WA225
REFERENCE.

The Medical Directory 2002

158th edition

Volume Two

informa
PROFESSIONAL

Published by Informa Professional, a division of Informa Group plc
Informa House
30-32 Mortimer Street
London W1W 7RE
Tel: +44 (0)20 7017 5375
Fax: +44 (0)20 7017 5221
Email: liz.godden@informa.com
Website: www.informalaw.com

First published 1845
158th edition published 2002

ISBN 1 84311 111 X

A catalogue record for this book is available from the British Library

Whilst every effort is made to ensure the accuracy of the entries, advertisements, listings and other material in this edition, neither the proprietors, Informa Group plc, nor the printers are to be liable in damages or otherwise for omissions or incorrect insertion, whether as to wording, space or position of any entry or advertisement.

Entry into this directory does not in any way serve as validation of a medical practitioner's fitness to practice – all such enquiries should be forwarded to the General Medical Council or the relevant registration body.

The publishers reserve the right of acceptance or rejection in respect of particulars, advertising copy, and listings submitted for insertion.

Informa Professional, a division of Informa Group plc
© Informa Professional 2002
All rights reserved. No part of this publication may be reproduced, stored in a retrieval system, or transmitted in any form or by any means, electronic, mechanical, photocopying, recording or otherwise without the prior written permission of the Publishers.

Database services and typesetting by MPG Dataworld Ltd.
Bound in Great Britain by Unwin Brothers Ltd, Old Woking.

Contents

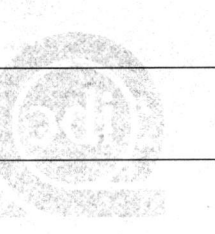

Volume One

Directory of Services	
Introduction	i
Foreword by Dame Deirdre Hine, President RSM	iii
Abbreviations	vii
Obituary List	xi
Part One: Medical Practitioners in the UK A-L	1

Volume Two

Medical Practitioners in the UK M-Z	2249
Index by Postal District: London	4148
Index by Town	4173
Part Two: Healthcare Organisations in the UK	4361
NHS Trusts and NHS Hospitals	4363
Health Authorities and Boards	4553
Independent Hospitals	4557
Educational Institutions	
Universities and Medical Schools	4570
Postgraduate Medical Centres	4622
Royal Colleges and Faculties	4642
Research Institutions	4645
Government and Statutory Bodies	4649
Coroners	4658
Medical Associations and Societies	4664
Index by Organisation Name	4683
Index of Hospitals by Town	4707

 **Healthcare Conferences**

Visit our web site for more information **www.healthcare-info.co.uk**

Part of the Informa Group, IBC UK Conferences organise a wide range of respected conferences within the healthcare sphere. Recent events include:-

- NHS Management
- Nursing
- Cardiology
- Emergency Care
- Training & Education
- Day Surgery
- Bed Management
- Pathology
- Orthopaedics
- Pharmacy
- AHPs
- Independent Healthcare
- Paediatrics/Neonatology
- Older People
- Radiology
- Obstetrics & Gynaecology
- Information Management & Technology
- Medico-Legal

For further information on any of our events or sponsorship opportunities please call Nicola Scudamore on 020 7017 5160 or email nicola.scudamore@informa.com, or visit our web site at www.healthcare-info.co.uk.

Register for our no effort update **Healthcare E-Bulletins.** Specifically designed to give you a concise monthly run down on developments within healthcare and to let you know what relevant events and publications are available.

To register simply visit our homepage at **www.healthcare-info.co.uk** and fill in your name and email address in the boxes supplied.

Abbreviations

Abbreviation	Full Form
AB	Bachelor of Arts
ABPsS	Associate British Psychological Society
ADMS	Assistant Director Medical Services
AE	Air Efficiency Award
AFC	Air Force Cross
AFOM	Associate Faculty of Occupational Medicine
AFPM	Associate Faculty Pharmaceutical Medicine
AHA	Associate Institute of Hospital Administrators
AKC	Associate King's College (London)
AM	Albert Medal
AMQ	American Medical Qualification
AMS	Army Medical Service
AO	Officer Order of Australia
ARIC	Associate Royal Institute of Chemistry
BA	Bachelor of Arts
BAc	Bachelor of Acupuncture
BAO	Bachelor of the Arts of Obstetrics
BASc	Bachelor of Applied Science
BC, BCh	Bachelor of Surgery
BChir	Bachelor of Surgery
BChD	Bachelor of Dental Surgery
BDA	British Dental Association
BDS	Bachelor of Dental Surgery
BDSc	Bachelor of Dental Science
BDentSc	Bachelor of Dental Science
BEM	British Empire Medal
BHy	Bachelor of Hygiene
BHyg	Bachelor of Hygiene
BM	Bachelor of Medicine
BMA	British Medical Association
BMedBiol	Bachelor of Medical Biology
BMedSc	Bachelor Medical Science
BMedSci	Bachelor of Medical Science
BPharm	Bachelor of Pharmacy
BS	Bachelor of Surgery
BSc	Bachelor of Science
BSc (MedSci)	Bachelor of Science (Medical Sciences)
Bt	Baronet
BVMS	Bachelor of Veterinary Medicine & Surgery
CAA	Civil Aviation Authority
CAS Applied Immunol	Certificate of Advance Study in Applied Immunology
CB	Companion Order of the Bath
CBE	Commander Order of British Empire
CC	County Council
CCFP	Certificate College of Family Physicians
CChem	Chartered Chemist
CD	Canadian Forces Decoration
Cert AvMed	Certificate in Aviation Medicine
CH	Companion of Honour
ChB	Bachelor of Surgery
CIH	Certificate in Industrial Health
CM, ChM	Master of Surgery
CMF	Christian Medical Fellowship
CMG	Companion Order of St Michael & St George
CMS	Church Missionary Society
CPH	Certificate in Public Health
CRAMC	Commander Royal Army Medical Corps
CRCP	Certificant Royal College of Physicians
CRCS	Certificant Royal College of Surgeons
CStJ	Commander Order of St John
CTCM&H	Certificate in Tropical Community Medicine & Hygiene
CVO	Commander Royal Victorian Order
DA	Diploma in Anaesthetics
DADMS	Deputy Assistant Director Medical Services
DADH	Deputy Assistant Director of Health
DAP & E	Diploma in Applied Parasitology & Entomology
DAvMed	Diploma in Aviation Medicine
DBE	Dame Commander Order of British Empire
DipBMS	Diploma in Basic Medical Sciences
DC	District Council
DCC	Diploma of Chelsea College
DCCH	Diploma in Child & Community Health
DCD	Diploma in Chest Diseases
DCDH	Diploma in Community Dental Health
DCh	Doctor of Surgery
DCH	Diploma in Child Health
DChD	Doctor of Dental Surgery
DCHT	Diploma in Community Health in the Tropics
DCL	Doctor of Civil Law
DCM	Distinguished Conduct Medal
DCMT	Diploma in Clinical Medicine of Tropics
DCP	Diploma in Clinical Pathology
DCPath	Diploma College of Pathologists
DDerm	Diploma in Dermatology
DDM	Diploma in Dermatological Medicine
DDMS	Deputy Director Medical Services
DDO	Diploma in Dental Orthopaedics
DDR	Diploma in Diagnostic Radiology
DDS	Doctor of Dental Surgery
DDSc	Doctor of Dental Science
DFC	Distinguished Flying Cross
DFHom	Diploma Faculty of Homoeopathy
DFM	Distinguished Flying Medal
DFM	Diploma in Forensic Medicine
DGDP	Diploma in General Dental Practice
DGM	Diploma in Geriatric Medicine
DGMS	Director-General Medical Services
DGO	Diploma in Gynaecology & Obstetrics
Dip GU Med	Diploma in Genitourinary Medicine
DHA	District Health Authority
DHMSA	Diploma in History of Medicine, Society of Apothecaries
DHyg	Doctor of Hygiene
DIC	Diploma of Membership of Imperial College of Science & Technology (London)
DIH	Diploma in Industrial Health
Dip IMC RCS Ed	Diploma in Immediate Medical Care, Royal College of Surgeons, Edinburgh
DL	Deputy Lieutenant
DLO	Diploma in Laryngology & Otology
DM	Doctor of Medicine
DMC	District Medical Committee
DMD	Director of Dental Medicine
DMedRehab	Diploma Medical Rehabilitation
DMHS	Director Medical & Health Services
DMJ	Diploma in Medical Jurisprudence
DMO	District Medical Officer
DMR	Diploma in Medical Radiology
DMRD	Diploma in Medical Radio-Diagnosis
DMRE	Diploma in Medical Radiology & Electrolysis

ABBREVIATIONS

Abbreviation	Full Form
DMRT	Diploma in Medical Radio-Therapy
DMS	Director Medical Services or Doctor of Medicine & Surgery
DMSA	Diploma in Medical Services Administration
DMSS	Director Medical & Sanitary Services
DMV	Doctor of Veterinary Medicine
DO	Diploma in Ophthalmology
DObst	Diploma Obstetrics
Dobst RCOG	Diploma Royal College Obstetrics & Gynaecology
DOMS	Diploma in Ophthalmic Medicine & Surgery
DOrth	Diploma in Orthodontics
DPA	Diploma in Public Administration
DPath	Diploma in Pathology
DPD	Diploma in Public Dentistry
DPhil	Doctor of Philosophy
DPhilMed	Diploma in Philosophy of Medicine
DPhysMed	Diploma in Physical Medicine
Dip Pract Derm	Diploma of Practical Dermatology
DPH	Diploma in Public Health
DPM	Diploma in Psychological Medicine
DPMSA	Diploma in Philosophy of Medicine Society of Apothecaries
DrAc	Doctor of Acupuncture
DR	Diploma in Radiology
DRACOG	Diploma Royal Australian College of Obstetrics & Gynaecology
DFACR	Diploma Royal Australasian College of Radiologists
DRCOG	Diploma Royal College of Obstetrics & Gynaecology
DRCPath	Diploma Royal College of Pathologists
DRM	Diploma in Radiation Medicine
DRS	Doctorandus
DS	Doctor of Surgery
DSC	Distinguished Service Cross
DSc	Doctor of Science
DSM	Diploma in Social Medicine
DSO	Companion Distinguished Service Order
DSSc	Diploma in Sanitary Science
DStJ	Dame Order of St John
DTCD	Diploma in Tuberculosis & Chest Diseases
DTCH	Diploma in Tropical Child Health
DTD	Diploma in Tuberculous Diseases
DTM & H	Diploma in Tropical Medicine & Hygiene
DTPH	Diploma in Tropical Public Health
DV & D	Diploma in Venereology & Dermatology
ECFMG	Education Council for Foreign Medical Graduates
ED	Efficiency Decoration
EMAS	Employment Medical Advisory Service
EMS	Emergency Medical Service
ENT	Ear, Nose & Throat
ERD	Emergency Reserve Decoration
ESMI	Elderly Subnormal Mentally Infirm
FACA	Fellow American College of Anesthetists
FACC	Fellow American College of Cardiologists
FACDS	Fellow Australian College of Dental Surgeons
FACG	Fellow American College of Gastroenterology
FACMA	Fellow Australian College of Medical Administrators
FACO	Fellow American College of Otolaryngology
FACOG	Fellow American College of Obstetrics & Gynecology
FACP	Fellow American College of Physicians
FACR	Fellow American College of Radiologists
FACS	Fellow American College of Surgeons
FACTM	Fellow American College of Tropical Medicine
FAGO	Fellow in Australia in Obstetrics & Gynaecology
FANZCP	Fellow Australian & New Zealand College of Psychiatrists
FBIM	Fellow British Institute of Management
FBCO	Fellow British College of Ophthalmic Opticians
FBPsS	Fellow British Psychological Society
FCAP	Fellow College of American Pathologists
FCCP	Fellow American College of Chest Physicians
FCGP	Fellow College of General Practitioners
FCOphth	Fellow College of Ophthalmology
FCMS	Fellow College of Medicine & Surgery
FCPath	Fellow College of Pathologists
FCP	Fellow College of Clinical Pharmacology or Fellow College Physicians
FCPS	Fellow College of Physicians & Surgeons
FCS	Fellow Chemical Society
FCRA	Fellow College of Radiologists of Australia
FDS	Fellow in Dental Surgery
FFA	Fellow Faculty of Anaesthetists
FFCM	Fellow Faculty of Community Medicine
FFCMI	Fellow Faculty of Community Medicine in Ireland
FFDS	Fellow Faculty of Dental Surgery
FFFP	Fellow Faculty of Family Planning
FFHom	Fellow Faculty of Homeopathy
FFOM	Fellow Faculty of Occupational Medicine
FFPath	Fellow Faculty of Pathology
FFPHM	Fellow Faculty of Public Health Medicine
FFPM RCP (UK)	Fellow Faculty of Pharmaceutical Medicine Royal College of Physicians UK
FFR	Fellow Faculty of Radiologists
FIHA	Fellow Institute of Hospital Administrators
FIBiol	Fellow Institute of Biology
FICS	Fellow International College of Surgeons
FKC	Fellow King's College London
FLCO	Fellow London College of Osteopathy
FLCOM	Fellow London College of Osteopathic Medicine
FLEXLic(USA)	Federal Licensing Examination (USA)
FLS	Fellow Linnean Society
FMC	Fellow Medical Council
FMCGP (Nigeria)	Fellow Medical Council of General Practitioners (Nigeria)
FOM	Faculty of Occupational Medicine
FPA	Family Planning Association
FPC	Family Practitioner Committee
FPHM	Faculty of Public Health Medicine
FPS	Fellow Pharmaceutical Society
FRACDS	Fellow Royal Australasian College of Dental Surgery
FRACGP	Fellow Royal Australasian College of General Practitioners
FRACO	Fellow Royal Australasian College of Ophthalmologists
FRACOG	Fellow Royal Australian College of Obstetricians & Gynaecologists
FRACP	Fellow Royal Australasian College of Physicians
FRACR	Fellow Royal Australasian College of Radiologists
FRACS	Fellow Royal Australasian College of Surgeons
FRAI	Fellow Royal Anthropological Institute
FRANZCP	Fellow Royal Australian & New Zealand College of Psychiatrists
FRCA	Fellow Royal College of Anaesthetists
FRCD	Fellow Royal College of Dentists
FRCGP	Fellow Royal College of General Practitioners
FRCOG	Fellow Royal College of Obstetricians & Gynaecologists
FRCP	Fellow Royal College of Physicians
FRCPA	Fellow Royal College of Pathologists Australasia
FRCPath	Fellow Royal College of Pathologists
FRCPC	Fellow Royal College of Physicians of Canada
FRCPI	Fellow Royal College of Physicians of Ireland
FRCPS	Fellow Royal College of Physicians & Surgeons
FRCPsych	Fellow Royal College of Psychiatrists
FRCR	Fellow Royal College of Radiologists
FRCRA	Fellow Royal College of Radiologists of Australasia
FRCS	Fellow Royal College of Surgeons
FRCSI	Fellow Royal College of Surgeons of Ireland
FRES	Fellow Royal Entomological Society

ABBREVIATIONS

Abbreviation	Full Form
FRFPS	Fellow Royal Faculty of Physicians & Surgeons
FRIC	Fellow Royal Institute of Chemistry
FRIPHH	Fellow Royal Institute of Public Health & Hygiene
FRMS	Fellow Royal Microscopical Society
FRS	Fellow Royal Society
FRSC	Fellow Royal Society of Chemistry
FRSE	Fellow Royal Society of Edinburgh
FRSH	Fellow Royal Society of Health
FSS	Fellow Royal Statistical Society
FZS	Fellow Zoological Society
GBE	Knight/Dame Grand Cross Order of the British Empire
GC	George Cross
GCB	Knight/Dame Grand Cross Order of the Bath
GCMG	Knight Grand Cross Order of St Michael and St George
GCSI	Knight Grand Commander Order of the Star of India
GCStJ	Knight Grand Cross Venerable Order of St John of Jerusalem
GCVO	Knight/Dame Grand Cross Royal Victorian Order
GM	George Medal
GMC	General Medical Council
GP	General Practitioner
HA	Health Authority
HDD	Higher Dental Diploma
HSE	Health & Safety Executive
IAMC	Indian Army Medical Corps
i/c	In Charge
IC	Intensive Care
ICRF	Imperial Cancer Research Fund
ICU	Intensive Care Unit
IMA	Irish Medical Association
IMS	Indian Medical Service
ISO	Imperial Service Order
JCC	Joint Committee on Contraception
JCHMT	Joint Committee for Higher Medical Training
JCPTGP	Joint Committee on Postgraduate Training in General Practice
JHMO	Junior Hospital Medical Officer
JP	Justice of the Peace
KBE	Knight Commander British Empire
KCB	Knight Commander Order of the Bath
KCMG	Knight Commander Order of St Michael and St George
KCSI	Knight Commander Order of the Star of India
KCVO	Knight Commander Royal Victorian Order
KCSG	Knight Commander Order St Gregory the Great
KM	Knight of Malta
KStJ	Knight of Justice Order of St John
LAH	Licentiate Apothecaries Hall, Dublin
LCPS	Licentiate College of Physicians & Surgeons
LDSc	Licentiate in Dental Science
LDS	Licentiate in Dental Surgery
LicAc	Licentiate in Acupuncture
LIHSM	Licentiate of Institute of Health Services Management
LLB	Bachelor of Laws
LLCO	Licentiate London College of Osteopathy
LLCOM	Licentiate London College of Osteopathic Medicine
LLD	Doctor of Laws
LLM	Master of Laws
LM	Licentiate in Midwifery
LMC	Local Medical Committee
LMCC	Licentiate Medical Council of Canada
LMS	Licentiate in Medicine & Surgery
LMSSA	Licentiate in Medicine & Surgery Society of Apothecaries London
LRCP	Licentiate Royal College of Physicians
LRCPI	Licentiate Royal College of Physicians of Ireland
LRCPS	Licentiate Royal College Physicians & Surgeons
LRCS	Licentiate Royal College of Surgeons
LRCSI	Licentiate Royal College of Surgeons of Ireland
LRFPS	Licentiate Royal Faculty of Physicians & Surgeons
LSA	Licentiate Society of Apothecaries London
LSM	Licentiate School of Medicine
LVO	Lieutenant Royal Victorian Order
M	Member
MA	Master of Arts
MACD	Member Australasian College of Dermatology
MACGP	Member Australasian College of General Practitioners
MACO	Member Australian College of Ophthalmologists
MACR	Member American College of Radiology
MANZCP	Member Australian & New Zealand College of Psychiatrists
MAO	Master of the Art of Obstetrics
MAustCOG	Member Australian College Obstetrics & Gynaecology
MB	Bachelor of Medicine
MBA	Master in Business Administration
MBAcA	Member British Acupuncture Association
MBE	Member Order of British Empire
MC	Military Cross
M-C	Medico-Chirurgical
MC, MCh, MChir	Master of Surgery
MCB	Master of Clinical Biochemistry
MCCM	Member College of Community Medicine (New Zealand)
MCCP	Member Ceylon College of Physicians
MCDH	Mastership in Community Dental Health
MCFP	Member College of Family Practitioners
MCh	Master of Surgery
MChir	Master of Surgery
MChD	Master of Dental Surgery
MChOrth	Master of Orthopaedic Surgery
MChOtol	Master of Otology
MCISc	Master of Clinical Science
MClinPsychol	Master of Clinical Psychology
MCommH	Master of Community Health
MCPA	Member College of Pathologists of Australia
MCPath	Member College of Pathologists
MCPS	Member College of Physicians & Surgeons
MCRA	Member College of Radiologists of Australia
MD	Doctor of Medicine
MDD	Doctor of Dental Science
MDentSc	Master of Dental Surgery
MDS	Master of Dental Surgery
MDSc	Master of Dental Science
MFCM	Member Faculty of Community Medicine
MFCMI	Member Faculty of Community Medicine, Ireland
MFFP	Member Faculty of Family Planning
MFHom	Member Faculty of Homoeopathy
MFOM	Member Faculty of Occupational Medicine
MFPaedRCPI	Member Faculty of Paediatrics, Royal College of Physicians of Ireland
MFPM	Member Faculty Pharmaceutical Medicine
MFPHM	Member Faculty Public Health Medicine
MFPM RCP (UK)	Member Faculty Pharmaceutical Medicine Royal College Physicians UK
MGDS	Member in General Dental Surgery
MHyg	Master of Hygiene
MIBiol	Member Institute of Biology
MICGP	Member of Irish College of General Practitioners
MIH	Master of Industrial Health
MLCO	Member London College of Osteopathy
MLCOM	Member London College of Osteopathic Medicine
MM	Military Medal
MMed	Master of Medicine
MMedSc	Master of Medical Science
MMF	Member Medical Faculty
MMSA	Master of Midwifery Society of Apothecaries

ABBREVIATIONS

Abbreviation	Full Form	Abbreviation	Full Form
MMSc	Master of Medical Science	**NUI**	National University of Ireland
MO	Master of Obstetrics	**OBE**	Officer Order of British Empire
MOD	Ministry of Defence	**OM**	Order of Merit
MO & G.	Master Obstetrics & Gynaecology	**OSJ**	Knight Sovereign Order of St John
MObstG		**OStJ**	Brother Officer Order of St John
MOH	Medical Officer of Health	**PAMC**	Pakistan Army Medical Corps
MPhil	Master of Philosophy	**PC**	Privy Councillor, Pharmaceutical Chemist
MPH	Master of Public Health	**PhD**	Doctor of Philosophy
MPS	Member Pharmaceutical Society	**PHLS**	Public Health Laboratory Service
MPSI	Member Pharmaceutical Society of Ireland	**PMO**	Principal Medical Officer
MPsy	Master of Psychiatry	**QC**	Queen's Counsel
MPsychMed	Master of Psychological Medicine	**QGM**	Queen's Gallantry Medal
MRACGP	Member Royal Australasian College of General Practitioners	**QHP**	Queen's Honorary Physician
		QHS	Queen's Honorary Surgeon
MRACO	Member Royal Australasian College of Ophthalmologists	**QJM**	Queen's Jubilee Medal
		QSM	Queen's Service Medal
MRACP	Member Royal Australasian College of Physicians	**QSO**	Queen's Service Order
MRACR	Member Royal Australasian College of Radiologists	**RADC**	Royal Army Dental Corps
		RAMC	Royal Army Medical Corps
MRad(D)	Master of Radiodiagnosis	**RAuxAF**	Royal Auxiliary Air Force
MRad(T)	Master of Radiotherapy	**RCAMC**	Royal Canadian Army Medical Corps
MRANZCP	Member Royal Australian & New Zealand College of Psychiatrists	**RCOG**	Royal College of Obstetricians & Gynaecologists
		RCP	Royal College of Physicians
MRC	Medical Research Council	**RCS**	Royal College of Surgeons
MRCGP	Member Royal College of General Practitioners	**RD**	Reserve Decoration
MRCOG	Member Royal College of Obstetricians & Gynaecologists	**RNVR**	Royal Naval Volunteer Reserve
		SA	College of Medicine of South Africa
MRCP	Member Royal College of Physicians	**SBStJ**	Serving Brother Order of St John
MRCPA	Member Royal College of Pathologists Australasia	**ScD**	Doctor of Science
		SHO	Senior House Officer
MRCPath	Member Royal College of Pathologists	**SHMO**	Senior Hospital Medical Officer
MRCPI	Member of Royal College of Physicians of Ireland	**SJM**	Silver Jubilee Medal
MRCPsych	Member Royal College of Psychiatrists	**SSStJ**	Serving Sister Order of St John
MRCS	Member Royal College of Surgeons	**SMO**	Sovereign Military Order
MRCVS	Member Royal College of Veterinary Surgeons	**TAVR**	Territorial & Army Volunteer Reserve
MRNZCGP	Member Royal New Zealand College General Practitioners	**TC Dub**	Trinity College Dublin
		TD	Territorial Decoration
MRO	Member Register of Osteopaths	**TDD**	Tuberculosis Diseases Diploma
MRSH	Member Royal Society of Health	**UGM**	Unit General Manager
MS	Master of Surgery	**VAD**	Voluntary Aid Detachment
MSc	Master of Science	**VC**	Victoria Cross
MScD	Master of Dental Science	**VD**	Volunteer Decoration
MSSc	Master of Surgical Science	**VQE**	Visa Qualifying Examination USA
MSMF	Member of State Medical Faculty	**VRD**	Volunteer Reserve Decoration
MVO	Member Royal Victorian Order	**VTS**	Vocational Training Scheme
NHI	National Health Insurance	**VTSO**	Vocational Training Scheme Organiser
NHS	National Health Service	**WHO**	World Health Organisation

The Medical Directory 2002

Part One

Medical Practitioners in the UK
M-Z

Informa Professional **Medico-Legal Titles**

Do **you** need **regular** medico-legal **updates?**

If so then **Informa** has a **portfolio** of titles to **suit your** needs

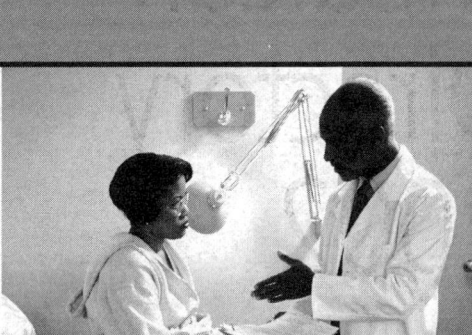

Personal and Medical Injuries Law Letter (PMILL)

..has been the most highly regarded title within its field for nearly 20 years and is a must for those needing a brief background to current clinical negligence and personal injury cases. In 10 issues a year, you will receive concise and informed updates by a leading consultant editorial team and hear of ground-breaking judgements as soon as they are reached.

10 issues - £294

Medical Law Monitor

... is essential reading for both medical and legal professionals who need to understand the details and implications of recent developments in medical law. Topics regularly covered include; malpractice, patient confidentiality, clinical negligence, medical ethics, mental health, NHS complaints and professional regulation.

12 issues - £265 – discounts are available to NHS employees

Lloyds Law Reports: Medical

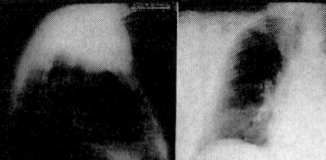

.... provide expert case selection and incisive commentaries from 3 Sergeants' Inn. It aims to provide lawyers and medical experts with authoritative reports of all the major legal cases in this field and includes judgements on clinical negligence litigation, medical ethical cases, mental health, judicial review and doctor's discipline. Bound volumes are available of cases dating back until 1989.

10 issues - £212 – Bound volumes £109 per annum – full set £835

For further information or a **free sample copy** please contact **Emma Cox** on **tel: 020 7017 5441** or **email: emma.cox@informa.com** quoting reference **PPM0005A**

informa PROFESSIONAL

www.informabookshop.com

***M A ICHIHASHI, Rica Farah** 50 Hollybush Hill, London E11 1PX — BM BS 1998 Nottm.

M'ALLISTEV, Kay Forbes The Sandyford Initiative, 2-6 Sandyford Place, Sandriehall St., Glasgow G3 7NB Tel: 0141 211 8130 Fax: 0141 211 8139 — MB ChB 1989 Glas.; MRCOG 1994. Cons. Community Gynaecol. The Sandyford Initiative Glas.

M'CAW, Revd. Dr. Stephen Aragorn (retired) 23 Canons Close, Thetford IP24 3PW — MB BS 1986 Lond.; MA Camb. 1987; FRCS Eng. 1990; MRCGP 1992; DRCOG 1991. Prev: GP Wickham Market Suff.

M'MUNORU, Minna Maarika Flat 3, Lindsey Mansions, 11 Warrior Square Terrace, St Leonards-on-Sea TN37 6BN Fax: 01424 465448 — State Exam Med 1991 Tübingen.

MA, Richard Maung Min Naing 4C Wilberforce Road, London N4 2SW — MB ChB 1995 Sheff.

MA, Ronald Ching Wan 23 Woodsford Square, London W14 8DP Tel: 020 7602 4086 Fax: 020 7602 7673 — MB BChir 1994 Camb.; MA Camb. 1995; MRCP 1997. (Univ. Camb. & UMDS Schools Guy's & St. Thos.) Med. Off., (Dept. of Med. & Therap.), P. of Wales Hosp. Hong Kong. Prev: SHO (Neurol. & Dermol.) St. Mary's Hosp. Lond.; SHO Hammersmith Hosp. Lond.; SHO (Renal Med. & Transpl.) St. Mary's Hosp. Lond.

MA-FAT, Roger 18 Crawley Road, Timperley, Altrincham WA15 7ST — MB ChB 1983 Manch.

MAAITA, Maher Elias Khaled Department of Obstetrics & Gynaecology, Queen Mary's Hospital, Sidcup DA14 6LT — MB BS 1991 Lond.

MAALAWY, Maalawy Mikhail Rawlinson Street Surgery, 128 Rawlinson Street, Barrow-in-Furness LA14 2DG Tel: 01229 820221 Fax: 01229 824948 — MB BCh 1965 Cairo; MRCS Eng. LRCP Lond. 1979. Socs: BMA; Med. Protec. Soc. Prev: SHO (Geriat. & Med.) High Carley Hosp. Ulverston; SHO (Gen. Surg.) N. Lonsdale Hosp. Barrow-in-Furness; SHO (Urol.) Salford Roy. Hosp.

MAALOUF, Elia Fares 21 Wellington Court, Mayfield Road, London W12 9LT Tel: 020 8743 1034 Email: emaolouf@rpms.ac.uk — MB ChB 1989 Dundee; MRCP (UK) 1994. Regist. (Paediat.) Hammersmith Hosp. Lond. Socs: BMA.

MAAN, Shamsher Singh (retired) 7 Long Meadow, Stafford ST17 9DP Tel: 01785 256299 — MB BS Lucknow 1954; DPM Eng. 1969. Prev: Cons. St Geo.'s Hosp. Stafford.

*MAAN, Zafar 16 The Spiert, Stone, Aylesbury HP17 8NJ — MB BS 1998 Lond.

MAAROUF, Mr Abdel Salam Mohamed Shafik 17 Woodside Terrace, Inverness IV2 3YW Tel: 01463 220167 — MB BCh 1972 Cairo; FRCS Glas. 1986.

MAARTENS, Mr Nicholas Francois Department of Neurological Surgery, Radcliffe Infirmary, NHS Trust, Woodstock Road, Oxford OX2 6HE Tel: 01865 311188 Fax: 01865 224898 — MB ChB 1986 Cape Town; FRCS 2001 (SN); FRCS 1994. (Cape Town) Cons. Neurosurg., Roy. Melbourne Hosp. Socs: BMA; Brit. Soc. Neurol. Surgs.; Int. Soc. Pituitary Surgs. Prev: Regist. (Neurosurg. & Neurol.) Groote Schuur Hosp. Cape Town; Specialist Regist. (Neurosurg.) Radcliffe Infirm. Oxf.

*MAASSARANI, Faisal 1 The Serpentine, Garston, Liverpool L19 9DT — MB ChB 1998 Sheff.

MAASSARANI, Hassan Ali Tower Hill Health Centre, Highfield, Towerhill, Kirkby, Liverpool L33 1XD Tel: 0151 546 9955 Fax: 0151 549 1037 — MB ChB 1969 Liverp.

MABADEJE, Abdul Fatai Biola c/o Dr M A Oshodi, 122 Cholmley Gardens, London NW6 1AA — MB BS 1963 Lond.; MRCP Ed. 1967.

MABBOTT, Jennifer Lesley Scunthorpe Community Health Care NHS Trust, Goole & District Hospital, Woodland Avenue, Goole DN14 6RX Tel: 01405 720720 Fax: 01405 768993; The Yews, 6 Pontefract Road, Snaith, Goole DN14 9JS Tel: 01405 861026 — MB BS 1968 Newc.; MSc Lond. 1990; DCH RCP Lond. 1987. (Newc.) SCMO Scunthorpe Community Health Care NHS Trust. Socs: Fell. Roy. Coll. Paediat. & Child Health; Brit. Acad. Forens. Sci. Prev: Med. Off. W. Riding CC; SHO (Psychiat.) St. Geo. Hosp. Morpeth; Ho. Off. Ashington Gen. Hosp.

MABERLY, Dion Jonathan (retired) Allergy Centre, Farfield House, North Street, Keighley BD21 3AA Tel: 01535 603966 Fax: 01535 655456 — MB BS Lond. 1962; FRCP Lond. 1994; FRACP 1976, M 1967. Prev: Cons. Phys. (Chest Dis.) Airedale Gen. Hosp.

MABEY, Professor David Christopher William London School of Hygiene & Tropical Medicine, Keppel St., London WC1E 7HT Tel: 020 7927 2297 Fax: 020 7637 4314; 10 St. Germans Place, London SE3 0NN Tel: 020 8858 3164 Email: david.mabey@lshtm.ac.uk — BM BCh 1974 Oxf.; DM Oxf. 1994; FRCP Lond. 1993; MRCP (UK) 1978. (St Thomas's) Prof. Communicable Dis. Lond. Sch. Hyg. & Trop. Med.; Cons. Phys. Hosp. for Trop. Dis. Lond. Socs: Roy. Soc. Trop. Med. & Hyg.; Assn. Phys.; Med. Soc. Study VD. Prev: Sen. Clin. MRC Laborat., The Gambia.

MABEY, Mrs Denise Margaret Sth. Wing Eye Department, St Thomas' Hospital, Lambeth Palace Road, London SE1 7EH — MRCS Eng. LRCP Lond. 1975; FRCOphth Lond. 1991. (St Thos.) Cons. Ophth. Guy's & St Thomas' Trust Hosp. Lond. Socs: Internat. Soc. for Geographic & Epidemiol. Ophth.; UK Soc. for Cataract & Refractive Surg.; Roy. Soc. Med.

MABIN, David Charles Paediatric Department, West Suffolk Hospital, Hardwick Lane, Bury St Edmunds IP33 2QZ Tel: 01284 713000 Fax: 01284 713407 Email: david.mabin@wsh-tr.anglox.nhs.uk — MB ChB 1982 Dundee; MD Dundee 1995; MRCP (UK) 1988; T(M)(Paediat.) 1994. Cons. Paediat. W. Suff. Hosp. Bury St. Edmunds; Vis. Cons. in Paediat. Allergy, Addenbrooke's Hosp. Camb. Prev: Regtl. Med. Off. 1st Bn. Gordon Highlanders.

MABLEY, Alison Mary 44 Park Hill Road, Harborne, Birmingham B17 9HJ — MB ChB 1988 Birm.; MRCGP 1995. Asst. GP Warley. Prev: Trainee GP/SHO Kidderminster Gen. Hosp. VTS; Ho. Off. (Med.) Gen. Hosp. Birm.

MABROOK, Mr Abbas Fadhil 28 Dartmouth Street, Walney, Barrow-in-Furness LA14 3AS; 11 Ennismore Gardens, Thames Ditton KT7 0YS — MB ChB 1974 Basrah; FRCS Ed. 1982.

MCADAM, Mr Andrew Hamilton (retired) 35 Castle Rising Road, King's Lynn PE30 3JA Tel: 01553 671557 Email: andrewmcadam@doctors.org.uk — MB ChB 1958 St. And.; MA Glas. 1960; FRCS Ed. 1969; DO Eng. 1965. Prev: Cons. Ophth. Surg. King's Lynn & Wisbech Hosps.

MACADAM, Arthur David (retired) Old Carpenters, Dares Lane, Ewshot, Farnham GU10 5BS Tel: 01252 850401 — MA, MB Camb. 1958, BChir 1957; MRCS Eng. LRCP Lond. 1957; MRCGP 1965.

*MCADAM, Catherine Anne Flat 2F2, 35 Spottiswoode St., Edinburgh EH9 1DQ — MB ChB 1998 Ed.; MB ChB Ed 1998.

MACADAM, Charles Francis Cannington Health Centre, Mill Lane, Cannington, Bridgwater TA5 2HB Tel: 01278 652335 Fax: 01278 652453; Willowbrook, Pightly Road, Spaxton, Bridgwater TA5 1BU Tel: 01278 671824 — MB ChB 1979 Bristol; MRCGP 1984; DRCOG 1983; Cert. Family Plann. JCC 1983. Prev: Trainee GP Som. VTS; SHO (Psychiat.) Bristol; Ho. Off. Taunton.

MCADAM, Elspeth Katharine Bethel Child & Family Centre, Mary Chapman House, Hotblack Road, Norwich NR2 4HN Tel: 01603 421421 Fax: 01603 421990; 49 Elm Quy Court, 30 Nine Elms Lane, London SW8 5DF Tel: 020 7622 2732 — MB BChir 1972 Camb.; Registration Supervisor 1995; UKCP Therapist 1995; MA Camb. 1973; MRCPsych 1982; FRCPsych 1998. (Middlx.) Cons. Child & Family Psychiat. Bethel Child & Family Centre Norwich; Cons. to BUP Clinics in Köping Eskilstuna & Gothenberg, Sweden (Projects on Anorexia, Psychosis & Child Abuse); Tutor & Supervisor Kensington Cons. Centre Dip. Systemic Ther..; Cons. to Norf. Ment. Health Trust. Socs: BMA; RC Psychiat.s; Kesington Consultation Centre.

MCADAM, Helen Bayne Raikesfield, 11 Raikes Avenue, Skipton BD23 1LP Tel: 01756 3359 — MB ChB 1959 St. And.; DObst RCOG 1961.

MCADAM, John Gordon 47 Antrim Road, Ballynahinch BT24 8AN — MB BCh BAO 1982 Belf.; MB BCh Belf. 1982.

MCADAM, Julie Anne 71 Main Road, Fenwick, Kilmarnock KA3 6DU — MB ChB 1995 Glas.

*MCADAM, Karen Frances 41 Richmond Road, Cambridge CB4 3PP — MB BS 1986 Lond.; MRCP (UK) 1990.

MCADAM, Professor Keith Paul William James Medical Research Council (UK) Laboratories, Fajara, PO Box 273, Banjul, Gambia Tel: 00 220 496715 Fax: 00 220 496513 Email: kmcadam@mrc.gm; Oakmead, 70 Luton Lane, Redbourn, St Albans AL3 7PY Tel: 01582 792833 Fax: 01582 792833 — MB BChir 1969 Camb.; MA 1967 Camb.; BA Camb. 1966; FRCP Lond. 1984;

MCADAM

MRCP (UK) 1971; Dip. Amer. Bd. Allergy & Clin. Immunol. 1980; Dip. Amer. Bd. Internal Med. 1978. (Cam. Middl.) Director MRC (UK) Laborats. Banjul, Gambia; Wellcome Prof. Trop. Med. Lond. Sch. Hyg. & Trop. Med. Socs: Fell. Roc. Soc. Trop. Med. & Hyg.; (E. Pres) Internat. Med. Club. Prev: Assoc. Prof. Med. New. Eng. Med. Center, Tufts Univ. Boston, Mass., USA; Vis. Scientist Immunol. Br. Nat. Cancer Inst. NIH Bethesda, USA; Vis. Prof. Stellenbosch Univ. S Afr. 1995.

MCADAM, Louise Anne Elizabeth 27 Wellington Street, Kilmarnock KA3 1DW Tel: 01289 331710 — MB ChB 1990 Manch.; MRCGP 1994; DRCOG 1993.

MCADAM, Michelle Susan 44 Main Road, Marsh Lane, Sheffield S21 5RH — MB BS 1990 Lond.

MCADAM, Norena Winifred Kirriemuir Health Centre, Tannage Brae, Kirriemuir DD8 4ES Tel: 01575 573333; Old Kennels Cottage, Pearsie, Kirriemuir DD8 4RP Tel: 01575 540250 — MB BCh BAO 1980 Belf.; MRCGP 1985; Cert. Family Plann. JCC 1985; DRCOG 1984; DCH Dub. 1983; Cert. Av. Med. 1994. C.A.A. Aviat. Med. Examr. Socs: Ulster Med. Soc. Prev: Med. Off. Falkland Is. S. Atlantic for Overseas Developm. Admin.

MACADAM, Robert Crawford Alexander 43 Osborne View Road, Fareham PO14 3JW — MB ChB 1990 Leeds.

MCADAM, Sheena Ruth Dundonald Medical Practice, 9 Main Street, Dundonald, Kilmarnock KA2 9HF Tel: 01563 850496 Fax: 01563 850426; 15 Noran Crescent, Troon KA10 7JF — MB ChB 1984 Glas.; MB ChB Glas. 1984; MRCGP 1988.

***MCADAM, Timothy Kerr** 67 Deanfield, Bangor BT19 6NX — MB BCh BAO 1995 Belf.

MCADAM, Mr William Archibald Frame (retired) Silverdale, Raikeswood Crescent, Skipton BD23 1ND Tel: 01756 793359 — MB ChB St. And. 1959; FRCS Glas. 1965; FRCS Ed. 1965. Prev: Cons. (Gen. Surg.) Airedale Gen. Hosp. Steeton.

MCADOO, Hugh McCrone (retired) 85 Framingham Road, Sale M33 3RH Tel: 0161 973 6640 — MB BCh BAO 1947 Belf.; MRCGP 1954. Prev: Ho. Surg. & Ho. Phys. Roy. Vict. Hosp. Belf.

MACAFEE, Mr Alastair Lowry (retired) 142 Warren Road, Donaghadee BT21 0PQ — MB BCh BAO 1959 Belf.; MD Belf. 1962; FRCSI 1988; FRCS Eng. 1967. Prev: Cons. Orthop. Surg. Ulster Community & GreenPk. Trusts.

MACAFEE, Mr Charles Andrew Jeremy (retired) 10 Guilford Road, Stoneygate, Leicester LE2 2RB Tel: 0116 2770 7770 Fax: 0116 210 9613 — MD 1960 Belf.; MB BCh BAO 1956; FRCS Glas. 1964; MFFP 1964; FRCOG 1977, M 1964. Prev: Cons. O & G Leicester Roy. Infirm.

MACAFEE, David Alastair Lowry 6 Bramcote Lane, Wollaton, Nottingham NG8 2ND Tel: 0115 928 6738 Fax: 0115 928 6738 — BM BS 1998 Nottm.; BM BS Nottm 1998; BMedSci. Nottm. 1996. (Nottm.) PRHO (Gen./Thoracic Surg.) Nottm. City Hosp. Prev: PRHO (Med.) Blackpool Vic. Hosp.

MCAFEE, Lewis Alexander 3a Townfield Road, West Kirby, Wirral CH48 7EY Tel: 0151 625 5350 — MRCS Eng. LRCP Lond. 1942; MA Camb. (Camb. & St. Bart.) JP. Prev: Surg. Lt. RNVR; Sen. Ho. Surg. St. Bart. Hosp.; Ho. Phys. Birkenhead Gen. Hosp.

MCALAVEY, Andrew John 12 Wood Lane, Greasby, Wirral CH49 2PT — MB ChB 1992 Liverp.

MCALAVEY, Pauline Susan Glenmill Medical Centre, 1191 Royston Road, Glasgow G33 1EY Tel: 0141 770 4052 Fax: 0141 770 4255; 15 Heriot Road, Lenzie, Glasgow G66 5AX Tel: 0141 776 6867 — MB ChB 1978 Glas.; MRCGP 1984; DCH; DRCOG. (Glasgow)

MCALEA, Philomena Marie 41 Killeaton Crescent, Dunmurry, Belfast BT17 9HB — MB BCh BAO 1991 Belf.

MACALEENAN, Frank Aloysius Ardgowan, 13 Old Belfast Road, Downpatrick BT30 6SG Tel: 01396 2503 — MB BCh BAO 1958 Belf.; MD Belf. 1963, MB BCh BAO 1958; FRCP Lond. 1986, MRCP 1965. Cons. Phys. Ulster Hosp. Dundonald & Downe Hosp. Downpatrick. Socs: Fell. Ulster Med. Soc.; BMA. Prev: Sen. Med. Regist. Roy. Vict. Hosp. Belf.; Tutor Path. Qu. Univ. Belf.; Ho. Off. Mater Hosp. Belf.

MACALEENAN, Nuala Anne James Street Practice, 40 James Street, Crossgar, Downpatrick BT30 9JU; Ardgowan, Old Belfast Road, Downpatrick BT30 6SG Tel: 01396 612503 — MB BCh BAO 1966 Belf.; DCH RCPS Glas. 1968.

MCALEER, Angela Pauline 133 Clogherney Road, Beragh, Omagh BT79 0RE — MB BCh BAO 1990 NUI.

MCALEER, Bernard Gerard Anthony Erne Hospital, Enniskillen BT74 6AY Tel: 01365 324711; Levaghy, Enniskillen BT74 6DN — MB BCh 1984 Belf. (Queen's. Univ. Belfast) Staff Phys. Erne Hosp. Enniskillen, N. I. Prev: Staff Phys. Mid Ulster Hosp. Magherafelt, N. I.

MCALEER, Gerard Ward, CStJ, CBE Poynings Park Road, Wokingham RG11 2AH Tel: 01734 782211 — MB BCh BAO 1926 NUI; DTM & H Eng. 1936. Prev: PMO Far E. Air Force.

MCALEER, James Joseph Anthony U Floor, Belfast City Hospital, Lisburn Road, Belfast BT9 7A Tel: 028 9069 9315 — MB BCh BAO 1981 Dublin; BA Dub. 1981; MD Belf. 1992; FRCP Ed. 1996; FRCR 1988. Sen. Lect. & Cons. Radiother. & Oncol. Belf. City Hosp. Belf.

MCALEER, Matthew The Health Centre, 203 Main Street, Barrhead G78 1HG Tel: 0141 880 6161 Fax: 0141 881 7063 — MB ChB 1972 Glas.; MRCGP 1976.

MCALEESE, Mr Gerard Anthony 21 Royal Crescent, Coventry CV3 3DY — MB BCh BAO 1988 NUI; FRCS Ed. 1995; LRCPSI 1988.

MCALEESE, Jonathan James 4 Wilshere Drive, Belfast BT4 2GP Tel: 01232 768465 — MB ChB 1996 Ed.; MA Cantab. 1996, BA 1993.

MCALEESE, Mr Paul Joseph Gregory 34 Chaldon Way, Coulsdon CR5 1DB — MB BCh BAO 1985 NUI; FRCS Ed. 1989; FRCSI 1989; LRCPI & LM LRCSI & LM 1985; DTPH RCSI 1985; Cert. Sports Med. RCSI 1985; Cert. Diagnostic. Radiol. RCSI 1985.

***MCALINDEN, Claire** 23 Highholm Street, Port Glasgow PA14 5HN — MB ChB 1995 Glas.

MCALINDEN, Eileen Sonniva Tynan Surgery, 15 Dartan Ree, Tynan, Armagh BT60 4QT Tel: 028 3756 8214 Fax: 028 3756 8837; 9 Bracken Lodge, Portadown, Craigavon BT63 5XD — MB BCh BAO 1990 Belf.; MRCGP 1994; DRCOG 1993; DGM RCPS Glas. 1992. Socs: RCGP. Prev: Trainee GP Co. Armagh.; SHO (Med.) & Ho. Off. Craigavon Area Hosp.

MCALINDEN, Jacqueline Mary Faith Donard, Windsor Hill, Newry BT34 1HS — MB BCh BAO 1990 Belf.; MB BCh Belf. 1990.

MCALINDEN, Mr Michael Gavan 18 Laganvale Manor, Stranmillis, Belfast BT9 5BE — MB BCh BAO 1990 Belf.; BSc (Anat.) Belf. 1987; FRCS Eng. 1995; MPhil 1997. (Queens University Belfast) Regist. (Orthop. Surg.) Musgrave Pk. Hosp. Belf.; Hon. Research Assoc. Qu. Univ. Belf. Socs: Irish Orthop. Trainees Assn.; Brit. Orthop. Train. Assn.; Assoc. Mem. BOA. Prev: Regist. (Fract. Surg.) Roy. Vict. Hosp. Belf.

MCALINDEN, Paula Mary Armagh & Dunganon HSS Trust, Victoria House, Tower Hill, Armagh BT61 9DR Tel: 02837 414529 Email: pmcalinden@adhsst.n-i.nhs.uk; 17 Derrymacash Road, Lurgan, Craigavon BT66 6LG — MB BCh BAO 1982 Belf.; FRCPCH 1997; MRCGP 1989; DCH RCPI 1988; DRCOG 1987; DA (UK) 1985. Cons. Paediat. Community Child Health Armagh & Dungannan HSS Trust. Socs: BACCH; ARICD. Prev: SCMO Armagh, Dungannon Unit of Managem.

MCALINDON, Mark Edward P Floor, Royal Hallamshire Hospital, Glossop Road, Sheffield S10 2JF — BM BS 1987 Nottm.; BMedSci Nottm. 1985; MRCP (UK) 1990; DM 1998. (Nottm.) Cons. (Phys. / Gastroent.) Roy. Hallamshire Hosp, Sheff.; Brit. Digestive Foundat. Research Train. Fell. Univ. Hosp. Nottm. Socs: Brit. Soc. of Gastroenterol. Prev: Regist. (Gastroenterol.) Univ. Melbourne W.. Hosp. Melbourne, Vict., Austral.; Career Regist. (Gastroenterol. & Med.) City Gen. Hosp. N. Staffs. Roy. Infirm. Stoke-on-Trent; SHO Rotat. (Med.) City Gen. Hosp. & N. Staffs Roy. Infirm. Stoke-on-Trent.

MCALINDON, Shane 39 The Graylings, Boston PE21 8EB — MB ChB 1988 Leic.

MCALINDON, Timothy Edward Rheumatology Unit, St. Thomas' Hospital, London SE1 Tel: 020 7928 9292; c/o 29 Gladstone Street, London SE1 6EY — BM 1982 Soton.; MRCP (UK) 1985. Sen. Regist. (Rheum.) St. Thos. Hosp. Prev: Research Regist. (Rheum.) Bristol Roy. Infirm.

MCALINNEY, Patrick Gerard 52 Lower Sloane Street, London SW1W 8BP — MB BCh BAO 1974 Belf.; MRCS Eng. LRCP Lond. 1974. Prev: Cas. Off. & Ho. Off. Downe Hosp. Downpatrick; SHO (Anaesth.) Mater Infirm. Hosp. Belf.

MACALLISTER

MCALISKEY, Damian Patrick 39 Kanes Road, Derrylaughan, Dungannon BT71 4QY — MB BCh BAO 1992 Belf.

MACALISTER, Anne Old Mill Surgery, 100 Old Mill Road, Uddingston, Glasgow G71 7JB Tel: 01698 817219; 3 Ravenscourt, Thorntonhall, Glasgow G74 5AZ — MB ChB 1977 Glas.; MFHom RCP Lond. 1989.

MACALISTER, Anthea Margaret The Wistaria Practice, 32 St. Thomas' Street, Lymington SO41 9NE Tel: 01590 672212; Highfield Ridge, 6 Highfield, Lymington SO41 9GB Tel: 01590 675004, 01590 75004 — MB BS 1966 Lond.; MRCS Eng. LRCP Lond. 1966; MRCGP 1974. (St. Bart.) Socs: Mem. of Roy. Coll. of Gen. Practitioners. Prev: SHO (Paediat.) St. Mary's Gen. Hosp. Portsmouth; Ho. Off. Whipps Cross Hosp. Lond.

MACALISTER, Carole Anne 25 Avondale Place, Edinburgh EH3 5HX Tel: 0131 343 2719 — MB ChB 1988 Ed.; MRCGP 1994; DRCOG 1995; DFFP 1993. (Edinburgh) Prev: Trainee GP Edin. & Musselburgh; SHO (Geriat. Med.) Roy. Vict. Hosp. Edin.; SHO (O & G) Ealing Hosp. Lond.

MACALISTER, Elizabeth Dorman (retired) Coldstone Beck, Burley-in-Wharfedale, Ilkley LS29 7AB — MB ChB 1939 Glas.; MRCOG 1944. Prev: Research Schol. Hosp. Wom. Leeds.

MACALISTER, Heather Moira The Old Sunday School, Noke Common, Newport PO30 5TY Email: heather@mcalister.demon.co.uk — MB ChB 1993 Dundee; BMSc (Hons.) Dund 1992. Staff Grade (Psychiat.) Newcroft Hosp. IOW. Prev: SHO (Psychiat.) Newcroft Hosp. I. of Wight; SHO (Psychiat). St. James Hosp. Portsmouth; SHO (Psychiat). St. Ann's Hosp. Poole.

MACALISTER, Ian (retired) Clunaig, Dean Road, Hawick TD9 7HU — MB ChB 1940 Ed.

MCALISTER, James The Surgery, 4/5 Avondale Court, Onchan IM9 1LN — MB BCh BAO 1984 Belf.; MRCGP 1989.

MACALISTER, James Charles Ashvale, Roses Lane Ends, Ballindery, Lisburn BT28 2LE — MB BS 1993 Lond.; BSc (Hons.) Lond. 1992.

MACALISTER, Susan May, Capt. RAMC Group Practice, Bengal Road, Bulford Camp, Salisbury Tel: 01980 672201; 101 Tongham Road, Aldershot GU12 4AT — MB BS 1993 Lond.; BSc Lond. 1991. GP Regist. Gp. Pract. Bulford. Prev: SHO (Med.) Camb. Milit. Hosp. Aldershot.

MACALISTER HALL, Margaret Sheila (retired) Gallanach Cottage, Lochgair, Lochgilphead PA31 8SD — MB ChB 1947 Ed.

MCALL, Frances Ashburner Mooring Bignell Wood, Lyndhurst SO43 7JA Tel: 01703 812239 — LRCP LRCS Ed. LRFPS Glas. 1939. (Roy. Colls. Ed.) Socs: Med. Wom. Federat. (Ex-Pres. Wessex Assn.).

MCALL, Mr Graham Lonsdale Gerald Devonshire Green Medical Centre, 126 Devonshire Street, Sheffield S3 7SF Tel: 0114 272 1626; Perhentian, 28 Highcliffe Drive, Sheffield S11 7LU — MB BChir 1977 Camb.; MA, MB Camb. 1977, BChir 1976; FRCS Ed. 1982; MRCGP 1991; Cert. Family Plann. JCC 1991. Socs: Christ. Med. Fell.sh. Prev: Lect. (Anat. & Surg.) Univ. Med. Sci. Penang, Malaysia; Regist. (Surg.) Warwick Hosp.; Head Dept. Surg. Univ. Sains Kelantan, Malaysia.

MACALLAN, Colin Roy Ambrose Avenue Surgery, 76 Ambrose Avenue, Colchester CO3 4LN Tel: 01206 549444 Fax: 01206 369910; Surrey Villa, 22 Lexden Road, Colchester CO3 3NH — BMedSci (Hons.) Nottm. 1976, BM BS 1978; MRCGP 1991; DCH RCP Lond. 1983; DRCOG 1981.

MACALLAN, Derek Clive Dept of Infectious Diseases, St Georges' Hospital Medical school, London SW17 0RE — MB BS 1983 Lond.; PhD Lond. 1994; MA Oxf. 1993, BA 1980; R Nutr 2000; FRCP 2001 UK; DTM & H 1998. Sen. Lect. (Infec. Dis.) St. Geo. Hosp. Sch. Lond.; Hon. Cons. Div. Infect. Dis. St. Geo. Hosp. Med. Sch. Lond.

MCALLEN, Christoph James Peter 27 Sydney Buildings, Bath BA2 6BZ Tel: 01225 442897 — MB ChB 1992 Bristol; FRCS 1997.

MCALLEN, Monica Kathleen (retired) 7 Deanway, Chalfont St Giles HP8 4JH Tel: 01494 872178 — MB BS Lond. 1943; MD Lond. 1945; FRCP Lond. 1974, M 1945; MRCS Eng. LRCP Lond. 1942. Prev: Cons. Phys. (Respirat. Med.) Univ. Coll. Hosp. Lond.

MCALLEN, Philip Michael (retired) 7 Dorchester Road, Stratton, Dorchester DT2 9RU — MD Lond. 1948, MB BS 1941; FRCP Lond. 1968, M 1947; MRCS Eng. LRCP Lond. 1941. Prev: Cons. Phys. W. Middlx. Hosp. Isleworth.

MCALLION, Susan Jean Ashludie Hospital, Monifieth, Dundee DD5 4HQ Tel: 01382 527830; 3 Haldane Street, Dundee DD3 0HP Tel: 01382 826678 Email: jmcallion@aol.com — MB ChB 1973 Dundee; MB ChB Dund.1973; MFHom Glas. 1984. (Dund.) Clin. Asst. (Geriat. Psychiat. & Homoeop.) Tayside Primary Care NHS Trust; Clin. Research Fell. Univ. Dundee. Socs: Treas. Socialist Health Assn. Scott. Br.; Treas. Fac. of Homoeopathy Tayside Gp.

MACALLISTER, Andrew Samuel 2 Mountcoole Park, Belfast BT14 8JR — MB BCh BAO 1991 Belf.; MRcP (UK) 1994; DTM & H Liverp 1998, DRCOG 1998. (The queens Univ. of Belfast)

MACALLISTER, Charles 50 Lisshefield Road, Loughgall, Armagh BT61 8QB — MB BCh BAO 1982 NUI; LRCPI & LM, LRCSI & LM BAO 1982; MRCPI 1987.

MACALLISTER, D P 127a Lowedges Road, Sheffield S8 7LE.

MACALLISTER, Daniel Martin Granville House Medical Centre, Granville Street, Adlington, Chorley PR6 9PY Tel: 01257 481966 Fax: 01257 474655 — MB ChB 1982 Manch.; MRCGP 1988; DA (UK) 1985.

MACALLISTER, Dermot (retired) Sarum View, Down Barn Road, Winterbourne Gunner, Salisbury SP4 6JN — LRCPI & LM, LRSCI & LM 1952; LRCPI & LM, LRCSI & LM 1952.

MACALLISTER, Donald James Chirnside Medical Practice, South Crofts, Chirnside, Duns TD11 3UH Tel: 01890 818253 Fax: 01890 818595; Baravaig, Ferney Castle, Reston, Eyemouth TD14 5LU Tel: 018907 61381 — MB ChB 1984 Glas.; BSc (Hons.) Glas. 1979; MRCGP 1988; DRCOG 1986. (Glasgow) Prev: Trainee GP Glas. VTS.

***MCALLISTER, Gail** 16 Gartcows Road, Falkirk FK1 5QT — MB ChB 1994 Glas.

MACALLISTER, Mr James Alexander Princess Margaret Hospital, 38-42 Osborne Road, Windsor SL4 3SJ Tel: 01753 743419 Fax: 01753 743435 Email: eyemac@supanet.com — MB ChB 1971 St. And.; FRCS Ed. 1981. p/t Cons. Ophth. P. Chas. Eye Unit, King Edwd. VII Hosp. Windsor. Socs: FRCS; FRCOPH; FAAO.

MACALLISTER, Mr John Cunningham Ross Farnborough Orthopaedic Centre, Farnborough Hospital, Orpington BR6 8ND Tel: 01689 877855 Fax: 01689 814058 — MB BS Lond. 1983; FRCS Ed. 1990; FRCS (Orth) 1997; FRCS (Orth) 1999. (The London Hospital, Whitechapel) Cons. Orthop. Surg. to Bromley Hosps. Socs: Brit. Orthop. Assn.; Roy. Soc. Med. Prev: Sen. Regist. (Orthop.) Roy. Nat. Orthop. Hosp. Stanmore.

MACALLISTER, Jonathan George Castle Practice, Carrickfergus Health Centre, Taylors Avenue, Carrickfergus BT38 7HT Tel: 028 9336 4193 Fax: 028 9331 5947; 4 Bradford Gardens, Marshallstown Road, Carrickfergus BT38 9EH Tel: 01960 367726 — MB BCh BAO 1987 Belf.; MRCGP 1992; DRCOG 1993; DMH Belf. 1990. Socs: Med. Sickness Soc.; Med. Defence Union. Prev: Trainee GP/SHO Rotat. (Psychiat., Cas., Gen. Surg. & Paediat.) Whiteabbey Hosp. Co. Antrim VTS; SHO (O & G) Belf. City Hosp.

***MCALLISTER, Jonathan Mark** 66 Westcroft, Honley, Huddersfield HD9 6JP — MB ChB 1996 Liverp.

MCALLISTER, Jordana Marie Main X-Ray Department, Royal Victoria Hospital, Grosvenor Road, Belfast BT12 6BA Tel: 01232 240503 Ext: 4350; 41 Marlborough Park Central, Belfast BT9 6HN Tel: 01232 682711 — MB BCh BAO 1990 Belf.; MB BCh Belf. 1990. Specialist Regist. (Radiol.) Roy. Vict. Hosp. Belf. Socs: Fell. Roy. Coll. Radiologists; Roy. Coll. Radiol. BrE. Gp.; Ulster Med. Soc.

***MCALLISTER, Moyra Anne** 119 Caiyside, Swanston, Edinburgh EH10 7HR — MB ChB 1996 Ed.

MCALLISTER, Patricia Dawn Lee House Surgery, Eves Corner, Danbury, Chelmsford CM3 4QA Tel: 01245 225522 Fax: 01245 222196 Email: triciamcallister@hotmail.com — BM 1982 Soton.; MRCGP 1986; DRCOG 1986. Prev: SHO Trainee GP E.bourne VTS.

MCALLISTER, Peter David, Maj. RAMC Defence Services Psychiatric Centre, Duchess of Kent Hospital, Horne Road, Catterick Garrison DL9 4DF Fax: 01748 873612 Email: petemcal@dsca.gov.uk — MB BS 1992 Lond.; BSc Lond. 1989, MB BS 1992; MRC Psych 1999. (Kings Lond.) Specialist Regist. in Psychiat. Defence Servs. Psychiat. Centre, Catterick Garrison. Prev: SHO in Psychiat. DSPC; RMO 1 Highlanders, Lond. Derry; RMO Lond., Derry.

MACALLISTER, Raymond John Centre for Clinical Pharmacology, University College London Medical School, The Rayne Institute, 5 University St., London WC1E 6JJ Tel: 020 7209 6174 Email: r.allister@ucl.ac.uk; 21 Chesfield Road, Kingston upon Thames KT2 5TH — MB BS 1987 Lond.; MA Camb. 1988, MD 1995; MRCP (UK) 1990. Sen. Lect. & Hon. Cons. Clin. Pharmacol. Univ.

MCALLISTER

Coll. Lond. Med. Sch. Prev: Sen. Regist. (Clin. Pharmacol.) St. Geo. Hosp. Lond.

MCALLISTER, Mr Ronald Murdoch Ross 82 Chapel Street, Billericay CM12 9LS Tel: 01277 625271 Fax: 01277 625271 Email: rmrm@telinco.com — MB BS 1985 Lond.; BSc Lond. 1983; FRCS Eng. 1990. (St. Thos. Hosp.) Socs: Fell. Roy. Soc. Med.

MCALLISTER, Ruth Hester Trevor Gibbons Unit, Maidstone Hospital, Hemriatge Lane, Maidstone ME16 9QQ Tel: 01622 723194 Fax: 01622 723174 — MB ChB 1981 Sheff.; BSc 1978 (Hon.) Sheff.; MD 1993; MRCP (UK) 1985; MRCPsych 1993. Cons. Forens. Psychiat. Kent Forens. Psychiat. Serv.; Hon. Sen. Lect. Guy's, King's and St Thomas's Sch. of Med. Prev: SHO (Neurol.) Roy. Free Hosp. Lond.; Regist. (Psychiat.) Maudsley Hosp.; Research Fell. (Neurol.) Middlx. Hosp.

MCALLISTER, Timothy William John 1 Sandown Close, Tunbridge Wells TN2 4RL — MB BS 1993 Lond.; Biochemistry BSc Honours 1987; DCH 1995; DMG 1996; DRCOG 1996; DFFP 1998; DTM & H 1998; MRCGP 1998. (UCL)

MCALLISTER, Victor Lionel Department of Neuroradiology, Newcastle General Hospital, Westgate Road, Newcastle upon Tyne NE4 6BE Tel: 0191 273 8811 Fax: 0191 273 1613; Bermar, Horsley, Newcastle upon Tyne NE15 0NS Tel: 01661 853813 — MB BS 1966 Lond.; MRCS Eng. LRCP Lond. 1966; FRCR 1972; DMRD Eng. 1970. (Univ. Coll. Hosp.) Cons. & Head Neuroradiol. Regional Neurol. Centre Newc. Gen. Hosp.; Hon. Clin. Lect. (Neuroradiol.) Univ. Newc. Socs: Assoc. Mem. Brit. Soc. Neuroradiol.; (Pres. Elect) Brit. Soc. Neuroradiol. Prev: Clin. Dir. Neurosci. Regional Neurosci. Centre Newc. Gen. Hosp.; Nat. Delegate & Sec. & Treas. Brit. Soc. Neuroradiol.

***MCALLISTER, Victoria Doreen Marjory** 25 Kenilworth Avenue, Reading RG30 3DL — MB BS 1994 Lond.

MCALLISTER, William Archibald Charles Royal Surrey County Hospital, Egerton Road, Guildford GU2 7XX; The Compasses, East Lane, West Horsley, Leatherhead KT24 6LQ — MB BS 1973 Lond.; MD Lond. 1986; FRCP Lond. 1993; MRCP (UK) 1976; MRCS Eng. LRCP Lond. 1973. (Guy's) Cons. Phys. Roy. Surrey Co. Hosp. Guildford. Socs: Brit. Thorac. Soc. Prev: Sen. Regist. W.minster Hosp. Lond.; Sen. Regist. Brompton Hosp. Lond.; Clin. Lect. (Clin. Pharmacol.) Cardiothoracic Inst. Lond.

MCALLISTER, Mr William James 34 Chaldon Way, Coulsdon CR5 1DB — MB BChir 1992 Camb.; BA Camb. 1988; FRCS Eng. 1995. (Univ. Camb.) Research Fell. (Urol.) Roy. Lond. Hosp.

MCALLISTER, William Tait Baillie (retired) 21 Le May Avenue, London SE12 9SU Tel: 020 8857 6196 — LRCP LRCS 1939 Ed.; LRCP LRCS Ed. LRFPS Glas. 1939. Governor Salvation Army Men's Social Servs. Brit. & Irel. Prev: Chief Med. Off. S.A. Cath. Booth & MacRobt. Hosps. India & P S.A. Chikankata Hosp., Zambia.

MCALONAN, Grainne Mary 124 Providence Square, London SE1 2ED — MB BS 1996 Lond.

MCALOON, Jarlath Department of Paediatrics, Antrim Hospital, 45 Bush Road, Antrim BT41 2RL Tel: 02894 424000 — MB BCh BAO 1978 Belf.; MPhil Belf. 1994; FRCP Lond. 1995; MRCP (UK) 1983; FRCPCH 1996; T(M) (Paed.) 1991; DRCOG 1982; DCH RCPSI 1980. (Qu. Univ. Belf.) Cons. Paediat. United Hosps. Trust, Antrim.

MCALPIN, Patricia Giuliana Roberta Beverley Road Surgery, 151 Beverley Road, Hull HU3 1TY Tel: 01482 328861 Fax: 01482 321223 — MB ChB 1975 Leeds; Cert. Family Plann. JCC 1984. (Leeds University Medical School)

MCALPINE, Alison Cameron Apsley Street Surgery, 14 Apsley Street, Glasgow G11 7SY Tel: 0141 339 2960 — MB ChB 1982 Glas.; MRCGP 1987; DRCOG 1986.

MCALPINE, Christine Helen Stobhill Hospital, Balornock Road, Glasgow G21 3UW Tel: 0141 201 3000 Fax: 0141 201 3218; 29 Birnam Crescent, Bearsden, Glasgow G61 2AU Tel: 0141 942 7223 Email: christine.mcalpine@northglasgow.scot.nhs.uk — MB ChB 1980 Glas.; MRCP (UK) 1983; FRCP Glas. 1993. Cons. Phys. (Geriat. Med.) Stobhill Hosp. Prev: Cons. Phys. Geriat. Med. Stirling Roy. Infirm.

MCALPINE, Cynthia Joan (retired) 168 Southbrae Drive, Glasgow G13 1TX Tel: 0141 954 6670 — MB ChB 1949 Glas.; MB ChB (Commend.) Glas. 1949; FRCP Glas. 1983, M 1980; FRCP Lond. 1982 M 1952; DObst RCOG 1951. Mem. of Exec. Comm. of Erskine Hosp. Bishopton; Cons. Phys. (Geriat. Med.) P.ss Louise

Scott. Hosp. Erskine; Chairm. of Healthcare Comm. of Erskine Hosp. Bishopton. Prev: Mem. Med. Appeals Tribunal.

MCALPINE, David Martin 29 Calside, Paisley PA2 6DB — MB ChB 1978 Glas.

MCALPINE, Gwendyth Anne (retired) Adams, Wrotham Road, Meopham, Gravesend DA13 0JH Tel: 01474 813586 — MB ChB 1959 Ed. Prev: Regist. (Anaesth.) Dartford Gp. Hosps.

MCALPINE, Howard McPherson Victoria Infirmary, Langside, Glasgow G42 Tel: 0141 649 4545 — MB ChB 1979 Glas.; FRCP Glas. 1994; MRCP (UK) 1981. Cons. Phys. Vict. Infirm. Glas.

MCALPINE, Jacqueline Ann c/o 1 Castle Crescent, Doune FK16 6BX Tel: 01786 841315 — MB ChB 1988 Aberd.; MRCGP 1995. (Aberdeen) Prev: GP ChristCh. New Zealand; Trainee GP Tryst Med. Centre StenHo.muir; Regist. (Cas.) Ipswich Hosp. Qu.sland, Austral.

MCALPINE, Joseph Kenneth Tel: 01224 556319 Fax: 01224 556339; 1 Cromar Gardens, Kingswells, Aberdeen AB15 8TF Tel: 01224 746658 — MB ChB 1982 Ed.; BSc (Hons.) St. And. 1976, BSc Med Sci 1979; MRCP (UK) 1986. (Edin.) Cons. Phys. (Med. For Elderly) Grampian Univ. Hosps. NHS Trust Woodend Hosp. Aberd.; Hon. Clin. Sen. Lect. Univ. Aberd. Socs: Brit. Geriat. Soc.; RCPS Glas.; RCP Edin. Prev: Cons. Phys. (Med. for Elderly) Roy. Alexandra Hosp. Paisley; Sen. Regist. (Geriat. Med.) Lightburn Hosp. & Glas. Roy. Infirm. Glas.; Hon. Clin. Sen. Lect. Univ. Glas.

MCALPINE, Kenneth William Hand Browning Fermanagh House, 41 Tandragee Road, Portadown, Craigavon BT62 3BQ — LM 1954 Rotunda; MA Dub. 1953, BA 1950, MB BCh BAO 1952. (TC Dub.)

MCALPINE, Lawrence George Department of Medicine, Monklands Hospital, Airdrie ML6 0JS Tel: 01236 748748 Fax: 01236 713152 Email: lawrence.mcalpine@laht.scot.nhs.uk; 29 Birnam Crescent, Bearsden, Glasgow G61 2AU Tel: 0141 942 7223 — MB ChB 1980 Glas.; FRCP 2001 London; BSc (1st cl. Hons. Path.) Glas. 1978; FRCP Glas. 1995; MRCP (UK) 1983. p/t Cons. Phys. (Gen. & Respirat. Med.) Monklands Hosp. Airdrie; Hon. Cons. Phys. (Respirat. Med.) W.. Infirm. & Gartnavel Gen. Hosp. Glas.; Hon. Clin. Sen. Lect. (Med.) Univ. of Glas. Socs: Brit. Thorac. Soc.; Amer. Thoracic Soc.; Europ. Respirat. Soc. Prev: Sen. Regist. (Gen. & Respirat. Med.) W.. Infirm. & Gartnavel Gen. Hosp. Glas.; Regist. (Respirat. Med.) W.. Infirm. & Kt.swood Hosp. Glas.; MRC Train. Fell. Wolfson Laborat. for Molecular Path. Beatson Inst. for Cancer Research Bearsden.

MCALPINE, Stuart Gemmell (retired) 168 Southbrae Drive, Glasgow G13 1TX Tel: 0141 954 6670 Email: stuart.mcalpine@tinyworld .co.uk — MB ChB 1949 Glas.; MD (Commend.) Glas. 1959; FRCP Lond. 1975, M 1955; FRCP Glas. 1965, M 1962; FRFPS Glas. 1954. Med. Adviser Army Pens. Off. MoD. Prev: Cons. Phys. Roy. Alexandra Hosp. Paisley.

MCALPINE, William Arthur Gatehead Road Surgery, Gatehead Road, Crosshouse, Kilmarnock KA2 0HU Tel: 01563 521506 Fax: 01563 573695; 1 South Hamilton Street, Kilmarnock KA1 2DN — MB ChB 1978 Dundee; MRCGP 1982; DCH RCP Lond. 1984; DRCOG 1980. Prev: Trainee GP Perth & Kinross Dist. VTS.

MCANALLEN, Cora McAnallen and McAnallen, The Health Centre, Tavanagh Avenue, Portadown, Craigavon BT62 3BU Tel: 028 3835 1347 — MB BCh BAO 1977 NUI. Socs: MICGP.

MCANALLEN, James Gerard McAnallen and McAnallen, The Health Centre, Tavanagh Avenue, Portadown, Craigavon BT62 3BU Tel: 028 3835 1347; The Health Centre, Tavanagh Avenue, Portadown, Craigavon BT62 3BU Tel: 01762 351347 — MB BCh BAO 1974 NUI; MRCGP 1980; MICGP. Socs: Amer. Acad. Family Phys.s.

MCANALLY, David 40 Danemere Street, London SW15 1LT — MA (Hnrs. Nat. Sc. Trip.) MB BChir Camb. 1942. (Camb. & Middlx.) Prev: Ho. Surg. E. Suff. & Ipswich Hosp.; Lt. RAMC.

MACANDIE, Christine Flat 5, 29 Springkell Gardens, Pollokshields, Glasgow G41 4BP — MB ChB 1993 Glas.; FRCS Ed. 1997. Specialist Regist. Otolaryngol. Vict. Infirm. NHs Trust Glas. Prev: SHO Otolaryngol. Vict. Infirm. Glas.; SHO Gen. Surg. S. Ayrsh. Hosp. NHS Trust, AYR; SHO Rotat. (Surg.) W.. Infirm. Glas.

MACANDIE, Kerr Southern General Hospital NHS Trust, 1345 Govan Road, Glasgow G51 4TF Tel: 0141 201 1100; Flat 5, 29 Springkell Gardens, Pollokshields, Glasgow G41 4BP Tel: 0141 423 7896 Email: kmacandie@aol.com — MB ChB 1993 Glas. SHO

(Ophth.) S.. Gen. Hosp. Glas. Socs: Med. & Dent. Defence Union Scotl.; BMA. Prev: SHO (Ophth.) Ayr Hosp.; Ho. Off. (Gen. Med.) Roy. Infirm. Glas.; Ho. Off. (Gen. Surg.) Stobhill Hosp. Glas.

MCANDREW, Mr Andrew Richard Flat 3, 127 Milbrook Road E., Southampton SO15 1HQ — MB BS 1990 Lond.; FRCS Ed. 1995. (St. Georges Hospital Medical School London) Specialist Regist. (Orthop.) Wessex Rotat.

MCANDREW, Estelle Marie 509 Brook Street, Broughty Ferry, Dundee DD5 2EA — MB ChB 1985 Dundee; MRCGP 1989; DRCOG 1989. Princip. GP Cowley.

MCANDREW, Fiona Catherine Mary 36 Fabian Road, London SW6 7TZ — MB ChB 1992 Manch.

MCANDREW, Gordon Miller Bishop's House, 4 Lansdowne Crescent, Edinburgh EH12 5EQ Tel: 0131 225 9128 — MB ChB 1957 Aberd.; FRCP Lond. 1986, M 1966; FRCP Ed. 1975, M 1962. Socs: Scott. Soc. Phys.

MCANDREW, Helen Fiona 4 Upton Lane, Nursling, Southampton SO16 0XY — MB BS 1989 Lond. SHO (Surg.) Alder Hey Hosp. Liverp.

MCANDREW, Ian William British Nuclear Fuels plc, Sellafield, Seascale CA20 1PG Tel: 019467 71436 Fax: 019467 71452; South Winds, Outrigg, St Bees CA27 0AN Tel: 01946 822326 — MB ChB St. And. 1968. (St. And.) Sen. Med. Off. Brit. Nuclear Fuels Plc Sellafield, Seascale. Prev: GP Egremont; SHO (Med., Surg. & Obst.) W. Cumbld. Hosp.; SHO (ENT) Dundee Roy. Infirm.

MCANDREW, Leonora Janet Hunter Bishop's House, 4 Lansdowne Crescent, Edinburgh EH12 5EQ Tel: 0131 225 9128 — MB ChB 1959 Aberd. SCMO (Community Rehabil.) Edin. Socs: (Pres.) Scott. Soc. Rehabil. Prev: Research Fell. (Rehabil. Studies Unit) Edin. Univ.

MCANDREW, Neil Anthony Wrexham Maelor Hospital, Croesnewydd Road, Wrexham LL13 7TD Tel: 01978 727018 Email: neil.mcandrew@new-tr.wales.nhs.uk; Wrexham Maelor Hospital, Croesnewydd Road, Wrexham LL13 7TD Tel: 01978 727018 Email: neil.mcandrew@new-tr.wales.nhs.uk — BM BCh 1992 Oxf.; CCST (Resp. & Gen. Intenal Med.) 2001; BA (Hons.) Oxf. 1989; MRCP (UK) 1995. (Oxf.) Cons. Phys. with interest in Respirat. Med., Wrexham Maelor. Socs: BMA; BTS; ERS. Prev: Specialist Regist (Thoracic & Gen. Med.) Llandough Hosp. Cardiff; Regist. Rotat. (Gen., Geriat. & Respirat. Med.) Glan Clwyd; SHO Rotat. (Med. & ITU) Nottm. City Hosp.

MCANDREW, Paul Edward Dryburn Hospital, North Road, Durham DH1 5TW Tel: 0191 386 4911; 136 Houghton Road, Hetton Le Hole, Houghton-le-Spring DH5 9PL — MB BS 1989 Newc. SHO (Anaesth.) Dryburn Hosp. Durh.

MCANDREW, Mr Peter Gilchrist Maxillofacial Unit, Rotherham District General Hospital, Rotherham S60 2UD Tel: 01709 824459 Fax: 01709 824459; Morthen Lodge, Morthen Hall Lane, Rotherham S66 9JL Tel: 01709 702023 Fax: 01709 702023 — MB BS Lond. 1970; BDS Lond. 1965; FRCS Ed. 1986; MRCS Eng. LRCP Lond. 1970; FDS RCS Eng. 1969. (Guy's) Cons. Maxillofacial Surg. Rotherham Gen. Hosp. & Chas. Clifford Dent. Hosp. Sheff.

MCANDREW, Sarah Elizabeth 2 Turberville Place, Canton, Cardiff CF11 9NX Tel: 01222 226728 — BM BCh Oxf. 1993; MRCGP 1997; DRCOG 1996; DCH RCP Lond. 1995. (Oxf.) Clin. Asst. (Genito Urin. Med.) Roy. Gwent Hosp. Card.

MCANDREW, Sean Victor The Surgery, 15 Haden Road, Old Hill, Warley B64 6ER Tel: 01384 566688 — LRCPI & LM, LRSCI & LM 1957; LRCPI & LM, LRCSI & LM 1957; LAH Dub. 1958; LM Coombe 1958.

MCANDRY, Simon Paul Southern Group Practice, Surgery, Bridson St, Port Erin IM9 6AN Tel: 01624 832226; Sunnymount, Bradda Road, Port Erin IM9 6PS Tel: 01624 836248 — MB BS 1982 Lond.; BSc (Hons. Pharmacol.) Lond. 1979, MB BS 1982; MRCGP 1986; DRCOG 1985. (St. Thos.)

MCANENA, Mr Oliver James Niel Patrick Surgical Professorial Unit, The Royal London Hospital, Whitechapel Road, London E1 1BB — MB BCh BAO 1979 NUI; MCh NUI 1985; FRCSI 1983.

MACANESPIE, Harry (retired) 3 South Glassford Street, Milngavie, Glasgow G62 6AT Tel: 0141 956 1302 — MB ChB 1955 Glas.; MFCM 1974; DPH Glas. 1961. Cons. Pub. Health Med. Gtr. Glas. HB. Prev: Cons.Pub.Healyth Med. GTR.Glas.HB.

***MACANOVIC, Srdjan** 17 Humberstone Road, Cambridge CB4 1JD — LMSSA 1994 Lond.

MCANULTY, Gregory Raymond St. Georges Hospital, Department of Anaesthetics, Blackshaw Road, London SW17; 16 Barmouth Road, London SW18 2DN — MB BS 1982 Sydney; BA (Hons.) Sydney 1989; FRCA 1990. Regist. (Anaesth.) St. Geo. Hosp. Lond.

MACARA, Sir Alexander Wiseman Elgon 10 Cheyne Road, Stoke Bishop, Bristol BS9 2DH Tel: 0117 968 2838 Fax: 0117 968 4602 — FFOM 2000; MB ChB Glas. 1958; FRCP Lond. 1991; FFPHM RCP (UK) 1990; FRCGP 1982; FFCM 1974, M 1972; DPH (Hecht Prize) Lond. 1960; FRCP Ed 1997; DSc (Hon.) 1998; F Med Sci 1997. (Glas.) Cons. Health Manpower Developm. & Med. Educat. WHO 1970-; Hon. Visit. Prof. Health Studies Univ. York.; Chairm. Nat. Heart Forum; Mem. Nat. Task Force on Coronary Heart Dis. Socs: Fell. (Past Chairm. Counc.) BMA; Elected Mem. GMC; Chairm. Pub. Health Med. Consultative Comm. Prev: Cons. Sen. Lect. (Epidemiol. & Pub. Health Med.) Univ. Bristol 1963-1997/Co-Dir. WHO Collaborating Centre Environm. Health Promotion & Ecology 1989-97; Hon. Doctor Pub. Health Sch. Pub. Health Athens 1991; Ho. Surg. Roy. Matern. & Wom. Hosp. Glas.

MCARA, Ann Christine The Middlesex Hospital, Anaesthetic Department, Mortimer St., London W1T 3AA Tel: 020 7380 9013 Fax: 020 7380 9604 Email: anaesec@academic.uclh.nthames.nhs.uk; 79 De Beauvoir Road, Kingsland, Hackney, London N1 4EL Tel: 020 7254 1491 Email: robert.ford4@virgin.net — MB BS Lond. 1963; MRCS Eng. LRCP Lond. 1963; FFA RCS Eng. 1971; DCH RCPS Glas. 1965. (St. Mary's) Cons. Anaesth. UCL Hosps. Trust. Socs: BMA; Assn. Anaesth. Prev: Sen. Regist. (Anaesth.) Hosp. Sick Childr. Gt. Ormond St. & Univ. Coll. Hosp.

MACARA, Lena Mary The Queen Mothers Hospital, Yorkhill NHS Trust, Yorkhill, Glasgow G3 8SJ; 38 Craignethan Road, Whitecraigs, Glasgow G46 6SH — MB ChB 1987 Glas.; MD Glas. 1995; MRCOG 1992. (Glas.) Cons. O & G Qu. Mothers Hosp. Prev: Research Regist. (Perinatal Biol.) Glas. Roy. Infirm. & Irvine Centr. Hosp. Arysh.; Regist. (O & G) Qu. Mothers Hosp. Glas.

MACARDLE, Breege Mary Royal National Throat Nose &Ear Hospital, Grayh Inn, London WC1X 8DA Tel: 0207 915 7641 Email: breege.macardle@rfh.nthames.nhs.uk; 34 Birchington Road, London N8 8HP — MB BCh BAO 1975 NUI; MSc Lond. 1997; FRCP Lond. 1995; MRCP (UK) 1981; FRCPCH 1997. (Univ. Coll. Dub.) Cons. (Audiol. Med.) The Roy. Nose, Throat & Ear Hosp. Lond. Prev: Cons. Paediat. N.wick Pk. Hosp. Harrow Middlx.

MCARDLE, Brian (retired) Park Cottage, Greville Park Road, Ashtead KT21 2QT Tel: 01372 276823 — MB BS 1934 Lond.; MD Lond. 1937; FRCP Lond. 1960, M 1936; MRCS Eng. LRCP Lond. 1933; DCH Eng. 1935. Prev: on Extern. Scientif. Staff, MRC.

MCARDLE, Professor Colin Stewart University Department of Surgery, Royal Infirmary, Edinburgh Tel: 0131 536 3812 Fax: 0131 228 2661; 6 Collylinn Road, Bearsden, Glasgow G61 4PN — MB ChB Glas. 1963; MD Glas. 1977; FRCS Glas. 1980; FRCS Eng. 1969; FRCS Ed. 1968. Prof. Surg. Univ. Edin. Prev: Cons. & Hon. Prof. Gen. Surg. Roy. Infirm. Glas.; Cons. Gen. Surg. Vict. Infirm. Glas.; Sen. Regist. W.. Infirm. Glas.

MCARDLE, John Maclachlan Spa Surgery, 205 High Street, Boston Spa, Wetherby LS23 6PY Tel: 01937 842842 Fax: 01937 841095; Fontwell House, Clifford, Wetherby LS23 6JQ Tel: 01937 843405 Fax: 01937 841095 — MB ChB 1958 Ed.; MRCOphth 1989; DO Eng. 1974. (Ed.) Hosp. Med. Pract. (Ophth.) Gen. Infirm. Leeds.

MCARDLE, Leo 55 Andersonstown Road, Belfast BT11 9AG Tel: 028 613436 — MD 1959 Belf.; PhD Belf. 1969, MD 1959, MB BCh BAO 1947; FFA RCSI 1961; DA RCPSI 1951. (Belf.) Cons. Anaesth. Mater Infirm. Hosp. Belf. Prev: Asst. Anaesth. Mater Hosp. Belf.; Anaesth. Regist. Shotley Bridge Hosp.

MCARDLE, Maureen Teresa Wythenshawe Health Care Centre, Stancliffe Road, Sharston, Manchester M22 4PR Tel: 0161 946 0065 — MB BCh BAO 1985 NUI; MRCP (UK) 1991; DCH RCPS Glas. 1989. Cons. Paediat. (Community Child Health) Mancunian Community Trust. Socs: Fell. NCPCH; BACCH; Manch. Med. Soc. Paediatric Div. Prev: Sen. Regist. (Community Paediat.) NW Manch. HA.

MCARDLE, Paul Augustine Fleming Nuffield Unit, Burdon Terrace, Newcastle upon Tyne NE2 3AE Tel: 0191 281 6177; 57 Kenton Road, Gosforth, Newcastle upon Tyne NE3 4NJ Tel: 0191

MCARDLE

284 1483 — MB BCh BAO 1978 NUI; MRCPI 1982; MRCPsych 1985. Sen. Lect. & Cons. Child & Adolesc. Psychiat. Fleming Nuffield Unit Roy. Vict. Infirm. Gp. Hosps. Trust.

MCARDLE, Mr Paul John Maxillofacial Unit, Poole General Hospital, Longfleet Rd, Poole BH15 Tel: 01202 665511 — MB ChB 1994 Bristol; BDS Manch. 1986; FDS RCS Eng. 1990; FRCS 1998 Eng. (Bristol) SHO (Orthop.) W.on Gen. Hosp. W.on Super Mare, Specialist Regist. Wessex Region, oral & Rotat. maxillofacial Surg.

***MCARDLE, Peter Alexander** Fernlea, 6 Collylinn Road, Bearsden, Glasgow G61 4PN — MB ChB 1998 Glas.; MB ChB Glas 1998.

MCARDLE, Theresa Frances National Children's Hospital, Harcourt St., Dublin, Republic of Ireland Tel: 00 353 1 4752355; c/o 33 Telford Road, Inverness IV3 8JA Tel: 0463 221027 — MB ChB 1981 Ed.; MRCP (UK) 1989; MRCGP 1985; DTM & H Liverp. 1987; DCH RCPS Glas. 1984. Cons. Community Paediat. S. Birm. Prev: Sen. Regist. (Community Paediat.) W. Birm.; Sen. Regist. (Med. Research Counc.) The Gambia, W. Afr.

***MCAREAVEY, Fiona Eileen** 62 Marlborough Park S., Belfast BT9 6HN — MB BCh BAO 1995 Belf.

MCAREAVEY, Martin John Rosedene, Douglastown, Forfar DD8 1TL; Rosedene, Douglastown, Forfar DD8 1TL — MB ChB 1993 Dundee; BSc (Hons.) Dund 1990; DFFP 1997; DGCOG 1998. GP Regist. W.gate Health Centre, Dundee. Socs: BMA. Prev: SHO (Comm. Paediat.) Strathmaifice Hosp. Dundee; SHO (O & G) Ninewells Hosp. Dundee; SHO (Path.) Ninewells Hosp. Dundee.

***MCAREE, Simon James** 26 Thomson Street, Aberdeen AB25 2QQ — MB ChB 1998 Aberd.; MB ChB Aberd 1998.

MACARI, Angela Catherine Liberton Medical Group, 55 Liberton Gardens, Edinburgh EH16 6JT Tel: 0131 664 3050 Fax: 0131 692 1952 — MB ChB 1993 Aberd.

MACARTHUR, Agnes Doreen Drummond, MBE (retired) 1 Skaterigg Drive, Jordanhill, Glasgow G13 1SR Tel: 0141 951 2642 Email: add.macarthur@aol.com — MB ChB 1941 Glas.; MB ChB (Commend.) Glas. 1941; DCH Eng. 1946. Prev: Regist. (Med.) Roy. Hosp. Sick Childr. Glas.

MCARTHUR, Alan Anderson Braidcraft Medical Centre, 200 Braidcraft Road, Glasgow G53 5QD Tel: 0141 882 3396 Fax: 0141 883 3224 — MB ChB 1980 Glas.; MRCGP 1986.

MACARTHUR, Alastair (retired) 4 Craigweil Manor, The Drive, Craigweil, Bognor Regis PO21 4AP — LMSSA 1946 Lond.; MRCGP 1953; DObst RCOG 1949. Prev: Sen. Resid. Off. (Obst.) St. Mary's Hosp. Lond.

MCARTHUR, Alexander Sycamore Lodge, Cover Hill Road, Grotto, Oldham OL4 5RF Tel: 0161 624 2062 — MB ChB 1932 Glas. (Univ. Glas.)

MCARTHUR, Calum James Gibb, Surg. Cdr. RN SOI PC, MDGINI, South Terrace, HMNB, Portsmouth PO1 3LR Tel: 02392 720380 Email: calummcarthur@hotmail.com — MB BCh BAO 1980 NUI; LRCPI & LM, LRCSI & LM 1980; MRCGP 1986; Dip. Occ. Med. RCP Lond. 1995; DRCOG 1990. SOI PC MDGINI. Prev: SMO HQ3 CDOBSE RM; Princip. Med. Off. MHS Warrior N.wood.

MCARTHUR, Craig Andrew Tweeddale Medical Practice, High Street, Fort William PH33 6EU — MB ChB 1991 Glas.; MRCGP 2001; DFFP 1996; DRCOG 1995. GP Partner Fort William. Prev: Assoc. GP Tarbert; Trainee GP Norwich VTS.

MACARTHUR, David John Porch Surgery, Beechfield Road, Corsham SN13 9DL Tel: 01249 712232 Fax: 01249 701389 — BChir 1974 Camb.; MB; MRCGP 1980; DCH Eng. 1977.

***MCARTHUR, David Ross** 20 Leavesden Grove, Birmingham B26 3AU — MB ChB 1998 Birmingham.

MACARTHUR, Derek Glyn Dimple Lane Medical Centre, Dimple Lane, Crich, Matlock DE4 5BQ Tel: 01773 852035 Fax: 01773 857247; The Orchard, Hinderstitch Lane, Whatstandwell, Matlock DE4 — MB ChB 1970 Manch.; MRCGP 1985; DA Eng. 1973.

MACARTHUR, Mr Donald Cormack Dept of Neurosurgery, Queens Medical Centre, Nottingham NG7 2UH Email: donald.macarthur@nottingham.ac.uk — MB ChB 1991 Ed.; BSc (Hons.) Neurosci. Ed. 1989; FRCS Glas. 1996. Specialist Regist. Neurosurg. Dept. Qu.'s Med. Centre Nottm.; Stanhope Research Fell. in Neurosurg./Acad. Radiol. Univ. of Nottm. Socs: Fell.(Past Pres.) Roy. Med. Soc. Edin. Prev: SHO (Gen. Surg. & Intens. Care Unit) W.. Gen. Hosp. Edin.

MCARTHUR, Donald Robert Abbey Medical Centre, Lonend, Paisley PA1 1SU; 3 Kaimhill Road, Bridge of Weir — MB ChB 1970 Glas.; LMCC (Nova Scotia) 1982; MRCGP 1981; DObst RCOG 1972.

MACARTHUR, Gillian E Govanhill Health Centre, 233 Calder Street, Glasgow G42 7DR Tel: 0141 531 8385 Fax: 0141 531 4432 — MB ChB 1982 Glasgow; MB ChB 1982 Glasgow.

MACARTHUR, Hilary Claire (retired) 73 Ashley Road, Epsom KT18 5BN Tel: 01372 725888 — MB BS 1946 Lond.; MRCS Eng. LRCP Lond. 1946. Prev: Med. Off. Ewell, Croydon, Carshalton & Wallington Family Plann. Clinics.

MCARTHUR, James Bell Hill (retired) Windle Dale, 34 Hartington Road, St Helens WA10 6AQ Tel: 01744 27145 — MB BS 1935 Lond.; FRCP Ed. 1994; MRCP Ed. 1947; MRCS Eng. LRCP Lond. 1934. Prev: Cons. Chest Phys. St. Helens Area.

MCARTHUR, James Gemmell Health Services Clinic, Firs Entry, Bannockburn, Stirling FK7 0HW Tel: 01786 813435 Fax: 01786 817545 Email: james.mcarthur@gp25600.forth-hb.scot.nhs.uk — MB ChB 1972 Glas. (Glasgow) Hosp. Practitioner (Diabetes).

MACARTHUR, John (retired) 90 Findon Road, Worthing BN14 0AQ Tel: 01903 62978 — MB ChB 1925 Aberd.

MCARTHUR, John Duncan Department of Cardiology, Western Infirmary, Glasgow G11 6NT Tel: 0141 211 1903 Fax: 0141 211 1908 Email: john.mcarthur.wg@northglasgow.scot.nhs.uk; 8 Durness Avenue, Bearsden, Glasgow G61 2AQ Tel: 0141 563 9068 Fax: 0141 942 7330 Email: jd.mcarthur@ntlworld.com — MB ChB 1963 Glas.; MB ChB (Hons.) Glas. 1963; DM (Cardiol.) Madras 1970; BSc (1st cl. Hons. Biochem.) Glas. 1960; FRCP Ed. 1994, M 1967; FRCP Glas. 1980, M 1966; MRCP Lond. 1966; DObst RCOG 1965. (Glas.) Cons. Cardiol. W.ern Infirm. Glas.; Hon. Clin. Sen. Lect. Univ. Glas. Socs: Brit. Cardiac Soc.; Scott. Cardiac Soc.; Scott. Soc. Phys. Prev: Sen. Regist. Glas. Teach. Hosps.; Reader (Cardiol.) Christian Med. Coll. Hosp. Vellore, India.

MCARTHUR, Kathleen Maria Boyce (retired) Meadowside, 202 Little Marlow Road, Marlow SL7 1HX — MRCS Eng. LRCP Lond. 1921; MA Camb. Prev: Ho. Surg. Out-pat. Dept. & Res. Obst. Off. St. Mary's Hosp.

***MACARTHUR, Mairi** 13 Glenburn Drive, Inverness IV2 4ND — MB ChB 1998 Aberd.; MB ChB Aberd 1998.

MACARTHUR, Malcolm Drummond 16 Keir Circle, Westhill, Westhill AB32 6RE Tel: 01224 741402 — MB ChB 1972 Glas.; MRCP (UK) 1977. Cons. (Geriat. Med.) Grampian Health Bd. Prev: Sen. Regist. (Geriat. Med.) S. Lothian Health Dist.; Med. Regist. Roy. Alexandra Infirm. Paisley; Jun. Ho. Off. (Med.) Glas. Roy. Infirm.

MACARTHUR, Mary Margaret Castlerigg Close, West Bridgeford, Nottingham NG2 6RN — MB ChB 1991 Ed. Trainee GP/SHO (Psychiat.) Qu. Margt. Hosp. Dunfermline VTS. Prev: SHO (A & E) Dunfermline & W. Fife Hosp.; SHO (Infec. Dis.) Cameron Hosp. Windygates; Ho. Off. (Gen. Surg. & Orthop.) Dunfermline & W. Fife Hosp.

MCARTHUR, Mr Paul Andrew 9 Hillsboro Avenue, Frodsham, Warrington WA6 7QY Tel: 01928 739014 Email: paul@mcarthurpa.freeserve.co.uk — MB BS 1990 Newc.; FRCS Ed. 1994; FRCS Ed. 1992. Specialist Regist. (Plastic & Reconstruc. Surg.) Mersey Deanary; SHO Gen Surg NGH/RVI Newc.; Specialist Regist. (Plastic Surg.) Morriston, Swansea; BAPS Research Fell. Sheff.; SHO Plastics NGH Sheff.; SHO Plastics RUI Newc. Prev: SHO. Off. (A & E) Newc. Gen. Hosp.; SHO. Off. (Orthop.) Qu. Eliz. Hosp. Gateshead; SHO. Off. (Plastic & Reconstruc. Surg.) Roy. Vict. Infirm. & Newc. Gen. Hosp.

MCARTHUR, Pauline 10 The Close, Salisbury SP1 2EB — MB BS Lond. 1947; MRCS Eng. LRCP Lond. 1947; FFA RCS Eng. 1956; DA Eng. 1951. (Roy. Free)

MCARTHUR, Sheila Mary Abbey Medical Centre, Lonend, Paisley PA1 1SU Tel: 0141 889 4088; 3 Kaimhill Road, Bridge of Weir — MB ChB 1973 Glas.; LMCC 1983; MRCGP 1981.

MACARTNEY, Bruce Wallace Murray (retired) 1 Knowles Close, Brampton, Huntingdon PE28 4PN Tel: 01480 52871 — BM BCh 1952 Oxf.; MFCM RCP (UK) 1974; DPH Lond. 1966; DCH Eng. 1961; DObst RCOG 1960. Prev: SCM (Child Health) Cambs. AHA (T).

***MACARTNEY, Christine Alexandra** 1 Dorchester Park, Belfast BT9 6RH Tel: 01232 661641 — MB BCh 1998 Belf.; MB BCh Belf 1998.

MACARTNEY, Clive Willow Tree Farm, 53 Cockhill Road, Ballymena BT42 2JP — MB BCh 1998 Belf.; MB BCh Belf 1998.

MACARTNEY, Fergus James 2 Tenison Court, Tenison Road, Cambridge CB1 2EF; Angsteloord 46, Abcoude 1381 EG, Netherlands — MB BChir 1967 Camb.; MB BChir Camb. 1966; MA Camb. 1984, BA 1963; FRCP Lond. 1977, M 1968. (St. Thos.) Prof. Paediat. Cardiol. Acad. Med. Centre Amsterdam; Europ. Paediat. Cardiol. Scientif. Sec. Assn. Europ. Paediat. Cardiol. Socs: Brit. Cardiac Soc. & Assn. Prev: Vandervell Prof. Paediat. Cardiol. Inst. Child Health Lond.; Hon. Cons. Paediat. Cardiol. Hosp. Sick Childr. Lond.; Consult. in Paediat. Cardiol. Killingbeck Hosp. Leeds.

MACARTNEY, James Carey Department of Pathology, Walsgrave Hospital, Clifford Bridge Road, Coventry CV2 2DX Tel: 024 76 538855 Fax: 024 76 538715 — MB ChB 1971 Birm.; BSc Birm. 1968, MD 1980; MRCPath 1977. Cons. Histopath. Walsgrave Hosp. Coventry; Hon. Sen. Lect. (Path.) Birm. Univ. Socs: Path. Soc.; Internat. Assn. Pathol. Prev: Med. Dir. Alexander Hosp. Redditch; Sen. Lect. (Histopath.) United Med. & Dent. Sch. Lond.; Lect. (Path.) Univ. Birm.

MACARTNEY, James Howitt (retired) The Mannamead Surgery, 22 Eggbuckland Road, Plymouth PL3 5HE Tel: 01752 223652 Fax: 01752 253875 — MB ChB 1959 Glas. Clin. Asst. ENT Dept. Plymouth Gen. Hosp. Prev: Ho. Off. Surg. & SHO Urol. W.. Infirm. Glas.

MACARTNEY, Mairi Margaret St Triduanas Medical Practice, 54 Moira Park, Edinburgh EH7 6RU Tel: 0131 657 3341 Fax: 0131 669 6055; 8 Succoth Gardens, Edinburgh EH12 6BS Tel: 0131 337 0093 — MB ChB 1979 Glas.; MRCGP 1985; FRCGP 1996. (University of Glasgow)

MACARTNEY, Nicholas John Derick Intensive Care Unit, Chase Farm Hospital, The Ridgeway, Enfield EN2 8JL Email: nick@macartney.org; Tel: 020 7241 1028 Fax: 020 7241 1032 — MB BS 1982 Lond.; FFA RCS 1988. Cons. (Anaesth.) Chase Farm Hosp. Socs: Intens. Care Soc. & Assn. Anaesth.; Europ. Soc. of Intesive Care Med. Prev: Sen. Regist. (Anaesth.) Middlx. & Lond. Chester Hosp.; Regist. (Anaesth.) Univ. Coll. & Middlx. Hosps.

MACARTNEY, Simon Ian 11 Thorn Park, Plymouth PL3 4TG — MB ChB 1994 Sheff. SHO (Orthop.) Mt. Gould Hosp. Plymouth. Prev: Ho. Off. (Gen. Med. & Gen. Surg.) Roy. Hallamsh. Hosp. Sheff.

MACASKILL, Iain Angus Macleod 526 King Street, Aberdeen AB24 5SS Tel: 01224 40324 & 821701 — MB ChB 1975 Aberd.; BMedBiol (Hons.) 1973. Clin. Asst. (Genito-Urin.) Med. Aberd. Roy. Infirm. Prev: Lect. (Pathol.) Edin. Univ.

MACASKILL, John Napier (retired) Ravensdale, Corpach, Fort William PH33 7JJ — MB ChB Glas. 1967; DObst RCOG 1969. Prev: Med. Off. Arjo Wiggins.

MACASKILL, Norman Duncan 52 Linden Avenue, Sheffield S8 0GA Tel: 0114 281 7561 Fax: 0114 281 7561; Southfield House, 40 Clarendon Road, Leeds LS2 9PJ Tel: 0113 295 5430 Fax: 0113 295 5431 — MB ChB 1973 Aberd.; BMedBiol (Hons.) 1970; MRCPsych 1977; Dip. Psychother. Aberd. 1979. (Aberd.) Sen. Lect. (Psychother.) Univ. Leeds. Prev: Cons. Psychother. Nottm.; Cons. Psychiat. (s/i Psychother.) Sheff.; Sen. Regist. Ross Clinic Aberd.

MACASKILL, Sarah (retired) 72 Goodwins Road, King's Lynn PE30 5PD Tel: 01553 775527 — MB ChB 1942 Glas.; FRCOG 1970, M 1950. Prev: Cons. (O & G) Qu. Eliz. Hosp. King's Lynn.

MCASPURN, Michelle Veronica 2 Newtoon Terrace, Glasgow G3 7PJ — MB ChB 1994 Glas.

MCATAMNEY, Dominic Gerard 26 Locksley Park, Belfast BT10 0AR — MB BCh BAO 1990 Belf.; FRCA 1995.

MCATEER, Charles Oscar Ballyclare Group Practice, Ballyclare Health Centre, George Avenue, Ballyclare BT39 9HL Tel: 028 9332 2575 Fax: 028 9334 9897; 22 Lower Ballyboley Road, Ballyeaston, Ballyclare BT39 9SW — MB BCh BAO 1974 Belf.; MRCOG 1979, DObst RCOG 1976; MRCGP 1980; MICP 1994; FRCOG 1997. (Queen's University, Belfast)

MCATEER, Dympna Susan Dept of Radiology, Aberdeen Royal Infirmary, Aberdeen AB25 2ZN Tel: 01224 681818 Ext: 652178 Email: d.mcateer@abdn.ac.uk; 12 Richmond Terrace, Aberdeen AB25 2RL — MB BCh BAO 1989 Dub.; BA (Hons.) Dub. 1989; MRCP (UK) 1993; M. Rad (UK) 1996; FRCR 1998. (Dub.) Regist. (Radiol.) Aberd. Roy. Infirm.; Cons./Radiol./Grampian Univ. Hosp. Trust. Socs: Scott. Radiol. Soc. Prev: SHO (Med.) Whiteabbey Hosp. & Belf. City Hosp.; SHO (Cardiol. & Med.) Roy. Vict. Hosp.

MCATEER, Eamonn Joseph Craigmore Manse, 7 Orken Lane, Aghalee, Craigavon BT67 0ED — MB BCh BAO 1981 Belf.

MCATEER, Edward John Flat 58, Dunbar Wharf, 126-134 Narrow St., London E14 8BD — MB ChB 1976 Glas.; FFA RCS Eng. 1980.

MCATEER, Emer Mary Dept. of Anaesthesia, D-Floor, Jubilee Building, Leeds General Infirmary, Great George St., Leeds LS1 3EX Tel: 0113 392 6345 — MB BCh BAO 1975 Belf.; LLB (Hons.) Lond. 1995; FFA RCSI 1979. (Queen's Univ. Belfast) Cons. Anaesth. Gen. Infirm. Leeds. Prev: Cons. Anaesth. Roy. Vict. Hosp. Belf.; Cons. Anaesth. & Asst. Prof. Univ. Kuwait.

MCATEER, Helen Mary 27 Dublin Road, Newry BT35 8DA — MB BCh BAO 1990 Belf.

MCATEER, James An Cuilfionn, Newry Tel: 01693 2613 — MB BCh BAO 1949 NUI. (Univ. Coll. Dub.)

MCATEER, John Anthony 16 Balmoral Avenue, Belfast BT9 6NW — MB BCh BAO 1990 Belf. SHO (Gen. Med.) MusGr. Pk. Hosp. Belf. & Daisy Hill Hosp. Newry. Prev: SHO Belf. City Hosp.; Ho. Off. Daisy Hill Hops. Newry.

MCATEER, Mary Patricia 535 Oldpark Road, Belfast BT14 6QU — MB BCh BAO 1974 Belf.; DA Eng. 1978.

MCAUGHEY, Jennifer Margaret Skegoneill Health Centre, 195 Skegoneill Avenue, Belfast BT15 3LL Tel: 028 9077 2471 Fax: 028 9077 2449 — MB BCh BAO 1980 Belf.

MCAUGHTRIE, Alison Elizabeth (retired) Mansfield House, Kirkton of Kinnettles, Forfar DD8 1TQ Tel: 01307 820233 — MB ChB 1972 Ed.; BSc Ed. 1969, MB ChB 1972; MRCPsych 1977. Prev: Cons. Child & Adolesc. Psychiat. Stratheden Hosp. Cupar.

MACAULAY, Alastair 3 Murrayfield Avenue, Edinburgh EH12 6AU — MB ChB 1950 Ed. (Ed.)

MACAULAY, Alexander Collingwood Clinic, St. Nicholas Hospital, Gosforth, Newcastle upon Tyne NE3 3XT Tel: 0191 273 6666; 17 Bondene Way, Cramlington NE23 3GU Tel: 01670 590416 — MB ChB 1988 Aberd.; MRCGP 1993; DCH RCP Lond. 1993; DRCOG 1991. Trainee GP/SHO Rotat. (Psychiat.) Newc. Prev: Trainee GP. N.umbria VTS.

MACAULAY, Andrew John Cardinal Clinic, Oakley Green, Windsor SL4 5UL Tel: 01753 869755 Fax: 01753 842852 — MB BS 1976; MD Lond. 1988; MSc (Clin. Psychother.) Lond. 1985; MRCS Eng. LRCP Lond. 1976; MRCPsych 1981; MD 1988 Lond. (Char. Cross) Cons. Psychiat. Wexham Pk. Hosp. Slough. Prev: Regist. (Psych.) Char. Cross Hosp. Lond.; Regist. (Psych.) St. Bernard's Hosp. S.all; Research Fell. (Psychiat. & Urodynamics) St. Geo. Hosp. Lond.

MCAULAY, Antoinette Hazel Poole Hospital NHS Trust, Longfleet Road, Poole BH15 2JB Tel: 01202 665511 Fax: 01202 442822 Email: amcaulay@poole-tr.swest.nhs.uk; 54 Twemlow Avenue, Poole BH14 8AN Email: mca@cwcom.net — MB ChB Bristol 1982; MD Bristol 1990; MRCP (UK) 1985; FRCPCH 1997. Cons. Paediat. Poole Hosp. NHS Trust. Socs: Brit. Soc. Paediat. Endrocrin. & Diabetes. Prev: Sen. Regist. (Paediat.) Roy. Manch. Childr. Hosp.; Regist. (Paediat.) S.mead Hosp. Bristol; Novo Research Fell. Roy. Hosp. Sick Childr. Bristol.

MACAULAY, Calum Zachary Lodgehill Road Clinic, Lodgehill Road, Nairn IV12 4RF Tel: 01667 452096 Fax: 01667 456785; Cawdor Villa, 7 Wellington Road, Nairn IV12 4RE Tel: 01667 455451 — MB ChB 1985 Aberd.; MRCGP 1990; Cert Family Plann. JCC 1989. Prev: SHO (O & G) CrossHo. Hosp. Kilmarnock; SHO (ENT) Vict. Infirm. Glas.; SHO (A & E) Dumfries Roy. Infirm.

MACAULAY, David Daniel Robert Sandwell Hospital, Anaesthetic Office, Lyndon, Sandwell, West Bromwich B71 4HJ Tel: 0121 553 1831; 79 Primrose Lane, Hall Green, Birmingham B28 0JN Tel: 0121 745 3018 — MB ChB 1974 Bristol; FFA RCS Eng. 1979.

MACAULAY, Diane Enaldine Sarian Occupational Health Service, BT Centre, PPB2M, 81 Newgate St, London EC1A 7AJ Tel: 020 7356 5125 Fax: 020 7356 6568 Email: diane.macaulay@bt.com — MB BS 1977 Lond.; MSc (Clin. Trop. Med.) Lond. 1985; AFOM RCP Lond. 1990; Cert. Family Plann. JCC 1985; DTM & H RCP Lond. 1984; MFOM RCP Lond. 1998. (Univ. Coll. Hosp.) Sen. Occupat.al Phys. e-peopleserve Occupat.al Health Serv. Socs: Soc. Occupat. Med.; Fell. Roy. Soc. Med. Prev: Sen. Regist. (Occupat. Med.) Kings Coll. Hosp. Lond.; Med. Off. STC Telecommunications Lond.; Regist. (Occupat. Med.) Roy. Free Hosp. Lond.

MACAULAY

MACAULAY, Donald Health Clinic, Ashgrove, Blackburn, Bathgate EH47 7LL Tel: 01506 652956 Fax: 01506 634790; 47 Braid Avenue, Edinburgh EH10 6DS — MB ChB 1976 Ed.; BSc (Med. Sci.) Ed. 1973, MB ChB 1976; MRCGP 1980; DRCOG 1980. GP Blackburn.

MCAULAY, Eileen Margaret Nithsdale Road Surgery, 162 Nithsdale Road, Glasgow G41 5RU Tel: 0141 424 1831 Fax: 0141 423 7422 — MB ChB 1989 Glas.; MRCGP 1993; DFFP 1993; Cert. Prescribed Equiv. Exp. JCPTGP 1993.

MACAULAY, Mr Ewan Macdonald Raigmore Hospital, Inverness IV2 3UJ Tel: 01463 704000; 11 Castle Street, Black Isle, Fortrose IV10 8TH Tel: 01381 621498 Email: esmcaulay@enterprise.net — MB BCh BAO 1988 Dub.; FRCS Glas. 1992. (Trinity Coll. Dub.) Specialist Regist.N. E. Scot.

MACAULAY, Flora Macdonald Portrigh, Carradale, Campbeltown PA28 6SE — MB BCh 1943 Wales; BSc, MB BCh Wales 1943. (Cardiff) Prev: Regist. (Orthop.) Newport & S. Mon. Gp. Hosps.; Ho. Surg. Glos. Roy. Infirm.; Capt. RAMC.

MACAULAY, Ian Innes AON Occupational Health, Foresterhill Road, Aberdeen AB25 2ZP Tel: 01224 669036 Fax: 012240 669030; 68 Cairncry Road, Aberdeen AB16 5LE Tel: 01224 495218 Fax: 01224 669030 — MB ChB 1959 Aberd.; AFOM RCP Lond. 1982; DObst RCOG 1961. (Aberd.) Screening Phys. AON Aberd. Socs: Undersea Med. Soc.; Soc. Occupat. Med. Prev: Med. Adviser Brit. Gas A.G.I.P. Karachaganak, Kazakhstan; Ship's Surg. RRS Discovery; Manager Med, Serv. BP Exploration, Europe.

MCAULAY, James St Andrews Surgery, 166 Market Street, Eastleigh SO50 5PT Tel: 023 8061 2472 Fax: 023 8061 1717 Email: dr.jim.mca@yahoo.co.uk; 5 Brooklyn Close, Otterbourne, Winchester SO21 2EF Tel: 01962 712857 Email: dr.jim.mca@yahoo.co.uk — MB ChB 1971 Ed.; BSc Ed. 1968; DObst RCOG 1974. (University of Edinburgh) GP E.leigh Hants. Prev: GP Laurieston Stirlingsh.; SHO (Paediat.) Stirling Roy. Infirm.; SHO (Geriat.) Roy. Vict. Hosp. Edin.

MACAULAY, John Henry North Tees General Hospital, Hardwick, Stockton-on-Tees TS19 8PE Tel: 01642 617617; Heathwaite, Thirsk Road, Yarm TS15 9UJ — MB BS 1982 Lond.; MD Lond. 1995; MRCOG 1987. Cons. O & G N. Tees Gen. Hosp. Stockton-on-Tees.

MACAULAY, John Roy (retired) Lightcliffe, Swordale, Isle of Lewis HS2 0BP Tel: 01851 870223 Email: jroymac@aol.com — MB ChB Ed. 1957.

MACAULAY, Kenneth Edwin Charles Rosyth Health Centre, Park Road, Rosyth, Dunfermline KY11 2SE Tel: 01383 418931 Fax: 01383 419007; 3 Glamis Gardens, Dalgety Bay, Dunfermline KY11 9TD Tel: 01383 823050 Fax: 01383 419007 Email: k.macaulay@virgin.net — MB ChB 1977 Dundee; MRCGP 1982; Dip. Occ. Med. 1997. (Dundee Univ.) GP Inverkeithing/Rosyth. Prev: Regist. (Med.) Ninewells Hosp. & Med. Sch. Dundee; SHO (Med.) N. Tees Gen. Hosp. Stockton; Ho. Surg. Lewis Hosp. Stornoway.

MACAULAY, Lesley Mearns Medical Centre, 3 Eaglesham Road, Newton Mearns, Glasgow G77 5BE Tel: 0141 639 2753 Fax: 0141 616 2403; 206 Fenwick Road, Giffnock, Glasgow G46 6UE — MB ChB 1989 Glas.; MRCGP 1993; DRCOG 1992.

MACAULAY, Margaret Ellen Rhyl PHL, Glan Clwyd District General Hospital, Rhyl LL18 5UJ Tel: 01745 583737 Fax: 01745 584179 — MB ChB 1962 Manchester; MBA Open 1995; MSc Sheff. 1990; BA Open 1980; MD Manch. 1977; MRCPath 1986Dip. Bact. Manch. 1970. (Manchester) Cons. Med. Microbiol. Pub. Health Laborat. Serv.

MACAULAY, Olatunde Olaosebikan Gainsborough Practice, Warfield Medical Centre, White Grove, Bracknell RG42 3JP — MB BS 1979 Lagos; MSc Leeds 1987; MRCOG 1993; DRCOG 1993; DFFP 1993; Cert. Family Plann. JCC 1989. Staff Grade (Gyn.) Roy. Berks. Hosp. Reading. Socs: BMA; Med. Protec. Soc. Prev: Regist. (O & G) Barnsley Dist. Gen. Hosp. & Sunderland Dist. Gen. Hosp.; SHO (O & G) Bassetlaw Dist. Gen. Hosp.

MACAULAY, Robert Allan Angus 57 St Stephen Street, Edinburgh EH3 5AH Tel: 0131 225 3240 — MB ChB Ed. 1967; MRCPath 1975. (Ed.) Med. Asst. Pk.inson's Assessm. Clinic Edin. Prev: Res. Pathol. Stanford Univ. Med. Sch. Palo Alto, USA; Jun. Asst. Pathol. Univ. Camb.; Lect. (Forens. Med.) Univ. Edin.

MACAULAY, Roderick Bernadette (retired) 17 St Peter's Road, Broadstairs CT10 2AG Tel: 01843 861708 — LRCPI & LM, LRSCI & LM 1953; LRCPI & LM, LRCSI & LM 1953.

MACAULAY, Valentine Moya 36 Eton Road, Datchet, Slough SL3 9AY Tel: 01753 543889 — MB BS 1979 Lond.; PhD Lond. 1995, BSc (Hons.) 1979, MD 1989; MRCP (UK) 1982; MRCS Eng. LRCP Lond. 1979. (Char. Cross) MRC Clin. Scientist ICRF Laborats. Inst. Molecular Med. Oxf. Prev: Sen. Regist. Ch.ill Hosp. Oxf.; Research Fell. Chester Beatty Laborat. Lond.; Research Regist. Inst. Cancer Research Sutton.

MACAULEY, Anne Maire (retired) 4 Norton Drive, Malone Road, Belfast BT9 6ST Tel: 01232 661840 — MB BCh BAO 1952 NUI; DO Eng. 1955.

MCAULEY, (Barbara) Christine The Groves Medical Centre, (surg.) 72 Coombe Road, New Malden KT3 4QT Tel: 020 8336 2222 Fax: 020 8336 0297; 15 High Drive, New Malden KT3 3UJ Email: a261563@infotrade.co.uk — MB BS Lond. 1961; MRCS Eng. LRCP Lond. 1961; DCH Eng. 1964; DObst RCOG 1962. (St. Mary's) Socs: BMA. Prev: Ho. Surg. Paddington Gen. Hosp.; Resid. Off. (Obst.) St. Mary's Hosp.; Ho. Off. (Paediat.) Evelina Childr. Hosp. Lond.

MCAULEY, Daniel Francis 19 Strandview Street, Belfast BT9 5FF Tel: 01232 209986 — MB BCh BAO 1992 Belf.; MD Belf. 1997; MRCP (UK) 1995. Specialist Regist. (Gen. Med.) Mater Hosp. Belf.

MCAULEY, Daniel J (retired) 4 Norton Drive, Malone Road, Belfast BT9 6ST Tel: 01232 661840 — MB BCh BAO 1952 NUI; CPH 1954; LM Coombe 1953.

MCAULEY, David Edward Mandalay Medical Centre, 933 Blackburn Road, Bolton BL1 7LR Tel: 01204 302228 Fax: 01204 597949; 12 Wincanton Drive, Springfield Heights, Sharples, Bolton BL1 7PG — MB ChB 1981 Manch.; MRCGP 1985; DRCOG 1983.

MCAULEY, Mr David John 26 Ashdene Road, Moneyreagh, Newtownards BT23 6DD — MB BCh BAO 1991 Belf.; FRCSI 1995. (Queen's University Belfast) Specialist Regist. (Neurosurg.) Roy. Vict. Hosp. Belf.

MCAULEY, Dermot Martin Clyde Street Medical Centre, 1A Clyde Street, Leicester LE1 2BG Tel: 0116 262 8368; 7 Patrick Street, Strabane BT82 8DQ Tel: 01504 882144 — MB BCh BAO 1989 Belf.; Cert. Family Plann. JCC 1994.

MCAULEY, Professor Domhnall Ciaran Hillhead Family Practice, 33 Stewartstown Road, Belfast BT11 9FZ Tel: 028 9028 6800 Fax: 028 9060 2944 — MB BCh BAO 1980 NUI; FRCGP 1999; 2000 FFPHNI; MD Dub. 1994; MFPHMI 1994; MRCGP 1984; DPH Belf. 1993; Dip. Sports Med. Soc. Apoth. 1990; MICGP 1985; DRCOG 1983; Dip. Sports Med. 1991. (Univ. Coll. Dublin) Prof. of Prim. Care (Research); Assoc. Zeletor SMJ. Socs: Brit. Assn. Sport & Med.; Amer. Coll. Sports Med.; Fell. Inst. Sports Med. Lond. Prev: Lect. (Physiol. & Sports Med.) St. Mary's Coll. Educat. Belf.; Trainee GP Univ. Exeter VTS; Hon. Research Fell. (Epidemiol. & Pub. Health) Qu. Univ. Belf.

MCAULEY, Duncan James Crabtree House, Meres Lane, Five Ashes, Mayfield TN20 6JS — BChir 1994 Camb.

MCAULEY, Dympna Mary 49 Ravenhill Park, Belfast BT6 0DG — MD 1984 Belf.; MD (Hons.) Belf. 1984, MB BCh BAO 1973; FFA RCSI 1978. Cons. Anaesth. Ulster Hosp. Dundonald.

MCAULEY, Eileen Margaret Jane Finaghy Health Centre, 13-25 Finaghy Road South, Belfast BT10 0BX Tel: 028 9062 8211; 56 Deramore Park, Belfast BT9 5JU — MB BCh BAO 1980 Belf.; MRCGP 1984; DCH RCPSI 1982; DRCOG 1983. Socs: Ulster Med. Soc.

MCAULEY, Francis Thomas Queen Elizabeth Hospital, Department of Anaesthetics, Sheriff Hill, Gateshead NE9 6SX Tel: 0191 403 2176 Fax: 0191 403 2827; 93 Dene Road, Wylam NE41 8HB — MB ChB 1988 Aberd.; FRCA 1995. Cons. (Anaesth.).

MCAULEY, John Henry Royal London Hospital, Whitechapel, London E1 Tel: 020 7377 7472 — MB BChir 1989 Camb.; BA (Hons)1987 Camb.; CCST (neurology) 2000; MD Camb. 1996, MA 1990; MRCP (UK) 1992. Cons. (Neurol.) Roy. Lond. Hosp.; Cons. NeUrol., King Geo. Hosp. Redbridge. Socs: Assoc. Physiological Soc.; Assn. Brit. Neurol. (Ordinary). Prev: Research Regist. Inst. Neurol. Qu. Sq. Lond.

MCAULEY, John Joseph Whitby Group Practice, Spring Vale Medical Centre, Whitby YO21 1SD; Woodend, Main Road, Aislaby, Whitby YO21 1SW — MB ChB 1983 Manch.; DFFP 1993; DA (UK) 1991; Dip. IMC RCS Ed. 1990; DRCOG 1990. Clin. Asst. A/E ScarBoro. Trust; Maj. RAMC (U); Hosp. Practitioner Anaesthetics,

ScarBoro. Trust. Prev: Regist. (Anaesth. & ICU) Treliske Hosp. Truro; M.O.S.S. Oamary Hosp., NZ; GP Wigtown, Scotl.

MCAULEY, Maeve Rose Apartment 1, Ceara Court, 46 Windsor Avenue, Belfast BT9 6EJ — MB BCh BAO 1984 Belf.; MB BCh Belf. 1984.

MACAULEY, Mark Richard 33 Shan Slieve Dr, Newcastle BT33 0HN — MB BCh BAO 1997 Belf.

MCAULEY, Patricia Ann 16 Driffield Road, Prescot L34 1LH — MB ChB 1996 Liverp. SHO Paediat. Mersey Rotat.

MCAULEY, Raymond Thomas 25 Ballymullan Road, Lisburn BT27 5PJ — MB BCh BAO 1994 Belf.

MCAULEY, Reginald George Kilrea Medical Centre, 36 Garvagh Road, Kilrea, Coleraine BT51 5QP Tel: 028 2954 0231 Fax: 028 2954 0851 — MB BCh BAO 1982 Belf.; MB BCh Belf. 1982.

MCAULEY, Robert Roger 20 Cooks Brae, Kircubbin, Newtownards BT22 2SQ — MB BCh BAO 1969 Belf.

MCAULEY, Stephen Michael 112A Gilford Road, Lurgan, Craigavon BT66 7AB Tel: 017622 23324 — MB BCh BAO 1981 Belf.

MCAULEY, William John 24 Fernmore Road, Bangor BT19 6DY — MB BCh BAO 1990 Belf.

MCAULIFFE, Fionnuala Mary 73 Abbotswood Road, East Dulwich, London SE22 8DJ — MB BCh BAO 1991 NUI; MRCPI 1997; MRCOG 1996; DCH RCPI 1993. (Univ. Coll. Dub.) Research Regist. (Obst.) Harris Birthright Research centre for Fetal Med. King's Coll. Hosp. Sch. Med. Lond. Prev: Specialist Regist. (OBST. & Gyn) N. Trent Region.

MCAULIFFE, Georgina Lucy Spencer House, Little St., Sulgrave, Banbury OX17 2SG — MB BS 1987 Lond.; FRCA 1992.

MACAULIFFE, Richard Joseph (retired) The Hollies, Victoria Terrace, Saltburn-by-the-Sea TS12 1HN Tel: 01287 22385 — MB BCh BAO 1942 NUI; BSc (Pub. Health) NUI 1944, MD 1949; DPH NUI 1944; LM Rotunda 1942. Prev: Resid. Med. Off. St. Vincent's Hosp. Dub. & Co. Sanat. & Isolat. Hosp. Leicester.

MCAULIFFE, Romayne Lesley Fleur House, 7 The Drive, Coombe Hill, Kingston upon Thames KT2 7NY — MB BS 1968 Sydney; FFA RCS Eng. 1976; DA Eng. 1972. (Sydney) Cons. Anaesth. Moorfields Hosp. Lond. Prev: Sen. Regist. (Anaesth.) St. Geo. Hosp. Lond.

MCAULIFFE, Mr Thomas Bernard Holly House Hospital, High Road, Buckhurst Hill IG9 5 Tel: 020 8498 9931 — MB BS 1979 Lond.; MB BS (Hons.) Lond. 1979; MA Camb. 1976; FRCS Eng. 1984. (Univ. Coll. Hosp.) Cons. Orthop. Surg. Whipps Cross Hosp. Socs: Fell. BOA. Prev: Lect. (Orthop.) Inst. Orthop.; Sen. Regist. (Orthop.) Roy. Nat. Orthop. Hosp. Lond.; Regist. (Orthop.) The Lond. Hosp.

MACAUSLAN, Alan David Rowan (retired) Hill House, Denston, Newmarket CB8 8PW Tel: 01440 820203 — MB BChir 1947 Camb.; MA, MB BChir Camb. 1947; AFOM RCP Lond. 1980.

MACAUSLAN, Karen Margaret Perry Hill Surgery, 145 Perry Hill, London SE6 4LR Tel: 020 8699 1062 — MB BS 1978 Lond.; MA Oxf. 1974.

MCAUSLANE, Sharon Elizabeth Leith Mount, 46 Ferry Road, Edinburgh EH6 4AE; 56 Stirling Road, Edinburgh EH5 3JD — MB ChB 1989 Glas.; MRCGP 1994.

MCAVINCHEY, Rita Patricia Marringdean, St. Leonards Park, Horsham RH13 6EG — MB BS 1982 Lond.; MSc (Nuclear Med.) Lond. 1993, MB BS 1982; MRCP (UK) 1986; FRCR 1990. Cons. Diagn. Radiol. E. Surrey Hosp. Redhill; Sen. Regist. (Diag. Radiol.) Roy. Lond. Hosp. Prev: Regist. (Diag. Radiol.) Lond. Hosp. Whitechapel; SHO (Gen. Med.) St. Bart. Hosp. Lond.

MACAVINEY, Margaret Anne Marie Netherton Health Centre, Halesowen Road, Dudley DY2 9PU Tel: 01384 253673 Fax: 01384 457979 — MB ChB Birm. 1961; DObst RCOG 1964. (Birm.) Prev: Ho. Phys. & Ho. Surg. St. Kevin's Hosp. Dub.; Ho. Surg. Rotunda Hosp. Dub.

MACAVOCK, Patrick Joseph 213 Wingrove Road, Newcastle upon Tyne NE4 9DB — LRCPI & LM, LRSCI & LM 1944; LRCPI & LM, LRCSI & LM 1944.

MCAVOY, Brian John Timothy 14 Waldron Road, Broadstairs CT10 1TB Tel: 01843 862378 — MRCS Eng. LRCP Lond. 1958; Cert. Av. Med. 1977. (St. Thos.) Auth. Med. Examr. Civil Aviat. Auth. Prev: Res. Phys. Amer. Hosp. Paris; Sen. Obst. Ho. Surg. Ramsgate Hosp.

MCAVOY, Professor Brian Ramsay University of Newcastle, Department of Primary Health Care, The Medical School, Framlington Place, Newcastle upon Tyne NE2 4HH Tel: 0191 222 8761 Fax: 0191 222 7892 Email: brian.mcavoy@ncl.ac.uk; Apartment 9, Lintzford Mill, Rowlands Gill NE39 1NB Tel: 01207 544041 Fax: 01207 544041 — MB ChB 1972 Glas.; MB ChB (Hons.) Glas. 1972; BSc (Hons.) Glas. 1970; MD Leicester 1990; FRCP Lond. 1992; MRCP (UK) 1975; FRCGP 1988, M 1976; MRNZCGP 1991. (Univ. Glas.) William Leech Prof. Primary Heath Care Univ. Newc. u. Tyne; Primary Care Policy Adviser N.. & Yorks. RHA. Prev: Prof. Gen. Pract. Univ. Auckland, NZ; Sen. Lect. (Gen. Pract.) Univ. Leicester.

MCAVOY, John Page Hall Medical Centre, 101 Owler Lane, Sheffield S4 8GB Tel: 0114 261 7245 Fax: 0114 261 1643; 2 Linden Avenue, Woodseats, Sheffield S8 0GA — MB ChB 1979 Birm.

MCAVOY, Norma Claire 43 Cromarty Road, Airdrie ML6 9RL — MB ChB 1998 Glas.; MB ChB Glas 1998.

MCAVOY, Pauline Anne 8 Swinburne Place, Summerhill Square, Newcastle upon Tyne NE4 6EA Tel: 0191 230 3494 Fax: 0191 261 0405 — MB ChB 1973 Glas.; MRCGP 2001; MRNZCGP 1991; FRNZCGP 1998. (Glas.Univ.) Chief Exec. Prev: Med. Dir. Newc.City Health Trust; GP Leicester; Sub Dean (Acad.) Univ. of Auckland & GP Auckland, NZ.

MCBAIN, Archibald Patrick (retired) 3 Deveron Terrace, Banff AB45 1BB Tel: 01261 812958 — MB ChB Aberd. 1953. Prev: GP Banff.

MCBAIN, Catherine Anne 31 Georgian Villas, Omagh BT79 0AT — MB ChB 1994 Manch.

MACBAIN, Mr Gordon Campbell 1 Bank Avenue, Milngavie, Glasgow G62 8NG — MB ChB 1962 Glas.; FRCS Ed. 1966. (Glas.) Cons. Surg. S.. Gen. Hosp. Glas.

MCBAIN, Ian (retired) 75 Duncan Drive, Elgin IV30 4NH — MB ChB Glas. 1966; DObst RCOG 1969.

MACBAIN, Katharin Helen Flat T/R, 25 Shathblane Road, Milngavie, Glasgow G62 8DL — MB ChB 1989 Glas.

MCBAIN, Roderick Hugh Balgownie, Bonar Crescent, Bridge of Weir PA11 3EH Email: mcbainr@hotmail.com — MB ChB 1991 Glas.

MCBAY, Iain William Sheepridge, Kenton, Exeter EX6 8LN — MB BS 1984 Lond.

MACBEAN, Anthea Lilian 16 St Marys Grove, Canonbury, London N1 2NT Tel: 020 7226 3546 Fax: 020 7704 9312 — MB ChB 1949 St. And.

MACBEAN, Ian James (retired) 92 Gayton Road, King's Lynn PE30 4ER Tel: 01553 774884 — MB ChB St. And. 1955; FRCA 1965; DA Eng. 1960; DObst RCOG 1958. Prev: Sen. Cons. Anaesth. W. Norf. HA.

MCBEAN, James Bell (retired) Old Convent Farmhouse, Reading St., Broadstairs CT10 3AX Tel: 01843 65919 — MB ChB 1942 Glas.; MRCGP 1956. Prev: Ho. Surg. W.. Infirm. Glas. & Glas. Roy. Matern. & Wom. Hosp.

MACBEAN, Lena May (retired) 16 Strathspey Drive, Grantown-on-Spey PH26 3EY Tel: 01479 2039 — MB ChB 1952 St Andrews; MD Dundee 1970; DPH 1959; DCH Eng. 1955; MD 1970 Dundee. Prev: Med. Off. & Lect. (Health Educat.) Dundee Coll. Educat.

MCBEAN, Mercy Sonja (retired) Old Convent Farmhouse, Reading St., Broadstairs CT10 3AX Tel: 01843 65919 — MB BS 1939 Lond. Prev: Research Asst. Roy. Hosp. Sick Childr. Glas.

MACBEAN, Susan Margaret Cefn Coed, Llangranog, Llandysul SA44 6AE — MB BS 1994 Lond.

MCBEATH, Helen Alexandra St Clements Surgery, 39 Temple Street, Oxford OX4 1JS Tel: 01865 248550; The Ridings, High St, Beckley, Oxford OX3 9UU Tel: 01865 351623 — MB BS 1976 Lond.; MRCS Eng. LRCP Lond. 1976; MRCGP 1980; DCH RCP Lond. 1981; DRCOG 1979. (Roy. Free) Socs: BMA; RCGP. Prev: Research fell. (Family Med.) Univ. Toronto, Canada.

MCBEATH, Janet Irvine Trimite Ltd., Arundel Road, Uxbridge UB8 2SD Tel: 01895 251234 Fax: 01895 254321; Templemead, Templewood Lane, Stoke Poges, Slough SL2 4AP Tel: 01753 645432 — MB BS 1971 Lond.; MRCS Eng. LRCP Lond. 1971; DObst RCOG 1973. (Roy. Free) Med. Off. Trimite Ltd. Uxbridge. Socs: BMA & Soc. Occupat. Med. Prev: Med. Off. Slough Family

MACBEATH

Plann. Clinic; Cas. Off. St. Thos. Hosp. Lond.; Ho. Surg. (Gyn. & Obst.) Centr. Middlx. Hosp.

MACBEATH, John Thomson (retired) 12 Morville Road, Chorlton-cum-Hardy, Manchester M21 0UR Tel: 0161 881 4151 Fax: 0161 881 4151 Email: jmacbeath@aol.com — MB ChB 1962 Ed.; FFA RCS Eng. 1969. Hon. Clin. Tutor Univ. Manch. Med. Sch. Prev: Cons. Anaesth. Salford AHA (T).

MACBEATH, Marjorie Catherine Elizabeth (retired) 15 Rowmore Quays, Rhu, Helensburgh G84 8TA Tel: 01436 821175 Email: mmacbeath@doctors.org.uk — MB ChB 1952 Glas.; DPH Glas. 1964.

MACBETH, Alison Jane 1 Lodge Court, The Nook, Staining, Blackpool FY3 0EH; 30 Kippen Drive, Clarkston, Glasgow G76 8JG Tel: 0141 644 2105 — MB ChB 1992 Manch.; BSc Med. Sci. St. And 1989. (Manchester) SHO (Paediat.) GP Train. Scheme Blackpool Vict. Hosp. Socs: BMA; MDU. Prev: Staff Grade (A & E) Blackpool Vict. Hosp.; SHO (A & E) Blackpool Vict. Hosp.

MCBETH, Christine 1 The Avenue, Llandaff, Cardiff CF5 2LP Tel: 029 2057 7791 — MB BS 1989 Lond.; BA Oxf. 1985; FRCA 1994. Cons. (Anaesth.) Univ. Hosp. of Wales Cardiff. Socs: Assn. Anaesth.; Fell. Roy. Coll. Anaesth.; Neuroanaesth. Soc. Prev: Sen. Regist. (Anaesth.) Univ. Hosp. Cardiff Wales.

MACBETH, Fergus Robert Velindre Hospital, Whitchurch CF14 2TL Tel: 02920 316232 Fax: 02920 316267 — BM BCh 1973 Oxf.; MA 1973, DM Oxf. 1987; FRCP Glas. 1989; FRCP Lond. 1997; FRCR 1986; T(M) 1991; MBA Stirling 1999. (Oxford and King's Coll. Hospital) Cons. Oncol. Velindre NHS Trust, Cardiff. Prev: Dir. Clin. Effectiveness Support Unit (Wales); Cons. Clin. Oncol. W.. Infirm. Glas.; Sen. Regist. (Radiother. & Oncol.) Addenbrooke's Hosp. Camb.

MACBETH, John Nigel (retired) Greenbury, 22 Writtle Green, Chelmsford CM1 3DU Tel: 01245 420078 — BM BCh Oxf. 1943; MRCGP 1953. Prev: Indust. Med. Off. Marconi Co. Ltd.

MACBETH, Mary Oxford Street Surgery, 20 Oxford Street, Workington CA14 2AL Tel: 01900 603302 — MB BS 1972 Newcastle; MB BS Newc. 1972. (Newcastle) GP Workington, Cumbria.

MCBIRNIE, Miss Julie Mary Princess Margaret Rose Orthopaedic Hospital, Frogston Road W., Fairmile Head, Edinburgh EH10 7ED Tel: 0131 536 4600 Fax: 0131 536 4600 Email: julie@jmcbirnie.freeserve.co.uk; 23 Belford Mews, Edinburgh EH4 3BT Email: julie@jmcbirnie.freeserve.co.uk — MB BCh 1988 Witwatersrand; FRCS (Orth.) Ed. 1997; FRCS Ed. 1993; FRCS Glas. 1993. (Witwatersrand, JHB, RSA) Cons. (Orthop. Surg.). Socs: Fell. BOA; ATLS Instruc.; Mem. of the Brit. Elbow and Shoulder Soc. (BESS). Prev: Sen. Regist. (Orthop. Surg.) P.ss Margt. Rose. Hosp. Edin.; Career Regist. (Orthop.) Edin.; Basic Surgic. Trainee Rotat. (Gen. Surg.) Edin.

MCBLANE, Alexander Crossan (retired) Hayfield, Blebocraigs, Cupar KY15 5UF — MB ChB 1954 Glas.; MRCGP 1968. Prev: Princip. Med. Off. Scott. Home & Health Dept.

MCBLANE, James Hood (retired) The Medical Centre, 12 East King Street, Helensburgh G84 7QL Tel: 01436 672277 Fax: 01436 674526 — MB ChB 1962 Glas.; MRCGP 1970; DObst RCOG 1964.

MCBOYLE, John Rae, OBE (retired) 515 Fulwood Road, Sheffield S10 3QB — MB ChB 1938 Aberd.

MACBRAYNE, James Dr MacBrayne and Partners, 19 Dinmont Road, Shawlands, Glasgow G41 3UJ Tel: 0141 632 8883 Fax: 0141 636 0654 — MB ChB 1966 Glas.

MACBRAYNE, Janet Findlay Govanhill Health Centre, 233 Calder Street, Glasgow G42 7DR Tel: 0141 531 8385 Fax: 0141 531 4432; 27 Paidmyre Crescent, Newton Mearns, Glasgow G77 5AQ Tel: 0141 639 5686 — MB ChB 1966 Glas. (Glas.)

MACBRAYNE, John Thom MacBrayne and Partners, The Oakley Surgery, Addington Way, Luton LU4 9FJ Tel: 01582 574954 Fax: 01582 561808 — MB ChB 1973 Glas. Chairm. Luton PCG. Socs: Osler Club Lond.

MCBREEN, Grania Mary Magdalen 50 Victoria Square, Rostrevor, Newry BT34 3EU — MB BCh BAO 1990 Belf.

MCBRIDE, David F Motherwell Health Centre, 138-144 Windmill Street, Motherwell ML1 1TB Tel: 01698 275567 Fax: 01698 252147 — MB ChB 1970 Glasgow; MB ChB 1970 Glasgow.

MCBRIDE, David Iain 52 King Street, Newcastle BT33 0HB — MB BCh BAO 1981 Belf.

MCBRIDE, Mr Donald James 540 Etruria Road, Basford, Newcastle-under-Lyme ST5 0SX Tel: 01782 614419 Fax: 01782 663 0270; Manesty, 6 Snape Hall Close, Whitmore Heath, Newcastle ST5 5HD Tel: 01782 680107 — MB ChB 1981 Glas.; FRCS (Orth.) 1994; FRCS Ed. 1987; FRCS Glas. 1988. (Glas.) Cons. Orthop. Surg. N. Staffs. Hosp. & Hartshill Orthop. Hosp. Stoke-on-Trent; Hon. Sen. Lect. (Orthop.) Keele Univ. Socs: BMA; Brit. Orthop. Foot Surg. Soc.; Fell. BOA. Prev: Sen. Regist. Rotat. (Orthop.) W. Midl. RHA; Trainee Regist. (Orthop.) W.. Infirm. Glas.; SHO (Gen. Surg.) & Research Regist. (Orthop.) Glas. Roy. Infirm.

MCBRIDE, Douglas David Hilltops Medical Centre, Kensington Drive, Great Holm, Milton Keynes MK8 9HN Tel: 01908 568446 — MB ChB 1969 Glas.; MRCGP 1976.

MCBRIDE, Elizabeth 12 Towerhill Avenue, Cradlehall, Inverness IV2 5FB — MB ChB 1995 Aberd.; DRCOG 1997. (Aberdeen) GP VTS.

MCBRIDE, Eve Mere Surgery, Dark Lane, Mere, Warminster BA12 6DT Tel: 01747 860001 Fax: 01747 860119; George's Barn, Brixton Deverill, Warminster BA12 7EL — BM 1980 Soton.; DRCOG 1985.

MCBRIDE, Evelyn Veronica 92 Newbridge Road, St. Ann's, Bristol BS4 4DL — MB BCh BAO 1983 NUI.

MCBRIDE, Gerard Patrick St Bede's Medical Centre, Lower Dundas Street, Sunderland SR6 0QQ Tel: 0191 567 5335; 34 Woodlands, Gosforth, Newcastle upon Tyne NE3 4YL Tel: 0191 285 3343 — MB BCh BAO 1982 NUI; MRCGP 1987; DRCOG 1986. GP Tutor Sunderland Area. Socs: BMA.

MCBRIDE, Hamish McNeil Inzievar Surgery, 2 Kenmore Street, Aberfeldy PH15 2BL Tel: 01887 820366 Fax: 01887 829566; Comelybank, Aberfeldy PH15 2EF Tel: 01887 840355 — MB ChB 1970 Glas.; DA Eng. 1974. Clin. Tutor Univ. Dundee.; Co. Phys. Tayside Health Bd.

MCBRIDE, Iain Milne Cos Lane Medical Practice, Woodside Road, Glenrothes KY7 4AQ Tel: 01592 752100 Fax: 01592 612692; 45 High Street, Markinch, Glenrothes KY7 6DQ — MB ChB 1981 Ed.; BSc St. And. 1978. Clin. Asst. (Geriat. Med.) Glenrothes Hosp.

MCBRIDE, Jane Gatehead Road Surgery, Gatehead Road, Crosshouse, Kilmarnock KA2 0HN Tel: 01563 521506 Fax: 01563 573695; 67 London Road, Kilmarnock KA3 7AH — MB ChB 1985 Glas.; DRCOG 1988.

MCBRIDE, John Brendan The Oaks Family Medical Centre, 48 Orritor Road, Cookstown BT80 8BH Tel: 028 7976 2249 Fax: 028 7976 6793 — MB BCh BAO 1976 Belf.; MRCGP 1981; DRCOG 1980; DCH RCPSI 1978.

MCBRIDE, Mr John Malcolm Avenue House, Church Hill, Easingwold, York YO61 3HF — MD 1954 Glas.; MD (High Commend.) Glas. 1954, MB ChB 1937; FRCOG 1959. M 1947; FRFPS Glas. 1948; FRCS Glas. 1962. (Glas.) Socs: Glas. Obst. Soc. Prev: Cons. Gyn. Roy. Samarit. Hosp. for Wom. Glas.; Cons. Obst. Qu. Mother's Hosp. Glas.; Squadron Ldr. RAF.

MCBRIDE, Julia Elizabeth 18 Thornleigh Gardens, Cleadon Village, Sunderland SR6 7PX — MB 1984 Camb.; BChir 1983; FRCS Ed. 1991.

MCBRIDE, Keith Roborough Surgery, 1 Eastcote Close, Southway, Plymouth PL6 6PH Tel: 01752 701659 Fax: 01752 773181; Long Barn, Week, Dartington TQ9 6DZ Tel: 01803 840232 Email: keithmcbride@doctorupdate.net — MB BS 1964 Lond.; MRCS Eng. LRCP Lond. 1964; DObst RCOG 1966. (Char. Cross) Prev: SHO (Obst.) St. Mary's Hosp. Kettering; Ho. Phys. Hosp. St. John & Eliz. Lond.; Ho. Surg. Char. Cross Hosp. Lond.

MCBRIDE, Kevin Niels The Avenue Surgery, 14 The Avenue, Warminster BA12 9AA Tel: 01985 846224 Fax: 01985 847059; George's Barn, Brixton Deverill, Warminster BA12 7EL — BM 1980 Soton.; DA (UK) 1985; MRCGP 1987; DRCOG 1985.

MCBRIDE, Michael Edward La Boisserie, Le Varines, St Saviour, Jersey JE2 7SB — MB BCh BAO 1972 Belf.

MCBRIDE, Michael Oliver Department of Genitourinary Medicine, Royal Victoria Hospital, Grosvenor Road, Belfast BT12 6BA Tel: 01232 320159 Fax: 01232 322303 Email: michael.mcbride@royalhospitals.n-i.nhs.uk — MB BCh BAO 1986 Belf.; MRCP (UK) 1989; FRCP Lond. 1998. (Queen's University Belfast) Cons. Phys. Genitourin. Med. Roy. Vict. Hosp. Belf.; Director of Educat. and Train. Roy. Hosp.s. Socs: Coun. Mem. MSSVD; Ulster Med. Soc.; Coun. Mem. Assn. Genitourin. Med. Prev: Sen. Regist.

MCCABE

(Genitourin. Med. & Communicable Dis.) St. Mary's Hosp. Lond.; Research Fell. & Hon. Regist. St. Mary's Med. Sch. Lond.; Regist. (Genitourin. Med.) Roy. Vict. Hosp. Belf.

MCBRIDE, Mollie, MBE (retired) 61 Hough Green, Chester CH4 8JW Tel: 01244 675108 Fax: 01244 678191 Email: molliemcbride@compuserve.com — MB ChB (2nd cl. Hons.) Liverp. 1954; FRCGP 1980, M 1970; AFOM RCP Lond. 1980; MICGP 1987. Prev: Hon. Sec. RCGP.

MCBRIDE, Pamela Ann 18 Hanbury Road, Bristol BS8 2EP; Top Flat, 15 Hanbury Road, Clifton, Bristol BS8 2EW Tel: 0117 923 9163 — MB ChB 1989 Glas.; DA (UK) 1993. SHO (Anaesth.) Bristol Roy. Infirm. Socs: Train. Mem. Assn. Anaesth.; BMA. Prev: SHO (Anaesth.) Guy's Hosp. & Lewisham Hosp. Lond.; SHO (A & E) St. Geo. Hosp. Lond.; SHO (Geriat.) Bolingbroke Hosp. Lond.

MCBRIDE, Paul Martin Carmel Ampleforth Abbey, Ampleforth, York YO62 4EN — MB ChB 1990 Ed.

MCBRIDE, Richard John 3 Sunnybrook, Ballyrobert Road, Crawfordsburn, Bangor BT19 1HT — MB BCh BAO 1971 Belf.; MPhil (Med. Ethics & Law) Belf. 1994; FFA RCSI 1975. Cons. Anaesth. Roy. Vict. Hosp. Belf. Socs: Assn. Anaesth. GB & Irel. Prev: Sen. Regist. & Sen. Tutor (Anaesth.) Roy. Vict. Hosp. & Qu. Univ. Belf.

MCBRIDE, Samuel James 77 Killyfaddy Road, Armagh BT60 2PG Tel: 01861 531619; 153 Hillhall Road, Lisburn BT27 5JA Tel: 01846 666393 — MB BCh BAO 1987 Belf.; BSc (Hons. Med. Microbiol.) Belf. 1984; MRCP (UK) 1992. Specialist Regist. (A & E) Greenwich Dist. Hosp. Lond. Socs: Collegiate Mem. Roy. Coll. Phys. Lond.; Assoc. Mem. Brit. Assn. Accid. & Emerg. Med. Prev: Regist. (Clin. Biochem. & Clin. Path.) Roy. Vict. Hosp. Belf.; Regist. (Cardiol.) Antrim Area Hosp. Co. Antrim; SHO (Gen. Med.) Belf. & Ballymena.

MCBRIDE, Sandra Robyn Department of Dermatology, Royal Victoria Infirmary, Newcastle upon Tyne NE1 4LP Tel: 0191 232 5131 Email: s.r.mcbride@ncl.ac.uk; 5 Sackville Road, Heaton, Newcastle upon Tyne NE6 5SY Tel: 0191 240 1579 — MB BS 1991 Newc.; MRCP (UK) 1994. Clin. Research Assoc. Univ. of Newc.; Specialist Regist. (Dermat.) Roy. Vict. Infirm. Newc. upon Tyne. Socs: Brit. Assn. of Dermatol.; Brit. Soc. of Investigative Dermat.; (Train. Mem.) BMA. Prev: SHO (Med.) Dryburn Hosp. Durh.

MCBRIDE, Simon Thomas 36 Grange Road, Bangor BT20 3QQ — MB BCh BAO 1994 Belf.

MCBRIDE, Thomas Mary Kingswood Centre, Turner Road, Colchester CO4 5YJ — MB BCh BAO 1984 NUI.

MCBRIDE, Timothy Peter 3 Oldfield Grove, Sale M33 2AZ — MB ChB 1986 Manch.

MCBRIDE, William Thomas Department of Clinical Anaesthesia, Royal Victoria Hospital, Belfast BT12 6BA Tel: 01232 240530 ext 4006; 212 Hillsborough Old Road, Lisburn BT27 5QE Tel: 01846 670842 Email: 106177.173@compuserve.com — MB BCh BAO 1987 Belf.; MD Belf. 1995; BSc (Hons.) Belf. 1984; FFA RCSI 1992; FRCA 1992. (Queens Univ.) Cons. (Cardiol. Anaesth.) Roy. Vict. Hosp. Belf. Prev: Sen. Regist. (Anaesth.) Roy. Vict. Hosp. Belf.; Assoc. Prof. Anaesthesiol. Duke Univ. Durh. NC, USA; Fell. (Cardiac Anaesth.) Roy. Vict. Hosp. Belf.

MCBRIEN, Andrew 1 Brook Road, Liverpool L31 3EG — MB ChB 1988 Bristol.

MCBRIEN, David John (retired) Gaywood, Colebrook Lane, Watersfield, Pulborough RH20 1NA — MB BS 1952 Lond.; FRCP Lond. 1973, M 1954. Prev: Cons. Phys. Worthing Gp. Hosps.

MCBRIEN, Fergus Edgar Francis Flat C, 20 Courthill Road, London SE13 6HB — MB BCh BAO 1982 Belf.; FRCA 1993; MRCGP 1987. Prev: Assoc. Specialist (Sleep Disorders & Anaesth.) Roy. Nat. Throat, Nose & Ear Hosp. Lond.; GP Princip Wigan; Regist. (Anaesth.) Wrexham.

MCBRIEN, Hamilton Stanley 25 Dromore Road, Hillsborough BT26 6HS — MB BCh BAO 1994 Belf.

MCBRIEN, James Joseph Sheridan 16 Lagan Vale, Larganare Road, Lisburn BT28 2XA — MB BCh BAO 1992 Belf. (Qus. Univ. Belf.)

MCBRIEN, Michael Edmund 24 Lylehill Green, Templepatrick, Antrim BT41 0BF Email: mmcb@dnet.co.uk — MB ChB 1988 Ed.; FRCA 1993. Cons. Regist. Anaesth. Roy. Vict. Hosp. Belf. Prev: Regist. (Anaesth.) John Radcliffe Hosp. Oxf.; SHO (Anaesth.) St. John's Hosp. Livingston & W.. Gen. Hosp. Edin.

MCBRIEN, Mr Michael Patrick The Nuffield Hospital, Bury St Edmunds IP33 2AA Tel: 01284 701371 Fax: 01284 769998; Stanton House, Norton, Bury St Edmunds IP31 3LQ Tel: 01359 30832 Fax: 01359 231266 Email: mandtmcb@hotmail.com — MB BS 1960 Lond.; MS Lond. 1973, MB BS 1960; FRCS Eng. 1967; DObst RCOG 1962. (St. Thos.) Cons. Surg. InDepend. Pract.; Clin. Teach. Fac. Med. Univ. Camb.; Examr. Surg. Univ. Camb.; Univ. Lond.; Sec. Ct. of Examrs. RCS Eng.; Extern. Examr. RCS Edin., Colombo Sri Lanka, & Cairo. Socs: Fell. Assn. Surgs.; Assoc. Mem. BAUS; Ct. Exam. RCS Eng. Prev: Sen. Regist. & Lect. St. Thos. Hosp. Lond.; Regist. (Surg.) Soton. Hosp. Gp.; Cas. Off. & Ho. Surg. (Orthop. & Plastic Surg.) St. Thos. Hosp. Lond.

MCBRYAN, Daniel Damian Riverview Medical Centre, 6/8 George St., Johnstone PA5 8SL Tel: 01505 320151 Fax: 01505 322543 — MB ChB Glas. 1987; MRCGP 1991. Dep. Trainer (Gen. Pract.) Renfrewsh.; LMC Mem. (Argyll & Clyde); Asst. Med. Co-Ordinator, Renfrewsh. Emerg. Med. Serv. Out of Hours Serv. for GPs; Clin. Asst. in Subst. Abuse Clinic, Renfrewsh. (Assoc. Specialist). Prev: Mem. GP Sub-Comm. Area Audit Comm. Argyll & Clyde HB.

MCBRYDE, Callum Wilson 54 Witchford Road, Ely CB6 3DP — MB ChB 1998 Manch.; MB ChB Manch 1998.

MCBRYDE, Hugh McGillivray (retired) Church Farm, Church St., Semington, Trowbridge BA14 6JS — MB ChB 1950 Glas.; FRCPsych. 1981, M 1971; DPM Eng. 1957. Prev: Cons. Psychiat. Roundway Hosp. Devizes Wilts.

MCBURNIE, Paul Richard Ralphs Ride Practice, Ralphs Ride Surgery, Ralphs Ride, Bracknell RG12 9LH Tel: 01344 454626 Fax: 01344 303929 — MB BS 1986 Lond.; MRCGP 1993; DRCOG 1990; DCH RCP Lond. 1989.

MCBURNIE, Veronica Anne 2/L, 37 Beechwood Drive, Broomhill, Glasgow G11 7ET — MB ChB 1990 Glas.

MCCABE, Calum George Tams Brig Surgery, 107 New Road, Ayr KA8 8DD Tel: 01292 262697 Fax: 01292 265926; 4 Coila Avenue, Prestwick KA9 2BW Tel: 01292 74737 — MB ChB 1983 Aberd.; MRCGP 1987; DRCOG 1986. Prev: Trainee GP Ayrsh. & Arran VTS; Ho. Phys. Woodend Hosp. Aberd.; Ho. Surg. Roy. Infirm. Aberd.

MCCABE, Christopher Roscoe School Road Surgery, School Road, Praze-An-Beeble, Camborne TR14 0LB Tel: 01209 831386; Parc Clies, Trevarrack, Gulval, Penzance TR18 3DB Tel: 01736 362954 — MA; BM BCh Oxf. 1969.

MCCABE, Desmond John Mary 28 Bron Vardre Avenue, Deganwy, Conwy LL31 9UU — MB BCh BAO 1984 NUI.

MCCABE, Edmund Joseph 44 Rosemary Hill Road, Sutton Coldfield B74 4HJ Tel: 0121 353 2124; 73 Walsall Road, Little Aston, Sutton Coldfield B74 3BA Tel: 0121 353 2124 — MB ChB Ed. 1951; MRCOphth 1992; DO Eng. 1954. (Ed.) Socs: Midl. Ophth. Soc.

MCCABE, Edward Aloysius (retired) 6 Dunbeth Avenue, Coatbridge ML5 3JA — MB ChB Glas. 1957. Indep. Tribunal Serv. Glas.

MCCABE, Elaine Marie Westbank Day Unit, West Bridge St., Falkirk FK1 5RQ Tel: 01324 624111 Fax: 01324 611738; 32 Heugh Street, Falkirk FK1 5QR Email: emccabe@compuserve.com — MB ChB 1979 Dundee; MRCPsych 1984; MFPHM 1989; MPH Glas. 1986. Staff Psychiat. (Gen. Psychiat.) W.bank Day Unit Falkirk. Prev: Cons. Pub. Health Med. Forth Valley HB.

MACCABE, Mr James Jeffrey 152 Harley Street, London W1N 1HH Tel: 020 7935 3834 Fax: 020 7224 2574; 113 Dulwich Village, London SE21 7BJ Tel: 020 8693 2127 Fax: 020 8693 2127 — MB ChB Ed. 1951; FRCS Ed. 1961. (Ed.) Prev: Cons. Neurosurg. King's Coll. Hosp.; Emerit. Cons. Neurosurg. Bethlem Roy. & Maudsley Hosps. Lond.

MCCABE, Janet Alison 3 Westcroft, Comberton, Cambridge CB3 7EJ — MB BS 1974 Lond. SCMO (Palliat. Med.) Arthur Rank Hse. Brookfields Hosp. Camb.

MCCABE, John Gerald Flat 3, Williamson House, Raleigh Park, Barnstaple EX31 4HX — MB BCh BAO 1993 Belf.; BSc (Hons.) Belf. 1991; MRCP 1996. SHO (GP VTS) Barnstaple.

MCCABE, Margaret Mary Elizabeth 24 Village Lane, Washington NE38 7HU — MB ChB 1992 Manch.

MCCABE, Martin Gerard 24 Village Lane, Washington NE38 7HU — BChir 1994 Camb.

MCCABE, Mr Michael John Accident Department, Morriston Hospital, Swansea SA6 6NL Tel: 01792 703415 Email:

MCCABE

michael.mccabe@morrnhst-tr.wales.nhs.uk — MB BCh BAO 1981 Dub.; BA (Biochem.) Dub. 1978; FRCS Ed. 1988; FRCSI 1988; MRCPI 1985; FFAEM 1993. (Dub.) Cons. A & E Morriston Hosp. Swansea. Socs: Brit. Assn. Accid. & Emerg. Med.; BMA. Prev: Sen. Regist. (A & E) Cardiff Roy. Infirm.; Regist. (A & E) N.wick Pk. Hosp. Harrow; Demonst. (Anat.) Trinity Coll. Dub.

MCCABE, Michael Joseph (retired) The Bramlings, Morton, Gainsborough DN21 3AQ Tel: 01427 2949 — MB BCh BAO 1943 NUI; LM Coombe 1944. Treas. Med. Off. Prev: Gen. Pract. Anaesth. John Coupland Hosp. GainsBoro.

MCCABE, Niamh Elizabeth Eva c/o 41 Ardmore Avenue, Belfast BT10 0JP — MB BCh BAO 1987 NUI.

MCCABE, Robert James Raimondo Southfield House, Mearnskirk Hospital, Glasgow G77 5RY Tel: 0141 211 9435; 51 Buchanan Drive, Rutherglen, Glasgow G73 3PF — MB ChB 1977 Glas.; MPhil Univ. Ed. 1983; MRCPsych 1982. Cons. Adolesc. Psychiat. S.field Ho. Adolesc. & Family Psychiat.; Cons. Adolesc. Psychiat. Family Psychiat. Unit Mearnskirk Hosp. & Gartnavel Adolesc. Unit Gartnavel Roy. Hosp. Glas. Prev: Sen. Regist. (Child & Adolesc. Psychiat.) Dept. of Child & Family; Psychiat. Roy. Hosp. Sick Childr. Edin. & Young People's Unit Roy.; Edin. Hosp.; Regist. Roy. Edin. Hosp.

MCCABE, Ruth Elizabeth 42 The Meadow, Antrim BT41 1EY — MB BCh BAO 1997 Belf.

MCCABE, Shane Edward Thomas 13 Charlton Crescent, Plymouth PL6 5EQ — MB BS 1994 Lond.

MCCABE, Siobhan The Health Centre, Loch Road, Tranent, Edinburgh EH3 2JX — MB BCh BAO 1987 NUI.

MCCABE, Stephen David Portree Medical Centre, Portree IV51 9BZ Tel: 01478 612013 Fax: 01478 612340 — MB ChB 1988 Ed.; MRCGP 1993; DFFP 1994. (Ed.) Med. Off. Portree Community Hosp. Socs: BMA; Fac. PreHosp. Care RCS Edin. Prev: Assoc. GP Bowmore, Islay & Isle of Jura.

MCCABE, Mr Stephen Edward Braeside, Longridge, Sheepscombe, Stroud GL6 7QU — MB ChB 1978 Glas.; FRCPS Glas. 1983; FRCS Ed. 1982.

MCCABE, Thomas James (retired) 46 Talbot Park, Londonderry BT48 7TA Tel: 02871 51262 — MB BCh BAO 1951 Belf.; LRCP LRCS Ed. LRFPS Glas. 1950. Mem. Indust. Med. Off. N. Irel. Fire Auth. Of Nortrthern Irel. Prev: Resid. Ho. Off. (Surg. ENT, Ophth., Cas. & Obst.) Mater Infirm. Hosp. Belf.

MCCADDON, Andrew Nadra and Partners, The Surgery, Gardden Road, Rhosllanerchrugog, Wrexham LL14 2EN Tel: 01978 840034 Fax: 01978 845782; 7 Trem-y-Nant, Coed-y-Glyn, Wrexham LL13 7QL — MB ChB 1987 Sheff.; BSc (Hons.) Sheff. 1983; MRCGP 1991. (Sheff.) Prev: Trainee GP Rotherham VTS.; Ho. Off. (Surg. Med. & Neurosurg.) Roy. Hallamsh. Hosp. Sheff.

MCCAFFERTY, Francis Gerard 234 Limestone Road, Belfast BT15 3AR — MB BCh BAO 1977 Belf.

MCCAFFERTY, H The Surgery, The Limes, Hawley Street, Margate CT9 1PU Tel: 01843 227567 Fax: 01843 230167 — MB ChB 1979 Glas.

MCCAFFERTY, Ian James Queen Elizabeth Hospital, Department of Imaging, Edgbaston, Birmingham B15 2T Email: l.mccafferty@usa.net — MB BS 1989 Lond.; BSc (Hons) Lond. 1986; MRCP (UK) 1992; FRCR 1996. Cons. (Radiol.) Univ. Hosp. Birm. Prev: Sen. Regist. (Radiol.) W. Midl. HA.

MCCAFFERTY, Ian James 129 Roundways, Coalpit Heath, Bristol BS36 2LU — BM 1992 Soton.

MCCAFFERTY, James Brian County Hospital Lincoln, Sewell Road, Lincoln LN2 5QY Tel: 01522 512512; 18 Rostrop Road, Nocton, Lincoln LN4 2BT — MB BS 1958 Durh.; FFR 1973; DMRD Eng. 1967. Cons. Radiol. Lincoln Co. Hosp. Socs: Fell. Roy. Coll. Radiol.; BMA. Prev: Radiol. RAF Hosps. Wegberg, Germany, Nocton Hall & Changi, Singapore.

MCCAFFERTY, James Deans 1 Leelands, Lymington SO41 8EY — LRCPI & LM, LRSCI & LM 1957; LRCPI & LM, LRCSI & LM 1957.

MCCAFFERTY, Jean Innes Maternity Out-Patients, Royal Lancaster Infirmary, Ashton Road, Lancaster LA1 4RP; 61 Borrowdale Road, Lancaster LA1 3EU Tel: 01524 65531 — MB ChB 1971 Aberd. Clin. Asst. (Colposcopy) Roy. Lancaster Acute Hosps. NHS Trust; Clin. Med. Off. Community Well-Wom. Serv. Lancaster Priority Servs. NHS Trust. Socs: BSCCP.

MCCAFFERY, Kevin Flat 3/3, 15 Apsley St., Patrick, Glasgow G11 7ST — MB ChB 1993 Aberd.

MCCAFFERY, Teresa Maria 40 Erskine Street, Aberdeen AB24 3NQ — MB BS 1969 Lond.; FRCS Eng. 1975.

MCCAFFREY, Benedict James 20 Watery Lane, London SW20 9AD — MB BS 1994 Lond.

MCCAFFREY, John Edward 23 Colenso Pde, Belfast BT9 5AN — MB BCh BAO 1997 Belf.

MCCAFFREY, Margaret Josephine Derry Lodge, 29 Lough Road, Lurgan, Craigavon BT66 6JL — LRCPI & LM, LRSCI & LM 1946; LRCPI & LM, LRCSI & LM 1946. (RCSI) Prev: Ho. Surg. & Ho. Phys. Jervis St. Hosp. Dub.; Capt. R.A.M.C.

MCCAFFREY, Patricia Marian 58 Derryleckagh Road, Newry BT34 2NL — MB BCh BAO 1979 Belf.; FRCP Glas. 1994.

MCCAFFREY, Paul Edward Ballyhullagh, Lisnaskea, Enniskillen BT92 5FG — MB BCh 1998 Belf.; MB BCh Belf 1998.

MCCAFFREY, Silvana 20 Watery Lane, London SW20 9AD — MB BS 1994 Lond.

MCCAHILL, James Patrick 17 Kingswood Place, Corby NN18 9AF — MB ChB 1994 Leic.

MCCAHON, Mr Ian Albert (retired) 8 Gaten by Garth, Alne Road, Easingwold, York YO61 3QT — MB BCh BAO 1957 Belf.; FRCS Ed. 1963.

MCCAHON, Robert Alexander 27 Ashley Heights, Armagh BT60 1HG — MB ChB 1997 Manch.

MCCAHY, Helen Jane 67 Greenloons Drive, Liverpool L37 2LX — MB BS 1989 Lond.

MCCAHY, Mr Philip James 141 Salters Road, Gosforth, Newcastle upon Tyne NE3 1DU — MB BS 1987 Newc.; FRCS Ed. 1992. N. Region Continuum in Urol. Prev: Demonst. (Anat.) Univ. Newc.; Research Fell (Surg.) Univ. Newc.

MCCAIE, Charlotte Pelham Brannams Medical Centre, Brannams Square, Kiln Lane, Barnstaple EX32 8AP Tel: 01271 329004 Fax: 01271 346785 — MB ChB 1976 Ed.; MRCP (UK) 1978; MRCGP 1986.

MCCAIG, Mr John X-Ray Department, Warrington Hospital NHS Trust, Lovely Lane, Warrington WA5 1QG Tel: 01925 662359 Fax: 01925 662052 — MB ChB 1984 Liverp.; BSc (Hons. Physiol.) Liverp. 1979; FRCS Ed. 1991; FRCR 1996; DRCOG 1988. (Liverp.) Cons. Radiologist Warrington Hosp. NHS Trust; Cons. Radiologist BUPA N. Chesh. Hosp. Prev: Sen. Regist. (Radiol.) N. Staffs. Hosp. NHS Trust; Regist. (Radiol.) N. Staffs. HA; SHO (Radiother. & Oncol.) Clatterbridge Hosp. Wirral.

MACCAIG, John Norman (retired) 7 Cherry Tree Drive, Landkey, Barnstaple EX32 0UE Tel: 01271 831020 Fax: 01271 831020 — MB ChB Manch. 1955; FRCP Lond. 1975, M 1960. Prev: Cons. Phys. N. Devon Clin. Area.

MCCAIG, Ronald Harry 1 Dawson Drive, Chester CH2 1AL — MB ChB 1976 Ed.; MFOM RCP Lond. 1985; DIH Soc. Apoth. Lond. 1982. Sen. Employm. Med. Adviser Health & Safety Exec. Bootle. Socs: Soc. Occupat. Med. & Ergonomics Soc. Prev: Employm. Med. Adviser EMAS Birm.; Med. Off. W. Midl. Indust. Health Servs. Ltd. W. Bromwich; Med. Off. (Research) Army Personnel Research Establ. Roy. Aircraft Establ. FarnBoro..

MCCALDIN, Alexander Mark, Maj. RAMC Heron House, 2 Aldcliffe Mews, Aldcliffe, Lancaster LA1 5BT — MB BS 1993 Newc.; MRCGP 2000; Dip. Child Health Care (RCP) 1998; Dip. Roy. Coll. Obst. & Gyn. 1998. (Newc.U.Tyne.) St Anthony's Health Centre, Walker, Newc.-upon-Tyne; Hon. Clin. Lect. Dept. Of Primary Care Newc. Univ. Prev: Roy. Army Med. Corps. (1994-2001).

MCCALDIN, Michael Dermot Bradgate Surgery, Ardenton Walk, Brentry, Bristol BS10 6SP Tel: 0117 959 1920 Fax: 0117 983 9332 — MB ChB 1986 Cape Town; MRCGP 1993; DCH RCP.

MCCALISTER, Mr Alexander, TD (retired) 20 Burnside Park, Crawfordsburn, Bangor BT19 1JW Tel: 02891 852338 — MB BCh BAO 1948 Belf.; MCh Belf. 1962; FRCS Eng. 1954; FRCSI 1953. Prev: Cons. Surg. Ulster Hosp. Dundonald.

MCCALISTER, Bridget Bonnybridge Health Centre, Larbert Road, Bonnybridge FK4 1ED Tel: 01324 812315 Fax: 01324 814696 — MB ChB 1987 Ed.; MRCGP 1991; DRCOG 1991.

MCCALISTER, Peter William Bonnybridge Health Centre, Larbert Road, Bonnybridge FK4 1ED Tel: 01324 812315 Fax: 01324 814696 Email: peter.mccalister@gp25192_forth-hb.scot.nhs.uk —

MCCALLUM

MB ChB 1987 Ed.; MRCGP 1991; DRCOG 1991; DCCH 1998. (Edinburgh) GP Bennybridge. Prev: Staff Grade (Community Paediat.) Stirling; SHO (Cas.) St. John's Hosp. Broxburn; SHO (O & G) Dunfermline.

MCCALL, Alastair Arthur Alexander (retired) Inverfheoran, 2 Old Evanton Road, Dingwall IV15 9RA Tel: 01349 862256 — MB ChB 1960 Ed.; FRCGP 1993, M 1968; DObst RCOG 1962. Prev: Ho. Phys. & Ho. Surg. Dumfries & Galloway Roy. Infirm.

MCCALL, Alastair Charles Meeks Road Surgery, 10 Meeks Road, Falkirk FK2 7ES Tel: 01324 619930 Fax: 01324 627266; 41 South Broomage Avenue, Larbert FK5 3LF — MB ChB 1989 Glas.; MRCGP 1993.

MCCALL, Allison 84 Etive Crescent, Bishopbriggs, Glasgow G64 1EY — MB ChB 1992 Glas.

MCCALL, Andrew 15 Chestnut Av, Holbeach, Spalding PE12 7NE — MB ChB 1997 Birm.

MCCALL, Andrew William 23 Cowleaze Road, Kingston upon Thames KT2 6DZ — MB ChB 1984 Glas.

MACCALL, Callum A Murray Royal Hospital, Muirhall Road, Perth PH2 7BH Email: callumamaccall@ukgateway.net — MB ChB 1997 Aberd.; BSc. Med. Sci (Hons) 1997; MRCPsych 2001; MB, CLB. Aberd. 1997. (Aberdeen) SpR Forens./Gen. Psychiat. Prev: SHO (Psychiat.) Roy. Cornhill Hosp., Aberd.

MCCALL, Christopher John 216a Wareharm Road, Corfe Mullen, Wimborne BH21 3LN Tel: 01202 694721 Fax: 01202 658957 — MRCS Eng. LRCP Lond. 1976; BSc Lond. 1973, MB BS 1976; DRCOG 1981; MRCGP 1982; DCH RCP Lond. 1982.

MCCALL, Iain William Department of Radiology, Robert Jones & Agnes Hunt Orthopaedic & District NHS Trust, Oswestry Tel: 01691 404546 Fax: 01691 404057; Holly Lodge, Kinton, Nesscliff, Shrewsbury SY4 1AZ Tel: 01743 741329 — MB ChB 1967 Birm.; FRCR 1975; DMRD 1971. Cons. Radiol. Robt. Jones & Agnes Hunt Orthop. Hosp. OsW.ry; Prof. of Radiological Sci.s Univ. of Keele. Socs: Pres. Elect Internat. Skeletal Soc.; Exec. Bureau Europ. Assn. of Radiol.; Union of Europ. Med. Specialists (Pres. Radiol. Sect.).

MCCALL, Jacqueline Ruth 36 Belfast Road, Holywood BT18 9EL — MB BCh BAO 1994 Belf.

MCCALL, James Chelsea & Wesminster Hospital, 369 Fulham Road, London SW10 9NH Tel: 020 8746 8570 Fax: 020 8764 8588 Email: jmccall@lc.ac.uk; 4 Cleveland Road, London W4 5HP — MB BS 1983 Univ. Lond.; FRCR 1991; MRCP Roy. Coll. Phys. 1987; BSc Univ. Lond. 1980. Cons. Radiol. Chelsea & W.minster Hosp. Lond. Socs: BSIR; CIRSE.

MCCALL, James Montgomerie 62 Croftdown Road, London NW5 1EN — MB BS 1983 Lond.; MRCP (UK) 1987; FRCR 1991.

MCCALL, James Stein Galston Surgery, 5A Henrietta Street, Galston KA4 8JW Tel: 01563 820424 Fax: 01563 822380 — MB ChB 1974 Glas.; MRCGP 1978; DRCOG 1977.

MCCALL, Jane Windrush, Flaxton Road, Strensall, York YO32 5XQ — MB ChB Birm. 1968; DA Eng. 1972. (Birm.)

MCCALL, Janice Margaret Clydebank Health Centre, Kilbowie Road, Clydebank G81 2TQ Tel: 0141 531 6475 Fax: 0141 531 6478; 12 Fifth Avenue, Glasgow G12 0AT — MB ChB 1990 Glas.; MRCGP 1995.

MCCALL, Joanna Dovecote House, 38 Wollaton Road, Beestan, Nottingham NG9 2NR; 572 Adams Hill, Derby Road, Nottingham NG7 2GZ — BM BS 1991 Nottm.; MRCGP 1995; DCH 1996 DCH 1996; DRCOG 1995; DFFP 1998. (Nottm) Staff Grade (Comm. Paediat.) Nottm.

MCCALL, John 23 Haining Road, Renfrew PA4 0AB — MB ChB 1959 Glas.

MCCALL, John Good Station Road Surgery, 2 Station Road, Prestwick KA9 1AQ Tel: 01292 671444 Fax: 01292 678023 — MB ChB 1973 Glas.; MRCGP 1979; DRCOG 1978.

MCCALL, Joyce Madeliene Stewart (retired) 14 Mullinure Park, Portadown Road, Armagh BT61 Tel: 01861 524498 — LRCPI & LM, LRSCI & LM 1950; LRCPI & LM, LRCSI & LM 1950.

MCCALL, Karin Elizabeth 21 Westfield Avenue, Hayling Island PO11 9AG — MB ChB 1997 Manch. SHO (A & E) N. Manch. Gen. Hosp.

MCCALL, Peter David Tudor House Surgery, 43 Broad Street, Wokingham RG40 1BE Tel: 0118 978 3544 Fax: 0118 977 0420; 43 Broad Street, Wokingham RG40 1B — MB BS 1968 Lond.;

MRCS Eng. LRCP Lond. 1967. (Westm.) Med. Off. RMNS Bearwood Coll. Wokingham; Med. Off. Oakfields Hosp. Wokingham.

MCCALLAN, Susan Elizabeth 133 Ochiltree, Dunblane FK15 0PA — MB BCh BAO 1977 Belf.; MRCP (UK) 1981; MRCGP 1983; DCH RCPSI 1979. Clin. Asst. (Diabetes/Rehabil.) Stirling Roy. Infirm. NHS Trust. Socs: BMA. Prev: GP Princip. & Trainer Dunblanc.

MCCALLION, James 4 Holm Road/, Crossford, Carluke ML8 5RG — MB ChB 1981 Glas.; MRCP (UK) 1985. Cons. Geriat. Law Hosp. Lanarksh.

MCCALLION, Judith Susan 4 Holm Road, Crossford, Carluke ML8 5RG — MB ChB 1981 Glas.; DRCOG 1990; Dip. Pract. Dermat. Wales 1991.

MCCALLION, Mr Kevin 23 North Parade, Ormeau Road, Belfast BT7 2GF Tel: 01232 208067 Email: k.mccallion@qub.ac.uk — MB BCh BAO 1992 Belf.; BSc (Hons.) Belf. 1989. Specialist Regist. Surg. N. Irel. Rotat. Socs: Fell. Roy. Coll. Surgs. Eng.; Fell. Roy. Coll. Surgs. Irel.

MCCALLION, Nial Eugene Waterside Health Centre, Glendermot Road, Londonderry BT47 6AU Tel: 028 7132 0100 Fax: 028 7134 9323 — MB BCh BAO 1984 Belf.; BSc (Hons.) Belf. 1981; MRCGP 1988; DFFP 1994; DRCOG 1987; DCH RCPSI 1987; DGM RCP Lond. 1986. Prev: Dir. Business Servs. Altnagelvin Gp. Hosps. W.. HSSB; Trainee GP Lond.derry; Trainee GP/SHO & Ho. Off. Altnagelvin Area Hosp. Lond.derry.

MCCALLION, William Omagh Health Centre, Mountjoy Road, Omagh BT79 7BA Tel: 028 8224 3521 — MB BCh BAO 1974 Dub.; MRCGP 1983; DRCOG 1979.

MCCALLION, William Alexander 14 Upton Avenue, Finaghy, Belfast BT10 0LU Tel: 01232 301254 — MB BCh BAO 1987 Belf.

MACCALLUM, Alexander Gordon Riverbank Medical Centre, Dodsley Lane, Midhurst GU29 9AW Tel: 01730 812121 Fax: 01730 811400; Woodstock, Vanzell Road, Easebourne, Midhurst GU29 9BA — MB BS 1986 Lond.; BSc Lond. 1983; MRCP (UK) 1989; DRCOG 1990. (Lond.) Prev: Acting Regist. (Gen. Med.) Roy. Sussex Co. Hosp. Brighton; SHO (Med.) Roy. Sussex Co. Hosp. Brighton.

MCCALLUM, Alexander Symon Ross Dingle House, Belmont Road, Bromley Cross, Bolton BL7 9QR Tel: 01204 53254 — MB ChB 1968 Ed.; DObst RCOG 1970. (Ed.) Med. Adviser FHSA Rochdale Family Health Servs. Auth.

MCCALLUM, Alison Elizabeth 129A Victoria Road, Kirkcaldy KY1 1DH Tel: 01592 263332 Fax: 01592 644288; 23 Townsend Crescent, Kirkcaldy KY1 1DN Email: alisonemac@aol.com — MB ChB 1975 Ed. (Ed.) GP Kirkcaldy.

MCCALLUM, Alison Katherine East & North Hertfordshire Health Authority, Charter House, Parkway, Welwyn Garden City AL8 6JL Tel: 01707 361274 Fax: 01707 361295; 5 Liverpool Road, St Albans AL1 3UN Email: alisonkm@study.v-net.com — MB ChB 1983 Glas.; MSc Newc. 1990; MFPHM 1991; FFPHM 1998. Dir. Pub. Health & Health Strategy E. & N. Herts. HA Charter Ho., Pk.way, Welwyn Gardon City Herts.; Sen. Lect. (Pub. Health Med.) Lond. Prev: Cons. Pub. Health Med. Enfield & Haringey HA.

MCCALLUM, Archibald Ian (retired) Duncraoibhan, Lochgilphead PA31 8QX Tel: 01546 2899 — MB ChB 1939 Glas. Prev: Ho. Phys. W.. Infirm. Glas.

MCCALLUM, Catriona Anne 10 Ketilstown Grove, Linlithgow EH49 6PP — MB ChB Ed. 1987.

MCCALLUM, Charles John Dept. of Haemotology, Victoria Hospital, Kirkcaldy KY2 5AH Tel: 01592 643353; 23 Townsend Crescent, Kirkcaldy KY1 1DN — MB ChB 1974 Ed.; MRCP (UK) 1976; MRCPath. 1982. Cons. (Haemat.) Fife Area Laborat. Kirkcaldy. Prev: Lect. (Haemat.) Welsh Nat. Sch. Med. Cardiff; Regist. (Haemat.) Roy. Infirm. Edin.; Research Schol. Dept. Therap. Edin. Univ.

MCCALLUM, David Shaw 44 Peel Street, Dundee DD2 3TZ — MB ChB 1983 Aberd.

MCCALLUM, Mr Derek Alexander Lawrence Anchorfield House, Perth Road, Dunblane FK15 0BS — MB ChB 1966 Glas.; FRCS Glas. 1972. (Glas.) Cons. ENT Surg. Forth Valley Health Bd. Socs: Glas. M-C Soc. & Scott. Otol. Soc.

MCCALLUM, Eileen MacFarlane Greencroft Medical Centre (North), Greencroft Wynd, Annan DG12 6BG; Grovewood, Plumdon Road, Annan DG12 6SJ — MB ChB 1979 Glas.

MACCALLUM

MACCALLUM, Elizabeth Ann 52 Marlborough Road, Broomhill, Sheffield S10 1DB — MB ChB 1998 Sheff.; MB ChB Sheff 1998.

MACCALLUM, Fiona Elizabeth Anaesthetics Department, Aberdeen Royal Hospitals NHS Trust, Foresterhill House, Ashgrove Road W., Aberdeen AB25 4ZN — MB ChB 1993 Ed.

MACCALLUM, Harrison Shaw 2 The Craigs, Newark St., Greenock PA16 7UU Tel: 01475 21922 — MB ChB 1947 Glas.; DObst RCOG 1951. (Univ. Glas.)

MACCALLUM, Helen Morag Morris (retired) 26 Victoria Road, Brookfield, Johnstone PA5 8UA Tel: 01505 20290 — MD 1963 Glas.; MB ChB 1950; FRCPath 1977, M 1965. Prev: Lect. in Path. Univ. Glas. & W.. Infirm. Glas.

MACCALLUM, Huntly Gill 6 West Saville Terrace, Newington, Edinburgh EH9 3DZ Tel: 0131 667 0179 — MB ChB 1981 Ed.; MRCGP 1988. Prev: Regist. (Gen. Med.) Cross Ho.s Hosp. Shrewsbury.

MACCALLUM, James Marshall Newland Medical Practice, Bathgate Primary Care Centre, Whitburn Road, Bathgate EH48 2SS Tel: 01506 655155 Fax: 01506 636263 Email: james.mccallum@cult.scot.nhs.uk; 10 Ketil'stoun Grove, Linlithgow EH49 6PP Tel: 01506 670820 Email: james.catriona@virgin.net — MB ChB 1987 Ed.; MRCGP 1992; DRCOG 1991. (Edinburgh University) GP Princip. Prev: Assoc. Locality Co-ordinator W. Lothian; Trainee GP Penicuik VTS.

MACCALLUM, Janet Elizabeth Priory Medical Group, 19 Albion Road, North Shields NE29 0HT Tel: 0191 257 0223; Tel: 0191 284 7257 — MB BS Newc. 1991; MRCGP 1995. (Newc.) Socs: Brit. Med. Assn.

MCCALLUM, Mr John Rankine Napier House, 8 Colinton Road, Edinburgh EH10 5DS — MB ChB 1945 Ed.; FRCS Ed. 1954.

MACCALLUM, Mr John Ross Raeberry, Havelock St., Helensburgh G84 7HB — MB ChB 1963 Ed.; FRCS Ed. 1969. Cons. Gen. Surg. Vale of Leven Dist. Gen. Hosp. Alexandria. Prev: Govt. Med. Off. Zambia; Regist. (Surg.) W.. Infirm. Glas.; Research Fell. Peter Bent Brigham Hosp. Boston U.S.A.

MACCALLUM, Kathryn Jane Mary 92 Queens Road, Aberdeen AB15 4YQ — MB ChB 1985 Ed.

MACCALLUM, Kay Storm 7 Little Causeway, Forfar DD8 2AD — MB ChB 1985 Dundee. Trainee GP Asst. Forfar.

MACCALLUM, Linda Reid Lauriston Place Surgery, 32 Lauriston Place, Edinburgh EH3 9EZ — MB ChB 1978 Glas.

MACCALLUM, Malcolm Iain Duncan Department of Anaesthetics, Salisbury District Hospital, Odstock Road, Salisbury SP2 8BJ Tel: 01722 425050 Fax: 01722 414143 — MB ChB 1976 Glas.; FFA RCS Eng. 1980. Cons. Anaesth. & IC & Chairm. Dept. Anaesth. Salisbury Dist. Hosp. Prev: Sen. Regist. Nuffield Dept. of Anaesth. Oxf.; SHO & Regist. (Anaesth.) W.. Infirm. Glas.; Sen. Clin. Research Fell. (Med.) Univ. W.. Ontario, Canada.

MACCALLUM, Mary Fordingbridge Surgery, Bartons Road, Fordingbridge SP6 1RS Tel: 01425 652123 Fax: 01425 654393 — MB 1981 Camb.; BSc (Hons.) Sussex 1970; MA Camb. 1982, MB 1981, BChir 1980; MRCGP 1985; DRCOG 1983. (Addenbrookes)

MACCALLUM, Mary McNee 4 Hornshill Farm Road, Stepps, Glasgow G33 6DE — MB ChB 1970 Glas.

MACCALLUM, Niall Samy 31 White House, Vicarage Crescent, London SW11 3LJ Tel: 0410 078321 Email: nsm@dial.pipex.com — MB BS 1995 Lond. (UMOS Guy's & St. Thos. Hosps.)

MACCALLUM, Peter Kenneth MRC Epidemiology & Medical Care Unit, St. Bart. & Royal Lond. School Med. & Dent., Charterhouse Sq, London EC1M 6BQ Tel: 020 7982 6203 Fax: 020 7982 6262 Email: pkmaccallum@mds.qmw.ac.uk; 41 Collingwood Avenue, London N10 3EE — MB ChB 1981 Sheff.; MD Sheff. 1995, BMedSci (Hons.) 1980; MRCP (UK) 1985; MRCPath 1993. (Sheff.) Sen. Lect. & Hon. Cons. Haemat. Roy. Hosps. NHS Trust. Prev: Sen. Regist. (Haemat.) St. Bart. Hosp. Lond.; Regist. (Haemat.) Manch. Roy. Infirm.; Ho. Off. (Gen. Med.) Roy. Hallamsh. Hosp. Sheff.

MACCALLUM, Mr Richard Daniel Accident & Emergency, Victoria Infirmary, Langside Road, Glasgow G42 9TY Tel: 0141 201600 Email: r.maccallum@virgin.net; 27 Ayr Road, Whitecraigs, Glasgow G46 6SB Tel: 0141 201 6000 — MB ChB 1988 Ed.; MBA Ed. 1994; FRCS Glas. 1993; FFAEM 1997. (Edinburgh) Cons. (A & E) Vict. Infirm. Glas. Socs: Fell. (Life Mem.) Roy. Med. Soc. Prev: Sen. Regist. (A & E) Dundee Roy. Infirm.; Regist. (A & E) Vict.

Infirm. Glas. & Roy. Infirm. Edin.; SHO (Cardiol.) W.. Gen. Hosp. Edin.

MCCALLUM, Professor Robert Ian, CBE 4/1 Chessels Court, 240 Canongate, Edinburgh EH8 8AD Tel: 0131 556 7977 Email: ian.mccallum@which.net — MB BS 1943 Lond.; DSc Lond. 1971, MD 1946; FRCP Ed. 1985; FRCP Lond. 1970, M 1944; FFOM RCP Lond. 1979, M 1978. (Guy's) Emerit. Prof. Occupat. Health Univ. Newc.; Hon. Cons. Inst. Occupat. Med. Edin. Socs: Fell. Roy. Soc. Med.; Soc. Occupat. Med. Prev: Dean Fac. Occupat. Med. RCP Lond. 1984-86; Rockefeller Trav. Fell. Med. MRC 1953-54 USA; Ho. Phys. Guy's Hosp. Lond. & Brompton Hosp. Lond.

MCCALLUM, Roland William 45B Bellshaugh Gardens, Kelvinside, Glasgow G12 0SA — MB ChB 1995 Glas.; BSc (Hons.) Immunol. Glas. 1992. (Glas.) SHO (Gen. Med.) W.. Infirm. Glas.

MACCALLUM, Rosalind Flat 3, Shabden Park, 2 High Road, Coulsdon CR5 3SF — MB ChB 1993 Birm. SHO (O & G) Roy. Sussex Co. Hosp. Brighton. Prev: SHO (A & E) Russells Hall Hosp. Dudley W. Midl.; Ho. Off. (Surg.) City Hosp. Birm.

MACCALLUM, Seonaid Margaret 36 Briar Road, Kirkintilloch, Glasgow G66 3SA — MB ChB 1992 Glas.

MACCALLUM, Shona Jayne Birchcliffe, Tonacliffe Road, Rochdale OL12 8SJ Tel: 01706 345741 — MB BS 1993 Lond.; MRCP (UK) 1996. (UMDS) Specialist Regist. Rotat. (Respirat. Med.) Fazakerley Hosp., Roy. Liverp. Hosp. & BRd.green Cardiothoracic Centre Liverp. Prev: SHO (Med.) Blackburn Roy. Infirm.

MACCALLUM, Stewart, MC Wilby House, 111 Loughborough Road, Kirkcaldy KY1 3DD — LRCP LRCS 1933 Ed.; LRCP LRCS Ed. LRFPS Glas. 1933; LDS Glas. 1932. Socs: BMA. Prev: Ho. Surg. E. Suff. & Ipswich Hosp.; Ho. Phys. Herefordsh. Gen. Hosp.; Maj. RAMC.

MACCALLUM, Susan Katharine Woodstock, Vanzell Road, Easebourne, Midhurst GU29 9BA — MB BS 1986 Lond.; DRCOG 1988. Trainee GP Brighton.

MACCALLUM, William Andrew Gordon (retired) 7 Tweskard Park, Belfast BT4 2JY Tel: 01232 63149 — MB BCh BAO 1954 Belf.; FRCPI 1972, M 1961; FRCPsych 1974, M 1971; DPM RCPSI 1958. Sen. Cons. Psychiat. Purdysburn Hosp. Belf.; Fell. Ulster Med. Soc. Prev: Cons. Psychiat. St. Luke's Hosp. Armagh.

MCCAMILY, Julie 60 Thornyflat Road, Ayr KA8 0LY — MB ChB 1989 Glas.

MCCAMMON, Leonard Charles Hillhead Health Centre, 50 Hillhead, Stewartstown, Dungannon BT71 5HY Tel: 028 8773 8648 Fax: 028 8773 8648 — MB BCh BAO 1981 Belf.

MCCAMMON, William Jeremy 24 Greenhill Park, Newcastle BT33 0HP — MB BCh BAO 1995 Belf.

MCCANCE, Alastair John Department of Cardiology, Derby City General Hospital, Derby DE22 3NE Tel: 01332 40131 — BM BCh 1980 Oxf.; MA Camb. 1981; DM Oxf. 1990, BM BCh 1980; MRCP (UK) 1983. Cons. Cardiol. Derby City Gen. Hosp. Socs: Brit. Cardiac Soc. & Med. Research Soc. Prev: Brit. Heart Foundat. Jun. Research Fell. John Radcliffe Hosp. Oxf.; Sen. Regist. (Cardiol.) Groby Rd. Hosp. Leicester.

MCCANCE, David Robert Metabolic Unit, Royal Group Hospitals, Belfast BT12 6BA Tel: 01232 894922; 1 The Spires, Church Road, Holywood BT18 9DY Tel: 01232 894922 — MB BCh BAO 1982 Belf.; BSc (1st cl. Hons.) Belf. 1979; MD Belf. 1990; MRCP (UK) 1985; DCH RCPSI 1984; FRCP (Ed) 1997; FRCP (L) 1998. (Qu. Univ. Belf.) Cons. Phys. Sir Geo. E. Clark Metabol. Unit Roy. Vict. Hosp. Belf. Socs: Brit. Diabetic Assn.; Endocrine Soc.; Eur. Assn. for Study Diabetes.

MCCANCE, Janet Margaret Church Street Surgery, 1 Church Street, Newtownards BT23 4FH Tel: 028 9181 6333 Fax: 028 9181 8805; 6 Massey Park, Stormont, Belfast BT4 2JX — MB ChB 1984 Ed.; MRCGP 1989; DCH RCPS Glas. 1988.

MCCANCE, Katherine Jane Deeside Lodge, Charleston Road, Aboyne AB34 5EL — MB ChB 1985 Sheff.; MRCGP 1989; DCCH RCP Ed. 1990; DRCOG 1988. (Sheff.) Staff Grade Community Child Health Aberd. Prev: Trainee GP Aylesbury VTS.

MCCANCE, Pamela Frances (retired) House of Strachan, Banchory AB31 6NN Tel: 01330 850273 — MB BS 1953 Lond.; MRCS Eng. LRCP Lond. 1953; MRCPsych 1972; DPM Ed. 1971. Prev: Cons. Psychiat. Roy. Cornhill Hosp. Aberd.

MCCANCE, Sylvia Louise Psychiatry Unit, Derby City General Hospital, Uttoxeter Road, Derby DE22 3NE Tel: 01332 625588 —

MCCANN

BM BCh 1980 Oxf.; MRCPsych 1986. Cons. (Gen. Adult Pschiatry) S.ern Derbysh. Ment. Health NHS Trust.

MCCANDLESS, William Banbridge Medical Group Centre, Linenhall Street, Banbridge BT32 3EG — MB BCh BAO 1975 Belf.; DRCOG 1977.

MCCANDLISH, Hannah Elizabeth Flat 2/1, 32 Stewartville St., Glasgow G11 5PJ — MB ChB 1995 Glas.

MCCANE WHITNEY, John Anthony (retired) 30 Wingfield Road, Alfreton DE55 7AN Tel: 01773 832431 — MB ChB 1959 Sheff. Prev: GP Derbysh.

MCCANN, Brendan Gabriel Histopathology Department, Norfolk & Norwich Hospital, Brunswick Road, Norwich NR1 3SR; 8 The Mews, Arlington Lane, Norwich NR2 2BY Tel: 01603 632772 — MB BCh BAO 1966 NUI; FRCPath 1985, M 1973. (Univ. Coll. Dub.) Cons. Path. Norf. & Norwich Hosp. Socs: Internat. Acad. Path. & Assn. Clin. Pathol. Prev: Sen. Lect. (Histopath.) Char. Cross Hosp. Med. Sch. Lond.; Instruc. Path. Washington Univ. St. Louis, USA; Lect. (Path.) Univ. Birm.

MCCANN, Brian Henry George McCann and Morgan, Rathfriland Health Centre, John Street, Rathfriland, Newry BT34 5QH Tel: 028 4063 0666 Fax: 028 4063 1198; The Bungalow, Cross Heights, Rathfriland, Newry BT34 5QU — MB BCh BAO 1980 Belf.

MCCANN, Caron Bridget 21 Evelyn Road, Sheffield S10 5FE — MB ChB 1995 Sheff. Socs: BMA; MPS.

MCCANN, Clare Marie Ardoch Medical Centre, 6 Ardoch Grove, Cambuslang, Glasgow G72 8HA Tel: 0141 641 3827; 22 Gowanlea Drive, Giffnock, Glasgow G46 6HN Tel: 0141 637 3182 — MB ChB 1975 Glas.; DCH RCPS Glas. 1978.

MCCANN, David John Luson Surgery, Wellington TA21 8AG Tel: 01823 662836 Fax: 01823 660955 — MB BS 1976 Lond.; MRCP (UK) 1980. (New Lond. Hosp.) GP Princip., Wellington, Som.

MCCANN, Denis George (retired) Peacock Tree, North Roundabout, Pulborough RH20 Tel: 0190 663124 — MB ChB 1942 Ed.; BA Camb.

MCCANN, Desmond Francis Madeira Road Surgery, 1A Madeira Road, Parkstone, Poole BH14 9ET Tel: 01202 741345; 7 Mount Grace Drive, Lilliput, Poole BH14 8NB Tel: 01202 700030 Fax: 01202 700030 Email: dmccann3@compuserve.com — MB ChB 1978 Glas.; MBA Bournemouth 1993; MRCGP 1983; DRCOG 1984. (Glasgow University) GP Princip.; Med. Dir. Poole Hyperbaric Centre.

MACCANN, E London Lane Clinic, Kinnaird House, 37 London Lane, Bromley BR1 4HB Tel: 020 8460 2661 Fax: 020 8464 5041.

MCCANN, Emma 10 Druminally Road, Portadown, Craigavon BT62 1QS — MB BCh BAO 1993 Belf.

***MCCANN, Fiona Jane** 1 Helidon Cottages, The Coombe, Streatley, Reading RG8 9QN — MB BS 1998 Lond.; MB BS Lond 1998.

MCCANN, George Alexander (retired) The Moorings, Killowen Vill., Rostrevor, Newry BT34 3RS Tel: 016937 38538 — MB BCh BAO 1951 Belf. Prev: GP Rathfriland.

MCCANN, Gerald Department of Medicine & Therapeutics, Gardiner Institute, Western Infirmary, Glasgow G11 6NT Tel: 0141 211 2897 Fax: 0141 339 2800 Email: gmc8v@clinmed.gla.ac.uk; 89 Norse Road, Scotstoun, Glasgow G14 9EF Tel: 0141 576 1897 Fax: 0141 339 2800 — MB ChB 1992 Glas.; BSc Glas. 1989; MRCP (UK) 1995; Dip. Sports Med. Roy. Coll. Scot. 1997. (Univ. Glas.) Clin. Research Fell. (Sports Med. & Cardiol.) Gardiner Inst. W.. Infirm. Glas.; Vis. Specialist Lect. Glas. Caledonian Univ. Prev: Regist. (Med.) Napier Pub. Hosp., NZ; SHO Rotat. (Gen. Med.) W.. Infirm. Glas.

MCCANN, Gillian Jane 22 Ballyhannon Grove, Portadown, Craigavon BT63 5SD — MB ChB 1997 Glas.

MCCANN, Jerome Joseph 134 Curr Road, Beragh, Sixmilecross, Omagh BT79 0QT; 58 Mill Lane, Lymm WA13 9SQ — MB BCh BAO 1988 Belf.; DA (UK) 1993; FRCA 1996. Socs: BMA; Assn. Anaesth. Gt. Brit. & Irel.; Liverp. Soc. Anaesth.

MCCANN, Joan Kathleen (retired) The Stocks, Start Lane, Whaley Bridge, High Peak SK23 7BP Tel: 01663 732907 — MB ChB 1954 Liverp.; 1989 FFPHM 1989; 1988 FFOM RCP Lond.; 1985 FFCM; 1962 DIH Soc. Apoth. Lond.; 1974 MFCM; 1980 MFOM. Prev: Cons. Occupat. Health & Dir. of Occupat. Health Servs. Stockport HA.

MCCANN, John Joseph 26 Springfield Road, Warrenpoint, Newry BT34 3NW — MB BCh BAO 1994 Belf.

MCCANN, John Patrick Royal Victoria Hospital, Grosvenor Road, Belfast BT12 6BA Email: john.maccann@royalhospitals.n-i.nhs.uk — MB BCh BAO 1977 Belf.; MD Belf. 1986; FRCP Lond. 1996; FRCP Ed. 1995; MRCP (UK) 1981; FRCPI 1998. (Qu. Univ. Belf.) Cons. Phys. (Rehabil. Med.) Roy. Vict. Hosp. Belf. Socs: Brit. Soc. Rehabil. Med.; Internat. Med. Soc. Paraplegia.

MCCANN, Kathryn May Ystrad Mynach Hospital, Caerphilly Road, Hengoed CF82 7XU Tel: 01443 812201; 2 East Rise, Llanishen, Cardiff CF14 0RJ Tel: 01222 741 7646 — MB ChB 1984 Glas.; DCH RCPS Glas. 1988; MSc Univ. of Wales Coll. Of Med.1999. Assoc. Specialist Community Paediat., Gwent NHS Trust. Socs: BACCH; RCPaediat. Prev: Regist. (Paediat.) Roy. Matern. Hosp. Glas.; Regist. (Paediat.) & SHO (Obst.) Roy. Alex. Hosp. Paisley.

MCCANN, Kirsty Rallt, Ceunant, Caernarfon LL55 4RT — MB ChB 1992 Liverp.; MRCGP 1997; DRCOG 1996; DFFP 1996. (Liverpool)

MCCANN, Margaret Ann Castle Craig Clinic, Blyth Bridge, West Linton EH46 7DH Tel: 01721 752625 Fax: 01721 752662 Email: g657@dial.pipex.com; Hope Burn House, Castle Craig, Blyth Bridge, West Linton EH46 7DH Tel: 01721 752270 — MB BCh BAO 1974 NUI. (National University Ireland) Med. Dir. (Alcoholism) Castle Craig Treatm. Clinic; Mem. Med. Counc. on Alcohol. Prev: Regist. (Anaesth.) Belf. City Hosp. & St. Bart. Hosp. Lond.

MCCANN, Mary Josephine (retired) Sunningdale, 7 Albany Avenue, Eccleston Park, Prescot L34 2QN Tel: 0151 426 5083 — LRCPI & LM, LRCSI & LM 1950.

MCCANN, Mr Michael Charles The Willows, Horners Lane, Rostrevor, Newry BT34 3EJ — MB BCh BAO 1982 NUI; FRCSI 1990. Assoc. Specialist (A & E) Daisy Hill Hosp. Newry. Socs: BMA & Brit. Assn. A & E Med.

MCCANN, Michael Gerard Occupational Health Dept, Glaxo Wellcome, Temple Hill, Dartford DA1 5AH Tel: 01322 223488 Fax: 01322 390460; 3 Dene Close, Chipstead, Coulsdon CR5 3NW Tel: 01737 553153 Fax: 01737 554852 Email: mikemccann@compuserv.com — MB BCh 1973 Dub.; MFOM 1993; AFOM 1987; Dip. Indust. Health Lond. 1984. (Trinity Coll. Dubl.) Occupat. Health Manager, Glaxo Wellcome Dartford. Socs: Soc. Occupat. Med.; Med. Co. Alcoholism (Mem. Publ. Health & Educat. Comm.); BMA. Prev: Chief Med. Off. SAPPI-SAICCOR S. Africa.

MCCANN, Neil Dept. of Anaesthetics, Univ. Hospital Of Wales, Health Park, Cardiff CF14 4XW Tel: 029 207 43107 Fax: 029 207 43251 Email: sue.donovan@uhw-tr.wales.nhs.uk; 2 East Rise, Llanishen, Cardiff CF14 0RJ — MB ChB 1985 Glas.; FRCA 1992; BSc 1982 (Hons.). Cons. Anaesth., Univ. Hosp. Of Wales, Cardiff. Socs: IASP; Pain Soc.; Welsh Pain Soc. Prev: Lect (Anaes) UHW, Cardiff; Regist., Anaesthetics, Glas.

MCCANN, Peter 4 West End, Penwortham, Preston PR1 0JD — MB ChB 1998 Leeds.

MCCANN, Richard John Riversdale Surgery, Riversdale House, Merthyrmawr Road, Bridgend CF31 3NL Tel: 01656 766866 Fax: 01656 668659; 33 Merthyr Mawr Road, Bridgend CF31 3NN — MB ChB 1979 Manch.; MRCGP 1987; DRCOG 1987.

MCCANN, Rosemary Anne Department Public Health Medicine, Salford and Trafford Health Authority, Peel House, Albert Street, Eccles, Manchester M30 0NJ Tel: 0161 787 0066 — MB BCh BAO 1982 NUI; MSc (Community Med.) Lond. 1987; MFPHM RCP (UK) 1990; MRCGP 1986; DCH RCP Lond. 1985; DRCOG 1985. (Dublin) Cons. Communicable Dis. Control Salford & Trafford HA.

MCCANN, Simon James 19 Ledcameroch Road, Bearsden, Glasgow G61 4AE — MB ChB 1995 Manch.

MCCANN, Simon Joseph Rickmansworth Road Surgery, 35 Rickmansworth Road, Watford WD1 7HL Tel: 01923 223232 Fax: 01923 243397 — MB BS 1983 Lond.; MSc Lond. 1994; MRCGP 1988; DRCOG 1987; DCH RCP Lond. 1987. (West. Med. Sch. Lond.) GP; Bd. Mem. & Clin. Governance Lead Watford & Three Rivers PCG. Prev: Tutor (Gen. Pract.) Watford Postgrad. Med. Centre.

MCCANN, Simon Robert Duns Medical Practice, The Knoll, Station Road, Duns TD11 3EL Tel: 01361 883322 Fax: 01361 882186 — MB ChB 1985 Ed.; MRCGP 1989; DCCH RCP Ed. 1990. Gen. Practitioner Duns; GP Community Hosp., Minor Injuries Unit.

MCCANN, Vincent John Bryn Teg, Capel y Graig, Bangor LL57 2SJ — MB BCh BAO 1991 Dub.

MCCANN, Wendy c/o Cole, 58 Endrick Gardens, Balfron, Glasgow G63 0RD — MB ChB 1992 Glas.

MCCANNELL

MCCANNELL, Elizabeth Scott Kirkside House, Sorn, Mauchline KA5 6HT — MB ChB 1985 Glas.; MRCGP 1990.

MCCAREY, Alexander Geddes 1 Bryanston Road, Birkenhead CH42 8PT Tel: 0151 608 3544 — MD 1951 Glas.; MB ChB 1943; DMRD Eng. 1951; DR Liverp. 1951. (Glas.)

MCCAREY, David William 7 Lyle Road, Greenock PA16 7QT — MB ChB 1997 Glas.

MCCARLIE, Isabel Southbank Road Surgery, 17-19 Southbank Road, Kirkintilloch, Glasgow G66 1NH Tel: 0141 776 2183 Fax: 0141 777 8321; Woodbourne House, Seven Sisters, Lenzie, Glasgow G66 3AW Tel: 0141 776 1791 — MB ChB 1977 Glas.; MFFP 1993; MRCGP 1985.

MCCARLIE, John (retired) c/o Logan, 2 Sandringham, Largs KA30 8BT — MB ChB 1944 Glas.

MCCARROLL, Connor Patrick 18 Alderwood Close, Purdysburn Road, Belfast BT8 6YZ — MB BCh BAO 1994 Belf.

MCCARROLL, Sheila Elizabeth Reform Street Health Centre, Reform Street, Beith KA15 2AE Tel: 01505 502888 Fax: 01505 504151 — MB ChB 1981 Glas. GP Beith.

***MCCARRON, Beth Kirstie** Helmsdale Cottage, Tregenna Lane, Blisland, Bodmin PL30 4JS — BM BS 1997 Nottm.

MCCARRON, Brendan Noel 73 Craigend Drive, Coatbridge ML5 5TG — MB ChB 1985 Glas.

MCCARRON, Emer Eilish Trade Winds, Malmesbury Road, Kington Langley, Chippenham SN14 6BQ — MB ChB 1997 Manch.

MCCARRON, Mark Owen 8 Fir Road, Londonderry BT48 8NB — MB BChir 1992 Camb.; MB (Hons.) Camb. 1992, BChir 1991, BA (Hons.) 1989, MA (Hons.) 1993; MRCP (UK) 1994. Regist. (Neurol.) S.. Gen. Hosp. Glas.; Patrick Berthoud Research Fell. Prev: SHO Rotat. (Med.) Roy. Vict. Hosp. Belf.

MCCARRON, Peter Gerard Dept of Social Medicine, University of Bristol, Bristol BS8 2PR — MB BCh BAO 1989 Dub.; MB BCh Dub. 1989.

MCCARRON, Siobhan Bernadette 160 Belldoo, Strabane BT82 9QL — MB BCh BAO 1993 Belf.

MCCARRY, Maria Elizabeth 43 Priors Way, Dunvant, Swansea SA2 7UH — MB ChB 1992 Birm.; ChB Birm. 1992.

MCCARRY, Neil William 57 Galbraith Drive, Milngavie, Glasgow G62 6LZ — MB ChB 1960 Glas.

MCCARTER, Douglas Henry Alexander 23 Kensington Gate, Dowanhill, Glasgow G12 9LQ Tel: 0141 334 1234 — MB ChB 1985 Glas.; MRCP (UK) 1991; DRCOG 1990; DCH RCPS Glas. 1988; FRCR 1995. Cons. Radiol. Glas. Roy. Infirm. Socs: Roy. Coll. Radiol.; Scott. Radiol. Soc. Prev: Sen. Regist. Rotat. (Diagn. Radiol.) Glas. E.

MCCARTER, James David Sandy Lane, Hanmer, Whitchurch SY13 3DL Tel: 01948 830223 Fax: 01948 830103; Pendle House, Hanmer, Whitchurch SY13 3DL — MB BCh BAO 1960 Dub.; MA Dub. 1960; LAH Dub. 1960; DObst RCOG 1963; LM Rotunda 1962. (T.C. Dub.) Clin. Asst. Penley Hosp.; Racecourse Med. Off., Diving Med. Ref. Socs: BMA. Prev: Clin. Clerk Rotunda Hosp. Dub.; Cas. Off. & Ho. Surg. Sir P. Dun's Hosp. Dub.

MCCARTHY, Andrew Laurence Department of Obstetrics & Gynaecology, Wycombe General Hospital, Queen Alexandra Road, High Wycombe HP11 2TT Tel: 01494 526161 — MB BCh BAO 1982 NUI; MD NUI 1995; MRCPI 1988; MRCOG 1988. Cons. O & G Wycombe Hosp. Bucks. Prev: Lect. (O & G) Roy. Postgrad. Med. Sch., Hammersmith Hosp. & Qu. Charlotte Hosp. Lond.; Regist. & Research Regist. St. Thos. Hosp. Lond.

MCCARTHY, Anna Helen Stoodley Sweet Briars, East Dean Road, Lockerley, Romsey SO51 0JQ — MB BS 1991 Lond.

MCCARTHY, Anna Maria (retired) 22 Grove Road, Sheffield S7 2GZ — MB BCh BAO 1945 NUI. Prev: Princip. Clin. Med. Off. (Audiol. Clinic) Sheff. Centr. Health Dist.

MCCARTHY, Basil 18 Coalway Avenue, Penn, Wolverhampton WV3 7LT — MB BCh BAO 1953 NUI. (Galw.) Prev: Ho. Phys. & Ho. Surg. Centr. Hosp. Galway; Sen. Ho. Off. Booth Hall. Childr. Hosp. Manch.

MCCARTHY, Benita Therese 27 Hillhead Crescent, Stewartstown Road, Belfast BT11 9FS — MB BCh BAO 1989 Belf.

MACCARTHY, Brendan Francis (cons.) 44 Fitzjohn's Avenue, London NW3 Tel: 020 7794 2624; 19 Willow Road, London NW3 1TJ Tel: 020 7435 7006 — MD 1965 NUI; MSc NUI 1951,

MD 1965, MB BCh BAO 1952; FRCPsych 1976, M 1971; DPM Eng. 1955. (Univ. Coll. Dub.) Dir. Lond. Clinic Psychoanal. Lond. Socs: Brit. Psychoanalyt. Soc. Prev: Cons. Psychother. Portman Clinic; Cons. Child Psychiat. Tavistock Clinic.

MCCARTHY, Brendan Patrick Ronan 8 Emery Close, Stockport SK4 4AY — MB ChB 1973 Manch.

MCCARTHY, Brian Edward Tanworth Lane Surgery, 2 Tanworth Lane, Shirley, Solihull B90 4DR Tel: 0121 744 2025 Fax: 0121 733 6890 — MB BCh BAO 1983 NUI; MRCGP 1990; DCH RCPS Glas. 1989; DObst RCPI 1989. GP. Prev: Trainee GP Worcester VTS.

MCCARTHY, Brian Gerald (retired) 1 Almond Avenue, Ickenham, Uxbridge UB10 8NA — MB BCh BAO 1953 NUI; MRCGP 1966. Prev: Med. Off. Brit. Red Cross Soc.

MACCARTHY, Charles Desmond (retired) 35 Queen's Road, Brentwood CM14 4HE Tel: 01277 218312 — MB BCh BAO Dub. 1941.

MCCARTHY, Cornelia Ann Manor Brook Medical Centre, 117 Brook Lane, London SE3 0EN Tel: 020 8856 5678 Fax: 020 8856 8632; 20 Foxes Dale, Blackheath, London SE3 9BQ — MB BS Lond. 1970; MRCS Eng. LRCP Lond. 1970; DCH Eng. 1973. (Guy's) Princip. in Gen. Pract.

MCCARTHY, Cornelius Gerrard Tel: 01473 719112 Email: mccarthy91@fsnet.co.uk; 137 Tuddenham Road, Ipswich IP3 9BN Tel: 01473 255141 — MB BCh BAO 1983 NUI; MRCGP 1988; DCH RCP Lond. 1987; DRCOG 1987; DA (UK) 1985; DMJ 1999 Soc Apoth. (University College Cork) GP Princip.; Police Surg. Suff. Constab. Prev: Trainee GP/SHO Ipswich VTS; Ho. Off. (Med. & Surg.) Mallow Gen. Hosp.

MCCARTHY, Daniel Anthony 3 Park Hill Medical Practice, Torquay TQ1 2AL Tel: 01803 605123; 13-15 Sherwell Valley Road, Chelston, Torquay TQ2 6EJ — MB BCh BAO 1964 NUI. (Univ. Coll. Cork) Prev: Sen. Ho. Phys. St. Kevin's Hosp. Dub.; SHO Erinville Matern Hosp. Cork; Ho. Phys. & Ho. Surg. St. Finbarr's Hosp. Cork.

MCCARTHY, Daniel Peter Justin, TD The Surgery, 328 Clapham Road, London SW9 9AE Tel: 020 7622 2006 — MB ChB Aberd. 1967. (Aberd.) Private Gen. Practitioner; Barrister-at-Law Inner Temple 1978. Socs: BMA & Med.-Leg. Soc.; FRSM; Soc. Doctors in Law. Prev: Regist. (Community Med.) S.W. Thames RHA; Regist. (Anaesth.) St. Helier Hosp. Carshalton; Ho. Phys. Bethnal Green Hosp. Lond.

MCCARTHY, David Terence Tel: 0117 966 9724 Fax: 0117 953 2604 — MB ChB 1968 Bristol.

MCCARTHY, Denis Francis 104 grange Road, Birmingham B24 0EU — MB BCh BAO 1945 NUI.

MCCARTHY, Denis Kevin The Limes Medical Centre, 8-12 Hodge Road, Worsley, Manchester M28 3AT Tel: 0161 790 8621 Fax: 0161 703 8670.

MACCARTHY, Desmond 11 Fir Tree Lane, Scarvagh, Craigavon BT63 6NY — MB BCh BAO 1980 NUI.

MACCARTHY, Diarmuid Anthony (retired) 85 Woodlands Road, Charfield, Wotton-under-Edge GL12 8LT Tel: 01453 511101 — LRCPI & LM, LRSCI & LM 1949; LRCPI & LM, LRCSI & LM 1949.

MCCARTHY, Mr Donal Martin Department of Orthopaedic Surgery, Homerton Hospital, Homerton Row, London E9 6SR Tel: 020 8919 7955 Fax: 020 8919 7474; 190 Warner Road, Walthamstow, London E17 7EA — MB BCh BAO 1981 NUI; FRCSI 1987. Cons. Orthop. Homerton Hosp. Lond.; Hon. Lect. St. Bart. Hosp. Lond. Prev: Hon. Fell Univ. Pittsburgh, USA.

MCCARTHY, Mr Donal O'Beirn Department of Surgery, Glan Clwyd Hospital, Bodelwyddan, Rhyl LL18 5UJ Tel: 01745 534229 (Secr.), 01745 583910 Email: donal.mccarthy@cd-tr.wales.nhs.uk — MB ChB Leeds 1968; FRCS Eng. 1974. (Leeds) Cons. Gen. & BrE. Surg. Glan Clwyd Hosp. N. Wales. Socs: Fell. Assn. Surgs. Of GB and Irel.; Brit. Assn. of Surg. Oncol. Prev: Sen. Cons. Surg. Camb. Milit. Hosp. Aldershot Hants.; Sen. Regist. (Profes. Surg. Unit) St. Bart. Hosp. Lond.; Regist. Rotat. (Surg.) Roy. Vict. Infirm. Newc.

MCCARTHY, Fiona Jane Frances Slaithwaite Health Centre, New Street, Slaithwaite, Huddersfield HD7 5AB Tel: 01484 846674; 13 Varley Road, Slaithwaite, Huddersfield HD7 5HL — MB ChB 1988 Dundee. Doctor (Family Plann.) Huddersfield.

MCCARTHY, Florence Justin (Surgery) 54 Trentham Road, Longton, Stoke-on-Trent ST3 4DW Tel: 01782 315547; 696 Lightwood Road, Longton, Stoke-on-Trent ST3 7HE — LRCPI & LM,

LRSCI & LM 1948; LRCPI & LM, LRCSI & LM 1948. (RCSI) Prev: Ho. Phys. & Ho. Surg. Bolton Roy. Infirm.; Ho. Surg. (Ophth.) Derbysh. Roy. Infirm.

MCCARTHY, Geraldine Mary Teresa Academic Unit, B4P, Dept of Psychological Medicene, University Hospital of Wales, Heath Park, Cardiff CF4 4XN Tel: 029 2074 3058 Email: mccarthygm@cardiff.ac.uk — MB BCh BAO 1988 NUI; MRCPsych 1996; DCH NUI 1990. (Univ. Coll. Dub.) Specialist Regist. (Psychiat. Of Old Age) S.wead Hosp. Bris.; Clin. Lect., Univ. of Bris. Prev: Clin. Research Fell. (Neuropsychiat. Genetics) Univ. Hosp. Wales, Cardiff.

MCCARTHY, Gerard James Accident & Emergency Department, Royal Gwent Hospital, Cardiff Road, Newport NP20 2UB — MB BCh BAO 1983 Belf. Cons. (Accid. & Emerg.) Roy. Gwent Hosp.

MCCARTHY, Gillian Ann The Wolverton Centre, Kingston Hospital NHS Trust, Galsworthy Road, Kingston upon Thames KT2 7QB Tel: 020 8974 9331 Fax: 020 8481 0078 — MB BS 1984 Lond.; MSc Surrey 1978; BSc (Hons.) Lond. 1977, MB BS 1984; MRCP (UK) 1988; MRCGP 1991; FRCP 2000 UK. (Royal Free) Cons. Phys. GUM/HIV The Wolverton Centre, Kingston Hosp. NHS Trust. Socs: Soc. Study VD., AGUM: Prev: Sen. Regist. (HIV & Genitourin. Med.) UCL Hosps. Lond.; Regist. (HIV & Genitourin. Med.) St. Stephens & W.m. Hosp. Lond.

MCCARTHY, Gillian Theresa (retired) Chailey Heritage Clinical Services, Beggarswood Road, North Chailey, Lewes BN8 4JN Tel: 01825 722112 Fax: 01825 723544 — MB ChB Sheff. 1963; FRCP Lond. 1985; MRCP (UK) 1970; DObst RCOG 1967; DCH Eng. 1966; FRCPCH. Hon. Cons. Neuropaediat. Chailey Heritage Clin. Servs. Lewes. Prev: Med. Dir. & Cons. Neuropaediat. Chailey Heritage Rehabil. & Developm. Centre Lewes E. Sussex.

*MCCARTHY, Hugh James 54 Handen Road, London SE12 8NR — MB BS 1998 Lond.; MB BS Lond 1998.

MCCARTHY, Ide Mary Gerardine Maclean, Isaac, Moore & McCarthy, Carisbrooke Health Centre, 22 Carisbrooke High St., Newport PO30 1NR — MB BCh BAO 1985 NUI; T(GP) 1992; DObst RCPI 1990; DCH RCPSI 1987.

MCCARTHY, James Francis Sett Valley Medical Centre, Hyde Bank Road, New Mills, Stockport SK22 4BP Tel: 01663 743483; Tir na Nog, Station Road, Furness Vale, High Peak SK23 7QA Tel: 01663 747030 — MB ChB 1976 Manch.; MB ChB (Hons.) Manch. 1976; BSc (Hons.) Newc. 1970; MSc Leeds 1971; MRCGP 1980; DCCH RCP Ed., RCGP & FCM 1983; DRCOG 1980; DCH Eng. 1978; FRIPHH 1987. GP Trainer Derbysh. Prev: Clin. Med. Off. Stockport HA.

MCCARTHY, James Justin Mayfield Surgery, 54 Trentham Road, Longton, Stoke-on-Trent ST3 4DW Tel: 01782 315547; 4 Rectory Close, Church Leigh, Leigh, Stoke-on-Trent ST10 4PR — MB BCh BAO 1984 NUI; LRCPI & LM, LRCSI & LM 1984; MRCGP 1988.

MCCARTHY, Jane Mary Northgate and Prudhoe NHS Trust, Prudhoe Hospital, Prudhoe NE42 5NT Tel: 01661 514393 Fax: 01661 514592; 82 Mariners Wharf, Quayside, Newcastle upon Tyne NE1 2BJ — MB ChB 1982 Leeds; MRCPsych 1990; MRCGP 1987. (Leeds University) Cons. Psychiat. (Learning Disabil.) N.gate & Prudhoe NHS Trust; Sen. Lect. Newc. Univ. Prev: Cons. Psychiat. (Learning Disabil.) Hinchingbrooke NHS Trust; Lect. (Developm. Psychiat.) Univ. Coll. Lond.

MACCARTHY, Joan Marie (retired) 32 Torkington Road, Gatley, Cheadle SK8 4PR Tel: 0161 428 2515 — MB BCh BAO 1950 NUI; BSc NUI 1947; DPH Manch. 1956; DPH Eng. 1956; DCH RCPSI 1953. Sen. Med. Off. S. Manch. HA. Prev: Ho. Phys. Mater Hosp. Dub.

MCCARTHY, John Langley Health Centre, Common Road, Slough SL3 8LE Tel: 01753 544288 Fax: 01753 592415; 55 Old Slade Lane, Iver SL0 9DX — MB ChB 1960 Glas. (Glas.) Socs: Fell. Roy. Soc. Med.; Oxf. Inst. Psychiat. Prev: Squadron Ldr. RAF Med. Br.; Ho. Surg. E.. Dist. Hosp. Glas.; Ho. Phys. Heathfield Hosp. Ayr.

MCCARTHY, John Haydon Department of Pathology, District Laboratory, South Tyneside District Hospital, Harton Lane, South Shields NE34 OPL Tel: 0191 454 8888 Fax: 0191 202 4145; The Beeches, Whickham Park, Whickham, Newcastle upon Tyne NE16 4EH Tel: 0191 488 3458 — MB BS 1974 Newc.; FRCPath 1993, M 1982; DMJ Soc. Apoth. Lond. 1988. Cons. Histopath. S. Tyneside HA; Hon. Clin. Lect. Univ. Newc.; Home Office Apptd. Forens. Path. N. Eng. Socs: Founder Mem. Brit. Assn. Ophth. Path.; Founder Mem. Internat. Soc. of Ophth. Path. Prev: Lect. (Path.) Univ. Newc. u Tyne.

MCCARTHY, John James The Health Centre, West Pottergate, Norwich NR2 4BX Tel: 01603 877911 Fax: 01603 877912; 262 Unthank Road, Norwich NR2 2AJ Tel: 01603 504158 — MB BS 1977 Lond.; MRCS Eng. LRCP Lond. 1977; DRCOG 1982; DA Eng. 1980. (Guy's) Clin. Asst. MFE Norf. Univ. Hosp. Trust. Prev: Trainee GP Som. VTS; SHO (Anaesth.) Roy. Sussex Co. Hosp. Brighton.

MCCARTHY, John Philip 6 Southey Cl, Littleborough OL15 0RD — MB ChB 1997 Liverp.

MACCARTHY, Joseph Aidan, OBE, GM Central Medical Establishment, Kelvin House, Cleveland St., London W1P 6AU Tel: 020 7636 4651 — MB BCh BAO 1939 NUI. (Cork) Civil. Med. Pract. RAF Centr. Med. Estab. Lond.

MACCARTHY, Joseph Paul Employee Health Services, White Rose House, 28a York Place, Leeds LS1 2EZ Tel: 0113 244 7245 — MB ChB 1980 Dundee; MRCP (UK) 1986; MFOM RCP Lond. 1997. Area Med. Adviser Employee Health Servs. N. E. Area.

MCCARTHY, Julie Elizabeth 31A Glenmore Road, London NW3 4BY — MB BCh BAO 1990 NUI; LRCPSI 1990.

MCCARTHY, Justin Peter 79 Winstanley Road, Orrell, Wigan WN5 7XE — MB ChB 1990 Birm.; ChB Birm. 1990.

MCCARTHY, Kathleen (retired) Bromley Hospital, Cromwell Avenue, Bromley BR2 9AJ — MB BS 1962 Lond.; MRCS Eng. LRCP Lond. 1962; FFA RCS Eng. 1966. Prev: Cons. Anaesth. Bromley NHS Trust.

MCCARTHY, Kathleen Joyce (retired) 44 Camberwell Grove, London SE5 8RE Tel: 020 7703 3888 — MRCS Eng., LRCP Lond. 1937; DCH Eng. 1948. Prev: Asst. Med. Off. Pub. Health Dept. LCC.

MCCARTHY, Kathryn 12 Disraeli Road, Christchurch BH23 3NB — MB BS 1998 Lond.; MB BS Lond 1998.

MCCARTHY, Kathryn Helen 55 Ashburnham Grove, London SE10 8UJ — MB BS 1988 Lond. Regist. (O & G) King's Coll. Hosp. Lond.

MCCARTHY, Keith Paul Department of Histopathology, Cheltenham General Hospital, Sandford Road, Cheltenham GL53 7AN Tel: 01242 222222 Fax: 01242 226255; Nutfield House, Bromesberrow, Ledbury HR8 1RS Tel: 01531 650114 Fax: 01531 650793 Email: bromesberrowmacs@netscapeonline.co.uk — MB BS 1984 Lond.; MD Lond. 1993; MRCPath 1993. Cons. Histopath. Cheltenham Gen. Hosp. & Gloucester Roy. Hosp. Socs: Brit. Lymphoma Path. Gp.; Assn. Clin. Path.; Brit. Div. Internat. Acad. Path. Prev: Cons. Histopath. Roy. Marsden Hosp. Lond.; Sen. Regist. St. Geo. Hosp. Lond.; Clin. Research Fell. Roy. Marsden Hosp. Sutton.

MCCARTHY, Kevin Well Hall Surgery, 174-180 Well Hall Road, Eltham, London SE9 1JB Tel: 020 8850 1615 Fax: 020 8294 1486 — MB BCh BAO 1977 NUI; DCH RCP Lond. 1981; DObst 1979. Forens. Med. Examr. Metrop. Police Lond.

MCCARTHY, Professor Kevin (retired) Department of Medical Microbiology, University of Liverpool, PO Box 147, Liverpool L69 3BX — MB ChB Liverp. 1944; MD Liverp. 1951; FRCPath 1970. Hon. Sen. Fell. Med. Microbio. Univ. Liverp. Prev: Prof. Med. Microbiol. Univ. Liverp.

MCCARTHY, Mr Liam Sean Lloyd 19 Weald View Road, Tonbridge TN9 2NG — MB BS 1990 Lond.; FRCS Ed. 1994.

MCCARTHY, Margaret Anne Dunglascar, 19 Dunlady Road, Dundonald, Belfast BT16 1TT — MB BCh BAO 1974 Belf.; DCH RCPSI 1976.

MCCARTHY, Marie Elizabeth Stokewood Surgery, Fair Oak Road, Fair Oak, Eastleigh SO50 8AU Tel: 023 8069 2000 Fax: 023 8069 3891 — MB ChB 1971 Otago. (Otago) GP E.leigh, Hants.

MCCARTHY, Marion Elin 2 Cae'rbont, Swansea Road, Fforestfach, Swansea SA5 4NS — MB BCh 1991 Wales; MRCGP 1995.

MCCARTHY, Mark Ian Unit of Metabolic Medicine, Imperial College School of Medicine, London W2 1NY Tel: 020 7886 1235 Fax: 020 7886 1790 Email: m.mccarthy@ic.ac.uk — MB BChir 1984 Camb.; MA Camb. 1984, MD 1995; FRCP (UK) 1999. (St. Thos. Hosp. Lond.) Reader (Molecular Genetics) Imperial Coll. Sch. Med. Lond.; Hon. Cons. Phys. St. Mary's Hosp. Lond. Prev: MRC Trav. Fell. Lond. Hosp. Med. Coll.; Lect. (Med.) Lond. Hosp.

MCCARTHY, Professor Mark James Department of Epidemiology and Public Health, University College London, 1-19 Torrington

MCCARTHY

Place, London WC1E 6BT Tel: 020 7391 1711 Fax: 020 7813 0280 Email: m.mccarthy@ucl.ac.uk; 37 Downshire Hill, London NW3 1NU — MB BChir Camb. 1970; PhD (Econ.) Lond. 1991; MSc 1974; MA Camb. 1970; FRCP Lond. 1994; MRCP (UK) 1971; FFCM 1987; M 1974. (Univ. Coll. Hosp.) Prof. Pub. Health; Hon. Cons. in Pub. Health Camden & Islington HA. Socs: Europ. Pub. Health Assoc. Prev: Dir. Pub. Health Camden & Islington Health Auth.

MCCARTHY, Mr Mark John Lilac Cottage, 5 West Lane, Billesdon, Leicester LE7 9AP Tel: 0116 259 6738 Email: mjm25@leicester.ac.uk — MB ChB 1990 Birm.; ChB Birm. 1990; FRCS Ed. 1994. (Birmingham) Clin. Lect. (Gen. Surg.) Univ. of Leicester. Socs: Affil. Mem. Vasc. Surg. Soc.; Affil. Assn. Surgs. GB & Irel.; Surg. Research Soc. Prev: Wellcome Clin. Research Fell. Univ. of Leicester; Specialist Regist. (Gen. Surg.) Birm. Heartlands Hosp.

MCCARTHY, Mary Elizabeth Frances Mayfield Surgery, 54 Trentham Road, Longton, Stoke-on-Trent ST3 4DW Tel: 01782 315547; Lorien, Lightwood Road, Rough Close, Stoke-on-Trent ST3 7PW Tel: 01782 396045 — MB BS 1981 Lond.

MCCARTHY, Mary Rose 17 Poulett Gardens, Twickenham TW1 4QS — MB BCh BAO 1984 NUI.

MCCARTHY, Mary Ursula Belvidere Medical Practice, 23 Belvidere Road, Broseley SY2 5LS Tel: 01743 363640 Fax: 01743 357400; 2 Lexden Gardens, Belle Vue, Shrewsbury SY3 7NL Tel: 01743 350786 — MB BS 1964 Lond. (Roy. Free) Hosp. Practitioner Diabetic Unit Roy. Shrewsbury Hosp. & P.ss Roy. Hosp. Telford; Clin. Asst. Fertil. Unit Roy. Shrewsbury Hosp. Socs: Eur. Assoc. Study Diabetes; BDA; RCGP. Prev: GP Broseley; Clin. Asst. Shrops. Diabetic Serv.; GP Welwyn Garden City.

MCCARTHY, Matthew Joseph Peel House Medical Centre, Avenue Parade, Accrington BB5 6RD Tel: 01254 237231 Fax: 01254 389525; Hillside, 209 Manchester Road, Accrington BB5 2PF — MB BCh BAO 1981 Dub.

MCCARTHY, Michael Basil Chipping Surgery, 1 Symn Lane, Wotton-under-Edge GL12 7BD Tel: 01453 842214; 57 Amberley Way, Wickwar, Wotton-under-Edge GL12 8LW Tel: 01453 842214 — MB BCh BAO 1979 Dub.

MCCARTHY, Michael David Wood 79 Winstanley Road, Billinge, Wigan WN5 7XE — MB ChB 1997 Leeds.

MCCARTHY, Michelle Joy 4 Furrow Close, Stanway, Colchester CO3 5YN — BM BS 1989 Nottm.

MCCARTHY, Michelle Marie Department of Gastroenterology, St. Thomas' Hospital, London SE1 7EH Tel: 020 7928 9292; 83 Burlington Lane, Grove Park, Chiswick, London W4 3ET — MB BS 1989 New South Wales; FRACP 1997. (Univ. New South Wales Sydney, Austral.) Specialist Regist. in Gastroenterol. at St. Thomas Hosp., Lond. Socs: BSG; BASL; AGA.

MCCARTHY, Miriam Dolores Senior Medical Officer, Castle Buildings, Stormont, Belfast BT4 3SF Tel: 028 90 520744 Fax: 028 90 520725 Email: miriam.mccarthy@dhsspshligor.uk — MB BCh BAO 1981 Belf.; MPH 1995; MRCGP 1985; DRCOG 1984. Sen. Med. Off. Med. + allied Br. DHSSPS, N. Irel..

MACCARTHY, Nicholas Eugene The Surgery, Carisbrooke House, Stockleigh Road, St Leonards-on-Sea TN38 0JP Tel: 01424 423190/432925 Fax: 01424 460473; 8 Old House Gardens, Hastings TN34 2JS Tel: 01424 428783 — MB ChB 1977 Liverp.; DRCOG 1979; Dip. Occ. Med. 1997. GP Tutor. Socs: SOM.

MCCARTHY, Nicholas Rae Highdown Surgery, 1 Highdown Avenue, Worthing BN13 1PU Tel: 01903 265656 Fax: 01903 830450 — MRCS Eng. LRCP Lond. 1978; MB BS Lond. 1979, BDS 1971; FDS RCPS Glas. 1982. (Univ. Coll. Hosp.) Adviser on Surg. List. & Princip. Mem. Disciplinary Panel Sussex FHSA; Chief Med. Off. Lond. & Edin. Insur. Co. Socs: Anglo-French Med. Soc.; Brit. Acad. Experts.; Roy. Soc. Med. Prev: Regist. (Oral Surg.) St. Richard's Hosp. Chichester & Univ. Coll. Hosp. Dent. Sch. Lond.

MCCARTHY, Owen Rourke (retired) 54 Handen Road, London SE12 8NR — MB BCh BAO 1952 Dub.; FRCP Lond. 1986, M 1966; FRCP Ed. 1982, M 1962; DHMSA 1996. Prev: Cons. Phys. Newham Health Dist.

MCCARTHY, Patrick Hugh Vernon Birchwood Hall Community Centre, Storridge, Malvern WR13 5EZ Email: hhc@durcon.co.uk; 14 Baxendale Street, London E2 7BY — MB BS 1981 Lond.; DCH RCP Lond. 1986. Mem. Hoxton Health Collective Lond.

MACCARTHY, Patrick Richard High Street, 16 High Street, Great Baddow, Chelmsford CM2 7HQ Tel: 01245 473251 Fax: 01245 478394 — MB BS 1972 Lond. Socs: BMA. Prev: Med. Adviser Centr. Elec. Generat. Bd. (SE Region); Trainee GP P'boro. VTS.; Ho. Phys. Lond. Hosp.

MCCARTHY, Paul Martin Caldicot Medical Group, Gray Hill Surgery, Woodstock Way, Caldicot, Newport NP26 4DB Tel: 01291 420282 Fax: 01291 425853 — MB BCh 1970 Wales.

MACCARTHY, Philip Andrew Kings College Hospital, Denmark Hill, London — MB ChB 1991 (Hons.) Bristol; PhD 2000 Wales; BSc Bristol 1988; MRCP (UK) 1994. Specialist Regist. (Cardiol.) King's Coll. Hosp. Lond. Socs: Brit, Cardiovasc. Interven. Soc.; Brit. Soc. Cardiovasc. Research; Internat. Soc. Heart Research. Prev: Regist. (Cardiol.) Univ. Hosp. Wales Cardiff; SHO (Med.) John Radcliffe Hosp. Oxf.; MRC Clin. Train. Fell. Cardiff.

MCCARTHY, Robert John Leafield, Higher Downs Road, Torquay TQ1 3LD — MB BS 1992 Lond.; FRCS Eng. 1996. (Roy. Lond. Hosp.) Specialist Regist. Gen. Surg. Yeovil Dist. Hosp.

MCCARTHY, Rona Department of G. U. M., Ninewells Hospital, South Block, Dundee DD1 9ND; West Cottage, Glen Duckie, By Newburgh, Cupar KY14 6JF — MB ChB 1988 Aberd.; DRCOG 1995; DFFP 1995. (Aberdeen) Clin. Asst., G. U. M. Dept., Ninewells Hosp., Dundee; Clin. Asst., G. U. M. Dept., Vict. Hosp., Kirkgaldy; Clin. Med. Off., Family Plann., Drumhar HC, Perth. Prev: GP Partner, Newburgh,Fife.

MCCARTHY, Sally Anne 540A Holburn Street, Aberdeen AB10 7LL — MB ChB 1992 Aberd.

MCCARTHY, Sean Patrick 39 Salford Road, London SW2 4BL; 15 Pronkwood Lawns, Aylesbury Estate, Tallaght, Dublin, Republic of Ireland — MB BCh BAO 1978 NUI; DObst. RCPI 1982; DCH Dub. 1982; MICGP 1988. GP FirHo..

MCCARTHY, Shaun Francis (retired) 20 Dorchester Close, Headington, Oxford OX3 8SS — MB BCh BAO NUI 1956; DCH RCPSI 1959; DObst RCOG 1960; MA Philosphy of Health Care (Wales) 1993.

MCCARTHY, Stephen William Thornley Street Surgery, 40 Thornley Street, Wolverhampton WV1 1JP Tel: 01902 26843 Fax: 01902 688500; 14 Parkdale W., Parkdale, Wolverhampton WV1 4TE Tel: 01902 562885 Email: stephen_mccarthy@parkdalewest.freeseerve.co.uk — MB ChB 1984 Birm.; DRCOG 1987. (Birm.) Non-Exec. Dir. Wolverhampton HA. Prev: GP Walsall; Trainee GP Walsall VTS.

MCCARTHY, Steven Penistone Group Practice, 19 High St., Penistone, Sheffield S36 6BR Tel: 01226 762257; 7 All Saints Close, Silkstone, Barnsley S75 4LQ Tel: 01226 790579 — MB BCh 1991 Wales; MRCGP 1995; DFFP 1994; DRCOG 1993. (UWCM (Cardiff)) Prev: Trainee GP Abergavenny.

MCCARTHY, Terence John The Surgeries, Grafton Road, Canvey Island SS8 7BT Tel: 01268 682277 — MB BS 1961 Lond.; MRCS Eng. LRCP Lond. 1961; DObst RCOG 1963. (Lond. Hosp.) Socs: BMA.

MCCARTHY, Thomas Paul 16 Waterford House, Thorney Mill Road, West Drayton UB7 7DL Tel: 01895 421372 Fax: 020 8990 4357 Email: tpm59499@glaxowellcome.co.uk — MB BS Lond. 1969; MRCS Eng. LRCP Lond. 1969; DA Eng. 1972; MRCPCH 1996. (Guy's) Assoc. Med. Dir. Glaxo Wellcome UK. Socs: Brit. Thorac. Soc.; W Kent Medico-Chir. Soc.; GP Asthma Gp. Prev: Audit Advisor Suff. MAAG; Ho. Phys. (Paediat.) & SHO (Anaesth.) W.m. Hosp. Lond.; Regist. (Anaesth.) Greenwich Dist. Hosp. Lond.

MCCARTHY, Timothy 69A Craneford Way, Twickenham TW2 7S8 — MB BS 1992 Lond.

MCCARTHY, Timothy James Queens Park Medical Centre, Farrer Street, Stockton-on-Tees TS18 2AW Tel: 01642 679681 Fax: 01642 677124 — MB BCh BAO 1975 NUI.

MCCARTHY, William Edward, Maj. RAMC Retd. 11 Adam Court, Henley-on-Thames RG9 2BJ — MB BS 1962 Lond. (St. Bart.)

MCCARTIE, Brenden St John 31 Victoria Road, Londonderry BT47 2PT — LRCPI & LM, LRCSI & LM 1949; DPH NUI 1953.

MCCARTIE, John David Basement Flat, 57 Brook Green, London W6 7BJ — MB ChB 1984 Otago.

MCCARTIE, Kathleen Mary 7 Margaret Avenue, Trentham, Stoke-on-Trent ST4 8EE — MRCS Eng. LRCP Lond. 1952; DObst RCOG 1955.

MCCARTNEY, Carol Anne 3 Wyverne, Berners End, Barnston, Great Dunmow, Dunmow CM6 1LY — MB BS 1984 Lond.

MCCARTNEY, Colin John Lindsay 15 Errol Road, Invergowrie, Dundee DD2 5AG — MB ChB 1991 Ed.

MCCARTNEY, David James Maryhill Health Centre, 41 Shawpark Street, Glasgow G20 9DR Tel: 0141 531 8897 Fax: 0141 531 8863 — MB ChB 1983 Glas.; MRCGP 1987; DRCOG 1986. (Glasgow) GP Princip. & Clin. Tutor Glas. Univ.

MCCARTNEY, Elinor Marie 18 Laganvale Manor, Stranmills, Belfast BT9 5BE — MB BCh BAO 1991 Belf.; MRCGP 1995; DGM RCPS Glas. 1994; DCH RCPSI 1994. SHO (Dermat. & Rheum.) Belf. Prev: Trainee GP Randalstown.

MCCARTNEY, Irene Margaret Gurney Surgery, 101-103 Magdalen Street, Norwich NR3 1LN Tel: 01603 448800 — MB BCh BAO 1984 Belf.; MB BCh BAO Belf. 1984; MRCGP 1991; DRCOG 1991.

MCCARTNEY, Kelley Noelle Muckamore Abbey Hospital, Antrim BT41 3BE — MB BCh BAO 1990 Belf.; DMH; MRCPsych. (Queen's University Belfast) Sen. Regist. Learning Disabil. (Psychiat.).

MCCARTNEY, Mark Tel: 0115 924 9924/41136 Fax: 0115 970 9706 — BM BS 1990 Nottm.; Diploma in Cognitive Therapy 1998 Newcastle/Durham; BMedSci Nottm. 1988; MRCPsych 1995. Cons. Gen. Adult Psychiat., Nottm. Prev: Sen. Regist. - Gen. Adult Psychiat. Mid-Trent (Nottm.) Rotat.; Specialist Regist. - Cognitive and Behavioural Psychother. (Nottm.).

MCCARTNEY, Mark Robert Pensilva Health Centre, School Road, Pensilva, Liskeard PL14 5RP Tel: 01579 362249 Fax: 01579 363323 — MB ChB 1982 Bristol; MRCGP 1988; DRCOG 1985.

MCCARTNEY, Maureen Department of Public Health, EHSSB, 12-22 Linenhall St., Belfast BT1 — MB BCh BAO 1983 Belf.; MB BCh BAO Belf.1983.

MCCARTNEY, Michael Ground Floor Left, 18 Bentinck St., Greenock PA16 7RN — MB ChB 1991 Glas.; DFFP 1996. (University of Glasgow) GP Princip., Port Glas. Health Centre. Prev: GP Regist.; Sen. Health Off., Psychiat. Ravenscraig Hosp. Greenock; Sen. Health Off., Med. for the Elderly, Paisley.

MCCARTNEY, Michael David 14 Meadowlands, Portstewart BT55 7FG — MB BCh BAO 1990 Belf.

MCCARTNEY, Peter Russell St Peters Street Medical Practice, 16 St Peters Street, London N1 8JG Tel: 020 7226 7131 Fax: 020 7354 9120; 23 Belitha Villas, London N1 1PE Tel: 020 7607 4442 — MB BS 1982 Lond.; MSc Med. Stats. Lond. 1973, BSc ARCS 1972. (St. Bart.) Research Fell. Lond. Sch. Hyg. & Trop. Med. Prev: Trainee GP Middlx. Hosp. VTS; Ho. Surg. Hackney Hosp. Lond.; Ho. Phys. St. Bart. Hosp. Lond.

MCCARTNEY, Rory Norman Jonathan Ballymoney Health Centre, Robinson Memorial Hospital, 21 Newal Road, Ballymoney BT53 6HB Tel: 028 2766 0300 Fax: 028 2766 0321; 49 Kirk Road, Ballymoney BT53 8HB Tel: 012656 64649 — MB BCh BAO 1983 Dub.; MRCGP 1987; DGM RCP Lond. 1987; DCH RCPSI 1986; DRCOG 1985. Prev: SHO (Paediat., Surg., O & G & Med.) Daisy Hill Hosp. Newry; SHO (Geriat. Med.) Lagan Valley Hosp. Lisburn.

MCCARTNEY, Sara Ann 19 Ella Road, London N8 9EL — MB BS 1988 Lond.

MCCARTNEY, William Alexander (retired) Glenmalure, 50 Semicock Road, Ballymoney BT53 6PY Tel: 028 2766 2196 — MB BCh BAO Belf. 1948; FRCGP 1981, M 1969. Prev: Hosp. Med. Off. Lond.derry & Gransha Hosp.

MCCARTY, David 98 Belmont Church Road, Belfast BT4 2DA — MB BCh BAO 1997 Belf.

MCCARTY, Heather Anne 98 Belmont Church Road, Belfast BT4 2DA — MB BCh 1998 Belf.; MB BCh Belf 1998.

MCCARTY, Moira Department of Radiology, James Cook University Hospital, Marton Road, Middlesbrough TS4 3BW — MB BS 1983 Lond.; FRCP 2000; MRCP (UK) 1986; FRCR 1989. (Royal Free) p/t Cons. Diagn. Radiol. S. Cleveland Hosp. Middlesbrough. Prev: Sen. Regist. (Diagn. Radiol.) St. Mary's Hosp. Lond.

MCCASKIE, Andrew William 121 Carisbrooke Road, Leicester LE2 3PG — MB ChB 1987 Leeds.

MCCATHIE, Neal James 58 Wigorn Road, Bearwood, Warley B67 5HG — BM BS 1998 Nottm.; BM BS Nottm 1998.

MCCAUGHAN, John Francis Gerard The Occupational Health Unit, Seapark, 151 Belfast Road, Carrickfergus BT38 8PL Tel: 0289 700718 Fax: 02890 700731; Email: mccaughen@nireland.com — MB BCh BAO 1981 Belf.; MRCGP 1987; FFOM (RCPI) 2001; DRCOG 1986; MFOM RCP Lond. 1997. (Qu. Univ.) Med. Adviser to N. Irel. Civil Serv. Belf.; Med. Adviser to Harland & Wolff Heavy Industries, Belf.; Div. Surg. Abbey Div. St. John's Ambul. Socs: Soc. Occupat. Med. Prev: Indust. Med. Off. Harland & Wolff & BT Belf.; Trainee GP Sandhead SW Scotl.

MCCAUGHAN, Ursula Mary 60 Glenshesk Road, Brackney, Ballycastle BT54 6PY Tel: 012657 63436 — MB BCh BAO 1984 Belf.; MRCGP 1989; DCH Dub. 1990; DGM RCP Lond. 1989; DRCOG 1988.

MCCAUGHERN, Jean Maine Medical Practice, Old Mill Park, Main Street, Cullybackey, Ballymena BT42 1GP Tel: 028 2588 2222 Fax: 028 2588 3900; Tel: 028 2588 1211 — MB BCh BAO 1989 Belf.; MRCGP 1994; DFFP 1994; DRCOG 1992; DCH Dub. 1991. (Queen's University, Belfast) GP Cullybackey Ballymena; GP SHO Course Organizer Antrim Hosp. Socs: N. Irel. Assn. Family Plann. Doctors; RCGP. Prev: Trainee GP Ahoghill Ballymena.

MCCAUGHERN, Sarah Georgina Shankill Road Surgery, 136-138 Shankill Road, Belfast BT13 2BD Tel: 028 9032 4524 — MB BCh BAO 1984 Belf.; DRCOG 1989; DCH Dub. 1988. Princip. (Gen. Pract.). Socs: BMA. Prev: Trainee GP Belf.

MCCAUGHEY, Conall Padraig Joseph Regional Virus Laboratory, The Royal Hospitals, Belfast BT12 6BN Tel: 01232 894628 Fax: 01232 439181 Email: c.mccaughey@qub.ac.uk; 23 Manse Park, Carryduff, Belfast BT8 8RX — MB BCh BAO 1987 Belf.; BSc Belf. 1987; MD 1997; MRCPath 1993. (Queen's Belf.) Cons. (Virol.) Regional Virus Lab. Roy. Hosps. Socs: MRCPath.; Soc. Gen. Microbiol. Prev: Sen. Regist. (Virol.) Regional Virus Laborat. Roy. Vict. Hosp.

MCCAUGHEY, Elizabeth Susan Department Community Child Health, Bitterine Health Centre, Commercial St., Southampton SO18 6BT Tel: 02380 420420 Fax: 02380 448920; Slab Farm, Slab Lane, West Wellow, Romsey SO51 6BY Tel: 01794 323844 — BM 1977 Soton.; MRCP (UK) 1980. Cons. Paediat. (Community Child Health). Prev: Soton. Community Health Serv. Trust.

MCCAUGHEY, Malcolm Neillsbrook Road Surgery, 5 Neillsbrook Road, Randalstown, Antrim BT41 3AE Tel: 028 9447 2575 Fax: 028 9447 3653; 1 The Hermitage, Randalstown, Antrim BT41 3EA Tel: 01849 472820 — MB BCh BAO 1972 Belf.; MICGP 1986; MRCGP 1985; DObst RCOG 1974.

MCCAUGHEY, Manus 18 Knockbracken Cr, Carryduff, Belfast BT8 8DB — MB BCh BAO 1997 Belf.

MCCAUGHEY, William Bannview, 61 Banbridge Road, Gilford, Craigavon BT63 6DL Tel: 028 38 831761 Email: wmccaughey@cahgt.n-i.nhs.uk — MD 1982 Belf.; MB BCh BAO 1966; 1969 FFA RCS Eng. 1970; 1970 FFA RCSI 1969. (Belf.) Cons. Anaesth. Craigavon Hosp.; Lect. (Anaesth.) Qu. Univ. Belf. Prev: Sen. Tutor (Anaesth.) Qu. Univ. Belf.; Ho. Off. Roy. Vict. Hosp. Belf.

MCCAUL, James Anthony 3 Upland Road, Glasgow G14 9BG Email: jmccau@aol.com — BDS 1991 Glas.; BDS (Hons.) Glas. 1991; MB ChB Glas. 1997; FDSRCPS Glas. 1994. SHO (Gen. Surg.) W. of Scotl. Basic Surgic. Train. Scheme. Socs: BAOMS; BMA W. of Scotl. JDC Mem. Prev: Res. (Surg.) W.ern Infirm. Glas.; Locum Cons. Maxillofacial Surg. Monklands Dist. Gen. Hosp.; Locum Regist. Monklands Dist. Gen. Hosp.

MCCAUL, John Alexander 12 Ildersly Grove, Dulwich, London SE21 8EU — MB BS 1972 Lond.; FFOM RCP Lond. 1994, MFOM 1984; DIH Eng. 1980. (Univ. Coll. Hosp.) Chief Med. Off. Innogy plc. Socs: Soc. Occupat. Med. & Roy. Soc. Med. Prev: Ho. Surg. Univ. Coll. Hosp. Lond.; Ho. Phys. Whittington Hosp. Lond.; Sen. Med. Off. Ford Motor Co. Ltd.

MCCAULEY, Adrian Anthony Martin The Surgery, 137 Ormeau Rd, Belfast BT7 1SN Tel: 028 9031 1118 Fax: 028 9032 5615; 19 Maryville Park, Malone Road, Belfast BT9 6LN Tel: 02890 664804 — MB BCh BAO 1982 Belf.; MRCGP 1986; DRCOG 1986; DCH NUI Dub. 1988. Socs: BMA.

MCCAULEY, Deirdre Aine 3 Shandon Park, Londonderry BT48 8AW — MB BS 1998 Lond.; MB BS Lond 1998.

MCCAULEY, Patricia Mary Josephine The Courtyard, East Block, A Floor, Queens Medical Centre, Derby Road, Nottingham NG7 2UH — MB BCh BAO 1978 NUI; MRCPsych 1987.

MCCAULEY, Peter (retired) 103 The Thoroughfare, Woodbridge IP12 1AS — MB BCh BAO 1939 NUI; DPM 1948. Cons. Psychiat.

MCCAULEY

Ipswich Hosp. Gp.; Psychother. Prev: Jun. Asst. Phys. Mapperley Hosp. Nottm.

MCCAULEY, William John 15 Sperrin Park, Londonderry BT47 6NG — MB BCh BAO 1992 Belf.

MCCAVERT, Michael Omagh Health Centre, Mountjoy Road, Omagh BT79 7BA Tel: 028 8224 3521 — MB BCh BAO 1976 Belf.; BSc (Physiol.) Belf. 1973, MB BCh BAO 1976; MRCP (UK) 1983; MRCGP 1983; DRCOG 1982. GP Omagh.

MCCAW, Colin John Irvinestown Health Centre, 20 Church Street, Irvinestown, Enniskillen BT94 1EH Tel: 028 6862 1212 Fax: 028 6862 8624 — MB BCh BAO 1985 Belf.; MRCGP 1990; T(GP) 1991.

MCCAW, Thomas The Strand, 21 Shore Road, Killyleagh, Downpatrick BT30 9UE — MB BCh BAO 1985 Belf.; MRCGP 1989; DTM & H Liverp. 1990; DRCOG 1987.

MCCAY, David Alexander Wye Valley Surgery, 2 Desborough Avenue, High Wycombe HP11 2RN Tel: 01494 521044 Fax: 01494 472770; 40 Maybrook Gardens, High Wycombe HP13 6PJ Tel: 01494 529356 — BM BCh 1964 Oxf.; MRCS Eng. LRCP Lond. 1964. (Oxf. & Guy's)

MCCAY, Natalie Jennifer Patricia 17 Muscovey Close, Lyneham, Chippenham SN15 4QB — MB BS 1996 Lond.

MCCAY, Noreen Mary Ballygomartin Road Surgery, 17 Ballygomartin Road, Belfast BT13 3BW; 41 Warren Gardens, Lisburn BT28 1EA Tel: 661269 — MB BCh BAO 1978 Belf.

MCCHEYNE, Alan James 5 Oldcroft Place, Aberdeen AB16 5BT — MB ChB 1998 Aberd.; MB ChB Aberd 1998.

MCCHEYNE, Joanne 5 Oldcroft Place, Aberdeen AB16 5BT — MB ChB 1998 Aberd.; MB ChB Aberd 1998.

MACCLANCY, John Roderick O'Connor (retired) 5 Baldock Road, Letchworth SG6 3LB Tel: 01462 675724 — MB BCh BAO 1945 NUI.

MCCLATCHEY, Alan Wrington Vale Medical Group, Station Road, Wrington, Bristol BS40 5NG Tel: 01934 862532 Fax: 01934 863568; Daniells Farm, Churchill Grove, Churchill, Bristol BS25 5QH — BSc Ed.1978, MB ChB 1981; MRCP (UK) 1986; DCH RCP Lond. 1986; DRCOG 1983.

MCCLATCHEY, Samuel Jones (retired) 7 Barons Mead, Henley-on-Thames R99 2DL — MB BCh BAO 1939 Belf.; DPH 1941; MFCM 1974. Med. Ref. E. Hampstead Crematorium. Prev: Community Phys. E. Berks. Health Dist.

MCCLATCHEY, William Tennant (retired) 8 Glebe Terrace, Perth PH2 7AG Tel: 01738 626697 — MD Belf. 1954, MB BCh BAO 1940; FRCPsych 1971; DPM RCPSI 1950. Prev: Gp. Phys. Supt. Murray Roy. & Murthly Hosps. Perth.

MCCLAUGHLIN, Julie 2 Duncan Street, Horwich, Bolton BL6 6BL — BM BS 1986 Nottm.; MRCPsych 1994.

MCCLAY, Andrew Oswald Old Stables, 3 Great Austins, Farnham GU9 8JG Tel: 01252 713924 — MB BCh BAO 1941 Belf. (Qu. Univ. Belf.)

MCCLAY, Mary Jane 69 Glenmore Park, Altnagelvin, Londonderry BT47 2JY — MB BCh BAO 1991 Belf.

MCCLAY, William John Adam Stannix Medical Practice, 77-81 Scotland Road, Carlisle CA3 9HL Tel: 01228 525768 Fax: 01228 592965 — MB ChB 1982 Glas.; DA (UK) 1986. Prev: GP Longtown, Cumbria.

MCCLEAN, Andrew Nicholas, RD (retired) Department of Genitourinary Medicine, Royal United Hospital, Combe Park, Bath BA1 3NG Tel: 01225 824617 — MB BS Lond. 1959. Civil Cons. Genitourin. Med. RN; Surg. Lt.-Cdr. RNR Retd. Prev: Cons. Genitourin. Phys. Roy. United Hosp. Bath.

MCCLEAN, Edward Graham (retired) 21 East Drive, Angmering, Littlehampton BN16 4JH Tel: 01903 775601 Email: mccleans@talk21.com — MB BCh BAO 1947 Belf. Prev: Med. Off. Brit. Aerospace, Stevenage.

MCCLEAN, Honor Jane Mary 97 Hillsborough Road, Lisburn BT28 1JN Tel: 0184 62 78870 — MB BCh BAO 1956 Belf. (Belf.) Med. Asst. E. Special Care Muckamore Abbey. Socs: Affil. RCPsych; Ulster Med. Soc.

MCCLEAN, Hugo Laurence Hull Royal Infirmary, Anlaby Road, Hull HU3 2JZ Tel: 01482 674760 Fax: 01482 674858 — MB BCh BAO 1985 Belf.; MRCPI 1992; DFFP 1993. (Belf.) Cons. Phys. (Genitourin. Med.) Hull Roy. Infirm. Socs: Soc. Study VD; Assn. Genitourin. Med.; Brit. Soc. Study of Vulval Dis. Prev: Sen. Regist. (Genitourin. Med.) Glas. Roy. Infirm.; SHO Guy's Hosp. Lond. & Belf. City Hosp.

MCCLEAN, John Raymond Bayview Medical Centre, 3 Bayview Terrace, Derry, Londonderry BT48 7EE Tel: 01504 377027; 32 Aberfoyle Crescent, Londonderry BT48 7PG Tel: 02871 263991 — LRCPI & LM, LRCSI & LM 1958. GP Derry City. Prev: Med. Off. Du Pont (UK) Ltd.

MCCLEAN, Maeve 4 Clontarf Heights, Omagh BT78 5BL — MB ChB 1996 Liverp.

MCCLEAN, Mark Shankill Health Centre, 135 Shankill Parade, Belfast BT13 1SD Tel: 028 9024 7181; 8 Neill's Lane, Greenisland, Carrickfergus BT38 8UD Tel: 01232 869956 — MB BCh BAO 1982 Belf.; MRCGP 1987; DRCOG 1986. GP Belf.

MCCLEAN, Patricia Department of Paediatrics, St. James' University Hospital, Beckett St., Leeds LS9 7TF Tel: 0113 206 6880 Fax: 0113 206 6691 — MB BCh BAO 1980 Belf.; MD Belf. 1989; MRCP (UK) 1985. Cons. Paediat. St. Jas. Univ. Hosp. Leeds; Cons. Paediatric Hepatologist & Gastroenterologist. Socs: BSPGN; BMA; BPA.

MCCLEANE, Gary John 58 Kensington Manor, Dollingstown, Craigavon BT66 7HR Tel: 028 3834 9799 Fax: 028 3834 9799 Email: gary@mccleane.freeserve.co.uk — MB BCh BAO 1984 Belf.; MD Belf. 1990; Dip IMC RCS Eng. 1989; FFA RCSI 1988; DA (UK) 1987. Cons. Anaesth. & Pain Managem. Lagan Valley Hosp., Lisburn. Prev: Sen. Regist. (Anaesth.) Craigavon Area Hosp.

MCCLEARY, Alistair John 91 Carnreagh, Hillsborough BT26 6LJ — BM BCh 1989 Oxf.

MCCLEARY, Susan Elizabeth (Ramsden) — BM BS 1989 Nottm.; MRCGP 1993; DRCOG 1992. p/t Trainee GP Centr. Notts. VTS.; GP retainer, Whickham Health Centre, Newc.-Upon-Tyne.

MCCLEARY, Winston Lawrence Aishling House, 18 Marshfield Road, Castleton, Cardiff CF3 2UU — MB BCh BAO 1990 NUI; LRCPSI 1990.

MCCLEERY, Andrew John 22 Cairnshill Park, Belfast BT8 6RG — MB BCh 1998 Belf.; MB BCh Belf 1998.

MCCLEERY, Christopher Hugh (Surgery), 22 Prospect Road, Ossett WF5 8AN Tel: 01924 274123; Thornfield House, Springstone Avenue, Ossett WF5 9EH Tel: 01924 275149 — MB BS 1958 Lond.; DPM Eng. 1975. (St. Thos.) Socs: BMA. Prev: Head of Med. Div. RAS Lanuf, Libya; Med. Appts. Tanzania, Malawi, Libya, Sudan & Home Offices (Prison Med. Dept.).

MCCLEERY, Jenny Mackie University Department of Psychiatry, Warneford Hospital, Headington, Oxford OX3 7JX — MB BS 1992 Lond.; MRCPsych 1997. Wellcome Ment. Health Train. Fell. Oxf. Univ. Dept. of Psychiat. Oxf.

MCCLEERY, Mark Robert 1 Village Court, Belfast BT8 7XJ — MB BCh BAO 1991 Belf.

MCCLEERY, Muriel 45 The Meadows, Broughshane, Ballymena BT43 7NG — MB BCh BAO 1988 Belf.

MCCLEERY, William Finlay Bovally Medical Centre, 2 Rossair Road, Limavady BT49 0TE Tel: 028 7776 6354 — MB BCh BAO 1975 Belf.; DRCOG 1977.

MCCLEERY, William Noel Colvan Penclose House, Manor Lane, Baydon, Marlborough SN8 2JD Tel: 01672 305958 — MB BCh BAO 1952 Belf.; FFA RCS Eng. 1960; DA Eng. 1957. (Qu. Univ. Belf.) Cons. Anaesth. Sheff. AHA (T); Hon. Clin. Lect. Sheff. Univ. Socs: Assn. Anaesth. Gt. Brit. & BMA. Prev: Asst. Anaesth. Montreal Neurol. Inst.; Sen. Regist. Belf. Hosp. GP.

MCCLELLAN, Alison 13 Craigbarnet Road, Milngavie, Glasgow G62 7RA Tel: 0141 956 6073 — MB BS 1985 Newc.; MRCGP 1989; DRCOG 1989. Prev: GP Retainer Scheme Glas.; Trainee GP Cleveland VTS.

MCCLELLAN, Eileen Stoke College, Stoke-by-Clare, Sudbury CO10 8HP — MB BCh BAO 1970 Belf.

MCCLELLAND, Alan James The Health Centre, Stokenchurch, High Wycombe HP14 3TG Tel: 01494 483633 Fax: 01494 483690; 5 Westminster Close, Daws Hill Lane, High Wycombe HP11 1QR — MB ChB 1980 Glas.; MRCGP 1986; DRCOG 1983.

MCCLELLAND, Alexander (retired) 71 Monument Road, Ayr KA7 2UF Tel: 01292 264929 — MB ChB 1946 Glas.; DPH 1954; MRCPsych 1971; DPM Eng. 1956. Cons. Psychiat. Ayrsh. & Arran Health Bd. Prev: Sen. Ho. Off. Psych. Dept. S.. Gen. Hosp. Glas.

MCCLELLAND, Anne Margaret 12 Meadow Park, Crawfordsburn, Bangor BT19 1JN — MB BCh BAO 1994 Belf.

MCCLELLAND, Averil Tel: 01524 842884 Fax: 01524 844839; Glebe House (Old Vicarage), Chapel Lane, Ellel, Lancaster LA2 0PW Tel: 01524 751254 Email: averilmcclelland@talk21.com — MB ChB 1981 Manch.; MRCGP 1985; DRCOG 1997; DCH RCP Lond. 1984. (Manch.) p/t GP.

MCCLELLAND, Mr Charles Joseph Ard Garran, 1 Nursery Grove, Antrim BT41 1QT Tel: 01849 64573 — MB BCh BAO 1972 Belf.; FRCS Ed. 1976. (Belf.) Lect./Cons. (Orthop. Surg.) Musgrave Pk. Hosp. Belf. Prev: Sen. Regist. (Orthop. Surg.) Musgrave Pk. Hosp. Belf.

MCCLELLAND, Damian 2 Home Farm Cottages, Swynnerton, Stone ST15 0RA — MB BS 1994 Lond.; BSc (Hons.) Lond. 1991. SHO Rotat. (Surg.) N. Staffs. Roy. Infirm. Prev: Ho. Off. Basingstoke Dist. Hosp. & N. Staffs. Hosp.

MCCLELLAND, David Brian Lorimer Regional Blood, Transfusion Centre, Royal Infirmary, Edinburgh EH3 9HB Tel: 0131 536 5351 Fax: 0131 536 5353 Email: d.mcclelland@snbts.nhs.scot.uk — MD Leiden 1977; BSc (Hons.) Ed. 1965, MB ChB 1968; FRCP Ed. 1980; MRCP (UK) 1971; MRCPath 1990. (Edin.) Dir. S.E. Scotl. Regional Blood Transfus. Serv.; Sen. Lect. Dept. Clin. Pharmacol. Univ. Edin. Socs: Brit. Blood Transfus. Soc. & Brit. Soc. Haemat.

MCCLELLAND, Hamish Anderson (retired) 38 Nuns Moor Crescent, Newcastle upon Tyne NE4 9BE Tel: 0191 273 9354 — MB BS 1952 Durh.; DPM 1963; FRCP Lond. 1976, M 1961; FRCPsych 1974, M 1971; DCH Eng. 1958; DObst RCOG 1957. Psychiat. Mem. Parole Bd. 1996. Prev: Cons. Psychiat. Newc. DHA. Sen. Regist. (Psychol. Med.) Roy. Vict. Infirm. Newc.

MCCLELLAND, Helen Katherine 6 Dangan Road, London E11 2RF — MB ChB 1988 Leic.; Dip Pract Derm 1999; MRCGP 1992; DRCOG 1996. Prev: Clincal Asst. Dermat. Whipps Cross Hosp.; GP Wanstead, Lond. Retainer Scheme.

MCCLELLAND, Henry Raymond 62 Ballybentragh Road, Antrim BT41 2HJ — MB BCh BAO 1979 Belf.; MRCOG 1984.

MCCLELLAND, Jennifer Anne Elizabeth Donaghadee Health Centre, 3 Killaughey Road, Donaghadee BT21 0BU; 33 Moira Drive, Bangor BT20 4RW Tel: 01247 454508 — MB BCh BAO 1972 Belf.; DObst. RCPI 1991.

MCCLELLAND, Lisa Cathryn Wonford House Hospital, Dryden Road, Exeter EX2 5AF Tel: 01392 403444 — MB BS Lond. 1986; BSc (Hons.) Lond. 1981; MRCPsych 1991. (St Thomas's London) Cons. Psychiat. Wonford Ho. Hosp. Exeter. Prev: Cons. Psychiat. W.bourne Scott Hosp. Plymouth; Clin. Lect. (Psychiat.) St. Geo. Hosp. Med. Sch. Lond.; Regist. (Psychiat.) Maudsley Hosp. Lond.

MCCLELLAND, Mr Martin Raymond Tel: 0114 271 5645 Fax: 0114 271 5649; 74 Whirlow Lane, Sheffield S11 9QF Tel: 0114 235 2840 — MB BCh BAO 1976 Belf.; BSc (Hons.).Belf. 1973; FRCS Eng. 1980. (Qu. Univ. Belf.) Cons. Spinal Injuries P.ss Roy. Spinal Injuries Unit N. Gen. Hosp. Sheff. Prev: Sen. Regist. (Spinal Injuries) Robt. Jones & Agnes Hunt Orthop. Hosp.; Research Fell. (Orthotics) & Regist. (Orthop. Surg.) Robt. Jones & Agnes Hunt Hosp. OsW.ry.

MCCLELLAND, Peter 5 Shrewbridge Road, Nantwich CW5 5TG — MB ChB 1980 Liverp.

MCCLELLAND, Richard Leeper (retired) 27 Claylands Road, London SW8 1NX Tel: 020 7735 1678 Fax: 020 7582 3012. — MB BCh BAO 1945 Dub.; BA Dub. 1945; MA Dub.L.c. 2000. Prev: Ho. Phys. & Ho. Surg. Meath Hosp. Dub.

MCCLELLAND, Professor Roy Queens University, Belfast BT9 5 Tel: 01232 335790 Fax: 01232 324543 Email: r.j.mcclelland@qub.ac.uk; 4 Malone View Park, Belfast BT9 5PN — MB BCh BAO Belf. 1967; PhD Lond. 1982; MD Belf. 1971; FRCPsych 1985, M 1974; DIC 1983. (Lond.) Prof. Ment. Health Belf. City Hosp. & Qu. Univ. Belf. Socs: Soc. for Clin. Neurophysiol.; BMA. Prev: Sen. Lect. (Ment. Health) Qu. Univ. Belf.; Sen. Regist. St. Barts. Hosp. Lond.; Regist. Bethlem Roy. & Maudsley Hosps.

MCCLELLAND, Suzanne Maureen Dept. of Radiology, Perth Royal Infirmary, Taymount Terrace, Perth PH1 1NX Tel: 01738 473640 — MB ChB 1987 Ed.; MRCP (UK) 1990; FRCR 1995; DMRD Ed. 1994. (Edin. Univ.) Cons. (Radiol.) Perth Roy. Infirm. Perth. Socs: Fell. Roy. Coll. Of Radiol.; Scott. Radiol. Soc.; Brit. Med. Ultrasound Soc. Prev: Sen. Regist. (Radiol.) Aberd. Roy. Infirm.;

Regist. (Radiol.) Lothian HB Edin.; Regist. (Gen. Med. & Endocrinol.) Roy. Infirm. Edin.

MCCLELLAND, William Morris Northern Ireland Blood Transfusion Service, Belfast City Hospital Complex, Lisburn Road, Belfast BT9 7TS Tel: 01232 321414 Fax: 01232 439017; 103 Osborne Park, Belfast BT9 6JQ Tel: 01232 666724 — MB BCh BAO 1971 Belf.; FRCPath 1977. Chief Exec. & Med. Dir. N. Irel. Blood Transfus. Serv. Socs: Internat. Soc. Blood Transfus. & Brit. Soc. Haematol.; Brit. Blood Transfus. Soc.

MCCLEMENT, Bernard John Department of Accident & Emergency, Sandwell General Hospital, Sandwell, West Bromwich B71 4HJ; Flat 11, Block 4, Hallam Close, West Bromwich B71 4HU — MB ChB 1994 Cape Town. SHO (A & E) Sandwell Gen. Hosp. Birm. Socs: Med. Defence Union; BMA.

MCCLEMENTS, Brian Martin Mater Hospital, Crumlin Road, Belfast BT14 6AB Tel: 02890 741211 Fax: 02890 741342; 16 Meadowbank, Jordanstown, Newtownabbey BT37 0UP Tel: 02890 364366 Email: brian.mcclements@ntlworld.com — MB BCh BAO 1985 Belf.; MD Belf. 1991; MRCP (UK) 1988; FRCP 1999 Edinburgh. Cons. Cardiol. Mater Hosp. Belf. Socs: Roy. Coll. Phys.; Brit. Cardiac Soc.; Irish Cardiac Soc. Prev: Sen. Regist. (Cardiol.) Belf. City Hosp. & Roy. Vict. Hosp. Belf.; Research & Clin. Fell. (Cardiol.) Mass. Gen. Hosp. Boston, USA.

MCCLEMENTS, Philip Gordon Ardclinis, 21 Tullynagardy Road, Newtownards BT23 4UQ Tel: 01247 812512 — MB BCh BAO 1964 Belf.; BSc Belf. 1961, MB BCh BAO 1964; MFPHM 1990; MRCGP 1971; DObst RCOG 1967. (Belf.) Princip. Med. Off. DHSS N. Irel. Prev: Ho. Off. Roy. Vict. & Roy. Matern. Hosps. Belf.; Ship's Surg. S.S. Arkadia.

MCCLEMONT, Elizabeth Jean Watson Department of Rehabilitation Medicine, Ashby Ward, Lincoln District Healthcare Trust, Lincoln LN1 1FS Tel: 01522 577165 Fax: 01522 577172; Lowfield, Mill Lane, Welton, Lincoln LN2 3RH Tel: 01673 861481 Fax: 01673 861481 — MB ChB Aberd. 1967; FRCP Lond. 1995; DCH RCPS Glas. 1969. Cons. Rehabil. Med. St. Geo. Hosp. Lincoln; Clin. Dir. Community Unit Lincoln. Socs: Brit. Soc. Rehabil. Med.; Assistive Technol. s/i Gp. Prev: Cons. Spinal Injuries Lothian HB; Research Fell. (Child Life & Health) Univ. Edin.

MCCLEMONT, James Michael Farra Lincoln County Hospital, Sewell Road, Lincoln LN2 5QY Tel: 01522 573749 — MB ChB 1967 Ed.; MRCPath 1978. Cons. Path. Lincoln Co. Hosp. Prev: Sen. Regist. W. Gen. Hosp. Edin.; Ho. Off. (Surg. & Med.) Bishop Auckland Gen. Hosp.

MCCLEMONT, William Ferguson (retired) 26 St James's Square, Bath BA1 2TT Tel: 01225 424648 — MB ChB Glas. 1941. Prev: Ho. Surg. Roy. Samarit. Hosp. Wom. Glas.

MCCLENAHAN, Alexandra Faris Medical Centre, Princess Royal Barracks, Deepcut, Camberley GU16 6RW Tel: 01252 340858; Oakdene, The Maultway, Camberley GU15 1QF — MB BCh BAO 1970 Belf.; Cert. FPA JCC 1974; DObst RCOG 1973. (Qu. Univ.) Civil. Med. Pract. P.ss Roy. Barracks Deepcut. Socs: Brit. Soc. Med. & Dent. Hypn. Prev: Ho. Off. Roy. Vict. Hosp. Belf.; Ho. Off. (O & G) St. Stephens Hosp. Lond.; Clin. Med. Off. W. Surrey & NE Hants. Health Dist.

MCCLENAHAN, Martin Cooke Coleraine Health Centre, Castlerock Road, Coleraine BT51 3HP Tel: 028 7034 4833 Fax: 028 7032 8746; Salem Lodge, 33 Millburn Road, Coleraine BT52 1QT — MB BCh BAO 1974 Belf.; DRCOG 1978. (Queens University Belfast) GP Coleraine. Prev: SHO (O & G) Craigavon Area Hosp.; SHO (Paediat.) Roy. Belf. Hosp. Sick Childr.; SHO (Med.) Roy. Vict. Hosp. Belf.

MCCLINTOCK, Charles Paul Cairnsmore Medical Practice, Creebridge, Newton Stewart DG8 6NR Tel: 01671 403609 Fax: 01671 404008 — MB BS 1989 Lond.; MRCGP 1993; DCH RCP Lond. 1993; DRCOG 1992.

MCCLINTOCK, Cyril Beranick Henry Moore Clinic, 26 Smawthorne Lane, Castleford WF10 4EN Tel: 01977 552007 Fax: 01977 604176; 79 Ferrybridge Road, Castleford WF10 4JP Tel: 01977 552290 — MB BCh BAO 1945 Belf.; MB BCh BAO (2nd cl. Hons.) Belf. 1945; DA Eng. 1963. (Qu. Univ. Belf.) Prev: Ho. Surg. Roy. Vict. Hosp. Belf. & Belf. Hosp. Sick Childr.

MCCLINTOCK, Cyril Lawson Tait, CB, OBE, OStJ, Surg. Rear-Admiral 5 Ambleside Court, Crescent Road, Alverstoke, Gosport PO12 2DJ Tel: 01705 503648 — MRCS Eng. LRCP Lond. 1940;

MCCLINTOCK

MFCM 1974. Prev: Cons. ENT Surg. Hamilton, Bermuda; Med. Off. i/c RN Haslar.

MCCLINTOCK, Ian Robert 20 Ivy Road, Gosforth, Newcastle upon Tyne NE3 1DB — MB ChB 1991 Ed.

MCCLINTOCK, Janet Elizabeth 55 Ackworth Road, Pontefract WF8 3PG — MB ChB 1975 Dundee; DRCOG 1977.

MCCLINTOCK, John Henry Neil 55 Ackworth Road, Pontefract WF8 3PG — MB ChB 1975 Dundee.

MCCLINTOCK, Margo Joan 11 St Ronans Circle, Cutler, Aberdeen — MB ChB 1996 Ed.

MCCLINTOCK, Rosemary 50 Kilbride Road, Doagh, Ballyclare BT39 0SA — MB BCh BAO 1993 Belf.

MCCLINTOCK, Thomas Lynn Poplar House, 2 Deronda Road, London SE24 9BG — MB BCh BAO 1989 Belf. Regist. Rotat. (Psychiat.) St. Geo. Hosp. Lond. Prev: Regist. (Forens. Psychiat.) W. Pk. Hosp. Epsom.

MCCLINTON, Mr Samuel 1 Primrosehill Road, Cults, Aberdeen AB15 9ND — MB BCh BAO 1980 Dub.; MD Dub. 1993; FRCS Ed 1995; FRCSI 1986.

MCCLOGHRY, Fergus James P.J. Kaye and Partners, Northwick Surgery, 36 Northwick Park Road, Harrow HA1 2NU Tel: 020 8427 1661 Fax: 020 8864 2737 — MB BS 1981 Lond.; BSc (Human Genetics) Lond. 1979, MB BS 1981; MRCGP 1985; DRCOG 1984; DCH RCP Lond. 1983. Princip. GP Harrow. Prev: Trainee GP N.wick Pk. Hosp. VTS; Ho. Surg. Univ. Coll. Hosp. & Roy. Ear Hosp. Lond.; Ho. Phys. N.ampton Gen. Hosp.

MCCLOSKEY, Anita Mary 20 Kings Road, Newtownabbey BT37 0DA — MB BCh BAO 1994 Belf.

MCCLOSKEY, Professor Bernard Gerald 4 Birds Cottages, Uphampton, Ombersley, Droitwich WR9 0JS Tel: 01905 620387 Fax: 01905 621568 Email: b.mccloskey@worc.ac.uk — MB,BCh BAO 1976 Dub.; MD Dub. 1988; FFPHM RCP (UK) 1995, M 1989; MFCM 1988. (Trinity Coll. Univ. Dub.) Dir. (Pub. Health) Worcs. HA; Prof. Pub. Health Fac. of Health and Exercise Sci.s Univeristy Coll. Worcester. Socs: (Pres.) Assn. Directors Pub. Health. Prev: Dir. (Pub. Health) Worcester & DHA; Specialist (Community Med.) Worcester & DHA.

MCCLOSKEY, Brian Vincent 34 Old Coach Avenue, Upper Malone, Belfast BT9 5PY — MB BCh BAO 1988 Belf.

MCCLOSKEY, Carmel Louise 14 Moneyneana Road, Draperstown, Magherafelt BT45 7EU — MB BCh BAO 1995 Belf.

MCCLOSKEY, Eugene Vincent Beechvale, 11 Quarterlands Road, Drumbeg, Lisburn BT27 5TN — MB BCh BAO 1983 Dub.; MRCP (UK) 1987. MRC Train. Fell.sh. & Research Regist. (Human Metab. & Clin. Biochem.) Univ. Sheff.

MCCLOSKEY, Louise Elizabeth 59 Vale Road, Eglington, Londonderry BT47 3BL — BM BS 1998 Nottm.; BM BS Nottm 1998.

MCCLOSKEY, Margaret 32 Gallagh Road, Toomebridge, Antrim BT41 3QU — MB BCh BAO 1991 Belf.

MCCLOSKEY, Martin Eugen Aberfoyle Terrace Surgery, 3-5 Aberfoyle Terrace, Strand Road, Londonderry BT48 7NP Tel: 028 7126 4868; 20 Griffith Park, Londonderry BT48 8PE Tel: 01504 354773 Email: derrymccloskey@msn.com — MB BCh BAO 1980 Dub.; MRCGP 1984; DCH RCPSI 1983; DRCOG 1983.

MCCLOSKEY, Mary Anne Racecourse Medical GP., Shantallow H.C., Londonderry; 109 Chapel Road, Waterside, Londonderry BT47 2BG — MB BCh BAO 1981 NUI; MRCGP (Ed.) 1987; DCH (Glas.) 1984. GP Shantallow H.C. Derry (p/t).

MCCLOSKEY, Michael Seamus Albert Street Health Centre, Albert Street, Belfast BT12 4JR Tel: 028 9032 0777 — MB BCh BAO 1985 Belf.; DGM RCP Lond. 1988.

MCCLOSKEY, Patricia Maria — MB BCh BAO 1992 Belf.; MRCGP 1996; DFFP 1996; DCH RCPSI 1995; DMH Belf. 1995; DRCOG 1994. (Queens University, Belfast) Prev: SHO (Paediat.) Ulster Hosp. Dundonald; SHO (Psychiat. & Med.) Ards Hosp.

MCCLOSKEY, Roisin Mary Helen Lucy Summertown Group Practice, 160 Banbury Road, Oxford OX2 7BS Tel: 01865 515552 Fax: 01865 311237 — MB ChB 1989 Glas.; MRCGP 1995. GP Princip. Socs: MRCGP.

MCCLOSKEY, Scott Marshall 12 Carmond Dr, Larne BT40 2DB — MB BCh BAO 1997 Belf.

MCCLOUD, Jonathan Mark Flat 5, Block 3, Royal Shrewsbury Hospital Flats North, Mytton Oak Road, Shrewsbury SY3 8XQ — MB ChB 1994 Sheff.

MCCLOY, Elizabeth Carol (retired) — MB BS Lond. 1969; BSc Lond. 1966; FRCP Lond. 1995; MRCS Eng. LRCP Lond. 1969; FFOM RCP Lond. 1993, MFOM 1987, AFOM 1986. Prev: Chief Exec. & Dir. Civil Serv. Occupat. Health & Safety Agency Centre. Off. Edin.

MCCLOY, James Wallace (retired) 15 Berwick Road, Shrewsbury SY1 2LL Tel: 01743 57444 — MB BS 1950 Lond.; MRCS Eng. LRCP Lond. 1950; FFA RCS Eng. 1958; DA Eng. 1953. Cons. Anaesth. Shrewsbury Gp. Hosps. & Robt. Jones & Agnes Hunt Orthop. Hosp. OsW.ry. Prev: Sen. Regist. (Anaesth.) Aberd. Hosps.

MCCLOY, Mary Patricia 18 St Albans Gardens, Belfast BT9 5DR — MB BCh BAO 1990 Belf.

MCCLOY, Mr Rory Francis Clough View Farm, New Row, Bacup OL13 8RA — MRCS Eng. LRCP Lond. 1969; MD Lond. 1982, BSc 1966, MB BS 1969; FRCS Eng. 1974. (Westm.) Sen. Lect. & Hon. Cons. Surg. Manch. Roy. Infirm. Socs: Brit. Soc. Gastroenterol. & Surg. Research Soc. Prev: Vis. Surg. & Endoscopist H.M. Prison, Wormwood Scrubs Lond.; Sen. Surg. Regist. Gen. Hosp. N.ampton & Roy. Postgrad. Med. Sch.; Hammersmith Hosp. Lond.

MCCLUGGAGE, Heather Louise Community Paediatric Department, Strabane Health Centre, Strabane BT82 Tel: 01504 384114; The Manse, 5 Nancy's Lane, Strabane BT82 8LA — MB BCh BAO 1982 Belf.; MFFP 1994; MRCGP 1991; DRCOG 1988. (Queen's University Belfast) Clin. Med. Off. (Community Paediat.) Foyle Community Trust.

MCCLUGGAGE, John Robert Northern Ireland Council for Postgraduate Medical & Dental, Education, 5 Annadale Avenue, Belfast BT7 3JH Tel: 02890 492731 Fax: 02890 427032; Apartment 2, Woodlodge, Croft Road, Holywood BT18 0QB Tel: 02890 427032 — MB BCh BAO 1965 Belf.; FRCPI 1995; FRCP Ed. 1994; FRCGP 1984, M 1971; DObst RCOG 1967. Chief Exec. & Postgrad. Dean N. Irel. Counc. for Postgrad. Med. & Dent. Educat. Prev: Sen. Lect. (Gen. Pract.) Qu. Univ. Belf.

MCCLUGGAGE, Michele Jane 100 Ballybarnes Road, Newtownards BT23 4TD; 18 Bristol Road, Wavertree, Liverpool L15 9HH — MB ChB 1993 Aberd. SHO (Paediat.) St. Helens & Knowsley NHS Trust.

MCCLUGGAGE, Wilson Glenn 18 Sandringham Place, Carrickfergus BT38 9EQ — MB BCh BAO 1987 Belf.

MCCLUMPHA, Alistair Ian The Strand Practice, 2 The Strand, Goring-by-Sea, Worthing BN12 6DN Tel: 01903 243351 Fax: 01903 705804; 2 Cissbury Avenue, Findon Valley, Worthing BN14 0DN — MB BS Lond. 1991; MRCGP 1995; DFFP 1995.

MCCLUNE, Jean Benson Tel: 028 9079 8294 — MB BCh BAO 1979 Belf.; M Phil (Med Law & Ethics) 1995 Belfast; MRCGP 1985; DRCOG 1981. PIT Gen. Pract. Shegoneill Health Centre. Belf.

MCCLUNEY, Neil Andrew 170 Carniny Road, Ballymena BT43 5NJ — MB BCh 1998 Belf.; MB BCh Belf 1998.

MCCLUNG, Allyson Rae 6 Church Avenue, Newmains, Wishaw ML2 9BH — MB ChB 1988 Glas.

MCCLUNG, James Paul Dobbin Lane Health Centre, Dobbin Lane, Armagh BT61 7QG Tel: 028 3752 3165 — MB BCh BAO 1988 Belf.; MRCGP 1992; DCCH RCGP 1992; DRCOG 1991.

MCCLURE, Alex 5 Mayfield Road, Inverness IV2 4AE — MB ChB 1980 Liverp.; MRCS Eng. LRCP Lond. 1980.

MCCLURE, Anne McNeil Department Child & Family Psychiatry, South Tyneside District Hospital, Harton Lane, South Shields NE34 0PL Tel: 0191 202 4023 Fax: 0191 202 4180 Email: ane.mcclure@eem.sthct.northy.nhs.uk; 54 Melville Grove, High Heaton, Newcastle upon Tyne NE7 7AR Tel: 0191 240 3563 Email: david_mcclure@cableinet.co.uk — MB ChB 1977 Glas.; MRCPsych 1985; MRCGP 1981; DRCOG 1980. (University of Glasgow) Cons. Child & Adolesc. Psychiat. S. Tyneside Dist. Hosp. Prev: Sen. Regist. (Child & Adolesc. Psychiat.) Nuffield Psychol. & Psychiat. Unit Fleming Memor. Hosp. Newc.; Sen. Regist. (Child & Adolesc. Psychiat.) Hosp. Sick Childr. Edin.

MCCLURE, David Department of Chemical Pathology, Freeman Hospital, Freeman Road, Heaton, Newcastle upon Tyne NE7 7DN Tel: 0191 284 3111 — MB ChB 1982 Dundee; BSc Glas. 1973; PhD Strathclyde 1977; C Chem.MRSC 1978. Assoc. Specialist (Chem. Path.) Freeman Hosp. Newc. u. Tyne. Prev: Regist. (Clin. Chem.) Roy. Infirm. Edin.

MCCLURE, Elizabeth Alison Northgate Village Surgery, Northgate Avenue, Chester CH2 2DX Tel: 01244 390396 Fax: 01244 370762; 135 Queens Road, Vicars Cross, Chester CH3 5HF Tel: 01244 346144 — BM BCh 1973 Oxf.; MA Camb. 1973; MRCGP 1977; DObst RCOG 1976. GP Chester.

MCCLURE, Eve Caroline 4 Woodcroft Avenue, Broomhill, Glasgow G11 7HU — MB BS 1998 Lond.; MB BS Lond 1998.

MCCLURE, Iain Maurice 4 Kirklee Terrace, Glasgow G12 0TQ — MB BS 1990 Newc. Socs: Roy. Coll. Psychiat.

MCCLURE, Mr Ian Alexander 1 Ewenfield Park, Ayr KA7 2QG Tel: 01292 268907 — MB ChB 1955 Ed.; BA (Hons.) Camb. 1952; FRCS Ed. 1966. (Camb. & Ed.) Cons. ENT Surg. Ayrsh. & Arran Health Bd. Socs: Scott. Otolaryng. Soc.; Fell. Roy. Soc. Med. Prev: Cons. ENT Surg. W.. Infirm. Glas.; Sen. Regist. ENT Surg. Glas. Roy. Infirm.

MCCLURE, Ian James Department of Oral Surgery, Perth Royal Infirmary, Perth PH1 1NX Tel: 01738 623311 Ext: 3791; 18 Oakbank Road, Perth PH1 1DG Tel: 01738 634601 — MRCS Eng. LRCP Lond. 1985; MDS Sheff. 1981; BDS Lond. 1971; FDS RCS Eng. 1974, LDS 1970; FDS RCS Ed. 1998. Cons. Oral Surg. Perth Roy. Infirm.; Hon. Sen. Lect. Dundee Dent. Sch.

MCCLURE, Ian Richardson Hanscombe House Surgery, 52A St. Andrew Street, Hertford SG14 1JA Tel: 01992 582025 Fax: 01992 305511; 28 Holden Close, Hertford SG13 7JU — BM BS 1985 Nottm. GP Hertford.

MCCLURE, Jason Rox 25b Main Road, Fairlie, Largs KA29 0DL — MB ChB 1995 Glas.

MCCLURE, John Hayden Department of Anaesthetics, Royal Infirmary, Lauriston Place, Edinburgh EH3 9YW Tel: 0131 536 3652 Fax: 0131 536 3672 Email: john.mcclure@ed.ac.uk; 4 Priestfield Road N., Edinburgh EH16 5HS — MB ChB 1974 Ed.; BSc (Hons.) Physiol. Ed. 1971; FRCA 1978. (Univ. Ed.) Cons. Anaesth. Roy. Infirm. Edin. & Simpson Memor. Matern. Pavil.; Hon. Sen. Lect. Univ. Edin. Socs: (Hon. Treas. GB & Irl.) Europ. Soc. of Regional Anaesth. Prev: Cons. Anaesth. Elsie Inglis Memor. Matern. Hosp.

MCCLURE, John Lawe Priory Hospital, North london, Southgate, London N14 6RA Tel: 020 8882 8191 Fax: 020 8447 8138; BUPA Hospital (Harpenden), Ambrose Lane, Harpenden AL5 4BP Tel: 01582 763191 Fax: 01582 763191 — MB BS 1955 Lond.; MRCP Lond. 1961; FRCPsych 1981, M 1972; DPM Eng. 1964. (Lond. Hosp.) Cons. Psychiat. Priory Hosp. Nth Lond., S.gate & BUPA Hosp. Harpenden. Socs: Fell. Roy. Soc. Med. Prev: Cons. Psychiat. Qu. Eliz. II Hosp. Welwyn Gdn. City; Sen. Regist. Maudsley & Bethlem Roy. Hosps.; Regist. (Med.) & Ho. Surg. Lond. Hosp.

MCCLURE, John Pender 34 Doonfoot Road, Ayr KA7 4DN Tel: 01292 267687 — MB ChB 1966 Glas.; FRCP Ed. 1987; FRCP Glas. 1983; MRCP (UK) 1972; DCH RCPS Glas. 1969; DObst RCOG 1968. Med. Dir. & Cons. Paediat. N. Ayrsh. & Arran NHS Trust. Prev: Sen. Regist. (Paediat.) Roy. Hosp. Sick Childr. Glas.; Regist. (Med.) Falkirk Roy. Infirm.; SHO (Obst.) Glas. Roy. Matern. Hosp.

MCCLURE, Kathleen Anne Ligoniel Health Centre, 74A Ligoniel Road, Belfast BT14 8BY Tel: 028 9039 1690; 25 Broomhill Park, Belfast BT9 5JB Tel: 01232 660841 — MB BCh BAO 1978 Belf.; MRCGP 1982; DRCOG 1980.

MCCLURE, Kenneth Richmond Queens Crescent Surgery, 10 Queens Cresent, Glasgow G4 9BL Tel: 0141 332 3526 Fax: 0141 332 1150 — MB ChB 1964 Glas.; DObst RCOG 1966. (Glas.)

MCCLURE, Louise Jesmond Dene, 86 Duchy Road, Harrogate HG1 2HA Tel: 01423 531187 — MB ChB 1980 Manch.; MRCGP 1985; DPM Eng. 1990; DCH RCP Lond. 1984; DCCH RCP Ed. 1984; DRCOG 1982; Cert. Family Plann. JCC 1982.

MCCLURE, Mark Jonathan Irby Hall, Irby Road, Irby, Wirral CH61 2XF — MB BCh BAO 1991 Belf.; FRCR 1998; MRCPI 1995. Cons. Radiologist.

MCCLURE, Mary Cupples 18A Ardenlee Avenue, Belfast BT6 0AA Tel: 028 458759 — MB BCh BAO 1945 Belf.

MCCLURE, Professor Neil Royal Maternity Hospital, Grosvenor Road, Belfast BT12 6BB Tel: 028 9089 4600 Fax: 028 9032 8247 Email: n.mcclure@qub.ac.uk; Clifden House, 15 Bangor Road, Holywood BT18 0NU Tel: 028 90 421948 — MB BCh BAO 1983 Belf.; MD Belf. 1994; MRCOG 1989. (Belfast) Prof. (O & G) Qu. Univ. Belf. Roy. Gp. Hosps. Trust. Socs: Fell. Ulster Med. Soc.; Soc. Study Fertil.; Gyn. Vis. Soc. Prev: Fell. (Reproduc. Med.) Brown Univ. Rhode Is., USA; Sen. Regist. & Lect. (Reproduc. Med.) Monash Univ. Melbourne, Austral.

MCCLURE, Nicola Anne 16-17 The Links, Shepherds Bush Centre, London W12 8PP Tel: 020 8749 1882 Fax: 020 8749 4278; 83 Devonshire Road, London W5 4TS Tel: 020 8840 9462 — MB BS 1976 Lond.; MRCS Eng. LRCP Lond. 1976. (Char. Cross) Prev: SHO (Gen. Med.) Char. Cross Hosp. & Qu. Mary's Hosp. Lond.

MCCLURE, Patrick Somerled 3 Ferndown Gardens, Cobham KT11 2BH — LMSSA 1950 Lond.; BA Oxf. (Westm.)

MCCLURE, Patrick Thomas 2 Carsons Avenue, Ballygowan, Newtownards BT23 5GD — MB BCh BAO 1990 Belf.

MCCLURE, Robert James Addenbrookes Hospital, Hills Road, Cambridge CB2 2QQ Tel: 01223 586629 Fax: 01223 217064 — MB ChB 1987 Leeds; MRCP Lond. 1991; MD 1999 Leeds. Cons. Neonatologist Addenbrooke's Hosp. NHS Trust Camb.; Cons. Paediat. with an Interest in Paediatric Gastroenterol.

MCCLURE, Ronald Henry 135 Queens Road, Vicars Cross, Chester CH3 5HF Tel: 01244 390396 — MB ChB 1950 Ed.; MA Oxf. (Oxf. & Ed.) Prev: Ho. Surg. Chester Roy. Infirm.; Ho. Phys. Roy. Cornw. Infirm. Truro; Sen. Ho. Off. (O & G) Bedford Gen. Hosp.

MCCLURE, Samuel John Freeman Hospital, High Heaton, Newcastle upon Tyne NE7 7DN Tel: 0191 284 3111 Email: s.j.mcclure@ncl.ac.uk; 160 Great Western Road, Glasgow G4 9AE Tel: 0141 333 1809 — MB ChB 1992 Ed.; BSc (Hons.) Ed. 1990, MB ChB 1992; MRCP 1996. Specialist Regist. Cardiol. Freeman Hosp. Prev: Clin.Research.Fell.Cardiol.Univ.Glas.

MCCLURE, Shona Kinmylies Medical Practice, Assynt Road, Inverness IV3 6PB — MB BS 1988 Newc.; MRCGP 1992; DRCOG 1990. p/t GP Retainer.

MCCLURE, Timothy Cardwell 8 Ballyhannon Park, Portadown, Craigavon BT63 5SF — MB BCh BAO 1995 Belf.

MCCLUSKEY, Anthony Department of Anaesthetics, Steppinghill Hospital, Stockport SK2 7JE Tel: 0161 419 5869; 58 Albert Road, Bollington, Macclesfield SK10 5HS Tel: 01625 576344 Fax: 01625 576344 Email: amccluskey@mcmail.com — MB ChB 1986 Manch.; BSc (Hons.) Manch. 1983; FRCA 1992. (Manch.) Cons. Anaesth. Stepping Hill Hosp. Stockport. Socs: Manch. Med. Soc.; Assn. NW Intens. Care Units; Assn. Anaesth. Prev: Sen. Regist. (Anaesth.) Stepping Hill Hosp. Stockport, Univ. Hosp. S. Manch. & Roy. Manch. Childr. Hosp.

MCCLUSKEY, Christopher Joseph (retired) 12 Mayfield Gardens, Milnathort, Kinross KY13 9GD Tel: 01577 865792 — MB ChB Ed. 1965; FRCOG 1987, M 1974; T(OG) 1991; DObst RCOG 1971. Prev: Cons. O & G RAF Med. Br.

MCCLUSKEY, Constantine 19 Lisburn Road, Belfast BT9 7AA — MB BCh BAO 1939 NUI; LM Nat. Matern. Hosp. (Univ. Coll. Dub.) Prev: Ho. Phys. & Ophth. Ho. Surg. Rochdale Infirm.; Ho. Surg. Beckett Hosp. Barnsley.

MCCLUSKEY, David Rolande Department of Medicine, Royal Victoria Hospital, Belfast BT12 6BA Email: dmccluskey@qub.ac.uk; The Mill, 7 Ballievey Road, Banbridge BT32 3RX Tel: 018206 69885 — MD 1983 Belf.; MB BCh BAO Belf. 1976; MD (Hons.) Belf. 1983; FRCP Lond. 1997; FRCPI 1995; FRCP Ed. 1989; MRCPI 1994; MRCP (UK) 1979. (Queen's Belfast) Cons. Phys. & Clin. Immunol. Roy. Victory Hosp. Belf.; Sen. Lect. (Med.) Qu. Univ. Belf.; Asst. Head Sch. Clin. Med. Qu.'s Univ. Belf. Socs: Fell.Roy. Coll. Phys.s Edin.; Fell.Roy. Coll. Phys.s Irel..; Fell.Roy. Coll. Phys.s Lond.

MCCLUSKIE, Maureen Agnes Fitzgerald (retired) 16 Waterside Gardens, Carmunnock, Clarkson, Glasgow G76 9AL Tel: 0141 644 1797 — MB ChB 1949 Glas.; DObst RCOG 1952.

MCCLUSKIE, Mr Philip John Adam 6 Mary Vale, Godalming GU7 1SW — MB ChB 1969 Glas.; FRCS Eng. 1979.

MCCLUSKIE, Mr Robert Aloysius (retired) 16 Waterside Gardens, Carmunnock, Clarkston, Glasgow G76 9AL Tel: 0141 644 1797 — MB ChB 1944 Glas.; FRCS Ed. 1948. Cons. Thoracic Surg. Hairmyres Hosp. E. Kilbride. Prev: Cons. Surg. Thoracic unit Hairmyres Hosp. E. Kilbride.

MCCLYMONT, Calum Medical Specialist Group, Guernsey GY1 3EX Tel: 020 823 8565 Email: cmguernsey@supanet.com — MB ChB Aberd. 1982; FANZCA 1992; FCAnaesth. 1989. (Aberdeen) Cons. Anaesth. Guernsey. Socs: Assn. of Anaesth.s; BMA; Pain Soc.

MCCLYMONT, Mr Leo George Department of Otolaryngology, Raigmore Hospital, Inverness IV2 3UJ Tel: 01463 704000 Fax:

MCCLYMONT

01463 711322; 137 Culduthel Road, Inverness IV2 4EF — MB ChB 1980 Glas.; MD Glas. 1991; FRCS Ed. 1985. Cons. ENT Raigmore Hosp. Inverness. Socs: Brit. Assn. Otol. & Roy. Soc. Med. Prev: Sen. Regist. (ENT) Vict. Infirm. Glas.

MCCLYMONT, William Department of Anaesthesia, Ninewells Hospital and Medical School, Dundee DD5 9SY Tel: 01382 660111 Fax: 01382 644914; 3 Palnackie Road, Monifieth, Dundee DD5 4TZ Tel: 01382 535571 Email: w.mcclymont@dundee.ac.uk — MB ChB 1983 Glas.; FRCA 1989; FFA RCSI 1988. Cons. Anaesth. Ninewells Hosp. Dundee; Hon. Clin. Sen. Lect. Univ. Dundee. Socs: Scott. Soc. Anaesth.; Assoc. Mem. Assn. Anaesth. GB & Irel. Prev: Sen. Regist. (Anaesth.) Ninewells Hosp. Dundee; Regist. (Anaesth.) W.. Infirm. Glas.; Research Fell. Scott. Home & Health Dept.

MCCOACH, Antonette Wishaw Health Centre, Kenilworth Avenue, Wishaw ML2 7BQ Tel: 01698 357766 — MB ChB 1985 Glas.; MRCGP 1989; DRCOG 1988; DCH RCPS Glas. 1987.

MCCOACH, Gwladys Noeline (retired) Manor Surgery, Middle St., Beeston, Nottingham NG9 1GA — MB ChB 1950 Birm.; DObst RCOG 1955. Prev: Tutor in Gen. Pract. Nottm. Univ.

MCCOLE, Louise Catherine 16 Surrey Close, Burbage, Hinckley LE10 2NY — MB ChB 1987 Leics.

MCCOLGAN, Bernard Joseph 38 Gallan Road, Newtownstewart, Omagh BT78 4DG — MB BCh BAO 1988 Dub.

***MCCOLGAN, Catherine Claire** 4 Hillington Gardens, Glasgow G52 2TP — MB ChB 1994 Glas.

MCCOLGAN, Ciara Mary Josephine 126 Desswood Place, Aberdeen AB15 4DQ — MB ChB 1993 Ed.

MCCOLL, Rt. Hon. Lord Guy's Hospital Nuffield House, London SE1 1YR Tel: 020 7955 4466 Fax: 020 7407 6615 Email: mccollii@parliament.uk — MB BS 1957 Lond.; MS Lond. 1966; FRCS Ed. 1962; FRCS Eng. 1962; MRCS Eng. LRCP Lond. 1957; FACS 1975. (Guy's) Prof. of Surg. Univ. of Lond. Socs: Amer. Gastroenterol. Assn.; (Ex-Honarary Sec.) Brit. Soc. Gastroenterol. Prev: Parliamentary Private Sec. to Prime Minister; Honarary Cons. Surg. to the Army; Mem. Bd. of Governors Amer. Coll. Surgs. - Governor at Large Eng.

MCCOLL, Alastair James 8 Avenue Road, Fulflood, Winchester SO22 5AQ — MB BS 1984 Lond.; MSc Soton. 1990; MRCGP 1988; DCH RCP Lond. 1989; DRCOG 1986. (Guy's) Lect. (Pub. Health Med.) UMDS St. Thos. & Guy's Hosp. Lond. Prev: SHO Avon GP VTS; Ho. Surg. Guy's Hosp. Lond.; Ho. Phys. Lewisham Hosp. Lond.

MCCOLL, Alison Dorothy 34 Easter Currie Terrace, Currie EH14 5LE Tel: 0131 449 3686; 34 Kings Road, Mount Roskill, Auckland 1004, New Zealand Tel: 00 64 96208977 — MB ChB 1988 Dundee. Regist. (Psychiat.) The Cottage Community Ment. Health Clinic. Otara, Auckland NZ. Socs: Roy. Austral. & NZ Coll. Psychiats.

MCCOLL, Angus Wade Portugal Place Health Centre, Portugal Place, Wallsend NE28 6RZ Tel: 0191 262 5252 Fax: 0191 262 5252 — MB ChB 1978 Ed. GP Wallsend Tyne & Wear.

MCCOLL, Caroline Lennox 5 The Heights, Foxgrove Road, Beckenham BR3 5BY — MB BS 1986 Lond.; MB BS (Hons. Path.) Lond. 1986; MRCGP 1990; DCH RCP Lond. 1989; DRCOG 1988. Prev: GP FarnBoro. Hosp. VTS.

MCCOLL, Catriona Margaret 17 Seton Terrace, Skelmorlie PA17 5AY Tel: 01475 521086 — MB ChB 1994 Glas. Medico-Legal Adviser, MDU.

MCCOLL, David James 17 Seton Ter, Skelmorlie PA17 5AY — MB ChB 1997 Glas.

MCCOLL, Donald (retired) Carmadon, 10 Mearnscroft Road, Newton Mearns, Glasgow G77 5QH Tel: 0141 577 6409 — MB ChB Glas. 1943; BSc (Pure Sci.) Glas. 1940; MFOM RCP Lond. 1978. Prev: Works Med. Off. Aberd. Nobel Div. ICI Ltd Stevenson Ayrsh.

MACCOLL, Eileen Mairi, MBE (retired) Laggan, Main St., Killin FK21 8UT Tel: 01567 820563 — MB ChB 1952 Glas.; DObst RCOG 1956.

MCCOLL, Hugh (retired) Parkside, Vanzell Road, Midhurst GU29 9BA Tel: 01730 814353 — MRCS Eng. LRCP Lond. 1941; MA Camb. 1947, BA 1938, MB BChir 1942; DObst RCOG 1947. Prev: Surg. Lt. RNVR.

MCCOLL, Jean Lennox Priority Care Unit (Child Health), Elizabeth Blackwell House, Avonley Road, New Cross, London SE14 5BH — MB BS 1958 Lond.; MRCS Eng. LRCP Lond. 1958; DCH Eng. 1960;

DObst RCOG 1960. (Guy's) Hon. Lect. Surg. Profess. Unit Guy's Hosp.; Clin. Med. Off. Lewisham & N. S.wark HA & Camberwell HA. Prev: Ho. Phys. Guy's Hosp. & Evelina Childr. Hosp. (Guy's Hosp.); Obst. Ho. Off. St. Alfege's Hosp. Greenwich.

MCCOLL, Professor Kenneth Edward Louis 3 Bridgegait, Fairways, Milngavie, Glasgow G62 6NT Tel: 0141 956 5619 — MD 1981 Glas.; MD (Hons. & Bellahouston Medal) Glas. 1981, MB ChB (Commend.) 1974; FRCP Glas. 1987, M 1976. Prof. Med. Univ. Glas.; Hon. Cons. Phys. & Gastroenterol. Gtr. Glas. HB. Socs: Brit. Soc. Gastroenterol. & Assn. Phys. Prev: Lect. (Mat. Med.) Univ. Glas.; MRC Trav. Fell. (Gastroenterol.) Univ. Calif., USA; Watson Prize Lect. RCPS Glas.

***MACCOLL, Lorna Jean** 2 Goodwood Avenue, Bridgnorth WV15 5BD — MB ChB 1996 Birm.

MCCOLL, Martin Thomas Carew Greenways, Balmer Lawn Road, Brockenhurst SO42 7TT Tel: 01590 24194; Brookvale Adolescent Service, 30 Brookvale Road, Southampton SO17 1QR — MB ChB 1984 Sheff.; MRCPsych 1988. Prev: Sen. Regist. (Child & Adolesc. Psychiat.) St. Geo. Hosp. Lond.

MCCOLLAM, James (retired) Corry, Belleer, Enniskillen BT93 3EZ Tel: 0136 565611 — LRCPI & LM, LRSCI & LM 1941; LRCPI & LM, LRCSI & LM 1941.

MCCOLLAM, Mary Patricia 18 Mill Street, Cushendall, Ballymena BT44 0RR — MB BCh BAO 1994 Belf.

MCCOLLUM, Amanda North End Medical Centre, 211 North End Road, West Kensington, London W14 9NP Tel: 020 7385 7777 Fax: 020 7386 9612; 109 Kelmscott Road, London SW11 6PU — MB ChB 1990 Birm.; DRCOG 1993.

***MCCOLLUM, Amanda Samantha** 3 Belmont Place, Coleraine BT52 1QH — MB BCh BAO 1994 Belf.

MCCOLLUM, Professor Charles Nevin Research & Teaching Building, University Hospital of South Manchester, Nell Lane, Manchester M20 2LR Tel: 0161 447 3841/3840 Fax: 0161 447 3846 Email: cnmcc@fs1.with.man.ac.uk; Birtles Old Hall, Birtles, Macclesfield SK10 4RS Tel: 01625 860106 — MB ChB 1972 Birm.; MD Birm. 1981; FRCS Eng. 1976; FRCS Ed. 1976. (birm) Prof. Surg. Univ. Manch. S. Manch/Hon Cons.S.manch.Univ.Hosp.Trust. Socs: Assn. of Surg. GB & Irel.; Vasc. Surg. Soc. Prev: Reader (Surg.) Char. Cross & W.m. Med. Schs. Lond.; Lect. (Surg.) Univ. Birm.

MCCOLLUM, David Hugh, MC (retired) Preston Cottage, Levedale Road, Penkridge, Stafford ST19 5AT Tel: 0178 712577 — MB BCh BAO Belf. 1940.

MCCOLLUM, David Hugh The Edgbaston Health Clinic, 24 Somerset Road, Edgbaston, Birmingham B15 2QD Tel: 0121 456 1435 Fax: 0121 454 3909; Parsonage, Ambersley, Droitwich WR9 0HP Tel: 01905 620004 — MB ChB 1972 Birm. Med. Off. Edgbaston Health Clinic; Med. Adviser Bass Tavern, Kelper Recoro, Forward Trust, Deloitte Touche & Others. Socs: Occupat.al Med. Soc. Prev: GP Stafford; Med. Off. LTA, AAA, Test & Co. Cricket Bd.; Police Surg. Cannock.

MCCOLLUM, Deborah 29 Watt Avenue, Armadale, Bathgate EH48 2LB — MB ChB 1998 Dund.; MB ChB Dund 1998. Jun. Ho. Off. Surg., Ninewells Hosp. Dundee. Prev: Jun. Ho. Off. Med. Kings Cross Hosp. Dundee.

MCCOLLUM, John Parlane Kinloch Creywell Surgery, Creywell, Wark, Hexham NE48 3LQ Tel: 01434 230654 Fax: 01434 230059 — MB BS 1966 Newc.; MSc (Lond.) 1975; MRCP (U.K.) 1970; MRCPCH 1997 Lond. (Newc.) GP N.d.; Clin. Asst. Child Health Hexham Gen. Hosp.; Lect. Primary Health Care Newc Univ. Socs: BMA & Paediat. Res. Soc. Prev: Lect. (Child Health) Inst. Child Health.& Hosp. for Sick Childr. Gt. Ormond St. Lond.; Regist. (Child Health) Hammersmith Hosp. Lond.; Ho. Phys. Roy. Vict. Infirm. Newc.

MCCOLLUM, John Sydney Charles Dpartment of Clinical Anaesthetics, Belfast City Hospital, Belfast BT9 7AB Tel: 01232 329241; 20 Drumbo Road, Lisburn BT27 5TX — MB BCh BAO 1978 Belf.; FFA RCSI 1983. Cons. Anaesth. Belf. City Hosp. Socs: Intens. Care Soc.; N. Irel. Soc. Anaesth. Prev: Sen. Regist. (Anaesth.) Roy. Vict. Hosp. Belf.; Sen. Regist. (Anaesth.) Roy. N. Shore Hosp. St. Leonards NSW, Austral.

MCCOLLUM, Margaret Phyllis Pennine Drive Surgery, 6-8 Pennine Drive, London NW2 1PA Tel: 020 8455 9977; 29 Parliament Hill, London NW3 2TA Tel: 020 7794 5333 — MB BS 1972 Lond.; BSc (Hons. Physiol.) Lond. 1969; DCH Eng. 1976;

DObst RCOG 1974. (Univ. Coll. Hosp.) Sch. DR to Univ. Coll. Sch. Sch. (Jun. foranch), Holly Hill, Lond. NW3; On interviewing for UCL/UCH/RFH Med. Sch. applicants voluntry. Prev: SHO (Obst.) Univ. Coll. Hosp. Lond.; SHO (Paediat.) Guy's Hosp. Lond.; SHO (Cas.) Univ. Coll. Hosp. Lond.

MCCOLLUM, Professor Peter Thomas Academic Surgical Unit, Ward 100, Hull Royal Infirmary, Hull HU3 2JZ Tel: 01482 328631 Email: p.t.mccollum@medschool.hull.ac.uk; Westpoint, 11 Brimley, Molescroft, Beverley HU17 7EE Tel: 01482 882857 Email: peter.mccollum@virgin.net — MB BCh BAO 1977 Dub.; MCh Dub. 1986; FRCS Ed. 1996; FRCSI 1981. (Univ. Dub.) Prof. Vasc. Surg. Univ. of Hull; Hon. Cons. Vasc. Surg. Hull Roy. Infirm. Hull. Socs: (Counc.) Vasc. Surgic. Soc.; Surgic. Research Soc.; Eur. Soc. Vasc. Surg. Prev: Cons. Vasc. Surg. Ninewells Hosp. Dundee; Sen. Regist. (Surg.) Meath Hosp. Dub.; Sen. Regist. (Vasc. Surg.) Repatriation Hosp. Concord, Sydney, Austral.

MCCOLLUM, Rachel Deborah Westpoint, 11 Brimley, Molescroft, Beverley HU17 7EE Tel: 01482 882857 — MB BCh BAO 1979 Dub.; DCH RCPI 1981; DObst. RCPI 1980; Cert. Family Plann. JCC 1980. Clin. Med. Off. (Family Plann.); Clin. Asst. (GUM) Castlehill Hosp. Hull. Prev: Endoscopist; Sen. Research Fell. (Med).

MCCOLLUM, Richard William, RD Blyth Health Centre, Thoroton Street, Blyth NE24 1DX Tel: 01670 396500 Fax: 01670 396516 — MB BS 1970 Newc.; MRCGP 1980; DRCOG 1979. Prev: Trainee GP. Leicester VTS; Ho. Phys. Sunderland Gen. Hosp.; Surg. Lt. RN.

MCCOLLUM, William Robert Keith Dorman, Dorman, Chambers, McCollum and Fearon, Willowbank Surgery, Crossmore Road, Keady, Armagh BT60 3RL Tel: 028 3753 1248 Fax: 028 3753 1404 — MB BCh BAO 1986 Belf.

MCCOLM, Juliet Ann 19 Walton Street, St Albans AL1 4DQ Tel: 01727 864702; Clinical Pharmacology Unit, Level 7, Northwick Park Hospital, Watford Road, Harrow HA1 3UJ Tel: 020 8966 3531 Fax: 020 8422 6070 — MB BCh 1990 Wales; DPM 1997. Clin. Research Phys. N.wick Pk. Hosp. Harrow.

MCCOMB, David Wesley Holywood Arches Health Centre, Westminster Avenue North, Belfast BT4 1NS Tel: 028 9056 3336 Fax: 028 9056 3356; 1 Glenmachan Drive, Cairnburn Road, Belfast BT4 2RE Tel: 028 9076 0377 — MB BCh BAO 1973 Belf.; DObst RCOG 1976; DCH RCPSI 1975. (Queens University Belfast)

MCCOMB, Janet Mary Department of Cardiology, Freeman Hospital, Newcastle upon Tyne NE7 7DN Tel: 0191 284 3111 — MB BCh BAO 1975 Belf.; MD (Hons.) Belf. 1981; FRCP Lond. 1992; MRCP (UK) 1978. Cons. Cardiol. Freeman Hosp. Newc. u. Tyne. Prev: Sen. Lect. (Cardiol.) Univ. Newc.

MCCOMB, Mary Clarke (retired) 3 new Forge Grange, Belfast BT9 5QB Tel: 028 906 6317 — MB BCh BAO Belf. 1949.

MCCOMB, Patricia Eleanor Freda 49 Foreland Road, Bembridge PO35 5XN — MB ChB 1977 Bristol.

MCCOMB, Thomas Norman (retired) Pennywise, Hyndford Bridge, Lanark ML11 — MB ChB 1955 Glas.; DA Eng. 1958. Prev: Cons. Anaesth. Law Hosp. Carluke.

MCCOMBE, Mr Andrew Wightman Frimley Park Hospital, Portsmouth Road, Frimley, Camberley GU16 7UJ Tel: 01276 604604 — MB ChB 1985 Ed.; MD Ed. 1994; FRCS (Orl) 1993; FRCS Eng. 1991; FRCS Ed. 1989. (Edinburgh) Cons. ENT Surg. Frimley Pk. Hosp. Surrey; Hon. Cons. Roy. Surrey Co. Hosp. Guildford and N. Hants. Hosp. Basingstoke. Prev: Sen. Regist. Rotat. SW Region; TWJ Research Fell. Toronto; Regist. Rotat. (ENT) Mersey Region.

MCCOMBE, Brian Hugh (retired) 208 Thorpe Road, Peterborough PE3 6LB Email: mccombe@cyberwave.co — MB BS Lond. 1955; MRCS Eng. LRCP Lond. 1955. Prev: GP P'boro.

MCCOMBIE, Claire 81 Rokeby Terrace, Newcastle upon Tyne NE6 5SU — MB BS 1998 Newc.; MB BS Newc 1998.

MCCOMBIE, Peter Munro Medical Centre, West Elloe Avenue, Spalding PE11 2BY Tel: 01775 766181 Fax: 01775 766168; Riversend, 56 St. Thomas's Road, Sunfleet Reservoir, Sunfleet Seas End, Spalding PE11 4DJ — MB ChB 1972 Aberd.; MRCGP 1976; DObst RCOG 1975. (University of Aberdeen) Clin. Asst. (Haemat.) Johnson Hosp. Spalding. Prev: Trainee GP Inverness VTS; Ho. Phys. City Hosp. Aberd.; Ho. Surg. Roy. Aberd. Childr. Hosp.

MCCOMISH, Peter Bartholomew (retired) 14 Herbert Road, Hornchurch RM11 3LA Tel: 01708 445024 — MB BS Lond. 1955; FFA RCS Eng. 1962; DA Eng. 1959. Prev: Cons. Anaesth. Essex.

MCCOMISKEY, Colin Alexander (retired) c/o National Westminster Bank, 49 Sandygate Road, Folkestone CT20 1RU — MB BCh BAO 1933 Belf.; DTM & H Eng. 1936. Prev: Med. Off. Colon. Med. Serv.

MCCONACHIE, Catriona Frances Jean Blackgate, Scotland Road, Dry Drayton, Cambridge CB3 8BX — MB ChB 1969 Glas. Community Med. Off. Camb.

MCCONACHIE, Ian William Blackpool Victoria Hospital, Whinney Heys Road, Blackpool FY3 8NR Tel: 01253 300000 — MB ChB 1982 Aberd.; FFA RCS Eng. 1987. Cons. Anaesth. & Intens. Blackpool Vict. Hosp. Socs: Intens. Care Soc. Prev: Lect. (Anaesth.) Univ. Manch.

MCCONACHIE, James William (retired) 18 Burnett Road, Sutton Coldfield B74 3EJ Tel: 0121 353 7443 — MRCS Eng. LRCP Lond. 1944; DPH Eng. 1948. Prev: Clin. Asst. (Paediat.) King Geo. V Hosp. Ilford.

MCCONACHIE, Mrs (Jean) Margaret (retired) The Laggan, Stotfield, Lossiemouth IV31 6QP Tel: 0134 381 3131 — MB ChB 1946 Aberd.

MCCONACHIE, John Alexander (retired) The Laggan, Lossiemouth IV31 6QP Tel: 01343 812480 — MB ChB 1944 Aberd.; FRCP Ed. 1976, M 1950.

MCCONACHIE, Norman Stewart University Hospital, Queens Medical Centre, Nottingham NG7 2UH Tel: 01159 709949 Fax: 01158 493311 Email: nsmccon@doctors.net.uk; Ash Tree House, Main St, Wysall, Nottingham NG12 5QS Tel: 01509 881795 — MB ChB 1984 Aberd.; FRCR 1991; T(R) (CR) 1992. Cons. Neuroradiol. Univ. Hosp. & Qu. Med. Centre Nottm. Socs: Eur. Soc. Neuroradiol.; Brit. Soc. Neuroradiol.; World Federat. Interven. Therap. Neurorad. Prev: Sen. Regist. (Neuroradiol.) Beaumont Hosp. Dub.; Sen. Regist. (Diag. Radiol.) Dundee Gp. Hosps.; Regist. (Diag. Radiol.) Nottm. Gp. Hosps.

MCCONAGHY, Martin Damian 36 North Circular Road, Lurgan, Craigavon BT67 9EB Tel: 01762 325530 — MB BCh BAO 1997 Belf. (Queen's Univ. Belf.) Socs: Roy. Coll. Surg.; Brit. Assoc. Sports Med.

MCCONAGHY, Paul Martin 7 Tiscallen Lane, Aghagallon, Craigavon BT67 0AF — MB BCh BAO 1988 Belf.

MCCONKEY, Brian 81 Harborne Road, Edgbaston, Birmingham B15 3HG Tel: 0121 455 9496 Fax: 0121 455 0288; 11 Dyott Road, Moseley, Birmingham B13 9QZ Tel: 0121 449 2064 — BM BCh Oxf. 1946; DM Oxf. 1959; FRCP Lond. 1971, M 1947. (Oxf.) Hon. Cons. Phys. City Hosp. NHS Trust Birm.; Postgrad. Clin. Tutor Birm. Med. Inst. Socs: Brit. Soc. Rheum. & Midl. Rheum. Soc.; W Midl. Phys. Assn. Prev: Sen. Specialist (Med.) RAMC; Sen. Regist. (Med.) Cardiff Roy. Infirm.; Ho. Phys. Radcliffe Infirm. Oxf.

MCCONKEY, Christopher David 66 Killowen Street, Belfast BT6 8NG — MB BCh 1998 Belf.; MB BCh Belf 1998. SHO, Gen. Med., Craigavon Area Hosp.

MCCONKEY, Graham Neil The Surgery, High Street, Heathfield TN21 8JD Tel: 01435 864999/862192 Fax: 01435 867449; Woodside Cottage, Rushlake Green, Heathfield TN21 9QR — MB BS 1987 Lond.; MRCGP 1991; DCH RCP Lond. 1989. Prev: GP Tunbridge Wells VTS.

MCCONKEY, Katherine Joyce 23B Chapelhill Drive, Blackley, Manchester M9 8FJ — MB ChB 1993 Manch.; Dip. Trop. Med. & Hyg. (Distinct.) 1997. Socs: Christ. Med. Fell.sh.; MRCGP.

MCCONKEY, Kevin 2 Briar Crescent, Newtownabbey BT37 0FR Tel: 01232 854430 — MB BCh BAO 1986 Belf.; MRCGP 1992; DGM RCP Lond. 1991; DRCOG 1988. (Qu. Univ. Belf.) Staff Grade (A & E) Whiteabbey Hosp. Co. Antrim, N. Irel. Prev: Trainee GP/SHO Rotat. Mid Ulster Hosp.; SHO Greenls./Whiteabbey Hosp.; Trainee GP Sandhead VTS.

MCCONKEY, Matthew James 12 Knockburn Park, Belfast BT5 7AY — MB BCh 1998 Belf.; MB BCh Belf 1998.

MACCONNACHIE, Alisdair Angus 43 Torridon Road, Broughty Ferry, Dundee DD5 3JH — MB ChB 1998 Aberd.; MB ChB Aberd 1998.

MCCONNACHIE, Mr James Stewart (retired) Norlands, Clytha Park Road, Newport NP20 4NA Tel: 01633 264 5535 — MB ChB 1938 Aberd.; MB ChB (Hons.) Aberd. 1938; BSc Aberd. 1935; FRCS Eng. 1946; MRCS Eng. LRCP Lond. 1939. Surg. Nevillhall Hosp. Abergavenny. Prev: Sen. Regist. (Surg.) Aberd. Roy. Infirm.

MCCONNACHIE

MCCONNACHIE, William (retired) Moorwell, Brampton Road, Alston CA9 3AA — MB BChir 1957 Camb.; DObst RCOG 1961. Prev: Ho. Surg. Middlx. Hosp.

MCCONNELL, Albert Arthur McGown Doonvarna, Tobermore Road, Magherafelt BT45 — MD 1948 Belf.; MB BCh BAO 1942; FRCPI 1968, M 1950. (Belf.) Phys. Mid Ulster Hosp. Magherafelt. Socs: Fell. Ulster Med. Soc. Prev: Regist. N. Irel. Fev. Hosp. Belf. & Belf. City Hosp.; Surg. Lt. RNVR.

MCCONNELL, Alfred Terence Netherbank, Watery Lane, Barbon, Kirby, Lonsdale, Carnforth LA6 2LN — LRCPI & LM, LRSCI & LM 1972; LRCPI & LM, LRCSI & LM 1972.

MCCONNELL, Archibald Allison Clinical Biochemistry Department, Inverclyde Royal Hospital, Greenock PA16 0XN Tel: 01475 633777 Fax: 01475 637340 — MB ChB 1980 Glas.; PhD Glas. 1971, BSc (1st cl. Hons. Chem.) 1967; LLB Strathclyde 1996; MRCPath 1990. (Glas.) Cons. Chem. Path. Inverclyde Roy. Hosp. Greenock; Hon. Clin. Sen. Lect. Glas. Univ.; Mem. Fac. of Med. Glas. Univ. Socs: Fell. Roy. Soc. Chem.; Sec. Scott. medico-legal soc. 1999-2001; Assn. Clin. Path. Prev: Sen. Regist. S.mead Hosp. Bristol; Regist. Glas. Roy. Infirm.

MCCONNELL, Charles Anthony Glan Clwyd Hospital, Bodelwyddan, Rhyl LL18 5UJ Tel: 01745 583910; Ty Cerrig, Tremeirchion, St Asaph LL17 0UP Tel: 01745 582923 — MB ChB 1974 Liverp.; MRCP (UK) 1977; FRCR 1981; DMRD Liverp. 1979. Cons. (Radiol.) Glan Clwyd Hosp. Prev: Sen. Regist. (Radiol.) Roy. Liverp. Hosp.; Sen. Regist. (Radiol.) Alder Hey Hosp. Liverp.; Regist. (Med.) Walton Hosp. Liverp.

MCCONNELL, David Leslie, Group Capt. RAF Med. Br. HQ Personnel & Training Command, RAF Innsworth, Gloucester GL3 1EZ Tel: 01452 712612 — MB ChB 1974 Dundee; MSc Lond. 1993; DAvMed FOM RCP Lond. 1985; DObst RCOG 1976. (Dundee) Dep. Dir. Primary Health Servs. Prev: Med. P1 RAF Defence Servs. Med. Directorate; Command Ft. Med. Off. HQ RAF Support Command; Sen. Med. Off. RAF Valley, RAF Kinloss & RAF Gatow.

MCCONNELL, Dora Ann 42 Rannoch Road, Holywood BT18 0NB — MB ChB 1983 Liverp.; MRCGP 1989.

MCCONNELL, Dynes Tracey Aberdeen Maternity Hospital, Cornhill Road, Aberdeen AB25 2ZL — MB ChB 1984 Otago; MRCOG 1992.

MCCONNELL, Edith Mavis (retired) 21 Llys y Tywysog, Tremeirchion, St Asaph LL17 0UL Tel: 01745 710588 — MD 1949 Liverp.; MB ChB (Hons.) 1944; FRCPath 1968, M 1963. Prev: Cons. Path. Liverp. HA & Mersey RHA.

MCCONNELL, Elizabeth Mae 113 Nettlehill Road, Lisburn BT28 3HF — MB BCh BAO 1992 Belf.

MCCONNELL, Eugene (retired) 117 Bessbrook Road, Mountnorris, Armagh BT60 2TZ Tel: 01861 507220 — MB BCh BAO NUI 1959. Prev: Asst. Psychiat. Gransha Hosp. Lond.derry.

MCCONNELL, Fiona Kathryn The Surgery, Cross Road, Sacriston, Durham DH7 6LJ Tel: 0191 371 0232 — MB BS 1985 Newc.; MRCGP 1989; DRCOG 1988.

MCCONNELL, Huw David Smithyman Cedar House, Alton St., Ross-on-Wye HR9 5JJ — MB ChB 1998 Dund.; MB ChB Dund 1998.

MCCONNELL, Miss Joanne 4 Canvey Road, Leigh-on-Sea SS9 2NN — BM BS 1988 Nottm.

MCCONNELL, John Paul McConnell, Carson and Mathews, The Health Centre, Tavanagh Avenue, Portadown, Craigavon BT62 3BU — MB BCh BAO 1975 Belf.; BSc (Physiol.) Belf. 1970. Forens. Med. Off. Lurgan & Craigavon.

MCCONNELL, John Robert Lawson The Medical Centre, Well St., Biddulph, Stoke-on-Trent ST8 6HD Tel: 01782 512822; The Homestead, John St, Biddulph, Stoke-on-Trent ST8 6BB — MB ChB 1958 Glas.

MCCONNELL, Joseph Matthew Stewartville Street Surgery, 5 Stewartville Street, Glasgow G11 5PE Tel: 0141 339 0902 Fax: 0141 339 0132; 1 Upland Road, Scotstoun, Glasgow G14 9BG — MB ChB 1982 Glas.; DCH RCPS Glas. 1987; MRCGP 1988. Prev: SHO (O & G) Rutherglen; Trainee GP Irvine VTS; SHO (Infect. Dis.) Ruchill.

MCCONNELL, Kenneth Douglas 8 Victoria Road, West Ferry, Dundee DD5 1BD — B Med Newc. NSW 1987.

MACCONNELL, Linda Elizabeth Sinclair The Surgery, 5 Queen Street, Portsea, Portsmouth PO1 3HL Tel: 023 9281 2033 Fax: 023 9287 1077 — MB ChB 1966 Glas. (Glas.) Hosp. Pract. (Dermat.) St. Mary's Hosp. Portsmouth. Socs: Scott. Dermat. Soc. Prev: Lect. (Dermat.) Univ. Glas. & W.. Infirm. Glas.

MCCONNELL, Lisa Ann 43 Lancedean Road, Belfast BT6 9QP — MB ChB 1992 Birm.; ChB Birm. 1992.

MCCONNELL, Margaret Bridget Compass House Medical Centres, 25 Bolton Street, Brixham TQ5 9BZ Tel: 01803 855897 Fax: 01803 855613; Shrublands, Huxtable Hill, Torquay TQ2 6RN Tel: 01803 605746 — MB BCh BAO NUI 1981; MRCGP 1987.

MCCONNELL, Pamela Ross-Thomson Unit, Route Hospital, 8 Coleraine Road, Ballymoney BT53 6BU; 24 Market Street, Limavady BT49 0AA Tel: 015047 22596 — MB BCh BAO 1984 Dub.; MRCPsych 1992; DMH Belf. 1991; MD Belf. 1999. Staff Grade (Psychiat.) Causeway HSS Trust, Route Hosp. Ballymoney. Socs: BMA. Prev: Locum Cons.; Sen. Regist. (Gen. Psychiat.) N.. Irel. Train. Scheme; Research Assoc. (Ment. Health) Qu. Univ. Belf.

MCCONNELL, Richard Bonar, TD 2 Countisbury Drive, Liverpool L16 0JJ Tel: 0151 722 4426 — MD Liverp. 1955, MB ChB 1942; FRCP Lond. 1967, M 1949. (Liverp.) Emerit. Cons. Phys. Roy. Liverp. Hosp. Socs: Hon. Mem. (Ex-Pres.) Brit. Soc. Gastroenterol.; (Ex-Pres.) Liverp. Med. Inst.; Assn. Phys. Prev: Cons. Phys. Roy. Liverp. Hosp. & Brd.green Hosp. Liverp.; Squadron Ldr. RAF Med. Serv.; Col. RAMC TA.

MCCONNELL, Robert George Clive Chapman and Partners, 370-372 Cregagh Road, Belfast BT6 9EY — MB BCh BAO 1969 Belf.

MCCONNELL, Rosemary The Health Centre, University of Sussex, Falmer, Brighton BN1 9RW Tel: 01273 679434 Fax: 01273 675689; 8 Clermont Road, Brighton BN1 6SG Tel: 01273 502389 Email: rosy@unimed.co.uk — MB ChB 1975 Birm.

MCCONNELL, Sandra Margaret 43 Duns Crescent, Wishaw ML2 8SD — MB ChB 1997 Glas. SHO (Gen. Med.) CrossHo. Hosp. Kilmarnock.

MCCONNELL, Thomas Francis Betts Avenue Medical Centre, 2 Betts Avenue, Newcastle upon Tyne NE15 6TQ Tel: 0191 274 2767 Fax: 0191 274 0244 — MB BCh BAO 1978 NUI; MRCPI 1987.

MCCONNELL, Thomas James Davison Leyfield Surgery, 2 Eckington Road, Staveley, Chesterfield S43 3XZ Tel: 01246 473321 Fax: 01246 477303; Norbriggs House, 18 Worksop Road, Mastin Moor, Chesterfield S43 3BN Tel: 01246 474449 — MB ChB 1969 Sheff. Socs: Chesterfield Med. Soc.; BMA. Prev: Med. Off. i/c Gizo Hosp. W.. Solomon Is.s; Med. Off. (O & G) Centr. Hosp. Honiara, Brit. Solomon Is.s; SHO (O & G) Scarsdale Hosp. Chesterfield.

MACCONNELL, Thomas Joseph Department of Cardiology, Taunton & Somerset Hospital, Musgrove Park, Taunton TA1 5DA Tel: 01823 342709; 58 Stonegallows, Taunton TA1 5JS — MB ChB 1984 Glas.; MRCP (UK) 1987; FRCP 1999. (Univ. Glas.) Cons. Cardiol. Taunton & Som. Hosp. Prev: Sen. Regist. Bristol Roy. Infirm.; Regist. (Cardiol.) Bristol Roy. Infirm.; Regist. (Med.) Vict. Infirm. Glas.

MCCONNELL, Vicky Ann 122 Munro Road, Jordanhill, Glasgow G13 1SE — MB ChB 1998 Glas.; MB ChB Glas 1998.

MCCONNELL, Vivienne Priscilla Margaret 33 Crewcatt Road, Richill, Armagh BT61 8QN — MB BCh BAO 1987 Belf.; MRCGP 1992. Clin. Med. Off. (Community) Armagh. Socs: MDU; Brit. Assn. Community Child Health; DRCOG.

MCCONNELL, Wallace (retired) 2A Fulwood Park, Liverpool L17 5AG — MRCS Eng. LRCP Lond. 1940.

MCCONNELL, William Brian 5 Beresford Row, The Mall, Armagh BT61 9AU — MB BCh BAO 1954 Belf.; MRCPI 1964; FRCPsych 1983, M 1971; DPM RCPSI 1957. Med. Supt. St. Lukes Hosp. Armagh; Cons. Craigavon Area Hosp. Prev: Sen. Tutor & Sen. Regist. (Ment. Health) Qu. Univ. Belf.; Regist. Purdysburn Hosp. Belf.; Ho. Off. Roy. Vict. Hosp. Belf.

MCCONNELL, William David Dorset County hospital, Williams Avenue, Dorchester DT1 2JY Tel: 01305 255270 Email: willmcconnell@doctors.org.uk — BM BCh 1991 Oxf.; MA Camb. 1992; MRCP (UK) 1994. (Oxford) Cons., Gen. & Respirat. Med. Dorset Co. Hosp. Dorchester. Socs: Brit. Thorac. Soc.

MCCONNOCHIE, Kathryn Ann Pendragon Chambers, 124 Walter Road, Swansea; Email: ylt45@dial.pipex.com — MB ChB 1976 Manch.; BSc St. And. 1973; MRCP (UK) 1980; LLB. Cardiff 1996. Barrister, Pendragon Chambers. Prev: Clincal Scientist Med. Research Counc. Pneumoconiosis Unit Llandough Hosp.; Penarth;

Regist. (Med.) Roy. Liverp. Hosp.; Lect. & Hon. Sen. Regist. Llandough Hosp. Penarth.

MCCONVILLE, Anne Elizabeth North Derbyshire Health, Scarsdale, Newbold Road, Chesterfield S41 7PF Tel: 01246 231255 Fax: 01246 206672; The Hollows, 4 Vernon Green, Buxton Road, Bakewell DE45 1DT — MB ChB 1980 Birm.; MRCGP 1984; MFPHM RCP (UK) 1989; DRCOG 1983; Cert. Family Plann. JCC 1983; FFPHM (UK) 1999. (Birmingham) Dir. (Pub. Health) N. Derbysh. Health. Prev: Dir. (Pub. Health) E. Birm. HA; Sen. Med. Off. NHS Exec.

MCCONVILLE, John Paul Turcarra, Woodview, Armagh BT61 8RH — MB BChir 1994 Camb.

MCCONVILLE, Joseph Martin Turcarra, Woodview, Armagh BT60 8RH — MB BCh BAO 1985 Belf.; MRCGP 1989; DCH RCPS Glas. 1988; DRCOG 1989.

MCCONVILLE, Kevin Francis 13 Kelly Gardens, Lurgan, Craigavon BT67 9HB — MB ChB 1998 Dund.; MB ChB Dund 1998.

MCCONVILLE, Mary Tracey 12 Chestnut Grove, Lurgan, Craigavon BT66 6AJ — MB BCh BAO 1989 Belf.; MB BCh Belf. 1989.

MCCONVILLE, Michael Eoin 6 Laurelvale Court, Old Rossorry, Enniskillen BT74 7LZ — MB BCh BAO 1983 Belf.

MCCONVILLE, Pauline Mary Clinical Research Centre, Royal Cornhill Hospital, Cornhill Road, Aberdeen AB25 2ZH Tel: 01224 663131 Ext: 57400 Fax: 01224 620751 Email: p.mcconville@abdn.ac.uk; 30 Morningside Drive, Edinburgh EH10 5LZ Tel: 0131 447 1571 — MB ChB 1989 Ed. (Ed.) Clin. Lect. Univ. Aberd.; Hon. Specialist Regist. (Psychiat.). Prev: SHO Rotat. (Psychiat.) Fife HB; Ho. Off. (Med.) Falkirk & Dist. Roy. Infirm.; Ho. Off. (Surg.) E.. Gen. Hosp. Edin.

MCCONVILLE, Raymond John Royal Devon & Exeter Hospital, Barrace Road, Exeter EX2 5DW Tel: 01392 411611; 70 Lewis Crescent, Exeter EX2 7TD Email: raymond.mcconville@virgin.net — MB ChB 1990 Glas. (Glas.) Staff Grade (Emerg. Med.); Police Surg. To Devon & Cornw. Constab. Socs: Assn. Police Surg.

MCCONVILLE, Richard Mayne 47 Ballynafern Road, Ballinaskeagh, Banbridge BT32 5BW — MB BCh 1998 Belf.; MB BCh Belf 1998.

MCCONWAY, James Henry Francis 82 Trench Park, Belfast BT11 9FG — MB BCh 1998 Belf.; MB BCh Belf 1998.

MCCOOL, Hamish John 51 Crosswood Crescent, Balerno, Edinburgh EH14 7LX — MB ChB 1996 Ed.

MCCORD, Francis Brian Altnagelvin Area Hospital, Londonderry BT47 6SB Tel: 01504 345171 — MB BCh BAO 1979 Belf.; MRCP (UK) 1983; DCH RCPSI 1982. Cons. Paediat. Lond.derry.

MCCORD, Nicola 19 Dalziel Place, Edinburgh EH7 5TP — BM BCh 1996 Oxf.

MCCORD, William Clifford, MBE (retired) Granary, Aughnacloy Tel: 01662 557121 — MB BCh BAO 1950 Dub.; MA 1998 Trinity College, Dublin.

MCCORD, William David George Sydney Lane Surgery, 2 Sydney Lane, Aughnacloy BT69 6AF Tel: 028 8555 7234 — MB BCh BAO 1979 Belf.; MRCGP 1983; DRCOG 1982.

MCCORKELL, Lucy Monsell The Old Schoolhouse, Dunsyre, Carnwath, Lanark ML11 8NG — BM BCh 1983 Oxf.

MCCORKELL, Stuart Alexander 15 Bellew Street, London SW17 0AD — MB BS 1992 Lond.

MCCORKINDALE, Clare Margaret Catherine The Surgery, 53 Burnbank Road, Hamilton ML3 9AQ Tel: 01698 281407; 104 Speirs Road, Bearsden, Glasgow G61 2LA — MB ChB 1987 Aberd.

MCCORKINDALE, James William Welman House, Golf Road, Altrincham WA15 8AE Tel: 0161 928 6311; 26 Valdene Road, Worsley, Manchester M28 7GA — MB ChB 1981 Aberd.; AFOM RCP Lond. 1990; MRCGP 1986; DRCOG 1985. Regional Med. Adviser Brit. Gas. plc. Socs: Soc. Occupat. Med. Prev: Med. Off. Brit. Gas; Capt. RAMC.

MCCORKINDALE, Rhona Ann 1A Endfield Close, Exeter EX1 3BB — MB ChB 1992 Manch.

MCCORKINDALE, Sheila Manchester Road Surgery, 39 Manchester Road, Walkden Worsley, Manchester M28 3NS Tel: 0161 702 8595 Fax: 0161 702 8592 — MB ChB 1978 Manch.; MRCGP 1982; DRCOG 1983.

MCCORMACK, Deirdre Helen Pauline Tempany St Marys Surgery, 37 St. Mary's Street, Ely CB7 4HF Tel: 01353 665511 Fax: 01353 669532; 14 Egremont Street, Ely CB6 1AE Tel: 01353 666808 — MB BS 1983 Lond.; MRCGP 1988.

MCCORMACK, Derek John Taybank Medical Centre, 10 Robertson St., Dundee DD4 6EL Tel: 01382 461588; Millburn, Tealing, Dundee DD4 0QZ — MB ChB 1984 Dundee. Clin. Asst. (A & E) Dundee Roy. Infirm.; Med. Off. Dundee United Football Club. Prev: Clin. Med. Off. (Community Paediat.) Greenock; SHO (Psychiat.) Roy. Dundee Liff Hosp.; SHO (O & G) Law Hosp. Carluke.

MCCORMACK, Graham Eugene Oakham Medical Practice, Cold Overton Road, Oakham LE15 6NT Tel: 01572 722621/2; 12 Cross Lane, Preston, Rutland, Oakham LE15 9NQ — MB ChB 1985 Leic.; DRCOG 1989. Prev: Trainee GP/SHO Leicester VTS.

MACCORMACK, James Maurice (retired) 43 Milton Crescent, Ravenshead, Nottingham NG15 9BA — MB ChB 1938 Glas.; DA Eng. 1947. Prev: RAF 1940-45.

MCCORMACK, Joanne Ruth Sarah Padgate Medical Centre, 12 Station Road South, Padgate, Warrington WA2 0RX Tel: 01925 815333 Fax: 01925 813650 — MB ChB 1986 Manch.; MRCGP 1990; DRCOG 1988.

MCCORMACK, John Gerard The Surgery, Kinmel Avenue, Abergele LL22 7LP Tel: 01745 833158 Fax: 01745 822490 — MB BCh BAO 1986 NUI; MRCGP 1992; DObst RCPI 1991; DCH NUI 1989.

MACCORMACK, Jon Gordon 29 Morar Place, Broughty Ferry, Dundee DD5 3HL — MB ChB 1998 Dund.; MB ChB Dund 1998.

MCCORMACK, Katherine Georgina Lonsdale House, 133 Cumberworth Lane, Lower Cumberworth, Huddersfield HD8 8PG — MB ChB 1979 Ed.

MCCORMACK, Kieran 89 High Street, Eckington, Sheffield S21 4DJ — MB BS 1989 Lond.; BSc Lond. 1986, MB BS 1989; MRCGP 1994; DFFP 1994; DRCOG 1993.

MCCORMACK, Mary 60 Church Path, London W4 5BJ Tel: 020 8995 4931 — MB BS 1993 Lond.; PhD Lond. 1988, MSc 1985; BSc Dub. 1984.

MCCORMACK, Mary Catherine 59 Derrycrew Road, Loughgall, Armagh BT61 8PW — MB BCh BAO 1989 Dub.; MB BCh Dub. 1989.

MCCORMACK, Mary Leitch 826 Liverpool Road, Ainsdale, Southport PR8 3SL — MB ChB 1948 Ed.

MCCORMACK, Mary Patricia Churchtown Medical Centre, 137 Cambridge Road, Southport PR9 7LT Tel: 01704 224416 Fax: 01704 507168 — MB ChB 1986 Liverp.; MRCGP 1993; DRCOG 1992; DCH RCP Lond. 1990; DA (UK) 1989.

MCCORMACK, Michael James Countess of Chester Hospital, Liverpool Road, Chester CH2 1BQ Fax: 01244 365003; Highfield, 39 Newton Lane, Chester CH2 2HJ Fax: 01244 321656 Email: jim.mccormack@virgin.net — MB BCh BAO 1982 Belf.; MD Belf. 1992; FRCOG 1987. Cons. O & G Countess of Chester Hosp. Prev: Lect. Birm. Matern. Hosp.

MCCORMACK, Mr Michael John (retired) 19 Oaklands Drive, Newtonmassey, Newtownabbey BT37 0XE — MB BCh BAO 1981 NUI; MB BCh NUI 1981; BSc (Hons.) NUI 1983; FRCSI; MSc (Hons.) Orth. Lond. 1993. Cons. Orthop. Surg. (NHS).

MCCORMACK, Nicola Wyn Lodge Surgery, Lodge Road, Chippenham SN15 3SY Tel: 01249 660667 Fax: 01249 447350 — MB ChB 1979 Manch.; MRCGP 1983; DRCOG 1983. p/t Gen. Practitioner Princip. Lodge Surg. Chippenham. Prev: GP Macclesfield; GP Littleport, Ely; GP Berkhamsted.

MCCORMACK, Paraic Michael 42 The Summit, Wallasey CH44 1AZ — MB BS 1994 Lond.

MCCORMACK, Patricia D R Kapil & Partners, 291 Ashby Road, Scunthorpe DN16 2AB Tel: 01724 864426; Glencrest, Ermine Street, Scawby, Brigg DN20 9NB Tel: 01652 657768 — MB BCh BAO 1982 Belf.; MB BCh Belf. 1982; DRCOG 1986; DCH Dub. 1985; Cert. Family Plann. JCC 1986. Prev: Trainee GP Brigg VTS.

MCCORMACK, Patricia Madeleine (retired) Richmond House, 124 Aldenham Road, Bushey, Watford WD23 2ET Tel: 01923 238461 Fax: 01923 256630 — MB BS 1960 Lond.

MCCORMACK, Peter 44 The Avenue, Nunthorpe, Middlesbrough TS7 0AR — MB 1957 Camb.; BChir 1956; FRCP Lond. 1976, M 1961. (Camb. & St. Mary's) Hon. Cons. S. Tees Hosp. Prev: Cons.

MCCORMACK

Phys. S. Tees Hosp. Gp.; Ho. Phys. Med. Unit St. Mary's Hosp. Lond.; Ho. Surg. Canad. Red Cross Memor. Hosp. Taplow.

MCCORMACK, Roger Fullerton (retired) Whinfield, 261 Upper Batley Lane, Batley WF17 0AR Tel: 01924 441000 — MRCS Eng. LRCP Lond. 1954; MRCGP 1964. Prev: Hosp. Pract. (A & E) Dewsbury Dist. Hosp.

MCCORMACK, Sheena Mary Geraldine MRC Clinical Trials Unit, 222 Euston Road, London NW1 2DA Tel: 0207 670 4708 Fax: 0207 670 4818 Email: s.mccormack@ctu.mrc.ac.uk — MB BS 198 Lond.; MRCP (UK) 1985; Dip. Ven. Lond. 1987; FRCP (UK) 1999; MSc 1997. Cons. Genitourin. Med. Roy. Devon & Exeter Hosp.; Sen. Clin. Research Fell., MRC Clin. Trials Unit; Cons. Phys. HIV/GVM Chelsea & W.minster NHS Trust; Hon. Cons. Phys., HIV/GVM St Mary's NHS Trust; Hon. Cons. Phys., HIV/GVM Camden & Islington Community Healthcare Trust; Cons. GU/HIV Phys. At Vict. Clinic os Sexual Health, Chelsea & W.minster NHS Trust Lond. Prev: Cons. Genitourin. Med.) Roy. Devon & Exeter Hosp.; Sen. Regist. (Genitourin. Med.) Char. Cross Hosp. Lond.; Regist. (Genitourin. Med.) Char. Cross Hosp. Lond.

MCCORMACK, Stephen Robert Edgar North Parade Surgery, 6 North Parade, Belfast BT7 2GG — MB BCh BAO 1990 Belf.; MRCGP 1995; DRCOG 1993; DGM RCPS Glas. 1992.

MACCORMACK, Stuart Michael 156 Ifield Road, West Brompton, London SW10 9AF — MB BS 1994 West. Austral.

MCCORMACK, Terence Whitby Group Practice, Spring Vale Medical Centre, Whitby YO21 1SD Tel: 01947 820888 Fax: 01947 603194; Plantation House, Thorpe Lane, Robin Hood's Bay, Whitby YO22 4RN Tel: 01947 880530 — MB BS 1982 Lond.; DRCOG 1985; DA Eng. 1984. (St. Marys) Socs: Assn. Anaesth. Prev: SHO (Obst.) ScarBoro. Gen. Hosp.; SHO (Anaesth.) P.ss Margt. Hosp. Swindon; SHO (A & E) Roy. Berks. Hosp. Reading.

MCCORMICK, Mr Alastair James Alan 1 The Saltings, Shaldon, Teignmouth TQ14 0BT — MB ChB 1942 Ed.; FRCS Ed. 1954; DOMS Eng. 1949.

MACCORMICK, Alistair Stevenson Murray Road Surgery, 50 The Murray Road, East Kilbride, Glasgow G75 0RT Tel: 01355 225374 Fax: 01355 239475; Cir Mhor, 5 Glen Quoich, East Kilbride, Glasgow G74 2JE Tel: 01355 229718 — MB ChB Glas. 1965; DObst RCOG 1967. (Glas.)

MCCORMICK, Anna Guilford (retired) Shepherd's Spring, Hardington Mandeville, Yeovil BA22 9PP — MB ChB 1959 Bristol; FFPHM RCP (UK) 1987, M 1980; DObst RCOG 1961; BSc 2000 Open. Prev: Cons. Med. Statistician Off. Populat. Censuses & Surveys.

MCCORMICK, Mrs Anne Rosamunde 2 Stallibrass Mews, High St., Barkway, Royston SG8 8EG — MB ChB 1963 Ed. (Ed.) Prev: SCMO Child Assessm. Unit Roy. Shrewsbury Hosp.; Deptm. Med. Off. Salop CC; Ho. Phys. & Ho. Surg. Falkirk Infirm.

MCCORMICK, Bruce Andrew Department of Anaethesia, Bristol Royal Infirmary, Marlborough Street, Bristol BS2 8HW — MB BS 1992 Lond.

MCCORMICK, Carol Gillian Sheena Moore Street Health Centre, 77 Moore Street, Bootle L20 4SE Tel: 0151 944 1066 Fax: 0151 933 4715 Email: carolmccormick@pccbsefton-ha.nhs.uk; 5 Firs Crescent, Freshfield, Liverpool L37 1PT — MB ChB 1981 Liverp.; DRCOG 1983.

MCCORMICK, Christina Sara Frances Department of Histopathology, Derriford Hospital, Derriford Road, Plymouth PL6 8DH Tel: 01752 763533 — MB BCh BAO 1988 Belf.; MRCPath 1995. (QUB, NI) Cons. (Histopath.) Derriford Hosp. Plymouth. Socs: RCP; BMA.

MCCORMICK, Clare Veronica Main Street Surgery, 31 Main Street, Lochwinnoch PA12 4AH Tel: 01505 842200 Fax: 01505 843144 — MB BS 1970 London; MB BS Lond. 1970; MRCS Eng LRCP Lond. 1970. (London) GP Lochwinnoch, Renfrewsh.

MCCORMICK, Colin James Department of Cellular Pathology, Royal Berkshire Hospital, London Road, Reading RG1 5AN — MB BS 1985 Lond.; MRCPath 1993. Cons. Histopath. Roy. Berks. Hosp. Reading. Prev: Sen. Regist. (Histopath.) Roy. Berks. Hosp. Reading.

MCCORMICK, David Craig 25 Belvoir Road, London SE22 0QY — MB ChB 1985 Otago; MRCP (UK) 1989.

MCCORMICK, Deirdre Anne Department of Histopathology Level E, Queen Alexandra Hospital, Cosham, Portsmouth PO6 3LY; Hilston, Bowes Hill, Rowlands Castle PO9 6BS — MB BCh BAO 1981 NUI; MRCPI 1985; MRCPath 1991; FRCPath 1999. (University College Dublin) Cons. Histopath. & Cytol. Qu. Alexandra Hosp. Cosham.

MCCORMICK, Isobel Anne Orchard Croft Medical Centre, 2A Westfield Road, Horbury, Wakefield WF4 6LL Tel: 01924 271016 Fax: 01924 279459; 18 Silcoates Drive, Wrenthorpe, Wakefield WF2 0UR — MB ChB 1984 Leeds.

MCCORMICK, Mr John St Clair Ivy Cottage, Kirkpatrickdurham, Castle Douglas DG7 3HG — MB ChB 1964 Ed.; FRCS Ed. 1967. Cons. Surg. Dumfries & Galloway Roy. Infirm. Prev: Cons. Surg. Dunfermline & W. Fife Hosp.; Sen. Surg. Regist. Roy. Infirm. & Chalmers Hosp. Edin.

MCCORMICK, Justin Kelly 117 Dundrum Road, Newcastle BT33 0LN — MB BCh BAO 1993 Belf.

MCCORMICK, Kenneth Peter Bolton 15 Sandringham Road, South Gosforth, Newcastle upon Tyne NE3 1QB Tel: 0191 284 8372 — MB ChB 1988 Ed. SHO (Paediat.) Newc. Gen. Hosp. Prev: SHO (Paediat.) Roy. Hosp. Sick Childr. Glas.

MCCORMICK, Martin Francis 189 Hamilton Road, Rutherglen, Glasgow G73 3BE — MB ChB 1998 Glas.; MB ChB Glas 1998.

MCCORMICK, Mr Maxwell Stewart 27 Rodney St, Liverpool L1 9EH Tel: 0151 709 8416; 334 Telegraph Road, Heswall, Wirral CH60 6RW Tel: 0151 342 7960 — MB ChB 1973 Liverp.; FRCS Eng. 1979. Cons. Surg. (ENT) Roy. Liverp. & BRd.green Univ. Trust; Alder Hey Childr. Hosp. Trust. Socs: Roy. Soc. Med.; Brit. Assn. Otol.; Irish Otol. Soc. Prev: Sen. Regist. Mersey HA; Regist. Radcliffe Infirm. Oxf.; Regist. Groote Schuur Hosp., Cape Town.

MCCORMICK, Michael Thomas 24 Kilbroney Road, Rostrevor, Newry BT34 3BJ — MB BCh BAO 1997 Belf.

***MCCORMICK, Paul Jonathan** 11 East Mead, Aughton, Ormskirk L39 5ES — MB ChB 1997 Liverp.

MCCORMICK, Peter Anthony Dryland Surgery, 1 Field St., Kettering NN16 8JZ Tel: 01536 518951; 19 Warkton, Kettering NN16 9XL — MB ChB 1963 Ed.; DCH Eng. 1965.

MCCORMICK, Robert Neill Shepherd's Spring, Hardington Mandeville, Yeovil BA22 9PP Tel: 01935 862481 — MB BS 1993 Lond.

MCCORMICK, Simon Richard Dept of A&E, Sheffield Children's Hospital, Sheffield S10 2TH; 154 Bole Hill Road, Walkley, Sheffield S6 5DE Tel: 0114 233 6169 — MB ChB 1993 Sheff. Specialist Regist. Sheff. Childr.'s Hosp.

MCCORMICK, Stewart Incle Street Surgery, 8 Incle Street, Paisley PA1 1HR Tel: 0141 889 8809 Fax: 0141 849 1474; Mountstuart, 43 Main Road, Elderslie, Johnstone PA5 9BA Tel: 01505 324900 — MB ChB 1967 Glas.; BSc (Hons.) Glas. 1964, MB ChB 1967. (Glas.) GP Trainer; Hon. Phys. St. Mirren Football Club. Prev: Ho. Phys. Roy. Alexandra Infirm. Paisley; Ho. Surg. W.. Infirm. Glas.

MCCORQUODALE, Linda Jane (retired) 20 Buckingham Drive, Ely CB6 1DR — MB BS 1997 Lond.

MCCORRY, Angela 426 Street La, Leeds LS17 6RL — MB ChB 1997 Leic.

MCCORRY, Richard Lewis (retired) 9 Earlswood Road, Belfast BT4 3DY Tel: 02890 655733 — MB BCh BAO 1947 Belf.; FRCPI 1963, M 1953; FRCPath 1969, M 1963. Prev: Hon. Cons. Chem. Path. Ulster Hosp., Dundonald.

MCCOSH, Claire Robin Close, The Hedgerows, Balance Hill, Uttoxeter ST14 8TP — MB BCh 1987 Wales.

MCCOUBREY, Iain Addison Waitrose Ltd, Bracknell RG12 8YA Tel: 01344 842337 Email: iain_mccoubrey@waitrose.co.uk — MB ChB 1970 Glas.; MRCGP 1975; DAvMed Eng. 1976; FFOM RCP Lond. 1994, MFOM 1984, AFOM 1978. (Glas.) Dep. Chief Med. Adviser John Lewis Partnership. Socs: Assoc. Fell. Aerospace Med. Assn.; Soc. Occupat. Med. Prev: Dir. Plans & Personnel Defence Secondary Care Agency; Commanding Off. P.ss Alexandra's RAF Hosp. Wroughton; Dir. Med. Organisation (RAF) MOD.

MCCOUBREY, Mark Antony 63 Donaghadee Road, Bangor BT20 4QY — MB ChB 1997 Dundee.

MCCOUBRIE, Malcolm Department of General Practice, St. Georges Hospital Medical School, Cranmer Terrace, London SW17 0RE Email: m.mccoubrie@sghms.ac.uk; 5 Stagbury Avenue, Chipstead, Coulsdon CR5 3PA — MB BS Lond. 1964; FRCGP 1985, M 1979. p/t Sen. Lect. (Community Based Med. Educat.) St. Geo. Hosp. Med. Sch. Lond.; Acad. Gen. Practitioner, Streatham, Lond.

Prev: CME Tutor Calderdale HA; Ment. Health Act Commiss. 1984-6.; Course Organiser Halifax VTS.

MCCOUBRIE, Paul Flat 11, Block 1, 5 Beech Hill Road, Sheffield S10 2RA — MB BS 1996 Lond.

MCCOURT, Barbara Ann Central Surgery, 22 Cowley Hill Lane, St Helens WA10 2AE Tel: 01744 24849 Fax: 01744 456497; 2 Crescent Green, Aughton, Ormskirk L39 5DR Tel: 01695 423061 — MB ChB 1983 Sheff.; DRCOG 1985.

MCCOURT, Killian Charles Department of Clinical Anaesthesia, Royal Victoria Hospital, Grosvenor Road, Belfast BT12 6BA Tel: 0123890325725 Fax: 012890 9032 5725 Email: killian.mccourt@royalhospitals.n-i.nhs.uk; 22 Laganvale Court, Stranmillis, Belfast BT9 5BH Tel: 02890 664828 Fax: 02890 334 9984 Email: killian@opus-one.org — MB BCh BAO 1988 Belf.; FRCA 1994; MD 1999 Belfast. (Qu. Univ. Belf.) Cons. Anaesth. The Roy. Gp. of Hosp.s Belf. Prev: Sen. Regist. & Research Fell. (Anaesth.) Qu. Univ. Belf.

MCCOURT, Margaret Yvonne 11 Broadwater Park, The Willows, Aghalee, Craigavon BT67 0EW — MB BCh BAO 1980 Belf.

MCCOURT, Maureen Winifred Goretta Knockanore, Ballyaran Hill, Portadown, Craigavon BT62 — MB BCh BAO 1979 NUI.

MCCOURTNEY, Mr James Stephen Royal Alexandra Hospital, Corsebar Rd, Paisley PA2 9PN Tel: 0141 580 4883; Shamiana, 62 Ferndale Road, Burgess Hill RH15 0HG — MB ChB 1988 Glas.; MD Glas. 1998; FRCS 1998 (Gen. Surg.); MD 1998 Glas; FRCS (Gen Surg) 1998; BSc (Hons.) Glas. 1985; FRCS Glas. 1992. (Univ. Of Glasgow) Cons. Cororectal Surg., Roy. Alexandra Hosp. Paisley; Cons. Colorectal Surg., Roy. Alexandra Hosp. Paisley. Socs: Sec. of W. Scott. Surgic. Assn.; Sec. of W. Of Scott. Surgic. Assn. Prev: Specialist Regist. (Gen. Surg.) Glas. Roy. Infirm., Stobhill Hosp. & W.. Infirm. Glas.; Res. Surgic. Off., St Mark's Hosp. Harrow; Resid. Surg. Off., St Mark's Hosp., Harrow.

MACCOWAN, Hamish Arthur Scott Ryehill Health Centre, St. Peter Street, Dundee DD1 4JH Tel: 01382 644466 Fax: 01832 646302 — MB ChB 1977 Dundee; MRCGP 1982.

MACCOWAN, Jean Sutherland Russell Chapel Street Medical Centre, Chapel Street, Ashton-under-Lyne OL6 6EW Tel: 0161 339 9292 Fax: 0161 339 7808; Bramber, 98 Thornfield Grove, Ashton-under-Lyne OL6 6RJ Tel: 0161 330 6788 — MB ChB 1964 Glas. Clin. Asst. (Ultrasonogr.) Tameside & Glossop HA.

MCCOWAT, Lorna Catherine 1 Ardmore Avenue, Broughty Ferry, Dundee DD5 2TU — MB ChB 1998 Ed.; MB ChB Ed 1998.

MCCOWEN, Caroline Margaret (retired) Cogden House, 34 Market Place, Ripon HG4 4EF Tel: 01765 689257 Email: caroline@cogden.freeserve.co.uk — BA Oxf. 1962, BM BCh 1965; FRCP Lond. 1991; FRCP Ed. 1990; MRCP (UK) 1981; DCH Eng. 1978. Prev: Cons. Paediat. N. Tees Hosp. Stockton Cleveland.

MCCOWEN, Eleanor Mary 3FR, 3 Cambridge Street, Edinburgh EH1 2DY Tel: 0131 229 5272 — MB ChB 1997 Ed.; BSc (Hons) 2:1 Med. Microbiol Ed. 1997. St Geo.'s Healthcare NHS Trust Paediat. SHO. Prev: SHO Paediat. Kircaldy Acute Hosp.; Surg. Ho. Off. Falkirk & Distrist RI; Med Ho. Off. W.ern Gen. Edin.

MCCOY, Bernard Gerard Hillhead Health Centre, 50 Hillhead, Stewartstown, Dungannon BT71 5HY Tel: 028 8773 8648 Fax: 028 8773 8648 — MB BCh BAO 1984 Belf.; MB BCh Belf. 1984.

MCCOY, Brigid Teresa Lleifior, Lon St Ffraid, Trearddur Bay, Holyhead LL65 2BJ — MB BCh BAO 1975 Belf.; DCH Dub. 1978. Clin. Med. Off. (Community Health) Gwynedd HA.

MCCOY, Mr David Richard (retired) Ave. House, High St, Iron Acton, Bristol BS37 9UH Tel: 01454 228874 — MB BS Lond. 1958; FRCS Ed. 1964; FRCS Eng. 1964; FRCOG 1980, M 1967. Prev: Cons. (Obst. & Gyn) S.mead Hosp. Gp. Bristol.

MCCOY, Eamon Paul Royal Victoria Hospital, Belfast BT12 6BA Tel: 01232 240503 Fax: 01232 325725 Email: eamonmccoy@ireland.com; 5 Cranmore Avenue, Malone, Belfast BT9 6JH Tel: 01232 669774 Fax: 01232 325725 — MB BCh BAO 1986 NUI; MD Belf. 1995; FFA RCSI 1990. Cons. Anaesth. Roy. Vict. Hosp. Belf. Prev: Sen. Regist. (Anaesth.) Roy. Vict. Hosp. Belf.; SHO Roy. Vict. Hosp. Belf.; Intern. Cork Regional Hosp.

MCCOY, Mr Gerald Francis Mary 87 Balmoral Avenue, Belfast BT9 6NZ — MB BCh BAO 1976 Belf.; MD Belf. 1985; FRCSI 1980. Cons. (Orthop. Trama Surg.) Roy. Vict. Hosp. Belf. Socs: Brit. Orthop. Assn.; Brit. Trauma Soc.; Irish. Orthop. Assn. Prev: Research Fell. Dept. Orthop. Surg. Qu.'s Univ. Belf.

MCCOY, Kevin James 49A Cushendall Road, Ballymena BT43 6HA — MRCS Eng. LRCP Lond. 1981.

MCCOY, Rachel Nola 16 Stodmarsh House, Cowley Road, London SW9 6HH — MB ChB 1991 Otago.

MCCOY, Mrs Yvette (retired) 433 Budshead Road, Whitleigh, Plymouth PL5 4DU Tel: 01752 734492 — MRCS Eng. LRCP Lond. 1947; MRCGP 1966; DObst RCOG 1952. Prev: Ho. Phys. & Ho. Surg. Metrop. Hosp.

MCCOYE, Andrew Joseph 164 Haven Lane, Moorside, Oldham OL4 2QQ — MB ChB 1998 Sheff.; MB ChB Sheff 1998.

MCCRACKEN, Adrian Lees Avenue Road Surgery, 28A Avenue Road, Malvern WR14 3BG Tel: 01684 561333 Fax: 01684 893664 Email: practice.m81039@gp-m81039.nhs.uk; Wyche End, 23 King Edwards Road, Malvern WR14 4AJ — MB BCh BAO 1966 Belf.; DObst RCOG 1968. Socs: Travel Med. Internat. Prev: SHO (Paediat.) Worcester Roy. Infirm.; SHO (O & G) The Route Hosp. Ballymoney; Ho. Phys. & Ho. Surg. Roy. Vict. Hosp. Belf.

MCCRACKEN, Alistair John 9A Gloucester Lane, Edinburgh EH3 6ED — MB ChB 1979 Ed.; DRCOG 1982.

MCCRACKEN, Dermot (retired) 76 The Dell, Westbury-on-Trym, Bristol BS9 3UG — MB BCh 1942 Wales; MB BCh (Distinc. Pharmacol. & Hyg.) Wales 1942; BSc Wales 1939; FRCP Lond. 1973, M 1945. Prev: Phys. Univ. Leeds Stud. Health Dept.

MCCRACKEN, Diane Department of Medical Microbiology & Public Health Lab., University Hospital of Wales, Heath Park, Cardiff CF14 4XW — BM BCh 1993 Oxf.; MRCP (UK) 1996. Specialist Regist. (Med. MicroBiol.) Pub. Health Laborat. Serv. Cardiff.

MCCRACKEN, Fiona Margaret The Health Centre, High Street, Arnold, Nottingham NG5 7BG Tel: 0115 926 7257 — BM BS 1990 Nottm.; BMedSci. Nottm. 1988; MRCGP 1995; DRCOG 1992. (Nottm.) GP Part Time, Nottm. Prev: Trainee GP/SHO (Cas.) Derby Roy. Infirm.; Trainee GP Stoke Mandeville Hosp. Aylesbury VTS.

MCCRACKEN, James Spowart, MBE (retired) 17 Arlington Drive, Mapperley Park, Nottingham NG3 5EN Tel: 0115 960 7971 Fax: 0115 960 7971 — MB ChB 1957 Aberd.; FRCGP 1986, M 1965; DCH RCPS Glas. 1968; DObst RCOG 1960. Prev: Sen. GP Nottm.

MCCRACKEN, Jean (retired) 12 Bay Tree Avenue, Worsley, Manchester M28 2NW Tel: 0161 794 2693 — MB ChB 1953 Manch.; DA Eng. 1960. Prev: Assoc. Specialist (Anaesth.) Salford AHA (T).

MCCRACKEN, Margaret (retired) 76 The Dell, Westbury-on-Trym, Bristol BS9 3UG — MB ChB 1944 Manch.

MCCRACKEN, Mary 113C Harleston Road, Northampton NN5 7AQ — MB BS 1977 Lond.; BSc Lond. 1974, MB BS 1977; FFA RCS Eng. 1984. (Univ. Coll. Hosp.) Clin. Asst. (Anaesth.) N.ampton Gen Hosp.

MCCRACKEN, Norman 10 Beechill Park E., Santfield Road, Belfast BT8 4NY — MB BCh BAO 1975 Belf.

MCCRACKEN, Stuart Robert Crozier 290 Comber Road, Dundonald, Belfast BT16 1UR — BM BS 1998 Nottm.; BM BS Nottm 1998.

MCCRAE, Anne Fiona Dept. Anaesthetics, Royal Infirmary, Edinburgh EH3 9YW Tel: 0131 536 3651 Fax: 0131 536 3672 Email: a.mccrae@ed.ac.uk — MB ChB 1981 Ed.; FFA RCSI 1989; DRCOG 1985. (Ed.) Cons. Anaesth. Roy. Infirm. Edin. Prev: Sen. Regist. & Regist. (Anaesth.) Roy. Infirm. Edin.

MCCRAE, Fiona Catherine Department of Rheumatology, Queen Alexandra Hospital, Cosham, Portsmouth PO6 3LY Tel: 023 9228 6000 Fax: 023 9228 6862 — MB ChB 1980 Manch.; FRCP 1997, M (UK) 1983. p/t Cons. Rheum. Qu. Alexandra Hosp. Portsmouth. Socs: BMA; Brit. Soc. Rheum.; Nat. Osteoporosis Soc.

MCCRAE, John Stewart, CBE, MBE(Mil) (retired) The Retreat, 87 Walton Road, Clevedon BS21 6AW Tel: 01275 871470 — MB ChB Glas. 1939. Prev: Chairm. Nat. Med. Consult. Comm. & Scott. Counc. BMA.

MCCRAE, William Morrice (retired) Seabank House, Aberdour, Burntisland KY3 0TY Tel: 01592 860452 — MB ChB 1955 Glas.; MSc Ed. 1996; FRCP Glas. 1968, M 1962; FRFPS Glas. 1960; FRCPCH 1997; FRCP Ed. 1967, M 1962. Prev: Cons. Phys. Roy. Hosp. Sick Childr. Edin.

MCCRAITH, John Anthony (retired) 2 Broadtree Close, Mellor, Blackburn BB2 7PW Tel: 01254 812363 — MB BS 1950 Durh.; DObst RCOG 1952.

MCCRAITH

MCCRAITH, Kennedy Henry (retired) Rannochbrae, Garelochhead, Helensburgh G84 0DB — MB BS 1958 Lond.; MRCS Eng. LRCP Lond. 1958; DObst RCOG 1960. Prev: Surg. Cdr. RN.

MCCRAITH, Nicholas Stuart St Marys Health Centre, Cop Lane, Penwortham, Preston PR1 0SR Tel: 01772 744404 Fax: 01772 752967; 23 Hurst Park, Penworthham, Preston PR1 9BD — MB ChB 1978 Aberd.; MRCGP 1982; DRCOG 1981.

MCCRANN, Ursula Grace 64 Sir Harry's Road, Edgbaston, Birmingham B15 2UX Tel: 0121 440 4452 Email: umcran@hotmail.com — MB BCh 1995 Wales. (UWCM)

MCCREA, Anthony Philip 2nd Floor, Frizzell House, 8 High St., Holywood BT18 9AZ Tel: 028 90 427427 Fax: 02890 427425 Email: philip.mccrea@ohcni.com — MB BCh BAO 1982 Belf.; MD Belf. 1989; MRCP (UK) 1985; MFOM RCP Lond. 1992; MFOM RCPI 1991. (Queen's Belfast) Indep. Occupat.al Health Specialist. Prev: Med. Off. N.. Irel. Electricity Bd. Belf.; Regional Med. Off. BT N. Irel.

MCCREA, Daniel 1 Cork Square, Vaughan Way, Wapping, London E1W 2NH — MB BS 1982 Lond. Regist. (Med.) Chelmsford Gp. Hosps. Prev: Ho. Phys. & Ho. Surg. & SHO/Regist. Rotat. Lond. Hosp.

MCCREA, Danny Winston Kieron 59 Addiscombe Road, Croydon CR8 1EU Tel: 020 8668 3699 — MB BS 1975 Newc.; DRCOG 1979; MRCGP 1980. (Newcastle upon Tyne)

MCCREA, George Windsor Castlereagh Medical Centre, 220 Knock Road, Belfast BT5 6QF Tel: 028 9079 8308 Fax: 028 9040 3776; (Surgery) 220 Knock Road, Belfast BT5 6QD — MB BCh BAO 1961 Belf.

MCCREA, John Daniel Department of Rheumatology, West Cumberland Hospital, Whitehaven CA28 8JG Tel: 01946 523005 Fax: 01946 523504 Email: jdmcc@doctors.org.uk — MD 1984 Belf.; MD (Hons.) Belf. 1984; MB BCh BAO Belf. 1976; MRCP (UK) 1980; T(M) 1991; FRCP Lond. 1996; FRCP Glas. 1998. (Queen's University Belfast) Cons. Rheum. & Gen. Med. W. Cumbld. Hosp. Socs: Brit. Soc. Rheum.; BMA; Scientif. Advis. Comm. Nat. Osteoporosis Soc. (1997). Prev: Michael Mason Memor. Fell. (ARC) Rheum. Univ. Sydney Roy. N. Shore Hosp., Australia; Hon. Sen. Regist. & Research Fell. (Med. & Rheum.) Hammersmith Hosp. & Roy. Postgrad. Med. Sch. Univ. Lond.; Sen. Regist. (Rheum.) Musgrave Pk. & City Hosps. Belf.

MCCREA, Julia 16 Oldfield Road, Bath BA2 3ND — MB BCh 1966 Wales. (Cardiff) Clin. Asst. (Geriat.) St. Martins, Bath; Asst GP Bath.

MCCREA, Julia Anne Sharon 1 Wilson Crescent, Ballymena BT42 3BW — MB BCh BAO 1980 Belf.

MCCREA, Kathryn Jayne 24 Donaghedy Road, Bready, Strabane BT82 0DA Tel: 01504 841374 — MB ChB 1994 Glas.; MRCP 1997. SHO Roy. Hosp. Sick Childr. Yorkhill Glas.

MCCREA, Madalina 2F3 1 Roseburn Avenue, Edinburgh EH12 5PD — MB ChB 1998 Ed.; MB ChB Ed 1998.

MCCREA, Paul Hilary Mental Health Services, Rotherham District General Hospital, Moorgate Road, Rotherham S60 2UD Tel: 01709 304335 — MB BCh BAO 1988 Belf.; MRCPsych 1992; DMH Belf. 1990. Cons. (Psychiat.) Rotherham Dist. Gen. Hosp.

MCCREA, Robert Ronald 346 Grimshaw Lane, Middleton, Manchester M24 2AU; 14 West Crescent, Middleton, Manchester M24 4DA Tel: 0161 643 8989 — MB BCh BAO Belf. 1947.

MCCREA, Roderick Denis 1 Cherryhill, Rostrevor, Newry BT34 3BD — MB BS 1985 Lond.

MCCREA, William (retired) 22 Shore Road, Aberdour, Burntisland KY3 0TU — MB BCh BAO 1973 Belf.; MRCPsych 1978. Cons. Psychiat. Ment. Handicap Servs. Fife HB. Prev: Cons. Psychiat. Roy. Scott. Nat. Hosp. Larbert.

MCCREA, William Arthur Princess Margaret Hospital, Okus Road, Swindon SN1 4JU Tel: 01793 426906 Fax: 01793 426661 — MB BCh BAO 1980 NUI; FRCP 1999 London; LRCPI 1980. (Royal College of Surgeons (Dublin)) Cons. Cardiol. P.ss Margt. Hosp. Swindon; Hon. Cons. Cardiol. Bristol Roy. Infirm. Bristol. Socs: Brit. Cardiac Soc.; Brit. Soc. of Echocardiography; Irish Cardiac Soc. Prev: Sen. Regist. (Cardiol.) Kings Coll. Hosp. Lond. & SE Thames Regional Cardiothoracic Unit Brook Hosp. Lond.

MCCREADIE, Mr Dominic William James Accident & Emergency Department, New Cross Hospital, Wednesfield Road, Wolverhampton WV10 0QP Tel: 01902 307999 — MB ChB Glas. 1975; FRCS Ed. 1984; FFAEM 1993. (Glas.) Cons. (A & E) New Cross Hosp. Socs: Fell. Fac. Accid. & Emerg. Med.; Brit. Assn. Accid. & Emerg. Med.; Milit. Surg. Soc. Prev: Cons. A & E & Trauma Surg. Warwick Hosp.; Sen. Regist. (A & E Med.) Basingstoke Dist. Hosp.; Maj. RAMC (Gen. Surg.) Wroughton RAF Hosp.

MCCREADIE, Janice Elizabeth 7 The Crest, Kingshill, Ware SG12 0RR — MB ChB 1982 Manch.; BSc MedSci St. And. 1979; Cert. Prescribed Equiv. Exp. JCPTGP 1986; Cert. Family Plann. JCC 1985. CMO (Child Health) E. Herts. HA. Prev: GP Ware Herts.; CMO (Child Health) N. Herts. HA; Trainee GP N. Middlx. Hosp. Lond. VTS.

MCCREADIE, Maureen Ann 15 Ashfield Road, Kenilworth CV8 2BE — MB ChB 1976 Glas. Clin. Asst. (Psychiat.) Warwick Centr. Hosp. & St. Michael's Hosp. Warwick. Prev: SHO (Psychiat.) Pk. Prewett Hosp. Basingstoke.

MCCREADIE, Professor Robin Graeme Crichton Royal Hospital, Dumfries DG1 4TG Tel: 01387 244000 Fax: 01387 257735 Email: rgmccreadie-crh@compuserve.com; East Cluden Hill, East Cluden, Dumfries DG2 0JA Tel: 01387 721169 — DSc Glas. 1993, BSc 1962, MD 1972, MB ChB 1965; FRCPsych 1985, M 1972; DPM Ed. & Glas. 1968. (Glas.) Dir. Clin. Research & Cons. Psychiat. Crichton Roy. Hosp. Dumfries.; Hon. Prof. of Clin. Psychiat. Univ. of Aberd. Prev: Cons. Psychiat. Crichton Roy. Hosp. Dumfries; Cons. Psychiat. Gartnavel Roy. Hosp. Glas.; Lect. Glas. Univ. Dept. Psychol. Med. S.. Gen. Hosp. Glas.

MCCREADIE, Stuart Lamont Kilwinning Medical Practice, 15 Almswall Road, Kilwinning KA13 6BO Tel: 01294 554591 Fax: 01294 557300; 5 Brodick Close, Kilwinning KA13 6RN Tel: 01294 54591 — MB ChB Glas. 1963.

MCCREADY, Dean Victor 5 Ballyloughan Brow, Ballymena BT43 6PW — MB BCh BAO 1984 Belf.

MCCREADY, Professor Victor Ralph Royal Marsden Hospital, Downs Road, Sutton SM2 5PT Tel: 020 8642 6011 Fax: 020 8642 7694 Email: ralph@icr.ac.uk; Tel: 020 8643 3120 — MB BCh BAO Belf. 1960; DSc Belf. 1986, BSc 1957; MSc Lond. 1964; MRCP Lond. 1974; FRCR 1975; Hon. FFR RCSI 1992; DMRD Eng. 1963. Prof. Radiol. Sci. Inst. Cancer Research Lond.; Hon. Cons. Roy. Marsden Hosp. Lond. & Sutton; Civil. Cons. RN.

MACCREANOR, Catherine Mary 22 Ballymote Road, Glenavy, Crumlin BT29 4NS — MB BCh BAO 1985 Belf.

MCCREARY, Robert D Hillsborough Health Centre, Ballynahinch Street, Hillsborough BT26 6AW Tel: 028 9268 2216 Fax: 028 9268 9721 — MB BCh 1978 Belfast; MB BCh 1978 Belfast.

MCCREATH, Brian James Flat 3/2, 14 Oban Drive, Glasgow G20 6AF — MB ChB 1995 Glas.; BSc (Hons.) Anat. Glas. 1993. Specialist Regist. in Anaesth. based at S.ern Gen Hosp, Glas.

MCCREATH, Catriona Munro 11 Quadrant Road, Newlands, Glasgow G43 2QP — MB ChB 1995 Glas.

MCCREATH, Georgina Torrance Stobhill Hospital NHS Trust, 133 Balornock Road, Glasgow G33 Tel: 0141 201 3625; 11 Quadrant Road, Newlands, Glasgow G43 2QP Tel: 0141 637 1972 — MB ChB Glas. 1969; FRCR 1975; DMRD Eng. 1973. Cons. (Radiodiag.) Stobhill NHS Trust Glas. Prev: Cons. (Radiodiag.) S.. Gen. Hosp. Glas.; Cons. (Radiodiag.) W.. Infirm. Glas.; Sen. Regist. (Radiodiag.) S.. Gen. Hosp. Glas.

MCCREATH, Mr Stewart William Neidpath, 3 Torridon Avenue, Dumbreck, Glasgow G41 5LA Tel: 0141 427 1536 Fax: 0141 427 1536 Email: smccreath@msn.com — MB ChB 1967 Glas.; BSc Glas. 1964; FRCS Glas. 1972. (Univ. Glas.) Cons. Orthop. Surg. S.. Gen. Hosp. Glas.; Clin. Tutor Nat. Centre for Train. & Educat. in Prosth.s & Orthotics Univ. Strathclyde. Socs: Fell. BOA; BMA. Prev: Sen. Regist. (Orthop.) Addenbrooke's Hosp. Camb.; Regist. (Surg.) Stobhill Gen. Hosp. Glas.

MCCREDIE, Janet Elizabeth Bellingham Green Surgery, 24 Bellingham Green, London SE6 3JB Tel: 020 8697 7285 Fax: 020 8695 6094; 26 Sportsbank Street, Catford, London SE6 2EX Tel: 020 8697 3603 — MB BS 1982 Lond.; MRCGP 1987. Prev: Trainee GP Dartford VTS; SHO (Psychiat.) W. Middlx. Hosp. Isleworth.

MCCREE, Terence Slaidburn Health Centre, Slaidburn, Clitheroe BB7 3EP Tel: 0120 06 229 — MB BS 1954 Durh. Socs: BMA. Prev: Ho. Phys. Sunderland Gen. Hosp.; Ho. Surg. (Midw. & Gyn.) & Sen. Ho. Off. (Surg.) S. Shields Gen.; Hosp.

MCCREEDY, Ann Elizabeth Main Street Surgery, 11 Main Street, Loughbrickland, Banbridge BT32 3NQ Tel: 028 4066 2692 Fax: 028 4066 9517; 36 Hilltown Road, Rathfriland, Newry BT34 5NA Tel:

01820 630388 — MB BCh BAO 1983 Belf.; MRCGP 1988; DRCOG 1992; DCH RCPS Glas. 1991. (Qu. Univ. Belf.)

MCCREERY, Joanna Brook Street Surgery, 9 Brook Street, Holywood BT18 9DA Tel: 028 9042 6984 Fax: 028 9042 6656; Ballygrot House, 16 Kathleen Avenue, Helens Bay, Bangor BT19 1LF — MB BCh BAO 1984 Belf.; MRCGP 1989; T(GP) 1991; DCH RCPSI 1987; DRCOG 1986.

MCCREERY, William Cecil Charles (retired) Trengganu, 11 Pledwick Crescent, Sandal, Wakefield WF2 6DF Tel: 01924 250615 — MB BCh BAO Dub. 1944; MA Dub. 1968, BA 1940, MD 1965. Prev: Cons. Venereol. Clayton Hosp. Wakefield & Gen. Hosp. Dewsbury.

MCCREESH, Geraldine Anne McDonnell and Partners, 139-141 Ormeau Road, Belfast BT7 1DA Tel: 028 9032 6030 — MB BCh BAO 1986 Belf.; MRCGP 1990; DRCOG 1990.

MCCRIMMON, Fiona Elizabeth 4 Homington Court, Albany Park Road, Kingston upon Thames KT2 5SP Tel: 020 8549 0886; 20 Sherbourne Place, 57 The Chase, Stanmore HA7 3UH — MB BS 1993 Lond.; BSc Lond. 1990; DCH RCP Lond. 1995; DRCOG 1996; DGMRCP Lond. 1997; DFFP 1996. (Roy. Free, Hamstead) Trainee GP/SHO N.wick Pk. Hosp. Harrow VTS. Socs: RCGP; BMA; FFP.

MCCRINDLE, David Cumming 4 Oxton House, Kenton, Exeter EX6 8EX — MB ChB 1992 Cape Town. SHO (Psychiat.) Centr. Hosp. Hatton.

MCCRIRRICK, Alastair Bryce Laregan, France Lynch, Stroud GL6 8LZ — BM 1983 Soton.; FCAnaesth 1989. Cons. (Anaesth. & IC) Gloucester Roy. Hosp.

MCCRONE, Catherine Cameron (retired) West House, West Road, Dunfermline KY12 9UN Tel: 01383 852217 — MB ChB Glas. 1955.

MCCRONE, Colin John (retired) West House, West Road, Saline, Dunfermline KY12 9UN Tel: 01383 852217 — MB ChB Glas. 1955.

MCCRONE, Helena Elizabeth Maitland 58 Westover Road, London SW18 2RH — MB BS 1978 Lond.; BA Camb. 1966. (Roy. Free)

MCCRONE, James Wallace Lancelyn Precinct Practice, 1 Lancelyn Precinct, Spital Road, Wirral CH63 9JP Tel: 0151 334 4019 Fax: 0151 346 1063; 4 Dunraven Road, Little Neston, South Wirral CH64 9QU Tel: 0151 336 2833 — MB ChB 1970 Ed.; BSc (Med. Sci.) Ed. 1967, MB ChB 1970; MRCP (UK) 1974; MRCGP 1979. Princip. GP Merseyside; Sessional Dr. BUPA Med. Centre Murrayfield Hosp. Wirral.

MCCRONE, Lesley Anne Royal Cornhill Hospital, Cornhill Road, Aberdeen AB25 2ZH Tel: 01224 557276; Corrennie, St. Arnauds, Raemoir Road, Banchory AB31 4EJ Tel: 01330 823423 — MB ChB 1978 Aberd.; MRCPsych 1983. Cons. Psychiat. Roy. Cornhill Hosp. Aberd.

MCCRONE, Martin Gerrard Banchory Group Practice, The Surgery, Bellfield, Banchory AB31 5XS Tel: 01330 822121 Fax: 01330 825265; Corrennie, St. Arnauds, Raemoir Road, Banchory AB31 4EJ Tel: 01330 823423 Email: mmccrone@aol.com — MB ChB 1978 Aberd.; MRCGP 1982; DRCOG 1981; FRCGP 1997. (Aberd.) Chairm. Deeside LHCC.

MCCRORY, Colin Alexander William 84 Raw Brae Road, Whitehead, Carrickfergus BT38 9SX — MB BCh BAO 1985 Belf.

MCCRORY, Connell Roger Leonard 41 Woodbury Road, Halesowen B62 9RH; 41 Woodberry Road, Halesowen B62 9RH — MB BCh BAO 1988 NUI; LRCPSI 1988.

MCCRORY, Mr David Camillus 111 Upper Lisburn Road, Belfast BT10 0LG — MB BCh BAO 1983 Belf.; FRCSI 1987.

MCCRORY, Graeme William Toberargan Surgery, 27 Toberargan Road, Pitlochry PH16 5HG Tel: 01796 472558 Fax: 01796 473775; 31 Bonnethill Road, Pitlochry PH16 5ED — MB ChB 1990 Dundee; MRCGP 1995; DRCOG 1992. (Dundee) GP Princip. Pitlochry. Prev: Hospice Phys. Inverness.

MCCRORY, James Wilfred Noble's Hospital, Westmoreland Road, Douglas — MB BS 1979 Newc.; FFA RCS Eng. 1986. Cons. Anaesth. Noble's Hosp. Douglas I. of Man. Prev: Sen. Regist. (Anaesth.) Roy. Vict. Infirm. Newc.; Regist. (Anaesth.) Freeman Rd. Hosp. Newc. u Tyne.

MCCRORY, Mark 28 Liscorran Road, Lurgan, Craigavon BT67 9JR — MB BCh BAO 1995 Belf.

MCCROSSAN, Lawrence Anthony 8 Aigburth Drive, Liverpool L17 3AA — MB ChB 1988 Glas.

MCCROSSAN, Pamela Janet Mather Avenue Practice, 584 Mather Avenue, Liverpool L19 4UG Tel: 0151 427 6239 Fax: 0151 427 8876 — MB ChB 1993 Liverp.

MACCROSSAN, William Rae (retired) Kincraig, 82 Leven Road, Lundin Links, Leven KY8 6AJ Tel: 01333 320482 — MB ChB 1945 Glas. Squadron Ldr. RAFVR.

MCCROSSON, Fiona Margaret 5 Varna Road, Jordanhill, Glasgow G14 9NE — MB ChB 1998 Glas.; MB ChB Glas 1998.

MCCRUDEN, Douglas Campbell Vale of Leven Hospital, Alexandria G83 0UA Tel: 01389 754121 Fax: 01389 603919; Craigview, Lusset Road, Old Kilpatrick, Glasgow G60 5LU — MB ChB 1972 Glas.; BSc (Hons.) Glas. 1970; FRCP Glas. 1995; FRCP Ed. 1990; MRCP (UK) 1975. (Glas.) Cons. Phys. Vale of Leven Hosp. Alexandria; Hon. Clin. Sen. Lect. Univ. Glas. Prev: Sen. Regist. (Gen. Med., Diabetes & Endocrinol.) Roy. & W.. Infirm. Glas.; Regist. (Gen. Med.) W.. Infirm. Glas.; Ho. Off. (Gen. Med.) W.. Infirm. Glas.

MCCRUDEN, Elizabeth Ann Blin University of Glasgow, Institute of Virology, Church St., Glasgow G11 5JR Tel: 0141 330 4017 Email: e.mccruden@bio.gla.ac.uk; Craigview, Lusset Road, Old Kilpatrick, Glasgow G60 5LU Tel: 01389 890608 — MB ChB 1972 Glas.; BSc (Hons.) Glas. 1970; MRCPath 1988; FFA RCS Eng. 1976. Sen. Lect. Hon. Cons. (Virol.) Inst. Virol. Glas. Socs: Brit. Soc. Study of Infec.; (Comm.) Clin. Virol. Gp. Soc. for Gen. Microbiol.; Assn. Clin. Paths. Prev: Sen. Regist. (Virol.) Regional Virus Laborat. Ruchill Hosp. Glas.; Regist. (Anaesth.) Vale of Leven Dist. Gen. Hosp. Alexandria; Clin. Off. W. Scotl. Blood Transfus. Serv.

MCCRUM, Anne Crimond, Crifty Craft Lane, Churchdown, Gloucester GL3 2LL Tel: 01452 712016 — MB ChB 1977 Bristol; MRCOG 1983. Prev: Regist. (O & G) Birm. HA.

MCCRUM, David Wishaw Health Centre, Kenilworth Avenue, Wishaw ML2 7BQ Tel: 01698 357766; 11 Powforth Close, Larkhall ML9 1NU Tel: 01698 889641 — MB ChB 1985 Glas.; MRCGP 1989.

MCCRUM, John Conal St John's Avenue Surgery, 24 St. John's Avenue, Churchdown, Gloucester GL3 2DB Tel: 01452 713036 Fax: 01452 714726; Crimond, Crifty Craft Lane, Churchdown, Gloucester GL3 2LL Tel: 01452 712016 — MB ChB 1977 Bristol; MRCP (UK) 1980; MRCGP 1984.

MCCRYSTAL, David John 41 Clarence Street, Ton Pentre, Pentre CF41 7LP — MB BS 1991 Queensland.

MCCUBBIN, Alan Thomas Grant Seaton Hirst Health Centre, Norham Road, Ashington NE63 0NG Tel: 01670 813167 Fax: 01670 523889 — MB ChB 1988 Ed.; MRCGP 1994; DRCOG 1994. (Edin.) NHS GP Princip. Prev: Regtl. Med. Off. 1st Bn. Devonsh. & Dorset Regt.; MOIC Barker Barracks Med. Centre; Trainee GP/SHO BMH Rinteln.

MCCUBBIN, Thomas Dalziel Department of Anaesthesia, Western Infirmary, Glasgow G11 6NT Tel: 0141 211 2069 Fax: 0141 211 1806; 71 Newlands Road, Glasgow G43 2JP Tel: 0141 649 0092 — MB ChB 1970 Glas.; FFA RCS Eng. 1975; DObst RCOG 1972. Cons. Anaesth. & Pain Managem. N. Glas. Univ. Hosps. NHS Trust; Postgrad. Tutor W. Glas. Hosps.; Hon. Clin. Sen. Lect. Univ. Glas. Socs: Assn. Anaesth.; Pain Soc.; N. Brit. Pain Assn. Prev: Sen. Regist. (Anaesth.) W.. Infirm. Glas.; Regist. (Anaesth.) Roy. Infirm. Glas.; Fell. (Anaesth.) Baroness Erlanger Hosp. Chattanooga, USA.

MACCUE, Elspeth Campbell 29 Russell Drive, Bearsden, Glasgow G61 3BB — MB ChB 1977 Ed.; BSc (Med. Sci.) Ed. 1974, MB ChB 1977; MRCPsych. 1983; MRCGP 1981; DRCOG 1979. Cons. Psychiat. Argyll & Clyde Health Bd.

MACCUE, Miss Jane Louise Queen Elizabeth II Hospital, Howlands, Welwyn Garden City AL7 4HQ Tel: 01707 328111 Fax: 01707 365127 — MB BS 1981 Lond.; MS Lond. 1993; FRCS Eng. 1985. (St. Bart.) Cons. Colorectal Surg. Qu. Eliz. II Hosp. Welwyn Garden City. Prev: Sen. Regist. (Gen. Surg.) St. Mary's Hosp. Lond.; Lect. (Surg.) St. Bart. Hosp. Lond.

MACCUISH, Allison Stonehaven Medical Group, Stonehaven Medical Centre, 32 Robert Street, Stonehaven AB39 2EL; Laurel Bank, Woodcot Lane, Stonehaven AB39 2GJ Tel: 01569 64039 — MB ChB 1974 Aberd.; MRCGP 1978; DRCOG 1978.

MACCUISH, Angus Carstairs 21 Poplar Avenue, Newton Mearns, Glasgow G77 5QZ Tel: 0141 639 3163 — MD 1983 Ed.; MB ChB 1965; FRCP Ed. 1977, M 1969; FRCP Glas. 1982, M 1979. (Ed.) Cons. Phys. (Med. & Diabetes) Glas. Roy. Infirm & Glas. Roy.

MACCUISH

Matern. Hosp.; Hon. Sen. Lect. Med. Univ. Glas. Socs: Assn. Phys. Gt. Brit. & Irel.; Brit. Diabetic Assn. Prev: Sen. Regist. (Gen. Med.) Edin. Roy. Infirm.

MACCUISH, Sandra Karen Farne Drive Surgery, 59 Farne Drive, Glasgow G44 5DQ Tel: 0141 637 9828 Fax: 0141 633 5284; 46 Aursbridge Crescent, Barrhead, Glasgow G78 2TJ Tel: 0141 880 8956 — MB ChB 1986 Glas.; DRCOG 1989.

MCCULLAGH, Anthony Graham 9 Aberdeen Terrace, London SE3 0QX — MB 1974 Camb.; BA Camb. 1970, MB 1974, BChir 1973.

MCCULLAGH, Catriona Denise 7 Ridgeway Street, Belfast BT9 5FB — MB BCh BAO 1993 Belf.

MCCULLAGH, Geraldine Maria 72 Camden Mews, London NW1 9BX — MB BS 1989 Lond.

MCCULLAGH, Majella Margaret Mary 214 Brockley Grove, London SE4 1HG — MB BCh BAO 1980 Dub.; MCh Dub. 1992; FRCS (Paediat.) 1996; FRCSI 1984. Cons. Paediat. Surg. Univ. Hosp. Lewisham Lond. Socs: Brit. Assn. Paediat. Surg.

MCCULLAGH, Mary Rose Albert Street Health Centre, Albert Street, Belfast BT12 4JR Tel: 028 9032 0777 — MB BCh BAO 1985 Belf.; DRCOG 1988. Trainee GP Belf.

MCCULLAGH, Michael Gerard Orchard Medical Practice, Orchard Street, Ipswich IP4 2PU Tel: 01473 213261 — MB BCh BAO 1982 NUI; FRCGP 1993, M 1987. (Univ. Coll. Dub.) Commrs. E. Suff.; Vice Chairm. Suff. MAAG; Chaim. GP Professional Developm. Gp. for Suff.; Commiss.er E. Suff.; Primary Care Research Co-ordinator Suff.

MCCULLAGH, Paul Joseph Department of Histopathology, Royal Devon & Exeter Hospital, Church Lane, Exeter EX2 5AD — MB BCh BAO 1989 NUI; MSc Lond. 1993; BDS Belf. 1981; MRCPath 2000. Cons. Histopath., Roy. Devon & Exeter Hosp. Exeter. Socs: Path. Soc. Prev: Clin. Research Fell. ICRF Med. Oncol. Unit St. Bart. Med. Coll. Lond.; Clin. Lect. Histopath. Univ. Coll. Lond.; Cons. Histopath., MusGr. Pk. Hosp., Taunton.

MCCULLAGH, William Douglas (retired) 28 Gateacre Rise, Gateacre, Liverpool L25 5LA Tel: 0151 428 1698 — MB BCh BAO 1932 Belf. Prev: Ho. Surg. David Lewis N. Hosp., Walton Hosp. & Alder Hey Hosp. Liverp.

MCCULLEN, Mark Andrew c/o Medical Secretaries, Level F, Queen Alexandra Hospital, Cosham, Portsmouth PO6 3LY Tel: 023 92 379451; 262 Innsworth Lane, Innsworth, Gloucester GL3 1EB — MB BS 1988 Lond.; BSc Lond. 1985, MB BS 1988; MRCP (UK) 1992. Regist. Rotat. (Gastroenterol. & Gen. Med.) Qu. Alexandra Hosp. Portsmouth & Soton. Gen. Hosp. Prev: SHO Rotat. (Med.) Bournemouth & Poole.

MCCULLINS, Mary Elizabeth 15 Glencregagh Drive, Belfast BT6 0NJ — MB ChB 1994 Ed.; MA (Hons) Physiol. Camb 1991; MRCP (Ed.) 1997. (Cambridge/Edinburgh) GP Locum. Socs: MRCP; MRCGP. Prev: SHO (Med. & Renal) Roy. Infirm. Edin.

MCCULLOCH, Alan Jackson General Hospital, Bishop Auckland; Churchside, Ingleton, Darlington DL2 3HS — MD 1984 Ed.; BSc 1970, MB ChB 1973; FRCP Lond. 1990; FRCP Ed. 1987; MRCP (UK) 1976. Cons. Phys. Bishop Auckland Gen. Hosp.

MCCULLOCH, Alan Smith Department of Radiology, Ninewells Hospital, Ninewells, Dundee DD2 1UB Tel: 01382 60111 — MB ChB 1979 Dundee; FRCR 1988. Cons. Radiol. & Hon. Sen. Lect. Radiol. Univ. Dundee.

MCCULLOCH, Alison Erica 43 Willow Road, West Bridgford, Nottingham NG2 7AY Tel: 0115 923 1405 — MB ChB 1981 Dundee. Clin. Asst. (Psychiat.) Mapperley Hosp. Nottm. Prev: Trainee GP MarlBoro..; Regist. (Psychiat.) Bassingstoke.

***MCCULLOCH, Andrew Charles** 49 Lavender Drive, East Kilbride, Glasgow G75 9JH — MB ChB 1998 Dund.; MB ChB Dund 1998.

MCCULLOCH, Mr Archibald Bruce 30 Upper Dicconson Street, Wigan WN1 2AG Tel: 01942 242366; Dornoch House, 92 Orrell Road, Orrell, Wigan WN5 8HB Tel: 01942 222254 — MB ChB Ed. 1942; FRCS Ed. 1948. (Ed.) Socs: Fell. BOA. Prev: Cons. Orthop. Surg. Wigan & Leigh Hosp. Gp.; Cons. Orthop. Surg. S.W. Durh. Hosp. Gp.; Sen. Regist. (Orthop.) Roy. Vict. Infirm. Newc. u. Tyne.

***MCCULLOCH, Corrin Jane** Kinnen Dell, Bathgate EH48 4NJ — MB ChB 1995 Manch.

MCCULLOCH, Dori Ann Keeper's Cottage, Betton Wood, Market Drayton TF9 4BQ — MD 1987 Northweston U, USA. Cons. Anaesth. Stafford Dist. Gen. Hosp.

MCCULLOCH, Elizabeth Ellen Health Centre, Holme Lane, Cross Hills, Keighley BD20 7LG Tel: 01535 632147 Fax: 01535 637576 — MB ChB 1981 Dundee; MRCGP 1986.

MCCULLOCH, George Morrison (retired) 2 Cedar Avenue, Stirling FK8 2PF — MB ChB 1954 Ed.; DObst RCOG 1962; MRCGP 1974. Prev: GP Stirling.

MCCULLOCH, Gordon James Durham Road Surgery, 25 Durham Road, Edinburgh EH15 1NY Tel: 0131 669 1153 Fax: 0131 669 3633 — MB ChB 1979 Ed.; MRCGP 1984; CIH Dund 1987. Prev: Civil. Phys. US Army Munich.

MCCULLOCH, Ian Michael The Long House, 73-75 East Trinity Road, Edinburgh EH5 3EL Tel: 0131 552 4919; 3 Royston Terrace, Edinburgh EH3 5QU Tel: 0131 552 2696 — MB ChB 1982 Aberd.; MRCP (UK) 1986; MRCGP 1989. Prev: Regist. (Med.) King's Cross Hosp. Dundee; SHO (O & G) Perth Roy. Infirm.; SHO (Med.) Aberd. Roy. Infirm.

MCCULLOCH, Ian Norman (retired) The Coppice, Station Road, Cardross, Dumbarton G82 5NL Tel: 01389 841886 — MB ChB 1952 Glas. Prev: Capt. RAMC.

MCCULLOCH, Ian William Lindsay, Maj. RAMC Retd. Musters Medical Practice, 214 Musters Road, West Bridgford, Nottingham NG2 7DR Tel: 0115 981 4124 Fax: 0115 981 3117; 43 Willow Road, West Bridgford, Nottingham NG2 7AY Tel: 0115 914 5560 — MB ChB 1981 Dundee; MRCGP 1985; DRCOG 1987. Prev: SHO (Psychiat.) Pk. Prewett Hosp. Basingstoke; SHO (Paediat., O & G & A & E) Camb. Milit. Hosp. Aldershot.

MCCULLOCH, James Allen Thomson Argyll and Bute Hospital, Lochgilphead PA31 8LD Tel: 01546 602323 Fax: 01546 606452; Camus Beag, Lochgair, Lochgilphead PA31 8SD Tel: 01546 886386 — MB ChB 1975 Glas.; FRCPsych 1997; MRCPsych 1979. Cons. Psychiat. Argyll & Bute Hosp. Lochgilphead.

MCCULLOCH, Joan Elizabeth (retired) 2 Cedar Avenue, Stirling FK8 2PF Tel: 01786 75343 — MB ChB 1954 Ed. Prev: Clin. Med. Off. Forth Valley HB.

MCCULLOCH, Joan Mary Department of Obstetric Ultrasound, Ninewells Hospital and Medical School, Dundee DD1 9SY Tel: 01382 660111; 45 Wemyss Crescent, Monifieth, Dundee DD5 4RA Tel: 01382 535303 — MB ChB 1979 Dundee; DRCOG 1981. (Dundee)

MCCULLOCH, John (retired) Flat 1C 1 Hutchison Court, Berryhill Road, Giffnock, Glasgow G46 7NN Tel: 0141 638 8556 — LRCP LRCS 1948 Ed.; LRCP LRCS Ed. LRFPS Glas. 1948; MRCGP 1962. Prev: Res. Med. Off. Stobhill Hosp. Glas.

MACCULLOCH, Professor Malcolm John University of Wales College of Medicine, Heath Park, Cardiff CF14 4XN Tel: 029 2074 7747 Fax: 029 2074 7839; Inglewood, Lisvane Road, Lisvane, Cardiff CF14 0SF — MD 1969 Manch.; MB ChB 1960; FRCPsych 1977, M 1971; DPM Manch. 1965. (Manch.) Prof. Forens. Psychiat. Univ. Wales Coll. Med. Cardiff; Hon. Cons. Forens. Psychiat. Bridgend & Dist. NHS Trust. Prev: Med. Dir. Pk. La. Special Hosp.; Sen. Princip. Med. Off. Ment. Health Div. DHSS; Sen. Lect. Dept. Psychiat. Univ. Liverp.

MCCULLOCH, Nicholas Alan The Surgery, St. Mary Street, Thornbury, Bristol BS35 2AT Tel: 01454 413691 Fax: 01454 411141 — MB BS 1985 Lond.; MA Oxf. 1982; MRCGP 1990; DRCOG 1989.

MCCULLOCH, Paul (retired) 8 Brookview Court, 38 Village Road, Enfield EN1 2HE Tel: 020 8363 1936 — MB ChB 1944 Glas.; BSc Glas. 1941; AFOM RCP Lond. 1979. Prev: Indust. Med. Off. Everest Double Glazing Company.

MCCULLOCH, Mr Peter George Academic Unit of Surgery, Clinical Sciences Centre, Lower Lane, Liverpool L9 7AL Tel: 0151 529 5887 Fax: 0151 529 5888 — MB ChB 1980 Aberd.; MD Aberd. 1988; FRCS Ed. 1984; FRCS Glas. 1984. Sen. Lect. (Surg.) Univ. Liverp.; Hon. Cons. Surg. Univ. Hosp. Aintree. Socs: Sec. Brit. Oesophago-gastric Cancer Gp.; Brit. Assn. Surg. Oncol.; Soc. of Acad. & Research Surg.s. Prev: Regist. (Surg.) Gtr. Glas. HB; Lect. (Surg.) Univ. Glas.; Cas. Off. Sheff. AHA.

MCCULLOCH, Thomas Scott 6 Stewarton Crescent, Kilmarnock KA3 6BP — MB ChB 1995 Glas.

MCCULLOCH, William James Daer Walsgrave Hospital, Coventry CV2 2DX; The Grange, 16 Guys Cliffe Avenue, Leamington Spa CV32 6LY — MB BS 1976 Lond.; FFA RCS Eng. 1983. (St. Bartholomews) Cons. Anaesth. Walsgrave Hosp. Coventry. Socs:

Mem. of Vasc. Anaestheisa Soc.; Mem. of Assn. of Anaesth.s of Gt. Britain and Irel. Prev: Sen. Regist. (Anaesth.) Edin. Roy. Infirm.; Regist. (Anaesth.) St. Bart. Hosp. Lond.

MCCULLOCH, William John Director of Health Safety & Environment, United Biscuits, Church Road, West Drayton UB7 7PR Tel: 01895 432277 Fax: 01895 43226 Email: bill_mcculloch@biscuits.com; 4 Rydal Gardens, West Bridgford, Nottingham NG2 6JR Tel: 0115 923 4592 Fax: 0115 945 2670 — MB ChB 1975 Dundee; BSc St. And. 1972; FRCP Glas. 1991; MRCP (UK) 1980; FFOM RCP Lond. 1994, MFOM 1986; MRCGP 1981. Gp. Dir. of Health, Safety & Environment United Biscuits W. Drayton. Socs: Inst. Occupat. Safety & Health; Soc. Occup. Med.; Amer. Coll. Occupat. Environm. Med. Prev: Chief Occupat. Phys. Mars; Med. Off. Nat. Coal Bd. W. Area; Regist. (Med.) Falkirk & Dist. Roy. Infirm.

MCCULLOUGH, Adrian Maurice Dumfries & Galloway Royal Infirmary, Bankend Road, Dumfries DG1 4AP Tel: 01387 246246; Mount Pleasant, Broadchapel Road, Lochmaben, Lockerbie DG11 1RL Tel: 01387 810854 — MB BCh BAO 1977 Belf.; MRCS Eng. LRCP Lond. 1977; FRCOG 1996, M 1983; T(OG) 1991. (Qu. Univ. Belf.) Cons. O & G Dumfries & Galloway Roy. Infirm. Socs: BMA; ISSVD; BSCCP. Prev: Cons. O & G P.ss Mary's RAF Hosp. Akrotiri & BMH Rinteln; Hon. Sen. Regist. Qu. Mother's Hosp. Glas.; Sen. Specialist (O & G) Camb. Milit. Hosp. Aldershot.

MCCULLOUGH, Allen Ingram 8 Carnhill Gardens, Carmoney, Newtownabbey BT36 6LQ — MB BCh BAO 1990 Belf.

MCCULLOUGH, Bernard Edward Paul c/o Westminster Bank, Berkeley Square, London W1 — MB ChB 1936 New Zealand; DA Eng. 1940. (Otago) Socs: Fell. Roy. Soc. Med.; BMA. Prev: Res. Surg. Off. Samarit. Hosp. Wom. Lond.; Sen. Res. Anaesth. St. Mary's Hosp. Lond.; Specialist Anaesth. Nos. 1 & 2 Maxillofacial Units MEF.

MCCULLOUGH, Bernard Lawrence (retired) 4 Glendale Avenue, Eastbourne BN21 1UU Tel: 01323 732558 — MB BS 1962 Lond.; MRCS Eng. LRCP Lond. 1962; Cert. Family Plann. JCC 1985; DTM & H Eng. 1968; DObst RCOG 1963. Prev: Ho. Surg. Middlx. Hosp. Lond.

MCCULLOUGH, Christian Thomas Flat 1F2 18 Roseneath Terrace, Edinburgh EH9 1JN Tel: 020 84 228 9404 Email: drctmcc@aol.com — MB ChB 1998 Ed.; MB ChB (Hons) Ed 1998; BSc (Hons) 1995 Edin. (Edin.) Med. Fac. Research Fell. Dept. Path. Uni. Edin. Med. Sch. Edin. Prev: Ho. Off. c/o Elderly Roy. Infirm. Edin; Ho. Off. Orthop. + Mepatobiliary Surg. Roy. Infirm. Edin.

MCCULLOUGH, Mr Christopher John Northwick Park Hospital, Watford Road, Harrow HA3 1UJ Tel: 020 8869 2635 — MB BChir 1971 Camb.; BChir 1970; MA Camb. 1971; FRCS Eng. 1975. (Camb. & Univ. Coll. Hosp.) Cons. Orthop. Surg. N.wick Pk. Hosp. Harrow. Socs: Fell. BOA; Fell. Brit. Soc. Surg. of the Hand. Prev: Sen. Regist. (Orthop.) Nuffield Orthop. Centre Oxf.; Regist. (Surg.) Univ. Hosp. Wales; SHO Trauma Unit Univ. Coll. Hosp. Lond.

MCCULLOUGH, Derreck Allen Department of Clinical Biochemistry, St John's Hospital at Howden, Howden Road W., Livingston EH54 6PP Tel: 01506 419666 Ext: 3342 Fax: 01506 460301 Email: derreck.mccullough@wlt.scot.nhs.uk — MB BCh BAO 1971; MD 1977 Belf.; MRCPath 1983. (Queens University Belfast) Cons. Chem. Path. St. John's Hosp. Livingston W. Lothian; Clin. Pharmacologist, Beechams Pharmaceut., Epsom, Surrey. Prev: Sen. Regist. (Chem. Path.) Roy. Vict. Hosp. Belf.; Lect. (Phys.) Qu. Univ. Belf.

MCCULLOUGH, Fiona Wallace Hunters Way Medical Centre, Hunters Way, Kimbolton, Huntingdon PE28 0JF Tel: 01480 860205 Fax: 01480 861590 — MB BChir 1979 Camb.; MA 1983 Camb.; MRCGP 1990; MFFP 1993; DRCOG 1983. GP, Kimbolton Med. Centre; Med. Manager, Family Plann., Hinchingbrooke Health Care NHS Trust. Socs: Chairm., E. Anglian Gp. of Family Plann. Doctors. Prev: Trainee GP Camb. VTS.; Hosp. Practitioner, Colposcopy, Hinchingbrooke.

MCCULLOUGH, Mr George Wellesley The Willows, Beanstown Road, Lisburn BT28 — MB BCh BAO 1964 Belf.; FRCS Ed. 1972.

MCCULLOUGH, Heather Jayne (retired) 30 Drumahoe Road, Londonderry BT47 3SD Tel: 01504 301428 — MB BCh BAO 1986 Belf.; MRCGP 1990.

MCCULLOUGH, Hugh Clement Pitsmoor Surgery, 151 Burngreave Road, Sheffield S3 9DL Tel: 0114 272 8228 — MB BCh BAO 1981 Dub.; MRCGP 1985; DRCOG 1985; DCH RCP Lond. 1984.

MCCULLOUGH, Isabel Margaret (retired) 175 Whitecoates Lane, Walton, Chesterfield S40 3HJ Tel: 01246 236197 — LRCPI & LM, LRSCI & LM 1949; LRCPI & LM, LRCSI & LM 1949; DObst RCOG 1955; DCH Eng. 1952. Prev: GP Chesterfield.

MCCULLOUGH, Jean Bernadette Department of Histopathology, Ninewells Hospital & Medical School, Dundee DD1 9SY Tel: 01382 60111 — MB ChB 1983 Manch.; BSc St. And. 1980; MRCPath 1993. Cons. & Hon. Sen. Lect. Histopath. Ninwells Hosp. Dundee. Prev: Clin. Lect. & Hon. Sen. Regist. (Histopath.) Ninewells Hosp. Dundee; Regist. (Histopath.) Bradford Roy. Infirm.; SHO (Path.) N. Manch. Gen. Hosp.

MCCULLOUGH, Justine 13 Broadbent Close, Whetstone, Leicester LE8 6NN Tel: 0116 286 4571 — MB ChB 1993 Leic.; FRCS (Eng.) 1997.

MCCULLOUGH, Keith Alexander 632 George Street, Aberdeen AB25 3XN — MB ChB 1998 Aberd.; MB ChB Aberd 1998.

MCCULLOUGH, Michael Edward (retired) Garthland, 49 Grahams Dye Road, Bo'ness EH51 9ED — MB ChB 1955 Ed. Prev: Ho. Surg. Orthop. Dept. & Ho. Phys. Edin. Roy. Infirm.

MCCULLOUGH, Sharon Hanson's Bank, Spurgrove, Frieth, Henley-on-Thames RG9 6PB Tel: 01494 882264 Email: smccullough@zygian.com — MB BS 1984 Lond.; MBA City 1990; BSc Lond. 1981; Dip. Pharm. Med. RCP (UK) 1994. (Univ. Coll. Lond.) Dir. Zygian Pharmaceut. Med. Consultancy. Prev: Dir. Med. Affairs, Innovex Assoc. Med. Dir., Glaxo Wellcome UK.

MCCULLOUGH, Sonya Ruth c/o 32 Beanstown Road, Lisburn BT28 3QS; 34 Lowestoft Drive, Burnham Gate, Slough SL1 6PF Tel: 01628 668918 — MB BCh BAO 1991 Belf.; MRCOG 1996. Specialist Regist. Genito Urin. Med. Chelsea & W.m. Hosp. Fulham Rd. Lond. Socs: RCOG; Ulster Obst. Soc. Prev: Regist. Acute Obst. Groote Schuur, Cape Town.

MCCULLOUGH, Stafford Clugston (retired) 52 Venn Grove, Hartley, Plymouth PL3 5PH Tel: 01752 772921 — MB ChB BAO 1948 Belf. Prev: Med. Off. RAMC Merebrook Camp, Malvern.

MCCULLOUGH, Timothy Kourosh 4A Lynwood Avenue, Epsom KT17 4LQ — MB BS 1996 Lond.

MCCULLOUGH, Mr Wesley Linton Northampton General Hospital, Cliftonville, Northampton NN1 5RD — BM 1982 Soton.; FRCS Ed. 1990; MRCOG 1995. (Southampton) Cons.s in Obst. and Gyn.

MCCUNE, Catherine Anne 14 East End, Marshfield, Chippenham SN14 8NU — MB BS 1992 Lond.; BSc (Hons.) 1988; MRCP (UK) 1995. (University College London) Specialist Regist. (Gastroenterol.) Bristol.

MCCUNE, Graham Scott 5 Kindleton, Great Linford, Milton Keynes MK14 5EA — MB ChB 1969 Glas.; MRCOG 1976, DObst 1971. Cons. (O & G) Milton Keynes Hosp. Prev: Sen. Regist. (O & G) Gtr. Glas. Health Bd.

MCCUNE, Mr Kenneth Harold 17 Fortwilliam Park, Belfast BT15 4AL; 17 Fortwilliam Park, Belfast BT15 4AL — MB ChB 1989 Dundee; FRCS Ed. 1996. Socs: BMA; Assn. of Surg.s of GB and I; Assn. of Surg.s in Train.

MCCUNE, Noel Samuel Charles Child & Family Clinic, Bocombra Lodge, 2 Old Lurgan Road, Portadown, Craigavon BT63 5SQ Tel: 01762 392112 Fax: 01762 361968 — MB BCh BAO 1976 Dub.; MRCPsych 1982. Cons. Child Psychiat. S.. Health & Social Servs. Bd.

MCCUNE, Ronald Edward The Hambleden Clinic, Blanchedown, London SE5 8HL Tel: 020 7274 3939 — MB BS 1970 Lond.; MRCS Eng. LRCP Lond. 1970. Hon. Orthop. Surg. King's Coll. Hosp. Lond.; Med. Off. Surrey Co. Cricket Club. Prev: Sen. Regist. (Cas.) King's Coll. Hosp. Lond.

MCCURDIE, Ian Michael, Lt.-Col. RAMC 32 Holly Lane W., Banstead SM7 2BB — MB BS 1983 Lond.; MSc (Sports Med.) Lond. 1996; MRCP (UK) 1994; MRCGP 1990; DRCOG 1988. (King's Coll. Hosp. Lond.)

MCCURDIE, Michael John Huntley Mount Medical Centre, Huntley Mount Road, Bury BL9 6JA Tel: 0161 761 6677 Fax: 0161 761 3283 — MB ChB 1983 Cape Town.

MCCURDY, Alexander Matthew (retired) 30 Seapatrick Road, Craigavon Area Hospital, Banbridge BT32 4PH Tel: 018206 62069 — MB BCh BAO 1956 Dub.; MA Dub. 1960, MD 1965; MB BCh

MCCURDY

BAO 1956; DMRD Eng. 1963. Prev: Cons. Radiol. Craigavon Area Hosp.

MCCURDY, David Lloyd Department Sexual Health, Clinic 11, Ipswich Hospital NHS Trust, Heath Road, Ipswich IP4 5PD Tel: 01473 254718 — MB BS 1963 Lond.; MRCS Eng. LRCP Lond. 1963; DObst RCOG 1967. (Lond. Hosp.) Clin. Asst. Sexual Health Matern. Dept. Ipswich Hosp. Socs: Ipswich Clin. Soc.

MCCURDY, John Frederick 1 Hadleigh Court, Marine Parade E., Clacton-on-Sea CO15 6JJ — LMSSA 1967 Lond.

MCCURDY, Robert Nigel Charles (retired) Chy an Rudhak, Tanhouse Road, Lostwithiel PL22 0DL Tel: 0779 630 5792 — MB ChB Ed. 1941; DPH Lond. 1949. Prev: Stationsarzt Landesversicherungsanstalt, Nassau, Lahn, Germany.

MCCURLEY, John 263 Nithsdale Road, Glasgow G41 5AW Tel: 0141 427 3330 Fax: 0141 427 3330 — MB ChB 1961 Glas.; FRCPsych 1986, M 1971; DPM Ed. & Glas. 1964. Hon. Cons. Psychiat. Renfrewsh. Healthcare NHS Trust. Prev: Med. Dir. Renfrewsh. Healthcare NHS Trust; Phys. Supt. Dykebar & Merchiston Hosps. Paisley.

MCCURRACH, David McNaughton (retired) 135 Ochiltree, Dunblane FK15 0PA Tel: 01786 824603 — LRCP LRCS Ed. LRFPS Glas. 1948. Prev: GP Bathgate.

MCCUSKER, Charles Dennis Midlochhead Cottage, Kilbirnie Road, Lochwinnoch PA12 4DX Tel: 01505 842634 — MB ChB 1956 Glas.; MRCGP 1975; DCH RCPS Glas. 1974.

MCCUSKER, Dorothy Patricia Portglenone Health Centre, 17 Townhill Road, Portglenone, Ballymena BT44 8AD Tel: 028 2582 1551 Fax: 028 2582 2539 — MB BCh BAO 1990 (O&G and Child Health) Belf.; MRCGP 1994; DMH (Distinc.) Belf. 1993; DRCOG 1993; DCH RCP Lond. 1993; DGM RCP Lond. 1992. (Qu. Univ. Belf.) Socs: Brit. Med. & Dent. Hypn. Soc.

MCCUSKER, Ellen Tempo, Enniskillen BT94 3PA — MB BCh BAO 1941 NUI. (Univ. Coll. Dub.) Prev: Ho. Surg. Noble's Isle of Man Gen. Hosp.

MCCUSKER, Fiona Elizabeth McCracken 44 Kippington Road, Sevenoaks TN13 2LJ — MB ChB 1978 Ed.; MRCGP 1982; DRCOG 1981.

MCCUSKER, John Anthony Tempo Medical Centre, Main Street, Edenmore Tempo, Enniskillen BT94 3LU Tel: 028 8954 1216 — MB BCh BAO 1977 NUI.

MCCUSKER, Patrick 29 Glasgow Road, Paisley PA1 3PA Tel: 0141 889 3732 — MB ChB 1944 Glas.; DA RCPSI 1973. (Univ. Glas.) Prev: Ho. Surg. Roy. Infirm. Bradford; Regist. Dept. Anaesth. S.. Gen. Hosp. Glas.; Asst. Surg. Roy. Alexandra Infirm. Paisley.

MCCUSKER, Teresa Mary Majella 34 Collinbridge Gardens, Glengormley, Newtownabbey BT36 7SU — MB BCh BAO 1986 Belf.; MRCGP 1990; DCH RCP Glas. 1989. GP Antrim.

MCCUTCHAN, James Donald Shaw Department of Orthopaedic Surgery, Worthing Hospital, Park Road, Worthing BN11 2DH — MB BCh 1981 Wales; FRCS (Orth.) Eng. 1993; FRCS Eng. 1987. Cons. Orthop. Worthing Health Auth.; Med. Dir., The Back Pain Centre, King Edwd. VII Hosp., Midhurst. Socs: Fell.Brit. Orthop. Assoc.; Brit. Orth. Research Soc.; Brit. Orth. Spine Soc. Prev: Sen. Regist. (Orthop.) Leeds; Regist. (Orthop.) Sheff.; Specialist (Surg.) RAMC.

MCCUTCHEON, Alexander Robert (retired) 15 Dalziel Drive, Pollokshields, Glasgow G41 4JA Tel: 0141 427 0281 — MB ChB 1956 Glas.; FRCGP 1978, M 1967; DObst RCOG 1961. Prev: Ho. Phys. & Ho. Surg. Vict. Infirm. Glas.

MCCUTCHEON, Andrew Holywood Arches Health Centre, Westminster Avenue, Belfast BT4 1NS Tel: 028 9056 3354 Fax: 028 9065 3846 — MB BCh BAO 1985 Belf.; MRCGP 1990; DMH Belf. 1989; DRCOG 1988.

MCCUTCHEON, Catriona 12A Ainslie Place, Edinburgh EH3 6AS Tel: 0131 220 5646 Fax: 0131 220 5646 Email: cat@ednet.co.uk — MB ChB 1998 Ed.; MB ChB Ed 1998; BSc Med. Sci. (Phyol) Edin. 1995. (Edin.) Ho. Off. Gen. Med. Card. Weoterl Gen. Hosp. Edin.; A & E Roy. Infirm. Edin. Socs: BMA; MDDUS. Prev: Ho. Off. Gen. Sug. Borders Gen. Melose, Roxburghsh.

MCCUTCHEON, Marion Ruth Mersey Care Trust, Arunddel House, Sefton General Hospital, Smithdown Road, Liverpool L9 7JP Tel: 0151 330 8013 — MB ChB 1986 Leic.; MRCPsych 1991. Cons. (Psychiat.).

MCCUTCHION, Archibald (retired) Flat 2, 95 Banks Road, Sandbanks, Poole BH13 7QQ Tel: 01202 701485 — MB ChB 1954 Glas.; DPH Glas. 1958; MFCM 1974. Prev: Sen. Med. Off. Dorset AHA.

MCCUTCHION, Rosemary Poole Community Health Clinic, Shaftesbury Road, Poole BH15 2NT Tel: 01202 683363 — MB ChB 1954 Ed. (Ed.) SCMO E. Dorset Healthcare Trust. Prev: Ho. Phys. Law Hosp. Carluke; Ho. Surg. Stobhill Hosp. Glas.; Ho. Off. Univ. Coll. Hosp. W. Indies.

MCDADE, Gerard Tameside General Hospital, Ashton-under-Lyne OL6 9RW Tel: 0161 331 5067 — MB ChB 1980 Manch.; MSc Manch. 1993; BSc (Med. Sci.) St. And. 1977; MRCP (UK) 1985; MRCPsych 1989. Cons. Gen. Psychiat. Tameside Gen. Hosp. Socs: Brit. Neuropsychiat. Assn. Prev: Sen. Regist. (Psychiat.) N. W.. RHA; Research Regist. David Lewis Centre Epilepsy Chesh.; Regist. (Gen. Med.) Blackburn Roy. Infirm.

MCDADE, Hugh Brownlie Foxes Hollow, 2 Round Heads End, Forty Green, Beaconsfield HP9 1YB Tel: 01494 677932 Fax: 01494 678487 — MB ChB 1971 Glas.; MRCP (UK) 1975; FRCPS Glas. 1991. Dir. Antiviral Clin. Research Glaxo Wellcome Research & Devlopm. Greenford. Prev: Regist. (Med.) Gartnavel Gen. Hosp. Glas.

MCDAID, Peter Delaval Avenue Surgery, Dunelm, 1 Delaval Avenue, Whitley Bay NE25 0EF Tel: 0191 237 1148 Fax: 0191 298 0290 — MB BS 1979 Newc.

MCDANIEL, Daniel 12 Green Road, Ardglass, Downpatrick BT30 7UA Tel: 02844 841091 — MB BCh BAO 1946 Belf. Socs: Roy. Coll. Gen. Pract.

MCDANIEL, William Hanson (retired) 5 Atwater Court, Lenham, Maidstone ME17 2PW — MD Belf. 1948, MB BCh BAO 1945; FRCPI 1974, M 1950.

MCDARMAID, Elizabeth Jane Tanworth Cottage, The Green, Tanworth-In-Arden, Solihull B94 5AL — MB BS 1998 Lond.; MB BS Lond 1998.

MCDERMID, George Royal Edinburgh Hospital, 151 Morningside Place, Edinburgh EH10 5E — MB ChB 1990 Dundee; BMSc Dund 1987.

MACDERMOT, Professor John Section on Clinical Pharmacology, Division of Medicine, Imperial College School of Medicine,, Hammersmith Hospital, London W12 0NN Tel: 020 8383 3221 Fax: 020 8383 2066 Email: j.macderm@rpms.ac.uk — MB BS 1971 Lond.; PhD (Biochem.) Lond. 1977, MSc (Biochem.) 1973, MD 1979; FRCP Lond. 1989; MRCP (UK) 1975; DIC 1973; F Med Sci 1999. (Char. Cross) Prof. Clin. Pharmacol. Univ. Lond. Prev: Prof. Pharmacol. Med. Sch. Univ. Birm.; Wellcome Sen. Research Fell. & Hon. Cons. Roy. Postgrad. Med. Sch. Lond.

MACDERMOT, Kvetuse Drahuse 48 Fairhazel Gardens, London NW6 3SJ — MRCS Eng. LRCP Lond. 1972; MPhil Lond. 1988; MRCP Lond. 1980. (Char. Cross) Sen. Lect. & Cons. Genetics Roy. Free Hosp. Sch. Med. Lond. Prev: Sen. Regist. (Genetics.) MRC N.wick Pk. Hosp. Harrow; SHO (Med.) Char. Cross Hosp. Lond.; Resid. (Genetics) NIH Bethesda Md. & Johns Hopkins Univ. Baltimore USA.

MACDERMOT, Violet Denise Colstock, 43 High St., Ditchling, Hassocks BN6 8SY Tel: 01273 844248 — MRCS Eng. LRCP Lond. 1941. (King's Coll. Hosp.)

MACDERMOTT, Anthony Joseph 55 Amersham Road, London SE14 6QQ — BM BCh 1979 Oxf.; MRCS Eng. LRCP Lond. 1979; DAvMed FOM RCP Lond. 1990.

MACDERMOTT, Barbara Ann Lisnaskea Health Centre, Drumhaw, Lisnaskea, Enniskillen BT92 0JB Tel: 02867 721566 Fax: 02867 722526; Cloghtogle, Lisbellaw, Enniskillen BT94 5EJ Tel: 02866 387049 Fax: 0286 638 7141 Email: cloghtogle@ireland.com — MB BCh BAO 1976 NUI; DFFP 1996; DObst RCPI 1984. (NUI) GP. Socs: Diplomatic & Family Plann. & Reproductive Health.

MCDERMOTT, Bridghe Marie Lorraine 21 Diamond Road, Aldergrove, Crumlin BT29 4DB — MB BCh BAO 1989 Belf.; MRCGP 1994; DCH Dub. 1995; DGM RCP Lond. 1993; DMH Belf. 1993.

MCDERMOTT, Mr Bruce Christopher, CBE, Brigadier late RAMC Retd. (retired) 1 Shrewsbury Lane, Woolwich, London SE18 3JE — MB BS Lond. 1956; FRCS Eng. 1961; MRCS Eng. LRCP Lond. 1956. Prev: Cons. Adviser Burns & Plastic Surg. (Army).

MCDERMOTT, Catherine Mary (retired) 7 Kirk Edge Drive, Worrall, Sheffield S35 0AZ Tel: 0174 286 2559 — MB BCh BAO NUI 1951.

*MCDERMOTT, Catherine Rebecca Mary 21 Highbury Villas, Bristol BS2 8BY — MB ChB 1995 Bristol.

MCDERMOTT, Celice Amber Old Hill Farm, Carmmenellis, Redruth TR16 6PR — MB ChB 1995 Bristol. Prev: SHO (O & G) Bedford; SHO (Surg.) Taunton; SHO (Med.) Truro.

*MCDERMOTT, Christopher John 48 Bedford Drive, Birkenhead CH42 6RU — MB ChB 1994 Leeds.

MCDERMOTT, Damian Tower House Practice, St. Pauls Health Centre, High Street, Runcorn WA7 1AB Tel: 01928 567404; 18 Moughland Lane, Runcorn WA7 4SE — MB ChB 1980 Liverp.; MRCGP 1984; DRCOG 1982. GP Princip.

MCDERMOTT, Mr Damien Michael 48 The Downs, Silverdale, Nottingham NG11 7DY — MB 1987 Dundee; FRCS Glas. 1994.

MCDERMOTT, Mr David Charles Patrick 26 Forest Drive, Standish, Wigan WN6 0SG — MB BCh BAO 1987 NUI; FRCS Glas. 1992.

MCDERMOTT, Dermot Joseph (retired) 65 Springfield Road, Warrenpoint, Newry BT34 3NW Tel: 016937 73770 — LRCPI & LM, LRCSI & LM 1946. Prev: Med. Off. DHSS N. Irel.

MACDERMOTT, Domhnall (retired) Health Centre, Great James St., Londonderry BT48 — MB BCh BAO NUI 1948; MRCGP 1968.

MCDERMOTT, Edward John 47 Herschell Street, Leicester LE2 1LE — MB ChB 1998 Leic.; MB ChB Leic 1998.

MCDERMOTT, Elizabeth Mary Bethany, Derby Road, Mansfield NG18 5BJ Tel: 01623 625983; 58 Bailey Crescent, Mansfield NG19 6JF Tel: 01623 621338 — MB BS 1989 Lond.; MRCP (UK) 1994; DM Nottm 1999. Specialist Regist. (Immunol.) Univ. Hosp. NHS Trust Nottm. Prev: Research Regist. (Clin. Immunol.) Univ. Hosp. NHS Trust Nottm.; Regist. (Rheum.) Nottm. City Hosp.; SHO (Gen. Med.) King's Mill Centre Mansfield.

MCDERMOTT, Eulalia 46 Hale Lane, Mill Hill, London NW7 3PR — MB ChB 1964 Leeds; DCH Eng. 1968. Clin. Med. Off. Barnet Healthcare Trust.

MCDERMOTT, Hilary Winifred The Simpson Health Centre, 70 Gregories Road, Beaconsfield HP9 1PS Tel: 01494 671571 Fax: 01494 680219; Penn Surgery, Elm Road, Penn, High Wycombe HP10 8LQ Tel: 01494 817144 — MB BS 1978 Lond.; MRCGP 1986; DRCOG 1981. GP Trainer High Wycombe. Prev: Trainee GP S.end-on-Sea; Ho. Phys. Black Notley Hosp. Braintree; Ho. Surg. Rush Green Hosp. Romford.

MCDERMOTT, Ian Tel: 0113 295 3180 Fax: 0113 295 3181 — MB ChB 1989 Leeds; MRCGP 1993.

MCDERMOTT, Ian Douglas 30 Park Way, Ruislip HA4 8NU — MB BS 1992 Lond. SHO (A & E) P'boro. Dist. Hosp. Prev: Ho. Off. (Gen. Med.) P'boro. Dist. Gen. Hosp.; Ho. Off. (Surg.) S.end Dist. Gen. Hosp.

MACDERMOTT, Mr James Paul Anthony Urology Department, Bradford Royal Infirmary, Bradford BD9 6RJ Tel: 01274 42200; 4 Byeway, Tranmere Park, Guiseley, Leeds LS20 8JP — MB BCh BAO 1979 NUI; FRCSI 1984. Regist. (Urol.) Bradford Roy. Infirm.

MCDERMOTT, John Martin 135 Westland Drive, Glasgow G14 9PF — MB ChB 1995 Glas.

MACDERMOTT, Keith John 18 Wenlock Terrace, York YO10 4DU Tel: 0904 646861; 9 Kilburn Road, York YO10 4DF Tel: 0904 638101 — MB BChir 1976 Camb.; BA, MB Camb. 1976, BChir 1975.

MCDERMOTT, Margaret Eileen 6 Higweek Village, Newton Abbot TQ12 1QB — MB ChB 1996 Liverp.

MCDERMOTT, Margaret Grace Pennys Lane Surgery, Pennys Lane, Cranborne, Wimborne BH21 5QE Tel: 01725 517272 Fax: 01725 517746; 72 Manor Road, Verwood BH31 6EA Tel: 01202 824339 — MB BS 1965 Lond.; MRCS Eng. LRCP Lond. 1965; DCH Eng. 1967. (Roy. Free) Prev: Med. Asst. Leicester Area Geriat. Serv. Hillcrest Hosp.; Ho. Surg. Leicester Roy. Infirm.; Ho. Phys. Leicester Gen. Hosp.

MCDERMOTT, Mary Agnes 17 Campsie Road, Omagh BT79 0AE Tel: 01662 240898 Fax: 01662 251128 — MB BCh BAO 1983 NUI; MMedSc (Psychoather.) Dub. 1996; MRCPsych 1991; DCH RCP Dub. 1986. (Univ. Coll. Dub.) Cons. Child & Adolesc. Psychiat. Rivendell Child & Adolesc. Serv. Omagh.

MCDERMOTT, Mary Gerardine 187 Blackfort Road, Fintona, Omagh BT78 2JA — MB BCh BAO 1989 Belf.

*MCDERMOTT, Melissa Jane Dolter's Rendenies, Nottingham City Hospital, Nottingham NG5 1PB; 6/7 Hadden Farm Cottages, Sprenita, Kelso TD5 8HU Tel: 01890 830304 — MB ChB 1998 Glas.; MB ChB Glas 1998.

MACDERMOTT, Neil John Gerard 8 Braddan Avenue, Sale M33 3WP — MB BCh BAO 1973 NUI; MRCP (U.K.) 1976; MRCPI 1975.

MCDERMOTT, Mr Peter James Campbell Lismore House, 22 Loom Lane, Radlett WD7 8AD — MB BChir 1985 Camb.; MA Camb. 1984; FRCS Ed. 1990; BDS Lond. 1974; FDS RCS Eng. 1988. (Guy's) Cons. Oral & Maxillofacial Surg. Barnet and Chase Farm Hosp.s NHS Trust. Prev: Sen. Regist. (Oral & Maxillofacial Surg.) Mt. Vernon Hosp. N.wood; Regist. (Oral & Maxillofacial Surg.) Univ. Coll. Hosp. Lond.; Regist. (Oral Surg.) Roy. Free & Whittington Hosps. Lond.

MCDERMOTT, Ramon Alexander Mayfield Road Surgery, 125 Mayfield Road, Edinburgh EH9 3AJ Tel: 0131 668 1095 Fax: 0131 662 1734 — MB BCh BAO 1988 NUI; MRCGP 1993.

MCDERMOTT, Richard Paul Bitterne Park Surgery, 28 Cobden Avenue, Bitterne Park, Southampton SO18 1BW Tel: 023 80585 655/6 Fax: 023 8055 5216; 34 Milbury Court, Southampton SO18 5EH — BM BS 1991 Nottm. GP Soton.

*MCDERMOTT, Richard Paul 39 Eskdale Avenue, Bramhall, Stockport SK7 1DU — MB BS 1996 Lond.

MACDERMOTT, Robert Ian Joseph 84 Ridgeway, Leeds LS8 4DF — MB ChB 1984 Leeds; MRCOG 1990. Regist. (O & G) Leeds. Prev: Regist. (O & G) Bradford.

MCDERMOTT, Sandra Margaret Shantallow Health Centre, Racecourse Road, Londonderry BT48 8NL Tel: 01504 351350; 35 Bayswater, Londonderry BT47 6JL Tel: 01504 47514 — MB BCh BAO 1984 Belf.; Cert. Family Plann. JCC 1989; DRCOG 1988. Community Med. Off. (Child Health) Shantallow Health Centre Lond.derry.

MACDERMOTT, Sarah Jane St Martins Practice, 319 Chapeltown Road, Leeds LS7 3JT Tel: 0113 262 1013 Fax: 0113 237 4747 — MB ChB 1986 Leeds.

MCDERMOTT, Ultan 18 Harberton Park, Belfast BT9 6TS — MB BCh BAO 1994 Belf.; BMedSci (Hons.) 1992.

MCDERMOTT, Una Mary Concepta 9A Elm Grove, London W5 3JH — MB BCh BAO 1980 NUI; LRCPI & LM, LRCSI & LM 1980.

MCDEVITT, Alan Gregory The Green Medical Practice, Kilbowie Road, Clydebank G81 2TQ Tel: 0141 531 6425 — MB ChB 1985 Glas.; MRCGP 1989; DRCOG 1987. GP Practitioner; Chairm. Clydebank LHCC; Vice Chairm. Glas. LMC; Asst. Med. Sec. Glas. LMC.

MCDEVITT, Claire Sarah 18 Brandon Terrace, Edinburgh EH3 5DZ Tel: 0131 557 2850 — MB ChB 1992 Ed. (Edinburgh) Socs: MRCGP. Prev: Trainee GP/SHO (O & G.) Perth VTS.

MCDEVITT, Denis Gordon Department of Clinical Pharmacology & Therapeutics, University of Dundee, Ninewells Hospital & Medical School, Dundee DD1 9SY Tel: 01382 632180 Fax: 01382 644972; 1 Godfrey Street, Barnhill, Dundee DD5 2QZ Tel: 01382 739483 — MB BCh BAO 1962 Belf.; MB BCh BAO (Hons.) Belf. 1962; FRS Ed. 1996; DSc Belf. 1978, MD 1968; FRCP Ed. 1985; FRCP Lond. 1978, M 1966; FRCPI 1977, M 1965; FFPM RCP (UK) 1990. (Belf.) Prof. Clin. Pharmacol. Univ. Dundee; Cons. Phys. Ninewells Hosp. Dundee; Civil Cons. (Clin. Pharmacol.) RAF. Socs: Brit. Pharm. Soc.; Hon. Mem. Assn. Phys. Prev: Dean, Fac. Med. & Dent, Univ. Dundee; Prof. Clin. Pharmacol. Qu. Univ. Belf.; Merck Internat. Fell. (Clin. Pharmacol.) Vanderbilt Univ. Nashville, USA.

MCDEVITT, Helen 34 Fullarton Street, Kilmarnock KA1 2QT — MB ChB 1997 Glas.

MCDEVITT, Jonathan Mark 1 Godfrey Street, Barnhill, Dundee DD5 2QZ; Flat 4, Room 11, Astor House, Belgarth Square, Carlisle CA2 7PH — MB ChB 1996 Dundee. SHO Rotat. (Gen. Med.) Tayside; SHO Med. Rotat., Carlisle Hosp. NHS Trust.

MCDEVITT, Joyce 10 Ledcameroch Crescent, Bearsden, Glasgow G61 4AD — MB ChB 1986 Glas.

MCDEVITT, Michael William St Nicholas Health Centre, Saunder Bank, Burnley BB11 2EN Tel: 01282 831249 Fax: 01282 425269 — MB ChB 1975 Leeds; MB ChB 1975 Leeds.

MCDEVITT, Robert Laughlan 1 Torridon Gardens, Newton Mearns, Glasgow G77 5NQ — MB ChB 1970 Glas.; FFA RCS Eng.

MACDIARMAID-GORDON

1977; LMCC 1973. Cons. (Anaesth.) & Postgrad. Tutor Roy. Alexandra Infirm. Paisley.

MACDIARMAID-GORDON, Adam Robert Department of Medicine, University Hospital of South Manchester (Withington), Nell Road, Manchester M20 8LR Tel: 0161 445 8111; 19 Lincoln Grove, Sale M33 2JG Tel: 0161 973 1967 — MB ChB 1984 Liverp.; MB ChB (Hons.) Liverp. 1984; MRCP (UK) 1989. Research Fell. (Med.) Univ. Hosp. S. Manch. Socs: Renal Assn. & Med. Research Soc. Prev: Regist. & SHO Univ. Hosp. S. Manch.; SHO Roy. Liverp. Teach Hosp.

MCDIARMID, Alastair James Anaesthetic Department, Aberdeen Royal Infirm., Grampian University Hospital Trust, Aberdeen AB25 2ZN Tel: 01224 681818 — MB ChB 1988 Glas.; FRCA 1994. Cons. (Anaesth.) Grampian Univ. Hosp. Aberd. Prev: Regist. (Anaesth.) Ninewells Hosp. Dundee.

MACDIARMID, Duncan 26 Liston Road, London SW4 0DF Tel: 020 7652 5815 Fax: 020 7498 3553 — MB BS 1972 Lond.; MRCS Eng. LRCP Lond. 1971; FRCPsych 1993, M 1975. Sen. Fell. UMDS Guy's & St. Thos. Hosps. Prev: Dir. C.G. Jung Clinic Lond.; Cons. Psychother. Guy's Hosp. Lond.; Sen. Lect. (Psychother.) Middlx. Hosp. Med. Sch.

MACDIARMID, Fiona Mary Moors Farmhouse, Black House Lane, Gt Cornard, Sudbury CO10 0NL — MB BS 1996 Lond.

MACDIARMID, Iain Robertson 67 London Road, Kilmarnock KA3 7AH — MB ChB 1969 Glas.; FFA RCS Eng 1974.

MCDIARMID, Mr James George Milton c/o Department of Plastic Surgery, Canniesburn Hospital, Bearsden, Glasgow G61 1QL Tel: 0141 211 5600 Fax: 0141 211 5652 Email: james.mediarmid@virgin.net; 15 Braids Walk, Kirkella, Hull HU10 7PB Tel: 01482 651257 — MB ChB 1990 Aberd.; MSc (Hons.) Lond. 1996; FRCS (Eng.) 1994; FRCS (Plast.) 1999. (Aberd.) Specialist Regist. (Plastic Surg.) Canniesburn Hosp. Glas.; Hand Surg. Fell. Kleinert Inst. For Head Microsurg. Louisville, KY, USA. Socs: Train. Assoc. Brit. Assoc. Plast. Surg.; Sec. Sen. Reg. Travel. Club in Plast. Surg. Prev: Research Regist. (Plastic Surg.) Univ. Coll. Lond. Hosps.; SHO (Plastic & Reconstruc. Surg.) Addenbrooke's Hosp. Camb.; SHO Rotat. (Surg.) Roy. United Hosp. Bath.

MCDIARMID, Margaret Hunter (retired) 4 St Ninian's Road, Edinburgh EH12 8AW Tel: 0131 334 4151 — MB ChB 1937 Ed. Prev: GP Edin.

MCDIARMID, Maria Katherine Springhead Medical Centre, 376 Willerby Road, Hull HU5 5JT Tel: 01482 352263 Fax: 01482 352480 — MB ChB 1990 Manch.; MB ChB (Hons.) Manch. 1990; BSc St. And. 1987; MRCGP (Distinc.) 1994; DCH RCP Lond. 1993; DRCOG 1993.

MACDIARMID, Norman Gilbert Cos Lane Medical Practice, Woodside Road, Glenrothes KY7 4AQ Tel: 01592 752100 Fax: 01592 612692; 16 Newtown, Cupar KY15 4DD — MB BChir 1987 Camb.; MSc Glas. 1982, BSc (Hons.) 1975; BSc St. And. 1984. Prev: SHO (Paediat.) Ninewells Hosp. Dundee; SHO (A & E) Perth Roy. Infirm.; Clin. Med. Off. (Community Child Health) Dundee.

MCDICKEN, Ian Wilson 75 Chatsworth Road, Ainsdale, Southport PR8 2QQ — MB ChB 1962 Glas.; MRCPath 1970.

MCDONAGH, Andrew Joseph Gerard Department of Dermatology, Royal Hallamshire Hospital, Glossop Road, Sheffield S10 2JF Tel: 0114 271 3796 Fax: 0114 271 3763 — MB ChB 1982 Liverp.; FRCP Lond. 1997; MRCP (UK) 1985. Cons. Dermat. Sheff. Hosps. Socs: Brit. Assn. Dermat.; Eur. Hair Research Soc. Prev: Cons. Dermat. Bradford & Airedale Hosps.; Sen. Regist. (Dermat.) Roy. Hallamsh. Hosp. Sheff.; Hon. Clin. Tutor (Dermat.) Univ. Sheff.

MCDONAGH, Colette Marie Flat 3, Kingston Court, Kingston Road, Manchester M20 2RZ — MB ChB 1993 Manch.

MCDONAGH, Florence Mary Celine 98 The Drive, Alwoodley, Leeds LS17 7QQ — MB BCh BAO 1979 NUI; LRCPI & LM, LRCSI & LM 1979.

MACDONAGH, Gillian Rosemary Struan (retired) Wild Orchard, South Harting, Petersfield GU31 5PY — MB ChB 1948 Aberd.; DObst RCOG 1951. Med. Expert Witness S.ern Circuit. Prev: Cons. (A & E Med.) Qu. Alexandra Hosp. Cosham.

MACDONAGH, Ian Robert Joseph Lee Health Centre, 2 Handen Road, London SE12 8NP Tel: 020 8852 2611 Fax: 020 8297 8221 — MB ChB 1972 St. And. Prev: Ho. Phys. (Paediat.) Brook Gen.

Hosp. Lond.; Ho. Surg. (Gen. Surg. & Urol.) St. Geo. Hosp. Lond.; Ho. Phys. (Gen. Med.) St. Nicholas Hosp. Lond.

MCDONAGH, Janet Edith 29 Roxburgh Place, Heaton, Newcastle upon Tyne NE6 5HU Tel: 0191 265 9172; 22 Bannvale, Coleraine BT51 3JD — MB BS 1986 Newc.; MRCP (UK) 1989. Research Regist. (Rheum.) Free Man Hosp. Newc. u Tyne & Roy. Vict. Infirm. Prev: Regist. (Rheum.) Freeman Hosp. Newc. u Tyne; Regist. (Med.) N. Tees Gen. Hosp. Stockton on Tees.

MCDONAGH, Laura Mary (retired) 4 Golden Cross Mews, Portobello Road, London W11 1DZ Tel: 020 7243 3394 Fax: 020 7243 3394 Email: mcdonagh@compuserve.com — MB BS Lond. 1984; FRCS Ed. 1993; MRCP (UK) 1991.

MCDONAGH, Michael Francis Nithsdale Dental Centre, 8 Nithsdale Road, Glasgow G41 2AN Tel: 0141 423 1505 Fax: 0141 423 0616; 3 Oak Avenue, Bearsden, Glasgow G61 3HD Tel: 0141 470 0344 — MB ChB 1983 Glas.; DA 1987. (Glasgow) Partner Nithsdale Dent. Centre. Socs: Assn. Anaesth.; Assn. Dent. Anaesth.; BMA. Prev: Staff Grade (Anaesth.) Vale of Leven Hosp.

MCDONAGH, Michael Joseph 99 Clapham Common, South Side, London SW4 9SQ Tel: 020 8673 2481 — MB BCh BAO 1950 NUI.

MCDONAGH, Michael Joseph Department of Anaesthesia, Hospital of St Cross, Barby Road, Rugby CV22 5PX — MB BCh BAO 1986 NUI.

MCDONAGH, Nicholas John St Dunstan's Park Health Centre -, St Dunstan's Park, Melrose TD6 9RX Tel: 01896 822161 Fax: 01896 823151 — MB ChB 1985 Ed.

MACDONAGH, Mr Ruaraidh Peter Department of Urology, Taunton and Somerset Hospital, Musgrove Park, Taunton TA1 5DA Tel: 01823 333444; Rosehill, Broomfield, Bridgwater TA5 2EL — MB BS 1982 Lond.; MD Sheff. 1992; FRCS Ed. 1987. Cons. Urol. Taunton & Som. Hosp.; Sen. Clin. Lect. (Surg.) Univ. Bristol. Socs: Brit. Assn. Urol. Surgs. Prev: Sen. Regist. Rotat. (Urol.) SW Region; Research Fell. (Spinal Injuries) Lodge Moor Hosp. Sheff.; Regist. (Urol.) E.bourne Dist. Gen. Hosp.

MCDONAGH, Theresa Anne 25F Hughenden Gardens, Glasgow G12 9XZ Tel: 0141 341 0336 Fax: 0141 211 1791 Email: t.mcdonagh@biomed.gla.ac.uk — MB ChB 1987 Ed.; FRCP 2002 Glasgow; 2000 FRCPE; MD 1999 University of Edinburgh; BSc (Hons.) Ed. 1985; MRCP (UK) 1990. Sen. Lect. & Hon. Cons. Cardiol. Univ. of Glas. Prev: Lect. & Hon. Sen. Regist. (Cardiol.) Univ. Glas.; Research Fell. (Cardiol.) W.ern Infirm. Glas.; Regist. (Gen. Med.) Roy. Infirm. Edin.

MCDONALD, Agnes Mary (retired) Fern Lea, Crosthwaite, Kendal LA8 8HX — MB ChB 1956 Ed. Prev: GP Bonnyrigg Lothian.

MACDONALD, Alan The Medical Centre, Main St., Brough, Kirkby Stephen CA17 4AY Tel: 017683 41294 Fax: 017683 72385; 23 Hothfield Drive, Appleby-in-Westmorland CA16 6HJ Tel: 0176 83 52816 — MB ChB 1982 Aberd.

MACDONALD, Alan Aird Department of Microbiology, Lister Hospital, Coreys Mill Lane, Stevenage SG1 4AB Tel: 01438 314333 ext 5425; 124 Ridge Road, Letchworth SG6 1PT — MB ChB 1984 Ed.

MACDONALD, Alan George Aberdeen Royal Infirmary, Foresterhill, Aberdeen AB25 2ZN Tel: 01224 554614 Email: alan.macdonald@arh.grampian.scot.nhs.uk; 43 Derbeth Park, Kingswell, Aberdeen AB15 8TU — MB ChB 1986 Glas.; MRCP (UK) 1989; FRCP Glas. 1998. Cons. (Rheumat.) Aberd. Roy. Infirm. Prev: Sen. Regist. (Rheum. & Med.) Roy. Liverp. Univ. Hosp.; Regist. (Med. & Rheum.) Glas.; Regist. (Med.) Aberd.

MACDONALD, Alan Gordon Department of Anaesthesia, Victoria Infirmary, Langside, Glasgow G42 9TY Tel: 0141 201 6000; 29 Newlands Road, Glasgow G43 2JD Tel: 0141 632 3990 — MB ChB 1960 Aberd.; FRCP Glas. 1993; FRCA. 1965. (Aberd.) Cons. Anaesth. Vict. Infirm. Glas.; Hon. Clin. Sen. Lect. (Anaesth.) Univ. Glas. Prev: Lect. (Anaesth.) Univ. Glas. W.. Infirm. Glas.; Sen. Regist. (Anaesth.) Dundee Gps. Hosps.; Regist. (Anaesth.) Glas. Roy. Infirm.

MACDONALD, Alan Graham 29 Newlands Road, Glasgow G43 2JD — MB ChB 1994 Glas.; MB ChB (Hons.) Glas. 1994; BSc (Hons.) Glas. 1991; MRCP (UK) 1997.

MCDONALD, Alan John Ley Mill Surgery, 228 Lichfield Road, Sutton Coldfield B74 2UE Tel: 0121 308 0359 Fax: 0121 323 2682 — MB ChB Cape Town 1973; MRCGP 1980. GP Tutor Good Hope Hosp. Sutton Coldfield.

MCDONALD

MCDONALD, Alan Ronald The Surgery, 6 Huddersfield Road, Barnsley S70 2LT Tel: 01226 203355 Fax: 01226 731245; 16 Harden Close, Pogmoor, Barnsley S75 2JJ — MB ChB 1974 Ed.; BSc (Med. Sci.) Ed. 1971, MB ChB 1974; MRCGP 1980. (Ed.) Prev: Ho. Phys. City Hosp. Edin.; Ho. Surg. Roy. Infirm. Edin.

MACDONALD, Alasdair Cameron, VRD (retired) 9 Redlands Road, Glasgow G12 0SJ Tel: 0141 339 1694 — MB ChB 1939 Glas.; FRCP Lond. 1973, M 1948; FRCP Glas. 1964, M 1962; FRFPS Glas. 1947. Prev: Cons. Phys. W.. Infirm. Glas. & Gartnavel Gen. Hosp. Glas.

MACDONALD, Alasdair James Carleton Clinic, Chmwhinton Drive, Carlisle CA1 3SX Tel: 01228 602000 Fax: 01228 597987 — MB ChB Glas. 1970; FRCPsych 1994; T(Psych) 1991; DPM Ed. & Glas. 1974; DCH RCPS Glas. 1972. p/t Hon Cons. Psychiat. Psychotherapist N. Cumbria menatl health & learning Disabilities trust - Carlisle; Project Director, Ment. health institue, st. martins Coll. Prev: Cons. Psychiat. Psychotherapist Dumfries & Galloway HB; Cons. Adult Ment. Illness W.on-Super-Mare Gen. Hosp.; cons Psychiat, psychotherapist, N. Cumbria.

MCDONALD, Alastair Hugh 16 Woodway Crescent, Harrow HA1 2NQ — MB ChB 1962 Ed.; BSc Ed. 1959, MB ChB 1962; FRCP Lond. 1978, M 1966; MRCP Ed. 1965. (Univ. Ed.) Cons. Cardiol. Lond. Hosp.; Sen. Lect. Cardiol. Lond. Hosp. Med. Coll. Socs: Brit. Cardiac Soc.; Fell. Roy. Soc. Med. Prev: Sen. Regist. Cardiac Dept. Lond. Hosp.; Regist. Nat. Heart Hosp. Lond.; Asst. Lect. Dept. Med. Roy. Infirm. Edin.

MACDONALD, Professor Alastair John Douglas 100 Turney Road, London SE21 7JH — MD 1986 Glas.; MB ChB 1973; FRCPsych 1993. (Glas.) Prof. (Psychiat. of Old Age) Lond.; Hon. Cons. (Psychiat. of Old Age) Lewisham & Guy's Ment. Health Trust Lond. Prev: Lect. Inst. Psychiat. Lond.

MACDONALD, Alastair Wray Department of Histology, Castle Hill Hospital, Cottingham HU16 5JQ Tel: 01482 623299 Fax: 01482 623290 — MB BCh BAO 1983 Dub.; BDS Ed. 1977; MRCPath 1989.

MACDONALD, Alexander Farquharson 8 Salisbury Terrace, Aberdeen AB10 6QH — MB ChB 1952 Ed.; DMRD 1959; FFR 1962; FRCP Ed. 1974, M 1961. (Ed.)

MACDONALD, Alexander John Anthony Group Practice Surgery, Green Street, Forfar DD8 3AR Tel: 01307 462316 Fax: 01307 463623; Braedounie, Gowanbank, Forfar DD8 2SU — MB ChB 1971 Glas.; MRCGP 1975; DObst RCOG 1975. Prev: Ho. Phys. & Ho. Surg. W.. Infirm. Glas.; Ho. Surg. Qu. Mother Hosp. Glas.; Ho. Phys. Roy. Hosp. Sick Childr. Glas.

MACDONALD, Alexander John Ranald 19 Richmond Hill, Bristol BS8 1BA Tel: 0117 973 6331 Fax: 0117 973 9477 — MB BS 1966 Lond.; DLO Eng. 1971. (St. Thos.) Socs: Intractable Pain Soc.; Internat. Assn. Study of Pain; Roy. Soc. Med. Prev: Clin. Asst. Pain Relief Clinic Char. Cross Hosp.; Surg. Lt. RN.

MCDONALD, Mr Alexander Malcolm 21 Cambridge Avenue, New Malden KT3 4LD — MB BS 1968 Lond.; FRCS Eng. 1973; MRCS Eng. LRCP Lond. 1968; T(S) 1991. (Univ. Coll. Hosp) Sen. Surg. Regist. Univ. Coll. Hosp. Lond. Socs: BMA. & Brit. Assn. Surg. Oncol. Prev: Research Fell. (Cancer Research Campaign) King's Coll. Hosp. Med.; Sch. Lond.; Surg. Regist. Univ. Coll. Hosp. Lond.

MCDONALD, Alison Dawn Holmes Chapel Health Centre, London Road, Holmes Chapel, Crewe CW4 7BB Tel: 01477 533100 Fax: 01477 532563 — MB BS 1986 Newc.; MRCGP 1990. Prev: Trainee GP Holmes Chapel.

MCDONALD, Alison Joan (retired) Westhill, Jurby Road, Ramsey IM7 2EA Tel: 01624 812073 Fax: 01624 811921 — MB Camb. 1967, BChir 1966; FFA RCS Eng. 1970. Prev: Assoc. Specialist Anaesth., IOM.

MACDONALD, Alison Marjorie Department of Anaesthetics, William Harvey Hospital, Kennington Road, Willesborough, Ashford TN24 0LZ Tel: 01233 610641/2; 15 Churchill Road, Canterbury CT1 3EB Tel: 01227 456529 Email: doctorallymacd@aol.com — MB BChir 1975 Camb.; MA Camb. 1975; FRCA 1978. (King's Coll. Hosp.) Cons. Anaesth. William Harvey Hosp. Ashford; Cons. Anaesth. Kent & Canterbury Hosp. Socs: Assn. Anaesths.; Soc. Orthop. Anaesth.; Obst. Anaes. Assn. Prev: Cons. Anaesth. Q. Eliz. Q. Mother Hosp. Margate; Lect. & Hon. Cons. Univ. Dept. Anaesth. Manch. Roy. Infirm.; Sen. Regist. Glas. Roy. Infirm.

MCDONALD, Alistair 11 Fowler Place, Polmount, Falkirk FK2 0XQ — MB ChB 1977 Aberd.; FFA RCS Eng. 1981. (Aberd.) Cons. Anaesth. Falkirk & Dist. Roy. Infirm.

MACDONALD, Alistair Cameron (retired) 10 Millside, Morpeth NE61 1PN Tel: 01670 512796 Email: aandfmacdonald@compuserve.com — MB ChB Aberd. 1948; FRCGP 1984, M 1974. Prev: GP Mem. Dist. Managem. Team, N. Tees HA.

MACDONALD, Alistair Mitchell, Maj. RAMC (retired) Ballagan House, Strathblane, Glasgow G63 9AE Tel: 01360 70850 — MD 1941 Ed.; MD (Gold Medal) Ed. 1941, MB ChB 1935; FRCP Ed. 1943, M 1939; FRCP Glas. 1966, M 1962; FRCPath 1963. Prev: Rockefeller Fell. 1947.

MACDONALD, Alistair Peter (retired) Wildfield House, Clenchwarton, King's Lynn PE34 4AH Tel: 01553 772332 — MB ChB 1955 Glas.; FRCOG 1975, M 1962; DObst RCOG 1959. Prev: Cons. O & G King's Lynn & Wisbech Hosps. NHS Trust.

***MACDONALD, Allan Angus** 28 Gogoside Road, Largs KA30 9LU — MB ChB 1998 Glas.; MB ChB Glas 1998.

***MACDONALD, Andrew John** 47 Keir Street, Bridge of Allan, Stirling FK9 4QJ — MB ChB 1998 Glas.; MB ChB Glas 1998.

MACDONALD, Andrew Keir 15 Tavistock Way, Wakefield WF2 7QS — MB ChB 1988 Ed.

MACDONALD, Angus Monkland District General Hospital, Monkscourt Road, Airdrie — MB ChB 1984 Glas.; FRCS Glas; MD Glasgow 1996. Cons. Colorectal Surg.

MACDONALD, Mr Angus Coombe Manor Farm, Coombe Lane, Wadhurst TN5 6NU — MB BS 1992 Lond.; FRCS (Lond). (Lon. Hosp. Med. Sch.)

MACDONALD, Angus Coombe Manor Farm, Wadhurst TN5 6NU Tel: 0189 288 2552 — MB ChB 1959 Ed.; MRCP Glas. 1964; FRCP Lond. 1981, M 1965. (Ed.) Cons. Dermat. Tunbridge Wells, Sevenoaks & E. Grinstead; Roy. Soc. Med. (Mem. Sect. Dermat.) & St. John's Hosp. Dermat. Soc. Prev: Med. Regist. N. Middlx. Hosp. Lond; Ho. Phys. W.. Gen. Hosp. Edin.; Sen. Regist. Dept. Dermat. St. Mary's Hosp. Lond.

MACDONALD, Angus Graham 13 Ashbrook Lawns, Ennis Road, Limerick, Republic of Ireland; Rosecot, Bromley Lane, Wellpond Green, Standon, Ware SG11 1NW Tel: 01279 843031 — MB BS 1986 Lond.; MRCGP 1992; DRCOG 1992; DCH RCP Lond. 1990.

MACDONALD, Angus Norman Portree IV51 9BZ — MB ChB 1976 Edinburgh; DCH; LMCC; DRCOG. (Glasgow) GP Portree, Isle of Skye; GP Princip.; Clin. Asst., Portree Hosp.

***MCDONALD, Anna Elizabeth** Blaidwood, South Road, Durham DH1 3TQ — MB BS 1998 Lond.; MB BS Lond 1998.

MACDONALD, Anne (retired) 224 Sheen Lane, London SW14 8LB Tel: 020 8876 4223 — MB ChB 1946 St. And.; MFCM RCP (UK) 1974; DCH RCP Lond. 1951. Prev: Princip. Med. Off. Hammersmith & Fulham HA.

MACDONALD, Anne 50 Pinewood Avenue, Kirkintilloch, Glasgow G66 4EQ — MB ChB 1975 Birm.; MRCPsych 1980.

MCDONALD, Anne Rosemary 89 Gubbins Lane, Harold Wood, Romford RM3 0DR Tel: 01708 346666 — BM BCh 1977 Oxf.; MA Camb. 1978; MRCGP 1980; DFFP 1993; DRCOG 1979. Prev: Windsor VTS Trainee GP; Hon. Off. Phys. Radcliffe Infirm. Oxf.; Hon. Off. Surg. Radcliffe Infirm. Oxf.

MCDONALD, Archibald Francis, TD, CStJ (retired) 2 Yew Tree Close, Rayleigh Road, Hutton, Brentwood CM13 1AH Tel: 01277 213348 — MB ChB 1934 Glas. Prev: Res. Asst. Surg. W.. Infirm. Glas.

MCDONALD, Bernard Side Suite, 10 Cariad Court, Cleeve Road, Goring, Reading RG8 9BT — MB BCh BAO 1950 NUI; LAH Dub. 1950.

MCDONALD, Beverley Anne The Grove Medical Practice, Richford Gate Primary Care Centre, Richford St., London W6; Flat 5, 20 Cleveland Square, London W2 6DG Tel: 020 7706 2318 Fax: 020 7706 2318 Email: latchman@oxford.com — MB ChB 1991 Leic.; DCH Lond. 1994; MRCGP 1997. (Leicester) GP Partner. Socs: BMA.

MCDONALD, Brendan Department Neuropathology, Radcliffe Infirmary, Woodstock Road, Oxford OX2 6HE Tel: 01865 228497 Fax: 01865 228496; Cherry Cottage, Main St, North Newington, Banbury OX15 6AJ Tel: 01295 730797 — MB ChB 1982 Liverp.; BSc (Hons.) Liverp. 1977; MRCPath 1993; MFFP 1995. (Liverp.)

MCDONALD

Cons. Neuropath. Radcliffe Infirm. Oxf. Prev: Sen. Regist. (Neuropath.) Radcliffe Infirm. Oxf.; Wellcome Research Train. Fell. Nuffield Dept. Path. & Bacteriol. John Radcliffe Hosp. Oxf.; Hon. Sen. Regist. (Histopath.) John Radcliffe Hosp. Oxf.

MCDONALD, Brendan Thomas Omagh Health Centre, Mountjoy Road, Omagh BT79 7BA Tel: 028 8224 3521 — MB BCh BAO 1980 Belf.

MCDONALD, Brian James St Barnabas Hospice, 36 Nettleham Road, Lincoln LN2 1RE Tel: 01522 511566 Fax: 01522 520877 — MB ChB 1972 Glas.; MSc (Community Health) Ed. 1987; MRCGP 1977. Med. Dir. St Barnabas Hospice Lincoln. Socs: Austral. & NZ Soc. Palliat. Med. Prev: Palliat. Med. Alfred Hosp. Melbourne Vict.; Med. Dir., Caritas Christi Hospice, Melbourne, Vict.

MACDONALD, Brian Nicholas Barrington Medical Centre, 68 Barrington Road, Altrincham WA14 1JB Tel: 0161 928 9621 Fax: 0161 926 9317 — MB ChB 1983 Manch.; MRCGP 1988; DRCOG 1986. GP Altrincham. Prev: Trainee GP Timperley Health Centre Altrincham; SHO (Paediat.) Wigan HA; SHO (Med. for Elderly) Lancaster HA.

MACDONALD, Bridget Kathryn Department of Neurology, Kings College Hospital, Denmark Hill, London SE5 9RS — MB BS 1989 Lond.; BSc Lond. 1986; MRCP (UK) 1993. Cons. (Neurol.) King's Coll. Hosp. Prev: Specialist Regist. (Neurol.) (KCH).

MACDONALD, Bruce Robertson Duke Street Surgery, 4 Duke Street, Barrow-in-Furness LA14 1LF Tel: 01229 820068 Fax: 01229 813840 — MB ChB 1978 Dundee; MRCGP 1982.

***MCDONALD, Calum Ewan** 606 George Street, Aberdeen AB25 3XN — MB ChB 1998 Aberd.; MB ChB Aberd 1998.

MACDONALD, Carol Joan Rosedale, Balvaird Road, Muir of Ord IV6 7QX — MB ChB 1987 Aberd.

MACDONALD, Caroline Helen 57 Skibo Avenue, Glenrothes KY7 4PX — MB ChB 1995 Glas. (Glasgow) SHO (Anaesth.) Norf. & Norwich Hosp.

MACDONALD, Carolyn Margaret 10 Fintry Gardens, Bearsden, Glasgow G61 4RJ — MB ChB 1984 Glas.; BSc (Hons.) Glas. 1982; MRCGP 1988; DRCOG 1987; DCH RCPS Glas. 1986. Clin. Asst. (Dermat.) Roy. Hosp. Sick Childr. Glas.

MACDONALD, Catherine Margaret Trethowell Cottage, Porthkea, Truro TR3 6AH — MB BS 1925 Lond.; MRCS Eng. LRCP Lond. 1924. (Univ. Coll. Lond.)

MACDONALD, Catherine Wilton (retired) Darquhillan, Gleneagles, Auchterarder PH3 1NG Tel: 0176 462476 — MB ChB 1950 Ed. Prev: Clin. Med. Off. Community Health Surrey AHA.

MCDONALD, Catriona Ford The Gainsborough Practice, Warfield Medical Centre, 1 County Lane, Whitegrove, Bracknell RG42 3JP Tel: 01344 428742 Fax: 01344 428743; 3 Minorca Avenue, Deepcut, Camberley GU16 6TT — MB ChB 1978 Sheff.; MRCGP 1994; DRCOG 1991; DCH RCPS GLas. 1983; DTM & H RCP Lond. 1981.

MACDONALD, Charles Ewing Dr McElhone and Partners, Townhead Surgery, 6-8 High St., Irvine KA12 0AY Tel: 01294 273131 Fax: 01294 312832 — MB ChB 1976 Glas.; MRCGP 1986; DRCOG 1979.

MACDONALD, Christopher Ewen Cumberland Infirmary, Newton Road, Calise CA2 7HY Tel: 01228 814184 Email: chris.macdonald@ncumbria-acute.nhs.uk; Tel: 016977 46637 Email: chrismacdonald@msn.com — MB ChB 1989 Glas.; BSc (Hons.) Glas. 1987; MRCP (UK) 1992. Cons. (Gastroenterol & gen. Med.) Cumbld. Infir. Socs: Brit. Soc. Gastroenterol.; La. Donian Gastroenterol. Prev: Regist. (Gastroenterol. & Gen. Med.) Derby City Gen.

MCDONALD, Christopher Iain AstraZeneca R&D, Charnwood, Bakewell Road, Loughborough LE11 5RH Tel: 01509 644996 Fax: 01509 645545 Email: chris.mcdonald@astrazeneca.com — MB ChB 1976 Ed.; FFOM RCP Lond. 1993, M 1984, A 1981; JCPTGP 1989; JCHMT 1984; DIH Soc. Apoth. Lond. 1981; MIOSH 1996. Dir. Safe Hlth. & Envir. AstraZeneca R&D charnwood. Socs: Soc. Occupat. Med. Prev: Chief Med. Off. Fisons plc; SMO BP Oil; Surg. Lt. Cdr. RN (SM).

MACDONALD, Christopher James York Road Group Practice Surgery, York Road, Ellesmere Port, South Wirral CH65 0DB Tel: 0151 355 2112 Fax: 0151 356 5512; 11 Telfords Quay, South Pier Road, Ellesmere Port, South Wirral CH65 4FL Tel: 0151 356 9063 Email: cjmac@aol.com — MB ChB 1989 Liverp.; DCH RCP Lond. 1993; DRCOG 1991. (Liverpool University)

MCDONALD, Christopher John 10 Percheron Close, Impington, Cambridge CB4 9YX Tel: 01223 235320 — MB BS 1982 Newc.; AFPM RCP Lond. 1993; MRCOphth 1988; DO RCS Eng. 1988. (Newcastle-upon-Tyne) Prev: SHO (Ophth.) Auckland Hosp., NZ; Ho. Off. Profess. Med. Unit Roy. Vict. Infirm. Newc. u. Tyne.

MCDONALD, Claire Fiona Grange Medical Group, 1 Beaufort Road, Edinburgh EH9 1AG Tel: 0131 447 1646 Fax: 0131 447 8192 — MB ChB 1981 Ed.; MRCGP 1986.

MCDONALD, Clare Frances Maureen 28 Ladeside Close, Newton Mearns, Glasgow G77 6TZ — MB ChB 1984 Glas.; MB ChB Glas. 1984.

MACDONALD, Colin Alexander The Surgery, Miaraig, Uig, Isle of Lewis HS2 9HE Tel: 01851 672283 Fax: 01851 672233 — MB ChB 1973 Aberd.; DObst RCOG 1975. (Aber.) Princip.

MACDONALD, Colin Michael Wynne Hill Surgery, 51 Hill Street, Lurgan, Craigavon BT66 6BW; 2 Stewart Avenue, Portadown, Craigavon BT63 5DA — MB BCh BAO 1982 Belf.; MB BCh Belf. 1982; MRCGP 1986; DRCOG 1985; DCH RCPSI 1984.

MACDONALD, Cristabel 21 Montague Row, Inverness IV3 5DX Tel: 01463 230548 — MB ChB 1963 Aberd.; DCH RCPS Glas. 1969. (Aberd.) Assoc. Specialist (Ment. Handicap) Craig Phadrig Hosp. Inverness. Socs: BMA. Prev: Regist. (Paediat.) Inverness Gp. Hosps.; Resid. Med. Off. Childr. Hosp. Birm.

MACDONALD, Mr David Alastair St James's University Hospital, Leeds LS9 7TF Tel: 0113 243 3144 Email: hamish_kirsty@email.msn.com; Email: hamish_kirsty@email.msn.com — MB BS 1982 Lond.; FRCS Eng. 1986. (Char. Cross) Cons. Orthop. St. Jas. Univ. Hosp.; Hon. Sen. Clin. Lect. Leeds Univ. Socs: Fell. BOA; Brit. Orthop. Research Soc.; Brit. Hip Soc. Prev: Sen. Regist. (Orthop.) Yorks. HA; Lect. (Orthop.) Univ. Glas. W.. Infirm. Glas.

MCDONALD, David Ernest 45 Woodlands Road, Sonning Common, Reading RG4 9TD Tel: 01189 722654 Fax: 01189 722654 — MB BCh Wales 1969; MRCPsych 1975; DPM Eng. 1973. (Cardiff) Cons. Psychiat. S. Oxon. Community, The Pk. Hosp. for Childr. Oxf. & The Home Office; Hon. Cons. St. Luke's Hosp. for Clergy Lond. Socs: BMA. Prev: Cons. Child. & Family Psychiat. & Psychiat. Ment. Handicap. Oxf. RHA; Sen. Regist. (Child Adolesc. & Family Psychiat.) Soton. & S.W. Hants. Health Dist.; Sen. Regist. (Forens. Psychiat.) Wessex RHA.

MACDONALD, David Jack Findlay (retired) 1 Shaw Road, Milngavie, Glasgow G62 6LU Tel: 0141 956 3327 — MB ChB 1956 St. And.; DTM & H Liverp. 1958; FFA RCS Eng. 1964; DA Eng. 1960. Prev: Cons. Anaesth. Glas. Roy. Infirm.

MACDONALD, Mr David Moffat Hampshire Place, Ridgeway Lane, Lymington SO41 8AA Tel: 01590 675672 — LRCP LRCS Ed. LRFPS Glas. 1937; FRCS Glas. 1962; FRCS Ed. 1948; FRFPS Glas. 1948; FDS RCPS Glas. 1967, LDS 1935. (Glas.) Cons. Dent. Surg. Emerit. Guy's Hosp. & Orpington & Sevenoaks Hosps. Socs: Fell. Brit. Assn. Oral & Maxillofacial Surg.; Fell. Roy. Soc. Med. Prev: Sen. Regist. Lond. Hosp.; Maj. RAMC, Surg. Specialist; Med. Off. Plastic & Jaw Injury Unit, Bangour EMS Hosp.

MACDONALD, David Robert The Surgery, Shaw Lane, Albrighton, Wolverhampton WV7 3DT Tel: 01902 372301 — BM 1981 Soton.; MRCGP 1986; DCH RCP Lond. 1984; DRCOG 1983. (Southampton) GP; Hosp. Pract. (Diabetes) New Cross Hosp. Wolverhampton.

MACDONALD, David William Robertson 2 Woodthorne Road, High West Jesmond, Newcastle upon Tyne NE2 3PB — MB BS 1980 Lond.; PhD Lond. 1976, MB BS 1980; BSc Ed. 1972. Sen. Regist. (Clin. Biochem. & Metab. Med.) Roy. Vict. Infirm. Newc. Socs: Assoc. RCPath; Biochem. Soc. Prev: Regist. (Chem. Path.) Roy. Postgrad. Med. Sch. Hammersmith Hosp. Lond.; SHO (Gen. Med./Gastroenterol.) St. Jas. Hosp. Lond.; SHO (Renal Med.) St. Helier Hosp. Carshalton.

MCDONALD, Desmond Gerald 5 Richmond House, Hillside Park, Ascot SL5 9RP — MB BCh BAO 1947 NUI. (Univ. Coll. Dub.)

MACDONALD, Donald Beecholme, Westfield Road, Cupar KY15 5DS Tel: 01334 652955 — MB ChB 1949 Glas. (Glas.) Prev: Ho. Surg. & Ho. Phys. Vict. Infirm. Glas.; Ho. Surg. Bellshill Matern. Hosp.

MACDONALD, Donald 27 Bourtree Brae, Lower Largo, Leven KY8 6HX — MB ChB 1943 Glas. (Glas.) Prev: Princip. Lect. (Health Educat.) & Med. Off. Jordanhill Coll. Educat. Glas.; Hon. Maj. RAMC.

MACDONALD, Donald 74 Port Vale, Hertford SG14 3AF — BM BCh 1996 Oxf.

MACDONALD, Donald Hugh Charles Department of Haematology, Charing Cross Hospital, Fulham Palace Road, London W6 8RF Tel: 020 8846 7122 Fax: 020 8846 7111 Email: d.h.macdonald@ic.ac.uk — MB ChB 1982 Sheff.; MD Sheff. 1991; MRC Path 1993; FRCP 1997. Cons. Haemat. Char. Cross Hosp. Lond. Prev: Sen. Regist. (Haemat.) Hammersmith Hosp. Lond.

MACDONALD, Donald John 44C Kevock Vale Caravan Park, Lasswade EH18 1LY — MB ChB 1982 Glas.; T(GP) 1994.

MACDONALD, Donald Michael Keats House, Guy's Hospital, London SE1 9RT Tel: 020 7955 4584 Fax: 020 7955 4584; Ash Court, Maidstone Road, Hothfield, Ashford TN26 1AN Tel: 01233 625320 — MB BChir 1970 Camb.; MB Camb. 1970, BChir 1969; MA Camb. 1969; FRCP Lond. 1982, M 1972; FRCPath 1991. Cons. Dermat. Guy's Hosp. Lond. Prev: Sen. Regist. (Histopath.) Inst. Dermat. St John's Hosp. Dis. Skin Lond.; Sen. Regist. (Dermat.) King's Coll. Hosp. Lond.; Regist. (Dermat.) St. Geo. Hosp. Lond.

MACDONALD, Mr Donald Murray (retired) 6 Craiglockhart Grove, Edinburgh EH14 1ET Tel: 0131 455 8777 Email: dmmacdoanld@freescotcoll.ac.uk — MB ChB 1967 Ed.; FRCS Ed. 1972. Prev: Med. Sup. Lakhnadon Christian Hosp. Madhya Pradesh, India.

MACDONALD, Donald William (retired) 51 Meadows Avenue, Thornton-Cleveleys FY5 2TW Tel: 01253 822637 Fax: 08707 065176 Email: dwm@donaldmacdonald.co.uk — MB ChB Ed. 1955. Prev: Clin. Asst. (Cardiol.) Vict. Hosp. Blackpool.

MACDONALD, Douglas John Hector George Street Surgery, 16 George Street, Alderley Edge SK9 7EP Tel: 01625 584545 — MB 1977 Camb.; BChir 1976; MRCGP 1981; DRCOG 1979.

MACDONALD, Duncan (retired) Pines Cottage, Hooton Road, Willaston, Neston, South Wirral CH64 1SE Tel: 0151 327 4560 — MB ChB 1951 St. And.

MACDONALD, Duncan, MBE (retired) The Gantocks, Fort William PH33 6RL Tel: 01397 2050 — MB ChB 1938 Glas. Prev: Med. Adviser Scott. Pulp & Paper Mills Lochaber.

MCDONALD, Duncan Stewart Alban House, Holly Hill Lane, Southampton SO31 6AG — MB BS 1988 Lond.

MCDONALD, Edward Lawson King Edward VII's Hospital for Officers, Beaumont St., London W1G 6AA Tel: 020 7486 4411 Ext: 4306 Fax: 020 7467 4312; 9 Bentinck Mansions, Bentinck St, London W1U 2ER Tel: 020 7935 7101 — 2001 FAHA; MB BChir Camb. 1946; MA Camb. 1946, MD 1952; FRCP Lond. 1961, M 1949; MRCS Eng. LRCP Lond. 1942; FACC 1968. (Camb. & Middlx.) Hon. Cons. Cardiol. Nat. Heart Hosp. Lond.; Fell. Emerit. Amer. Coll. of Cardiol.; Emerit. Fell. Amer. Heart Assn.; Mem. Most Honourable Order of the Crown of Sohore. Socs: Internat. Fell. Counc. Clin. Cardiol. Amer. Heart Assn.; Assn. Phys. & Brit. Cardiac Soc.; Amer. Coll. of Cardiol. Prev: Rockefeller Trav. Fell. (Med.) Peter Bent Brigham Hosp., Boston & Harvard Univ. 1952-3; Asst. Dir. Inst. Cardiol. Univ. Lond.; Cons. Cardiol. King Edwd. VII's Hosp. for Offs. Lond. & Roy. Lond. Hosp.

MACDONALD, Elisabeth Anne (retired) 103 Devonshire Mews S., London W1G 6QS Tel: 07811 064854 Fax: 020 7486 9702 Email: eamsears@aol.com — MB BS 1969 Lond.; MA (Med. Law & Ethics) Lond. 1989; MRCS Eng. LRCP Lond. 1969; FRCR 1975; DMRT Eng. 1972. Cons. Clin. Oncologist Cromwell Hosp.; Cons. Clin. Oncologist Harley St. Oncol. Unit 81 Harley St. Lond. Prev: Cons. Radiother. Guys & St Thomas NHS Trust.

MACDONALD, Elizabeth 88 Brenfield Road, Muirhead, Glasgow G44 3JR — MB ChB 1984 Glas.; MRCP UK. 1987.

MACDONALD, Elizabeth (retired) 50 Blinkbonny Road, Edinburgh EH4 3HX Tel: 020 8332 5840 — MB ChB 1946 Glas.; DPH 1953; DObst RCOG 1949.

MACDONALD, Elizabeth Charlotte Tigh-Scoile, Onich, Fort William — MB ChB 1973 Aberd.; DRCOG 1983.

MCDONALD, Elizabeth Mary Patricia Maudsley Hospital, Denmark Hill, London SE5 8AF; 6 Dalmore Road, West Dulwich, London SE21 8HB Tel: 020 8670 8783 — MB BCh BAO 1982 NUI; MPhil Lond. 1993; MRCPsych 1986; Dip.Cog Behavioural

Psychother, Inst. Psychiatry 1997. (Uni. Coll. Cork. NUI) Sen. Regist. Maudsley Hosp. Lond. Prev: Research Fell. Inst. Psychiat. & Hon. Sen. Regist. Maudsley Hosp.

MACDONALD, Elizabeth Mhairi 3 Woodlands Cottage, Dumfries DG2 0HZ — MB ChB 1988 Glas.

MACDONALD, Elspeth Ann Path House Medical Practice, Path House, Nether Street, Kirkcaldy KY1 2PG Tel: 01592 644533 Fax: 01592 644550; 20 Townsend Crescent, Kirkcaldy KY1 1DN Tel: 01592 643701 — MB ChB 1979 Ed.

MACDONALD, Elspeth Taylor 11 Landsborough Drive, Kilmarnock KA3 1RY — MB ChB 1972 Glas.; MRCP (U.K.) 1974. Clin. Asst. Ayrsh. Centr. Hosp. & Biggart Day Hosp. Prev: Jun. Ho. Off. Roy. Infirm. Glas.; SHO Welsh Nat. Sch. Med. Cardiff & Brompton Hosp. Lond.

MACDONALD, Esme Jean (retired) Southwinds, Hatton Road, Kinnoull, Perth PH2 7DB Tel: 01738 622765 — MB ChB 1948 Ed.; Dip. Psychiat. Ed. 1962; DObst RCOG 1950. Prev: Cons. Psychiat. Stratheden Hosp. Cupar.

***MACDONALD, Euan Ruairidh** 4 Merchiston Bank Gardens, Edinburgh EH10 5EB — MB ChB 1998 Manch.; MB ChB Manch 1998.

MACDONALD, Evelyn Morag 36 Princess Meadow, Gosforth, Newcastle upon Tyne NE3 4RZ — MB BCh 1990 Wales; BSc (Hons.) St. And. 1985; BA (Hons.) Open 1988; DRCOG 1995; DCH RCPS Glas. 1993.

MACDONALD, Ewan Beaton Department of Public Health, University of Glasgow, 2 Lilybank Gardens, Glasgow G12 8RZ Tel: 0141 330 4038 Fax: 0141 330 5018 Email: ebmd1t@udcf.gla.ac.uk; Callandale, 45 Gallowhill Road, Lenzie, Glasgow G66 4AL — MB ChB 1971 Glas.; FRCP Ed. 1996; FRCP Lond. 1994; FRCP Glas. 1992; MRCP (UK) 1975; FFOM RCP Lond. 1988, MFOM 1983; DIH Eng. 1978. Sen. Lect. (Occupat. Health) Univ. Glas.; Cons. Occupat. Phys. Monklands Bellshill NHS Trust; Dir. of Salus Occupat. Health & Safety Serv.; Mem. of GMC Performance Assessm. Implementation Gp. Socs: Soc. Occupat. Med.; BMA (Occupat. Health Comm.); Sec. UEMS Sect. of Occupat. Med. Prev: Dean of Fac. Occupat. Med. Roy. Coll. Phys. Lond.; Chief Med. Off. IBM (UK) Ltd Portsmouth; Princip. Med. Off. Yorks. Nat. Coal Bd.

***MACDONALD, Finlay Iain** Blackford House, Macclesfield Road, Alderley Edge SK9 7BH — MB ChB 1998 Manch.; MB ChB Manch 1998.

MCDONALD, Fiona Anne 54 Brooklands Way, Redhill RH1 2BW; 36B Nightingale Lane, London SW12 8TD — MB ChB 1991 Dundee; MRCP (UK) 1996. Specialist Regist. Paediat. Guys Hosp. Lond. Socs: RCPCH.

MCDONALD, Fiona Elizabeth 31 Centurion Way, Heddon-on-the-Wall, Newcastle upon Tyne NE15 0BY — MB ChB 1990 Dundee.

***MCDONALD, Fiona Mary Alison** 4, Gloucester Place, London NW1 5AB — MB BS 1997 Lond.

MACDONALD, Fiona Reay (retired) 4 Rysland Drive, Fenwick, Kilmarnock KA3 6EY Tel: 01560 600441 — MB ChB 1960 Glas.; DA Eng. 1965. Prev: Assoc. Specialist Anaesth. Vict. Infirm. Glas.

MACDONALD, Garry (retired) Springfield, Southdown Road, Shawford, Winchester SO21 2BY Tel: 01962 713113 — MB ChB 1957 Manch.; FRCP Ed. 1992; FFPM RCP (UK) 1992, M 1990; MRCGP 1977; DObst RCOG 1962. Prev: Med. Dir. Bayer plc Newbury.

MCDONALD, George Alexander (retired) 11 Pinecrest Drive, Bieldside, Aberdeen AB15 9FJ Tel: 01224 867595 Fax: 01224 867595 — MD 1960 Aberd.; MB ChB 1954; FRCP Glas. 1972, M 1968; FRCPath 1976, M 1963. Hon. Lect. (Haemat.) Univ. Glas.; Cons. Haematologist Glas. Roy. Infirm.; Hon. Cons. (Haemat.) Univ. Strathclyde; Vis. Prof. Med. Fac., Kuwait Univ.; Pres. Leukaemia Research Fund - Scott. Region. Prev: Ho. Phys. & Ho. Surg. Aberd. Roy. Infirm.

MCDONALD, George Edmund Stewart (retired) Blaidwood, South Road, Durham DH1 3TQ Tel: 0191 384 6900 — MRCS Eng. LRCP Lond. 1963. Prev: SHO Paediat. Derbysh. Childr. Hosp.

MACDONALD, George James 197 Maxwell Avenue, Bearsden, Glasgow G61 1HS — MB ChB 1990 Glas.

MCDONALD, Gillian Elizabeth 18 Furnston Grove, Emsworth PO10 8NP — MB BChir 1994 Camb.

MCDONALD

MCDONALD, Graeme Harding Mater Infirmorum Hospital, Crumlin Road, Belfast BT14 6AB; 33 Viewfort Park, Upper Malone, Belfast BT17 9JY — MB BCh BAO 1981 Belf.; MRCPsych 1985. Cons. Psychiat. Mater Infirmorum Hosp. Roy. Vict. Hosp. Belf. Prev: Cons. Psychiat. Purdysburn Hosp. Roy. Vict. Hosp. Belf.

MCDONALD, Hamish John (retired) 50 Greenhill Road, Coalville, Leicester LE67 4RH Tel: 01530 832940 — MB ChB Ed. 1952. Prev: GP Leicester.

MACDONALD, Hamish Neil (retired) Springbank, 11 Hall Drive, Bramhope, Leeds LS16 9JF — PhD Leeds 1973; MB ChB Glas. 1958; FRCOG 1978, M 1966, DObst 1959. Prev: Med. Dir. St. Jas. Univ. Hosp. Leeds.

MACDONALD, Hazel Elizabeth 15 Ailsa Drive, Giffnock, Glasgow G46 6RL — MB ChB 1989 Glas.; MRCGP 1993.

MACDONALD, Helen (retired) 20 Leegate Gardens, Stockport SK4 3NR — MB BS Lond. 1955. Prev: GP Manch.

MACDONALD, Helen Jean 252 Manchester New Road, Middleton, Manchester M24 1JS — MB ChB 1993 Liverp.

MACDONALD, Helen Lindsay Eskhill Lodge, 17 Inveresk Village, Musselburgh EH21 7TD — MB ChB 1976 Ed.; FRCR 1983; DMRD Ed. 1982.

MACDONALD, Helen Mary Health Centre, Ferry Road, Dingwall IV15 9QS — MB ChB 1988 Aberd.; DFFP, 1996; MRCGP 1992; DRCOG 1993. (Aberdeen) p/t Retainer, GP.

MACDONALD, Helen Watson 4 Merchiston Bank Gardens, Edinburgh EH10 5EB — MB ChB 1971 Aberd.; BSc Aberd. 1971; MRCGP 1982; MFFP 1995; DCCH RCP Ed. 1985; DObst RCOG 1973. (Aberd.) Sen. Clin. Med. Off. (Family Plann.) Lothian HB; Clin. Med. Off. (Child Health) Lothian HB. Prev: GP Trainee (Guy's Prof. Unit.) Galleons Reach Health Centre; Clin. Med. Off. (Child Health) Greenwich & Bexley AHA.

MCDONALD, Henry Francis THe Surgery, 89 Gubbins Lane, Harold Wood, Romford RM3 0DR Tel: 01708 346666 Fax: 01708 381300 — BM BCh 1977 Oxf.; MA Oxf. 1979; MRCGP 1980; DFFP 1993; DRCOG 1978. Prev: Trainee GP Pract. Reading VTS; Ho. Phys. Radcliffe Infirm. Oxf.; Ho. Surg. Co. Hosp. Hereford.

MACDONALD, Hugh (retired) 6 Westbourne Crescent, Highfield, Southampton SO17 1EE Tel: 023 8055 6908 — MB ChB 1952 Ed.; DMRT ed. 1958; FRCR 1975; FFR 1961. Prev: Cons. Radiother. & Oncol. Soton. Univ. Hosps. Trust.

MCDONALD, Mr Hugh Alexander (retired) 6 Cliff Lane, Gorleston, Great Yarmouth NR31 6JY Tel: 01493 662480 — MRCS Eng. LRCP Lond. 1937; FRCS Eng. 1944; FRCS Ed. 1941. Prev: Cons. Surg. Gt. Yarmouth & Gorleston Gen. Hosp.

MACDONALD, Iain Orr Regional Medical Adviser, C/O FCO (Moscow), King Charles Street, London SW1A 2AH Email: i-mcdonald@dfid.gov.uk; c/o Know How Fund Section, British Embassy, Kutusovsky Prospekt 7/4, Moscow 121248, Russia Tel: +7095 956 7477 Fax: +7095 956 7480 Email: iain.mcdonald@nailsea.net — MB ChB 1977 Bristol; MRCGP 1983; DRCOG 1980. (Bristol) Health Adviser, Russia Know How Fund, Brit. Embassy, Moscow. Socs: BMA; RCGP. Prev: Travel Fell. Russia, GP Qu.'s Univ. Belf.; GP. Princip., Nailsea Family Pract., Nailsea, Bristol.

MACDONALD, Iain Smith, CB (retired) 4 Skythorn Way, Falkirk FK1 5NR Tel: 01324 625100 — MB ChB 1950 Glas.; MD (Commend.) Glas. 1958; FRCP Ed. 1979, M 1978; FFPHM RCP (UK) 1978; DPH Glas. 1955; DObst RCOG 1954. Prev: Chief Med. Off. Scott. Home & Health Dept.

MACDONALD, Ian Wheatley and Macdonald, 163 Birmingham Road, Allesley Village, Coventry CV5 9BD Tel: 024 7640 3250 Fax: 024 7640 5009 — MB ChB 1976 Birm.; BSc (Hons.) Anat. Birm. 1973, MB ChB 1976; FRCGP 1994, M 1984.

MACDONALD, Professor Ian Hillside, Fountain Drive, London SE19 1UP Tel: 020 8670 3055 Fax: 020 8670 3055 Email: rosian@cwcom.net — MB BS 1944 Lond.; PhD Lond. 1953, DSc 1966, MD 1959; FIBiol. 1971; DObst RCOG 1948. (Guy's) Emerit. Prof. Applied Physiol. Univ. Lond. Socs: (Vice-Pres.) Brit. Nutrit. Foundat.; (Ex-Pres.) Nutrit. Soc.; Amer. Soc. Clin. Nutrit. Prev: Prof. Applied Physiol. & Head, Dept. Physiol. Guy's Hosp. Lond.; Chairm. Jt. WHO/FAO Expert Comm. on Dietary Carbohydrates; Chairm. Brit. Nutrit. Foundat.

MCDONALD, Ian Alexander Linden Lea, 5 Caledonian Road, Peebles EH45 9DJ — MB ChB 1969 Aberd.; FRCP Ed. 1993; FFCM 1987, M 1978; DSM Ed. 1974.

MACDONALD, Ian Anthony Russell Westhall, Lerwick, Shetland ZE1 0RN — MB ChB 1981 Ed.; BSc. Ed. 1978; MRCP (UK) 1984. Socs: Brit. Paediat. Assn.; Brit. Assn. Emerg. Med.; BMA. Prev: Specialist Regist. (Paediat.) Roy. Vict. Infirm. Newc.; Sen. Regist. (Paediat.) P'boro. Dist. Hosp.

MACDONALD, Ian Duncan 56 Greenbank Crescent, Edinburgh EH10 5SW — MB ChB 1986 Glas.; MRCP (UK) 1992.

MACDONALD, Ian Martin Nithsdale Road Surgery, 162 Nithsdale Road, Glasgow G41 5RU Tel: 0141 424 1831 Fax: 0141 423 7422; 5 Merrylee Road, Glasgow G43 2SH — MB ChB 1974 Glas.; DObst RCOG 1976; MRCGP 1981; MSc. (Med Sci.) Sports Med. Univ. Glas. 1999.

MACDONALD, Ian Somerled (retired) Llanddewi, 11 Glynderwen Crescent, Derwen Fawr, Swansea SA2 8EH Tel: 01792 280286 Fax: 01792 280286 Email: abertanejock@compuserve.com — MB BS Lond. 1959; MRCS Eng. LRCP Lond. 1959. Prev: Med. Off. Colonial Med. Serv. Basutoland.

MACDONALD, Miss Iona Kathleen Grant 36 Roman Court, Bearsden, Glasgow G61 2HS Tel: 0141 943 0091 — MB ChB 1988 Aberd.; MRCGP 1994; DGM RCP Lond. 1990. SHO (Dermat.) S.. Gen. Hosp. Glas. Prev: Trainee GP Bishopbriggs; SHO (Psychiat.) Pk.head Hosp. Glas.; SHO (PAediat.) CrossHo. Hosp. Kilmarnock.

MACDONALD, Isabelle Wilma Claire Department of Pathology, Pontefract Hospitals NHS Trust, Pontefract WF8 1PL Tel: 01977 606386 Fax: 01977 606868 Email: claire.macdonald@panp_tr.northy.nhs.uk; 63 Ackworth Road, Pontefract WF8 3PG Tel: 01977 709268 — MB ChB 1975 Glas.; BSc (Hons.) Biochem. Glas. 1971; FRCPath 1994, M 1982. Cons. Path. Pontefract Gen. Infirm.; Dir. Pathol. Pinderfields & Pontefract Hosps. NHS Trust. Prev: Lect. (Path.) Aberd. Med. Sch.; Sen. Regist. (Path.) Victory Infirm. Glas.; Regist. (Path.) W.ern Infirm. Glas.

MACDONALD, Isobel (retired) Craig Mhor, North Road, Dunbar EH42 1AX Tel: 01368 863396 — MB ChB 1952 Ed.; DObst RCOG 1963.

MACDONALD, Jacqueline 67 Ashley Terrace, Edinburgh EH11 1RU — MB ChB 1979 Glas.

MCDONALD, Jacqueline McCrindle 4A Kirkhill Gardens, Penicuik EH26 8JE — MB ChB 1978 Ed.; MRCGP 1982; DRCOG 1981.

MCDONALD, Jacqueline McKenzie Department of Community Child Health, Grampian Healthcare NHS Trust, Berrryden Road, Aberdeen; Gushet-Neuk, Gauch Hill, Kintore, Inverurie AB51 0XQ — MB ChB 1978 Aberd. Staff Grade in Comm. Paediat. Grampain Healthcare NHS Trust.

MCDONALD, James Flat 40, Rivermill, 151 Grosvenor Road, London SW1V 3JN — MB BCh BAO 1980 NUI.

MCDONALD, James Douglas (retired) 60 Frenchgate, Richmond DL10 7AG Tel: 01748 823223 Fax: 01748 823223 — MB ChB Ed. 1950. Prev: GP.

MACDONALD, James Hugh Budge Masterton Health Centre, 74 Somerville Street, Burntisland KY3 9DF Tel: 01592 873321 Fax: 01592 871338 — MB ChB 1968 Ed. (Ed.) GP Burntls.

MACDONALD, James Kennedy (retired) Frithwood, London Common Road, Little Burstead, Billericay CM12 9SY — MB BS 1965 Lond.; DObst RCOG 1967. Prev: GP Romford.

MCDONALD, James Ronald (retired) Westhill, Jurby Road, Ramsey IM7 2EA Tel: 01624 812073 Fax: 01624 812073 — MB ChB Ed. 1961; DObst RCOG 1964.

MACDONALD, James Stewart (retired) Darquhillan, Gleneagles, Auchterarder PH3 1NG Tel: 01764 662476 Fax: 01764 661086 — MB ChB Ed. 1950; DMRD Ed. 1956; FRCP Ed. 1979, M 1973; FRCR 1975; FFR 1960. Prev: Dir. (Diagn. Radiol.) Roy. Marsden Hosp. Lond.

MACDONALD, Jamie 14 Braeface, Alness IV17 0QP — MB ChB 1993 Aberd.

MACDONALD, Jancis Clare Birchetts, Stockland Green, Speldhurst, Tunbridge Wells TN3 0TY — MB BS 1959 Lond.; DA Eng. 1962. (Middlx.)

MACDONALD, Janine Adèle Houndlaw Park Health Centre, Houndlaw Park, Eyemouth TD14 5DA; 8 Wester Row, Greenlaw, Duns TD10 6XE Tel: 01361 810337 — MB ChB 1975 Ed.; LFHom 1996. Socs: Accred. Mem. BMAS; BMDHS (Scotl.).

MCDONALD, Jean Mary 18 Osprey Rise, E. Hunsbury, Northampton NN4 0TA — MB BS 1963 Lond.; MRCS Eng. LRCP Lond. 1963; MRCPsych. 1982; DCH Eng. 1965. (Roy. Free)

MACDONALD

MACDONALD, Jean Murray (retired) Snow's Green House, Shotley Bridge, Consett DH8 0EW Tel: 01207 502008 — MB ChB Ed. 1952. Assoc. Specialist (Radiother.) Newc. AHA (T). Prev: Cas. Off. Farnham Hosp.

MACDONALD, Jeanie Clark 7 Byron Court, Bothwell, Glasgow G71 8TW Tel: 0141 853552 — MB ChB 1932 Glas.

MCDONALD, Jill (retired) Westhall, Lerwick ZE1 0RN — MB ChB 1950 Ed.; DObst RCOG 1954. Prev: Chief Admin. Med. Off. Shetland Health Bd.

MCDONALD, John Pencraig, 10 Beaufort Avenue, Langland, Swansea SA3 4NU Tel: 01792 69184 — MB ChB 1952 Glas.; MA Glas. 1944, MB ChB 1952; DPM Eng. 1958. (Glas.) Cons. Child Psychiat. Welsh Hosp. Bd.; Psychiats. Socs: Roy. Med.-Psych. Assn. Mem. Assn. Child Psychols. & Child. Prev: Ho. Phys. S.. Gen. Hosp. Glas.; Ho. Surg. Ballochmyle Hosp. Mauchline.

MCDONALD, John Department of Paediatrics, Raigmore Hospital, Inverness IV2 3UJ Tel: 01463 704000 Email: john.mcdonald@raigmore.scot.nhs.uk; 73 Stratherrick Road, Inverness IV2 4LL — MB ChB Glas. 1967; FRCP (Ed.) 1996; FRCP Glas. 1988; MRCP (U.K.) 1970; FRCPCH 1997; DObst RCOG 1969; DCH RCPS Glas. 1969. (Glas.) Cons. Paediat. Raigmore Hosp. Inverness.; Clin. Sen. Lect. Univ. Aberd. Prev: Lect. Child Health Univ. Dept. Child Health Roy. Hosp. Sick Childr.; Glas.; Ho. Off. Med. Glas. Roy. Infirm.

MACDONALD, John Alexander Cropwell Bishop Surgery, Fern Road, Cropwell Bishop, Nottingham NG12 3BU Tel: 0115 989 2287; 2 Springfield Close, Cropwell Bishop, Nottingham NG12 3GJ Tel: 0115 989 2174 Fax: 0115 989 0166 — MB BS 1989 Lond.; MB BS (Distinc. Surg.) Lond. 1989; MRCGP 1993; BPharm (Hons.) 1983; DFFP 1993; DRCOG 1993; Dip IMC RCS Ed. 1992. Socs: Roy. Pharmaceut. Soc. GB; Nottm. M-C Soc. Prev: SHO (O & G, A & E Med., Gen. Respirat. & Gastroenterol.) Univ. Hosp. Nottm.

MACDONALD, Mr John Arthur Ernest 47 Keir Street, Bridge of Allan, Stirling FK9 4QJ Tel: 01786 833868 — MB ChB 1965 Glas.; FRCS Glas. 1994; FRCS Ed. 1970. (Glas.) Cons. Surg. Falkirk & Dist. Roy. Infirm. Socs: Scott. Soc. Hist. Med. & Scott. Soc. Experim. Med. Prev: Sen. Regist. (Gen. Surg.) Edin. Roy. Infirm.; Research Asst. & Regist. (Surg.) W.. Infirm. Glas.

MACDONALD, John Borthwick 23 Glasgow Road, Kilmarnock KA3 1TJ — MD 1979 Camb.; MB 1969, BChir 1968; FRCP Glas. 1985; MRCP (UK) 1972. (Univ. Coll. Lond.) Cons. Phys. CrossHo. Hosp. Kilmarnock. Socs: Brit. Thoracic Soc. Prev: Cons. Phys. Centr. Hosp. Irvine & Ballochmyle Hosp. Ayrsh.; Sen. Regist. City Hosp. Nottm.; Med. Regist. Welsh Nat. Sch. Med. Cardiff.

MACDONALD, John Charles Mackie (retired) Findrassie Lodge, Elgin IV30 5PS Tel: 01343 543060 — MB ChB Aberd. 1942; DA Eng. 1959. Prev: GP (Anaesth.) Dr Grays Hosp. Elgin.

MCDONALD, John Clive Hammett (retired) 66 Grenville Drive, Cambuslang, Glasgow G72 8DP Tel: 0141 583 1639 Email: jch.mcdonald@net.ntl.com — MB ChB 1953 Glas.; DObst RCOG 1958. Prev: GP Glas.

MCDONALD, Professor John Corbett Department of Occupational & Environmental Medicine, National Heart & Lung Institute, Dovehouse St., London SW3 6LY Tel: 020 7351 8934 Fax: 020 7351 8091; 4 Temple West Mews, West Square, London SE11 4TJ Tel: 020 7582 9084 — MB BS Lond. 1947; DPH Lond. 1949; MSc Harvard 1951; MD Lond. 1949; FRCP Lond. 1976, M 1964; FRCP Canada 1970; MRCS Eng. LRCP Lond. 1942; FFOM 1978; FFCM 1976; DIH Eng. 1950. (St. Mary's) Emerit. Prof. Dept. Occup. & Env. Med. Nat. Heart & Lung Inst. Univ. Lond.; Emerit. Prof. Dept. Occupat. Health McGill Univ. Montreal. Prev: Prof. & Head Sch. Occupat. Health McGill Univ. Montreal; Prof. & Head, TUC Centenary Inst. Occupat. Health Univ. Lond.; Prof. & Chairm. Dept. Epidemiol. & Health McGill Univ. Montreal.

MACDONALD, John Douglas (retired) Shingle Sound, Seabank Road, Nairn IV12 4HA Tel: 01667 452710 Fax: 01667 452710 — MB ChB 1956 Aberd.; FRCGP 1980, M 1964; DObst RCOG 1960. Prev: GP Nairn.

MCDONALD, John Ewan 1 Beech Crescent, Newton Mearns, Glasgow G77 5BN Tel: 0141 639 4679 Email: jmd24n@clinmed.gla.ac.uk — MB ChB 1994 Glas.; BSc (Hons); MRCP Glas. (Glasgow) Res. Fell. (Cardiol.) W.ern NHS Trust. Glas. Socs: BMA. Prev: SHO (Cardiol.) W.rn NHS Trust Glas.; Med. Rotat. W.ern NHS Trust Glas.

MACDONALD, John Hamish (retired) 37 Salford Road, Ainsdale, Southport PR8 3JX Tel: 01704 78253 — LMSSA 1970 Lond. Med. Off. DSS.

MACDONALD, John Knox Fallin, Cowie and Airth Medical Practice, Stirling Road, Fallin, Stirling FK7 7JD Tel: 01786 812412 Fax: 01786 817496; Woodlands, 21 Harviestoun Road, Dollar FK14 7HG Tel: 01259 743710 — MB ChB 1982 Dundee; BSc, MB ChB Dund 1982; MRCGP 1986; DRCOG 1982.

MACDONALD, John Maxwell Brogan and Partners, The O'Connel Street Medical Centre, 6 O'Connell Street, Hawick TD9 9HU Tel: 01450 372276 Fax: 01450 371564 — MB ChB 1979 Ed.; MRCGP 1984.

MACDONALD, John William Alexander Wigtown Medical Practice, High Vennel, Wigtown, Newton Stewart DG8 9JQ Tel: 01988 402210 Fax: 01988 403482 Email: john@718131.dghb.scot.nhs.uk; Woodside, Wigtown, Newton Stewart DG8 9EE Email: joanne@bladnech.demon.co.uk — MB ChB 1976 Ed.; BSc (Hons.) Ed. 1972; DRCOG 1979. (Ed.)

MACDONALD, Jonathan Beaton Girthill, Warlock Road, Bridge of Weir PA11 3SR — MB ChB 1975 Glas.; MRCP (UK) 1980.

MCDONALD, Joseph William The Barnes Unit, Durham Road, Sunderland SR3 4AF Tel: 0191 522 7739 Email: joe@adolescentpsychiatry.co.uk — BM BS 1985 Nottm.; BMedSci. (Hons.) Nottm. 1983; MRCPsych 1990. (Nottm.) Adolesc. Psychiat. Sunderland; Hon. Sen. Lect. Newc. Univ. Prev: Cons. (Child. & Adolesc. Psychiat.) Gateshead.

MACDONALD, Judith Lesley Granary Cottage, Wakerley Road, Harringworth, Corby NN17 3AH — MB BS 1991 Newc.; MRCGP 1995; Cert. Prescribed Equiv. Exp. JCPTGP 1995. SHO (Psychiat.) NW Anglia Healthcare Trust P'boro.

MCDONALD, Judith Margaret 1 Cairnhill Gardens, St Andrews KY16 8QY Tel: 01334 472793 — MB ChB Aberd. 1974; DCH RCPS Glas. 1976; MRCGP 1978.

MCDONALD, Judith Pamela Handforth Health Centre, The Green, 166 Wilmslow Road, Handforth, Wilmslow SK9 3HL Tel: 01625 529421; Little Orchard, Cross Lane, Wilmslow SK9 2DB Tel: 01625 527053 — MB ChB 1971 Liverp.; DA Eng. 1977; DObst RCOG 1973.

MACDONALD, June Sheila 36 Roman Court, Bearsden, Glasgow G61 2HS — MB ChB 1957 Liverp.; MRCS Eng. LRCP Lond. 1957; DA Eng. 1959. (Liverp.) Socs: BMA. Prev: Regist. (Anaesth.) Roy. Alexandra Infirm. Paisley; Ho. Surg. Roy. Hosp. Sick Childr. Glas.; Sen. Ho. Off. (Anaesth.) Aberd. Gen. Hosps.

MCDONALD, Katrina Eileen Kymberlea, Reskadinnick, Camborne TR14 0BH — MB BS 1988 Lond.

MACDONALD, Kay Martin Lincoln Lodge, Chalfont Lane, Chorleywood, Rickmansworth WD3 5PR — MB BS 1996 Lond.

***MACDONALD, Kendon** Nurses Cottage, Farr, Inverness IV2 6XJ — MB ChB 1998 Aberd.; MB ChB Aberd 1998.

MACDONALD, Kenneth James (retired) Sleasdaraidh, Bonar Bridge, Ardgay IV24 3AT Tel: 01863 766354 — MB ChB 1954 Aberd.; DObst RCOG 1959. DOH Employee. Prev: Surg. Lt. RN.

MCDONALD, Kenneth John 3/2 138 Fergus Drive, Glasgow G20 6AT — MB ChB 1995 Glas.; BSc (Hons) Glas. 1992; MRCP (UK) 1998.

MCDONALD, Kenneth Walter Huddersfield Road Surgery, 6 Huddersfield Road, Barnsley S70 2LT Tel: 01226 287589 Fax: 01226 731245 — MB ChB 1974 Ed.; BSc (Med. Sci.) Ed. 1971. (Ed.) Sec. Barnsley LMC. Prev: Vice-Chairm. Barnsley FHSA.

MCDONALD, Kevin Ambrose Belvedere, Wrexham Road, Rhostyllen, Wrexham LL14 4DH Tel: 01978 840034; Belvedere, Wrexham Road, Rhostyllen, Wrexham LL14 4DH Tel: 01978 840034 — MB BCh BAO 1945 NUI; LM Coombe 1949. (Univ. Coll. Dub.) Chairm. Min. of Social Security Bd. Socs: Wrexham & Dist. Clin. Soc. Prev: Ho. Phys. War Memor. Hosp. Wrexham; Ho. Phys. & Ho. Surg. St. Kevin's Hosp. Dub.

MACDONALD, Kirsteen Margaret 37 Whitehall Place, Aberdeen AB25 2RH — MB ChB 1994 Aberd.

MACDONALD, Kirsten Lesley West End Medical Practice, 21 Chester Street, Edinburgh EH3 7RF Tel: 0131 225 5220 Fax: 0131 226 1910; 14 Woodhall Terrace, Juniper Green, Edinburgh EH14 5BR Tel: 0131 442 4821 — MB ChB 1991 Aberd.; MRCGP 1996; DRCOG 1994. GP Princip. W. End Med. Pract. Edin.

MACDONALD

MACDONALD, Laura Stewart 4 Pinewood Court, Kirkintilloch, Glasgow G66 4JW — MB ChB 1995 Glas.

MCDONALD, Lesley Ann Boyd 18 Meikleriggs Drive, Paisley PA2 9NP — MB ChB 1993 Glas.

MACDONALD, Lesley Anne Crewe Medical Centre, 135 Boswall Parkway, Edinburgh EH5 2LY Tel: 0131 552 5544 Fax: 0131 551 5364; 10 Queens Avenue S., Edinburgh EH4 2BU Tel: 0131 332 3378 — MB ChB 1978 Ed.; MRCGP 1982; DRCOG 1981. GP Edin.

MACDONALD, Lesley June 2 The Vineys, Sandhurst Lane, Sandhurst, Gloucester GL2 9NX — MB ChB 1981 Glas.; MRCGP 1986; DRCOG 1986.

MACDONALD, Lesley Margaret Radiology Department, St Thomas's Hospital, London SE1 7EH Tel: 020 7928 9292 Email: lesley.macdonald@gsttsthames.nhs.uk; 205 Spice Quay Heights, 32 Shad Thames, London SE1 2YL — MB BS 1970 Lond.; FRCR 1977; DMRD Eng. 1974; FRCPCH. (St. Thos.) Cons. Radiol. St. Thos. Hosp. Lond. Prev: Regist. (Radiol.) & Sen. Regist. (Radiol.) St. Thos. Hosp. Lond.; Sen. Regist. (Radiol.) W.m. Hosp. Lond.

MACDONALD, Lesley Margaret North Hill Surgery, 18 North Hill, Colchester CO1 1DZ Tel: 01206 578070 Fax: 01206 769880; 1 Heathside, West Bergholt, Colchester CO6 3JT — MB ChB 1980 Manch.; BSc (Med. Sci.) St. And. 1977; MRCGP 1984. Prev: Civil. Med. Practitioner, Garrison Med. Centre, P.ss Roy. Barracks; Clin. Med. Off. (Child Health) SW Herts. HA; RAF Med. Off.

MACDONALD, Lesley Marjorie Fife Health Board, Springfield House, Cupar KY15 5UP; 13 Louisville Avenue, Aberdeen AB15 4TT — MB ChB Aberd. 1970; MFPHM RCP (UK) 1993; FFPHM RCP (UK) 1998. Dir. Pub. Health & CAMO Fife Health Bd. Prev: Cons. Pub. Health Med. Highland HB.

MCDONALD, Linda Judith 20 Balfour Avenue, Whitehead, Carrickfergus BT38 9RD — MB BCh BAO 1994 Belf.

MACDONALD, Linsey Tarrel Dr Anne Spooner & Associates, Beach Centre, 33 Beach Road, Repulse Bay, Hong Kong, China Tel: 00 852 2542 9000; Tel: 01383 720634 — MB ChB 1994 Ed.; DRCOG; MRCGP 1998. (Edinburgh) GP Dr Anne Spooner & Assoc.s, Hong Kong. Prev: GP Regist., Stockbridge HC, Edinburgh.

MACDONALD, Lucinda Jane Westover Surgery, Western Terrace, Falmouth TR11 4QJ Tel: 01326 212120 Fax: 01326 212080; Riverdale, Perranwell Station, Truro TR3 7PR Tel: 01872 862937 — MB BChir 1988 Camb.; MA Camb. 1989,MB BChir 1988. GP. Prev: Trainee GP Perranporth.

MCDONALD, Lynne 35 Allan Place, Inverurie AB51 4TD — MB ChB 1988 Aberd.

MCDONALD, Malcolm Chapelthorpe Surgery, Hall Lane, Chapelthorpe, Wakefield WF4 3JE Tel: 01924 255166 Fax: 01924 257653; Grove House Farm, The Balk, Walton, Wakefield WF2 6JY Tel: 01924 253429 — MB ChB 1979 Leeds; MRCGP 1983. Clin. Asst. (ENT) Clayton Hosp. Wakefield. Prev: Ho. Surg. & Ho. Phys. Wharfedale Gen. Hosp. Otley.

MACDONALD, Mrs Margaret 40 Grafton Terrace, London NW5 4HY Tel: 020 7485 5814 — MB BS Lond. 1954; MRCS Eng. LRCP Lond. 1954; DO Eng. 1965; Dip Med. Acupunc 1995. (Roy. Free) Socs: Brit. Med. Acupunct. Soc. Prev: Hon. Clin. Asst. (Pain Clinic) Roy. Free Hosp. Lond.; Ophth. Specialist RAF; Govt. Med. Off., Zimbabwe.

MACDONALD, Margaret Evelyn Carradale, 29 Newlands Road, Glasgow G43 2JD Tel: 0141 632 3990 — MB ChB 1964 Glas. (Glas.) Prev: Ho. Off. Glas. Roy. Infirm. & King's Cross Hosp. Dundee.

MACDONALD, Margaret Grant Lyndon, 1 Abertay Gardens, Banhill, Dundee DD5 2RR — MB ChB 1968 Aberd. (Aberd.) Clin. Med. Off. Community Child Health Tayside Health Bd.

MACDONALD, Margaret Jean, MBE (retired) 11 Ashburnham Gardens, South Queensferry EH30 9LB Tel: 0131 331 4217 Fax: 0131 331 3663 Email: maggiejmacdonald@lineone.net — MB ChB Ed. 1969; FRCS Ed. 1975; FCOphth 1989; DO Eng. 1974; MBA Ed. 1998. Prev: Cons. Ophth. Qu. Margt. Hosp. NHS Trust.

MACDONALD, Margaret Laird (retired) 22 Viewpark, Glasgow Road, Milngavie, Glasgow G62 6HH Tel: 0141 956 1391 — LRCP LRCS Ed. LRFPS Glas. 1948; DPH Glas. 1962; DObst RCOG 1951. Prev: Sen. Clin. Med. Off. Gt.er Glas. Health Bd.

MACDONALD, Margaret Russell Sinclair Eynord, Bowmore PA43 7JF — MB ChB 1946 Glas.; DPA 1946. Prev: Ho. Off. (Gen. Med. & Dermat.) Roy. Hosp. Sick Childr. Glas.; S.. Gen. Hosp. Glas. & W.. Gen. Hosp. Midw. Glas.

MACDONALD, Marion Scotsburn Road Health Centre, Scotsburn Road, Tain IV19 1PR Tel: 01862 892203 Fax: 01862 892165; The Firs, Loandhu, Fearn, Tain IV20 1RS Tel: 01862 832457 — MB ChB 1982 Glas.

MACDONALD, Marjorie Graham (retired) Ballagan House, Strathblane, Glasgow G63 9AE Tel: 01360 70850 — MB ChB 1947 Glas.; DCH Eng. 1951.

MCDONALD, Mark Ireland Drumcarro, Windygates Road, Leven KY8 4DW — MB ChB 1989 Dundee.

MACDONALD, Martin Russell Eynord, Bowmore PA43 7JF — MB ChB 1979 Glas.

MACDONALD, Mary Kynoch (retired) 1 Grant Avenue, Edinburgh EH13 0DS Tel: 0131 441 3508 — MB ChB 1945 Ed.; FRCP Ed. 1964, M 1948; FRCPath 1975. Prev: Reader Path. Dept. Univ. Edin.

MCDONALD, Mary Roddie (retired) 20 Lomond Road, Wemyss Bay PA18 6BD Tel: 01475 522074 — MB ChB 1950 Glas. Prev: SCMO Renfrew Health Centre.

MACDONALD, May Fraser Urquhart Torwood, Corrie Road, Muir of Ord IV6 7TL Tel: 01463 870377 — MB ChB 1925 St. And. (St. And.) Prev: Hon. Med. Off. Dundee SPCC; Ho. Phys. Childr. Dept. & Ho. Surg. ENT Dept. Dundee Roy. Infirm.

MCDONALD, Michael 25 Partridge Way, Merrow Park, Guildford GU4 7DW — MB ChB 1976 Ed.; MRCP (UK) 1980; DPM Eng. 1985.

MCDONALD, Michael Alexander (retired) Summer Barn, Back Lane, Tollerton, York YO61 1PZ Tel: 01347 830086 — MRCS Eng. LRCP Lond. 1953; FFOM RCP Lond. 1983, MFOM 1978; DIH Soc. Apoth. Lond. 1973; DIH Eng. 1973; DObst RCOG 1955. Prev: Chief Med. Off. Post Office.

MACDONALD, Moraig Windyedge, Muirhall Road, Kinfauns, Perth PH2 7LL — MB ChB 1986 Aberd.; MRCGP 1990.

MACDONALD, Natalie-Jane BUPA, 15-19 Bloomsbury Way, London W1A 2BA; 1 Essex Road, Thame OX9 3LT — MB ChB 1984 Glas.; MRCP (UK) 1987; MBA, Lond. Bus. Sch. 1997. (Glasgow) head of Healthcare Policy & Dev. BUPA UIC. Prev: Asst. Med. Dir. BUPA Health Servs. Lond.; Head Internat. Dept. & Head of Med. Ethics BMA Lond.; Lect. (Gen. Med. & Clin. Pharmacol.) Dept. Med. & Therap. Univ. Glas.

MACDONALD, Mr Neil (retired) 20 Leegate Gardens, Stockport SK4 3NR Tel: 0161 432 3377 — MB BS 1950 Lond.; MB BS (Hons. Surg.) Lond. 1950; FRCS Eng. 1957; MRCS Eng. LRCP Lond. 1950. Prev: Cons. Surg. Wythenshawe Hosp.

MACDONALD, Neil (retired) The Surgery, Tarbert PA29 6UL Tel: 01880 820219 Fax: 01880 820401 — MB ChB 1963 Ed. Prev: Obst. Ho. Off. Raigmore Hosp. Inverness.

MCDONALD, Neil Hamish The Surgery, Greenwich Avenue, Hull HU9 4UX Tel: 01482 374415 Fax: 01482 786462; 89 Hull Road, Coniston, Hull HU11 4LD Tel: 01482 813438 Fax: 01482 813033 Email: neil@mcdonald-hull.demon.co.uk — MB ChB 1978 Manch. (Manchester)

MACDONALD, Neil James, MBE (retired) Carnelrig, Aviemore PH22 1PZ Tel: 01479 810707 — MB ChB 1961 Ed.; FRCP Ed. 1997; DObst RCOG 1963. Prev: GP Aviemore.

MACDONALD, Nicola Dawn 5 Chaee Close, Glastonbury BA6 9PT — MB BS 1994 Lond.

MCDONALD, Nicola Jane The Old Rectory, Leckhampstead Road, Akeley, Buckingham MK18 5HH — MB BS 1994 Lond.

MCDONALD, Noel Gerard Regional Medical Centre, RAF Coltishall, Norwich NR10 5AJ Tel: 01603 737361 Ext: 7241; Corofin, Cross Road, Swanston Abblt, Norwich NR10 5DT Tel: 01692 538196 Email: corofin@waitrose.com — MB ChB 1981 Sheff.; MRCGP 1985; MICGP 1987; DRCOG 1984; DAvMed. 1998. (University of Sheffield Medical School)

MCDONALD, Patrick Andrew Ellerslie, Stanlawe Road, Formby, Liverpool L37 1LD Tel: 01704 879669; Preston Acute Hospitals Trust, Department of Medicine for Elderly, Sharoe Green Lane, Preston PR2 9HT Tel: 01772 711302 Fax: 01772 711368 — MB ChB Liverp. 1986; MRCP (UK) 1990. Cons. (Phys. w. Special Responsibil. for Elderly) Preston Acute Hosps. Trust, Lancs. Socs: Brit. Geriat. Soc.; Roy. Coll. Phys. Lond.; Brit. Assn. Stroke Phys. Prev: Sen. Regist. Geriat.s Liverp.

MACDONALD

MCDONALD, Paula Anne 29 Lansdowne Road, Belfast BT15 4AA — MB BCh BAO 1987 Belf.

MCDONALD, Paula Claire Communicable Disease Unit, PHLS, Countess of Chester Health Park, Liverpool Road, Chester CH2 1UL Tel: 01244 366766 Fax: 01244 366777 — MB ChB 1980 Liverp.; MSc Manchester 1994; MRCGP 1985; MFPHM 1996. (Liverpool MBChB) p/t Head ofCommunicable Dis. Unit Chesh. & Wirral. Prev: SCMO (Adult Health) S. Manch. HA; GP Manch.

MACDONALD, Peter Ashley G G c/o J. & P. Lewis, 34 Newhailes Crescent, Musselburgh EH21 6EG Email: paggmacdonald@hotmail.com — MB ChB 1992 Dundee. Socs: Amer. Acad. Of Family Pract. Prev: Res. Genesis Regional Health Cen. Michigan, USA; Casualty Off. Roy. Albert Edwd. Infirm. Wigan, Lancs.

MACDONALD, Peter David Department of Paediatrics, Southern General Hospital, Glasgow G51 4TF Tel: 0141 201 2228 Fax: 0141 201 2774 — MB ChB 1983 Manch.; BSc St. And. 1980; MRCP (UK) 1987. (Manchester) Cons. Paediat. & Neonatol. Roy. Hosp. Sick Childr. & S.. Gen. Hosp. Glas. Socs: FRCPCh; Roy. Coll. Phys.s & Surg. of Glas.; Brit. Associaiton of Perinatal Med. Prev: Sen. Regist. (Paediat.) Roy. Hosp. Sick Childr. Glas.; Fell.sh. (Neonat.. Intens. Care) Monash Med. Centre Melbourne, Austral.; Regist. (Paediat.) Roy. Matern. Hosp. & Roy. Hosp. for Sick Childr. Glas.

MACDONALD, Mr Peter John Department of Gastroenterology, Northwick Park and St Mark's Hospitals, Watford Road, Harrow HA1 3UJ Tel: 020 8869 2627 — MB BS 1975 Lond.; MS Soton. 1984; FRCS Eng. 1980. Cons. Gastroenterol. Surg. N.wick Pk. Hosp. & St. Mark's Hosp.; Hon. Lect. Univ. Lond. Socs: Assn Surgs.; Roy. Soc. Med. (Surg. & Coloproctol. Sects.); Assn. Coloproctol. Prev: Resid. Surg. Off. St. Mark's Hosp. Lond.; Lect. & Sen. Regist. (Surg.) Univ. Soton.; Fell. (Colorectal) Cleveland Clinic Ohio, USA.

MACDONALD, Peter John West Denburn Medical Practice, West Wing, Denburn Health Centre, Rosemount Viaduct, Aberdeen AB25 1QB Tel: 01224 642955 Fax: 01224 637736; 15 Oakhill Road, Aberdeen AB15 5ER — MB ChB 1974 Aberd.; FRCP Ed. 1995; MRCP (UK) 1977; Cert. Family Plann. JCC 1979. Clin. Tutor Aberd. Prev: Regist. (Gen. Med.) S. Grampian Health Dist. & Clin. Tutor (Med.) Univ. Aberd.; Lect. (Med.) Univ. Aberd.

MCDONALD, Philip Francis 15 Litten Terrace, Chichester PO19 4SA Tel: 01243 538861; Department of Anaesthetics, St. Richard's Hospital, Chichester PO19 4SE Tel: 01243 788122 Email: 73754.2417@compuserve.com — MB ChB 1984 Liverp.; MB ChB Liverp. l984; FRCA 1990. (Liverpool) Cons. Anaesth. St. Richard's Hosp. Chichester.

MACDONALD, Phyllis Margaret Sleasdaraidh, Bonar Bridge, Ardgay IV24 3AT — MB ChB 1955 Aberd.

MACDONALD, Reginald William Donald (retired) Hawthorne, Low Askomil, Campbeltown PA28 6EP Tel: 01586 52013 — MB ChB Glas. 1951.

MACDONALD, Mr Robert Campbell Ridgemoor, 64 Beaumont Park Road, Huddersfield HD4 5JH Tel: 01484 645451 Fax: 01484 645451 — MB ChB 1972 Ed.; BSc (Med. Sci.) Ed. 1969, ChM 1986, MB ChB (Hons.) 1972; FRCS Eng. 1990; FRCS Ed. 1976. (Ed.) Cons. Gen. Surg. Huddersfield HA. Socs: Brit. Soc. Gastroenterol.; Assn. Surg.; Assn. Upper G.I. Surg. Prev: Lect. Surg. Univ. Leeds.

MACDONALD, Mr Robert Duncan 96 Longmead Av, Bishopston, Bristol BS7 8EF — MB ChB 1991 Bristol; MRCOG 1998. Sen. Reg. S.mead Hosp. Bristol (O&G). Prev: Regist. Gloucester Roy. Hosp., Gloucester (O & G).

MACDONALD, Robert Park Cumming, VRD (retired) Brook House, Lower Stoke, Rochester ME3 9RE Tel: 01634 270394 — MB BS 1948 Lond.; MRCS Eng. LRCP Lond. 1945; DMRD Eng. 1950. Prev: Surg. Lt.-Cdr. RNR.

MACDONALD, Robin James Martin Blackwater Medical Centre, Princes Road, Maldon CM9 7DS Tel: 01621 854204 Fax: 01621 850246 — MB BS 1965 Lond.; DObst RCOG 1968. (Lond. Hosp.) Clin. Asst. (Rheum.) Chelmsford & Essex Hosp. Chelmsford.

MACDONALD, Roderic Sinclair 106 Wellesley Road, Chiswick, London W4 3AP Tel: 020 8994 1701 — MB BS 1966 Lond.; MRCP (UK) 1972; DMS Med. Soc. Apoth. Lond. 1993; MLCOM 1979; DObst RCOG 1968. (King's Coll. Hosp.) Research Worker (Back Pain) & Clin. Tutor Lond. Coll. Osteop. Med. Socs: Hon. Sec. Brit. Osteop. Assn.; Soc. Back Pain Research. Prev: Regist. (Med.) Epsom Dist. Hosp. & Worcester Roy. Infirm.; Inst. Human Performance Univ. Coll. Lond.

MCDONALD, Roderick Duncan St Dunstan's Park Health Centre -, St Dunstan's Park, Melrose TD6 9RX Tel: 01896 822161 Fax: 01896 823151 — MB ChB 1979 Ed.

MACDONALD, Mr Roderick John Macpherson, Lt.-Col. RAMC Retd. St. Johns Hospital, Howden, Howden Road W., Livingston EH54 6PP Tel: 01506 419666; 4 Merchiston Bank Gardens, Edinburgh EH10 5EB Tel: 0131 447 1570 — MB ChB 1971 Aberd.; FRCS Ed. 1979. Cons. Orthop. Surg. St Johns Hosp. Howden & P.ss Margt. Rose Hosp. Edin. Prev: Sen. Cons. Orthop. Surg. Camb. Milit. Hosp. Aldershot; Hon. Sen. Specialist (Orthop.) Childr. Hosp. Gt. Ormond St. Lond. & P.ss Margt. Rose Hosp. Edin.

MCDONALD, Ronald James 24 Truro Close, Lichfield WS13 7SR — MB ChB 1968 Glas.; MRCP (UK) 1973.

MACDONALD, Mr Ronald Robert (retired) 4 Shawdene, Burton Crescent, Leeds LS6 4DN Tel: 01132 789573 Fax: 01132 789573 — MB ChB 1951 Glas.; MD (Commend.) Glas. 1962; FRCS Ed. 1965; FRCOG 1970, M 1959, DObst 1957. Medico-legal Cons. Leeds. Prev: Sen. Clin. Lect. (O & G) Univ. Leeds.

MCDONALD, Ronald Stewart, OBE, Surg. Capt. RN (retired) Frenchman's Cove, 2 Sun Hill, Cowes PO31 7HY Tel: 01983 296660 — MRCS Eng. LRCP Lond. 1943; DMRD Eng. 1961. Prev: Ho. Governor & Med. Supt. King Edwd. VII Convalesc. Home Offs. I. of Wight.

MCDONALD, Rosalind Mary (retired) Frithwood, Laindon Common Road, Little Burstead, Billericay CM12 9SY Tel: 01277 659582 — MB BS 1962 Lond. Prev: SHO (O & G) & Ho. Phys. Rush Green Hosp. Romford.

MACDONALD, Rosemary Gillespie University Department for NHS Postgrad. Med. & Dent. Educat., 2 Willow Terr. Road, University of Leeds, Leeds LS2 9JT Tel: 0113 233 1500 Fax: 0113 233 1530; Springbank, 11 Hall Drive, Bramhope, Leeds LS16 9JF Tel: 0113 203 7374 — FRCP 2000; MB ChB Glas. 1967; PhD Bradford 1976; FFCA Eng. 1971. (Univ. Glas.) Postgrad. Dean (Yorks.) Univ. Leeds N. & Yorks. NHS. Socs: Yorks. Soc. Anaesth.; Assn. of Anaesth. Prev: Cons. Anaesth. St. Jas. Hosp. Leeds; Lect. (Anaesth.) Univ. Leeds Dent. Sch.; Sen. Regist. (Anaesth.) Leeds RHB.

MACDONALD, Ruth Mairi 63 Gardner Street, Glasgow G11 5BZ — MB ChB 1989 Manch.; BSc St. And 1986; DRCOG 1993.

MACDONALD, Sheena Lindsay Leader Medical Group, Kidgate, Earlston TD4 6DW Tel: 01896 849684 Email: sheena.macdonald@leader.borders.scot.nhs.uk; Rhymers Cottage, Kidgate, Earlston TD4 6DW Tel: 01896 849245 — MB ChB 1982 Ed.; BSc (Med. Sci.) Ed. 1979; FRCGP 2000; MRCGP 1987; DCH RCPS Glas. 1985; DRCOG 1984. (Edinburgh) GP Earlston; Trainer. Prev: SHO (O & G) Falkirk & Dist. Roy. Infirm.; SHO (Paediat. Med.) Roy. Hosp. Sick Childr. Glas.; SHO (Geriat. Med.) Roy. Vict. Hosp. Edin.

MACDONALD, Simon Thomas 3 Bavelaw Cr, Penicuik EH26 9AX — BM BCh 1997 Oxf.

***MCDONALD, Stephen Edward** 63 Withert Avenue, Wirral CH63 5NE — BM BCh 1997 Oxf.

MCDONALD, Stephen Jeremy, RD (retired) 2 Drew Close, Talbot Village, Poole BH12 5ET — MB BS Lond. 1960; PhD Lond. 1965; FRCP Lond. 1979, M 1967; MRCS Eng. LRCP Lond. (Handcock Prize RCS) 1960. Surg. Lt.-Cdr. RNR Retd. Prev: Cons. Phys. Roy. Bournemouth Hosp.

MACDONALD, Stephen Patrick John 59 Auchingane, Edinburgh EH10 7HU Tel: 0131 441 7906 Fax: 0131 441 7906 Email: spjmacdonald@hotmail.com — MB ChB 1994 Ed.; BSc (Hons.) Ed. 1992; MRCP (UK) 1997. Regist. (Emerg. Med.) Sir Chas. Gardner Hosp. Perth W.ern Australia.

MACDONALD, Stuart Forbes 20 North Circular Road, Lisburn BT28 3AH — MB BCh BAO 1993 Belf.

MCDONALD, Stuart William Laboratory of Human Anatomy, University of Glasgow, Glasgow G12 8QQ Tel: 0141 330 4185 Fax: 0142 330 4299 Email: s.mcdonald@bio.gla.ac.uk — MB ChB 1983 Glas.; PhD Glas. 1989, BSc (Hons. Anat.) 1980, MB ChB 1983. Lect. (Anat.) Univ. Glas. Socs: (Hon. Sec.) Brit. Assn. Clin. Anat.; BMA. Prev: Ho. Off. Gartnavel Gen. Hosp. & W.. Infirm. Glas.

MACDONALD, Susan Elizabeth Lache Health Centre, Hawthorn Road, Lache, Chester CH4 8HX Tel: 01244 671991 Fax: 01244

MCDONALD

680729; 2 Kinnerton Court, Lower Kinnerton, Chester CH4 9EA — MB ChB 1986 Sheff.; MRCGP 1992; DRCOG 1991.

MCDONALD, Willa Victoria 23 Lloyd Baker Street, London WC1X 9AZ — MB ChB 1992 Dundee; MRCP (Paediat.) Lond. 1996; DRCOG Lond. 1998; DFFP Lond. 1998. GP. Prev: GP VTS Whittington Hosp. Lond.

MACDONALD, William Cos Lane Surgery, Glenrothes KY7 4AQ Tel: 01592 2100; 15 Carnoustie Gardens, Glenrothes KY6 2QB Tel: 01592 752950 — MB ChB 1959 Aberd. Prev: SHO (O & G) E. Dist. Hosp. Glas.; Maj. RAMC; Resid. Ho. Off. Aberd. Roy. Infirm.

MACDONALD, William George (retired) Whinnyknowe, Lesmurdie Road, Elgin IV30 4HP Tel: 01343 542800 — MB ChB 1950 Aberd. Prev: Ho. Surg. Tredegar Hosp.

MCDONALD, Professor William Ian (retired) Royal College Of Physicians, 11 St Andrews Place, London NW1 4LE Tel: 020 7935 1174 Ext: 311 Fax: 020 7486 3729 Email: ian-mcdonald@rcplondon.ac.uk — MB ChB 1962 New Zealand; Hon. DSc 2000 Otago; 1999 F med Sci; PhD 1962 New Zealand; BMedSc 1955 NZ; FRCOphth 1989 (hons, 1999); FRACP 1968; MRCP 1964 Lond; FRCP 1972 Lond.; MRACP 1963. Harveian Librarian, RCP. Prev: Prof. & Head Univ. Dept. Clin. Neurol. Lond.

MACDONALD, William Paul Guidepost medical Group, North Parade, Guidepost, Choppington NE62 5RA — MB BS 1988 Lond.; BSc (Hons.) Dunelm 1976; MRCGP 1993; T(GP) 1994; DCCH RCP Lond. 1994; DFFP 1994. (Char. Cross & Westm.) Gen. practitioner. Socs: BMA; Roy. Coll. of Gen. Practitioners. Prev: SHO (Psychiat.) Forth Valley HB Bellsdyke Hosp. Larbert; Trainee GP Links Med. Centre II Edin.; SHO (O & G, & Neonat. Paediat.) E.. Gen. Hosp. Edin.

MACDONALD-BROWN, Andrew James Clanricarde Medical entre, Clanricarde Road, Tunbridge Wells TN1 1PJ Tel: 01892 01892 546422 Fax: 01892 533987 Email: andrew.macdonald-brown@gp-g82035.nhs.uk — MB BS 1974 Lond.; MRCS Eng. LRCP Lond. 1974; MRCGP 1979; DFFP 1996; DRCOG 1976. (Lond. Hosp.) Prescribing Lead - S. W. Kent PCT. Prev: Trainee GP Winchester VTS; SHO Roy. Hants. Co. Hosp. Winchester.

MACDONALD BURNS, David Christopher Marlborough Department, Royal Free Hospital, Pond St., Hampstead, London NW3 2QG Tel: 020 7794 0500 Fax: 020 7830 2587; 2 Malden Place, London NW5 4JL Tel: 020 7482 0655 — MB BS Lond. 1964; MRCS Eng. LRCP Lond. 1963; FRCOG 1989, M 1970; DObst RCOG 1966. (King's Coll. Hosp.) Sen. Cons. Sexually Transm. Dis. Roy. Free Hampstead NHS Trust. Socs: (Vice-Pres.) Harveian Soc.; BMA (Chairm. Hampstead Div.); Internat. AIDS Soc. Prev: Sen. Regist. St. Bart. Hosp. Lond.; Regist. (O & G) N.wick Pk. Hosp. Harrow; Resid. Med. Off. Qu. Charlotte's Hosp. Lond.

MACDONALD HULL, Susan Patricia Dept of Radiology, Pontefract General Infirmary, Pontefract WF8 1PL Tel: 01977 606244; 15 Charville Gardens, Shadwell, Leeds LS17 8JL Tel: 0113 273 7293 — MB ChB 1972 Liverp.; FRCP 1998; MD Leeds 1999. Cons. Dermat. Pontefract Gen. Infirm. Socs: Eur. Hair Research Soc.; Fell Roy. coll. Of Phys.s; Brit. Assoc. Dermatol.s. Prev: GP Croydon; Sen. Regist. (Dermat.) Leeds Gen. Infirm.

MACDONALD-SMITH, Kenneth Alexander Radio House, John Wilson Business Park, Whitstable CT5 3QP Tel: 01227 772666 Fax: 01227 772444; Havisham House, Harbledown, Canterbury CT2 9BL Tel: 01227 456681 — MB BChir Camb. 1960; MA Camb. 1961; AFOM RCP Lond. 1981; DA Eng. 1963; DObst RCOG 1962. (Camb. & Middlx.) Socs: BMA. Prev: Chairm. Exec. Health Care Ltd.; Med. Advisor Canad. Pacific Ships Lond.; Mem. Active Staff King Edwd. VII Hosp., Bermuda.

MACDONALD-SMITH, Wilhelmina Mary Grace (retired) Barley, Royston SG8 8 Tel: 01763 996 84 655 — MB ChB 1927 Ed.; MB ChB (Hons.) Ed. 1927.

MACDONALD SPEIRS, Norma Anne Hurford Child & Family Centre, Hawkhead Hospital, Hawkhead Road, Paisley PA2 7BL Tel: 0141 889 8151; Wraes Farm, Neilston Road, Barrhead, Glasgow G78 1TY — MB ChB 1966 Ed.; MRCPsych 1973; DPM Ed. & Glas. 1972; DObst RCOG 1968. (Ed.) Cons. Child Psychiat. Child & Family Centre Hawkhead Hosp. Paisley. Socs: BMA. Prev: SHO (O & G) W.. Gen. Hosp. Edin.; SHO Roy. Edin. Hosp.; Sen. Regist. Roy. Hosp. Sick Childr. Glas.

MACDONALD-WATSON, Archibald 1 Old Cottages, Stroud Common, Shamley Green, Guildford GU5 0TB — MB ChB 1959 Glas.

MCDONNELL, Alexander (Alasdair) McDonnell and Partners, 139-141 Ormeau Road, Belfast BT7 1DA Tel: 028 9032 6030; 22 perry Volgie Avenue, Belfast BT9 6DN Tel: 02890662170 Fax: 02890 683203 — MB BCh BAO 1974 NUI; DRCOG 1977; DCH RCPSI 1976. (Univ. Coll. Dub.) Mem. N.ern Irel. Assembly. Prev: SHO (Obst.) Roy. Matern. Hosp. Belf.; SHO (Gen. Med.) Belf. City Hosp.; SHO (Paediat.) Ulster Hosp. Dundonald.

MCDONNELL, Anne Patricia 20 Mount Eden Park, Malone Road, Belfast BT9 6RA — MB BCh BAO 1986 Dub.; MB BCh BAO NUI Dub. 1986. Socs: MRCPsych.

MACDONNELL, Anthony John Randal West Kingsdown Medical Centre, London Road, West Kingsdown; Sevenoaks TN15 6EJ Tel: 01474 855000 Fax: 01474 855001; 34 Woodclyffe Drive, Chislehurst BR7 5NT Tel: 01474 855015 Email: tonymacd@cityscape.co.uk — MB BS 1981 Lond.; BSc Lond. 1978. Med. Dir. DAGDOC Co-op. Kent.

MCDONNELL, Catherine Mary 94 Bellvedere Park, Stranmillis, Belfast BT9 5GS — MB BCh BAO 1986 NUI.

MCDONNELL, Catherine Teresa Banbury Road Surgery, 172 Banbury Road, Oxford OX2 7BT Tel: 01865 515731 Fax: 01865 510711 — MB BCh BAO 1983 NUI.

MCDONNELL, David Stephen Meadowside Medical Practice, 1-3 Meadowside, Lancaster LA1 3AQ Tel: 01524 32622 Fax: 01524 846353; 26 Knowe Hill Crescent, Hala, Lancaster LA1 4JY — MB ChB 1990 Leic.; MRCGP 1994.

MCDONNELL, Eoin Dermot Department of Accident and Emergency, Royal Sussex County Hospital, Eastern Road, Brighton BN2 5BE — MB BS 1998 Lond.; MB BS Lond 1998.

MCDONNELL, Gavin Vincent 48 Andersonstown Road, Belfast BT11 9AN — MB BCh BAO 1990 Belf.; MRCP (UK) 1993. Socs: Fell. Roy. Soc. Med.; Ulster Med. Soc.

MCDONNELL, Professor Harry (retired) 5 Willow Grove, Beverley HU17 8DS Tel: 01482 868686 — MB ChB 1958 Ed. Prev: Dir. & Prof. Inst. Health Studies Univ. Hull.

MCDONNELL, Joanna Hilary Wychall Lane Surgery, 11 Wychall Lane, Kings Norton, Birmingham B38 8TE Tel: 0121 628 2345 Fax: 0121 628 8282; 82 Oakham Road, Birmingham B17 9DG Tel: 0121 427 4063 — MB BS 1980 Lond.; MRCGP 1984; DRCOG 1983. (St. Thos.) Prev: Princip. GP Lond.

MCDONNELL, John Gerard 58 Green Lane, Standish, Wigan WN6 0TX — MB ChB 1985 Liverp.; MSc Liverp. 1980, BSc 1979, MB ChB 1985.

MCDONNELL, John Michael Priory House, 134 St John's Road, Newbold, Chesterfield S41 8TW Tel: 01246 455187 — MB ChB 1972 Manch.; FRCOG 1990, M 1978. Cons. (O & G) Chesterfield Roy. Hosp. Trust; Clin. Dir. (Matern., Child Health & Gyn.) Chesterfield Roy. Hosp. Trust.

MCDONNELL, Juan Jose 8 Morris Way, London Colney, St Albans AL2 1JL — MB BS 1992 Lond.

MCDONNELL, Mary Perpetua c/o Anaesthetic Department, Wexham Park Hospital, Slough SL2 4HL; 7 The Grange, Church Road, Old Windsor, Windsor SL4 2PS — MB BCh BAO 1978 NUI.

MCDONNELL, Michael William (retired) Old School, North-A-Voe, Yell, Shetland ZE2 9DA Tel: 01957 702431 Fax: 01957 702172 — MB ChB Glas. 1964; FRCGP 1994, M 1974; DTM & H Liverp. 1968; DObst RCOG 1966. Prev: Dist. Med. Off. Brit. Solomon Isles.

MCDONNELL, Norma Patricia KCHospital, Bessemer Road, London SE5 9RS — MB BS 1988 Lond.; FRCA 1994. Cons. (Anaesth. & Int. Care) King's Coll. Hosp. Lond.

MCDONNELL, Olivia Lucia 1 Brannock Heights, Newry BT35 8DH — MB BCh 1998 Belf.; MB BCh Belf 1998.

MACDONNELL, Patrick Terence (retired) Southover, Bronshill Road, Torquay TQ1 3HD Tel: 01803 37100 Fax: 01803 316295 — MB BCh BAO 1957 Dub.; BA, MB BCh BAO Dub. 1957; DObst RCOG 1961; DTM & H Eng. 1962. Prev: Med. Off. Federat. Rhodesia & Nyasaland & The Uganda Co.

MCDONNELL, Mr Peter Joseph Tel: 0121 455 8066 Fax: 0121 454 7960 — MB BS 1978 Lond.; MA Oxf. 1980; FRCS Eng. 1983; MRCP (UK) 1981; FRCOphth 1988; DO Eng. 1982; FRCP Lond. 1998. (Oxf. & St. Thos.) Cons. Ophth. Surg. Birm. & Midl. Eye

Centre City Hosp. & Univ. Hosp. Trust, Birm.; Hon. Sen. Clin. Lect. (Surg.) Univ. Birm.; Hon. Cons. Ophth. Surg., Childr. Hosp. Birm. Socs: UK & Irel. Soc. Cataract & Refractive Surgs.; Birm. Medico-Legal Soc.; Bowman Club. Prev: Sen. Regist. (Ophth.) St. Thos. Hosp. Lond.; Resid. Surg. Off. Moorfields Eye Hosp. Lond.

MCDONNELL, Peter Wyndham 2 St. James Lodge, 219 Clifton Drive South, Lytham St Annes FY8 1ES Tel: 01253 722831 — MB BCh BAO 1947 NUI; MFHom 1950. (NUI)

MACDONNELL, Sean Patrick Jerome Department of Anaesthetics, Colchester District General Hospital, Turner Road, Colchester CO4 5JL Tel: 01206 853535 — MB BS 1987 Lond.; FRCA 1993; FFA RCSI 1993; DA (UK) 1989. Cons. Anaesth. Essex Rivers Healthcare Trust. Prev: Sen. Regist. (Anaesth.) Roy. Hosps. Trust.

MCDONNELL, Teresa Catherine Donnington Medical Practice, Wrekin Drive, Donnington, Telford TF2 8EA Tel: 01952 605252 Fax: 01952 677010; 46 Cote Road, Shawbirch, Telford TF5 0NQ — MB BCh BAO 1983 NUI; MRCGP 1988. Clin. Asst. (Rheum.) P.ss Roy. Hosp. Telford.

MCDONOGH, Brian Athol 45 Keats Close, Horsham RH12 5PL Tel: 01403 241527 Email: brian@medix-uk.com; 45 Keats Close, Horsham RH12 5PL Tel: 01403 241527, 01403 259899 Email: brian@medix-uk.com — MB ChB 1982 Pretoria; 1997 T (GP) Lond.; MSc 2001 Nutri Med; 1979 B Med Sci Pretoria. Specialist in Nutrit.al Med. Horsham, W. Sussex. Socs: BSAENM - Brit. Soc. for Allergies, Environm. & Nutrit.al Med.

MCDONOUGH, Belinda Mary 100 Windmill Lane, Widmer End, High Wycombe HP15 6AU — MB BCh BAO 1993 Belf. (Qu. Univ. Belf.) GP Regist. Edin. Prev: SHO (Genitourin. Med.) Roy. Infirm. Edin.; SHO (O & G) Route Hosp. Ballymoney.

MCDONOUGH, Helen Margaret Whitehouse Surgery, 189 Prince of Wales Road, Sheffield S2 1FA — MB ChB 1994 Sheff.

MCDONOUGH, Julian 130 Industry Street, Sheffield S6 2WX — MB ChB 1992 Sheff.; BMedSci 1989.

MCDONOUGH, Stephen Berkeley 100 Windmill Lane, Widmer End, High Wycombe HP15 6AU — BM BS 1990 Nottm.; BMedSci (Hons.) Mottm. 1988; MRCGP 1995. (Nottm.)

MCDOUALL, Sara Frances Medical Staffing, General Medicine, Queens Med Centre, Nottingham Tel: 0115 924 9924; 9 Ganton Close, Mapperley, Nottingham NG3 3ET Tel: 0115 958 3628 — BM BCh 1997 Oxf.; MA Bm Bch. Oxf. 1998. (Oxford) SHO (Gen. Med.), Qu.s Med centre Nottm. Prev: SHO(A+E), Salisbury Dist. Hosp.; Jun. Ho. Off. (Med.), Oxf.

MCDOUGALD, Margaret 39 London Road, Newark NG24 1RZ Tel: 01636 79490 Email: mgcmcdougald@netscape.com — BM BS 1984 Nottm.; PhD Leeds 1968, BSc 1962; BMedSci 1981; MRCOG 1997. (Nottingham) Regist. Ldr. Gen. Infirm. Prev: Regist. Nottm. City Hosp.; SSHO Kings Mill Sutton-in-Ashfield; SHO Doncaster Roy. Infirm.

MCDOUGALL, Alan 2 Oliver Road, Horsham RH12 1LH — MB ChB 1984 Glas.; MRCGP 1988; DRCOG 1986. Med. Affairs Manager Novo Nordisk Ltd; Hon. Clin. Lect. Univ. Glas. Prev: Clin. Asst. (Diabetes) Gartnavel Gen. Hosp. Glas.; GP.

MACDOUGALL, Alasdair Iain, RD (retired) 6 Kelvin Crescent, Bearsden, Glasgow G61 1BT Tel: 0141 942 2850 — MB ChB 1950 Glas.; BSc Glas. 1947; FRFPS Glas. 1960; FRCP Glas. 1971, M 1962; FRCP Ed. 1964; MRCP Ed. 1973. Prev: Cons. Phys. Stobhill Gen. Hosp. Glas.

MCDOUGALL, Allan Colin (retired) 87 Lower Radley, Abingdon OX14 3BA Tel: 01235 526510 Fax: 01865 242606 — MB ChB 1946 Ed.; MD Ed. 1958; FRCP Ed. 1994; FRCP Lond. 1979, M 1959; MRCP Ed. 1951; FRFPS Glas. 1951; DObst RCOG 1949. Prev: Hon. Cons. Leprosy (Dermat.) Ch.ill Hosp. Oxf.

MCDOUGALL, Ann Varee The Bacon Lane Surgery, 11 Bacon Lane, Edgware HA8 5AT Tel: 020 8952 7876; 40 The Highlands, Edgware HA8 5HL — MB ChB 1980 Dundee; MRCGP 1986; DRCOG 1984.

MCDOUGALL, Mr Archibald 2 Hutchison Court, Berryhill Road, Glasgow G46 7NN Tel: 0141 638 9573 — MB ChB 1938 Glas.; FRCS Ed. 1947; FRFPS Glas. 1946. (Univ. Glas.) Sen. Orthop. Surg. Vict. Infirm. Glas. & Assoc. Hosps.; Lect. Anat. Foot Hosp. Glas. Socs: Hon. Fell. Chiropody Soc.; E. Afr. Surg. Assn. Prev: Ho. Surg. Roy. Cancer Hosp. Glas.; Res. Med. Off. Port Sunlight Hosp.; Squadron Ldr. RAF.

MCDOUGALL, Archibald Neil Victoria Infirmary, Langside, Glasgow G42 9TY Tel: 0141 201 5376 Fax: 0141 201 5094; 10 Newton Place, Newton Mearns, Glasgow G77 5PG Tel: 0141 616 0683 — MB ChB 1969 St. And.; FRCOG 1987, M 1974. (St. And.) Cons. O & G Gen. Hosp., Glas. & Vict. Infirm. Glas. and at S.; Hon. Clin. Sen. Lect. Univ. Glas. Socs: Blair Bell Res. Soc.; Glas. Obst. & Gyn. Soc.; Glas. S.. Med. Soc. Prev: Cons. (O & G) Rutherglen Matern. Hosp.; 1st Asst. (O & G) Univ. Newc.; Sen. Regist. (O & G) MRC Unit Growth & Reproduc. P.ss Mary Matern Hosp. Newc.

MACDOUGALL, Barbara Kate College House, Bishop Middleham, Ferryhill DL17 9DR — MB ChB 1984 Birm; DRCOG 1990.

MCDOUGALL, Catherine Mary 32 Beechwood Gardens, Ilford IG5 0AE — MB ChB 1997 Aberd.

MCDOUGALL, Claire 16 Coldstream Dr, Rutherglen, Glasgow G73 3LQ — MB ChB 1997 Glas.

MCDOUGALL, Colin Market Street Health Centre, Market Street, Ullapool IV26 2XE Tel: 01854 612015/612595 Fax: 01854 613025; 15 Custom House Street, Ullapool IV26 2XF Tel: 01854 612837 — MB ChB 1988 Glas.; MRCGP 1993; T(GP) 1992. (Glas.) GP Partner Ullapool Med. Pract. Socs: BMA. Prev: Dist. Med. Off. Nkotakota Dist. Hosp., Malawi.; Trainee GP Gairloch & Aultbea & Isle of N. Uist; SHO (Paediat.) Raigmore Hosp. Inverness.

MACDOUGALL, Colin Francis Medical School, Univesity of Warwick, Coventry CV4 7AL Tel: 024 7652 3523 Fax: 024 7646 1606 — MB BS 1992 Newc.; MRCP (UK) 1996. (Newc. u. Tyne) Sr. Lect.. Med. Educat., Univ. of Warwick, Coventry; Mem. Roy. Coll. Paediat. & Child Health; Hon. Cons. (Peaddiat.) Walsgrave Gen. Hosp. Walsgrave on Sowe, Coventry. Socs: BMA. Prev: SHO (Neonat. Intens. Care) Roy. Vict. Infirm. Newc.; SHO Rotat. (Paediat.) N. Tees Gen. Hosp. Stockton & Roy. Vict. Infirm. Freeman Hosp. Newc. u.Tyne; Specialist Regist. Rotat. Newc. u. Tyne.

MACDOUGALL, David Alexander 5 Burns Avenue, Muir of Ord IV6 7TQ Tel: 01463 870573 — MB ChB 1991 Ed.; BSc (Hons.) Ed. 1989; MRCP (UK) 1995. (University of Edinburgh) Research Fell. (Cardiol.) Glas. Roy. Infirm. Socs: BMA; Med. & Dent. Defence Union Scotl. Prev: SHO III (Med.) Falkirk & Dist. Roy. Infirm.; SHO (Thoracic Med., Gastroenterol. & Gen. Med.) Fazakerley Hosp. Liverp.; SHO (A & E) Roy. Liverp. Univ. Hosp.

MACDOUGALL, Donald Hunter (retired) 3 The Ridgeway, Fareham PO16 8RF — MB ChB St. And. 1962; FFA RCS Eng. 1972; DA Eng. 1966. Prev: Cons. Anaesth. Portsmouth Gp. Hosps.

MCDOUGALL, Fiona Morrison Stranraer Health Centre, Edinburgh Road, Stranraer DG9 7HG Tel: 01776 706566; Alticry Lodge, Port William, Newton Stewart DG8 9RT Tel: 01581 500269 — MB ChB 1985 Ed.; MRCGP 1989; DRCOG 1988.

MACDOUGALL, Gillian Margaret Department of Otolaryngology, Royal Infirmary of Edinburgh, 1 Lauriston Place, Edinburgh EH3 9YW Tel: 0131 536 1000; 67 Restalrig Road, Edinburgh EH6 8BG — MB ChB 1987 Ed.; FRCS Ed. 1992; FRCS (Orl.) 1998. (Edinburgh) Sen. Regist. (Otolaryngol.) Roy. Infirm. Edin.

MACDOUGALL, Iain Cumming Renal Unit, King's College Hospital, East Dulwich Grove, London SE22 8PT Tel: 020 7346 6234 Fax: 020 7346 6472 Email: icm-kru@globalnet.co.uk; 18 Piermont Road, East Dulwich, London SE22 0LN — MB ChB 1983 Glas.; MD Glas. 1991, BSc (Hons.) 1980; MRCP 1999. (Glas.) Cons. Nephrol. King's Coll. Hosp. Lond. Socs: Renal Assn.; Eur. Renal Assn.; Amer. Soc. Nephrol. Prev: Sen. Regist. (Nephrol.) Renal Unit, St. Bart. Hosp. Lond.; Clin. Research Fell. (Nephrol.) Inst. Nephrol. Cardiff. Roy. Infirm.; Regist. (Med.) Gtr. Glas. HB.

MACDOUGALL, Ian Alexander (retired) 10 Beech Grove, Maltby, Middlesbrough TS8 0BL Tel: 01642 596845 — MB ChB 1962 Glas.

MACDOUGALL, Ian Somerled Springtails, 82 Fairmile Lane, Cobham KT11 2DA Tel: 01932 867722 — MB BS 1955 Lond. (Guy's) Local Treasury Med. Off. Prev: Sen. Ho. Off. (Paediat.) & Ho. Phys. Kingston Hosp.; Ho. Surg. Roy. Hants. Co. Hosp. Winchester.

MACDOUGALL, Jean Weir (Surgery), 109 Egilsay St., Glasgow G22 7JL Tel: 0141 772 1183; 33 Tofthill Avenue, Bishopbriggs, Glasgow G64 3PB — MB ChB 1946 Glas. (Glas.) Lect. St. John Ambul. Brig. & Brit. Red Cross Soc. Socs: BMA. Prev: Ho. Phys. Derbysh. Hosp. Sick Childr.; Asst. Sch. Med. Off. City Nottm.; Asst. Med. Off. Heref. CC.

MACDOUGALL, Jean Yates (retired) 713 Coatbridge Road, Bargeddie, Baillieston, Glasgow G69 7PH Tel: 01236 423487 — MB ChB 1952 Glas.; MD Glas. 1971; FRCP Glas. 1982; MRCP Glas.

MCDOUGALL

1976; DObst RCOG 1958; DCH Eng. 1957. Prev: SCM (Child Health) Lanarksh. Area HB.

MCDOUGALL, John Biddulph (retired) 23/1 Roseneath Place, Edinburgh EH9 1JD — MB ChB 1954 Ed.

MACDOUGALL, Mr John Campbell 35 S. Beach, Troon KA10 6EF Tel: 01292 311746 — LRCP LRCS 1935 Ed.; BSc Glas. 1964, HDD 1956, LDS 1934; FRCS Glas. 1962; FDS RCS Ed. 1970; FDS RCPS Glas. 1967; LRCP LRCS Ed. LRFPS Glas. 1935. Emerit. Prof. Dent. Surg. Glas. Dent. Hosp. Univ. Glas.

MCDOUGALL, John Lindsay (retired) Oakview, 5 The Avenue, Moulton, Northampton NN3 7TL Tel: 01604 495423 — MB ChB 1945 St. And. Prev: Hosp. Pract. Isebrook Hosp. WellingBoro.

MACDOUGALL, Kathleen Mary Maitland (retired) 50 Windsor Road, Doncaster DN2 5BT — MRCS Eng. LRCP Lond. 1945; MRCS Eng., LRCP Lond. 1945; FFA RCS Eng. 1963; DA Eng. 1954.

MCDOUGALL, Lynne Dundonald Medical Practice, 9 Main Street, Dundonald, Kilmarnock KA2 9HF Tel: 01563 850496 Fax: 01563 850426 — MB ChB 1986 Ed.

MACDOUGALL, Malcolm William John 18 Ross Road, Newington, Edinburgh EH16 5QN — MB ChB 1996 Ed.

MACDOUGALL, Margaret Jane Consultant Obstetrician & Gynaecologist, Addenbrooke's Hospital, Cambridge CB2 2SW Tel: 01223 245151 Email: jane.macdongall@adenbrookes.nhs.uk, jane.mcdougall@msexc.addenbrookes.anglox.nhs.uk — MB BChir 1982 Camb.; FRCOG 2000; MA 1979 Camb.; MD 1995; MRCOG 1988; MA (Hons.) Camb. 1979, MD 1995; MRCOG 1988; FRCOG 2000. (Univ. Camb. & St. Thos. Hosp.) Cons. O & G Addenbrooke's Hosp. Camb.; Dir. Studies Clin. Med. Newnham Coll. Camb. Univ.; Dir. Postgrad. Edu. Addenbrooke's Hosp.; Coll. Tutor (RCOG); Convenor Train. the Trainers Courses (Rcog); Mem. Specialist Train. Socs: Brit. Fertil. Soc.; Amer. Fertil. Soc.; Eur. Soc. Human Reproduc. & Embryol. Prev: Sen. Regist. (O & G) Univ. Coll., Middlx. & Whittington Hosps. Lond.; Research Regist. (Repoduc. Endocrinol.) Middlx. Hosp. Lond.; Regist. Rotat. (O & G) Brighton Hosps., Soho Hosp. Wom. Middlx.& Univ. Coll. Hosp. Lond.

MACDOUGALL, Marion St Andrew's Glebe Health Centre, St. Andrew's Glebe, Tongue, Lairg IV27 4XB Tel: 01847 611213 Fax: 01847 611382; Ardveg, Bettyhill, Thurso KW14 7SS — MB ChB 1983 Aberd.

MACDOUGALL, Mary Couper (retired) 6 Kelvin Crescent, Bearsden, Glasgow G61 1BT Tel: 0141 942 2850 — MB ChB 1951 Glas.; MB ChB (Commend.) Glas. 1951; BSc (Hons.) Glas. 1947, MD (Hons.) 1959. Prev: Stud. Counsellor Univ. Glas.

MACDOUGALL, Moira Elizabeth Tudor House Surgery, 43 Broad Street, Wokingham RG40 1BE Tel: 0118 978 3544 Fax: 0118 977 0420; Holme House, 12 South Drive, Wokingham RG40 2DH — MB BS 1981 Lond.; DRCOG 1984. (Westm.) GP Partner.

MACDOUGALL, Moragh Hilary 40 Chilton Road, Bath BA1 6DR Tel: 01225 336635 — BM 1990 Soton.; MRCGP 1995. (Univ. Soton.) GP Asst. Melkeham.

MCDOUGALL, Neil (retired) 33 Tofthill Avenue, Bishopbriggs, Glasgow G64 3PB Tel: 0141 772 3131 — MB ChB 1946 Glas. Prev: Ho. Phys. W.. Infirm. Glas.

MACDOUGALL, Peter William (Surgery), Ashfield House, Forest Road, Annesley Woodhouse, Mansfield NG18 9JB Tel: 01623 752295 Fax: 01623 759350 — MB ChB 1976 Liverp.; DRCOG 1980. (Liverpool) GP Princip. Annesley. Socs: Mansfield Med. Soc. Prev: SHO (Med.) Walton Hosp. Liverp.; SHO (Paediat. & O & G) Notts. AHA (T).

MCDOUGALL, Robert Davidson (retired) 70 Newark Street, Greenock PA16 7TF Tel: 01475 787362 — MB ChB Glas. 1955. Prev: Med. Adviser Med. Research Dept. Sandoz Ltd. Basel, Switz.

MACDOUGALL, Mr Robert Hugh Department of Clinical Oncology, Western General Hospital, Edinburgh EH4 2XU Tel: 0131 537 2208 Fax: 0131 537 1029; 23 Belgrave Crescent, Edinburgh EH4 3AL — MB ChB 1972 St. And.; FRCP Ed. 1996; FRCS Ed. 1977; FRCR 1982; DMRT Ed. 1979. (St. And.) Clin. Dir. (Clin. Oncol.) W.. Gen. Hosp. Edin.; Hon. Sen. Lect. (Clin. Oncol.) Univ. Edin.; Hon. Sen. Lect. (Experim. Path.) Univ. St. And. Fife. Socs: Eur. Soc. Therap. Radiol. & Oncol.; BMA. Prev: Cons. Radiother. & Oncol. Ninewells Hosp. & Med. Sch. Dundee; Lect. (Clin. Oncol.) Univ. Edin.

MCDOUGALL, Roy Stewart Flat 3, 11 The Steils, Edinburgh EH10 5XD — MB ChB 1998 Aberd.; MB ChB Aberd 1998.

MCDOUGALL, Sandra Jean Rutherglen Health Centre, 130 Stonelaw Road, Glasgow G73 2PQ — MB ChB 1995 Glas.; DFFP 2000; DRCOG; MRCGP 1999. (Glasgow) p/t GP Princip. Glas. Prev: SHO (A & E) S.ern Gen. NHS Trust Glas.; SHO (O & G) S.ern Gen. NHS Trust Glas.; SHO (Med./Geriat.) S.ern Gen. NHS Trust Glas.

MCDOUGALL, Sheila Hood (retired) 52 Fitz Roy Avenue, Harborne, Birmingham B17 8RJ Tel: 0121 427 1648 — MB ChB 1956 Glas. SCMO N. Birm. HA; Hon. Sen. Clin. Lect. Inst. Child Health Univ. Birm.

MCDOUGALL, Stanley Morton (retired) Meadow Corner, 19 Dukes Meadow, Stapleford, Cambridge CB2 5BH Tel: 01223 842081 — MB ChB Glas. 1960; FRCP Glas. 1993; MRCP (UK) 1990; FFPHM 1989; FFCM 1979, M 1974; DMSA Ed. 1962; PhC Glas. 1952. Cons. Pub. Health Med. E. Anglian RHA. Prev: SCM Cambs. HA.

MACDOUGALL, Valerie Margaret Eaglesham Surgery, 30 Gilmour Street, Eaglesham, Glasgow G76 0AT Tel: 01355 302221 Fax: 01355 302907; 400 Clarkston Road, Muirend, Glasgow G44 3QG Tel: 0141 637 2391 Fax: 0141 637 1967 — MB ChB 1982 Glas.; MRCGP 1986; DRCOG 1988.

MACDOUGALL, Mr William Waddell (retired) 52 Fitz Roy Avenue, Harbourne, Birmingham B17 8RJ Tel: 0121 427 1648 Email: william@wmedougall.freeserve.co.uk — MB ChB Glas. 1956; FRCS Ed. 1964; FRCOG 1975, M 1961. Prev: Cons. O & G Dudley Rd. Hosp. Birm.

MCDOUGLE, Margaret Dean Russell The Old Forge, South Newbald Road, Newbald, York YO43 4SX Tel: 01430 827578 — MB ChB 1939 Ed.; DObst RCOG 1948. (Univ. Ed.)

MCDOWALL, Arthur Wynn Tremenheere (retired) 38 Blacklow Road, Warwick CV34 5SX — MB ChB 1962 Glas.; FRCPsych 1987, M 1972; DPM Eng. 1966. Prev: Sen. Regist. United Birm. Hosps.

MCDOWALL, Duncan John Aberlour Health Centre, Queens Road, Aberlour AB38 9PR Tel: 01340 871210 Fax: 01340 871814; Firhill, Mary Avenue, Aberlour AB38 9PL — MB ChB 1981 Aberd.; MRCGP 1985.

MCDOWALL, Fiona Jane 38 Blacklow Road, Warwick CV34 5SX — MB BS 1994 Lond. SHO (Gen. Adult Psychiat.) Chase Farm Hosp. Enfield.

MCDOWALL, Gwen Katherine Lister House, The Common, Hatfield AL10 0NL Tel: 01707 268822; 10 Lowlands, Hatfield AL9 5DY Tel: 01707 890873 Email: peter@habdon2000.fsnet.co.uk — MB ChB 1989 Glas.; DRCOG 1992. (Glasgow) GP. Prev: Trainee GP/SHO Rotat. Vict. Infirm. Glas. VTS.

MCDOWALL, Jean Lea-Rig, Crede Lane, Bosham, Chichester PO18 8PD Tel: 01243 572482 — MB BS 1955 Lond.; DCH Eng. 1959. (St. Geo.) Prev: Ho. Surg. Vict. Hosp. Childr. Chelsea; Ho. Phys. Whittington Hosp. Lond.

MACDOWALL, Jennifer Elizabeth 42 East Lancashire Road, Worsley, Manchester M28 2TH — MB ChB 1993 Manch.

MCDOWALL, Katherine Mary 11 Elm Bank Drive, Nottingham NG3 5AL — BM BS 1986 Nottm.

MCDOWALL, Morag Shelagh North House Surgery, 28 North Street, Ripon HG4 1HL Tel: 01765 690666 Fax: 01765 690249; Hencliffe Fold, Low Grantley, Ripon HG4 3PH — MB ChB 1986 Leeds; MRCGP 1991; T(GP) 1991. (Leeds) Princip. GP; Med. Off. (Coll. Ripon & York St. John's) Leeds Univ.; Med. Off. (Ripon Cathedral Choir Sch.); Clin. Asst. (Ripon Community Hosp.). Socs: Roy. Coll. Gen. Pract.; BMA.

MCDOWALL, Nicholas Alexander The Health Centre, Rikenel, The Park, Gloucester GL1 1XR Tel: 01452 891110 Fax: 01452 891111; Whitehouse Farm, Hartpury Lane, Highleadon, Newent GL18 1HH Tel: 01452 790742 — MB BCh 1977 Wales; MRCGP 1982.

MACDOWALL, Patrick 24 Hazeldean Crescent, Oban PA34 5JT — MB ChB 1989 Aberd.

MCDOWALL, Mr Robert Andrew Woodman Odstock Regional Plastic Surgery Unit, Salisbury District Hospital, Salisbury SP2 8BJ Tel: 01722 336262 Ext: 2343; The Priory, Rockbourne, Fordingbridge SP6 3NA Tel: 01725 518487 Fax: 01725 518487 — MB BChir 1965 Camb.; MChir Camb. 1976, MA, MB BChir 1965; FRCS Eng. 1968. (Camb. & St. Bart.) Cons. Plastic Surg. Wessex Regional Plastic Surg. Centre Odstock Hosp. Salisbury. Socs: (Ex Treas.) Brit. Assn. Plastic Surgs.; Brit. Soc. Surg. Hand; Brit. Assn. Aesthetic Plastic Surgs. Prev: Sen. Regist. (Plastic Surg.) Qu. Vict.

Hosp. E. Grinstead; Regist. (Gen. Surg.) Roy. Berks. Hosp. Reading; Regist. St. Bart. Hosp.

MACDOWELL, Andrew David 18 Scarborough Close, Anston, Sheffield S25 4DS — MB BChir 1994 Camb.

MCDOWELL, Daniel Kevin 29 Dowhills Road, Blundellsands, Liverpool L23 8SJ — MB BCh BAO 1968 NUI; BSc (Physiol.) NUI 1970, MB BCh BAO 1968; FRCP Lond. 1988; MRCP (U.K.) 1973; MRCPI 1972. Cons. Phys. Walton & Fazakerley Hosps. Liverp.

MCDOWELL, David Blair Courtside Surgery, Kennedy Way, Yate, Bristol BS37 4D2 Tel: 01454 313874 Email: davidmcd@doctors — MB BS 1988 Lond.; BSc Lond. 1985; MRCGP 1995; DFFP 1995; DRCOG 1994. (Univ. Coll. & Middlx. Sch. Med.) Socs: Assoc. Mem. Soc. of Orthopaedic Med.

MCDOWELL, David Paul The Barn House, Oaklands, Church St., Barrowfield, Nelson BB9 6QU — MB ChB 1983 Manch.; FFARCS 1988. Cons. in Pain Managem. & Anaesth. Hope Hosp. Salford.

MCDOWELL, Gillian Anne 28 Princes Road, Newcastle upon Tyne NE3 5AL — MB ChB 1987 Ed.; MRCGP 1994.

MCDOWELL, Heather Prudence Mawhinney Royal Liverpool Children NHS Trust, Alder Hey, Eaton Road, Liverpool L12 2AP Tel: 0151 252 5294 Fax: 0151 252 5676 — MB BS 1977 Lond.; FRCP Lond. 1996; MRCP (UK) 1983; DCH RCP Lond. 1983; PhD Liverp. 1998; FRCPCH 1998. (Charing Cross) Cons. Paediat. Oncol. Alder Hey Hosp. Trust. Socs: Med. Wom. Federat. (Pres. Merseyside Br.); Liverp. Med. Instit.

MCDOWELL, Helen Mary 3 Ashgrove Avenue, Newry BT34 1PR — MB BCh BAO 1976 Belf.; MRCP (UK) 1979. Cons. Phys. w. Responsibil. for Elderly Daisy Hill Hosp. Newry.

MCDOWELL, Ian Frederick William Department Medical Biochemistry, University Hospital of Wales, Cardiff CF4 4XW — BM BCh 1983 Oxf.; MD 1993 Belf.; MRCP 1986 UK; BA 1979; FRCPath 1990. Sen. Lect. & Cons. Univ. Wales Coll. Med. Prev: Sen. Regist. (Chem. Path.) Roy. Vict. Hosp. Belf.

MCDOWELL, Ian Roger 25 Mount Pleasant, Maldon CM9 6EQ — MB BCh BAO 1991 Belf. Trainee GP/SHO Whiteabbey Hosp. Newtownabbey.

MCDOWELL, John Desmond, SBStJ (retired) 12 Marlborough Crescent, Grappenhall, Warrington WA4 2EE Tel: 01925 265671 — MB BCh BAO 1952 Belf.

MCDOWELL, John Forbes Eden Medical Group, Port Road, Carlisle CA2 7AJ Tel: 01228 24477 — MB BCh BAO 1984 Belf.; MRCGP 1991; DFFP 1993; DCH RCP Lond. 1991; DRCOG 1989; DMH Belf. 1989. Prev: Trainee GP Jedburgh.

MCDOWELL, Margaret Jean Julia Cottage, Stalling Down, Cowbridge CF71 7DT Tel: 01446 772866 — MB BCh BAO 1983 Belf.; DRCOG 1985. Clin. Asst. (Infertil.) BUPA Hosp. Cardiff.

MCDOWELL, Marion Jane The Orchard Medical Centre, Fairmead, Cam, Dursley GL11 5NE Tel: 01453 548666 Fax: 01453 548124; Far Green Cottage, Coaley, Dursley GL11 5EL — MB ChB 1986 Bristol; MRCGP 1991; DRCOG 1991.

MCDOWELL, Michael James 14 Racecourse Close, Downpatrick BT30 6US — MB BCh BAO 1991 Belf.; MB BCh Belf. 1991.

MCDOWELL, William Arnold 19 Rushfield Avenue, Belfast BT7 3FP — MB BCh BAO 1982 Belf.; MB BCh Belf. 1982.

MCDOWELL, Zoe Caroline Flat 2/1, 24 Brougham Place, Edinburgh EH3 9JU — MB ChB 1998 Ed.

MACDUFF, Andrew 11/8 Sienna Gardens, Edinburgh EH9 1PQ — MB ChB 1998 Ed.; MB ChB Ed 1998.

***MACE, Alasdair Day** 52 Whielden Street, Old Amersham, Amersham HP7 0HU — MB BS 1995 Lond.

MACE, Alastair Thomas Matthew 51 Polwarth Street (Flat 2/R), Glasgow G12 9TH — MB ChB 1996 Glas. Surg. Ho. Off. Glas. Roy. Infirm.; Med. Ho. Off. Newc. Freeman Hosp. Prev: Glas. Basic Surg. Train. Scheme.

MACE, Christopher John Department Postgraduate Medical Education, Universtiy of Warwick, Coventry CV4 7AL Fax: 01203 524225 Email: psras@csv.warwick.ac.uk — MB BS 1980 Lond.; BSc Lond. 1977, MB BS 1980, MD 1998; MRCPsych 1984. Cons. Psychother. S. Warks. HA; Sen. Lect. (Psychother.) Univ. Wark. Socs: Fell. Roy. Soc. Med.; Brit. Neuropsychiat. Assn.; Comm. Mem. Amer. Psychiatric Assn. Prev: Sen. Regist. St. Geo. Hosp. Lond.; Lect. (Neuropsychiat.) Inst. of Neurol. Lond.; Regist. Maudsley Hosp. Lond.

MACE, Malcolm Whickham Health Centre, Rectory Lane, Whickham, Newcastle upon Tyne NE16 4PD Tel: 0191 488 5555 Fax: 0191 496 0424 — MB ChB Ed. 1966; MRCGP 1977; DCH RCPS Glas. 1969; MA (Med. Ethics) 1996.

MACE, Mr Martin Charles 90 Harley Street, London W1N 1AF Tel: 020 7935 2249 Fax: 020 7224 4158 Email: m.mace@which.net; Crown Farm House, Whielden St, Amersham HP7 0HU Tel: 01494 434421 Fax: 01494 434421 — MB BS 1973 Lond.; MRCS Eng. LRCP Lond. 1973; BDS Lond. 1968; LDS RCS Eng. 1967; FDS RCS Eng. 1975. (Guy's) p/t Cons. Oral & Maxillofacial Surg. Stoke Mandeville Hosp.; Hon. Clin. Tutor United Med. & Dent. Sch. Guy's & St. Thos. Hosp. Socs: Fell. Brit. Assn. Oral & Maxillofacial Surg.; Craniofacial Soc. (Pres. 2000); Chairm. Dentists Provident Soc. Prev: Sen. Regist. (Oral Surg.) Guy's Hosp. Lond. & Qu. Vict. Hosp. E. Grinstead; Regist. (Oral Surg.) E.man Dent. Hosp. & Inst. Dent. Surg. Lond.

MACE, Peter James Edgerton 6 Christ Church Avenue, Tunbridge Wells TN1 1UW Tel: 01892 518859 Email: performance@hotmail.com — MB ChB 1976 Birm.; MRCP (UK) 1979. Prev: Regist. (Diabetic Med.) Kings Coll. Hosp. Lond.; Research Regist. (Cardiol.) E. Birm. Hosp.; GP Hampton in Arden.

MCEACHAN, Jane Elisabeth 3 Lansdowne Crescent, Glasgow G20 0TG — MB ChB 1988 Glas. SHO Rotat. (Surg.) St. Geo. Hosp. Lond.

MACEACHEN, Melanie Leigh 19 Covesea Road, Elgin IV30 4JX — MB ChB 1998 Aberd.; MB ChB Aberd 1998.

MACEACHERN, Mr Alastair Glen Mount Stuart Hospital, St. Vincents Road, Torquay TQ1 4UP Tel: 01803 321614 Fax: 01803 311498 — MB ChB 1971 Sheff.; FRCS Eng. 1976. (Sheff.) Cons. Orthop. Surg. Torbay Hosp. Torquay; Hon. Cons. Orthop. Surg. Roy. Devon. & Exeter Hosp. Exeter; SW Ref. Spec. Adv. In Trauma & Orthop. Socs: Brit. Assn. Knee Surg. Prev: Sen. Regist. (Orthop.) P.ss Eliz. Orthop. Hosp. Exeter; Sen. Regist. (Orthop.) Roy. Cornw. Hosp. Truro; Regist. (Orthop., Neurosurg. & Surg.) Sheff. HA.

MACEACHERN, Deirdre Anne Manor Cottage, Barston Lane, Eastcote, Solihull B92 0HS — MB ChB 1973 Dundee; DCCH 1990. SCMO (Community Paediat.) Solihull Healthcare NHS Trust.

MACEDO, Chrystalla 86 St Johns Road, Isleworth TW7 6PG Tel: 020 8232 8277 — MB BS 1997 Lond.; BSc Bris.1991. (St. George's Hosp. Med. Sch.) SHO (Med.) St. Peter's Hosp. Chertsey.

***MACEDO, Patricia** 26 Northway Road, London SE5 9AN — MB BS 1998 Lond.; MB BS Lond 1998.

MCELDERRY, Elisabeth Mary Litchdon Medical Centre, Landkey Road, Barnstaple EX32 9LL Tel: 01271 23443 Fax: 01271 25979 — MB BCh 1974 Wales. Socs: Medact & BMA.

MCELDERRY, Robert Knox (retired) 10 Sequoia Heights, Old Manse Road, Newtownabbey BT37 0QX Tel: 01232 851281 — MB BCh BAO 1939 Belf.; FRCGP 1978, M 1964. Prev: Flight Lt. RAFVR Med. Br. 1940-6.

MCELDOWNEY, Una Josephine 46 Upper Malone Gardens, Belfast BT9 6LY — MB BCh BAO 1993 Belf.

MCELEARNEY, Noel Leo Gerard The Wellcome Foundation Ltd., Temple Hill, Dartford DA1 5AH; 26 Highlands Park, Seal, Sevenoaks TN15 0AQ — MB BCh BAO 1980 NUI; MSc (Occupat. Med.) Lond. 1988; LRCPI & LM, LRCSI & LM 1980; MFOM RCP Lond. 1990, A 1988; DCH Dub. 1984. Sen. Occupat. Health Phys. Wellcome Foundat. Socs: Fell. Roy. Soc. Med.; (Hon. Treas.) Soc. Occupat. Med. Prev: Med. Off. Brit. Airways; Med. Off. A. Guinness & Co. Dub.; Regist. (Psychiat.) St. Patricks Hosp. Dub.

MCELENY, Kevin Robert 1 Rosecroft Road, Weymouth DT4 9EG — BM 1994 Soton.

MCELENY, Paul Charles Antony Road Surgery, 16 Antony Road, Torpoint PL11 2JW Tel: 01752 813277 Fax: 01752 815733; The Rosery, Wilcove, Torpoint PL11 2PQ — BM 1986 Soton.; MRCGP 1993; DRCOG 1991. Prev: Trainee GP Salisbury VTS; PHO Mackay Hosp. Qu.sland, Austral.

MCELHENNY, Bronagh Elizabeth 40 University Avenue, Belfast BT7 1GY — MB BCh BAO 1989 Belf.

MCELHENNY, Clodagh 7 Seymour Road, Bangor BT19 1BL — MB BCh BAO 1997 Belf.

MCELHERON, Mary Louise 89 Brentwood Way, Newtownards BT23 8RY — MB BCh BAO 1997 Belf.

MCELHINNEY, Andrew Stanley James Carronbank Medical Practice, Denny Health Centre, Carronbank House, Denny FK6 6GD

MCELHINNEY

Tel: 01324 822382 Fax: 01324 826675 — MB BCh BAO 1987 NUI; LRCPSI 1987; MRCGP 1993.

MCELHINNEY, Bernadette Rose 15 Curley Hill Road, Strabane BT82 8LP; Omega, 44 Clonallan Road, Warrenpoint, Newry, County Down BT34 3PH, Republic of Ireland Tel: 01693 773879 Email: joe&bernieathome@bt.com — MB BCh BAO 1991 Belf.

MCELHINNEY, Donald James Burlington Road Surgery, 14 Burlington Road, Ipswich IP1 2EU Tel: 01473 211661 Fax: 01473 289187; 115 Anglesea Road, Ipswich IP1 3PJ Tel: 01473 250949 — MB BChir 1976 Camb.; BA Camb. 1972, MA, MB BChir 1976.

MCELHINNEY, Ian Patrick Martin Coquet Medical Group, Amble Health Centre, Percy Drive, Amble, Morpeth NE65 0HD Tel: 01665 710481 Fax: 01665 713031; 3 Old Barns Morwick Road, Warkworth, Morpeth NE65 0TG Tel: 01665 711628 Fax: 01665 713031 — MB BCh BAO 1974 NUI; MRCGP 1978; DRCOG 1977. (Cork) Clin. Governance Lead N. N.d. PCG. Socs: Newc. & N.ern Cons. Med. Soc.; N. N.umberland Div. BMA. Prev: Trainee GP Newc.VTS; Hon. Off. Mercy Hosp. Cork.

MCELHINNEY, Jacqueline Mary University of London, Central Institution Health Service, 20 Gower St., London WC1E 6DP — MB BCh BAO 1985 NUI.

MCELHINNEY, John Hartley North Glen Medical Practice, 1 Huntsmans Court, Glenrothes KY7 6SX Tel: 01592 620062 Fax: 01592 620465; 27 Mactaggart Way, Glenrothes KY7 6FA — MB BCh BAO 1979 Belf.

MCELHOLM, Adrian Raymond 4 Ardmore Avenue, Omagh BT78 5AS — MB BCh BAO 1997 Belf.

MCELHONE, James Peter Stephen Dr McElhone and Partners, Townhead Surgery, 6-8 High St., Irvine KA12 0AY Tel: 01294 273131 Fax: 01294 312832 — MB ChB 1972 Glas.

MCELHONE, John Joseph The Lodge, Holmwood, Netherlee Road, Glasgow G44 3YG Tel: 0141 637 4590 — MB ChB 1945 Glas. (Univ. Glas.)

MCELLIGOTT, Andrew John 64 Briar Road, London SW16 4LX — MB ChB 1992 Leeds.

MCELLIGOTT, Geraldine Maire Frances Whipps Cross Hospital, London E11 — MB BS 1974 Lond.; MRCP (UK) 1982; MRCS Eng. LRCP Lond. 1974. (Char. Cross) Cons. Phys. Dept. Med. for Elderly Whipps Cross Hosp. Lond. Prev: Sen. Regist. Middlx. Hosp.

MCELLIGOTT, Humphrey Francis (retired) The Grange, 48A Gally Hill Road, Fleet GU52 6QE — MB BCh BAO Dub. 1946; FFCM 1977, M 1972; DPH Lond. 1958; DIH Eng. 1958; DTM & H Eng. 1957. Prev: CMO EMR DMSD MoD.

MCELNAY, Rosemary Elizabeth Armagh Health Centre, Dobbin Lane, Armagh BT61 7QG Tel: 028 3752 3165 Fax: 028 3752 2319 — MB BCh BAO 1981 Belf.; MRCGP 1985; DFFP 1993; DCH Dub. 1984; DRCOG 1983. (Qu. Univ.) GP Armagh Health Centre. Socs: BMA; Ulster Med. Soc. Prev: Clin. Med. Off. Armagh Health Centre.

MCELROY, Bernard John 22 Ravenswood Avenue, Rock Ferry, Birkenhead CH42 4NX — MB ChB 1984 Liverp.

MCELROY, Catherine Elizabeth Mary 34 Pinewood Close, Leicester LE4 1ER — MB ChB 1996 Leic.

MCELROY, Colette Alicia Judge, McElroy and Thompson, 15 Sefton Road, Litherland, Liverpool L21 9AH Tel: 0151 928 4820 — MB ChB 1985 Liverp.; DRCOG 1988.

MCELROY, Helen 63 Merchants Quay, Salford M5 2XF — MB ChB 1993 Manch. SHO (Paediat.) Birm. Heartlands Hosp.

MCELROY, John Henry The Cottage, Park View, Hetton-le-Hole, Houghton-le-Spring DH5 9JH — MB BCh BAO 1970 NUI.

MCELROY, Katherine 32 Ashiestiel Court, Cumbernauld, Glasgow G67 4AU — MB ChB 1998 Glas.; MB ChB Glas 1998.

MCELROY, Mary Margaret Patricia The Cottage, Park View, Hetton-le-Hole, Houghton-le-Spring DH5 9JH — MB BCh BAO 1969 NUI; FRCR 1976. Cons. Radiol. Bishop Auckland Gen. Hosp. & Darlington Memor. Hosp. Prev: SHO (Med.) & Regist. (Med.) St. Finbarr's Hosp. Cork; Sen. Regist. Radiol. Roy. Vict. Infirm. Newc.

MCELROY, Ruth Grace Rushfield, Bridgetown, Castlederg BT81 7PX — MB BCh BAO 1984 Belf.; MB BCh Belf. l984; MRCGP 1989; DCH RCPSI 1988; DRCOG 1987. Socs: BMA.

MCELVANNEY, Andrena Marie 47 Whittingehame Drive, Glasgow G12 0YH — MB ChB 1987 Glas.; FRCS Ed. 1992; FCOphth 1992. Socs: MLLOSA (Counc. Mem.); BLLA (Counc. Mem.); UKISCRS. Prev: Moorfields Eye Hosp. Lond.; Formerly Sen. Regist.; St. Geo.s Hosp. Lond.

MCELWAINE, Alison Valerie 76 Marlborough Park S., Belfast BT9 6HW Tel: 01232 667015 — MB BCh BAO 1973 Belf.; Cert JCC Lond. 1980. Med. Off. (Dermat.) Ulster Hosp. Dundonald; Clin. Asst. (Dermat.) Belf. City Hosp. Prev: SHO (Dermat.) Roy. Vict. Hosp. Belf.

MCELWAINE, John Gerard 27 Grindley Hill Court, City General Hospital, Newcastle Road, Sheffield ST4 6QG — MB ChB 1997 Sheff.

MCELWEE, Celia Sarah Elizabeth 12 Malone View Road, Belfast BT9 5PH — MB BCh BAO 1993 Belf.; BSc Belf. 1992. SHO (Gen. Psychiat.) Lond.

MCENEANEY, David John 74 Marlborough Park South, Belfast BT9 6HW — MB BCh BAO 1987 Belf.; BSc (Med. Microbiol.) Belf. 1985; MD Belf. 1995; MRCP (UK) 1990. Cons. Cardiol. Craigavon Area Hosp. Co. Armagh N. Irel. Prev: Sen. Regist. (Cardiol.) Roy. Vict. Hosp. Belf.

MCENERY, Gerald (retired) 50 Northchurch Road, London N1 4EJ Tel: 020 7254 8652 Fax: 020 7923 2945 Email: chessells.mcenery@virgin.net — MB BS Lond. 1962; FRCP Lond. 1985, M 1967; MRCS Eng. LRCP Lond. 1962; FRCPCH 1997, M 1996; DCH Eng. 1965. Prev: Cons. Community Paediat. Forest Health Care Trust.

MCENERY, Rachel Sarah Karen 16 Kingsway Drive, Harrogate HG1 5NJ Tel: 01423 569108 — MB ChB 1998 Birm.; MBChB Birm. 1998. (Birm.)

***MCENROE, Geraldine** 365 Reddish Road, Stockport SK5 7EW — MB ChB 1994 Bristol.

MCENTEE, Siobhan Helena Hillhead Family Practice, 33 Stewartstown Road, Belfast BT11 9FZ Tel: 028 9028 6800 Fax: 028 9060 2944 — MB BCh BAO 1988 Belf.

MCENTEGART, Anne 1 Kylepark Avenue, Uddingston, Glasgow G71 7DF Tel: 0141 813691 — MB ChB 1990 Glas. Regist. (Rheum.) Glas. Roy. Infirm.

MCENTEGART, Margaret Bridget 1 Threshold Park, East Kilbride, Glasgow G74 4HP — MB ChB 1997 Glas.

MCERLAIN, Michael Joseph 10 Belfield Road, Bournemouth BH6 4JB — MB ChB 1993 Aberd.; BSc (Med. Sci.) Aberd. 1992. SHO (Plastic Surg.) Roy. Hosp. Haslar Gosport. Socs: BMA; MPS. Prev: SHO (Orthop.) Duchess of Kents Hosp. Catterick N. Yorks.

MCERLANE, Flora Eileen 33 Bideford Gardens, Gateshead NE9 6XE — MB ChB 1998 Liverp.; MB ChB Liverp 1998.

MCERLANE, James Richard Christopher Maloney 14 Gransha Avenue, Glen Road, Belfast BT11 8AJ — MB BCh BAO 1966 Belf.

MCERLEAN, Peter Maple Lodge, Southwick Road, Denmead, Waterlooville PO7 6LA Tel: 01705 255947 — MB BS 1959 Lond.; MRCS Eng. LRCP Lond. 1959. (Univ. Coll. Hosp.) Med. Off. HM Prison Portsmouth. Socs: BMA. Prev: Regist. (ENT) Portsmouth Hosp. Gp.; SHO (ENT) Kingston Hosp.; Ho. Surg. Centr. Middlx. Hosp. Pk. Roy. & Birm. Accid. Hosp.

MACEROLA, Giuseppe Eaton Wood Medical Centre, 1128 Tyburn Road, Erdington, Birmingham B24 0SY Tel: 0121 373 0959 Fax: 0121 350 2719; 2 The Green, Wylde Green Road, Sutton Coldfield B72 1NB — MB BS 1981 Lond.; MRCP (UK) 1985. GP Birm.

MCEVEDY, Mr Brian Victor (retired) Crabtree Corner, Little Compton, Moreton-in-Marsh GL56 0RS Tel: 01608 674411 — BM BCh 1947 Oxf.; MA Oxf. 1947, MCh 1956; FRCS Eng. 1952. Mem. Ct. of Examrs. RCS Eng. Prev: Cons. Surg. Roy. Vict. Infirm. Newc.

MCEVEDY, Christopher John Beresford Paterson Centre, St. Mary's Hospital, 20 South Wharf Road, London W2 1PD — MB BS 1988 Lond.; MRCPsych 1992. Cons. Psychiat. St. Mary's Hosp. Lond. Prev: Lect. (Psychiat.) Char. Cross Hosp. Lond.

MCEVEDY, Colin Peter 7 Caithness Road, London W14 0JB Tel: 020 7603 8797 — BM BCh 1955 Oxf.; DM Oxf. 1970, BM BCh 1955; FRCPsych. 1981, M 1972; Acad. DPM Univ. Lond. 1963. Cons. Psychiat. St. Bernard's Hosp., & Ealing & S.all-Norwood Hosps. Prev: Sen. Regist. Psychiat. Dept. Middlx. Hosp. Lond.; Regist. Maudsley Hosp. Lond.

MCEVEDY, Mark Beresford 2 Clarence Road, Tunbridge Wells TN1 1HE Tel: 01892 26777 — BM BCh 1946 Oxf.; MA, BM BCh Oxon. 1946; FFR 1958; DMRT Eng. 1953; DObst RCOG 1950. (Oxf.) Cons. Radiotherap. Pembury Hosp. Prev: Ho. Surg. & Obst. Ho. Surg. Radcliffe Infirm. Oxf.

MCEVEDY, Peter Anthony Station Medical Group, Gatacre Street, Blyth NE24 1HD Tel: 01670 396540 Fax: 01670 396517; Westlands, Front St, Earsdon, Whitley Bay NE25 9JX Tel: 0191 251 5529 — MB BS 1984 Newc. GP Blyth, N.d.; Mem. N.d. LMC. Prev: Ho. Off. Freeman Roy. Hosp. Newc.; Ho. Surg. Roy. Vict. Infirm. Newc.

MCEVETT, Caroline Alice Clonallon, 12 Mill St., Steventon, Abingdon OX13 6SP — MB BCh BAO 1940 Dub.

MCEVETT, Frederick Charles 6 Cedar Drive, Loddon, Norwich NR14 6LE — MB BCh BAO 1962 Dub.; MRCPsych 1972; DPM Eng. 1971. (TC Dub.) Cons. Psychiat. St. Nicholas Hosp. Gt. Yarmouth. Prev: Sen. Regist. (Psychiat.) Warley Hosp. Brentwood; Regist. (Psychiat.) Qu. Eliz. II Hosp. Welwyn Gdn. City; Asst. Med. Off. St. Patrick's Hosp. Dub.

MCEVOY, Mr Andrew William 120 Deyes Lane, Maghull, Liverpool L31 6DW — MB BS 1990 Lond.; BSc (Hons.) Lond. 1987; FRCS Eng. 1994.

MCEVOY, Ann Winifred 116 Fagley Road, Bradford BD2 3JJ — MB BCh 1976 Wales; MRCP (UK) 1979.

MCEVOY, Mr Anthony Hope Hospital, Eccles Old Road, Salford M8 6HD Tel: 0161 789 7373; 7 Glastonbury Drive, Middlewich CW10 9HR Tel: 01606 835064 — MB ChB 1988 Manch.; BSc (Hons.) St. And. 1985; FRCS Glas. 1993. Wishbone Research Fell. (Orthop. Surg.) Hope Hosp. Salford. Prev: SHO (Orthop.) Blackburn Roy. Infirm. & Trafford Gen. Hosp.

MCEVOY, Charles William Rickard Greystones, Sharow Lane, Sharow, Ripon HG4 5BG Email: charles@oath.com — BChir 1996 Camb.; MB Camb. 1997.

MCEVOY, Daniel Martin (retired) 57 Hampton Lane, Solihull B91 2QD — MB BCh BAO 1952 NUI; LAH Dub. 1952.

MCEVOY, Helen Mary The Health Centre, Madeira Road, West Byfleet KT14 6DH Tel: 01932 336933 Fax: 01932 355681; Orleton, Aviary Road, Pyrford, Woking GU22 8TH — MB BS 1984 Lond. (St. Geo.) Clin. Asst. Ashford Hosp. Middlx. Prev: Clin. Asst. (Rheumat.) Ashford Hosp. Middlx.; SHO (Med.) E. Surrey Hosp. Redhill; SHO Dorking Gen. Hosp.

MCEVOY, Jane Frances 116 Fagley Road, Bradford BD2 3JJ — MB BCh 1980 Wales.

MCEVOY, Joseph Damian 686 Saintfield Road, Carryduff, Belfast BT8 8BU Tel: 01232 813124; 32 Clooney Terrace, Waterside, Londonderry BT47 6AR Tel: 01504 47844 — MB BCh BAO 1987 Belf.; MRCGP 1992; DRCOG 1993; DGM RCP Lond. 1989.

MCEVOY, Louise Helen Cons. Physician, Bassetlaw DGH, Kilton Hill, Worksop S81 0BD Tel: 01224 638502, 01909 500990 Fax: 01909 502798 Email: louisemcevoy@yahoo.co.uk — MB ChB 1993 Aberd. p/t Specialist Regist. (Anaesth.) Aberd.

MCEVOY, Maire Deirdre 14 Glenmachan Drive, Belfast BT4 2RE — MB BCh BAO 1976 Belf.; MRCGP 1980.

MCEVOY, Michael Paul Celestine 61 Victoria Road, Armagh BT61 9DY — MB BCh BAO 1967 NUI.

MCEVOY, Michael William Harrogate District Hospital, Lancaster Park Road, Harrogate HG2 7SX Tel: 01423 885959; 69B Shoorers Hill Road, Blackheath, London SE3 7HU Tel: 01423 781618, 020 8853 4847 Email: slphillips@btinternet.com — MB ChB 1966 Birm.; FRCPath (Haemat.) 1986, M 1974. (Birm.) Cons. Haemat. Harrogate Hosp. Prev: Sen. Regist. (Haemat.) Coventry Gp. Hosps., Nat. Blood Transfus.; Serv. Birm. & Birm. Childrs. Hosp.

MCEVOY, Patrick Joseph Aberfoyle Terrace Surgery, 3-5 Aberfoyle Terrace, Strand Road, Londonderry BT48 7NP Tel: 028 7126 4868; 14 Shandon Park, Londonderry BT48 8AW Tel: 01504 268774 Fax: 01504 260919 Email: pmcevoy14@tianet.com — MB BCh BAO 1971 Belf.; FRCGP 1993, M 1976; DObst RCOG 1976. (Qu. Univ. Belf.) GP Aberfoyle Med. Pract. Derry.; Course Organiser N.. Irel. VTS Altnagelvin Hosp. Lond.derry. Socs: BMA; Assn. Course Organisers (Mem. Exec. Counc.). Prev: SHO Roy. Matern. Hosp. Belf.; SHO Belf. City Hosp.; Med. Off. Friends Hosp. Kaimosi, Kenya.

MCEVOY, Patrick Mark Newry Health Village, Newry BT35 6BW Tel: 02830 265853; 68 Clonallon Road, Warrenpoint, Newry BT34 3PH Tel: 02841 772953 — MB BCh BAO 1980 NUI; MRCGP 1984; DRCOG 1982.

MCEVOY, Penelope Ann Elizabeth Greystones, Sharow Lane, Sharow, Ripon HG4 5BG Email: penny@oath.com — BChir 1996 Camb.; MB Camb. 1997.

MCEVOY, Rachel Clare 14 Haroldstone Close, Haverfordwest SA61 1LP — MB BCh 1993 Wales.

MCEVOY, Susan Clair First Floor Flat, 175 Redland Road, Bristol BS6 6YQ — MB ChB 1990 Bristol.

MCEWAN, Alan, OBE, OStJ London Hospital Medical College Staff Clinics, Turner Street, London E1 2AD; 8 Wellington Road, Hampton Hill, Hampton TW12 1JR Tel: 020 8977 6170 — LRCP LRCS Ed. LRFPS Glas. 1956; FRCGP 1980, M 1974; MFCM 1974; DTM & H Eng. 1963. GP Harley St. Lond.; Gp. Med. Adviser Financial Times; Med. Adviser Channel 4 TV, Booker plc, Total Oil Marine, Goldman Ltd., Chas. Barker Gp., John Swire & Sons & Nat. Theatre; Hon. Med. Adviser to SSAFA Counc. Socs: Fell. Med. Soc. Lond.; Fell. Roy. Soc. Med.; Brit. Acupunc. Soc. Prev: Surg. Capt. RN, Adviser (Gen. Pract.) Mem. Med. Counc. Hong Kong; Mem. GP Advis. Counc. & Postgrad. Counc. for Med. Educat. Eng. & Wales; Resid. Med. Off. HM Tower of Lond.

MCEWAN, Mr Alec Stephen Holly Cottage, The Mews, Market Place, Deddington, Banbury OX15 0SB Email: alecmcewan@barclays.net — BM BCh 1993 Oxf.; MRCOG 1998 (Nov.). (Oxf.) Specialist Regist. (Obstet. & Gyn.) Oxf. Deanery.

MCEWAN, Alistair Stewart Flat 8 Lamerton Lodge, 228 Kew Road, Richmond TW9 3JX — MB BCh BAO 1985 Dub.; MRCGP 1990.

MCEWAN, Amanda Jennifer Dr Forbes and Partners, East Calder Medical Practice, 147 Main Street, East Calder, Livingston EH53 0EW Tel: 01506 882882 Fax: 01506 883630; 7 Abinger Gardens, Edinburgh EH12 6DE — MB ChB 1988 Glas.; MRCGP 1992; DRCOG 1991.

MCEWAN, Mr Andrew James 36 Aytoun Road, Glasgow G41 5HN Tel: 0141 423 2504 — MB ChB 1961 Glas.; FRCS Glas. 1967; FRCS Eng. 1967. Cons. Surg. Roy. Alexandra Hosp. Paisley; Hon. Clin. Sen. Lect. Univ. Glas.; Examr. RCPS Glas. Prev: Clin. Dir. (Surg.) Roy. Alexandra Hosp. Paisley; Sen. Regist. (Surg.) W.. Infirm. Glas.; Research Fell. Univ. Dept. Surg. Glas.

MCEWAN, Anthea 30 Manor Way, South Croydon CR2 7BS Tel: 020 8688 8916 — MB BS 1958 Lond. (Lond. Hosp.) Med. Off. Stud. Health Lond. Hosp. Med. Coll.

MCEWAN, Mr Arthur Bruce Coilla-Na-Lochan, 152 Whalley Road, Blackburn BB1 9LJ — MB ChB 1961 Glas.; FRCS Ed. 1968. (Glas.) SHO Glas. Roy. Infirm. Prev: Sen. Ho. Off. Orthop. Killearn Hosp. Glas.

MCEWAN, Christina, MBE (retired) 46 Turretbank Drive, The Oaks, Crieff PH7 4LW — MB ChB 1951 Glas.; MD Glas. 1965, MB ChB 1951, DPH (Mackinlay Prize); FFCM 1981, M 1974. Prev: Sen. Med. Off. (Pub. Health Med.) Forth Valley HB.

MCEWAN, George Alexander (retired) 4 Wellbrae Drive, Strathaven ML10 6JR Tel: 01357 521359 — MB ChB 1958 Ed. Prev: Assoc. Specialist (Surg.) StoneHo. Hosp.

MCEWAN, George Murdoch (retired) — MB ChB Glas. 1944. Prev: Coroner to the Roy. Ho.hold.

MCEWAN, Gordon Dickson c/o Lloyds Bank, Cranbrook Branch, Woodside, High St., Cranbrook TN17 3DJ — MB ChB 1971 Glas.; MRCGP 1977; DObst RCOG 1975. (Glasgow) Prev: Maj. RAMC; SHO Seafield Childr. Hosp. Ayr; Ho. Off. (Med.) Raigmore Hosp. Inverness.

MCEWAN, Gregor James 30 Manor Way, South Croydon CR2 7BS — MB BS 1986 Lond.

MCEWAN, Helen Purdie 47 Westland Drive, Glasgow G14 9PE Tel: 0141 959 2018 — MD 1970 Glas.; MB ChB 1959; FRCS Glas. 1980; FRCOG 1976, M 1963, DObst 1961; FRCP Ed. 1995. Cons. O & G Gt.er Glas. HB; Cons. Obst. Roy. Matern. Hosp. & Roy. Infirm. Glas.; Hon. Clin. Sen. Lect. Univ. Glas.; Hon. Cons. Strathclyde Univ. Socs: Roy. Med. Chir. Soc. Glas. (Ex-Pres.); (Ex-Pres.) Glas. Obst. Soc. Prev: Research Schol. Gyn. & Ho. Surg. W. Infirm. Glas.; Sen. Regist. (Obst & Gyn.) Glas. Teach. Hosps.

MACEWAN, Hugh Douglas 8 Paget Road, Ipswich IP1 3RP — MB ChB 1955 Glas.; DObst. RCOG 1957. Prev: Ho. Phys. & Ho. Surg. Glas. Roy. Infirm.; Obst. Ho. Surg. Ipswich & E. Suff. Hosp.

MCEWAN, Iain Michael, Surg. Cdr. RN Retd. Birken Hillock, Shore Road, Cove, Helensburgh G84 0NU Tel: 01436 842101 — MB ChB 1972 Glas.; MSc (Occupat. Med.) Lond. 1976; MFOM RCP Lond. 1981; DIH Eng. 1976. (Glas.) Socs: Fac. Occupat. Med.; Soc. Occupat. Med. Prev: PMO HM Naval Base Rosyth; Staff Med. Off.

MCEWAN

Submarine Sea Train.; SHO 3rd & 10th Submarine Squadrons & Med. Off. HMS Resolution (Portsmouth).

MCEWAN, Ian Paul (retired) 132 Newmarket Road, Norwich NR4 6SB Tel: 01603 502610 — MB ChB Manch. 1958; FFA RCS Eng. 1964. Prev: Cons. Anaesth. Norf. and Norwich Hosp.

MCEWAN, James, Col. late RAMC Retd. 21 Highbanks Close, Welling DA16 3ES Tel: 020 8855 2176 — MB ChB Glas. 1950; FFA RCS Eng. 1974. Prev: Anaesth. Qu. Eliz. Milit. Hosp. Lond.

MCEWAN, Jean Rigley Cardiovascular Directorate, The Middlesex Hospital, Mortimer Street, London W1N 8AA Tel: 020 7380 9656 Email: j.mcewan@ucl.ac.uk; Cannonbury, Potash Road, Billericay CM11 1HH Tel: 01277 650699 — MB ChB 1980 Glas.; PhD (Pharm.) Lond. 1989; BSc (Hons.) Glas. 1978; FRCP Lond. 1996; FRCP Ed. 1994; MRCP (UK) 1983. Reader & Cons. Cardiol. Univ. Coll. Lond. Med. Sch. & Univ. Coll. Lond. Hosps. Socs: Brit. Cardiac Soc. Prev: MRC Jun. Train. Fell. Hammersmith Hosp. Lond.

MCEWAN, John Alexander (retired) South East London Family Planning Training Unit, Optimum St Giles, St Giles Road, London SE5 7RN Tel: 020 7635 1112 Fax: 020 7582 2916 Email: john.mcewan@btinternet.com — MB BChir Camb. 1953; FFFP 1996, M 1993; FRCOG ad eundem 1995; FRCGP 1977, M 1966. Hon. Cons. Optimum NHS Trust; Trustee Simon Populat. Trust; Mem. Populat. Investig. Comm. (Represen. Fac. FPRHC); Mem. Edit. Advis. Bd. Jl. Family Plann. & Repro. Hlth. Care. Prev: Hon. Dir. SE Lond. Family Plann. Train. Unit.

MCEWAN, John Aloysius Michael c/o ENT Medical Secretaries, Charing Cross Hospital, Fulham Palace Road, London W6 8RF — MB BS 1988 New South Wales.

MCEWAN, Karen Lindsay Chadderton (Town) Health Centre, Middleton Road, Chadderton, Oldham OL9 0LH Tel: 0161 628 4543 Fax: 0161 284 1658; 19 Overbrook Drive, Prestwich, Bury, Manchester M25 0AB Tel: 0161 798 7374 — MB ChB 1993 Manch.; DFFP 1995; DRCOG 1995; MRCGP 1997. (Manch. Univ.) Socs: Roy. Coll. Gen. Pract.

MCEWAN, Laura Miranda Health Centre, Llanfairpwllgwyngyll LL61 5YZ Tel: 01248 714388 Fax: 01248 715826; Merlyns, Llanfaes, Beaumaris LL58 8RF — MB BS 1978 Lond.; DRCOG 1983.

MCEWAN, Margaret Anderson Wormiston Farm, Eddleston, Peebles EH45 8PP — MB ChB 1966 Ed.

MCEWAN, Peter Neil 33 Clifford Road, North Berwick EH39 4PP — MB ChB 1993 Aberd. (Aberd.) Locum Appointment in Train. (Paediat.) Roy. Vict. Infirm. Newc. Socs: MRCPCH. Prev: SHO (Paediat.) Airedale Gen. Hosp.f; SHO (Paediat.) Leeds Gen. Infirm. & Singleton Hosp. Swansea; Ho. Off. Aberd. Roy. Infirm.

MCEWAN, Sarah Campbell (retired) c/o Bank of Scotland, 1 High St., Renfrew PA4 8QJ — MB ChB 1946 Glas.; MFCM 1974; DPH Glas. 1961; DObst RCOG 1952. Prev: Dep. MOH Dunfermline.

MCEWAN, Thomas Edward (retired) 30 Manor Way, South Croydon CR2 7BS Tel: 020 8688 8916 — MB BS Lond. 1957; FRCA 1969; DA Eng. 1965. Prev: Cons. Anaesth. E.man Dent. Hosp. Lond.

MACEWAN, Thomas Hood Dept. of Psychiatry, Gartnavel Royal Hospital, Great Western Road, Glasgow G12 0XH — MB ChB 1991 Ed.; MRC Psych 1995. Specialist Regist. W. of Scotl. Psychiat.

MCEWEN, Abayomi Mojisola River Surgery, 16 Rous Road, Buckhurst Hill IG9 6BN Tel: 020 8504 7364 Fax: 020 8559 0269; Ayodele, 17 Roding Lane, Buckhurst Hill IG9 6BJ Email: abayomi.mcewen@virgin.net — MB BS 1977 Lond.; MRCS Eng. LRCP Lond. 1976. (Roy. Free) Tutor (Gen. Pract.) W. Essex. Prev: Mem. Med. Pract. Comm.

MCEWEN, Ailsa Jean 18 Well Brae, Pitlochry PH16 5HH — MB ChB 1985 Manch.; BSc (Med. Sci.) St. And. 1982; DRCOG 1989.

MACEWEN, Alexander Campbell (retired) 2 Transy Place, Dunfermline KY12 7QN Tel: 01383 724473 — MB ChB Ed. 1932; MRCGP 1953.

MCEWEN, Andrew Wiliam Priors Cottage, Main Road, Brightstone, Newport PO30 4AH Tel: 01983 742410 — BM 1983 Soton.; FCAnaesth. 1990. Cons. Anaesth. St. Mary's Hosp., Isle of Wight. Socs: Fell. Roy. Coll. Anaesth.; Assn. Anaesth.; Intens. Care Soc. Prev: Cons. Anaesth. Morecambe Bay Healthcare Trust; Sen. Regist. & Regist. (Anaesth.) Sheff. Hosps.; Regist. (Anaesth.) Green La. Hosp. Auckland, NZ.

MACEWEN, Caroline Jan Ninewells Hospital, Perth Road, Dundee DD1 9SY — MB ChB 1981 Dundee; MD Dundee 1994; FRCS Ed. 1986; FRCOphth 1988; MD 1994 Dundee. Cons. Ophth. Ninewells Hosp. & Med. Sch. Dundee; Hon. Sen. Lect. Univ. Dundee.

MCEWEN, Ewen Alasdair Moray Young People's Centre, 10 College Gardens, Belfast BT9 6BQ Tel: 01232 661825 Fax: 01232 666792; Morenish, 10 Magheralanve Court, Lisburn BT28 3BY — MB BCh BAO 1975 Belf.; MRCPsych 1981. Cons. (Adolesc. Psychiat.) E. Health & Social Servs. Bd.

MACEWEN, Gordon Lawrence The Surgery, High Street, Moffat DG10 9HL Tel: 01683 220062 Fax: 01683 220453 — MB ChB 1975 Dundee; MB ChB (Commend.) Dundee 1975; DRCOG 1977; MRCGP 1979.

MCEWEN, Helen Catherine Weir View, Wargrave Road, Henley-on-Thames RG9 3HX Tel: 01491 576314; Weir View, Wargrave Road, Henley-on-Thames RG9 3HX Tel: 01491 576314, 02476 715716 Fax: 01491 573683 — MB BS 1959 Lond.; MRCGP 1975. (Univ. Coll. Hosp.) Private Practitioner in Allergy Henley-on-Thames. Socs: Brit. Soc. Allergy & Clin. Immunol.; Brit. Soc. Allergy & Environm. Med. Prev: Clin. Asst. (Allergy) Roy. Berks. Hosp. Reading; Princip. GP. Sonning Common Health Centre.

MCEWEN, Professor James Department of Public Health, University of Glasgow, 2 Lilybank Gardens, Glasgow G12 8RZ Tel: 0141 330 5013 Fax: 0141 330 5018; 25A Mansionhouse Road, Langside, Glasgow G41 3DN Tel: 0141 649 1537 Fax: 0141 649 1537 — MB ChB St. And. 1963; FRCP Glas. 1991; FFPHMI (Hon.) 1997; FFCM 1982, M 1974; FFOM RCP Lond. 1990, MFOM 1978; DIH Soc. Apoth. Lond. 1968. (St. And.) Henry Mechan Prof. of Pub. Health Univ Glas.; Pres. Fac. Pub. Health Med. Prev: Prof. & Head Dept. Community Med. King's Coll. Sch. Med. & Dent. Lond.; Chief Med. Off. Health Educ. Counc.; Sen. Lect. (Community Health) Univ. Nottm.

MCEWEN, Jean MacKinlay (retired) 7 Roman Road, Kirkintilloch, Glasgow G66 1EE Tel: 0141 578 3468 Email: j.me5580906@aol.com — MB ChB Glas. 1951; MRCGP 1965; DPH Glas. 1961. Prev: SCMO N.allerton HA.

MCEWEN, John DDS Medicines Research Ltd., Ninewells Hospital & Medical School, Dundee DD1 9SY Tel: 01382 646317 Fax: 01382 645606; 1 Osborne Place, Dundee DD2 1BE — MB ChB 1966 St. And.; PhD Dundee 1977; FRCP Ed. 1988; MRCP (UK) 1970; FFPM RCP (UK) 1989. (St. And.) Med. Dir. Drug Developm. (Scotl.) Ltd. Ninewells Hosp. Dundee; Hon. Cons. Clin. Pharmacol. Tayside HB; Hon. Prof. Clin. Pharmacol. Univ. Dundee. Socs: Med. Res. Soc. & Brit. Pharmacol. Soc. Prev: Head Clin. Pharmacol. Hoechst UK Milton Keynes; Hon. Lect. Clin. Pharmacol. St. Bart. Hosp. Lond.; Research Fell. Vanderbilt Univ. Nashville, USA.

MCEWEN, Jonathan Roy 1 Osborne Place, Dundee DD2 1BE — MB ChB 1993 Ed.; DCH RCPS Glas. 1996.

MCEWEN, Judith Phillippa Jane 31 North Street, Stirling FK9 5NB — MB ChB 1993 Ed.

MCEWEN, Leonard Maitland Weir View, Wargrave Road, Henley-on-Thames RG9 3HX — BM BCh 1959 Oxf. (Univ. Coll. Hosp.) Socs: Brit. Soc. Allergy & Clin. Immunol.; Brit. Soc. Allergy & Environm. Med. Prev: Sen. Lect. (Applied Pharmacol.) St. Mary's Hosp. Med. Sch. Lond.

MCEWEN, Leonie Maureen Rosewood, Broadway, Edington, Bridgwater TA7 9JP Tel: 01278 722716 — MB BS 1960 Lond.; MRCS Eng. LRCP Lond. 1960. (Roy. Free) Prev: Clin. Med. Off. S.end H.A.; Ho. Surg. Roy. Hants. Co. Hosp., Winchester; Med. Off. Wantage, Basingstoke & S.end Family Plann. Clinics.

MCEWEN, Michael John (retired) 30 The Close, Norwich NR1 4DZ Tel: 01603 624386 Fax: 01603 624386 Email: mmcewen@which.net — MB 1969 Camb.; BChir 1968; DObst RCOG 1970. Prev: GP Norwich.

MCEWEN, Murray The Health Centre, George St., Uxbridge UB8 1UB Tel: 01895 231925; 7 Pinewood Close, Iver Heath, Iver SL0 0QT Tel: 01753 654295 — MB BS Lond. 1969; MRCS Eng. LRCP Lond. 1969; DA (UK) 1972. (St. Mary's) Prev: Ho. Surg. St. Mary's Hosp. Harrow Rd.; Ho. Phys. Hillingdon Hosp. Uxbridge; SHO (Cas. Dept.) Hillingdon Hosp. Uxbridge.

MCEWEN, Thomas Hamilton Chawton House Surgery, St. Thomas Street, Lymington SO41 9ND Tel: 01590 672953 Fax: 01590 674137 — MRCS Eng. LRCP Lond. 1974; BSc (Hons.) Lond. 1972, MB BS 1975; DRCOG 1978.

MCEWING, David James Budshead Health Centre, 433 Budshead Road, Whitleigh, Plymouth PL5 4DU Tel: 01752 773492 Fax: 01752 775657; Gas House, Modbury, Ivybridge PL21 0SP Tel: 01752 790682 — MB ChB 1976 Ed.; DA Eng. 1980. GP Plymouth.

MCFADDEN, John Alexander Vaughan Bunfield Medical Practice, Harris Road, Inverness IV2 3 Tel: 01463 220077 — MB ChB 1988 Ed.; Dip. Obst. Otago 1991; MRCGP 1996; Dip. Sports Med. Scot. 1998. (Edinburgh)

MCFADDEN, Patricia Mary (retired) Waite, McFadden and Brown, 35 George Street, Dumfries DG1 1EA Tel: 01387 53724 Fax: 01387 259780 — MB ChB 1963 Aberd.

MCFADYEAN, Kenneth Michael (retired) 7 Barrack Square, Winchelsea TN36 4EG Tel: 01797 226422 — MRCS Eng. LRCP Lond. 1950; MA, MB BChir Camb. 1950; DObst RCOG 1953. Prev: Act. Squadron Ldr. RAF Med. Br.

MCFADYEN, Anne Child & Family Department, The Tavistock Clinic, 120 Belsize Lane, London NW3 5BA Tel: 020 7447 3735; Leopald Muller Department Child & Family Mental Health, Royal Free Hospital School of Medicine, Rowland Hill St, London NW3 2PF Tel: 020 7830 2270 — MB ChB 1980 Glas.; MSc Brunel Univ. 1991; MRCPsych 1984. Sen. Lect. (Child & Adolesc. Psychiat.) Roy. Free Hosp. Sch. Med. & Tavistock Clinic Lond.; Hon. Cons. Roy. Free Hosp. NHS Trust & Tavistock Clinic. Prev: Sen. Lect. (Child & Adolesc. Psychiat.) Univ. Dundee; Cons. Child & Adolesc. Psychiat. Tayside HB; Sen. Lect. (Child Psychiat). Univ. Leicester.

MCFADYEN, Edmund Paul Back Road Surgery, 7 Back Road, Dailly, Girvan KA26 9SH Tel: 01465 811224 Fax: 01465 811518; 69 Patna Road, Kirkmichael, Maybole KA19 7PJ Tel: 0165 55 466 — MB ChB 1980 Glas.; MRCGP 1984; DCH RCPS Glas. 1982; Cert. Family Plann. JCC 1984. Prev: Resid. Paediat. Grenfell Regional Health Servs. Newfld., Canada; SHO (O & G) Matern. Hosp. Dunfermline; SHO (Paediat.) Seafield Hosp. Ayr.

MCFADYEN, Iain Ross Univ. of Liverpool, Department of Obstetrics & Gynaecology, Liverpool Womens Hospital, Crown St., Liverpool L8 7SS Tel: 0151 702 4100 Fax: 0151 702 4024 — MB ChB Glas. 1955; FRCOG 1975, M 1962. (Glas.) Hon. Sen. Research Fell. & Hon. Cons.; Coordinator Clin. Audit Mersey RHA; Foundat. Vis. Prof. Obst. & Gyn. Univ. Missouri Kansas, USA; IDA Scudder Oration, Christian Med. Coll., Vellore, India. Socs: (Ex-Hon. Sec.) Blair Bell Research Soc.; (Ex-Pres.) Developm. Path. Soc.; (Ex-Chairm. Harrow Br.) Brit. Med. Assn. Prev: Sen. Lect. & Hon. Cons. O & G Roy. Liverp. Wom.s Hosp.; Cons. O & G N.wick Pk. Hosp. & Clin. Research Centre Harrow; Sen. Lect. (O & G) St. Thos. Hosp. Med. Sch. Lond.

MCFADYEN, Ida Jean 4 Chessel's Court, The Royal Mile, Edinburgh EH8 8AD — MD 1986 Glas.; MB ChB 1961; FRCP Glas. 1993; MRCP Glas. 1967; DObst RCOG 1963.

MCFADYEN, Morag B 12 Sandbank Avenue, Maryhill, Glasgow G20 0DB — MB ChB 1988 Dundee; MRCP Glas. 1994; DCH Dub. 1990. Paediat. Regist. Yorkhill Rotat. Glas. Socs: MRCPCH; BMA. Prev: Neonat. Regist. Glas. Roy. Matern. Hosp.; Neonat. Research Fell. Qu. Mothers Hosp. Glas.; SHO III Roy. Aberd. Childr. Hosp. & Matern. Unit.

MACFADYEN, Robert John Cardiac Unit, 7th Floor, Raigmore Hospital, Inverness IV2 3UJ Tel: 01463 704000 Ext: 5943 Email: r.macfadyen@abdn.ac.uk; 3 Kingsmill Park, Inverness IV2 3RE Tel: 01463 230714 Email: rjmacf@aol.com — MD 1993 Glas.; PhD Strathclyde 1982; BSc (Hons.) Glas. 1978, MD 1993, MB ChB 1987; MRPharms 1979; MRCP (UK) 1991. (Glas.) Cons. (Phys./Cardiol.) Raigmore Hosp. Inverness. Socs: Brit. Pharm. Soc.; Brit. Cardiac Soc.; Roy. Coll. Phys. Prev: Lect. Med. Ninewells Hosp. Dundee; Sen. Research Fell. (Med. & Therap.) W.. Infirm. Glas.; Regist. (Med.) W.. Infirm. Glas.

MCFADYEN, Thomas Erskine Hospital, Erskine Hospital, Bishopton, Erskine PA7 5PU Tel: 0141 812 1100 Fax: 0141 812 0514 — MB ChB 1964 Glas. (Glas.) Dir. (Med. Serv.) Erskine Hosp. Socs: BMA; Brit. Geriat. Soc. Prev: Sen. Med. Off. Erskine Hosp.; Regist. (Med.) Roy. Alexandra Infirm. Paisley.

MACFADYEN, Una Margaret Stirling Royal Infirmary, Livilands, Stirling FK8 2AU Tel: 01786 434000 Fax: 01786 434199; 35 Randolph Terrace, Stirling FK7 9AF — MB ChB 1975 Ed.; BSc 1972 Ed.; FRCP Lond. 1991; FRCP Ed. 1987; MRCP (UK) 1979; DCH Eng. 1979; FRCPCH 1997. (Edinburgh) Cons. Paediat. Forth Valley Acute Hosp.s NHS Trust. Socs: Brit. Assn. of Perinatal Med.; Neonat. Soc.; Brit. Paediatric Respirat. Soc. Prev: Cons. Paediat. Leicester Roy. Infirm.

MACFADYEN, William Agnew Laws (retired) Flat 2, Old Grammar School, High St., Chipping Campden GL55 6HB Tel: 01386 840501 — MB ChB 1936 Ed.; MD Ed. 1949; FRCP Ed. 1954, M 1947. Prev: Cons. Phys. Blackburn & Dist. Hosp. Gp.

MCFADZEAN, Irene Elizabeth (retired) Dalblair, Wheatland Drive, Lanark ML11 7Q Tel: 01555 3715 — MB ChB 1947 Glas.

MCFADZEAN, James Anderson (retired) Court Cottage, 46 St James St, South Petherton TA13 5BN Tel: 01460 242390 — MB ChB Glas. 1948; DSc Strathclyde 1989; MD (Commend.) Glas. 1954; FRCP Glas. 1982, M 1980; FRSE 1985. Prev: Dir. Research Rhone-Poulenc Ltd. Dagenham.

MCFADZEAN, Jillian 22 Ewart Drive, Dumfries DG2 7LT — MB ChB 1990 Glas.

MACFADZEAN, John Adam Craig 48 London Road, Carlisle CA1 2EL Tel: 01228 27559 Fax: 01228 594434; 6 Etterby Scaur, Carlisle CA3 9NX Tel: 0228 23013 — MB BS 1965 Newc.; DObst RCOG 1968. Clin. Asst. (Dermat.) Cumbld. Infirm. Carlisle; Hon. Med. Off. Carlisle Rugby Union Football Club. Socs: Carlisle Med. Soc. Prev: SHO Newc. Gen. Hosp; Regist. (O & G) Dryburn Hosp. Durh.

MCFADZEAN, William Alexander, Lt.-Col. RAMC Retd. 4 Mary Twill Lane, Langland, Swansea SA3 4RB — MB BS 1978 Lond.; FFA RCSI 1988; DA (UK) 1986. (Roy. Free Hosp. Lond.) Cons. Anaesth. Welsh Regional Centre for Burns & Plastic Surg. Morriston Hosp. NHS Trust Swansea. Prev: Sen. Lect. (Anaesth. & Resusc.) to Army; Cons. Anaesth. 23 Parachute Field Ambul.

MCFALL, Ephraim (retired) Oldbury Health Centre, Albert St., Oldbury, Warley B69 4DE Tel: 0121 552 6665 — MB BCh BAO 1950 Belf. Prev: Ho. Phys. Ulster Hosp. Childr. & Wom. Belf.

MCFALL, Ida Crampton Sandrina, Wormington, Broadway WR12 7NL — LRCPI & LM, LRSCI & LM 1947; LRCPI & LM, LRCSI & LM 1947; CPH Wales 1950; Cert FPA 1964; Cert Child Health Developm. Welsh Nat. Sc. Med 1975. (RCSI) Sen. Med. Off. Hereford & Worcester AHA. Prev: Med. Off. N. Gwent Health Dist.; Clinic Med. Off. Soweto Township (Baragwanath Hosp. Serv.), S.; Africa.

MCFALL, Malcolm Worthing Hospitals NHS Trust, Lyndhurst Road, Worthing BN11 2DH; 22 Prior's Acre, Boxgrove, Chichester PO18 0ER Tel: 01243 776987 — MB ChB 1998 Bristol; FRCS 2000 Edinburgh; FRCS 2000 London; FDS 1993 London. Research Fell., Worthing Hosp.s NHS Trust.

MCFARLAN, Charles Stuart Bensfield, Beech Hill, Wadhurst TN5 6JR — MB BS 1992 Lond.

MCFARLAND, Alan Robert 19 Ogles Grove, Culcavey Road, Hillsborough BT26 6RS Tel: 01846 683951 — MB BCh BAO 1983 Belf.; MRCGP 1991; DRCOG 1991.

MCFARLAND, Albert John Black Plumbridge, Omagh BT79 8AA — MB BCh BAO 1941 Dub. (TC Dub.) Prev: Med. Off. R.A.F. 1942-46.

MCFARLAND, David 34 Pond Park Road, Lisburn BT28 3LF — MB BCh BAO 1989 Belf.

MCFARLAND, Gillian Louise Moyard, Ballyhanwood Road, Dundonald, Belfast BT16 1XP — MB ChB 1996 Ed.

MCFARLAND, John Robert Lithgow Ballymena Health Centre, Cushendall Road, Ballymena BT43 6HQ Tel: 028 2564 2181 Fax: 028 2565 8919; Ballymena Health Centre, Ballymena BT43 6HQ — MB BCh BAO 1977 Belf.; MRCGP 1981; DRCOG 1979.

MCFARLAND, Maureen Adelaide The Surgery, Drumart Square, Belvoir Est., Belfast BT8 7EY Tel: 01232 645746 Fax: 01232 642516 Email: jr.rutherford@p148.gp.n-i.nhs.uk; 13 University Avenue, Belfast BT7 1GX Tel: 01232 328823 Email: blake@unite.co.uk — MB BCh BAO Belf. 1982; MRCGP 1987; MFFP RCP (UK) 1993; DRCOG 1986; MIPM 1999. (Queens Uni. Belfast) G.P Belvoir Est.; Clin. Med. Off. (Family Plann.) E.. Health & Social Servs. Bd. Socs: BMA; Brit. Menopause Soc.; SASH. Prev: GP Ballymoney.

MCFARLAND, Patricia Elizabeth Vera (retired) 31 Limberlost Close, Butlers Road, Handsworth Wood, Birmingham B20 2NU Tel: 0121 554 7187 — MB BCh BAO 1946 Dub.; BA Dub. 1946; DPH Lond. 1955; LM Rotunda 1946. Prev: SCMO Birm. AHA.

MCFARLAND, Robert James Moyard, 27 Ballyhanwood Road, Dundonald, Belfast BT16 1XP — MB BCh BAO 1970 Belf.; BSc (1st

MCFARLAND

cl. Hons.) Belf. 1967, MB Bch BAO 1970; FRCP Lond. 1989; FRCP Glas. 1986; MRCP (UK) 1973. Cons. Phys. (Gastroenterol.) Ulster Hosp., Dundonald.; Dir. of Med. Servs. UNDAH Trust. Prev: Sen. Lect./Cons. Dept. Med. Qu. Univ. Belf.

MCFARLAND, Mr Robert John Epsom General Hospital, Dorking Road, Epsom KT18 7EG Tel: 01372 735735; 7 Thorkhill Gardens, Thames Ditton KT7 0UP Tel: 0208 398 9736 Email: bobmcf@7thorkhill.freeserve.co.uk — MB BChir 1973 Camb.; BA Camb. 1970; MChir Camb. 1989; FRCS Eng. 1981. Cons. Vasc. Surg. Epsom Gen. Hosp.; Cons. Vasc. Surg. St. Geo.s Hosp. SW17. Socs: Vasc. Surg. Soc.; Eur. Soc. Vasc. Surg.; Assn. Surg. Prev: Sen. Regist. (Surg.) St. Geo. Hosp. Lond.

MACFARLANE, Mr Adrian Ian Kent County Ophthalmic Hospital Maidstone ME14 1DT Tel: 01622 673444 — MB 1977 Camb.; BChir 1976; FRCS Ed. 1982; FCOphth 1989. Cons. Ophth. Surg. Kent Co. Ophth. Hosp. Maidstone. Prev: Cons. Ophth. Surg. Milton Keynes Gen. Hosp.; Resid. Surg. Off. & Sen. Regist. Moorfields Eye Hosp. Lond.

MCFARLANE, Alan Thomas Seawood Cottage, 14 The Bartletts, Hamble, Southampton SO31 4RP Tel: 02380 457341 — MB BS 1994 Lond.; BSc (Hons.) Lond. 1988, MB BS 1994. (St. Barts. Lond.) Dip. Podiatric Med. Lond. Foot Hosp. 1982.; GP Locum. Prev: Ho. Off. (Endocrinol.) St. Bart. Hosp. Lond.

MCFARLANE, Mr Alexander Gerald Hasland, Duncrievie Road, Glenfarg, Perth PH2 9PA Tel: 0468 830276 Fax: 07001 830276 Email: alex@hasland.demon.co.uk; PO Box 7331, Perth PH2 9YA Tel: 07051 830276 Fax: 07001 830276 Email: 3ma@sol/co/uk — MB BS 1978 Lond.; FRCS Eng. 1982; MRCGP 1994; DFFP 1995; DCCH RCP Ed. 1992; DRCOG 1991. (Westm.) Socs: BMA; Guild Catholic Doctors; Scot. Catholic Med. Assn.

MACFARLANE, Alexander John (retired) Martins Close, 11 Wycombe Road, Princes Risborough HP27 0EE Tel: 01844 343004 — MB BS 1958 Lond.

MCFARLANE, Alexander Roberts Telfer Edenfield Road Surgery, Cutgate Shopping Precinct, Edenfield Road, Rochdale OL11 5AQ Tel: 01706 344044 Fax: 01706 526882; Bethany Farm, Bethany Lane, Newhey, Rochdale OL16 3TB — MB ChB 1979 Manch.; BSc Med. Sc. St. And 1976.

MCFARLANE, Andrea Sigune Urania 18 Turretbank Drive, Crieff PH7 4LW — MB ChB 1989 Aberd.

MCFARLANE, Andrew Raigmore Hospital, Inverness IV2 3UJ; Mole House, Woodside, Blackpark, Leachkin, Inverness Tel: 01463 715747 — MB ChB Ed. 1987; DRCOG 1995. Staff Grade (Renal Med.) Inverness. Prev: SHO (Psychiat.) Inverness; GP Trainee Inverness; SHO (Med.) Cardiff Roy. Infirm, Univ. Hosp. Wales & Roy. Gwent Hosp.

MACFARLANE, Andrew William Ysbyty Gwynedd, Bangor LL57 2PW Tel: 01248 384337 Email: andy.macfarlane@nww-tr.wales.nhs.uk; Cefn Cana, Llanddaniel Fab, Gaerwen LL60 6EF — MB ChB 1979 Liverp.; FRCP 1998. Cons. Dermat. Ysbyty Gwynedd Bangor. Prev: Sen. Regist. (Dermat.) Roy. Liverp. Hosp.

MACFARLANE, Anne Elizabeth The Medical Centre, 24 Laurie Grove, London SE14 6NH Tel: 020 8692 6427 Fax: 020 8691 9698; 6 Brookway, Blackheath, London SE3 9BJ — MB BS 1972 Lond.; MRCS Eng. LRCP Lond. 1972. (Guy's)

MACFARLANE, Arthur 70 Walkley Crescent Road, Walkley, Sheffield S6 5BB — MB ChB 1988 Sheff.

MACFARLANE, Arthur Ian Hill (retired) Clythers, Church Road, Swallowfield, Reading RG7 1TJ Tel: 01734 883332 — MB BS 1955 Lond. Prev: Ho. Surg. & Ho. Surg. Gyn. & Obst. St. Stephen's Hosp. Lond.

MACFARLANE, Bruce John Mt Vernon & Watford NHS Trust, Vicarage Road, Watford WD18 0HB Tel: 01923 217317 Fax: 01923 217727 Email: bsknmac@aol.com; 2 Woodfield Avenue,), Northwood HA6 3EA Tel: 01923 823314 Email: bsknmac@aol.com — MB BCh 1982 Witwatersrand; MRCP (UK) 1990; PhD Witwatersrand 1990; CCST (Gastroenter. & Gen. Internal Med.) 1996. (Uni. Witwatersrand, Johannesburge) Cons. E.roenterovogist, Mt Vernon & Watford NHS Trust. Socs: Brit. Sco. Gastroen. - Ordinary; BMA. Prev: Lect. Roy, Free Hosp. Sch. Med.

MACFARLANE, Catherine Sarah View Cottage, Hallmoor Road, Darley Dale, Matlock DE4 2HF — MB BS 1993 Lond.; BSc 1990; MRCP Lond. 1998. (UMDS)

MCFARLANE, Cecilia Great Western Road Medical Group, 327 Great Western Road, Aberdeen AB10 6LT Tel: 01224 571318 Fax: 01224 573865 — MB ChB 1981 Ed.; MRCP (UK) 1985; MRCGP 1989.

MCFARLANE, Colin Department of Anaesthetics, Dr Grays Hospital, Elgin IV30 1SN — MB ChB 1982 Glas.; FCAnaesth 1989. (Glas.) Cons. Anaesth. Dr Gray's Hosp. Elgin. Socs: Scott. Soc. Anaesth. Prev: Sen. Regist. (Anaesth.) Roy. Infirm. Edin.

MACFARLANE, Colin Peter Shotts Health Centre, 36 Station Road, Shotts ML7 5DS Tel: 01501 822099 Fax: 01501 826622 — MB ChB 1982 Glas.

MACFARLANE, David Bixter Health Centre, Langbiggin, Bixter, Shetland ZE2 9NA Tel: 01595 810202 Fax: 01595 810493; The Back, Sandsound, Bixter, Shetland ZE2 9LU Tel: 01595 810496 Fax: 01595 810700 Email: dave.mac@zetnet.co.uk — MB ChB 1978 Dundee.

MACFARLANE, Mr David Aloysius (retired) Wythburn, 4 Wilbury Avenue, Cheam, Sutton SM2 7DU Tel: 020 8642 6974 — MB BCh 1944 Wales; BSc Wales 1941, MCh 1956, MB BCh 1944; FRCS Glas. 1986; FRCS Ed. 1985; FRCS Eng. 1949. Hon. Cons. Surg. St. Stephen's Hosp. Lond. & Sutton Hosp.; Teach. (Surg.) Univ. Lond.; Hon. Surg. St. Anthony's Hosp. Cheam; Surg. Tutor St. Bart. Hosp. Lond.; Examr. (Surg.) RCS Eng. & RCS Glas. & Univs. Liverp., Lond. & Glas. Prev: Research Fell. in Surg. Harvard Med. Sch.

MACFARLANE, David William 3 Norbreck Drive, Giffnock, Glasgow G46 6AF — MB ChB 1983 Glas.

MACFARLANE, David William Roy Anaesthetic Department, Queen Elizabeth Hospital, Edgbaston, Birmingham B15 2TY Fax: 0121 697 8340; 25 St. Mary's Road, Harborne, Birmingham B17 0EY Fax: 0121 681 2898 — MB ChB 1965 Birm.; FFA RCS Eng. 1970. Cons. Anaesth. Univ. Hosp. Birm. NHS Trust.

MCFARLANE, Denise Elaine Dr Gray's Hospital, Elgin IV30 Tel: 01343 543131; 33 Woodlands Crescent, Bishopmill, Elgin IV30 4LY Tel: 01343 551275 — MB ChB 1987 Glas.; DCH RCP Lond. 1992; DRCOG 1991. Staff Paediat. Dr. Gray's Hosp. Elgin. Prev: Staff Paediat. Falkirk & Dist. Roy. Infirm.; Trainee GP/SHO (Paediat.) Dumfries Roy. Infirm.

MACFARLANE, Diana Geraldine Maidstone and Tunbridge Wells NHS Trust, Rheumatology Unit, The Homoeopathic Hospital, Church Road, Tunbridge Wells TN1 1JU Tel: 01892 542977 Fax: 01892 542244 Email: drdgmacfarlane@cs.com; Kiln Cottage, Bletchinglye Lane, Rotherfield, Crowborough TN6 3NN Tel: 01892 852877 — MB BS 1973 Lond.; MB BS (Hons.) Lond. 1973; FRCP Lond. 1994; MRCP (UK) 1975. (Middlx.) Cons. Phys. (Rheum.) Maidstone and Tunbridge Wells NHS Trust; Hon. Research Fell. (Anat.) Guy's Hosp. Med. Sch. Lond. Socs: Fell. Roy. Soc. Med.; Brit. Soc. Rheum. Prev: Cons. & Sen. Lect. (Rheum.) Lewisham Hosp. & Guys Hosp. Med. Sch. Lond.; Sen. Regist. Univ. Dept. Med. Bristol Roy. Infirm.

MCFARLANE, Donald Bryce (retired) 14 Kelvin Court, Glasgow G12 0AB Tel: 0141 357 2195 — MB ChB Glas. 1957; MRCGP 1968; DObst RCOG 1961. Clin. Dir. Lasercare Clinic S.ern Gen. Hosp. Glas. Prev: GP Glas.

MACFARLANE, Doniert Alexis 63 Fentiman Road, London SW8 1LH — MB BS 1998 Lond.; MB BS Lond 1998.

MACFARLANE, Elisabeth Raigmore Hospital, Perth Road, Inverness IV2 3UJ Tel: 01463 704000; Lilyfield, Loch Flemington, Gollanfield, Ardersier, Inverness IV2 7QR Tel: 01667 461067 — MB ChB 1991 Aberd. (Aberdeen) GP Trainee. Socs: BMA; Med. & Dent. Defence Union Scotl. Prev: Regist. (Gen. Pract.) Nairn; Regist. (A & E) Jersey Gen. Hosp.; SHO (Gen. Surg.) Law Hosp. Carluke.

MCFARLANE, Elizabeth Anne Raigmore Hospital, Inverness IV2 3UJ; Mole House, Woodside, Blackpark, Leachkin, Inverness IV3 6PW Tel: 01463 715747 — MB BCh 1994 Wales; BSc (Hons.) Zool. Wales 1988; DRCOG 1996; DCH RCP Lond. 1997; MRCGP 1998. SHO (Med.). Prev: SHO (Palliat. Care & Med.) Inverness VTS; SHO (Paediat.) Inverness VTS; GP Regist. Inverness.

MACFARLANE, Elizabeth Stark (retired) Rookwood, Donaldfield Road, Bridge of Weir PA11 3JG — MB ChB 1928 Glas.

MACFARLANE, Gary John ARC Epidemiology Unit, School of Epidemiology & Health Sciences, Stopford Building, University of Manchester, Manchester M13 9PT Tel: 0161 275 5046 Fax: 0161 275 5043 Email: g.macfarlane@man.ac.uk — MB ChB 1990 Glas.; PhD Bristol 1994; BSc (Hons.) Glas. 1985. Prof. (Epidemiol.). Socs:

Roy. Soc. Med. Prev: Dep. Dir. Epidemiol. & Biostatistics Europ. Inst. Oncol.; Sen. Lect. (Epidemiol.) Univ. Manch.

MACFARLANE, Gary Preston, MBE Doctors Surgery, 18 Union Street, Kirkintilloch, Glasgow G66 1DJ Tel: 0141 776 1238 Fax: 0141 775 2786; 10 Broom Gardens, Kirkintilloch, Glasgow G66 4EH Tel: 0141 578 6995 Fax: 0141 775 2786 Email: garym@union-docs.co.uk — MB ChB 1978 Glas.; MRCGP 1983; DRCOG 1982. Prev: Clin. Asst. (Diabetes) Monklands Dist. Gen. Hosp. Airdrie.

MACFARLANE, Grace Ness 34 Sherbrooke Drive, Glasgow G41 5AA Tel: 0141 427 2959 — MB ChB 1956 Glas.

MCFARLANE, Harry John 19 Louisville Avenue, Aberdeen AB15 4TT — MB ChB 1976 Aberd.; FFA RCSI 1981; FRCS 2000 Edinburgh. Cons. Anaesth. Aberd. Roy. Infirm. Prev: Sen. Regist. Brompton, W.m. & Char. Cross Hosps. Lond.; Regist. Mater Hosp. Dub.

MCFARLANE, Mr Harry William Heather Brae, 110 Whitaker Road, Derby DE23 6AP Tel: 01332 345174 Fax: 01332 345174 — MB ChB 1952 St. And.; FRCS Ed. 1961; FRCS Eng. 1961. (St. And.) Cons. ENT Surg. Derby. Socs: Fell. Roy. Soc. Med. (Mem. Sects. Otol. & Laryng.); Midl. Inst. Otol.; Soc. ENT Advances in Childr. Prev: Cons. ENT Surg. Derbysh. Roy. Infirm., Derbysh. Childr. Hosp. & Roy. Sch. for the Deaf Derby; Sen. Regist. (ENT.) Roy. Infirm. Aberd. & Clin. Tutor Univ. Aberd.; Regist. (ENT) Aberd. Roy. Infirm.

MACFARLANE, Helen Dora (retired) Colts Paddock, 24 Aveley Lane, Farnham GU9 8PR — MB BS Lond. 1954; DPH Singapore 1965.

MACFARLANE, Ian Andrew Univ. Hospital Aintree, Walton Hospital, Rice Lane, Liverpool L9 1AE — MB ChB 1973 Sheff.; MD (with Commendation) Sheff. 1981; FRCP 1991. Cons. Phys. & Endocrinol. Univ. Hosp. Aintree, Liverp.; Hon. Cons. Endocrinol. Regional Neurosci. Unit Walton Hosp. Liverp.; Hon. Reader of Med., Dept of Med., Univ. of Liverp. Prev: Sen. Regist. (Diabetic Clin.) Gen. Hosp. Birm.; Lect. (Med.) Roy. Infirm. Manch.; Research Fell. Christie Hosp. Manch.

MACFARLANE, James Aidan 6 Cobden Crescent, Oxford OX1 4LJ Tel: 01865 226781 Fax: 01865 226773 — MB 1965 Camb.; BChir 1964; FRCP Lond. 1985; MRCP (UK) 1972. Cons. Pub. Health & Health Policy Oxf.; Sen. Clin. Lect. (Paediat.) Oxf.; Dir. Nat. Adolesc. & Stud. Health Unit. Socs: Brit. Paediat. Assn. Prev: Cons. Paediat. (Child Health) & Clin. Lect. (Paediat.) Oxf. HA.

MACFARLANE, James Brand, OStJ (retired) Bedford House, John St., Elland HX5 0AW Tel: 01422 372148 — MB ChB 1950 Ed. GP W. Yorks. Prev: Dep. Police Surg. W. Yorks. Constab.

MACFARLANE, James Falkland Imperial Road Surgery, 8 Imperial Road, Matlock DE4 3NL Tel: 01629 583249 — MB BChir 1968 Camb.; MA Camb. 1970; AFOM RCP Lond. 1987; DObst RCOG 1969. (Camb. & St. Thos.) Prev: Ho. Off. (Obst.) & Ho. Surg. St. Thos. Hosp.; Ho. Phys. (Gen. Med.) Kingston Hosp. Kingston upon Thames.

MACFARLANE, Jan Lennox Pensilva Health Centre, School Road, Pensilva, Liskeard PL14 5RP Tel: 01579 362249 Fax: 01579 363323; Halwihnick Cottage, Linkinhorne, Callington PL17 7NS — MB ChB 1980 Glas.; MRCGP 1985; DCH RCP Lond. 1984.

MACFARLANE, Jane Avis Curtis Kinkell Bowling Green Road, Cupar KY15 4HD — MB ChB 1992 Dundee; BDS 1982; FDS RCPS Glas. 1988. Regist. (Oral & Maxillofacial Surg.) City Hosp. Edin. Socs: Assoc. Mem. Brit. Assn. Oral & Maxillofacial Surgs.

MCFARLANE, Jeannette Harriet Department of Forensic Medicine & Science, University of Glasgow, Glasgow G12 8QQ Tel: 0141 330 4574 — MB ChB 1983 Manch.; BSc Manch. 1980, MB ChB (Hons.) 1983; MRCPath (Histopath.) 1990. Cons. Forens. Path. Univ. Glas. Prev: Sen. Regist. (Histopath.) NW RHA.

MACFARLANE, Mr John Alan (retired) Coach House, Belhaven Est., Wishaw ML2 7PE — MB ChB 1941 Ed.; FRCS Ed. 1947. Prev: Cons. Surg. Law Hosp.

MACFARLANE, John Alexander (retired) 65 Blandy Road, Henley-on-Thames RG9 1QB — MB ChB 1942 Glas.

MACFARLANE, John Clarkson (retired) 10 St Edmunds Close, Allestree, Derby DE22 2DZ Tel: 01332 558432 — MB ChB 1925 Aberd. Prev: Obstetr. Nightingale Matern. Home Derby.

MCFARLANE, John Oakley 8 Park Avenue S., Northampton NN3 3AA — MB BS 1961 Lond.; MRCS Eng. LRCP Lond. 1961. (Univ. Coll. Hosp.) Prev: Ho. Phys. Univ. Coll. Hosp. Lond.; Ho. Surg. (Surg. & Gyn.) & SHO (Obst.) St. John's Hosp. Chelmsford.

MACFARLANE, Mr John Robert Kinglassie House, By Kinglassie, Lochgelly KY5 0UN — MB ChB 1974 Glas.; FRCS Ed. 1979. Cons. Urol. Qu. Margt. Hosp. Dunfermline.

MACFARLANE, John Thomson Nottingham City Hospital, Hucknall Road, Nottingham NG5 1PB Tel: 0115 962 7723 Fax: 0115 962 7723 Email: john.macfarlane@nottingham.ac.uk; Middlebeck Farm, Gray Lane, Halam, Newark NG22 8AL Tel: 01636 812583 Fax: 01636 816969 — BM BCh 1973 Oxf.; DM Oxf. 1983, MA, BM BCh 1973; FRCP Lond. 1989; MRCP (UK) 1976; MRCGP 1999. (Oxf.) Cons. Phys. & Respirat. Phys. City Hosp. Nottm. Socs: (Counc.) Brit. Thoracic Soc.; Assn. Phys. Prev: Sen. Regist. (Gen. & Respirat. Med.) Nottm. AHA (T); Regist. Ahmadu Bello Univ. Hosp. Zaria, Nigeria; SHO Brompton Hosp. Lond.

MACFARLANE, Jonathan Peter 5 Shoe Lane, East Hagbourne, Didcot OX11 9LW Email: jon.mcfarlane@btinternet.com — MB BChir 1991 Camb.; FRCS Lond. 1995. Specialist Regist. Urol. Battle Hosp. Readin; Specialist Regist. (Radiol.) Ch.ill Hosp. Oxf.

MCFARLANE, Kathryn June Chantrell Bennetts End Surgery, Gatecroft, Hemel Hempstead HP3 9LY Tel: 01442 63511 Fax: 01442 235419 — MB ChB 1987 Sheff.; MRCGP 1991; DRCOG 1991; Cert. Family Plann. JCC 1990.

MACFARLANE, Laura May Scotstown Medical Centre, Cairnfold Road, Bridge of Don, Aberdeen AB22 8LD Tel: 01224 702149 Fax: 01224 706688; Waverly Lodge, High Cross Avenue, Melrose TD6 9SF Tel: 0189682 2078 — MB ChB 1992 Aberd. Trainee GP Aberd. Socs: Assoc. Mem. Roy. Coll. Gen. Practs. Prev: SHO (O & G) Aberd. Roy. Infirm.

MACFARLANE, Lorna 8 Maywood Avenue, East Didsbury, Manchester M20 5GR — MB ChB 1987 Glas.; MSc Manch. 1996; MRCPath 1997.

MACFARLANE, Malcolm Peter 43 Almoners Avenue, Cambridge CB1 8NZ — MB ChB 1988 Manch.

MCFARLANE, Margaret (retired) 14 Allanshaw Street, Hamilton ML3 6NJ Tel: 01698 421595 — MB ChB 1952 Glas.

MCFARLANE, Marjory Nan (retired) 2 Burlington Crescent, Headington, Oxford OX3 8DY — MD 1945 St. And.; MD (Hnrs. & Univ. Gold Medal) St. And. 1945, MB; ChB 1940. Prev: Asst. Pathol. Dundee Roy. Infirm. & St. And. Univ.

MACFARLANE, Neil David 12 Ransfield Road, Manchester M21 9QH — MB BS 1986 Lond.; BA Camb. 1983; MRCPsych 1994. (Guy's)

MCFARLANE, Peter Allan 323 Glasgow Road, Paisley PA1 3BA — MB BChir 1989 Camb.

MACFARLANE, Peter Iain Rotherham District General Hospital, Moorgate Road, Rotherham S60 2UD Tel: 01709 820000 Fax: 01709 824101 Email: peter.macfarlane@rgh-tr.trent.nhs.uk; 51 Whirlow Lane, Whirlow, Sheffield S11 9QF — MB ChB 1977 Manch.; FRCP Glas. 1994; MRCP (UK) 1980; FRCPCH 1996; DME 1989. (Manchester) Cons. Paediat. Rotherham Gen. Hosp.; Lect. in Child Health. Socs: Brit. Thorac. Soc.; BMA; Brit. Paediat. Respirat. Gp. Prev: Tutor (Child Health) Univ. Manch.

MACFARLANE, Peter Stewart (retired) 3 Mannofield, Bearsden, Glasgow G61 4AY Tel: 0141 942 4289 — MB ChB 1944 Glas.; MB ChB (Commend.) Glas. 1944; FRCP Glas. 1972, M 1969; FRCP Ed. 1965, M 1955; FRCPath 1969, M 1963. Prev: Cons. Pathol. Glas. Roy. Infirm. & W.. Infirm. Glas.

MACFARLANE, Mr Robert Department of Neurosurgery, Addenbrooke's Hospital, Cambridge CB2 2QQ Tel: 01223 217289 Fax: 01223 274645 — MD 1992 Camb.; MA Camb. 1983, MD 1992, MB BChir 1982; FRCS Eng. 1986. Cons. Neurosurg. Addenbrooke's Hosp. Camb. Prev: Cons. Neurosurg. Roy. Lond. Hosp.; Sen. Regist. (Neurosurg.) Addenbrooke's Hosp. Camb.; Research Fell. (Neurosurg.) Harvard Med. Sch. Mass. Gen. Hosp. Boston, USA.

MACFARLANE, Robert Goudie, MBE, Maj.-Gen. late RAMC Retd. 6 Redholm, Greenheads Road, North Berwick EH39 4TB — MB ChB Glas. 1940; MD Glas. 1955; FRCP Ed. 1964, M 1957; FRCP Lond. 1979, M 1971. (Glas.) Prev: Hon. Phys. to HM the Qu.; Cons. Phys. to the Army; Cons. Phys. BAOR.

MACFARLANE, Robert Martin 1 Beaufort Road, Edinburgh EH9 1AG Tel: 0131 447 1646 — MB BS 1979 Lond.; MRCGP

MACFARLANE

1986; DGM RCP Lond. 1990. (Westm.) Prev: Regist. (Geriat. Med.) Longmore Hosp. Edin.

MACFARLANE, Roy Christopher (retired) Red Syke, Hall Santon, Holmrook CA19 1UU Tel: 019467 26390 — MB BS 1958 Lond.; DObst RCOG 1960; DA Eng. 1960. Prev: Regist. Anaesth. Char. Cross Hosp.

MACFARLANE, Sarah Emma 18 Rathmena Avenue, Ballyclare BT39 9HX — MB BCh 1998 Belf.; MB BCh Belf 1998.

MCFARLANE, Stewart Hamish Laindon Health Centre, Laindon, Basildon SS15 5TR Tel: 01268 546411 Fax: 01268 491248 — MB ChB 1980 Ed.; MRCGP 1984; DRCOG 1982.

MCFARLANE, Susan Mary The Surgery, All Saints House, 39 All Saints Road, Lightwater GU18 5SQ Tel: 01276 472248 Fax: 01276 473873; 11 Keswick Drive, Lightwater GU18 5XD Tel: 01276 476789 — MB BS 1975 Lond. (The Middlesex Hospital) Socs: BMA.

MCFARLANE, Thomas 9 Edgehill Road, Bearsden, Glasgow G61 3AD Tel: 0141 942 4118 — MB ChB 1950 Glas.

MCFARLANE, Thomas Alexandra Hospital, Mill Lane, Cheadle SK8 2PX Tel: 0161 428 3656 Fax: 0161 487 3492; Highfield House, 442 Buxton Road, Stockport SK2 7JB Tel: 0161 483 9512 — MB ChB 1967 Glas.; BSc Glas. 1962, MB ChB 1967; MRCOG 1975. Cons. O & G Stockport HA.

MACFARLANE, Valerie Alexandra Shotts Health Centre, 36 Station Road, Shotts ML7 5DS Tel: 01501 822099 Fax: 01501 826622; East Lodge, 60 Allanton Road, Allanton, Shotts ML7 5DF Tel: 01501 821393 — MB ChB 1985 Dundee.

MCFARLANE, Victoria Judith (Roughton) Seawood, Wessex Radiotherapy Centre, Royal South Hants Hospital, Bintons Terrace, St Marys, Southampton — BM 1993 Soton.; MRCP 1997. Specialist Regist. (Radiother. & Oncol.) Wessex Radiother. Centre Roy. S. Hants, Hosp. Soton.

MACFARLANE, Wendy Forrest 32 Avonbridge Drive, Hamilton ML3 7EJ — MB ChB 1992 Glas.; MRCGP 1996; DRCOG 1994.

MCFARLANE, Xola Alan 57 Link, Department of Gastroenterology, Royal Liverpool University, Prescott St., Liverpool L7 8XP Tel: 0151 706 2000; 40 Milner Road, Heswall, Wirral CH60 5RZ — MB BS 1986 W. Indies; MD Bath 1996; MRCP (UK) 1990. (University West Indies) Lect. & Sen. Regist. (Med. & Gastroenterol.) Roy. Liverp. Univ. Hosp. Socs: Brit. Soc. Gastroenterol.

MACFARQUHAR, Iain Alexander, MBE (retired) Aloha, 19 Wittet Drive, Elgin IV30 1SE Tel: 01343 547904 — MB ChB Aberd. 1959; DObst RCOG 1961. Prev: GP.

MCFATTER, Fiona Baker 8 Poets View, Kirkintilloch, Glasgow G66 3HT — MB ChB 1997 Glas.

MCFAUL, Christopher David 28 Acer Leigh, Fullwood Green, Aigburth, Liverpool L17 5BN — MB ChB 1996 Liverp.

MACFAUL, John Philip The Surgery, Houghton Lane, Shevington, Wigan WN6 8ET Tel: 01257 253311; 391 Gathurst Road, Orrell, Wigan WN5 0LL Tel: 01942 213262 — MB BCh BAO 1958 NUI; DObst RCOG 1960. (Univ. Coll. Dub.) Prev: Clin. Asst. (Obst.) Billinge Hosp. Wigan; Regist. (O & G) Billinge Hosp. Wigan.

MACFAUL, Mr Peter Alexander Bunker & Co. Solicitors, 7 The Drive, Hove BN3 3JS — MB BS 1959 Lond.; FRCS Eng. 1966; DO Eng. 1963. (Middlx.) Prev: Cons. Ophth. Surg. Middlx. Hosp. Lond., Roy. Nat. Orthop. Hosp. Lond.; & Roy. Marsden Hosp. Lond.; Lect. Inst. Ophth. Lond.; Hon. Cons. Surg. W.. Ophth. Hosp. Lond.

MCFAUL, Peter Bertram Department of Obstetrics & Gynaecology, Belfast City Hospital, Belfast BT9 7AB Tel: 01232 329241; 9 Sequoia Park, Lambeg, Lisburn BT27 4SJ — MB BCh BAO 1980 Belf.; MD 1989; MRCOG 1985; DRCOG 1982. Cons. Sen. Lect. Belf. City Hosp. Trust & Qu. Univ. Belf.

MACFAUL, Roderick Woodmoor House, Wood Lane, Newmillerdam, Wakefield WF2 7SR — MB ChB 1968 Leeds; MB ChB (Distinc. Med.) Leeds 1968; FRCP Lond. 1986; MRCP (UK) 1973; DCH RCPS Glas. 1970. Cons. Paediat. Pinderfields Hosp. Wakefield. Prev: Sen. Specialist in Paediat. RAMC; Ho. Surg. Gen. Hosp. Otley; Ho. Phys. Proffess. Paediat. Unit Seacroft Hosp. Leeds.

***MCFEE, Lindsey Laura Margaret** 23 Mortonhall Road, Edinburgh EH9 2HS — MB ChB 1997 Manch.

MCFEELY, Denis Francis 7 St Juliens Mount, Cawthorne, Barnsley S75 4EX — LRCPI & LM, LRSCI & LM 1950; LRCPI & LM, LRCSI & LM 1950.

MCFEETERS, James Ian (retired) Baranduin, 2 Butt Lane, Tattershall, Lincoln LN4 4NL — BM BCh 1953 Oxf.; BA Oxf. 1950, MA, BM BCh 1953; MRCGP 1968. Local Treasury Med. Off. Prev: Hosp. Pract. (Orthop.) Pilgrim Hosp. Boston.

MCFERRAN, Dermot Hugh 35 Newmarket Road, Norwich NR2 2HN Tel: 01603 666217 — MB BS 1950 Lond.; MFOM RCP Lond. 1980; MFCM 1974; DPH Lond. 1962; DIH Soc. Apoth. Lond. 1962; DTM & H Eng. 1961. (Char. Cross) Prev: Cas. Off. Char. Cross Hosp. Lond.; Ho. Surg. (Orthop.) St. Alphege's Hosp. Greenwich; SHO Lewisham Gp. Hosps.

MCFERRAN, Mr Donald John Essex County Hospital, Lexden Road, Colchester CO3 3NB Tel: 01206 744493 Fax: 01206 744439 Email: donmcferran@compuserve.com; Parsonage Farm, Boxted, Colchester CO4 5ST Tel: 01206 852927 — MB BChir 1982 Camb.; 1998 FRCS (ORL-HNS) Intercollegiate exam; MA Camb. 1983; FRCS Eng. (ENT) 1989. Cons. ENT Surg., Essex Rivers Healthcare Trust, Colchester. Prev: Sen. Regist. (ENT) Norf. & Norwich Hosp.; Specialist Regist. (ENT) Addenbrooke's Hosp. Camb.

MCFERRAN, Kevin Ballyowen Health Centre, 179 Andersonstown Road, Belfast BT11 9EA Tel: 028 9061 0611 Fax: 028 9043 1323; 6 Cranmore Avenue, Belfast BT9 6JH — MB BCh BAO 1980 Belf.; MRCGP 1985; DRCOG 1984.

MCFETRICH, Andrew James 12 Cheyne Gardens, Bournemouth BH4 8AS — MB ChB 1997 Sheff. Basic Surg. Trainee Sheff.

MCFETRIDGE, Lynne Denise 149 Carrowreagh Road, Garvagh, Coleraine BT51 5JL Tel: 012665 40306; 149 Carrowreagh Road, Garvagh, Coleraine BT51 5JL Tel: 012665 40306 — MB BS 1996 Newc. (Univ. of Newc.-u-Tyne) SHO (Neonates) Birm. Wom.'s Hosp. Edgbaston, Birm. Socs: BMA; Full Mem. MPS; Christ. Med. Fell.sh. Prev: SHO (Comm. Paediat.) Stanley Co. Durh.; SHO (Paediat.) Dryburn Hosp. Durh.; SHO (A & E Med.) Mater. Hosp. Belf.

MACFIE, Alexander James Haxby & Wigginton Health Centre, Wigginton, York YO32 2LL Tel: 01904 760125 Email: docs@myer-partners.demon.co.uk; Bolingbroke, Coxwold, York YO61 4AA Tel: 01937 86845 Email: sam@haxby.demon.co.uk — MB BS 1974 Lond.; MRCGP 1981. GP Princip. Wigginton.; Forth Valley PCG Research. Prev: Med. Off. Chas. Johnson Memor. Hosp. Nqutu, Zululand; Cas. Off. & SHO (Gen. Med.) York Dist. Hosp.

MACFIE, Jack Alexander 55 Murrayfield Gardens, Edinburgh EH12 6DH — MB ChB 1971 Ed.; BSc Ed. 1968; MRCGP 1989; DCH 1976; DObst RCOG 1973. (Ed.)

MACFIE, Janet Lavinia Bowman Leven Terrace Surgery, 6 Leven Terrace, Edinburgh EH3 9LT — MB ChB 1970 Glas.; MRCGP 1978; DCH RCPS Glas. 1973; DObst RCOG 1972; Cert FPA 1973. (Glas.)

MACFIE, Mr John Scarborough Hospital, Woodlands Drive, Scarborough YO12 6QL Tel: 01723 368111 Fax: 01723 354031; Mallard Green, 25 Hall Garth Lane, West Ayton, Scarborough YO13 9JA Tel: 01723 862733 — MB ChB 1974 Birm.; MD Birm. 1982; FRCS Eng. 1978. Cons. Surg. ScarBoro. Gen. Hosp. & Bridlington Hosp.; Regional Adviser Gen. Surg. Yorks.; Mem. Ct. of Examr.s (Roy. Coll. Surg.s of Eng.); Co. Director Combined Gastroenterol. Research Unit ScarBoro. Socs: Brit. Assn. Paren. & Ente. Nutrit.; Eur. Soc. Parenteral & Enteral Nutrit.; Assn. of ColoProctol. of GB & Irel. Prev: Sen. Regist. Yorks. RHA; Sen. Lect. & Cons. Univ. Auckland, NZ.

MACFLYNN, Edward James (retired) 61 Bells Hill, Limavady BT49 0DQ Tel: 028 7776 2206 — MB BCh BAO NUI 1939; DPH Belf. 1941. Prev: Resid. Ho. Phys., Ho. Surg. & Gyn. Mater Infirm. Hosp. Belf.

MACFLYNN, Geraldine Mary Patricia Central Scotland Healthcare, Dunrowan, 37 Maggieswood Loan, Falkirk FK1 5EH — MB BCh BAO 1973 Belf.; MRCPsych 1978.

MACFOY, Donald 64 Egerton Road N., Manchester M21 0QY — MB ChB 1979 Manch.

MCGAAHAN, Cathryn 3 Wyresdale Dr, Leyland, Preston PR25 3DP — MB ChB 1997 Leeds.

MCGAHAN, Anita Margaret 15 College Park, Coleraine BT51 3HE Tel: 01265 43996; 82 Chapel Street, Cookstown BT80 8QD Tel: 016487 62032 — MB BCh BAO 1986 Belf.; MB BCh Belf. 1986; MRCGP 1990; DRCOG 1990; DMH Belf. 1989.

MCGAHEY, David Torrance 61 Sunningdale Park, Ballymena BT43 5NQ — MB BCh BAO 1991 Belf.

MCGALLIARD, Catherine Ann Patricia 26 Glenwood Court, Kirkintilloch, Glasgow G66 4JL — MB ChB 1997 Glas. SHO (O &

G) Stobhill NHS Trust Glas. Prev: SHO Obst. Qu. Mothers Hosp. Glas.

MCGALLIARD, Mr James Noel Ophthalmology Department, Royal Liverpool University Hospital, Prescot St., Liverpool L7 8XP Tel: 0151 709 2000 — MB BCh BAO 1981 Belf.; BSc (Anat.) Hons. Belf. 1978, MB BCh BAO 1981; FRCS Ed. 1987; FCOphth. 1989; DO RCPSI 1985. Cons. Ophth. Liverp. HA. Socs: N. Eng. Ophth. Soc. & Liverp. Med. Inst. Prev: Sen. Regist. (Ophth.) St. Pauls Eye Hosp. Liverp.; Regist. (Ophth.) Roy. Vict. Hosp.

MCGALLOWAY, Barbara Ann 42 Pilrig Street, Edinburgh EH6 5AL — MB ChB 1978 Dundee.

MCGARITY, Joseph Francis (retired) 1 Pinefield, Inchmarlo, Banchory AB31 4AF Tel: 01330 824946 — MB BS Durh. 1940; DPH Durh. 1950; FFCM RCP (UK) 1980, M 1974. Prev: Regional Med. Specialist (Capital Developm.) Trent RHA.

MCGARITY, Kenneth Leo 1 Turner Road, Wellingborough NN8 4UT Tel: 01933 673456 Fax: 01933 402869; 2 Manor Court, Little Harrowden, Wellingborough NN9 5BZ Tel: 01933 673456 — MB ChB 1975 Aberd.; MRCGP 1983; DRCOG 1979.

MCGARRIGLE, Alina Phoebe St Davids Clinic, Bellevue Terrace, Newport NP20 2LB Tel: 01633 251133 Fax: 01633 221096; 19 Ffos y Fran, Caerphilly Road, Bassaleg, Newport NP1 0LU — MB ChB 1984 Bristol; DCH RCP Lond. 1990; DGM RCP Lond. 1989; DA (UK) 1987.

MCGARRITY, Charles Fosse Medical Centre, 344 Fosse Road N., Leicester LE3 5RR Tel: 0116 253 8988; The Sycamores, 2 Church St, Blaby, Leicester LE8 4FA — MB ChB 1981 Leic.; BSc Leic. 1978, MB ChB 1981; MRCGP 1985; DRCOG 1983.

MCGARRITY, Mr Gerald Inverclyde Royal Hospital, Greenock PA16 0XN Tel: 01475 633777 — BSc Glas. 1965, MB ChB 1969; FRCS Glas. 1974. (Glas.) Cons. Orthop. Surg. Inverclyde Roy. Hosp. Greenock.

MCGARRITY, John David Flemington House, 7 Glasgow Road, Uddingston, Glasgow G71 7AR — MB ChB 1986 Aberd.; MRCGP 1992.

MCGARRITY, Kathleen Margaret 9 Edinburgh Drive, Gourock PA19 1AG — MB ChB 1995 Glas.

MCGARRITY, Margaret Flemington Hosue, 7 Glasgow Road, Uddingston, Glasgow G71 7AR — MB ChB 1988 Aberd.

MCGARRITY, Susan Josephine Holywood Road Surgery, 54 Holywood Road, Belfast BT4 1NT Tel: 028 9065 4668; 9 Barnetts Crescent, Belfast BT5 7BQ Tel: 01232 489347 — MB BCh BAO 1982 Belf.; MRCGP 1988; DCH NUI 1986; DRCOG 1985.

MCGARRY, Conor Joseph Patrick 480 Lisburn Road, Belfast BT9 6GU — MB BCh BAO 1992 Belf.; MB BCh Belf. 1992.

MCGARRY, Fiona Jane 335 Albert Drive, Glasgow G41 5HJ — MB ChB 1993 Dundee.

MCGARRY, Gerald William Department of Otolaryngology, Glasgow Royal Infirmary, Glasgow G31 2ER Tel: 0141 211 4330 — MB ChB 1984 Glas.; MD Glas. 1997; FRCS ORL HNS 1993; FRCS (Orl.) Ed. 1990; FRCS Glas. 1988; FRCS Ed. 1988. (Glasgow) Cons. Otolaryngol. Glas. Roy. Infirm. Socs: Otorhinolaryngol. Soc.; Brit. Assn. Otolarynol. Head & Neck Surgs.; Scott. Otolaryngol. Soc. Prev: Sen. Regist. (Otolaryngol.) Glas. Teachg. Hosps.

MCGARRY, James Alexander (retired) 57 Fotheringay Road, Glasgow G41 4NN Tel: 0141 423 0938 — MB ChB 1954 Glas.; FRCOG 1974, M 1961. Prev: Cons. O & G S.. Gen. Hosp. Glas.

MCGARRY, John Michael (retired) Calthorpe Clinic, 4 Arthur Road, Edgbaston, Birmingham B15 2UE Email: admin@calthorpe-clinic.co.uk — MB ChB 1961 Bristol; MFFP 1993; FRCOG 1986, M 1968; DObst RCOG 1964. Mem. Gen. Counc. Bar Professional Conduct Comm. Prev: Med. Dir. Calthorpe Clinic Birm. & Med. Dir. S. Manch. Private Clinic.

MCGARRY, Mary Bridget Anne 9 Shrewsbury Road, Brooklands, Sale M33 3TW — MB BCh BAO 1973 NUI.

MCGARRY, Philip Joseph Mater Hospital, Crumlin Road, Belfast BT14 6AB Tel: 028 90 802402; 16 Dorchester Park, Belfast BT9 6RH — MB BCh BAO 1981 Belf.; MRCPsych 1986. (Qu. Univ. Belf.) Cons. Gen. Adult Psychiat. Mater Hosp. & Roy. Vict. Hosps. Belf.

MCGARVA, Mr John 1 Atholl Place, Dunblane FK15 9AQ Tel: 01786 822139 — MB ChB 1980 Glas.; FRCS Glas. 1984; FRCS (ENT) Ed.1987. Cons. Otolaryngol. Forth Valley HB. Prev: Regist.

(ENT) Vict. Infirm. Glas.; Sen. Regist. Rotat. (Otolaryngol.) Leeds; Regist. (Gen. Surg.) W. Scotl. Surg. Train. Scheme.

MCGARVEY, Lorcan Patrick Augustine 13 Church Avenue, Dunmurry, Belfast BT17 9RS — MB BCh BAO 1990 Belf.

MCGARVEY, Niamh 45 Stockman's Lane, Belfast BT9 7JD — MB BCh 1998 Belf.

MCGAUGHEY, David Gibson Church Street Surgery, 1 Church Street, Newtownards BT23 4FH Tel: 028 9181 6333 Fax: 028 9181 8805 — MB ChB 1981 Bristol.

MCGAULEY, Gillian Anne Department of Psychotherapy, Richard adds Centre, Broadmoor Hospital, Crowthorne RG45 7EG Tel: 01344 754396 — MB BS 1983 Lond.; BSc Lond. 1980; MRCPsych 1987. (St Bart's) Cons. & Sen. Lect. in Forens. Psychother. W. Lond. Ment. Health NHS Trust. Socs: Brit. Med. Assn. (Mem.); Roy. Coll. of Psychiat.s (Mem.).

MCGAVIGAN, Andrew Douglas Flat 1/1, 122 Beith St., Glasgow G11 6HD — MB ChB 1995 Glas.

MCGAVIGAN, James Arncliffe, Glasgow Road, Kilsyth, Glasgow G65 9AD — MB ChB 1968 Glas.; FRCPath 1988, M 1977. (Glas.) Cons. Bact. Forth Valley Health Bd. Prev: Cons. Glas. Roy. Matern. Hosp. & Glas. Roy. Infirm.; Cons. & Sen. Regist. Glas. Roy. Infirm.

MCGAVIGAN, Maureen Elizabeth 66 Mainswood, Park Mains, Erskine PA8 7JW — MB ChB 1990 Glas.

MCGAVIGAN, Peter Paul Pentland Medical Centre, 44 Pentland View, Currie EH14 5QB Tel: 0131 449 2142 Fax: 0131 451 5855; Garden Cottage, 40 Johnsburn Road, Balerno, Edinburgh EH14 7BB Tel: 0131 449 3995 — MB ChB Glas. 1970; MRCGP 1975; DCH RCPS Glas. 1973; DObst RCOG 1972. Socs: BMA.

MCGAVIN, Clive Roderick Plymouth Chest Clinic, Derriford Hospital, Derriford Road, Plymouth PL6 8DH Tel: 01752 763862 Fax: 01752 763864 Email: clive.mcgavin@phnt.swest.nhs.uk — MA Camb. 1971. MD 1981, MB 1970, BChir 1969; FRCP Lond. 1987. Cons. Gen. & Thoracic Phys. Plymouth Hosp. NHS Trust; Hon. Sen. Lect. Univ. Plymouth. Prev: Sen. Regist. (Med.) St. Jas. Hosp. Balham & Roy. Brompton Hosp.; Regist. City Hosp. Edin.

MCGAVIN, David Blackthorn Medical Centre, St. Andrews Road, Barming, Maidstone ME16 9AL Tel: 01622 726277 Fax: 01622 725774 — MB BS 1970 Lond.; MRCGP 1977; MFHom. 1982; DCH Eng. 1976. (Lond. Hosp.) Med. Off. Blackthorn Trust (Med. Charity Serving Seriously & Chronically Ill).

MCGAVIN, Mr David Douglas Murray Department of Preventive Ophthalmology, Institute of Ophthalmology, Bath St., London EC1V 9EL Tel: 020 7608 6909 Fax: 020 7250 3207; Canniesbum, 71 Brickhill Drive, Bedford MK41 7QE — MB ChB Glas. 1962; MD (Hons.) Glas. 1975; FRCS Ed. 1968; FRCOphth 1988; DO Eng. 1968; DCH RCPS Glas. 1966; DObst RCOG 1964. (Glas.) Assoc. Sen. Lect. (Preven. Ophth.) Inst. Ophth. Lond.; Med. Dir. Internat. Resource Centre; Edr. Community Eye Health. Prev: Project. & Med. Dir. N.O.O.R. Eye Inst. Kabul & Herat. Ophth. Centre; Sen. Regist. Tennent Inst. Ophth. Glas.

MCGAVIN, Mr Donald Burns Dolphin House, Weston by Welland, Market Harborough LE16 8HS — MB BChir 1931 Camb.; MA, MChir Camb. 1939, MB BChir 1931; FRCS Eng. 1934; MRCS Eng. LRCP Lond. 1933. (Camb. & St. Bart.) Surg. Emerit. Leicester Roy. Infirm. Socs: Fell. Assn. Surgs. Gt. Brit.; Leicester Med. Soc. Prev: Chief Asst. Surgic. Unit, St. Bart. Hosp.; Surg. Regist. Roy. Nat. Orthop. Hosp. Lond.

MCGAVIN, James Grant (retired) Glentyn, Coalport Road, Madeley, Telford TF7 5BN Tel: 01952 585769 — MRCS Eng. LRCP Lond. 1941.

MCGAVOCK, Elizabeth Four Winds, 55 Culcrum Road, Cloughmills, Ballymena BT44 9NJ Tel: 01265 638258 Fax: 01265 638258 — MB BCh BAO 1965 Belf.; MB BCh BAO (Hons.) Belf. 1965. (Belf.) Indep. Med. Specialist Child, Adolesc. & Family Ment. Health. Socs: BMA Ulster Sub-Div. (Ex. Chairm.); Ulster Med. Soc. Prev: Phys. i/c Child Guid. Clinic Ballymoney Health Centre Co. Antrim; Regist. (Psychiat.) Holloway Sanat. Virginia Water & Long Gr. Hosp. Epsom; Ho. Off. Roy. Vict. Hosp. Belf.

MCGAVOCK, Professor Hugh Biomedical Sciences, Univ. of Ulster, Coleraine BT52 1SA Tel: 01265 44141; Four Winds, 55 Culcrum Road, Cloughmills, Ballymena BT44 9NJ Tel: 01265 638258 Fax: 01265 638258 — MB BCh BAO 1964 Belf.; BSc (Physiol. Hons.) Belf. 1961, MD 1977, MB BCh BAO 1964; FRCGP 1990. (Belf.) Prof. Prescribing Sci., Univ. Ulster; Course Organizer

MCGAWLEY

(Cont. Professional Developm.); NI Counc. Postgrad. Med. & Dent. Educ.; Mem. Comm. on Safety of Med.; Mem. Comm. of UK DURG. Socs: Hon. Life Mem. UK DURG; Fell. (ad eundem) Roy. Coll. GPs; BMA. Prev: GP & Clin. Tutor Qu.'s Univ. Belf.; Maj. RAMC Sen. Specialist (Human Physiol.); Dir. Drug. Utilization Research Unit Qu. Univ. Belf.

MCGAWLEY, Cecilia Mary Primrose Avenue Surgery, 1 Primrose Avenue, Urmston, Manchester M41 0TY Tel: 0161 747 2424 Fax: 0161 747 7344 — MB ChB 1978 Manch.

MCGEACHIE, John Francis 5 Devon Drive, Diggle, Saddleworth, Oldham OL3 5PP — MB ChB 1977 Glas.; FFA RCS Eng. 1982. Cons. Anaesth. Oldham HA. Socs: Europ. Soc. Regional Anaesth.; Assn. Anaesth. Gt. Brit. & Irel. Prev: Sen. Regist. (Anaesth.) N. W.. RHA; Regist. (Anaesth.) W.. Infirm. Glas.; Regist. (Anaesth.) Palmerston N. Hosp. New Zealand.

MCGEACHY, Donald James 1A Crescent Road, Heybridge, Maldon CM9 4SJ Tel: 01621 842245 Fax: 01621 842245 Email: dmcgeachy@hotmail.com — MB ChB Glas. 1978.

MCGEACHY, Julie Elizabeth Tillingham Medical Centre, 61 South Street, Tillingham, Southminster CM0 7TH Tel: 01621 778383 Fax: 01621 778034; 102 Imperial Ave, Mayland, Chelmsford CM3 6AJ Tel: 01621 740030 Fax: 01621 740030 — BMedSci 1985 Nottm.; BM BS Nottm. 1997; MRCGP 1991. Princioal GP, Tillingham Med. Centre, Essex. Prev: Princip. GP, Roxburgh, New Zealand.

MCGECHAEN, Kenneth Wilson Sunfield Medical Centre, Sunfield Place, Stanningley, Pudsey LS28 6DR Tel: 0113 257 0361 Fax: 0113 236 3261 — MB ChB 1987 Leeds; BSc (Hons.) Path. Leeds 1984, MB ChB 1987; DRCOG 1992; DA (UK) 1992. Prev: Trainee GP Leeds VTS.

MCGEE, Andrew Murray 74 Stanley Road, Hoylake, Wirral CH47 1HZ — MB ChB 1993 Birm.

MCGEE, Cameron Thomas 3 Hazel Lea, 44 Lansdown Road, Cheltenham GL51 6PU — MB BS 1996 Lond.

MCGEE, Fergus Christopher 49 Pear Tree Lane, Bexhill-on-Sea TN39 4RQ — MB BS 1986 Lond.; DCH RCP Lond. 1994; DRCOG 1993.

MCGEE, Henry Mary Jude Royal Oldham Hospital, Rochdale Road, Oldham OL1 2JH — MB BCh BAO 1976 NUI.

MCGEE, Professor James O'Donnell Nuffield Department of Pathology & Bacteriology, Level 4, Academic Block, John Radcliffe Hospital, Headington, Oxford OX3 9DU Tel: 01865 220549 Fax: 01865 220078 Email: jamesmcgee@ndp.ox.uk; 17 Cadogan Park, Woodstock OX20 1UW Tel: 01993 811556 Fax: 01993 813664 — MB ChB 1962 Glas.; PhD Glas. 1969, MD (Hons.) 1973; MA Oxf. 1975; FRCP Glas. 1989; FRCPath 1986, M 1974. Prof. Morbid Anat. Univ. Oxf. Head Nuffield Dept. Path. & Bact. John Radcliffe Hosp Oxf; Hon. Cons. Oxf. DHA; Fell. Linacre Coll. Prev: Sen. Lect. & Hon. Cons. (Path.) Roy. Infirm. Glas.

MCGEE, Janet Ann TY Perllan, Vicarage Park, Redlynch, Salisbury SP5 2JZ — BM BCh 1985 Oxf.; BA Oxf. 1981; MRCP (UK) 1988; MRCGP 1990; DRCOG 1990.

MCGEE, Maria Teresa 221 Manchester New Road, Middleton, Manchester M24 1JT — MB ChB 1979 Manch.

MCGEE, Patricia Jane 2 Frenshaw Way, Pewsey SN9 5HA — MB BS 1996 Lond. (St Mary's Hospital Medical School) SHO (Anaesth.) MusGr. Pk. Hosp. Taunton Som.

MCGEE, Shaun Gerard Gregory Department of Clinical Radiology, Salisbury District Hospital, Salisbury SP2 8BJ Tel: 01722 336262 — MB BS 1985 Lond.; BA Oxf. 1980; MRCP (UK) 1989; FRCR 1993. Cons. Radiol. Salisbury Dist. Hosp. Salisbury Healthcare NHS Trust. Prev: Vis. Prof. Radiol. Duke Univ. Med. Centre N. Carolina, USA; Sen. Regist. (Diag. Radiol.) Welsh Train. Scheme Univ. Hosp. Wales Cardiff.; Research Fell. (Gastrointestinal Radiol.) St. Mark's Hosp. Lond.

MCGEE, Thomas Campbell Barns Street Surgery, 3 Barns Street, Ayr KA7 1XB Tel: 01292 281439 Fax: 01292 288268 — MB ChB 1978 Glas.; MRCGP 1983; DFFP 1993; DRCOG 1981. (Univ. Glas.) Princip./Trainer in Gen. Pract.; Company Med. Adviser to Aerostructure Manufacturer.

MCGEECHAN, Anne Teresa Ninewells Hospital & Medical School, Dundee Tel: 01382 660111; The Old School House, Drimmie, Bridge of Cally, Blairgowrie PH10 7JS — MB ChB 1987 Ed.; MRCP Ed. 1992. (Ed.) Staff Grade Gen. Paediat./ Paediat. Neurol.

MCGEECHAN, Peter 17 Main Street, Stewarton, Kilmarnock KA3 5BS Tel: 01560 2531 — MB ChB 1963 Glas.

MCGEEHAN, Mr Daniel Francis Accident & Emergency Unit, Stafford District General Hospital, Weston Road, Stafford ST16 3SA Tel: 01785 257731; 60 Sneyd Avenue, Westlands, Newcastle ST5 2PY Tel: 01782 712488 Fax: 01785 203111 Email: dannymac@netcentral.co.uk — MB ChB 1973 Leeds; FRCS Ed. 1980. (Univ. Leeds) Socs: Fell. Fac. A & E Med.; Brit. Trauma Soc.; Brit. Assn. Accid. & Emerg. Med.

MCGEOCH, Mr Christopher McGregor 39 Berwick Road, Shrewsbury SY1 2LS Tel: 01743 240030 Fax: 01743 350393 Email: chris@mcgeoch.fsnet.co.uk — MB ChB 1973 Glas.; FRCS Ed. (Orth.) 1983; FRCS Ed. 1978. (Glasgow) Sen. Arthroplasty Specialist Robt. Jones & Agnes Hunt Orthop. Hosp. OsW.ry. Prev: Regist. (Orthop.) Robt. Jones & Agnes Hunt Orthop. Hosp. OsW.ry.; Cons. (Orthop.) Roy. Shrewsbury Hosp.

MACGEOCH, Colin Maxwell, MBE (retired) Maes Araul, Penslade, Fishguard SA65 Tel: 01348 872824 — MRCS Eng. LRCP Lond. 1928. Prev: Ho. Surg. Childr. Hosp. Birm.

MCGEOCH, Kenneth Lennie 19 Stanely Avenue, Paisley PA2 9LB Tel: 0141 884 4813 Fax: 0141 884 7149 Email: k.l.mcgeoch@btinternet.com — MB ChB Glas. 1955; FFOM RCP Lond. 1995, MFOM 1992, AFOM 1982; MRCGP 1968; DObst RCOG 1959. Cons. Hand & Arm Vibration Syndrome HAVS Test Centre Mitsui Babcock Ltd.

MCGEOCH, Paul Duncan 7C Bruce Road, Glasgow G41 5EL — MB ChB 1998 Aberd.; MB ChB Aberd. 1998.

MCGEORGE, Mr Alistair Department of Urology, Burnley General Hospital, Casterton Avenue, Burnley BB10 2PQ Tel: 01282 425071; 3 Wood Close, Roughlee, Nelson BB9 6PQ Tel: 01282 695009 — MB ChB 1972 Glas.; FRCS Ed. 1976; FRCS Glas. 1976. Cons. Urol. Burnley Gen. Hosp.

MCGEORGE, Anne Patricia EEG Department, Institute Neurological Sciences, Southern General Hospital, Glasgow G52 4TF Tel: 0141 201 1100; 37 Charlotte Street, Helensburgh G84 7SE Tel: 01436 673790 — MB ChB 1969 Glas.; DObst RCOG 1972. Assoc. Specialist (EEG) Inst. Neurol. Sc. S.. Gen. Hosp. Glas.

MCGEORGE, Mr Douglas Donald Department of Plastic & Reconstructive Surgery, Countess of Chester Hospital, Chester CH2 1UL Tel: 01244 365988 Fax: 01244 366277 — MB ChB 1980 Manch.; FRCS (Plast Surg.) Ed. 1992; FRCS Ed. 1984. p/t Cons. Plastic Surg. Countess of Chester Hosp. Prev: Sen. Regist. (Plastic Surg.) Qu. Mary's Hosp. Roehampton; Regist. (Plastic Surg.) Whiston Hosp.

MCGEORGE, Ronald Samuel (retired) Rodos, 2 St Annes Way, Fence, Burnley BB12 9HL Tel: 01282 693947 — MB ChB 1935 Glas.

MCGEOUGH, Patrick Thomas Salisbury Medical Centre, 474 Antrim Road, Belfast BT15 5GF Tel: 028 9077 7905; 43 Lismoyne Park, Belfast BT15 5HE Tel: 01232 777759 — MB BCh BAO 1966 Belf.; MPhil Belf. 1994; MSc (Immunol.) Lond. 1987. (Belf.) Socs: FRCGP.

MCGEOWN, James Graham 56 Deramore Park, Belfast BT9 5JU — MB BCh BAO 1982 Belf.; MB BCh Belf. 1982.

MCGEOWN, Mark Francis James 12 Seafield Park, Portstewart BT55 7JU — MB BCh BAO 1985 Belf.

MCGEOWN, Professor Mary Graham, CBE (retired) Queen's University of Belfast, Room31, Whitla medical Building 97 Lisburn Road, Belfast BT9 7BL Tel: 01232 272241 Fax: 01232 438346 Email: mmcgowan@qub.ac.uk — MB BCh BAO (Hons.) 1946; PhD Belf. 1953, MD 1950; Hon. DSc Ulster 1983; FRCPI Dub. 1982; FRCP Lond. 1978, M 1978; FRCP Ed. 1969, M 1967; Hon. DMedSci Belf. 1991. Cons. Nephrol. Belf. City Hosp.. Prev: Profess. Fell.sh. Qu. Univ. Belf. 1988.

MCGEOWN, Philip Thomas 5 Charnwood Court, Belfast BT15 5DJ — MB BCh 1998 Belf.

MCGETTIGA, Helen 158 Thistle Grove, Welwyn Garden City AL7 4AQ — MB BS 1996 Lond. Med. SHO Rotat. Qu. Eliz. II Hosp. Welwyn Garden City Herts. Prev: SHO (A & E) N.wick Pk. Hosp. Harrow Middlx.

MCGETTIGAN, Clare Patricia 40 Kendal Drive, Liverpool L31 9AZ — MB ChB 1994 Sheff.

MCGETTIGAN, Hugh Christopher Straderry, 5 Hamden Way, Papworth Everard, Cambridge CB3 8UG Tel: 01480 830236 — MB

BS 1994 Lond.; MRCP (Lond.) 1997. (St. Thos.) SHO Neurol. Diabetes & Endocrinol. Guy's Hosp. Lond. Prev: SHO (Gastroenterol., Endocrinol. & Gen. Med.) Qu. Eliz. II Hosp. Welwyn Garden City; SHO (A & E) Kent & Canterbury Hosp.

MCGETTIGAN, Josephine Therese Topps Park, Fintry Road, Denny FK6 5JF Tel: 01324 826221 — MB ChB 1987 Aberd.; MRCGP 1992; DRCOG 1991; DFFP 1994; DPD 1997. Community Med. Off. (Palliat. Care) Hospice Phys. Denny. Prev: Trainee GP Boston VTS; Regist. (Med.) W.. Austral.; Clin. Asst. (Dermat.) Stirling.

MCGETTRICK, Sheila Margaret Prince & Princess of Wales Hospice, 71 Carlton Place, Glasgow G5 9TD Tel: 0141 429 5599 Fax: 0141 429 8780 Email: ppwhclinical @aol.com; 11 Coylton Road, Newlands, Glasgow G43 2TA Tel: 0141 637 5382 Fax: 0141 569 5129 — MB ChB 1974 Glas.; Dip. Palliat. Med. Wales 1993; Dip. Ethics Cancer & Palliat. Care Keele 1999. Med. Dir. (Palliat. Med.) P. & P.ss of Wales Hospice Glas.; Hon. Cons. (Palliat. Med.) Vict. Infirm. NHS Trust; Hon. Clin. Sen. Lect. Glas. Univ. Socs: Assn. Palliat. Med. Prev: Clin. Asst. P. & P.ss Wales Hospice Glas.

MCGHEE, Alastair George Peartree Lane Surgery, 110 Peartree Lane, Welwyn Garden City AL7 3UJ Tel: 01707 329292; 30 Guessens Road, Welwyn Garden City AL8 6RA Tel: 01707 396608 — MB BS 1987 Lond.; BSc (Hons.) Lond. 1984; MRCGP 1996; DRCOG 1990. Course Organiser Welwyn Gdn. City VTS & GP Trainer. Prev: Trainee GP Qu. Eliz. II Hosp. Welwyn Gdn. City VTS; Ho. Phys. Univ. Coll & Middlx. Hosp. Lond.

MCGHEE, Mr Alastair Robertson 10 Laverock Park, Linlithgow EH49 6AT; 2 Baronshill Court, Linlithgow EH49 7SP — MB ChB 1992 Ed.; FRCS Ed. (A&E) 1998. (Universiy of Edinburgh) SHO III (A & E) Monklands Dist. Gen. Hosp.

MCGHEE, Professor Charles Ninian John University of Dundee, Department of Ophthalmology, Ninewells Hospital & Medical School, Dundee DD1 9SY Tel: 01382 632714 Fax: 01382 660130 Email: l.e.rose@dundee.ac.uk — MB ChB 1983 Glas.; BSc (Hons.) Glas. 1981; FRCS Glas. 1988; FRCOphth 1989; PhD Dundee 1999. (Glas.) Prof. (Ophth.) & Head Dept. Univ. Dundee; Hon. Cons. (Ophth. Surg.) Ninewells Hosp. & Med. Sch. Dundee. Socs: Ex-Pres Brit. Excimer & Keratorefractive Laser Soc.; Counc. Mem. UK & Irel. Cataract & Refractive & Refractive Soc. Prev: Cons. (Ophth.) Prof. Ocular Therap. Sunderland Eye Infirm.; Sen. Reg. Oprithalmology, Tennent Inst. Glas.

MCGHEE, Chrystine 21 Bantaskine Street, Falkirk FK1 5ES Tel: 01324 23966 — MB ChB 1976 Glas.; DRCOG 1978.

MCGHEE, Daniel Patrick Townhead Health Centre, 16 Alexandra Parade, Glasgow G31 2ES Tel: 0141 531 8972 Fax: 0141 531 8980; 21 Gartconnell Road, Bearsden, Glasgow G61 3BW Tel: 0141 942 0656 Fax: 0141 531 8980 — MB ChB 1972 Glas.; FRCGP 1993, M 1979; FFA RCSI 1978. Hon. Lect. (Physiol. & Pharmacol.) Strathclyde Univ. Prev: Regist. (Anaesth.) W.. Infirm. Glas.; SHO (Med. Paediat.) Roy. Hosp. Sick Childr. Glas.; SHO (O & G) S.. Gen. Hosp. Glas.

MCGHEE, Kenneth James Seaford Health Centre, Dane Road, Seaford BN25 1DH Tel: 01323 490022 Fax: 01323 492156; Raphael, 36 Headland Avenue, Seaford BN25 4PZ Email: mcghee@fastnet.co.uk — MB BS 1971 Lond.; MRCS Eng. LRCP Lond. 1976; Cert. JCC Lond. 1977; DFFP 1996. (St. Mary's) Hosp. Pract. (Respirat. Med.) S. Downs Health Trust; Police Surg. E. Downs Sussex Police. Socs: Fell. Roy. Soc. Med.; Brit. Thorac. Soc. & Assn. Police Surgs. Prev: SHO St. Mary's Hosp. Lond.; Regist. (Cardiothoracic Med.) Centr. Middlx. Hosp. & Willesden Chest Clinic; SHO Norf. & Norwich Hosp. Norwich.

MCGHEE, Michael 53 Borough Street, Castle Donington, Derby DE74 2LB Tel: 01332 810241; Davaar, Grange Farm, Main St, Hemington, Derby DE74 2TJ Tel: 01332 811077 — MB BS 1975 Lond.; D.Occ.Med 1999; MFFP 1996; MRCS Eng. LRCP Lond. 1975; MRCGP 1980; DRCOG 1977. (St. Mary's) Sen. Part. Derby. Prev: Squadron Ldr. RAF Retd.

MCGHEE, Thomas David Department of Anaesthesiology, Newham Hospital, Glen Road, London E13 8SL — MB ChB 1967 Ed.; FFA RCSI 1976; T(Anaes) 1991.

MCGHIE, Alan Stephen Trevaylor Road Health Centre, Trevaylor Road, Falmouth TR11 2LH Tel: 01326 317317 — MB ChB Glas. 1977; MRCGP 1984; D.Occ.Med. RCP Lond. 1996; DA Eng. 1981; DRCOG 1979.

MCGHIE, Fiona Jane The James Cochrane Practice, Maude Street/Helme Chase Surgeries, Kendal LA9 Tel: 01539 722124 — MB ChB 1991 Glas.; MRCGP 1995; DFFP 1995. Asst. GP Kendal. Prev: Trainee GP Paisley.

MCGHIE, Jonathan 82 Larch Drive, East Kilbride, Glasgow G75 9HG — MB ChB 1998 Glas.; MB ChB Glas 1998.

MCGIBBEN, Barbara Frances 15 Windsor Avenue, Belfast BT9 6EE — MB BCh BAO 1969 Belf.

MCGIBBEN, Laurence James 17 Rufus Close, Lewes BN7 1BG — MB BCh BAO 1972 Belf.; MRCPsych 1986; DPM RCPSI 1985. Cons. Child & Adolesc. Psychiat. Community Servs. Centre Hailsham. Prev: Sen. Regist. (Child & Adolesc. Psychiat.) Hollymoor Hosp. Birm.; Sen. Regist. (Child & Adolesc. Psychiat.) Child Psychiat. Unit Gulson Hosp. Coventry; Med. Off. Trust Dub.

MCGIBBEN, Patricia Dianne 15 Ardlee Avenue, Holywood BT18 9LT — MB BCh BAO 1980 Belf.; FRCPath 1997; MRCPath 1990. Cons. Histopath. Belf. link Labs, Belf. City Hosp. Prev: Cons. Histopath. Antrim Laborat. Antrim Hosp.

MCGIBBON, Alasdair Fram 71 Finedon Road, Irthlingborough, Wellingborough NN9 5TY Tel: 01933 260 — MB BS 1960 Lond.; MRCS Eng. LRCP Lond. 1960; DObst RCOG 1963. Socs: BMA. Prev: Sen. Ho. Off. St. Mary's Hosp. Kettering; Ho. Surg. (ENT) King's Coll. Hosp.; Ho. Phys. Dulwich Hosp.

MACGIBBON, Barbara Haig, CB (retired) 5 Liverpool Road, Kingston upon Thames KT2 7SX Tel: 020 8541 0168 — BM BCh Oxf. 1953; BA (Hons.) Oxf. 1950; MRCPath 1972. Prev: Sen. Lect. & Hon. Cons. Haemat. St. Thos. Hosp. & Med. Sch. Lond.

MCGIBBON, Cyril Quarry Court, Quarry St., Woolton, Liverpool L25 6DY — MD 1945 Liverp.; MB ChB 1937. (Liverp.) Socs: N. Eng. Dermat. Soc.; Brit. Assn. Dermat. Prev: Cons. (Dermat.) Liverp. Regional Hosp. Bd.

MCGIBBON, David Hugh 8 Pickfords Wharf, Clink St., London SE1 9DG — MB ChB 1969 Liverp.; FRCP Lond. 1986; MRCP (UK) 1974. Cons. Dermat. Greenwich Dist. Hosp. & St. Thos. Hosp. Lond.

MCGIBBON, Ian The Surgery, Gib Lane, Sudbury, Derby DE6 5HY Tel: 01283 585215 Fax: 01283 585069; The Health Centre, Monk St, Tutbury, Burton-on-Trent DE13 9NA Tel: 01283 812455 — MB ChB 1964 Glas.; MRCGP 1985. Socs: Brit. Assn. Sport and Med. (Chair. E. Midls. Region); Brit. Soc. Allergy & Clin. Immunol. Prev: Med. Off. RAF.

MCGIBBON, James Shaw Laidlaw 'Invergarry', 176 Ayr Road, Newton Mearns, Glasgow G77 6ED Tel: 0141 639 2831 — M.B., Ch.B. Glas. 1934. (Glas.)

MACGIBBON, Robert 25 Montague Road, Cambridge CB4 1BU Tel: 01223 515917 Fax: 01223 515917 — MB BS Lond. 1966; MSc (Occupat. Med.) Lond. 1973; MRCS Eng. LRCP Lond. 1965; MRCGP 1976; FRCGP 1999. (Char. Cross) Socs: RCGP (Hon. Treas. E. Anglia Fac.); BMA. Prev: Lect. GP Unit Univ. Coll. Hosp. Sch. Med. Lond.; GP Tutor Whittington Hosp. Postgrad. Centre Lond.

MCGIBBON, Shaun Patrick 66 Bangor Road, Holywood BT18 0LN Tel: 0123 174430 — MB BCh BAO 1946 Belf.

MCGIBBON, Shaun Patrick 42 Cranmore Gardens, Belfast BT9 6JL — MB BCh 1983 Wales.

MCGIBBON, Shauna Barwell Medical Centre, 39 Jersey Way, Barwell, Leicester LE9 8HR Tel: 01445 842981; 3 Cadle Close, Stoney Stanton, Leicester LE9 4HD — MB ChB 1990 Glas.; DRCOG 1994. GP Undergrad. Tutor, Leicester Univ.; Hosp. Undergrad. Tutor, Leicester Univ. Socs: BMA & Brit. Assn. Sports Med. Prev: Trainee GP Burton-on-Trent; SHO Burton Dist. Hosp. VTS.

MCGIBNEY, David Park House., Church Lane, Barham, Canterbury CT4 6QR Tel: 01227 830494 — MB ChB 1977 Leeds; BSc Leeds 1974, MB ChB 1977; MRCP (UK) 1979; FFPM 1993. Vice-Pres. Europ. Clin. Research Pfizer Centr. Res. Sandwich. Socs: Med. Res. Soc. Prev: Dir. Pfizer Centr. Res. Sandwich.

MACGILCHRIST, Alastair John Scottish Liver Transplant Unit, Royal Infirmary, Edinburgh EH3 9YW Tel: 0131 536 1620 Fax: 0131 536 1520 Email: alastair.macgilchrist@cs.com; 7A Tantallon Place, Edinburgh EH9 1NY Tel: 0131 668 4364 Email: amacgilchrist@compuserve.com — MB ChB 1979 Glas.; MRCP (UK) 1982; MD Glas. 1988; FRCP (Glas). 1994; FRCP (Ed.) 1998. (Glas.) Cons. Gastroenterol. & Hepatologist Roy. Infirm. of Edin. Socs: Brit. Soc. Gastroenterol.; Amer. Assn. Study Liver Dis.; Scott. Soc. Phys.

MCGILCHRIST, John Morrison (retired) 2 New Place, London Road, Sunningdale, Ascot SL5 9SD Tel: 01344 621441 — MB ChB

MACGILL

1947 St. And.; MB ChB (Commend.) St. And. 1947; FFPM RCP (UK) 1989. Prev: Med. Dir. Dow-Lepetit Ltd., Warner-Lambert (UK) Ltd. & E.R. Squibb & Sons. Ltd.

MACGILL, Alexander New Street Health Centre, New Street, Stevenston KA20 3BB Tel: 01294 464413 Fax: 01294 604234; 2 Kinnis Vennel, Woodside, Kilwinning KA13 6UB — MB ChB 1985 Glas. Prev: Trainee GP Airdrie; SHO (Psychiat.) Woodille Hosp. Lenzie; SHO (Obst.) Bellshill Matern. Hosp.

MCGILL, Andrew Michael Mardale, Florence Drive, Kilmacolm PA13 4JN — MB ChB 1998 Ed.; MB ChB Ed 1998.

MCGILL, Brian Walker Motherwell Health Centre, 138-144 Windmill Street, Motherwell ML1 1TA Tel: 01698 265193 Fax: 01698 253324; 14 Alloway Gardens, Hamilton ML3 9XZ — MB ChB 1977 Manch.

MCGILL, David (retired) Hill House, 170 Stepney Road, Scarborough YO12 5NH Tel: 01723 503162 — MB ChB 1943 Glas.

MCGILL, David James 632 George Street, Aberdeen AB25 3XN — MB ChB 1998 Aberd.; MB ChB Aberd 1998. PRHO (Gen. Med). Aberd. Roy. Inf. Aberd. Prev: PRHO Surg. Aberd. Roy. Inf. Aberd.

MCGILL, Denis Aubrey Francis Old Farm House, Cripstead Lane, St Cross, Winchester SO23 9SE — MRCS Eng. LRCP Lond. 1952; MD Lond. 1958, MB BS 1952; FRCP Lond. 1971, M 1955. (Guy's) Cons. Phys. Roy. Hants. Co. Hosp. Winchester. Socs: Fell. Roy. Soc. Med. & Med. Soc. Lond. Prev: Sen. Med. Regist. Guy's Hosp. Lond.

MCGILL, Eileen Veronica Abercrombie (retired) 4 Porth-y-Castell, Barry CF62 6QA Tel: 01446 732679 — LRCP LRCS Ed. LRFPS Glas. 1945; MRCGP 1958; DObst RCOG 1950. Prev: Ho. Surg. Roy. N.. Infirm. Inverness & Simpson Matern. Pavil. Roy. Infirm. Edin.

MCGILL, Fiona Joy 7 Sketty Park Drive, Sketty, Swansea SA2 8LN — MB BCh 1994 Wales.

MCGILL, Glenys Mary (retired) Kilmeny Surgery, 50 Ashbourne Road, Keighley BD21 1LA Tel: 01535 606415 Fax: 01535 669895 — MB ChB 1974 Leeds. Prev: Clin. Asst. (Diabetes) Airedale Gen. Hosp. Steeton.

MCGILL, Helen Lesley Castle Street Surgery, 39 Castle Street, Luton LU1 3AG Tel: 01582 729242 Fax: 01582 725192; The Bungalow, Ringshall, Berkhamsted HP4 1ND Tel: 01442 843532 Fax: 01442 843532 Email: chloetweed@mcmail.com — MB BS 1983 Lond.; BDS (Hons.) Lond. 1976; Pharmacol. (Hons.). (Middlesex Hospital London) Bd: Mem. Luton PCG.

MCGILL, Ian Gordon (retired) 17 Lisburne Square, Torquay TQ1 2PT Tel: 01803 294248 Fax: 01803 299576 Email: ian@lisburnedoc.demon.co.uk — BM BCh Oxf 1960; MA Oxf. 1960; FRCP Lond. 1979, M 1963. Prev: Cons. Phys., S. Devon Healthcare Torbay Hosp. Torquay.

MCGILL, James Glynn Eborall and Partners, Fountain Medical Centre, Sherwood Avenue, Newark NG24 1QH Tel: 01636 704378/9 Fax: 01636 610875; Box Tree Farm House, Main St, Norwell, Newark NG23 6JN Email: mcgill@boxtreefarm.demon.co.uk — MB BChir 1971 Camb.; MA Camb. 1972, MB BChir 1971; MRCP (U.K.) 1974; MRCGP 1980; Dip. Occ. Med. 1998. (Cambridge and St. George)

MCGILL, Mr James Iggleden (cons. rooms) Chalybeate Hospital, Tremona Road, Southampton SO16 6UY Tel: 02380 775544 Email: mcgill@tcp.co.uk; Keeping Farm, Beaulieu, Brockenhurst SO42 7XA Tel: 01590 616322 Fax: 01590 616322 Email: mcgill@tcp.co.uk — BM BCh 1967 Oxf.; BA 1962 Oxf.; DPhil 1965 Oxf.; MA 1966 Oxf.; FRCS Eng. 1971; FRCOphth 1988. (Middlx.) Cons. Ophth. Surg. Soton. Univ. Hosp.; Reader Opth. Soton. Univ. Hosps. Socs: Fell. Roy. Soc. Med.; Oxf. Ophth. Soc. Prev: Sen. Resid. Moorfields Eye Hosp. (City Rd. Br.) Lond.; Ho. Surg. Surgic. Unit & Ho. Phys. (Neurol.) Middlx. Hosp. Lond.; SHO W.. Ophth. Hosp. Lond.

MCGILL, John Ultan Downpatrick Road Surgery, 14 Downpatrick Road, Killyleagh, Downpatrick BT30 9RG Tel: 028 4482 8746 Fax: 028 4482 1458; 46 Tullykin Road, Killyleagh, Downpatrick BT30 9TW Email: ulty@msn.com — MB BCh BAO 1982 Belf.; FRCP Ed. 1995; MRCP Ed. 1985; MRCGP 1988; DCH RCPSI 1987.

MCGILL, Neil Andrew 31 St Ledgers Road, Queens Park, Bournemouth BH8 9BA — BM 1989 Soton.

MCGILL, Patrick Paul Benedict 214 Park Road N., Birkenhead CH41 8BU — MB BCh BAO 1946 NUI. (NUI)

MCGILL, Paul Edward 14 North Campbell Avenue, Milngavie, Glasgow G62 7AA Tel: 0141 956 6381 — MD 1974 Glas.; MB ChB 1964; FRCP Glas. 1992; FRCP Ed. 1979, M 1968; DObst RCOG 1966. (Glas.) Cons. Phys. Stobhill Hosp. Glas.

MCGILL, Ronald Kilmeny Surgery, 50 Ashbourne Road, Keighley BD21 1LA Tel: 01535 606415 Fax: 01535 669895 Email: rmcgill@bradford-ha.northg.nhs.uk; Hob Lane Farm, Stanbury, Keighley BD22 0HW Tel: 01535 646797 Email: ron.mcgill@talk21.com — MB ChB 1974 Leeds; MRCGP 1978. Prev: Course Organiser Airendale Vocational Train. scheme. Airedale Gen. Hosp. Keighley.

MCGILL, Rory Michael St Budeaux Health Centre, Stirling Road, St. Budeaux, Plymouth PL5 1PL Tel: 01752 361010 Fax: 01752 350675; 6 Looseleigh Park, Plymouth PL6 5JL — MB BCh 1982 Wales.

MCGILL, Rosemary Elspeth Thurston (retired) 35 Kilnford Crescent, Dundonald, Kilmarnock KA2 9DW Tel: 01563 850861 Email: rosemary@romemcgill.freeserve.co.uk — MB ChB Ed. 1949. Prev: Assoc. Specialist (Microbiol.) CrossHo. Hosp. Kilmarnock.

MCGILLIGAN, Mr James Anthony 101B Liverpool Road, London N1 0RG — MB BS 1987 Lond.; FRCS Ed. 1992.

MCGILLIGAN, Joseph Marshall Patrick Flat 1, 23 Essendine Road, Maida Vale, London W9 2LT Tel: 020 7286 0863 — MB ChB 1990 Birm.; ChB Birm. 1990; MRCGP 1994. (Birmingham) GP Asst.

MCGILLIGAN, Rachel Celia Flat 1, 23 Essendine Road, Maida Vale, London W9 2LT Tel: 020 7286 0863 — MB BS Lond. 1989; MRCGP 1994; DRCOG 1993. (St. Bart. Lond.)

MACGILLIVRAY, Alastair The Brooke Surgery, 20 Market Street, Hyde SK14 1AT Tel: 0161 368 3312 Fax: 0161 368 5670 — MB ChB 1972 Manch. (Manch.) Princip. GP.

MACGILLIVRAY, Barron Bruce (retired) 21 The Avenue, Wraysbury, Staines TW19 5EY Tel: 01784 482304 Email: bmacg@dircon.co.uk — BSc (Hons.) Witwatersrand 1949; MB BS Lond. 1962; FRCP Lond. 1973, M 1959; MRCS Eng. LRCP Lond. 1955. Prev: Phys. i/c Dept. Clin. Neurophysiol. Roy. Free Hosp. Lond.

MACGILLIVRAY, Donald c/o 1 Speed House, Barbican, London EC2Y 8AT — MB BCh 1989 Witwatersrand.

MCGILLIVRAY, Doreen (retired) 16 Atholl Drive, Giffnock, Glasgow G46 6QR Tel: 0141 571 7810 — MB ChB 1948 Aberd.; DPH 1951. Prev: Ho. Surg. (ENT) & Cas. Off. Aberd. Roy. Infirm.

MACGILLIVRAY, Douglas Armadale Group Practice, 18 North Street, Armadale, Bathgate EH48 3QD Tel: 01501 730432 — MB ChB 1985 Ed.

MACGILLIVRAY, Gay (retired) 28 India Street, Edinburgh EH3 6HB — MB ChB Glas. 1967; DPM Manch. 1977. Prev: Assoc. Specialist (Psychiat.) Vict. Hosp. Blackpool.

MACGILLIVRAY, Ian (retired) Errogie, 35A Coombe Lane, Stoke Bishop, Bristol BS9 2BL Tel: 0117 940 0478 — MD 1953 Glas.; MB ChB 1944; FRCP Glas. 1972, M 1972; FRCOG 1959, M 1949. Prev: Regius Prof. O & G Univ. Aberd.

MCGILLIVRAY, Jennifer Louise 4 Grange Cl, Crowborough TN6 1YD — MB ChB 1997 Sheff.

MACGILLIVRAY, John Balfour (retired) 23 Farington Street, Dundee DD2 1PF — MB ChB 1952 St. And.; FRCPath 1976, M 1964; DCP Lond 1960. Prev: Cons. Pathol. Nine Wells Hosp. & Hon. Sen. Lect. Univ. Dundee.

MACGILLIVRAY, Karen 11 Lingholme, Whitehall Park Estate, Chester-le-Street DH2 2TP — MB ChB 1996 Liverp.

MACGILLIVRAY, Mr Neil (retired) 28 India Street, Edinburgh EH3 6HB — MB ChB 1964 Ed.; FRCS Ed. 1972. Prev: Sen. Regist. (Otolaryngol.) United Manch. Hosps.

MACGILLIVRAY, Ronald Charles (retired) 30 Ashcroft Avenue, Lennoxtown, Glasgow G66 7EN Tel: 01360 310973 — MB ChB Ed. 1946; FRCP Glas. 1965; FRFPS Glas. 1948; FRCPsych 1971; DPM Lond. 1951. Prev: Phys. Supt. Lennox Castle Hosp.

MACGILLIVRAY, Ruth Marjorie (retired) 21 The Avenue, Wraysbury, Staines TW19 5EY Tel: 01784 482304 Fax: 01784 482304 Email: bmacg@dircon.co.uk — MB ChB Manch. 1954; BSc Manch. 1951; MRCGP 1971. Prev: GP New Malden.

MCGILLIVRAY, Mr William Harthill (retired) 16 Atholl Drive, Giffnock, Glasgow G46 6QR — MB ChB 1942 Aberd.; FRCS Ed. 1951. Prev: Cons. ENT Surg. Lanarksh.

MCGIVERN

MCGILLOWAY, Margaret Mary Eimir 14 Heathfield, Culmore Road, Londonderry BT48 8JD Tel: 02871 351787; Flat 5, 3 Anerley Hill, Crystal Palace, London SE19 2BA Tel: 020 8776 9851 Fax: 020 8776 9851 Email: emcgilloway@hotmail.com — MB BCh BAO 1990 Belf.; MRCP (UK) 1993. Socs: Mem. Roy. Coll. of Pysicians. Prev: Regist. (Neurol.) St. Jas. Hosp., Adelaide & Beaumont Hosps. Dub.

MCGILP, Henry Craig (retired) 54 Fox Street, Greenock PA16 8QS — MB ChB 1948 Glas. Prev: GP Greenock.

MCGILP, Robert Henry — MB ChB 1986 Glas.; MRCPsych 1991. Cons. Psychiat., Gt.er Glas. Primary Care NHSTrust. Prev: Regist. (Psychiat.) Leverndale Hosp. Glas.

MCGILVRAY, Ian (retired) 7 The Woodlands, Eccleston Park, Prescot L34 2TN Tel: 0151 426 6615 — MB ChB Liverp. 1952.

MCGIMPSEY, John Murdoch Brook Street Surgery, 9 Brook Street, Holywood BT18 9DA Tel: 028 9042 6984 Fax: 028 9042 6656; 3 Lynwood Park, Holywood BT18 9EU — MB ChB 1976 Manch.

MCGIMPSEY, Stuart John Willowbrook House, 23 Burnside Road, Dunadry, Antrim BT41 2HZ — MB BCh 1998 Belf.; MB BCh Belf 1998.

MCGIMPSEY, William Derek Rosehall Surgery, 2 Mallusk Road, Newtownabbey BT36 4PP Tel: 028 9083 2188 Fax: 028 9083 8820 — MB BCh BAO 1968 Belf.; MRCGP 1972; DCH RCPSI 1971; DObst RCOG 1970. (Belf.)

MCGIMPSEY, William Murdock Montgomery 2 West Circular Road, Cultra, Holywood BT18 0AT — MB BCh BAO 1948 Belf.

MCGINLEY, Anne Louise 4 Ailsa Drive, Langside, Glasgow G42 9UL Tel: 0141 649 8909 — MB ChB 1988 Glas.; MRCGP 1993. Med. Off. GDPS Ruchill Hosp. Glas. Prev: SHO (O & G) Rutherglen Matern. Hosp.; SHO (A & E) Yorkhill Roy. Hosp. Sick Childr.; SHO (Geriat.) Stobhill Gen. Hosp.

MCGINLEY, Eileen Psychotherapy Unit, Maudsley Hospital, London SE5 8AF Tel: 020 7919 2385 Email: E.Mcginley@slam-tr.nhs.uk; Email: eileenmcginley@compuserve.com — MB ChB 1976 Glas.; MRCP (UK) 1979; MRCPsych 1986; FRCP Glas. 1997. p/t Cons. Psychother. Maudsley Hosp. Lond. Socs: Mem., Internat. Psychoanalytic Assn.; Assoc. Mem., Brit. Psychoanalytic Soc. Prev: Sen. Regist. (Psychiat.) Univ. Coll. Hosp. & Middlx. Hosp. Lond.; Regist. (Psychiat.) Maudsley Hosp. Lond.; Fell. (Renal) P. Henry's Hosp. Melbourne, Austral.

MCGINLEY, Ian Gerard Waterside Health Centre, Glendermolt Road, Londonderry BT47 6AU Tel: 028 7132 0100 — MB BCh BAO 1990 Belf.

MCGINLEY, Josephine Frances Breenagh, Penlan Road, Carmarthen SA31 — MB BCh BAO 1945 NUI.

MCGINN, Catherine Mary Stella 61 Dunlambert Park, Belfast BT15 3NL Tel: 01232 778516 — MB BCh BAO 1989 Belf.; MRCP 1993; FRACP 1998. (Queen's University Belfast) Socs: Australasian Soc. Nephrol.

MCGINN, Elizabeth Priscilla Grantham Health Centre, Grantham Road, London SW9 9DL Tel: 020 7733 6191 Fax: 020 7737 2870 — MB BS 1980 Lond.; BA (Anthropol.) Camb. 1977; MRCGP 1986; DRCOG 1986.

MCGINN, Mr Francis Peter (retired) Department of General Surgery, Southampton University Hospitals Unit Trust, Southampton General Hospital, Tremona Road, Southampton SO16 6YD Tel: 02380 794636 — MB BS 1963 Lond.; MPhil Lond. 1970, MS 1976; FRCS Eng. 1970; MRCS Eng. LRCP Lond. 1963; DObst RCOG 1965. Cons. Gen. Surg. (Endocrinel) Soton. Univ. Hosp. Unit Trust & Lymington Hosp. Prev: Lect. & Hon. Sen. Regist. (Surg.) Univ. Soton. Med. Sch.

MCGINN, Gordon Hart Ardgour, Woodrow Avenue, Kilmacolm PA13 4QF — MB ChB 1988 Glas.

MCGINN, Mairead Teresa Anne Tel: 90 798477; Tel: 90 798477 — MB BCh BAO 1994 Belf.; MRCP (UK) 1998; MRCPCH. (Qu. Univ. Belf.) SpR Paediat., Our Lady's Hosp. for Sick Childr., Crumlin. Socs: MRCPCH; Fac. of Paediat., Roy. Coll. of Phys.s Irel.; Brit. Assn. for Community Child Health.

MCGINN, Orna Margaret Sandown Lodge, Littleworth Common Road, Esher KT10 9UE — MB BS 1995 Lond.

MCGINNITY, Francis Gerard Mater Infirmorum Hospital, Belfast BT14 6AB — MB BCh BAO 1980 Belf.

MCGINNITY, Maria Goretti Anne Muckamore Abbey Hospital, 1 Abbey Road, Antrim BT41 4SH; 51 Richmond Park, Stranmillis, Belfast BT9 5EF Tel: 01232 669057 — MB BCh BAO 1976 Belf.; MA 2001 Queen's Belfast; FRCPsych 2000; MRCPsych 1982. (Queen's Belfast) Cons. (Psychiat.) (Learning Disabil.) Belf. Socs: FRCPsych.

MCGINTY, Andrew David 17 Auchendoon Crescent, Ayr KA7 4AS — MB ChB 1992 Manch.

MCGINTY, Frank The White House, Dinedor, Hereford HR2 6LQ Tel: 01432 870376 — MB ChB 1965 Sheff.; BMedSci Sheff. 1970; MRCPath 1974. (Sheff.) Cons. Path. Hereford Co. Hosp.

MCGINTY, Helen Jessica 12 Angel Meadows, Odiham, Hook RG29 1AR — MB ChB 1977 Bristol; MRCGP 1982; DRCOG 1980.

MCGINTY, Mary Joanna Keepers Cottage, Newhouse Road, Earls Colne, Colchester CO6 2PE — MB BS 1983 Lond.; BSc Lond. 1980; FRCA 1992. Cons. Anaesth. Colchester Gen. Hosp.

MCGINTY, Melba Rosemary The White House, Dinedor, Hereford HR2 6LQ Tel: 01432 870376 Fax: 01432 870376 — MB ChB 1965 Sheff.; MRCPCH 1994; DFFP 1993. (Sheff.) Cons. Community Paediat. Heref. Primary Care Trust; Med. Co-Dir. Child Developm. Centre Hereford. Socs: BMA; BPA; Fac. Community Health.

MCGIRR, Brian Patrick The Simpson Health Centre, 70 Gregories Road, Beaconsfield HP9 1PS Tel: 01494 671571 Fax: 01494 680219 — MB BS 1987 Lond.; MRCGP 1991; DCH RCP Lond. 1991; DRCOG 1990. (St. Mary's Padding.)

MCGIRR, Professor Edward McCombie, CBE Anchorage House, 3 Orchard Avenue, Bothwell, Glasgow G71 8NF Tel: 0141 852194 — MB ChB (Hons.) Glas. 1940; Hon. FACP 1971; FFPHM RCP (UK) 1989; FFCM 1972; MD (Hons. & Ballahouston Medal) Glas. 1960; FRSE; BSc Glas. 1937, MD (Hons. & Bellahouston Medal) 1960; Hon. DSc 1994; FRCP Ed. 1962, M 1960; FRCP Glas. 1962; FRCP Lond. 1961, M 1948; FRFPS Glas. 1947. (Glas.) Emerit. Prof. Med. Univ. Glas. Socs: Hon. Mem. Assn. Phys.; Corr. Mem. Amer. Thyroid Assn. Prev: Dean Fac. Med. & Dean of Fac. Univ. Glas.; Chairm. Scott. Health Serv. Plann. Counc.; Chairm. Scott. Counc. Postgrad. Med. Educat.

MCGIRR, Gareth Patrick 10 Edenvale Park, Omagh BT78 5EB — MB BCh BAO 1995 Belf.

MCGIRR, Paul William Finney Lane Health Centre, Heald Green, Cheadle SK8 3DG Tel: 0161 436 8384; 29 Hampton Gardens, Belfast BT7 3DF Tel: 01232 691623 — MB BCh BAO 1984 Belf. Trainee GP Cheadle, Chesh. Prev: SHO (Neurol. & Geriat. Med.) Roy. Vict. Hosp. Belf.; SHO (Gen Med.) Mater Infikmorium Hosp. Belf.; SHO Regional Med. Cardiol. Centre, Roy. Vict. Hosp. Belf.

MCGIVERN, Andrina 15 John Street, Rathfriland, Newry BT34 5QH Tel: 018206 38664; 15 John Street, Rathfriland, Newry BT34 5QH Tel: 018206 38664 — MB BCh 1998 Belf.; MB BCh (Hons) Belf 1998. (Queen's Univ. Belf.) Jun. Ho. Off. Antrim Hosp.

MCGIVERN, Anna Maria Warrenpoint Health Centre, Summerhill, Warrenpoint, Newry BT34 3JD — MB BCh BAO 1988 Belf.; MRCGP 1992; DCH Dub. 1991; DRCOG 1991; DGM RCP Lond. 1990.

MCGIVERN, Carol Battlefield Road Surgery, 148 Battlefield Road, Glasgow G42 9JT Tel: 0141 632 6310 Fax: 0141 636 1180; 35 Merlinford Crescent, Renfrew PA4 8XW Tel: 0141 886 3616 — MB ChB 1992 Glas.; DFFP 1996; MRCGP 1996; DCH 1995; DRCOG 1994. (Glas.) GP Princip. Socs: BMA; MDDUS. Prev: GP Regist.

MCGIVERN, Damian Vincent Chest Unit, Castle Hill Hospital, Castle Road, Cottingham HU16 5JQ Tel: 01482 623011 Fax: 01482 623255; Tel: 01482 328541 Fax: 01482 675061 — BM 1977 Soton.; DM Nottm. 1987; MRCP (UK) 1979. Cons. Thoracic & Gen. Med. Castle Hill Hosp. & Hull Roy. Infirm. Prev: Sen. Med. Regist. Bristol Roy. Infirm. & Frenchay Hosp. Bristol.; Med. Regist. Nottm. City Hosp.; SHO (Med.) Soton. Gen. Hosp.

MCGIVERN, Delia Flat 0/3, 34 St Andrews Square, Glasgow G1 5PP — MB ChB 1997 Glas.

MCGIVERN, Joseph 26 Rushall Manor Road, Walsall WS4 2HF — MB BCh BAO 1942 NUI. (Dub.)

MCGIVERN, Joseph Warrenpoint Health Centre, Summerhill, Warrenpoint, Newry BT34 3JD — MSc Dub. 1977, BA 1982, MB BCh BAO 1982; BSc (Hons.) (1st cl.) Salford 1976; MRCGP 1986; DCH RCP Lond. 1985; DRCOG 1984.

MCGIVERN, Thomas Anthony Glanaber, Lodgebrymbo, Wrexham LL11 4PS — MB BCh BAO 1949 NUI; LAH Dub. 1948.

MCGIVNEY

MCGIVNEY, Mr Ronan Ciaran Vincent 8 The Starkies, Manchester Road, Bury BL9 9QR — MB BCh BAO 1979 NUI; FRCSI 1988; LRCPI & LM, LRCSI & LM 1979.

MCGLADDERY, John Arthur Rectory Road Surgery, 41 Rectory Road, Hadleigh, Benfleet SS7 2NA Tel: 01702 558147; 41 Rectory Road, Hadleigh, Benfleet SS7 2NA Tel: 01702 558147 Fax: 01702 558863 — MB BS Lond. 1956. (St. Bart.) Prev: Ho. Off. (Paediat. & Obst.) Farnham Hosp.; Ho. Surg. & Ho. Phys. Gen. Hosp. Rochford.

MCGLADE, Derek Robert 14 Springwell Road, Durham DH1 4LR — MB ChB 1982 Aberd.; MRCGP 1987; DCW (RCP) Lond. 1996; DRCOG 1989.

MCGLADE, John Francis Xavier Coleraine Health Centre, Castlerock Road, Coleraine BT51 3HP Tel: 028 7034 4834 Fax: 028 7035 8914 — LRCPI & LM, LRSCI & LM 1958; LRCPI & LM, LRCSI & LM 1958. Prev: Ho. Off. St. Kevin's Hosp. Dub.

MCGLADE, Kieran John McGlade, Holmes and Jones, 1 Dunluce Avenue, Belfast BT9 7HR Tel: 028 9024 0884; 6 Ogles Grove, Hillsborough BT26 6RS Tel: 01846 682810 — MD 1989 Belf.; MSc Belf. 1993, MD 1989, MB BCh BAO 1981; MRCGP 1985; DRCOG 1983. Sen. Lect. (Gen. Pract.) Qu. Univ. Belf. Socs: Ulster Med. Soc. Prev: Lect. (Gen. Pract.) Qu. Univ. Belf.; Sen. Regist. (Gen. Pract.) Qu. Univ. Belf.; Clin. Research Fell. (Gen. Pract.) Qu. Univ. Belf.

MCGLADE, Mary Patricia (retired) Oakroyd, Foxholes Road, Horwich, Bolton BL6 6AS Tel: 01204 697883 — MB ChB Manch. 1943, DPH 1948. Prev: Ho. Phys. City Hosp. Chester.

MCGLASHAM, Gordon Medical Centre, Cambridge Avenue, Bottesford, Scunthorpe DN16 3LG Tel: 01724 842415 Fax: 01724 271437; 10 Westcliff Gardens, Scunthorpe DN17 1DT — BSc (1st cl. Hons.) (Chem. Path.) Leeds 1980, MB ChB 1983; T(GP) 1991; Cert. Family Plann. JCC 1987. (Leeds)

MCGLASHAN, Ian Archibald (retired) Kerrys, Causeway End, Felsted, Dunmow CM6 3 Tel: 01371 820511 — MB BS Lond. 1958; Cert FPA 1974. Med. Off. William Julian Ct.auld Hosp. Braintree. Prev: Ho. Surg & Ho. Phys. Black Notley Hosp. Braintree.

MCGLASHAN, Mr Julian Andrew Department of Otorhinolayngology, Queen's Medical Centre, Nottingham NG7 2UH Tel: 0115 924 9924 Fax: 0115 970 9748 Email: julian.mcglashan@nottingham.ac.uk — MB BS 1983 Lond.; FRCS Eng. 1990. (St. Thos. Hosp.) Sen. Lect. Nottm. Univ.; Hon. Cons. Qu. Med. Centre Nottm. Socs: Brit. Assn. Otol.; Brit. Assn. of Performing Arts Med.; Brit. Voice Assn. Prev: Sen. Regist. (ENT) Guy's Hosp. Lond.; Regist. (ENT) Guy's Hosp. Lond.; SHO (ENT) Roy. Nat. ENT Hosp. Lond.

MCGLASHAN, Katherine Anne Kerrys, Causeway End, Felstead, Dunmow CM6 3LU — MB BS 1989 Lond. SHO (Rheum. Rehabil.) Norwich HA. Socs: BMA & Brit. Assn. Sports Med. Prev: SHO (A & E) Kent & Sussex Hosp. Tunbridge Wells; Ho. Surg. Timaru Pub. Hosp. NZ.

MCGLASHON, Donald Wargrave House, St. Owen St., Hereford Tel: 01432 272285; Burlton Court, Burghill, Hereford HR4 7RQ — MB ChB 1970 St. And.; DObst RCOG 1972. Princip. Police Surg. W. Mercia. Prev: SHO (Obst.), SHO (Paediat.) & Ho. Off. (Med. & Surg.) Hereford Co.; Hosp.

MCGLEENON, Bronagh Mary 126 Agincourt Avenue, Belfast BT7 1QD — MB BCh BAO 1993 Belf.

MCGLENNON, Deidre Mary 41 Riverdale Park N., Belfast BT11 9DL — MB BCh BAO 1989 NUI.

MCGLENNON, Matthew Meadowville, 9 Crownfields, Woodbridge IP13 6EY — MB ChB 1981 Sheff.; MPH Leeds 1985; Cert. Family Plann. JCC 1984; MFPHM 1991. Cons. Pub. Health Med. E. Suff. HA. Prev: Sen. Regist. (Community Med.) Bradford HA; Hon. Research Fell. Clin. Epidemiol. Unit Bradford Univ.; Regist. (Community Med.) Harrogate HA.

MCGLEW, James Martin 93 Dromore Road, Ballynahinch BT24 8HU — MB BCh 1998 Belf.; MB BCh Belf 1998.

MCGLINCHEY, Iain Vale of Leven Hospital, Alexandria G83 0UA Tel: 01389 754121 — MB ChB 1985 Glas.; FRCS Glas. 1989; FRCR 1996. Cons. Radiol. Vale of Leven Dist. Gen. Hosp. Alexandria. Prev: Sen. Regist. (Radiol.) W.. Infirm. Glas.; Regist. Rotat. (Surg.) Vict. Infirm. Glas.

MCGLINCHEY, Paul Gerard 12 Sperrin View, Tamlaght Road, Omagh BT78 5BJ — MB BCh BAO 1995 Belf.

MACGLONE, Calum Michael James MacDuff 47 Dunvegan Avenue, Kirkcaldy KY2 5TG — MB ChB 1992 Aberd.

MCGLONE, Gerard Corbett Baillieston Health Centre, 20 Murside St., Baillieston, Glasgow G69; 69 Stewarton Drive, Cambuslang, Glasgow G72 8DQ — LRCP LRCS 1950 Ed.; LRCP LRCS Ed. LRFPS Glas. 1950. Prev: Ho. Surg. Perth Roy. Infirm.; Sen. Ho. Phys. Lymington & Dist. Gen. Hosp.; Sen. Ho. Surg Matern. Hosp. S. Shields.

MCGLONE, Katherine Jane 7 Oaks Forstal, Sandhurst, Cranbrook TN18 5JR — MB BS 1998 Lond.; MB BS Lond 1998.

MCGLONE, Laura 3A Tay Sq, Dundee DD1 1PB — MB ChB 1997 Dundee.

MCGLONE, Michelle Carmel Baillieston Health Centre, 20 Muirside Road, Baillieston, Glasgow G69 7AD Tel: 0141 531 8050 Fax: 0141 531 8067 — MB ChB 1973 Glas. Clin. Med. Off. E. (Glas.) Health Dist.

MCGLONE, Peter (Surgery) 6/8 High Street, Irvine KA12 0AY; 167 Bank Street, Irvine KA12 0NH — MB ChB 1965 Glas. (Glas.) Prev: RAMC.

MCGLONE, Raymond Gerard Accident & Emergency Department, Lancaster Royal Infirmary, Ashton Road, Lancaster LA1 4RP Tel: 01524 583004 Fax: 01524 583010 Email: ray.mcglone@laht.nwest.nhs.uk; 16 Derwent Road, Lancaster LA1 3ES Tel: 01524 64772 — MB BS 1980 Lond.; FRCS (A&E) Ed. 1987; FRCP (UK) 1997, MRCP (UK) 1983; FFAEM 1993; ATLS 1997. (London) Cons. A & E Lancaster Roy. Infirm. Socs: Catholic Doctors Guild; Christian Med. Fell.ship; Brit. Assn. of A&E Med. Prev: Sen. Regist. (A & E) Yorks. RHA; SHO & Regist. Rotat. (A & E) Trent RHA; Regist. (Med.) Roy. Gwent Hosp. Newport.

MCGLYNN, Jacqueline Mary 53 Longdales Avenue, New Carron Village, Falkirk FK2 7HZ Tel: 01324 613921 — MB ChB 1991 Ed. Trainee GP Falkirk Unit Forth Valley HB VTS.

MCGLYNN, Stephen John 40 Kennedy Drive, Airdrie ML6 9AW — MB ChB 1998 Dund.

MCGOLDRICK, Alicia Nuala 6 Courtlands, Billericay CM12 9HX Tel: 01277 56230 — MB BCh BAO 1967 NUI. (Univ. Coll. Dub.) Socs: BMA. Prev: Med. Off. Govt. Nigeria Med. Serv.; Med. Off. Govt. Singapore Med. Serv.

MCGOLDRICK, Hugh Patrick Mary Hannah and McGoldrick, Health Centre, Pound Lane, Downpatrick BT30 6HY — MB BCh BAO 1980 NUI.

MCGOLDRICK, Mr Patrick Joseph Dunleary, Off Street Lane, Roundhay, Leeds LS8 1DF Tel: 0113 269 0154 — MD 1991 Belf.; MB BCh BAO 1981; FRCS Ed. 1985. Cons. Cardiothoracic Surg. Gen. Infirm. Leeds & Sen. Lect. Univ. Leeds. Socs: Soc. Cardiothoracic Surg. of Gt. Brit. & Irel.; Specialist Advisory Comm.; Roy. Coll. Surgs. (Cardiac Surg.). Prev: Sen. Regist. (Cardiac. Surg.) Papworth Hosp.

MCGOLDRICK, Susan 68A Downham Road, London N1 5BG — MB ChB 1992 Ed.

MCGOLDRICK, Vivienne Maria Clare Craigavon Area Hospital Group HSS Trust, 68 Lurgan Road, Craigavon BT63 5QQ Tel: 01762 334444 Fax: 01762 350068 — MB BCh BAO 1990 Belf. Staff Phys. Craigavon Area Hosp. Socs: BMA; Brit. Assn. Sport & Med.; Irish Soc. Rheumat.

MCGONAGLE, Denis Gerard Flat 2, 38 Hyde Terrace, Leeds LS2 9NZ — MB BCh BAO 1990 NUI.

MCGONIGAL, Aileen Flat F, 255 Kelvindale Avenue, Glasgow G12 0QU — MB ChB 1994 Glas.; MRCP (UK) 1997. (University of Glasgow) Specialist Regist. Clin. Neurophysiol. Glas.

MCGONIGAL, Gerard The Beeches, 78A Hatch Lane, Basingstoke RG24 7EF — MB ChB 1986 Glas.; MD Glas. 1993; MRCP (UK) 1990. Cons. Geriat. Med. N. Hants. Hosp. Basingstoke.

MCGONIGAL, Judith Aileen 19 Shoregate, Crail, Anstruther KY10 3SU; 19 Shoregate, Crail, Anstruther KY10 3SU — MB ChB 1998 Ed.; MB ChB Ed 1998; BSc Med Sci 1997. (Edinburgh) PRHO Freeman Hosp. Prev: PRHO Yorkhill Hosp.

MCGONIGLE, Richard Jonathon Scott Hoo Meavy House, Hoo Meavy, Yelverton PL20 6JE — MRCS Eng. LRCP Lond. 1975; MD Lond. 1987, MB BS 1975; MRCP (UK) 1978; FRCP 1999. Cons. Phys. and Nephrologist Plymouth.

MCGONIGLE, Robert Joseph 39 Upper Green, Dunmurry, Belfast BT17 0EL — MB ChB 1993 Glas.; DGM 1996; DRCOG 1997; MRCGP 1998. (Glas.) Partership, Gen. Prac. Dumbarton Health Centre, Station Rd, Dumbarton, G82 1PW. Prev: GP Princip., Renfrew Health Centre, Renfrew.

MCGONIGLE, Thomas Paul 48 Moss Lane, Whitefield, Manchester M45 8NQ — BM BS 1997 Nottm.

MCGOOGAN, Euphemia Department of Pathology, University Medical School, Teviot Place, Edinburgh EH8 9AG Tel: 0131 650 2894 Fax: 0131 650 6528; 51 Caiyside, Edinburgh EH10 7HW Tel: 0131 477 1333 — MB ChB 1973 Aberd.; FRCPath 1992. Hon. Cons. Path. & Clin. Dir. (Path. Servs.) RIE NHS Trust; Sen. Lect. (Path.) Univ. Edin. Socs: Internat. Acad. Cytol. (Exec. Counc. Mem.).

MCGORRIGAN, Jeanette Lesley Le Riche Buchanan Road Surgery, 72 Buchanan Road, Sheffield S5 7AL Tel: 0114 245 6679; 59 Dransfield Road, Crosspool, Sheffield S10 5RP Tel: 0114 230 2369 — MB ChB 1977 Sheff.; MRCGP 1981; DRCOG 1979. Socs: BMA; Inst. Psychosexual Med.

MCGORRY, Karen Mary Hassocks Health Centre, Windmill Avenue BN6 8LY Tel: 01273 843563 — MB BS 1994 Lond.; MRCGP 2000; DFFP 2000; 2000 LoC IUD; MRCOG I 1996; DRCOG 1998. (Royal Free Hospital) GP, Hassocks Health Centre; Family Plann. Doctor, Exchange Rd., Crawley.

MCGOUGH, John Gerard Church Farm, Victoria Road, Aldeburgh IP15 5EB; Mill Edge, 28 Victoria Road, Aldeburgh IP15 5EG Tel: 01728 453188 Email: john@mcgough.enta.net — MB ChB 1974 Manch.; MB ChB (Hons.) Manch. 1974; BSc (Hons.) Liverp. 1965; MRCGP 1979.

MCGOURAN, Rory Charles Martin The Close, East Rudham, King's Lynn PE31 8SU Tel: 01485 528925 Fax: 01553 766266 — MD 1981 Lond.; MB BS 1969; FRCP Lond. 1989; MRCP (UK) 1975. (St. Thos.) Cons. Phys. Qu. Eliz. Hosp. Kings Lynn. Socs: Brit. Soc. Gastroenterol. Prev: Sen. Regist. (Med.) St. Geo. Hosp. Lond.

MCGOURTY, Ethna Christina 19 Ailesbury Road, Belfast BT7 3FH — MB BCh BAO 1980 Dub.; MRCPI 1982.

MCGOURTY, John Charles Queen Elizabeth Hospital, Gayton Road, King's Lynn PE30 4ET Tel: 01553 613613 Fax: 01553 613900 Email: john.mcgourty@klshosp.anglox.nhs.uk; The Old Rampant Horse, The Green, Shouldham, King's Lynn PE33 0BY — MB ChB 1980 Sheff.; BSc (Hons. Physiol.) Sheff. 1976; FRCP Lond. 1994; MRCP (UK) 1983. Cons. Geriat. Med. Qu. Eliz. Hosp. Kings Lynn. Prev: Research Regist. (Med.) Hypertens. Unit Clatterbridge Hosp. Bebington; Regist. (Med.) Roy. Hallamsh. Hosp. Sheff.; Sen. Regist. Roy. Devon & Exeter Hosp. Exeter.

MCGOURTY, Linda Jane 50 Dunvegan Avenue, Kirkcaldy KY2 5TG — MB ChB 1995 Glas.

MCGOVERN, Alan Watson Nethertown Surgery, Elliot Street, Dunfermline KY11 4TF Tel: 01383 623516 Fax: 01383 624254 — MB BS 1978 Newc.; MRCGP 1986.

***MCGOVERN, Anna Elizabeth** 2 Ashley Gardens, Belfast BT15 4DN — MB BCh BAO 1994 Belf.

MCGOVERN, Anthony James 126 Elizabeth Street, Blackpool FY1 3QN Tel: 01253 28949 — MB BS 1964 Durh.; DObst RCOG 1965. Socs: BMA. Prev: Ho. Off. (Med. & Surg.) Roy Vict. Infirm. Newc.; Ho. Off. (Obst.) Glenroyd Matern. Hosp. Blackpool.

MCGOVERN, Clare Frances Mary The Middlesex Hospital, Mortimer St., London W1T 3AA Tel: 020 7380 9013; 5A Crogsland Road, London NW1 8AY — MB BS 1993 Lond.; BSc Nottm. 1983; MSc Lond. 1984, MB BS 1993; DA (UK) 1995, Roy Coll Anaesth.; FRCA 1999. (St Barts. Hosp. Med. Coll.) Specialist Regist. (Anaesth.) UCL Hosps.

MCGOVERN, Dermot Anthony 71 Wentworth Road, Harborne, Birmingham B17 9SS — MB ChB 1974 Birm.; MPhil Birm. 1996; FRCPsych 1997, M 1980. (Birm.) Cons. Psychiat. N. Birm. Ment. Health Trust. Prev: Cons. Psychiat. BromsGr. & Redditch HA.

MCGOVERN, Dermot Patrick Bracher DerrifordHospital, Plymouth PL6 8DH Tel: 01752 777111; Kent House, Mary Tavy, Tavistock PL19 9PR Tel: 01872 810090 — MB BS 1993 Lond.; MRCP (UK) 1996. (St. Mary's Hosp. Med. Sch. Lond.) Specialist Regist. (Gastroenterol. & Gen. Internal Med.) SW Region (plymth). Prev: SHO Rotat. (Med. & ITU) Frenchay Hosp. Bristol; SHO Rotat. (Med.) Gloucester Roy. Hosp.; Specialist Regist. (Gastroenterol. & Gen. Internal Med.) SW Region (Truro).

MCGOVERN, Dominic John Lloyd Old Hall Grounds Health Centre, Old Hall Grounds, Cowbridge CF7 7AH Tel: 01446 772383 Fax: 01446 774022 — MB ChB 1991 Dundee.

MCGOVERN, Donald Ormsby Magdalen Medical Practice, Lawson Road, Norwich NR3 4LF Tel: 01603 475555 Fax: 01603 787210; 25 Thorpe Hall Close, Norwich NR7 0TH — MB ChB 1979 Dundee; DRCOG 1983; DA Eng. 1983.

MCGOVERN, Gerald Patrick (retired) 41 Gilmour Road, Edinburgh EH16 5NS Tel: 0131 667 2604 — MB ChB 1952 Ed.; FRCP Ed. 1971, M 1958; FRCPsych 1985, M 1971; DPM Eng. 1959.

MCGOVERN, Grace Josephine McMaster 15 Fortwilliam Drive, Belfast BT15 4EB Tel: 01232 771549 — MB BCh BAO 1959 Dub.

MCGOVERN, Helen 34 Beechcroft Gardens, Wembley HA9 8EP Tel: 0208 904 5444 Fax: 0208 904 7063 — MB BS 1990 Lond.; MRCP (UK) 1996; MRCGP 1997. GP Princip.

MCGOVERN, Ian 21 Royal Victor Place, Old Ford Road, London E3 5SS — MB BS 1993 Lond.

MCGOVERN, John Martin 149 Cavehill Road, Belfast BT15 5BL — MB BCh BAO 1985 Belf.

MCGOVERN, Mary Claire Royal Belfast Hospital for Sick Children, Belfast BT12 6BE — MB BCh BAO 1988 Belf.; MRCP (UK) 1993.

MCGOVERN, Michael 71 Roupell Street, London SE1 8SS — MB BCh BAO 1974 Dub.; MRCPI 1981; MRCPath 1984.

MCGOVERN, Sheila Margaret Mary 28 Upper Malone Park, Belfast BT9 6PP — MB BCh BAO 1991 Belf.

MCGOVERN, Thomas Desmond 15 Fortwilliam Drive, Belfast BT15 4EB Tel: 01232 771549 — MB BCh BAO 1958 NUI.

MCGOVERN, Ursula Brigid 7 First Avenue, London W3 7JP — MB ChB 1998 Leic.; MB ChB Leic 1998; BSc (Hons) Liverp 1993.

MCGOVERN, Vincent Michael 17 Knightsbridge Manor, Belfast BT9 5ET Tel: 01232 683088 — MB BCh BAO 1981 Belf.; MRCGP 1989; DRCOG 1987. Clin. Asst. (A & E) Ulster Hosp. Dundonald; Clin. Asst. Asthma Clinic Roy. Belf. Hosp. for Sick Childr. Socs: Ulster Paediat. Soc.

MACGOWAN, Alasdair Peter Department Microbiology, Southmead Hospital, Westbury-on-Trym, Bristol BS10 5NB Tel: 0117 959 5652 Fax: 0117 959 3154 Email: macgowan_a@southmead.swest.nhs.uk; Elmside, Stone, Berkeley GL13 9LB Tel: 01453 520236 — MB ChB Aberd. 1983; MD Bristol 1990; BMedBiol (Hons.) (Immunol.) Aberd. 1980; MRCPath 1991; FRCPath 1999. (Aberd.) Cons. Med. MicroBiol. N. Bristol NHS Trust S.mead Hosp.; Clin. Reader MicroBiol. Bristol. Socs: Hon. Gen. Sec. Brit. Soc. Antimicrobial Chemother. Prev: Sen. Regist. (Med. MicroBiol.) S. W.. RHA; Regist. (Med. MicroBiol.) S.mead DHA; Lect. (Path.) Univ. Aberd.

MCGOWAN, Alastair Accident & Emergency Department, St. James's University Hospital, Beckett St., Leeds LS9 7TF — MB ChB 1977 Ed.; FRCS 2000 Ed.; FRCP Ed. 1990; FRCP Lond. 1992. Cons. A & E Med. St. Jas. Hosp. Leeds.

MCGOWAN, Alison Kim Blackford House Medical Centre, 137 Croft Lane, Hollins, Bury BL9 8QA Tel: 0161 766 6622 Fax: 0161 786 2748; 24 Lodge Mill Lane, Turn Village, Edenfield, Bury BL0 0RW Tel: 01706 824913 — MB ChB 1992 Manch.; BSc (Hons.) Leeds 1986; MRCGP 1996; T(GP) 1996; DFFP 1994. (Univ. Manch.) Mem. Bury & Rochdale LMC. Prev: GP/Regist. Minden Health Centre Bury; SHO Blackburn VTS.

MCGOWAN, Angela Rosemary 38 Langside Drive, Glasgow G43 2QQ — MD 1975 Glas.; MB ChB 1961. (Glas.)

MCGOWAN, Barbara Maria Christina 9 Heathside Road, Moor Park, Northwood HA6 2EE — MB BS 1998 Lond.

MCGOWAN, Catherine Margaret 47 Church Cr, Newtownabbey BT36 6ES — MB ChB 1997 Liverp.

MCGOWAN, Damien Joseph Springfield Road Surgery, 44-46 Springfield Road, Belfast BT12 7AH Tel: 028 9032 1454 Fax: 028 9020 1106 — MB BCh BAO 1986 Belf.

MCGOWAN, Donald Wilson 41 Whitefauld Road, Dundee DD2 1RJ — MB ChB 1993 Manch.

MCGOWAN, Fiona Jane St Brycedale Surgery, St. Brycedale Road, Kirkcaldy KY1 1ER — MB ChB 1989 Ed.; MRCGP 1993; DRCOG 1991. Prev: Trainee GP Kirkcaldy VTS.

MCGOWAN, Graham Kemp, Maj. RAMC Retd. (retired) Awel y Mor, Lon Bridin, Morfa Nefyn, Pwllheli LL53 6BY Tel: 01758 721027 — BM BCh 1939 Oxf.; BA Oxf. 1935; FRCPath 1963. Prev: Cons. Chem. Path. Bristol Roy. Infirm.

MCGOWAN, Ian Michael Anthony Gilead Sciences, 333 Lakeside Drive, Foster City CA 94404, USA Tel: 00 1 650 574 3000 Fax: 00 1 650 572 6626 Email: ian_mcgowan@gilead.com; Flat D, 37

MCGOWAN

MCGOWAN Woodville Road, London W5 2SE — MB ChB 1985 Liverp.; DPhil Oxf. 1995; MRCP (UK) 1988. Sen. Clin. Research Phys. Glaxo Wellcome Greenford, Middlx.; Assoc. Dir. Gilead Scis.; Hon. Sen. Lect. Med. King's Coll. Sch. Med. Dent. Lond. Socs: RSM Lond.

MCGOWAN, James Howatson 99 Glasgow Road, Strathaven ML10 6NF — MB ChB 1993 Glas.

MCGOWAN, Janet Filmer Court Lodge Oast, Warbleton, Heathfield TN21 9BD Tel: 01435 831120 — MB BS 1975 Lond.; MRCS Eng. LRCP Lond. 1975; FFA RCS Eng. 1979. Cons. Anaesth. E.bourne Dist. HA. Socs: Intractable Pain Soc.; Assn. Anaesth. Prev: Sen. Regist. (Anaesth.) E.bourne Dist. HA; Sen. Regist. (Anaesth.) Bristol Health Dist. (T); Regist. (Anaesth.) Bristol Dist. (T).

MACGOWAN, Joanna Rachel Flat 2, 35 Kings Avenue, London N10 1PA — MB BS 1991 Lond.; BSc (Hons.) Lond. 1987.

MCGOWAN, John David Coatbridge Medical Practice, Coatbridge Health Centre, 1 Centre Park Court, Coatbridge ML5 3AP.Tel: 01698 422950 Fax: 01698 437787 — MB ChB 1962 Glas.

MCGOWAN, Joyce Janet Coulter Elizabeth 9 Fields Park Court, Newport NP20 5BD — MB ChB 1966 Glas. Socs: BMA. Prev: Clin. Med. Off. N. Gwent Health Dist.; SHO (Rheum.) Univ. Hosp. Wales Cardiff; Ho. Surg. Robroyston Hosp. Glas.

MCGOWAN, Julie Maria Moorcroft Medical Centre, 10 Botteslow Street, Hanley, Stoke-on-Trent ST1 3NJ Tel: 01782 281806 Fax: 01782 205755; Holdenby, Denford Road, Longsdon, Stoke-on-Trent ST9 9QG Tel: 01538 399565 — MB BS 1983 Lond.; MRCGP 1988; DRCOG 1989. (St. Bart.)

MCGOWAN, Karen Therese 5 Sandown Close, Ipswich IP1 6RF — MB BCh BAO 1991 NUI.

MCGOWAN, Marian Elizabeth Lucinda Community House, Trust Head Quarters, Fountain Drive, Carshalton SM5 4NR Tel: 020 8770 8335 Fax: 020 8770 8424 — MB BCh 1975 Wales; FRCP Lond. 1995; FRCPCH 1997. (Welsh Nat. Sch. Med.) Cons. Paediat. Epsom & St Helier NHS Trust. Prev: SCMO Camberwell HA; Research Regist. (Paediat. Neurol.) King's Coll. & Guy's Hosps. Lond.; Regist. (Paediat.) Roy. Free Hosp. Lond.

MCGOWAN, Mary Pauline Springburn Health Centre, 200 Springburn Way, Glasgow G21 1TR Tel: 0141 531 9641 Fax: 0141 531 9642 — MB BCh BAO 1976 Belf.; DCh Belf. 1979, MB BCh 1976; MRCGP 1980; DRCOG 1978.

MCGOWAN, Mervyn Thomas Sea Mills Surgery, 2 Riverleaze, Sea Mills, Bristol BS9 2HL Tel: 0117 968 1182 Fax: 0117 962 6408 — MB BCh BAO 1978 Belf.; MRCGP 1985; DRCOG 1984.

MCGOWAN, Michelle Bridget Boultham Park Medical Practice, Boultham Park Road, Lincoln LN6 7SS Tel: 01522 874444; 9 Limelands, Greetwell Road, Lincoln LN2 4AR Tel: 01522 568825 — MB ChB 1987 Leeds; BSc Hons. Leeds 1984, MB ChB 1987; MRCGP 1992; Cert. Family Plann. JCC 1990; DRCOG 1990. (Leeds) GP Partner Boultham Pk. Socs: Lincoln Med. Soc. Prev: Partner Birchwood Med. Pract.; SHO (A & E) Leeds Gen. Infirm.; SHO (Med. for Elderly & O & G) St. James' Univ. Hosp. Leeds.

MCGOWAN, Neil James 11 Kirkfield W., Livingston Village, Livingston EH54 7BD — MB ChB 1998 Glas.; MB ChB Glas 1998.

MCGOWAN, Patrick Francis Grange House Surgery, 22 Grange Road, Hartlepool TS26 8JB Tel: 01429 272679 Fax: 01429 861265; Tel: 01480 861311 Fax: 01480 861352 — MB BCh BAO 1985 Dub.; BA Dub. 1985; MRCGP 1990; Cert. Family Plann. JCC 1989; Dip. AGP 1998 (Newcastle University). (Trinity Coll. Dub., Ireland) Socs: BMA; MRCGP. Prev: Trainee GP Preston VTS; SHO (ENT Surg.) W. Wales Gen. Hosp. Carmarthen; SHO (O & G) S. Cleveland Hosp.

MCGOWAN, Patrick Hugh (retired) 11 Portlock Avenue, Liverpool L16 9JT Tel: 0151 722 7364 — LRCPI & LM, LRCSI & LM 1942; DPH NUI 1946.

MCGOWAN, Patrick Joseph Aloysius 4 Castlewood, Castlecoole Road, Enniskillen BT74 6HZ — MB BCh BAO 1984 NUI.

MCGOWAN, Patrick Robert Department of Anaesthesia, Barnet and Chase Farm Hospitals NHS Trust, Barnet EN5 3DJ Tel: 020 8216 5283 Fax: 020 8216 5297 Email: painclinic@eggconnect.net — MB ChB 1988 Liverp.; LMSSA Lond. 1988; FRCA 1993; DA (UK) 1991. Cons. (Anaesth. & Pain Managem.) Barnet and Chase Farm Hosp.s NHS Trust. Prev: Sen. Regist. (Anaesth.) NE Thames; Regist. Rotat. (Anaesth.) Mersey Region; Assoc. Vis. Prof. Texas Tech. Univ. Health Sci. Center.

MCGOWAN, Paul Joseph Alma Street Medical Centre, Alma Street, Stockton-on-Tees TS18 2AP Tel: 01642 607248 Fax: 01642 612968 — MB BCh BAO 1984 Dub.; MRCGP 1988; DCCH RCP Ed. 1988; DRCOG 1988; DGM RCP Lond. 1986. (Trinity Coll. Dub.) Socs: BMA.

MACGOWAN, Mr Simon William Department of Cardiac Surgery, Royal Victoria Hospital, Grosvenor Road, Belfast BT12 6BA Tel: 01232 263000 Fax: 01232 894918 Email: smacg@iol.ie — MB BCh BAO 1983 NUI; BSc NUI 1985; FRCSI 1987; LRCPI & LM, LRCSI & LM BAO 1983; MCh NUI 1995. (Roy. Coll. Surgs. Irel.) Cons. Cardiac Surg. Roy. Vict. Hosp. Belf. Socs: Soc. Cardiothoracic Surgs. GB & Irel.

MCGOWAN, Stephen William 37 Gallowstree Lane, Newcastle ST5 2QR — BM BCh 1990 Oxf.

MCGOWAN, Stuart Watson (retired) 41 Whitefauld Road, Dundee DD2 1RJ Tel: 01382 65281 — MB ChB 1952 Glas.; FFA RCS Eng. 1960; DA Eng. 1957. Prev: Cons. Anaesth. Dundee Teachg. Hosps.

MCGOWAN, Wesley Alexander Wolsey 153 Mountsandel Road, Coleraine BT52 1TA — MB BCh BAO 1972 Belf.; MD Belf. 1979; FFA RCSI 1977. Cons. Anaesth. The Route Hosp. Ballymoney; Med. Dir. Causeway HSS Trust. Socs: Assn. Anaesth. GB & Irel. & Mem. N. Irel. Soc. Anaesth.

MCGOWN, Anne Dora 22 Ellesmere Road, Bow, London E3 5QX — MB BChir 1992 Camb.; BA Camb. 1988; MRCP (UK) 1995. Regist. (Chest Med.) Chase Farm Hosp. Socs: Brit. Thorac. Soc. Prev: Regist. (Chest Med.) Roy. Lond. Hosp.; Regist. (Chest Med.) Newham Gen. Hosp.; SHO (Cardiol.) Lond. Chest Hosp.

MCGOWN, Douglas Stewart 39 Thrums Av., Bishopbriggs, Glasgow G64 1ER — MB ChB 1991 Glas.

MCGOWN, Frank McLaren (retired) Rectory House, Stondon Massey, Brentwood CM15 0EJ Tel: 01277 823198 — MD Camb. 1951, MB BChir 1939; FRCP Lond. 1969, M 1946; MRCS Eng. LRCP Lond. 1939. Prev: Phys. OldCh. Hosp., Romford & St. Geo. Hosp. HornCh.

MCGOWN, Margaret Pamela (retired) Rectory House, Stondon Massey, Brentwood CM15 0EJ — MB BS Lond. 1953.

MCGOWRAN, David Paterson (retired) 4 Jumpers Road, Christchurch BH23 2JR Tel: 01202 484356 — MB ChB Ed. 1952; DA Eng. 1965. Prev: Assoc. Specialist (Anaesth.) Bournemouth & E. Dorset Hosp. Gp.

MCGRADY, Brendan Joseph 2 Salney Park, Saul Road, Downpatrick BT30 6PH — MB BCh BAO 1984 Belf.

MCGRAND, Mr James Cull Bereweeke, 30 Bereweeke Road, Winchester SO22 6AJ Tel: 01962 867853 — MB BCh BAO 1958 Belf.; FRCOphth; FRCS Ed. 1966; FRCS Eng. 1967; DO RCS Eng. 1963; DObst RCOG 1960. Cons. Ophth. Surg. Roy. Hants. Co. Hosp. Winchester. Socs: Ophth. Soc. UK & Roy. Soc. Med. Prev: Demonst. (Anat.) Qu.'s Univ. Belf.; Ho. Off. & Sen. Regist. Roy. Eye Hosp. Lond.

MCGRANE, Catherine Elizabeth 85 Clare Road, Bootle L20 9LZ — MB ChB 1985 Manch.

MCGRANE, Conor Thomas 2 Monea Close, Bangor BT19 1AL — MB BCh BAO 1994 NUI.

***MCGRANE, David James** 24 Braedale Avenue, Motherwell ML1 3DX — MB ChB 1998 Glas.; MB ChB Glas 1998.

MCGRANE, Michael 85 Clare Road, Bootle L20 9LZ — MB ChB 1985 Manch.

MCGRANE, Stuart 24 Braedale Avenue, Motherwell ML1 3DX — MB ChB 1998 Glas.; MB ChB Glas 1998.

MCGRANN, Patrick John Beech Tree Surgery, 68 Doncaster Road, Selby YO8 9AJ Tel: 01757 703933 Fax: 01757 213473; Cramond, Burn Hall Close, Burn, Selby YO8 8LS Tel: 01757 270285 — MB ChB 1974 Liverp.; MRCGP 1978; DRCOG 1976. Prev: SHO (Paediat.) Seacroft Hosp. Leeds; SHO (O & G) St. Jas. Hosp. Leeds; Ho. Surg. Harrogate Gen. & Dist. Hosps.

MCGRATH, Alice Mary 11 Gardenside Avenue, Uddingston, Glasgow G71 7BU — MB ChB 1985 Glas.; MRCPsych 1992; MRCGP 1989; DRCOG 1988. Sen. Regist. (Child Adolesc. Psychiat.) DCFP Yorkhill Hosp. Glas. Prev: Trainee GP Paisley VTS; Sen. Regist. (Gen. Psychiat.) Community & Ment. Health Trust Glas.; Regist. (Psychiat.) Dykebar Hosp. Paisley.

MCGRATH, Alison Emma 8 Dawn Close, Thatto Heath, St Helens WA9 5JB — MB BS 1994 Lond.; MRCP 1997. (St Marys)

MCGRATH, Brendan Anthony Prickley Green Cottage, Prickley Green, Martley, Worcester WR6 6QQ — MB ChB 1997 Sheff. Ho. Off. (Gen. Surg.) Orth. Worcs.

MCGRATH, Carol Mary P 39 London Road, Shardlow, Derby DE72 2GR — MB BCh BAO 1982 Dub.; DRCOG 1989; DCCH 1989.

MCGRATH, Conor 9 Clontarf Heights, Omagh BT78 5BL — MB ChB 1996 Liverp.

MCGRATH, Corinne Catherine Bernadette 80 Hubert Road, Birmingham B29 6EG — MB ChB 1992 Birm.

MCGRATH, Daniel (retired) 37 Thornburn Road, Weston Favell, Northampton NN3 3DA — MB BCh BAO 1944 NUI; BA, MB BCh BAO NUI 1944; MRCPsych 1971; DPM RCPSI 1947. Prev: Cons. Psychiat. St. Crispin Hosp. Duston.

MCGRATH, Daniel Desmond (retired) 22 Westminster Drive, Wrexham LL12 7AU Tel: 01978 290693 — MB BCh BAO Dub. 1944. Prev: Flight Lt. RAFVR Med. Br.

MCGRATH, Daniel Ronald 3 Ballycairn Road, Coleraine BT51 3HU Tel: 0410 447151 Email: daniel.mcgrath@tesco.net — MB BCh BAO 1995 Belf. SHO (Basic Surg. Rotat.) E.bourne DGH E.bourne. Prev: PRHO, Roy. Gp. Hosps. Belf.; SHO (Surg) Craigavon Area Hosp. Craigavon.

MCGRATH, Edgar Parkinson (retired) 27 Rowallane Dale, Saintfield, Ballynahinch BT24 7LE — MB BCh BAO 1947 Belf.; DPH 1950; FFCM 1981, M 1974; DPA Lond. 1965. Prev: Community Phys. EHSSB Co. Down.

MCGRATH, Graeme John Department of Psychotherapy, Gaskell House, Swinton Grove, Manchester M13 0EU Tel: 0161 273 2762 Fax: 0161 273 4876 Email: gmcgrath@doctors.org.uk — MB BS 1977 Lond.; MA, DPhil Oxf. 1973; FRCPsych 1982. Cons. Psychother. Manch.; Hon. Clin. Lect. Univ. Manch. Prev: Cons. Psychiat. Manch.; Lect. (Adult Psychiat.) Univ. Manch.; Sen. Regist. (Psychiat.) Manch. NW RHA.

MCGRATH, Mrs Helen Jane The Health Centre, Gibson Lane, Kippax, Leeds LS25 7JN Tel: 0113 287 0870 Fax: 0113 232 0746; Ashfield House, 96 Carleton Road, Pontefract WF8 3NQ Tel: 01977 702990 — MB ChB 1963 Liverp. (Liverp.) Prev: Sch. Med. Off. Derbysh. CC; Regist. (Anaesth.) N. Staffs. Hosp. Centre.

MCGRATH, Helen Mary 1 Imperial Terrace, Town Moor, Doncaster DN2 5BU — MB BCh BAO 1969 NUI; MRCP (UK) 1972. (Cork) Cons. Dermat. Doncaster Roy. Infirm.

MCGRATH, Mr James 146 Harley Street, London W1G 7LF Tel: 020 7486 1969 — MB BCh BAO 1959 NUI; MAO 1967; FRCS Ed. 1967; FRCOG 1978, M 1965. (Galw.) Cons. O & G Kingston & Esher DHA. Socs: Fell. Hunt Soc. & Roy. Soc. Med. Prev: Regist. Rotunda Hosp. Dub.; Lect. TC Dub.; Sen. Regist. Inst. O & G Hammersmith Hosp. Lond.

MCGRATH, James Justin Ormonde 119 Circular Road, Jordanstown, Whiteabbey, Newtownabbey BT37 0RE Tel: 01231 64289 — MB BCh BAO 1971 Belf.

MCGRATH, Jane Catherine 23 Hartlebury Way, Charlton Kings, Cheltenham GL52 6YB — MB BS 1985 Lond.; MRCGP 1990; DRCOG 1988.

MCGRATH, John Alexander St. John's Institute of Dermatology, St. Thomas's Hospital, London SE1 7EH Tel: 020 7928 9292 Fax: 020 7922 8175 Email: j.mcgrath@umds.ac.uk; 22 Herald's Place, Renfrew Road, Kennington, London SE11 4NP Tel: 020 7582 5400 — MB BS 1985 Lond.; MD Lond. 1994; MRCP (UK) 1988. (UMDS). Sen. Lect. (Dermat. Molecular Genetics) & Hon. Cons. Dermatol. St. John's Inst. Dermat. Lond. Prev: Sen. Regist. St. John's Inst. Dermat. Lond.; Post Doctoral Research Fell. Jefferson Med. Coll. Philadelphia, USA; SHO & Research Fell. St. John's Inst. Dermat. Lond.

MCGRATH, John Gregor 2 Tower Green, HM Tower of London, London EC3N 4AB — MB BS 1962 Queensland; MRCP (UK) 1972; AFOM RCP Lond. 1980. Med. Adviser to Mirror Gp.; Resid. Med. Off. HM Tower of Lond.; Austral Govt. Med. Off.

MCGRATH, John Samuel 80 Carnvue Road, Newtownabbey BT36 6RQ — BM BS 1994 Nottm.

MCGRATH, Kevin Joseph Department of Anaesthetics, Royal Victoria Hospital, Grosvenor Road, Belfast BT12 6BA — MB BCh BAO 1981 NUI.

MCGRATH, Lois Ruth 9 Sackville Road, Crookes, Sheffield S10 1GT — MB ChB 1990 Sheff.

MCGRATH, Malvida Elena Room 626, The Adelphi, 1-11 John Adam St., London WC2 Tel: 020 7962 8045 Fax: 020 7962 8785; 2 Tower Green, HM Tower of London, London EC3N 4AB Tel: 020 7488 5690 — MB BS 1964 Queensland. Sec. Disabil. Living Allowance Adivs. Bd.

MCGRATH, Martin Marcus 87 Whoberley Avenue, Coventry CV5 8ES Tel: 01203 711097 — MB ChB 1995 Birm.; ChB Birm. 1995. SHO (Med.) Warwick Hosp.

MCGRATH, Michael Brian Joseph (retired) Aslan, Lymm Marina, Warrington Lane, Lymm WA13 0SW — MB BS 1960 Lond.; Acad. Dip. Gen. Biochem. 1967. Prev: Clin. Asst. (Ment. Handicap) Cranage Hall Hosp.

MCGRATH, Patrick Gerard, CB, CBE (retired) 18 Heathermount Drive, Crowthorne RG45 6HN Tel: 01344 774552 — MB ChB 1939 Glas.; FRCPsych 1971; DPsych Ed. 1955. Prev: Hon. Lt.-Col. RAMC.

MCGRATH, Patrick Joseph Tel: 028 9756 2929 — MB BCh BAO 1970 Belf.; MPhil (Med. Ethics & Law) Qu. Univ. Belf. 1993; MRCGP 1976; DObst RCOG 1976. (Qu. Univ. Belf.) Hosp. Pract. (ENT & Dermat. Surg.) Downe Hosp. Co. Down; Forens. Med. Off. Co. Down. Socs: Assn. Police Surg.; Medico-Legal Soc. N. Irel.; Downe Med. Soc.

MCGRATH, Mr Peter Anthony (retired) Ashfield House, 96 Carleton Road, Pontefract WF8 3NQ Tel: 01977 702990 Email: petermcgrath18@hotmail.com — MB BCh BAO NUI 1955; FRCSI 1966. Prev: Cons. Orthop. Surg. Pontefract & Goole Gp. Hosps.

MCGRATH, Peter Desmond Patrick 4 Highgrove Park, Teignmouth TQ14 8FA — BM BCh 1953 Oxf.; DObst RCOG 1956; LMCC 1956. (Oxf. & Univ. Coll. Hosp.)

MCGRATH, Philippa Jane Tarleton Group Practice, Gorse Lane, Tarleton, Preston PR4 6UJ Tel: 01772 812205; 11 Moss Lane, Hesketh Bank, Preston PR4 6AA Tel: 01772 814621 — MB ChB 1986 Dundee; MRCGP 1990; T(GP) 1993. Partner in Gen. Pract. Prev: Trainee GP Tayside VTS.

MCGRATH, William David 106 Lanark Road W., Currie EH14 5LA.

MCGRATH ROSS, Linda 9 Swanston Avenue, Inverness IV3 8QN Tel: 01463 221498 — MB ChB 1981 Aberd. Med. Adviser Benefits Agency Med. Servs. Inverness.

MCGRATTAN, Barry Malachy 15 Belgravia Road, Bangor BT19 6XJ — MB BCh 1998 Belf.; MB BCh Belf 1998.

MCGRAW, Mary Elizabeth Bristol Royal Hospital for Children, Upper Maudlu Street, Bristol BS2 8BJ Tel: 0117 342 8879 Fax: 0117 342 8810 — MB ChB 1976 Bristol; FRCP Lond. 1993; MRCP (UK) 1979; DCH Eng. 1980. Cons. Paediat. Nephrol. S.mead Hosp. Bristol.

MCGRAW, Simon James 214 Bannerdale Road, Sheffield S11 9FE — MB ChB 1992 Sheff.

MCGREAD, Anthony John 34 Harbeton Park, Belfast BT9 6TS — MB BCh BAO 1984 Belf.; MB BCh BAO Belf. 1984; MRCGP 1989; DCH RCP Dub 1988; DRCOG 1987; AFOM London 1998. (Queens University - Belfast) Socs: BMA & Soc. Occupat. Med.; Assoc. of FOM.

MACGREEVY, Brian Irial Patrick 6A Palace Gate, London W8 5NF Tel: 020 7589 2478 Fax: 020 7584 4595 — MB BS 1981 Lond.; MRCP (UK) 1985. (Westm.) Prev: Regist. (Med.) Liver Unit KCH & Roy. Surrey Co. Hosp. Guildford.

MACGREEVY, Bronagh Mary Catherine Health Services, Citibank NA, Cottons Centre, Hays Lane, London SE1 2QT Tel: 020 7500 5004 Fax: 020 7500 2172; 30 Dorville Crescent, London W6 0HJ Tel: 020 8741 9022 Fax: 020 8741 9023 — MB BS 1981 Lond.; MRCS Eng. LRCP Lond. 1981; MRCGP 1986. (Char. Cross) Assoc. Corporate Phys. Citibank NA. Socs: Soc. Occupat. Med. Prev: GP Lond.

MCGREEVY, Niall Gerard James Street Grove Practice, James Street, Workington CA14 2DF Tel: 01900 62241 Fax: 01900 603385; Highgarth, 75 High St, Workington CA14 4EU — MB BCh BAO 1983 NUI; MRCGP 1988; DObst RCPI 1987; DCH NUI 1986.

MACGREGOR, Agnes Murray (retired) 10D Brisbane Court, Braidpark Drive, Giffnock, Glasgow G46 6LX Tel: 0141 633 3781 — MB ChB 1943 Glas.; FRCPS Glas. 1997; DMRD Ed. 1949. Prev: Asst. Specialist (Ultrasonics) Hobhill Hosp. Glas.

MCGREGOR, Aileen Janet Portland Surgery, 1 Dukes Road, Troon KA10 6QR Tel: 01292 312489 Fax: 01292 317837; 9 Sarazen Drive, Troon KA10 6JP Tel: 01292 316055 — MB ChB 1983 Glas.;

MACGREGOR

MRCGP 1987; DRCOG 1985. GP Princip. Prev: Retainer GP; GP Bellshill; Trainee GP Vict. Infirm. Glas. VTS.

MACGREGOR, Ailsa Mary 18 Richmond Terrace, Dundee DD2 1BQ — MB ChB 1996 Dundee. SHO (Gen. Med.) Glas.

MACGREGOR, Professor Alan Duncan Morriston Hospital, Morriston, Swansea SA6 6NL Tel: 01792 703871 Fax: 01792 703737 Email: colette@swansea-tr.wales.nhs.uk; 49 New Road, Llanelli SA15 3DP Tel: 01554 754224 Email: maral@globalnet.co.uk — MB ChB Aberd. 1976; 1987 MD Aberd. 1987; 1986 FRCS (Plast Surg.)1986; 1980 FRCS Glas. 1980; 1997 FRCS Eng. 1997. Cons. Plastic Surg. Morriston Hosp. Swansea; Prof. Reconstruc. Surg. Sch. Biol. Sci. Univ. Wales Swansea. Socs: Brit Assoc of Plastic Surg.s; Brit Assoc of Head and Neck Oncologists; Brit Assoc of Clin. Anatomists. Prev: Sen. Regist. Regional Plastic & Jaw Surg. Unit Mt. Vernon Hosp. & Char. Cross Hosp. Lond.; Regist. (Plastic & Maxillofacial Surg.) Roy. Perth Hosp., W. Austral.; Research Fell. (Microsurg.) Dept. Plastic Surg. Klinikum Rechts der Isar, Munich W. Germ.

MACGREGOR, Professor Alan Michael Department of Medicine, Kings College School of Medicine, Denmark Hill, London SE5 8RX Tel: 020 7346 3013 Fax: 020 7346 3313; 2 Rollscourt Avenue, Herne Hill, London SE24 0EA — MB BChir 1975 Camb.; MD, MA Camb. 1980, BA 1971; FRCP Lond. 1985; MRCP (UK) 1977. (Camb. & Middlx.) Prof. Med. Kings Coll. Sch. of Med. Lond.; Cons. Phys. King's Healthcare. Prev: Wellcome Sen. Fell. (Clin. Sc.) & Sen. Lect. & Hon. Cons. Phys. (Med.) Univ. Wales Coll. Med.; MRC Train. Fell. & Sen. Regist. (Med.) Roy. Vict. Infirm. Newc.; Berkeley Trav. Fell. NIH Bethesda, USA.

MACGREGOR, Mr Alasdair Bruce Royal Infirmary, Lauriston Place, Edinburgh EH5 9YW Tel: 0131 536 1611 Fax: 0131 536 1511; 8 East Castle Road, Edinburgh EH10 5AR Tel: 0131 229 4621 — MB ChB Ed. 1964; BA Camb. 1961; FRCS Ed. 1967. (Ed.) p/t Cons. Surg. Roy. Infirm. Edin.; Hon. Treas. Roy. Coll. of Surg.s, Edin. Socs: Fell. Assn. Surgs.; Assn. Coloproctol.; BMA. Prev: Sen. Regist. (Surg.) W.. Gen. Hosp. Edin.; Regist. (Surg.) Hammersmith Hosp. Lond.; Sen. Research Fell. Univ. Toronto, Canada.

MACGREGOR, Professor Alexander Hamilton (retired) Bron Hwylfa, Llannefydd, Denbigh LL16 5EF Email: rogergcam@bronhwylfa.freeserve.co.uk — LRCP LRCS Ed. LRFPS Glas. 1956; FRCS Eng. 1972; FACOG 1964. Prev: Assoc. Prof. O & G Med. Coll., Ohio, USA.

MACGREGOR, Alexander James 26 Evelyn Drive, Pinner HA5 4RU — MB BS 1984 Lond.

MACGREGOR, Alexander MacNaught The Surgery, Station Road, Fortrose IV10 8SY Tel: 01381 620909 Fax: 01381 620505; Sonas, Precincts Road, Fortrose IV10 8TS Tel: 01381 620751 — MB ChB 1969 Glas.; BSc (Hons.) Glas. 1964.

MACGREGOR, Alexander Rankin (retired) 54 Terregles Avenue, Glasgow G41 4LX Tel: 0141 423 1664 — MB 1943 Glas.; MB, ChB Glas. 1943.

MACGREGOR, Alison New Craigs Hospital, Leachkin Road, Inverness IV3 8NP Tel: 01463 242860; 17 Hawthorn Close, Horsham RH12 2LH Tel: 01403 263133 Fax: 01403 263133 Email: hadihuda@yahoo.com — MB ChB 1976 Glas.; MRCPsych 1981. Cons. Psychiat. Highland Communities NHS Trust.

MACGREGOR, Andrew Robert 10 Woodlands Wald, Mannings Heath, Horsham RH13 6JG — MB ChB 1973 Sheff.; AFOM 1982; DIH 1982. Occupat. Phys. Brit. Airways Health Servs. Heathrow Airport. Prev: Sen. Occupat. Health Phys. Private Pats. Plan.; Med. Dir. (Occupat. Health) Internat. Aylesbury; Med. Dir. Healthright Med. Screening Milton Keynes.

MACGREGOR, Angus (retired) Withyholt, 26 Lyttleton Road, Droitwich WR9 7AA Tel: 01905 776077 — MB BChir 1950 Camb.; MA, MD Camb. 1958; FRCP Lond. 1986; FFCM 1974; DPH Liverp. 1956. Prev: Regional Med. Off. W. Midl. RHA.

MACGREGOR, Angus Hamilton Department of Pathology, University of Edinburgh, Medical School, Teviot Place, Edinburgh EH8 9AG Tel: 0131 650 3001 Fax: 0131 650 6528 Email: amg@srv4.med.ed.ac.uk; 3 Waverley House, Main St, West Linton EH46 7EE Tel: 01968 661219 — MB ChB 1992 Ed.; BSc 1990 Ed. (Edinburgh)

***MACGREGOR, Anna Elizabeth** 101 Countess Street, Stockport SK2 6HB — MB ChB 1997 Manch.

MACGREGOR, Anna Fulton Scobie (retired) 54 Terregles Avenue, Glasgow G41 4LX Tel: 0141 423 1664 — MB ChB 1943 Glas.

MACGREGOR, Archibald McKenzie (retired) 5 Charlton Avenue, Aboyne AB34 5GL — MB ChB 1949 Aberd.; MRCGP 1961. Prev: Princip. GP Turriff Aberd.shire.

MACGREGOR, Barbara Leontine 23 High St., Sandgate, Folkestone CT20 3AH — MB BS 1956 Lond.; MRCS Eng. LRCP Lond. 1956. (Roy. Free)

MACGREGOR, Brian Email: BLMDH1@aol.com — MB ChB 1987 Leeds; T(GP) 1992. Non- Princip. GP; Prescribing GP Compass Drug Dependency Clinic. Socs: Sec. of LMC Dist. Sub-Comm.

MACGREGOR, Campbell North Wing, Denburn Health Centre, Rosemount Viaduct, Aberdeen AB25 1QB Tel: 01224 642757 Fax: 01224 404989; 8 Earlswells View, Cults, Aberdeen AB15 9LF Tel: 01224 867430 — MB ChB 1968 Aberd. (Aberd.) p/t Clin. Asst. Rehabil. Med., Vasc. Unit, Aberd. Roy. Infirm.; N.ern Pract., Denburn Health Centre, RoseMt. Viaduct, Aberd. AB25 1QB. Socs: Aberd. M-C Soc. & Assoc. Mem. RCGP. Prev: Ho. Off. (Obst. & Paediat.) Aberd. Special Hosps.; Ho. Off. (Med. & Surg.) Aberd. Gen. Hosps.

MACGREGOR, Carol Anne 19 Poplar Avenue, Bishopton PA7 5AD — MB ChB 1994 Glas.; BSc (Hons.) Glas, 1991.

MACGREGOR, Catherine Helen The Medical Centre, Tanhouse Lane, Church Hill, Redditch B98 9AA Tel: 01527 67715; Carthouse Farm, Hollowfields Road, Hanbury, Redditch B96 6RD — MB ChB 1988 Birm.; MRCGP 1993; DRCOG 1990. (Birm.) Princip. in Gen. Pract., Ch. Hill Med. Centre, Redditch. Socs: BMA; RCGP.

MACGREGOR, Catriona Mary Dept. Comm. Child Health, Ayrshire Central Hospital, Irvine KA12 8SS Tel: 01294 323441; 3 Braehead Terrace, Kilmaurs, Kilmarnock KA3 2TP Tel: 01563 532489 — MB ChB 1981 Dundee. Staff Grade (Comm. Paed) Ayrsh. & Arran Health Care Trust. Prev: Trainee GP W. Lothian VTS.; Clin. Med. Off. Child Health Ayrsh. & Arran Health Bd.

***MACGREGOR, Catriona Rose** Camserney Cottage, Aberfeldy PH15 2JG — MB ChB 1998 Manch.; MB ChB Manch 1998.

MACGREGOR, Christine Mary New Craigs Hospital, 6-16 Leachkin Road, Inverness IV3 8NP — MB BCh 1980 Wales; MRCPsych 1990. Cons. Psychiat. (Gen. Adult Psychiat.).

MACGREGOR, Christopher Alan James Dells Farm, Dells Common, Stokenchurch, High Wycombe HP14 3UR — MB BS 1998 Lond.; MB BS Lond 1998.

MACGREGOR, Christopher John Orchard Medical Practice, Innisdoon, Crow Hill Drive, Mansfield NG19 7AE Tel: 01623 400100 Fax: 01623 400101; Birchwood House, Clipstone Drive, Forest Town, Mansfield NG19 0JH Tel: 01623 635200 — BM BS 1986 Nottm.

MACGREGOR, Claire 20 High Street, Frome BA11 1ER — MB ChB 1984 Bristol.

MACGREGOR, Claire Susan Monica 16 Honister Avenue, High West Jesmond, Newcastle upon Tyne NE2 3PA — MB BS 1992 Newc.; FRCA 1999.

MACGREGOR, Colin James Colinton Surgery, 296B Colinton Road, Edinburgh EH13 0LB Tel: 0131 441 4555 Fax: 0131 441 3963; 296B Colinton Road, Edinburgh EH13 0LB Tel: 0131 441 4555 Fax: 0131 441 3963 — MB ChB 1976 Liverp.; DRCOG 1980. Socs: Brit. Soc. Med. & Dent. Hypn. (Scotl. Br.).

MACGREGOR, David Hugh Occupational Health Department, British Nuclear Fuels PLC, Sellafield Works, Seascale — MB ChB 1982 Aberd.; MFOM RCP Lond. 1997; MRCGP 1990; DRCOG 1988; DCH RCP Lond. 1988. (Aberdeen University)

MACGREGOR, Diana Mairi Accident & Emergency Department, Royal Aberdeen Childrens Hospital, Foresterhill, Aberdeen AB25 2ZG Tel: 01224 681818 Fax: 01224 840937; 88D Station Road, Ellon AB41 9AY Tel: 01358 724071 Fax: 01358 724071 — MB ChB 1975 Aberd.; Cert. Family Plann. JCC 1983. Staff Grade Post (A & E) Roy. Aberd. Childr. Hosp. Aberd.; Hon. Clin. Tutor Univ. Aberd. Prev: GP Ellon; Occupat. Phys. RGIT Survival Unit Aberd.

MACGREGOR, Donald Finlay Perth Royal Infirmary, Perth PH1 1NX Tel: 01738 473381; 44 Rose Crescent, Perth PH1 1NT Tel: 01738 473201 — MB ChB 1981 Manch.; BSc St. And. 1978; MRCP (UK) 1984. Cons. Paediat. Perth & Kinross Healthcare. Socs: Eur. Soc. Paediat. Research; Papua New Guinea Med. Soc.; Canad.

Paediat. Soc. Prev: Sen. Lect. Child Health Univ. Dundee; Hon. Research Fell. Lancaster Univ.; Sen. Regist. (Paediat. Neurol.) Roy. Hosp. Sick Childr. Edin. & Hon. Lect. (Child Life & Health).

MCGREGOR, Donald Roy James Wigg Group Practice, Kentish Town Health Centre, 2 Bartholomew Road, London NW5 2AJ Tel: 020 7530 4747 Fax: 020 7530 4750 — MB BChir 1979 Camb.; MRCGP 1982. Prev: Europ. Corr. Med. News Network TV; Company Doctor TV AM.

MCGREGOR, Dugald McColl (retired) Camserney Cottage, Aberfeldy PH15 2JG Tel: 01887 20965 — MB ChB 1949 Glas.; FRCPsych 1980, M 1975; DPM Leeds 1955. Prev: Cons. Psychiat. Stratheden Hosp. & W.on Day Hosp. Cupar.

MCGREGOR, Duncan (retired) Cul-na-Shee, 4 Holly Close, Bramble Ridge, Ellesmere SY12 9ES Tel: 01691 622367 Email: drd.macgregor@virgin.net — MB ChB 1952 Ed.; DObst RCOG 1956. Chairm. Shrops. Family Pract. Comm.

MCGREGOR, Mr Duncan Buchanan Carse of McCorriston, Thornhill, Stirling FK8 3QE — MB ChB 1958 Glas.; FRCS Glas. 1962; FRCS Ed. 1963.

MCGREGOR, Elisabeth Anne The City of London Migraine Clinic, 22 Charterhouse Square, London EC1M 6DX Tel: 020 7490 2183 — MB BS 1986 Lond.; MFFP 2000; DIPM 1998; DFFP 1993. Director of Clin. Research, City of Lond. Migraine Counc.; Sen. Clin. Med. Off., Dept. of Sexual Health, St. Bart. Hosp., Lond.; Clin. Asst., Dept. of Gyn., St. Bart. Hosp., Lond.; Med. Adviser, Margt. Pyke Memor. Trust, Lond. Socs: Gen. Sec., Internat. Headache Soc.

MCGREGOR, Elizabeth Moira 3 Crawford House, 132 North St., St Andrews KY16 9AF Tel: 01334 474897 — MB ChB 1966 St. And.

MCGREGOR, Ellon Ann Renal Unit, Western Infirmary, Glasgow G11 5HF; 60 Roseangle, Flat 6, Dundee DD1 4NB — MB ChB 1983 Glas.; MRCP (UK) 1986. Regist. (Renal Med.) W.. Infirm. Glas.

MCGREGOR, Esther Myrtle Old Irvine Road Surgery, 4 Old Irvine Road, Kilmarnock KA1 2BD — MB ChB 1990 Glas.; MRCGP 1994 Glas.; DRCOG 1993. Gen. Practitioner, Kilmarnock; CrossHo. Hosp., Kilmarnock; Clin. Asst., Diabetic Clinic. Socs: BMA; Mem. Of The Roy. Coll. of Gen. Practitione; Diplomat of Roy. Coll. of Obst.s. Prev: SHO (A & E O & G & Gen. Med.) Roy. Alexandra Hosp. Paisley.; Locum Staff Grade, Law Hosp., Lamarkshire; Med. SHO Roy. Alexandra Hosp. Paisley.

MCGREGOR, Miss Fiona Buchanan Department of Otolaryngology, Head & Neck Surgery, Gartnavel General Hospital, 1053 Gt Western Road, Glasgow G12 0YN Tel: 0141 211 3212 Fax: 0141 357 4725 — MB ChB 1986 Ed.; FRCS (Orl.) 1996; FRCS Ed. 1991. (Edinburgh) Cons. OtoLaryngol. Gartnavel Gen. Hosp. Glas. & Roy. Hosp. for Sick Childr. Glas. Prev: Sen. Regist. Glas.; Regist. Roy. Nat. Throat, Nose & Ear Hosp. Lond.; Research Fell. Hammersmith Hosp. Lond.

MCGREGOR, Fiona Mary (retired) 5 Cromwell Close, Swaffham PE37 7TT — MB ChB 1957 Glas.; DPM Eng. 1965.

MCGREGOR, Fiona Mary 21 Cleghorn Road, Lanark ML11 7QR — MB ChB 1978 Ed.

MCGREGOR, Frances Mary (retired) 7 Ledcameroch Road, Bearsden, Glasgow G61 4AB Tel: 0141 942 3419 — MB BCh BAO 1955 Belf.; FRCPath 1978, M 1966. Lect. (Path.) Univ. Glas. Prev: Tutor (Path.) Qu. Univ. Belf.

MCGREGOR, Gary Summerside Medical Centre, 29B Summerside Place, Edinburgh EH6 4NY Tel: 0131 554 3533 Fax: 0131 554 9722; 10 Ulster Drive, Edinburgh EH8 7JF Tel: 0131 661 2162 — MB ChB 1969 Ed. (Ed.) Prev: Ho. Off. (Surg. & Med.) Deaconess Hosp. Edin.; Ho. Off. (O & G) Bangour Gen. Hosp.

MCGREGOR, Gerald Alastair (retired) 31 Epsom Road, Guildford GU1 3LA Tel: 01483 502009 — MB BS 1943 Lond.; MRCP Lond. 1946; MRCS Eng. LRCP Lond. 1943. Prev: Cons. Phys. Guildford Hosp. Gp.

MCGREGOR, Gordon G/L60 Airlie Street, Glasgow G12 9SW — MB ChB 1994 Glas.

MCGREGOR, Gordon Strachan Bishopgate Medical Centre, 178 Newgate Street, Bishop Auckland DL14 7EJ Tel: 01388 603983 Fax: 01388 607782 — MB ChB 1974 Glas.

MCGREGOR, Graeme Alistair (retired) 47 Coroners Lane, Widnes WA8 9JB Tel: 0151 424 5285 Email: graeme.mcgregor@virgin.net — MB ChB Liverp. 1961; DObst RCOG 1964.

MCGREGOR, Professor Graham Alexander Blood Pressure Unit, Department of Medicine, St George's Hospital Medical School, London SW17 0RE Tel: 020 8725 2989 Fax: 020 8725 2959 Email: g.macgregor@sghms.ac.uk — MB Camb. 1968, BChir 1967; MA Camb. 1968; FRCP Lond. 1982. (Camb. & Middlx.) Prof. Cardiovasc. Med. Blood Pressure Unit. Dept. Med. St. Geo. Hosp. Med. Sch.; Phys. St. Geo. Hosp. Lond. Socs: Treas. Euro. Counc. High Blood Pressure; Pres. Brit. Hypertens. Soc. (Past. Treas.); Chairm. Blood Pressure Assn. Prev: Sen. Lect. & Hon. Cons. Phys. Char. Cross Hosp. Lond.

MCGREGOR, Helen Mary Howe of Fife Medical Practice, 27 Commercial Road, Ladybank, Cupar KY15 7JS Tel: 01337 830765 Fax: 01337 831658 — MB ChB 1975 Manch.

MCGREGOR, Hugh Torquil Rameldry, Millbank, Kingskettle, Cupar KY15 7TY — MB ChB 1972 Glas.

MCGREGOR, Ian 1 Newton Avenue, Elderslie, Johnstone PA5 9BB — MB ChB 1955 Glas.

MCGREGOR, Ian George 10 Carrongrove Avenue, Falkirk FK2 8NG — MB ChB 1982 Glas.

MCGREGOR, Ian Graham (retired) Great Field, Cleabarrow, Windermere LA23 3ND Tel: 015394 42599 — MB ChB 1940 Ed.

MCGREGOR, James Alloa Health Centre, Marshill, Alloa FK10 1AQ Tel: 01259 216701; 107 Claremont, Alloa FK10 2DN Tel: Alloa 722050 — MB ChB 1978 Glas.

MCGREGOR, James Anderson (retired) Ard Coille, 1 Chapel Brae Gardens, Ballater AB35 5WP Tel: 01339 741919 — MB ChB Aberd. 1949; MRCGP 1964. Prev: GP Edin.

MCGREGOR, James Duncan, OBE (retired) 74 Glasgow Road, Perth PH2 0PG Tel: 01738 624493 Fax: 01738 624493 Email: jdmac74@aol.com — MB ChB St. And. 1950; MD (High Commend.) St. And. 1968; FFPHM 1980, M. 1974; DPH Lond. 1966; DTM & H Ed. 1955. Prev: Med. Off. Perth & Kinross Unit Tayside HB.

MCGREGOR, Jane Margaret Dept Photobiology, St Johns Institute of Dermatology, St Thomas' Hospital, London SE1 7EH — MB BChir 1985 Camb.

MCGREGOR, Janet Elizabeth, OBE, Capt. RAMC Retd. (retired) 22 Ovington Square, London SW3 1LR — MB ChB 1943 Glas.; BSc Glas. 1940, MD (Commend.) 1963; FRCOG 1986; FRCPath 1982, M 1979. Hon. Dir. Harris Birthright Research Centre, Univ. Aberd.; Hon. Research Fell. (Obst. & Gyn.) Univ. Aberd. Prev: Sen. Lect. (Cytol.) Univ. Aberd.

MCGREGOR, John Charles Radiology Department, Royal Lancaster Infirmary, Lancaster LA1 4RR — MB ChB 1977 Manch.; MRCP (UK) 1981; FRCR 1985; FRCP Ed.; BSc (Hons) 1999. (Manchester) Cons. Diagn. Radiol. Roy. Lancaster Infirm. Prev: Cons. Diagn. Radiol. Sperrin Lakeland AE Trust; Cons. Diagn. Radiol. Blackburn & Ribble Valley Healthcare Trust.

MCGREGOR, Mr John Cummack Murrayfield Hospital, 122 Corstorphine Road, Edinburgh EH12 6UD Tel: 0131 334 0363 Fax: 0131 334 7338; Murrayfield Hospital, 122 Corstorphine Road, Edinburgh EH12 6UD Tel: 0131 334 0363 Fax: 0131 334 7338 — MB ChB 1969 (Commend) Glas.; BSc (Hons.) Glas. 1967; FRCS Ed. 1983; FRCS Eng. 1974. (Glas.) Cons. Plastic Surg. Lothian HB; Hon. Cons. Inveresk Res. Centre Edin. Socs: Brit. Assn. Plastic Surg.; Brit. Assn. Aesthetic Plastic Surgs.; Brit. Burns Assn. Prev: Sen. Regist. (Plastic Surg.) Bangour Gen. Hosp.; Regist. (Plastic Surg.) Nottm. City Hosp. & Canniesburn Hosp. Glas.

MCGREGOR, Mr John Robert Department of Surgery, Crosshouse Hospital, Kilmarnock KA2 0BE Tel: 01563 521133 Fax: 01563 577974 Email: jrmcgregor@nayrshire.scot.nhs.uk; Cranley, 9 Sarazen Drive, Troon KA10 6JP Email: jrmcgregor@compuserve.com — MB ChB 1983 Glas.; MD Glas. 1989; FRCS Glas. 1989; FRCS (Gen.) 1994. (University of Glasgow) Cons. Surg. N. Ayrsh. & Arran NHS Trust; Postgrad. Tutor N. Ayrsh. & Arran NHS Trust; Hon. Sen. Lect. Univ. of Glas. Socs: Surg. Research Soc.; Assn. Endoscopic Surgs.; Nat. Assn. Clin. Tutors. Prev: Lect. (Surg.) W.. Infirm. Univ. Glas.; Hon. Sen. Regist. (Surg.) Gt.er Glas. Health Bd.; Regist. W. Scotl. Jt. Rotat. Train. Scheme Surg.

MCGREGOR, John Ross Gatesgarth, 3 Cowrakes Road, Lindley, Huddersfield HD3 3LA Tel: 01484 651816 — MB BS 1949 Durh.; DObst RCOG 1953. (Newc.) Socs: BMA & Huddersfield Med. Soc. Prev: Ho. Phys. Roy. Infirm. Sunderland; Ho. Surg. Gen. Hosp. Sunderland; O & G Ho. Off. Lewisham Hosp.

MACGREGOR

MACGREGOR, Kathleen Elizabeth 91 Baronald Drive, Kelvindale, Glasgow G12 0HP — MB ChB 1988 Glas. Socs: BMA.

MACGREGOR, Kathleen Leslie (retired) 343 Perth Road, Dundee DD2 1LQ Tel: 01382 660567 — MB ChB 1952 Ed.

MCGREGOR, Kenneth Alistair Drymen Road Surgery, 96 Drymen Road, Bearsden, Glasgow G61 2SY Tel: 0141 942 9494; 96 Drymen Road, Bearsden, Glasgow G61 2SZ — MB ChB 1975 Glas.; MRCP (UK) 1979; MRCGP 1984.

MACGREGOR, Malcolm Eliot (retired) Pittern Hill Farm, Kineton, Warwick CV35 0JF Tel: 01926 640234 — MB BS (Hons. Med.) 1938; MD Lond. 1946; FRCP Lond. 1960, M 1943; DCH RCP Lond. 1947. Prev: Vis. Sen. Clin. Lect. Univ. Warwick.

MACGREGOR, Malcolm Fraser Clovelly, Mounthill Avenue, Chelmsford CM2 6DB — MB BS 1984 Lond.

MCGREGOR, Margaret McGregor (retired) 5 Charlton Avenue, Aboyne AB34 5EL — MB ChB 1949 Aberd.; MRCGP 1961. Prev: Princip. GP Turriff Aberd.shire.

MACGREGOR, Mark Steven Renal and Transplant Unit, Western Infirmary, Glasgow G11 6NT Tel: 0141 2112883 Email: mark.s.macgregor@talk21.com — MB ChB 1990 Glas.; BSc (Hons.) Glas. 1987; MRCP (UK) 1993. (Glasgow) Specialist Regist. in Nephrol, Spr in Nephrology & Gen. Med., W.ern Infirm., Glas. Socs: Brit. Transpl. Soc.; Renal Assn.; Scott. Renal Assn. Prev: Nat. Kidney Research Fund Train. Fell., Univ. of Glas.; Sen. Ho. (Med. & Nephrol.) W.ern Infirm. Glas.; Ho. off. (Med.) Glas. Roy. Infirm.

MCGREGOR, Mary Bell Brock 2 Millburn, Well Road, Moffat DG10 9BP — MB ChB Ed. 1949; FRCR 1975; FFR 1966; DMRD Eng. 1960; DCH Eng. 1952; CRCP (Canada). (Edinburgh University) Prev: Emerit. Cons. Diag. Radiol. Lincoln N. HA.

MCGREGOR, Pamela Gail Biggar Health Centre, South Croft Road, Biggar ML12 6BE Tel: 01899 220383 Fax: 01899 221583 — MB ChB 1986 Glas. Trainee Community Child Health Edin.

MCGREGOR, Pauline Anne 500 Manchester Road, Rochdale OL11 3HE — MB ChB 1997 Manch.

MACGREGOR, Robert Gordon Scott (retired) Chyverton, Mawnan Smith, Falmouth TR11 5HE — BM BCh 1927 Oxf.; BA Oxf (Hons.) 1924, MA, DM 1940, BM BCh 1927; MD (Hon. Causa) Malaya 1951; MRCS Eng. LRCP Lond. 1926. Prev: King Edwd. VII Prof. Physiol. Univ. Malaya.

MCGREGOR, Robert Roy Department of Anaesthetics, Eastbourne District General Hospital, Kings Drive, Eastbourne BN21 2UD Tel: 01323 417400 — MB BS 1987 Lond.; FRCA 1994. Cons. Anaesth. E.bourne Dgn. Prev: Sen. Regist. (Anaesth.) Roy. Free Hosp.; Regist. (Anaesth.) St. Thos. Hosp. Lond. & Conquest Hosp. Hastings; SHO (Anaesth.) Roy. Sussex Co. Hosp. Brighton.

MCGREGOR, Rosalind Mary Valentine Royal London Homoeopathic Hospital, Gt. Ormond St., London WC1N 3HR Tel: 020 7837 8833; Brook House, Red Lane, Hopesay, Craven Arms SY7 8HD — MB BS 1978 Lond.; MFHom 1988; DCH RCP Lond. 1982; DRCOG 1980. (St. Mary's Hosp. Med. Sch.) Clin. Asst. Homoeop. Hosp. Lond.

MACGREGOR, Ruth Josephine Staff Paediatrician, Community Child Health, Musgrove park Hospital, Taunton; St. Andrew's Cottage, 40 North St, Ottery St Mary EX11 1DR Tel: 01404 814907 — MB BS 1986 Lond.; MRCP Ed. 1991; DCH RCP Lond. 1990. (King's Coll. Hosp. Med. Sch. Lond.) Staff Grade (Paed) Taunton. Prev: Community Med. Off. (Child Health) Leeds; Sen. SHO Rotherham Dist. Gen. Hosp.; Community Med. Off. & SHO (Paediat.) Leeds Gen. Infirm.

MCGREGOR, Scott Laurie The Manse, Tulliebelton Road, Bankfoot, Perth PH1 4BS — MB ChB 1996 Ed.

MACGREGOR, Susan Elizabeth Department of Dermatology, Hairmyres Hospital, E. Kilbride, Glasgow — MB ChB 1980 Manch.; BSc St. And. 1978. Clin. Asst. (Dermat.) Lanarksh. Health Bd.

MACGREGOR, Walter (retired) Ardross Cottage, Kinlockard, Stirling FK8 3TL Tel: 01877 387287 — MB ChB 1937 Ed. Prev: Ho. Surg. & Ho. Phys. Roy. Infirm. Sunderland.

MACGREGOR, William Lindsay 55A Spa Road, Weymouth DT3 5EP Tel: 01305 782177 — MB ChB 1940 Glas. (Glas.)

MCGREGOR, Mr William Stewart Petrie, OBE, Lt.-Col. RAMC 63 Hutton Avenue, Hartlepool TS26 9PP Tel: 01429 72250 — MB ChB 1958 Aberd.; FRCS Ed. 1967. Cons. Surg. RAMC. Prev: Ho. Phys. Gen. Hosp. Nottm.; Ho. Surg. Aberd. Roy. Infirm.

MACGREGOR-MORRIS, Rosanne Lower Shilston, Throwleigh, Okehampton EX20 2HX; Lower Shilston, Throwleigh, Okehampton EX20 2HX — MB BS 1991 Lond. Specialist Regist., Forens. Psychiat., Ravenswood Ho. Medium Secure Unit.

MCGRIGOR, Mr Angus Buchanan (retired) Warningore House, Plumpton, Lewes BN7 3AT Tel: 01273 890371 — MRCS Eng. LRCP Lond. 1942; MA Camb. 1942, MB BChir 1951; FRCS Eng. 1955; DMRD Eng. 1957. Prev: Cons. Radiol. Brighton, Lewes, Cuckfield & Haywards Heath Hosps.

MCGRIGOR, Victoria Susan Central Health Clinic, East Park Terrace, Southampton SO14 0YL Tel: 02380 902562; The Old Vicarage, Common Road, Whiteparish, Salisbury SP5 2SU Tel: 01794 884937 — MB BS 1972 Lond.; FRCPCH 1996; MRCS Eng. LRCP Lond. 1972; DCH RCP Lond. 1984. Cons. Paediat. (Community Child Health) Soton.

MCGROARTY, Vanessa 22 Holbeck Park Avenue, Barrow-in-Furness LA13 0RG — MB ChB 1996 Liverp.

MCGROGAN, Liam Patrick Avenue Medical Centre, 51-53 Victoria Avenue, Blackley, Manchester M9 6BA Tel: 0161 720 8282 Fax: 0161 740 7991 — MB ChB 1974 Leeds; BSc (Hons.) Biochem. Leeds 1974, MB ChB (Hons.) 1977; MRCGP 1986. Tutor Gen. Pract. Univ. Manch. Prev: Clin. Asst. Lipid Clinic Univ. Hosp. S. Manch.; Resid. Med. Off. N. Manch. Gen. Hosp.; Ho. Off. (Med.) Profess. Med. Unit St. Jas. Hosp. Leeds.

MCGROGAN, Paraic James 13 Sans Souci Park, Belfast BT9 5BZ — MB ChB 1987 Ed.

MCGRORY, Francis (retired) Tay Court Surgery, 50 South Tay Street, Dundee DD1 1PF — MB ChB 1960 St. And.; DPH St. And. 1963. Prev: Asst. Med. Off. Fife CC.

MCGROTHER, Catherine Winefride Department of Epidemiology & Public Health, University Leicester, 22-28 Princess Road W., Leicester LE1 6TP Tel: 0116 252 3197 Fax: 0116 252 5423 Email: cm45@ie.ac.uk; 209 Leicester Road, Markfield, Leicester LE67 9RF Tel: 01530 244667 — MB BS 1975 Newc.; MFPHM RCP (UK) 1986. Sen. Lect. (Epidemiol.) Univ. Leicester. Socs: Soc. Social Med.

MCGROUTHER, Professor Duncan Angus Department of Plastic Surgery, South Manchester University Hospitals, Wythenshawe Hospital, Southmoor Road, Manchester M23 9LT Tel: 0161 291 6327 Fax: 0161 291 6301 — MD (Hons.) Glas. 1988, MB ChB 1969; MSc Strathclyde 1975; FRCS Ed. 1993; FRCS Eng. 1973; FRCS Glas. 1973. Prof. Plastic & Reconstrvc. Surg. Univ. of Manch.; Visiting Cons. Plastic Surg., Jersey Gen. Hosp., St Helier, Jersey, CI. Socs: Brit. Assn. Plastic Surg. & Brit. Soc. Surg. Hand. Prev: Cons. Plastic Surg. Shotley Bridge Hosp. Fleming Memor. Childr. Hosp. & Sunderland Dist. Gen. Hosp.; Cons. Plastic Surg. Canniesburn Hosp. Bearsden Glas.; Prof. Plastic and Reconstrvc. Surg., Univ. Coll., Lond.

MCGROUTHER, Ronald Iain Charlotte Street Surgery, 1 Charlotte Street, Dumfries DG1 2AG Tel: 01387 267626 Fax: 01387 266824; Rowanbank, Craigs Road, Dumfries DG1 4QJ Tel: 01387 256083 — MB ChB 1982 Ed.; MRCGP 1986; DRCOG 1985. Prev: Trainee GP N. Lothian VTS.

MCGUANE, Kevin Francis, CStJ (retired) Avoca, 45 Dryden Road, Scunthorpe DN17 1PW Tel: 01724 840989 — MB BCh BAO 1949 NUI. Prev: Capt. RAMC.

MCGUCKEN, Pamela Bell 55 Waringfield Avenue, Moira, Craigavon BT67 0FA — MB BCh BAO 1994 Belf.

MCGUCKEN, Richard Brian 12 Chorley Road, Hilldale, Parbold, Wigan WN8 7AL Tel: 0125 76 462058 — MB BCh BAO 1965 Belf.; MRCP (U.K.) 1970; FRCP Lond. 1984; DCH RCPS Glas. 1967. (Belf.) Cons. Paediat. Wigan & Leigh Health Servs. NHS Trust. Prev: Cons. Paediat. Wesley Guild Hosp. Ilesha, Nigeria; Regist. (Paediat.) Ulster Hosp. Dundonald; Ho. Off. Roy. Vict. Hosp. Belf.

MCGUFFIE, Adam Crawford 16 Beechwood Paddock, Loans, Troon KA10 7LX — MB ChB 1989 Glas.

MCGUFFIE, Gwendoline Mary (retired) Grange Fell House, Fernleigh Road, Grange-over-Sands LA11 7HN Tel: 015395 32904 — MB ChB 1941 St. And. Prev: Flight Lt. RAF Med. Br.

MCGUFFIN, Katherine Maeve 130 Earlswood Road, Belfast BT4 3EB — MB ChB 1989 Liverp.

MCGUFFIN, Professor Peter SGDP Research Centre, Institute of Psychology, 111 Denmark Hill, London SE5 5AF Email: p.mcguffin@iop.kcc.ac.uk — MB ChB 1972 Leeds; PhD Lond. 1984; FRCP 1988; MRCP (U.K.) 1976; FRCPsych 1990, M 1978; DPM

MCGUIRE

Leeds 1977. Dir. & Prof. Of Psychiat. Genetics, Social Genetics & Developm. Psychiat. Research Centre. Inst. of Psychiat. . Lond.; Hon. Cons. Psychiat. S. Glam HA. Socs: Pres. Internat. Soc. Psychiat. Genetics; Founding Fell. Acad. Med. Sci. Prev: Prof. (Psychol. Med.) Univ. Wales Coll. Med.; Sen. Lect. & MRC Sen. Clin. Fell. Inst. Psychiat. Lond.; Hon. Cons. Psychiat. Maudsley Hosp. Lond. & King's Coll. Hosp. Lond.

MCGUGAN, Elizabeth Ann TFL, 111 Willowbank Road, Aberdeen AB11 6XJ — MB ChB 1994 Glas.

MCGUIGAN, Christopher Charles Astley Ainslie Hospital, Edinburgh EH9 2HL; 9/2 Ettrick Road, Edinburgh EH10 5BJ Tel: 0131 229 5678 — MB ChB 1993 Ed.; BA Camb. 1985. SHO (Rehabil. Med.) Astley Ainslie Hosp. Edin.

MCGUIGAN, James Adrian 10 Smeaton Park, Moira, Craigavon BT67 0NF — MB BCh BAO 1976 Belf.

MCGUIGAN, James Robert 30 Stratford Road, Neston, South Wirral CH64 0SH — MB ChB 1998 Manch.; MB ChB Manch 1998.

MCGUIGAN, Lorraine Anne 22M Riverside Drive, Aberdeen AB11 7DF — MB ChB 1997 Aberd.

MCGUIGAN, Patrick Stephen Davidsons Mains Medical Centre, 5 Quality Street, Edinburgh EH4 5BP Tel: 0131 336 2291 Fax: 0131 336 1886 — MB BCh BAO 1986 Belf.; MRCGP 1992; T(GP) 1992.

MCGUINESS, Caroline Nancy 21A Cadogan Gardens, London SW3 2RW — MB BS 1990 Lond.

MCGUINESS, Aidan Patrick 23 Five Acres, Strabane BT82 9JD — MB BCh BAO 1993 Belf.

MCGUINNESS, Anne Marie Accident & Emergency Department, Royal Free Hospital, Pond St., London NW3 2QG Tel: 020 7794 0500 Fax: 020 7830 2985; 2 Gubyon Avenue, London SE24 0DX Tel: 020 7274 2049 — MB BCh BAO 1979 Belf.; FRCS Ed. 1983; FFAEM 1993. Cons. A & E Med. Roy. Free Hosp. Lond. Socs: Fell. Med. Soc. Lond. & Library Comm. Mem.; Brit. Assn. of Accid. & Emerg. Med.; Assn. Cas. Surgs.

MCGUINNESS, Anthony John 44 Woodland Road, Upton, Wirral CH49 8HW — MB ChB 1998 Birm.; ChB Birm. 1998.

MCGUINNESS, Bernadette Millhouse, 41 Derryvale Rd, Coalisland, Dungannon BT71 4PB — MB BCh BAO 1997 Belf.

MCGUINNESS, Professor Brian William (retired) Courtlands, Norwich Road, Swaffham PE37 8DE Tel: 01760 720416 Email: brian@bmguinness.freeserve.co.uk — MB ChB 1956 Liverp.; MD Liverp. 1959; MFFP 1993; FRCGP 1973, M 1966; DCH RCPS Glas. 1964; DObst RCOG 1962; Cert. Family Plann. JCC 1962 & 1972. Prev: Prof. Primary Health Care Univ. of Keele.

MCGUINNESS, Carol Tel: 01865 311188 Fax: 01865 224917 Email: carol.mcguinness@orh.nhs.uk; 88 Cunliffe Close, Oxford OX2 7BL — MB BS 1970 Lond.; MRCS Eng. LRCP Lond. 1971; FRCA 1975. (Royal Free Hosp. Sch. Med.) Cons. Anaesth. Nuffield Dept. Anaesth. John Radcliffe Hosp. Oxf. Socs: Assn. Anaesth. & Neuroanaesth. Soc. GB & Irel.; BMA; Intens. Care Soc. Prev: Specialist (Anaesth.) Adelaide Med. Centre for Wom. & Childr. Austral.

MCGUINNESS, Miss Catharine Louise Dept. of Surgery, St Thomas Hospital, Lambeth Palace Rd, London SE1 7EH Tel: 020 7928 9292; Fax: 01483 222795 — MB BS 1987 Lond.; FRCS Eng. 1992. (St Georges Hospital, London) Specialist Regist. Medway Hosp. Socs: Assn Surg.s; SRS; VSS. Prev: Lect. (Surg.) St. Thomas Hosp. Lond.; Regist. (Surg.) St. Thos. Hosp. Lond., Kent & Canterbury Hosp. & Qu. Mary's Hosp. Sidcup.

MCGUINNESS, Catherine Louise Langley House Surgery, 27 West St., Chichester PO19 1RW — MB ChB 1989 Manch.; MRCGP 1995. (Manch.) p/t GP Partnership.

MCGUINNESS, Jacqueline Ann 202 Westbourne Avenue, Princes Avenue, Hull HU5 3JB — MB BS 1997 Lond. SHO Psychiat. - Wexham Pk. Hosp. - Slough.

MCGUINNESS, Joan Frances St Lukes Hospital, Learning Disability Directorate, Loughgall Road, Armagh BT7 1DY Tel: 01861 522381 — MB BCh BAO 1987 Belf.; MRCPsych 1994; DMH Belf. 1992; MA 1999 Belfast. (Queens Uni. Belfast) Cons. Psychiatrist Learning Disabil.

MCGUINNESS, John Burnett (retired) 60 Lanton Road, Glasgow G43 2SR Tel: 0141 637 4146 — MB ChB 1972 Glas.; MD Glas. 1972, MB ChB 1951; FRCP Lond. 1975, M 1957; FRCP Glas. 1968, M 1962. Prev: Cons. Phys. Vict. Infirm. Glas.

MCGUINNESS, Oonagh Elizabeth 6 Crediton Hill, London NW6 1HP — BSc (Hons.) Lond. 1987, MB BS 1990; DCH RCP Lond. 1994. SHO (Paediat.) Lond.

MCGUINNESS, Patrick Joseph Noel Shanklin House, Aston Lane, Birmingham B20 — MB ChB 1954 Birm. Prev: Ho. Surg. Little Bromwich Hosp.; Ho. Phys. & Obst. Ho. Surg. Selly Oak Hosp.

MCGUINNESS, Peter David 29 North Park Road, Sedgefield, Stockton-on-Tees TS21 2AP — MB ChB 1982 Manch.

MCGUINNESS, Shay Patrick 107 Walkley Crescent Road, Walkley, Sheffield S6 5BA — MB ChB 1990 Sheff.

MCGUIRE, Anne Young (retired) South Beach Practice, 17 South Crescent, Ardrossan KA22 8EA Tel: 01294 463011 Fax: 01294 462790 — MB ChB 1982 Glas.; MRCGP 1986; DRCOG 1984. GP S. Beach Surg. Ardrossan VTS.

MCGUIRE, Barry Ewan Firhill, Hatton Road, Perth PH2 7DB Tel: 01738 560301; 15 Hunters Mews, Wilmslow SK9 2AR Tel: 01625 548321, 01738 560301 — MB ChB 1990 Ed.; MRCGP 1994; DRCOG 1992; FRCA 1996. Cons. (Anaesth.) Ninewells Hosp. Dundee. Prev: Trainee GP Dumfries & Galloway VTS.

MCGUIRE, Dennis Patrick 'Kirkleatham', Carlton-in-Cleveland, Middlesbrough TS9 7DJ Tel: 01642 710948 Fax: 01642 815761 — MB ChB 1971 Ed.; MFOM 1985, A 1981; DIH Dund 1976; DTM & H Liverp. 1973. (Ed.) Cons. Occupat. Health Phys. S. Tees HA. Prev: Occupat. Health Phys. Stockport HA; Staff Phys. Esso Standard Libya Inc.; Sen. Med. Off. N.C.C.M. Konkola Div. Chililabombwe Zambia.

MCGUIRE, Edward John (retired) The Bricklayers, Clay Hill, Goudhurst, Cranbrook TN17 1AB Tel: 01580 211277 — MB BS 1949 Lond.; FFCM 1980, M 1974; MFOM RCP Lond. 1980. Prev: Dir. Pub. Health Tunbridge Wells HA.

MCGUIRE, Joanne Naughton 34 Borland Road, Bearsden, Glasgow G61 2ND — MB ChB 1995 Glas.

MCGUIRE, John 6 Regency Park, Ingleby Barwick, Stockton-on-Tees TS17 0QR Tel: 01642 769495 Fax: 01642 769495 Email: john@peelhall.u-net.com; The Health Centre, Trenchard Avenue, Thornaby, Stockton-on-Tees TS17 0DD Tel: 01642 762921 Fax: 01642 760608 — MB ChB 1988 Glas.; BSc (Hons.) Glas. 1986; MRCP (UK) 1991; JCPTGD 1998. (Glas. Univ.) GP Princip. Prev: GP Regist. Peter Hse. Surg. Bolton; Sen. Regist. & Clin. Lect. (Nephrol. & Gen. Med.) Manch. Roy. Infirm.; Regist. (Gen. & Renal) Manch. Roy. Infirm.

MACGUIRE, John Dillon Dr. J. MacGuire and Partners, Meadows Surgery, Temple Grove, Burgess Hill RH15 9XN Tel: 01444 242866 Fax: 01444 870496; 1 Roeheath, Cinder Hill, North Chailey, Lewes BN8 4HR Tel: 01825 723052 — MRCS Eng. LRCP Lond. 1970; DA Eng. 1974. (Univ. Dub.) Clin. Asst. Vasc. Surg. Dept. P.ss Roy. Hosp., Haywards Heath. Socs: Primary Care Rheum. Soc.; Brighton & Sussex M-C Soc. Prev: Regist. (Anaesth.) Torbay Hosp. Torquay; SHO (Obst.) Roy. Sussex Co. Hosp. Brighton.

MCGUIRE, Lawrence Conran 11 Ivanhoe Crescent, Wishaw ML2 7DZ Email: larry@meguirel.freeserve.co.uk — MB ChB 1989 Glas.; MRCP (UK) 1997. Specialist Regist. (A&E), The John Radcliffes, Oxf.. Socs: BAEM; Fac. Accid. & Emerg. Med.

MCGUIRE, Martin RGIT Ltd, Occupational Health Services, Culham Science Centre, Abingdon OX14 3 Tel: 01235 463397 Email: harwell@rgit.co.uk; 10 Gaynor Avenue, Loanhead EH20 9LT Tel: 0131 440 0656 — MB ChB 1990 Dundee. Occupat. Health Phys., A. E. A. Harwell Oxon. Socs: Soc. of Occupat. Med. Prev: Lect (Path.) Foresterhill Aberd. Univ.; SHO (Histopath.) BRd.green Hosp. Liverp.; Trainee GP Stornoway.

MCGUIRE, Maureen 11 Crathie Drive, Ardrossan KA22 8HQ — MB ChB 1984 Glas.

MACGUIRE, Michael Henry Queen Alexander Hospital, Southwick Hill Road, Cosham, Portsmouth PO6 3LY Tel: 02392 286000; Crossfields, The Drive, Bosham, Chichester PO18 8JG — MB BCh BAO 1972 NUI; FRCR 1983; DMRD Eng. 1982. Cons. Radiologist. Qu. Alexandra Hosp.. Portsmouth. Prev: Cons. Radiol. St. Mary's Hosp. Portsmouth.; Asst. Surg., P&O Shipping Company; Cons. Radiol. Redhill & E. Surrey Hosp.

MCGUIRE, Mr Neil Gilbert (retired) Heatherdene, Cricket Hill Lane, Yateley GU46 6BQ — MB BS 1943 Lond.; FRCS Eng. 1949; DLO Eng. 1954; MRCS Eng. LRCP Lond. 1943. Prev: Cons. ENT Surg. Roy. Berks. Hosp. Reading.

MCGUIRE, Philip Kevin Institute of Psychiatry, De Crespigny Park, Denmark Hill, London SE5 8AF Tel: 020 7919 3752 Fax: 020 7701

MCGUIRE

9044 Email: p.mcguire@iop.kcl.ac.uk — MB ChB 1986 Ed.; PhD Univ. of Lond. 1998; BSc Ed. 1984, MD 1993; MRCPsych 1992. Sen. Lect. (Psychol. Med.) Inst. Psychiat. Lond.; Hon. Cons. Psychiat. Maudsley Hosp. Lond. Socs: Soc. Neurosci.; Organisation for Human Brain Mapping; Internat. Early Psychnosis Assn. Prev: Wellcome Train. Fell. Inst. Psychiat. & MRC Cyclotron Unit Hammersmith Hosp. Lond.; Hon. Lect. Inst. Psychiat. Lond.; Post Doctoral Fell. (Neuroanat.) Yale Univ.

MCGUIRE, William 15 Youngsdale Place, Newport-on-Tay DD6 8DL — MB ChB 1987 Glas.

MCGUIRK, Simon Prosser 30 Lower Packington Road, Ashby-de-la-Zouch LE65 1GD — MB BS 1997 Newcastle.

MCGURK, Colm Timothy 5 Strandview Street, Stranmillis, Belfast BT9 5FF — MB BCh BAO 1990 Belf.

MCGURK, David Andrew 1 Newhaven Grove, Largs KA30 8NS — MB ChB 1998 Glas.; MB ChB Glas 1998.

MCGURK, Mr Francis Myrle 2 Mill Road, Bothwell, Glasgow G71 8DQ Tel: 0141 852283 Fax: 001 807 343 1548 Email: fmcg32@hotmail.com — MB ChB Ed. 1956; BSc Ed. 1953; FRCP Ed. 1982, M 1960; FRCS Ed. 1964; LMCC 1978; FRCR 1975; FFR 1965; DMRT Ed. 1962. (Ed.) Staff Radiat. Oncologist N.W. Ontario Cancer Centre Thunder Bay Ontario. Socs: Roy. Med. Soc. Edin.; M-C Soc. Glas. Prev: Cons. Radiother. & Oncol. Belvidere Hosp. Glas.; Fell. Radiother. Ontario Cancer Inst. Toronto, Canada; Staff Radiat. Oncol. Dr H. Bliss Murphy Cancer Centre, St. John's, Newfld.

MCGURK, Grainne Maire Kilrea Medical Centre, 36 Garvagh Road, Kilrea, Coleraine BT51 5QP Tel: 028 2954 0231 Fax: 028 2954 0851; 30 Lisnagrot Road, Kilrea, Coleraine BT51 5SE Tel: 01265 41183 — MB BCh BAO 1982 NUI; MB BCh BAO NUI 1981; BA (Hons.) NUI 1975; MRCGP 1985; DCH RCP Lond. 1982. (NUI) GP Kilrea.

MCGURK, John Columba (retired) 45 Manse Road, Kilkeel, Newry BT34 4BN Tel: 028 4176 2728 — LAH Dub. 1963. Prev: GP Newry.

MCGURK, Professor Mark Guy's Dental School, Guy's Hospital, London SE1 Tel: 020 7955 4342 Fax: 020 7955 4165; 12 Wallside, Monkwell Square, London EC2Y 5BL Tel: 020 7920 9401 Fax: 020 7628 9395 — MB ChB 1984 Sheff.; BDS Sheff. 1976; MD Sheff. 1989; FRCS Ed. 1989; FDS RCS Eng. 1980; FDS RCPS Glas. 1980; FDS RCS Ed. 1980. Prof. Oral & Maxillofacial Surg. Guy's Dent. Sch. UMDS Guy's & St. Thos. Hosp. Lond. Socs: Brit. Assn. Head & Neck Surg.; Brit. Skull Base Soc.; Brit. Assn. Surgic. Oncol.

MCGURK, Michael Neil Washington House Surgery, 77 Halse Road, Brackley NN13 6EQ Tel: 01280 702436; Washpool Farm House, Marston St. Lawrence, Banbury OX17 2DE Tel: 01295 711526 — MB BS 1971 Lond.; DObst. New Zealand 1977. (St. Mary's) Prev: GP Dora Cheek Med. Centre N.S.W.; Regist. (Paediat.) Hastings Hosp.

MCGURK, Simon Francis 2 Mill Road, Bothwell, Glasgow G71 8DQ; La Casita, 11 Pitgaveny Quay, Lossiemouth IV31 6TW Tel: 01343 815057 — MB ChB 1995 Ed.; BSc Med. Sci. (Hons Neuroscience). (Edinburgh) SHO (Surg.) Glas. Roy. Infirm. Prev: SHO (Med.) Aberd. Roy. Infirm.; SHO (A & E & Orthop.) Dr Grays Hosp. Elgin.

MCGURN, Brian Flat 2F1, 40 Strathearn Road, Edinburgh EH9 2AD — MB ChB 1993 Ed.

MACHACEK, Karel Antonin (retired) 39 Lionel Road, Canvey Island SS8 9DE Tel: 01268 683439 — MD Czechoslovakia 1943. Prev: GP Canvey Is.

MACHADO, Mr Fidelis Rosario Christie Convatec (Europe), Swakeleys House, Milton Road, Uxbridge UB10 8NS Tel: 01895 678888 — MB BS 1970 Ceylon; FRCS Eng. 1977; FICS 1989. Vice-Pres. World Wide Med. Affairs Convatec Bristol Myers Squibb. Prev: Europ. Med. Dir. Convatec Bristol Myers Squibb; Cons. Surg. & Sen. Regist. (Gen. Surg.) Beneden Hosp.; Regist. (Gen. Surg.) Croydon Gen. Hosp.

MACHADO, Mr Francisco Roberto Da Silva Old Road Surgery, Old Road, Abersychan, Pontypool NP4 7BH Tel: 01495 772239 Fax: 01495 773786; Ty Estoril, 2 White House Gardens, Little Mill, Pontypool NP4 0HW Email: fran@abersycham.demon.co.uk — MB BS 1987 Lond.; MS BS Lond. 1987; BSc (Hons.) Lond. 1984; MRCP (UK) 1990; MRCGP 1993; DCH RCP Lond. 1991; DRCOG 1991. (University College Lond.) GP Pontypool; Clin. Asst. (Cardiol.) Pontypool; Mem. RCGP (S.E. Wales Fac.) Dep. Rep. Centr. Coun.

Prev: Trainee GP N. Gwent VTS; SHO (A & E) P. Chas. Hosp. Merthyr Tydfil.

MCHAFFIE, Gavin Sinclair 5 Front Street, Corbridge NE45 5AP — MB ChB 1995 Aberd.; BSc (Hons) Med Sci 1993 (Aberdeen); MRCP 1999. (Edinburgh). Prev: SHO (Nephrol.) Roy. Infirm. Edin.

MCHALE, Duncan Philip 35 Oakwell Crescent, Roundhay, Leeds LS8 4AF — MB BS 1991 Newc.; BMedSci (Hons.) 1990; MRCP (UK) 1994. Prev: SHO (Med.) Freeman Hosp. Trust Newc.; Ho. Off. (Med.) N. Tees Gen. Hosp.; Ho. Off. (Surg.) Jersey Gen. Hosp.

MACHALE, Mr James Joseph (retired) 1C School Lane, Emsworth PO10 7ED Tel: 01243 370707 — MB BCh BAO (1st cl. Hons.) NUI 1938; FRCS Eng. 1947; FRCSI 1940. Hon. Cons. E. Birm. Hosp. Mem. Soc. Thoracic Surgs. & Thoracic Soc. Prev: Thoracic Surg. Birm. RHB.

MCHALE, Joseph Gerard Anthony Jude Mourneside Medical Centre, 1A Ballycolman Avenue, Strabane BT82 9AF Tel: 028 7138 3737 Fax: 028 7138 3979 — MB BCh BAO 1980 NUI.

MCHALE, Julie Frances Eelfield, Church Lane, Willoughby-on-the-Wolds, Loughborough LE12 6SS — MB ChB 1989 Manch.

MCHALE, Mary Joanna 35 Oakwell Crescent, Roundhay, Leeds LS8 4AF — MB BS 1990 Newc. Prev: SHO (Paediat. Cardiol.) Freeman Hosp.; SHO (Paediat. Surg.) Roy. Vict. Infirm.

MCHALE, Nigel Paul The Surgery, 6 Lambley Lane, Burton Joyce, Nottingham NG14 5BG Tel: 0115 931 2500 Fax: 0115 931 2118; 25 Church Road, Burton Joyce, Nottingham NG14 5GE — BM BS 1987 Nottm.; MRCGP 1991.

MACHALE, Sarah Joanne 8 The Green, Widdington, Saffron Walden CB11 3SD — BM BCh 1994 Oxf.

MCHALE, Sean Patrick 1 Woodfield Cottages, Marlpit Lane, Oving, Chichester PO20 6BP — MB BS 1986 Lond.; BSc (Hons.) Birm. 1981; FRCA 1991; DA (UK) 1988. Cons. Anaesth. St. Richard's Hosp. Chichester. Prev: Regist. (Anaesth.) Hammersmith Hosp. Lond.; SHO (A & E) Ealing Gen. Hosp. S.all.

MCHALE, Sharon Joy Whin Park Medical Centre, 6 Saughton Road, Edinburgh EH11 3RA Tel: 0131 455 7999 Fax: 0131 455 8800 — MB ChB 1988 Ed.; MRCGP 1992; DRCOG 1991; DCH RCPS Glas. 1990. (Edinburgh) GP.

MACHALE, Siobhan Maria Dept. of Psychological Medicene, Royal Infirmary of Edinburgh, Lauriston Place, Edinburgh EH3 9LA Tel: 0131 536 2875; 7 Ralvelrig Park, Balerno, Edinburgh EH14 7DL — MB BCh BAO 1988 NUI; MPhil Psych. 1996; MRCPI 1991; MRCPsych 1994. (Univ. Coll. Dub.) Cons. (Liaison Psychiat.).

MCHARDY, Clarinda 1 Todrig Drive, Kilmarnock KA1 4UN Tel: 01563 27786 — MB ChB 1977 Glas. Asst. Gen. Pract. Kilmarnock; Clin. Med. Off. Sexual Reproductive Health Care Serv. Ayrsh. & Arran Primary Care Trust. Prev: SHO (Paediat.) Stobhill Hosp. Glas.; SHO (Obst.) Glas. Roy. Matern. Hosp.; Ho. Off. (Med.) Glas. Roy. Infirm.

MCHARDY, Derek Alexander The Viaduct Medical Practice, Denburn Health Centre, Rosemount Viaduct, Aberdeen AB25 1QB Tel: 01224 644744 Fax: 01224 627115 — MB ChB 1980 Aberd.; MRCP (UK) 1983; MRCGP (Distinc.) 1986. Assoc. GP Strathdon & Rhynie. Socs: BMA & Christian Med. Fell.sh. Prev: Regist. (A & E) Aberd. Roy. Infirm.; Regist. (Med.) Aberd. Teachg. Hosps.; Trainee GP Elmbank Pract. Aberd.

MCHARDY, Fiona Esther 2 St Ronans Crescent, Peterculter AB14 0RL — MB ChB 1990 Ed.

MCHARDY, George Jamieson Ross 6 Ettrick Road, Edinburgh EH10 5BJ Tel: 0131 229 9026 Fax: 0131 229 9026 Email: rmchardy@btinternet.com — MSc Oxf. 1987, MA 1956, BA 1953, BSc 1955, BM BCh 1957; FRCP Lond. 1973, M 1961; FRCP Ed. 1970, M 1969; DObst RCOG 1958. (Oxf. & Middlx.) Mem. Injuries Compensation Appeals Panel, Pens. Appeal Tribunal (Scotl.) & Criminal. Socs: Assn. Phys.; Brit. Thorac. Soc.; Scot. Thoracic Soc. (Ex-Pres.). Prev: Cons. Phys. Respirat. Physiol. Lothian Health Bd.; Internat. Postdoctoral Fell. US Pub. Health Serv. Johns Hopkins Univ. Baltimore, U.S.A.; Sen. Regist. Hammersmith Hosp. Lond.

MCHARDY, James Ayrshire & Arran Health Board, Boswell House, 10 Arthur St., Ayr KA7 1QJ Tel: 01292 611040 Fax: 01292 885890 Email: mchardyj@aapct.scot.nhs.uk; 1 Todrig Drive, Kilmarnock KA1 4UN Tel: 01563 527786 Email: jim.mchardy@btinternet.com — MB ChB 1973 Glas.; MFCM 1980; MFPHM 1990; DPH Glas. 1977; FFPHM 1999. (Univ. Glas.) Cons. Pub. Health Med. Ayrsh. & Arran HB. Socs: BMA; Fac. Pub. Health Med. Prev: Fell. (Community

Med.) Cancer Surveillance Unit Glas. & W.. (Glas.) Health Dist.; Med. Off. Kuluva Hosp. Arua, Uganda.

MCHARDY, Kenneth Charles Wards 27/28, Royal Infirmary, Foresterhill, Aberdeen AB25 2ZN Tel: 01224 681818; 12 Coull Gardens, Kingswells, Aberdeen AB15 8TQ Tel: 01224 744735 — MB ChB 1978 Aberd.; MD Aberd. 1990; FRCP Ed. 1995; MRCP (UK) 1981. Cons. Gen. Phys. & Diabetol. Roy. Aberd. Hosps. NHS Trust; Hon. Clin. Sen. Lect. Dept. Med. & Therap. Univ. Aberd.; Postgrad. Tutor Postgrad. Med. Centre Foresterhill Aberd. Socs: Brit. Diabetic Assn. (Med. & Scientif. Sect.); Eur. Assn. Study Diabetes; Soc. Endocrinol. Prev: Lect. (Human Nutrit. & Metab.) Dept. Med. & Therap. Univ. Aberd.; Cruden Research Fell. Rowett Inst. Aberd.; Regist. (Gen. Med.) S. Grampian (Aberd.) Health Dist.

MCHARDY, Roslyn Francis 11 Orford Road, Walthamstow, London E17 Tel: 020 8520 8971; 19 Lansdowne Road, South Woodford, London E18 2AZ Tel: 020 8530 4370 — MB BS 1974 Melbourne; DRCOG 1980; DA Eng. 1977. Cons. Community Paediat. Forest Health Care Trust Lond. Socs: Brit. Paediat. Assn.

MCHARDY, Valentine Urie Meadows Medical Practice, 9 Brougham Place, Edinburgh EH3 9HW Tel: 0131 229 7709 Fax: 0131 229 0765 — MB ChB 1967 St. And. (St. And.) GP Edin. Prev: Research Asst. (Respirat. Dis.) Univ. Edin.; Ho. Phys. City Hosp. Edin.; Ho. Surg. Bridge of Earn Hosp.

MCHARG, Anne McDougall Tayside Primary Care Trust, Gowrie House, Royal Dundee Liff Hospital, Dundee DD2 5NF Tel: 01382 423105 — MB ChB 1973 Dundee; FRCPsych 1992, M 1977. Cons. Psychiat. Dundee Psychiat. Serv.; Hon. Sen. Lect. Univ. Dundee.

MCHARG, James Fleming, VRD (retired) 33 Hazel Avenue, Dundee DD2 1QD Tel: 01382 566153 — MB ChB 1940 Ed.; 1940 MB ChB Fd.; 1959 MD (Commend.) Fd.; 1950 FRCP Fd.; 1971 FRCPsych; 1948 DPM Eng.; 1950 MRCP Ed. Prev: Cons. Psychiat. Roy. Dundee Liff Hosp.

MCHATTIE, Adam Grant Portland Surgery, 1 Dukes Road, Troon KA10 6QR Tel: 01292 312489 Fax: 01292 317837 — MB ChB 1981 Glas.; MB ChB. Glas. 1981.

MCHATTIE, Ian (retired) 12 Kirkdene Place, Newton Mearns, Glasgow G77 5SB Tel: 0141 639 1809 — MB ChB Glas. 1944; BSc Glas. 1941; FRCR 1975; FFR 1965; DMRT Eng. 1950. Prev: Cons. Glas. Inst. Radiother. & Oncol. W.. Infirm. Glas.

MACHELL, Richard John (retired) Boswinney Church Lane, Lelant, St Ives TR26 3HY — MB BS Lond. 1969; MRCS Eng. LRCP Lond. 1969; DObst RCOG 1971; MRCP (UK) 1973; MA Camb. 1977; FRCP Lond. 1990. Mem. (Chairm.) Cornw. Gastrointestinal Cancer Appeal. Prev: Cons. Phys. Roy. Cornw. Hosps. NHS Trust.

MACHELL, Roger Keys The Mill House, Mill Lane, Caunton, Newark NG23 6AJ Tel: 01636 636263 — MB ChB St. And. 1947; FFPHM RCP (UK) 1974; DPH 1952. Prev: Co. MOH & Princip. Sch. Med. Off. I. of Wight 1959-74; Dep. Co. Med. Off. Cumbld. CC 1956-9; Emerit. Cons. Pub. Health Med. N. Notts. HA.

MACHEN, Janice Margaret Bannold Road Surgery, Rosalind Franklin House, Bannold Road, Waterbeach, Cambridge CB5 9LQ Tel: 01223 860387 Fax: 01223 576259; 23 Lode Avenue, Waterbeach, Cambridge CB5 9PX — MB ChB 1977 Liverp.; DRCOG 1981.

MACHEN, John The Surgery, Regal Chambers, 50 Bancroft, Hitchin SG5 1LL Tel: 01462 453232; Ashdown, Newlands Close W., Hitchin SG4 9BA Tel: 01462 458352 — MB BS 1973 Lond.; FRCP 2001 UK; MRCS Eng. LRCP Lond. 1973; MRCGP 1978; DObst RCOG 1975. (St. Marys) GP Tutor N. Herts. Prev: Regist. (Med.) Harold Wood Hosp.; Ho. Surg. St. Mary's Hosp. Lond.

MACHENDER, Kakkar Sundon, 2 Windsor Road, Saltburn-by-the-Sea TS12 1BQ Tel: 01287 622393; 9 The Wynd Marske, Marske, Redcar TS11 7LD Tel: 01642 477133 — MB BS 1967 Osmania; Cert. Family Plann. JCC 1980. Prev: SHO (Dermat.) Carter Bequest Hosp. Middlesbrough; SHO (Psychiat.) St. Luke's Hosp. Middlesbrough.

MCHENRY, Christopher John The Surgery, Church Lane, Elvington, York YO41 5AD — MB ChB 1969 Liverp.

MCHENRY, Elaine 33 Firmount, 581 Antrim Road, Belfast BT15 4HZ — MB BCh 1998 Belf.

MCHENRY, Elizabeth Anne 216 Friern Road, London SE22 0BB Fax: 020 8516 6305 Email: liz@mchenrys.demon.co.uk — MB BS 1973 Lond.; MFFP. (Middlx.) Clin. Med. Off. (Fam. Plg.) King's Healthcare; Clin. Asst. (GUH) King's Healthcare.

MCHENRY, Felix Anthony (retired) 21 Droghadfayle Park, Port Erin IM9 6ER Tel: Ex Dir — MB BCh BAO NUI 1971. Prev: Assoc. Assn. Clin. Path.

MACHENRY, John Christopher Robert Maurice Glendower, Ballynorthland Park, Dungannon BT71 6BT — MD 1979 Belf.; MB BCh BAO 1970; T(OG) 1991; FRCOG 1990 M 1975, DObst 1972. Cons. (O & G) S.. Health & Social Servs. Bd.

MCHENRY, Michelle Therese 44 Stranmillis Road, Belfast BT9 5AA — MB BCh BAO 1997 Belf.

MCHENRY, Pamela Margaret Department of Dermatology, Western Infirmary, Dumbarton Road, Glasgow G11 6NT Tel: 0141 211 2540 — MB BCh BAO 1985 Belf.; MD Belf. 1995; MRCP (UK) 1988. (Queen's Belf.) Cons. Dermat. W.. Infirm. & Roy. Hosp. for Sick Child. Glas. Socs: BMA & Brit. Assn. Dermat.; Roy. Coll. Phys. & Surgs. Glas. Prev: Clin. Lect. (Dermat.) Univ. Glas.

MCHENRY, Sean Martin 28 Willesden Park, Belfast BT9 5GX — MB BCh BAO 1993 Belf.

MACHERIANAKIS, Alexis Flat D, 12 Fulwood Park, Liverpool L17 5AH — Ptychio latrikes 1991 Thessalonika. (Aristotelio Univ. Thessaloniki) Staff Grade (Comm. Paediat.) Alder Hey Hosp. Liverp. Socs: Liverp. Med. Inst.; Internat. Coll. Paediat. & Child Care.

MACHESNEY, Mr Michael Robert RAFT Institute of Plastic Surgery, Mount Vernon Hospital, Northwood HA6 2RN Tel: 01923 844260 Fax: 01923 844081 Email: m.r.machesney.mds.qmc.ac.uk; 59 Arcadia Court, 45 Old Castle St, London E1 7NY — MB BS 1990 Lond.; MB BA LOnd. 1990; BSc (Immunol.) Lond. 1987; FRCS Eng. 1994. (Univ. Coll. Lond.)

MACHETA, Anthony Thadeus Department of Pathology, Furness General Hospital, Dalton Lane, Barrow-in-Furness LA14 4LF Tel: 01229 870870; 3 Stoneleigh Close, Barrow-in-Furness LA13 9UR Tel: 01229 812572 Email: tonymach@aol.com — MB ChB 1979 Manch.; BSc (Hons.) Path. Manch. 1977; FRCPath 1998; FRCP 1996. Cons. Haemat. Furness Gen. Hosp. Barrow-in-Furness. Prev: Sen. Regist. (Haemat.) Manch. Roy. Infirm.; Regist. (Haemat.) Dudley Rd. Hosp. Birm. & Worc. Roy. Infirm.; SHO (Gen. Med.) Hope Hosp. Salford.

MACHETA, Marian Paul 53 Beech Grove, Sale M33 6RT — MB ChB 1987 Ed.; MRCP (UK) 1991; DRCPath 1996. (Ed.) Leukaemia Research Fell. Manch. Roy. Infirm. Socs: Brit. Soc. Haematol. Prev: Regist. (Haemat.) St. Jas. Univ. Hosp. Leeds & Bradford Roy. Infirm.; SHO Rotat. (Med.) Withington & Christie Hosps. Manch.

MACHIN, Antonia Jane The Surgery, 54 Thorne Road, Doncaster DN1 2JP Tel: 01302 361222 — MB BS 1983 Newc.; MRCGP 1987; DRCOG 1988; Cert. Family Plann. (RCOG & RCGP) 1988. Prev: Trainee GP Doncaster VTS.; Ho. Off. (Med.) Doncaster Roy. Infirm.; SHO (O & G) P.ss Mary Matern. Hosp. & Roy. Vic. Infirm. Newc. u. Tyne.

MACHIN, Clive Valentine Road Surgery, Valentine Road, Hunstanton PE36 5DN Tel: 01485 532859 Fax: 01485 534608; Aysgarth, 13 Wodehouse Road, Old Hunstanton, Hunstanton PE36 6JD — MB ChB 1973 Leeds; DRCOG 1977; Cert JCC Lond. 1976. (Leeds) Socs: Fell. RSM 1997.

MACHIN, Mr Derek Grenville 48 Rodney Street, Liverpool L1 9AA Tel: 0151 709 2079 Fax: 0151 709 2727; Tree Tops, Kings Drive, Caldy, Wirral CH48 2JE Tel: 0151 625 5820 — MB ChB 1972 Liverp.; FRCS Eng. 1977. (Univ. Liverp.) Cons. Urol. Surg. Fazakerley Hosp. Liverp. Socs: (Hon. Sec.) NW Eng. Urol. Club; Liverp. Med. Inst.; Brit. Assn. Urol. Surgs. Prev: Sen. Regist. (Urol.) Roy. Liverp. Hosp.; MAKR Fell. & Hon. Sen. Regist. (Urol.) Roy. Liverp. Hosp.; Sen. Demonst. (Anat.) Univ. Liverp.

MACHIN, John Richard Raigmore Hospital, Old Perth Road, Inverness IV2 5BG Tel: 01463 235596; Inshes House, Inshes, Inverness IV2 5BG Tel: 01463 234151 — MB ChB 1969 Ed.; BSc (Hons. Physiol.) Ed. 1966, MB ChB 1969; FFA RCS Eng. 1975; DObst RCOG 1971; MBA 1998. (Edinburgh University) Med. Dir.; Cons. in Anaesth./ ITV. Socs: Scott. Soc. Anaesth.

***MACHIN, Mark Gordon Adam** c/o Goldman Sachs International, Peterborough Court, 133 Fleet St., London EC4A 2BB; Flat 83, St. Joan's Court, 76 MacDonnell Road, Mid Levels, Hong Kong Tel: 00 852 29780265 Fax: 00 852 2978 0306 Email: mark.machin@gs.com — BChir 1990 Camb.; BA Oxf. 1987; BM Camb. 1990.

MACHIN, Pamela Lesley Priory Medical Centre, Belmont Grove, Liverpool L6 4EW Tel: 0151 260 9119 Fax: 0151 260 3035; Tree

MACHIN

Tops, Kings Drive, Caldy, Wirral CH48 2JE — MB ChB 1972 Liverp.; FRCGP 1996, M 1978; DFFP 1995; Cert. Family Plann. JCC 1980; DCH RCPSI 1975; DObst RCOG 1974. (Liverp.) Princip. GP; Hon. Clin. Tutor (Course Organiser GP VTS); Dept. of Primarycare, Fac. of Med., Univ. of Liverp. Socs: (Ex-Vice Pres.) Liverp. Med. Inst.

MACHIN, Paul The Surgery, 90 Church Road, Sheldon, Birmingham B26 3TP Tel: 0121 743 3409 — MB BChir 1981 Camb.; LMSSA Lond. 1980; MRCGP 1988; DRCOG 1983.

MACHIN, Professor Samuel John Department of Haematology, University College of London, Gower St., London WC1E 6BT Tel: 020 7380 9884 Fax: 020 7380 9886; Rosslyn, Latchmoor Grove, Gerrards Cross SL9 8LN Tel: 01753 884136 Fax: 01753 891531 — MB ChB 1971 Sheff.; FRCPath 1989, M 1977; MRCP (UK) 1992. Prof. Haemat. Univ. Coll. & Middlx. Sch. Med.; Cons. Haemat. Middlx. Hosp. Lond. Prev: Lect. (Haemat.) Middlx. Hosp. Lond.; Research Fell. K.U. Leuven, Belgium; SHO (Path.) Manch. Roy. Infirm.

MACHIN, Vanessa Gay 12 Stondon Park, Forest Hill, London SE23 1LA Tel: 020 8699 7284 — MB BS 1988 Lond.; BSc (Jt. 1st cl. Hons.) Lond. 1983; FRCS Eng. 1993; AKC 1983. Regist. (Cardiothoracic Surg.) Cardiothoracic Centre Liverp. Prev: Regist. (A & E) St. Thos. Hosp. Lond.; Regist. (Cardiothoracic) Brook Hosp. Lond.; SHO (Cardiothoracic) St. Mary's Hosp. Lond.

MACHRAY, Alastair John Ralphs Ride Practice, Ralphs Ride Surgery, Ralphs Ride, Bracknell RG12 9LH Tel: 01344 454626 Fax: 01344 303929; Tile House, Tilehurst Lane, Bracknell RG42 5JR Tel: 01344 425119 — MRCS Eng. LRCP Lond. 1969; BA Camb. 1965. (Middlx.)

MCHUGH, Alice Teresa Lakeside Lodge, Skipton Road, Foulbridge, Colne BB8 7NW — LRCPI & LM, LRCSI & LM 1950; DPH Liverp. 1953; DCH Dub. 1952. Assoc. Specialist Ment. Handicap Calderstones Hosp. Burnley.

MCHUGH, Catriona Frew Terrace Surgery, 9 Frew Terrace, Irvine KA12 9DZ Tel: 01294 272326 — MB ChB 1989 Glas.; MRCGP 1994; LF Hom Glas. 1998. p/t GP Partner The Surg. Irvine.

MCHUGH, Conor John Springfield Road Surgery, 44-46 Springfield Road, Belfast BT12 7AH Tel: 028 9032 1454 Fax: 028 9020 1106; 25 Malone Meadows, Belfast BT9 5BG — MB BCh BAO 1981 Belf.; DRCOG 1983.

MCHUGH, Damian Francis Department of Emergency Medicine, Hope Hospital, Salford M6 8UD; 10 Taylor Street, Heywood OL10 1EF — MB ChB 1990 Manch.; MRCGP 1994; T(GP) 1994; DFFP 1993; DCH RCP Lond. 1993; DRCOG 1992. SHO (A & E) Hope Hosp. Salford. Socs: Assoc. Mem. BAEM; Internat. Collegiate Mem. ACEP. Prev: SHO (A & E) W.. Cumbld. Hosp. Whitehaven.; Trainee GP Heywood.

MCHUGH, Fiona Claire Church View, 45 New Road, Linslade, Leighton Buzzard LU7 2LS — MB ChB 1998 Birmingham; ChB Birm 1998.

MCHUGH, Francis Joseph 5 Oakleigh, Gough's Lane, Knutsford WA16 8QW Tel: 01565 52113 — MB BCh BAO 1950 Dub.; BA, MB BCh BAO Dub. 1950. (T.C. Dub.) Med. Off. Manch. United Football Club. Prev: Ho. Surg. Roy. City Dub. Hosp.

MCHUGH, George The Three Oaks, 43 Forest Rose, Kirby, Muxloe, Leicester Tel: 0116 239 3392 — MB ChB 1942 Glas.; BSc, MB ChB Glas. 1942, DPH 1962; MFCM 1974; DTM & H Eng. 1948; DIH St. And. 1967. (Univ. Glas.) Sen. Med. Off. Leics. AHA (T). Prev: PMO Ghana Govt.

MCHUGH, Geraldine Teresa 33 Harborough Road, Oadby, Leicester LE2 4LE Tel: 0116 271 2674 — MB BS 1982 Newc.; MRCGP 1987; DRCOG 1988.

MACHUGH, James Iain Roderick Toberargan Surgery, 27 Toberargan Road, Pitlochry PH16 5HG Tel: 01796 472558 Fax: 01796 473775 — MB ChB 1983 Manch.; BSc St. And. 1980; MRCGP 1988; DRCOG 1988; Cert. Family Plann. JCC 1987. Princip. GP Pitlochry; Asst. GP Irvine Memor. Hosp. Pitlochry. Socs: Brit. Assn. Rally Doctors; Assoc. Mem. BASICS. Prev: GP Bo'ness; Trainee GP Fort William VTS.

MCHUGH, John Priors Field Surgery, 24 High Street, Sutton, Ely CB6 2RB — MB BS 1988 Lond.; MRCGP 1992; DRCOG 1993.

MCHUGH, John Alphonsus (retired) 32 The Green, Dunmurry, Belfast BT17 0QA Tel: 01232 613384 — MB BCh BAO 1945 Belf.; MRCGP 1968.

MCHUGH, Mr John Dominic Anthony 73 Harley Street, London W1N 1DE Tel: 020 7935 5874 Fax: 020 7224 5210; Email: dommch@msn.com — MB BS 1980 Lond.; MD Lond. 1991; FRCS Ed. 1987; FRCOphth 1988; DO RCS Eng. 1986. (Middlx Hosp. Med. Sch.) Cons. Ophth. King's Coll. Hosp. Lond. Socs: Amer. Acad. Ophth.; Assn. Research Vision & Ophth. Prev: Vitreoretinal Fell. Moorfields Eye Hosp.; Sen. Regist. Moorfields Eye Hosp. Lond.; Vision Research Fell. Moorfields Eye Hosp. & St. Thos. Hosp. Lond.

MCHUGH, John Gerard (retired) Carrington House, 97 Buxton Road, Weymouth DT4 9PP — MB ChB 1956 Glas.; FRCP Ed. 1980, M 1962; DCH Eng. 1960. Prev: Cons. Phys. Geriat. W. Dorset Health Dist.

MCHUGH, John Oliver Plunket Carrick Hill Medical Centre, 1 Carrick Hill, Belfast BT1 2JR Tel: 028 9043 973 — MB BCh BAO 1961 Belf.

MCHUGH, John Paul 88 Hollywood Avenue, Gosforth, Newcastle upon Tyne NE3 5BR — MB BS 1984 Newc.

MCHUGH, Kieran Radiology Department, Hospital for Sick Children, Great Ormond St., London WC1N 3JH; 26 Lucas Road, High Wycombe HP13 6QG — MB BCh BAO NUI 1982; FRCPI 1995, M 1985; LMCC 1994; FRCR 1989; DCH Dub. 1986. Prev: Fell. Roy. Alexandra Hosp. Childr. Sydney, Austral. & Hosp. Sick Childr. Toronto; Regist. (Radiol.) Soton. Gen. Hosp. Hants.

MCHUGH, Linda Ann Number 18 Surgery, 18 Upper Oldfield Park, Bath BA2 3JZ Tel: 01225 427402 Fax: 01225 484627; 6 Somerset Lane, Lansdown, Bath BA1 5SW Tel: 01225 422552 — MB ChB 1980 Otago; DObst Auckland 1982.

MCHUGH, Loretto Mary The Surgery, Station Road, Knebworth SG3 6AP; Coombe Cottage, King Edward Road, Shenley, Radlett WD7 9BY — MB BCh BAO 1977 NUI; MRCPI 1984; MRCGP 1985; DObst. RCPI 1985; DCH RCPSI NUI 1984.

MCHUGH, Luke Joseph New Family Surgery, Caerau Lane, Ely, Cardiff CF5 5; 132 Pencisely Road, Llandaff, Cardiff CF5 1DR — MB BCh BAO 1950 NUI. (Galway) Prev: Ho. Phys. Merthyr Gen. Hosp. Merthyr Tydfil; Ho. Surg. Neath Gen. Hosp.; SHO (Orthop. & Cas.) Morriston Hosp.

MCHUGH, Neil John Royal National Hospital for Rheumatic Diseases, Upper Borough Walls, Bath BA1 1RL Tel: 01225 465941 Fax: 01225 473435 Email: prsnjm@bath.ac.uk; 6 Somerset Lane, Lansdown, Bath BA1 5SW Tel: 01225 422552 — MB ChB 1978 Otago; FRACP 1986. Cons. Rheum. Roy. Nat. Hosp. Rheum. Dis. Bath; Sen. Lect. Univ. Bath. Socs: Brit. Soc. Immunol.; Brit. Soc. Rheum.; Internat. Mem. Amer. Coll. Rheum. Prev: Sen. Regist. (Rheum.) Roy. Nat. Hosp. Rheum. Dis. Bath; Postdoctoral Fell. Yale Univ.

MCHUGH, Owen Christopher Townhead Health Centre, 16 Alexandra Parade, Glasgow G31 2ES Tel: 0141 531 8972 Fax: 0141 531 8980 — MB ChB 1987 Glas.

MCHUGH, Patricia Mary 40 West Road, Bridgend CF31 4HD Tel: 01656 55825 — MB BCh 1961 Wales. (Cardiff)

MCHUGH, Patrick James Francis Department of Haematology, Kingston Hospital, Galsworthy Road, Kingston upon Thames KT2 7QB — MB BS Lond. 1970; FRCPath 1988, M 1976. Cons. Haemat. Kingston Hosp. NHS Trust. Socs: Brit. Assn Med. Managers; Fell. Roy. Soc. Med. Prev: Lect. (Haemat.) St. Geo. Hosp. Med. Sch. Lond.; Regist. (Haemat.) King's Coll. Hosp. Lond.

MCHUGH, Patrick Joseph Mary Department of Anaesthesia, Leeds General Infirmary, Great George St., Leeds LS1 3EX Tel: 0113 243 2799 Email: pmochugh@ulth.northy.nhs.uk; Email: patrickmchugh@netscapeonline.co.uk — MB BCh BAO 1981 NUI; FFA RCS 1988; FFA RCSI 1988; DA (UK) 1986. Cons. Anaesth. Leeds Gen. Infirm. Prev: Cons. Paediat. (Intens. Anaesth.) Leeds Gen. Infirm.; Sen. Regist. Mersey RHA; Sen. Regist. (Intens. Care) Roy. Hallamsh. Hosp. Sheff.

MCHUGH, Robert John 40 West Road, Bridgend CF31 4HD — MB BCh 1995 Wales.

MCHUGH, Roisin 10 Ashburn Park, Castlederg BT81 7BA — MB BS 1998 Lond.; MB BS Lond 1998.

MCHUGH, Seamus Joseph Alphonsus Crumlin Road Health Centre, 130-132 Crumlin Road, Belfast BT14 6AR Tel: 028 9074 1188 — MB BCh BAO 1980 Belf.

MCHUGH, Stephen Oldcastle Surgery, South St., Bridgend CF31 3ED — MB BCh 1963 Wales; MRCGP 1973. (Cardiff)

MCHUGH, Thomas Michael Anthony D'Mello and Partners, The Health Centre, Curtis Street, Hucknall, Nottingham NG15 7JE Tel: 0115 963 2535 Fax: 0115 963 2885; 21 Devon Drive, Sherwood, Nottingham NG5 2ET Tel: 0115 960 9649 — MB BCh BAO 1983 NUI; MRCGP 1989.

MCHUGO, Josephine Margaret Birmingham Womens Hospital, QEMC, Edgbaston, Birmingham B15 2TG Tel: 0121 627 2680 Fax: 0121 627 2616 — MB BS 1973 Lond.; FRCP; FRCPCH; MRCP (U.K.) 1976; FRCR 1982. Cons. (Radiol.) Birm. Wom. Hosp. Birm.; Hon. Sen. Lect. Birm. Univ. Prev: Sen. Regist. (Radiol.) W. Midl. RHA.

MCHUTCHON, Andrew Department of Anaesthesia, Queen Elizabeth Hospital, Gateshead NE9 6SX Tel: 0191 403 2176 Fax: 0191 403 2827 Email: andrew.mchutchon@ghnt.nhs.uk; 19 Lily Crescent, Newcastle upon Tyne NE2 2SP Tel: 0191 281 2255 Email: amchutchon@compuserve.com — MB ChB 1977 Dundee; FFA RCS Eng. 1981. Cons. Anaesth. Qu. Eliz. Hosp. Gateshead. Socs: Assn. Anaesth.; Obst. Anaesth. Assn.; Intens. Care Soc. Prev: Sen. Regist. (Anaesth.) N.. RHA; Regist. Rotat. (Anaesth.) Sheff. AHA.

MACIEJCZAK, Danuta 2D Queen Anne Avenue, Bromley BR2 0SB Tel: 020 8460 7325 — Lekarz 1958 Wroclaw; MRCPsych 1983; DPM Eng. 1975. Cons. Psychiat. Ment.ly Handicap. N. Herts. DHA. Socs: Polish Med. Assn. Prev: Sen. Regist. St. Thomas's Lond. & Surrey HA.

MACIEJEWSKA, Elzbieta Maria Merchiston Surgery, Highworth Road, Swindon SN3 4BF Tel: 01793 823307 Fax: 01793 820923; 21 Westlecot Road, Swindon SN1 4EZ Tel: 01793 525781 Email: hv86@dial.pipex.com — MB ChB 1973 Birm.

MACIEJEWSKI, Andrzej (retired) 43 Woodfield Road, Coventry CV5 6AJ — MD Bologna 1947; FFA RCS Eng. 1960; DA Eng. 1955; Cons. Anaesth. Coventry Hosp. Gp. Prev: Sen. Hosp. Med. Off. Anaesth. S.. Gen. Hosp. Glas.

MCILFATRICK, Sheena Douglas Newtownards health Centre, 17 Frederick St., Newtownards BT23 4LS; 8 Laurel Park, Conlig, Newtownards BT23 7PE — MB BCh BAO 1977 Belf.; DCH RCPSI 1980; DRCOG 1979.

MCILHENNY, Craig Flat Six, 53 Kent Road, Glasgow G3 7BL Tel: 0141 204 3419 Email: d2202213@infotrade.co.uk — MB ChB 1994 Glas.; FRCS (Ed) 1998. (Glasgow University) Research Fell. Gen. Surg.

MCILHINNEY, Stephen William The Health Centre, 20 Cleveland Square, Middlesbrough TS1 2NX Tel: 01642 245069 Fax: 01642 230388; 9 Sandy Flatts Lane, Acklam, Middlesbrough TS5 7YY Tel: 01642 322584 Email: stevemcilh@aol.com — MB BS 1979 Newc.; DRCOG 1982; MRCGP 1983. GP Partner Middlesbrough. Prev: Trainee GP Cleveland VTS.

MCILHINNEY, Susan Elizabeth Byrne, Langham, Apps, Finnie and McIlhinney, 186 Neasham Road, Darlington DL1 4YL Tel: 01325 461128 Fax: 01325 469123; 49 Flora Avenue, Darlington DL3 8PF — MB ChB 1982 Manch.; MRCGP 1986; DRCOG 1985. Socs: BMA. Prev: GP Darlington; SHO (Obst.) Middlesbrough Matern. Hosp.; SHO (Gen. Med. & Paediat.) Memor. Hosp. Darlington.

***MCILHONE, Paul** 18 Lattimore Road, St Albans AL1 3XW — MB BS 1998 Lond.; MB BS Lond 1998.

MCILLMURRAY, Malcolm Barron Royal Lancaster Infirmary, Ashton Road, Lancaster LA1 4RP Tel: 01524 65944; Beech House, Over Kellet, Carnforth LA6 1DL — MB BS Lond. 1968; DM Nottm. 1978; FRCP Lond. 1985; MRCP (UK) 1970. (Lond. Hosp.) Cons. Med. Oncol. & Palliat. Care Roy. Lancs. Infirm. & W.morland Gen. Hosp. Kendal; Med. Dir. St. John's Hospice Lancaster.; Hon. Prof. Univ. of Lancaster. Prev: Lect. (Therap.) Univ. Nottm.

MCILMOYLE, Carolyn Anne 26 Ballywee Road, Parkgate, Ballyclare BT39 0DW Tel: 01960 323099 — MB BCh BAO 1979 Belf.; DMH Belf. 1996. (Queens University - Belfast)

MCILMOYLE, Edith Lindsay Brookhill, 51 Ballinderry Road, Ballinderry Upper, Lisburn BT28 2NS Tel: 01232 457862 — MB BCh BAO 1975 Belf.; MD Belf. 1982.

MCILMOYLE, James Royal Lancaster Infirmary, Ashton Road, Lancaster LA1 4RP Tel: 01524 65944; 398 Craigs Road, Rasharkin, Ballymena BT44 8RD — MB BCh BAO 1992 Belf.; MRCP (UK) 1996.

MCILMOYLE, Norma Anne 102 Dowland Road, Limavady BT49 0HR Tel: 015047 64363 — MB BCh BAO 1994 Belf.; DRCOG 1996; DMH 1997. GP Regist. Mt.sandel Surg. Coleraine. Prev: SHO (Gen. Med.); SHO (Ment. Health); SHO (O & G).

MCILRATH, Edwin Maynard 28 Cleaver Park, Belfast BT9 Tel: 01232 666517 — MB BCh BAO 1956 Belf.; FFR 1962; DMRD Eng. 1959. (Belf.) Sen. Lect. in Radiol. Qu. Univ. Belf.; Cons. Roy. Vict. Hosp. Belf.

MCILRATH, James Patrick 2A Rathmena Gardens, Ballyclare BT39 9HU — MB BCh BAO 1985 Belf.; MRCGP 1991; T (GP) 1992; DRCOG 1991.

MCILRATH, Robert Alexander (retired) 45 Castlehill Road, Belfast BT4 3GN — MB BCh BAO 1942 Belf. Prev: Vis. Med. Off. Madame Curie Home.

MCILROY, Alan James Larne Health Centre, Gloucester Avenue, Larne BT40 1PB Tel: 028 2826 1924 Fax: 028 2826 1940 — MB BCh BAO 1984 Belf.; MB BCh Belf. 1984.

MCILROY, Mr Brendan Stephen 21 The Green, Caldy, Wirral CH48 2LA Tel: 0151 625 0109 — MB ChB 1987 Liverp.; FRCS 1997; FRCS Eng. 1991. Sen. Regist. (Gen. Surg.) NW Deanery.

MCILROY, David Ian Farnham Road Surgery, 301 Farnham Road, Slough SL2 1HD Tel: 01753 520917 Fax: 01753 550680 — MB ChB 1976 Ed.; MRCGP 1981; DCH RCP Lond. 1981; DRCOG 1979.

MCILROY, David John 112 Carrickfergus Road, Larne BT40 3JX — MB ChB 1998 Dund.; MB ChB Dund 1998. PRHD Surg. Perth Roy. Infir. Perth; SHO A & E Perth Roy. Infir. Perth. Prev: PRHO Med. Cumbld. Infir. Carlisle.

MCILROY, Eileen Annie (retired) 2A Ramsay Court, Eaglesham Road, Newton Mearns, Glasgow G77 5DJ — MB ChB Glas. 1945.

MCILROY, Gordon Henry Corbett Neillsbrook Road Surgery, 5 Neillsbrook Road, Randalstown, Antrim BT41 3AE Tel: 028 9447 2575 Fax: 028 9447 3653; Roughan House, 51 New St, Randalstown, Antrim BT41 3LA Tel: 018494 73931 — MB BCh BAO 1981 Belf.; MRCGP 1985; DCH Dub. 1985; DRCOG 1984.

MCILROY, Heather Anne Balvicar Centre, 46 Balvical St., Glasgow G42 6QU; Flat 7, 7 Netherlee Place, Glasgow G44 3YL — MB ChB 1977 Glas. Staff Grade (Community Paediat.) Yorkhill NHS Trust Glas. Prev: Clin. Med. Off. (Community Child Health) Gtr. Glas. HB.

MCILROY, Janet Hamilton Department of Chemical Pathology, St James's University Hospital, Beckett Street, Leeds LS9 7TF Tel: 0113 203 4818; 3 Lidgett Mount, Roundham, Leeds LS8 1EX Tel: 0113 266 5874 — MB ChB 1986 Glas.; MRCPath 1998; MRCP (UK) 1990; Dip. RCPath 1996. Cons. in Chem. Path., Leeds Teachg. Hosps. NHS Trust.

MCILROY, Philip William John Occupational Health Unit, 1-3 Bryn Eirias Close, Colwyn Bay LL29 8AR; Tel: 0113 269 6158 Email: kate@kate66.fsnet.co.uk — MB BCh BAO 1987 Belf.; DRCOG 1991; DCH 1990; 2000 D Occ Med; MRCGP 1991; T(GP) 1991. Force Med. Off., Occupat.al Health, N. Wales Police, Colwyn Bay; Gen. Practitioner, Amlwch.

MCILROY, Robert James 17 Bardney Road, Hunmanby, Filey YO14 0LX Tel: 01723 892959 Fax: 01723 892959 — MB ChB 1945 Glas. Prev: Med. Off. Falkland Is.s Govt.; GP Hunmanby N. Yorks.; Med. Off. Tasmanian Govt.

MCILROY, Ruth Lyn 20 Manse Road, Castlereagh, Belfast BT6 9SB — MB BCh BAO 1988 Belf.

MCILROY, Sadie Stevenson Holly Cottage, Caythorpe, Grantham NG32 3DR — MB BCh BAO 1960 Belf.; FFPHM RCP (UK) 1991. Dir. (Pub. Health) S. Lincs. HA.

MCILROY, William Henry Halliday (retired) Westfield Nursing Home, 405 Hagley Road, Edgbaston, Birmingham B17 8BL — MB BCh BAO 1937 Belf. Prev: Gen. Pract. Partner, Newc.-u-Lyme, Staffs.

MCILVEEN, Donald Joseph Sibley (retired) Sunday's Hill, Whinfield Road, Dodford, Bromsgrove B61 9BG Tel: 01527 831074 — MB ChB 1942 Birm.; BDS Birm. 1939. Prev: Cons. i/c Geriat. Med. Dept. BromsGr. Gen. Hosp.

MCILVEEN, Sheila Mary (retired) Sunday's Hill, Whinfield Road, Dodford, Bromsgrove B61 9BG Tel: 01527 831074 — MB ChB 1951 Birm.; DObst RCOG 1953. Prev: Ho. Phys. Qu. Eliz. Hosp. & Childr. Hosp. Birm.

MCILVEEN, William Henderson (retired) Touchstone, Cliffords Mesne, Newent GL18 1JT Tel: 01531 820404 — MB ChB Birm. 1947. Prev: Asst. Res. Med. Off. Gen. Hosp. Birm.

MACILWAIN

MACILWAIN, Ian Fraser Royal Cornhill Hospital, Cornhill Road, Aberdeen AB25 2ZH Tel: 01224 557278 Fax: 01224 557709 — MB ChB 1972 Aberd.; MRCPsych 1976. Cons. Psychother. Grampian HB Aberd. Socs: MRCPsych.; Pub. Ed. Off. RCPsych. N.. Scott.; Elected Mem. of Counc. & Fac. Prev: Cons. Psychother. E. Surrey HA & St. Geo. Hosp. Lond.; Psychiat. Dept. Health P. Edwd. Is. Canada; Sen. Res. (Psychiat.) St. Michael's Hosp. Toronto.

MCILWAIN, Mr Jeffrey Clifford Clinical Risk Management, Whiston Hospital, Warrington Road, Prescot L35 5DS Tel: 0151 430 1564 Fax: 0151 430 1218 — MD 1988 Belf.; MB BCh BAO 1977; FRCS Eng. 1982. (Queens Belfast) Cons. Clin. Risk Managem. Whiston Hosp. Prescot. Socs: Brit. Assn. Otol. Prev: Sen. Regist. (ENT) Roy. Vict. Hosp. Belf.; Conacher Fell. Toronto, Canada 1986.

MCILWAIN, Leonard Ian Michael Cameron Grafton Medical Centre, 208A-208B North Row, Buckingham Square, Central Milton Keynes, Milton Keynes MK9 3LQ Tel: 01908 695070; 18 Towcester Road, Old Stratford, Milton Keynes MK19 6AQ Tel: 01908 561017 — MRCS Eng. LRCP Lond. 1974. (Middlx.) Prev: Regist. (Paediat.) Ipswich Hosp.; SHO Whittington Hosp. Neonat. Unit; SHO W.m. Childr. Hosp.

MCILWAINE, Mr Gawn Graham 12 Lonsdale Terrace, Edinburgh EH3 9HN — MB BCh BAO 1981 Belf.; FRCS Glas. 1988; FCOphth 1990.

MCILWAINE, Gillian Marjorie Dept. Obstetrics, University of Edinburgh, Edinburgh; 26 Albert Place, Stirling FK8 2RF Tel: 01786 475199 Email: gillian.mcilwaine@which.net — MB ChB 1964; FRCOG 1997 Adeurden; PhD Glas. 1975; MD Aberd. 1969; FFCM 1982, M 1977; DObst RCOG 1966; MD 1969 Aberd. (Aberd.) Research Fell. Dept. of Obst. Univ. of Edin. Prev: Cons. Pub. Health Med. Wom. Health Gtr. Glas. HB.; Edpidemiol. Social Paediat. Obst. Research Unit Univ. Glas.; Instruc. (Obst.) State Univ. New York Downstate Med. Center Brooklyn.

MCILWAINE, Judith Elizabeth Jane Waterside Health Centre, Glendermot Road, Londonderry BT47 6AU Tel: 028 7132 0100 Fax: 028 7132 0107; 4 Glenaden Hill, Altnagelvin, Londonderry BT47 2LJ Tel: 028 7134 4723 — MB BCh BAO 1976 Belf.; DCH RCPSI 1979; DRCOG 1978.

MCILWAINE, Julie Ruth Carnoch, Balnafoich, By Farr, Inverness IV1 2XG Tel: 01808 521274; 20A Upper Toberhewny, Lurgan, Craigavon BT66 7EF Tel: 01762 325518 — MB ChB 1994 Ed. (Ed.) GP Regist. Ardlarich Med. Pract. Inverness. Prev: SHO (Psychiat.) Craig Dunain Hosp. Inverness; SHO (Med.) Belford Hosp. Fort William; Ho. Off. (Med.) Dumfries & Galloway Roy. Infirmm.

MCILWAINE, Louisa Marjorie Shu Haeinalology, Directorate of Laboratory, Medicine and Clinical Physics, Western Infirmary, Dumbator Road, Glasgow G11 Tel: 0141 412008; 2a Albert Place, Stirling FK8 2RF Tel: 01786 475199 — MB ChB 1995 Aberd.; MRCP (UK) 1998. (Aberdeen University) SHO(Haemat.) W.en Infiray, Glas. Prev: SHO (Gen. Med.) Aberd. Roy. Infirm.

MCILWAINE, Ronald John (retired) 26 Albert Place, Stirling FK8 2RF Tel: 01786 475199 Fax: 01786 479247 Email: r.j.mci@which.net — MB BCh BAO 1958 Belf.; MRCPsych 1971; DPM Eng. 1962. Prev: Cons. Psychiat. Bellsdyke Hosp. Larbert.

MCILWAINE, Werner Jon 10 Ballyrogan Park, Newtownards BT23 4SD Tel: 02891 816644 Email: wjmcilwaine@doctors.org.uk — MD 1984 Belf.; MB BCh BAO 1975; MRCP (UK) 1978; FRCP (UK) 1996. Cons. Gen. Phys. Ulster Community & Hosps. Trust Dundonald Belf. Socs: Ulster Soc. Intern. Med.; Diabetes UK.

***MCILWEE, Carl Alister** 11 Ballynacooley Road, Randalstown, Antrim BT41 3NB Tel: 01849 472930 — MB BCh BAO 1995 Belf.

MCILWRAITH, George Robert The Maidstone Hospital, Maidstone ME16 9QQ Tel: 01622 729000 Fax: 01622 720807; Noah's Ark Farm House, Headcorn, Ashford TN27 9PS Tel: 01622 891278 — MB ChB St. And. 1966; FRCP Lond. 1988; MRCP (UK) 1972. Cons. Phys. Maidstone Hosp. Socs: Brit. Thorac. Soc.; Brit. Geriat. Soc.; Eur. Respirat. Soc. Prev: Asst. Prof. Internal Med. (Pulm. Div.) Univ. Michigan Med. Sch. Ann Arbor Michigan, USA; Hon. Sen. Regist. King's Coll Hosp. Lond.

MCILWRAITH, William The Medical Centre, 2 Francis St., Doncaster DN1 1JS Tel: 01302 349431; 96 Thorne Road, Doncaster DN2 5BJ Tel: 01302 368793 — LRCP LRCS 1948 Ed.; LRFPS Glas. 1948. (Glas.)

MCILWRICK, Winifred Margaret (retired) Green Lane House, 1 Green Lane, Davenham, Northwich CW9 8HT — MB ChB 1946 Manch.

MCINALLY, Joseph 64 Hartburn Avenue, Stockton-on-Tees TS18 4HB — MB ChB 1945 Ed. (Ed.)

MCINDOE, Mr Gerald Angus James Institute of Obstetrics & Gynaecology, Hammersmith Hospital, Du Cane Road, London W12 0NN Tel: 020 8383 3268 Fax: 020 8383 8065; 9 Grosvenor Gardens, Muswell Hill, London N10 3TB Tel: 020 8365 4880 Fax: 020 8365 4889 — MB ChB 1980 Auckland; PhD Lond. 1993; BSc Auckland 1976; FRCS Eng. 1985; MRCOG 1987. Cons. Gyn. Oncol. Hammersmith Hosps. NHS Trust Lond. Socs: Brit. Gyn. Cancer Soc.; Brit. Soc. Colpos. & Cerv. Path. Prev: Sen. Regist. Addenbrooke's Hosp. Camb.; Gyn. Oncol. Train. Fell. St. Mary's Hosp. Lond.; Clin. Research Fell. Imperial Cancer Research Fund. Lond.

MACINDOE, Neil Lyle 39 Frogston Road W., Edinburgh EH10 7AH — MB ChB 1983 Otago.

MCINDOE, Sheila Elizabeth 8 Dudley Drive, Hyndland, Glasgow G12 9SD; 8 Redcliffe Road, Chelsea, London SW10 9NR — MB ChB 1987 Glas.

MACINDOE, William Lindsay (retired) 9 Langside Drive, Comrie, Crieff PH6 2HR Tel: 01764 670274 — MB ChB 1953 Glas.; DObst RCOG 1959.

MCINERNEY, Bernadette Ann Millbrook, Kingsmill Hospital, Sutton-in-Ashfield Tel: 01623 22515; Chessy, Kinvarra, Galway, Republic of Ireland — MB BCh BAO 1984 NUI; MRCPsych 1991.

MCINERNEY, Gillian Margaret 4 Grove Villas, Inchbrook, Stroud GL5 5EZ — MB BS 1992 Lond. Trainee GP Roy. United Hosp. Bath.

MCINERNEY, Joanne Lesley Cheviot Lodge, Dixon Terrace, Yealmpton, Plymouth PL8 2NB — MB ChB 1986 Liverp.; DRCOG 1993.

MCINERNEY, John Randall and Partners, 494 Liverpool Street, Salford M6 5QZ Tel: 0161 736 1745 Fax: 0161 661 0588 — MB BCh BAO 1986 Dub.; MB BCh Dub. 1986. (Trinity College Dublin)

MCINERNEY, Linda Joyce 44 High Street, Easton on the Hill, Stamford PE9 3LN — MB BS 1991 Lond.

MCINERNEY, Maeve Anne Rosser and Partners, Crewkerne Health Centre, Middle Path, Crewkerne TA18 8BX Tel: 01460 72435 Fax: 01460 77957 — MB BCh BAO 1986 Dub.; MRCGP 1993.

MCINERNEY, Mr Paul Desmond Derriford Hospital, Derriford Road, Plymouth PL6 8DH; Cheviot Lodge, Dixon Terrace, Yealmpton, Plymouth PL8 2NB — MB ChB Liverp. 1980; MD Liverp. 1995; FRCS (Urol.) 1994; FRCS Ed. 1984. Cons. Urol. Derriford Hosp. Plymouth.

MCINERNY, Deborah Ann Regional Postgraduate Institute of Medicine & Dentistry, University Newcastle upon Tyne, 10/12 Framlington Place, Newcastle upon Tyne NE2 4AB Tel: 0191 222 7389 Fax: 0191 232 8533 Email: d.a.mcinerny@ncl.ac.uk — MB BS 1977 Newc.; FRCS Ed. 1982; MFPHM RCP (UK) 1990; MFCM 1989; FFPHM 2000. Assoc. Postgrad. Dean Univ. Newc.; Hon. Cons. Pub. Health Med. N. & Yorks. Regional Office. Prev: Cons. Pub. Health Med. N.. RHA; Sen. Regist. (Community Med.) N.d. HA; Sen. Regist. (A & E) Newc. Gen. Hosp.

MCINERNY, Timothy Mark Department of Forensic Psychiatry, Maudsley Hospital, Denmark Hill, London SE5 8AZ Tel: 020 7703 6333 — MB BS 1988 Lond.; BA Oxf. 1985; MRc Psych. 1995. Hon. Cons. Phys. BRd.moor Hosp. Crowthorne; Clin. Tutor Dept. of Forens. Psychiat. Lond. Prev: Sen. Regist. Forens. Psychiat. Maudsley Hosp. Lond.

MCINNES, Alastair Archibald 45 Brook Street, Raunds, Wellingborough NN9 6LL Tel: 01933 622545 — MB BChir 1948 Camb.; MA Camb. 1965, MB BChir 1948; MRCGP 1960. (Middlx.) Prev: Ho. Surg. N.ampton Gen. Hosp.

MCINNES, Alison Jane 9 Chestnut Avenue, Hessle HU13 0RH — MB BS 1992 Newc.

MCINNES, Archibald McCallum Brechin Health Centre, Infirmary Street, Brechin DD9 7AY Tel: 01356 624411 Fax: 01356 623259 — MB ChB 1986 Ed.; MRCGP 1991; DRCOG 1990. Prev: Occupat. Phys. Angus.

MACINNES, Archibald Neil The Surgery, 45 Main Street, Calderbank, Airdrie ML6 9SG Tel: 01236 767704 Fax: 01236 759186 — MB ChB 1974 Glas.

MCINTOSH

MACINNES, Brian Neil 73 Glasserton Road, Newlands, Glasgow G43 2LN — MB BS 1989 Lond.; MRCP (UK) 1992.

MCINNES, Diana Catherine 56 Burbage Road, Herne Hill, London SE24 9HE Tel: 020 7274 1226 Email: diana_m@ukgateway.net — MB BS 1975 Lond.; MSc Lond. 1991; MRCGP 1979; DCH Eng. 1979; DRCOG 1977. (Uni. Coll. Hosp. Med. Sch. Lond.) Princip. Med. Off. DoH Lond. HQ. Prev: Sen. Med. Off. DoH Lond. HQ; Clin. Med. Off. Lambeth S.wark Lewisham DHA; Princip. GP Lewisham.

MACINNES, Duncan Strathyre, 523 High St., Newarthill, Motherwell ML1 — MB ChB 1938 Glas.; DPH 1949; MRCGP 1953; DIH RFPS Glas. 1948. (Glas.)

MACINNES, Duncan Calum High Street Surgery, 60 High Street, Newarthill, Motherwell ML1 5JU Tel: 01698 860246 Fax: 01698 861641 — MB ChB 1978 Manch.; BSc (Hons.) Manch. 1975, MB ChB 1978; MRCGP 1982.

MACINNES, Duncan Jack Scapa Medical Group, Health Centre, New Scapa Road, Kirkwall KW15 1BQ Tel: 01856 885445 Fax: 01856 873556; Orka Howe, Holm, Orkney KW17 2RZ Tel: 0185678 _282 — MB ChB 1974 Aberd.; MRCGP 1978; DRCOG 1979. Med. Off. Balfour Hosp. Kirkwall.

MCINNES, Elizabeth Gray 36 Stourton Avenue, Feltham TW13 6LG — MB ChB 1975 Manch.; MRCP (UK) 1982; DCH Eng. 1977.

MCINNES, George Campbell Department of Radiology, Victoria Infirmary NHS Trust, Langside Road, Glasgow G42 9TY Tel: 0141 201 5551 Fax: 0141 201 5497; 19 The Steils, Edinburgh EH10 5XD Email: 106225.1456@compuserve.com — MB ChB 1983 Glas.; MRCGP 1987; FRCR 1991. Cons. Radiol. Vict. Infirm. NHS Trust; Hon. Sen. Lect. Univ. Glas. Prev: Sen. Regist. (Radiol.) Aberd. Roy. Infirm.; Regist. (Radiol.) Glas. Roy. Infirm.; Trainee GP Paisley VTS.

MCINNES, Gordon Kenneth Camelon Medical Practice, 3 Baird Street, Camelon, Falkirk FK1 4PP Tel: 01324 622854 Fax: 01324 633858 — MB ChB 1984 Ed.

MCINNES, Gordon Thomas University Department of Medicine & Therapeutics, Western Infirmary, Glasgow G11 6NT Tel: 0141 211 2319 Fax: 0141 339 2526 Email: g.t.mcinnes@clinmed.gla.ac.uk; 12 Kilpatrick Drive, Bearsden, Glasgow G61 4RH Tel: 0141 943 0225 — MB ChB 1971 Glas.; MD Glas. 1984, BSc (Hons.) Physiol. 1969; FRCP Ed. 1993; FRCP Glas. 1987, M 1975; FFPM RCP (UK) 1992. (Glas.) Sen. Lect. (Med.) & Hon. Cons. Phys. Univ. Dept. Med. & Therap. Gardiner Inst. W.. Infirm. Glas. Socs: Brit. Hypertens. Soc.; Clin. Sect. Brit. Pharmacol. Soc.; Assn. Phys. Prev: Lect. (Med.) & Hon. Sen. Regist. Univ. Dept. Med. Gardiner Inst. W..Infirm. Glas.; Searle Research Fell. (Clin. Pharmacol.) Searle & Co. High Wycombe; SHO (Med.) Hammersmith Hosp. Lond.

MCINNES, Iain Blair T/L 89 Novar Drive, Glasgow G12 9SS — MB ChB 1989 Glas.

MCINNES, Ian Campbell (retired) 81 Cae Du, Abersoch, Pwllheli LL53 7DJ Tel: 01758 713820 Fax: 01758 713820 — MB ChB Manch. 1960; DA Eng. 1964. Prev: Assoc. Specialist N. Manch. Gp. Hosps.

MCINNES, Joanne Clare 1 Coopers Cottage, Calder St., Lochwinnoch PA12 4DD — MB ChB 1991 Aberd.; MRCP (UK) 1995. Career Regist. (Med. Paediat.) Stirling Roy. Infirm. NHS Trust. Socs: Brit. Paediat. Assn.; Scott. Paediat. Soc.

MCINNES, Katherine Elizabeth Thornrigg, Samuelston Crossroads, Haddington EH41 4HE — MB ChB 1991 Aberd. Trainee GP Lothian.

MACINNES, Lindsay Elizabeth 72 Prebend Gardens, London W6 0XU Tel: 020 8741 2053 — MB ChB 1972 Sheff.; MRCGP 1978.

MCINNES, Paula Beverly 140 Malden Road, Sutton SM3 8RA Tel: 020 8644 3739 — MB ChB 1986 Glas. (Univ. Glas.) Clin. Asst. Beta Cell Unit Qu. Mary's Hosp. Lond. Prev: Clin. Asst. W. of Scotl. Regional Blood Transfs. Serv.; Clin. Asst. Diabetic Clinic Gartnavel Gen. Hosp. Glas.; Clin. Asst. Oxf. Regional Blood Transfs. Serv.

MACINNES, Pauline Alloa Health Centre, Marshill, Alloa FK10 1AQ Tel: 01259 216476 — MB ChB 1988 Ed.

MACINNES, Peter Kilbirnie Medical Practice, 2 Kirkland Road, Kilbirnie KA25 6HP Tel: 01505 683333 Fax: 01505 683591; Broomhill, 4 Largs Road, Kilbirnie KA25 7AT Tel: 01505 684665 — MB ChB 1964 Glas.; MRCGP 1970; DObst RCOG 1966. (Glas.)

Socs: BMA. Prev: Ho. Phys. Kilmarnock Infirm.; Ho. Surg. Vict. Infirm. Glas.; Ho. Surg. (Obst.) Glas. Roy. Matern. Hosp.

MACINNES, Robert Elliot 1 Shaftesbury Avenue, Bedford MK40 3SA — MB ChB 1985 Aberd.

MACINNES, Robert John Tel: 01296 424435 Fax: 01296 434139 — BM BCh 1977 Oxf.; MRCGP 1983; Dip Pris 2000 (Med); DCH Lond. 1980. Prison Med. Off. HM Prison Grendon, Grendon Underwood, Bucks.

MCINNES, Roger Cannon Street, Oldham OL9 6EP; 9 Bagnall Close, Uppermill, Oldham OL3 6DW — MB ChB 1981 Manch.; BSc St. And. 1978.

MACINNES, Ronella Janet Newton Health Centre, New Scapa Road, Kirkwall KW15 1BX Tel: 01856 885445 — MB ChB 1974 Aberd.; DFFP 1993; DRCOG 1977; Cert. Contracep. & Family Plann. RCOG RCGP &; Cert FPA 1976. (Aberd.) Non Princip. GP (Employed); Pract. Manager, Scapa Med. Gp., Kirkwall. Socs: Scott. Family Plann. Med. Soc. (Inst. of Healthcare Managem.).

MCINNES, Russell Mintlaw Group Practice, Newlands Road, Mintlaw, Peterhead AB42 5GP Tel: 01771 623522 Fax: 01771 624349; Wester Clerkhill, Kinmundy Road, Peterhead AB42 2AE — MB ChB 1982 Ed.; MRCGP 1986; DRCOG 1986.

MCINNES, Susan Jane Detling, 53 Caldene Avenue, Hebden Bridge HX7 5AJ — MB BS 1998 Newc.; MB BS Newc 1998.

MCINROY, Bruce Kilwinning Medical Practice, 15 Almswall Road, Kilwinning KA13 6BO Tel: 01294 554591 Fax: 01294 557300 — MB ChB 1970 Glas.; MRCGP 1974; DObst RCOG 1972.

MCINROY, David Campbell (retired) 3 Burnside Avenue, Kirkintilloch, Glasgow G66 1EP Tel: 0141 776 3081 — MB ChB 1962 Glas.; FRCPsych 1991, M 1975; DPM Eng. 1973. Prev: Hon. Clin. Sen. Lect. (Psychol. Med.) Univ. Glas.

MCINROY, John (retired) 27 Lewis Street, Stranraer DG9 7AB Tel: 01776 702036 — MB ChB 1936 Glas.; MB ChB (Hons.) Glas. 1936; DPH Glas. 1939.

MCINROY, Ronald Allan (retired) West Royd, 112 Allerton Road, Bradford BD8 0AQ Tel: 01274 487711 — MB ChB 1943 St. And.; BSc (Hons. Path.) St. And. 1940; FRCPath 1967; DTM & H Liverp. 1947. Cons. Path. St. Luke's Hosp. Bradford.

MCINTOSH, Alastair Ballingall (retired) 11 Alston Road, Middleton-in-Teesdale, Barnard Castle DL12 0UU Tel: 01833 640384 — MB ChB 1945 Ed.

MCINTOSH, Alastair David (retired) 14B Drumalin, Drummond Road, Inverness IV2 4NB — MB ChB 1944 Ed.; FRCOG 1969, M 1952. Prev: Cons. O & G Raigmore Hosp. Highland Health Bd.

MCINTOSH, Alastair Hogg McIntosh, Gourlay and Partners, 1 India Place, Edinburgh EH3 6EH Tel: 0131 225 9191 Fax: 0131 226 6549; 32 Ormidale Terrace, Edinburgh EH12 6EF — MB ChB 1974 Manch.; BSc (Med. Sci.) St. And. 1971; MRCGP 1979. (St. And. & Manch.) Socs: RCGP.

MCINTOSH, Alexander Wilson (retired) West Winds, The Gowans, Sutton-on-the-Forest, York YO61 1DL Tel: 01347 810483 Email: rubislaw@aol.com — MB ChB Aberd. 1950; MD Aberd. 1962; FFPHM 1978, M 1972; DPH Aberd. 1956. Prev: Cons. Pub. Health Med. Yorks. RHA.

MCINTOSH, Andrew Fraser 108 Montgomery Street, Edinburgh EH7 5HE Tel: 0131 557 1866 — MB ChB 1987 Aberd.

MCINTOSH, Andrew Mark Kennedy Tower, Royal Edinburgh Hospital, Morningside Park, Edinburgh EH10 5HF Tel: 0131 537 6000 Email: andrew.mcintosh@ed.ac.uk; Tel: 0131 449 5327 — MB ChB 1995 Aberd.; MPhil 2001 Edin.; BSc (Hons.) Aberd. 1992; MRCPysch. 1999. (Univ. Aberd.) Research Fell. (Hon Spr) Univ. of Edin. Socs: Brit. Assn. Psychopharmacol. Prev: SHO (Forens. Psychiat.) State Hosp. Coustairs; SHO (Child Psychiat.) St. John's Hosp. Livingston; (Wellcome) Research Regist. Univ. of Edin.

MCINTOSH, Carol Ann 14 Saxe Coburg Street, Edinburgh EH3 5BW — MB ChB 1981 Aberd.; FRCS Ed. 1986.

MCINTOSH, Cathryn Sian 1 Oxford Road, Redhill RH1 1DT Tel: 01737 762902 — MB BS 1990 Lond.; MRCP 1995; DFFP 1995; 1995 JCPTGP cert. Of Prescirbed Experience; BSc (anatomy) Lond. 1987; DRCOG 1993. Full Time Gen. Pract.; Clin. Assit Dermat., E. Surrey Hosp. Redhill.

MCINTOSH, Christine Anne Block Lane Surgery, 158 Block Lane, Chadderton, Oldham OL9 7SG Tel: 0161 620 2321 Fax: 0161 628 5604; 48 Rishworth Rise, Shaw, Oldham OL2 7QA — MB ChB 1979 Manch.; MRCGP 1983; DRCOG 1981.

MCINTOSH

MCINTOSH, Christopher Gordon McIntosh, Trounce and Harvey, Health Centre, Orchard Way, Chillington, Kingsbridge TQ7 2LB Tel: 01548 580214 Fax: 01548 581080; Old Barton, Higher Coleridge, Chillington, Kingsbridge TQ7 2JG Tel: 01548 580549 — MB BS 1979 Lond.; MRCP (UK) 1982; MRCGP 1989; DRCOG 1989. (St. Mary's Hosp.)

MCINTOSH, Claire Elizabeth 52/8 Laichpark Road, Edinburgh EH14 1XB — MB ChB 1995 Dundee; MRC Psych 1999. SHO (Psychiat.) Roy. Edin. Hosp. Prev: Ho. Off. (Med.) Dumfries & Galloway Roy. Infirm.; Ho. Off. (Paediat. Surg.) Roy. Aberd. Childr. Hosp.

MCINTOSH, Colin Stephen, TD 4 The Downsway, Sutton SM2 5RN Tel: 020 8642 3470 Email: colin@mcintoshc.fsnet.co.uk — MB ChB 1964 Aberd.; MD Aberd. 1975; FRCP Lond. 1985; MRCP (UK) 1970. Cons. Phys. Chelsea & W.m. Hosp. Lond. Socs: Diabetes UK; Internat. Diabetes Federat.; Roy. Soc. Med. Prev: Sen. Regist. (Med.) W.m. Hosp. Lond.; Cons. Phys. Qu. Mary's Hosp. Lond.; Lect. (Nephrol.) Med. Coll. St. Bart. Hosp. Lond.

MACINTOSH, Corinna Mary Arderne 31 Hayfield Road, Oxford OX2 6TX — MB ChB 1997 Bristol.

MCINTOSH, Dawn Marie 120 Bellingham Road, London SE6 2PR — MB BS 1994 Lond.

MCINTOSH, Diana Marie Flat 2/3, 237 Bearsden Road, Anniesland, Glasgow G13 1DH — MB ChB 1998 Glas.

MCINTOSH, Edwin David Senior Medical Adviser, Wyeth, Huntercombe Lane South, Taplow, Maidenhead SL6 0PH Tel: 01628 414814 Fax: 0168 414802 Email: mcintod@wai.wyeth.com; 36B King Henry's Road, London NW3 3RP Tel: 020 7483 1652 Email: edgmci@aol.com — PhD Sydney 1997; MPH Sydney 1986; FRACP 1993; DObst RCOG 1984; DCH RCP Lond. 1984; FAFPHM Sydney 1990; MRCP & CH Lond. 1996. (Univ. Sydney) Sen. Med. Adviser; Vis. Lect. 1st Fac. of Med. Chas. Univ., Prague, Czech RePub.; Sen. Lect. Fac. of Med., Imperial Coll. Socs: Fell. Roy. Soc. Trop. Med. & Hyg.; Mem. Brit. Assn. of Pharmaceutical Phys.s. Prev: Hon. Clin. Asst. & Sen. Regist. Dept. Paediat. St. Mary's Hosp. Lond.; Hon. Clin. Lect. Imperial Coll. Sch. of Med. at St Mary's; SmithKline Fell. (Prevent. Med.) The Childr. Hosp. Sydney.

MCINTOSH, Elizabeth Ann St Serf's Medical Practice, Loch Leven HC, Lathro — MB ChB 1986 Glas.; MRCGP 1993; DA (UK) 1993. p/t GP Retainer, St Serf's Med. Pract. Loch Leven Health Centre Lathro Kinross. Socs: Roy. Coll. Gen. Pract. Prev: GP Partnership: Harden, Prentice, Powell, Chapman.

MCINTOSH, George Douglas, MC (retired) 4 Mayfield Road, Inverness IV2 4AE — MB ChB 1937 Ed.

MCINTOSH, George Ewan Haylodge Health Centre, Neidpath Road, Peebles EH45 8JG Tel: 01721 720380 Fax: 01721 723430 — MB ChB 1978 Aberd.; MRCGP 1985; DRCOG 1981. GP Peebles.

MCINTOSH, Gillian Dorothea 23 Glenmoor, Hebburn NE31 1DE — MB ChB 1989 Manch.

MCINTOSH, Graham Henderson, MBE Stonehaven Medical Group, Stonehaven Medical Centre, 32 Robert Street, Stonehaven AB39 2EL Tel: 01569 762945 Fax: 01569 766552; Greywalls, Stonehaven AB39 2HB Tel: 01569 763532 Fax: 01569 764903 Email: drgmci@aol.com — MB ChB 1967 Aberd.; MRCGP 1975; DObst RCOG 1971. (Aberd.) Chairm. Scott. Med. Practs Comm. Socs: Aberd. M-C Soc. Prev: Resid. Ho. Off. (Surg. & Med.) & SHO (Anaesth.) Aberd. Roy. Infirm.; Resid. Obst. Aberd. Matern. Hosp.

MCINTOSH, Mr Gregor Scott 119 Bouverie Avenue S., Salisbury SP2 8EA — MRCS Eng. LRCP Lond. 1976; MS Lond. 1988, MB BS 1976; FRCS Eng. 1980. (Lond. Hosp.) Cons. Surg. Urol. Salisbury Dist. Hosp. Socs: Brit. Assn. Urol. Surgs.; Eur. Assn. Urol. Prev: Sen. Regist. (Surg. & Urol.) Roy. Free Hosp. Lond.; Sen. Regist. (Urol.) St. Peter's Hosp. Inst. Urol. Lond.; Wellcome Trust Surgic. Research Fell. Roy. Free Hosp. Sch. Med. Lond.

MCINTOSH, Heather Yvonne Downpatrick Road Surgery, 14 Downpatrick Road, Killyleagh, Downpatrick BT30 9RG Tel: 028 4482 8746 Fax: 028 4482 1458 — MB BCh BAO 1977 Belf.; MRCGP 1982.

MCINTOSH, Iain Blackwood (cons. rooms), Tornio Shirras Brae, Stirling FK7 0AY Tel: 01786 464242 Fax: 01786 464242 — MB ChB 1963 Ed.; DGM RCP Lond. 1986; DObst RCOG 1965. Train. Assessor W. Scotl. Postgrad. Centre; GP Train. Cons. Dementia Servs. Developm. Centre Univ. Stirling; Assoc. Edr. Travel Med. Internat. & Jl. Travel Med; Edr. Scott. Med. & Jl. Brit. Soc. Med. & Dent. Hypn. (Scotl.). Socs: Fell. (Ex-Pres.) Brit. Soc. Med. & Dent. Hypn. (Scotl.); Founding Mem. Brit. Travel Health Assn. Prev: Hosp. Pract. (Geriat.) Stirling Roy. Infirm.; GP Forth Valley HB; Lect. Stirling Univ. 1995 & Glas. Univ. 1994.

MACINTOSH, Iain Donald 18 Stirling Drive, Bishopbriggs, Glasgow G64 3AL — MB ChB 1991 Ed.

MCINTOSH, Iain Menzies Feastfield Medical Centre, King St., Pateley Bridge, Harrogate HG3 5AT Tel: 01423 711369 Fax: 01423 712482 Email: mcintosh@btinternet.com; Cabin Lane, Dacre Banks, Summerbridge, Harrogate HG3 4EE Tel: 01423 780486 — MB ChB 1975 Ed.; DA Eng. 1978.

MCINTOSH, Ian Douglas The Health Centre, Coachmans Drive, Broadfield, Crawley RH11 9YZ Tel: 01293 531951 — MB BCh BAO 1970 Dub.

MCINTOSH, James Stuart Kensington Road Surgery, 148 Kensington Road, Coventry CV5 6HY Tel: 024 7667 2466 Fax: 024 7671 7311; 27 Asthill Grove, Coventry CV3 6HN — MB ChB Aberd. 1958; DObst RCOG 1964. (Aberd.) Prev: Res. Med. Off. Aberd. Roy. Infirm.; Med. Off. Gen. Hosp. Tasmania & Roy. Wom. Hosp. Melb. Australia.

MCINTOSH, Mr James Wilson (retired) Cornwall House Clinic, Sandy Lane, Newcastle-under-Lyme ST5 0LZ Tel: 01782 714600 Fax: 01782 714609 — MB ChB Glas. 1956; MD Glas. 1965; FRCS Eng. 1963; FRCS Ed. 1961. Cons. Neurosurg. in Private Pract. Prev: Cons. Neurosurg. N. Staffs. Hosp. Trust Stoke-on-Trent.

MCINTOSH, Jamie Woodlands, Pyotts Hill, Old Basing, Basingstoke RG24 8AP — MB ChB 1998 Bristol.

MCINTOSH, Katherine Jane Tel: 01452 617295 Fax: 01452 617296; 16 Kingsholm Square, Gloucester GL1 2QJ — BM BS 1994 Nottm.; MRCGP 2000; DFFP 1997. GP Regist. Hucclecote Surg. Gloucs; GP Partner, Hucclecote Surg., Glos. Prev: SHO (A & E) Cheltenham Gen. Hosp.; SHO (Paediat.) Gloucs. Roy. Hosp.; SHO (O & G) Glos. Roy. Hosp.

MCINTOSH, Katherine Rachel Bridge Medical Centre, Wassand Close, Three Bridges, Crawley RH10 1LL Tel: 01293 526025; 95 Ashdown Drive, Tilgate, Crawley RH10 5ED Tel: 01293 543591 — MB BS 1978 Lond.; MRCGP 1990; DRCOG 1981. GP Crawley; Clin. Asst. Dermat., Cranley Hosp. Prev: GP VTS Hemel Hempstead; SHO (Accid. & Orthop.) Barnet Gen. Hosp.; SHO (O & G) Centr. Middlx. Hosp.

MACINTOSH, Kenneth Campbell, TD, Lt.-Col. 8 St Matthews Terrace, Leyburn DL8 5EL Email: kennethmacintosh@hotmail.com — MB ChB 1967 Leeds; FFA RCS Eng. 1974. (Leeds) Cons. Anaesth. MDHU (N) Friarge Hosp. N.allgrion, N.Yorks. Prev: Sen. Regist. (Anaesth.) Sheff. AHA (T); Capt. RAMC, Specialist Anaesth.; Cons. Anaesth. Norf. & Norwich 1976 - 2000.

MCINTOSH, Ludovic Grant Roslin Surgery, 6 Main Street, Roslin EH25 9LE Tel: 0131 440 2043 Fax: 0131 448 2558 — MB ChB 1974 Ed.; MRCP (UK) 1982. (Edinburgh)

MACINTOSH, Mary Christina Munro Fairfield, Woodlands Drive, Apperley Bridge, Bradford BD10 0PP — MB ChB 1980 Sheff.; MB ChB (Hons.) Sheff. 1980; MA Camb. 1974, MD 1995; MRCOG 1985. Dir. CESDI (Confidential Enquiries into Stillbirths & Deaths in Infancy) Lond.; Cons. Obst. Homerton Hosp. - Lond. Prev: Cons. Obst. & Med. Care Epidemiol. Leeds Gen. Infirm.

MCINTOSH, Neil Department Child Life & Health, University Edinburgh, 20 Sylvan Place, Edinburgh EH9 1UW Tel: 0131 536 0801 Fax: 0131 536 0821 Email: neil.mcintosh@ed.ac.uk; 32 Queen's Crescent, Edinburgh EH9 2BA Tel: 0131 667 5173 — MB BS 1968 Lond.; DSc (Med.) Lond. 1995; BSc Soton 1963; FRCP Ed. 1988; FRCP Lond. 1985; MRCP (UK) 1970; MRCS Eng. LRCP Lond. 1968. (Univ. Coll. Hosp.) Prof. Child Life & Health Univ. Edin. Socs: (Pres.) Europ. Soc. Paediat. Research; Neonat. Soc.; Brit. Assn. of Perinatal Med. Prev: Sen. Lect. & Cons. Paediat. St. Geo. Hosp. Lond.; Sen. Regist. (Paediat.) Univ. Coll. Hosp. Lond.; Research Fell. (Paediat. Endocrinol.) Univ. Calif., San Francisco.

MCINTOSH, Rebekah Elizabeth 43 Hurst Rise Road, Oxford OX2 9HE Tel: 01865 862642 — MB ChB 1995 Birm.; MBChB Birm. 1995. (Birmingham) GP VTS Dorset Co. Hosp. Dorchester. Prev: SHO (Paediat.) Alexandra Hosp. Redditch; RMO Bundaberg Base Hosp. Qu.sland, Australia.

MCINTOSH, Robert Ewing (retired) Torridon, 3 Graham Avenue, Stevenston KA20 4AD Tel: 01294 462433 — MB ChB 1957 Glas.; MRCGP 1968. Prev: GP Saltcoats.

MACINTYRE

MCINTOSH, Sandra Anne 23 Rubislaw Terrace, Aberdeen AB10 1XE Tel: 01224 643665 Fax: 01224 625197 Email: sandra.mcintosh@rubislawterrace, grampian.scot.nhs.uk; Gillahill Croft, Kingswells, Aberdeen AB15 8PR Tel: 01224 741057 — MB ChB 1968 Aberd. (Aberd.) Prev: Cas. Off. & Ho. Surg. Roy. Aberd. Childr. Hosp.; Ho. Phys. Woodend Gen. Hosp. Aberd.

MCINTOSH, Shona Jane 2 School Court, St. Mary's St., Boston Spa, Wetherby LS23 6BP — MB ChB 1986 Leeds; MRCP (UK) 1989. Cons. c/o Elderly St. Jas. Univ. Hosp. Leeds. Prev: Regist. (Gen. Med.) Bradford Roy. Infirm.

MCINTOSH, Simon Paul 21 Penwethers Lane, Truro TR1 3PW — MB ChB 1998 Bristol.

MCINTOSH, Mr Stuart Andrew 32A Clarence Street, Edinburgh EH3 5AF Tel: 0131 225 4341 — MB ChB 1993 Ed.; FRCS Ed. 1997. (Edinburgh) Research Fell. Dept. of Surg. W.ern Infirm. Glas. Prev: SHO (Cardiothoracic Surg.) Roy. Infirm. Edin.

MCINTOSH, Stuart Lloyd 31 Hacketts Lane, Woking GU22 8PP — BM BS 1995 Nottm.

MCINTOSH, William Grant (retired) 82 Duddington Road W., Edinburgh EH15 3PU — MB ChB Ed. 1945; FRCS Ed. 1950; FRCGP 1978; DTM & H Antwerp 1952. Hon. Maj. RAMC.

MACINTYRE, Alexander Dunelm Medical Practice, 1-2 Victor Terrace, Bearpark, Durham DH7 7DF Tel: 0191 373 2077 Fax: 0191 373 6216 — MB ChB 1964 Ed. (Ed.)

MACINTYRE, Alison Ruth Whalebridge Practice, Health Centre, Carfax Street, Swindon SN1 1ED Tel: 01793 692933; Wykeham House, Hyde Lane, Purton, Swindon SN5 4DU — MB ChB 1986 Leic.; MRCGP 1990; DRCOG 1988.

MCINTYRE, Alistair James Priory Court Surgery, 1 High Street, Beauly IV4 7BY Tel: 01463 782214 Fax: 01463 782129; 7 Broallan, Kilmorack, Beauly IV4 7AH Tel: 01463 782731 — MB ChB 1985 Aberd.; MRCGP 1990. GP. Prev: Trainee GP Highland Region.

MCINTYRE, Alistair Stewart Wycombe Hospital, High Wycombe HP11 2TT Tel: 01494 425595 Fax: 01494 425597 — MB BS 1981 Lond.; BSc (Hons.) Lond. 1978, MD 1990. (St. Bart.) Cons. Gen. Internal Med. & Gastroenterol. And Hepat. Wycombe Hosp. High Wycombe. Socs: Fell. Roy. Coll. Phys.; Brit. Soc. Gastroenterol. Prev: Sen. Regist. Univ. Hosp. Nottm.

MCINTYRE, Andrew George Applemead, Church St., Stonesfield, Oxford OX29 8PS — MB ChB 1990 Dundee.

MACINTYRE, Anne Elizabeth Robina 5 Metford Place, Bristol BS6 7LE Tel: 0117 924 6216 — MB ChB 1965 Ed.; DO Eng. 1980; DCH RCPS Glas. 1967.

MCINTYRE, Archibald Dewar, CBE (retired) Birchlea, 43 Falkirk Road, Linlithgow EH49 7PH Tel: 01506 842063 — MB ChB Ed. 1950; FRCP (Ed.) 1986, M 1983; FFCM 1979, M 1974; DIH Soc. Apoth. Lond. 1960; DPH Ed. 1960; DTM & H Ed. 1956. Prev: PMO Scott. Home & Health Dept.

MCINTYRE, Christopher William Little Loddenden, High St., Staplehurst, Tonbridge TN12 0AD — MB BS 1990 Lond.

MCINTYRE, Mr Donald (retired) 12 Greenside Drive, Hale, Altrincham WA14 3HX Tel: 0161 928 8697 — MB ChB Ed. 1951; FRCS Eng. 1959; FRCS Ed. 1961. Prev: Cons. Urol. Salford Roy. Hosp., Christie Hosp. Manch., N. Manch. Gen. Hosp. & Roy. Manch. Childr. Hosp.

MACINTYRE, Donald James 6 (2FR) Bruntsfield Gardens, Edinburgh EH10 4EA Tel: 0131 229 8311 Email: djmacintyre@clara.net — MB ChB 1996 Ed.; BSc (Med. Sci.) 1994. (Edinburgh) Socs: Life Mem. Roy. Med. Soc.

MCINTYRE, Douglas Hendry Hilly Fields Medical Centre, 172 Adelaide Avenue, London SE4 1JN — MB ChB 1971 St. And.

MCINTYRE, Duncan (retired) 11 Faires Close, Borrowash, Derby DE72 3XP — MB ChB 1961 Ed. Prev: GP Derby.

MACINTYRE, Duncan Victoria Infirmary, Glasgow G42 9TY Tel: 0141 649 4545; 74 Montgomery Street, Eaglesham, Glasgow G76 0AU Tel: 0176 729 2884 — MB 1974 Camb.; BChir 1973; FRCP Glas. 1988. Cons. Phys. (Gen. & Respirat. Med.) Vict. Infirm. Glas.

MCINTYRE, Elizabeth Ann 5 Abigail Court, Sandringham Road, South Gosforth, Newcastle upon Tyne NE3 1PP — MB ChB 1993 Glas.; MRCP (UK) 1997; DRCOG 1995.

MCINTYRE, Fiona Jane Durnford Medical Centre, 113 Long Street, Middleton, Manchester M24 6DL Tel: 0161 643 2011 Fax: 0161 653 6570; 12 Greenside Drive, Hale, Altrincham WA14 3HX — MB ChB 1993 Manch.; DFFP 1996; DRCOG 1996. Clin. Asst. (Cardio-Respirat. Med.) Hope Hosp. Salford.

MCINTYRE, George Bell East riding HA, Grange Pute Lane, Willerby, Hull HU10 6DT Tel: 01482672040 Fax: 01482 267 2060; 12 Hay Lane, Scalby, Scarborough YO13 0SP Tel: 01723 368994 Fax: 01723 507976 Email: george.mcintyre@lineone.net — MB ChB 1967 Ed.; MRCGP 1974; Cert. Community Paediat. Hull 1978; DObst RCOG 1973; DCH RCPS Glas. 1971. Dir.Primary Care E. Riding HA. Prev: GP ScarBoro.; SCMO ScarBoro. HA; Regist. (Paediat.) Newc. Hosp. Gp.

MCINTYRE, Heather 27 Alms Hill Road, Sheffield S11 9RR — MB BS 1981 Lond.; MRCP (UK) 1984; DCH RCP Lond. 1983. Med. Co-ordinator Christian Outreach Sudan. Prev: Regist. (Paediat.) Roy. Berks. Hosp. Reading & John Radcliffe Hosp. Oxf.; SHO (Paediat.) Guy's Hosp. & King's Coll. Hosp. Lond.

MCINTYRE, Hugh Farrell The Conquest Hospital, The Ridge, St Leonards-on-Sea TN37 7RD Tel: 01424 755255 Fax: 01424 757048; South View, Salehurst, Robertsbridge TN32 5PT Tel: 01580 880405 Fax: 01580 881522 Email: hfm@i-forth.com — MB BS 1984 Lond.; MA Oxf. 1992, BA 1981; MD Lond. 1994; FRCP 2000 UK. (Oxford and Westminster) Cons. Phys. The Conquest Hosp. Hastings; Hon. Cons. Cardiol. The Brompton Hosp. Sydney St. Lond.; Heart Failure Adviser The family Heart Assn. Lond. Socs: BMA; Brit. Soc. Heart Failure; Brit. Assn. Med. Managers. Prev: Sen. Regist. Rotat. (Med.) Guy's & Hastings Hosps.; Regist. (Med.) Kingston Hosp. Surrey & St. Thos. Hosp. Lond.; Brit. Heart Foundat. Research Fell. St. Thos. Hosp. Lond.

MACINTYRE, Professor Iain William Harvey Research Institute, St. Bartholomew's & Royal London School Medicine, & Dentistry, Charterhouse Square, London EC1M 6BQ Tel: 020 7882 6168 Fax: 020 7882 6162 Email: i.macintyre@qmul.ac.uk; Great Broadhurst Farm, Broad Oak, Heathfield TN21 8UX Tel: 01435 883515 Fax: 01435 883611 Email: calc@broadoak.demon.co.uk — MB ChB 1947 Glas.; Hon. MD 2002 Sheffield; FRS 1996; PhD Lond. 1960, DSc 1970; Hon. MD Turin 1985; FRCP Lond. 1977, M 1969; FRCPath 1971, M 1963; Mem. Assn. Amer. Phys.; F Med Sci 1998. (Univ. Glas.) Research Dir. William Harvey Research Inst. St. Bart. & Roy. Lond. Sch. Med. & Dent., Qu. Mary Coll. Univ. of Lond. Dept. Of Clin. Pharmacol. Socs: Biochem. Soc.; Physiol. Soc.; Endocrine Soc. Prev: Dir. Dept. Chem. Path. & Endocrine Unit Roy. Postgrad. Med. Sch. Lond.; Vis. Sci. Nat Inst. Health Bethesda, USA; Mem. MRC Clin. Research Bd. Grants Comm. 1972-76.

MCINTYRE, Mr Iain Gavin 15 Barwell Road, Sale M33 5FE — MB BChir 1990 Camb.; MD 2000 Manchester; MA Camb. 1992; FRCS Eng. 1995. (Univ. Camb.) Specialist Regist. Rotat. (Urol.) Manch. Socs: Jun. Mem. BAUS.

MACINTYRE, Mr Iain Melfort Campbell, QHS General Surgical Unit, Western General Hospital, Edinburgh EH4 2XU Tel: 0131 537 1548 Fax: 0131 537 1018 — MB ChB 1968 Ed.; MD Ed. 1992; FRCS Ed. 1973. (Ed.) Cons. Surg. W.. Gen. Hosp. Edin. Socs: (Counc.) RCS Edin.; Assn. Surg.; Brit. Soc. Gastroenterol. Prev: Cons. Surg. Leith Hosp. Edin.; Lect. (Clin. Surg.) Univ. Edin.

MCINTYRE, James Clark (retired) 12 Barnton Park Drive, Edinburgh EH4 6HQ Tel: 0131 336 1010 Email: clark_mcintyre@virgin.net — MB ChB 1956 Ed.; FFA RCS Eng. 1965; DA Eng. 1958. Prev: Cons.Anaesth City Hosp.Edin.

***MCINTYRE, James Duncan** 24 Rosemary Road, Sprowston, Norwich NR7 8ER — MB BS 1996 Lond.

MCINTYRE, James Eadie Glenesk, Brownburn Road, Airdrie ML6 9QG Tel: 0123 64 68080 — MB ChB 1964 Glas.; DObst RCOG 1966. (Glas.)

MACINTYRE, Jane Margaret Princes Street Surgery, 155 Princes Street, Dundee DD4 6DG Tel: 01382 461090 Fax: 01382 461091; Tayside Cottage, 5 West Lights, Tayport DD6 9AW — MB ChB 1972 St. And.

MCINTYRE, Janie Morrison (retired) 23 Lothian Drive, Clarkston, Glasgow G76 7NA Tel: 0141 638 3117 — MB ChB 1955 Glas.; FFA RCS Eng. 1968; DA Eng. 1960; DObst RCOG 1958.

MCINTYRE, Jean Weir (retired) 12 Greenside Drive, Hale, Altrincham WA14 3HX Tel: 0161 928 8697 — MB ChB 1957 Glas.; DA Eng. 1960. Prev: Clin. Asst. Nat. Blood Auth. N.. Zone.

MACINTYRE, John (retired) Silverwells, 29 Ness Bank, Inverness IV2 4SF Tel: 01463 234754 — MB ChB 1950 Glas.; LMCC 1967;

MACINTYRE

MRCPsych 1971; Cert (Psychiat.) RCP Canada 1968; DPM Eng. 1958. Prev: Cons. Psychiat. Craig Dunain Hosp. Inverness.

MACINTYRE, John Craig (retired) 25 Moray Place, Edinburgh EH3 6DA Tel: 0131 226 6972 — MB ChB 1954 Glas.; FFA RCS Eng. 1972; DA Eng. 1957. Prev: Civil. Cons. Anaesth. Camb. Milit. Hosp. Aldershot.

MCINTYRE, John Winston Academic Division of Child Health, Derbyshire Children's Hospital, Uttoxeter Road, Derby DE22 3NE Tel: 01332 625635 Fax: 01332 625636 Email: john.mcintyre@nottingham.ac.uk; 19 Hillside, Kingsbury, Tamworth B78 2ND Tel: 01827 872731 — MB ChB 1987 Liverp.; BSc (Hons.) Liverp. 1984; DM Nottm. 1994; MRCP (UK) 1990. Sen. Lect. in Child Health. Prev: Sen. Regist. (Paediat.) Camb.; Lect. Univ. Hosp. Nottm.; Research Fell. Qu. Med. Centre Nottm.

MCINTYRE, Julie Mairi Airdrie Health Centre, Monkscourt Avenue, Airdrie ML6 0JU Tel: 01236 768181; 15 Troon Gardens, Westerwood, Cumberland, Glasgow G68 0JW Tel: 01236 732593 — MB ChB 1989 Glas.

MCINTYRE, June Mary Flat 3/3, 17 James Gray St., Glasgow G41 3BS — MB ChB 1997 Manch.

MCINTYRE, Katharine Elspeth 77 Station Road, Impington, Cambridge CB4 9NP — MB BS 1991 Lond.; BSc (Hons.) Lond. 1988.

MCINTYRE, Kathleen Rosemary 82 Chartfield Road, Cambridge CB1 9JY — MB ChB 1987 Glas.

MCINTYRE, Keith John North Avenue Surgery, 18 North Avenue, Cambuslang, Glasgow G72 8AT Tel: 0141 641 3037 Fax: 0141 646 1905; Methlic, 41 Stewarton Drive, Cambuslang, Glasgow G72 8DQ Tel: 0141 641 6970 — MB ChB 1989 Glas.; MRCGP 1993; DFFP 1993; T(GP) 1993; DRCOG 1991; Cert. Family Plann. JCC 1991. GP Princip.; Med. Assessor, Indep. Tribunal Serv.; Hon. Lect. Dept. Pharmacol. Univ. Strathclyde. Prev: Clin. Asst. (A & E) & SHO (Gen. Med. & Psychiat.) Roy. Alexandra Hosp. Paisley.

MCINTYRE, Lesley Anne Portland Road Surgery, 34 Portland Road, Kilmarnock KA1 2DL Tel: 01563 522411 Fax: 01563 573556; Aldersie, 16 Kirkton Road, Fenwick, Kilmarnock KA3 6DH — MB ChB 1980 Glas.; DRCOG 1983.

MCINTYRE, Letitia Lila Sarah (retired) 8 Gladstone Place, Stirling FK8 2NN Tel: 01786 473456 Email: lila@oceangas.com — MB ChB 1951 Glas.; MRCPsych 1978. Prev: Cons. Psychiat. Gtr. Glas. HB.

MCINTYRE, Linda Taylor (retired) Hyval, Cairston Road, Stromness KW16 3J — MB ChB 1976 Glas.; MRCGP 1983; DA Eng. 1982; BSc (Hons.) 1996; MSc Appl. Stats. Sheff. Hall. Univ. 1999. Ind. Researcher.

MCINTYRE, Lisa Marie 41 Blair Road, Coatbridge ML5 1JQ — MB ChB 1997 Glas.

MCINTYRE, Malcolm Rowan Northumberland Heath Medical Centre, Hind Crescent, Northumberland Heath, Erith DA8 3DB Tel: 01322 336556 Fax: 01322 351475; 18 Norlands Crescent, Chislehurst BR7 5RN Tel: 020 8325 6147 Email: rockingdoc@msn.com — MB BS 1981 Lond.; MRCGP 1986; DRCOG 1985. (Univ. Coll. Hosp.) Prev: Trainee GP Sidcup VTS.

MCINTYRE, Margaret Ann Department of Pathology, Western General Hospital, Crewe Road, Edinburgh EH4 2XU — MB ChB 1960 Aberd.; MRCPath 1977; FRCPath 1987. Cons. (Path.) W.. Gen. Hosp. Edin.

MCINTYRE, Martin Department of Diabetes & Endocrinology, Royal Alexandra Hospital, Paisley PA2 9PN Tel: 0141 580 4433 Fax: 0141 889 1931 Email: martin.mcintyre@rah.scot.nhs.uk; 26 Torridon Avenue, Dumbreck, Glasgow GU1 5AU — MB ChB 1990 Glas.; BSc Glas. 1987; MRCP (UK) 1993; PhD Glasgow 1998. (University of Glasgow) Cons. Gen. Med. Diabetes & Endocrinol., Roy. Alexandra Hosp. Paisley.

MACINTYRE, Martin Gerard Tigh A Bhuachaille, Stilligarry, Lochboisdale HS8 — MB ChB 1988 Aberd.

MCINTYRE, Michael Patrick Joseph Department of Microbiology, Wexham Park Hospital, Slough SL2 4HL Tel: 01753 633000 Ext: 3469 Fax: 01753 633965 — MB BS 1981 Lond.; MA Camb. 1982; FRCPath 1997. (Camb. & King's Coll. Lond.) Cons. Microbiol. Heatherwood & Wexham Pk. Hosp. NHS Trust.

MCINTYRE, Professor Neil University Department Medicine, Royal Free Hospital, Pond St., London NW3 2QG Tel: 020 7794 0500 Fax: 020 7794 4688 — MB BS 1958 Lond.; BSc (1st cl. Hons. Physiol.) Lond. 1955, MD 1967; MB BS (Hons.) 1958; FRCP Lond.

1972, M 1963. (King's Coll. Hosp.) Prof. & Chairm. Dept. Med. Roy. Free Hosp. Lond. Socs: Internat. Assn. Study of Liver; Med. Res. Soc. Prev: Flight Lt. RAF Med. Br.; MRC Trav. Fell. Mass. Gen. Hosp. & Harvard Med. Sch., USA; Ho. Phys. & Cas. Off. King's Coll. Hosp. Lond.

MCINTYRE, Owen Bernard Laburnham Cottage, Rhosesmor Road, Halkyn, Holywell CH8 8DL — MB BCh 1997 Wales.

MACINTYRE, Paul Alan Methilhaven Road Surgery, 361 Methilhaven Road, Methil, Leven KY8 3HR Tel: 01333 426913 Fax: 01333 422300 — MB ChB 1978 Dundee.

MACINTYRE, Paul Dominic 2309 Great Western Road, Old Dunchapel, Glasgow G15 6RT Tel: 0141 944 4472 — MB ChB 1987 Glas.; MSc Glas. 1991, BSc 1984; MRCP (UK) 1990. Lect. (Sports Med. & Cardiol.) W.. Infirm. Glas.

MCINTYRE, Paul Gerard 32 Hatton Road, Luncarty, Perth PH1 3UZ — MB ChB 1987 Glas.

MACINTYRE, Peter Alexander Anaesthetic Department, Royal Brisbane Hospital, Herston Road, Brisbane Qld, Australia; 14 Dunelm Court, Durham Tel: 0191 386 3907 — MB BS 1989 Lond.; FRCA 1994. (St. Thos. Hosp. Lond.) Fell. (Anaesth.) Roy. Brisbane Hosp. Prev: Specialist Regist. Middlx. Hosp.; Regist. Gt. Ormond St.; Regist. St Geo. Hosp. Lond.

MCINTYRE, Peter Bruce Queen Elizabeth II Hospital, Welwyn Garden City AL7 4HQ — MB ChB 1976 Glas.; MD Glas. 1985; FRCP Lond. 1994; FRCP Glas. 1992; MRCP (UK) 1979. Cons. Phys. & Gastroenterol., Qu. Eliz. II Hosp, Welwyn Gdn. City & Hertford Co. Hosp. Socs: BMA & Brit. Soc. Gastroenterol. Prev: Sen. Regist. (Med.) Char. Cross & W. Middlx. Univ. Hosp.; Research Regist. (Gastroenterol.) St. Mark's Hosp. Lond.

MCINTYRE, Mr Robert Division of Surgery, Dr Gray's Hospital, Elgin IV30 1SN Tel: 01343 543131 Fax: 01343 552612 Email: mcinty@arh.grampian.scot.nhs.uk; 10 Jock Inksons Brae, Elgin IV30 1QE Tel: 01343 542677 — MB ChB 1982 Glas.; BSc (Hons.) Glas. 1979, MD 1990; FRCS (Gen.) 1995; FRCS Glas. 1987. (Glas.) Cons. Gen. Surg. Dr. Gray's Hosp. Elgin. Prev: Sen. Regist. (Gen. Surg.) Aberd. Roy Infirm.

MACINTYRE, Siobhan Christina 52/6 Polwarth Gardens, Edinburgh EH11 1LL — MB ChB 1993 Ed.

MCINTYRE, Waveney 44A Herga Court, Sudbury Hill, Harrow on the Hill, Harrow HA1 3RT — MB BS 1994 Lond.; MA (Engin. Sci.) Oxf. 1993; DCH RCP Lond. 1997; DRCOG 1996. (Roy. Free Hosp. Sch. Med.) GP Regist. & SHO (c/o the Elderly) N.wick Pk Hosp. Harrow.

MCINTYRE, William (retired) Cruachan, 89 Lowndes Park, Driffield YO25 5BE Tel: 01377 253436 — MB ChB 1950 Aberd.

MCINTYRE, William Quartermaine 24 Darnley Gardens, Glasgow G41 4NG Tel: 0141 423 2491 — MB ChB 1939 Glas.; BSc 1936, MB ChB Glas. 1939. (Univ. Glas.) Socs: Tuberc. Soc. Scotl. Prev: Jt. Med. Supt. St. Andrews Home, Millport.

MACIOLEK, Janusz Stanley The Surgery, 939 Green Lanes, Winchmore Hill, London N21 2PB Tel: 020 8360 2228 — MB BS 1975 Lond.; MCOphth 1990; DRCOG 1978. Princip. Gen. Med. Pract. Ophth. Lond.

MACIPE, Maria Eugenia Bristol Eye Hospital, Lower Maudlin St., Bristol BS1 2LX Tel: 0117 928 4691 Fax: 0017 928 4686; 13 Broadway Avenue, Henleaze, Bristol BS9 4SU Tel: 0117 962 2049 — LMS 1973 Madrid; DO RCS Eng. 1988. (Univ. Complutense Madrid) Assoc. Specialist.

MCIRVINE, Mr Andrew James Department of Surgery, Darent Valley Hospital, Dartford DA2 8DA Tel: 01322 428625 Fax: 01322 428635; 35 Elsie Road, Dulwich, London SE22 8DX Tel: 020 8693 3803 Fax: 020 8693 7920 Email: jekyll@atlas.co.uk — MB BS 1974 Lond.; FRCS Eng. 1978. (St. Thos.) Cons. Gen. & Vasc. Surg. Dartford & Gravesham HA. Socs: Assn. Surg.; Vasc. Surg. Soc.; Roy. Soc. Med. Sect. Surg. (Vice-Pres.). Prev: Sen. Regist. (Surg.) King's Coll. Hosp. Lond.; Lect. (Trauma & Gen. Surg.) Groote Schuur Hosp. Univ. Cape Town S. Afr.; Research Fell. (Surg.) Brigham & Wom. Hosp. Harvard Med. Sch.

MACISAAC, Alison Brewster Nethertown Surgery, Elliot Street, Dunfermline KY11 4TF Tel: 01383 623516 Fax: 01383 624254; 5 Alison Grove, Crossford, Dunfermline KY12 8YU — MB ChB 1984 Ed.; MRCGP 1990; DRCOG 1988; DCH RCP Glas. 1988. Prev: SHO (Geriat.) Roy. Vict. Hosp. Edin.; SHO (Obst.& Gyn.) Glas. Roy. Matern. Hosp.; SHO (Paediat.) Yorkhill Hosp. Glas.

MCIVER, Anne (retired) Tigh An Cu, Craigerne Lane, Peebles EH45 9HQ — MB ChB Ed. 1968. Assoc. Specialist (Genitourin. Med.) Roy. Infirm. Edin. NHS Trust.

MCIVER, Bryan 3 Kenilworth Avenue, Helensburgh G84 7JR — MB ChB 1988 Ed.; PhD Vermont USA 1985; BSc (Hons.) Ed. 1981, MB ChB 1988; MRCP (UK) 1992. Regist. (Diabetes, Endocrinol. & Gen. Med.) Roy. Infirm. Edin.

MACIVER, Catriona Alexandra 23 Barley Road, Great Chishill, Royston SG8 8SB — MB ChB 1988 Ed.; MRCP (Lond.) 1996.

MACIVER, David Hunter Department of Cardiology, Musgrove Park Hospital, Taunton & Somerset NHS Trust, Taunton TA1 5DA Tel: 01823 342130 Fax: 01823 342709 Email: david.maciver@tauntonsom-tr.swest.nhs.uk — MB BS 1982 Lond.; MD Leic. 1990; MRCP (UK) 1985; T(M) 1994; FRCP (UK) 1999. (St. George's Hospital, London) Cons. Cardiol. MusGr. Pk. Hosp.

MACIVER, Duncan Kenneth Flat A, 8 Strafford Road, Twickenham TW1 3AE — MB ChB 1979 Birm.

MACIVER, Elizabeth Marjorie (retired) Flowerburn Mains, Fortrose IV10 8SJ Tel: 01381 20339 — LRCP LRCS 1951 Ed.; LRCP LRCS Ed. LRFPS Glas. 1951. Prev: Ho. Surg. Roy. Infirm. Edin.

MACIVER, Ishbel 44 Knock, Point, Isle of Lewis HS2 — MB ChB 1988 Glas.

MACIVER, John Edward (retired) Ingleton, 55 Stamford Road, Bowdon, Altrincham WA14 2JN — MD 1959 Camb.; MB BChir 1948; FRCP Ed. 1983; FRCPath 1968. Cons. (Haemat.) Manch. Roy. Infirm.; Hon. Lect. (Clin. Haemat.) Univ. Manch. Prev: Hon. Cons. Haemat. Centr. Manch. HA.

MACIVER, Malcolm 252 Liverpool Road Sth., Burscough, Ormskirk L40 7RF Tel: 01704 894880 Email: compuserve@101712.310 — MB ChB 1971 Liverp.; MD Liverp. 1980; FRCP Lond. 1995; MRCP (UK) 1976. Cons. Phys. N. W. RHA.

MACIVER, Mary 3 Lewin Road, London SW16 6JZ Tel: 020 8516 8800 — MB ChB Aberd. 1951. Prev: GP Brooke La. Med. Mission Bromley, Kent; Asst. MoH Inverness, Scotl.; GP Lewis St. Stornoway, Scotl.

MCIVER, Michael Scott 10 Aberfoyle Park, Belfast BT10 0DY — MB BCh BAO 1993 Belf.

MACIVER, Norman 2 Stonefield Avenue, Crosland Moor, Huddersfield HD4 5QG Tel: 01484 51023 — MB ChB 1963 Glas.; MFCM 1974; DPH Glas. 1966. (Glas.) Sen. Sch. Med. Off. Huddersfield Co. Boro. Socs: BMA. Prev: Regist. Psychiat. Towers Hosp. Leicester; SHO Dermat. Stobhill Hosp. Glas.; Asst. Sch. Med. Off. Birm. Corpn.

MCIVER, Norman Keith Ian, OSJ Central Surgery, Sussex Road, Gorleston-on-Sea, Great Yarmouth NR31 6QB Tel: 01493 414141 Fax: 01493 656253; Priory Lodge, 52 Church Road, Gorleston, Great Yarmouth NR31 6LN Tel: 07808 177311 Email: 100662.650@compuserve.com — MB BS 1965 Lond.; MRCS Eng. LRCP Lond. 1965; FFOM RCP Lond. 1993. (Westm.) Princip. GP; Apptd. Doctor (Offshore Installations Diving Operats.) Health & Safety Exec.; Clin. Dir. James Paget Hosp. Hyperbaric Unit 1995-date; Extern. Examr. to Inst. of Environm. and Occupat.al Health, Aberd. Univ. Socs: Fell. Roy. Soc. Med.; Diving Med. Advis. Comm.; Undersea Med. Soc., BMA, & Europ. Undersea Biomed. Soc. Prev: Ho. Surg. Gordon Hosp. (W.m. Hosp.) Lond.; Ho. Phys. St. Stephen's Hosp. Chelsea; Maj. RAMC, Regtl. Med. Off. 6th Gurkha Rifles.

MCIVER, Sian Newton Lodge, Regional Secure Unit, Ouchthorpe Lane, Wakefield WF1 3TD Tel: 01924 327378 — MB ChB 1992 Leeds; MRCPsych 1996. Specialist Regist. in Forens. Psychiat.

MACIVER, Suzanne Amanda Hunter 61 Dumbuck Crescent, Dumbarton G82 1EH — MB ChB 1988 Glas.; 2000 Plymouth; MRCP (UK) 1992; MRCGP 1996. p/t GP. Prev: GP/Regist. Riverside Med. Pract. Inverness; Med. Off. Brit. Antarctic Survey.

MCIVOR, Cresson Caldwell Mark 17 Falcon Heights, Newtownards BT23 4GF Tel: 01247 812824 — MB BCh BAO 1990 Belf.; MRCGP 1995; DCCH RCP Ed. 1996; DRCOG 1992. (Belf.) Socs: BMA.

MCIVOR, Diane Elizabeth Laura 99 Newmills Road, Donaghey, Dungannon BT71 4BY — MB BS 1988 Lond. Trainee GP Cheltenham VTS.

MCIVOR, Elizabeth Mary Hassard 13 Kincora Avenue, Belfast BT4 3DW Tel: 01232 657619; PO Box 1, Makwasa, Malawi Tel: 00 265 474217 Fax: 00 265 474315 — MB BCh BAO 1964 Belf.; DFFP 1993. Chief Exec. Thandizani Moyo Thyolo Malawi.

MCIVOR, Jacqueline Eleanor Matilda Northgate Medical Practice, 1 Northgate, Canterbury CT1 1WL Tel: 01227 463570 Fax: 01227 786147; Four Acres, Bekesbourne Lane, Canterbury CT4 5DY — MB BS 1986 Lond.; DA (UK) 1988. Prev: Trainee GP Canterbury VTS.

MCIVOR, James (retired) 39 Rosedew Road, London W6 9ET Tel: 020 8478 7853 — MB ChB Glas. 1963; BDS Glas. 1958; FRCR 1975; FFR 1971; FDS RCS Eng. 1965; DMRD Eng. 1969. Prev: Cons. Radiol. Char. Cross Hosp. Lond. & Chief of Serv. (Radiol.) Hammersmith Hosps. NHS Trust.

MCIVOR, Patricia Cardine Antoinette 3 Dunvale Park, Londonderry BT48 0AU — MB BCh BAO 1990 Belf.

MCIVOR, Paul Joseph 20 Hopefield Avenue, Belfast BT15 5AP — MB BCh BAO 1993 Belf.

MCIVOR, Ronan John Tel: 020 7740 5569 Fax: 020 7740 5552 Email: ronan.mcivor@slam-tr.nhs.uk — MB BCh BAO 1986 NUI; MRCPsych 1991. (Uni. Coll. Dublin) Cons. (Psychiat.) Maudsley Hosp. Lond.

MACK, Alison Ethel, MBE (retired) 9 Merrylee Road, Glasgow G43 2SH Tel: 0141 637 1673 — MB ChB Glas. 1960; MFFP 1991. Asst. Med. Off. Univ. Strathclyde. Prev: Occupat. Phys. Marks & Spencer Glas.

MACK, Mr Alistair John (retired) 9 Merrylee Road, Glasgow G43 2SH Tel: 0141 637 1673 — MB ChB Glas. 1960; MSc Glas. 1965; FRCS Ed. 1965; FRCS Glas. 1965. Prev: Apptd. Dir. (Med. Servs.) Vict. Infirm. NHS Trust Glas.

MACK, Damien John 64 Myddleton Avenue, London N4 2FG — MB BS 1995 Queensland.

MACK, Douglas Sommerville Rogell House, 51 Hamilton Avenue, Glasgow G41 4HB Tel: 0141 427 1623 — MB ChB 1968 Glas.; FRCOG 1986, M 1972. Cons. (O & G) S. Glas. Univ. Hosp. NHS Trust. Socs: BMA & Glas. Obst. & Gyn. Soc. Prev: Sen. Regist. (O & G) Glas. Roy. Matern. Hosp. & Roy. Infirm.; Glas.- Hall Fell. & Regist. Glas. Roy. Matern. Hosp. & Glas. Roy.; Infirm.

MACK, Helen Maureen Harbord (retired) Kenfield, St. Thomas Road, Trowbridge BA14 7LU Tel: 01225 765731 — MB ChB 1943 Sheff. Prev: SCMO Community Health Wilts. AHA.

MACK, Helen Noel The Surgery, High Street, Kemnay, Inverurie AB51 5NB Tel: 01467 642289; 15 Milton View, Kemnay, Inverurie AB51 5EW Tel: 01467 643937 — MB ChB 1974 Ed.; MRCGP 1978. p/t GP; CMO (Family Plann.).

MACK, Ian James Koopowitz and Partners, Watlington Medical Centre, Rowan Close, Watlington, King's Lynn PE33 0TU Tel: 01553 810253 Fax: 01553 811629 — MB BS 1984 Lond.; T(GP) 1991; DGM RCP Lond. 1988. Prev: Trainee GP Wroxham Norf. VTS; Regist. (Geriat. Med.) Qu. Eliz. Hosp. Kings Lynn; SHO (Gen. Med.) Heatherwood Hosp. Ascot.

MACK, Kenneth McGlashan York Place Surgery, 10-12 Union Street, Kirkintilloch, Glasgow G66 1DG Tel: 0141 776 1273 Fax: 0141 776 4060 — MB ChB 1973 Glas.; MRCGP 1977; DRCOG 1977.

MACK, Miles Bradley Ferry Road Health Centre, Ferry Road, Dingwall IV15 9QS Tel: 01349 863034 Fax: 01349 862022 — MB ChB 1989 Ed.

MACK, Paul Department of Clinical Oncology, St. George's Hospital, Long Leys Road, Lincoln LN1 1EF Tel: 01522 512512; Manor Court House, King Edward St, Kirton in Lindsey, Gainsborough DN21 4NQ — MB BS 1981 Lond.; BSc Theoretical Physics Hull 1976; MRCP (UK) 1985; FRCR 1990; FRCP (Lond.) 1998. (King's Coll. & Westm.) Cons. Clin. Oncol. Lincoln Hosps. NHS Trust & NE Lincs. NHS Trust. Prev: Sen. Regist. (Clin. Oncol.) Velindre Hosp. Cardiff; Regist. (Radiother. & Oncol.) Qu. Eliz. Hosp. Birm.; Ho. Phys. W.m. Hosp. Lond.

MACK, Peter Robert Queens Park and Moredon Surgeries, 146 Drove Road, Swindon SN1 3AG Tel: 01793 487394 Fax: 01793 342011 — MB BCh 1986 Wales; MRCGP 1991.

MACK, Robert Henry Health Centre, St. Marys Place, Townend, Kirkcudbright DG6 4BJ Tel: 01557 330755 Fax: 01557 330917; Roslyn, 84 St Mary St, Kirkcudbright DG6 4EJ Tel: 01557 332399 — MB ChB 1976 Ed.; BSc Ed. 1973; MRCGP 1981; DRCOG 1981. (Ed.) Non-Exec. Dir. Dumfries & Galloway HB.

MCKAIGUE, James Patrick Royal Belfast Hospital for Sick Children, 180 Falls Road, Belfast BT12 6BE Tel: 028 9026 3056 Fax: 028 9026 3294; 179 Malone Road, Belfast BT9 6TB — MB

MCKAIGUE

BCh BAO 1982 Belf.; MD Belf. 1992; FFA RCS (Irel.) 1986. (Queen's Belfast) Cons. Anaesth. The Roy. Hosps. Belf. Socs: N. Irel. Soc. Anaesth.; Assn. Paediat. Anaesth.; Assn. of Anaesth. GB & Irel. Prev: Fell. (Cardiac Anaesth.) Freeman Hosp. Newc.; Sen. Regist. (Anaesth.) EHSSB; Research Fell. (Therap. & Pharmacol.) Qu. Univ. Belf.

MCKAIGUE, Oonagh Josephine Conway Road Health Centre, Conway Road, Sale M33 2TB Tel: 0161 962 7321 Fax: 0161 973 1151 — MB BCh BAO 1984 Belf.; MB BCh Belf. 1984; MRCGP 1989; DGM RCP Lond. 1987.

MCKAIL, Thomas John 144 Hamilton Road, Glasgow G32 9QR Tel: 0141 778 1546 — MB ChB 1922 Glas. (Glas.) Prev: Med. Off. Ment. Serv. Glas. Corp.; Res. Surg. Off. Roy. Infirm. Preston; Ho. Surg. & Ho. Phys. Glas. Roy. Infirm.

MCKAIN, Alexander Donald Southern Medical Group, 322 Gilmerton Road, Edinburgh EH17 7PR Tel: 0131 664 2148 Fax: 0131 664 8303 — MB ChB 1980 Dundee; MRCGP 1985; DRCOG 1982.

MCKALL, Kay Carol Square Surgery, 23 The Square, Martlesham Heath, Ipswich IP5 3SL Tel: 01473 610028 Fax: 01473 610791; 114 Rushmere Road, Ipswich IP4 4JX Tel: 01473 725737 — MD 1972 Manitoba; BSc Manitoba 1972; Dip. Sports Med. Soc. Apoth. Lond. 1993. (Univ. Manitoba) Socs: Soc. Orthop. Med. & Brit. Med. Acupunc. Soc.

MCKANE, Joseph Patrick Leverndale Hospital, 510 Crookston Road, Glasgow G53 7TU Tel: 0141 211 6479 — MB ChB 1978 Glas.; MRCPsych 1983.

MCKANE, William Roland Ulster Hospital, Ulster, North Down & Ards Hospital Trust, Dundonald, Belfast BT16 1RH Tel: 01232 484511 Fax: 01232 481166; 2 Beechmount Road, Manse Road, Carryduff, Belfast BT8 8AD — MB BCh BAO 1983 Belf.; BSc 1980; MD 1991; MD Belf. 1991; MRCP (UK) 1986; FRCP 1997. Cons. Phys. & Rheum. Ulster Hosp. Belf. Prev: Regist. (Rheum.) Musgrave Pk. Hosp. Belf.

MCKANE, William Smith 2A Odsey Villas, Umfreville Road, London N4 1RX — MB BChir 1991 Camb.

MACKANESS, Charlotte Rosemary Derby City Gen. Hospital, Ottoxter Road, Derby DE22 3NE Tel: 01332 340131 Fax: 01332 290559 — MB BS 1990 Lond.; FRCA 1996; DA (UK) 1992. Cons. Anaes. S.Derbysh. NHS Trust. Prev: SHO (Anaesth., Med. & Intens. Care) Qu. Med. Centre Nottm.; Specialist Regist. (Anaesth.) Nottm.

MCKAVANAGH, Marie 17 Firbeck Gardens, Crewe CW2 8UP — MB BCh BAO 1982 Belf.; MRCGP 1989. GP Nantwich.

MCKAY, Agatha Paula 51 Saintfield Road, Ballynahinch BT24 8UZ Email: apmckay@iol.ie — MB BCh BAO 1982 Dub.; MA 2000 Dub.; FRCPI 1998; MRCPI 1984.

MCKAY, Alan Charles 33 Tweskard Park, Belfast BT4 2JZ — MD 1981 Belf.; MB BCh BAO 1970; FFA RCSI 1975. Cons. Anaesth. Belf. City Hosp.

MCKAY, Mr Alan John 33 Lubnaig Road, Newlands, Glasgow G43 2RY — MB ChB 1973 Glas.; FRCS Glas. 1978. Cons. (Gen. & Vasc. Surg.) Gartnavel Gen. Hosp. & W.. Infirm.

MACKAY, Alasdair Miles (retired) Department Pathology, Countess of Chester Hospital NHS Trust, Liverpool Road, Chester CH2 1UL Tel: 01244 365000 — MB ChB 1960 Glas.; BSc (Hons.) Glas. 1957, MD (Hons.) 1970,; FRCPath 1982, M 1970. Cons. Histopath. Countess of Chester Hosp. NHS Trust. Prev: Reader in Path. & Hon. Cons. Inst. Cancer Research & Roy. Marsden Hosp. Lond.

MACKAY, Alec David Good Hope Hospital NHS Teaching Trust, Rectory Road, Sutton Coldfield B75 7RR Tel: 0121 378 2211 Fax: 0121 378 6095 — MB BCh 1973 Wales; MD Wales 1983; FRCP Lond. 1993; MRCP (UK) 1975. (Univ. Wales) Cons. Phys. (Gen. & Respirat. Med.) Good Hope Hosp. NHS Teachg. Trust Sutton Coldfield; Med. Dir. Socs: Med. Res. Soc.; Brit. Thorac. Soc.; Eur. Respirat. Soc. Prev: Cons. Phys. Sandwell Dist. Gen. Hosp.; Vis. Research Physiol. Cardiovasc. Research Inst. Univ. Calif. & Sen. Regist. (Gen. & Thoracic Med.) N. Staffs. Hosp. Centre; Lect. (Med.) & Brit. Thoracic Assn. Research Fell. Univ. Soton.

MACKAY, Alexander Bath Lodge Practice, Bitterne Health Centre, Commercial Street, Bitterne, Southampton SO18 6BT Tel: 023 8044 2111 Fax: 023 8042 1316 — MB BS 1976 Newc.; MRCGP 1984.

MCKAY, Alexander Roland Old Machar Medical Practice, 526 King Street, Aberdeen AB24 5RS Tel: 01224 480324 Fax: 01224 276121 — MB ChB 1981 Aberd.; MRCGP 1985.

MACKAY, Alison 64 Oxgangs Road, Fairmilehead, Edinburgh EH10 7AY — MB ChB 1985 Aberd.

MACKAY, Alison Jill 2/2, 89 Hyndland Road, Glasgow G12 9JE — MB ChB 1991 Glas.; MRCP (UK) 1995. Clin. Research Fell. (Med. & Therap.) W.. Infirm. Glas.; Specialist Regist. Diabetes & Endocrinol. Hairmyres Hosp., E. Kilbride. Prev: Lect. in Med., W.ern Infirm. Glas.; Sen. Health Off. (Med.) Gartnavel Gen. Hosp. Glas.

MACKAY, Andrew David Dept of Microbiology, Queen Elizabeth Hospital, Stadium Road, Woolwich SE18 4QM Fax: 020 8312 6025 — MB BS 1984 Lond.; MA Camb. 1984; MRCP (UK) 1990; MRCPath 1997. Cons. (Med. Microbiol.) Qu. Eliz. Hosp. Lond.; Lead Clinic. In Path. Prev: Sen. Regist. (Med. Microbiol.) Univ. Coll. Lond. Hosps.; Sen. Regist. (Med. Microbiol.) Hosp for Childr. Gt. Ormond St. Lond.; Regist. (Med. Microbiol.) Roy. Free Hosp. Lond.

MACKAY, Andrew Ross St Triduanas Medical Practice, 54 Moira Park, Edinburgh EH7 6RU Tel: 0131 657 3341 Fax: 0131 669 6055 — MB ChB 1993 Glas.; DRCOG 1997; MRCGP 1998. (Glasgow) GP Regist. Milton Surg. Prev: SHO (Psychiat.) St. John's Hosp. Livingston; SHO (A & E) St. John's Hosp. Livingston; SHO (O & G) S.ern Gen. Hosp. Glas.

MACKAY, Angus Victor Peck, OBE Argyll and Bute Hospital, Lochgilphead PA31 8LD; Tigh-An-Rudha, Ardrishaig, Lochgilphead PA30 8ER Tel: 01546 603272 — MB ChB 1969 Ed.; PhD Camb. 1974, MA 1977; BSc (Hons. Pharmacol.) Ed. 1966; FRCP Ed. 1990, M 1985; FRCPsych 1983, M 1976; T(Psychiat.) 1991. Phys. Supt., Clin. Dir., Clin. Tutor & MacIntosh Lect. Univ. Glas.; Mem. Comm. on Safety of Meds. DoH; Hon. Sen. Lect. (Psychol.) Univ. St. And.; Mem. NHS Policy Bd. Scotl.; Chairm. Ment. Health Refer. Gp. Scotl.; Research Chairm. & Clin. Sect. RCPsych. (Scotl.); Chairm. Crag/Scotmeg Working Party Ment. Health Servs. Scotl.; Chairm. Area Psychiat. Audit Comm. Prev: Dep. Dir. MRC Neurochem. Pharm. Unit Camb.; Hon. Cons. Camb. Health Dist. (T); Lect. (Pharmacol.) Trinity Coll. Camb.

MACKAY, Ann Marie Gerard Invermay, 5 Station Terrace, Longside, Peterhead AB42 4UE — MB BCh BAO 1987 NUI.

MCKAY, Anne Flat 2/3, 18 Oban Drive, Glasgow G20 6AF — MB ChB 1994 Glas.

MACKAY, Calum (retired) 24 Miller Place, Scrabster, Thurso KW14 7UH Tel: 01847 893465 — MB ChB 1960 Aberd. Prev: Ho. Off. (Med. & Surg.) Woodend Hosp. Aberd.

MCKAY, Carolyn Mary The Medical Centre, 7 Hill Place, Arbroath DD11 1AE Tel: 01241 431144 Fax: 01241 430764 — MB ChB 1980 Ed.; MRCGP 1984. (Edin.) GP Arbroath.

MCKAY, Christina Elizabeth c/o MacLean, 14 Argyll Place, Aberdeen AB25 2EL — MB ChB 1971 Aberd.; FRCP(C) (Psychiat.) 1977. Assoc. Specialist (Child & Family Psychiat.) Roy. Aberd. Childr. Hosp. Socs: Corr. Mem. Canad. Acad. Child Psychiat. & Canad. Psychiat. Assn. Prev: Cons. Child Psychiat. Childr. Hosp. E. Ontario, Canada; Lect. Univ. Ottawa.

MACKAY, Mr Colin (retired) 73 Buchanan Drive, Bearsden, Glasgow G61 2EP Tel: 0141 942 8759 Fax: 0141 942 8759 — MB ChB 1961 Glas.; MB ChB (Commend.) Glas. 1961; BSc (Hons.) Glas. 1958; FRCS Eng. 1966; FRCS Glas. 1966; FRCS Ed. 1965. Prev: Cons. Surg. Gartnavel Gen. Hosp. W.ern Infirm. Glas.

MCKAY, Colin John House 3, Ranfurly Church, Prieston Road, Bridge of Weir PA11 3AJ — MB ChB 1987 Glas.; FRCPS Glas. 1991. SHO (Gen. Surg.) Gtr. Glas. Health B. Prev: SHO (Orthop.) Glas. Roy. Infirm.

MACKAY, Colin John Epsom Hospital, Dorking Road, Epsom KT18 7 Tel: 01372 735735; Tighnabruaich, 16 Links Brow, Fetcham, Leatherhead KT22 9DU Tel: 01372 379043 — MB BS 1984 Lond.; FRCA 1990. (St. Geo.) Cons. Anaesth. Epsom Hosp. Prev: Sen. Regist. (Anaesth.) Char. Cross. Hosp. Lond.; Regist. Rotat. (Anaesth.) St. Geo. Hosp.

MACKAY, Mr Colin Kenneth Flat 1/1, 101 Marlborough Avenue, Glasgow G11 7LD — MB ChB 1990 Glas.; FRCS Glas. 1994.

MCKAY, David Alexander 17 Airds Drive, Dumfries DG1 4EW Tel: 01384 262093 Email: david mckay@doctors.or.uk — MB ChB 1994 Glas.; MRCP UK 1999. SHO, Med. Borders Gen. Hosp. Melrose.

MACKAY

MACKAY, David Calder 21 Lindale Avenue, Whickham, Newcastle upon Tyne NE16 5QT — MB ChB 1988 Aberd.

MACKAY, David John (retired) Beechwood, Lochawe, Dalmally PA33 1AH Tel: 01838 200323 — MD 1963 Glas.; MB ChB 1951; FRCOG 1971, M 1958. Cons. O & G Bellshill Matern. Hosp. & Hairmyres Hosp. E. Kilbride.

MCKAY, Derek James Ramanathan, McKay and Kearney, The Health Centre, 2-4 Bay Street, Port Glasgow PA14 5EW Tel: 01475 745321 Fax: 01475 745587; 4 Station Road, Langbank, Port Glasgow PA14 6YA — MB ChB 1984 Glas.; DCH RCPS Glas. 1987.

MCKAY, Diana Rose 29 Cromford Road, London SW18 1NZ — MB BS 1990 Sydney.

MACKAY, Donald Eric, Surg. Capt. RN Retd. (retired) 14 Nidd Rise, Birstwith, Harrogate HG3 3AP — MD Glas. 1966, MB ChB 1951; FFOM RCP Lond. 1989, M 1979; DPH Lond. 1965. Prev: Surg. Capt. Roy. Navy.

MACKAY, Donald Ian Ellon Group Practice, Health Centre, Schoolhill, Ellon AB41 9AH Tel: 01358 720333 Fax: 01358 721578; Inverglebe, 6 Castle Road, Ellon AB41 9EY Tel: 01358 723095 — MB ChB 1972 Aberd.; MB ChB Aberd 1972; DCH RCPS Glas. 1976; DObst RCOG 1974. (Aberd.)

MACKAY, Donald James, CStJ, Surg. Capt. RN Pennyroyal, Buckingham Road, Ryde PO33 2DP Tel: 01983 563450 — Lic. Med., Lic. Surg. Dub. 1961; MFOM RCPI 1981; MRCGP 1974. Princip. Med. Off. HMS Nelson Portsmouth; Cdr. St. John Ambul. I. of Wight. Prev: Princip. Med. Off. HMS Drake; Staff Med. Off. to Flag Off. Submarines; Head of Undersea Med. RN.

MACKAY, Donald Melvin (retired) 6 Grammar School Lane, Northallerton DL6 1BP Tel: 01609 772738 — MB ChB Ed. 1946; DObst RCOG 1951.

MACKAY, Duncan Henry Walker Greyfriars, 28 Beach Road, Barassie, Troon KA10 6SG Tel: 01292 312924 — MB ChB Glas. 1966; MRCOG 1971. (Glas.) Cons. (O & G) Ayrsh. Centr Hosp. & CrossHo. Hosp. Kilmarnock. Socs: Brit. Fertil. Soc.; Glas. Obst. & Gyn. Soc. Prev: Sen. Regist. (O & G) Stobhill Gen. Hosp. Glas.; Res. Ho. Off. (Obst.) Glas. Roy. Matern. Hosp.; Res. Ho. Phys. S.. Gen. Hosp. Glas.

MACKAY, Edward Hugh Dept. Of Pathology, University Hospital of Leicester NHS Trust, Leicester General Hospital, Gwendolen Road, Leicester LE5 4PW Tel: 0116 258 4556 Fax: 0116 258 4666; 68 Leicester Road, Markfield, Leicester LE67 9RE Tel: 01530 243770 — MB ChB 1964 Bristol; FRCPath 1986, M 1974; DObst RCOG 1966. (Bristol) Cons. Histopath. Leicester Gen. Hosp. Socs: BMA; Leic. Med. Soc.; Vice-Pres. 1998-2001 Assn. Clin. Path. Prev: Tutor (Path.) Harkness Laborat. Radcliffe Infirm. Oxf.; Lect. (Path.) Gibson Laborat. Radcliffe Infirm. Oxf.; Regist. (Path.) Frenchay Hosp. Bristol.

MACKAY, Eoin Vonde (retired) 26 Ayot Green, Welwyn AL6 9AB — MRCS Eng. LRCP Lond. 1942; MA Camb.

MCKAY, Eric (retired) Shenaghan, Check Bar, Nigg, Aberdeen AB12 4LP Tel: 01224 780225 — MD Aberd. 1965, MB ChB 1948; FRCP Ed. 1971, M 1956; MRCPsych 1971.

MACKAY, Eric John (retired) 4 Conifer Place, Lenzie, Glasgow G66 4EJ Tel: 0141 776 3992 Fax: 0141 776 3992 Email: emak305@aol.com — MB ChB St. And. 1951; FRCGP 1981, M 1964; DObst RCOG 1956. Prev: GP Kirkintilloch.

MCKAY, Fiona Helen 16 Edgehill, Llanfrechfa, Cwmbran NP44 8UA — BM 1988 Soton.

MCKAY, Fiona Margaret Anne Inverurie Medical Group, Health Centre, 1 Constitution Street, Inverurie AB51 4SU Tel: 01467 621345 Fax: 01467 625374; Lower Glenhead, Kemnay, Inverurie — MB ChB 1986 Aberd.; MRCGP 1990; DRCOG 1990. Prev: Trainee GP Aberd. VTS.

MACKAY, Frank Whitelaw 47 Daly Road, Ardrossan KA22 7LB — MB ChB 1986 Glas.

MACKAY, George Hugh 94 Newbridge Hill, Bath BA1 3QB Tel: 01225 26710 — MB ChB 1960 Ed.; MRCPsych 1975; DObst RCOG 1962; DPM Eng. 1972. (Ed.) Cons. Psychiat. St. Martins & Roy. United Hosps. Bath.

***MCKAY, Gerard Anthony** 17 Fife Avenue, Glasgow G52 3EW — MB ChB 1994 Glas.

MACKAY, Mr Gordon (retired) The Coulard, 17 Rock Lodge Road, Sunderland SR6 9NX — MB ChB Ed. 1958; FRCOG 1980, M 1967. Prev: Cons. O & G S. Tyneside Health Care Trust.

MACKAY, Gordon Matheson Stirling Royal Infirmary, Stirling — MB ChB 1987 Glas.; BSc St. And. 1984; Dip. Sports Med. Lond 1990; FRCS Glas. 1992; MD 1997; FRCS (T & Orth.) 1998. Cons. Orthop. Surg. Stirling Roy. Infirm. Stirling Scotl. Socs: Brit. Orthop. Sports Trauma Assn.; BASM; BOA.

MACKAY, Gordon Robert 29 Paisley Gardens, Edinburgh EH8 7JN — MB ChB 1981 Ed.

MACKAY, Grace Violet (retired) 5 Edenhall Grove, Newton Mearns, Glasgow G77 5TS Tel: 0141 616 2831 — MB ChB Glas. 1959. Prev: Sen. Clin. Med. Off. Community Child Health Glas.

MACKAY, Helen Jane c/o Hollowstones, Borrowdale, Keswick CA12 5UY — MB ChB 1990 Ed.; MRCP (UK) 1993.

MACKAY, Helen Margaret Warbrick-Smith and Partners, The Moat House Surgery, Beech Close, Warboys, Huntingdon PE28 2RQ Tel: 01487 822230 Fax: 01487 823721 — MB BS 1984 Newc.; MB BS (Hons.) Newc. 1984; MRCGP 1989; DRCOG 1989.

MACKAY, Helen McLachlan 77 St Andrews Drive, Bearsden, Glasgow G61 4NW — MB ChB 1994 Glas.

MACKAY, Helen Paul Geriatric Day Hospital, Knightswood Hospital, Glasgow G14 Tel: 0141 211 6922; 73 Buchanan Drive, Bearsden, Glasgow G61 2EP Tel: 0141 942 8759 — MB ChB 1964 Glas.; BSc Glas. 1961. (Glas.) Assoc. Phys. (Geriat.) Gtr. Glas. HB. Prev: Ho. Surg. & Ho. Phys. W.. Infirm. Glas.; Hall Tutorial Fell. in Med. W.. Infirm. & Univ. Glas.

MCKAY, Mr Iain 124 Allander Street, Glasgow G22 5JH Tel: 0141 336 8038; 57 Mitre Road, Glasgow G14 9LH Tel: 0141 959 1739 — MB ChB 1963 Glas.; FRCS Ed. 1972. Surg. i/c Orthotic Clinic PossilPk. HC Glas. Prev: Regist. (Surg.), Ho. Surg. & Ho. Phys. Glas. Roy. Infirm.; SHO (Surg.) E.. Dist. Hosp. Glas.

MACKAY, Iain Mackenzie Parkhead Hospital, Salamanca St, Glasgow G53 7TU Tel: 0141 211 8300 Email: ianmackay@ukonline.co.uk; Flat 2R, 126 Novar Drive, Hyndland, Glasgow G12 9SY Tel: 0141 357 1630 — MB ChB 1992 Glas.; MRC Psych 1998. Specialist Regist. Gen. Psych. With Subst. Misuse.

MACKAY, Iain Ronald 11 Threshold Park, E. Kilbride, Glasgow G74 4HP — MB ChB 1981 Dundee.

MACKAY, Ian Gibson Kirkside, 1-3 Claremount Avenue, Giffnock, Glasgow G46 6UT — MB ChB 1979 Ed.; BSc Hons. (Path.) Ed. 1976; FRCP Glas. 1993; MRCP (UK) 1981. Socs: Med. Res. Soc. Prev: Cons. Phys. Gen. Med. & Nephrol. CrossHo. Hosp. Kilmarnock; Sen. Regist. (Gen. Med. & Nephrol.) S.mead Hosp. Bristol; Regist. (Med.) Roy. Infirm. Edin.

MACKAY, Ian Innes Rose Garden Medical Centre, 4 Mill Lane, Edinburgh EH6 6TL Tel: 0131 554 1274 Fax: 0131 555 2159 — MB ChB 1983 Glas.; MRCGP 1992; DRCOG 1991. (Glas.) Socs: Brit. Soc. Antimicrob. Chemother.; Roy. Coll. GPs (Hon. Sec. Treas. - SE Scotl. RCGP); Brit. Soc. Study of Infec. Prev: Regist. (Bacteriol.) Roy. Infirm. Glas.

MACKAY, Mr Ian Stuart 55 Harley Street, London W1G 8QR Tel: 020 7580 5070 Fax: 020 7323 5401 Email: ian@mackay.netkonect.co.uk — MB BS Lond. 1968; FRCS Eng. 1974; MRCS Eng. LRCP Lond. 1968. (Roy. Free) Cons. ENT Surg. King. Edwd VII Hosp. for Offs., Roy. Brompton, Nat. Heart & Char. Cross. Hosps. Lond.; Hon. Sen. Lect. (Rhinol.) Roy. Nat. Throat Nose & Ear Hosp. Lond. Socs: Pres. Brit. Assn. Otolaryngol. - Head & Neck Surg.

MACKAY, Isobel Robertson (retired) 25 Brian Road, Harlington, Dunstable LU5 6NH — MB ChB Ed. 1960; FFA RCS Eng. 1967. Prev: Cons. Anaesth. Luton & Dunstable Hosp.

MACKAY, James 2 Stirling Place, Upper Achintore, Fort William PH33 6UW — MB ChB 1978 Aberd.; FFA RCS Eng. 1984. Cons. Anaesth. Belford Hosp. Fort William.

MACKAY, James University of Cambridge, Department of Oncology, Addenbrooke's Hospital, Box 193, Hill's Road, Cambridge CB2 2QQ Tel: 01223 336800 Fax: 01223 412213; 16 Town Green Road, Orwell, Royston SG8 5QL Tel: 01223 207346 — MB ChB 1983 Ed.; MA Camb. 1980; MD Ed. 1989; MRCP (UK) 1993; FRCP Ed 1999. (Univ. Ed.) Sen. Research Assoc. Univ. Camb. Sch. Clin. Med.; Hon. Cons. Clin. Oncol. Addenbrooke's Hosp. Camb.; Hon. Cons. Cancer Genetics Roy. Marsden Hosp. Lond. & Roy. Hosps. NHS Trust Lond; Hon. Cons. (Cancer Genetics) Derby City Hosp. Derby. Socs: Assn. Cancer Phys.; Brit. Assn. Cancer Research; Amer. Assn. Advancem. of Sci. Prev: Sen. Regist. (Med. Oncol.) W.. Gen.

MACKAY

Hosp. Edin.; Regist. (Gen. Med.) Roy. Berks. Hosp. Reading; Research Fell. MRCS Human Genetics Unit Edin.

MACKAY, James Finlayson (retired) 35 Queen Victoria Park, Inchmarlo, Banchory AB31 4AL Tel: 01330 826235 — MB ChB 1937 Aberd. Prev: Cons. Venereol. N. Lancs. & S. Cumbria Areas.

MACKAY, James Hugh (retired) 8 Douglas Drive, Newton Mairns, Glasgow G77 6HR Tel: 0141 639 2226 — MB ChB Glas. 1957; DPath Eng. 1963; FRCPath. 1970, M 1967. Prev: Cons. Path. Hairmyres Hosp. E. Kilbride Lanarksh.

MACKAY, James Ross Mintlaw Group Practice, Newlands Road, Mintlaw, Peterhead AB42 5GP Tel: 01771 623522 Fax: 01771 624349; Invermay, 5 Station Terrace, Longside, Peterhead AB42 4UE — MB ChB 1987 Aberd.; MRCGP 1995; DFFP 1994.

MACKAY, Jane Elizabeth The Surgery, 1 Manor Place, London SE17 3BD Tel: 020 7703 3988 Fax: 020 7252 4002; 60 Cambria Road, London SE5 9AS — MB BS Lond. 1970; MRCGP 1982; DObst RCOG 1974. (Westm.) Socs: BMA; RCGP. Prev: GP Trainer Lond.; Trainee GP Lambeth, S.wark & Lewisham AHA; Med. Developm. Off. Volun. Serv. Overseas.

MACKAY, Jean Elizabeth The Teaching Centre, Norfolk & Norwich Hospital, Brunswick Road, Norwich NR1 3SR — MB BS 1984 Lond.; BDS 1975; MRCP 1997. (Kings Coll. Lond.)

MACKAY, Jennifer Mary 6 Bridge Lane, Little Shelford, Cambridge CB2 5HE — MB BChir 1976 Camb.; DRCOG 1981.

MACKAY, John Wishaw Health Centre, Kenilworth Avenue, Wishaw ML2 7BQ Tel: 01698 372888; The Beeches, 8 Coronation St, Wishaw ML2 8LF — MB ChB 1977 Glas.

MACKAY, John, OBE (retired) Moorholm, Barr's Brae, Kilmacolm PA13 4DE Tel: 01505 873234 — MB ChB 1949 Glas.; FRCGP 1975, M 1954. Prev: Med. Ref. Benefits Agency Med. Serv.

MACKAY, John 7 Burges Terrace, Southend-on-Sea SS1 3BD — MB ChB 1956 Glas.; AFOM RCP Lond. 1983; CIH Dund 1982. Occupat. Health Phys. Aramco Med. Dept. Saudi Arabia. Socs: BMA & Soc. Occupat. Med.

MACKAY, John Alexander Ford Medical Practice, Gorsey Lane, Ford, Liverpool L21 0DF — MB ChB 1991 Dundee.

MACKAY, John Charles Shafto Grangewood Surgery, Chester Road, Shiney Row, Houghton-le-Spring DH4 4RB Tel: 0191 385 2898; 10 Cherry Banks, Chester-le-Street DH3 4AX — MB BS 1985 Newc.

MACKAY, John Joseph Thomas Street Surgery, 57 Thomas Street, Dungannon BT70 1HW — MB BCh BAO 1974 Dub.

MACKAY, John Murray Ardblair Medical Practice, Ann Street, Blairgowrie PH10 6EF Tel: 01250 872033 Fax: 01250 874517 — MB ChB 1970 Glas.; BSc (Hons.) Glas. 1968, MB ChB (Commend.) 1970; MRCP (U.K.) 1973; MRCGP 1980; DObst RCOG 1975.

MCKAY, John Phillips Westwyn, 6 Spital Heyes, Wirral CH63 9NF Tel: 0151 334 5596 — MB ChB 1966 Liverp. (Liverp.) Clin. Asst. Clatterbridge Hosp. Wirral. Socs: Liverp. Psychiat. Soc. Prev: Clin. Asst. W. Chesh. & Moston Hosps. Chester; SHO Profess. Unit Rainhill Hosp. Liverp.; Regist. E. Liverp. Psychiat. Day Hosp. & Rainhill Hosp. Liverp.

MCKAY, John Stephen Leighton Hospital, Crewe CW1 4QJ Tel: 01270 255141; 14 Park Road, Nantwich CW5 7AQ — MD 1987 Aberd.; MB ChB 1973; FRCP Lond. 1992; MRCP (UK) 1976. Cons. Phys. Leighton Hosp.

MACKAY, Jonathan Angus 9 West Road, Annfield Plain, Stanley DH9 7XT Tel: 01207 231112 — MB ChB 1977 Manchester; MB ChB Manch. 1977. (Manchester) GP Stanley, Co. Durh.

MACKAY, Jonathan Donald Victoria Hospital, Blackpool FY3 8NR; 7 Croyde Road, St Annes-on-Sea, Lytham St Annes FY8 1EX — MB BChir 1972 Camb.; MD Camb. 1991; FRCP Lond. 1994; MRCP (UK) 1974. Cons. Phys. Vict. Hosp. Blackpool. Prev: Sen. Regist. (Med.) Manch. Roy. Infirm. & Withington Hosp. Manch.

MACKAY, Jonathan Hickey Papworth Hospital, Papworth Everard, Cambridge CB3 8RE Tel: 01480 364406 Email: jon.mackay@papworth-tr.angloz.nhs.uk; 14 High Street, Brampton, Huntingdon PE28 4TG Email: jonmackay@doctors.org.uk — MB BS 1982 Newc.; MRCP (UK) 1986; FRCA 1990.

MACKAY, Joyce Elisabeth (retired) 4 Conifer Place, .Lenzie, Glasgow G66 4EJ Tel: 0141 776 3992 — MB ChB 1955 St. And. Prev: Med. Asst. Roy. Scott. Nat. Hosp. Larbert.

MACKAY, Judith Alexandra 11 Loudoun Road, London NW8 0LP Tel: 020 7624 5551 — MB BS 1981 Lond.; PhD Lond. 1988, MB BS 1981; MRCP (UK) 1986. Research Phys. (Clin. Pharmacol.) Glaxo Gp. Research. Prev: Regist. (Med.) Hillingdon Hosp.

MCKAY, Katherine 52 Mosshead Road, Bearsden, Glasgow G61 3HL Tel: 0141 942 2337 — MB ChB 1984 Glas.; MRCPI (Paediat.) 1992; DCH RCPS Glas. 1990; DRCOG 1988. Sen. Regist. (Paediat.) Roy. Hosp. Sick Childr. Glas. Socs: BMA & Community Paediat. Gp. Scott. Prev: Regist. (Paediat.) Ninewells Hosp. Dundee; SHO (Paediat. & A & E) Roy. Hosp. Sick Childr. Glas.; Regist. (Neonat. Med.) Rutherglen Matern. Hosp. Glas.

MACKAY, Kathleen Heather Enfield PCT, Holbrook House, Cockfosters Road, Barnet EN4 0DR Tel: 0208 272 5500; 47 The Crosspath, Radlett WD7 8HP Tel: 01923 856177 — MB ChB 1975 Glas.; MSc (Community Med.) Ed. 1990; MFPHM RCP (UK) 1994. Cons. Pub. Health Med., Enfield Primary Care Trust; Hon. Sen. Lect. Roy. Free Hosp. Sch. of Med. Prev: GP Edin.; Dep. Director Pub. Health Med. Barnet HA.

MACKAY, Kathleen Margaret Woodlands Hospital, Craigton Road, Cults, Aberdeen AB15 9PR Tel: 01224 551513 Fax: 01224 404018; Old Smiddy, West Fingask, Oldmeldrum, Inverurie AB51 0EA Tel: 01651 873225 — MB ChB 1979 Aberd.; MRCPsych 1988; DRCOG 1981. Cons. Psychiat. (Learning Disabil.) Woodlands Hosp. Aberd.; Hon. Sen. Clin. Lect. Univ. Aberd.

MACKAY, Keith (retired) Park House, Harbottle, Morpeth NE65 7BD Tel: 01669 50325 — MB BS 1947 Durh. Prev: Clin. Asst. (Geriat.) Sunderland Gen. Hosp.

MACKAY, Kenneth Boyle (retired) The Oast House, Shrub Lane, Burwash, Etchingham TN19 7EB — MRCS Eng. LRCP Lond. 1943.

MACKAY, Kenneth Mackenzie Hospital Hill Surgery, 7 Izatt Avenue, Dunfermline KY11 3BA Tel: 01383 731721 Fax: 01383 623352 — MB ChB 1970 Ed.

MACKAY, Kerry Maria 16A Peebles Road, Penicuik EH26 8LU — MB ChB 1993 Ed.

MACKAY, Kim Elizabeth Henderson Wishaw Heath Centre, Kenilworth Avenue, Wishaw ML2 7BQ Tel: 01698 361716 — MB ChB 1980 Glas.; DRCOG 1983. (Glasgow) Socs: BMA.

MACKAY, Kirsten Robyn Alban House, Cefn Mount, Dinas Powys CF64 4AR; 2 Wyndham Way, Oxford OX2 8DF Email: kirsten.mackay@well.ox.ac.uk — MB ChB 1989 Bristol; MRCP (UK) 1993. ARC Clin. Research Fell. Wellcome Trust Centre for Human Genetics Oxf. Socs: BMA; BSR.

MACKAY, Kirsty Joanne 208 Aurs Glen, Barrhead, Glasgow G78 2LJ — MB ChB 1997 Glas.

MCKAY, Lesley Anne 3 Tigh-Na-Mara Court, Wemyss Bay Road, Wemyss Bay PA18 6AE — MB ChB 1984 Glas.

MACKAY, Louisa Jane 3 Beresford Park, Sunderland SR2 7JT — MB ChB 1973 Aberd.; FFA RCS Eng. 1979.

MCKAY, Malcolm (Surgery), Denewell House, Low Fell, Gateshead NE9 5HD Tel: 0191 482 4000; The Manse, Church Road, Low Fell, Gateshead NE9 5XE Tel: 0191 487 9945 — MB BS 1958 Durh. (Newc.) Trainer N.umbria VTS; Med. Adviser N.E. Dyslexia Assn. Socs: BMA. Prev: Surg. Lt.-Cdr. RNR; Med. Off. Brit. Trawler Fleet Icelandic Support Operat.

MACKAY, Margaret Macleod 7 Park Road, Great Sankey, Warrington WA5 3BY — MB ChB 1968 Aberd.; DPM Eng. 1971. (Aberd.)

MACKAY, Marion Elizabeth (retired) 14 Merlewood Drive, Swinton, Manchester M27 0ER Tel: 0161 794 4264 — MB ChB 1953 Aberd.; MRCP Lond. 1965; FRCPsych 1986, M 1971; DPM Eng. 1968. Cons. Psychiat. Prestwich Hosp. Manch.

***MACKAY, Miss Miriam Liza** 1 Townhead Cottage, Ardoe, Aberdeen AB12 5XX — MB ChB 1997 Aberd.; BSc (Med. Sci.).

***MCKAY, Neil Douglas** 25 Tower House, Tower St., Newcastle upon Tyne NE1 2HW — MB BS 1997 Newc.

MACKAY, Mr Neil Nelson Scott (cons. rooms), Mount Stuart Hospital, St Vincent's Road, Torquay TQ1 4UP Tel: 01626 352081 Fax: 01626 352091 — MB BS Lond. 1965; FRCS Eng. 1971; MRCS Eng. LRCP Lond. 1965. (Univ. Coll. Hosp.) Cons. Orthop. Surg. Mt. Stuart Hosp. Torqay; Cons. Orthop. Surg. Nuffield Hosp. Exeter. Socs: Fell. BOA; Roy. Soc. Med.; Fell. Brit. Assoc. Surg. Knee Jt. Prev: Sen. Regist. Rotat. (Orthop.) Univ. Coll. Hosp. Lond., W.m. Hosp. & Roy. Nat. Orthop. Hosp. Lond.; John Marshall Fell. & Atkinson Morley Schol. Univ. Lond.; Hon. Cons. Orthop. Surg. Torqay Hosp. S. Devon Healthcare Trust Torquay.

MACKAY, Neil Sinclair Davis Surgery, 75 Bank Street, Alexandria G83 0NB Tel: 01389 752626 Fax: 01389 752169 — MB ChB 1981 Glas. GP Alexandria.

MCKAY, Niall Patterson Limes Medical Centre, Limes Avenue, Alfreton DE55 7DW Tel: 01773 833133 Fax: 01773 836099 — MB ChB 1989 Glas.; MRCGP 1993. Clin. Asst. in Gen. Pract.

MACKAY, Professor Norman, CBE Dunolly, 4 Erskine Avenue, Dumbeck, Glasgow G41 5AL Tel: 0141 427 0900 — MD Glas. 1973, MB ChB 1959; FRCS Ed. 1994; FRCP Glas. 1992; FRCP Ed. 1975, M 1963; FRCP Glas. 1973, M 1962; FRCGP 1993. Socs: FCPS (Pakistan). Prev: Dean Postgrad. Med. & Prof. Postgrad. Med. Educat. Univ. Glas.

MACKAY, Norna Medical Centre, Thurso Tel: 01847 3321 — MB ChB 1958 Aberd. SCMO (Child Health) Highland Health Bd. (N. Dist.). Prev: Surg. Ho. Off. Woodend Hosp. Aberd.; Ho. Phys. & JHMO Radiother. Unit Aberd. Roy. Infirm.

MCKAY, Pamela Jane Royal Alexandra Hospital, Corsebar Road, Paisley PA2 9PN Tel: 0141 580 4225 Fax: 0141 580 4112 Email: pammckay@rah.scot.nhs.uk — MB ChB 1984 Glas.; FRCPath 2000 U.K; MRCP (UK) 1987; MRCPath 1992; FRCP (UK) 1998. Cons. Haemat. Roy. Alexandra Hosp. NHS Trust Paisley. Socs: Roy. Coll. Phys. & Surg. Glas.; Fell.Roy. Coll. of Pathologists. Prev: Sen. Regist. & Regist. (Haemat.) W.. Infirm. Glas.

MACKAY, Patricia Christine (retired) 5 Ravelston Park, Edinburgh EH4 3DX Tel: 0131 332 4199 — MB ChB 1950 Ed.; FRCS Ed. 1963; FRCOG 1973, M 1958, DObst 1952. Prev: Cons. O & G Doncaster Roy. Infirm.

MACKAY, Peigi Smith 130 Rosemount Place, Aberdeen AB25 2YU — MB ChB 1998 Aberd.; MB ChB Aberd 1998.

MACKAY, Peter Malcolm Department of Paediatrics, Dewsbury & District Hospital, Halifax Road, Dewsbury WF13 4HS Tel: 01924 512000 ext. 4004 Fax: 01924 816175 — MB BS 1978 Lond.; MRCP (UK) 1987; MRCS Eng. LRCP Lond. 1978; MRCGP 1984; FRCPCH 1998. (St. Bart.) Cons. Paediat. Dewsbury Dist. Hosp. Prev: Sen. Regist. (Paediat.) King's Coll. Hosp. Lond.; Regist. (Paediat.) Leeds Gen. Infirm.; SHO (Paediat.) Guy's Hosp. Lond.

MACKAY, Peter William Norwich Road Surgery, 199 Norwich Road, Ipswich IP1 4BX Tel: 01473 289777 Fax: 01473 289545 — MB BCh BAO 1988 Belf.; MRCGP 1994. GP Princip.

MCKAY, Rebecca Jayne Tocil House, Main St., Polebrook, Peterborough PE8 5LN — BM BCh 1998 Oxf.; BM BCh Oxf 1998.

MACKAY, Robert Hope St John's Avenue Surgery, 24 St. John's Avenue, Churchdown, Gloucester GL3 2DB Tel: 01452 713036 Fax: 01452 714726; 45 Broad Leys Road, Barnwood, Gloucester GL4 3YW Tel: 01452 614514 Email: ros.mackay@btinternet.com — MRCS Eng. LRCP Lond. 1971; MRCGP 1981. (Guy's) Course Organiser Glos. VTS.

MACKAY, Robert Hugh Larch Villa, St. John's Road, Annan DG12 — MB ChB 1952 Glas.; BSc Glas. 1946, MB ChB 1952; DObst RCOG 1955. Med. Off. Brit. Nuclear Fuels Plc. Chapelcross Works Annan. Prev: Ho. Surg. Greenock Roy. Infirm.; Ho. Phys. Larkfield Hosp. Greenock; Ho. Gynaecol. David Elder Infirm. Glas.

MACKAY, Robert Ian (retired) 229 Bramhall Lane S., Bramhall, Stockport SK7 3EP Tel: 0161 439 2618 — MB ChB 1940 Manch.; MB ChB (2nd cl. Hons.) Stephen Lewis Prize Manch. 1943; BSc Manch. 1940; FRCP Lond. 1971, M 1947; DCH Eng. 1944. Hon. Foundat. Fell. Roy. Coll. Paediat. & Child Health. Prev: Hon. Cons. Paediat. Roy. Manch. Childr. Hosp.

MACKAY, Roderick Macdonald (retired) 3 Beech Hill Avenue, Hadley Wood, Barnet EN4 0LW — MB ChB 1932 Ed.

MCKAY, Ronald Eric Southover Medical Practice, Bronshill Road, Torquay TQ1 3HD Tel: 01803 327100 Fax: 01803 316295 — LRCPI & LM, LRSCI & LM 1969; LRCPI & LM, LRCSI & LM 1969. (RCSI)

MACKAY, Ronald Kennedy Soddy 1A Links Road, Wilmslow SK9 6HQ Tel: 01625 583714 Email: ken@mackayk.freeserve.co.uk — MB ChB 1964 Glas.; DObst RCOG 1966. Socs: Glas. Roy. M-C Soc. Prev: Chairm. E. Chesh. PCG; Sen. Partner Kenmore Med. Centre, Wilmslow; Med. Adviser NW REG H.A.

MACKAY, Ronald Tod (retired) 75 Stratherrick Road, Inverness IV2 4LL Tel: 01463 232624 — MB ChB 1955 Ed.; DMRD Eng. 1960. Prev: Cons. Radiol. Highland Area HB Inverness.

MACKAY, Ruth Margaret 14 Elm Gardens, Perth PH1 1ES Tel: 01738 629538 Fax: 01738 447673 — MB ChB 1972 Glas.; DObst RCOG 1974. Clin. Med. Off. (Community Health) Perth & Kinross Dist.; Staff Grade (Obst.& Ultrasound) Perth Roy. Infirm.

MACKAY, Sarah Evelyn 16 Links Brow, Fetcham, Leatherhead KT22 9DU — MB BS 1984 Lond.; DRCOG 1988. (St. Geo.)

MCKAY, Sheila Elizabeth 2 Ailsa Court, 20 Dirleton Drive, Glasgow G41 3BQ — MB ChB 1983 Glas.

MACKAY, Sheila Gillian Doctors Surgery, Pembroke Road, Framlingham, Woodbridge IP13 9HA Tel: 01728 723627 Fax: 01728 621064; 95 College Road, Framlingham, Woodbridge IP13 9EU Tel: 01728 723544 — MB ChB 1964 Glas. (Glas.) Med. Off. Ipswich Family Plann. Socs: BMA. Prev: Clin. Asst. (Geriat.) Ipswich Hosp.

*****MCKAY, Simon Jonathon** 6 Spital Heyes, Bebington, Wirral CH63 9NF — MB ChB 1996 Liverp.

MACKAY, Stanley Gordon Malcolm (retired) 22 Mitchell Avenue, Newcastle upon Tyne NE2 3LA Tel: 0191 811421 — MB BS 1937 Durh. Prev: Capt. RAMC.

MCKAY, Suzanne 5 Burn Road, Blaydon-on-Tyne NE21 6EB — MB BS 1998 Newc.; MB BS Newc 1998.

MACKAY, Suzanne Kathleen Rosyth Health Centre, Park Road, Rosyth, Dunfermline KY11 2SE Tel: 01383 418931 Fax: 01383 419007; 47 North Larches, Dunfermline KY11 4NX — MB ChB 1992 Aberd.; MRCGP 1996; DFFP 1996; DRCOG 1995. (Aberd.) Princip GP Rosyth Health Centre.

MACKAY, Thomas Ian Britton and Partners, 10 Spencer Street, Carlisle CA1 1BP Tel: 01228 29171 — MB ChB 1972 Liverp.

MACKAY, Thomas William Royal Infirmary, Laurston Place, Edinburgh EH3 9YW Tel: 0131 536 1000 Fax: 0131 536 2362; Southfield House, 71/3 Carnibee Avenue, Edinburgh EH16 6GA Tel: 0131 664 1648 Fax: 0131 664 1964 Email: tomwmackay@hotmail.com — MB ChB 1984 Ed.; BSc (Hons.) Ed. 1981; FRCP Ed. 1996; MRCP (UK) 1988. (Univ. Ed.) Cons. Phys. (Respirat., Sleep & Gen. Med.) Roy. Infirm. Edin. Socs: Scott. Thoracic Soc.; Brit. Thorac. Soc.; BMA. Prev: Cons. Phys. (Gen. & Respirat. Med.) Roy. Alexandra Hosp. Paisley; Sen. Regist. St. Mary's & Centr. Middlx. Hosps. Lond.; Lect. (Med.) Roy. Infirm. Edin.

MCKAY, Veronica 2 Left, 11 Dryburgh Gardens, Glasgow G20 6BT — MB ChB 1987 Glas.

MACKAY, Viola Edythe 5 North Lodge, Chester-le-Street DH3 4BA Tel: 0191 388 6080 — MB BS Durh. 1944; MSc Manch. 1976; MFPHM RCP (UK) 1989; MFCM 1977; T(PHM) 1991. (Newc.) Med. Ref. Durh. Crematorium. Socs: Foundat. Assoc. RCGP; BMA; RSM. Prev: SCM (Social Servs.) Cleveland HA; Specialist (Community Med.) SW Durh. HA; Specialist Pub. Health Med.. NW.Durh. HA.

MACKAY, William George (retired) 14B Riverside Gardens, Gourock PA19 1RX Tel: 01475 38741 — MB ChB 1926 Glas.; MB ChB Glas. (Commend.) 1926; FRCOG 1951. Prev: Cons. O & G Renfrewsh. Area.

MCKAY, William Graham (retired) Rheda, Frizington CA26 3TE — MB ChB Aberd. 1951.

MACKAY, William Patrick 29 Seaton Drive, Standens Barn, Northampton NN3 9SS — MB ChB 1977 Glas.

MACKAY-JAMES, Maxim Alexander The Middlemarsh Clinic, Middlesmarsh Street, Poundbury, Dorchester DT2 0ET Tel: 01305 262626 — MB BS 1987 Lond.; MA Camb. 1973. Indep. GP Dorset.

MACKEACHAN, Donald Cameron, TD (retired) 7 Broomfield, Largs KA30 8HH Tel: 01475 675491 — MB ChB 1951 Glas.

MACKEACHAN, Fiona 20 Napiershall Street, Glasgow G20 6HA — MB ChB 1979 Glas.

MCKEAGNEY, Krystine Elizabeth 149 Main Street, Fivemiletown BT75 0PG — MB BCh BAO 1993 Belf.

***MCKEAGUE, Gerard Patrick Bernard** 1 Innisfayle Park, Belfast BT15 5HS — MB BCh BAO 1997 Belf.

MCKEAN, Anita Marie 71 Cross Green, Otley LS21 1HE — MB ChB 1994 Ed.

MCKEAN, Carl William Fortescue (retired) 84 Bargates, Leominster HR6 8QS Tel: 01568 612466 — MB BChir 1942 Camb.; MB BChir. Camb. 1942; MA Camb. 1942; MRCS Eng. LRCP Lond. 1939. Prev: Phys. Lond. Skin Hosp.

MCKEAN, Colin Douglas Greenbank Drive Surgery, 8 Greenbank Drive, Sefton Park, Liverpool L17 1AW Tel: 0151 733 5703 — MB ChB 1969 Liverp.; MRCP (U.K.) 1975.

MCKEAN

MCKEAN, Douglas McDonald (retired) 212 Saltshouse Road, Hull HU8 9HH — MB ChB Glas. 1947. Prev: GP Hull.

MCKEAN, Edward John Gustavus New Cross Street Surgery, Bradford Tel: 01274 733232; 3 Appleby Court, Knaresborough HG5 9LU — MB ChB BAO 1948 Belf. (Belf.)

MCKEAN, John Mackintosh Westmoreland GP Centre, Fazakerley Hospital, Longmoor Lane, Fazakerley, Liverpool L9 7AL Tel: 0151 525 6286 Fax: 0151 525 9070; Lowood, Lyndhurst Road, Mossley Hill, Liverpool L18 8AU Tel: 0151 724 1209 Fax: 0151 724 3242 — MB ChB 1984 Liverp.; MRCGP 1988; DRCOG 1987; D.Occ.Med. RCP Lond. 1995. Socs: Vice-Pres. Liverp. Med. Inst. Prev: SHO (O & G) Wom.s Hosp. Liverp. & Liverp. Matern. Hosp.; SHO (Paediat. & Psychiat.) Whiston Hosp. St. Helens; SHO (Cas.) Walton Hosp. Liverp.

MCKEAN, John Robertson Lochgelly Health Centre, David Street, Lochgelly KY5 9QZ Tel: 01592 782783; 21 Deanpark Gardens, Kirkcaldy KY2 6XX Tel: 01592 644967 — MB ChB 1982 Ed.; BSc (Hons.) (Path.) Ed. 1979, MB ChB 1982; DRCOG 1986. Prev: Resid. (Med. & Surgic.) Roy. Infirm. Edin.; Lect. (Path.) Edin. Univ. & Roy. Infirm. Edin.; Trainee GP Fife VTS.

MCKEAN, Mary Elizabeth Department of Pathology, Medical Buildings, Foresterhill, Aberdeen AB25 2ZD Tel: 01224 553002 Fax: 01224 663002 Email: m.e.mckean@abdn.ac.uk — MB ChB 1976 Glas. (Glasgow University) Cons. Cytopath. Aberd. Roy. Hosps. NHS Trust. Prev: Sen. Regist. Glas. Roy. Infirm.

MACKEAN, Melanie Jane Lothian University NHS Trust, Western General Hospital, Crewe Road, Edinburgh EH4 2XU Tel: 0131 537 1000; 10a Dick Place, Edinburgh EH9 2JL Tel: 0131 667 5369 Email: melanie@mackean.com — MB ChB 1988 Ed.; MRCP (UK) 1991; MSc 1996. (Edinburgh) Cons., Med. Oncol., W.ern Gen. Hosp., Edin.; Hon. Sen. Lect., W.ern Gen. Hosp., Edin.

MCKEAN, Michael Charles Linden Lea, 2A Woodley St., Ruddington, Nottingham NG11 6EP — MB ChB 1992 Manch.

MCKEAN, Susan Jane Calder Allander Street Surgery, 124 Allander Street, Glasgow G22 5JH Tel: 0141 336 8038 Fax: 0141 336 3440 — MB ChB 1984 Glas.; MRCP (UK) 1990; DRCOG 1994; DFFP 1994. (Glasgow)

MACKEAN, William George The Castle Medical Group, Pendleside Medical Practice, Clitheroe Health Centre, Railway View Road, Clitheroe BB7 2JG Tel: 01200 421900 Fax: 01200 421902 — MB ChB 1987 Liverp.; DFFP 1999; MRCGP 1993; Cert. Family Plann. JCC 1992; DRCOG 1991. (Liverp.) GP Princip., The Castle Med. Gp., Clitheroe. Prev: Assoc. GP Slaidburn, Lancs.; Trainee GP Clitheroe; SHO (Psychiat.) Burnley Gen. Hosp.

MACKEAN, William Mackintosh, RD Lowood, Lyndhurst Road, Mossley Hill, Liverpool L18 8AU Tel: 0151 724 1209 Fax: 0151 724 3242 — MB ChB 1951 Liverp.; FRCGP 1982, M 1963; AFOM RCP Lond. 1983. (Liverp.) Med. Off. Metal Box plc, J.F. Renshaw Ltd; Asst. Div. Med. Off. Civil Serv. Liverp.; Local Civil Serv. Med. Off. Liverp. Socs: Soc. Occupat. Med.; (Ex-Pres.) Liverp. Med. Inst. Prev: Ho. Phys. St. Catherines Hosp. Birkenhead; Ho. Surg. & Cas. Off. Sefton Hosp. Liverp.; Surg. Cdr. RNR.

MCKEAN, Mr William Patrick Nithsdale Road Surgery, 162 Nithsdale Road, Glasgow G41 5RU Tel: 0141 424 1831 Fax: 0141 423 7422 — MB ChB 1972 Glas.; FRCS Glas. 1977.

MCKEAN, William Thomas Sinclair (retired) High Hedges, Orchard Hill, Bideford EX39 2QY — MB BCh BAO 1940 Belf. Prev: Med. Staff Bideford & Dist. Hosp.

MCKEATING, Edward Grant Royal Infirmary of Edinburgh, 1 Lauriston Place, Edinburgh EH3 9YW Tel: 0131 229 2477; 2FL, 15 Lauderdale Street, Marchmont, Edinburgh EH9 1DF Tel: 0131 452 8449 — MB ChB 1989 Ed. SHO (Anaesth.) Roy. Infirm. Edin. Prev: SHO (Anaesth.) Fife; SHO (Med.) Vict. Hosp. Kirkcaldy; SHO (A & E) Roy. Vict. Infirm. Newc. u. Tyne.

MCKEATING, John Brendan Medical Centre, HMS Warrior, Sandy Lane, Northwood HA6 3HS — BM BCh 1988 Oxf.

MCKEATING, Sarah Helen Newbyres Medical Group, Gorebridge Health Centre, Gorebridge EH23 4TP Tel: 01875 820405 Fax: 01875 820269 — MB ChB 1989 Ed.; MRCGP 1994; DFFP 1993; DRCOG 1991. (Edinburgh) GP. Prev: GP Edin. Retainer Scheme.

MCKECHAN, Kathryn Frances Flat 3/7, 17 Stewartville St., Partick, Glasgow G11 5HR — MB ChB 1984 Glas.

MCKECHNIE, Alasdair Alner (retired) 13 Jocks Hill Crescent, Linlithgow EH49 7BJ Tel: 01506 842293 — MB ChB 1960 Aberd.; MD Aberd. 1978; FRCP Ed. 1990; FRCPsych 1980, M 1972; DPM Ed. & Glas. 1966. Prev: Phys. Supt. & Cons. Psychiat. Bangour Village Hosp. Broxburn.

MCKECHNIE, Ann Back Lane Surgery, Back Lane, Colsterworth, Grantham NG33 5NJ Tel: 01476 860243 Fax: 01476 860200; The Old Rectory, North Witham, Grantham NG33 5LQ — MB ChB 1973 Dundee; DCH Eng. 1976. Prev: Clin. Med. Off. (Community Child Health) Lothian Health Bd.; Leukaemia Research Fell. (Hon. Regist.) Hosp. Sick Childr. Gt. Ormond St.; SHO (Path.) & SHO (Paediat. Neonat.) Roy. Free Hosp. Lond.

MACKECHNIE, Mr Donald William Macleod Eriskay, 210 Dundee Lane, Ramsbottom, Bury BL0 9HF — MB ChB 1976 Glas.; FRCS Glas. 1980; FFAEM 1993. Cons. A & E Rochdale NHS Trust. Prev: Cons. A & E Bury Gen. Hosp.; Sen. Regist. (A & E) Manch. Roy. Infirm. & Vict. Hosp. Blackpool; Regist. Rotat. (Surg.) W. Scott. Jt. Train. Scheme.

MCKECHNIE, Eileen Patricia Bridge House, 13 Cadehill Road, Stocksfield NE43 7PB Tel: 01661 842718 — MB BS 1968 Newc.; DObst RCOG 1970. (Newc.) Med. Off. (Occupat. Health) Derwent Valley Foods Ltd., Consett Co. Durh.

MCKECHNIE, Elizabeth Jane Paediatric Department, Royal United Hospital, Coombe Park, Bath BA1 Email: ejmck@hotmail.com; 75 Septon Park Road, Bristol BS7 9AN Tel: 0117 942 2749 — MB BS 1990 Lond.; MRCP (UK) 1996; MRCPCH. (St. Thos. Lond.) Specialist Regist. (Paediat.) S. W. Region (Bath).

MCKECHNIE, Elspeth Mavor, CBE 10 Holly Court, Palatine Road, Manchester M20 3JE Tel: 0161 445 3383 — MRCS Eng. LRCP Lond. 1942. (Manch.) Prev: Ho. Surg. St. Mary's Hosp. Manch. & Roy. Infirm. Manch.

MCKECHNIE, Mr Ian (retired) Rectory Cottage, Marlholm, Peterborough PE6 7JA — LRCP LRCS 1942 Ed.; FRCS Ed. 1956; LRCP LRCS Ed. LRFPS Glas. 1942. Prev: Sen. Orthop. Regist. Roy. Infirm. Aberd.

MCKECHNIE, Jennifer Margaret Well Woman & Family Planning Services, Nithbank, Dumfries DG1 2SA Tel: 0345 023687; 37 Gilloch Crescent, Dumfries DG1 4DW Tel: 01387 261918 — MB ChB 1970 Glas.; MFFP 1993. Dir. Well Wom. & Family Plann. Servs. for Dumfries & Galloway NHS Trust. Socs: Assoc. Mem. Inst. Psychosexual Med.

MCKECHNIE, Mr John Southend Hospital, Prittlewell Chase, Westcliff on Sea SS0 0RY Tel: 01702 348911; 7 Greyfriars, Mount Avenue, Shenfield, Brentwood CM13 2XB — MB BChir 1979 Camb.; BDS St. And. 1972, BSc 1976; FRCS Ed. 1985; MRCS Eng. LRCP Lond. 1979; FDS RCS Eng. 1984; FFD RCSI 1982. Cons. Oral & Maxillofacial Surg. S.end, Basildon, Orsett & St. And. Hosp. Billericay. Socs: Fell. Brit. Assn. Oral & Maxillofacial Surg.; Fell. Roy. Soc. Med. Prev: Sen. Regist. (Oral & Maxillofacial Surg.) Roy. Lond. Hosp.; Regist. (Oral Surg.) N. Staffs. HA; SHO (Orthop. & A & E) St. Richards Hosp. Chichester.

MCKECHNIE, Martin David James 26 Woodcroft Avenue, Glasgow G11 7HY — MB ChB 1990 Glas.

MCKECHNIE, Roger Nettleton Esso Petroleum Co. Ltd., Occupational Health Department, Mailpoint 04, Esso House, Ermyn Way, Leatherhead KT22 8UX Tel: 01372 222005 Fax: 01372 223612; 96 Tilt Road, Cobham KT11 3HQ — MB ChB 1992 Aberd.; DRCOG 1994; MRCGP 1997; DFFP 1997. Trainee Occupat. Phys. Esso Petrol. Co.Ltd. Leatherhead. Prev: SHO (A & E) Raigmore Hosp. NHS Trust Inverness; SHO (Gen. Med.) Raigmore Hosp. NHS Trust Inverness; SHO (Psychiat.) Craig Dunain Hosp. Inverness.

MCKECHNIE, Ronald Livingstone, VRD 7 Collingwood Drive, Great Barr, Birmingham B43 7NS — MB ChB Glas. 1958; MRCGP 1974.

MCKECHNIE, Samuel Ardvaar House, Wemyss Bay Road, Wemyss Bay PA18 6AD Tel: 01475 520836 — MB ChB 1946 Glas.; FRCA 1993; FFA RCS Eng. 1954; DA Eng. 1952. (Glas.) Socs: Assn. Anaesths. & BMA. Prev: Med. Dir. Ardgowan Hospice Greenock; Cons. Anaesth Argyll & Clyde HB; Cons. Anaesth. Sheff. HA.

MCKECHNIE, Sheila Anne Mount Florida Medical Centre, 183 Prospecthill Road, Glasgow G42 9LQ Tel: 0141 632 4004 Fax: 0141 636 6036; 39 Lubnaig Road, Newlands, Glasgow G43 2RY Tel: 0141 632 1143 — MB ChB 1981 Glas.; MRCGP 1985; DRCOG 1984. (Glas. Univ.) GP Shawlands, Glas. Retainer Scheme; GP Mt. Florida Glas. FT.

MCKEE, Alexander George Ivybank, Helsdale, Sunderland — MB ChB 1971 Aberd.; MRCP (U.K.) 1974; DA Eng. 1978. Regist. (Renal Med.) St. Jas. Hosp. Leeds. Prev: Regist. (Gen. Med.) Roy. N.. Infirm. Inverness; SHO (Gen. Med.) Pembury Hosp.

MCKEE, Angus Hugh 526 Anniesland Road, Glasgow G13 1YA Tel: 0141 954 1992 — MB ChB 1969 Ed.; FFA RCS Eng. 1974. Cons. Anaesth. Stobhill Gen. Hosp. Glas.

MCKEE, Charles Henry Wilson Castlereagh Road Surgery, 50 Castlereagh Road, Belfast BT5 4NH — MB BCh BAO 1982 Belf.; MRCGP 1986; DTMM & H 1988; DCH RCP Lond. 1985; DRCOG 1984.

MCKEE, Professor Clifford Martin Health Services Research Unit, London Schoolof Hygine & Tropical Medicine, Keppel St., London WC1E 7HT Tel: 020 7927 2229 Fax: 020 7580 8183 Email: m.mckee@ishtm.ac.uk — MB BCh BAO 1979 Belf; MB BCh BAO Belf. 1979; MSc Lond. 1986; FRCPI 1997; FRCP Lond. 1995; MRCP (UK) 1982; FFPHM RCP (UK) 1994; MFCCM1998; Belf. (Belf.) Prof. Europ. Pub. Health Lond. Sch. Hyg. & Trop. Med.; Hon. Cons. N Thames NHS Exec. & Kensington, Chelsea & W.m. HA; Cons. Adviser RAF; Research Dir., Europ. Observatory on Health Car Systems. Socs: BMA & Roy. Soc. Med. Prev: sen. Regist. (Pub. Health Med.) Islington HA; Resist. (Lcommunity Med.) NHSSB; Regist. (Gen. Med.) Roy. Vict. Hosp. Belf.

MCKEE, Colin Nairn Surrey Fire & Rescue Service, Wray Park Centre, 70 Wray Park Road, Reigate RH2 0EJ Tel: 01323 502200/503240 Fax: 01323 500527 Email: cnmckee@btinternet.com; Downscroft, 3 The Dene, Wannock Lane, Eastbourne BN20 9SY Tel: 01323 486325 — MB ChB 1971 Glas.; DOcc Med. GP Occupat.al Phys., Surrey Fire and Rescue Serv., Reigate, Surrey; Hon. Med. Adviser E.bourne Lifeboat; Co. Med. Adviser E. Sussex CC Lewes; Med. Adviser E. Sussex Fire Brig. Lewes; Med. Adviser Brighton Univ. Prev: GP E.bourne.

MCKEE, David Hugh 19 Woodside Drive, Wrenthorpe, Wakefield WF2 0NA — MB BS 1993 Lond.

MCKEE, Mr Gary John 18 Cotswold Gardens, Nigh Heaton, Newcastle upon Tyne NE7 7AE — MB BCh BAO 1985 Belf.; MD 1996; MB BCh BAO (Hons.) Belf. 1985; BSc (Hons.) Belf. 1982; FRCS Eng. 1991; FRCS Ed. 1990; FRCS (Orl) 1996. (Belf.) Cons. Freeman Hosp. Newc. Socs: Otorhinolaryngol. Research Soc.; Dysphagia Research Soc. Prev: Sen. Regist. Altnagelvin Area Hosp. N. Irel.; Sen. Cons. Groote Schuur Hosp., Cape Town; Regist. (ENT) Roy. Gwent Hosp. Newport.

MCKEE, Heather Jean Charing Cross Hospital, Fulham Palace Road, London W6 8RF Tel: 020 8846 1509 Fax: 020 8846 1133 — MB BCh BAO 1971 Belf.; MRCPsych 1975.

MCKEE, Ian Hume Wester Hailes Health Centre, 7 Murrayburn Gate, Edinburgh EH14 2SS Tel: 0131 537 7300 Fax: 0131 537 7337; 37 Fernielaw Avenue, Edinburgh EH13 0EF Tel: 0131 441 5827 Fax: 0131 441 6253 Email: mckee@cableinet.co.uk — MB ChB Ed. 1965; DFFP 1993; DObst RCOG 1970; Cert. FPA 1967. (Ed.) Publ. Scott. Med. Jl., Edin. Med. & Scott. Med. Socs: BMA; GP Writers Assn.; MJA. Prev: Ho. Surg. Ingham Infirm. S. Shields; Ho. Phys. Roy. Infirm. Edin.; Flight Lt. RAF Med. Br.

MACKEE, Mr Ian William ENT Department, Royal Infirmary, New Durham Road, Sunderland SR2 7JE — BM BCh 1972 Oxf.; MA, BM BCh Oxf. 1972; FRCS Eng. 1977. Cons. ENT Surg. Roy. Infirm. Sunderland.

MCKEE, Keith James 1 Mercier Road, Putney, London SW15 2AW Tel: 020 8780 9725 Fax: 020 8789 4878 — MB BS 1964 Lond.; MRCS Eng. LRCP Lond. 1964. (St. Mary's) Hon. Med. Cons. Roy. Theatrical Fund; Med. Examr. Allied Dunbar, Lond., WFE, Legal & Gen. & other Insur. Cos.; Med. Adviser Cameron Mackintosh Ltd. & Really Useful Gp. Prev: SHO (O & G) Roy. Postgrad. Med. Sch. Hammersmith Hosp. Lond.; SHO (Cas.) & Ho. Surg. St. Mary's Hosp. Lond.

MCKEE, Lesley Anne 36 Baskerville Gardens, Dog Lane, London NW10 1PF — MB ChB 1993 Glas.

MCKEE, Linda Alison Rubislaw Place Medical Group, 7 Rubislaw Place, Aberdeen AB10 1QB Tel: 01224 641968 Fax: 01224 645738 — MB ChB 1983 Leeds.

MCKEE, Maurice James Braeside, Moneymore, Magherafelt — LAH Dub. 1968.

MCKEE, Nigel Duncan The Derby Medical Centre, 8 The Derby Square, Epsom KT19 8DW Tel: 01372 726361; 29 Ruden Way, Epsom Downs, Epsom KT17 3LL — MB BS 1980 Lond.; MRCS Eng. LRCP Lond. 1980; DRCOG 1983. Prev: Trainee GP Stroud; Attend. Phys. L'Hôpital Notre Dame Manitoba Canada.

MCKEE, Paul Bernard 14 Mulberry Road, Newlands, Glasgow G43 2TR — MB ChB 1974 Glas.; DPH Glas. 1978. Socs: BMA.

MCKEE, Paul James William 3 Mingarry Street, Glasgow G20 8NP — MB BCh BAO 1982 Dub.; MRCPI 1987.

MCKEE, Robert Hastings Mountain View Surgery, 585A Crumlin Road, Belfast BT14 7GB Tel: 028 9039 2392 Fax: 028 9039 2392; 21 Downview Avenue, Belfast BT15 4EZ Tel: 01232 777604 — MB BCh BAO 1972 Belf.; BA (Econ. & Business Admin.) Belf. 1988; MFCH 1978. (Queen's University Belfast) GP Belf.; Dir. Community Med. Servs. N. & W. Belf. Health & Social Serv. Trust; Dir. E.ern Multifund; Company Sec. Assoc. of Belf. Doctors on Call. Socs: Soc. Community Med.

MCKEE, Ruth Fraser Consultant Colorectal Surgeon, Glasgow Royal Infirmary, 16 Alexander Parade, Glasgow G32 2ER Tel: 0141 211 4286 Fax: 0141 211 4991; 526 Anmesland Road, Glasgow G13 1YA Tel: 0141 954 1992 — MB ChB 1980 Glas.; BSc Glasgow 1979, MB ChB Glas. 1980; FRCS Glas 1984; MD 1989 Glasgow. (Glasgow) Regist. (Surg.) Roy. Infirm. Glas.; Cons. Colorectal Surg., Glas. Roy. Infirm.; Hon. Sen. Lect. Univ. of Glas. Socs: Assn. ColoProctol. of Gt. Britain & Irel. (Counc. Mem.); Assoc. of Surg.s; Brit. Soc. of Gastroenterol. Prev: Resid. Surgic. Off., St Marks Hosp. Lond.; Sen. Regist., Aberd. Teachg. Hosps.

MCKEE, Mrs Sarah Nicola Kirstin 26 Beaconsfield Road, London SE3 7LZ Tel: 020 8858 2959 Email: tomtom@pobox.com; 38 Circus Street, London SE10 8SN Tel: 020 8858 2959 Email: kirstin@pobox.com — MB BS 1996 Lond. (Roy. Free Lond.)

MCKEE, Shane Alexander Clinical Genetics Unit, Birmingham Women's Hospital, Edgbaston, Birmingham B15 2T Tel: 0121 627 2630 Fax: 0121 627 2618 Email: shane@dna1.dnet.co.uk; 1 Glenview Crescent, Glenville Road, Whiteabbey, Newtownabbey BT37 0TW Tel: 01232 364620 Email: shane@mckee.dnet.co.uk — MB BCh BAO 1994 Belf.; BSc (Med. Genetics) Belf. 1991; MRCP (Ed.) 1997. (Queen's Univ. Belf.) Specialist Regist. (Clin. Genetics) Birm. Wom.'s Hosp. Socs: BMA. Prev: SHO (Paediat.) Roy. Belf. Hosp. Sick Childr.; SHO (Gen. Med.) & Ho. Off. Roy. Vict. Hosp. Belf.

MCKEE, Thomas Alexander Department of Pathology, Division of Virology, Tennis Court Road, Cambridge CB2 1QP Tel: 01223 257027 Fax: 01223 336926 Email: tam@mole.bio.cam.ac.uk — MB ChB 1985 Glas.; PhD Glas. 1990, BSc 1982; MRCPath 1993. Lect. (Clin. Virol.) Univ. Camb.; Hon. Sen. Regist. (Clin. Virol.) Addenbrooke's Hosp. Camb. & PHLS. Prev: Post-Doctoral Fell. Scripps Research Foundat. San Diego, USA; MRC Train. Fell. Inst. Virol. Glas.

MCKEE, William Bernard Walton Surgery, 301 High Street, Walton, Felixstowe IP11 9QL Tel: 01394 278844 Fax: 01394 284438 Email: billy.mckee@grp-d83082.nhs.uk — MB BCh BAO 1982 Belf.; BSc (Joint Hons.) Belf. 1979; MRCGP 1988; DRCOG 1987.

MCKEE, William James Ernest, QHP (retired) Morningdale, 22A Bereweeke Avenue, Winchester SO22 6BH Tel: 01962 861369 — MB BChir Camb. 1955; MA Camb. 1955, MD 1963; MRCS Eng. LRCP Lond. 1955; FFCM 1974. Prev: Hon. Phys. to HM The Qu.

MCKEEVE, George Kinning Park Medical Centre, 42 Admiral Street, Glasgow G41 1HU Tel: 0141 429 0913 Fax: 0141 429 8491 — MB ChB 1982 Glas.

MCKEEVER, Christopher Stuart Taylor 7 St Lawrence Road, St. John's, Colchester CO4 4LG — MB BCh BAO 1975 Belf.

MCKEEVER, Gabrielle Teresa Mary Loy Medical Centre, 8 Loy Street, Cookstown BT80 8PE Tel: 028 8676 3030 Fax: 028 8676 1400; 12 Clagg. Place, Cookstown — MB BCh BAO 1986 Belf.; MRCGP 1992; T(GP) 1992.

MCKEEVER, Geraldine Hoo St Werburgh Practice, 98 Bells Lane, Hoo Street, Werburgh, Rochester ME3 9RA Tel: 01634 250523; 16 Thames Avenue, High Halstow, Rochester ME3 8TE Tel: 01634 253219 — MB BS 1980 Newc.; MRCGP 1985; DRCOG 1983.

MCKEEVER, Gerard Joseph Karl c/o 2nd Term SHOS, Royal Belfast Hospital for Sick Children, 180 - 184 Falls Road, Belfast BT12 6BE — MB BCh BAO 1994 Belf.

MCKEEVER, Mary Ann Monica (retired) — MB BCh BAO 1979 NUI; MRCGP 1984; DObst. RCOG 1982; DCH RCPI 1982.

MCKEEVER

MCKEEVER, Patricia Ann Department of Pathology, Clinical Sciences Building, Leicester Royal Infirmary, PO Box 65, Leicester LE2 7LX Tel: 0116 252 3228 Fax: 0116 252 3274; Woodcote Farm, Smisby Road, Smisby, Asby-de-la-Zouch LE65 2UH Tel: 01530 564896 — MB BCh BAO 1974 Belf.; MRCPath 1985. Sen. Lect. (Paediat. Path.) Leicester Univ.

MCKEIGUE, Paul Matthew Department of Epidemiol. & Population Health, London School of Hyg. & Trop. Med., London WC1E 7HT Tel: 020 7927 2312 Fax: 020 7580 6897; 52 Clapham Manor Street, London SW4 6DZ — MB BChir 1979 Camb.; PhD Lond. 1990, MSc 1984; FFPHM RCP (UK) 1995, M 1988. Reader (Metab. & Genetic Epidemiol.). Prev: Wellcome Research Fell. Univ. Coll. Lond.; Brit. Heart Foundat. Research Fell. Univ. Coll. Lond.

MCKEIGUE, Sarah Jane Uxbridge Road Surgery, 337 Uxbridge Road, Acton, London W3 9RA Tel: 020 8993 0912 — MB BS 1974 Lond.; MRCS Eng. LRCP Lond. 1974; DRCOG 1978; DCH Eng 1977. (Westminster) GP Lond.

MCKEITH, David Douglas Dr McElhone and Partners, Townhead Surgery, 6-8 High St., Irvine KA12 0AY Tel: 01294 273131 Fax: 01294 312832 — MB ChB 1979 Ed.; MRCGP 1983; DCCH RCP Ed. 1987; DRCOG 1983. Princip. GP Irvine.

MCKEITH, Professor Ian Grant Institute for Ageing Health, Wolfson Research centre, Newcastle General Hospital, Newcastle upon Tyne NE4 6BE Tel: 0191 273 8811 Fax: 0191 273 1156 Email: i.g.mckeith@ncl.ac.uk; Email: i.g.mckeith@ncl.ac.uk — MB BS 1977 Newc.; MD Newc. 1993; FRCPsych 1995, M 1982. Prof. Old Age Psychiat. Univ. Newc. Prev: MRC Clin. Scientist; Sen. Lect. & 1st Asst. (Psychiat.) Univ. Newc.

MACKEITH, James Alexander Culpin P.O.Box 20824, London SE22 8WS Tel: 020 7362 0100 Fax: 020 8693 4125 Email: jamesacmal@hotmail.com — MB BCh BAO 1965 Dub.; MA, MB BCh BAO Dub. 1965; FRCPsych. 1992, M 1972; DPM Eng. 1971. (T.C. Dub.) Emerit. Cons. Psychiat. Bethlem Roy & maudsley Hosps, S. Lond. and Maudsley NHS Trust. Prev: Cons. Psychiat. BRd.moor Hosp. Crowthorne; Regist. Bethlem Roy. & Maudsley Hosps. Lond. & Exchange Resid. John Hopkins Hosp.

MACKELL, Kathleen Anne Sheepcot Medical Centre, 80 Sheepcot Lane, Garston, Watford WD25 0EA Tel: 01923 672451 Fax: 01923 681404 — MB BS 1983 Newc.; DCH RCP Lond. 1988; DPD (Distinc.) Cardiff 1997. GP; Clin. Asst. (Dermat.) Watford Gen. Hosp.

MCKELLAR, Adrienne Kay Yorkleigh Surgery, 91 St. George's Road, Cheltenham GL50 3ED Tel: 06 835 4999; Tel: 01452 613676 — MB ChB 1994 Glas.; MRCGP 1998 (Edin.); DRCOG 1996. (Glas.) GP Principle, Cheltenham. Prev: GP City Med., Napier, New Zealand; Sen. Health Off. Ophth., Glas.; GP Regist., Connell, Argyll.

MACKELLAR, Barry Norminton Orchard House, 14 High St., Gravenhurst, Bedford MK45 4HY — LLM 1991 Wales; MB ChB Liverp. 1971; DObst RCOG 1974. Head Internat. Med. Servs. Med. Protec. Soc. Prev: Ho. Off. Roy. S.. Hosp. Liverp.; SHO Alder Hey Childr. Hosp. Liverp.; SHO Mill Rd. Matern. Hosp. Liverp.

MACKELLAR, Douglas Duncan Brown 41 Glenn Way, Shardlow, Derby DE72 2GZ Tel: 01332 792852 — MB ChB 1961 Glas.; MFHom 1975. Indep. Homoeop. Derby. Prev: Dispensing Phys. Glas. Homoeop. Disp.; SHO Glas. & W. Scotl. Neurosurg. Unit Killearn Hosp. Glas.; Ho. Phys. Stobhill Gen. Hosp. Glas.

MCKELLAR, Jack Barron Murdoch Primrose Cottage, Main St., Drymen, Glasgow G63 0BQ — MB ChB Glas. 1967; FRCA Eng. 1972. (Glas.) Cons. (Anaesth.) Stobhill Hosp. Glas. Socs: Assn. Anaesths. Prev: Sen. Regist. (Anaesth.) Vict. Infirm. Glas.

MCKELLAR, Nimmo James (retired) Flat 5/E, Southwood Place, Rosemount Avenue, Newton Mearns, Glasgow G77 5TN Tel: 0141 616 3380 — MB ChB Glas. 1949; DMRD Eng. 1956; Cons. Radiol. Roy. Infirm. Glas.

MCKELLICAN, James Fergusson 20 Kilnburn, Newport-on-Tay DD6 8DE Tel: 01382 665711 — MB ChB 1963 St. And.; MRCGP 1974; MICGP 1987. Clin. Asst. Drug Developm. (Scott.) Ltd. Ninewells Hosp. Dundee; Hon. Cons. Gen. Pract. Centre for Med. Educat. Univ. Dundee; Designated Med. Pract. Austral. & Canad. High Commiss. UK. Socs: BMA & ASME. Prev: GP Dundee; Lect. (Health Educat.) & Asst. Med. Off. Dundee Coll. of Educat.; Ho. Phys. Falkirk & Dist. Roy. Infirm.

MCKELVEY, Miss Audrey 1 Purdysburn Village, Belfast BT8 8LJ — MB BCh BAO 1995 Belf.; FRCSI.

MCKELVEY, Ian Alexander The Surgery, Trekenning Road, St Columb Major, St Columb TR9 6R Tel: 01637 880359 Fax: 01637 881482; St. Anthonys, St. Maurgan, Newquay TR8 4EU Tel: 01637 860665 — MB BS 1989 Lond.; MRCGP 1992; DRCOG 1992.

MCKELVEY, James Moorhead (retired) Saintfield Health Centre, Fairview, Saintfield, Ballynahinch BT24 7AD Tel: 028 9751 0575 Fax: 028 9751 1895 — MB BCh BAO Belf. 1958. GP Advisor Down/Lisburn Trust.

MCKELVEY, John Cullybackey Health Centre, Tober Park, Cullybackey, Ballymena BT42 1NR Tel: 028 2588 0505 Fax: 028 2588 1916 — MB BCh BAO 1947 Belf.; MB BCh BAO (2nd Cl. Hons.) Belf. 1947. (Belf.) Socs: BMA. Prev: Ho. Off. Roy. Vict. Hosp. Belf.

MCKELVEY, Mr John Alan William (retired) Trelawney Heights, 11 Epworth Close, Truro TR1 1UP Tel: 01872 270565 — MB BCh BAO Belf. 1955; MD Belf. 1962; FRCS Eng. 1973; DCH Eng. 1959; DObst RCOG 1957. Prev: Cons. Ophth. Surg. Roy. Cornw. Hosp.

MCKELVEY, John Knox 42 Shelling Hill Road, Cullybackey, Ballymena BT42 1NR Tel: 01266 880159 — MB BCh BAO 1977 Belf.; DRCOG 1979.

MCKELVEY, Maighread Ann c/o Medical Staffing Department, Altnagelvin Hospital, Londonderry BT47 6SB; 24 Garden City, Londonderry BT48 7SN — MB BCh BAO 1992 NUI.

MCKELVEY, Robert David Cullybackey Health Centre, Tober Park, Cullybackey, Ballymena BT42 1NR Tel: 028 2588 0505 Fax: 028 2588 1916; 75 Hillmount Road, Cullybackey, Ballymena BT42 1NZ Tel: 01266 881345 — MB BCh BAO 1978 Belf.; MRCGP 1984; DRCOG 1981; DTM & H Liverp. 1980.

MCKELVEY, Mr Samuel Thomas Donnan 31 Harberton Park, Belfast BT9 6TX Tel: 01232 665356 — MCh Belf. 1971, MB BCh BAO 1962; FRCS Eng. 1968; FRCS Ed. 1967; DObst RCOG 1965. Cons. Surg. Ulster Hosp. Belf. Socs: Assn. Surgs. Gt. Brit. & Irel.; Brit. Soc. Gastroenterol. Prev: 1st Asst. (Surg.) Univ. Newc.; Sen. Lect. in Surg. Qu. Univ. Belf.

MCKELVEY, Thomas Patrick Hubert, Brigadier late RAMC Retd. 9 Perifield, Croxted Road, West Dulwich, London SE21 8NG Tel: 020 8670 8089 — MB BChir 1937 Camb.; MA Camb. 1938, MB BChir 1937; FRCP Lond. 1971, M 1954. (Camb. & Char. Cross) Socs: Fell. Roy. Soc. Med.; BMA. Prev: Dir. Army Med. & Cons. Phys. to the Army; Hon. Phys. to HM the Qu.; Cons. Phys. Far E. Land Forces.

MCKELVIE, Mr George Bennett, OBE (retired) 18 Airlie Court, Auchterarder PH3 1SA Tel: 01764 663156 Fax: 01764 664120 Email: gbmckelvie@aol.com — MB ChB 1952 Glas.; FRCS Glas. 1980; FRCS Ed. 1958. Cons. Urol. Forth Valley HB. Prev: Cons. Surg. & Urol. Stirlingsh. Area.

MCKELVIE, James Donald The Medical Centre, Feorlin Way, Gareloch Head, Helensburgh G84 0GD Tel: 01436 810370 — MB BCh BAO 1986 NUI; MA St. And. 1976; LRCPI & LM, LRCSI & LM 1986; DFFP 1993. (RCSI) Scott. Opera Med. Advisor; Team Doctor Lond. Scott. RFC.

MCKELVIE, Karen Park Flat 5, 11 Abbotsford Road, Blundellsands, Liverpool L23 6UX — MB ChB 1987 Glas.; BSc (Hons.) Glas. 1984. Staff Grade (A & E) Ninewells Hosp, Dundee. Prev: Clin. Asst. (A & E) Whiston Hosp. Prescot.; SHO (Gen. Surg.) Arrowe Pk. Hosp. Wirral; Reg. Med. Halton Hosp. Halton.

MCKELVIE, Margaret Gibson (retired) Silent Springs, Nosterfield, Bedale DL8 2QW Tel: 01677 470929 — MB ChB St. And. 1965. Prev: Ho. Surg. Hillingdon Hosp.

MCKELVIE, Mr Peter (retired) 9 Farm Way, Northwood HA6 3EG Tel: 01923 823544 — MB ChB 1956 Manch.; MD Manch. 1970, ChM 1964; FRCS Ed. 1988; FRCS (Otol.) Eng. 1962; DLO Eng. 1962. Prev: Cons. ENT Surg. Lond. Hosp. & St. Bart. Hosp.

MCKEMEY, Michael John Purton Surgery, High Street, Purton, Swindon SN5 4BD Tel: 01793 770207 Fax: 01793 772662; Mayflower House, Charlham Lane, Down Ampney, Cirencester GL7 5RQ Tel: 01793 751780 — MB BS 1982 Lond.; MRCGP 1987; DGM RCP Lond. 1986; DCH RCP Glas. 1986; DRCOG 1985. (St. Thos.) Clin. Asst. (Ophth.) P.ss Margt Hosp. Swindon. Socs: Christ. Med. Fell.sh. Prev: SHO (Ophth.) Mid. Counties Eye Infirm. Wolverhampton; Trainee GP/SHO Aylesbury VTS.

MCKENDRICK, Anderson Dan Carnoustie Medical Group, The Health Centre, Dundee Street, Carnoustie DD7 7RB Tel: 01241 859888 Fax: 01241 852080; 41 Maule Street, Carnoustie DD7 6EU

Tel: 01241 859594 — MB ChB 1971 Ed.; FRCGP 1992, M 1975. (Edinburgh) Hon. Lect. (Gen. Pract.) Univ. Dundee. Prev: Assoc. Regional Adviser (Gen. Pract.) E. Scotl.; Trainee GP Bristol VTS; Hon. Off. Leith Hosp. Edin.

MCKENDRICK, Charles Stewart Flat 2, No. 1, Ibbotson's Lane, Liverpool L17 1AL Tel: 0151 724 6339 — MB BChir 1943 Camb.; MA, MD Camb. 1955; FRCP Lond. 1967, M 1948. (Camb. & Liverp.) JP. Socs: Assn. Phys. & Brit. Cardiac Soc. Prev: Sen. Phys. Liverp. Regional Cardiac Centre; Dir. of Cardiol. Studies Univ. Liverp.; Emerit. Phys. Roy. Liverp. Hosp.

MCKENDRICK, Claire Flat 2/2, Crow Road, Glasgow G11 7LA — MB ChB 1997 Glas.

MCKENDRICK, Fowler Yates (retired) Well House, 26 Croftway, Sherburn-in-Elmet, Leeds LS25 6BW Tel: 01977 682373 — MB ChB 1938 Glas. Prev: Clin. Asst. (Orthop.) Pontefract & Castleford Dist. Hosps.

MCKENDRICK, George Donald William (retired) Goatsmoor Hall, Goatsmoor Lane, Stock, Ingatestone CM4 9RS Tel: 01277 840394 Fax: 01277 840394 Email: dmckendrick@freeserve.co.uk — BM BCh Oxf. 1943; MA Oxf. 1943, BA (Hons.) 1939; FRCP Lond. 1967, M 1950. Med. Columnist Saga Magazine; Smallpox Cons. DHSS. Prev: Cons. Phys. St. Ann's Hosp. Lond.

MCKENDRICK, Helen Margaret Vauxhall Health Centre, Limekiln Lane, Liverpool L5 8XR Tel: 0151 298 2246 — MB ChB 1986 Liverp.

MCKENDRICK, John Forrigan, Newnham Hill, Henley-on-Thames RG9 5TJ Tel: 01491 641250 Fax: 01491 641250 Email: forrigan@aol.com — MB ChB Ed. 1959; FRCGP 1981, M 1973; DObst RCOG 1962. Socs: Fell. Roy. Med. Soc. Edin. Prev: Ho. Phys. Roodlands Gen. Hosp. Haddington; Ho. Surg. Roy. Edin. Hosp. Sick Childr.; Ho. Surg. (O & G) Bangour Gen. Hosp. Broxburn.

MCKENDRICK, Lorna Flat 1, 9 Clarendon Place, Glasgow G20 7PZ — MB ChB 1994 Glas.

MCKENDRICK, Malcolm Niall 1 Campfield Villas, The Avenue, Truro TR1 1HR — MB ChB 1990 Aberd.; DCH RCP Lond. 1995. SHO (O & G) Roy. Cornw. Hosps. Treliske. Prev: SHO (Paediat., ENT & Med.) Roy. Cornw. Hosp. Truro; SHO (A & E) & Ho. Phys. Roy. Cornw. Hosp. Truro; Ho. Off. (Surg.) Dumfries & Galloway Roy. Infirm.

MCKENDRICK, Michael William Department of Infection & Tropical Medicine, Sheffield Teaching Hospitals, NHS Trust, Royal Hallamshire Hospital, Sheffield S10 2JF Tel: 0114 271 3561 Fax: 0114 275 3061 — MB BS 1972 Lond.; FRCP Lond. 1989; MRCP (UK) 1975; FRCP 1998 Glasgow. (Middlx.) Cons. Phys. (Infec. Dis.and Trop. Med.) Roy. Hallamsh. Hosp. Sheff.; Hon. Sen. Clin. Lect. Univ. Sheff. Socs: Brit. Soc. for Antimicrobial Chemother.; Infec. Dis.s Soc. of Amer.; Europ. Soc. for Clin. MicroBiol. and Infec. Dis.s. Prev: Sen. Regist. (Infec. Dis.) E. Birm. Hosp.; Regist. (Med.) Birm. Gen. Hosp. & Ipswich Hosp.

MCKENDRICK, Olive Mary (retired) Flat 2, 1 Ibbotson's Lane, Liverpool L17 1AL Tel: 0151 724 6339 — MB ChB Liverp. 1947. Hon. Research Assoc. (Child Health) Univ. Liverp. Prev: SCMO (Comm. Child Health) Liverp. AHA.

MCKENDRICK, Thomas (retired) 87 Woodlands Road, Aigburth, Liverpool L17 0AN Tel: 0151 727 2700 — MB BS 1948 Lond.; FRCP Lond. 1974, M 1958; MRCS Eng. LRCP Lond. 1949; DCH Eng. 1954; DPH Lond. 1955. Hon. Cons. Paediat. Roy. Liverp. Childr. Hosp. Alder Hey Br. Prev: Ho. Phys. (Childr.) Univ. Coll. Hosp.

MCKENNA, Alison Mary Bondgate Surgery, Infirmary Close, Alnwick NE66 2NL — MB ChB 1976 Dundee.

MCKENNA, Anthony The Surgery, Tennant Street, Stockton-on-Tees TS18 2AT Tel: 01642 613331 Fax: 01642 675612; 5 The Poplars, Wolviston, Billingham TS22 5LY — MB BS 1980 Lond.; BSc (Pharm.) Lond. 1977, MB BS 1980; MRCGP 1986; DRCOG 1982. (Univ. Coll. Hosp.) GP Trainer Cleveland VTS. Prev: Trainee GP Medway VTS; Ho. Surg. Whipps Cross Hosp. Lond.; Ho. Phys. Univ. Coll. Hosp. Lond.

MCKENNA, Barry Joseph The Petersgate Medical Centre, 99 Amersall Road, Scawthorpe, Doncaster DN5 9PQ Tel: 01302 390490; 5 Ellers Road, Bessacarr, Doncaster DN4 7BE — MB ChB 1978 Sheff.; MRCGP 1982; DRCOG 1981. Princip. GP Scawthorpe & Bentley; Police Surg. Doncaster. Prev: Trainee GP Doncaster VTS.

MACKENNA, Beverly Robertson (retired) 3 Seafield Avenue, Bearsden, Glasgow G61 3LB Tel: 0141 942 4588 — MB ChB 1956 Glas.; PhD Glas. 1962, MB ChB 1956; FRCP Glas. 1992; MRCP (UK) 1990. Prev: Sen. Lect. (Physiol.) Glas. Univ.

MCKENNA, Charles Joseph Dept. Of Cardiology, John Radcliffe Hospital, Oxford OX3 9DT; 39 Lenaghan Park, Belfast BT8 7JB — MB ChB 1988 Ed.; MD 1999; MRCP 1991 (UK); BSc 1984. Internat. Fell. Socs: RCP Edinburgh; AHA Scientif. Counc.; Brit. Cardiac Interconvention. Prev: Mayo. Clinic - Internat. Fell.

MCKENNA, Clare Louise Department of Psychological Medicine, Hammersmith Hospital, Du Cane Road, London W12 0NN — MB BS 1976 Melbourne; MB BS Melbourne; BA Melbourne 1994; FRANZCP 1988. Socs: Eur. Soc. Communicative Psychother.

MCKENNA, Daniel John Joseph 88A Malone Road, Belfast BT9 5HP — MB BCh BAO 1993 Belf.

MCKENNA, Deirdre Marie Pathology Dept, Chesterfield and North Derbyshire Royal Hospital, NHS Trust, Calow, Chesterfield S44 5BL Tel: 01246 277271 Ext: 2260 Fax: 01246 552536; Wheat Hay, Shatton, Bamford, Hope Valley S33 0BG — MB BCh BAO 1983 Dub.; FRCPath 1999; MRCPI 1985; MRCPath 1990. (Trinity Coll. Dubl.) Cons. Histopathol. Chesterfield & N. Derbysh. NHS Trust; Hon. Clin. Lect. Univ. Sheff. Med. Sch. Socs: Path. Soc.; Brit. Div. Internat. Acad. Path.; Brit. Soc. Gastroenterol. Prev: Lect. (Pathol.) Univ. Sheff.; Lect. (Pathol.) Trinity Coll. Dubl.

MCKENNA, Mr Douglas Murray Department of Obstetrics & Gynaecology, Salisbury District Hospital, Salisbury SP2 8BJ Tel: 01722 425212 Fax: 01722 325373 — MB ChB 1977 Ed.; BSc Ed. 1973; FRCS Ed. 1988; MRCOG 1983. (Ed.) Cons. O & G Salisbury Dist. Hosp.; Trustee Salisbury Hospice Care Trust; Mem. Wessex Gyn. Oncol. Gp. Socs: Salisbury Med. Soc.; Brit. Soc. Cervical Cytol. & Path. Prev: Sen. Regist. (O & G) Univ. Hosp. Wales Cardiff; Regist. (O & G) P.ss Anne Hosp. Soton.; SHO (O & G) Roy. Infirm. Edin.

MCKENNA, Edward Andrew 20 Glasgow Road, Uddingston, Glasgow G71 7AS — MB ChB 1962 Glas. (Glas.)

MCKENNA, Frank Trafford General Hospital, Davyhulme, Manchester M41 5SL Tel: 0161 746 2395 Fax: 0161 746 2399; 87 Palatine Road, Manchester M20 3JQ Tel: 0161 445 9434 — MB ChB 1976 Sheff.; MD Sheff. 1989; FRCP Lond. 1994; MRCP (UK) 1981; MRCS Eng. LRCP Lond. 1976. Cons. Phys. & Rheum. Trafford Gen. Hosp. Manch.; Hon. Clin. Lect. Univ. Manch.

MCKENNA, Geraldine Lucy The Group Surgery, 257 North Queen Street, Belfast BT15 1HS Tel: 028 9074 8317 Fax: 028 9075 4438; 10 Rosemary Park, Belfast BT9 6RF Tel: 01232 664791 — MB ChB BAO 1984 NUI; DMH Belf. 1991; DObst RCPI 1989; DCH RCPSI 1988. GP Princip. Lagan Valley Hosp. Lisburn. Socs: BMA. Prev: SHO (Paediat.) Roy. Belf. Hosp. Sick Childr.; SHO (Med. & O & G) S. Tyrone Hosp. Dungannon.

MCKENNA, John Bernard Brook House, Hovingham, York YO62 4JX — MB BCh BAO 1940 NUI. (Univ. Coll. Cork)

MCKENNA, John Francis 14 Slievemoyne Park, Belfast BT15 5GZ — MB BCh BAO 1960 Belf.; FRCP Lond. 1992; FRCPI 1991; FRCP Ed. 1990; FFCM 1979, M 1974; FFCMI 1978; DPH Belf. 1966. (Belf.) Prev: Chief Med. Off. DHSS N. Irel.; Chiet Admin. Med. Off. EHSS Bd.; Chief Admin. Med, Off. NHSS Bd. Princip. Asst.

MCKENNA, John Fraser Baslow Road Surgery, 148-150 Baslow Road, Totley, Sheffield S17 4DR Tel: 0114 236 9957 Fax: 0114 262 0756 — MB ChB 1974 Sheff.; BSc Lond. 1969; FFA RCS Eng. 1979; DRCOG 1977.

MCKENNA, John Gordon c/o GU Medicine Department, Raigmore Hospital, Inverness IV2 3UJ Tel: 01463 704202 Fax: 01463 705770; Bhraclach, Glaickmore, Tore, Muir of Ord IV6 7SD — MB ChB 1983 Glas.; BSc (Hons.) Glas. 1980, MB ChB 1983; MRCP (UK) 1986; FRCP 1996; FACSHP 1992. Cons. Phys. (Genito-Urin. Med.) Inverness. Prev: Sen. Regist. (Genito-Urin. Med.) Roy. Infirm. Edin.

MCKENNA, John Terence Guild Lodge, Guild Park, Whittingham Lane, Goosnargh, Preston PR3 2AZ Tel: 01772 406617 Fax: 01772 406629 — MB BS 1986 Lond.; BSc Lond. 1982; MRCPsych 1991; MA Manchester 2000. Cons. Forens. Psychiat. (Rehabil.) Guild Lodge Preston. Prev: Sen. Regist. (Forens. Psychiat.) Prestwich Hosp. Manch.

MCKENNA

MCKENNA, Kevin The Bondgate Practice, Bondgate Surgery, Infirmary Close, Alnwick NE66 2NL Tel: 01665 510888 Fax: 01665 510581 — MB BS 1974 Newc.; MRCGP 1986.

MCKENNA, Kevin Eamon 130 Newry Road, Banbridge BT32 3NB — MB BCh BAO 1985 Belf.; MRCP (UK) 1988. Sen. (Dermat.) Roy. Vict. Hosp. Belf. Socs: BMA & Irish Assn. Dermat.

MCKENNA, Kieran John Top Right, 28 Bellwood St., Glasgow G41 3ES — MB ChB 1989 Aberd.

MCKENNA, Margaret Anne 829 Chorley Old Road, Bolton BL1 5SL — MB ChB 1980 Liverp.

MCKENNA, Margaret Jean Bhraclach, Glackmore by Tore, Muir of Ord IV6 7SD — MB ChB 1981 Glas.; MRCGP 1985.

MCKENNA, Margaret Mary Tower Road, Sheffield S2 3RE; Wetherlaw, 5 Brutten Way, Mitchell Gardens, Chard TA20 2HB Tel: 01460 63348 — MB ChB 1987 Liverp.; MRCGP 1993.

MCKENNA, Margaret Philomena Baillieston Health Centre, 20 Muirside Road, Baillieston, Glasgow G69 7AD Tel: 0141 531 8050 Fax: 0141 531 8067 — MB ChB 1962 Glas.; DObst RCOG 1964. (Glas.) Socs: BMA & M-C Soc. Glas. Prev: Ho. Surg. E. Gen. Hosp. Glas. & Ayrsh. Centr. Hosp. Matern. Sect. Irvine; Ho. Phys. Roy. Infirm. Glas.

MCKENNA, Mary Louise (retired) — MB ChB 1978 Sheff.

MCKENNA, Mary Philomena 59 Locksley Park, Finaghy, Belfast BT10 0AS — MB BCh BAO 1975 NUI; FFA RCSI 1986; DCH RCPSI 1980.

MCKENNA, Michael Joseph (retired) 4 Newlands Road, Lytham St Annes FY8 4AU Tel: 01253 734303 — MB BCh BAO 1950 Belf.; DObst RCOG 1953. Prev: Ho. Surg. City Hosp. Belf.

MCKENNA, Michael Joseph 24 Linden Avenue, Altrincham WA15 8HA — MB ChB 1992 Glas. SHO (Orthop.) Vict. Infirm. Glas.

MCKENNA, Michael Joseph Francis 43 Norwood Grove, Beverley HU17 9HR — MB ChB 1996 Leeds.

MCKENNA, Michael Patrick 40 Denewood Park, Belfast BT11 8FS — MB BCh BAO 1992 Belf.

MCKENNA, Miriam Agnes, Lt.-Col. RAMC Retd. (retired) 9 Keepers Wood, Chichester PO19 4XU Tel: 01243 528665 — MB BS Lond. 1963; MRCS Eng. LRCP Lond. 1963; FFA RCS Eng. 1975; DObst RCOG 1968. Hon. Cons. (Palliat. Med.) Roy. W. Sussex Trust & Chichester Priority Care Sers. NHS Trust. Prev: Med. Dir. Macmillan Serv. King Edwd. VII Hosp. Midhurst.

MCKENNA, Moira Fay Ferry Road Health Centre, Ferry Road, Dingwall IV15 9QS Tel: 01349 863034 Fax: 01349 862022; Assynt Mill, Glenglass, Evanton, Dingwall IV16 9XW Tel: 01349 830444 — MB ChB 1990 Ed.; BSc Ed. 1988, MB ChB 1990; MRCGP 1994; DRCOG 1992. Prev: Trainee GP Highland HB; Ho. Off. (Surg.) St. John's Hosp. Livingston; Ho. Off. (Med.) Raigmore Hosp. Inverness.

MCKENNA, Patrick Hugh Lineside Health Centre, 10A Lineside, Coalisland, Dungannon BT71 4LP Tel: 028 8774 8555 — MB BCh BAO 1966 NUI; MRCGP 1972. (Univ. Coll. Dub.) Socs: BMA. Prev: Cas. Off. & Res. Surg. Off. Mater Infirm. Hosp. Belf.

MCKENNA, Mr Patrick Joseph Abbey Cottage, Horton, Wimborne BH21 7JA — MB BS 1993 Lond.; FRCS Eng. 1997. (UMDS London) Specialist Regist. in Trauma & Orthop. Surg., Wessex Rotat. Prev: SHO Plastic Surg., St Geo.s Hosp., Tooting, Lond.; Sen. SHO Orthop. Mayday Univ. Hosp., Croydon; SHO Gen. Surg., Chelsea & W.minster Hosp., Lond.

MCKENNA, Paul Clinical Chemistry Department, North Tyneside General Hospital, Rake Lane, North Shields NE29 8NH Tel: 0191 293 2546 Fax: 0191 293 2796 — MB BS 1984 Lond.; PhD Camb. 1980, MA 1980; MRCP (UK) 1987; MRCPath 1991. (London) Cons. Chem. Path. N.umbria Healthcare NHS Trust. Prev: Sen. Regist. (Clin. Chem.) Nottm. Hosps.; Regist. (Clin. Biochem. & Metab. Med.) Roy. Vict. Infirm. Newc.; SHO (Gen. Med.) Freeman Hosp. & Newc. Gen. Hosp. Newc.

MCKENNA, Peter John Fulburn Hospital, Cambridge CB1 5EF Tel: 01223 218814 Fax: 01223 218638 — MB ChB 1977 Birm.; BA 1974; MA 1982. (Birm) Cons. Psych.Fulburn Hosp.Cambs.

MCKENNA, Peter Joseph Sawston Health Centre, Link Road, Sawston, Cambridge CB2 4LB Tel: 01223 832711 Fax: 01223 836096; Ram House, 100 High St, Linton, Cambridge CB1 6JT — MB BS 1969 Lond.; MRCS Eng. LRCP Lond. 1969; MRCGP 1976. (St Barts.)

***MCKENNA, Ronan** 52 Holtby Road, Moston, Manchester M9 4AR — MB ChB 1994 Manch.

MCKENNA, Sarah Mary Michelle 35, Deramore Drive, Belfast BT9 3JR Tel: 01232 666183 Email: sarahmckenna@doctors.net.uk; 35, Deramore Drive, Belfast BT9 3JR Tel: 01232 666183 Email: sarahmckenna@doctors.net.uk — MB BCh BAO 1991 Belf.; MRCP 1993. SpR Med. Oncol.

MCKENNA, Terence Dominic 829 Chorley Old Road, Bolton BL1 5SL Tel: 01204 43737 — MB BCh BAO 1948 NUI. (Cork) Socs: Bolton Med. Soc. & BMA. Prev: Ho. Surg. City Hosp. York; Ho. Phys. Roy. Halifax Infirm. & Bolton Roy. Infirm.

MCKENNA, Una Michele 25 Jordanstown Road, Newtownabbey BT37 0QD — MB BCh BAO 1990 Belf.

MCKENNA, Professor William John Department of Cardiological Sciences, St. George's Hospital Medical School, Cranmer Terrace, London SW17 0RE Tel: 020 8725 5913 Fax: 020 8682 0944 Email: wmckenna@sghms.ac.uk; Flat 2, 23 Fitzjohn's Avenue, London NW3 5JY Tel: 020 7794 9704 Fax: 020 7431 7244 — MD 1974 CM McGill Univ. Montreal; BA Yale 1969; DSc 2001 Univ. of Lond. (McGill Uni.) BHF Prof. of Molecular Cardiovasc. Sci, St. Geprge's Hosp. Med. Sch.; Hon. Cons. Cardiol. St Geo. Hosp; Hon. Cons. Cardiol. Hosp. For Sick Childr. Gt. Ormond St. Lond. Socs: Fell. Amer. Coll. Cardiol.; Fell. Roy. Coll. Physic.; Founding Fell. Euro. Soc. Cardiol. Prev: Reader, Sugden Sen. Lect. & Hon. Cons. Cardiol. St. Geo. Hosp. Med. Sch. Lond.; Prof. Cardiac Med. St. Geo. Hosp. Med. Sch. Lond.; Hosp. Med. Sch., Lond.

MCKENNELL, Jack Tenter Croft, Savile Park Road, Halifax HX1 2ET Tel: 01422 52866 — MB ChB 1944 Leeds; MD Leeds 1947, MB ChB 1944; MRCGP 1973. (Leeds) Socs: Leeds M-C Soc & Bradford M-C Soc. Prev: Sen. Res. Med. Off. Gen. Hosp. Halifax; Ho. Phys. Gen. Infirm. Leeds; Res. Med. Off. City Hosp. Derby.

MACKENNEY, Paul James 93/9 Brunswick Street, Edinburgh EH7 5HR — MB ChB 1993 Ed.

MACKENNEY, Mr Robert Paul Cedars, The Avenue, Bushey, Watford WD23 2LL — MB ChB 1969 Ed.; BSc Ed. 1966, MB ChB 1969; FRCS Ed. 1974. Cons. (Orthop. Surg.) Watford Gen. Hosp. & St. Vincent's Hosp.

MCKENNING, Stephen Thomas The Surgery, 194 Allaway Avenue, Paulsgrove, Portsmouth PO6 4HJ Tel: 023 9237 7006 Fax: 023 9237 4263 — MB ChB 1972 Aberd.

MCKENNY, John Gregory Alvaston Medical Centre, 14 Boulton Lane, Alvaston, Derby DE24 0GE Tel: 01332 571322; Holly Lodge, 567A Burton Road, Littleover, Derby DE23 6FW Tel: 01332 760304 — MB BCh BAO 1950 Belf.; DTM & H. Eng. 1955; DPH Belf. 1954; DObst RCOG 1952.

MCKENNY, Niall Vincent Limavady Health Centre, Scroggy Road, Limavady BT49 0NA — MB BCh BAO Belf. 1968.

MCKENZIE, Aeron Anne Yew Tree Farm, Bridgewater Road, Highbridge TA9 4HP — MB ChB 1993 Bristol.

MCKENZIE, Mr Alan (retired) 1 Hillside Road, Heswall, Wirral CH60 0BJ Tel: 0151 342 4043 — MB ChB 1934 Glas.; FRCS Ed. 1938.

MACKENZIE, Alan George Lightburn Medical Centre, 930 Corntyne Road, Glasgow G32 6NB Tel: 0141 778 0111 Fax: 0141 778 0143; 930 Carntyne Road, Glasgow G32 6ND Tel: 0141 778 0111 Fax: 0141 778 0143 — MB ChB 1982 Glas. Prev: SHO (O & G) Stobill Hosp. Glas.; Trainee GP Craigshill Livingston; SHO (A & E) CrossHo. Hosp. Kilmarnock.

MCKENZIE, Alan Kenneth 5 Glebe Avenue, Kings Park, Stirling FK8 2HZ Email: alanmck@dotlink.v-net.com — MB ChB 1987 Glas.; MRCP (UK) 1992. Sen. Regist. (Geriat. Med.) Glas. Roy. Infirm.; Sen. Regist. (Geriat. & Gen. Med.) Glas. Roy. Infirm. Socs: Train. Rep. Scott. Br. Brit. Geriat. Soc. Prev: Career Regist. Rotat. (Geriat. Med.) Vict. Geriat. Unit Glas.

MACKENZIE, Alasdair David Colin The Surgery, High Street, Thorpe-le-Soken, Clacton-on-Sea CO16 0DY Tel: 01255 861850 Fax: 01255 860330 — MB BS 1975 Lond.; MRCS Eng. LRCP Lond. 1975. Prev: Trainee GP Kettering VTS.

MACKENZIE, Alexander (retired) Lismore, Foxcover Lane, Sunderland SR3 3TQ Tel: 0191 528 1085 — MB ChB 1941 St. And.; BSc St. And. 1938; FRCPath 1963. Prev: Cons. Pathol. Sunderland Hosp. Gp.

MACKENZIE, Alexander Gavin (retired) Bridge End House, Caldbeck, Wigton CA7 8EW Tel: 0169 74 78284 — MRCS Eng. LRCP Lond. 1944; BA Camb. 1942. Prev: Resid. Med. Off. & Cas. Off. St. And. Hosp. Dollis Hill.

MACKENZIE, Alexander John (retired) 20 Arnhall Drive, Dundee DD2 1LU Tel: 01382 665922 — MB ChB 1955 St. And.

MACKENZIE, Alexander Robertson The Infection Unit, Aberdeen Royal Hospitals NHS Trust, Foresterhill, Aberdeen AB25 2ZP Tel: 01224 681818 Fax: 01224 685307 Email: air.mackenzie@abdn.ac.uk; 67 Leggart Avenue, Aberdeen AB12 5UP Tel: 01224 873264 Email: a.r.mackenzie@abdn.ac.uk — MB ChB 1989 Aberd.; BMedBiol. Aberd. 1988; MRCP (UK) 1992; DTM & H Liverp. 1993. (Univ. Aberd.) Specialist Regist. (Infec. & Trop. Med.) Aberd. Roy. Infirm.; Clin. Lectyrer Univ. Aberd. Socs: BMA; Collegiate Mem. RCP Edin.; Fell. Roy. Soc. Trop. Med. & Hyg. Prev: Regist. (Med.) Groote Schuur Hosp. Cape Town, S. Afr.; Regist. (Microbiol. & Med.) Middlemore Hosp. Auckland, NZ; SHO (Med.) Aberd. Roy. Infirm. Aberd.

MACKENZIE, Alexander Stewart 95 Devonshire Road, Aberdeen AB10 6XP Tel: 01224 322543 — MB ChB 1959 Aberd. Examg. Med. Practitioner Benefits Agency Med. Servs. Aberd. Socs: (Counc. & Ex-Pres.) Aberd. M-C Soc. Prev: Area Med. Adviser Benefits Agency Med. Servs. Aberd.; Regional Med. Off. S.H.H.D.; GP Banff.

MACKENZIE, Alexandra Mary 46 Ravenswood Drive, Glasgow G41 3UH; Bridgeton Health Centre, 201 Abercromby St, Glasgow G40 2DA Tel: 0141 531 6620 Fax: 0141 531 6626 — MB ChB 1981 Manch.; BSc (Med Sci.) St. And. 1978; MRCGP 1986; DRCOG 1984.

MCKENZIE, Alfred Wilson (retired) 50 Bracondale, Norwich NR1 2AP Tel: 01603 623575 — MB ChB Ed. 1955; FRCP Lond. 1975, M 1959. Prev: Cons. Dermat. Norf. & Norwich Hosp.

MCKENZIE, Alisdair 9 Duddingston Crescent, Edinburgh EH15 3AS — MB ChB 1975 Ed.

MACKENZIE, Alison Jane Burlington House, Sefton Health Authority, Burlington House, Crosby Road North, Liverpool L22 0QB Tel: 0151 920 5056 Fax: 0151 920 1035 Email: alison.mackenzie@sefton-ha.nhs.uk — MB ChB 1989 Bristol; MPH Birm. 1997; MFPHM 1999. (Univ. of Bris.) Cons. In Pub. Hlth. Med. Sefton & Liverp. Hlth. Auth. Liverp. Socs: Fac. Of Pub. Health Med.; Brit. Med. Assoc.; UK Pub. Hlth. Assn. Prev: Sen. Regist. (Pub. Health Med.) NW Pub. Health Train. Scheme; SHO (Pub. Health Med.) Som. HA; Regist. (Gen. Med. & ITU) Goldcoast Hosp. Qu.sland, Austral.

MACKENZIE, Alistair Tigh An Rudha, Plockton IV52 8TL — MB BS 1943 Durh.; FFA RCS Eng. 1953; DA Eng. 1948. (Durh.) Prev: Cons. Anaesth. Roy. Vict. Infirm. Newc.; 1st Asst. in Anaesth. Dept. Anaesth. King's Coll. Univ. Durh.

MACKENZIE, Alistair Anthony James Ship Street Surgery, Ship Street, East Grinstead RH19 4EE Tel: 01342 325959 Fax: 01342 314681 Email: alistair.mackenzie@gp-h82008.nhs.uk — MB BS 1979 Lond.; MRCGP 1984; DRCOG 1983; DCH Glas. 1982. (Char. Cross) GP Partnership with Fisher, Bellamy, Hill, Berkovitch & Byrne. Prev: Trainee GP Torbay VTS.

MCKENZIE, Alistair Graham Department of Anaesthetics, Royal Infirmary of Edinburgh, Lauriston Place, Edinburgh EH3 9YW Tel: 0131 536 1000 Fax: 0131 536 3672; 9 Craiglockhart Avenue, Craiglockhart, Edinburgh EH14 1HN Tel: 0131 443 5487 — LRCP LRCS 1982 Ed.; MB ChB Zimbabwe 1982; Glas. 1982; FCAnaesth 1990. (Univ. Zimbabwe) Cons. (Anaesth.) Roy. Infirm. Ed. & P.ss Margt. Rose Orthop. Hosp. Ed. Socs: BMA; Counc. Mem. Hist. of Anaesth. Soc.; Assn. Anaesths. - Hon. Librarian. Prev: Cons. (Anaesth.) E. Gen. Hosp. Edin.; Cons. Anaesth. Harare & Parirenyatwa Hosps. Harare, Zimbabwe; Hon. Lect. (Anaesth.) Univ. Zimbabwe.

MACKENZIE, Alistair Grant The James Cochrane Practice, Maude Street, Kendal LA9 4QE Tel: 01539 722124 Fax: 01539 734995; Castlesteads, Oxenholme, Kendal LA9 7PR Tel: 01539 732613 — MB ChB 1979 Ed.; BSc Ed. 1976; MRCGP 1984; DRCOG 1985; DCH RCP Lond. 1983; Dip. Occ. Med. 1996. (Edinburgh) Hosp. Pract. (Obstet. & Gyn.) W.moreland Gen. Hosp. Kendal; Clin. Asst. (Psychiat.) W.moreland Gen. Hosp. Kendal; Clin. Asst. (A & E) W.moreland Gen. Hosp. Kendal; Med. Off. Axa/Provincal Insur.; LMC Vice-Chairm. Prev: Med. Underwriter Scott. Provident.

MACKENZIE, Alistair Ian (retired) 2 Lanark Road, Carluke ML8 4HD Tel: 01555 772145 — MB ChB 1944 Glas.; FFA RCS Eng. 1955; DA Eng. 1946. Prev: Cons. Anaesth. Law Hosp, Carluke.

MCKENZIE, Andrew Ian 172 Whitham Road, Sheffield S10 2SR Tel: 0114 266 2112 Fax: 0114 268 4071; 48 Ribblesdale Drive, Ridgeway, Sheffield S12 3XE Tel: 0151 677 1625 — MB ChB 1977 Sheff.; Advanced Diploma in Occupational Medicine 1999 Manchester University. Indep. GP Sheff.; Med. Off. to various companies. Socs: Soc. Occupat. Med. Prev: Clin. Asst. (Orthop.) N.. Gen. Hosp.; Med. Off. Sheff. Ice Hockey Club; Med. Off. Sheff. Rugby Club & Sports Injuries Clinic.

MACKENZIE, Angus Alexander City Hospital NHS Trust, Dudley Road, Birmingham B18 7QH Tel: 0121 507 5603 Fax: 0121 507 4349; Wayside, Woodfield Lane, Belbroughton, Stourbridge DY9 9UT Tel: 01562 710480 Email: angus@romsley.demon.co.uk — MB ChB 1981 Birm.; FFA RCS Eng. 1986. Cons. Anaesth. City Hosp. NHS Trust. Prev: Sen. Regist. (Anaesth.) Midl. Area Train. Scheme.

MACKENZIE, Angus MacLeod (retired) 59 Underwood Road, Rutherglen, Glasgow G73 3TF — MB ChB Glas. 1952.

MCKENZIE, Ann Barbara 10 Rhylstone Mount, Bradford BD7 2QB — MB ChB 1984 Dundee. Clin. Med. Off. Bradford HA.

MACKENZIE, Anne Catherine Mary The Surgery, High St., South Milford, Leeds LS25 5AA; Rowardennan, Well Farm, Lumby, Southmilford, Leeds LS25 5JA — MB ChB Glas. 1982; MRCGP 1986; DRCOG 1985.

MACKENZIE, Anne Rosemary The Health Centre, Rothesay PA20 9JL Tel: 01700 502290 Fax: 01700 505692; Port Ban, Ardencraig Lane, Rothesay PA20 9EZ Tel: 01700 502843 — MB ChB 1966 Ed.; DPhysMed Eng. 1975. (Ed.) Clin. Dir. Argyle & Bute Trust.

MCKENZIE, Bruce Cameron 12 Gladstone Road, Chesterfield S40 4TE Email: 75337.2274@compuserve.com — MB ChB 1992 Otago. (Univ. Otago)

MACKENZIE, Calum John Robert Flat 5, 64 Broughton St., Edinburgh EH1 3SA Tel: 0131 556 7415 — MB ChB 1986 Ed.; MRCGP 1991.

MACKENZIE, Caroline Anne Sheffield Children's Hospital NHS Trust, Western Bank, Sheffield S10 2TH Tel: 0114 271 7160 Fax: 0114 273 0522; The Mission, Sheephill Road, Sheffield S11 7TU Tel: 0114 230 8989 — MB ChB 1984 Dundee; MD Sheff. 1994; MRCP (UK) 1987; FRCPCH 1997; DCCH RCP Ed. 1987. (Dundee) Cons. Paediat. Sheff, Childr. Hosp.; Med. Dir. Sheff. Childs. Hosp. Socs: BPRS; BSPE; RCPCH. Prev: Lect. & Hon. Sen. Regist. (Paediat.), Clin. Research Asst. & Hon. Regist. Sheff. Childr. Hosp.

MCKENZIE, Catherine Helen Keston House medical Practice, 70 Brighton Road, Purley CR8 2LJ — MB BS 1994 Lond.; BSc Basic Med. Scs. & Physiol. (1st cl. Hons.) Lond. 1991; DRCOG 1997; Dip. Family Plann 1997; MRCGP 1998. (St Georges)

MACKENZIE, Charlotte Patricia Deecroft, Oldfield Drive, Heswall, Wirral CH60 6SR — MB BS 1976 Lond.; DLO Eng. 1979; MSc Manch. 1998. (Guy's) Staff Grade Paediat. Wirral Hosp. Trust. Prev: Clin. Med. Off. Wirral HA.; SHO ENT Unit St. Mary Abbot's Hosp. Lond.; Med. Asst. (A & E) W.. Gen. Hosp. Edin.

MCKENZIE, Mr Christopher Gurney (retired) Kintail House, Pathfields Close, Haslemere GU27 2BL Tel: 01428 641041 Fax: 01428 641041 — MB BS 1959 Lond.; FRCS Eng. 1962; FRCR 1975; FFR (Rohan Williams Medal) 1973; DMRT Eng. 1972. Prev: Cons. Radiother. Hammersmith Hosp. Lond.

MCKENZIE, Christopher Iain The Family Surgery, 7 High Street, Green Street Green, Orpington BR6 6DE Tel: 01689 850231 Fax: 01689 862746; 19 Station Road, Orpington BR6 0RZ Tel: 01689 812455 — MB BS 1976 Lond.; MRCS Eng. LRCP Lond. 1975; MRCP (UK) 1984; DTM & H RCP Lond. 1985; DRCOG 1985.

MCKENZIE, Christopher Jason 66 Melbourne Road, Bolton BL3 5RN — MB BS 1994 Lond. (RFHSM) SHO (Med.) Qu. Eliz. Hosp. King's Lynn, Norf.

MCKENZIE, Claire Louise 17 Cassie Cl, Cove Bay, Aberdeen AB12 3WE — MB ChB 1997 Aberd.; BSc MedSci (Hons) Aberd. 1998. (Aberd.) SHO (Gen. Pract. VTS) Aberd. Socs: MDDUS; BMA.

MACKENZIE, Colin Tennant Street Surgery, Stockton-on-Tees TS18 2AT Tel: 01642 613331 Fax: 01642 675612 — MB ChB 1954 Aberd.; FRCGP 1985, M 1977.

MACKENZIE, Colin Drummond Craiglockhart Surgery, 161 Colinton Road, Edinburgh EH14 1BE Tel: 0131 455 8494 Fax: 0131 444 0161; 28 Granby Road, Edinburgh EH16 5NL — MB ChB 1978 Ed.; MRCGP 1985; DRCOG 1981.

MACKENZIE

MACKENZIE, Davina Lakshimi 15B St Albans Road, Kingston upon Thames KT2 5HQ — MB ChB 1998 Manch.; MB ChB Manch. 1998.

MCKENZIE, Donald James Putneymead Medical Centre, 350 Upper Richmond Road, London SW15 6TL Tel: 020 8788 0686; 33 Castelnau, Barnes, London SW13 9RS — MB BS 1981 Sydney; MB BS (2nd. Cl. Hons.) Sydney 1981; DRCOG 1986; DCH RCP Lond. 1984.

MACKENZIE, Donald John Medicover Medical Centre, 16 Street Eugen Lovinescu, Sector 1, Bucharest, Romania Tel: 00 401 2233055 Fax: 00 401 2233676; Hawkchurch House, Hawkchurch, Axminster EX13 5XD Tel: 01297 678209 — MB BS 1962 Lond.; MRCS Eng. LRCP Lond. 1962; DObst RCOG 1965; DA (UK) 1964. Med. Off. Medicover Med. Centre Bucharest, Romania. Socs: BMA; Med. Protec. Soc. Prev: Sen. Med. Off. Shell Romania Exploration BV Bucharest, Romania; Sen. Med. Off. Canad. OcciDent. Petroleum Ltd. Aden, RePub. of Yemen; Med. Off. Shell Internat. Petroleum Company (Brunei, Papua New Guinea, Oman & Nigeria.

MACKENZIE, Donald Yardley (retired) South Strand Cottage, 5 The Drive, Angmering-on-Sea, Littlehampton BN16 1QH Tel: 01903 784868 — MB BS Lond. 1947; MD Lond. 1952; FRCP Lond. 1979, M 1954; MRCS Eng. LRCP Lond. 1947; DPhysMed. Eng. 1960; DCH Eng. 1953. Prev: Cons. Phys. (Rheum.) Roy. Surrey Co. Hosp. and SW Surrey Health Dist.

MACKENZIE, Douglas Graham 64 Inverleith Row, Edinburgh EH3 5PX — MB ChB 1995 Ed.

MACKENZIE, Duncan Neil 2 Waterperry, Wheatley, Oxford OX33 1LD — MB BS 1991 Lond.

MACKENZIE, Duncan Sherwood St John's Group Practice, 1 Greenfield Lane, Balby, Doncaster DN4 0TH Tel: 01302 854521 Fax: 01302 310823 — MB ChB 1987 Sheff.; DCH RCP Lond. 1990.

MACKENZIE, Elizabeth Adelaide 7 Moorings Close, Poole BH15 4AL — MB BS 1998 Lond.; MB BS Lond 1998.

MACKENZIE, Elizabeth Frances Dudley Department of Cytology, BUPA Hospital, Redland Hill, Bristol BS6 6UT Tel: 0117 973 2562 Fax: 0117 923 7211; 2 Merchants Quay, Bristol BS1 4RL Tel: 0117 929 4622 Fax: 0117 929 0836 — MB BS 1957 Lond.; FRCPath 1992; DPH Eng. 1962. (St. Bart.) Cons. Cytopath. BUPA Hosp. Bristol; Manager BUPA Cervical Screening Progr. Socs: Fell. Internat. Acad. Cytol.; (Ex-Pres.) Brit. Soc. Clin. Cytol.; Assn. Clin. Path. Prev: Cons. Cytopath. & Manager Avon Cervical Cytol. Screening Servs.; Director Regional Cytol. Train. Centre.

MCKENZIE, Elizabeth Mysie Binnie 20 Hazelwood Road, Duffield, Belper DE56 4DQ Tel: 01332 841070 — MB ChB 1956 Manch.; DA Eng. 1959. Clin. Asst. (ENT) S. Derbysh. HA. Prev: Clin. Asst. (Anaesth.) Derbysh. AHA.

MACKENZIE, Elma Moira (retired) Ridgewood, 15 Old Mill Road, Inverness IV2 3HR Tel: 01463 717007 — MB ChB Aberd. 1948. Assoc. Specialist. (Ment. Handicap) Craig Phadrig Hosp. Inverness. Prev: Asst. GP Inverness.

MACKENZIE, Esther Clare The Rectory, 13 Ersham Road, Canterbury CT1 3AR — MB ChB 1997 Sheff.

MACKENZIE, Evan Pratt (retired) Flat 19 Park Gate, Park Place, Cheltenham GL50 2QE Tel: 01242 262073 — MRCS Eng. LRCP Lond. 1946; FRCGP 1976, M 1962. Prev: Ho. Surg. Lond. Hosp.

MACKENZIE, Fergus Alastair Ferguson, Surg. Capt. RN Retd. (retired) 7 Old Rectory Gardens, Thurlestone, Kingsbridge TQ7 3PD Tel: 01548 560671 Fax: 01548 560671 — MB ChB Glas. 1945; FRCR 1975; FFR 1967; DMRD Eng. 1955. Prev: Cons. Radiol. MusGr. Pk. Hosp. Taunton.

MACKENZIE, Fiona Anne The Rivermead Unit, Northern General Hospital, Herries Road, Sheffield S5 7AU Tel: 01142 271 4967 Fax: 01142 271 5444 — MB ChB 1986 Leic.; BSc (Med. Sci.) Leic. 1983; MRCPsych 1992. Cons. Psychiat. (Learning Disabil.) Community Health Sheff. Prev: Sen. Regist. (Psychiat. Learning Disabil.) Notts. Train. Scheme.

MACKENZIE, Fiona Mackinnon Barn Cottage, Shilton, Burford OX18 4AB — BM 1998 Soton.; BM Soton 1998.

MACKENZIE, Fiona Margaret Princess Royal Maternity Unit, Glasgow Royal Infirmary, 16 Alexandra Parade, Glasgow G31 2ER Tel: 0141 211 5400 — MB ChB 1984 Leeds; MRCOG 1990. Cons. O & G Glas. Roy. Matern. Hosp. & Stobhill Hosp., Glas.

MCKENZIE, Fiona Ross Airedale General Hospital, Skipton Road, Steeton, Keighley BD20 6TD — MB ChB 1978 Aberd.; MRCPsych 1986; DRCOG 1982. Cons. Psychiat. Airedale Gen. Hosp. Prev: Sen. Regist. (Psychiat.) Yorks. RHA.

MACKENZIE, Forbes Alexander (retired) 24 Woodstock Drive, Worsley, Manchester M28 2WW Tel: 0161 794 2243 — MB ChB 1954 Aberd. Prev: Med. Off. GB Rugby League.

MACKENZIE, Gary David 103 Vera Avenue, London N21 1RN — MB BS 1997 Lond.

MACKENZIE, Geoffrey Frazer (retired) High Croft, School Meadow, Thame Road, Chilton, Aylesbury HP18 9LL — MB ChB 1953 Sheff.; MRCS Eng. LRCP Lond. 1953; MFOM RCP Lond. 1981; DA Eng. 1967. Med. Adviser Yorks. Water Auth.; Occupat. Phys. Hickson & Welch Plc. Castleford. Prev: GP Darrington.

MACKENZIE, George Donald (retired) Caberfeidh, 38 Beesfield Lane, Farningham, Dartford DA4 0BZ Tel: 01322 865393 — MB ChB Glas. 1957. Prev: GP Swanley Kent.

MACKENZIE, George Kenneth (retired) Flat 29, Royal Marine Apts., Marine Foad, Nairn IV12 4EN Tel: 01667 453060 — MB ChB 1936 Ed.; MD Ed. 1951. Prev: Resid. Med. Off. (Infec. Dis.) Hosp. Inverness.

MCKENZIE, Glen Gordon Jenkins Attic Flat, 16 Rosslyn Terrace, Dowanhill, Glasgow G12 9NA — MB ChB 1998 Glas.

MACKENZIE, Graeme Merrie The Medical Centre, St. Pauls Square, Carlisle CA1 1DG; 35 Brunstock Close, Carlisle CA3 0HL — MB ChB 1982 Aberd.; DRCOG 1984. Prev: Jun. Ho. Phys. & Jun. Ho. Surg. Stirling Roy. Infirm.

MACKENZIE, Graham Douglas Palms Medical Centre, 97-101 Netley Road, Newbury Park, Ilford IG2 7NW Tel: 020 8554 9551 Fax: 020 8518 2045 Email: grahammackenzie@gp-86009.nhs.uk; 62 Birkbeck Road, Rush Green, Romford RM7 0QP Tel: 01708 788530 — MB ChB Aberd. 1979; MRCGP 1984; DRCOG 1981. Prev: Vocational Trainee GP Neath Gen. Hosp.; Trainee GP Port Talbot Health Centre; Ho. Phys. & Ho. Surg. Falkirk Roy. Infirm.

MCKENZIE, Hamish Department of Medical Microbiology, University Medical Buildings, Foresterhill, Aberdeen AB25 2ZD Tel: 01224 552446 Email: h.mckenzie@abdn.ac.uk — MB ChB 1982 Glas.; PhD Strathclyde 1975, BSc 1970; FRCPath 1998. Sen. Lect. & Hon. Cons. Univ. Aberd. & Grampian HB. Prev: Assoc. Dean (UnderGrad. Med.).

MCKENZIE, Helen Jeanne Motherwell Health Centre, 138-144 Windmill Street, Motherwell ML1 1TA Tel: 01698 265193 Fax: 01698 253324; 8 Malcolm Street, Motherwell ML1 3HY — MB ChB 1979 Glas.; MRCGP 1984; DRCOG 1981.

MACKENZIE, Hugh Melville (retired) Dunraven, 70 Bonnethill Road, Pitlochry PH16 5ED Tel: 01796 472372 Email: hugh@bonnethill.oik.co.uk — MB ChB 1955 Ed.; FRCGP 1980, M 1966; DObst RCOG 1959. Prev: SHO Forth Pk. Matern. Hosp. Kirkcaldy.

MACKENZIE, Mr Iain 46 Beechlands Drive, Clarkston, Glasgow G76 7XB — MB ChB 1969 Glas.; FRCS Glas. 1974. Cons. Surg. Monklands Dist. Gen. Hosp. Lanarksh. Prev: Sen. Surg. Regist. Vict. Infirm. Glas.

MCKENZIE, Ian RAF Hospital, Wegbeg BFPO 40 — MB ChB 1981 Auckland.

MACKENZIE, Ian Alexander Ross, TD (retired) Cockyhoop Cottage, Peddars Way, Hillington, King's Lynn PE31 6DS Tel: 01485 520321 — MB ChB 1939 Aberd.

MACKENZIE, Ian Donald Cogges Surgery, 12 Cogges Hill Road, Witney OX8 6FP Tel: 01993 700505 — MB ChB 1986 Dundee; BSc Hons. (Physiol.) St. And. 1981; MRCGP 1990. Prev: Trainee GP E. Cumbria VTS; Ho. Surg. & Ho. Phys. Stracathro Hosp. Brechin.

MACKENZIE, Ian Fraser Cornwall & Isles of Scilly Health Authority, John Keay House, St Austell PL25 4NQ Tel: 01726 77777 Fax: 01726 71777 Email: ian.mackenzie@ciosha.cornwall.nhs.uk — MB BS 1976 Lond.; FFPHM 2001; BSc (Pharmacol. Hons.) Lond. 1974; MRCS Eng. LRCP Lond. 1975; MFPHM RCP (UK) 1995; AFOM RCP Lond. 1993; MRCGP (Distinc.) 1984; DCH RCP Lond. 1981; DRCOG 1980; FRCGP 1999. (Guy's) Cons. Pub. Health Med. (Primary Care) Cornw. & I. of Scilly HA St. Austell. Socs: Soc. Occupat. Med. Prev: Primary Care Med. Adviser Cornw. & I. of Scilly HA St. Austell; Dir. Clin. Policy Durh. FHSA; GP Saltash.

MACKENZIE, Mr Ian James Centre for Human Communication, Humanities Building, University of Manchester, Oxford Road,

Manchester M13 9PL Tel: 0161 275 3786 Fax: 0161 275 3373 Email: mackenzie@fs1.ed.man.ac.uk; Deecroft, Oldfield Drive, Heswall, Wirral CH60 6SR Tel: 0151 342 4061 — MRCS Eng. LRCP Lond. 1975; BDS Lond. 1970; MSc Manch. 1993; MD Manch. 1997; FRCS Ed. 1979; FDS RCS Eng. 1983, LDS 1969. (Guy's) p/t Cons. Neuro-otol. Walton Centre For Neurosci., Fazakerly Hosp., Liverp.; Lect. Audiological Med. Univ. Manch.; Hon. Reader, Walton Centre, Univ. of Liverp.; Paediat. Cons. Audiolog. Phys. Olham NHS Trust; Cons. Audiolog. Phys. Aintree NHS Trust. Socs: Otorhynolaryng. Research Soc.; Brit. Soc. Of Audiol.; Fell. Roy. Soc. Med. Prev: Sen. Lect. & Cons. Otorhinolaryng. Liverp. Univ.; Sen. Regist. (ENT) Lothian Health Bd.; Regist. (ENT) Ninewells Hosp. Dundee.

MACKENZIE, Ian Zem Nuffield Department of Obstetrics & Gynaecology, John Radcliffe Hospital, Oxford OX3 9DU Tel: 01865 221006 Fax: 01865 69141; 2 Waterperry, Oxford OX33 1LD — MB ChB 1967 Bristol; DSc Oxf. 1994, MA 1981; MD Bristol 1981; FRCOG 1986, M 1973. Clin. Reader & Hon. Cons. Nuffield Dept. O & G Univ. Oxf.; Profess. Fell. St. Hugh's Coll. Oxf. Prev: Clin. Lect. (O & G) John Radcliffe Infirm. Oxf.; Research Fell. (O & G) John Radcliffe Hosp. Oxf.; Regist. (O & G) Newc. Gen. Hosp.

MCKENZIE, Immanuel Peter Glen Acre Child & Family Service, 21 Acre House Avenue, Lindley, Huddersfield HD3 3BB Tel: 01484 342141 Fax: 01484 342136; Westfield House, Westfield, Chat Hill Road, Thornton, Bradford BD13 3AP — MB ChB 1987 Leic.; MRCPsych 1991. Cons. (Child Psychiat.) Yorks. Region. Prev: Sen. Regist. (Child Psychiat.) Yorks. Region.

MACKENZIE, Isla Shelagh 44 Newtonhill Road, Newtonhill, Stonehaven AB39 3PX — MB ChB 1997 Aberd.

MACKENZIE, Isobel Raigmore Hospital, Inverness IV2 3UJ Tel: 01463 704000 — MB ChB 1974 Glas.; FFA RCS Eng. 1980. Cons. Anaesth. Raigmore Hosp. Trust Inverness; Hon. Clin. Sen. Lect. Aberd. Univ. Socs: Counc. Mem. Scott. Soc. of Anaethetists. Prev: Cons. Anaesth. Caithness Gen. Hosp. Wick; Sen. Regist. (Anaesth.) Wessex RHA.

MCKENZIE, Isobel Fiona Yorkleigh Surgery, 93 St. Georges Road, Cheltenham GL50 3ED Tel: 01242 519049 Fax: 01242 253556; 2 King Henry Close, Charlton Park, Cheltenham GL53 7EZ Tel: 01242 519566 — MB ChB 1983 Dundee; MRCGP 1988; DRCOG 1989. (Univ. Dundee) Police Surg. Prev: Trainee GP Gt. Yarmouth VTS; SHO (Community Health & Paediat.) Tower Hamlets HA.

MCKENZIE, Mr James Wolverhampton Nuffield Hospital, Wood Road, Tettenhall, Wolverhampton WV6 8LE Tel: 01902 741704; Norton Grange, 33 Norton Road, Stourbridge DY8 2AG Tel: 01384 396432 — MB ChB Aberd. 1944; FRCS Eng. 1961; DLO Eng. 1956. (Aberd.) Cons. ENT Surg. Wolverhampton, Dudley & Worcester/Hereford AHAs. Socs: Fell. Roy. Soc. Med. Prev: Sen. Regist. (ENT) Wolverhampton Hosp. Gp.; Regist. (ENT) Manch. Roy. Infirm.; Capt. RAMC.

MCKENZIE, James Watatu Developments, Haselbech Hall, Maidwell Road, Haselbech, Northampton NN6 9LG Fax: 01604 686335 Email: watatu@usa.net — BM BCh 1997 Oxf.; BA Oxf. 1994. (Oxford University) SHO (A&E) Roy. Lond. Prev: PRHO Gen. Med. N.ampton; PRHO Surg./Trauma/Orthop. York.

MACKENZIE, James Anderson Boyd Maryhill Health Centre, 41 Shawpark Street, Glasgow G20 9DR Tel: 0141 531 8800 Fax: 0141 531 8851; Wellbank, 45 Strathblane Road, Milngavie, Glasgow G62 8HA — MB ChB 1979 Glas.; BSc (Physiol.) (Hons.) Glas. 1976; MRCP (UK) 1984; MRCGP 1986. (Glas.)

MCKENZIE, James Angus (retired) 68 Seafield Road, Broughty Ferry, Dundee DD5 3AQ Tel: 01382 779173 — MB ChB 1965 St. And. Prev: GP Dundee.

MACKENZIE, James Campbell, RD Department of Renal Medicine, Southmead Hospital, Westbury-on-Trym, Bristol BS10 5NB Tel: 0117 950 5050 — MB 1958 Camb.; BA Camb. 1953, MB 1958, BChir 1957; FRCP Ed. 1979, M 1963; AFOM RCP Lond. 1980; DObst RCOG 1959; DIH Soc. Apoth. Lond. 1961. (St. Bart) Dir. Renal Unit S.mead Hosp. Bristol; Civil. Cons. (Renal Med.) RN; Surg. Cdr. RNR. Socs: Fell. Roy. Soc. Med.; Internat. Soc. Nephrol. Prev: Pres. Brit. Renal Soc.; Sen. Regist. & Ho. Phys. St. Bart. Hosp. Lond.

MACKENZIE, James Carswell 13 Stoney Brae, Potterhill, Paisley PA2 7TG — MB ChB 1993 Aberd.

MACKENZIE, James Mackintosh Department of Pathology, Aberdeen Royal Infirmary, Foresterhill, Aberdeen AB25 2ZD Tel: 01224 552442 Fax: 01224 663002 Email: j.m.mackenzie@abdn.ac.uk — MB ChB 1980 Ed.; BSc (Hons.) (Physiol.) Ed. 1977; MRCPath 1986. Cons. Neuropath. & Histopath. Aberd. Roy. Infirm. Prev: Cons. Neuropath. Walton Hosp. Liverp.; Sen. Regist. (Neuropath.) Leeds Gen. Infirm.; Trainee Path. Univ. Ed. & Roy. Infirm. Ed.

MCKENZIE, James Richard William 83 Parkhill Road, London NW3 2XY — MB BS 1997 Lond.

MACKENZIE, James Wallace Department of Genitourinary Medicine, St Bartholomew's Hospital, West Smithfield, London EC1M Tel: 020 7601 8090; 102A Richmond Avenue, Barnsbury, Islington, London N1 0LS Tel: 020 7837 4893 — MB BS 1990 Lond. (St. Bartholomew's London) Clin. Asst. St. Bart. Hosp. Lond. Socs: Assn. Genitourin. Med.

MACKENZIE, Jane 61 Merchiston Crescent, Edinburgh EH10 5AQ Tel: 0131 229 8846; Morningside Medical Practice, 2 Morningside Place, Edinburgh EH10 5ER Tel: 0131 452 8406 — MB ChB 1986 Aberd.; MRCGP 1994; DRCOG 1993. Retainer GP Morningside Med. Pract. Edin. Prev: Research Regist. City Hosp. Edin.; Trainee GP Glas.; Regist. & SHO (Med.) Monklands Dist. Gen. Hosp.

MACKENZIE, Jeanetta Ruth Surrenden Lodge, 23 Cammo Crescent, Edinburgh EH4 8DZ — MB ChB Ed. 1966; FRCP (Glas) 1996; FRCR 1976; DMRD Ed. 1973; DCH RCPS Glas. 1970; FRCPCH 1997. Cons. Radiol. Roy. Hosp. Sick Childr. Glas. Roy. Matern. Hosp. Socs: Eur. Soc. Uroradiol.; Europ. Soc. Paediat. Radiol.; Brit. Nuclear Med. Soc.

MACKENZIE, Jennifer Amanda Dumbarton Health Centre, Station Road, Dumbarton G82 1PW Tel: 01389 602633 Fax: 01389 602623 — MB ChB 1968 Liverpool; MB ChB Liverp. 1968. (Liverpool)

MACKENZIE, Jennifer Elaine 68 Marchmont Crescent, Edinburgh EH9 1HD — MB ChB 1991 Aberd.

MACKENZIE, Jeremy 21 Anthony Drive, Caerleon, Newport NP18 3DT — MB BS 1998 Lond.; MB BS Lond 1998.

MACKENZIE, Jessie Patricia Montrose Hillview, Upper Carnoch, Glencoe, Ballachulish PH49 4HU — MB ChB 1943 Glas.

MACKENZIE, Joan Wyeside, The Park, Bakewell DE45 1ET Tel: 01629 812357 — MB ChB 1940 Sheff. (Sheff.)

MACKENZIE, John Donald 43 Hazledene Road, Aberdeen AB15 8LB — MB ChB 1976 Aberd.; FFA RCS Irel. (Aberdeen University) Cons. Anaesth. Aberd. Roy. Infirm. Socs: Scott. Soc. Experimen. Med.; Scott. Soc. Anaesths.; Assn. Cardio Thoracic Anaesths. Prev: REA Grampian; Pres. NE Scot. Soc. of Anaesths.

MACKENZIE, John Fraser Royal Infirmary, Glasgow G4 0SF Tel: 0141 304 4968; 20 Campbell Drive, Bearsden, Glasgow G61 4NE Tel: 0141 942 6245 — MB ChB 1968 Liverp.; FRCP Ed. 1991; FRCP Glas. 1989; MRCP (UK) 1972. Cons. Phys. Glas. Roy. Infirm.; Hon. Clin. Sen. Lect. Univ. Glas. Socs: Brit. Soc. Gastroenterol. (Oesoph. Sect.); BMA. Prev: Sen. Regist. (Med.) Glas. Roy. Infirm.; Research Fell. Glas. Roy. Infirm.; Regist. (Med.) Walton Hosp. Liverp.

MACKENZIE, John Frazer Highcroft, School Meadow, Thame Road, Chilton, Aylesbury HP18 9LL Tel: 01844 208928 — MB ChB 1977 Sheff.; AFOM RCP Lond. 1987. Head (Occupat. Health & Safety) Rothmans of Pall Mall (Internat.) Ltd. Socs: Soc. Occupat. Health & Roy. Soc. Med. Prev: Area Med. Off. Nat. Power plc; Co. Med. Adviser Scott. Power plc.

MACKENZIE, John William Bantry House, Woodland Avenue, Windsor SL4 4AG Tel: 01753 858698 — MB BChir 1981 Camb.; MA Camb. 1982, MB BChir 1981; MRCP (UK) 1985; FFARCS 1988. Cons. Anaesth. W. Berks. HA. Socs: Assn. Anaesth. GB & Irel. Pain Soc. Prev: Sen. Regist. (Anaesth.) Oxf. HA; Regist. (Anaesth.) Roy. Berks. Hosp. Reading; SHO (Anaesth.) St. Thos. Hosp. Lond.

MCKENZIE, Jolanta Gabriela 1 Regency Close, Bishop's Stortford CM23 2NP — MB BS 1981 Lond.

MCKENZIE, Joyce 150 Riddell Street, North Drumry, Clydebank G81 2HD — MB ChB 1991 Glas.

MACKENZIE, Judith Margaret H.M.P. Grendon, Grendon Underwood, Aylesbury — MB ChB Manch. 1972; DPM Eng. 1976. Visit. Psychiat. to the Home Office.

MACKENZIE, Julie The Village Practice, Mere Lane, Armthorpe, Doncaster DN3 2DB Tel: 01302 300322 Fax: 01302 300737 — MB ChB 1987 Sheff. Prev: Trainee GP Rotherham VTS.

MCKENZIE

MCKENZIE, Kathryn Joy Department of Pathology, Royal Hospital for Sick Children, 2 Rillbank Crescent, Edinburgh EH9 1LF Tel: 0131 536 0447 Fax: 0131 536 0455 Email: kathryn.mackenzie@ed.ac.uk — MB ChB 1989 Glas.; BSc Glas. 1987; MRCPath 1996. (Univ. Glas.) Cons. Paediat. Histopath. Roy. Hosp. for Sick Childr. Edin. Socs: Assn. Clin. Paths.; Internat. Acad. Path.; BRIPPA. Prev: Sen. Regist. (Histopath.) W.. Infirm. Glas.

MACKENZIE, Mr Kenneth 171 Queen Victoria Drive, Scotstounhill, Glasgow G14 9BP Tel: 0141 959 3217 — MB ChB 1978 Dundee; FRCS Ed. 1982. Sen. Regist. (Otorhinolaryngol.) Glas. Hosps.

MACKENZIE, Kenneth Arthur (retired) Bridge House, Flookburgh, Grange-over-Sands LA11 7JS Tel: 01539 559094 — MB ChB 1936 Ed.; DMR 1944; FRCR 1977. Prev: Cons. Radiother. Highland HB.

MACKENZIE, Kenneth Gerald Powell Peamore House, Alphington, Exeter EX2 9SJ — MRCS Eng. LRCP Lond. 1951; MA (2nd cl. Hons. Nat. Sc. Trip. Pts. I & II); MB BChir Camb 1951; DCH Eng. 1954. (Camb. & Guy's) Socs: BMA & Doncaster Med. Soc. Prev: Res. Med. Off. P.ss Louise Kens. Hosp. Childr. & Roy. Devon & Exeter Hosp.; Med. Regist. Roy. Hants. Co. Hosp.

MACKENZIE, Kenneth Michael Gaughton House, Fornham All Saints, Bury St Edmunds IP28 6JY Tel: 01284 766908 — MD 1949 Lond.; MB BS 1944; FRCP Lond. 1978, M 1949; MRCS Eng. LRCP Lond. 1943. (St. Mary's) Prev: Cons. Phys. W. Suff. Gen. Hosp.; Ho. Phys. St. Mary's Hosp. & Brompton Hosp.; RAMC 1944-47.

MACKENZIE, Mr Kenneth Roderick Manchester Royal Eye Hospital, Oxford Road, Manchester M13 9WH Tel: 0161 276 1234 Fax: 0161 273 2028; 10 Roundcroft, Romiley, Stockport SK6 4LL — MB ChB 1984 Manch.; FRCS Ed. 1989; FCOphth 1989. Community Eye Phys. Manch. Centr. Hosp. & Community Care NHS Trust. Prev: Research Fell. (Ophth.) Manch. Roy. Eye Hosp.; Regist. (Ophth.) Roy. Vict. Infirm. Newc.

MACKENZIE, Kenneth Sutherland 64 Burneoge Fold Road, Grasscroft, Saddleworth, Oldham OL4 4EE Tel: 01457 871977 — MB ChB Glas. 1950. (Glas.) Div. Surg. Gt.er Manch. Police; Div. Surg. Gtr. Manch. Police. Socs: Assn. Police Surg. Prev: Ho. Phys. & Ho. Surg. Glas. Roy. Infirm.; Med. Off. Roy. Scots Greys.

MCKENZIE, Kenneth Thomas Clyde (retired) 14 The Crescent, Solihull B91 1JP — MB ChB 1948 Birm. Prev: Former partner in McKenzie, Hill, Travis, Stockdale, Terry, Leyton, & StenHo., Solihull.

MACKENZIE, Kenneth William Linlithgow Health Centre, 288 High Street, Linlithgow EH49 7ER Tel: 01506 670027 — MB ChB 1976 Ed.; BSc (Med. Sci.) Ed. 1973, MB ChB 1976. (Ed.) GP Linlithgow.

MCKENZIE, Kwame Julius 20 Beauval Road, London SE22 8UQ Tel: 020 8299 1165 — BM 1987 Soton.; MRCPsych 1994. Prev: Clin. Research Fell. Inst. Psychiat. King's Coll. Hosp. Lond.; Regist. Maudsley Hosp. Lond.; SHO (A & E) Lewisham Hosp.

MACKENZIE, Lindsay Elise Patel and Partners, 4 Bedford Street, Bletchley, Milton Keynes MK2 2TX Tel: 01908 377101 Fax: 01908 645903 — MB BS 1991 Lond. Trainee GP/SHO Milton Keynes Hosp. VTS.

MACKENZIE, Lisa Mairi 4 Newtonhill Road, Newtonhill, Stonehaven AB39 3PX — MB ChB 1996 Aberd.

MACKENZIE, Margaret Elizabeth Fraser 43 Southside Road, Inverness IV2 4XA Tel: 01463 236536; 22 Auldcastle Road, Inverness IV2 3PZ — MB ChB 1946 Aberd.

MACKENZIE, Marianne Shaw Newton House, 13 Milbank Road, Darlington DL3 9NJ — MB ChB 1977 Aberd.; MRCGP 1981. Clin. Asst. (Ophth.) Dryburn Hosp. Durh.

MACKENZIE, Marion Enid Townsend (retired) Leiston Old Abbey, Leiston IP16 4RF Tel: 01728 832053 — MB BS 1931 Lond MB BS (Distinc. in Midw.) Lond. 1931; MRCS Eng. LRCP Lond. 1931; FRCPsych 1972, M 1971. Hon. Cons. Child Psychiat. (Childr. & Parents) Tavistock Clinic Lond. Prev: Ho. Surg. (O & G) Roy. Free Hosp. Lond.

MACKENZIE, Mr Martin West Cornwall Hospital, Penzance TR18 2PF — MB ChB 1966 Glas.; FRCS Ed. 1972. Cons. Surg. W. Cornw. Hosp. Penzance.

MACKENZIE, Martine Helene Ormskirk & District General Hospital, Wigan Road, Ormskirk L39 2AZ — MB ChB 1984 Manch.; MSc Fac. Med. Manch. 1992; MRCPsych 1988. Cons. Gen. Psychiat. Ormskirk & Dist. Gen. Hosp. Prev: Sen. Regist. (Forens. Psychiat.)

Prestwich Hosp. Manch.; Lect. (Psychiat.) Manch. Univ.; Sen. Regist. (Psychiat.) Rehabil. Dept. Prestwich Hosp.

MCKENZIE, Mary Alexandra Norton Grange, 33 Norton Road, Stourbridge DY8 2AG Tel: 01384 396432 — MB ChB Aberd. 1944. (Aberd.) Dept. Med. Off. Worcs. CC. Prev: Asst. Sch. Med. Off. Rochdale; Res. Med. Off. Roy. Infirm. Aberd.

MACKENZIE, Michael Flat Top Right, 36 Airlie St., Glasgow G12 9TP — MB ChB 1995 Glas.

MACKENZIE, Naomi Ann Royal Preston Hospital, Sharoe Green Lane, Fulwood, Preston PR2 9HT Tel: 01772 716565; 5 Water Street, Egerton, Bolton BL7 9SS — BM 1988 Soton.; FRCS Ed. 1992. Regist. (Gen. Surg.) Roy. Preston Hosp. Prev: Regist. (Gen. Surg.) Blackburn Roy. Infirm.; SHO (Gen. Surg.)) Qu. Alexandra Hosp. Portsmouth & I. of Wight.

MACKENZIE, Neil 1 Scotswood Terrace, Dundee DD2 1PA — MB ChB 1976 Ed.; FFA RCS Eng. 1982. Cons. Anaesth. Ninewells Teach. Hosp. Dundee.

MACKENZIE, Niall Caville Rydon House, Taunton TA2 7AZ Tel: 01823 333438 Fax: 01823 333287 — MB ChB 1962 Otago; MA Oxf. 1969; BA NZ 1954; DPM Eng. 1967. Tutor (Psychol. of Religion) Fac. of Theol. Oxf. Univ. Socs: Brit. Soc. Hist. of Med.; Hellenic Med. Soc. Prev: Princip. GP Oxf.; Hon. Psychiat. Slade Hosp. & (Clin. Neurol.) Ch.ill Hosp. Oxf.; Sen. Regist. (Psychiat.) Littlemore Hosp. Oxf.

MACKENZIE, Niall Thomas Department of Radiology, Royal Victoria Infirmary, Newcastle upon Tyne NE1 4LP; 20 Appleby Park, North Shields NE29 0PL — MB ChB 1994 Dundee. Specialist Regist. (Clin. Radiol.) Newc. u. Tyne. Prev: SHO (Gen. Med.) Coleraine Hosp. Co. Derry.

MACKENZIE, Nigel Charles Institute of Psychiatry, De Crespigny Park, Denmark Hill, London SE5 8AF Tel: 020 7703 5411; 36 Wood Lane, Highgate, London N6 5UB Tel: 020 8340 1602 — MB BS 1989 Lond.; MA Oxf. 1968; DPhil Sussex 1970; MPhil Lond. 1979. Clin. Lect. & Hon. Sen. Regist. Inst. Psychiat. Lond. Socs: Roy. Coll. Psychiat. Prev: Sen. Regist. (Neuropsychiat.) Maudsley Hosp. Lond.

MACKENZIE, Pamela Margaret Newton Cottage, 10 Isles St., Newmilns KA16 9DP — MB ChB 1991 Glas.; MB ChB (Commend.) Glas. 1991; MRCP (UK) 1995. Staff Grade Nephrol., CrossHo. Hosp. Socs: BMA; Med. Dent. & Defence Union. Scotl.; Roy. Coll. Phys. Prev: SHO (Nephrol.) Stobhill Hosp. Glas.; SHO (Med.) Glas. Roy. Infirm.; SHO (A & E) S.. Gen. Hosp. Glas.

MACKENZIE, Patricia Campbell 46 Beechlands Drive, Clarkston, Glasgow G76 7XB — MB ChB 1976 Glas.

MACKENZIE, Percy Arthur Paul, TD 102 Mayfield Court, 27 West Savile Terrace, Edinburgh EH9 3DR — LRCP LRCS Ed. LRFPS Glas. 1952; CIH Dund 1974; Assoc. Fac. Occupat. Med. RCP Lond. 1979. (Roy. Colls. & Univ. Ed.) CStJ; Maj. RAMC (T & AVR); Mem. BASM & BASICS. Prev: Ho. Surg. Surgic. Out-Pat. Dept. Roy. Infirm. Edin.; Cas. Off. Childr. Wing St. Geo. Hosp. Lond.; Ho. Phys. Perth Roy. Infirm.

MACKENZIE, Peter Alexander Department of Anaesthesia, Victoria Infirmary, Langside Road, Glasgow G42 9TY Tel: 0141 201 5320 Fax: 0141 201 5318; 8 Laurel Park Close, The Laurels, Jordanhill, Glasgow G13 1RD Tel: 0141 954 1526 Email: pete@mackenzie19.freeserve.co.uk — MB ChB 1985 Glas.; FRCA 1994; MRCGP 1989; DRCOG 1989. Cons. (Anaesth.) Vict. Infirm., Glas.. Socs: MDU; BMA & Assn. Anaesth.; Scott. Soc. Anaesth. Prev: Sen. Regist. in (Pain Managem.), Flinders Med. Centre, Adelaide; Specialist Regist., W. of Scotl. Sch. of Anaesths.; Career Regist. & SHO (Anaesth.) Glas. Roy. Infirm.

MACKENZIE, Peter John Oxford Radcliffe Hospital, Nuffield Department of Anaesthetics, John Radcliffe Hospital, Oxford OX3 9RP Tel: 01865 741166 Fax: 01865 220027 Email: peter.mckenzie@nda.ox.ac.uk; 13 Turnpike Road, Cumnor Hill, Oxford OX2 9JQ Tel: 01865 862509 — MD 1984 Glas.; MB ChB 1972; FFA RCS Eng. (Prize) 1976. (Glas.) Cons. Anaesth. Nuffield Dept. Anaesth. John Radcliffe Hosp.; Hon. Sen. Clin. Lect., Univ. of Oxf. Socs: BMA; Assn. Anaesth. Prev: Sen. Regist. (Anaesth.) W.. Infirm. Glas.; Regist. (Anaesth.) Glas. Roy. Infirm.; Ho. Surg. Glas. Roy. Infirm.

MACKENZIE, Peter William Medical Protection Society, 33 Cavendish Square, London W1G 0PS Tel: 020 7399 1300; 15 Church End, Newton Longville, Milton Keynes MK17 0AG Tel: 01908 648002 — MB BS 1987 Lond.; Pg. Dip. (Law); MA Camb.

1987, BA 1984; MRCGP 1993; DRCOG 1993. (Guy's Hosp. Med. Sch.) Medico-Legal Adviser to Med. Protec. Soc.

MACKENZIE, Rachel Jane 3 Braeside Avenue, Newtownabbey BT36 6AR — BM BS 1995 Nottm.

MACKENZIE, Rebecca Jane Curran and Partners, Manor Health Centre, 86 Clapham Manor Street, London SW4 6EB Tel: 020 7411 6866 Fax: 020 7411 6857 — MB BS 1994 Lond.

MACKENZIE, Miss Rhoda Katharine Email: rhodamackenzie@yahoo.com — MB ChB 1992 Aberd.; FRCS Ed. 1996. Specialist Regist., Gen. Surg., Aberdeen Roy. Infirm. Socs: BMA; RCS Edin.; Europ. Venous Forum. Prev: Research Fell., Vasc. Surg., Aberd. Roy. Infirm.; SHO Surgic. Rotat., Aberd. Roy. Infirm.

MACKENZIE, Richard Alexander Wellington House Practice, Wades Field, Straton Road, Princes Risborough HP27 9AX Tel: 01844 344281 Fax: 01844 274719 — MB BS 1970 Lond.; MRCS Eng. LRCP Lond. 1970; MRCGP 1974; DObst RCOG 1972. (Roy. Free)

MACKENZIE, Mr Robert John 108 Old Glasgow Road, Uddingston, Glasgow G71 7QA — MB ChB 1963 Glas.; FRCS Ed 1971; DObst RCOG 1965.

MACKENZIE, Roberta Ann 1 Campsie Drive, Milngavie, Glasgow G62 8HX — MB ChB 1998 Glas.; MB ChB Glas 1998.

MACKENZIE, Ronald Mackinnon Bampton Surgery, Landells, Bampton OX18 2LJ Tel: 01993 850257; Barn Cottage, Shilton, Oxford OX1 5JQ Tel: 01993 842177 — MRCS Eng. LRCP Lond. 1970; BSc (Physiol) Lond. 1967, MB BS 1971; DObst RCOG 1971.

MACKENZIE, Rory Ewen Department of Anaesthesia, Monklands District General Hospital, Monkscourt Avenue, Airdrie ML6 0JS Tel: 01236 748748 Fax: 01236 746224; 9 Randolph Road, Stirling FK8 2AJ — MR ChB 1987 Ed.; FRCA 1992. Cons. (Anaesth.) Monklands Dist. Gen. Hosp. Lanarksh. Prev: Sen. Regist. (Anaesth.) W.. Infirm. Glas.; Research Fell. (Anaesth.) W.. Infirm. Glas.; Career Regist. (Anaesth.) W.. Infirm. Glas.

MCKENZIE, Ruth Joan c/o Anaesthetic Department, Singleton Hospital, Sketty, Swansea SA2 8QA — MB ChB 1987 Pretoria.

MACKENZIE, Samuel Drummond Tigh-na-Mara, Ardrishaig, Lochgilphead PA30 8EU Tel: 01546 2114 — MB ChB 1947 Glas.

MACKENZIE, Sarah Elizabeth Westburn Medical Group, Forester Hill Health Centre, Wetburn Road, Aberdeen AB25 2AY Tel: 01224 559595 Fax: 01224 559597 Email: sarh.mackenzie@westburn.grampian.scot.nhs.uk; 35 The Park, St. Albans AL1 4RU Fax: 01224 559597 Email: sarh.mackenzie@westburn.grampian.scot.nhs.uk — MB BS 1983 Lond.; BSc (Hons.) Lond. 1980; MRCGP 1990; DRCOG 1990. (St. Bart.) Prev: GP Forfar; GP Chingford.

MACKENZIE, Sarah Jane Greyswood Practice, 238 Mitcham Lane, London SW16 6NT Tel: 020 8769 0845/8363 Fax: 020 8677 2960; Flat 2, 32 Narbonne Avenue, London SW4 9JS Tel: 020 8673 7095 — MB BS 1989 Lond.; MRCGP 1994; DRCOG 1993. GP Princip. Streatham. Prev: Asst. GP Ealing; SHO (Psychiat.) Kingston Hosp.; Trainee GP Mitcham.

MACKENZIE, Scott 78 Kilmardinny Crescent, Bearsden, Glasgow G61 3NW — MB ChB 1995 Aberd.

MACKENZIE, Scott David 55 Thistlewaite Road, London E5 0QG — MB BS 1996 Lond.

MACKENZIE, Sheila Agnes 69 Gordon Road, South Woodford, London E18 1DT Tel: 020 8505 7481 Email: mckenzie@+htch.demon.co.uk; An Sithean, Lairg Road, Bonar Bridge, Ardgay IV24 Tel: 01863 766461 Email: vasdias@msn.com — MB ChB 1969 Ed.; MD Ed. 1993; FRCP Ed. 1989; FRCP Lond. 1989; MRCP (UK) 1972; DCH RCPS Glas. 1971. (Ed.) Cons. Paediat. & Hon. Sen. Lect. Qu. Eliz. Childrs. Serv., Roy. Lond. Hosp., Whitechapel, Lond.; Assoc. Dir. of Postgrad. Educat. (Paediat.). Socs: Brit. Paediat. Assn. (Regional Adviser); Brit. Thorac. Soc. Prev: Cons. Paediat. Romford, OldCh. & Rushgreen Hosps.; Sen. Regist. (Paediat.) Hammersmith Hosp. Lond.; Regist. (Paediat.) Edgware Gen. Hosp. & Roy. Free Hosp. Lond.

MACKENZIE, Sheila Ann Simpson (retired) 68 Seafield Road, Broughty Ferry, Dundee DD5 3AQ Tel: 01382 779173 — MB ChB 1962 St. And.

MACKENZIE, Sheila Patricia (retired) 2 Warford Drive, Great Warford, Alderley Edge SK9 7TR Tel: 01565 872254 Email: smacke9555@aol.com — MB BCh BAO 1960 Dub.; LAH Dub. 1960. Assoc. Specialist (Ment. Handicap & Community Care) Soss

Moss Hosp. Macclesfield.; Assoc. Specialist (Learning Disabil., Psychiat. Community Care, & Psychother.) Soss Moss Hosp, Macclesfield. Prev: Regist. (Gen. Surg.) Chesterfield Roy. Hosp.

MACKENZIE, Shireen Natasha 17 Stone Mill Court, Leeds LS6 4RQ — MB ChB 1998 Leeds.

MACKENZIE, Shirley Ann 3 Brownsville Road, Heton Moor, Stockport SK4 4PE Tel: 0161 432 2042 — MB ChB 1957 Cape Town; BSc Rhodes 1953. (Cape Town)

MACKENZIE, Shonag Beatrice Penelope 1st Floor Flat, 41 Great King St., Edinburgh EH3 6QR — MB ChB 1990 Sheff. SHO (O & G) N. Gen. Hosp. Sheff.

MACKENZIE, Simon Ian Pierson 54 Bear Street, Nayland, Colchester CO6 4HX Tel: 01206 263490 — MB BS 1974 Lond.; FFA RCS Eng. 1985; DRCOG 1978. Cons. Anaesth. & ITU Colchester Gen. Hosp. Socs: Eur. Soc. Regional Anaesth.; Assn. Anaesth.; Assn. Low Flow Anaesth. Prev: Clin. Fell. W.mead Hosp. Univ. Sydney, Australia; Sen. Regist. W.minster & Char. Cross Hosp. Lond.; Regist. St. Bart. Hosp. Lond.

MACKENZIE, Simon James 74 Morningside Drive, Edinburgh EH10 5NU — MB ChB 1983 Ed.; FRCA 1989. Cons. Anaesth. & Intens. Ther. Roy. Infirm. Edin. Prev: Cons. Anaesth. & Intens. Ther. W.. Gen. Hosp. Edin.; Sen. Regist. (Anaesth.) Roy. Infirm. Glas.

MACKENZIE, Stephanie Royal Hospital for Sick Children, 9 Sciennes Road, Edinburgh EH9 1LF Tel: 0131 536 0253; 14 Cluny Avenue, Edinburgh EH10 4RN Tel: 0131 536 0260 — MB ChB 1974 Aberd.; FRCR 1981; DMRD Lond. 1979. Cons. (Paediat. Radiol.) Roy. Hosp. For Sick Childr., Edin. Prev: Sen. Regist. (Radiol.) Bris. Roy. Infirm.; Regist. (Radiol.) Plymouth.

MACKENZIE, Stuart Alan Northumberland Community Health, The Health Centre, Civic Precinct, Forum Way, Cramlington NE23 6QN Tel: 01670 712821 — MB BS 1971 Newc.; DA (UK) 1979; DObst RCOG 1973.

MACKENZIE, Susan 45 Cramond Glebe Road, Edinburgh EH4 6NT — MB ChB 1976 Ed.

MACKENZIE, Susan Eileen 2 Beagle Spinney, Stamford Bridge, York YO41 1BE — MB BS 1981 Newc.; MRCGP 1985; DRCOG 1984.

MACKENZIE, Thomas Hunter Maclauchlan 20 Stephenson Drive, Burnley BB12 8AJ — MB ChB 1983 Manch.; BSc St. And. 1980. Prev: Regist. (Gen. Med.) Burnley Gen. Hosp.; SHO (Dermat.) Newc. Roy. Vict. Infirm.; SHO (Gen. Med.) Hope Hosp. Salford HA.

MACKENZIE, Thomas Meikleham 35 Kingsley Avenue, Melton Park, Newcastle upon Tyne NE3 5QN Tel: 0191 236 3740 — MB BS 1953 Durh.

MACKENZIE, Tracy Christina 6 Kingsdale Park, Belfast BT5 7BY — MB BCh 1998 Belf.

MACKENZIE, Valerie Frances The Corner Cottage, 45 Stratton Road, Beaconsfield HP9 1HR — MB BS 1962 Lond.; MRCS Eng. LRCP Lond. 1962. (St. Mary's) Clin. Asst. N. Lond. BrE. Screening Serv. & Surgic. BrE. Clinic N.wick Pk Hosp Harrow. Socs: BMA; Med. Wom. Federat.; Assn. BrE. Clinicians. Prev: Clin. Asst. (O & G) Eliz. G. Anderson Hosp. Lond.; Regist. (Obst.) St. Mary's Hosp. Lond. (Harrow Rd. Br.); Regist. (O & G) Hillingdon Hosp. Middlx.

MACKENZIE, William (retired) Hillview Glencoe, Ballachulish PA39 4HT Tel: 0185 52 265 — LRCP LRCS 1943 Ed.; LRCP LRCS Ed. LRFPS Glas. 1943.

MACKENZIE, William Cameron Ferniehill Road Surgery, 8 Ferniehill Road, Edinburgh EH17 7AD Tel: 0131 664 2166 Fax: 0131 666 1075; Lyndean, St Leonards, Lasswade EH18 1LR — MB ChB 1971 Ed.

MACKENZIE, William Donald, Surg. Lt.-Cdr. RN Retd. Lauriston House, 40 Carpool Lane, Whitby YO22 4JE Email: ex. dir — MB ChB 1945 St. And.; MB ChB (Commend.) St. And. 1945; MFOM RCP Lond. 1979. (St. And.) Socs: (Ex-Dep. Sec. Gen.) Internat. Acad. Aviat. & Space Med. Prev: Cons. Med. Advisor Cyprus Airways; PMO (Overseas) Brit. Airways Med. Serv.; Surg. Lt.-Cdr. RN.

MACKENZIE, William Ewen 4 Herbert Austin Drive, Marlbrook, Bromsgrove B60 1RA — MD 1989 Ed.; MB ChB 1975; MRCOG 1981, D 1979; FRCOG. (University of Edinburgh) Cons. O & G Birm. Heartlands Hosp.; Hon. Sen. Lect. Univ. Birm. Socs: Blair Bell Res. Soc. Prev: Cons. O & G Marston Green Hosp. Birm.; Lect. (Obst.& Gyn.) Univ. of Birm.

MCKENZIE

MCKENZIE, Yvonne Eden Medical Group, Port Road, Carlisle CA2 7AJ Tel: 01228 524477 Fax: 01228 553809; 19 Marlborough Gardens, Carlisle CA3 9NQ — MB ChB 1983 Glas.; MRCGP 1989. (Glasgow) GP Princip. Prev: Trainee GP E. Cumbria VTS. Dumfries.

MACKENZIE CROOKS, David John Watercress Cottage, 1 Oldbury Lane, Wick, Bristol BS30 5RJ Tel: 0117 937 3018 — MB BS Lond. 1965; MRCP Lond. 1969; MRCS Eng. LRCP Lond. 1965; FFR 1974. (Westm.) Indep. Cons. Radiol. Bristol. Prev: Cons. Radiol. Frenchay Hosp. Bristol; Head of Dept. (Radiol. & Nuclear Med.) Riyadh Milit. Hosp., Saudi Arabia.

MACKENZIE ROSS, Alastair Dudley Blythe Muse Misbourne Avenue, Chalfont St Peter, Gerrards Cross SL9 0PD — BChir 1996 Camb.; MB Camb. 1997; MA Camb. 1998. (Cambridge)

MACKENZIE-ROSS, Catherine Jane (retired) April Cottage, French St., Westerham TN16 1PW — MB ChB 1952 Ed.; DCH Eng. 1955.

MACKENZIE-ROSS, Ronald Keith (retired) The Coppice, Rowhills, Heath End, Farnham GU9 9AU — MB BChir 1962 Camb.; MA, MB Camb. 1962, BChir 1961; MRCS Eng. LRCP Lond. 1960; MRCGP 1974; DObst RCOG 1963. Prev: Ho. Surg. (Obst.) Kingston Hosp. Kingston-on-Thames.

MCKEOGH, John Cottage Farm, Wield, Alresford SO24 9RU Tel: 01420 63188 — LRCPI & LM, LRSCI & LM 1941; LRCPI & LM, LRCSI & LM 1941; DOMS Eng. 1950. (RCSI) Sen. Hosp. Med. Off. Roy. Eye Hosp. & Ophth. Dept. St. Jas. Hosp. Balham.

MCKEOGH, Maeve Mary Mildmay Mission Hospital, 2 Hackney Road, London E2 7NA Tel: 020 7739 2331 Fax: 020 7613 0773; Willowfield Lodge, Milkwood Road, London SE24 0HY — MB BCh BAO 1985 NUI; MRCPI 1992. Cons. Palliat. Med. Mildmay Mission Hosp. Lond.

MCKEOGH, William Kevin (retired) Kincora, Nant Mawr Road, Buckley CH7 2BS Tel: 01244 550882 Email: rubislaw@aol.com — LRCPI & LM, LRCSI & LM 1947. Prev: GP Buckley Clwyd.

MCKEON, Jacqueline Teresa 7 Burnhead Road, Glasgow G43 2SU — MB ChB 1989 Glas.

MCKEON, Shauna Clare 53 Newlands Road, Glasgow G43 2JP — MB ChB 1990 Glas.

MCKEOWN, Anne Cecilia 13 Cadder Road, Bishopsbriggs, Glasgow G64 3JH — MB ChB 1994 Aberd.

MCKEOWN, Anne June Patricia 57 Thornleigh Drive, Lisburn BT28 2DA — MB ChB 1989 Glas.; FRCS Glas. 2001; FRCS Glas. 1994. Regist (Cardiothoracic Surg.) Roy P. Alfred Hosp., Sydney, Australia. Socs: Mem. of the Soc. Of Cardiothoracic Surg.s Of Gt. Brit. And N. Irel. Prev: Specialist Regist. (Cardiothoracic Surg.) Glas. Roy. Infirm.; Specialist regist. (Cardiothoracic Surg.) W.ern Infirm. Glas.; Specialist Regist. (Cardiothoracic Surg.) Hosp. For Sick Childr., Yorkhul, Glas.

MCKEOWN, Barbara Jane Peterborough District Hospital, Thorpe Road, Peterborough PE3 6; 5 The Grove, Hartford, Huntingdon PE29 1YD — MB BCh BAO 1984 NUI; MRCPI 1987; FRCR 1991. Cons. (Radiol.) PeterBoro. Hosps. NHS Trust, Cambs. Prev: Sen. Regist. (Radiol.) Guy's Hosp. Lond.; Sen. Regist. (Radiol.) Hammersmith Hosp. Lond.; Cons. Radiol. Mayday Univ. Hosp. Surrey.

MCKEOWN, Carole Margaret Eve Birmingham Women's Hospital, Birmingham B15 2TG Tel: 0121 627 2632 Fax: 0121 627 2618 Email: carole.mckeown@bham-womens.thenhs.com; 34 Reddings Road, Moseley, Birmingham B13 8LN — BM BCh 1975 Oxf.; MA, MSc Oxf. 1975; FRCP Lond. 1994; MRCP (UK) 1979; DCH Eng. 1977. (Oxford University and The London Hospital) Cons. Clin. Genetics. Birm. Wom.'s. Hosp. Prev: Sen. Regist. (Clin. Genetics) St. Mary's Hosp. Manch.; Clin Research Fell. Inst. Child Health Birm.

MCKEOWN, Christopher Owen The Manor House Surgery, Braidwood Road, Normanby, Middlesbrough TS6 0RE — MB BS 1968 Lond.; Cert Family Planning; MRCS Eng. LRCP Lond. 1968; DObst RCOG 1970; DCH Eng. 1972; ECFMG Cert 1969.

MCKEOWN, Colin James (retired) 2 Windmill Road, Nuneaton CV10 0HL Tel: 01203 341717 Fax: 01203 341717 Email: mckeo56@tinyonline.co.uk — MB ChB 1959 Ed.

MCKEOWN, Daniel Francis Gerard 49 Old Manse Road, Jordanstown, Newtownabbey BT37 0RX — MB BCh BAO 1980 Belf.; MRCGP 1985.

MCKEOWN, David Samuel Porter Mount Oriel Surgery, 2 Mount Oriel, Belfast BT8 7HR Tel: 028 9070 1653 — MB BCh BAO 1963 Belf.; MRCGP 1972; DObst RCOG 1967; DCH RCPS Glas. 1969.

MCKEOWN, Dermot William Ward 15 ICU, Royal Infirmary, Lauriston Place, Edinburgh EH3 9YW Fax: 0131 536 1515 Email: dermot.mckeown@ed.ac.uk; Email: dermotmckeown@doctors.net.uk — MB ChB 1977 Ed.; FFA RCS Eng. 1981. (Ed.) Cons. in Anaesthesia and Intens. Care and Hon. Clin. Sen. Lect. Univ. of Edin. Socs: Eur. S. Regional Anaesth.; Intens. Care Soc. Prev: Sen. Regist. & Research Fell. (Anaesth.) Roy. Infirm. Edin.; Sen. Regist. (Pain & Intens. Care) Flinders Med. Centre S. Austral.

MCKEOWN, Elizabeth Florence 19 Malone View Road, Belfast BT9 5PH Tel: 01232 776040 — MD 1945 Belf.; DSc Belf. 1966, MD 1945, MB BCh BAO 1942; FRCP Lond. 1974; FRCPath 1964. (Belf.) Musgrave Prof. Path. Qu. Univ. Belf.; Cons. Pathol. Roy. Vict. Hosp. & City Hosp. Belf. Socs: Path. Soc. Gt. Brit. & Brit. Cardiac Soc.

MACKEOWN, Isobel Louise 31 Long Down, Petersfield GU31 4PD; 6 Castle Gardens, Petersfield GU32 3AG — BM BCh 1994 Oxf.; MA Camb. 1995, BA (Hons.) 1991. Prev: Ho. Off. (Surg.) Plymouth.

MCKEOWN, Jane Margaret Isabel St. Aubyns, 2 Woodlands Road, Great Shelford, Cambridge CB2 5LW Tel: 01223 842262 Fax: 01223 842262 — MB BS 1966 Lond.; MA Cantab. 1977; FRCPsych 1997, MRCPsych 1973; DPM Eng. 1972. (St. Bart.) Retd. from NHS February 2000 continuing in Private Pract. Prev: Sen. Regist. (Psychiat.) United Camb. Hosps.; SHO (Path.) Soton. Gen. Hosp.; Ho. Surg. (Obst.) St. Bart. Hosp. Lond.

MCKEOWN, Kenneth Dudley Pond House, 2 Croft Road, Hurworth on Tees, Darlington DL2 2JE — MB BS 1969 Lond.; D. Occ. Med. 2000; MRCS Eng. LRCP Lond. 1969; DCH RCPS Glas. 1974; DA Eng. 1973; DObst RCOG 1973. (St. Bart.)

MCKEOWN, Martha Elizabeth The Health Centre, Lisburn BT28 1LU Tel: 018462 665181; Garvey Heights, 32 Plantation Avenue, Lisburn BT27 5BL Tel: 018462 663166 — MB BCh BAO 1950 Belf.; DPH 1955. (Qu. Univ. Belf.)

MCKEOWN, Mary Ethel The Square Surgery, 16A The Square, Comber, Newtownards BT23 5AP Tel: 028 9187 8159; 16 Waddel's Hill, Castle Espie, Comber, Newtownards BT23 JWJ Tel: 01247 873009 — MB BCh BAO Belf. 1976.

MCKEOWN, Michael David The Surgery, 7 Kynance Place, Gloucester Road, London SW7 4QS Tel: 020 7581 3040 Fax: 020 7584 0506 — MB BS 1972 Lond.; BSc Lond. 1964, MB BS 1972; LRCPI & LM, LRCSI & LM 1972.

MCKEOWN, Pascal Patrick Joseph Mountshalgus, Staffordstown Road, Randalstown, Antrim BT41 3LE — MD 1991 Belf.; MB BCh BAO 1984; MRCP (UK) 1987. (Queens University of Belfast) Cons./Sen. Lect. In Cardiol. - Roy. Vict. Hosp. - Belf. & the Qu.s Univ. of Belf. Socs: Brit. Cardiac Soc.; UK Alexander von Humboldt Assn. Prev: Sen. Regist. (Cardiol.) Belf. City Hosp.; Sen. Regist. (Cardiol.) Roy. Vict. Hosp. Belf.; Regist. (Nephrol.) Belf. City Hosp.

MCKEOWN, Paul Benedict 20 Parkmount Road, Belfast BT15 4EQ — MB BCh BAO 1949 Belf. (Qu. Univ. Belf.)

MCKEOWN, Peadar Francis 25 Bernagh Gardens, Dungannon BT71 4AP — MB BCh 1998 Belf.; MB BCh Belf 1998.

MCKEOWN, Rhona Catherine Doctors Surgery, 18 Union Street, Kirkintilloch, Glasgow G66 1DJ — MB ChB 1992 Glas.; MRCGP 1996; DCH RCPS Glas. 1995; DRCOG 1994. (Glasgow) GP Princip. Prev: SHO (O & G) Gtr. Glas. HB.; SHO (Paediat.) Roy. Alexandra Hosp. Paisley; SHO (Geriat.) Gartnavel Gen. Hosp. Glas.

MCKEOWN, Ronan Michael Eugene 2A Catherine Street, Newry BT35 6JG — MB BCh BAO 1994 Belf.

MCKEOWN, Ruth Priscilla Ormeau Park Surgery, 281 Ormeau Road, Belfast BT7 3GG Tel: 028 9064 2914 Fax: 028 9064 3993 — MB BCh BAO 1972 Belf.; DObst RCOG 1976.

MACKEOWN, Simon Timothy 25 Silverhill Road, Ecclesall, Sheffield S11 9JG — MB ChB 1989 Sheff.

MCKEOWN, Stephen Patrick Cheadle Royal Healthcare, 100 Wilmslow Road, Cheadle SK8 3DG Tel: 01565 755225 Fax: 0161 428 2457 Email: mckeownsp@aol.com; The White House, Carrwood Road, Wilmslow SK9 5DN — MB BS 1973 Lond.; MRCPsych 1978; Hon. FFOM 1998. (Middlx.) Med. Dir. Cheadle Roy. Healthcare; Cons. Ment. Health Zeneca Pharmaceut.; Assoc. Med. Dir. BUPA. Socs: Fell. Roy. Soc. Med.; (Pres). UK Br. of

Internat. Stress & Managem. Assn.; MRCPsych. (Hon. Sec.) Private Pract. s/i Gp. Prev: Med. Dir. Altrincham Priory Hosp.; Research Psychiat. Oxf. Univ.

MCKEOWN, Susanna Joan 13 Sepentine Road, Harborne, Birmingham B17 9RD — MB ChB 1976 Birm.

MCKERACHER, Roy Duncan Brimmond Medical Group, 106 Inverurie Road, Bucksburn, Aberdeen AB21 9AT Tel: 01224 713869 Fax: 01224 716317; 4 Burnside Road, Rutherglen, Glasgow G73 4SA — MB ChB 1983 Aberd.; MRCGP 1987.

MCKERAN, Ronald Orville 192 Harestone Valley Road, Caterham CR3 6BT — MB BS 1968 Lond.; MSc (Biochem.) Lond. 1974, BSc (Hons.) 1965, MD 1982; FRCP Lond. 1984; MRCP (UK) 1971; MRCS Eng. LRCP Lond. 1968. (Univ. Coll. Hosp.) Cons. Neurol. St. Geo. & Atkinson Morley's Hosps. Lond. & St. Helier Hosp. Carshalton; Hon. Cons. Neurol. Roy. Marsden Hosp.; Hon. Sen. Lect. St. Geo. Hosp. Med. Sch. Prev: Sen. Regist. (Neurol.) Nat. Hosp. Nerv. Dis. & Univ. Coll. Hosp. Lond.; Clin. Research Fell. & Hon. Sen. Regist. (Internal Med.) MRC.

MCKERCHAR, Duncan James Ellon Group Practice, Health Centre, Schoolhill, Ellon AB41 9AH Tel: 01358 720333 Fax: 01358 721578 — MB ChB 1975 Aberd.; BMedBiol Aberd. 1972, MB ChB 1975; MRCGP 1979; DRCOG 1978.

MACKERETH, Alastair Ian The Caxton Surgery, Oswald Road, Oswestry SY11 1RD Tel: 01691 654646 Fax: 01691 670994; Minffordd, Hengoed, Oswestry SY10 7EH Tel: 01691 658878 — MB ChB 1983 Manch.; DRCOG 1986.

MACKERETH, Annette Claire 4 Brookroyd Gardens, Batley WF17 0ER — MB ChB 1992 Sheff.

MACKERETH, Rachel Mary Llysmeddyg, Castle St., Conwy LL32 8AY — BM 1987 Soton.

MACKERETH, Stephen William Llys Meddyg Surgery, Llys Meddyg, 23 Castle Street, Conwy LL32 8AY Tel: 01492 592424 Fax: 01492 593068 — BM 1987 Soton.

MCKERLIE, Linda Catherine Ward 16, Monklands & Bellshill Hospitals NHS Trust, Monkscourt Avenue, Airdrie ML6 0JS; 107 Lomondside Avenue, Glasgow G76 7UH — MB ChB 1994 Glas. SHO (Dermat.) Monklands & Bellshill Hosps. NHS Trust. Socs: Med. & Dent. Defence Union Scotl.; BMA. Prev: SHO (Geriat. & A & E) S.. Gen. Hosp. Glas.; Ho. Off. (Med.) Law Hosp. Carluke; Ho. Off. (Surg.) Hairmyres Hosp. E. Kilbride.

MCKERNAN, Angela Mary Department of Haematology, Derbyshire Royal Infirmary, London Road, Derby DE1 2QY; 40 Main Road, Whatstandwell, Matlock DE4 5HE — MB ChB 1982 Manch.; MD Manch. 1990; MRCP (UK) 1985; MRCPath 1992. Sen. Regist. Rotat. (Haemat.) Mersey RHA. Prev: Regist. Rotat. (Haemat.) W. Midl. RHA; Research Regist. & SHO (Path.) Withington Hosp. Manch.

MCKERNAN, Claire 57 Wango Lane, Aintree, Liverpool L10 8JQ — MB ChB 1996 Liverp.

MCKERNAN, Michael Francis 74 Fruithill Park, Belfast BT11 8GF — MB BCh BAO 1988 Belf.

MCKERRELL, William, MBE (retired) Kildalton Cottage, North Cvan Ferry, Isle of Seil, Oban PA34 4RB Tel: 01852 300406 — MB ChB 1947 Glas.; MRCGP 1963.

MCKERRON, Colin Gordon (retired) Apple Tree Cottage, Middleton, Saxmundham IP17 3NF Tel: 01728 648205 — MB BS 1958 Lond.; FRCP Lond. 1972; MRCP (UK) 1964. Hon. Cons. Phys. Kings Coll. Hosp. Prev: Cons. Phys. King's Coll. Hosp. & Greenwich HA.

MCKERROW, Anderson Herdman, TD (retired) 52 South Street, St Andrews KY16 9JT Tel: 01334 473811 — MB ChB 1944 Ed.; MRCGP 1965. Maj. RARO. Prev: Ho. Surg. Roy. Infirm. & Roy. Hosp. Sick Childr. Edin.

MCKERROW, Mrs Elisabeth Kitchen Ground, Irton, Holmrook CA19 1YP Tel: 0194 04 238 — MB BChir 1949 Camb.; MRCS Eng. LRCP Lond. 1949; DCH Eng. 1951; DObst RCOG 1951.

MCKERROW, Malcolm Brunlees 3 Chalfont Lane, Chorleywood, Rickmansworth WD3 5PR Tel: 01923 283087 — MB BS 1953 Lond.; DObst RCOG 1955; DCH Eng. 1955. (St. Bart.) Assoc. RCGP. Prev: Ho. Phys. Childr. Dept. & Ho. Surg. O & G Dept. St. Bart.; Hosp.; Ho. Phys. St. And. Hosp. Dollis Hill.

MCKERROW, Margaret Mary, MBE (retired) 5 Ashley Court, Morpeth Terrace, London SW1P 1EN Tel: 020 7828 3751 — MB BS 1957 Lond.; MRCS Eng. LRCP Lond. 1957; DPhysMed Eng.

1969. Prev: Med. Dir. Rowcroft Hse. The Hospice for Torbay & S. Devon.

MCKERROW, Neil (retired) 51A Stainburn Road, Workington CA14 1SS — MB ChB 1953 Ed. Prev: Ho. Off. (Phys.) Ashford Hosp. Kent.

MCKERROW, Mr William Sangster Department of Otolaryngology, Raigmore Hospital, Inverness IV2 3UJ Tel: 01463 704000 Fax: 01403 711322; Scotsburn House, Drummond Road, Inverness IV2 4NA Tel: 01463 223917 Email: bill.mckerrow@quista.net.uk — MB ChB 1973 Aberd.; FRCS Glas. (Orl.) 1984; FRCS Ed. 1980; MRCGP 1977. (University of Aberdeen) Cons. Otolaryngol. Raigmore Hosp. Inverness NHS Trust; Clin. Sen. Lect. Univ. Aberd. Socs: Fell. Roy. Soc. Med.; Brit. Assn. Otol. Head & Neck Surg.; BMA Scott. Comm. Hosp. Med. Serv.s. Prev: Sen. Regist. (Otolaryngol.) Grampian HB; TWJ Fell. Univ. Calif., San Francisco (1986).

MACKERSIE, Angela Mary Great Ormond Street Hospital for Children, Great Ormond St., London WC1 Tel: 020 7829 8865 — MB BS 1971 Lond.; BSc (Hons.) Physiol. Lond. 1967, MB BS 1971; FRCA 1976. Cons. Anaesth. Gt. Ormond St. Childr. Hosp. Lond. Prev: Sen. Regist. Univ. Coll. Hosp. & Nat. Hosp. Nerv. Dis. Lond.; Regist. (Anaesth.) Univ. Coll. Hosp. Lond.; SHO (Anaesth.) N.wick Pk. Hosp. Harrow.

MCKESSACK, John James (retired) 91 Wickersly Road, Rotherham S60 3PU — MRCS Eng. LRCP Lond. 1963. Prev: Deptm. Med. Off. Sheff. HA (T).

MACKETT, John, SBStJ 67 High Street, Wootton Bridge, Ryde PO33 4LU Tel: 01983 882000 — MB BS 1951 Lond.; MRCS Eng. LRCP Lond. 1951; DA Eng. 1958. (King's Coll. Lond. & St. Geo.) Socs: Fell. Brit. Soc. Med. & Dent. Hypn.; Fell. Roy. Soc. Med. Prev: Regist. (Anaesth.) St. Geo. Hosp. & Luton & Dunstable Hosp.; Asst. Anaesth. I. of Wight AHA; Ho. Phys. Roy. I. of Wight Co. Hosp.

MCKEVENEY, Paul Joseph 15 Lake Street, Lurgan, Craigavon BT67 9DT — MB BCh BAO 1993 Belf.

MCKEVITT, Fiona Mary Royal Hallamshire Hospital, Sheffield S10 2JF; 88 Edgedale Road, Nether Edge, Sheffield S7 2BR — MB ChB 1994 Sheff.; MRCP (UK) 1998.

MCKEVITT, Nicolas Laurence 3 Wood View, Wimborne BH21 7BP Tel: 01202 840207 Email: nmckevitt@pond.com.au; 16 Holmesbrook Street, Ashgrove, Brisbane, Queensland 4060, Australia Tel: 0061 7 33667750 Fax: 0061 7 33667750 — MB ChB 1987 Birm.; FANZCA 1996. Specialist Anaesth. Cardiac Anaesth. P.ss Alexandra Hosp. Brisbane Australia; Specialist Anaesth. Wesley, Holy Spirit, St Andrew's, Roy. Brisbane Hosp.s Brisbane, Australia. Socs: Austral. Med. Assn.; Austral. Soc. of Anaesth.s; Anaesth. Adv. Comm. Wesley Hosp. Brisbane. Prev: Regist. (Anaesth.) Gold Coast Hosp. & Roy. Brisbane Hosp. Qu.sland, Austral.; Fell. in Cardiothoracic Anaesth. P. Chas. Hosp. 1996 Brisbane Australia.

MACKEY, Clyde John Rectory Cottage, Monks Horton, Ashford TN25 6DT — MB BS 1981 Queensland.

MACKEY, James Peter Pugin (retired) Pescotts, Crawley Down, Crawley RH10 4HG Tel: 01342 712223 — MB ChB Birm. 1938; FRCPath 1964; Dip. Bact. Lond 1950; DTM & H RCP Lond. 1947; DPH Eng. 1946. Prev: Mem. BMA & Hosp. Infec. Soc.

MACKEY, Paul Martin 19 Chestnut Drive, Porthcawl CF36 5AD — BM 1992 Soton.; FRCS 1997. SpR. All Wales Rotat. Socs: BMA.

MACKEY, Simon Philip 132A Westbourne Terrace, London W2 6QJ — MB BS 1998 Lond.; MB BS Lond 1998.

MACKEY, William Trevor 9 Wicklow Avenue, ytham, Lytham St Annes FY8 4TD — MB BCh BAO 1976 Belf.; BSc (Hons.) Belf. 1973; MRCPsych 1983. Staff Grade (Psychiat.) Vict. Hosp. Blackpool.

MCKIBBIN, Alistair Richard Rowden Surgery, Rowden Hill, Chippenham SN15 2SB Tel: 01249 444343 Fax: 01249 446797 — MB BS 1983 Lond.; MRCGP 1989; DRCOG 1988; DCH RCP Lond. 1986. GP Chippenham.

MCKIBBIN, Mr Andrew, OBE (retired) Erne Hospital, Enniskillen BT74 6AY — MB BCh BAO Belf. 1960; FRCSI 1969. Prev: Cons. Surg. Erne Hosp. Enniskillen.

MCKIBBIN, Professor Brian 4 Kingswear Court, Castle Road, Kingswear, Dartmouth TQ6 0DX Tel: 01803 752646 Fax: 01803 752646 Email: brianmck@aol.com — MB ChB Leeds 1955; MSc (Surg.) Univ. Illinois 1963; MD Leeds 1969; FRCS Eng. 1960. (Leeds

MCKIBBIN

& Oxf.) Emerit. Prof. Traum. & Orthop. Surg. Univ. Wales Coll. Med. Socs: Fell. (Ex-Pres.) BOA; (Ex-Mem. Counc.) Roy. Coll. Surgs. Eng.; Ex-Pres Brit. Orthop. Research Soc. Prev: Cons. Orthop. Surg. S. Glam. HA; Sen. Lect. & Head Dept. Orthop. Univ. Sheff.; Hon. Cons. Surg. United Sheff. Hosps.

MCKIBBIN, Charles The Valley Medical Centre, 20 Cooneen Road, Fivemiletown BT75 0ND Tel: 028 8952 1326; The Old Rectory, Cooneen, Fivemiletown BT75 0NJ — MB BCh BAO 1970 Belf.; MRCGP 1989; DRCOG 1990. Sen. Partner The Valley Med. Pract. Fivemiletown. Prev: Med. Supt. Ochadamu Med. Centre Nigeria.

MCKIBBIN, Colin Midgley The Surgery, John Street, Bellshill ML4 1RJ Tel: 01698 747195; 20 Holmwood Avenue, Uddingston, Glasgow G71 7AJ — MB ChB 1978 Glas.

MCKIBBIN, Martin Andrew Eye Clinic, St. James' University Hospital, Beckett Street, Leeds LS9 7TF; Fax: 0161 789 2556 — MB BS 1989 Newc.; FRCOphth 1994. Cons. Ophth. St. James' Univ. Hosp., Leeds.

MCKIBBIN, Victor Paul Chorlton Health Centre, 1 Nicolas Road, Manchester M21 9NJ — MB BCh BAO 1985 Belf.

MACKICHAN, Alastair Hugh Tyrell The Bridge Street Surgery, 30-32 Bridge Street, Downham Market PE38 9DH Tel: 01366 388888 Fax: 01366 383716 — MB BS 1974 Lond.

MACKICHAN, Ian Duncan (retired) 35 High Street, Braunston, Daventry NN11 7HR Tel: 01788 890881 — MB BChir 1947 Camb.; MA Camb. 1947; MRCS Eng. LRCP Lond. 1947; DObst RCOG 1949. Prev: Clin. Asst. (Occupat. Health) Hosp. of St. Cross Rugby.

MACKICHAN, Neil Duncan (retired) Aros, Towerside, Whittingham, Alnwick NE66 4RF — MB BChir 1953 Camb. Prev: GP & SCMO Occupat. Health N. Tyneside DHA.

MACKICHAN, Roderick Ian Haresfield House Surgery, 6-10 Bath Road, Worcester WR5 3EJ Tel: 01905 763161 Fax: 01905 767016; 4 Sparrowhall Lane, Colletts Green, Powick, Worcester WR2 4SG Tel: 01905 830849 — MB ChB 1979 Bristol; MRCGP 1985; DRCOG 1984. (Bristol)

MCKIDDIE, Margaret Trudie (retired) Kimsbury Cottage, Upton Hill, Upton, St Leonards, Gloucester GL4 8DF Tel: 01452 813670 — MB ChB (Hons.) St. And. 1962; MD Dundee 1969; FRCP Lond. 1979, M 1966; FRCP Glas. 1976, M 1965; DObst RCOG 1964. Prev: Cons. Phys. Glos. Roy. Hosp.

MACKIE, Alasdair David Ramsay Diabetes & Endocrine Centre, Northern General Hospital NHS Trust, Sheffield S5 7AV; 1 Woodend, Grenoside, Sheffield S35 8RR — FRCP 2001 London; MB ChB Ed. 1984; MRCP (UK) 1987; DRCOG 1987; MD (Edin.) 1997; FRCP 1999 Edinburgh. (Edinburgh) Cons. Phys. Gen. Med. (Diabetes Mellitis). Socs: Diabetics.U.K; Soc. Endocrinol. Prev: Sen. Regist. Gen. Med. (Diabetes & Endocrinol.) Addenbrooke's Hosp. Camb. & Ipswich Hosp.

MACKIE, Alastair James (retired) — MB ChB 1969 Aberd.; MRCPsych 1975; Dip. Psychother. Aberd. 1979. Cons. Psychiat. Adolesc. Unit N. Gen. Hosp. Sheff. Prev: Sen. Regist. Ross Clinic Aberd. & Stratheden Hosp. Fife.

MACKIE, Alison Poppy 3 Stairs Hill Cottages, Empshott, Liss GU33 6HP — MB ChB 1994 Bristol.

MCKIE, Allison Jane 19 Skaterigg Gardens, Glasgow G13 1ST — MB ChB 1997 Glas.

MACKIE, Anne West Kent HA, Preston Hall, Aylesford ME20 7NJ — MB BS 1985 Lond.; MFPHM RCP Lond. 1995. Director of Pub. Health W. Kent HA.

MACKIE, Catherine Frances Sighthill Health Centre, 380 Calder Road, Edinburgh EH11 4AU Tel: 0131 453 5335; 142 Lanark Road W., Currie EH14 5NY Tel: 0131 449 3541 — MB ChB 1956 Glas.

MACKIE, Charles Macmillan Larcombe Farmhouse, Exford, Minehead TA24 7PF — MB ChB 1963 Birm.; DObst RCOG 1970. Surg. Chief Off. Roy. Fleet Auxil. Prev: Ho. Phys. Roy. Hosp. Wolverhampton; Ho. Surg. Gen. Hosp. Birm.; Surg. Lt. RN.

MACKIE, Christina Maria Flamily Planning and Sexual Health, 2 Claremont Terrace, Glasgow G3 7XR Tel: 0141 211 8155 Fax: 0141 211 8139; 2 Beech Avenue, Cambuslang, Glasgow G72 8AU Tel: 0141 641 1240 — MB ChB 1972 Glas.

MACKIE, Mr Colin Robert Univ. Hospital Aintree, Longmoor Lane, Liverpool CH49 7AL; 59 Manor Drive, Upton, Wirral CH49 6LG — MB ChB 1970 St. And.; 1984 MD Dundee 1984; 1991 FRCS Eng. 1991; 1975 FRCS Ed. 1975. Cons. Surg. (Gen. & Colorect.) Aintree Hosp. Liverp.; Clin. Dir. Gen. Surg. Aintree

Hosps. Liverp. Socs: Assn. Coloproctol.; Assn. Surg. GB & Irl. Prev: Sen. Lect. (Clin.) Dept. Surg. Univ. Liverp.; Sen. Regist. (Surg.) Ninewells Hosp. Dundee.; Research Assoc. & Instruc. Univ. Chicago, Illinois, USA.

MACKIE, Colin Skene The Surgery, Lorne Street, Lochgilphead PA31 8LU Tel: 01546 602921 Fax: 01546 606735; Caol Ila, Lochgilphead PA31 8SZ — MB ChB 1976 Aberd.; MRCGP 1982. Prev: GP Trainee Highland Health Bd.; SHO Balfour Hosp. Kirkwall; Ho. Surg. Birm. Accid. Hosp.

MACKIE, Mr David Bonar (retired) Flint Cottage, Stratford-sub-Castle, Salisbury SP1 3LG Tel: 01722 336352 — MB 1961 Camb.; MChir Camb. 1970, MB 1961, BChir 1960; FRCS Eng. 1965. Prev: Cons. Surg. Salisbury Health Dist.

MCKIE, Dorothy Jane Chapel End, Kidderminster Road, Ombersley, Droitwich WR9 0DP; SEMA Medical Services, Five Ways Complex, Frederick Road, Edgbaston, Birmingham B15 1ST Tel: 0121 626 3190 Fax: 0121 626 3210 — MB ChB St. And. 1966; DObst RCOG 1968. (St. And.) Med. Adviser Sema Med. Servs. to Benefits Agency Birm.

MACKIE, Elizabeth Macgregor (retired) 76 Whittinghame Court, 1300 Great Western Road, Glasgow G12 0BH Tel: 0141 339 7396 — MB ChB 1943 Glas.; DPA 1955, DPH 1968; MFCM 1972; DCH Eng. 1949. Prev: Sen. Med. Off. Community Health Servs. Gtr. Glas. HB.

MACKIE, Erica Jane Dept of Paediatric Oncology G Level, Southampton General Hospital, Tremona Road, Southampton SO16 6YD Tel: 02380 794101 Email: ejm1@soton.ac.uk — MB ChB 1982 Liverp.; MRCP (UK) 1986. p/t Cons. Paediatric Oncologist S.ampton Gen. Hosp.; Research Asst. Dept. of Paediatric Oncol. Soton. Univ.; Trustee Naomi Ho. Childr.'s Hospice Winchester. Prev: Sen. Regist. (Paediat. Oncol.) Roy. Manch. Childr. Hosp.; Lect. (Paediat.) Univ. Sc. & Technol. Kumasi, Ghana; Regist. Alder Hey Childr. Hosp. Liverp.

MACKIE, Fiona Dawn 15 Arden Court, Court Leet, Binley Woods, Coventry CV3 2NA — MB BS 1994 Lond.

MACKIE, George Hillcrest, Littlegain Hilton, Bridgnorth WV15 5PA Tel: 01746 710389 — MB ChB 1961 Birm.; FRCR 1995; DMRD Eng. 1969. Cons. Radiol. Wolverhampton Hosps. & BridgN. Infirm. Prev: Specialist in Med. RAF.

MACKIE, George Edward 16 Crossfield Terrace E., Haltwhistle NE49 9JB; 72 Montgomery Street, Edinburgh EH7 5JA — MB ChB 1993 Glas. Prev: SHO (Orthop. & A & E) N. Tyneside Gen. Hosp.

MACKIE, Graeme Clifford (retired) 1 Heathfield, Reigate RH2 8QR Tel: 01737 222015 — LRCP LRCS Ed. LRFPS Glas. 1946. Prev: Capt. RAMC.

MACKIE, Halldis Aslaug Insch Health Centre 2, Rannes Street, Insch AB52 6JJ Tel: 01464 820707 Fax: 01464 820707; Westertown, Rothienorman, Inverurie AB51 8US Tel: 01467 671253 — MB ChB 1963 Aberd.; DRCOG 1977; DCH RCPS Glas. 1969. (Aberd.) Princip. Gen. Pract. Insch Health Centre, Insch; Med. Dir. Insch War Memor. Hosp. Socs: BMA; Assoc. Mem. RCGP.; Garioch Med. Assn. Prev: SHO (O & G) Raigmore Hosp. Inverness; Ho. Off. (Cas. Outpat.) Roy. Aberd. Infirm.; Ho. Off. Roy. Aberd. Hosp. Sick Childr.

MACKIE, Helen Jean Gardner (retired) Viewfield, Mauchline KA5 5AP — MB ChB 1947 Glas. Med. Asst. (Geriat.) Ayrsh.

MACKIE, Mr Ian Alexander 99 Harley Street, London W1N 1DF Tel: 020 7935 3035 Fax: 020 7224 1723; 28 Kensington Gate, London W8 5NA Tel: 020 7584 0942 — MB ChB 1954 Aberd.; FRCS Eng. 1983; DO Eng. 1958; FRCOphth. 1988. (Aberd.) Socs: Fell. Roy. Soc. Med.; Ex-Pres. Med. Contact Lens. Assn. Prev: Assoc. Specialist Extern. Eye Dis. Clinic Moorfields Eye Hosp. Lond.; Ho. Phys. Aberd. Roy. Infirm.; Ho. Surg. Woodend Gen. Hosp. Aberd.

MACKIE, Mr Ian Grant 114 Ely Road, Llandaff, Cardiff CF5 2DA — MB BS 1974 Lond.; FRCS Eng. 1979; MRCS Eng. LRCP Lond. 1974.

MACKIE, James Farquharson (retired) 5 King Duncan's Place, Birnam, Dunkeld PH8 0QD Tel: 01350 727595 — MB ChB 1947 Aberd.; MRCGP 1958. Prev: Sen. Partner Mackie, O'Callaghan, McLinteck, & Chundun, Walthamstow.

MACKIE, James George Institute of Occupational Health, University of Birmingham, Edgbaston, Birmingham B15 2TT Tel: 0121 414 6030 Fax: 0121 414 6217 Email: mackiej@ioh.bham.ac.uk; Greenfields, Norton Cannon, Hereford

HR4 7BH Tel: 01544 318899 Email: james.mackie@lineone.net — MB ChB 1990 Birm.; ChB Birm. 1990; MRCGP 1996; DRCOG 1993; DFFP 1993. (Birm.) Clin. Lect. (Occupat. Med.) Univ. of Birm. Socs: Herefordsh. Med. Soc.; Soc. of Occup. Med. Prev: GP Princip. Clin. Asst. (Med.) Worcester Roy. Infirm.

MACKIE, James Ian Queensbery W., Admin. Block, The Crichton Royal Hospital, Dumfries Tel: 01387 244000 — MB ChB 1987 Ed.; BSc (1st cl. Hons.) Med. Sci. Psych. Ed. 1985; MRC Psych 1992; MPsy 1998. Cons. Gen. Adult Psych, with s/i in Psychother., The Crichton Roy. Hosp. Dumfries. Prev: Specialist Regist. Gen. Psychiat. of Psychother., Yorks.; Regist. & SHO Roy. Edin. Train. Scheme.

MACKIE, Jane Helen The Winlaton & Ryton Medical Partnership, 19 Front St., Winlaton, Blaydon-on-Tyne NE21 4RD — MB ChB 1988 Ed.; MRCGP 1993; DCCH RCP Ed. 1994; DRCOG 1990. (Ed.)

MACKIE, Joan Edith Warner (retired) 22 Mortonhall Road, Edinburgh EH9 2HN Tel: 0131 667 2566 — MB ChB 1942 Ed.; FRCOG 1962, M 1947. Prev: Cons. Obstetr. & Gynaecol. Elsie Inglis Matern. Hosp. & Bruntsfield.

MACKIE, John Rowan Croft, Sandy Lane, Out Rawcliffe, Preston PR3 6BQ Tel: 01995 671220 Fax: 01995 671220 Email: mackiejohn@talk21.com — MB ChB Ed. 1956; FRCGP 1990, M 1977. (Ed.) Cons. Med. Off. Initial Shorrock Security, Blackburn, Lancs - CMO Scott. Equitable plc, Lytham, Lancs. Socs: BMA & Assur. Med. Soc. Prev: GP TheFylde, Lancs.; CMO Guardian Financial Servs.; Clin. Asst. (Diabetic Clinic) Roy. Preston Hosp.

MACKIE, John Hugh Kerr (retired) 191 Cooden Sea Road, Bexhill-on-Sea TN39 4TR — MB BS 1954 Lond.; DObst RCOG 1959.

MCKIE, Judith Mary 96A Stoke Newington High Street, London N16 7NY; 117 Stanmore Road, 6 Mount Florida, Glasgow G42 9AL Tel: 0141 636 5940 Email: jmckie@hgmp.mrc.ac.uk — MB ChB 1988 Glas.; PhD Lond. 1998. SHO (Psychiat.) Lanarksh. Rotat.al Train. Scheme. Prev: Research Fell., Molecular Med. Unit, Instit. Of Child Health, Lond.

MACKIE, Lewis (retired) Marine Cottage, Collieston, Ellon AB41 8RS Tel: 01358 751317 Email: drlmackie@lineone.com — MB ChB 1944 Aberd.; FRCGP 1983, M 1963. Prev: Clin. Asst. Kingseat Hosp. Newmachar.

MCKIE, Mr Lloyd Douglas Mater Hospital, Crumlin Road, Belfast BT14 6AB Tel: 028 9080 3107 Fax: 028 9080 2242 Email: lmckie@mater.n-i.nhs.uk — MB BCh BAO 1984 Belf.; MD Belf. 1995; FRCS Ed. 1989; FRCSI 1988. Cons. (Surg.) Gen. Surg. Mate Hosp. Belf.

MACKIE, Moira Russell (retired) 52 Castle Court, Newton Mearns, Glasgow G77 5JD — MB ChB 1952 Glas.; DPH 1954.

MACKIE, Niall Fraser Thomson Drongan Surgery, 74 Mill O'Shields Road, Drongan, Ayr KA6 7AY Tel: 01292 591345 Fax: 01292 590782 Email: niall.mackie@aapct.scot.nhs.uk; Viewfield, 27 Cumnock Road, Mauchline KA5 5AP Tel: 01290 550421 — MB ChB 1979 Glas.; MRCGP 1985; DCH RCP Lond. 1984; DRCOG 1981.

MCKIE, Nigel Ian Paul Stone Well Place, Edgeworth, Stroud GL6 7JQ Tel: 01285 821483; 33 Chester Way, London SE11 4UR Tel: 020 7820 1951 — MB ChB 1966 St. And.; MSc Occupat. Med. Lond. 1979; FFOM RCP Lond. 1993; DIH Eng. 1979. Indep. Cons. Occupat. Phys. Glos. Socs: Fell. Austral. Coll. Occupat. Med.; Fell. Austral. Fac. Occupat. Med. Prev: Chief Med. Off. Shell UK Ltd.; Sen. Med. Adviser Overseas Shell Internat. Petroleum Co. Lond.; Sen. Med. Off. Shell UK Ltd. Stanlow Refinery Ellesmere Port.

MACKIE, Norman (retired) 18 Sutherland Drive, Newcastle-under-Lyme, Newcastle ST5 3NB — MB ChB 1954 Liverp. Prev: Ho. Off. (Med.) Denbighsh. Infirm.

MACKIE, Peter Howard HRH Princess Christian's Hospital, Clarence Road, Windsor SL4 5AG Tel: 01753 633417 Fax: 01753 633406 Email: phm@btinternet.com — BM BCh 1972 Oxf.; MA Oxf. 1972; FRCP Lond. 1995; MRCP (UK) 1978; FRCPath 1993, M 1981. (Oxf.) Cons. Haemat. Heatherwood & Wexham Pk. Hosp. Trust. Socs: Brit. Soc. Haematol. (Regional Represen.); Ex-Counc. Mem. Windsor and Dist. Med. Soc. Prev: Sen. Regist. (Haemat.) John Radcliffe Hosp. Oxf.; Clin. Lect. (Immunol.) Univ. Birm. Med. Sch.

MACKIE, Professor Rona McLeod Department of Dermatology, Glasgow University, Glasgow G12 8QQ Tel: 0141 339 8855 Fax: 0141 330 4008; 62 Russell Drive, Bearsden, Glasgow G61 3BB — MD 1970 Glas.; FRSE 1983; DSc Glas. 1994, MD (Commend.) 1970, MB ChB 1963; FRCP Lond. 1985; FRCP Glas. 1978; MRCP (UK) 1971; FRCPath 1983, M 1980. Prof. Dermat. Univ. Glas. Prev: Consult. Dermat. W.. RHB (Scotl.); Lect. (Dermat.) Univ. Glas.; Ho. Phys. W.. Infirm. Glas.

MACKIE, Shiona Elizabeth Ross Ladywell Medical Centre, 26 Featherwall Avenue, Edinburgh EH12 7UN Tel: 0131 334 5000 Fax: 0131 334 8410; Braeburn Stable Cottage, Blinkbonny Road, Currie EH14 6AQ — MB ChB 1972 Aberd.; MRCGP 1988. (Aberd.) Clin. Dir. (p/t) NW Edin. Local Health Care Co-op. Prev: GP Locality Co-Ordinator, NW Edin.

MACKIE, Stuart 307 Tudor Drive, Kingston upon Thames KT2 5PF — MB ChB 1986 Glas.

MACKIE, Thomasin Catherine Margaret 72 Montgomery Street, Edinburgh EH7 5JA — MB BS 1993 Newc.; DCH 1996; MRCGP 1998; DFFP 1998. (Newc.) p/t GP Polwarth Surg., Edin. Prev: Trainee GP Newc.u.Tyne VTS.

***MACKIE, Valerie Susan** Nith Hill, 3 Lovers Walk, Dumfries DG1 1LR — MB ChB 1987 Ed.

MACKIE, Victoria Jane Belmont Medical Centre, Eastholme Avenue, Belmont, Hereford HR2 7XT; Greenfields, Norton Canon, Hereford HR4 7BH Tel: 01544 318899 — MB ChB 1990 Birm.; ChB Birm. 1990; DRCOG 1993; DFFP 1993. (Birm.) Asst. GP Hereford.

MCKIERNAN, Mr David Charles 3 Jessel House, Regency Street Dwellings, London SW1P 4BH — MB BS 1989 Lond.; FRCS Eng. 1995.

MCKIERNAN, Eamonn Patrick 5 Parklands Avenue, Penwortham, Preston PR1 0QL — MB ChB 1979 Manch.; FFA RCS Eng. 1985. Cons. Anaesth. Preston & Chorley HAs. Prev: Sen. Regist. (Anaesth.) NW RHA; Regist. (Anaesth.) Soton HA.

MCKIERNAN, Michael John EEF, Broadway House, Tothill St., London SW1H 9NQ Tel: 020 7222 7777 Fax: 020 7222 4963; 8 Chadwick Manor, Chadwick End, Knowle, Solihull B93 0AT — MB ChB 1966 Birm.; FRCP Lond. 1996; FFOM RCP Lond. 1988; DIH Eng. 1976. Dir. Occup. Policy. Socs: Fell. Roy. Soc. Med.; Soc. Occupat. Med.; Fell. Austral Fac. Occupat. Med. Prev: Health & Safety Commiss.er 1996; Head Occupat. Med. HCF Sydney, Austral.

MCKIERNAN, Mr Michael Vincent Department of Plastic Surgery, Royal Preston Hospital, Fulwood, Preston PR2 9HT Tel: 01772 716565; Cahercalla Road, Ennis, County Clare, Republic of Ireland Tel: 00 353 65 24768 — MB BCh BAO 1986 NUI; MMedSci NUI 1992; FRCS Ed. 1990; FRCSI 1990. Sen. Regist. (Plastic Surg.) Roy. Preston Hosp. Socs: Fell. Roy. Acad. Med. Irel.; Brit. Burns Assn.; Founder Mem. Irish Soc. Surgic. Oncol. Prev: Regist. (Plastic Surg.) Newc. Gen. Hosp.; Regist. (Plastic Surg.) Shotley Bridge, W. Norwich Hosp. & Regional Hosp. Galway.

MCKIERNAN, Patrick James Liver Unit, Birmingham Children's Hospital NHS Trust, Steelhouse Lane, Birmingham B4 6NH Tel: 0121 333 8254 Fax: 0121 333 8251 Email: pat.mckiernan@bhamchildrens.wmids.nhs.uk; 132 Salisbury Road, Moseley, Birmingham B13 8JZ Tel: 0121 449 6787 — MB BCh BAO 1983 Belf.; MRCP (UK) 1986; T(M) (Paediat.) 1994; FRCPCH 1999. Cons. Paediat. (Paediat. Hepatol.) Birm. Childr. Hosp. NHS Trust; Hon. Sen. Lect. In Child Health, Univ. of Birm.

MCKILLEN, Jacqueline Mary 103 Lislaban Road, Cloughmills, Ballymena BT44 9HZ — MB BCh BAO 1997 Belf.

MCKILLOP, Alison Catherine 111, 268 Crow Road, Glasgow G11 7BG — MB ChB 1988 Glas.

MACKILLOP, Andrew Joseph James 23 Parkside Avenue, Bromley BR1 2EJ Email: a.mackillop@calk21.com — MB ChB 1994 Sheff. SHO N. Trent Anaesth. Rotat. 1996-1999; Specialist Regist. Rotat. (Anaesth.). Socs: BMA RCAnaesth.

MCKILLOP, Graham Fax: 0131 536 2950 Email: grahammckellop@doctors.org.uk; 24 Kettilstoun Cres, Linlithgow EH49 6PR Tel: Ex directory — MB ChB 1983 Glas.; MRCP (UK) 1986; FRCR 1992. (Glasgow) Cons. Radiol. Edin. Roy. Inf. Prev: Cons. Radiol. Vict. Infirm. Glas.; Sen. Regist. (Radiol) Edin. Roy. Infirm.; Reg. (Car. Rad. Med.) Vict. Infirm. Glas.

MCKILLOP, Helen Teresa 68 Agnew Avenue, Airdrie ML6 9AA — LRCP LRCS 1945 Ed.; LRCP LRCS Ed. LRFPS Glas. 1945. (Anderson & St. Mungo's Colls. Glas.) Prev: Ho. Surg. Roy. Infirm. Glas.; Med. Off. Co. Fev. Hosp. Motherwell & Matern. Hosp. Bellshill.

MCKILLOP

MCKILLOP, Professor James Hugh University Department of Medicine, Royal Infirmary, Glasgow G31 2ER Tel: 0141 552 4014 Fax: 0141 552 2953; 10 Kirklee Circus, Glasgow G12 0TW Tel: 0141 339 7000 — MB ChB 1972 Glas.; PhD Glas. 1979, MB ChB 1972, BSc (Hons.) 1970; FRCP Lond. 1992; FRCP Ed. 1990; FRCP Glas. 1986; MRCP (UK) 1975; FRCR 1994. Muirhead Prof. Med. & Hon. Cons. Phys. Univ. Dept. Med. Roy. Infirm. Glas. Socs: Assn. Phys.; Brit. Nuclear Med. Soc. Prev: Sen. Lect. (Med.) Glas. Roy. Infirm.; Harkness Fell. of the Commonw. Fund of New York Stanford Med. Center, Calif., USA.

MCKILLOP, Keith David 43 Langmuir Avenue, Kirkintilloch, Glasgow G66 2JQ — MB ChB 1992 Glas.

MCKILLOP, Margaret Elspeth Raigmore Hospital, Inverness IV2 3UJ Tel: 01463 704000; 8 Devlin Crescent, Inverness IV2 4LH Tel: 01463 222927 — MB ChB Glas. 1964; DObst RCOG 1966. Assoc. Specialist (Med. Elderly) Highland HB. Prev: Regist. (Chest Med.) Culduthel Hosp. Inverness.

MACKILLOP, Neil Alexander 78 Berkeley Street, Glasgow G3 7DS Tel: 0141 221 1775 — MB ChB 1946 Glas.; DPH 1963. Prev: Res. Med. Off. Vict. Fev. Hosp. & Sanat, Kirkcaldy; Ho. Surg. Glas. W.. Infirm.; Regist. (Med.) Roy. Lond. Homoeop. Hosp.

MACKILLOP, Neil Graham 33 Lindsey Close, Bessacarr, Doncaster DN4 7JD — MB ChB 1983 Manch.; BSc (Med. Sci.) St. And. 1980. SHO/Trainee GP Doncaster Gen. Infirm. VTS. Socs: Assur. Med. Soc. Prev: Ho. Surg. Glan Clwyd Hosp. Bodelwyddan; Ho. Phys. Hope Hosp. Manch.

MCKIM, Donald Stewart Top Flat, 4 Alfred St., Bath BA1 2QU — MB BS 1987 Lond.

MCKIM, Mr Robert Stewart (retired) 52 Warminster Road, Bath BA2 6RX — MB BChir Camb. 1954; MA Camb. 1955; FRCS Eng. 1961; DLO Eng. 1958. Prev: Hon. Cons. ENT Surg. Bath HA.

MCKIMMIE, Patricia Lucy Frances (retired) 5 Beechwood Court, 24 Drymen Road, Bearsden, Glasgow G61 2RY Tel: 0141 943 0724 — MRCS Eng. LRCP Lond. 1942.

MCKIMMIE, Siona Jane 15 Riselaw Terrace, Edinburgh EH10 6HW; 7 Conway Close, Caterall, Garstang, Preston PR3 0QE Tel: 01995 601983 — MB ChB 1995 Manch. SHO (Obs+Gynae) GP Regist.

MCKIMMON, William James (retired) 12 Lenamore Avenue, Newtownabbey BT37 0PF Tel: 028 9085 2748 — MB BCh BAO 1948 Belf.; FRCGP 1984, M 1957; DObst RCOG 1950.

MACKIN, Elspeth Alice Latchford Medical Centre, 5 Thelwall Lane, Latchford, Warrington WA4 1LJ Tel: 01925 637508 Fax: 01925 654384 — MB ChB 1981 Manch.; BSc (Hons.) St. And. 1978; DRCOG 1984.

MACKIN, James Robert Church End Medical Centre, Church End, Old Leake, Boston PE22 9LE Tel: 01205 870666 Fax: 01205 870971; School House, Benington, Boston PE22 0BT — MB ChB 1976 Ed.; MRCGP 1980; DCH Eng. 1980.

MACKIN, John Gerard 110 Caw Hill Park, Londonderry BT47 6XX — MB BS 1989 Lond.

MCKINLAY, Alastair William Wards 3 & 4, Aberdeen Royal Infirmary, Forresterhill, Aberdeen AB25 2ZN Tel: 01224 681818 Fax: 01223 685307; 26 Roseberry Street, Aberdeen AB15 5LL — MB ChB 1982 Ed.; BSc (Hons.) Ed. 1979; MRCP (UK) 1985. Cons. Phys. & Gastroenterol. Aberd. Roy. Hosp. Trust. Socs: Brit. Soc. Gastroenterol. Prev: Sen. Regist. (Gen. Med. & Gastroenterol.) Aberd. Roy. Infirm.; Regist. (Gastroenterol.) Glas. Roy. Infirm.

MACKINLAY, Carolyn Isobel 2 Church Street, Great Bedwyn, Marlborough SN8 3PE — MB ChB 1991 Ed.

MCKINLAY, David Michael 221 Upper Chorlton Road, Whalley Range, Manchester M16 0DE — MB ChB 1986 Liverp.

MACKINLAY, George Brian Leith Mount, 46 Ferry Road, Edinburgh EH6 4AE Tel: 0131 554 0558 Fax: 0131 555 6911; 2 Cramond Glebe Road, Edinburgh EH4 6AF Tel: 0131 336 4567 — MB ChB 1963 Ed.; DObst RCOG 1966.

MCKINLAY, Mr George Campbell, DSC (retired) Lochinver, Arthurlie Drive, Uplawmoor, Glasgow G78 4AH Tel: 01505 850384 — MB ChB 1939 Glas.; FRCS Ed. 1947; MB ChB (Hons.) Glas. 1939. Prev: Sen. Cons. Surg. ENT Dept. W.. Infirm. Glas.

MACKINLAY, Mr Gordon Alexander The Royal Hospital For Sick Children, Sciennes Road, Edinburgh EH9 1LF Tel: 0131 536 0662 Fax: 0131 536 0665; Marhaba, Johnsburn Park, Balerno EH14 7NA Tel: 0131 449 5979 Email: mackinlays@msn.com — MB BS Lond. 1969; FRCS Eng. 1976; FRCS Ed. 1976; MRCS Eng. LRCP Lond. 1969. (Char. Cross Hosp. Univ. Lond.) Sen. Lect. (Clin. Surg.) Univ. Edin. & Cons. Surg. Roy. Hosp. for Sick Childr. Edin.; Dir. Surg. Anaesth. & ITU Edin. Sick Childr. NHS Trust. Socs: Fell. Roy. Soc. Med.; BMA; UKCCSG. Prev: SHO (Surg.) Hosp. for Sick Childr. Gt. Ormond St. Lond.; SHO (Surg.) Char. Cross Hosp. Lond.; Ho. Phys. Char. Cross Hosp. Lond.

MCKINLAY, Ian Alexander Mackay Gordon Centre, Royal Manchester Childrens Hospital, Pendlebury, Manchester M27 4HA Tel: 0161 727 2340 Fax: 0161 727 2340; 6 Godfrey Road, Irlams O'th' Height, Salford M6 7QP Tel: 0161 736 4820 Fax: 0161 736 4820 — MB ChB 1969 Ed.; BSc (Hons.) Ed. 1966; FRCP Lond. 1983; MRCP (UK) 1972; FRCPCH 1996; DCH RCPS Glas. 1971. (Ed.) Sen. Lect. (Community Child Health) Univ. Manch. Mackay-Gordon Centre Roy. Manch. Childr. Hosp.; Hon. Mem. Assn. Paediat. Chartered Physiother.; Mem. Disabil. Living Allowance Advis. Bd. Socs: Brit. Paediat. Neurol. Assn. Prev: Cons. Paediat. Neurol. Booth Hall & Roy. Manch. Childr. Hosps.; Sen. Regist. (Paediat. Neurol.) Booth Hall & Roy. Manch. Childr. Hosps.

MCKINLAY, James Joseph 61 High Road, Saltcoats KA21 5SA; Springburn Health Centre, 200 Springburn Way, Glasgow G21 1TR — MB ChB 1990 Glas.; BSc (Hons.) Glas. 1985; MRCGP 1996; DRCOG 1995. Princip. (Genereal Pract.). Prev: Higher Professional Train. Fell. (Gen. Pract.).

MACKINLAY, Mr James Young Grasmere, Blow Row, Epworth, Doncaster DN9 1HP Tel: 01427 872495 — MB ChB 1975 Glas.; FRCS Glas. 1981; FRCR 1987; DMRD Ed. 1985; DRCOG 1977. (Glas.) Cons. Radiol. Doncaster Roy. Infirm. Socs: Fell. Roy. Soc. Med.; Brit. Soc. Interven. Radiol.; Cardiovasc. & Interven. Radiol. Soc. Europe. Prev: Sen. Regist. (Diag. Radiol.) W. Midl. RHA; Regist. (Diag. Radiol.) W.. Gen. Hosp. & Roy. Infirm. Edin.; Regist. (Vasc. Surg.) Roy. Infirm. Edin.

MCKINLAY, Justin 4 Norfolk Terrace, Chapel Allerton, Leeds LS7 4QW Tel: 0113 269 6660 Email: justin@mckim67.freeserve.co.uk — BM BCh 1992 Oxf.; MA 1993; FRCA 1998. (Oxford) Specialist Regist. (Anaesth.).

MCKINLAY, Kenneth Hunter Department of Anaesthesia, Western Infirmary Dumbarton Road, Glasgow G11 Tel: 0141 211 2000; Top Left, 78 Novar Drive, Glasgow G12 9TZ Tel: 0141 334 4911 — MB ChB 1995 Glas. Sen. Health Off. (Anaesth.) W. Glagow Hosps. Univ. NHS Trust. Socs: Glas. & W. Scot. Soc. Anaesth.; Scott. Soc. of Anaesth.

MCKINLAY, Kevin Peter, Wing Cdr. RAF Med. Br. Retd. The North Hampton Hospital, Aldermaston Road, Basingstoke RD24 7DS Tel: 01256 313636 Fax: 01256 313634; 17 Priory Gardens, Old Basing, Basingstoke RG24 7DS Tel: 01256 321260 Fax: 01256 321260 Email: kpmck@lineone.net — MB BS 1980 Lond.; MRCP (UK) 1984; MRCS Eng. LRCP Lond. 1980; FRCP 2000. (Guy's) Cons. Phys. N. Hants. Hosp. Basingstoke; Recognised Teach. (Thoracic Med.) Univ. Soton.; UnderGrad. Clin. Tutor N. Hants. Hosp.; Lead Clinician for Cancer N. Hants. Hosp. Socs: Brit. Thoracic Soc. Sub-Comm. on Guidelines for Passengers with Respirat. Dis. on Flying. Prev: Cons. Adviser Thoracic Med. RAF; Cons. Phys. King Edwd. VII Hosp. Midhurst; Hon. Sen. Regist. (Thoracic Med.) Roy. Brompton & Nat. Heart Hosp. Lond.

MCKINLAY, Margaret Isabel (retired) 45 St James Close, Pangbourne, Reading RG8 7AP — LM 1935 Rotunda; MB ChB Ed. 1926, DPH 1931. Prev: Asst. Admin. MOH Matern. & Child Welf., & Ment. Health Birm.

MACKINLAY, Marna Elizabeth 28 Mabarry Street, Aberdeen AB25 1NB Email: marnamack@aol.com — MB ChB 1998 Aberd.; MB ChB Aberdeen 1998; BSc (Hons) Aberdeen 1993. (Aberdeen University) PRHO in Gen. Med., Aberd. Roy. Infirm. Prev: PRHO in Gen. Surg./Urol.

MACKINLAY, Morag Grace Raigmore Hospital, Bearsden, Inverness IV2 3UJ — MB ChB 1988 Ed.; MRCP (Paediat.) (UK) 1995; MRCGP 1993; DObst Otago 1991. (Edinburgh) Regist. (Med. Paediat.) Inverness. Socs: BMA; RCPCH; RCGP. Prev: SHO (Med. Paediat.) Aberd. Hosps. Trust; Trainee GP Highland HB.

MCKINLAY, Robert Gray 1 Court View, Tennis Drive, The Park, Nottingham NG7 1AE Tel: 01159 441573 — MRCS Eng. LRCP Lond. 1969; FFPM RCP (UK) 1992; Dip. Pharm. Med. RCP Ed. 1980; DA Eng. 1973; DObst RCOG 1972. (Sheff.) Head Med. Serv.

Boots PLC Nottm. Prev: Clin. Research Dept. Ciba-Geigy Basle; Med. Dir. Zyma B.V. Holland.

MCKINLAY, Robert Greig Campbell Stirling Royal Infirmary NHS Trust, Livilands, Stirling FK8 2AU Tel: 01786 434476 Fax: 01786 434499; The Mine House, Bridge of Allan, Stirling FK9 4DY Tel: 01786 832361 — MB ChB 1968 Glas.; FRCA 1973; Dip. Palliat. Med. Wales 1995; FFA RCSI 1973. (Glasgow University) Cons. Anaesth. (Anaesth. & Pain Managem.) The Stirling Roy. Infirm. NHS Trust. Socs: Pain Soc.; Assn. Anaesth. Prev: Cons. Anaesth. & Pain Managem., Guernsey; Cons. Anaesth. Argyll & Clyde HB; Sen. Specialist (Anaesth.) RN Hosp. Haslar.

MCKINLAY, Sonya Department of Anaesthesia, Western Infirmary, Dumbarton Road, Glasgow G11 6NT Tel: 0141 211 2000; Top Left, 78 Novar Drive, Glasgow G12 9TZ Tel: 0141 334 4911 — MB ChB 1995 Glas. SHO (Anaesth.) W. Glas. Hosps. Univ. NHS Trust. Socs: W Scotl. Soc. of Anaesth. (Trainee Rep.); Scott. Soc. of Anaesth. Prev: SHO (Anaesth.) Monklands Hosp. Airdrie.

MCKINLAY, William John David Pendleside Medical Practice, Clitheroe Health Centre, Railway View Road, Clitheroe BB7 2JG Tel: 01200 421888 Fax: 01200 421887; Claremont, 53 Pendle Road, Clitheroe BB7 1JQ Tel: 01200 425032 Fax: 01200 429983 — MB BS Newc. 1969; MRCP 2001; DFFP 1993; FRCGP 1987, M 1973; DHMSA 1990; DObst RCOG 1974; DCH Eng. 1973. (Newcastle upon Tyne) Dir. of Postgrad. Gen. Pract. Educat. Unviersity of Manch. & N. W. Regional Office, NHS-E; Mem. of JCPT-GP (Int Comm. for Postgrad. Train. For Gen. Pract.). Socs: Manch. Med. Soc.; Blackburn Med. & Dent. Soc.; Yorks. Med. & Dent. Hist. Soc. Prev: Provost NW Fac RCGP; Course Organiser Blackburn & Burnley VTS; Convenor JT. Hosp.Vis.RCOP. 1992-2000.

MCKINLEY, Miss Aileen Joyce Raigmore Hospital, Old Perth Road, Inverness IV2 3YW Tel: 01463 704000; 28 St. Magdalenes, Linlithgow EH49 6AQ — MB ChB 1991 Ed.; BSc (Neurosci.) 1st cl. Hons. Ed. 1989; FRCS Ed. (Ed.) Specialist Regist. Surg. Raigmore Hosp. Inverness. Socs: Fell. Roy. Med. Soc.

MCKINLEY, Andrew George 3 Grange Valley, Saintfield, Ballynahinch BT24 7NW — MB BCh BAO 1985 Belf.

MCKINLEY, Neil Patrick 30 Bedwin Street, Salisbury SP1 3UT — MB BS 1988 Lond.

MCKINLEY, Patrick Martin 10 Glenmakeeran Road, Ballycastle BT54 6PU — MB BCh BAO 1990 Belf.

MCKINLEY, Robert Kee The East Leicester Medical Practice, 131 Uppingham Road, Leicester LE5 4BP Tel: 0116 276 7145 Fax: 0116 246 1637 — MB BCh BAO Belf. 1982; MD Belf. 1992; MRCP (UK) 1985; MRCGP 1988. Sen. Lect. (Gen. Pract.) Univ. Leicester.

MCKINLEY, William John 91 Whitefield Crescent, Houghton-le-Spring DH4 7QU — MB BS 1972 Newc.

MCKINNA, Fiona Elisabeth Mid Kent Oncology Centre, Maidstone Hospital, Hermitage Lane, Maidstone ME16 9NN Tel: 01622 729000; 46 Yewland Close, Banstead SM7 3DB — MB BS 1986 Lond.; MRCP (UK) 1990; FRCR 1994. Cons. (Clin. Oncol.).

MCKINNA, Mr James Alan 14 Elliott Square, London NW3 350 Tel: 01797 225125 Fax: 01797 222812 Email: amckinna@doctors.org.uk — MB BS 1956 Lond.; BSc Lond. 1953; FRCS Eng. 1964. (St. Bart.) Emerit. Cons. Surg. Cromwell Hosp. Lond. (Retd.). Socs: BMA; Brit. Assn. Surgic. Oncol.; Harveian Soc. Prev: Cons. Surg. Roy. Marsden Hosps. Lond. & Sutton; Sen. Lect. Inst. Cancer Research Lond.; Hon. Cons. Surg. Chelsea Hosp. Wom. Lond.

MCKINNEL, Simon Robert 402 Pinhoe Road, Exeter EX4 8EH — MB BS 1979 Lond.

MCKINNELL, Thomas Harald 86 Bonnygate, Cupar KY15 4LB — MB ChB 1998 Manch.

MCKINNEY, Angela Anna Gertrud 8 Glencroft, Magheralin, Craigavon BT67 0GL Tel: 01846 613569 Email: awmckin@aol — State Exam Med 1988 Aachen; DFFP 1994; MRCOG 1997. Specialist Regist. (O & G) Belf. City Hosp.

MCKINNEY, Caroline Anne Helena Email: ben027397@aol.com — MB BCh BAO 1987 Belf.; MRCGP 1992; DRCOG 1993; DGM RCP Lond. 1989. (Queen's University Belfast) Prev: Trainee GP Belf. VTS.

***MCKINNEY, Catherine Frances** 33 Barleyhill Road, Bridgehill, Consett DH8 8JS — MB BS 1996 Newc.

MCKINNEY, Conor Anthony Thomas (retired) 24 Reeds Avenue, Earley, Reading RG6 5SR — MB BCh BAO 1956 NUI; DObst RCOG 1961. Prev: Regist. (Surg.) N.ampton Gen. Hosp.

MCKINNEY, Jane Patricia (retired) 24 ReedsAvenue, Earley, Reading RG6 5SR Tel: 01189 874440 — MB BCh BAO 1956 NUI. Prev: Clin. Med. Off. W. Berks. HA.

MCKINNEY, Karen Aileen Department of Obstetrics and Gynaecology, The Queen's University of Belfast, Institute of Clinical Science, Grosvenor Road, Belfast BT12 6BJ Tel: 01232 894600 Fax: 01232 328247; 2 Kernan Park, Portadown, Craigavon BT63 5QY — MB ChB 1986 Dundee; MD Belf. 1996; MRCOG 1991. (Lect. (Obst. & Gyn.) Qu. Univ. Belf.) Prev: Fell. (Reproduc. Endocrinol. & Infertil.) Oregon Health Sci.s Univ. Portland, USA.

MCKINNEY, Mr Leslie Alan 1 Riverbridge, Drumahoe, Londonderry BT47 3YH — MB BCh BAO 1979 Belf.; FRCS Ed. 1983.

MCKINNEY, Maurice Stanley The Ulster Hospital, Dundonald, Belfast BT16 1RH Tel: 028 9058 4511 Email: maurice.mckinney@nda.n-i.nhs.uk; 29B Saintfield Road, Ballygowan, Newtownards BT23 6HB Tel: 028 9752 8999 — MD 1993 Belf.; MB BCh BAO 1982; FFA RCSI 1986.

MCKINNEY, Nicola Mary University Hospital (GMC), Nottingham NG7 2UH Tel: 0115 924 9924; 55 Woodland Grange, Belfast BT11 9QT Tel: 01232 616134 — BM BCh 1996 Oxf.; MA Contab 1993; MRCP UK 1999. (Uni. Camb. & Uni. Oxf.) SHO (Dermat.) Qeens Med. Centre, Notts. Prev: Sen. Ho. Off. (Gen Med. Rot.) Torbay Hosp. Torquay.

MCKINNEY, Norman Hugh Moore Morecambe Health Centre, Hanover St., Morecambe LA4 5LY Tel: 01524 418418 — BM BCh 1958 Oxf.; MA, BM BCh Oxf. 1958; MRCGP 1968; DObst RCOG 1962. (Oxf.) Socs: BMA. Prev: Ho. Phys., Ho. Surg. & Obst. Ho. Surg. Radcliffe Infirm. Oxf.; Capt. RAMC.

MACKINNON, Ailie Serena Rosemary Ramsbottom Health Centre, Carr Street, Ramsbottom, Bury BL0 9DD Tel: 01706 824413 Fax: 01706 821196 — MB ChB 1976 Ed.; Dip Practical Dermatology 2000. (Edinburgh) Gen. Practitioner. Socs: Brit. Menopause Soc.; Fam. Plann.

MACKINNON, Alan Duncan Montgomery Baillieston Health Centre, 20 Muirside Road, Baillieston, Glasgow G69 7AD Tel: 0141 531 8040 — MB ChB 1971 Glas.; MSc (Sports Med.) Glas. 1997.

MACKINNON, Mr Alan Ewen Sheffield Childrens Hospital, Western Bank, Sheffield S10 2TH Tel: 0114 271 7000 Fax: 0114 276 8419 Email: conaem@sheffch_tr.trent.uk; 12 Dore Road, Dore, Sheffield S17 3NB Tel: 01142 365967 Fax: 01142 353105 — MB BS Lond. 1965; FRCS Glas. 1971; FRCS Eng. 1970; FRCPCH 1998. (Middlx.) Cons. Paediat. Surg. Sheff. Childr. Hosp. Sheff. Prev: Sen. Regist. (Paediat. Surg.) Roy. Manch. Childr. Hosp.; Regist. W.. Infirm. Glas.; Ho. Phys. Middlx. Hosp.

MACKINNON, Alastair Graham 31 Langford Green, London SE5 8BX — MB BS 1996 Lond.

MACKINNON, Alexander Gordon, TD (retired) Dun Ringill, 70 Woolton Hill Road, Gateacre, Liverpool L25 4RF Tel: 0151 428 5486 — MB ChB 1948 Liverp.; FRCA 1994; FFA RCS Eng. 1955. Prev: Cons. Anaesth. Liverp. HA (T) & Sefton HA.

MACKINNON, Andrew David Osborne House, Preston, Cirencester GL7 5PR — MB BS 1996 Lond.

MACKINNON, Angus Joseph Anthony, Maj. RAMC (retired) Balcult, Campsie Dene Road, Blanefield, Glasgow G63 9BN Tel: 01360 771048 Email: angusandpaddy@supanet.com — MB ChB 1965 Glas.; DObst RCOG 1967.

MACKINNON, Ann Jennifer Community Child Health, Strathmartine Hospital, Dundee DD3 0PG Tel: 01382 858334 Fax: 01382 828311; 14 Inchcape Road, Broughty Ferry, Dundee DD5 2LL Tel: 01382 731329 — MB ChB 1984 Dundee. SCMO (Community Child Health); Hon. Lect. Dundee Univ. & Med. Sch. Socs: RCPCH; BACDA; BACCH.

MACKINNON, Anne Lee Department of Diagnostic Radiology, Worthing Hospital, Park Avenue, Worthing BN11 2DH Tel: 01903 205111 Fax: 01903 285045 Email: anne.mackinnon@wash-tr.sthames.nhs.uk; Ivy Cottage, Mouse Lane, Steyning BN44 3LP Tel: 01903 813550 — MB ChB 1976 Aberd.; MRCP (UK) 1983; FRCR 1989. Cons. Radiol. Worthing & S.lands Hosps. Trust. Prev: Regist. & Sen. Regist. (Diagn. Radiol.) St. Bart. Hosp. Lond.

MCKINNON

MCKINNON, Carol Castlemilk Health Centre, 71 Dougrie Drive, Glasgow G45 9AW Tel: 0141 531 8585 Fax: 0141 531 8596 — MB ChB 1986 Glas.

MCKINNON, Charlotte Jane 58 Saxby Ave, Bromley Cross, Bolton BL7 9NX — BM BS 1997 Nottm.

MCKINNON, David Livingston (retired) 2 Saddler Avenue, Aston Lodge, Stone ST15 8YH Tel: 01785 818402 — MB ChB 1946 Ed.; MFOM RCP Lond. 1978; DIH Eng. 1959.

MCKINNON, Mr David Michael 69 Harley Street, London W1N 1DE Tel: 020 7487 5407 Fax: 020 7224 2264; 98 Old Park Ridings, Winchmore Hill, London N21 2EP Tel: 020 8360 1403 — MB ChB 1957 Manch.; FRCS Eng. 1966; FRCS Ed. 1965. (Manch.) Cons. ENT Surg. W. Roding, Bloomsbury & Islington Health Dists.; Hon. Cons. ENT Surg. Hosp. St. John & St. Eliz. Lond. Socs: Fell. Roy. Soc. Med.; Assn. Head & Neck Oncol. Prev: Sen. Regist. (ENT) Middlx. & Mt. Vernon Hosps.; Demonst. (Anat.) Univ. Edin. Med. Sch.; Regist. Manch. Roy. Infirm.

MCKINNON, Donald (retired) The Windsor Apartment, 1 Dukes Wharf, Terry Avenue, York YO23 1JE Tel: 01904 611442 — MRCS Eng. LRCP Lond. 1945; MD Lond. 1951, MB BS 1945; FRCPath 1965, M 1964. Prev: Cons. Pathol. York Hosp. Gp.

MACKINNON, Duncan Alisdair Glebe View, Maxton, Melrose TD6 0RL — MB BS 1984 Sydney.

MACKINNON, Fiona Mary Little Penquite, Lostwithiel PL22 0HX — MB BCh 1984 Wales.

MACKINNON, Gordon Ramsbottom Health Centre, Carr Street, Ramsbottom, Bury BL0 9DD Tel: 01706 824413 Fax: 01706 821196 — MB ChB 1976 Glas.; MRCGP 1994; FRACGP 1989; DRCOG 1980.

MACKINNON, Harriet Blainey An Airigh, 20 Borden Road, Glasgow G13 1QX Tel: 0141 959 3230 Fax: 0141 954 2007 — MB ChB 1956 Glas.; FRCGP 1981, M 1969; DObst RCOG 1958; Dip. Autogenic Psychotherapy 1997; L.F.Hom 1995. (Glas.) Med. Hypnotherap., Private Pract. Socs: Brit. Soc. Med. & Dent. Hypn. Scotl.; Brit. Autogenic. Soc.; Assoc. Fac. Homeop.

MACKINNON, Heather Susan Whittington Hospital, Highgate Hill, London N19 5NF Tel: 020 7272 3070 Fax: 020 7288 5215; 8 Bryanstone Road, Crouch End, London N8 8TN Tel: 020 8348 9096 — MB ChB 1974 Manch.; FRCP Lond. 1996; MRCP (UK) 1978; DCH Eng. 1976; FRCPCH. (Manchester) Cons. Paediat. Whittington Hosp. Lond. Prev: Sen. Regist. (Paediat.) Univ. Coll. Hosp. Lond.; Regist. (Paediat.) Whittington Hosp. Lond.; SHO Rotat Booth Hall Childr. Hosp. Manch.

MACKINNON, Helen Fraser Department of Public Health Medicine, Lothian Health, 148 Pleasance, Edinburgh EH8 9RS Tel: 0131 536 9000 — MB ChB 1985 Ed.; MSc Ed. 1996; MA (Hons.) Aberd. 1976; DRCOG 1987. Regist. (Pub. Health Med.) Lothian HB. Prev: Clin. Asst. Edin. BrE. Unit. W.. Gen. Hosp.; Research Regist. (MRC Study) Dept. O & G W.. Gen. Hosp. Edin.; SHO (O & G) W.. Gen. Hosp. Edin.

MACKINNON, Helen Lindsay Blackhall Medical Centre, 51 Hillhouse Road, Edinburgh EH4 3TH Tel: 0131 332 7696 Fax: 0131 315 2884; 138 Craigleith Road, Edinburgh EH4 2EQ — MB ChB 1987 Leeds; MRCGP 1991; DCCH RCP Ed. 1992.

MACKINNON, Helen Margaret Lake House, Prestbury, Cheltenham GL52 3BH Tel: 01242 251585 — MB BS 1981 Lond.; MA Oxf. 1981; MRCGP 1985; DRCOG 1985. Prev: Trainee GP Nailsea VTS; Trainee GP Oxf. VTS.

MACKINNON, Jacob 17 Wimpole Street, London W1M 7AD Tel: 020 7631 0811 Fax: 020 7323 9126 — MB BS 1970 Lond.; MRCP (U.K.) 1973; FRCPCH 1997; Acad. Dipl. Gen. Biochem. (Distinc.) Univ. Lond 1967; FRCP 1998. (St. Bart.) Cons. Paediat. Lond. Prev: Cons. Paediat. Sydenham Childr. Hosp. Lond.; Sen. Regist. (Paediat.) S. Camden (Univ. Coll.) Health Dist. (T); Regist. Hosp. Sick Childr. Gt. Ormond St. Lond.

MACKINNON, James Robert Osbourne House, Preston, Cirencester GL7 5PR — MB ChB 1998 Birm.; ChB Birm. 1998.

MACKINNON, Jane Ross Department of Ophthalmology, Aberdeen Royal Infirmary, Forresterhill, Aberdeen AB25 2ZD — MB ChB 1991 Glas.; FRCOphth 1995. (Glasgow) Specialist Regist. (Ophth.) Aberd. Roy. Infirm. Prev: Specialist Regist. (Ophth.) Raigmore Hosp. Inverness; SHO (Ophth.) P.ss Alexandra Eye Pavil. Roy. Infirm. Edin.

MCKINNON, Jean 2 Longlands Park Crescent, Sidcup DA15 7NE — MB BS 1961 Lond.; MRCS Eng. LRCP Lond. 1961.

MACKINNON, Joanna Elizabeth 74 Trouville Road, London SW4 8QP — MB BS 1996 Lond.

MACKINNON, John (retired) 3 Golden End Drive, Knowle, Solihull B93 0JP Tel: 01564 775614 — MD Sheff. 1954, MB ChB 1945; FRCP Lond. 1968, M 1950. Hon. Cons. Cardiol. W. Birm. HA. Prev: Cons. Cardiol. E. & W. Birm. Health Dists.

MACKINNON, John Christopher Department of Anaesthetics, Kent & Canterbury Hospital, Ethelbert Road, Canterbury CT1 3NG Tel: 01227 783007 Fax: 01227 783152 — MB ChB 1981 Glas.; FFA RCS Eng. 1987. Cons. Anaesth. Kent & Canterbury Hosp. Prev: Sen. Regist. (Anaesth.) Soton. Univ. Hosp. NHS Trust; Clin. Fell. (Intens. Care) Toronto W.. Hosp., Canada; Regist. (Anaesth.) Roy. Infirm. Edin.

MACKINNON, Mr John Grant Cotswold Nuffield Hospital, Talbot Road, Cheltenham GL51 6QA Tel: 01242 251585 — BM BCh 1981 Oxf.; MA, BM BCh Oxf. 1981; ChM Bristol 1991; FRCS Ed. 1985; FRCS Eng. 1985. Cons. Orthop. & Trauma Surg. E. Glos. NHS Trust; Lillie Research Fell. Dept. Orthop. Univ. Brist. Prev: Sen. Regist. Rotat. (Orthop. & Trauma) Bristol; Regist. (Orthop. & Trauma) Bristol Roy. Infirm.; SHO (Surg.) Glos. Roy. Hosp.

MCKINNON, Kathryn Ann Foxwood, York Dr, Bowdon, Altrincham WA14 3HF — MB ChB 1997 Manch.

MACKINNON, Mairi Donalda Child Health Offices, St. Georges Road, Cheltenham GL50 3EW Tel: 01242 516235 Fax: 01242 234527; 12 Celandine Bank, Woodmancote, Cheltenham GL52 9HZ Tel: 01242 675018 — MB ChB 1969 Glas. SCMO E. Glos. NHS Trust.

MACKINNON, Malcolm William Bruce 87 Windmill Crescent, Halifax HX3 7DG — MB ChB 1994 Glas.

MACKINNON, Marian Flat F, 4 Grovepark Gardens, Glasgow G20 7JB — MB ChB 1997 Aberd.; BSc (Med Sci) Hons 1995. SHO (Med.) W.ern Infirm. Glas.

MCKINNON, Marjory Grace McKenzie Howden Health Centre, Livingston EH54 6TP Tel: 01506 418518; 10 Forkneuk Road, Uphall, Broxburn EH52 6BL — MB ChB 1959 Ed.; FRCS Ed. 1965; MRCOG 1970; MRCGP 1975. Hosp. Pract. (O & G) Bangour Gen. Hosp. Prev: Regist. Elsie Inglis Matern. Hosp. Edin.; Regist. (Surg.) Bruntsfield Hosp. Edin.

MCKINNON, Michael Douglas Occupational Health Department, Ford Motor Company, Eagle Way, Brentwood CM13 3BW Tel: 01268 402341 Fax: 01268 405723 Email: mmckinno@ford.com; 101 Vanbrugh Park, Blackheath, London SE3 7AL — MB BS 1980 Lond.; MSc (Occupat. Med.) Lond. 1988; MFOM RCP Lond. 1993, AFOM 1989; DO RCPSI 1986; DRCOG 1983. Sen. Med. Off. Ford Motor Company Dunton Small Vehicle Centre. Socs: Fell. Roy. Soc. Med.; Soc. Occupat. Med. Prev: Regist. (Occupat. Health) Roy. Free Hosp. Lond.; Trainee GP St. Geo. Hosp. Lond. VTS; Ho. Surg. King's Coll. Hosp. Lond.

MCKINNON, Morag Eleanor St Paul's Cottage Surgery, 88a Augustus Road, London SW19 6EW Tel: 020 8788 8880 Fax: 020 8287 8905 — MB BS 1987 Lond.; BSc Newc. 1966; PhD Lond. 1978.

MACKINNON, Mr Neil Athol Countess of Chester Hospital NHS Trust, Liverpool Road, Chester CH2 1 Tel: 01244 366328 — MB BS 1965 Lond.; FRCS Eng. 1972; MRCS Eng. LRCP Lond. 1965. (Middlx.) Cons. Surg. ENT Countess of Chester Hosp. NHS Trust.

MACKINNON, Norman Alan Macaskill (retired) 11 Hawkcraig Road, Aberdour, Burntisland KY3 0XB — MB ChB 1932 Ed.; DPH Ed. & Glas. 1936.

MACKINNON, Pamela Corran Boyd St. Hilda's College, Oxford OX4 1DY Tel: 01865 76884; 27 Norham Road, Oxford OX2 6SQ Tel: 01865 57637 — MB BS 1948 Lond.; MA Oxf. 1964; PhD Lond. 1957, MB BS 1948. (King's Coll. Hosp.) Emerit. Fell. St. Hilda's Coll. Oxf.; Lect. (Human Anat.) New. Coll. Oxf. Socs: Life Mem. Anat. Soc. & Soc. Endocrinol. Prev: Lect. (Human Anat.) Univ. Oxf.; Ho. Phys. King's Coll. Hosp.; Demonst. (Anat.) Middlx. Hosp. Med. Sch.

MACKINNON, Ralph James 178 Moss Lane, Bramhall, Stockport SK7 1BD — MB ChB 1994 Manch.

MACKINNON, Ranald Scott Dept. Of General Surgery, Blackpool Victoria Hospital, Whinney Heys Road, Blackpool FY3 8NR Tel: 01253 300000, 01483 224993 — MB BCh BAO Belf. 1957;

MACKINTOSH

FRCPsych 1992, M 1972; T (Psych.) 1991; DPM Eng. 1967. p/t Cons. Psychiat. (Alcohol & Subst. Misuse, & PTSD Managem. Progr.) Holy Cross Hosp. Haslemere; Cons. Child & Adult Psychiat. Grafham Grange Special Ed Trust Bramley; Regional Cons. Psychiat. Ex-Servs. Ment. Welf. Soc. N.. Irel. & S.. Regions. Prev: Command Cons. Psychiat. HQ NI BFPO 825; Assoc. Dir. (Family Ther.) Childr. & Adolesc. Servs. Edmonton, Canada; Cons. Child & Adolesc. Psychiat. Woking Child Guid. Clinic.

MACKINNON, Rebecca Eleanor Church Road Surgery, Church Road, Kyle IV40 8DD Tel: 01599 534257 Fax: 01599 534107; Eishort, 1/2 of 1, Heaste, Broadford, Isle of Skye IV49 9BN Tel: 01471 822450 — MB BChir 1987 Camb.; MA Camb. 1989, BA (Hons.) 1985, MB BChir 1987. (Camb.) GP Partner Kyle of Lochalsh. Prev: SHO (Obste. & Gyn.) Raigmore Hosp. Inverness; SHO (Gen. Med.) Raigmore; SHO (A & E) Belford Hosp. Fort William.

MACKINNON, Roderick Kenneth John Morningside Medical Practice, 2 Morningside Place, Edinburgh EH10 5ER Tel: 0131 452 8406 Fax: 0131 447 3020 — MB ChB 1970 Glas.

MACKINNON, Stephen Sandygate, Fulmer Road, Gerrards Cross SL9 7EE — MB ChB 1980 Glas.; MRCP (UK) 1983.

MCKINNON, Susan Stormonth 13 Edinburgh Drive, Gourock PA19 1AG — MB ChB 1989 Glas. SHO (Med. Paediat.) Yorkhill Hosp. Glas. Prev: SHO (Anaesth.) Stobhill Hosp. Glas.

MCKINSTRY, Ann Reid Castlereagh Medical Centre, 220 Knock Road, Belfast BT5 6QF Tel: 028 9079 8308 Fax: 028 9040 3776 — MB BCh BAO 1975 Belf.; MRCGP 1979; DRCOG 1977.

MCKINSTRY, Brian Hubert Ashgrove HC, Bladebuan, Bathgate EH47 7LL Tel: 01506 634798, 01506 652956, 01752 894103 Email: brian.mckinstry@ed.ac.uk, peter.riov@btinternet.com; Tel: 0131 449 5875 Fax: 0131 538 5181 Email: brian.mckinstry@blueyonder.co.uk — MB ChB 1978 Ed.; FRCGP 1998; MRCP (UK) 1981; MRCGP (Distinc.) 1982; MD Ed. 1998. (Edinburgh) Princip. In Gen. Pract.; Director of Research, SE. Scotl..; Director of Lothian Primary Care Research Network; Sen. Researcher, Dept. Community Health Sci., Ed. Univ. Socs: BMA; Assn. Course Organisers; Fell. Roy. Coll. Gen. Practitioners. Prev: Assoc. Adviser S. E. Scotl.

MCKINSTRY, Caleb Eccles 72 Watcombe Road, Bournemouth BH6 3LX — BM 1993 Soton.; MRCP (UK) 1996. (Soton.)

MCKINSTRY, Charles Steven 14 Deramore Park S., Belfast BT9 5JY — MB BCh BAO 1979 Belf.; FRCR 1984. Cons. Neuroradiol. Roy. Vict. Hosp. & Grosvenor Rd. Belf. Socs: Brit. Inst. Radiol. & Soc. Magnetic Resonance Med. Prev: Research Fell. NMR Unit Roy. Postgrad. Med. Sch. Hammersmith Hosp. Lond.; Sen. Regist. Dept. Neuroradiol. Regional Neurol. Centre Newc. Gen. Hosp.

MCKINSTRY, Thomas Herbert West Moors Village Medical Centre, 164 Station Road, West Moors, Wareham BH22 0JB Tel: 01202 877185 Fax: 01202 892080; 72 Watcombe Road, Southbourne, Bournemouth BH6 3LX Tel: 01202 421269 — MB BCh BAO 1979 Belf.; Cert. Prescribed Equiv. Exp. JCPTGP 1988; Cert. Family Plann. JCC 1988; BSc. (King's Coll. Lond. & Belf.) GP Bournemouth. Socs: Fell. Belf. Roy. Acad.; (Counc.) BMA; Life Mem. Assn. Psychiat. in Train. Prev: Regist. (Psychiat.) St. Ann's Hosp. Bournemouth.; Clin. Asst. (in c/o the Elderly), Aldenay & St. Leonards'Hosp.

MACKINTOSH, Alan Finlay Department of Cardiology, St. James's University Hospital, Beckett St., Leeds LS9 7TF Tel: 0113 243 3144; 15 Charville Gardens, Shadwell, Leeds LS17 8JL Tel: 0113 273 7293 Fax: 0113 232 9730 — MD 1980 Camb.; MA Camb. 1973, MB BChir 1972; FRCP Lond. 1988; MRCP (U.K.) 1975. (Camb. & Westm.) Cons. Cardiol. St. Jas. Univ. Hosp. Leeds & Leeds Gen. Infirm. Socs: Fell. Europ. Soc. Cardiol. Prev: Sen. Regist. (Cardiol.) Camb. AHA; Regist. (Med.) King's Coll. Hosp. Lond.; Regist. (Med.) Roy. Sussex Co. Hosp. Brighton.

MACKINTOSH, Christopher John Hunter Health Centre, Andrew Street, East Kilbride, Glasgow G74 1AD Tel: 01355 906611 Fax: 01355 906615; 38 Buchanan Drive, Cambuslang, Glasgow G72 8BB Tel: 0141 641 3029 — MB ChB 1982 Aberd. Socs: MRCGP.

MACKINTOSH, Claire Louise 4 Lochknowe Street, Braidwood, Carluke ML8 5PW — MB ChB 1997 Ed.

MACKINTOSH, Colin Edward 50 Harley Street, London W1N 1AD Tel: 020 7255 1889 Fax: 020 7436 3365 Email: colinm713@aol.com — MB ChB 1959 Ed.; FRCS Ed. 1963; FFR 1969; FRCR 1975; DMRD Eng. 1965. (Ed.) Cons. Radiol. Roy. Free Hosp. Lond. Socs: Brit. Soc. Gastroenterol.

MACKINTOSH, Darren James 148 Harrow Road, Leicester LE3 0JX — MB ChB 1996 Leic.

MACKINTOSH, Dorothy Jane Caol Clinic, Kilmallie Road, Caol, Fort William PH33 7DZ Tel: 01397 702258; Craigdhu, Banavie, Fort William PH33 7PB Tel: 01397 772070 Fax: 01397 772056 — MB ChB 1968 Aberd. (Aberd.) Assoc. Specialist (Community Child Health) Highland Communites NHS Trust. Socs: Scott. Community Paediat. Gp.; BMA. Prev: Clin. Med. Off. Highland HB; GP Glas. & Surrey.

MACKINTOSH, Mr Graeme Ian Stewart Cheltenham General Hospital, Sandford Rd, Cheltenham GL53 7AN — MB ChB 1979 Ed.; BSc (Hons.) Ed. 1976; FRCS Ed. 1986; FRCOphth 1989; DO RCS Eng. 1985. (Edin.) Cons. Ophth. Surg. Cheltenham Gen. Hosp.; Clin. Tutor FRCOphth.; Clin. Director. Socs: BMA (Hon. Sec. Glos.). Prev: Sen. Regist. (Ophth.) Roy. Infirm. Edin.

MACKINTOSH, Gregor James Foyers Medical Centre, Foyers, Inverness IV2 6YB Tel: 01456 486224 Fax: 01456 486425; Glenhinnisdale, Foyers, Inverness IV2 6XU Tel: 01456 486341 — MB ChB 1978 Aberd.

MACKINTOSH, Ian Eden House, Edenbridge TN8 5DB; 129A Gloucester Road, Hereford Square, London SW7 4TH Tel: 020 7370 5368 — MB ChB 1927 Aberd. (Aberd.) Sen. Med. Adviser Shell UK Ltd., Fell. Hunt. Soc. Socs: Osler Club. Prev: Res. Ho. Surg. Robt. Jones & Agnes Hunt Orthop. Hosp. OsW.ry; Mem. Malaria Advis. Bd. Malaya.

MACKINTOSH, John Finlay Robert Street Surgery, 140 Robert Street, Milford Haven SA73 2HS Tel: 01646 690690 Fax: 01646 690402; Bulford Cottage, Bulford Road, Johnston, Haverfordwest SA62 3ET Tel: 01437 890341 — MB ChB 1976 Manch.; BSc St. And. 1973; MRCGP 1980; DRCOG 1980. GP Milford Haven.

MACKINTOSH, Kenneth Duncan (retired) The Surgery, 16 Victoria St., Newport-on-Tay DD6 8DJ Tel: 01382 543251 Fax: 01382 542052 — MB ChB 1954 (Commend.) St. And. Prev: Res. Ho. Phys. & Res. Ho. Surg. Dundee Roy. Infirm.

MACKINTOSH, Lesley Elizabeth Foyers Medical Centre, Foyers, Inverness IV2 6YB Tel: 01456 486224 Fax: 01456 486425; Glenhinnisdale, Foyers, Inverness IV2 6XU Tel: 01456 486341 — MB ChB 1978 Aberd.

MACKINTOSH, Lesley Norah Margaret Williamwood Medical Centre, 85 Seres Road, Clarkston, Glasgow G76 7NW Tel: 0141 638 7984 Fax: 0141 638 8827; 38 Buchanan Drive, Cambuslang, Glasgow G72 8BB — MB ChB 1983 Aberd.; MRCGP 1987; DCH RCPS Glas. 1986.

MACKINTOSH, Lindsey Ann Little Thatches, Ashley, Kings Somborne, Stockbridge SO20 6RH — MB ChB 1993 Bristol.

MACKINTOSH, Martin Meddygfa Rhiannon, Northfield Road, Narberth SA67 7AA Tel: 01834 860237 Fax: 01834 861625; Hauly-Bore, Kensington Close, Templeton, Narberth SA67 8SF Email: mmackintosh@doctorsnet.uk — MB BCh 1986 Wales; MRCGP 1993; DCH RCP Lond. 1990; Dip. IMC RCS Ed. 1989. (University Wales College Medicine) Princip. GP Narberth. Prev: Princip. GP Merthyr Tydfil.

MACKINTOSH, Melanie Anne Southmead Health Centre, Ullswater Road, Bristol BS10 6DF Tel: 0117 950 7150 Fax: 0117 959 1110; 66 Chesterfield Road, St. Andrews, Bristol BS6 5DP Tel: 0117 924 9057 — MB ChB 1983 Bristol. Prev: GP Ruthin Clwyd; Trainee GP Clwyd VTS & Salop HA VTS.

MACKINTOSH, Neil John Tayview Medical Practice, 16 Victoria Street, Newport-on-Tay DD6 8DJ Tel: 01382 543251 Fax: 01382 542052; 66 Bay Road, Wormit, Newport-on-Tay DD6 8LZ — MB ChB 1985 Dundee; MRCGP 1989. (Dundee) Tutor (Gen. Pract.) Newport. Socs: BMA.

MACKINTOSH, Nola Brough Little Thatches, Ashley, Kings Somborne, Stockbridge SO20 6RH Tel: 01264 388248 — MB ChB 1961 Ed. Clin. Med. Off. (Child Psychiat. & Comm. Health), Basingstoke Health Dist.

MACKINTOSH, Terence Frederick Peter Little Thatches, Ashley, Kings Somborne, Stockbridge SO20 6RH Tel: 01794 388248 — MB ChB 1961 Ed.; FRCP Ed. 1975, M 1964. (Ed.) Cons. Paediat. Winchester & Centr. Hants. & Basingstoke & N. Hants.

MACKINTOSH

MACKINTOSH, Ursula Department of Accident & Emergency Medicine, Stirling Royal Infirmary, Stirling FK8 2AU — MB BS 1984 Lond.; DAvMed 1998; FFAEM 1995; FRCS Ed. 1990; MRCP (UK) 1987. (St. Mary's) Cons. A & E Stirling Roy. Infirm. Socs: Fell. Fac. A & E Med. Prev: Cons. (A & E) Dundee Roy. Infirm.; Sen. Regist. (A & E) Roy. Infirm. Edin.

MACKINTOSH, William Alexander 10 Drumbeg Loan, Killearn, Glasgow G63 9LG — MB ChB 1967 Glas.; DObst RCOG 1969.

MCKINTY, Marion Catherine Child Health Centre, Caroline St., Hartlepool Tel: 01429 276701; 26 Acle Meadows, Rushyford Grange, Newton Aycliffe DL5 4XD — MB BS 1984 Newc.; MRCGP 1988; DRCOG 1988. p/t Sen. Clin. Med. Off., Community Paediat. Socs: BMA.

MCKINTY, Robert Martin Tel: 01325 313289 Fax: 01325 301428; 26 Acle Meadows, Rushyford Grange, Newton Aycliffe DL5 4XD — MB BCh BAO 1984 NUI; MRCGP 1989; DFFP 1993. (Univ. Coll. Dublin) Bd. Mem. Sedgefield PCG; Ment. Health LEAD PCG.

MACKIRDY, Mr Hugh Campbell Albany Road Medical Centre, 24 Albany Road, Roath, Cardiff CF24 3YY Tel: 029 2048 6561 Fax: 029 2045 1403 — MB ChB 1965 Glas.; PhD Glas. 1970; FRCS Glas. 1979; FRCS Eng. 1981. (Glas.) p/t Hosp. Pract. Surg. Unit Univ. Hosp. Wales. Prev: Lect. Inst. Physiol. Glas. Univ.

MACKIRDY, Jane Elspeth The Laurels Surgery, 73 Church Street, Flint CH6 5AF Tel: 01352 732349 Fax: 01352 730678; 1 Moel View, Wern Road, Rhosesmor CH7 6PY — MB ChB 1979 Dundee; DRCOG 1982.

MCKIRDY, Mairi Lindsay 52 Dan-y-Coed Road, Cardiff CF23 6NE Tel: 029 2075 8687 — BM 1992 Soton.; BM (Hons.) Soton. 1992. SHO (Paediat. & Surg.) Qu. Med. Centre Nottm. Prev: SHO (Gen. Surg.) Nottm. City Hosp.; SHO (Orthop. & A & E) Qu. Med. Centre Nottm.; Demonst. (Anat.) Nottm. Univ. Med. Sch.

MCKIRDY, Michael John 14 Viewpark Drive, Rutherglen, Glasgow G73 3QD — MB ChB 1985 Glas.; FRCPS Glas. 1991.

MCKIRDY, Stuart Wilson 37 Caistor Close, Manchester M16 8NW — MB ChB 1994 Manch.

MCKITTERICK, Emily Clare Suthergery House Medical Centre, 37a St Johns Road, Watford WD1 1LS Tel: 01923 224424 — MB BS 1993 Newc.; DRCOG 1999; MRCP 1997. Salaried Asst. in Gen. Pract., Watford. Prev: GP VTS Watford; SHO Renal Roy. Free Hosp.a; SHO (Med.) Blackpool.

MCKITTERICK, Malcolm John Health Centre, Mid St., Bathgate EH48 1PT Tel: 01506 54444 Fax: 01506 635931; 7 Craigleith Crescent, Edinburgh EH4 3JJ Tel: 0131 332 7115 — MB ChB 1967 Ed.; FFA RCS Eng. 1973; LMCC 1976. (Ed.) Prev: Trainee Gen. Pract. Livingston Vocational Train. Scheme; Family Pract. Melfort, Sask, Canada.

MCKITTRICK, Mhairi 102 Bentley Lane, Leeds LS6 4AJ — MB ChB 1995 Leeds.

MACKLE, Celestine Patrick 14 Woodville Avenue, Lurgan, Craigavon BT66 6JP — MB BCh BAO 1949 NUI. (Univ. Coll. Dub.) Socs: BMA. Prev: Ho. Phys. & Ho. Surg. St. Kevin's Hosp. Dub.; Obst. Ho. Surg. Tyrone Co. Hosp.; Sen. Ho. Off. & Cas. Off. Bridgwater & Dist. Gen. Hosp. Som.

MACKLE, Mr Edward (Eamon) John Craigavon Area Hospital, 68 Lurgan Road, Portadown, Craigavon BT63 5QQ Tel: 028 3833 4444 Fax: 028 3833 2065 Email: emackle@cahgt.n-i.nhs.uk; 34 Gilford Road, Portadown, Craigavon BT63 5EF Tel: 02838 335261 Fax: 02838 335261 Email: emackle@aol.com — MB BCh BAO 1980 Belf.; MCh Belf. 1991; FRCSI 1984. Cons. Surg. Craigavon Area Hosp. Prev: Sen. Regist. Rotat. (Gen. Surg.) N.. Irel.

MACKLE, John 174 Kylepark Drive, Uddingston, Glasgow G71 7EA — MB ChB 1993 Glas.

MACKLE, Mary Geraldine Elizabeth Cornmarket Surgery, 6 Newry Health Village, Monaghan Street, Newry BT35 6BW Tel: 028 3026 5838 Fax: 028 3026 6727; 65 Moss Road, Ballinaskeagh, Banbridge BT32 3NZ — MB BCh BAO 1978 Belf.; MRCGP 1982.

MACKLE, Ronan Aloysius The Health Centre, Tavanagh Avenue, Portadown, Craigavon BT62 3BU Tel: 01762 359909; No. 21 Lynden Gate, Ballyhannon Road, Portadown, Craigavon BT63 5YH — MB BCh BAO 1984 Belf.; MB BCh Belf. 1984; MRCGP 1989; DRCOG 1987. Exec. Mem. S. LMC; Mem. S.. Area Primary Care Audit Sub Comm.

MACKLIN, Alan Scott Aberdeen Industrial Doctors, 56 Carden Place, Aberdeen AB10 1UP Tel: 01224 624314; 340 Holburn Street, Upper Flat, Aberdeen AB10 7GX — MB ChB 1984 Aberd.; MRCGP 1988. Med. Off. (Occupat. Health) Aberd. Indust. Doctors Aberd. Socs: BMA. Prev: GP Aberd.

MACKLIN, Andrew Vincent 132 Whitstable Road, Canterbury CT2 8EG — BM 1990 Soton. SHO (Med.) Norf. & Norwich Hosp. Prev: SHO (Med.) Gillingham.

MACKLIN, Mr Christopher Paul 132 Whitstable Road, Canterbury CT2 8EG Tel: 01227 463804; 14 Chandos Avenue, Roundhay, Leeds LS8 1QU Tel: 0850 193456 Email: chris@cpmdoc.demon.co.uk — BM BS 1992 Nottm.; BMedSci Nottm. 1990, BM BS 1992; FRCS Eng. (Nottingham) Surg. Research Regist. Leeds Gen. Infirm. Prev: SHO Rotat. (Surg.) Leeds Gen. Infirm.; Demonst. (Anat.) Roy. Free Hosp. Lond.; Resid. Med. Off. Clementine Ch.ill Hosp. Harrow.

MACKLIN, Helen Rachel Flat 4, Regency Court, 135 Osborne Road, Newcastle upon Tyne NE2 2TB — MB BS 1992 Newc.

MACKLIN, Jonathan Paul 20 Vernon Road, Harrogate HG2 8DE — MB ChB 1998 Dund.; MB ChB Dund 1998.

MACKLIN, Sean Christopher Hayes, Exbourne, Okehampton EX20 3RT — MB BS 1993 Lond.

MACKLON, Anthony Francis High Staples, Steel, Hexham NE47 0HA — MB BS 1971 Newc.; FRCP Lond. 1989; MRCP (UK) 1975. Cons. Phys.Uniersity Hosp. of N. Durh., Durh.; Cons. Phys. Shotley Bridge Gen. Hosp. Consett.

MACKLON, Nicholas Stephen Department of Obstetrics & Gynaecology, Erasmus University Medical Centre Rotterdam, Glasgow Royal Infirmary, Glasgow Tel: 0141 304 4706; Tel: 0031 10 452 4205 — MB ChB Ed. 1987; MRCOG 1992; MD 1996 Edinburgh. Sen. Lect. and Cons. (O&G) EMCR Rotterdam. Socs: Ed. Obst. Soc. & Glas. Obst. & Gyn. Soc.; ESHRE. Prev: Lect. & Hon. Sen. Regist. (O & G) Glas. Roy. Infirm.; Regist. (O & G) Qu. Mothers Hosp. Glas.; Research Fell. Univ. Glas.

MACKMAN, Catherine Janette Falconers Cottage, Clevelode, Malvern WR13 6PB — MB BS 1998 Lond.; MB BS Lond 1998.

MACKNEY, Philip Henry The Meanwhile Garden Medical Centre, Unit 5, 1-31 Elkstone Road, London W10 5NT Tel: 020 8960 5620 Fax: 020 8964 1964; 2A Woodsome Road, London NW5 1RY Tel: 020 7482 0362 — MB BS 1980 Lond. (Royal Free Hospital School of Medicine) Princip. GP; Clin. Asst. (Med. Oncol.) Roy. Free Hosp.

MCKNIGHT, Alexander German (retired) 19 Old Coach Road, Belfast BT9 5PR Tel: 01232 604655 — MB BCh BAO 1950 Belf.; FRCGP 1976, M 1965; DObst RCOG 1952. Prev: GP Belf.

MCKNIGHT, Charles Kennedy 3 West Avenue, Benton, Newcastle upon Tyne NE12 9PA — MB ChB 1976 Glas.; FFA RCS 1981.

MCKNIGHT, Diana Overton (retired) 8 Earl Richards Road N., Exeter EX2 6AG Tel: 01392 275440 — MB BS Lond. 1952, DPH 1959; MFCM 1974; DCH Eng. 1956. Prev: SCM N. Devon HA.

MCKNIGHT, Douglas William Arran, 40 Admiral Street, Glasgow G41 1HU Tel: 0141 429 2626 Fax: 0141 429 2331 — MB ChB 1984 Glas.; MRCGP 1988; DRCOG 1988; Cert. Family Plann. JCC 1987. GP Glas.

MCKNIGHT, Frances Elizabeth Carstairs Health Centre, The School House, School Road, Carstairs, Lanark ML11 8QF Tel: 01555 870512; Violin Villa, Lanark Road, Ravenstruther, Lanark ML11 7SS — MB BCh BAO 1975 Belf.; MRCGP 1979.

MCKNIGHT, Frances Elizabeth Wilson (retired) 19 Old Coach Road, Belfast BT9 5PR — MB BCh BAO Belf. 1950; DObst RCOG 1952.

MCKNIGHT, Janice Miles Bridgeview Centre, 59 Ruchill St., Glasgow G20 Tel: 0141 945 3449 — MB ChB 1973 Glas.; MRCPsych 1978. Cons. Psychiat. Stobhill Hosp., Glas.; Sect. 98 Dr - Ment. Welf. Commiss. for Scotl.; Mem. SHAS Panel; Hon. Clin. Sen. Lect. (Psychol. Med.), Univ. of Glas. Prev: Sen. Regist. (Psychiat.) Gt.er Glas. Health Bd.

MCKNIGHT, Jean 4 Barn Road, Carrickfergus BT38 7EU — MB BCh BAO 1987 Belf.

MCKNIGHT, John Alexander Metabolic Unit, Western General Hospital, Edinburgh EH4 2XU Tel: 0131 537 3072 Fax: 0131 537 3071 Email: john.mcknight@talk21.com — MB BCh BAO 1983 Belf.; MD Belf. 1989; FRCP (Ed.). (The Queen's University of Belfast) Cons. Phys. (Diabetes & Gen. Med.) W.. Gen. Hosp. Lothian Univs.

MACLACHLAN

NHS Trust Edin.; Hon. Sen. Lect. Univ. Edin. Socs: Brit. Diabetic Assn.; Eur. Assn. Study Diabetes; Amer. Diabetes Assn. Prev: Research Fell. (Med.) Brigham & Wom. Hosp. Harvard Med. Sch., Boston, USA; Sen. Regist. N. Irel.

MCKNIGHT, John Edward (retired) 2 Helen's Court, Helen's Bay, Bangor BT19 1TJ Tel: 01247 852267 — MB BCh BAO 1940 Belf.; FRCP Ed. 1980, M 1973; MFCM 1974; FRCGP 1970, M 1964. Prev: Sec. N. Irel. Counc. Postgrad. Med. Educat.

MCKNIGHT, Karen Margaret 80 Ravensworth Gardens, Cambridge CB1 2XN — BM BCh 1997 Oxf.

MCKNIGHT, Michael McKnight, Clanrye Surgery, Newry Health Village, Monaghan Street, Newry BT35 6BW Tel: 028 3026 0949 Fax: 028 3025 7414 — MB BCh BAO 1979 Belf.; AFOM RCP Lond. 1988; MRCGP 1984; DRCOG 1983.

MACKRELL, Mr David Robert Woodland Road Surgery, 20 Woodland Road, St Austell PL25 4QY Tel: 01726 63311; Ledrah House, 57 Ledrah Road, St Austell PL25 5HG Tel: 01726 75993 — MB BChir 1977 Camb.; MA Camb. 1978; FRCS Eng. 1981. (Camb. & Westm.) Socs: BMA. Prev: Trainee GP Lostwithiel; Regist. (Gen. Surg.) Roy. Cornw. Hosp. (Treliske) Truro; SHO (Psychiat.) St. Lawrence's Hosp. Bodmin.

MACKRELL, Jane Rosemary South Hill Crescent Surgery, 4 South Hill Crescent, Sunderland SR2 7PA Tel: 0191 567 5571 Fax: 0191 510 2810; Stratford House, Ferndale Lane, Off Sunderland Road, East Boldon NE36 0NA Tel: 0191 536 7823 — MB ChB 1978 Glas.; MRCGP 1984.

MACKRILL, Martyn John Robert (retired) High View, Bigsby Road, Retford DN22 6SE Tel: 01777 707653 — MRCS Eng. LRCP Lond. 1950. Prev: Ho. Surg. (Obst.) Upton Hosp. Slough & W. Hill Hosp. Dartford.

MACKRODT, Kathleen Mary Woodrising, 49 Arthog Road, Hale, Altrincham WA15 0LU — MB ChB 1967 Birm.; BSc (Anat.) Birm. 1964, MB ChB 1967.

MACKWAY-JONES, Mr Kevin Charles Emergency Department, Manchester Royal Infirmary, Oxford Road, Manchester M13 9WL — BM BCh 1981 Oxf.; FRCS Ed. 1987; MRCP (UK) 1985; FFACM 1993; FRCP 1997.

MACKWORTH GEE, Nicola Claudine 21 Colehill Gardens, Fulham, London SW6 6SZ Tel: 020 7736 7205 — MB BS 1998 Lond.; MB BS Lond 1998.

MACKWORTH-YOUNG, Charles Gerard Department of Rheumatology, Charing Cross Hospital, Fulham Palace Road, London W6 Tel: 020 8746 8442 Fax: 020 8746 8440 — MB BChir 1979 Camb.; MA Camb. 1979, BA 1975, MD 1987, MB 1979, BChir 1978; FRCP 1995; MRCP (UK) 1980. (Cambridge) Cons. Phys. Rheum. & Gen. Med. Char. Cross, Chelsea & W.m. Hosp. Lond.; Phys. K. Edwd. VII Hosp. for Off's Lond. Socs: Amer. Coll. of Rheum.; Brit. Soc. of Rheum.; Brit. Soc. of Immunol. Prev: Sen. Regist. (Rheum. Clin. Immunol. & Gen. Med.) Hammersmith Hosp., Lond.; Research Fell. Cancer Research Center, Tufts Univ., USA; Regist. (Rheum. & Gen. Med.) Hammersmith Hosp. Lond.

MCLACHLAN, Adrian James The New Surgery, 31-35 Linom Road, London SW4 7PB Tel: 020 7274 4220 Fax: 020 7737 0205; 39 Carver Road, London SE24 9LS Tel: 020 7737 6072 Email: amclachlan@compuserve.com — MB BS 1983 Lond.; BA (Hons.) Camb. 1980. (King's London)

MCLACHLAN, Alastair Neil Baldwin and Partners, Hucknall Road Medical Centre, off Kibworth Close, Nottingham NG5 1FX Tel: 0115 960 6652 Fax: 0115 969 1746; 6 Cocker Beck, Lambley, Nottingham NG4 4QP Tel: 0115 931 3689 Fax: 0115 931 3689 — MB BS 1979 Lond.; MRCGP 1983; DCH 1983; DRCOG 1981. (Westminster) GP Trainer Nottm. HA.; VTS Course Organiser Nottm.

MACLACHLAN, Allan Cameron (retired) Steadings, Church Lane, Oving, Aylesbury HP22 4HL Tel: 01296 641643 — MB ChB 1953 Glas.; MRCGP 1976; DPH Glas. 1965; DIH Soc. Apoth. Lond. 1963. Prev: GP Aylesbury.

MCLACHLAN, Brian The Medical Centre, 12 East King Street, Helensburgh G84 7QL Tel: 01436 672277 Fax: 01436 674526; 18 Redclyffe Gardens, Helensburgh G84 9JJ — MB ChB 1983 Glas.; MRCGP 1988. Princip. GP Helensburgh. Prev: SHO (Gen. Med.) Vict. Infirm. Glas.; SHO (Geriat.) Vict. Geriat. Unit Glas.; SHO (O & G) Paisley Matern. Hosp.

MCLACHLAN, Christopher James Henderson Bewdley Medical Centre, Dog Lane, Bewdley DY12 2EG Tel: 01299 402157 Fax: 01299 404364; Leystile Farm, Heightington, Bewdley DY12 2XP Tel: 01299 826355 — MB BS 1966 Lond.; BSc Lond. 1963, MB BS (Hons. Surg. & Obst. & Gyn.) 1966; DCH Eng. 1970; DObst RCOG 1970. (Univ. Coll. Hosp.) Med. Adviser Hereford & Worcs. FHSA. Prev: Med. Unit Univ. Coll. Hosp.; SHO (Paediat.) Jenny Lind Hosp. Norwich; Ho. Phys. (Med.) & Ho. Surg. Univ. Coll. Hosp.

MACLACHLAN, David Connor 6/5 Craigleith Avenue S., Ravelston, Edinburgh EH4 3LQ — MB ChB 1966 Aberd.; BDS Glas. 1955; FFA RCSI 1975; DA Eng. 1969. (Aberd.) Socs: NE Scotl. Soc. Anaesths.

MCLACHLAN, Douglas David Eaglesham Surgery, 30 Gilmour Street, Eaglesham, Glasgow G76 0AT Tel: 01355 302221 Fax: 01355 302907; 13 Polnoon Street, Eaglesham, Glasgow G76 0BH — MB ChB 1977 Glas.; DRCOG 1980.

MCLACHLAN, Helen Anne 10 Redmere Drive, Heswall, Wirral CH60 1YF — MB ChB 1996 Liverp.; MB ChB (Hons.) Liverp. 1996. (Liverp.) SHO (A & E Med.) Derbysh. Roy. Infirm. Derby.

MACLACHLAN, Iain Stewart Moir (retired) 3 Mingarry Street, Glasgow G20 8NP — MB ChB 1974 Glas.

MACLACHLAN, James 12 Ravelston Dykes, Edinburgh EH4 3ED Tel: 0131 332 1921 — MB ChB 1944 Glas.; AFOM RCP Lond. 1982; MFCM 1974; DIH St. And. 1963; DPH Glas. 1948. (Univ. Glas.) Specialist Community Med. Common Servs. Agency Edin. Socs: FRSH; Soc. Occup. Med. & BMA. Prev: MOH Cos. Midlothian & Peebles; Res. Ho. Surg. Roy. Infirm. Glas.; Sen. Res. Ho. Phys. Vict. Infirm. Glas.

MCLACHLAN, James Ian (Surgery), 470 Hucknall Road, Nottingham NG5 1FX Tel: 0115 960 6652; Primrose Cottage, 58 Main St., Lambley, Nottingham NG4 4PP — MB BS 1969 Lond.; MRCS Eng. LRCP Lond. 1969; DCH Eng. 1972; DObst RCOG 1971. (Westm.) Hosp. Pract. (Genetic Counselling) Nottm. City Hosp.

MACLACHLAN, James Stewart 78 Cantieslaw Drive, Calderwood, East Kilbride, Glasgow G74 3AH — MB ChB 1974 Glas.

MCLACHLAN, Jennifer Kim, Surg. Lt. RN 58 Main Street, Lambley, Nottingham NG4 4PP Tel: 0115 931 3823; 41 Shaftesbury Cottages, North Hill, Plymouth PL4 8JE Tel: 01752 228205 — MB ChB 1994 Ed. (Univ. Ed.) SHO (Anaesth.) Roy. Hosp. Hasler, Gosport, Hants. Prev: RN. Med. Off. Roy. Naval Air Station Yedvilton Ilchester Som.; RN Med. Off. HMS Soton. BFPO 389; Ho. Off. (Surg.) Qu. Margt. Hosp. Dumfermline.

MCLACHLAN, Karen Patricia Walsgrove hospital, Clifford Bridge Road, Walsgrove, Coventry CV2 2DX Tel: 02476 602020; Damson Cottage, 134 Lodge Road, Knowle, Solihull B93 0HF Tel: 01564 771985 — MB BS 1991 Lond.; MRCP (UK) 1994. (Char. Cross & Westm.) p/t Cons. Paediat. WalGr. Hosp. Coventry. Prev: Regist. Paediat. WalsGr. Hosp.; Regist. (Paediat.) Birm. Childr. Hosp.; SHO (Paediat.) Nottm. City Hosp.

MACLACHLAN, Karina Grace The Royal Berkshire Hospital, London Road, Reading 5AN Tel: 0118 987 7065 — MB BS 1991 Lond.; FRCA 1997 Fell. Of the Roy. Coll. Of Anaesthetics Lond.; BSc Lond. 1988; AKC 1988. Specialist Regist. (Anaesth.) St. Geo. Hosp. Lond., Cons. (Anaesth.) The Roy. Berks. Hosp. Reading. Socs: BMA; Obst. Anaesth. Assn.; AAGBI. Prev: SPR (Anaesth.) Oxf. Sch. of Anaesth., Oxf.; SPR (Anaest.) St. Geo.s Hosp. Tooting, Lond.

MCLACHLAN, Kathryn Ruth Bank Street Surgery, 46-62 Bank Street, Alexandria G83 0LS Tel: 01389 752020 Fax: 01389 755549 — MB ChB 1986 Glas.; MRCGP 1990; DRCOG 1988.

MACLACHLAN, Kenneth Euan, Squadron Ldr. RAF Med. Br. (retired) Mallard Czottage, 46 North St, Emsworth PO10 7DJ Tel: 01243 431334 — MB BS 1951 Lond.; MRCS (Eng.) LRCP (Lond.) 1950. Prev: GP.

MACLACHLAN, Neil Andrew General Hospital, St Helier, Jersey JE2 3QS Tel: 01534 622660 Fax: 01534 622895; La Campagne, Rue des Alleurs, Rozel, St Martin, Jersey JE3 6AZ Tel: 01534 857808 Fax: 01534 858391 Email: maclac@psilink.caihe.co.je — MB BS 1979 Lond.; MRCOG 1985; DCH RCP Lnd. 1983. (Guy's) Cons. O & G Gen. Hosp. St Helier Jersey. Socs: Brit. Med. Ultrasound Soc.; Europ. Soc. Human ReProduc. & Embryol. & Brit. Fertil. Soc. Prev: Lect. Qu. Charlotte's & Chelsea Hosp. for Wom. Lond.; Regist. (O & G) Rotat. Ashford Hosp. & St. Thos. Hosp. Lond.; SHO (O & G) Guy's Hosp. Lond.

MACLACHLAN

MACLACHLAN, Robert Stewart (retired) 2160 Paisley Road WeStreet, Glasgow G52 3SH Tel: 0141 882 6630 — MB ChB 1945 Glas.; MRCGP 1959.

MACLACHLAN, Ronald Edgar 3 Cocker Beck, Lambley, Nottingham NG4 4QP — MRCS Eng. LRCP Lond. 1940; MRCGP 1953. (Manch.) Prev: RAF; Ho. Surg. Roy. Infirm. Sheff.

MACLACHLAN, Sally 38 Nightingale Square, London SW12 8QN Tel: 020 8673 4494 Fax: 020 8675 9436 — MRCS Eng. LRCP Lond. 1976. Barrister-At-Law Gray's Inn.

MACLACHLAN, Sean Guthrie 2 Rock Cottages, Farnham Green, Belper DE56 2JP; Kingsway Hospital, Kingsway, Derby DE22 3LZ — MB ChB 1992 Leeds.

MCLAGGAN, James Gavin (retired) Glenfield, The Street, Detling, Maidstone ME14 3JU Tel: 01622 738109 Fax: 01622 738109 — MB 1959 Camb.; BChir 1958; DObst RCOG 1960. Chairman of Trustees The Heart of Kent Hospice Maidstone. Prev: GP Maidstone.

MCLAIN, Alison Jane Silbrook, 30 Heol Don, Cardiff CF14 2AU — MB BCh 1988 Wales.

MCLAIN, Bruce Irving 1 Western Avenue, Castle Hill, Prudhoe NE42 6NU — MB BS 1982 Nottm.

MCLAIN, Mr Maurice William (retired) Gayton House, Baker St., Gayton, Northampton NN7 3EZ Tel: 01604 859640 — MB BCh BAO 1959 Belf.; MD Belf. 1964; FRCS Eng. 1967. Prev: Cons. Surg. (Accid. & Orthop.) N.ampton Gen. Hosp. & Manfield Orthop. Hosp.

MACLAINE, Edmund, OBE(Mil) (retired) 69 Thorpe Park Road, Peterborough PE3 6LJ Tel: 01733 567001 — MB BCh BAO Belf. 1940.

MACLAINE, Gale Newton Currie Road Health Centre, Currie Road, Galashiels TD1 2UA Tel: 01896 754833 Fax: 01896 751389 — MRCS Eng. LRCP Lond. 1966; BSc (Anat.) Lond. 1963, MB BS 1966; MRCP (U.K.) 1970. SHO (Med.) & Ho. Phys. & Ho. Surg. Harold Wood Hosp.; Ho. Phys. Lond. Hosp.

MCLANNAHAN, Ivan Francis Gordon (retired) Woodlands, Killochan, Girvan KA26 9Ff Tel: 01673 860827 Email: drmac@weldun.freeserve.co.uk — MRCS Eng. LRCP Lond. 1950.

MACLARAN, Sarah Jane Astrid 9 Asbury Road, Balsall Common, Coventry CV7 7QN — BM 1997 Soton. (Southampton) SHO (Med.) Solihull Hosp. Prev: SHO (A & E) Warwick Hosp. Warwick; Med. Ho. Off. St Mary's Hosp. Portsmouth; Surg. Ho. Off. P.ss Margt. Hosp. Swindon.

MCLARDY, Geoffrey The Halliwell Surgery, Lindfield Drive, Bolton BL1 3RG Tel: 01204 23813; 26 Waddington Close, Bury BL8 2JB Tel: 0161 764 5219 — MB ChB 1977 Manch.; MRCGP 1984; DRCOG 1979; DCH 1982.

MACLARDY, Iain Hamish (retired) Casa Roja, 207 West Main St., Broxburn EH52 5LJ Tel: 01506 853901 — MB ChB 1944 Ed. Police Surg. Lothian & Borders Constab. Prev: Ho. Surg. Orthop. Dept. Roy. Infirm. Edin.

MCLARDY, James Priory Court Surgery, 1 High Street, Beauly IV4 7BY Tel: 01463 782214 Fax: 01463 782129 — MB 1977 Camb.; BChir 1976; MRCGP 1981.

MCLARDY SMITH, Mr Peter David Nuffield Orthopaedic Centre, Headington, Oxford OX3 7LD — MB BS 1975 Lond.; MA Oxf. 1976; FRCS Eng. 1981. Cons. Orthop. Surg. Nuffield Orthop. Centre Oxf. Socs: Fell. BOA; Hon. Sec. Girdlestone Orthop. Soc. Prev: SHO (Surg.) Bristol Roy. Infirm.; Clin. Lect. (Orthop. Surg.) Univ. Oxf.

MCLAREN, Alexander Douglas 14 Mochrum Road, Newlands, Glasgow G43 2QE — MB ChB 1970 Glas.; FFA RCS Eng. 1975; DObst RCOG 1972. Cons. Anaesth. W.. Infirm. Glas. Socs: Scott. Soc. Anaesth. & Glas. & W. Scott. Soc. Anaesth.

MCLAREN, Alison Anne Alexandra Gillygate Surgery, 28 Gillygate, York YO31 7WQ Tel: 01904 624404 Fax: 01904 651813; 11 Station Road, Upper Poppleton, York YO26 6PX Tel: 01904 788270 — MB ChB 1981 Ed.; MA (Hons.) Oxf. 1975; MRCP (UK) 1984. (Oxf. & Ed.) Partner in GP, York. Socs: (Comm.) York Med. Soc. - Comm.; Roy. Coll. Phys. Prev: Regist. (Geriat. Med.) Tayside HA.

MCLAREN, Mr Andrew James Greenacres, Nicker Hill, Keyworth, Nottingham NG12 5ED Tel: 0115 937 4224 — BM BCh 1991 Oxf.; BA Oxf. 1988; FRCS Lond. 1995. Specialist Regist. Surg., Oxf. Prev: Research Regist., Nuff. Dept. Surg., Oxf..

MCLAREN, Andrew Robert Henry 2 Eccleston Street, London SW1W 9LL Tel: 020 7730 4948 — MRCS Eng. LRCP Lond. 1975; MB BS Lond. 1975, BDS 1970; DDS UCLA 1984. (Char. Cross) Dir. Special Dent. Unit (HIV) Riverside HA Lond. Prev: Ho. Surg. Profess. Unit Surg., Ho. Surg. ENT Dept. & Ho. Phys. (Neurol. & Neurosurg.) Char. Cross Hosp.

MCLAREN, Andrew Thomas Bailiffs Cottage, West Thirston, Morpeth NE65 9EF — MB BS 1991 Newc.

MACLAREN, Antoinette Marie The Rumney Surgery, 842 Newport Road, Rumney, Cardiff CF3 4LH Tel: 029 2079 7751; 68 Fidlas Road, Llanishen, Cardiff CF14 0ND — MB BCh 1983 Wales; BSc Lond. 1978.

MACLAREN, Atholl Hutchison, MBE (retired) 27 Main Street, Bradmore, Nottingham NG11 6PB Tel: 0115 921 3227 — MB ChB 1942 Aberd.; FRCGP 1981, M 1963. Prev: Vice-Chairm. Nottm. DHA.

MACLAREN, Carla Frances 3/1 Greendyke Street, Glasgow G1 5PU — MB ChB 1997 Glas.

MCLAREN, Mr Charles Angus Norrie Department of Surgery, York District Hospital, Wiggington Rd, York YO31 8HE — MB ChB 1980 Ed.; BSc (Med. Sci.) 1977; FRCS Eng. 1985; FRCS Ed. 1984. Cons. Orthop. Surg. N. Yorks. HA. Prev: Sen. Regist. (Orthop. Surg.) Tayside HA; Regist. (Orthop. Surg.) Salop. HA.

MCLAREN, Colin Alban Bryant, QHP, OStJ, Air Commodore RAF Med. Br. (retired) 12 Broadacres, Broad Town, Wootton Bassett, Swindon SN4 7RP Email: c.mclaren@eidosnet.co.uk — MB ChB 1951 Birm.; FFA RCS Eng. 1961. Prev: Cons. Anaesth. & Cons. Adviser Anaesth. RAF.

MACLAREN, David Martin Moidart House, Chapel Lane, Bodicote, Banbury OX15 4DA Tel: 01295 261839 — MB BS Lond. 1956; MA Aberd. 1950; MD Lond. 1967; FRCP Ed. 1980, M 1963; MRCS Eng. LRCP Lond. 1956; FRCPath 1978, M 1965. (Guy's) Emerit. Prof. Clin. Bacteriol. Free Univ. Amsterdam. Prev: Lect. (Bact.) Guy's Hosp. Med. Sch. Lond.; Cons. Path. Stockport & Buxton Hosp. Gp.; Ho. Off. Guy's Hosp.

MCLAREN, Donald Pennfields, 11 Barassie Court, Bothwell, Glasgow G71 8UH Tel: 0141 854289 — MB ChB 1959 Glas. (Glas.)

MCLAREN, Donald Stewart International Centre For Eye Health, Institute of Ophthalmology, London EC1V 9EL Tel: 020 7608 6800 Fax: 020 7250 3207 Email: e.cartwright@ucl.ac.uk — MB ChB Ed. 1947; PhD Lond. 1957; MD Ed. 1955; FRCP Ed. 1982, M 1980; DTM & H Eng. 1949. (Ed.) Head Nutrit. Blindness Preven. Progr. Internat. Centre Eye Health Lond. Socs: Fell. Roy. Med. Soc. Edin.; BMA; Fell. Amer. Soc. Nutrit.al Scis. Prev: Reader (Clin. Nutrit.) Roy. Infirm. Edin.; Prof. (Clin. Nutrit.) Sch. Med. Amer. Univ. Beirut, Lebanon; Reader (Physiol.) Edin. Univ. Med. Sch.

MCLAREN, Duncan Bruce Western General Hospital, Crewe Road, Edinburgh EH4 2XL Tel: 0131 537 2215 Fax: 0131 537 2219; The Farmstead, 9 The Courtyard, Easter Broomhouse, Dunbar EH42 1RD — MB BS 1989 Lond.; BSc (Clin. Sci.) Lond. 1988, MB BS 1989; MRCP (UK) Lond. 1992; FRCR 1995. (St. Mary's London) Cons. Clin. Oncol. W.ern Gen. Hosp. Edin.; Regist. (Clin. Oncol) Velindre Hosp. Socs: Counc. Scott. Radiol. Soc.; Mem. Scott. Standing Comm. Prev: Clin. Fell. Brit. Columbia Cancer Agency Vancouver; Specialist Regist. Clin. (Oncol.) Velindre Hosp. Cardiff; SHO (Med.) Qu.s Med. Centre Nottm.

MCLAREN, Eon Hamish, TD Stobhill Hospital, Glasgow G21 3UW Tel: 0141 210 3309 Fax: 0141 201 3888 Email: hamish.mclaren@northglasgow.scot.nhs.uk; 40 Sherbrooke Avenue, Glasgow G41 4EP Tel: 0141 427 0704 Fax: 0141 419 0036 — MB ChB Ed. 1967; BSc Ed. 1965; FRCP Glas. 1979; FRCP Ed. 1981; MRCP (UK) 1970. (Ed.) Cons. Phys. Stobhill Gen. Hosp. Glas.; Clin. Director Acute Med., N. Glas. Univ. Hosp. NHS Trust. Socs: Med. & Scientif. Sect. Brit. Diabetic Assn. & Caledonian Soc. Endocrinol. Prev: Regist. (Endocrinol.) Groote Schuur Hosp. Cape Town, S. Afr.; Sen. Regist. N.. Gen. Hosp. Sheff. & Roy. Hosp. Sheff.

MCLAREN, Evelyn Jane Royal Dundee Liff Hospital, Liff, Dundee DD2 5NF; Viewbank House, Moredun Terrace, Perth PH2 0DA — MB ChB 1987 Aberd.; DRCOG 1993; DCH RCPS Glas. 1989; MRCGP 1996. SHO (Psychiat.) Roy. Dundee Liff Hosp. Dundee.

MACLAREN, Fiona Barbara 3 Minto Street, Edinburgh EH9 1RG — MB ChB 1964 Ed.; DObst RCOG 1967. (Ed.)

MCLAREN, George Ian The Surgery, Station Road, Bridge of Weir PA11 3LH Tel: 01505 612555 Fax: 01505 615032; East Brannochlie, Prieston Road, Bridge of Weir PA11 3AN — MB ChB 1977 Glas.

MCLAREN, George Stuart Leven Health Centre, Victoria Road, Leven KY8 4ET Tel: 01333 425656 Fax: 01333 422249; 55B Main Street, Lower Largo, Leven KY8 6BN Tel: 01333 320130 Email: docstu@globalnet.co.uk — MB ChB 1981 Dundee; MRCGP 1986.

MCLAREN, Gordon Leonard 97 Cardigan Road, Bridlington YO15 3JU — MB ChB 1982 Leeds; MRCGP 1987; DRCOG 1984.

MACLAREN, Mr Iain Ferguson (retired) 3 Minto Street, Edinburgh EH9 1RG Tel: 0131 667 3487 — MB ChB Ed. 1949; FRCP Ed. 1995; FRCS Ed. 1955; FRCS Eng. 1960. Prev: Cons. Surg. Roy. Infirm. Edin. & Deaconess Hosp. Edin.

MCLAREN, Iain Macdonald Department of Anaesthetics and Intensive Care, Leicester Royal Infirmary, Leicester LE1 5WW Tel: 0116 254 1414 Fax: 0116 258 5026; 4 Bonner Close, Oadby, Leicester LE2 4UZ Tel: 0116 271 0684 — MB ChB 1984 Manch.; BSc (Med. Sci.) Hons. St. And. 1981; FRCA 1990. Cons. Intens. Care & Anaesth. Leicester Roy. Infirm.; Hon. Clin. Teach. Univ. Leic. Socs: Intens. Care Soc.; Assn. Anaesth. GB & Irel.; Leic. Med. Soc. Prev: Sen. Regist. (Anaesth.) Leicester Hosps.; Lect. (Anaesth. & Intens. Care) Chinese Univ., Hong Kong.; Regist. (Anaesth.) P'boro. Dist. Hosp.

MACLAREN, Iain Robertson (retired) 34 Westbourne Gardens, Glasgow G12 9PF Tel: 0141 357 5152 — MB ChB 1955 Glas.; BA Open 1983. Prev: GP Drymen.

MCLAREN, Ian c/o Accident & Emergency Department, Monklands District General Hospital, Airdrie ML6 0JS Tel: 01236 748748 Fax: 01236 713138, 01236 755480 Email: ian.mclaren@laht.scot.nhs.uk; 35 Falkland Street, Hyndland, Glasgow G12 9QZ Tel: 0141 339 4850 — MB ChB 1976 Glas.; MRCGP 1982; FFAEM 1996. (University of Glasgow) Cons. A & E Monklands Dist. Gen. Hosp. Airdrie.; Med. Off. Brit. Assoc. Ski Patrollers. Prev: Sen. Regist. Warrington Dist. Gen. Hosp.; Regist. W.. Infirm. Glas.

MCLAREN, James 17 Broadwood Drive, Kings Park, Glasgow G44 5UP — MB ChB 1988 Glas.

MCLAREN, Mr James Ewan Drummond (retired) Parkfield, Crown East, Worcester WR2 5TU Tel: 01905 425667 — MB BChir 1959 Camb.; BA Camb. 1956, MB BChir 1959; FRCS Ed. 1971. Prev: Cons. ENT Surg. S. Worcs. & Hereford Hosps.

MCLAREN, Janet Elizabeth 25 Cheadle Road, Cheadle Hulme, Cheadle SK8 5HL Tel: 0161 485 4068 — MB ChB 1971 Ed.; DFFP 1993; DRCOG 1973. Staff Grade (Comm. Paediat. Child health) Manch. Comm. NHS Trust. Prev: Staff Grade Community Paediat. Mancunian Community Health NHS Trust.

MCLAREN, Mr John Anderson Stockbridge Health Centre, 1 India Place, Edinburgh EH3 6EH — MB ChB 1974 Ed.; FRCS Ed. 1979.

MCLAREN, John Malcolm (retired) 33 Pennant Hills, Bedhampton, Havant PO9 3JZ — MB BS 1957 Lond.

MCLAREN, John Stuart Paderewski Building, Rheumatic Diseases Unit, Western General Hospital, Crewe Road S., Edinburgh EH4 2XU Tel: 0131 537 1000 Fax: 0131 537 1051 Email: john.mclaren@ed.ac.uk; 28 High Cross Avenue, Melrose TD6 9SU Tel: 01896 822510 Email: jmclaren@abel.co.uk — MB ChB 1993 Aberd.; MB ChB (Commend.) Aberd. 1993; BSc Hons. (Med. Sci.) Aberd. 1992; MRCP (UK) 1996. (Univ. Aberd.) Clin. Lect., Rheumatic Dis.s Unit, Univ. of Edin., Edin.; Hon. Specialist Regist. (Rheum.) W.ern Gen. Hosp. Edin. Socs: BMA; Collegiate Mem. RCPE. Prev: Regist. (Gen. Med.) Raigmore Hosp. Inverness; Regist. (Gen. Med.) Tauranga Hosp., NZ; SHO (Gen. Med.) Aberd. Roy. Infirm.

MCLAREN, Judith Ann Orchard House Surgery, Fred Archer Way, Newmarket CB8 8NU Tel: 01638 663322 Fax: 01638 561921 — MB BS 1977 Lond.; MRCS Eng. LRCP Lond. 1977; MRCGP 1984; DCH Eng. 1979; DRCOG 1980. (Char. Cross) GP Newmarket.

MCLAREN, Kathryn Mary Department of Pathology, University of Edinburgh Medical School, Teviot Place, Edinburgh EH8 9AG — MB ChB 1974 Ed.; BSc (Hons. Path.) Ed. 1972, MB ChB 1974; FRCP Ed. 1994; FRCS Ed. 1994; FRCPath. 1993.

MCLAREN, Mr Magnus Ian Bower House, Station Road, Soberton, Southampton SO32 3QU Tel: 01489 877254 — MB BS 1977 Lond.; MS Soton. 1986; FRCS Eng. 1982. Cons. Orthop. Surg. Portsmouth. Prev: Sen. Regist. (Orthop.) Sheff.

MACLAREN, Mary Helen Stuart 33 Muirfield Road, Inverness IV2 4AY — MB ChB 1985 Aberd.; MRCGP 1990; DRCOG 1988. Staff Grade in Indep. Hospice (P/T).

MCLAREN, Monica Mary (retired) Bohereen, Bath Road, Nailsworth, Stroud GL6 0QJ Tel: 01453 832943 — MB ChB 1954 Bristol; DObst RCOG 1960. Prev: SHO (O & G) Leicester Gen. Hosp.

MCLAREN, Pamela Jayne 39 Fairways, Frodsham, Warrington WA6 7RU — BM BS 1991 Nottm.; MRCGP 1995; DCH 1995; DRCOG 1994; DFFP 1993. GP. Prev: Research Fell. Vancouver, Canada; GP/Regist., Cardiff; SHO (A & E) S. Warks. Hosp. Warwick.

MCLAREN, Paul Martin Oakdene, Camden Park, Tunbridge Wells TN2 5AA — MB BS 1984 Lond.

MCLAREN, Rebecca 24 York Gardens, Wolverhampton WV3 9BY — MB BS 1998 Lond.; MB BS Lond 1998.

MCLAREN, Robert (retired) 6 Royal Gardens, Stirling FK8 2RJ Tel: 01786 473866 — MB ChB St. And. 1955; MFOM RCP Lond. 1978; DPH Glas. 1957 DIH Eng. 1962. Prev: Chief Med. Off. Gtr. Manch. Transport.

MCLAREN, Robert Craik 26 Dundas Street, Edinburgh EH3 6JN Tel: 0131 556 7180 — MB ChB 1941 Ed. (Univ. Ed.) Civil. Med. Pract. Min. of Defence. Socs: Life Mem. BMA. Prev: GP Methlick, Aberd.sh.; GP Edin.; Capt. RAMC.

MACLAREN, Mr Robert Edward Merton College, Oxford OX1 4JD Tel: 01865 276397 Fax: 01865 276361 Email: robert.maclaren@merton.ox.ac.uk — MB ChB 1990 Ed.; DPhil Oxf. 1995; FRCS Ed. 1998. Specialist Regist. (Ophth.) Moorfield Eye Hosp. & NW Lond. Rotat. Prev: SHO (Ophth.) Radcliffe Infirm., Oxf. & Lect. Merton Coll. Univ. Oxf.; Med. Off. 16 Armoured Field Ambul. RAMC; MRC Clin. Research Fell.

MCLAREN, Robert John Henderson (retired) Cardigan House, 97 Cardigan Road, Bridlington YO15 3JU Tel: 01262 674112 — MB ChB Ed. 1964; DObst RCOG 1966. Prev: Ho. Surg. Edin. Roy. Infirm.

MACLAREN, Roy Barrie (retired) 32 Wordsworth Road, High Wycombe HP11 2UR Tel: 01494 526624 — MB ChB 1956 St. And.; DIH (Chadwick Medal) 1967; MFOM RCP Lond. 1979. Prev: Cons. Aviat. Phys. Brit. Airways Health Servs.

MCLAREN, Ruth Diane 64 Simplemarsh Road, Addlestone, Weybridge KT15 1QJ — MB ChB 1991 Bristol; MRCGP 1995; DCH RCP Lond. 1994; DRCOG 1993; Dip. Pall. Med. Cardiff 1997. (Bristol) Specialist Regist. (Palliat. Med.) Wales Train. Prog.

MCLAREN, Sally Anne Una 7 Grove Mews, London W6 7HS — MB ChB 1991 Auckland.

MCLAREN, Stuart The Tarns, Huishlane End, Tedburn St Mary, Exeter EX6 6EQ — MB BS 1981 Lond.; MRCPsych 1985.

MCLARNON, Jillian Fiona 124A Moneynick Road, Randalstown, Antrim BT41 3HU — MB ChB 1989 Ed.

MACLARNON, Kay Hunter 34 Priory Road, Loughborough LE11 3PP — BM BCh 1985 Oxf. SHO (A & E) King Geo. Hosp. Ilford.

MACLARNON, Patrick Gerard 20 Union Road, Magherafelt BT45 5DF Tel: 01648 32331 — MB BCh BAO 1946 Belf.

MCLARNON, Robert Stanley Wilson 45 Downview Park W., Belfast BT5 5HP — MB BCh BAO 1951 Dub.

MCLARTY, Eric Winston Redfern Health Centre, Shadycombe Road, Salcombe TQ8 8DJ — MRCS Eng. LRCP Lond. 1967; BSc Lond. 1964; MB BS 1967; DObst RCOG 1971. (Univ. Coll. Hosp.)

MCLARTY, Esther Springfield, Lower Batson, Salcombe TQ8 8NH — MB ChB 1995 Birm.; ChB Birm. 1995.

MACLARTY, Helen Jackson The Whitehouse, Auchterarder PH3 1ND Tel: 01764 3742 — MB ChB 1980 Glas.; BSc (Hons.) Glas. 1977, MB ChB 1980.

MCLARTY, Isobel Jean 12 Magdala Crescent, Edinburgh EH12 5BD Tel: 0131 337 7683 — MB ChB 1939 Ed.; MFCM 1974. (Univ. Ed.) Prev: Sen. Med. Off. (Child Health) Worcs. CC; Asst. Sch. Med. Off. Sheff.; Med. Off. (Matern. & Child Welf.) Dept. Pub. Health Dept. Sheff.

MCLASKEY, Sheila Bedgrove Surgery, Brentwood Way, Aylesbury HP21 7TL Tel: 01296 330330 Fax: 01296 399179; 10 Webster Road, The Furlongs, Aylesbury HP21 7FJ Tel: 01296 82618 — MB ChB 1969 Leeds; MRCGP 1986; DCH Eng. 1972; DObst RCOG 1971. (Leeds) Med. Off. Aylesbury Family Plann. Clinic Bucks. HA. Prev: Clin. Asst. Manor Ho. Hosp. Aylesbury.

MCLATCHIE

MCLATCHIE, Professor Gregor Robertson 57 Hylton Road, Hartlepool TS26 0AH Tel: 01429 266654 Ext: 2329 Fax: 01429 422987 — MB ChB 1974 Glas.; FRCS Glas. 1978; Dip. Sports Med. Scotl. 1997. Cons. Surg. (Gen. Surg.) Gen. Hosp. Hartlepool; Vis. Prof. Surg. Scs. & Sports Med. Sch. Health Scs. Univ. Sunderland; Vis. Prof. Sch. Social Scs. Univ. Greenwich. Socs: Fell. Inst. Sp. Med.; BASO; Assn. Surg. Prev: Dir. Nat. Sports Med. Inst. Lond.; Sen. Regist. (Gen. Surg.) S. Gen. Hosp. Glas.; Regist. (Gen. Surg.) Glas. Roy. Infirm. & Monklands Dist. Gen. Hosp. Airdrie.

MCLAUCHLAN, Alan Edward (retired) 60 Friars Street, Sudbury CO10 2AG Tel: 01787 373177 — MB BS 1949 Lond. Exam. Med. Off. DHSS; Sen. Med. Off. ABA. Prev: GP Sudbury.

MCLAUCHLAN, Alan James Wilson 55 Wittet Drive, Elgin IV30 1TB — MB ChB 1977 Aberd.

MCLAUCHLAN, Mr Christopher Alan James Emergency Department, Royal Devon & Exeter Hospital (Wonford), Barrack Road, Exeter EX2 5DW Tel: 01392 402305 Fax: 01392 402313; 17 Dince Hill Close, Whimple, Exeter EX5 2TE — MB BS 1977 Lond.; MRCS Eng. LRCP Lond. 1977; DRCOG 1979; FRCP Lond. 1997; FFAEM 1994; FRCS Ed. 1988. (Guy's) Mem. Resusc. Counc. (UK). Prev: Sen. Regist. (A & E) Derriford Hosp. Plymouth; Research Regist. St. Bart. City Life Saver Resusc. Scheme St. Bart. Hosp. Lond.

MCLAUCHLAN, David George 38 Warren Avenue, Cheadle SK8 1ND — MB BS 1979 Newc.

MCLAUCHLAN, Donald (retired) Corn Rigs, Castle Drive, Kilmarnock KA3 1TN Tel: 01563 25731 — MB ChB 1947 St. And. Prev: GP Kilmarnock.

MCLAUCHLAN, Mr George James 12 Cameron Knowe, Philpstoun, Linlithgow EH49 6RL Tel: 01506 834119 Email: george_louise@compuserve.com — MB ChB 1989 Manch.; BSc (Med. Sci.) St. And. 1986; FRCS Glas. 1994. Specialist Regist. Rotat. (Orthop.) P.ss Margt. Rose Hosp. Edin. Socs: BMA; Assoc. Mem. BOA. Prev: SHO (Plastic Surg.) St. John's Livingston; SHO (Orthop.) P.ss Margt. Rose. Hosp. Edin.; SHO (Cardiothoracic) Roy. Infirm. Edin.

MCLAUCHLAN, Ian Edward Johnston (retired) 2 Firs Court, The Green, Hardingstone, Northampton NN4 6TB Tel: 01604 702095 — MB ChB Birm. 1949; MRCS Eng. LRCP Lond. 1949; MRCPsych 1971. Prev: Cons. Psychiat. St. And. Hosp. N.ampton.

MCLAUCHLAN, Mr James 12 Bellenden Walk, Milltimber AB13 0EY — MB BS 1961 Lond.; ChM Aberd. 1976; FRCS Ed. 1969; MRCS Eng. LRCP Lond. 1961. (Lond. Hosp.) Cons. Orthop. Surg. Grampian Health Bd.; Hon. Reader (Orthop. Surg.) Univ. Aberd. Prev: Ho. Surg. Neurosurg. Dept. Lond. Hosp.; Lect. Anat. King's Coll. Hosp.; Surg. Regist. Bethnal Green Hosp.

MCLAUCHLAN, John Hamilton Peel View Medical Centre, 45-53 Union Street, Kirkintilloch, Glasgow G66 1DN Tel: 0141 211 8270 Fax: 0141 211 8279; 38 Victoria Road, Lenzie, Kirkintilloch, Glasgow G66 5AN Tel: 0141 211 8270 Fax: 0141 211 8279 — MB ChB 1976 Dundee; MRCP (UK) 1979; MRCGP 1981; DRCOG 1981; FRCP Glas 1996. (Dundee) Clin. Asst. (c/o the Elderly) Lenzie Hosp. Glas. Socs: Fell. Roy. Coll. Phys. & Surgs. Glas.

MCLAUCHLAN, Maria Anne 14 Cunnigar Hill View, Mid Calder, Livingston EH53 0SG Tel: 01506 439786 — MB ChB 1990 Dundee.

MCLAUCHLAN, Sylvia June (retired) 7 Holmwood Close, East Horsley, Leatherhead KT24 6SS Tel: 01483 285144 Fax: 01483 285144 Email: derek@mclauchland.freeserve.co.uk — MB ChB 1959 Bristol; 1959 MB ChB Bristol; 1980 MSc Manch.; 1990 FFPHM RCP (UK); 1981 MFCM. Chair. Primary Care Facilitation Trust; Trustee E. Thames Care; Gov. Lord Mayor Treloar Sch. Prev: Dir. Gen. Stroke Assn. Lond.

MACLAUGHLAN, Catrin Aerona 42 Lyric Way, Thornhill, Cardiff CF14 9BP — MB BCh 1994 Wales.

MCLAUGHLAN, Derek John 2/2, 39 Falkland St., Glasgow G12 9QZ — BM BS 1998 Nottm.; BM BS Nottm 1998.

MCLAUGHLIN, Adrian Gerard Beaconsfield Road Surgery, 1 Beaconsfield Road, Widnes WA8 9LB Tel: 0151 424 3232/3986 Fax: 0151 424 1009; 142 Mossbank Road, Moss Bank, St Helens WA11 7DH — MB ChB 1972 Liverp.

MCLAUGHLIN, Andrew James 3 Linden Court, Holyoake Road, Headington, Oxford OX3 8AS — BM 1994 Soton. Socs: Med. Defence Union; RCAnaesth. Prev: SHO (Anaesty) Portsmouth NHS Trust, SHO (Neonate) Brighton NHS Trust; SHO (Gen. Paediat.) Brighton NHS Trust; SHO (Cas.) Soton. NHS Trust.

MCLAUGHLIN, Anthony Bernard No. 1 Glenmiskan, Rostrevor, Newry BT34 3FF Tel: 0169 37 38823 — LRCPI & LM, LRSCI & LM 1947; LRCPI & LM, LRCSI & LM 1947.

MCLAUGHLIN, Caroline Anne Lakeside House, 45 Home Park Road, London SW19 7HS Tel: 020 8946 4294 — MB ChB 1966 Glas.; DObst RCOG 1971. Employm. Med. Adviser Health & Safety Exec. SE Area E. Grinstead. Socs: Fell. Roy. Soc. Med.; Soc. Occupat. Med. Prev: Occupat. Phys. St. Helier Hosp. Carshalton; Med. Adviser Merton & Sutton Local Auths.

MCLAUGHLIN, Catherine Grangewood Surgery, Chester Road, Shiney Row, Houghton-le-Spring DH4 4RB Tel: 0191 385 2898 — MB BS 1985 Lond.; MRCGP 1989; DRCOG 1988. GP Houghton-le-Spring.

MCLAUGHLIN, Clare Frances 15 Jedburgh Place, Perth PH1 1SJ — MB ChB 1997 Ed.

MCLAUGHLIN, Darren Michael 24 Chestnut Grove, Lurgan, Craigavon BT66 6AJ — MB BCh BAO 1997 Belf.

MCLAUGHLIN, Eamon 12 Sunningdale Wynd, Bothwell, Glasgow G71 8EQ — MB ChB 1974 Glas.; BSc (Hons. Biochem.) Strathclyde 1969. GP Glas. Med. Off. Blood Transfus. Serv.

MCLAUGHLIN, Florence Kathleen 97 Fotheringay Road, Glasgow G41 4LH Tel: 0141 423 2906 — MB BCh BAO 1937 NUI.

MCLAUGHLIN, Henry Greenwood, 21 Cloughmore Road, Rostrevor, Newry BT34 3EN — MB BCh BAO 1985 Belf.

MCLAUGHLIN, Ian Michael 3 Kirklee Gardens, Glasgow G12 0SG Tel: 0141 334 6852 — MB ChB 1989 Glas.; MRCP (UK) 1993; FRCR 1997.

MCLAUGHLIN, Mr Ian Stirling 13 Courthill, Bearsden, Glasgow G61 3SN Tel: 0141 942 5979 — MB ChB 1963 Glas.; FRCS Ed. 1968; FRCS Canada 1978. (Glas.) Socs: Brit. Assn. Urol. Surgs. Prev: Cons. Urol., Stobhil Hosp., Glas.

MCLAUGHLIN, James Anthony 15 Rathbeg Drive, Limavady BT49 0BB — MB BCh BAO 1992 Belf.

MCLAUGHLIN, James Erswell 3 Florence Road, Ealing, London W5 3TU — MB BS 1964 Lond.; BSc Lond. 1961; FRCPath 1984, M 1972. (St. Bart.) Cons. Histopath. Roy. Free Hosp. Lond. Prev: Lect. Dept. Morbid Anat. Lond. Hosp.; Regist. Dept. Histopath. Roy. Free Hosp. Lond.; Resid. Clin. Path. St. Mary's Hosp. Lond.

MCLAUGHLIN, John, OStJ 4 St Nicholas Avenue, Sabden, Clitheroe BB7 9HR Tel: 01282 773772 — MB ChB 1951 Glas. (Glas.) Socs: Blackburn & Dist. Med. Soc. & Dent. & Med. Soc. Study Hypn. Prev: Ho. Phys. S.. Gen. Hosp. Glas.; Ho. Surg. Gen. Hosp. King's Lynn.

MCLAUGHLIN, John 53 Belraugh Road, Garvagh, Coleraine BT51 5HB Tel: 01265 868552 — MB BCh BAO 1992 Belf.; DRCOG 1995; DCH RCP Lond. 1995.

MCLAUGHLIN, John Thomas 55 St Marys Road, Bamber Bridge, Preston PR5 6TE — MB ChB 1990 Manch.

MCLAUGHLIN, Kevin James 12 Rosepark Avenue, Uddingston, Glasgow G71 6JD Tel: 01698 814775; 3/1 James Gray Street, Shawlands, Glasgow G41 3BS Tel: 0141 649 1922 — MB ChB 1989 Ed.; MB ChB (Hons.) Ed. 1989; MRCP Ed. 1992. (Ed.) Sen. Regist. (Nephrol.) Roy. Infirm. Glas. Prev: Regist. (Med.) StoneHo. Hosp.; SHO (Renal) Roy. Infirm. Edin.; SHO (Med.) Milesmark Dunfermline.

MCLAUGHLIN, Maria Elizabeth 23 Dundonald Road, Glasgow G12 9LL Tel: 0141 357 4606 Email: mia_mclaughlin@compuserve.com — MB BCh BAO 1989 NUI; MRCPsych 1998. (University College Galway) Specialist Regist. (Psychiat.) Roy. Alexander Hosp. Paisley. Prev: SHO (Psychiat.) Gartnavel Roy. Hosp. Glas.

MCLAUGHLIN, Martin Francis Flat 0/1, 40 Hector Road, Glasgow G41 3QD — MB ChB 1997 Glas.

***MCLAUGHLIN, Michael Mark** 1 Crossroad Cottages, Marvington, Gifford, Haddington EH41 4JP — MB ChB 1998 Ed.; MB ChB Ed 1998.

MCLAUGHLIN, Michael Robert Springburn Health Centre, 200 Springburn Way, Glasgow G21 1TR Tel: 0141 531 9641 Fax: 0141 531 9642 — MB ChB 1970 Glas.; DObst RCOG 1971. (Glas.)

MCLAUGHLIN, Neil Philip McLaughlin and Partners, 27-29 Derby Road, North End, Portsmouth PO2 8HW Tel: 023 9266 3024 Fax:

023 9265 4991 Email: drnmelaughlin@hotmail.com — MB BCh BAO 1978 NUI. Clin. Asst. Ave. Hse. Portsmouth.

MCLAUGHLIN, Mr Philip Joseph John St Joseph's Private Nursing Home, Garden Hill, Sligo, Republic of Ireland Tel: 00353 71 62649 — MB BCh BAO 1983 Dub.; MA Dub. 1987, BA Dub. 1981, MB BCh BAO 1983; FRCSI 1987; FRCSE 1987. Cons. (Gen. Surg.) St. Joseph's Nursing Home Sligo. Prev: Cons. Surg. Sligo Gen. Hosp.; Regist. (Urol.) Univ. Coll. Hosp. Galway.

MCLAUGHLIN, Russell Edward 2 Abbeyhill Way, Newtownabbey BT37 0YG — MB BCh BAO 1995 Belf.

MCLAUGHLIN, Stella Fiona 35 Watson Avenue, Rutherglen, Glasgow G73 2NL Tel: 0141 647 9500 — MB ChB 1993 Glas. SHO (Anaesth.) Roy. United Hosp. Bath. Socs: BMA; MDDUs.

MCLAUGHLIN, Tracy 47 Frankfort Street, Glasgow G41 3XF; 42 Frankfort Street, Glasgow G41 3XF — MB ChB 1997 Aberd.

MCLAUGHLIN, William Joseph, DFM (retired) 27 Laleham Court, Woking GU21 4AX — MB ChB 1951 Glas.; MFOM RCP Lond. 1980; DIH St. And. 1964; DPH Glas. 1956. Prev: Med. Off. Gtr. Glas. Health Bd.

MACLAURIN, James Richard Colin Sunbury Health Centre Group Practice, Green Street, Sunbury-on-Thames TW16 6RH Tel: 01932 713399 Fax: 01932 713354; 6 Burnside Close, Twickenham TW1 1ET Tel: 020 8892 8476 — MB ChB 1954 New Zealand; Dip. Obst. Auckland 1973.

MACLAURIN, John Carruthers (retired) 42 North Grange Road, Bearsden, Glasgow G61 3AF — MB ChB 1953 Glas.; MD (Hons.) Glas. 1967; FRCP Ed. 1981, M 1960; FRFPS Glas. 1962; FRCP Glas. 1971, M 1962. Cons. Paediat. Roy. Matern. Hosp. & Roy. Hosp. Sick Childr. Glas.

MACLAURIN, Remo Earle 5 Grovewood Close, Chorleywood, Rickmansworth WD3 5PU Tel: 01923 282990 — MB BS 1956 Lond.; FFA RCS Eng. 1962; DA Eng. 1958. (Middlx.) Cons. Anaesth. Harefield Hosp. Socs: Assn. Anaesths. Prev: Cons. Anaesth. Mt. Vernon Hosp.; Sen. Regist. (Anaesth.) Middlx. Hosp.; Ho. Phys. Med. Unit Middlx. Hosp.

MACLAVERTY, Caoilin 84 Eccleston Road, London W13 0RL — MB ChB 1991 Liverp.

MCLAVERTY, Deirdre Marie 15 Glenhill Park, Glen Road, Belfast BT11 8GA — MB BCh BAO 1983; DCH Dub. 1987; DRCOG 1985.

MACLAVERTY, Keith Graeme John Donnybrook House Group Practice, Clarendon Street, Hyde SK14 2AH Tel: 0161 368 3838 Fax: 0161 368 2210; 17 Oaklands Road, Hyde SK14 3DD Tel: 0161 367 8799 — MB ChB 1984 Liverp.

MCLAY, Arthur Laurence Cunningham Clinical Laboratories, Hairmyres Hospital, E. Kilbride, Glasgow G75 8RG Tel: 0141 572560; 275 Cumbernauld Road, Muirhead, Chryston, Glasgow G69 9HW Tel: 0141 779 2316 Email: mclay@btinternet.com — MB ChB 1970 Glas.; MRCPath. 1987; FRCPath 1997. Cons. Path. Hairmyres Hosp. E. Kilbride. Prev: Lect. (Path.) Glas. Roy. Infirm.

MCLAY, Clare Kerry Alice 122 Bailielands, Linlithgow EH49 7TF — MB ChB 1989 Aberd.; MRCGP 1994; DFFP 1997; DCCH RCP Ed. 1996; T(GP) 1994; Cert. Family Plann. JCC 1993. (Aberd.) GP. Socs: Med. & Dent. Defence Union Scotl.; BMA; MSS. Prev: Partner GP Bathgate; Clin. Asst. Gogarburn Hosp. Ed.; SHO Rotat. (Gen. Med.) Stoke Mandeville Hosp. Aylesbury.

MACLAY, Elisabeth 66 Sutherland Avenue, Orpington BR5 1RB Tel: 01689 602245 Fax: 01689 602245 — MB BS 1963 Lond.; MRCS Eng. LRCP Lond. 1963; MRCPsych 1972; DPM Eng. 1971. (Roy. Free) Clin. Asst. Psychother. Univ. Coll. Hosp. Lond.; Treas. SE Psychother. Gp. Socs: Assoc. Mem. Brit. Assn. Psychother.

MCLAY, Ian Alexander Bruce Bramblys Grange, Bramblys Drive, Basingstoke RG21 8UW Tel: 01256 467778 Fax: 01256 842131 — MB ChB 1972 Ed.; BSc Ed. 1969; DA Eng. 1976; DObst RCOG 1975.

MCLAY, James Stuart 7 St Marks Road, Bush Hill Park, Enfield EN1 1BG — MB ChB 1983 Aberd.

MCLAY, Mr Kenneth (retired) 8 Moray Place, Edinburgh EH3 6DS Tel: 0131 225 8561 — MB ChB 1945 Ed.; FRCS Ed. 1951. Hon. Sen. Lect. Otolaryngol. Univ. Edin. Prev: Cons. Surg. ENT Dept. Roy. Infirm. Edin. & City Hosp. Edin.

MCLAY, Mr Kenneth Andrew Lennox Lodge, 7 Arduthie Road, Stonehaven AB39 2EH — MB ChB 1969 Glas.; FRCS Glas. 1974; DObst RCOG 1971. Cons. Otolaryngol. Grampian Health Bd.

(Aberd.). Socs: Scott. Otolaryngol. Soc. & Assn. Head & Neck Oncol. GB.

MCLAY, Roderick Kerr Wellhall Medical Centre, 4 Hillhouse Road, Hamilton ML3 9TZ Tel: 01698 285818; Bothwell, Glasgow G71 8UW — MB ChB 1981 Dundee; MRCGP 1985; DRCOG 1984.

MCLAY, Mr William David Shanks, OBE Strathclyde Police Occupational Health & Welfare Unit, Glasgow Caledonian University, 70 Cowcaddens Road, Glasgow G4 0BA Tel: 0141 332 4925 Fax: 0141 332 4931; Wester Rackets, Main St, Houston, Johnstone PA6 7EL Tel: 01505 613916 — MB ChB 1961 Glas.; LLB Glas. 1972; FRCS Glas. 1968. Chief Med. Off. Strathclyde Police; Hon. Clin. Sen. Lect. (Forens. Med.) Glas. Univ. Socs: Fell. Roy. Soc. Med.; (Ex-Pres.) Assn. Police Surgs.

MACLAY, William Paton, Lt.-Col. RAMC Retd. Springtime, 9 Carlyon Close, Farnborough GU14 7BX Tel: 01252 543404 — MB ChB 1950 Glas.; DTM & H Eng. 1960. Fell. St. John's Hosp. Dermat. Soc. Socs: Brit. Pharmacol. Soc. Prev: Ho. Phys. W.. Infirm. Glas.; Dermatol. Camb. Milit. Hosp. Aldershot & Brit. Milit. Hosp.; Singapore.

MCLEAN, Adam George Department of Nephrology, Dialysia & Transplantation, Royal Free Hospital, Pond St., London NW3 2QG — MB BS 1984 Lond.; BA Oxf. 1981; MRCP (UK) 1988. Regist. (Renal Unit) Roy. Free Hosp.

MACLEAN, Agnes Margaret 29A Church Lane, Uxbridge UB8 2XE — MB BS 1954 Lond.; MRCP (UK) 1960; DCH RCP Lond. 1957.

MCLEAN, Alan Fisher Ferguson 14 Prestwick Close, Tytherington, Macclesfield SK10 2TH — MB ChB 1952 Glas. (Univ. Glas.) Prev: Ho. Phys. & Ho. Surg. Ballochmyle Hosp.; Ho. Surg. Matern. Sect. Ayrsh. Centr. Hosp. Irvine.

MCLEAN, Alan Neil Queen Elizabeth National Spinal Injuries Unit, Southern General Hospital, Glasgow GS1 4TF; 3 Broomknowe Terrace, Kilmacolm PA13 4HT — MB ChB 1987 Aberd.; MRCP (UK) 1990. (Aberd.) Cons. (Spinal Injuries) S.ern Gen. Hosp. Glas. Socs: Brit. Thorac. Soc.; Scott. Thoracic Soc. Prev: Regist. (Med.) Gartnavel Gen. Hosp. Glas.; Regist. (Med.) Roy. Cornw. Hosp. Truro.

MACLEAN, Alasdair Barry Alverthorpe Surgery, Balne Lane, Wakefield WF2 0DP — MB ChB 1978 Dundee.

MCLEAN, Alasdair Duncan 7 Lychgate Green, Stubbington, Fareham PO14 3LL — MB ChB 1989 Manch.; BSc St. And. 1986; FRCS Ed. 1997. Regist. (Gen. Surg.) Pk. Hosp.

MACLEAN, Alasdair Rhuairidh Clifton House, 7 Furlong Road, Stoke Ferry, King's Lynn PE33 9SU — MB BS 1987 Lond.; BSc (Hons.) Lond. 1984. SHO (Anaesth.) ScarBoro. Gen. Hosp. Prev: Ho. Surg. Wanganui Base Hosp., NZ.

MACLEAN, Alastair 73 Bagley Wood Road, Kennington, Oxford OX1 5LY Tel: 01865 730237 — MB ChB 1947 Glas.; DPH 1957; MFOM RCP Lond. 1978. (Glas.) Mem. DHSS. Bd.ing Panel. Socs: Soc. Occupat. Med. & Brit. Occupat. Hyg. Soc. Prev: Regional Med. Off. Rover Gp. Ltd. Oxf.

MACLEAN, Alastair Donald (retired) Bourton House, Elmhurst Road, Gosport PO12 1PG Tel: 0170 17 80922 — MB ChB St. And. 1940; DObst RCOG 1947. Hon. Med. Off. Gosport War Memor. Hosp., Blake Matern. Home Gosport Blackbrook Ho. Matern. Home Fareham; Med. Off. St. Geo. Barracks, Gosport. Prev: O & G Regist. OldCh. Hosp. Romford.

MCLEAN, Alexander Christopher John Bannold Road Surgery, Rosalind Franklin House, Bannold Road, Waterbeach, Cambridge CB5 9LQ Tel: 01223 860387 Fax: 01223 576259 — MB BS 1965 Lond.

MACLEAN, Mr Alexander David Willard 18 Upper Wimpole Street, London W1G 6LX Tel: 020 7935 3575 — MB BS 1958 Lond.; FRCS Eng. 1967; FRCS Ed. 1967. (Westm.) Cons. Surg. The Lond. Hosp.; Sub-Dean Admissions Lond. Hosp. Med. Coll.; Examr. Surg. Univ. Lond. & RCS Eng. Prev: Asst. Dir. Profess. Surg. Unit Lond. Hosp.; Surg. Regist. W.m. Hosp. Teachg. Gp.; Regtl. Med. Off. 1st Bn. Coldstream Guards.

MACLEAN, Alexander Fitzroy Ardencaple, Banchory AB31 4AE — MB ChB 1965 Aberd.; MRCGP 1975; DObst. RCOG 1968. Socs: BMA & Aberd. M-C Soc. Prev: GP Bellfield, Banchory.

MCLEAN, Alison Margaret Brunton Place Surgery, 9 Brunton Place, Edinburgh EH7 5EG Tel: 0131 557 5545 — MB ChB 1979 Aberd.; MRCGP 1983.

MCLEAN

MCLEAN, Alison Mary 16 Courthope Road, London NW3 2LB Tel: 020 7267 6341 — MB 1975 Camb.; BChir 1974; MRCP (UK) 1977; FRCR 1980; DMRD Eng. 1979; FRCP 1998. (Middlx.) Cons. Radiol. St. Bart. Hosp. Lond. Socs: BMUS; BSG. Prev: Sen. Regist. (Diag. Radiol.) St. Bart. Hosp. Lond.; Clin. Fell. (Radiol.) New Eng. Med. Centre Hosp. Boston, Mass. USA.

MCLEAN, Alison Morag 11 Garden Court, Denmore Park, Bridge of Don, Aberdeen AB23 8FF Tel: 01224 703407 — MB ChB 1988 Dundee; DRCOG 1995. Clin. Med. Off. (Family Plann. & Community Gyn.) Aberd. Retainer Scheme. Prev: GP Aberd. Retainer Scheme; Trainee GP Perth VTS.

MCLEAN, Professor Allan Bruce University Department of Obstetrics & Gynaecology, The Royal Free Hospital School of Medicine, Rowland Hill St., London NW3 2PF Tel: 020 7794 0500 Fax: 0174 830 2261 — MB ChB 1971 Otago; BMedSc Otago, MD 1984; FRCOG 1990, M 1978. (University of Otago, New Zealand) Prof. O & G Roy. Free Hosp. Sch. Med. Socs: Chairmen, Brit. Soc. for the Study of Vulval Dis.; Brit. Gyn. Cancer Soc., Mem.; Brit. Soc. colposcopy & gervical Path. Prev: Sen. Lect. (O & G) Univ. Glas.

MCLEAN, Allan Charles (retired) Broomfield, 5 North Feus, Upper Largo, Leven KY8 6ER Tel: 01333 360668 — MB ChB Ed. 1951; MFOM RCP Lond. 1978; DIH Eng. 1976; DObst RCOG 1961. Prev: Sen. Med. Off. Shell Stanlow Refinery Ellesmere Port.

MCLEAN, Mr Allan Hunter Queen Alexandra Hospital, Cosham, Portsmouth PO6 3LY Tel: 023 92 286000 Fax: 023 92 286440; The Crossways, Blind Lane, Wickham, Fareham PO17 5HD — MB ChB 1986 Ed.; FRCS Ed. 1992; FRCOphth 1992. (Edinburgh) Cons. (Ophth. Surg.) Qu. Alexandra Hosp. Portsmouth. Prev: SHO (Ophth. Surg.) P.ss Alexandra Eye Pavil. Edin.; Regist. (Ophth. Surg.) P.ss Alexandra Eye Pavilion Edin.; Sen. Regist. (Ophth. Surg.) Roy. Vict. Infirm. Newc.

MCLEAN, Andre Ernest Michael Laboratory of Toxicology & Pharmacokinetics, School of Medicine, University College London, 5 University St., London WC1E 6JJ Fax: 020 7380 1530 Email: andre.mclean@btinternet.com; Toxicology Consultants, 97 Albert St, London NW1 7LX Tel: 020 7209 3847 Fax: 020 380 1530 Email: andre.mclean@btinternet.com — BM BCh 1957 Oxf.; PhD Lond. 1960; FRCPath 1982, M 1978. (Univ. Coll. Hosp. & Oxf.) p/t Prof. Toxicol. Univ. Coll. Lond.; Hon. Cons. (Toxicol.) UCH Lond.; Chairm. UCLH Ethics of Human Research Comm.; Mem. Food Standards Agency Comm. on Minerals And Vit.s. Prev: Mem. Scientif. Staff MRC Toxicol. Research Unit Carshalton; Asst. Prof. Chicago Med. Sch., USA; Mem. Scientif. Staff MRC Trop. Metab. Research Unit Jamaica.

MCLEAN, Mr Andrew Bruce (retired) Greenfoot, Sebergham, Carlisle CA5 7HP Tel: 01697 476233 Fax: 01697 476233 — MB ChB Glas. 1942; FRCS Eng. (ad eund.) 1978; FRCS Glas. 1962; FRCS Ed. 1948; FRFPS Glas. 1947. Hon. Cons. Surg. E. Cumbria HA. Prev: Regional Adviser Surg. RCS Eng.

MCLEAN, Andrew Hamilton Medical Services, Coronna House, 29 Cadogan St., Glasgow G2; 7 E Monkton Court, Prestwick KA9 1EN — MB ChB 1972 Glas.; MRCGP 1976; DRCOG 1977. Med. Adviser & Disabil. Analyst, Med. Servs., Glas. Prev: GP Princip., Greenhills Health Centre, E. Kilbride.

MCLEAN, Angus Charles Willard Birchgrove Surgery, 104 Caerphilly Road, Cardiff CF14 4AG Tel: 029 2052 2344 Fax: 029 2052 2487 — MB BS 1988 Lond.; MRCGP 1993.

MCLEAN, Anna Cyncoed Road Medical Centre, 350 Cyncoed Road, Cardiff CF23 6XH Tel: 029 2076 2514 Fax: 029 2076 4262 — MB BS 1988 Lond.

MCLEAN, Arja Tiina Maria 15 South Crescent, Durham DH1 4NF — MB BS 1990 Newc.

MCLEAN, Barbara Smith (retired) 69 Drury Road, Colchester CO2 7UU — MB ChB 1952 Glas. Prev: Clin. Asst. Severalls Hosp. Colchester.

MCLEAN, Brendan Norbert The Royal Cornwall Hospital, Treliske, Truro TR1 3LJ Tel: 01872 252715 Fax: 01872 253128; Chyvogue House, Perranwell Station, Perranwell, Truro TR3 7IX — MB ChB 1980 Ed.; BSc (Hons.) Ed. 1977, MD 1992; FRCP Lond. 1997; MRCP (UK) 1985. (Ed.) Cons. Neurol. Roy. Cornw. Hosp. Truro. Prev: Sen. Regist. (Neurol.) Frenchay Hosp. Bristol; Lect. (Clin. Neurochem.) Inst. Neurol. Lond.

MACLEAN, Brian Neil Kingsmills Medical Practice, 18 Southside Road, Inverness IV2 3BG Tel: 01463 235245 Fax: 01463 01443 714400 — MB ChB 1988 Ed.; MRCGP 1992; DRCOG 1991.

MCLEAN, Bruce 25c Bolton Gardens, London SW5 — MB ChB 1958 N.Z.

MCLEAN, Catherine Margaret Una 7 Albert Terrace, Edinburgh EH10 5EA Tel: 0131 447 7416 Fax: 0131 447 7416 — MB ChB 1949 Ed.; PhD Ed. 1967, MD 1965; FRCP Ed. 1994; FFCM 1975, M 1974; DPH Ed. 1964. (Ed.) Reader (Community Med.) Univ. Edin. Socs: Soc. Social Med. Prev: Sen. Research Asst. Ibadan Cancer Register Univ. Ibadan, Nigeria; Mem. MRC Unit For Research on Epidemiol. of Ment. Illness Dept. Psychol. Med. Univ. Edin.

MCLEAN, Catriona Mairi 12 Powside Place, Inchture, Perth PH14 9RJ — MB ChB 1990 Dundee; MRCGP 1994; T(GP) 1995; DRCOG 1993; DCH RCPS Glas. 1992.

MCLEAN, Catriona Mary Department of Radiation Oncology, Western General Hospital, Edinburgh — MB BS 1985 Lond.; MRCP (UK) 1989; FRCR 1993. Cons. (Clin. Oncol.) W.ern Gen. Hosp. Edin.; Hon. Sen. Lect. 1997.

MCLEAN, Charles Dargaville Thomson Glencoe, The Merge, Rockcheffe, Dalbeattie DG5 4QH — MB ChB 1942 Glas.; MD Glas. 1954; FRCP Ed. 1971, M 1951; DMRD Eng. 1948. Hon. Cons. Radiol. Char. Cross Hosp. Socs: Roy. Coll. Radiols. Prev: Sen. Regist. (Radiodiag.) Lond. Hosp.; Ho. Surg. & Clin. Asst. (Med.) Glas. Roy. Infirm.

MCLEAN, Christina Margaret 331 Woodstock Road, Oxford OX2 7NX Tel: 01865 511927 — MB ChB 1997 Sheff.

MCLEAN, Christopher John 12C Westbourne Terrace Road, London W2 6NG — MB BS 1989 Lond.

MCLEAN, Mr Christopher Richard 33 Milton Road E., Lowest Office, Suffield, Lowestoft NR32 1NU Tel: 01502 568296 Email: chrisrmclean@yahoo.com — MB BS 1995 Lond.; MRCS Glasg. July 1999. (Lond. Hosp. Med. Coll.) SHO Rotat. (Surg.) Epsom Dist. Gen. Hosp. Prev: Ho. Off. (Med.) Heatherwood Hosp. Ascot; Ho. off (Surg.) P.ss Alexander Hosp. Harlow.

MCLEAN, David Smyth (retired) Greystones, 31 Pinehill Road, Drumbo, Lisburn BT27 5TU Tel: 01232 826392 Fax: 01232 826392 — MB BCh BAO 1957 Belf.; FFOM RCPI 1992; AFOM RCP Lond. 1983; MRCGP 1961; DCH RCPS Glas. 1964; DObst RCOG 1959. Dep. Sen. Med. Off. Stud. Health Dept. Qu. Univ. Belf.

MCLEAN, Denis Foster Ardoran, Carberry Park, Leven KY8 4JG — MB ChB 1974 Dundee; BSc St. And. 1971. Cons. Radiol. Ninewells Teachg. Hosps. Dundee. Socs: Fell. RCP Canada; FRCR. Prev: Cons. Radiol. Qu. Margt. Hosp. & Vict. Hosp. Fife.

MCLEAN, Derek Greenacre, 75 Dundee Road, West Ferry, Dundee DD5 1NA Tel: 01382 776931 — MB ChB 1965 St. And.; PhD St. And. 1969; FRCP Lond. 1981; MRCP (UK) 1969; FRCP Ed. 1980. (Dundee) Med. Dir. Tayside Univ. Hosps. NHS Trust; Hon. Sec. Lect. (Pharmacol. & Therap.) Univ. Dundee. Prev: Dir. Med. Servs. Dundee Teachg. Hosps. NHS Trust; Sen. Lect. (Pharmacol. & Therap.) & Lect. (Med.) Univ. Dundee; Research Fell. (Med.) Harvard Med. Sch. & Peter Bent Brigham Hosp. Boston, USA.

MCLEAN, Donald Grant Kildalton, Bonar Crescent, Bridge of Weir PA11 3EH Tel: 01505 612499 — MB ChB Ed. 1942; FFAEM 1994. (Ed. University of Edinburgh)

MCLEAN, Douglas (retired) Southernwood, 17 Quarry Heads Lane, Durham DH1 3DY Tel: 0191 386 4033 — MB BS 1937 Durh.; DCH Eng. 1946. Prev: Ho. Surg. & Asst. Resid. Med. Off. Roy. Vict. Infirm. Newc.

MCLEAN, Douglas Alexander Charden, Chapel Lane, Curdridge, Southampton SO32 2BB Tel: 0148 92 787363 — MB BS 1967 Lond.; MRCOG 1975; DObst 1972. (St. Geo.) GP Fair Oak Winchester. Prev: Research Fell. & Hon. Sen. Regist. Nuffield Dept. O & G Univ.; Oxf.; Ho. Surg. St. Geo. Hosp. Lond.

MCLEAN, Mr Duncan Alexander Western Isles Hospital, Macaulay Road, Stornoway HS1 2AF Tel: 01851 704704; 18 Goathill Crescent, Stornoway HS1 2TB Tel: 01851 702618 Fax: 01851 702618 — MB ChB 1964 Ed.; FRCS Ed. 1968. (Edinburgh) Cons. Surg. W.ern Isles Hosp. Stornoway. Socs: Fell. Ass. Surg. GB & Irel.; Viking Surg. Club; BMA. Prev: Lect. (Surg.) Univ. Edin.; Regist. Regional Surg. Paediat. Serv. Edin.; Regist. Edin. Hosps. Rotat. Scheme.

MCLEAN, Mrs Elizabeth Kathleen (retired) — BM BCh 1957 Oxf.; BA (1st cl. Nat. Sc.) Oxf. 1954; DM 1973; FRCPsych 1986, M

MCLEAN

1975; DPM Eng. 1973. Hon. Sen. Lect. Psychiat. St. Geo. Med. Sch. Lond. Prev: Regist. Bethlem Roy. & Maudsley Hosp. Lond.

MCLEAN, Emma Kirsty 16 Rydon Lane, Countess Wear, Exeter EX2 7AW Tel: 01392 877430; 16 Rydon Lane, Countess, Wear, Exeter EX2 7AW — MB BCh 1998 Wales. (UWCM) Med. SHO E. Glam. LGen. Hosp., Ch. Village NR. Pontypndd, Mid Glam.

MACLEAN, Eoin Swan (retired) 24 Lylefoot Crescent, Greenock PA16 7TJ Tel: 01475 721405 — MB ChB 1952 Glas.; MRCGP 1968. Prev: GP Greenock.

MACLEAN, Gillian Patricia Queens Drive Surgery, 181 Queens Drive, Glasgow G42 8QD Tel: 0141 423 3474 — MB ChB 1974 Glas.; DObst RCOG 1976.

MCLEAN, Gillian Suzanne Falkirk & District Royal Infirmary, Major's Loan, Falkirk FK1 5QE Tel: 01324 624000 Fax: 01342 616447 Email: gmclean@fvpc.scot.nhs.uk; 1 Woodburn Avenue, Clarkston, Glasgow G76 7TZ — MB ChB 1982 Glas.; BSc (Hons.) Glas. 1977; MRCPsych 1990; DRCOG 1984. Cons. Psychiat. Falkirk & Dist. Roy. Infirm.; Hon. Clin. Lect. Univ. Glas. Socs: Exec. Comm. Old Age Psychiat. Scott. Div. (Meetings Sec.). Prev: Sen. Regist. (Psychiat.) Gartnavel Hosp. Glas. & Bellsdyke Hosp. Larbert.

MCLEAN, Gladys Frances Agnes (retired) 71 Victoria Road, Horwich, Bolton BL6 5ND Tel: 01204 68247 — MB ChB 1924 Manch.; DPH 1926. Prev: Asst. MOH Preston Co. Boro.

MACLEAN, Graham Douglas (retired) Dunryber, 243 Queen's Road, Aberdeen AB15 8DL Tel: 01224 310494 — MB ChB Aberd. 1962; MRCGP 1973. Prev: GP Aberd.

MACLEAN, Graham Edward 2 Sebbys Gardens, Terling, Chelmsford CM3 2PS — MB BS 1982 Lond.

MACLEAN, Hamish The Rowans, Dunglass Road, Maryburgh, Conon Bridge, Dingwall IV7 8ET — MB ChB 1948 Ed. (Ed.) Prev: Ho. Surg. & Ho. Phys. Roy. Infirm. Edin.; Obst. Off. Raigmore Hosp. Inverness.

MACLEAN, Henry Ross Colquhoun (retired) 9 The Butts, Brentford TW8 8BJ Tel: 020 8560 6667 — MB ChB Aberd. 1944. GP Brentford.

MCLEAN, Hugh (retired) The Sheerings, Honeysuckle Lane, High Salvington, Worthing BN13 3BT Tel: 01903 66629 — MB ChB 1961 Glas.

MACLEAN, Hugh Cameron Muir Carisbrooke Health Centre, 22 Carisbrooke Road, Newport PO30 1NR Tel: 01983 522150 Fax: 01983 825902 — MB ChB 1972 Glas. Clin. Asst. (Dermat.) St. Mary's Hosp. Newport I. of Wight.; Chairm. Is. Health Care Consortium; Nat. Chairm. Assoc. Indep. Multifunds. Prev: SCMO (Family Plann.) I. of Wight AHA; SHO (Med.) Stobhill Gen. Hosp. Glas.; SHO (O & G) St. Mary's Hosp. Newport I. of Wight.

MCLEAN, Iain Cran The Surgery, 3 St. John Street, Whithorn, Newton Stewart DG8 8PS Tel: 01988 500218 Fax: 01988 500737 — MB ChB 1986 Aberd.; BSc (Hons.) Aberd. 1976; MRCGP 1990; DRCOG 1990.

MACLEAN, Iain Grant (retired) Glaich-Na-Goire, Loaneckheim, Kiltarlity, Beauly IV4 7JQ Tel: 01463 741471 — MB ChB Ed. 1943.

MACLEAN, Iain Matheson (retired) Sonachan, Rootfield, Muir of Ord IV6 7RF Tel: 01349 862580 — MB ChB 1962 Aberd.; DObst RCOG 1966. Prev: Med. Off. Falkland Is.s.

MACLEAN, Iain Michael Urmston Group Practice, 154 Church Road, Urmston, Manchester M41 9DL Tel: 0161 755 9870 Fax: 0161 755 9896; 21 Harrow Road, Sale M33 3TJ — MB ChB 1985 Manch.; MRCGP 1989.

MCLEAN, Ian Fortescue College Road Surgery, 50/52 College Road, Maidstone ME15 6SB Tel: 01622 752345 Fax: 01622 758133; The Oast House, Rectory Lane, Barming, Maidstone ME16 9NG Tel: 01622 726229 — MB BS 1973 Lond.; MRCGP 1977. (Kings Coll. Hosp.) Assoc. Adviser Postgrad. Gen. Pract. Educat., S. Thames (E.). Prev: Ho. Off. (Orthop., NeuroSurg., A & E & Dermat.) King's Coll. Hosp. Lond.

MACLEAN, Ian Hamish The Grove, Irongray, Dumfries DG2 9TN Tel: 01387 721037 — MB ChB 1971 Dundee; FFCM 1989, M 1982. Chief Admin. Med. Off. & Dir. Pub. Health Isle of Man Govt. Prev: Dir. of Pub. Health Dimfries & Galloway HB; Community Med. Specialist Borders HB; Sen. Regist. (Community Med.) N.Id. & N. Tyneside AHAs.

MCLEAN, Ian Paul Princess Margaret Rose Orthopaedic Hospital, Edinburgh EH10 7ED Tel: 0131 536 4600 Fax: 0131 536 4601 — MB ChB 1984 Manch.; MB ChB Manch. 1987; BSc (Physiol.)

Manch. 1984; FRCPS Glas. 1992; Dip. Sports Med. Scotl. 1995. Regist. (Trauma & Orthop.) Lothian Region Higher Train. Scheme. Prev: Mersey Region Basic Surgic. Train. Scheme.

MACLEAN, Isabella Forrester (retired) 11 Den Close, Beckenham BR3 6RP Tel: 020 8650 8428 — MB ChB 1951 Glas. Prev: Sen. Med. Off. Bromley AHA.

MACLEAN, Jackson (retired) 12 Douglas Street, Hamilton ML3 0BP Tel: 01698 286262 — MB ChB 1956 Glas. Prev: GP Hamilton.

MCLEAN, James Alexander Forbes (retired) 25 Kelston Road, Ilford IG6 2EJ Tel: 020 8551 8781 — MB ChB 1937 Aberd.; MB ChB (Hons.) Aberd. 1937; FRCPath 1965, M 1964; DPH Aberd. 1941.

MACLEAN, James Curdie Russel Foxhill Farm, Catfoot Lane, Lambley, Nottingham NG4 4QH Tel: 0115 926 9579 — MB ChB 1951 St. And. (St. And.)

MCLEAN, James Douglas Farquhar (retired) 31 Ellenabeich, Easdale, Oban PA34 4RQ Tel: 01852 300385 Email: jdmclean@globalnet.co.uk — MB ChB Ed. 1949. Prev: Med. Off. TynePk. List Sch. & Lothian Ho. Trust Templedean.

MACLEAN, Mr James Gordon Bruce Perth Royal Infirmary, Perth PH1 1NX; Tibbermore House, Tibbermore, Perth PH1 1QJ — MB ChB 1981 Dundee; FRCS (Orth.) Glas. 1993; FRCS Glas. 1986. Cons. Perth Roy. Infirm.; Hon. Lect. Univ. of Dundee Med. Sch.; Cons. Ninewells Hosp. (Childr. Orthop.). Socs: Brit. Orthopaedic Assn.; Brit. Soc. for Childr.'s Orthop. Prev: Cons. & Research Fell. Univ. Cape Town; Sen. Regist. Norf. & Norwich Hosp.; Regist. (Orthop.) Raigmore Hosp. Inverness.

MACLEAN, Jane Kay (Surgery) 10 Russell Place, 4 Chessel Avenue, Bitterne, Southampton SO17 1NU; 10 Russell Place, Southampton SO17 1NU Tel: 01703 557649 — MB ChB 1962 Ed. (Ed.)

MCLEAN, Jean 3 Great Minster Street, Winchester SO23 9HA — MB ChB 1957 Ed.; MA Ed. 1951, MB ChB 1957.

MCLEAN, Joan Ann 6 Grove Crescent, Aberdeen AB16 5DW — MB ChB 1960 Aberd.

MACLEAN, John (retired) 1 Sunway Grove, Coventry CV3 6GR Tel: 024 7641 5021 — MB ChB 1946 Ed.

MACLEAN, John 37 Imrie Place, Penicuik EH26 8LF — MB ChB 1975 Ed.; MRCGP 1981.

MACLEAN, John Anderson Allison and Partners, Maryhill Health Centre, 41 Shawpark Street, Glasgow G20 9DR Tel: 0141 531 8840 Fax: 0141 531 8848; 63 Lubnaig Road, Newlands, Glasgow G43 2RX Tel: 0141 571 0693 — MB ChB 1981 Glas.; MRCGP 1987. Clin. Lect. (Sports Med.) Univ. Glas. Socs: Brit. Assn. Sport & Med.; Brit. Assn. Trauma in Sport.

MCLEAN, John Graeme Murray James Paget Hospital, Lowestoft Road, Gorleston, Great Yarmouth NR31 6LA Tel: 01493 452452; Crosswinds, The Drive, Acle, Norwich NR13 3RF — MB BS 1965 Durh.; FRCOG 1982, M 1969. (Newc.) Clin. Dir. (O & G & Paediat.) Jas. Paget Hosp. Gt. Yarmouth. Socs: N. Irel., N. Eng. & Scott. Obst. Soc. & E. Anglian Obst. Soc. Prev: Cons. O & G Jas. Paget Hosp. Gt. Yarmouth; Sen. Regist. (O & G) Univ. Hosp. Wales Cardiff; Regist. (O & G) Roy. Matern. Hosp. & Roy. Samarit. Hosp. Glas.

MCLEAN, John Harvey Readesmoor Group Practice, 29 West St., Congleton CW12 1JN Tel: 01266 27661; 1 Wood Lane, Buglanton, Congleton CW12 3PX Tel: 01260 279908 — MB ChB 1954 Glas. (Glas.) Prev: Ho. Phys. Roy. Infirm. Glas.; Ho. Surg. Stobhill Gen. Hosp. Glas.; Jun. Specialist Obst. RAF Med. Br.

MACLEAN, John Lachlan (retired) 2 Parklands, Eynsham Road, Farmoor, Oxford OX2 9TA Tel: 01865 864467 — MB ChB 1940 Manch. Prev: Ho. Surg. Crumpsall Hosp. Manch.

MCLEAN, John Michael 24 St Brannock's Road, Chorlton, Manchester M21 0UP Tel: 0161 881 4967 Fax: 0161 881 4967 — MD Newc. 1968; BSc (Hons.) Durham. 1961, MB BS (Hons.) 1959. (King's Coll. Newc.) Sen. Lect. Anat. Manch. Univ. Prev: Ho. Phys. & Ho. Surg. Roy. Vict. Infirm. Newc.; Postgrad. Schol., Physiol. Dept. Durh. Univ.; Lect. Anat. Newc. Univ.

MCLEAN, Joseph Campbell 100 Strand Road, Portstewart BT55 7PG — MB BCh BAO 1950 Dub.; BA Dub. 1946, MB BCh BAO 1950; LAH Dub. 1950. (TC Dub.) Sen. Asst. Med. Off. Coleraine Ballymoney & Moyler Dists. N.; Health & Social Serv. Bd. Asst. Co. Med. Off. Antrim Co. Health Comm.

MACLEAN

MACLEAN, Joseph Robson (retired) 49 Lidgett Park Road, Leeds LS8 1JN — MB ChB 1949 Glas. Prev: Ho. Surg. Roy. Infirm. Glas.

MCLEAN, Julia Beatrice Ellen Ladycroft Cottage, Hebden, Skipton BD23 5DX — MB ChB 1995 Birm.; ChB Birm. 1995.

MCLEAN, Katharine Anne Department of Medicine for the Elderly, Derbyshire Royal Infirmary, London Road, Derby DE1 2QY — MB ChB 1983 Manch.; BSc Med. Sc. St. And. 1980; MRCP (UK) 1986; FRCP 1998. Cons. Phys. Med. for Elderly Derbysh. Roy. Infirm. Socs: Derby Med. Soc. Prev: Sen. Regist. (Gen. Med.) Roy. Hallamsh. Hosp. Sheff.; Regist. (Gen. Med.) N. Manch. Gen. Hosp.; Regist. (Geriat.) Withington Hosp. Manch.

MCLEAN, Katherine Anne 3 The Oval, Brooksfield, Middlesbrough TS5 8ET — MB ChB 1998 Ed.; MB ChB Ed 1998.

MCLEAN, Kenneth (retired) Ardchattan, 12 Park Road, Eskbank, Dalkeith EH22 3DF Tel: 0131 663 2216 — MB ChB 1956 Aberd.; MRCGP 1972; Dip Soc Med Ed. 1969.

MCLEAN, Kenneth Andrew Department of Genitourinary Medicine, Charing Cross Hospital, Fulham Palace Road, London W6 8RF Tel: 020 8846 1578 Fax: 020 8846 7582; Flat 2, 28 Telford Avenue, Streatham, London SW2 4XF — MB ChB 1979 Glas.; FRCP Ed. 1995; MRCP (UK) 1984. (Glas.) Cons. Genitourin. Med. Char. Cross Hosp. Lond.

MCLEAN, Kenneth Fraser Carronbank Medical Practice, Denny Health Centre, Carronbank House, Denny FK6 6GD Tel: 01324 822382 Fax: 01324 826675; Bankside, Denny FK6 5NA — MB ChB 1976 Aberd.; MRCGP 1980. Prev: Trainee GP Aberd. Hosp. Gp. VTS.

MACLEAN, Kenneth Smedley 7 Ice House Wood, Oxted RH8 9DN Tel: 01883 716652 — MB BChir Camb. 1939; MA Camb. 1942, MD 1948; FRCP Lond. 1954, M 1946; MRCS Eng. LRCP Lond. 1939. (Guy's) Cons. Med. Off. Hannover Life Re (UK) formerly Skandia Re (UK) 1978 to date; Emerit. Cons. Phys. Guy's Hosp. Lond. Socs: Assn. Phys. & Med. Soc. Lond.; (Ex-Pres.) Assur. Med. Soc. Prev: Ex-Chairm. Univ. Hosps. Assn.; Dir. Dept. Med. & Sub-Dean Postgrad. Studies Guy's Hosp. Lond.; Surg. Lt.-Cdr. RNVR.

MCLEAN, Lesley Mair Dept. of Radiology, Royal Victoria Infirmary, Newcastle upon Tyne NE1 4LP Tel: 0191 232 5131 — MB ChB 1975 Glas.; FRCR 1983; DMRD Eng. 1979; DRCOG 1977. Cons. Radiol. i/c Mammography Screen. Unit, Roy. Vict. Infirm. Newc. Prev: Cons. Radiol. Chichester; Sen. Regist. (Radiol.) King's Coll. Hosp. Lond.; Sen. Regist. (Radiol.) Brist. Roy. Infirm.

MCLEAN, Malcolm Downie Weare House, 16 Rydon Lane, Countess Wear, Exeter EX2 7AW — MB ChB 1972 St. And.; FRCR 1979. Cons. Radiol. Exeter Health Dist. Prev: Sen. Regist. (Radiol.) Bristol & W.on Health Dist. (T).

MACLEAN, Malcolm Hugh 20 Rothesay Terrace, Edinburgh EH3 7RY Tel: 0131 225 1701 — MRCS Eng. LRCP Lond. 1969; BChir Camb. 1965, MB 1966.

MACLEAN, Malcolm Hugh Tel: 01382 534301 Fax: 01382 535959 — MB ChB Ed. 1982; LRCP LRCS Ed. LRCPS Glas 1982.

MCLEAN, Malcolm Stuart Henfield Medical Centre, Deer Park, Henfield BN5 9JQ Tel: 01273 492255 Fax: 01273 495050; 12 Gresham Place, Henfield BN5 9QJ Tel: 01273 493964 — BA Hons. Camb. 1975, MB BChir 1979; MRCGP 1987; DCH RCP Lond. 1987; DRCOG 1986.

MCLEAN, Margaret Elizabeth (retired) 12 Grants Avenue, Paisley PA2 6AZ — MB ChB (Commend.) Glas. 1950; DObst RCOG 1952; MRCGP 1959.

MCLEAN, Margaret Elizabeth 1/Fl, 51 Marchmont Rd, Edinburgh EH9 1HT — MB ChB 1996 Ed.

MCLEAN, Margaret Louise 92 Drakies Avenue, Inverness IV2 3SD — MB ChB 1994 Ed.

MCLEAN, Margaret Rosemary (retired) 25 Culduthel Road, Inverness IV2 4AP Tel: 01463 238110 — MB ChB Aberd. 1961. Med. Asst. (Cytol.) Raigmore Hosp. Inverness.

MCLEAN, Marjory Anne Hairmyres Hospital, Department Gynaecology, Eaglesham Road, East Kilburn, London Tel: 0141 569 8034; 7 Springfield Park Road, Burnside, Glasgow G73 3RG — MB ChB 1982 Manch.; Diploma Obstetric Ultrasound; BSc St. And. 1979; MD Manch. 1993; MRCOG 1988; DRCOG 1985. Assoc. Specialist Obst. and Gynae, 6 sessions, locum Cons. 2 sessions. Prev: Locum Cons (Obst.) Bellshill Mat.; Locum Cons. (O & G) Vict. Infirm. NHS Trust Glas.; Sen. Regist. Rotat. (O & G) W. Scotl.

MACLEAN, Michael John Bosmere Medical Practice, PO Box 41, Civic Centre Road, Havant PO9 2AJ Tel: 023 9245 1300 Fax: 023 9294 2524 Email: bosmeremedical@cs.com; Lowerford Cottage, Kingsmead, Wickham, Fareham PO17 5AU Tel: 01329 835941 — MB BS 1972 Lond.; MRCGP 1980.

MCLEAN, Michelle Jayne North Road Medical Practice, 182 North Road, Cardiff CF14 3XQ Tel: 029 2061 9188 Fax: 029 2061 3484 — MB ChB 1991 Leic.

MACLEAN, Morag 13 Camuscross, Isle Ornsay, Isle of Skye IV43 8QS Tel: 01471 833241 — Dip Sports Med 2000 (Distinction); MB ChB Ed. 1989; BSc (Hons.) Ed. 1986; MRCGP 1994; DRCOG 1993. (Univ. Ed.) Assoc. GP Sleat, Skye.

MACLEAN, Murdo, RD (retired) The Cottage, St. Catherines, Cairndow PA25 8AZ — MB ChB 1952 Glas. Prev: Surg. Lt.-Cdr. RNR.

MACLEAN, Murdoch Neil Department of Obstetrics & Gynaecology, Aberdeen Royal Hospitals (NHS) Trust, Aberdeen Tel: 01224 681818; 11 Garden Court, Denmore Park, Bridge of Don, Aberdeen AB23 8FF Tel: 01224 703407 — MB ChB 1988 Aberd.; BMedBiol (Comm.) Aberd. 1988; MRCOG 1993. (Aberd.) Specialist Regist. (O & G) Aberd. Roy. Hosps. Trust. Prev: Career Regist. (O & G) Aberd. Roy. Hosps. Trust & Raigmore Hosp. Inverness; SHO (O & G) Aberd. Roy. Hosps. Trust; SHO (Surg. & O & G) Grampian HB.

MACLEAN, Murdoch William (retired) 25 Culduthel Road, Inverness IV2 4AP Tel: 01463 238110 — MB ChB Aberd. 1961; FRCOG 1980, M 1967, DObst 1963. Prev: Cons. (O & G) Highland Health Bd.

MCLEAN, Murray Jack (retired) Sonachan, 8 Camstradden Drive E., Bearsden, Glasgow G61 4AH Tel: 0141 942 0896 — MB ChB 1959 Ed.; DA Eng. 1962; DObst RCOG 1961. Prev: Anaesth. Paisley & Dist. Hosps.

MCLEAN, Nancy Patricia (retired) Ardchattan, 12 Park Road, Eskbank, Dalkeith EH22 3DF Tel: 0131 663 2216 — MB ChB 1957 Aberd.

MACLEAN, Mr Neil (retired) 1 Lennox Street, Edinburgh EH4 1QB Tel: 0131 332 1714 — MB ChB 1934 Ed.; FRCS Ed. 1983; FRCP Ed. 1963, M 1938; DPH Manch. 1940; FRCPath 1973, M 1963. Prev: Cons. Path. N. Lothian Health Dist.

MACLEAN, Neil Ash Mount, 5 St Brydes Terrace, Lockerbie DG11 2EJ — MB ChB 1964 St. And.

MCLEAN, Neil Mackinnon Holmfield, Duntocher Road, Clydebank G81 3LN Tel: 0141 952 5245 — MB ChB 1961 Glas.; MRCGP 1972 DMJ Soc. Apoth. Lond. 1971; FRCGP 1988. Socs: Medico-Legal Soc. & Assn. Police Surgs. Gt. Brit.

MCLEAN, Mr Neil Robert Nuffield Hospital, Clayton Road, Jesmond, Newcastle upon Tyne NE2 1JP Tel: 0191 281 6131 — MD 1991 Glas.; MB ChB 1976 Glas.; BSc 1974 Glas.; FRCS Glas. 1980. (University of Glasgow) Cons. Plastic & Reconstruc. Surg. Roy. Vict. Infirm. Newc. Socs: Coun. Mem. Brit. Assn. Plastic Surg.; Brit. Assn. Head & Neck Oncol.; Brit. Assn. Oncol. Prev: Regist. (Plastic Surg.) St. Lawrence Hosp. Chepstow; Sen. Regist. (Plastic Reconstruc. & Burns Surg.) Qu. Mary's Hosp. Roehampton Lond. and The Roy. Marden Hosp., Lond.

MACLEAN, Norman, OBE, TD Flanshaw House, Flanshaw Lane, Wakefield WF2 9JE Tel: 01924 74839 — MB ChB 1951 Ed. (Ed.)

MACLEAN, Pamela Joyce (retired) Greenacre, 75 Dundee Road, Broughty Ferry, Dundee DD5 1NA Tel: 01382 776931 — MB ChB 1965 St. And.; MCOphth 1991; DO Eng. 1968. Prev: Assoc. Specialist (Ophth.) Dundee Teachg. Hosps. NHS Trust.

MCLEAN, Peter 7 Hazelbank Terrace, Edinburgh EH11 1SL — MB ChB 1997 Ed.

MCLEAN, Peter Stewart 6 Broomhill Avenue, Glasgow G11 7AE — MB ChB 1997 Glas.

MCLEAN, Philip Charles Wells Road Centre, Wells Road, Nottingham NG3 3AA Tel: 0115 952 9422 Fax: 0115 952 9421 Email: pcm@nadt.org.uk — MB ChB 1967 Ed.; FRCPsych 1989, M 1973; DPM Ed. 1973. Cons. Psychiat. Nottm.shire Healthcare NHS Trust; Clin. Teach. (Psychiat.) Univ. Nottm. Prev: Sen. Regist. Roy. Edin. Hosp.

MCLEAN, Rhona Murray 61A Romilly Road, Cardiff CF5 1FL — MB ChB 1991 Aberd. Lect. Univ. Wales Coll. Med.

MCLEAN, Mr Robert Donald (retired) The Croft, Wollaston Court, Wollaston, Stourbridge DY8 4SQ Tel: 01384 372343 — MB ChB

1957 Birm.; FRCOG 1978, M 1964, DObst 1959. Cons. O & G Dudley AHA. Prev: Regist. (O & G) S. Shields Hosp. Gp.

MACLEAN, Rona (retired) Penberth, Oakfield Road, Ashtead KT21 2RD Tel: 01372 272317 — MB BS 1951 Lond.; FRCPsych 1984, M 1972; DFFP 1993; DPM Eng. 1965; DObst RCOG 1955. Prev: Research Regist. (Psychol. Med.) St. Bart. Hosp. Lond.

MACLEAN, Ronald Alexander Stuart Eaglesham Surgery, 30 Gilmour Street, Eaglesham, Glasgow G76 0AT Tel: 01355 302221 Fax: 01355 302907; 400 Clarkston Road, Glasgow G44 3QG Tel: 0141 637 2391 Fax: 0141 637 1967 — MB ChB 1960 St. And.; FRCGP 1991, M 1975; DObst RCOG 1963. Socs: (Ex-Pres.) Glas. S.. Med. Soc.; Roy. Soc. Med.

MCLEAN, Mr Ronald Donald Woods Cullion, Londonderry Tel: 0150 489256 — MB BCh BAO 1962 Belf.; FRCS Ed. 1967. (Belf.) Cons. Surg. Altnagelvin Hosp. Lond.derry; Postgrad. Clin. Tutor W.. Health & Social Servs. Bd. Socs: BMA & Assn. Surgs. Gt. Brit. & Irel. Prev: Ho. Surg. Roy. Vict. Hosp. Belf.; Regist. (Cardiothoracic Surg.) Hammersmith Hosp. Lond.; Sen. Regist. (Thoracic Surg.) W.. Hosp. Soton.

MACLEAN, Sarah Ann Flat 2/1st Floor, 6 Broomhill Avenue, Glasgow G11 7AE — MB ChB 1997 Glas.

MCLEAN, Sheila Margaret Royal Dundee Liff Hospital, By Liff, Dundee DD2 5NF Tel: 01382 423000; The Coach House, 4 Balruddery Meadows, Invergowrie, Dundee DD2 5LJ — MB ChB 1969 St. And. (Dundee & St. And.) SCMO (Psychiat. of Old Age) Roy. Dundee Liff Hosp. Socs: Affil. Mem. Roy. Coll. Psychiat. Prev: GP Princip. Glas.; Ho. Off. (Med.) King's Cross Hosp. Dundee; Ho. Off. (O & G) Stobhill Hosp. Glas.

MACLEAN, Sheila Scott (retired) 5 Suffolk Road, Edinburgh EH16 5NR Tel: 0131 667 4866 — MB ChB 1949 Ed.; DCCH RCP Ed, RCGP & FCM 1984. Prev: SCMO Lothian HB.

MACLEAN, Tearlach Sonachan, Rootfield, Muir of Ord IV6 7RF — MB ChB 1995 Glas. Ho. Off. (Surg.) Ayr Hosp.

MCLEAN, Thomas William Barry 40 Tullywest Road, Crumlin BT29 4SP Email: tom.mclean@nireland.com — MB BCh BAO 1982 Belf. Gen. Med. - Antrim Area Hosp. - Antrim.

MACLEAN, Valerie Mary Mansefield, Station Road, Drumlithie, Stonehaven AB39 3YT Email: valmaclean@cheerful.com — MB ChB 1987 Glas.; BSc (Hons.) Glas. 1985; MRCP (UK) 1990. Specialist Regist. (A & E) Aberd. Roy. Infirm. Prev: Staff Grade (A & E) Aberd. Roy. Infirm.; Regist. (Med.) King's Cross Hosp. & Ninewells Hosp. Dundee; SHO (Med.) Ninewells Hosp. Dundee.

MACLEAN, William Ewan, OBE (retired) Oaklea, 23 Kippington Road, Sevenoaks TN13 2LJ Tel: 01732 451738 — MB ChB 1935 St. And.; FRCP Ed. 1994; MRCP Ed. 1948; DCH Eng. 1947. Prev: Regist. & Receiv. Room Phys. Hosp. Sick Childr. Gt. Ormond St. Lond.

MACLEAN, William Kenneth (retired) 31 Grange Road, Edinburgh EH9 1UG Tel: 0131 667 3102 — LRCP LRCS Ed. LRFPS Glas. 1950. Prev: Admiralty Surg. & Agent.

MCLEARIE, Mr Matthew (retired) 39 Ashfield Road, Leicester LE2 1LB Tel: 0116 270 7081 — MB ChB 1938 Glas.; FRCS Ed. 1946; FRCS Glas. 1962; FRFPS Glas. 1944. Prev: Orthop. Surg. Leicester AHA.

MCLEARIE, Stephen 4 Norbreck Drive, Giffnock, Glasgow G46 6AF — MB ChB 1993 Glas.

MCLEAY, Gordon Forbes St Margaret's Health Centre, St Margaret's Drive, Auchterarder PH3 1JH — MB ChB 1986 Aberd.; FRCP 2000 Glas.; MSc Glas. 1993; MRCGP 1996; DRCOG 1995. GP Auchterarder; Hon. Lect. Tayside Centre for GP Dundee; Assoc. Adviser Tayside. Prev: Regist. (Radiother., Oncol. & Med.) Gtr. Glas. HB.

***MACLEAY, Kenneth Mark** 79 Kenworth Road, London E9 5RB — MB BS 1998 Lond.; MB BS Lond 1998.

MCLEES, David James Stuart Wallace House Surgery, 5-11 St. Andrew Street, Hertford SG14 1HZ Tel: 01787 550541 — MB BS 1988 Lond.; BSc (Hons.) Biochem. Lond. 1985; MRCGP 1993; DRCOG 1992. Prev: Trainee GP Lond Hosp. VTS; Primary Health Care Seychelles; Ho. Surg. S.end Hosp.

MCLEISH, David George Garth (retired) 45 Langdale Road, Hove BN3 4HR Tel: 01273 726959 — MB ChB 1952 Liverp.; DObst RCOG 1955. Prev: Cas. Off. & Ho. Surg. (Obst.) Sefton Gen. Hosp. Liverp.

MCLEISH, Ian Stanley (retired) 44 Norwood Park, Bearsden, Glasgow G61 2RZ Tel: 0141 942 6330 — MB ChB 1950 Glas.; MRCGP 1959. Prev: GP Clydebank.

MCLEISH, Ruby Dora McIlvride (retired) 44 Norwood Park, Bearsden, Glasgow G61 2RZ — MB ChB 1950 Glas. Prev: Clin. Med. Off. (Community Health) Gtr. Glas. HB.

MCLELLAN, Ailsa Elizabeth High Clere, 7 Coppy Wood Drive, Ilkley LS29 0DX — MB ChB 1992 Ed.

MCLELLAN, Alastair Robert Department of Medicine & Therapeutics, Western Infirmary, Glasgow G11 6NT Tel: 0141 211 2880 Fax: 0141 339 2800; 39 Lubnaig Road, Newlands, Glasgow G43 2RY Tel: 0141 632 1143 — MB ChB Glas. 1981; MD Glas. 1991; FRCP Glas. 1994; MRCP (UK) 1984. Cons. Phys. & Endocrinol. W.. Infirm. Glas. Socs: Soc. Endocrinol.; Caledonian Endocrine Soc.; Amer. Soc. Bone & Mineral Research. Prev: Clin. Scientist MRC Blood Pressure Unit Glas.; Lect. (Med.) Gardiner Inst. W.. Infirm. Glas.; Regist. (Endocrinol.) W.. Infirm. Glas.

MCLELLAN, Anne Department of Obstetrics & Gynaecology, Ninewells Hospital, Dundee DD1 9SY; 10 Balruddery Meadows, Invergowrie, Dundee DD2 5LJ — MB ChB 1986 Glas.; MRCOG 1994. Specialist Regist. (O & G) Ninewells Hosp. Dundee.

MCLELLAN, Professor David Lindsay University of Southampton, Southampton General Hospital Mail print 874, Southampton SO16 6YD Tel: 02380 796466 Fax: 02380 794943 Email: dlm@soton.ac.uk; Coles Farm cottage, Awbridge Hill, Romsey SO51 0HF Tel: 01794 522402 Fax: 01794 523993 — MB BChir 1966 Camb.; PhD Glas. 1975; MA Camb. 1966; FRCP (UK) 1982, M 1970. (Camb. & St. Thos.) Prof. Rehabil. Univ. Soton.; Hon. Cons. Neurol. & Rehabil. Med. Soton. Univ. Hosps. NHS Trust. Socs: Soc. Research Rehabil.; Brit. Soc. Rehabil. Med.; Assn. Brit. Neurol. Prev: Sen. Lect. (Neurol.) Univ. Soton.; Sen. Regist. (Neurol.) Lond. Hosp.; Lect. (Neurol.) Univ. Glas.

MCLELLAN, Dina 37 Amisfield Street, Maryhill, Glasgow G20 8LB — MB ChB 1988 Glas.

MCLELLAN, Dougal Murdo 26 Florence Drive, Giffnock, Glasgow G46 6UN — MB ChB 1991 Glas.

MCLELLAN, Douglas Richard Pathology Department, The Victoria Infirmary, Langside, Glasgow G42 9TY Tel: 0141 201 5676 Fax: 0141 201 5663 — MB ChB 1977 Glas.; MD Glas. 1989; FRCPath 1997, MRCPath 1987; Dip. Forens. Med. Glas 1991. (Glas.) Cons. Path. Vict. Infirm. Glas.; Hon. Clin. Sen. Lect. Univ. Glas. Socs: Internat. Acad. Path. (Brit. Div.); Assn. Clin. Pathol.; S.. Med. Soc. (Hon. Sec.). Prev: Sen. Regist. (Path.) W.. Infirm. Glas.; Hon. Sen. Regist. (Neuropath.) Inst. Neurol. Scs. Glas.; Regist. (Path.) S.. Gen. Hosp. Glas.

MCLELLAN, Duncan Graham 8 Ondine Road, London SE15 4EB — MB BS 1991 West. Austral.

MCLELLAN, Elaine Margaret Bridgeton Health Centre, 201 Abercromby Street, Glasgow G40 2DA Tel: 0141 550 3822 — MB ChB 1987 Glas.; 1998 M.Phil Law and Ethics in Medicine, Glas.; LLB 1994. (Glas.) GP Princip. Galsgow; Dip. Legal Pract. Univ. Strathclyde Law Sch. Prev: Asst. GP Kirkintilloch; Regist. (Geriat. Med.) Law Hosp. Carluke; Trainee GP Glas.

MCLELLAN, Fiona Molly Wellands, Letcombe Bassett, Wantage OX12 9LP — MB ChB 1993 Glas.

MCLELLAN, George Iain Murie 29 Tavistock Court, Nottingham NG5 2EH — MB BChir 1962 Camb.; BA Camb. 1953, MA 1962; MRCS Eng. LRCP Lond. 1958. (Camb. & Birm.) Prev: Ho. Phys. Geo. Eliot Hosp. Nuneaton; Ho. Surg. Hosp. of St. Cross, Rugby; Ho. Surg. (Obst.) Bushey Matern. Hosp.

MACLELLAN, Mr Gordon Edward Oldchurch Hospital, Romford RM7 0BE Tel: 01708 708095 Fax: 01708 708095; Salmonds Farm House, Salmonds Grove, Ingrave, Brentwood CM13 3RS Tel: 01277 810945 Fax: 01277 812839 Email: gembones25@hotmail.com — MB BS 1969 Lond.; FRCS Eng. 1974. (St. Geo.) p/t Cons. Orthop. Surg. Barking, Havering & Redbridge NHS Trust. Socs: Roy. Soc. Med.; Brit. Orthop. Assn.; SICOT. Prev: Sen. Regist. (Orthop.) Roy. Nat. Orthop. Hosp. Lond.; Resid. Orthop. Mass. Gen. Hosp. Boston, USA; Ho. Surg. St. Geo. Hosp. Lond.

MCLELLAN, Gordon Stephen Moore Farfield Group Practice, St. Andrew's Surgeries, West Lane, Keighley BD21 2LD Tel: 01535 607333 Fax: 01535 611818 — MB ChB 1975 Leeds; DRCOG 1977. (Leeds)

MCLELLAN

MCLELLAN, Iain Campbell (retired) 25 Hest Bank Lane, Hest Bank, Lancaster LA2 6DG Tel: 01524 822013 Fax: 01524 824663 — MB BChir Camb. 1961; MA Camb. 1962; MRCS Eng. LRCP Lond. 1960; T(GP) 1991; DObst RCOG 1963. Prev: GP Lancaster.

MCLELLAN, Iain Stewart Dorema Surgery, Dorema, Bridge of Weir Road, Kilmacolm PA13 4AP Tel: 01505 872155 Fax: 01505 874191; Cairngorm, Rowantree Hill Road, Kilmacolm PA13 4NP Tel: 01505 872927 — MB ChB 1969 Glas.; MFHom 1984; DA Eng. 1973; DObst RCOG 1971; MCPS Sask. 1973. Med. Pract. Glas. Homoeop. Hosp. Prev: Ho. Off. Glas. Roy. Infirm.; Regist. (Anaesth.) Roy. Free Hosp. Lond.; Active Staff St. Peters Hosp. Melville, Canada.

MCLELLAN, Ian 31 Western Park Road, Leicester LE3 6HQ Tel: 0116 857188 — MB BS 1968 Lond.; MRCS Eng. LRCP Lond. 1968; FFA RCS Eng. 1973. (St. Bart.) Cons. Anaesth. Leicester Roy. Infirm. & Leicester Cardio-Thoracic Unit Groby Rd. Hosp.

MCLELLAN, James Weir (retired) 2 Auchneagh Road, Greenock PA16 9HX Tel: 01475 723406 — MB ChB Glas. 1952; DObst RCOG 1958.

MCLELLAN, Jean Marion The New Surgery, The Nap, Kings Langley WD4 8ET Tel: 01923 261035 Fax: 01923 269629; 208 Abbots Road, Abbots Langley WD5 0BP Tel: 01923 265800 — MB ChB 1972 Leeds; MRCGP 1976; LMCC 1977; DCH Eng. 1975; DObst RCOG 1974; Cert. Family Plann. JCC 1974. (Leeds) GP (Family Plann.) Psychosexual Clinics & Child Protec. Team; Psychosexual Counsell. Clinic. Hemel Hempstead & Watford. Socs: Inst. Psychosexual Med.; Dip. Fac. Family Plann. Prev: GP Trainer King's Langley; GP Fort Nelson Brit. Columbia, Canada; Fact. Doct Racals Acoustics.

MCLELLAN, Jessica Foxcombe End, Foxcombe Lane, Boar's Hill, Oxford OX1 5DH Tel: 01865 735182 — MB ChB 1988 Cape Town.

MACLELLAN, Linda Dorothy Childrens Services, Terrapin Building, Raigmore Hospital, Inverness IV2 3UJ Tel: 01463 701307 Fax: 01463 701320 Email: linda.maclellan@hpct.scot.nhs.uk — MB ChB 1981 Manch.; FRCPCH; MRCP (UK) 1988; MRCGP 1986; DRCOG 1985; DCH RCP Lond. 1985. Cons. Paediat. Community Child Health Highland Region. Prev: Sen. Regist. (Paediat.) Edin.

MCLELLAN, Neil James Children's Department, The London Hospital, Whitechapel, London E1 1BB — MB BS 1975 Lond.; BSc (Hons.) Lond. 1971, MB BS 1975; MRCP (UK) 1979. (Univ. Coll. Hosp.) Lect. Paediat. Neonat. Research Gp. Acad. Dept. Child Health The Lond. Hosp. Med. Coll.

MACLELLAN, Peter Desmond (retired) Corner Cottage, Whim Road, Gullane EH31 2BD — MB BChir Camb. 1939; MA Camb. 1940; MRCS Eng. LRCP Lond. 1939; MRCGP 1954. Prev: Sen. Resid. Med. Off. Sutton & Cheam Hosp.

MCLELLAN, Stuart Andrew Lower Flat, 16 Merchiston Gardens, Edinburgh EH10 5DD — MB ChB 1991 Ed.; BSc Bact. 1988; MRCP (UK) 1994.

MACLELLAN-SMITH, Ian Cheadle Medical Practice, 1-5 Ashfield Crescent, Cheadle SK8 1BH; 2 Plattwood Cottage, Lyme Park, Disley, Stockport SK12 2NT — MB ChB Manch. 1970; MRCGP 1978; Dip. Palliat. Med. Wales 1995. Asst. Med. Director, Willow Wood Hospice, Willow Wood Cl., Mellor Rd., Ashton-under-Lyne, Lancs., OL6 6SL; Racecourse Med. Off. Haydock Pk. Racecourse. Socs: Racecourse Med. Offs. Assn.; Assur. Med. Soc. Prev: Clin. Med. Off. (Palliat. Care) St. Ann's Hospice Chesh.

MCLELLAND, Janet Dermatology Department, Royal Victoria Infirmary, Newcastle upon Tyne NE1 4LP Tel: 0191 232 5131; Tel: 0191 285 0153 — MB BS (Hons.) Lond. 1981; BSc Lond. 1978, MD 1990; MRCP (UK) 1984. (Univ. Coll. Hosp.) Cons. Dermat. Roy. Vict. Infirm. Newc. u. Tyne. Prev: Cons. Dermat. Sunderland & S. Tyneside; Sen. Regist. (Dermat.) Roy. Vict. Infirm. Newc.; Research Fell. Roy. Postgrad. Med. Sch. Lond.

MCLEMAN, Daniel Ernsdaal, 3 Rectory Drive, Strichen, Fraserburgh AB43 6TU Tel: 01771 637369 — MB ChB Aberd. 1955; MRCGP 1966; DCH Eng. 1962; DObst RCOG 1960; LMCC 1960. (Aberdeen) Prev: Flight Lt. RAF Med. Br.; Ho. Phys. Roy. Aberd. Childr. Hosp.; Smith Clinic Ontario, Canada.

MCLENACHAN, James Meek Department of Cardiology, Leeds General Infirmary, Leeds LS1 3EX Tel: 0113 292 6476; 2 Parkwood Avenue, Roundhay, Leeds LS8 1JW Tel: 0113 266 6397 — MD 1988 Glas.; MB ChB 1980; MRCP (UK) 1983; FRCP Glas. 1993; FRCP Lond. 1996. (Glasgow) Cons. Cardiol. Leeds Gen. Infirm.

MCLENACHAN, William McLay 6 Roman Place, Bellshill ML4 2AU Tel: 01698 747195 — MB ChB 1955 Glas. (Glas.)

MACLENNAN, Alexander The Schoolhouse, Clunas, Nairn IV12 5UT Tel: 0166 77 672 — MB ChB 1946 Ed. (Ed.) Prev: Ho. Phys. N.. Gen. Hosp. Edin.; JHMO Stapleton Hosp. Bristol; Research Asst. Gen. Infirm. Leeds.

MACLENNAN, Alexander Charles Department of Radiology, Royal Hospital Sick Children, Yorkhill NHS Trust, Glasgow G3 8NJ Tel: 0141 201 0098 Fax: 0141 201 0098; Westwind, Milton, Dumbarton G82 2SG — MB ChB 1985 Aberd.; MRCP (UK) 1990; FRCR 1993; DRCOG 1989; DGM RCP Lond. 1988. (Aberdeen) Cons. (Paediat. Radiol.) Roy. Hosp. Sick Childr. Glas. Prev: Clin. Fell. Univ. Brit. Columbia Vancouver; Sen. Regist. (Radiol.) Glas. Roy. Infirm.; Regist. (Radiol.) Glas. Roy. Infirm.

MCLENNAN, Alistair James Top Flat, 156 Wilton St., Glasgow G20 6BS — MB ChB 1995 Glas.

MCLENNAN, Andrew Cameron 58 Ruthin Road, London SE3 7SH — MB BS 1988 New South Wales; MRCOG 1995.

MCLENNAN, Andrew Stuart 105 Cookridge Lane, Cookridge, Leeds LS16 7NE — MB ChB 1992 Leeds; BChD 1982; FDS RCPS Glas. 1987.

MACLENNAN, Ann Kinloch (retired) Bracken Lodge, Tower Brae, Westhill, Inverness IV2 5BW Tel: 01463 791572 — MB ChB Glas. 1944; MFCM 1974; DPH Glas. 1949. Prev: SCM Highland Health Bd.

MACLENNAN, Bruce Alexander 78 Malone Avenue, Belfast BT9 6ES — MB BCh BAO 1975 NUI; MRCP (UK) 1978.

MACLENNAN, Christine Rankin Archway Medical Practice, 16 Francis Street, Stornoway HS1 2XB Tel: 01851 703588 Fax: 01851 706338; 54 Macaulay Road, Stornoway, Isle of Lewis HS1 2TT Email: christine@tarlas.com — MB ChB 1976 Glas.; MRCGP 1995; DCH Eng. 1979. (Glas.) Prev: Clin. Med. Off. (Child Health) Vale of Leven.

MCLENNAN, Colin 63 Great George Street, Glasgow G12 8LA — MB ChB 1994 Glas.

MACLENNAN, David James 2 Ross Way, Whitley Bay NE26 3EJ — MB BS 1997 Lond.

MACLENNAN, Donald Neil Beaumont Street Surgery, 19 Beaumont Street, Oxford OX1 2NA Tel: 01865 240501 Fax: 01865 240503 — MB BS Lond. 1968; MRCGP 1975; DObst RCOG 1971; DCH Eng. 1970.

MACLENNAN, Iain Ross, Surg. Lt.-Cdr. RN Office of the Flag Officer Sea Training, Grenville Block, HMS Drake, Plymouth PL2 2BG Tel: 01752 557753; c/o ARNO, 70 Porchester Terrace, Bayswater, London W2 3TP Tel: 0958 418078 — MB ChB 1981 Manch.; DTM & H Liverpl 1997; DCH RCP Lond. 1985; MRCGP 1999. (Manch.) Sen. Off. (Health) to Cinfleet; Sen. Med. Off. to Fost. Prev: GP Portsmouth & Ipswich.

MACLENNAN, Mr Ian Surgical Unit 10, Manchester Royal Infirmary, Manchester M13 9WL Tel: 0161 276 4170 Fax: 0161 276 4530; 23 Anson Road, Manchester M14 5BZ Tel: 0161 224 1512 — MB ChB 1967 Manch.; FRCS Eng. 1972; FRCS Ed. 1971. (Manch.) Cons. Surg. Manch. Roy. Infirm.; Dean Clin. Studies Manch. Univ. Med. Sch. Socs: Fell. Manch. Med. Soc.; Fell. Roy. Soc. Med. (Counc. Sect. Coloproctol.); N. Eng. Gastroenterol. Soc. Prev: Research Fell. & Instruc. Harvard Med. Sch. Boston, U.S.A.

MACLENNAN, Professor Ian Calman Muir University of Birmingham, MRC Centre for Immune Regulation, Edgbaston, Birmingham B15 2TT Fax: 0121 414 3599 Email: i.c.m.maclennan@bham.ac.uk — FMedSci; MB BS Lond. 1965; PhD Lond. 1970, BSc (Anat.) 1962; FRCP Lond. 1995; MRCP (UK) 1989; MRCS Eng. LRCP Lond. 1964; FRCPath 1985, M 1973; FAMS 1998. Prof. Immunol. Univ. Birm. & Hon. Cons. Univ. Hosp. Trust; Dir. MRC Centre Immune Regulat. Univ. of Birm.; Mem. MRC Counc.; Chairm. MRC Molecular & Cellular Med. Bd. Socs: Brit. Soc. Immunol.; Amer. Assn. Immunol.; Hon. Life Mem. Scand.n Soc. for Immunol. Prev: SHO MRC Rheum. Unit Canad. Red Cross Memor. Hosp. Taplow; Lect. Nuffield Dept. Clin. Med. Univ. Oxf. & Hon. Cons. Oxon. AHA (T).

MACLENNAN, Ian Patrick Bethune 2 Lansdowne Gardens, London SW8 2EG — MB BCh BAO 1966 NUI. Regist. Dept. Venereol. St. Mary's Hosp. Lond.

MCLENNAN, Jacqueline Victoria 17 Minorca Road, Deepcut, Camberley GU16 6ST — MB ChB 1995 Leic.

MCLENNAN, Jane Mary Royal Victoria Hospital, Craigleith Road, Edinburgh EH4 2DN Tel: 0131 537 5016 Fax: 0131 537 5141; Tel: 0131 334 1628 — MB ChB 1984 Aberd.; MRCPsych 1989. Cons. Psychiat. (Old Age) Lothian Primary Care Trust.

MACLENNAN, Jean MacDonald (retired) Bonnington Nursing Home, 205 Ferry Road, Edinburgh EH6 4NN Tel: 0131 555 0780 — MB ChB 1930 Ed.; MD Ed. 1937; LMCC 1948; Cert. Paediat. RCPS Canada 1952; DPH Ed. & Glas. 1934. Prev: Clin. Instruc. (Paediat.) Univ. Brit. Columbia, Canada.

MCLENNAN, Keith Michael Fernbank Surgery, 18 Church Road, Lytham, Lytham St Annes FY8 5LL Tel: 01253 736453; Freckleton Health Centre, Douglas Drive, Freckleton, Preston PR4 1RY — MB ChB 1975 Manch. Clin. Asst. Diabetic Serv. Vict. Hosp. Blackpool. Prev: SHO (Paediat., Obst. & Gen. Med.) Vict. Hosp. Blackpool.

MACLENNAN, Kenneth Angus Department of Pathology, St James University Hospital, Beckett St., Leeds LS9 7TF — MB BS 1976 Lond.; DM Nottm. 1989; MRCPath 1983.

MACLENNAN, Sara Anne 13 Moreton Road, Oxford OX2 7AX — MB BS 1968 Lond.; DO Eng. 1978.

MACLENNAN, Sheila Leeds Blood Centre, Bridle Path, Leeds LS15 7TW Tel: 0113 214 8638 Fax: 0113 214 8696 Email: sheila.maclennan@nbs.nhs.uk — MB BS 1979 Lond.; MRCP (UK) 1982; MRCPath 1994. (Univ. Coll. Hosp.) Cons. Haemat. Nat. Blood Serv. Leeds Centre. Socs: Brit. Blood Transfus. Soc.; Brit. Soc. Haematol.; Amer. Assn. Blood Banks. Prev: Sen. Regist. (Haemat.) Nat. Blood Serv. Yorks. & N. Lond. Blood Transfus. Centre.

MACLENNAN, Mr William Donald Aros House, Templar Place, Gullane EH31 2AH Tel: 06120 843314 — LRCP LRCS 1945 Ed.; FRCS Ed. 1966; LRCP LRCS Ed., LRFPS Glas. 1945; FDS RCS Ed. 1952; FDS RCPS Glas. 1967. (Roy. Colls. Ed.) Prof. Emerit. Oral Surg. Univ. Edin. Socs: BDA & Brit. Assn. Oral & Maxillo-Facial Surgs. Prev: Surg. Lt. (D) RNVR 1945/48.

MACLENNAN, Professor William Jardine 26 Caiystone Avenue, Fairmilehead, Edinburgh EH10 6SG Tel: 0131 445 1755 — MB ChB 1964 Glas.; MD (Hons.) Glas. 1973; FRCP Ed. 1981; FRCP Glas. 1980, M 1968; FRCP Lond. 1980, M 1968. (Glas.) Emerit. Pof. (Geriat. Med.) Univ. Ed. Socs: Brit. Geriat. Soc. Prev: Prof. Geriat. Med. Univ. Edin.; Reader (Geriat. Med.) Univ. Dundee; Lect. (Mat. Med.) Glas. Univ.

MACLEOD, Alan John 78 Kingfisher Way, Upton, Wirral CH49 4PS — MB ChB 1993 Liverp.

MACLEOD, Alasdair Robert (retired) Schoolwaters House, Millbrow, Barrow-in-Furness LA13 0PE Tel: 01229 62608 — MB ChB 1956 Ed. Prev: Med. Off. Remploy Ltd.

MACLEOD, Alastair Ian (retired) 3 Seavale Mews, Seavale Road, Clevedon BS21 7QB Tel: 01275 874350 — MB BChir 1943 Camb.; MA Camb. 1943; MRCGP 1953. Prev: Ho. Phys. & Med. 1st Asst. Lond. Hosp.

MACLEOD, Alexander 18 Durward Court, Shawlands, Glasgow G41 3RZ — MB ChB 1981 Glas.; MSc Glas. 1988; FFA RCS Eng. 1986.

MACLEOD, Alexander Aldenham Cottage, Ardingdrean, Loch Broom, Garve IV23 2SE — MB ChB 1967 Ed.

MACLEOD, Alexander Andrew Manse Road Surgery, 142 Manse Road, Ardersier, Inverness IV2 7SR — MB ChB 1968 St. And.; DObst RCOG 1970; DA Eng. 1972.

MACLEOD, Mrs Alison A&E Department, Middlesbrough General Hospital, Ayresome Green Lane, Middlesbrough TS5 5AZ Tel: 01642 850850; 115 Nunsmoor Road, Fenham, Newcastle upon Tyne NE4 9BA Tel: 0191 272 5500 Email: allyali@lineone.net — BM BCh 1990 Oxf.; FRCS Ed. 1995. (Oxf.) Specialist Regist. (A & E) N. Region. Socs: Assoc. Mem. Brit. Assoc. for A&E Med. Prev: SHO (Gen. Med.) Wansbeck Gen. Hosp. Ashington; SHO Rotat. (Gen. Surg.) N.. HA; SHO (Orthop. & A & E) Walton & Fazakerley Hosp. Liverp.

MACLEOD, Alison Jane Morecambe Health Centre, Hanover Street, Morecambe LA4 5LY Tel: 01524 418418 Fax: 01524 832584 — MB ChB 1985 Manch.; MRCGP 1991; DRCOG 1988. (Manch.) Socs: Assoc. Mem. Brit. Acupunc. Soc.

MACLEOD, Alison Jean Department of Obstetrics and Gynaecology, Ward 12, St John's Hospital at Howden, Howden Road, Livingston Tel: 01506 419666; Westfield House, Westfield, Bathgate EH48 3DF — MB ChB 1987 Aberd.; MRCOG 1993. Cons. (O & G).

MACLEOD, Professor Alison Murray Department of Medicine & Therapeutics, Medical School, Foresterhill, Aberdeen AB25 2ZD Tel: 01224 681818 Fax: 01224 699884; 43 Forest Road, Aberdeen AB15 4BY Tel: 01224 646072 — MD 1984 Aberd.; MD (Hons.) Aberd. 1984, MB ChB 1975, BMedBiol 1972; FRCP Ed. 1993; FRCP Lond. 1993; MRCP (UK) 1979. Prof. (Med.) Univ. Aberd. & Hon. Cons. Phys. Nephrol. Grampian Univ. Hosp.s Trust. Prev: Hon. Cons. (Psysician. Nephrol.) Aberd. Roy. Hosps. Trust; Sen. Lect. (Med.) Univ. Aberd.; Lect. (Med.) Univ. Aberd.

*MACLEOD, Alison Ruth** 35 Knollwood, Seapatrick, Banbridge BT32 4PE — MB BCh 1998 Belf.; MB BCh Belf 1998.

MACLEOD, Alistair (retired) — MB ChB Glas. 1964; BSc (Hons.) Glas. 1961; FRCP Lond. 1995; FRCP Glas. 1980, M 1968. Prev: Cons. Cardiol & Phys. Dist. Gen. Hosp. E.bourne.

MACLEOD, Alistair David 1 Beaufort Road, Edinburgh EH9 1AG; Laverock, 13 Wyvern Park, Edinburgh EH9 2JY Tel: 0131 668 3832 Fax: 0131 668 3832 — MB ChB 1972 Glas.; MRCGP 1979. (Univ. Glas.) Sen. Partner; Occupat. Health Adviser Edin. Socs: BMA; JMT. Prev: SHO (O & G) E. Gen. Hosp. Edin.; Med. Off. Brit. Antarctic Survey; Ho. Surg. Belford Hosp. Fort William.

MACLEOD, Alistair Gordon (retired) 8 Shanter Way, Alloway, Ayr KA7 4PF Tel: 01292 441449 — MB ChB Glas. 1941; DObst RCOG 1947. Prev: Capt. RAMC.

MACLEOD, Alistair Tormod 1 Langley Lawnes, 79 Langley Park Road, Sutton SM2 5HD — MB BS 1994 Lond.; DFFP 1999; BSc (Hons.) Aberd. 1987; DRCOG 1998.

MACLEOD, Alister Ian (retired) 3 Holmwood Drive, Formby, Liverpool L37 1PG Tel: 01704 876587 — MB ChB 1945 Aberd.

MACLEOD, Allison Lorna Gartmore Road Surgery, 2 Old Gartmore Road, Drymen, Glasgow G63 0DP Tel: 01360 660203; 1 Garmarten Farm Cottages, Gartmore, Stirling FK8 3RT Email: allisonm@uk.packardbell.org — MB BS 1982 Lond. (Charing Cross Hospital Medical School)

MCLEOD, Andrew Alasdair Poole General Hospital, Longfleet Road, Poole BH15 2JB Tel: 01202 665511 Fax: 01202 442754; Deepdene, 32 Bury Road, Branksome Park, Poole BH13 7DG Tel: 01202 707932 — MB BChir 1974 Camb.; B 1970, MD 1984, MB 1974, BChir 1973; FRCP Lond. 1989; MRCP (UK) 1975; FESC 1998. Cons. Cardiol. & Med. Poole Gen. Hosp. Socs: Counc. Mem. Brit. Cardiac Soc.; (Steering Gp.) Brit. Assn. of Cardiac Rehabil. Prev: Cons. Cardiol. King's Coll. & Dulwich Hosps.; Hon. Sen. Lect. Univ. Lond.; Assoc. Fac. Med. Duke Univ. Med. Center Durh., NC, USA.

MCLEOD, Andrew Douglas Mitford 48 Kilner House, Clayton St., London SE11 5SE — MB BS 1992 Lond.; FRCA 1998. Specialist Regist. (Anaesth,) N Thames Scheme.

MACLEOD, Andrew Forbes Royal Shrewsbury Hospital, Mytton Oak Road, Shrewsbury SY3 8XQ Tel: 01743 261021 Fax: 01743 261388 — MB BS 1992 Lond.; MA Oxf. 1985, BA 1971; MD Lond. 1992; FRCP (UK) 1997; MRCP 1978. Cons. Phys. Shrops. HA. Socs: Diabetes U.K.; ABCD (Assoc of Brit. Clin. Diabetologists); Fell. Roy. Soc. Med. Prev: Lect. (Med.) United Med. & Dent. Sch. Lond.; Regist. (Med.) Kingston & St. Thos. Hosps. Lond.

MACLEOD, Mr Andrew John Moir Radiology Department, Raigmore Hospital, Inverness IV2 3UJ Tel: 01463 704000 — MB ChB 1988 Aberd.; FRCS Glas. 1993; FRCR 1996; Mrad Aberd. 1996. (Univ. Aberd.) Cons. (Radiol.) Raignore Hosp. Prev: Specialist Regist. (Radiol.) X-Ray Dept. Aberd. Roy. Infirm.

MACLEOD, Angus Hugh Auckland Medical Group, 54 Cockton Hill Road, Bishop Auckland DL14 6BB Tel: 01388 602728 — MB ChB 1947 Glasgow; MB ChB Glas. 1947. (Glasgow) GP Bishop Auckland, Co. Durh.

MACLEOD, Angus Iain, SBStJ (retired) 13 Hunt Court, York YO1 7DE Tel: 01904 655636 Fax: 01904 655636 Email: dmacyork@aol.com — MB ChB Glas. 1947. Hon. Med. Off. York City Football Club. Prev: Ho. Surg. W.. Infirm. Glas.

MACLEOD, Annabelle Mary Stafford District General Hospital, Weston Road, Stafford ST16 3SA Tel: 01785 257731 — MB ChB 1981 Birm.; MRCP (UK) 1984; FRCR 1987. Cons. Radiol. Stafford Dist. Gen. Hosp. Prev: Sen. Regist. & Regist. (Radiol.) W. Midl. Train. Scheme.

MACLEOD, Anne Eastbourne & County Health Care Trust, Child Health Department, The Firs, The Drive, Hellingly, Hailsham BN27 4ER Tel: 01323 440022; 78 Upper Ratton Drive, Eastbourne

MACLEOD

BN20 9DJ — MB ChB 1966 Glas. (Glas.) Clin. Med. Off. (Child Health) E.bourne & Co. Health Care Trust.

MACLEOD, Anne (retired) Bryntirion, 35 Meliden Road, Prestatyn LL19 9SD Tel: 01745 886219 — MB ChB Glas. 1948; MFFP 1993. Prev: GP Prestatyn.

MACLEOD, Anne Colleen Dermatology Department, Raigmore Hospital, Inverness Tel: 01463 704000 — MB ChB 1975 Aberd. Assoc. Specialist (Dermat.) Raigmore Hosp. Inverness. Socs: Scot. Dermat. Soc.; Brit. Assn. Dermatol. Prev: Trainee GP Inverness; Research Asst. (Chest Med. & Bact.) Culduthel Hosp. Inverness.

MCLEOD, Mr Bruce Kenvyn Sussex Eye Hospital, Eastern Road, Brighton BN2 5BF Tel: 01273 606126 Fax: 01403 732752; Richmond House, Rye Farm Lane, Barns Green, Horsham RH13 7QB Tel: 01403 732752 Fax: 01403 732752 Email: bkmc@breathe.co.uk — MB BS 1974 Lond.; FRCS Lond. 1986; MRCS Eng. LRCP Lond. 1974; FRCOphth 1989. Cons. Ophth. Surg. The Sussex Eye Hosp. Brighton NHS Trust; Cons. Ophth. Surg. The P.ss Roy. Hosp. Haywards Heath W. Sussex. Prev: Lect. (Ophth.) Leicester Univ.

MACLEOD, Mr Calum Macleod Baird 2 Bellflower Grove, East Kilbride, Glasgow G74 4TB — MB ChB 1988 Aberd.; FRCS Ed. 1994. Specialist Regist. (Orthop.) W. of Scotl. Train. Scheme. Socs: BMA. Prev: Trauma Fell. Glas. Roy. Infirm.

MACLEOD, Catherine The Medical Centre, 12 East King Street, Helensburgh G84 7QL Tel: 01436 672277 Fax: 01436 674526; 50B Glasgow Street, Helensburgh G84 8YH Tel: 01436 71249 — MB ChB 1979 Glas.; MRCGP 1987; DRCOG 1983; Dip. Pract. Dermat. Wales 1997.

MCLEOD, Catriona Douglas Tanyard Cottage, 12 Bridge Square, Farnham GU9 7QR Tel: 01252 715586 — MB ChB 1951 St. And.; DObst RCOG 1954. (St. And.)

MACLEOD, Christina Martin 78/BF1 Harrison Gardens, Edinburgh EH11 1SB — MB ChB 1997 Ed.

MACLEOD, Christine Anne Cambridgeshire Health Authority, Public Health Directorate Kingfisher House, Kingfisher Way, Huntingdon PE29 6FH Tel: 01480398604 Fax: 01480 398501 Email: christine.macleod@cambs-ha.nhs.uk; 27 Lewes Gardens, Werrington, Peterborough PE4 6QN Tel: 01733 579274 Email: c.macleod@btinternet.com — MB ChB 1979 Aberd.; FFPHM 1999; MSc Newc. 1989; MRCP (UK) 1985; MFPHM RCP (UK) 1991; FRCP 2000 Edinburgh. Dep. Director of Pub. Health/Head of Informat. Strategy Camb.shire Health Auth.; Cons. in Pub. Health Med. S. PeterBoro. Primary Care Trust, St Johns PeterBoro. Socs: Fac. Adviser (Pub. Health Med.) E.ern Region. Prev: Cons. Pub. Health Med. N. W. Anglia Health Auth. PeterBoro.; Cons. Pub. Health Med. NHS Exec. (Trent); Cons. Pub. Health Med. Trent RHA.

MACLEOD, Christine Lee Hunter Eoropie, Easterton, Dalcross, Inverness IV2 7JE Tel: 01667 462412 — MB ChB 1948 Glas.; LM Nat. Matern. Hosp. Dub. 1953. (Glas.) Prev: GP Kt.swood Glas.; Med. Off. & Lect. (Health Educat.) Craigie Coll. Educat. Ayr; Assoc. Specialist (Rehabil.) Raigmore Hosp. Inverness.

MCLEOD, Professor David University Department of Ophthalmology, Manchester Royal Eye Hospital, Oxford Road, Manchester M13 9WH Tel: 0161 276 5620 Fax: 0161 273 6354; Langdale, 370 Chester Road, Woodford, Stockport SK7 1QG Tel: 0161 440 0737 — BSc (Hons.) Physiol. Ed. 1966, MB ChB (Hons.) 1969; FRCS Eng. 1974; FCOphth 1989. Prof. Ophth. Univ. Manch.; Hon. Cons. Ophth. Surg. Manch. Roy. Eye Hosp.; Civil. Cons. Ophth. RAF. Socs: (Exec. Comm.) Club Jules Gonin; Vice-Pres. RCOphth.; Internat. Mem. Amer. Acad. Ophth. Prev: Cons. Ophth. Surg. Moorfields Eye Hosp. Lond.; Clin. Lect. Inst. Ophth. Lond.; Hon. Sen. Lect. Roy. Postgrad. Med. Sch. Lond.

MACLEOD, David Brett, Surg. Lt. RN 1 Linden Villas, High St., Soberton, Southampton SO32 3PN — MB BS 1986 Lond.

MACLEOD, Dominic Paul London Chest Hospital, Bonner Road, London E2 9JX Tel: 020 8980 4433 Fax: 020 8983 2279 Email: thoracic@lchresp.demon.co.uk — MB BS 1985 Lond.; BSc (Hons.) Lond. 1982; MD 1997; MRCPI 1991. (Univ. Coll. Hosp.) Sen. Regist. (Gen. & Respirat. Med.) Roy. Lond. Hosp. Prev: Sen. Regist. (Gen. & Respirat. Med.) Whipps Cross Hosp. Lond.; Lect. (Clin. Med.) Trinity Coll. Dub.; Clin. Research Fell. Soton. Gen. Hosp.

MACLEOD, Donald Angus (retired) 49 Plantation Road, Harlow Hill, Harrogate HG2 0DB Tel: 01423 508668 — MB ChB 1946 Manch.; MD Manch 1962; MRCGP 1953; DCH Eng. 1953; DObst RCOG 1950. Prev: Sen. Med. Off. Univ. Bradford.

MACLEOD, Mr Donald Angus David (retired) The Lister Institute, 11 Hill Square, Edinburgh EH8 9DR Tel: 0131 650 2613 — MB ChB 1965 Ed.; FRCP Ed. 1996; FRCS Ed. 1969. Assoc. PostGrad. Dean (Surg.) S.-E. Scotl.; Hon. Med. Adviser Scott. Rugby Union & Internat. Rugby Football Bd.; Mem. Scott. Med. Roy. Coll. Bd. for Sports Med.; Vice-Pres. Roy. Coll. of Surg.s of Edin.; Chairm., Intercollegiate Acad. Bd. for Sport and Exerare Med. Pressdeut, Brit. Assn. for Sport and Exerare Med. Prev: Cons. Gen. Surg. St John's Hosp. Langston.

MACLEOD, Donald Campbell Queen Margaret Hospital, Whitefield Road, Dunfermline KY12 0SU Tel: 01383 623623 — MB ChB 1982 Ed.; PhD Ed. 1993; FRCPE 1997. Cons. Cardiol. Qu. Margt. Hosp. Dunfermline. Prev: Sen. Regist. (Cardiol.) W.ern Gen. Hosp. Edin.

MACLEOD, Donald John 10 Redhills View, Campsie Rise, Lennoxtown, Glasgow G66 7BL Tel: 0141 312368 — MB ChB 1941 Glas.

MACLEOD, Donald Macrae Westwood House, Kinellar, Aberdeen AB21 0SR Tel: 01224 790840 — MB ChB 1979 Aberd.; FFA RCSI 1984. Cons. Anaesth. Aberd. Roy. Infirm. Grampian HB; Hon. Sen. Lect. (Anaesth.) Univ. Aberd. Prev: Lect. (Anaesth.) Lond. Hosp. Med. Sch.; Vis. Assoc. Anaesthiology Duke Univ. Med. Center.

MACLEOD, Donna 2/L, 5 Garrioch Quadrant, Glasgow G20 8RT — MB ChB 1991 Glas.

MACLEOD, Doris Sarah Te-Yung North Glen Medical Practice, 1 Huntsmans Court, Glenrothes KY7 6SX Tel: 01592 620062 Fax: 01592 620465 — MB ChB 1985 Ed.; DRCOG 1988.

MACLEOD, Mr Douglas, OStJ (retired) 4 Tudor Avenue, Prestatyn LL19 9HN Tel: 01745 857675 — MB ChB Glas. 1945; FRCS Glas. 1962; MRCGP 1957. Prev: Regist. (Surg.) S.. Gen. Hosp. Glas.

MCLEOD, Douglas William Fitzalan Medical Centre, Fitzalan Road, Littlehampton BN17 5JR Tel: 01903 733277 Fax: 01903 733773; 26 Ash Lane, Rustington, Littlehampton BN16 3BT — BSc Lond. 1978, MB BS 1981; MRCGP 1990; DRCOG 1984; DCH RCP Lond. 1983. (Guy's) Staff Littlehampton & Zachery Merton Community Hosps. Prev: Trainee GP I. of Thanet VTS; SHO (A & E) Greenwich Dist. Hosp.; Ho. Off. (Gen. Med.) Lewisham Hosp.

MCLEOD, Dwight Thomas Sandwell Healthcare NHS Trust, West Bromwich B71 4HJ Tel: 0121 607 3414 Fax: 0121 607 3245; 87 Station Road, Wylde Green, Sutton Coldfield B73 5JY Tel: 0121 240 7868 — MB ChB Manch. 1977; MD Manch. 1986; FRCP Lond. 1994; MRCP (UK) 1980. Cons. Phys. Sandwell Healthcare NHS Trust; Med. Tutor, 3rd & 5th Year Med. Stud.s. Prev: Sen. Regist. Freeman Hosp. & Roy. Vict. Infirm. Newc.; Sen. Regist. N. Tees Gen. Hosp. Stockton-on-Tees; Regist. (Respirat. Med.) City Hosp. Edin.

MACLEOD, Mrs Elizabeth Helen Menzies 30 Spencer Place, Kirkcaldy KY1 2AX — MB ChB 1967 Ed.

MACLEOD, Evalyn Lucy (retired) Broughton House, Broughton Crossing, Aylesbury HP22 5AR Tel: 01296 88175 — MB ChB 1963 Glas. Prev: Ho. Phys. & Ho. Surg. Lewis Hosp. Stornoway.

MACLEOD, Evelyn Foresterhill Health Centre, Ullswater Centre, Aberdeen AB25 2AY Tel: 01224 696848; 21 Burnside Drive, Bridge-of-Don, Aberdeen AB23 8PL Tel: 01224 703377 — MB ChB 1961 Aberd. (Aberd.)

MCLEOD, Ewen Donald John Glass and McLeod, 13 Provost Craig Road, Ballater AB35 5NN Tel: 013397 55686 Fax: 013397 53510 Email: ewen.mcleod@ballater.grampian.scot.nhs.uk; Fairview, 9 Monaltrie Close, Ballater AB35 5PT — MB ChB 1985 Aberd.; MRCGP 1989; DFFP 1996; Dip IMC RCS Ed. 1991; DRCOG 1989. (Aberd.) Med. Off. (A & E) Aberd. Roy. Infirm. Prev: Regist. (A & E) Aberd. Roy. Hosps. NHS Trust; Trainee GP/SHO Aberd. VTS; SHO (A & E) Roy. Aberd. Childr. Hosp.

MCLEOD, Fiona 2 James Watt Road, Milngavie, Glasgow G62 7JY — MB ChB 1991 Glas.

MACLEOD, Fiona Silver Springs, Roy Bridge PH31 4AN — MB ChB 1998 Aberd.; MB ChB Aberd 1998.

MACLEOD, Fiona Katharine 2A Church Street, Broughton, Kettering NN14 1LU — BM BS 1991 Nottm.; MRCP (UK) 1994; FRCR 1998. Regist. (Radiol.) Manch.

MCLEOD, Fraser Neil 7 Percival Road, Clifton, Bristol BS8 3LE Tel: 0117 974 1396 Fax: 0117 973 3809; 3 Druid Stoke Avenue, Stoke Bishop, Bristol BS9 1DB Tel: 0117 968 7100 — MB BS 1975 Lond.; MBWI (Expert Witness Inst.) 1989; MRCS Eng. LRCP Lond. 1974; FRCOG 1993, M 1980. (St. Bart.) Cons. O & G Frenchay &

S.mead Hosps. Bristol. Socs: SW Obst. & Gyn. Soc.; Founder Mem. Brit. Soc. Gyn. Endoscopy.; Brit. Menopause Soc. Prev: Sen. Regist. (O & G) S.mead Hosp. Bristol; Lect. & Hon. Sen. Regist. (O & G) Roy. Free Hosp. Lond.; Regist. (O & G) S.mead Hosp. Bristol.

MACLEOD, George Finlay 24 Risborrow Close, Etwall, Derby DE65 6HY — MB ChB 1973 Aberd.; FFA RCS Eng. 1978. Cons. (Anaesth.) Derby Hosps.

MACLEOD, George Leslie (retired) Herons Reach, West end, Glan Conwy, Colwyn Bay LL28 5SY — MB ChB 1950 Ed.; MFOM RCP Lond. 1980; DIH Eng. 1964. Prev: Gp. Med. Adviser Tate & Lyle Ltd.

MACLEOD, Gillian Anne Rood Lane Medical Centre, 10 Rood Lane, London EC3M 8BN Tel: 020 7283 4028; 8 Eynella Road, London SE22 8XF Tel: 020 8693 4057 — MB ChB 1982 Bristol; MRCP (UK) 1985. Prev: Regist. (Med.) Roy. Free Hosp. Lond.

MCLEOD, Mr Gordon George Campfield, Comrie, Crieff PH6 2HB Tel: 01764 670996 — MB ChB 1980 Ed.; BSc Hons. (Physiol.) Ed. 1977, MB ChB 1980; FRCS Ed. 1985. Cons. Orthop. Surg. Perth Roy. Infirm. Prev: Lect. & Sen. Regist. (Orthop.) Dundee Roy. Infirm.; Regist. (Orthop.) Lothian HB.

MACLEOD, Graeme Alistair Kildrum Health Centre, Afton Road, Cumbernauld, Glasgow G67 2EU Tel: 01236 721354 Fax: 01236 727549 — MB ChB 1985 Aberd.; MRCGP 1990. (Aberd.)

MCLEOD, Harpur Neil 46B Tamlough Road, Randalstown, Antrim BT41 3DP — MB BCh BAO 1984 Belf.; MA OXON. 1982; FFA RCSI 1988; FCAnaesth 1988.

MACLEOD, Helen Ty Sion, 10 Y Fron Estate, Cemaes Bay LL67 0LW — MB ChB 1992 Birm.

MACLEOD, Helen Elizabeth 5 Gardenside Avenue, Uddingston, Glasgow G71 7BU Tel: 0141 818310 — MB ChB 1979 Aberd.; MRCGP 1983; DRCOG 1984.

MCLEOD, Herbert Roderick Thomas Amphlett, Surg. Capt. RN Retd. (retired) Willow Cottage, Antingham Hill, North Walsham NR28 0NH Tel: 01692 403820 — MB BS 1955 Lond.; MRCS Eng. LRCP Lond. 1955. Prev: Civil. Med. Pract., HMS Nelson Portsmouth.

MACLEOD, Hugh Murdoch (retired) 3 Forrester Road, Corstorphine, Edinburgh EH12 8AA Tel: 0131 334 4978 — MB ChB 1947 Ed.; FRCP Ed. 1968, M 1953. Prev: Princip. Med. Off. Scott. Widows' Fund & Life Assur. Soc.

MACLEOD, Hugh Sime Matheson (retired) Summerwells, Fearn, Tain IV20 1RR Tel: 01862 832439 — MB ChB 1964 Aberd.

MACLEOD, Iain Cameron 22 Shore Street, Hilton, Tain IV20 1XD — MB ChB 1985 Aberd.

MCLEOD, Iain Charles East Calder Health Centre, 147 Main St., E. Calder, Livingston EH53 0EW Tel: 01506 882882; Beaconsfield Cottage, Main St, Mid Calder, Livingston EH53 0AN — MB ChB 1984 Ed.; MRCGP 1990; Cert. Family Plann. JCC 1990. (Edinburgh) Prev: Princip. GP Edin.; Regist. (Geriat.) Roy. Vict. Hosp.; Trainee GP Lothian HB.

MACLEOD, Iain Hamish The Surgery, High St., Moffat DG10 9JP Tel: 01683 220062 Fax: 01683 220453; Rosebery House, Old Carlisle Road, Moffat DG10 9QJ Tel: 01683 220314 — MB ChB 1964 Ed.; FRCGP 1983, M 1975; Dip. IMC RCS Ed. 1995. Socs: BMA; Brit. Assn. Immed. Care Schemes. Prev: Maj. RAMC TAVR (3); Chairm. Brit. Assn. Immediate Care; Ho. Surg. (Thoracic Surg.) City Hosp. Edin.

MACLEOD, Iain Robb St Saviours Surgery, Merick Road, Malvern Link, Malvern WR14 1DD Tel: 01684 572323 Fax: 01684 891067; 3 The Old Barn, Hall Court, Bishops Frome, Worcester WR6 5BY Tel: 01885 490540 — MB ChB 1984 Dundee. Clin. Asst. (Subst. Misuse) Worcester Roy. Infirm. Prev: Trainee GP Croydon HA VTS.

MCLEOD, Mr Ian Cairdell, 40 Malcolm's Mount W., Stonehaven AB39 2TF — MB ChB 1987 Dundee; FRCS Ed. 1993. Clin. Research Fell. (Orthop. Surg.) Aberd.

MACLEOD, Ian Frew Terrace Surgery, 9 Frew Terrace, Irvine KA12 9DZ Tel: 01294 272326 Fax: 01294 314614 — MB ChB 1948 Aberd. (Aberd.) Prev: Jun. Cas. Off. Aberd. Roy. Infirm.; RAMC 1948-9.

MACLEOD, Mr Ian Alexander 25 West Chapelton Crescent, Bearsden, Glasgow G61 2DE Tel: 0141 942 2094 — MB BS 1971 Glas.; MB ChB Glas. 1971; MD Glas. 1983; FRCS Glas. 1976; FRCR 1988; FFR RCSI 1987. Cons. Radiol. Stobhill NHS Trust Hosp. Glas.; Hon. Clin. Sen. Lect. Glas. Univ. Socs: Scott. Radiol. Soc. Prev: Sen.

Regist. (Diag. Radiol.) Gtr. Glas. HB; Research Fell. (Surg.) Roy. Infirm. Glas.; Regist. (Gastroenterol.) W.. Infirm. Glas.

MACLEOD, Mr Ian Buchanan (retired) Derwent House, 32 Cramond Road N., Edinburgh EH4 6JE Email: ian@imacleod.freeserve.co.uk — MB ChB 1957 Ed.; MB ChB (Hons.) Ed. 1957; BSc Ed. 1954; FRCS Ed. 1962. Prev: Hon. Sec. Roy. Coll. Surgs. Edin.

MACLEOD, Ian Norman Clowes The Surgery, Corse, Staunton, Gloucester GL19 3RB Tel: 01452 840228 — MB ChB 1984 Bristol.

MACLEOD, Ian St Clair Scott Compton Health Centre, Compton, Ashbourne DE6 1DA Tel: 01335 343784 Fax: 01335 300782; The Old Vicarage, Belle Vue Road, Ashbourne DE6 1AT Tel: 01335 46283 — MB ChB 1982 Dundee; MRCGP 1986; DRCOG 1985.

MACLEOD, Iona Colquhoun Department of Obstetrics & Gynaecology, Northern General Hospital, Sheffield S5 7AU Tel: 0114 243 4343 — MB ChB 1983 Aberd.; MRCOG 1989. Regist. (O & G) N. Gen. Hosp. Sheff. Prev: Research Regist. Univ. Dept. Jessop Hosp for Wom. Sheff.

MCLEOD, Jacqueline Ann DR J Mc Loed, The Vale Medical Centre, 195-197 Perry Vale, London SE23 2JF Tel: 020 8291 7007 Fax: 020 8291 5111 — MB ChB Ed. 1988; Cert. Prescribed Equiv. Exp. JCPTGP 1993; DFFP 1993. (Ed.) GP Assit. The Vale Med. Centre, Lond. Prev: SHO (Gyn.) W.m. Hosp. Lond.; SHO UCH Lond.; SHO UCH Lond.

MACLEOD, James Parkview Surgery, 28 Millfield Avenue, Hull Road, York YO10 3AB Tel: 01904 413644 Fax: 01904 431436; 18 Bootham Terrace, Bootham, York YO30 7DH Tel: 01904 639483 — MB 1979 Camb.; MA Camb. 1983, BA 1975, MB 1979, BChir 1978; MRCGP 1986; DRCOG 1982. Prev: Trainee GP Skipton, N. Yorks.; SHO (Psychiat.) Claybury Hosp.; Gen. Med. Off. Rabaul E. New Brit. Papua New Guinea.

MCLEOD, Jane Burnaby Arnewood Practice, Milton Medical Centre, Avenue Road, New Milton BH25 5JP Tel: 01425 620393 Fax: 01425 624219 — MB BS 1982 Lond.; MRCGP 1988; DA (UK) 1987. SHO (A & E) N.ampton Gen. Hosp. Prev: SHO (O & G) Marston Green Hosp. Birm.; SHO (Anaesth.) N.ampton Gen. Hosp.; SHO (Paediat.) Good Hope Hosp. Sutton Coldfield.

MACLEOD, Jean Margaret Department of Medicine, University Newcastle upon Tyne, The Medical School, Framlington Place, Newcastle upon Tyne NE2 4HH Tel: 0191 222 6000; 29 Otterburn Avenue, Gosforth, Newcastle upon Tyne NE3 4RR — MB ChB 1985 Ed.; MRCP (UK) 1988. Clin. Research Assoc. Univ. Newc. u. Tyne; Hon. Regist. (Med.) Newc. Teach. Hosps. & Middlesbrough Gen. Hosp. Prev: Regist. (Med.) Aberd. Teach. Hosps.

MACLEOD, John Dept of Anaesthetics, City Hospital, Dudley road, Birmingham B18 7BH Tel: 0121 507 4344 Fax: 0121 507 4349, dr.john.macleod@virgin.net — MB ChB 1985 Ed.; FRCA 1991. Cons. (Anaesth.) City Hosp. NHS Trust Birm.

MACLEOD, John Alasdair Johnston Lochmaddy Surgery, Lochmaddy HS6 5AE Tel: 01876 500333 Fax: 01876 500877 — MB ChB Glas. 1963; FRCGP 1993, M 1982; DCH RCPS Glas. 1965; DObst RCOG 1965; FRCP Glas. (Glas.) Vis. Prof. Dept. Family Med. Univ. N. Carolina; D.L. W.. Isles. Socs: Fell. Roy. Soc. Med.; BMA. Prev: Sen. Regist. Middlx. Hosp. Lond.; Ho. Surg. Glas. Roy. Infirm.; Ho. Phys. Stobhill Gen. Hosp. Glas.

MACLEOD, John David Alexander Royal Hampshire County Hospital, Romsey Road, Winchester SO22 5DG Tel: 01962 863535 — MB BS 1987 Newc.; FRCOphth 1991. Cons. Ophth. Roy. Hants. Co. Hosp. Winchester.; Hon. Cons. Uptholmologist, S.ampton Eye Unit, S.ampton Gen. Hosp. Prev: Sen. Regist. (Ophth.) Soton. Eye Unit; Lect. (Ophth.) Soton. Eye Hosp.; Regist. (Ophth.) Qu.s Med. Centre Nottm.

MACLEOD, John George 43 Dick Place, Edinburgh EH9 2JA Tel: 0131 667 6309 — MB ChB 1938 Ed.; FRCP Ed. 1947, M 1941. (Ed.) Prev: Cons. Phys. W.. Gen. Hosp. Edin., Roy. Edin. Hosp. & Rheum. Clinic Roy. Infirm. Edin.; Chairm. Univ. Dept. Med. W.. Gen. Hosp. Edin.

MCLEOD, June Margaret (retired) Windrush, Battery Lane, Portishead, Bristol BS20 7JD Tel: 01275 848042 — MB ChB Bristol 1956; DCH Eng. 1959; DObst RCOG 1960.

MCLEOD, Karen Alicia 27 Royal Park Terrace, Edinburgh EH8 8JB — MB ChB 1987 Ed.; BSc Ed. 1985, MB ChB 1987. Ho. Off. (Med.) E. Gen. Hosp. Edin.; Ho. Off. (Surg.) Profess. Unit. Roy. Infirm. Edin.

MACLEOD

MACLEOD, Kathleen Gillean (retired) Derwent House, 32 Cramond Road N., Edinburgh EH4 6JE Tel: 0131 336 1541 — MB ChB 1959 Ed.

MACLEOD, Kenneth George Allan Dept. of Anaesthetics, St Mary's Hospital, Praed St, London W2 1NY Tel: 020 7886 1248 Fax: 020 7886 6360 Email: ken.macleod@stmarys.nhs.uk; 38 Woodville Gardens, Ealing, London W5 2LQ Tel: 020 8997 1548 — MB BS 1974 Lond.; MRCS Eng. LRCP Lond. 1974; FFA RCS Eng. 1980. (St. Mary's) Cons. Anaesth. St. Mary's Hosp. Paddington Lond.

MACLEOD, Kenneth MacIntyre Department of Diabetes and Vascular Medicine, Royal Devon & Exeter Hospital, Barrack Road, Exeter EX2 5DW Tel: 01392 403035 Fax: 01392 403007 Email: k.m.macleod@exeter.ac.uk; Bicton Lodge, 1 Bicton Place, Mont le Grand, Exeter EX1 2PF — MB ChB 1986 Aberd.; MD 1997; MRCP (UK) 1989. (Aberdeen) Cons. Phys. Roy. Devon & Exeter NHS Trust; Sen. Lect. (Med.) Exeter Univ.; Collge Tutor (Med.); Undergrad. Teachg. CoorDir. Socs: Diabetes UK; Brit. Endocrine Soc.; Brit. Thyroid Assn. Prev: Research Regist. (Diabetes) Univ. Edin. & Hon. Regist. Lothian HB; Regist. (Med.) Aberd. Roy. Infirm.; SHO Rotat. Aberd. Teach. Hosp.

MACLEOD, Kenneth Russell Hinchingbrooke Hospital, Huntingdon PE29 6NT Tel: 01480 416416 Fax: 01480 416561 Email: kenmacleod@doctors.org.uk; 36 Green End, Great Stukeley, Huntingdon PE28 4AE Tel: 01480 412803 — MB BS Lond. 1968; MRCS Eng. LRCP Lond. 1968; FFA RCS Eng. 1979; DA Eng. 1972; DObst RCOG 1970. (St. Mary's) Cons. Anaesth. Hinchingbrooke Hosp. Huntingdon. Socs: Treas. E. Anglian Assn. of Anaesth.

MCLEOD, Lorna Sophia Western Infirmary, Dumbarton Road, Glasgow G11 6NT Email: campbellscl@hotmail.com; 38 Ballantyne Palace, Livingston EH54 6TG — MB ChB 1990 Ed.; FRCS Ed. 1995; Dip IMC RCS Ed. 1998. Specialist Regist. (A & E) W. of Scotl. Socs: Fell. Roy. Med. Soc. Edin. Prev: SHO (A & E) Roy. Infirm. Edin.

MACLEOD, Lucile Janette The Haining, Woodlands Park, Livingston EH54 8AT Tel: 01506 411092 — MB ChB 1965 Ed.; DCCH RCP Ed. 1984. (Ed.) Assoc. Specialist (Community Child Health) St John's Hosp. Livingston.

MACLEOD, Malcolm Robert Western General Hospital, Edinburgh EH4 2XU Tel: 0131 332 2525; 15 Kings Stables Lane, Edinburgh EH1 2LQ — MB ChB 1991 Ed.; BSc (Hons.) Ed. 1988. SHO W.. Gen. Hosp. Edin.

MACLEOD, Margaret Ann First Floor Flat, 47 Comely Bank Place, Edinburgh EH4 1ER — MB ChB 1991 Glas. SHO (Gen. Med.) Aberd. Roy. Infirm.

MACLEOD, Margaret Macdonald The Group Practice, Health Centre, Stornoway, Isle of Lewis HS2 Tel: 01851 706138 Fax: 01851 706138; Ramadale, 9 Goathill Crescent, Stornoway, Isle of Lewis HS2 — MB ChB 1987 Ed. Prev: Trainee GP Argyll VTS; SHO (Med.) Co. Hosp. Oban.

MACLEOD, Margrit 3 Benside, North Tolsta, Isle of Lewis HS2; Gleann Mor, Leurbost, Isle of Lewis HS2 9JP — MB ChB 1990 Glas.

MACLEOD, Mary Taighe na Greine, Ardendrain, Kiltarlity, Beauly IV4 7HS — MB ChB 1962 Ed.; MRCPsych 1975; DPM Eng. 1973. Cons. Psychiat. Craig Dunain Hosp. Inverness. Prev: Cons. Psychiat. Dingleton Hosp. Melrose.

MACLEOD, Mary Catherine (retired) Easthaven, 13 Admiralty St., Portknockie, Buckie AB56 4NB — MB BS 1956 Lond.; MB BS (Hons. Surg., Path.) (Univ. Medal) Lond. 1956; DObst RCOG 1958. Prev: GP Applecross.

MACLEOD, Mary Joan 16 Cottown of Balgownie, Bridge of Don, Aberdeen AB23 8JQ Tel: 0141 357 1548 — MB ChB 1989 Glas.; BSc (Hons.) Glas. 1986, MB ChB 1989; MRCP (UK) 1992.

MACLEOD, Melanie Jane Dormers, Hayes Close, Bromley BR2 7BZ — MB ChB 1993 Liverp.

MACLEOD, Melville Christie (retired) Catriona, Sparkford Close, Winchester SO22 4NH Tel: 01962 854605 — MB ChB 1947 Glas.; MD (Hon.) Glas. 1955; DPH Glas. 1950. Prev: Area Med. Off. Beds. AHA.

MCLEOD, Mhairi Elizabeth The Clinic, 4 Firs Entry, Bannockburn, Stirling FK7 0HW Tel: 01786 813435 Fax: 01786 817545 — MB ChB 1973 Glas.

MACLEOD, Moira Catherine Mary Baillieston Health Centre, 20 Muirside Road, Baillieston, Glasgow G69 7AD Tel: 0141 531 8050 Fax: 0141 531 8067 — MB ChB 1980 Glas.; MRCGP 1986; DRCOG 1985; Cert. Family Plann. JCC 1985. GP Glas. Prev: Trainee GP Glas. VTS.

MACLEOD, Morag Fiona St John's Hospital, Livingston Tel: 01506 419666 — MB ChB 1987 Ed.; MRCPsych 1992. Cons. in Adult Psychiat.

MACLEOD, Morton, Surg. Capt. RN Retd. Rosehill, Cargreen, Saltash PL12 6NF Tel: 01752 846520 — MB ChB 1967 Glas.; MRCP (UK) 1975.

MACLEOD, Murdo (retired) Dunvegan, 5 Thorns Drive, Greasby, Wirral CH49 3PU Tel: 0151 630 2080 — MB ChB 1952 Ed.; FRCGP 1981. Prev: Ho. Phys. Walton Hosp. Liverp.

MACLEOD, Murdo Donald Aldershot Health Centre, Wellington Avenue, Aldershot GU11 1PA Tel: 01252 324577 Fax: 01252 324861; Dolphins, 72A Upper Hale Road, Farnham GU9 0NZ Tel: 01252 737282 Email: mmacleod@librykim.demon.co.uk — MB ChB Aberd. 1970; MRCGP 1977. Clin. Asst. PLD Servs. N.field Aldershot.

MACLEOD, Murdoch Assynt, Surg. Capt. RN Retd. (retired) Department of Nuclear Medicine, Royal Hospital Haslar, Gosport PO12 2AA Tel: 01705 584255 Fax: 01705 762363 — MB ChB 1960 Ed.; MSc (Radiat. Biol.) Lond. 1969; MD Ed. 1976. Prev: SHO (Surg.) Dundee Roy. Infirm.

MCLEOD, Nairn William 66 Craigleith View, Edinburgh EH4 3JY — MB ChB 1998 Manch.; MB ChB Manch 1998.

MCLEOD, Neil Alexander Glover Street Medical Centre, 133 Glover Street, Perth PH2 0JB Tel: 01738 639748 Fax: 01738 635133 — MB ChB 1983 Dundee. (Dundee) GP Perth.

MCLEOD, Patricia Mary Department of Clinical Oncology, Derriford Hospital, Plymouth PL6 8DH Tel: 01752 763980 Email: pat.macleod@phnt.swest.nhs.uk — MB ChB 1976 Manch.; FRCR 1984. Cons. Clin. Oncol. Plymouth. Prev: Sen. Regist. (Radiother.) Plymouth Gen. Hosp.

MACLEOD, Pearl Anna Inglis (retired) Karitane, 30 Netheredge Close, Knaresborough HG5 9BZ — MB ChB 1941 Glas.; BSc 1937, MB ChB Glas. 1941; FRFPS Glas. 1948; FRCS Glas. 1962; FRACS 1954. Prev: Cons. (Orthop. Surg.) Harrogate Gen. Hosp.

MACLEOD, Rachel Abigail Lisa 42 Daisy Road, Edgbaston, Birmingham B16 9DZ — MB ChB 1994 Birm.; ChB Birm. 1994; BSc Birm. 1993. SHO (Paediat.) Roy. Brompton Hosp. Lond. Prev: SHO (Paediat.) Birm. childr. Hosp.; SHO (Paediat.) City Hosp. Birm.

MACLEOD, Robert Carswell (retired) Rowanbrae, Garelochhead, Helensburgh G84 0AN Tel: 01436 810268 — MB ChB 1947 Glas. Prev: GP Garelochhead.

MACLEOD, Robert Dewar Murray c/o Gray's Hospital, Elgin IV30 1SN — MB ChB Aberd. 1960; FRCP Ed. 1981, M 1965; DObst RCOG 1962. (Aberd.) Cons. Phys. & Geriat. Dr. Gray's Hosp. Elgin. Socs: Brit. Geriat. Soc.

MACLEOD, Roderick Medical Centre, Loan Fern, Ballachulish PH49 4JB Tel: 01855 811226 Fax: 01855 811777; Craigleven, Ballachulish PH49 4JQ Tel: 0185 52 226 — MB ChB 1970 Aberd. (Aberd.) GP Ballachulish; Med. Off. Glencoe Hosp. Prev: Capt. RAMC; Regtl. Med. Off. 1st Bn The Gordon Highlanders.

MACLEOD, Roderick John Tel: 0141 632 4962 Fax: 0141 636 6651; 20 Calderwood Road, Newlands, Glasgow G43 2RP Tel: 0141 571 0322 — MB ChB 1968 Glas.; MRCGP 1972; DObst RCOG 1970. (Glas.) Socs: BMA; Glas. M-C Soc. Prev: SHO (Med.) S.. Gen. Hosp. Glas.; Jun. Ho. Off. (Med.) & (Surg.) Glas. Roy. Infirm.

MACLEOD, Roderick Samuel MacVicar and MacLeod, The Surgery, Keppoch Road, Culloden, Inverness IV2 7LL Tel: 01463 793777 Fax: 01463 792143; Milton of Ness-side, Inverness IV2 6DH Tel: 01463 231608 Email: macleods@talk21.com — MB ChB 1984 Aberd.; MRCGP 1988; DCCH RCP Ed. 1989; DRCOG 1987. GP Princip. Culloden Med. Pract., Inverness. Prev: Trainee GP Grantown-on-spey Moraysh.; SHO (A & E & O & G) Raigmore Hosp. Inverness.

MACLEOD, Rona Kenland House Surgery, 37 Station Road, Milngavie, Glasgow G62 8BT Tel: 0141 956 1005 Fax: 0141 955 0342; 7 Dunmore Drive, Milngavie, Glasgow G62 6NZ Tel: 0141 956 6147 — MB ChB 1966 Glas.; DA Eng. 1970. (Glas.) Clin. Asst. (Bone Densitometry) Stobhill Gen. Hosp. Glas. Socs: Bearsden & Milngavie Med. Soc. Prev: Med. Off. (Family Plann.) Ayrsh. & Arran HB; Regist. (Anaesth.) S.. Gen. Hosp. Glas.

MCLOUGHLIN

MACLEOD, Ronald Crum (retired) Metcombe Barton, Metcombe, Ottery St Mary EX11 1RS Tel: 01404 813431 — MB ChB Glas. 1936; MD Glas. 1955; MFCM 1974; DTM & H Eng. 1947; DPH Glas. 1938.

MCLEOD, Shaun Raymond 2 The Terrace, Dalton, Lockerbie DG11 1DS — MB ChB 1997 Aberd.

MCLEOD, Sheila 5 Old Forge Manor, Belfast BT10 0HY — MB BCh BAO 1971 Belf.

MACLEOD, Sheila Margaret Baillie (retired) Elleray, Knockinkelly, Whiting Bay, Brodick KA27 8RQ Tel: 01770 700268 — MB ChB 1960 Ed.; FFA RCS Eng. 1967; DObst RCOG 1963. p/t Cons. Anaesth. Arran War Memor. Hosp. Prev: Specialist (Anaesth.) Arran War Memor. Hosp.

MACLEOD, Sheila Robertson 13 Northumberland Avenue, Gosforth, Newcastle upon Tyne NE3 4XE — MB ChB Glas. 1983; MRCGP 1992; FFA RCSI 1988; DRCOG 1991; DA (UK) 1985. Prev: Trainee GP Kilmacolm; Regist. (Path.) Stobhill Gen. Hosp. Glas.; Regist. (Anaesth.) Vict. Infirm. Glas.

MACLEOD, Sheona Mary Compton Health Centre, Compton, Ashbourne DE6 1DA Tel: 01335 343784 Fax: 01335 300782; The Old Vicarage, Belle Vue Road, Ashbourne DE6 1AT — MB ChB 1983 Glas.; MRCGP 1987; D.Occ.Med. RCP Lond. 1995; DCH RCPS Glas. 1986; DRCOG 1985.

MACLEOD, Shona Margaret Cherry Lodge, Kilmichael, Lochgilphead PA31 8QA — MB ChB 1990 Glas.

MCLEOD, Susan Anne 19 Kings Gate, Aberdeen AB15 4EL — MB ChB 1994 Aberd.

MACLEOD, Susan Elizabeth 66 Souter Drive, Inverness IV2 4XG Tel: 01463 716068 — MB ChB Aberd. 1968; T(GP) 1996; DFFP 1995; DRCOG 1972. GP Locum in Highland region. Socs: BMA. Prev: GP Asst. Inverness (Long Term Locum); Trainee GP Inverness.

MACLEOD, Susan Kathleen Kingsmills Medical Practice, 18 Southside Road, Inverness IV2 3BG Tel: 01463 235245 Fax: 01463 01443 714400 — MB ChB 1981 Glas.

MACLEOD, Mr Thomas Michael RAFT Institute, Mount Vernon Hospital, Northwood HA6 2RN — MB BS 1993 Lond.; BSc (Hons) 1991 Lond.; FRCS. (Lond. Hosp. Med. School) Research Regist., Plastic Surg./Mt. Vernon Hosp. Socs: BMA; MDU. Prev: Plastic Surg. Nottm. City Hosp.; Gen. Surg. Nottm. City Hosp.; Orthop. Qu.s Med. Surg. Nottm.

MCLEOD, Tina Jacqueline 85 Blythesway, Alvechurch, Birmingham B48 7NB — MB BS 1985 Lond.; DA (UK) 1990. Regist. Rotat. (Anaesth.) S. Midl. HA. Socs: Jun. Mem. Assn. Anaesth.; MRCAnaesth.

MACLEOD, Torquil Hector Rees 20 Carlton Road, Seaford BN25 2LE Tel: 01323 892759 — MB BS 1955 Lond.; FRCPsych 1986, M 1973; DPM Eng. 1961. (Char. Cross) Cons. Psychiat. (Psychogeriat.) Sutton Hosp. Socs: Brit. Geriat. Soc.; World Psychiat. Assn. (Sect. Geriat. Psychiat.). Prev: Cons. Psychiat. Rainhill Ment. & BRd.green Gen. Hosps. Liverp.; Regist. (Psychiat.) Char. Cross Hosp.; Lect. (Psychiat.) Univ. Liverp.

MACLEOD, Torquil Neil Nicolson Old Machar Medical Practice, 526 King Street, Aberdeen AB24 5RS Tel: 01224 480324 Fax: 01224 276121; Braehead Way, Bridge of Don, Aberdeen AB22 Tel: 01224 821701 Fax: 01224 823481 — MB ChB 1976 Aberd.; MRCGP 1982. Clin. Tutor (Gen. Pract.) Univ. Aberd.; Police Surg. Grampian Police; Clin. Asst. (A & E) Grampian HB; Med. Off. Offshore Med. Support; Chairm. GP Audit Comm. Prev: SHO (Gen. Orthop. & Cardiothoracic Surg. & Anaesth.) Aberd. Roy. Infirm.

MACLEOD, Una Margaret Shettleston Health Centre, 420 Old Shettleston Road, Glasgow G32 7JZ Tel: 0141 531 6220 Fax: 0141 5316298 — MB ChB 1988 Glas.; 2001 PHD Univ. Glasg; MRCGP 1996; Dip. Palliat. Care Glas. 1996. (Glas.) p/t GP Princip. and Lect. Univ. Glas. Prev: SHO (Med.) CrossHo. Hosp. Kilmarnock; SHO (Radiat. Oncol.) W.. Infirm. Glas.; CRC Clin. Research Fell. (primary care Oncol.) Univ. Glas.

MACLEOD, William Alexander Poltonbank House, Lasswade EH18 1JH — MB ChB 1994 Ed.

MCLEOD, William Jardine (retired) 16 Flush Park, Belfast BT6 0GD Tel: 01232 642475 — MB BCh BAO 1939 Belf.; MD Belf. 1948, MB BCh BAO 1939; DPH 1942. Prev: Dist. Admin. Med. Off. Lisburn.

MACLEOD, Wilma Joan Jack Murrayfield, Castletown, Thurso KW14 8TY — MB ChB 1985 Aberd.; DRCOG 1992.

MCLINDON, John Paul c/o Mr B. McLindon, 110 Reevy Road, Wibsey, Bradford BD6 3QF — MB ChB 1986 Liverp.

MCLINTOCK, Derek Graeme Queen Elizabeth II Hospital, Howlands, Welwyn Garden City AL7 4HQ Tel: 01707 328111; Deards Farm, Sally Deards Lane, Rabley Heath, Welwyn AL6 9UE Tel: 01438 821997 Fax: 01438 821997 Email: gynae@deardsfarm.demon.co.uk — MB BS 1971 Lond.; BSc Lond. 1968; FRCOG 1996, M 1977. (Middlx.) Cons. O & G E. Herts. NHS Trust. Socs: Fell. Roy. Soc. Med. Prev: Sen. Regist. (O & G) Mayday Hosp. Croydon; Lect. (O & G) W.m. Med. Sch.; Regist. (O & G) Qu. Mary's Hosp. Roehampton.

MCLINTOCK, Donald McKenzie The Surgery, Station Road, Hemyock, Cullompton EX15 3SF Tel: 01823 680206 Fax: 01823 680680 — MB ChB 1978 Glas.; MRCGP 1983. p/t Gen. Practitioner; Med. Teach. Socs: ASME; AMEE. Prev: Clin. Research Fell & Facilitator; Secondary Preven. of Coronary Heart Dis. N. & E. Devon; Trainee GP Exeter VTS.

MCLINTOCK, Lorna Ann 11 Monksrig Road, Penicuik EH26 9JH — MB ChB 1995 Glas.

MCLINTOCK, Margaret Gillian Hillfolds, Drybridge, Buckie AB56 5JY — MB ChB 1972 Ed. (Ed.)

MACLINTOCK, Roslyn Mary Lyons and Partners, Shoreham Health Centre, Pond Road, Shoreham-by-Sea BN43 5US Tel: 01273 440550 Fax: 01273 462109; 2 Radinden Manor Road, Hove BN3 6NH Tel: 01273 556553 — MB BS 1970 Lond.; MRCGP 1978; DRCOG 1977. (St. Mary's) Prev: Ho. Phys. St. Mary's Hosp. Lond.

MCLINTOCK, Traven Thomson Christison Glasgow Royal Ingirmary, Directorate of Anaesthesia, Castle St, Glasgow G4 0SF Tel: 0141 211 4621 Fax: 0141 211 4622 Email: traven.mclintock@northglasgow.scot.nhs.uk; 7 Manor Road, Jordanhill, Glasgow G14 9LG — MB ChB 1980 Glas.; FFA RCS Eng. 1985. Cons. Anaesth. Glas. Roy. Infirm.; Hon. Clin. Sen. Lect. Univ. of Glas. Socs: Assn. Anaesth.; Soc. Computing & Technol. in Anaesth.

MCLISTER, Mary Suzanne Ballycastle Health Centre, Dalriada Hospital, 1A Coleraine Road, Ballycastle BT54 6BA Tel: 028 2076 2684 Fax: 028 2076 9891 — MB BCh BAO 1978 NUI.

MACLLAN, Roderick 37 Bellfield, Invergordon IV18 0JS — MB ChB 1991 Ed.; BSc (Med. Sci.) (Hons.) 1988; MSc Middlx. 1992; MRCGP 1996; DFFP 1996. (Ed.)

MCLOONE, Jacqueline Abbey Medical Centre, Lonend, Paisley PA1 1SU; 178 Seaforth Gardens, Stoneleigh, Epsom KT19 0NW — MB ChB 1991 Glas.; BSc (Hons.) Glas. 1989.

MCLOONE, Mary Bridget Elsie 3 Turnpike Drive, Luton LU3 3RA — MB BS 1996 Lond.

MCLORINAN, Gregory Christopher 88 Cloona Park, Dunmurry, Belfast BT17 0HF — MB BCh BAO 1997 Belf.

MCLOUD, Karen Hazel 22 Hillview Crescent, Corstorphine, Edinburgh EH12 8QG Tel: 0131 334 3771 — MB ChB 1992 Ed. Staff Grade Geriat. Med. Roy.. Vic. Hosp. Edin.

MCLOUGHLIN, Claire Mary 134 Malone Road, Belfast BT9 5LH — MB BCh BAO 1983 Belf. SHO (O & G) Mater Infirm. Belf. Prev: SHO (Gen. Med.) Belf. City Hosp.; SHO (Geriat. & Rheum.) Musgrave Pk. Hosp.

MCLOUGHLIN, Cormac Coburn 15 Beechwood Grove, Belfast BT8 7UR — MD 1991 Belf.; MB BCh BAO Dub. 1982; FFA RCSI 1986. Cons. Anaesth. Belf. City Hosp.

MCLOUGHLIN, David Cyril 88 Lurgan Road, Portadown, Craigavon BT63 5QS — MB BCh BAO 1990 Belf.

MCLOUGHLIN, Evelyn Therese Mary Laburnum House, Laburnum Avenue, Kirkby in Ashfield, Nottingham NG17 8LQ — MB BCh BAO 1974 Belf.

MCLOUGHLIN, Mr Gerard Anthony Roscoe House, 27 Rodney St., Liverpool L1 9EH Tel: 0151 709 4600 — MB BS (Hons.) Durh. 1966; MS DUrh. 1974, MD 1980; FRCS Eng. 1972; FRCS Ed. 1971. (Durh.) Lect. (Surg.) Univ. Liverp. Socs: Boston Med. Soc. & Vasc. Soc. GB & Irel. Prev: Cons. Surg. Roy. Liverp. Hosp.; Sen. Regist. Liverp. Roy. Infirm.; Clin. Instruc. (Vasc. Surg.) Harvard Med. Sch. & Peter Bent Brigham Hosp. Boston, USA.

MCLOUGHLIN, Ian James 9 Stratford Grove, Heaton, Newcastle upon Tyne NE6 5AT — MB BS 1979 Newc.

MCLOUGHLIN

MCLOUGHLIN, Imelda Catherine 14 Studd Street, London N1 0QJ — MB BS 1991 Lond.; BA Oxf. 1988. Trainee GP/SHO Roy. Lond. Trust Hosp. VTS.

MCLOUGHLIN, James Christopher Mater Infirmorum Hospital, Crumlin Road, Belfast BT14 6AB — MD 1977 Belf.; MB BCh BAO (2nd Cl. Hons.) 1971; FRCP Lond. 1989; MRCP (U.K.) 1974; FRCPI 1996. (Queens University of Belfast) Cons. Phys. Mater Infirm. Hosp. Belf.; Med. Dir. Socs: Brit. Soc. Gastroenterol.; Irish. Soc. Gastroenterol; Corrigan Club. Prev: Ho. Off. Mater Infirm. Hosp. Belf.; Regist. & Tutor Belf. City Hosp.; Research Fell. Roy. Vict. Hosp. Belf.

MCLOUGHLIN, Mr John Department of Urology, West Suffolk Hospital, Hardwick Lane, Bury St Edmunds IP33 2QZ Tel: 01284 712549 — MB BS 1983 Lond.; MS Lond. 1992; FRCS Eng. 1987; FRCS (Urol.) 1993. (St Mary's) Cons. (Urol.) Dept. of Urol. W. Suff. Hosp. Bury St. Edmunds. Socs: BAUS; Brit. Prostate Gp. Prev: Sen. Regist. & Bristol & S. W. Rotat.

MCLOUGHLIN, John Gerard Cliff Villages Medical Practice, Mere Road, Waddington, Lincoln LN5 9NX Tel: 01522 720277 Fax: 01522 729174 — MB BS 1988 Lond.

MACLOUGHLIN, John Herbert (retired) Seascape, 61A Shore Road, Greenisland, Carrickfergus BT38 8TZ — MB BCh BAO Belf. 1936; MFCM 1974; DObst RCOG 1948; DPH Belf. 1938. Prev: Dist. Admin. Med. Off. N.. Health & Social Servs. Bd.

MCLOUGHLIN, John Stephen 3 Harberton Avenue, Belfast BT9 6PH — MB BCh BAO 1975 Belf.; FRCR 1983; DMRD Eng. 1980. Cons. (Radiol.) Mater Infirm. Hosp. Belf.

MCLOUGHLIN, Julian Neil Felpham and Middleton Health Centre, 109 Flansham Park, Felpham, Bognor Regis PO22 6DH Tel: 01243 582384 Fax: 01243 584933; 85 Crossbush Road, Felpham, Bognor Regis PO22 7NA Tel: 01243 584392 Fax: 01243 584933 Email: mcl@gatewaysl.demon.co.uk — MB ChB 1971 Leeds; DCH Eng. 1975.

MCLOUGHLIN, Kathleen Heather, Wing Cdr. RAF Med. Br. 39 Demesne Avenue, Ballymena BT43 7BE — MB BCh BAO 1979 Belf.; MB BCh BAO (Hons.) Belf. 1979; FFARCSI 1984. Cons. Anaesth. P.ss Alexandria Hosp. RAF Wroughton Swindon. Socs: Assn. Anaesths.; Eur. Resusc. Counc. Prev: Cons. Anaesth. P.ss of Wales Hosp. RAF Ely Cambs.; Med. Off. P.ss Mary Hosp. RAF Akrotiri, Cyprus; Hon. Sen. Regist. Addenbrooke's & Papworth Hosps. Camb.

MCLOUGHLIN, Kathryn Claire 3 Libra Cl, Liverpool L14 9LX — MB ChB 1997 Liverp.

MCLOUGHLIN, Lisa Marie 18 Dingwall Drive, Wirral CH49 1SG — MB ChB 1998 Liverp.

MCLOUGHLIN, Mary Kathleen 8 Ty Brith Gardens, Usk NP15 1BY Tel: 01291 672477 — MB ChB 1966 Liverp. SCMO Nevill Hall & Dist. NHS Trust Abergavenny. Socs: MRCPCH. Prev: SCMO Gwent HA Pontypool; Clin. Med. Off.

MCLOUGHLIN, Matilda Katarzina 74 Kingslea Road, Solihull B91 1TL — MB ChB 1994 Leeds.

MCLOUGHLIN, Noel Patrick Thomas St Isan Road Surgery, 46 St. Isan Road, Heath, Cardiff CF14 4LX Tel: 029 2062 7518 Fax: 029 2052 2886; 11 Heol Waun-Y-Nant, Whitchurch, Cardiff CF14 1JZ Email: nptmack@aol.com — MB BCh 1984 Wales; MRCGP 1992. Socs: BMA.

MACLOUGHLIN, Paul Vincent Anthony 47 Weymouth Street, London W1G 8NE — MRCS Eng. LRCP Lond. 1966. (Univ. Coll. Lond. & Roy. Free) Socs: Fell. Roy. Soc. Med. & Roy. Anthropol. Inst. Prev: Research Fell. Roy. Postgrad. Med. Sch. Lond.; Ho. Phys. Univ. Coll. Hosp. Lond.; Ho. Surg. Roy. Free Hosp. Lond.

MACLOUGHLIN, Peter John Corner Place Surgery, 46A Dartmouth Road, Paignton TQ4 5AH Tel: 01803 557458 Fax: 01803 524844 — MB BCh BAO 1977 Belf.; MRCP (UK) 1982; MRCGP 1984; DRCOG 1983. Mem. Roy. Coll. Phys. Ed. Socs: Roy. Coll. Gen. Pract.

MCLOUGHLIN, Peter Leo 163 Pitville Avenue, Liverpool L18 7JH — MB ChB 1993 Liverp.

MCLOUGHLIN, Mr Philip Martin Maxillofacial Department, Ninewells Hospital, Dundee DD1 9SY Tel: 01382 35590; Airdit, Balmullo, St. Andrews KY16 0AL Tel: 01629 584031 Email: phjil@mcloughlinpm.freeserve.co.uk — MB BS 1988 Lond.; BDS Lond. (Hons.) 1981; FDS RCS Eng. 1991; FRCS Ed. 1991. (Univ. Coll. Lond.) Cons. (Oral & Maxillofacial) Ninewells Hosp., Dundee. Socs: Brit. Assn. Oral & Maxillofacial Surg.; Assn. Head & Neck Oncol. Prev: Sen. Regist. (Maxillofacial Surg.) Univ. Coll. Hosps. Lond.; Sen. Regist. (Maxillofacial) Qu. Vict. Hosp. E. Grinstead; Regist. (Maxillofacial) N. Wales Hosps.

MCLOUGHLIN, Rachel 33 Pollard Road, Liverpool L15 7JD — MB ChB 1997 Liverp.

MCLOUGHLIN, Mr Stephen James Cumberland House, 1 Cumberland Avenue, Blackpool FY1 5QL Tel: 01253 699444 Fax: 01253 699555 — MB ChB 1980 Manch.; FRCS (Orth.) Ed. 1990; FRCS Ed. 1984. Cons. Orthop. Surg. Blackpool. Socs: Internat. Arthroscopy Assn.; Arthroscopic Assn. of N. Amer.; BOA. Prev: Clin. Fell.sh. (Sports Injuries) N. Amer., USA; Regist. (Orthop.) Pk. Hosp. & Roy. Preston Hosp. Manch.; Regist. (Surg.) Manch. Roy. Infirm.

MCLOUGHLIN, Susan Jean 24 Knighton Drive, Leicester LE2 3HB — MB ChB 1987 Sheff.; BSc Sheff. 1982, MB ChB 1987.

MCLOUGHLIN, Thomas Anthony William 16 Arbour Way, Highwoods, Colchester CO4 4BD — MB BS 1983 Lond.

MCLOUGHLIN, Una Marie Main Street Surgery, 40 Main Street, Coalisland, Dungannon BT71 4NB Tel: 028 8774 8853; 8 Kalendra Court, Bush Road, Dungannon BT71 6EB — MB BCh BAO 1983 Belf.; MRCGP 1989; DRCOG 1989.

***MCLOUGHLIN, Wendy Ellen** 628 Dowbridge, Kirkham, Preston PR4 2YL — MB BS 1994 Lond.

MCLUCKIE, Angela Department of Intensive Care, St Thomas's Hospital, London SE1 7EH Tel: 020 7960 5846 Fax: 020 7960 5842 Email: angela.mcluckie@gstt.sthames.nhs.uk — MB BS 1982 Lond.; FFA RCS Lond. 1987. (Guy's) Cons. Dept. of Intens. Care Guy's and St Thomas' Hosp. Trust. Socs: Intens. Care Soc.; Austral. & NZ Intens. Care Soc.; Eur. Intens. Care Soc. Prev: Sen. Regist. (Anaesth.) Guy's Hosp. Lond.; Sen. Regist. (Intens. Care) Roy. Melbourne Childr. Hosp.; Regist. (Intens. Care) Sir Chas. Gairdner Hosp. Perth, Austral.

MCLUCKIE, Karen Louise Findlay Farm Cottage, Bridge of Don, Aberdeen AB23 8AX — MB ChB 1997 Aberd.

MCLUCKIE, Shaughna Lindsay Greenacres, Monkshill Road, Faversham ME13 9EH — MB ChB 1988 Aberd.

MACLULLICH, Alasdair Maurice Joseph 18 Melville Terrace, Edinburgh EH9 1LY — MB ChB 1993 Ed.; BSc (Hons.) Ed. 1990; MRCP (UK) 1996. SHO (Rehabil. Med.) Astley Ainslie Hosp. Edin.

MACLURE, Alison Mary Russell 8 Fraser Street, Aberdeen AB25 3XS — MB ChB 1981 Aberd.

MCLURE, Clare Elaine The Whittington Hospital, Department of Rheumatology, London N19 5NF Tel: 020 7272 5259 — MB BChir 1990 Camb.; MA Camb. 1990; MRCP (UK) 1993.

MACLURE, Mr Gordon Malcolm (retired) 36 The Avenue, Linthorpe, Middlesbrough TS5 6PD Tel: 01642 888208 — MB ChB St. And. 1958; FRCOphth 1988; DO Eng. 1965. Hon. Cons. Ophth. N. Riding Infirm. Middlesbrough. Prev: Sen. Regist. Birm. & Midl. Eye Hosp. & Selly Oak Hosp. Birm.

MCLURE, Hamish Angus Flat 5, 35 Hamilton Road, London W5 2EE — MB ChB 1990 Manch.; FRCA 1994. Regist. Rotat. (Anaesth.) Char. Cross Hosp. Lond.

MACLURE, Ian Romiley Health Centre, Chichester Road, Romiley, Stockport SK6 4QR Tel: 0161 430 2573 Fax: 0161 406 7237; 16 Werneth Road, Glossop SK13 6NF — MB ChB 1982 Manch.; BSc (Hons.) Med. Biochem. Manch. 1979; MRCGP 1986; DRCOG 1985; MFHom 1996. (Manch.)

MACLURE, William Alastair (retired) Deloraine Court, 4 James St., Lincoln LN2 1QE Tel: 01522 528480 — MB ChB 1941 Glas.; BSc Glas. 1938; MRCP Lond. 1945; MRCGP 1953. Prev: Med. Off. Eng. Electric Valves Ltd. Lincoln.

MACLURG, Katherine Margaret 23 Moulsham Lane, Yateley GU46 7QX — MB BCh BAO 1987 Belf.; MRCGP 1993; DRCOG 1991; Cert. Family Plann. JCC 1990.

MCLUSKEY, Peter William 27 Durness Avenue, Bearsden, Glasgow G61 2AH — LRCP LRCS 1951 Ed.; LRCP LRCS Ed. LRFPS Glas. 1951. (St. Mungo's Coll.) Socs: BMA. Prev: Med. Resid. Glas. Roy. Infirm.; Med. Off. RAF; Resid. in Obst. Bellshill Matern. Hosp.

MCLUSKIE, John Warren Farm House, Great Missenden HP16 — MB BS 1947 Lond.; DCH Eng. 1950. (St. Mary's) Prev: Ho. Phys. Paediat. Dept. St. Mary's Hosp. & Centr. Middlx. Hosp.; Obst. Ho. Surg. Kent & Canterbury Hosp.

MCLUSKY, Evan Gavin Cooper 11 Ripon Road, Killinghall, Harrogate HG3 2DG Tel: 01423 503218 — MB ChB 1968 Leeds.

MACLUSKY, Kevin Andrew 34 Hitchin Road, Stotfold, Hitchin SG5 4HP — MB BS 1985 Lond.

MCMAHON, Andrew James 4 Gypsy Wood Close, Leeds LS15 9DY — MB ChB 1994 Ed.

MCMAHON, Mr Andrew James Department of Surgery, Stobhill Hospital, Glasgow G21 3UW Tel: 0141 201 4136 Fax: 0141 557 5507 Email: andrew.mcmahon@northglasgow.scot.nhs.uk — MB ChB 1985 Glas.; MD Glas. 1994; FRCS (Gen.) 1995; FRCS Glas. 1989; FRCS Ed. 1989. (Glas.) Cons. Gen. Surg. Stobhill Hosp. Glas.; Hon. Sen. Lect. Glas. Univ. Socs: Assn. of Surg.s ASGBI; Assn. of Colocopectology ACPGBI; Assn. of Endoscopic Surg. AESGBI. Prev: Sen. Regist. Rotat. (Gen. Surg.) Ed.; Career Regist. (Gen. Surg.) W. of Scotl. Higher Surgic. Train. Scheme; Research Fell. (Surg.) W.. Infirm. Glas.

MACMAHON, Bronagh Mary Aberfoyle Terrace Surgery, 3-5 Aberfoyle Terrace, Strand Road, Londonderry BT48 7NP Tel: 028 7126 4868 — MB BCh 1964 N U Irel. (N U Irel) GP Lond.derry.

MCMAHON, Catriona Carol Freeman Hospital, High Heaton, Newcastle upon Tyne NE7 7DN Tel: 0191 284 3111; 14A Pioneer Terrace, Bedlington Station, Bedlington NE22 5PW Tel: 01670 826329 Email: trina_mcmahon@msn.com — MB ChB 1989 Ed.; BSc (Hons.) Ed. 1987; FRCA 1994. (Ed.) Specialist Regist. Intens. Care Med. N. Deanery N.ern & Yorks. RHA. Socs: Intens. Care Soc. (Comm. Mem. Trainees Subdiv.); Train. Mem. Assn. AnE.h. Prev: Research Fell. (Anaesth.) Freeman Hosp. Newc.; Regist. (Anaesth.) Freeman Hosp. Newc.; SHO (Anaesth.) Ashington Hosp. N.d. HA.

MCMAHON, Charles Patrick Renfrew & Inverclyde Primary Health Care Trust, Dykebar Hospital, Grahamston Road, Paisley PA2 7DE Tel: 0141 884 5122 — MB BCh BAO 1983 Belf.; MRCPsych 1990. Cons. (Psychiat.) Dykebar Hosp. Paisley.

MCMAHON, Christopher The Surgery, Marsh Lane, Misterton, Doncaster DN10 4DP Tel: 01427 890206 Fax: 01302 891794; Moorcroft, Brickenhole Lane, Walkeringham, Doncaster DN10 4HX Email: cmcma36406@aoc.com — MB ChB 1975 Sheff.

MCMAHON, Clare Meadway Health Centre, Meadway, Sale M33 4PS Tel: 0161 905 2850; 11 Harewood Avenue, Sale M33 5BX Tel: 0161 969 4601 — MB ChB BAO 1979 NUI; MICGP 1987; MRCGP 1986; DObst RCPI 1984; DCH RCSI 1983. (Galway) Prev: GP St. Helens; Trainee GP Sale VTS; Regist. (Geriat. Med.) Merlin Pk. Regional Hosp. Galway.

MCMAHON, David Jeremy c/o Department of Oral & Maxillofacial Surgery, Canniesburn Auxiliary Hospital, Switchback Road, Bearsden, Glasgow G61 1QL — MB ChB 1992 Auckland.

MCMAHON, Dorothy Jane 7 Ridgepark Drive, Lanark ML11 7PG — MB ChB 1998 Glas.; MB ChB Glas 1998.

MACMAHON, Douglas Graham Camborne - Redruth Hospital, Barncoose Terrace, Redruth TR15 3ER Tel: 01209 881631 Fax: 01209 881715 Email: doug.macmahon@cornwall.nhs.uk; Email: dgm@doctor.com — MB BS 1973 Lond.; FRCP Lond. 1991; MRCP (UK) 1976; MRCS Eng. LRCP Lond. 1973. (King's Coll. Hosp.) Cons. Phys. Camborne - Redruth Hosp. & Treliske Hosp. Truro; Hon. Sen. Lect. Univ. Plymouth. Socs: Brit. Geriat. Soc. (Chair Policy Comm.); Pk.insons Dis. Soc. (Counc.). Prev: Sen. Regist. (Med. & Geriat. Med.) John Radcliffe Hosp. Oxf.; Regist. (Med.) Stoke Mandeville Hosp. Aylesbury; SHO (Med. & Geriat.) Portsmouth & SE Hants. Health Dist.

MACMAHON, Eithne Mary Edana Department of Infection, Virology Section, Guy's & St Thomas' Hospital, Lambeth Palace Road, London SE1 7EH Tel: 020 7928 9292 Ext: 8167 Fax: 020 7922 8387 Email: eithne.macmahon@kcl.ac.uk — MB BCh BAO 1982 NUI; MRCPI 1985; DCH RCPSI 1986; MD 1997; MRCPath 1998. (University College Dublin (NUI)) Cons. in Virol., Guy's & St. Thomas' Hosp. Trust, Lond.; Hon. Sen. Lect. Guy's, King's & St. Thos. Hosps. Sch. of Med. Socs: IDSA; Internat. Assn. Research on Epstein-Barr Virus & Assoc.d Dis.; Europ. Soc. for Clin. Virol. Prev: Clin. Lect. & Honarary Sen. Regist. (Virol.) Roy. Free Hosp. Sch. Med. Lond.; Research Assoc. (Neurol.) Univ. Minnesota, USA; Fell. (Infec. Dis.s) Johns Hopkins Hosp. Baltimore, MD USA.

MCMAHON, Jessie Millar 7 Ridgepark Drive, Lanark ML11 7PG Tel: 01555 663844 — MB ChB 1957 Glas.; DObst RCOG 1959. (Glas.) Prev: Clin. Med. Off. (Community Servs). S> Lanarksh, Healthcare NHS Trust.

MCMAHON, Mr John Brian 29 Low Greens, Berwick-upon-Tweed TD15 1LZ — MB ChB 1986 Aberd.; FRCS Glas. 1991.

MCMAHON, John Edgar Matunda, Barrington, Bristol BS40 7AA — MRCS Eng. LRCP Lond. 1960.

MACMAHON, Joseph 40 Lisnabreeny Road, Castlereagh, Belfast BT6 9SR — MB BCh BAO 1972 Belf.; FRCP Ed. 1991; MRCP (UK) 1976. Cons. Phys. Belf. City Hosp.

MCMAHON, Judith Marian Riverside Surgery, 48 Worthing Road, Horsham RH12 1UD Tel: 01403 264848 Fax: 01403 275158; Winchmore, 53 Worthing Road, Horsham RH12 1TD — MB ChB 1972 Liverp.; MFCM RCP (UK) 1980; DFFP 1995. Dir. Community Servs. Surrey & Sussex NHS Trust.

MCMAHON, Leo Frederick William (retired) Firethorn Cottage, Llanfrynach, Brecon LD3 7BZ — MB BS 1957 Durh.; FRCGP 1979, M 1965. Prev: GP Cardiff.

MACMAHON, Marcus Thomas Chiltern House, Bells Hill, Stoke Poges, Slough SL2 4EG Tel: 01753 642222 Fax: 01753 647030; Littlemead, Carmen St, Great Chesterford, Saffron Walden CB10 1NR Tel: 01799 30339 — MB BS 1960 Lond.; MRCP Lond. 1964; MRCS Eng. LRCP Lond. 1960; Dip. Pharm. Med. RCP (UK) 1986. (St. Marys) Med. Dir. Chiltern Internat. Slough; Hon. Cons. Phys. Wexham Pk. Hosp. Slough; Mem. Pharmaceut. Phys. Socs: Fell. Roy. Soc. Med.; Brit. Soc. Gastroenterol.; Fell. Fac. Pharmaceut. Phys. Prev: Gastroenterol. Winston Salem Health Care N. Carolina, USA; Clin. Research Dir. Special Project Unit Sandoz Pharmaceut.; Cons. Phys. Wycombe DHA.

MACMAHON, Margaret Department of Geriatric Medicine, Freeman Group of Hospital, Freeman Road High Heaton, Newcastle upon Tyne NE7 7DN — MB BCh BAO 1984 NUI; MRCPI 1988.

MCMAHON, Marie Flat 2/2, 41 Caird Drive, Glasgow G11 5DX — MB ChB 1997 Glas.

MCMAHON, Professor Michael John Department of Surgery, The General Infirmary, Leeds Tel: 0113 392 3466 Fax: 0113 392 6305 Email: mjmcmahon@compuserve.com — MB ChB 1966 Sheff.; PhD Birm. 1973; ChM Sheff. 1982; FRCS Eng. 1973. Cons. (Surg.) Gen. Infirm. Leeds; Prof. (Surg.) Univ. Leeds.

MCMAHON, Michael John Dumfries & Galloway Royal Infirmary, Bankend Road, Dumfries DG1 4AP Tel: 01387 246246 Fax: 01387 241192 — MB ChB 1984 Manch.; BSc St. And. 1981; MRCP (UK) 1989; FRCP Glas 1999. Cons. Phys. Dumfries & Galloway Roy. Infirm. Prev: Sen. Regist. (Rheum.) Withington Hosp. Manch.; Sen. Regist. & Regist. (Rheum.) Rhem. Dis. Centre Hope Hosp. Salford; Regist. (Gen. Med.) Roy. Preston Hosp.

MCMAHON, Nuala Marie 1 Sunningdale Park, Belfast BT14 6RU — MB BCh BAO 1997 Belf.

MCMAHON, Paul Joseph Thomas Northgate Hospital, Northgate St, Great Yarmouth NR30 1BU Tel: 01493 337600 — MB BCh BAO 1979 NUI; MRCPsych 1983. Cons. Psychiat. Gt. Yarmouth & Waveney HA.

MCMAHON, Raymond Francis Thomas Laboratory Medicine Academic Group, The Medical School, Stopford Building, Oxford Road, Manchester M13 9PT Tel: 0161 275 5295 Fax: 0161 275 5289 Email: ray.mcmahon@man.ac.uk — MB BCh BAO 1979 NUI; BSc NUI 1982, MD 1992; FRCPath 1997; MRCPath 1986. (NUI (Galway)) Sen. Lect. (Path.) Univ. Manch.; Hon. Cons. Path. Centr. Manch. Healthcare NHS Trust. Socs: Path. Soc.; Internat. Acad. Path. (Brit. Div.); Brit. Soc. Gastroenterol. Prev: SHO & Regist. (Histopath. & Morbid Anat.) Regional Hosp. Galway.

MCMAHON, Robertson 28 The Loaning, Alloway, Ayr KA7 4QL Email: rmcm178075@aol.com — MB ChB 1967 Glas.; FFA RCS Eng. 1972. Cons. Anaesth. Ayrsh. & Arran Health Bd. Socs: Scott. Soc. Anaesth. & Glas. & W. Scotl. Soc. Anaesth. Prev: Sen. Regist., Regist. & SHO Dept. Anaesth. Glas. Roy. Infirm.

MCMAHON, Rosemary Joan (retired) Matunda, Burrington, Bristol BS40 7AA Tel: 01761 462438 — MRCS Eng. LRCP Lond. 1958; DRCOG 1959. Prev: Train. Coordinator WHO.

MCMAHON, Ross 1 Sunningdale Park, Belfast BT14 6RU — MB BCh 1998 Belf.; MB BCh Belf 1998.

MCMAHON, Sorcha Mary 10 Stonehey Drive, Wirral CH48 2HS — MB ChB 1994 Liverp.

MCMAIN, Sheena Stuart Meanwood Group Practice, 548 Meanwood Road, Leeds LS6 4JN Tel: 0113 295 1737 Fax: 0113 295 1736 — MB ChB 1980 Ed.; MMed Sc 2000 (Primary Health Care) Leeds; MRCP (UK) 1984; MRCGP 1988. Princip. in Gen. Pract., The Mantwood Gp. Pract., Leeds; VTS Course Organiser,

MCMAIN

Leeds GDEC, Post Grad. Centre St James Univ. Hopital, Leeds, LS9 7TF.

MCMAIN, Thomas Stuart Health Centre, 288 High St., Linlithgow EH49 7ER Tel: 01506 670027; 76 Bailielands, Linlithgow EH49 7TF — MB ChB 1983 Ed.; MRCGP 1987; DRCOG 1986. GP Linlithgow; Asst. Team Doctor Falkirk Football Club.

MACMANAWAY, Patrick James Westbank Natural Health Centre, Strathmiglo, Cupar KY14 7QP Tel: 01337 868945 Fax: 01337 868945 — MB ChB 1990 Ed. Indep. Pract. (Complementary Med.) W.bank Natural Health Centre Strathmiglo. Socs: Brit. Holistic Med. Assn. Prev: SHO (Surg. & Accid.) Balfour Hosp. Kirkwall, Orkney; Ho. Off. (Med.) Falkirk & Dist. Roy. Infirm.; Ho. Off. (Surg.) Dunfermline & W. Fife Hosp.

MCMANN, Pamela Margaret Kepplehills Road, Bucksburn, Aberdeen AB21 9DG; 122 Inverurie Road, Bucksburn, Aberdeen AB21 9AU — MB ChB 1981 Aberd.; MRCGP 1986; DCH RCPS Glas. 1986; DRCOG 1985. GP Dyce Aberd.. Prev: Trainee GP, Kemnay, Aberd.sh.; SHO Aberd. Matern. Hosp.; SHO (Paediat.) N. Ayrsh. Dist. Gen. Hosp.

MCMANNERS, Angus John Whitley Road Health Centre, Whitley Road, Whitley Bay NE26 2ND Tel: 0191 253 1113; 15 Northumberland Terrace, Tynemouth, North Shields NE30 4BA — MB BS 1978 Newc.; MRCGP 1982.

MCMANNERS, Deborah Louise 187 London Road N., Merstham, Redhill RH1 3BN — MB BS 1983 Lond.

MCMANNERS, Joseph (retired) Valley Downe, Earls Drive, Lowfell, Gateshead NE9 6AB — MB BS 1948 Durh.

MCMANNERS, Mr Joseph Oral & Maxillofacial Department, Falkirk & District Royal Infirmary, Majors Loan, Falkirk FK1 5QE Tel: 01324 24000 — MB ChB 1984 Birm.; BDS Birm. 1974; FRCS Ed. 1987; FDS RCS Eng. 1984. (Birm.) Cons. Oral & Maxillofacial Surg. Falkirk & Dist. Roy. Infirm.; Cons. Oral & Maxillofacial Surg. Stirling roy. Infirm.; Hon. Sen. Lect. (Oral & Maxillofacial Surg.) Glas. Dent. Sch. Socs: Fell. Brit. Assn. Oral & Maxillofacial Surg. Prev: Sen. Regist. (Oral Surg. & Med.) Glas. Dent. Hosp.

MCMANNERS, Mary Michele 15 Northumberland Terrace, Tynemouth, North Shields NE30 4BA — MB BS 1978 Newc.; MRCGP 1984.

MCMANNERS, Robert Auckland Medical Group, 54 Cockton Hill Road, Bishop Auckland DL14 6BB Tel: 01388 602728; West House, 5 Etherley Lane, Bishop Auckland DL14 7QR Tel: 01388 602180 — MB BS 1971 Newc.; MRCGP 1975; MA Med. Ed. Durham 1998. Course Organizer, N.umbria UTS.

MCMANNERS, Thomas The Old Rectory, Barlings, Lincoln LN3 5DG Tel: 01522 29921 — MB ChB 1964 Leeds; FRCR 1975; FFR 1970; DMRD Eng. 1969; DObst RCOG 1966. (Leeds) Cons. Radiol. Lincoln Co. Hosp.

MCMANUS, Breda Mary Carrick House, Carrickmacusker, Lisnaskea, Enniskillen BT92 5EH Email: bmcmanus@fs1.sdr.man.ac.uk; 7 Higher Downs, Altrincham WA14 2QL — MB BCh BAO 1990 Belf.; MRCP 1995; FRCR Part I Lond. 1997. (Belf.) Specialist Regist. Rotat. (Diagnostic Radiol.) N W Manch. Regional Heatlh Auth. Prev: Regist. (Gen. Med., Diabetes & Endocrinol.) Manch. Healthcare Trust; SHO (Cardiol.) Ulster Hosp. Dundonald; SHO (Gen. Med.) Roy. Vict. Hosp. Belf. & Belf. City Hosp.

MCMANUS, Bruce Neil Burnbrae House, Ecchinswell, Newbury RG20 4UQ — MB BS 1998 Lond.; MB BS Lond 1998.

MCMANUS, Christopher John 4 Ashbury Drive, Haydock, St Helens WA11 0FA — MB BS 1996 Newc.

MCMANUS, Damian Terence 12 Newton Heights, Belfast BT8 6HA — MB BCh BAO 1989 Belf.; MRCPath 1994. (Qu. Univ. Belf.)

MCMANUS, David Kenneth Cleland Park Surgery, 2 Cleland Park, Bangor BT20 3EB; 38 Deanfield, Bangor BT19 6NX — MB BCh BAO 1982 Belf.; MRCGP 1986; DRCOG 1985. (Qu. Univ. Belf.) Med. Off. Motorcycle Union of Irel.; Med. Off. (A & E) Ulster Hosp. Dundonald; Mem. Med. Advis. Panel to N.. Irel. Ambul. Serv.; Vice-Pres. Internat. Med. Panel (CMI) Federat. InterNat.e Motocycliste. Socs: Brit. Assn. of Immed. Care Schemes.

MCMANUS, Eileen Maura High Street Surgery, 48 High Street, Chalgrove, Oxford OX44 7SS Tel: 01865 890760 Fax: 01865 400226; Willowbeck House, Berrick Salone, Wallingford OX10 6JD — MB ChB 1987 Dundee; MRCGP 1992; DRCOG 1991; DTM & H Liverp. 1990; DCH RCP Lond. 1989. Prev: Trainee GP Oxf. VTS; Health UnLtd. Work S.. Sudan; Relief Fund for Romania.

MCMANUS, Francis Bernard Rex Duchess of Kent's Psychiatric Hospital, Horne Road, Catterick Garrison DL9 4DF Tel: 01748 873612 Email: elizhouse@osca.gov.uk — MB BS 1976 Lond.; MRCPsych 1983. (Royal Free Hospital) Director of Defence Psychiat.; Hosp. Cdr DKPH Catterick; Med. Mem. Pens. Appeal Tribunals. Prev: Cons. Psychiat. Psychiat. Centre, P.ss Alexandra Hosp. RAF Wroughton.; Tri-Serv. Director of Community Psychiat.; Cons. in Community Psychiat. RAG Coll. Cranwell.

MCMANUS, Professor Ian Christopher University College London, Gower Street, London WC1E 6BT Tel: 020 76795390 Fax: 020 74364276 Email: i.mcmanus@ucl.ac.uk; 43 Kelvin Road, Highbury, London N5 2PR — MB ChB 1975 Birm.; 1972 BA Camb.; PhD Camb. 1979; MD Lond. 1985; FRCP Lond. 1998. (Birmingham) Prof. Psychol. & Med. Educat. Univ. Coll. Lond. Prev: Prof. Psych. Imperial Coll. Sch. Med. at St Mary's Hosp. Lond.

MCMANUS, Joanne 11 Piney Hills, Belfast BT9 5NR — MB BCh BAO 1988 Belf.

MCMANUS, John Brendan Weavers Medical Centre, 50 School Lane, Kettering NN16 0DH Tel: 01536 513494 Fax: 01536 416521; 7 Headlands, Kettering, Kettering NN15 7ER Tel: 01536 515058 Email: mcmanus@nildram.co.uk — MB BS 1990 Lond.; DRCOG 1994; MRCGP 1998.

MCMANUS, Kathleen Mary (retired) c/o Lloyds Bank, 125 Balham High Road, London SW12 9AT — LRCPI & LM, LRSCI & LM 1952; LRCPI & LM, LRCSI & LM 1952.

MACMANUS, Michael Patrick Northern Ireland Centre of Clinical Oncology, Belvoir Park Hospital, Hospital Road, Belfast BT8 8JR Tel: 01232 491942; 5 Coolnasilla Avenue, Belfast BT11 8LD — MB BCh BAO Belf. 1983; MD Belf. 1989; MRCP (UK) 1986; FRCR 1993; FFR RCSI 1993. Regist. (Radiother. & Oncol.) N. Irel. Radiother. Centre.

MACMANUS, Niall Leonard Manus (retired) 83 Oliver's Battery Road S., Winchester SO22 4JQ — MRCS Eng. LRCP Lond. 1944. Prev: Cas. Off. St. John's Hosp. Lewisham & Gravesend & N. Kent Hosp.

MCMANUS, Orla Bernadette 85 Layde Road, Cushendall, Ballymena BT44 0NH — BM 1998 Soton.; BM Soton 1998.

MCMANUS, Richard James Magnus 21 Ridley Road, London NW10 5UB — MB BS 1991 Lond.

MCMANUS, Terence Edward Carrick House, Carrickmacusker, Lisnaskea, Enniskillen BT92 5EH — MB BCh BAO 1997 Belf.

MCMANUS, Thomas Joseph Department of Genitourinary Medicine, King's College Hospital, London SE5 Tel: 020 7346 3470; 142 Culford Road, London N1 4HU — MB ChB 1972 Glas.; FRCOG 1992, M 1977. Cons. Dir. (Genitourin. Phys.) King's Coll. Hosp. Lond. Socs: (Sec.) Soc. Study VD. Prev: Sen. Regist. (Genitourin. Med.) St. Mary's Hosp. Lond.

MCMANUS, Winifred Helen 10 Westcott Road, South Shields NE34 0QZ — MB ChB 1981 Manch.

MCMASTER, Albert Brian Malcolm (retired) Penn Hill Surgery, St. Nicholas Close, Yeovil BA20 1SB — BM BCh 1958 Oxf.; Cert G.A.M 1976; FRCP 1998; MRCP Lond. 1965. Prev: Ho. Surg. & Ho. Phys. Med. Unit St. Bart. Hosp. Lond.

MCMASTER, Anne Watt 17 Roughan Road, Broughshane, Ballymena BT42 4QX — MB ChB 1997 Ed.

MCMASTER, David Stuart 9 Julian Way, Widnes WA8 9AB Tel: 0151 424 6093 — MB ChB 1989 Liverp.; BSc Liverp. 1986, MB ChB 1989. Trainee GP/SHO Countess of Chester Hosp. VTS.

MACMASTER, Hugh Linden Park, Hawick TD9 8SU Tel: 01450 2550 — MB ChB 1957 Ed.; DObst RCOG 1960. Prev: Ho. Off. Aberd. Matern. Hosp.; Ho. Phys. Edin. Roy. Infirm.; Cas. Ho. Surg. Leith Hosp.

MCMASTER, Ian James Mountsandel Surgery, 4 Mountsandel Road, Coleraine BT52 1JB Tel: 028 7034 2650 Fax: 028 7032 1000 — MB ChB 1972 Ed.; MRCGP 1976; DA Eng. 1979; DRCOG 1976.

MCMASTER, James Ian DHSS, Room C3.13, Castle Buildings, Stormount, Belfast BT4 3PP — MB BCh BAO 1985 Belf.; MRCPsych 1992; Dip. Addic. Behaviour Lond. 1995; DMH Belf. 1990; DRCOG 1987. Med. Off. DHSS N. Irel.

MCMASTER, Mr John Michael 20 Cavendish Crescent N., Flat 3, The Park, Nottingham NG7 1BA Tel: 0115 988 1473; Biomechanics

MCMILLAN

Laboratory, Department of Orthopaedic and Accident Surgery, Queen's Medical Centre, Nottingham NG7 2UH Tel: 0115 951 3277 Fax: 0115 951 3278 Email: john.mcmaster@nottingham.ac.uk — MB ChB 1993 Ed.; FRCS (Ed.) 1997. (Univ. of Ed.) Research Fell. (Orthop.) Dept. of Orthop. & Accid. Surg. Univ. of Nottm.

MCMASTER, Mr Michael John Princess Margaret Rose Orthopaedic Hospital, Edinburgh EH10 7ED Tel: 0131 536 4600 Fax: 0131 536 4601; 345 Lanark Road W., Edinburgh EH14 5RS Tel: 0131 449 3133 — MB BCh BAO 1964 Belf.; MD Belf. 1979; FRCS Ed. 1968. (Belf.) Cons. Orthopaedic Spine Surg. Edin. Spinal Deformity Centre P.ss Margt. Rose Orthopaedic Hosp. Edin.; Cons. Orthop. Surg. Roy. Hosp. Sick Child. Edin.; Hon. Sen. Lect. (Orthop.) Univ. Edin. Socs: Fell. BOA; Brit. Scoliosis Soc.; Spine Soc. Of Europe. Prev: Cons. Orthop. Surg. P.ss Margt. Rose Orthop. Hosp. Edin.; Sen. Lect. (Orthop.) Univ. Edin.; Assoc. Cons. Mayo Clinic Rochester, USA.

MCMASTER, Patrick David Bruce Paediatric Intensive Care Unit, City General North Staffordshire Hospital, Newcastle Road, Stoke-on-Trent ST5 6QQ Tel: 01782 715444 Fax: 01782 553851 Email: paddymcmaster@doctors.org.uk; 19 Oaktree Road, Trentham, Stoke-on-Trent ST4 8KF Tel: 01782 641111 Email: paddymcmaster@doctors.org.uk — MB ChB 1989 Bristol; MRCP (UK) 1993. (Bristol Univ.) Cons. (Paediat.) Paediat. Intens. Care N. Staffords. Hosp. Stoke-on-Trent. Prev: Lect. (Paediat.) Port Moresby, Papua New Guinea; Fell. (Paediat. Infect. Dis.) The New Childr.s Hosp. Sydney Aus.; Fell. (Paediat. Infect. Dis.) Roy. Childr.s Hosp. Melb. Aus.

MCMASTER, Mr Paul Queen Elizabeth Hospital (Liver Unit), Edgbaston, Birmingham B15 2TH Tel: 0121 627 2413 Fax: 0121 414 1833; 13 St. Agnes Road, Moseley, Birmingham B13 9PH — MB ChB 1966 Liverp.; MA Camb. 1976; ChM Liverp. 1979, MB ChB 1966; FRCS Eng. 1971. (Liverp.) Cons. Hepatobiliary Surg. & Transpl. Surg. Qu. Eliz. Hosp. Birm.; Vis. Prof. Rome, Geneva, Conception Chile; Pres. Europ. Soc. Organ Transpl., Counsellor Transpl. Soc. Socs: Brit. Transpl. Soc. (Ex.-Pres.).

MCMASTER, Thomas Dumbarton Health Centre, Station Road, Dumbarton G82 1PW Tel: 01389 602633 Fax: 01389 602623 — MB ChB 1981 Glas.; MRCGP 1985; Dip. Pract. Dermat. Wales 1994; DCH RCPS Glas. 1989; DRCOG 1983. (Glas.) Socs: BMA.

MCMASTER, Victoria Jane Bath University, Medical Centre, Quarry House North Road, Bath BA2 7AY Tel: 01225 462395 Fax: 01225 826489 — BM 1985 Soton.; BM Soton 1985. Ships Surg. Roy. Fleet Auxil. Socs: Comm. Anglo-French Med. Soc.

MCMATH, William Kenneth Twining Little Firs Surgery, The Avenue, Ascot SL5 7LY Tel: 01344 882871 Fax: 01344 890254 — MRCS Eng. LRCP Lond. 1965. (Char. Cross) Prev: Regist. (Infec. Dis. & Gen. Med.) W. Hendon Hosp. Lond.; Ho. Phys. (Paediat. & Infec. Dis.) Brook Gen. Hosp. Lond.; Ho. Surg. (Obst.) City of Lond. Matern. Hosp.

MCMECHAN, Stephen Robert 43 Roddens Crescent, Belfast BT5 7JN — MB BCh BAO 1989 Belf.

MCMEEKIN, Barbara Anne 40 Foregate, Fulwood, Preston PR2 8LA — MB ChB 1960 Bristol; DObst RCOG 1963. (Bristol) Clin. Med. Off. (Audiol.) Lancs. AHA. Prev: SHO Med. Llwynypia Hosp. Rhondda; Asst. MOH Mon. CC.

MCMEEKIN, Kate 37 The Drive, Gosforth, Newcastle upon Tyne NE3 4AJ — MB ChB 1993 Glas.

MCMEEKIN, Nigel Hugh Pendleside Medical Pratice, Clitheroe Health Centre, Clitheroe BB7 2JG Tel: 01200 421888 — MB BCh 1991 Wales; MRCGP; DCH. GP Partner. Prev: Asst. GP Pendleside Med. Pract. Clitheroe Lancs.

MCMENAMIN, James Joseph 6 Ewing Court, Hamilton ML3 8UX — MB ChB 1987 Glas.; MRCP (UK) 1990. Regist. (Infec. Dis., Trop. Med., HIV & AIDS) Ruchill Hosp. Glas.

MCMENAMIN, Michelle 37 Woodlands Road, Aigburth, Liverpool L17 0AJ — MB ChB 1991 Liverp.

MCMENEMIE, Fiona Mary Elizabeth 30 Hunters Road, Gosforth, Newcastle upon Tyne NE3 1SE — MB ChB 1990 Ed.

MCMENEMIN, Ian McCulloch Taybank, 60 Colquhoun St., Helensburgh G84 9JN Tel: 01436 673702; Department of Anaesthesia, Western Infirmary, Dumbarton Road, Glasgow G11 6NT Tel: 0141 211 2069 Fax: 0141 211 1806 Email: ianmcm@compuserve.com — MB ChB 1981 Glas.; FFA RCS Eng.

1985. Cons. Anaesth. W.ern Infirm. Glas.; Hon. Sen. Lect. Univ. of Glas.

MCMENEMIN, Lindsay Stewart 9 Carters Place, Irvine KA12 0BU — MB ChB 1986 Glas.

MCMENEMIN, Rhona Margaret Beatson Oncology Centre, Western Infirmary, Glasgow G11 6NT Tel: 0141 211 2000 Fax: 0141 211 6356 Email: rmcmenemin@wght_nhs.org.uk; T/L 32 Woodcroft Avenue, Broomhill, Glasgow G11 7JA — MB ChB 1988 Glas.; MRCPI 1994; MSC Glas. 1999. (Univ. of Glas.)

MCMENEMY, Pauline Louise 65 Moygashel Park, Moygashel, Dungannon BT71 7RN — MB BCh BAO 1993 Belf.

MCMENZIE, Angela Jane Northenden Group Practice, 489 Palatine Road, Manchester M22 4DH Tel: 0161 998 3206 — MRCGP 1997; MB ChB Manch. 1993. Gen. Practitioner.

MCMICHAEL, Andrew James Midsummer Cottage, Church St., Beckley, Oxford OX3 9UT — MB BChir 1969 Camb.; FRS 1992; PhD CNAA 1974; FRCP Lond. 1985; MRCP (UK) 1971. (St. Mary's) MRC Clin. Research Prof. of Immunol. Oxf. Univ. Prev: Lect. (Med.) Oxf. Univ.; Wellcome Sen. Research Fell. Nuffield Dept. Surg. Radcliffe Infirm.; MRC Trav. Fell. Stanford Univ. Calif., USA.

MCMICHAEL, Professor Anthony John Department of Epidemiology and Population Health, London School of Hygiene and Tropical Medicine, Keppel St., London WC1E 7HT Tel: 020 7927 2254 Fax: 020 7580 6897 Email: t.mcmichael@lshtm.ac.uk — MB BS Adelaide 1967; PhD Melbourne 1972; FFPHM RCP (UK) 1996; FRCP (UK) 1997; FAFPHM 1996; F Med. Sci. 1999. Prof. Epidemiol. Lond. Sch. Hyg. & Trop. Med. Prev: Prof. Occupat. & Environm. Health Univ. of Adelaide (S. Australia); Sen. Princip. Research Scientist, Div. Human Nutrit. CSIRO (Australia).

MCMICHAEL, Catherine Margaret Stannary House, Stainland Road, Stainland, Halifax HX4 9HA; The Old Sunday School, Jagger Green, Halifax HX4 9DQ — MB ChB 1980 Sheff.; MRCGP 1986; DRCOG 1985; DCH RCPS Glas. 1984.

MCMICHAEL, Christian Fullerton Yew Tree House, Sunningwell, Abingdon Tel: 01865 739606 — MB ChB 1952 Glas. (Glas.)

MACMICHAEL, Clare Jane Balham Park Surgery, 92 Balham Park Road, London SW12 8EA Tel: 020 8767 8828 Fax: 020 8682 1736 — MB ChB 1988 Bristol; MRCGP 1992.

MACMICHAEL, Florence Hazle Windward, Greenfield Court, Balfron, Glasgow G63 0QG Tel: 0141 40586 — MB ChB 1944 Ed.; DObst RCOG 1948. (Univ. Ed.)

MCMICHAEL, Hugh Bignell (retired) Huntingdon House, Sheepy Road, Sibson, Nuneaton CV13 6LE Tel: 01827 881252 Fax: 01827 881252 — MB BS 1960 Lond.; MD Lond. 1974; FRCP Lond. 1979, M 1963. Hon. Research Fell. (Med.) Univ. Bristol; Mem. Brit. Psychosocial Oncol. Gp. Prev: MacMillan Cons. Sen. Lect. (Palliat. Med.) Univ. Bristol.

MACMICHAEL, Mr Ian Milroy (retired) Bon Air Consulting Rooms, La Rue du Froid Vent,St Saviour, St Helier, Jersey JE2 7LJ Tel: 01534 24847 Fax: 01534 80709 — MB ChB 1964 Ed.; FRCS Ed. 1969; FCOphth 1988; DO Eng. 1968. Exec. Comm. Med. Advis. Bd. Orbis Internat. NY, USA. Prev: Sen. Regist. (Ophth.) Roy. Infirm. Edin.

MCMICHAEL, James Lees Cestria Health Centre, Whitehill Way, Chester-le-Street DH2 3DJ Tel: 0191 388 7771 Fax: 0191 387 1803 — MB ChB 1981 Dundee; MRCGP 1985.

MCMICHAEL, Jane Ford 87 Mossgiel Road, Glasgow G43 2DA — MB ChB 1988 Glas.; MRCGP 1993; DRCOG 1991. Trainee GP/SHO (ENT) Stobhill Hosp. Glas. VTS.

MCMICHEN, Hamish Urquhart Stewart Basuto Medical Centre, 29 Basuto Road, London SW6 4BJ Tel: 020 7736 7557; 2 Bowerdean Street, London SW6 3TW Tel: 020 7736 4912 — MB BS 1972 Lond.; MRCS Eng. LRCP Lond. 1972; MRCGP 1977.

MCMICHEN, Iain Kissock Stewart c/o 2 Bowerdean Street, London SW6 3TW Tel: 020 7736 4912 — MB BS 1976 Lond.; MRCS Eng. LRCP Lond. 1976; DRCOG 1979. (St. Mary's)

MACMILLAN, Mr Alasdair Iain Macaulay 4 Bucklers Wynd, Kellas, Broughty Ferry, Dundee DD5 3TP — MB ChB 1989 Ed.; FRCS Eng. 1995. Specialist Regist. (Gen. Surg.) Tayside. Prev: Research Fell. (Surg.) Univ. of Dundee; SHO (Gen. Surg.) Vict. Hosp. Kirkcaldy; SHO (Gen. Surg.) Sandwell Dist. Gen. Hosp. W. Bromwich.

MCMILLAN, Alexander 29/6 Merchiston Gardens, Edinburgh EH10 5DD Tel: 0131 337 8107 Email: sandy@warts.demon.co.uk

MCMILLAN

— MB ChB 1971 Ed.; MD Ed. 1980; FRCP Lond. 1995; FRCP Ed. 1984; MRCP (UK) 1974. (Univ. Ed.) Cons. Phys. (Genitourin. Med.) Lothian HB & Edin. Roy. Infirm.; Sen. Lect. Univ. Edin. Socs: Brit. Soc. Study of Infec.; Med. Soc. Study VD. Prev: Edr. Genitourin. Med.; Sen. Regist. & Ho. Surg. Roy. Infirm. Edin.; Ho. Phys. Raigmore Hosp. Inverness.

MCMILLAN, Alexandra Honor Kirsty 97 Greenwood, Walters Ash, High Wycombe HP14 4XB — MB BS 1990 Lond.; BSc (Pharm.) Lond. 1987; DRCOG 1994; DCH RCP Lond. 1993.

MACMILLAN, Alistair Hamish McGregor, QHP, Brigadier late RAMC c/o Royal Bank of Scotland, 393 Sauchiehall St., Glasgow G2 3ND — MB ChB 1974 Glas.; MFPHM RCP (UK) 1993; MPH Glas. 1993. Cdr. Med. HQ, Land Command; Defence Cons. adviser in Pub. Health. Socs: Fell. Roy. Inst. of Pub. Health.; Fell. Roy. Soc. Of Health; Fell. Roy. Soc. Of Med. Prev: Cdr. (Med.) 1st (UK) Armoured Div.; Chief of Staff Army Med. Directorate; Dep. Asst. Chief of Staff (Med.) Permanent Jt. HQ.

MCMILLAN, Andrew Kenneth Dept. Of Haematology, Nottingham City Hospital, Hucknall Road, Nottingham NG5 1PB Tel: 0115 969 1169 Email: amcmilla@ncht.trent.nhs.uk — MB BS 1983 Lond.; FRCP 2000; PhD Lond. 1995; MA Camb. 1984; MRCP (UK) 1986; MRCPath 1994. (St. Thos.) Cons. Haemat. Nottm. City Hosp. Prev: Cons. Haemat. Mt. Vernon & Watford Hosps. NHS Trust & Sen. Lect. Univ. Coll. Lond.; Sen. Regist. (Haemat.) Roy. Free Hosp. Lond.; Clin. Lect. & Hon. Sen. Regist. (Clin. Haemat.) Univ. Coll. & Middlx. Sch. Med. Univ. Coll. Lond.

MACMILLAN, Angus Leith (retired) Trethewey, Foxes Lane, Mousehole, Penzance TR19 6QQ Tel: 01736 731343 — BM BCh 1958 Oxf.; MA Oxf.; BSc 1959 Oxf.; FRCP Lond. 1988, M 1965. Prev: Cons. Dermat. S.end Hosp.

MCMILLAN, Ann Edwards Dyfed Road Health Centre, Dyfed Road, Neath SA11 3AP Tel: 01639 635331 Fax: 01639 641016; 86 Cimla Road, Neath SA11 3TS Tel: 01639 637731 — MB BCh 1974 Wales; MRCGP 1978; DRCOG 1977.

MCMILLAN, Avril Christina Maryhill Health Centre, 41 Shawpark Street, Glasgow G20 9DR Tel: 0141 531 8897 Fax: 0141 531 8863 — MB ChB 1972 Glas.; MRCGP 1987; DObst RCOG 1974.

MCMILLAN, Carol Sarah Agnes 74 Main Street, Leuchars, St Andrews KY16 0HE Tel: 01382 660111 Email: csmacmillan@doctors.org — MB ChB 1991 Dundee; Diploma in Intensive Care Medicine 2201; MRCP (UK) 1994; FRCA 1997. Specialist Regist. (Anaesth.) Ninewells Hosp. Dundee; Lect.

MCMILLAN, Catherine Flat 2/2, 21 Cartha St., Glasgow G41 3HH — MB ChB 1991 Glas.

MCMILLAN, Craig Howard Department of Clinical Oncology, The General Hospital, Northampton NN1 5BD Tel: 01604 545225 Fax: 01604 545225 — MB ChB 1981 Leeds; FRCP 1999; MRCP (UK) 1984; FRCR 1988; T(R)(CO) 1991. Cons. Clin. Oncol. N.ampton Gen. Hosp. Prev: Sen. Regist. (Clin. Oncol.) Nottm. Gen. Hosp.; Regist. (Clin. Oncol.) Middlx. & Mt. Vernon Hosp.

MCMILLAN, Cynthia (retired) 7 Beacon Park, Penrith CA11 7UB Tel: 01768 863194 — MB ChB 1950 Leeds; MRCS Eng. LRCP Lond. 1950. Prev: Ho. Off. (Obst.) Staincliffe Gen. Hosp. Dewsbury.

MACMILLAN, Donald John, OBE (retired) Brushwood, 4B Coach House, Springfield Road, Plymstock, Plymouth PL9 8JS Fax: 01752 481021 — MB ChB 1939 Birm. Prev: Temp. Surg. Lt.-Cdr. RNVR.

MCMILLAN, Douglas Middleton Royal Surrey County Hospital, Egerton Road, Guildford GU2 7XX Tel: 01483 571122; Rivendell, 50 Speedwell Close, Merrow Park, Guildford GU4 7HE Tel: 01483 533019 Fax: 01483 533019 — MB BS Lond. 1966; FRCS Eng. 1970; MRCS Eng. LRCP Lond. 1965. (St. Thos.) Assoc. ENT Surg. Roy. Surrey Co. Hosp.

MCMILLAN, Duncan Lindsay 17 Wimpole Street, London W1G 8GB Tel: 020 7631 0914 Fax: 020 7323 9126 Email: 106411.2460@compuserve.com; 41 Primrose Avenue, Enfield EN2 0SZ — MB BCh 1969 Witwatersrand; MRCOG 1977. Cons. O & G Whipps Cross Hosp.; Hon. Sen. Lect. St. Bart. Lond. Socs: Internat. Soc. Gyn. Endoscopy; Eur. Soc. Gyn. Endoscopy.

MCMILLAN, Elizabeth (retired) 27 Bonaly Drive, Colinton, Edinburgh EH13 0HB Tel: 0131 441 4431 — MB ChB 1950 Glas. Prev: Clin. Med. Off. Lothian HB.

MCMILLAN, Elizabeth Joan c/o The Royal Bank of Scotland plc, 231 Bramhall Lane, Stockport SK2 6JF — MB ChB 1993 Liverp.

MACMILLAN, Fergus Noel Central Surgery, King Street, Barton-upon-Humber DN18 5ER Tel: 01652 635435 Fax: 01652 636122; Brown Gables, Westfield Road, Barton-upon-Humber DN18 5AB Tel: 01652 636312 Email: fergusmacmillan@cs.com — MB ChB 1980 Aberd.; MRCGP 1984; DRCOG 1984.

MACMILLAN, Fiona Kathleen 6 Oak Crescent, Eye IP23 7BY — MB ChB 1980 Aberd.

MACMILLAN, Fiona Theresa 16 Pimmcroft Way, Sale M33 2LA Tel: 0161 976 2143 — MB ChB 1990 Manch.; BSc (Hons.) Chem. Manch. 1983; DRCOG 1993.

MCMILLAN, Professor George Harrison Grant, QHP, Surg. Cdr. RN MDG (N), Victory Building, HM Naval Base, Portsmouth PO1 3LS Tel: 02392 727803 Fax: 02392 727805; Alveron, 17 Ashburton Road, Alverstoke, Gosport PO12 2LH Tel: 02392585084 Email: drgrantmcmillan@aol.com — MB ChB Glas. 1969; MSc (Occupat. Med.) Univ. Lond. 1975, MD 1983; FRCP Lond. 1989; FRCP Glas. 1987, M 1980; FFOM RCP Lond. 1986. Dep. Med. Director Gen. (Naval); Adjunct Asst. Prof. Prevent. Med. Uniformed Servs. Univ. Washington DC, USA; Vis. Prof. Occupat. Med. Univ. Bradford. Socs: Fell. Med. Soc. Lond.; Fell. Roy. Soc. Med.; Soc. Occupat. Med. Prev: Med. Off. i/c Inst. of Naval Med.; Dean of Naval Med.; Prof. Naval Occupat. Med.

MACMILLAN, Gordon Sinclair Tel: 01903 882972 — MB ChB 1967 Liverp.; DObst RCOG 1972; DA Eng. 1971. (Liverp.) Clin. Med. Off. (Remote Areas) Ruwais Hosp. Abu Dhabi; Clin. Asst. (Acute Psychiat.) Epsom Gen. Hosp. & W. Pk. Hosp. Epsom. Socs: Sussex Postgrad. Soc.; N.A.N.P; Sussex Obst. Prev: Clin. Director King Kahled Airport Hosp. Riyadh, Saudi Arabia; Resid. (Anaesth.) Guy's Hosp. Lond.; Resid.(Anaesth.) Farnham Hosp.

MCMILLAN, Graham John Smeaton Chigwell Medical Centre, 300 Fencepiece Road, Hainault, Ilford IG6 2TA Tel: 020 8500 0066 Fax: 020 8559 8670 — MB BS 1987 Lond.; DRCOG 1992; T(GP) 1991. (London Hospital Medical College) Prev: Trainee GP/SHO Newham Gen. Hosp. Lond. VTS; Ho. Surg. Chelmsford & Essex & Broomfield Hosp. Chelmsford; Ho. Phys. Broomfield Hosp. Chelmsford.

MCMILLAN, Graham Stuart Flat 2/3, 61 Glenapp St., Pollokshields, Glasgow G41 2NQ — MB ChB 1998 Glas.

MACMILLAN, Iain Macalpine Macrae Ladywell Medical Centre (West), Ladywell Road, Edinburgh EH12 7TB Tel: 0131 334 3602 Fax: 0131 316 4816 — MB ChB 1965 Ed.; FRCGP 1983, M 1971. (Ed.) Fact. Med. Off.; Lect. Edin. Sch. Chiropody. Socs: M-C Soc. Edin. & Edin. Clin. Club.

MCMILLAN, Jacquelyn Flat 1/L, 7 Dolphin Road, Pollokshields, Glasgow G41 4LE Tel: 0141 423 8064 — MB ChB 1987 Glas.; FRCS Ed. 1992; FRCS (Orth.) Ed. 1998.

MCMILLAN, James Alan 91 Cupar Street, Belfast BT13 2LJ Tel: 01232 327613; 125 Castlehill Road, Belfast BT4 3GQ Tel: 01232 760808 — MB BCh BAO 1977 Belf. SCMO (Child Health) E. HB Belf. Socs: Fell. Roy. Coll. Paediat. and Child Health.

MCMILLAN, James Clifford Department of Dermatology, Wing D, Tower Block, City Hospital, Lisburn Road, Belfast BT9 7AB Tel: 02890 263898 Fax: 02890 263898; 14 Inishanier, Whiterock, Newtownards BT23 6SU Tel: 02897 541715 — MB BCh BAO 1978 Belf.; FRCP Ed. 1992, M 1981. Cons. Dermat. Belf. City Hosp.; Consultant Dermatol. Mater Hosp. Belf. Socs: Pres. Irish Assn. Dermat.; Brit. Assn. Dermat. Prev: Brit. Assn. of Dermatol.s Exec. Comm. Mem. and Area Represen. RePub. of Irel.

MCMILLAN, Janet Fiona St. Edwards Hospital, Cheddleton, Leek ST13 7EB Tel: 01538 360421 — MB ChB 1975 Ed.; BSc (Med. Sci.) Ed. 1972, MD 1986; MRCPsych 1979. (Ed.) Cons. Psychiat. St. Edwd.s Hosp. Leek; Sen. Clin. Lect. Univ. Keele. Prev: Sen. Lect. (Psychiat.) Univ. Birm.; Lect. (Psychiat.) Univ. Edin.; Hon. Sen. Regist. N.wick Pk. Hosp.

MCMILLAN, Jennifer Fiona 48 Raith Drive, Kirkcaldy KY2 5NR — MB ChB 1998 Ed.; MB ChB Ed 1998.

MCMILLAN, John Alexander (retired) 14 Old Street, Fareham PO14 3HU — MB BS 1954 Lond.; MRCS Eng. LRCP Lond. 1954; FRCPath 1977, M 1965; DPath Eng. 1959. Prev: Cons. Path. & Cytol. Portsmouth & SE Hants. Health Dist. Path. Serv.

MACMILLAN, John Crichton c/o 41 Jesmond Avenue, Bridge of Don, Aberdeen AB22 8UD — MD 1991 Aberd.; MB ChB 1983; MRCP (UK) 1987. Lect. (Clin. Genetics) Inst. Genetics Univ. Wales Coll. Med. Cardiff.

MCMILLIN

MACMILLAN, John David Roderick Dudley Lane Village Surgery, Dudley Lane, Cramlington NE23 6US Tel: 01670 712821 Fax: 01670 730837; 3 Whitegates, Longhorsley, Morpeth NE65 8UJ — MB ChB 1980 Sheff.; MRCGP 1984; DRCOG 1983; Dip. Practical Dermatology 1999. GP Cramlington, N.d.; Clin. Asst. Dernatology, Roy. Vict. Infirm., Newc. Prev: Course Organiser, E. Cumbria VTS, Cumbld. Infirm., Carlisle.

MCMILLAN, Joseph Hill (retired) 27 Bonaly Drive, Colinton, Edinburgh EH13 0HB Tel: 0131 441 4431 — MB ChB 1949 Ed.; MSc (Comm. Med.) Ed. 1979, MB ChB 1949; FFCM 1986; MFCM 1982. Prev: SCM Lothian Health Bd.

MCMILLAN, Karen 1 Borland Crescent, Eaglesham, Glasgow G76 0JA — MB ChB 1997 Glas.

MCMILLAN, Linda Jean Douglas 5 Woodburn Road, Glasgow G43 2TN Tel: 0141 637 1441 — MB ChB 1978 Glas.; BSc (Hons.) Glas. 1973. Assoc. Specialist (Gyn.) Vict. Infirm. NHS Trust Glas.; Clin. Asst. (Gyn.) Glas. W.ern NHS Trust. Socs: S.. Med. Soc. Glas.; Brit. Menopause Soc. Prev: SCMO Gyn. Ultra Sound Roy. Vict. Infirm. Glas.

MCMILLAN, Margaret Anne Renal Unit, Western Infirmary, Glasgow G11 6NT Tel: 0141 211 2178 Fax: 0141 211 1711; Windyhaugh, South Beach, Troon KA10 6EH — MB ChB 1979 Glas.; MD (Hons.) Glas. 1986; FRCP Glas. 1992; MRCP (UK) 1981. Cons. Nephrol. W.. Infirm. Glas.; Hon. Clin. Sen. Lect. (Med.) Univ. Glas. Prev: Cons. Nephrol. Stobhill Gen. Hosp. Glas.

MACMILLAN, Margaret Gaye Victoria Hospital, Hayfield Road, Kirkcaldy KY2 5AH Tel: 01592 648045 Fax: 0192 647090; 38A Shore Road, Aberdour, Burntisland KY3 0TU Tel: 01383 860056 — MB ChB Ed. 1968; FRCP Ed. 1987; MRCP (UK) 1975. Cons. Paediat. Kirkcaldy Acute Hosps. NHS Trust. Prev: Sen. Regist. (Med. Paediat.) Grampian HB.

MCMILLAN, Mrs Mary (retired) High Trees, Promenade de Verdun, Purley CR8 3LN Tel: 020 8660 4422 — MB ChB 1950 Leeds; MB ChB (Hons.) Leeds 1950; PhD (Biochem.) Leeds 1943, MD (Distinc.) 1957; BPharm Lond. 1941; FRCPath 1972, M 1963. Prev: Cons. Chem. Pathol. Lewisham Gp. Laborat.

MACMILLAN, Mary Adams Bisset (retired) Flat 5, 3 Craigend Park, Edinburgh EH16 5XY Tel: 0131 672 1832 — MB ChB 1955 Aberd.; DObst RCOG 1958; DA Eng. 1958. Prev: (Anaesth.) Perth & Kinross Health Dist.

MCMILLAN, Mrs Maureen Pearson (retired) Flatt Walks Clinic, Whitehaven Tel: 01946 5551 — MB ChB 1956 Manch.

MACMILLAN, Mildred Farnham Medical Centre, 435 Stanhope Road, South Shields NE33 4JE Tel: 0191 455 4748 — MB ChB 1962 Liverp. Prev: Ho. Phys. & Ho. Surg. Roy. S.. Hosp. Liverp.

MCMILLAN, Millicent Iris 10 Clontoncally Road, Carryduff, Belfast BT8 8AG — MB BCh BAO 1976 Belf.; MRCGP 1980; DCH RCPSI 1979; DRCOG 1978.

MACMILLAN, Neil Cameron (retired) Homelands, Pye Alley Lane, Whitstable CT5 3AX Tel: 01227 272549 — MB BChir Camb. 1962; FRCGP 1985, M 1975; DObst RCOG 1963. Prev: GP Tutor Canterbury Postgrad. Centre.

MCMILLAN, Nigel Charles Department of Radiology, Western Infirmary, Glasgow G11 6NT Tel: 0141 211 2218 Fax: 0141 337 3416 Email: n.c.mcmillan@clinmed.gla.ac.uk; 5 Woodburn Road, Glasgow G43 2TN Tel: 0141 637 1441 Email: nigelmcmillan@compuserve.com — MB ChB 1973 Glas.; FRCR 1982; DMRD 1980; MRCP (Glas.) 1995; FRCP (Glas.) 1997. Cons. (Radiol.) W.ern Infirm. & Gartnaval Gen. Hosp. Glas.; Hon. Clin. Sen. Lect. Univ. Glas. Socs: Ordinary Mem. Brit. Inst. Radiol.; Internat. Soc. Magnetic Resonance Med.; Counc. Mem. Roy. Medico-Chirurgical Soc. Glas.

MCMILLAN, Philip John Mid Kent Healthcare Trust, Hermitage Lane, Maidstone ME16 9; Saddlehurst Farm, Tenterden Road, Cranbrook TN17 3PB Tel: 01580 715336 — MB BS 1976 Lond.; FRCR 1985. Cons. Radiol. Mid Kent Trust. Prev: Cons. Radiol. Nottm. HA.

MCMILLAN, Rhona Margaret Incle Street Surgery, 8 Incle Street, Paisley PA1 1HR Tel: 0141 889 8809 Fax: 0141 849 1474 Email: rhona.mcmillan@gp87471.ac-hb.scot.nhs.uk; 6 Woodland Avenue, Paisley PA2 8BH Tel: 0141 884 8525 — MB ChB 1984 Glas.; MRCGP 1988; DRCOG 1986. Princip. in Gen. Pract.; Assoc. Adviser CD Dept. of PG Med. Glasow Univ. Prev: Clin. Asst. Asthma Clinic Paisley.

MACMILLAN, Robert Douglas 8 Beaumont Avenue, Southwell NG25 0BB — MB ChB 1988 Glas.; FRCS Glas. 1994. Lect. (Surg.) Univ. Nottm.

MACMILLAN, Robert Macaulay 23 Overnewton Square, Glasgow G3 8RW — MB ChB 1994 Glas.; BSc (Hons.) Glas. 1991. Cas. Off. (A & E) Stirling Roy. Infirm.

MACMILLAN, Robin Reid Jesmond, 3 Albany Avenue, Eccleston Park, Prescot L34 2QN Tel: 0151 426 6134 Fax: 0151 426 9505 — MB ChB 1974 Dundee; BSc St. And. 1972; FFA RCS Eng. 1980. Cons. Anaesth. & Intens. Care St. Helens & Knowsley Hosps. NHS Trust & Whiston Hosp. Prescot; Exec. Med. Dir. St. Helens & Knowsley NHS Trust; Europ. Dip. IC Med. 1990. Socs: Eur. Soc. Intens. Care Med.; (Treas.) Assn. Merseyside Intens. Care Units; UK & Europ. Intens. Care Socs. Prev: Sen. Regist. Rotat. (Anaesth.) Mersey Region; Sen. Resid. Med. Off. Long Reach, Qu.sland, Austral.

MCMILLAN, Ruth Lorraine 10 Portstewart Road, Portrush BT56 8EQ — MB BCh BAO 1997 Belf.

MCMILLAN, Sarah Anne Firrhill Medical Centre, 167 Colinton Mains Drive, Edinburgh EH13 9AF Tel: 0131 441 3119 Fax: 0131 441 4122; 13 Cluny Avenue, Edinburgh EH10 4RN — MB ChB 1984 Ed.; MRCGP 1989; DRCOG 1988. (Edin.) Princip. GP Firrhill Med. Centre Edin.

MACMILLAN, Stuart James East Lynne Medical Centre, 3-5 Wellesley Road, Clacton-on-Sea CO15 3PP Tel: 01255 220010 Fax: 01255 476350; 77 Holland Road, Clacton-on-Sea CO15 6EU — MB ChB 1981 Glas.; DRCOG 1983.

MACMILLAN, Susan Jane Sinclair 15 Pitstruan Place, Aberdeen AB10 6PQ — MB ChB 1991 Aberd.; MRCOG 1996.

MACMILLAN, Suzanne Burns Flat 1, 38 Broomhill Drive, Glasgow G11 7AA Tel: 0141 357 2061 — MB ChB 1994 Glas. SHO (Anaesth.) Monklands Dist. Gen. Hosp. Airdrie.

MACMILLAN, Sylvia Irene Ethel (retired) The Old Port House, Layer-de-la-Haye, Colchester — MB BS 1941 Lond.; MRCS Eng. LRCP Lond. 1941; DPH Lond. 1947. Prev: SCMO Colchester Health Dist.

MCMILLAN, Thomas Mowbray Colinton Surgery, 296B Colinton Road, Edinburgh EH13 0LB Tel: 0131 441 4555 Fax: 0131 441 3963; 18A Merchiston Park, Edinburgh EH10 4PN — MB ChB 1980 Ed.; BSc (Med. Sci.) 1977; MRCGP 1984; DRCOG 1984.

MCMILLEN, George Victor Jordanthorpe Farm, Norton, Sheffield S8 8JR Tel: 0114 237 2138 — MB BCh BAO Belf. 1948. (Belf.) Prev: Ho. Phys. Bootle Gen. Hosp. Liverp.

MCMILLEN, Helen Kathleen Community Paediatrics and Child Health, Holywood Arches Health Centre, Westminster Avenue N., Belfast BT4 1NS Tel: 01232 563373 Fax: 01232 563327; 11 Glenariff Drive, Comber, Newtownards BT23 5HA — MB BCh BAO Belf. 1970; DCH RCPS Glas. 1972. SCMO (Community Paediat. & Child Health) S & E. Belf. Health & Social Servs. Trust. Socs: BMA; Assoc. Mem. BPA; Ulster Paediat. Soc.

MCMILLEN, Julie Elizabeth 91 Harpers Lane, Smithills, Bolton BL1 6HU — MB ChB 1982 Manch.

MCMILLEN, Robert McClelland United Hospitals Health & Social Services Trust, Antrim Hospital, 45 Bush Road, Antrim BT41 2RL Tel: 028 9442 4280 Fax: 028 9442 4195 Email: robert.mcmillen@uh.n-i.nhs.co.uk; 19 Straid Road, Ballyclare BT39 9PY Tel: 028 9335 2390 Email: rmccmcm@aol.com — MB BCh BAO 1975 Belf.; MB BCh (2nd cl. Hons.) Belf. 1975; MPhil Belf. 1993; FRCOG 1993, M 1980, D 1977; DCH RCPSI 1981. (Qu. Univ. Belf.) Cons. O & G Antrim Hosp.; Dir. of Wom. & Child Health United Hosps. Trust Antrim. Socs: Fell. Ulster Med. Soc.; N. Irel. Medico-Legal Soc. Prev: Cons. O & G Moyle Hosp. Larne; Cons. Gyn. Whiteabbey Hosp.; Sen. Regist. & Regist. (O & G) N.. Health & Social Servs. Bd.

MCMILLIN, William Patrick Castlereagh Medical Centre, 220 Knock Road, Belfast BT5 6QF Tel: 028 9079 8308 Fax: 028 9040 3776; Hillcrest, 47 Lisnabreeny Road E., Castlereagh, Belfast BT6 9SS Tel: 01232 448559 Fax: 01232 448559 — MB BCh BAO Belf. 1954; LFOM RCPI 1979; FRCGP 1984, M 1963. (Belf.) Mem. Gen. Pract. Comm. (NI); Med. Off. Brit. Oxygen Company. Socs: Brit. Med. Acupunct. Soc.; BMA; Ulster Med. Soc. Prev: Chairman GMSc (NI) 1986-97; Vice-Chairm. BMA Counc. N. Irel.; Dep. Indust. Med. Off. Belf. Corpn.

MCMINN

MCMINN, Anna Maria Clara 58 Newick Road, Lower Clapton, London E5 0RR Tel: 01442 833380 Fax: 020 8986 2894 — MB BS 1974 Lond.; BSc Biochem. (Hons.) Lond. 1971; MRCP (UK) 1979; MRCS Eng. LRCP Lond. 1974. (Roy. Free) Dir. Archway Developm. & Consultancy Ltd; Pract. Manager: Archway Surg. Socs: Biochem. Soc.; Roy. Coll. Phys. (Lond.). Prev: GP Fund Holding Manager Allum Pract. Lond.; Regist. (Gen. Med.) Whipps Cross Hosp. Lond.; SHO (Nephrol.) St. Bart. Hosp. Lond.

MCMINN, Charles Scott The Health Centre, Wardlaw Way, Oakley, Dunfermline KY12 9QH Tel: 01383 850212 — MB ChB 1982 Glasgow. (Glasgow) GP Dunfermline, Fife.

MCMINN, David Joseph Stewart 179 Ballysnod Road, Larne BT40 3NN — MB ChB 1997 Dundee.

MCMINN, Mr Derek James Wallace Calcot Farm, Calcot Hill, Clent, Stourbridge DY9 9RX Tel: 01562 710817 Fax: 01562 710825 — MB BS 1977 Lond.; MRCS Eng. LRCP Lond. 1977; FRCS Eng. 1981; FRCS Ed. 1981. (St. Thos.) Cons. Orthop. Surg. Birm. Nuffield Hosp.; Edit. Bd. Hip Internat. Jl. Socs: Fell. BOA; (Sec.) Brit. Hip Soc.; Brit. Orthop. Research Soc. Prev: Med. Dir. Roy. Orthop. Hosp. Birm.; Cons. Orthop. Surg. Roy. Orthop. Hosp. & City Hosp. Birm.

MCMINN, Frank James (retired) 92 Handsworth Wood Road, Birmingham B20 2PL — MB ChB 1956 Ed.

MCMINN, Jeremy Bruce The Old Stables, Eaton-on-Tern, Market Drayton TF9 2BX Tel: 01952 541645 — MB BS 1992 Newc. SHO (A & E & Psychiat.) Jas. Paget Hosp. Socs: BMA & Med. Protec. Soc. Prev: Ho. Off. (Surg.) Newc. Gen. Hosp.; Ho. Phys. (Med.) Sunderland Dist. Gen. Hosp.

MCMINN, Louise Dumbledore Surgery, High Street, Haywards Heath RH17 6BN — MB ChB 1984 Glas.; DRCOG 1986.

MCMINN, Margaret Grieve (retired) Achnafuaran, Ardfern, Lochgilphead PA31 8QN Tel: 01852 500274 — MB ChB; MB ChB Glas. 1946; DA Eng. 1968. Prev: Clin. Asst. (Anaesth.) S. W. Thames RHA.

MCMINN, Margaret Rose Alder Hey Childrens Hospital, Eaton Road, Liverpool L12 Tel: 0151 228 4811; 11 Fawley Road, Liverpool L18 9TE Tel: 0151 724 4896 — MB BS 1960 Lond.; MRCS Eng. LRCP Lond. 1960. (Roy. Free) SCMO Liverp. AHA. Prev: Clin. Med. Off. Essex AHA; Med. Off. Dept. Matern. & Child Health Rabaul Terr., Papua New Guinea.

MCMINN, Marion Elizabeth 4 Park Rise, Leatherhead KT22 7HZ — MB BS 1974 Lond.; BSc Lond. 1971; MRCS Eng. LRCP Lond. 1974. (Westm.)

MCMINN, Melanie Jane Calcot Farm, Calcot Hill, Clent, Stourbridge DY9 9RX — MB ChB 1976 Birm.; FRCS Eng. 1982; FRCR 1986. Cons. Radiol. Dudley Rd. Hosp. Birm.; Dir. BrE. Screening Serv. W. N. & E. Birm. HAs.

MCMINN, Professor Robert Matthew Hay (retired) Achnafuaran, Ardfern, Lochgilphead PA31 8QN Tel: 01852 500274 — MB ChB Glas. 1947; PhD Sheff. 1956; MD (Commend.) Glas. 1958; FRCS Eng. 1978; MB ChB 1947 Glasgow. Prev: Sir William Collins Prof. Anat. RCS Eng.

MCMINN, Simon Gregor Erskine Yorkleigh Surgery, 93 St. Georges Road, Cheltenham GL50 3ED Tel: 01242 519049 Fax: 01242 253556 — MB BS 1968 Lond.; MRCS Eng. LRCP Lond. 1968; MRCGP 1974. (St. Thos.) Partner (Princip.) in GP. Socs: Bristol Medico-Historical Soc.; Fell. Roy. soc. Med. Prev: Ho. Phys. Lister Hosp. Hitchin; Ho. Surg. Worthing Hosp.; Jun. Med. Off. (O & G) RAF Hosp. Nocton Hall.

MCMINN, Stephen Alexander Bangor Health Centre, Newtownards Road, Bangor BT20 4LD Tel: 028 9146 9111; 40 Bryansglen Avenue, Bangor BT20 3RU — MB BCh BAO 1981 Belf.; MRCGP 1986; DRCOG 1985.

MCMINN, Timothy Gavin The Surgery, 20 Sackville Road, Hove BN3 3FF Tel: 01273 778585/736030 Fax: 01273 724648; Flat 2, 53 The Drive, Hove BN3 3PF — MB BS 1986 Lond.; MRCGP 1991; DRCOG 1991. Prev: Trainee GP E.bourne VTS.

MACMONAGLE, Patrick Joseph 128 Wolseley Road, Rugeley WS15 2ET Tel: 01889 582418 — MB BCh BAO 1944 NUI. (Univ. Coll. Dub.)

MCMONAGLE, Thomas Michael Mario Gwynedd Hospital, Hergest Unit, Bangor LL57 2PW Tel: 01248 384384 — MB BCh BAO 1990 NUI. Regist. (Psychiat.) Gwynedd Community Health Trust Bangor.

MCMORDIE, Eveline Alice Maud (retired) 127 Knock Road, Belfast BT5 6LG — MB BCh BAO 1929 Belf.; DPH 1939. SCMO (Pub. Health) Belf.

MCMORDIE, Hilary Christine c/o Healthcall, 152 London Road, Leicester LE2 1ND Tel: 0116 255 3387; Drumhillery, 10 Wexford Close, Oadby Grange, Leicester LE2 4TE — MB BCh BAO 1981 Belf.; Cert. Family Plann. JCC 1988; Cert. Prescribed Equiv. Exp. JCPTGP 1986; DRCOG 1984. Socs: Assoc. Mem. RCGP; MPS; BMA.

MACMORLAND, Lesley Ann Bredon Hill Surgery, Kemerton Road, Bredon, Tewkesbury GL20 7QN Tel: 01684 73444; 8 The Dell, Bredon, Tewkesbury GL20 7QP — MB BS 1982 Lond.; DRCOG 1988; DA (UK) 1985.

MACMORLAND, Timothy David Lamont The Bredon Hill Surgery, Kemerton Road, Bredon, Tewkesbury GL20 7QN Tel: 01684 73444; 8 The Dell, Bredon, Tewkesbury GL20 7QP — MB BS 1983 Lond.; BSc (Hons.) Sussex 1977; MRCGP 1988; DRCOG 1987; DCH RCP Lond. 1985.

MCMORRAN, James Philip 27 Sidelands Road, Stratford-upon-Avon CV37 9DT — BM BCh 1993 Oxf.

MCMORRAN, Pamela Mary (retired) 4 George Street, Thurso KW14 7JG Tel: 01847 893396 — MB BS 1952 Lond.; MRCS Eng. LRCP Lond. 1951.

MCMORRAN, Stewart Hamish 27 Sidelands Road, Stratford-upon-Avon CV37 9DT — BChir 1994 Camb.

***MCMORRIS, Ewan Leslie James** Ealing Hospital, Uxbridge Road, Southall UB1 3HW — MB BS 1997 Lond.

MCMORRIS, Sheilah Alexander Child & Family Clinic, 83 Blair Road, Coatbridge ML5 2EP Tel: 01236 422663; 9 Garngaber Avenue, Lenzie, Glasgow G66 4LJ Tel: 0141 776 1247 — MB ChB Ed. 1963; MRCPsych 1977; DCH RCPS Glas. 1968; DObst RCOG 1965. (Ed.) Cons. Child Psychiat. Lanarksh. HB. Socs: BMA. Prev: Sen. Regist. (Child Psychiat.) & Regist. (Paediat.) Roy. Hosp. Sick Childr. Glas.; Regist. (Neonat. Paediat.) Glas. Roy. Matern. Hosp.

MCMORROW, John Francis Paul (retired) 26 Kilmorie Road, Cannock WS11 1HZ Tel: 0154 35 574574 — MB BCh BAO 1952 NUI. Prev: Ho. Surg. & Ho. Phys. Tyrone Co. Hosp. Omagh.

MCMORROW, Susannah Marie c/o Mortimer Market Centre, London WC1E 6JB — MB BS 1990 Lond.

MCMULLAN, Andrew Daniel Verney Close Family Practice, Verney Close, Buckingham MK18 1JP Tel: 01280 822777 Fax: 01280 823541 — MB ChB 1990 Dundee. Prev: Trainee GP/SHO (A & E & Geriat.) Perth Roy. Infirm. VTS.

MCMULLAN, Catherine Anne High Clandon N., East Clandon, Guildford GU4 7RP — MB ChB 1975 Bristol; BSc Bristol 1971, MB ChB 1975.

MCMULLAN, Eamon Anthony Omagh Health Centre, Mountjoy Road, Omagh BT79 7BA Tel: 028 8224 3521; 116 Dublin Road, Omagh BT78 1TU — MB BCh BAO 1987 NUI; DObst RCPI 1990.

MCMULLAN, Francis Hugh The Health Centre, Omagh BT79 7BA Tel: 01662 3521; 2 Lissan View, Omagh BT78 1TR — MB BCh BAO 1942 Belf. (Qu. Univ. Belf.)

MCMULLAN, James Edward Tynan Surgery, 15 Dartan Ree, Tynan, Armagh BT60 4QT Tel: 028 3756 8214 Fax: 028 3756 8837; 232 Garron Road, Waterfoot, Glenariffe, Ballymena BT44 0RB — MB BCh BAO 1991 Belf.; MB BCh Belf. 1991; MRCGP (Ed.) 1995; DRCOG 1993.

MCMULLAN, Jeanine Suzanne 52 Oaklea Avenue, Hoole, Chester CH2 3RE — MB ChB 1997 Liverp.

MCMULLAN, John Joseph, RD (retired) 43 Whielden Street, Amersham HP7 0HU Tel: 01494 726842 — MB BChir 1951 Camb.; MD Camb. 1957; FRCGP 1978, M 1968; DIH Eng. 1965. Prev: Civil Med. Pract. (Occupat. Health) Civil Serv. Dept. RAF HQ Strike Command.

MCMULLAN, Martin Joseph Carrick Hill Medical Centre, 1 Carrick Hill, Belfast BT1 2JR Tel: 028 9043 973; 118 Saintfield Road, Lisburn BT27 5PG Tel: 01232 627643 — MB BCh BAO 1986 Belf.; MRCGP 1992; DRCOG 1991; DMH Belf. 1989. Prev: Trainee GP Stockport; Med. Supt. Palm Is. Qu.sland, Austral.

MCMULLAN, Michael George 232 Garron Road, Glenariffe, Ballymena BT44 0RB — MB BCh BAO 1995 Belf.

MCMULLAN, Neville James 85 Old Galgorm Road, Ballymena BT42 1DQ; 5 Old Mill Close, Dundonald, Belfast BT16 1WA — MB BCh 1998 Belf.; MB BCh Belf 1998.

MCMULLAN, Mr Patrick John de Ville c/o Department of Neurosurgery, The Queen Elizabeth Hospital, Birmingham; 55 Meadway, London NW11 6PP Tel: 020 8455 7280 — MB BChir 1991 Camb.; MA Camb. 1990; FRCS Ed. 1994. Career Regist. Rotat. (Neurosurg.) Birm.

MCMULLAN, Peter Francis 4 Church Avenue, Carrduff, Belfast BT8 8DU — MB BCh BAO 1973 Belf.; MRCOG 1978, DObst 1976.

MCMULLAN, Ronan 9 The Quay, Strangford, Downpatrick BT30 7NH — MB BCh 1998 Belf.; MB BCh Belf 1998.

MCMULLAN, Tristan Francis Wallace Elm Cottage, Station Road, Goring, Reading RG8 9HA — BChir 1994 Camb.; MA 1997; MB 1995; MRCOPHTH parts I & II. (Addenbrooke's) SHO (Ophth.) Salisbury Dist. Hosp. Salisbury.

MCMULLEN, Brian John 2 Burnside, Kinloss, Forres IV36 3XL — MB ChB 1975 Ed.; MRCGP 1979; DRCOG 1978.

MCMULLEN, Mr David John Sandown Medical Centre, Melville Street, Sandown PO36 8LD Tel: 01983 402464 Fax: 01983 405781 — MB 1974 Camb.; BChir 1973; FRCS Eng. 1978.

MCMULLEN, Elizabeth Anne 22 Rosemary Park, Belfast BT9 6RG — MB BCh BAO 1993 Belf.

MCMULLEN, Mr Hugh Lister (retired) Little Chestnuts, 15 Holland Road, Frinton-on-Sea CO13 9DH Tel: 01255 676771 — MB BChir 1942 Camb.; BA Camb. 1938; FRCS Eng. 1943; MRCS Eng. LRCP Lond. 1941. Prev: Cons. Orthop. Surg. Vict. Hosp. Worksop & Assoc. Hosps.

MCMULLEN, Ian Douglas Halliburton Len Valley Practice, Tithe Yard, Church Square, Lenham, Maidstone ME17 2PJ Tel: 01622 858341 Fax: 01622 859659; Gloucester House, Dully Hill, Doddington, Sittingbourne ME9 0BY Tel: 01795 886134 — MB BS 1968 Lond.; MRCGP 1977; DObst RCOG 1970. (Middlx.) Prev: Ho. Surg. Middlx. Hosp. Lond.

MCMULLEN, John Victor Gilford Health Centre, Castleview, Gilford BT63 6JS Tel: 028 831225; 1A Monroe Avenue, Lurgan, Craigavon BT66 7BR — MB BCh BAO 1978 Belf.; MRCGP 1983; DRCOG 1982.

MCMULLEN, Kathleen Wendy Dept. of Obstetrics & Gynaecol., Stirling Royal Infirmary, Livilands, Stirling FR8 2AU — MB BS 1984 Lond.; FRCS Eng. 1990; FRCS Ed. 1990; MRCOG 1992. (Middlx. Hosp. Lond.) Cons. O & G Stirling Roy. Infirm. Prev: Sen. Regist (O & G) Edin. Roy. Infirm.

MCMULLIN, Geoffrey Peter (retired) Yew Tree Plat, German St., Winchelsea TN36 4EN Tel: 01797 226315 Fax: 0179 227837 — MB ChB 1960 Ed.; FRCP Lond. 1983, M 1967. Prev: Cons. Paediat. Warrington & Halton Health Dists.

MCMULLIN, Mary Frances Department Haematology, Institute of Clinical Science, Queens University of Belfast, Royal Victoria Hospital, Grosvenor Road, Belfast BT12 6BA Tel: 01232 240503 Fax: 01232 325272 Email: m.mcmullin@qub.ac.uk; 44 Crofthill, Cairnshill Road, Belfast BT8 6GX Tel: 01232 402607 — MD 1987 Belf.; MB BCh BAO 1980; MRCP (UK) 1983; MRCPath. 1988. Cons. Haemat. Roy. Hosp. Trust Belf.; Sen. Lect. (Haemat.) Qu. Univ. Belf. Socs: Fell. Roy. Coll. Phys. Edin.; Fell. Roy. Coll. Path.; Fell. Roy. Coll. Phys. Irel. Prev: Sen. Regist. Hammersmith Hosp. Lond.; Sen. Regist. Roy. Vict. Hosp. Belf.

MCMURDO, Lydia (retired) c/o Sherrington, 48 The Street, Old Costessey, Norwich NR8 5DD — MRCS Eng. LRCP Lond. 1941; MFPHM 1974; DPH Manch. 1960. Prev: Sen. Med. Off. Norf. AHA.

MCMURDO, Professor Marion Elizabeth Taylor Ageing & Health, Department of Medicine, Ninewells Hospital, Dundee DD1 9SY Tel: 01382 660111 Fax: 01382 660675 Email: m.e.t.mcmurdo@dundee.ac.uk; 13 Rockfield Crescent, Dundee DD2 1JF — MB ChB 1980 Dundee; CBiol FIBiol; FRCP London 2000; MD Dundee 1988; FRCP Ed. 1992; MRCP (UK) 1984; FRCP Glas. 1997. Prof. (Ageing & Health) Univ. Dundee; Hon. Cons. Med. For the Elderly Primary Healthcare Trust. Socs: Brit. Geriat. Soc.; Brit. Pharm. Soc.; African Gerontological Soc. Prev: READER (Ageing & Health Med.) Univ. Dundee.

MCMURRAY, Mr Arthur Hamilton 27 Bally Grainey Road, Holywood BT18 0HE Tel: 01232 428234 — MB BCh BAO 1973 Belf.; FRCS Ed. 1977; BDS (Belf.) 1968. Cons. Surg. Antrim Area Hosp. Socs: Assn. Surg.; Ulster Med. Soc. Prev: Regist. Groote Schuur Hosp. Cape Town, S. Afr.

MCMURRAY, David Anthony 2/L 253 Garrioch Road, North Kelvinside, Glasgow G20 8PQ Tel: 0141 946 2395 — MB BCh BAO 1992 Belf.; MRCOG 1998. Specialist Regist. (Ostetrics & Gyn.) Roy. Alexandra Hosp. Paisley. Prev: Specialist Regist. (O & G) S.ern Gen. Hosp. Glas.; Clin. Research Fell. (Med.) W.ern Gen. Hosp. Edin.; Regist. (O & G) Bellshill Hosp. Glas.

MCMURRAY, David Henry Mark 178 Stainbeck Lane, Leeds LS7 2EA — MB ChB 1998 Dund.

MCMURRAY, Hazel Rosemary 9 Winchester Avenue, Sheffield S10 4EA — MB BCh 1989 Wales.

MCMURRAY, John Health Needs, 110 High Road W., Felixstowe IP11 9AD Tel: 01394 270493 Fax: 01394 277881; 110 High Road W., Felixstowe IP11 9AD Tel: 01394 270493 Fax: 01394 277881 — MB BCh BAO 1986 Belf.; DGM RCP Lond. 1991; DRCOG 1991. (Queens University) Private GP; Sen. Med. Off. Communityu Drugs Team E. Suff.

MCMURRAY, Professor John Joseph Valentine Western Infirmary, Glasgow G11 6NT Tel: 0141 330 6588 Fax: 0141 330 6588 Email: j.mcmurray@bio.gla.ac.uk; 5 Thorn Drive, Bearsden, Glasgow G61 4PS Tel: 0141 942 2724 Fax: 0141 942 6858 — MB ChB 1983 Manch.; MB ChB (Hons.) Manch. 1983; BSc (Hons.) Manch. 1980, MD 1990; FRCP Glas. 1996; MRCP (UK) 1986; FESC 1996. (Univ. Manch.) Prof. of Med. Cardiol., Univ. Glas.; Hon. Cons. Cardiol., W.ern Infirm., Glas. Socs: Brit. Cardiac Soc.; Fell. Europ. Soc. Cardiol.; Fell. Amer. Coll. Cardiol. Prev: Cons. Cardiol. W.. Gen. Hosp. Edin.; Regist. (Cardiol.) W.. Infirm. Glas.; SHO (Med.) Roy. Infirm. Edin.

MCMURRAY, Paul Constantine 32 Caird Gardens, Hamilton ML3 0AT — MB ChB 1981 Glas.; FFA RCSI 1987.

MCMURRAY, Raymond Grant Lower Brook Street Surgery, 6 Lower Brook Street, Oswestry SY11 2HJ Tel: 01691 655844 Fax: 01691 671864; 8 Lower Hafor, Oswestry SY11 1UX — MB ChB 1986 Ed.; BSc (Hons.) Ed. 1983; DRCOG 1989.

MCMURRY, Sarah Amanda 72 Haverstock Hill, Belsize Park, London NW3 2BE — MB ChB 1993 Manch. Roy. Free Hosp., N. Thames Rotat. Prev: Kings Coll. Hosp.

MCMURTRIE, Fiona c/o Palmeiras, 76 Dundonald Road, Kilmarnock KA1 1TH — MB ChB 1998 Glas.; MB ChB Glas 1998.

MCMURTRY, Hugh James 75 Strand Road, Portstewart BT55 7LX — MB ChB 1992 Manch.; MRCP (UK) 1996. Specialist Regist. (Gastroenterol.) Manch.

MCMURTRY, Ian Andrew 8 Manning Court, Eastbury Road, Watford WD19 4PX — MB BCh BAO 1990 Belf.; MB BCh Belf. 1990.

MCMURTRY, Joanne Lesley Nottingham City Hospital, Hucknall Road, Nottingham NG5 1PB Tel: 0115 969 1169; 12 Prospect Gardens, Carrickfergus BT38 8QX Tel: 01960 365512 — BM BS 1997 Nottm.; BMedSci Nottm. 1995. (Nottm.) SHO A&E.

MACNAB, Andrew 9 Temperance Hill, Woolley Moor, Alfreton DE55 6FJ — MB ChB 1990 Liverp. SHO (A & E) Countess of Chester Hosp.

MCNAB, Andrew Lowe (retired) Gorse Cottage, Queen Hoo Lane, Tewin, Welwyn AL6 0LR Tel: 01438 798240 — MB ChB 1947 Glas. Prev: Cas. Surg. Roy. Alexandra Infirm. Paisley.

MACNAB, Anita Wythenshaw Hospital, Southmoor Road, Nythenshawe, Manchester M23 9LT; 29 Tall Trees, Mersey Road, Manchester M20 2PE — MB ChB 1991 Manch.; MRCP, 1995. Specialist Regist. Cardiol. Wythenshawe Hosp., Manch.

MCNAB, David Andrew The Hartington Wing, Chesterfield & North Derbyshire Royal Hospital, Calow, Chesterfield S44 5BL — MB ChB 1975 Glas.; MRCPsych 1979.

MCNAB, Duncan Stuart 8 Old Hall Drive, Newton Stewart DG8 6HZ — MB ChB 1998 Glas.; MB ChB Glas 1998. PRHO Med. W.ern INF Glas. Prev: PRHC Surgury Vict. INF Glas.

MACNAB, Ena Brunton Darroch, 15 Elder Road, Killearn, Glasgow G63 9RX Tel: 01360 550385 Email: emacnab@aol.com — MB ChB 1965 Glas. (Glas.) Cons. Paediat. (Community), Yorkhill NHS Trust Glas. Socs: Fell.of Roy. Soc. Pub. Health & Hyg.; Brit. Assn. Comm. Child Health; FRCPCH & BMA.

MACNAB, Gavin c/o Sunderland Royal General Hospital, Kayll Road, Sunderland SR4 7TP Tel: 0191 565 6256 Fax: 0191 569 9218 — MB ChB 1973 Dundee; MRCOG 1980; FRCOG 1991. Cons. O & G CHST Sunderland. Prev: Lect./Hon. Sen. Regist. Univ. Leic.

MACNAB

MACNAB, Geraldine Marie The Health Centre, 20 Duncan Street, Greenock PA15 4LY Tel: 01475 724477 Fax: 01475 727140 — MB ChB 1978 Glas.

MACNAB, Graham William (retired) Flat 1, 87 South Beach, Troon KA10 6EQ Tel: 01292 312759 — MB ChB 1953 Glas.; FFA RCS Eng. 1961; DA Eng. 1956. Mem. Scott. Anaesth. Prev: Cons. Anaesth. CrossHo. Hosp. Ayrsh. & Arran HB.

MACNAB, Hamish Kellar The Medical Centre, Station Avenue, Bridlington YO16 4LZ Tel: 01262 670690; Normanby Lodge, 9 St. Chad Road, Bridlington YO16 4DY — MB ChB 1977 Manch.

MCNAB, Mr Ian Stuart Hugh Department of Truama and Orthopaedics, The Royal London Hospital, Whitechapel, London E1 — MB BS 1989 Lond.; FRCS Eng. 1993; FRCS (Orth.) 1998. Sen. Regist. (Orthop.) The Roy. Lond. Hosp. Socs: Assoc. Mem. BOA; Assoc. Mem. Brit. Soc. Surg. Hand; Roy. Soc. Med. Prev: Sen. Regist. (Orthop.) Gt. Ormond St. Hosp.; Sen. Regist. (Orthop.) Nuffield Orthop. Centre Oxf.; Sen. Regist. (Orthop.) Norf. & Norwich Hosp.

MACNAB, Jane Louise Simpson Memorial Maternity Pavilion, 1 Lauriston Place, Edinburgh EH3 GYW Tel: 0131 536 1000 — MB ChB 1991 Ed.; BSc (Med. Sci.) (Hons.) Ed. 1989; MRCOG 1996. (Ed.) p/t Specialist Regist. (O & G) Roy. Infirm. Edin. & Simpsons Memor. Matern. Pavil. Prev: Specialist Regist. (O & G) Borders Gen. Hosp. Melrose.; Specialist Regist. (O & G) E.ern Gen. Hosp. Edin.; Specialist Regist. (O & G) Roy. Infirm. Edin. & Simpsons Memor. Matern. Pavil.

MCNAB, Johan Margaret 7 Avontoun Park, Linlithgow EH49 6QG — MB ChB 1979 Dundee; DO RCS Eng. 1985.

MCNAB, Mr John Winton 4 Melrose Place, Perth PH1 1SD — MB ChB Aberd. 1967; BSc Aberd. 1960; FRCS Ed. 1973; FFR RCSI 1977; DMRD Aberd. 1975. Socs: Eur. Soc. Neuroradiol.; Brit. Soc. Neuroradiol.; (Ex-Pres.) Scott. Radiol. Soc. Prev: Cons. Neuroradiol. Ninewells Hosp. Dundee; Sen. Regist. (Radiol.) Ninewells Hosp. Dundee; Regist. (Gen. Surg.) Roy. N.. Infirm. & Raigmore Hosp. Inverness.

MACNAB, Margery Shearer Paton 9 Skaithmuir Crescent, Falkirk FK2 8BP — MB ChB 1974 Dundee.

MCNAB, Marion Anne 25 Park Road, Lower Weston, Bath BA1 3EE — MB ChB 1993 Bristol.

MCNAB, Mary Jane Walker Health Centre, Park Drive, Stenhousemuir, Larbert FK5 3BB Tel: 01324 552200 Fax: 01324 553623; The Neuk, 2 Carrongrange Gardens, Larbert FK5 3DY Tel: 01324 562433 — MB ChB 1984 Aberd.; MRCGP 1988. Clin. Asst. Roy. Scott. Nat. Hosp. Larbert. Prev: Cas. Off. Stirling Roy. Infirm.; Jun. Ho. Phys. Woodend Hosp. Aberd.; Jun. Ho. Surg. Dumfries & Galloway Roy. Infirm.

MCNAB, Sheila Margaret 31 Sinclair Gardens, Bishopbriggs, Glasgow G64 1NU — MB ChB 1990 Glas.

MACNAB, William Ross 15 Elder Road, Killearn, Glasgow G63 9RX Tel: 0141 550385 — MB ChB 1993 Manch.; BSc St And. 1990. SHO (A & E) Roy. Preston Hosp. Prev: SHO (A & E) Booth Hall Childr. Hosp. & N. Manch. Gen. Hosp.

MCNAB JONES, Mr Robin Francis The Consulting Suite, The Princess Grace Hospital, 45-52 Nottingham Place, London W1M 3FD Tel: 020 7486 1234 Fax: 020 7935 2198; 91 Barnfield Wood Road, Beckenham BR3 6ST Tel: 020 8650 0217 — MB BS 1945 Lond.; FRCS Eng. 1952. (St. Bart.) Socs: Fell. Roy. Soc. Med. (Mem. Counc. & Ex-Pres. Sect. Laryngol.). Prev: Cons. Surg. (ENT) St. Bart. Hosp. Lond.; Co-opted Mem. Otolaryng. Counc. RCS Eng.; Dean Inst. of Laryng. & Otol. Lond.

MCNAB JONES, Susan Eluned 20 Harrop Road, Hale, Altrincham WA15 9BZ; 325 Woodstock Road, Oxford OX2 7NX — MB BS 1976 Lond.

MCNABB, Sally Jane 96 Alderbrook Road, Solihull B91 1NS — BM BS 1995 Nottm.

MCNABB, William Robinson 4 Warbank Lane, Kingston upon Thames KT2 7ES — MB BChir 1974 Camb.; MB BChir. Camb. 1974; MA Camb. 1975; MD Lond. 1985; FRCP Lond. 1992; MRCP (UK) 1977. Cons. Phys. (Gen. Med. & c/o Elderly) Kingston & Dist. Community NHS Trust.

MCNABOE, Mr Edward James Dominic 66 Garland Hill, Manse Road, Newtownbreda, Belfast BT8 6YL Tel: 028 90 797091 Fax: 028 38 331947 — MB BCh BAO 1989 Belf.; FRCS Ed (ORL-HNS) Ed. 1994; FRCS Glas. 1994. Cons. Ent & Head & Neck Surg. Craigavon Area Hosp. N. Irel.

MACNAIR, Alexander Lewis (retired) Cae'n Y Bwlch, Talsarnau LL47 6YB Tel: 01766 780812 Fax: 01766 780812 — MB ChB St. And. 1959; DObst RCOG 1961.

MCNAIR, Alistair Neville Bruce Email: a.mcnair@ntlworld.com — MB BChir 1985 Camb.; PhD Lond. 1994; MA Camb. 1986; MRCP (UK) 1988. (Camb.) Cons. (Gastroenterol.) Qu. Elizabeth Hopsital, Lond.; Hon. Sen. Lect. Guy's Hosp. Lond. Prev: Lect. (Gastroenterol.) King's Coll. Hosp. Lond.

MACNAIR, Andrew Duncan Ivy House, Market Hill, Foulsham, Dereham NR20 5RU Tel: 01362 683372 Fax: 01362 683372 Email: admacnair@aol.com — MB 1971 Camb.; MA Camb. 1972, MB 1971, BChir 1970; MRCP (UK) 1976; DObst RCOG 1972; DTM & H Liverp. 1972. (Camb. & Middlx.) Prev: SHO (Med.) Doncaster Roy. Infirm.; Dist. Med. Off. Lesotho; Ho. Surg. (Orthop.) Middlx. Hosp. Lond.

MACNAIR, Christine Fraser The Health Centre, 2 The Tanyard, Cumnock KA18 1BF Tel: 01290 422723 Fax: 01290 425444; 15 Kings Drive, Cumnock KA18 1AG Tel: 01290 421375 — MB ChB 1970 Glas. (Glas.) Prev: Ho. Off. (Obst.) & Regist. (Chest Med.) Ayrsh. Centr. Hosp. Irvine.

MACNAIR, David Malcolm Blacklie 15 Kings Drive, Cumnock KA18 1AG — MB ChB 1997 Glas.

MACNAIR, Duncan Ritchie 97 London Road, Gloucester GL1 3HH — MB BS 1960 Lond.; DCH Eng. 1964. Prev: Med. Regist. Soton. Gen. Hosp.; Ho. Surg. Middlx. Hosp. Lond.; Ho. Phys. Dept. Gastroenterol. Centr. Middlx. Hosp. Lond.

MACNAIR, Jacqueline Ann 15 Kings Drive, Cumnock KA18 1AG — MB ChB 1990 Glas.

MACNAIR, James Malcolm The Health Centre, 2 The Tanyard, Cumnock KA18 1BF Tel: 01290 422723 Fax: 01290 425444; 15 Kings Drive, Cumnock KA18 1AG Tel: 01290 21375 — MB ChB 1970 Glas.; DObst RCOG 1973. (Glas.) Prev: Regist. (Gen. Med.) Kilmarnock Infirm.; Regist. (Chest & Infec. Dis.) & SHO (Obst.) Ayrsh. Centr. Hosp. Irvine.

MACNAIR, John Derek Tranent Medical Practice, Loch Road, Tranent EH33 2JX Tel: 01875 610697 Fax: 01875 615046; 2 Lochbridge Road, North Berwick EH39 4DN Tel: 01620 895187 — MB ChB 1974 Ed.; BSc Ed. 1971; MRCGP 1978; DRCOG 1977. (Ed.) Prev: SHO Edin. Roy. Infirm.; Ho. Surg. (Gen. Surg.) Falkirk Roy. Infirm.; Ho. Phys. (Gen. Med.) Bangour Gen. Hosp. Broxburn.

MACNAIR, Mrs Margaret Elizabeth (retired) 29 Gilston Road, The Boltons, London SW10 9SJ Tel: 020 7352 7735 Fax: 020 7352 7684 — MB ChB Ed. 1945; MRCGP 1965.

MCNAIR, Margaret Murray St. Mary's Hospital, Praed St., London W2 — MB ChB 1963 Glas.; FRCR 1975; FFR 1970; DMRD Eng. 1967. (Glas.) Clin. Asst. (Radiol.) St. Mary's Hosp. Lond. Prev: Cons. Radiol. King's Coll. Hosp. Lond.; Cons. Radiol. St. Chas. & St. Mary's Hosps. Lond. & Roy. Hosp. Sick; Childr. Glas.

MACNAIR, Patricia Ann Tel: 01428 713471 — MB ChB 1982 Bristol; DA 1984 UK; MA 2001 (Medical Ethics & Medical Law) King's Coll. Lond. (Bristol) Med. Writer & BRd.caster Lond. Socs: Assn. BRd.casting Doctors.; Media Medics. Prev: SHO (Renal Med.) St Heliers Hosp. Carshalton; SHO (Chest & Gen. Med.) Kingston Gen. Hosp. Surrey; SHO (Anaesth.) St Mary's Hosp. Lond.

MCNAIR, Sybil Monteith Dick (retired) Easter Carrick, Chapel Green, Earlsferry, Leven KY9 1AD Tel: 01333 330244 — MB ChB Ed. 1949. Prev: Sen. Lect. (Path.) Univ. Edin.

MCNALLY, Anne Marie Govanhill Health Centre, 233 Calder Street, Glasgow G42 7DR Tel: 0141 531 8370 Fax: 0141 531 4431 — MB ChB 1977 Glas.

MCNALLY, Damien Patrick Gerald 46 Baronscourt Road, Belfast BT8 8BQ Tel: 01232 814656 — MB BCh BAO 1993 Belf.; Dip. Ment. Health Belf. 1997; DRCOG 1996. (Queen's University Belfast)

MCNALLY, Dermot Martin Flat 12, 33 Kent Road, Charing Cross, Glasgow G3 7BY — MB BCh BAO 1993 Belf.

MCNALLY, Eugene Gerard Department of Radiology, Nuffield Orthopaedic Centre, Oxford OX3 7LD Tel: 01865 227345; The Willow House, Barton Lane, Oxford OX3 9JW — MB BCh BAO 1983 NUI; MA NUI 1983; MRCPI 1985; FRCR 1990; T(R) (CR) 1992; FRCPI 1999. Cons. Radiol. Nuffield Orthop. Centre & Oxf. Radcliffe Hosp.; Hon. Sen. Lect. Univ. Oxf.

MCNALLY, Jeremy Dennis Department of Rheumatology, Northwick Park & St. Mark's NHS Trust, Harrow HA1 3UJ — MB BS 1989 Lond. Specialist Regist., Dept. of Rheum., N.wick Pk., Harrow.

MCNALLY, John Ronan Anthony Radiology Department, Ulster Hospital, Dundonald, Belfast Email: ronan.mcnally@bigfoot.com — MB BCh BAO 1991 Belf.; FRCR 1998; MRCP (UK) 1994. Cons. Radiol. Socs: BMA; Fell. of Roy. Coll. Radiol.; MDV. Prev: Specialist Regist. (Radiol.) Belf.

MCNALLY, Lisa Marina 10 Oakley Yard, 48/52 Bacon St., London E2 6DU Tel: 020 7256 1405 Email: lisa.mcnally@virgin.net — MB BS 1993 Lond.; BSc (Hons.) Lond. 1990; MRCP (UK) 1996; MRCPCH 1997; DTM & H 1998. (St Bartholomew's Medical College) Specialist Regist. Whipps Cross Hosp. Lond.; Hon. Research Fell. Centre for Internat. Child Health Lond. Prev: SHO (Paediat. Infect. Dis./Immunol.) Gt. Ormond St. Hosp.; SHO (Paediat.) Guy's Hosp. Lond.; SHO (Neonate) Homerton Hosp. Lond.

MCNALLY, Margaret Susan Friary Surgery, Dobbin Lane, Armagh BT61 7QG Tel: 028 3752 3165 Fax: 028 3752 1514 — MB BCh BAO 1986 Belf.; DRCOG 1989.

MCNALLY, Mr Martin Austin Nuffield Orthopaedic Centre, Windmill Road, Headington, Oxford OX3 7LD Tel: 01865 227250, 01865 227480 — MB BCh BAO 1986 Belf.; MD Belf. 1996; FRCS Ed. (Orth.) 1996; FRCS Ed. 1990. (Qu. Univ. Belf.) Cons. (Limb Reconstruction) Nuffield Orthopaedic Centre, Oxf.; Hon. Sen. Lect. in Orthopaedic Surg., Univ. of Oxf.; Hon. Cons. in Trauma Surg., John Radcliffe Hosp., Oxf. Socs: Brit. Orthopaedic Assn. Fell.; Brit. Limb Reconstruction Soc.; Brit. Orthopaedic Research Soc. Prev: Cons. in Trauma Surg. John Radcliffe Hosp., Oxf.; Fell. (Limb Reconstuctive Surg.) Nuffield Dept. Orthop. Surg. Univ. Oxf.; Sen. Regist. (Orthop. Surg.) Lisburn.

MCNALLY, Mr Patrick Kennoch House, St. Quivox, Ayr KA6 5HJ Tel: 01292 74353 — MB ChB 1968 Glas.; FRCS Glas. 1973. (Glas.) Cons. Orthop. Surg. Ayr Co. Hosp. Prev: Sen. Regist. (Orthop. Surg.) W.. Infirm. Glas.; Regist. (Orthop. Surg.) Glas. Roy. Infirm.

MCNALLY, Patrick John, Group Capt. RAF Med. Br. Retd. 25 Cambridge Road, Marlow SL7 2NR — MB BCh BAO 1927 NUI; DPH Eng. 1936.

MCNALLY, Paul Gerard Department of Diabetes & Endocrinology, Leicester Royal Infirmary NHS Trust, Leicester LE1 5WW Tel: 0116 258 6182 Fax: 0116 258 6992; 16 Church Street, Braunston, Oakham LE15 8QT Tel: 01572 757147 — BM BS 1983 Nottm.; MD Leicester 1991; BMedSci Nottm. 1981; MRCP (UK) 1986; FRCP 1998. Cons. Phys. (Diabetes & Endocrinol.) Leicester Roy. Infirm. Socs: Brit. Diabetic Assn.; Brit. Endocrine Soc. Prev: Sen. Regist. (Diabetes & Endocrinol.) Leicester Roy. Infirm.; Regist. (Med.) Leicester Roy. Infirm.; Trav. Research Fell (Endocrinol.) Austin Hosp. Univ. Melbourne, Austral.

MCNALLY, Samantha Jane 18 Hartley Hall Gardens, Gowan Road, Manchester M16 8LP — MB ChB 1995 Manch.

MCNALLY, Sara Anne 2 Highland Drive, Bushey, Watford WD23 4LH — MB BS 1997 Lond.

MCNALLY, Scarlett Armorel 40 Princess Terrace, Brighton BN2 5JS — MB BChir 1990 Camb.; FRCS Eng. 1994.

MCNALLY, Stephen Justin Kennoch House, St Quivox, Ayr KA6 5HJ — MB ChB 1997 Aberd.

MCNALLY, Steven Richard Banks Health Centre, Hoole Lane, Banks, Southport PR9 8BD Tel: 01704 227348 Fax: 01704 227380; 22 West Lane, Formby, Liverpool L37 7BA Tel: 01704 874218 Email: stevenmcnally@compuserve.com — BM BS 1985 Nottm.; BMedSci Nottm. 1983; MRCGP 1990; DRCOG 1990; DCH RCP Lond. 1989; Dip. Occ. Med. 1997. (Nottm.) Socs: Brit. Assn. Sport & Med.

MACNAMARA, Mr Aidan Francis Mary Hartfield, Maxstoke Lane, Meriden, Coventry CV7 7ND — MB BCh BAO 1988 NUI; FRCS Ed. 1993.

MCNAMARA, Catherine Mary Kyle House, Thornhill Road, Benton, Newcastle upon Tyne NE12 9PD — MB BS 1987 Lond.

MCNAMARA, Colin West Winds, 2 Abington Drive, Ashton, Preston PR2 1EY Tel: 01772 72639 — MB ChB 1951 Liverp.; AFOM RCP Lond. 1983; DIH Lond. 1982. Med. Off. Roy. Ordnance Chorley.

MCNAMARA, Henry Ian Crown Avenue Surgery, 12 Crown Avenue, Inverness IV2 3NF Tel: 01463 710777 Fax: 01463 714511; 24 Southside Road, Inverness IV2 3BG Tel: 01463 235706 — MB BS Lond. 1969; BSc (Physiol.) (1st cl. Hons.) Lond. 1966; FRCGP 1988, M 1974; DCH RCPS Glas. 1973; DObst RCOG 1973. (St. Mary's) Dir. Postgrad. Gen. Pract. Educat. (N. Scotl.); Hon. Sen. Lect. Dept. of Gen. Pract. & Primary Care Univ. of Aberd. Socs: Highland Med. Soc. Prev: SHO (Paediat.) Roy. N.. Infirm. Inverness; Ho. Phys. (Med.) St. Mary's Hosp. Lond.; Ho. Surg. Barnet Gen. Hosp.

MCNAMARA, Henry Pearson (retired) 9 Queen Parade, Harrogate HG1 5PW Tel: 01423 503618 — MB BS 1933 Durh.; FRCGP 1994, M 1953. Prev: Hon. Regist. (Med.) Coventry & Warks. Hosp.

MCNAMARA, John Francis Occupational Health Unit, Baguley House, Wythenshawe Hospital, Southmoor Road, Manchester M23 0LT Tel: 0161 291 2674 Fax: 0161 291 2674; Upway, Parkhill Road, Hale, Altrincham WA15 9JX Tel: 0161 980 5054 Fax: 0161 980 5054 Email: mcnamara@tinyworld.co.uk — MRCS Eng. LRCP Lond. 1970; DObst RCPI 1973; FRCP Ed. 1997; LLM Wales 1994; FRCP Glas. 1994; MRCP (UK) 1979; MFFP 1993; MFOM RCP Lond. 1983, AFOM 1981; MRCGP 1975; DIH Eng. 1981; DObst RCOG 1973. (Leeds) Dir. & Cons. Phys. Occupat. Health S. Manch. Univ. Hosps., W. Chesh. & Halton Gen. Hosp. NHS Trusts; Hon. Clin. Lect. Univ. Manch.; Occupat. Med. Adviser Steripak Pharmaceut. Ltd Runcorn; Mem. Med. Appeals Tribunals. Socs: Soc. Occupat. Med.; Assur. Med. Soc.; Assn. Nat. Health Occupat. Phys. (Mem. Managem. Comm.). Prev: Sen. Med. Off. Brit. Nuclear Fuels Ltd. Risley; SHO (Rheum. & Physical Med.) Univ. Hosp. Wales Gp. Hosps.; Occupat. Health Phys. City of Salford.

MCNAMARA, John Timothy The Stables, Hunters Yard, Riseley, Bedford MK44 1EN — MB BS 1989 Lond.; FRCA 1995. (St. Geo. Hosp. Med. Sch. Lond.) Cons. Bedford. Hosp. Prev: Regist. (Anaesth.) Char. Cross Hosp. Lond.; SHO (Anaesth.) Frimley Pk. Hosp.

MCNAMARA, Laurie (retired) 7 Devitt Close, Ashtead KT21 1JS Tel: 0137 22 75157 — MB BS 1937 Madras; DPH Lond. 1956. Prev: Clin. Med. Off. & Deptm. Med. Off. Merton, Sutton & Wandsworth.

MACNAMARA, Mrs Marcelle Alpheda Maria Birmingham Heartlands Hospital, Bordesley Green East, Bordesley, Birmingham B9 5SS Tel: 0121 424 2339 Fax: 0121 424 1353 — MB BS 1985 Lond.; MA Oxf. 1985; MPhil Keele 1996; FRCS (Orl) 1995; FRCS (ENT) 1991; FRCS Eng. 1989. (Univ. Coll. Hosp. Lond.) Cons. ENT Surg. Birm. Heartlands Hosp.; Hon. Sen. Lect. Univ. of Birm.; Lead Clinician Head & Neck Oncol. Socs: Roy. Soc. Med.; Brit. Assn. of Head & Neck Oncol.; Midl. Inst. OtorhinoLaryngol. Prev: Sen. Regist. (ENT) W. Midl. Rotat.; Regist. (ENT) Roy. Ear Hosp. Univ. Coll. Hosp. Lond.

MCNAMARA, Martin John 419 Harborne Road, Edgbaston, Birmingham B15 3LB — BM BS 1991 Nottm.; BMedSci Nottm. 1989; DA (UK) 1995.

MACNAMARA, Michael Apple Tree Cottage, Husseys Lane, Lower Froyle, Alton GU34 4LX — MB BCh BAO 1949 NUI; LAH Dub. 1949; MRCGP 1963.

MCNAMARA, Neil Joseph 133 Kylepark Drive, Uddingston, Glasgow G71 7DD — MB ChB 1998 Ed.; MB ChB Ed 1998.

MACNAMARA, Oswald Danvers (retired) Worsley House, Abberley, Worcester WR6 6BQ Tel: 01299 896262 — MB BChir 1941 Camb.; MA Camb. 1941; DMRD Eng. 1953; DTM & H Ed. 1947. Prev: Cons. W. Midl. RHA.

MCNAMARA, Patrick Joseph 5 Wethesfield Way, Wickford SS11 8XX — MB BCh BAO 1993 Belf.

MCNAMARA, Paul John Gerald St. Oswald's Hospice, Regent Avenue, Gosforth, Newcastle upon Tyne NE3 1EE Tel: 0191 285 0063 Fax: 0191 284 8004; Shandon, Causey Hill, Hexham NE46 2DL Tel: 01434 604536 — MB ChB 1981 Manch.; MRCGP 1986; DRCOG 1984. Med. Director, St. Oswald's Hospice Newc. u. Tyne; Hon. Clin. Lect. (Primary Health Care) Univ. Newc.; Hon. Cons. Palliat. Med. N.umbria Health Care. Socs: Assn. Palliat. Med. Prev: Asst. Med. Dir. St. Catherine's Hospice Crawley; Clin. Fell. Sir Michael Sobell Hse. Oxf.; Regist. Trinity Hospice Lond.

MCNAMARA, Paul Stephen Institute of Child Health, University of Liverpool, Eaton Road, Liverpool L12 2AP Tel: 0151 228 4811 Ext: 2703 Email: mcnamara@iv.ac.uk — MB BS 1992 Lond.; MRCP Lond. 1996. (Kings Coll. Lond.) Research Fell., Univ. of Liverp.; Hon.

MCNAMARA

Specialist Regist. (Paed.) Alder Hey Hosp., Liverp. Prev: Specialist Regist. (Paediat.) Alder Hey Hosp.

MCNAMARA, Penelope Ann St John's Sue Ryder Care, Moggerhanger, Bedford MK44 3RJ — MB BS 1989 Lond.; MRCGP 1994; MA (Ethics) Keele 1998. (St George) Cons. Palliat. Med. St John, Moggerhanger and Bedford NHS Trust. Socs: RSM; APM; BMA. Prev: Sen. Regist. P.ss Alice Hosp. Esher, Surrey; Regist. (Palliat. Med.) St. Catherine's Hospice Crawley.

MCNAMARA, Samuel Antoine Frederic Ozanam (retired) Mount House, 11 Station Road, Buntingford SG9 9HT Tel: 01763 273623 — MB BS 1958 Lond.; MRCS Eng. LRCP Lond. 1958; DObst RCOG 1962. Prev: GP Buntingford.

MCNAMEE, Basil Thompson Craigavon Area Hospital, 68 Kurgan Road, Craigavon BT63 5QQ Tel: 02838 34444; 11 Killyniell Road, Dungannon BT71 6LL Tel: 028 877 24528 — MB BCh BAO Belf. 1962; FRCP Glas. 1981, M 1967; DObst RCOG 1964. (Queens University Belfast) Cons. Cardiol., Craigavon Area Hosp.

MCNAMEE, David Anthony 15 Loughview Drive, Belfast BT6 0NU — MB BCh BAO 1993 Belf.

MCNAMEE, Gerard George 195 Common Road, Wombourne, Wolverhampton WV5 0LS Tel: 01902 5289 — MB BCh BAO 1935 NUI. (Univ Coll. Dub.) Div. Surg. St. John Ambul. Brig. Socs: BMA.

MCNAMEE, Heather Margaret 52 Ashton Park, Finaghy, Belfast BT10 0JQ — MB ChB 1989 Ed. SHO (Paediat.) Edin.

MCNAMEE, Raymund Neil Dumbarton Health Centre, Station Road, Dumbarton G82 1PW Tel: 01389 602644 Fax: 01389 602624; 77 Bon Hill Road, Dumbarton G82 2DU — MB ChB 1966 Glas.

MCNAMEE, Sarah Alison 77 Bon Hill Road, Dumbarton G82 2DU — MB ChB 1967 Glas.

MCNARRY, Alistair Ferris 5 Dundela Gardens, Belfast BT4 3DH — MB BChir 1994 Camb.

MCNAUGHT, Alan Stuart Department of Psychiatry, Royal Free Hospital, Pond St., London NW5 2QG — MB ChB 1988 Aberd.; MRCPsych 1993. Cons. (psych.) Roy. Free Hosp. Lond. Prev: Regist. (Psychiat.) Roy. Free Hosp. & Gt. Ormond St. Hosp. Lond.; Sen. Regist.(Psychiot.) Mandslen Hosp, Lond.

MCNAUGHT, Mr Andrew Ian Department of Ophthalmology, Cheltenham General Hospital, Sandford Road, Cheltenham GL53 7AN Tel: 01242 222222 Fax: 01242 273652; The Old Vicarage (Nth Wing), The Green, Edge, Stroud, Gloucester GL5 6PB Tel: 01452 812059 Fax: 01452 814800 Email: amcnaught@compuserve.com — MB BS 1986 Lond.; MD (Lond.) 1997; FRCOphth. 1991. Cons. Ophth. Cheltenham Eye Unit. Gen. Hosp. Cheltenham, Gloucestershire. Socs: Assn. Research Vision & Ophth.; Amer. Acad. of Ophth.; Europ. Glaucoma Soc. Prev: Sen. Regist. Ophth. W.ern Eye. Hosp. Lond. W2; Glaucoma Fell., Roy. Vic. Eye & Ear Hosp., Roy. Hobart Hosp. Australia; Reg. Ophth., Moorfields Eye Hosp. Lond.

MCNAUGHT, Ella Isobel (retired) Malin, 5 Carmunnock Road, Clarkston, Glasgow G76 8SY — MB ChB Glas. 1947; MD Glas. 1958; FRCS Glas. 1980; FRCOphth. 1989; DO Eng. 1950. Prev: Cons. Ophth. Surg. Law Hosp. Lanarksh.

MCNAUGHT, Mr Gordon Herbert Dargavel, VRD (retired) Clova, 11 Manor Road, Hartlepool TS26 0EH Tel: 01429 266918 Fax: 01429 266918 — MB ChB Ed. 1944; FRCS Ed. 1948. Prev: Cons. Surg. Hartlepool HA.

MCNAUGHT, Jennifer Ann Lymington Infirmary, East Hill, Lymington SO41 9ZJ Tel: 01590 676081 Fax: 01590 670749 — MB BCh 1987 Wales. Clin. Asst. Lymington Infirm.

MCNAUGHT, Philip Leo Kings Park Surgery, 274 Kings Park Avenue, Glasgow G44 4JE Tel: 0141 632 1824 Fax: 0141 632 0461; 15 Briar Gardens, Glasgow G43 2TF — MB ChB 1976 Glas.; Dip. Forens. Med. Glas. Univ. 1987.

MCNAUGHT, Rosemary Sheffield Health, 5 Old Fulwood Road, Sheffield S10 3TG Tel: 0114 271 1100 Fax: 0114 271 1101; The Old Rectory, Church St, Eckington, Sheffield S21 4BG — MB ChB 1979 Sheff.; BSc Sheff. 1976; MFPHM RCP (UK) 1992. Cons. Pub. Health Med. & Communicable Dis. Control Sheff. HA.

MACNAUGHTAN, Mr Ian Philip Jackson 20 Cottown of Balgownie, Bridge of Don, Aberdeen AB23 8JQ Tel: 01224 703266 — MB ChB 1934 Ed.; FRCS Ed. 1937. (Univ. Ed.) Prev: Sen. Cons. Otolaryngol. N. E. RHB (Scotl.); Clin. Sen. Lect. Dis. ENT Univ. Aberd.; Maj. RAMC Specialist Otol. (1939-45).

MCNAUGHTON, Alastair Ronald 38 Clifton Avenue, Hartlepool TS26 9QN — MB ChB 1951 Aberd.

MCNAUGHTON, Elaine 5 Collingwood Crescent, Barnhill, Dundee DD5 2SX — MB ChB 1981 Dundee.

MCNAUGHTON, Elizabeth Louise 15B Cranmer Road, Cambridge CB3 9BL — MB BS 1977 Monash.

MCNAUGHTON, Fiona Jean Dykes Hall Medical Centre, 156 Dykes Hall Road, Sheffield S6 4GQ Tel: 0114 232 3236; 50 Barncliffe Road, Sheffield S10 4DF — MB ChB Sheff. 1978.

MCNAUGHTON, Gordon William Accident & Emergency Department, Royal Alexandra Hospital, Paisley PA7 9PN Tel: 0151 580 4304 Email: gordon.mcnaughton@vol.scot.nhs.uk — MB ChB 1988 Glas.; MRCP (UK) 1993; FFAEM 1996. (University of Glasgow) Cons. A&E Roy.Alex.Hosp.Paisley. Socs: Fac. Accid. & Emerg. Med.; BAEM; BMA. Prev: Sen. Regist. (A&E) Glas. Roy. Infirm.; Regist. (A & E) W.. Infirm. Glas.; SHO (A & E & Med.) W.. Infirm. Glas.

MCNAUGHTON, Ian Charles Green Street Clinic, 118-122 Green Street, Eastbourne BN21 1RT Tel: 01323 722908 Fax: 01323 723136; Old Mill House, Old Mill Lane, Wannock, Polegate BN26 5NQ Tel: 01323 483315 Email: ianmcnaughta72@freeserve.co.uk — MB BS 1978 Lond.; DRCOG 1983.

MACNAUGHTON, Professor Sir Malcolm Campbell Beechwood, 15 Boclair Road, Bearsden, Glasgow G61 2AF Tel: 0141 942 1909 — MD 1970 Glas.; FRSE 1983; FRSE 1983; MB ChB 1948; FRCP Glas. 1972, M 1971; FRCOG 1966, M 1954; Hon. FRACOG 1987; Hon. FRCA 1987; Hon. FACOG 1986; LLD 1988; Hon. FSLCOG 1986. Emerit. Prof. O & G Univ. Glas.; Muirhead Prof. O & G Univ. Glas. Roy. Matern. Hosp. & Roy. Infirm. Glas. Socs: Fell. (Ex-Pres.) Roy. Coll. Obst. & Gyn.; Soc. Endocrinol. & Roy. Soc. Med. Prev: Cons. O & G Dundee Roy. Infirm. & Maryfield Hosp.; Sen. Lect. (O & G) Univ. St. And. & Univ. Dundee; Lect. (Midw. & Gyn.) Univ. Aberd.

MACNAUGHTON, Peter David Department of Anaesthetics, Derriford Hospital, Derriford, Plymouth PL6 8DH Tel: 01752 777111 Email: peter.macnaughton@phnt.swest.nhs.uk — MB BS 1982 Lond.; BSc Lond. 1979; MD Lond. 1993; MRCP (UK) 1985; FRCA 1988. (Westm.) Cons. Anaesth. & Head Clinician ICU Derriford. Hosp. Plymouth. Socs: Intens. Care Soc.; Eur. Intens. Care Soc.; Soc. Devon. Intens. Ther. Prev: Sen. Regist. (Intens. Care) W.mead Hosp. Sydney; Sen. Regist. (Anaesth.) Frenchay Hosp. Bristol; MRC Train. Fell. Nat. Heart & Lung Inst. Lond.

MACNAUGHTON, Rosemary Jane 6 Kelso Street, Yoker, Glasgow G14 0JZ; 2 Hillhead Street, Glasgow G12 8PS — MB ChB 1988 Glas.; MA Glas. 1982, MB ChB 1988; MRCGP 1992; DRCOG 1994.

MCNAUL, William Donald (retired) Monanton, 41 Strand Road, Portstewart BT55 7LU Tel: 01265 832376 — MB BCh BAO 1949 Dub.; BA Dub. 1948, MB BCh BAO 1949; FFA RCSI 1977; FFA RCS Eng. 1962. Prev: Cons. Anaesth. N. Down Gp. Hosps.

MCNAY, Margaret Bryce (retired) Auchineden Farmhouse, Blanefield, Glasgow G63 9AX Tel: 01360 771026 Fax: 01360 771026 Email: gmgibb@compuserve.com — MB ChB Glas. 1969; MPhil Glas. 1992; MRCP (Glas.) 1988; FRCOG 1989, M 1974. Prev: Cons. Obst. Ultrasound Qu. Mother's Hosp. Yorkhill NHS Trust Glas.

MCNEAL, Allan David Merrow Down House, 30 Upton Road, Ryde PO33 3HE Tel: 01983 564123 — MB BS 1964 Lond.; MRCS Eng. LRCP Lond. 1964; FRCOG 1986, M 1974, DObst 1966. (King's Coll. Hosp.) Cons. O & G I. of Wight AHA. Prev: Sen. Regist. St. Geo. Hosp. Lond.; Sen. Regist. (O & G) Soton. Gen. Hosp.; Specialist (O & G) Brit. Milit. Hosp. Munster.

MCNEE, Andrew Barrhead Health Centre, 201 Main St., Barrhead, Glasgow G78 1SD Tel: 0141 880 6161; North Park, Lowndes St, Barrhead, Glasgow Tel: 0141 881 5315 — MB ChB 1973 Glas.; BSc Glas. 1968, MB ChB 1973. Prev: Regist. (Infec. Dis.) Hawkhead Hosp. Paisley; SHO (Obst.) Ayrsh. Centr. Hosp.; Ho. Off. (Med. & Surg.) Ballochmyle Hosp. Mauchline.

MCNEE, Philip Andrew James Pinckneys House, 17 High St., Durrington, Salisbury SP4 8AE — MB ChB 1997 Dundee.

MACNEE, Professor William Elegi Colt Laboratories, Wilkie Building, University of Edinburgh, Medical School, Teviot Place, Edinburgh EH8 9AG Tel: 0131 651145 Fax: 013 651 5495 Email: wmacnee@ed.ac.uk; Tel: 0131 664 3301 — MB ChB 1975 Glas.; MRCP (UK) 1978; MD Glas. 1985; FRCP(Ed.) 1990; FRCR Glas.

1989. (Glas.) Prof. of Respirat. & Environm. Med., Univ. of Edin. & Hon. Cons. Phys. The Lothian Univ. Hosps. NHS Trust.; Vis. Prof. (Biological Scis.) Napier Univ. Edin.; Pat. Serv. Director, Lothian Univ. Hosp. NHS Trust. Socs: Assn. Phys.; Hon. Sec. Brit. Lung Foundat. Scotl.; Chairm. Brit. Thoracic Soc. Europe Resp. Soc. Scientif. Comm. Prev: Reader (Med.) Univ. of Edin.; Lect. (Respirat. Med.) Univ. of Edin.; MRC Trav. Fell. Univ. of Brit. Columbia.

MCNEELA, Mr Bartley James 16 The Parklands, Ingleby Arncliffe, Northallerton DL6 3LT Tel: 01609 882345 Email: bmcneela@neos.demon.co.uk — MB ChB 1977 Liverp.; FRCS Eng. 1982; FRCOphth. 1989. Cons. (Ophth.) N. Riding Infirm. Middlesbrough. Socs: Hon. Sec. N. Eng. Ophthalmol. Soc.

MCNEELA, Helen Elizabeth 16 The Parklands, Ingleby Arncliffe, Northallerton DL6 3LT — MB ChB 1978 Manch.

MCNEICE, Roy Archibald Gallows Street Surgery, 50 Gallows Street, Dromore BT25 1BD Tel: 028 9269 2758; Emdale, 48 Ballymacormick Road, Dromore BT25 1QR — MB BCh BAO 1978 Belf.; MICGP 1986; DRCOG 1981.

MCNEIL, Aideen Frances St Andrews House, Waterloo Road, Stalybridge SK15 2AU Tel: 0161 338 3181 Fax: 0161 303 1208; Heaps Farm, Mottram Old Road, Stalybridge SK15 2TE — MB BS 1972 Newc.; MRCGP 1977; Cert. JCC Lond. 1977; DObst RCOG 1976. Prev: SHO (Psychiat.) St. Nicholas Hosp. Gosforth; SHO (O & G) Roy. Vict. Infirm. & P.ss Mary Matern. Hosp. Newc.

MACNEIL, Alisdair Southcote, 41 Southside Road, Inverness IV2 4XA — MB ChB 1978 Glas.; FFA RCS Eng. 1983; FFA RCSI 1983. Cons. Anaesth. Raigmore Hosp. Inverness.

MCNEIL, Andrew James John Department of Psychiatry, Royal Free Hospital, Pond St., Hampstead, London NW3 Tel: 020 7794 0500; 66 Putney Park Lane, London SW15 5HQ Tel: 020 8876 6636 — MB BChir 1993 Camb.; MA (Natural Sci.) Camb. 1994. SHO (Gen. Adult Psychiat.) Roy. Free Hosp. NHS Trust. Lond. Prev: SHO (Gen. Psychiat.) St. Anne's Hosp. Lond.; Ho. Off. (Gen. Med.) W. Suff. Hosp.; Ho. Off. (Surg. & Urol.) P'boro. Gen. Hosp.

MCNEIL, Byron David Meddygfa Taf, North Road, Whitland SA34 0AT Tel: 01994 240195 Fax: 01994 241138 — MB BCh 1986 Wales.

MACNEIL, Catriona 44 Milton Road W., Edinburgh EH15 1QU — MB ChB 1994 Glas.

MCNEIL, Helen Alison Lea Medical Centre, Calderwood, East Kilbride, Glasgow G74 3BE Tel: 01355 261666 — MB ChB 1989 Glas.; MRCGP 1993; DRCOG 1991. (Glasgow)

MCNEIL, Iain Donald Courtyard Surgery, The Courtyard, London Road, Horsham RH12 1AT Tel: 01403 253100 Fax: 01403 267480; 1 Nightingale Road, Horsham RH12 2NW Tel: 01403 260237 Fax: 01403 267480 — MB ChB 1981 Dundee; MRCGP 1985; Dip. IMC RCS Ed. 1993; DRCOG 1983. (Dundee) GP Princip.; Med. Dir., Surrey Ambul. Serv. NHS Trust; Chairm. BASICS. Socs: BASICS; BAEM; FPHCRCS (Ed.) (Speciality Advisery Bd.). Prev: Trainee GP S. Clwyd VTS.

MCNEIL, Iain Robert Ramage 17 Muirhill Avenue, Muirend, Glasgow G44 3HP Tel: 0141 637 2477 — MB ChB 1962 Glas.; FRCPath 1986, M 1974. (Glas.) Cons. Haemat. S.. Gen. Hosp. Glas.; Hon. Sen. Clin. Lect. Univ. Glas. Socs: Brit. Soc. Haematol.; BMA; Assn. Clin. Pathols. Prev: Sen. Regist. Univ. Dept. Haemat. W.. Infirm. Glas.; Regist. Laborat. Med. Vict. Infirm. Glas.; MRC Schol.

MCNEIL, Ian Andrew 39 Middleton Road, Bottesford, Scunthorpe DN16 3NW — MB BS 1989 Lond.

MCNEIL, Neil Claddach, 25 Waterfoot Road, Newton Mearns, Glasgow G77 5RU Tel: 0141 639 5165 — MB ChB 1956 Glas.; FFCM 1980, M 1974; DPA Glas. 1965, DPH 1962; Dr. Mackinlay Prize Univ. Glas. 1962. (Univ. Glas.) Dist. Med. Off. Hamilton & E. Kilbride Health Dist.; Hon. Clin. Lect. Dept. of Community Med. Univ. Glas. Socs: Scott. Soc. Experim. Med. Prev: Sen. Med. Off. Scott. Home & Health Dept.; Cons. Epidemiol. Ruchill Hosp. Glas. & Hon. Clin. Lect. Depts. Mat.; Med. & Community Med. Univ. Glas.

MCNEIL, Neil Charles Hood St Andrews House, Waterloo Road, Stalybridge SK15 2AU Tel: 0161 338 3181 Fax: 0161 303 1208; Heaps Farm, Mottram Old Road, Stalybridge SK15 2TE Tel: 0161 338 3181 — MB BS 1972 Lond.; MRCS Eng. LRCP Lond. 1972; MRCGP 1976; DA Eng. 1976. (Guy's) Prev: Trainee GP Newc. VTS; SHO (O & G) Hexham Gen. Hosp.; SHO (Anaesth.) Newc. Gen. Hosp.

MCNEIL, Neil Ian Ealing Hospital, Uxbridge Road, Southall UB1 3HW; 20 Nower Hill, Pinner HA5 5QS — MB BChir 1971 Camb.; MD Camb. 1980, MA 1971; FRCP Lond. 1991; MRCP (UK) 1972. (Camb. & Guy's) Cons. Phys. & Gastroenterol. Ealing Hosp. S.all. Socs: Brit. Soc. Gastroenterol. Prev: Lect. (Med.) Univ. Coll. Hosp. Med. Sch. Lond.

MCNEIL, William Townley (retired) 19 Western Avenue, Halesowen B62 8QH Tel: 0121 422 2002 — MB ChB Birm. 1954; FFA RCS Eng. 1960. Prev: Cons. Anaesth. Midl. Centre Neurosurg. & Neurol. Smethwick & Hallam Hosp. W. Bromwich.

MCNEIL, William Young The Health Centre, 20 Duncan Street, Greenock PA15 4LY Tel: 01475 724477 Fax: 01475 727140 — MB ChB 1971 Glas.

MCNEILL, Aine (Patricia Paula) Dunblane HC, Well Place, Dunblane FK15 9AL Tel: 01786 855295; 16 Coldstream Avenue, Dunblane FK15 9JN Tel: 01786 825192 — MB BCh BAO NUI 1990; DRACOG 1995. (Univ. Coll. Dublin) Princip. GP DunbLa. Socs: BMA.

MCNEILL, Alan Ian Neil Havant Health Centre Suite D, Suite D, Havant Health Centre, Civic Centre Road, Havant PO9 2AP Tel: 023 9247 5010 Fax: 023 9249 2392 — MB ChB 1979 Liverp.; DTM & H Liverp. 1985.

MACNEILL, Alastair Duncan (retired) Flat 2/1, 21 Prince Albert Road, Glasgow G12 9JU Tel: 0141 579 7041 — MB ChB 1944 Glas.; FFHom 1985. Prev: Assoc. Specialist Glas. Homoeop. Hosp.

MCNEILL, Albert John Altnagelvin Area Hospital, Londonderry BT47 6SB Tel: 02871345171 Fax: 02871 611218 Email: amcneill@alt.n-i.nhs.uk — MB BCh BAO 1982 Belf.; MD Belf. 1988; FRCP Ed. 1996; MRCP (UK) 1985; FESC 1995; FRCP Lond. 1997; FRCPI 1999. Cons. Phys. Altnagelvin Area Hosp. Lond.derry; Hon. Cons. Phys. Roy. Vict. Hosp. Belf. Socs: Brit. Cardiac Soc.; Irish Cardiac Soc. Prev: Sen. Regist. Waveney Hosp. Ballymena; Sen. Regist. Roy. Vict. Hosp. Belf.; Brit. Heart Foundat. Fell. Thoraxcenter, Rotterdam.

MCNEILL, Mr Alexander Duncan (retired) 12 Drummond Place, Stirling FK8 2JE Tel: 01786 461867 — MB ChB 1956 Glas.; FRCS Glas. 1963; FRCS Ed. 1963; DObst RCOG 1960. Prev: Cons. Surg. Stirling Roy. Infirm.

MACNEILL, Andrew Lorimer Community Health Sheffield, Fulwood House, Old Fulwood Road, Sheffield S10 3TH Tel: 0114 271 6715 Fax: 0114 271 6378 Email: andrewm@chsheff-tr.trent.nhs.uk; Tel: 0114 262 1032 Email: macneill@legend.co.uk — MB ChB 1971 Glas.; MRCPsych 1975; DPM Ed. & Glas. 1974. Cons. Psychiat. Community Health Sheff.; Med. director Community Health Sheff. NHS Trust. Socs: Roy. Coll. Psychiat.; BMA; Bd. Mem. Assn. of Trust Med. Directors. Prev: Lect. Dept. Psychol. Med. Univ. Glas. at S.. Gen. Hosp. Glas.

MACNEILL, Angus Aviemore Medical Centre, Aviemore PH22 1SY Tel: 01479 810258 Fax: 01479 810067 — MB ChB 1971 Aberd.

MCNEILL, Avril 2 Kilogan Court, Hilden Road, Lambeg, Lisburn — MB BCh BAO 1977 Belf.

MACNEILL, Carolyn Edith (retired) Altramhullin, Manse Brae, Lochgilphead PA31 8RA — MB ChB 1960 Glas.; DTM & H Liverp. 1961. Prev: Med. Off. Baptist Miss. Soc. Hosp. Bolobo-sur-Fleuve, Zaire & CBFZ Disp. Kinshasa, Zaire.

MCNEILL, Carolyn Margaret 28 Beech Crescent, Larbert FK5 3EY — MB ChB 1987 Glas.

MCNEILL, Desmond Lorne Marcus (retired) Beechdene, 11 Purberry Grove, Ewell, Epsom KT17 1LU Tel: 020 8224 8333 Fax: 020 8224 8333 Email: desmac@cwcom.net — MRCS Eng. LRCP Lond. 1947; FRCPsych. 1981, M 1971; DPM Eng. 1959. Prev: Cons. Psychiat. Horton Hosp. Epsom.

MCNEILL, Donald Castletown Medical Practice, Murrayfield, Castletown, Thurso KW14 8TY Tel: 01847 821205 Fax: 01847 821540; Tansfield House, Castletown, Thurso KW14 8UA — MB ChB 1979 Dundee. GP Castletown Caithness. Prev: GP Duns Berwicksh.; SHO Rotat. (Surgic.) Monklands Dist. Gen. Hosp.; SHO (O & G) Warrington Dist. Gen. Hosp.

MACNEILL, Donald (retired) — MB ChB 1951 Aberd. Cons. Orthop. Surg. Stracathro Hosp. Brechin. Prev: GP Hosp. Pract. (Orthop.) Stracathro Hosp. Brechin.

MCNEILL, Mr Donald Cragg 24 Milford Street, Salisbury SP1 2AP Tel: 01722 321735 Fax: 01722 321732 Email: acms@btinternet.com; Mayor Ivie House, Ivy St, Salisbury SP1 2AY

MACNEILL

Tel: 01722 338077 Fax: 01722 321732 — MB BS 1958 Lond.; FRCS (Eng.); FRCS (Ed.) 1968; MRCS Eng. LRCP Lond. 1959; DObst RCOG 1960. (St. Mary's) Hon. Cons. Wessex Regional Centre for Plastic & Maxillofacial Surg. Salisbury; Indep. Pract. Salisbury, S.ampton, Bournemouth, Jersey, Guernsey. Socs: Brit. Inst. Managem.; Brit. Assn. Aesth. Plastic Surg.; Amer. Medicol. Assn. Prev: Cons. Wessex Regional Centre for Plastic Surg; Sen. Lect. Soton. Univ.; Sen. Regist. (Plastic & Maxillofacial Surg.) Hammersmith Hosp. & Wessex Regional Centre Odstock Hosp. Salisbury.

MACNEILL, Dugald Roderick Argyle Street Surgery, 1119 Argyle Street, Glasgow G3 8ND Tel: 0141 248 3698 Fax: 0141 221 5144 — MB ChB 1988 Glas.; MRCGP 1995; DRCOG.

MCNEILL, Elizabeth Trewinnard Cottage, Quay Road, St Agnes TR5 0RT — MB ChB 1991 Glas.

MCNEILL, Emma Jay Marie 5 Manston Approach, Leeds LS15 8BQ — MB BS 1998 Newc.; MB BS Newc 1998.

MACNEILL, Miss Fiona Anne Breast Unit, Essex County Hospital, Colchester CO3 3NB Tel: 01206 744464 Fax: 01206 744654; 12 Beverley Road, Colchester CO3 3NG Tel: 01206 364079 Email: 113631352@compuserve.com — MB BS 1983 Lond.; MD Lond. 1994; FRCS Eng. 1988. (St. Bart.) Clin. BrE. Surg. Colchester Essex. Socs: BASO; MWF; WIST.

MCNEILL, Geraldine Department of Medicine & Therapeutics, University of Aberdeen, Foresterhill, Aberdeen AB25 2ZD Email: g.mcneill@abdn.ac.uk — MB ChB 1980 Birm.; MSc Lon.1982; PhD Lon. 1986. Univ. of Aberd. (Dept. of Med. & Therap.). Socs: Nutrit. Soc.; Assoc. for the study of Obesity; BMA. Prev: Sen. Scientif. Off., Rowett Research Inst., Aberd.; Research Assoc., Lond. Sch. of Hyg. & Trop. Med.

MCNEILL, Graeme Peter Bendochy House, Coupar Angus, Blairgowrie PH13 9BU — MB ChB 1968 St. And.; PhD Dundee 1974; FRCP Ed. 1985; MRCP (UK) 1972. Cons. Cardiol. Ninewells Hosp. Dundee. Prev: Lect. (Med.) Ninewells Hosp. Dundee; Lect. (Cardiol.) McGill Univ. Montreal, Canada.

MCNEILL, Harold George South Tyrone Hospital, Dungannon BT71 4AU Tel: 018687 22821; 14 Quarry Lane, Dungannon BT70 1HX Tel: 018687 23270 — MB BCh BAO 1968 Dub.; FFA RCSI 1976. Cons. Anaesth. S.. Health & Social Serv. Bd. Craigavon. Socs: BMA. & Assn. Anaesth. Gt. Brit. & Irel.

MCNEILL, Iain Stewart Prestonpans Health Centre, Preston Road, Prestonpans EH32 9QS Tel: 01875 810736 Fax: 01875 812979; The Health Centre, Avenue Road, Cockenzie, Prestonpans EH32 Tel: 01875 811011 — MB ChB St. And. 1971; MRC Psych. 1978; MRCGP 1979; DCH RCPS Glas. 1973.

MCNEILL, Mr Ian Fletcher (retired) 14 Westfield Grove, Gosforth, Newcastle upon Tyne NE3 4YA Tel: 01632 52031 — MB BS 1949 (Hons.) Durh.; MS Durh. 1963; FRCS Eng. 1955. Cons. Surg. Roy. Vict. Infirm. Newc. Prev: 1st Asst. Profess. Surg. Unit & Sen. Regist. Roy. Vict. Infirm. Newc.

MCNEILL, Jane Margaret High Street Surgery, 15 High Street, Overton, Wrexham LL13 0ED Tel: 01978 710666 Fax: 01978 710494 (Call before faxing); Clemhill Cottage, New Marton, Oswestry SY11 3HR Tel: 01691 690314 — MB ChB 1978 Ed.

MCNEILL, Jane May 21A Woodford Road, South Woodford, London E18 2EL — MB ChB 1984 Aberd.; FRCA 1990. Cons. Anaesth. Roy. Lond. Hosp.

***MCNEILL, Janette** 4 Tudor Avenue, Newtownabbey BT37 0RS — MB BCh BAO 1993 Belf.

MCNEILL, Jean Johnston (retired) 12 Drummond Place, Stirling FK8 2JE Tel: 01786 461867 — MB ChB 1957 Aberd.; DObst RCOG 1959. Prev: Clin. Asst. (Dermat.) Glas. Roy. Infirm.

MCNEILL, Karalyn Elizabeth McLaren Strathmore Surgery, 19 Jessie Street, Blairgowrie PH10 6BT Tel: 01250 872552 Fax: 01250 874504 — MB ChB 1970 Dundee; DObst RCOG 1972. Princip. GP Blairgowrie Perthsh.

MCNEILL, Lesley Anne Shenaval, Knockbain, Munlochy IV8 8PG — MB ChB 1983 Aberd.

MCNEILL, Owen Anthony 24 Glendun Road, Cushendun, Ballymena BT44 0PX — MB BCh 1998 Belf.; MB BCh Belf 1998.

MCNEILL, Robert James Cumbernauld Road Surgery, 144-146 Cumbernauld Road, Stepps, Glasgow G33 6HA Tel: 0141 779 2330 — MB ChB 1977 Glas.

MCNEILL, Ronald Hay Cumberland Infirmary, X-Ray Department, Newtown Road, Carlisle CA2 7HY Tel: 01228 523 3444 Email: rmcneill@carlh_tr.demon.co.uk — MB ChB 1971 Ed.; FRCR 1978; DMRD Ed. 1975. (Edinburgh) Cons. Radiol. Cumbld. Infirm. Carlisle.

MCNEILL, Ronald Stewart (retired) 64 Bonhard Road, Scone, Perth PH2 6QB Tel: 01738 553113 — MD Ed. 1959, MB ChB 1944; FRCP Ed. 1962, M 1951. Prev: Cons. Phys. Perth Roy. Infirm.

MCNEILL, Sandra Isabel 8 Malone View Park, Belfast BT9 5PN — MB BCh BAO 1989 Belf.

MCNEILL, Mr Stuart Alan Dept. of Urology, Western General Hospital, Crewe Road S., Edinburgh EH12 6ES Tel: 0131 537 1000 Fax: 0131 537 1019; 10 Murrayfield Road, Edinburgh EH12 6EJ — BM BS 1989 Nottm.; BMedSci Nottm. 1987; FRCS Eng. 1994; FRCS Ed. 1994; FRCS (Urol.) 1999. (Nottm) Cons. Urol., W. Gen. Hosp. Edin. Socs: Brit. Assoc. of Urol. Surg.; Europ. Assoc. of Urol.

MCNEILL, Wendy Tansfield House, Castletown, Thurso KW14 8UA — MB ChB 1979 Dundee. Staff Grade Community Paediat. Caithness & Sutherland NHS Trust. Prev: Clin. Med. Off. (Family Plann.) Highland HB.

MCNEILLAGE, Jennifer Anne 201 Mayfield Road, Edinburgh EH9 3BD — MB ChB 1994 Aberd.

MCNEILLIS, Nicholas James Dominic 172 Central Hill, Upper Norwood, London SE19 1DY — MB BS 1993 Lond.

MCNEILLY, James Craig, MBE (retired) 38 Greenleafe Drive, Barkingside, Ilford IG6 1LL — MB BCh BAO 1938 Dub.

MCNEILLY, Paul McNeilly, McKenna and Fearon, 529 Warrington Road, Rainhill, Prescot L35 4LP Tel: 0151 426 2141 Fax: 0151 430 6210 — BM BS 1979 Nottm.; MRCGP 1983; DRCOG 1982; DCH RCP Lond. 1981. GP Prescot. Prev: Govt. Med. Off., Falkland Is.s; GP, Hinckley; Trainee GP Macclesfield VTS.

MCNEILLY, Robert Andrew Bupa Wellness, Battlebridge House, 300 Grays Inn Rd, London WC1X 8DU Tel: 0207 656 2000 — MB BS 1984 Lond.; MRCGP 1988; DCH 1988. Asst. Med. Director BUPA Wellness; Vis. Med. Off., The Priory Gp. Prev: SHO (O & G) Odstock Hosp.; Trainee GP Univ. Exeter VTS.; Ho. Off. (Med.) Qu. Marys Hosp. Roehampton.

MCNEILLY, Robert Henry 19 Park Lane, Woodstock OX20 1UD — MB BCh BAO 1963 Belf.; MSc Lond. 1973; MD Belf 1967; FFCM 1979, M 1974; DObst RCOG 1965. Dir. UK Med. Servs. United Med. Enterprises Lond. Prev: SCM Oxf. RHA.

***MCNEIR, Caroline** 9 Upper Lansdowne Mews, Bath BA1 5HG — MB ChB 1996 Birm.

MCNEISH, Professor Alexander Stewart St. Bartholomew's & Royal London School Medicine & Dentistry, West Smithfield, London EC1 7BE Tel: 020 7601 8806 Fax: 020 7329 2363 Email: a.s.mcneish@qmw.ac.uk; 128 Westfield Road, Edgbaston, Birmingham B15 3JQ Tel: 0121 454 6081 Fax: 0121 456 5465 — MB ChB 1961 Glas.; MSc Birm. 1972; FRCP Glas. 1984; FRCP Lond. 1977, M 1964; MRCP Glas. 1965; FRCPCHC 1996; F Med. Sci. 1998. (Glas.) Warden St. Bart. & Roy. Lond. Sch. Med. & Dent. Lond. Prev: Dir. MRC Clin. Sci. Centre Lond.; Leonard Parsons Prof. of Paediat. & Child Health Birm. Univ.; Foundat. Prof. Child Health Univ. Leicester.

MCNEISH, Christine Isabella Margaret Lightburn Medical Centre, 930 Carntyne Road, Glasgow G32 6NB Tel: 0141 778 0440 Fax: 0141 778 0143 — MB ChB 1977 Glas.; MRCGP 1982; DRCOG 1979.

MCNEISH, Gordon Kenilworth Medical Centre, 1 Kenilworth Court, Greenfaulds, Cumbernauld, Glasgow G67 1BP Tel: 01236 727816 Fax: 01236 726306 — MRCGP 1981; MB ChB 1974 Glasgow; MB ChB 1974 Glasgow.

MCNEISH, Iain Alexander CRC Institute for Cancer Studies, Clinical Research Block, University Birmingham, Birmingham B15 2TA Tel: 0121 414 3291 Fax: 0121 414 3263 Email: i.mcneish@bham.ac.uk; 15 Serpentine Road, Harborne, Birmingham B17 9RD Tel: 0121 426 3247 — BM BCh 1992 Oxf.; BM BCh Oxf. 1922; MA Oxf. 1994, BA 1989; MRCP (UK) 1995. Clin. Research Fell. CRC Inst. for Cancer Studies Univ. Birm. Socs: Assn. Cancer Phys.; Brit. Assn. Cancer Research. Prev: SHO (Med.) W.. Infirm. Glas.

MCNICHOLAS, Fiona Christine Patricia 13C Vanbrugh Hill, Blackheath, London SE3 7UE Tel: 020 8858 7259 — MB BCh BAO 1985 Dub.; MRCPsych 1990; Dip. Psychother. Univ. Lond. 1989.

MCNIE

MCNICHOLAS, James Joseph Kevin 32 Willow Crescent, Great Houghton, Northampton NN4 7AP — MB BS 1994 Lond.; MA Cambs. 1994. SHO (Anaesth.) Roy. Hosp. Haslar Gosport.

MCNICHOLAS, Jane Louise 80 Hunningley Lane, Stairfoot, Barnsley S70 3DT Tel: 01226 244069 Fax: 01226 299402; 113 Ashborne Crescent, Huyton, Bootle L30 4JJ Tel: 0151 481 0784 — MB ChB 1996 Liverp. SHO (Neurosurg.) Walton Centre for Neurol. & Neurosurg.

MCNICHOLAS, Mr Michael James University Department of Orthopaedic & Trauma Surgery, Dundee Royal Infimary, Dundee DD1 9ND Tel: 01382 322803 Fax: 01382 202460 Email: mmcnich732@aol.com; 26 Doocot Road, St Andrews KY16 8QP Tel: 01334 478602 — MB ChB 1989 Manch.; BSc (Med. Sci.) St. And. 1986; FRCS Glas. 1994; FRCS Ed. 1994. Clin. Lect. & Hon. Specialist Regist. (Orthop. & Trauma Surg.) Dundee. Socs: Brit. Orthop. Train. Assn.; Brit. Orthop. Research Soc.; Assoc. Mem. BOA. Prev: Edin. Knee Fell.; Research Fell. (Orthop.) Dundee Roy. Infirm.; Regist. (Orthop.) Stracathro Hosp. Angus.

MCNICHOLAS, Mr Thomas Anthony Department of Urology, Lister Hospital, North Hertfordshire Trust, Corey's Mill Lane, Stevenage SG1 4AB Tel: 01438 781095 Fax: 01438 781270; Elm Tree House, Letchworth Lane, Letchworth SG6 3ND Tel: 01462 683814 Fax: 01462 683815 Email: mcnic@globalnet.co.uk — MB BS 1977 Lond.; FRCS Eng. 1982. (St. Bartholomews) Cons. (Urol. Surg.) Lister Hosp. Stevenage. Socs: Fell. Europ. Bd. Urol.; Fell.Roy. Soc. Med. (Sec. Elect. 2002/3); Brit. Assn. Urol. Surgs. (Mem. of Counc. 1997-2000). Prev: Sen. Regist. St. Peter's Hosps. Lond.; Lect. Acad. Unit Inst. Urol. Lond.; Regist. (Surg.) Univ. Coll. Hosp. Lond.

MCNICHOLAS, Timothy James Fulham Medical Centre, 146 Fulham Road, London SW6 1BG Tel: 020 7385 6001 Fax: 020 7385 3755 — MB ChB 1991 Manch.

MCNICHOLL, Brian Peter Gerald 1.8E Left, Royal Victoria Hospital, Belfast BT12 6BA — MB BCh BAO 1985 NUI; MRCPI 1987.

MCNICHOLL, Feargal Patrick Briery Hill, 9 Shore Road, Faughanvale, Greysteel, Londonderry BT47 3XH — MB BCh BAO 1995 Belf.; MRCP (UK) 1998. SHO Med. Rotat. Roy. Vict. Hosp. Belf. Prev: SHO (Med.) Altnagelvin Area Hosp. Derry.

MCNICHOLL, Anne Marie University Department of Pathology, Royal Infirmary, Castle St., Glasgow G4 0SF Email: a.m.mcnicol@clinmed.gla.ac.uk — MB ChB 1971 Glas.; BSc (Hons. Path.) Glas. 1969, MD (Hons.) 1985, MB ChB 1971; FRCP Glas. 1987; MRCP (UK) 1973; MRCPath 1983; FRCPath 1995. (Glasgow) Reader & Hon. Cons. (Path.) Glas. Roy. Infirm. Socs: Ex-Comm. Mem. Path. Soc. Gt. Brit. & Irel.; Past Pres. Internat Pitutiary Path Club; Internat. Endoarine Path. Soc. Prev: Ho. Surg. Glas. Roy. Infirm.; Ho. Phys. Stobhill Gen. Hosp. Glas.; Ure Schol. Univ. Dept. Med. Glas. Roy. Infirm.

MCNICOL, David Kilmoluag, Appin PA38 4DD — MB ChB 1940 Glas.

MCNICOL, Duncan (retired) 18 Garscadden Road, Glasgow G15 6UN Tel: 0141 944 7214 — MB ChB 1950 Aberd.

MCNICOL, Evelyn Mary (retired) 2 Menzies Drive, Fintry, Glasgow G63 0YG Tel: 01360 860325 — MB ChB Glas. 1952; FRCOG 1984, M 1971; DObst RCOG 1953. Prev: Cons. Obst. Bellshill Hosp.

MCNICOL, Frances Jacqueline 16 Fairlawn Avenue, London N2 9PS; 18 Ballbrook Ave, Didsbury, Manchester M20 3JG — MB ChB 1998 Manch.; MB ChB Manch 1998. SHO (Surg.) Hope Hosp. Manch.

MCNICOL, Professor George Paul, CBE 17 Barton Farm, Cerne Abbas, Dorchester DT2 7LF Tel: 01300 341758 — MB ChB 1952 Glas.; PhD Glas. 1965, MD (Hons. & Bellahouston Medal) 1964; Hon. LLD Aberd. 1992; FRCP Lond. 1977, M 1971; FRCP Ed. 1968, M 1957; FRCP Glas. 1967, M 1962; FRFPS Glas. 1957; Hon. FACP 1972; FRCPath 1977, M 1969. Socs: Hon. Mem. Assn. Phys.; Foreign Correspond. Mem. Roy. Acad. Med. Belgium. Prev: Princip. & Vice-Chancellor Univ. Aberd.; Prof. (Med.) & Cons. Phys. Leeds Gen. Infirm.; Harkness Fell. Commonw. Fund At Washington Univ. St. Louis, Mo.

MCNICOL, Iain David The Surgery, Port Appin, Appin PA38 4DE Tel: 01631 730271 Fax: 01631 730533 — MB ChB 1940 Glasgow; MB ChB Glas 1940. (Glasgow) GP Appin, Argyll.

MCNICOL, Ian Fraser Drongan Surgery, 74 Mill O'Shields Road, Drongan, Ayr KA6 7AY Tel: 01292 591345 Fax: 01292 590782; 18 Hillhead, Coylton KA6 6JR — MB ChB 1973 Glas. GP, Coylton, Ayrsh.

MCNICOL, Irene Janette (retired) 124 Allander Street, Glasgow G22 5JH Tel: 0141 336 8038 — MB ChB Glas. 1957; DObst RCOG 1960.

MCNICOL, John Anderson (retired) 3 Drumchapel Gardens, Glasgow G15 6QD Tel: 0141 944 8641 — MB ChB Glas. 1940.

MCNICOL, Kenneth Martin (retired) Woodwych, Crossways Road, Grayshott, Hindhead GU26 6HD Tel: 01428 604832 Email: mmcm@btconnect.com — MB BChir 1947 Camb.; DObst RCOG 1951. Prev: Med. Adviser Surrey FHSA.

MCNICOL, Leslie Roderick Department of Anaesthesia, Yorkhill NHS Trust, Glasgow G3 8SJ Tel: 0141 201 0186 Fax: 0141 201 0821; 34 Heather Avenue, Bearsden, Glasgow G61 3JE Tel: 0141 942 4656 Fax: 0141 942 9526 Email: amrod@compuserve.com — MB ChB 1969 Glas.; FRCA 1973. Cons. Anaesth. Roy. Hosp. Sick Childr. & Roy. Infirm. Glas.; Hon. Clin. Sen. Lect. Univ. Glas.; Examr. Roy. Coll. Anaesth. Socs: Scott. Soc. Anaesth.; (Counc.) Assn. Paediat. Anaesth. Ex. Treas.; (Counc.) Assn. Anaesth. Gt. Brit. Irel. Prev: Ho. Surg. Glas. Roy. Infirm.; Ho. Phys. S.. Gen. Hosp. Glas.; Regist. (Anaesth.) Glas. Roy. Infirm.

MACNICOL, Mr Malcolm Fraser Red House, 1 South Gillsland Road, Edinburgh EH10 5DE Tel: 0131 447 9104 — MB ChB 1969 Ed.; BSc Ed. (Hons. Pharmacol.) 1966, MB ChB 1969; MChOrth Liverp. 1979; FRCS Ed. 1973; FRCS Ed. (Orth.) 1980; Dip. Sports Med. 1998 (RCS Ed). (Ed.) Cons. Surg. & Sen. Lect. (Orthop.) Edin. Univ.; Scott. Coll. Represen. Special Advis. Gp. Comm. in Orthop. Surg.; Naughton Dunn Lect. Brit. Orthopaed. Assn. Socs: Fell. BOA; Hon. Treas. Roy. Coll. Surgs. Edin.; Brit. Orthop. Research Soc. Prev: Sen. Lect. (Orthop.) Univ. W.. Austral.; Lect. (Orthop.) Edin. Univ.; Research Fell. Harvard Med. Sch.

MCNICOL, Margo Fraser Lindsay and Partners, 1413 Pollokshaws Road, Glasgow G41 3RG Tel: 0141 632 9141 Fax: 0141 636 1288 — MB ChB 1991 Dundee.

MCNICOL, Martin Wilkinson, OBE (retired) 5 Oaklands, somerford Road, Cirencester GL7 1FA — MB ChB 1953 Glas.; FRCP Lond. 1971; FRCP Ed. 1969; FRCP Glas. 1967. Co-ordinator for Know How Fund Samara Health Systems Reform Progr. Prev: Chairm. Centr. Middlx. Hosp. NHS Trust.

MCNICOL, Roderick Andrew 43 Castleton Drive, Newton Mearns, Glasgow G77 5LE — MB ChB 1994 Ed.

***MCNICOL, Ruth Margaret** 27 Marchmont Gardens, Bishopbriggs, Glasgow G64 3DJ — MB ChB 1998 Glas.; MB ChB Glas 1998.

MCNICOL, Susan Moira (retired) 17 Barton Farm, Cerne Abbas, Dorchester DT2 7LF Tel: 01300 341758 — MB ChB 1958 Glas. Prev: Med. Off. Grampian & S. Yorks. Regional Blood Transfus. Serv.

MCNICOLL, Ian Thow Erskine View Clinic, Old Kilpatrick, Glasgow G60 5JG; 108 Prestonfield, Milngavie, Glasgow G62 7PZ — MB ChB 1981 Aberd.

MCNICOLL, Mr William Dudley, Surg. Cdr. RN Retd. The Park Hospital, Sherwood Lodge Drive, Arnold, Nottingham NG5 8RX Tel: 0115 967 0670; The Oaks, 278 Eakring Road, Mansfield NG18 3ES Tel: 01623 644774 — MRCS Eng. LRCP Lond. 1967; FRCS Glas. 1976; DLO Eng. 1971. (Guy's) Cons. Otorhinolaryng. Kings Mill Hosp. Sutton in Ashfield, Mansfield. Socs: Midl. Inst. Otol. & Nottm. M-C Soc. Prev: Cons. & Head Dept. Otorhinolaryng. Roy. Naval Hosp. Haslar; Sen. Regist. Head & Neck Unit & Roy. Marsden Hosp. Lond.; Specialist (Otorhinolaryng.) RN Hosp. Plymouth.

MCNIE, Dhuie John McGregor (retired) — MB BS 1965 Lond.; MRCS Eng. LRCP Lond. 1965. Prev: Paediat. Regist. Qu. Charlotte's Matern. Hosp. Lond.

MCNIE, Mrs Helen Elmbank, 54 South St., Fochabers IV32 7EF — MB ChB 1931 Ed.; TDD Wales, 1937.

MCNIE, Helen Mary McGregor Greenwich District Hospital, Vanbrugh Hill, London SE10 9HE — MB BS 1959 Lond.; MRCS Eng. LRCP Lond. 1959; FRCOG 1981, M 1968. (Roy. Free) Cons. (O & G) Woolwich & Greenwich Dist. Hosps. Prev: Sen. Regist. (O & G) Roy. Free Hosp. Lond.; Regist. Taunton & Som. Hosp.; SHO Jessop. Hosp. Wom. Sheff.

MCNIFF

MCNIFF, Cathal Gerard Patrick 16 Golf Links, Dundrum Road, Newcastle BT33 — MB BCh BAO 1983 Belf.; MRCP (UK) 1986.

MCNINCH, Andrew William The Paediatric unit, Royal Devon and Exeter Hospital, Barrack Road, Exeter EX2 5DW Tel: 01392 452676 — MB BS 1973 Lond.; BSc Lond. 1970; FRCP Lond. 1993; DCH Eng. 1979; FRCPCH; FRCPCH. (St. Bart.) Cons. Paediat. Roy. Devon & Exeter Hosp. Exeter. Socs: Brit. Paediat. Assn. & Brit. Soc. Paediat. Endocrinol. Prev: Sen. Regist. & Regist. (Paediat.) Roy. Hosp. Sick Childr. Bristol; Sen. Regist. (Paediat.) Roy. Devon & Exeter Hosp. Exeter.

MCNIVEN, Archibald Colin Blackhall Medical Centre, 51 Hillhouse Road, Edinburgh EH4 3TH Tel: 0131 332 7696 Fax: 0131 315 2884 — MB ChB 1982 Ed.; DRCOG 1988. GP Edin.

MCNULTY, Cliodna Ann Public Health Laboratory, Gloucestershire Royal Hospital, Great Western Road, Gloucester GL1 3NN Tel: 01452 305334; Villa Vinaria, 95 London Road, Gloucester GL1 3HH Tel: 01452 522334 — MB BS 1981 Lond.; MRCPath 1987; FRCPath 1997. Cons. Microbiol. Gloucester Pub. Health Laborat.

MCNULTY, Ivan Christopher McNulty and Partners, Torkard Hill Medical Centre, Farleys Lane, Shieldfield, Nottingham NG15 6DY Tel: 0115 963 3676 Fax: 0115 968 1957; Farley House, 61 Farleys Lane, Hucknall, Nottingham NG15 6DT — MB BCh BAO 1968 NUI. (Galway) Clin. Asst. (Haemat.) Nottm. City Hosp. Socs: Notts. M-C Soc. Prev: SHO (Paediat.) Derbysh. Childr. Hosp.; SHO (Med.) Derbysh. Roy. Infirm.; SHO (Obst.) Derby City Hosp.

***MCNULTY, Jane Marie** 8 Baslow Road, Leicester LE5 5HD — MB ChB 1995 Leic.

MCNULTY, John Francis Whickham Health Centre, Rectory Lane, Whickham, Newcastle upon Tyne NE16 4PD Tel: 0191 488 5555 Fax: 0191 496 0424 — MB BS 1977 Lond.; BSc Lond. 1974, MB BS 1977; MRCGP 1982. GP Whickham.

MCNULTY, Orla Maire Clare 57 Moyle Road, Ballycastle BT54 6LG — MB BCh BAO 1987 NUI.

MCNULTY, Rebecca Rose 25 Hannington Road, Bournemouth BH7 6JT — MB ChB 1995 Liverp.

MCNULTY, Sarah Jane 66 Liverpool Road, Cadishead, Manchester M44 5AF — MB ChB 1997 Leeds.

MCNULTY, Steven John St. Helens and Knowsley Trust, Liverpool L35 5DN Tel: 0151 426 1600 Fax: 0151 430 1900; 11 Druidsville Road, Allerton, Liverpool L18 3EL Email: sid@doctors.org.uk — MB ChB 1992 Liverp.; MPCP (UK) Glas. 1996. Specialist Regist. (Diabetes) Endo & Gim; Cons. Phys., Diabetologist, Endocrinologist. Socs: Diabetes UK; BMA; MDU.

MCNULTY, Susie Maria 14 Egerton Road, Monton, Eccles, Manchester M30 9LR — MB ChB 1998 Liverp.; MB ChB Liverp 1998.

MCNUTT, Andrew Paul William Health Clinic, Mid Street, Bathgate EH48 1PT Tel: 01506 655155; 2 Low Brae, Torphichen, Edinburgh EH48 4LW Tel: 01506 655252 — MB ChB 1989 Ed.; MRCGP 1994; T(GP) 1994.

MCNUTT, Ann Rosemary Josephine Elms Medical Centre, 31 Hoole Road, Chester CH2 3NH Tel: 01244 351000 — MB BS 1983 Lond. Prev: Trainee GP Guildford VTS; Ho. Off. St. Thos. Hosp. Lond.; Ho. Off. Worthing Hosp. W. Sussex.

MCNUTT, Charles Edward The Ulster Hospital, Dundonald, Belfast BT16 1RH; Roscah House, Kesh, Enniskillen BT93 1RE — MB ChB 1991 Ed.

MCNUTT, Donald Campbell, MBE (retired) Gipsy Meadow, 26 Monckton Road, Gosport PO12 2BQ Tel: 01705 580199 — MB ChB 1950 Ed.; MRCGP 1974; DAvMed Eng. 1968. Prev: GP Gosport.

MCNUTT, Norman Richard 182 Gilford Road, Lurgan, Craigavon BT66 7AH — MB BCh BAO 1950 Dub. (T.C. Dub.) Socs: BMA.

MCOMIE, Heather (retired) 16 Richmond Hill, Bristol BS8 1AT Tel: 0117 973 7887 — MB ChB 1947 Wales; BSc, MB ChB Wales 1947; FFA RCS Eng. 1954; DA Eng. 1951. Prev: Assoc. Hosp. Specialist S. W.. RHA.

MACONOCHIE, Ian Kristen Academic Department of Paediatrics, St. Mary's Hospital, Padington, London W2 1NY Tel: 020 7725 6377; 3 Kingswood Road, London SW2 4JE — MB BS 1984 Lond.; MB BS, LMSSA Lond. 1984; MRCPI 1992. Research Fell. (Paediat.) St. Mary's Hosp. Lond. Prev: Regist. (Cardiac Intens. Care) Gt. Ormond St. Lond.; Clin. Med. Off. W. Lambeth.

MACOUN, Stephen James Robert (retired) 4 Lewes Crescent, Kemptown, Brighton BN2 1FH Tel: 01273 697636 — MA Camb. 1966, BA 1938, MB; BChir 1942; FRCP Lond. 1970, M 1943; MRCS Eng. LRCP Lond. 1942; FRCPCH 1997. Prev: Cons. Paediat. S.W. Thames RHA.

MACOUSTRA, Stuart Alexander Swindon Health Centre, Carfax Street, Swindon SN1 1ED Tel: 01793 692062; Woolstanton, Ham Road, Liddington, Swindon SN4 0HH Tel: 01793 709100 — MB ChB 1976 Liverp.; DRCOG 1979; Cert Family Plann 1979; D. Occ. Med. 1996. Police Surg.; Med. Adviser W. H. Smith Ltd Swindon. Socs: Soc. Occup. Med. Prev: SHO (O & G.) Walton & Fazakerley Hosps. Liverp.; N. Gwent VTS Abergavenny.

MCOWAN, Alan Gordon The Victoria Clinic for Sexual Health, 82 Vincent Square, London SW1P 2PF — MB BS 1989 Lond.; MRCP (UK) 1994; DFFP 1998. Cons. (GUM/HIV Med.) Chelsea & W.m. Healthcare. Socs: Internat. AIDS Soc.; Med. Soc. Study VD; BMA. Prev: Sen. Regist. (GUM/HIV Med.) Mortimer Market Centre Lond.

MCOWAN, Margaret McMillan Richmond Surgery, Richmond Close, Fleet GU52 7US Tel: 01252 625466; The Kyles, Victoria Hill Road, Fleet GU51 4LG Tel: 01252 617215 — MB ChB 1962 Glas. (Glas.) Med. Off. Family Plann. Clin. Fleet Hosp.; Med. Off. Family Plann. Camberley Health Centre. Prev: Asst. Sch. Med. Off. Bordon.

MCPARLAND, Monica Grace 17 Chepstow Villas, London W11 3DZ — MB BCh BAO 1984 Belf.

MCPARLAND, Penelope Clare 58 King Street, Enderby, Leicester LE9 5NT — MB BS 1992 Newc.

MCPARLIN, Michael James 23 Downing Drive, Morpeth NE61 2YB — MB ChB 1993 Manch.

MCPARTLIN, Mr David Walter 25 The Cedars, St. Stephen's Road, Ealing, London W13 8JF — MB BS 1992 Lond.; FRCS Eng. 1997; FRCS (Oto.) Eng. 1998. (London Hospital Medical College)

MCPARTLIN, Gerald Maurice 54 Moira Park, Edinburgh EH7 6RU; Tel: 0131 667 8224 — MB BS 1978 Lond.; BSc St. And. 1966; FRCGP 1999. Sen.Lect. Lect. Dept. Gen. Pract. Edin. Univ.

MCPARTLIN, Mr John Francis 6 Radnor Cliff, Folkestone CT20 2JN Tel: 01303 248381 — BM BCh 1962 Oxf.; BA 1962; FRCS Eng. 1969. (Lond. Hosp.) Cons. Gen. Surg. Kent Health Trust. Socs: BMA; Ass. SNRG. G.B & I. Prev: Sen. Regist. (Surg.) Lond. Hosp.

MCPARTLIN, Shona 9/3 Grange Manor, South Oswald Road, Edinburgh EH9 2HQ — MB ChB 1998 Glas. (Glas. Univ.)

MCPEAKE, James Richard Department of Medicine, Royal Alexander Hospital, Paisley PA2 9PN Tel: 0141 580 4391 Fax: 0141 887 6701 Email: james.mcpeake@rah.scot.nhs.uk; 12 Grosvenor Crescent, Glasgow G12 9AF Tel: 0141 337 2422 — MB BS 1985 Lond.; FCRA 2001 Glas.; MRCP (UK) 1989. (Guy's Hosp. Lond.) Cons. Phys. & Gastroenterol. Roy. Alexandra Hosp. Paisley; Hon. Clin. Sen. Lect. Med. Glas. Univ. Socs: Brit. Soc. Gastroenterol.; Brit. Assn. Study Liver; Scott. Soc. Phys. Prev: Sen. Regist. (Med.) W.ern Infirm. Glas.; Clin. Research Fell. Liver Unit & Inst. Liver Studies King's Coll. Hosp. Lond.; Regist.(Med.) Kent & Canterbury Hosp.

MCPHADEN, Allan Russell Department of Pathology, Glasgow Royal Infirmary, Glasgow G4 0SF Tel: 0141 211 4224 Fax: 0141 211 4884 — MB ChB 1982 Glas.; BSc (Hons.) Glas. 1980, MD 1991; MRCPath 1992. Sen. Lect. & Cons. Histopath. Univ. Dept. Path. Glas. Roy. Infirm.

MCPHAIL, Alastair Lewin 14 Moorside Road, West Moors, Ferndown BH22 0EJ — BM 1997 Soton.

MACPHAIL, Alison Katrina 3Greenfield Court, Balfron, Glasgow G63 0QG — MB ChB 1994 Aberd.

MACPHAIL, Carol Victoria 162 Newton Road, Great Barr, Birmingham B43 6BU Tel: 0121 358 1595 — MB BS Durh. 1966; DObst RCOG 1970; DCH Eng. 1969. (Newc.) Sen. Med. Off. Sandwell Healthcare NHS Trust.

MACPHAIL, Donald Ian Clackmannan and Kincardine Medical Practice, Health Centre, Main Street, Clackmannan FK10 4JA Tel: 01259 723725 Fax: 01259 724791 — MB ChB 1980 Dundee. (Dundee) Socs: MRCH.

MACPHAIL, Hugh Norman (retired) 17 Kingsburgh Road, Edinburgh EH12 6DZ Tel: 0131 337 2009 — MB ChB 1950 Aberd.; MRCGP 1966. Prev: Med. Adviser Bank Scotl.

MCPHAIL, Iain James The Stable House, Reswallie, Forfar DD8 2SA — MB ChB 1995 Dundee.

MACPHAIL, Ian (retired) Muirfield, London Road, Hook RG27 9EQ Tel: 01256 763381 — MB ChB Ed. 1937; FFA RCS Eng. 1956; DA Eng. 1954. Prev: Mem. Assn. Anaesths. & BMA.

MACPHAIL, John Barrie (retired) 19 Fieldhouse Close, Hepscott, Morpeth NE61 6LU — MB ChB 1962 Glas. Prev: GP Morpeth.

MCPHAIL, Lorna Martin The Cockit Hat, Clathy/Gask, Crieff PH7 3PH Tel: 0173 873215 — MB BS 1963 Lond.; Dip. Forens. Med. Glas 1993. (St. Bart.) Prev: GP & Police Surg. Perth.

MACPHAIL, Malcolm 22 Houndsden Road, Winchmore Hill, London N21 1LT Tel: 020 8360 5799 — MB ChB St. And. 1959. Socs: BMA. Prev: Med. Regist. Hackney Hosp. & Bethnal Green Hosp.

MACPHAIL, Mary Marjorie Vue De L'Hyvreuse, Candie Road, St Peter Port, Guernsey GY1 1U — MB ChB 1933 Glas. Socs: BMA.

MCPHAIL, Neil John c/o Gilvear, 56 Ballochney St., Airdrie ML6 OLE — MB ChB 1998 Glas.; MB ChB Glas 1998.

MCPHAIL, Patricia Mary Anwoth, Erskine Road, Gullane EH31 2DQ Tel: 01620 843216 — MB ChB 1980 Ed.; DRCOG 1984. (Ed.) Clin. Asst. (Diabetes) Roy. Infirm. Edin.

MACPHAIL, Sheila Department of Obstetrics & Gynaecology, 4th Floor, Leazes Wing, Royal Victoria Hospital, Newcastle upon Tyne NE7 7LS Tel: 0191 232 5131 Fax: 0191 222 5066 Email: sheila.macphail@ncl.ac.uk; 29 The Cloisters, Gosforth, Newcastle upon Tyne NE7 7LS Tel: 0191 285 7688 — BM 1981 Soton.; PhD Newc. 1993; MRCOG 1986. Sen. Lect. (O & G) Univ. Newc.; Clin. Sub-Dean, Med. Sch. Newc. Univ. Socs: Soc. Perinatal Obst.; Brit. Assn. Perinatal Med. Prev: Sen. Regist. N.. RHA; Matern. Fetal Med. Fell. Univ. Toronto, Canada.

MCPHATE, Gordon Ferguson School of Biomedical Sciences, Bute Medical Buildings, University of St Andrews, St Andrews KY16 9TS Tel: 01334 463597 Fax: 01334 463600 Email: gfm1@st.and.uk — MB ChB 1974 Aberd.; FRCP Ed. 1997; MSc Surrey 1986; MA Camb. 1981, BA 1977, MD 1988; MTh Edin 1994. Sen. Lect. (Physiol. & Path.) Univ. St. And.; Hon. Cons. Chem. Path. Fife Hosps. Socs: Assn. Clin. Biochem.; Assoc. Mem. RCPath. Prev: Lect. (Physiol.) Guy's Hosp. Med. Sch. Lond.; Regist. (Chem. Path.) St. Luke's Hosp. Guildford.

MCPHATER, Archibald 3 Rysland Crescent, Newton Mearns, Glasgow G77 6EB — MD 1943 Glas.; MB ChB (Hons. Distinc. Surg. & McEwan Medal) 1936; FRCP Glas. 1964; FRFPS Glas. 1941. Prev: Cons. Phys. Vict. Infirm. Glas.

MCPHEAT, Anne Summers 40 Provost Smith Crescent, Inverness IV2 3TG — MB ChB 1978 Glas.; DRCOG 1980. (Glas. Univ.) Clin. Med. Off., Community Child Health,. Prev: Doctors Retainer Scheme Gen. Pract.; Sessional Community Med. Off. Community Child Health Sch. Serv.

MACPHEE, Graeme James Andrew Department of Medicine for the Elderly, Southern General Hospital, 1345 Govan Road, Glasgow G51 4TF; 17 Burnside, Bearsden, Glasgow G61 4PX — MB ChB 1979 Dundee; FRCP Glas. 1993; MRCP (UK) 1983. Cons. Phys. (Geriat. Med.) S.. Gen. Hosp. Glas.; Hon. Clin. Sen. Lect. Univ. Glas. Prev: Sen. Regist. Vict. Geriat. Unit Glas.; Regist. (Med.) W.. Infirm. Glas.

MACPHEE, Iain Angus MacGregor Division of Renal Medicine, St. George's Hospital Med. School, Cranmer Terrace, London SW17 0RE Tel: 020 8725 5035 Fax: 020 8725 5036 Email: imacphee@sghms.ac.uk — BM BCh 1991 Oxf.; DPhil Oxf. 1988; BSc (Hons.) Glas. 1985; MRCP (UK) 1994; CCST Renal Med 1998. (Univ. Oxf.) Sen. Clin. Res. Fell. St. Geo.'s Hosp. Med. Sch.; Hon. Cons. Nephrologist, St. Geo.'s Hosp. Lond. Prev: Sen. Regist. In Renal Med. St. Geo.'s. Hosp. Lond.; Career Regist. (Nephrol.) W.. Infirm. Glas.; Regist. (Med.) Stirling Roy. Infirm.

MCPHEE, Kevin 35 Millston Close, Naisberry Park, Hartlepool TS26 0PX — MB ChB 1998 Glas.

MCPHEE, Stuart Gerard The Turret Medical Centre, Catherine Street, Kirkintilloch, Glasgow G66 1JB Tel: 0141 211 8260 Fax: 0141 211 8264 — MB ChB 1990 Dundee.

MACPHEE, Susan Jane Department of Public Health Medicine, NHS Grampian, Summerfied House, 2 Eday Road, Aberdeen AB15 6RE Tel: 01224 558476 Fax: 01224 558609; Clayford, Insch AB52 6PS — MB ChB 1977 Manch.; BSc St. And. 1974; MFCM 1989; FFPHM 2000. Cons. Pub. Health Med. NHS Grampian.

MACPHEE, William Peter Parkhead Health Centre, 101 Salamanca Street, Glasgow G31 5BA Tel: 0141 531 9058 Fax: 0141 531 9026; 42 Stirling Drive, Bearsden, Glasgow G61 4NT — MB ChB 1982 Glas.; BDS Glas. 1976. Hon. Clin. Sen. Lect., Dept. of Gen. Pract., Univ. of Glas.

MACPHERSON, Agnes Cochrane (retired) Ben Alder, 15 Lubnaig Road, Newlands, Glasgow G43 2RY Tel: 0141 632 0723 — MB ChB 1946 Glas.; DPH 1949; MFCM 1974. Community Med. Specialist Argyll & Clyde Health Bd. Prev: Dep. MOH Burgh E. Kilbride.

MACPHERSON, Alan Gordon Henry Whin Park Medical Centre, 6 Saughton Road, Edinburgh EH11 3RA Tel: 0131 455 7999 Fax: 0131 455 8800 — MB ChB 1976 Edinburgh; MB ChB Edin 1976. (Edinburgh) GP Edin.

MACPHERSON, Alyson Maxine Addington Street Surgery, 69 Addington Street, Ramsgate CT11 9JQ Tel: 01843 593544 Fax: 01843 594310 — MB BS 1991 Lond. (Roy. Free Hosp.) GP.

MCPHERSON, Andrew Maryhill Practice, Elgin Health Centre, Maryhill, Elgin IV30 1AT Tel: 01343 543788 Fax: 01343 551604; Cockmuir House, Longmorn, Elgin IV30 8SL Tel: 01343 806227 — MB ChB 1980 Aberd.; MRCGP 1984. (Aberdeen) Assoc. advisor Gen. Pract.

MACPHERSON, Andrew James Sacre Institute of Experimental Immunology, Universitatsspital, Schmelzbergstrasse 12, CH8091,, Zurich, Switzerland Tel: 1 255 3785 (+41) (lab), 1 255 4139 (+41) Fax: 1 255 4420 Email: amacpher@pathol.unizh.ch; 43 Pathfield, Torrington EX38 7BX — MB BChir 1985 Camb.; MA Camb. 1983, PhD 1982, MPhil 1980, MB BChir 1985; MRCP (UK) 1987. MRC Clin. Sci. & Hon. Cons. Phys. Med. King's Coll. Hosp. Lond. Prev: MRC Train. Fell. & Hon. Sen. Regist. (Med.) King's Coll. Hosp. Lond.; Hon. Regist. (Med.) MRC Clin. Research Centre. N.wick Pk. Hosp. Lond.; SHO Leicester Roy. Infirm.

MCPHERSON, Angus Francis (retired) 4 Shepherds Croft, Southview Road, Findon, Worthing BN14 0UA — MB BS 1970 Lond.; MRCPsych 1977. Cons. Psychiat. Acre Day Hosp. Worthing. Prev: Cons. Psychiat. Graylingwell Hosp. Chichester.

MACPHERSON, Ann, CBE Beaumont Street Surgery, 19 Beaumont Street, Oxford OX1 2NA Tel: 01865 240501 Fax: 01865 240503 Email: maclennan@beaumont19.oxongps.co.uk; 25 Norham Road, Oxford OX2 6SF Tel: 01865 558743 Fax: 01865 463474 Email: ann.mcpherson@dphpc.ox.ac.uk — MB BS 1968 Lond.; FRCP 2001; FRCGP 1978, M 1993; DCH Eng. 1971. (St. Geo.) p/t GP; Lect. Univ. Dept. of Primary Care, Univ. of Oxf. Socs: BMA; MDU; Oxf. Med. Soc. Prev: Med. Off. John Radcliffe Hosp. Oxf.; Med. Off. (Dermat.) Slade Hosp. Oxf.

MCPHERSON, Barbara The Surgery, Back Lane, Stillington, York YO61 1LL Tel: 01347 810332; 3 Woodyard Court, Easingwold, York YO61 3QR — MB ChB 1984 Aberd.; MRCGP 1990; DRCOG 1989.

MACPHERSON, Barbara Christine Mitchell Department of Radiology, Wishaw General Hospital, 50 Netherton Street, Wishaw ML2 0DP Tel: 01698 366516; 11 Tinto Road, Glasgow G43 2AP Tel: 0141 637 1636 — MB ChB 1984 Glas.; MRCP (UK) 1987; FRCR 1990; FRCP (Glas) 1998; MBA (Keele) 1999. Cons. Radiol., Wishaw Gen. Hosp., Wishaw; Hon. Clin. Sen. Lect. Univ. of Glas. Prev: Sen. Regist. (Radiol.) Roy. Infirm. Glas.

MACPHERSON, Catherine 64 Ashley Avenue, Belfast BT9 7BU — MB BCh BAO 1987 Belf.; MRCGP 1992.

MACPHERSON, Catherine Keith 5 Camstradden Drive W., Bearden, Glasgow G61 4AJ Tel: 0141 942 0506 — MB ChB 1970 Glas.

MACPHERSON, Christine Margaret Hollybush Villa, 42 Cathkin Road, Langside, Glasgow G42 9UH Tel: 0141 632 2970; Toberaie, Nethy Bridge PH25 3EE — MB ChB 1986 Glas.

MACPHERSON, Mr David Symon Benenden Hospital, Cranbrook TN17 4AX Tel: 01580 240333 Fax: 01580 240021 — BM BCh 1972 Oxf.; MD Leic. 1984; FRCS Eng. 1978; DObst RCOG 1976. (Univ. Oxf.) Cons. Gen. Surg. Benenden Hosp. Kent. Socs: Vas. Surg. Soc. GB & Irel.; Fell. Assn. Surgs. Prev: Cons. Gen. & Vasc. Surg. Leicester; Regist. (Surg.) Leicester Roy. Infirm.; SHO (Gen. Surg.) Nuffield Dept. Surg. Radcliffe Infirm. Oxf.

MACPHERSON, Mr David William St Richards Hospital, Chichester PO19 4SE Tel: 01243 788122 Fax: 01243 831544; Summit House, Torton Hill Road, Arundel BN18 9HF — MB BS 1984 Lond.; FDS RCS 1986 Eng.; BDS 1974 Lond.; FRCS 1988 Ed. (Roy. Free) Cons. Maxillofacial Surg. St Richard's Hosp. Chichester & Worthing Hosp. Trusts. Socs: Fell. Brit. Assn. Oral & Maxillofacial

MCPHERSON

Surg.; BMA; Roy. Soc. Med. Prev: Sen. Regist. Rotat. SW Thames; Regist. (Maxillofacial Surg.) Univ. Coll. Hosp. Lond.

MCPHERSON, Derek (retired) Orchard Cottage, Maypole, Monmouth NP25 5QH Tel: 01600 715195 — MB BS 1964 Lond.

MACPHERSON, Duncan Andrew Richmond House, 79 Whitehall, London SW1A 2NL Tel: 020 7210 5769; The Fountain House, 7 South St, Lewes BN7 2BT Tel: 01273 471592 — MB BS 1965 Lond.; DA Eng. 1970; DObst RCOG 1969. (St. Bart.) Head of Emerg. Plann. Unit, Dept. of Health. Prev: Regional Med. Off. DHSS S.. Div.; GP Harwich & DoverCt.; Med. Off. Zambia Flying Doctor Serv.

MACPHERSON, Elizabeth Seonag Coldside Medical Practice, 129 Strathmartine Road, Dundee DD3 8DB Tel: 01382 826724 Fax: 01382 884129 — MB ChB 1984 Dundee; MRCGP 1988; DRCOG 1987.

MACPHERSON, Elizabeth Steele 3 Derinilla Lane, Dundrum, Newcastle BT33 0SY — MB BCh BAO 1976 Belf. Cas. Off. Moyle Hosp. Larne.

MCPHERSON, Emma Anne Accident and Emergency Department, Glasgow Royal Infirmary, 84 Castle Street, Glasgow G4 0SF — MB ChB 1995 Glas.

MCPHERSON, Ewan Cameron Isla Mount, Coupar Angus, Blairgowrie PH13 9AU — MB ChB 1968 St. And.; DA Eng. 1971.

MACPHERSON, George Gordon Sir William Dunn School of Pathology, South Parks Road, Oxford OX1 3RE Tel: 01865 57321 — BM BCh 1966 Oxf.; DPhil Oxf. 1973, BM BCh 1966. (Oxf.) Univ. Lect. Experim. Path. Univ. Oxf.; Fell. & Tutor in Med. Oriel Coll. Oxf. Socs: Brit. Soc. Immunol. & Brit. Transpl.. Soc. Prev: 1st Florey Fell. Biomed. Research John Curtin Sch. Med. Research; Canberra, Australia; MRC Jun. Research Fell. Sir William Dunn Sch. Path. Oxf.

MACPHERSON, George Robert (retired) 15 Culduthel Road, Inverness IV2 4AG Tel: 01463 234361 — MB ChB 1944 Aberd.; DObst RCOG 1953. Prev: Ho. Phys. Woodend Hosp. Aberd. & City Hosp. Aberd.

MCPHERSON, Mr Gilbert Alexander Dobbie Peppard House, Forty Green Road, Beaconsfield HP9 1XL — BM BCh 1973 Oxf.; MA (Phys.) Oxf. 1973, MCh, DM Oxf. 1986; FRCS Eng. 1978. (Oxf. & Univ. Coll. Hosp.) Cons. Surg. S. Bucks. NHS Trust; Surg. Tutor Wycombe Dist. 1989; Lead Clinician Cancer SBNHS Trust 1997; Lead BrE. Cancer 1996-. Socs: Fell. Roy. Soc. Med. & Assn. Surgs.; Ct. Exam. RCS Eng.; Vasc. Surg. Soc. & Assn. Coloproctol. Prev: Sen. Regist. & Resid. Surgic. Off. Hammersmith Hosp. Lond.; Sen. Regist. (Surg.) Roy. Berks. & Battle Hosps. Reading.; Ho. Surg. Surg. Unit Univ. Coll. Hosp. Lond.

MACPHERSON, Gordon (retired) The Retreat, Mill Lane, Hooe, Battle TN33 9HS Tel: 01424 893008 — MB BS 1955 Lond. Edr. Black's Med. Directory. Prev: Dep. Edr. BMJI.

MACPHERSON, Gordon Hugh Alexandra Hospital, Redditch B98 7UB Tel: 01527 503030 Fax: 01527 517432; 20 Marlborough Avenue, Bromsgrove B60 2PF Tel: 01527 879474 Fax: 01527 879474 — MB ChB 1967 Glas.; FRCOG 1993, M 1973. Cons. O & G Alexandra Hosp. Redditch. Prev: Lect. (O & G) Univ. Dundee.

MCPHERSON, Harry 2 Edgehill Road, Aberdeen AB15 5JH — MB ChB 1959 Aberd.

MACPHERSON, Helen Mary The Surgery, 20 Low Road, Debenham, Stowmarket IP14 6QU Tel: 01728 860248 Fax: 01728 861300 — MB BS 1983 Lond.; BSc (Hons.) Lond. 1980, MB BS 1983; DRCOG 1987.

MACPHERSON, Herbert The Croft, Croft Hill Road, Elleker, Brough HU15 2DE Tel: 01430 423814 — LRCP LRCS 1941 Ed.; LRCP LRCS Ed. LRFPS Glas. 1941; AFOM RCP Lond. 1988; DIH Soc. Apoth. Lond. 1961. (Manch.) Gp. Med. Adviser Ideal Standard Ltd. Hull; Med. Adviser United Towing Ltd. & Horlands Printers Hull. Prev: Med. Adviser Stelrad.

MACPHERSON, Hilary Dawn Department of Obstetrics and Gynaecology, Edinburgh Royal Infirmary, Edinburgh EH3 9YW; 85 Trinity Road, Edinburgh EH5 3JX — MB ChB 1979 Ed.; MRCOG 1984; DCH RCP Lond. 1982; MBA 1998. Cons. O & G Edin. Roy. Infirm. Prev: Cons. O & G Falkirk & Dist. Roy. Infirm.

MACPHERSON, Iain 5 Camstradden Drive W., Bearsden, Glasgow G61 4AJ Tel: 0141 942 0506 — LRCP LRCS 1966 Ed.; LRCP LRCS Ed. LRCPS Glas. 1966.

***MACPHERSON, Iain Roderick James** Edgehill, Brighton Road, Cupar KY15 5DH — MB ChB 1998 Glas.; MB ChB Glas 1998.

MACPHERSON, Ian (retired) 65 Drakies Avenue, Inverness IV2 3SD — MB ChB 1952 Glas. Prev: Regist. (Med.) & Assoc. Specialist. (Bact.) Raigmore Hosp. Inverness.

MCPHERSON, Ian Stuart Hayman House, 8 Tivoli St., Cheltenham GL50 2UW Tel: 01242 519990 Fax: 01242 576570 Email: ian_mcpherson@msn.com — MB BS 1978 Lond.; MRCGP 1985; MFFP 1993; DRCOG 1984; Cert. Family Plann. JCC 1984; DA Eng. 1980; Cert. Av. Med. 1992. (St. George's) Assoc. GP BRd.way Worcs; Sen. Clin. Med. Off. (Family Plann.) E. Glos. & Severn NHS Trusts; Lect. (Obst. & Gyn.) Birm. Med. Sch. Prev: Unit Med. Off. RAF Innsworth Gloucester.; SCMO (Gyn.) E. Glos. NHS Trust.

MACPHERSON, James Hector Keresley Road, 2 Keresley Road, Coventry CV6 2JD Tel: 024 7633 2628 Fax: 024 7633 1326; 2 Keresley Road, Coventry CV6 2JD — MRCS Eng. LRCP Lond. 1977.

MCPHERSON, James John Sunny Bank Cottage, Stock Green, Redditch B96 6TA — MB BS 1975 Lond.; FFA RCS Eng. 1980. (St. Thos.) Cons. Anaesth. Alexandra Hosp. Redditch. Prev: Sen. Regist. (Anaesth.) Univ. Hosp. Wales, Cardiff; Regist. (Anaesth.) Univ. Hosp. Wales Cardiff & Roy. Berks. Hosp.; Reading.

MCPHERSON, James Ritchie Morar, 139 Queens Road, Fraserburgh AB43 9PU — MB ChB 1945 Aberd.

MACPHERSON, Jane Isabel (retired) 65 Drakies Avenue, Inverness IV2 3SD — MB ChB 1960 Aberd. Prev: GP Inverness.

MACPHERSON, Janet Elizabeth Muckamore Abbey Hospital, 1 Abbey Road, Muckamore, Antrim BT41 4SH Tel: 018494 63333 — MB BCh BAO 1988 Belf.; MRCPsych 1993; DMH Belf. 1991. Cons. Psychiat. (Learning Disabil.) Muckamore Abbey Hosp. Co. Antrim.

MCPHERSON, Jeffrey Stuart Godden Green Clinic, Godden Green, Sevenoaks TN15 0JR Tel: 01732 763491 Fax: 01732 763160 — MRCS Eng. LRCP Lond. 1976; MRCPsych 1984; DRCOG 1978. (Rhodesia) Cons. Psychiat. Godden Green Clinic, Sevenoaks. Socs: BMA; Marcé Soc.; Fell. Roy. Soc. Med. Prev: Cons. Psychiat. S. Derbysh. Ment. Health Trust; Sen. Lect. (Psychiat.) RAMC Millbank; Sen. Specialist (Psychiat.) Qu. Eliz. Milit. Hosp. Woolwich.

MCPHERSON, Jennifer Vivienne (Hardman) 3 Monmouth Gardens, Ashurst Bridge, Southampton SO40 2QN Tel: 02380 860529 — MB ChB 1992 Manch.; FRCR 2000; MRCP (UK) 1995. (Manch.) Specialist Regist. (Radiol.) Soton. Gen. Hosp. Wessex. Prev: Regist. (Gen. Med. & Gastroenterol.) Jersey Gen. Hosp.; SHO (Gen. Med.) Manch. Roy. Infirm.; SHO (Gen. Med.) N. Manch. Gen. Hosp.

MACPHERSON, Jessie Blair Cytology Department (Pathology Department), Medical School, Forresterhill, Aberdeen AB25 2ZD Tel: 01224 681818 Fax: 01224 663002; 15 Crollshillock Place, Newtonhill, Stonehaven AB39 3RF Tel: 01569 730963 — MB ChB 1975 Aberd. Med. Off. (Cytol.) Aberd. Roy. Hosps. NHS Trust. Prev: Clin. Med. Off. (Child Health & Family Plann.) Grampian Healthcare NHS Trust.

MACPHERSON, John James Donald (retired) Heath Cottage, Uplands Road, Bromborough, Wirral CH62 2BY — MB ChB 1951 Liverp.; MRCS Eng. LRCP Lond. 1951. Prev: Med. Off. Cammell Laird & Co. Birkenhead.

MACPHERSON, John Martin Templehill Surgery, 23 Templehill, Troon KA10 6BQ Tel: 01292 312012 Fax: 01292 317594; Southlands, Bentinck Crescent, Troon KA10 6JN — MB ChB 1980 Dundee; BSc 1976 (Hons.) Dundee; MRCGP 1984; DRCOG 1983.

MACPHERSON, John Niall Diabetic Day Centre, Crosshouse Hospital, Kilmarnock KA2 0BE Tel: 01563 521133 Email: niall.macpherson@aaaht.scot.nhs.uk — MB ChB 1971 Ed.; BSc (Hons.) Ed. 1968, MB ChB 1971; FRCP Glas. 1992; FRCP Ed. 1988; MRCP (UK) 1975. Cons. Phys. CrossHo. Hosp. Kilmarnock. Prev: Sen. Regist. (Med.) Ninewells Hosp. Dundee.

MACPHERSON, Lesley Katharine Ruth Radiological Department, Birmingham Children's Hospital NHS Trust, Steelhouse lane, Birmingham B4 6NH Tel: 0121 333 9736 — MB ChB 1990 Sheff.; FRCR 1997. Cons. Paediatric Radiologist, Birm. Childr.'s Hosp., SteelHo. La., Birm. Prev: Paediatric NeuroRadiol. Fell. (Hosital for Sick Childr., Toronto); Paediaric Radiol. Fell. (Roy. Childr.s Hosp., Melbourne); Specialist Regist. Radiol. (W. Midl.s Radiol. Rotat.).

MACPHERSON, Margaret Crawford (retired) 21 Westbourne Crescent, Bearsden, Glasgow G61 4HB Tel: 0141 942 3785 — MB ChB Glas. 1943. Prev: Clin. Med. Off. Community Health Glas. Pub. Health Dept.

MACPHERSON, Margaret Murchison 34 Byron Court, 26 Mecklenburg Square, London WC1N 2AG Tel: 020 7837 9552 —

MB ChB 1958 Glas.; DA RCPSI 1963. Airport Med. Off. Health Control Unit Lond. Airport (Heathrow). Prev: Staff Anaesth. Wilhelmina Gasthuis Univ. Amsterdam; Med. Adviser Wellcome Foundat. Ltd. Scand. & Netherlands; Med. Off. MRC Head Office Lond.

MACPHERSON, Marion Barr Allison 11 Regent Street, Nottingham NG1 5BS Tel: 0115 947 5475 — MB ChB 1974 Aberd.; DM Nottm. 1989; MRCOG 1981; DRCOG 1977; FRCOG 1994. (Aberdeen) Cons. O & G Univ. Hosp. Nottm. Socs: Birm. & Midl. Gyn. Res. Soc.; Birm. & Midl. Obst. & Gyn. Soc.; Gyn. Res. Soc.

MCPHERSON, Marjorie Rae (retired) 9 Abbey Road, Westbury-on-Trym, Bristol BS9 3QN — MB ChB 1947 Ed. Prev: Clin. Asst. Geriat. Day Hosp. Frenchay Hosp. Bristol.

MACPHERSON, Michael James Peter Culduthel Road Surgery, Ardlarich, 15 Culduthel Road, Inverness IV2 4AG Tel: 01463 712233 Fax: 01463 715479; 41B Dores Road, Inverness IV2 4QU — MB ChB 1980 Ed.; LLB Ed. 1973; BSc Ed. 1977, MB ChB 1980, MRCGP 1984. Prev: Ho. Off. City Hosp. Edin.; SHO Psychiat. Roy. Edin. Hosp.; SHO Med. Deaconess Hosp. Edin.

MACPHERSON, Murray James 22 Viewpark Drive, Rutherglen, Glasgow G73 3QD — MB ChB 1993 Glas.

MACPHERSON, Peter (retired) Ben Alder, 15 Lubnaig Road, Newlands, Glasgow G43 2RY Tel: 0141 632 0723 — LRCP LRCS Ed. LRFPS Glas. 1947; FRCP Glas. 1984, M 1982; FRCR 1975; FFR 1969; DMRD Eng. 1967; DTCD (Distinc.) Wales 1960. Cons. Neuroradiol. Inst. Neurol. Sci. Glas. Prev: Sen. Regist. (Radiodiag.) W.. Infirm. Glas.

MACPHERSON, Rhona Isabel The Surgery, 111 Pembroke Road, Clifton, Bristol BS8 3EU Tel: 0117 973 3790 — MB ChB 1981 Bristol; MRCGP 1987; DFFP 1993; Dip. Obst. Otago 1988. (Bristol) SCMO (Family Plann.) United Bristol Healthcare Trust. Socs: Bristol M-C Soc. Prev: SHO (O & G) ChristCh., NZ; SHO (Psychiat.) Barrow Hosp. Bristol; SHO (Gen. Med.) Frenchay Hosp. Bristol.

MACPHERSON, Robert Buchanan Mountfield Cottage, Staple St., Hernhill, Faversham ME13 9TY Tel: 01227 750468 — MB ChB 1952 Ed.; DObst RCOG 1956; MRCGP.

MACPHERSON, Robertson Wotton Lawn, Horton, Gloucester GL1 3PX Tel: 01452 395741 — MB ChB 1986 Leic.; MD Bristol 1995; MRCPsych 1990. Cons. Psychiat. (Gen. & Rehabil. Wotton Lawn Severn NHS Trust Gloucester.

MCPHERSON, Mr Roger James Eoin Univ. Hosp. of Wales, Heath Park, Cardiff CF14 4XW Fax: 029 2074 8240 Email: mcpherson.org.uk; 20 Winchester Avenue, Penylan, Cardiff CF23 9BT Fax: 029 2074 8240 Email: mcpherson@doctors.org.uk — BM 1986 Soton.; FRCOphth 1995. (Soton. Univ.) Cons. Ophth., Cardiff eye Unit, Univ. Hosp. of Wales. Socs: EVRS (Europ. Vitreoretinal Soc.); UKISCRS (United Kingdom & Irel. Soc. of Cataraten & refractive Surgens); BEAVRS (Brit. & Irel. Assciation of Vitreo retinal surgens). Prev: Fell. (Vitreoretinal), Roy. Vict. Eye & Ear Hosp., Melbourne, Australia; Specialist Regist. (Ophth.) Univ. Hosp. of Wales, Cardiff; Specialist Regist. (Ophth.) Singleton Hosp. Swansea.

MACPHERSON, Sean Angus 8 Ivy Place, Dunshalt, Cupar KY14 7HA — MB ChB 1998 Glas.; MB ChB Glas 1998.

MACPHERSON, Sheila Cranmer West of Scotland Breast Screening Clinic, 205 Calder St., Glasgow G42 7PH Tel: 0141 531 4400; 50 Queens Park Avenue, Glasgow G42 8BT Tel: 0141 423 1758 Email: sheilamacpherson@msn.com — MB ChB 1989 Glas.; FRCS Glas. 1993. Regist. (Radiol.) Glas.

MCPHERSON, Simon John 11 Park Drive, Harrogate HG2 9AY — MB BS 1985 Lond.; BSc Lond. 1982; MRCP (UK) 1989. Regist. (Diag. Radiol.) Addenbrooke's Hosp. Camb. Prev: Resid. (Internal Med.) Med. Univ. S. Carolina, USA.

MACPHERSON, Stephen Graeme 34 Montague Street, Glasgow G4 9HX Tel: 0141 339 4971 Email: stephmac@doctors.org.uk — MB ChB 1986 Aberd.; DCCH 1998 Edin.; DCH RCPS Glas. 1993.

MACPHERSON, Professor Stuart Gowans Lister postgraduate Institute, 11 hill Square, Edinburgh EH8 9DR Tel: 0131 650 2609 Fax: 0131 662 0580 Email: stuartmacpherson@scpmde.scot.nhs.uk; 33/4 Blackford Road, Edinburgh EH9 2DT Tel: 0131 668 4574 — MB ChB 1968 Glas.; FRCS Glas. 1972. Postgrad.Dean. Prof.Postgrad.med.Ed.Univ.Edin; Assoc. Dean. Postgrad Med. Glas. Socs: (Comm.) Brit. Transpl. Soc.; Transpl.ation Soc.;

Counc.mem.ASME. Prev: Sen.lect.Surg.Univ.Glas. & hons.Surg.W.Glas.Hosps.Univ.NHS Trust; Assoc.PG.Dean Univ.Glas; Assoc.Undergrad.Dean.Univ Glas.

MACPHERSON, Thomas David The Surgery, 3 Glasgow Road, Paisley PA1 3QS Tel: 0141 889 2604 Fax: 0141 887 9039 — MB ChB 1982 Glas.

MACPHERSON, Thomas Stewart Strathpeffer Medical Practice, The Surgery, Strathpeffer IV14 9BA Tel: 01997 421455 Fax: 01997 421172; Flat 5, The Old Jail, Jubilee Park Road, Dingwall IV15 9QZ Tel: 01349 862574 — MB ChB 1984 Glas.; MRCGP 1996. (Glasgow) GP Strathpeffer; Gen. Pract. Audit Facilitator Highland HB. Prev: Trainee GP Strathpeffer; Regist. (O & G) Gtr. Glas. HB. Glas.; Dist. Health Off., Malawi.

MACPHERSON, Timothy John 17 The Limes, Ingatestone CM4 0BE Tel: 01277 354681 — MB BS 1982 Newc.

MACPHIE, Duncan Love, QHS, Maj.-Gen. late RAMC Retd. 139 Shooters Hill Road, London SE3 8UQ — MB ChB 1957 Glas. Socs: BMA. Prev: Exec. Dir. St. John Ambul. Lond.; Cdr. Med. BAOR; Chief Med. Plans & Policy Br. SHAPE.

MCPHIE, James Langley Department of Pathology, Raigmore Hospital NHS Trust, Perth Road, Inverness IV2 3UJ Tel: 01463 70400 Fax: 01463 705648; Nyhavn, 14 Leys Park, Inverness IV2 3JD Tel: 01463 220357 — MB ChB Aberd. 1969; FRCPath 1991, M 1979. Cons. Path. Raigmore Hosp. Inverness; Hon. Sen. Lect. (Path.) Aberd. Univ. Prev: Lect. (Path.) Aberd. Univ.; Hon. Sen. Regist. (Path.) S. Grampian Health Dist.

MACPHIE, Jane Catherine 70 Lamberton Avenue, Broomridge, Stirling FK7 7TT — MB ChB 1979 Ed.

MACPHIE, Samuel Anlaby Road Surgery, 497 Anlaby Road, Hull HU3 6DT Tel: 01482 342282, 01482 353997; Highlands, 14 Acorn Way, Tranby Park, Hessle HU13 0TB — MB ChB 1977 Manch.; BSc (Med. Sci.) St. And. 1974. Princip. in Gen. Med. Pract. and Sen. Partner. Socs: BMA; Hull Med. Soc.

MCPHILLIPS, Maeve Assumpta Department of Diagnostic Radiology, Royal Hospital for Sick Children, Sciennes Road, Edinburgh EH9 1LF Tel: 0131 536 0000 — MB BCh BAO 1980 NUI; FRCR 1987. Cons. Diagn. Radiol. Roy. Hosp. Sick Childr. Edin. Prev: Paediat. Radiol. Montreal; Diagn. Radiol. Zurich & Hong Kong; Sen. Regist. & Regist. (Diagn. Radiol.) Yorks. RHA.

MCPHILLIPS, Michael Antony 31 Rivercourt Road, London W6 9TF Tel: 020 8748 4518 Fax: 020 8748 4518 — MB BS 1987 Lond.; BA (Hons.) Camb. 1984; MRCP (UK) 1990; MRCPsych 1994. Lect. (Psychiat.) Imperial Coll. Lond.; Sen. Regist. (Subst. Misuse) Riverside Subst. Misuse Serv. W. Lond. Prev: Regist. Rotat. (Psychiat.) Char. Cross Lond.

MCPHILOMY, Sinead Claire 3 Darnley Place, Glasgow G41 4NA — MB ChB 1997 Glas.

MCQUADE, Brian Nicholl (retired) 82 London Street, Chertsey KT16 8AJ Tel: 01932 564300 Email: bnmcq@aol.com — BM BCh Oxon. 1950; DObst RCOG 1952. Prev: Cas. Off. & Ho. Surg. Surgic. Unit St. Thos. Hosp.

MCQUADE, Elaine 56 Drumlee Road, Dungannon BT71 7QD — MB BCh BAO 1997 Belf.

MCQUADE, Jacqueline Ann (retired) Bodriggy Health Centre, 60 Queens Way, Bodriggy, Hayle TR27 4PB Tel: 01736 753136 Fax: 01736 753467 — MB BCh BAO 1968 NUI; MRCP (UK) 1973; MRCGP 1976; DCH Eng. 1970. Prev: Regist. (Paediat.) Roy. Cornw. Hosp. Truro.

MCQUADE, Paul Richard 39 Spinney Hill Drive, Loughborough LE11 3LB — MB BS 1977 Lond.

MCQUAID, Arthur Kneesworth House Hospital, Bassingbourn, Royston SG8 5JP Tel: 01763 242911 Fax: 01763 242011 — MB ChB 1955 Glas.; FRCPsych 1986, M 1971; DPM Eng. 1960. (Glas.) Cons. Psychiat. Kneesworth Ho. Hosp. Royston. Prev: Cons. Psychiat. Murray Roy. Hosp. Perth; Cons. Psychiat. Scott. Home & Health Dept.; Hon. Sen. Lect. (Psychiat.) Univ. Dundee.

MCQUAIL, Paul Anthony Department of Child Psychiatry, Alder Hey Hospital, Alder Road, Liverpool L12 2AP — MB BS 1986 Lond.; MRCPsych 1992.

MCQUAKER, Ian Grant Department of Haematology, Glasgow Royal Infirmary, Castle St., Glasgow G4 Tel: 0141 211 4672 — MB ChB 1987 Glas.; MRCP (UK) 1990; MRC Path 1998; DM Nottm. 1998. Cons. Haematologist. Socs: Scott. Soc. Experim. Med.; Brit.

MCQUATTIE

Soc. of Haemat. Prev: SP Registrar Nottm. city Hosp.; Sp Registrar Univ. Hosp. Nottm.; Clin. Research Fell., City Hosp. Nottm.

MCQUATTIE, Anne 49 The Avenue, Kew, Richmond TW9 2AL Tel: 020 8940 4551 — MB ChB 1969 Glas.

MCQUAY, Henry John Pain Relief, Chuchill Hospital, Oxford OX3 7JN Tel: 01865 226161; Holywell Manor, Manor Road, Oxford OX1 3UH — BM BCh 1974 Oxf.; DM 1985; FFA RCS Eng. 1979. Clin. Reader Pain Relief Univ. Oxf.

MCQUAY, Thomas Alexander Ireland 14 Sinnels Field, Shipton-under-Wychwood, Oxford OX7 6EJ Tel: 01865 831149 — MB BCh BAO 1945 Belf. (Belf.)

MCQUEEN, Alexander Flat 7/A, Southwood Place, Rosemount Avenue, Newton Mearns, Glasgow G77 5TN — MB ChB 1950 Glas.; MRCPath 1968. (Glas.) Sen. Lect. (Path.) Anderson Coll. Univ. Glas.; Hon. Cons. Path. W.. Infirm. Glas. Socs: Assn. Clin. Pathols. & N. Brit. Dermat. Soc. Prev: Sen. Regist. (Neuropath.) Inst. Neurol. Sc. Glas.

MCQUEEN, Daniel 71 Lothrop Street, London W10 4JD — MB ChB 1994 Sheff.; BMedSci 1991; MRCP 1998.

MCQUEEN, David Kilncroft, 43 Ayr Road, Douglas, Lanark ML11 0PX Tel: 01555 851333 — MB ChB 1976 Ed.; MRCOG 1985. Cons. O & G Falkirk & Dist. Roy. Infirm.

MCQUEEN, Fiona 38 Norwood, Newport-on-Tay DD6 8DW — MB ChB 1984 Aberd.

MCQUEEN, Iain Norman Fanshawe 44 Cyncoed Road, Cyncoed, Cardiff CF23 5SH Tel: 029 2048 3505; 44 Cyncoed Road, Cyncoed, Cardiff CF23 5SH — BSc (Med. Sci.), MB ChB Ed. 1970; FRCP Lond. 1994; FRCP Ed. 1986; MRCP (UK) 1974. Cons. Neurol. Univ. Hosp. Wales; Clin. Teach. Univ. of Wales Coll. Med.; Clin. Dir. Neuroscis Univ. Hosp. Wales. Socs: Assn. Brit. Neurols.; Soc. Phys. Wales. Prev: Sen. Regist. (Neurol.) Univ. Hosp. Wales Cardiff; Regist. (Neurol.) Inst. Neurol. Scs. S.. Gen. Hosp. Glas.; Regist. (Med.) Leith Hosp. Edin.

MCQUEEN, Janet Elizabeth Abernethy House, 70 Silver Street, Enfield EN1 3EP Tel: 020 8366 1314 Fax: 020 8364 4176 — MB BS 1984 Lond.; BA Lond. 1990, BSc 1981; MRCP (UK) 1988; MRCGP 1995; DRCOG 1988; DCH RCP Lond. 1987. (Middlx.)

MCQUEEN, Mr John Sloane Hospital, 125 Albemarle Road, Beckenham BR3 5HS Tel: 020 8325 3623; Downs View, Heritage Hill, Keston BR2 6AU Tel: 01689 859058 Fax: 01689 860965 — MB BChir 1967 Camb.; MA Camb. 1967; FRCS Eng. 1972; FRCOG 1985, M 1973, DObst 1969; DCH Eng. 1968. (St. Thos.) Cons. (O & G) FarnBoro. Hosp. Bromley Kent. Socs: BMA. Prev: Sen. Regist. Qu. Charlottes Hosp. & Chelsea Hosp. Wom. Lond.; Regist. (O & G) Middlx. Hosp. Lond.; SHO (Surg.) Kingston Hosp.

MCQUEEN, Mr Kenneth James The Surgery, Victoria Gardens, Lockerbie DG11 2BJ Tel: 01576 203665 Fax: 01576 202773; The Green, Arthur's Place, Lockerbie DG11 Tel: 01576 202862 Email: kmmargne@aol.com — MB ChB 1967 Glas.; FRCS Glas. 1972. (Glas.) Prev: Ho. Phys. Glas. Roy. Infirm.; Anat. Demonst. Univ. Edin.; Surg. Regist. Glas. Roy. Infirm.

MCQUEEN, Margaret Murray Edinburgh Trauma Unit, Royal Infirmary of Edinburgh, Edinburgh Tel: 0131 536 3721 Fax: 0131 536 3413 Email: mcqueenm@telemedicine.dh.ed.ac.uk — MB ChB 1977 Ed.; BSc (Med. Sci.) Ed. 1974; MD Ed. 1995; FRCS Ed. (Orth.) 1987; FRCS Ed. 1981. Cons. Trauma Surg. Roy. Infirm. Edin. Trust; Sen. Lect. Univ. of Edin. Prev: Sen. Lect. & Lect. (Orthop.) Surg. Univ. Edin.; Regist. (Orthop.) P.ss Margt. Rose Orthop. Hosp. & Roy. Infirm. Edin.

MACQUEEN, Mirjam Edinburgh Sick Children's Trust, Community Child Health Services, 10 Chalmers Crescent, Edinburgh EH10 1TS Tel: 0131 536 0000; 7 Kingsburgh Road, Edinburgh EH12 6DZ — MB ChB 1981 Glas.; MRCGP 1989; DCCH RCP Ed. 1988. Staff Grade (Community Child Health) Edin. Sick Childr. Trust. Prev: Clin. Med. Off. (Child Health) Fife HB.

MCQUILLAN, Brendan Joseph Bovally Medical Centre, 2 Rossair Road, Limavady BT49 OTE Tel: 028 7776 6352; 10 Scriggan Road, Limavady BT49 0DH Tel: 015 47 65035 — MB BCh BAO 1984 Dub.; MRCGP 1988; DObst RCPI 1988; DCH RCPSI 1987. Princip. (Gen. Pract.). Socs: Roy. Coll. Gen. Pract. Prev: Trainee GP Derby VTS; Ho. Off. (Med. & Surg.) St. Jas. Hosp. Dub.

MCQUILLAN, Colleen 29 Ballynadrentagh Road, Aldergrove, Crumlin BT29 4AR — MB BCh BAO 1997 Belf. (Queens Uni. Belfast)

MCQUILLAN, Eamon Joseph The Surgery, 30 Bloomsbury Street, Nechells, Birmingham B7 5BS Tel: 0121 359 1539 — MB BCh BAO 1982 Belf.; MB BCh Belf. 1982; MRCGP 1988; DRCOG 1985. Prev: Trainee GP Staffs.

MCQUILLAN, James Dunlop Ballymena Health Centre, Cushendall Road, Ballymena BT43 6HQ Tel: 028 256 42181 Fax: 028 25 632360 — MB BCh BAO 1981 Belf.; MRCGP 1985; DCH RCPI 1984; DRCOG 1983. (Qu. Univ. Belf.)

MACQUILLAN, John Gabriel 23 Leinster Road, London N10 3AN — MB BCh BAO 1946 NUI.

MCQUILLAN, Orla Marie Anne Windrush, Vyse Rd, Boughton, Northampton NN2 8RP — MB ChB 1997 Leic.

MCQUILLAN, Peter Jerome Department of Intensive Care Medicine, Queen Alexandra Hospital, Cosham, Portsmouth PO6 3LY Tel: 023 92 286000 Fax: 023 92 286967; 3 Kinnell Close, Emsworth PO10 7HF Tel: 01243 370389 — MB BS 1980 Newc.; FFA RCS Eng. 1986; FANZCA (Intens. Care) 1992. Cons. Intens. Care & Anaesth. Qu. Alexandra Hosp. Portsmouth. Prev: Sen. Regist. (Anaesth.) Qu. Alexandra Hosp. Portsmouth; Research Fell. Intens. Care Unit John Radcliffe Hosp. Oxf.; Regist. (Anaesth.) Newc. HA.

MCQUILLAN, Siobhan 20 Hornby Park, Liverpool L18 3LL — MB ChB 1991 Liverp.

MCQUILLAN, Steven Trevor Norwood Medical Centre, 99 Abbey Road, Barrow-in-Furness LA14 5ES Tel: 01229 822024 Fax: 01229 823949 — MB BS 1988 Newc.

MCQUILLAN, William Joseph Windrush, Vyse Road, Boughton, Northampton NN2 8RP Tel: 01604 843635 — MB BCh BAO 1951 NUI; DPH (Hons.) 1955; FFCM 1974; DCH RCPSI 1956. Socs: BMA. Prev: Chief Exec. N.ampton DHA; Area Med. Off. N.ants. AHA; Hon. Phys. to HM the Qu.

MCQUILLIN, Melville James (retired) Beechcroft, Fawdon Walk, Newcastle upon Tyne NE13 7AW Tel: 0191 286 7787 — MB BS 1963 Durh. Prev: SHO (Med.) Gen. Hosp. Bishop Auckland.

MACQUIRE-SAMSON, Inthea Marion Priscilla Janet Bristol Priory Hospital, Heath House Lane, Off Bell Hill, Bristol BS16 1EQ Tel: 01179 525255 — MB BS 1974 Lond.; MRCPsych. 1982. (Charing Cross) Cons. Psychiat. Priory Hosp. Bristol. Prev: Cons. Psychiat. & Sen. Regist. (Psychiat.) Barrow Hosp. Bristol; Clin. Asst. Barrow Hosp. Bristol.

MACQUISTEN, Susan Tyn y Buarth, Llangaffo, Gaerwen LL60 6LY — MB BChir 1979 Camb.; BSc (Hons. Physiol.) St. And. 1975; MFPHM RCP (UK) 1994; DTM & H Liverp. 1983; DRCOG 1981.

MCQUITTY, Andrew Francis Accident & Emergency Department, Southampton General Hospital, Southampton SO16 6YD Tel: 02380 796220; 14 Drakes Court, Quayside Walk, Marchwood, Southampton SO40 4AA Tel: 02380 663655 — MB ChB 1973 Dundee. Staff Grade Phys. A & E Soton. Gen. Hosp. Socs: BMA. Prev: Staff Grade Phys. A & E Douglas I. of Man.

MCQUITTY, Eoin Leonard (retired) Westcourt Farmhouse, Burbage, Marlborough SN8 3BW Tel: 01672 810189 — MB ChB 1941 St. And.; MB ChB (Cum Laude) St. And. 1941; MRCGP 1964.

MCQUONEY, Patricia Ann Air Balloon Surgery, Kenn Road, St George, Bristol BS5 7PD Tel: 0117 909 9914 Fax: 0117 908 6660 Email: tmcquoney@airballoon.cix.co.uk — MB ChB 1981 Glas.; M.F. HOM 2001 Bristol; MRCGP 1985; Cert. Family Plann. JCC 1985; DRCOG 1983; L.F. HOM 97; DFFP. (Glasgow University)

MCQUONEY, Quentin John Renfrew Health Centre, 103 Paisley Road, Renfrew PA4 8LL Tel: 0141 886 2455 Fax: 0141 855 0457; Crofton Hill, Mousebank Road, Lanark ML11 7RA Tel: 01555 662411 — MB ChB 1967 Glas. (Glas.)

MACRAE, Alasdair Russell 14 Waverley Avenue, Helensburgh G84 7JU — MB ChB 1998 Dund.; MB ChB Dund 1998.

MACRAE, Alexander Donald Kings College, Cambridge CB2 1ST — MB ChB 1986 Glas.

MACRAE, Alexandra Jane Royal Berkshire & Battle Hospital NHS Trust, 3 Craven Road, Reading RG1 5LF Tel: 01189 315800 Fax: 01189 750297; 10 College Road, Reading RG6 1QB Tel: 01189 267286 — MB BS 1973 Lond.; MRCP (UK) 1978; FRCP (UK) 1997; FRCPCH 1997; DCH Eng. 1977; DRCOG 1976. Cons. Paediat. (Community Child Health) Roy. Berks. & Battle Hosps. NHS Trust.

MACRAE, Alison Margaret Tranent Medical Practice, Loch Road, Tranent EH33 2JX Tel: 01875 610697 Fax: 01875 615046 — MB ChB 1988 Glas.; MRCGP 1995.

MCRAE, Mr Andrew Robert Lincoln County Hospital, Greetwell Road, Lincoln LN2 5QY Tel: 01522 512512; 9 Greetwell Lane, Netteham, Lincoln LN2 2PN Tel: 01522 753262 Fax: 01522 753262 Email: andymcrae@msn.com — MB ChB Sheff. 1976; FRCS Eng. 1982; T(S) 1991. Cons Otolaryngol. Lincoln Hosp. Prev: Cons. Otolaryngol. RAF Hosp. Wroughton; Hon. Sen. Regist. Roy. Marsden Hosp. Lond.; Sen. Specialist (Otolaryngol.) Inst. Aviat. Med. RAF FarnBoro..

MACRAE, Ann Sheila 57 Dalry Road, Kilwinning KA13 7HN — MB ChB 1992 Aberd.

MACRAE, Calum Archibald Conon Lodge, Uig, Portree IV51 9XP — MB ChB 1985 Ed.; MRCP (UK) 1988.

MACRAE, Calum Og Medical Centre, Portree; Conon Lodge, Uig, Portree IV51 9XP Tel: 0147 042202 — MB ChB 1953 Aberd. (Aberd.) Phys. Supt. Portree Hosp.

MACRAE, Catriona Murray Eaglesham Surgery, 30 Gilmour Street, Eaglesham, Glasgow G76 0AT Tel: 01355 302221 Fax: 01355 302907 — MB ChB 1986 Aberd.; MRCGP 1990; DRCOG 1988. Gen. Practitioner. Prev: Trainee GP Raigmore Hosp. Inverness VTS; SHO (A&E) Vict. Infirm., Glas.

*MCRAE, Christine Ada High Gree, Lochlibo Road, Burnhouse, Beith KA15 1LH — MB ChB 1997 Aberd.

MACRAE, Duncan James, MC (retired) Tir nan Og, 3 Big Sand, Gairloch IV21 2DD Tel: 01445 2150 — MB ChB 1939 St. And. Prev: Capt. RAMC.

MACRAE, Duncan John Royal Brompton Hospital, Sydney St., London SW3 6NP Tel: 020 7351 8545 Fax: 020 7829 8802 Email: d.macrae@rbh.nthames.nhs.uk — MB ChB 1980 Dundee; BMSc (Hons.) Dund 1977; FFA RCS Eng. 1984. Dir. Paediat. Intens. Care, Roy. Brompton Hosp. Lond. Socs: Paediat. Intens. Care Soc. (Counc.); Eur. Soc. Paediat. Intens. Care(UK Counc. Mem.); Fell.Roy. Coll. Paediat. Child Health. Prev: Cons. Paediat. Intens. Care Gt. Ormond St. Hosp. Lond.; Regist. (Intens. Care) Roy. Childr. Hosp. Melbourne, Austral.; Sen. Regist. (Anaesth.) Char. Cross & Brompton Hosps. Lond.

MACRAE, Eithne Maire Rosaleen Kenneth Macrae Medical Centre, 32 Church Road, Rainford, St Helens WA11 8HJ Tel: 01744 882606 — MB ChB 1988 Manch.; BSc (Med. Sci.) St. And. 1985; DCH RCP Lond. 1992; DRCOG 1991. Socs: BMA. Prev: Trainee GP Aviemore; SHO (Med. for Elderly) Cumbld. Infirm. Carlisle; SHO (O & G) Fairfield Hosp. Bury.

MCRAE, Fergus Campbell Broxburn Health Centre, Holmes Road, Broxburn EH52 5JZ Tel: 01506 852016 — MB ChB 1981 Ed.; MRCGP 1985; DRCOG 1983.

MCRAE, Ferguson (retired) Kiprig, west Torphin, West Calder EH55 8RT Tel: 01506 871361 — MB ChB 1952 Glas.

MACRAE, Fiona Langwood, Langlands Road, Hawick TD9 7HL; 21 Old Coach Avenue, Belfast BT9 5PY Tel: 01232 628211 — MB BCh BAO 1992 Belf.; BSc (Hons.) Physiol. Aberd. 1987; DRCOG 1995; DCH Dub. 1995. GP Regist. Belf. Socs: BMA. Prev: SHO (Paediat., Med. & Geriat.) Craigavon Area Hosp.; SHO (O & G) Mater Infirm. Belf.

MACRAE, Fiona Mary Helen 97 Woolton Hill Road, Liverpool L25 4RE — MB ChB 1984 Liverp.

MACRAE, Iain Alastair (retired) North Farm, Murton, Seaham SR7 9RP Tel: 0191 526 3073 — MB BS 1962 Durh.; DObst RCOG 1964. Prev: Ho. Surg. & Ho. Phys. Roy. Vict. Infirm. Newc.

MACRAE, Ian Fotheringham The Surgery, Astonia House, High Street, Baldock SG7 6BP Tel: 01462 892458 Fax: 01462 490821; Brierley, 3 Croft Lane, Letchworth SG6 1AS — MB BS 1960 Lond.; MRCS Eng. LRCP Lond. 1960. (Guy's) Prev: Hosp. Pract. (Rheum.) Lister Hosp. Stevenage; Research Fell. (Med.) Univ. Leeds; Clin. & Research Fell. (Med.) Mass. Gen. Hosp., USA.

MACRAE, Mr John Angus Macdonald 6 Elm Park, Inverness IV2 4WN Tel: 01463 220305 — MB ChB 1972 Dundee; FRCS Ed. 1977; FRCOphth 1988; DO Eng. 1976. Cons. Ophth. Raigmore Hosp. Inverness. Socs: Scott. Ophth. Club; UK & Irel. Soc. Cataract & Refractive Surgs. Prev: Sen. Regist. (Ophth.) Ninewells Hosp. Dundee; Regist. (Ophth.) Ninewells Hosp. Dundee.

MACRAE, Karen Anne Hunter Health Centre, Andrew Street, East Kilbride, Glasgow G74 1AD Tel: 01355 906622 Fax: 01355 906629 — MB ChB 1984 Glas.

MCRAE, Kenneth Alistair (retired) The Glade, Little Bealings, Woodbridge IP13 6LX Tel: 01473 622005 — MB ChB 1942 Ed.

MACRAE, Malcolm John Kingsmills Medical Practice, 18 Southside Road, Inverness IV2 3BG Tel: 01463 235245 Fax: 01463 01443 714400 — MB ChB 1983 Ed.; MRCGP 1987; DRCOG 1989; DCH RCPS Glas. 1987.

MCRAE, Malcolm Macdonald Bank Street Medical Centre, 46-62 Bank Street, Alexandria G83 0LS Tel: 01389 756029 Fax: 01389 710049; 14 Waverley Avenue, Colgrain, Helensburgh G84 7JU Tel: 01436 676064 Fax: 01436 676064 Email: malcolm@m3doc.demon.co.uk — MB ChB 1973 Glas.; MRCGP 1978; DRCOG 1977. Hosp. Practitioner (Psychiat.) Valedeleven Dist. Gen. Hosp. Alexandra. Prev: Med. Off. (Psychogeriat.) Cottage Day Hosp. Dumbarton.

MACRAE, Mary Catherine Hill House, Oxton, Lauder Tel: 0157 85 224 — LRCP LRCS 1948 Ed.; LRCP LRCS Ed. LRFPS Glas. 1948; LDS RCS 1947. (Ed.) Med. Asst. Dept. Venereol. Roy. Infirm. Edin.

MACRAE, Mary Elizabeth 32 Thornwood Terrace, 2nd Floor Right, Glasgow G11 7QZ — MB ChB 1991 Aberd.

MACRAE, Mary Elizabeth Shaw (retired) Caladh na Sithe, Balmacara, Kyle IV40 8DN Tel: 01599 566246 — MB ChB 1949 Ed.; DCH Eng. 1952. Prev: Jun. Hosp. Med. Off. Roy. Hosp. Sick Childr. Glas.

MCRAE, Michael Bruce 16 Crozier House, 17 Wilkinson St., London SW8 1DQ — MB ChB 1983 Cape Town.

MACRAE, Monica Teresa 48 Church Road, Rainford, St Helens WA11 Tel: 0174 488 2606 — MB ChB 1950 Liverp.; DA Eng. 1954. (Liverp.) Prev: Vis. Anaesth. Providence Hosp. St. Helens; Regist. Anaesth. Sefton Gen. Hosp. & Alder Hey Childr. Hosp. Liverp.

MCRAE, Mr Robert Duncan Roderick Colchester General Hospital, Turner Road, Colchester CO4 5JL — MB BS 1984 Lond.; FRCS 1995 (Orl); FRCS Lond. 1990. Cons. (OtoLaryngol.) Cochester Gen. Hosp. Prev: SHO (Neurosurg. & Neurol.) Addenbrooke's Hosp. Camb.; Demonst. (Anat.) Univ. of Camb.; SHO (ENT) St. Bart. Hosp. Lond.

MCRAE, Roderick Anthony Dr McElhone and Partners, Townhead Surgery, 6-8 High St., Irvine KA12 0AY Tel: 01294 273131 Fax: 01294 312832; 4 Greenfield Drive, Irvine KA12 0ED — MB ChB 1977 Dundee. Prev: Regist. (Geriat. Med.) Vict. Geriat. Unit Glas.; SHO (Surg./Orthop. Surg.) Yeovil Dist Hosp. Som.

*MCRAE, Roderick Coll Blagdon, Sandersfield Gardens, Banstead SM7 2DQ — MB BS 1996 Lond.

MCRAE, Mr Ronald Kenneth (retired) The Cedars, 22 Moorfield Road, Gourock PA19 1DD Tel: 01475 632623 Fax: 01475 632623 Email: ronaldmcrae@compuserve.com — MB ChB 1949 Glas.; FRCS Glas. 1984; FRCS Eng. 1960. Prev: Cons. Orthop. Surg. Ross Hall Hosp. Glas.

MACRAE, Rosemary Anne Duncan Kenneth Macrae Medical Centre, 32 Church Road, Rainford, St Helens WA11 8HJ Tel: 01744 882606 — MB ChB 1986 Manch.

*MACRAE, Sara Lillian Conon Lodge, Uig, Portree IV51 9XP — MB ChB 1988 Aberd.

MCRAE, Sheena Clare Chadwick Finsbury Circus Medical Centre, 5 London Wall Buildings, Finsbury Circus, London EC2M 5NS Tel: 020 7638 0909 Fax: 020 7638 9211 — MB BS 1984 Lond.; BSc (Hons.) Lond. 1980, MB BS 1984; MRCGP 1993; Dip. Occ. Med. 1998.

MACRAE, Susan Eleanor 18 Otter Close, Salhouse, Norwich NR13 6SF — MB ChB 1993 Leic. GP Norwich.

MACRAE, William Andrew The Pain Service, Ninewells Hospital, Dundee Tel: 01382 60111 — MB ChB 1971 St. And.; FFA RCS Eng. 1978; DObst RCOG 1975. Cons. Anaesth. Ninewells Hosp. Dundee.

MACRAE, William John (retired) Achnahannait, Glen Lonan, Taynuilt PA35 1HY Tel: 01866 822224 Fax: 01866 822224 — MB ChB 1954 Aberd.

MACRAE, William John Department of Anaesthetics, Stobhill Hospital, 133 Balornock Road, Glasgow G21 3UW Tel: 0141 201 3005 — MB ChB 1986 Aberd.

MACRAE, William Rennie (retired) 4 Corrennie Gardens, Edinburgh EH10 6DG Tel: 0131 447 1112 Fax: 0131 447 9956 Email: 100775.372@compuserve.com — MB ChB Ed. 1957; FRCS Ed. 1994; FRCA 1992; FFARCSI (Hon) 1998. Prev: Cons. Anaesth. Edin. Roy. Infirm.

MACREADY

MACREADY, Douglas Narrowcliff Surgery, Narrowcliff, Newquay TR7 2QF Tel: 01637 873363 Fax: 01637 850735 — MB BS 1985 Lond.; BSc (Hons.) Lond. 1982, MB BS 1985. GP Princip. Newquay Cornw.

MACREADY, Lynne Old Orchard Surgery, South Street, Wilton, Salisbury SP2 0JN Tel: 01722 744775 — MB ChB 1991 Bristol; DRCOG 1996; MRCGP 1997; DFFP 1996. (Bristol) p/t GP Retainer Dr. A. Hall & Partners Old Orchard Surg. Wilton Salisbury. Prev: Research GP Med. Research Counc. Soton.; Clin. Asst. (Rheum.) Salisbury Dist. Hosp.; GP Regist. Stockbridge.

MACRITCHIE, Donald Malcolm The Surgery, 40 Manse Road, Forth, Lanark ML11 8AJ Tel: 01555 811200; 40 Manse Road, Forth, Lanark ML11 8AJ — MB ChB 1974 Aberd.; MB ChB Aberd 1974.

MCRITCHIE, Hamish Andrew Department of Radiology, Borders General Hospital, Melrose Tel: 01896 826000 Fax: 01896 826438 — MB ChB 1983 Ed.; BSc; DMRD; FRCR. (Edinburgh) Cons. Radiol.

MACRITCHIE, James Donald 39 Kinstone Avenue, Glasgow G14 0EB — MB ChB 1974 Glas.

MACRITCHIE, Karine Anne Nicolson Department of Psychiatry, Royal Victoria Infirmary, Newcastle upon Tyne NE1 4LP — MB ChB 1991 Glas. Specialist Regist. Psychiat. Roy. Vict. Infirm. Newc. upon Tyne.

MACRITCHIE, Pamela Agnes The Surgery, 40 Manse Road, Forth, Lanark ML11 8AJ Tel: 01555 811200; 40 Manse Road, Forth, Lanark ML11 8AJ — MB ChB 1974 Aberd.

MCRITCHIE, Robert Liddell (retired) 39 Whitney Drive, Stevenage SG1 4BQ Tel: 01438 314816 — MB ChB Glas. 1956; DObst RCOG 1959. Prev: Company Med. Off. OcciDent. of Libya Oil Company.

MCROBBIE, Ian Andrew Cowdenbeath Medical Practice, 173 Stenhouse Street, Cowdenbeath KY4 9DH Tel: 01383 518500 Fax: 01383 518509 — MB ChB 1976 Aberd.; MRCGP 1980.

MCROBBIE, Ian Simpson, SBStJ (retired) Moordale, Broadgait Green, Gullane EH31 2DW Tel: 01620 843558 — MB ChB 1952 Ed.; FFOM RCP Lond. 1992, M 1979; DIH Eng. 1976; DObst RCOG 1957. Prev: Scott. Area Med. Adviser Post Office.

MCROBERT, Moira Somerville The Surgery, Gaywood House, North St, Bedminster, Bristol BS3 3AZ Tel: 0117 966 1412 Fax: 0117 953 1250 — MB ChB 1980 Glas.; MRCGP 1985.

MCROBERT, Rose 58 Coolshinney Road, Magherafelt BT45 5JF — MB ChB 1998 Glas.; MB ChB Glas 1998.

MCROBERTS, Maureen Theresa Henley-in-Arden Medical Centre, Prince Harry Road, Henley in Arden, Solihull B95 5DD Tel: 0156 42 793333 — MB ChB 1960 Manch.; DA Eng. 1963. (Manch.)

MCROBERTS, Randal John 13 Downshire Gardens, Carrickfergus BT38 7LW — MB ChB 1994 Dundee. (Med. Off. Brit. Antarctic Survey)

MCROBERTS, William (retired) Hillcroft, 638 Thornton Road, Thornton, Bradford BD13 3PZ — MB ChB 1948 Glas.; MPhil Bradford 1981; DIH Soc. Apoth. Lond. 1970; CIH Dund 1970.

MCROBIE, Emma Rachel 18 Dulverton Avenue, Westlands, Newcastle ST5 3NJ — MB ChB 1995 Bristol.

MCRORIE, Anne Penicuik Health Centre, 37 Imrie Place, Penicuik EH26 8LF; 24 Carfrae Park, Blackhall, Edinburgh EH4 3SN Tel: 0131 336 2909 — MB ChB 1986 Glas.; MRCGP 1993; DRCOG 1992; DA (UK) 1989.

MCRORIE, Euan Robert Western General Hospital, Crewe Road, Edinburgh EH4 2XU Tel: 0131 537 1016 Fax: 0131 537 0151 — MB ChB 1986 Glas.; FRCP 2001 Glas.; FRCP 2000 Edinburgh.

MCRORIE, John Strathearn, Swordale Road, Evanton, Dingwall IV16 9UZ Tel: 01349 830474 — MB ChB 1974 Ed.; MRCGP 1987; DRCOG 1981; DA Eng. 1977.

MACRORIE, Norman Dallas The Surgery, 50 Highcroft Villas, Brighton BN1 5PT Tel: 01273 552063 Fax: 01273 555836 — MB ChB 1956 Glas.; DObst RCOG 1973; Cert Amer. Bd. Psychiat. & Neurol. 1969. GP Brighton. Prev: Ho. Surg. Roy. Infirm. Edin.; Staff Psychiat. Qu.'s Hosp. Center New York, U.S.A.; SHO (O & G) Roy. W. Sussex Hosp. Chichester.

MACRORIE, Roderick Andrew 50 Highcroft Villas, Brighton BN1 5PT — BA (Physiol. Sci.) Oxf. 1982, BM BCh 1985; MRCGP 1992; DRCOG 1991; DCH RCP Lond. 1989; DTM & H Liverp. 1989. Internat. Nepali Med. Mission Off. Socs: Christ. Med. Fell.sh. & BMA. Prev: SHO (Cas.) St. Jas. Hosp. Leeds; SHO (Paediat.) Roy. Liverp. Childr. Hosp.; SHO (Gen. Med.) Hull Roy. Infirm.

MCRORY, Joseph Patrick (retired) The Ollands, 51 St Johns Road, Bungay NR35 1DH — MB BCh BAO 1948 Belf.; MRCGP 1962; DPH Lond. 1961. Prev: Clin. Asst. Norf. & Norwich Hosp.

MACROSTIE, Jacqueline Anne (Sneary) Abbey Surgery, 28 Plymouth Road, Tavistock PL19 8BU — MB BS 1989 Lond.; DRCOG 1993; MRCGP 1993; Cert. Family Plann. JCC 1993.

MACROW, Peter John Pinderfields Hospital, Aberford Road, Wakefield WF1 4DG Tel: 01924 213912 Fax: 01924 214147; Cobble Cottage, 38 School Hill, Newmillerdam, Wakefield WF2 7SP Tel: 01924 255736 — MB ChB 1983 Liverp.; MD Manch. 1995; MRCOG 1990. Cons. (O & G) Pinderfields Hosp. Wakefield. Socs: Eur. Soc. Human Reproduc. & Embryol.; Brit. Fertil. Soc. Prev: Sen. Regist. (O & G) S. Trent RHA; Regist. Rotat. (O & G) N. W.. RHA; Research Fell (Reproduc. Med.) Univ. Hosp. S. Manch.

MACRURY, Sandra Mary Raigmore Hospial NHS Trust, Inverness IV2 3UJ Tel: 01463 704000 — MD 1990 Glas.; FRCP 1995 Glas.; FRCP 1997 Edin.; MB ChB 1981; MRCP (UK) 1984. Cons. Phys. Raigmore Hosp. NHS Trust Inverness. Prev: Sen. Regist. (Gen. Med.) Gtr. Glas. HB; Regist. (Gen. Med.) Glas. Roy. Infirm.

MCRUVIE, Gordon Murray 35 Grove Crescent, Aberdeen AB16 5DU — MB ChB 1979 Aberd.

MCSHANE, Aine Marie Moy Health Centre, 40 Charlemont Street, Moy, Dungannon BT71 7SL; 1 Laurelview, Killyneill Road, Dungannon BT71 6UA — MB BCh BAO 1987 Belf.; MFFP 1994; MRCGP (Distinc.) 1991; DCH RCSI 1991; Cert. Family Plann. JCC Belf. 1990. (Queen's University, Belfast) p/t Princip. in Gen. Pract.; Course Organiser Vocational Train. in Gen. Pract. Socs: BMA & Nat. Assn. Family Plann. Doctors. Prev: SHO Roy. Matern. Hosp., Roy. Vict. Hosp. & Hosp. Sick Childr. Belf.

MCSHANE, Charles Brian Glebe House, Litton Cheney, Dorchester DT2 9AD Tel: 01308 482373 — MB BCh BAO 1953 Belf.; DObst RCOG 1962; DTM & H Eng. 1969. (Qu. Univ. Belf.) Socs: Fell. Roy. Soc. Trop. Med. & Hyg.; BMA. Prev: Ho. Surg. & Ho. Phys. Roy. Vict. Hosp. Belf.; Resid. Med. Off. Roy. Matern. Hosp. Belf.; Lt.-Col. RAMC.

MCSHANE, Christina Donna 30 Southvale Road, Blackheath, London SE3 0TP Tel: 020 8297 2345 — MB ChB 1991 Ed. Regist. (Community Paediat.) Lond. Prev: SHO (Paediat.) Roy. Brompton Hosp., Roy. Postgrad. Med. Sch. Lond. & Roy. Hosp. Sick Childr. Edin.

MCSHANE, Helen Irene 397 Banbury Road, Oxford OX2 7RF — MB BS 1991 Lond.; BSc Lond. 1988, MB BS 1991; MRCP 1994. MRC Clin. Train. Fell. Oxf. 1997. Prev: SHO Rotat. (Med.) Brighton Health Care.

MCSHANE, Joseph Aloysius (retired) Glencroft, 213 Wythenshawe Road, Manchester M23 9DB Tel: 0161 998 3511 — MB ChB Glas. 1956. Prev: Ho. Surg. & Ho. Phys. Glas. Roy. Infirm.

MCSHANE, Linda Janice Dunblane Medical Practice, Well Place, Dunblane FK15 9BQ Tel: 01786 822595 Fax: 01786 825298; 43 Abbey Mill, Riverside, Stirling FK8 1QS Tel: 01786 446020 — MB ChB 1988 Glas.; MRCGP 1995. (Glas. Univ.) Staff Phys. Stirling Roy. Infirm.; (Jobsharing) GP. Socs: Brit. Med. Acupunct. Soc. Prev: SHO (Med.) Roy. Cornw. Hosp. Truro; SHO Bath Roy. United Hosp.; Ho. Off. Glas. Roy. Infirm.

MCSHANE, Lucy Marie 158 Alcester Road S., Kings Heath, Birmingham B14 6AA Tel: 0121 444 1186 — MB BCh BAO 1982 NUI; MRCGP 1990.

MCSHANE, Mr Martin David Eckington Health Centre, Gosber Road, Eckington, Sheffield S21 4BZ — MB BS 1981 Lond.; MS Lond. 1989, BSc 1978, MB BS 1981; FRCS Eng. 1985; MRCGP 1992.

MCSHANE, Michael Anthony Dept. of Paediatrics, The John Radcliffe Hospital, Headley Way, Oxford OX3 9DU Tel: 01865 220951 — MB BCh BAO 1981 Belf.; MRCP (UK) 1986; T(M) (Paediat.) 1992. Cons. Paediat. Neurol. John Radcliffe Hosp. Oxf. Prev: Sen. Regist. (Paediat. Neurol.) Hosp. for Sick Childr. Gt. Ormond St. Lond.

MCSHANE, Rachel The Health Centre, University of East Anglia, Norwich NR18 0RZ Tel: 01603 592172 — MB ChB 1989 Bristol; BSc Bristol 1986; DCH RCP Lond. 1992. GP Norf.

MCSHANE, Rupert Hector Fulbrook Centre, Churchill Hospital, Oxford OX3 7JU Tel: 01865 223841 Fax: 01865 223842 Email: rupert.mcshane@oxmhc_tr.anglox.nhs.uk — MB BChir 1989 Camb.

Cons. (Psychiat. of Elderly)Oxf. Ment. Healthcare Trust. Prev: Clin. Lect. (Psychiat. of Elderly) Warneford Hosp. Oxf.

MACSHARRY, Charles Gerald (retired) Nazareth House, Ashton Road, Lancaster LA1 5AQ Tel: 0524 63098 — LM 1957 Rotunda; BAgrSc. NUI 1942, MB BCh BAO 1950; LAH Dub. 1957. Prev: Assoc. Specialist (Psychiat.) Roy. Albert Hosp. Lancaster.

MACSHARRY, Mary Julie 91 Lichfield Road, Stone ST15 8QD — MB ChB 1984 Manch.; MRCGP 1995; DRCOG 1993. GP Princip. Homcroft Surg. Stafford. Prev: Trainee GP BromsGr.; SHO (Paediat.) Leighton Hosp. Crewe.

MCSHERRY, Gerard Joseph Frew Terrace Surgery, 9 Frew Terrace, Irvine KA12 9DZ Tel: 01294 272326 Fax: 01294 314614; 227 Bank Street, Irvine KA12 0YB Tel: 01294 274004 Fax: 01294 274004 — MB ChB 1967 Glas.; DObst RCOG 1969. (Glas.)

MACSORLEY, Donall Thomas (retired) 20 Lethbridge Road, Southport PR8 6JA — MB BCh BAO 1950 NUI; DPM Eng. 1957. Prev: Cons. (Psychiat.) S.port Gen. Infirm. & Pinel Unit Greaves Hall.

MCSORLEY, Frances Alison 32 Cairngorm Crescent, Glengormley, Newtownabbey BT36 5EW — MB BCh BAO 1990 NUI.

MACSORLEY, Frederick James Church Walk Surgery, 28 Church Walk, Lurgan, Craigavon BT67 9AA Tel: 028 3832 7834 Fax: 028 3834 9331; 53 Ballyhannon Road, Portadown, Craigavon BT63 5SE — MB BCh BAO 1978 Belf.; DIP IMC RCS Ed. 1990; DRCOG 1982.

MCSORLEY, John Dominic 225 Newtonsaville Road, Eskra, Omagh BT78 2RW — MB ChB 1992 Manch.; MRCP Lond. 1996; DTM & H Liverp. 1996; Dip GUM Lond. 1999. (Manch.)

MACSORLEY, Michael Patrick Antrim Road Surgery, 515 Antrim Road, Belfast BT15 3BS Tel: 028 9077 6600 Fax: 028 9077 3165 — MB BCh BAO 1987 NUI.

MCSORLEY, Peter Dominic Falkirk & District Royal Infirmary, Majors Loan, Falkirk FK1 5QE — MB BS 1968 Lond.; FRCP Glas. 1988; MRCP (UK) 1971. Cons. Phys. Falkirk & Dist. Roy. Infirm. Socs: Scott. Soc. Phys.; Brit. Cardiac Soc. & Scott. Cardiac Soc. Prev: Lect. (Med.) & Clin. Pharm. Soton. Univ.

MACSORLEY, Peter Joseph Antrim Road Surgery, 515 Antrim Road, Belfast BT15 3BS Tel: 028 9077 6600 Fax: 028 9077 3165; Lugano, 781 Antrim Road, Newtownabbey BT36 7PW — MB BCh BAO 1979 Belf.; MRCGP 1983; DRCOG 1987.

MCSPARRAN, Alexander John McDonnell Glens of Antrim Medical Centre, Gortaclee Road, Cushendall, Ballymena BT44 0TE Tel: 028 2177 1411; Coiscib, Cushendall, Ballymena BT44 0PB Tel: 028256 71411 — MB BCh BAO 1969 Belf.

MCSPARRAN, John Archibald Glens of Antrim Medical Centre, 2 Gortaclea Road, Cushendall, Ballymena BT44 0TE Tel: 012667 71411; Agola Lodge, 47 Knocknacarry Road, Cushendun, Ballymena BT44 0NS Email: john@agola.freeserve.co.uk — MB BCh BAO 1992 Belf.; DMH Belf. 1994. GP Asst. Glens of Antrim Med. Centre Cushendall. Prev: GP/Regist. Ballymena.

MCSPARRON, Rachel Anne 25 Broadleys Avenue, Bristol BS9 4LY — BM 1994 Soton.

MCSTAY, Bernard Bewicke Health Centre, 51 Tynemouth Road, Wallsend NE28 0AD Tel: 0191 262 3036 Fax: 0191 295 1663; 1 Alexandra Garth, Meadow Lane, Beadnell, Chathill NE67 5AQ Tel: 01665 720860 — MB BS 1956 Durh.; MD Newc. 1972; MRCGP 1968. (newcastle upon tyne) Local Med. Off. Civil Serv. Dept. Med. Advis. Serv. Prev: Clin. Asst. (Med. & Paediat.) Preston Hosp. N. Shields.

MCSTAY, Kevin Curtis Cumberland Infirmary, Carlisle CA2 7HY Tel: 01228 523444; 8 Butterburn Close, Carlisle CA3 0PT Tel: 01228 810196 — MB BS 1988 Newc. Staff Grade (Elderly Care) Cumbld. Infirm. Carlisle.

MCSTAY, Mary Kathleen Gemma Flat 11, Mission Bldg., 747 Commercial Road, London E14 7LE — MB BS 1994 Lond.

MCSWAN, Elizabeth 4/14 Succoth Court, Succoth Park, Edinburgh EH12 6BZ Tel: 0131 346 8297 Fax: 0131 346 8297 — MB ChB 1963 Glas.; DObst RCOG 1965. (Lond.) Hon. Med. Adviser to Commonw. Games (Counc. for Scotl.). Socs: BMA; Brit. Assn. Sport & Med. Prev: Med. Off. Moray Hse. Inst. Educat. Edin.; Ho. Surg. S.. Gen. Hosp. & Redlands Hosp. Wom. Glas.; Ho. Phys. Glas. Roy. Infirm.

MACSWEEN, Karen Fiona Pennyfield, Penicuik EH26 0NN; Prestondene, Pathhead EH37 5UH — MB ChB 1989 Aberd.; BMedBiol. (Hons.) Aberd. 1988; MRCP (UK) 1992; MSc 1998; DTM & H 1999. Research.Fell. Univ.Edin. Prev: Regist. (Infec. Dis.) Lothian HB.; Sen.Reg.Microbiol.UCL.

MACSWEEN, Marjory Pentland (retired) 32 Calderwood Road, Newlands, Glasgow G43 2RU Tel: 0141 637 4355 — MB ChB 1959 Glas. Prev: Clin. Asst. (Dermat.) S.. Gen. Hosp. Glas. & Roy. Infirm. Glas.

MACSWEEN, Penrose Jane Morvern, 1 Manor Gardens, Shepshed, Loughborough LE12 9BD — MB ChB 1968 St. And.; DCH Eng. 1971. (St. And.) Clin. Med. Off. Leics. HA. Prev: Regist. & SHO (Paediat.) N. Staffs. Hosp. Centre; Ho. Off. Dundee Roy. Infirm.

MACSWEEN, Roderick Norman McIver 32 Calderwood Road, Newlands, Glasgow G43 2RU — MD 1974 Glas.; FRSE 1985; BSc Glas. 1956, MD (Hons.) 1974, MB ChB 1959; FRCP Ed. 1974, M 1964; FRCP Glas. 1972, M 1964; FRCPath. 1979, M 1967; FIBiol. 1988. (Glas.) Prof. Path. Glas. Univ. Glas.; Edr. Histopathol. Socs: Internat. Assn. for Study of Liver; Path. Soc. Gt. Brit. & Irel. Prev: SHO Med. Glas. Roy. Infirm.; Regist. (Path.) Glas. W.. Infirm.; Clin. Research Asst. & Demonst. Dept. Path. Univ. Colorado Med.

MACSWEEN, Ruth Margaret 32 Calderwood Road, Newlands, Glasgow G43 2RU Tel: 0141 637 4355; 63 Main Street, West Leake, Loughborough LE12 5RF Email: ruth_macsween@msn.com — MB BChir 1990 Camb.; BSc (Hons.) St. And. 1987; MRCP (UK) 1994; FRCPC. Regist. (Dermat.) Qu. Med. Centre Nottm. Prev: SHO (Gen. Med.) Walsgrave Hosp. Coventry; SHO Hammersmith Hosp. & Guy's Hosp. Lond.; Ho. Phys. Addenbrooke's Hosp. Camb.

MACSWEEN, Mr William Alexander Wishaw General Hospital, Wishaw ML2 0DP Tel: 01698 361100; Kerrera, 18 Columbine Way, Carluke ML8 5AY Tel: 01555 771248 — MB ChB 1968 St. And.; FRCS Ed. 1974. Cons. Orthop. Surg.Wishaw Gen. Hopsita, Wishaw. Prev: Sen. Regist. Harlow Wood Orthop. Hosp. Mansfield; Rotating Surg. Regist. Dumfries & Aberd. Gps. Hosps.; Regist. (Orthop.) Nottm. Gen. Hosp.

MACSWEENEY, David Anthony Flat 30, King Edward Mansions, 629 Fulham Road, London SW6 5UH Tel: 020 7736 6498 — MB BS 1966 Lond.; MA (Experim. Psychol.) Camb.; MRCS Eng. LRCP Lond. 1966; MRCPsych 1976; DPM Eng. 1970. (St. Thos.) Cons. Psychiat. Community Psychiat. Redbridge Trust; Sen. Lect. Roy. Lond. Med. Coll.; Clin. Dir. Servs. for the Community Redbridge HA. Socs: Roy. Coll. Psychiat. & Brit. Assn. Behavioural Psychother. Prev: Lect. Psychiat. Acad. Dept. Psychiat. Middlx. Hosp. Lond.; Recognised Teach. Univ. Lond.; on Sen. Staff MRC Neuropsychiat. Unit W. Pk. Hosp. Epsom.

MCSWEENEY, Eoghan Emmanuel (retired) Whitehill Lodge, Brinsworth, Rotherham — MB BCh BAO 1950 NUI; LAH Dub. 1949.

MACSWEENEY, Josephine Emer MedTel Open MRI Centres, 64 Harley St., London W1G 7HB Tel: 020 7299 0500 Fax: 020 7636 4227 Email: emacsweeney@medtel.com — MB BS 1983 Lond.; BSc Lond. 1980; MRCP (UK) 1987; FRCR 1992. (Middlx. Hosp. Med. Sch.) Cons. Neuroradiologist and Med. Director, MedTel UK Ltd., Wideopen MRI Centres, 64 Harley St., Lond.; Hon. Cons. Neuroradiologist, Atkinson Morley's Hosp., St. Geo.s Hosp. Health Care Trust, Lond. Socs: Mem. Brit. Soc. of Neuroradiologists. Prev: Sen. Regist. (Neuroradiol.) Nat. Hosp. Neurol. & Neurosurg. Qu. Sq. Lond.; Reg/SR (Radiol.) Hammersmith Hosp./Chelsea W.m. Hosp.; SHO Nat. Hosp. Nerv. Dis. Lond./Hammersmith Hosp./Roy. Brompton Hosp.

MCSWEENEY, Katherine Geraldine Pauline The Flat, Maes-y-Felin, St. Mellons Road, Lisvane, Cardiff CF14 0SH — MB BCh BAO 1983 NUI; MRCOG 1991.

MCSWEENEY, Mr Luke Ysbyty Gwynedd, Bangor LL57 2PW Tel: 01248 384384; 1 Pentre DU Cottages, Aber, Llanfairfechan LL33 0HU — MB ChB 1979 Liverp.; MChOrth 1988; FRCS Glas. 1986. Cons. Orthop. Surg. Ysbyty Gwynedd Bangor Gwynedd.

MACSWEENEY, Mr Shane Terence Robin 40 Canford Road, London SW11 6PD — MB BChir 1985 Camb.; MA, MB Camb. 1985, BChir 1984, MChir 1991; FRCS Eng. 1988. Sen. Regist. (Surg.) Char. Cross Hosp. Lond. Prev: Lect. (Surg.) Char. Cross Hosp. Lond.

MCSWIGGAN, George Vincent Lomea, The Droveway, St Margaret's Bay, Dover CT15 6DE Tel: 01304 852778 — LRCPI & LM, LRSCI & LM 1951; LRCPI & LM, LRCSI & LM 1951. (RCSI)

MCSWINEY

MCSWINEY, Michael Morgan Homewood, Harp Hill, Charlton Kings, Cheltenham GL52 6PU — MB BS 1985 Lond.; FRCA 1990; FFARCSI 1990.

MCTAGGART, Anne London Road Medical Practice, 12 London Road, Kilmarnock KA3 7AD Tel: 01563 523593 Fax: 01563 573552 — MB ChB 1984 Glas.; MRCGP 1989; DRCOG 1988. (Glas.) Prev: Trainee GP Largs VTS; SHO (Ophth.) Gartnavel Gen. Hosp. Glas.

MACTAGGART, Douglas Keith (retired) Sundial Lodge, Parkhill Road, Torquay TQ1 2EA Tel: 01803 292889 — MA (Hons. Hist.) Aberd. 1944, MB ChB 1949; FFCM 1982, M 1974; DPH Lond. 1952. Prev: DMO Bury Health Auth.

MCTAGGART, Helen Hunter Health Centre, Andrew Street, East Kilbride, Glasgow G74 1AD Tel: 01355 906655 — MB ChB 1979 Glas.

MCTAGGART, John 27 Muirfield Street, Kirkcaldy KY2 6SY — MB ChB 1986 Ed.

MCTAGGART, John Christopher Stranraer Health Centre, Edinburgh Road, Stranraer DG9 7HG Tel: 01776 706566.

MACTAGGART, Mrs June Mary (retired) Broadwater, Warren Road, Torquay TQ2 5TL Tel: 01803 295225 — MB ChB 1948 Aberd.; MFCM 1974; DPH Lond. 1952. Prev: SCM Devon HA.

MACTAGGART, Margaret Mary (retired) 10 The Causeway, Duddingston Village, Edinburgh EH15 3PZ — MB ChB 1943 Ed.

MACTAGGART, Mary Rose 40 West Lane, Ripon HG4 2NP — MB ChB 1950 Glas.

MCTAGGART, Wilson Alexander Drongan Surgery, 74 Mill O'Shields Road, Drongan, Ayr KA6 7AY Tel: 01292 591345 Fax: 01292 590782 — MB ChB 1990 Glas.; BSc (Hons) Anat. Glas. 1987; MRCGP 1994. (Glasgow) p/t Clin. Asst. Anticoagulant Servs. Ayrsh. Acute Hosp. Trust. Socs: BMA; RCGP. Prev: Trainee GP Argyll & Clyde HB.

MCTAGUE, Laura 86 Ranby Road, Sheffield S11 7AL — MB ChB 1994 Sheff.

MACTAVISH, Anna Shiela (retired) 32 Weymouth Drive, Glasgow G12 0LX Tel: 0141 339 0635 Fax: 0141 339 0635 — MB ChB Glas. 1946.

MCTAVISH, James Connell 26 Nicholls Avenue, Leuchars, St Andrews KY16 0LQ — MB BChir 1993 Camb.

MCTAVISH, Kim 139 Scott Road, Sheffield S4 7BH — MB ChB 1981 Sheff.

MCTAVISH, Sarah Fiona Bethel Psychopharmacology Research Unit, Warneford Hospital, Warneford, Oxford OX3 7JX Tel: 01865 741717 Fax: 01865 251076 — MB BChir 1988 Camb.; BA Oxf. 1986; MRCPsych 1993. (Oxford (preclinical) Cambridge (clinical)) MRC Clin. Train. Fell.sh. Hon. S.R. Status Psychiat. Univ. Oxf. Little more Hosp. Prev: Regist. Rotat. (Psychiat.) Oxf.; SHO Rotat. (Psychiat.) Oxf. & Camb. HA.

MACTAVISH, Siobhan Dorothy 11 Walters Mead, Ashtead KT21 2BP — MB BS 1996 Lond. (St. Bart's Lond.)

MACTIER, Fiona Claire Anne 3 Oaks Corner, Arlington Avenue, Leamington Spa CV32 5XJ — BChir 1992 Camb.

MACTIER, Helen Culdene, 11 Camstradden Drive W., Bearsden, Glasgow G61 4AJ Tel: 0141 570 0749 — MD 1988 Glas.; MB ChB 1981; MRCP (UK) 1984. Cons. Neonat.ogist. Prev: Sen. Regist. (Paediat.).

MACTIER, Robert Alexander Renal Unit, Stobhill General Hospital, Glasgow G21 3UW Tel: 0141 201 3645 Fax: 0141 557 0468 — MB ChB 1979 Glas.; MB ChB Glas.1979; MD Glas. 1988; FRCP Glas. 1994; MRCP (UK) 1982. Cons. Gen. Med. & Nephrol. Gtr. Glas. HB. Socs: Renal Assn.; Internat. Soc. Nephrol.; Eur. Renal Assn. Prev: Sen. Regist. (Gen. Med. & Nephrol.) Tayside HB.

MACULLOCH, Sheila Margaret 3 Kiltongue Cottages, Monkscourt Avenue, Airdrie ML6 — MB ChB 1977 Glas.; DCH RCPS Glas. 1980; DRCOG 1981.

MACVE, John Stuart The Surgery, Bramblys Grange, Basingstoke RG21 8UW Tel: 01256 470464 Fax: 01256 57289; The Backwater, Paddock Fields, Old Basing, Basingstoke RG24 7DB Tel: 01256 24544 — MB BChir 1960 Camb.; MA, MB Camb. 1960, BChir 1959. (St. Thos.) Prev: Resid. Med. Off. Gen. Hosp. Burton-on-Trent; Regist. (Cardiol.) Harefield Hosp.

MCVEAN, Angus Edward Liberton Medical Group, 55 Liberton Gardens, Edinburgh EH16 6JT Tel: 0131 664 3050 Fax: 0131 692 1952 — MB ChB 1991 Ed.; MRCGP 1995; DRCOG 1994.

MCVEIGH, Catherine Mary 11 Quetta Park, Church Crookham, Fleet GU52 8TG; 17 Gaza Road, Bulford, Salisbury SP4 9BA — MB BCh BAO 1982 Belf.; MRCGP 1987; DRCOG 1986.

MCVEIGH, Gary Eugene 14A Adelaide Park, Belfast BT9 6FX — MD 1987 Belf.; MB BCh BAO 1981; MRCP (UK) 1984.

MCVEIGH, Gwendolyn 2A Parkview, Ayr KA7 4QG — MB ChB 1997 Aberd.

MCVEIGH, Joseph Enda Drumenagh, Killyman, Dungannon BT71 6RJ — MB BCh BAO 1988 Belf.; MB BCh Belf. 1988. Socs: MRCOG.

MCVEIGH, Linda Mary Kilcoroon, Quarry Road, Glenmachan, Belfast BT4 2NP Tel: 01232 768015 — MB BCh BAO 1978 Belf. Clin. Med. Off. Belf.

MCVERRY, Bernard Anthony 7 Dunstarn Gardens, Adel, Leeds LS16 8EJ Tel: 0113 267 0436 — MB BCh BAO 1968 NUI; MRCP (UK) 1976; MRCPath 1977.

MCVERRY, David Nicholas Kidsgrove Medical Centre, Mount Road, Kidsgrove, Stoke-on-Trent ST7 4AY Tel: 01782 784221 Fax: 01782 781703; 194 Crewe Road, Alsager, Stoke-on-Trent ST7 2JF Tel: 01270 877017 — MB BCh BAO 1973 NUI; DCH RCPSI 1978. (Univ. Coll. Dub.)

MCVERRY, Mr Eugene Anthony Glen House, Colby, Castletown IM7 1HN — LRCPI & LM, LRSCI & LM 1946; LRCPI & LM, LRCSI & LM 1946; FRCSI 1950; FRCS Eng. 1953.

MCVERRY, Ian Thomas Bernard McVerry-McEvoy Medical Centre, Newry Health Village, Monaghan Street, Newry BT35 6BW Tel: 028 3026 1220/5853 Fax: 028 3025 1804; 1 Avoca Lawns, Warrenpoint, Newry BT34 3RJ Tel: 016937 72628 — MB BCh BAO 1974 Belf.; DCH NUI 1978.

MCVERRY, Mary Michele Jane McVerry-McEvoy Medical Centre, Newry Health Village, Monaghan Street, Newry BT35 6BW Tel: 028 3026 1220/5853 Fax: 028 3025 1804 — MB BCh BAO 1979 Dub.

MCVERRY, Michael Gerard 7 John Mitchel Place, Newry BT34 2BP — MB BCh BAO 1939 NUI. (NUI) Prev: Ho. Surg. Walsall Gen. Hosp.; Res. Med. Off. Kewstoke Emerg. Hosp.; Ho. Surg. Camborne & Redruth Miners' Gen. Hosp.

MCVERRY, Raymond Gerrard McVerry-McEvoy Medical Centre, Newry Health Village, Monaghan Street, Newry BT35 6BW Tel: 028 3026 1220/5853 Fax: 028 3025 1804 — MB BCh BAO 1981 Dub.; MB BCh Dub. 1981; DRCOG 1983.

MCVEY, Fiona Kathleen Department of Anaesthesia, Southmead Hospital, Westbury-on-Trym, Bristol BS10 5NB Tel: 0117 959 5114; 30 Lansdown Road, Redland, Bristol BS6 6NS Tel: 0117 974 1862 — MB ChB 1982 Bristol; MRCP (UK) 1987; FCAnaesth. 1989. Cons. Anaesth. S.mead Hosp. Bristol.

MCVEY, Rhona Janet 13 Gillbrook Road, Didsbury, Manchester M20 6WH Tel: 0161 434 2209 — MB ChB 1991 Manch. Specialist Regist. (Histopath.) N. W. Region. Prev: SHO (Histopath.) Manch. Roy. Infirm.; Ho. Off. (Med.) N. Manch. Gen. Hosp.; Ho. Off. (Surg.) Manch. Roy. Infirm.

MCVEY, Timothy John Newton Surgery, Park Street, Newtown SY16 1EF Tel: 01686 626221/626224 Fax: 01686 622610; Pen-y-Garreg, Upper Dolfor Road, Newtown SY16 3AD Tel: 01686 627743 — MB ChB 1978 Birm.; MRCGP 1986; DRCOG 1980. Prev: Trainee GP Som.; Off i/c Div. Health Aitape, Papua New Guinea.

MCVEY, Vivienne Margaret The Simpson Health Centre, 70 Gregories Road, Beaconsfield HP9 1PS Tel: 01494 671571 Fax: 01494 680219; Springtime, 11 Baring Road, Beaconsfield HP9 2NB Tel: 01494 672444 — MB BChir 1987 Camb.; MRCGP 1992; DRCOG 1991; DCH RCP Lond. 1991. Prev: Lect. (Primary Health Care) Univ. Coll. & Middlx. Sch. Med. Lond.

MACVICAR, Angus David Lees 27 Allendale Close, Camberwell, London SE5 8SG — MB BChir 1980 Camb.

MACVICAR, Clare Victoria 17A Rydens Avenue, Walton-on-Thames KT12 3JB Tel: 01932 224532 Fax: 01932 232 2539 Email: simon.clarke.kane@xtra.co.nz — MB ChB 1991 Birm.; ChB Birm. 1991. Paediat. Regist., Wllington, NZ.

MACVICAR, Donald (retired) 49 Fairefield Crescent, Glenfield, Leicester LE3 8EJ Tel: 0116 287 1858 — MB ChB 1944 Ed.; MD Ed. 1953; FRCOG 1968, M 1951. Prev: Cons. O & G Leicester Roy. Infirm. & LoughBoro. Gen. Hosp.

MACVICAR, Donald MacVicar and MacLeod, The Surgery, Keppoch Road, Culloden, Inverness IV2 7LL Tel: 01463 793777 Fax:

01463 792143; Sithean Mor, 28 Moray Park Terrace, Culloden, Inverness IV2 7RW Tel: 01463 792389 — MB ChB 1978 Glas.; MRCP (UK) (Paediat.) 1982; MRCGP 1986. (Glas.)

MCVICAR, Elin Mary Danyrallt House, Llangadog SA19 9DD — BM BCh 1984 Oxf.; MA Camb. 1988; MRCGP 1988; DRCOG 1988; DCH 1986.

MCVICAR, Elizabeth Helen Farndon Green Medical Centre, 1 Farndon Green, Wollaton Park, Nottingham NG8 1DU Tel: 0115 928 8666 Fax: 0115 928 8343; 57 Moor Road, Papplewick, Nottingham NG15 8EN Tel: 0115 963 2891 — BM BS 1988 Nottm.; BMedSc Nottm. 1986; MRCGP 1993; DGM RCP Lond. 1993; DRCOG 1991. Prev: Trainee GP Nottm. VTS; SHO (O & G & Paediat.) St. Richard's Hosp. Chichester.

MACVICAR, Mr Frank Turner Fairwinds, Margnaheglish, Lamlash, Brodick KA27 8LE — MB ChB 1952 Glas.; FRCS Glas. 1962; FRCS Ed. 1963. (Glas.)

MACVICAR, George Wern Fechan, Beulah Road, Rhiwbina, Cardiff CF4 — MRCS Eng. LRCP Lond. 1941. (Guy's) Prev: Ho. Surg. Lewisham Gen. Hosp.; Ophth. Ho. Surg. Guy's Hosp.; Surg. Lt. RNVR.

MCVICAR, Mr Iain Hamilton Maxillofacial Unit, 30 The Ropewalk, Nottingham NG1 5DW Tel: 0115 924 9924 Ext: 48915 Fax: 0115 948 5552 Email: ihmcvicar@qmcnottingham.freeserve.co.uk; 57 Moor Road, Papplewick, Nottingham NG15 8EN Tel: 0115 963 2891 Fax: 0115 968 0330 Email: iainhmcvicar@msn.com — BM BS 1988 Nottm.; BMedSci Nottm. 1986; BDS Sheff. 1981; FRCS Ed. 1991; FRCS Eng. 1991; FDS RCS 1986, LDS 1981. Cons. Maxillofacial Surg. Qu. Med. Centre Univ. Hosp. NHS Trust Nottm. Socs: Fell. Brit. Assn. Oral & Maxillofacial Surg.; Eur. Assn. Cranio-Maxillo. Surg.; Internat. Assn. Oral & Maxillofacial Surg. Prev: Sen. Regist. (Oral & Maxillofacial Surg.) Trent RHA; Regist. (Maxillofacial Surg.) St. Richards Hosp. Chichester; SHO Rotat. (Surg.) Nottm. HA.

MCVICAR, Jane Therese 59 Grange Avenue, West Derby, Liverpool L12 9JR — MB ChB 1993 Manch.

MACVICAR, Professor John 39 Guilford Road, Leicester LE2 2RD Tel: 0116 270 7827 — MB ChB 1950 Glas.; MD Glas. 1959; FRCS Glas. 1972; FRCOG 1967, M 1955. (Glas.) Prof. Emerit. Univ. Leicester. Prev: Prof. O & G Univ. Leicester; Sen. Lect. (Midw.) Univ. Glas.

MACVICAR, John The Surgery, Croyard Road, Beauly IV4 7BT Tel: 01463 782794 Fax: 01463 782111 — MB ChB 1977 Glas.

MACVICAR, Lindsay Clare Druim House, Stratherrick Road, Inverness IV2 4LQ — MB ChB 1985 Aberd.; MRCGP 1989; DRCOG 1987. Trainee GP/SHO Inverness VTS.; Highland GP Retainer Scheme. Prev: SHO (A & E) Raigmore Hosp. Inverness; Trainee GP Highland VTS.

MACVICAR, Maureen Benachally, Yeaman St., Rattray, Blairgowrie PH10 7DW — MB ChB 1983 Dundee.

MACVICAR, Ronald Culduthel Road Surgery, Ardlarich, 15 Culduthel Road, Inverness IV2 4AG Tel: 01463 712233; Druim House, Stratherrick Road, Inverness IV2 4LQ — MB ChB 1981 Glas.; FRCGP 1994, M 1986; DRCOG 1983; DCCH RCP Ed. 1989. GP Inverness.

MACVICAR, Stephen Health Centre, New Street, Beaumaris LL58 8EL Tel: 01248 810818 Fax: 01248 811589; Plas Hyfryd, Rating Row, Beaumaris LL58 8AF Tel: 01248 810624 — MB ChB 1981 Birm.; MRCGP 1986; DRCOG 1986.

MACVICAR, Susan Marjorie 36 Moorfoot Way, Bearsden, Glasgow G61 4RL — MB ChB 1976 Glas.; FFA RCS (Eng.) 1981. Cons. Anaesth. Monklands Dist. Gen. Hosp. Airdrie.

MCVICKER, James Douglas (retired) Craignamaddy, 126 Moycraig Road, Ballymoney BT53 8QZ — MB BCh BAO Dub. 1962. Prev: GP Stow, Selkirksh.

MCVICKER, James Thomas Central Abacus, 40-46 Dale Street, Liverpool L2 5SF Tel: 0151 284 2500 Fax: 0151 293 2005; 14 Cole Crescent, Aughton, Ormskirk L39 5AJ Tel: 01695 422957 Email: jmcvicker@doctors.org.uk — MB BCh BAO 1978 Belf.; MRCGP 1995; MFFP 2000; T(GP) 1994. Assoc. Specialist in Family Plann. & Reprod. Health Care, Wotten's Health Directorate, Centr. Abacus; Hon. Clin. Lect., Dept. of Obst. & Gyn., Liverp. Univ. Socs: BMA; Brit. Menopause Soc.; N. W. Soc. Of Serual Med. & Family Plann.

MCVICKER, John Matthew 11 Delhi Parade, Ormeau Road, Belfast BT7 3AU — MB BCh BAO 1983 Belf.; MRCGP 1989.

MACVICKER, Katherine Mary (retired) Forest House Farm, Gallowsclough Lane, Oakmere, Northwich CW8 2TG Tel: 01606 883652 — MB BS 1957 Lond.; MRCS Eng. LRCP Lond. 1957; DObst RCOG 1960. Prev: Clin. Med. Off. Warrington Health Dist.

MCVIE, Duncan Hunter (retired) 4A Merchiston Park, Edinburgh EH10 4PN Tel: 0131 229 5919 — MB ChB 1950 Ed.; FRCGP 1979, M 1958; DObst RCOG 1952. Prev: Phys. i/c Edin. Univ. Health Serv.

MCVIE, Hilary Margaret The Kyles, 44 Victoria Hill Road, Fleet GU51 4LG — MB ChB 1995 Leic.

MCVIE, James Lachlan 3 South Street, West Rainton, Houghton-le-Spring DH4 6PA — MB BS 1992 Newc.

MCVIE, Professor John Gordon Director General, Cancer Research Campaign, 10 Cambridge Terrace, Regents Pk., London NW1 4JL Tel: 020 7224 1333 Fax: 020 7224 2399 Email: gmcvie@crc.org.uk — MB ChB Ed. 1969; DSc (Hon.) Nott. 1997; DSc (Hon.) Portsmouth 1999; DSc (Hon.) Abertay, Dund 1996; MD Ed. 1978; FRCP (Lond.) 1997; FRCPS Glas. 1987; FRCP Ed. 1981; MRCP (UK) 1971; F Med Sci 1998; FRCSE 2000. (Edinburgh) Dir. Gen. Cancer Research Campaign Lond.; Vis. Prof. Brit. Postgrad. Med. Federat. Lond. Univ.; Vis. Prof. Glas. Univ.; Europ. Edr. Jl. for the Natioanl Cancer Inst.; Bd. Mem. Phot-Therap. Ltd; Bd. Mem. Cancer Source; Bd. Mem. Cancer Research Campaign Technologies Ltd. Socs: Pres. and Bd. Mem. Treatm. of Cancer Europ. Org. for Res.; Bd. Mem. and Chairm. Fell.sh. Progr. Union Internat.e Contre le Cancer. Prev: Scientif. Dir., Cancer Research Campaign; Scientif. Dir. (Clin.) Nat. Cancer Inst., Netherlands; Sen. Lect. (Oncol.) Glas. Univ.

MACVIE, Mrs Marion Hamilton (retired) Raymond Priestley House, 114 Bromford Lane, Erdington, Birmingham B24 8BZ — MB ChB 1924 Glas.; Dip. Bact. Manch. 1925.

MCVIE, Mary Walker 4A Merchiston Park, Edinburgh EH10 4PN Tel: 0131 229 5919 — MB ChB 1950 Ed.; BSc Ed. 1946. (Ed.) Prev: Lect. Edin. Univ. Gen. Pract. Teachg. Unit; SHO (Med.) Edin. Roy. Infirm.; Ho. Surg. (O & G) W.. Gen. Hosp. Edin.

MACVIE, Sheila Irene (retired) 1 Addison Crescent, London W14 8JP Tel: 020 7603 4488 — BSc Lond. 1947, MB BS 1956, DCP 1961; MRCPath 1971. Prev: Cons. Haemat. Mid Downs DHA.

MCVITIE, David Robison Craig Roundhay Wing, St. James University Hospital, Beckett St., Leeds LS9 7 Tel: 0113 243 3144 Fax: 0113 234 6856 — MB ChB St. And. 1969; MRCPsych 1974; DPM Ed. & Glas. 1973. Cons. Psychiat. St. Jas. Univ. Hosp. Leeds; Sen. Clin. Lect. Univ. Leeds. Prev: Cons. Psychiat. Stanley Royd Hosp. Wakefield.

MCVITTIE, Claire Helen 3/2, 54 Polwarth St., Glasgow G12 9TL — MB ChB 1995 Glas.; MRCP (UK) 1999. SHO (A&E) W.ern Infirm. Glas.

MCVITTIE, Clare Jemma The Maisonette, 1 Margarets Bldg., Bath BA1 2LP — MB ChB 1997 Ed.

MCVITTIE, Steven Gordon St Michael's House, 54 Holloway Hill, Pershore WR10 1HP Tel: 01386 554625 Email: sgmcrittie@aol.com — MB BChir 1979 Camb.; MA Camb. 1980; AFOM 1997; MRCGP 1991; DRCOG 1986; DA (UK) 1982. Occupat. Phys. Socs: Soc. Occ. Med.; Medico-Legal Soc.

MACWALTER, Ronald Siller Ninewells Hospital and Medical School, Dundee DD1 9SY Tel: 01382 660111 Fax: 01382 660675 Email: ronald.macwalter@tuht.scot.nhs.uk; Ellangowan, 8 Hillcrest Road, Dundee DD2 1JJ Tel: 01382 566125 Email: rsmacwalter@blueyonder.co.uk — MB ChB 1978 Dundee; FRCP 1992 Ed; FRCP 1993 Glas; MRCP 1982 UK; BMSc 1975 (Hons) Dund. Cons. Phys. & Sen. Lect. (Gen. Med.) Ninewells Hosp. & Med. Sch. Dundee. Socs: Scott. Soc. Phys.; Brit. Geriat. Soc. (Counc. Scott. Br.); Brit. Assn. Stroke Phys. Prev: Cons. Phys. & Sen. Lect. (Med. for Elderly) Roy. Vict. Hosp. & Ninewells Hosp. Dundee; Sen. Regist. (Gen. & Geriat. Med.) Nuffield Dept. Med. John Radcliffe Hosp. Oxf.; Regist. (Gen. Med. & Haemat.) Ninewells Hosp. & Med. Sch. Dundee.

MCWATT, P J Parkfield Health Centre, Sefton Road, New Ferry, Wirral CH62 5HS Tel: 0151 644 0055 Fax: 0151 643 1679.

MCWATTERS, The Hon. Mrs Veronica The Grove, Dundry, Bristol BS41 8JG Tel: 0117 964 1334 — MRCS Eng. LRCP Lond. 1960. (Roy. Free) GP Bristol. Prev: Ho. Surg. Roy. Free Hosp. Lond.; Ho. Phys. Stamford & Rutland Hosp.

MACWHANNELL

MACWHANNELL, Alan Sheene House, Church Lane, Sheriffhales, Shifnal TF11 8DH — MB BS 1977 Lond.

MCWHINNEY, Mr Norman Arthur Department of Obstetrics & Gynaecology, St Helier Hospital, Wrythe Lane, Carshalton SM5 1AA Tel: 020 8644 4343 Fax: 020 8641 4546; Highfield, 1 Chalgrove Road, Sutton SM2 5JT — MB BCh BAO 1973 Dub.; BA, MB BCh BAO Dub. 1973; FRCS Ed. 1980; FRCOG 1994, M 1978. (Trinity College, Dublin) Cons. Obst. & Gyn. St. Helier Hosp. Carshalton; Hon. Sen. Lect. St. Geo. Med. Sch. Prev: Sen. Regist. (O & G) N.wick Pk. Hosp. Harrow & Hammersmith Hosp.; Regist. (O & G) John Radcliffe Hosp. Oxf.; Regist. (Urol.) Hammersmith Hosp. Lond.

MCWHINNEY, Paul Henry Morgan Medical Admissions Unit, Bradford Royal Infirmary, Bradford BD9 6RJ Tel: 01274 382047/68 Fax: 01274 364283 Email: paul@mcwhinney.freeserve.co.uk; 54 Ellingham Road, Harden, Bingley BD16 1LQ Tel: 01535 271395 Fax: 0870 063 6399 — MB BS 1983 Lond.; MA Camb. 1984; MRCP (UK) 1986; DCH RCP Lond. 1989. Cons. Phys., Infec. Dis.s. Socs: Brit. Infec. Soc.; Brit. Soc. for Med. Myocology; Europ. Soc. of Clin. MicroBiol. and Infec. Dis.s. Prev: Sen. Regist. (Infec. Dis.s), Seacroft Hosp., Leeds; Research Fell. (Communicable Dis.) Roy. Free Hosp. Lond.; Regist. (Med.) York Dist. Hosp.

MCWHINNIE, Alexander James 16 Cupar Road, Newport-on-Tay DD6 8DF — MB BS 1985 Lond.

MCWHINNIE, Mr Douglas Leslie Milton Keynes General Hospital, Standing Way, Eaglestone, Milton Keynes MK6 5LD Tel: 01908 243153 Fax: 01908 243153 — MB ChB 1977 Glas.; MB ChB Glas. (Commend) 1977; MD (Hons.) Glas. 1989; FRCS Glas. 1981; FRCS Eng. 1997. Cons. Gen. & Vasc. Surg. Milton Keynes Gen. Hosp. Prev: Tutor (Surg.) Univ. Oxf.

MCWHINNIE, Robert Nicholas The Surgery, 1 Kimberworth Road, Rotherham S61 1AH Tel: 01709 561442/562319 Fax: 01709 740690 — MB ChB 1982 Sheff.

MACWHIRTER, Gilbert Ian Highover, Bracken Lane, Storrington, Pulborough RH20 3HS — MB BS 1957 Lond.; FFA RCS Eng. 1967; DA Eng. 1964.

MCWHIRTER, James Holman McWhirter, Barton and Silver, The Surgery, Wanbourne Lane, Nettlebed, Henley-on-Thames RG9 5AJ Tel: 01491 641204 Fax: 01491 641162; 8 Watlington Street, Nettlebed, Henley-on-Thames RG9 5AA Tel: 01491 641999 Fax: 01491 641999 Email: mcwhirter@lineone.net — MB ChB 1977 Liverp.; MA Oxf. 1972; MRCGP 1982; DRCOG 1982. (Liverp.) GP Sen. Part.

MCWHIRTER, James Wyllie Galston Surgery, 5A Henrietta Street, Galston KA4 8JW Tel: 01563 820424 Fax: 01563 822380; Westwood, 29 Cessnock Road, Galston KA4 8LR — MB ChB 1981 Ed.

MCWHIRTER, Malcolm Francis Forth Valley Health Board, 33 Spittal St., Stirling FK8 1DX Tel: 01786 457254 Fax: 01786 446327; 133 Ochiltree, Dunblane FK15 0PA — MB BCh BAO 1977 Belf.; MBA Strathclyde 1990; MRCP (UK) 1981; FFPHM RCP (UK) 1993; MFCM 1985; MPH Glas. 1982; FRCP (Ed.) 1998. Dir. of Pub. Health Forth Valley HB; Hon. Sen. Clin. Lect. (Pub. Health) Univ. Glas. Prev: Cons. Pub. Health Med. Forth Valley HB.

MCWILLIAM, Agnes Janet Hamilton (retired) 49 Lower Milehouse Lane, Newcastle ST5 9BE Tel: 01782 611409 Fax: 01782 611409 — MB ChB Glas. 1950; MSc Keele 1993; DPMC 1992.

MCWILLIAM, Andrew Gwynne 36 Whinney Heys Road, Blackpool FY3 8NP — MB ChB 1997 Aberd.

MCWILLIAM, Christopher Ribbleton Hospital, Miller Road, Ribbleton, Preston PR2 6LS Tel: 01772 401613 — MB ChB 1979 Liverp.; MA Keele 1992; MRCPsych 1984. Cons. Psychiat. Guild Health Care Trust; Hon. Sen. Lect. Univ. Centr. Lancs. Socs: Fell.Roy. Soc. for Promotion of Health (FRSH). Prev: Sen. Lect. & Cons. Psychiat. Univ. of Wolverhampton; Cons. Psychiat. & Clin. Lect. Univ. of Liverp.; Lect. & Hon. Sen. Regist. Univ. of Liverp.

MCWILLIAM, Joan Margaret (retired) 48A Dreghorn Loan, Edinburgh EH13 0DD Tel: 0131 441 1269 — MB ChB 1941 Ed.; MFCM 1973; MRCPath 1964; DPH Ed. 1950. Prev: SCM Lothian Health Bd.

MCWILLIAM, Jonathan 8 Sandringham Road, Walton-le-Dale, Preston PR5 4QN — MB ChB 1982 Liverp.

MACWILLIAM, Kathleen Margaret (retired) Downlands, Rectory Road, Streatley, Reading RG8 9LE Tel: 01491 872169 — MB BCh BAO 1953 Dub.; BA, MB BCh BAO Dub. 1953; MRCP Ed. 1959; DCH Eng. 1956. Prev: Clin. Med. Off. W. Berks. HA.

MCWILLIAM, Lorna Jean Clayton Fold Farm, Kettleshulme, Whaley Bridge, High Peak SK23 7EJ — MB ChB 1979 Sheff.; MRCPath 1986.

MCWILLIAM, Lorna Suzanne 23 Victoria Street, Forfar DD8 3BA — MB ChB 1992 Aberd. (Aberd.) SHO (Psychiat.) Roy. Dundee Liff Hosp. Dundee. Prev: SHO (Psychiat.) Sunnyside Roy. Hosp. Montrose; GP/Regist. Kirriemuir Health Centre; SHO (Med. for Elderly) Ashludie Hosp. Dundee.

MCWILLIAM, Patricia Jane (retired) Contin Manse, Contin, Strathpeffer IV14 9ES Tel: 01997 421380 Email: gmc77@dial.pipex.com — MB ChB 1963 Glas.; DObst RCOG 1965.

MCWILLIAM, Peter Kenneth Angus (retired) Greystone Gables, 103 Pontefract Road, Ackworth, Pontefract WF7 7EL Tel: 01977 704940 Email: pkamcwilliam@lineone.net — MB ChB Leeds 1954; DCH Eng. 1957; DCH RCPS Glas. 1957. Prev: Hosp. Pract. (Paediat.) Pontefract HA.

MCWILLIAM, Robert Charles Fraser of Allander Neurosciences Unit, Royal Hospital for Sick Children, Yorkhill, Glasgow G3 8SJ Tel: 0141 201 0134 Fax: 0141 201 9270 Email: rmcwillian@compuserve.com; Pleanbank Farm House, By Plean, Stirling FK7 8BB Tel: 01786 816412 — MB ChB 1974 Ed.; FRCP Glas. 1989; MRCP (UK) 1976; FRCPCH 1997. Cons. (Paediat. Neurol.) Roy. Hosp. Sick Child. Yorkshill NHS Trust Glas. Prev: Cons. Paediat. & Paediat Neurol. Forth Valley Health Bd.

MCWILLIAM, Robert John (retired) 4 Torridon Avenue, Glasgow G41 5LA Tel: 0141 427 1204 — MB ChB Glas. 1945; FRFPS Glas. 1950; FRCP Glas. 1966, M 1962; FRCOphth. 1988; DO Eng. 1953. Prev: Civil Cons. Ophth. RN in Scotl.

MCWILLIAM, William Nicholson (retired) 14 Crofton Road, Ipswich IP4 4QS — MB BCh BAO 1950 Belf. Prev: GP Ipswich.

MCWILLIAMS, Mr Daniel Joseph 22 St Lane, Leeds LS8 2ET Tel: 0113 237 1356 Fax: 0113 237 0319; Chalgrove, 9 Old Pk Road, Leeds LS8 1JT Tel: 0113 266 8800 — MB BCh BAO 1955 Belf.; FRCS Ed. 1960. Cons. Orthop. Surg. St. Jas. Hosp. Leeds. Prev: Sen. Regist. Roy. Vict. Hosp. Belf.; Regist. Musgrave Pk. Hosp. Belf.

MCWILLIAMS, Donal Michael (retired) 11 Deanfield Road, Henley-on-Thames RG9 1UG — MA Dub. 1961, MB BCh BAO 1953; FFA RCS Eng. 1959; DA Eng. 1956. Prev: Cons. Anaesth. Reading & Dist. Hosp. Gp.

MCWILLIAMS, Edward Adrian 14 Broughshane Road, Ballymena BT43 7DX Tel: 01266 3016 — MB BCh BAO 1953 Belf.; DO Eng. 1956. SHMO N. Irel. Hosps. Auth. Prev: Regist. Addenbrooke's Hosp. Camb.; SHO St. Paul's Eye Hosp. Liverp.

MCWILLIAMS, Helen 6 Ivy Court, Hixon, Stafford ST18 0FF — MB BS 1998 Lond.

MCWILLIAMS, Jane Elizabeth Winlaton and Ryton Medical Partners, 10 Front Street, Winlaton, Blaydon-on-Tyne NE21 4RD Tel: 0191 414 2339 Fax: 0191 414 4779 — MB BS 1994 Newc.

MCWILLIAMS, Lionel Francis, MC (retired) Oak Tree Platt, Mill Lane, Blue Bell Hill, Chatham ME5 9RB Tel: 01634 861467 — MB BCh BAO 1938 Belf.; DPH 1947; MFCM 1974. Prev: Med. Adviser (Occupat. Health Serv.) Dartford & Gravesham HA.

MCWILLIAMS, Marianne Julia Woodthorpe, 4 Ryecroft Road, Heswall, Wirral CH60 1XB — MB ChB 1990 Manch.; MRCGP 1994. Prev: SHO (Geriat.) Newton Gen. Hosp. Leeds; SHO (O & G) & Cas. Off. Trafford Hosp. Manch.

MCWILLIAMS, Mr Richard Gregory Woodthorpe, 4 Ryecroft Road, Heswall, Wirral CH60 1XB — MB BCh BAO 1986 Dub.; FRCS Eng. 1990; FRCR 1995. Cons. Interven.al Radiol. Roy. Liverp. Univ. Hosp. Prev: Sen. Regist. (Radiol.) Leeds & Bradford.

MCWILLIAMS, Ronald Nigel New Dover Road Surgery, 10 New Dover Road, Canterbury CT1 3AP Tel: 01227 462197 Fax: 01227 786041 — MB BS 1982 Lond.; MRCGP 1987; DCH RCP Lond. 1986; DRCOG 1985. (St. Mary's)

MCWILLIAMS, Royussell North Lodge, 53 Downshire Road, Newry BT34 1EE Tel: 01693 63119 — MB BCh BAO 1964 Belf.; FRCOG 1985, M 1971.

MCWILLIAMS, Sarah Elizabeth 1 Stanley Avenue, Beckenham BR3 6PU — MB BS 1988 Lond.; MB BS (Distinc.) Lond. 1988; MRCP (UK) 1991; FRCR 1995. Cons. Radiol. - Guy's & St. Thomas's Hosp. - Lond. Prev: Sen. Regist. (Radiol.) Kings Coll. Hosp.

MCWILLIAMS, Timothy Guy 3 Crawshaw Villa, Crawshaw Road, Pudsey LS28 7UB — MB BS 1992 Lond.

MADAGAN, Nigel George 9 Sandpiper Close, Stratford-upon-Avon CV37 9EY — MB BS 1991 Lond.

***MADAN, Anil Kumar** 232 Queens Promenade, Blackpool FY2 9HA — MB ChB 1994 Liverp.

MADAN, Arvind Kumar The Hurley Clinic, Ebenezer House, Kennington Lane, London SE11 4HJ Tel: 020 7735 7918 Fax: 020 7587 5296; 287 Beulah Hill, London SE19 3UZ — MB ChB 1991 Leic.; MRCGP 1996; DRCOG 1994. (Leic.)

MADAN, Asha Child & Family Clinic, Bocombra Lodge, 2 Old Lurgan Road, Portadown, Craigavon BT63 5SQ Tel: 01762 392112; The Beeches, 41 Cultra Avenue, Holywood BT18 0AY Tel: 01232 427564 — MB ChB Leeds 1965; MRCPsych 1972; DPM Lond. 1971. Cons. Child Psychiat. Craigavon & Banbridge Community HSS Trust. Prev: Cons. Child Psychiat. Worcester Roy. Infirm.

MADAN, Ashu 31 Banstead Road S., Sutton SM2 5LG — MB ChB 1992 Leic.

MADAN, Chand Karan Rawdon Surgery, 11 New Road Side, Rawdon, Leeds LS19 6DD Tel: 0113 295 4234 Fax: 0113 295 4228; Farwake Hill Farm, Grantley, Ripon HG4 3PT — MB BS 1963 Delhi.

MADAN, Harvinder 19 Leamington Road, Coventry CV3 6GF — MB ChB 1984 Liverp.

MADAN, Ira Lower Waiting Hall, Houses of Parliament, London SW1 0AA Tel: 020 7219 5757; 20A Broadwater Down, Tunbridge Wells TN2 5NR Email: madan@roltanet.com — MB BS 1985 Lond.; MB BS (Hons.) Lond. 1985; MRCP (UK) 1988; MFOM RCP Lond. 1992; FRCP 1999; FFOM 2000. (UMDS) p/t Cons. Occupat.al Phys. Guy's and St Thomas's NHS Trust Lond.; Med. Adviser Ho.s of Parliament. Socs: Soc. Occupat. Med. Prev: Cons. Occupat. Phys. S.mead NHS Trust; Sen. Clin. Lect. (Occupat. Med.) Univ. Bristol; Lect. (Occupat. Med.) UMDS Univ. Lond.

MADAN, Krishna Kumar Bispham Road Surgery, 154 Bispham Road, Blackpool FY2 0NG Tel: 01253 352066 — MB BS 1961 Punjab; MB BS Punjab (India) 1961. (Med. Coll. Amritsar)

MADAN, Larvinder Singh The Surgery, 4 Stowe Drive, Southam Tel: 01926 812577 — MB BS 1987 Lond.; MRCGP (Distinc.) 1994. GP Princip.

MADAN, Mr Manmohan York District Hospital, Wigginton Road, York YO31 8HE — MB ChB 1984 Glas.; FRCS Eng. 1992; FRCS Gen. 1997. (Glasgow) Cons. (Surg. & Vascul.) York Dist. Hosp. Prev: St James Univ. Hosp., Leeds Specialist Regist.; Regist. (Surg.) S.. Gen. Hosp. Glas.; Lect. (Anat.) Univ. Glas.

***MADAN, Nisha** 2 Hatchlands, Horsham RH12 5JX — MB ChB 1998 Manch.; MB ChB Manch 1998.

MADAN, Raman Flat 40, Elizabeth Newcomen House, 38 Newcomen St., London SE1 1YZ — MB BS 1977 Delhi; FFA RCS Eng. 1988; FFA RCSI 1987.

MADAN, Santosh Windmill Health Centre, Mill Green View, Leeds LS14 5JS Tel: 0113 273 3733; Shiraz, Betteras Hill Road, Hillam, Leeds LS25 5HB Tel: 01977 684564 Fax: 0113 232 3202 — MB BS 1963 Delhi; BSc Meerut 1958; DMRT Eng. 1971. (Maulana Azad Med. Coll.)

MADAN, Santosh Bispham Road Surgery, 154 Bispham Road, Blackpool FY2 0NG Tel: 01253 352066 — MB BS 1962 Punjab; BSc (Hons.), MB BS Punjab 1962.

MADAN, Yogesh Nath (retired) Lyndhurst, 48 George St., Sedgley Park, Prestwich, Manchester M25 9WS Tel: 0161 773 8053 — MB BS 1955 Agra. Prev: GP Salford.

MADAN BENARJI, Tatineni 1 Greenfield Gardens, Doncaster DN4 6TF Tel: 01302 531921 — MB BS 1968 Mysore; MRCOG 1981. Staff Grade (O & G) P.ss Margt. Hosp. Swindon.

MADANAYAKE, Sirinatha Kumaradasa Rose Farm, Station Road, Lydiate, Liverpool L31 4HA Tel: 0151 526 0530 — MRCS Eng. LRCP Lond. 1960. (Liverp.)

MADAR, Robert Ivan (retired) 123 Cheriton Road, Folkestone CT19 5HD Tel: 01303 850585 — MD 1951 Budapest; LRCP LRCS Ed. LRFPS Glas. 1959; MFFP 1994; MRCOG 1967. Prev: GP Kent.

MADAR, Robert John Derriford Hospital, Plymouth PL6 8OH Tel: 01752 777111 Email: john.madar.@phnt.swest.nhs.uk — BM 1985 Soton.; MRCP (UK) 1990; FRCPCH. Cons. Neonatol. Derriford Hosp. Plymouth. Prev: Sen. Regist. (Paediat.) Roy. Hosp. Sick Childr. Glas.

MADDAFORD, Karen Jane 8 Pent Vale Close, Folkestone CT19 5LQ Email: 065021713@compuserve.com — MB ChB 1987 Ed.; DFFP 1996. Prev: SHO (Gen. Med., Co-op. Care & Rheum.) Roy. Lond. Trust; SHO (Paediat.) St. Johns Hosp. Chelmsford; SHO (Gen. Med.) Kettering Gen. & Maidstone Hosps.

MADDAMS, David John East Street Surgery, 6-7 East Street, Ware SG12 9HJ Tel: 01920 468777 Fax: 01920 484892; 2 Musleigh Manor, Widbury Gardens, Ware SG12 7AT — MB ChB 1983 Sheff.; MRCGP 1987. Prev: Trainee GP Basildon & Thurrock VTS; Ho. Phys. Luton & Dunstable Hosp.; Ho. Surg. Rotherham Dist. Gen. Hosp.

MADDEN, Annabel Mary Doonholm, Alloway, Ayr KA6 6BL Tel: 01292 442690 — MB BS 1986 Lond. Staff Grade (A & E) Ayr Hosp. Prev: SHO (Orthop. & A & E) Roy. Alexandra Hosp. Paisley; SHO (Paediat. Surg.) Yorkhill Hosp. Glas.

MADDEN, Anthony Paul Department of Anaesthesia, North Bristol NHS Trust, Southmead Hospital, Bristol BS10 5NB Tel: 0117 950 5050 Email: anthony.madden@north-bristol.swest.nhs.uk; 33 Kingsweston Road, Henbury, Bristol BS10 7QT Tel: 0717 950 6038 — BM BCh 1S73 Oxf.; MA Oxf. 1974; FRCA 1978 England. (Oxf. & St. Bart.) Cons. Anaesth. S.mead Hosp., N. Bristol NHS Trust. Socs: Assn. Anaesths.; Anaesth. Res. Soc.; Soc. Computing & Technol. Anaesth. Prev: Sen. Regist. (Anaesth.) St. Thos. Hosp. Lond.; Regist. (Anaesth.) Hosp. Sick Childr. Gt. Ormond St. Lond.; Anaesth. St. Bart. Hosp. Lond.

MADDEN, Brendan Patrick Cardiothoracic Unit, St. Georges Hospital, Blackshaw Road, Tooting, London SW17 0QT Tel: 020 8672 1255 Fax: 020 8725 0360; 27 Auburn Road, Johnstown, Dun Laoghaire, Republic of Ireland — MB BCh BAO 1984 NUI; MD NUI 1991; MSc Applied Immunol. Brunel 1992; FRCPI 1995, M 1987; FRCP Lond. 1997. (University College Dublin) Cons. Thoracic, Intens. Care and Transpl.. Phys. St. Geo. Hosp. Lond.; Reader in Cardiothoracic Med. Socs: Brit. Thorac. Soc.; Intens. Care Soc. Prev: Sen. Regist. (Cardiopulm. Transpl.) Brompton Hosp. & Nat. Heart & Lung Inst. Lond.; Regist. (Cardiopulm. Transpl.) Harefield Hosp. Middlx.; Regist. (Nephrol.) & Clin. Tutor Meath Hosp. Dub.

MADDEN, Mr Brian Knight (retired) The Manor House, Chilthorne Domer, Yeovil BA22 8RD — MB BChir 1949 Camb.; FRCS Eng. 1957. Prev: Cons. Orthop. Surg. Yeovil Gen. Hosp.

MADDEN, Catherine Anne Avenue House Surgery, 109 Saltergate, Chesterfield S40 1LE Tel: 01246 272139 Fax: 01246 556336; Grove Farm, Loads Road, Holymoorside, Chesterfield S42 7HW — MB ChB 1982 Leeds; MRCGP 1987; DCH RCP 1987.

MADDEN, Daphne Alexandra Frances (retired) Tara, Queen's Road, Oswestry SY11 2JB Tel: 01691 653287 — MB BCh BAO 1951 Dub. Prev: Ho. Phys. S. Lond. Hosp. Wom. & Childr.

MADDEN, Edward John (retired) 48 Jenner House, Hunter St., London WC1N 1BL — BM BCh 1947 Oxf.; MA Oxf. 1948, BM BCh 1947. Lond. Med. Off. AER Lingus. Prev: Ho. Phys. Radcliffe Infirm. Oxf.

MADDEN, Fergus James Finch Department of Oncology, Leicester Royal Infirmary, Infirmary Square, Leicester LE1 5WW; Willow House, Stanford Dingley, Reading RG7 6LX Tel: 01189 744654 — BM BCh 1966 Oxf.; FRCP Lond. 1990; MRCP (UK) 1971; FRCR 1976; DMRT Eng. 1975. Cons. Radiother. & Oncol. Leicester Roy. Infirm.

MADDEN, Mr Gerard James 12 Cawley Road, Chichester PO19 1UZ Tel: 01243 787669 Fax: 01243 787669 Email: gerrymadden@btinternet.com — MB BS 1981 Lond.; BSc (Hons.) Lond. 1978; FRCS Eng. 1987. Cons. Otolaryngol. Portsmouth Hosps. Prev: Sen. Regist. (ENT Surg.) St. Mary's Hosp. Lond.; Regist. (ENT Surg.) Roy. Free Hosp. Lond.; SHO (Gen. Surg.) Roy. Marsden Hosp. Lond.

MADDEN, James Warren Cuthbert Ampleforth Abbey, York YO62 4EN Tel: 014393 766751 Fax: 014393 788330 — MB BS 1978 Lond.; MRCP (UK) 1982. (Middlx.)

MADDEN, John Spencer (retired) Grosvenor and Nuffield Hospital, Wrexham Road, Chester CH4 7QP Tel: 01244 680444 Fax: 01244 680812 — MB BCh BAO NUI 1951; FRCP Ed. 1973, M 1960; FRCPsych 1971; DPM Eng. 1956. Cons. Psychiat. W. Chesh.; Vice Chair. Med. Counc. Alcoh.; Chairm. Jl. Comm. Alcohol & Alcoholism; Asst. Ed. Jl. of Psychiat. Prev: Sen. Regist. Rainhill Hosp. Liverp.

MADDEN

MADDEN, Marie Goretti Histopathology Department, Altnagelvin Hospital, Londonderry BT47 6SB Email: mmadden@alt.n-l.nhs.uk — MB BCh BAO 1975 NUI; BSc (Path.) NUI 1979; FRCPath 1996. Cons. Histopath. Socs: Fell. Roy. Coll. Pathologists; Assn. Clin. Pathologist; Fell. Roy. Acad. Med. Dub.

MADDEN, Mary Patricia 3 Barn Hey, Moels Drive, Hoylake, Wirral CH47 4DF; 37/4 Dean Path, Dean Village, Edinburgh EH4 3AY — MSc 1989; MB BCh BAO NUI 1962; MFPHM 1992; Dip Travel Med. 1997. Sen. Med. Off. Scott. Off. Edin. Prev: Sen. Regist. (Community Med.) Mersey RHA.

MADDEN, Mr Nicholas Paul Chelsea & Westminster Hospital, 369 Fulham Road, London SW10 9NH Tel: 020 8746 8696 Fax: 020 8746 8644 Email: n.madden@ic.ac.uk; 15 Bridgefield Road, Cheam, Sutton SM1 2DG Tel: 020 8661 7528 Email: madboddy@globalnet.co.uk — BM BCh 1974 Oxf.; MA Oxf. 1974; FRCS Eng. 1980. Cons. Paediat. Surg. Chelsea & W.m. Hosp. & St. Mary's Hosp. Lond. Socs: Brit. Assn. Paediat. Surg. Prev: Cons. Paediat. Surg. W.m. Childr. Hosp. Lond.; Sen. Regist. (Paediat. Surg.) Leeds Gen. Infirm. & St. Jas. Hosp. Leeds.

MADDEN, Peter Lawrence Roycroft, Madden and Thomas, Chelford Surgery, Elmstead Road, Chelford, Macclesfield SK11 9BS Tel: 01625 861316 Fax: 01625 860075; Somerford, 10 Henbury Rise, Henbury, Macclesfield SK11 9NW Tel: 01625 611260 — MB ChB 1981 Manch.; BSc (Med. Sci.) St. And. 1978; FRCGP 1995, M 1985; DRCOG 1984. Hon. Sec. S. Chesh. LMC.

MADDEN, Thomas Bowman (retired) Tara, Queens Road, Oswestry SY11 2JB Tel: 01691 653287 — LM 1952 Rotunda; MD Dub. 1952, MB BCh BAO 1948; DCH RCPSI 1951. Prev: Anaesth. OsW.ry & Dist. Hosp.

MADDERS, Denis Joseph 25 Highcroft Avenue, Oadby, Leicester LE2 5UH — MB BCh BAO 1974 NUI. (Cork) Sen. Regist. (Histopath.) Leicester Roy. Infirm. Prev: Regist. (Path.) BRd.green Hosp. Liverp.

MADDICK, Graham Creywell Surgery, Creywell, Wark, Hexham NE48 3LQ Tel: 01434 230654 Fax: 01434 230059 — MB BS 1966 Durh.; DObst RCOG 1968.

***MADDINENI, Satish Babu** Accident and Emergency Department, Glasgow Royal Infirmary, 84 Castle Street, Glasgow G4 0SF — MB ChB 1996 Ed.

MADDISON, Antony Derek BaNbury Road Medical Centre, 172 Banbury Road, Oxford OX2 7BX Tel: 01865 515731 Fax: 01865 510711 — MB ChB 1991 Leic. GP Princip.

MADDISON, Bernard, MBE (retired) Cherry Trees, 131 Church Green Road, Bletchely, Milton Keynes MK3 6DE Tel: 01908 373204 — MRCS Eng. LRCP Lond. 1938; MRCGP 1953. Prev: Ho. Phys. Co. Hosp. Lincoln.

MADDISON, Beryl West Low Row, Cornsay, Durham DH7 9EG — MB BS 1962 Durh.

MADDISON, Geoffrey Michael Chastleton Surgery, Newton Drive, Framwellgate Moor, Durham DH1 5BH Tel: 0191 384 6171 Fax: 0191 386 3743 — MB BS 1962 Durh.

MADDISON, Ian David Department of Radiology, Central Middlesex Hospital Trust, Park Royal, London NW10 7NS Tel: 020 8453 2272 Fax: 020 8453 2783; 12 Rede Place, London W2 4TU — BM BCh 1969 Oxf.; MA; MRCP (U.K.) 1973; FRCR 1978; DMRD Eng. 1976. Cons. (Radiol.) Centr. Middlx. Hosp. Lond.

MADDISON, Joan Eleanor (retired) Quarry House, Tosside, Skipton BD23 4SY Tel: 01200 446274 — MB BS 1949 Durh.

MADDISON, John Langton 2 White's Terr, Bradford BD8 8NR — MB ChB 1957 St. And.; Mem. BMA. Prev: Ho. Phys. & Orthop. Ho. Surg. Friarage Hosp. N.allerton.

MADDISON, John Stanley 52 Jasmin Close, Northwood HA6 1DQ — MB ChB 1965 Sheff.; DObst RCOG 1967. Prev: Asst. Cas. Off. Roy. Hosp. Sheff.; Ho. Phys. Bedford Gen. Hosp.; Ho. Surg. O & G OldCh. Hosp. Romford.

MADDISON, Paul 6 Roslin Way, Cramlington NE23 7XB Tel: 01670 714795 Fax: 01865 790493 Email: paul.maddison@clinical-neurology.ox.ac.uk; 3 Ogilby Mews, Holmsley Grange, Woodlesford, Leeds LS26 8WF Fax: 0113 246 5231 Email: paul@piglet2.demon.co.uk — MB BS 1993 Newc.; MRCP (UK) 1996; MD (commendation) 1999. (Newc.) Specialist Regist. (Neurol.), St. Jas. Univ. Hosp. Leeds. Prev: SHO (Med.) Middlesbrough Gen. Hosp. Cleveland; Research Fell. Univ. of Oxf. Dept. of Neurol.

MADDISON, Peter John Gwynedd Rheumatology Service, Ysbyty GWynedd, Bangor LL57 2PW Tel: 01248 385097 Fax: 01248 384343 — MB BChir 1971 Camb.; MA Camb. 1970; MD Camb. 1981; FRCP Lond. 1987; MRCP (UK) 1974. (Camb. & St. Bart.) Cons. Rheum. Gwynedd Hosps. NHS Trust. Socs: Brit. Soc. Rheum. Prev: Prof. Bone & Jt. Med. Univ. Bath; Cons. Rheum. Wessex RHA; Asst. Prof. & Fell. (Rheum. & Immunol.) State Univ. New York Buffalo Sch. USA.

MADDISON, Tina Jayne Rayment 30 Bozward Street, St. Johns, Worcester WR2 5DE — MB ChB 1990 Birm.

MADDOCK, Catherine Alice Mary 14 Killyvilly Heights, Tempo Road, Enniskillen BT74 4DS — MB BCh BAO 1991 Dub.

MADDOCK, Clement Roy (retired) King's Mill Hospital, Sutton-in-Ashfield NG17 4JL Tel: 01623 22515 — MB BChir 1962 Camb.; MRCP Ed. 1958; MRCS Eng. LRCP Lond. 1951; DA Eng. 1966. Cons. Paediat. Mansfield Gp. Hosps. Prev: Phys. Edin. Med. Miss. Soc. Hosp. Nazareth, Israel.

MADDOCK, Elaine Faith Stenhouse Medical Centre, Furlong Street, Arnold, Nottingham NG5 7BP Tel: 0115 967 3877 Fax: 0115 967 3838 — MB BS 1984 Lond.; MA Camb. 1984; MRCGP 1988; DRCOG 1987. Asst. GP Retainer Scheme Harlow.

MADDOCK, Huw Morriston Hospital NHS Trust, Morriston, Swansea SA6 6NL Tel: 01792 703280 — BM 1985 Soton.; FRCA 1993. (Soton.) Cons. (Anaesth.) Morriston Hosp. NHS Trust Swansea.

MADDOCK, Jonathan Paul Snaith Health Centre, Snaith, Goole; Plot 2, Station Road, Howden, Goole DN14 7AF — MB ChB 1984 Leeds; MRCGP 1989. Prev: Trainee GP N. Humberside VTS.

***MADDOCK, Miranda Sophie Clementine** Top Flat, 20 Halfmoon Lane, Herne Hill, London SE24 9MU Tel: 020 7274 1110 Email: c.maddock@nmds.ac.ak — MB BS 1998 Lond.; MB BS Lond 1998; BSc (Hons) Immunol Lond 1996.

MADDOCK, Rosemary Anne The Surgery, 87 Allport Lane, Bromborough, Wirral CH62 7HL — MB ChB 1979 Liverp.; DRCOG 1982.

MADDOCK, Simon John Rokeby Millview Surgery, 1A Goldsmith Street, Mansfield NG18 5PF Tel: 01623 649528 Fax: 01623 624595; 34 Swinton Rise, Ravenshead, Nottingham NG15 9FR Email: sjrmaddock@aol.com — MB BS 1983 Lond.; MRCGP 1996. (Roy. Lond. Hosp.) Princip. GP. Prev: GP Harlow.

MADDOCKS, Anne Catherine The Small House, Willow Grove, Chislehurst BR7 5BS — BM BCh 1960 Oxf.; FRCPath 1980, M 1968. Sen. Lect. Dept. Bacteriol. St. Mary's Hosp. Lond.

MADDOCKS, Jane Old Station Surgery, 39 Brecon Road, Abergavenny NP7 5UH Tel: 01873 859000 Fax: 01873 850163 — MB BS 1981 Lond.; BSc Lond. 1978, MB BS 1981; DRCOG 1984.

MADDOCKS, Jane Alison Swansea NHS Trust, 21 Orchard St., Swansea SA1 5AT Tel: 01792 517911 Fax: 01792 517042 Email: alison.maddocks@swansea-tr.wales.nhs.uk — MB BCh 1973 Wales; BSc Wales 1970; FRCP 1997, M 1978; MRCGP 1982; DCH RCP Lond. 1976; FRCPCH 1997. (Wales) Cons. Paediat. Swansea NHS Trust; Sen .Lect. Sch. of Health Sci. Swansea Univ.; Designated Dr. Child Protec., IMH; Forens. Med. Examr. Socs: Welsh Paediat. Soc.; Brit. Assn. Preven. of Child Abuse & Neglect; Child Protec. s/i Gp.

MADDOCKS, John Leyshon 49 Chelsea Road, Brincliffe, Sheffield S11 9BQ — MRCS Eng. LRCP Lond. 1964; MD Lond. 1973; MB BS 1964; FRCP Lond. 1981, M 1968. (St. Geo.) Reader (Clin. Pharmacol.) Univ. Sheff.; Hon. Cons. Phys. Roy. Hallamsh. Hosp. Sheff. Socs: Med. Research Soc., Renal Assn., Brit. Pharmacol. Soc. & Int.; Soc. Immunopharmacol. Prev: Lect. Inst. Dis. Chest Brompton Hosp. Lond.; Lect. Renal Med. & Hon. Sen. Regist. Kruf Inst. Cardiff; Ho. Phys., & SHO (Med.) St. Geo. Hosp. Lond.

MADDOCKS, Peter Dobell 47 Alma Road, Windsor SL4 3HH Tel: 01753 851551 Fax: 01753 858569 — MB BS 1958 Lond.; MRCP Lond. 1965; FRCPsych 1984, M 1972; DPM Eng. 1966; DObst RCOG 1960. (Middlx.) p/t Cons. Psychiat. Cardinal Clinic Windsor. Prev: Cons. Psychiat. Wexham Pk. Hosp. Slough & Maidenhead Hosp.; Chief Asst. (Psychol. Med.) St. Thos. Hosp. Lond.; Regist. (Med.) St. Helier Hosp. Carshalton.

MADDOCKS, Williamina Thelma Astrid Department of Psychiatry, Wexham Park Hospital, Wexham, Slough SL2 4HL Tel: 01753 634212; Ellington Lodge, Ellington Road, Taplow, Maidenhead SL6 0BA — MB BS 1959 Lond.; MRCPsych 1983; DPM Eng. 1980. (Middlx.) Assoc. Specialist (Psychiat.) Wexham Pk.

Hosp. Slough. Socs: BMA & Windsor Med. Soc. Prev: Med. Off. Slough & Dist. Family Plann. Clinic; Regist. (Psychiat.) Wexham Pk. Hosp. Slough; Med. Off. FPA To St. Helier Hosp. Carshalton & Shotfield Clinic Wallington.

MADDOX, Andrew John 5 Grantsfield, Maxton, Melrose TD6 0RR — MB ChB 1991 Manch.

MADDOX, Anthony John Mt. Vernon Hospital, Rickmansworth Road, Northwood HA6 2RN Tel: 01923 844210 Fax: 01923 844067 Email: tmaddox500@netscapeonline.co.uk; 70B Benthal Road, London N16 7DA Tel: 020 8806 7394 Email: tmaddox500@netscapeonline.co.uk — MB BS 1988 Lond.; 1982 MSc Lond.; 1980 BA Oxf.; MRCPath 1996. Cons. (Histopath.) W. herts. Hosps. N.wood (Mt. Vernon) & Watford. Socs: Path. Soc.; Brit. Div. Internat. Acad. Path.; Assn. Clin. Path. Prev: Sen. Regist. (Histopath.) Roy. Free Hosp. Lond.; Regist. (Histopath.) Char. Cross Hosp. Lond.

MADDOX, Barbara Ruth Anne Viewfield Medical Centre, 3 Viewfield Place, Stirling FK8 1NJ Fax: 01786 463388; Longriggs Farm, Coalsnaughton, Tillicoultry FK13 6LG — MB ChB 1967 Bristol. Full Time GP Princip., Stirling, Scotl.

***MADDOX, Josephine Claire** Glandwr, Rudry Road, Lisvane, Cardiff CF14 0SN — BM 1994 Soton.

MADDOX, Mr Paul Raymond Royal United Hospital, Combe Park, Bath BA1 3NG Tel: 01225 824801 Fax: 01225 824801; Quarry Cottage, Quarry Farm, Claverton Down,, Bath BA2 6EE — MB BCh 1980 Wales; MCh Wales 1990; BSc (Hons.) Liverp. 1975; FRCS Ed. 1986; FRCS Eng. 1986. (Wales) Cons. Gen. Surg. (BrE. & Endocrine Surg.) Roy. United Hosp. Bath. Socs: BASO-BrE. Specialty Gp.; Brit. BrE. Gp.; BAES-Exec. Comm. Mem. Prev: Sen. Regist. (Gen. Surg.) S. Glam. & Clwyd HA's; Regist. (Surg.) Morriston Hosp. Swansea; Research Fell. & Regist. (Surg.) Cardiff.

MADDULA, Manohar Rao Queen Street Surgery, Whittlesey, Peterborough PE3 1AY; 3 Stanford Walk, Peterborough PE3 9UU Tel: 01733 263088 Email: smanyam2.aol.com — MB BS 1979 Nagarjuna, India; DLO RCS Eng. 1986. (Guntur Med. Coll., India) GP Princip.; Clin. Assit. Rheum., Edith Cavell Hosp. Prev: SHO (Paediat. & Obst.) P'boro. Dist. Hosp. VTS; GP/Regist. Wansford Surg. P'boro.

MADDY, Adele The Grange Practice, Allerton Clinic, Wanstead Crescent, Allerton, Bradford BD15 7PA Tel: 01274 541696; 10 Woodhall Croft, Calverley, Pudsey LS28 7TU — MB BS 1983 Lond.; DRCOG 1987.

MADDY, Paul James Hillfoot Surgery, 126 Owlcotes Road, Pudsey LS28 7QR Tel: 0113 257 4169 Fax: 0113 236 3380 — MB BS 1983 Lond.; Dip. Ther. Newc. 1995; DRCOG 1987.

MADEJ, Tamara Henryka Tel: 01904 725399; 31 Penleys Grove Street, York YO31 7PW Tel: 01904 628671 — BM BCh 1979 Oxf.; BA Camb. 1976; FFA RCS Eng. 1983. p/t Cons. Anaesth. York Dist. Hosp. Socs: BMA; YMS; OAA. Prev: Lect. (Anaesth.) Leeds Univ.; Lect. (Anaesth.) Univ. Calgary; Sen. Regist. (Anaesth.) Yorks. RHA.

MADELEY, Professor Charles Richard (retired) Burnfoot, Stocksfield NE43 7TN Tel: 01661 842649 Fax: 01661 844514 Email: dickmadeley@aol.com — MB ChB Aberd. 1961; MD (Commend.) Aberd. 1965; FRCPath 1984, M 1979. Prev: Prof. Clin. Virol. Univ. Newc. & Cons. Virol. PHLS.

MADELEY, Jean Roberta The Manor Surgery, Middle Street, Beeston, Nottingham NG9 1GA Tel: 0115 925 6127 Fax: 0115 967 8612; 18 Wollaton Vale, Wollaton, Nottingham NG8 2NR Tel: 0115 925 5606 — MB BS 1971 Lond.; BSc Lond. 1968, MB BS 1971; DObst RCOG 1974.

***MADELEY, Nicola Jane** 84 Dalkeith Grove, Stanmore HA7 4SF — MB ChB 1997 Manch.

MADELEY, Richard John Department of Public Health Medicine & Epidemiology, University of Nottingham Medical School, Queens Medical Centre, Clifton Boulevard, Nottingham NG7 2UH Tel: 0115 970 9305 Fax: 0115 970 9316 Email: richard.madeley@nottingham.ac.uk; 18 Wollaton Vale, Nottingham NG8 2NR Tel: 0115 925 5606 — MB BS Lond. 1969; MSc (Social Med.) Lond. 1974; DM Nottm. 1985; FFCM 1985, M 1977. (Univ. Coll. Hosp.) Prof. & Head Sch. of Community Health Sci., Univ. Nottm. Med. Sch.; Hon. Specialist (Pub. Health Med.) Nottm. HA; Edr. Jl. Pub. Health Med.; Pres. Assoc. of Sch. of Pub. Health Europ. Region (ASPHER). Socs: SSM; IEA. Prev: Cons. Smallpox Eradication

WHO; Cons. Matern. & Child Health, WHO Geneva; Cons. World Bank Estonia Health Project.

MADELIN, Stephen Karel Oldcastle Surgery, South Street, Bridgend CF31 3ED Tel: 01656 657131 Fax: 01656 657134; 3 Parklands, Corntown, Bridgend CF35 5BE Tel: 01656 656028 — MB BCh 1977 Wales; MRCGP 1988.

MADEN, Anthony Department of Forensic Psychiatry, Institute of Psychiatry, De Crespigny Park, London SE5 8AF Tel: 020 7703 5411; Denis Hill Unit, Bethlem Royal Hospital, Monks's Orchard Road, Beckenham BR3 3BX Tel: 020 8777 6611 Fax: 020 8777 4933 Email: sphdanm@iop.bpmf.ac.uk — MB BS 1982 Lond.; MD Lond. 1992; MRCPsych 1987. Cons. Forens. Psychiat. Bethlem Roy. & Maudsley Hosp. Lond.; Sen. Lect. Inst. Psychiat. Lond.

MADER, Ute Cornelia Ormskirk & District General Hospital, Wigan Road, Ormskirk L39 2AZ — State Exam Med 1986 Tubingen.

MADEVITT, Katharine Elizabeth Margaret 7 Moorhouse Cottages, Westerham TN16 2ES — MB BS 1997 Newc.; BA Durham 1992. (Newcastle) SHO Paediat. Kent Canterbury.

MADGE, Adrian Francis (retired) Acorn House, Evesham St., Alcester B49 5DS Tel: 01798 762417 — MB BChir 1953 Camb. Prev: GP Alcester.

MADGE, Sara Jane 35B Newington Green, London N16 9PR — MB BS 1986 Lond.

***MADGE, Simon Nicholas** Drummermire, Troutbeck, Windermere LA23 1PL Tel: 015394 33030 — BM BCh 1997 Oxf.; BA (Camb.) 1994.

MADGWICK, Mr John Colin Alexander (retired) 4 Taylor Avenue, Kew Gardens, Richmond TW9 4ED Tel: 020 8255 1148 — MB BS (Hons., Distinc. Surg.) Lond. 1954; FRCS Eng. 1961. Prev: Cons. Orthop. Surg. Hosp. St. John & St. Eliz. Lond.

MADGWICK, Julia Margaret 10 Chelwood Road, Earley, Reading RG6 5QG Tel: 0118 961 1275 Email: madg@madgwickj.freeserve.co.uk — MB ChB 1977 Manch.; MRCP (UK) 1981; DCH Eng. 1980. Prev: GP Retain. Brookside Med. Gp., Reading; GP Princip. Brookside Surg., Reading; GP Train. Wistoria, Lymington, Hants.

MADGWICK, Stephen Alan Brookside Group Practice, Brookside Close, Gipsy Lane, Earley, Reading RG6 7HG Tel: 0118 966 9222 Fax: 0118 935 3174; 10 Chelwood Road, Earley, Reading RG6 5QG Tel: 01734 611275 — MB ChB 1978 Cape Town.

MADHAV, Rohit Thakor 28 Heathdene Road, London SW16 3PD Email: rohit.madhav@virgin.net — MB BS 1991 Lond.; FRCS (Ed) 1995. (St George's Hosp. Med. Sch.) Specialist Regist. Hammersmith. Rot. (N/W Thames Region). Prev: Trauma Research Fell. (Lower Limb Recons.) Imper. Coll. Char. Cross Hosp.

***MADHAVAN, Beenu** 95 Sutherland Road, Croydon CR0 3QL — MB BS 1998 Lond.; MB BS Lond 1998.

MADHAVAN, Mr Padmanabhan 36A Tyn yr Heol Road, Bryncoch, Neath SA10 7EA — MB BS 1969 Kerala; FRCSI 1982.

MADHAVAN, Thekkinkattil Shakespeare Avenue Surgery, 75 Shakespeare Avenue, Hayes UB4 0BE Tel: 020 8573 6042 Fax: 020 8569 3293 — MB BS 1973 Mysore. (Kasturba Med. Coll. Manipal)

MADHOK, Minoo The Belmont Medical Centre, 53-57 Belmont Road, Uxbridge UB8 1SD Tel: 01895 233211 Fax: 01895 812099; 64 The Drive, Ickenham, Uxbridge UB10 8AQ Tel: 01895 270617 — MB BCh 1988 Wales; MRCGP 1992. (University of Wales Coll. Og Medicine) p/t Partner.

MADHOK, Rajan Centre for Rheumatic Diseases, Glasgow Royal Infirmary NHS Trust, Glasgow G4 0SF Tel: 0141 211 4410 Fax: 0141 552 4862 Email: gcl103@clinmed.gla.ac.uk; 135 Springkell Avenue, Glasgow G41 4EY — MB ChB 1980 Glas.; FRCP Glas. and Edin.; MD Glas. 1989; MRCP (UK) 1983. Cons. Gen. Med. & Rheum. Glas. Roy. Infirm. Socs: Fell. Roy. Coll. Phys. & Surgs. Glas.; Roy. Soc. Med. Prev: Cons. Gen. Med. & Rheum. Gartnavel Gen. Hosp. Glas.; Lect. & Hon. Sen. Regist. (Rheum.) Glas. Roy. Infirm.

MADHOK, Mr Rajan Gateshead & South Tyneside Health Authority, Horsley Hill Road, South Shields NE33 3BN Tel: 0191 401 4535 Fax: 0191 401 4520 Email: 100446.3347@compuserve.com — MB BS 1979 Delhi; MSc Newc. 1990; FRCS Glas. 1985; Dip. Biomechanics Glas. 1988; MFPHM 1990. Dir. Pub. Health Gateshead & S. Tyneside HA; Hon. Lect. (Epidemiol. & Pub. Health) Med. Sch. Newc.; Hon. Fell. (Orthop. Surg.) Univ. Edin. Prev: Cons. Pub. Health Med. S. Tees HA; Sen.

MADHOK

Regist. (Pub. Health Med.) Newc. u. Tyne; Special Project Assc. Mayo Clinic, USA.

MADHOK, Virinder Kumar Battlefield Road Surgery, 208 Battlefield Road, Glasgow G42 9NH Tel: 0141 649 5878 Fax: 0141 636 6690; 40 Dalziel Drive, Glasgow G41 4HY Tel: 0141 427 7555 Fax: 0141 429 4247 — LRCP LRCS Ed. LRCPS Glas. 1983. Prison Med. Off. Glas. Prev: Clin. Med. Off. (A & E) Roy. Hosp. Sick Childr. Glas.

MADHOTRA, Ravi 103 Friary Road, Handsworth Wood, Birmingham B20 1BA — MB BS 1987 Himachal Pradesh; MRCP (UK) 1995.

MADHU, Kopparamachandra Rao Jasmine Grove Surgery, 64 Jasmine Grove, Coventry CV3 1EA; 3 Cedar Avenue, Ryton-on-Dunsmore, Coventry CV8 3QB Tel: 02476 511811 Email: madhu_koppa@yahoo.com — MB BS 1970 Bangalore; Cert. Indust. Med. Surrey 1988; Dip. Thoracic Med. Lond. 1985; DTM & H RCP Lond. 1985; DGM RCP Lond. 1985. (Bangalore Med. Coll.) Clin. Asst. (Gen. Med.) Geo. Eliot Hosp. Nuneaton. Socs: Fell. Roy. Soc. Med.; Soc. Occupat. Med.; Fell. Roy. Soc. of Health. Prev: Trainee GP, Lochmaddy, I. of N. Wist; Regist. (Med.) Nobles Hosp., Douglas, I. of Man; Regist. (Med.) Hairmyres Hosp, E. Kilbride.

*****MADHUSUDAN, Mysore Gangadhararae** 39 Drummond Way, Macclesfield SK10 4XJ — MB BS 1983 Bangalor; MB BS Bangalore 1983; MS (Orthop.) Mysore 1988.

MADI, Ahmed Mohammed 20/3, 123 Petershill Drive, Glasgow G21 4QU — MB ChB 1983 Libya; MRCP (UK) 1991.

MADI, Mabrouk Saad 17 Rannock Avenue, Kinsbury, London NW9 7JS — MB BCh 1982 Al Fateh; MRCP (UK) 1990.

MADI, Salem Ibrahim 5 Judeland, Astley Village, Chorley PR7 1XJ — MB BCh 1981 Al Fateh; MRCP (UK) 1991.

MADIGAN, Elizabeth Anne Lansdowne Surgery, Waiblingen Way, Devizes SN10 2BU Tel: 01380 722278 Fax: 01380 723790 — MB BS 1980 Lond.; MRCS Eng. LRCP Lond. 1980.

MADIGAN, Margaret Marion c/o Dr Nadini Close, Left, 61 Lymburn St., Glasgow G3 8PD — MB BCh BAO 1993 NUI.

MADIGAN, Mr Michael Roebourne (retired) Greenacre, Pine Grove, Bishop's Stortford CM23 5NR Tel: 01279 653070 — MB BS 1952 Adelaide; BSc Adelaide 1953, MB BS. 1952; FRCS Ed. 1959; FRCS Eng. 1959. Prev: Cons. Gen. Surg. Bishop Stortford & Hertford Hosps.

MADILL, Stephen Anthony 42 Berkeley Crescent, Dartford DA1 1NH — MB BS 1996 Lond.; BSc Vision and Perception Lond. 1995. (St. Bart. Hosp. Med. Coll.) SHO (Ophth.) Salisbury Dist. Hosp.

MADINA, T The Surgery, 138 London Road, Hackbridge, Carshalton SM5 7HF Tel: 020 8647 3711 Fax: 020 8773 8577 — MB BS 1965 Punjab; MB BS 1965 Punjab.

MADIPALLI, Sudha Glen Road Medical Centre, 1-9 Glen Road, London E13 8RU Tel: 020 7476 3434 Fax: 020 7473 6092; 10 Bressey Grove, Southwoodford, London E18 2HP Tel: 020 8989 5366 — MB BS 1981 Osmania; MRCS Eng. LRCP Lond. 1986; MRCOphth 1991. Prev: SHO (Psychiat.) Pastures Hosp. Derby; SHO (A & E) Newham Gen. Hosp.

MADIRA, Webster Mutimurefu The Lodge, Forest Drive, Kirby Muxloe, Leicester LE9 2EA; Department of Chemical Pathology, Leicester Royal Infirmary, Leicester LE1 5WW Tel: 0116 258 6550 Fax: 0116 258 6550 — MRCS Eng. LRCP Lond. 1982; PhD Lond. 1983, BSc 1974; MRCPath 1996. (St. Mary's) Cons. Leicester Roy. Infirm.

MADISETTI, Mr Pandurangam (retired) 65 The Drive, Morden SM4 6DH Tel: 020 8648 7554 — MB BS Osmania 1951; FRCS Ed. 1969; LMSSA Lond. 1962.

MADKOUR, Mr Mohamed Bahaa El-Din Ysbyty Gwynedd, Penrhosgarnedd, Bangor LL57 2PW Tel: 01248 370007 ext. 423; Y Graig, Lon Graig, Llanfairpwllgwyngyll LL61 5NX — MB BCh 1972 Ain Shams; FRCS Glas. 1986; DLO RCS Eng. 1984. Cons. ENT Surg. Gwynedd HA. Socs: Brit. Assn. Otolaryng. & N. Eng. ENT Soc.

MADOC-JONES, John Christopher Middle Lane Surgery, Middle Lane, Denbigh LL16 3UW Tel: 01745 816481 Fax: 01745 816153 — MB BCh 1968 Wales; MRCGP 1986; DObst RCOG 1972. (Welsh Nat.) Socs: Inst. Of Reactionary Med. (Life Pres.); Cymdeithas Meddygol (AELOD); BMA.

MADON, Pervez Keki (retired) 25 Albert Bridge Road, Battersea, London SW11 4PX — LRCPI & LM, LRSCI & LM 1968; MRCGP 1984; DGM RCP Lond. 1988; DCCH RCP Ed. 1987; DRCOG 1987; DCH RCP Lond. 1986. GP Princip. Prev: Ho. Phys. (Paediat.) Roy. Alexandra Hosp. Brighton.

MADSEN, Karen Ellen 14 Monkgate Cloisters, York YO31 7HY — MB ChB 1953 Leeds.

MADSEN, Sheila Tigh Na Lus, 43 Woodside Road, Beith KA15 2BU Tel: 01505 502893 Email: sheila@jmadsen.globalnet.co.uk — MB ChB 1973 Glas.; FFA RCS Eng. 1981; DObst RCOG 1975. Cons. Anaesth. Roy. Alexandra Hosp. Paisley.

MADZIWA, David 66 The Crescent, Croydon CR0 2HN — MB ChB 1979 Zimbabwe; MB ChB U Zimbabwe 1979; MRCPath 1987.

MAECKELBERGHE, Willy Eduard Hendrik (retired) Roscadghill, Penzance TR20 8TD — MB BS Lond. 1952; DObst RCOG 1955.

MAENDL, Andrew Christian John Helios Medical Centre, 17 Stoke Hill, Stoke Bishop, Bristol BS9 1JN Tel: 0117 982 6060 — MB BS 1961 Lond. (Univ. Coll. Hosp.) Prev: Ho. Surg. Nat. Temperance Hosp. Lond.; Ho. Phys. Brighton Gen. Hosp.; Obst. Ho. Surg. St. Alfeges Hosp. Greenwich.

MAENPAA, Garath Alan Orchard House, 11 High St., Catworth, Huntingdon PE28 0PF — MB ChB 1992 Sheff.

MAFFULLI, Professor Nicola Department of Orthopaedics Surgery, Keele University School of medicine, Thoruborrow Drive ST4 7QB Tel: 01782 554995 Fax: 01782 412236 Email: mimajjulli@keele.ac.uk — State DMS 1983 Naples; MD 1998 Aberdeen; PhD Lond. 1992, MS 1994; FRCS (Orth.) 1993; FRCS Ed. 1995; Dip. Sports Med. Scott. 1991; Dip Sports Med. . Lond. 1990; MIBiol. 1992. (Univ. Napoli, Italy) Prof. of Truma and Orthopeidic Surg., Honary Cons.; keele univ; Prof. (Orthop. Surg.) Chinese Univ. of HK. Socs: Fell. BOA; Eur. Soc. Sports Traumatol. Knee Surg. & Arthroscopy; Bd. of Directors Internat. Soc. Knee Surg. Prev: Assoc. Prof. Orthop. Surg. Chinese Univ. Hong Kong; Sen. Regist. Rotat. (Orthop.) & Hon. Clin. Lect. (Orthop.) Univ. Aberd. Med. Sch.; Clin. Lect. (Sports Med.) Inst. Child Health Lond.

*****MAFHAM, Marion Marjorie** 2F2 13 Bruntsfield Avenue, Edinburgh EH10 4EL — MB ChB 1998 Ed.; MB ChB Ed 1998.

MAGAHY, Frederick David Inverannaty House, 24 Bonhard Road, Scone, Perth PH2 6QN — MB ChB 1972 Ed.; FFA RCS Eng. 1980.

MAGANAS AGUILERA, Isabel Department of Anaesthetics, Morriston Hospital NHS Trust, Heol Maes Eglwys, Cwmrhydyceirw, Swansea SA6 6NL — LMS 1988 Barcelona.

MAGAPU, Viswanathan Hunts Croft, Allens Lane, Marchington, Uttoxeter ST14 8LA — MB BS 1973 Osmania; MRCPsych 1986.

MAGARA, Geraldine 29A Chevening Road, London NW6 6DB — MRCS Eng. LRCP Lond. 1990.

MAGAURAN, Miss Denise Mary, DStJ Epsom and St Helier NHS Trust, Sutton Hospital, Cotswold Road, Sutton SM2 5NF Tel: 020 8296 2000 Fax: 020 8770 7051 Email: stjohn@palnet.com; 25 Alexandra Road, Epsom KT17 4BP Tel: 01372 722466 Email: denise magauran@aol.com — MB BS 1963 Lond.; FRCS Eng. 1971; MRCS Eng. LRCP Lond. 1963; FRCOphth. 1988; DO Eng. 1966. (Char. Cross) Locum Cons. Ophth. Epseom/St Helier NHS Trust. Socs: Fell. Roy. Soc. Med.; Ophth. Soc. UK. Prev: Cons. Ophth. & Chief Surg. St. John Ophth. Hosp., Jerusalem; Asst. Surg. St. John Ophth. Hosp., Jerusalem; Sen. Regist. (Ophth.) St. Paul's Eye Hosp. Liverp.

MAGAURAN, Peter Stanley Oakdene, Brickhouse Lane, Newchapel, Lingfield RH7 6HY Tel: 01342 836148 Fax: 01342 836148 — MB BChir Camb. 1968; LMSSA Lond. 1968; FFA RCSI 1973; T (GP) 1991; DA Eng. 1970; Spec. Reg. (Anaesth.) 1997. (St. Bart.) Cons. Anaest. N. Downs Hosp., Caterham, Surrey. Socs: Fell. Roy. Soc. Med.; Liveryman Soc. Apoth.; PHTLS/BASICS. Prev: SHO Anaesth. St. Geo. Hosp. Lond.; Anaesth. Regist. St. Mary's Hosp. Lond.; Reg. St Geo. Hosp. Lond.

MAGBADELO, Jonathan Adekunle (retired) 31 St Andrews, Grantham NG31 9PE — MB BCh BAO 1973 Dub.; MA Dub. 1973, BA (Hons. Biochem) 1968; DRCOG 1984; DObst RCPI 1984. Prev: Staff Grade (A & E) Newark Gen. Hosp.

MAGEE, Alan Gordon 9 Kingswood Road, London SW19 3ND — BSc 1980, MB BCh BAO 1983; MRCP (UK) 1986; DCH RCPS Glas. 1986.

MAGEE, Alexandra Christine Regional Genetics Service - Floor A, Belfast City Hospital Tower, Lisburn Road, Belfast BT9 7AB Tel: 02890 263873 Fax: 02890 236911 Email: alex.magee@bch.n-i.nhs.uk — MB BCh BAO 1978 Belf.; MD Belf. 1996; MRCGP

1982; DCCH RCP Ed. 1985; DCH RCPS Glas. 1980. (Queens University Belfast) Cons. (Clin. Genetics) Belf. City Hosp. Socs: Brit. Hum. Genetic Soc.

***MAGEE, Brendan Joseph** 40 Owenvarragh Park, Belfast BT11 9BE — MB BCh 1998 Belf.; MB BCh Belf 1998.

MAGEE, Brian Joseph Christie Hospital, Wilmslow Road, Manchester M20 — MB BCh BAO 1980 Belf.; MRCP (UK) 1983; FRCR 1986. Cons. Radiother. & Clin. Oncol. Christie Hosp.

MAGEE, Cliona Mary 15 Greenhill Road, Moseley, Birmingham B13 9SR — MB BCh BAO 1985 Dub.

***MAGEE, Conor James** 9 Percy Street, Liverpool L8 7LT — MB ChB 1994 Liverp.

MAGEE, David John Rathfriland Health Centre, 37 Newry Street, Rathfriland, Newry BT34 5PY Tel: 028 4063 0034 Fax: 028 4063 1446 — MB BCh BAO 1984 NUI; MRCGP 1988; DRCOG 1986. Prev: Princip. GP Cuffley Village Surg. Herts.

MAGEE, Derek Brian Havant Health Centre Suite B, PO Box 43, Civic Centre Road, Havant PO9 2AQ Tel: 023 9248 2124 Fax: 023 9247 5515 Email: brian.magee@gp-j82196.nhs.uk; 4 Tudor Avenue, Emsworth PO10 7UG — MB BChir 1975 Camb.; MA Camb. 1975; MRCS Eng. LRCP Lond. 1974; MRCGP 1980. (Camb. Univ. and King's Coll. Hosp. Med. Sch.) Prev: SHO (Paediat.) Roy. Sussex Co. Hosp. Brighton; SHO (O & G) St. Mary's Hosp. Portsmouth; SHO (Med.) Roy. Portsmouth Hosp.

MAGEE, Mr Gerald Damian 18 Oakwood Park, Belfast BT9 6SE — MB BCh BAO 1985 Belf.; FRCSI 1989. Regist. (Surg.) Belf.

MAGEE, Joseph Robert Gatehead Road Surgery, Gatehead Road, Crosshouse, Kilmarnock KA2 0HU Tel: 01563 521506 Fax: 01563 573695; 12 Alder Place, Kilmarnock KA1 2HR Tel: 01563 572005 — MB ChB 1976 Glas.; DRCOG 1978. (Glasgow) Med. Off. Kilmarnock FC. Socs: Kilmarnock Med. Soc.; BMA.

MAGEE, Kenneth John Brookside Health Centre, Brookside Road, Freshwater PO40 9DT Tel: 01983 753433 Fax: 01983 753662 — MB BCh BAO 1979 Dub.; MRCGP 1986; DObst. RCPI 1983; DCH RCPSI 1986.

MAGEE, Margaret Anne Richmond Medical Centre, Moor Lane, North Hykeham, Lincoln LN6 9AY Tel: 01522 500240 Fax: 01522 500232; Grangefield House, 318 Hykeham Road, Lincoln LN6 8BW Tel: 01522 686607 Fax: 01522 686607 — MB ChB 1976 Sheff.; MRCGP 1994; DRCOG 1979.

***MAGEE, Nicholas David** 78 Waterloo Road, Lisburn BT27 5NW Tel: 01846 603762 — MB BCh BAO 1997 Belf.

MAGEE, Norma Elizabeth (retired) Greensands, Toys Hill, Westerham TN16 1QE Tel: 01732 750381 — MB BCh BAO 1951 Dub.; MFFP 1993. Instruct. Doctor Family Plann. Assn. Prev: Clin. Med. Off. (Community Health) Camberwell, E. Surrey & Tunbridge Wells HAs.

MAGEE, Mr Patrick Gabriel 50 Wimpole Street, London W1G 8SG Tel: 020 7486 8962 Fax: 020 7486 7918 Email: patrick.magee@btinternet.com; 52 Barnsbury Street, London N1 1ER Tel: 020 7609 3717 Fax: 020 7609 3717 — MB BCh BAO 1971 NUI; FRCS Lond. Ad eundem; FRCSI 1976; BSc (Anat.) NUI 1973; FRCS Ed. 1976. (Univ. Coll. Dub.) Cons. Cardioth. Surg. Lond. Chest Hosp. Barts & The Lond. NHS Trust Lond.; Cons. Surg. King Edwd. VII Hosp. for Offs. Lond. Socs: Exec. Mem. Soc. Cardiothoracic Surg. GB & Irel.; Eur. Assn. Cardiothoracic Surg.; Chairm. SAC on Cardioth. Surg. Prev: Sen. Regist. Nat. Heart & Chest Hosps.; Fell. Cardiac Surg. Johns Hopkins Hosp., USA.

MAGEE, Patrick Terence Department of Anaesthesia, Royal United Hospital, Bath BA1 3NG Email: ptmagee00@aol.com; Tel: 01225 825057 Email: ptmagee00@aol.com — MB BS 1981 Lond.; MSc (Biomechanics) Surrey 1975; BSc (Engin Sc.) Durh. 1974; FFA RCS Eng. 1987. (Westminster university of London) Conultant Anaesth. Roy. United Hosp. Bath.; Hon. Sen. Lect. in Postgrad. Med., Univ. of Bath; HSE Approved Underwater Med. Specialist; Vis. Sen. Lecturer Dept. of Mechanical Engin. Univ. of Bath.

MAGEE, Sara Elizabeth Elsa 5 Clear Water, Londonderry BT47 6BE — MB BCh BAO 1971 Belf.; MRCOG 1977.

MAGEE, Stephen Kenneth 10 Swilly Park, Portstewart BT55 7FL — MB BCh BAO 1987 Belf.

MAGEE, Teresa Marea Wellfield Resource Centre, 22 Wellfield Road, Carmarthen SA31 1DS Tel: 01267 236017 Fax: 01267 238503 — MB BCh BAO 1978 NUI; MRCPsych 1987. Sen. Regist. (Psychiat.) St. David's Hosp. Carmarthen.

MAGEE, Thomas Finbar 81 Kingsmill Road, Whitecross, Armagh BT60 2SX — MB BCh BAO 1985 Belf.

MAGEE, Mr Timothy Raymond Department of Surgery, Royal Berkshire Hospital, Reading RG1 5AN Tel: 0118 987 7773 Fax: 0118 987 7881 — MB ChB 1983 Bristol; MD Bristol 1996; FRCS Eng. 1989; FRCS Ed. 1988. (University of Bristol) Cons. Gen. Surg. Roy. Berks. Hosp. Reading. Socs: Vasc. Surg. Soc. GB & Irel.; Assn. Surg. Prev: Sen. Regist. Rotat. (Gen. Surg.) John Radcliffe Hosp. Oxf.; Research Fell. (Vasc. Surg.) Bristol Roy. Infirm. & Roy. United Hosp. Bath; Regist. (Surg.) Roy. Devon & Exeter Hosp.

MAGEE, William Houston Keith Limavady Health Centre, Scroggy Road, Limavady BT49 0NA Tel: 028 7776 6641; 1 Scriggan Road, Limavady BT49 0DH — MB BCh BAO 1981 Belf.; MRCGP 1987 Edin. Chairm. 'Roe Doc' [Local out of hours co-op arrangement].

MAGEEAN, Aine Maire 69 Maryville Park, Belfast BT9 6LQ — MB BCh BAO 1985 Belf.; MRCGP 1992.

MAGEEAN, Robert James Loughview Surgery, 2 Main Street, Kircubbin, Newtownards BT22 2SP Tel: 028 9173 8532 — MB BCh BAO 1982 Belf.

MAGELL, Mr Jack (retired) The Barn, Old Back Lane, Wiswell, Whalley, Blackburn BB7 9BS Tel: 01254 822599 — MB BCh 1950 Wales; FRCS Eng. 1959. Prev: Cons. Surg. Roy. Infirm. Blackburn & Vict. Hosp. Accrington.

MAGENNIS, Claire Elizabeth 13 Ballygallum Road, Downpatrick BT30 7DA Tel: 01396 614084 — MB BCh BAO 1977 Belf.

MAGENNIS, Dorothy Ann (retired) Troutbeck, 1 Chestnut Avenue, Great Crosby, Liverpool L23 2SY Tel: 0151 924 6807 — MB ChB Liverp. 1961. Prev: Ho. Surg. & Ho. Phys. BRd.green Hosp. Liverp.

MAGENNIS, Helen Maria 12 Myrtlefield Park, Belfast BT9 6NE — MB BCh BAO 1977 Belf.; BSc Belf. 1972; MRCPath 1988.

MAGENNIS, James Kevin 21 Porter Brook View, Sheffield S11 8ZJ Tel: 0114 268 5074 — MB BCh BAO Belf. 1943.

MAGENNIS, Mr James Patrick Mary Regional Maxillofacial Unit, Fazakerley Hospital, Long Lane, Liverpool L9 7AL Tel: 0151 525 5980 Fax: 0151 529 3239 Email: mfufazak@globalnet.co.uk — MB BCh BAO 1992 Belf.; BDS Belf. 1988; FRCSI 1995; FDS RCPS Glas. 1988; FDS RCS Ed. 1988; FFD RCSI 1988; FRCSI 1999. (Qu. Univ. Belf.) Specialist Regist. Oral & Maxillofacial Unit Walton Hosp. Liverp. Socs: Jun. Fell. Brit. Assn. Oral & Maxillofacial Surg.; Internat. Assn. Maxillofacial Surg. Train.; Eur. Assn. Cranio-Maxillo. Surg. Prev: Lect. & Higher Surgic. Trainee (Oral & Maxillofacial Surg.) Roy. Lond. Hosp. Med. Coll.; SHO Roy. Vict. Hosp. Belf.; SHO Rotat. Belf.

MAGENNIS, Joyce Arrowe Park Hospital, Upton, Wirral CH49 5PE Tel: 0151 604 1068, 0151 604 7171; Irby Hall, Irby Road, Irby, Wirral CH61 2XF — MB ChB 1975 Glas.; FRCR 1984; LMCC 1977; DMRD Liverp. 1980. Cons. Radiol. Arrowe Pk. Hosp. Wirral. Socs: FRCR. Prev: Med. Off. Internat. Grenfell Assn. Labrador Canada; Child Health Off. W.. Newfld.

***MAGENNIS, Rachel Fiona** 26 Westbourne Grove, Manchester M20 1JA — MB ChB 1994 Manch.

MAGENNIS, Sean Patrick Michael Manor Health Centre, Liscard Village, Wallasey CH45 4JG Tel: 0151 638 8221 Fax: 0151 639 6512; Irby Hall, Irby Road, Wirral CH61 2XF Tel: 0151 648 7584 — MB ChB 1983 Liverp.; BDS Glas. 1974; MRCGP 1987. Lect. (Gen. Pract.) Liverp. Univ.

MAGER-JONES, Janet Alrewas Surgery, Exchange Road, Alrewas, Burton-on-Trent DE13 7AS Tel: 01283 790316 Fax: 01283 791863; The Old Bath House, Tatenhill Lane, Rangemore, Burton-on-Trent DE13 9RW Tel: 01283 711880 — MB ChB 1987 Sheff.; DA (UK) 1988. (Sheff.) GP. Prev: SHO (Anaesth.) Derbysh. Roy. Infirm.

MAGFHOGARTAIGH, Lonan Gall Michel Fintona Medical Centre, 33 Dromore Road, Fintona, Omagh BT78 2BB Tel: 028 8284 1203 Fax: 028 8284 0545 — MB BCh BAO 1979 Belf.

MAGGIORI, Lucy Anne Elizabeth Dumeries - Galloway Royal Infirmary, Bankend Road, Dumfries DG1 4AP Tel: 01387 246246 — MB ChB 1992 Glas.; MRCGP 1996. Clin. Asst. In Rheum., Nov 99. Prev: Locum Staff Grade Cardiol.; SHO Gen. Med.

MAGGIORI, Terence Kevin Greencroft Medical Centre (North), Greencroft Wynd, Annan DG12 6BG — MB ChB 1992 Ed.; MBChB (Edin) 1992. GP; Med. Off. BNFL. Socs: BMA.

MAGGS

*MAGGS, Alexandra Genevieve 53 Queens Road, Sketty, Swansea SA2 0SB — MB BS 1995 Lond.

MAGGS, Anthony Fergus Patrick Ground Floor Flat, 5 West Road, Newport-on-Tay DD6 8HH — MB ChB 1982 Leeds.

MAGGS, Margaret Jean Tel: 01761 413334 Fax: 01761 411176; 39 Church Road, Abbots Leigh, Bristol BS8 3QT Tel: 01275 372624 — MB BCh Wales 1970; DObst RCOG 1972.

*MAGGS, Nicola Mary 86 Linwood Close, London SE5 8UX — MB BS 1998 Lond.; MB BS Lond 1998.

MAGGS, Richard Grafton 11 Kingston Road, Sketty, Swansea SA2 0ST — MB BS 1993 Lond.

MAGGS, Roderick Frank (retired) Old Post Cottage, Cookley Green, Henley-on-Thames RG9 6EN Tel: 01491 641768 — MB ChB 1941 Cape Town; FRCP Ed. 1972, M 1949; FRCP Glas. 1972; FRFPS Glas. 1949; DCH Eng. 1947. Prev: Cons. Paediat. Dept. Paediat. & Child Health Univ. Cape Town.

MAGID, Yagoub Mohamed Abdel Pontefract General Infirmary, Friarwood Lane, Pontefract WF8 1PL Tel: 01977 600600 — MB BS 1979 Khartoum; MB BS Khartoum Sudan 1979; MRCOG 1991.

*MAGILL, Catherine Clare 4 The Brambles, Trumpington, Cambridge CB2 2LY — BM BCh 1996 Oxf.; MA Cantab. 1993.

MAGILL, Eleanor Ann Royal Belfast Hospital for Sick Children, Belfast BT12 6BE Tel: 01232 263056 Fax: 01232 235340; 11 Mount Carmel, Somerton Road, Belfast BT15 4DQ Tel: 01232 776946 — MB BCh BAO Belf. 1966; DCH RCPS Glas. 1969; DObst RCOG 1968. (Belf.) Assoc. Specialist (Parenteral Nutrit.) Roy. Belf. Hosp. Sick Childr.

MAGILL, Henry George (retired) St. Thomas Health Centre, Cowick St., Exeter EX4 1HJ Tel: 01392 78031 — MB BCh BAO 1935 Belf.; DPH Eng. 1947.

MAGILL, Michael John Bridgnorth Medical Practice, Northgate House, 7 High St., Bridgnorth WV16 4BU Tel: 01746 767121; 5 Old Bury Wells, Bridgnorth WV16 5JE — MB ChB 1990 Birm.; MRCGP (Distinc.) 1995; DRCOG 1993.

MAGILL, Patrick John Nuffield Department of Obstetrics & Gynaecology, The Women's Centre, John Radcliffe Hospital, Headington, Oxford OX3 9DU Tel: 01865 221011 Fax: 01865 769141 Email: patrick.magill@obs-gyn.ox.ac.uk — MB ChB 1971 Bristol; PhD Lond. 1983; FRCPath 1989, M 1977; FFPM RCP (UK) 1994. Fell. Pharmaceut. Med. Nuffield Dept. O & G Wom. Centre John Radcliffe Hosp. Headington. Prev: Head Clin. Research Hoechst UK Ltd.; Lect. (Chem. Path.) St. Thos. Hosp. Lond.; Sen. Regist. (Chem. Path.) N.wick Pk. Hosp. Harrow.

MAGILL, Raymond Benedict (retired) 1 Ballytrustan Road, Downpatrick BT30 7AQ — MD 1941 Belf.; MB BCh BAO 1938; FRCPI 1977, M 1975; FRCP Lond. 1965, M 1941. Prev: Sen. Cons. Phys. Mater Infirm. Hosp. Belf.

MAGIN, Sabine Christine 4 Blackford Hill View, Edinburgh EH9 3HD Tel: 0131 667 1976 — State Exam Med 1986 Cologne.

MAGINN, Mr Paul Musgrave Park Hospital, Belfast BT9 7JB Tel: 01232 669501; 8 Scotstown Road, Lisburn BT28 3ST Tel: 01846 648168 — MB BCh BAO 1982 Belf.; MB BCh Belf. 1982; FRCS Ed. 1987. (Qu. Univ. Belf.) Cons. Orthop. Surg. Musgrave Pk. Hosp. Belf. Prev: Sen. Regist. (Hand Surg.) St. And. Hosp. Billericay.

MAGINN, Sarah 1 Manor Mews, Ringwould, Deal CT14 8HT — MB ChB 1990 Manch.

MAGINNES, Joseph John Daniel Chiswick Health Centre, Fisher's Lane, London W4 1RX Tel: 020 8994 2408 — MB BCh BAO 1957 NUI; DObst RCOG 1959.

MAGINNESS, John Michael Francis Tyrone County Hospital, Omagh BT79 0AP Tel: 01662 245211 Fax: 01662 246293; 63 Brookmount Road, Omagh BT78 5HY Tel: 01662 245211 — MB BCh BAO 1972 Belf.; FFA RCSI 1976; EDA 1986; Specialist Accredit. RCSI 1980. (Queen's Univ. Belf.) Cons. Anaesth. Tyrone Co. Hosp. Omagh; Cons. Anaesth. Sperrin Lakeland H&SS Trust. Socs: Assn. Anaesth. GB & Irel.; BMA; Intens. Care Soc. Irel. Prev: Sen. Regist. (Anaesth.) Erasmus Univ. Hosp. Rotterdam, Holland; Sen. Regist. (Anaesth.) Roy. Vict. & City Hosps. Belf.; Ho. Off. Mater Infirmorum Hosp. Belf.

MAGINNIS, Claire Marie 14 Highfield Road, Derby DE22 1GZ Tel: 01332 369726 — MB ChB 1989 Ed.; MRCGP 1994. Specialist Regist. (Occupat. Med.) Rolls Royce plc Derby. Prev: SHO (ENT) City Hosp. Edin.; GP/Regist. Edin.; SHO (Med. & Geriat.) Haddington.

MAGNAGO, Tatiana Sophia Isabella Falt 1, 72 Musters Road, West Bridgford, Nottingham NG2 7PS — MB ChB 1991 Bristol. SHO (Med.) Derbysh. Roy. Infirm. Derby.

MAGNALL, Rachel Jane Flat B, 214 Cavendish Road, London SW12 0BY — MB ChB 1992 Sheff.

MAGNAY, Andrew Richard The Institute of Child Health, Nuffield Building, Francis Road, Birmingham B16 8ET Tel: 0121 454 4851 Fax: 0121 454 5383 — MB BChir 1983 Camb.; MA, BA Camb. 1980, MB 1983, BChir 1982; MRCP (UK) 1986. (Camb.) Lect. (Paediat. & Child Health) Inst. Child Health Univ. Birm.; Hon. Sen. Regist. (Paediat.) Birm. Childr. Hosp. Socs: Paediat. Intens. Care Soc. & Nutrit. Soc. Prev: Regist. (Paediat.) Birm. Childr. Hosp.; SHO (Cardiol.) Hosp. Sick Childr. Gt. Ormond St. Lond.; SHO (Paediat.) Addenbrooke's Hosp. Camb.

MAGNAY, Dorothy Eileen 153 Darras Road, Ponteland, Newcastle upon Tyne NE20 9PQ — MB BS 1963 Durh.; MSc Newc. 1993; Dip. Amer. Bd. Pediat. 1972. (Newc.) SCMO Newc. AHA. Socs: BMA & Clin. Genetics Soc. Prev: Fell. (Human Genetics) Johns Hopkins Univ. Baltimore, USA; Fell. Child Developm. Center Univ. Miami, USA; Fell. John. F. Kennedy Inst. Baltimore, USA.

MAGNAY, Kate Louise 17 Rodbourne Road, Harborne, Birmingham B17 0PN — MB ChB 1994 Birm.; ChB Birm. 1994. SHO (O & G) Birm. Heartlands Hosp. Prev: Ho. Off. (Surg.) Worcester Roy. Infirm.; Ho. Off. (Med.) City Hosp. NHS Trust Birm.

MAGNER, Edward Hugh 56 Western Avenue, London W3 7TY Tel: 020 8743 4133 — MB BCh BAO 1960 NUI. (Univ. Coll. Dub.)

MAGNER, Valerie Claire (retired) 203 Crowborough Road, London SW17 9QE Tel: 020 8672 8569 — MB BCh BAO 1952 NUI; DCH Eng. 1955. Indep. Psychotherapist Lond. Prev: Sen. Med. Off. (Adopt. & Fostering) Wandsworth HA.

MAGNIER, Maurice Robert Bridge Street Medical Centre, 30 Bridge Street, Londonderry BT48 6LA Tel: 028 7126 1137; 9 Clearwater, Caw, Londonderry BT47 6BE Tel: 01504 344281 — MB BCh BAO 1974 NUI; DCH RCPSI 1978; DRCOG 1976. (U.C.D) Mem. City of Derry Pract.; Indust. Injuries Exam. Off.

MAGNIFICO, Fabiola 4 Beresford Terrace, London N5 2DH — State Exam Rome 1993.

MAGNUS, Iain Allingham Pear Tree Cottage, Mount Bures, Bures CO8 5BA Tel: 01787 227455 — MB BChir 1945 Camb.; MA Camb. 1963, MD 1963; FRCP Lond. 1967, M 1949; MRCS Eng. LRCP Lond. 1944. (Camb. & St. Thos.) Emerit. Prof. Photobiol. Inst. Dermat. Lond. Socs: Roy. Soc. Med.; Brit. Photobiol. Soc. Prev: Regist. (Skin) Guy's Hosp. Lond.; Research Fell. Guy's Hosp. Med. Sch. Lond.; Regist. (Med.) Miller Gen. Hosp. Lond.

MAGNUSDOTTIR, Ebba Margret 12/7 Sienna Gardens, Edinburgh EH9 1PQ — Cand Med et Chir Reykjavik 1993.

MAGNUSSEN, Mr Peter Alex The Guildford Nuffield, Stirling Road, Guildford GU2 7RF Tel: 01483 555842 Fax: 01483 555844 Email: peteramagnussen@uk-consultants.co.uk; Hemingford, Prey Heath Road, Worplesdon, Woking GU22 0RN Tel: 01483 232156 Email: peteramagnussen@uk.home.co.uk — MB BS 1977 Lond.; MSc (Orthop.) Lond. 1985; FRCS Eng. 1983; FRCS Ed. 1983. (Middlx. Hosp. Med. Sch.) Cons. Orthop. Surg. & Hand Surg. Roy. Surrey Co. Hosp. Guildford. Prev: Cons. Orthop. & Hand Surg. Rowley Bristow Orthop. Unit St. Peter's Hosp. Chertsey; Sen. Regist. (Orthop. Surg.) Bristol Roy. Infirm. & Winford Orthop. Hosp. Bristol; Lect. (Orthop. Surg.) Leicester Roy. Infirm.

*MAGNUSSON, Anna 19 Park Lane, Newmarket CB8 8AX — MB BS 1997 Lond.

MAGONET, Hyman The Cottage, 44 Streatham Hill, London SW2 4RA Tel: 020 8674 4499 — LMS 1936 Nova Scotia; BSc 1933, MD, C M Dalhousie 1936. (Dalhousie) Prev: Med. Regist. St. John's Hosp. Dis. Skin; Phys. Nat. Pk.s, Canada; Obst. Ho. Surg. Brit. Postgrad. Med. Sch.

MAGORRIAN, Mark Thomas 71 Mill Hill, Castlewellan BT31 9NB — MB BCh BAO 1996 Belf.; MRCP (UK) 1999.

MAGOS, Adam Laszlo Minimally Invasive Therapy Unit & Endoscopy Training Centre, University Department of Obst. & Gyn., The Royal Free Hospital, Pond St., London NW3 2QG Tel: 020 7431 1321 Fax: 020 7431 1321 Email: amagos@rfc.ucl.ac.uk — MB BS 1978 Lond.; BSc Lond. 1975, MD 1986; MRCOG 1986; FRCOG 1998. (King's Coll. Hosp.) Cons. O & G Roy. Free. Hosp. Lond.; Cons. Gyn. King Edwd. VII Hosp. for Offs. Beaumont St. Lond. Socs: Eur. Soc. Hysteroscopy; Brit. Soc. Gyn. Endoscopy; Blair Bell Res.

Soc. Prev: Sen. Lect. & Hon. Cons. Acad. Dept. O & G Univ. Lond. Roy. Free Hosp. Lond.; Clin. Lect. & Hon. Sen. Regist. Nuffield Dept. O & G Univ. Oxf. & John Radcliffe Hosp. Oxf.; Regist. (O & G) King's Coll. & Dulwich Hosps. Lond.

MAGOVERN, Patrick Michael John 126 Harley Street, London W1N 1AH Fax: 00 353 1 678 5905; 126 Harley Street, London W1N 1AH Tel: 020 7935 2030/3 — MB BCh BAO 1980 NUI; MICGP 1984; DObst RCPI 1984; LMCC 1986. (Univ. Coll. Dub.) Socs: Amer. Acad. Environm. Med.; Brit. Soc. Allergy Environm. and Nutrit. Med.; Amer. Acad. of Med. Acupunc.

MAGOWAN, Brian Alexander Department of Obstetrics & Gynaecology, Borders General Hospital, Melrose TD6 9BS Tel: 01896 826000 Fax: 01896 826728; Email: magowan@compuserve.com — MB ChB 1987 Ed.; MRCOG 1994; MRCGP 1991; DCH RCPS Glas. 1989. (Ed.) Cons. O & G Borders Gen. Hosp. Melrose. Prev: Lect. & Hon. Sen. Regist. (O & G) Univ. Glas.; Regist. Rotat. (O & G) Simpson Memor. Hosp. Edin.

MAGOWAN, John Lisleen, Leek Road, Endon, Stoke-on-Trent ST9 9HQ Tel: 01782 502227 — MB BCh BAO 1940 Belf.

MAGOWAN, Mary Caroline Ballymena Health Centre, Cushendall Road, Ballymena BT43 6HQ Tel: 028 2564 2181 Fax: 028 2564 9138 — MB BCh BAO 1974 Belf.

MAGOWAN, Terence Desmond Ballymena Health Centre, Cushendall Road, Ballymena BT43 6HQ Tel: 028 2564 2181 Fax: 028 2564 9138; 26 Aughnadore Road, Lisnamurrican, Broughshane, Ballymena BT42 4QB — MB BCh BAO 1974 Belf.; MRCGP 1982; DRCOG 1978.

MAGOWAN, William Stanley (retired) 5 Park Grove Avenue, Giffnock, Glasgow G46 6HT Tel: 0141 637 0066 — MB ChB 1942 Glas.; BSc Glas. 1939. Prev: Clin. Asst. Vict. Infirm. Glas.

MAGRATH, Antony (retired) 45 Newmarket Road, Norwich NR2 2HN — MB BS 1958 Lond.; MRCS Eng. LRCP Lond. 1958; DObst RCOG 1962.

MAGRATH, Beryl Helene Doris, MBE Alderbrook, Southill Road, Chislehurst BR7 5EE Tel: 020 8467 8473 Fax: 020 8467 8473 Email: beryl.magrath@tinyworld.co.uk — MB BS 1963 Lond.; MRCS Eng. LRCP Lond. 1963; FFA RCS Eng. 1968; DObst RCOG 1965; DA Eng. 1965. (Lond. Hosp.) Cons. Anaesth. Socs: Assn. Anaesths. & Roy. Soc. Med.; Fell. Roy. Soc. Med.; Anaesth. Counc. Prev: Cons. Anaesth. Regional Plastic Unit S.E. Essex Gp. Hosps.; Med. Director S. Bromley Hosp. Care; Cons.Anaesth. & Med. Director Bromely Hosp.

MAGRATH, Helene Patricia Alderbrook, Southill Road, Chislehurst BR7 5EE — MB BChir 1994 Camb.; BA Camb. 1992; MRCP UK 1998. (Univ. Camb.) SHO (A&E) Nelson Hosp. New Zealand. Prev: SHO Rotat. (Med.) Birm. Heartlands Hosp.; SHO (A & E) Derbysh. Roy. Infirm.; Ho. Off. (Surg.) Addenbrooke's Hosp. Camb.

MAGRATH, Ian Malcolm Histopathology Department, Shirley Oaks Hospital, Croydon CR9 8AB Tel: 020 8655 2255; Alderbrook, Southill Road, Chislehurst BR7 5EE Tel: 020 8467 8473 — MB BS 1962 Lond.; MRCS Eng. LRCP Lond. 1962; FRCPath 1982, M 1970. (St. Geo.) Cons. Histopath. Shirley Oaks Hosp. Croydon. Socs: BMA & Assn. Clin. Pathols.; Croydon Med. Soc.; Croydon Medico-Legal Soc. Prev: Sen. Regist. (Morbid Anat.) Univ. Coll. Hosp. Lond. & Lewisham Hosp.; Regist. (Path). St. Stephen's Hosp. Lond.; Cons. Histopath. Mayday Hosp. Thornton Heath.

***MAGRATH, Morag** 90 Wentworth Road, Harborne, Birmingham B17 9SY — MB ChB 1997 Manch.

MAGRI, Mr Joseph (retired) 60 Wise Lane, Mill Hill, London NW7 2RG Tel: 020 8906 8430 — MD 1949 Malta; FRCS Eng. 1958; BSc Open 1993. Prev: Sen. Regist. St. Peter's & St. Pauls' Hosps. Lond.

MAGRILL, Lesley Honor Esher Community Support Team, Elmbridge Lodge, Western Green Road, Thames Ditton KT7 0HY Tel: 020 8398 8019 Fax: 020 8398 9327; 9 Westmead, London SW15 5BH Tel: 020 8789 6797 — MB ChB 1973 Manch.; MRCPsych 1979; Dip. Family Ther. (Distinc.) St. Geo. Hospital 1993. (St. Georges) cons. (Psychiat. of Learning Disabil.) Kingston & Dist. Community Trust Surrey. Socs: Roy. Coll. Psychiat.; Assn. Family Ther. & Systemic Pract.; Assn. Child Psychol. & Psychiat. Prev: Sen. Regist. (Psychiat. of Learning Disabil.) St Geo.s; Regist. (Child Psychiat.) St Geo.s.

MAGRO, Mr Joseph John Terra Nova House Medical Practice, 43 Dura Street, Dundee DD4 6SW Tel: 01382 451100 Fax: 01382 453679 — MRCS Eng. LRCP Lond. 1977; FRCS Ed. 1982; MRCGP 1985.

MAGSON, Celia Rosemary Littlehampton Health Centre, Fitzalan Road, Littlehampton BN17 5HG; 5 Old Rectory Close, Westbourne, Emsworth PO10 8UB Tel: 01243 374458 Email: ce.shannon@virgin.net — MB BS Lond. 1966; MFFP 1995; DFFP 1993; Cert. Family Plann. JCC 1990; Cert. FPA 1969. (St. Geo.) Clin. Med. Off. (Community Health) Worthing Health Trust & Portsmouth Trust. Socs: Fac. Fam. Plann. & Reproduc. Health; Brit. Menopause Soc.; S. Hants & W Sussex Family Plann. Doctors Gp.

MAGUET, Henri 35 St James Road, Melton, North Ferriby HU14 3HZ — LMS 1986 Santander.

MAGUINESS, Mr Stephen David The Princess Royal Hospital, Saltshouse Road, Hull HU8 9HE Tel: 01482 676842 — MB BCh BAO 1981 Belf.; MD Belf. 1992; MRCOG 1986. Cons. O & G Hull & E. Yorks. NHS Trust; Med. Dir. Hull IVF Unit; Hon. Sen. Lect. Socs: Brit. Fertil. Soc.; Brit. Soc. Gyn. Endoscopy; ESHRE. Prev: Sen. Regist. (O & G) Yorks. RHA; Regist. Newham Gen. Hosp.

MAGUIRE, Aideen Maria Patricia 322 Stockport Road, Marple, Stockport SK6 6ET — MB ChB 1988 Leeds.

MAGUIRE, Ailsa Catherine 29 Elm Bank Gardens, Barnes, London SW13 0NU — MB BS 1989 Lond.; BSc Lond. 1988; MRCP (UK) 1992; DRCOG 1995. GP Regist. Lond.

MAGUIRE, Alan Antony 14 Baronswood, Gosforth, Newcastle upon Tyne NE3 3UB Tel: 0191 284 4841; Branch End Surgery, Stocksfield NE43 7LL Tel: 01661 842626 — MB BS 1990 Newc.; MRCGP Newc. 1997. GP Stocksfield, N.d.

MAGUIRE, Anne (cons. rooms), 23 Harley St., London W1N 1DA Tel: 020 7436 5262; (cons. rooms), 17 Wellington St., St. John's, Blackburn BB1 8AF Tel: 01254 59910 — MB BS Lond. 1946; FRCP Lond. 1974, M 1956; MRCS Eng. LRCP Lond. 1946; Dip. Analyt. Psychol. C. G. Jung Inst. Zürich 1976. (Lond. Sch. Med. Wom.) Socs: Fell. Roy. Soc. Med. (Mem. Dermat. Sect.); Intern. Assn. Analyt. Psychol. Zurich; Brit. Assn. Dermatol. Prev: Hon. Cons. Phys. Dis. of Skin Blackburn & Dist. & Burnley & Dist. Hosp Gps.; Sen. Regist. Univ. Coll. Hosp. Lond.; Regist. Guy's Hosp. Lond.

MAGUIRE, Anne Marie Bridgeton Health Centre, 210 Abercromby Street, Glasgow G40 2DA Tel: 0141 531 6630 Fax: 0141 531 6626 — MB ChB 1981 Glas. Clin. Med. Off. Gtr. Glas. HB.

***MAGUIRE, Breege** 28 Tates Av, Belfast BT9 7BY — MB BCh BAO 1997 Belf.

MAGUIRE, Brian Gerard 64 Meadowfield, Gosforth, Seascale CA20 1HU — MB ChB 1973 Manch.; FRCR 1979; DMRD Eng. 1977. Cons. (Diag. Radiol.) W. Cumbld. Hosp. Hesingham. Prev: Lect. (Anat.) Univ. Manch.; Regist. (Diag. Radiol.) & Sen. Regist. (Diag. Radiol.) Manch. AHA.

MAGUIRE, Briegeen Mary Maphoner Surgery, Maphoner Road, Mullaghbawn, Newry BT35 9TR; Innisfree, Lurgyvallen, Armagh BT61 8BE Tel: 01861 522310 — MB BCh BAO 1988 Belf.; MRCGP 1992; DMH Belf. 1992; DRCOG 1991. (Queen's University Belfast) GP. Socs: BMA; ASADOC. Prev: Trainee GP Lisburn; SHO (Med., Surg. & Cas.) S. Tyrone Hosp. Dungannon; Ho. Off. Belf. City Hosp.

MAGUIRE, Mr Charles James Frederick (retired) Achadara, Shallany, Lisnarick, Enniskillen BT94 1PX — MB BCh BAO 1954 Belf.; FRCS Eng. 1966; DO Eng. 1961. Prev: Ophth. Surg. Roy. Vict. Hosp. Belf. & Moyle Hosp. Larne.

***MAGUIRE, Deirdre** 322 Stockport Road, Marple, Stockport SK6 6ET — MB ChB 1997 Sheff.

MAGUIRE, Dermot Francis Clifton Street Surgery, 15-17 Clifton Street, Belfast BT13 1AD Tel: 028 9032 2330 Fax: 028 9043 9812 — MB BCh BAO 1992 Belf.

MAGUIRE, Donna Marie Meddyfga Taf, North Road, Whitland SA34 0AT Tel: 01994 240195 Fax: 01994 241138 — MB BCh 1985 Wales.

MAGUIRE, Edward Shepherd East Wing, Esk Medical Centre, Ladywell Way, Musselburgh EH21 6AA Tel: 0131 665 2267 Fax: 0131 653 2348; 18 Blackford Road, Edinburgh EH9 2DS — MB ChB 1966 Ed.; ECFMG Cert 1966. (Ed.) Med. Off. Loretto Sch. Musselburgh. Socs: BMA & Med. Off. Sch. Assn. Prev: SHO (O & G) Cresswell Hosp. Dumfries; Ho. Surg. & Ho. Phys. Qu. Eliz. Hosp. Gateshead.

MAGUIRE

MAGUIRE, Gavin Robert The Old Vicarage, Bardsea, Ulverston LA12 9QU — MB ChB 1993 Manch.

MAGUIRE, Helen Claire Frances CDSC (Thames), 40 Eastbourne Terrace, London W2 3QR Tel: 020 7725 2734 Fax: 020 7725 2712 — MB BCh BAO 1978 NUI; MPH (NUI) 1985; MFPHMI 1992; MFPHM RCP (UK) 1990; DO RCPI (RCPI) 1981; DCH (RCP) Lond. 1980; FFPHM RCP (UK) 1997. Cons. Regional Epidemiol. Pub. Health Laborat. Serv. Communicable Dis. Surveillance Centre (Thames) Lond.; Hon. Sen. Lect. (Pub. Health Scis.) St. Geo. Hosp. Med. Sch. Lond. Prev: Sen. Regist. (Pub. Health Med.) PHLS Communicable Dis. Surveillance Centre Lond.; Sen Regist. (Community Med.) SW Thames Region HA.

MAGUIRE, James (retired) Innisfree, Lurgyvallen, Armagh BT61 8AU Tel: 01861 522310 — MB BCh BAO Belf. 1954; MFCMI 1987; FFCM RCP (UK) 1980, M 1972; DPH 1958; DObst RCOG 1957. Prev: Dir. (Pub. Health) S.. HSSB N. Irel.

MAGUIRE, James Cuthbert Market Street Surgery, 92 Market Street, Dalton-in-Furness LA15 8AB Tel: 01229 462591 Fax: 01229 468217; The Old Vicarage, Bardsea, Ulverston LA12 9QU Tel: 01229 869508 — MB ChB 1965 Liverp. (Liverp.) Hosp. Pract. (Dermat.) Furness Gen. Hosp.; Police Surg. Prev: Ho. Surg. & Ho. Phys. BRd.green Hosp. Liverp.; Demonst. (Anat.) Univ, Liverp.; SHO (Cas. & Orthop.) Liverp. Roy. Infirm.

MAGUIRE, John Mitchell (retired) 2 Larch Road, Glasgow G41 5DA Tel: 0141 427 0902 — MB ChB 1958 Glas.; MRCGP 1977; DObst RCOG 1960.

MAGUIRE, John Paul 42 Staups Lane, Shibden, Halifax HX3 7AB — MB ChB 1992 Leeds.

MAGUIRE, Joseph Stillmoor House Surgery, Dennison Road, Bodmin PL31 2JJ Tel: 01208 72489; Stillmoor House, Dennison Road, Bodmin PL31 2JJ — MB BS 1971 Lond.; MRCS Eng. LRCP Lond. 1971; DRCOG 1977; DA (UK) 1973.

MAGUIRE, Joseph 23 Gayton Parkway, Wirral CH60 3SZ — MB ChB 1980 Glas.

MAGUIRE, Kelly Maria 9 St George's Hill, Bathampton, Bath BA2 6RN — MB BCh BAO 1996 Belf. GP VTS SHO.

MAGUIRE, Kenneth Gilmour (retired) 293 Old Glenarm Road, Larne BT40 1TU — MB BCh BAO 1954 Belf.

MAGUIRE, Mary 14 Fernshaw Road, Chelsea, London SW10 0TF Tel: 020 8778 6202 — MB BS 1955 Lond. (Roy. Free) Prev: Ho. Surg. Roy. Free Hosp.; Ho. Phys. Roy. Sussex Co. Hosp. Brighton; Ho. Off. Vict. Matern. Hosp. Barnet.

***MAGUIRE, Michael Fletcher** The Old Vicarage, Bardsea, Ulverston LA12 9QU Tel: 01229 869508 Email: mfmaguire69@hotmail.com; The Old Vicarage, Bardsea, Ulverston LA12 9QU Tel: 01229 869508 — BM BCh 1998 Oxf.; BM BCh Oxf 1998; MA (CANTAB) 1999.

MAGUIRE, Michael John, TD North Glamorgan NHS Trust, c/o Prince Charles Hospital, Merthyr Tydfil CF47 9DT Tel: 01685 721721 Fax: 01685 388001 Email: dr.maguire@nglam-trwoles.nhs.uk; 1 The Grove, Merthyr Tydfil CF47 8YR Email: mjmaguire@doctors.org.uk — BChir 1971 Camb.; MA Camb. 1972, BChir 1971, MB 1972; FRCP Lond. 1991; MRCP (UK) 1973; FRCPCH 1997. (Camb.) Cons. Paediat. N. Glam. NHS Trust; Hon. Lect. Child Health WWCM. Prev: Cons. Paediat. UTH Lusaka; Hon. Lect. Child Health UNZA.

MAGUIRE, Niamh Moira Postgraduate Medical Centre, Falkirk & District Royal Infirmary, Majors Loan, Falkirk FK1 5QE — MB ChB 1993 Aberd.

MAGUIRE, Olivia Teresa 16 Cambourne Park, Belfast BT9 6RL — MB BCh BAO 1955 Belf.

MAGUIRE, Pamela Amy Borders General Hospital, Melrose TD6 9BS — MB BCh BAO 1971 Belf.; MRCP (UK) 1979; DObst RCOG 1975; FRCP 1995. Cons. Phys. Responsibil. Elderly Borders Gen. Hosp. Prev: Sen. Regist. (Gen. Med.) Belf. City Hosp.; Sen. Regist. (Rehabil. Med. & Geriat. Med.) Roy. Vict. Hosp. Belf.; Regist. (Nephrol) St. Vincent's Hosp. Dub.

MAGUIRE, Peter Bernard The Haven, 21 Camlough Road, Newry BT35 6JP Tel: 01693 66817 Fax: 01693 63713 Email: docgasman@aol.com — MB BCh BAO 1993 NUI; LRCPSI 1993; FFA RCSI 1998. (Roy. Coll. Surgs. Dub.) Specialist Regist. (Anaesth.) Belf. City Hosp. Prev: SHO (Anaesth.) Roy. Vict. Hosp. Belf.; SHO (Gastroenterol.) Jas. Connolly Memor. Hosp. Dub.; SHO (Anaesth.) Daisy Hill Hosp. Newry.

MAGUIRE, Sabine Ann Royal Gwent Hospital, Glen Hafren Trust, Cardiff Road, Newport NP20 2UB Tel: 01633 252244; The Mill House, Pontcanna Field, Llandaff, Cardiff CF5 2AX — MB BCh BAO 1984 NUI; MRCPI 1988; LRCPI & LM LRCSI & LM 1984. Cons. Paediat. Roy. Gwent Hosp. Gwent. Socs: Paediat. Research Soc. & Brit. Paediat. Assn.; Brit. Soc. Paediat. Gastroenterol. & Nutrit.

***MAGUIRE, Sarah Rachel Grace** 2 Dromore Road, Lurgan, Craigavon BT66 7HN — MB BCh BAO 1997 Belf.

MAGUIRE, Sean Henry 11 Gilford Road, Portadown, Craigavon BT63 5ED — MB ChB 1989 Manch.

MAGUIRE, Stephanie Frances Flat 1/2, 13 Rupert St., Glasgow G4 9AP — MB ChB 1994 Glas.

MAGUIRE, Suzanne Mary 176 Tandragee Road, Newry BT35 6LP — MB BCh BAO 1990 NUI; MRCP (UK) 1993; LRCPSI 1990. SHO (Med.) Roy. Hosps. Trust Belf.

MAGUIRE, Thomas Kevin 11 Everest Drive, Crickhowell NP8 1DH Tel: 01873 810865 — MB BCh BAO NUI 1946. (Univ. Coll. Dub.) Prev: Med. Off. Tuberc. Dept. Newsham Gen. Hosp. Liverp.; Lt.-Col. RAMC.

MAGUIRE, Thomas Matthew (retired) Robin Hill, 18 Murdoch Road, Wokingham RG40 2DE Tel: 01734 787027 Email: tmasu44278@aol.com — MB BCh BAO 1954 Dub.; FRCPsych 1980, M 1971; DPM Durham. 1959; DMJ Soc. Apoth. Lond. 1970. Prev: Cons. Psychiat. BRd.moor Hosp. Crowthorne.

MAGUIRE, Winifred Ann 32 Orpen Park, Finaghy, Belfast BT10 0BN — MB BCh BAO 1978 Belf.

MAGUS, Simon Robert 52 Summerhill Avenue, Newport NP19 8FP — MB BS 1990 Lond.

MAH, Michael Seng Lee 51 Froggatts Ride, Walmley, Sutton Coldfield B76 2TQ; 59 Tingkat TAMAN, Ipoh 7, Ipoh Garden S., Ipoh, Perak 31400, Malaysia — MB BCh BAO 1988 Belf.; MB Bch BAO Belf. 1998; DA (UK) 1997; MRCPI Dub. 1998. (Qu. Univ. Belf.) Clin. Pharm. Phys. Guys Drug Research Unit, Lond.; SHO (Genitourin. Med.) Roy. Hallowshire Hosp. Sheff.; SHO (Gen. Med.) Qu.'s Hosp. Burton-Upon-Trent; SHO (Gen. Med.) Staff. Gen. Hosp. Socs: BMA. Prev: SHO (Gen. Med.) Qu.'s Hosp. Burton-upon-Trent.

MAHAD, Don Joseph 15 Melyd Avenue, Prestatyn LL19 8RN — MB ChB 1993 Sheff.

***MAHADANAARACHCHI, Jude Chaminda** 15 Melyd Avenue, Prestatyn LL19 8RN — MB ChB 1998 Liverp.; MB ChB Liverp 1998.

MAHADESHWAR, Shridhar Sakharam 39 Friern Watch Avenue, London N12 9NY — MB BS 1976 Bombay; MSc Keele 1991; MRCPsych 1983. Cons. Psychiat. (Ment. Handicap) Wolverhampton & Walsall HAs.

MAHADEVA, Ravindran 18 Eastfields Road, London W3 0AD — MB BS 1988 Lond. SHO (Gen. Med. & Chest Med.) St. Helier Hosp. Hastings.

MAHADEVA, Sanjiv Scarborough General Hospital, Woodlands Drive, Scarborough YO12 6QL — MB BS 1993 Newc. Specialist Regist. (Gastroenterol.) ScarBoro. Prev: SHO (Med.) Leeds; SHO (Hepat.) Leeds.

MAHADEVA, Sanmugam (retired) 117 Clarence Avenue, New Malden KT3 3TY — MB BS Ceylon 1957. Prev: Lect. Dept. Clin. Pharmacol. & Therap. Char. Cross & W.m. Med. Sch. Univ. Lond.

MAHADEVA, Ula — MRCPath 2000; MB BS Lond. 1994; BSc (Molecular Biol. & Basic Med. Sci.) Lond. 1991. (Univ. Coll. Lond. Med. Sch.) Locum Cons. Histo/Cytopatologist, St. Mary's Hosp., Lond. until 02/11/01. Socs: Middlx. Hosp. Med. Soc. Prev: Specialist Regist. (Histopath.) N.wick Pk. & St Mark's NHS Trust; SHO (Histopath.) St. Mary's Hosp. NHS Trust Lond.; Specialist Regist. (Histopath.) St Mary's NHS Trust Lond.

MAHADEVAN, Daruka 38 Bishops Park Road, Norbury, London SW16 5TS — MB BS 1990 Lond.

MAHADEVAN, Jayanthy Sorrento, Station Road, Staplehurst, Tonbridge TN12 0PZ Tel: 01580 240333 — MB BS 1982 Delhi; FFA RCSI 1989; DA Eng. 1984. Cons. Anaesth. (long term locum) Maidstone Hosp. Prev: Clin. Asst. (Anaesth.) Tunbridge Wells Area Health.

MAHADEVAN, Mayurathy 16 Calverley Road, Stoneleigh, Epsom KT17 2NX — MB ChB 1993 Birm.

***MAHADEVAN, Mellini Manjula** Flat 4, 6 King's Stables Road, Edinburgh EH1 2JY — MB ChB 1996 Ed.

MAHADEVAN, Neila 3 Midhurst Gardens, Luton LU3 1UG — MB BS 1979 Lond.; MRCOG 1987. Sen. Regist. (O & G) Chelsea & W.m. Hosp. Lond.

MAHADEVAN, Satchidanandan 4 Haworth Bank, Moorgate, Rotherham S60 3BP — MB BS 1959 Madras; MFCM 1980; DPH Calcutta 1961. (Madras Med. Coll.) Specialist (Community Med.) Rotherham HA. Prev: Sen. Regist. (Community Med.) N.. RHA.

MAHADEVAN, Subramaniam Benenden Hospital, Benenden, Cranbrook TN17 4AX — MD 1978 Poona; MD Poona India 1978, MB BS 1975; MRCOG 1983. Assoc. Specialist Benenden Hosp. Prev: Regist. (O & G) Sunderland Dist. Gen. Hosp.

MAHADY, Ian William Carlton House, Healey Mount, Burnley BB11 4HS Tel: 01282 23182 — MB ChB 1966 St. And.; FRCOG 1989, M 1973; Cand. Med. et Chir. Copenhagen 1969. (St. And.) Cons. (O & G) Burnley Gen. Hosp. Prev: Reservelaege (O & G) Afdeling Centr.sygehuset, Nykøbing Falster, Denmark; Regist. (O & G) Roy. Berks. Hosp. Reading; Sen. Regist. NW RHA.

MAHADY, Valerie Elizabeth Carlton House, Healey Mount, Burnley BB11 4HS — MB ChB 1976 Manch.

MAHAFFEY, Ann Miriam Arbury Road Surgery, 114 Arbury Road, Cambridge CB4 2JG Tel: 01223 364433 Fax: 01223 315728 — MB BS 1981 Lond.; MRCGP 1991; DCH RCP Lond. 1985. Prev: Regist. (Med.) St. Luke's Hosp. Sydney, Austral.; Resid. Med. Off. Roy. N. Shore Hosp. Sydney, Austral.; Ho. Surg. Roy. Free Hosp. Lond.

MAHAFFEY, Mr Peter John Department of Plastic & Reconstructive Surgery, Lister Hospital, Stevenage SG1 4AB Tel: 01438 314333 Fax: 01438 360091 — MB BCh BAO 1973 NUI; FRCS Ed. 1981; FRCS Eng. 1981. Cons. Plastic Surg. Lister Hosp. Stevenage & Bedford Gen. Hosp. Socs: Brit. Soc. Surg. Hand. Prev: Regist. Regional Plastic Surg. Unit St. And. Hosp. Billericay; Regist. (Plastic Surg.) Canniesburn Hosp. Glas.; Sen. Regist. (Plastic Surg.) Withington Hosp. Manch.

MAHAFFY, Mr Ronald Gibson (retired) Ordhill Farm, Peterculter AB14 0LT — MB ChB 1952 Ed.; FRCS Ed. 1959; FRCR 1975; FFR 1964; DMRD Ed. 1962. Prev: Cons. Radiol. Roy. Infirm. Aberd.

MAHAFZA, Tareq Al c/o ENT Department, Wythgenshawe Hospital, Sputhmoor Road, Manchester M23 9LT — Vrach 1981 1st Leningrad Med. Inst. USSR.

MAHAI, Amrit Pal Kaur 8 Kingsbrook Way, Wirral CH63 5NG Tel: 0151 644 1277 — BM Soton. 1988; MRCGP 1993; T(GP) 1993; DFFP 1993; Cert. Prescribed Equiv. Exp. JCPTGP 1993; DRCOG 1992. (Univ. Soton.) Assoc. GP Wirral. Socs: BMA; Med. Protec. Soc.; Non-Princip. Rep. Wirral LMC. Prev: Trainee GP Skimped Hill Health Centre Bracknell; SHO Roy. Canberra Hosp. N. & S. Canberra, Austral.; SHO (O & G) St. Helier Hosp. Carshalton.

MAHAJAN, Abhijit Jogannath 30 Knightcott Road, Banwell, Weston Super Mare BS29 6HA — MB BS 1984 Bombay.

MAHAJAN, H R Bridge Street Surgery, 48 Bridge Street, Newton-le-Willows WA12 9QS Tel: 01925 225755.

MAHAJAN, Jugnu 35 Sandringham Drive, Bramcote Hills, Nottingham NG9 3ED Tel: 0115 925 3952 — MB BS 1984 Meerut, India; MD Chandigarh, India 1986; MRCP (UK) 1992.

MAHAJAN, Om Prakash 19 Field Street, Trelewis, Treharris CF46 6AW — MB BS 1957 Calcutta; BSc Calcutta 1949, MB BS 1957; DTM & H Eng. 1957. Prev: Chief Med. Off. W.. Dooars & Chulsa Med. Assn., India.

MAHAJAN, Ravi Prakash Department of Anaesthesia, University Hospital, Queens Medical Centre, Nottingham NG7 2UH Tel: 0115 924 9924 Fax: 0115 970 0739; The Cedars, Chesterfield Road, Tibshelf, Alfreton DE55 5NP Tel: 01773 875913 — MB BS 1981 Meerut, India; FFA RCSI 1990. Sen. Lect. & Hon. Cons. Socs: Eur. Soc. Anaesth.; Assn. Anaesth. GB & Irel.; Brit. Soc. Intens. Care.

MAHAJAN, Tripti Abhijit 30 Knightcott Road, Banwell, Weston Super Mare BS29 6HA — MB BS 1988 Bombay; MRCP (UK) 1993.

MAHAJAN, Vitthal Das Docklands Medical Centre, 100 Spindrift Avenue, Isle of Dogs, London E14 9WU Tel: 020 7537 1444; 11 Dickens Drive, Chislehurst BR7 6RU — MB BS 1969 Vikram.

***MAHAL, Kulbinder Kaur** 167 Saltwell Road, Gateshead NE8 4TJ — MB ChB 1997 Leic.

MAHAL, Palvinder Singh Central Health Centre, North Carbrain Road, Cumbernauld, Glasgow G67 1BJ Tel: 01236 731738; 15 Gullace Crescent, Cumbernauld, Glasgow G68 0HR — MB ChB 1985 Glas.; MRCGP 1991; DRCOG 1991.

MAHALINGAM, Mekala Branston & Heighinton Family Practice, Station Road, Branston, Lincoln LN4 1LG Tel: 01522 793081; Email: mekala@tinyonline.co.uk — MB ChB 1994 Glas.; MRCGP 1998. (Univ. of Glas.) p/t Gen. Practitioner (employed), Branston, Lincoln; Clin. Med. Off., Family Plann., Newark FP Clinic, Mansfield Dist. PCT. Socs: Diploma, Fac. of Familing Plann.

MAHALINGAM, Saraswathi 66 Dorchester Avenue, Glasgow G12 0ED Tel: 0141 334 0590 — MB BS 1962 Madras. (Stanley Med. Coll.) Clin. Med. Off. (Child & Sch. Health), Lanarksh. Healthcare NHS Trust (Airdale Dist.) Motherwell. Prev: Regist. (Cas.) N. Manch. Gen. Hosp.; Clin. Med. Off. (Child Health) Lanarksh. Health Bd.

***MAHAN, Jaishan Kumaresh,** Lt. RAMC 5 Filbert St E., Leicester LE2 7JG — MB ChB 1997 Leic.

MAHANTY, Swaroop Kumar Eastmoor Health Centre, Windhill Road, Wakefield WF1 4SD Tel: 01924 327625 Fax: 01924 298488; 8 Pinders Grove, Wakefield WF1 4AH Tel: 01924 379264 — MB BS 1963 Calcutta; BSc, MB BS Calcutta 1963. (Calcutta) Hosp. Pract. Dept. Otorhinolaryng. & Radiother. & Oncol. Clayton Hosp. Wakefield. Prev: Regist. Dept. Oncol. & Radiother. Cookridge Hosp. Leeds.

MAHAPATRA, Jasbir St Brides Medical Centre, Tredegar House Drive, Duffryn, Newport NP10 8UX Tel: 01633 815161 Fax: 01633 810900 — MB BS 1967 Bombay; MB BS 1967 Bombay.

MAHAPATRA, Kali Sankar Stonecross Surgery, 25 Street End Road, Chatham ME5 0AA Tel: 01634 842334; Merrihill, Caring Lane, Leeds, Maidstone ME17 1TJ — MB BS 1971 Calcutta. (R.G. Kar Med. Coll. Calcutta) Prev: Trainee GP Walthamstow; SHO (Geriat.) Middx. Hosp. Lond.; SHO (Gen. Med.) R.G. Kar Med. Coll. & Hosp. Calcutta, India.

MAHAPATRA, Kesaba Chandra 106 Folders Lane, Burgess Hill RH15 0DX — MB BS 1971 Berhampur; DA Eng. 1978.

MAHAPATRA, Prabhat Kumar Care Principles, Cedar House, Dover Road, Canterbury CT4 6PW Tel: 01227 833711 Fax: 01227 833701 Email: pk.m@virgin.net; 2 Filmer Road., Bridge, Canterbury CT4 5NB Tel: 01227 832095 Fax: 01227 832095 — MB BS 1990 Utkal; MD (Psychiat.) Banaras Hindu Univ. 1993; MRCPsych 1997; Dip. Psychiat. Manch. 1996. (S.C.B. Med. Coll. Cuttack, India) Cons. Psychiat., Care Principles, Canterbury. Socs: Indian Psychiat. Soc.

MAHAPATRA, Sasi Bhusan Harrogate Clinic, 23 Ripon Road, Harrogate HG1 2JL Tel: 01423 500599 Fax: 01423 531074; Woodlands Grange, Woodlands Drive, Apperley Bridge, Bradford BD10 0NX — MB BS 1958 Utkal; FRCP Lond. 1982, M 1963; FRCPsych 1978, M 1971; DPM Eng. 1964. (S.C.B. Med. Coll. Orissa) Cons. Psychiat. & Med. Dir. Harrogate Clinic N. Yorks; Hon. Cons. Psychiat. Leeds Community & Ment. Health Serv. Trust. Prev: Cons. Psychiat. St. Jas. Univ. Hosp. Leeds; Sen. Clin. Lect. (Psychiat.) Univ. Leeds; Sen. Regist. Rotat. Runwell Hosp. Wickford, St. Clement's Hosp. Lond. & Lond. Hosp.

MAHAPATRA, Mr Tapan Kumar Department of Surgery, Castle Hill Hospital, University of Hull, Castle Road, Cottingham HU16 5JQ Tel: 01482 624013 Fax: 01482 62650; 3 Alma Close, Kirk Ella, Hull HU10 7LH Tel: 01482 659494 Fax: 01482 659494 Email: tmahapatra@hotmail.com — MB BS 1978 Delhi, India; DA Delhi 1980; FRCS Ed. 1983; Dip. Urol. Lond 1993; FRCS 1999. Cons. Surg., Hull & E. Yorks. Hosp. NHS Trust. Socs: Brit. Assn. Surg. Oncol.; BMA. Prev: Clin. Fell. in BrE. Surg., Acad. Surgic. Unit, Univ. of Hull; Cons. Barnsley Dist. Gen. Hosp. NHS Trust; Assoc. Specialist Surg. Barnsley Dist. Gen. Hosp. NHS.

MAHAR, Mr Pir Bux 99 Inglehurst Gardens, Ilford IG4 5HA — MB BS 1975 Sind; FRCSI 1986.

MAHARAJ, Aruna Camille Sharma Flat 11 Spreadbury Close, Harborne, Birmingham B17 8TQ Tel: 0121 420 3758 Fax: 0121 420 3758 Email: aruna_maharaj@hotmail.com — MB BS 1995 West Indies. (The Univ. of The W. I. Trinidad) SHO City Hosp. NHS Trust, Birm. Socs: BMA. Prev: SHO Eric Williams Med. Sci.s Complex, Trinidad, W.I.; Ho. Off. San Fernando Gen Hosp. Trinidad, W.I.

MAHARAJ, Mr Ashok Kumar c/o Mr Andy Pascoe, Sergeant & Collins, 25 Oswald Road, Scunthorpe DN15 7PS — MB BS 1972 Bombay; FRCS Glas. 1981; FRCS Ed. 1981.

MAHARAJ, Veena 2 Sycamore Close, Leicester LE2 2RN — MB BS 1983 Lond.; MRCP (UK) 1989.

MAHATANE

MAHATANE, Juliet Rose 46 Melrose Avenue, Willesden Green, London NW2 4JS — MB BS 1990 Lond.; BSc Lond. 1988.

MAHATME, Devendra Amol Shradhanand St Giles Road Surgery, St. Giles Road, Watton, Thetford IP25 6XG Tel: 01953 889134 Fax: 01953 885167 — MB ChB 1985 Leeds; MRCGP 1990; DRCOG 1988.

MAHATME, Sarala Shradhanand (retired) The Surgery, Kelvin Grove, Wombwell, Barnsley S73 0DL Tel: 01226 752361 — MB BS 1960 Bombay; DA Eng. 1963.

MAHATME, Mr Shradhanand Bhasker Parklands, 100 Wood Walk, Wombell, Barnsley S73 0NE — MB BS 1957 Bombay; FRCS Ed. 1965. (Grant Med. Coll.) Cons. Otolaryngol. Barnsley Gp. Hosps. Socs: N. Eng. Otolaryng. Soc. Prev: Sen. Regist. ENT Dept. Liverp. RHB & United Liverp. Hosps.

***MAHAWISH, Lena** 21 St Vincent's Road, Fulwood, Preston PR2 8YU — MB ChB 1998 Manch.; MB ChB Manch 1998.

MAHAY, Gurmit Ram Poplars Medical Centre, Third Avenue, Low Hill, Wolverhampton WV10 9PG Tel: 01902 733 1195 Fax: 01902 656466; 135 Lea Road, Pennfields, Wolverhampton WV3 0LQ Tel: 01902 335314 — MB ChB 1986 Birm.

MAHDI, Mr Atief Mahmoud 85 Eversley Road, London SE19 3QS — MB BCh BAO 1985 NUI; FRCSI 1991; LRCPSI 1985.

MAHDI, Gamal El Din Mohamed Department of Paediatrics, Hull Royal Infirmary, Anlaby Road, Hull HU3 2JZ — MB BCh 1973 Ain Shams; MRCPI 1990; DTCH Liverp. 1986; DCH Dub. 1981. Cons. Paediat. Gastroenterol. Hull Roy. Infirm.; Fell.sh. Paediat. Gastroenterol. Univ. Brit. Columbia Canda 1995. Prev: Lect. & Sen. Regist. Bristol Hosp. Sick Childr.; Regist. (Paediat.) Ninewells Hosp. & Med. Sch. Dundee.

MAHDI, Mr Kassim Salman Bishop Auckland General Hospital, Cockton Hill Road, Bishop Auckland DL14 6AD Tel: 01388 454080 Fax: 01388 454136; 8 Holywood, Wolsingham, Durham DL13 3HE Tel: 01388 526791 — MB ChB Baghdad 1970; FRCS Ed. 1984; FRCSI 1984; FRCS Glas. 1982. Cons. Orthop. Surg.

MAHDI, Mr Shahab Gerlan, Stryt Las, Rhosllanerchrugog, Wrexham LL14 2HF — MB BS 1981 Karachi; FRCS Glas. 1986.

MAHENDRA, Bala 10 Harley Street, London W1N 1AA Tel: 0207 467 8300 Email: mahen@supanet.com — MB BS 1975 Sri Lanka; LLB Lond. 1992; MRCPsych 1980. Barrister Gray's Inn.; Sen. Tutor Law Tutors Partnership. Prev: Hon. Sen. Lect. Univ. Warwick; Cons. Psychogeriat. Geo. Eliot Hosp. Nuneaton & Prestwich Hosp. Manch.

MAHENDRA, Christian Chelliah (retired) 4 Teesdale Gardens, Isleworth TW7 6AT Tel: 020 8560 1569 Fax: 0208 400 7552 — MB BS 1956 Ceylon; PhD Lond. 1969. Prev: Chief (Nutrit.) Med. Research Inst. Colombo, Sri Lanka.

MAHENDRA, Meena Manickam (retired) 4 Teesdale Gardens, Isleworth TW7 6AT Tel: 020 8560 1569 Fax: 020 8400 7552 — MB BS Ceylon 1956; FRCPath 1980, M 1968; DPath Eng. 1966. Prev: Cons. Microbiol. W. Middlx. Univ. Hosp. Isleworth.

MAHENDRA, Premini Department of Haematology, Queen Elizabeth Hospital, Edgbaston, Birmingham B15 2TH Tel: 0121 627 2480 Fax: 0121 697 8401 Email: prem.mahendra@university-b.wmds.nhs.uk; 31 Richmond Hill Road, Edgbaston, Birmingham B15 3RR Tel: 0121 603 8464 Fax: 0121 604 9330 — MB ChB 1985 Glas.; MD Glas. 1995; MRCP (UK) 1988; MRCPath 1994; FRCP 2000. (Glas.) Cons. Haematologist Univ. Hosp. Birm. NHS Trust. Prev: Cons. Haemat. Mt. Vernon Hosp. Middlx.; Leukaemia Research Fund Fell. & Hon. Sen. Regist. Addenbrooke's NHS Trust Camb.; Sen. Regist. (Haemat.) Addenbrooke's NHS Trust Camb.

MAHENDRA-YOGAM, Mr Palapillai Granbrook Surgery, 465 Granbrook Road, Gants Hill, Ilford IG2 6EW Tel: 020 8554 7111 Fax: 020 8491 6374; 48 Buntingbridge Road, Ilford IG2 7LR Tel: 020 8518 5730 — MB BS 1972 Ceylon; FRCS Ed. 1982. (Ceylon)

MAHENDRAN, Bhanu 57 Redcliffe Gardens, London SW10 9JJ Tel: 020 7370 2120 Fax: 020 7373 9293 — MB BS Sri Lanka 1978; FRCA 1982; T(Anaesth) 1991. Indep. Cons. Anaesth. Lond.; Hon. Cons. Anaesth. St. Luke's Hosp. for Clergy Lond. Prev: Cons. Anaesth. (long-term locum) St. Thos. Hosp. Lond.; Sen. Regist. (Anaesth.) Guy's Hosp. Lond.; Clin. & Research Fell. (Anaesth.) Univ. Hosp., Univ. W.. Ontario, Canada.

MAHENDRAN, Dhushyanthan 58 Haycroft Drive, Matson, Gloucester GL4 6XX — MB ChB 1986 Manch.; BSc (Hons.) Manch. 1983, MB ChB 1986.

MAHENDRAN, Muttucumarasamy Stantonbury Health Centre, Purbeck, Stantonbury, Milton Keynes MK14 6BL Tel: 01908 316262 Fax: 01908 221432; 55 Gartcombe, Great Holm, Milton Keynes MK8 9EA Tel: 01908 569737 Email: m.mahendran@btinternet.com — MB BS 1978 Ceylon; MRCP 1982 (UK); FRCP 1998 (Lond.); MRCGP 1990. p/t Hosp. Pract. (Cardiol.) Milton Keynes Gen. Hosp.; CHD Lead Clinician, Milton Keynes PCT, Milton Keynes. Socs: Roy. Coll. of Phys.s, Lond. (standing Comm.). Prev: Regist., Gen. Med., Milton Keynes Dist. Gen. Hosp., Milton Keynes, 1985-1987.

MAHENDRAN, Rajini 12 The Avenue, Wembley HA9 9QJ — MB BS 1991 Lond.

MAHENDRAN, Saverimuttu Michael Royal Lancaster Infirmary, Ashton Road, Lancaster LA1 4RP; 11 Cathedral Drive, Heaton with Oxcliffe, Morecambe LA3 3RE — MB BS 1979 Colombo; MRCOG 1986. Staff Grade Doctor (O & G) Roy. Lancaster Infirm.

MAHENDRAN, Mr Sinnadurai Shrewsbury Road Health Centre, Shrewsbury Road, London E7 8QP Tel: 020 8586 5111 Fax: 020 8586 5046; 44 Highland Gardens, Ilford 1G1 3LD Tel: 020 8554 1689 Email: doemahen@aol.com — MB BS Ceylon 1970; FRCS Ed. 1982. (University of Leylon) GP Princip. City & E. Lond. H/A; Minor Surg. Facilitator Endoscopist. Prev: Chairm. - Newham Med. Soc.

MAHENDRARAJAH, A Pickhurst Surgery, 56 Pickhurst Lane, Bromley BR2 7JF Tel: 020 8462 2880 Fax: 020 8462 9581.

MAHER, Bridget 31 Garden Lane, Liverpool L9 9DZ — MB ChB 1994 Liverp.; MRCP 1997. (Liverp.) Lect. (Clin. Pharmacol.) Hon. Specialist Regist. Dept. Pharmacol. & Therap. Univ. Liverp. Prev: SHO (Gen. Med.) N.. Gen. Hosp. Sheff.; SHO (Gen. Med.) Roy. Liverp. Univ. Hosp.; Ho. Off. Roy. Liverp. Univ. Hosp.

MAHER, Dermot Paul Global Tuberculosis Programme, World Health Organisation, CH-1211 Geneva 27, Switzerland Tel: 00 41 22 7912626 Fax: 00 41 22 7914199 Email: maherd@who.ch; 16 Roby Road, Huyton, Liverpool L36 4HE Tel: 0151 489 3773 — BM BCh 1983 Oxf.; MA Camb. 1991, BA (Hons.) 1980; MRCS Eng. LRCP Lond. 1983; MRCP (UK) 1988; MRCGP 1988; DTM & H Liverp. 1991; DRCOG 1987; DCH RCP Lond. 1987. (Univ. Camb., Univ. Oxf. Sch. of Clin. Med.) Med. Off. Global Tuberc. Progr. WHO, Geneva; Hon. Fell. Liverp. Sch. Trop. Med. Socs: Fell. Roy. Soc. Trop. Med. & Hyg.; BMA; Med. Assn. Malawi. Prev: Med. Specialist Govt. Malawi & Clin. Lect. (Med.) Univ. Malawi.

MAHER, Professor Eamonn Richard Division of Medical and Molecular Genetics, Department of Paediatrics & Child Health, Birmingham Women's Hospital, Birmingham B15 2TG Tel: 0121 627 2642 Fax: 0121 627 2618 Email: ermaher@hgmp.mrc.ac.uk — MB ChB 1980 Manch.; MB ChB (Hons.) Manch. 1980; BSc (1st cl. Hons. Physiol.) Manch. 1977, MD 1988; FRCP Lond. 1996; MRCP (UK) 1983; FRCP 1996. (Manchester) Prof. & Hon. Cons. Med. Genetics Univ. Birm. & W. Midl. Regional Genetics Serv.; Edr. Jl. of Med. Genetics. Prev: Lect. & Cons. Med. Genetics Univ. Camb. & E. Anglian Regional Genetics Serv.; Clin. Lect. & Sen. Regist. (Med. Genetics) Univ. Camb.; Regist. (Med.) Univ. Coll. & Whittington Hosps. Lond.

MAHER, Elizabeth Ann (retired) Grovebury House, The St, Horringer, Bury St Edmunds IP29 5SN Tel: 01284 735330 — MB ChB 1965 Birm.; FFA RCS Eng. 1970; DA Eng. 1968. Prev: Cons. Anaesth. W. Suff. Hosps. Trust, Bury St Edmunds.

MAHER, Elizabeth Jane Mount Vernon Cancer Treatment, Northwood HA6 2RN Tel: 01923 844681 Fax: 01923 844172; 25 Silver Crescent, London W4 5SF Tel: 020 8747 3122 — MB BS 1976 Lond.; FRCR 1982; FRCP (UK) 1997, M 1979; FRCP Ed 1998. Cons. Clin. Oncol. Mt. Vernon Centre for Cancer Treatm. N.wood; Cons. Hillingdon & Wexham Pk. Hosps.; Sen. Clin. Lect. Univ. Coll.& Middlx. Med. Sch.; Chief Med. Off. Macmillan Cancer Relief 1998 (p/t). Socs: Roy. Soc. Med. (Counc. Mem. Div. Oncol.). Prev: Sen. Regist. Middlx. & Roy. Marsden Hosps. Lond.; Clin. Fell. Massachussetts Gen. Hosp. & Harvard Med. Sch., USA.

MAHER, Henry Austin 28 Mount Avenue, Westcliff on Sea SS0 8PT Tel: 01702 712121 — MB ChB 1952 St. And.; DA Eng. 1958. (St. And.) Prev: Cas. Off. Roy. Infirm. Dundee; Ho. Surg. Matern. Hosp. Hull; Anaesth. Regist. Mansfield Gen. Hosp.

***MAHER, Joanna** Shanboe, Claremont Av, Bristol BS7 8JD — MB ChB 1997 Sheff.

MAHER, John 28 Sandycombe Road, Richmond TW9 2DY — MB BCh BAO 1987 Dub.; BA (Med.) Dub. 1984; MRCP (UK) 1990;

MRCPI 1989. (Univ. Coll. Dub.) Research Fell. (Haemat.) Roy. Postgrad. Med. Sch. Lond.

MAHER, Mary McLeod Cameron Veric (retired) Flat 4B, South Lodge Court, Race Course Road, Ayr KA7 2TA — MB ChB Glas. 1937.

MAHER, Mathew Gerard (retired) 20 Ampton Road, Edgbaston, Birmingham B15 2UJ Tel: 0121 454 3388 — MB BCh BAO NUI 1948.

MAHER, Oxana Aesthetics Department, Dewsbury and District Hospital, Halifax Road, Dewsbury WF13 4HS — MB ChB 1973 Manch.; FFARCS Eng. 1984. Cons. Anaesth. Dewsbury Dist. Hosp. W. Yorks.

MAHER, Sarah Patricia The Westgate Medical Centre, Braddon Close, Morecambe LA4 4UZ Tel: 01524 832888 Fax: 01524 832722 — MB ChB 1988 Manch.; MRCGP 1993. Gen. Practitioner, The W.gate Med. Pract. Morecambe; Sessional Doctor Family Plann., Morecombe Bay Primary Care Trust.

MAHER, Stephen John 16 Roby Road, Huyton, Liverpool L36 4HE — BChir 1978 Camb.

MAHER, Thomas Vincent 55 Priestnall Road, Stockport SK4 3DL Tel: 0161 432 1889 — MB BCh BAO 1952 NUI; LM Coombe 1954.

*****MAHER, Toby Michael** Landabethick, Blisland, Bodmin PL30 4QZ — BM 1998 Soton.; BM Soton 1998.

*****MAHERU, Arvind Kaur** 14 Sherrans Dell, Wolverhampton WV4 6RW — MB BS 1996 Lond.

MAHESAN, Glory Suguna 153 Aurelia Road, Croydon CR0 3BF — MB BS 1979 Sri Lanka; LRCP LRCS Ed. LRCPS Glas. 1983.

MAHESH, Dr 2 Copperfield Way, Chislehurst BR7 6RY Tel: 020 8467 9766; (Surgery), 31-32 Telemann Square, Kidbrooke, London SE3 9YR Tel: 020 8586 4167 — MB BS 1966 Banaras Hindu; DCH Eng. 1970. (Inst. Med. Scs. Varanasi)

MAHESH BABU, Raghavan Nair St Johns Hospital, Wood St., Chelmsford CM2 9BG Tel: 01245 440761 Fax: 01245 513313; 40 Main Road, Danbury, Chelmsford CM3 4NQ — MB BS Kerala 1982; MRCP (UK) 1987; DCH RCP Lond. 1987; FRCPCH 1988. Cons. Paediat. St John's Hosp. Chelmsford. Socs: BMA & Roy. Coll. Paediat. & Child Health. Prev: Sen. Regist. Univ. Hosp. Wales Cardiff; Regist. (Paediat.) Qu Charlottes Hosp. Lond. & Jas. Paget Hosp. Gt. Yarmouth.

MAHESHWARAN, Satkurunathan 104 Dora Road, Wimbledon Park, London SW19 7HJ Tel: 020 8946 7890 — MRCS Eng. LRCP Lond. 1986; MRCP (UK) 1989; FRCR 1992. Cons. Diagn. Radiol. Mayday Univ. Hosp. Thornton Heath Surrey. Prev: Sen. Regist. (Diag. Radiol.) W. Midl. Train. Scheme; Trainee Regist. (Radiol.) W. Midl. Train. Scheme; SHO (Med.) Roy. Shrewsbury Hosp.

MAHESHWARAN, Mr Shunmuga Sundaramarthandan 25 Roedean Drive, Eaglescliffe, Stockton-on-Tees TS16 9HT — MB BS 1978 Karnatak; MChOrth Liverp. 1989; FRCS Ed. 1984. Cons. Orthop. Socs: Fell. BOA; Brit. Soc. Surg. Hand; Brit. Soc. Surg. Knee.

MAHESHWER, Mr Conjeevaram Bhasker Queen Elizabeth Hospital, Gayton Road, King's Lynn PE30 4ET; 5 Ox Close, North Bretton, Peterborough PE3 8JR — MB BS 1986 Madras; MCh Orthop. Liverp. 1994; FRCSI 1990. Prev: Regist. (Orthop.) Fazakerley Hosp. Liverp.; Regist. (Orthop.) P'boro. Dist. Hosp.

MAHESON, Aria Copsewood Medical Centre, 95 Momus Boulevard, Coventry CV2 5NB Tel: 024 7645 7497 Fax: 024 7663 6395; 9A Fairlands Park, Coventry CV4 7DS — MB BS 1961 Ceylon.

MAHESON, Mr Marcellino Valeriano Surendran Department of Trauma &Orthopaedics, University Hospital of Wales, Heath Park, Cardiff CF14 4XW Tel: 029 2074 3254 Fax: 029 2074 5399 — MB ChB 1983 Sheff.; FRCS Eng. 1988; FRCS Ed. 1988; FRCS (Orth.) 1992. Cons. Orthopedist & Trauma Surg. Univ. Hosp. of Wales Cardiff. Socs: Brit. Orth. Assn.; Brit. Hip Soc. & Europ. Hip Soc. Prev: Sen. Regist. (Orthop. & Trauma) Cardiff Teachg. Hosps. S. Glam.; Regist. Rotat. (Surg.) Cardiff Teachg. Hosps.; SHO (Surg.) Qu.'s Med. Centre Univ. Hosp. Nottm.

MAHESON, Mr Vallipuram Subramaniam (retired) Acapulco, Parker St., Newark NG24 1RB Tel: 01636 605087 Fax: 01636 605087 — MB BS 1955 Ceylon; FRCS Eng. 1963; FRCS Ed. 1963. Cons. Surg. Newark & Grantham Hosps. Prev: Assoc. Specialist Newark Hosp.

MAHESWARAN, Catherine Margaret Sheffield Community NHS Trust, Child Heath Services, 55 Osbourne Road, Sheffield S11 9BF Tel: 0114 271 6636; 25 Newfield Street, Dore, Sheffield S17 3DB Tel: 0114 236 5623 — MB ChB 1982 Sheff.; MRCP (Paediat.) (UK) 1987. (Sheffield) Staff Grade (Comm. Paediat.) Sheff. Comm. NHS Trust (P/T). Socs: RCPCH.

MAHESWARAN, Muttuvelu Medical Examination Centre, 30 Drysdale St., London N1 6LT Tel: 020 7749 7085 Fax: 020 7729 8264; 84 Glebelands Avenue, Newbury Park, Ilford IG2 7DL Tel: 020 8220 8079 Fax: 020 8491 3535 — MB BS Ceylon 1962; DPH Liverp. 1974. (Univ. Ceylon) Med. Examr. Hoxton. Prev: SCMO S. Essex HA; Regist. (Psychiat.) ColdE. Hosp. Soton.; Dist. Med. Off. Francistown, Botswana.

MAHESWARAN, Ravindra University of Sheffield, Section of Public Health, ScHARR Uni. Sheffield, Regent Court, 39 Regent St., Sheffield S1 4DA Tel: 0114 222 0681 Fax: 0114 222 0791 Email: r.maheswaran@ic.ac.uk; 25 Newfield Lane, Sheffield S17 3DB Tel: S17 3DB — MB ChB 1981 Sheff.; MD Sheff. 1990; MRCP (UK) 1984; MFPHM 1996. (Sheff.) Sen. Clin. Lect. (Pub. Health Med.) Uni. Sheff. Sheff. Prev: Sen. Regist. (Pub. Health Med.) W. Sussex Health Commiss., Clin. Lect. (Epidemiol & Pub. Health Med.) Imper. Coll. Sch. Med.; Regist. Rotat. (Med.) St. Geo. Hosp.; Research Regist. Dudley Rd. Hosp. Birm.

MAHESWARAN, S The Surgery, 1 Gillmans Road, Orpington BR5 4LA Tel: 01689 822022 Fax: 01689 897929.

MAHESWARAN, Vijayasundari 36 Greenhill Road, Birmingham B13 9SR — MB ChB 1985 Sheff.

MAHESWARAN, Wyramuttoo Thangarajah 7 Audrey Gardens, Wembley HA0 3TF Tel: 020 8904 1789; 276 Cricklewood Lane, Cricklewood, London NW2 2PU Tel: 020 8452 8822 — MB BS 1974 Sri Lanka; MRCOG 1984.

MAHFOUZ, Mona 85 Park View, Moulton, Northampton NN3 7UZ — MB ChB 1983 Sheff.

MAHFUTH, Zuleikha Said 1 Heather Bank, Eltham, London SE9 1NN Tel: 020 8856 6181 — MB BCh 1967 Cairo.

MAHIDA, Professor Yashwant Ranchhodsinh Division of Gastroenterology, University Hospital, Queen's Medical Centre, Nottingham NG7 2UH — MB ChB 1980 Liverp.; MD Liverp. 1990; FRCP Lond. 1996; MRCS Eng. LRCP Lond. 1980; MRCP (UK) 1984. (Univ. Liverp.) Prof. in Med. Qu. Med. Centre Nottm. Socs: Brit. Soc. Gastroenterol.; Med. Res. Soc.; Amer. Gastroenterol. Assn. Prev: Reader Qu. Med. Centre Nottm.; Sen. Lect. Qu. Med. Centre Nottm.; Research Fell. Mass. Gen. Hosp. Boston, USA.

MAHINDRAKAR, Mr Naganath Hanamanthrao (cons. rooms) Beaumont Hospital, Old Hall Clough, Chorley New Road. Lostock, Bolton BL6 4LA; 208 Chorley New Road, Bolton BL1 5AA Tel: 01204 840131 — MB BS 1956 Bombay; FRCS (Orl.) Eng. 1967; FRCS Ed. 1961; DLO Eng. 1961. (Seth G.S. Med. Coll. Bombay) Cons. ENT Surg. Bolton HA. Socs: Fell. Manch. Med. Soc.; N. Eng. Otolaryng. Soc. Prev: Sen. Regist. Manch. Roy. Infirm.; Lect. (Otolaryng.) Univ. Manch.

MAHIR, Mr Mahir Shakir Department of Surgery, Newham General Hospital, Glen Road, Plaistow, London E13 8SL Tel: 020 7476 4000 Fax: 020 7363 8102 — MB ChB 1977 Baghdad; PhD Lond. 1989; FRCS Ed. 1986. Cons. Gen. Surg. Newham Gen. Hosp. Lond. Socs: Fell. Roy. Soc. Med.; Surg. Research Soc. Prev: Regist. (Surg.) Blackburn Roy. Infirm.; Regist. (Surg.) Roy. Marsden Hosp. Lond, Roy. Hants. Co. Hosp. & St. Richards Hosp. Chichester.

*****MAHIR, Shah Abdulla** 53 Armitage Road, London NW11 8QT — MB BS 1998 Lond.

MAHLATI, Sylvester Samuel Gilimamba 744 Julian Crossley Court, William Goodenough House, Mecklenburgh Square, London WC1N 2AN — MB ChB 1982 Natal.

MAHLER, Professor Robert Frederick Royal College of Physicians, Regent's Park, London NW1 4LE Tel: 020 7935 1174 Fax: 020 7487 5218; 14 Manley Street, London NW1 8LT Tel: 020 7586 1198 — MB ChB Ed. 1947; BSc Ed. 1946; FRCP Lond. 1968; FRCP Ed. 1968. (Univ. Ed.) Edr. Emerit. Jl. Roy. Coll. Phys. Socs: Assn. Phys. & Med. Research Soc.; Brit. Diabetic Assn. Prev: Cons. Phys. N.wick Pk. Hosp. Harrow.; Prof. Med. & Hon. Cons. Phys. Welsh Nat. Sch. Med. & United Cardiff Hosps.; Reader (Experim. Med.) Guy's Hosp.

MAHMANDI, Nasir Ahmed Khan (retired) 7 Ryton Way, Stirchley, Telford TF3 1EP Tel: 01952 419218 — MB BS 1956

MAHMOOD

Panjab; TDD 1960; DETC (PRAUGE) 1970; DTCD Wales 1965; DTM & H Liverp. 1964; Cert. Community Paediat. Warwick 1986. SCMO Shropsh. DHA. Prev: Cons. TB Chest Dis. Kaduna, Nigeria.

MAHMOOD, Abid The Tannahill Centre, 76 Blackstown Road, Paisley PA3 1NT Tel: 0141 889 7631 Fax: 0141 889 6819; The Albany Mansions, 347 Renfrew St, Glasgow G3 6UW — MB ChB 1984 Glas.; DCH RCPS Glas. 1989.

MAHMOOD, Ahmad St Michael's Hospital, St Michael's Road, Warwick CV34 5QW Tel: 01926 406732 Fax: 01926 406702 Email: ahmadm47@hotmail.com — MB BS 1977 Punjab; MA Keele 1995; MRCPsych 1985; DPM Eng. 1983. Cons. Psychiat. of Old Age St Michaels Hosp. Warwick & Dir. of Memory Clinic, S. Warks. Socs: Med. Protec. Soc. Prev: Sen. Regist. Rotat. W. Midl.

MAHMOOD, Arshad Maindiff Court Hospital, Abergavenny NP7 8NF — MB BS 1982 Quaid-i-Azam.

MAHMOOD, Asif 55 Sundridge Drive, Chatham ME5 8HT — MB BS 1981 Punjab.

***MAHMOOD, Asif** 20 Swanage Road, Birmingham B10 9ES — MB ChB 1995 Birm.; ChB Birm. 1995.

***MAHMOOD, Asif** 64 Courtenay Road, Woking GU21 5HQ — MB ChB 1995 Leic.

MAHMOOD, Azhar (retired) 11 Roseworth Avenue, Gosforth, Newcastle upon Tyne NE3 1NB Tel: 0191 285 7463 — MB BS 1959 Punjab, Pakistan; PhD Lond. 1965; MRCP Ed. 1965; FRCPath 1984, M 1971; DTM & H RCP Lond. 1962. Prev: Cons. Haemat. Dist. Laborat. Gen. Hosp. S. Shields.

MAHMOOD, Babur 38 Salters Close, Rickmansworth WD3 1HH — BM 1995 Soton.

MAHMOOD, Dhia Ahmed Royal Preston Hospital, Sharoe Green Lane, Fulwood, Preston PR2 9HT; 7 Brookview, Fulwood, Preston PR2 8FG — MB ChB 1977 Basrah, Iraq; PhD Lond. 1988, MSc 1982; MRCPI 1992. Cons. Paediat. Roy. Preston Hosp. Prev: Sen. Regist. Hillingdon Hosp. Uxbridge; Regist. Roy. Preston Hosp.

MAHMOOD, Khalid The Surgery, 341 Kilburn High Road, London NW6 7QB Tel: 020 7624 4414 Fax: 020 7328 5158 — MB BS 1964 Punjab; MB BS Punjab (Pakistan) 1964; FRCPI 1984; FRCPath 1986, M 1975; FFPath RCPI 1984. (Nishter Med. Coll. Multan) Socs: Brit. Soc. Clin. Cytol.; BMA & Internat. Acad. Path. (Brit. Div.). Prev: Cons. Histopath NE Thames RHA Lond.; Chief Resid. Path. Univ. Pittsburgh USA; Assoc. Prof. King Saud Univ. Riyadh.

MAHMOOD, Khalid 17 Manor Way, Todwick, Sheffield S26 1HR Tel: 01909 770886 Fax: 0114 242 6553; 160 Firth Park Road, Sheffield S5 6WP Tel: 0114 242 6553 Fax: 0114 242 6553 — MB BS 1965 Peshawar; DA RCSI 1969; MRCGP 1997. Hosp. Pract. (Med. for Elderly) N. Gen. Hosp. Sheff. Socs: Med. Protec. Soc.; BMA; ODA.

MAHMOOD, Mazhar 232 Hampton Road, Ilford IG1 1PP — MB ChB 1991 Glas.; DFFP Glas. 1996. (Glas.) GP Illford. Socs: MDU.

MAHMOOD, Mohammad White's Terrace Surgery, 27 White's Terrace, Bradford BD8 7LN Tel: 01274 544915 Fax: 01274 821999; 19 Northcroft Rise, Bradford BD8 0BW — MB BS 1964 Dacca.

MAHMOOD, Mr Mohammed Zafar 6 Firshill Avenue, Sheffield S4 7AA — MB BS 1974 Patna; FRCSI 1990; FRCS Ed. 1990.

MAHMOOD, Mr Nasir c/o Mr Waheed Ahmed, 40 Carwood, Halebarn, Altrincham WA15 0EW — MB BS 1983 Punjab; FRCSI 1991.

MAHMOOD, Nilofer Cardiothoracic Directorate, Derriford Hospital, Derriford Road, Plymouth PL6 8DH; 127 Midsummer Avenue, Hounslow W., Hounslow TW4 5AZ — MB BS 1982 Karachi; MRCP (UK) 1987; FRCA. 1992. Cons. (Cardiothoracic Anaesth.). Socs: Fell. Assn. Anaesth. GB & Irel.; Fell. RSM; Assn. Cardiothoracic Anaesth.

MAHMOOD, Rafeek Hosny Broadleaves, Meols Drive, West Kirby, Wirral L48 5DS Tel: 0151 632 5467 — MB BCh 1969 Ain Shams; FRCPsych 1991, M 1976; DPM Eng. 1975; DPM RCPSI 1975. (Ain Shams Cairo) Cons. (Psychiat. & Psychother.) Clatterbridge Hosp. Bebington; Specialist Tutor (Psychother.) Univ. Liverp.; Mem. W. Midl. Inst. Psychother.

***MAHMOOD, Sajjad** 22 Byron Street, Bradford BD3 0AD — BChir 1997 Camb.

MAHMOOD, Shahid Thomas House, 12A Eastbridge Road, Dymchurch, Romney Marsh TN29 0PF Tel: 01708 873156 — MB BS 1964 Punjab; MB BS Punjab (Pakistan) 1964.

MAHMOOD, Sheikh Mosehuddin 223 Old Brompton Road, Earl's Court, London SW5 0EA Tel: 020 7373 4102; 76 Scott House, Woolmer Road, London N18 2JJ — MB BS 1960 Dacca; LM 1967.

MAHMOOD, Tahir Ahmed Department of Obstetrics & Gynaecology, Forth Park Hospital, Kirkcaldy KY2 5RA Tel: 01592 643355 Fax: 01592 648171; Tel: 01592 269017 — MB BS Punjab 1978; BSc Punjab 1978; MD Aberd. 1990; FRCPI 1994, M 1993; MFFP 1993; FRCOG 2000; DObst RCPI 1982. (King Edwd. Med. Coll. Lahore) Cons. O & G Forth Pk. Hosp. Kirkcaldy; Clin. Dir. Wom. & Childrs. Directorate, Fife Acute NHS Hosps. Trust; Hon. Sen. Lect. (Biol. Scis.) St. And. Univ.; Clin. Sen. Lect. (Obst & Gyn.) Univ Edin.; Clin. Sen. Lect. Univ. Aberd. Socs: Obst. & Gyn. & Neonat. Med. Soc. (Ex-Hon. Sec. Fife Div.); Chairm. N.. E. Scotl. Obst. & Gyn. Soc.; Coun. Memebr Scott. BMA. Prev: Sen. Regist. & Clin. Lect. Aberd. Matern. Hosp.; Regist. Forth Pk. Matern. Hosp. Kircaldy; Regist. Glas. Roy. Matern. Hosp. & Bellshill Matern. Hosp.

MAHMOOD, Tariq 68 Thornbury Drive, Bradford BD3 8JE Tel: 01274 667391 — MB BS 1984 Lond.; BSc Punjab 1982; LMSSA Lond. 1988; MRCPI 1991; FRCP Irel. 1996; Cert. Av. Med. 1987. Locum Cons. Phys. / Gastroenterol. Worthing Hosp. Socs: Brit. Soc. Gastroenterol. Prev: Cons. Phys. (Gastroenterol. & Hepat.) GNP Hosp., Jeddah; Sen. Regist. (Med. & Gastroenterol.) SETME Guy's Hosp. Lond. for Jeddah; Regist. & SHO (Gen. Med.) Roy. Oldham Hosp.

MAHMOOD, Tariq 45 Beresford Road, Longsight, Manchester M13 0GT — MB ChB 1987 Dundee.

***MAHMOOD, Tariq** 137 Kitson Hill Road, Mirfield WF14 9EG — MB ChB 1995 Leeds.

MAHMOOD, Yahya 4 Hillfield Road, Birmingham B11 3LJ — MB ChB 1994 Leic.

MAHMOOD, Zeenath Ziama 11 Meliden Way, Stoke-on-Trent ST4 5DZ — MB ChB 1991 Aberd.

MAHMOUD, Ahmed Mohamed Ahmed 8 Riverbank Close, Nantwich CW5 5YF — MB BCh 1987 Cairo.

MAHMOUD, Mouneer Abdel-Rahman 21 Springvale Avenue, Bournemouth BH7 7EP; 21 Springvale Avenue, Littledown, Bournemouth BH7 7EP — MB BCh 1977 Cairo; MB BCh Cairo, Egypt 1977; FFA RCSI 1989.

MAHMOUD, Mr Nabil Abdel Hafez Fitzwilliam Hospital, Milton Way, South Bretton, Peterborough PE3 9AQ Fax: 01733 261119 Email: nam4ent@hotmail.com; Email: nobel.man@nam34.freeserve.co.uk — MB BCh 1957 Cairo; FRCS Eng. 1975; FRCS Ed. 1971; LMSSA Lond. 1975. (KASR.AL.AINI (Cairo)) Cons. ENT Surg. Fitzwilliam Hosp. S. Bretton, PeterBoro. Socs: Brit. Assn. Otol.; Roy. Soc. Med. Prev: Sen. Regist. (ENT) W.m. Hosp. Lond.; Regist. (ENT) Chester Roy. Infirm.; Cons. ENT Surg. Edith Cavell Hosp. P'boro.

MAHMOUD, Omar Abdul Rahman Flat D4, 72 St Vincent Terrace, Glasgow G3 8XA — MB ChB 1974 Mosul; LRCP LRCS Ed. LRCP Glas. 1979.

MAHMOUD, Omar Mohamed Mohamed 207 London Road, Twickenham TW1 1EJ Tel: 020 8892 3912 — MB BCh 1962 Cairo; MRCS Eng. LRCP Lond. 1977; FFA RCS Eng. 1973; Dip. Med. Cairo 1967; DA Cairo 1965. (Cairo) Cons. Anaesth. W. Middlx. Hosp. Isleworth. Prev: Sen. Regist. & Regist. W. Middlx. Hosp.; Cons. Anaesth. Nkana Hosp. Kitwe, Zambia.

MAHMOUDI, Mohammed 24 Craford Rise, Flat 8, Maidenhead SL6 7LS — MB BS 1996 Lond.; BSc 1993.

***MAHMUD, Kabir** Flat C, 64 Warren St., London W1T 5NZ — LMSSA 1997 Lond.

MAHMUD, Shamsul Zamri Anaesthetic Department, Medway Hospital, Windmill Road, Gillingham ME7 5NY — MB BCh 1994 Wales.

MAHMUD, Sultan The New Trap Surgery, 5 Dean Street, Aberdare CF44 7BN Tel: 01685 872045 Fax: 01685 870625; Ynyswendraeth Farm, Penderyn Aberdare, Mid Glam. Ret., Aberdare CF44 OYX Tel: 01685 810859 — MB BS 1964 Peshawar. (Khyber Med. Coll.)

MAHMUD, Talac 10 Elvaston Place, South Kensington, London SW7 5QG; 292 Munster Road, Fulham, London SW6 6BQ Tel: 020 7385 5728 Email: talaco1@hotmail.com — MB BS 1996 Lond.; MB BS Lond. 1995; BSc Lond. 1992. (King's Coll. Lond.) GP Regist. Socs: MDU. Prev: Med. SHO Maryday Hosp.; Ho. Off. Med. Bromley Hosp.; A & E Bromley Hosp.

MAHOMED, Essak Kassim 21 Lynette Avenue, London SW4 9HE Tel: 020 8673 2052 Fax: 020 8675 1378 — LRCPI & LM, LRCSI &

LM 1964. (RCSI) Private GP. Prev: Regist. (Paediat.) Chelsea & Kensington Gp. Hosps; Ho. Off. (Paediat.) Oldham & Dist. Gen. Hosp.; Ho. Surg. & Ho. Phys. (Paediat.) Harari Hosp. Salisbury & Harare Hosp.Zimbabwe.

MAHOMED, Mr Ishtiyak 2 The Boundary, The Wickets, Allerton Road, Bradford BD8 0BQ — MB BCh 1986 Witwatersrand; FRCS Ed. 1993.

MAHOMED KESHAVJEE, Shaukatalli Noor Kingston & District Community Mental Health Trust, Barnes Hospital, South Wordle Way, Barnes, London SW14 8SU Tel: 020 8878 4981; 7 Clydesdale Gardens, Richmond TW10 5EG Tel: 020 8876 9312 Fax: 020 8241 1321 — LRCPI & LM, LRCSI & LM 1968; MRCPsych 1978; DPM Eng. 1978. (RCSI) Cons. Psychiat. Barnes Hosp. Prev: Abraham Conley Unit Chertsey Surrey#; Cons. Psychiat. Lister Hosp. Stevenage; Sen. Regist. Qu. Mary's Hosp. Roehampton & Netherne Hosp. Coulsdon.

MAHON, Andrew Highfield, Horeb Road, Five Roads, Llanelli SA15 5YY — MB BCh 1993 Wales.

***MAHON, Caroline Margaret** Kingsley, 50 Sussex Place, Slough SL1 1NR — MB BS 1998 Lond.; MB BS Lond 1998.

MAHON, Christine Helen — MB ChB 1981 Liverp.; DRCOG 1984. Private Practitioner. Prev: GP Liverp.; Med. Adviser Med. Serv.s/Benefits Agency) Bootle.

MAHON, Christopher Charles William 256 Turney Road, London SE21 7JP — MB ChB 1991 Birm.; MB ChB (Hons.) Birm. 1991; BSc (Hons.) Birm. 1988; FRCS Eng 1995.

MAHON, David 35 Coquet Avenue, Bramley, Rotherham S66 1TU — MB ChB 1993 Sheff.

MAHON, Irene Marie Brechin Health Centre, Infirmary Street, Brechin DD9 7AY Tel: 01356 624411 Fax: 01356 623259 — MB ChB 1988 Dundee; MRCGP 1992.

MAHON, Jarlath Patrick 15 Beauty Bank, Cradley Heath, Cradley Heath B64 7HY — MB BCh BAO 1982 NUI.

MAHON, Jasper Nicholas Nightingale Practice, 10 Kenninghall Road, Clapton, London E5 8BY Tel: 020 8985 8388 Fax: 020 8986 6004 — MB BS 1991 Lond.

MAHON, Simon Victor Cardiothoracic Unit, Morriston Hospital NHS Trust, Morriston, Swansea SA6 6NL Tel: 01792 703491 Fax: 01792 704141 Email: simon.mahon@mornhst-tr.wales.nhs.uk; Pen y Fedwr, Whitemill, Carmarthen SA32 7HG — MB ChB 1989 Liverp.; FRCA 1994. Cons. Cardiothoracic Anaesth. Morriston Hosp. NHS Trust, Swansea. Socs: Assn. Cardiothoracic Anaesth.; Intens. Care Soc.; Anaesth. Res. Soc. Prev: Clin. Lect. (Cardiothoracic Anaesth.) Cardiothoracic Centre Liverp.

MAHON-DALY, Linda Margareta Elisabeth Shrub End Road Surgery, 122 Shrub End Road, Colchester CO3 4RY Tel: 01206 573605 Fax: 01206 200219; Park House, Bounstead Road, Colchester CO2 0DF — MB BS 1982 Lond.; MRCGP 1987.

MAHONEY, Allan 36 Glade Road, Marlow SL7 1DY — MB BS 1982 Lond.

MAHONEY, Celia Frances Kathleen (retired) 24 Woodcrest, Wilpshire, Blackburn BB1 9PR — MB BCh 1960 Wales; DCH Eng. 1963. Prev: Clin. Asst. (Paediat.) Hyndburn & Ribble Valley HA.

MAHONEY, Air Commodore Maurice, Air Commodore RAF Med. Br. (retired) Strathnaver Cottage, Dorchester Road, Cerne Abbas, Dorchester DT2 7JS Tel: 01300 341171 — MB ChB 1960 Glas.; FRCS Glas. 1973. Prev: Cons. Surg. MoD (Air).

MAHONEY, Michael Peter (retired) West Winds, 24 Woodcrest, Wilpshire, Blackburn BB1 9PR Tel: 0125249777 — MB BCh 1958 Wales; FRCP Lond. 1977; MRCP Lond. 1963. Prev: Phys. Roy. Infirm. Blackburn.

MAHONEY, Peter Francis Leonard Cheshire Centre, 4 Taviton Street, London WC1H 0BT — MB BS 1985 Newc.; FFA RCSI 1994; FRCA 1994; DMCC Soc. Apoth. Lond. 1996; Dip. IMC RCS Ed. 1992; DA (UK) 1989; T (Anaesth.) 1998. (Newc. u. Tyne) Hon. Sen. Lect., Leonard Chesh. Dept of conflict Recovery. Prev: Sen. Regist. (Anaesth.) Trent Region; Regist. Helicopter Emerg. Med. Servs. Lond.; Regist. (Anaesth.) N.. Region.

MAHONEY, Sarah Beckington, 12 Moor Farm Lane, Hereford HR4 0NT — MB ChB 1997 Liverp.

MAHONY, John Barton Surgery, Barton, Horn Lane, Plymouth PL9 9BR Tel: 01752 407129 Fax: 01752 482620; Picket Rook, Renney Road, Heybrook Bay, Plymouth PL9 0BG Tel: 01752 862595 — MB ChB 1980 Bristol; MRCGP 1986.

MAHONY, John Desmond Howard (retired) 50 Marine Parade, Tankerton, Whitstable CT5 2BD — MD Belf. 1961, MB BCh BAO 1945; FRCP Glas. 1976, M 1967; MMSA Lond. 1960; DObst RCOG 1948; DCH RFPS Glas. 1961. Cons. (Venereol.) Maidstone Hosp. Prev: Cons. (Venereol.) Roy. Vict. Hosp. Belf., E. Kent Gp. & King's Coll. Hosp.

MAHOOD, Charles Vernon Martin (retired) Lulworth, 49 Park Grove, Westbury-on-Trym, Bristol BS9 4LG Tel: 0117 962 0678 — LRCPI & LM, LRCSI & LM 1944; LM Rotunda 1945.

MAHOOD, John Meredith Waydale Farm House, Little Brington, Northampton NN7 4HS — MB BChir 1975 Camb.; MA, MB Camb. 1975, BChir 1974; FRCP 1996 UK. (St. Mary's) Cons. Dermat. N.ampton & Kettering DHAs. Prev: Sen. Regist. (Dermat.) Roy. Hallamsh. Hosp. Sheff.

MAHOOD, Kathleen Mary 21 Belfast Road, Carrickfergus BT38 8BY Tel: 01960 363712 — MB BCh BAO 1995 Belf. (Queens University - Belfast)

MAHRAN, Raouf Mohamed Ahmed Block D, Queen's Hospital, 66A Queen's Road, Croydon CR9 2PQ — MB BCh 1974 Mansoura; LRCP LRCS Ed. LRCPS Glas. 1985.

MAHROOF, Haja Mohideen 57 Bickersteth Road, London SW17 9SH — MB BS 1967 Ceylon.

MAHROOF, Mohamed Razeen Westering House, Milton Lilbourne, Pewsey SN9 5LQ Tel: 0411 627962 Email: dr_raz@hotmail.com — BM 1998 Soton.; BM Soton 1998. (Univ. of Soton.) SHO (Med.) Basildon Hosp. Socs: BMA; MPS. Prev: PRHO (Surg.) Soton. Gen. Hosp.; PRHO (Med.) P.ss Margt. Hosp.

***MAHTANI, Devendra Gobind** 1 Haslemere Gardens, London N3 3EA — MB ChB 1998 Leeds.

MAHTO, Nand Kishore Patel and Partners, Thornley Road Surgery, Thornley Road, Wheatley Hill, Durham DH6 3NR Tel: 01429 820233 Fax: 01429 823667 — MB BS 1975 Delhi. (Delhi) GP Durh.

MAHTO, Mr Ram Swaroop Granville Lodge, Weston Road, Bath BA1 2XU Tel: 01225 24860 — MB BS 1957 Bihar; MS Bihar 1959, MB BS 1957; FRCS Ed. 1970; DO Eng. 1963. (Darbhanga Med. Coll.) Assoc. Ophth. Roy. United Hosp. Bath. Socs: Fell. Coll. Ophth.; S.W. Ophth. Soc. Prev: SHO (Ophth.) N.Riding Infirm. Middlesbrough; Regist. (Ophth.) W. Suff. Gen. Hosp. Bury St. Edmunds; Regist. (Ophth.) N.ampton Gen. Hosp.

MAHY, David John (retired) Ferry Lane Cottage, Uckinghall, Tewkesbury GL20 6ER Tel: 01684 594468 Fax: 01684 594468 Email: djmahy@aol.com — MB ChB 1957 Bristol; DMRT Eng. 1960; FRCR 1964. Prev: Cons. Clin. Oncol. E. Glos. NHS Trust.

MAHY, Ian Richard John Department of Cardiology, Aberdeen Royal Infirmary, Foresterhill, Aberdeen AB25 2ZN — MB BS 1985 Lond.; MA Camb.1986, BA 1982; MD Lond. 1996; MRCP (UK) 1988. (Westm.) Sen. Regist. (Cardiol.) Aberd. Roy. Infirm.; Clin. Lect. Univ. Aberd. Prev: Clin. Research Fell. Clin. Microvasc. Research Laborat. Univ. Exeter; Regist. (Cardiol.) Lond. Chest Hosp.; Regist. (Med.) W.m. Hosp. Lond.

MAHY, Nicolas John Pathology Department, Oxford Radcliffe Hosps. NHS Trust, Oxford Road, Banbury OX16 9AL Tel: 01295 229232 Fax: 01295 229225; Fresh Fields, The Green, Barford St Michael, Oxford OX15 0RN Tel: 01869 337963 — MB BS 1977 Lond.; MRCP (UK) 1981; MRCPath 1987; FRCPath 1998. Cons. Histopath. Oxf. Radcliffe Hosps. NHS Trust Banbury. Prev: Sen. Regist. (Histopath.) Univ. Wales Cardiff.

MAHYOUB ABBAS, Mahfoodh Abdulla 50 Gloucester Road, Patchway, Bristol BS34 6QA — MB BS 1993 Lond.

MAIBAUM, Anja 31 Huntsmill, Fulbourn, Cambridge CB1 5RH — State Exam Med. Frankfurt 1991; MRCP (UK) 1995. Specialist Regist. Radiol.

MAIDEN, Mr Adib 19 Mayfield Avenue, Lower Parkstone, Poole BH14 9NY — MD 1975 Damascus; FRCS Glas. 1981. Assoc. Specialist (Traum. & Orthop. Surg.) Poole Gen. Hosp. Prev: Clin. Asst. (Accid. & Orthop.) Poole Gen. Hosp.; Regist. (Orthop.) Poole Gen. Hosp.; SHO (Orthop.) Qu. Eliz. Hosp. King's Lynn.

MAIDEN, Hannah Kirsten 19 Linwood Close, Camberwell, London SE5 8UT — MB ChB 1997 Birm. SHO GP VTS Guys & St Thomas NHS Trust Lond. Prev: Jun. Ho. Off. Surg. St Johns Hosp. Livingston; Jun. Ho. Off. Med. City Hosp Birm.

MAIDEN, Laurence Peter 136 Rempstone Road, Wimborne BH21 1SX — MB BS 1993 Lond.

MAIDEN

MAIDEN, Nicola Lindsay Creinch, Alexandria G83 8NL — MB ChB 1993 Ed.

MAIDLOW, William Marson (retired) 50 Batts Park, Taunton TA1 4RE Tel: 01823 332960 — MRCS Eng. LRCP Lond. 1938; FFA RCS Eng. 1953; DA Eng. 1939. Prev: Cons. Anaesth. S.mead Hosp. Bristol.

MAIDMENT, Charles Geoffrey Haylock 15 Fairfield Lane, Farnham Royal, Slough SL2 3BX Tel: 01753 643991 — MB BS 1971 Lond.; MD Lond. 1987; FRCP Lond. 1993; MRCP (UK) 1974; DObst RCOG 1973. (Lond. Hosp.) Cons. Phys. Wexham Pk. Hosp. Slough & Heatherwood Hosp. Ascot; Hon. Sen. Lect. (Cons.) Dept. Med. Roy. Postgrad. Med. Sch. Hammersmith Hosp. Socs: Fell. Roy. Soc. Med.; Renal Assn. Prev: Sen. Regist. (Med.) Addenbrooke's Hosp. Camb.; Sen. Regist. (Med.) Norf. & Norwich Hosp.; Regist. (Med.) Univ. Coll. Hosp. Lond.

MAIDMENT, Graeme 66 Danville Road, Seaburn, Sunderland SR6 8EY — BM BCh 1989 Oxf.; MA Oxf. 1991, BM BCh 1989. Prev: Ho. Surg. Sunderland Roy. Infirm.; Ho. Phys. Roy. Vict. Infirm. Newc. u. Tyne.

MAIDMENT, John Charles Haylock (retired) Meadows, Straight Lane, Harleston IP20 9HZ Tel: 01379 852320 — MB BS 1940 Lond.; MD Lond. 1949; MRCS Eng. LRCP Lond. 1940. Prev: Outpat. Ho. Phys. Lond. Hosp.

MAIDMENT, Peter Richard Bilbrook Medical Centre, Brookfield Road, Bilbrook, Wolverhampton WV8 1DX Tel: 01902 847313 Fax: 01902 842322; The Farthings, 38 Keepers Lane, Codsall, Wolverhampton WV8 2DP Tel: 01902 843655 — MB 1978 Camb.; MA 1978 Camb.; FRCGP 2001; BChir 1977; MRCGP 1982. (St. Mary's) Vocational Train. Course Organiser Wolverhampton.

MAIER, A E 23 Old Lane, Rainford, St Helens WA11 8JE — Med. State Exam. (University Heidelberg)

MAIER, Michael Imperial College School of Medicine, Charing Cross Campus, Fulham Palace Road, London W6 8R Tel: 020 8967 5786; Department of Psychiatry, St. Bernard's Wing, Ealing, Hammersmith & fulham NHS, Southall UB1 3EU Tel: 020 8967 5786 Fax: 020 8967 5676 Email: micheal.maier@ic.ac.uk — MB BS 1988 Lond.; BSc Lond. 1973; DPhil 1977; MRCPsych 1992. (Char. Cross & Westm. Med. Sch.) Sen. Lect. Divison of Neurosci. & Psychol. Med. Imperial Coll. Sch. of Med.; Hon. Cons. Ealing, Hammersmith & Fulham NHS Trust; Hon. Lect. Nat. Hosp. Neurol. & Neurosurg. Lond.; Hon. Sen. Lect. Inst. of Psychiat. Lond. Prev: Sen. Regist. Maudsley Hosp. Lond.; Wellcome Research Fell. & Hon. Sen. Regist. Nat. Hosp. Neurol. & Neurosurg. Lond.; Regist. & SHO Bethlem Roy. & Maudsley Trust.

MAILE, Christopher James Drayson Hatfield Mount, Hatfield Lane, Norton, Worcester WR5 2PZ Tel: 01905 820267 — MB BChir 1976 Camb.; MA Camb. 1976; FRCA 1980. (Camb. & Guy's) Cons. Anaesth. Worcester Roy. Infirm. Prev: Sen. Regist. (Anaesth.) Leics. HA; Regist. (Anaesth.) Hosp. Sick Childr. Gt. Ormond St. & St. Mary's Hosp. Lond.

MAILE, Louise Jane The Surgery, 2A St. Wilfrids Square, Calverton, Nottingham NG14 6FP Tel: 0115 965 2294 Fax: 0115 965 5898 — BMedSci Nottm. 1977, BM BS 1979; DCH RCP Lond. 1983; MRCGP 1983; DRCOG 1982. Clin. Med. Off. (Paediat.). Nottm. HA.

MAILE, William Burgess Drayson (retired) Prinsted Grange, Prinsted, Emsworth PO10 8HT — MB BChir 1941 Camb.; MA, Camb., MD 1946, MB BChir 1941; FRCP Lond. 1974, M 1948; MRCS Eng. LRCP Lond. 1940; DMRD Eng. 1953. Prev: Cons. Radiol. Portsmouth Hosp. Gp.

MAILOO, Rohan Jeyaratnam St Georges Medical Centre, 7 Sunningfields Road, Hendon, London NW4 4QR Tel: 020 8202 6232 Fax: 020 8202 3906 — MB BChir 1991 Camb.

MAIMARIS, Mr Christos Varnava Accident and Emergency Department, Addenbrooke's Hospital, Cambridge CB2 2QQ Tel: 01223 217116 Fax: 01223 217057; Hill Lodge, Hildersham, Cambridge CB1 6DB — MB ChB 1980 Birm.; FRCS Ed. 1986; FFAEM 1993. Asst. Lect. & Cons. A & E Addenbrooke's Hosp. Camb.; Clin. Dir. Socs: Fell. Fac. Accid. & Emerg. Med.; Brit. Assn. Accid. & Emerg. Med. Prev: Sen. Regist. (A & E Med.) Guy's, Kent & Canterbury Hosps.; Regist. (A & E) Roy. Infirm.

MAIN, Mrs Agnes Mary 6 Sherwood Close, Barnes, London SW13 0JD Tel: 0208 788 1696 — MB BS 1936 Durh.; MRCPsych 1972. (Newc.) Socs: Assoc. Mem. Brit. Psychoanal. Soc. Prev: Dir.

Twickenham Child & Family Clinic; Regist. Tavistock Clinic; Asst. Med. Off. Gateshead Ment. Hosp. Stannington.

MAIN, Alistair Norman Hunter Housman's Barn, Valley Road, Bournheath, Bromsgrove B61 9HY Tel: 01527 837429 Fax: 0121 627 2204 Email: alistairmain@compuserve.com — MB ChB 1973 Ed.; BSc (Med. Sci.) Ed. 1970, MD 1989; FRCP Lond. 1992; MRCP (UK) 1977. (Ed.) Cons. Geriats. & Clin. Co-ordinator (Acute Elderly Med.) Univ. Hosp. Birm. NHS Trust; Sen. Clin. Lect. Univ. Birm.; Clin. Dir. S. Birm. CHT; Specialist Adviser HAS 2000. Socs: Brit. Soc. Gastroenterol.; Brit. Geriat. Soc. (Exec. Mem. Engl.). Prev: Sen. Lect. (Geriat.s Med.) Univ. Birm.; Sen. Regist. (Gen. & Geriat. Med.) W. Midl. Train. Scheme; Regist. (Gastroenterol. & Gen. Med.) Roy. Infirm. Glas.

MAIN, Angela de la Condamine (retired) 4 Queen Anne Drive, Claygate, Esher KT10 0PP Tel: 01372 466380 — MB BS 1956 Lond. Prev: SCMO (Family Plann.) Richmond, Twickenham & Roehampton Healthcare NHS Trust.

MAIN, Anthony Castle Hill Hospital, Castle Road, Cottingham HU16 5JQ — MB ChB 1983 Ed.; DA Eng. 1986; FRCA 1991. Cons. Anaesth. Cardiothoracic Unit.

MAIN, Mr Brian Joseph (retired) Eslincote, Stows Hill, Cockfield, Bury St Edmunds IP30 0JB Tel: 01284 828016 Fax: 01284 828715 — MB BChir 1963 Camb.; MA Camb. 1977, BA 1959, MChir 1978, MB 1963, BChir 1962; FRCS Eng. 1967; MRCS Eng. LRCP Lond. 1962. Prev: Cons. Orthop. Surg. W. Suff. Hosp. Bury St. Edmunds.

MAIN, Gavin Radiology Department, Ninewells Hospital and Medical School, Dundee DD1 9SY Tel: 01382 360714 Ext: 32651 Email: gavin.main@tuht.nhs.scot.uk; Tel: 01382 360714 — MB ChB 1982 Dundee; MRCP (UK) 1985; FRCR 1993. Cons. & Hon. Sen. Lect. (Clin. Radiol.) Ninewells Hosp. & Med. Sch. Dundee. Prev: Sen. Regist. (Radiol.) S.. Gen. Hosp. & W.. Infirm. Glas.; Regist. (Radiol.) Glas. Roy. Infirm. & S.. Gen. Hosp.; Regist. (Cardiol. & Med.) Ninewells Hosp. Dundee.

MAIN, Janice Department of Medicine, St. Mary's Hospital, Praed St., London W2 1NY Tel: 020 7886 1926 Fax: 020 7724 9369 Email: j.main.@ic.ac.uk — MB ChB 1980 Dundee; FRCP Lond. 1995; FRCP Ed. 1993; MRCP (UK) 1983. Sen. Lect. (Med. & Infec. Dis.) St. Mary's Hosp. & St. Chas. Hosp. Lond. Prev: Sen. Regist. (Med. & Infec. Dis.) St. Mary's Hosp. Lond.

MAIN, John McGregor South Cleveland Hospital, Marton Road, Middlesbrough TS4 3BW Tel: 01642 850850 Fax: 01642 286001 — MD 1990 Ed.; FRCP (UK) 1997, M 1983; MB ChB 1980. (Edinburgh) Cons. Phys. & Nephrol. S. Cleveland Hosp. Middlesbrough. Prev: Sen. Regist. (Nephrol.) Roy. Vict. Infirm. & Freeman Hosp. Newc.; Regist. (Gen. Med.) Aberd. Teach. Hosp.

MAIN, Mr John Mein (retired) Harden, Lochloy Road, Nairn IV12 5AF Tel: 01667 452732 — MB ChB Ed. 1952; FRCS Ed. 1959. Prev: Cons. Surg. Rochdale & Dist. Hosp. Gp.

MAIN, Joy Annette Hartcliffe Health Centre, Hareclive Road, Bristol BS13 0JP Tel: 0117 964 2839 Fax: 0117 964 9628; 2 Rodney Cottages, Clifton Down Road, Clifton, Bristol BS8 4AJ Email: pmain@cix.compulink.co.uk — MB BChir 1973 Camb.; MB BChir Camb. 1972; MA Camb. 1973, BA 1969; MRCGP 1978; DObst RCOG 1974; Cert. Family Plann. RCOG RCGP & FPA 1976. (Camb. & King's Coll. Hosp.) Princip. GP; Trainer Bristol Univ. VTS; Teach. (Gen. Pract.) Bristol Univ. Socs: BMA; Bristol M-C Soc. Prev: SCMO (Epidemiol.) Avon AHA; SHO (Terminal Care & Geriat.) St. Christopher's Hospice Sydenham; Ho. Phys. King's Coll. Hosp. Lond.

MAIN, Katherine Helen (retired) Harden, Lochloy Road, Nairn IV12 5AF Tel: 01667 452732 — MB ChB Ed. 1958.

MAIN, Monica Maitland Brora Health Centre, Station Square, Brora KW9 6QJ Tel: 01408 621320 Fax: 01408 621535 — MB ChB 1975 Aberd.; MRCGP 1979; DRCOG 1978.

MAIN, Paul Graeme Neilson Hartcliffe Health Centre, Hareclive Road, Bristol BS13 0JP Tel: 0117 964 2839 Fax: 0117 964 9628; 2 Rodney Cottages, Clifton Down Road, Clifton, Bristol BS8 4AJ Email: p.main@cix.compulink.co.uk — MB BChir 1974 Camb.; MB BChir Camb. 1973; BA Camb. 1969, MA 1973; MRCGP 1979; Cert. Family Plann. JCC 1977; DRCOG 1976. (Camb. & King's Coll. Hosp.) Princip. GP; Teach. (Gen. Pract.) Bristol Univ.; Trainer & Course Organiser Bristol Univ. VTS; Assoc. Regional Adviser (Gen. Pract.) Dept. of Postgrad.; Med. Educat. Univ. of Bristol; Cons. Primary Healthcare Kazakstan (Know How Fund). Socs: BMA;

(Treas.) Bristol M-C Soc.; Assn. Course Organisers. Prev: Regist. GP Bristol Univ. VTS; SHO (Obst.) S.mead Hosp. Bristol; Ho. Surg. King's Coll. Hosp. Lond.

MAIN, Sir Peter Tester, ERD (retired) Ninewells House, Chirnside, Duns TD11 3XF Tel: 01890 818191 Email: petermain@mainsir.demon.co.uk — MB ChB 1948 Aberd.; Hon. LLD 1986; MD Aberd. 1963; FRCP Ed. 1982, M 1981. Prev: Chairm. The Boots Co. plc.

MAIN, Robert Allardyce (retired) Tullich, Beaconhill Road, Milltimber AB13 0JR Tel: 01224 867042 — MB ChB 1949 St. And.; FRCP Ed. 1970, M 1956. Cons. Dermat. Aberd. Roy. Infirm.; Reader Clin. (Dermat.) Univ. Aberd. Prev: Sen. Regist. (Dermat.) Dundee Roy. Infirm.

MAIN, Robert Ernest Wigmore (retired) 13 Balmoral Avenue, Bedford MK40 2PT Tel: 01234 365344 — MB ChB 1961 Ed.; MRCGP 1969. Prev: GP Bedford.

MAIN, Stephen John Church Plain Surgery, Loddon, Norwich NR14 6EX Tel: 01508 520222 Fax: 01508 528579 — MB BChir 1981 Camb.; PhD Reading 1976; MRCGP 1991; DA (UK) 1986; DRCOG 1986.

MAIN, Thomas David 57 Howdenhall Road, Edinburgh EH16 6PL Tel: 0131 664 3766 — MB ChB 1968 Ed.; DObst RCOG 1970. (Ed.) Med. Sec. Local Med. Advisory Comm. Edin. BMA Deputising Serv. Socs: BMA & Edin. Clin. Club. Prev: SHO (O & G) Simpson Memor. Matern. Pavil. Edin.; SHO (Paediat.) Roy. Hosp. Sick Childr. Edin.

MAIN, Thomas James Flaxton Farm, Bunwell Road, Besthorpe, Attleborough NR17 2LN — MB BS 1996 Lond.

MAINDS, Mr Colin Campbell 17 Monreith Road, Glasgow G43 2NY — MB ChB 1979 Glas.; FRCS Glas. 1983.

MAINE, Ian Howard (retired) Toi et Moi, Route Orange, St Brelade, Jersey JE3 8GP Tel: 01534 745777 — MRCS Eng. LRCP Lond. 1951.

MAINEY, Vincent Gerard, Squadron Ldr. RAF Med. Br. Retd. Withnell Health Centre, Railway Road, Withnell, Chorley PR6 8UA Tel: 01254 830311 Fax: 01254 832337; Landau Chapel Lane, Hoghton, Preston PR5 0RY Tel: 01254 853605 Fax: 01254 851362 Email: mainey@doctors.org.uk — MB BS 1972 Newc.; MRCGP 1977; DRCOG 1977. (Newcastle upon Tyne) Socs: Brit. Med. Acupunct. Soc. & Counc. Mem. Psionic Med. Soc.

MAINGAY, Christopher Hugh Sighthill Health Centre, 380 Calder Road, Edinburgh EH11 4AU Tel: 0131 537 7320 Fax: 0131 537 7005; 1 Castlelaw Road, Edinburgh EH13 0DN Tel: 0131 441 5009 — MB BCh BAO 1965 Dub.; MRCGP 1977; DObst RCOG 1968. Trainer (Gen. Pract.) Edin. Prev: SHO (O & G) Simpson Matern. Pavil. Edin.; Ho. Surg. Roy. Infirm. Edin.; Ho. Phys. N.ampton Gen. Hosp.

MAINI, Arvind Kumar The Group Surgery, 257 North Queen Street, Belfast BT15 1HS Tel: 028 9074 8317 Fax: 028 9075 4438 — MB BCh BAO 1977 Belf.; MRCGP 1984; DCH RCPSI 1985; DRCOG 1979.

MAINI, Ashok The Surgery, 57 Sydney Street, London SW3 6PX Tel: 020 7362 8031 Fax: 020 7351 3726 — MB ChB 1981 Manchester; MB ChB 1981 Manchester.

MAINI, Bharat C/o Anaesthetic Department, Leicester Royal Infirmary, Leicester LE1 5WW Tel: 0116 254 1414; 8 Milton Avenue, High Barnet, Barnet EN5 2EX Tel: 020 8440 3974 — MB BS 1984 Lond.; MA Camb. 1985; DA (UK) 1987. (St. Geo.) Regist. (Anaesth.) Leicester Roy. Infirm. Socs: BMA; Assn. Anaesth. of Gt. Brit. & Irel. Prev: SHO (Anaesth.) Barnet Gen. Hosp.; SHO (Geriat.) Barnet Gen. Hosp.; SHO (Cas.) Basildon Hosp.

MAINI, Dinesh Lenton Medical Centre, 266 Derby Road, Lenton, Nottingham NG7 1PR Tel: 0115 941 1208 — MB ChB 1991 Leic.

MAINI, Mala Department of STD's, Mortimer Market Centre, off Capper St., London WC1E 6AU Tel: 020 7387 9600 Ext: 8706 Fax: 020 7380 9669 Email: m.maini@ucl.ac.uk; Flat 6, 2 Gainsford St, London SE1 2NE Tel: 020 7378 9341 — MB BS 1986 Lond.; MRCP (UK) 1991; DTM & H RCP Lond. 1990; PhD (Immunology) 1998. Sen. Lect., Dept. of STD's & Immunol., UCL. Prev: MRC Clin. Train. Fell., UCL; Sen. Regist. (Genitourin. Med.) UCLMS Lond.; Regist. (Genitourin. Med.) Middlx. Hosp.

MAINI, Manoj Health Centre, Pasley Road, Eyres Monsell, Leicester LE2 9BU — MB BS 1993 Lond.

*****MAINI, Pankaj** 21 Latham Road, Bexleyheath DA6 7NW — MB BS 1994 Lond.

MAINI, Rajiv 77 Barnfield Wood Road, Beckenham BR3 6ST — MB BS 1991 Lond.; BSc (Hons.) Lond. 1988; FRCOphth 1996.

MAINI, Professor Ravinder Nath The Kennedy Institute of Rheumatology, 1 Aspenlea Road, London W6 8LH Tel: 020 8383 4444 Fax: 020 8383 4499 Email: r.maini@ic.ac.uk — MB BChir 1962 Camb.; FRCP Ed. 1994, MRCP 1966; FRCP Lond. 1977, M 1966. (Guy's) Prof. Rheum. & Dir. Kennedy Inst. Rheum. Imperial Coll. Sci. & Med.; Hon. Cons. Phys. Rheum. Char. Cross Hosp. Socs: Assn. Phys.; Brit. Soc. Rheum.; Hon. Mem. Amer. Coll. Rheum. Prev: Prof. Immunol. Rheum. Dis. Char. Cross Hosp. & W.m. Med. Sch. Lond.; Cons. Phys. St. Stephens Hosp. Lond.; Regist. & Ho. Phys. Guy's Hosp. Lond.

MAINI, Ritu The Bowery Medical Centre, Elephant Lane, St Helens WA9 5PR Tel: 01744 816837 Fax: 01744 850800 — MB ChB 1989 Manch.; DRCOG 1994.

MAINI, Sunil Lancaster Gate Medical Centre, 20-21 Leinster Terrace, London W2 3ET Tel: 020 7706 9750 Fax: 020 7479 9751; 135 Hammersmith Grove, London W6 0NJ — MB ChB 1979 Manch.; BSc St. And. 1976; MRCGP 1984; DRCOG 1982.

MAINI, Vikram Claypath Medical Practice, 26 Gilesgate, Durham DH1 1QW Tel: 0191 333 2830 Fax: 0191 333 2836; Fairway, Newcastle Road, Crossgate Moor, Durham DH1 4HZ — MB BS 1974 Newc.; MRCGP 1979; DRCOG 1977. GP Tutor Durh. Prev: SHO (Paediat.) Dryburn Hosp. Durh. & Cherry Knowle Hosp. Sunderland; Ho. Off. (O & G) Dryburn Hosp. Durh.

***MAINIE, Inder Mohan Lal** 92 Ashley Avenue, Belfast BT9 7BU — MB BCh BAO 1995 Belf.

MAINPRIZE, Mr Karl Steven — MB BChir 1990 Camb.; FRCS Eng. 1993. Cons. Colorectal & GI Surg., Milton Keynes, Gen. Hosp., milton keynes. Prev: Ivo Fuchs Colorectal Cancer Research Fell. (Gen. Surg.) John Radcliffe Hosp. Oxf.

MAINWARING, Arthur Robert (retired) Hope Hospital, Eccles Old Road, Salford M6 8HD — MB BS 1954 Lond.; FRCPath 1975, M 1964. Prev: Sen. Lect. (Path.) & Lect. Path. Univ. Manch.

MAINWARING, Courtney Jason Michael John Royal Hampshire County Hospital, Romsey Road, Winchester SO22 5DG Tel: 01962 825663 — MB ChB 1986 Liverp.; MRCP (UK) 1990; MRCPath (Haemat.) 1997; Dip. RCPath 1994. Cons. (Haemat.) Roy. Hants. Co. Hosp. Winchester. Socs: Brit. Soc. Haematol.; MDU; BMA. Prev: Regist. (Haemat.) Roy. United Hosp. Bath, Sen. Reg.(Haemat) Roy. Hallamshire - Sheff.; Regist. (Gen. Med.) Harrogate Dist. Gen. Hosp. Yorks.; SHO (Haemat.) St. Jas. Hosp. Leeds.

MAINWARING, Daniel Gareth Windyridge, 196 Feinfoel Road, Llanelli SA15 3NJ Tel: 01554 772556 — MB BS 1964 Lond.; MRCS Eng. LRCP Lond. 1964. (Lond. Hosp.)

MAINWARING, Dorothy (retired) Abbey House, Abbey Walk, Shaftesbury SP7 8BB Tel: 01747 852226 — MB ChB 1955 Leeds; DCH Eng. 1958; DObst RCOG 1957. Prev: Clin. Research Asst. Alder Hey Childr. Hosp. Liverp.

MAINWARING, John Toft (retired) 18 Mulberry Lane, Cosham, Portsmouth PO6 2QU Tel: 02392 378295 — MB Camb. 1957, BChir 1956. Prev: Sen. Partner in Gen. Pract. Cosham Portsmouth.

MAINWARING, Paul Norman Department of Medicine, Royal Marsden Hospital, Fulham Road, London SW3 6JJ — MB BS 1989 Sydney.

MAINWARING, Philippa Jane Parkbury House Surgery, St. Peters Street, St Albans AL1 3HD Tel: 01727 851589 — MB BS 1984 Lond.; MRCGP 1989; DRCOG 1989; DCH RCP Lond. 1988.

MAIR, Alison Lemons Farm, Atherington, Umberleigh EX37 9HY Tel: 01769 560566 Email: alison@lemfarm.demon.co.uk — MB BS 1984 Lond.; FRCA 1992. Assoc. Specialist (Anaesth.) N. Devon Dist. Hosp. Prev: Regist. (Anaesth.) Leics. Hosps.

MAIR, Borge Ulrik (retired) Causewell Cottage, The Street, Darsham, Saxmundham IP17 3QA — MB BS Lond. 1940; MRCS Eng. LRCP Lond. 1939; DPH Lond. 1947; DCH Eng. 1943.

MAIR, Bruce Magnus The Aldergate Medical Practice, The Mount, Salters Lane, Tamworth B79 8BH Tel: 01827 54775 Fax: 01827 62835 — MB ChB 1971 Ed.; MRCGP 1975; DObst RCOG 1975.

MAIR, Christopher Jeffery Creich Surgery, Cherry Grove, Bonar Bridge, Ardgay IV24 3EP Tel: 01863 766379 Fax: 01863 766768; Carn Salachaidh, Bonar Bridge, Ardgay IV24 3EB Tel: 018632 502 — MB BS 1981 Lond.; MSc Birm. 1974; MA Oxf. 1973; MRCP (UK)

MAIR

1984; DA (UK) 1986. (St. Mary's) Clin. Asst. (Psychogeriat. & c/o Elderly) Sutherland; Hosp. Practioner (Anaesth.) Sutherland. Prev: GP Devon.

MAIR, David John Corgarff Ward, Royal Cornhill Hospital, Aberdeen AB25 2ZH Tel: 01224 681818; 1 Airyhall Crescent, Aberdeen AB15 7QS Tel: 01224 311807 — MB ChB 1990 Aberd. Staff Grade (Psychiat.) Roy. Cornhill Hosp. Aberd. Prev: Clin. Asst. Stroke Rehabil. Centre Aberd.

MAIR, Dianne Rhoda 61 Louisville Avenue, Aberdeen AB15 4TT — MB ChB 1991 Aberd.

*MAIR, Fiona 4 Willowgrove Gardens, Kinellar, Aberdeen AB21 0XW — MB ChB 1997 Aberd.

MAIR, Frances Susanne Department of Primary Care, The Whelan Building, University of Liverpool, PO Box 147, Liverpool L69 3BX Tel: 0151 794 5597 Fax: 0151 794 5604 Email: f.s.mair@liv.ac.uk — MB ChB 1985 Glas.; MRCGP 1989; DRCOG 1988. (Univ. Glas.) Sen. Clin. Lect. (Gen. Pract.) Dept. Primary Care Univ. Liverp. Prev: Research Fell. (Family Med.) Univ. Kansas Med. Center, USA; Med., Off. & Quality Assur. Phys. Adviser US Navy Med. Clinic. Lond.; Trainee GP/SHO Gtr. Glas. HB VTS.

MAIR, Frank Fentie Banchory Group Practice, The Surgery, Bellfield, Banchory AB31 5XS Tel: 01330 822121 Fax: 01330 825265; Muiresk, Raemoir Road, Banchory AB31 4ER Tel: 01330 822670 Fax: 01330 822670 — MB ChB 1969 Aberd.; Lf Hom. Glas. 2000. GP Princip., Homeopathy.

MAIR, Geoffrey Ian The Surgery, Market Place, Halesworth IP19 8BA Tel: 01986 874136 Email: zoffrey@msn.com — MB BS 1968 Lond.; MRCGP 1974; DObst RCOG 1971. (Univ. Coll. Hosp.) Trainer (Gen. Pract.) Norwich VTS. Prev: Trainee GP Ipswich VTS; Med. Off. Zambia Flying Doctor Serv.

MAIR, Graeme Hunter McDonald 53 Green Hill Road, Otford, Sevenoaks TN14 5RR Tel: 0195 922586 — MB ChB 1966 Glas.; FRCR 1975; FFR 1974; DMRT Eng. 1973. (Glas.) Cons. (Radiother. & Oncol.) Lond. Hosp. Prev: Sen. Regist. (Radiother.) W. Infirm. Glas. & MRC Fast Neutron; Clinic Hammersmith Hosp. Lond.; Regist. (Radiother.) Roy. Beatson Memor. Hosp. Glas.

MAIR, Hazel Elizabeth (retired) 4 Priors Walk, Kirkhill, Morpeth NE61 2RE — MB BS 1948 Durh.; DA Eng. 1978.

MAIR, Helen Elizabeth, OBE (retired) Kintaline House, Kintaline Mill Farm, Benderloch by Oban, Oban PA37 1QS Tel: 01631 720653 Fax: 01631 720223 Email: drmair@kintaline.co.uk — MB ChB Manch. 1948; FRCP Lond. 1985; FRCPsych 1980, M 1974; FFCM 1976, M 1972; DPH Manch. 1954. Prev: Dir. Pub. Health Med. Medway HA.

MAIR, Ian Michael Jaques (retired) 1 Cowley Road, Middlesbrough TS5 7EU Tel: 01642 818802 — MB BChir Camb. 1953; FFA RCS Eng. 1960; DA Eng. 1958. Prev: Cons. Anaesth. S. Tees Health Dist.

MAIR, James Morton 40 South Road, Kingswood, Bristol BS15 8JQ — MB ChB 1971 Aberd.; MRCGP 1975.

*MAIR, James Ulrik Well Cottage, Walpole, Halesworth IP19 9AX Tel: 07803 052631 — MB BS 1998 Lond.; MB BS Lond 1998.

MAIR, Jan Hilary Dale Cornerways, Oxford St., Lee Common, Great Missenden HP16 9JL Tel: 01494 837348 — MB BS 1968 Lond.; Dip. Ven. Soc. Apoth Lond. 1987; DObst RCOG 1970. (Univ. Coll. Hosp.) Assoc. Specialist (Genitourin. Med.) Wycombe Gen. Hosp. High Wycombe; Sen. Clin. Med. Off. Amersham Family Plann. Clinic. Prev: SHO (Cas.), Ho. Phys. & Ho. Surg. Dreadnought Seaman's Hosp.; Ho. Surg. (Obst.) S. Lond. Hosp. Wom. Clapham.

MAIR, Janet Mary Creich Surgery, Cherry Grove, Bonar Bridge, Ardgay IV24 3EP Tel: 01863 766379 Fax: 01863 766768; Carn Salachaidh, Bonar Bridge, Ardgay IV24 3EB Tel: 01863 766502 — MB BS 1984 Lond.; MBA 2001; Dip. Ther. 1997. (St Mary;s Lond.) GP Princip., Creich Surg. Bonan Bridge Sutherland; Hosp. Pract. Lawson community Hosp. Sutherland.

MAIR, John Magnus (retired) 67 Elliot Road, Hendon, London NW4 3EB — MB ChB 1937 Aberd.; MFCM 1971; DPH Ed. 1946.

MAIR, Jonathan Alfred The Surgery, 51-52 Roker Avenue, Sunderland SR6 0HT — MB BS 1975 Newc.

MAIR, Marie Isobel 15 Mariscat Road, Pollokshields, Glasgow G41 4NJ — MB ChB 1940 Aberd.; DCH RCPS Glas. 1965. (Aberd.) SCMO Argyll & Clyde Health Bd.

MAIR, Robert Maclean Paisley Road West Surgery, 1314 Paisley Road West, Glasgow G52 1DB Tel: 0141 882 4567 Fax: 0141 882 4548; 14 Fairlie, Oakwood Park Est., Stewartfield, Glasgow G74 4SE Tel: 01355 265453 — MB ChB 1987 Glas.; MRCGP 1991. (Glasgow) GP; Clin. Asst. (A & E) Glas. Roy. Infirm. Prev: SHO (O & G) Rutherglen Matern. Hosp. Glas.; SHO (Geriat. & A & E) Vict. Infirm. Glas.; SHO (Psychiat.) Leverndale Hosp. Glas.

MAIR, Stuart John 51 The Kyles, Kirkcaldy KY1 2QG Tel: 01592 641767 — MB ChB 1990 Aberd.; DRCOG 1994. Clin. Research Phys. Inveresk Clin. Research Ltd. Socs: Med. & Dent. Defence Union Scotl.; BMA. Prev: Trainee GP Fife VTS; SHO (Infec. Dis.) Vict. Hosp. Kirkcaldy.

MAIR, William Brown Stirling Royal Infirmary, Livilands, Stirling FK8 2AU Tel: 01786 434000; 30 Snowdon Place, Stirling FK8 2JN Tel: 01786 451415 Fax: 01786 451415 — MB ChB 1978 Aberd.; FFA RCS Eng. 1983; T(Anaesth.) 1991. Cons. Anaesth. Stirling Roy. Infirm.

MAIR, William George Parker (retired) 3 Seafield Street, Portnockie, Buckie AB56 4LX Tel: 01542 840499 Email: wa16@dial.pipex.com — MB ChB Aberd. 1936; MD Aberd. 1956; FRCPath 1968. Prev: Cons. Neuropath. Nat. Hosp. for Nerv. Dis. Lond.

MAIR, Mr William Stark Johnstone Hurst House Farmhouse, Hurstwood Lane, Haywards Heath RH17 7QX; Le Massitrou, Nedde 87120, France — MB ChB St. And. 1968; FRCS Eng. 1973; FRCS Ed. 1973; DObst RCOG 1971. (St. And.) Cons. Gen. Surg. P.ss Roy. Hosp. Hayward. Heath. Socs: BMA; Assn. Surg. Prev: Cons. Gen. Surg. Doncaster AHA; Sen. Regist. (Surg.) Yorks. RHA; Lect. (Surg.) Univ. Leeds.

MAIRS, Adrian Philip Department of Health & Social Services, Castle Buildings, Upper Newtownards Road, Belfast BT4 3SJ Tel: 01232 520615 Fax: 01232 520725 Email: adrian.mairs@dhssni.gov.uk; 14 Garland Hill, Manse Road, Castlereagh, Belfast BT8 6YL — MB BCh BAO 1983 Belf.; FRCS Ed. 1987; MFPHM RCP (UK) 1995; MRCGP 1991; DPH Belf. 1993; T(GP) 1991; DRCOG 1991; Dip. IMC RCS Ed. 1990. Sen. Med. Off. - DHSS Belf. Socs: Fac. Publ. Health Med.

MAIRS, Jeanne Greig (retired) 39 Deanwood Avenue, Netherlee, Glasgow G44 3RH Tel: 0141 637 6633 — LRCP LRCS 1948 Ed.; LRCP LRCS Ed. LRCPS Glas. 1948.

MAIRS, M Lorna Ambergate, Hutwood Road, Chilworth, Southampton SO16 7LL Tel: 02380 769116 — MB BCh BAO 1969 Belf.; MA Birm. 1979; BA (Theol.) Soton. 1978. (Belf.) Insur. Med. Examr. Prev: Lect. Inst. Ophth. Lond.; Clin. Teach. (Primary Med. Care) Soton. Univ.; EMP Ben Agy Med Serv.

MAIRS, Philip Paul 19A Noctorum Dell, Birkenhead CH43 9UL — MB BS 1993 Lond.

MAIRS, Thomas David 9 Goldfinch View, Loggerheads, Market Drayton TF9 2QH — MB BCh BAO 1973 Belf.; DObst RCOG 1976.

MAISELS, Catriona Margaret (retired) Loch Tummel House, Strathtummel, Pitlochry PH16 5RX — MB ChB Ed. 1949; DPH Ed. 1954. Prev: Asst. MOH & Asst. Sch. Med. Off. City Oxf.

MAISELS, Mr David Oliver (retired) Loch Tummel House, Strathtummel, Pitlochry PH16 5RX — MB ChB Ed. 1951; FRCS Eng. 1974; FRCS Ed. 1956. Prev: Cons. Plastic Surg. Mersey RHA.

MAISEY, Anthony Robin Cross Keys Practice, High Street, Princes Risborough HP27 0AX Tel: 01844 344488 Fax: 01844 274714; Thimbles, Crowbrook Road, Askett, Princes Risborough HP27 9LR Tel: 01844 345527 Fax: 01844 345527 Email: tonymaisey@aol.com — MB ChB Liverp. 1969; MRCGP 1975; DObst RCOG 1971; DCH Eng. 1971. Div. Surg. Oxon. St. John Ambul.; Med. Off. Molins Ltd. Saunderton; Asst. Police Surg. Thames Valley Police. Socs: Soc. Occupat. Med.

MAISEY, David Nichol Norfolk and Norwich University Hospital, Colney Lane, Norwich NR4 7UY Tel: 01603 288009 Fax: 01603 288571 Email: lesley.turner@norfolk-norwich.thenhs.com; 384 Unthank Road, Norwich NR4 7QE Tel: 01603 506762 — MB BS 1972 Lond.; MA Camb. 1978; BSc Lond. 1969; FRCP Lond. 1994; MRCP (UK) 1975. (St. Thos.) Cons. Geriat. Med. Norf. & Norwich Hosp. Socs: Brit. Geriat. Soc. Prev: Sen. Regist. (Geriat. & Med.) Roy. Devon & Exeter Hosps.; Clin. Lect. (Med.) Addenbrooke's Hosp. Camb.; Regist. (Gen. Med.) Roy. United Hosp. Bath.

MAISEY, Irene Charlotte (retired) 17 Eliot Vale, Blackheath, London SE3 0UW — MB BS Lond. 1964; MRCS Eng. LRCP Lond. 1964. Med. Off. Marks & Spencer plc. Prev: SHO (Anaesth.), Ho. Surg. & Ho. Phys. Lewisham Hosp.

MAISEY, Professor Michael Norman Department Radiological Sciences, Guy's Hospital, London SE1 9RT Tel: 020 7955 4531 Fax: 020 7955 4532 Email: m.maisey@umds.ac.uk — MB BS 1964 Lond.; BSc Lond, 1960, MD 1971, MB BS 1964; FRCP Lond. 1978, M 1966; MRCS Eng. LRCP Lond. 1964; FRCR 1983; Dip. Amer. Bd. Nuclear Med. 1972. (Guy's) Prof. Radiol. Sc. Guy's, Kings St. Thomas Sch. Med.; Cons. Phys. Nuclear Med. Guy's & St. Thos. Hosp. Lond.; Hon. Cons. Nuclear Med. to the Army. Socs: (Ex-Pres.) Brit. Nuclear Med. Soc.; Vice-Pres. Brit. Inst. Radiol. Prev: Cons. Phys. (Nuclear Med. & Endocrinol.) Guy's Hosp. Lond.; Regist. (Med.) & Sen. Regist. (Endocrinol.) Guy's Hosp. Lond.; Research Fell. (Nuclear Med.) Johns Hopkins Med. Sch., USA.

MAISEY, Nicholas Robert 104A Lewisham Way, London, SE14 6NY — MB BS 1993 Lond.

MAISTER, Anthony Ross Nathaniel St. Mary's Surgery, Church St., Somersham, Huntingdon PE28 3EG; The Walnut Trees, 38 High St, Bluntisham, Huntingdon PE28 3LA Tel: 01480 842221 — MRCS Eng. LRCP Lond. 1962; DCH Eng. 1973.

MAISTER, Margaret Brenda St Mary's Surgery, 6A Church Street, Somersham, Huntingdon PE28 3EG Tel: 01487 841300 Fax: 01487 740765; The Walnut Trees, 38 High St, Bluntisham, Huntingdon PE28 3LA — Artsexamen 1973 Groningen. (State Univ. Groningen) Prev: SHO (Gen. Med. & Intens. Care) Windhoek, SW Africa; SHO (Gen. Med. & Cardiol.) Tygerberg Hosp., S. Africa; SHO (O & G) Johannesburg Gen. Hosp., S. Africa.

MAITI, Harisadham Hertford County Hospital, North Road, Hertford SG14 1LP Tel: 01707 373358 — MB BS 1969 Calcutta; FRCOG 1993, M 1977; Dip. GU Med. Soc. Apoth Lond. 1983. Cons. Genitourin. Med. Hertford Co. Hosp.

MAITI, Sunil Kumar James Street Surgery, 53 James Street, Blackburn BB1 6BE Tel: 01254 52005 — MB BS 1972 Calcutta; MB BS 1972 Calcutta.

MAITLAND, Anne Hilary Castle View Cottage, Smithy Lane, Mouldsworth, Chester CH3 8AR Tel: 01928 740363 — BM BCh Oxf. 1958; BA Oxf. 1958; DObst RCOG 1960. (Univ. Coll. Hosp. Lond.) Clin. Asst. (Obst.) Chester Halton Community Care for Health; Clin. Asst. (Gyn. & Diabetes) Halton Gen. Hosp.

MAITLAND, Bryant William (retired) Willow Tree Farm, Palmer St., Walsham-le-Willows, Bury St Edmunds IP31 3BZ Tel: 01359 258062 Fax: 01359 258062 — MB BS 1959 Lond.; MRCS Eng. LRCP Lond. 1958; DObst RCOG 1960. Prev: Med. Dir. Suff. Family HAs.

MAITLAND, Helen Mary 125 Morriston Road, Elgin IV30 4NB Tel: 01343 544901 — MB ChB 1953 Aberd.; MRCGP 1968. (Aberd.) Med. Off. Community Med. Grampian Health Bd. W. Unit. Socs: Med. Wom. Federat.; BMA. Prev: Regist. (Anaesth.) Derbysh. Roy. Infirm. & Derby City Hosp.; Sen. Ho. Off. (Anaesth.) Roy. Infirm. Aberd.

MAITLAND, James Macdonald Rosemount Medical Practice, 1 View Terrace, Aberdeen AB25 2RS Tel: 01224 638050 Fax: 01224 627308; 12 Northcote Avenue, Aberdeen AB15 7TN — MB ChB 1981 Aberd.; MRCGP 1985; DRCOG 1984. GP Aberd.; Clin. Research Fell. Univ. Aberd. Prev: Research Fell. MSD Foundat.; Trainee GP Aberd. VTS; Research Fell. (Gen. Pract.) Aberd. Univ.

MAITLAND, Jennifer Anne Department of Haematology, Kingston Hospital, Galsworthy Road, Kingston upon Thames KT27 7QB Tel: 020 8546 7711 Ext: 3154 Fax: 020 8549 2450 — MB BS 1977 Lond.; MRCS Eng. LRCP Lond. 1977; FRCP Lond. 1996; FRCPath 1997; MRCPath 1986. (St. Bartholomew's London) Sen. Lect. (Haemat.) Imperial Coll. Med. Sch. Lond. & Hon. Cons. Haemat. Kingston Hosp. Socs: Brit. Soc. Haematol. Prev: Sen. Lect. (Haemat.) Imperial Coll. Med. Sch. Lond. & Hon. Cons. Haemat. Qu. Mary's Univ. Hosp. Roehampton; Sen. Regist. (Haemat.) Roy. Marsden Hosp. Lond.

MAITLAND, John, RD, QHP Tarbert Medical Practice, School Road, Tarbert PA29 6UL Tel: 01880 820219 Fax: 01880 820104 Email: administrator@gp8474.ac_hb.scot.nhs.uk; Glenakil, West Loch, Tarbert PA29 6XX Tel: 01880 820150 Fax: 01880 820199 — MB BS Newc. 1973; MRCGP 1977; Dip. Pract. Dermat. Wales 1995. (Newc. Univ.) Princip. GP Tarbert. Socs: BMA; PCDS. Prev: Dir. Med. Reserves 1995-98; Qu.'s Hon. Phys. 1955-98; Clin. Asst. (Dermat.) Kent & Canterbury Hosp.

MAITLAND, Julian Edward 34 Kingsway Park, Belfast BT5 7EW — MB BS 1980 Lond.; MRCS Eng. LRCP Lond. 1979; MPH Glas. 1991; DRCOG 1986; DA Eng. 1982; MFPHM Lond. 1995. (Char. Cross) Sexual Health & Alliance Manager, LoughBoro.; Clin. Asst. (Gum Dept.) Roy. Vict. Hosp. Belf. Prev: Sen. Regist. (Pub. Health Med.) WHSSB Lond.derry.; Med. Off. Save Childr. Fund Nakhon Phanom N.E. Thailand.

MAITLAND, Richard Ian (retired) 51 Burnett Road, Crownhill, Plymouth PL6 5BH Tel: 01752 773117 — MB BS Lond. 1947; MRCS Eng. LRCP Lond. 1947; MRCGP 1962; DObst RCOG 1953. Prev: Ho. Surg. St. Bart. Hosp. & Luton Matern. Hosp.

MAITLAND-WARD, Kathryn Merchiston Surgery, Highworth Road, Swindon SN3 4BF Tel: 01793 823307 Fax: 01793 820923; 3 Hunter's Piece, Bourton, Swindon SN6 8JR Tel: 01793 783793 — MB BS 1981 Lond.; MRCGP 1985; DRCOG 1983.

MAITRA, Mr Asit Kumar Tel: 0191 281 2636 Fax: 0191 281 2397; 23 Park Drive, Melton Park, Gosforth, Newcastle upon Tyne NE3 5QB Fax: 01347 888339 Email: a.k.maitra@ncl.ac.uk — MB BS 1958 Calcutta; FRCS Eng. 1968; FRCS Ed. 1965. (Nilratan Sircar Med. Coll.) Emerit. Cons. A&E. Newe. NHS Hosp. Trust; Mem. Med. Edr.ial Advis. Bd., Hosp. Doctor, Reed Health Care Publishing. Socs: Med. Protec. Soc. Prev: Consult. (A & E Med.) Roy. Vict. Infirm. Newc.; Clin. Lect. Orthop. & Trauma Surg. Univ. Newc.

MAITRA, Begum Child & Family Consultation Service, 1 Wolverton Gardens, London W6 7DY Tel: 020 8846 7806; 38 Nant Road, London NW2 2AT — MD 1983 Bombay; MD (Psych.) Calcutta 1983, MB BS 1976; MRCPsych 1987; DPM Calcutta 1979. Cons. Child & Adolesc. Psychiat. Riverside Ment. Health Trust Lond.

MAITRA, Mr Debasish Whiston Hospital, Warrington Road, Prescot L35 5DR — MB BS 1980 Calcutta; FRCS Glas. 1986.

MAITRA, Dilip Kumar Park Farm Surgery, 1 Alder Rd, Folkstone CT19 5BZ Tel: 01303 851021 Fax: 01303 226743 — MB BS (DCH) Calcutta, India. (Calcutta Nat. Med. Coll.) GP. Prev: Med. Off. In Fam. Plan.; Clin. Med. Off.

MAITRA, Ketaki c/o Drive K. Mythili, 72 Argyle Gardens, Upminster RM14 3EX — MB BS 1967 Dibrugarh.

MAITRA, Mr Soumyen 64 Acacia Avenue, Huyton, Liverpool L36 5TP Tel: 0151 489 5173 — MB BS 1963 Calcutta; FRCS Ed. 1970.

MAITRA, Tapas Kumar 22 Lakeside Drive, Silica Lodge, Scunthorpe DN17 2AG — MB BS 1972 Calcutta.

MAITRA, Mr Tilak Bhupal Scunthorpe General Hospital, Cliff Gardens, Scunthorpe DN15 7BH — MB BS 1977 Poona; FRCS Ed. 1980.

MAITY, Mr Pulin Behari Burbage Surgery, Tilton Road, Burbage, Hinckley LE10 2SE Tel: 01455 634879 Fax: 01455 619860; Rosewood, Sketchley Lane, Burbage, Hinckley LE10 2NG Tel: 01455 636929 — MB BS 1962 Calcutta; MS 1975, MB BS Calcutta 1962; DPhysMed Eng. 1970. (Nilratan Sircar Med. Coll.) GP. Hinckley, Leics. Prev: Regist. Dept. Physical Med. & Rheum. Coventry & Warks. Hosp.; SHO Dept. Physical Med. & Rheum. Whitley Hosp. Coventry.

MAITY, Santanu 1 Kenwick Gardens, Louth LN11 8EZ — MB ChB 1993 Manch.

MAIZELS, David Warren Bursted Wood Surgery, 219 Erith Road, Bexleyheath DA7 6HZ Tel: 020 8303 5027 Fax: 020 8298 7735; 113 Blackbrook Lane, Bickley, Bromley BR1 2LP Tel: 020 8467 1600 — MRCS Eng. LRCP Lond. 1974.

MAJA, Oladipo 10 Symons Street, London SW3 2TJ Tel: 020 7730 1929 — LRCP LRCS 1954 Ed.; LRCP LRCS Ed. LRFPS Glas. 1954. (Ed.) Prev: GP Med. Off. Maja Hosp. Lagos, Nigeria.

MAJDNEYA, Mr Ebadollah 14 Kings Road, Westcliff on Sea SS0 8LL — MD 1973 Tabriz; FRCS Ed. 1985; DO RCPSI 1978.

MAJEED, Mr Ali Waqar K-Floor, Royal Hallamshire Hospital, Sheffield S10 2JF Tel: 0114 271 1900 Fax: 0114 271 3791 Email: a.w.majeed@sheffield.ac.uk; 131 Rustlings Road, Sheffield S11 7AB Tel: 0114 266 7971 — MB BS 1984 Punjab; MD Sheff. 1995; FRCS Ed. 1989; FRCS (Gen.) 1997. Sen. Lect. (Surg.) Hon. Cons. Surg. Roy. Hallamsh. Hosp. Sheff. Socs: ASGBI; SRS. Prev: Lect. (Surg.) & Hon. Sen. Regist. Roy. Hallamsh. Hosp. Sheff.

MAJEED, Diana Moorfield House Surgery, 35 Edgar Street, Hereford HR4 9JP Fax: 01432 341942; Green Acres, Roman Road, Bobblestock, Hereford HR4 9QW — MB ChB 1981 Ed.; DIP. Ther. 2001; DFFP 1993; DRCOG 1984. (Ed.)

MAJEED, F A A Earle Road Surgery, 131 Earle Road, Liverpool L7 6HD Tel: 0151 734 3535.

MAJEED

MAJEED, Farrukh Azeem Curran and Partners, Manor Health Centre, 86 Clapham Manor Street, London SW4 6EB Tel: 020 7411 6866 Fax: 020 7411 6857; 14 Lake Close, London SW19 7EG — MB BCh 1985 Wales; MD Wales 1996; MFPHM RCP (UK) 1993; MRCGP 1990. Sen. Lect. (Gen. Pract.) Univ. Coll. Lond.; Med. Epidemiologist Office for Nat. Statistics Lond.

MAJEED, Gulnaz Syed 96A St Michaels Hill, Bristol BS2 8BQ — MB BS 1987 Punjab.

MAJEED, Joohi Fraz The West Suffolk Hospital, Hardwick Lane, Bury St Edmunds IP33 2QZ Tel: 01284 713000 Fax: 01284 713406 Email: joohi.majeed@wsufftrust.org.uk; 14 Cool Oak Lane, London NW9 7BJ — MB BS 1985 Nigeria; MRCP (UK) 1990. (Lagos) Cons. Phys. (Gen. Med.) Diabetes & Endocrinol. W. Suff. Hosp. Bury St. Edmunds. Prev: Sen. Regist. (Diabetes & Endocrinol.) Addenbrooke's Hosp. Camb.; Research Fell. (Diabetes & Endocrinol.) Univ. Hull; Regist. (Diabetes & Endocrinol.) Roy. Liverp. Univ. Hosp.

MAJEED, Mr Laith Jalal Abdul Green Acres, Roman Road, Bobblestock, Hereford HR4 9QW — MB ChB 1972 Mosul; FRCS Glas. 1982; Dip. Biomechanics Strathclyde 1997. Assoc. Specialist (Orthop.) Gen. Hosp. Hereford. Socs: Brit. Orthop. Assn.; BMA; Herefordsh. Med. Soc. Prev: Regist. Rotat. (Orthop.) Robt. Jones & Agnes Hunt Hosp.; Regist. (Orthop.) Leighton Hosp. Crewe; SHO Rotat. (Gen. Sur., Orthop. & A & E) Medway Hosp. Gillingham.

MAJEED, Qamar Flat 1, Tilney Court, 2 Catherine Road, Surbiton KT6 UJB — MB BS 1957 Punjab.

MAJEED, Mr Syed Mohammad Kamran Flat 4, Eaton House, 41 St Peter's Road, Margate CT9 1TJ Tel: 01843 225544; 28 Kenver Avenue, Finchley, London N12 OPG Tel: 020 8445 5404 — MB BS 1982 Punjab; FRCS Ed. 1987; FMGEMS 1984.

MAJEED, Tahir Royal Preston Hospital, Sharoe Green Lane N., Fulwood, Preston PR2 9HT Tel: 01772 710556 Fax: 01772 718746 — MB BS 1985 Punjab; PhD Glas. 1996; MRCPI 1991; FRCPI 1997; FRCPG 1998. (King Edwd. Med. Coll. Lahore, Pakistan) Cons. Neurol. Roy. Preston Hosp.; Cons. Lancaster Roy. Infirm. Prev: Clin. Lect. (Neurol.) Univ. Glas.; Regist. (Neurol.) Cork Regional Hosp.

MAJEKODUNMI, Maureen Joy Tel: 01782 502227 Fax: 01782 541068 — MB BS 1979 Lagos; MRCS Eng. LRCP Lond. 1982; MRCGP 1985; DRCOG 1983. p/t GP.

MAJEKODUNMI, Oladapo Olafimihan 36 Waldeck Road, Ealing, London W13 8LZ — MB BCh BAO Dub. 1962; MD Dub. 1969; Dip. Path. Lond. 1969.

MAJER, Raymond Vaughan Haematology Department, Prince Phillip Hospital, Dafen, Llanelli SA14 8QF — MB BS 1976 Lond.; MRCP (UK) 1983; MRCPath 1988. Cons. Haemat. E. Dyfed HA.

MAJEVADIA, Dhirajlal Kurji Hamstead Road Surgery, Handsworth, Birmingham B20 2BT Tel: 0121 523 5111 — MB BS 1966 Bombay. (Grant Med. Coll.)

MAJEVADIA, Sheetal Kumar 76 Fred Lee Grove, Coventry CV3 5NN — MB BS 1995 Lond.; DCH 1997; DRCOG 1997; DFFP 1999. (Univ. Coll. Lond.) GP Non Princip. Prev: GP Regist. Rallsalc Common, coventry; SHO Gen. Med. WalsGr. Hosp. Coventry.

MAJEWSKI, Andrzej Antoni 9-10 Havergal Villas, Green Lane, London N15 3DY Tel: 020 8888 6662 Fax: 020 8881 6350 — MB BCh BAO NUI 1969; MICGP 1987; DRCOG 1972. Socs: Polish Med. Assn.

MAJI, Sankarprasad Marsh Lane Surgery, 68 Marsh Lane, Fordhouses, Wolverhampton WV10 6RU Tel: 01902 398111 Fax: 01902 680078; Pendeford Health Centre, Whitburn Close, Wolverhampton WV9 5NJ Tel: 01902 680078 — MB BS 1972 Calcutta.

MAJID, Abdul Warley Hospital, Warley Hill, Brentwood CM14 5HQ Tel: 01277 302731 Fax: 01277 302734; Deyne House, 2a Ayldlfs Walk, Hornchurch RM11 2RD Tel: 01708 454313 Fax: 01708 454313 — MB BS 1966 Dhaka; MRCPsych 1972; FRCPsych 1993; DPM Lond. 1972. Cons. Psychiat. NELMHT, NHS Trust, Brentwood, Essex. Socs: BMA & World Federat. for Ment. Health.; (Vice-Pres.) Bangladesh Med. Assn. in UK. Prev: Cons. Psychiat. St. Luke's Hosp. Middlesbrough.; Cons. Psychiat. Admin. i/c Dept. Adult Psychiat. Hastings HA; Serv. Director/ Assoc. Med. Director. BHB NHS Trust, Brentwood, Essex.

MAJID, Mr Abdul 14 Hillcrest Rise, Leeds LS16 7DL — MB BS 1956 Patna; FRCS Glas. 1973; MRCS Eng. LRCP Lond. 1975. (Patna Med. Col.)

MAJID, Arshad 5 Branksome Crescent, Bradford BD9 5LD — MB ChB 1993 Glas.

MAJID, Asad 46 Dene Road, Northwood HA6 2DE — MB ChB 1991 Manch. SHO Wythenshawe Hosp. Manch.

MAJID, Faruk Hilly Fields Medical Centre, 172 Adelaide Avenue, London SE4 1JN Tel: 020 8314 5552 Fax: 020 8314 5557 — BSc Liverp. 1979, MB ChB 1984; DCH RCP Lond. 1986; MRCGP 1989; DRCOG 1989; DIP Med. Acupunc. 1997. GP; GP Tutor Lewisham LMC Mem. for Lewisham Clin. Lect. KCH; Bd. Mem. & Clin. Governance Lead N. Lewisham PCG. Socs: Brit. Med. Acupunc. Soc.

***MAJID, Imran** 1 Dronfield Road, Salford M6 7FN — MB ChB 1995 Manch.

MAJID, Mahseeman Self-Realization Healing Centre, Laurel Lane, Queen Camel, Yeovil BA22 7NU — MB ChB 1983 Leic.; MRCP (UK) 1987. (Univ. Leicester)

MAJID, Mohammed Azhar 29 Ridgehill, Bristol BS9 4SB — MB ChB 1993 Bristol. (Bris.) Res Fell. Bris. Eye Hosp. Prev: SHO (Ophth.) Roy. Liver. Hosp.; SHO (Ophth.) Taunton & Som. Hosp.

MAJID, Nahida Akhtar 115 Oakdale Road, Nottingham NG3 7EJ — MB BS 1992 Lond.

MAJID, Saleh Mohammed 2 Roxby Street, Bradford BD5 7NU — MB ChB 1993 Leeds.

MAJID, Sarah 7 Woodville Road, London NW11 9UH — BChir 1992 Camb.

MAJID, Zaheeda 34 Greenford Road, Manchester M8 0NW — MB ChB 1991 Sheff.

MAJKOWSKI, Mr Richard Stephen Gloucestershire Royal NHS Trust, Gloucestershire Royal Hospital, Great Western Road, Gloucester GL1 3NN Tel: 01452 528555; The Little House, Sandy Lane Road, Charlton Kings, Cheltenham GL53 9DA Tel: 01242 521284 — MB BChir 1981 Camb.; BA Camb. 1978; FRCS (Orth.) 1993; FRCS Eng. 1985. Cons. Orthop. Surg. Glos. Roy. Hosp. Socs: Fell. BOA; BMA. Prev: Sen. Regist. (Orthop. Surg.) Nottm.; Tutor (Orthop. Surg.) Univ. Bristol; Regist. (Orthop. Surg.) Bristol Roy. Infirm. & Cheltenham Gen. Hosp.

MAJMUDAR, Nikhil Gaurang 9 Fairhill Crescent, Perth PH1 1RR — MB ChB 1989 Ed.

MAJOE, Philip Fox's Den, Tai Penylan, Capel Llanilltern, Cardiff CF5 6JH Tel: 029 2089 0119 — MB ChB 1981 Zimbabwe.

***MAJOR, Andrew** 14 Thurlow Road, Clarendon Park, Leicester LE2 1YE Tel: 0116 270 1971 — MB ChB 1998 Leic.; MB ChB Leic 1998.

MAJOR, Anoosh 17 Glenalmond House, Manor Fields, Putney Hill, London SW15 3LP Tel: 020 8788 4960 — MD 1956 Tehran; MD Tehran Univ. 1956; DO RCS Eng. 1963. Ophth. Med. Pract. Lond. Socs: Coll. Ophth. Prev: Cons. Ophth. Min. Health Iran.

***MAJOR, Barnaby Spencer** Uplyme, Wells Road, Eastcombe, Stroud GL6 7EE — MB BS 1998 Lond.; MB BS Lond 1998.

MAJOR, Edward Intensive Therapy Unit, Morriston Hospital, Swansea SA6 6NL Tel: 01792 703470 Fax: 01792 703470 — MB BS 1972 Lond.; FFA RCS Eng. 1976. (Lond. Hosp.) Dir. Intens. Ther. Morriston Hosp. Swansea. Socs: FRCA; Welsh Intens. Care Soc.; Intens. Care Soc. Prev: Sen. Lect. & Hon. Cons. Anaesth. Lond. Hosp. Med. Coll.; Sen. Regist. (Anaesth.) Lond. Hosp. & Hosp. Sick Childr. Gt. Ormond St. Lond.

MAJOR, Grenville Raymond 31 Broadlands Close, Plymouth PL7 1JP — MB ChB 1980 Cape Town.

MAJOR, Heather Gillian The Medical Advisory Branch, DVLA, Longview Road, Morriston, Swansea SA99 1TU Tel: 01792 783782 — MB BS 1974 Lond.; BSc Lond. 1971, MB BS 1974. Med. Adviser to Dept. of Transport Swansea. Prev: Princip. GP Ilford & Swansea; Ho. Phys. (Cardiac) & SHO (Emerg. & Accid.) Lond. Hosp.

MAJOR, Karen Anne 52 Liggars Place, Dunfermline KY12 7XZ — MB BCh 1982 Wales; MRCGP 1986; DRCOG 1986.

MAJOR, Kathleen Jane 154 Malone Road, Belfast BT9 5LJ Tel: 01232 668881 — MB BCh BAO 1961 Belf.; DObst RCOG 1963; DCH RCPS Glas. 1965. (Belf.) Assoc. Specialist (Paediat.) Ulster Hosp. Dundonald.

MAJOR, Rolf Gabor Bodowen Surgery, Halkyn Road, Holywell CH8 7GA Tel: 01352 710529 Fax: 01352 710784; Plas yn Llan, Llanasa, Holywell CH8 9NE — MB ChB 1987 Manch.; MRCGP 1993; DRCOG 1992.

MAJOR, Stella Claire Department of Family Medicine, American University of Beirut, Beirut, Lebanon Tel: 00 961 1 352040 Fax: 00 1 212 4781995 Email: sm09@aub.edu.lb; c/o 17 Glenalmond House, Manor Fields, Putney Hill, London SW15 3LP Tel: 020 8 788 4960 — MB BS 1990 Lond.; MRCGP 1995; DRCOG 1992; DCH RCP Lond. 1991. (Char. & Westm.) Instruc. (Family Med.) Amer. Univ. Beirut, Lebanon. Prev: Trainee GP N.wick Pk. Hosp. Harrow VTS.

MAJOR, Professor Valerie 34 Uplands Crescent, Llandough, Penarth CF64 2PR — MB BS 1959 Lond.; MRCS Eng. LRCP Lond. 1959; FFA RCS Eng. 1964. (Roy. Free Hosp. Sch. Med.) Prof. Anaesth. Christian Med. Coll. & Hosp. Vellore, S. India.

MAJUMDAR, Abdullah A W Newmains Health Centre, 17 Manse Road, Newmains, Wishaw ML2 9AX Tel: 01698 381074 — MB BS 1972 Punjab; MB BS 1972 Punjab.

MAJUMDAR, Asokkumar Mapleton, 22 Preston Avenue, North Shields NE30 2BS — MB BS 1973 Calcutta.

MAJUMDAR, Mrs Bhaswati 18 Garfield Road, Ryde PO33 2PT Tel: 01983 565103 Fax: 01983 617288 — MBBS 1982; LMSSA 1989 London; MRCGP 1993 London. Occupat.al Health Phys.

MAJUMDAR, Mr Biswajit Spring Cottage, 478 Burton Road, Derby DE23 6AL Tel: 01332 371209 — MB BS 1969 Calcutta; FRCS Eng. 1978; FRCS Ed. 1976; DLO Eng. 1977. (N.R.S. Med. Coll. Calcutta) Cons. ENT Surg. Roy. Infirm. Derby; Clin. Teachg. (OtoLaryngol.) Univ. Nottm.. Socs: Fell.Roy. Soc. of Med.; Otolaryngological Research Soc. UK; Fell.Internat. Coll. of Surg.s. Prev: Sen. Regist. (OtoLaryngol.) United Sheff. Hosps. & Univ. Hosp. Nottm.; Regist. (OtoLaryngol.) W. Infirm. Glas. & Univ. Hosp. Wales Cardiff.

MAJUMDAR, Gautam Doncaster Royal Infirmary, Thorne Road, Doncaster DN2 5LT Tel: 01302 366666 Fax: 01302 553209 Email: gautam@majumdar.demon.co.uk — MB BS 1972 Calcutta; FRCP 1999; FRCPath 1997; MD (AIMS) 1977; MBBS (Calcutta) 1972. (NRS Medical College, Calcutta) Cons. Haemat. Doncaster Roy. Infirm.

MAJUMDAR, Kallol Garfield Road Surgery, 18 Garfield Road, Ryde PO33 2PT Tel: 01983 565103 Fax: 01983 617288 — MB BS 1974 Calcutta.

MAJUMDAR, Kusha Nilminie 3 The Mount, Edenthorpe, Doncaster DN3 2JL — MB BS 1980 Colombo.

MAJUMDAR, Mr Pratip Greystones, 20 Broom Lane, Rotherham S60 3EL Tel: 01709 363793 — MB BS 1956 Calcutta; FRCS Ed. 1959. (Calcutta) Cons. Pk.field Private Hosp. Rotherham. Prev: Cons. Orthop. Surg. Rotherham Dist. Hosp.

MAJUMDAR, Rupendra Kumar Olivet, 3 Penygroes, Groesfaen, Pontyclun CF72 8PA — MB BS 1960 Calcutta; DPH Liverp. 1963. (Calcutta Nat. Med. Coll.)

***MAJUMDAR, Samit** 16 Ariel Close, Basford, Nottingham NG6 0EH — BM BS 1998 Nottm.; BM BS Nottm 1998.

MAJUMDAR, Swadhin Kumar Pant Street Health Clinic, Pant Street, Aberbargoed, Bargoed CF81 9BB Tel: 01443 831185 Fax: 01443 839146 — MB BS 1971 Calcutta.

***MAJUMDER, Anjalina** 99 Brian Avenue, Cleethorpes DN35 9DF — MB BS 1998 Lond.; MB BS Lond 1998.

MAJUMDER, Mr Arun Kumar The Surgery, 14 Eleanor Street, Grimsby DN32 9DT Tel: 01472 355640 — MB BS 1961 Calcutta; FRCS Eng. 1977. (R.G. Kar Med. Coll.) Prev: Regist. (Surg.) Scunthorpe Gen. Hosp.; Vasc. Surg. Trainee & Surg. Nutrit. Research Worker Boston Med. Sch.; U.S.A.

MAJUMDER, Mr Bimalesh Chandra 30A Margaret Street, Greenock PA16 8BU Tel: 01475 727138 Fax: 01475 727140 — MB BS 1962 Calcutta; FRCS Glas. 1981; DLO RCS Eng. 1972; DLO Calcutta Univ. 1966. Prev: Regist. & Clin. Asst. (ENT) Inverclyde Roy. Hosp. Greenock; SHO (ENT) Halifax Roy. Infirm.

MAJUMDER, Jnanendra Lal 22 Garden Close, Banstead SM7 2QB Tel: 01737 356979 — MB BS 1960 Calcutta; DCH Calcutta 1962; DPM 1964. (Calcutta Med. Coll.) Assoc. Specialist Riverside HA Lond. Socs: BMA; Affil. Mem. Roy. Coll. Psychiat. Prev: Regist. Friern Hosp. Lond. & W. Pk. Hosp. Epsom; Med. Asst. Oakwood Hosp. Maidstone & Banstead Hosp.

MAJUMDER, Sanjib 1 Sandgate Drive, Kippax, Leeds LS25 7EX — MB BS 1989 West Indies.

MAJUPURIA, Ajai Normanby Road Surgery, 502-508 Normanby Road, Normanby, Middlesbrough TS6 9BZ Tel: 01642 452727/440501 Fax: 01642 466723; 5 Lingdale Drive, Seaton Carew, Hartlepool TS25 2AJ — MB BS 1975 Jiwaji. (Gajra Raja Med. Coll. Gwalior) GP Middlesbrough.

***MAJURAN, Vinayakamoorthy** 65 Revell Road, Kingston upon Thames KT1 3SL — MB BS 1998 Lond.; MB BS Lond 1998.

MAJURY, Clive William 96 Warren Road, Donaghadee BT21 0PQ — MB BCh BAO 1978 Belf.; FRCR 1984; DMRD Eng. 1983. David Porter Prize 1985; Cons. Diag. Radiol. Ulster Hosp. Belf. Socs: BMA.

MAJURY, Nigel Tod Silverbirch Medical Practice, 39A Silverbirch Road, Bangor BT19 6EU Tel: 028 9145 5000 — MB BCh BAO 1981 Belf.; DRCOG 1984; Cert. Family Plann. JCC 1984. Prev: Med. Off. (A & E) Ulster Hosp. Dundonald; SHO (O & G) Ards Hosp. Newtownards.

MAJUS, Reena Elliott Hall Medical Centre, 165-167 Uxbridge Road, Hatch End, Pinner HA5 4EA Tel: 020 8428 4019 Fax: 0208 420 1993 — MB BCh 1977 Witwatersrand; MRCP 1980; MRCGP 1988. (University of Witwatersrand)

MAJZLISZ, Anna 48 Maresfield Gardens, London NW3 5RX — LRCP LRCS 1946 Ed.; LRCP LRCS Ed. LRFPS Glas. 1946. (Surg. Hall Ed.) Prev: Ho. Surg. (Orthop.) Pk. Prewett Hosp. Basingstoke; Ho. Surg. Boro. Gen. Hosp. Soton.

MAK, Eric Yu-Kee 51 Hawksworth Road, Hawksworth Road, Horsforth, Leeds LS18 4JP — MB ChB 1992 Leeds.

MAK, Fiona 44 Kelcey Road, Quorn, Loughborough LE12 8UU Tel: 01509 413003; 16 Wilson Road, Jardine's Lookout, Hong Kong — MB ChB 1987 Leic.

MAK, Ian, Yeung Nung Department of Clinical Neurophysiology, Charing Cross Hospital, Fulham Palace Road, London W6 8RF Tel: 020 8846 1655 Fax: 020 8846 1300 Email: imak@doctors.org.uk — MB ChB 1987 Liverp.; MRCPI 1994; MRCP (UK) 1993; DGM RCP Lond. 1993. Cons. (Clin. Neurophy.) Char. Cross Hosp. & Chelsea & W.m. Hosp. Lond. Prev: Sen. Regist. Rotat. (Clin. Neurophysiol.) Qu. Eliz. Hosp. & Birm. & Selly Oak Hosp. Birm.; Regist. (Neurol., Neurophysiol. & Gen. Med.) New Cross Hosp. Wolverhampton; SHO (Haemat.) Qu. Eliz. Hosp. Birm.

MAK, Ian Yee Hwang 6 Knox Street, London W1H 1FT — MB BS 1994 Lond.

***MAK, Tony Wing Chung** Flat 6, 41 Belsize Park, London NW3 4EE — MB ChB 1997 Manch.

MAK, Vincent Hoi Fan Central Middlesex Hospital, Alton Lane, Park Royal, London NW10 7NS Tel: 020 8453 2143 Fax: 020 8453 2450; Flat 1 4 Alexandra Park Road, Muswell Hill, London NW2 2AA Tel: 020 8883 9744 Email: vince@macondo.demon.co.uk — MB BS 1983 Lond.; BSc Lond. 1980, MB BS 1983; MRCP (UK) 1986; FRCP 1999. (Guys) Cons. Phys. Prev: Lect. (Med.) St. Thos. Hosp. Lond; Research Fell. (Respirat. Med.) Rayne Inst. Univ. Coll. Hosp. Lond.

MAK, Vivienne Yuen Yee 90 Goldstone Crescent, Hove BN3 6BE — MB BS 1988 Lond.

***MAKAN, Jayesh** 130A Park Road, New Barnet, Barnet EN4 9QN — MB BS 1998 Lond.; MB BS Lond 1998.

MAKANJI, Hasmukh Woodcroft Medical Centre, Gervase Road, Burnt Oak, Edgware HA8 0NR Tel: 020 8906 0500 Fax: 020 8906 0700; 59 Valley Drive, Kingsbury, London NW9 9NJ Tel: 020 8204 5050 — MB ChB 1972 Birm.; MRCOG 1979. (Univ. Zimbabwe) Clin. Asst. (Gyn.) N.wick Pk. Hosp. & Clin. Research Centre Harrow. Prev: Regist. (O & G) Roy. Liverp. Hosp. & Mill Rd. Matern. Hosp. Liverp.; SHO (Surg.) N.wick Pk. Hosp. & Clin. Research Centre Harrow.

MAKANJUOLA, Akinwale David 44 Catterick Way, Borehamwood WD6 4QT Tel: 020 8386 1700 — MB BS 1987 Ibadan, Nigeria; MRCP (UK) 1993. (Univ. Ibadan Coll. of Med., Nigeria) Lect. (Nephrol.) Guy's Hosp. Lond. Prev: Regist. (Nephrol.) & SHO (Renal) Guy's & St. Thos. NHS Trust Lond.

MAKANJUOLA, Ayoola Oladeji Kapace & Partners, Theobald Medical Centre, 121 Theobald St., Borehamwood WD6 4PU Tel: 020 8953 3355; 81 Rivington Crescent, London NW7 2LF Tel: 020 8906 8184 Email: dejimaks@epulse.net — MB ChB 1981 Ife; BSc Ife 1978; DCH 1996; Accreditation 1998; FNML Path (1) Nig. Postgrad. Med. Coll. (Nigeria) Asst. Theobald Med. Centre Borehamwood Herts. Socs: BMA; Nigerian Med. Assn.

***MAKANJUOLA, Christabel Anne Olawumi** 58 Tyn y Cae, Pontardawe, Swansea SA8 3DL — MB ChB 1998 Bristol.

MAKAR

MAKAR, Adel Saleh c/o Orthopaedic Secretaries, King George Hospital, Barley Lane, Ilford IG3 8YB — MB BCh 1968 Cairo; MChOrth Liverp. 1990.

*MAKAR, Sonia 9 Killermont Road, Bearsden, Glasgow G61 2JB — MB ChB 1997 Glas.

*MAKATINI, Zinhle Nomusa 45 Tennyson Road, Sheffield S6 2WD — MB ChB 1998 Sheff.; MB ChB Sheff 1998.

MAKEN, Sadrudin Butty Piece Cottage, 4 Park Street Mews, Bath BA1 2SZ Tel: 01225 317261 — MB BCh 1963 Wales; MRCS Eng. LRCP Lond. 1963. (Cardiff) Clin. Asst. (Cardiol.) Bristol Roy. Infirm.; Capt. RAMC T & AVR. Socs: BMA; Med. Defence Union. Prev: Clin. Asst. (Plastic Surg.) Frenchay Hosp. Bristol; SHO (Thoracic Surg.) Frenchay Hosp. Bristol; SHO (Gen. Surg. & Accid.) Roy. United Hosp. Bath.

MAKEPEACE, Mr Alan Rutherford Centre for Cancer Treatment, Mount Vernon Hospital, Northwood HA6 2RN — MRCS Eng. LRCP Lond. 1977; BSc (1st cl. Hons.) Lond. 1971, MB BS 1977; FRCR 1985; FRCS Ed. 1981; FRCS Eng. 1981. (King's Coll.) Cons. Radiother. & Oncol. Mt. Vernon Hosp. Socs: BMA & Roy. Soc. Med. Prev: Sen. Regist. & Regist. (Radiother.) Middlx. & Mt. Vernon Hosps.; SHO (Plastic Surg.) Frenchay Hosp. Bristol; SHO (Gen. Surg.) Bristol Roy. Infirm.

MAKEPEACE, Donald James Woodlands, Delph Lane, Aughton, Ormskirk L39 5EB — MB BS 1977 Newc.; MRCGP 1983; DRCOG 1984.

MAKEPEACE, John Scott (retired) Holy Well House, Spaunton Bank Foot, Appleton Le Moors, York YO62 6TR Tel: 01751 417624 — MB BS Durh. 1949; MA York 1996.

MAKEPEACE, Penelope Ann Holly House, Bescar Lane, Ollerton, Newark NG22 9BS — MB BS 1982 Lond.; MRCOG 1989.

MAKEPEACE, William 3 West Cottages, Doxford, Chathill NE67 5DR — MB BS 1977 Newc.; PhD (Electrochem.) Newc. 1973; BSc (Chem.) 1966, MB BS 1977.

MAKEY, Mr Arthur Robertson 2 Beverley Close, Barnes, London SW13 0EH Tel: 020 8876 7347 — MB BS 1945 Lond.; MS Lond. 1951; FRCS Eng. 1948. (Char. Cross) Emerit. Cardiothorac. Surg. to Char. Cross Hosp.; Emerit. Thorac. Surg. to RAF. Socs: Soc. Thoracic. & Cardiothoracic Surgs. GB & Irel. Prev: Cons. In Thoracic Surg. To RAF; Cons. Cardiothoracic Surg. Char. Cross Hosp. & W. Middlx. Univ. Hosp.; Mem. (Ex-Chairm.) Ct. of Examrs. RCS Eng.

MAKGOBA, Malegapuru William Department of Chemical Pathology, Royal Postgraduate Medical School, Hammersmith Hospital, Du Cane Road, London W12 0HS — MB ChB 1977 Natal; MRCP (UK) 1980.

MAKHANI, Firozali Abdulhusein Kingsthorpe Medical Centre, Eastern Avenue South, Northampton NN2 7JN Tel: 01604 713823 Fax: 01604 721996 — MB BS 1974 Bombay; DRCOG 1977 RCOG Lond.; Cert. Family Plann 1975; Cert. Acupuncture 1980 BMS. GP; Clin. Asst. in PsychoGeriat. Socs: BMA; BMAS.

MAKHDOOM, Zahoor Ahmed 1 Fox Hill Road, Burton Joyce, Nottingham NG14 5DB Tel: 0115 931 3277 — MB BS 1982 Pakistan; MRCP (UK) 1990.

MAKHDUM, Rashida 17 Cabborns Crescent, Stanford-le-Hope SS17 0EA Tel: 01375 675632 — MB BS 1949 Punjab. (King Edwd. Med. Coll. Lahore) Clin. Med. Off. (Community Med.) Basildon & Thurrock Health Dist. Prev: Regist. (O & G) Lady Willingdon Hosp. Lahore, Pakistan; Maj. Pakistan AMC; Sen. Ho. Surg. Vict. Hosp. Deal.

MAKHECHA, Rasiklal Liladhar Sheaveshill Avenue Surgery, 25 Sheaveshill Avenue, Colindale, London NW9 6SE Tel: 020 8205 2336 — MB BS 1958 Bombay; MB BS 1958 Bombay.

MAKHIJA, Shashi Kanta The Bungalow, 29A Mount Pleasant, Alperton, Wembley HA0 1UA — MB BS 1960 Delhi.

*MAKIN, Alistair James The Orchard, 7 Blueberry Road, Bowdon, Altrincham WA14 3LS — MB BS 1988 Lond.

MAKIN, Andrew James City Hospital NHS Trust, Dudley Road, Birmingham B18 7QH Tel: 0121 554 3801; 51 Arosa Drive, Harborne, Birmingham B17 0SB Tel: 0121 427 6662 Email: 02223214@infotrade.co.uk — MB ChB 1996 Birm.; BEng. (Hons.) 1990. (Birmingham) SHO (Gen. Surg.). Prev: SHO (Trauma & Orthop.).

MAKIN, Andrew Philip 1st Floor Right, 13 Clarence Drive, Glasgow G12 9QL — MB ChB 1989 Dundee.

MAKIN, Miss Carol Audrey Arrowe Park Hospital, Upton, Wirral CH49 5PE Tel: 0151 678 5111 Fax: 0151 604 1760 Email: carol.makin@whnt.nhs.uk; Springvale, Moorside Lane, Parkgate, South Wirral CH64 6QP — MB BCh 1976 Wales; PhD Lond. 1985; FRCS Eng. 1980. (Cardiff) Cons. Surg. Wirral Hosp. Trust.; Director Informat. Serv.s Wirral Hosp. Trust. Socs: Vice-Pres. Roy. Soc. Med. Sec. Sect. Coloproctol.; Assn. Coloproct. Prev: Sen. Regist. & Lect. Roy. Liverp. Hosp.; Regist. (Surg.) W.m. Hosp. Lond.; Clin. Research Fell. St. Mark's Hosp. & ICRF.

MAKIN, Christopher Maxwell Ian Mile End Hospital, Bancroft Road, London E1 4DG — MB ChB 1981 Sheff.

MAKIN, Doreen 186 Canterbury Road, Davyhulme, Manchester M41 0GR Tel: 0161 747 1997; 34 Cornhill Road, Davyhulme, Manchester M41 5TD Tel: 0161 748 8228 — MB BS 1964 Lond.; MRCS Eng. LRCP Lond. 1964; DObst. RCOG 1966. (Roy. Free) Prev: Ho. Phys., Ho. Surg. & Ho. Surg. Obst. Pk. Hosp. Davyhulme.

MAKIN, Guy William James Academic Unit of Paediatric Oncology, Christie Hospital, Wilmslow Road, Manchester Email: guy. makin@mac.uk; 40 Newlyn Road, Sheffield S8 8SU Email: awgm@easynet.co.uk — BM BCh 1991 Oxf.; MRCP (UK) 1994. Clin. Lect. (Paediat. Oncol.) Christie Hosp. Manch. & Roy. Manch. Childr. Hosp.

MAKIN, John Sager Plympton Health Centre, Mudge Way, Plymouth PL7 1AD Tel: 01752 341474; The Lodge, 103 Fore St, Plympton St. Maurice, Plymouth PL7 1ND Tel: 01752 337572 — MB BS 1969 Lond.; MRCS Eng. LRCP Lond. 1969; MRCGP 1977; Dip. Occ. Med. RCP Lond. 1996; DObst RCOG 1971. (King's Coll. Hosp.) Prev: SHO Freedom Fields Hosp. Plymouth; Ho. Off. Dulwich & Plymouth Hosps.

MAKIN, Matthew Keith 143 Middleton Road, Oswestry SY11 2XX — MB ChB 1991 Birm.; MRCP (UK) 1994. (Univ. Birm. Med. Sch.) Specialist Regist. (Palliat. Med.) Mersey Region. Socs: RCP Ed.; Assn. Palliat. Med. Prev: Macmillan Fell. (Palliat. Care with Oncol.) Birm. Oncol. Centre.

MAKIN, Sheena Wight 58 Lucknow Drive, Nottingham NG3 5EU — MB ChB 1955 Ed.; FFA RCS Eng. 1961. (Ed.)

MAKIN, Wendy Philippa Christie Hospital NHS Trust, Wilmslow Road, Manchester M20 4BX Tel: 0161 446 3000 — MB ChB 1978 Birm.; MRCP (UK) 1982; FRCR 1990; FFR RCSI 1990; T(M) 1991; T(R) (CO) 1991; FRCP 1998. Macmillan Cons. Palliat. Care & Oncol. Christie Hosp. Manch. Socs: Assn. Palliat. Med. Prev: Cons. Palliat. Med. & Hon. Clin. Lect. (Oncol.) St. Oswalds Hospice Newc.

MAKINDE, Olusola 46 Belsize Avenue, Palmers Green, London N13 4TJ — MB BS 1989 Lond.

MAKINGS, Ellen Alison 213 Gilbert House, London EC2Y 8BD — MB BS 1991 Lond.

*MAKINS, Anita Elizabeth 3 Chapel Close, Commercial Road, Skelmanthorpe, Huddersfield HD8 9AT — BM BS 1998 Nottm.; BM BS Nottm 1998.

MAKINS, David John Bristow 6 Lower Moor, Birmingham B30 1TN — MB ChB 1952 Ed.

MAKINS, Richard John 6 Denys Court, Olveston, Bristol BS35 4DW — MB BS 1994 Lond.; MRCP (UK) 1997; BSc (Hons. Physiol. 1991. (St. Geos.)

MAKINSON, Donald Hindley (retired) Old Sidmouth House, Cotmaton Road, Sidmouth EX10 8ST Tel: 01395 577591 Fax: 01395 577591 — MB BChir 1943 Camb.; MA Camb. 1945; FRCP Lond. 1971, M 1946. Prev: Dir. & Dean (Postgrad. Studies) Univ. Wales Coll. Med. Cardiff.

MAKKAR, Bhagat Singh (retired) 33 The Priory, Priory Park, London SE3 942 Tel: 020 8297 0084, 020 8297 9076 — MB BS 1969 Rajasthan. Prev: GP 1974-.

MAKKER, Himender Kumar Chest Clinic, North Middlesex Hospital, London N18 1QX — MB BS 1982 Delhi; MRCP (UK) 1987.

MAKKISON, Ian Dept of Anaesthetics, Royal Hospital, Alow, Chesterfield S44 5BL Tel: 01246 277271; 40 Brookside Bar., Chesterfield S40 3PJ Tel: 01246 567259 Email: makkison@tesco.net — MB BS 1984 Newc.; BMedSc (Hons.) Newc. 1981; FRCA 1997; MRCGP 1993; DA (UK) 1987. (Univ. Newc.) Cons. Anaesth. with interest in Chronic Pain. Socs: Pain Soc.; Assn. Anaesth.; Fell. Roy. Coll. Anaesth. Prev: Med. Off. Brit. Antarctic Survey Med. Unit; SHO (Cardiol.) Freeman Rd. Hosp. Newc.; SRR Nottm. Rotat.

MAKOL, Om Prakash Princess Medical Centre, Princess Street, Woodlands, Doncaster DN6 7LX Tel: 01302 723406 Fax: 01302 723433 — MB BS 1966 Delhi.

MAKOMASKA, Mrs Anna Zofia Stanislawa (retired) 15 Knightswood Close, Reigate RH2 8BE Tel: 01737 245070 — MD 1950 Beirut; BA Beirut 1946. Cons. Chest Phys. S. W.. RHA; Worker in Cotswold Nuffield Hosp. Med. Checks Scheme. Prev: Assoc. Specialist S. W.. RHA.

MAKOMASKA, Barbara Miroslawa Anna 8 Seale Hill, Reigate RH2 8HZ — MB 1982 Camb.; BChir 1981; DRCOG 1984.

MAKOWER, Mr Richard Mortimer Accident & Emergency Department, Countess of Chester Hospital NHS Trust, Chester CH2 1UL Tel: 01244 365215 Fax: 01244 365225 Email: richard.makower@coch-tr.nwest.nhs.uk — MB BS 1980 Lond.; FRCS Ed. 1986; FFAEM 1994. (Lond. Hosp.) Cons. A & E Countess of Chester Hosp. NHS Trust. Socs: Brit. Assn. Accid. & Emerg. Med. Prev: Sen. Regist. (A & E) Kent & Canterbury Hosps. NHS Trust; Regist. (A & E) Glas. Roy. Infirm.; Regist. (Orthop. Trauma) Tayside HB.

MAKOWSKA, Marta Teresa Florey Unit, Royal Berkshire Hospital, London Road, Reading RG1 5AN Tel: 01734 877205 — MB ChB 1973 Ed.; MRCP (UK) 1977. (Edinburgh) Staff Phys. (Genitourin. Med.) Roy. Berks. Hosp.

MAKRIS, Andreas Mount Vernon Hospital, Rickmansworth Road, Northwood HA6 2RN Tel: 01926 844723 Fax: 01926 844167 — MD 1999 Sheff.; MA 1995 Oxf.; BA Oxf. 1982; MB ChB Sheff. 1985; MRCP (UK) 1988; FRCR (UK) 1992. Cons. (Clin. Oncol.) Mt. Vernon Hosp., Rickmansworth Rd., Middlx.; Sen. Lect. Clin. Oncol. UCL. Socs: Hon. Sec. of Brit. Oncol. Assoc. Prev: Sen. Regist. Roy. Marsden Hosp., Lond. 1995-1997; Research Fell. BrE. Unit, Roy. Marsden Hosp., Lond. 1993-1995; Regist., W.on Pk. Hosp., Sheff. 1989-1993.

MAKRIS, Michael Department of Haematology, Royal Hallamshire Hospital, Glossop Road, Sheffield S10 2JF Tel: 0114 271 2760 Fax: 0114 275 6126 Email: m.makris@sheffield.ac.uk — MB BS 1984 Lond.; MA Oxf. 1991, BA 1981; MD Sheff. 1995; MRCP (UK) 1987; MRCPath 1992. Sen. Lect. (Haemat.) Univ. Sheff.; Hon. Cons. Haemat. Roy. Hallamsh. Hosp. Sheff. Socs: Brit. Soc. Haematol.; Brit. Soc. Haemostasis & Thrombosis. Prev: Lect. (Haemat.) Univ. Sheff.; Regist. (Haemat.) Roy. Hallamsh. Hosp. Sheff.; SHO Rotat. (Med., Neurol., Nephrol. & Haemat.) Morriston Hosp. Swansea.

MAKSIMCZYK, Peter The Surgery, 13 Clarence Road East, Weston Super Mare BS23 4BP Tel: 01934 415080 Fax: 01934 612813; 13 Clarence Road E., Weston Super Mare BS23 4BP — MB BS 1976 Lond.; MRCS Eng. LRCP Lond. 1977. (Char. Cross) Socs: Guild of Catholic Doctors.; W.on-Super-Mare Dn. Sec. BMA; Guild Catholic Doctors. Prev: Clin. Asst. Geriat. W.on Gen. Hosp.; Trainee GP Axbridge; Regist. (Diagn. Radiol.) Bristol Roy. Infirm.

MAKULOLUWE, Charminie Lanka Kumari 17 Beechdale, London N21 3QE — MB BS 1994 Lond. (St. Geo. Hosp. Med. Sch.) SHO (Intens. Care Cardiol.) Whittington Hosp. NHS Trust Lond. Prev: SHO (Renal Med.) King's Coll. Hosp. Lond.; SHO (Gen. Med. & Gastroenterol.) St. Heller Hosp. Carshalton; SHO (Gen. Med. & c/o the Elderly) Frimley Pk. Hosp. Surrey.

MAKUNDE, Mr John Tichatonga Urology Department, St Mary's Hospital, Parkhurst Rd, Newport PO30 5TG Tel: 01983 534797 Fax: 01983 534596 Email: makunde@aol.com — MB BS 1979 Lagos; FRCS 1999 (Intercoll. Bd. Urol.); MSc 1997 (Urology) UCL; 2000 FEBU; FRCSI 1989; Dip. Urol. Lond 1992. Cons. Urol., IOW. Socs: BAUS; EAU; ICS. Prev: SHO (Urol.) Geo. Elliot Hosp. Nuneaton.; SpR in Urol. Russells Hall Hosp. 1998-1999; Locum cons. Urol. Worcs. Roy. Infirm. 1999-2000.

MAKWANA, Mr Nilesh Kumar 24 Grange Drive, Melton Mowbray LE13 1EY Tel: 01664 850730 Email: nilesh@bhanu.freeserve.co.uk — MB BS 1989 Lond.; FRCS Glas. 1993; FRCS Ed. 1993; FRCS Ed. (Orth.) 1999. Specialist Regist. Leicester S. Trent Region. Socs: Med. Defence Soc.

MAKWANA, Nitenkumar Vinesh 44 Watermeadow Drive, Watermeadow, Northampton NN3 8SS — MB ChB 1996 Birm.; ChB Birm. 1996; BSc (Hons.) Pharm. 1993; MRCPCH 1990. (Birmingham)

MAKWANA, Mr Ramniklal Devji The Health Centre, Trenchard Avenue, Thornaby, Stockton-on-Tees TS17 0DD Tel: 01642 762636 Fax: 01642 766464; Macwood, 1 Holme Lane, Seamer, Middlesbrough TS9 5LN Tel: 01642 710532 — MB BS 1968 Gujarat; FRCS Ed. 1975.

MALAIYA, Nilima 45 Kingsley Drive, Warrington WA4 5AF — MB BS 1976 Jiwaji.

MALAK, Mr Tawfik M Department of Obstetrics & Gynaecology, General Hospital, King's Drive, Eastbourne BN21 2UD Tel: 01323 417400 Email: r1tmm@yahoo.com; The Old Mill House, 85 Willingdon Road, Eastbourne BN21 1TZ Tel: 01323 735814 Fax: 01323 720790 — MB BCh 1980 Cairo; PhD Leicester 1995; MSc Cairo 1984; MRCOG 1988; DFFP 1999; FRCOG 2000. Cons. O & G E.bourne Gen. Hosp. Socs: Internat. Conf. Soc.; Internat. Urogynaecol. Soc.; Brit. Menopause Soc. Prev: Lect., Sen. Regist. & Clin. Research Fell. (O & G) Leicester Univ.; Regist. (O & G) Leicester Roy. Infirm.

MALAKI, Farzin 57 Ivor Court, Glossop Place, London NW1 6BN — MB ChB 1993 Glas.

MALAN, David Huntingford (retired) Parker's Close, Hartley Wintney, Hook RG27 8JG Tel: 01252 842502 — BM BCh Oxf. 1951; MA Oxf. 1953, BA (Chem.) 1943, DM 1962; FRCPsych 1973, M 1971; DPM Eng. 1956. Prev: Cons. Tavistock Clinic Lond.

MALAREE, Sergio Lorenzo Ferrari 77 Molesworth Road, Stoke, Plymouth PL1 5PG — Medico Cirujano Chile 1973. Prev: Regist. (Community Med.) Camb. HA; SHO (Paediat.) W. Yorks. & S. Tees HAs.

MALATA, Mr Charles Musonda Plastic & Reconstructive Surgery Department, Canniesburn Hospital, Switchback Road, Bearsden, Glasgow G61 1QL Tel: 0141 211 5600 Fax: 0141 211 5652; 18 Dirleton Gate, Bearsden, Glasgow G61 1NP — MB ChB 1984 Univ. Zambia; BSc Univ. Zambia 1981; FRCS Glas. 1990; MRCS Eng. LRCP Lond. 1988; FRCS 1997. Specialist Regist. (Plastic Surg.) Canniesburn Hosp. Glas.; Fell. (BrE. & Aesthetic Surg.) Geo.town Univ. Med. Centre Washington. Socs: Eur. Soc. Surg. Research.; Surgic. Research Soc. Prev: SHO (Plastic Surg.) Newc. Teachg. Hosps.; Regist. (Respirat. & Gen. Med.) Guy's Hosp. Lond.; SHO (Plastic Surg.) St. James Univ. Leeds.

***MALBON, Katherine Mary** 1 Gloucester View, Southsea PO5 4EB — MB ChB 1997 Manch.

MALCOLM, Agnes Jane Hattrick (retired) Shawbost, Brookfield, Johnstone PA5 8UE Tel: 01505 320255 — MB ChB 1950 Glas. Prev: Supernum. Non-Resid. Ho. Phys. Roy. Hosp. Sick Childr. Edin.

MALCOLM, Alasdair David (retired) Malcolm Consulting, Lake House, Copthorne Road, Felbridge, East Grinstead RH19 2QQ Tel: 01342 305 039 Fax: 01342 305 065 Email: admalcolm@compuserve.com — MB BS 1968 Lond.; MD Lond. 1987; MSc (Biophysics) Univ. West. Ontario 1975; FRCP Lond. 1985; MRCS Eng. LRCP Lond. 1968; MRCP (UK) 1971; FFPM 1997. Dir., Malcolm Consg. Prev: Regist. (Med.) Lond. Hosp.

MALCOLM, Professor Archibald Johnston North of England Bone Tumour Registry, University Department of Pathology, Royal Victoria Infirmary, Newcastle upon Tyne NE1 4LP Tel: 0191 232 5131 Fax: 0191 222 8100 Email: a.j.malcolm@ncl.ac.uk — MB ChB 1974 Glas.; FRCPath 1992, M 1980. (Glasgow) Prof. (Clin. Path.); Cons. Newc. u. Tyne NHS Trust; Chairm. ACP Counc.; Regional Adviser RCPath; Bd. Mem. CPA. Socs: Assn. Clin. Pathologists; Internat. Skeletal Soc.; Eur. Musculoskeletal Soc. Prev: Past Chairm. MRC Soft Tissue Sarcoma Panel.

MALCOLM, Brian Litchdon Medical Centre, Landkey Road, Barnstaple EX32 9LL Tel: 01271 23443 Fax: 01271 25979; Blakewell Mill Farm, Near Muddiford, Barnstaple EX31 4ES Tel: 01271 344918 — MB ChB 1981 Ed.; BSc Ed. 1978; MRCGP 1986; Dip. Pract. Dermat. Wales 1992; DCH RCP Lond. 1985; DRCOG 1984. (Ed.) Hosp. Pract. (Dermat.) N. Devon Dist. Hosp.; Trainer (Gen. Pract.) Barnstaple; Examr. Post. Grad. Dermat. Univ. of Wales Cardiff. Socs: Primary Care Dermatol. Soc. Prev: Trainee GP Mid Wales VTS; SHO Tadworth Ct. Childr. Hosp. Surrey; Ho. Phys. Falkirk Roy. Infirm. Scotl.

MALCOLM, David The Surgery, Scalloway, Shetland ZE1 0UH Tel: 01595 880219; Schiehallion, Berry Road, Scalloway, Lerwick ZE1 0UL Tel: 0154 588463 — MB ChB 1978 Ed. Prev: Trainee GP Wick.

MALCOLM, Mr George Pulteney Frenchay Hospital, Bristol BS16 1 — MB BS 1987 Lond.; BSc Lond. 1984; 1997 FRCS. (King's College) Cons. Neurosurg. Frenchay Hosp. Bristol.

MALCOLM

***MALCOLM, James Edward** 86 Osmaston Road, Birkenhead CH42 8LP — MB ChB 1994 Manch.

MALCOLM, Janet Margaret Rivoan, Alverston Avenue, Woodhall Spa LN10 6SN — MB BS 1986 Lond.; MRCGP 1992; DCH RCP Lond. 1990; DRCOG 1988. p/t Asst. GP Lincoln.

MALCOLM, John Bradford Eildonhurst, 500 Perth Road, Dundee DD2 1LS Tel: 01382 668058 — MB ChB 1940 St. And.; AFOM RCP Lond. 1979; MRCGP 1955; DIH Soc. Apoth. Lond. 1966.

MALCOLM, John Pulteney The Old Vicarage, Upton, Norwich NR13 6AR Tel: 01493 751228 Fax: 01493 751228 Email: jpm@malcolm.co.uk — MRCS Eng. LRCP Lond. 1966; DObst RCOG 1972; DCH Eng. 1970. (Guy's) Asst. Thoppewood Surg., Woodside, Norwich, NR7 9QL. Prev: Phys. Nakuru War Memor. Hosp. Kenya.; Partner Acle Med. Centre.

MALCOLM, Lesley Brimmond Medical Group, 106 Inverurie Road, Bucksburn, Aberdeen AB21 9AT Tel: 01224 713869 Fax: 01224 716317 — MB ChB 1988 Aberd.; MRCGP 1992; DCCH RCP Ed. 1993; DRCOG 1991. (Aberdeen University) p/t GP Partner.

MALCOLM, Margaret Reid Department of Psychiatry, Southern General Hospital, Govan Road, Glasgow G51 Tel: 0141 201 1921 Fax: 0141 201 1920; Brenfield, 180 Southbrae Drive, Glasgow G13 1TX Tel: 0141 959 3082 — MB ChB 1968 Glas.; FRCP Glas. 1988; MRCP (UK) 1971; FRCPsych 1990, M 1975. Cons. Psychother. S.. Gen. Hosp. Glas.; Hon. Sen. Lect. (Psychol. Med.) Univ. Glas. Socs: (Chairm.) Scott. Assn. Psychoanal. Psychother. Prev: Sen. Regist. (Psychiat.) Gtr. Glas. HB; Regist. (Psychiat.) Gartnavel Roy. & S.. Gen. Hosps. Glas.

MALCOLM, Marion Kerr 16 Polwarth Street, Hyndland, Glasgow G12 9TY — MB ChB Glas. 1941.

MALCOLM, Miles Timothy Clatterbridge Hospital, Clatterbridge Road, Bebington, Wirral CH63 4JY Tel: 0151 334 4000 — MB ChB 1966 Liverp.; MD Liverp. 1973; FRCPsych 1986, M 1972; DPM Eng. 1969. (Liverp.) Cons. Psychiat. Clatterbridge Hosp. Bebington. Prev: Sen. Regist. (Psychiat.) W. Chesh. Hosp. Chester; Regist. (Psychiat.) United Liverp. Hosps.; SHO Sefton Gen. Hosp. Liverp.

MALCOLM, Napier (retired) Kingswood House, Pilcorn St., Wedmore BS28 4AW Tel: 01934 712520 — MB BChir 1958 Camb.; MB Camb. 1958, BChir 1957; FRCP Lond. 1979, M 1963; MRCS Eng. 1958, LRCP Lond. 1959; T(M) 1991; DTM & H Liverp. 1964. Prev: Cons. Phys. W.on-super-Mare Gen. Hosp.

MALCOLM, Norman Paul 8 Granby Road, Headingley, Leeds LS6 3AS — MB ChB 1984 Leeds.

MALCOLM, Paul Napier Pilgrim Health NHS Trust, Pilgrim Hospital, Sibsey Road, Boston PE21 9QS Tel: 01205 364801 — MB BS 1986 Lond.; BSc Lond. 1983; MRCP (UK) 1989; FRCR 1994. Cons. Radiol. Pilgrim Hosp. Boston. Lincolnshire. Prev: Regist. (Gen. Med.) N.wick Pk. Hosp.; Specialist Regist. (Radiol.) Guys & St Thomas's Hosp. Lond.; MRI Fell. Mallinckrodt Inst. of Radiol. St Louis USA.

MALCOLM, Richard Burton (retired) 17 Brunenburg Way, Axminster EX13 5RD Tel: 01297 32477 — MB ChB St. And. 1955; DObst RCOG 1957.

***MALCOLM, Robert Graham** 86 Osmaston Road, Birkenhead CH42 8LP — MB ChB 1997 Ed.

MALCOLM, Robert Mackay Occupational Health Department, Tayside Police HQ, PO Box 59, West Bell St., Dundee DD1 9JU Tel: 01382 596300 — MB ChB 1977 Glas.; MRCGP 1988; MFOM RCP Lond. 1996, AFOM 1991; Dip. Forens. Med. Glas 1994; DCH RCPS Glas. 1980. Chief Med. Off. Tayside Police. Socs: Soc. Occupat. Med.; Assn. Police Surg.; Assn. Local Auth. Med. Advisers. Prev: Sen. Med. Off. Newc. Occupat. Health Agency.

MALCOLM, Russell Steven Centre for Integrative Medical Training, 11B North Claremont St., Glasgow G3 7NR Tel: 0141 331 0393 Fax: 0141 410163 Email: russelmalcolm@cimt.fsbusiness.co.uk; Battery House, 3 East Bay, North Queensferry, Inverkeithing KY11 1JX Tel: 01383 410163 Fax: 01383 410163 — MB ChB 1983 Dundee; BA Open 1987; MFHom 1987. Med. Dir. Centre for Integrative Med. Train. Glas.; Homeop. Phys. W. Glas. Hosps. Univ. NHS Trust. Socs: Fac. Homoeop. Prev: Dir. of Educat. Roy. Lond. Homoeop. Hosp. Trust; Cons. Homoeop. Med. Glas. Homoeop. Hosp.; Regist. (Med. & Homoeop.) Glas. Homoeop. Hosp.

MALCOLM, Stewart James Division of Ophthalmology, Royal Berkshire Hospital, London Road, Reading RG1 5AN — MB BS 1979 Melbourne, Australia.

MALCOLM, William Neil Department of Anaesthetics, Queen Margaret Hospital NHS Trust, Dunfermline KY12 0SU — MB ChB 1974 Dundee.

MALCOLM-SMITH, Nigel Andrew, RD (retired) 43 Craiglea Drive, Edinburgh EH10 5PB Tel: 0131 447 2572 — MB ChB 1960 Ed.; FFA RCS Eng. 1966. Hon. Fell. Anaesth. Roy. Infirm. Edin. Prev: Cons. Anaesth. Roy. Infirm. Edin. &P.ss Margt. Rose Orthop. Hosp.

MALCOLMSON, Sheila Elizabeth Glencairn, Brinckman Terrace, Westhill, Inverness IV2 5BL — MB ChB 1991 Aberd.

MALCOMSON, Colin Ian 49 Clogher Road, Lisburn BT27 5PQ — MB BCh BAO 1988 Belf.

MALCOMSON, David Herbert The Church Street Practice, David Corbet House, 2 Callows Lane, Kidderminster DY10 2JG Tel: 01562 822051 Fax: 01562 827251; Clovelly, 22 Wyre Hill, Bewdley DY12 2UE Tel: 01299 402179 — MB ChB 1974 Birm.; DA Eng. 1980; DObst Auckland 1977; DCH Eng. 1976. (Birm.) Clin. Asst. (Anaesth. & A & E) Worcs. Prev: SHO (Paediat.) City Gen. Hosp. Stoke-on-Trent; SHO (O & G) N. Staffs. Matern. Hosp. Stoke-on-Trent; SHO Auckland Hosp. Bd., NZ.

MALCOMSON, Elizabeth Jane The Church Street Practice, David Corbet House, 2 Callows Lane, Kidderminster DY10 2JG Tel: 01562 822051 Fax: 01562 827251 — MB ChB 1974 Birm.; Dip Obst Auckland 1977. (Birm.) Prev: SHO (Paediat.) City Gen. Hosp. Stoke-on-Trent; SHO (O & G) N. Staffs. Matern. Hosp. Stoke-on-Trent; Ho. Phys. Hereford Health Dist.

MALDE, Mr Girish Mulchandbhai Hilly Fields Medical Centre, 172 Adelaide Avenue, London SE4 1JN Tel: 020 8314 5552 Fax: 020 8314 5557; 254 Broad Walk, Blackheath, London SE3 8NQ Tel: 020 8856 5972 — MB BS 1980 Baroda; FRCS Glas. 1985; LRCP LRCS Ed. LRCPS Glas. 1985; DRCOG 1988; MSc. (GP.) Lond. 1998. (MS University of Baroda, India) GP.

MALDE, Kalpee Fort House Surgery, 32 Hersham Road, Walton-on-Thames KT12 1JX Tel: 01932 253055 Fax: 01932 225910; 20 Wauerley Road, weybridge KT13 8UT Tel: 01932 856214 — MB BS 1993 Lond.; DRCOG 1997; DCH UCL 1998. GP.

MALDE, Nikunj Shantilal Alperton Medical Centre, 32 Stanley Avenue, Wembley HA0 4JB Tel: 020 8903 2379 Fax: 020 8903 3027; 71Gordon Avenue, Stanmore HA7 3QR — MB ChB 1981 Aberd.; DCH RCP Lond. 1987. (Univ. Aberd.) Prev: Trainee GP Barnet HA VTS; SHO (Paediat.) Wexham Pk. Hosp. Slough; SHO (Gen. Med.) K. Edwd. VII Hosp. Windsor.

MALDEN, Mark Andrew 24 Furness Close, Bedford MK41 8RN — MB BS 1990 Lond.; DRCOG 1994; DCH RCP Lond. 1993.

MALDEN, Melanie Anne The Health Centre, Endeavour Practice, PO Box 101(a), The Health Centre, 20 Cleveland Square, Middlesbrough TS1 2NX Tel: 01642 242192 Fax: 01642 231809; Waitefield, 113 Roman Road, Linthorpe, Middlesbrough TS5 5QB Tel: 01642 823165 — MB BS 1984 Lond. (UCH/UCL) Prev: Asst. Police Surg. Cleveland Constab.

MALE, Alison Mary 12A Beech Court, 35 Grove Road, Sutton SM1 2AG — MB BS 1990 Lond. SHO (Paediat.) Qu. Mary's Hosp. Sick Childr. Carshalton.

MALE, Christopher Geoffrey 4 Chantry Road, Westlands, Newcastle-under-Lyme ST5 2EU Tel: 01782 617590 Email: cmale@compuserve.com — MB ChB 1968 Liverp.; MRCS Eng. LRCP Lond. 1969; FANZCA 1979; FRCA 1973. (Liverp.) p/t Cons. Anaesth. N. Staffs. Hosp. Trust. Socs: Assn. Anaesths. & Anaesth. Research Soc.; Internat. Trauma Anaesth. & Critical Care Soc.; Soc. Critical Care Med. Prev: Sen. Lect. (Anaesth.) ChristCh. Clin. Sch. Univ. Otago, NZ; Instruc. (Anesth.) Univ. Louisville, USA; Sen. Regist. (Anaesth.) Bristol Health Dist. (T).

MALE, David Alexander 12A Beech Court, 35 Grove Road, Sutton SM1 2AG — MB BS 1990 Lond.

MALE, Erica Jayne Leeway, Mount Hill Rise, Carmarthen SA31 2LA Tel: 01267 235910 — MB BCh 1995 Wales; DFFP. GP Regist. Bridgend VTS; SHO (Paediat.); SHO (Obst. & Gyn.).

MALE, Ian Austin Mackeith Centre, Royal Alexandra Children's Hospital, Dyke Road, Brighton BN1 3JN; 101B Leylands Road, Burgess Hill RH15 8AA Email: ian_and_cathy@lineone.net — MB BCh 1988 Wales; MRCP (UK) 1993. Locum Cons. Community Paediat., Brighton & Middlx. Socs: MRCPCH; MRCP. Prev: Regist.

MALIK

(Paediat.) Alder Hey Hosp. Liverp.; SHO (Paediat.) Llandough Hosp., Univ. Hosp. Wales Cardiff & Roy. Devon & Exeter Hosp.; Ho. Off. (Vasc. Surg.) Univ. Hosp. Wales.

MALE, P Thornbury Health Centre, Eastland Road, Thornbury, Bristol BS35 1DP Tel: 01454 412167 Fax: 01454 419522 — MB BS 1981 London; MB BS 1981 London. G.P Partner. Prev: G.P Tutor, S.mead Hosp.; PCG Prescribing Advisor.

MALEC, Martin John (retired) Freewood House, Freewood Street, Bradfield St George, Bury St Edmunds IP30 0AY Tel: 01284 388682 Email: mjm@doctors.org.uk — MB BS Lond. 1969; MRCS Eng. LRCP Lond. 1969.

MALEK, Batu 25 Heath Drive, Hampstead, London NW3 7SB Tel: 020 7431 1381 — MB BS 1960 Lond.; LMSSA Lond. 1959. (Westm.) Prev: Surg. Regist. St. Chas. Hosp. Lond.

MALEKI-TABRIZI, Anahita Yeovil District Hospital, Higher Kingston, Yeovil BA21 4AT Tel: 01935 707502 Fax: 01935 26850; Killone Cottage, Pembroke, Carlow, Republic of Ireland — MB BCh BAO 1990 NUI; LRCPSI 1990.

MALEKNIAZI, Daryoush 36 Springfield Gardens, Bickley, Bromley BR1 2LZ Tel: 020 8467 9016 Fax: 020 8467 9016 — MD 1969 Tehran; Mem. of Roy. Coll. of Psychiat.; BCPsych 1976 (Board Certificate in Psychiatry). Cons. Psychiat. Ashford Gen. Hosp. Middlx.; Bd. Cert. Psychiat. Iranian Bd. Med. Counc. 1976. Socs: BMA; MDU; Roy. Coll. of Psychiat. Prev: Cons. Psychiat. W. Middlx. Univ. Hosp.

MALEKOTTODJARY, Nina Maria 11a Church Close, Cottenham, Cambridge CB4 8SL — MB BChir 1989 Camb. Clin. Research Phys. Camb. Prev: Clin. Research Phys. Welwyn Gdn. City.; Ho. Off. (Gen. Surg.) Mt. Vernon Hosp.; Ho. Off. (Gen. Med.) W.m. Hosp. Lond.

MALENDA, Andrzej Narcyz Frank Swire Health Centre, Nursery Lane, Halifax HX2; The Croft, Water Hill Lane, Warley, Halifax HX2 7SG — LRCP LRCS 1973 Ed.; LRCP LRCS Ed. LRCPS Glas. 1973; Med. Dipl. Poland 1958; Cert Gen. Surg. Poland 1966. (Lodz) Clin. Asst. (Surg.) Roy. Halifax Infirm. Halifax. Socs: BMA. Prev: Sen. Asst. (Surg.) Dr. K. Jonscher Hosp. Lodz, Poland; Regist. Thoracic Surg. Thoracic Centre Killingbeck Hosp. Leeds; Regist. Gen. Surg. St. Jas. Hosp. Leeds.

MALES, Anthony George Newmarket Road Surgery, 125 Newmarket Road, Cambridge CB5 8HA Tel: 01223 364116 Fax: 01223 366088; 11 Redfern Close, Cambridge CB4 2DT Tel: 01223 355358 — MB BChir Camb. 1987; MA Camb. 1989; MRCGP 1992; DCH RCP Lond. 1991; DRCOG 1990; DLO RCS Eng. 1988. (Camb.) Asst. Dir. (GP Studies) Univ. Camb. Prev: Trainee GP Camb. VTS.

MALES, Rebecca 11 Redfern Close, Cambridge CB4 2DT — MB BChir 1994 Camb.; MSc Georgia 1986. (Camb. & Roy. Free Hosp.)

MALES, Sheena Mary 23 Freston Gadens, Cockfosters, Barnet EN4 9LX — MB BS 1987 Lond.; MRCGP Lond. 1993. p/t Asst. GP Lond. Enfield. Prev: Trainee GP Lecis. VTS.; SHO (Anaesth.) W.m. Hosp.

MALGWA, Arvind Malgwa and Malgwa, RJ Mitchell Medical Centre, 19 Wright Street, Butt Lane, Kidsgrove, Stoke-on-Trent ST7 1NY Tel: 01782 782215 Fax: 01782 774184 — MB BS 1972 Indore.

MALGWA, Pushpa Rani Malgwa and Malgwa, RJ Mitchell Medical Centre, 19 Wright Street, Butt Lane, Kidsgrove, Stoke-on-Trent ST7 1NY Tel: 01782 782215 Fax: 01782 774184 — MB BS 1972 Indore.

MALHAM, Patricia Anne Market Street Surgery, 102 Market Street, Newton-le-Willows WA12 9BP Tel: 01925 221457 — MB ChB 1981 Liverp.; DRCOG 1985.

MALHAS, Mazen Haider The Surgery, 2 Scarsdale Villas, London W8 6PR Tel: 020 7937 3343 Fax: 020 7937 3949 — MB ChB 1971 Baghdad; MB ChB 1971 Baghdad.

MALHAS, Susan Margaret The Surgery, 2 Scarsdale Villas, London W8 6PR Tel: 020 7937 3343 Fax: 020 7937 3949 — MB ChB 1977 Birm.; DRCOG 1979; Cert Family Plann JCC 1979. (Univ. Birm.) Tutor (Gen. Pract.) Cement Project.

MALHERBE, Charl Jacobus Flat 3, Hillsborough, Hilledson Road, Torquay TQ1 1QF — MB ChB 1991 Stellenbosch.

***MALHI, Arfan Mustafa** 40 Wadham Gardens, Greenford UB6 0BP — MB BS 1998 Lond.; MB BS Lond 1998.

MALHI, Gurjhinder 112C Lennard Road, Beckenham BR3 1QS — MB ChB 1990 Manch.; BSc (Hons.) Pharmacol. 1988.

MALHI, Mr Sardul Singh (Surgery), 63-65 Clarence Road, Derby DE23 6LR Tel: 01332 768912; 1A Fairview Close, Littleover, Derby DE23 7SF — MB BS 1957 Agra; FRCS Ed. 1969.

***MALHOMME DE LA ROCHE, Helena Julia Maria** 9 Hunter Road, London SW20 8NZ — MB BS 1998 Lond.; MB BS Lond 1998.

***MALHOTRA, Angeli Elizabeth Denise** 38 Kings Road, Steepleview, Basildon SS15 4AB — MB ChB 1997 Manch.

MALHOTRA, Anil Kumar Palmerston Road Surgery, 148 Palmerston Road, Walthamstow, London E17 6PY Tel: 020 8520 3059 — MB BS 1988 Lond.; MRCGP 1992; Cert. Family Plann. JCC 1992; DRCOG 1992. Prev: SHO St. Bart. & Homerton Hosps GP VTS; Ho. Off. (Med.) K. Geo. & Barking Hosps.; Ho. Off. (Surg.) Roy. Free Hosp. Lond.

MALHOTRA, Anmol Dept. of Diagnostic Imaging, Royal Hospitals NHS Trust, London E1 1BB; 2 Grove End House, Grove End Road, London NW8 9HS — MB BS 1994 Lond. Regist. (Radiol.) Roy. Hosps. NHS Trust Lond.

***MALHOTRA, Anshu** 40 Beresford Gardens, Hounslow TW4 5HW — MB BS 1995 Lond.

MALHOTRA, Aruna Radsham Medical Centre, 33-35 Butt Hill, Kippax, Leeds LS25 7JU Tel: 0113 286 1891 Fax: 0113 286 2550 — MB BS 1968 Sambalpur. (Sambalpur) GP Leeds.

***MALHOTRA, Dev Kumar** 152 Littleheath Road, South Croydon CR2 7SF — BM 1995 Soton.

MALHOTRA, Kumud 5 Deneside Court, Selborne Gardens, Jesmond, Newcastle upon Tyne NE2 1EZ Tel: 0191 281 9602; 13 Aplin Way, Isleworth TW7 4RJ Tel: 020 8580 1613 — MB BS 1991 Newc.; DCH RCP 1997; DRCOG 1998; MRCGP 1998. Prev: GP Regist. N.umbria VTS; SHO (Med.) Sunderland HA.

MALHOTRA, Meenee 29 Cranbourne Gardens, London NW11 0HS — MB ChB 1988 Glas.

***MALHOTRA, Paresh Arjun** Cliffe Lodge, Selby Road, Garforth, Leeds LS25 2AQ — BM BCh 1998 Oxf.; BM BCh Oxf 1998.

MALHOTRA, Prem Krishan Radsham Medical Centre, 33-35 Butt Hill, Kippax, Leeds LS25 7JU Tel: 0113 286 1891 Fax: 0113 286 2550 — MB BS 1959 Punjabi U. (Punjabi U) GP Leeds.

MALHOTRA, Raman 6 Westfield Park, Redland, Bristol BS6 6LT — MB ChB 1993 Bristol.

MALHOTRA, Ramesh Kumar Kensington Street Health Centre, Whitefield Place, Girlington, Bradford BD8 9LB Tel: 01274 496433 Fax: 01274 776466 — MB BS 1968 Allahabad. (Allahabad) GP Bradford, W. Yorks.

MALHOTRA, Usha Flat 3, 11 Lindfield Gardens, London NW3 6PX — MB BS 1960 Lucknow.

MALHOTRA, Vidja Bhushan Greystones Surgery, Greystones, Evie, Orkney KW17 2PQ Tel: 01856 751283 Fax: 01856 751452 — MB BS 1965 Panjab. (Panjab) GP Orkney.

MALI, Monira North Staffordshire Hospital Trust, Child Development Centre, City General, Newcastle Road, Stoke-on-Trent ST4 6QG Tel: 01782 552249 Fax: 01782 552676 — MB BS 1973 Karachi.

MALIK, Mr Adnan Pine Ridge, Beech Drive, Kingswood, Tadworth KT20 6PJ — MB BS 1979 Punjab; FRCS Ed. 1985; LRCP LRCS Ed., LRCPS Glas. 1985.

***MALIK, Ahmad Kamran** 24 Southbrae Drive, Glasgow G13 1PY — MB ChB 1998 Glas.; MB ChB Glas 1998.

MALIK, Ahmar Qaseem 7 Cadbury Road, Birmingham B13 9BH — MB ChB 1991 Dundee.

MALIK, Akila Shahin 104B Oxford Road, Reading RG1 7LL Tel: 0118 9677 200; 47 Plains Road, Nottingham NG3 5JU Tel: 0115 840 9370 — MB BS 1992 Lond. (King's Coll. Lond.) SHO (Obst.) Birm. Wom. Hosp.; Flexivle Train. Med. Prev: SHO (O & G) New Cross Hosp. Wolverhampton; SHO (A & E) John Radcliffe Hosp. Oxf.

MALIK, Mr Ala'a El Din Taha Mustafa 4 Orme Avenue, Colwyn Bay LL28 4LF — MB BS 1983 Khartoum; FRCS Ed. 1994.

MALIK, Ali Akhtar Leigh Infimary, Leigh WN7 1HS Tel: 01942 264546 Fax: 01942 264543; 10 Whiteacre, Shevington Moor, Standish, Wigan WN6 0SH — MB BS 1964 Punjab; MRCPsych 1974; DPM Eng. 1968. (Nishtar Medical College Punjab) Cons. Psychiat. Wigan HA. Prev: Sen. Regist. Roy. Vict. Infirm. Newc.

***MALIK, Amar** 6 Lawrence Road, London SE25 5AA — MB ChB 1995 Manch.

MALIK

*MALIK, Aneela Mushtaq 19 Beatrice Road, Southall UB1 1RJ — MB BS 1997 Lond.

MALIK, Mr Asif Department of Surgery, Edgware General Hospital, Edgware HA8 0AD Tel: 020 8952 2381 — MB BS 1983 Peshawar; FRCSI 1989. Regist. (Urol.) Edgware Gen. Hosp. Middx.

*MALIK, Asif Masood 66 Edmund Road, Birmingham B8 1HE — MB ChB 1998 Manch.; MB ChB Manch 1998.

MALIK, Ather Hameed 138 Allenby Road, Southall UB1 2HL Tel: 020 8575 1700 — MB BS 1981 Punjab; MRCPsych 1989.

MALIK, Bashir Ahmed 67 Meldon Avenue, South Shields NE34 0EL — MB BS 1970 Sind; MFCM (UK) 1982; DCH RCPS Glas. 1973; DPH RCPS Eng. 1972; DIH Soc. Apoth. Lond. 1972. (Liaquat Med. Coll.) Specialist (Community Med.) S. Tyneside HA. Prev: Sen. Regist. (Community Med.) Gwent, Mid. Glam. & S. Glam. HAs; Regist. (Paediat.) Gen. Hosp. S. Shields; Med. Off. Local Health Dept. Mombasa Kenya.

MALIK, D R Robson Street Medical Centre, 54 Robson Street, Liverpool L5 1TG Tel: 0151 263 2295.

MALIK, Deepak Town Hall Surgery, 112 King Street, Dukinfield SK16 4LD Tel: 0161 330 2125 Fax: 0161 330 6899; 6 Arley Close, Richmond Park, Dukinfield SK16 5RB Tel: 0161 343 3034 — MB BS 1978 Bangalor; MB BS Bangalore 1978; LRCP LRCS Ed. LRCPS Glas. 1984. (Bangalore Med. Coll.) Clin. Asst. Tameside Gen. Hosp. Ashton-u-Lyme. Prev: SHO (Psychiat., A & E & Geriat. Med.) Tameside Gen. Hosp. Ashton-u.-Lyne.

*MALIK, Farida Asifa 30 Crockerton Road, London SW17 7HG — MB BS 1996 Lond.

*MALIK, Farukh Rasheed 25 Philbeach Gardens, London SW5 9DY — BM BCh 1998 Oxf.; BM BCh Oxf 1998.

MALIK, Farzana Bellaire, 3 Tadcaster Road, Copmanthorpe, York YO23 3UL — MB BS 1970 Punjab; MB BS Punjab (Pakistan) 1970. (Fatimah Jinnah Med. Coll. Lahore)

*MALIK, Hammad Mehbub 169 Harrow View, Harrow HA1 4SU — MB BS 1994 Lond.

MALIK, Hassan Zakria 10 Lammermuir Gardens, Bearsden, Glasgow G61 4QZ — MB ChB 1992 Glas.; FRCS Glas. 1996.

MALIK, Iqbal Saeed 15 Spencer Road, South Croydon CR2 7EL — MB BChir 1991 Camb.; MA Camb. 1991 BChir 1990; MRCP (UK) 1994. Regist. (Cardiol.) Hammersmith Hosp. Lond. Prev: SHO (Gen. Med.) Roy. Lond. NHS Trust; Ho. Surg. Greenwich Dist. Hosp. Lond.; Ho. Phys. Lewisham & N. S.wark Trust Lond.

MALIK, Irfan Ahmed Black and Partners, Sherwood Health Centre, Elmswood Gardens, Sherwood, Nottingham NG5 4AD Tel: 0115 960 7127 Fax: 0115 985 7899 — MB ChB 1992 Birm.; MRCGP 1996; DRCOG Lond. 1997; DCCH Ed. 1998; DGM Lond. 1998; DFFP Lond. 1998. (Birm.)

MALIK, Jehan Zeb 588 Antrim Road, Belfast BT15 5GN — MB BS 1983 Peshawar; FFA RCSI 1992.

MALIK, Kemal Zulfiqar 80 Dolphin Road, Slough SL1 1TA — MB BS 1987 Lond.; BSc (Hons.) Lond. 1984, MB BS 1987; MRCP (UK) 1990.

MALIK, Manju Narindernath Garden Park Surgery, 225 Denbigh Surgery, Howdon, Wallsend NE28 0PW Tel: 0191 289 2525 Fax: 0191 262 3786 — MB BS 1974 Poona. (Armed Forces Med. Coll.) GP Wallsend, Tyne & Wear. Prev: SHO (Cas.) Orpington Hosp.; SHO (Orthop.) Orpington Hosp.; SHO (Plastic Surg.) W. Norwich Hosp., Norwich.

MALIK, Mohammad Azhar 6A Highgate West Hill, London N6 6JR — MRCS Eng. LRCP Lond. 1987. Trainee GP Univ. Coll. Hosp. Lond VTS.

MALIK, Mr Mohammad Haneef Khan 30 Crockerton Road, London SW17 7HG Tel: 020 8672 9091 — MB BS 1951 Punjab; MB BS Punjab (Pakistan) 1951; FRCS Eng. 1962; DO Eng. 1962. SHMO St. Thos. Hosp. Lond. Socs: Ophth. Soc. U.K. Prev: SHMO Roy. Eye Hosp. Lond.; Regist. St. Paul's Eye Hosp. Liverp.; SHO St. Paul's Eye Hosp. Liverp.

MALIK, Mohammed Iqbal Afzal 37 Castlehill Drive, Newton Mearns, Glasgow G77 5JZ Tel: 0141 639 6049 — MB ChB 1990 Dundee; MRCPI 1996.

MALIK, Mohammed Massaud Alam 17 Fernsway, Sunderland SR3 1YS Tel: 0191 528 2657 — MRCS Eng. LRCP Lond. 1962; DObst RCOG 1964; DCH RCPS Glas. 1965. (Leeds) Mem. LMC. Socs: BMA. Prev: SHO Childr. Hosp. Sunderland; Ho. Phys. & Ho. Surg. Roy. Infirm. Sunderland; Ho. Off. Sunderland Matern. Hosp.

MALIK, Mustansir Ahmed 29A Cherrington Road, London W7 3HL Email: mustansirmalik@yahoo.com — MB BCh 1993 Wales. (Univ. Wales Coll Med.) A & E - Ealing Hosp. Prev: SHO (Plastic Surg.) St. Thos. Hosp. Lond.; SHO (Orthop.) N.Middx Hosp.

MALIK, Nabeel Naseem 15 Irving Mansions, Queens Club Gardens, London W14 9SL — MB BS 1992 Lond.

MALIK, Naeem Mansoor 64 Christopher Road, Selly Oak, Birmingham B29 6QJ — MB ChB 1990 Birm.; ChB Birm. 1990.

MALIK, Nasir Saeed c/o Mr Akram, 64 Minet Drive, Hayes UB3 3JW — MB BS 1984 Pakistan.

MALIK, Naveed Anjum Department of Medicine for The Elderly, Poole General Hospital, Longfleet Road, Poole BH15 2 Tel: 01202 665511 Fax: 01202 442993; 85 Parkstone Avenue, Poole BH14 9LW Tel: 01202 734132 Email: su2976@eclipse.co.uk — MB BS 1979 Punjab, Pakistan; MRCP (UK) 1993. (King Edward, Pakistan) Specialist Regist. (Med. for Elderly) Soton. Gen. Hosp. Prev: Staff Phys. (Geriat.s) Roy. Bournemouth Hosp.; Regist. (Geriat.) Halifax Gen. Hosp.

MALIK, Nusrat Jahan 125 Broadway, Walsall WS1 3HB — MB BS 1975 Punjab; MB BS Punjab (Pakistan) 1975; MRCS Eng. LRCP Lond. 1978. (Fatima Jinnah Med. Coll. Wom. Lahore) SHO (Path.) Jessop Hosp. Wom. Sheff. Prev: SHO (Obst. &gyn.) Sir Ganga Ram Hosp. Lahore, Pakistan & PeterBoro.; Dist. Hosp.; Ho. Off. (Gen. Surg.) Manor Hosp. Walsall.

MALIK, Omar 19 Blakesley Av., London W5 2DN — MB BS 1991 Lond.

MALIK, Qaiser Kuzdafi 58 Marlborough Road, Slough SL3 7LH Tel: 0956 562784 — MB BS 1998 Lond.; MB BS Lond 1998; BSc (Hons), 1995. GP VTS Scheme, W. Middlx. Hosp. Prev: Ho. Phys., W. Middlx. Hosp.; Ho. Surg., W. Middlx. Hosp.

MALIK, Rakesh 44 Reachview Close, Baynes St., Camden Town, London NW1 0TY Tel: 020 7284 3843 — MB BS 1992 Lond. Regist. Rotat. (Child & Family Psychiat.) St. Thos. Hosp. Lond. Prev: Regist. (Gp. Psychother.) & SHO (Community & Rehabil. Psychiat.) Bexley Hosp. Kent; SHO (Gen. Acute Psychiat. & Old Age Psychiat.) St. Thos. Hosp. Lond.

MALIK, Rayaz Ahmed Department of Medicine (M7), Manchester Royal Infirmary, Oxford Road, Manchester M13 9WL Tel: 0161 276 8691 Fax: 0161 274 4740 Email: humza@f1.cmht.nwest.nhs.uk; Carter Villa, Clifton Bank, Rotherham S60 2NA Tel: 01709 361369 — MB ChB 1991 Aberd.; BSc (Hons.) Aberd. 1986, MB ChB 1991; MSc Aberd. 1990; MRCP 1996; PhD Manchester 1997. (Aberdeen) Clin. Lect. Centr. Manch. Hosps. Healthcare Trust; Clin. Lect. & Specialist Regist. Socs: Brit. Diabetic Assn. & Europ. Assn. Study Diabetes; Amer. Diabetes Assn.

*MALIK, Rifat Javed Ahmed 30 Crockerton Road, London SW17 7HG — MB BS 1994 Lond.

*MALIK, Rizwan 38 Allcroft Road, Birmingham B11 3EB — MB ChB 1998 Dund.; MB ChB Dund 1998.

MALIK, Rizwan Ahmed 12 Portland Road, Longsight, Manchester M13 0SA; 12 Portland Road, Longsight, Manchester M13 0SA — MB BS 1998 Lond.; MB BS Lond 1998; MA (CANTAB) 1999; BA (Hons) Camb. 1995. (UMDS Lond. & Pembroke Coll. Camb.) SHO (Med.) N. Manch. Gen. Hosp., Manch. Prev: Ho. Off. (Surg.) William Harvey Hosp. Kent; Ho. Off. (Med.) Qu. Mary's Hosp. Kent.

*MALIK, Rohail 2 Ventnor Av, Ward End, Birmingham B36 8ED — MB ChB 1997 Dundee.

MALIK, Salahuddin Downfield Surgery, 325 Strathmartine Rd, Dundee DD3 8NE Tel: 01382 812111 Email: drmalik@downfield.finix.org.uk — MB ChB 1989 Dundee; BSc (Hons.) Dund 1984; MRCGP 1995.

MALIK, Selma Naz Nuffield Road Medical Centre, Cambridge CB4 1GL Tel: 01223 423424 — MB ChB 1988 Leeds; MRCGP 1994. Retainee in Gen. Pract.; Locum in Gen. Pract. - Yorks. Region.

MALIK, Shabir Ahmad Internist & General Practitioner, Fairway Medical Centre, 7 The Fairway, Leigh-on-Sea SS9 4QN Tel: 01702 421333 Fax: 01702 420707; 253 Station Road, Leigh-on-Sea SS9 3BP Tel: 01702 713099 — MB BS 1974; MD 1980. (Medical College Srinagar Kashmir) Princip. Gen. Med. Practitioner.

MALIK, Shahid West Cheshire (NHS) Trust, Liverpool Road, Chester CH2 1UL Tel: 01244 365000 Fax: 01244 364106; The Conifers, Norlands Lane, Rainhill, Prescot L35 6NR — MB BS 1973

Ranchi; MRCPsych 1983; DPM Eng. 1985. Cons. Psychiat. Learning Disabil. s/i Epilepsy W. Chesh. NHS Trust. Chester. Socs: BMA.

MALIK, Shameem c/o Ashraf Barkat, 195 Pantback Road, Cardiff CF14 6AD — MB BS 1965 Pubjab; FRCOG 1988.

MALIK, Shazia 49 Fairfield Drive, Burnley BB10 2PU — MB ChB 1991 Liverp.

MALIK, Sikander Khan Tel: 0161 431 9339 Fax: 0161 431 5140 — MB BS. (Nagpur Medical College, India) Gen. Practitioner. Socs: BMA; GMC.

MALIK, Tahira Yasmin 18 Seymour Gardens, Hanworth Park, Feltham TW13 7PQ — MB ChB 1990 Manch.

MALIK, Tassadaque Hussain 9 Canford Grove, Allerton, Bradford BD15 7AT — MB ChB 1993 Manch.; BSc St. And. 1990. Lect. Sch. Biol Scis. Univ. Manch.

MALIK, Yog Darshan The Surgery, 32 Chinbrook Road, London SE12 9TH Tel: 020 8857 4660 Fax: 202 8857 6374; 63 Hayes Way, Beckenham BR3 6RR Tel: 020 8650 1652 — MD 1974 Delhi; MD (Paediat.) Delhi 1974; MB BS Gauhati 1969; DCH Eng. 1974. (Gauhati)

***MALIK, Zafar Iqbal** 138 Lovely Lane, Warrington WA5 1PQ — MB ChB 1994 Liverp.

MALIK, Zafar Iqbal Stainforth Road Surgery, 33 Stainforth Road, London E17 9RB Tel: 020 8521 8050 — MB BS 1965 Punjab. Phys. Ch.. Hill. Clin. Walthamstow. Prev: Regist. (Orthop. Surg.) Vict. Hosp. Worksop; Med. Asst. (Trauma & Orthop. Surg.) W.on-Super-Mare Gen. Hosp.

MALIK, Zarrar Mahmood 20 Larkspur Gd., Luton — MB BS 1980 Punjab.

MALIM, Philip Francis (retired) 36 The Strand, Topsham, Exeter EX3 0AY — MRCS Eng. LRCP Lond. 1938; BA Cantab. 1932. Prev: Ho. Phys. W. Hants. Hosp. Bournemouth.

MALIN, Adam Simon Clinical Sciences, London School of Hygiene & Tropical Medicine, London WC1E 7HT Tel: 020 7927 2457 Fax: 020 7637 4314; 78 Dukes Avenue, Muswell Hill, London N10 2QA Email: adam.malin@mcmail.com — MB ChB 1985 Bristol; BSc (Cell. Path.) Bristol 1982; MRCP (UK) 1989; DTM & H RCP Lond. 1990; PhD Lond. 1998. (Bristol) Specialist Regist. (Thoracic Med.) Lond. Chest Hosp., Lond.; Hon. Clin. Lect. (Clin. Sci.) Lond. Sch. Hyg. & Trop. Med. Socs: Fell. (Mem. Counc.) Roy. Soc. Trop. Med. & Hyg.; Brit. Thoracic Soc. Prev: Lect. (Clin. Pharmacol.) Univ. Zimbabwe, Harare; Regist. Hosp. Trop. Dis. Lond.; Regist. (HIV) Middlx. Hosp. Lond.

MALIN, David Robert The Surgery, 275 Ashby Road, Scunthorpe DN16 2AB Tel: 01724 843375 Fax: 01724 270101 Email: david.malin@gp-b81113.nhs.uk; 112 Glover Road, Scunthorpe DN16 2AB Tel: 01724 342510 — MB ChB 1982 Leeds; MRCGP 1986; DRCOG 1985. Course Organiser Doncaster VTS.

MALING, David John Bissoe Surgery, Bissoe Road, Carnon Downs, Truro TR3 6JD Tel: 01872 863221 Fax: 01872 864113; Penweir, Restronguet Weir, Falmouth TR11 5SS Tel: 01326 372723 — MB BS 1981 Lond.; DCH RCP Lond. 1984; DRCOG 1983. (St. Thomas')

MALING, John Allan, MC 8 Harland Way, Southborough, Tunbridge Wells TN4 0TQ Tel: 01892 529595 Fax: 01892 529595 — LMSSA Lond. 1954. (St. Thos.) Socs: BMA. Prev: Ho. Phys. Gravesend & N. Kent Hosp.; Ho. Surg. Ramsgate Gen. Hosp.; Obst. Ho. Surg. Kent & Canterbury Hosp.

MALINS, Andrew Francis Department of Anaesthetics, Queen Elizabeth Hospital, Edgbaston, Birmingham B15 2TH Tel: 0121 627 2060 Fax: 0121 627 2062; Arden House, 263 Blossomfield Road, Solihull B91 1TA — MB ChB 1974 Birm.; FFA RCSI 1979; FFA RCS Eng. 1979. Cons. Anaesth. Qu. Eliz. Hosp. & Wom. Hosp. Birm. Prev: Sen. Regist. (Anaesth.) S.W. RHA.

MALINS, David Middlemore Sarum House Surgery, 3 St. Ethelbert Street, Hereford HR1 2NS Tel: 01432 265422 Fax: 01432 358440; Quarry Bank, Callow, Hereford HR2 8DD — MB ChB 1978 Birm.; MRCP (UK) 1981; DRCOG 1984. Prev: Med. Supt. St. John's Hosp. Mzuzu Malawi.

MALINS, Dennis Frederick James (retired) Mayfield, Owl St., E. Lambrook, South Petherton TA13 5HF Tel: 01460 241652 — MB ChB Birm. 1949; MFCM 1974; DPH Bristol 1969. Prev: Specialist Community Phys. (Child Health) Dyfed HA.

MALINS, Mr Timothy John Church House, The Butts, Betley, Crewe CW3 9AS Tel: 01270 820778 Email:

100747.1634@compuserve.com — MB BS 1986 Lond.; FRCS Ed. 1989. (Charing Cross, Lond.) Cons., Oral & Maxillofacial Surg., N. Staffs. Trust, Stoke on Trent. Socs: Fell.Brit. Asso. Of Oral & Maxillofacial surgens.; Europ. Assn. Craniomaxillofacial Surgs.

MALIPHANT, Henry Brace Red Court, St. Peters, Carmarthen SA33 5DR Tel: 01267 7182 — MRCS Eng. LRCP Lond. 1945; FFA RCS Eng. 1978; DA Eng. 1947. (St. Geo.) Cons. Anaesth. W. Wales Hosp. Carmarthen. Socs: Assn. Anaesths. Prev: Asst. Res. Anaesth. St. Geo; Hosp.; Gp. Regist. Anaesth. Roy. Infirm. Preston.

MALISANO, Lawrence Pietro Royal National Orthopaedic Hospital, Brockley Hill, Stanmore HA7 4LP Tel: 020 8954 2300 — MB BS 1980 Queensland; FRACS 1988.

MALKAN, Mr Dilipkumar Hemchand 3 Sneyd Avenue, Westlands, Newcastle ST5 2QA Tel: 01782 717806 Fax: 01782 717806; Whitting Tree Farm, Dymock, Newent GL18 2AB Tel: 01531 890207 — MB BS 1980 Karnatak; FRCS Glas. 1986; MRCS Eng. LRCP Lond. 1986. Waiting List Initiative Surg. Leighton Hosp. Crewe. Prev: Regist. (Orthop.) Tameside Hosp. Ashton-under-Lyne, Stafford Dist. Gen. Hosp. & Lincoln Co. Hosp.

MALKHANDI, Anita Devi Four Seasons Medical Centre, Orford Clinic, Capesthrone Road, Orford, Warrington WA2 9AR Tel: 01925 419784 Fax: 01925 234221; The Surgery, 1 Manchester Road, Warrington WA1 3AD Tel: 01925 653218 Fax: 01925 244737 — MB ChB 1989 Liverp.; MRCGP 1994.

MALKI, Mr Abdalla Abd-El-Hamid Gabrel 6 Millar House, Merchant's Road, Clifton, Bristol BS8 4HA Tel: 0117 973 9739 Fax: 01454 201221 — MB BCh 1968 Cairo; FRCS Ed. 1980.

MALKI, Daniel Saba Edith Cavell Hospital, Bretton Gate, Peterborough PE3 9GZ Tel: 01733 330777; 32 Bowness Way, Gunthorpe, Peterborough PE4 7NG Tel: 01733 320953 — MB ChB 1975 Mosul; DLO RCS Eng. 1986. Staff Grade (ENT) Edith Cavell Hosp. P'boro. Socs: Assoc. Mem. Brit. Assn. Otolaryngol. Prev: Regist. & SHO (ENT) N.ampton Gen. Hosp.; SHO (Gen. Surg.) King's Mill Hosp.

***MALKIN, Christopher John** 26 Priory Road, West Bridgford, Nottingham NG2 5HU — MB ChB 1998 Sheff.; MB ChB Sheff 1998.

MALKIN, Jacqueline Carol 20 Coniger Road, London SW6 3TA Tel: 020 7731 5527 — MB BS Newc. 1969; DMJ 1994 Soc. of Apothecaries. Sen. Forens. Med. Exam. (Clin. Forens. Med.) Metrop. Polic. Serv. Lond. Socs: Fell. Roy. Soc. Med.; Hon. Sec. Sect. Clin. Forens. and Legal Med.

MALL, Keshaw Prasad Park Road Medical Centre, Bradford BD5 0SG Tel: 01274 721924 Fax: 01274 776466 — MB BS 1972 Kanpur.

MALLABAND, Brian Carvell (retired) Great Island House, Muchelney, Langport TA10 0DJ Tel: 01458 253333 — MRCS Eng. LRCP Lond. 1957; DObst RCOG 1965. Prev: GP Watford.

MALLABAND, Elizabeth Yelverton Surgery, Westella Road, Yelverton PL20 6AS Tel: 01822 852202 Fax: 01822 852260 — MB ChB 1977 Bristol; DRCOG 1979; MRCGP 1982. Prev: Asst. GP Plymouth.

MALLACE, Betty (retired) St. Mary's Cottage, Dunblane FK15 0EZ — MB ChB 1946 Ed.; MRCOG 1953. Prev: Cons. O & G Thornhill Matern. Hosp. Renfrewsh.

MALLADI, Krishna Sankar Flat 8 Block A, Broomfield Residences, Kennington Road, Willesborough, Ashford TN24 0LY — MB BS 1996 Lond.

MALLADI, Ram Kumar Flat 101, Ivy Lane, Osler Road, Headington, Oxford OX3 9DY Email: r_malladi@yahoo.com — MB BS 1996 Lond.; BA Camb. 1991. (King's College School of Medicine and Dentistry) SHO Rotat. (Med.) John Radcliffe Hosp. Oxf. Prev: SHO Gen. Med. & Cardiol. Frimley Pk. Hosp. Surrey; SHO Elderly care & Gen. Med. Frimley Pk. Hosp. Surrey; Ho. Off. (Surg.) Greenwich Dist. Hosp.

MALLAGH, Doreen Elizabeth (retired) 12 Sussex House, Hartington Place, Eastbourne BN21 3BH Tel: 01323 642042 — MB BCh BAO Dub. 1951; DObst RCOG 1954.

MALLAIAH, Shubha Department of Anaesthetics, Liverpool Women's Hospital, Crown St., Liverpool L8 7SS Tel: 0151 708 9988 Fax: 0151 702 4006; 4 Green Meadows, Lowton, Warrington WA3 1LW — MB BS 1979 Bangalore; FFA RCS Eng. 1983. Cons. Anaesth. Liverp. O & G Univ. Socs: Obst. Anaesth. Assn.; Eur. Soc. Regional Anaesth.

MALLAL

MALLAL, Gwendolen Maureen 30 Chelsea Crescent, Chelsea Harbour, London SW10 0XB Tel: 020 7376 5848 Fax: 020 7352 1731 — MB BS 1958 Malaya; DCH Lond. 1958. Socs: Life Mem. Malaysia Med. Assoc.

***MALLAM, Katherine Marie** 11 Church Street, Ribchester, Preston PR3 3XP — MB ChB 1996 Liverp.

MALLAM, William David Cave Westgate Surgery, 15 Westgate, Chichester PO19 3ET Tel: 01243 782866 — MB BS 1963 Lond.; DObst RCOG 1965. (St. Thos.) Med. Off. Roy. Milit. Police Chichester. Socs: Soc. Occupat. Med.; Med. Assur. Soc.; Soc. Expert Witness. Prev: Ho. Surg., Obst. Ho. Surg. & Cas. Off. St. Thos. Hosp. Lond.

MALLARD-SMITH, Rebecca Jane John Hampden Surgery, 97 High Street, Prestwood, Great Missenden HP16 9EU Tel: 01494 890900 — MB BS 1992 Lond.; DFFP 1996. GP; Family Plann. Doctor.

***MALLEN, Christian David** 6 Catherton Park, Cleobury Mortimer, Kidderminster DY14 8EA — BM BS 1998 Nottm.; BM BS Nottm 1998.

MALLENDER, Lilian Janet (retired) Highlands, Boxes Lane, Horsted Keynes, Haywards Heath RH17 7EJ — MB ChB 1944 Leeds; DMRT Eng. 1949. Prev: Cons. Radiotherap. Gen. Infirm. & Cookridge Hosp. Leeds.

MALLEPADDI, Nageswara Rao Belgrave Medical Centre, 116 Belgrave Road, Dresden, Stoke-on-Trent ST3 4LR Tel: 01782 593344 Fax: 01782 593344 — MB BS 1971 Andhra; MB BS 1971 Andhra.

***MALLERY, Erica Claudette** Old Stonelynk Edge, 63 Battery Hill, Fairlight, Hastings TN35 4AP — BM 1998 Soton.; BM Soton 1998.

MALLESON, Steven Miles 64 St James Lane, Muswell Hill, London N10 3RD — MB BS 1975 Lond.; MFOM RCP Lond. 1988.

MALLET, Catherine Moira 22 Hurrell Road, Cambridge CB4 3RH — MB BS 1985 Lond.; BA (Hons.) Camb. 1982; MRCGP 1994; DRCOG 1989; DCH RCP Lond. 1988; DFFP RCOG 1997.

MALLET, Mark Louis 22 Hurrell Road, Cambridge CB4 3RH Email: mmallet@clara.net — MB BS 1986 Lond.; MA Oxf. 1987; MRCP (UK) 1996. (Lond. Hosp. Med. Coll.) Specialist Regist. Geriat. Med. - E. Anglia; MDiv Washington DC 1993. Socs: Brit. Soc. Echocardiogr. Prev: SHO (Gen. Med.) W. Suff. Hosp. Bury St. Edmunds; SHO (Gen. Med.) Kettering Gen. Hosp.; Sho (Med/Cardio) Bedford Hosp.

MALLETT, Bernard Louis (retired) The Tilehouse, 27 Tilehouse St, Hitchin SG5 2DY Tel: 01462 432659 — MB BS 1952 Lond.; MB B (Hons.) Lond. 1952; MRCP Lond. 1956; MRCS Eng. LRCP Lond. 1952; FRCPsych 1983, M 1971; DPM Eng. 1957. Hon. Cons. Psychiat. Lister Hosp. Stevenage. Prev: Research Fell. (Ment. Health) Guy's Hosp. Lond.

MALLETT, Brenda Leoda Antony Road Surgery, 16 Antony Road, Torpoint PL11 2JW Tel: 01752 813277 Fax: 01752 815733 — MB BS 1974 Lond.; MRCGP 1983; DRCOG 1985. (Roy. Free) Prev: Med. Regist. P. of Wales Hosp. Tottenham; SHO (O & G) N. Middlx. Hosp. Lond.

MALLETT, David Stephen 39 Dale Bank Crescent, New Whittington, Chesterfield S43 2DN — MB ChB 1991 Sheff.

MALLETT, Eric (retired) Norrard, 8 Godwyn Road, Folkestone CT20 2LA — MB BS 1955 Lond.; MRCS Eng. LRCP Lond. 1955; MRCGP 1965; DObst RCOG 1957. Prev: Police Surg. Folkestone.

MALLETT, Jean Mary (retired) Pinehurst, Herbert Road, Salcombe TQ8 8HN Tel: 01548 842208 — MB ChB Manch. 1949; DPH Manch. 1964.

MALLETT, Michael Ian New Wortley Health Centre, 15 Green Lane, Tong Road, Leeds LS12 1JE Tel: 0113 231 0626 Fax: 0113 231 9428; Laurel Bank, Newlay Wood Road, Horsforth, Leeds LS18 4LF Tel: 0113 258 2398 — MB ChB 1965 Leeds. Dep. Med. Ref. Leeds.

MALLETT, Paul BKCW Trust, c/o 11-15 Brondesbury Road, London NW6 6BX Tel: 020 8937 6331 Fax: 020 8937 6333 Email: p.mallett@talk21.com; Flat 6, 37 Canfield Gardens, London NW6 3JN Tel: 020 7624 5633 — MB BS 1985 Lond.; MRCPsych 1989. (Guy's Hospital) Cons. Psychiat. BKCW Ment. Health Trust. Prev: Lect. (Psychiat.) Univ. Hosp. Wales Cardiff; Regist. (Psychiat.) St. Bart's Hosp. Lond.; Research Regist. Homerton Hosp. Lond.

MALLETT, Peter John Penthouse C, 48-66 Barkston Gardens, London SW5 0EL — MRCS Eng. LRCP Lond. 1977.

MALLETT, Reginald (retired) 44 Pinewood Road, Ferndown BH22 9RR — BD Lond. 1955; MB ChB Birm. 1970; FFCM 1985, M 1980. Prev: Dist. Gen. Manager Cheltenham & Dist. HA.

MALLETT, Richard Brendan Peterborough District Hospital, Thorpe Road, Peterborough PE3 6DA Tel: 01733 874000 Fax: 01733 874001; Brights Lodge, Luddington, Peterborough PE8 5QX — MB BS 1980 Lond.; MRCS Eng. LRCP Lond. 1979; MRCP (UK) 1985; FRCP 1999. (Guy's) Cons. Dermat. P'boro. Dist. Hosp. Socs: Fell. Roy. Soc. Med. Prev: Sen. Regist. (Dermat.) St. Geo. Hosp. Lond. & St. Helier Hosp. Carshalton; Regist. (Dermat.) Addenbrooke's Hosp. Camb.; Research SHO (Dermat.) W.m. Hosp. Lond.

MALLETT, Sophie Ann The Surgery, 95 Monks Road, Lincoln LN2 5HR Tel: 01522 530334; Church Farm House, Dumstom, Lincoln LN4 2EW — MB BS 1987 Lond. (Middlesex) GP Princip. The Surg. 95 Monklands Rd. Lincoln. Socs: Lincoln Med. Soc.

MALLETT, Susan Veronica Royal Free Hospital, Department Anaesthesia, Pond St., Hampstead, London NW3 2QG — MB BS 1979 Lond.; FFA RCS Lond. 1985. Cons. Anaesth. Roy. Free Hosp. Lond. Prev: Sen. Regist. Roy. Free Hosp. Lond.; Asst. Prof. Presby. Univ. Hosp. Pittsburgh PA., USA.; Fell. Liver Transpl. Anaesth. Pittsburgh PA., USA.

MALLETT, Vivienne Ann Heighington House, Heighington, Lincoln LN4 1RJ Tel: 01522 790704 — MB BS 1961 Lond. (St. Mary's) Socs: Lincoln Med. Soc.

MALLEY, Roy 34 Lodge Close, Hamsterley Mill, Rowlands Gill NE39 1HB Tel: 01632 542531 — MRCS Eng. LRCP Lond. 1954; BA Camb. 1950. (Univ. Coll. Hosp.)

MALLICK, Dipak Kumar 11 Badgemore Court, Two Mile Ash, Milton Keynes MK8 8AF Tel: 01908 567626 Fax: 01908 567626 — MB BS 1969 Calcutta; DTM & H Liverp. 1974; Cert JCC Lond. 1975; FRSH 1993; FRIPHH 1997. (N.R.S. Med. Coll.) Med. Adviser BAMS (DSS). Socs: BMA & Fac. for Comm. Health. Prev: SCMO Bucks. AHA; SHO (Geriat.) St. Margt.'s Hosp. Stratton St. Margt.'s; Sen. Ho. Off. (Psychiat.) Severalls Hosp., Colchester.

MALLICK, Golap High Road Surgery, 706-708 High Road, Leyton, London E10 6JP Tel: 020 8539 4707 Fax: 020 8539 1690 — MB BS 1962 Calcutta; MB BS 1962 Calcutta.

MALLICK, Jivinder Kaur 254 Amhurst Road, London N16 7UP Tel: 020 7254 5293 — MB BS 1960 Baroda.

MALLICK, Krishna Bhusan High Road Surgery, 706-708 High Road, Leyton, London E10 6JP Tel: 020 8539 4707 Fax: 020 8539 1690 — MB BS 1961 Calcutta.

MALLICK, Sir Netar Prakash Department of Renal Medicine, Royal Infirmary, Manchester M13 9WL Tel: 0161 276 4411 Fax: 0161 273 8022; 43 Porchfield Square, St Johns Gardens, Manchester M3 4FG Tel: 0161 279 1621 — MB ChB 1959 Manch.; BSc Manch. 1956; FRCP Ed. 1992; FRCP Lond. 1976, M 1965. (Manch.) Prof. Renal Med. Univ. Manch. & Cons. Phys. Manch. Roy. Infirm.; Med. Dir. Centr. Manch. Healthcare Trust. Socs: (Ex-Pres.) Renal Assn.; Eur. Renal Assn. (Ex-Chairm. Registration Comm. & Counc. Mem.). Prev: Cons. Phys. i/c Dept. Renal Med. Manch. Roy. Infirm.

MALLICK, Shahadat Hossain Bloxwich Hospital, Reeves St., Bloxwich, Walsall WS3 2JJ Tel: 01922 858600 Fax: 01922 858639; 186 Clarence Road, Four Oaks, Sutton Coldfield B74 4LD Tel: 0121 308 7563 — MB BS 1970 Dacca; DPM Eng. 1980. Sen. Community Med. Off. (Psychiat.) Broxwich Hosp. Walsall.

MALLICK, Mr Subhendu Nath (retired) 21 East Moor Road, Wakefield WF1 3RZ Tel: 01924 379786 — MB BS 1958 Calcutta; FRCS Eng. 1970; FRCS Ed. 1968. Med. Adviser & Assessor Indep. Tribunal Serv. NE Region. Prev: Retd. Gen. Surg. NHS.

MALLIGIANNIS, Pantelis Kings College Hospital, Harris Birthright Research Centre, Denmark Hill, London SE5 9RS — Ptychio Iatikes Athens 1984.

MALLIK, Arabinda Kumar Houghton Regis Medical Centre, Peel Street, Houghton Regis, Dunstable LU5 5EZ Fax: 01582 865483; 19 Hawthorn Close, Dunstable LU6 3BL Tel: 01582 518098 — MB BS 1968 Calcutta; BSc 1963; FRCOG 1991, M 1977, D 1976; DGO Calcutta 1971. GP Regist. Dunstable. Socs: Med. Protec. Soc. Prev: Cons. O & G Matern & Childr. Hosp. Damman, Saudi Arabia.

MALLIK, Debabrata (Surgery), 45 St John's Avenue, Harlesden, London NW10 4ED Tel: 020 8965 4347 Fax: 020 8965 4450; 6 Folly Close, Radlett WD7 8DR Tel: 0378 412993 — MB BS 1957

Calcutta; ECFMG Cert. 1968; Cert FPA 1969; MRCOG 1963; DObst RCOG 1960; DGO Calcutta 1959. (Nilratan Sarkar Med. Coll.) Clin. Asst. (Gyn.) Samarit. Hosp. Lond.; Vasectomy Surg. Pk.side HA; Med. Off. (Family Plann.) Ealing HA. Socs: BMA; Med. Defence Union. Prev: Regist. (O & G) Sunderland Gen. Hosp.; Regist. (O & G) W. Cumbld. Hosp. Hensingham.

MALLIK, Mr Manas Kumar Spring Bank West Surgery, 919 Spring Bank West, Hull HU5 5BE Tel: 01482 351219 Fax: 01482 351930 — MB BS 1964 Calcutta; FRCS Ed. 1973.

***MALLIK, Meeta** 54 Acton Avenue, Appleton, Warrington WA4 5PT — MB ChB 1998 Manch.; MB ChB Manch 1998.

MALLIK, Samarendranath 5 Birmingham Road, Walsall WS1 2LX Tel: 01922 20303 Fax: 01922 649526; 89 Belvidere Road, Walsall WS1 3AU Tel: 01922 24014 — MB BS 1962 Calcutta; MRCOG 1969; DGO Calcutta 1964. (Calcutta) Socs: BMA. Prev: Regist. (O & G) Manor Hosp. Walsall.; SHO (O & G & Med.) Warrington Gen. Hosp.

MALLIK, Subratakumar Clayponds Hospital, Sterling Place, South Ealing, London W5 4RN Tel: 020 8560 4011 Fax: 020 8568 7341; 22 South Way, Harrow HA2 6EP Tel: 0208 863 1529 — MD 1976 Calcutta; MRCP (UK) 1982; MB BS 1972. (NRS Medical College Calcutta) Clin. Asst. in Med. Stroke Rehabil. Clayponds Hosp. S. Ealing; Clin. Asst. in Med. Gastroentorology & Diabetes Ealing Hosp. Socs: Roy. Coll. Phys.s; Fell., Internat. Coll. of Angiology; Life Mem. Assn. Phys.s of India. Prev: Cons. Phys. Internal Med. P. Salman Hosp. Riyadh, Saudi Arabia; Regist. (Gen. Med.) Pontefract Gen. Infirm.; Regist. (Geriat. Med.) Wrexham Maelor Hosp.

MALLIK, Tushar Kanti 7 Brant Road, Scunthorpe DN15 7BS — MB BS 1973 Calcutta.

MALLIKARJUN, Mr Totalam Sreenivason Accident & Emergency Department, Stepping Hill Hospital, Poplar Grove, Stockport SK2 7JE — MB BS 1962 Mysore; FRCS Ed. 1970.

MALLINDER, Petrina Anne Department of Anaesthetics, Darlington Memorial Hospital, Hollyhurst Road, Darlington DL3 6HX Tel: 01325 380100 Fax: 01325 743875 Email: mallipa@hotmail.com; West Kirby, 208 Conisciffe Road, Darlington DL3 8PL Tel: 01325 362240 Email: mallipa@hotmail.com — MB BS 1988 Lond.; BSc (Biochem.) Lond. 1985; MRCP (UK) 1991; FRCA 1994. (London Hospital) Cons. Anaesth. & Director ITU Darlington Memor. Hosp. Socs: Assn. of Anaesth.s; Roy. Coll. of Anaesth.s; Brit. Soc. of Orthopaedic Anaesth.s. Prev: Regist. (Anaesth.) Middlesbrough Gp. Hosp.; SHO (Anaesth.) N.ampton Gen. Hosp. & S. Tees Acute Hosp. Trust; SHO (Med.) Darlington Memor. Hosp.

MALLINSON, Annette Campbell Department of Haematology, Western Infirmary, Glasgow G11 6NT Tel: 0141 211 2156 Fax: 0141 211 6296; 19 Kew Terrace, Glasgow G12 0TE Tel: 0141 334 6205 — MB ChB 1965 Glas. Assoc. Specialist Haemat. Dept. W.. Infirm. Glas.

MALLINSON, Christopher Niels 134 Harley Street, London W1N 1AH Tel: 020 7935 4849 Fax: 020 7935 6826; 6 Blackheath Park, London SE3 9RR Tel: 020 8852 9690 — MB BChir Camb. 1961; FRCP Lond. 1975, M 1963; MRCS Eng. LRCP Lond. 1960. Cons. Phys. & Gastroenterol. Univ. Hosp. Lewisham (Emerit.); Phys. Cons. in Med. Communication; Dir. Communications Research Gp. Univ. Hosp. Lewisham. Socs: Brit. Soc. Gastroenterol.; Assn. Phys.; Pancreatic Soc. Prev: Cons. Gastroenterol. Greenwich Dist. Hosp. & Lect. (Physiol.) Guy's Hosp. Med. Sch. Lond.; Research Fell. (Gastroenterol.) Pennsylvania Hosp., USA; Pres. Europ. Bd. Gastroenterol.

MALLINSON, Claire 135 Woodwarde Road, Dulwich, London SE22 8UP — MB BS 1990 Lond.; FRCA 1995. (Kings Coll. Hosp. Lond.) Cons. (Anaesth.) St. Thomas's Hosp. Socs: Assn. Anaesth. GB & Irel. (Chairm. Gp. Anaesth. in Train.). Prev: Specialist Regist. (Anaesth.) Middlx. Hosp. Lond.; Specialist Regist. Brompton Hosp. Lond.; Regist. (Anaesth.) Chase Farm Hosp. Enfield & Middlx. Hosp. Lond.

MALLINSON, Eileen Anne (retired) 20 Bunley Orchard, Staines Lane, Chertsey KT16 8PS Tel: 0193 28 61537 — MRCS Eng. LRCP Lond. 1933. Prev: Asst. Co. Med. Off. Kent.

MALLINSON, Lady (Margaret) 25 Wimpole Street, London W1M 7AD Tel: 020 7580 7919 — MB BS 1953 Lond.; BA (Hons.) Lond. 1942, MB BS 1953. (St. Geo.) Socs: Fell. Roy. Soc. Med. Prev: Admin. Med. Off. Med. Research Counc. Lond. 1955-70.; Ho. Surg. Childr. Dept. St. Geo. Hosp. Lond.; Resid. Surg. Off. Wimbledon Hosp. Lond.

MALLINSON, Robert Henry Department of Emergency Medicine, Emergency Assessment Unit, The Norfolk and Norwich University Hospital, Norwich Tel: 01603 287955; Crossways, Keswick Road, Cringleford, Norwich NR4 6UG — MB ChB 1989 Manch.; DGM; MRCP (UK) 1995. (Manchester) Cons. Gen. Med., Norf. and Norwich Univ. NHS Trust. Socs: RCP. Prev: Sen. Regist. (Med.) W. Suff. Hosp.; Sen. Regist. (MFE) W. Suff. Hosp.

MALLINSON, Thomas Jeffrey (retired) Conigre, 64 Ashby Road, Tamworth B79 8AD Tel: 01827 62940 — MB BS 1952 Durh.

MALLION, Jennifer Ann 37 Cliff Hill, Gorleston, Great Yarmouth NR31 6DQ — MB BCh BAO 1975 Dub.

***MALLIPEDDI, Rajeev** Yamuna, London Road, Binfield, Bracknell RG42 4AB — MB BS 1997 Lond.

MALLOCH, Andrew James Health Centre, 20 Duncan St., Greenock PA15 4LY — MB ChB 1986 Glas.

MALLOCH, Duncan Keith 17 Lyndhurst Road, Exeter EX2 4PA — MB ChB 1966 Ed.

MALLOCH, Mr John Donald (retired) 124 Kingsway, Chandlers Ford, Eastleigh SO53 5DW Tel: 023 8026 6316 — MB ChB 1944 Ed.; FRCS Ed. 1952. Prev: Orthop. Surg. Scunthorpe, Lincoln & GainsBoro. Hosps.

MALLOCH, Thomas Back Road Surgery, 7 Back Road, Dailly, Girvan KA26 9SH Tel: 01465 811224 Fax: 01465 811518 — MB ChB 1981 Glas.

MALLON, Eleanor Catherine 28 Alma Square, London NW8 9PY — MB BS 1987 Lond.; MRCP (UK) 1991. (St George's Hospital Medical School London)

MALLON, Elizabeth Ann 1012 Great Western Road, Glasgow G12 0NR — MB ChB 1984 Glas.

MALLON, James Henry Banbridge Medical Group Centre, Linenhall Street, Banbridge BT32 3EG; 5 Rugby Avenue, Banbridge BT32 3NA Tel: 018206 27062 — MB BCh BAO 1977 Belf.; DRCOG 1979.

MALLON, Julie Margaret Central Health Centre, North Carbrain Road, Cumbernauld, Glasgow G67 1BJ Tel: 01236 737214 Fax: 01236 781699 — MB ChB 1990 Glas.

MALLON, Maria Josephine Tempo Medical Centre, Main Street, Edenmore Tempo, Enniskillen BT94 3LU Tel: 028 8954 1216 — MB BCh BAO 1985 Belf.; MRCGP 1989; DRCOG 1990; DCH RCP Lond. 1990.

***MALLON, Patrick William Gerard** 6 Coolnasilla Park S., Glen Road, Belfast BT11 8LF — MB BCh BAO 1995 Belf.; BSc (Hons.) Leeds 1993.

MALLON, Timothy John Annandale Medical Centre, Mobberley Road, Knutsford WA16 8HR Tel: 01565 755222 Fax: 01565 652049 — MB ChB 1983 Manch.; MRCGP 1987; DRCOG 1987; DCH RCP Lond. 1985.

MALLORY, Su Hill House, Bridge Road, Leigh Woods, Bristol BS8 3PE — MB ChB 1993 Manch.

MALLOTT, Lavinia Mary (retired) 12 Georges Lane, Horwich, Bolton BL6 6RT — MB ChB 1949 Manch. Prev: GP.

MALLOWS, Harry Russell, CStJ, Surg. Rear-Admiral Retd. (retired) 1 Shear Hill, Petersfield GU31 4BB Tel: 01730 263116 — MB BChir Camb. 1945; MA Camb. 1946, MD 1959; FFOM RCP Lond. 1982, MFOM 1978; FFPHM RCP (UK) 1974; DPH Lond. 1957; DIH Soc. Apoth. Lond. 1957. Prev: Hon. Phys. to HM the Qu.

MALLOY, Nigel Philip Liverpool Road Surgery, 523 Liverpool Road, Irlam, Manchester M44 6ZS — MB BCh BAO 1985 Belf.

MALLUCCI, Mr Conor Laurence Walton Centre for Neurology & Neurosurgery, Lower Lane, Fazavevley, Liverpool L9 7LT Tel: 0151 529 5671 Fax: 0151 529 5090; Email: cons@msn.com — MB BS Lond. 1989; FRCS Eng. 1993; FRCS (SN) 1997. (Lond.) Cons. (Paediat. Neurosurg.) Walton Centre Neurol. & Neurosurg. & Aldehay Hosps. Liverp. Prev: Sen. Regist. (Neurosurg.) Qu. Med. Centre Nottm.; Regist. (Neurosurg.) Midl. Centre for Neurol. & Neurosurg. W. Midl.

MALLUCCI, Giovanna Rachele Department of Neurology, Hammersmith Hospital, Du Cane Road, London W12 0NN; 3 New End Square, London NW3 1LP — MB BS 1988 Lond.; BA (Hons.) Oxf. 1985; MB BS (Hons.) Lond. 1988; MRCP (UK) 1991. Regist. (Neurol.) Hammersmith Hosp. Lond.

MALLUCCI

MALLUCCI, Patrick Lawrence 20 Sunny Hill Court, Sunningfields Road, London NW4 4RB — MB ChB 1989 Leic.

MALLYA, Balamani 36 Fairdale Gardens, Upper Richmond Road, London SW15 6JW Tel: 020 8788 6481 — MB BS 1969 Kerala.

MALLYA, Jagadish Ullal 23 Overton Place, West Bromwich B71 1RL Tel: 0121 553 1831 ext. 3737 — MB BS 1978 Mysore; MRCP (UK) 1983.

MALLYA, Ramesh Kamalaksha Halton General Hospital, Hospital Way, Runcorn WA7 2DA Tel: 01928 714567 Fax: 01928 753119 Email: r.mallya@halton-tr.nwest.nhs.uk — MB BS 1970 Mysore; FACR 1998; FRCP (Ed) 1996; FRCP Lond. 1992; MRCP (UK) 1976; BSc (Hons) 1966. Cons. Phys. & Rheum. Halton Gen. Hosp. NHS Trust Runcorn. Socs: Fell.Roy. Soc. of Med. , Lond.; BMA. Prev: Sen. Regist. (Med. & Rheum.) Guy's Hosp. Lond.; Sen. Regist. (Rheum.) King's Coll. Hosp. Lond.; Regist. (Med.) W.minster Hosp. Lond.

MALLYA, Sheila Clinical Laboratories, Leighton Hospital, Middlewich Road, Crewe CW1 4QJ Tel: 01270 612236 Fax: 01270 250639 Email: sheila.mallya@mcht.nhs.uk — MB BS 1977 Bombay; FRCPath 1999; MD Bombay 1978; MRCPath 1991; FRCP 1999. Cons. Chem. Pathologist. Socs: Brit. Med. Assn.; Fell.of Roy. Coll. of Pathologists; Assn. of Clin. Biochem. Prev: Regist. Univ. Coll. Hosp. Lond.; Sen. Regist., Roy. Liverp. Hosp.; Sen. Regist., Aintree Hosp.

MALMBERG, Aslog Kristina 14 Eccleshall Road, Stone ST15 0HN — MB BS 1987 Lond.; BSc Lond. 1984, MB BS 1987; MRCPsych 1991. Sen. Research Regist. Univ. Dept. Psychiat. Warneford Hosp. Oxf. Prev: Regist. (Psychiat.) Maudsley Hosp. Lond.

MALNICK, Stephen David Howard 10 Kenmore Road, Kenton, Harrow HA3 9EL Tel: 020 8204 6604 Email: stevash@trendline.co.il — MB BS 1985 Lond.; MSc Weizmann 1982; MA Oxf. 1986. Sen. Dep. Head (Internal Med.) Kaplan Hosp. Rehovot, Israel; Lect. (Intern. Med.) Hebrew Univ. 1994. Socs: Israel Soc. Internal Med.; Israel Soc. Gastroenterol.; Eur. Assn. Study Liver Dis. Prev: Ho. Phys. Middlx. Hosp. Lond.; Ho. Surg. (Gen. Med.) N. Middlx. Hosp. Lond.

MALONE, Adrienne Honor Pingles, Chelmsford Road, Felsted, Dunmow CM6 3ET — MB BCh BAO 1971 Dub.; BA, MB BCh BAO Dub. 1971; DA Eng. 1977; DCH Eng. 1975; DObst RCOG 1975. (TC Dub.) Clin. Asst. (Anaesth.) Chelmsford Gp. Hosp. Prev: Regist. (Anaesth.) Char. Cross Hosp. Lond.; SHO (Anaesth.) Guy's Hosp. Lond.; SHO (O & G) Dorking Hosp.

MALONE, Alexander Andrew 127 Lauderdale Mansions, Lauderdale Road, Maida Avenue, London W9 1LY Email: alex_a_malone@hotmail.com — MB BS 1996 Lond.; BSc (Hons) Psych. 93. (St Mary's Hosp. Lond.) SHO Basic Surg. Train. Prev: Surg. Rot. St. Mary's. N.W.. Lond. NHS Trust.

MALONE, Anna Marie Albion Surgery, Pincott Road, Bexleyheath DA6 7LP Tel: 020 8304 8334 Fax: 020 8298 0408 — MB ChB 1991 Liverp.; DPD Cardiff. (Liverpool) GP Princip.; Clin. Asst. (Dermat.); Qu. Elizebeth's Woolwich. Socs: BMA & Med. Defence Union. Prev: SHO (O & G) Qu. Mary's Hosp. Sidcup; SHO (Geriat.) Qu. Mary's Hosp. Sidcup; SHO (Psychiat.) Bexley Hosp.

MALONE, Charles Michael (retired) Braefoot, Main St., Ringford, Castle Douglas DG7 2AL Tel: 01557 820314 — MB ChB 1959 Ed. Prev: Med. Off. Falkland Is. Govt. Serv.

MALONE, Clare Josephine Inwood Cottage, Inwood, All Stretton, Church Stretton SY6 6LA — MB ChB 1991 Liverp.

MALONE, David (retired) Aveland Park, Callender FK17 8EN Tel: 01877 30039 — MB ChB 1951 Ed.

MALONE, John Peter 1A Grosvenor Street, Hartlepool TS26 8DP Tel: 01429 7356 — MB ChB 1958 Glas. (Glas.) Prev: Ho. Surg., Ho. Phys. & SHO (O & G) Stirling Roy. Infirm.

MALONE, Judith Douglas Southmead NHS Trust, Gloucester House, Southmead Hospital, Westbury on Trym, Bristol BS10 5NB Tel: 0117 959 5807; 28 Nevil Road, Bishopston, Bristol BS7 9EQ Tel: 0117 942 4936 — MB ChB 1979 Bristol; Cert Cognitive Analytic Ther 1997. (Bristol) Clin. Asst. (Psychother.) S.mead Hosp. Bristol; GP Sessional Work Private Psychother. Socs: MDU.

MALONE, Keith Desmond Scott 2 Dalmeny View, Dalgety Bay, Dunfermline KY11 9LU — MB ChB 1989 Aberd.

MALONE, Mary Margaret Therese Department of Histopathology, Hospital for Sick Children, Great Ormond St., London WC1N 3JH Tel: 020 7405 9200 — MB BCh BAO 1977 NUI; MRCPath 1985. Cons. Hosp. Sick Childr. Gt. Ormond St. Lond. Socs: Internat. Acad. Pathol. (Brit. Div.); Paediat. Path. Soc. Prev: Lect. (Morbid. Anat.) Kings Coll. Hosp. Med. Sch. Lond.; Asst. Lect. (Morbid. Anat.) Lond. Hosp. Med. Coll.

MALONE, Michael John Simpson House Medical Centre, 255 Eastcote Lane, South Harrow, Harrow HA2 8RS Tel: 020 8864 3466 Fax: 020 8864 1002; 136 Locket Road, Harrow HA3 7NR — MB BS 1990 Lond.; MRCGP June 95. (GUYS)

MALONE, Moya Angela 62 Billy Mill Avenue, North Shields NE29 0QN — MB ChB 1984 Sheff. SHO (Paediat. Surg.) Fleming Memor. Childr. Hosp. Newc. Prev: SHO (Orthop. Surg. & A & E) N. Tyneside HA; Ho. Off. (Gen. Med. & Gastroenterol.) Rotherham Dist. Gen. Hosp.; Ho. Off. (Gen. Surg. & Neurosurg.) Roy. Hallamsh. Hosp. Sheff.

MALONE, Mr Padraig Colm (retired) 129 Viceroy Close, Edgbaston, Birmingham B5 7UY Tel: 0121 440 0342 Fax: 0121 440 0342 — MB BCh BAO NUI 1954; MD NUI 1986; FRCS Eng. 1964. Prev: GP Birm.

MALONE, Mr Padraig Seamus 8 St Aubins Avenue, Southampton SO19 8NW Tel: 02380 442734 Fax: 02380 794008 Email: pat.malone@suht.swest.nhs.uk — MB BCh BAO 1977 NUI; MCh NUI 1988; FRCSI 1981; T(S) 1991; FRCS 1988. (University College Dublin) Cons. Paediat. Urol. Soton. Gen. Hosp.; Hon. Cons. Paediat. Urol. St. Mary's Hosp. Portsmouth. Socs: Eur. Soc. Paediat. Urol.; Brit. Assn. Urol. Surgs.; Brit. Assn. Paediat. Urol.-Hon Sect. Prev: Cons. Paediat. Surg. & Paediat. Urol. Soton. Gen. Hosp.; Sen. Regist. Hosp. for Sick Childr. Gt. Ormond St. Lond.

MALONE, Mr Peter Richard IBH Berkshire Independent Hospital, Wensley Road, Reading RG1 6UZ Tel: 0118 902 8000 Fax: 0118 902 8125; Flexford House, Highclere, Newbury RG20 9PU Tel: 01635 254795 Email: flexford@aol.com — MB BS 1975 Lond.; MS Lond. 1988; FRCS Eng. 1980; FEBU 1992. (St. Geo. Hosp. Lond.) Cons. Urol. Battle Hosp. Reading. Socs: Brit. Assn. Urol. Surgs.; Eur. Assn. Urol.; Chairm. Brit. Prostate Gp. Prev: Sen. Regist. (Urol.) St. Geo. Hosp. Lond.; Sen. Regist. (Urol.) St. Peter's Gp. Hosp. Lond.

MALONE, Simona Tanja Hurst Place Surgery, 294A Hurst Road, Bexley DA5 3LH Tel: 020 8300 2826 Fax: 020 8309 0661 — MB ChB 1991 Birm.; ChB Birm. 1991; T(GP) 1996. Prev: GP/Regist. Eltham, Lond.; SHO (A & E) W.hill Hosp. Dartford; SHO (O & G) Solihull.

MALONE, Tessa Bridie Alexandra 127 Broomfield Avenue, Palmers Green, London N13 4JR — MB ChB 1985 Manch.; MRCGP 1991; DRCOG 1990.

MALONE, Timothy John Louis Demonstration Centre, Royal Devon & Exeter Hospital, Gladstone Road, Exeter EX1 2ED Tel: 01392 405171 Fax: 01392 405173 — MB BS 1987 Lond.; FRCA 1994; DA (UK) 1990. (St. Thomas' Hospital Medical School (UMDS))

MALONE-LEE, Professor James Gerard 48 Longley Road, Harrow HA1 4TH Tel: 020 8427 0249 Fax: 020 7383 3483 — MRCS Eng. LRCP Lond. 1975; MD Lond. 1991, MB BS 1975; FRCP Lond. 1993; MRCP (UK) 1980. (St. Thos.) Prof. (Geriat. Med.) Univ. Coll. Lond.; Dir. Div. (Geriat. Med. Dept. Med.) UCL; Chairm. Bd. Gov. St Vincents Hosp. Pinner. Socs: Internat. Continence Soc. & Brit. Geriat. Soc.; Physiol. Soc. Prev: Sen. Clin. Lect. & Clin. Lect. (Geriat. Med.) Univ. Coll. Hosp. Lond.; Vis. Prof. Bergen Univ.; Med. Off. RAMC.

MALONEY, Christopher Somerford Grove Practice, Somerford Grove Health Centre, Somerford Grove, London N16 7TX Tel: 020 7241 9700 Fax: 020 7275 7198 — MB ChB 1983 Leic.; BSc Leic. 1980; MRCPsych 1990; MRCGP 1987; DRCOG 1987. Princip. GP Somerford Gr. Health Centre Lond. Prev: Cons. Psychother. Heatherwood Hosp. Ascot.

MALONEY, Douglas John Lindsay Department of Pathology, Dryburn Hospital, North Road, Durham DH1 5TW Tel: 0191 333 2455; Lanchester House, 35 Front St, Lanchester, Durham DH7 0HT Tel: 01207 520260 — MB ChB 1978 Ed.; FRCPath 1997, MRCPath 1986. Cons. Histopath. Dryburn Hosp. Durh. Socs: Clin. Paths.; Brit. Thorac. Soc.; Brit. Soc. Cervical Cytol.

MALONEY, Emma Jane Elizabeth 30 High Street, Trumpington, Cambridge CB2 2LP — BM BCh 1993 Oxf.

MALONEY, Fenella Eunice 82 Cooden Sea Road, Bexhill-on-Sea TN39 4SP Tel: 01424 845477; 48 Charleston Road, Eastbourne BN21 1SF Tel: 01323 735223 — MB BS 1990 Lond.; MRCGP 1996; DRCOG 1995; DCH RCP Lond. 1994. (Guy's) GP E.bourne Retainer Scheme. Prev: Trainee GP Hastings VTS; SHO (Med.) St. Helens Hosp. Hastings; Ho. Off. (Med.) E.bourne Dist. Gen. Hosp.

MALONEY, Gillian Department of Occupational Health, Dryburn Hospital, North Road, Durham DH1 5TW Tel: 0191 333 2351 Fax: 0191 333 2353; Lanchester House, Lanchester, Durham DH7 0HT Tel: 01207 520260 — MB ChB 1978 Ed.; AFOM RCP Lond. 1994. Occupat. Health Phys. N. Durh. Acute Hosps. Trust. Socs: Soc. Occupat. Med.; Assn. Nat. Health Occupat. Phys.

MALONEY, Jane Deborah Mount House, Low St., Husthwaite, York YO61 4QA Tel: 01347 868235 — BM BS 1984 Nottm.; BMedSci (Hons.) Nottm. 1982; MRCGP 1990; DRCOG 1987. Prev: GP Basingstoke; Trainee GP Basingstoke VTS.

MALONEY, Mrs Julie Bernadette Cartrefle, Porthmadog Road, Y Groeslon, Caernarfon LL54 7ST — MB ChB 1991 Liverp. Staff Grade Community Paediat. Gwynedd Community Trust. Prev: GP.

MALOVIC-YEELES, Mira 30 Hayward Road, Oxford OX2 8LW Tel: 01865 556686 Fax: 01865 556686 — MD 1967 Zagreb; DCH Zagreb 1968; Neuropsychiat. Zagreb 1974; Jungian Analyst BAP Lond. 1992. (Zagreb, Croatia) Psychother. (private pract.). Socs: Assoc. Mem. BAP; IAAP; BMA. Prev: Assoc. Specialist (Psychiat.) Warneford Hosp. Oxf.

MALPAS, Christopher Andrew Coltishall Surgery, St John's Road, Rectory Road, Coltishall, Norwich NR12 7HL Tel: 01603 737593 Fax: 01603 737067; Court House, Great Hautbois Road, Colishall, Norwich NR12 7JN Tel: 01603 738629 — MB BS 1980 Lond.; BSc Lond. 1977; MRCOphth 1992; DRCOG 1987; DO RCS Eng. 1983. Hosp. Pract. (Ophth.) W. Norwich Hosp.

MALPAS, Clare Elizabeth Houghton Tower Farm, Ramsbrook Lane, Hale, Liverpool L24 5RP — MB BS 1998 Lond.

MALPAS, Professor James Spencer Department of Medical Oncology, St Bartholomews Hospital, West Smithfield, London EC1A 7BE Tel: 020 7601 7456 Fax: 020 7796 3979; Masters Lodge, Charterhouse Square, London EC1M 6AH Tel: 020 7253 0272 Fax: 020 7253 4012 — MB BS Lond. 1955; BSc Lond. 1952; DPhil Oxf. 1965; FRCPCH 1997; FRCP Lond. 1971, M 1961; FFPM RCP Lond. 1989; FRCR 1983. (St. Bart.) Emerit. Prof. Med. Oncol. & Hon. Cons. Phys. St. Bart. Hosp. Lond.; Examr. BM Oxf. Univ.; Examr. MB Lond. Univ.; Mem. (Ex. Vice-Pres.) St. Bart. Hosp. Med. Coll. Lond. Socs: (Pres.) Assn. Cancer Phys. Prev: Dir. Imperial Cancer Research Fund Dept. Med. Oncol. Unit St. Bart. Hosp. Lond.; Sen. Lect. & Sen. Regist. (Med.) St. Bart. Hosp. Lond.; Lect. (Med.) Nuffield Dept. Clin. Med. Radcliffe Hosp. Oxf.

***MALPAS, Lee** The Mews, Drakes Farm, Ide, Exeter EX2 9RL Tel: 01392 430850 — MB BS 1998 Lond.; MB BS Lond 1998.

MALPAS, Linda Christine Court House, Great Hautbois Road, Coltishall, Norwich NR12 7JN Tel: 01603 738629 — MB BS 1982 Lond.; DA Eng. 1984. Asst. GP Norwich; Clin. Asst. (Anaesth.) Norf. & Norwich Hosp.

MALPAS, Sandra May Pennys Lane Surgery, Pennys Lane, Cranborne, Wimborne BH21 5QE Tel: 01725 517272 Fax: 01725 517746; The Old Vicarage, Cranborne, Wimborne BH21 Tel: 01725 517253 Fax: 01725 575902 Email: ant1159@aol.com — MB BCh BAO 1972 Dub.; BA Dub. 1970. (TC Dub.) Partner, Cranborne Med. Pract.; Chairm. N. E. Dorset PCG.

MALPASS, Edward Lyn, Maj. RAMC (retired) The Surgery, 41 Lyndhurst Road, Barnehurst, Bexleyheath DA7 6DL Tel: 01322 525000 Fax: 03122 523123 — MB ChB 1975 Aberd.; MRCGP 1982; DRCOG 1980.

MALPASS, Tanya Stephannie Accident & Emergency Department, Wycombe General Hospital, High Wycombe; Pennhurst, Bernards Close, Great Missenden HP16 0BU — MB ChB 1977 Manch.; MRCP (UK) 1981; DCH Eng. 1979; FRCP. Cons. A & E S. Bucks. NHS Trust. Socs: Brit. Assn. of Accid. and Emerg. Med.; Christian Med. Fell.ship. Prev: Sen. Regist. (A & E) Guy's Hosp. Lond.; Regist. (Med.) Clwyd N. Wales; SHO (Anaesth.) Chester Roy. Infirm.

MALPICA, M G Eric Moore Health Centre, Tanners lane, Warrington WA2 7LY Tel: 01925 417252 Fax: 01925 417729 — LMS 1988 Santiago de Compostel; LMS 1988 Santiago de Compostel.

MALSEED, Geoffrey James (retired) 16 Burn Bridge Oval, Harrogate HG3 1LR Tel: 01423 870513 — MB BCh BAO 1951 Dub.; MA Dub. 1951; MFCM 1972; DPH Belf. 1966. Prev: Princip. Asst. Sen. Admin. Off. N. Irel. Hosps. Auth.

MALSTER, Margaret Gillian 82 Pengwern, Llangollen LL20 8AS — MB ChB 1970 Liverp.; MRCP Dub. 1978. Cons. Phys. (Geriat. Med.) Roy. Liverp. Hosp.; Clin. Lect. Univ. Liverp. Prev: Cons. Phys.

Halton & Warrington Health Dists.; Med. Regist. United Liverp. Hosps.; Ho. Off. Liverp. Roy. Infirm.

MALTBY, Mr Alfred Cecil Victor (retired) Knockloe, 10 Killyclogher Road, Omagh BT79 0AX Tel: 01662 242528 — MB BCh BAO 1943 Dub.; FRCSI 1949. Cons. Surg. W. Tyrone Gp. Hosps.; Surg. Lt. RNR. Prev: Regist. (Surg.) Roy. Berks. Hosp. Reading.

MALTBY, Mr Barrie Anson Medical Centre, 23 Anson Road, Victoria Park, Manchester M14 5BZ Tel: 0161 248 2011 Fax: 0161 248 2012; Sycamore House, 93 Cote Green Road, Marple Bridge, Stockport SK6 5EN — MB ChB 1965 Leeds; FRCS Ed. 1972. (Leeds) Hon. Cons. Orthop. Surg. Manch. Roy. Infirm. Prev: Lect. (Orthop. Surg.) Univ. Manch.; Sen. Regist. (Orthop.) Manch. Roy. Infirm.; Postgrad. Fell. (Orthop.) Research Mayo Clinic USA.

MALTBY, Mr John Wingate (retired) Howden Pines, Exeter Road, Tiverton EX16 5PH Tel: 01884 253089 Email: howpines@aol.com — MA, MB BChir Camb. 1955; FRCS Eng. 1959; MRCS Eng. LRCP Lond. 1954; DObst RCOG 1960. Prev: Clin. Asst. (Surg.) Tiverton & Dist. Hosp.

MALTBY, Julia Dawn 3 Lily Close, Kempshott, Basingstoke RG22 5NT — BChir 1990 Camb.

MALTBY, Karyn Peta 1 Hamilton Road, Twickenham TW2 6SN — MB BS 1984 Lond.; MRCP (UK) 1992. Regist. Train. NW Thames HA.

MALTBY, Sybil Dora Howden Pines, Tiverton EX16 5PH Tel: 01884 253089 — BSc Wales 1951, MB BCh 1954; DObst. RCOG 1957. SCMO Devon AHA. Prev: Ho. Surg. & Ho. Phys. Bridgend Hosp.; SHO O & G Poole Gen. Hosp.; Orthop. Regist. Cardiff. Roy. Infirm.

MALTHOUSE, Marina Elizabeth Whitegates, 29 Audley Park Road, Bath BA1 2XJ Tel: 01225 445762 — MB BS 1982 Lond.; LMSSA Lond. 1982.

MALTHOUSE, Simon Robin Whitegates, 29 Audley Park Road, Bath BA1 2XJ Tel: 01225 445762 — MB BS 1981 Lond.; FRCR Eng. 1988; MRCP (UK) 1985.

MALTZ, Milton Beer 48 Harley Street, London W1N 1AD Tel: 020 7323 9292 Fax: 020 7323 4484 Email: mccr@mccr.co.uk — MB BS 1979 Brazil; MD Brazil 1981, MB BS 1979; MPhil Cardiol. Lond. 1988; DGM Lond. 1982. (Brazil) Clin. Asst. & Med. Dir. (Cardiac Research) MCCR Ltd; Clin. Asst. (Cardiol.) Roy. Free Hosp. & Whipps Cross Hosp. Lond. Prev: Research Regist. St. Bartholomews Hosp. Lond.; Hon. Clin. Asst. (Cardiol.) St. Bartholomews Hosp. Lond.

MALVANKAR, Ganesh Kumar Janardan St Chad's Medical Centre, 4 St. Chad's Road, Tilbury RM18 8LA Tel: 01375 842396 Fax: 01375 840448; No. 5 Stanford House, Princess Margaret Road, Tilbury RM18 Tel: 01375 859688 — MB BS Banaras Hindu 1968. Clin. Asst. (Genitourin. Med.) Orsett Hosp. Prev: Regist. (Med.) Edgware Gen. Hosp. Lond. & Roodland Hosp. E. Lothian; SHO Sunderland Gen. Hosp.

MALVERN, Mr John 82 Harley Street, London W1G 7HN Tel: 020 7636 2766 Fax: 020 7631 5371; 30 Roedean Crescent, Roehampton, London SW15 5JU Tel: 020 8876 4943 Fax: 020 8876 4943 — MB BS Lond. 1963; BSc (1st cl. Hons.) Lond. 1960; FRCS Ed. 1968; MRCS Eng. LRCP Lond. 1963; FRCOG 1984, M 1970. (Lond. Hosp.) p/t Cons. O & G Qu. Charlottes & Chelsea Hosp. Lond. Emerit.; Hon. Cons. (Gyn.) KEVII's Hosp. for Offs.; Hon. Sen. Lect. Inst. Obst. & Gyn. Roy. Postgrad. Med. Sch.; Examr. Centr. Midw. Bd., Univs. Lond., Liverp. & Manch. Edin., Coll. of Surg.s of Pakistan & RCOG; Mem. Profess. Linguistic Assessm. Bd. Socs: Fell. Roy. Soc. Med. (Ex-Pres. Obst. & Gyn. Sect.); Gyn. Vis. Soc.; Internat. Continence Soc. Prev: Regist. (O & G) Middlx. Hosp. & The Hosp. for Wom. Lond.; Sen. Regist. Qu. Charlottes & Chelsea Hosps. Lond.; Res. Accouch. Lond. Hosp.

MAMALOUKAS, Evangelos c/o Chris Manderson, 64 Woodside Avenue, London N6 4ST Email: evangelosm@msn.com — Ptychio Iatrikes 1994 Thessalonika. SHO (Psychiat.) Tameside Gen. Hosp. Prev: SHO & Ho. Off. (Gen. Med. & Med. for Elderly) Bolton Gen. Hosp.

MAMATTAH, Jonathan Kwaku-Mensah (retired) 27 Mount Drive, Nantwich CW5 6JG Tel: 01270 625176 — MD Lond. 1972, MB BS 1962; Dip Bact Manch. 1968. Cons. Path. (Microbiol.) Leighton Hosp. Crewe. Prev: Temp. Lect. Bacteriol. Edin. Univ.

MAMDANI

MAMDANI, Gulam Haider Acorn Centre, Vale of Leven Hospital, Alexandria G83 0UA Tel: 01389 603929 Fax: 01389 603928 Email: haider.mamdani@vol.scot.nhs.uk — MB BS 1970 Poona; DCCH RCP Ed. 1985; DCH RCP Glas. 1984. Cons. Paediat. (Community Child Health) Lomond & Argyll Primary Care Trust.

MAMELOK, Jane Patricia Cheadle Medical Practice, 1-5 Ashfield Crescent, Cheadle SK8 1BH Tel: 0161 428 7575 Fax: 0161 283 8884; 29 Honiton Way, Altrincham WA14 4UW — MB BS 1986 Lond.; BSc (Hons.) Durham. 1981; MRCGP 1990; DFFP 1993; DRCOG 1988.

MAMISO, Julian Anofukei 18 Llwyn y Broden, Parc Gwern Fadog, Morriston, Swansea SA6 8TD Tel: 01792 790782 — MB BS 1978 Ibadan; MRCOG 1986.

MAMMAN, Isyaka 9 Acacia Grove, Wirral CH48 4DD — MB BS 1964 Lond.

MAMMAN, Parmjit Singh Castleton Health Centre, 2 Elizabeth Street, Castleton, Rochdale OL11 3HY Tel: 01706 658905 Fax: 01706 343990 — MB ChB 1989 Manch.; MRCGP 1993; DFFP 1993; DRCOG 1992.

MAMMEN, Catherine 23 Willow Drive, Kirkcaldy KY1 2LF Tel: 01592 643355 — MB BS 1984 Kerala; MRCOG 1993.

MAMMEN KORULLA, Babukutty Department of Anaesthetics, Ysbyty Gwynedd, Bangor LL57 2PW Tel: 01248 384384 — BSc Kerala 1972, MB BS 1978; DA (UK) 1987; DCH RCP Lond. 1982. Staff Doctor (Anaesth.) Ysbyty Gwynedd. Prev: Regist. (Anaesth.) Bangor; SHO (Anaesth.) Pontefract Gen. Infirm. & Hull Roy. Infirm.

MAMMO, May Abdul Rahim Bassetlaw District General Hospital, Kilton Road, Worksop S81 0BD Tel: 01909 500990 Email: maymammo@bhcs_tr.trent.nhs.uk — MB ChB 1973 Baghdad; MSc Liverp. 1985; MRCOG 1982; FRCOG 1998. (Baghdad Med. Sch.) Cons. O & G Bassetlaw Hosp. & Community Servs. NHS Trust. Socs: Brit. Menopause Soc.; Welsh Obst. & Gyn. Soc.; N. Eng. Obst. & Gyn. Soc. Prev: Locum Cons. Univ. Hosp. Wales; Specialist Ahmadi Hosp. Kuwait.

MAMODE, Nizam Glasgow Royal Infirmary, Alexandra Parade, Glasgow G31 2ER; Warwickdale Cottage, Overton Road, Kilmarnock KA2 0DN — MB ChB 1987 Glas.; BSc St And 1984; FRCPS Glas. 1991. (St Andrews, Glas.) Specialist Regist. (Gen. Surg.) Glas. Prev: Research Regist. (Vasc. Surg.) Glas. Roy. Infirm.

MAMOOWALA, Haider Ebrahim Bury General Hospital, Walmersley Road, Bury BL9 6PG Tel: 0161 764 6081 Fax: 0161 705 3249; 40 Freckleton Drive, Bury BL8 2JA — MB BS 1983 Bombay; MS Bombay 1988. (Grant Medical College, Bombay, India) Staff Orthop. Surg. Bury Gen. Hosp.

MAMPILLY, Mr Jojo The Surgery, Felmores Surgery, Felmores End, Basildon SS13 1PN Tel: 01268 728142 Fax: 01268 726567; 4 Russetts, Langdon Hills, Basildon SS16 6SH — MB BS 1964 Mysore; FRCS 1989 Glas. (Bangalore Med. Coll.)

MAMTORA, Hariprakash Little Orchard, Cross Lane, Wilmslow SK9 2DB Tel: 01625 527053 — MD 1982 Manch.; MB ChB 1972; FRCR 1979; DMRD Eng. 1978. Cons. Radiol. Hope Hosps. Socs: Fell. Manch. Med. Soc. Prev: Lect. Diag. Radiol. Manch. Univ.; Clin. Research Fell. (Diag. Radiol.) Manch. Univ.; Sen. Regist. (Radiol.) Manch. Roy. Infirm.

MAMTORA, Malakumari Pursotam Bhardwaj and Mamtora, Crawford Avenue Health Centre, Crawford Avenue, Wembley HA0 2HX Tel: 020 8903 6411; 219 Cannon Lane, Pinner HA5 1JA Tel: 020 8723 5579 — MB BS 1988 Lond.; DCH RCP Lond. 1992; Cert. Family Plann. JCC 1992. Prev: Trainee GP N.wood; SHO (Paediat. & Obst. Gyn.) Roy. Berks. Hosp. Reading.

MAMUJEE, Mr Abdullah Mulla Springfields, 151 The Street, Rushmere, Ipswich IP5 1DG Tel: 01473 272269 — MB BS 1960 Poona; FRCS Glas. 1966; FRCS Ed. 1964; FFAEM 1993. (B.J. Med. Coll. Poona) Cons. Surg. i/c A & E Ipswich Hosp. NHS Trust. Prev: Cons. Surg. & Hon. Sen. Lect. (Surg.) MoH & Fac. Med. Univ. Dar-es-Salaam, Tanzania; Regist. (Surg.) Ashford Hosp. Middlx.

MAMUJEE, Nalini Vaikunth Springfields, 151 The Street, Rushmere, Ipswich IP5 1DG Tel: 01473 272269 — MB BS 1959 Poona; FRCP Ed. 1994; MRCP Lond. 1966; MRCP Glas. 1966; FRCPath 1992; DTM & H Eng. 1962. (B.J. Med. Coll. Poona) Sen. Med. Microbiol. & Assoc. Specialist Pub. Health Laborat. Ipswich Hosp. Prev: Asst. Med. Microbiol. & Sen. Regist. Pub. Health Laborat. Ipswich Hosp.; Cons. Phys. MoH Health Dar-es-Salaam, Tanzania; Regist. (Path.) Mt. Vernon Hosp. N.wood.

MAMUJEE, Shaukat Akberally Albert House Clinic, 101 Normanby Road, South Bank, Middlesbrough TS6 6SE Tel: 01642 453049 Fax: 01642 464343; Shipcote, 1 Brooklands, Bishop Auckland DL14 6PW Tel: 01388 606467 — MB BS 1971 Ceylon; MB BS Colombo 1971; DRCOG 1993. (Colombo) Prev: Clin. Asst. (A & E) Bishop Auckland Gen. Hosp.; SHO (Psychiat.) Winterton Hosp. Sedgefield Cleveland; SHO (A & E) Dist. Gen. Hosp. Sunderland.

MAN, Alexander Cross Road Surgery, Cross Road, Rodwell, Weymouth DT4 9QX Tel: 01305 768844 Fax: 01305 760686; 5 Bincleaves Road, Rodwell, Weymouth DT4 8RL — BM 1987 Soton.; MRCGP 1991. Prev: SHO (Cas.) Weymouth & Dist. Hosp.

MAN, Fung Wah Alice 93 Granville Road, London N22 5LR Tel: 020 8888 0895 — MB BS 1996 Lond. (Imperial Coll. (St. Mary's)) SHO (Anaesth.) Luton & Dunstable Hosp. Luton. Prev: SHO (Cas.) Qu. Eliz. II Hosp. Welwyn Garden City.

MAN, Irene Wai-Ping Ninewells Hospital, Dundee DD1 9SY — MB ChB 1993 Dundee.

MAN, Kwong Wai Belsize Priory Medical Practice, 208 Belsize Rd, London NW6 4DJ Tel: 0207 530 2666 — BM BCh 1990 Oxf.; DFFP 1997; MA Camb. 1991.

MAN, Lung-Kwong 25 Hunters Place, Newcastle upon Tyne NE2 4PB — MB ChB 1991 Dundee.

MAN, William Ding-Cheong Dept. of Respiratory Medicine & Allergy, Guy's King's & St. Thomas's School of Medicine, King's Denmark Hill Campus, Bessemer Road, London SE5 9PJ Tel: 020 7346 4493 Fax: 020 7346 3589 Email: william.man@kcl.ac.uk. Med. Research Counc., Clin. Train. Fell. In Respirat. Med.

MAN SINGH, Mr Ajit Flat 16, Grovelands, Barracks Road, High Wycombe HP11 1QN — MB BS 1986 All-India Institute Med Sci; FRCS Ed 1994.

MANAKTALA, Kavitha Jane Rajam Abbey Practice, Family Health Centre, Stepgates, Chertsey KT16 8HZ Tel: 01932 565655; 7 Marriott Lodge Close, Addlestone, Weybridge KT13 2XD Tel: 01932 853596 — MB BS 1982 Lond.; MRCGP 1988; DRCOG 1988. (Roy. Free Hosp. Lond.) Prev: SHO (O & G) St. Geo. Hosp. Lond.; SHO (Geriat.) Redhill Gen. Hosp.; SHO (Neonates) Hammersmith Hosp. Lond.

MANAM, A Claremont Clinic, 459-463 Romford Road, Forest Gate, London E7 8AR Tel: 020 8522 0222 Fax: 020 8522 0444 — MB BS 1974 Andhra; MB BS 1974 Andhra.

MANAM, Venkata Rangam 9 Kinburn Street, London SE16 6DN — MB BS 1972 Osmania.

MANANDHAR, Lochan Devi Lincoln & Louth NHS Trust, Greetwell Road, Lincoln LN2 5QY; 11 Acer Close, Lincoln LN6 0RD — Vrach 1972 Peoples Friendship USSR; Peoples Friendship USSR. 1972; MD 1972; DFFP. Assoc. Specialist (Anaesth.) Lincoln & Louth NHS Trust.

MANARA, Alexander Richard Dept of Anaesthesia, Frenchay Hospital, Bristol BS16 1LE Tel: 0117 970 2020 Fax: 0117 957 4414; 15 Old Aust Road, Almondsbury, Bristol BS32 4HJ Tel: 01454 615761 — MB BCh 1981 Wales; MRCP (UK) 1985; FFA RCS Eng. 1986. Cons. Anaesth. & Intens. Care Frenchay Hosp. Bristol. Prev: Sen. Regist. (Anaesth.) Bristol Roy. Infirm.; Regist. (Anaesth.) Addenbrooke's Hosp. Camb.; SHO (Med., IC & Anaesth.) Whittington Hosp. Lond.

MANASEKI-HOLLAND, Semira Birmingham Health Authority, 213 Hagley Road St Chad's Court, Edgbaston, Birmingham B16 9RT Tel: 0121 695 2363; 29 Park Avenue, Stafford ST17 9RB — MB BS 1991 Newc.; MFPHM 2000; MSc 1997 (Epid. & Pub. Health); 1989 B.Med.Sci. Newc.; MRCP (Paediat.) (Ed.). (Newc.) Cons. In Child Health & Pub. Health, Pub. Health Directorate, B'ham Health Auth. Socs: BMA; (Paediat.) RCP; FPHM. Prev: Sen. Regist. (Pub. Health) S. Staffs. HA; Med. Off. At World Health Organisation HQ in Geneva '99-'00; Sen. Regist. Pub. Health at Birm. Health Auth. '97-'99.

MANASSE, Andrew Paul (retired) 462 Redmires Road, Sheffield S10 4LG Tel: 0114 230 7838 Fax: 0870 063 7908 Email: anasse@doctors.org.uk — MB BChir 1962 Camb.; MA Camb. 1967; MRCP Lond. 1967; MRCGP 1984; DObst RCOG 1968; DCH Eng. 1963.

MANASSES, Euthymia (Surgery) Station Road, Langbank, Port Glasgow PA14 6YA Tel: 01475 540404; 3 Broomknowe Terrace,

Kilmacolm PA13 4HT Tel: 01505 872279 — MB BS 1988 Lond.; MRCGP 1993. Prev: SHO Gartnavel Hosp. Glas.

MANCAIS, Penny Anne Pembury Hospital, Tunbridge Wells TN2 4QJ; 37 Dudley Road, Tunbridge Wells TN1 1LE — MB BS 1989 Lond.; MRCP (UK) 1996; DCH RCP Lond. 1995. SHO (Paediat.) Roy. Sussex Co. Hosp. Prev: SHO (Paediat.) Pembury Hosp. Tunbridge Wells; SHO (Paediat.) St. Thos. Hosp. Lond.

MANCERO, Susana Department of Oncology, Bristol Royal Infirmary, Marlborough St., Bristol BS2 8HW; 9 Codrington Road, Bishopston, Bristol BS7 8ET — D Med y Cir Quito, Ecuador 1975; DMRT Liverp. 1981.

MANCEY-BARRATT, William Alexander The Surgery, 18 Hove Park Villas, Hove BN3 6HG — MB BS 1986 Lond.; BA (Hons.) Oxf. 1982; MRCGP 1990. Clin. Asst. (Diabetes) Roy. Sussex Co. Hosp. Brighton; Clin. Asst. (Genitourin. Med.) Claude Nicol Centre Brighton. Prev: Med. Dir. St. Jude Hosp. St Lucia, WI; Trainee GP Brighton; Ho. Off. St. Bart. & Homerton Hosps. Lond.

MANCEY-JONES, Mr John Benedict 27 Oakwell Crescent, Oakwood, Leeds LS8 4AF — MB BS 1989 Lond.; FRCS Eng. 1993.

MANCEY-JONES, Marian Sophia Brixton Hill Group Practice, 22 Raleigh Gardens, London SW2 1AE Tel: 020 8674 6376 Fax: 020 8671 0283 — MB BS 1986 Newc.

MANCHANDA, Lisa Flat 3/2, 166 Great George St., Glasgow G12 8AJ — MB ChB 1995 Glas.

MANCHANDA, Simmie Wycombe Hospital, Queen Alexandra Rd, High Wycombe HP11 2TT Tel: 01494 526161 — MB BS 1988 Lond.; MSc 1998; MRCP 1993 UK. (King's College London) Cons. Phys., Wycombe Hosp., High Wycombe (GIM & Geriat). Prev: Sen. Regist. (Med. & Geriat.) Lister Hosp. Stevenage; Sen. Regist. (Med.) Chelsea & W.m. Hosp. Lond.; Regist. (Med.) Guy's Hosp. Lond.

MANCHE, Marioth 34 Meadowsway, Upton, Chester CH2 1HZ — MRCS Eng. LRCP Lond. 1977.

MANCHE, Richard (retired) 2 Kingsworthy Close, Dawson Road, Kingston upon Thames KT1 3ER Tel: 020 8549 6283 Email: rmanche@doctors.org.uk — MD 1957 Malta; BPharm 1952; MRCGP 1977. Prev: Civil. Med. Pract. & Trainer (Gen. Pract.) MoD.

MANCHESTER, David John Langley Group Surgery, Wood Street, Middleton, Manchester M24 5QL Tel: 0161 643 5385 Fax: 0161 653 6430; The Bungalow, Wardle Ford, Wardle, Rochdale OL12 9NF — MB BS 1983 Lond.

MANCHESTER, Keith (retired) 66 Pollard Lane, Bradford BD2 4RW Tel: 01274 636598 — MB BS Lond. 1962; BSc (Hons.) Lond. 1959; DSc (Hon.) Bradford. Med. Adv.; York. Child. Hosp. Fund. Prev: Vis. Lect. (Palaeopathol.) & Hon. Research Fell. Univ. Bradford.

MANCHESTER, Stephen Giles Laisterdyke Clinic, Moorside Lane, Bradford BD3 8DH Tel: 01274 662441 — MB BS 1993 Lond.

MANCHETT, Paul The Surgery, New Street, Stockbridge SO20 6HG Tel: 01264 810524 Fax: 01264 810591 — MB BS 1974 Lond.; DCH Eng. 1981. (Lond. Hosp.) Prev: Regist. (Paediat.) Roy. Aberd. Childr. Hosp.; SHO (Med.) Plymouth Gen. Hosps.

MANCHIP, Andrew John Rutherglen Health Centre, 130 Stonelaw Road, Rutherglen, Glasgow G73 2PQ Tel: 0141 531 6030 Fax: 0141 531 6031 — MB ChB 1987 Glas.; Dip. Forens. Med. Glas 1996; Dip Therapeutics (UWCM 1999). (Univ. Glas.) Socs: Scott. Medico-Legal Soc.; (Trustee) Rutherglen Practitioners Soc. Prev: Trainee GP E. Kilbride VTS; Ho. Off. (Med.) Glas. Roy. Infirm.; Ho. Off. (Surg.) Hairmyres Hosp.

MANCHIP, Simon Paul Savernake Hospital, Marlborough SN8 3HZ Tel: 01793 425417 — BM 1988 Soton.; MRCPsych 1994. Cons. in Old Age Psychiat., Savernake Hosp. MarlBoro.

MAND, Harbhajan Singh 11 Rye Street, Bishop's Stortford CM23 2HA Tel: 01279 657785 — MB BS 1967 Punjab. Prev: Trainee GP Bishop's Stortford.

***MANDAIR, Inderjit Singh** 67 Newton Road, Bitterne Park, Southampton SO18 1NJ — MB BS 1996 Lond.

MANDAL, Mr Anil Kumar Tel: 01226 730000 Fax: 01226 202859 — MB BS 1964 Calcutta; FRCS Ed. 1974; DO Eng. 1969; DOMS Calcutta 1967. (Nilratan Sircar Med. Coll.) Cons. Ophth. Barnsley AHA. Socs: Fell. Roy. Coll. Ophth.; Ophth. Soc. UK & N. Eng. Ophth. Soc. Prev: Sen. Regist. Nottm. Eye Hosp.; Regist. (Ophth.) W. Wales Gen. Hosp. Carmarthen; SHO (A & E & Ophth.) Hull Roy. Infirm.

MANDAL, Bibhat Kumar (retired) Res. Unit Department Infect. Dis., North Manchester General Hospital, Delanhays Road,

Manchester M8 5RB Tel: 0161 720 2845 Fax: 0161 720 2562 — MB BS 1959 Calcutta; FRCP Glas. 1978, M 1965; FRCP Ed. 1978, M 1966. Dir. Internat. Collab. Centre for Research in Trop. Infect. Manch. & Calcutta.; Hon. Cons. Phys. Dept. Inf. Dis. & Trop. Med. Nth. Manch. Gen Hosp. Manch. Prev: Cons. Phys. & Dir. Dept. of Infect. Dis. & Trop. Med. Nth. Manch. Gen Hosp. Manch.

MANDAL, Jayanta 11 Finch Avenue, Sandal, Wakefield WF2 6SE — MB BCh BAO 1993 NUI; LRCPSI 1993.

MANDAL, Mr Kajal Chandra Banff and Gamrie Medical Practice, Clunie Street, Banff AB45 1HY Tel: 01261 812221 Fax: 01261 818455; 13 Windy Brae, Banff AB45 1DG Tel: 01261 812113 — MB BS Calcutta 1965; BSc Calcutta 1957; FRCS Glas. 1980. (Nil Ratan Sircar Med. Coll.) GP Banff & Med. Pract. Chalmers Hosp. Banff. Socs: BMA. Prev: SHO (Cas. & Orthop.) Darlington Memor. Hosp.; SHO (Gen. Surg. & ENT) Bronglais Gen. Hosp. Aberystwyth; SHO (ENT) City Hosp. & Roy. Infirm. Edin.

MANDAL, Lal Bahadur Central Surgery, 1 Central Court, Central Avenue, Telscombe Cliffs, Peacehaven BN10 7LU; Hill view, 85 Dean Court Road, Rottingdean, Brighton BN2 7DL Tel: 01273 390985 Fax: 01273 390985 Email: lal_mandal@hotmail.com — LRCP LRCS Ed. LRCPS Glas. 1985; DCH RCPI 1989; DRCOG 1989. Full Time Princip. in Gen. Pract.

***MANDAL, Sema** 44D Harwood Road, London SW6 4PY — MB BS 1998 Lond.; MB BS Lond 1998.

MANDAL, Sisir Kumar (retired) 6 Perth Close, North Shields NE29 8DF — MB BS Calcutta 1955; FRCP Ed. 1985, M 1967; FRCP Glas. 1981, M 1966; DTM & H Liverp. 1966; TDD Calcutta 1958. Prev: Cons. Phys. N. Tyneside DHA.

MANDALIA, Harshvadan Natwarlal 43 Merrion Avenue, Stanmore HA7 4RY Tel: 020 8954 2167 — MB BS 1967 Gujarat; DO RCPSI 1971.

MANDALIA, I R The Surgery, 2-4 Halsbury Street, Leicester LE2 1QA — MB BS 1970 Rajasthan; MB BS 1970 Rajasthan.

MANDAVIA, Babulal Jadavji 4 Ashurst Drive, Gants Hill, Ilford IG2 6SQ Tel: 020 8554 2797 Fax: 020 8554 2797 — MB BS 1973 Saurashtra. (Shri M.P. Shah Med. Coll. Jamnagar) Clin. Asst. Ophth. Guy's Hosp. Lond. Socs: Med. Prot. Soc.

MANDAVILLI, S The Surgery, 1 Clements Road, East Ham, London E6 2DS Tel: 020 8472 0603 Fax: 020 8553 0211 — MB BS 1971 Andhra; MB BS 1971 Andhra.

MANDEL, John Eric 81 Harley Street, London W1 1DE Tel: 020 7935 6104 — MB BS 1947 Lond. (Guy's) Prev: Flight Lt. RAF; Ho. Surg. Joyce Green Hosp. Dartford; Paediat. Ho. Phys. Dist. Hosp. Pembury.

MANDELBROTE, Bertram Maurice 76 Lonsdale Road, Oxford OX2 7ER Tel: 01865 556531 — MB ChB 1945 Cape Town; MA Oxf. 1961, MSc (Research) 1948; FRCP Lond. 1964, M 1948; FRCPsych 1972; DPM Eng. 1951. (Cape Town) Clin. Lect. Univ. Oxf.; Hon. Cons. Psychiat. Oxf. HA; Mem. Green Coll. Oxf. Socs: BMA; Oxf. Med. Soc. Prev: Sen. Regist. Maudsley Hosp. Inst. Psychiat.; Rhodes Schol. Att. Dept. Neurol. Oxf.; Canad. Dominion Provin. Teach. & Research Fell. Inst. Psychiat.

***MANDER, Annabel Victoria Louise** Lewberry Close, Ashow, Kenilworth CV8 2LE — MB ChB 1995 Bristol.

MANDER, Anthony Michael Royal Oldham Hospital, Rochdale Road, Oldham OL1 2JH Tel: 0161 624 0420 Fax: 0161 627 8230; Private Rooms, Lancaster House, 174 Chamber Road, Oldham OL8 4BU Tel: 0161 652 1227 Fax: 0161 287 6595 — MB ChB 1970 Sheff.; FRCOG 1989, M 1975; Specialist Accredit. (Obst. & Gyn.) RCOG 1980. Cons. O & G Roy. Oldham Hosp.; Undergrad. Tutor Manch. Univ. Med. Sch. Roy. Oldham Hosp.; Dist. Tutor RCOG Oldham; Edit. Bd. Jl. Brit. Menopause Soc. Socs: Counc. Mem. Brit. Menopause Soc.; Brit. Soc. Immunol.; Brit. Assn. Cancer Research. Prev: Sen. Regist. (O & G) King's Coll. Hosp. Lond.; Mem. Jt. Cons. Comm.; Cancer Research Campaign Fell. Dept. Surg. Welsh Nat. Sch. Med.

MANDER, Mr Brian James 6 Providence Sq, London SE1 2EA Tel: 020 7237 9475 Fax: 020 7237 9475 Email: bjames@mander39.freeserve.co.uk; 6 Providence Sq, London SE1 2EA Tel: 020 7237 9475 Fax: 020 7237 9475 — MB BS 1989 Lond.; BSc Lond. 1986; FRCS Eng. 1993. Specialist Regist. (Gen. Surg.) SW Thames Rotat.; Res. Fell. Roy. Lond. Hosp. Prev: SHO (Surg.) W.m. & S.end Hosps.

MANDER

MANDER, David (retired) Westfield, Castleton Road, Hathersage, Sheffield S30 1AH Tel: 01433 50291 — MB ChB 1945 Sheff.; DObst. RCOG 1947. Prev: Res. Obst. Off. Crumpsall Hosp. Manch.

MANDER, Davinder Singh 18 Park View Road, London W5 2JB — MB BCh BAO 1990 NUI; LRCPSI 1990.

MANDER, Rajinder Singh The Surgery, Langshott, Horley RH6 9XY — BM 1987 Soton.

MANDERS, Duncan Nicholas Royal Hospital for Sick Children, Department of Child & Family Psychiatry, 3 Rill Bank Terrace, Edinburgh EH9 1LL Tel: 0131 447 2011 Email: duncan.manders@zoom.co.uk — BM BS 1989 Nottm.; BMedSci (Hons.) Nottm. 1986; MRCPsych 1994. Sen. Regist. (Child & Adolesc. Psychiat.) Roy. Edin. Hosp. Prev: Regist. (Psychiat.) Roy. Edin. Hosp.; SHO Roy. Edin. Hosp.; Sen. Regist. RHSC Edin.

MANDERSLOOT, Gerlinde Francisca 4 Chinnery Close, Forty Hill, Enfield EN1 4AX — MB ChB 1987 Pretoria.

MANDERSON, John Gregg 41 Windsor Hill, Hillsborough BT26 6RI — MB BCh BAO Belf.; MRCOG 1996. (Qu. Univ. Belf.) Specialist Regist. (O & G) Altnagelvin Area Hosp. Lond.derry; Sub Specialist Trainee in Matern. & Fetal Med., Roy. Maternity Hosp., Belf., BT12 6BA. Socs: Ulster Obstetricial and Gyn. Soc. Europ. Assn. for the study of Diabetes.

MANDERSON, Julie Elizabeth 28 Brookmeadows, Ballynure, Ballyclare BT39 0QF — MB BCh BAO 1993 Belf.

ANDERSON, Laurence Leonard 15 Wynchurch Road, Belfast BT6 0JH — MB BCh BAO 1990 Belf.; MB BCh Belf. 1990.

MANDERSON, William Greer 40 Arkleston Road, Paisley PA1 3TH Tel: 0141 849 1923 — MB ChB 1942 Glas.; Hon. LLD (Strathclyde) 1988; MD Glas. 1959; FRCP Lond. 1970, M 1951; FRCP Glas. 1964, M 1962; FRFPS Glas. 1948. (Univ. Glas.) Hon. Cons. Phys. Roy. Infirm. Glas.; Hon. Prof. Univ. Strathclyde. Socs: Sen. Mem. Assn. Phys. & Surg. Prev: Hon. Cons. Phys. Roy. Infirm. Glas.

***MANDEVILLE, Henry Campbell** 1 Ardlui Gardens, Milngavie, Glasgow G62 7RL — MB ChB 1997 Aberd.

MANDEVILLE, Joseph Elwin Fishponds Health Centre, Beechwood Road, Fishponds, Bristol BS16 3TD Tel: 0117 965 6281; Frenchay Surgery, 15 Stourdon Close, Frenchay, Bristol BS16 1JU Tel: 0117 956 5684 — MB BS Lond. 1961. (Univ. Coll. Hosp.) Prev: Ho. Phys. Univ. Coll. Hosp.; Ho. Surg. (O & G) Ronkswood Hosp. Worcester.

MANDEVILLE, Robert Parnell, MBE Possilpark Health Centre, 85 Denmark Street, Glasgow G22 5EG Tel: 0141 531 6170 Fax: 0141 531 6177 — MB BS 1970 Lond.; PhD (Memor. Univ. Newfld.) 1980; MRCP (UK) 1973; MRCS Eng. LRCP Lond. 1970; MRCPath 1980.

MANDL, Stefan Alexander 163 Picardy Road, Belvedere DA17 5QL — LRCP LRCS Ed. LRCPS Glas. 1968. (Warsaw Med. Acad.)

MANDOUR, Omer El Mahdi Ahmed Unit 002, Flat 78 Bootham Park Court, York YO31 8JT — MB BS 1983 Khartoum.

MANDRY, David Roberts (retired) Abernant, Llangoedmor, Cardigan SA43 2LD — MB BCh BAO 1958 Dub.; BA, MB BCh BAO Dub. 1958. Prev: SCMO Cardigan & Dist. Memor. Hosp.

MANEK, Neeta Microbiology Department, George eliot Hospital NHS Trust, College St, Nuneaton CV10 7DJ; 167 Tythe Barn Lane, Dickens Heath, Solihull B90 1PQ — MB ChB 1980 Manch.; MBA; MRCPath. 1986; FRCPath. (Manchester) Cons. Microbiol. Georg Eliot Hosp. Prev: Sen. Regist. (Microbiol.) Dudley Rd. Hosp. & Infect. Research Lab. Birm.; Sen. Regist. (Microbiol.) Sandwell Dist. Gen. Hosp. W. Brom.; Sen. Regist. (Microbiol.) Good Hope Hosp. Sutton Coldfield.

MANEK, Sanjiv Department of Cellular Pathology, John Radcliffe Hospital, Oxford OX3 9DU Tel: 01865 220520 Fax: 01865 220519 Email: smanek6014@aol.com — MB BS 1985 Lond.; Dip RC Path 1995; BSc Lond 1982; MRCPath 1994; DRCPath 1995. Cons. Cellular Path. John Radcliffe Hosp. Oxf. Socs: ACP Counc. Mem. & Meeting Sec.; BSCC; BGCS. Prev: Sen. Regist. (Histopath.) John Radcliffe Hosp. Oxf.

MANEKSHA, Sohrab Consulting Rooms, 24 Hermiston Avenue, Crouch End, Hornsey, London N8 8NL Tel: 020 8340 6832; Tel: 020 8340 6832 — MBBS 1959 Vikram; BSc (Hons.) Bombay 1954. (Mahatma Gandhi Memorial Medical Colege) InDepend. Anaesth. Socs: Fell. Roy. Soc. Med. (Anaesth. Sect.); Assn. Anaesth.; Brit.

Assn. Day Surg. Prev: Clin. Asst. (Anaesth.) Char. Cross Hosp. Lond.; Clin. Asst. Roy. Nat. Throat, Nose & Ear Hosp. Lond.; Asst. Anaesth. Roy. N.. Hosp. & City Lond. Matern. Hosp.

***MANEY, Julie-Ann** 4 Cairnshill, Newry BT34 2ST — MB BCh BAO 1997 Belf.

MANFIELD, Pauline Ann (retired) Chadwick House, 51 Hollyfield Road, Sutton Coldfield B75 7SE Tel: 0121 378 2727 Fax: 0121 378 2727 Email: pamanfield@tinyonline.co.uk — MB BS; MB BS Lond. 1954; FRCP Lond. 1980, M 1963; DObst RCOG 1957; DCH Eng. 1956; FRCPCH 1997. Prev: Cons. Paediat. Good Hope Gen. Hosp. Sutton Coldfield.

MANFORD, Mark Ralph Andrew Bedford Hospital, Kempston Road, Bedford MK42 9DJ Tel: 01234 792261 Fax: 01234 795713; Weelwrights, 30, Erimine St., Cambridge CB3 — MB BS 1985 Lond.; BSc (1st cl. Hons.) Lond. 1982, MD 1993; MRCP (UK) 1988; FRCP 2000 UK. (University College london) Cons. NeUrol. Bedford Hosp. Bedford and Addenbrooke's Hosp. Camb. Socs: Fell. Roy. Coll. Phys.s; Assn. Brit. NeUrol.s; Fell. Roy. Soc. Med. Prev: Sen. Regist. (Neurol.) Wessex Neurol. Centre Soton.; Clin. Research Fell. Inst. Neurol. Lond.; Regist. (Neurol.) Char. Cross Hosp. Lond.

MANGAL, Amarnauth Atkinson Health Centre, Market Street, Barrow-in-Furness LA14 2LR Tel: 01229 821556 Fax: 01229 827171; 7 Infield Park, Barrow-in-Furness LA13 9JL Tel: 01229 831348 — LRCPI & LM, LRSCI & LM 1973; LRCPI & LM, LRCSI & LM 1973. Princip. GP Cumbria; Sen. Med. Off. (Occupat. Health Med.) S. Cumbria HA; Sen. Police Surg. Cumbria Constab. Socs: Med. Defence Union.

MANGALESWARADEVI, Rajaratnam Ganeshalingam 23 Monkfrith Way, Southgate, London N14 5LY Tel: 020 8361 6705 — MB BS 1976 Sri Lanka; MRCOphth 1987.

MANGALESWARAN, Kumaradasan 59 Druid Road, Coventry CV2 4AU — MB BS 1972 Ceylon.

MANGALESWARAN, Somaskandasamy 20 Pitcairn Road, Mitcham CR4 3LL — MB BS 1976 Sri Lanka; MRCP (UK) 1994.

MANGAN, Brian Gerard 15 Bristow Park, Belfast BT9 6TF — MB BCh BAO 1985 Belf.

MANGAN, Catherine Mary 21 Larkfield Avenue, Belfast BT10 0LY — MB BCh BAO 1991 Belf.

MANGAN, Christine Melrose 159 Wellmeadow Road, London SE6 1HP Tel: 020 8698 5733 — MB ChB 1967 Manch.; DObst RCOG 1970. (Manch.) Med. Off. Kings Healthcare NHS Trust & Optimum Health Servs. Auths. Socs: Diplomate Fac. Family Plann. & Reproduc. Health Care. Prev: SHO (O & G) Whittington Hosp. Lond.; SHO (Paediat.) Birkenhead Childr. Hosp.; Ho. Off. (O & G) Hope Hosp. Salford.

MANGAN, Elizabeth Frances — MB ChB 1992 Liverp.; DCH RCP Lond. 1996; MRCGP Lond. 1997. (Univ. Liverp.) Salaried GP for Chester City Nursing Homes. Socs: Nat. Associaion of non-Princip.s coordinator of Chester non Princip. Gp. Prev: Regist. (Med.) Healthcare Hawkes Bay, NZ; SHO (Paediat.) Countess of Chester Hosp.; GP Regist. Buckley, N. Wales.

MANGAN, Michael Kevin St. Jude, 36 The Walk, Merthyr Tydfil CF47 8RS — LMSSA 1950 Lond.

MANGAN, Sally Ann Manor Farm Medical Centre, Manor Farm Road, Huyton, Liverpool L36 0UB Tel: 0151 480 1244 Fax: 0151 480 6047 — MB ChB 1980 Liverp.; DCH RCPS Glas. 1984; DRCOG 1983. (Liverpool)

MANGAR, Stephen Anthony Christie Hospital, Manchester M20 4BX Tel: 0161 446 3000; 10 Rosewarne Close, St. Michaels Wood, Liverpool L17 5BX Tel: 0151 727 8201 — MB ChB 1994 Liverp.; MRCP- Lond. 1999. (Liverp. Univ. Med. School) Specialist Regist. Christie Hosp. Manch.; Haemet./ Uncol. Med. Off. Cromwell Hosp. Lond. Prev: Off. (A & E) Roy. Liverp. Univ. Hosp. Liverp.; SHO (Haemat.) Roy. Free Hosp. Lond.

MANGAT, Har Bhajan Singh 18 Glynn Road, Peacehaven BN10 8AT — MB BS 1974 Delhi; DRCOG 1981; DTM & H Liverp. 1979.

MANGAT, Harbans Kaur The Medical Centre, 2-4 West End Road, Southall UB1 1JH Tel: 020 8843 2000; Renwick House, Hart Grove, London W5 3NB Tel: 020 8992 3355 — MB BS 1958 Rangoon; DCH RCSI 1961. Socs: BMA; Assoc. RCGP. Prev: Ho. Surg. Rangoon Dufferin Hosp. & Rangoon Gen. Hosp.

MANGAT, Hardeep Kaur The Gables, 119 Chestnut Lane, Amersham HP6 6DZ Tel: 01494 722839 — MB BS 1977 Lond.; BSc (Hons.) Lond. 1974, MB BS 1977; MRCGP 1982; DRCOG 1981.

MANGAT, Kamarjit Singh 64A Dorchester Way, Coventry CV2 2LX — MB BCh 1993 Wales. SHO (A & E) Good Hope Hosp. Birm. Prev: Ho. Off. (Surg.) Wycombe Gen. Hosp.; Ho. Phys. (Nephrol.) Qu. Nephrol. Qu. Eliz. Hosp. Birm.

MANGAT, Mr Khushbal Singh (retired) Oaklands Barn, Lugs Lane, Broome, Bungay NR35 2HT Tel: 01508 518397 — MB ChB Ed. 1962; FRCS Ed. 1968. p/t Med. Mem. InDepend. Tribunal Serv.s. Prev: Cons. ENT Surg. Norf. & Norwich Hosp., Jas. Paget Hosp. & Gt. Yarmouth & LoW.oft Clin. Area.

MANGAT, Kulraj Singh 62 Wood End Road, Erdington, Birmingham B24 8AD — MB ChB 1993 Leeds.

MANGAT, Louise Neelam Tarrant Manor Drive Surgery, 3 The Manor Drive, Worcester Park, London Tel: 020 8337 0545 Fax: 0208 335 3281 — MB BS 1993 Lond.; BSc 1991 Lond.; DRCOG 1995; DFFP 1998. (St Georges Hospital) GP Partner. Prev: GP Asst.; GP Regist.

***MANGAT, Nimrat Singh** General Medicine, Bromley Hospital, Bromley BR2 9AJ — MB BS 1998 Lond.; MB BS Lond 1998.

MANGAT, Niranjan Singh The Medical Centre, 2-4 West End Road, Southall UB1 1JH Tel: 020 8843 2000 — MB BS 1956 Rangoon; DO RCS Eng. 1961; FRSH 1964. GP S.all & Ealing; Ophth. Med. Pract. S.all; Mem. Hounslow Hammersmith & Ealing Family Pract. Comm. & LMC; Mem. Kensington, Chelsea & W.m. LMC. Socs: Fell. Roy. Soc. Health; Assoc. RCGP; BMA. Prev: Sen. Regist. & Chief Clin. Asst. Moorfields Eye Hosp. Lond.; SHMO Roy. Eye Hosp. Lond.; Cons. Refractionist Hosp. Sick Childr. Lond.

MANGAT, Pushpinder Singh ITU Department, Morriston Hospital, Swansea SA6 6NL Tel: 01792 703420 Fax: 01792 703470 Email: pushmagnat@hotmail.com; Woodlands, 4 Southward Lane, Swansea SA3 4QE Tel: 01792 360908 Fax: 01792 360908 — MB ChB 1983 Birmingham; DA (UK) 1987; FCAnaesth 1990. (Birmingham) Cons., Intens., Ther. & Anaesth., Morriston Hosp., Swansea. Socs: Intens. Care Soc.; Assn. Anaesth. Prev: Sen. Regist. Rotat. (Anaesth.), E. Anglia; Regist. Rotat. (Anaesth.), Swansea & Cardiff Health Auth.; Sen. Ho. Off. (Anaesth.) Centr. Birm. Health Auth., W. Glam. Health Auth.

MANGAT, Surjit Kaur 5 Cecil Road, Hounslow TW3 1NU Tel: 020 8572 2536 Fax: 020 8570 3197; 23 Beaconsfield Road, Southall UB1 1BW Tel: 020 8574 5943 Fax: 020 88113 8968 — MB BS 1972 Punjab; MB BS Punjabi 1972; T(GP) 1991. (Govt. Med. Coll. Patiala) Med. Off. Family Plann. Clinic Featherstone Clinic S.all. Prev: Ho. Phys. (Paediat.) & Ho. Surg. (Gen. Surg.) Selly Oak Hosp. Birm.; Res. Sen. Ho. Phys. (Paediat.) Solihull Hosp.

MANGAT, Swaran Singh 130 The Ridgway, Woddingdean, Brighton BN2 6PB Tel: 01273 304325 — MB BS 1967 Bombay.

MANGAT, Mr Teja Singh (retired) High Lodge Farmhouse, Iverley, Stourbridge DY7 6PP Tel: 01384 394583 — MB BS Lond. 1953; FRCS Eng. 1960. Prev: Cons. Orthop. Surg. Dudley & Stourbridge Hosp. Gp.

MANGAT, Tejina Kiran High Lodge Farmhouse, Iverley, Stourbridge DY7 6PP — MB BS 1986 Lond.

***MANGHAM, Catherine Mary Jane** 31 Mount Street, Aberdeen AB25 2QX — MB ChB 1998 Aberd.; MB ChB Aberd 1998.

MANGHAM, David Charles Department of Musculoskeletal Pathology, Royal Orthopaedic Hospital, Northfield, Birmingham B31 Tel: 0121 414 7641 Fax: 0121 414 7640 — MB ChB 1987 Manch.; BSc (Hons.) Manch. 1985; MRCPath 1993. (Univ. Manch.) Cons. & Hon. Sen. Lect. (Histopath.) Roy. Orthop. Hosp. Birm. Prev: Cons. (Histopath.) Qu. Eliz. Hosp. Birm.; Fell. (Path. & Orthop.) Mass. Gen. Hosp. Boston, USA; Lect. & Hon. Sen. Regist. (Histopath.) Univ. Birm.

***MANGHANI, Mona Kishu** 35A Shirley Road, Cardiff CF23 5HL — MB BCh 1998 Wales.

***MANGHAT, Nathan Eugene** 6 Tabarin Way, Rosebushes, Epsom KT17 3NZ — MB ChB 1995 Bristol.

MANGION, David c/o Pilgrim Hospital, Sibsey Road, Boston PE21 9QS — MRCS Eng. LRCP Lond. 1978; FRACP 1992; FRCP 1999. Cons. Gen. & Geriat. Med. Pilgrim Hosp. Boston.

MANGION, John (retired) 100 Gunnersbury Avenue, Ealing, London W5 4HB Tel: 020 8992 7565 — MD 1958 Malta; BSc. MD Malta 1958; MRCGP 1976; DMJ (Clin.) Soc. Apoth. Lond. 1972. Prev: Sen. Forens. Med. Examr. Metrop. Police.

MANGION, Pio Dryburn Hospital, Durham DH1 5TW Tel: 0191 333 2581; 14 Hill Meadows, High Skincliffe, Durham DH1 2PE — MD 1964 Malta; FRCP Lond. 1991; MRCP (UK) 1970. (Malta Med. Sch.) Cons. Rheum. N. Durh. NHS Health Trust. Socs: Brit. Soc. Rheum. Prev: Sen. Regist. (Rheum.) Roy. Free Hosp. Lond.; Regist. (Med. And Neuro.) Char. Cross Hosp. Lond.; Ho. Phys. Profess. Unit St. Luke's Hosp. Malta.

MANGNALL, Mr Roger (retired) Woodstock House, Fern Road, Pakenham, Bury St Edmunds IP31 2JS Tel: 01359 30475 — MB BChir 1952 Camb.; MA Camb. 1953, MB BChir 1952; FRCS Glas. 1962. Prev: Cons. Orthop. Surg. Bury St. Edmunds Health Dist.

MANGROLIA, Ram Dayal 15 Whiting Grove, Ladybridge, Bolton BL3 4PU Tel: 01204 655607 — MB BS 1965 Rajasthan. (S.M.S. Med. Coll. Jaipur) Assoc. Specialist (Orthop. & Accid.) Bolton AHA. Prev: Regist. (Orthop.) Bolton Roy. Infirm.; SHO (Gen. Surg.) Horton Gen. Hosp. Banbury; SHO (Orthop.) Heatherwood Hosp. Ascot.

MANGTANI, Punam Department of General Practice., Division of Community health, UMDS Guy's & St Thomas's Hospital (Guy's Campus), London SE1 9RT Tel: 020 7955 5000; 396 Bath Road, Hounslow TW4 7RP — BSc (Hons.) Lond. 1979, MB BS 1982; MRCP (UK) 1986; MRCGP 1990; DCH RCP Lond. 1987. Med. Research Counc. Train. Fell. (Health Serv. Research) UMDS Lond.

MANGWANA, Krishan Lal Fulham Road Surgery, 714 Fulham Road, London SW6 5SB Tel: 020 7736 6305 Fax: 020 7384 3153 — MB BS 1963 Panjab; MRCGP 1979.

MANHEIM, Vivienne Helen Staunton Group Practice, 3-5 Bounds Green Road, Wood Green, London N22 8HE Tel: 020 8889 4311 Fax: 020 8826 9100; 10 Ridings Close, Highgate, London N6 5XE Tel: 020 8341 5918 — MRCS Eng. LRCP Lond. 1965. (Roy. Free) Elected Mem. Lond. Boro. Haringey (Counc.lor).

MANHIRE, Adrian Ross 21 Troutbeck Crescent, Bramcote, Nottingham NG9 3BP — MB BS 1972 Lond.; BSc (Biochem.) Lond. 1969, MB BS 1972; MRCP (UK) 1976; FRCR 1983. (Middlx.) Cons. (Radiol.) City Hosp. Nottm. Prev: Sen. Regist. (Radiol.) Middlx. Hosp. Lond.; Regist. (Radiol.) Bristol Roy. Infirm.; Tutor in Radiol. Univ. Bristol.

MANI, Chinta 7 Clydebrae Drive, Bothwell, Glasgow G71 8SB — MB BS 1974 Punjabi; MRCPsych 1982.

MANI, Joseph (retired) 6 Chepstow Close, Bamford, Rochdale OL11 5TR — MB BS 1950 Madras; DTM & H Liverp. 1953. Prev: Regist. (Med.) St. Luke's Hosp. Bradford & Blackburn Roy. Infirm.

MANI, Venkateswaran Leigh Infirmary, The Avenue, Leigh WN7 1HS Tel: 01942 672333 Fax: 01942 677330; Westdene, 118 Junction Road, Bolton BL3 4NE Tel: 01204 656039 — MB BS 1962 Calcutta; FRCP Lond. 1992; FRCP Ed. 1980, M 1966. (Nat. Med. Coll. Calcutta) Cons. Gastroenterol. Leigh Infirm.; Hon. Clin. Teach. Lond. Univ. Socs: Brit. Soc. Gastroenterol.; Eur. Assn. for Gastroenterol. & Endoscopy. Prev: Cons. Phys. Leigh Infirm.; Sen. Regist. (Med.) Hope Hosp. Salford; Regist. (Med.) Hull Roy. Infirm. & Staincliffe Hosp. Dewsbury.

MANICKARAJAH, Mr Ponnusamy 7 St Mary's View, Kenton, Harrow HA3 8ED — MB BS 1972 Ceylon; FRCS Glas. 1981; FRCS Ed. 1982; MRCS Eng. LRCP Lond. 1979. Med. Off. Lond. N. Regional Off. DHSS. Prev: Regist. (Gen. Surg.) Scunthorpe HA; Regist. (A & E) Morriston Hosp. Swansea; SHO (GEn. Surg.) Corbett & Wordsley Hosps. W. Midl.

MANICKASAMY, Mr Thiruvenkata Ayyamperumal 35 Quilp Drive, Newlands Spring, Chelmsford CM1 4YA Tel: 01245 443569 — MB BS 1962 Madras; FRCS Ed. 1976. Socs: Med. Protec. Soc.; Hosp. Cons. & Spec. Assn.

MANIDAS, Sadanandan 1 Wadhurst Court, Wadhurst Close, Penge, London SE20 8TA Tel: 020 8659 0067 Fax: 020 7288 5699 Email: smanidas@hotmail.com — MB BS 1979 India; ATLS Cert. (Lond.) 2001; ALS Cert. (Lond.) 2001; Cert. Adv Life Support 1994; MRCS Eng. LRCP Lond. 1983; LMSSA Lond. 1983; FICS (USA) 1995; FICA (USA) 1991; DFFP 1993; T(GP) 1991; Cert. Family Plann. JCC 1988; Cert. Prescribed Equiv. Exp. JCPTGP 1988. (Trivandrum Med. Coll. Univ. Kerala) Staff Phys. A & E The Whittington Univ. Hosp./UCL Med. Sch., Lond. Socs: Fac. Hist. & Philosophy of Med. & Pharmacy of Soc. Apoth. Lond.; Migraine in Primary Care Advisers Gp. Surrey (MIPCA); Fell. Roy. Soc. Health Lond. Prev: Staff Phys. A & E Gen. Hosp. Kettering, N.ants; Staff

MANIERA

Phys. (A & E) Stoke Mandeville Hosp., Aylesbury, Bucks; Staff Phys. (A & E) Warwick Gen. Hosp., Warwick, Midl.s.

MANIERA, Djanan Meryem The Cambridge Street Surgery, 93 Cambridge Street, London SW1V 4PY Tel: 0207 834 5502 Fax: 0207 834 2350 Email: j.maniera@ic.ac.uk — MB BS 1986 Lond.; LMSSA Lond. 1985; MRCGP 1989; DRCOG 1989; DGM RCP Lond. 1987. (St. Thos.) Princip. GP; Hon. Sen. Lect. ICSM CX Campus. Socs: BMA; RCGP. Prev: SHO (O & G & Paediat.) St. Thos. Hosp. Lond.; SHO (Geriat. Med.) Richmond, Twickenham & Roehampton HA; Cas. Off. & Ho. Phys. Kingston Hosp.

MANIFOLD, Donald Kilvington 9 Lealands Avenue, Leigh, Tonbridge TN11 8QU — MB BChir 1990 Camb.

MANIFOLD, Ian Howard 122 Button Hill, Sheffield S11 9HJ — MB BChir 1975 Camb.; MD Sheff. 1984; MA, MB Camb. 1975, BChir 1974; MRCP (UK) 1976; FRCR 1984. (Lond. Hosp. & Camb.) Sen. Regist. (Radiotherap.) W. Pk. Hosp. Sheff. & Hon Tutor in Med.; Univ. Dept. Med. Roy. Hallamsh. Hosp. Sheff. Prev: Lect. (Med. & Clin. Oncol.) Univ. Dept. Med. Roy. Hallamsh. Hosp.; Sheff.; Ho. Phys. Lond. Hosp.

MANIFOLD, Nancy Jane 9 Lealands Avenue, Leigh, Tonbridge TN11 8QU — BChir 1991 Camb.

***MANIK, Kulvinder Singh** 24 Grange Av, Bradford BD3 7BB — MB ChB 1997 Leic.

MANIKON, Maria Isabel Flat 3, 29 Ousley Road, London SW12 8ED — MB BS 1996 Lond.

MANISALI, Mehmet 33 Ifield Road, London SW10 9AZ — MB BS 1992 Lond.; BDS Bristol 1982; FFD RCSI 1991.

MANISTRE, Stephen John St Peters Hill Surgery, 15 St. Peters Hill, Grantham NG31 6QA Tel: 01476 590009 Fax: 01476 570898 — MB BS 1975 Lond.; MRCGP 1980; DRCOG 1980. (Middlx.) Prev: Trainee GP I. of Thanet VTS.

MANJI, Mr Ajay Kumar Chorley & South Ribble District General Hospital, Chorley PR7 1PP Tel: 01257 261222 Fax: 01257 245309; 254 Garstang Road, Fulwood, Preston PR2 9QB Tel: 01772 462068 Fax: 01772 462068 — MB BS 1972 Calcutta; MS All India Inst. Med. Scs. 1976; FRCS Glas. 1982. (Nilratan Sircar Med. Coll., Calcutta) Specialist Surg. (A & E) Chorley & S. Ribble Dist. Gen. Hosp. Chorley Lancs. Socs: Brit. Assn. Accid. & Emerg. Med.; Fac. Pre-Hosp. Care; Assoc. Fell. Fac. A&E Med. Prev: Staff Grade Surg. (A & E Med.) W.morland Gen. Hosp. Kendal; Clin. Asst. (A & E) Llandudno Gen. Hosp.; Regist. (Neurosurg.) Roy. Preston Hosp.

MANJI, Hadi Department of Neurology, Ipswich Hospital, Heath Road, Ipswich IP4 5PD; 42 Wakehams Hill, Pinner HA5 3BQ — MB BChir 1982 Camb.; MA Camb. 1983, MD 1996; FRCP 2000 UK; DRCOG 1985. (Middlx.) Cons. Neurol. Ipswich Hosp. NHS Trust & Nat. Hosp. for Neurol. & Neurosurg. Lond. Prev: Sen. Regist. & Lect. (Neurol.) Roy. Free Hosp. Lond.; Regist. (Neurol.) Nat. Hosp. Neurol. & Neurosurg. Lond. & Middlx. Univ. Coll. Hosp. Lond.; Research Fell. (Neurol.) Middlx. Hosp. Lond.

MANJI, Hamid Hussain 141A Connor Hill, Oxford OX2 9JA — MB ChB 1991 Glas.

MANJI, Mavji University Hospital Birmingham NHS Trust Selly Oak Hospital, Raddlebarn Road, Selly Oak, Birmingham B29 6JD — MB BCh 1987 Wales; MRCP (UK) 1990; FRCA 1994. Cons. (IC Med. & Anaesth.) Univ. Hosp. Birm. NHS Trust. Prev: Sen. Regist. (Intens. Care & Anaesth.) Qu. Eliz. Hosp. Birm.; Regist. (Anaesth.) Warks.; Regist. (Chest & Renal Med.) E. Birm. HA.

MANJIANI, Jhaman Dass 8 Beulah Road, Thornton Heath, Croydon CR7 8JE Tel: 020 8771 6556 — MB BS 1970 Sind; MB BS Sind Pakistan 1970; FFA RCS Eng. 1980; DA (UK) 1978. Cons. - anE.hetist, Crawley Hosp. Prev: Sen. Regist. (Anaesth.) Poole Trust Hosp.; Assoc. Prof. Anaesth. Karachi.; Sen. Regist. (Anaesth.) NQu. Eliz. Hosp. Lond.

MANJOORAN, Francis Oswald Medical Centre, 296 Union Road, Oswaldtwistle, Accrington BB5 3JD Tel: 01254 236009 — MB BS 1963 Karnatak; MB BS 1963 Karnatak.

MANJOORAN, Thomas Oswald Medical Centre, 296 Union Road, Oswaldtwistle, Accrington BB5 3JD Tel: 01254 236009; Oswald Medical Center, 296 Union Road, Oswaldtwistle, Accrington BB5 3JD Tel: 01254 236009 & 232206 — MB BS 1963 Karnatak; MRCS Eng. LRCP Lond. 1978; MRCGP 1977. (Kasturba Med. Coll. Mangalore) Socs: BMA. Prev: SHO (Med.) Roy. Hosp. W.on-super-Mare.

MANJUBHASHINI, Sivanathan Botleys Park Hospital, Chertsey KT16 0QA Tel: 01932 2000; Sabarmat, 31 Fletcher Road, Ottershaw, Chertsey KT16 0JY Tel: 0193 287 3690 — MB BS 1973 Madras; DPM Eng. 1975. Cons. Psychiat. (Ment. Handicap) Botleys Pk. Hosp. Chertsey.

MANJULA, Govindshenoy c/o Dr B. Mallaya, 36 Fairdale Gardens, Upper Richmond Road, Putney, London SW15 6JW — MB BS 1984 Calicut, India; MRCP (UK) 1991.

MANJUNATH, Manjunath Rhos House Surgery, 55 Oxford Street, Mountain Ash CF45 3HD Tel: 01443 473214 Fax: 01443 473289 — MB BS 1970 Bangalore.

MANJUNATHA, Srikantaiah 3 Warrens Croft, Walsall WS5 3JX — MB BS 1978 Mysore; BSc Mysore 1970, MB BS 1978; MRCP (UK) 1989.

MANKAD, Mr Pankaj Shashikant Royal Infirmary, Lauvinston Place, Edinburgh EH3 9YW Tel: 0131 536 3692 Fax: 0131 536 3482 Email: pankaj.mankad@ed.ac.uk; Harvieston Mains, Gorebridge EH23 4LG Email: pankaj.mankad@ed.ac.uk — MB BS 1977 Baroda; MS Baroda 1980, MB BS 1977; FRCS Ed. 1984; FRCS (C Th) 1989. Cons. Cardiothoracic Surg. Roy. Infirm. Edin.; p/t Sen. Lect. (Cardiac Surg.) Edin. Univ. Prev: Sen. Regist. (Cardiothoracic Surg.) Gt. Ormond St. Hosp. Lond.

MANKIKAR, Ganesh Dattatray (retired) Connaught House, 16 Princes Square, Hove BN3 4GE Tel: 01273 729573 Fax: 01273 729844 — MB BS Karnatak 1965; FRCP Lond. 1986; FRCP Glas. 1986; FRCP Ed. 1984, MRCP 1971. Cons. Phys. Brighton Health Care NHS Trust; Hon. Lect. Univ. Brighton. Prev: Sen. Regist. Guy's Hosp. Lond.

MANKOO, Kirpal Singh Coldershaw Road Surgery, 168 Coldershaw Road, West Ealing, London W13 9DT Tel: 020 8567 0970; 4 Kerrison Road, Ealing, London W5 5NW Tel: 020 8567 9186 — MB BS 1956 Bombay; MLCOM 1982; DA (UK) 1966; DCH RCP Lond. 1961. (Grant Med. Coll.)

MANKTELOW, Mr Andrew Richard Jonathan 68 Crayford Road, London N7 0ND — MB BS 1989 Lond.; BSc Lond. 1986, MB BS 1989; FRCS Ed. 1993.

MANKTELOW, Claire 68 Crayford Road, London N7 0ND — MB BS 1992 Lond.

MANLEY, Anthony Francis Stoneycroft Medical Centre, Stoneville Road, Liverpool L13 6QD Tel: 0151 228 1138 Fax: 0151 228 1653; Boundary Farm, Graveyard Lane, Bickerstaffe, Ormskirk L39 9EE — MB ChB 1976 Liverp.

MANLEY, Carol Anne 12 Stephen Dr, Sheffield S10 5NX — MB ChB 1997 Birm.

MANLEY, Gerald William (retired) Department of Chemical Pathology, Torbay Hospital, Torquay TQ2 7AA Tel: 01803 614567 — MD 1963 Bristol; DPhil Oxf. 1966; MB ChB 1957; FRCPath 1981, M 1969. Cons. Chem. Path. Torbay Hosp. Devon & Hon. Research Fell. Univ. Exeter. Prev: Lect. (Cell Biol.) Univ. Exeter.

MANLEY, Miles Ewan Pearce Coalway Road Surgery, 119 Coalway Road, Penn, Wolverhampton WV3 7NA Tel: 01902 341409 Fax: 01902 620527 — MB ChB 1989 Manch.; BSc (Hons.) St. And. 1982.

MANLEY, Patrick Anthony Sperrin Lakeland Trust, Tyrone & Fermanagh Hospital, Omagh BT79 0NS Tel: 01662 245211 Email: pmanley@slt.n-i.nhs.uk — MB BCh BAO 1981 NUI; MRCPsych 1991; MRCGP 1986; DCH RCSI 1984; Dip. Obst. RCPI 1984. (University College Dublin) Cons. Gen. Adult Psychiat. Sperrin Lakeland NHS Trust Omagh Co. Tyrone. Socs: BMA. Prev: Sen. Regist. Maudsley Hosp. Lond.; Research Regist. St. Patrick's Hosp. Dub.; Regist. St. Patrick's Hosp. Dub.

MANLEY, Rachel 17 Vicarage Gardens, Marshfield, Cardiff CF3 2PS — MB ChB 1991 Bristol.

MANLEY, Robert Brooklyn Surgery, 65 Mansfield Road, Heanor DE75 7AL Tel: 01773 712552; 1 Hazel Close, Heanor DE75 7UB Tel: 01773 719522 — MB ChB 1985 Manch.; T(GP) 1993.

MANLEY, Rupert The Stennack Surgery, The Old Stennack School, St Ives TR26 1RU Tel: 01736 795237 Fax: 01736 795362; Paddock's End, Wheal Venture Road, St Ives TR26 2PQ — MB ChB 1986 Bristol; BSc Bristol 1983; MRCGP 1993; T(GP) 1994; DRCOG 1992; DGM RCP Lond. 1989. Clin. Asst. (Neurol.) Cornw. Prev: Trainee GP St. Ives Cornw. & Cornw. & Isles of Scilly VTS; SHO (Med.) Roy. Cornw. Hosp. Truro.

MANN

MANLEY, Susan Mary Alder Hey Childrens Hospital, Eaton Road, West Derby, Liverpool L12 2AP Tel: 0151 252 5294; Boundary Farm, Graveyard Lane, Bickerstaffe, Ormskirk L39 9EE — MB ChB 1976 Liverp.; MB ChB (Hons.) Liverp. 1976. Clin. Asst. (Paediat. Oncol.) Unit Alder Hey Childr. Hosp. Liverp.

MANLEY, Vanessa Claire Ridgacre House Surgery, 83 Ridgacre Road, Quinton, Birmingham B32 2TJ Tel: 0121 422 3111; 72 Cambridge Road, Moseley, Birmingham B13 9UD Tel: 0121 689 2781 — MB ChB 1989 Birm.; MRCGP 1994; DFFP 1994; DCH RCP Lond. 1992. Prev: Trainee GP/SHO Worcester Roy. Infirm. VTS.

MANLOW, Christopher John 44 Woodstock Road; Broxbourne EN10 7NT — MB BS 1993 Lond.

MANN, Alan John (retired) The Upper Flat, 27 Daglands Road, Fowey PL23 1JN Tel: 01726 833403 — MB BS 1956 Lond.; MRCS Eng. LRCP Lond. 1956.

MANN, Aman-Baksh 39 Lodge Hill Road, Selly Oak, Birmingham B29 6NU — MB ChB 1994 Birm.; ChB Birm. 1994.

MANN, Amar Paul Singh 110 Rosemary Avenue, Hounslow TW4 7JG — MB ChB 1992 Leeds.

MANN, Anna Louise The New Sheepmarket Surgery, Ryhall Road, Stamford PE9 1YA — MB ChB 1979 Sheff.

MANN, Anthony Howard 75 Chesil Court, Chelsea Manor St., London SW3 5QS — MB BChir 1966 Camb.; MA Camb. 1966, MD 1982; MPhil Lond. 1972; FRCP Lond. 1986, M 1968; FRCPsych 1984, M 1973. (St. Bart.) Prof. Epidemiol. Psychiat. Inst. Psychiat. Lond.; Hon. Cons. Maudsley Hosp. & Roy. Free Hosp. Lond.; Vis. Prof. Roy. Free Hosp. Med. Sch. Lond. Socs: Fell. Roy. Soc. Med. (Pres. Psychiat. Sect.).

MANN, Balvindar Singh Wishaw General Hospital, 50 Netherton St., Wishaw ML2 0DP — MB ChB 1974 Glas.; FRCPath 1993; MRCPath 1983. (Glas.) Cons. Histopath. Law Hosp. Carluke. Prev: Lect. (Histopath.) Roy. Free Hosp. Med. Sch. Lond.; Regist. (Histopath.) Hammersmith Hosp. Roy. Postgrad. Med. Sch. Lond.; Regist. & SHO (Histopath.) Stobhill Gen. Hosp. Glas.

MANN, Barbara Mary 599 Yarm Road, Eaglescliffe, Stockton-on-Tees TS16 9BN Tel: 01642 786344 — MB BS 1975 Lond.; MRCS Eng. LRCP Lond. 1974. (Roy. Free)

MANN, Bertram Tullis (retired) 4 Fern Court, 43 Hendon Lane, Finchley, London N3 1SF Tel: 020 8349 2082 — MD 1942 Glas.; BSc Glas. 1934, MD 1942, MB ChB 1937, DPH 1940. Cons. Chest Phys. Asberstosis Halifax Yorks. Prev: Cons. Chest Phys. Halifax Hosp. Gp.

MANN, Bhupinder Singh 38 St Joseph's Drive, Southall UB1 1RL Tel: 020 8574 6552; 38 St. Joseph's Drive, Southall UB1 1RL — MB BS 1991 Lond.; BSc Lond. 1987; MRCP I, II Lond. 1995; MSc 1999. (St. Mary's Hospital Medical School) Roy. Brompton Hosp., Lond. Prev: Specialist Regist. Gen. & Respirat. Med. W. Middlx. Hosp.

MANN, Carl Lee Ambrose 20 Grange Park Road, Bromley Cross, Bolton BL7 9YA — MB ChB 1992 Manch.; BSc (Hons.) Manch. 1990; MRCP (UK) 1996. (Manch.) Research Regist. (Neurol.) N. Staffs. Roy. Infirm.

MANN, Caroline Elizabeth 5 Cresta Gardens, Nottingham NG3 5GD — BM BS 1994 Nottm.

***MANN, Catherine** Garden Flat, 45 Upper Belgrave Rd, Clifton, Bristol BS8 2XN — MB ChB 1997 Bristol.

MANN, Catherine Mary Northampton General Hospital, Cliftonville, Northampton NN1 5BD; 17 Wyre Hill, Bewdley DY12 2UE — BM BCh 1997 Oxf. GP Voca. Train. Schm.

MANN, Mr Charles James Victor Deakin Goodcheap Farmhouse, Hinxhill Estate, Hinxhill, Ashford TN25 5NR Tel: 01233 635948 Email: vascmann@aol.com — MB BS 1988 Lond.; FRCS Ed. 1995; FRCS Eng. 1995. (Lond. Hosp. Med. Coll.) Career Regist. (Orthop.) St. Thos. Hosp. Lond.

MANN, Mr Charles Victor The Cosy, Basingstoke Road, Old Alresford, Alresford SO24 9DL Tel: 01962 735315 — BM BCh 1951 Oxf.; MCh Oxf. 1965; FRCS Eng. 1958. (Oxf. & St. Thos.) Emerit. Cons. N.wick Pk. & St. Mark's Hosp. Trust; Pres. Cons. Surg. Roy. Lond. Hosp. Trust. Socs: Assn. Colo-proctol. GB & Irel.; Roy. Soc. Med.; Soc. Apocatharies. Prev: Pres. Sect. Coloproctol. Roy. Soc. Med.; Postgrad. Sub-Dean Lond. Hosp. Med. Coll.; Dean Postgrad. Studies St. Marks Hosp. Lond.

MANN, Christine Gracombe House, Hornton Road, Horley, Banbury OX15 6BL Tel: 01295 738755 — MB BCh BAO 1979 Belf. Clin. Asst. (Genitourin. Med.) Stratford Hosp. & Warwick Hosp.

MANN, Mr Christopher Franz 15 York Close, Kings Langley WD4 9HX — MB BS 1991 Lond.; FRCS Eng. 1995. Specialist Regist. Rotat. (Orthop.) Yorks.

MANN, Christopher Howard Birmingham Women's NHS Trust, Edgbaston, Birmingham B15 2TG — MB ChB 1988 Leic. Specialist Regist. Birm. Wom.'s NHS Trust.

MANN, Clifford John Accident & Emergency Department, Musgrove Park Hospital, Taunton TA1 1RP Tel: 01823 333444 Email: cjmann@cjm3.demon.co.uk; 3 Richmond Terrace, Buckland Monachorum, Yelverton PL20 7LU Tel: 01822 854019 — MB BS 1986 Lond.; MB BS Lond. 1985; BSc (Hons.) Lond. 1983; MRCP (UK) 1990; MRCGP 1990; DA (UK) 1992; DCH RCP Lond. 1988; FFAEM 1997. (Charing Cross and Westminster) Cons. (A & E) MusGr. Pk. Hosp. Taunton. Prev: Regist. (A & E) Qu. Alexandra Hosp. Portsmouth, Sen. Regist. (A & E) Derriford Hosp. Plymouth; Regist. (Emerg. Med.) Auckland, NZ; SHO (Anaesth.) MusGr. Pk. Hosp. Taunton.

MANN, David Murray (retired) Clemens, Green Lane, Crantock, Newquay TR8 5RF Tel: 01637 830716 Email: david.mann@eggconnect.net — MB BS 1955 Lond.; DObst RCOG 1957. Prev: Ho. Surg. St. Giles' Hosp. Lond.

MANN, Dora Jeane (retired) 69 Beach Road, Barassie, Troon KA10 6SX Tel: 01292 313963 — MB ChB 1961 Glas.; MRCGP 1983; DObst RCOG 1963. Prev: GP Irvine Ayrsh.

MANN, Edgar John 38 Easedale Drive, Elm Park, Hornchurch RM12 Tel: 0140 24 51585 — MB BS 1949 Lond.; MRCS Eng. LRCP Lond. 1949; DMJ (Clin.) Soc. Apoth. Lond. 1970; DPH Eng. 1962; DObst RCOG 1951. (King's Coll. Hosp.) Assoc. RCGP; Police Surg. HornCh., Upminster & Rainham. Socs: Brit. Acad. Foren. Sc.; FRIPHH. Prev: Ho. Surg. Co. Hosp. York & Gyn. Dept. King's Coll Hosp.; Cas. Off. St. And. Hosp. Bow.

MANN, Emily Amelia 24 Forehill Road, Ayr KA7 3DT Tel: 01292 268111 — LRCP LRCS 1950 Ed.; LRCP LRCS Ed. LRFPS Glas. 1950; MFCM RCPI 1978; DPH Glas. 1961. Sen. Med. Off. (Community Med.) Renfrew Health Dist.

MANN, Evleen Theresa 42 Duchy Road, Harrogate HG1 2ER Tel: 01423 503513 Fax: 01423 538700 Email: evleen1@aol.com — MB BS 1979 Lond. (Roy. Free) p/t Clin. Asst. Eating Disorders, Searoft Hosp. Prev: GP Greenford & Highgate.

MANN, Felix Bernard 15 Devonshire Place, London W1G 6HF Tel: 020 7935 7575 — MB BChir 1955 Camb.; MA Camb. 1955; LMCC 1956. (Camb. & Westm.) Specialist (Acupunc.) Lond. Socs: Founder Mem. (Ex-Pres.) Med. Acupunc. Soc.

***MANN, Gurdeep Singh** 94 Berkswell Road, Coventry CV6 7DL — MB ChB 1996 Birm.; ChB Birm. 1996.

MANN, Mr Gurminder Singh Department of Urology, Nottingham City Hospital, Hucknall Road, Nottingham NG5 1PB — BM BS 1991 Nottm.; FRCS Eng. 1995.

MANN, Helen Macgregor Childa and Family Psychological Medicine, St Peter's Hospital, Guildford Rd, Chertsey KT16 0PZ Tel: 01932 722561 Fax: 0141 531 3302; 21 Herons Place, Isleworth TW7 7BE — MB ChB 1984 Ed.; MRCGP 1989; MRCPsych 1992; DRCOG 1988; DCCH RCP Ed. 1988. (Ed.) p/t Cons.Childa and Adolesc. Psychiat. N.-W. Surrey.

MANN, James Graham (retired) 69 Beach Road, Barassie, Troon KA10 6SX Tel: 01292 313963 — MB ChB 1950 Glas.; DObst RCOG 1951. Prev: Ho. Phys. Ayr Co. Hosp.

MANN, Jane Elizabeth The Croft, Kilcot, Newent GL18 1NZ Tel: 01989 720488 — MB BS 1978 Lond.; BSc Lond. 1974, MB BS 1978; MFFP 1994. (Roy. Free)

MANN, Jaspreet 19 Campion Road, Leamington Spa CV32 5XF — MB ChB 1992 Manch. (Manch.)

MANN, Jill Barbara Research Institute for the Care of the Elderly, St Martins Hospital, Midford Road, Bath BA2 5RP Tel: 01225 835866 Fax: 01225 840395; Ormond Lodge, 30 Sion Hill, Bath BA1 2UW — MB BS 1976 Lond.; MFFP 1993. (UCHMS Lond.) Sen. Clin. Research Fell. Research Inst. for c/o Elderly Bath. Prev: Clin. Med. Off. (Family Plann.) Bath & W. Community NHS Trust; Regist. (Clin. Bacteriol.) St. Mary's Hosp. Lond.

MANN, Professor Jillian Rose Oncology Department, Birmingham Childrens Hospital, Steelhouse Lane, Birmingham

MANN

B4 6NH Tel: 0121 333 8238 Fax: 0121 333 8241 Email: jillmann@bhamchildrenswmids.nhs.uk; 19 Rodman Close, Edgbaston, Birmingham B15 3PE Tel: 0121 455 8643 — MB BS Lond. 1962; FRCP Lond. 1980, M 1966; MRCS Eng. LRCP Lond. 1962; DCH Eng. 1964; FRCPCH 1997. (St. Thos.) Cons. Paediat. Oncol. Birm. Childr. Hosp.; Hon. Prof. Birm. Univ. Socs: (Ex-Sec & Ex-Chairm.) UK Childr. Cancer Study Gp.; BMA; Soc. Internat. d'Oncologie Pédiatrique. Prev: Cons. Paediat. Selly Oak Hosp.; SHO (Gen. Med.) Hosp. Sick Childr. Gt. Ormond St. Lond; Ho. Phys. St. Thos. Hosp. Lond.

MANN, John Hedley Wyke Regis Health Centre, Portland Road, Weymouth DT4 9BE Tel: 01305 782226 Fax: 01305 760549; Burgundy House, 40 Westhill Road, Wyke Regis, Weymouth DT4 9NB — MB BS Lond. 1969; MRCP (U.K.) 1973. (St. Geo.) GP Princip.; Clin. Asst. (Dermat.) Weymouth & Dist. Hosp. Prev: Ho. Surg. St. Geo. Hosp. Lond.; SHO (Med.) Weymouth & Dist. Hosp.; SHO (Paediat.) Dorset Co. Hosp. Dorchester.

MANN, John Richard Blue Dykes Surgery, Eldon Street, Clay Cross, Chesterfield S45 9NR Tel: 01246 862468 — MB ChB 1979 Sheff.; DRCOG 1983.

MANN, Jonathan Fleming Nuffield Unit, Burdon Terrace, Jesmond, Newcastle upon Tyne NE2 3AE; Hollyhurst, 118 Woodland Road, Darlington DL3 9LN — MB ChB 1985 Dundee; BMSc (Path.) Dund 1982; MRCPsych 1992. Sen. Regist. (Child & Adolesc. Psychiat.) Fleming Nuffield Unit Newc. u. Tyne.

MANN, Jonathan Nicholas 80 Roman Way, Andover SP10 5JJ Tel: 01264 351396 — MB BS 1993 Lond. (St. Mary's) Regist. (Gen. Psychiat.) Roy. Lond. Hosp. (St. Clements).

MANN, Jonathan Spencer New Cross Hospital, Wolverhampton WV10 0QP Tel: 01902 307999; 71 Wrottesley Road, Tettenhall, Wolverhampton WV6 8SQ — MB BS 1976 Lond.; DM Soton. 1987; FRCP Lond. 1994; MRCS Eng. LRCP Lond. 1976. (St. Bart.) Cons. Gen. Phys. (Respirat. Med.) New Cross Hosp. Wolverhampton; Chairm. Regional SpR Train. Comm. Respirat. Med. Socs: Brit. Thorac. Soc. Prev: Regional Roy. Coll. of Phys.s and BTS Represen.; Clin. Dir. (Med.); Sen. Regist. (Gen. & Thoracic Med.) Stoke City Gen. Hosp.

MANN, Kanwarinder Singh Friarsgate Practice, Friarsgate Medical Centre, Friarsgate, Winchester SO23 8EF Tel: 01962 854091 Fax: 01962 854956 Email: marton@friarsgatepractice.freesrve.co.uk — MB BS 1985 Lond.; MRCP (UK) 1992; MRCGP 1995; DTM & H RCP Lond. 1990. (The London Hospital Medical College) Prev: Regist. (Gen. Med.) Waikato Hosp. Hamilton, NZ; SHO (Gen. Med.) Burton Hosp.; Med. Off. Rubya Hosp., Tanzania.

MANN, Katherine Ellis (retired) Victoria Infirmary, Helensburgh G84 Tel: 01436 78142 — MB ChB 1960 Glas.; DCH RCPS Glas. 1973. Prev: SCMO Dumbarton Dist.

MANN, Keith Antony Elms Medical Practice, 5 Stewart Road, Harpenden AL5 4QA Tel: 01582 769393 Fax: 01582 461735 — BM BCh 1968 Oxf.; BA Oxf. 1964; MRCS Eng. LRCP Lond. 1967; DA Eng. 1971. (St. Geo.) Prev: Ho. Phys. (Paediat.) & Ho. Surg. (Genitourin.) St. Geo. Hosp. Lond.

***MANN, Kenneth Grant** 3 Fiddlers Walk, Wargrave, Reading RG10 8BA — MB ChB 1994 Cape Town.

MANN, Manjit Singh 1 Marlborough Road, Smethwick, Smethwick B66 4DN — BM 1990 Soton.

MANN, Margaret (retired) 15 Compass Court, North Drive, Wallasey CH45 0LZ Tel: 0151 638 4785 — MB ChB St. And. 1945.

MANN, Mary Sue Nuffield Department of Anaesthetics, Radcliffe Infirmary, Oxford Tel: 01865 811133; Wayside, Northfield Avenue, Lower Shiplake, Henley-on-Thames RG9 3PB Tel: 0118 940 2839 Fax: 0118 940 1597 — MD 1974 Wake Forest Univ., USA; BSc N. Carolina 1970; MRCS Eng. LRCP Lond. 1977; FFA RCS Eng. 1978; FRCPCH 1998. (Bowman Gray, Univ. N. Carolina, USA) Cons. Anaesth. Radcliffe Infirm. Oxf. Socs: Assn. Anaesth.; Plastic Surg. & Burns Anaesth. Assn.; Neuroanesth. Soc. Prev: Cons. (Anaesth.) Wexham Pk & Heatherod NHS Trust; Sen. Regist. (Anaesth.) Univ. Hosp. Nottm.; Regist. (Anaesth.) Roy. Free Hosp. Lond.

MANN, Maurice 93 Stumperlowe Hall Road, Sheffield S10 3QT — MB ChB 1980 Sheff.; LMSSA Lond. 1981; MRCOG 1986. Regist. (Pub. Health Med.) Trent RHA. Prev: Regist. (O & G) W.m. Hosp. Lond.; SHO Jessop Hosp. Sheff.; Ho. Off. Roy. Hallamsh. Hosp. Sheff.

***MANN, Md Haroon Azam** 86 Queens Drive, Mossley Hill, Liverpool L18 2DY — MB BS 1994 Lond.

MANN, Melanie Corinne Arrowside Unit, Alexandra Hospital, Woodrow Drive, Redditch B98 — MB ChB 1987 Birm.; MRCOG 1992. Cons. Contracep. and Reproductive Health. Prev: Sen. Regist. (Community Gyn.) Birm.

MANN, Michael St James Surgery, 89 Wash Lane, Clacton-on-Sea CO15 1DA Tel: 01255 222121; 41 Church Road, Clacton-on-Sea CO15 6BG Fax: 01255 223684 Email: mmann10@compuserve.com — MB BS 1977 Lond.; MRCGP 1981; DRCOG 1979.

MANN, Michael John, QHP, Surg. Capt. RN (retired) Braeside, Court Road, Newton Ferrers, Plymouth PL8 1BZ Tel: 01752 872057 — MB BS 1957 Lond.; MRCS Eng. LRCP Lond. 1957; FFA RCS Eng. 1966. Prev: Cons. Anaesth. RN Hosp. Plymouth.

MANN, Nicholas Gary 17 Barrett's Grove, Stoke Newington, London N16 8AP — MB BS 1990 Lond.; MRCGP 1995; DFFP 1993.

MANN, Nicholas Patrick Department of Paediatrics, Royal Berkshire Hospital, London Road, Reading RG1 5AN Tel: 0118 987 8668 Fax: 0118 987 8383; Wayside, Northfield Avenue, Lower Shiplake, Henley-on-Thames RG9 3PB — MB BS 1974 Lond.; MRCS Eng. LRCP Lond. 1975; MD Lond. 1984; DCH Eng. 1977; FRCP Lond. 1993; MRCP (UK) 1977; FRCPCH 1997. (Univ. Coll. Hosp.) Cons. Paediat. Roy. Berks. Hosp. Reading; Vice Chairm. Bicycle Helmet Initiative Trust, Reading; Commiss.ing Edr. Archiv.s of Dis. in Childh. BMJ Publishing, Lond. Socs: Brit. Soc. Paediat. Endocrinol. Prev: Sen. Regist. (Paediat.) City & Univ. Hosps. Nottm.; Diabetes Research Fell. Univ. Hosp. Nottm.; Ho. Phys. Hosp. Sick Childr. Gt. Ormond St.

MANN, Nicola Mary Christmas Maltings Surgery, Camps Road, Haverhill CB9 8HF Tel: 01440 702203 Fax: 01440 712198 — MB BS Lond. 1986; MRCGP 1991; DRCOG 1991.

MANN, Parveen The Church Street Practice, David Corbet House, 2 Callows Lane, Kidderminster DY10 2JG Tel: 01562 822051 Fax: 01562 827251 — MB ChB 1987 Manch.; BSc (Hons.) Med. Biochem. Manch. 1984. (Manchester) Prev: Ho. Surg. Preston Roy. Infirm.; Ho. Phys. Manch. Roy. Infirm.

MANN, Patricia Mary Kelsall Medical Centre, Church Street, Kelsall, Tarporley CW6 0QG Tel: 01829 751252 Fax: 01829 752593; Sunville, Four Lane Endds, Tiverton, Tarporley CW6 9MA Tel: Ex Dir — MB ChB 1972 Bristol; MRCGP 1976; DObst RCOG 1974; Cert JCC Lond. 1974. (Bristol)

MANN, Patrick James Todhillwood, Canonbie DG14 0TF — MB ChB 1983 Manch.; FRCOphth 1992. Sen. Regist. (Ophth.) Ninewells Hosp. Dundee.

MANN, Paul Graham (retired) The Old Vicarage, Southstoke, Bath BA2 7DU Tel: 01225 832080 — MRCS Eng. LRCP Lond. 1943; MD Camb. 1952, MB BChir 1943; FRCPath 1978, M 1964; Dip. Bact. Lond 1952. Prev: Hon. Cons. Bacteriol. Bath Health Dist.

MANN, Peter Gerald 12 Saltire Gardens, Broughton Heights, Salford M7 4BG — MRCS Eng. LRCP Lond. 1961.

MANN, Peter Thomas c/o Lloyds Bank Plc, 26 Hammersmith Broadway, London W6 7AH — MB BS 1994 Lond.

MANN, Rachel Sara Catherine Westbank Practice, Limes Surgery, Church Stile, Exminster, Exeter EX6 9DF Tel: 01392 833230 — MB ChB 1990 Leic.; MRCGP 1994; DFFP 1995; DRCOG 1995. GP Partner.

MANN, Rebecca Jane Rosehill, Broomfield, Bridgwater TA5 2EL — BM BS 1987 Nottm.; MRCP (UK) 1991; DCH RCP Lond. 1990. Sen. Regist. (Paediat.) Bristol. Prev: Research Regist. (Paediat.) S.mead Hosp. Bristol; SHO (Paediat.) Alderhey Childr. Hosp.

MANN, Richard Gregory A R Newton Dunn and Partners, 61 New Street, Salisbury SP1 2PH Tel: 01722 334402 Fax: 01722 410473; Barton Mead, Winterbourne Earls, Salisbury SP4 6HD — BM BS Nottm. 1986; BMedSci (Hons.) Nottm. 1984; MRCGP 1990; DCH RCP Lond. 1990. New Mell Hosp., Private Gen. Pract. Clinic, Salisbury. Prev: SHO/Trainee GP Derby VTS.

MANN, Richard Quentin The Surgery, Stocking Lane, Shenington, Banbury OX15 6NF Tel: 01295 678124; Gracombe House, Horley, Banbury OX15 6BL Tel: 01295 738755 — MB BCh BAO 1978 Belf.; MRCGP 1982; DRCOG 1981.

MANN, Robert Alexander Menzies 127 Corton Road, Lowestoft NR32 4PR Tel: 01502 561834 — MB ChB 1974 Aberd.; MBA Irel.

1993; FFA RCSI 1979; DA Eng. 1977. Cons. Anaesth. Gt. Yarmouth & Waveney Dist.

Roy. Infirm. Glas.; Sen. Regist. Bridge of Earn Hosp.; Regist. W.. Infirm. Glas.

MANN, Robert John Princess Margaret Hospital, Okus Road, Swindon SN1 4JU Tel: 01793 536231 — MB BChir 1974 Camb.; FRCP Lond. 1994; MRCP (UK) 1977. Cons. Dermat. Swindon & MarlBoro. NHS Trust. Socs: Fell. Roy. Soc. Med.; Brit. Assn. Dermat. Prev: Sen. Regist. (Dermat.) Bristol Roy. Infirm.; Regist. (Gen. Med.) York. Dist. Hosp.

MANNA, Vasant Kumar 51 Coleraine Road, London SE3 7PF — MB BS 1973 Lond.; MRCP (UK) 1978; MRCS Eng. LRCP Lond. 1973.

***MANN, Robin Yngve** 100 Harpenden Lane, Redbourn, St Albans AL3 7PD — MB BCh 1998 Wales.

MANN, Professor Ronald David 42 Hazleton Way, Waterlooville PO8 9BT Tel: 02392 597220 Fax: 02392 571073 Email: drmann@manorcottage.fsbusiness.co.uk; 42 Hazleton Way, Waterlooville PO8 9BT Tel: 02392 597220 Fax: 02392 571073 Email: drmann@manorcottage.fsbusiness.co.uk — MB BS Lond. 1952; MD Lond. 1969; FRCP Lond. 1993; FRCP Glas. 1988; MRCP (UK) 1986; MRCS Eng. LRCP Lond. 1952; FFPM RCP (UK) 1990; FRCGP 1988, M 1965; FCP (USA) 1974. (Westm. Univ. Lond.) Edr.-in-chief PharmacoEpidemiol. and Drug Safety (Wiley)/ Edr.-in-chief Jl. & Drug Eval. (Parthenon); Princip. Research Fell., Drug Safety Research Unit, Soton. Socs: Fell. Roy. Soc. Med.; BMA; Fell. Fac. Pharmaceut. Med. Prev: Med. Sec. Roy. Soc. Med.; Princip. Med. Off. DHSS Lond. & Med. Assessor Comm. Safety Med. Lond.; Internat. Med. Dir. Pfizer Internat. New York, USA.

MANN, Sheila Anne North Essex Mental Health Partnership Trust Headquarters, Cuton Hall Lane, Spungfield CM2 5PX Tel: 01245 318420 Fax: 01245 318401 Email: sheila.mann@nemhpt.nhs.uk — MB ChB Birm. 1965; MPhil (Psych.) Lond. 1970; FRCPsych 1980, M 1973. Med. Director, N. E. Ment: Health Partnership Trust; Cons. Psychiat. NE Essex Ment. Health Trust, Clacton on Sea. Prev: Cons. Psychiat. Univ. Coll. & Friern Hosps. Lond. & Frenchay HA; Mem. Extern. Scientif. Staff MRC Nat. Survey of Health & Developm. Dept. Community Health Univ. Bristol; Sen. Lect. St. Bart. & Roy. Lond. Sch. Med. & Dent. Lond. 1986-2001.

MANN, Simon Gideon Longfield Medical Centre, Princes Road, Maldon CM9 5DF Tel: 01621 856811 Fax: 01621 852627; Little London Farm House, Wash Lane, Goldhanger, Maldon CM9 8LX — MB BS 1980 Lond.

MANN, Stanley Lyall 4 New Walk, Beverley HU17 7AD Tel: 01482 870769 Email: stan@mannstanley.clemon.co.uk — MB ChB St. And. 1970; FRCR 1980; DMRD 1979. Cons. Radiol. Castle Hill Hosp.

MANN, Stephen James Worcester Street Surgery, 24 Worcester Street, Stourbridge DY8 1AW Tel: 01384 371616 — MB ChB 1986 Birm.; DCH RCP Lond. 1989.

MANN, Steven Craig 13 Duck Street, Elton, Peterborough PE8 6RQ — MB ChB 1988 Leic.

MANN, Steven David St Mary's Hospital, Watford Road, Harrow HA1 3UJ Tel: 020 8235 4160 Email: s.d.mann@ic.ac.uk; 2 Downhurst Court, Parson St, London NW4 1QT — MB ChB 1989 Manch.; MRCP (UK) 1993. (Univ. Manch.) Research Fell. (Gastroenterol.) St. Mark's Hosp. Lond. Prev: Regist. Rotat. (Gen. Med. & Gastroenterol.) N. Middlx., Whipp's Cross & St. Mark's Hosps. Lond.; SHO Rotat. (Med.) Roy. Lond. Hosp.

MANN, Sukhjinderpal Singh 39 Buckland Avenue, Slough SL3 7PJ Email: sodimann@yahoo.com — BM 1990 Soton.; MRCPsych 1996. Specialist Regist. (Forens. & Gen. Adult Psychiat.) Manch. Rotat.

***MANN, Susan Elizabeth** 14 Paties Road, Edinburgh EH14 1EF — MB ChB 1997 Manch.

MANN, Susan Nerina 90 Alleyn Road, London SE21 8AH — MB ChB 1988 Bristol. SHO (A & E) St. Mary's Hosp. Lond.

MANN, Thomas Andrew Nicholas 1 Fowlmere Road, Shepreth, Royston SG8 6QG — MB BS 1976 Lond.; BSc Lond. 1973, MB BS 1976; MRCP (UK) 1982. (Westm.)

MANN, Thomas Joseph Wigan & Bolton Health Authority, Bryan House, 61 Stondish Grds, Wigan WN1 1AH Tel: 01942 772829 Fax: 01942 820787; 42 Duchy Road, Harrogate HG1 2ER Tel: 01423 503515 — MB BS 1979 Lond.; MBA Keele 1994; MRCGP 1984. (Roy. Free) Chief Exec. Prev: Head Pub. Health NHS Exec.; Head Performance Managem. Team N. Eng.; Princip. GP Highgate.

MANN, Mr Thomas Strang Crofthill, 30 Drymen Road, Bearsden, Glasgow G61 2RG — MB ChB 1953 Glas.; FRCS Ed. 1960; FRFPS Glas. 1961. Socs: Fell. BOA. Prev: Cons. Orthop. & Traum. Surg.

MANNALL, Ivan Gordon (retired) Ryburn, Dudwell Grove, Halifax HX3 0SG Tel: 01422 357082 — MB ChB 1960 St. And.; FRCP Lond. 1986; MRCP (UK) 1971; DCH RCPS Glas. 1964. Prev: Cons. Paediat. Calderdale Healthcare NHS Trust Halifax.

MANNALL, Jean Agnes Melville (retired) Princess Royal Community Health Centre, Greenhead Road, Huddersfield Tel: 01484 545411 — MB ChB St. And. 1961; FRCPCH 1998. Prev: Princip. Clin. Med. Off. Huddersfield HA.

MANNALL, Jill 6 Woodhall Crescent, Hornchurch RM11 3NN Tel: 01708 509399 — MB BS 1964 Lond.; MSc (Pub. Health Med.) Lond. 1994; BSc (Hons.) Physiol. Lond. 1961; MRCS Eng. LRCP Lond. 1964; DIH (Eng.) 1984; DObst RCOG 1966. (Roy. Free) Occupat. Health Phys. Redbridge Healthcare Trust. Socs: BMA. Prev: SCMO (Pub. Health) ELCHA; SCMO (Child Health & Occupat. Health) Barking, Havering & Brentwood HA; Princip. GP Wanstead.

MANNAN, Mohammed Abdul 54 Worton Way, Isleworth TW7 4AT — MB BS 1958 Dacca; DTCD Wales 1968 DTM & H Liverp. 1965. Cons. Primary Care Phys. K. Fahd Milit. Med. Complex, Saudi Arabia. Socs: Fell. Roy. Inst. Pub. Health & Hyg. Lond.; Fell. Roy. Acad. Med. in Irel.; BMA. Prev: Specialist (Chest Dis. & Tuberc.) Govt. of Zambia; Sen. Med. Off. Govt. of Botswana; Clin. Asst. (Surg.) Dacca Med. Coll. Hosp. Bangladesh.

MANNAN, Mohammed Azharul 54 North Drive, Hounslow TW3 1PU — MB ChB 1992 Manch.

MANNAN, Mr Muhammad Abdul The Surgery, 48 Watson Road, Worksop S80 2BH Tel: 01909 480554 Fax: 01909 530195 — MB BS 1958 Calcutta; FRCS Eng. 1970; FRCS Ed. 1969. (Nilratan Sircal Med. Coll.) Gen. Surg. Regist. Vict. Hosp. Worksop. Socs: BMA. Prev: Anaesth. Regist. Darlington Memor. Hosp.; Regist. (Surg.) W.morland Co. Hosp. Kendal.

MANNAN, Vandana Long Street Medical Centre, 24 Long Street, Wigston LE18 2AH Tel: 0116 288 3314 Fax: 0116 288 6711 — MB BS 1990 Lond.; MRCGP 1995.

MANNAR, Ranga 48 Countisbury Drive, Childwall, Liverpool L16 0JJ — MB BS 1958 Andhra; FFA RCSI 1973; DA Osmania 1962. (Guntur Med. Coll.) Cons. (Anaesth.) Walton Hosp. Liverp.; Clin. Lect. (Anaesth.) Univ. Liverp.

MANNARI, Narasimhamurthy Shrinivasacharya Calfaria Surgery, Regent Street, Treorchy, Cardiff CF42 6PR Tel: 01443 773595 Fax: 01443 775067; 5 Dinham Park, Ton-Pentre Tel: 01443 442284 — MB BS 1973 Karnatak.

MANNERS, Brian Thomas Boot Woking Nuffield Hospital, Shores Road, Woking GU21 4BY Tel: 01483 763511; Thorndown Cottage, Thorndown Lane, Windlesham GU20 6DD Tel: 01276 73817 — MB BS 1963 Lond.; MRCP Lond. 1967; FRCPath 1984, M 1972; MRCGP 1969. (St. Mary's) Cons. Histopath. & Cytol. Roy. Surrey Co. Hosp. Guildford; Princip. SW Thames Bone Tumour Regist.; Mem. Nat. Bone Tumour Panel. Prev: SHO (Neurol. & Dermat.) & Regist. (Path.) St. Mary's Hosp. Lond.; Asst. Lect. (Path.) St. Thos. Hosp. Lond.

MANNERS, Caroline Elisabeth The Firs, Cadney Road, Howsham, Market Rasen LN7 6LA — MB ChB 1987 Birm.

MANNERS, Jennifer Helen Edith 9 Tile Fields, Hollingbourne, Maidstone ME17 1TZ — MB BS 1973 Lond.; DA Eng. 1977; AKC.

MANNERS, John Michael 70 Lakewood Road, Eastleigh SO53 5AA — MB ChB Leeds 1953; DObst RCOG 1955; FFA RCS Eng. 1962; DA Eng. 1959. Cons. Anaesth. Soton. Hosp. Gp.

MANNERS, John Stewart Flintfield House, 4 The Limes, St Nicholas Hill, Leatherhead KT22 8NH Tel: 01372 379216 — BM BCh 1959 Oxf.; MA Oxf. 1960; FRCP Lond. 1982, M 1969; FRCR 1975; FFR 1972; DMRD Eng. 1970; DObst RCOG 1962. (St. Thos.) Cons. Radiol. Shirley Oaks Hosp. Croydon; Cons. Emerit. & Radiol. Mayday Univ. Hosp. Croydon. Socs: Brit. Inst. Radiol.; Fell.RSM. Prev: Recognised Teach. Univ. Lond. (Kings Coll. Sch. Med. & Dent.); Hon. Cons. Radiol. Brompton Hosp. Lond.; Sen. Regist. (X-Ray) Middlx. Hosp. Lond. & Brompton Hosp. Lond.

MANNERS, Ruth Southampton Eye Unit, Southampton General Hospital, Tremona Road, Southampton SO16 6YD Tel: 02380 777222 Fax: 02380 794120 — MB BS 1984 Lond.; FRCS Eng.

MANNERS

1989; FRCOphth 1991; DO RCS Eng. 1989. Cons. Ophth. Soton. Eye Unit. Socs: Vice-Pres. Ophth. Sect. Roy. Soc. Med. Prev: Sen. Regist. Soton. Eye Hosp.; Fell. Moorfields Eye Hosp.

MANNERS, Thomas (retired) 6 The Crescent, Loansdean, Morpeth NE61 2DQ — MB BS Durh. 1945; MD Durh. 1953; FRCPath 1967; DPath Eng. 1959. Prev: Cons. Path. Ashington Hosp. N.d.

MANNING, Adrian Philip Bradford Royal Infirmary, Duckworth Lane, Bradford BD9 6RJ Tel: 01274 364548 Fax: 01274 366591 — MB ChB Bristol 1972; MD Bristol 1981; MRCP (UK) 1975. (Bristol) Cons. Phys. (Gastroenterol.) Bradford Roy. Infirm. & St. Luke's Hosp. Bradford. Socs: Brit. Soc. Gastroenterol.; BMA. Prev: Sen. Regist. (Med.) Yorks. RHA; Fell. (Gastroenterol.) Duke Univ. Med. Center Durh., USA; Regist. (Med.) Avon AHA (T).

MANNING, Albert David 63 The Drive, Edgware HA8 8PS Tel: 020 8958 5113; 63 The Drive, Edgware HA8 8PS Tel: 0208 958 5113 — MB ChB 1944 Leeds; FRCGP 1980, M 1963. (Leeds) Prev: Cas. Off. Harrogate & Dist. Gen. Hosp.; Ho. Surg. (Orthop.) Roy. Cornw. Infirm. Truro; RAMC.

MANNING, Alexander Geoffrey Vernon Frog Cottage, 27 High St., Sutton, Ely CB6 2RB — MB ChB 1992 Manch.

MANNING, Angela Aroza, 14 Heronstone Lane, Bridgend CF31 3DP — MB ChB 1981 Manch.

MANNING, Ann Nicola Oxford Radcliffe Hospital, Headington, Oxford OX3 9RP; 32 Park Town, Oxford OX2 6SJ — MB BS 1978 Lond.; MRCS Eng. LRCP Lond. 1978. (St. Bart) Assoc. Specialist (Prenatal Diag.) Dept. Obst. Oxf. Socs: Skeletal Dysplasia Gp.; Brit. Med. Ultrasound Soc. Prev: Staff Grade (Prenatal Diag.) Dept. Obst. Oxf.; SHO (Med. Genetics) Ch.ill Hosp. Oxf.; Ho. Surg. St. Bart. Hosp. Lond.

MANNING, Christopher James Ford Melville Street Surgery, 17 Melville Street, Ryde PO33 2AF Tel: 01983 811431 Fax: 01983 817215; Abbey View, 16 Newnham Lane, Binstead, Ryde PO33 4ED Tel: 01983 811088 — MRCS Eng. LRCP Lond. 1972; DObst RCOG 1973: (Guy's) Prev: SHO (O & G) Dorset Co. Hosp. Dorchester; Ho. Phys. Beckenham Hosp.; Ho. Surg. (Orthop.) Guy's Hosp. Lond.

MANNING, Christopher John Windrush Health Centre, Witney OX28 6JS Tel: 01993 702911 Fax: 01993 700931; Broad Hill House, Woodgreen, Witney OX28 1DL — BM BCh 1967 Oxf.; DObst RCOG 1969. (Oxf.) Prev: SHO (Gen. Med.) Roy. Cornw. Hosp. (Trelisk) Truro; Ho. Off. (Paediat. & Gen. Surg.) Radcliffe Infirm. Oxf.; Ho. Off. Sussex Matern Hosp. Brighton.

MANNING, Christopher Loyd Upstream Health Centre, 29 Park Road, Hampton Wick, Kingston upon Thames KT1 4AS Tel: 020 8977 7173 Fax: 020 8977 7173; 95 Langham Road, Teddington TW11 9HG Tel: 020 8977 5974 Fax: 020 8977 5974 Email: primhe1@compuserve.com — MB BS 1978 Lond.; MB BS (Hons.) Distinc. Pharmacol. & Therap. Lond. 1978; BSc (Biochem.) Sheff. 1973; MRCGP 1983; DRCOG 1981. (Middlx.) Founder Nat. Depression Care Train. Centre; Exec. Comm. Doctors Support Network; Dir. Upstream Healthcare; Vice-Chairm. Depression Alliance; Gen. Chair Primary Care Ment. Health Educat. Socs: Brit. Med. Acupunct. Soc.

MANNING, Derek Percy (retired) 341 Liverpool Road, Birkdale, Southport PR8 3DE Tel: 01704 573646 — MB ChB 1956 Liverp.; DSc Liverp. 1995; MD Liverp. 1971; FFOM RCP Lond. 1985; DIH Soc. Apoth. Lond. 1966. Prev: Sen. Med. Off. Ford Motor Co. Halewood.

MANNING, Diana Ruth Pryce Appleton Village Surgery, 2-6 Appleton Village, Widnes WA8 6DZ Tel: 0151 423 2990 Fax: 0151 424 1032; The Grange House, Grange Road, Ashton, Chester CH3 8AE Tel: 01829 51220 — MB ChB Liverp. 1966, Dip. Ven. 1968. Socs: Assoc. Mem. RCGP.

MANNING, Donal John Department of Paediatrics, Arrowe Park Hospital, Upton, Wirral CH49 5PE Tel: 0151 678 5111 Fax: 0151 604 7138; 4 Boundary Lane, Heswall, Wirral CH60 5RR Tel: 0151 342 6007 — MD 1990 NUI; MB BCh BAO 1977; MRCP (UK) 1981; DRCOG 1979; DCH NUI 1979; MSc Liverp. 1997. (University College Dublin) Cons. Paediat. Wirral Hosp. Trust. Socs: Brit. Paediat. Assn. & Neonat. Soc.; Brit. Assn. Perinatal Med.

MANNING, Eileen Mary Carmel Department of Clinical Chemistry, 4th Floor Duncan Building, Royal Liverpool University Hospital, Prescot St., Liverpool L7 8XP Tel: 0151 706 4244 Email: emanning@liv.ac.uk; Crosshills, 160 Liverpool Road, Birkdale, Southport PR8 4NS Tel: 01704 562924 — MB BCh BAO 1982 NUI; MRCP (UK) 1985; MRCPath 1994; FRCP 2000. (Univ. Coll. Cork) Cons. Chem. Path. (Clin. Chem.) Roy. Liverp. & BRd.green Univ. Hosp. Trust; Hon. Cons. Liverp. Wom. Hosp.; Hon. Clin. Tutor Liverp. Univ. Prev: Sen. Regist. & Regist. (Clin. Chem.) Roy. Liverp. Univ. Hosp.; SHO (Med.) N. Tees Gen. Hosp. Stockton-on-Tees & Cork Volun. Hosps.

MANNING, Mr Everard Alexander Dermot Niall B NW London Hospitals NHS Trust, Central Middlesex Hospital, Acton Lane, London NW10 7NS Tel: 020 8453 2410 Fax: 020 8453 2408; Ch'i-Lin, 72 Corringway, Ealing, London W5 3AD Tel: 020 8810 9503 Fax: 020 8810 9503 — MB BS Lond. 1974; FRCOG 1995, M 1982. (Middlx. Hosp. Med. Sch.) Cons. O & G Centr. Middlx. Hosp. Lond.; Hon. Sen. Clin. Lect. St. Mary's Hosp. Med. Sch. Lond. Socs: Brit. Soc. Colpos. & Cerv. Path.; Roy. Soc. Med. Forum Family Plann. Sexual Med. Prev: Sen. Regist. (O & G) Middlx. & Univ. Coll. Hosps. Lond.; Regist. (O & G) St. Helier Hosp. Surrey & Middlx. Hosp. Lond.

MANNING, Francis James, TD (retired) Heathstock Cleeve, Ford Road, Wiveliscombe, Taunton TA4 2RQ Tel: 01984 623513 — LRCPI & LM, LRSCI & LM 1936; LRCPI & LM, LRCSI & LM 1936; MRCPsych 1971. Col. RARO, Late RAMC; Forens. Cons. Psychiat. HM Prison Exeter; Hon. Cons. Psychiat. Tone Vale & Halse Manor, & Lynchfield Hosps. Bishops Lydeard; Vis. Psychother. Dartmoor Prison, P.town; Med. Off. Brit. Red Cross Soc. Prev: Cons. Psychiat. Tone Vale Hosp. Norton Fitzwarren.

MANNING, Frank Robert Cassels, AE (retired) Corner's, Howbourne Lane, Buxted, Uckfield TN22 4QB Tel: 01825733166 — MRCS Eng. LRCP Lond. 1941; MRCGP 1974.

MANNING, Garth Alexander Kenneth, Wing Cdr. RAF Med. Br. Retd. 35 Bridgefield Avenue, Wilmslow SK9 2JS Tel: 01625 549720 Fax: 01625 549721 Email: 106247.2471@compuserve.com — MB BCh BAO 1979 Belf.; MRCGP 1988; DRCOG 1982; DAvMed FOM RCP Lond. 1986. (Qu. Univ. Belf.) Freelance Med. Cons. Prev: Gp. Flight Med. Off. HQ 38 Gp.; Sen. Med. Off. RAF Akrotiri Cyprus; Sen. Med. Off. RAF N.olt.

MANNING, Geoffrey Claude (retired) 7 Spinnaker View, Glebe Park Avenue, Bedhampton, Havant PO9 3JD Tel: 01705 450764 — MB BCh 1947 Camb.; MA Camb. 1948, MD 1959; FRCP Lond. 1979, M 1954. Prev: Cons. Phys. Kingston Hosp.

MANNING, Mr Geoffrey Lewis Department of Dental & Oral Surgery, Central Out-Patients Department, Hartshill, Stoke-on-Trent Tel: 01782 44161; The Old Hall, Haughton, Stafford ST18 9HB Tel: 01785 780273 — MB ChB 1961 Birm.; BDS 1954; FDS RCS Eng. 1964, LDS 1953; FRCS Ed. 1986. (Birm.) Cons. Dept. Dent. & Oral Surg. N. Staffs. Hosp. Centre Stoke-on-Trent. Socs: Brit. Assn. Oral & Maxillo-Facial Surgs. & (Ex-Pres.) Oral Surg.Club. Prev: Sen. Regist. Dept. Jaw Surg., Plastic Surg. Centre Mt. Vernon Hosp.; N.wood & Centr. Middlx. Hosp. Lond.; Ho. Off. N. Staffs. Roy. Infirm.

MANNING, Gerald Francis Eric Moore Health Centre, Tanners Lane, Warrington WA2 7LY — MB BCh BAO 1956 NUI. Prev: Ho. Phys. Fermanagh Co. Hosp. Enniskillen; Ho. Surg. Mater Miser. Hosp. Dub.; Capt. RAMC.

MANNING, Geraldine Mary 18 York Road, Grappenhall, Warrington WA4 2EH; Orchard Cottage, 27 Cefn-y-Gwrych, Meliden, Prestatyn LL19 8LL — MB ChB 1991 Manch.; BSc (Med Sci.) St. And. 1988; MRCGP 1996; DCCH RCP Ed. 1996. (St. And. & Manch.) Staff Grade (Community Paediat.) Roy. Alexandra Hosp. Rhyl. Socs: BMA. Prev: Trainee GP Ysbyty Glan Clwyd Bodelwyddan Clwyd HA; Ho. Off. (Med.) Trafford Gen. Hosp.; Ho. Off. (Surg.) Glan Clwyd Hosp.

MANNING, Godfrey Louis 63 The Drive, Edgware HA8 8PS Tel: 0208 958 5113 — MB BS 1981 Lond.; BSc (1st cl. Hons.) Med. Statistics & Computer Sc. Lond. 1978. Indep. Med. Acupunc. Middlx.; Med. Off. Nat. Blood. Trans. Serv. Prev: Ho. Surg. Whittington Hosp. Lond.; Ho. Phys. Stoke Mandeville Hosp. Aylesbury.

MANNING, Helen Patricia Blundells Farm, West Monkton, Taunton TA2 8NW — MB BCh BAO 1950 Dub.

***MANNING, Jonathan James** Top/Right Flat, 1 Kersland St., Glasgow G12 8BN — MB ChB 1998 Glas.; MB ChB Glas. 1998.

MANNING, Julie Elizabeth Elmwood Health Centre, Huddersfield Road, Holmfirth, Huddersfield HD9 3TR Tel: 01484 681777 Fax:

01484 689603; 211 Huddersfield Road, Thongsbridge, Huddersfield HD9 3TT — BM BS 1980 Nottm.; MRCGP 1984; DRCOG 1984.

MANNING, Karen Linda Clifton Lodge, 17 Cheddon Road, Taunton TA2 7BL Tel: 01823 282151 Fax: 01823 326755 — MB ChB 1983 Birm.; MRCGP 1987; DRCOG 1985; Cert. Family Plann. ICC 1985. Socs: BMA. Prev: Trainee GP Henley in Arden & Kings Heath VTS; SHO (Paediat.) Warwick Gen. Hosp.

MANNING, Lucy Victoria Belgrave Medical Centre, 22 Asline Road, Sheffield S2 4UJ Tel: 0114 255 1184; 4 Roslin Road, Sheffield S10 1FA — BM BS Nottm. 1984, BMedSci (Hons.) 1982; MRCGP 1990; DCH RCP Lond. 1987.

MANNING, Marcus Francis (retired) The Barn, Little Targley, Wonersh, Guildford GU5 0PW Tel: 01483 575552 — MB BS 1947 Lond.; MRCS Eng. LRCP Lond. 1942; DCH Eng. 1948. Prev: Res. Med. Off. Seamen's Hosp. Greenwich.

MANNING, Margaret Elizabeth (retired) Crumstone, 70B Kent Road, Harrogate HG1 2NH Tel: 01423 508260 — MB ChB 1965 Manch. Prev: Child Welf. Med. Off. (Sessional) N. Yorks. CC.

MANNING, Mr Michael Patrick Rory Andrew Whiston Hospital, Prescot L35 5DR Tel: 0151 426 1600; 144 Rupert Road, Huyton with Roby, Liverpool L36 9TH Tel: 0151 489 5323 — MB ChB 1979 Liverp.; MB ChB (Hons.) Liverp. 1979, MChOrth 1986; FRCS Eng. 1983. Cons. Orthop. Surg. Whiston & St. Helens Hosps. Merseyside; Head Serv. Dept. Orthop. Socs: Fell. BOA; Liverp. Med. Inst. Prev: Sen. Regist. (Orthop.) Mersey RHA; Chief Resid. & Clin. Fell. Mass. Gen. & Assoc. Hosps. Boston, USA; Regist. (Surg.) Centr. Birm. HA.

***MANNING, Nia Angharad** Y Werydd, Penyranchor, Aberystwyth SY23 1BJ — MB BCh 1994 Wales.

MANNING, Niall Thomas Vale of Leven District General Hospital, Alexandria G83 0UA — MB BCh BAO 1971 NUI; FRCPI 1989, M 1977. Cons. Phys. Geriat. Med. Vale of Leven Dist. Gen. Hosp. Alexandria, Dunbartonsh.

MANNING, Mr Paul Andrew Department Orthopaedic and Accident Surgery, Queens Medical Centre, Nottingham NG7 2UH Tel: 0115 951 3277 Fax: 0115 951 3278 Email: p.manning@nottingham.ac.uk — BM BS 1992 Nottm.; BMedSci Nottm. 1990; FRCS 1996. (Nottm.) Specialist Regist. (Orthop. & Trauma Surg.) Nottm. Socs: BOA; BESS; BORS. Prev: Research Regist. (Orthop. Surg.) Univ. Nottm.; SHO Rotat. (Surg.) Qu. Med. Centre Nottm.; Ho. Off. (Surg.) Derby Roy. Infirm.

MANNING, Richard William Main Street Surgery, 29 Main Street, Eglinton, Londonderry BT47 3AB Tel: 028 7181 0252 Fax: 028 7181 1347 — MB BCh BAO 1983 Belf.; MRCGP 1988; DRCOG 1986; DCH Dub. 1986.

MANNING, Stewart Irwin Oakley Terrace Surgery, 12 Oakley Terrace, Leeds LS11 5HT Tel: 0113 272 0900 Fax: 0113 270 7300; 1 Shadwell Park Grove, Leeds LS17 8TU Tel: 0113 266 4951 — MB BS 1973 Lond.; MRCS Eng. LRCP Lond. 1973. (Westm.) Prev: SHO (Obst.) Univ. Coll. Hosp. Lond.; Ho. Phys. & Ho. Surg. Gordon Hosp. Lond.

MANNINGS, David John Lime Tree Surgery, Lime Tree Avenue, Findon Valley, Worthing BN14 0DL Tel: 01903 264101 Fax: 01903 695494; 217 Findon Road, Worthing BN14 0EP Tel: 01903 873013 — BSc (Med. Sci.) Lond. 1976, MB BS 1979; MRCGP 1985; T (GP) 1991; DCH RCP Lond. 1984. (St. Mary's) Prev: Trainee GP I. of Thanet Dist. Hosp. VTS.

MANNINGS, Henry William Paul 93 Telegraph Road, Deal CT14 9DF — MB BCh BAO 1976 Belf.

MANNINGS, Richard Arthur Dacres 9 Mallards, Alton GU34 2LB — MB BS 1986 Lond.

MANNION, Ethna Mary Department of Histopathology, Royal Marsden NHS Trust, Fulham Road, London SW3 6JJ — MB BCh BAO 1991 NUI.

***MANNION, Joanne Frances** 79 Wilbraham Road, Manchester M14 7DN — MB ChB 1994 Leeds.

MANNION, Michael Francis Holywell Hospital, Steeple Road, Antrim BT41 2RJ Tel: 01849 465211; 3 Roseville Avenue, Randalstown, Antrim BT41 2LZ — MB BCh BAO 1982 Dub.; MRCPsych 1987. Cons. Holywell Hosp. Antrim.

MANNION, Philip Thomas Chester Public Health Laboratory, Countess of Chester Health Park, Liverpool Road, Chester CH2 1UL — MB ChB 1980 Manch.; MSc Med. Microbiol. (Distinc.) Lond. 1987; MRCPath 1988. Dir. Cons. Med. Microbiol. Chester Pub.

Health Laborat. Chester; Cons. Communicable Dis. Control S. Chesh. HA. Prev: Sen. Regist. (Med. Microbiol.) Liverp. Pub. Health Laborat. Fazakerley Hosp.

MANNION, Richard Andrew John 32 Bankside Close, Upper Poppleton, York YO26 6LH — MB ChB 1986 Leeds; BSc (Hons.) Biochem. Leeds 1983; MRCP (UK) 1989; FRCR 1993. Cons. Radiol. York Dist. Hosp. Prev: Sen. Regist. (Diagn. Radiol.) Leeds Gen. Infirm.

MANNION, Mr Stephen John 24 Ullswater Road, Blackpool FY4 2BZ Tel: 01253 344287 Email: stevemannion@compuserve.com; 20 Stangate, Royal St, Southwark, London SE1 7EQ Tel: 020 7261 0835 — BChir 1990 Camb.; MA Camb. 1990; FRCS Glas. 1994; DMCC Soc. Apoth. Lond. 1995; DTM & H RCP Lond. 1992; Dip. Aviat. Healthcare Provider's 1994. Higher Surgic. Train. Rotat. (Orthop. Surg.) SE Thames; Regist. (Orthop. Surg.) Greenwich Hosp. Lond.; Assoc. Lect. (Conflict Med.) Univ. Coll. Lond; Trauma Surg. Med. Sans Frontieres UK. Socs: Fell. Roy. Soc. Trop. Med. & Hyg.; Fell. Roy. Geogr. Soc.; World Orthopaedic Concern. Prev: Regist. (Orthop. Surg.) Lewisham Hosp. Lond.; Regist. (Orthop. Surg.) Guy's Hosp. Lond.; Trauma Surg. Medecins Sans Frontiers N.. Sri Lanka.

MANNIS, Neil Derek 6 Stratford Road, Bangor BT19 6ZN; 34 Merok Gardens, Belfast BT6 9NA Tel: 01232 590581 — MB BCh 1998 Belf.; MB BCh Belf 1998. (QUB)

MANNIX, Kathryn Anne Newcastle Marie Curie Centre, Marie Curie Drive, Newcastle upon Tyne NE4 6SS Tel: 0191 219 5560 Fax: 0191 256 5719 — MB BS 1982 Newc.; MRCP (UK) 1986; FRCP 1999. (Newcastle-upon-Tyne) Cons. Palliat. Med. Marie Curie Centre; Cons. Palliat. Med. Roy. Vict. Infirm. Prev: Sen. Regist. (Palliat. Med.) St. Oswald's Hospice Newc.

MANNIX, Paul Anthony Neonatal Unit, The Royal London Hospital, Whitechapel, London E1 1BB Tel: 020 7377 7712 Fax: 020 7377 7712 Email: paul.mannix@bartsandthelondon.nhs.uk; 4 Finch Lane, Little Chalfont, Amersham HP7 9NE Tel: 01494 765057 Email: pman1365@aol.com — MB BS 1988 Lond.; MRCP (UK) 1993; MD 2000. (Lond. Hosp. Med. Coll.) Cons. (Neonatology) Roy. Lond. Hosp. Whitechapel Lond.; Hon. Sen. Lect. Dept. Cild Health; Clin. Dir. Obestetrics & Neonatol. Roy. Lond. Hosp. Socs: Neonat. Soc.; Roy. Coll. Paediatric & Child Health (Fell.); Brit. Assn. Perinatal Med. (BAPM). Prev: Lect. & Sen. Regist. (Child Health) St. Bartholomews & Roy. Lond. Sch. Med. & Dent.; Research Fell. (Neonate ICU) Homerton Hosp., Lond.; Neonat. Fell., Monash Med. Centre, Melbourne Australia.

***MANNS, Dudley Wilfred** Heather Cob, 48 Pilford Heath Road, Colehill, Wimborne BH21 2NB — MB ChB 1995 Glas.

MANNS, John Jaynes 41 The Downs, Altrincham WA14 2QG Tel: 0161 928 0611 Fax: 0161 927 9175; 33 Hillington Road, Sale M33 6GQ Tel: 0161 973 2493 — MB BCh 1964 Wales; FRCP Lond. 1983, M 1969. p/t Cons. Phys. Wythenshawe Hosp. Manch.; Hon. Assoc. Lect. Med. Univ. Manch. Prev: Sen. Regist. Dundee Teachg. Hosps.; Hon. Lect. Univ. Dundee.

MANNS, Robert Allan Princess Royal Hospital NHS Trust, Wellington, Telford TF1 6TF Tel: 01952 641222; 6 Rowallan Way, Priorslee, Telford TF2 9RX Tel: 01952 291937 — MB ChB 1981 Birm.; FRCR 1987. Cons. Radiol. P.ss Roy. Hosp. NHS Trust.

MANOCHA, Kishan Fitzgerald 53 Ravenscroft Avenue, Wembley HA9 9TE Tel: 0973 375199 Fax: 020 8904 1280 — MB BS 1991 Lond.; BSc (Hons.) Lond. 1987. (St. Bart. Hosp. Med. Sch. Lond.) Clin. Research Fell. & Hon. Regist. (Forens. Psychiat.) Springfield Hosp. Lond. Prev: Regist. (Psychiat.) Atkinson Morley's Hosp. Lond.; SHO (Psychiat.) Warlingham Pk. Hosp. & Sutton Hosp. Surrey; Ho. Phys. E. Surrey Hosp. Redhill.

MANOCK, Kirsten Jane Tinshill Lane Surgery, 8 Tinshill Lane, Leeds LS16 7AP Tel: 0113 267 3462 Fax: 0113 230 0402 — MB ChB 1985 Leeds; BSc (Hons.) Biochem. in Relation to Med. Leeds 1982; DRCOG 1990.

MANOHAR, Sumana No. 2 New Heath Close, New Cross Hospital, Wednesfield, Wolverhampton WV11 1XX — MB BS 1987 Sri Venkateswara; MRCOG 1993.

MANOHARAN, Ganesh 60 Sandhurst Drive, Belfast BT9 5AZ — MB BCh BAO 1993 Belf.

***MANOHARAN, Prakash** 3 Prospect House, Prospect Avenue, Kingsdown, Bristol BS2 8EH — MB ChB 1995 Bristol.

MANOHARAN, Sathananthambighaiammal 117 Winterbourne Road, Thornton Heath, Croydon CR7 7QZ — MB BS 1976 Sri Lanka.

MANOS, John Kings' College Hospital (Dulwich), East Dulwich Grove, London SE22 8PT Tel: 020 7346 6234; 120 St. George's Road, Sandwich CT13 9LD Tel: 01304 615368 — Ptychio Iatrikes 1971 Athens; MD 1981. (Athens - Greece) Staff Grade Nephrol. Dulwich Lond. Socs: Renal Assn.; EDTA; BTS. Prev: Staff Grade (Renal Med.) N.. Gen. Hosp. Sheff.; Med. Adviser Pfizer Ltd. Sandwich; Assoc. Specialist (Renal Med.) Manch. Roy. Infirm.

MANRAJ, Priya Rohini 1 Sandgate Drive, Kippax, Leeds LS25 7EX — MB BS 1989 West Indies.

MANS, Mathilde Child Health, Penrith Health Centre, Bridge Lane, Penrith CA11 8HX Tel: 01768 245267; 15 Glebe Close, Dalston, Carlisle CA5 7JE Tel: 01228 711149 Fax: 01228 711149 — MB ChB 1977 Cape Town; DCH Coll. Med. S. Afr. 1982; IHPRAX MED Med. Univ. S. Afr. 1989; FCP(SA) 1994. (College of Medicine of South Africa) Staff Grade (Comm. Paediat.) Penrith. Socs: MRCPCH; Coll. Med. S. Afr. Prev: Cons. Paediat. Cumbld. Infirm. Carlisle; Cons. Paediat. Addington Hosp. Durban S. Africa.

MANSBRIDGE, Bruce John Lordshill Health Centre, Lordshill District Centre, Lordshill, Southampton SO16 8HY Tel: 023 8073 8144 Fax: 023 8073 0722; 13 Woodview Close, Bassett, Southampton SO16 3PZ — MB BS 1971 Lond.; DObst RCOG 1973. (Univ. Coll. Hosp.) Prev: Ho. Phys. Univ. Coll. Hosp. Lond.; Ho. Surg. & SHO (O & G) Soton. Gen. Hosp.

MANSBRIDGE, Drummond Christopher (retired) 15 Briarcroft Place, Robroyston, Glasgow G33 1RF Tel: 0141 558 2700 Email: dcm4939@aol.com — MB ChB Glas. 1966. Prev: GP Lesmahagow, Lanark.

MANSEL, Professor Robert Edward University of Wales, College of Medicine, Heath Park, Cardiff CF14 4XN Tel: 029 2074 2749 — MB BS 1971 Lond.; MS Lond. 1988; FRCS Eng. 1975; MRCS Eng. LRCP Lond. 1971. (Char. Cross) Prof. Surg. Univ. Wales; Hon. Cons. Surg. S. Glam. AHA. Socs: Fell. Assn. Surgs.; BMA. Prev: Prof. Surg. Univ. Manch.; Sen. Lect. (Surg.) Welsh Nat. Sch. Med.

MANSELL, Alexandra Jane 42 Orchards Way, Highfield, Southampton SO17 1RE — MB BS 1986 Lond.; MRCGP 1990; DRCOG 1989.

MANSELL, Edwin John Byng (retired) 1 Boundary Court, Snells Park, Edmonton, London N18 2TB Tel: 020 8807 3126 — MRCS Eng. LRCP Lond. 1951. Prev: Surg. Regist. Highlands Hosp. Lond.

MANSELL, Martin Andrew Middlesex Hospital, Mortimer St., London W1T 3AA Tel: 020 7380 9191 Fax: 020 7380 9199 — MD 1982 Lond.; MB BS 1971; FRCP Lond. 1989; MRCP (UK) 1974. Cons. Nephrol. UCL Hosps. Lond. Prev: Cons. Renal Phys. St. Geo. & St. Jas. Hosp. Lond; Lect. (Nephrol.) St. Peter's Hosps. & Inst. Urol. Lond.; Regist. (Med.) N.wick Hosp. Lond.

MANSELL, Mary Elizabeth Women's Health, Whittington Hospital, London N19 5NF; 16 Rochester Terrace, London NW1 9JN — MB BChir 1964 Camb.; BA Camb. 1960, MA 1964; FRCOG 1990, M 1969. (St. Geo.) Assoc. Specialist Woms. Health Whittington Hosp. Trust Lond. Prev: Clin. Asst. Colposcopy Unit Roy. N.. Hosp. Lond.

MANSELL, Mr Nicholas John Dept. of Otolaryngology, Royal Berkshire Hospital, London Road, Reading RG1 5AN Tel: 0118 987511; 16 Ferny Close, Radley, Abingdon OX14 3AN Tel: o1235 522310 — MB ChB 1986 Bristol; FRCS 2000 Eng.; BSc (Hons.) Med. Microbiol. Bristol 1983; FRCS Eng. 1995; FRCS Ed. 1995; MRCGP 1991; DLO RCS Eng. 1992; DRCOG 1991; DCH RCP Lond. 1990. Specialist Regist. (ENT) Oxf. Socs: Fell. Roy. Soc. Med.; Brit. Assn. Otol. & Head & Neck Surg.; BMA. Prev: SHO, ENT, Char. Cross + Gt. Ormond St. Hosp. Childr. Lond. & (ENT & Neurosurg.) Radcliffe Infirm. Oxf.; SpR, ENT, Oxf. Region Rotat. (Radclive Infirm., Oxf.).

MANSELL, Peter Ian University Hospital, Nottingham NG7 2UH Tel: 0115 924 9924 Ext: 43834 Fax: 0115 970 1080 — MB ChB 1982 Bristol; DPhil, MA Oxf. 1978; DM Nottm. 1989; MRCP (UK) 1985; FRCP 1998. (Bristol) Cons. Phys. (Diabetes & Endocrinol.) Univ. Hosp. Nottm. Socs: Brit. Diabetic Assn.; Eur. Assn. Study Diabetes; Soc. Endocrinol. Prev: Cons. Phys. (Diabetes & Endocrinol.) Salisbury Dist. Hosp.; Sen. Regist. (Med.) Bath & Soton.; Regist. (Med.) Univ. Hosp. Nottm.

*****MANSELL, Robert Charles** 88 The Bargates, Leominster HR6 8QS — MB BS 1998 Lond.; MB BS Lond 1998.

MANSELL-WATKINS, Thomas Kings Road Surgery, 2-4 Kings Road, Mumbles, Swansea SA3 4AJ Tel: 01792 360933 Fax: 01792 368930; Ashglade House, Lime Kiln Bank, Oldway, Bishopston, Swansea SA3 3DH Tel: 01792 232287 — MB BS 1989 Lond.; MRCGP 1995. (Lond. Hosp. Med. Coll.) Princip. GP Kings Rd. Surg. Swansea.

MANSER, Inez Noreen 31 Brookside, West Coker, Yeovil BA22 9AD — MRCS Eng. LRCP Lond. 1942; MRCGP 1965. (Roy. Free)

MANSER, Richard Francis Cape Cornwall Surgery, Market Street, St. Just-in-Penwith, Penzance TR19 7HX Tel: 01736 788306 — MB BS 1967 Lond.; MRCS Eng. LRCP Lond. 1967. (Lond. Hosp.)

MANSER, Timothy Ivor Leatside Surgery, Baggage Road, Totnes TQ9 5JA Tel: 01803 862671 Fax: 01803 860309 Email: tim.manser@gp-l83043.nhs.uk; Whitelears, Bridgetown Hill, Totnes TQ9 5BN Tel: 01803 863876 — MB BS 1970 Lond.; DMJ Soc. Apoth. 1980; DObst RCOG 1974. (Westm.) GP Adviser, S. Devon Healthcare Trust, Torquay. Socs: Brit. Acad. Foren. Sci.; Roy. Soc. Med. (Sect. Clin. Forens. and Legal Med.). Prev: Police Surg. Devon & Cornw. Constab.

MANSFIELD, Professor Averil Olive Academic Surgical Unit, St. Mary's Hospital & Medical School, London W2 1NY Tel: 020 7886 1301 Fax: 020 7886 1810 — MB ChB 1960 Liverp.; ChM Liverp. 1973; Hon. MD Liverp. 1994; FRCP Glas. 1996; FRCS Eng. 1967; FRCS Ed. 1966; Hon. FRACS 1996. (Liverp.) Prof. Surg. Imperial Coll. St. Mary's Hosp. Lond.; Cons. Vasc. Surg. St. Mary's Hosp. Lond.; Hon. Sen. Lect. (Vasc. Surg.) Roy. Postgrad. Med. Sch. Lond. & Gt. Ormond St. Hosp Lond. Socs: (Ex-Pres.) Assn. Surgs.; (Pres.) Vasc. Surgic. Soc. (Ex-Sec.); Pres. Sect. Surg. Roy. Soc. Med. Prev: Cons. Surg. Roy. Liverp. Hosp.; Lect. (Surg.) Univ. Liverp.; Ex-Chairm. Ct. Examrs. RCS Eng.

MANSFIELD, Brian Geoffrey St. Luke's Surgery, St. Luke's Road, Beckington, Bath BA11 6SE Tel: 01373 830316 Fax: 01373 831261 Email: brian.mansfield@beckingtonfamilypractice.nhs.uk; 17 Linnet Way, Frome BA11 2UY — BM BCh 1982 Oxf.; MSc (Experim. Psychol.) Sussex 1979; MA (Physiol. Sci.) Oxf. 1982; MRCGP 1986; T(GP) 1991; DRCOG 1986. Prev: GP Dorset; Trainee GP Exeter; Ho. Off. N. Tees Gen. Hosp. Stockton-on-Tees.

MANSFIELD, Charles Leonard, TD (retired) — MRCS Eng. LRCP Lond. 1952; DObst RCOG 1958; MRCGP 1969. Med. Off. Norwood & Dist. Hosp. Lond. Prev: Ho. Off. Belgrave Hosp. Childr.

MANSFIELD, Colin Paul (retired) 38 Valley Road, Rickmansworth WD3 4DS Tel: 01923 771651 — MB BS 1957 Lond. Prev: Ho. Phys. Middlx. Hosp. Lond.

MANSFIELD, Darren John Edenfield Road Surgery, Cutgate Shopping Precinct, Edenfield Road, Rochdale OL11 5AQ Tel: 01706 344044 Fax: 01706 526882; 2 Beaumonds, Meadowcroft Lane, Rochdale OL11 5HN Tel: 01706 358492 — MB ChB 1986 Leic.; MRCGP 1992. (Leicester)

MANSFIELD, Mr David Colin Inverclyde Royal Hospital, Larkfield Road, Greenock PA16 0XN Tel: 01475 633777 Fax: 01475 656185; Tel: 01505 842689 — MB BChir 1985 Camb.; PhD Open 1985; MA Camb. 1985; FRCS Glas. 1989; FCOphth 1991. Cons. (Ophth.) Inverclyde Roy. Hosp. Greenock. Prev: Hon. Clin. Lect. Univ. Glas.; Regist. (Ophth.); SR & Reg jobs were at the Tennent Inst., W.ern Inf., Glas.

MANSFIELD, Hugh Naylor (retired) Springfield, Alcester Road, Wythall, Birmingham B47 6AP Tel: 01564 823352 — MRCS Eng. LRCP Lond. 1942; MD Lond. 1951, MB BS 1942; FRCOG 1962, M 1949. Prev: Cons. O & G Sorrento Matern. Hosp. & E. Birm. Hosp.

MANSFIELD, Jack Edgar Shirley Health Centre, Grove Road, Southampton SO4 3WU Tel: 02380 783611 Fax: 02380 783156 — MB BS 1957 Lond. (Univ. Coll. Hosp.) Nuffield Foundat. GP Schol. Prev: Med. Off. RAF; Ho. Off. Poole Gen. Hosp. & Soton. Gen. Hosp.

MANSFIELD, Jacqueline Diane Bounds Geen Group Practice, Bounds Green Group Practice, Gordon Road, New Southgate, London N11 2PF Tel: 020 8889 1961 Fax: 020 8889 7844; Dancers Hill Farm House, Dancers Lane, Barnet EN5 4RX — MB BS 1978 Lond.; DCH RCP Lond. 1982.

MANSFIELD, John Charles Royal Victoria Infirmary, Newcastle upon Tyne NE3 4DR Tel: 0191 282 0135 Fax: 0191 282 0135

MANSON

mail: j.c.mansfield@ncl.ac.uk; 2 Beechfield Road, Gosforth, Newcastle upon Tyne NE3 4DR Tel: 0191 285 6310 — MB BS 1986 Newc.; MA Oxf. 1988; MD Sheff. 1995; MRCP (UK) 1989. Cons. & Sen. Lect. (Gastroenterol.) Roy. Vict. Infirm. Newc. Socs: Brit. Soc. Gastroenterol. Prev: Sen. Regist. (Gen. Med. & Gastroenterol.) N. RHA; Regist. Rotat. (Gen. Med. & Gastroenterol.) J.. RHA; Research Regist. (Gastroenterol.) Roy. Hallamsh. Hosp. Sheff.

MANSFIELD, John Damien 20 Moreton Avenue, Stretford, Manchester M32 8BP — MB BS 1971 Adelaide.

MANSFIELD, John Raymond Burgh Wood Clinic, 34 Brighton Road, Banstead SM7 1BS Tel: 01737 361177 Fax: 01737 352245 — MRCS Eng. LRCP Lond. 1960; DObst RCOG 1964. (Guy's) Med. Dir. Burghwood Clinic Banstead. Socs: (Ex-Pres.) Brit. Soc. Allergy & Nvironm. Med. Prev: Police Surg. Epsom & Banstead; Intern. Mercy Hosp. Des Moines; Ho. Surg. Orpington Hosp.

MANSFIELD, Katherine Brenda (Kelly) West Walk Surgery, 21 West Walk, Yate, Bristol BS37 4AX Tel: 01454 272200; 7 Elm Close, Chipping Sodbury, Bristol BS37 6HE Tel: 01454 312575 Fax: 01454 312575 Email: katemansfield@doctors.og.uk — MB BS 984 Lond. (King's College) Asst. GP.

MANSFIELD, Lesley Elizabeth 127 Copers Cope Road, Beckenham BR3 1NY — MRCS Eng. LRCP Lond. 1976; MB BS Lond. 1976.

MANSFIELD, Martin David The Ipswich Hospital NHS Trust, Heath Road, Ipswich IP4 5PD Tel: 01473 712233; Applegarth, Wilmslow Avenue, Woodbridge IP12 4HW Tel: 01394 384370 — MB ChB 1987 Ed.; FRCA 1992. (Edin.) Cons. (Anaesth.) Ipswich Hosp. NHS Trust. Prev: Sen. Regist. (Anaesth.) Glas. Roy. Infirm.; Regist. & Research Fell. Glas. Roy. Infirm.; SHO (Anaesth.) Roy. Infirm. Edin., Ipswich Hosp. & Roy. Infirm. Glas.

MANSFIELD, Michael William St James's University Hospital, Beckett Street, Leeds LS9 7TF Tel: 0113 206 6963 Fax: 0113 206 5065 Email: michael.mansfield@gw.northy.nhs.uk; 20 West Park Avenue, Leeds LS8 2HG — BM BCh 1987 Oxf.; BA (Hons) Oxf. 1984; MRCP (UK) 1990; DM Oxf. 1998. Cons. Phys. in Diabetes nd Endocrinoloy St Jas. Univ. Hosp. Leeds. Prev: Lect. & Hon. Sen. Regist. (Diabetes & Gen. Med.) Gen. Infirm. Leeds.; Clin. Research Fell. & Hon. Regist. (Gen. Med. & Diabetes) Gen. Infirm. Leeds; Regist. (Gen. Med.) Leeds Gen. Infirm. & Airedale Gen. Hosp. Keighley.

MANSFIELD, Nicholas Charles West Walk Surgery, 21 West Valk, Yate, Bristol BS37 4AX Tel: 01454 272200; 7 Elm Close, Chipping Sodbury, Bristol BS37 6HE Tel: 01454 312575 — MB BS 1981 Lond.; BSc Lond. 1978; MRCGP 1985; DRCOG 1984. (Kings Coll.)

MANSFIELD, Patrick Alexander Tamworth House Medical Centre, 341 Tamworth Lane, Mitcham CR4 1DL Tel: 020 8288 1866 Fax: 020 8679 3621 — MB BS 1996 Lond.; 2001 DFFP; BSc Hons.) 1993. (Lond.) GP Salaried Partner. Socs: BMA; MPS. Prev: GP VTS St. Richards Hosp. Chichester; PRHO (Med.) Bournemouth; GP Regist. Wimbledon, Lond.

MANSFIELD, Peter John Good Healthkeeping, Thames St., Louth N11 7AD Tel: 01507 601655 Fax: 01507 606655 Email: pm@health uk.demon.co.uk; 84 Tinkle Street, Grimoldby, Louth LN11 8TF — MB Camb. 1969, BChir 1968; Cert. Av. Med. 1979. (Camb.) Dir. Good Health Keeping; Dir. & Trustee Templegarth Trust. Socs: Pres. Nat. Pure Water Assn.; Inst. Psionic Med.; Roy. Soc. Med. Prev: Research Fell. (Community Med.) Univ. Coll. Hosp. Med. Sch. Lond.; Ho. Off. Evelina Childr. Hosp. Guy's Hosp. Lond.; Ho. Phys. & Ho. Surg. Metrop. Hosp. Dalston.

MANSFIELD, Rebecca Mary 22 Gertrude Road, West Bridgeford, Nottingham NG2 5BY — BM BS 1992 Nottm.

MANSFIELD, Richard John Robert Millgate Cottage, Millagte, Masham, Ripon HG4 4EQ — MB ChB 1990 Leeds; BSc (Hons.) Leeds 1987; MRCP (UK) 1993.

MANSFIELD, Stephen David 21 Dryburn Park, Durham DH1 5AD — MB ChB 1993 Birm.

MANSFIELD, Timothy Guy Robert Coltishall Surgery, St John's Road, Rectory Road, Coltishall, Norwich NR12 7HL Tel: 01603 737593 Fax: 01603 737067; Tel: 01263 735053 — MB BS 1986 Lond.; MRCGP 1991; DRCOG 1990.

MANSHIP, Jacinta Margaret Marie 4 Dilstonhaugh Cottages, Corbridge NE45 5QY — MB BS 1990 Newc.

MANSI, Anthony Ronald Ernest 7 High Street, Green St. Green, Orpington BR6 6BG Tel: 01689 850231; Little Grange, 27 Crofton Avenue, Orpington BR6 8DU Tel: 01689 53990 — MB BS 1962 Lond.; MRCS Eng. LRCP Lond. 1962; DPM Eng. 1972. (Lond. Hosp.) Socs: BMA. Prev: Hosp. Pract. (Psychiat.) Greenwich Dist. Hosp.; Ho. Surg. FarnBoro. Hosp. Kent; Ho. Phys. Miller Gen. Hosp. Lond.

MANSI, Elizabeth Gabrielle 42 Felstead Road, Wanstead, London E11 2QJ — MB BS 1973 Lond.

MANSI, Janine Lucia Department of Oncology, St. George's Hospital, London SW17 0RE Tel: 020 8725 2955 Fax: 020 8725 1199; Herons Way, Wey Road, Weybridge KT13 8HS — MB BS 1979 Lond.; MD Lond. 1989; FRCP (UK) 1982. (King's College) Cons. Med. Oncol. St Geo. Hosp. Lond. Prev: Sen. Regist. Roy. Marsden Hosp. Sutton Surrey.

MANSI, Joseph Anthony (retired) Kent Lodge, 15 Glentrammon Road, Farnborough, Orpington BR6 6DE Tel: 01689 859255 — MRCS Eng. LRCP Lond. 1936.

MANSI, Mr Makram Nazir 6 Buckingham Court, Kensington Park Road, London W11 3BP Tel: 020 7221 1057 — MB BCh 1961 Cairo; FRCS Ed. 1981; ECFMG Cert 1975. (Kasr-el-Aini Fac. Med. Cairo) Prev: Med. Off. Iron & Steel Co. Cairo, Egypt; Post-Doctoral Fell. (Orthop.) Baylor Coll. Med. Houston, U.S.A.; Regist. (Orthop.) W. Middlx. Hosp. Isleworth.

MANSINGH, Mr Sanjay 2 Lime Avenue, Groby, Leicester LE6 0YE — MB BS 1979 Kanpur; FRCS RCPS Glas. 1986.

MANSON, Alice Jane 102 Fulham Palace Road, London W6 9PL Tel: 020 8846 9442 — MB BS 1991 Lond.; MRCP (UK) 1995. (Charing Cross & Westminster) Research Fell. (Neurol.) Nat. Hosp. for Neurol. & Neurosurg. & Middlx. Hosp. Lond. Socs: Med. Protec. Soc. Prev: Med. Regist. Luton & Dunstable Hosp.; SHO Neurol. St Barths. Hosp. Lond.; SHO N. Middlx. Hosp. Lond.

MANSON, Catherine Mary 3 Craigweil Avenue, Didsbury, Manchester M20 6JQ — MB ChB 1988 Manch.; BSc (Hons.) Manch. 1986, MB ChB 1988; MRC Path 1999. Regist. (Histopath.) N. W.. RHA. Prev: SHO (Path.) Manch. Roy. Infirm.; Ho. Off. Trafford Gen. Hosp.

MANSON, Charles Matheson Health Centre, Eaton Place, Bingham, Nottingham NG13 8BG Tel: 01949 837338; The Old Cottage, The Green, Orston, Nottingham NG13 9NZ Tel: 01949 50738 — MB ChB 1952 Ed. (Ed.) Socs: Nottm. & E. Midl. Edin. Med. Grad. Soc. & Nottm. M-C Soc. Prev: Ho. Surg. (Obst.) Raigmore Hosp. Inverness; Cas. Off., Ho. Phys. & Ho. Surg. Warneford Gen. Hosp. Leamington Spa.

MANSON, Emma Frances St Thomas Surgery, Ysyol Street, St. Thomas, Swansea SA1 8LH Tel: 01792 653992 — MB ChB 1988 Liverp.; DFFP 1994; DA (UK) 1993.

MANSON, George Inglis, OBE (retired) 12 Brothock Meadows, Letham Grange, Arbroath DD11 4QN Tel: 01241 890443 — MB ChB 1944 Aberd.

MANSON, Gregory Cossington House Surgery, 51 Cossington Road, Canterbury CT1 3HX Tel: 01227 763377 Fax: 01227 786908; The Old Barn, Mount Court Acrise, Folkestone CT18 8LQ — MB BCh 1992 Witwatersrand; DRCOG RCOG. 1996; OFFP Royal Coll Family Planning Nov 1992; MRCGP Royal coll. GP May 1998. GP Canterbury, Kent.

MANSON, Helen McGregor Kingstone Cottage, 67 William St., Herne Bay CT6 5NR Tel: 01227 740000; 2 Dukeswood, Radfall Road, Chestfield, Whitstable CT5 8PJ — MB ChB 1989 Dundee; MRCGP 1994. Prev: Asst. GP Herne Bay & Ashford; Trainee GP Wilmslow.

MANSON, Ian Wilson (retired) Poole Cottage, Hill Lane, Hurst Green, Clitheroe BB7 9QT Tel: 01254 826818 — MB ChB 1956 Manch.; FRCOG 1979, M 1964; DObst RCOG 1959. Cons. O & G Preston HA. Prev: Regist. Wythenshawe Matern. Hosp. Manch. & Roy. Lancaster Infirm.

MANSON, Mr James McKenzie Consultant Surgeon, Singleton Hospital, Sketty Lane, Swansea SA2 8QA Tel: 01792 285334 Fax: 01792 285334 Email: j.mck.manson@mumbles98.freeserve.co.uk; 2 The Mount, Swangland Bay Road, Mumbles, Swansea SA3 42J — MB ChB 1978 Manch.; BSc St. And. 1975; ChM 1989; FRCS Eng. 1982. Cons. Surg. (Gen. Surg. & Upper Gastrointestinal Surg.) Singleton Hosp. Swansea NHS Trust Swansea. Socs: Assn. Upper G.I. Surg.; Internat. Soc. Dis. of Oesophagus; Pancreatic Soc. Prev:

MANSON

Sen. Regist. NW Region; Research Fell. Harvard Sch. Med. Boston, USA.

MANSON, James Scott (retired) 7 Marchfield Park, Edinburgh EH4 5BW Tel: 0131 336 5741 — MB ChB Ed. 1951; AFOM RCP Lond. 1981. Prev: Regional Med. Adviser United Biscuits (UK) Ltd Edin.

***MANSON, Jessica Jane** 73 Corringham Road, London NW11 7DL Tel: 020 8455 6379 — MB ChB 1998 Manch.; MB ChB Manch 1998; BSc (Hons) Manch. 1995.

MANSON, Malcolm Donald The Health Centre, Buckley CH7 2JL Tel: 01244 550939; The New House, The Green, Higher Kinnerton, Chester CH4 9BZ Tel: Kinnerton 660785 — MB ChB 1955 Liverp.; MRCGP 1968. (Liverp.) Hosp. Pract. Meadowslea Hosp. Pennyffordd; Mem. Clwyd Local Med. Comm.; Mem. Clwyd Family Pract. Comm.; Mem. Med. Advis. Comm. Clwyd HA; UMR Clwyd S. Community Unit. Prev: SHO (O & G) Walton Hosp. Liverp.; Ho. Phys. & Ho. Surg. David Lewis N. Hosp. Liverp.

MANSON, Patrick George Campbell 6 Crumelknowes, Hawick TD9 0NL Tel: 01450 372636 — MB ChB 1977 Aberd.; MRCGP. 1981; DRCOG 1980. GP Trainer. Socs: (Sec. & Treas.) Hawick Med. Soc. Prev: GP LoughBoro.; Trainee GP Nottm. VTS; Ho. Surg. Woodend Gen. Hosp. Aberd.

MANSON, Peter Richard Connemara, 79 Wickersley Road, Rotherham S60 3PU Tel: 01709 70758 — LRCPI & LM, LRSCI & LM 1962; LRCPI & LM, LRCSI & LM 1962. (RCSI)

MANSON, Thomas Williamson 14 Church Hill, Edinburgh EH10 4BQ Tel: 0131 447 0901 Fax: 0131 447 0901; 14 Church Hill, Edinburgh EH10 4BQ Tel: 0131 447 0901 Fax: 0131 447 0901 — MB ChB Ed. 1952; MRCGP 1970; DIH Soc. Apoth. Lond. 1964. (Ed.) Cons. Occupat. Med. Edin. Socs: Soc. Occupat. Med. Prev: Employm. Med. Adviser Health & Safety Exec.; GP Edin.

MANSON, William George Campbell (retired) Correen, Hawthorn Place, Ballater AB35 5QH Tel: 013397 55371 — MB ChB Aberd. 1949. JP. Prev: G.P. Alford, Aberd.shire.

MANSON, William Giles 6 Warrender Park Terrace, Edinburgh EH9 1JA — MB ChB 1989 Ed.

MANSON-BAHR, Philip Gordon Patrick Long Stratton Health Centre, Flowerpot Lane, Long Stratton, Norwich NR15 2TS Tel: 01508 530781 Fax: 01508 533030 Email: gordon.manson-bahr@gp-d82037.anglox.nhs.uk; Bodon House, Hall Lane, Tharston, Norwich NR15 2YF Tel: 01508 530064 Fax: 01508 533030 Email: gordonmb@doctors.org.uk — MRCS Eng. LRCP Lond. 1970; DObst RCOG 1973. (St. Thos.) Prev: Regist. (Med.) Groote Schuur Hosp., Cape Town; SHO (Obst.) John Radcliffe Hosp. Oxf.; Ho. Phys. St. Thos. Hosp. Lond.

***MANSOOR, Ismail C** 209 Wennington Road, Southport PR9 7AH — MB ChB 1996 Liverp.

MANSOOR, Mohammad Athar Holderness Road Surgery, 1199 Holderness Road, Hull HU8 9EA Tel: 01482 799139; Hornbeams, 9 Greenways, North Ferriby HU14 3JN — MB BS 1964 Punjab; MB BS Punjab (Pakistan) 1964; MRCP (U.K.) 1973. (King Edwd. Med. Sch. Lahore) Clin. Asst. Psychiat. Hull Hosp.; Med. Off. HMP Hull.

MANSOOR, Mohammad Riaz Hull Royal Infirmary, Hull HU3 2JZ Tel: 01482 674741 Fax: 01482 674026 Mobile: 07887 562203 Email: riaz.mansoor@hey.nhs.uk; 2 Ella Park, South Ella Way, Kirkella, Hull HU10 7EP Tel: 01482 652830 — MB BS 1978 Punjab; MRCP Lond. 1990; CCST (UK) 1999. Cons. Phys. Hull Roy. Infirm. Socs: Pakistan Med. & Dent. Coun.; BS. Prev: Staff Grade Phys. (Gastroenterol.) Grantham & Kesteven Gen. Hosp.; Med. Specialist Punjab Employees Social Security Inst. Lahore, Pakistan.; Sen. Regist. (Gastroenterol.) Gwynedd Hosp. Bang.

MANSOOR, Syed Irwin Road Health Centre, Sutton, St Helens WA9 3UG — MB BS 1972 Bangalor; MB BS Bangalore 1972. (Bangalore Med. Coll.) Prev: Regist. (Anaesth.) Caern. & Anglesey Gen. Hosp. Bangor.; SHO S. Shields Gen. Hosp.

***MANSOOR, Wasat** 83 Greenhead Road, Huddersfield HD1 4EZ — MB BCh 1995 Wales.

MANSOR, Fadhilah Zowyah Lela Yasmin 52 Filey Road, Reading RG1 3QQ — MB BS 1982 Monash.

***MANSOUBI, Hatef** Flat 3, Birken Court, Rickmansworth Road, Northwood HA6 2GY — MB BS 1996 Lond.

MANSOUR, Diana Jane Ashton Graingerville Contraception & Sexual Health Clinic, Newcastle General Hospital, Westgate Road, Newcastle upon Tyne NE4 6BE Tel: 0191 219 5239 Fax: 0191 219 5232 Email: didnamansour@hotmail.com; Holtburn, Well Road, Stocksfield NE43 7QW — BM BCh 1982 Wales; MFFP 1993; MRCOG 1989; DRCOG 1985; T(OG) 1995. (Wales) Cons. Community (Gyn. & ReProduc. Healthcare) Newc.; Med. Adviser & Lect. Margt. Pyke Memor. Trust Lond.; Lect. Univ. Newc. 1997. Socs: Hon. Sec. Fac. Family Plann. & Reproduc. Healthc/o the Roy. Coll. Obst. & Gyn.; Brit. Menopause Soc.; Brit. Soc. Colpos. & Cerv. Path. Prev: Dep. Dir. Margt. Pyke Centre Lond.; Sen. Regist. (Reproduc. Health & Family Plann.) Lond.

MANSOUR, Dolores Margaret Katrina Tel: 01207 232384; Newbell House, 30 Villa Real Road, Consett DH8 6BH Tel: 01207 508865 — MB BS 1980 Newc.

MANSOUR, Farid Cromwell Hospital, Cromwell Road, London SW5 0TU Tel: 020 7460 2000 Fax: 020 7460 5555; 127 Woodsford Square, Addison Road, Holland Park, London W14 8DT Tel: 020 7603 9194 Fax: 020 7602 4009 — MD Beirut 1965; LMSSA Lond. 1972. (St. Joseph's Univ.) Indep. GP. Cromwell Hosp. Lond. VTS & Humana Hosp. Wellington Lond.; Mem. WHO Task Gp Asbestos & Other Mineral Fibres. Socs: Med. Advis. Panel Asbestos Internat. Assn. Paris. Prev: Regist. (Med.) Roy. Berks. Hosp. Reading; GP Reading; Cons. Med. Inst. for Applied Fibrous Dust Research, Neuss, W. Germany.

MANSOUR, Julie Thérèse Parsloes Farmhouse, Overtown, Wroughton, Swindon SN4 0SH Tel: 01793 814889 — MB BCh 1976 Wales; MRCP (UK) 1979; Dip. Palliat. Med. Wales 1995. Assoc. Specialist (Clin. Oncol.) P.ss Margt. Hosp. Swindon & Ch.ill Hosp. Oxf. Prev: Clin. Asst. (Radiother.) P.ss Margt. Hosp. Swindon; Regist. (Med.) S. Sefton & Liverp. HAs; SHO (Med.) S. Sefton HA.

***MANSOUR, Mark Robert** 127 Woodsford Sq, London W14 8DT — MB ChB 1997 Ed.

MANSOUR, Mr Mohamed Sayed Ahmed, Lt.-Col. RAMC Holtburn, Well Road, Stocksfield NE43 7QW — MB ChB Alexandria 1965; MFFP 1993; MRCOG 1985; T(OG) 1991; DGO 1971; FRCOG 1998. Cons. O & G Hexham Gen. Hosp. N.d. Socs: Brit. Menopause Soc.; Brit. Soc. Colpos. & Cerv. Path.; Eur. Soc. Obst. & Gyn. Prev: Cons. O & G RAMC Camb. Milit. Hosp. Aldershot; Cons. O & G Al-Salama Hosp. Alkhobar, Saudi Arabia; Sen. Regist. (O & G) Univ. Coll. Hosp. Lond.

MANSOUR, Nagui Youssef BUPA Alexandra Hospital, Impton Lane, Walderslade, Chatham ME5 9PG Tel: 01634 687166; Nagashee, 3A Vicary Way, Maidstone ME16 0EJ Tel: 01622 756404 — MB BCh 1962 Cairo; MRCS Eng. LRCP Lond. 1974; FFA RCS Eng. 1971; DA Cairo 1967. (Cairo) Cons. Anaesth. BUPA Alexandra Hosp. Chatham; Hon. Cons. Anaesth. Medway Health Dist.; Cons. Anaesth., Somerfield Hosp., Maidstone. Prev: Cons. Anaesth. Medway Health Dist.; Regist. (Anaesth.) Hastings Gp. Hosps.; Sen. Regist. (Anaesth.) Nottm. City Hosp. & United Sheff. Hosps.

MANSOUR, Nassif Samuel Nassif Oak Hill Health Centre, Oak Hill Road, Surbiton KT6 6EN Tel: 020 8399 6622 Fax: 020 8390 4470; 18 Warren Avenue, Richmond TW10 5DZ Tel: 020 8876 3186 — MB BS 1988 Khartoum; MRCGP 1996; DGM - RCP 1995; DRCOG 1995; DFFP 1994. (Faculty of Medicine, University of Khartoum, Sudan) GP Princip.; Hosp. Pract. (Neurol.) Kingston Hosp.; GP Research Fell. UMDS.

MANSOUR, Paul Department of Cellular Pathology, Southport District General Hospital, Town Lane, Southport PR8 6PN Tel: 01704 547471 Email: paul.mansour@mail.soh-tr.nwest.nhs.uk — MB ChB 1983 Sheff.; MRCPath 1991; FRCPath 1999. Cons. Histopath. S.port & Ormskirk Hosp. NHS Trust. Prev: Sen. Regist. (Histopath.) W. Midl. Regional Train. Scheme.

MANSOUR, Sahar Tel: 020 8725 0957 Fax: 020 8725 3444 Email: smansour@sghms.ac.uk — BM BS 1987 Nottm.; MSc (Genetics) (Distinc.) Lond. 1994; MRCP (UK) 1991. Regist. (Genetics) St. Geo. Hosp. Med. Sch. Lond.; Cons. geneticist, Dept. of Med. Genetics, St. Geo.'s Hosp., Lond. Socs: BMA. Prev: Regist. (Paediat.) Qu. Med. Centre Nottm.

MANSOUR, Samir Hassan Saleh Southdene Medical Centre, Front Street, Shotton Colliery, Durham DH6 2LT Tel: 0191 526 5811 Fax: 0191 526 7740 — MB BCh 1970 Ain Shams. (Ain Shams)

MANSOURI, Maher Auchinairn Road Surgery, 101 Auchinairn Road, Bishopbriggs, Glasgow G64 1NF Tel: 0141 772 1808 Fax: 0141 762 1274; Aldourie, 11 Collylinn Road, Bearsden, Glasgow G61 4PN Tel: 0141 942 2968 — MD 1974 Aleppo Syria. Clin. Asst. (A & E) Stobhill Gen. Hosp. Prev: Trainee GP/SHO (O & G)

Stobhill Gen. Hosps. Glas.; Regist. (Orthop. & A & E) Inverclyde Hosp.; SHO (Geriat.) Bridge of Weir & Ravenscraig Hosp.

MANSUETO, Vincent 111 Maidstone Road, Chatham ME4 6JA Tel: 01634 849501 Fax: 01634 811268 Email: v. mansueto@virgin.net — MD Malta 1958; BPharm Malta 1955; DObst RCOG 1964; DCH Eng. 1963. Med. Off. Remploy Rochester. Prev: Regist. (Paediat.) City Gen. Hosp. Stoke-on-Trent; SHO (Paediat.) Gen. Hosp. Kettering; Ho. Off. Obst. Beckenham Matern. Hosp.

MANSURI, Mohomedshafi Gulammohomed 3 Osborne Gardens, Thornton Heath, Croydon CR7 8PA — MB BS Gujarat 1961; DPM Bombay 1965. Med. Off. Home Office. Socs: Affil. RCPsych; MDU; Assoc. Mem. Brit. Acad. Foren. Sc. Prev: Med. Off. Home Office; Med. Asst. (Psychiat.) Morgannwg Hosp. Bridgend; Regist. (Psychiat.) Doncaster Roy. Infirm.

MANSY, Hatem Abdel Aziz Fencer House, Fencer Hill Park, Newcastle upon Tyne NE3 2EA — MB BCh 1974 Tanta; MRCPI 1983.

MANT, Professor Arthur Keith Linn Cottage, 29 Ashley Drive, Walton-on-Thames KT12 1JT Tel: 01932 225005 — MB BS Lond. 1949; MD (Path.) Lond. 1950; FRCP Lond. 1982, M 1977; MRCS Eng. LRCP Lond. 1943; FRCPath 1967, M 1964; DMJ (hon. causa) Soc. Apoth. Lond. 1979. (St. Mary's) Prof. Emerit. Forens. Med. Univ. Lond. Socs: (Ex-Pres.) Brit. Acad. of Forens. Sci.; (Emerit. Pres.) Internat. Assn. Accid. & Traffic Med.; (Ex-Pres.) Forens. Sci. Soc. Prev: Prof. & Head Forens. Med. Guy's Hosp. Univ. Lond.; Sen. Lect. (Forens. Med.) King's Coll. Hosp. Lond.; Maj. RAMC, Path. War Crimes Gp. 1945-48.

MANT, Professor David Clive Anthony University of Oxford, Department of Primary Health Care, Old Road, Oxford OX3 7LF Tel: 01865 226770 Fax: 01865 227036 Email: david.mant@dphpc.ox.oc.uk; 28 Portland Road, Oxford OX2 7EY Tel: 01865 516829 — MB ChB 1977 Birm.; MSc (Community Med.) Lond. 1983; MA Camb. 1973; MRCGP 1982; MFPHM 1984. Prof. Gen. Pract. Prev: Prof. Primary Care (Epid). Uni. S.hamp.; Dir. Research & Develop. NHSE S&W; GP S. Oxf. Health Centre.

MANT, Jonathan William French Deptartment of Primary Care And General Practice, Medical School, University of Birmingham, Edgbaston, Birmingham Tel: 0121 414 2657 Fax: 0121 414 6571 Email: j.w.mant@bham.ac.uk; 15 Cotton Lane, Moseley, Birmingham B13 9SA Tel: 0121 689 5540 — MB BS 1985 Lond.; MA Camb. 1985, BA 1982; MSc Lond. 1990, MB BS 1985; MFPHM 1994. Sen. Lect. (Gen. Pract.) Univ. Birm. Prev: Clin. Lect. (Pub. Health Med.) Univ. Oxf.; Regist. (Pub. Health Med.) Oxf. RHA; SHO Rotat. (Med) Roy. Devon. & Exeter Hosp.

MANT, Timothy George Keith Guy's Drug Research Unit, 6 Newcomen St., London SE1 1YR Tel: 020 7910 7700 Fax: 020 7910 7800 Email: tmant@qguy.quitvtiles.com — MB BS 1979 Lond.; BSc (Hons.) Lond. 1976; FRCP Lond. 1995; LMSSA Lond. 1979; MRCP (UK) 1983; FFPM RCP (UK) 1995. (Guy's) Med. Dir. Guy's Drug Research Unit Ltd. Lond.; Hon. Cons. Guy's & St. Thos. Hosp. Trust Lond.; Hon. Sen. Lect. Div. Phamacol. Scis. Guy's, Kings Coll & St Thos. Hosp. Med. & Dent. Sch. Prev: Lect. (Clin. Pharmacol.) Guy's Hosp. Lond.; Research Regist. Poisons Unit Guy's Hosp. Lond.; SHO (Med.) Hammersmith Hosp. Lond.

MANTAFOUNIS, Adriana Fulham Medical Centre, 146 Fulham Road, London SW6 1BG Tel: 020 7385 6001 Fax: 020 7385 3755 — MB BS 1985 Lond.; MRCGP 1990; DRCOG 1989; DCH RCP Lond. 1988. Prev: SHO Ealing GP VTS; SHO (Paediat.) & Ho. Surg. Char. Cross Hosp. Lond.; Ho. Phys. W. Middlx. Univ. Hosp. Lond.

MANTEL-COOPER, Nicola The Abbey Practice, The Family Health Centre, Stepgates, Chertsey KT16 8HZ Tel: 01932 561199 Fax: 01932 571842; 1 Sunnybank, 297 Guildford Road, Bisley, Woking GU24 9AG — MB BS 1991 Lond.; MRCGP 1996; DRCOG 1994. (St George's Hospital) Partner, Abbey Pract., Chertsey Family Health Centre. Prev: GP Asst. Lightwater Surg.

MANTELL, Alison Elizabeth 25 Wellington Buildings, Wellington Way, London E3 4NA — MB BS 1994 Lond.; BSc Lond. 1991, MB BS 1994.

MANTELL, Anne Jane 19 Manor Close, Notton, Wakefield WF4 2NH — MB ChB 1980 Liverp.; MRCS Eng. LRCP Lond. 1980; MRCGP 1987; DRCOG 1988.

MANTELL, Brian Stuart (retired) 10 Ferrings, College Road, Dulwich, London SE21 7LU Tel: 020 8693 8141 Fax: 020 8299 0538 Email: bsmantell@yahoo.co.uk — MB BS Lond. 1958; FRCP Lond. 1990, M 1963; FRCR 1975; FFR 1967; DMRT Eng. 1965. Prev: Hon. Cons. King Geo. Hosp. Ilford & Harold Wood Hosp. Romford.

MANTELL, Janet Medical GU, St Helier Hospital, Wrythe Lane, Carshalton SM5 1AA Tel: 020 8296 2848 Fax: 020 8296 2208 Email: jmantell@sthelier.sghms.ac.uk; 10 Ferrings, College Road, Dulwich, London SE21 7LU Tel: 020 8693 8141 — MB BS 1969 Lond.; BSc (Physiol., Hons.) Lond. 1966; FRCP Lond. 1996; MRCP (UK) 1984. (Lond. Hosp.) Cons. Genitourin. Med. St. Helier Hosp. Carshalton & St. Geo. Hosp. Tooting. Prev: Sen. Regist. (Genitourin. Med.) Lond. & Moorfields Eye Hosp.; Regist. (Path.) Whipps Cross Hosp. Lond.; Ho. Phys. Lond. Hosp.

MANTGANI, Abhinandan Bhupalrao Miriam Medical Centre, Laird Street, Birkenhead CH41 7AL Tel: 0151 652 6077; 50 Bidston Road, Birkenhead CH43 6UW — MB BS 1977 Mysore; LRCP LRCS Ed. LRCPS Glas. 1982.

MANTHRI, Praveen Ramdoss 5 Travebank Gardens, Monifieth, Dundee DD5 4ET — MB BS 1981 Osmania.

MANTHRI, Sushma 97 Abbey Road, Barrow-in-Furness LA14 5ES Tel: 01229 821048 Fax: 01229 821048 Email: sudheer_manthri@compuserve.com — MB BS 1977 Osmania; MRCOG 1990. GP. Socs: BMA; Roy. Coll. Obst. & Gyns.

MANTHY, Ibrahim 57 Steep Bank Side, Southowram Bank, Halifax HX3 9PX — LMS 1963 Makerere U Coll., E. Afr.; LMS Makerere U Coll., E. Africa 1963.

MANTIDES, George Emiliou 2 Muswell Hill Place, London N10 3RR — MB ChB 1992 Leeds.

***MANTLE, Damien** Ninewells Hospital, PO Box 120, Dundee DD1 9SY — MB ChB 1997 Dundee.

MANTLE, David John (retired) 43 Askrigg Avenue, Hadrian Park, Wallsend NE28 9YA — MRCS Eng. LRCP Lond. 1949; DPH Leeds 1970.

MANTLE, Mark X-Ray Department, New Cross Hospital, Wolverhampton WV10 0QP — MB BS 1981 Lond.; MA Oxf. 1984, BA 1978; MRCP (UK) 1985; T(R)(CR) 1991; FRCR 1988. Cons. Radiol., Roy. Wolverhampton Hosp. NHS; Cons. Radiologist. Kidderminster Gen Hosp. Prev: Sen. Regist. (Diag. Radiol.) W. Midl. Train. Scheme.; Sec. Gen. Roy. Wolverhampton Hosps. NHS Trust.

MANTLE, Mary (retired) 62 Storey's Way, Cambridge CB3 0DX Tel: 01223 359335 — MB BCh BAO NUI 1944. Prev: Ho. Surg. King Edwd. VII Hosp. Windsor.

MANTON, Andrew George Summerfield, Streetham Road, Palestine, Andover SP11 7EH — MB ChB 1987 Leeds.

MANTON, Helen Elizabeth The Manor Street Surgery, Manor Street, Berkhamsted HP4 2DL Tel: 01442 875935; Heath Cottage, Little Heath Lane, Potten End, Berkhamsted HP4 2RY Tel: 01442 876062 — MB BS 1986 Lond.; MRCGP 1991; DRCOG 1990.

MANTON, Hilary Claire 9 Tyning Place, Combe Down, Bath BA2 5HA — MB ChB 1988 Leic.; DFFP 1994; DLO RCS Eng. 1994. Staff Grade (ENT Surg.) Roy. United Hosp. Bath. Prev: GP Bath VTS.

MANTON, John Rodney Woodley Health Centre, Hyde Road, Woodley, Stockport SK6 1ND Tel: 0161 430 2466 Fax: 0161 406 8217; 74 Station Road, Marple, Stockport SK6 6NY Tel: 0161 427 4231 Fax: 0161 427 2569 — MB ChB 1966 Ed.; FRCGP 1990, M 1972. (Ed.) Assoc. Adviser (Gen. Pract.) NW Region. Socs: Gen. Pract. Writers Assn.

MANTOUDIS, Evripidis University College Hospital, Maternity & Obstetrics, Huntley St., London WC1E 6DH — Ptychio Iatrikes 1989 Athens.

MANTOURA, Olivia Anne Chard Road Surgery, Chard Road, St. Budeaux, Plymouth PL5 2UE Tel: 01752 363111 Fax: 01752 363611 — MB ChB 1975 Liverp. p/t GP Princip.; Police Surg. Plymouth.

MANTOVANI, Cathryn Paula 17 Kenlor Road, London SW17 0DG — MB BS 1993 Lond.

MANTRAVADI, Krishana Mohan Flat 18, 2 Hill Place, Edinburgh EH8 9DS — MB BS 1985 Punjab; FRCA 1994.

MANTTAN, Patricia Lee Harrison Department, Radcliffe Infirmary, Woodstock Road, Oxford OX2 6HE; 4 Wrightson Close, Horspath, Oxford OX33 1RR Tel: 0186 772818 — BM BCh 1963 Oxf. Assoc. Specialist (Genitourin. Med.) Oxf. Prev: GP Oxf.; Ho. Phys. & Ho. Surg. Radcliffe Infirm. Oxf.

MANU

MANU, Mangta 32 Beaudesert Road, Birmingham B20 3TG — MB ChB 1989 Birm.

MANUCHEHRI, Mr Kaykhosrov Birmingham and Midland Eye Centre, City Hospital, Dudley Road, Birmingham B18 7QU; 16 Springlawn Road, Blanchardstown, Dublin 15, Republic of Ireland Tel: 00 353 1 8203396 Email: 1064552425@compuserve.com — MB BCh BAO 1991 Dub.; MB BCh Hons BAO Dub. 1991; MRCO Path. Lond. 1996; FRCO Path. Lond. 1997. (Dublin) Specialist Regist. (Ophth.) W. Midl. Rotat. Socs: Midl. Ophthalm. Soc.; Roy. Soc. Med.

MANUDHANE, Varsha Vasant The Village Surgery, 49 High Street, Wolstanton, Newcastle ST5 0ET Tel: 01782 626172 — MB BS 1974 Poona.

MANUDHANE, Vasant Shivanarayan The Health Centre, Dunning Street, Tunstall, Stoke-on-Trent ST6 5AP Tel: 01782 577822 Fax: 01782 811024 — MB BS 1971 Nagpur. (Govt. Med. Coll. Napur)

MANUEL, Abraham Rajasingh Godfrey Cardiff Royal Infirmary, Newport Road, Cardiff CF24 0SZ Tel: 029 2049 2233; 52 Heath Park Avenue, Cardiff CF14 3RH Tel: 029 2075 4806 — MB BS Ceylon 1966; MRCOG 1981; Dip. Ven. Soc. Apoth. Lond. 1984; FRCOG Lond. 1991; MFFP Fac. Family Planning of RCOG (UK) 1993. Cons. Genitourin. Med. Cardiff Roy. Infirm. & Dewi Sant Hosp. Pontypridd. Prev: Sen. Regist. (Genitourin. Med.) Cardiff Roy. Infirm.; Regist. (Genitourin. Med.) Birm. Gen. Hosp.

MANUEL, Arthur Myrtle House, 154 Blackburn Road, Accrington BB5 0AE Tel: 01254 233651 Fax: 01254 391965; Langcliffe, Laund Road, Accrington BB5 2PP Tel: 01254 390418 — MB BCh BAO 1974 Dub.; BA, MB BCh BAO Dub. 1974; MRCGP 1980; DCH Eng. 1977; DRCOG 1976. (TC Dub.) Prev: SHO Brit. Milit. Hosp. Rinteln, W. Germany; Regtl. Med. Off. 26 Field Regt. RA; Regtl. Med. Off. 1st. Bn. Scots Guards.

MANUEL, Dilani Dushyanthi 52 Heath Park Avenue, Cardiff CF14 3RH Tel: 029 2045 4806 — MB BS 1994 Lond.; MRCP. UK, June 1998, Royal Coll. Of Physicians. Lond. (Charing Cross & westminster) Specialist Regist. Radio., Roy. Hallamshire Hosp. Sheff.

MANUEL, Howard Cranbrook, Pyrford Road, West Byfleet KT14 6RE Tel: 0193 23 46360 — MSc Lond. 1976; MB Camb. 1963, BChir 1962; DRCPath 1971; DTM & H Eng. 1965; DObst RCOG 1964.

MANUEL, Jennifer Bernadette 12 Kent House Lane, Beckenham BR3 1LF — MB ChB 1982 Leeds.

MANUEL, John The Mullberry House, Rous Lench, Evesham WR11 4UJ — MB BS 1952 Lond.; MRCS Eng. LRCP Lond. 1952; DObst RCOG 1954. (St. Bart.)

MANUEL, Peter David Medway Maritime Hospital, Windmill Road, Gillingham ME7 5NY Tel: 01634 825140/825208 Fax: 01634 825145; 82 Borstal Road, Rochester ME1 3BD Tel: 01634 841482 — MB BCh Wales 1969; FRCP Lond. 1989; MRCP (UK) 1973; FRCPCH 1997. Cons. Paediat.Medway NHS Trust; Clin. Dir. Child Life & Health Medway NHS Trust. Socs: Brit. Soc. Paediat. Gastroenterol. & Nutrit.

***MANUELPILLAI, Neil Lawrence** 38 Bromar Road, London SE5 8DL — MB BS 1994 Lond.

MANUJA, Mr Sohan Lal 117 Cronk Lianyr, Trumode Park, Douglas IM2 5LT Tel: 01624 624639 — MB BS Rajasthan 1965; FRCS Ed. 1975. Cons. Otorhinolaryng., Head & Neck Surg. & Facial Reconstruc. Surg. Noble's Hosp. Douglas I. of Man. Socs: Roy. Soc. Med.; N. Eng. Otolaryngol. Soc.

MANWELL, Carol Elizabeth Gwynne Tel: 01570 470010; Moyddin Fach, Gorsgoch, Llanybydder SA40 9TN Tel: 01570 470010 Email: e.manwell@lycos.com — MB BCh Wales 1969; Cert. Family Plann. JCC 1985. (Welsh Nat. Sch. Med.) p/t Clin. Med. Off. (Family Plann. & Cytol.) Aberaeron & Ceredigion Mid Wales NHS Trust; Locum Gen. Practitioner. Socs: BMA; Welsh F. P. Doctors. Prev: Locum GP; GP Telford; Regist. (Anaesth.) Singleton Hosp. Swansea & St. Helier Hosp. Carshalton.

MANWELL, Morna Kathleen Cummings Department of Child & Adolescent Psychiatry, Royal Belfast Hospital for Sick Children, 180 Falls Road, Belfast BT12 6BE Tel: 01232 240503; 11 Malone Park, Belfast BT9 6NH Tel: 01232 682586 — MB BCh BAO 1964 Belf.; MB BCh Belf. 1964; DPM Eng. 1968. Assoc. Specialist (Child Psychiat.) Roy. Belf. Hosp. Sick Childr. Socs: Medico-Legal Soc.; Assn. Child Psychol. & Psychiat.

MANYEULA, Reginah Tshegofatso 12 Talbot Crescent, Roundhay, Leeds LS8 1AL — MB ChB 1989 Leeds.

MANYWEATHERS, Vanessa Julie Castle Practice, 2 Hawthorne Road, Castle Bromwich, Birmingham B36 0HH Tel: 0121 747 2422 Fax: 0121 749 1196; 7 Hollyhurst, Water Orton, Birmingham B46 1PS — MB ChB 1989 Birm.; MRCGP 1994; DRCOG 1993.

MANZANERD - ESCARTI, Mr Ricardo Flat 1, 18 Marloes Rd, Kensington, London — MB BS 1987 Valencia. (Valencia, Spain)

MANZOOR, Azhar 24 Best Avenue, Burton-on-Trent DE15 9GU; 43 Linnet Close, Exeter EX4 5HF — MB BS 1984 Peshawar; MRCPI 1992.

MANZUR, Mr Khan Mohammad Anisuddin 150 Turner Road, Edgware HA8 6AR Tel: 020 7925 5362 — MB BS 1962 Dacca; FRCS Ed. 1975; DO Eng. 1965. (Dacca) Outpats. Med. Off. Moorfields Eye Hosp. Lond.; Clin. Asst. St. Albans City Hosp. Prev: Clin. Asst. W.. Ophth. Hosp. Lond.; SHO St. Paul's Eye Hosp. Liverp.; SHO Qu. Eliz. Hosp. Birm.

MAPARA, Rajeshkumar Fernville Surgery, Midland Road, Hemel Hempstead HP2 5BL Tel: 01442 213919 Fax: 01442 216433 Email: raj-mopara@gp-e82022.nhs.uk; 26, Wimscumbe Way, Stanmore HA7 3AU — MB BS 1983 Lond. (Distinc.); DCH RCP 1985 Lond.; DRCOG 1986; MB BS Lond. 1983 (Distinc.); MRCGP 1987 (Distinc.); MRCGP (Distinc.) 1987; DCH RCP Lond. 1985; DRCOG 1986.

MAPLE, Christine Blue Wing, Wallacetown Health Centre, Lyon Street, Dundee DD4 6RB Tel: 01382 458333 Fax: 01382 461833; 8 Piperdam Drive, Piperdam, Fowlis DD2 5LY — MB ChB 1989 Dundee; MRCP (UK) 1992. p/t Gen. Practitioner, Dundee. Prev: Research Regist. & SHO Rotat. (Med.) Tayside Health Dundee.

MAPSON, Elizabeth Ann The Dairy, 4 Towsington Court, Exeter EX6 8AY Tel: 01392 833627 — MB BS 1974 Lond.; MRCS Eng. LRCP Lond. 1974; MRCGP 1986. (Royal Free Hospital) Med. Off. (Prosth.s & Orthotics) Exeter Mobility Centre.

MAPSTONE, Bridget Bernard (retired) 2 Rushmere Way, Northampton NN1 5RW — MB BCh BAO 1940 NUI. Prev: Clin. Med. Off. p/t, S.W. Surrey HA.

MAPSTONE, James 1 Ermin Close, Baydon, Marlborough SN8 2JQ — BChir 1995 Camb.; MA Cantab. 1997; MB Cantab. 1996. (Uni. Camb.) Specialist Regist. N. Thames. Train. Region. Pub. Health Med. Socs: BMA. Prev: SHO Pub. Health Med. Croydon Health Auth.; SHO ITU N.ampt. Gen. Hosp.; SHO A+E Addenbrooke's Camb.

MAPSTONE, Nicholas Peter The Knoll, 18 Kings Road, Ilkley LS29 9AN Email: n.p.mapstone@leeds.ac.uk — MB ChB 1987 Liverp.; MRCPath 1994. Sen. Lect. (Path.) Univ. Leeds; Hon. Cons. Path. Leeds Gen. Infirm.

MAQBOOL, Hussain Sheikh 22 Over Mill Drive, Selly Park, Birmingham B29 7JL Tel: 0121 471 4174 — MB BS Punjab 1958; MFFP 1993; MFPHM RCP (UK) 1990; MFCM RCP (UK) 1974; MPH Baltimore 1965; T(PHM) 1993; DPH Punjab 1962. Cons. Pub. Health Med. Birm. HA; Chairm. Pub. Health Med. & Community Health Forum Overseas Doctors Assn. (UK). Prev: SCM & Acting Dist. Med. Off. S. Birm. HA; Sen. Med. Off. Notts. HA; Fell. John Hopkins Univ. Sch. Pub. Health.

MARA, Helen Kit-Man The Elms Medical Centre, Tilley Close, Main Road, Hoo, Rochester ME3 9AE Tel: 01634 250142 — BM 1983 Soton.; MRCGP 1987; DRCOG 1985. Prev: Trainee GP Dartford & Gravesham Auth. VTS; Ho. Off. (Surg.) Vict. Hosp. Blackpool; Ho. Off. (Med.) St. Mary's Hosp. Portsmouth.

MARAIS, Andre Du Randt c/o Nes International, PO Box 888, Dereham NR20 5TR — MB ChB 1974 Pretoria.

MARAJ, Mr Barry Hayden Charing Cross Hospital, Department Urology, Fulham Palace Road, London W6 8RF; 2 Blagdon Court, Golden Manor, Hanwell, Ealing, London W2 3EF Tel: 020 8567 4671 — MB ChB 1987 Glas.; FRCS Glas. 1993. Specialist Regist. (Urol.) Char. Cross Hosp. Lond. Prev: Research Fell. (Molecular Med. & Urol.) St. Jas. Univ. Hosp. Leeds; Hon. Regist. (Urol.) St. Jas. Hosp. Leeds.

MARAK, Winnie Khama 58A Burton Road, Repton, Derby DE65 6FN — MB BS 1966 Gauhati.

MARAN, Professor Arnold George Royal Infirmary, Edinburgh EH3 Tel: 0131 536 3743 Fax: 0131 229 8769; 27 Learmonth Terrace, Edinburgh EH4 1NZ Tel: 0131 332 0055 Fax: 0131 332 1717 Email: agmaran@compuserve.com — MB ChB 1959 Ed.; MD Ed. 1965; FDS (Hons.) RCS Ed. 1994; FRCS Eng. 1991; FRCP Ed.

1988; FRCS Ed. 1963; FCS (Hons.) S. Afr. 1996; FACS 1975. Pres. RCS (Ed.); Cons. Otolaryngol. Roy. Infirm. Edin. Socs: Fell. Roy. Soc. Med. (Pres. Laryngol. Sect.); (Pres.) Brit. Assn. Acad. Otolaryngol. Prev: Cons. Otolaryngol. Roy. Infirm. Dundee; Fell. (Head & Neck Surg.) Univ. Iowa; Prof. Otolaryngol. W. Virginia Univ. Morgantown, USA.

MARAN, Nicola Jane 1 Alva Street, Edinburgh EH2 4PH Tel: 0131 225 2284 — MB ChB 1985 Ed.; FRCA 1990; DA (UK) 1988. Lect. (Anaesth.) Univ. Edin. Prev: Regist. & SHO (Anaesth.) Roy. Infirm. Edin.

MARASCO, Mario 61 Sandringham Road, London N22 6RB — State Exam Naples 1992.

MARASHI, Latifa 5 Grassiees, Rickleton, Washington NE38 9JA Tel: 0191 417 7344 — MB ChB 1991 Liverp.

MARASHI, Muhammed Taque Houghton Health Centre, Church Street, Houghton-le-Spring DH4 4DN Tel: 0191 584 2154 — MB BS 1956 Karachi; LRCP LRCS Ed. LRFPS Glas. 1957; MRCP Ed. 1967; DCH RFPS Glas. 1960. (Dow Med. Coll.) Prev: JHMO (Gen. Med.) Dryburn Hosp. Durh.; Ho. Phys. & Ho. Surg., & Ho. Off. (Obst. & Gyn) S. Shields Gen. Hosp.

MARATHE, Ramesh Mahader Apsley House, 188 Waterloo Road, Burslem, Stoke-on-Trent ST6 3HF Tel: 01782 837498 Fax: 01782 833440 — MB BS 1964 Nagpur; MB BS 1964 Nagpur.

MARATOS, Jason The Group-Analytic Practice, 88, Montagu Mansions, London W1U 6LF Tel: 020 7935 3103 Fax: 020 7935 1397 Email: maratos@gapractice.org.uk; Briarwood Cottage, 4 Mitchell Walk, Amersham HP6 6NN — MPhil (Psychiat.) Lond. 1976; Ptychio Iatrikis Athens 1969; DPM Eng. 1976; MInstGA 1979; MCPsych 1998. (Athens) p/t Cons. Psychiat. & Gp. Analyst, Child & Adolesc. Psychiat., Psychother., The Gp.-Analytic Pract., Lond.; Cons. in Child and Adolesc. Psychiat., St. Mary's Hosp., Lond.; Cons. Psychiat., Internat. Centre for Eating Disorders, Aylesbury. Socs: Assn. Child Psychol. & Psychiat.; Gp. Analyt. Soc.; Roy. Coll. Psych. Prev: Sen. Regist. (Child Psychiat.) Roy. Free & Univ. Coll. Hosps. Lond.; Regist. (Neurol.) St. Bart. Hosp. Lond.; Regist. (Psychiat.) Lond. Hosp.

MARAZZI, Erminio (retired) 24/97 Southampton Row, London WC1B 4HH Tel: 020 7636 2764 — MD 1941 Parma; LAH Dub. 1954.

MARAZZI, Philip John Michael The Medical Centre, Kingston Avenue, East Horsley, Leatherhead KT24 6QT Tel: 01483 284151 Fax: 01483 285814 Email: phil.marazzi@profiad.com; The Gables, 87 The St, West Horsley, Leatherhead KT24 6BG — MB BS 1983 Lond.; DCH RCP Lond. 1986. (Westminster Medical School) Princip. in Gen. Pract., Dr V. Finnamore & Partners, E. Horsley.; Med. Adviser, Profiad Ltd, 20-24 Vachelrd, Reading, Berks. RG1 1NY.

MARBER, Michael Stephen Department of Cardiology, St Thomas' Hospital, London SE1 7EH Tel: 020 7922 8191 Fax: 020 7960 5659 Email: m/marber@umds.ac.uk — MB BS 1984 Lond.; MB BS Lond. 1983; PhD Lond. 1993, BSc (Hons.) 1981; MRCP (UK) 1987; FACC 1997; T(M) 1994. Sen. Lect. & Hon. Cons. (Cardiol.) UMCS & Guys & St Thos. Hosps. Trust; Head Dept. Cardiol. UMDS. Socs: Brit. Cardiac. Soc.; Amer. Heart Assn.; Brit. Soc. Cardiovasc. Research. Prev: Sen. Lect./Hon. Cons. (Cardiol.) UCL Med. Sch. & UCL Hosps. Trust; Vis. Fell. Cardiol. Univ. Calif. Trust at San Diego Med. Centre; Regist. (Cardiol. & Gen. Med.) St. Geo. Hosp. Lond.

*****MARCER, Hilary Jane** 4 Leopold Road, Leicester LE2 1YB — MB ChB 1997 Leic.

MARCH, Christina 153 Langtree Avenue, Muldura Vic. 3500, Australia; 13 Gloucester Place, Windsor SL4 2AJ — MB BS Lond. 1970; DObst RCOG 1973. (Univ. Coll. Hosp.) GP Vict. Australia. Socs: BMA. Prev: SHO (Gen. Med.) Chase Farm Hosp. Enfield; SHO (Obst.) & Ho. Phys. & Ho. Surg. Univ. Coll. Hosp. Lond.; GP, Windsor.

MARCHAM, Clive Douglas Rooley Lane Medical Centre, Rooley Lane, Bradford BD4 7SS Tel: 01274 770777; 28 Moor Road, Leeds LS6 4BJ Tel: 0113 275 6258 — MB ChB 1966 Liverp.; DA Eng. 1975; DPM Eng. 1971. (Liverp.)

***MARCHAND, Lucy Jane Camille** 9 Dudleston Heath Drive, Cowplain, Waterlooville PO8 8AR — BM 1998 Soton.; BM Soton 1998.

MARCHANT, Andrew Eric 19 Mauricewood Rise, Penicuik EH26 0BL — MB ChB 1989 Ed.

MARCHANT, Bradley Gerald Pfizer Global Research + Development, Ramsgate Road, Sandwich CT13 9NJ Tel: 01304 648999 Fax: 01304 658807 Email: bradley_marchant@sandwich.pfizer.com — MB BS 1985 Lond.; Dip Pharm Med; MD Lond. 1994; MRCP (UK) 1988. Exec. Director, Clin. Developm., Pfizer Global research and Developm. Socs: Brit. Cardiac Soc. Prev: Brit. Heart Foundat. Jun. Research Fell. Lond. Chest Hosp.; Regist. (Cardiol. Med.) King's Coll. Hosp. Lond.; Regist. (Med. & Cardiol.) St. Helens Hosp. Hastings.

MARCHANT, Dara Edulji (retired) 16 Queensland Avenue, Wimbledon, London SW19 3AD Tel: 020 8715 4599 Fax: 020 8715 4599 Email: betty.marchant@compuserve.com — MB BS 1945 Lucknow; DPH Eng. 1957; DIH Soc. Apoth. Lond. 1957; DTM & H Calcutta 1952. Prev: MOH Trinidad Govt.

MARCHANT, Jeanette 74 Roslyn Street, Leicester LE2 1BW — MB ChB 1991 Birm.; ChB Birm. 1991.

MARCHANT, John Michael (retired) Bryb Coed, Chirk, Wrexham LL14 5LN Tel: 01691 2110 — M.B., Ch.B. Liverp. 1938; M.B., B.Chir. Camb. 1940; F.F.A. R.C.S. Eng. 1954; D.A. Eng. 1948.

MARCHANT, Mary Kathleen (retired) 29 Druids Cross Gardens, Calderstones, Liverpool L18 3EB Tel: 0151 428 7102 — MB ChB 1948 Liverp.; FRCS Eng. 1957.

MARCHANT, Matthew James 25 King Edwards Avenue, Gloucester GL1 5DB — MB ChB 1992 Leic.

MARCHBANK, Mr Adrian John Dept. Of Cardiothoracic Surg., Derriford Hospital, Plymouth PL6 8DH Tel: 01752 517 527 Email: adrian.marchbank@phnt.swest.nhs.uk — MB BS 1988 Lond.; BSc Lond. 1985; FRCS Eng. 1992; FRCS (Cth) 1998. Cons. (Cardiothoracic Surg.) N. Thames. Prev: Tutor (Cardiothoracic Surg.) Nat. Heart & Lung Inst. Lond.; Regist. (Cardiothoracic Surg.) Roy. Lond. Hosp. Trust; SpR (Cardiothoracic Surg.) N. Thames.

MARCHBANK, Nigel David Peter Eastbourne District General Hospital, King's Drive, Eastbourne BN21 2UD Tel: 01323 417400 Ext: 4102 Fax: 01323 414933 Email: nigel.marchbank@ed.ebh-tr.sthames.nhs.uk; Heather Hurst, 52 St. John's Road, Eastbourne BN20 7NG Tel: 01323 640028 — MB BS 1987 Lond.; MRCP (UK) 1991; FRCR 1995. (Guy's) Cons. (Radiol.) E.bourne; Cons. Radiol., Esperance Private Hosp. Socs: Fell.Roy. Coll. Radiol.; BMA; Brit. Inst. Radiol. Prev: Sen. Regist. (Radiol.) St. Geo.'s Hosp. Lond.; Regist. (Radiol.) St. Geo.'s Hosp. Lond.

MARCHI, Clive Jeffrey Bruce Conway Road Health Centre, Conway Road, Sale M33 2TB Tel: 0161 962 7321 Fax: 0161 973 1151; 21 Wilcott Road, Gatley, Cheadle SK8 4DX — MB ChB 1983 Manch.; BSc St. And. 1980; MRCGP 1987; DRCOG 1987. Clin. Asst. Diabetic Clinic Pk. Hosp. Davyhulme; Chairm. Trafford MAAG.

MARCHMENT, Alfred Henry Coleridge Kilcrea, Poplar Avenue, Great Crosby, Liverpool L23 — MB BCh BAO 1938 NUI. (Cork) Chairm. Bootle Med. Gp. & Local Med. Comm. Socs: Bootle Exec. Counc.; Liverp. Inst. Prev: Med Asst. Med. Off. Lawn Ment. Hosp. Lincoln; Jun. Res. Med. Off. Cork Dist. Hosp.; Med. Off. Mersey Med. Serv.

MARCO MOLINA, Miss Maria Luz Manchester Royal Infirmary, Renal Transplant Unit, Manchester M13 Tel: 0161 276 4413; 33 Dundonald Road, Didsbury, Manchester M20 6RU Tel: 0161 446 2789 Fax: 0161 248 4668 Email: branbrun20002@yahoo.com — LMS 1988 Navarra; FRCSI 1995. Clin. Research Fell. Renal Transpl. Manch. Roy. Infirm., Manch. Socs: FRCS; WIST; Assoc. Surg.s in Train. Prev: SHO (Gen. Surg.) Roy. Oldham Hosp., Manch. Roy. Infirm. & Bolton Gen. Hosp.; SHO (Cas. & Orthop.) Roy. Oldham Hosp.; Specialist Regist. (Gen. Surg.) Arrowe Pk. Hosp.

MARCOOLYN, Geoffrey John Sowter Norwich Road Surgery, 199 Norwich Road, Ipswich IP1 4BX Tel: 01473 289777 Fax: 01473 289545; 263 Henley Road, Ipswich IP1 6RW Tel: 01473 232935 Email: geoffrey_marcoolyn@msn.com — MRCS Eng. LRCP Lond. 1971; FRCGP 1997, M 1976; DObst RCOG 1975. (Char. Cross) Prev: Trainee GP Ipswich VTS; SHO (Obst. & Neonat. Paediat.) Canad. Red Cross Memor. Hosp. Taplow.

MARCOVIC, Ljubisa The Bungalow, Dobson Close, Hall Lane, Appley Bridge, Wigan WN6 9EP — MD 1974 Belgrade, Yugoslavia; MD Belgrade Yugoslavia 1974.

MARCOVITCH, Harvey Horton Hospital, Banbury OX16 9AL Tel: 01295 229014 Fax: 01295 229043; Honeysuckle House, Balscote, Banbury OX15 6JW Tel: 01295 738100 Fax: 01295 738100 Email: h.marcovitch@btinternet.com — MB BChir Camb. 1967; MA Camb

MARCUCCILLI

1967; FRCP Lond. 1988; FRCPCH 1996; DObst RCOG 1968; DCH Eng. 1968. (Camb. & St. Mary's) Cons. Paediat. Oxf. Radcliffe Hosps.; Hon. Sen. Clin. Lect. Univ. Oxf.; Off. (Press & Pub. Relations) Roy. Coll. Paediat. & Child Health; Edr.-in-Chief Archiv. of Dis. in Childh. Socs: Assoc. Mem. Med. Jl.ists Assn.

MARCUCCILLI, Felice Coatbridge Health Centre, No. 1 Centre Park Court, Coatbridge ML5 3AP Tel: 01698 422311 Fax: 01698 437787 — MB ChB 1961 Glas.; DObst RCOG 1962. (Glas.)

MARCUCCILLI, Natalino Sergio Coatbridge Health Centre, 1 Centre Park Court, Coatbridge ML5 3AP Tel: 01236 422311; 33 Blairmill Street, Coatbridge ML5 1PG Tel: 01236 24157 — MB ChB 1985 Glas. SHO Bellshill Matern. Hosp. Socs: BMA.

MARCUS, Adrian Julian Radiology Department, Barnet General Hospital, Wellhouse Lane, Barnet EN5 3DT Tel: 020 8216 4000, 020 8455 9228 Email: ajmarcus@doctors.net.uk; 47 Southway Hamstead Garden Suburb, London NW11 Fax: 020 8455 9229 — MRCS Eng. LRCP Lond. 1979; MB ChB 1979; MD 1984 Liverp.; FRCS Ed. 1983; FRCR 1987. (Liverpool) Cons. (Radiol.) Barnet Gen. Hosp. Lond. Socs: Brit. Soc. Interven. Radiol.; Eur. Soc. Uroradiol.; Brit. Med. Ultrasound Soc. Prev: Sen. Regist. St. Bart. Hosp. Lond.; Asst. Prof. Radiol. Penn State Univ.; Regist. (Radiol.) King's Coll. Hosp. Lond.

MARCUS, Claude Robert Steiner NMR Unit, Hammersmith Hospital, Du Cane Road, London W12 0NN — MD 1986 Rheims.

MARCUS, Elkan 27 Belsize Road, London NW6 4RX — MB BCh BAO 1949 NUI. (NUI)

MARCUS, Neil Jonathan 20 Belgrave Gardens, Oakwood, London N14 4TT — MB BS 1993 Lond.; MB BS (Hons.) Clin. Pharmacol. Lond. 1993; BSc (Basic. Med. Scis. & Pharmacol.) Lond. 1990; MRCP (UK) 1996. (Char. Cross & Westm.)

MARCUS, Nisrin Kamal Kilingi Smith, Niemczuk, Woolrych and Marcus, 279-281 Mill Road, Cambridge CB1 3DG Tel: 01223 247812 Fax: 01223 214191; 15 Nightingale Avenue, Cambridge CB1 8SG Tel: 01223 248672 Email: n.marcus@btinternet.com — MB ChB 1969 Baghdad; 1999 FRCOG; MRCOG 1981. GP Princip., 281 Mill Rd., Camb. Socs: ESHRE; MPS; BMA. Prev: Cons. Gyn. Bourn Hall Clinic Camb.

MARCUS, Paul Marcus Ridley Associates Ltd, Newton House, Newton Lane, Lower Whitley, Warrington WA4 4JA Tel: 01925 730527 Fax: 01925 732903 Email: drpmar@cs.com — MD Sheff. 1972, MB ChB (Hons.) 1968; FFPM RCP (UK) 1994, M 1989; Dip. Pharm. Med. RCP (UK) 1982; DAVMed Eng. 1973. Dir. Marcus Ridley Assocs. Ltd. Socs: Fell. Roy. Soc. Med.; Med. Res. Soc. Prev: Head Internat. Med. & Technical Servs. Zeneca Pharmaceuts. plc Alderley Edge; Dir. Med. Affairs Armour Pharmaceut. Ltd. Shalford; Head of Cold Environm. Research RAF Inst. Aviat. Med. FarnBoro..

MARCUS, Mr Raphael (retired) 10 heathfielde, Lyttelton Road, London N2 0EE Tel: 020 8458 0464 Fax: 020 8301 4216 — MB ChB Liverp. 1937; ChM Liverp. 1948, MD 1950; FRCS Eng. 1946. Expert Surgic. Witness. Prev: Cons. Surg. Liverp. Regional Hosp. Bd.

MARCUS, Richard Laurence Roselands, 4 Middleton Road, Manchester M8 5DS Tel: 0161 795 9111 Fax: 0161 798 9892 Email: rickymarcus@compuserve.com; 8 Barnhill Road, Prestwich, Manchester M25 9NH Tel: 0161 773 9464 Fax: 0161 798 9892 — MB ChB 1966 Manch.; FFOM RCP Lond. 1983, M 1981; MRCGP 1977; DIH Soc. Apoth. Lond. 1971; DCH Eng. 1968. (Manch.) Cons. Occupat. Phys. Manch. Prev: Regional Speciality Advis. Occupat. Med. N. W.. RHA.

MARCUS, Mr Richard Thomas (retired) 46 Tiddington Road, Stratford-upon-Avon CV37 7BA Tel: 01789 292229 — MB ChB 1958 Bristol; BSc Bristol 1955, ChM 1967; FRCS Eng. 1964. Cons. Surg. S. Warks. Hosp. Gp. Prev: Sen. Regist. (Surg.) United Bristol Hosp.

MARCUS, Robert Edwin 230 Milton Road, Cambridge CB4 1LQ Tel: 01223 424352 Fax: 01223 217017 Email: cm242@cam.ac.uk — MB BS 1977 Lond.; FRCP; FRCPath; MRCP (UK) 1980; MRCPath 1986. (Univ. Coll. Hosp.) Cons. Haemat. Addenbrooke's Hosp. Camb.; Dir. E. Anglian Bone Marrow Transpl. Unit. Prev: Sen. Regist. (Haemat.) Roy. Free Hosp. Lond.; Research Fell. MRC Leukaemia Unit Roy. Postgrad. Med. Sch.; Clin. Lect. Dept. Haemat. Univ. Coll. Hosp.

MARCUS, Mr Samuel Fahim Bourn Hall Clinic, Cambridge CB3 7TR Tel: 01954 717228 Fax: 01954 718826; 15 Nightingale Avenue, Cambridge CB1 8SG Tel: 01223 248672 Fax: 01223 248672 Email: sfmarcus@virgin.net — MB ChB 1973 Cairo; FRCS Glas. 1983; MRCS Eng. LRCP Lond. 1985; FRCOG 1997, M 1982. Cons. Gyn. & Fertil. Bourn Hall Clinic Camb. Socs: Brit. Fertil. Soc.; Eur. Soc. Human Reproduc. & Embryol.; Amer. Soc. Reproduc. Med. Prev: Specialist (O & G & Infertil.) Infertil. Advis. Centre Lond. Indep. Hosp.; Specialist Regist. (Sen. Reg.) Ketering Genral Hosp.

MARCUSON, Mr Roger Wolff 14 St John Street, Manchester M3 4DZ Tel: 0161 834 4411 Email: roger.marcuson@virgin.net; Stenner Brow, Stenner Lane, Didsbury, Manchester M20 2RQ Tel: 0161 445 7080 Email: roger.marcuson@virgin.net — MB BChir 1962 Camb.; MChir Camb. 1975, MA 1962; FRCS Eng. 1965; FRCS Ed. 1965. (Middlx.) Private Pract. Prev: Cons. Vasc. Surg. Manch. Roy. Infirm.; Cons. Surg. Hope Hosp. Salford; Sen. Regist. (Surg.) Middlx. Hosp. Lond.

MARCZAK, Mr Janusz Boleslaw (retired) 8 Summerfield Road, Chapel Ash, Wolverhampton WV1 4PR Tel: 01902 429044 Fax: 01902 773920 — MB ChB 1962 Birm.; FRCS Eng. 1968. Cons. Surg. Roy. Hosp. Wolverhampton. & New Cross Hosp.

MARCZEWSKI, Andrew George The Orchard Surgery, Commercial Road, Dereham NR19 1AE Tel: 01362 692916 Fax: 01362 698347 — MB BS 1976 Lond.; BSc (Physiol.) Lond. 1973, MB BS 1976; DRCOG 1980; Cert. Family Plann. JCC 1980, Socs: Nat. Assn. Family Plann. Doctors. Prev: Trainee GP King's Lynn VTS.

MARCZEWSKI, Ludwik Zbigniew (retired) 21 Lynton Close, Ely CB6 1DJ Tel: 01353 664782 — Med. Dipl. 1939 Univ. Lwow. Prev: Asst. Psychiat. Stoke Pk. Hosp. Gp. Bristol.

MARDEL, Manuel Joseph Charles (retired) 24 Glen Eyre Road, Bassett, Southampton SO16 3GG Tel: 01703 678811 — LMSSA Lond. 1952. Prev: Princ. GP.

MARDEL, Mr Simon Nicholas, OBE Department of Accident & Emergency, Furness General Hospital, Dalton Lane, Barrow-in-Furness LA14 4LF Tel: 01229 491049 Fax: 01229 826765 Email: merdel@mcmail.com — MB BS 1980 Lond.; FRCS Ed. 1990; FFARCS Dub. 1986; DTM & H RCP Lond. 1987; MSc Aberd. 1998. (St Mary's, Lond.) Cons. (Accid. & Energ. Med.) Furness Gen. Hosp. Barrow in Furness. Socs: Fell. Roy. Soc. Trop. Med. & Hyg.; Brit. Assn. Accid. & Emerg. Med. Prev: Short Term Consultancies in Humanatarian Work Overseas; Sen. Regist. (A & E) Aberd. Roy. Infirm.; Regist. (A & E) Leicester Roy. Infirm.

MARDEN, Bernard John 17 Poplar Way, Bishopdown, Salisbury SP1 3GR Tel: 01722 330833 Email: docmarden@yahoo.uk.com — MB BS 1992 Lond.; BSc Lond. 1989; MRCP (UK) 1998; MB BS St George's 1992. (St. George's Hosp. Lond.) Specialist Regist. (Paediat.) Wessex Deanery. Socs: Roy. Coll. Paeds. And Child Health. Prev: SHO (Anaesth.) Salisbury; SHO (Paediat. Rotat.) Soton. & Salisbury; GP VTS Salisbury.

MARDEN, Jean Margaret Isabel 17 Heron Close, Lower Halstow, Sittingbourne ME9 7EF — MB ChB 1949 Leeds; DObst RCOG 1951. (Leeds) Prev: Asst. Sch. Med. Off. & Asst. Matern. & Child Welf. Off. Derbysh. CC; Sen. Ho. Off. O & G Geo. Eliot Hosp. Nuneaton; Gyn. Ho. Surg. S. Lond. Hosp. Wom. & Childr.

***MARDEN, Peter F** 154 Avenue Road, Acton, London W3 8QG — MB BS 1996 Lond.

MARDER, Elizabeth St Anns Health Centre, St Anns Well Road, Nottingham NG3 3PX Tel: 0115 948 0560 Fax: 0115 958 8493; 1 Kingsbridge Way, off Chilwell Lane, Bramcote, Nottingham NG9 3LW Tel: 0115 967 7554 — BM BS 1984 Nottm.; MRCP (UK) 1989. Cons. Paediat. Community Child Health. QMC Univ. Hosp. NHS Trust; Med. Adviser Downs Syndrome Assoc.; Clin. Tutor. Socs: Fell.Roy. Coll. Paediat.s & Child Health; Brit. Assn. Comm. Child Health; Down's Syndrome Med. Interest Grp. Prev: SCMO N. Derbysh. HA; Regist. (Childh. Ment. Handicap) Manch. HA.; Regist. (Community Paediat.) Nottm. HA.

MARDON, Jacqueline Margaret Top Flat, 31 Hyndland Road, Glasgow G12 9UY — MB BS 1986 Lond.; MPhil Camb. 1989; MRCGP 1994; MFFP 1994.

MARDON, Julie 53/10 Bread Street, Edinburgh EH3 9AH — MB ChB 1993 Ed.

MAREDIA, Mohamadbhai Noorbhai Villette Surgery, Suffolk Street, Hendon, Sunderland SR2 8AX Tel: 0191 567 9361 Fax: 0191 514 7476; 1 Millthorp Close, Sunderland SR2 7RE Tel: 0191 567 9361 — MB BS 1971 Gujarat. Socs: BMA. Prev: Trainee GP Newc. VTS; SHO Newc. Gen. Hosp. & (Obst. & Paediat.) Sunderland Dist. Gen. Hosp.

MARENAH, Christine Beatrice Department of Clinical Chemistry, City Hospital, Hucknall Road, Nottingham NG5 1PB Tel: 0115 969 1169 Fax: 0115 962 7606; 20 Tavistock Avenue, Mapperley Park, Nottingham NG3 5BD — MB BChir 1978 Camb.; PhD Lond. 1973, BSc (Hons.) 1970; MA Camb. 1979, BA 1975; MRCP (UK) 1980; MRCS Eng. LRCP Lond. 1978; FRCPath 1996, M 1985; FRCP 1998. (St. Thos.) Cons. Chem. Path. City Hosp. Nottm. Prev: Lect. (Chem. Path. & Metab. Disorders) St. Thos. Hosp. Med. Sch. Lond.

MARESH, Michael John Andrew 20 Elm Road, Manchester M20 6XD Tel: 0161 445 5541 — MB BS 1975 Lond.; BSc Exeter 1970; MD Lond. 1992; FRCOG 1992, M 1980. (Lond. Hosp.) Cons. (O & G) St. Mary's Hosp. Manch.; Hon. Sen. Lect. Univ. Manch. Prev: Lect. O & G St. Mary's Hosp. Med. Sch. Lond.; SHO (Obst.) Qu. Charlottes Matern. Hosp. Lond.; Research Asst. (Reproduc. Endocrinol.) Kings Coll. Hosp. Lond.

MARFELL, Kathryn Bradford Health Authority, New Mill, Victoria Road, Saltaire, Shipley BD18 3LD Tel: 01274 366007; 5 Marlborough Villas, Menston, Ilkley LS29 6DB Tel: 01943 875262 — MB ChB 1978 Liverp.; MFCM 1987; MPH Leeds 1986; FRCPCH 1997. Cons. Pub. Health Med. Bradford HA; Research Fell. (Clin. Epidemiol.) Bradford Univ. Socs: Soc. for Social Med. Prev: Hon. Research Fell. Clin. Epidemiol. Research Unit Univ. Bradford; Specialist (Community Med.) Bradford HA; Med. Off. (Environm. Health) Bradford MDC.

MARFLEET, Jean Caroline 11 Fitzwalter Road, Colchester CO3 3SY Tel: 01206 576768 — MB BS 1974 Lond.; MFFP & RHC. (Middlesex) Cons. Family Plann. & Reproductive Health, Colchester Gen. Hosp.

MARFLEET, Paul Tel: 01206 570371 Fax: 01206 369908; 11 Fitzwalter Road, Colchester CO3 3SY — MB BS 1973 Lond.; MRCGP 1979; DRCOG 1977; Dip. Sports Med. 1997 Glas. (Middlesex) Med. Off. Brit. Ultimate Federat. Colchester; Med. Adviser, Colchester Exercise Referral Scheme; Med. Adviser, N. Essex Exercise Referral Monitoring & Developm. Socs: Brit. Assn. Sports Med. (Chairperson E.ern Region).

MARGALLO LANA, Maria Luisa Winterton Hospital, Sedgefield, Stockton-on-Tees TS21 3EJ; c/o Drive M. M. Lana, Torrelavega, Cantabria, Spain Tel: 942 890906 — LMS 1987 Cantabria. SHO Rotat. (Psychiat.) P'boro. Dist. Hosp. Socs: BMA & MSP. Prev: SHO (Geriat.) St. And. Hosp. Billericay; Ho. Off. (Surg.) Horton Gen. Hosp. Banbury; Ho. Off. (Med.) Luton & Dunstable Hosp.

MARGARSON, Michael Philip Department of Anaesthetics, Chelsea & Westminster Hospital, 369 Fulham Road, London SW10 9NH; 8 Elizabeth Cottages, Kew Gardens, Richmond TW9 3NJ — MB BS 1987 Lond.; FRCA 1993. Clin. Lect. Char. Cross. & W.m. Hosp. Med. Sch.

MARGARY, James Justin Comeragh Lodge, Golf Club Road, Woking GU22 0LU — MB BS 1978 Lond.; FRCA 1983. Cons. Anaesth. St. Peter's Hosp. Chertsey. Prev: Sen. Regist. St. Geo. Hosp. Lond. & Hosp. Sick Childr. Gt. Ormond St. Lond.; Vis. Asst. Prof. Stanford Univ.

MARGERESON, Amanda Elizabeth Lodge Surgery, Normandy Road, St Albans AL3 5NP Tel: 01727 853107 Fax: 01727 862657 — MB BS 1989 Lond.

MARGERISON, Adrian Charles Frederick 15 Tweedsyde Park, Kelso TD5 7RF — MB 1973 Camb.; BChir 1972; MRCP (UK) 1979. Cons. Paediat. Borders HB. Prev: SHO (Paediat.) Kings Coll. Hosp. & Guy's Hosp. Lond.; Regist. (Paediat.) Kings Coll. Hosp. Lond. & All St.s Hosp. Chatham; Sen. Regist. (Paediat.) Selly Oak Hosp., Sorrento Matern. & Birm. Childr. Hosp.

MARGERISON, Jeremy Christopher Lee The Culverhay Surgery, Culverhay, Wotton-under-Edge GL12 7LS Tel: 01453 843252 — MRCS Eng. LRCP Lond. 1968; LDS RCS Eng. 1963; DObst RCOG 1971. (Guy's) Prev: Ho. Phys. Roy. Alexandra Hosp. Sick Childr. Brighton.

MARGERISON, Lawrence Neil St Pauls Medical Centre, St. Pauls Square, Carlisle CA1 1DG Tel: 01228 524354 Fax: 01228 616660 — MB ChB 1985 Leeds; MRCGP 1991; DCCH RCGP 1991.

MARGERISON, Michael Royle Wrose Health Centre, Kings Road, Wrose, Bradford BD2 1QG Tel: 01274 493623 — MB ChB 1962 Birm.

MARGERISON, Neil James Barnet Healthcare Trust, Barnet Hospital, Wellhouse Lane, Barnet EN5 3DN Tel: 020 8216 4640 Fax: 020 8216 4595 — MB BS 1979 Lond.; MA Camb. 1977; MRCPsych 1984. (King's Coll. Hosp.) Cons. Psychiat. Barnet Healthcare Trust. Prev: Sen. Regist. Middlx. Hosp. Lond. & Napsbury Hosp.; Regist. (Psychiat.) Maudsley Hosp. Lond.

MARGERRISON, Charles David Department of Histopathology & Morbid Anatomy, Bradford Royal Infirmary, Bradford BD9 6RJ Tel: 01274 542200; 19 Wilmer Drive, Heaton, Bradford BD9 4AR — MRCS Eng. LRCP Lond. 1965. (Leeds) Clin. Asst. (Histopath. & Morbid Anat.) Bradford Roy. Infirm.; Lect. (Path.) Sch. Med. Sci. Univ. Bradford.

MARGETTS, Betty Muriel (retired) The Horseman's Cottage, Milton St., Polegate BN26 5RW Tel: 01323 870394 — MB BS 1942 Lond.; MRCS Eng. LRCP Lond. 1941; DCH Eng. 1947.

MARGETTS, George 44 Broomfield Drive, Billingshurst RH14 9TN Tel: 01403 783214 Fax: 01403 782314 — MB BS 1963 Lond.; BPharm Lond. 1955, MSc 1960; MRCS Eng. LRCP Lond. 1963; FFPM RCP (UK) 1989. (Univ. Coll. Hosp.)

MARGETTS, Jane Patricia 44 Broomfield Drive, Billingshurst RH14 9TN — MB BS 1996 Newc.

MARGETTS, Lyn Janet Department of Anaesthesia, Bristol Royal Infirmary, Marlborough Street, Bristol BS2 8HW — MB ChB 1993 Bristol.

MARGETTS, Mr Michael John Hospital of St Cross, Barby Road, Rugby CV22 5PX Tel: 01788 545235 Fax: 01788 545204; Leazes End, Paddox Court, Rugby Road, Kilsby, Rugby CV23 8XX — MB BS 1979 Lond.; BSc (Physics in Med.) Lond. 1975; MCh (Orth.) Liverp. 1988; FRCS Ed. (Orth.) 1990; FRCS Ed. 1983; MRCS Eng. LRCP Lond. 1978. (Guy's) Cons. Orthop. Surg. Univ. Hosps. Coventry & Warks. NHS Trust. Socs: Fell. BOA; BMA; (Sec.) Rugby & Dist. Med. Soc. Prev: Regist. (Orthop.) Alder Hey Childr. Hosp. Liverp. & S.port & Formby Dist. Gen. Hosp.; Regist. (Orthop.) Walton & Fazakerley Hosps. Liverp.; Regist. Rotat. (Orthop.) Hammersmith & Cuckfield Hosps.

MARGHOOB, Mashkoor Ahmed (retired) 6A Hatchgate Gardens, Burnham, Slough SL1 8DD Tel: 01628 664698 — MB BS 1954 Karachi; DTCD Wales 1961; DTM & H Eng. 1960. Prev: GP Slough & Dist.

MARGHOOB, Mohammad Saad 6A Hatchgate Gardens, Burnham, Slough SL1 8DD — MB BChir Camb. 1986; MA Camb. 1987, MB BChir Camb. 1986. Resid. Anaesthesiol. Stoneybrook Hosp. NY, USA. Prev: SHO (Neurol. & Med.) OldCh. Hosp. Romford; SHO (A & E) P.ss Alexandra Hosp. Harlow.

MARGINSON, John Edwin Windward Group Practice, 68 Worsley Road, Worsley, Manchester M28 2SN Tel: 0161 794 1603 Fax: 0161 794 2371 — MB BS 1976 Lond.; MRCS Eng. LRCP Lond. 1976; MRCGP 1980; DRCOG 1979. (Guy's)

MARGISON, Frank Richard Department of Psychotherapy, Gaskell House, Manchester Royal Infirmary, Swinton Grove, Manchester M13 0EW Tel: 0161 273 2762 Fax: 0161 273 4876 Email: frankm@psy.cmht.nwest.nhs.uk — MB ChB 1974 Liverp.; MSc Manch. 1981; MRCPsych 1978. Cons. Psychother. Gaskell Hse. Manch. Roy. Infirm.; Mem. NW Inst. Dynamic Psychother. Socs: Brit. Psychol. Soc. Prev: Lect. (Psychiat.) Univ. Manch.; Sen. Regist. (Psychiat.) Univ. Hosp. S. Manch.

MARGO, Andrew Miles Goodmayes Hospital, Barley Lane, Ilford IG3 8XJ Tel: 020 8970 8439 Fax: 020 8970 5702 — MB BCh 1970 Witwatersrand; BSc (Med.) Witwatersrand 1967; FRCPsych 1987, M 1975. (Witwatersrand) Cons. Psychiat. Goodmayes Hosp. Lond. Prev: Sen. Regist. Maudsley Hosp. Lond.

MARGOLIS, Simon 25 St John Street, Manchester M3 4DT Email: simarg@mc.mail — MB ChB 1986 Manch.; BSc St And. 1983. Private GP.

MARGUERIE, Christopher Patrick Rheumatology Unit, Warwick Hospital, Lakin Road, Warwick CV34 5BN Tel: 01926 495321 Fax: 01926 482615 — MB BS 1983 Lond.; BSc (1st cl. Hons.) Lond. 1980, MB BS 1983; MRCP (UK) 1986; FRCP 1998. (Char. Cross) Cons. Phys. Med. & Rheum. Warwick Hosp. Prev: Sen. Regist. (Rheum.) St. Mary's, Char. Cross & Qu. Mary's Hosps. Lond.; ARC Research Fell. Rheum. Unit. Hammersmith Hosp. Lond.; Regist. (Rheum.) Hammersmith Hosp. Lond.

MARGULIES, Herman Hersch 25 High Sheldon, Sheldon Avenue, London N6 4NJ Tel: 020 8348 9473 — MD 1936 Masaryk Univ. Brno; MRCS Eng. LRCP Lond. 1946. (Masaryk Univ. Brno) Socs: BMA. Prev: Med. Off. i/c E.M.S. Hosp. Winchester; Asst. Med. Off. Hackney Hosp. (LCC); Non-Res. Cas. Off. Ashford Co. Hosp.

MARIEN

MARIEN, Brian James King Edward VII Hospital, Midhurst GU29 0BL Tel: 01730 812341 Fax: 01730 816333; Dumpford Farm House, Trotton, Petersfield GU31 5JN Tel: 01730 821309 Fax: 01730 821193 — MB BS 1977 Lond.; MSc (Health Psychol.) Univ. Surrey; MRCGP 1995; DCH Eng. 1980; DRCOG 1979. (St. Bart.) Med. Off. (Pain & Rehabil.) King Edwd. VII Hosp. Midhurst; Sen. Clin. Med. Off. St Bart's Hosp. Dept. of Psychol Med. Prev: GP Midhurst; SHO (Rotat.) St. Richard's Hosp. Chichester; Ho. Phys. Wexham Pk. Hosp. Slough.

MARIGOLD, James Henry Salisbury District Hospital, Salisbury SP2 8BJ Tel: 01722 336262; Saunton House, Upper Wooodford, Salisbury SP4 6PA Tel: 01722 782374 — BM BCh 1973 Oxf.; MA Lond. 1972, MSc 1982; DM Oxf. 1984, BM BCh 1973; FRCP Lond. 1993; MRCP (UK) 1977. Cons. Phys. Special Responsib. for Elderly Salisbury Dist. Hosp. Socs: Med. Res. Soc.; Brit. Soc. Gastroenterol.; Brit. Geriat. Soc. Prev: Cons. Phys. Special Responsibil. Elderly & Sen. Regist. (Gen. Med.) St. Thos. Hosp. Lond.

MARIMON ORTIZ DE ZARATE, Miguel Scarborough Hospital, Woodlands Drive, Scarborough YO12 6QL — LMS 1987 Bilbao.

MARINAKI, Paulina House 23 Western Court, 100 University Avenue, Glasgow G12 8SQ — Ptychio Iatrikes 1989 Athens.

MARINAKIS, Ioannis Block 5, Friars Field Nurses Home, Friars Road, Newport NP20 4EZ — Ptychio Iatrikes 1988 Athens.

MARINKER, Professor Marshall Leonard, OBE 6A Middleton Grove, London N7 9LU Tel: 020 7607 3139 Fax: 020 7607 4589 Email: mmarinker@compuserve.com — MB BS 1956 Lond.; Hon. MD Tampere, Finland 1982; FRCGP 1971, M 1966. (Middlx.) Vis. Prof. Gen. Pract. UMDS Guy's & St. Thos. Hosp. Lond.; Med. Educat. & Health Policy Adviser MSD Ltd.; Chairm. R & D Comm. High Security Psychiat. Servs. Commiss. Bd. NHSE. Prev: Prof. Gen. Pract. Univ. Leicester; Sen. Lect. (Gen. Pract.) St. Mary's Hosp. Med. Sch. Lond.; Chairm. Educat. Div. RCGP.

MARINO, Anthony 3 Redditch Road, Hopwood, Alvechurch, Birmingham B48 7TL — MB BS 1990 Lond.

MARIOTTI, Paola Top Flat, 37 Woodsome Road, London NW5 1SA Tel: 020 7485 7269 — State DMS 1976 Milan. Hon. Cons. Lond. Clinic Psychonalysis. Socs: Assoc. Mem. Brit. Psychoanalyt. Soc.

MARISWAMY, Saligrama Boranna Feeny Medical Centre, Main Street, Feeny, Londonderry BT47 4TD Tel: 028 7778 1501 Fax: 028 7778 1925; 101 Greystone Road, Limavady BT49 0ND — MB BS 1974 Mysore. (Kasturba Medical College Manipal) GP Feeny Med. Centre Lond.derry. Socs: Irish Coll. Gen. Pract.

MARIZ, Segundo Dimitri Manuel 69 Broomfield Rise, Abbots Langley WD5 0HH — MD 1995 Liege.

MARJOT, David Henry, Surg. Cdr. RN Retd. 16 Walton Lane, Weybridge KT13 8NF Tel: 01932 831913 — MB BS 1953 Lond.; MRCS Eng. LRCP Lond. 1952; FRCPsych 1981, M 1971; DPM Eng. 1960. (St. Mary's) Cons. Psychiat. Kaleidoscope Project, and Rivendell Health Care Chaucer Project; Hon. Cons. Psychiat. BRd.moor Hosp. Socs: Fell. Roy. Soc. Med.; BMA; Soc. Study Addic. Prev: Cons. Psychiat. (Alcohol & Addict. Unit) St. Bernard's Hosp. S.all; Cons. Psychiat. W. Middlx. Hosp. Isleworth; Cons. Psychiat. RN Hosp. Haslar.

MARJOT, Robert Royal United Hospital, Bath BA1 3NG Tel: 01225 825057 Fax: 01225 825061 — MB BS 1983 Lond.; FRCA 1988. (St. Mary's) Cons. Anaesth. Roy. United Hosp. Bath. Prev: Sen. Regist. Rotat. (Anaesth.) Leicester Hosp.; Sen. Regist. (Anaesth.) Perth, Austral.; Regist. (Anaesth.) King's Coll. Hosp. Lond.

MARK, Catherine Teresa The New Surgery, Buxton Road, Tideswell, Buxton SK17 8NS Tel: 01298 871292 Fax: 01298 872580; Summerhill, Nether Padley, Grindleford, Sheffield S32 2HE — MB BS 1972 Lond. (St. Mary's)

MARK, Mr Ian Reeves 69 Canterbury House, Royal St., London SE1 7LW — MB BS 1984 Delhi; FRCS Glas. 1990.

MARK, John Frederick Fort Corblets, Alderney GY9 3YJ — MB BCh BAO 1942 Belf.; DObst RCOG 1951. (Belf.) Socs: BMA & Kenya Med. Assn.

MARK, John Stephen Summerhill, Nether Padley, Grindleford, Sheffield S32 2HE — MRCS Eng. LRCP Lond. 1971; FFA RCS Eng. 1980. (St. Mary's) Cons. Anaesth. N. Derbysh. Roy. Hosp. Chesterfield. Prev: Sen. Regist. (Anaesth.) Avon HA; Regist. (Anaesth.) Sheff. AHA; Ho. Off. Qu. Eliz. II Hosp. Welwyn Gdn. City.

MARK, Julian Peter Department of Anaesthesia, Harrogate District Hospital, Lancaster Park Road, Harrogate HG2; 1 Appleby Grove, Knaresborough HG5 9NQ — MB ChB 1994 Leeds; BSc (Hons.) Leeds 1991. SHO (Anaesth.) Harrogate Dist. Hosp.

MARK, Margaret Clare 30 Cadogan Park, Belfast BT9 6HH Tel: 028 669606 — MB BCh BAO 1971 Belf.

MARK, Prunella Elizabeth 515 Wilbraham Road, Chorlton, Manchester M21 0UF Tel: 0161 881 6120 — MB ChB 1967 Bristol; MFHom 1990; MRCGP 1978. (Bristol) Prev: Ho. Phys. Frenchay Hosp. Bristol; Ho. Surg. Bristol Gen. Hosp.

MARK, Stephen Dwight 86B St Michaels Hill, Kingsdown, Bristol BS2 8BQ — MB ChB 1983 Otago.

MARKANDAY, Asha 35 Wessex Drive, Hatch End, Pinner HA5 4PX Tel: 020 8421 1980 — MB BS Calcutta 1962; DTM & H Eng. 1965. Clin. Asst. (Rheum. & Disabil. Servs.) Amersham Gen. Hosp.; Med. Acupunc. Middlx. Socs: Foundat. Mem. BBTS; BMAS. Prev: Med. Asst. N. Lond. Blood Transfus. Centre Edgware; Regist. (Path.) Edgware Gen. Hosp.; Regist. & SHO (Path.)) Guy's Hosp. Lond.

MARKANDOO, Puvaneswary 26 Homewood Drive, Whitehaven CA28 8JG — MB BS 1977 Madras; FRCS Ed. 1984.

MARKANDYA, Om Prakash (retired) 31 Flower Lane, London NW7 2JG — LRCP LRCS 1941 Ed.; LRCP LRCS Ed. LRFPS Glas. 1941; DMSA Ed. 1963. Prev: SCMO Berks. AHA. Sen. Med. Off. Uganda.

MARKAR, Hameen Rizvi Weller wing, Bedford General Hospital, Kempston Road, Bedford MK42 9DJ Tel: 01234 792006 — MB BS 1975 Sri Lanka; MPhil Edin 1991; FRCPsych 2000; FRCP 1999 Edinborough. Cons. Psychiat. Weller Wing, Bedford Gen. Hosp., Kempston Rd., Bedford; Clin. Dir. Beds. & Luton Community NHS Trust, Charter Ho., Luton; Assoc. Lect. Univ. Dept. of Psychiat., Addenbrooks Hosp. Camb. Socs: Examr. Roy. Coll. of Psychiat.s; Apptd. Doctor - Ment. Health Commiss. Prev: Chief of Psychiat., Bermuda; Cons. Psychiat. E. Herts. NHS Trust; Sen. Regist. Fulbourn & Addenbrookes Hosp. Camb.

MARKAR, Therese Nimal Hillend Hospital, St Albans Tel: 01727 55555; 245 Sandpit Lane, St Albans AL4 0BU Tel: 01727 812582 — MB BS 1976 Ceylon. SHO Hillend Hosp. St. Albans. Prev: Regist. (Geriat. Med. & Dermat.) P'boro. Dist. Gen. Hosp.

MARKBY, David Puckle Waterfront Garden Surgery, Jones Lane, Hythe, Southampton SO45 6AW Tel: 02380 841841 Fax: 02380 848084; Curtle House, Beaulieu, Brockenhurst SO42 7YB Tel: 01590 612451 — MB BS 1966 Lond.; MRCS Eng. LRCP Lond. 1966; MRCGP 1971; DObst RCOG 1970. (St. Thos.) Maj. RAMC (V). Prev: SHO Soton. Gen. Hosp., St. Mary's Hosp. Portsmouth & Poole Gen.; Hosp.

MARKER, Alison Jean Tel: 01223 217169; Truscott House, Burrell Way, Balsham, Cambridge CB1 6DY Tel: 01223 894036 — MB ChB 1986 Glas.; BSc Glas. 1983; MRCPath 1993; MD Lond. 1997. (Glasgow) Cons. Histopath. & Cytopath. Addenbrooke's NHS Trust. Socs: Assn. Clin. Path. & Internat. Assn. Path.; Brit. Soc. Clin. Cytol.; BMA. Prev: Cons. in Histopath. & Cytopath. S. Kent Hosps. NHS Trust; Lect. (Histopath.) King's Coll. Sch. Med. & Dent.; Regist. (Histopath.) W.. Infirm. Glas.

MARKER, Harold Royston (retired) 100 Springhall Lane, Lower Penn, Wolverhampton WV4 4TJ Tel: 0190238991 — MB BS 1954 Lond.; MRCS Eng. LRCP Lond. 1953. Med. Off. Roy. Sch. Wolverhampton; Med. Off. GB Disabled Olympic Team. Prev: Clin. Asst. (Diabetes) Roy. Hosp. & Eye Infirm. Wolverhampton.

MARKESON, Vivienne Ester 1 Beechpark Way, Watford WD17 3TY — MB BS 1973 Lond.

MARKEY, Andrew Clive St. Johns Institute of Dermatology, St. Thomas Hospital, Lambeth Palace Road, London SE1 7EH Tel: 020 7928 9292 Fax: 020 7922 8314; The Lister Hospital, Chelsea Bridge Road, London SW1W 8RH Tel: 020 7730 1219 Fax: 020 7730 1368 — MB ChB 1980 Manch.; MD Manch. 1990; MRCP (UK) 1984; T(M) 1991. Cons. Dermat. & Sen. Lect. (Dermat. Surg. & Laser Unit) St Johns Inst. Dermat. Lond. Socs: Fell. Amer. Soc. Dermat. Surg.; Fell. Amer. Coll. MOHS Micrographic Surg. and Cutaneous Oncol. Prev: Asst. Clin. Prof. (Dermat. Surg. & Laser Unit) Univ. Calif.; Sen. Regist. (Dermat.) St Johns Inst. Lond.; Regist. (Dermat. & Med.) Guy's Hosp. Lond.

MARKEY, Brendan Michael Shotton Lane Surgery, 38 Shotton Lane, Shotton, Deeside CH5 1QW Tel: 01244 812094 Fax: 01244 811728 — MB ChB 1979 Liverp.; MRCGP 1984; DRCOG 1982.

MARKEY, Geraldine Mary Haematology Department, Belfast City Hospital, Belfast BT9 7AB Tel: 01232 329251; 23 Deramore Drive, Belfast BT9 5JR — MB BCh BAO 1962 NUI; BSc NUI 1964, MD 1991; FRCPath 1982, M 1970. Assoc. Specialist (Haemat.) Belf. City Hosp. Prev: Research Assoc. & Sen. Regist. Belf. City Hosp.; SHO (Clin. Path.) Guy's Hosp. Lond.

MARKEY, Greg Stephen 2 Burghley Court, Stamford PE9 1EF — MB BS 1987 Lond.; MRCP (UK) 1993; FRCA 1994; DA (UK) 1990. Regist. (Anaesth.) Hammersmith Hosp. Lond. Prev: SHO (Med.) Gloucester Roy. Hosp.; SHO (Anaesth.) Roy. Berk. Hosp. Reading.

MARKEY, Paul Gerard Acorn Surgery, 39 Junction Lane, St Helens WA9 3JN Tel: 01744 813065 Fax: 01744 819441; 44 Forest Grove, Eccleston Park, Prescot L34 2RZ Tel: 0151 426 5459 — MRCS Eng. LRCP Lond. 1974. (Liverp.) Area Surg. St. John's Amb. Assn. St. Helens & Knowsley. Socs: Small Pract. Assn. Prev: St. John's Ambul. Assn., Bootle.

MARKEY, Timothy Edward Harcourt Medical Centre, Crane Bridge Road, Salisbury SP2 7TD Tel: 01722 333214 Fax: 01722 421643 — MB BS 1979 Lond.; MRCGP 1983; D.Occ.Med. RCP Lond. 1996; DRCOG 1982. (Roy. Free) Prev: Trainee GP Salisbury VTS.

MARKHAM, Alexander Fred West Riding Medical Research Trust, Molecular Medicine Unit, St James' University Hospital, University of Leeds, Leeds LS9 7TF Tel: 0113 206 5681 Fax: 0113 244 4475 Email: msj6afm@stjames.leeds.ac.uk; 307 Market Street, Droylsden, Manchester M43 7EA — MB BS 1985 Lond.; PhD Birm. 1974, BSc 1971, DSc 1992; MRCP (UK) 1994; FRCPath 1996, M 1989. Prof. Med. St. Jas. Univ. Hosp. Leeds; Hon. Cons. Phys. St. Jas. Univ. Hosp. Leeds.

MARKHAM, Bruce Herbert (retired) 15 Nightingale Road, Pakefield, Lowestoft NR33 7AX — MB BS 1954 Lond.; MRCS Eng. LRCP Lond. 1954; DObst RCOG 1957. Med. Off. HM Prison Blundeston. Prev: Cas. Off. Norf. & Norwich Hosp.

MARKHAM, Christopher Ridley (retired) 97 Great North Road, Brunton Park, Newcastle upon Tyne NE3 5LY Tel: 0191 236 2109 — MB BS 1952 Durh. Prev: Princip. GP Newc.

MARKHAM, D Clare Chapel Row Surgery, The Avenue, Bucklebury, Reading RG7 6NS Tel: 01189 713252 Fax: 01189 714161 — MB BS 1977 Lond. (King's College)

MARKHAM, Mr David Eric 1'2 Manor Close, Cheadle Hume, Cheadle SK8 7DJ Tel: 0161 485 3633 — MB ChB 1961 Sheff.; FRCS Eng. 1967. (Sheff.) Chairm. & Pres. of The Med. Defence Union Ltd. Socs: Fell. BOA. Prev: Cons. Orthop. Surg. Manch. Roy. Infirm.; Hon. Lect. (Clin. Orthop.) Univ. Manch.; Lect. Univ. Dept. Orthop. Roy. Infirm. Sheff.

MARKHAM, Deborah Hassana Department of General Surgery, Frenchay Hospital, Frenchay Park Road, Bristol BS16 1LE Tel: 01272 701212; Yew Tree Cottage, Marsha Lane, Burton, Chippenham SN14 7LP Tel: 01454 218146 — MB BS 1991 Lond.; LLB Soton. 1986. SHO (Gen. Surg.) Frenchay Hosp. Bristol. Socs: BMA. Prev: SHO (Neurosurg., Gen. Surg. & Orthop.) Frenchay Hosp. Bristol.

MARKHAM, Derrian Hilary Alice Louise 16 Bignal Drive, Leicester Forest East, Leicester LE3 3QE — BM BCh 1989 Oxf.

MARKHAM, Gillian Christine Radiology Department, Central Middlesex Hospital, Acton Lane, London NW10 7NS Tel: 020 8965 5733; 7 Meon Road, London W3 8AN Tel: 020 8993 3789 Email: gill.markham@talk21.com — MB ChB 1970 Liverp.; MRCS Eng. LRCP Lond. 1970; FRCR 1975; DMRD 1974; DObst RCOG 1972. (Liverp.) Cons. Radiologist N. W. Lond. Hosp.s Trust Centr. Middlx. Hosp. Lond. Socs: St. Helens Med. Soc.; (Vice-Pres.) Liverp. Med. Inst. Prev: Cons. Radiol. St. Helens & Knowsley AHA; Sen. Regist. (Radiol.) Roy. S.. Hosp. Liverp.; Ho. Off. (O & G) BRd.green Hosp. Liverp.

MARKHAM, John Edward ThE Elizabeth Courtauld Surgery, Factory Lane West, Halstead CO9 1EX Tel: 01787 475944 Fax: 01787 474506 — MB ChB 1981 Sheff.; DRCOG 1984.

***MARKHAM, Jospeh Edric Robin** 22 Lorne House, Weld Place, New Southgate, London N11 1QY Tel: 020 8361 6257 — MB BS 1981 West Indies.

MARKHAM, Julia Jane Argyle Surgery, 128 Argyle Road, Ealing, London W13 8ER Fax: 020 8991 2103 — MB BS 1989 Lond.

MARKHAM, Marilyn Victoria Berryfield House, Newton Farm Court, Sutton on the Forest, York YO61 1DZ — MB ChB 1974 Dundee.

MARKHAM, Mr Nicholas Ian North Devon District Hospital, Raleigh Park, Barnstaple EX31 4JB Tel: 01271 322577; Youldon House, Goodleigh, Barnstaple EX32 7NX — MB BS 1977 Lond.; MS Lond. 1986; FRCS Eng. 1983; FRCS Ed. 1982; MRCS Eng. LRCP Lond. 1977. (St. Bart.) Cons. Surg. N. Devon Health Care Trust & N. Devon Dist. Hosp. Prev: Lect. (Surg.) Roy. Free Hosp. Sch. Med. Univ. Lond.; Vis. Lect. (Surg.) Chinese Univ. & P. of Wales Hosp., Hong Kong.

MARKHAM, Rachel Ann 18 Lyndhurst Grove, Stone ST15 8TP Tel: 01785 815938 — MB ChB 1995 Manch. SHO (Anaesth.) N.wick Pk. Hosp. Harrow Middlx.

MARKHAM, Mr Richard Hugh Clement Litfield House, Clifton Down, Bristol BS8 3LS Tel: 0117 974 6421 Fax: 0117 973 3303 Email: markham@gifford.co.uk — MB BS Lond. 1969; FRCOphth 1989; FRCS Eng. 1975; MRCP (UK) 1974; FRCP 2000. (St. Bart.) Cons. Eye Surg. Bristol Eye Hosp. Socs: Fell. Roy. Soc. Med. Prev: Clin. Dir. (Ophth.) United Bristol Health Care NHS Trust; Sen. Regist. Eye Dept. St. Thos. Hosp. Lond.

MARKHAM, Robert John O'Sullivan Gillygate Surgery, 28 Gillygate, York YO31 7WQ Tel: 01904 624404 Fax: 01904 651813; Tel: 01347 810618 — MB ChB 1974 Dundee; MRCP (UK) 1980; DRCOG 1982. Exec. Comm. Chairm., Selby & York PCT. Socs: (Sec.) York & Selby Dist. GP Comm. Prev: Sec. York & Selby Dist. GP Committ.; Chairm., York PCG.

MARKHAM, Sara Linden Cottage, North Bovey, Newton Abbot TQ13 8RA — MB BS 1985 Lond.; LMSSA 1984. Staff Anaesth. Roy. Devon & Exeter Hosp. Prev: SHO (Anaesth.) Roy. Devon & Exeter Hosp. & High Wycombe Hosp.; Trainee GP Oxf. VTS.

MARKHAM, Sarah Jean 28 Easthorpe, Southwell NG25 0HY — MB ChB 1977 Sheff.; FFA RCS Eng. 1982. Cons. Anaesth. Centr. Notts. HA. Prev: Regist. (Anaesth.) Truro; SHO (Anaesth.) Nottm.; Ho. Off. (Gen. Med.) Leicester Roy. Infirm.

MARKIDES, Vias National Heart & Lung Institute, Imperial College School of Medicine, St Mary's Hospital, Praed Street, Paddington, London W2 1NY Tel: 020 7886 5131 Email: v.markides@virgin.net — MB BS 1992 Lond.; MRCP (UK) 1995. Specialist Regist. (Cardiol.) Hammersmith Hosp. Lond. Prev: Specialist Regist. (Cardiol.) Hammersmith Hosp.; Specialist Regist. (Cardiol.) St. Mary's Hosp. Lond.; Research Fell. IC St Thoma's Hosp.

MARKIEWICZ, Michael 23 Shirehall Close, London NW4 2QR Tel: 020 8202 1280 Fax: 020 8746 8635 Email: drlittle@bigfoot.com — MB BS 1982 Lond.; BSc (Hons.) Lond. 1979, MB BS 1982; MRCP (UK) 1986; FRCPCH 1997. (St Mary's Hospital London) Cons. Paediat. Chelsea and W.minster Hosp.; Hon. Sen. Clin. Lect. Imperial Coll. Schoool of Med. Lond. Prev: Sen. Lect. Child Health Imperial Coll. Lond.; Sen. Regist. (Paediat.) St. Mary's, Roy. Lond. & N.wick Pk. Hosps.; Clin. Lect. (Paediat.) Univ. Coll. Hosp. & Whittington Hosp. Lond.

MARKILLIE, Ronald Eric Douglas Swallowfield Park, Swallowfield, Reading RG7 1TG Tel: 01734 886163 — MB BS 1940 Lond.; MB BS Lond. 1939. DPM 1940; MRCS Eng. LRCP Lond. 1939; FRCPsych 1971. (St. Thos.) Hon. Cons. Psychiat. Leeds RHB. Socs: Assoc. Mem. Brit. Psychoanalyt. Soc. Prev: Cons. Psychiat. Leeds RHB; Lect. (Psychiat.) Univ. Leeds; Asst. Psychiat. Tavistock Clinic, Lond.

MARKLAND, Mr Colin George 183 Heene Road, Worthing BN11 4NN — BM BCh 1981 Oxf.; MA Oxf. 1978, BM BCh 1981; FRCS Eng. 1987; MFPM RCP Lond. 1993; Dip. Pharm. Med. RCP (UK) 1992. Sen. Med. Dir. Euro. Ligand, Pharmaeut. Inter. Inc. Kings Hill, Kent. Prev: Med. Dir. Rhône-Poulenc Rorer Ltd. E.bourne.; Head, Product Safety & Med. Informat. Schering Health Care Ltd. Burgess Hill W. Sussex; Regist. (Cardiothoracic Surg.) Middlx. & St. Geo. Hosp.

MARKLAND, William Edric Donald, VRD (retired) Romney Hoy, Madeira Road, Littlestone-on-Sea, New Romney TN28 8QP Tel: 01797 363403 — BM BCh 1948 Oxf.; MA Oxf. 1949. Med. Off. RNLI Littlestone-on-Sea. Prev: Ho. Surg. Accid. Serv. Radcliffe Infirm. Oxf.

MARKMAN, Philip (retired) Bandle, 1 Southern Crescent, Bramhall, Stockport SK7 3AQ Tel: 0161 439 5133 — MB ChB 1952 Cape Town; MD Cape Town 1981; FCP(SA) 1957; FRCP Lond.

MARKOS

1975, M 1958; FRCP Ed. 1973, M 1959. Prev: Cons. Phys. N. Manch. Gen. & N.. Hosps. Manch.

MARKOS, Atef Rizk Michael Staffordshire General Hospitals NHS Trust, Stafford ST16 3SA Tel: 01785 230264 Fax: 01785 230259; Tel: 01785 252600 — MB BCh 1977 Ain Shams; FRCOG 2000; MRCOG 1988. Cons. Genitourin. & Sexual Health Med. Staffs. Gen. Hosps., NHS Trust. Socs: Assoc. Mem. of RCP (Lond.); Med. Soc. Study VD; Brit. Soc. Colpos. & Cerv. Path. Prev: Sen. Regist. (Genitourin. Med.) N. Staffs. Hosp.; Regist. (Genitourin. Med.) Coventry & Warwick Hosp.; Regist. (Obst.& Gyn.) Walsgrave Hosp. Coventry.

***MARKOSE, George** 12 Montrouge Crescent, Epsom KT17 3PD — MB BS 1994 Lond.

MARKOSE, Varghese Madaparampil 12 Montrouge Crescent, Epsom Downs, Epsom KT17 3PD Tel: 01737 355952 — MB BS 1967 Bangalor; MB BS Bangalore 1967. (Bangalore) Prev: Regist. Hartwood Hosp. Shotts; SHO (Med.) Perth Roy. Infirm. & Morriston Hosp. Swansea.

MARKOVA, Ivana University of Hull, Faculty of Health, Coniston House, East Riding Campus, Willerby, Hull HU10 6NS Tel: 01482 466960 Email: ismarkova@psych.hi-net.co.uk; 21 Saxon Rise, Beverley HU17 7SN Tel: 01482 872355 Fax: 01482 872355 — MB ChB 1985 Glas.; MRCPsych 1990; M.Phil (Hist. & Philosophy of Sci.) Camb. 1996; MD Glas. 1998. (Glasgow) Sen. Lect. in Psychiat. Univ. of Hull; Hon. Cons. in Psychiat. Dept. of Psychol. Med. Hull Roy. Infirm. Prev: Cons. & Hon. Sen. Lect. (Psychiat.) P.ss Alexandra Hosp. Harlow; Sen. Regist. (Psychiat.) Fulbourn Hosp. Camb.; Regist. (Psychiat.) Fulbourn Hosp. Camb.

MARKOWE, Hugh Leonard John Department of Health, Skipton House, 80 London Road, London SE1 6LH Email: hugh.markowe@doh.gsi.gov.uk — MB BS 1977 Lond.; MSc Epidemiol. (Distinc.) Lond. 1981; BSc (1st cl. Hons.) Lond. 1974; FFPHM 1999. (Univ. Coll. Hosp.) Dir. Centr. Health Monitoring Unit Dept. Health, Lond.; Hon. Sen. Lect. (Epidemiol. & Pub. Health) UCL. Prev: Lect. (Clin. Epidemiol.) Lond. Sch. Hyg. & Trop. Med.

MARKS, Alexandra Jane 40 Ravensworth Road, London NW10 5NR — MB BS 1993 Lond.

MARKS, Annabella Mary Duchess of Kent House, Dellwood Hospital, Liebenrood Road, Reading RG30 2DX Tel: 0118 955 0457; Dunsden Lodge, Sonning Eye, Reading RG4 6TP Tel: 0118 969 2264 — MB BS 1972 Lond.; 1974 MRCP Lond.; 1979 FRCP Lond.; 1996 FRCP Lond.; 1969 BSc (Hue) London. (Guy's) Cons. Palliat. Med. Duchess of Kent Hse. Dellwood Hosp. Reading. Prev: Sen. Regist. (Radiother.) Mt. Vernon Hosp. N.wood.; Regist. (Radiother.) St. Bart. Hosp. Lond.; SHO Brompton Hosp. Lond.

MARKS, Anthony Peter 27 Westdown Road, Seaford BN25 2LD Tel: 01323 893804 Fax: 01323 893804 Email: anthonymarks@compuserve.com — MB BS 1958 Lond. (St. Bart.) GP (s/i occupat. health, med. acupunc.) & Treasury Med. Off. Socs: Brit. Med. Acupunct. Soc.; E.bourne Med. Soc. Prev: Ho. Surg. (O & G) Luton & Dunstable Hosp. Luton; Ho. Phys. Metrop. Hosp.; Sq. Ldr. RAF Med. Br.

MARKS, Anthony Simon Eagle House Surgery, 291 High Street, Ponders End, Enfield EN3 4DN Tel: 020 8351 1000 Fax: 020 8351 1007; 11 Alberon Gardens, London NW11 0AG — BSc (Hons.) Lond. 1976, MB BS 1979; MRCGP 1983; DRCOG 1982; DCH RCP Lond. 1983. (King's Coll. Hosp.) Prev: Trainee GP Centr. Middlx. Hosp. Lond. VTS; Ho. Surg. Bromley Hosp. Lond.; Ho. Phys. King's Coll. Hosp. Lond.

MARKS, Mr Christopher Guy The Guildford Nuffield Hospital, Stirling Road, Guildford GU2 7RF; White Beech, Chidding Fold, Godalming GU8 4XX — MB BChir 1968 Camb.; MChir Camb. 1979; FRCS Eng. 1971; MRCS Eng. LRCP Lond. 1967. (St. Thos.) Cons. Surg. Roy. Surrey Co. Hosp. Guildford; Vis. Prof. of Surgic. Oncol. Univ. of Surrey. Socs: Fell. Roy. Soc. Med.; BMA. Prev: Sen. Regist. (Surg.) Radcliffe Infirm. Oxf.; Regist. (Surg.) Soton. Gen. Hosp.; Resid. Surg. Off. St. Mark's Hosp. Lond.

MARKS, Clifton Michael Stamford Hill Group Practice, 2 Egerton Road, Stamford Hill, London N16 6UA Tel: 020 8800 1000 Fax: 020 8880 2402; 23 Bourne Avenue, London N14 6PA Tel: 020 8882 9963 Email: clifton.marks@ukgateway.net — MB BS 1982 Lond.; MRCGP 1995; DFFP 1994; DRCOG 1984. (Middlx.) Med. Off. (Family Plann. & Sub Fertil..) Enfield Community Care Trust; Tutor (Gen. Pract.) Med. Coll. St. Bartholewmews Hosp. & Roy. Lond.

Hosp.; Hon. Clin. Lect. Dept. Gen. Pract. QMW Coll. Univ. Lond.; Med. Adviser; Metrop. Housing Trust. Prev: Med. Off. Brook Advisory Centres; SHO (Dermat.) Middlx. Hosp. Lond.; Sen. Ho. Off. (O & G) Middlx. Hosp. & Hosp. for Wom. Lond.

MARKS, Colin Timothy Cyril The Surgery, 107 Brentwood Road, Romford RM1 2SH Tel: 01708 740244 Fax: 01708 731899; 14 Tudor Close, Chigwell IG7 5BG Tel: 020 8500 8232 — MB BS 1983 Lond.; MA Oxf. 1983; Cert. Family Plann. JCC 1985.

MARKS, David Ian Oncology Day Beds, Bristol Childrens Hospital, St Michaels Hill, Bristol BS2 8BJ Tel: 0117 928 5451 Fax: 0117 928 5682 Email: dmarks@nildram.co.uk; Tel: 0117 946 6396 — MB BS 1981 Melbourne; PhD Melbourne 1990; FRACP 1988. (University of Melbourne) Cons. in Haemat. & Bone Marrow Transpl.ation United Bristol Healthcare Trust. Socs: Clin. trials Comm.Brit. Soc. Bone Marrow Transpl.ation (Sec.); Brit. Soc. of haemetology. Prev: Asst. Prof. Div. of Hemat./Oncol. Hannemann Univ. Philadelphia; Hon. Sen. Regist. Haemat. Hammersmith Hosp.; Regist. Haemat. & Med. Oncol. Roy. Melbourne Hosp.

MARKS, Mr David Simon Royal Orthopaedic Hospital, Bristol Road, Northfield, Birmingham B31 2AP Tel: 0121 685 4085 Fax: 0121 685 4264; 3 Bellemere Road, Hampton-in-Arden, Solihull B92 0AN Tel: 01675 442283 Fax: 01675 443792 Email: david.smarks@talk21.com — MB BS 1985 Lond.; FRCS Eng. 1989; FRCS (Orth) 1996. (St. Bartholomews London) Cons. Orthopaedic Spinal Surg. Roy. Orthop. Hosp. Birm. & Birm. Childr. Hosp. Socs: Corr. Fell. Scoliosis Research Soc.; Brit. Scoliosis Soc.; Brit. Orthop. Assn. Prev: Wishbone & Dep. Trav. Fell.; Sen. Regist. Roy. Orthop. Hosp. Birm.

MARKS, Edward Newton (retired) Farne House, 30 Wheatlands Road E., Harrogate HG2 8PX Tel: 01423 504287 — MB ChB 1961 Liverp.; MB ChB (Distinc. Pub. Health) Liverp. 1961; MRCS Eng. LRCP Lond. 1950; MRCGP 1959. Prev: Regional Med. Off. DHSS.

MARKS, Frances Margarete (retired) 18 Quadrant Grove, London NW5 4JN — MB BS 1966 Lond.; MPhil Lond. 1974, BSc 1963, MB BS 1966; FRCPsych 1984, M 1973; DPM Eng. 1972. Prev: Cons. Child Psychiat. Lond. Hosp.

MARKS, Hannah Maude Rishworth (retired) 27 Castlegate Drive, Cockermouth CA13 9HD Tel: 01900 826608 — MB BCh BAO 1946 Dub.; MA Dub. 1997, BA 1942; MFCM RCP (UK) 1972; DPH Eng. 1970; DA Eng. 1956. Prev: Sen. Med. Off. (Community Child Health) E. Cumbria DHA.

MARKS, Professor Isaac Meyer Institute of Psychiatry, London SE5 8AF Tel: 020 7919 3365 Fax: 020 7740 5244 Email: i.marks@iop.bpmf.ac.uk — MB ChB Cape Town 1956; MD Cape Town 1963; FRCPsych 1976, M 1971; DPM Lond. 1963. Prof. Experim. Psychopath. Inst. Psychiat. Univ. Lond.; Dir. Clin. Computing Unit Inst. Psychiat. Univ. Lond.; Cons. Bethlem Roy. & Maudsley Hosp.

MARKS, Janet Mary (retired) 97 Burlington Court, Adderstone Crescent, Newcastle upon Tyne NE2 2HR Tel: 0191 281 0622 — BM BCh 1952 Oxf.; MA, DM Oxf. 1968, BM BCh 1952; FRCP Lond. 1972, M 1958. Prev: Sen. Lect. (Dermat.) Univ. Newc.

MARKS, Jeffrey Neville Flat 15, Elm Park Court, Elm Park Road, Pinner HA5 3LJ; Psychiatric Unit, Northwick Park Hospital, Harrow HA1 1UJ Tel: 020 8869 2307 Fax: 020 8869 2291 Email: jeffreymarks@bizonline.co.uk — MB ChB 1969 Manch; MB ChB Manch. 1969; MRCPsych 1973; DPM Manch. 1973; DPM Lond. 1972; FRCPsych 1995. (manchester) Cons. Psychiat. Harrow & Hillingdon NHS Healthcare Trust. Prev: Research Fell. (Psychiat.) Univ. Manch.; Hon. Sen. Regist. (Psychiat.) Univ. Hosp. S. Manch.; Regist. (Psychiat.) Manch. Roy. Infirm.

MARKS, Jeffrey Stanley (cons. rooms) Ryley Mount, 432 Buxton Road, Great Moor, Stockport SK2 7JQ Tel: 0161 483 9333; 53 Torkington Road, Gatley, Cheadle SK8 4PW Tel: 0161 428 3886 — BM BCh 1971 Oxf.; MA, BM BCh Oxf. 1971; FRCP Lond. 1991; MRCP (UK) 1974. (St. Thos.) Cons. Rheum. Stepping Hill Hosp. Stockport NHS Trust. Socs: Fell. Manch. Med. Soc.; Brit. Soc. for Rheum. Prev: Sen. Regist. (Rheumatol.) Manch. Roy. Infirm., Withington Hosp. Manch. & Wrightington Hosp.

MARKS, John (retired) The Dower, Bustlers Cottage, Duxford, Cambridge CB2 4RP Tel: 01223 833318 Fax: 01223 833318 — MB BS 1946 Lond.; MA Camb. 1949; MD Lond. 1949; FRCP Lond. 1972, M 1948; FRCPsych 1984, M 1977; FRCPath 1963. Prev: Elmore Research Stud. Univ. Camb.

MARKS, John Henry Brown Gables, Barnet Lane, Elstree, Borehamwood WD6 3RQ Tel: 020 8953 7687 Fax: 020 8953 7687 Email: johnmarks@browngables.demon.co.uk — MD Ed. 1974, MB ChB 1948; FRCGP 1975, M 1959; DObst RCOG 1953. Med. Dir. Nat. Med. Exam. Network. Socs: BMA (Ex-Chairm. of Counc.) & Assur. Med. Soc. (Mem. Counc.). Prev: Ho. Phys. & Ho. Surg. Wembley Hosp.; Ho. Surg. (Obst.) St. Martin's Hosp. Bath.

MARKS, Jonathan Emil Richard 15 Elm Park Court, Elm Park Road, Pinner HA5 3LJ — MB ChB 1995 Manch.

MARKS, Joseph (retired) 121 Heathwood Road, Cardiff CF14 4BJ Tel: 01222 336920 — MD Lond. 1949, MB BS (Hons.) 1940, Dipl. Bact. 1948; FRCP Lond. 1969, M 1941; FRCPath 1963. Prev: Dir., Tuberc. Ref. Laborat. Pub. Health Laborat. Serv.

MARKS, Kyla Anna Paddock Lodge, The Green, Hampton Court, East Molesey KT8 9BW — MB BS 1986 Lond.

MARKS, Leopold (retired) 20 Alexander Avenue, London NW10 3QS Tel: 020 8459 6860 — LRCPI & LM, LRCSI & LM 1945. Prev: Res. Med. Off. Roy. City Dub. Hosp.

MARKS, Linda Jane Disablement Services Centre, Royal National Orthopaedic Hospital Trust, Brockley Hill, Stanmore HA7 4LP Tel: 020 8954 0020 Fax: 020 8420 7439; Great Sarratt Hall Cottage, Sarratt, Rickmansworth WD3 4PD — MB BS 1973 Lond.; FRCP Lond. 1993; MRCP (UK) 1977. (Univ. Lond., Middlx. Hosp.) Cons. Rehabil. Med. Disablem. Serv. Centre Roy. Nat. Orthop. Hosp. Trust. Stanmore. Socs: (Ex-Pres.) Amputee Med. Rehabil. Soc.; Brit. Soc. Rehabil. Med.; Internat. Soc. Prosth.s & Orthotics. Prev: Sen. Med. Off. Disablem. Servs. Centre Roy. Nat. Orthop. Hosp. Trust Stanmore; Sen. Regist. (Rheumat.) Middlx. Hosp. Lond.; Regist. (Gen. Med.) Luton & Dunstable Hosp.

MARKS, Maurice Montie 9 Rowdon Avenue, Willesden, London NW10 2AJ Tel: 020 8459 2657 — LRCPI & LM, LRCSI & LM 1949. (RCSI) Prev: Ho. Surg. Ryhope Gen. Hosp. Nr. Sunderland; Sen. Res. O & G Off. St. Luke's Hosp. Bradford; Demonst. in Biol., Anat. & Physiol. Sch. of Surg. RCSI.

MARKS, Michael Francis David Place Medical Practice, 56 David Place, St Helier, Jersey JE1 4HY; La Plage Cottage, Rozel, St. Martin, Jersey JE3 6AN — MB BS 1969 Lond.; DObst RCOG 1974. (St. Mary's) Socs: BMA.; Inst. Trop. Child Health. Prev: SHO (O & G) Upton Hosp. Slough; SHO (Accid. & Orthop.) Battle Hosp. Reading; Ho. Phys. King Edwd. VII Hosp. Windsor.

MARKS, Mr Nicholas John Dunsden Lodge, Sonning Eye, Reading RG4 6TP — MRCS Eng. LRCP Lond. 1972; MS Lond. 1986, BSc 1969, MB BS 1972; FRCS Eng. 1978. (Guy's) Cons. ENT Surg. Roy. Berks. Hosp. Reading. Prev: Sen. Regist. Throat & Ear Dept. Guy's Hosp. Lond.

***MARKS, Nicola Adina** 119 The Avenue, London W13 8JT — BChir 1996 Camb.

MARKS, Mr Paul Vernon Department of Neurosurgery, The General Infirmary at Leeds, Great George St., Leeds LS1 3EX Tel: 0113 243 2799 Fax: 0113 392 5414 Email: pmarks4550@aol.com — MB BS 1980 Lond.; BA Open 1980; MD Lond. 1990; FRCS Eng. 1985; FRCPS Glas. 1984; Dip. Health Care Law Wales 1993; T(S) 1991; LLM Wales 1996. (Lond. Hosp. Med. Coll.) Cons. Neurosurg. Leeds Gen. Infirm.; Sen. Clin. Lect. (Neurosurg.) Univ. Leeds; Hunt. Prof. RCS Eng. Socs: Fell. Roy. Soc. Med.; Neurosurg. Soc. Australasia. Prev: Cons. Neurosurg. Auckland Hosp., NZ; Sen. Regist. Addenbrooke's Hosp. & Univ. Camb.; Reader Surg. Univ. Auckland, NZ.

MARKS, Peter 1 Maxted Road, London SE15 4LL — MB BCh BAO 1971 Dub.; MSc Lond. 1976; MRCP (UK) 1973; MRCS Eng. LRCP Lond. 1971. (Westm.) Prev: Lect. (Med.) Med. Unit King's Coll. Hosp. Lond.; Sen. Regist. (Research) Thoracic Unit, & Ho. Phys. (Cardiol.) & Ho. Surg. (Thoracic Surg.) W.m. Hosp. Lond.; SHO (Endocrinol.) Hammersmith Hosp.

MARKS, Peter John Health Centre, Midland St., Long Eaton, Nottingham NG10 1NY Tel: 0115 973 2370; 104 Long Moor Lane, Breaston, Derby DE72 3BD Tel: 013317 3783 — MB ChB 1977 Bristol; MRCGP 1981; DRCOG 1980. Course Organiser Derby VTS.

MARKS, Raymond Lawrence Chief Executives Office, Bootham Park, Bootham, York YO30 7BY Tel: 01904 454040 Fax: 01904 454439 Email: rmarksyhst@hotmail.com; 17 River View, Boston Spa, Wetherby LS23 6BA Tel: 01937 843859 Fax: 0937 843859 Email: rlmarks@easynet.co.uk — MB ChB Leeds 1961; FRCA 1968; DObst RCOG 1963. (Leeds) Exec. Med. Dir. York Health Servs. NHS

Trust; Cons. Anaesth. York Health Servs. NHS Trust. Socs: Assn. Anaesths.; Pain Soc.; Roy. Soc. Med. Prev: Sen. Regist. & Regist. (Anaesth.) United Leeds Hosps. & Leeds RHB; Regist. (Anaesth) Leeds 'A' & 'B' Hosp. Gps.

MARKS, Rex Richard David St Bartholomew's Hospital, West Smithfield, London EC1A 7BE Tel: 020 7601 7519; The Garden Flat, 160A Haverstock Hill, Belsize Park, London NW3 2AT Tel: 020 7586 5516 — MB ChB 1988 Liverp.; BSc (Hons) Med Cell Biology 1985; FRCA 1994; FFA RCSI 1993. Sen. Regist. Rotat. (Anaesth.) Roy. Lond. Hosps.; Lect. (Anaesth.) Lond. Hosp. Med. Coll.; Cons. Anaesth. (Cardiothoracic specialist) St Barth. & Lond. Chest Hosps. Socs: Fell. Roy. Coll. Anaesths.; UK Assn. Cardiothoracic Anaesth.; Anaesth. Res. Soc. Prev: Regist. (Anaesth.) St. Mary's Hosp. Lond. & Walton Hosp. Liverp.

MARKS, Richard Jeffrey 6 Grand Avenue, Muswell Hill, London N10 3AY Tel: 020 8883 5207 Email: rmarks@cix.compulink.co.uk — MB BS 1979 Lond.; MRCS Eng. LRCP Lond. 1979; FFA RCS Eng. 1984; T(Anaes.) 1991. (Westm.) Cons. (Anaesth.) Roy. Free Hosp. Lond. Prev: Cons. Anaesth. Gen. Hosp. Barnet Herts.; Sen. Regist. (Anaesth.) Brompton Hosp. & Roy. Free Hosp. Lond.; Vis. Prof. Anaesth. Duke Univ. Med. Centre Durh. NC, USA.

MARKS, Mr Robert Cornelius Department of Orthopaedics, Queen Margaret Hospital, Dunfermline KY12 0SU Tel: 01383 623623 Ext: 2441; 269 High Street, Burntisland KY3 9AQ Tel: 01592 874818 — MB ChB 1991 Edinburgh; MD Dundee 1991; MB ChB Ed. 1977; FRCS (Orth.) Ed. 1993; FRCS Ed. 1983. Cons. Orthop. Surg. Qu. Margt. Hosp. Dunfermline; Cons. (Orthop. Surg.) Vict. Hosp. Kirkcaldy.

MARKS, Robin Peter Moffett Department of Chemical Pathology, The Calderdale Roy. Hospital, Halifax HX3 0PW Tel: 01422 224196 Fax: 01422 222048 — MB BS 1974 Newc.; BA 1996 Open; BMedSc 1971 Newc.; FRCPath 1993. Cons. Chem. Path. Calderdale and Huddersfield NHS Trust. Prev: Sen. Regist. (Biochem.) S. Glam. AHA; SHO (Path.) Stockport AHA; Ho. Off. Durh. AHA.

MARKS, Ronald University of Wales College of Medicine, Department of Dermatology, Heath Park, Cardiff CF14 4XN Tel: 029 2074 2885 Fax: 029 2076 2314 — MB BS 1956 Lond.; MB BS (Hons.) Lond. 1959; BSc (Physiol. Hons.) Lond. 1956; FRCP Lond. 1977, M 1964; FRCPath 1985, M 1980; DTM & H Eng. 1961. (Guy's) Prof. Dermat. Univ. of Wales Coll. of Med. Cardiff. Socs: Fell. Roy. Soc. Med. & Roy. Coll. Path.; (Pres.) Internat. Soc. Bioeng. of Skin.

MARKS, Ronald Tollcross Medical Centre, 1101-1105 Tollcross Road, Glasgow G32 8UH Tel: 0141 778 2717 Fax: 0141 778 6880; Spinningdale, 7 Neidpath Road E., Giffnock, Glasgow G46 6TX Tel: 0141 639 4497 — MB ChB Glas. 1959; MRCGP 1966; DObst RCOG 1961. (Glas.) GP Princip.; Health Phys. (Occupat. Med.) Gtr. Glas. HB. Socs: BMA; MRCGP; SOM. Prev: Ho. Phys. Hairmyres Hosp. E. Kilbride & Bellshill Matern. Hosp.; Ho. Surg. Stobhill Hosp. Glas.; Ho. Off. Bellshill Matern. Hosp.

MARKS, Mr Sidney Michael Department of Neurosurgery, Middlesbrough General Hospital, Ayresome Green Lane, Middlesbrough TS5 5AZ Tel: 01642 850222; Meadowrise, Middleton on Lover, Yarm TS15 OJX — MB ChB 1974 Birm.; FRCP Lond. 1996; FRCP Glas. 1996; FRCS Eng. 1981. (Godfrey Huggins Sch. Med. Rhodesia) Cons. Neurosurg. Middlesbrough Gen. Hosp.; Examr. Intercollegiate Specialist Fell.sh. Neurosurg. FRCS (SN); Hon. Cons. Neurosurg. Newc. HA & N. Yorks. HA. Socs: Brit. Neurol. Surg. Soc.; N. Eng. Neurol. Soc.; Soc. Brit. Neurol. Surg. Prev: Sen. Regist. (Neurosurg.) Radcliffe Infirm. Oxf.; Hon. Capt. Rhodesian Army Med. Corps.

MARKS, Stephen David Dept. of Paediatrics, Northwick Park Hospital, Watford Road, Harrow HA1 3UJ Tel: 020 8864 3232 Ext: 329 Fax: 020 8869 2927; Flat 2, 28 Fellows Road, Swiss Cottage, London NW3 3LH Tel: 020 7722 7122 Email: s.marks@ich.ucl.ac.uk — MB ChB 1993 Glas.; MRCP(UK) 1996; DCH Lond. 1996; MRCPCH 1998. (Glas.) Specialist Regist. (Paediat.) N.wick Pk. Hosp. Harrow Middlx.; Paediat. Advanced Life Support Instruc. Socs: MDU. Prev: Regist. & Clin. Fell. (Med. Directorate) Gt. Ormond St. Hosp. Lond.; Regist. Mater Miser. Childr.'s Hosp. S. Brisbane Australia; SHO Rotat. (Paediat.) Univ. of Newc.

MARKS, Professor Vincent Dean of Medicine, EIHMS, University of Surrey, Stirling House, Surrey Research Park, Guildford GU2 7RF

MARKUS

Tel: 01483 450326 Fax: 01483 652893 Email: v.marks@surrey.ac.uk; Oriel House, Derby Road, Haslemere GU27 1BP Tel: 01428 643163 Fax: 01428 641940 Email: vincentmarks@bigfoot.com — BM BCh Oxf. 1954; DM Oxf. 1969; FRCP Lond. 1974, M 1969; FRCP Ed. 1970, M 1957; FRCPath 1973, M 1963. (Oxf. & St. Thos.) Adviser to the Dean Postgrad. Med. Sch. Univ. Surrey Guildford; Exec. Off. Assoc. Postgrad. Med. Sch.s Guildford. Socs: (Ex-Pres.) Assn. Clin. Biochems.; (Ex-Vice Pres.) Roy. Coll. Path. Prev: Dean Med. & Emerit. Prof. Clin. Biochem. Univ. Surrey; Emerit. Cons. Chem. Path. Roy. Surrey Co. & St. Luke's Hosps. Trust Guildford; Prof. Clin. Biochem. Univ. Surrey Guildford.

MARKUS, Andrew Charles Health Centre, East St., Thame OX9 3AU Tel: 01844 261066; Lashlake House, Thame OX9 3AU Tel: 01844 261414 Fax: 01844 260276 — BM BCh 1954 Oxf.; MA Oxf. 1955, BM BCh 1954; MRCP Lond. 1959; FRCGP 1979, M 1963. (Oxf. & Univ. Coll. Hosp.) Clin. Tutor (Community Med. & Gen. Pract.) Univ. Oxf. Socs: Fell. Green Coll. Oxf. Prev: Ho. Phys. Med. Unit & Ho. Surg. Surgic. Unit, Univ. Coll. Hosp.; Med. Off. Chest Div. RAF Hosp. Wroughton.

MARKUS, Hugh Stephen Flat 7, 1 Park Valley Road, The Park, Nottingham NG7 1BS Tel: 0115 941 4821 — BM BCh 1984 Oxf.; MA Camb. 1983; MRCP (UK) 1987. Regist. (Gen. Med.) Univ. Hosp. Nottm. Prev: SHO (Neurol.) St. Thos. Hosp. Lond.; SHO (Gen. Med.) John Radcliffe Hosp. Oxf.

MARKUS, Kathryn Calow and Brimington Practice, Brimington Medical Centre, Foljambe Road, Brimington, Chesterfield S43 1DD Tel: 01246 220166 Fax: 01246 208221 — MB ChB 1982 Sheff.

MARKUS, Patricia Josephine Mary Health Centre, East St., Thame Tel: 01844 261066; Lashlake House, Thame OX9 3AU — BM BCh 1954 Oxf.; MA Oxf. 1955, BM BCh 1954; DObst RCOG 1956. (St. Bart.) Prev: Ho. Surg. O & G Dept. & Ho. Surg. Centr. Middlx. Hosp. Pk.; Roy.; Ho. Phys. W. Middlx. Hosp. Isleworth.

MARKWELL, David Christopher 93 Wantage Road, Reading RG30 2SN Tel: 01734 584954 Fax: 01734 504464 — MB BS 1977 Lond.; MRCS Eng. LRCP Lond. 1977. (Guy's) Clin. Informat. Cons. Berks.; Mem. Computer Soc. Primary Health Care Gp. Prev: Technical Dir. Abies Informatics; GP Wye, Ashford Kent; Trainee GP Ashford VTS.

MARKWICK, Christopher Paul 17 Wingfield Road, Gravesend DA12 1BS — MB ChB 1992 Liverp.

MARLBOROUGH, John James Ciaran Montague Health Centre, Oakenhurst Road, Blackburn BB2 1PP Tel: 01254 268425 Fax: 01254 268450 — MB BCh BAO 1983 NUI. (Galway) GP Blackburn.

MARLBOROUGH, Marcus 68 Lilliput Road, Canford Cliffs, Poole BH14 8LA Tel: 01202 709662 Email: marc.marl@virgin.net — MB ChB 1943 Glas.; BSc Glas. 1940; FRCPC 1973; FFR 1958; DMRT Eng. 1949. (Glas.) Emerit. Cons. Bournemouth & E. Dorset Hosp. Gp. Prev: Cons. Radiother. Bournemouth & E. Dorset Hosp. Gp.; Assoc. Dir. & Sen. Radiother. Edmonton Cancer Clinic, Edmonton, Canada; Regist. (Radiother.) W.. Infirm. Glas.

MARLES, Paul Jason 11 GLendevon Close, Bolton BL3 4TZ — MB ChB 1992 Manch.

MARLETTA, Sylvia Ann (retired) The Haven, Windsor St., Shotts ML7 4DR Tel: 01501 821225 — MB ChB 1960 Ed. Locum Staff Grade Stroke Unit Hairmyres Hosp. Lanarksh. Hosp.s Trust. Prev: Assoc. Specialist (Geriat. Med.) Hairmyres & StoneHo. Hosps. Trust.

MARLEY, Jane Louise Rolling End, 6 Ivy Lane, Boston Spa, Wetherby LS23 6PP — MB BS 1993 Lond.; MRCOG 2000; LMSSA Lond. 1993. (St. Geos. Hosp. Med. Sch. Lond.) Specialist Regist. (Obst. &Gyn.)Centr. Sheff. Uni. Hosp. Prev: SHO (O & G) Nottm. City Hosp.; SHO (O & G) St. Peter's Hosp. Chertsey Surrey; SHO (Oncol.) the Middlx. Hosp. UCL Hosp.

***MARLEY, Justin Christian** Flat 5, 76 Auckland Road, London SE19 2DH — MB BS 1998 Lond.; MB BS Lond 1998.

MARLEY, Nicholas John Edward Department of Histopathology, Michael Darmady Laboratory, Queen Alexandra Hospital, Cosham, Portsmouth PO6 3LY Tel: 023 92 286494 Fax: 023 92 286493 — MB BS 1977 Lond.; BSc Lond. 1974; MRCP (UK) 1980; MRCPath 1985. Cons. Histopath. Portsmouth Hosps. NHS Trust. Prev: Sen. Regist. St. Thos. Hosp. Med. Sch. Lond.

MARLEY, Richard Thomas Coles 73 Oakley Road, London N1 3LW — BM BCh 1990 Oxf.; MRCP (UK) 1993. MRC Research

Fell. Hepat. Roy. Free Hosp. Sch. Med. Lond. Prev: Lect. (Gastroenterol.) Roy. Postgrad. Med. Sch. Hammersmith Hosp. Lond.

MARLOW, Anne-Marie Marlow and Partners, The Surgery, Bell Lane, Minchinhampton, Stroud GL6 9JF Tel: 01453 883793 Fax: 01453 731670 — MA, MB Camb. 1978, BChir 1977; MRCP (UK) 1980. (St. Geos.) Prev: Regist. (Med.) Cheltenham Gen. Hosp.; SHO (Infec. Dis.) St. Geo. Hosp. Lond.; SHO (Paediat.) & Ho. Phys. St. Geo. Hosp. Lond.

MARLOW, Clare Elizabeth 2 Bissell Close, Birmingham B28 0XX — MB BS 1994 Lond. (St. Geo. Hosp. Med. Sch. Lond.) SHO (Oncol.) Qu. Eliz. Hosp. Birm. Prev: Ho. Off. (Med.) New Cross Hosp. Wolverhampton; SHO (Med.) Worcester Roy. Infirm.; SHO (A & E) Good Hope Hosp. Sutton Coldfield.

MARLOW, Hilary Francis 5 Millhill, Pettaugh, Stowmarket IP14 4RT — BM BCh 1977 Oxf.; BSc (Pharm.) Rhodes 1962, BSc (Hons.) 1963; PhD Camb. 1967. Med. Advs. Cons. Pharm. Med.

MARLOW, John Henry 50 Hatherley Road, Cheltenham GL51 6EE — BM BS 1997 Nottm. SHO Med. Rotat. - Ipswich.

MARLOW, Karen Dorothy McIntosh 2 Breach Barn Cottage, Coalpit Lane, Wolvey, Hinckley LE10 3HD — MB ChB 1990 Liverp.; MRCGP 1995; DFFP 1995; DRCOG 1993. Prev: SHO (Psychiat.) Walsgrave Hosp. & Milton Keynes NHS Trust; SHO (O & G) Leicester Gen. Hosp.

MARLOW, Professor Neil Department of Child Health, University Hospital, Queens Medical Centre, Nottingham NG7 2UH Tel: 0115 942 1421 Fax: 0115 970 9382 Email: neil.marlow@nottingham.ac.uk; 22 Grantham Road, Bottesford, Nottingham NG13 0DF Tel: 01949 844567 Fax: 01949 844276 Email: neil.marlow@virgin.net — MB BS 1976 Lond.; BA (Hons.) Oxf. 1973, DM 1985; FRCP Lond. 1993; MRCP (UK) 1979; FRCPCH 1997. Prof. Neonat. Med. Qu. Med. Centre & City Hosp. Nottm. Socs: Brit. Assn. Perinatal Med. (Hon. Sec.). Prev: Cons. Sen. Lect. Child Health (Neonat. Med.) Univ. Bristol, St. Michael's & S.mead Hosp. Bristol.

MARLOWE, Gary Teejpaul Singh Aricon, Bromsash, Ross-on-Wye HR9 7PJ — MB BS 1987 Lond.

MARLOWE, Karl Hemant Singh Dual Team, 151 Blackfriars Road, London SE1 8EL — MSc 1999 Lond.; MB ChB Liverp. 1993. SpR in Addic.s. Socs: BMA; MDU; Roy. Soc. of Med.

MARLOWE, Martin James 2-4 Radnor Park Avenue, Folkestone CT19 5BW Tel: 01303 222422 — MB BS 1985 Lond.; MRCPsych 1991. Cons. Gen. Adult Psychiat. (Shepway Rural); Sen. Lect. (Psychiat.) United Med. & Dent. Sch. Guy's & St. Thos. Hosps. Lond.

***MARLOWE, Sharon Nalini Singh** 85 Sandringham Road, London E8 2LL — MB ChB 1994 Bristol.

MARMERY, Victor John (retired) Flat 2, 4 Oldfield Road, Bromley BR1 2LF Tel: 020 8467 5597 — MB BChir 1951 Camb.

MARMION, Damien Vincent BUPA, Staines TW18 4XF — MB BS 1991 Lond.; MBA Lond. 1995. Head of Hosp. Contracts - BUPA.

MARMION, Douglas Edward (retired) Well House, Lurgashall, Petworth GU28 9ET Tel: 01428 707339 — MA 1942, MD Camb. 1951, MB BChir 1941; MRCP Lond. 1947; MRCS Eng. LRCP Lond. 1941; DTM & H Eng. 1953. Prev: Med. Specialist, RAMC.

MARMION, Mr Vincent James St Mary's Private Hospital, Upper Byron Place, Clifton, Bristol BS8; 6 Norland Road, Clifton, Bristol BS8 3LP Tel: 0117 973 0640 — MB BCh BAO 1950 Belf.; FRCP Ed. 1982, M 1960; FRCS Ed. 1962; DO Eng. 1957; DOMS RCPSI 1957. Clin. Teach. (Ophth.) Univ. Bristol. Socs: RSM; Irish. Coll. Ophth.; Bristol Medico-Historial Soc. Prev: Cons. Surg. Bristol Eye Hosp.

MARMOT, Professor Sir Michael Gideon Department of Epidemiology & Public Health, University College London Medical School, University College, 1-19 Torrington Place, London WC1E 6BT Tel: 020 7391 1680 Fax: 020 7813 0280 Email: m.marmot@ucl.ac.uk; 17 North End, London NW3 7HR — MB BS 1969 Sydney; PhD Univ. Calif. 1975; BSc (Med.) Sydney 1967; FFCM 1989, M 1984; MPH Univ. Calif. 1972; FRCP 1996. (Sydney) Prof. Epidemiol. & Pub. Health Univ. Coll. Lond. Med. Sch.; Dir. Internat. Centre for Health & Soc.; Cons. Bloomsbury HA.; MRC Research Prof.sh.; Mem. Roy. Commiss. on Environm. Pollution. Prev: Sen. Lect. (Epidemiol.) Lond. Sch. Hyg. & Trop. Med.; Lect. (Sch. Pub. Health) Univ. Calif., Berkeley.

MARNANE, Conor Niall Royal National Nose, Throat & Ear Hospital, London WC1X 8EE — MB BCh 1993 Wales. SHO (Trauma

& Orthop.) Morriston Hosp. Swansea. Prev: SHO (Trauma & Orthop.) Morriston Hosp. Swansea; SHO (A & E) Cardiff Roy. Infirm.

MARNELL, Maria Bernadette Grove House Surgery, 80 Pryors Lane, Rose Green, Bognor Regis PO21 4JB Tel: 01243 265222/266413 Fax: 01243 268693 — MB BCh BAO 1984 NUI; Dip. Addic. Behaviour Lond. 1992; DCH RCPSI 1986. Prev: Trainee GP Lancing W. Sussex.

MARNER, Simon Peter Cater Street Surgery, 1 Cater Street, Kempston, Bedford MK42 8DR Tel: 01234 853461 Fax: 01234 840536; The Ovens, 2 High St, Blunham, Bedford MK44 3NL Tel: 01767 640020 — MB BS 1979 Lond. Socs: Assoc. Mem. Brit. Med. Acupunc. Soc. Prev: Trainee GP St. Michael's Surg. Glos.; Regist. (ENT) Char. Cross Hosp. & W.m. Hosp. Lond.

MARNEY, Yvonne Marie 1 Drumpellier Court, Cumbernauld, Glasgow G67 4NS — MB ChB 1990 Dundee; BMSc Dund 1987; MRCP (UK) 1993; FRCA (UK) 1997. Spcialist Regist. in Anaesth. (Wales). Prev: SHO (Anaesth.) S. Gwent.

MARNS, Rosalind Sheena 80 Hubert Road, Birmingham B29 6EG — MB ChB 1992 Birm.

MAROK, Inderjit Singh Rotton Park Medical Centre, 264 Rotton Park Road, Edgbaston, Birmingham B16 0LU Tel: 0121 429 2683; 278 Lordswood Road, Birmingham B17 8AN — BM 1984 Soton.; BSc (Hons.) Pharmacy Leic. 1978; MRCGP 1988; Cert. Family Plann. JCC 1988. Prev: SHO/GP Rotat. Dudley Rd. Hosp. Birm.; Ho. Phys. Soton. Gen. Hosp.; Ho. Surg. St. Mary's Hosp. Portsmouth.

MAROOF, Dr 62 Poplar Grove, London N11 3NL Tel: 020 8361 2238 — MB ChB 1969 Mosul; MB ChB Mosul, Iraq 1969; FRCS Ed. 1980; FRCS Glas. 1979.

MAROSSY, Agnes Eva 20 Birdwood Close, South Croydon CR2 8QG — MB BS 1987 Lond.; MRCGP 1993; DCH RCP Lond. 1992; DRCOG 1991. Public Health Doctor, Direcorate of Pub. Health, Croydon Health Auth. Prev: Gen. Practitioner Violet La. Med. Pract., Croydon.

MAROSSY, Dalma The Bell House, Messing, Colchester CO5 9UA — MB BS 1980 Lond.; MSc Lond. 1986, BSc 1977, MB BS 1980; MRCPath 1987. (St. Thos.) Cons. Med. Microbiol. Chelmsford Pub. Health Laborat.; Hon. Cons. Microbiol. Mid-Essex Hosp. Serv. NHS Trust. Socs: Hosp. Infec. Soc.; Brit. Soc. Antimicrob. Chem.; Assn. med. Microbiol.

MAROTTA, Salvatore 188 Downhills Park Road, London N17 6AP — State DMS 1985 Catania. SHO (Ophth.) Edgware Gen. Hosp. Prev: Clin. Asst. Roy. Lond. Hosp. & Moorfields Eye Hosp.

MAROUF, El Tayeb Saad Flat 5, 78 Fortis Green, London N2 9EX — MRCS Eng. LRCP Lond. 1987; MB BS Khartoum 1980. SHO (Gen. Med.) Co. Hosp. & St. Geo. Hosp. Lincoln; SHO Rotat. (Med.) Kettering Gen. Hosp. Prev: SHO (Gen. Med.) Khartoun Teachg. Hosp., Sudan; Ho. Off. (Gen. Surg. & Gen. Med.) Glas. Roy. Infirm.

MARPLE, James Barry 66 Park Avenue, Portobello, Edinburgh EH15 1JP Tel: 0131 657 5817 — MB ChB 1990 Ed.; BSc (Hons.) Ed. 1988; MRCGP 1995; DRCOG 1994. (Ed.) Locum.

MARPLES, David Duncan Ransford 54 Whitchurch Gardens, Edgware HA8 6PD — BM BCh 1990 Oxf.

MARPLES, Ivan Llewellyn The Bungalow, White House Farm, High Bradfield, Bradfield, Sheffield S6 6LJ — MB BS 1987 Lond.; FRCA 1994; DA (UK) 1991. SHO (Anaesth.) Roy. Infirm. Ed.

MARPLES, John Area Pathology Laboratory, Royal Albert Edward Infirmary, Wigan Lane, Wigan WN1 2NN Tel: 01942 822132 — MB ChB 1970 Manch.; FRCPath 1989, M 1977. Cons. Chem. Pathol. Wigan AHA.

MARPLES, Maria Cancer Research Centre, Weston Park Hospital, Sheffield S10 2SJ Tel: 0114 2265125 Fax: 0114 2265678 Email: m.v.marples@sheffield.ac.uk — BM BCh 1989 Oxf.; PHD (lond) 2001; MA Oxf. 1992, BA 1986; MRCP (UK) 1992. (Univ. Oxf. Med. Sch.) Sen. Lect./Hon. Cons. in Med. Oncol. Westn. Pk. Hosp. Sheff. Socs: Fell. Roy. Soc. Med.; Assn. Cancer Phys. Prev: Regist. (Med. Oncol.) Middlx. Hosp. Lond.; Regist. (Gen. Med.) Stoke Mandeville Hosp. Aylesbury.

MARQUAND, Peter Blondel Capsticks, 77-83 Upper Richmond Road, London SW15 2TT — MB BS 1987 Lond.; BSc (Anat.) Lond. 1984; MRCP (UK) 1990. Socs: Fell. Roy. Soc. Med.

MARQUIS, Anna Mary Macfie Clinical Assistant, Haem/Oncology, Royal Hampshire County Hospital, Winchester; Hill Farm, Sutton Scotney, Winchester SO21 3NT Tel: 01962 760810 Fax: 01962 760810 — MB ChB 1972 Aberd.; MRCGP 1976. (Aberd.) p/t Clin.

Asst., Haem/Oncol., Roy. Hants. Co. Hosp., Winchester, Hants. Prev: GP Hants. & Chandlers Ford; Trainee GP Banchory Kincardinsh.; Med. Off. Naomi Hse. Wessex Hospice for Childr.

MARR, Alexander William Auburn Cottage, Templand, Lockerbie DG11 1TG Tel: 01387 810734 — MB ChB 1957 Manch.; DCH RCPS Glas. 1967. (Manch.) Exam. Med. Pract. DSS. Prev: Sen. Med. & Health Off. Hong Kong Governm.; Sec. for Health Gilbert & Ellice Is.s.; Med. Off. HMOCS.

MARR, Ann Christina (retired) Ko-na-Mauri, 27 Churchill Road, Kilmacolm PA13 4NA Tel: 01505 873146 — MB BS Lond. 1966; MRCS Eng. LRCP Lond. 1966; MFPHM I 1978; Dip. Community. Med. Ed. 1976; DObst RCOG 1968. Cons. Pub. Health Med. Argyll & Clyde HB. Prev: Sen. Med. Off. (Community Med.) Argyll & Clyde HB.

MARR, Christopher Wellway Medical Group, The Surgery, Wellway, Morpeth NE61 6TB Tel: 01670 517300 Fax: 01670 511931; 4 The Crossway, Morpeth NE61 2DA — MB BS 1982 Newc.; MRCGP 1988; DRCOG 1987; DCCH RCP Ed. 1986.

MARR, Cyril Alexander Hutcheon (retired) 1 Rush Grove, Uppermill, Oldham OL3 6LD Tel: 01457 873910 — MB ChB St. And. 1953. Prev: GP Oldham.

MARR, David Henderson Hollies Surgery, 83 Birch Lane, Dukinfield SK16 4AJ Tel: 0161 330 2039 Fax: 0161 330 5149; The Old Toll House, 1 Oldham Road, Uppermill, Oldham OL3 6HY Tel: 01457 873636 — MB ChB 1979 Dundee; DA Eng. 1983.

MARR, Donald Cochran The Garth Surgery, Westgate, Guisborough TS14 6AT Tel: 01287 632206 Fax: 01287 635112 — MB BS 1967 Newc.; MRCGP 1973; DObst RCOG 1970. Prev: SHO (Obst.) Hexham Gen. Hosp.; SHO (Med.) Newc. Gen. Hosp.; Ho. Off. Roy. Vict. Infirm. Newc.

MARR, Miss Jane Elizabeth Birmingham & Midland Eye Centre, City Hospital NHS Trust, Dudley Road, Birmingham; 22 Broad Street, Bromsgrove B61 8LW Email: dr.jane@lineone.net — MB ChB 1991 Sheff.; FRCOphth. (Sheff.) Regist. (Ophth.) Birm. & Midl. Eye Centre City Hosp. NHS Trust.

MARR, Joseph 7 Rosamond's Cottages, Kingswood, Aylesbury HP18 0RG — MB BS 1987 Newc.

***MARR, Morag Mackinnon** Arthurlie, 19 South Avenue, Paisley PA2 7SP — MB ChB 1994 Ed.

***MARR, Sarah Anne Pamela** 19 South Avenue, Paisley PA2 7SP — MB ChB 1998 Ed.; MB ChB Ed 1998.

MARR, Sarah Theresa Pamela Arthurlie, 19 South Avenue, Paisley PA2 7SP — MB ChB 1964 Glas.

MARR, Thomas Cameron Kelly (retired) 56B Albany Road, Broughty Ferry, Dundee DD5 1NW Tel: 01382 330397 — MB BChir 1949 Camb.; BA (Hons.) Camb. 1946; FRCP Lond. 1977, M 1953. JP. Prev: Hall Tutorial Fell. in Med. Glas. W.. Infirm.

MARRAY, Philip John Oakengates Medical Practice, Limes Walk, Oakengates, Telford TF2 6JJ Tel: 01952 620077 Fax: 01952 620209; 45 Victoria Road, Shifnal TF11 8AE — MRCS Eng. LRCP Lond. 1982.

MARRE, Leonard (retired) 58 Brook Road, London NW2 7DN Tel: 020 8452 2301 — MRCS Eng. LRCP Lond. 1940. Med. Ref. Pearl Assur. Co. Prev: Exam. Med. Off. DHSS.

MARREN, Dora (retired) 14 Kersal Lawns, 115A Manchester Road, Sheffield S10 5DN Tel: 0114 266 0446 — MB BCh BAO 1949 NUI; DPH Liverp. 1957.

MARREN, Pauline Anne (retired) Department of Dermatology, Amersham Hospital, Amersham Tel: 01494 734648 Fax: 01494 734620 — MB BCh BAO 1982 NUI; MRCPI 1985. Cons. Dermat. Amersham & Wycombe Hosps.; Hon. Cons. Dermat. Ch.ill Hosp. Oxf. Prev: Sen. Regist. (Deramt.) Ch.ill Hosp. Oxf.

MARRETT, Henry Rex (retired) 7A The Firs, Kenilworth Road, Coventry CV5 6QD Tel: 024 7667 4706 — MRCS Eng. LRCP Lond. 1940; FFA RCS Eng. 1953; DA Eng. 1941. Prev: Cons. Anaesth. Coventry HA.

MARRETT, John Eric Clare House, Howe Green, Sandon, Chelmsford CM2 7TQ — MRCS Eng. LRCP Lond. 1945.

MARRIAGE, Stephen Christopher 73 Nightingale Lane, London N8 7RA — MB BS 1986 Lond.

MARRIAN, Valerie Jean (retired) 25 Hamilton Place, Perth PH1 1BD Tel: 01738 621018 — MB ChB 1955 Ed.; FRCP Ed. 1970, M 1959; FRCP Lond. 1977, M 1960; DCH Eng. 1958. Prev: Cons. Paediatr. Perth Roy. Infirm.

MARRINAN

MARRINAN, Mr Michael Timothy Department of Cardiothoracic Surgery, King's College Hospital, Denmark Hill, London SE5 9RS Tel: 020 7346 4365 Fax: 020 7346 3433; 72 Sunderland Road, Forest Hill, London SE23 2PY Tel: 020 8699 0596 Email: marrinan@mcmail.com — MB BCh BAO 1981 NUI; MB BCh BAO NUI 1981; FRCS Ed. 1985. Cons. Cardiothoracic Surg. King's Coll. Hosp. Lond. Prev: Sen. Regist. Guy's Hosp. Lond.; Fell. Mayo Clinic Rochester, USA; Lect. Roy. Lond. Hosp.

MARRINAN, Pamela Jane Mary Martin Surrey Docks Health Centre, Downtown Road, London SE16 6NP Tel: 020 7231 0207 Fax: 020 771 5650; 72 Sunderland Road, London SE23 2PY — MB BCh BAO 1977 NUI; MRCPI 1980; MRCGP 1988; DObst NUI 1981; DCH NUI 1979.

MARRIOTT, Alison Margaret Wood Lane Medical Centre, 2A Wood Lane, Ruislip HA4 6ER Tel: 01895 632677 Fax: 01895 634020; 75 Sharps Lane, Ruislip HA4 7HZ — MB BS 1967 Newc.; DCH Eng. 1969. (Newc.)

MARRIOTT, Caroline Margaret Muckamore Abbey Hospital, 1 Abbey Road, Muckamore, Antrim BT41 4SH Tel: 028 9446 3333 Fax: 028 9446 7730 Email: caroline.marriott@nwb.n-i.nhs.uk — MB BCh BAO 1976 Belf.; FRCPsych; MRCPsych 1983. Cons. Psychiat. Muckamore Abbey Hosp. Co. Antrim.; Med. Director (Hosp.); Muckamore Abbey Hosp.

MARRIOTT, Charles Michael The Avenue Surgery, 1 The Avenue, Cirencester GL7 1EH Tel: 01285 653122 Fax: 01285 650098; Barnfields, Sheephouse Lane, Ampney Crucis, Cirencester GL7 5DZ Tel: 01285 655581 — MB BS 1977 Lond.; MRCS Eng. LRCP Lond. 1977. Hosp. Pract. Elderly Care Unit Cirencester Hosp. Glos.

MARRIOTT, Mr Frederick Peter Sefton (retired) 229 Greenmont Lane, Bolton BL1 5JB Tel: 01204 841620 — MB ChB Ed. 1952; FRCS Ed. 1958. Prev: Cons. Surg. Bolton Gp. Hosps.

MARRIOTT, Jeremy David Queen Square Surgery, 2 Queen Square, Lancaster LA1 1RP Tel: 01524 843333 Fax: 01524 847550; 1 Escawbeck House, Crook of Lune, Caton, Lancaster LA1 1RP — MB ChB 1985 Birm.; MRCGP 1991.

***MARRIOTT, Joanna Clare** 4 Badgers Dene, Mill La, Rodmell, Lewes BN7 3HS — MB ChB 1997 Birm.

MARRIOTT, Joanna Mary Holt Medical Practice, Jacobs Place, High St., Holt NR25 6BH; 6 Glaven View Cottages, Holt Road, Thornage, Holt NR25 7QW — MB BS 1990 Lond.; MRCGP.

MARRIOTT, Mr John (retired) The Mill House, 13 Millway Road, Andover SP10 3EU Tel: 01264 338661 — MB BS 1964 Lond.; FRCS Eng. 1970; MRCS Eng. LRCP Lond. 1964; DObst RCOG 1969. Prev: Regist. (Surg.) Roy. Hants. Co. Hosp. Winchester.

MARRIOTT, Kenneth Noel 178 Heathfield Road, Southport PR8 3EW — MB BS 1976 Newc.

MARRIOTT, Philip John Saxonbury House, Croft Road, Crowborough TN6 1DP Tel: 01892 652266 Fax: 01892 668607; 2 Gillridge Green, Crowborough TN6 2UN Tel: 01892 663167 Fax: 01892 668607 — MB BChir 1972 Camb.; MA Camb. 1972; MRCP (UK) 1974; LMCC 1977. (Guy's) Socs: Fell. Roy. Soc. Med.; St. John's Hosp. Dermat. Soc.; Balint Soc. Prev: Regist. (Dermat.) St. Bart. Hosp. Lond.; Ho. Phys. Guy's Hosp. Lond.; Sen. Resid. (Paediat.) Qu. Univ. Canada.

MARRIOTT, Richard Gavin 52 Drift Road, Stamford PE9 1XA — MB ChB 1990 Sheff.; MRCP (UK) 1994. SHO (Psychiat.) Wakefield. Prev: Regist. (Gen. Med.) S.land Hosp. Invercargill, NZ; SHO (Gen. Med.) Doncaster Roy. Infirm. & Lodge Moor Hosp. Sheff.

MARRIOTT, Richard Marshall Red House Surgery, 96 Chesterton Road, Cambridge CB4 1ER Tel: 01223 365555 Fax: 01223 356848; 2 Hemington Close, Over, Cambridge CB4 5LX Tel: 01954 232552 Email: r.marriott@dial.pipex.com — MB BS 1986 Lond.; MRCGP 1992; DRCOG 1991.

MARRIOTT, Robert George Bewdley Medical Centre, Dog Lane, Bewdley, Dudley Tel: 01299 402157 Fax: 01299 404364 — MB ChB 1968 Birm.; BSc (Hons.) Birm. 1965, MB ChB 1968; MRCGP 1974; DObst RCOG 1970. (Birm.) Socs: BMA.

MARRIOTT, Samantha Elizabeth 37 Park Road, Radlett WD7 8EG Tel: 01923 854570 — MB ChB 1991 (Hons.) Birm.; MRCPsych 1996. (Univ. Birm.) Prev: Regist. (Psychiat.) Homerton Hosp. Lond.

MARRIOTT, Sarah Victoria Lowe Paterson Centre, South Wharf Road, London W2 1PD Tel: 020 7886 1644 Fax: 020 7886 1637 — MB BS 1986 Newc.; MRCPsych 1991. (Newc. u. Tyne) Cons. Psychiat. Paterson Centre Lond.; Hon. Sen. Lect. Dept. Pub. Ment. Health Imperial Coll. Lond. Prev: Sen. Regist. (Psychiat.) Maudsley Hosp. Lond.

MARRIS, Nicola Dawn c/o 2/24 Cranky Gardens, London SW7 3DD Tel: 020 7835 1907 — MB ChB 1990 Otago.

MARRIS, Russell 793 Harrow Road, London NW10 5PA — LMSSA 1960 Lond.

MARRIS, Susan Lilian Bassingham Surgery, Torgate Lane, Bassingham, Lincoln LN5 9HF Tel: 01522 788250 Fax: 01522 788180; Valley Farm, Collingham Road, Swinderby, Lincoln LN6 9JB Tel: 01522 868632 — MB ChB 1983 Liverp.; MRCGP 1987; DGM RCP Lond. 1987; DRCOG 1985.

***MARRON, Conor Damian** 8 Vaddegan Park, Newtownabbey BT36 7SR — MB BCh 1998 Belf.; MB BCh Belf 1998.

MARRON, Ellen Miriam (retired) 14 Braemore Court, Kingsway, Hove BN3 4FG Tel: 01273 720390 — MB ChB 1950 Bristol. Prev: Mem. Med. Bd. DHSS.

MARROTT, Seema New Hall Lane Practice, The Health Centre, Geoffrey Street, Preston PR1 5NE Tel: 01772 401730 Fax: 01772 401731 — MB ChB 1986 Manch. Community Med. Off. Preston. Socs: MRCGP.

MARROW, Mr Jonathan Arrowe Park Hospital, Upton, Wirral CH49 5PE Tel: 0151 678 5111 Fax: 0151 336 4599 Email: jonathan@marrow.com — MB BS Lond. 1968; FRCS Eng. 1979; FFAEM 1993. Cons. A & E Arrowe Pk. Hosp. Wirral. Socs: Brit. Assn. Accid. & Emerg. Med.; Emerg. Med. Research Soc.; Chairm. Jt. comm. On Higher Train. in A&E Med. Prev: Sen. Regist. (A & E) Hull Roy. Infirm.; Med. Off. Sekgoma Memor. Hosp. Serowe, Botswana.

MARRS, Timothy Clive Department of Health, Skipton House, 80 London Road, London SE1 6LH Tel: 020 7972 5328 Fax: 020 7972 5156 — MB BS 1968 Lond.; MSc Lond. 1973, DSc 1994, MD 1977; MRCS Eng. LRCP Lond. 1968; FRCPath 1987, M 1975; DRCPath (Toxicol) 1984; FIBiol 1988, M 1983. (Westm.) Sen. Med. Off. DoH. Socs: Soc. Toxicol. & Brit. Toxicol. Soc. Prev: Sen. Med. Off. Research Chem. Defence Estab.; Sen. Lect. & Sen. Regist. (Chem. Pathol.) W.m. Hosp.; SHO (Clin. Path.) W.m. Hosp. Lond.

MARS, John Simon Royal Albert Edward Infirmary, Wigan Lane, Wigan WN1 2NN Tel: 01942 822468; 2 Pheasant Close, Worsley, Manchester M28 1LA Email: imanmars@cs.com — BM 1985 Soton.; FRCOphth 1990. (Soton.) Cons. Ophth. Surg. Roy. Albert Edwd. Infirm. Wigan.

MARS, Philip Herbert Talygarn Hospital, Griffithstown, Pontypool NP4 5IA; 31 Waterside, Abergavenny NP7 5LJ — MB BCh 1973 Wales; MRCPsych. 1980. Cons. Psychiat. Talygarn Hosp., Griffithstown, Pontypool, Mon.

MARSDEN, Adrian Philip Highfield Family and Adolescent Unit, Warneford Hospital, Warneford Lane, Oxford OX3 7JX Tel: 01865 226285 Fax: 01865 226381 — MB BS 1984 Lond.; MA Camb. 1984, BA 1981; MRCGP 1990; T(GP) 1994; DRCOG 1989; MRC Psych 1998. (Guy's) Specialist Regist. in Child & Adolesc. Psychiat. Highfield Adolesc. Unit, Oxf. Socs: BMA. Prev: Resid. (Psychiat.) St. Brendan's Hosp. Paget, Bermuda; Resid. Dr. (Emerg. Med.) K. Edwd. VII Hosp. Hamilton, Bermuda; Trainee GP Cheltenham & Glos. VTS.

MARSDEN, Mr Andrew Kendall Scottish Ambulance Service, National Headquarters, Tipperlinn Road, Edinburgh EH10 5UU Tel: 0131 446 7015 Fax: 0131 446 7001 Email: amarsden@scotamb.co.uk; 38b Coates Garden, Edinburgh EH12 5LE Tel: 0131 346 4246 Fax: 0131 346 4246 Email: marsden@ednet.co.uk — MB ChB 1972 Leeds; FRCS Ed. 1977; FFAEM 1993; Fimc RCS Ed. 2001. Cons. Med. Dir. Scott. Ambul. Serv.; Mem. Bd. Immediate Med. Care RCS Edin.; Mem. Comm. Managem. Fac. Pre Hosp. Care. Socs: Counc. Mem. Brit. Assn. for Immediate Care; (Exec. Comm.) Resusc. Counc. UK. Prev: Cons. Emerg. Med. Pinderfields Gen. Hosp. Wakefield.

MARSDEN, Anne Rosemary 34 Green Walk, Timperley, Altrincham WA15 6JN — MB ChB 1985 Leeds.

MARSDEN, Mr Austin Joseph (retired) 7 Walton Road, St Helens WA10 6JJ Tel: 01744 22751 — MB ChB 1942 Liverp.; ChM Liverp. 1962, MB ChB 1942; FRCS Eng. 1947. Hon. Surg. Ormskirk Hosp. Gp. Prev: Surg. Providence Hosp. St. Helens.

MARSH

MARSDEN, Bruce (retired) Beechway, Coleford, Crediton EX17 5DG Tel: 01363 82947 — MB ChB 1945 Manch.; MRCS Eng. LRCP Lond. 1946. Prev: GP Bow, Crediton, Devon.

MARSDEN, Catherine Margaret Food for the Hungry Int/Bangladesh, PO Box 6097, Gulshan, Dhaka 1212, Bangladesh Email: kmarsden@fhl.net; 102 East Parade, Heworth, York YO31 7YH — MB ChB 1975 Glas.; BSc (Hons.) Microbiol. Glas. 1973, MB ChB 1975. (Glas. Univ.) Med. Advisor to FHI / Bangladesh. Prev: Staff Grade (Paed.) York Dist. Hosp.; Clin. Med. Off. York HA; Clin. Asst. (Paediat.) York Dist. Hosp.

MARSDEN, David Paul (retired) Gills Hill House, Bourn, Cambridge CB3 7TS Tel: 01954 719387 — MB ChB 1956 Sheff.; DObst RCOG 1963; MRCGP 1978. Prev: Hosp. Pract. (Urol.) Addenbrooke's Hosp. Camb.

MARSDEN, Debra Ann 1Pitch Pond Close, Knotty Green, Beaconsfield HPQ 1XY — MB BS 1986 Lond.; BSc Lond. 1983, MB BS 1986; MRCGP 1991; DRCOG 1989.

MARSDEN, Dorothy Joan (retired) 2 Plas Gwyn, 27 Hampton Park Road, Hereford HR1 1TH Tel: 01432 350720 — MB ChB Manch. 1952; DCH Eng. 1954. Prev: SCMO E. Herts. HA.

MARSDEN, Dorothy Margaret Westcliffe, 33 Watkin Road, Clayton-Le-Woods, Chorley PR6 7PU Tel: 012572 65995; Medical Directorate, Northgate Hospital, Morpeth NE61 3BP Tel: 01670 394081 — MB BS 1988 Lond.; BSc Basic Med. Scs. & Physiol. (Hons.) Lond. 1985; MRCP (UK) 1994; MRCS Eng. LRCP Lond. 1988; MRCPsych 1997; DGM RCP Lond. 1993; DCH RCP Lond. 1992. (King's Coll. Hosp. Sch. Med. & Dent.) Specialist Regist. (Psychiat. of Learning Disabilities) N.ern Region TS Newc. Socs: BMA Hon. Sec. Hexham Div. Prev: Regist. Rotat. (Psychiat.) N.. Region Train. Scheme Newc.; SHO Rotat. (Psychiat.) Newc. St Nicholas Hosp. Newc. u. Tyne; SHO (Geriat. & Psychiat.) W. Cumbld. Hosp.

MARSDEN, Helen Louise Urmston Group Practice, 154-156 Church Road, Urmston, Manchester M41 9DL — MB BS 1991 Lond.; MRCGP 1996; DCH RCP Lond. 1995; DRCOG 1994. (St. Geo. Hosp, Lond.) Socs: Med. Protec. Soc.; MSS. Prev: GP/Regist. St. And. Med. Centre Manch.

MARSDEN, Helen Louise 18 Gordons Walk, Harpenden AL5 1LQ Tel: 01582 460585 — MB BS 1996 Lond. (Royal Free Hospital. London) SHO (Psychiat.) W. Herts. GP VTS St Albans Herts. Prev: SHO (Accid. & Emegency); Ho. Off. (Surg.); Ho. Off. (Med.).

MARSDEN, Henry Basil (retired) 8 Shawdene Road, Northenden, Manchester M22 4BU Tel: 0161 998 2681 — MB ChB 1944 Manch.; MRCS Eng. LRCP Lond. 1945; FCPath 1969; DCH Eng. 1948, DPath 1953. Hon. Prof. Paediat. Path. Univ. Manch. Prev: Cons. Pathol. Roy. Manch. Childr. Hosp. Pendlebury, Booth Hall Childr. Hosp., Monsall Hosp. & Christie Hosp. (Dept. Epidemiol.).

MARSDEN, Jeremy Denis (Surgery) Rush View, Holme on Spalding Moor, York YO43 4BJ Tel: 01430 860221; (Surgery) Highfield Road, Bubwith, Selby Tel: 01757 288315 — MB BChir 1975 Camb.; MA, MB Camb. 1975, BChir 1974. Prev: Med. Off. Brit. Trawler Fleet (Icelandic Waters) Min. Agriculture; Fisheries & Food; SHO (O & G) Staincliffe Gen. Hosp. Densbury.

MARSDEN, Jeremy Robert Department of Dermatology, University Hospital NHS Trust, Selly Oak Hospital, Raddlebarn Road, Birmingham B29 6JD Tel: 0121 627 1627 Fax: 0121 627 8765 — BM BS 1976 Nottm.; FRCP Lond. 1994; MRCP (UK) 1979. Cons. Dermat. Uni. Hosp. Birm. NHS Trust. Prev: Sen. Regist. (Dermat.) Qu. Med. Centre Nottm.; MRC Train. Fell. (Dermat. & Clin. Pharmacol.) Roy. Vict. Infirm. Newc.; Regist. (Dermat.) Roy. Vict. Infirm. Newc.

MARSDEN, Joanne 303 Riverside Mansions, Garnet St., London E1W 3TB — MB BS 1989 Lond.

MARSDEN, Julian Kay Bradley and Partners, 30 Woodland Avenue, Luton LU3 1RW Tel: 01582 572239 Fax: 01582 494227; 2 Claygate Avenue, Harpenden AL5 2HF — MB ChB 1981 Liverp.; MRCGP 1988; DRCOG 1985. VTS Course Organiser Luton & Dunstable; Educat. Sec. Herts. & Beds. Fac. RCGP.

MARSDEN, Julie Helen Hyde Park Surgery, 3 Woodsley Road, Leeds LS6 1SG Tel: 0113 295 1235 Fax: 0113 295 1220; 24 Hillway, Tranmere Park, Guiseley, Leeds LS20 8HB — MB ChB 1981 Leeds; DRCOG 1985; Cert. Family Plann. JCC 1985. GP Leeds.

MARSDEN, Karen 84 Rowan Croft, Clayton Le Woods, Chorley PR6 7UX — MB ChB 1995 Leeds; DRCOG 1997. SHO & GP Regist. on VTS.

MARSDEN, Kenneth John The Boots Co. Plc., Occupational Health Service, D101 Surgery, Thane Road, Nottingham NG2 3AA Tel: 0115 959 3656; Talbenny, Park Avenue, Plumtree Park, Nottingham NG12 5LU — MB BS 1981 Lond.; MRCGP 1986; MFOM RCP Lond. 1993, AFOM 1989; DCH RCP Lond. 1986; DRCOG 1985. (King's College Hospital) Chief. Med. Off., The Boots Co. Plc.

MARSDEN, Mary Eileen (retired) Beechway, Coleford, Crediton EX17 5DG Tel: 01363 82947 — MB ChB 1945 Manch.; MRCS Eng. LRCP Lond. 1946. Prev: SHMO S. W.. RHB Blood Transfus. Serv.

MARSDEN, Michael Ruairidh 20 Beeches Avenue, Carshalton SM5 3LW — MB ChB 1996 Birm.; ChB Birm. 1996.

MARSDEN, Neville 29 Gisburn Road, Barrowford, Nelson BB9 8ND Tel: 01282 619582 — MRCS Eng. LRCP Lond. 1963; DObst RCOG 1969; Cert. Av. Med. 1981. (Manch.) Med. Adviser & Exam. Med. Pract. Benefits Agency. Socs: Fell. Manch. Med. Soc. Prev: Clin. Asst. (Orthop., Accid & Fract.) Burnley Gen. Hosp.

MARSDEN, Philip (retired) 51 Carson Road, London SE21 8HT Tel: 020 8670 9838 — BSc Lond. 1962, MD 1976, MB BS 1965; FRCP Lond. 1982, M 1968. Cons. Phys. Greenwich Dist. Hosp. Lond. Prev: Sen. Lect. (Med.) King's Coll. Hosp. Med. Sch. Lond.

MARSDEN, Philippa Jane University of North Durham, North Road, Durham DH1 5TW Tel: 0191 333 2333 — MB BS 1985 Newc.; MD 1999; MRCOG 1990. p/t Cons. Obst. & Gynaecologist Univ. Hosp. of N. Durh., N. Durh. Health Care Trust. Prev: Research Regist. (O & G) Newc. 1992-1995; Sen. Regist. - RH, Newc. 1995-1996; Sen. Regist. - Sunderland Roy. Hosp. 1997-1998.

***MARSDEN, Rachel** 288 Hill Lane, Upper Shirley, Southampton SO15 7NU — BM 1995 Soton.

MARSDEN, Robert Allan St. Georges Hospital, Blackshaw Road, London SW17 0QT Tel: 020 8725 1996 Fax: 020 8725 3297; 28 The Warren, Carshalton SM5 4EH Tel: 020 8661 0016 — MB ChB 1970 St. And.; FRCP Lond. 1987, M 1973. Phys. Skin Dept. St. Geo. Hosp. Socs: (Ex Hon. Sec.) Brit. Assn. Dermat.; Pres. Elect, Brit. Assn. Dermat. Prev: Chairm. Dermat. & Venereol. Sub Comm. of CCSC of BMA; Hon. Sec. Brit. Skin Foundat.

MARSDEN, Robert Barnby Beaumont Street Surgery, 27 Beaumont Street, Oxford City, Oxford OX1 2NR Tel: 01865 311500 Fax: 01865 311720; Cross Keys House, Manor Road, South Hinksey, Oxford OX1 5AS Tel: 01865 327447 — MB BS 1982 Lond.; LMSSA Lond. 1981; DRCOG 1988. (King's Coll. Hosp.) Hosp. Med. Represen. Oxf. Community Hosp. Socs: Oxf. Med. Soc.

MARSDEN, Stuart Neil Edson The Gardens, Lambton Park, Chester-le-Street DH3 4PN — MB BS 1982 Newc.; BMedSc Newc. 1979, MB BS 1982; MRCP (UK) 1985. Regist. (Diag. Radiol.) Newc. Hosps.

MARSDEN, Susan Mary Cantilupe Surgery, 49-51 St. Owen Street, Hereford HR1 2JB Tel: 01432 268031 Fax: 01432 352584 — MB ChB 1973 Liverp. Socs: Herefordsh. Med. Soc. Prev: GP Bristol; Trainee GP Gtr. Glas. HB; Ho. Phys. & Ho. Surg. Airedale Gen. Hosp.

***MARSDEN-WILLIAMS, Joanna** 47 Hereford Road, Monmouth NP25 3HQ — MB BS 1996 Lond.

***MARSH, Aidan John** 25 Courtenay Road, Winchester SO23 7ER — MB ChB 1995 Bristol.

MARSH, Alastair John Niall Stoke Mandeville Hospital, Mandeville Road, Aylesbury HP21 8AL — MB ChB 1995 Birm. (Univ. Birm.) SHO Rotat. (Surg.) Stoke Mandeville Aylesbury. Prev: SHO (A & E) Heartlands Hosp. Birm.; Ho. Off. (Surg.) Qu. Eliz. Hosp. Birm.

MARSH, Ann Marion 28 Lydon Road, London SW4 0HW Tel: 020 7720 9279 Fax: 020 7720 9279 — MB BS 1979 Lond.; MRCP (UK) 1982; FRCA 1985.

MARSH, Anthony James Marsh, Kennedy, Phipps, Chapman and Wilde, Netherfield Medical Practice, 2A Forester Street, Netherfield, Nottingham NG4 2NJ Tel: 0115 940 3775 Fax: 0115 961 4069 — BM BS 1976 Nottm.; MRCGP 1981; DRCOG 1980. GP Nottm.

MARSH, Antonia Margaret Blaise (retired) 31 Ouley Road, Ballinaskeagh, Banbridge BT32 5DD Tel: 0182 065 1277 — MB BCh BAO 1958 NUI; LM Coombe 1960; FFA RCSI 1970; DCH NUI

MARSH

1960. Cons. Anaesth. Craigavon, Lurgan, Banbridge & Dromore Hosps. Prev: SHO Coombe Lying-in Hosp. Dub.

MARSH, Brian Andrew Huntley Herons Ghyll, Porchfield, Newport PO30 4LW — BM BCh 1993 Oxf.

MARSH, Brian Thomas 100 Denham Lane, Chalfont St Peter, Gerrards Cross SL9 0QJ Tel: 01753 889072 Fax: 01753 890383 Email: btmarsh@compuserve.com — MB BS (Hons. Distinc. Surg.) Lond. 1962; BA Open 1991; MRCS Eng. LRCP Lond. 1962; FFPM RCP (UK) 1989; DObst RCOG 1965. (St. Bart.) Indep. Cons. Pharmaceut. Med. Socs: Liveryman Worshipful Soc. Apoth. Lond.; Fell. Roy. Soc. Med. (Ex-Pres. Pharmaceut. Med. Sect.); (Ex-Chairm.) Brit. Assn. Pharmaceut. Phys. Prev: Med. Dir. Leo Laboratories Ltd.; Ho. Surg. (Cas.) & Ho. Phys. St. Bart. Hosp. Lond.; Ho. Surg. (Obst.) Roy. Free Hosp. Lond.

MARSH, Carolyn Kendrick Paxton Green Health Centre, 1 Alleyn Park, Dulwich, London SE21; 16 Ildersly Grove, Dulwich, London SE21 8EU Tel: 020 8670 0856 — MB BS 1986 Lond.; MRCGP 1990; DRCOG 1989. Prev: Trainee GP Redhill VTS; Ho. Surg. St. Bart. Hosp. Lond.; Ho. Phys. Whipps Cross Hosp. Lond.

MARSH, Miss Catherine Sarah Eye Department, Queen Alexandra Hospital, Cosham, Portsmouth; 20 Charlton Road, Shirley, Southampton SO15 5FN Tel: 01703 226766 Email: cathmarsh@compuserve.com — MB ChB 1993 Bristol; BSc (Hons.) Bristol 1990; FRCOphth Lond. 1997. (Bristol) Specialist Regist. Rotat. (Ophth.) Wessex. Prev: Sen. Ho. Off. (Ophth.) Qu. Med. Centre Nottm.; Sen. Ho. Off. (Ophth.) W. of Eng. Eye Unit, Exeter.

MARSH, Christine Marion Grovehurst Surgery, Grovehurst Road, Kemsley, Sittingbourne ME10 2ST Tel: 01795 430444 Fax: 01795 410539; 17 Newton Road, Faversham ME13 8DZ Tel: 01795 539846 — MB BS 1979 Lond.; MRCP (UK) 1983; MRCGP 1984; DRCOG 1981. (Roy. Free Hosp. Sch. Med. Lond.)

MARSH, Christopher Roger 525 Chester Road S., Kidderminster DY10 1XH Tel: 01562 744036 — MB ChB 1982 Birm.; DA (UK) 1986. Staff Grade Anaesth. Cheltenham Hosp. Glos. Socs: Assn. Anaesth.; Obst. Anaesth. Assn. Prev: Regist. (Anaesth.) Gloucester Roy. Hosp.; Regist. (Anaesth.) Dudley Rd. Hosp. Birm. & Kidderminster Gen. Hosp.

MARSH, David Ian Studfall Medical Centre, Studfall Avenue, Corby NN17 1LG Tel: 01536 401372 Fax: 01536 401300; Old School House, Gretton, Corby NN17 3DE Tel: 01536 770682 — MB BS 1969 Lond. Clin. Asst. (Cardiol.) Nuffield Diag. Centre Kettering Gen. Hosp.

MARSH, David Max 63 Henlow Avenue, Kirkby, Liverpool L32 9RN Tel: 0151 549 2212 Fax: 0151 546 7875; 26 Blundell Drive, Southport PR8 4RG Tel: 01704 65639 — MRCS Eng. LRCP Lond. 1959; MB Camb. 1960, BChir 1959; MFOM RCP Lond. 1984; DIH Eng. 1973. (Camb.) Employm. Med. Adviser Dept. Employm. H & SE. Prev: Ho. Phys. & Ho. Surg. (Midw.) Sefton Gen. Hosp.

MARSH, David Raymond George Southern General Hospital, 1345 Govan Road, Glasgow G51 4TF Tel: 0141 201 1658 Fax: 0141 201 1321 Email: sgh.anaesthesia@virgin.net; 15 Laigh Road, Newton Mearns, Glasgow G77 5EX — MB ChB 1972 Glas.; FFA RCSI 1980; DObst RCOG 1974. Cons. Anaesth. S.. Gen. Hosp. Glas.; Hon. Clin. Sen. Lect. Glas. Univ. Prev: Sen. Regist. (Anaesth.) Sheff. Hosps.; Regist. & SHO (Anaesth.) Vict. Infirm. Glas.

MARSH, Professor David Russell QUB, Musculoskeletal & Research Unit, Musgrave Prak Hospital, Stockman's Lane, Belfast BT9 7JB Tel: 01232 669501 Ext: 2848 Fax: 01232 661112 Email: d.marsh@qub.ac.uk; 102 Princetown Road, Bangor BT20 3TG — MD 1990 Camb.; MA Camb. 1976, MB BChir 1976; FRCS Eng. 1980. (Churchill College Cambridge) Prof. of Trauma & Orthop. Surg. Qu.s Univ. Belf.; Hon. Cons. Roy. Vict. Hosp. & Musgrave Pk. Hosp. Belf. Socs: BORS; (Scientif. Sec.) ISFR (Internat. Soc. for Fractur Repair); BOA. Prev: Sen. Lect. (Orthop.) Manch. Univ.; Lect. (Orthop.) Manch. Univ.; Regist. (Orthop.) P'boro. Dist. Hosp. & Addenbrooke's Hosp. Camb.

MARSH, Deborah Frances 25 Courtenay Road, Winchester SO23 7ER — MB BS 1986 Lond.

MARSH, Deborah Jane 12 Clough Grove, Bryn, Wigan WN4 0LP Tel: 01942 201706; Northside, 14 East Downs Road, Bowdon, Altrincham WA14 2LQ Tel: 0161 929 0393 Email: debbiemarsh@hotmail.com — MB ChB 1989 Leeds; MRCGP 1994; DFFP 1993; DRCOG 1993. Socs: Brit. Menopause Soc. Prev: Trainee GP Manch.; SHO (Paediat.) Manch.; SHO (Gyn.) St. Mary's Hosp. Manch.

MARSH, Diane Lee Morston, St. Omer Road, Guildford GU1 2DA Tel: 01483 576762 — MB BCh 1986 Witwatersrand.

***MARSH, Felicity Joan** 8 Thornleigh Road, Jesmond, Newcastle upon Tyne NE2 3ET — MB BS 1996 Newc.

MARSH, Francis Patrick Renal Unit The Royal London Hospital, Whitechapel, London E1 1BB Tel: 020 7377 7367 Fax: 020 7377 7003; 28 Highfield Drive, Bromley E1 1BB Tel: 020 8460 6295 Fax: 020 7460 6295 — MB BChir Camb. 1960; MA Camb. 1961; FRCP Lond. 1976, M 1963. (Camb.) Cons. Phys. (Nephrol.) & Hon. Sen. Lect. (Med.) Roy. Lond. Hosp. Socs: Eur. Renal Assn.; Brit. Transpl. Soc.; Internat. Soc. Nephrol. Prev: Research Fell. & Regist. (Med.) Lond. Hosp.; Resid. Med. Off. Roy. Free Hosp. Lond.; SHO Kent & Canterbury Hosp.

MARSH, Mr Gavin David John Mayday Hospital, Department of Traumatic & Orthopaedic Surgery, Croydon CR7 7YE Tel: 020 8401 3455 Fax: 020 8401 3100; Ballards Mead, Ballards Lane, Limpsfield, Oxted RH8 0SN Tel: 01883 717432 Fax: 01883 717432 — MB BS 1984 Lond.; FRCS (Orth.) 1993; FRCS Ed. 1989. Cons. Orthop. Surg. Mayday Univ. Hosp. Thornton Heath. Prev: Sen. Regist. (Orthop. Surg.) King's Coll. Hosp. Lond.; Regist. (Orthop. Surg.) King's Coll. Hosp. Lond.; SHO (Plastic Surg.) Char. Cross Hosp. Lond.

MARSH, Geoffrey Norman, MBE (retired) The Old Vicarage, Bolam, Darlington DL2 2UP Tel: 01388 832499 — MB BS 1953 Durh.; MD Newc. 1974; FRCGP 1972, M 1965; Hon. MCFPC 1982; DObst RCOG 1958; DCH Eng. 1957. Fell. Centre for Health & Advanced Nursing Studies Univ. Durh. Prev: Vis. Prof. Family Pract. Univ. Iowa, USA.

MARSH, Heather Taunton & Somerset NHS Trust, Musgrove Park Hospital, Taunton TA1 5DA Tel: 01823 333444; Camelot, Trull, Taunton TA3 7EN Tel: 01823 272959 — MB ChB 1980 Sheff.; MD Bristol 1994; T(OG) 1992; MRCOG 1987; FRCOG 1999. (Sheffield University Medical School) Cons. O & G Taunton & Som. NHS Trust. Prev: Sen. Regist. (O & G) Arrowe Pk. Hosp. & Univ. Liverp.; Research Regist. (O & G) Bristol Matern. Hosp. & Bristol Roy. Infirm.; Regist. (O & G) Bristol Matern. & Bristol Gen. Hosps.

MARSH, Mr Henry Thomas 25 Dora Road, Wimbledon, London SW19 7EZ; Atkinson Morley's Hospital, Wimbledon, London SW20 0NE Tel: 020 8946 7711 Fax: 020 8947 8381 Email: henrymarsh@compuserve — MB BS 1979 Lond.; MB BS (Hons.) Lond. 1979; MA (1st cl. Hons.) Oxf. 1973; FRCS Eng. 1983. Cons. Neurosurg. Atkinson Morley's Hosp. Wimbledon; Hon. Cons. Neurosurg. Univ. Hosp. Wales, Cardiff; Assoc. Clin. Prof. Neurosurg. Univ. of Washington, Seattle, USA; Hon. Mem. Counc. Governors Emerg. Hosp. Kiev, Ukraine. Socs: Roy. Soc. Med. (Counc. Neurol. Sect.); (Advisory Counc. Soc.) Brit. Neurol. Surg.; Brit. Paediat. Neurosurg. Gp. Prev: Sen. Regist. (Neurosurg.) Nat. Hosp. Nerv. Dis. & Hosp. for Sick Childr. Lond.

MARSH, Howard Piers 86C College Place, London NW1 0DJ — MB ChB 1993 Bristol. Demonst. (Anat.) Guy's Hosp. Lond. Socs: BMA; MDU.

MARSH, Howard Stephen 103 Newport Road, Cardiff CF24 0AF Tel: 029 2048 5526; 40 Hollybush Road, Cyncoed, Cardiff CF23 6TA — MB BS 1981 Lond.; MRCP (UK) 1988; MRCGP 1987; DRCOG 1988. MacMillan Clin. Fell. (Gen. Pract.) Univ. Wales. Prev: Regist. (Palliat. Med.) Holme Tower Penarth; Regist. (Med.) Kent & Sussex Hosp. Tunbridge Wells.

MARSH, Mr Ian Bruce 86 Rodney Street, Liverpool L1 9AR Tel: 0151 707 1585 Fax: 0151 709 7509 Email: ian.marsh@virgin.net; 8 Bursar Close, Newton-le-Willows WA12 9JS Tel: 01925 227716 Fax: 01925 227716 — MB ChB 1978 Manch.; FRCS Ed. 1984; FRCOphth 1989. Cons. Ophth. Aintree Hosps. NHS Trust. Prev: Sen. Regist. NW RHA.

MARSH, Jacqueline Mary Health Centre, Greenside, Cleckheaton BD19 5AP Tel: 01279 242000 Fax: 01274 242001; High Meadows, Wellands Lane, Scholes, Cleckheaton BD19 6EY Tel: 01274 872386 — MB BCh Wales 1963; DObst RCOG 1966. (Welsh Nat. Sch. Med.) SCMO Dewsbury Health Care Trust; Family Plann. Instruc. Doctor W. Yorks. Prev: Ho. Phys. Llandough Hosp. Penarth.

MARSH, James Edward 27A Gardner Road, Guildford GU1 4PG — MB BS 1990 Lond.; MRCP Lond. 1993. SHO (Nephrol.) Guy's Hosp. Lond.

MARSH, Janette Isobel Carolside Medical Centre, 1 Carolside Gardens, Clarkston, Glasgow G76 7BS Tel: 0141 644 3511 Fax: 0141 644 5525; 15 Laigh Road, Newton Mearns, Glasgow G77 5EX Tel: 0141 639 7149 — MB ChB 1971 Glas. (Glas.) Clin Med. Off. (Child Health) Gtr. Glas. HB.

MARSH, Joanna Lucy TF1D, 1 Warrender Park Crescent, Edinburgh EH9 1DX — MB ChB 1997 Leic.

MARSH, Mr John David (retired) 59 Beauchamp Avenue, Leamington Spa CV32 5TB Tel: 01926 427239 Email: j-marsh@dircom.co.uk — MB BChir 1949 Camb.; MA Camb. 1950, BA (2nd cl. Pt. I Nat. Sc. Trip.; 1st cl. Pt. II Nat. Sc. Trip.) 1946, MChir 1959; FRCS Eng. 1956. Prev: Cons. Surg. S. Warw. Hosp. Gp.

MARSH, Judith Christine Watson Department of Haemotology, St George's Hospital, Cranmer Terrace, London SW17 0RE Tel: 020 8725 3545 Fax: 020 8725 0245 — MD 1976 Birm.; BSc (Med. Biochem. Studies) Birm. 1976; FRCP 1997; MRCP (UK) 1982; FRCPath 1997; MRCPath 1986; MB ChB 1979 Birmingham. (Birm. Univ.) Reader & Hon. Cons. Haemat. St Geo. Hosp. Med. Sch. Lond. Prev: Sen. Regist. (Haemat.) Roy. Postgrad. Med. Sch. Hammersmith Hosp. Lond.

***MARSH, Katharine Dora** 136 Park Road, London W4 3HP — MB ChB 1995 Glas.

MARSH, Kenneth Edwin 8 High Park Road, Broadstone BH18 9DE — MB BChir 1946 Camb. (Camb. & St. Geo.)

MARSH, Leela Fernanda 1 Chapel Lane, Lambley, Nottingham NG4 4PT — BM BS 1975 Nottm.

MARSH, Leesa Marie Rossarden House, Alexandria G83 8NU; Ross Arden House, Luss, Alexandria G83 8NU Tel: 01436 860619 Fax: 01436 860306 Email: ets@btinternet.com — MB ChB 1989 Bristol. Clin. Research Fell. Univ. Glas. Prev: SHO Roy. Cornw. Hosp. (Treliske) Truro.; Ho. Surg. Bristol Roy. Infirm.; Ho. Phys. Bristol Gen. Hosp.

MARSH, Marion Elizabeth (retired) 3 Parkwood Avenue, Esher KT10 8DE — MB BS 1956 Lond.; DCH Eng. 1960. Prev: Med. Off. Richmond, Twickenham & Roehampton HA.

***MARSH, Matthew James** Top Farm, The Tye, Barking, Ipswich IP6 8JD — BM 1997 Soton.

MARSH, Michael Harding (retired) The Willows, 3A Eastwood End, Wimblington, Peterborough PE15 0QQ Tel: 01354 740115 Fax: 01354 740115 Email: mhmarsh@tesco.net — LMSSA Lond. 1959; DObst RCOG 1965. Prev: Ho. Surg. Dorset Co. Hosp.

MARSH, Michael John Department of Paediatrics, Guys Hospital, St Thomas' St., London SE1 9RT Tel: 020 7966 5000 Fax: 020 7955 2563 Email: m.march@umds.ac.uk; 23 Glen House Road, Eltham, London SE9 1JH — MB BS 1986 Lond.; MRCP (UK) 1990. Cons. Paeediat. Intens. Care Guy's Hosp. Lond. Prev: Sen. Regist. (Paediat.) Guy's Hosp. Lond.; Research Regist. (Paediat.) St. Thos. Hosp. Lond.; SHO (Neonatol.) John Radcliffe Hosp. Oxf.

MARSH, Michael Newton University Department Medicine, Hope Hospital, Eccles Old Road, Salford M6 8HD Tel: 0161 787 4362 Fax: 0161 787 7432 Email: mmarsh@fsl.ho.man.ac.uk; 12 Grangeway, Handforth, Wilmslow SK9 3HZ Tel: 01625 525838 — BM BCh 1962 Oxf.; DSc Leeds 1992, BSc 1960; DM Oxf 1972; FRCP Lond. 1980, M 1967; DCH Eng. 1965; DObst RCOG 1965. Reader (Med.) Manch. Univ. & Cons. Phys. Hope Hosp. Salford; Vis. Prof. Univ. Nebraska Med. Centre Omaha, USA; Distinguished Vis. Schol. Univ. Adelaide, S. Austral.; Vis. Prof. Dept. Intern. Med. Gastroenterol. Univ. Iowa, USA; Vis. Prof. Dept. Med. Otago Univ. Med. Sch. Dunedin, New Zealand. Socs: Brit. Soc. Gastroenterol. & Brit. Soc. Immunol. Prev: Lect. (Med.) Univ. Soton.; MRC Trav. Fell. Boston Univ., USA; Regist. (Gastroenterol.) Hammersmith Hosp. Lond.

MARSH, Michael Stephen Academic Department of Obs. & Gynae., 9th Floor, Ruskin Wing, King's College Hospital, London SE5 9JP Tel: 020 7346 3629 — MB BS 1982 Lond.; MD Lond. 1995; MRCOG 1988; CCST 1997. (Guy's) Cons. / Sen. Lect. (Obst. and Gyn.) King's Coll. Hosp. Prev: Sen. Regist. (O & G) Roy. Free Hosp. Lond.; Research Fell. King's Coll. Hosp. Lond.; Regist. (O & G) St. Mary's Hosp. Lond. & Samarit. Hosp. for Wom. Lond.

***MARSH, Nicola Catherine** 23 Impstone Road, Pamber Heath, Tadley RG26 3EQ — MB ChB 1997 Birm.

MARSH, Philip John Microbiology Department, Bradford Royal Infirmary, Duckworth Lane, Bradford BD9 6RJ; Hollings Farm, 14 The Hollings, Hebden Bridge HX7 7DZ — MB ChB 1980 Ed.; MRCPath 1992. Cons. Med. Microbiologist Bradford Acute Hosps. (NHS) Trust.

MARSH, Philippa Julia Jane The Old Rectory, Wrington, Bristol BS40 5LD — MB BS Lond. 1970; MRCS Eng. LRCP Lond. 1970. (St. Bart. Hosp. Med. Coll.)

MARSH, Rachel Mary 22 Gregory Avenue, Coventry CV3 6DL — MB ChB 1993 Leic. SHO (Gen. Med.) Geo. Eliot Hosp. Nuneaton.

MARSH, Mr Ralph Lionel Radiology Department, Sunderland Royal Hospital, Kayll Road, Sunderland SR4 7TP Tel: 0191 565 6256 — MB BS 1983 Lond.; FRCS Ed. 1987; FRCR 1990. Cons. Radiol. Sunderland Roy. Hosp. Prev: Sen. Regist. & Regist. (Radiol.) Newc. Gp. Hosps.; SHO (Gen. Surg.) Roy. Shrewsbury Hosp.; SHO (Orthop., A & E) Univ. Hosp. Nottm.

MARSH, Richard Henry Kendal c/o Department of Anaesthetics, Northampton General Hospital, Cliftonville, Northampton NN1 5BD Tel: 01604 545671 Fax: 01604 545670 Email: richard.marsh@doctors.org.uk; New Barns, High St, Ravensthorpe, Northampton NN6 8EH Tel: 01604 770868 Fax: 01604 770944 — BM BCh 1975 Oxf.; MA Oxf. 1975; FRCA Eng. 1979. (Oxford and Guy's Hospital) Cons. Anaesth. N.ampton Gen. Hosp.; Dir. Intens. Ther. Unit N.ampton; Regional Adviser for Anaesth. Socs: Intens. Care Soc.; Hist. Anaesth. Soc.; Anaesth. Res. Soc. Prev: Sen. Regist. W.. Infirm. Glas.; Regist. Clin. Shock Study Gp. Glas.; Regist. Nuffield Dept. Anaesth. Oxf.

MARSH, Richard John 153 Hahnemann Court, Southwick, Sunderland SR5 2SQ Tel: 0191 548 1338 — BM BCh 1972 Oxf.; MRCGP 1994. Author. Socs: Brit. Soc. Allergy & Environm. Med.; Brit. Soc. Nutrit. Med. Prev: Dir. of Clin. Nutrit. Hosp. Santo Thomas, Rosarito Mexico; Med. Adviser Wyeth Laborat.

MARSH, Robert Durward Top Farm, Barkingtye, Ipswich IP6 8JD' — BM 1995 Soton. SHO Basic Surgic. Rotat., Ipswich Hosp. NHST, Ipswich.

MARSH, Robin Conon House, Church Lane, Curdridge, Southampton SO32 2DR Tel: 01489 782488 Fax: 01489 782470 — MB BChir Camb. 1959; MA Camb. 1959; MRCS Eng. LRCP Lond. 1959; MRCGP 1970; DObst RCOG 1962. (Guy's) Med. Advisor to Steven Yeadon Trust, 18, Sherwood Ave., Hedge End, Soton., SO30 0JY. Socs: BMA & Soton. Med. Soc.; Fell. Roy. Soc. Of Med. Prev: SHO (O & G) Hitchin Hosps.; Ho. Phys. & Ho. Surg. Lewisham Gen. Hosp.; Ho. Phys. Childr. Annexe, Luton & Dunstable Hosp.

MARSH, Mr Ronald John 149 Harley Street, London W1G 6DE Tel: 020 7935 4444 Fax: 020 7486 1592; 35 Cheam Road, Ewell, Epsom KT17 1QX Tel: 020 8394 0482 Fax: 020 8394 0482 — MB BS (Hons.) Lond. 1963; FRCS Eng. 1969; MRCS Eng. LRCP Lond. 1963; FRCOphth 1989; DO RCS Eng. 1967; MD 1999 London. (Lond. Hosp.) Hon. Cons. Moorfields Eye Hosp. Lond.; Hon. Cons. Ophth. St. Mary's Hosp. Lond. Socs: Fell. Roy. Soc. Med. (Past Pres. Ophth. Sect.). Prev: Sen. Regist. Moorfields Eye Hosp. Lond.; SHO W. Ophth. Hosp. Lond.; Ho. Phys., Ho. Surg. (Ophth.) Lond. Hosp.

MARSH, Selwyn George The Health Centre, Chagford, Newton Abbot TQ13 8BW Tel: 01647 433320 Fax: 01647 432425 — MB ChB 1962 Bristol; MRCGP 1974. (Bristol) Prev: SHO (Med.) Plymouth Gen. Hosp.; Ho. Phys. Frenchay Hosp. Bristol; Asst. Resid. Med. Off. Bristol Childr. Hosp.

***MARSH, Sian Fiona** 113 Cop La, Penwortham, Preston PR1 9AH — MB BS 1997 Lond.

MARSH, Mr Simon Keith The Breast Unit, Essex County Hospital, Lexden Road, Colchester CO3 3NB Tel: 01206 744410 Fax: 01206 744654; The Cottage, 24 Lower Road, Falkenham, Ipswich IP10 0RA — MB BChir 1988 Camb.; MA Camb. 1989; FRCS Eng. 1992; FRCS (Gen. Surg.) 1998; MD (CANTAB) 1998. (Camb.) Cons. (Gen. Surg.) Essex Rivers Health Care NHS Trust; Assoc. Cons. The Lond. BrE. Clinic 108 Harley St. Lond.; Surgic. Directory the Ivry St. Day Surg. Socs: BMA; BASO; RSM. Prev: Sen. Regist. (Gen. Surg.) Norf. & Norwich Hosp.; Research Fell. Imperial Coll. Sch. of Med. Char. Cross. Campus.

***MARSH, Suzanne Elizabeth** 11 Masons Rise, Broadstairs CT10 1AY — MB ChB 1997 Birm.

MARSH, Thomas Durward County Practice, Barking Road, Needham Market, Ipswich IP6 8EZ Tel: 01449 720666 Fax: 01449 720030; Top Farm, Barking Tye, Ipswich IP6 8JD Tel: 01473

MARSH

658583 — MB BS Lond. 1967; MRCS Eng. LRCP Lond. 1966; MRCGP 1980. (Lond. Hosp.)

MARSH, Valerie Christine The Scott Practice, 1 Greenfield Lane, Balby, Doncaster DN4 0TG Tel: 01302 850546 Fax: 01302 855338 — MB ChB 1970 Dundee; DObst RCOG 1972.

MARSH, William Gavin 61 Crawfordsburn Road, Newtownards BT23 4UH — MB BCh BAO 1988 NUI; MRCP (UK) 1991; FRCOphth 1995; MRCGP 1997. GP Cardiff. Prev: SHO Psychiat. Bristol; SHO (Ophth.) Bristol Eye Hosp. & Roy. Devon & Exeter Hosp.; SHO (Med.) S. Tyrone Hosp.

MARSHALL, Adrian John Felix House Surgery, Middleton Lane, Middleton St. George, Darlington DL2 1AE Tel: 01325 332235 Fax: 01325 333626 — MB BCh BAO 1980 Belf.; MRCGP 1985.

MARSHALL, Aileen Elizabeth 16 Gisborne Road, Cambridge CB1 3RZ — MB ChB 1994 Aberd.

MARSHALL, Alan Charles Department of Anaesthesia, Birmingham Heartlands Hospital, Bordesley Green E., Birmingham B9 5SS Tel: 0121 766 6611 Ext: 5153 Email: marshaa@heartsol.wmids.nhs.uk — MB BCh BAO 1988 Dub.; MB BCh BAO (Hons.) Dub. 1988; MRCP (UK) 1991; FRCA 1994. (Trinity College Dublin) Cons. in Anesthesia & IC. Birm. heartlands & Solihull NHST (Teachg.). Socs: Intens. Care Soc.; Assn. Anaesth.; BMA. Prev: Specialist Regist. (IC) UCL Hosps. NHS Trust Lond.; Regist. (IC) The Qu. Eliz. Hosp. Adelaide Australia; Specialist Regist. (Anaesth.) Rotat. UCL Hosps. NHS Trust Lond.

MARSHALL, Alexander Trianon, 7 Baird's Hill, Broadstairs CT10 3AA — MB ChB 1964 Ed.; FRCP Ed. 1980, M 1968. Cons. Phys. I. of Thanet & Kent & Canterbury Hosps. Socs: BMA & Brit. Diabetic Assn. Prev: Clin. & Research Fell. Indiana Univ.; Sen. Med. Regist. Roy. Infirm. Edin.

MARSHALL, Alexander James 22 Myrtle Drive, Kirkham, Preston PR4 2ZJ — MB BS 1986 Newc.

MARSHALL, Alexander John (retired) 21 Holohouse Road, Eaglesham, Glasgow G76 0JF Tel: 01355 301714 — MB ChB Glas. 1956. Prev: Capt. RAMC.

MARSHALL, Alexander Joseph Clova, Silverbirches Lane, Aspley Heath, Woburn Sands, Milton Keynes MK17 8TL Tel: 01908 583660 — MB ChB 1934 St. And. (St. And.) Prev: Ho. Surg. & Ho. Phys. Roy. Infirm. Dundee; Med. Off. Malayan Med. Serv.

MARSHALL, Aline Fiona 1/6 Windmill Pl, Edinburgh EH8 9XQ — MB ChB 1997 Ed.

MARSHALL, Alison Mary Brookside Group Practice, Brookside Close, Gipsy Lane, Earley, Reading RG6 7HG Tel: 0118 966 9222 Fax: 0118 935 3174; 36 Bulmershe Road, Reading RG1 5RJ Tel: 0118 668794 — MB BS 1979 Lond.; MRCGP 1984. (Middlx.)

MARSHALL, Alison Tarnya School Medicine, Health, Policy & Practice, University of East Anglia, Norwich NR4 7TJ Email: t.marshall@ued.dc.uk; 54B The Causeway, Cambridge CB5 0DU — MB BS 1992 Lond.; MRCP (UK) 1996. Sen. Research Assoc., Univ. of E. Anglia. Socs: BMA; BSR.

MARSHALL, Alistair Graeme Anaesthetic Department, Royal London Hospital, Whitechapel, London E1 1BB Tel: 020 7377 7793; 62 Parkgate Avenue, Hadley Wood, Barnet EN4 0NR — MB ChB Otago 1970; BSc NZ 1965; FFA RCS Eng. 1978. (Otago) Cons. Anaesth. (Cardiothoracic & Paediat.) Roy. Lond. Hosps. Trust.

MARSHALL, Allan Logie Aultbea and Gairloch Medical Practice, The Health Centre, Auchtercairn, Gairloch IV21 2BH Tel: 01445 712229; 9 The Croft, Poolewe, Achnasheen IV22 2JY Tel: 01445 781326 — MB ChB 1969 Ed.; DA Eng. 1973; DObst RCOG 1975. (Ed.) Socs: BMA; Highland Med. Soc.; Inducement Practs. Assn. Scott. Prev: SHO (Anaesth.) & SHO (Gen. Med.) Torbay Hosp. Torquay.

MARSHALL, Ana Maria 13 Park House Lane, Prestbury, Macclesfield SK10 4HZ Tel: 01625 828134 — LMS 1977 Barcelona; MSc (Parasitol. & Med. Entomol.) Liverp. 1991; LRCP LRCS Ed. LRCPS Glas. 1985; DTM & H Liverp. 1990. (Universidad Autonoma De Barcelona) Prev: GP/Regist. The Health Centre Holmes Chapel Chesh.

MARSHALL, Andrew Plot 87, Byeways Est., Muxton, Telford TF2 — MB ChB 1992 Birm.

MARSHALL, Andrew Geoffrey 10 Glenholm Road, Liverpool L31 7BD — MB ChB 1993 Manch.

MARSHALL, Andrew Gregory Carn Ingli, Love Lane, Denbigh LL16 3LY — MB ChB 1991 Otago.

MARSHALL, Andrew Hugh 14 Brandling Park, Newcastle upon Tyne NE2 4RR Tel: 0191 281 4091 Fax: 0191 281 4091 — MB BS 1994 Lond.; BSc Lond. 1991. (Lond. Hosp. Med. Coll.) SHO Basic Surgic. Train. N. Region. Prev: Demonst. anat. Univ. Newc.; Hse. Surg. Roy. Lond. Hosp.

MARSHALL, Andrew Huw Portland Road Surgery, 31 Portland Road, Kilmarnock KA1 2DJ Tel: 01563 522118 Fax: 01563 573562 — MB ChB 1978 Glas.

MARSHALL, Andrew Jamieson Department of Cardiology, Derriford Hospital, Plymouth PL6 8DH Tel: 01752 777111; Chubb Tor, Yelverton PL20 6JA — MB BS 1967 Lond.; MD Bristol 1977; FRCP Lond. 1986; MRCP (UK) 1970. (Westm.) Cons. Cardiol. Derriford Hosp. Plymouth; Civil. Cons. Cardiol. RN Hosp. Plymouth; Hon. Sen. Lect. Plymouth Postgrad. Med. Sch. Socs: Brit. Cardiac Soc.; Brit. Pacing & Electrophysiol. Gp. Prev: Sen. Regist. (Med.) Bristol Roy. Infirm.; Tutor (Med.) Univ. Bristol.

MARSHALL, Andrew John Regent Square Group Practice, 8-9 Regent Square, Doncaster DN1 2DS Tel: 01302 819999 Fax: 01302 369204; 237 Bawtry Road, Doncaster DN4 7AL — MB ChB 1978 Sheff.; MB ChB (Distinc. Surg.) Sheff. 1978; DRCOG 1981. Med. Off. Peglers Ltd. & RFS Engin. Doncaster. Socs: Brit. Soc. Med. & Dent. Hypn. & Roy. Coll. Gen. Pract.

MARSHALL, Andrew John Broomhill Practice, 41 Broomhill Drive, Glasgow G11 7AD Tel: 0141 339 3626 Fax: 0141 334 2399; 50 Edgehill Road, Glasgow G11 7JD Tel: 0141 334 3982 — MB ChB 1986 Glas.; MRCGP 1990; DCH RCPS Glas. 1990; DRCOG 1989. GP Glas.

MARSHALL, Andrew Martin, TD Yeadon Health Centre, 17 South View Road, Yeadon, Leeds LS19 7PS — MB ChB 1981 Leeds; BSc Leeds 1978; MRCGP 1985; DRCOG 1983.

MARSHALL, Andrew Stephen Manchester Road Surgery, 484 Manchester Road, Sheffield S10 5PN Tel: 0114 266 8411 — MB ChB 1990 Sheff.

MARSHALL, Ann Elizabeth 12 Essex Close, Powick, Worcester WR2 4PX — MB ChB 1995 Sheff.

MARSHALL, Ann Elizabeth Isobel (retired) 23 Glastonbury Grove, Jesmond, Newcastle upon Tyne NE2 2HB — MB BS 1963 Durh. Prev: Assoc. Specialist (Anaesth.) Freeman Hosp. Trust Newc.

MARSHALL, Anne Katharine Department of Pathology, Oldchurch Hospital, Romford RM2 0BE Tel: 01708 746090; 7 Deepdene Road, London SE5 8EG Tel: 020 7733 2559 — MB BS 1960 Lond.; MRCS Eng. LRCP Lond. 1960; FRCPath 1980, M 1968. Cons. (Neuropath.) OldCh. Hosp. Romford; Hon. Lect. The Lond. Hosp. Prev: Lect. in Morbid. Anat. Roy. Free Hosp. Med. Sch.; Sen. Regist. Univ. Coll. & Whittington Hosps. Lond.; Sen. Regist. (Morbid Anat.) Kings Coll. & Maudsley Hosps. Lond.

MARSHALL, Anne Mochrie Pollock Health Centre, 21 Cowglen Road, Glasgow G53 6EW; Manse of Camphill, 30 Glencairn Drive, Glasgow G41 4PW — MB ChB 1954 Glas.

MARSHALL, Anne Roberta East Lancashire Health Authority, 31-33 Kenyon Road, Lomeshaye Estate, Nelson BB9 5SZ Tel: 01282 610216 Fax: 01282 610213; 27 Spa Garth, Clitheroe BB7 1JD — MB BS 1981 Newc.; MSc Ed. 1988; MFPHM RCP (UK) 1992. Cons. Communicable Dis. Control E. Lancs. HA. Prev: Sen. Regist. (Pub. Health Med.) PHLS Communicable Dis. Surveillance Centre Lond.; Regist. (Pub. Health Med.) Lothian HB; Regist. (Infec. Dis.) Fazakerley Hosp. Liverp.

MARSHALL, Antony David Roy The Health Centre, Duke Street, Hoyland, Barnsley S74 9QS Tel: 01226 743208 Fax: 01226 742557 — MB ChB 1978 Sheff.; MA Camb. 1987; MRCGP 1982.

MARSHALL, Mr Arthur Thomas (retired) Elm Court, Wychbold, Droitwich WR9 0DF Tel: 01527 861237 — MB ChB 1938 Birm.; FRCS Ed. 1955; FRCOG 1964, M 1950. Prev: Cons. O & G S. Worcs. Hosp. Gp.

MARSHALL, Austin Stephen The Surgery, 32 Kingsland Road, West Mersea, Colchester CO5 8RA Tel: 01206 382015 Fax: 01206 385593 — MRCS Eng. LRCP Lond. 1977; BPharm Lond. 1966, MB BS 1977. (Char. Cross) Prev: Course Organiser Colchester & N.E. Essex VTS.; Ho. Phys. (Gen. Med. & Rheumat.) Char. Cross Hosp. Lond.; Ho. Surg. Frimley Pk. Hosp.

MARSHALL, Barbara Ann Holywood Arches Health Centre, Westminster Avenue North, Belfast BT4 1NS Tel: 028 9056 3394 Fax: 028 9065 3846; 10 Cairnburn Road, Knock, Belfast BT4 2HR Tel: 02890 761632 — MB BCh BAO 1977 Belf.; MRCGP 1985.

MARSHALL

MARSHALL, Barbara Sylvia Mary (retired) Fairview House, 25 Hailes St., Winchcombe, Cheltenham GL54 5HU Tel: 01242 603179 — MB ChB 1956 Birm.; FFCM 1981, M 1974. Prev: Med. Dir. Fosse Health Trust.

MARSHALL, Barry Martin Stuart Causeway Hospital, 4 Newbridge Road, Coleraim BT52 1HS Tel: 028 70327032 Fax: 028 70346125 Email: barry.marshall@chsst.n-i.nhs.uk; Cullycapple House, 19 Cullyapple Road, Aghadowey, Coleraine BT51 4AR Tel: 02870 868911 — MB BCh BAO 1980 Belf.; FRCOG 2001; MRCOG 1985; DRCOG 1983. (Queen's University, Belfast) p/t Cons. Obs& Gynac, Causeway Hosp. Coleraine; Cons. Obs& gynae Nrth Wst InDepend. Hosp, Bally Kelly. Socs: Ulster Obst. & Gyn. Soc.; Ulster Med. Soc.; BMA. Prev: Sen. Tutor Roy. Matern. Hosp. Belf.; Lect. Nat. Univ. Hosp., Singapore.

MARSHALL, Basil Yasil (retired) Hampden Cottage, The Green, Horsted Heath, Haywards Heath RH17 7AW Tel: 01825 790372 — MB BCh BAO 1942 Dub.; BA, MB BCh BAO Dub. 1942; MRCGP 1953. Prev: Phys. Caterham & Dist. Hosp. & Oxted Cottage Hosp.

MARSHALL, Benjamin Giles Southampton University Hospitals NHS Trust, Tremona Road, Southampton SO16 6YT Tel: 02380 796228 Fax: 02380 794585 Email: ben.marshall@suht.swest.nhs.uk; 29 Elm Bank Gardens, Barnes, London SW13 0NU Tel: 020 8876 9162 — MB BS 1988 Lond.; MB BS (Hons. Surg.) Lond. 1988; MRCP (UK) 1991; DTM & H RCP Lond. 1992. (St. Mary's Hosp. Med. Sch.) Cons. Phys. Respirat.& Gen. Internal Med. S.amp. Univ. Hosp. S.amp. Socs: BMA; Brit. Soc. Study of Infec.; Roy. Soc. Trop. Med. & Hyg. Prev: Specialist Regist. (Respirat. Med.) St. Mary's Hosp. Lond.; Clin. Research Fell. (Respirat. Med.) St. Mary's Hosp. Lond.; Regist. (Infec. Dis.) Lister Unit N.wick Pk. Hosp. Harrow.

MARSHALL, Bernard Aloysius (retired) Branksome, Warnington Drive, Doncaster DN4 6ST — MB ChB St. And. 1943; DOMS Eng. 1948. Cons. Ophth. Roy. Infirm. Doncaster. Prev: Graded Ophth. RAMC.

MARSHALL, Brenda Elizabeth The Lindens, Barrington Road, Altrincham WA14 1HZ; Lavender Cottage, 37 Lime Grove, Timperley, Altrincham WA15 6PJ Tel: 0161 980 1399 — MB ChB 1976 Glas.

MARSHALL, Brian Symbister Surgery, Symbister, Whalsay, Shetland ZE2 9AE Tel: 01806 56619 — MB BS 1967 Newc. Prev: SHO (O & G) Ashington Hosp.; SHO (Paediat.) Qu. Eliz. Hosp. Gateshead.

MARSHALL, Bryan 93 High Street, Belmont, Bolton BL7 8AJ — MB ChB 1990 Dundee; MSc Manch. 1996; DRCPath 1995. Specialist Regist. (Med. MicroBiol.) Pub. Health Laborat. Roy. Preston Hosp. Preston. Prev: Regist. (Med. Microbiol.) Hope Hosp. Salford.

MARSHALL, Caroline Ann Department of Anaesthetics, Southampton University Hospitals Trust, Tremona Road, Southampton SO16 6 — MB BS 1981 Lond.; MRCP (UK) 1984; FFA RCS Eng. 1988. (Middlesex) Cons. Anaesth. Soton. Univ. Hosp. Trust. Prev: Cons. Anaesth. & Hon. Sen. Lect. Roy. Free Hosp. Lond.

MARSHALL, Catherine Anne 2 Cairnshill Avenue, Belfast BT8 6NR — MB BCh BAO 1992 Belf. SHO Belf. City Hosp.

MARSHALL, Catherine Isobel Harlestone Road Surgery, 117 Harlestone Road, Northampton NN5 7AQ Tel: 01604 751832 Fax: 01604 586065 — MB BChir 1972 Camb.; MA Camb. 1972; DFFP 1995. GP The Surg., 117 Harlestone Rd, N.ampton.

***MARSHALL, Catherine Jane** 19 Albert Road, Brookfield, Johnstone PA5 8UE — MB ChB 1998 Glas.; MB ChB Glas 1998.

MARSHALL, Catriona Elisabethe Haus Saron, 106 Greenock Road, Largs KA30 8PG Tel: 01475 673162 Fax: 01475 686244 — MB ChB 1993 Glas. GP Trainee Horsham W. Sussex.

MARSHALL, Cecilia Mary Foundry House, The Oval, Stead Land, Bedlington — MB BS 1984 Newc.; MRCPsych 1994; MRCGP 1988; DRCOG 1989. Cons. in Elderly Psychiat., N.umberland Ment. Health Trust. Socs: Mem. of The Roy. Coll. of Psychiat.s; BMA.

MARSHALL, Charles Frederick 12 Scarsdale Road, Victoria Park, Manchester M14 5PS; 12 Scarsdale Road, Victoria Park, Manchester M14 5PS — MB ChB 1988 Dundee; FRCA 1994. Cons Anaesth.

MARSHALL, Christine Blyth 119 Wren Way, Farnborough GU14 8TA Tel: 01252 541884 Fax: 01252 511410 Email: christine.marshall@gp-j82181.nhs.uk; 4 The Sycamores, Farnborough GU14 7BE Email: dr.c.marshall@ntlworld.com — MB BS 1977 Lond.; MRCP (UK) 1979; MRCGP 1981. (Middlesex Hospital Medical School) Course Organiser Frimley Pk. VTS.

MARSHALL, Christopher Duncan Ward 26 Fairlawns, Langley Road, Watford WD17 4UH — MB BS 1979 Lond.; MRCP (UK) 1983; MRCGP 1986; DRCOG 1986.

***MARSHALL, Christopher Graham** Threshers Hall, Wangford Road, Reydon, Southwold IP18 6SJ — MB BS 1997 Lond.

***MARSHALL, Clare** 52 Wallheath Crescent, Walsall WS9 9HT — BM BS 1995 Nottm.

MARSHALL, Colette 29 Kingswood Avenue, High West Jesmond, Newcastle upon Tyne NE2 3NS — BM 1990 Soton.; BM (Hons. & Distinc. in Med. Sci.) Soton. 1990; BSc (Molecular & Cell Biol. Soton. 1989; FRCS Eng. 1994. Research Fell. (Vasc. Surg.) Roy. Vict. Infirm. Newc. u. Tyne. Prev: SHO (Surg.) Freeman Hosp., Roy. Vict. Infirm. & Gen. Hosp. Newc. u. Tyne.

MARSHALL, David — MB BS 1992 Lond.

MARSHALL, David Antony Scott Inverclyde Royal Hospital NHS Trust, Larkfield Road, Greenock PA16 0XN Tel: 01475 633777 Fax: 01475 656142 Email: marshall@davidas.freeserve.co.uk; Windyridge, Torr Road, Quarriers Village, Bridge of Weir PA11 3RZ Tel: 01505 690063 — MB ChB 1984 Glas.; MRCP (UK) 1987; FRCP Glas. 1996; FRCP Ed 1999. Cons. (Phys. & Rheum.) Inverclyde Roy. Hosp. NHS Trust; Clin. Dir. (Med. Servs.); Hon. Clin. Sen. Lect. Univ. Glas. Socs: Brit. Soc. Rheum.; Scott. Soc. Experim. Med. Prev: Sen. Regist. (Rheum. & Med.) Hope Hosp. Salford.

MARSHALL, David Chisholm (retired) Hawkhill Medical Centre, Hawkhill, Dundee DD1 5LA Tel: 01382 669589 Fax: 01382 645526 — MB ChB 1961 St. And.; DObst RCOG 1964; DMJ Soc. Apoth. Lond. 1969. Prev: Med. Adviser Tayside Regional Counc. Dundee Dist. Counc.

MARSHALL, David Ernest West Walk Surgery, 21 West Walk, Yate, Bristol BS37 4AX Tel: 01454 272200 — MRCS Eng. LRCP Lond. 1973; MRCGP 1989; DA Eng. 1978; DObst 1976. GP Bristol.

MARSHALL, Mr David Frederick Department of Paediatric Surgery, Royal Belfast Hospital for Sick Children, 180 Falls Road, Belfast BT12 6BE — MB BCh BAO 1991 Belf.; FRCSI 1995. (Qu. Univ. Belf.) Specialist Regist. (Paediat. Surg.) Roy. Belf. Hosp. Sick Childr. Socs: Soc. Research Into Hydrocephalus & Spina Bifida; Asso. Mem. Brit. Assn. Paed. Surg.; Assoc. of Surg.s in Train. Prev: Research Fell.; Paediat. Surg. Roy. Belf. Hosp. Sick Childr.

MARSHALL, David Ian Mocketts Wood Surgery, Mocketts Wood House, Hopeville Avenue, St Peter's, Broadstairs CT10 2TR Tel: 01843 862996 Fax: 01843 860126 — MB BS 1971 Lond.; MRCS Eng LRCP Lond 1971.

MARSHALL, David Lindsay Phoenix House, Priory Park, Glastonbury Road, Wells BA5 1TH Tel: 01749 683327 Fax: 01749 683376 Email: david.marshall@sompar.nhs.uk — MB BS Lond. 1979; MRCPsych 1983. Cons. Psychiat. Som. Partnership NHS and Social Care Trust. Prev: Sen. Regist. Rotat. (Adult Psychiat.) Guy's & Bexley Hosps.; Rotat. Train. Scheme Psychiat. St. Geo. Hosp. Med. Sch. Lond.; Clin. Research Fell. & Hon. Sen. Regist. St. Geo. Hosp. Med. Sch. Lond.

MARSHALL, Denis Arthur (retired) Strines, Beacon Hill, Upton, Pontefract WF9 1DB Tel: 01977 645316 — MB ChB Leeds 1956. Prev: Ho. Surg. & Ho. Phys. St. Jas. Hosp. Leeds.

MARSHALL, Doreen Louisa Patricia (retired) 45 Northfield Road, Newcastle upon Tyne NE3 3UN Tel: 0191 285 2243 — MB BS Durh. 1952; FRCPsych 1992, M 1978; Dip. Psychother. Leeds 1982. Prev: Med. Dir. N.d. Ment. Health NHS Trust.

MARSHALL, Dorothy Margaret (retired) Poplar Cottage, Kippford, Dalbeattie DG5 4LN Tel: 01556 620274 — MB ChB Glas. 1943; DObst RCOG 1948. Prev: Regist. O & G Padd. Hosp.

MARSHALL, Drew St John 15 High Street, Silsoe, Bedford MK45 4DR Tel: 01525 61481 — MRCS Eng. LRCP Lond. 1976; BSc (Hons.) Lond. 1973, MB BS 1976; DRCOG 1980. (Roy. Free) Prev: SHO Cuckfield Hosp. Haywards Heath; Ho. Phys. & Ho. Surg. Luton & Dunstable Hosp.; Mid Sussex VTS.

MARSHALL, Elizabeth Jane Addiction Sciences Building, 4 Windsor Walk, London SE5 8AF Tel: 020 7703 5411; The Maudsley Hospital, Denmark Hill, London SE5 8AZ Tel: 020 7919 2345 Fax: 020 7919 2345 — MB BCh BAO 1979 Dub.; MRCPI 1981; MRCPsych 1985; DCH Dub. 1980. Cons. Psychiat. & Sen. Lect. Maudsley Hosp. Lond. Prev: Sen. Regist. Bethlem Roy. & Maudsley

MARSHALL

Hosps. & Inst. Psychiat. Lond.; Regist. (Psychol. Med.) St. Bart. Hosp. Lond.; Regist. (Psychiat.) St. Patrick's & St. Jas. Hosps. Dub.

MARSHALL, Ernest Clatterbridge Centre for Oncology, Bebington, Wirral L63 3JY Tel: 0151 334 4000; Ashfield, Northwich Road, Lower Stretton, Warrington WA4 4NZ — MB ChB 1986 Manch.; MD Manch. 1997; MRCP (UK) 1989. (Manch.) Tutor (Oncol.) Christie Hosp. Univ. Manch.; McMillan Cons. (Med. Oncol.). Socs: Brit. Oncol. Assn.; Assn. Cancer Phys. Prev: SHO (Med.) Roy. Preston Hosp.

MARSHALL, Fleur Tiffany, Surg. Lt. RN Blenheim House, Old Warden, Biggleswade SG18 9HQ — MB ChB 1995 Bristol. (Bristol) Med. Off. RN. Prev: Ho. Off. (Surg. & Orthop.) Derriford Hosp. Plymouth; Ho. Off. (c/o Elderly & Gen. Med.) S.mead Hosp. Bristol.

MARSHALL, Francis Paul Fitzroy Whitegates, Newton St Cyres, Exeter EX5 5AQ — MB 1973 Camb.; BChir 1972; FFA RCS Eng. 1978.

***MARSHALL, Gail** 14 Tambowie Avenue, Milngavie, Glasgow G62 7AR — MB ChB 1998 Glas.; MB ChB Glas 1998.

***MARSHALL, Gayle Isobel** Meadowspott, Waverley Road, Dalkeith EH22 3DG — MB ChB 1994 Aberd.

MARSHALL, George Frederick Glenwell (retired) Madisa Court, Littleworth Lane, Rossington, Doncaster DN11 0HB Tel: 01302 867469 — MB BS 1948 Durh.; DObst RCOG 1952. Prev: Ho. Surg. (O & G) Coventry & Warw. Hosp.

MARSHALL, George Pigott McCay Knockspeare, Knockintern, Coleraine — MD Ed. 1937, MB ChB 1931; DPH Lond. 1934. (Ed.)

MARSHALL, Grace Shannon Botley Health Care Centre, Mortimer Road, Botley, Southampton SO32 2UG Tel: 01489 783422 Fax: 01489 781919 — MB BChir 1989 Camb.; MA Camb. 1990; MRCGP 1993; DFFP 1993; DRCOG 1992. (Camb. & St. Bart. Hosp. Lond.) Prev: Trainee GP N.ampton VTS; Ho. Surg. Ronkswood Hosp. Worcs.; Ho. Phys. W. Suff. Hosp. Bury St. Edmunds.

MARSHALL, Graham Brian 2 Newlands Close, Edwalton, Nottingham NG12 4FH — MB BS 1982 Lond.; MSc Lond. 1975; B Soc Sc. (Hons.) Birm. 1972; MFPM RCP (UK) 1991; Dip. Pharm. Med. RCP (UK) 1988. (Univ. Coll. Hosp.) Head of Med. Serv. - The Boots Company plc Nottm. Prev: Ho. Phys. Warneford Hosp. Leamington Spa; Ho. Surg. Whittington Hosp. Lond.

MARSHALL, Guy Eland Cyncoed Road Medical Centre, 350 Cyncoed Road, Cardiff CF23 6XH Tel: 029 2076 2514 Fax: 029 2076 4262; 30 Lake Road E., Roath Park, Cardiff CF23 5NN Tel: 029 2076 5088 Email: dr.guy.marshall@lineone.net — MB BCh 1985 Wales; MRCGP 1990; DRCOG 1987. (Univ. Wales Coll. Med.) (Undergrad) Hon. Tutor Dept. Gen. Pract. Univ. Wales Coll. Med. Socs: Roy. Coll. Gen. Pract.

MARSHALL, Heather 13 Cordiners Land, 70 West Port, Edinburgh EH1 2LF — MB ChB 1988 Ed.

MARSHALL, Howard James 41 Ulleries Road, Solihull B92 8DX — MB ChB 1988 Leeds. SHO (A & E) Roy. Preston Hosp. Fulwood.

MARSHALL, Mr Hugh Fraser White Lodge, 23 Glastonbury Grove, Newcastle upon Tyne NE2 2HB Tel: 0191 281 4091 Fax: 0191 281 8183 — MB BS Durh. 1961; FRCS Eng. 1967; DObst RCOG 1963. (Durh.) Emerit. Cons. Otolaryngol. & Head & Neck Surg. Freeman Hosp. Trust Newc. u. Tyne; Med. Chairm. Pens. Appeal Tribunal; Med. Mem. Med. Appeal Tribunal. Socs: Fell. Roy. Soc. Med. (Sect. Mem. Otol. & Laryngol.). Prev: Lect. (Otolaryngol.) Univ. Newc. u.Tyne; Chief Resid. (Otolaryngol.) Univ. Toronto, Canada; Sen. Regist. (ENT) Roy. Vict. Infirm. Newc.

MARSHALL, Ian Bruce Barbican Healthcare, 3 White Lyon Court, The Barbican, London EC4 8EA — MB BS 1971 Newc.; MRCGP 1975; FRACGP 1988.

MARSHALL, Isabel Jane East Wing, Esk Medical Centre, Ladywell Way, Musselburgh EH21 6AA Tel: 0131 665 2267 Fax: 0131 653 2348; 64 Victoria Terrace, Musselburgh EH21 7LW Tel: 0131 665 2832 — MB ChB 1986 Sheff.; MRCGP 1990. Clin. Asst. Inveresk Clin. Research Edin. Prev: Trainee GP Cleveland VTS.

MARSHALL, Jacqueline Ruth The Surgery, 81 Oxgate Gardens, London NW2 6EA Tel: 020 8208 0291 Fax: 020 8208 1753 — MB BS 1985 Lond.; MRCP (UK) 1988; MRCGP 1992.

MARSHALL, Jacquelyne Anne Beech House, Old College Gardens, Northleach, Cheltenham GL54 3HJ — MB BCh 1986 Wales.

MARSHALL, James Alastair George, Maj. RAMC 2 Redford Neuk, Edinburgh EH13 0AW — MB ChB 1986 Glas.; BSc St. And. 1982; MRCGP 1994; DRCOG 1992. Med. Off. Garrison Med. Centre BFPO 47.

MARSHALL, James Rennie, Col. late RAMC (retired) Mill End Cottage, Damerham, Fordingbridge SP6 3HU — MB BCh BAO Dub. 1955; BA Dub. 1952; FRCPI 1977, M 1970; FRCPCH 1997; DCH RCP Lond. 1963; DTM & H RCP Lond. 1962. Prev: Cons. Adviser Paediat. Army Camb. Milit. Hosp. Aldershot.

MARSHALL, James Stewart 21 Manor Road, Bramhall, Stockport SK7 3LX — MB ChB 1946 Glas. (Glas.) Prev: GP Bramhall; Ho. Surg. Ballochmyle EMS Hosp. & StoneHo. Co. Orthop. Hosp.; Squadron Ldr. RAFVR Med. Br.

MARSHALL, James William Valsler 1/L 46 Polwarth Street, Hyndland, Glasgow G12 9TJ — MB ChB 1990 Glas.

MARSHALL, Jane October Cottage, Old Gloucester Road, Knapp, Thornbury, Bristol BS35 3UF — BM 1991 Soton.; DCH RCP Lond. 1994; MRCGP 1997.

MARSHALL, Jane Margaret Govan Health Centre, 5 Drumoyne Road, Glasgow G51 4BJ Tel: 0141 531 8460 Fax: 0141 531 8451 — MB ChB 1984 Glas.; MRCGP 1988; DRCOG 1986. Prev: Ho. Phys. & Ho. Surg. Vict. Infirm. Glas.; W.. Infirm. GP Train. Scheme.

MARSHALL, Janet Rachel The Surgery, High Street, Fenny Compton, Leamington Spa CV47 2YG Tel: 01295 770855 Fax: 01295 770858; The Surgery, Stocking Lane, Shenington, Banbury OX15 6NF Tel: 01295 678124 — MB ChB 1988 Sheff.; MRCGP 1992; DCH RCP Lond. 1991; DRCOG 1990. (Sheffield) Prev: Trainee GP S. Warks. VTS.

MARSHALL, Janet Rosemary (retired) 12 Churchfields Avenue, Weybridge KT13 9YA Tel: 01932 849513 — MB BS 1969 Lond. Prev: Clin. Asst. (Young Phys. Disabled) Weybridge Hosp.

MARSHALL, Janet Ruth 5A Granville Road, Jesmond, Newcastle upon Tyne NE2 1TP — MB BS 1992 Newc. Trainee GP N.d. VTS.

MARSHALL, Jean Helen X-Ray Department, Peterborough District Hospital, Peterborough PE3 6DA — MB ChB 1974 Ed.; FRCR 1980; DMRD Eng. 1978. Cons. Radiol. PeterBoro. Dist. Hosp. Prev: Cons. Radiol. Middlx. Hosp. Lond.

MARSHALL, Jennifer Anne Dept. of Theraputics, Queens Medical Centre, Nottingham NG7 2UH Tel: 0115 924 9924 Email: jennifer marshall@nottingham.ac.uk; Flat 1, 10 Peveril Drive, The Park, Nottingham NG7 1DE — BM BS 1995 Nottm.; MRCP (UK) 1998. Specialist Regist. Qu.s Med. Centre Notting.

MARSHALL, Jennifer Kirsty 47 Bidborough Ridge, Bidborough, Tunbridge Wells TN4 0UU — MB BS 1993 Lond.

MARSHALL, Jeremy Michael Holt Tinkers Lane Surgery, High Street, Wootton Bassett, Swindon SN4 7AT Tel: 01793 852131 Fax: 01793 848891 — MB ChB 1987 Bristol. Prev: SHO (Gen. Med.) P.ss Margt. Hosp. Swindon.

MARSHALL, Jeremy Simon St Pauls Road Medical Centre, 248 St Pauls Road, London N1 2LJ; 1 Turner Close, London NW11 6TU — MB BS 1981 Lond.; MRCGP 1986; DRCOG 1986; DCH RCP Lond. 1985. Lect. Acad. Dept. Primary Care Univ. Coll. & Middlx. Hosp. Med. Sch.; Clin. Med. Off. (Paediat. Community) Whittington Hosp. Lond. Prev: SHO (Paediat.) W.m. Childr. Hosp.; SHO Rotat. (Med.) W.m. Hosp. Roehampton & Watford Gen. Hosp.; Ho. Phys. W.m. Hosp. Roehampton.

MARSHALL, Joan (retired) Town Farm, Lapford, Crediton EX17 6QH — MB BS 1949 Lond.; MRCS Eng. LRCP Lond. 1948; FRCOG 1972, M 1950, DObst 1950. Prev: Clin. Asst. (Gyn.) N.wood, Pinner & Dist. Hosp. & Mt. Vernon Hosp N.wood.

MARSHALL, Professor John, CBE 203 Robin Hood Way, London SW20 0AA Tel: 020 8942 5509 — MB ChB 1946 Manch.; DSc. Manch. 1981, MD 1951; FRCP Lond. 1966, M 1948; FRCP Ed. 1957, M 1956; DPM Lond. 1952. (Manch.) Emerit. Prof. Clin. Neurol. Univ. Lond. Socs: Assn. Brit. Neurols. & Phys. GB. Prev: Chairm. Disabled Living Allowance Bd.; Sen. Lect. (Neurol.) Univ. Edin.; Lt.-Col. RAMC Sen. Med. Specialist.

***MARSHALL, John Anthony** 2 Cromarty Square, Heywood OL10 3NN — MB ChB 1994 Liverp.

MARSHALL, John Edward (retired) Old Greyhound, Grosmount, Abergavenny NP7 8EP Tel: 01981 240572 Fax: 01981 240572 — MB ChB Leeds 1959; FFA RCS Eng. 1968. Cons. Anaesth. Shrewsbury & OsW.ry Hosp. Gps. Prev: Ho. Surg. Leeds Gen. Infirm.

MARSHALL, John Graham (retired) Ivy Cottage, Kirkcowan, Newton Stewart DG8 0HQ Tel: 01671 830469 Fax: 01671 830469 — MB ChB Glas. 1951. Prev: Local Med. Off.

MARSHALL, Mr John Haydn Department Orthopaedics, Torbay Hospital, Lawes Bridge, Torquay TQ2 7AA Tel: 01803 65422 — MRCS Eng. LRCP Lond. 1982; FRCS (Orth.) 1995; FRCS Ed. 1988. (Liverp.) Cons. Trauma & Orthop. Surg. Torbay Hosp. Prev: Sen. Regist. Rotat. (Orthop.) Birm.

MARSHALL, Jonathan Charles Walter Bridleway House, Goring-on-Thames, Reading RG8 0HS — MB BS 1988 Lond.

MARSHALL, Jonathan Paul The Health Centre, Aylesbury Road, Wendover, Aylesbury HP22 6LD Tel: 01296 623452 — BM 1986 Soton.; BM Soton 1986; MRCGP 1992; DCH Lond. 1990; DRCOG 1988. (Southhampton) GP; PCG Bd. Mem.

MARSHALL, Joy Catherine Brookside Health Centre, Freshwater PO40 9DT Tel: 01983 753433 Fax: 01983 753662 — MB BS 1981 Lond.; MFFP 1993. (Roy. Free) Sen. Clin. Med. Off. (Family Plann.) Barnet. Prev: SCMO Coll. Health Serv. Bloomsbury HA Lond.; GP Retainer Scheme Borehamwood.

MARSHALL, Katharine Mary Dobbin Lane Health Centre, Dobbin Lane, Armagh BT61 7QG Tel: 028 3752 3165 — MB BCh BAO 1984 Belf.; MRCGP 1988; DRCOG 1987; Cert. Family Plann. JCC 1987; DCH Dub. 1986. Socs: BMA; RCGP. Prev: SHO (Gen. Med., Paediat. & O & G & Psychiat.) Craigavon Area Hosp.; Trainee GP Belf.

MARSHALL, Kenneth Coid Birchfield Road Surgery, 2 Birchfield Road, Cheadle Heath, Stockport SK3 0SY Tel: 0161 428 7768 Fax: 0161 491 6931; 10 Cliffmere Close, Cheadle Hulme, Cheadle SK8 5JH Tel: 0161 485 2485 — MB BS 1969 Monash. (Monash) Socs: BMA; Small Pract.s Assn.

MARSHALL, Laura Scott Gleann Mor, Lochs, Isle of Lewis HS2 9JP — MB ChB 1988 Aberd.; MRCGP 1993; DCCH RCP Ed. 1994; DRCOG 1992. (Aberd.) GP Princip. N. Lochs Med. Pract. Leurbost. Socs: RCGP Rural Drs Gp. Prev: Trainee GP/SHO (Psychiat.); Assoc. GP.

***MARSHALL, Lisa Jane** 1 Hamilton Close, Hinckley LE10 0TS — MB BCh 1998 Wales.

MARSHALL, Lorna Jane Burnbank Medical Centre, 18 Burnbank Road, Hamilton ML3 0NQ Tel: 01698 286555 Fax: 01698 286686 — MB ChB 1993 Glas.; BSc (Hons.) Glas. 1987; MRCGP 1997; DRCOG 1995; DFFP 1997. GP Hamilton. Prev: Clin. Med. Off., Family Plann., Hamilton.

MARSHALL, Margaret Alison Blackader Lynwood, Maidstone Road, Hadlow, Tonbridge TN11 0HR Tel: 01732 850125 — MB BS Lond. 1936; MRCS Eng. LRCP Lond. 1936; DPH Lond. 1939. (Lond. Sch. Med. Wom.)

MARSHALL, Marion Jacqueline The Medical Centre, Brunel University, Uxbridge UB8 3PH Tel: 01895 234426 Fax: 01895 270964 — MB BS 1990 Lond.; BSc (Hons.) Ed. 1985.

MARSHALL, Martin Neil Mount Pleasant Health Centre, Mount Pleasant Road, Exeter EX4 7BW Tel: 01392 430132 Email: m.n.marshall@exeter.ac.uk; Thorns Cottage, Flower Lane, Woodbury, Exeter EX5 1LS Tel: 01395 232838 — MB BS 1987 Lond.; MSc Exon 1994; BSc Lond. 1984, MB BS 1987; MD Lond. 1997; DCH 1991; FRCGP 1998; DRCOG 1990. (Char. Cross & Westm.) Sen. Lect. (Gen. Pract.) Univ. Exeter; Hon. Research Fell. Nat. Prim. Care R & D Centre.

MARSHALL, Mary The Surgery, St. Couan Crescent, Kirkcowan, Newton Stewart DG8 0HH Tel: 01671 830206 Fax: 01671 404163; Hazelfield, 12 Blair Way, Newton Stewart DG8 6HX Tel: 01671 403420 — MB ChB 1983 Glas.; MRCGP 1988. Socs: Roy. Coll. Gen. Pract.

MARSHALL, Matthew 6 Camphill Park, Toome Road, Ballymena BT42 2DQ — MB ChB 1985 Bristol.

MARSHALL, Merlin 8 Mill Street, Crook DL15 9BE — MB BChir 1950 Camb.; FFA RCS Eng. 1956. (Univ. Coll. Hosp.) Cons. Anaesth. Newc. Gen. Hosp.

MARSHALL, Mr Michael North Ormesby Health Centre, Elizabeth Terrace, North Ormesby, Middlesbrough TS3 6EN Tel: 01642 277000 Fax: 01642 281000; 16 Marton Avenue, Middlesbrough TS4 3SQ Tel: 0642 320290 — MB BS 1969 Newc.; BSc Newc. 1966, MB BS 1969; FRCS Eng. 1975.

MARSHALL, Michael Adrian 4 Kings Court, Hoylake, Wirral CH47 1JE — MB ChB 1968 Liverp.; ECFMG Cert 1968; LMCC 1975; FFA RCS Eng. 1974; FFA RCSI 1971. (Liverp.) Cons. (Anaesth.) Whiston Hosp. Prescot. Socs: Liverp. Soc. Anaesth. & Liverp. Med. Inst. Prev: Research Fell. (Anaesth.) Hosp. Sick Childr.

Toronto, Canada; Sen. Regist. (Anaesth.) David Lewis N.. Hosp. Liverp.; SHO Walton Hosp. Liverp.

MARSHALL, Michele Mary 6 Broadwater Road, Southampton SO18 2EB — MB BS 1991 Lond.; BSc 1988 (Hon.) Lond.; MRCP (UK) 1994. Cons. Radiologist, Intestinal Imaging Centre, St Mark's Hosp., Harrow, UK. Prev: SHO Rotat. (Gen. Med.) N. Middlx. Hosp.; Ho. Off. (Gen. Surg.) Middlx. Hosp. Lond.; Ho. Off. (Gen. Med.) Chase Farm. Hosp. Enfield.

MARSHALL, Montague Frank Poynton 14 Park Close, Eastbourne BN20 8AG Tel: 01323 727654 Fax: 01323 727654 Email: jmarshal@netcouk.co — MRCS Eng. LRCP Lond. 1948. (Lond. Hosp.) Ophth. Med. Pract.; Authorised Med. Examr. Civil Aviat. Auth. Socs: Fell. Roy. Aeronautical Soc.; BMA; Fell. Roy. Soc. Med. Prev: Ho. Phys. St. Clement's Hosp.; Squadron Ldr. RAF; Clin. Asst. (Ophth.) E.bourne Hosp. Gp.

MARSHALL, Moyra (retired) Hawkhill Medical Centre, Hawkhill, Dundee DD1 5LA Tel: 01382 669589 Fax: 01382 645526 — MB ChB 1963 St. And. Prev: Ho. Off. (Surg. & Geriat.) Maryfield Hosp. Dundee.

MARSHALL, Neil Edwin Valsler Central Surgery, 463A Scalby Road, Newby, Scarborough YO12 6UB Tel: 01723 375343 & 500238 Fax: 01723 501582 — MB ChB 1959 Glas. (Glas.) Med. Off. Yorksh. RHA Nat. Blood Transfus. Serv. Socs: BMA. Prev: Surg. Lt. RN; SHO (O & G) & Sen. Ho. Phys. Torbay Hosp. Torquay.

MARSHALL, Neil William Deepings Practice, Godsey Lane, Market Deeping, Peterborough PE6 8DD Tel: 01778 579000 Fax: 01778 579009 Email: neil.marshall@lineone.net; Devonshire Cottage, Ashton, Stamford PE9 3BA Tel: 01780 740823 Fax: 01780 740192 — MB BChir 1971 Camb.; MA Camb. 1971, BA 1967. (Westm. Hosp.) GP (Diagn. Ultrasound) P'boro.

MARSHALL, Neil William (retired) 27 Defoe House, Barbican, London EC2Y 8DN — MB BS Lond. 1963; MRCGP 1974; DO RCS Eng. 1985; DObst RCOG 1970. Prev: Clin. Asst. (Ophth.) Bristol Eye Hosp.

MARSHALL, Mr Nicholas Charles 4 The Penns, Clevedon BS21 5AN — MB BS 1990 Lond.; BSc Lond. 1987, MB BS 1990; FRCS Eng. 1994; FRCS Ed. 1994. Lect. (Surg.) Roy. Lond. Hosp.

MARSHALL, Ninian 14 Buckley Road, London NW6 7NA Tel: 020 7624 1687; 57 Bainton Road, Oxford OX2 7AG Tel: 01865 553845 — MA Oxf. 1957, BA 1953; MB BS Lond. 1959. (Char. Cross) Socs: Brit. Psychol. Soc. Prev: Psychiat. Bowden Ho. Clinic.

MARSHALL, Noel Charles Dobbin Lane Health Centre, Dobbin Lane, Armagh BT61 7QG Tel: 028 3752 3165 — MB BCh BAO 1957 Belf.; DObst RCOG 1961. (Belf.)

MARSHALL, Pamela Northland Surgery, 79 Cunninghams Lane, Dungannon BT71 6BX Tel: 028 8772 752 Fax: 028 8772 7696 — MB BCh BAO 1971 Dub.; BA Dub. 1969, MB BCh BAO 1971. (Tc Dub.) GP Dungannon.

MARSHALL, Patricia Frances The Health Centre, Westfield Walk, Leominster HR6 8HD Tel: 01568 612084 Fax: 01568 610340; Pastoral, Churchway, Sutton St. Nicholas, Hereford HR1 3BD Tel: 01432 880661 — MB BS 1963 Lond.; MRCS Eng. LRCP Lond. 1963. (Roy. Free) Prev: Paediat. SHO & Ho. Off. Med. Dryburn Hosp. Durh.; Ho. Surg. Eliz. G. Anderson Hosp. Lond.

MARSHALL, Patricia Rosalind (retired) Spring Gables Surgery, Clint Bank, Birstwith, Harrogate HG3 3DW — MB ChB 1971 Leeds; MB ChB (Hons.) Leeds 1971; MRCS Eng. LRCP Lond. 1973; FFA RCS Eng. 1975. Locum GP. Prev: Clin. Asst., Regist & SHO (Anaesth.) Leeds Gen. Infirm.

MARSHALL, Mr Paul David Department of Orthopaedics, Royal Lancaster Infirmary, Ashton Road, Lancaster LA1 4RP Tel: 01524 583504 Fax: 01524 583506 — MB ChB 1985 Sheff.; BMedSci (Hons.) Sheff. 1984; FRCS (Orth.) 1994; FRCS Ed. 1990. (Sheff.) Cons. Orthop. Surg. Roy. Lancaster Infirm. W.morland Gen. Hosp. Socs: Fell. BOA; Brit. Soc. Childr. Orthop. Surg. Prev: Sen. Regist. (Orthop. Surg.) NW RHA; Regist. (Orthop.) Cardiff Roy. Infirm.; Regist. Rotat. (Surg.) Roy. Hallamsh. Hosp. Sheff.

MARSHALL, Paul Frank — MB BS 1978 Lond.; BSc Lond. 1975; MRCGP 1982. (St. Geo.)

MARSHALL, Penelope Anne 2 Erle Harvard Road, West Bergholt, Colchester CO6 2LH Tel: 01206 241137 Fax: 01206 241901; Holly Tree, Polestead St, Stoke by Nayland, Colchester CO6 4SA — MB ChB 1990 Bristol; DRCOG 1994. GP Retainer. Prev: GP/Regist.

MARSHALL

Lond.; SHO (Palliat. Med.) N. Lond. Hospice; SHO (O & G, Paediat. & Geriat.) Frimley Pk. Hosp.

MARSHALL, Peter John October Cottage, Old Gloucester Road, Knapp, Thornbury, Bristol BS35 3UF — MB ChB 1991 Sheff.

MARSHALL, Peter Jonathan Brookside Group Practice, Brookside Close, Gipsy Lane, Earley, Reading RG6 7HG Tel: 0118 966 9222 Fax: 0118 935 3174; 36 Bulmershe Road, Reading RG1 5RJ Tel: 0118 966 8794 Email: peter@brookgp.demon.co.uk — MB BS 1979 Lond.; MRCGP 1984. (Middlx.)

MARSHALL, Philip David Cefn Coed Hospital, Swansea SA2 0GH Tel: 01792 561155 — BM BCh 1976 Oxf.; MA Camb. 1977; MRCPsych 1980. Cons. Psychiat. Cefn Coed Hosp. Swansea. Prev: Sen. Regist. St. Thos. Hosp. Lond.

***MARSHALL, Philippa Mary** Bankfield House, Chevin Road, Belper DE56 2UN — MB BS 1994 Lond.

MARSHALL, Richard David (retired) Highfield, Moulton Road, Pitsford, Northampton NN6 9AU Tel: 01604 882150 Fax: 01604 882150 — MB BS 1959 Lond.; MRCS Eng. LRCP Lond. 1959; FFA RCS Eng. 1964; DA Eng. 1961. Prev: Cons. Anaesth. N.ampton Gen. Hosp. NHS Trust.

MARSHALL, Richard Peter 6 Broadwater Road, Southampton SO18 2EB — MB BS 1991 Lond.; BSc (Hons.) Lond. 1988; MRCP (UK) 1994. Research Fell. (Med.) Univ. Coll. Lond. Prev: Regist. (Chest Med.) Frimley Pk. Hosp. Camberley; SHO (Gen. Med.) OldCh. Hosp. Romford; Ho. Off. (Gen. Med.) Edgware Gen. Hosp.

MARSHALL, Robert Raybarrow Farm, Nettleton, Chippenham SN14 7NN Tel: 01249 782257 — MB BChir 1947 Camb.; MA Camb. 1948, MD 1956; FRCP Lond. 1972, M 1948. (Camb. & St. Bart.) Prev: Reader (Chest Dis.) Univ. Oxf.

MARSHALL, Robert Andrew (retired) Rose Park, Aglionby, Carlisle CA4 8AD Tel: 01228 513079 — MB ChB 1954 Ed.; MRCGP 1968; DTM & H Liverp. 1955. Prev: Med. Off. Bornu Provin. Leprosy Settlem. N.. Nigeria.

MARSHALL, Mr Robert Erik Keith 225A Stephendale Road, London SW6 2PR — MB BS 1988 Lond.; FRCS Eng. 1992. (St. Thos.) Regist. Rotat. (Gen. Surg.) Brook Hosp. Greenwich. Prev: SHO (Cardiothoracic Surg.) Roy. Brompton Nat. Heart & Lung Hosp.; SHO (A & E) Co. Hosp. Guildford; SHO (Gen. Surg.) St. Helier Hosp. Carshalton.

MARSHALL, Robert John Hawkes Point House, Hawkes Point, Carbis Bay, St Ives TR26 2NY — MB BS 1979 Lond.; MA Oxf. 1978; DM Soton. 1990; FRCPath 1995, M 1985. Cons. Histopath. Roy. Cornw. Hosp. (Treliske) Truro.

MARSHALL, Mr Robert William Orthopaedic Department, Royal Berkshire Hospital, Reading RG1 5AN Tel: 01734 875111; Whistlers House, 6 Whistlers Lane, Silchester, Reading RG7 2NE Tel: 01734 700203 — MB BCh 1974 Witwatersrand; FRCS Eng. 1981. Cons. Orthop. Surg. Roy. Berks. Hosp. Reading. Socs: Fell. BOA; Roy. Soc. Med. Prev: Sen. Regist. Rotat. (Orthop.) St. Mary's Hosp.; Regist. Rotat. (Orthop.) Char. Cross Hosp. Kingston.

MARSHALL, Robert William 4 Heathfield Park, Woodman's Corner, Yelverton PL20 6JJ — MB BS 1996 Lond.; BSc (Hons.) Lond. 1993. (UMDS of Guy's & St. Thos.) SHO (Med.) Derriford Hosp. Plymouth. Prev: SHO (Gen. Med.) c/o the Elderly Kingston Hosp. Glasworthy Rd. Kingston-upon-Thames; Pre-Reg. H. O. (Respirat. Med.) (Kingston Hosp.); PRHO (Orthop.) (Guy's Hosp.).

MARSHALL, Robin Lorimer (retired) 3 Kirkdene Grove, Newton Mearns, Glasgow G77 5RW Tel: 0141 639 5284 — MB ChB Ed. 1963; FFCA Eng. 1968; DObst RCOG 1965. Prev: Cons. Anaesth. Vict. Infirm. Glas.

MARSHALL, Ruth Bronia Laindon Health Centre, Laindon, Basildon SS15 5TR Tel: 01268 546411 Fax: 01268 491248 — MB ChB 1978 Sheff.

MARSHALL, Ruth Elizabeth 33 Deramore Street, Rusholme, Manchester M14 4DT; 30 Woodville Road, Morden SM4 5AF — MB ChB 1988 Birm. SHO (Psychiat. Rehabil.) Withington Hosp. Manch. Prev: SHO (Gen. Psychiat.) Stepping Hill Hosp. Stockport; SHO (Gen. Psychiat. & Cas.) Withington Hosp. Manch.

MARSHALL, Ruth Elizabeth Northview Farm, Beaumont, Carlisle CA5 6EF — MB ChB 1988 Sheff.; MRCP (UK) 1992; CCST 1997. Cons. (A&E) Roy. Alexandra Hosp. Paisley. Prev: Sen. Regist. (A & E) S.. Gen. Hosp. Glas.; Career Regist. & SHO (A & E) Glas. Roy. Infirm.; SHO (Med.) Morriston Hosp. Swansea.

MARSHALL, Ruth Helen 7 Clarborough Drive, Arnold, Nottingham NG5 7LL — MB BS 1996 Lond.

MARSHALL, Sally Margaret Department of Medicine, University of Newcastle upon Tyne, Newcastle upon Tyne NE2 2HH Tel: 0191 222 7149 Fax: 0191 222 7019 Email: s.m.marshall@newcastle.ac.uk — MD 1990 Glas.; MB ChB 1978, BSc (Hons.) 1975; FRCP Glas. 1994; MRCP (UK) 1981; FRCP 1994. Reader (Diabetes) Univ. Newc.; Hon. Cons. Phys. Newc. upon Tyne NHS Hosps. Trust. Socs: Brit. Diabetic Assn. (Chair, Professional Advis. Comm.).

MARSHALL, Samuel Gray 3 West Park, Inshes, Inverness IV2 5BY — MB ChB 1966 Glas.; MRCGP 1972; DObst RCOG 1969.

MARSHALL, Sarah Ann 29/154 Rathmines Road, Hawthorn East, Victoria 3123, Australia Tel: 00 61 3 98877929; 50 Woodmans Place, Droitwich WR9 9ER Tel: 01905 775571 — MB BS 1990 Lond. Regist. Rotat. (Emerg. & Anaesth.) Maroon Day Hosp. Ringwood, Vict., Austral. Prev: SHO (Emerg. & Med.) Worthing Gen. Hosp. W. Sussex.

MARSHALL, Sarah Jane 35 Gosberton Road, Wandsworth, London SW12 8LE — MB BS 1989 Lond.

MARSHALL, Sarah Jane 15 Middlegate, Morpeth NE61 2DD — MB BS 1990 Lond.; BA (Hons.) Oxf. 1987.

MARSHALL, Scott Ian 34 Cheswick Drive, Newcastle upon Tyne NE3 5DT — MB ChB 1988 Aberd.

MARSHALL, Scott Robert 4 Woodside, Hexham NE46 1HU Mobile: 07973 785225 Email: scott.r.marshall@doctors.org.uk — MB ChB 1996 Ed.; MRCP; BSc (Hons.) Immunol. (Edinburgh) Specialist Regist. in Haemat. N.. Region. Socs: MDDUS; Roy. Coll. of Phys.s, Lond.; Assn. of Clin. Pathologists. Prev: SHO Rotat. (Gen. Med.) Newc. Teachg. Hosps; Ho. Off. (Surg. & Med.) Wycombe Gen. Hosp.; LAT SpR N.ern Region.

MARSHALL, Shaun Andrew, Wing Cdr. RAF Med. Br. 43 High Street, Caythorpe, Grantham NG32 3DR — MB BCh BAO 1960 Belf.

MARSHALL, Sheila Rayna 24 Pelham Court, Bishopric, Horsham RH12 1TW Tel: 01403 218021 Fax: 01403 218021 — MB ChB 1953 Cape Town; FRCP 1981 Edinburgh; MRCP 1957 Edinburgh; DCH 1955 London. (Univ. of Cape Town) Cons. Paediat. Prev: Cons. Paediat. Learning Assessm. Centre, Horsham; Lect. Developm.al and Learning Disorders Univ. of Cape Town and Univ. of W.ern Cape; Cons. Paediat. Groote Scuiar Hosps., Cape Town.

MARSHALL, Simon Richard The Health Centre, Thornton Dam Lane, Gilberdyke, Brough HU15 2UL Tel: 01430 440225 Fax: 01430 440646 — MB BS 1983 Newc.; MRCGP 1987; DRCOG 1986. (Newcastle upon Tyne)

MARSHALL, Stuart Alan Guy's & St Thomas NHS Trust, Dept. of Anaesthetics, Guy's Hospital, St Thomas Street,, London SE1 9RT — MB ChB 1987 Aberd.; MB ChB (Commend.) Aberd. 1987; MRCP (UK) 1990; FRCA 1993. (Aberdeen) Cons. (anaesth.) Guy's & St. Thomas Hosp. Lond. Prev: Sen. Regist. (Anaesth.) Vict. Infirm. Glas.; Regist. (Anaesth.) W.ern Infirm. Glas.; SHO (Anaesth.) Lanarksh. HB.

MARSHALL, Stuart Duncan 6 Leicester Road, Groby, Leicester LE6 0DJ — MB ChB 1995 Sheff.

MARSHALL, Susan Ann P.J. Kaye and Partners, Northwick Surgery, 36 Northwick Park Road, Harrow HA1 2NU Tel: 020 8427 1661 Fax: 020 8864 2737 — MB BS 1979 Lond. (Charing Cross Hospital Medical School)

MARSHALL, Susan Elizabeth Mabel 42 Waldek Road, Chiswick, London W4 3NP — MB BS 1983 Lond.; MSc Lond. 1985. Freelance Med. Adviser. Prev: Med. Adviser Smithkline Beecham Pharmaceut. Harlow; Med. Adviser Bios Consultancy Bagshot.

MARSHALL, Susan Rose 18 Derby Street, Ormskirk L39 2BY; 93 Moss Delph Lane, Aughton LA2 5DY Tel: 01695 421028 — MB ChB 1977 Liverp.; DPD 1995 (Dip. Prac. Dermat) Cardiff. GP Princip. Ormskirk.

MARSHALL, Mr Sydney Glen Erne Hospital, Enniskillen BT74 6AY Tel: 01365 324711; Willoughby House, Enniskillen BT74 7EX — MB BCh BAO 1983 Belf.; FRCS Ed. 1987. Cons. (Gen. Surg.) Erne Hosp. Enniskillen. Socs: BMA; Assn. Surg.; Ulster Med. Soc.

MARSHALL, Tara Jane 135 Old Mansfield Road, Derby DE21 4SA — MB ChB 1997 Leic.

MARSHALL, Terry Lewis The Orchard, Clayton Road, Clayton, Newcastle ST5 4DH Tel: 01782 621366 — MB ChB 1967 Sheff.;

BA (Law) N. Staffs. Polytechnic 1983; MRCPath 1973. Prev: Cons. Histol. Sultanate of Oman; Cons. Histol. N. Staffs. Hosp. Centre.

MARSHALL, Thomas Geoffrey 38 Craighouse Avenue, Morningside, Edinburgh EH10 5LN — MB ChB 1977 Birm.; MRCP Lond. 1982.

MARSHALL, Thomas James Department of Radiology, Norfolk & Norwich NHS Healthcare Trust, Norwich NR1 3SR Tel: 01603 286286 Email: tmarshall@pactec.demon.co.uk; Boarded Gates Farm, High Oak Road, Wicklewood, Wymondham NR18 9QS — MB BS 1989 Lond.; MA Oxf. 1992; MRCP (UK) 1992; FRCR 1995. (Westm. & Char. Cross Hosp. Lond. & Univ. Coll. Oxf.) Cons. Radiol. Norf. & Norwich NHS Healthcare Trust Norwich. Socs: BMA; Brit. Skeletal Radiol. Soc. Prev: Sen. Regist. (Radiol.) Addenbrooke's Hosp.; Regist. (Radiol.) Addenbrooke's Hosp. Camb.; SHO (Med.). Addenbrooke's Hosp. Camb. & W.m. Hosp. Lond.

MARSHALL, Thomas Kenneth, CBE (retired) 27 Deramore Drive, Belfast BT9 5JR Tel: 028 9066 5264 Fax: 028 9066 5264 — MB ChB 1948 Leeds; FRCPath 1970, M 1963; MD 1959 Leeds. Prev: State Pathol. N.. Irel./Prof. Foren. Med. Qu. Univ. Belf./Cons. (Path.) N.. Irel. Health & Social Servs. Bds.

MARSHALL, Tom Patrick 6 Astrop Road, Kings Sutton, Banbury OX17 3PG — MB ChB 1987 Ed.; MSc (Pub. Health) Lond. Sch. Hyg. & Trop. Med. 1995; MSc (Health Economics) York 1992; MRCGP 1994. Regist. (Pub. Health Med.) Banbury. Socs: Assoc. Mem. Fac. Pub. Health Med.

MARSHALL, Vanessa 4 Heathfield Park, Woodhan's Corner, Yelverton PL20 6JJ — MB BS 1997 Lond.; BSc (Hons.) Experim. Pathol. Lond. 1995. (UMDS Guy's & St. Thos.) Prev: Ho. Off. (Med.) William Harvey Hosp. Lond.; Ho. Off. (Surg.) Guy's Hosp. Lond.

MARSHALL, Vicki Elizabeth Halton House, High St., Charlton-on-Otmoor, Kidlington OX5 2UG — MB ChB 1973 Liverp.; DObst RCOG 1975.

MARSHALL, Victoria Louise Spring House, NR Allendale, Hexham NE47 9PA — MB ChB 1997 Glas.; FRCP 1997.

MARSHALL, Walter 56 Richardsons Road, East Bergholt, Colchester CO7 6RR Tel: 01206 298272 Fax: 01206 299010; Ashfield, Gaston St, East Bergholt, Colchester CO7 6SD Tel: 01206 298643 — MB ChB 1956 Glas.; DObst RCOG 1957. Prev: RAMC, Families Med. Off. Colchester.

MARSHALL, William (retired) Arundale, Birtwith, Harrogate HG3 2JA Tel: 01423 770524 — MB ChB 1943 Leeds; MRCS Eng. LRCP Lond. 1944. Admiralty Surg. & Agent; Local Treasury Med. Off. Prev: Graded Surg. RAMC, Transjordan Frontier Force.

MARSHALL, William Dean Dalkeith Medical Centre, 22-26 St Andrews St., Dalkeith EH22 1AP Tel: 0131 561 5500 Fax: 0131 561 5555; Wellwood, 12 Golf Course Road, Bonnyrigg EH19 2EX Tel: 0131 654 0852 Email: wellwood12@aol.com — MB ChB 1988 Aberd.; MRCGP 1993.

MARSHALL, William Jasper Department of Clinical Biochemistry, King's College Hospital Campus, Guy's, King's and St Thomas' School of Medicine, London SE5 9PJ Tel: 020 7346 3275 Fax: 020 7737 7434 Email: william.marshall@kcl.ac.uk; 4 Myton Road, London SE21 8EB Tel: 020 8761 3180 — MB BS 1975 Lond.; MB BS (Hons. Path.) Lond. 1975; PhD Lond. 1970, MSc 1979; BA (1st cl. Nat. Sci., Biochem) Oxf. 1967, MA 1970; FRCP Ed. 1996; FRCP Lond. 1993, M 1979; FRCPath 1992, M 1980. (King's Coll. Hosp.) Reader (Chem. BioChem.) Guy's, King's & St Thomas' Sch. of Med. Lond.; Hon. Cons. Chem. Path. KCH; Chairm. UnderGrad. Bd. of Examr.s Guy's, King's & St. Thos' Sch. of Med. Lond.; Treas. Roy. Coll. Path. Socs: BMA; Assn. Clin. Biochem.s; Med. Writers Gp. (Soc. of Authors). Prev: Sen. Regist. (Chem. Biochem.) Lewisham & King's Coll. Hosps.

MARSHAM, Sheila Margaret (retired) Fairfield, Eskdale Green, Holmrook CA19 1UA Tel: 019467 23252 — MB ChB 1956 Liverp. Lect. Examr. Brit. Red Cross Soc. Prev: Ho. Surg. & Ho. Phys. Walton Hosp. Liverp.

MARSHMAN, Mr Laurence Adrian Guy 5 Baker's Lane, Lingfield RH7 6HE Tel: 01342 836196 — MB ChB 1987 Glas.; FRCS Glas. 1993. Socs: BMA. Prev: SHO (Gen. Surg.) Crawley Hosp. & Bolton Roy. Infirm.; SHO (Neurosurg.) Hope Hosp. Manch.

MARSHMAN, Robert Ian Marsh Street Surgery, 25A Marsh Street, Rothwell, Leeds LS26 0AG Tel: 0113 282 1571 Fax: 0113 282 4720; 27 Bideford Avenue, Leeds LS8 2AE Tel: 0113 225 7316 Email: ianmarshman@cwcom.net — MB ChB 1986 Leeds; BSc (Pharmacol.) Leeds 1983, MB ChB 1986; MRCGP 1990; DRCOG 1989. (Leeds)

MARSLAND, Alan 16 Waverley Road, Middleton, Manchester M24 6JG Tel: 0161 643 2437 — MB ChB Manch. 1943; DLO Eng. 1953. (Manch.) Assoc. Specialist (ENT) Macclesfield Hosp. Gp. Socs: Fell. Manch. Med. Soc. Prev: Chief Asst. (ENT) N. Manch. Hosp. Gp.; Regist. (ENT) Rochdale & Oldham Roy. Infirms.

MARSLAND, Margaret Longden (retired) 16 Waverley Road, Middleton, Manchester M24 6JG Tel: 0161 643 2437 — MRCS Eng. LRCP Lond. 1945; MFCM 1972. Prev: SCM (Child Health) Oldham AHA.

MARSON, Anthony Guy (retired) 44 The Beeches, Calderstones, Liverpool L18 3LT — MB ChB 1990 Liverp.; MRCP (UK) 1993.

MARSON, Beryl Winifred (retired) 3 Fiddlers Green, Hampton-in-Arden, Solihull B92 0EZ — MB ChB 1947 Birm.; DCH Eng. 1950. Prev: SCMO E. Birm. HA.

***MARSON, Brigitta Stephanie** 12 Palace Green, Addington, Croydon CR0 9AG — BM BS 1998 Nottm.; BM BS Nottm 1998.

MARSON, Diane Sevenposts Surgery, 326A Prestbury Road, Prestbury, Cheltenham GL52 3DD Tel: 01242 244103 — MB BS 1987 Lond.; BSc Lond. 1984, MB BS 1987; DRCOG 1991. (Middlesex Hospital and UCL London) GP Seven Posts Surg. Cheltenham. Socs: BMA.

MARSON, Jennifer Mary The Hawthorns, Church Lane, Skelton, York YO30 1XT — MB ChB 1982 Bristol; DRCOG 1986. Prev: GP Hawes, N. Yorks.

MARSON, Kerry Louise 44 The Beeches, Liverpool L18 3LT — MB ChB 1990 Liverp.

MARSON, Miss Lorna Palmer Easter Bankhead Farmhouse, Path of Condie, Forgandenny, Perth PH2 9DW — MB BS 1990 Lond.; FRCS Eng. 1994.

MARSON, Steve Old Mill Surgery, Marlborough Road, Nuneaton CV11 5PQ Tel: 024 7638 2554 Fax: 024 7635 0047 Email: mailto:steve@marson.co.uk — MB BS 1979 Lond.; MRCS Eng. LRCP Lond. 1979. (St. Bart.) GP Nuneaton Warks.

MARSON, William Stuart, MBE (retired) 103 Kidbrooke Grove, London SE3 0LQ Tel: 020 8858 0660 — MB ChB Glas. 1961; FRCGP 1982, M 1972; DObst RCOG 1964. Prev: GP Lambeth.

MARSON-SMITH, Roger Andrew Grosvenor Street Surgery, 4 Grosvenor Street, St Helier, Jersey JE1 4HB Tel: 01534 30541 Fax: 01534 887948 — MB BS 1989 Lond.; MRCGP 1995.

MARSTON, Derek John Wilson Pittenweem Surgery, 2 Routine Row, Pittenweem, Anstruther KY10 2LG Tel: 01333 311307 Fax: 01333 312520; 1 Seaview Row, Pittenweem, Anstruther KY10 2PQ — MB ChB 1986 Ed.; MRCGP 1990; DCCH RCP Ed. 1992. (Edinburgh)

MARSTON, Geoffrey Michael Riverhouse, Gulson Hospital, Gulson Road, Coventry CV1 2HR Tel: 02476 559758 — BM BS 1988 Nottm.; BMedSc Nottm. 1986. Cons. Psychiat. for People with Learning Disabil. Coventry. Socs: Roy. Coll. Psychiat. 1995.

MARSTON, Mr Jeffery Adrian Priestley 4 Hereford Square, London SW7 4TT Tel: 020 7373 7678 Fax: 020 7373 3753 Email: amar576837@ad.com — BM BCh 1951 Oxf.; MA Oxf. 1951, DM, MCh 1964; Hon. MD Nice 1981; FRCS Eng. 1958. (Oxf. & St. Thos.) Indep. Practitioner; Emerit. Surg. Middlx. & Univ. Coll. Hosps. Lond. Socs: (Ex-Pres.) Assn. Surgs.; (Ex-Pres.) Vasc. Surg. Soc.; Fell. Roy. Soc. Med. (Ex-Pres. Sect. Surg.). Prev: Vice-Pres. Roy. Coll. Surgs.; Cons. Surg. Roy. N.. Hosp., Manor Hse. Hosp. & Nat. Heart Hosp.; Dean. Roy. Soc. Med.

MARSTON, John Anthony Brannams Medical Centre, Brannams Square, Kiln Lane, Barnstaple EX32 8AP Tel: 01271 329004 Fax: 01271 346785; Gorwell House, Barnstaple EX32 7JP — MB BChir 1973 Camb.; MA, MB BChir Camb. 1973.

MARSTON, Michael Sidney (retired) 22 Foye House, Bridge Road, Leigh Woods, Bristol BS8 3PE Tel: 0117 973 3755 — MB BS Lond. 1958. Prev: GP Bristol.

MARSTON, Mr Robert Addenbrooke Department of Orthopaedics, The Princess Grace Hospital, 42-52 Nottingham Place, London W1U 5NY Tel: 020 7486 9571 Fax: 020 7486 2348 Email: n.marston@londonorthopaedics.co.uk; Consulting Rooms, Princess Grace Hospital, 42-52 Nottingham Place, London W1U 5NY Tel: 020 7486 9571 Fax: 020 7486 2349 — MB BS 1985 Lond.; BSc (Hons.) Lond. 1982; FRCS Eng. 1990; FRCS Ed. 1990; 1995 FRCS (Orthopaedics). (St. Thos.) p/t Cons. Orthopaedic Surg., St. Mary's

MARSTON

Hosp., Lond.; Cons. Orthopaedic Surg. to English Nat. Ballet; Med. Adviser to Dance UK; Hon. Cons. to St. Lukes Hosp. for the Clergy, Fitzroy Sq. Socs: Chelsea Clin. Soc.; InDepend. Doctors Forum; Brit. Orthop. Assn. Prev: Sen. Regist. (Orthop.) Middlx. Hosp., Roy. Nat. Orthop. Hosp. & Univ. Coll. Hosp.; Regist. (Orthop.) Roy. Nat. Orthop. Hosp., Chase Farm & Whipps Cross Hosps.; SHO Rotat. (Surgic.) United Norwich Hosps.

MARSTON, Mrs Sylvie 4 Hereford Square, London SW7 4TS Tel: 020 7373 7678 Fax: 020 7373 3753 — BM BCh Oxf. 1958; MA Oxf. 1951; MRCP (UK) 1977. (St. Geo.) Phys. i/c PUVA/Patch Testing Clinic Lond. Socs: Brit. Assn. Dermat. & St. John's Hosp. Dermat. Soc.; RSM. Prev: Regist. (Dermat.) W. Middlx. Hosp. Isleworth; Ho. Phys. Med. Unit & Cas. Off. St. Geo. Hosp. Lond.

MARSZALEK, Halina Barbara (retired) 25 Hoadly Road, London SW16 1AE — MB ChB 1948 Polish Sch. of Med. Prev: Princip. GP Lond.

MART, Doris Ivy (retired) 209 Ballard Lane, London N3 — MB BS 1924 Lond.; MRCS Eng. LRCP Lond. 1924; DPH Eng. 1927. Clin. Asst. Maudsley Hosp. Nerv. Dis.; Med. Off. Bethnal Green Infant Welf. Centres & Belgrave Hosp. Infant Welf. Centres; Examr. & Lect. Health Subjects LCC Evening Insts. & Brit. Red Cross Soc.; Mem. Indust. Med. Bds. Prev: Ho. Surg. (Surgic.) Roy. N.. Hosp. Lond.

MARTEN, Robert Humphrey (retired) The White House, School Road, Chislehurst BR7 5PQ Tel: 020 8467 5844 — BM BCh 1944 Oxf.; FRCP Lond. 1968, M 1949. Cons. Dermat. King's Coll. Hosp. Lond. Prev: Sen. Regist. Skin Dept. King's Coll. Hosp. Lond. & Middlx. Hosp.

MARTENS, Moira Jean (retired) Tillingham, Beckley Furnace, nr. Brede, Rye TN31 6ET Tel: 01424 882497 — MB BCh Witwatersrand 1952; DCH Eng. 1954.

MARTIN, Adam Maudlay's Cottage, Gretton Fields, Gretton, Cheltenham GL54 5HQ — MB BS 1994 Lond.

MARTIN, Adrienne Anaest. Dept, Bromley Hosp, Cromwell Avenue, Bromley BR2 9AJ — MB BS 1981 Lond.; FFA RCS Eng. 1987. (St Bartholomews Hospital) Cons. Anaesth.& Intens. Care Bromley Hosps. Trust. Socs: BMA; Assn. Anaesth.; Intens. Care Soc.

MARTIN, Ailsa Christine 6 Coronation Way, Bearsden, Glasgow G61 1DF Tel: 0141 942 4297 — MB ChB 1963 Glas.; DRCOG 1964. Med. Adviser S. Lanarksh. Counc.

MARTIN, Alasdair Robert Avon Medical Centre, Academy Street, Larkhall ML9 2BJ Tel: 01698 882547 Fax: 01698 888138; 19 Machan Road, Larkhall ML9 1HX — MB ChB 1977 Glas.; FRCP Glas. 1995; MRCP (UK) 1981; MRCGP 1984. Assoc. Adviser (Gen. Pract.) Lanarksh.; Hon. Clin. Sen. Lect. Univ. Glas.

***MARTIN, Alastair James Lindsay** 57 Daines Way, Thorpe Bay, Southend-on-Sea SS1 3PQ — MB ChB 1997 Bristol.

MARTIN, Albert (retired) Thornhill, 13 Beresford Park, Sunderland SR2 7JU Tel: 0191 565 9900 — MB ChB 1954 Birm.; FFCM 1981, M 1972; DPH Eng. 1959. Prev: Chief Med. Off. & Dir. Pub. Health Sunderland HA.

***MARTIN, Alexander George Murray** Alla Rectory, 87 Cumber Rd, Claudy, Londonderry BT47 4JA — MB BCh BAO 1997 Belf.

MARTIN, Alexander Millar Tel: 01292 886622 Fax: 01292 614303; 1 Craigstewart Crescent, Doonbank, Ayr KA7 4DB Tel: 01292 445158 — MB ChB 1972 Glas.; MRCGP 1977; DObst RCOG 1974; DCH RCPS Glas. 1974. GP Ayr; Local Civil Serv. Med. Off. Ayr.

MARTIN, Mr Alexandra Gabrielle 2 Windsor Terrace, Clifton, Bristol BS8 4LW — MB ChB 1988 Bristol; FRCS Ed. 1992.

MARTIN, Alison Mary 110 Chadderton Park Road, Chadderton, Oldham OL9 0QP Tel: 0161 620 7019; Westley Hall, Homestead Drive, Langdon Hills, Basildon SS16 5PE Tel: 01268 546389 — MB ChB 1987 Manch.; BSc (Hons. Experim. Immunol. & Oncol.) Manch. 1984. Prev: SHO (Med.) Bolton Gen. Hosp.

MARTIN, Alison Mary BP International Ltd., Chertsey Road, Sunbury-on-Thames TW16 7LN Tel: 01932 764038 Fax: 01932 763572 Email: martina3@bp.com; Tillies, Munstead Heath Road, Godalming GU8 4AR — MB BS Newc. 1969; MFOM RCP Lond. 1986; DIH Eng. 1982; DObst RCOG 1972. (Newc. u. Tyne) Med. Dir. Gp. HSE Resource. Socs: Soc. Occupat. Med.; UK Forum Organisational Hlth. Prev: Force Med. Advisor City of Lond. Police; Sen. Med. Adviser Unilever plc.

MARTIN, Alistair Anderson Attleborough Surgeries (Station Road), Station Road, Attleborough NR17 2AS Tel: 01953 452394

Fax: 01953 453569; Beech House, Wattlefield, Wymondham NR18 9LE — MB BS 1978 Lond.; DRCOG 1981. (Middlx.) Prev: Trainee GP Norf. & Norwich VTS; Ho. Phys. Norf. & Norwich Hosp.; Ho. Surg. Ipswich Hosps.

MARTIN, Alistair John Department of Anaesthesia, Leighton Hospital, Middlewich Road, Crewe CW1 4QJ Tel: 01270 255141; 7 Oak Farm, Long Lane, Haughton, Tarporley CW6 9RN — MB BS 1982 Newc.; FFA RCS Eng. 1987; DA Eng. 1984. Cons. Anaesth. Mid. Chesh. Hosp. Trust. Prev: Sen. Regist. (Anaesth.) NW RHA; Lect. Anaesthia, Foothills Hosp., Calgary, Canada 1990.

MARTIN, Andrea Patricia South Barn, 16 Church Lane, Isleham, Ely CB7 5SQ — MB BS 1987 Lond. Community Med. Off. P'boro. HA.

MARTIN, Andrew Charles 35 University Mansions, Lower Richmond Road, London SW15 1EP — MB BS 1991 Lond.

MARTIN, Andrew Edward Crieff Health Centre, King Street, Crieff PH7 3SA Tel: 01764 652456 Fax: 01764 655756; The Croft, Pitkellony St, Muthill, Crieff PH5 2AF Tel: 01764 81320 — MB ChB 1976 Aberd. Med. Off: Brit. Limbless Ex-Serv.mans Assn. Socs: Brit. Med. Acupunct. Soc.; Fac. Homoeop.

MARTIN, Mr Andrew James Department of Neurosurgery, King's College Hospital, London SE5 9RS; 40A Gloucester Gardens, London W2 6BN Email: anar@glgdns.freeserve.co.uk — MB BS 1991 Lond.; BSc Lond. 1990; FRCS Eng. 1995. (St. Bart. Hosp. Med. Sch.) Specialist Regist. (Neurosurg.) King's Coll. Hosp. Lond.; RCS Research Fell. in Neuro-Oncol., Inst. of Psychiat., Lond. Socs: Fell. Roy. Soc. Med. Prev: SHO Rotat. (Surg.) Hammersmith Hosp. Lond.; SHO (Neurosurg.) Roy. Free Hosp. Lond.; Demonst. (Anat.) & SHO (A & E) King's Coll. Hosp. Lond.

MARTIN, Angela Mary College Surgery, College Road, Cullompton EX15 1TG Tel: 01884 32373 Fax: 01884 35541; Corinthian House, Bradninch, Exeter EX5 4QS Tel: 01392 881069 Fax: 01392 881973 — MB BS 1965 Lond.; MRCS Eng. LRCP Lond. 1965; DA Eng. 1968. (King's Coll. Hosp.) Exam. Med. Off. DSS Devon.; Resid. Med. Woodmill Hosp. Cullompton. Prev: Med. Off. DHSS Devon; SHO (Anaesth.) Roy. Devon & Exeter Hosp.; Ho. Surg. King's Coll. Hosp. Lond.

MARTIN, Anna Cecilia 5 Hampton Park, Belfast BT7 3JL Tel: 028 48922 — MB BCh BAO 1941 Belf.; DPH NUI 1945. (Belf.) Socs: BMA & Med. Wom. Federat. Prev: Jun. Hosp. Med. Off. Whiteabbey Hosp. Belf.; Ho. Phys. Forster Green Hosp. Consump. Belf.; Ho. Surg. St. Mary's Hosp. Manch.

MARTIN, Anne Caroline 39 Woodburn Terrace, Morningside, Edinburgh EH10 4ST — MB ChB 1994 Aberd. (Univ. Aberd.) SHO (O & G) St. John's Livingston. Prev: SHO (Psych. & A & E) St John's Livingston.; SHO (Paediat. & Med.) St. John's Livingston; Ho. Off. (Surg.) Stirling Roy. Infirm.

MARTIN, Anne Catherine 17 Waldon Point, St. Lukes Road, Torquay TQ2 5YE — MB BS 1990 Lond.

MARTIN, Anne Mary Eileen 14 Elm Grove, Hartlepool TS26 8LZ — MB BCh BAO 1978 NUI; LRCPI & LM, LRCSI & LM 1977.

MARTIN, Anne Mary Eileen Friarwood Surgery, Carleton Glen, Pontefract WF8 1SU Tel: 01977 703235 Fax: 01977 600527 — MB ChB 1978 N U Irel.; MB BCh N U I 1978; L LM RCP Irel L LM RCS Irel 1977. (N U Irel.) GP Pontefract, W. Yorks.

MARTIN, Anthea Flat 1, Woodlee, Abercromby Drive, Bridge of Allan, Stirling FK9 4EA — MB ChB 1995 Dundee.

MARTIN, Anthony Rehabilitation Unit, Queen Victoria Hospital, Holtye Road, East Grinstead RH19 3DZ — MRCS Eng. LRCP Lond. 1963; MD Lond. 1974, MB BS 1963; FRCP Ed. 1989. (Guy's) Cons. Phys. P.ss Roy. Hosp., Haywards Heath and Qu. Vict. Hosp., E. Grinstead; Chairm. Crawley & Jersey Research Unit. Socs: Brit. Geriat. Soc. Mem; Roy. Soc Mem Fell.; Amer. soc Gerict.cardiol Fell. Prev: Cons. Phys. Gen. Hosp. St. Helier Jersey; Cons. Phys. Geriat. Crawley & Horsham Hosps. Sussex; Attend. Phys. Cook Co. Hosp. Chicago & Assoc. (Med.) Chicago Med. Sch., USA.

***MARTIN, Anthony Gwynne** 18 Cotswold Drive, Sheffield S26 2GT; 19 Maes Y Crofft, Morganstown, Cardiff CF15 8FE — MB BCh 1995 Wales.

MARTIN, Anthony John Park Lane Surgery, Park Lane, Woodstock OX20 1UD Tel: 01993 811452; Green Close, Tackley, Kidlington OX5 3AF Tel: 01869 331234 — MB BS 1966 Lond.; MRCS Eng. LRCP Lond. 1966; DCH Eng. 1969; DObst RCOG 1969. (King's Coll.

Hosp.) Prev: SHO (Paediat. & O & G) & Ho. Phys. Plymouth Gen. Hosp.

MARTIN, Professor Anthony Myles, RD Sunderland Royal Hospital, Sunderland SR4 7TP Tel: 0191 565 6256; 235 Darras Road, Ponteland, Newcastle upon Tyne NE20 9AJ — PhD Strathclyde 1980; MB ChB St. And. 1963; FRCP Lond. 1986; FRCP Ed. 1975. Cons. Phys. Nephrol. Sunderland Dist. Hosps.; Hon. Fell. Fac. Pharm. Univ. Sunderland; Vis. Med. Cons. Khartoum, Sudan.; Prof. Med. Univ. Sunderland; Examr. RCP Lond. & Edin. Prev: Sen. Regist. Dept. Therap. Roy. Infirm. Edin.; Sen. Research Fell. Bioengin. Unit Strathclyde Univ. Glas.

MARTIN, Mr Arthur 25 Mimosa Street, Fulham, London SW6 4DS — MRCS Eng. LRCP Lond. 1961; FRCS Eng. 1971; FRCS Ed. 1969. (Guy's) Prev: Regist. (Gen. & Vasc. Surg.) St. Stephens Hosp. Chelsea & St. Thos. Hosp. Lond.; Cons. (Gen. & Vasc. Surg.) MoH Riyadh Saudi Arabia.

MARTIN, Audrey Mary (retired) 20 Barton End, Alton GU34 1LD Tel: 01420 87946 — MB BS 1942 Lond.; MRCS Eng., LRCP Lond. 1942; DA Eng. 1945. Prev: Maj. RAMC, Anaesth. Specialist.

MARTIN, Avril Argyll House, 78 West Street, Ryde PO33 2QJ Tel: 01983 562955 Fax: 01983 883481; 134 High Street, Wootton Bridge, Ryde PO33 4LZ Tel: 01983 882424 Fax: 01983 883481 — MB ChB 1981 Dundee; MRCGP 1986; DRCOG 1986.

MARTIN, Branwen Anne Helsby Health Centre, Lower Robin Hood Lane, Helsby, Warrington WA6 0BW Tel: 01928 723676 Fax: 01928 725677 — MB ChB 1987 Manch.; MRCGP 1991; DRCOG 1991; Dip. Pract. Dermat. Cardiff 1998. p/t GP Helsby; Hosp. Practitioner Dermat. Halton Gen, Hosp. Chesh. Prev: Trainee GP Eccles; Ho. Off. Pk. Hosp. Davyhulme VTS.

MARTIN, Brendan Joseph Hairmyres Hospital, East Kilbride, Glasgow G75 8RG Tel: 0141 220292 Fax: 0141234064; 2 Brigside Gardens, Hamilton ML3 7BG — MB ChB 1977 Glas.; MD Glas. 1994; MRCP (UK) 1982; FRCPS Glas. 1991; DRCOG 1979. Cons. Phys. (Geriat. Med.) & Speciality Advisor Hairmyres Hosp. E. Kilbride; Hon. Sen. Lect. Univ. Glas.

MARTIN, Bruce William 2 Haseley Close, Poynton, Stockport SK12 1PJ — MB ChB 1994 Sheff.

MARTIN, Cameron William 6 Loanfoot Park, Aberuthven, Auchterarder PH3 1JF — MB ChB 1992 Aberd.

MARTIN, Cathal John Flat 3, The Grove, 41 Alan Road, Manchester M20 4WG — MB BCh BAO 1990 Dub.

MARTIN, Catherine Bridget 72 Parkway, London NW1 7AH — MB BS 1993 Lond.; CFPA New Zealand 1996.

MARTIN, Cathryn Ann 162 Long Street, Dordon, Tamworth B78 1QA Tel: 01827 822893 Fax: 01827 331420; 1 Bishops Cleeve, Austrey, Atherstone CV9 3EU Tel: 01827 830867 — MB ChB 1987 Glas.; MRCGP 1991. (Glasgow) GP Warks. Prev: GP Warks.

MARTIN, Charles Stirling Anaesthetic Department, Crosshouse Hospital, Kilmarnock KA2 0BE Tel: 01563 521133 Fax: 01563 577171; 71 Bentinck Drive, Troon KA10 6HZ Tel: 01292 315953 — MB ChB 1982 Glas.; FFA RCSI 1986. Cons. CrossHo. Hosp. Kilmarnock. Socs: Internat. Assn. Study of Pain. Prev: Sen. Regist. (Anaesth.) Mersey RHA; Regist. (Anaesth.) W.. Infirm. Glas. & Monklands Dist. Gen. Hosp. Airdrie; Ho. Off. Glas. Roy. Infirm.

MARTIN, Cheryl Lindy 1 Kenmure Road, Giffnock, Glasgow G46 6TU — MB BCh 1984 Witwatersrand.

MARTIN, Christine Martin, Barr and Stewart, Eastwick Park Avenue, Great Bookham, Leatherhead KT23 3ND Tel: 01372 452081 Fax: 01372 451680 — MB BS 1980 Lond.; MRCGP 1986; DRCOG 1985.

MARTIN, Christine McLeod Kinmylies Medical Practice, Charleston Court, Assynt Road, Inverness IV3 6PB Tel: 01463 239865 Fax: 01463 711218 — MB ChB 1975 Dundee; DFFP 1995; DA Eng. 1979.

MARTIN, Christopher Edward George The Borchordt Medical Centre, 62 Whitchurch Road, Withington, Manchester M20 1EB Tel: 0161 445 7475; 10 Redclyffe Road, Withington, Manchester M20 3JR Tel: 0161 283 8315, 0161 445 1340 — MB ChB 1978 Bristol; BA Oxf. 1975; DRCOG 1981.

MARTIN, Christopher John 17 Longmead Avenue, Hazel Grove, Stockport SK7 5PG Tel: 0161 456 7620 Fax: 0161 292 2436 — MB ChB 1970 Manch.; MRCGP 1978. (Manch.) Freelance Private Med. Practitioner Stockport; Health Screening Cons. BUPA Regency Hosp. Macclesfield; Obesity Clinic Cons. Med. Specialists Ltd. Manch. and Bury. Prev: Princip. GP Stockport; Ho. Phys. & Ho. Surg. Stepping Hill Hosp. Stockport.

MARTIN, Christopher John Laindon Health Centre, Laindon, Basildon SS15 5TR Tel: 01268 546411 Fax: 01268 491248; 10 Stephens Crescent, Hordon-on-the-Hill, Stanford-le-Hope SS17 8LZ Tel: 01375 643518 Fax: 01375 642518 — MB ChB 1987 Manch.; BSc St. And. 1984; DRCOG 1991; DCH 1991; MRCGP 1992. Prev: SHO (Med.) Roy. Lancaster Infirm.

MARTIN, Mr Christopher Patrick 33 Cecil Road, Hale, Altrincham WA15 9NT — MB ChB 1993 Manch.; BSc (Med. Sci.) St. And. 1990; FRCS Eng. 1997. Dept. Orthop. & Trauma Stepping Hill Hosp. Stockport.

MARTIN, Clifford John New Street Health Centre, New Street, Stevenston KA20 3BB Tel: 01294 464141 Fax: 01294 466408; 110 Eglington Road, Ardrossan KA22 8NN Tel: 01294 602044 — MB BCh BAO 1982 Belf.

MARTIN, Clive Munro Northdown Surgery, St Anthony's Way, Cliftonville, Margate CT9 2TR Tel: 01843 296413 Fax: 01843 231231; 42 The Ridings, Cliftonville, Margate CT9 3EJ — MB BS 1976 Lond.; MRCS Eng. LRCP Lond. 1976; DRCOG 1979. (Guy's) Clin. Asst. (Colposcopy) Thanet Dist. Gen. Hosp. Margate; Mem. Kent LMC.

MARTIN, Colin Brian 15 Fairmead Close, Hounslow TW5 9JB — BM 1990 Soton.

MARTIN, Colin Bruce Nufield Department Anaesthesia, John Radcliffe Hospital, Headington, Oxford OX2 6HE Tel: 01865 741166; Tel: 01235 868691 Fax: 01235 868691 — MB BS 1984 Lond.; 2001 Bd. Certified USA Perioperative Transesophageal Echocardiography; MRCGP 1992; FRCA 1996; DRCOG Lond. 1988; DTM & H RCP Lond. 1988; DCH RCP Lond. 1987. (Roy. Free Univ. Lond.) Vis. Instruc. Dept. Anaesthesiology Univ. of Michigan Med. Center, Ann Arbor, Michigan, USA. Socs: BMA; Assn. Anaesth.; Soc. Cardio-thoracic Anaesth. Prev: Princip. GP Newquay Cornw.

MARTIN, David (retired) Barrholme, The Wynd, Muthill, Crieff PH5 2AP Tel: 01764 681482 — MB ChB 1942 Glas.

MARTIN, David Gordon Dept of Anaesthesia, King George Hospital, Barley Lane, Goodmayes, Ilford IG3 8YB Tel: 020 8970 8158; Tel: 020 8508 9534 Email: d_g_martin@hotmail.com — MB BCh 1979 Wales; BSc Wales 1976, MB BCh 1979; MRCP (UK) 1984; FFA RCS Eng. 1986. Cons. Anaesth. & IC King Geo. Hosp. Ilford Essex. Prev: Cons. Anaesth.and IC Morriston Hosp. Swansea.

***MARTIN, David James** Wilbeth, Quarry Lane, Eaglesham, Glasgow G76 0BD — MB ChB 1998 Glas.; MB ChB Glas 1998.

MARTIN, David John (retired) Fircroft, 112 Heath Road, Petersfield GU31 4EL Tel: 01730 264117 — MB BS 1961 Lond.; DObst RCOG 1969.

***MARTIN, David John** 360 Caledonian Road, London N1 1DU — MB BS 1997 Lond.

MARTIN, Mr David Leslie Department of Plastic Surgery, Chelsea and Westminster Hospital, 369 Fulham Road, London SW10 9HT Tel: 020 8237 2777 Fax: 020 8237 2784 — MB ChB 1979 Ed.; FRCS Ed. 1984. Cons. Plastic Surg. Hand Surg., Chelsea & W.minster Hosp., Lond. Socs: Brit. Assn. of Plastic Surgs.; Brit. Assn. Aesth. Plastic Surg. Prev: Sen. Regist. (Plastic Surg.) St. Jas. Univ. Hosp. Leeds & St. Lukes Hosp. Bradford; Regist. City Hosp. Nottm.; Fell. Louisville Hand Surgs. Kentucky, USA.

MARTIN, David Ronald Barnwood Road Surgery, 51 Barnwood Road, Gloucester GL2 0SE Tel: 01452 523362 Fax: 01452 387931; Ty-Yothwch, Church Lane Sandhurst Lane, Sandhurst, Gloucester GL2 9NP — MB BS 1972 Lond.; MRCS Eng. LRCP Lond. 1972; DObst RCOG 1975; MRCGP 1977. Prev: SHO (Paediat.), SHO (A & E) & SHO (Dermat., Neurol. & Gen.; Med.) Glos. Roy. Hosp. Gloucester.

MARTIN, Denis Christopher Charlton Lane Centre, Charlton Lane, Cheltenham GL53 9DZ Tel: 01242 272104 — MB ChB 1973 Birm.; BA Open 1991; BChD, LDS Leeds 1966; MRCPsych 1983; Dip. Palliat. Med. Wales 1995; DPM Eng. 1981; Dip Pract. Dermat. 1998. Staff Grade (Psychiat. of Old Age) Charlton La. Centre Cheltenham. Prev: Regist. (Psychiat.) Roy. United Hosp. Bath; SHO (Dent.) Midl. Regional Plastic Surg. Centre Wordsley Hosp.; Ho. Surg. Dudley Rd. Hosp. Birm.

MARTIN, Denis Holt Altnagelvin Area Hospital, Londonderry BT47 6SB Tel: 02871 345171 Fax: 02871 611401; 2 Macrory Park,

MARTIN

Londonderry BT47 6LW Tel: 02871 349257 — MB BCh BAO 1967 Belf.; FRCOG 1986, M 1972, DObst 1972. (Qu. Univ. Belf.) Cons. O & G Altnagelvin Area Hosp. Lond.derry. Socs: BMA; (Ex-Pres.) Ulster Obst. & Gyn. Soc.

MARTIN, Derek James Parkhall Surgery, Parkhall Road, Somersham, Huntingdon PE28 3EU Tel: 01487 740888 Fax: 01487 843635 — MB BChir 1980 Camb.; BSc (Hons.) CNAA 1977. SHO (Cardiol., Dermat. & Chest Med.) Addenbrookes & Papworth Hosps. Cambs. Prev: Ho. Surg. Addenbrooke's Hosp. Camb.; Ho. Phys. Newmarket Hosp.

MARTIN, Derrick Frank 304 Wilbraham Road, Chorlton cum Hardy, Manchester M21 0UU — MB ChB 1972 Birm.; FRCP Lond. 1994; MRCP (UK) 1976; FRCR 1985; DObst RCOG 1974. Cons. Radiol. S. Manch. Univ. Hosps. Withington Hosp. Prev: Lect. (Radiol.) Univ. Manch.; Hon. Cons. Withington Hosp. Manch.

MARTIN, Desmond Anthony (retired) Ashdown Forest Health Centre, Lewes Road, Forest Row RH18 5AQ Tel: 01342 822131 Fax: 01342 826015 — MB ChB 1967 Glas.; MRCGP 1974; DObst RCOG 1974; DA Eng. 1973. Prev: Surg. Lt. RN.

MARTIN, Diana Lillian 21 Kings Park, Longniddry EH32 0QL — MB ChB 1978 Ed.; DRCOG 1981.

MARTIN, Diana Margaret (retired) 1 Woodland Close, Clapham Village, Worthing BN13 3XR Tel: Patching 388 — MRCS Eng. LRCP Lond. 1949; DA Eng. 1953. Prev: Clin. Asst. (Ophth.) Worthing Hosp.

MARTIN, Donal 14 Greystown Avenue, Belfast BT9 6UJ — MB BCh BAO 1991 Dub.; MB BCh Dub. BAO 1991.

MARTIN, Eileen Emily Violet 296 Main Road, Romford RM2 6LU Tel: 01708 42164 — MB ChB 1939 Liverp. (Liverp.) Asst. PMO Med. Adviser's Dept. GLC. Prev: Asst. MOH Barking; RAMC; Res. Surg. Off. York Matern. Hosp.

MARTIN, Elaine Gray (Watson) West Lothian NHS Trust, St Johns Hospital, Livingston EH54 6PP Tel: 01906 419666 — MB ChB 1986 Glas.; FRCA 1993. Cons.(Anaes.) St John's Hosp. W.Lothian NHS Trust. Prev: SHO (Anaesth.) Roy. Alexandra Hosp. Paisley & W.. Infirm. Glas.; Sen. Regist. (Anaesth.) Edin. Roy. Infirm. Regist., Glas. Roy. Infirm. & W.. Infirm. Glas.

MARTIN, Elaine Rachel Monkwearmouth HC, Dundas St., Sunderland SR6 0AB Tel: 0191 514 0431 Fax: 0191 510 3443; 2 Granville Drive, Forest Hall, Newcastle upon Tyne NE12 9LA Tel: 0191 270 1340 — MB ChB 1982 Leic. Assoc. Specialist (Community Child Health) City Hosps. Sunderland. Socs: BMA; Brit. Assn. Community Child Health; Roy. Coll. Paediat. and Child Heath. Prev: Clin. Med. Off. (Community Paediat.) N. Tyneside HA; Clin. Med. Off. (Adolesc. Psychiat.) Newc.; Regist. Rotat. (Paediat.) Newc.

***MARTIN, Elizabeth Ann** 6 Dowlans Road, Bookham, Leatherhead KT23 4LE — MB ChB 1994 Bristol.

MARTIN, Elizabeth Carole Department of Public Health Medicine, Kingston & Richmond HA, 22 Hollyfield Road, Surbiton KT5 9AL Tel: 020 8339 8005; 18a Elm Bank Gardens, Barnes, London SW13 0NT Tel: 020 8392 1984 — MB BCh BAO 1970 Belf.; MSc (Soc. Med.) Lond. 1975; FFCM 1987, MFCM 1977. Dir. Pub. Health Med. Kingston & Richmond HA. Prev: Community Phys. Riverside HA.

MARTIN, Elizabeth Maria 47 Bryan Street, Farsley, Pudsey LS28 5JP — MB ChB 1980 Leeds.

MARTIN, Else Juel 15 Station Road, Verwood BH31 7PY; Moorside Cottage, 35 St. Stephens Lane, Verwood BH31 7BQ Tel: 01202 822106 — MB BS Lond. 1967; MRCS Eng. LRCP Lond. 1965; Cert. Family Plann. JCC 1974. (Roy. Free) Socs: Brit. Soc. Med. & Dent. Hypn. Prev: Ho. Surg. & Cas. Off. Hampstead Gen. Hosp. Lond.; Ho. Phys. Eliz. G. Anderson Hosp. Lond.

MARTIN, Elspeth Paterson Rhu Grianach, Kingussie Road, Newtonmore PH20 1AY Tel: 01540 673938 Fax: 01540 673934 Email: elspeth.martin@bt.internet.com — MB ChB 1969 Ed.; MRCP (UK) 1975; MRCGP 1981; DCH Eng. 1974. (Edin.) GP Highland Region. Prev: GP Lond.; CMO Kensington Chelsea W.minster. HA; GP Edin.

MARTIN, Finbarr Callaghan St Thomas Hospital, London SE1 7EH Tel: 020 7922 8039 Fax: 020 7928 2339 Email: finbarr.martin@gstt.sthames.nhs.uk; 62 Woodbourne Avenue, London SW16 1UT Tel: 020 8769 1380 Email: fcmartin@easynet.co.uk — MB BS 1974 Lond.; MD Lond. 1984, MSc 1982, BSc (Hons.) 1970; FRCP Lond. 1990; MRCP (UK) 1977;

Hon. Fell. Roy. Coll. Speech and Language Therapists 1997. (Char. Cross Lond.) Cons. Phys. St. Thos. Hosp. Lond.; Clin. Dir. Acute Med. & Elderly Care Guy's & St. Thos. Hosps. NHS Trust. Socs: Brit. Geriat. Soc. (Chairm. Policy Comm.); Growth Hormone Res. Soc. Prev: Sen. Regist. Hammersmith Hosp. Lond.; Hon. Sen. Regist. N.wick Pk. Hosp. & Clin. Research Centre Harrow; Ho. Phys. Char. Cross Hosp. Lond.

***MARTIN, Fiona Jennifer** The Cottage, 1 The Green, Saltwood, Hythe CT21 4PS — MB BS 1998 Lond.; MB BS Lond 1998.

MARTIN, Frances Elizabeth (retired) 8 Meadowcroft Road, Meols, Wirral CH47 6BG — MB ChB 1939 Liverp.; DPH Leeds 1942. Prev: Asst. Med. Off. Liverp. Matern. & Child Welf. Dept.

MARTIN, Frances Jane Boscathnoe Farmhouse, Penzance TR20 8RY Tel: 01736 351971 Email: narmjam@aol.com — MB BCh BAO 1981 Dub.; MRCPI 1984; MRCGP 1988; DObst RCSI 1987; DCH NUI 1982. (Trinity Coll. Dublin) Prev: Trainee GP Mullion VTS.

MARTIN, Mr Francis William North Riding Infirmary, Newport Road, Middlesbrough TS1 5JE Tel: 01642 854063 Email: fwmnri@hotmail.com; Long Acres, 57 The Grove, Marton, Middlesbrough TS7 8AL — MB BS 1971 Lond.; FRCS Eng. 1975; MRCS Eng. LRCP Lond. 1970. Cons. Otolaryngol. Cleveland AHA. Socs: Fell.of RSM; Brit. Assn. of OtoLaryngol., Head and Neck Surg.

MARTIN, Francis Xavier, Col. late RAMC Retd. (retired) 33 Cambridge Road W., Farnborough GU14 6QA Tel: 01252 512545 — MD Malta 1952; BSc Malta 1948, PhC 1945; MFPHM 1989; MFCM 1974; DTM & H Eng. 1958. Prev: ADMS HQ S. W. Dist.

MARTIN, Gail Gillian 14 Compton Drive, Maidenhead SL6 5JS — MB BS 1992 Lond. (SHO (Psychiat.) Tolworth Hosp. Surrey)

MARTIN, George Lowry Collingwood, Pinehill Road, Ballycairn, Lisburn BT27 5TU — MB BCh BAO 1969 Belf.

MARTIN, Gerald Ewart Latham House, Sage Cross St., Melton Mowbray LE13 Tel: 01664 60101 — MB ChB 1961 Ed.; DObst RCOG 1964. Clin. Asst. (Geriat.) Framland Hosp. Melton Mowbray & St. Mary's; Mem. Leics. & Rutland Local Med. Comm. & Leics. Family Pract. Comm. Prev: Ho. Phys. E. Gen. Hosp. Edin.; Ho. Surg. Roy. Infirm. Edin.; O & G Ho. Surg. Ipswich & E. Suff. Hosp.

MARTIN, Geraldine Plum Tree Cottage, Rogerstown, Holtye Common, Cowden, Edenbridge TN8 7EJ — BChir 1977 Camb.; MB 1978.

MARTIN, Geraldine Mary (retired) Woodridge, Cross Common Road, Penarth CF64 3UU Tel: 029 2070 1627 — MB ChB 1961 Glas.; DObst RCOG 1963. Prev: GP Penarth.

MARTIN, Gillian Mary 136 Halfway Street, Sidcup DA15 8DB Tel: 020 8300 1274 — MB BS 1973 Lond.; DObst RCOG 1975.

MARTIN, Gillian Rebecca Catherine 140 Sydenham Avenue, Belfast BT4 2DU — MB BCh BAO 1982 Belf.

MARTIN, Glen City Way Surgery, 67 City Way, Rochester ME1 2AY Tel: 01634 843351 Fax: 01634 830421; 2 Orion Road, Rochester ME1 2UL Tel: 01634 841803 — MB BS 1984 Lond.

MARTIN, Gordon MacVicar Maryhill Health Centre, 41 Shawpark Street, Glasgow G20 9DR Tel: 0141 531 8897 Fax: 0141 531 8863 — MB ChB 1979 Glas.; MRCGP 1983; Cert. Family Plann. JCC 1982; Cert. Av Med. 1989; DRCOG 1982. Phys. Supt. E. Pk. Childr. Home Maryhill, Glas.

MARTIN, Graham David Ross Greenwood and Sneinton Family Medical Centre, 249 Sneinton Dale, Sneinton, Nottingham NG3 7DQ Tel: 0115 950 1854 Fax: 0115 958 0044; 5 Kilmalcolm Close, Prenton CH43 9QT Tel: 0151 652 4775, 07812 040509 Email: davetragen@hotmail.com — MB ChB 1978 Sheff.; MRCGP 1986; DRCOG 1984. Private Practitioner in Cosmetic Med.

MARTIN, Graham Howy Blyth (retired) 244 The Long Shoot, Nuneaton CV11 6JN Tel: 02476 383176 Fax: 012476 642036 Email: graham-martin@redroofs31.freeserve.co.uk — MB ChB 1962 St. And.; MD Dundee 1975; FRCGP 1994, M 1975; DObst RCOG 1970; DTM & H Liverp. 1965. Prev: Sen. Partner Red Roofs Surg. Nuneaton Warwicks.

MARTIN, Harry Wotzilka (retired) 'Eversheds', Carron Lane, Midhurst GU29 9LD Tel: 0173 081 6122 — MD 1937 Prague; MRCS Eng. LRCP Lond. 1945. Prev: Local Treasury Med. Off.

MARTIN, Hazel May Caer Ffynnon Surgery, Caer Ffynnon, Springfield Street, Dolgellau LL40 1LY Tel: 01341 422431 Fax: 01341 423717 — MB BS 1978 Lond.; BSc Lond. 1974; DRCOG 1982.

MARTIN, Heather Margaret 115 Craigentinny Road, Edinburgh EH7 6QN — MB ChB 1996 Sheff.

MARTIN, Helen 1 Knockgreenan Park, Omagh BT79 0DD — MB ChB 1995 Ed.

MARTIN, Helen Mary Wolverhampton Road Surgery, 13 Wolverhampton Road, Stafford ST17 4BP Tel: 01785 258161 Fax: 01785 224140 — MB ChB 1984 Leic.

MARTIN, Helena Catherine Willaston Surgery, Greenbank, Neston Road, Willaston, South Wirral CH64 2TN Tel: 0151 327 4593 Fax: 0151 327 8618; 75 Springcroft, Parkgate, South Wirral CH64 6SF — MB BCh 1986 Wales; MRCGP 1990.

MARTIN, Helene Sandra 14A Stonehenge Road, Amesbury, Salisbury SP4 7BA — MB BS 1980 Lond.

MARTIN, Henry de Val (retired) 14 Bourne Avenue, Salisbury SP1 1LS Tel: 01722 335973 — MB BS 1962 Lond. Prev: Med. Off. (Research) Min. of Defence.

MARTIN, Hilary Margaret 23 Arlington Gardens, Attleborough NR17 2NH — MB BS 1993 Lond.

MARTIN, Howard The Jubilee Medical Group, Cobblers Hall Surgery, Cobblers Hall, Burn Lane, Newton Aycliffe DL5 4SE Tel: 01325 311300 Fax: 01325 301389; 2 Hickstead Rise, Woodham Village, Newton Aycliffe DL5 4TP Tel: 01325 311300 — MB ChB 1958 Liverp.; MRCOG 1972, DObst 1964. (Liverp.) Prev: Lt.-Col. RAMC; Cons. (O & G) RAMC; Ho. Off. BRd.green Hosp. Liverp.

MARTIN, Hugh Alistair Daniel Grange Street Surgery, 2 Grange Street, St Albans AL3 5NF Tel: 01727 851136 Fax: 01727 847961; 8 Offa Road, St Albans AL3 4QR Tel: 01727 865244 — MB BS 1988 Lond.; DRCOG 1992. (Char. Cross & Westm.) Prev: Trainee GP Roy. Hants. Co. Hosp. Winchester; SHO (A & E) Whittington Hosp. Lond.; Ho. Surg. Char. Cross Hosp. Lond.

MARTIN, Hugh Philip Luscombe Haycart Barn, Marshfield Farm, Marsh Gibbon, Bicester OX27 0AG — MB BS 1980 Lond.; MRCGP 1985; DRCOG 1985. (Royal Free London) GP Princip. Socs: BMA.

MARTIN, Iain Gregory 42 Fairview Drive, Hythe, Southampton SO45 5GY — MB ChB 1987 Leeds.

MARTIN, Ian Cameron Duff (retired) 61 Belhaven Terrace, Wishaw ML2 7AY — MB ChB 1958 Glas. Prev: GP Wishaw.

MARTIN, Ian Charles Aitchison (retired) 12 Southend Avenue, Darlington DL3 7HL Tel: 01325 463214 Fax: 01325 463214 — MB ChB 1958 Leeds; FRCPsych 1979, M 1971; DPM Eng. 1963. Indep. Cons. Darlington. Prev: Cons. Psychiat: Dept. Psychiat. Memor. Hosp. Darlington.

MARTIN, Mr Ian Cliffe Department of Oral & Facial Surgery, Sunderland Royal Hospital, Sunderland SR4 7TP Tel: 0191 569 9132 Fax: 0191 569 9231; Hayfield House, 4 Whaggs Lane, Whickham, Newcastle upon Tyne NE16 4PF Fax: 0191 421 6402 Email: ian@martini.demon.co.uk — MB BS 1986 Lond.; BDS Lond. 1979; FRCS Eng. 1990; FRCS (Max Facl) Ed. 1990; FDS RCS Eng. 1984; LDS 1980; LLM 1998. (King's Lond.) Cons. Surg. Sunderland Roy. Hosp.; Cons. Dryburn Hosp. Durh.; Sen. Lect. Univ. Newc.; Chairm. SAC (Oral & Maxillo Facial Surg.); Clin. Co-ord. NCEPOD. Socs: Counc. Mem. Brit. Assn. Oral & Maxillofacial Surg.; Counc. Mem. Brit. Assn. Head Neck Oncologists; Counc. Mem. N. of Eng. Medico-Legal Soc. Prev: Sen. Regist. (Maxillofacial Surg.) Qu. Vict. Hosp. E. Grinstead; Regist. Mersey Region Serv. for Maxillofacial Surg.; SHO Rotat. (Surg.) Derriford Hosp. Plymouth.

MARTIN, Ian John 7 Cambridge Court, 4 Earlham St., Covent Gardens, London WC2H 9RZ — MB BS 1992 Adelaide.

MARTIN, Ian Revington The Berrow, Thurston Lane, Sardis, Milford Haven SA73 1LD Tel: 01646 601472 Fax: 01646 601477 Email: ianmartin@clara.net; Department of Radiology, Withybush Hospital, Haverfordwest SA61 2PQ Tel: 01437 773385 Fax: 01437 773450 — MB BS 1977 Lond.; BSc (Hons.) Lond. 1974; FRCR 1985. (Guy's) Cons. Diagn. Radiol. Withybush Gen. Hosp. HaverfordW. Pembrokesh.; Cons. (Radiol.) Werndale Hosp. Bancyfelin Carmarthenshire. Socs: Brit. Nuclear Med. Soc.; Gp. Roy. Coll. Radiol. (BrE. Gp.); SE Wales Radiol. Gp. Prev: Sen. Regist. (Diagn. Radiol.) Addenbrooke's Hosp. Camb.; Regist. (Radiol.) & SHO (Renal.) Guy's Hosp. Lond.

MARTIN, Ione Marina (retired) 15 Brattle Wood, Sevenoaks TN13 1QS Tel: 01732 464184 — MB BS 1953 Durh. Prev: Research (Paediat.) Guy's Hosp. Lond.

MARTIN, Iorwerth Owen (retired) 1A Harford Court, Sketty Green, Swansea SA2 8DE — MRCS Eng. LRCP Lond. 1926; BSc Wales 1923, MB BCh 1927. Prev: Ho. Surg. & Ho. Phys. Roy. Infirm. Cardiff.

MARTIN, James Clason 71 Dan-y-Bryn Avenue, Radyr, Cardiff CF15 8DQ — MB ChB 1986 Glas.; MD (Glas) 1997; MRCP (UK) 1990. (Glasgow) Cons. (Rheum.) Roy. Glam. Hosp., Llantrisant, Mid Glam., Wales. Socs: Brit. Med. Assn.; Brit. Soc. for Rheum.; Nat. Osteoporosis Soc. Prev: Sen. Regist. (Rheum.) Univ. Hosp. of Wales, Cardiff; Clin. Research Fell (Rheum.) City Hosp., Aberd.; Sen. Regist. (Rheum.) Wrexham Meelor Hosp., Wrexham.

MARTIN, James Douglas Cutlack The Laurels, Broad St., New Radnor, Presteigne LD8 2S — MB BChir 1969 Camb.; MA, MB Camb. 1969, BChir 1968; MRCS Eng. LRCP Lond. 1968; DObst RCOG 1971. (Camb. & St. Bart.) Prev: SHO Cas. & Orthop. Battle Hosp. Reading; SHO (Obst.) Roy. Berks. Hosp. Reading; SHO (Paediat.) Addington Hosp. Durban, S. Afr.

MARTIN, James Robert Campbell 88 Yeolland Park, Ivybridge PL21 0YP — MB BS 1986 Lond.; BSc Lond. 1984, MB BS 1986; MRCGP 1992; DRCOG 1990. Trainee GP Portsmouth. Prev: SHO Qu. Alexandra Hosp. Portsmouth.

MARTIN, Jamie Richard John 3 Manor Park, Staines TW18 4XE — MB BCh 1994 Wales.

MARTIN, Jane Christine Tel: 0161 794 0875 Fax: 0161 727 8661 Email: thredhouse@psychotherapy-mhss-tr.nwest.nhs.uk — MB ChB 1988 Manch.; BA (Hons.) Manch. 1973; MRCPsych 1995. (Manchester) Cons. Psychiat. in Psychother., The Red Ho., Ment. health Servs. of Salford, Mancester. Prev: Clin. Research Fell. (Psych.) Manch. Roy. Infirm.; Specialist Regist. Psychother. Gaskell Hse. Psychother. Centre Manch.; Regist. (Psychother.) Gaskell Hse. Manch.

MARTIN, Jane Helen 10 Bramley Place, Lenzie Kirkintilloch, Glasgow G66 5LU Tel: 0141 775 0839 — MB ChB 1994 Glas.; DRCOG 1997. (Glas.) GP Regist. Glas. Prev: SHO (Med. Geriat.) S.. Gen. Hosp. Glas.; SHO (Obstet. & Gyn.) S.. Gen. Hosp. Glas.; SHO (Paediat. Med.) Roy. Hosp. Sick Childr. Glas.

MARTIN, Janet Irene Lightburn Day Hospital, Carntyne Road, Glasgow G32 6ND; Flat 3/2, 1 Broompark Drive, Dennistoun, Glasgow G31 2DA — MB ChB 1974 Glas.; DObst RCOG 1975. Clin. Asst. (Geriat.) Lightburn Day Hosp. Glas. Prev: Clin. Asst. (Psychogeriat.) Gartloch & Pk.head Hosps. Glas.

***MARTIN, Jennifer Louisa** Avonside, Dark Lane, Malmesbury SN16 0BB — MB BS 1996 Lond.

MARTIN, Jennifer Valerie (retired) Pathology Laboratory, Royal Oldham Hospital, Rochdale Road, Oldham OL1 2JH — MB BS 1963 Lond.; FRCPath 1986, M 1974. Cons. Chem. Path. Oldham HA. Prev: Sen. Regist. (Chem. Path.) United Sheff. Hosps.

***MARTIN, Jessica Sarah** Raith Cottage, Old Portkil, Kilgregan, Helensburgh G84 0LF — BM BS 1998 Nottm.; BM BS Nottm 1998.

MARTIN, Joan, MBE (retired) Flat 2, 66 Kensington Church St., London W8 4BY Tel: 020 7229 0911 — MB BS Lond. 1944; MRCS Eng. LRCP Lond. 1942. Prev: Sen. Med. Off. Kensington, Chelsea & W.m. HA (T).

MARTIN, Joan Esmé Lowercrowsnest Farm, Kiln Lane, Milnrow, Rochdale OL16 3TR — MB ChB 1976 Manch.

MARTIN, Professor Joanne Elizabeth Department Morbid Anatomy & Histopathology, Institute of Pathology, The Royal London Hospital, London E1 1BB Tel: 020 7377 7347 Fax: 020 7377 0949 Email: j.e.martin@qmul.ac.uk — MB BS 1984 Lond.; MA Camb. 1981; MRCPath 1993; PhD Lond. 1997. Prof. (Histopath.) Roy. Lond. Hosp. Prev: Sen. Lect. (Neuropath.) Roy. Lond. Hosp.

MARTIN, John Friarsfield House, Friars Lane, Lanark ML11 9EL — MB ChB 1978 Glas.; BSc (Hons.) Glas. 1976, MB ChB 1978; FFA RCS Eng. 1982.

MARTIN, John 44 The Yonne, Chester CH1 2NH Tel: 01244 310132 — MB BS Lond. 1958; FRCP Lond. 1975, M 1963; MRCS Eng. LRCP Lond. 1958; DObst RCOG 1960; DCH Eng. 1961; FRCPCH 1998. (St. Bart.) Emerit. Cons. Paediat. Oncologist Roy. Liverp. Childr. Alder Hey. Prev: Vis. Cons. Paediat. I. of Man Health Serv. Bd.; Clin. Lect. Dept. Child Health Univ. Liverp.; Sen. Med. Regist. Hosp. Sick Childr. Gt. Ormond St. Lond.

MARTIN, John Angus McLeod 8 Eriskay Road, Inverness IV2 3LX Tel: 01463 31384 — MB ChB Ed. 1950. (Ed.) Med. Asst. Anaesth. N. Region. Hosp. Bd.

MARTIN

MARTIN, Mr John Antony Michael (retired) Drimla Cottage, Kildonan, Brodick KA27 8SE Tel: 01770 820229 Email: jantym@surfaid.org — MB BS Lond. 1950; FRCS Eng. 1961; DLO Eng. 1954. Clin. Dir. & Cons. Audiol. Med. Roy. Nat. Throat, Nose & Ear Hosp. Lond.; Hon. Sen. Lect. Inst. Laryng. & Otol. Univ. Coll. & Middlx. Sch. Med.; Prof. Assoc. Univ. Brunel. Prev: Dir. Nuffield Hearing & Speech Centre Lond.

MARTIN, Mr John Bryson Accident and Emergency, Ulster Hospital, Dundonald, Belfast BT16 1RH — MB BCh BAO 1984 Belf.; BSc NUU 1973; FRCS (A&E) Ed. 1990; FRCS Ed. 1989. Cons. (A & E) Ulster Hosp. Dundonald Belf. Prev: Cons. (A & E) Roy. Vict. Hosp. Belf.

MARTIN, John Clement 3 High Beeches Close, Great Woodcote Park, Purley CR8 3QU — MB BS 1964 Durh.

MARTIN, John David St James House Surgery, County Court Road, King's Lynn PE30 5SY Tel: 01553 774221 Fax: 01553 692181 — MB BS 1969 Lond.; MRCP (U.K.) 1972; FRCGP 1992, M 1977. (Lond. Hosp.)

MARTIN, Professor John Francis Department of Medicine, Kings Coll. School of Med. & Dentistry, Denmark Hill, London SE5 9PJ Tel: 020 7326 3013; 21 West Square, London SE11 4SN Tel: 020 8670 7822 — MD 1980 Sheff.; MB ChB 1973; FRCP Lond. 1989; MRCP (UK) 1977. Brit. Heart Foundat. Prof. of Cardiovasc. Sci. & Hon. Cons. Phys. Kings Coll Sch. Med. & Dent. Lond.; Head Cardiovasc. Research Wellcome Foundat. Research Laborat. Kent. Socs: Assn. Phys.; Pres. Mem. Europ. Soc. Clin. Investig. Prev: Sen. Lect. & Hon. Cons. Phys. (Med.) Roy. Hallamsh. Hosp. Sheff.; Sen. Lect. Univ. Melbourne, Austral.; MRC Train. Fell.

MARTIN, Mr John Leonard 132 Welling Way, Welling DA16 2RS — MRCS Eng. LRCP Lond. 1981; BSc (Hons.) Lond. 1978, MB BS 1981; FRCS Ed. 1986.

MARTIN, John Marshall (retired) Dalziel House, 19c Wells Road, Penn, Wolverhampton WV4 4BQ Tel: 01902 336805 — MB ChB Glas. 1956.

MARTIN, John Niall 10 Woodlands Court, Lisburn BT28 2XP — MB BCh BAO 1992 Belf.; MRCGP 1996; DCH Dublin 1994; DRCOG Lond. 1997; DGM Glas. 1995.

***MARTIN, John Nicholas** Chy Karenza, Lane End, St Gluvias, Penryn TR10 9AX — MB BS 1997 Lond.

MARTIN, Mr John Patrick (retired) Field Place, Shaugh Prior, Plymouth PL7 5HB Tel: 01752 839350 — MB BS 1961 Lond.; FRCS Ed. 1970; MRCS Eng. LRCP Lond. 1961; FRCOphth 1988; DO Eng. 1968. Prev: Cons. Ophth. Surg. Roy. Eye Infirm. Plymouth.

MARTIN, John Paul Flat 5, 24 Belsize Park, London NW3 4DU Tel: 020 7794 2241; Endoscopy Unit, St Mark's Hospital, Watford Road, Harrow HA1 3UJ Tel: 020 8235 4136 — MB BChir 1990 Camb.; MRCP UK) 1993. Regist. (Gastroenterol.) N.wick Pk. Hosp. Lond.; Regist. (Gastroenterol.) St. Mark's Hosp. Lond. Prev: Regist. (Gastroenterol.) N.wick Pk. Hosp. Lond.; Regist. (Gastroenterol.) Hillingdon Hosp. Lond.

MARTIN, John Philip DSS, Five Ways House, Frederick Road, Edgbaston, Birmingham B15 1ST — MB ChB Birm. 1961; T(GP) 1991. (Birm.) Med. Adviser DSS Birm. Prev: Med. Off. HM Prison Birm.; Attached Med. Off. BRd.moor Special Hosp. Crowthorne; Ho. Phys. Roy. Hosp. Wolverhampton & Profess. Unit Childr. Hosp. Birm.

MARTIN, John Robert Fairfield Road Surgery, 22a Abban Street, Inverness IV3 8HH Tel: 01463 713939; 10 Kingsmills Gardens, Inverness IV2 3LU Tel: 01463 710818 — MB ChB 1973 Dundee; FRCGP 1995, M 1977; DObst RCOG 1976. (St Andrews and Dundee)

MARTIN, John Russell 111 Wickham Way, Beckenham BR3 3AP — MB ChB 1992 Birm.; 2000 (JCPTGP); 1999 DRCOG RCOG. (Birmingham University Medical School) p/t GP; Asst. Gen. Pract., Beverly, E. Yorks. Prev: Principle in Gen. Practise, Beverley, E. Yorks.

MARTIN, John Stirling Litcham Health Centre, Manor Drive, Litcham, King's Lynn PE32 2NW Tel: 01328 701568 Fax: 01328 700632 — MB BCh BAO 1967 Dub.; MA Dub. 1969, MB BCh BAO 1967; MRCGP 1975; Dip. Midw. COG S. Afr. 1971; DCH Eng. 1970; DTM & H Liverp. 1969. Prev: Regist. (Obst.) Mpilo Hosp. Bulawayo, Zimbabwe; SHO Myrtle St. Childr. Hosp. Liverp.; Ho. Off. Sir Patrick Dunn's Hosp. Dub.

MARTIN, John William 8 Oak Road, Barton-under-Needwood, Burton-on-Trent DE13 8LR Tel: 01283 712015 Email: docmart@argonet.co.uk — MB ChB 1971 Ed.; FRCA 1978.

(Edinburgh) Cons. Anaesth. Burton-on-Trent Hosps. Socs: BMA & Assoc. Anaesth.; Intens. Care Soc.

MARTIN, Jonathan R Department of Primary Care & Population Sciences, Archway Resource Centre, 2nd Floor, Holborn Union Building, Highgate Hill, London N19 5NF Tel: 020 7288 3470 Fax: 020 7281 8004 Email: jonathan.martin@pcps.ucl.ac.uk — BM BS 1989 Nottm.; DRCOG 1993; MRCGP 1994; DFFP 1995; BMedSci 1987; MMSc. (Nottingham) p/t Clin. Lect. (Primary Care & Populat. Sci.), Roy. Free & Univ. Coll., Med. Sch., UCL; GP Partner.

MARTIN, Joyce Rona (retired) 121 Oakham Road, Tividale, Oldbury B69 1QH — MB ChB Birm. 1959; MRCGP 1968; DObst RCOG 1961. Prev: GP Sandwell.

***MARTIN, Julia Karen** Moonfleet, Strawberry Hill, Clevedon BS21 6AF — BM 1994 Soton.

MARTIN, Katharine Louise Yardley Green Medical Centre, 73 Yardley Green Raod, Birmingham B9 5PU Tel: 0121 773 3838 Fax: 0121 506 2005; 66 Meriden Road, Hampton-in-Arden, Solihull B92 0BT Tel: 01675 443411 — MB BS 1987 Lond.; DRCOG 1991; MRCGP 1992. (Guy's Hosp. Med. Sch.)

MARTIN, Katherine Childhealth Department, County Offices, St George's Road, Cheltenham GL50 3EW Tel: 01242 516235 Fax: 01242 234527 Email: kate.martin@egnhst.org.uk; Tel: 01865 881322 Email: kate.martin@doctors.org.uk — MB BChir 1986 Camb.; MRCP Lond. 1990. Cons. Paediatrician Community Child Health, E. Gloucestershire NHS Trust, Cheltenham. Prev: MRC Clin. Sci. UCL Med. Sch., Lond.; Regist. (Paediat.) SW Thames RHA Lond.; Specialist Regist. (Paediat.) Oxf. Radcliffe Hosp. NHS Trust. Hon. Sen. Regist. (Paediat. Rheum.) Gt. Ormond St. Hosp. for Child. Lond.

MARTIN, Keith Robert Graham Main Street Surgery, 60A Main Street, Donaghcloney, Craigavon BT66 7NL — BM BCh 1993 Oxf.

MARTIN, Mr Kenneth Whittle (retired) 4 North Pallant, Chichester PO19 1TJ Tel: 01243 784026 — MB BS 1940 Lond.; MS Lond. 1952; FRCS Eng. 1946; MRCS Eng. LRCP. Lond. 1940. Cons. Surg. Worthing Health Dist.; Fell. Roy. Soc. Med. Prev: Res. Asst. Surg., Regist. & Ho. Surg. & Cas. Off. St. Thos. Hosp.

MARTIN, Konrad Josef 19 Green End, Comberton, Cambridge CB3 7DY Tel: 01223 262600 — MD 1956 Munich; PhD McGill 1962; MA Camb. 1966; Lic. Newfld. Med. Bd. 1968. (Munich) Univ. Lect. Dept. Pharmacol. Univ. Camb.

MARTIN, Laurence John, CBE Department of Health, Wellington House, 133-155 Waterloo Road, London SE1 8UG Tel: 020 7972 4551 Fax: 020 7972 4791; 17 Watery Lane, Merton Park, London SW20 9AA Tel: 020 8542 8979 Fax: 020 8542 8979 — MB BS Lond. 1958. (Westm.) HM Insp. Anat. DoH Lond.; Vice-Pres. & Hon. Fell. Inst. Anat. Scis. Prev: Head Emerg. Plann. Co-ordinating Unit DoH; Cons. i/c A & E St. Stephen's Hosp. Lond.; Capt. RAMC.

MARTIN, Lawrence Vaughan Hunter (retired) 6 Frogston Road E., Edinburgh EH17 8AD Tel: 0131 664 8332 — MB ChB 1955 Ed.; 1955 MB ChB Ed.; 1964 FRCA; 1960 DA Eng.; 1959 DObst RCOG. Cons. Anaesth. Roy. Infirm. Edin.; Hon. Sen. Lect. Univ. Edin. Prev: Sen. Regist. (Anaesth.) Edin. Roy. Infirm.

MARTIN, Mr Lee 8 Bold Place, Liverpool L1 9DN — MB ChB 1989 Liverp.; FRCS Ed. 1993.

MARTIN, Mr Lee Marvill 34 Lawson Terrace, Porthill, Newcastle ST5 8NZ Tel: 01782 635901 — MB BS 1982 West Indies; FRCS Ed. 1992. SHO (Neurosurg.) Wakefield HA. Socs: BMA & Med. Assn. Jamaica.

***MARTIN, Leigh Elizabeth** 22 Torridon Way, Hinckley LE10 0UH — MB ChB 1998 Leic.; MB ChB Leic 1998.

MARTIN, Leonard Geoffrey Cadoux (retired) — MB BS 1941 Lond.; FRCP Glas. 1978, M 1962; FRFPS Glas. 1961; MRCS Eng. LRCP Lond. 1941. Prev: Phys. Maj. Qu.'s Own Yeomanry.

MARTIN, Lindsay Claire Alexandra Unit Palliative Care Unit, Dumfries & Galloway Royal Infirmary, Dumfries DG1 4AP Tel: 01387 241347 Fax: 01387 241347; Castlebank, Glencaple Road, Dumfries DG1 4AS Tel: 01387 253376 — MB ChB 1977 Leeds; MRCGP 1981; Cert. Family Plann. JCC 1981. Cons. Palliat. Med. Dumfries & Galloway Roy. Infirm. Socs: Assn. Palliat. Med.

MARTIN, Lionel Philip The Shrubbery, 65A Perry Street, Northfleet, Gravesend DA11 8RD Tel: 01474 356661 Fax: 01474 534542; Solway, 365 Singlewell Road, Gravesend DA11 7RL Tel: 01474 352206 Fax: 01474 322036 Email: rah30@dial.pipex.com — MB BChir Camb. 1961; MA Camb. 1961; DObst RCOG 1962.

(St. Thos.) Prev: SHO (Paediat.) All St.s' Hosp. Chatham; Ho. Surg. Peace Memor. Hosp. Watford; Ho. Phys. Shrodells Hosp. Watford.

MARTIN, Lois Margaret Biggart Hospital, Biggart Road, Prestwick KA9 2HQ Tel: 01292 470611 — MB ChB Ed. 1963; MRCP (UK) 1979; BSc Open Univ 1998. (Ed.) Cons. Phys. (Geriat. Med.) S. Ayrsh. NHS Hosp. Trust. Prev: Sen. Regist. (Geriat.) Longmore Hosp. Edin.

MARTIN, Louisa Jane 17 Ailsa Drive, Giffnock, Glasgow G46 6RL — MB ChB 1992 Manch.

MARTIN, Lynda Ann Old Feu House, 4 High St., Elie, Leven KY9 1BY — MB ChB 1979 Dundee. GP Kyle of Lochalsh Ross-sh.

MARTIN, Lynda Margaret Oakcroft, Heath Road, Soberton, Southampton SO32 3QH — MB ChB 1978 Liverp.; MRCGP 1983; DRCOG 1984.

MARTIN, Margaret Graham (retired) 4 Cromwell Road, Falkirk FK1 1SF Tel: 01324 622421 — MB ChB Ed. 1944, DPH 1952; MFCM 1974; DCH Eng. 1951. Prev: Resid. (Disp. & Admission Hall) Yorkhill Hosp. Glas.

MARTIN, Margaret Melville Rae West Suffolk Hospital, Hardwick Lane, Bury St Edmunds IP33 2QZ Tel: 01284 713151; 91 Duchess Drive, Newmarket CB8 8AJ Tel: 01638 662002 — MB ChB Ed. 1965; FRCS Ed. 1972; FRCOG 1985, M 1971. (Ed.) Cons. O & G W. Suff. Hosp. Trust. Socs: Med. Wom. Federat.; Fell. Edin. Obst. Soc.; Eur. Assn. Obst. & Gyn. Prev: Specialist (O & G) St. Paul's Hosp. Addis Ababa, Ethiopa; Regist. (O & G) Aberd. Gen. Gp. Hosps.; Regist. Glas. Roy. Matern. Hosp.

MARTIN, Mark David 18A Allingham Court, London NW3 2AH — MB BS 1993 Lond.

MARTIN, Mark Stephen Crowhurst Farm Cottages, Crowhurst Lane, West Kingsdown, Sevenoaks TN15 6JE Tel: 01474 854546 Fax: 01474 854546 — BM 1986 Soton.; DA 1988. Regist. (Anaesth.) Ealing Hosp. Prev: Ho. Off. (Gen. Med. & Haemat.) Boscombe Hosp. Dorset; Ho. Off. (Gen. Surg. & Orthop.) Qu. Alexandra Hosp. Portsmouth; SHO (Anaesth.) Ealing Hosp.

MARTIN, Mary Elizabeth 3 Manor Park, Staines TW18 4XE — MB BCh 1995 Wales.

MARTIN, Mary Frances Thérèse 14 Greystown Avenue, Belfast BT9 6UJ — MB BCh BAO 1978 Belf.; MRCPI (Paediat.) 1986; DTCH Liverp. 1993; DCH RCPSI 1982. Prev: Paediat. Kitovu Hosp. Masaka, Uganda; Paediat. Concern (Med. Progr. for Refugee Childr.) Renk, Sudan.

MARTIN, Mary Simpson 23 Cliff Terrace, Buckie AB56 1LX Tel: 01542 834927 — MB ChB 1942 Aberd. (Aberd.)

MARTIN, Michael Anthony Stockport NHS Trust, Stepping Hill Hospital, Stockport SK2 7JE Tel: 0161 483 1010 Fax: 0161 419 5903; 25 Ogden Road, Bramhall, Stockport SK7 1HJ Tel: 0161 439 9068 Fax: 0161 439 9068 Email: mick.martin@lineone.net — MD Sheff. 1981; MB BS Lond. 1970; FRCP Lond. 1990; MRCP (UK) 1973; MRCS Eng. LRCP Lond. 1970. (King's Coll. Hosp.) p/t Cons. Phys. (Med. & Cardiol.) Stepping Hill Hosp. Stockport. Socs: Med. Research Soc.; Brit. Cardiac Soc.; Brit. Soc. of Echocardiography. Prev: Sen. Regist. (Gen. Med.) Yorks. RHA; Research Sen. Regist. (Cardiol. & Therap.) Roy. Infirm. Sheff.; Regist. (Gen. Med.) Nottm. City Hosp.

MARTIN, Michael Frederick Roy 26 Duchy Road, Harrogate HG1 2ER Tel: 01423 509307 — MB 1974 Camb.; MA MB Camb. 1974, BChir 1973; FRCP Lond. 1992; MRCP (UK) 1978. (St. Bart.) Cons. Rheum. St. Jas. Univ. Hosp. Trust; Hon. Clin. Sen. Lect. Leeds Univ. Socs: Fell. Roy. Coll. Phys.; Brit. Soc. Rheum. Prev: Sen. Regist. (Rheum. & Rehabil.) Leeds Gen. Infirm.; Regist. (Med.) Roy. Cornw. Hosp. Treliske; Ho. Phys. St. Bart. Hosp. Lond.

MARTIN, Michael John Department of Microbiology, Royal Bournemouth Hospital, Castle Lane E., Bournemouth BH7 7DW Tel: 01202 704849 Fax: 01202 309975 — MB BS 1985 Lond.; MSc Clin. Microbiol. Lond. 1990; MRCPath 1992. (Guy's Hosp.) Cons. Microbiol. Roy. Bournemouth Hosp. Socs: Brit. Soc. Antimicrob. Chemother.; Path. Soc.; Hosp. Infec. Soc. Prev: Sen. Regist. (Microbiol.) St. Richards Hosp. Chichester; Regist. (Microbiol.) Guy's Hosp.

MARTIN, Michael John Anaesthetic Department, Newill Hall Hospital, Abergavenny NP7 9EG — MB ChB 1988 Ed.; FRCA 1994. Cons. Anaesth.

MARTIN, Michael Robert Corinthian House, Bradninch, Exeter EX5 4QS — MRCS Eng. LRCP Lond. 1966; MRCGP 1974; DObst RCOG 1968. (St. Geo.) Prev: Clin. Asst. ENT Tiverton & Dist. Hosp.; Clin. Asst. Dept. Neurol. Roy. Devon & Exeter Hosp.; Div. Surg. St. John Ambul. Brig.

MARTIN, Michelle Hope Highfield Surgery, Garton Avenue, Blackpool FY4 2LD — MB ChB 1993 Manch.; MRCGP 1997. (Manch.) GP, Highfield Surg., Blackpool.

MARTIN, Monica Kathleen 8 Stamford Road, Oakham LE15 6JA — MB BS 1953 Lond. (Lond. Hosp.)

***MARTIN, Neil** 11 Glenside, Glynn, Larne BT40 3HD — MB ChB 1998 Ed.; MB ChB Ed 1998.

MARTIN, Neil David Tait (retired) — MD 1987 Lond.; MB BS 1977; FRCP Lond. 1993; MRCP (UK) 1981; FRCP (UK) 1992. Cons. Paediat. Kent & Canterbury Hosp. Canterbury.; Clin. Dir. Prev: Sen. Regist. (Paediat.) Guy's Hosp. Lond.

MARTIN, Niall Aidan John Yardley Green Medical Centre, 75 Yardley Green Road, Bordesley Green, Birmingham B9 5PU Tel: 0121 773 3737; 46 St. Bernard's Road, Olton, Solihull B92 7BA Tel: 0121 706 3525 — LRCPI & LM, LRSCI & LM 1975; DRCOG 1979; MRCGP 1982. (RCSI) Clin. Asst. (Med. Ophth) Birm. Heartlands Hosp.]. Socs: BMA. Prev: Mem. W. Midl. Fac. Bd. RCGP (E. Birm. Dist. Represen.); Postgrad. Tutor (Gen. Pract.) E. Birm. Dist. Hosp.

***MARTIN, Niamh Maria** 152 Priests Lane, Shenfield, Brentwood CM15 8HN — MB ChB 1996 Liverp.

MARTIN, Nicholas Elmwood Health Centre, Huddersfield Road, Holmfirth, Huddersfield HD9 3TR Tel: 01484 681777 Fax: 01484 689603 — BM BS 1980 Nottm.; BMedSci Nottm. 1978, BM BS 1980; MRCGP 1984; DRCOG 1981.

MARTIN, Nicola Shettleston Health Centre, Shettleston Health Centre, 420 Old Shettleston Road, Glasgow G32 7JZ Tel: 0141 531 6250 Fax: 0141 531 6216; 20 Minister's Park, Kittoch Muir, Castleglen, East Kilbride, Glasgow G74 5BX — MB ChB 1990 Glas.; DRCOG 1996. (University of Glasgow) Partner Shettleston Health Centre Glas. Socs: BMA; MDDUS.

MARTIN, Nigel Paul Cae Glas Doctors Surgery, 34 Church Street, Oswestry SY11 2SP Tel: 01691 652929 Fax: 01691 670175; Penygarres House, Penygarres Lane, Pant, Oswestry SY10 9JS Tel: 01691 831289 Fax: 01691 831289 Email: nigmartin@cs.com — MB ChB 1981 Birm.; DRCOG 1985. (Birm.) Med. Off. Hope Hse. Childr. Respite Hospice.

MARTIN, Noel Jeremy Chisnall Tottington Health Centre, 16 Market Street, Tottington, Bury BL8 4AD Tel: 01204 885106 Fax: 01204 887717; 54 Lowercroft Road, Bury BL8 2EZ — MB ChB 1978 Manch.; MFFP 1994 RCOG.

MARTIN, Pamela The New Surgery, 296 Queens Road, London SE14 5JN Tel: 020 7639 5528 — MB BS 1982 Lond.; MRCGP 1986; DCH RCP Lond. 1986; DRCOG 1985. GP Lond. Prev: Trainee GP Luton & Dunstable Gen. Hosp. VTS.

MARTIN, Pamela Carole Doncaster Royal Infirmary, Armthorpe Road, Doncaster DN2 5LT Tel: 01302 366666 Ext: 4196; 25 Rectory Mews, Boat Lane, Sprotbrough, Doncaster DN5 7LG — MB ChB 1969 Ed.; FRCR 1981; DMRD Eng. 1978; DObst RCOG 1973. (Edinburgh) Cons. Radiol. Doncaster Roy. Infirm. Socs: Roy. Coll. Radiol.; Chairm. N. Engl.1994-1998 Brit. Inst. Radiol.; RSM. Prev: Cons. Radiol. Barnsley Dist. Gen. Hosp.; Sen. Regist. (Radiol.) Sheff. AHA (T); Regist. (Radiol.) N. & S. Nottm. Health Dists. (T).

MARTIN, Patricia (retired) 2 Partridge Green, New Milton BH25 5RS — MB BS 1945 Punjab; DPH Eng. 1955; DObst RCOG 1954. Prev: Sen. Med. Off. Herts. CC.

MARTIN, Paul Henry Department of Anaesthesia, Queen's Medical Centre, Nottingham NG7 2UH Tel: 0115 924 9924; 28 Chartwell Grove, Mapperley, Nottingham NG3 5RD — MB ChB 1985 Birm.; FRCA 1992; DA (UK) 1987. (Birm.) Cons. Anaesth. Qu. Med. Centre Nottm. Prev: Sen. Regist. (Anaesth.) Nottm. Hosps.; Regist. (Paediat. Anaesth.) Roy. Liverp. Childr. Hosp.; Regist. (Anaesth.) Nottm. Hosps.

MARTIN, Paul John 36 Byng Road, Tunbridge Wells TN4 8EJ — MB BS 1976 Lond.; DRCOG 1980; DCH Eng. 1978. (St. Geo.) Assoc. Specialist S. Thames Blood Transfus. Serv.

MARTIN, Paul Johnston (retired) Hurst House, Hurst Lane, Bollington, Macclesfield SK10 Tel: 01625 72360 — PhD (Pharmacol.) Lond. 1963, BSc (Physiol.) 1961,; MB BS 1967; MRCS Eng. LRCP Lond. 1967; MRCPath 1974. Prev: Cons. Chem. Path. Stepping Hill Hosp. Stockport.

MARTIN

MARTIN, Paul Lawrey (retired) Chesterton, 1 Woodland Close, Clapham Vill., Worthing BN13 3XR — MB ChB 1951 Glas.; DObst RCOG 1953. Prev: Res. Ho. Phys. Glas. Roy. Infirm.

MARTIN, Paul Stuart Failsworth Health Centre, Oldham, Manchester M35 0HN; 33 Norford Way, Bamford, Rochdale OL11 5QS — MB ChB Birm. 1965; DA Eng. 1968. (Birm.) Prev: Regist. (Anaesth.) E. Birm. Hosp.; Cas. Off. E. Birm. & Birm. Gen. Hosps.

MARTIN, Pauline Sandra 5A Windsor Avenue N., Belfast BT9 6EL — MB BCh 1972 Belf.

MARTIN, Peter 8 Belfast Road, Comber, Newtownards BT23 5EW — MB BCh BAO 1987 Belf.

MARTIN, Peter Alan Boddington The Health Centre, Crammavill Street, Stifford Clays, Grays RM16 2AP Tel: 01375 377127 Fax: 01375 394520 — MB BS 1983 Lond.; MRCGP 1987; DRCOG 1986.

MARTIN, Peter Boddington Westley Hall, Homestead Drive, Langden Hills, Basildon SS16 5PE — MB BS 1956 Lond.; MRCS Eng. LRCP Lond. 1956; MRCGP 1965. (King's Coll. Hosp.) Prev: Ho. Phys. Belgrave Hosp. Childr.; Ho. Surg. Swindon Vict. Hosp.; Med. Off. i/c Med. Div. RAF Hosp. St. Athan.

MARTIN, Peter Bradley St. Peters Hospital NHS Trust, Childrens Unit, Guildford Road, Chertsey KT16 0PZ Tel: 01932 872000 Fax: 01932 875171; 23 Wexfenne Gardens, Lower Pyrford Road, Pyford, Woking GU22 8TH — MB BS 1985 Lond.; MRCP (UK) 1991; DCH RCP Lond. 1988. Cons. Paediat. St. Peters Hosp. Chertsey. Prev: Sen. Regist. (Paediat.) Derby Childr. Hosp. & Nottm. City Hosp.; Regist. (Paediat.) Bristol Roy. Hosp. Sick. Childr. & Plymouth Gen. Hosp.; SHO (Special Care Baby Unit) Bristol Matern. Hosp.

MARTIN, Peter James Department of Neurology, Box 83, Addenbrooke's Hospital, Cambridge CB2 2QQ Tel: 01223 217534 — BM BCh 1989 Oxf.; MD 1994; MA Camb. 1990; MRCP (UK) 1992. Cons.NeUrol., Addenbrooke's Hosp. Camb.

***MARTIN, Peter Stephen** 2 Prospect Court, Ballygowan, Newtownards BT23 6LN — MB BCh BAO 1996 Belf.

***MARTIN, Philip Jeffrey** 25 Park Road, Buxton SK17 6SG — MB ChB 1995 Birm.

MARTIN, Philip Louis Patel and Partners, Broom Lane Medical Centre, 70 Broom Lane, Rotherham S60 3EW Tel: 01709 364470 Fax: 01709 820009; 95 Clough Road, Masbrough, Rotherham S61 1RG Tel: 01709 553664 — MB ChB 1984 Leeds; MSc Aberd. 1979, BSc (Hons.) Manch. 1978; MRCGP 1988. (Leeds) Princip. in Gen. Pract., Rotherham; Hon. Med. Off. to Rotherham Ltd. Football Club. Prev: Trainee GP Wakefield HA VTS.

MARTIN, Rachel Margaret 4 Stalbridge Avenue, Liverpool L18 1EX — MB ChB 1997 Liverp. Med. SHO; Whiston Hosp., Prescot, Merseyside.

MARTIN, Rankin (retired) 2 Chiltern Manor Park, Great Missenden HP16 9BL Tel: 01494 864499 — LRCP LRCS Ed. LRFPS Glas. 1951; Cert. Av Med. 1974.

MARTIN, Rebecca Katherine Scruschloch House, Kilry, Blairgowrie PH11 8HZ — MB ChB 1989 Ed.

MARTIN, Rebecca Victoria 12 Burrell Road, Birkenhead CH42 8NH — BM BS 1992 Nottm.

MARTIN, Richard Collins (retired) Mountview, 13 Caerau Crescent, Newport NP20 4HG Tel: 01633 264733 — MB BS 1960 Lond.; MRCS Eng. LRCP Lond. 1960; DObst RCOG 1963.

MARTIN, Mr Richard Hartley (retired) Bridle Cottage, Pownall Park, Wilmslow SK9 5PZ Tel: 01625 524488 — MB ChB Liverp. 1942; FRCS Ed. 1957; MRCS Eng. LRCP Lond. 1942; FRCOG 1965, M 1951. Hon. Cons. O & G Wythenshawe Hosp. Manch. Prev: Sen. Regist. United Liverp. Hosps. & Liverp. RHB.

***MARTIN, Richard John** 18 Rose Road, Birmingham B17 9LJ — MB ChB 1994 Liverp.

MARTIN, Richard Kennedy Flat 2, 46 Court Road, London SE9 5NP — MB BS 1992 Lond.

MARTIN, Richard Michael Drug Safety Research Unit, Burgledon Hall, Blundell Lane, Bursledon, Southampton SO31 1AA Tel: 02380 406122 Fax: 02380 406551 Email: drmann@dsru.u-net.com; 71 Firle Road, Eastbourne BN22 8EQ — BM BS 1990 Nottm.; BMedSci Nottm. 1988; MRCGP 1994; DRCOG 1993; DCH RCP Lond. 1992. Clin. Research Fell. Drug Safety Research Unit Soton. Prev: Clin. Research Fell. (Gen. Pract.) St. Geo. Hosp. Med. Sch. Lond.

MARTIN, Robert Frederick (retired) Offa's View, Malthouse Lane, Trefonen, Oswestry SY10 9DQ Tel: 01691 655449 — MB ChB 1945 Birm.; MRCS Eng., LRCP Lond. 1946. Med. Adviser Triplex Safety Glass Ltd. Birm. Prev: Ho. Surg. Gen. Hosp. Birm.

MARTIN, Robert Henry 12 The Common, Parbold, Wigan WN8 7DA — MB ChB 1973 Bristol; FRCOG 1990, M 1978. Cons. (O & G) Wigan HA. Prev: Research Fell. (O & G) Univ. Leeds.

MARTIN, Robert William Bennett Gould & Partners Ltd., 3rd Floor, CI Tower, St George's Square, New Malden KT3 4HG Tel: 020 8949 1100 — MB BS 1979 Lond.; MA Oxf. 1979, BA 1976. (St. Mary's) Med. Off. Bennett Gould & Partners Ltd. Surrey. Prev: GP Surbiton.

MARTIN, Robert William Young Brechin Health Centre, Infirmary Street, Brechin DD9 7AY Tel: 01356 624411 Fax: 01356 623259; Rosehill, North Latch Road, Brechin DD9 6LF Tel: 01356 624388 — MB BChir 1970 Camb.; MA, MB Camb. 1970, BChir 1969; MRCGP 1976; DObst RCOG 1971; DCH Eng. 1971. (St. Thos.)

MARTIN, Roberta Eileen 26 Woodlands, Knockmore Road, Lisburn BT28 — MB BCh BAO 1987 Belf.

MARTIN, Robin Peter Department of Cardiology, Bristol Royal Hospital for Sick Children, St Michael's Hill, Bristol BS2 8BJ Tel: 0117 928 3323 Fax: 0117 928 3341 Email: rob.martin@ubht.swest.nhs.uk; 9 Coates Grove, Nailsea, Bristol BS48 1SU Tel: 01275 851559 — MB ChB 1979 Birm.; FRCP Lond. 1996; MRCP (UK) 1982; FRCPCH 1997. (Univ. Birm.) Cons. Paediat. (Cardiol.) Roy. Hosp. for Sick Childr. Bristol. Socs: Brit. Paediat. Cardiac Assn.; Brit. Cardiac. Soc. Prev: Sen. Regist. (Paediat. Cardiol.) Roy. Liverp. Childr. Hosp.; Regist. (Cardiol.) Harefield Hosp. Middlx.; Research Fell. Guy's Hosp. Lond.

MARTIN, Mr Roger (retired) 11 Victoria Street, Norwich NR1 3QX — MB BS 1962 Lond.; FRCS Ed. 1970; FRCOG 1983, M 1969; DCH Eng. 1964. Prev: Cons. O & G Norf. & Norwich Hosp.

MARTIN, Roger Ellis Mitcheldean Surgery, Brook Street, Mitcheldean GL17 0AU Tel: 01594 542270 Fax: 01594 544897; Rosedean, Tibbs Cross, Littledown, Cinderford GL14 3LJ Tel: 01594 826115 Fax: 01594 822411 Email: rogermartin3@compuserve.com — BSc (Biochem.) Lond. 1966, MB BS 1969.

MARTIN, Roger Hugh St Lawrence Medical Centre, 4 Bocking End, Braintree CM7 9AA Tel: 01376 552474 Fax: 01376 552417 — MB ChB 1965 Bristol; MRCGP 1983; DCH Eng. 1973; DTM & H Sydney 1970; DObst RCOG 1967. Socs: BMA. Prev: SHO (Paediat.) Sydenham Childr. Hosp.; SHO (Paediat.) Torbay Hosp.; Gen. Med. Off. Papua, New Guinea.

MARTIN, Ronald Dennis (retired) 43 Trebarwith Crescent, Newquay TR7 1DX Tel: 01637 878230 Email: ronmartin@doctors.org.uk — MB BS 1957 Lond.; MRCGP 1970. Med. Off. RMS St Helena; Hon. Med. Off. JST's for STS St Helena & STS Tenacious.

MARTIN, Rosemary Brenda 10 Redclyffe Road, Manchester M20 3JR Tel: 0161 283 8315 — MB ChB 1977 Aberd.

MARTIN, Rosemary Janet (retired) St John's Cottage, Little St John St, Chester CH1 1RE — MB ChB 1949 Liverp. Prev: Adjudicating Med. Off. DHSS Merseyside Region.

MARTIN, Rosemary Patricia 190 Loughan Road, Coleraine BT52 1UD — MB BCh BAO 1973 Belf.; FRCS Ed. 1980; FCOphth 1990. Assoc. Specialist (Ophth.) Causeway Trust N. Irel.

MARTIN, Roswell James 5 Cheyne Close, Bromley BR2 8QA — MB BChir 1988 Camb.

MARTIN, Russell Dickson (retired) Gean Cottage, 11 Harelaw Road, Colinton, Edinburgh EH13 0DR Tel: 0131 441 3242 — MB ChB 1923 Glas.; DPH 1933. Prev: MOH Burgh of Clydebank.

***MARTIN, Ruth** 368 Perth Road, Dundee DD2 1EN — MB ChB 1998 Dund.; MB ChB Dund 1998.

MARTIN, Samuel Wesley 27 Dalvennan Avenue, Patna, Ayr KA6 7NA; Tel: 01292 282307 — MB BCh BAO 1981 Belf.; MRCGP 1987; DRCOG 1985; DCH Dub. 1984. Princip. Police Surg., R Div., Strathclyde Police, Ayr; GP Trainer. Prev: Trainee GP Ayr.

MARTIN, Sarah Manor Farm Close Surgery, 8 Manor Farm Close, Drayton, Norwich NR8 6DN Tel: 01603 867532; The Granary, Pound Green Lane, Shipdham, Thetford IP25 7LF — MB ChB 1980 Leic.; MRCGP 1987; DRCOG 1984.

***MARTIN, Sarah Victoria** 127 Kennington Road, Kennington, Oxford OX1 5PE — MB BS 1994 Lond.

*MARTIN, Sarita Ann 34 Churchmore Road, London SW16 5XB — LMSSA 1997 Lond.

MARTIN, Sheila Helen (retired) 4 Cotton Lane, Moseley, Birmingham B13 9SA Tel: 0121 449 1161 — MB ChB 1947 Ed.; LMCC 1948; DA Eng. 1954. Prev: Assoc. Specialist Birm. (W.) AHA (T).

MARTIN, Sheila Mary (retired) 13 Farm Avenue, London NW2 2EE — MB BChir 1945 Camb.; MRCS Eng., LRCP Lond. 1944. Prev: Res. Med. Off. Hosp. Wom. Soho Sq. & Qu. Charlotte's Hosp.

*MARTIN, Sian Katharine 35 Uffington Road, London SE27 0RW Tel: 020 8766 7692 Fax: 020 8670 6171 Email: help@fertilityuk.org — MB BS 1987 Lond.

MARTIN, Simon Lewis Northgate House, 7 High St., Bridgnorth WV16 4BU — MB ChB 1976 Birm.; DRCOG 1978.

MARTIN, Stanley 15 Calder View, Thornes Park, Rastrich, Brighouse HD6 3DQ — MB ChB 1989 Leeds.

MARTIN, Stephen Charles Manor Practice, James Preston Health Centre, 61 Holland Road, Sutton Coldfield B72 1RL Tel: 0121 354 2032 Fax: 0121 321 1779; 216 Rectory Road, Sutton Coldfield B75 7RU — MB ChB 1971 Birm.

MARTIN, Professor Stephen David Sycamore Ward, Middleton St. George Hospital, Darlington DL2 1TS Tel: 01325 333192 Fax: 01325 333883 — MB BS 1987 Newc.; MRCPsych 1991. Hon. Sen. Research Fell. Univ. Durh. Socs: Chairm. N. and Yorks. Region Special Care Forum. Prev: Cons. Psychiat. (Special Care & Ct. Diversion) St. Lukes Hosp. Middlesbrough; Cons. Psychiat. & Head of Research Cherry Knowle Hosp. Sunderland; Hon. Lect. Univ. Exeter.

MARTIN, Stephen John 34 Belle Vue Road, Ashbourne DE6 1AT — MB ChB 1990 Bristol.

MARTIN, Stephen John Scott The County Hospital, Durham DH1 4ST Tel: 0191 333 6262 Ext: 3478 Fax: 0191 333 3400; 198 Gilesgate, Durham DH1 1QN Tel: 0191 384 1903 — BM BCh 1975 Oxf.; BA Oxf. 1972, BM BCh 1975; MRCP (UK) 1979; MRCPsych 1985. (Kings Coll.) Cons. Psychiat. Co. Hosp. Durh. Prev: Sen. Regist. (Psychiat.) Middlx. Hosp. Lond.; Regist. (Psychiat.) N.wick Pk. Hosp. Harrow; Regist. (Neurol.) Walton Hosp. Liverp.

MARTIN, Stephen Joseph Castle Street Surgery, 39 Castle Street, Luton LU1 3AG Tel: 01582 729242 Fax: 01582 725192; 5 Alders End Lane, Harpenden AL5 2HL — MB BS 1974 Lond. (King's Coll. Hosp.)

MARTIN, Steven Carl Department of Chemistry, Wes Suffolk Hospital, Bury St Edmunds IP33 2QZ Tel: 01284 713417 Email: s.c.martin@doctors.org.uk — MB ChB 1983 Glas.; Dr. Med. Sci. Uppsala 1990; BSc Glas. 1980; DRC Path. 1997; MRC Path. 1998. Cons. Chem. Pathologist W. Suff. Hosp. Bury St. Edmunds; Cons. Chem. Pathologist Addenbrooke's Hosp. Camb. Prev: Sen. Regist. (Chem. Path.) Heartlands Hosp. Birm.; Regist. (Chem. Path.) Dudley Rd. Hosp. Birm.; Clin. Lect. Univ. Glas. Dept. Path. Biochem. Glas. Roy. Infirm.

MARTIN, Stuart Anderson Shipdham Surgery, Shipdham, Thetford IP25 7LA Tel: 01362 820225 Fax: 01362 821189; The Granary, Pound Green Lane, Shipdham, Thetford IP25 7LF — MB ChB 1983 Leic.; BSc Leics. 1974; MB ChB Leics. 1983; DRCOG 1990. Prev: Maj. RAMC.

*MARTIN, Susan 16 Perran Road, London SW2 3DL — MB BS 1998 Lond.; MB BS Lond 1998.

MARTIN, Susan Elizabeth The Hazeldene Medical Centre, 97 Moston Lane East, New Moston, Manchester M40 3HD Tel: 0161 681 7287 Fax: 0161 681 7438 — MB ChB 1984 Manch.; 2001 Dip Primary Care Rhematology; MRCGP 1990; DRCOG 1989.

MARTIN, Susan Grace Oakham Medical Practice, Cold Overton Road, Oakham LE15 6NT Tel: 01572 722621/2; Manortoft, 12 Main St, Market Overton, Oakham LE15 7PL Tel: 01572 767284 — MB BS 1983 Lond.; MRCGP 1988; DRCOG 1987; DCH RCP Lond. 1986. (Westm.)

MARTIN, Susan Jennifer Priory Medical Centre, Cape Road, Warwick CV34 4JP — BM BS 1987 Nottm.; DRCOG.

MARTIN, Susan Mary Grasmere Street Health Centre, Grasmere Street, Leigh WN7 1XB Tel: 01942 672811 Fax: 01942 680883 — MB ChB 1984 Bristol; MRCGP 1988. GP.

MARTIN, Terence Elwin DERA Centre for Human Sciences, Farnborough GU14 6TD Tel: 01252 393354 Fax: 01252 392525; 399 London Road, Clanfield, Waterlooville PO8 0PJ Fax: 01252 392097 Email: temartin@dra.hmg.gb — MB BS 1982 Lond.; MSc Lond. 1996, BSc 1979; MRCS Eng. LRCP Lond. 1982; DFFP 1993; DAvMed FOM RCP Lond. 1990; Dip. IMC RCS Ed. 1990; DRCOG 1986. Sen. Med. Adviser DERA Centre for Human Sci.s FarnBoro.; Assoc. Fell. Fac. A & E Med. Socs: Aerospace Med. Assn. Prev: Regist. (Helicopter Emerg. Med. Serv.) Roy. Lond. Trust; Med. Off. RAF.

MARTIN, Thomas Dawson Masson (retired) Hayfields, Pangbourne, Reading RG8 — MRCS Eng. LRCP Lond. 1934; FRCPath 1963. Prev: Cons. Path. W. Berks. Health Dist.

MARTIN, Thomas Gavin Hamilton (retired) 17 Aldersyde Court, Dringhouses, York YO24 1QN Tel: 01904 705855 — MB ChB 1926 Glas.; BSc, MB ChB Glas. 1926.

*MARTIN, Thomas Nicholas Rosehill 15 North Latch Road, Brechin DD9 6LF; 2F2, 11 Rosemount Viaduct, Aberdeen AB25 1NE — MB ChB 1997 Ed.

*MARTIN, Timothy John Mitchell Bow End House, Betley, Crewe CW3 9AB — ChM 1996 Birm.; ChB Birm. 1996.

MARTIN, Tony Stuart Brandram House, Park Road, Broadstairs CT10 1ED — MB ChB 1984 Leic.

MARTIN, Tristan John Wells City Practice, 22 Chamberlain Street, Wells BA5 2PF Tel: 01749 673356 Fax: 01749 670031; 43 Ash Lane, Wells BA5 2LW — MB ChB 1983 Zimbabwe; LRCP LRCS Ed. LRCPS Glas. 1983; MRCGP 1994; DRCOG 1992; DCH RCP Lond. 1991.

MARTIN, Una University Department of Therapeutics, Queen Elizabeth Hospital, Edgebaston, Birmingham B15 2TT Tel: 0121 414 6874 Fax: 0121 414 1355 Email: u.artin@bhan.ac.uv — MB BCh BAO 1983 NUI; MB ChB BAO 1983 NUI; FRCPI 1998; BSc 1985 NUI; PhD 1992 Edinburgh; MRCPI 1986. Sen. Lect., Qu. Eliz. Hosp., Birm. Socs: Brit. Pharmacological Soc.; Brit. Hypertens. Soc. Prev: Sen. Lect. in Clin. Pharmacol. Univ. of Birm.; Lect. (Clin. Pharmacol.) Univ. of S.ampton.; Research Fell. Clin. Pharmacolgy, Univ. of Edin.

MARTIN, Vaughan Carroll 42 Waveney Road, Keynsham, Bristol BS31 1RU Tel: 0117 986 4610 — MB ChB 1970 Bristol; BSc Bristol 1967, MB ChB 1970; FFA RCS Eng. 1974. (Bristol) Cons. Anaesth. Roy. United Hosp. Bath & St. Martins Hosp. Bath. Prev: Sen. Regist. (Anaesth.) Sheff. AHA (T); Regist. (Anaesth.) United Bristol Hosps. & SW RHB; SHO (Anaesth.) Soton. Univ. Gp. Hosps.

MARTIN, Vivian Max Cromwell Hospital, Cromwell Road, London SW5 0TU Tel: 020 7460 2000 Fax: 020 7460 5555; Consulting Rooms, 8 Upper Wimpole St., London W1M 7TD Tel: 020 7486 2365 Fax: 020 7224 0034 — MB BS Monash 1968; MRCP (UK) 1978. (Univ. Monash) Cons. Rheum. Cromwell. Hosp. Lond. Socs: Fell. Roy. Soc. Med.; Brit. Soc. Rheum. Prev: Cons.Rheum.Manor Hse.Hosp.Lond; Sen. Regist. (Rheum.) Univ. Coll. Hosp. Lond.; Regist. Whittington Hosp. Lond.

MARTIN, Vivien Hannah Park Road West Surgery, 11 Park Road West, Crosland Moor, Huddersfield HD4 5RX Tel: 01484 642020/642044 Fax: 01484 460774 — MB ChB 1983 Leeds. GP Huddersfield.

MARTIN, William Gilmour Old Mill Surgery, 100 Old Mill Road, Uddingston, Glasgow G71 7JB Tel: 01698 817219 — MB ChB 1984 Ed.; MRCGP 1988.

MARTIN, William Laurence Doctor's Mess, Nottingham City Hospital, Hucknall Road, Nottingham NG5 1PB; 28 Breckhill Road, Woodthrope, Nottingham NG5 4GP — BM BS 1986 Nottm.

MARTIN, William Millar Craig Department of Clinical Oncology, Norfolk & Norwich Hospital, Norwich NR1 3SR Tel: 01603 287674 Fax: 01603 287463 Email: clare.wilson@norfolk-norwich.thenhs.com; 14 Poplar Avenue, Norwich NR4 7LB Tel: 01603 452819 — MB BChir Camb. 1970; MB BCh BAO Belf. 1970; PhD Lond. 1981; MA Camb. 1971; FRCP Lond. 1992; MRCP (UK) 1973; FRCR 1978; FFR RCSI 1977; DMRT Eng. 1976. Cons. Clin. Oncol. Norf. & Norwich Hosp.; Hon. Sen. Lect. Univ. E. Anglia; Cons.Clin Oncol.J Paget Hosp.Gt Yarmouth. Socs: Eur.Soc.Therap.Radiol & Oncol. Prev: WHO Cons. Radiother. & Oncol. Parirenyatwa Hosp., Harare; Sen. Specialist Med. Off. (Radiother. & Oncol.) Angau Memor. Hosp., Papua New Guinea; Prof. Clin. Oncol. Chinese Univ., Hong Kong.

MARTIN

MARTIN, William Nicholas 328 Kennington Road, London SE11 4LD — MB ChB 1994 Bristol; FRCS Ed 1997. SHO (Gen. Surg.) MusGr. Pk. Hosp. Taunton.

MARTIN, Winston Adolphus 33 Devon Road, Bedford MK40 3DF — MB BS 1990 Lond.; MRCP (UK) 1994.

MARTIN-BATES, Charles Robert Dr D J McNie and Partners, 4 St. Barnabas Road, Caversham, Reading RG4 8RA Tel: 0118 478123; 30 Alexandra Road, Reading RG1 5PF Tel: 0118 926 2127 — MB BS 1975 Lond.; BA (Hons.) Kent 1969; MRCP (UK) 1979; MRCGP 1980; DCH Eng. 1978; DRCOG 1978. (St Thomas' Hospital) Socs: Roy. Coll. Phys.

MARTIN DELGADO, Raquel 45 Sydney Road, Sheffield S6 3GG — LMS 1993 Granada.

MARTIN GONZALEZ, Jose Enrique Bolton General Hospital, Minerva Road, Farnworth, Bolton BL4 0JR — LMS 1993 Valencia.

MARTIN HIERRO, Manuel Enrique 19 Boundary Lane, Heswall, Wirral CH60 5RP — LMS 1991 Santiago de Compostela.

MARTIN-HIRSCH, Dominic Paul 15 Adwalton Green, Moorlands, Drighlington, Bradford BD11 1DQ — BM BS 1987 Nottm.

MARTIN-HIRSCH, Pierre Leonard 14 Hannah Lodge, Avoncourt Drive, Didsbury, Manchester M20 8QY — MB ChB 1986 Manch.

MARTIN MARTINEZ, Jose Gonzalo 19 Hawthorn Road, Bexleyheath DA6 7AF — LMS 1990 U Autonoma Madrid.

MARTIN MIGUEL, Maria del Carmen 48 Rutland Court, London SW14 — LMS 1991 Madrid; LMS U Complutense Madrid 1991.

MARTIN OLIVER, Maria Jose 4 Jellicoe Court, Atlantic Wharf, Schooner Way, Cardiff CF10 4AJ — LMS 1987 Malaga.

MARTIN-ORTIZ, Roberto 61 George Loveless House, Diss St., London E2 7QZ — LMS 1990 Salamanca.

MARTIN PALMA, Elia 21 Martynside, The Concourse, London NW9 5UT — LMS 1988 Barcelona; FRCA 1994.

MARTIN-SCOTT, Ian, VRD (retired) Netherclay House, Bishops Hull, Taunton TA1 5EE Tel: 01823 284127 — MB ChB 1936 Glas.; MB ChB (Commend.) 1936; MD (Commend.) Glas. 1941. Prev: Cons. Dermat. W. Herts. Hosp. Hemel Hempstead, Peace Memor, Hosp. Watford & Luton & Dunstable Hosp.

MARTIN-SMITH, Michael Hugh Anthony Sydenham House Surgery, Boulevard, Hull HU3 2TA Tel: 01482 326818 Fax: 01482 218267; Sydenham House, Boulevard, Hull HU3 2TA — MB BS 1973 Lond.; BSc, MB BS Lond. 1973; MRCGP 1978; DRCOG 1977; Cert. Family Plann. JCC 1978.

MARTIN UCAR, Antonio 55 Ha'penny Bridge Way, Ocean Boulevard, Victoria Dock, Hull HU9 1HD Tel: 01482 219924 — LMS 1994 Basque Provinces. SHO (Cardiothoracic Surg.) Castle Hill Hosp. Cottingham E. Yorks.

MARTINDALE, Andrew David 148 Whitcliffe Lane, Ripon HG4 2LD — BM BCh 1993 Oxf.

MARTINDALE, Anne (retired) 5 Beach Lawn, Waterloo, Liverpool L22 8QA Tel: 0151 928 2714 — MB ChB 1958 Liverp.; MRCS Eng. LRCP Lond. 1958; DA Eng. 1962. Prev: Cons. Anaesth. BRd.green Hosp. Liverp. & N. Mersey Community NHS Trust.

MARTINDALE, Brian Victor Psychotherapy Dept, John Connolly Wing, Ealing, Hammersmith & Fulham Mental Health NHS Trust, Southall UB1 3EV Tel: 020 8354 8935 Fax: 020 8354 8142 Email: brian.martindale@cableinet.co.uk; 31 Nassau Road, Barnes, London SW13 9QF Tel: 020 8255 0181 Fax: 020 8255 0181 — MB BS 1971 Lond.; MRCP (UK) 1975; MRCS Eng. LRCP Lond. 1971; FRCPsych 2000. (Guy's) Cons. Psych.PyschoTher. Socs: Assoc.Mem.Brit.Psycho-Analytic.Soc.; Euro Rep of Psychiat. to World Psych. Assn.; Bd. mem.Internat.Soc.Pyscho.Treatm.s.Schizophrenia. Prev: Sen. Regist. (Psychother.) Cassel Hosp. Richmond; Regist. (Psychiat.) Maudsley Hosp. Lond.; Cons.Psychiat.PyschoTher., Pk.side Clinic & St Chas. Hosp.Lond.

MARTINDALE, Elizabeth Anne Tel: 01204 883205; 13 Mayfield Close, Holcombe Brook, Bury BL0 9TL Tel: 01204 883205 Fax: 01204 882129 Email: liz.dawson@virgin.net — MB ChB 1985 Liverp.; MFFP 1993; MRCOG 1991. Cons. (O & G) Qu.'s Pk. Hosp. B'burn. Socs: NW Obst. & Gyn. Soc.; Brit. Med. Ultrasound Soc. Prev: Sen. Regist. Roy. Bolton Hosp.; Sen. Regist. Fairfield Hosp. Bury; Regist. (O & G) Bolton Gen. Hosp.

MARTINDALE, Helen Claire 21/7 Parkside Terrace, Edinburgh EH16 5XW — MB ChB 1994 Ed.

MARTINDALE, Mr Jeremy Peter Tayside University Hospitals NHS Trust, Ninewells Hospital and Medical School, Dundee DD1 9SY Tel: 01382 660111; Estirbogsid, Alyth, Blairgowrie PH11 8HJ — MB ChB 1982 Ed.; FRCS Ed. 1988. Cons. Orthop. Surg. Dundee Roy. Infirm. Prev: Lect. (Orthop.) Univ. Nottm.; Regist. (Orthop.) Derbysh. Roy. Infirm.; Regist. Rotat. (Trauma) Dundee.

MARTINDALE, John Haydn (retired) 5 Beach Lawn, Waterloo, Liverpool L22 8QA Tel: 0151 928 2714 — MB ChB 1960 Liverp.; FRCPath 1979, M 1967. Prev: Hon. Clin. Lect. (Haemat.) Univ. Liverp.

MARTINDALE, Morag McHoull Ardblair Medical Practice, Ann Street, Blairgowrie PH10 6EF Tel: 01250 872033 Fax: 01250 874517; Estirbogsid, Alyth, Blairgowrie PH11 8HJ — MB ChB 1982 Ed.; BSc (Med. Sci.) Ed. 1979; Cert. Family Plann. Ed. 1986; DRCOG 1986. Prev: Clin. Med. Off. Angus NHS Trust Forfar.

MARTINDALE, Sarah Jane 3 Surrey Road, Bristol BS7 9DJ — MB BS 1991 Lond.

MARTINEAU, Adrian Ralph 28 Lonsdale Road, London SW13 9EB — MB BS 1996 Newc.; BMedSc Newc 1995; Dip Trop. Med. 1997.

MARTINEAU, Jennifer Gay Castle Hill Surgery, Castle Hill Gardens, Torrington EX38 8EU Tel: 01805 623222 Fax: 01805 625069 — MB BS 1988 Lond.; BSc Lond. 1985, MB BS 1988; DRCOG 1993; MRCGP 1998. (Roy. Free Hosp.) Prev: Trainee GP Glos. VTS.

MARTINEZ, Anna Elizabeth College Hall, St. Bartholomew's Medical College, Charterhouse Square, London EC1M 6BQ; 73 Kynaston Road, London N16 0EB — MB BS 1991 Lond.

MARTINEZ, Delia Briery Wood Farm, Hebers Gyll Drive, Ilkley LS29 9QQ — MB BS 1982 Newc.; MRCP (UK) 1985; FRCR 1988. Cons. Radiol. Clarendon Wing X-Ray Leeds Gen. Infirm. Prev: Sen. Regist. (Radiol.) Leeds.

MARTINEZ, Giselle Cardiff Community Healthcare NHS Trust, Whitchurch Hospital, Park Road, Cardiff CF14 7XB — MB BS 1985 Lond.; MRCPsych. 1991; DGM RCP Lond. 1989. Cons. Psychiat. Cardiff. Prev: Sen. Regist. (Psychiat.) S. Wales.

MARTINEZ, Joan 24 Stuart Road, Acton, London W3 6DG Tel: 020 8992 7210 — MB ChB 1936 Liverp.; DA Eng. 1940. (Liverp.) Prev: Cons. Anaesth. Highlands Hosp. & Wood Green Hosp. Lond.

MARTINEZ-ALIER, Nuria Gabriela 56A Beversbrook Road, London N19 4QH — BM BCh 1994 Oxf.; BSc (Hons.) Applied Biol. Lond. 1989. SHO (Paediat.) Gt. Ormond St. Lond. Socs: Pres. Gt. Ormond St. Hosp. Prev: SHO (Paediat.) St. Geo. Hosp. Lond.; SHO (Paediat.) Whittington Hosp. Lond.; Ho. Off. (Gen. Surg.) Roy. United Hosp. Oxf.

MARTINEZ BURGUI, Jesus Angel 10 Craven Hill, London W2 3DT — LMS 1990 Navarre.

MARTINEZ CAMPOS, Elisa 52 Sinclair Road, London W14 0NH — LMS 1994 Alcala de Henares.

MARTINEZ DEL CAMPO, Miguel Oaktree Cottage, Oakshade Road, Oxshott, Leatherhead KT22 0LF — LMS 1994 Barcelona.

MARTINEZ DEVESA, Pablo ENT Department, Wexham Park Hospital, Wexham St., Wexham, Slough SL2 4HL — LMS 1993 U Complutense Madrid.

MARTINEZ FERNANDEZ, Isabel 5 Black Swan Court, Priory St., Ware SG12 0HY — LMS 1987 Santander.

MARTINEZ HERNANDEZ, Agueda Flat 2, 267 Walmersley Road, Bury BL9 6NX; 7 Cavendish Gardens, Cavenish Road, Disbury, Manchester M20 1LA — LMS Granada 1987. GP Regist. Prev: Ho. Off. S. Manch. NHS.

MARTINEZ PASCUAL, Rosa Maria Doctor's Residence, West Wales Hospital, Carmarthen SA31 2AF Tel: 01267 235151 — LMS 1991 Zaragoza.

MARTINEZ ROMERO, Francisco Javier 93 Oxford Road, Flat 3, Banbury OX16 9AJ — LMS 1992 Saragossa.

MARTINEZ SAENZ, Juan Antonio Department of Obstetrics & Gynaecology, Princess Anne Hospital, Coxford Road, Southampton SO16 5YA — LMS 1993 Basque Provinces.

MARTINI, Ms Helen Claire Cools, South Ronaldsay, Orkney KW17 2RJ — MB BS 1980 Lond.; FRCS Ed. 1985. Staff Grade Surg. Balfour Hosp. Orkney.

MARTINS, Catherine Ann Benefits Agency Medical Services (Personnel), Quarry House, Quarry Hill, Leeds LS2 7UA; 7

Devonshire Road, Lytham St Annes FY8 2NX — MB ChB 1984 Manch.; BSc St. And. 1981. Med. Off. Benefits Agency Med. Servs. Lond.

MARTINS, Stella Lourdes 12 Chasewood Avenue, Enfield EN2 8PT Tel: 020 8363 0086 — MB BS 1965 Bombay; DPH Bombay 1966. (Grant Med. Coll.) Clin. Asst. (Psychiat.) Chase Farm Hosp. Enfield. Prev: SHO (Psychiat.) Chase Farm Hosp. Enfield; Med. Off. Convent of Jesus & Mary Sch. Bombay, India; Jun. Lect. (Preven. & Social Med.) Grant Med. Coll. Bombay.

MARTINUS, Pia Matilda 69 Fore Street, Chudleigh, Newton Abbot TQ13 0HT Email: pia@doctors.org.uk; 69 Fore Street, Chudleigh, Newton Abbot TQ13 0HT — BM 1989 Soton.; DFFP 1994; MRCGP 1996. GP Retainer, Albany St. Surg., Newton Abbot (p/t). Prev: SHO (O & G) Derriford Hosp. Plymouth; Trainee GP Saltash Cornw.; SHO (Psychiat.) Derriford Hosp. Plymouth.

MARTIS, Pamela Dolores Prospect Place Medical Group, Prospect Place, Newcastle upon Tyne NE4 6QD Tel: 0191 273 4201; 9 Murray Place, Stonehaven AB39 2GG Tel: 01569 763859 — MB ChB 1992 Ed.; DRCOG 1996. Trainee GP N.d. VTS. Socs: BMA. Prev: Ho. Off. (Med.) Roy. Infirm. & City Hosp. Edin.; Ho. Off. (Surg.) Whitehaven.

MARTLAND, Christopher Paul Dalton Surgery, 364A Wakefield Road, Dalton, Huddersfield HD5 8DY Tel: 01484 530068 — MB ChB 1986 Leeds.

MARTLAND, Timothy Richard 19 Bath Terrace, Newcastle upon Tyne NE3 1UH — MB ChB 1986 Ed.

MARTLEW, Kenneth George Everest House Surgery, Everest Way, Hemel Hempstead HP2 4HY Tel: 01442 240422 Fax: 01442 235045; 102 Gravel Lane, Hemel Hempstead HP1 1SB Tel: 01442 61525 Email: 100625.472@compuserve.com — MB BS 1966 Lond.; MRCS Eng. LRCP Lond. 1966; DObst RCOG 1971. (St. Thos.) Socs: BMA.

MARTLEW, Robert Andrew 7 Leechfield Road, Galgate, Lancaster LA2 0NX Tel: 01524 751492 — MB BS 1981 Newc.; FCAnaesth 1990. Cons. Anaesth. Preston Acute Hosps. Trust. Prev: Sen. Regist. (Anaesth.) NW Region.; Clin. Instruc. UCI Med. Centre, Irvine Calif., USA.

MARTLEW, Robert Howard (retired) 7 Mockbeggar Drive, Wallasey CH45 3NN — MD 1955 Liverp.; FRCPsych 1971; DPM Eng. 1951; MB ChB 1944 Liverpool. Prev: Cons. Psychiat. Rainhill & St. Helens Hosps.

MARTLEW, Vanessa Joan Royal Liverpool Hospital, Prescot St., Liverpool L7 8XP Tel: 0151 706 4322 Fax: 0151 706 5810 Email: vmartlew@rlbuhtr-nwest.nhs.uk; 6 Bayswater Gardens, Wallasey CH45 8LB Tel: 0151 638 0246 Email: vanessa.martlew@talk21.com — MB ChB 1975 Liverp.; FRCP Lond. 1995; FRCPath 1995; T(M) 1991; T(Path) 1991. Cons. Haemat. Roy. Liverp. Univ. Hosps. NHS Trust; Hon. Lect. (Haemat.) Univ. Liverp. Prev: Cons. Haemat. & Dir. Mersey Regional Blood Transfus. Serv.; Cons. Haemat. NW Regional Transfus. Serv.

MARTYN, Charles John 23 Ardmore Road, Holywood BT18 0PJ — MB BCh BAO 1983 NUI.

MARTYN, Christopher Neville MRC Environmental Epidemiology Unit, Southampton General Hospital, Southampton SO16 6YD — MB ChB 1977 Ed.; DPhil Oxf. 1979, MA 1979; FRCP Lond. 1994; FRCP Ed. 1992. Mem. Scientif. Staff MRC Environm. Epidemiol. Unit Soton. Gen. Hosp.; Hon. Cons. Neurol. Sci. Wessex Neuro. Centre Soton. Gen. Hosp. Prev: Lect. (Neurol.) Roy. Infirm. Edin.

MARTYN-JOHNS, David White City Health Centre, Australia Road, London W12 7PH Tel: 020 8743 3090 Fax: 020 8749 4188; 29 Elm Grove Road, Ealing Common, London W5 3JH Tel: 020 8567 2362 — MB ChB 1951 Birm.; MRCS Eng. LRCP Lond. 1951. (Birm.) Prev: RAF Med. Br.; Ship's Surg. Orient Line & Union Castle Line.

***MARTYN-SIMMONS, Claire Louise** Salisbury District Hospital, Odstock Road, Salisbury SP2 8BJ — MB BS 1998 Lond.; MB BS Lond 1998.

MARTYR, Joanne Wendy Park Practice, Brodrick Close, Hampden Park, Eastbourne BN22 9NQ Tel: 01323 502200 Fax: 01323 440970, 01323 500527 — MB ChB 1979 Birm. Retainee. Prev: Trainee GP Coventry; Ho. Off. (Med. & Surg.) Warneford Gen. Hosp. Leamington Spa.

MARTYROSSIAN, John (retired) 330 Myton Road, Leamington Spa CV31 3NY — MB ChB 1957 Bristol. Prev: Ho. Phys. Roy. Hosp. Sick Childr. Bristol.

MARTYS, Cedrick Reginald Applecross, Wyedale Crescent, Bakewell DE45 1BE — MD 1979 Sheff.; MB ChB 1968; MRCGP 1976.

***MARTYS, Miss Sarah Jennie** Applecross, 38 Wyedale Crescent, Bakewell DE45 1BE Tel: 01629 813234 — MB BS 1998 Newc.; MB BS Newc 1998.

MARU, Leena 211 The Quadrangle, Cambridge Square, London W2 2PJ — MB BS 1993 Lond.

MARUS, Anthony Giulio Francis 45 Holmhurst Road, Belvedere DA17 6HW Tel: 01322 441370 — MB BS 1958 Lond. (Lond. Hosp.) Hosp. Pract. (Gastroenterol.) Brook Hosp. Lond. Socs: BMA & Brit. Soc. Gastroenterol.

***MARUTHAINAR, Kunalan** 12 Hale Drive, London NW7 3DU — MB BS 1998 Lond.; MB BS Lond 1998.

MARUTHAINAR, Nimalan 8 Shakespeare Road, London NW7 4BB — MB BS 1993 Lond.; FRCS 1997. (Roy. Hosp. Sch. Med. Lond.) Specialist Regist., Roy. Nat. Orthop. Hosp. Rotat. Socs: BMA. Prev: SHO (Orthop.) Roy. Nat. Orthop., Norwich; SHO (Surg. Rotat.) Norwich; Demonst. (Anat.) Leeds Univ.

MARUTHAPPU, Jayalini 84 London Road, Stanmore HA7 4NS — MB BS 1974 Sri Lanka; MRCP (UK) 1983; MRCS Eng. LRCP Lond. 1985. Assoc. Specialist Ealing Hosp. & Clayponds Hosp. Lond.

MARVAL, Michael John St. Mary's Surgery, Church Close, Andover SP10 1DP Tel: 01264 361424 Fax: 01264 336792; The Old Stores, Goodworth Clatford, Andover SP11 7RE Tel: 01264 365637 — MB ChB 1963 Bristol; DObst RCOG 1966. (Bristol) Prev: Ho. Phys. S.mead Hosp. Bristol; Ho. Surg. Bristol Roy Infirm.

MARVAL, Paul David Cairns Cottage, Little London Lane, 3 Main Street, Wysall, Nottingham NG12 5QS — BM BS 1994 Nottm.

MARVASTI-ALIM, Ahmad Mideast Polyclinic, P.O. Box 55742, Dubai, United Arab Emirates Tel: 009714 221 6888 Fax: 009714 222 9387; Flat 56, The Quadrangle, Sussex Gardens, London W2 2RW Tel: 0207 402 0536 Fax: 0207 402 3706 Email: marvasti@emirates.net.ae — MD 1974 Teheran. Cons. Surg. and Med. Director MidE. Polyclinic, Dubai, United Arab Emirates. Socs: Fell. Internat. Coll. Surg. 1984; Fell. BMA, Roy. Soc. Med. & Med. Soc. Lond.; Internat. Soc. of Surg. Prev: Clin. Asst. (Surg.) Guy's Hosp. Lond.; Regist. (Surg.) Guy's Hosp. Lond.

MARVEN, Mr Sean Stuart Paediatric Surgical Unit, Sheffield Children's Hospital, Western Bank, Sheffield S10 2TH Tel: 0114 271 7000 Fax: 0114 276 8419 Email: s.s.marven@sheffield.ac.uk; 8 Byron Road, Nether Edge, Sheffield S7 1RY — MB ChB 1987 Leic.; FRCS Ed. 1991. Regist. (Paediat. Surg.) Sheff. Childr. Hosp.; Jun. Mem. UK Childr. Cancer Study Gp. Socs: Assoc. Mem. Brit. Assn. Paediat. Surgs.; Paediat. Intens. Care Soc. Prev: Regist. (Paediat. Surg.) Liverp.; SHO (Neonat.) Liverp. Matern. Hosp.; SHO (Gen. Surg.) Walton Liverp.

MARVIN, Cynthia Mary NHS Executive Headquarters, Quarry House, Quarry Hill, Leeds LS2 7UE Tel: 0113 254 5000; 32 Northern Common, Dronfield Woodhouse, Dronfield S18 8XJ — MB ChB Sheff. 1966; FFPHM 1989; MFCM 1985. Sen. Med. Off. NHS Exec. HQ; Med. Adviser to NHS locum agency. Socs: BMA. Prev: Cons. Pub. Health Med. Trent RHA; GP Chesterfield; SHO (Anaesth.) Sheff. Roy. Infirm.

MARWAH, Karamjit Singh The Surgery, 25 Greenwood Avenue, Beverley HU17 0HB Tel: 01482 881517 Fax: 01482 887022; 1 The Lawns, Molescroft, Beverley HU17 7LS — MB BS 1978 Rajasthan.

MARWAHA, Sarjit Singh Holmside Medical Group, 142 Armstrong Road, Benwell, Newcastle upon Tyne NE4 8QB Tel: 0191 273 4009 Fax: 0191 273 2745; 142 Armstong Road, Benwell, Newcastle upon Tyne NE4 8QB Tel: 0191 273 4009 — MB BS 1974 Aligarh; BSc Punjab 1968; LMSSA Lond. 1977. GP Newc.u.Tyne; Clin. Asst. (Gyn.) Newc.u.Tyne.

MARWAHA, Shaleen 12 Glamorgan Road, Kingston upon Thames KT1 4HP — MB ChB 1986 Manch.

***MARWAHA, Steve** 26 Palace Court, 250 Finchley Road, London NW3 6DN — MB BS 1996 Lond.

MARWICK, David Milne Rubislaw Place Medical Group, 7 Rubislaw Place, Aberdeen AB10 1QB Tel: 01224 641968 Fax: 01224 645738 — MB ChB 1992 Aberd.; DRCOG 1996; MRCGP 1997.

MARWICK, Kareen Elizabeth 40 Holme Road, West Bridgeford, Nottingham NG2 5AA — MB BS 1993 Lond.; BA 1983 Cantab.;

MARWICK

MSc Imper. Coll. Lond. 1984, Envirn. Techn. (Charing Cross & Westminster Med. School) GP Retainer, Nottm.

***MARWICK, Sarah Margaret** Merton Lodge, Binfield Rd, Wokingham RG40 1SL — MB ChB 1997 Birm.

MARWICK, Timothy Peter Beech Hill Medical Practice, 278 Gidlow Lane, Wigan WN6 7PD Tel: 01942 821899 Fax: 01942 821752 — MB ChB 1986 Liverp.

MARWOOD, Mr Roger Paul 96 Harley Street, London W1N 1AF Tel: 020 7637 7977 Fax: 020 7486 2022; 210 Peckham Rye, London SE22 0LU Tel: 020 8693 1250 Fax: 020 8693 0597 — MB BS 1969 Lond.; MSc (Med. Demography) Lond. 1974; FRCOG 1989, M 1977. (King's Coll. Hosp.) p/t Cons. O & G Chelsea & W.m. Hosp.; Hon. Cons. Gyn. King Edwd. VII Hosp. for Offs. Lond.; Clin. Director Wom. & Childr.s Servs. Socs: Pres. Roy. Soc. Med. Obst. & Gyn. Sect. Prev: Sen. Regist. St. Mary's Hosp. Med. Sch. Lond.; Lect. (O & G) Guy's Hosp. Med. Sch.

MARX, Clare Lucy Trauma & Orthopaedic Dept., Ipswich Hospital NHS Trust, Ipswich IP4 5PD Tel: 01473 702030 Fax: 01473 702094; Tel: 01473 737749, 0207 731 5790 Fax: 01473 737227 — MB BS 1977 Lond.; FRCS Eng. 1981. Cons. Orthop. Surg. Ipswich Hosp. NHS Trust. Socs: Fell. Roy. Soc. Med.; Fell. BOA. Prev: Cons. Orthop. Surg. St. Mary's Hosp. Lond.; Sen. Regist. W.m. & Univ. Coll. Hosps. & Roy. Nat. Orthop. Hosp. Stanmore; Regist. (Orthop.) W.m. Hosp. & W.m. Childr. Hosp.

MARX, Helen Margaret 4 Radford Rise, Solihull B91 2QH; 4 Radford Rise, Solihull B91 2QH Tel: 0121 705 2116 — MB BCh 1990 Wales; MRCGP 1994; DRCOG 1993. SHO (O & G) Derriford Hosp. Plymouth. Prev: SHO (O & G) W.on Gen. Hosp. W.on-super-Mare & St. Michael's Hosp. Bristol; Ho. Off. (Surg.) Morriston Hosp. Swansea; Ho. Off. (Med.) P.ss of Wales Hosp. Bridgend.

MARY, Adil Salman Georges Department of Cardiovascular Studies, Leeds University, Leeds LS2 9JT Tel: 0113 233 4810 Fax: 0113 233 4803 — MB ChB 1960 Baghdad; PhD Leeds 1977; FRCP Lond. 1985, M 1969; MRCS Eng. LRCP Lond. 1970. (Baghdad Med. Coll.) Sen. Lect. (Cardiovasc. Studies) Leeds Univ. Prev: Lect. (Cardiovasc. Studies) Leeds Univ.; Lect. (Physiol.) Guy's Hosp. Med. Sch. Lond.; Research Fell. (Cardiovasc. Studies) Leeds Univ.

MARY, Barbara Lettice Willow House, St. Mary's Hospital, Greenhill Road, Leeds LS12 Tel: 0113 279 0121; 51 North Park Grove, Leeds LS8 1EW — MB BS 1966 Lond.; MRCS Eng. LRCP Lond. 1966; DCCH RCP Ed. 1985; DObst RCOG 1968. (Roy. Free) SCMO (Child Health) Leeds Community & Ment. Health Trust. Socs: Soc. Pub. Health (Fac. Community Health). Prev: Clin. Med. Off. (Child Health & Family Plann.) Leeds HA; Ho. Surg. Hampstead Gen. Hosp.; Ho. Surg. (O & G) St. Mary Abbot's Hosp. Kensington.

MARY, Jamal Salman Georges Tel: 01384 573771; Lakeside District Surgery, Rannoch Close, Withymoor Village, Brierley Hill DY5 3RP Tel: 01384 892505 — MRCS Eng. LRCP Lond. 1969. (Sheff.) Socs: BMA & Overseas Doctors Assn.; Assoc. MRCGP. Prev: Ho. Surg. S. Sheilds Gen. Hosp.; Ho. Off. (Midw.) Chase Farm Hosp. Enfield.

MARY DAS, Thyveetil Antony Department of Anaesthesia & Intensive Care, Royal Berkshire Hospital, Reading RG1 5AN Tel: 0118 987 7065; 3 Edenham Close, Lower Earley, Reading RG6 3TH Tel: 0118 966 9678 Email: dasthyveetil@compuserve.com — MB BS 1980 Bangalore; BSc (Zool.) Kerala 1974; FFA RCSI 1990; DA (UK) 1985. Assoc. Specialist Anaesth. Roy. Berks. Hosp.; Mem. Coll. Anaesth. Socs: BMA; Med. Defence Union.

MARYNICZ, Paul Kelso Road Health Centre, Kelso Road, Coldstream TD12 4LG Tel: 01890 882711 Fax: 01890 883547 — MB ChB 1984 Glas.; MRCGP 1990; BSc (Glas.) 1979. Princip. GP.

MARYON-DAVIS, Alan Roger Lambeth, Southwark & Lewisham Health Authority, 1 Lower Marsh, London SE1 7NT Tel: 020 7716 7000 Fax: 020 7716 7018 Email: alan.maryondavis@ob.lslha.sthames.nhs.uk; 4 Sibella Road, London SW4 6HX Tel: 020 7720 5659 Fax: 020 7498 7929 — MB BChir Camb. 1970; MSc (Soc. Med.) Lond. 1978; MA Camb. 1970; MRCP (UK) 1972; MRCS Eng. LRCP Lond. 1969; MFCM 1978; FFPHM 1986. (St. Thos.) Cons. Pub. Health Med. Lambeth, S.wark & Lewisham HA; Sen. Lect. (Pub. Health Med.) King's Coll., Lond. Socs: Fell. (Mem. Counc.) Roy. Inst. Pub. Health & Hyg.; Soc. for Social Med. Prev: Sen. Med. Advisor Health Educat. Auth. Lond.; Chief Med. Off. & Dir. of Health Sci. Health Educat. Counc. Lond.

MARYOSH, Mr Jalal Abdul Aziz 64 New Dover Road, Canterbury CT1 3DT — MB ChB 1973 Baghdad; FRCS Ed. 1984.

***MASACORALE, Sarah Vinita** 3 Vyvyan Terrace, Clifton, Bristol BS8 3DF — MB ChB 1997 Bristol.

MASAND, Mahesh 47 Magpie Hall Road, Chatham ME4 5NE — MB BS 1976 Indore.

MASANI, Mr Hoshang Mehernosh, OStJ Meadowlands, 100 Newton Road, Burton-on-Trent DE15 0TT Tel: 01283 568215 — MB BS Bombay 1952; FRCS Ed. 1972. (Grant Med. Coll. Bombay) Assoc. Specialist Burton Dist. Hosp. Centre Burton-on-Trent. Prev: Orthop. Regist. Roy. Vict. Hosp. Boscombe & Bournemouth & E. Dorset; Hosp. Gp.

MASANI, Isobel Maria 31A Blackford Road, Edinburgh EH9 2DT — MB ChB 1993 Manch.; BSc (Med.Sci) St. And 1990; MRCP (UK) 1995; FRCR 1 1998. Specialist Regist. in(Radiolgy), S. E. Scott. Socs: BMA; Edin. Radiological Soc. Prev: SHO Rotat. (Med.) Manch.Roy. Infirm.; SHO Rotat. (Med.) Blackburn Hosp.; SHO (Neurol.) Walton centre for Neurol. & Neurosurg.

MASANI, Jhanbux Jamshed Noshirwanadil Consult. Suite, Wellington Hospital S., Wellington Place, London NW8 9LE Tel: 020 7686 5199 Fax: 020 7686 5199 Email: masani@doctors.org.uk; Ground Floor Flat, 125 St. Johns Way, London N19 3RQ — MB BS 1974 Mysore. (Kasturba Med. Coll. Manipal) Clin. Asst. Div. Traumatol. Milton Keynes Hosp.; Co. Surg. St. John Ambul. Assn. Aylesbury. Socs: Roy. Soc. Med. Prev: SHO (Gen. Surg.) Yeovil Dist. Hosp.; Govt. Med. Off. Univ. Teach. Hosp. Lusaka; Med. Off. RN Hosp. Plymouth.

MASANI, Keki Rustomji 10 Brook Lane, Haywards Heath RH16 1SG Tel: 01444 414300 — MRCS Eng. LRCP Lond. 1933; FRCPsych 1979, M 1971; DPM Eng. 1936. (Univ. Coll. Hosp.) Cons. Child Psychiat. N. Tees Gen. Hosp. Stockton; Founder (Ex-Pres.) Indian Counc. Ment. Hyg. Socs: Brit. Assn. Social Psychiat. Prev: Hon. Prof. Psychiat. & Head Dept. of Psychiat. Grant Med. Coll. & J.J.; Hosp. Gp. Bombay; Dir. Ind. Inst. Ment. Health & Human Relations; Bombay; Cons. Psychiat. Child Guid. Clinic Tata Inst. Social Scs.

MASANI, Navroz Dady Coedhirion, 8 Wallston Road, Wenvoe, Cardiff CF5 6AW — MB BS 1987 Lond.; MRCP (UK) 1990. Research Regist. (Cardiol.) Univ. Hosp. Wales Cardiff. Prev: Regist. (Cardiol.) St. Thos. Hosp. Lond.; Regist. (Med.) Medway Hosp.; SHO (Med.) Kent & Canterbury Hosp.

MASANI, Vidan Dady 36 Byron Avenue, London E18 2HQ — MB BS 1993 Lond.; MRCP (UK) 1997. Specialist Regist. (Respirat.) P.ss Margt. Hosp. Swindon. Socs: Brit. Thorac. Soc.; Brit. Med. Assoc. Prev: LAT (Respirat.) Roy. Bournemouth Hosp.

MASANJIKA, John Patrick Ophthalmolgy Department, Burnley General Hospital, Casterton Avenue, Burnley BB10 2PQ — MB ChB 1978 Manch.

MASCARENHAS, Felicia Josephine Oaklands Avenue, 30 Oaklands Avenue, Sidcup DA15 8NB Tel: 020 8300 1798 Fax: 020 8309 1727 — MB BCh BAO 1967 NUI. (Univ. Coll. Dub.) Princip. in Gen. Pract. Greenwich & Bexley FPC; Princip. in Gen. Pract. Bromley FPC & Kent FPC; Med. Off. GP Unit Qu. Mary's Hosp. Sidcup. Socs: BMA; Med. Defence Union. Prev: SHO (Paediat.) Sydenham Childr. Hosp. Lond.; SHO (Paediat. & O & G) City Gen. Hosp. Stoke-on-Trent.

MASCARENHAS, Mr Lawrence Joslin Dept. of Obs. & Gyn., St. Thomas' Hospital, Lambeth Palace Rd, London SE1 7EH Tel: 0207 928 9292 — MD 1986 Tours; 1998 M Ed (Camtab.); MD 1996 Birmingham; MFFP 1994; MRCOG 1991. (Univ. Of Tours, France) Cons., Dept. of Obs. & Gyn, Guy's & St Thomas Hosp. Lond. Socs: Brit. Fertil. Soc.; Brit. Soc. For Cynaecological Endoscopy; Roy. Soc. Of Med.

MASCARENHAS, Ninnette Noel 15 Cambridge Avenue, Welling DA16 2PJ — LRCPI & LM, LRSCI & LM 1971; LRCPI & LM, LRCSI & LM 1971. (RCSI) Co. MOH Kaofjord. Prev: Asst. Co. MOH Olderdalen, Norway; Ho. Phys. & Ho. Surg. Qu. Mary's Hosp. Sidcup; SHO (Psychiat.) Gaustad Sykehus, Oslo, Norway.

MASCARENHAS, Raul Armando 4 Cumberland Avenue, Helensburgh G84 8QF — MB ChB 1991 Glas.

MASCARENHAS, Ravik Francis 13 Kenilworth Avenue, Southcote, Reading RG30 3DL Email: ravik25@hotmail.com — BM BS 1998 Nottm.; BM BS Nottm 1998; BMedSci. (notts) SHO Med. Roy. Devon & Exeter hosp. Exeter. Socs: MPS.

MASCARI, Anthony Joseph, MBE, OStJ 2 Woodgate Close, Cotgrave, Nottingham NG12 3JL — MD 1934 Univ. West. Ontario; LMCC 1934; LMS Nova Scotia 1935. (Univ. West. Ont.) Hon. Med. Off. Nottm. Life Saving Assn.; Area Commr. St. John Ambul. Brig. Socs: BMA. Prev: Ho. Surg. (Orthop.) Guest Hosp. Dudley; Resid. (Med. & Surg.) St. Joseph's Hosp. Lond., Canada; Resid. Surg. Off. (Orthop.) Bolton Roy. Infirm.

MASCARI, Richard John Trent Bridge Family Medical Practice, 28A Henry Road, West Bridgford, Nottingham NG2 7NA Tel: 0115 914 6600 — MB BS 1976 Lond. (St. Bart.) Socs: M-C Soc.; Nottm. Small Pract. Assn. Prev: Trainee GP Nottm. VTS; Ho. Surg. & Ho. Phys. Centr. Notts. Health Dist. (T).

MASCIE-TAYLOR, Bryan Hugo Leeds Teaching Hospitals, NHS Trust, Leeds LS9 7TF Tel: 0113 206 5192 Fax: 0113 206 4954 — MRCS Eng. LRCP Lond. 1974; FRCP Lond. 1994; FRCPI 1992, M 1983; MHSM 1996; A.DIP.C 1997. (Leeds) Med. Dir. Leeds Teachg. Hosps. Trust; Sen. Clin. Lect. Univ. of Leeds; Vis. Fell. Univ. of York; Mem. Med. Sch. Bd., Univ. of Leeds; Mem. Med. Sch. Exec. Univ. of Leeds. Prev: Med. Dir. & Dir. Of Commiss.ing Leeds Health Auth.; Dir. Strategic Developm. CMH Trust Leeds; Cons. Phys. & Clin. Dir. St. Jas. Univ. & Seacroft Hosps.

MASCOTT, Annabelle The Crookes Practice, 203 School Road, Sheffield S10 1GN Tel: 0114 266 0677 Fax: 0114 266 4526 — MB BS 1985 Lond.; MRCGP 1991; DCH RCP Lond. 1991; DRCOG 1991.

MASCUNAN PEREZ, Pedro The Maudsley Hospital, Denmark Hill, London SE5 8AZ Tel: 020 7703 6333 Fax: 020 7703 0179; 44A Price of Wales Mansions, Prince of Wales Drive, London SW11 4BH — LMS 1982 Murcia. Research Regist. Maudsley Hosp. Special HA. Prev: Regist. (Psychiat.) St. Thos. Hosp. Lond.; Research Fell. Univ. Lond.

MASDING, Jennifer Elizabeth King Edward VII Hospital, Midhurst GU29 0BL Tel: 01730 812341; White Lea W., Guildford Road, Rudgwick, Horsham RH12 3BG Tel: 01403 822486 Fax: 01403 823949 — MB BS Lond. 1969; BSc (Physiol.) Lond. 1966; MRCS Eng. LRCP Lond. 1969; FRCR 1978. (Westm.) Med. Off. BrE. Clinic King Edwd. VII Hosp. Midhurst.; Cons. Macmillan Serv. (Palliat. Med.). Prev: Sen. Regist. & Regist. (Radiother.) & SHO (Gen. Med.) St. Luke's Hosp. Guildford.

MASDING, Michael Gerard 214A Capstone Road, Bournemouth BH8 8RX — MB BS 1992 Lond.; MRCP (UK) 1996. (St. Mary's Hosp. Med. Sch.) Specialist Regist. (Diabetes & Endocrinol.) Wessex Region Soton. Gen. Hosp.

MASEL, Philip John Unit 2 Block D, 54 Grainger Park Road, Newcastle upon Tyne NE4 8RQ — MB BS 1985 Queensland.

MASEY, Sally Ann Tel: 0117 928 2163 — MB BS 1975; DPMSA 1998; MRCS Eng. LRCP Lond. 1975; F RCA Eng. 1980; BSc Lond. 1972. (Westm.) Cons. (Anaesth.) Bristol Roy. Infirm. Prev: Sen. Regist. (Anaesth.) Brompton Hosp. Lond.; Regist. (Anaesth.) Hosp. Sick Childr. Gt. Ormond St.; Regist. Nuffield Dept. Anaesth. Radcliffe Infirm. Oxf.

MASH, Claire Heather — MB BS 1993 Lond.; MRCP (UK) 1997. Specialist Regist. (Med. & c/o the Elerly) N. W. Thames Deanery.

MASH, Katherine Mary Barcroft Medical Practice, Barcroft Medical Centre, Amesbury, Salisbury SP4 7DL Tel: 01980 623983 Fax: 01980 625530 — MB BS 1987 Lond.; DRCOG 1991. (St. Georges) p/t GP Barcroft Pract. Amesbury. Prev: GP Trainee Cuckfield VTS; SHO & HO. (Geriat.) Qu. Eliz. Hosp. Kings Lynn.

MASHARANI, Umesh Bhogilal 20 Regent Street, Lutterworth LE17 4BD — MB BS 1982 Lond.

MASHARANI, Vipul Lutterworth Health Centre, Gilmorton Road, Lutterworth LE17 4EB Tel: 01455 552346 — MB BCh 1982 Wales.

MASHEDER, Sally Montpelier Health Centre, Bath Buildings, Montpelier, Bristol BS6 5PT Tel: 0117 942 6811 Fax: 0117 944 4182; 6 Tyne Road, Bishopston, Bristol BS7 8EE Tel: 0117 924 8819 — MB ChB 1987 Bristol; MRCGP 1991; DRCOG 1989. Asst. GP.

MASHETER, Harry Crossley (retired) Waterbeck, Islet Road, Maidenhead SL6 8LD Tel: 01628 625950 Fax: 01628 625950 — MB BChir 1954 Camb. Prev: Cons. Pharmaceut. Med. Maidenhead.

MASHETER, Stewart Nicholas Hall Floor Flat, 2/9 Waverley Grove, Southsea PO4 0PZ — BM 1993 Soton.

MASHHOODI, Mr Nasser 26 Odell Place, Priory Road, Birmingham B5 7RQ — MD 1974 Tehran; FRCS Ed. 1983; DO RCS Eng. 1980.

MASHRU, Mahendra Kumar King Edwards Medical Centre, Toogoom, 19 King Edwards Road, Ruislip HA4 7AG Tel: 01895 632021 — MB BChir 1982 Camb.; MSc 1989; MRCS Eng. LRCP. Lond. 1982; LMSSA Lond. 1982; MRCGP 1986. Med. Adviser Gen. Pract. Brent & Harrow Family Pract. Comm.; Gen. Pract. Clin. Tutor Hillingdon Hosp.

MASIH, Harnek Northamptonshire Healthcare NHS Trust, Trust HQ Yorke House, Isebrook Hospital, Wellingborough NN8 1LP Tel: 01933 440099; 4 Gurston Rise, Rectory Farm, Northampton NN3 5HY Tel: 01604 409130 — MB BS Punjab 1969; MRCPsych 1982; DPM Eng. 1979. (Medical College Amritsar Punjab University India) Cons. Psychiat. P.ss Marina Hosp.; Clin. Dir. Directorate of the Psychiat. of Learning Disabilities. Prev: Cons. Psychiat. York Health Servs. NHS Trust; Cons. Psychiat. Lanarksh. Health Care (NHS) Trust Lanarksh. Scotl.

MASILAMANI, Mr Nithyanand Samuel 2 Arrowhead House, Rushgreen Hospital, Dagenham Road, Romford RM7 0YA Tel: 01708 746066 — MB BS 1985 Madras; FRCS Eng. 1991.

MASINA, Meherbanoo Hormasji (retired) 9 Grantchester Street, Newnham, Cambridge CB3 9HY Tel: 01223 361527 — MRCS Eng. LRCP Lond. 1948; MA Camb. 1948.

MASINGHE, Nimalka Ranjani North Riding Infirmary, Newport Road, Middlesbrough TS1 5JE; 52 Mallowdale, Nunthorpe, Middlesbrough TS7 0RG Tel: 01642 319180 — MB BS Ceylon 1970; DO (Lond.) 1979 - Royal College of Surgeon London; MS (Sri Lanke) 1994 - University of Colombo Sri Lanke. Staff Grade.

MASIP OLIVERAS, Teresa 180 Minster Court, Edge Hill, Liverpool L7 3QF — LMS 1994 Barcelona; LMS Barcelona 1991. (Univ. Med. Barcelona) SHO (O & G) Fairfield Gen. Hosp. Bury. Socs: Med. Defence Union. Prev: SHO (O & G) Sharoe Green Hosp. Preston & King's Mill Centre Mansfield.

MASKA, Mariusz Ramsey Group Practice Centre, Grove Mount South, Ramsey IM8 3EY Tel: 01624 813881 Fax: 01624 811921 — MB ChB 1982 Dundee; LMCC 1991; DA (UK) 1986. (Dundee) Chairm. Isle of Man GP Gp.; Mem. Med. Exec. Isle of Man. Socs: Isle of Man Med. Soc.

MASKELL, Mr Andrew Paul Orthopaedic Department, Blackburn Royal Infirmary, Infirmary Road, Blackburn BB2 3LR Tel: 01254 263555 Fax: 01254 294572; 93 The Rydings, Langho, Blackburn BB6 8BQ Tel: 01254 246605 Fax: 01254 246607 Email: andymaskell@amaskell.demon.co.uk — MB BS 1982 Lond.; FRCS (Orth.) 1996; FRCS Ed. 1987. (Middlx.) Cons. Orthop. Surg. Blackburn Roy. Infirm. Prev: Sen. Regist. NW RHA.

MASKELL, Anne Margaret Bodriggy Health Centre, 60 Queens Way, Hayle TR27 4PB Tel: 01736 753136 Fax: 01736 753467; Pipers Barn, Harris's Hill, Penpol, Feock, Truro TR3 6RU Tel: 01872 864930 Email: gmas239595@aol.com — MB BS 1988 Lond.; MRCGP 1995; DRCOG 1994; DFFP 1994; DCH RCP Lond. 1993; DGM RCP Lond. 1992. (Guy's Hosp.) Gen. Practitioner. Prev: Trainee GP Cornw. & Isles of Scilly VTS.

MASKELL, Giles Francis Royal Cornwall Hospital (Treliske), Truro TR1 3JW; Pipers Barn, Penpol, Feock, Truro TR3 6RU — MB BS 1980 Lond.; MRCP (UK) 1985; FRCR 1989. Cons. Radiol. Roy. Cornw. Hosp. (Treliske) Truro. Prev: Sen. Regist. (Diagn. Radiol.) Addenbrooke's Hosp. Camb.; Regist. (Diagn. Radiol.) Guy's Hosp. Lond.

MASKELL, Nicholas Anthony 4 Elmwood, Maidenhead Court Park, Maidenhead SL6 8HX — BM BS 1993 Nottm.

MASKELL, Rosalind Mary (retired) 84 Bowes Hill, Rowlands Castle, Portsmouth PO9 6BS Tel: 023 9241 3729 — BM BCh 1953 Oxf.; MA Oxf. 1962, BA 1950, DM 1985; FRCP Eng. 1992; MRCP (UK) 1985; DObst RCOG 1955. Prev: Sen. Med. Microbiol. Pub. Health Laborat. & Clin. Asst. Renal Unit Portsmouth.

MASKELL, Trevor William Cardiac X-Ray Department, Glenfield Hospital, Groby Road, Leicester LE3 9QP — MB ChB 1984 Leic.; FRCR 1993. Cons. Radiol. Univ. Hosps. of Leicester.

MASKERY, Judith Joan The Surgery, 292 Derby Road, Lenton, Nottingham NG7 1QG Tel: 0115 947 4002 Fax: 0115 924 0783; 26 Windermere Road, Beeston, Nottingham NG9 3AS Tel: 0115 922 1624 — MB ChB 1985 Leic.; MRCGP 1989; T(GP) 1991; DRCOG 1988. (Leic.) GP Trainer Nottm. VTS.

MASKEY

MASKEY, Sean Paul Christopher Great Ormond Street Hospital, Great Ormond St., London WC1N 3JH Tel: 020 7405 9200 Email: sean.maskey@gosh-tr.nthcemes.nhs.uk — MB BS 1981 Lond.; MRCS Eng. LRCP Lond. 1980; MRCPsych 1985. (Westm.) Cons. Child & Adolesc. Psychiat., Mildred Creak Unit, Gt. Ormond St.; Hon. Sen. Lect., Inst. of Child Health, Lond. Prev: Hon. Sen. Regist. Char. Cross Hosp. Lond.; Cons. Child & Adolesc. Psychiat. Guildford, Surrey; Cons. Child Psychiat. Collingham Gdns. Child Psychiat. Unit Riverside Ment. Health Trust Lond.

MASKILL, Christine Susan 4 Vineyard Mews, Preston Place, Richmond TW10 6DD Tel: 020 8332 9029 — MB BChir 1990 Camb.; DCH RCP Lond. 1993. (Cambridge) Locum GP. Socs: RCGP. Prev: Trainee GP/SHO Hinchingbrooke Hosp. VTS.; Ho. Off. (Gen. Med.) Hinchingbrooke Hosp.; GP Regist. Cranleigh Surrey.

MASKILL, Jon Michael 43 Silhill Hall Road, Solihull B91 1JX — MB ChB 1992 Sheff.

MASKREY, Neal National Prescribing Centre, The Infirmary, 70 Pembroke Palce, Liverpool L69 3GF Tel: 0151 794 8135 Email: neal.maskrey@talk21.com — MB ChB 1975 Leeds; MSc 2001 Liverp.; FRCGP 1992, M 1979; DRCOG 1978; 1989 Dip. Prescrib. Sci. Liverp. Med. Dir. Nat. Prescribing Centre; Course Organiser Yorks. Region MRCGP. Prev: GP ScarBoro. and Bridlington; Trainee GP N. Humberside VTS; Ho. Surg. & Ho. Phys. N. Staffs. HA.

MASLEN, Michael John Edwards and Partners, Wargrave House, 23 St. Owen Street, Hereford HR1 2JB Tel: 01432 272285 Fax: 01432 344059; Rosebank, Rectory Road, Hampton Bishop, Hereford HR1 4JX Tel: 01432 870270 Email: maslenatrosebank@aol.com — MB BS 1977 Lond.; FRCS Eng. 1983.

***MASLEN, Timothy Peter James** Flat 3, 59 Webber St., London SE1 0RD — MB BS 1995 Lond.

MASLIN, Paul Stuart Cross Pain Surgery, 84 Bulford Road, Durrington, Salisbury SP4 8DH Tel: 01980 652221 — BM 1991 Soton.; MRCGP 1996; DCH RCP Lond. 1994. Partner in Gen. Pract. Prev: GP/Regist. Salisbury.

MASLIN, Mr Simon Christopher Scunthorpe General Hospital, Cliffgardens, Scunthorpe DN15 7BH Tel: 01724 290111; 36 Packman Lane, Kirkella HU10 7TL Tel: 01482 656018 — MB ChB 1972 St. And.; FRCS Eng. 1978; FRCR 1993. (St Andrews) Cons. Radiol. N.ern Lincs. & Goole NHS Trust. Prev: Sen. Regist. (Radiol.) Hull Roy. Infirm.

***MASOLI, Matthew Peter Dominic** 8 Averill Street, London W6 8EB — MB BS 1997 Lond.

MASON, Alan Strathmore Medical Practice, 26-28 Chester Road, Wrexham LL11 7SA Tel: 01978 352055 Fax: 01978 310689; 50 Chester Road, Wrexham LL11 2SD — MB ChB 1969 Liverp. Prev: Ho. Off. David Lewis N.: Hosp. Liverp.; SHO W. Pk. Hosp. Macclesfield; Regist. (Paediat.) Stockport & Buxton Gp. Hosps.

MASON, Alan Bremner King Street Surgery, 84 King Street, Maidstone ME14 1DZ Tel: 01622 756721/756722/3; Pitts Farm House, Vanity Lane, Maidstone ME17 4BP Tel: 01622 744227 Email: abmason@orchards.u_net.com — MB ChB 1975 Glas.; MRCP (UK) 1986; MRCGP 1991; DRCOG 1992. (Glasgow)

MASON, Alan David 138 Halifax Road, Brighouse HD6 2QA — MB ChB 1974 Leeds.

MASON, Alan Peter Houndlaw Park Health Centre, Houndlaw Park, Eyemouth TD14 5DA Tel: 018907 50383 Fax: 018907 51749 — MB ChB 1976 Manch.; DRCOG 1979.

MASON, Alastair Michael Stuart 125 Upper Westwood, Bradford-on-Avon BA15 2DH Tel: 01225 868277 — MB BS 1967 Lond.; FRCP Lond. 1993; MRCP (UK) 1969; MRCS Eng. LRCP Lond. 1967; FFPHM RCP (UK) 1990; MFCM 1977. (Lond. Hosp.) Partner Care Bath. Prev: Regional Med. S. W.. RHA; Head Secretariat NHS/DHSS Health Servs. Informat. Steering Gp.; Sen. Med. Off. Plann., Organisat., Informat. & Med. Manpower Divs. DHSS.

MASON, Albert Abraham Flat 7, St Edmunds Court, St Edmunds Terrace, London NW8 7QL; 1009 North Beverly Drive, Beverly Hills CA 90210, USA Tel: 00 1 310 5500127 Fax: 00 1 310 5501811 — MB BS 1949 Lond. Clin. Prof. Psychiat. USC Sch. Med., Los Angeles, USA; Train. Analyst (Pres.) Psychoanal. Centre of Calif. Socs: Internat. Psychoanal. Assn.; Amer. & Internat. Psychoanal. Assns. Prev: Psychiat. W. Lond. Hosp.; Sen. Regist. Qu. Vict. Hosp. Surrey.

MASON, Alison Margaret 38 Chesham Road, Kingston upon Thames KT1 3AQ — MB BS 1992 Lond.

MASON, Andrew Maurice The Old Rectory, Norton, Bury St Edmunds IP31 3NB Tel: 01359 230426 Email: ammason@tesco.net — MB BS 1971 Lond.; MRCS Eng. LRCP Lond. 1971. (St. Bart.) p/t Phys. (Occupat. Health) Baxter Healthcare Ltd.; Brit. Assn. Immediate Care Accredit. Specialist 1998; Sen. RCMO Newmkt. Racecourses 1999; Attend. Phys., Shrubland Hall Health Clinic, Ipswich, 1996. Socs: Brit. Assn. Immed. Care; Suff. Accid. Rescue Serv. (Exec. Comm.); Med. Equestrian Assn. Prev: Med. Dir. Gershom Centre Bury St. Edmunds; GP Bury St. Edmunds; Demonst. (Anat.) Univ. Camb.

MASON, Andrew Richard Derwent House Surgery, Derwent House, Wakefield Road, Cockermouth CA13 0HZ Tel: 01900 822345 Fax: 01900 828469; 9 Fern Bank, Cockermouth CA13 0DF Tel: 01900 825001 Email: 100410.1712@compuserve.com — MB ChB 1980 Dundee; MRCGP 1989. (Univ. Dundee) Prev: Regist. (Gen. Med.) Stafford Dist. Gen. Hosp.; SHO (O & G) W. Cumbld. Hosp. Whitehaven; Med. Supt. Panguma Hosp. Sierra Leone.

MASON, Annabel Jane Maud 26 Callis Street, Clare, Sudbury CO10 8PX Tel: 01787 278620 — MB BS 1955 Lond.; MRCS Eng. LRCP Lond. 1955; FFA RCS Eng. 1965; DA Eng. 1960; DObst RCOG 1956. (St. Thos.) Socs: Assn. Anaesths. (Anaesth. Sect.); Roy. Soc. Med. Prev: Cons. Anaesth. Roy. Homoeop. Hosp.; Sen. Regist. (Anaesth.) St. Geo. Hosp.; Regist. (Anaesth.) Addenbrookes Hosp. Camb.

MASON, Anne Street Farmhouse, The Street, Troston, Bury St Edmunds IP31 1EW — MB ChB 1988 Sheff.

MASON, Arnold Denis 4 Mallory Rise, Moseley, Birmingham B13 9YE Tel: 0121 777 9832 — MRCS Eng. LRCP Lond. 1951.

***MASON, Benjamin Peter** 2 (1F2) Blackwood Crescent, Edinburgh EH9 1QY; 11 St. Leonards Drive, Nottingham NG8 2BB — MB ChB 1997 Ed.

MASON, Bernard Elmley Orchard, Hallow, Worcester WR2 6PE Tel: 01905 640453 — MB ChB 1962 Bristol; FRCP Lond. 1982, M 1967; FRCP Ed. 1978, M 1967; MRCPCH 1996; FRCPCH 1997. (Bristol) Socs: Fell. Roy. Soc. Med.; BMA; Anglo-French Med. Soc. Prev: Cons. Paediat. Worcester Roy. Infirm. & Kidderminster Gen. Hosp.; Sen. Regist. Dundee Roy. Infirm.; Ho. Phys. Profess. Med. Unit & Ho. Surg. Profess. Surg. Unit. Bristol.

MASON, Brendan Willys 89 King's Road, Llandybie, Ammanford SA18 2TL — MB ChB 1988 Leic.; MFPHM RCP (UK) 1996. (Leicester) Cons. Pub. Health Med. Iechyd Morgannwg Health Swansea.

MASON, Mr Brian Edward 48 Freeburn Causeway, Coventry CV4 8FQ Tel: 024 76 711447 — MB ChB 1966 Sheff.; FRCS Ed. 1977; MRCS Eng. LRCP Lond. 1967. (Sheff.) Prev: Regist. (Surg.) Centr. Hosp. Kitwe, Zambia & Sharoe Green Hosp.; Fulwood; Res. Surg. Off. Brompton Hosp. Lond.

MASON, Bridgett Ann (retired) 10 Meadowcroft, Chalfont St Peters, Gerrards Cross SL9 9DH Tel: 01494 581999 Fax: 01753 885255 Email: bamason@ctu.es — MB BS 1960 Lond.; MRCS Eng. LRCP Lond. 1960. Research Asst. Metab. Unit St. Mary's Hosp. Paddington; Clin. Asst. (Obst. & Gyn.) Middlx. Hosp. & Soho Hosp. Wom. Lond. Prev: Med. Dir. Bourn Hall & Hallam Med. Centre Margt. Pyke Centre.

MASON, Caroline Frances Merrywood Practice, William Budd Health Centre, Knowle West Health Park, Knowle, Bristol BS4 1WH — MB BS 1984 Lond.; DCH RCP Lond. 1988; DRCOG 1986. GP Princip. Bristol.

***MASON, Caroline Jessica** 34 Smoke Lane, Reigate RH2 7HJ — MB ChB 1997 Sheff.

MASON, Cherry Jane Anaesthetic Department, Birch House, Stepping Hill Hospital, Poplar Grove, Hazel Gr., Stockport SK7 1LJ Tel: 0161 419 5869; 8 Graham Drive, Didsley, Stockport SK12 2JJ — MB ChB 1977 Birm.; FFA RCS Eng. 1982. Cons. Anaesth. & Clin. Dir. (Anaesth. & ITU) Stepping Hill Hosp. Stockport; Hon. Lect. Univ. Manch. Socs: Assn. Anaesth.; MRCAnaesth.; BMA. Prev: Sen. Regist. (Anaesth.) N. W.. RHA; Regist. (Anaesth.) Birm. Centr. Health Dist. (T).

***MASON, Christine Ann** 12 Kingsway, Tynemouth, North Shields NE30 2LY — MB ChB 1998 Ed.; MB ChB Ed 1998.

MASON, Mr Christopher 5 Burlington Court, George V Avenue, Worthing BN11 5RG Email: drchrismason@hotmail.com — MB BS 1994 Lond.; MB BS Lond. 1994 1st Class Hons: Clin. Sci. Imperial

Coll. Lond. 1993; FRCS Irel. 1999; FRCS Eng. 1999. (St Thomas's Hosp. Med. School, Lond)

MASON, Christopher Howard Department of Histopathology, Easbourne District Hospital, Kings Drive, Eastbourne BN21 2UD Tel: 01323 417400 Fax: 01323 413752; 10 Pashley Road, Eastbourne BN20 8DU — BM BCh 1980 Oxf.; MA Camb. 1982; FRCPath 1997; MRCPath 1987. Cons. Histopath. E.bourne Dist. Hosp. Prev: Sen. Regist. (Histopath.) N.ampton Gen. Hosp.; Clin. Lect. (Histopath.) John Radcliffe Hosp. Oxf.

MASON, Christopher James The Firs, Naemoor Road, Crook of Devon, Kinross KY13 0UH — MB ChB 1993 Ed.

MASON, Christopher Michael Pudsey Health Centre, 18 Mulberry Street, Pudsey LS28 7XP Tel: 0113 257 6711 Fax: 0113 236 3928 — MB ChB 1985 Leeds; MRCGP 1990. Princip. Gen. Pract. Pudsey.

MASON, Colin Andrew Seymour (retired) D.M.P, Employment of Social Security, P.O Box 55, La Motte Street, Jersey JE4 8PE Tel: 01534 280000 Email: casmason200@hotmail.com — MB BS 1961 Lond.; MRCS Eng. LRCP Lond. 1960; DCH Eng. 1964. Designated Med. Practitioner. Prev: Regist. W.m. Childr. Hosp.

MASON, Colin Huw Oldcastle Surgery, South Street, Bridgend CF31 3ED Tel: 01656 657131 Fax: 01656 657134; Broadway House, 84 Broadway, Llanblethian, Cowbridge CF71 7EY — MB BS 1981 Lond.; MRCS Eng. LRCP Lond. 1980; MRCGP 1991; DRCOG 1985; DA (UK) 1984. (Westm.) CME Tutor OGWR HA. Prev: SHO (Anaesth.) S.mead Hosp. Bristol; Ho. Phys. St. Stephens Hosp. Lond.; Ho. Surg. Gordon Hosp. Lond.

MASON, David George Nuffield Department of Anaesthetics, John Radcliffe Hospital, Headington, Oxford OX3 9DU; Watergrasshill, High St, Charlton-On-Otmoor, Kidlington OX5 2UQ — MB BS 1983 Lond.; FFA RCS Eng. 1988; DA (UK) 1985. Cons. Anaesth. John Radcliffe Hosp. Oxf.

MASON, Professor Sir David Kean (retired) Greystones, Houston Road, Kilmacolm PA13 4NY Tel: 0150 587 2001 — MB ChB 1962 Glas.; Hon. FFD RCSI 1988; FDS RCPS Glas. 1967; FDS RCS Ed, 1956; FRCPath 1976, M 1967; Hon D. Univ. Glas. 1998; MD Glas. 1967; FRCS Glas. 1973; Hon. FRCS Ed. 1995; BDS St. And. 1952, LDS 1951; Hon. DSc Lond. Ontario 1997; Hon. LLD Dundee 1993; Hon. FDS RCPS Glas. 1990; Hon. DChD Wales 1991. Hon. Sen. Research Fell. (Oral Surg. & Oral Med.) Univ. Glas. Prev: Prof. Oral Med. & Hon. Cons. Dent. Surg. Univ. Glas.

MASON, David York Haematology Department, Level 4, John Radcliffe Hospital, Oxford OX3 9DU — BM BCh 1966 Oxf.; DM Oxf. 1977, BM BCh 1966; FRCPath 1986, M 1973.

MASON, Deborah Lee Department of Forensic Medicine, St Nicholas' Hospital, Jubilee Road, Gosforth, Newcastle upon Tyne NE3 3XT — MB ChB 1988 Glas.; MRCPsych 1993.

MASON, Elizabeth Anne 51 St Helen's Way, Adel, Leeds LS16 8LP — MB ChB 1976 Leeds; MRCGP 1981; DCH RCP Lond. 1983; DRCOG 1981.

MASON, Elizabeth Mary 31 Richmond Road, Solihull B92 7RP Tel: 0121 706 4064 — MB ChB 1976 Leeds; MSc (Community Med.) Lond. 1984; MFPHM RCP (UK) 1990; DCH RCP Lond. 1980.

MASON, Emma Elizabeth Grange Road Surgery, Grange Road, Bishopsworth, Bristol BS13 8LD Tel: 0117 964 4343 — MB ChB 1992 Birm. p/t GP Retainer, Grange Rd. Surg., Bristol (p/t).

MASON, Fiona Louise Broadmoor Hospital, Crowthorne RG45 7EG Tel: 01344 773111 Fax: 01344 754179 Email: f.l.m@btinternet.com — MB BS 1987 Lond.; MRCPsych 1992; Dip. Forens. Psychiat. Lond. 1995. (Middlesex Hospital Medical School) Cons. (Forens. Psychiat.) BRd.moor Hosp. Prev: Sen. Regist. (Forens. Psychiat.) Maudsley; Lect. (Victimology & Forens. Psychiat.) & Hon. Sen. Regist. Maudsley Hosp.; Regist. (Psychiat.) Roy. Free Hosp. Lond.

MASON, Fiona Mary St Giles Clinic, 67 St Giles St, Northampton NN1 1JF Tel: 01205 351193, 01604 620673 Email: edlizabsoud@doctors.org.uk; Tel: 01280 850439 — MB BS 1980 Lond.; Cert. Family Plann. JCC 1983; MFFP 1992. (King's Coll. Hosp. Lond.) Cons. Family Plann. N.ampton Healthcare; Clin. Asst. (Genitourin. Med.) Milton Keynes. Prev: Community Med. Off. Family Plann. Milton Keynes; Community Med. Off. Family Plann. Oxf.shire.

MASON, George Peter Hugh Orchard Surgery, Cope Road, Banbury OX16 2EJ Tel: 01295 256201 Fax: 01295 277783;

Woodlands, Milton, Banbury OX15 4HH Tel: 01295 720900 — MB BS 1968 Lond.; MRCS Eng. LRCP Lond. 1967; MFFP 1993. (St. Geo.) Prev: SHO St. Christopher's Hospice Sydenham.

MASON, Gerald Clare Clarendon Wing, The General Infirmary at Leeds, Belmont Grove, Leeds LS2 9NS Tel: 0113 392 6829 Fax: 0113 392 6531 Email: gerald.mason@leedsth.nhs.uk; Hillrise, Avenue des Hirondelles, Pool-in-Wharfedale, Otley LS21 1EY Email: mansonhillrise@aol.com — MB ChB 1981 Manch.; MD Manch. 1993; MRCOG 1986; FRCOG 1998. Cons. FetoMatern. Med. Clarendon Wing Leeds Gen. Infirm. Prev: Lect. (O & G) St Jas. Hosp. Leeds.

MASON, Graham John The Cannonhill Lane Medical Practice, 153 Cannon Hill Lane, Raynes Park, London SW20 9BZ Tel: 020 8542 5201 Fax: 020 8540 9049 — MB BS 1987 Lond. Prev: SHO (A & E) W.m. Hosp. Lond.; Ho. Phys. St. Richards Hosp. Chichester; Ho. Surg. Lond. Hosp. Whitechapel.

MASON, Gwyn Meirion (retired) 8 Mangotsfield Road, Mangotsfield, Bristol BS16 9JQ Tel: 0117 956 5122 — MB ChB Liverp. 1953; MRCGP 1963. Prev: Civil. Med. Pract. MoD.

MASON, Hamish Keil 55 Paddock Gardens, Lyminton, Lymington SO41 9ES Tel: 01590 610494 Mobile: 07710 435009; 55 Paddock Gardens, Lymington SO41 9ES Tel: 01590 610494 Mobile: 07710 435 009 — MB ChB 1952 Glas. (Glas.) Socs: Windsor & Dist. Med. Soc.; BMA. Prev: Squadron Ldr. RAF Med. Br., Sen. Med. Off. RAF Lindholme; Ho. Surg. (ENT, Cas., Fract. & Orthop.) W.. Infirm. Glas..

MASON, Harriet Mary Courtenay 20 Well Walk, Hampstead, London NW3 1LD Tel: 020 7435 2308 — MRCS Eng. LRCP Lond. 1960. (Middlx.) Assoc. Specialist (ENT) Ealing Hosp. S.all. Prev: Regist. ENT Dept. Centr. Middlx. Hosp. Lond.; Ho. Surg. ENT Dept. Middlx. Hosp. Lond. & Roy. Nat. Throat, Nose & Ear Hosp. Lond.

MASON, Hazel Valerie Diss Health Centre, Mount St, Diss IP22 4WG Tel: 01379 642021; The Limes, Market Place, Norwich NR16 2AH Tel: 01953 887666 Email: james.frost@virgin.net — MB BChir 1991 Camb.; 1999 Dip. Tra. Med. Glas.; BSc (Hons.) St. And. 1988; MRCGP 1995.

MASON, Helen Christine — MB ChB 1974 Leeds; AFOM RCP Lond. 1990; MFOM RCP Lond. 1998. Indep. Cons. Occupat.al Phys. Prev: Occupat. Phys. Zeneca Pharmaceut.; Occupat. Phys. ICI Chem.s & Polymers; Assoc. Specialist in Occupat. Med., Roy. Oldham Hosp.

MASON, Helen Clarissa Sian 64 Haverscroft Close, Taverham, Norwich NR8 6LU — MB ChB 1988 Manch.

MASON, Iain Harold Clarkson Surgery, De-Havilland Road, Wisbech PE13 3AN Tel: 01945 583133 Fax: 01945 464465; 8 Clarkson Avenue, Wisbech PE13 2EF Tel: 01945 589665 — MB ChB 1976 Sheff.; MRCGP 1986; DRCOG 1983; DCH RCP Lond. 1982; DA Eng. 1980. Socs: BMA.

MASON, Ian Logan The Surgery, The Old Orchard, Limekilns, Dunfermline KY11 3HS Tel: 01383 872201 Fax: 01383 873121; 16 Kingseat Road, Dunfermline KY12 0DD Tel: 01383 624722 Fax: 01383 624722 Email: ianmason@aol.com — MB ChB Ed. 1978; BSc Med. Sci. Ed. 1975; MRCGP 1982.

MASON, Ian Sutherland 19 St James Street, Paisley PA3 2HQ Tel: 0141 889 5505 Fax: 0141 848 9190 — MB ChB 1978 Glas.; DRCOG 1981.

MASON, James King's Lodge, Kew Green, Richmond TW9 3AA Tel: 020 8940 1773 — LMSSA 1943 Lond. (Liverp.)

MASON, James, MBE, ERD, TD (retired) 34 Town Street, Duffield, Belper DE56 4EH Tel: 01332 842022 — BM BCh Oxf. 1937. Prev: Ho. Phys., Ho. Surg. (ENT & Ophth.) & Cas. Off. St. Geo. Hosp. Lond.

MASON, James Stephen Department of Anaesthetics, King's Mill Hospital, Sutton-in-Ashfield NG17 4JL Tel: 01623 22515 Fax: 01623 676027; Walnut Tree House, 75a Westgate, Southwell NG25 0LD — MB BS 1973 Lond.; MRCS Eng. LRCP Lond. 1973; FFA RCS Eng. 1980; DA Eng. 1977. (Roy. Free) Socs: BMA & Assn. Anaesth. Prev: Sen. Regist. & Hon. Clin. Teach. Nottm. Univ. Fac. Med.; Anaesth. Sophia Kinderziekenhuis, Rotterdam Univ. Netherlands; Ho. Surg. Roy. Free Hosp. Lond.

MASON, Jane Rosemary The Old Rectory, Church Lane, Norton, Bury St Edmunds IP31 3NB Tel: 01359 230426 — MB BS 1971 Lond.; MRCS Eng. LRCP Lond. 1971; Dip. Addic. Studies Leeds 1997; REIKI I &II 1999. (St. Bart.) Socs: Soc. Study Addic. Prev: Clin. Asst. (Obst. & Ultrasound) W. Suff. Hosp. Bury St. Edmunds;

MASON

Ho. Surg. (Gen. Surg.) W. Suff. Gen. Hosp. Bury St. Edmunds; Med. Off. W. Suff. Drug Advisory Serv. Bury St. Edmunds.

MASON, Jayne Elizabeth Farm Mill, Dymock GL18 2DD — MB BS 1987 Lond.; PhD Liverp. 1980, BSc 1976. Prev: SHO (O & G) Glos.; Trainee GP Staunton; Trainee GP York.

MASON, Jeremy Harold 133 Orchard Grove, London SE20 8DW — MB ChB 1985 Leeds. SHO (Orthop.) Kingston Hosp. Surrey. Socs: Assoc. Mem. BMA. Prev: SHO (A & E) N. Manch. Gen. Hosp.; Ho. Phys. Hull HA; Ho. Surg. Huddersfield Roy. Infirm.

MASON, Jill Beverley Pudsey Health Centre, 18 Mulberry St., Pudsey LS28 7XP Tel: 0113 257 0711 Fax: 0113 236 3928 — MB ChB 1985 Leeds; DRCOG 1988. GP Pudsey Retainer Scheme.

MASON, John Coldthorn Cottage, Coldthorn Lane, Hailsham BN27 3PJ Tel: 01323 842656 — MB ChB Manch. 1957; MRCS Eng. LRCP Lond. 1957; DObst RCOG 1960; FFPM 1990. (Manchester) Indep. Med. Cons. E. Sussex. Socs: Fell. Fac. Pharm. Med. Prev: Dir. Med. Serv. Rorer Health Care Ltd., E.bourne; Asst. Med. Dir. Bayer (UK) Ltd Newbury; GP Buxton Derbysh. & Hailsham Sussex.

MASON, John Christopher 156 Brantingham Road, Manchester M21 0TS — MB ChB 1988 Manch.

MASON, John Dutton 12 West Street, Ringwood BH24 1DZ; Monmouth House, West St, Ringwood Tel: 0142 544171 — MB ChB 1955 Manch.; LDS RCS Eng. 1961.

MASON, Professor John Kenyon French, CBE Faculty of Law, Old College, South Bridge, Edinburgh EH8 9YL Tel: 0131 650 2051 Fax: 0131 650 6317 Email: ken.mason@ed.ac.uk; 66 Craiglea Drive, Edinburgh EH10 5PF Tel: 0131 447 2301 Fax: 0131 447 4137 — MB BChir 1943 Camb.; MA 1944; LLD Ed. 1987; MD Camb. 1961; FRCPath 1974, M 1963; DMJ Soc. Apoth. Lond. 1963; DTM & H Eng. 1962; DCP Lond 1950. (Camb. & St. Bart.) Emerit. Prof. & Hon. Fell. Fac. Law. Old Coll. Edin. Socs: Fell.Roy. Soc. of Edin. Prev: Regius Prof. Forens. Med. Univ. Edin.; Pres. Brit. Assn. Forens. Med.; Gp. Capt. RAF Med. Br.

MASON, John McKay (retired) Westcroft, 42 Albert Road, Dumfries DG2 9DN Tel: 01387 54417 — MB ChB 1956 Ed.; FFA RCS Eng. 1968. Prev: Cons. Anaesth. Dumfries Roy. Infirm.

MASON, Joseph Flat 2, 32 St Petersburgh Place, London W2 1ZZ — MB BCh BAO 1989 Dub.

MASON, Mr Joseph Ian Campbell (retired) 32 Westella Way, Kirkella, Hull HU10 7LW Tel: 01482 659009 — MB BS 1935 Lond.; FRCS Eng. 1941; MRCS Eng. LRCP Lond. 1935. Prev: Surg. Hull & E. Riding Hosp. Gps.

MASON, Josephine Jane (retired) Greenhill, Shotley Bridge, Consett DH8 0NJ Tel: 01207 504032 — MB ChB 1964 Ed. Prev: Princip. GP Rowlands Gill Med. Centre Tyne & Wear.

MASON, Juan Corlett Renal Unit, St. Mary's Hospital, Portsmouth PO3 6AD Tel: 023 92 822331; Poor Cottage, Chidham Lane, Chidham, Chichester PO18 8TF — BM BCh 1976 Oxf.; MA, DPhil Oxf. 1976; FRCP Lond. 1995; MRCP (UK) 1979. Cons. Phys. St. Mary's & Qu. Alexandra Hosps. Portsmouth; Dir. Wessex Renal & Transpl. Unit. Prev: Sen. Regist. & Regist. St. Thos. Hosp. Lond.; SHO Brompton Hosp. Lond., Nat. Hosp. Qu. Sq. & Lond. Chest Hosp.

MASON, Justin Charles Rheumatology Unit, Hammersmith Hospital, Du Cane Road, London W12 0NN Tel: 020 8383 1622 Fax: 020 8743 3109 Email: j.mason@rpms.ac.uk — MB BS 1986 Lond.; BSc (Hons.) Lond. 1983; PhD Lond. 1996; MRCP (UK) 1989. (Char. Cross & Westm.) Clin. Sci. Fell. (Arthritis & Rheum.) & Hon. Cons. Rheum., Hammersmith Hosp. Lond.; Assoc. Tutor RCP Lond. Prev: Sen. Regist. (Rheum. & Gen. Med.) Hammersmith Hosp. Lond.; MRC Train. Fell. (Rheum.) Roy. Postgrad. Med. Sch. Lond.; Regist. (Rheum. & Gen. Med.) Hammersmith Hosp. Lond.

MASON, Kenneth Accident & Emergency Department, St Helens Hospital, Marshall Cross Road, St Helens WA9 3DA — MB ChB 1976 Liverp.

MASON, Lynn Elizabeth 138 Halifax Road, Brighouse HD6 2QA — MB ChB 1974 Leeds.

MASON, Professor Malcolm David Velindre Hospital, Velindre Road, Cardiff CF14 2TL Tel: 029 2061 5888 Fax: 029 2052 9625 Email: masonmd@cf.ac.uk — MB BS 1979 Lond.; MD Lond. 1991; MRCP (UK) 1984; FRCP 1997; FRCR 1987. (St. Bart.) Prof. Clin. Oncol. Univ. Wales Coll. Med. Prev: Cons. Clin. Oncol. Velindre Hosp. Cardiff.; Lect. (Radiother. & Oncol.) Inst. Cancer Research & Roy. Marsden Hosp.

MASON, Margaret Joan Mount Street Surgery, 69 Mount Street, Coventry CV5 8DE Tel: 024 7667 2277 Fax: 024 7671 7352; 48 Freeburn Causeway, Canley, Coventry CV4 8FQ Tel: 024 76 711447 — MB ChB 1971 Sheff.; MRCGP 1991; FRCGP (Assess.) 1998. (Sheff.) GP Coventry. Prev: Ho. Off. (Accid. & Orthop.) N.. Gen. Hosp. Sheff.; SHO (Paediat.) Roy. Hosp. Chesterfield; Gen. Duties Med. Off. Nkana Mine Hosp. Kitwe, Zambia.

MASON, Margaret Ruth Norden House Surgery, Avenue Road, Winslow, Buckingham MK18 3DW Tel: 01296 713434; 11 Anstey Brook, Weston Turville, Aylesbury HP22 5RT Tel: 01296 613531 — BM BS 1985 Nottm.; BS Nottm. 1985; MRCGP 1991; DRCOG 1990. (Nottm.) p/t GP. Prev: Trainee GP Aylesbury VTS.

MASON, Margaret Ruth Hazelwood Cottage, Cardross Road, Dumbarton G82 5DH — MB ChB 1996 Ed.

MASON, Mark John 37 Ebury Road, Rickmansworth WD3 1BL — MB BS 1988 Lond.; MRCP (UK) 1993. (Char. Cross & Westm.) Regist. (Cardiol.) Harefield Hosp. Harefield.

MASON, Michael The Old Surgery, 39 Moor Lane, Watcombe, Torquay TQ2 8NU Tel: 01803 314888 — MB BS 1950 Lond.; MRCS Eng. LRCP Lond. 1950. (Guy's) Doctor & Ldr. Himalayan & Europ. Mt.ain Trekking. Prev: RAF Med. Br.; Ho. Phys. & Ho. Surg. E. Suff. & Ipswich Hosp.; Ho. Surg. (Obst.) Perth Roy. Infirm.

MASON, Mr Michael Andrew The Accident Centre, Medway Maritime Hospital, Windmill Road, Gillingham ME7 5NY Tel: 01634 833974 Fax: 01634 815751 Email: medwayae@btinternet.com; Lennox House, 3 Matts Hill Road, Hartlip, Sittingbourne ME9 7XA Email: masons.home@barclays.net — MB BS 1972 Lond.; FRCS Eng. 1981; MRCS Eng. LRCP Lond. 1972; FFAEM 1993. (Roy. Free) Dir. & Cons. A & E Servs. Medway HA. Socs: Brit. Assn. for Accid. & Emerg. Med.; BMA; RSM. Prev: Sen. Regist. (A & E) Oxf. RHA; Regist. (Orthop.) Roy. Free Hosp. Lond.; Regist. (Gen. Surg.) Univ. Coll. Hosp. Lond.

MASON, Mr Michael Christopher Hunter's Hollow, Penmaen, Swansea SA3 2HQ Tel: 0144 125 371602 — BM BCh 1963 Oxf.; BSc (Hons.) Leeds 1961; FRCS Eng. 1972. (Leeds & Oxf.) Cons. (Gen. Surg.) Singleton & Morriston Hosps. Swansea. Socs: Surg. Research Soc. & Vasc. Surg. Soc. Prev: Surg. Regist. York 'A' Hosp. Gp.; SHO Accid. Serv. Radcliffe Infirm. Oxf.; Ho. Surg. Profess. Unit, Gen. Infirm. Leeds.

MASON, Michael John McCleery 29 Grindlestone Hurst, Colne BB8 8BF Tel: 01282 859063 — MB ChB 1995 Manch.

MASON, Michael Knight (retired) 4 Blackthorn Lane, Burn Bridge, Harrogate HG3 1NZ — MB BS 1950 Lond.; MD Lond. 1963; MRCS Eng. LRCP Lond. 1950; FRCPath 1976, M 1963. Prev: Cons. Path. St. Jas. Hosp. Leeds.

MASON, Nicholas Charles (retired) 56 Hartford Road, Huntingdon PE29 3RP — MB 1971 Camb.; MSc Lond. 1986; BChir 1970; MFOM RCP Lond. 1986, AFOM 1983; DAvMed Eng. 1979. Prev: Cons. Occupat. Med. MoD.

***MASON, Nicolette Catherina** 7 Carlton Road, Sidcup DA14 6AQ — MB ChB 1996 Glas.

MASON, Nora Holmwood, Kents Bank Road, Grange-over-Sands LA11 7EY Tel: 014484 2226 — MB ChB 1945 Manch.; MD Yale 1944. (Manch. & Yale Med. Sch. New Haven) Med. Off. Family Plann. Assn. Barrow in Furness. Socs: B.M.A. Prev: Rotating Intern Med. Coll. Virginia; Ho. Surg. Roy. Infirm. Manch.

MASON, Pamela Georgina Walsh 34 Goodwood Court, Devonshire St., London W1W 5EF — MB BS 1950 Lond.; MRCS Eng. LRCP Lond. 1949; FRCPsych 1973; DPM Eng. 1957. (Roy. Free) Vice-Chairm. Taunton & Som. NHS Trust. Socs: Fell. Roy. Soc. Med.; Internat. Acad. Law & Ment. Health. Prev: Hon. Phys. HM the Qu.; Sen. Princip. Med. Off. DHSS; Cons. Psychiat. Childr. Dept. Home Office.

MASON, Paul John Portland Group Practice, The Health Centre, Park Estate Road, Easton, Portland DT5 2BJ Tel: 01305 820422 Fax: 01305 824143; 58 Buxton Road, Weymouth DT4 9PN — BM 1981 Soton.; MRCGP 1986; DRCOG 1984. (Southampton) GP Portland Gp. Pract. Prev: Trainee GP Hythe Med. Centre Soton. VTS; Med. Off. St. Francis Hosp. Katete, Zambia.

MASON, Paul Scott 12 Springfield Road, Hinckley LE10 1AN — MB BS 1990 Lond.

MASON, Mr Peter Francis, Wing Cdr. RAF Med. Br. Edith Cavell Hospital, Bretton Gate, Peterborough PE3 9GZ Tel: 01733 875199 Fax: 01733 875001; Stowe Corner, Stowe Road, Langtoft, Peterborough PE6 9NG Tel: 01778 561137 — MB ChB 1983 Liverp.; FRCS Ed. 1989; DAvMed FOM RCP Lond. 1993; FRCS (Gen) 1996 Intercoll Bd Gen Surg. Cons. Surg. Socs: Vasc. Surg. Soc. Prev: Sen. Regist. Kent & Canterbury Hosp.; Sen. Regist. RAF Hosp. Wroughton; Sen. Regist. P'boro. Dist. Hosp.

MASON, Peter Robert 23 Annes Close, Nottingham NG3 6DB — BM BS 1987 Nottm.

MASON, Mr Peter William 106 Harley Street, London W1N 1AF Tel: 020 7935 7952; 31 Warwick Avenue, London W9 2PS Tel: 020 7286 5397 — MB ChB 1972 Bristol; FRCS Ed. 1980; MRCOG 1978. Cons. O & G St. Mary's Hosp. Lond.; Cons. Gyn. Oncol. Samarit. Hosp. Lond.

MASON, Philip David Tingewick House, Upper St., Tingewick, Buckingham MK18 4QJ Email: phil.mason%mailgate.jrz@ox.ac.uk — MB BS 1976 Lond.; BSc (Hons.) Lond. 1976, MB BS (Hons.) (Med.; Surg., Pharmacol. & Therap.) 1979, PhD 1992; FRCP 1997, MRCP (UK) 1982. (Guy's) Cons. (Nephrol.) Oxf. Radcliffe Hosp. Trust; Hon. Sen. Lect. Oxf. Univ. Prev: Sen. Lect. Roy. Postgrad. Med. Sch.; Lect. RPMS.

***MASON, Phillipa** Dills, Combe Batch, Wedmore BS28 4DU — MB ChB 1998 Leeds.

MASON, Raymond Keith (retired) Amberley House, 38 Holland Road, Plymstock, Plymouth PL9 9BN Tel: 01752 402522 — MB BChir 1948 Camb.; BA, MB BChir Camb. 1948.

MASON, Rebecca Ann Beck House, Community Mental Health Team for Children & Families, 3 West Parade Road, Scarborough YO12 5ED Tel: 01723 352522; 20 High Street, Sherburn, Malton YO17 8LA — MB ChB 1981 Sheff.; MRCPsych 1986; MPsychother Leeds 1992. Cons. Child & Adolesc. Psychiat. Community Ment. Health Team for Childr. & Families ScarBoro. Prev: Sen. Regist. Rotat. (Child & Adolesc. Psychiat.) Yorks. RHA; Regist. & SHO Rotat. (Psychiat.) Nottm. Train. Scheme.

MASON, Richard Colin St Helier Hall End House, Hall End, Wootton, Bedford MK43 9HJ Tel: 01234 766123 Fax: 01234 766123 Email: rsthmason@aol.com — MB BS 1994 Lond.; BSc (Hons.) Immunol. Lond. 1991; MB BS (Hons) 1994; MRCP (UK) 1997. (St. Bart's Hosp. Med. Coll.) Specialist Regist. (A&E) N.wick Pk. Hosp. Middx. Prev: SHO (Med.) Rotat. Char. Cross Hosp. Lond.

MASON, Mr Richard Ray 136 Harley Street, London W1N 1AH Tel: 020 317 2790 Fax: 020 7436 7059; Oaklawn, 65 Dennis Lane, Stanmore HA7 4JU Tel: 020 8954 7448 Fax: 020 8420 7158 — MB BS 1972 Sydney; BSc (Med.) Sydney 1970; FRCS Eng. 1976; FRCP (UK) 1999; FRCR Eng. 1981; DMRD Eng. 1979. (Sydney) Cons. Radiol. Middlx. Hosp. Lond. Socs: Fell. Roy. Soc. Med. Prev: Med. Adviser Health Serv. Commiss.er for Eng. Scotl. & Wales; Sen. Regist. & Regist. (Radiol.) Middlx. Hosp. Lond.; Regist. (Surg.) Albury Base Hosp. Austral.

MASON, Mr Robert Charles 17 Kidbrooke Grove, London SE3 0LE — MB ChB 1976 Manch.; BSc (1st cl. Hons. Anat.) Manch. 1973, MD 1981, ChM 1989; FRCS Eng. 1991; FRCS Ed. 1980. Cons. Upper GI Surg. Guy's & St. Thos. Trust Lond.; Asst. Med. Director Guys & St. Thos. Trust Lond. Socs: Brit. Soc. Gastroenterol.; Assn. Surg.; Assn. Upper G.I. Surg. Prev: Sen. Regist. (Surg.) Guy's Hosp. Lond.; MRC Train. Fell. & Hon. Regist. (Surg.) Edin. Roy. Infirm.; Assit. PostGrad. Dean Kings Coll. Lond.

MASON, Roger John (retired) 327 Norton Way S., Letchworth SG6 1SZ Tel: 0462 676091 — MB BS 1960 Lond.; DA Eng. 1974; DObst RCOG 1962. Prev: Clin. Med. Off. (Anaesth.) Community Dent. Serv. Herts. & Beds. DHAs.

MASON, Rosalind Edna Ann Over Haddon, Bakewell DE45 1JE — MB BS 1961 Lond.; MRCS Eng. LRCP Lond. 1961; DFFP 1993; DMRT Eng. 1967. (Middlx.) Prev: Sen. Regist. Christie Hosp. & Holt Radium Inst. Manch.; Regist. S. Wales Radiother. Centre Cardiff; Ho. Surg. (Surgic. Studies) Middlx. Hosp. Lond.

MASON, Rosemary Anne Singleton Hospital, Sketty Lane, Swansea SA2 8QA Tel: 01792 205666 Fax: 01792 208647; Hunter's Hollow, Penmaen, Swansea SA3 2HQ Tel: 01792 371602 Fax: 01792 371602 Email: 106405.446@compuserve.com — MB ChB 1967 Leeds; MB ChB (Hons.) Leeds 1967; FRCA 1972; DObst RCOG 1969. Cons. Anaesth. Swansea NHS Trust; Asst. Edr. Assn. Anaesth. Socs: Assn. Anaesth.; Soc. Anaesth. Wales; Difficult Airway Soc. Prev: Sen. Regist. (Anaesth.) Univ. Hosp. Wales & Swansea Hosp.

MASON, Royston (retired) 100 Clifton Road, Ruddington, Nottingham NG11 6DE Tel: 0115 921 1672 — MRCS Eng. LRCP Lond. 1955. Prev: Med. Off. RAF (Nat. Serv.).

MASON, Rupert Bernard Stuart Parsonage Piece, Old Warden, Biggleswade SG18 9HQ Tel: 01767 627085 — MB BS 1971 Lond.; MRCS Eng. LRCP Lond. 1971. (Lond. Hosp.) Scientif. Dir. Bioglan Pharma PLC, Man. Dir. Bioglan Laborat. Ltd. Prev: Regist. (Physical Med.) Auckland Hosp., NZ; Cas. Off. King Edwd. VII Memor. Hosp., Bermuda; Ho. Off. Lond. Hosp.

MASON, Ruth Helena 50 Chipstead Close, Sutton SM2 6BE; Manor Hospital, Moat Road, Walsall WS2 9PS Tel: 01922 721172 — MB BS 1992 Lond. SHO Surg. Rotat. Manor Hosp. Walsall.

MASON, Sally Joanne Northfield Avenue Surgery, 61 Northfield Avenue, West Ealing, London W13 9QP Tel: 020 8567 1612 Fax: 020 8579 2593 — MB BS 1984 Lond.; DCH RCP Lond. 1987; MRCGP 1988; DRCOG 1987. Prev: Trainee GP Ealing Gen. Hosp. S.all VTS.

MASON, Sarah Joan Bronwydd, Windsor Road, Radyr, Cardiff CF15 8BQ Tel: 029 2084 2424 — MB BCh 1943 Wales; BSc 1940, MB BCh Wales 1943; DOMS Eng. 1947. (Cardiff) Prev: Asst. Ophth. Surg. Newport & E. Mon.; Ho. Phys. Llandough Hosp. Cardiff; Sen. Ho. Surg. Roy. Eye Hosp. Lond.

MASON, Stanley Arthur Front Orchard, Stileway, Meare, Glastonbury BA6 9SH Tel: 01458 860626 — AKC 1942; MB BS Lond. 1942; MRCS Eng. LRCP Lond. 1941; FFA RCS Eng. 1953, DA Eng. 1947; FRCA Eng 1992. (King's Coll. Hosp.) Socs: Hon. Fell. Indian Assn. Anaesths.; Hon. Mem. (Ex-Pres.) Assn. Anaesths. GB & Irel. Prev: Cons. Anaesth. King's Coll. Hosp.; Regist. (Anaesth.) King's Coll. Hosp.; Maj. RAMC, Anaesth. Specialist 1942-47.

***MASON, Stephanie Jane** 16 Larkfield, Eccleston, Chorley PR7 5RN — MB ChB 1994 Ed.

MASON, Susan Ann Principal's House, 18 St Pauls St., Stamford PE9 2BE Tel: 01780 756120; Department of Child Health, Eastgate Ward, Memorial Wing, Peterborough District Hospital, Peterborough PE3 6DA Tel: 01733 67451 — MB BS 1973 Newc.; MSc (Aud. Med.) Manch. 1998. Staff Grade (Community Paediat.) NWA Health Care Trust. Socs: Fell. RSM; BSA; Brit. Assn. Community Drs in Audiol. Prev: SCMO (Adult Ment. Handicap) N. Tyneside HA; Clin. Med. Off. Newc. HA & W. Berks. HA & Lancaster & N.d. HA; Staff Grade N. Downs Community Health Trust.

MASON, Miss Suzanne Margaret The Old Rectory, Church Lane N., Old Whittington, Chesterfield S41 9QY — MB BS 1990 Lond.; FRCS Glas. 1994. (Univ. Lond.) Specialist Regist. (A & E Med.) Sheff. Socs: Brit. Assn. Accid. & Emerg. Med.; BMA; Assoc. Mem. Fac. Accid. & Emerg. Med. Prev: Research Fell. (A & E Med.) Sheff.; SHO (A & E) N.. Gen. Hosp. Sheff.; Surg. SHO Rotat. Chesterfield Roy. Hosp. Trust.

MASON, Walter (retired) Derwent, Common Lane, River, Dover CT17 0PN Tel: 01304 823362 — MB ChB 1963 Ed.; DCH RCPS Glas. 1966; DObst RCOG 1965. Prev: Regist. (Paediat.) Roy. Vict. Infirm. Newc.

***MASON, William Thomas Matthew** Farr House, Lowgill, Wray, Lancaster LA2 8RA Tel: 015242 61382 Email: will.mason@virgin.net — BChir 1996 Camb.; MB 1997; MA 1998.

***MASON, Yvette Claire** 29 Forsyth Road, West Jesmond, Newcastle upon Tyne NE2 3DB — MB BS 1997 Newc.

MASON-APPS, Sally Patricia 16B Craigleith Drive, Edinburgh EH4 3HQ — MB ChB 1996 Ed.

MASON BROWN, David (retired) Moresby House, 12 Cromwell Road, North Berwick EH39 4LZ Tel: 01620 892995 Fax: 01620 890169 Email: dmasbrown@aol.com — MB ChB 1966 Ed. Indep. Psychother. & Stress Managem.; Med. Dir., Eqilibrium Assoc. Ltd, Edin.; Hon. Med. Off., Edinb. MESH (CFS Fell. Self Help Gp.). Prev: GP N. Berwick & Dunbar.

MASON-WALSHAW, Kenneth Roy (retired) Herons March, New Road, Instow, Bideford EX39 4LN Tel: 01271 860979 — MRCS Eng. LRCP Lond. 1950; MA Camb. 1944. Prev: Ho. Surg. St. Bart. Hosp. Lond.

MASON-WILLIAMS, John Tyn-y-Coed Surgery, 20 Merfield Close, Bryncethin, Bridgend CF32 9SW Tel: 01656 720334 Fax: 01656 721998 — MB BCh 1975 Wales.

MASOOD

MASOOD, Ahmed Bertram Road Surgery, 21 Bertram Road, Bradford BD8 7LN Tel: 01274 547763 — MB BS 1975 Madras.

***MASOOD, Junaid** 5 Christchurch Gardens, Epsom KT19 8RU — MB BS 1995 Lond.

MASOOD, Mohammad 21 Michael Drive, Edgbaston, Birmingham B15 2EL — MB BS Dacca 1956; MRCPsych 1976; DPM Eng. 1970. (Dacca Med. Coll.) Prev: Cons. Psychiat. Walsall Community Health Trust.

MASOOD, Muhammad Rashid The Surgery, Gardiners Lane, Ashwell, Baldock SG7 5PY — MB BS 1981 Karachi.

MASOOD, Muneera Begum 21 Bertram Road, Bradford BD8 7LN Tel: 01274 547763 — MB BS 1968 Madras. GP Bradford, W. Yorks.

MASOOD, Syed Kamil 122 Great West Road, Hounslow TW5 9AP — MB BS 1987 Karachi.

MASOOD, Mr Tahir 5 Ellis Avenue, Slough SL1 2RD Tel: 01753 527205 Email: gs71@dial.pipex.com — BM 1988 Soton.; FRCS Eng. 1994; DRCOG 1996.

***MASOOD, Umair** 5 Christchurch Gardens, Epsom KT19 8RU — MB BS 1995 Lond.

MASOODI, Musharraf Nazir c/o Department of Anaesthetics, West Wales General Hospital, Glangwiliw, Carmarthen SA31 2AF — MB BS 1980 Kashmir.

MASOTINA, Angelo Flat 2, 14 Dittons Road, Eastbourne BN21 1DW — State DMS 1990 Padua.

MASOUD, Raed Singleton Hospital, Sketty, Swansea SA2 8QA — MB BCh BAO 1993 NUI; LRCPSI 1993.

***MASOUMI-RAVANDI, Mashallah** 38 Southwark Close, Yateley GU46 6QG — MB BS 1995 Lond.

MASRI, Ziad 81 The Grove, Marton, Middlesbrough TS7 8AN Tel: 01642 316957 — MD 1965 Damascus; FFA RCSI 1977; DA Eng. 1972. (Damascus) Cons. (Anaesth. & Intens. Therap. Unit) N. RHA, Cleveland AHA; S. Tees Health Dist. & Middlesbrough Gen. Hosp. Prev: Sen. Regist. (Anaesth.) Newc. AHA (T).

MASROOR, Talat Department of Obstetrics & Gynaecology, Royal Maternity Hospital, Grosvenor Road, Belfast BT12 6BB — MB BS 1983 Karachi.

MASS, Michael Elliot Preston Medical Centre, 23 Preston Road, Wembley HA9 8JZ Tel: 020 8904 3263; 16 Sherwood Road, Hendon, London NW4 1AD — MB ChB 1967 Liverp.

MASSAM, Michael 66 Lawe Road, South Shields NE33 2AJ — MB ChB 1972 Manch.; FRCP (Lon.) 1997; MRCP (U.K.) 1976; FRCPCH 1997; DCH Eng. 1974.

MASSAR, Catherina Geertrudes Flat 2, 33 Clarendon Road, Birmingham B16 9SD — Artsexamen 1992 Amsterdam.

MASSARANO, Albert Alan Tameside General Hospital, Ashton-under-Lyne OL6 9RW Tel: 0161 331 6000 Fax: 0161 331 5255; 10 Lancaster Drive, Prestwich, Manchester M25 0HZ Tel: 0161 773 6282 — MB ChB 1979 Leeds; MD Leeds 1991; MRCP (UK) 1985; DCH Eng. 1981; FRCP 1997; FRCPCH 1997. Cons. Paediat. Tameside Gen. Hosp. Socs: Brit. Soc. Paediat. Endocrinol. Prev: Lect. & Sen. Regist. Univ. Manch.; Research Asst. (Paediat.) Middlx. Hosp. Lond.

***MASSEY, Adrian Peter** 47A Hanbury Road, Droitwich WR9 8PR — BM 1997 Soton.

MASSEY, Alexandra Mary Orgill 17 New Road, Chatteris PE16 6BJ — MB BS 1983 Lond.

MASSEY, Brynnen David The Surgery, Highfield Road, North Thoresby, Grimsby DN36 5RT — MB BS 1983 Lond.; MRCGP 1989; DCCH Ed. 1988.

MASSEY, Mr Charles Ian Wyncote, 19 Sibsey Road, Boston PE21 9QY — MB BS 1963 Durh.; BSc. (Hons.) Durham. 1960, MB BS 1963; FRCS Ed. 1968; FRCS Eng. 1969. Cons. (Gen. Surg.) Pilgrim Hosp. Boston. Prev: Sen. Regist. Derbysh. Roy. Infirm. Derby & Nottm Gen. Hosp.; Cons. (Gen. Surg.) Pilgrim Hosp. Boston.

MASSEY, Christopher John 14 Bath Terrace, Newcastle upon Tyne NE3 1UH — MB BS 1990 Newc.; MRCPsych 1994. (Newcastle Upon Tyne) Sen. Regist. (Psychiat.) N. RHA.

MASSEY, Edwin Herbert (retired) 18 Clive Place, Penarth CF64 1AY — MB BCh 1954 Wales; BSc Wales 1950, MB BCh 1954; MFCM 1972; DPH Eng. 1963, DIH 1964. Prev: Dep. MOH, Princip. Sch. Med. Off. & Port Med. Off. Newport Co. Boro.

MASSEY, Edwin James Ryall Herbert 18 Clive Place, Penarth CF64 1AY — MB ChB 1990 Bristol.

***MASSEY, Glenn Steven** 9 Kent Avenue, Formby, Liverpool L37 6BE — MB ChB 1998 Liverp.; MB ChB Liverp 1998.

MASSEY, Henrietta Jayne Orgill Maritime House, Linton Road, Barking IG11 8HF Tel: 020 8594 5522; 18 Birchwood Avenue, Muswell Hill, London N10 3BE — MB BS 1985 Lond.; MRCGP 1989; DRCOG 1988. Employm. Med. Adviser Health & Safety Exec. Barking. Prev: SHO (Ophth.) Roy. United Hosp. Bath; SHO (Psychiat.) Coney Hill Hosp.; SHO (Cas.) Cheltenham Gen. Hosp.

MASSEY, Jane Bernadette Clackmannan County Hospital, Ashley Terrace, Alloa FK10 2BE Tel: 01259 723840 Fax: 01259 724740; Iona, 55 The Firs, Bannockburn, Stirling FK7 0EG — MB ChB 1974 Aberd. Staff Grade (Psychiat.) Centr. Scotl. Healthcare NHS Trust Larbert. Socs: BMA.

MASSEY, Jillian Mary 19 Sibsey Road, Boston PE21 9QY — MB ChB 1972 Sheff.; FFA RCS Eng. 1977.

MASSEY, Mr John Adrian Whiston Hospital, Prescot L35 5DR Tel: 0151 430 1976 Fax: 0151 430 1405; 236 Moss Delph Lane, Aughton, Ormskirk L39 5BJ Tel: 01695 423196 — MB BS 1970 Lond.; MD Bristol 1986; FRCS Eng. 1978; MRCS Eng. LRCP Lond. 1972. (Univ. Coll. Hosp.) Cons. Urol. St. Helens & Knowsley NHS Trust. Prev: Sen. Regist. (Urol.) Manch. Roy. Infirm.; Research Fell. (Urol.) Ham Green Hosp. Pill Bristol.

***MASSEY, Karen Barbara** 61 Barrowburn Green, Ingleby Barwick, Stockton-on-Tees TS17 0FF — MB BCh BAO 1994 Belf.

MASSEY, Kathryn Commonfield Road Surgery, 156 Commonfield Road, Woodchurch, Birkenhead CH49 7LP Tel: 0151 677 0016; Tower House, School Lane, Little Neston, South Wirral CH64 4DG — MB ChB 1977 Liverp.; DRCOG 1981. GP Wirral.

MASSEY, Linda Jane Sandy Lane Surgery, Sandy Lane, Leyland, Preston PR25 2EB Tel: 01772 909915 Fax: 01772 909911 — MB ChB 1992 Leeds. Trainee GP Preston VTS.

MASSEY, Michael Robert Trevenna Cottage, St. Neot, Liskeard PL14 6NR — MB ChB 1972 Bristol.

MASSEY, Neil 45 Stainton Road, Endcliffe Park, Sheffield S11 7AX — MB ChB 1987 Sheff. SHO (ENT Surg.) Rotherham Gen. Hosp.

MASSEY, Nicholas John Alexander 326 Millhouses Lane, Sheffield S11 9JD — MB BS 1981 Lond.; FFA RCS Eng. 1987.

MASSEY, Paul Mackintosh Orgill (retired) Unst House, 80 Linthurst Road, Barnt Green, Birmingham B45 8JJ Tel: 0121 447 7622 — MB BChir 1953 Camb.; MD Camb. 1958, MA (Hons.), MB BChir 1953; MFOM RCP Lond. 1979; DIH Soc. Apoth. Lond. 1965. Prev: Sen. Med. Adviser CEGB Midl. Region.

MASSEY, Mr Ravi Ranjan Accident & Emergency Department, Royal Liverpool Childrens Hospital, Alder Hey Childrens Hospital, Eaton Road, Liverpool L12 2AP Tel: 0151 252 5583 Fax: 0151 252 5033 Email: paulmasseyhotmail.com; Fax: 0151 252 5033 — MB BS 1981 Punjab; MSc Orthop. Lond. 1988; MCh (Orth.) Liverp. 1995; MS Orthop. Punjab 1985; FRCPCH 1997; FFAEM 1996. (Christian Med. Coll. Ludhiana, India) Cons. & Hon. Clin. Lect. (Paediat. A & E) Alder Hey Childr. Hosp. Liverp. Socs: Fell. Fac. A & E Med.; BMA (Ex. Comm. Liverp. Div.). Prev: Staff Grade (Orthop. Paediat. Surg.) Alder Hey Childr. Hosp. Liverp.

MASSEY, Robinson Michael 218 Court Farm Road, Mottingham, London SE9 4JZ Tel: 020 8857 3322; 9 Kingsmead Court, London Road, Bromley BR1 3SY Tel: 020 8313 9174 — MB BS 1963 Sind. (Liaquat Med. Coll. Hyderabad) Socs: Affil. RCPsych; Fell. Roy. Soc. Med. Prev: Regist. (Psychol. Med.) S.. Gen. Hosp. Glas.; SHO (O & G) Liaquat Med. Coll. Hosp. Hyderabad, Pakistan; SHO (Paediat.) Dept. Child Health Roy. Liverp. Childr. Hosp.

MASSEY, Ruth Diana Orgill Ladies Walk, Butleigh, Glastonbury BA6 8SJ Tel: 01458 314 — MB BS 1962 Lond.; DObst RCOG 1964. (Middlx.) Prev: Ho. Surg. Middlx. Hosp. Lond.; Ho. Phys. Roy. Portsmouth Hosp.; Ho. Off. St. Mary's Hosp. HarBoro. Magna.

MASSEY, Simon Robert 26 Parrys Lane, Bristol BS9 1AA — MB BCh 1984 Wales; MRCP (UK) 1990; FRCA 1994.

MASSIE, Alan Tweeddale Medical Practice, High Street, Fort William PH33 6EU Tel: 01397 703136 Fax: 01397 700139; Erradale, Corpach, Fort William PH33 7LT Tel: 01397 772888 — MB ChB 1979 Aberd.; DRCOG 1983. Prev: Trainee GP Inverness.

MASSIE, Jennifer Anne 103A Byrons Lane, Macclesfield SK11 7JS Tel: 01625 431680 — BChir 1994 Camb.

MASSIE, Richard Reid 27 Buchan Road, Fraserburgh AB43 9WE — MB ChB 1979 Aberd.; MRCGP 1983.

MASSIL, Helen Yvonne Department of Reproductive Health, St Giles Road, London SE5 7RN Tel: 020 7771 3330 Fax: 020 7771 3338 Email: helen.massil@chsltr.sthames.nhs.uk — MB ChB 1978 Sheff.; MFFP 1993; MRCOG 1990. Cons. Reproductive Health; Hon. Sen. Lect. (OLG) GKST Lond.; Hon. Cons. (Obst. & Gyn.) Lewisham Hosp. Lond.

MASSON, Alastair Hugh Bailey (retired) 28 Beechmount Park, Edinburgh EH12 5YT — MB ChB 1947 Ed.; DA Eng. 1952; FFA RCS Eng. 1954; BA Open Univ. 1980; FRCS Ed. 1981; FRCA 1990. Hon. Archiv. RCS Ed. Prev: Cons. Anaesth. Roy. Infirm. Edin.

MASSON, Ewan Alastair 1 Redcliff Drive, North Ferriby HU14 3DP Tel: 01482 634302 Email: e.a.masson@medschool.hull.ac.uk — MB ChB 1982 Manch.; BSc St. And. 1979; MD Manch. 1989; FRCP Lond. 1997; MRCP (UK) 1986. (Manch.) Sen. Lect. (Med.) Univ. Hull & Hon. Cons. Phys. Roy. Hull Hosps.; Coll. Tutor RCP Lond. Socs: BMA (N. Ferriby Rep.); BDA.

MASSON, Geraldine North Staffordshire Hospital NHS Trust, Newcastle Road, Stoke-on-Trent ST4 6QG Tel: 01782 552447; 3 Anvil Close, Sandbach CW11 3RF Email: gmasson@tinyonline.co.uk — MB ChB 1987 Dundee; MRCOG 1992. Cons. (O & G) N. Staffs. Hosp. NHS Trust. Prev: Sen. Regist. (O & G) Liverp. Wom. Hosp.

MASSON, Harish 39 Moorsyde Cr, Sheffield S10 1QJ — MB ChB 1997 Sheff.

MASSON, Kamlesh Kumar Milton Road Surgery, 12 Milton Road, Grays RM17 5EZ Tel: 01375 381612 Fax: 01375 392366; Paddock House, Rectory Road, Orsett, Grays RM16 3JT Tel: 01375 892556 — MB BS 1969 Utkal. (S.C.B. Med. Coll. Cuttack) Prev: SHO (Cas. & Orthop.) W. Norf. & King's Lynn Gen. Hosp.

MASSON, Linda Jane Lane End Surgery, 2 Manor Walk, Benton, Newcastle upon Tyne NE7 7XX Tel: 0191 266 5246 Fax: 0191 266 6241 — MB ChB 1983 Dundee; MRCGP 1988; DCH RCP Lond. 1987; DRCOG 1986.

MASSON, Marjorie Nan (retired) 28 Beechmount Park, Edinburgh EH12 5YT Tel: 0131 337 5686 — MB ChB Ed. 1949. Prev: SCMO Lothian HB.

MASSON, William David (retired) Allt an Dorran, Salen, Acharacle PH36 4JN Tel: 01967 431255 — MB ChB 1955 Aberd.; FRCP Ed. 1989, M 1969; DCH RCPS Glas. 1964; DTM & H Lond 1963. Prev: GP Ardnamurchan.

MASSOUD, Ahmed Faris Northwick Park & St Mark's Hospitals, NHS Trust, Watford Road, Harrow HA1 3UJ Tel: 020 8869 2642 Fax: 020 8869 2927 Email: ahmed.massoud@nwlh.nhs.uk; 36 Blockley Road, Wembley HAO 3LR Tel: 020 8904 9551 — MB BS 1987 Lond.; FRCPCH 2001 UK; MRCP (UK) 1991; MD Lond. 1997. (University College London) Cons.(Paediat. and Endocrinol.) N.wick Pk. & St Marks Hosp. Harrow, Middx.; Sen. Lect. (Paediat.) Imp. Coll. Of Sci.,Tech. & Med. Socs: Roy. Coll. Paediat. & Child Health; Brit. Soc. Paediat. Endocrinol. & Diabetes; Eur. Soc. Paediat. Endocrinol. Prev: Sen. Regist. (Paediatric Endocrinol.) Gt. Ormond St. Hosp.; Lect. (Paediat. Endocrinol. & Gen. Paediat.) Middlx. Hosp. Lond. & Edgware Gen. Hosps.en. Regist. (Paediat. Endocrinol.) Gt. Ormond St. Hosp.; Clin. Research Fell. (Paediat. Endocrinol.) Middlx. Hosp. Lond.

MASSOUD, Mamdouh Samy 108 Addiscombe Road, Croydon CR0 5PQ Tel: 020 8654 9536 Fax: 020 8406 8218 — MB BCh 1971 Ain Shams; Dip. Sports Med. Scotl. 1996 Roy.Coll. Surg & Phys. Of Scot.; Dip. IMC RCS Ed. 1995 RCS Ed. (Ain Shams Univ. Cairo) SCMO (A & E) St. Helier Hosp. Carshalton; Chief Med. Adv. Inter. Med Rescue. Socs: Brit. Assn. Immed. Care Schemes; Founder Mem. Fac. Pre-Hosp. Care RCS Ed.; Brit. Assn. Sport & Med. Prev: Assoc. Specialist (A & E) St. Helier Hosp. Carshalton.

MASSOUD, Massoud Abou Khalaf West Middlesex University Hospital, Twickenham Road, Isleworth TW7 6AF Tel: 020 8847 4951 — MB BCh 1978 Cairo; MRCOG 1992.

MASSOUH, Hassan Rosewood, Long Hill, The Sands, Farnham GU10 1NG Tel: 01252 781435 — MD 1972 Damascus; FRCR 1982; DMRD Eng. 1980. (Lond.) Cons. Radiol. Frimley Pk. Hosp. Camberley.

MASSY, John Royds (retired) Hazel Lodge, Hensting Lane, Fishers Pond, Eastleigh SO50 7HH — MB BS 1960 Lond.; MRCS Eng. LRCP Lond. 1960. Prev: Ho. Phys. & Ho. Surg. Roy. S. Hants. Hosp. Soton.

MASTER, Bacha Rustom 5 The Mead, Clevelands, London W13 8AZ Tel: 020 8998 7466 — MB BS 1964 Poona; FFA RCS Eng. 1970; DA Eng. 1966. (B.J. Med. Sch. Poona) Cons. Anaesth. Char. Cross Hosp. Lond. Prev: Sen. Regist. Char. Cross Hosp.; Regist. Middlx. Hosp.; Clin. Fell. Johns Hopkins Hosp. USA.

MASTER, Dinshaw Rustam Guy's Hospital, Thomas Guy House, York Clinic, 47 Weston St., London SE1 3RR Tel: 020 7955 4278 Fax: 020 7407 0912 Email: dmaster@slam-tr.sthames.nhs.uk; 215 Kings Hall Road, Beckenham BR3 1LL Tel: 020 8778 2606 Fax: 020 8659 4900 Email: dinshaw.master@ukgateway.net — MB BS Lond. 1970; LLM Wales 1992; FRCP Lond. 1994; MRCP (UK) 1974; FRCPsych 1991, M 1977. (Middlx.) Jt. med dir S. Lond & Maudsley NHS Trust. Prev: Lect. Inst. Psychiat. Lond.; Sen. Regist. & Regist. Maudsley & Bethlem Roy. Hosps. Lond.

*****MASTER, Nicholas James** 215 Kings Hall Road, Beckenham BR3 1LL — MB BS 1998 Lond.; MB BS Lond 1998.

MASTER, Roshan Framroze (retired) 30 Eldon Road, Blackburn BB1 8BE Tel: 01254 261653 — MB BS 1948 Punjab; MB BS East Punjab (India) 1948; DA Eng. 1962. Prev: GP Blackburn.

MASTERMAN, Mr Ernest Bertram Zeller (retired) No. 12 Swallowfield Park, Swallowfield, Reading RG7 1TG Tel: 01189 882315 — MRCS Eng. LRCP 1934 Lond.; MD Camb. 1939, BChir 1936; FRCS Ed. 1947; MRCS Eng LRCP Lond. 1934. Prev: Surg. City Hosp. Nottm.

***MASTERMAN, Kathryn Louise** Greenways, Gussage All Saints, Wimborne BH21 5ET — MB ChB 1997 Sheff.

MASTERS, Adam Paul Department of Anaesthesia, Colchester General Hospital, Turner Road, Colchester CO4 5JL Tel: 01206 853535 — MB ChB 1981 Bristol; FFA RCS Eng. 1987. Cons. Anaesth. Essex Rivers Health Care Trust Colchester.

MASTERS, Amanda Jeanne Watercress Medical Group, Dean Surgery, Ropley, Alresford SO24 0BQ Tel: 01962 772340 Fax: 01962 772551 — MB BS 1982 Lond.; DCH RCP Lond. 1986; DRCOG 1985; Cert. Family Plann. JCC 1985. (Charing Cross) GP Princip.; GP Tutor. Prev: Trainee GP Winchester VTS; Ho. Phys. Char. Cross Hosp. E. Lond.; So. Surg. Worthing & S.lands Hosp. Essex.

MASTERS, Arnavaz Bomanshaw 13 Trinity Court, Queen's Avenue, Winchmore Hill, London N21 3JF Tel: 020 8360 0957 — MB BS 1952 Karachi; BSc Bombay 1947; LRCP LRCS Ed. LRFPS Glas. 1954; DCH Eng. 1962. (Dow Med. Coll. Karachi) Prev: Sen. Regist. (Paediat.) Beaumont Hosp. Lancaster; Cons. (Paediat.) Holy Family Hosp. & Lady Dufferin Hosp. Karachi, Pakistan.

MASTERS, D K 198 Court Farm Road, Mottingham, London SE9 4JS.

MASTERS, David The Clock Tower Practice, 50-66 Park Road, Crouch End, London N8 8SU Tel: 020 8348 7711 — MB ChB 1984 Manch.; MRCGP 1988.

MASTERS, Gillian Lois The New Surgery, Lindo Close, Chesham HP5 2JN Tel: 01494 782262; Swyllmers Barn, The Lee, Great Missenden HP16 9NA Email: masters@nildram.co.uk — MB BS 1976 Lond.; MRCS Eng. LRCP Lond. 1976. (St. Bart.)

MASTERS, Henrietta Clare Newbury Street Practice, Newbury Street, Wantage OX12 7AY Tel: 01235 763451; Larkrise, Coopers Lane, Wantage OX12 8HQ — BM BS 1990 Nottm.; MRCGP 1995; DFFP 1995; T(GP) 1994; DRCOG 1993. (Univ. Nottm.) Socs: BMA. Prev: Trainee GP Chipping Norton; SHO (A & E, Dermat. & Med.) Horton Gen. Hosp.

MASTERS, Jonathan Edward Angel Hill Surgery, 1 Angel Hill, Bury St Edmunds IP33 1LU Tel: 01284 753008 Fax: 01284 724744 — MB BS 1980 Lond.; BSc (Hons.) Lond. 1977; MRCGP 1987; DRCOG 1984. Prev: Trainee GP Brighton VTS; Ho. Surg. Guy's Hosp. Lond.; Ho. Phys. Lewisham Hosp.

MASTERS, Mr Jonathan Grenville 35 Woodlands Grange, Forest Hall, Newcastle upon Tyne NE12 9DG — BM BCh 1989 Oxf.; FRCS Eng. 1994. Higher Urol. Trainee N. & Yorks. Region. Socs: Brit. Assn. Urol. Surg.

MASTERS, Keith William (retired) 378 Birmingham Road, Walsall WS5 3NX Tel: 01922 623828 Fax: 01922 649075 Email: k.m.masters@btinternet.com — MB ChB Birm. 1961; FRCOG 1984, M 1972. Hon. Sen. Lect. Obst. & Gyn. Birm. Med. Sch. Prev: Cons. Adviser Jt. Study Gp. of FIGO/ICM Midw. Train. & Overseas.

MASTERS

MASTERS, Mandy West Farm Avenue Surgery, 381 West Farm Avenue, Longbenton, Newcastle upon Tyne NE12 8UT Tel: 0191 266 1728 Fax: 0191 270 1488 — BM BCh 1989 Oxf.

MASTERS, Nigel James Highfield Surgery, Highfield Way, Hazlemere, High Wycombe HP15 7UW Tel: 01949 813396 Fax: 01949 814107; 27 Tilsworth Road, Beaconsfield HP9 1TR — MB BS 1978 Lond.; BSc (Hons.) Lond. 1974; MRCGP 1983; DFFP 1993; DRCOG 1981. (Guy's) Prev: Adviser Cameron-Price Med. Div.; Lect. (Gen. Pract.) UMDS Lond.; Clin. Asst. (Dermat.) Erith Hosp.

MASTERS, Paul Wesley Chesterfield & N. Derbyshire Royal Hospital, Calow, Chesterfield S44 5BL Tel: 01246 277271 Fax: 01246 552231; Fawn House, 2 Fawn Close, Wingerworth, Chesterfield S42 6PZ Tel: 01246 279441 — MB ChB 1988 Leeds; MB ChB (Hons.) Leeds 1988; BSc (Hons.) Leeds 1985; MRCPath 1996, D 1993. (Leeds) Cons. Chem. Path. Chesterfield Roy. Hosp. Socs: Assn. Clin. Biochem. Prev: Sen. Regist. (Chem. Path.) Nottm. City Hosp.; Regist. (Chem. Path.) Yorks. RHA; SHO (Path.) Manch. Roy. Infirm.

MASTERS, Rachel Clare 17 Shire Close, Paignton TQ4 7SW — MB ChB 1988 Bristol.

MASTERS, Robert Richard Frondeg, Myndd Bodafon, Llanerchymedd LL71 8BG — MB ChB 1976 Sheff.

MASTERSON, Elizabeth Govan Health Centre, 5 Drumoyne Road, Govan, Glasgow G51 4BJ Tel: 0141 531 8470 Fax: 0141 531 8471; 102 Beech Ave, Newton Mearns, Glasgow G77 5BL — MB ChB 1988 Glas. (Glasgow) Clin. Asst. Cardiol.

MASTERSON, Gerard Robert 3 Canal Bank, Appley Bridge, Wigan WN6 9AW — MB BChir 1989 Camb.

MASTERSON, Mary 25 Maes-y-Nant, Creigiau, Cardiff CF15 9EJ — MB ChB Glas. 1988; T(GP) 1992.

MASTERSON, Sean William 15 Regina Road, London N4 3PT — MB ChB 1992 Bristol.

MASTERTON, George Department of Psychological Medicine, Edinburgh Royal Infirmary, Edinburgh Tel: 0131 536 2875 Fax: 0131 536 3408; 48 Ravelston, Dykes, Edinburgh EH4 — MD 1982 Glas.; BSc 1978, MB ChB 1975; MRCPsych 1979. Cons. Psychiat. Roy. Infirm. Edin. Socs: Fell.Roy. Coll. of Psychiat.s. Prev: Cons. Psychiat. Yeovil Dist. Hosp. & Tone Vale Hosp.; Lect. Dept. Psychol. Med. Glas. Univ. & Gartnavel Roy. Hosp.

MASTERTON, George (retired) 124 Haggs Road, Pollokshields, Glasgow G41 4AT — MB ChB St. And. 1940; DPH Ed. 1948. Prev: Cons. Venereol. Gtr. Glas. & Lanarksh. Health Bds.

MASTERTON, Jacqueline Wood 2 Prentis Road, Streatham, London SW16 1XU Tel: 020 8769 5002 Fax: 020 8677 1800; 87 Northwood Road, Thornton Heath, Croydon CR7 8HW — MB ChB Dundee 1978.

MASTERTON, Jean Gilmour Bishopton Health Centre, Greenock Road, Bishopton PA7 5AW Tel: 01505 863223 Fax: 01505 862798; Tir-Nan-Og, 26 Glencairn Road, Langbank, Port Glasgow PA14 6XL Tel: 0147 554 0378 Fax: 01505 862798 — MB ChB 1973 Glas.; DObst RCOG 1975; LFHom (Med) 1998. (Glas.)

MASTERTON, Robert Gardner Western General Hospital, Department of Clinical Microbiology, Crewe Road, Edinburgh EH4 2XU Tel: 0131 537 1934 Fax: 0131 537 1024; Ashburnham House, 1 Ashburnham Gardens, South Queensferry EH30 9LB Tel: 0131 331 1799 — MB ChB 1977 Glas.; BSc (Hons.) Glas. 1975; FRCPath 1996, M 1985; DGM RCP Lond. 1988; DTM & H Liverp. 1984; FRCP Ed 1998. (Glasgow) Cons. Microbiol. W.. Gen. Hosp. Edin.; Dep. Med. Dir. Prev: Cons. Microbiol. RAF.

MASTIHI, Angelique Flat 1, 63 Haven Lane, London W5 2HZ — MB BS 1993 Lond.

MASTON, Jean Community Health Office, St. Mary's Hospital, Greenhill Road, Armley, Leeds LS12 3QE Tel: 0113 279 0121; 21 Raines Meadows, Grassington, Skipton BD23 5NB Tel: 01756 752761 — MB ChB 1976 Leeds; DCH Eng. 1978. SCMO (Child Health) Leeds Community & Ment. Health NHSTrust. Socs: BMA. Prev: Clin. Med. Off. (Community Child Health) W. Leeds HA; Clin. Med. Off. (Community Health) Bristol & W.on HA.

***MASTRANTONIO, Maria Giuseppina** 11 Primrose Lane, Arlesey SG15 6RD — MB BS 1996 Lond.; BSc Lond. 1993; DRCOG 1999.

MASUD, Hamid The Surgery, 77 Sandy Lane, Mansfield NG18 2LT Tel: 01623 656055 Fax: 01623 424898 — MRCS Eng. LRCP Lond. 1986; MB BS Punjab, Pakistan 1978.

MASUD, Parveen Fatima Mawney Medical Centre, 34 Mawney Road, Romford RM1 4HN Tel: 01708 743627 — MB BS 1988 Lond.; DCH RCP Lond. 1993; DRCOG 1991.

***MASUD, Syed Parvez** 8 Swift House, Chigwell Road, South Woodford, London E18 1TP — MB BS 1997 Lond.; Dip. IMC RCS (Ed).

MASUD, Tahir City Hospital NHS Trust, Nottingham NG5 1PB Tel: 01602 691169 — MB BS 1985 Lond.; BA Physiol. Sci. Oxf. 1982; MRCP (UK) 1988; FRCP 1999 UK. (St Bart's Hospital) Cons. Phys. City Hosp. NHS Trust Nottm. Socs: Nat. Osteoporosis Soc.; Brit. Geriat. Soc.; Physical Activity for the Preven. of Osteoporosis, Falls and Fract.s (PAPOFF). Prev: Lect. & Hon. Sen. Regist. (Med. & Geriat.) St. Bart. Hosp. Med. Coll. Lond.

MASUDUZZAMAN, Mohammad (retired) 20 shrubbery Close, Sutton Coldfield B76 1WE Tel: 0121 384 7462 — MB BS 1952 Calcutta; FRCP Ed. 1980, M 1959; DTM & H Liverp. 1956. Cons. Phys. (Geriat. Med.) New Cross Hosp. Wolverhampton.

MASZADRO, Zdzislaw 46 Ludlow Avenue, Luton LU1 3RW Tel: 01582 28809 — MB BCh BAO 1954 NUI; LM Coombe 1955. (Galw. & W. Lond.) Prev: Regist. Psychiat. Hill End Hosp. St. Albans; Sen. Ho. Off. E.. Fev. Hosp. Lond.; Ho. Phys. Hammersmith Hosp. Lond.

***MAT ALI, Mohd Ezam** 17 Newall Dr, Beeston, Nottingham NG9 6NU — BM BS 1997 Nottm.

MATA, Sanjiv Kumar 53 Fowlers Walk, London W5 1BQ — MB BS 1980 Lond.

MATA, Sara Louise 91 Kington-st-michael, Chippenham SN14 6HX — MB BS 1993 Lond.

***MATAI, Rinku** 24 Newlands Quay, London E1W 3QZ — MB ChB 1998 Sheff.; MB ChB Sheff 1998.

***MATAI, Vandana** 24 Newlands Quay, London E1W 3QZ — MB BS 1994 Lond.

***MATAKIDOU, Athena** Flat 11, Westwood Court, Westwood Rd., Portswood, Southampton SO17 1UX — BM 1998 Soton.; BM Soton 1998.

MATANHELIA, Mr Shyam Sunder Royal Preston Hospital, Sharoe Green Road, Preston PR2 9HT Tel: 01772 716565; 36 Hight Street, Foxton, Cambridge CB2 6RS Tel: 01223 871838, 01257 234221 Email: k.beardsall@btinternet.com — MB BS 1977 Kanpur; MS Kanpur 1981; FRCS (Urol.) Ed. 1994; FRCS Ed. 1984; Dip. Urol. Lond 1986. (Kampur India) Cons. Urol. Roy. Preston Hosp. Lancs.; Cons.Urol.Chorley & Dist. Gen Hosp. Lancs. Socs: BAUS. Prev: Sen. Regist. (Urol.) Univ. Hosp. Wales Cardiff; Sen. Regist. (Urol.) Gwent Hosp. Newport; Temp. Sen. Regist. (Paediat. Surg. & Urol.) Roy. Vict. Infirm. Newc. u. Tyne.

MATCHAM, Nicola Jane Thorn Cottage, Brook Lane, Woodgreen, Fordingbridge SP6 2AZ — MB BS 1993 Lond.; MRCP (Lond.) 1997.

MATCHETT, Andrew Alexander Arnside Medical Practice, The Surgery, Orchard Road, Arnside, Carnforth LA5 0DP Tel: 01524 761311 Fax: 01524 762470; Old Orchard, Orchard Road, Arnside, Carnforth LA5 0DP — MB ChB 1969 Glas.; DObst RCOG 1972; DFFP. (Glasgow) GP Arnside. Socs: Soc. of Orthopaedic Med. Prev: Ho. Off. Stobhill Gen. Hosp. Glas.; Surg. Lt. RN.

MATE, John Derek New Medical Centre, Crossley Street, Wetherby LS22 6RT Tel: 01937 543200 Fax: 01937 588689; New Medical Centre, Crossley St., Wetherby LS22 6RT — MB ChB 1977 Manch.; MRCGP 1981; DRCOG 1980.

MATEAR, Elizabeth Anne Newbyres Medical Group, Gorebridge Health Centre, Gorebridge EH23 4TP Tel: 01875 820405 Fax: 01875 820269 — MB ChB 1982 Glas. GP Edin.

MATEOS DURAN, Luis Maria Riding Edge, Scotland Lane, Horsforth, Leeds LS18 5SF — LMS 1991 Cadiz.

MATEU-LOPEZ, Enrique St. George's Hospital, Corporation St., Stafford ST16 3AG Tel: 01785 257888 Fax: 01785 221591 — LMS 1961 Valencia; LAH Dub. 1968; MRCPsych 1972; DMJ Soc. Apoth. Lond. 1970; DPM Eng. 1966. (Valencia, Spain) Cons. Psychiat. Addic. Unit St. Geo. Hosp. Stafford.; Vis. Cons. Forens. Psychiat. Home Off.; Med. Vis. for the Ct. of Protec. Socs: Brit. Med. Acupunct. Soc. & Cannock Med. Soc.; Soc. Expert Witness. Prev: Sen. Regist. (Psychiat.) Mapperley Hosp. Nottm.; Psychiat. St. Brendan's Hosp. Dub.

MATHAI, Mr Joseph Thomas 28 Mandeville Way, Broomfield, Chelmsford CM1 7HN — MB BS 1978 Bombay; FRCS Glas. 1988.

*MATHAI, Mathew 45 Beverley Hills, Bangor BT20 4NB — MB BCh BAO 1997 Belf.

MATHALONE, Mr Michael Bruce Ronald 96 Harley Street, London W1N 1AF Tel: 020 7935 9555 Fax: 020 8399 5810; 2 Woodlands Road, Surbiton KT6 6PS Tel: 020 8399 5810 Fax: 020 8399 5810 — MB BChir Camb. 1958; FRCS Eng. (Ophth.) 1964; FRCS Ed. (Ophth.) 1963; MRCS Eng. LRCP Lond. 1957; FRCOphth 1989; DO Eng. 1960. (St. Mary's) Cons. Ophth. W.m. & Chelsea Hosp. & Roy. Eye Unit Kingston. Socs: Internat. & Europ. Strabismologic. Socs.; UK & Europ. Implant Soc. Prev: Sen. Regist. Guy's Hosp.; Resid. Surg. Off. Moorfields Eye Hosp. City Rd.; SHO W.. Ophth. Hosp. Lond.

MATHAMS, Mr Alan James Shrubbs Hill, Five Ashes, Mayfield TN20 6HY — MB BS 1977 Lond.; FRCS Eng. 1981; MRCS Eng. LRCP Lond. 1977; MRCGP 1986; DRCOG 1985. (Westm.) GP Mayfield. Prev: Regist. (Gen. Surg.) St. Jas. Hosp. Lond.; Regist. (Gen. Surg.) Epsom Dist. Hosp.

MATHAROO, Harpal 144 Station Road, Kings Heath, Birmingham B14 7TD Tel: 0121 680 6598 Email: h.s.matharoo@bham.ac.uk; 24 Blossom Waye, Heston, Hounslow TW5 9HD — MB ChB 1991 Manch.; FRCS (Eng.) 1996. (Manch.) Research Fell. (Urol.) Univ. Birm. Qu. Eliz. Hosp. Prev: SHO (Surg.) Russells Hall Hosp.; SHO (Urol.) Dudley Rd. Hosp.; SHO (Surg.) Dudley Rd. Hosp.

MATHARU, Gurminder Singh Dept. of Epidemiology & Public Health, University of Leicester, 22-28 Princess Road West, Leicester LE1 6TP Tel: 0116 252 5446 Email: gm56@le.ac.uk; 72 Parkland Drive, Oadby, Leicester LE2 4DG Tel: 01873 812124 Email: gmatharu66@tiscali.co.uk — MB ChB 1991 Liverp.; MRCOG. Clin. Research Fell., Dept. Of Epidemiol. & Pub. Health, Univ. of Leicester; SPR (O & G) Leic. Roy. Infirm. Socs: Med. Protec. Soc. Prev: Specialist Regist. (O & G) Lincoln Co. Hosp.; Regist. (O & G) Wycombe Hosp. High Wycombe.

MATHARU, Gurmit Singh Queen's Hospital, Burton Hospitals (NHS) Trust, Belvedere Road, Burton-on-Trent DE13 0RB Tel: 01283 66333 Fax: 01283 567579; 10 Brookside Close, Repton, Derby DE65 6FG Tel: 01283 701883 — MB ChB 1974 Birm.; BSc (Hons. Physiol.) Birm. 1971; FRCP Lond. 1994. Cons. Phys. (Responsible for Elderly) Qu.'s Hosp., Burton-on-Trent. Socs: Brit. Geriat. Soc.; Brit. Thoracic Soc. Prev: Sen. Regist. (Geriat. Med.) Dulwich Hosp. Lond. & Qu. Mary's Hosp. Sidcup; Regist. (Med.) N. Manch. Gen. Hosp.

MATHARU, Manjit Singh Flat 2, 6 Durham Road, East Finchley, London N2 9DN Tel: 020 8883 8092 — MB ChB 1994 Manch.; BSc (Pharm. & Physiol.) Manch. 1991; MRCP Lond. 1998. (Manchester Medical School) Res. Fell. Inst. Of Neurol., Lond. Prev: SHO (Neurol.) Nat. Hosp. For Neurol. & Neurosurg.; SHO (IC Med.) St. Thomas' Hosp. Lond.; SHO (Neurol. & Endocrinol.) The Middlx. Hosp. Lond.

MATHARU, Manmohan Singh, OBE Kaponda, Maypole St., Maughan's, Monmouth NP25 5QG — LRCPI & LM LRCSI & LM 1959; MFCM 1974; DPH Wales 1966; FFAEM FFPHM 1995. (RCSI) Cons. Pub. Health Med., Princip. Sch. Med. Off & Med. Advisor Social Servs. Gwent. Prev: MoH Monmouth Boro. & RD, Chepstow UD & RD & Port Med. Off. Chepstow; Asst. MoH with Special (Ment. Health) Responsibil. Newport Co. Boro.

MATHARU, Nicholas Mark Kaponda, Maypole, St Maughans, Monmouth NP25 5QG; Flat 5, 51 Fern Bank Road, Redland, Bristol BS6 6PX — MB ChB 1994 Bristol; BSc (Hons.) Bristol 1991. SHO (Surg.) Bristol Roy. Infirm. Prev: Demonst. (Anat.) Camb.; Research Assoc. Corpus Christie Coll. Camb.

MATHARU, Rupinder Singh 152 Martindale Road, Hounslow TW4 7HQ Tel: 01958 423617 Fax: 020 8572 6186 Email: rsmatharn@hotmail.com — MB BS 1996 Lond. (St. Bart. Hosp. Med. Coll.)

MATHARU, Santokh Singh 346 St Paul's Road, Smethwick, Smethwick B66 1EU — MB ChB 1976 Leeds.

MATHEN, Mr George Department of Ophthalmology, Lancaster Moor Hospital, Lancaster LA1 3JR Tel: 01524 586509 — MB BS 1969 Madras; FRCS Ed. 1995; FWACS 1990; MRCOphth 1993. (Christian Med. Coll. Vellore, India) Clin. Asst. (Ophth.) Lancaster Acute Hosps. NHS Trust.

MATHEN, Lucy Celine 8 Battledean Road, London N5 1UZ Tel: 020 7359 1315 Fax: 020 7354 1215 Email: lucymathen@adapsys.demon.co.uk — MB BS 1994 Lond.; BA (Hons.) Lond. 1973. (St Georges' Hosp. Med. Sch.) SHO (Ophth.) Lond.; SHO (Ophth.) W.ern eye Hosp. Lond. Socs: BMA & Med. Defence Union. Prev: Ho. Off. (Gen. Surg.) Homerton Hosp. & St. Bart. Hosp. Lond.; Ho. Off. (Gen. Med.) Barnet Gen. Hosp.

MATHEOU, Nikolaos Dept. of Orthalmology, Birmingham Heartlands Hospital, Bordesley Green E., Birmingham B9 5SS — MD 1994 Louvain. (Glaucoma Clin. Research Fell.), Birm. Heartlands, Solihull Hosp. & Birm. Midl. centre.

MATHER, Abdul Aziz Askew Avenue Surgery, 143A Askew Avenue, Hull HU4 6NH Tel: 01482 354251; 2 Headlands Drive, Hessle HU13 0JR Tel: 01482 640430 — MB BS 1970 Kerala. (Med. Coll. Trivandrum)

MATHER, Andrew James 102 Ack Lane W., Cheadle Hulme, Cheadle SK8 7ES — MB ChB 1965 Liverp.

MATHER, Charles Edward The Surgery, Recreation Drive, Billinge, Wigan WN5 7LY; Sandyforth Farm, Winstanley, Wigan WN5 7XZ — MB ChB 1962 Liverp. Prev: Ho. Phys. & Ho. Surg. Whiston Hosp. Prescot.

MATHER, Christopher Michael Periam Department of Anaesthetics, Cheltenham General Hospital, Sandford Road, Cheltenham GL53 7AN; South Barn, Laddingford, Maidstone ME18 6BX — MB ChB 1983 Bristol; FCAnaesth 1990. Cons. Anaesth. Cheltenham Gen. Hosp. Prev: Sen. Regist. (Anaesth.) Soton.; Acting Asst. Prof. Anaesth. Univ. Washington, Seattle, USA; Regist. Rotat. (Anaesth.) Bristol.

MATHER, Diana Charlotte 15c Woodside, London SW19 7AR — MB BS 1989 Lond.

*MATHER, Edward Peran Herbert Villa, Bosinver Lane, Polgooth, St Austell PL26 7BA — MB BCh 1998 Wales.

MATHER, Elizabeth Anne Freshfields, Llandow, Cowbridge CF71 Tel: 01656 890479; Paper Mill Farm, Paper Mill Lane, Bramford, Ipswich IP8 4DE Tel: 01473 830414 — BM 1990 Soton.; BSc (Hons.) Soton. 1989; DRCOG 1996; DFFP 1993. Trainee GP/SHO (Psychiat.) Bridgend VTS. Socs: MPS; BMA. Prev: Med. Off. RN.

MATHER, Frances Elizabeth (retired) 14 Marklands, Julian Road, Sneyd Park, Bristol BS9 1NP Tel: 0117 968 2074 — MB BS Lond. 1951; MRCS Eng. LRCP Lond. 1950. Prev: Clin. Asst. Burden Neurol. Hosp.

MATHER, Frances Mabel de Ville (retired) 25 York Road, Harrogate HG1 2QL Tel: 01423 503117 — MB ChB 1939 Manch. Prev: Ho. Surg. Manch. N.. Hosp.

MATHER, Gregory Ian 122 Dovedale Avenue, Long Eaton, Nottingham NG10 3HU — MB 1993 Lond.; BSc (Haemat. & Basic Med. Scis.) Lond. 1993, MB BS 1994. SHO Psychiat. Sheff. Community Hosps. NHS Trust Sheff. Prev: Ho. Off. (Surg.) Wexham Pk. Hosp.

MATHER, Harold Gordon (retired) 14 Marklands, Julian Road, Sneyd Park, Bristol BS9 1NP Tel: 0117 968 2074 — MB BChir Camb. 1946; MD West. Reserve, Cleveland 1945; MD Camb. 1954, MA 1946; FRCP Lond. 1965, M 1950; MRCS Eng. LRCP Lond. 1946. Cons. Phys. Bristol Clin. Area; Clin. Lect. (Med.) Univ. Bristol. Prev: Sen. Regist. (Med.), Ho. Surg. & Ho. Phys. King's Coll. Hosp. Lond.

MATHER, Hugh Maurice Ealing Hospital, Uxbridge Road, Southall UB1 3HW Tel: 020 8967 5489; 23 Amherst Avenue, London W13 8NQ Tel: 020 8997 7691 Email: hmather@onetel.net.uk — MD Camb. 1981, MB 1971, BChir 1970; FRCP Lond. 1990; MRCP (UK) 1974. (Cambridge and Westminster) Cons. Phys. Ealing Hosp. Middlx. Prev: Sen. Regist. (Gen. Med.) St. Geo. Hosp. Lond.; Med. Regist. Mayday Hosp. & St. Geo. Hosp. Lond.

MATHER, James Gabriel 400 Kilmarnock Road, Glasgow G43 2DJ Tel: 0141 649 3539 — LAH Dub.1954. (Univ. Coll. Dub.) Police Surg. City of Glas.

MATHER, James McLeod The Court Road Surgery, Court Road, Malvern WR14 3BL Tel: 01684 573161 Fax: 01684 561593; Court Road Surgery, Court Road, Malvern WR14 3BL — MB ChB 1988 Birm.; MRCGP 1992; DRCOG 1991. (Birmingham) Clin. Asst. (Dermat. & Diabetes Med.); Med. Off. Malvern Girls Coll.

MATHER, Jean Stewart 94 Cleveland Avenue, Darlington DL3 7BE Tel: 01325 252659 — MB BS 1977 Newc. Cons. (Family Plann. & Reproductive Health Care) S. Durh. Healthcare NHS Trust.

MATHER, Joan Margaret 14 Kingsley Road, St Helens WA10 6JN — MRCS Eng. LRCP Lond. 1957. GP Merseyside.

MATHER

MATHER, John Sherwood (retired) 1 Cedar Court, Upper Hall, Worcester Road, Ledbury HR8 1JA Tel: 01531 634390 — MB BChir 1960 Camb.; BA Camb. 1956, MB, 1960, BChir 1959; MRCS Eng. LRCP Lond. 1959; FFA RCS Eng. 1964. Cons. Anaesth. Qu. Eliz. Hosp. Birm.

MATHER, Joseph Forster (retired) Burrbanks, Nedderton Village, Bedlington NE22 6AS — BSc (Physics) Durham. 1939, MB BS 1951, DPH 1960.

MATHER, Judith Margaret Rochdale Infirmary, Whitehall Street, Rochdale OL12 0NB Tel: 01706 517406 — MB ChB 1984 Sheff.; FRCR 1992; T(R) (CR) 1993. Cons. Diag. Radiol. Rochdale NHS Trust. Prev: Sen. Regist. (Diag. Radiol.) Centr. Manch. Hosps.; Regist. (Diag. Radiol.) N. Staff. Hosp. Centre.

MATHER, Katherine Lucy Swithewood, Horsted Keynes, Haywards Heath RH17 7BP — MB BS 1993 Lond.; DCH 1998; DFFP 1997; DRCOG 1996. (St. Georges Hosp. Med. Sch. Lond.) GP Retainer. Socs: Brit. Med. Acupunc. Soc. Prev: GP Regist.

***MATHER, Marian Forster** 16/4 Tankerville Terrace, Newcastle upon Tyne NE2 3AH — MB BS 1997 Newc.

MATHER, Martin James Cossor The Medical Centre, Ilfracombe EX34 0JA Tel: 01271 863840 Fax: 01271 866681 — MB BS 1971 Lond. (St. Mary's) N. Devon, PCT Bd. Exec. Socs: CMF; BMA; GPIAG.

MATHER, Mary Market St Health Centre, Market St., Woolwich, London SE18 6QR Tel: 020 8855 2697 Fax: 020 8855 2689 Email: marymather@doctors.org.uk; Email: marymather@doctors.org.uk — MB ChB (Hons.) Leeds. 1972; BSc (Hons.) Physiol. Leeds 1969; FRCP 1997; FRCPCH 1997. Cons. Community Paediat. Greenwich Primary Care Trust. Socs: BMA; Roy. Coll. Paediat. & Child Health; Fac. Community Health. Prev: Clin. Chair. Community & Primary Care Greenwich Healthcare Trust; SCMO Thameslink NHS Trust; Clin. Med. Off. (Community Paediat.) Greenwich HA.

MATHER, Maud Lovett (retired) Rough Lee, 41 Beech Lane, Romiley, Stockport SK6 4AF Tel: 0161 430 5993 — MB ChB 1941 Ed.; DObst RCOG 1944. Prev: Med. Off. Family Plann. Manch. HA (T) & Derbysh. HA.

MATHER, Northage John de Ville (retired) 25 York Road, Harrogate HG1 2QL Tel: 01423 503117 — MB ChB 1937 Manch.; BA (Hons.) Oxf. 1933, MA 1939; FRCPsych 1971; DPM Eng. 1946. Prev: Lect. Foren. Psychiat. Univ. Manch.

MATHER, Rebecca Ann Lindsey Oxfordshire Mental Healthcare Trust, Department of Psychiatry of Old Age, Fulbrook Centre, Churchill Hospital, Oxford OX3 7LJ Tel: 01865 223800 Fax: 01865 223836 Email: rebeccamather@oxmhc-tr.anglox.nhs.uk; 12 Bardwell Road, Oxford OX2 6SW Tel: 01865 310280 — BM BCh 1977 Oxf.; MA Oxf. 1977; MRCPsych. 1983. Cons. Psychiat. (Old Age Psychiat.) Fulbrook Centre Ch.ill Hosp. Oxf. & Moorview Witney. Prev: Sen. Regist. (Psychiat.) Oxf. RHA; Regist. Psychiat. Oxf. RHA; Ho. Phys. Radcliffe Infirm. Oxf.

MATHER, Richard Hedley Herbert Villa, Bosinver Lane, Polgooth, St Austell PL26 7BA — BM BS 1995 Nottm.

MATHER, Richard James Swithewood, Horsted Keynes, Haywards Heath RH17 7BP — MB BChir 1952 Camb.; DObst RCOG 1958. (Lond. Hosp.) Prev: Ho. Phys. Lond. Hosp.; Obst. Ho. Surg. Bromley Hosp.; Res. Med. Off. Sydenham Childr. Hosp.

MATHER, Robert John North Oxford Medical Centre, 96 Woodstock Road, Oxford OX2 7NE Tel: 01865 311005 Fax: 01865 311257; 12 Bardwell Road, Oxford OX2 6SW Tel: 01865 310280 — BM BCh 1976 Oxf.; MA; MRCGP 1980; DRCOG 1977. Socs: Chairm. Oxon. LMC. Prev: SHO (Obst.) N.wick Pk. Hosp. Harrow; SHO (Paediat.) & Ho. Surg. & Ho. Phys. Radcliffe Infirm. Oxf.

MATHER, Mr Roy Fraser 1 West Drive, Longridge, Berwick-upon-Tweed TD15 2YW — MB ChB St. And. 1963; FRCS Ed. 1970.

MATHER, Sandra Diane Grove House Surgery, 80 Pryors Lane, Rose Green, Bognor Regis PO21 4JB Tel: 01243 265222/266413 Fax: 01243 268693; 20 Shelley Road, Bognor Regis PO21 2SN Tel: 01243 863357 Fax: 01243 865793 — MB BS Lond. 1970; MRCS Eng. LRCP Lond. 1970; MRCGP 1987; DFFP 1993; DObst RCOG 1973. (Char. Cross) GP; GP Tutor W. Sussex. Socs: BMA; RCGP; Asst. Sec. NAGPT. Prev: Cas. Off., SHO (O & G) & Ho. Off. Roy. W. Sussex Hosp.

MATHER, Stephen Howard Polkyth Surgery, 14 Carlyon Road, St Austell PL25 4EG Tel: 01726 75555 — MB ChB 1983 Birm.; MRCGP 1987; DCH RCP Lond. 1986. Prev: SHO (Gen. Med.)

BromsGr. Gen. Hosp.; SHO (Paediat. & O & G) BromsGr. Gen. Hosp.; SHO (A & E) Gen. Hosp. Birm.

MATHER, Stephen James Department of Anaesthesia, Bristol Royal Infirmary, Bristol BS2 8HW Tel: 0117 928 2163 Fax: 0117 928 2098 Email: stephen.mather@ubht.swest.nhs.uk — MB BS 1974 Lond.; MRCS Eng. LRCP Lond. 1974; FRCA Eng. 1979; DRCOG 1976. (Lond. Hosp.) Cons. (Anaesth.) Bristol Roy. Infirm.; Hon. Clin. Lect.. Univ. Bristol; Examr. Roy. Coll. of Anaesth.s; Chairm. Managem. Bd. of BristolMed. Simulation Centre. Socs: Treas. Europ. Soc. for Simulation in Applied Med.; Counc. Mem. Brit. Ophth. Anaesth. Soc. Prev: Sen. Regist. (Anaesth.) Sheff. AHA (T); Regist. (Anaesth.) Bristol United Hosps.; Hon. Tutor Univ. Sheff.

MATHER, Stephen Peter The Laurels, Norton Lindsey, Warwick CV35 8JA; Warwick Hospital, Lakin Road, Warwick CV34 5BW Tel: 01926 495321 — MB ChB 1977 Dundee; FFA RCS Eng. 1982. Cons. Anaesth. S. Warks. DHA. Socs: Assn. Anaesth.; Intract. Pain Soc. Prev: Sen. Regist. (Anaesth.) Yorks. RHA.

MATHERS, Alan Moncreiffe Princess Royal Maternity, Glasgow Royal Infirmary, 16 Alexandra Parade, Glasgow G31 2ERNA Tel: 0141 211 5218 Fax: 0141 211 5200 Email: alan.mathers@northglasgow.nhs.scot.uk — MB ChB 1979 Glas.; MRCOG 1986. Cons. (O & G), Hon. Sen. Lect. Glas. Roy. Infirm. Univ. NHS Trust; Clin. Dir. Gyn. & Perinat. Socs: Glas. Obst. & Gyn. Soc.; Brit. Med. Ultrasound Soc. Prev: Cons. O & G Vict. Infirm. NHS Trust, Glas.; Sen. Regist. Glas. Teachg. Hosp.

MATHERS, Angela Central Street Health Centre, Central Street, Countesthorpe, Leicester LE8 5QJ Tel: 0116 277 6336 — MB BS 1985 Lond.; DRCOG 1992; DCH RCP Lond. 1990; AKC 1985. Prev: Regist. (Paediat.) Bolton Gen. Hosp.; SHO Med. Profess. Unit Hosp. Sick. Childr. Gt. Ormond St. Lond.

MATHERS, Carola Birgit Barbro Sutton Hospital, Chiltern Wing, Cotswold Road, Sutton SM2 5NF Tel: 020 8296 4182 Fax: 020 8296 3957 Email: cmathers@swlstg-tr.nhs.uk — MB BS 1980 Lond.; BSc Lond. 1977; MRCPsych 1984. (Roy. Free Hosp. Lond.) p/t Cons. Psychother. Sutton Hosp.; Private Pract. Psychoanal./Psychother. Socs: Coll. Tutor, Roy. Coll. of Psychiat.s. Prev: Sen. Regist. (Psychother.) St. Geo. Hosp. Lond.; Regist. Rotat. (Psychiat.) Maudsley Hosp. Lond.

MATHERS, Dale 63 Briarwood Road, Clapham, London SW4 9PJ Tel: 020 7720 5681 Email: dalemathers@compuserve.com — MB BS 1982 Lond.; BSc Lond. 1979; MRCPsych 1986. Indep. Pract. Jungian Analyst Lond. Prev: Psychiat. Adviser Studs. Lond. Sch. Economics; Sen. Regist. (Psychiat.) St. Geo. Hosp. Lond.

MATHERS, George Crosthwaite Longcroft, Taynton, Gloucester GL19 3AR Tel: 01482 79282 — MB BS 1948 Lond.; MB BS (Hnrs. Med. Obst. & Gyn.) Lond. 1948; MRCS Eng. LRCP Lond. 1948; AFOM RCP Lond. 1980; DObst RCOG 1949. (Univ. Coll. Hosp.) Sen. Police Surg. N. Glos.; Med. Adviser Dowty PLC. Prev: Assoc. Specialist (ENT) Gloucester Roy. Hosp.; Specialist (Obst.) RN Malta; Ho. Surg. (Obst.) Univ. Coll. Hosp.

MATHERS, Jay Dale (retired) Tidewells, 15 Harold Avenue, Westgate-on-Sea CT8 8QU Tel: 01843 31231 — MB BCh BAO 1954 Belf.

***MATHERS, Jo-Anne Edwina Mary** 4 Coverley Garth, Yeadon, Leeds LS19 7WD — MB ChB 1997 Leeds.

***MATHERS, Marie Elaine** Tarool, Bowling Green Lane, Cupar KY15 4HD — MB ChB 1995 Aberd.

MATHERS, N J Bluebell Medical Centre, 356 Bluebell Road, Sheffield S5 6BS Tel: 0114 242 1406 Fax: 0114 261 8074.

MATHERS, Patricia Mary Antoinette 186 School Road, Sheffield S10 1GL — MB ChB 1992 Sheff.

MATHERS, Richard George The Surgery, 2 Crescent Bakery, St. Georges Place, Cheltenham GL50 3PN Tel: 01242 226336 Fax: 01242 253587; 135 Hales Road, Cheltenham GL52 6ST Fax: 01242 254979 — MRCS Eng. LRCP Lond. 1975; DRCOG 1982; DA Eng. 1979.

MATHERS, Ruth Penlon (retired) Sandgate House, The Esplanade, Sandgate, Folkestone CT20 3DX Tel: 01303 243313 — MB BS 1938 Lond.; MRCS Eng. LRCP Lond. 1938. Prev: Sen. Med. Off. Kensington, Chelsea & W.m. AHA (T).

MATHERS, Stephen Bruce Ian Charles Cottage Hospital, The Health Centre, Castle Road East, Grantown-on-Spey PH26 3HR Tel: 01479 872484 Fax: 01479 873503; Ar-Dachaidh, Woodside Avenue, Grantown-on-Spey PH26 3JR Tel: 01479 873316 — MB

MATHEW

ChB 1982 Aberd.; MRCGP 1989; DFFP 1994; DRCOG 1985. Socs: Assoc. Brit. Med. Acupunc. Soc.; Brit. Soc. Med. & Dent. Hypn.

MATHESON, Agnes Marjory Holtby House, Holtby, York YO19 5UD Tel: 01904 489250 — MRCS Eng. LRCP Lond. 1945. (Lond. Sch. Med. Wom.) Socs: Med. Wom. Federat. & York Med. Soc. Prev: Phys. (Occupat. Health) York Health Dist.; Med. Off. Rowntree Mackintosh Ltd. York.

MATHESON, Alan Christopher Walter Accident & Emergency Department, Wexham Park Hospital, Slough SL2 4HL Tel: 01753 634012 Fax: 01753 633902 — MB BS 1969 Lond.; FRCP 1999; FAEM; MSc (Nuclear Med.) Lond. 1982; MRCP (UK) 1977; MRCS Eng. LRCP Lond. 1968. (Guy's) Clin. Director, Accid. & Emerg. Healthewood & Wrexham Pk. Hosp.s NHS Trust, Slough & Berks.; Regional Adviser in Accid. & Emerg. Med., Oxf. Deanery. Socs: Brit. Assn. Accid. & Emerg. Med.; Fac. of Accid. & Emerg. Med.

MATHESON, Alan John Netherton, The Elms, Plymouth PL3 4BR — MB ChB 1934 Bristol; DPM Eng. 1939. (Bristol)

MATHESON, Mr Alasdair Burnett, OBE 27 Deeside Crescent, Aberdeen AB15 7PT Tel: 01224 321174; Accident and Emergency Department, Aberdeen Royal Infirmary, Foresterhill, Aberdeen AB25 2ZB Tel: 01224 681818 — MB ChB 1964 Aberd.; FRCS Ed. 1972; FFAEM 1993. (Aberd.) Cons. (A & E Care) Aberd. Roy. Infirm. Prev: Sen. Regist. (A & E) Aberd. Roy. Infirm.; Regist. (Surg.) Cumbld. Infirm. Carlisle; Demonst. (Physiol.) Univ. Newc.

MATHESON, Anne Rivermead, 4 Kemplay Foot, Eamont Bridge, Penrith CA10 2BD — MB BS 1979 Newc.; DRCOG 1997.

MATHESON, Desmond John Chainsbridge Medical Partnership, Chainbridge House, The Precinct, Blaydon-on-Tyne NE21 5BT Tel: 0191 414 2856 Fax: 0191 499 0449; 17 Brandling Park, Jesmond, Newcastle upon Tyne NE2 4RR Tel: 0191 281 3676 — MB BS 1978 Newc.; BSc Newc. 1973; DRCOG 1980. (Newca.)

MATHESON, Mr Duncan Mackenzie Macclesfield D.G.H, Victoria Road, Macclesfield SK10 3BL Tel: 01625 661310; Church View Cottage, Pott Shrigley, Macclesfield SK10 5SA Tel: 01625 574983 — BM BCh 1970 Oxf.; FRCS Eng. 1975. (Oxford) Cons. Surg. Macclesfield HA. Socs: BASO; Assn. Surg.; Vasc. Surg. Soc. Prev: Sen. Regist. (Surg.) Birm. AHA; Regist. (Surg.) Selly Oak Hosp. Birm. & United Birm. Hosps.

MATHESON, George Henry 56 Inverleith Row, Edinburgh EH3 5PX Tel: 0131 552 3870 — MB ChB 1949 Ed. (Ed.) Med. Ref. DHSS; Med. Off. Fettes Coll. Prev: Ho. Surg. St. Luke's Hosp. Bradford; Ho. Phys. Roy. Halifax Infirm.; Obst. Ho. Surg. Halifax Gen. Hosp.

MATHESON, Helen Anne Christine (retired) — MB ChB 1962 Glas.; FFA RCS Eng. 1973. Hon. Med. Off. Dog Shows: Crufts, Kelso, Exeter. Prev: Cons. (Anaesth.) Vict. Hosp. Blackpool.

MATHESON, Iain Charles Cope 42 Wellington Street, Millom LA18 4DE Tel: 01229 772123 — MB BS 1965 Lond.; MRCS Eng. LRCP Lond. 1965; DObst RCOG 1967. (St. Bart.) Socs: BMA. Prev: Ho. Off. (Obst.) Rochford Hosp.; SHO Accid. Serv. Luton & Dunstable Hosp.; Regist. (Med.) Friarage Hosp. N.allerton.

MATHESON, Iain Urquhart Old Bank House, Bank St., Cromarty IV11 8YE — MB ChB 1986 Aberd.

MATHESON, Ian Donald c/o 89 Fallowfield, Wellingborough NN9 5YY — MB BS 1974 Lond.

MATHESON, John Alexander (retired) 43 Millersneuk Avenue, Lenzie, Kirkintilloch, Glasgow G66 5HU — MB ChB 1970 Ed.; MRCGP 1980.

MATHESON, John Gunn (retired) 32 Newlands Road, Newcastle upon Tyne NE2 3NT Tel: 0191 284 4504 — MB ChB 1941 Aberd.; FFA RCS Eng. 1954; DA Eng. 1947. Cons. Anaesth. Newc. Gen. Hosp. & Hosp. Sick Childr. Prev: Cons. Anaesth. Shotley Bridge Hosp.

MATHESON, John Kenneth — MB ChB 1995 Aberd.; MRCGP 2000; DRCOG 1997; DFFP 1997.

MATHESON, Mr John Mackenzie, OBE, TD, Maj.-Gen. late RAMC Retd. (retired) 2 Orchard Brae, Edinburgh EH4 1NY Tel: 0131 332 1424 — MB ChB Ed. 1936; MD Ed. 1945; FRCP Ed. 1972, M 1939; FRCS Eng. 1962; FRCS Ed. 1946. Prev: Postgrad. Dean Fac. Med. Univ. Edin.

MATHESON, Kwee Hoon West Suffolk Hospital, Hardwick Lane, Bury St Edmunds IP33 2QZ Tel: 01284 713000 Fax: 01284 713100 — MB BS Melbourne 1967; LMCC 1970; FFA RCS Eng. 1972.

Cons. (Anaesth.) W. Suff. Hosp. Bury St. Edmunds. Prev: Sen. Regist. (Anaesth.) Lond. Hosp.

MATHESON, Lillian Mary Edinburgh Cancer Centre, Western General Hospital, Crewe Road, Edinburgh EH4 2XU Fax: 0131 537 1029 — MB ChB 1978 Glas.; FRCP 1991 Glas.; FRCR 1989; DMRT 1985; BSc (Hons.) Glas. 1976; MRCP (UK) 1981. (Glasgow Univ.) Cons. Clin. Oncologist, W.. Gen. Hosp. Edin. Socs: BMA; SRS; ECCO. Prev: Sen. Regist. Mt. Vernon Hosp. Lond.; Regist., Stobhill Hosp. Glas.

MATHESON, Lindsey Anne Cambridge Pharma Consultancy Ltd., 1 Quayside, Bridge St., Cambridge CB5 8AB — MB BS 1979 Lond.; MRCP (UK) 1983. Dir. Camb. Pharma Consult.

MATHESON, Margery (retired) 56 Inverleith Row, Edinburgh EH3 5PX — MB ChB 1949 Ed. Prev: GP Edin.

MATHESON, Mhairi Lindsay (retired) 9 Harris Road, Inverness IV2 3LS — MB ChB 1957 Aberd. Prev: GP Pk. St. Surg. Falkirk.

MATHESON, Mr Norman Alistair, MBE (retired) Head of Wood, Milltimber AB13 0HX Tel: 01224 868515 — MB ChB Aberd. 1956; ChM Aberd. 1965; FRCS Eng. 1961; FRCS Ed. 1961. Prev: Cons. Surg. Grampian HB.

MATHESON, Norman Ross (retired) 7 Newlyn Road, Meols, Wirral CH47 7AR — M.B., Ch.B. Bristol 1937, CPH 1946.

MATHESON, Pamela North Court, Chilham, Canterbury CT4 8AU Tel: 01227 730307 — MB BS Lond. 1954. (St. Bart.) Prev: Clin. Asst. Kent & Canterbury Hosp.; Ho. Surg. & Ho. Phys. Fulham. Hosp.

MATHESON, Philip James 16 Farrant Ave, London N22 6PB — MB ChB 1991 Otago.

MATHESON, Roderick Macrae Adelaide Medical Centre, 36 Adelaide Road, Andover SP10 1HA Tel: 01264 351144 Fax: 01264 358639 — BM BCh 1972 Oxf.; MRCGP 1978; DRCOG 1977; DA Eng. 1975.

MATHESON, Mr Thomas Swan, VRD (retired) Holtby House, Holtby, York YO19 5UD Tel: 01904 489250 — MB ChB 1943 Ed.; FRCS Eng. 1982; FRCS Ed. 1948. Prev: Cons. Surg. Ilkley & Otley Hosp. Gp. & York Hosp. Gp.

MATHESON, William Murchison (retired) 31 Netherblane, Blanefield, Glasgow G63 9JW Tel: 01360 771132 — MB ChB 1959 Glas.; DObst RCOG 1962. Vis. Med. Off. Jordanhill Campus Univ. Strathclyde.

MATHEW, Anna Dept. of Paediatrics, Worthing Hospital, Worthing BN11 2DH Tel: 01903 205111; 56 Arlington Avenue, Goring-by-Sea, Worthing BN12 4SR — MB BS Lagos 1982; MRCP (UK) 1992; DCH RCPS Glas. 1987. Cons. (Paed) Worthing Hosp, Worthing.

MATHEW, Mr Bruce Gordon Eastfield House, 44 Beverley Road, South Cave, Brough HU15 2AU Tel: 01430 422304 Fax: 01482 674636 — MB ChB 1979 Cape Town; ChM Bristol 1994; FRCS (SN) Ed. 1989; FRCS Ed. 1985. Cons. Neurosurg. Hull Roy. Infirm. Prev: Sen. Regist. (Neurosurg.) Roy. Vict. Hosp. Belf.

MATHEW, Elamma Kaleeckal, 14 Coppice Close, Wakefield WF1 4TA — MB BS 1976 Calicut.

MATHEW, George Community Unit, 305 Ware Road, Hailey, Hertford SG13 7PG Tel: 01992 444411; 58 Lancaster Road, St Albans AL1 4ET Tel: 01727 838472 — MB BS 1973 Bangalor; MB BS Bangalore 1973; MRCPsych 1985; DPM Eng. 1982. Cons. Psychiat. E. and N. Herts. NHS Trust. Prev: Sen. Regist. Cell Barnes Hosp. St. Albans.

MATHEW, Mr George 86 Sheaveshill Avenue, London NW9 6RX — MB BS 1975 Kerala, India; FRCS Glas. 1981.

MATHEW, Gizzy 21 Kiltongue Cottages, Monkscourt Avenue, Airdrie ML6 0JS — MB BS 1988 Madras.

MATHEW, Halley 14 Coppice Close, Pinders Heath, Wakefield WF1 4TA Tel: 01924 364627 — MB BS 1975 Kerala; MRCPsych 1981; DPM Leeds 1980. (Med. Coll. Trivandrum) Cons. Psychiat. Dewsbury Health Care. Socs: BMA & Soc. Clin. Psychiat. Prev: Sen. Regist. Tone Vale Hosp. Taunton; Regist. (Psychiat.) Naburn Hosp. York; Regist. (Psychiat.) High Royds Hosp. Menston.

MATHEW, Joseph Department of Histopathology, Royal Cornwall Hospital, Treliske, Truro TR1 3LT Tel: 01872 252550 Email: liver12@hotmail.com — MB BS 1981 Lagos; FMCPath 1988 Nigeria; MRCPath 1993 UK; Cert. TLHE 1997 UK. (College of Medicine University of Lagos Nigeria) Cons. in Histopath., Treliske, Cornw. Socs: Brit. Assn. for the Study of the Liver; Brit. Div., Internat. Acad. of Path.; Assn. Clin. Path. Prev: Lect. in Histopath.,

MATHEW

Univ. of Newc. upon Tyne, UK; Sen. Regist. in Histopath., Roy. Vict. Infimary, Newc. upon Tyne; Regist. in Histopath., Roy. Vict. Infirm., Newc. upon Tyne.

MATHEW, Malcolm Cecil Felton 126A Amyand Park Road, St. Margarets, Twickenham TW1 3HP — MB BS 1986 Lond.

MATHEW, Nirmala George 86 Sheaveshill Ave, Colindale, London NW9 6RX — MRCS Eng. LRCP Lond. 1978.

MATHEW, Mr Peter 17A Roseangue, Dundee DD1 4LP — BM BS 1983 Nottm.; FRCS Eng. 1988; FRCS (SN) 1995; DTM & H 1999. Cons. (Neurosurg.) Internat. Comm. of the Red Cross; Sen. Clin. Teach. Dundee Teachg. Hosps.; Neurosurg. Air Transportable Surgic. Squadron RAF Lenchars Fife. Socs: Soc. Brit. Neurol. Surg.

MATHEW, Pulickal Mathai Daisy Hill Hospital, Newry BT35 8DR — MB BS 1964 Calcutta.

MATHEW, Rowena Taliesin Surgery, Taliesin, Lampeter SA48 7AA Tel: 01570 422665 Fax: 01570 423810; Troedybryn, Ffarmers, Llanwrda, Llandeilo SA19 8JG — MB BS 1973 Lond.; DCH Eng. 1976; DRCOG 1978. (St. Bart.)

MATHEW, Shaji A-1 Musgrave House, Royal Bolton Hospital, Minerva Road, Farnworth, Bolton BL4 0JR — MB BS 1982 Bangalore.

MATHEW, Sindhu Harperbury Hospital, Harper Lane, Radlett WD7 7HU Tel: 01923 854861; 58 Lancaster Road, St Albans AL1 4ET Tel: 01727 838472 — MB BS 1974 Kerala. Clin. Asst. Harperbury Hosp. Radlett.

MATHEW, Thazathedathu Koshy Willowbrook Medical Practice, Brook Street, Sutton-in-Ashfield NG17 1ES Tel: 01623 440018; 8 Twin-Oaks Drive, Sutton-in-Ashfield NG17 1FN — MB BS 1962 Madras. Prev: Regist. (Gen. Med. & Chest Unit) W. Middlx. Hosp. Isleworth.

MATHEW, Professor Vallakalil Mathew Thames Gateway NHS Trust, Stone House, Cotton Lane, Dartford DA2 6PD Tel: 01322 622222 Fax: 01322 622110 Email: bmheb@aol.com; 2 The Coppice, Bexley DA5 2EA Tel: 01322 553310 Fax: 01322 553310 — MB BS 1978 Kerala; MPhil Lond. 1991; MRCPsych 1990; DTM & H Liverp. 1981; DPM Eng. 1988. Cons. Psychiat. & Sen. Lect. Thames Gateway NHS Trust; Hon. Vis. Prof. MG Univ., Kerala, India; Mem. (Gen. Psychiat. Represen.) Health Adviser GP Chem. Contamination Accid.s. Socs: Roy. Coll. Psychiat. (Exec. Comm. Specialist Sector Gen. Psychiat.). Prev: Hon. Vis. Prof. MG Univ. Kerala, India; Regist. (Psychiat.) & Staff Regist. Stone Hse. Hosp.; Hon. Regist. (Psychiat.) Char. Cross Hosp. Lond.

MATHEW, Verghese 66 St Isan Road, Heath, Cardiff CF14 4LY Tel: 029 2069 4326; 16 Kenneth Avenue, Ilford IG1 2ED — MB BS 1981 Delhi; MRCPI 1994.

MATHEWS, Brian Hugh (retired) Rose Cottage, Wellhouse Lane, Betchworth RH3 7HH Tel: 01737 845213 Fax: 01737 845213 — MB BS 1978 Lond.; Dip. Med. Educat. 1995; MM Ed. 1998 Dundee. Lect. St. Geo.'s Hosp. Med. Sch.; Med. Adviser Hospice Home Care Dorking. Prev: Research Fell. S. Thames W. Region.

MATHEWS, Carol Jane North Lodge, Akeley Wood, Buckingham MK18 5BN Tel: 01280 822457 — BM 1985 Soton.; MRCGP 1989; DRCOG 1989; DCH RCP Lond. 1987. (Soton.)

MATHEWS, Catherine Jane 6 Longwood Drive, London SW15 5DL — BChir 1995 Camb.; MB Camb. (Cambridge) SHO Rotat. (Med.) Birm. Heartlands Hosp.

MATHEWS, Cleeve Amherst Cornerways Medical Centre, Parkers Close, Gorley Road, Poulner, Ringwood BH24 1SD Tel: 01425 476688 Fax: 01425 470030 — MB ChB 1964 Bristol; DCH Eng. 1966; DObst RCOG 1969. (Bristol)

MATHEWS, Mr Clittus John 6 Mandeville Road, Hertford SG13 8JG — MB BS 1983 Kerala; FRCS Ed. 1990; FRCSI 1990. Regist. (Gen. Surg.) Lister Hosp. Stevenage.

MATHEWS, Colin Wallace McConnell, Carson and Mathews, The Health Centre, Tavanagh Avenue, Portadown, Craigavon BT62 3BU Tel: 028 3835 1145 Fax: 028 3839 2628; Email: c.mathews@btinternet.com — MB BCh BAO Belf. 1979; MRCGP 1983; Dip. GU Med. Soc. Apoth. Lond. 1990; DRCOG 1982. Hosp. Pract. (Genitourin. Med.) Clinics Roy. Vict. Hosp. Belf. & Daisy Hill Hosp Newry; GP Tutor, S. Bd. N. I. Socs: Fell. Ulster Med. Soc.; Soc. Study Sexuality Transm. Dis. in Irel; Soc. Advancem. of Sexual Health.

MATHEWS, Mr Dudley Dayre (retired) 120 Minster Road, Minster-on-Sea, Sheerness ME12 3JH Tel: 01795 872663 — MB BS 1959 Lond.; MD Lond. 1980; FRCS Ed. 1965; FRCOG 1978, M 1964; MRCS Eng. LRCP Lond. 1959. Cons. O & G Medway Health Dist. Prev: Lect. Inst. O & G Lond.

MATHEWS, Edward Terence 54 Selly Wick Road, Selly Park, Birmingham B29 7JB Tel: 0121 472 2904 — MB ChB 1949 Birm.; MRCS Eng. LRCP Lond. 1949; FFA RCS Eng. 1954. (Birm.) Cons. Anaesth. United Birm. Hosps.; Clin. Lect. Anaesth. Univ. Birm. Prev: Sen. Anaesth. Regist. Qu. Eliz. Hosp. Birm.; Anaesth. Regist. Warneford Hosp. Leamington Spa; Ho. Surg. Gen. Hosp. Birm.

MATHEWS, Elizabeth Diana The Laurels Surgery, 73 Church Street, Flint CH6 5AF Tel: 01352 732349 Fax: 01352 730678; Moel View, Ruthin Road, Gwernymynydd, Mold CH7 5LQ — MB ChB 1978 Liverp.; MRCGP 1987; DRCOG 1980.

MATHEWS, Hilary Mary Linton Mater Hospital, Crumlin Road, Belfast BT14 6AB Tel: 01232 741211 Email: hmlmatthews@doctors.org.uk; Silverdale, 17 My Lady's Mile, Holywood BT18 9EW Tel: 01232 425525 — MB ChB 1977 Bristol; FFA RCS Eng. 1983; DCH Eng. 1980; DRCOG 1979. (Bristol) Cons. Anaesth. Mater Hosp. Belf. Job Share; Postgrad. Tutor Mater Hosp. Belf.; Hon. Clin. Lect. in Anaesthetics Qu.s Univeristy Belf. Socs: Assn. Anaesth.; N. Irel. Soc. Anaesth.; Assn. Obst. Anaesth. Prev: Sen. Regist. Ulster Hosp.; Research Fell.sh. Qu. Univ. Belf.

MATHEWS, James Kenneth Tel: 01603 408275 Fax: 01603 401389; 54 Taverham Road, Drayton, Norwich NR8 6RY Tel: 01603 861254 — MB BCh BAO 1978 Belf.; DRCOG 1983. (Queen's University Belfast)

MATHEWS, James Wallace Maymount, 7 Killycomain Road, Portadown, Craigavon BT63 5BT Tel: 01762 2303 — MB BCh BAO 1942 Belf. (Qu. Univ. Belf.) Prev: Res. Surg. Off. Ards Dist. Hosp.; RNVR.

MATHEWS, John Alan Department of Rheumatology, St. Thomas' Hospital, London SE1 7EH Tel: 020 7928 9292 ext 2171 Fax: 020 7922 8362; 67 Walpole House, 126 Westminster Bridge Road, London SE1 7UN Tel: 020 7401 8187 — MB BChir 1957 Camb.; MA Camb. 1958, MD 1985; FRCP Lond. 1979, M 1966; MRCP Ed. 1965; MRCS Eng. LRCP Lond. 1957; DObst RCOG 1960; MB 1958. (Camb. & Guy's) Emeritis & Hon.Cons. Phys. (Rheum.) St. Thos. Hosp. Lond. Socs: Fell. Roy. Soc. Med. (Ex-Pres. Sect. Rheum. & Rehabil.); Brit. Soc. Rheum.; Amer. Coll. Rheum. Prev: Sen. Regist. (Physical Med.) St. Thos. Hosp. Lond.; Regist. (Physical Med. & Rheum.) Lond. Hosp.; Regist. (Med.) St. Peter's Hosp. Chertsey.

MATHEWS, Mathews 1 East Close, Pontefract WF8 3NS — LMSSA 1976 Lond.

MATHEWS, Robert Henry (retired) 1 Cavendish Avenue, Sheffield S17 3NJ Tel: 0114 236 2915 — MB ChB 1956 Sheff.; DObst RCOG 1957.

MATHEWS, Stuart Robin Verney Close Family Practice, Verney Close, Buckingham MK18 1JP Tel: 01280 822777 Fax: 01280 823541; North Lodge, Akeley Wood, Buckingham MK18 5BN Tel: 01280 822457 — MB ChB 1980 Cape Town; MRCGP 1987; DRCOG 1986; DCH S. Afr. 1984.

MATHEWS, Thomas Bourn Hall Clinic, Bourn, Cambridge CB3 7TR Tel: 01954 717235 Fax: 01954 717259 Email: tmatthews@talk21.com; 20 Granta Close, Witchford, Ely CB6 2HR Tel: 01353 667135 — MB BS 1971 Madras; MD Panjab 1975; FRCOG 1997, M 1985; DGO Panjab 1974. (Christian Med. Coll. Vellore) Head of Med. Func., Assisted Conception Unit, Bourn Hall Clinic. Socs: Brit. Fertil. Soc. & Brit. Androl. Soc.; Eur. Soc. Human Reproduc. & Embryology. Prev: Dep. Med. Director Fertil. Servs. Unit The Pk. Hosp. Nottm.; Cons. & Sen. Regist. (Invitro Fertilization) Bourn Hall Clinic; Regist. (Obst. & Gyn.) Roy. Infirm. Stirling.

MATHEWS, Walter Graham (retired) Town End House, Kirkby Lonsdale, Carnforth LA6 2AE Tel: 015242 71520 — MB ChB 1955 St. And. Prev: GP Kirkby Lonsdale.

MATHEWS, Mr William (retired) 15 Charnwood Park, Coleraine BT52 1JZ Tel: 01265 42517 — MB BCh BAO 1940 Belf.; FRCS Ed. 1949. Cons. ENT Surg. Coleraine & N. Antrim Hosp. Gps. Prev: Maj. RAMC.

MATHEWSON, Alexander MacKechnie (retired) Davaar, Grange Road, Earlsferry, Elie, Leven KY9 1AL Tel: 01333 330428 — MB ChB Glas. 1947; MRCGP 1964. DL. Prev: Chairm. BMA (Lanarksh. Div.).

MATHEWSON, Ian Byrne The Health Centre, 68 Pipeland Road, St Andrews KY16 8JZ Tel: 01334 476840 Fax: 01334 466516;

Feddinch Brae Cottage, St Andrews KY16 8NR Fax: 01334 466516 — MB ChB 1977 Manch.; BSc St And. 1974; MRCGP 1981; DRCOG 1980. (St Andrews and Manchester) Community Hosp. Adviser, N. E. Fife, LHCC; Hon. Lect. (Med. Scis.) Univ. St Andrews; Specialist Practitioner, Palliat. Care, St Andrews Memor. Hosp.

MATHEWSON, James Samuel Young (retired) 3 Morningside, Ballynahinch Road, Lisburn BT27 5PY — MB BCh BAO Belf. 1952; DObst RCOG 1954.

MATHEWSON, Kerry George Main Street Surgery, 171 Main Street, Callander FK17 8BJ Tel: 01877 331000 Fax: 01877 330864; West Cottage, Leny Road, Callender FK17 8AL Tel: 01877 331674 — MB ChB 1988 Ed.; MRCGP 1996; DRCOG 1993. (University of Edinburgh) Sen. Princip. Gen. Practitioner, Gen. Pract., Drs Mathewson and Gibson, Callander, Perthshire; Clin. Asst., Cardiol., Stirling Roy. Infirm., Stirling. Socs: BMA; RCGP. Prev: SHO (Psychiat.) Roy. Edin. Hosp.; SHO (Paediatric A&E and Surg.) Roy. Hosp. for Sick Childr. Glas.; SHO (Infec. Dis.) City Hosp. Edin.

MATHEWSON, Robert Charles Lavens High Lane Medical Centre, The Village Green, Buxton Rd, Stockport SK6 8DR Tel: 01663 762222 Fax: 01663 766566 Email: hlmc@mail.com; The Square House, 19 Stoneheads, Whaley Bridge, High Peak SK23 7BB — MB ChB 1977 Manch.; MRCGP 1985; DRCOG 1984.

MATHEWSON, William Bisset The Medical & Dental Defence Union of Scotland, 120 Blythwood St., Glasgow G2 4EA Tel: 0141 221 5858 Fax: 0141 228 1208 Email: wbm@mddus.com; 4 Kinnaird Avenue, Newton Mearns, Glasgow G77 5EL Tel: 0141 639 3262 Fax: 0141 639 3262 — MB ChB Ed. 1965; MPhil Glas. 1992; MRCGP 1974; Dip. Forens. Med. Glas. 1989; DGM RCP Lond. 1986; FRCP Ed 1998; FRCGP 1998. Dep. Chief Exec. & Dir. of Med. Servs. The Med. & Dent. Defence Union of Scotl. Socs: BMA. Prev: GP Scotl.; Surg. Specialist RAF Med. Br.; Hosp. Pract. (Geriat. Med.) City Hosp. Edin.

MATHEWSON, Zelda Martha Balnagar, Tealing, Dundee DD4 0QZ Tel: 0182 621463 — MB BCh BAO 1977 Belf.; MD (Hons.) Belf. 1985; MFPHM 1989; MFCM 1988. (Belf.) Cons. Pub. Health Med. Tayside HB. Socs: BMA & Ulster Med. Soc.

MATHIALAHAN, Thiriloganathan 3 Hawthorne Gardens, Adel Meadows, Leeds LS16 7TP Email: t.mathialahan@btopenworld.com — MB ChB 1992 Birm.; MRCP (UK) 1996. (Univ. Birm.)

MATHIAS, Professor Christopher Joseph Neurovascular Medicine Unit (Pickering Unit), Div. of Neurosci. & Psycho. Med., Imperial Coll. Sch of Med., at St Mary's Hospital, Praed St., London W2 1NY Tel: 020 7886 1468 Fax: 020 7886 1540 Email: c.mathias@ic.ac.uk; Meadowcroft, West End Lane, Stoke Poges, Slough SL2 4NE Fax: 01753 645566 — MB BS 1972 Bangalore; 2001 (Fmed Sci); DSc Lond. 1995; DPhil Oxf. 1976; FRCP Lond. 1987; MRCP (UK) 1978; LRCP LRCS Ed. LRCPS Glas. 1974. (St. John's Med. Coll. Bangalore) Prof. Neurovasc. Med. & Cons. Phys. St. Mary's Hosp., Imperial Coll. Sc. Technol. Med. Lond. & Autonomic Unit Nat. Hosp. Neurol. & Neurosurg., Inst. Neurol. Univ.Coll.Lond; Dir. Autonomic Unit Univ. Dept. Clin. Neurol. Inst. Neurol. Nat. Hosp. Neurol & Neurosurg Lond & Dir. Pickering Unit (Neuro Vasc. Med. Unit) St Mary's Hosp. Lond. Socs: Physiol. Soc.; Assn. Phys.; Assn. Brit. Neurols. Prev: Wellcome Trust Sen. Lect. (Med.) & Cons. Phys. St. Mary's Hosp. Med. Sch. & Univ. Dept. Clin. Neurol., Inst. Neurol, Nat. Hosp. Lond.; Wellcome Trust Sen. Clin. Research Fell., Hon. Sen. Regist. & Lect. (Med.) St. Mary's Hosp. Med. Sch. Lond.; Rhodes Schol. Research Off. & Hon. Regist. (Neurol.) Ch.ill Hosp. & Univ. Oxf.

MATHIAS, Mr David Bentley (retired) Gatehouse, Ninebanks, Hexham NE47 8HJ Tel: 01434 345206 Email: mathias@gatehouse.demon.co.uk — MB BS Lond. 1966; FRCS Eng. 1971; MRCS Eng. LRCP Lond. 1966. Prev: Sen. Regist. (ENT) Guy's Hosp. Lond.

MATHIAS, David Henry (retired) Fairways, Chase Ct., Quebec Road, Dereham NR19 2DE Tel: 01362 693260 — MB BChir 1954 Camb.; MRCS Eng. LRCP Lond. 1954; DObst RCOG 1956; MRCGP 1965. JP. Prev: Ho. Phys. Addenbrooke's Hosp. Camb.

***MATHIAS, Helen Claire** Glen View, 3 Lilac Close, Milford Haven SA73 1DF — MB BS 1998 Lond.; MB BS Lond 1998.

MATHIAS, Isobel Margaret Jean (retired) Gatehouse, Ninebanks, Hexham NE47 8HJ — MB BS Lond. 1966; MRCS Eng. LRCP Lond. 1966; FFA RCS Eng. 1973; DA Eng. 1968. Cons. (Anaesth.) Gateshead AHA. Prev: Sen. Regist. (Anaesth.) Guy's Hosp. Lond.

MATHIAS, Mr Jawahar Charles 60 Russell House, Cambridge St., Pimlico, London SW1V 4EQ Tel: 020 7821 0087 — MB BS 1985 Bangalor; MB BS Bangalore 1985; FRCS Ed. 1992; FRCS Glas. 1992.

MATHIAS, John Alexander (retired) 87 Willfield Way, London NW11 6YH Tel: 020 8455 7334 Email: j.matthias@ntlworld.com — MB BS 1959 Lond.; FFA RCS Eng. 1966. Prev: Cons. Anaesth. & Sen. Regist. St. Thos. Hosp. Lond.

MATHIAS, Richard Douglas St. James Surgery, 89 Wash Lane, Clacton-on-Sea CO15 1DA Tel: 01255 222121; 2 Third Avenue, Clacton-on-Sea CO15 5AP Tel: 01255 434090 — MB ChB 1958 St. And.; MRCGP 1968; DObst RCOG 1960.

MATHIAS, Stephen Robert 117 Rose Way, Cirencester GL7 1PS — MB BS 1984 Lond.; DCH RCP Lond. 1987.

MATHIAS, Tania Wyn 4 Glentham Gardens, London SW13 9JN Email: tania.mathias@btinternet.com — MB BCh 1988 Oxf.

MATHIAS, Thomas Grayson The Croase Orchard Surgery, Kingsland, Leominster HR6 9QL Tel: 01568 708214 Fax: 01568 708188; Great Oaks, Eyton, Leominster HR6 0AQ — MB BS 1980 Lond.; MRCS Eng. LRCP Lond. 1979; MRCGP 1987; DRCOG 1984; DLO RCS Lond. 1982. (Guy's)

MATHIAS, Zoe Tel: 01594 598020 — MB BS 1993 Lond.; DCCH 1996; DRCOG Lond. 1997. (Univ. Coll. Lond.) Trainee GP/SHO Airedale Hosp. VTS.

MATHIE, Adrian Gordon Kingston Hospital, Galsworthy Road, Kingston upon Thames KT2 7QB Tel: 020 8546 7711 Fax: 0870 054 7796 Email: adrian.mathie@stat.demon.co.uk — MB BS 1987 Lond.; MA Camb. 1986; FRCS Eng. 1996; FRCR 1996. (Camb. Univ. & Guys Hosp.) Cons. Radiologist Kingston Hosp. Socs: Fell. Roy. Coll. Surg.; Fell. Roy. Coll. Radiologists; Soc. Cardiovasc. & Interven.al Radiol. Prev: Cons. Radiol. W. Suff. Hosp. Bury St Edmunds; Fell. (Interven.al Radiol.) Sunnybrook Health Sci.s Centre Toronto.

MATHIE, Anthony George Hamilton House, 24 Pall Mall, Liverpool L3 6AL Tel: 0151 236 2637 Fax: 0151 236 3122 Email: tony.mathie@liverpool-ha.nhs.uk; Tibidabo Welshmans Lane, Nantwich CW5 6AB Tel: 01270 624722 Fax: 01270 629945 — MB BS Lond. 1969; MRCS Eng. LRCP Lond. 1969; FRCGP 1992, M 1975; Dip Med. Educat. Dund 1989; Cert. Family Plann. JCC 1972; DObst RCOG 1971. (Lond. Hosp.) Dir. Postgrad. Gen. Pract. Educat. NW Regional Office NHS Exec. & Univ. Liverp.; Hon. Treas. RCGP; Armed Serv.s GP approval Bd. Prev: GP Chesh.; Trainee GP Wessex RHB VTS; Ho. Off. Lond. Hosp.

MATHIE, David Stevenson Burnbank Medical Centre, 18 Burnbank Road, Hamilton ML3 0NQ Tel: 01698 286555 Fax: 01698 286686; 16 Sheepburn Road, Uddingston, Glasgow G71 7DX Tel: 01698 810383 — MB ChB 1982 Glas. (Glas.) Med. Dir. Healthcall Lanarksh.; Med. Off. Hamilton Pk. Racecourse. Prev: Trainee GP Muirhead VTS; SHO (O & G, Orthop. & Cas.) Gtr. Glas. HB.

MATHIE, Iain Hugh The Health Centre, Wardlaw Way, Oakley, Dunfermline KY12 9QH Tel: 01383 850212 — MB ChB 1989 Aberd.; BMedBiol 1986. Trainee GP Durh. VTS. Socs: BMA. Prev: SHO (Med.) Dryburn Hosp. Durh.

MATHIE, Ian Kenneth (retired) 11 Lapwing Lane, Norton, Stockton-on-Tees TS20 1LT Tel: 01642 553268 Email: ikmrailway@aol.com — MB ChB 1954 Ed.; FRCOG 1976, M 1963. Cons. O & G N. Tees Hosp. Gp. Prev: Sen. Regist. Inst. O & G Hammersmith Hosp. Lond. (Comb. Appt. with Portsmouth Hosp. Gp.).

MATHIE, Yvonne Mabel 12 Pleasance Brae, Cairneyhill, Dunfermline KY12 8FA; The Health Centre, Wardlaw Way, Oakley, Dunfermline KY12 9QH — MB BCh BAO 1984 Belf.; MRCGP 1988; T(GP) 1991; DRCOG 1986. GP; Clin. Asst. (Dermat.). Prev: GP Reading; SHO (O & G & Med.) Mid. Ulster Hosp. Magherafelt; SHO (Infec. Dis.) Belvoir Pk. Hosp.

MATHIESON, Alan Gordon The Turret Medical Centre, Catherine Street, Kirkintilloch, Glasgow G66 1JB Tel: 0141 211 8260 Fax: 0141 211 8264; 40 Kingsborough Gardens, Hyndland, Glasgow G12 9NL Tel: 0141 334 4410 — MB ChB 1963 Glas.; MFHom 1979. (Glas.) Hosp. Practitioner Glas. Homoeop. Hosp. & Lenzie Hosp. Glas. (Gemat.). Socs: Fac. Homoeop. Prev: Regist. (Dermat.) & Ho. Off. Roy. Infirm. Glas.; Ho. Off. Vict. Infirm. Glas.

MATHIESON

MATHIESON, Alice Mary (retired) 24 Spoutwells Drive, Scone, Perth PH2 6RR Tel: 01738 551976 — MB ChB Leeds 1947. Prev: Med. Off. Perth Family Plann. Clinic.

MATHIESON, Anne Elizabeth Thornton Wraysholme, Millans Park, Ambleside LA22 9AD Tel: 015394 32309 — MB ChB Leeds 1950; DObst RCOG 1953. (Leeds) Cons. Hypnother. & Psychosomatic Med. Ambleside; Mem. Inst. Psychosexual Med. Socs: Fell. Roy. Soc. Med. (Late Pres. Sect. Hypn., & Psychosomatic Med.). Prev: Med. Off. Psychosexual Problem Clinic & Family Plann. Clinic St. And. Hosp. Billericay; Ho. Phys. York Co. Hosp.; Ho. Surg. Leeds Matern. Hosp. & Hosp. Wom. Leeds.

***MATHIESON, Annie Kirk** 58 Catherine Drive, Galston KA4 8BS — MB ChB 1995 Glas.

MATHIESON, Christopher Boyd 17 The Old Market, Yarm TS15 9BX — MB ChB 1992 Dundee.

MATHIESON, Denys Avril Mary Appin House, Appin PA38 4BN Tel: 01631 730207 Fax: 01631 730567 — MB ChB Ed. 1965; MRCGP 1983; DCH NUI 1974. Partner Port Appin Surg.; Clin. Med. Off./Schs. Argyll & Bute NHS Trust. Socs: BMA; RCGP. Prev: Assoc. GP Port Appin; Primary Care Cons. Riyadh Milit. Hosp. Saudi Arabia; Princip. WAH Ayrsh. & Arran HB.

MATHIESON, Derek Cults Medical Group, Cults Medical Centre, South Avenue, Cults, Aberdeen AB15 9LQ Tel: 01224 867740 Fax: 01224 861392; 9 Oldfold Drive, Milltimber AB13 0JZ — MB ChB 1979 Aberd.

MATHIESON, Diana Mary 24 Crewy's Road, London SE15 2BH — MB BCh 1991 Wales.

MATHIESON, John Broomwell, 24 Henrietta St., Girvan KA26 9AL Tel: 01465 712412 — MB ChB Glas. 1943.

MATHIESON, Mary Allison 33 Westbourne Gardens, Glasgow G12 9PF — MB ChB 1976 Glas.; FRCS Glas. 1981.

MATHIESON, Professor Peter William Academic Renal Unit, Southmead Hospital, Westbury-on-Trym, Bristol BS10 5NB Tel: 0117 959 5438 Fax: 0117 959 5438 Email: p.mathieson@bris.ac.uk — MB BS 1983 Lond.; MB BS (Hons.) Lond. 1983; PhD Camb. 1991; MRCP (UK) 1986; FRCP 1998; F Acad. Med. Sc. 1999. (London Hospital Medical College) Prof. Renal Med. Univ. Bristol & Hon. Cons. Nephrol. S.mead Hosp. Bristol. Socs: Renal Assn. & Brit. Soc. Immunol.; Assn. Phys. Prev: MRC Clinician Sci. & Hon. Sen. Regist. (Nephrol.) Dept. Med. Addenbrooke's Hosp. Camb.; MRC Train. Fell. Camb.; Regist. (Nephrol.) Hammersmith Hosp. Lond.

***MATHIEU, Nicholas** 13 Maywater Close, South Croydon CR2 0RS — MB BS 1997 Lond.

MATHISON, Mr Andrew Clive 4 Enderleigh Gardens, Churchill, Bristol BS25 5NU — FRCS Ed. 1982.

MATHISON, Christopher David Newtownards Health Centre, Frederick Street, Newtownards BT23 4LS Tel: 028 9181 6880 Fax: 028 9181 1429; 21 Helensview Crescent, Newtownards BT23 4QN Tel: 01247 814977 — MB BCh BAO 1970 Belf.; MRCGP 1974; DObst RCOG 1973.

MATHISON, Diane Margaret 4 Enderleigh Gardens, Churchill, Bristol BS25 5NU — MB ChB 1976 Liverp.; DRCOG 1979.

MATHUR, Anthony 18 Hampstead Gardens, London NW11 7EU — MB BChir 1991 Camb.

MATHUR, Mr Arun Chandra Glan Clwyd Hospital, Bodelwyddan, Rhyl LL18 5UJ Tel: 01745 583910 Fax: 01745 583143; 9 Bryn Coed, Mount Road, St Asaph LL17 0DQ Tel: 01745 584630 — MB BS 1963 Vikram; FRCS Eng. 1977; FRCS Ed. 1977. (G.R. Med. Coll. Gwalior) Assoc. Specialist (Gen. Surg.) Glan. Clwyd Dist. Gen. Hosp. Socs: Assoc. Mem. BMA. Prev: Regist. (Surg.) Clwyd N. Heath Dist.; Sen. Specialist (Surg.) MoH Najran, Saudi Arabia; Regist. (Surg.) Chelmsford HA.

MATHUR, Azad Bhushan Jenny Lind Children's Department, Norfolk and Norwich Hospital, Brunswick Road, Norwich NR1 3SR — MB BS 1975 Rajasthan.

MATHUR, Chandra Prabha 37 Hawthorne Avenue, Harrow HA3 8AG — MB BS 1968 Vikram; FFA RCS Eng. 1978; DA Eng. 1976. (G.R. Med. Coll. Gwalior) Prev: Sen. Regist. (Anaesth.) Roy. Marsden Hosp.; Regist. Roy. Free Hosp.

MATHUR, Gyaneshwar Narayan Dewsbury and District Hospital, Dewsbury WF13 4HS; 7 Perran Grove, Cusworth, Doncaster DN5 8UJ Tel: 01924 512000 — MB BS 1958 Osmania; FRCPsych 1987, M 1972; DPM Eng. 1971. (Osmania Med. Coll. Hyderabad) Cons. Psychiat. Dewsbury and Dist. Hosp. Dewsbury Yorks. Socs: Fell. Indian Psychiatric Soc.; Fell. Manch. Med. Soc. Prev: Med. Asst. & Sen. Regist. Rainhill Hosp. Liverp.; Regist. Lancaster Moor Hosp.

MATHUR, Mr Pawan 11 Inveresk Gardens, Worcester Park KT4 7BB Tel: 020 8873 2501 Fax: 020 8746 8321 Email: pawan@icr.ac.uk — MB BS 1990 Lond.; FRCS 1995. (St Thomas' Hosp. UMDS) Specialist Surg. Reg. Gen Surg. Lon.; Research Fell. Socs: Asso. Surg. Of GB & Irel.; Asso. Surg. In Train. Asso.; Roy. Soc. Med. Prev: Specialist Regist. Gen. Surg. Bedford Hosp. Beds; Specailist Reg. Gen. Surg. Lister Hosp. Stevenage.

MATHUR, Pratibha Victoria Health Centre, 1 Queens Road, Barking IG11 8GD Tel: 020 8594 5625 Fax: 020 8594 1816 — MB BS 1968 Rajasthan; MB BS 1968 Rajasthan.

MATHUR, Rajat 32 Mayfields, Wembley HA9 9PS — MB BS 1984 All India Inst. Med. Sciences; MB BS All India Institute of Medical Sciences 1984; MRCP (UK) 1989.

MATHUR, Shiv Behari Warley Hospital, Brentwood CM14 5HQ Tel: 01708 464218 Fax: 01708 464306; 190 Southend Road, Stanford-le-Hope SS17 7AH — MB BS 1962 Rajasthan; BSc Rajasthan 1957; DPM Eng. 1971; MRCPsych Lond. 1973. (SMS Med. Coll. Jaipur) Cons. Psychiat. (c/o the Elderly) Warley Hosp. Brentwood.; Serv. Director (Care fo the Elderly) Warley Hosp. Brentwood. Socs: Fell.of the Roy. Coll. of Psychiat.s (1976). Prev: Sen. Regist. Warley Hosp. Brentwood.

MATHUR, Sunil 25 Davenport Avenue, Hessle HU13 0RL — MB BS 1996 Lond.; BA (Hons) Oxf 1993. (St Geos. Hosp. Med. Sch. Lond.)

MATICH, Maurice Dominic 109 Liverpool Road, Bickerstaffe, Ormskirk L39 0EQ — MB ChB 1977 Otago.

MATIN, Mohammed Abdul 6 Field End Close, Mottram Rise, Stalybridge SK15 2UF — MB BS 1955 Dacca; MRCPI 1975; MRCS Eng. LRCP Lond. 1967; FRCPI 1987; DTM & H Eng. 1962. (Dacca Med. Coll.) Cons. Phys. (Geriat. Med.) Tameside Gen. Hosp. Ashton-under-Lyne. Prev: Sen. Regist. (Geriat. Med.) Withington Hosp. S. Manch.; Sen. Regist. (Geriat. Med.) N. Manch. Gen. Hosp.; Regist. (Gen. Med.) Roy. Alexandra Hosp. Rhyl.

***MATIN, Mohammed Waziullah** 4 Fairmead Crescent, Edgware HA8 8YQ — MB BS 1995 Lond.

MATIN, Momtaz Parveen Delamere Street Health Centre, 45 Delamere Street, Crewe CW1 2ER Tel: 01270 214046 — MB ChB 1984 Sheff. GP. Socs: BMA.

MATIN, Muhammad Abdul Invicta Care NHS Trust, The Courtyard, Pudding Lane, Maidstone ME14 1PA; 1 Mungo Parkway, Orpington BR5 4EE — MB BS 1967 Dacca; MRCPsych 1977; T(Psych) 1977; DPM Eng. 1976. (Sir Salim Ullah Med. Coll.) Cons. Psychiat. Leybourne Grange Hosp. W. Malling; Sen. Clin. Tutor Dept. Psychol. Med. KCH Lond.

MATIN-SIDDIQI, Shaikh Abdul 12 The Combe, Ratton, Eastbourne BN20 9DB — MB BS 1958 Karachi. (Dow Med. Coll. Karachi) GP Polegate; GP Trainer E.bourne VTS. Prev: Med. Regist. (Paediat.) Alder Hey Childr. Hosp. Liverp.; Med. Regist. (Gen. Med. & Paediat.) Hastings Hosp. Gp.; Ho. Phys. (Gen. Med. & Paediat.) St. Mary's Hosp. E.bourne.

MATISCHEN, Gregory Michael Rydings Hall Surgery, Church Lane, Brighouse HD6 1AT Tel: 01484 715324 Fax: 01484 400847; Oakdale, Leeds Road, Halifax HX3 8NH — MB ChB 1982 Leeds. Prev: Trainee GP Otley VTS.; Regist. (Infec. Dis.) Seacroft Hosp. Leeds; SHO (A & E) Leeds Gen. Infirm.

MATITI, Henry Herbert Liquorpond Street Surgery, 10 Liquorpond Street, Boston PE21 8UE Tel: 01205 362763 Fax: 01205 358918 — MB ChB 1976 Nairobi; MRCP (UK) 1987.

MATKOVIC, Zelko Radcliffe Infirmary, Woodstock Road, Oxford OX2 6HE Tel: 01865 311188 — MB BS 1984 Melbourne; FRACP 1991. Regist. (Neurol.) Radcliffe Infirm. Oxf. Socs: Austral. Assn. Neurol.

MATLHAGA-NYONI, Batsile Maitshupo Ophthalmology Department, Royal United Hospital, Combe Park, Bath BA1 3NG — MB ChB 1985 Otago.

MATLIN, Abraham Julius 16 Eccleston Place, Park St., Salford M7 4NH — LRCPI & LM, LRSCI & LM 1948; LRCPI & LM, LRCSI & LM 1948. (RCSI)

MATRAVERS, Paul John Kanala, Western Road, Hailsham BN27 3EE — MB BS 1993 Lond.; BSc Lond. 1990; FRCS Ed. 1997. (King's Coll. Lond.) Specialist Regist. Radiol. N.wick Pk. & St. Marks. Prev: SHO (Gen. Surg.) Crawley Hosp.; SHO (A & E) King's Coll.

Hosp. Lond.; Prosector (Anat.) UMDS Guy's & St. Thos. Hosps. Lond.

MATSAKIS, Marios 27 Mayfield Road, London N8 9LL — MB BChir 1985 Camb.; PhD Lond. 1982, BSc 1976; MPhil Glas. 1992; DMJ(Path) Soc. Apoth. Lond. 1993; Dip. Forens. Med. Glas. 1990. Lect. (Forens. Med.) Char. Cross & W.m. Med. Sch. Lond.

MATSIKO, Katono Shekaniya Hinchingbrooke Hospital NHS Trust, Hinchingbrooke Park, Huntingdon PE17 8NT Tel: 01480 416416; Greenwood House, 9 Greenwood Close, Bury, Huntingdon PE26 2NZ Tel: 01487 814992 Fax: 01487 814992 Email: skmatsiko@aol.com — MRCS Eng. LRCP Lond. 1983; MRCPI 1990; DTM & H RCP Lond. 1982. Cons. Phys. Hinchingbrooke Hosp. Cambs. Prev: Sen. Regist. Addenbrookes Hosp. Camb.; Regist. (Med.) Aberd. Teach. Hosp. & Hon. Clin. Tutor Univ. Aberd.; Regist. (Med.) Enfield Dist. Hosp.

MATSON, Alexandra Margarethe West Middlesex University Hospital Trust, Twickenham Road, Isleworth TW7 6AF Tel: 020 8565 5824 Fax: 020 8565 5826 Email: amatson@doctors.org.uk; 8 Cambridge Park, Twickenham TW1 2PF Tel: 020 8892 1555 Email: amatson@doctors.org.uk — MB BS 1983 Lond.; BSc (Hons.) Physiol. Lond. 1980; FACA 1988 Eng. (Westm.) Cons. Anaesth. W. Middlx. Hosp. Isleworth. Socs: Brit. Med. Assn.; Roy. Coll. of Anaesth.s; Assn. of Anaesth.s. Prev: Sen. Regist. (Anaesth.) Char. Cross Hosp. Lond.; Regist. (Anaesth.) Roy. Nat. Throat, Nose & Ear Hosp. Lond.; Regist. (Anaesth.) St. Geo. Hosp. Lond.

MATSON, Ian Campbell Trust Headquaters, Merchiston Hospital, Brookfield, Johnstone PA5 8TY Tel: 01505 384000 Fax: 01505 384001 Email: ian.matson@renfrewshire-tr.scot.nhs.uk; 50 Bellahouston Drive, Glasgow G52 1HQ Tel: 0141 882 2094 — MB ChB 1979 Glas.; BSc Glas. 1974, MB ChB 1979; MRCPsych 1984. (Glas.) Cons. Psychiat. Merchiston Hosp Brookfield By Johnstone; Med. Dir., Renfrewsh. & Inverclyde Primary Care NHS Trust.

MATSON, Jonathan Stuart Spa Road Surgery, Spa Road East, Llandrindod Wells LD1 5ES Tel: 01597 824291 / 842292 Fax: 01597 824503; Dwyfnant, Newbridge on Wye, Llandrindod Wells LD1 6HP — MB ChB 1980 Liverp.; MRCS Eng. LRCP Lond. 1980; MRCGP 1991; AFOM RCP Lond. 1989; DTM & H Liverp. 1986; DCH RCPS Glas. 1986; DA Eng. 1984; DRCOG 1984. (Liverp.)

MATSON, Matthew Buckingham Barts And The London NHS Trust, Department of Radiology, Royal London Hospital, Whitechapel Road, London E1 Tel: 020 7377 7000 Fax: 020 7377 7094 Email: m.matson@bigfoot.com — MB BS 1988 Lond.; MRCP (UK) 1991; FRCR 1997. (St. Barth.) Socs: BMA & Roy. Soc. Med.; Brit. Soc. of Interven.al Radiol. Prev: Sen Regist., Radiol.) St Geo.s, Hosp. Lond; Specialist Regist., Radiol., Guys & St Thomas' Hosp. Lond.; Regist., (med.) Brook, Len Hosp.

MATSUDA, Takeshi 10 Hamilton Road, London SW19 1JF — MB ChB 1987 Leic.

MATTA, Mr Amir Shafik Quaker Lodge, Sidgreaves Lane, Lea Town, Preston PR4 0RD — MB ChB 1970 Alexandria; FRCS RCPS Glas. 1984.

MATTA, Hilal 16 Snaithing Lane, Ranmore, Sheffield S10 3LG — MB ChB 1983 Sheff.

MATTAR, Mr Muhammad Hassan Sandwell General Hospital, Lyndon, West Bromwich B71 4HJ Tel: 0121 607 3303 Fax: 0121 607 3374; 26 Rednet Road, Kings Norton, Birmingham B38 8DR Tel: 0121 458 2379 Fax: 0121 607 3558 — MB ChB 1973 Basrah; FRCOG 2000; Iraq 1973; MRCOG 1985; DO RCPSI 1982. Cons. O & G Sandwell Gen. Hosp. Lyndon, W. Bromwich. Socs: Med. Protec. Soc.; BMA; Eur. Soc. Obst. & Gyn. Prev: Sen. Regist. & Regist. (O & G) Erinville Hosp. Cork.

MATTAR, Mr Raymond George Sparkbrook Health Centre, Sparkbrook, Birmingham B11 — MRCS Eng. LRCP Lond. 1966; FRCS Ed. 1964.

MATTEUCCI, Paolo Luciano Scarborough General Hospital, Woodlands Drive, Scarborough YO12 6QL — MB ChB 1997 Leeds. SHO Rotat. (Basic Surg.) ScarBoro. Gen. Hosp.

MATTHAI, Mercy Susan Gloucestershire Royal Hospital, Great Western Road, Gloucester GL1 3NN Tel: 01452 528555 — MB BS Benin Nigeria 1986; MRCP (UK) 1993; DCH RCP Lond. 1992. Cons. Paediat. Glo. Roy. Hosp. Prev: Sen. Regist. (Paediat.) Alder Hey Hosp. Liverp.

MATTHEE, Michael Robert Royal Shrewsbury Hospital South, Mytton Oak, Shrewsbury SY3 8BR — MB ChB 1984 Manch. SHO (O & G) Roy. Shrewsbury Hosp. Prev: SHO (Anaesth.) Vict. Hosp. Blackpool.; SHO (Gen. Med.) Roy. Shrewsbury Hosp; SHO (Paediat.) Ysbyty Gwynedd Bangor.

MATTHES, Jean Wendy Anne Department of Child Health, Singleton Hospital, Swansea SA2 8QA Tel: 01792 205666 Fax: 01792 285244; 1 Blackthorn Rise, West Cross, Swansea SA3 5RQ — MB BCh 1980 Wales; MD 1996; FRCP 1997; FRCPCH. Cons. Paediat. Singleton Hosp. Swansea. Prev: Sen. Regist. (Paediat.) Cardiff.

MATTHES, Penelope Ann The Surgery, 32 Kingsland Road, West Mersea, Colchester CO5 8RA Tel: 01206 382015 Fax: 01206 385593 — MB ChB 1984 Glas.; T(GP) 1991. Clin. Asst. (Genitourin. Med.) Essex Rivers Health Care Colchester.

***MATTHEW, Aneurin Nathan Joseph** 43 Harley Crescent, Harrow HA1 4XH — MB ChB 1998 Leeds.

MATTHEW, Anne Muriel 10 Lampards Close, Allerton, Bradford BD15 9AZ — MB ChB 1981 Ed.

MATTHEW, Graeme Kerr, MBE (retired) Amnis House, Coln St Dennis, Cheltenham GL54 3JY Tel: 01285 720353 — MB Camb. 1957, BChir 1956; FFPHM RCP Lond. 1985, M 1972; DTM & H Eng. 1963. Prev: PMO DH.

MATTHEW, Jacob Department of Anaesthetics, Ashford Hospital, Ashford TW15 3AA — MB BS 1979 Kerala; DA (UK) 1986.

MATTHEW, John Low (retired) Alpine House, 61 Sheepwalk Lane, Ravenshead, Nottingham NG15 9FD Tel: 01623 792654 — MB ChB 1954 Aberd. Hon. Obst. King's Mill Hosp. Sutton-in-Ashfield; Med. Adviser Benefits Agency.

MATTHEW, Thomas Barrie Murray Road Surgery, 50 The Murray Road, East Kilbride, Glasgow G75 0RT Tel: 01355 225374 Fax: 01355 239475; 59 Borthwick Drive, East Kilbride, Glasgow G75 8YR Tel: 01355 243781 — MB ChB 1977 Glas.; DRCOG 1980.

MATTHEWMAN, Mr Philip John Prince of Wales Road Surgery, 87-89 Prince of Wales Road, London NW5 3NT Tel: 020 7284 3888 — MB ChB 1979 Bristol; FRCS Eng. 1984; FP Cert. 1988. UnderGrad. Tutor at Roy. Free Hosp. Sch. of Med.

MATTHEWS, Alan Eric St Margarets Health Centre, St. Margaret's Drive, Auchterarder PH3 1JH Tel: 01764 662614/662275 Fax: 01764 664178; Rossie Law, Townhead, Muckhart Road, Dunning, Perth PH2 0RW — MB ChB 1982 Dundee; MRCGP 1986; DRCOG 1986. (Univ. Dundee)

MATTHEWS, Alan Reginald 5 Kinilworth Terrace, Elford St., Ashby-de-la-Zouch LE65 1HH — LMSSA Lond. 1954.

MATTHEWS, Alan William (retired) 36 Botley Road, Park Gate, Southampton SO31 1AJ Tel: 01489 575263 — MB BS 1960 Lond.; MD Lond. 1976; FRCP Lond. 1982; MRCP (UK) 1970; DObst RCOG 1962. Prev: Cons. Phys. Portsmouth & SE Hants. Health Dist.

MATTHEWS, Alastair Grant Department of Clinical Radiology, Royal Infirmary of Edinburgh, Lauriston Place, Edinburgh EH3 9 Tel: 0131 536 2900; 75 Spottiswoode Street, Edinburgh EH9 1DL Tel: 0131 447 1794 — MB ChB 1991 Ed.; MRCP (UK) 1996. (Edinburgh) Specialist Regist. (Clin. Radiol.) S. E. Scotl. Train. Scheme.

MATTHEWS, Alison Jayne Plot 7 The Bridleway, The Alexandra Hospital, Woodrow Drive, Redditch Tel: 01527 503030; 10 Hazel Drive, Hollywood, Birmingham B47 5RJ Tel: 0121 430 7051 — BM BS 1989 Nottm.; BMedSci. 1987.

MATTHEWS, Alistair Robert 12 Rosemount Avenue, Kirkcaldy KY2 6SP — MB ChB 1989 Ed.

MATTHEWS, Allyson June 107 Bonaly Rise, Edinburgh EH13 0QY — MB ChB 1976 Ed.

MATTHEWS, Andrew John Department of Anaesthesia, University Hospital, Queen's Medical Centre, Nottingham NG7 2UH Tel: 0115 924 9924 Fax: 0115 978 3891; Woodland Cottage, Westhorpe, Southwell NG25 0NE Tel: 01636 812953 Email: andym1000@aol.com — MB ChB 1977 Bristol; FFA RCS Lond. 1981. Cons. Paediat. Anaesth. Qu. Med. Centre & City Hosp. Nottm. Socs: Assn. Paediat. Anaesth. & Paediat. Intens. Care Soc. Prev: Sen. Regist. (Anaesth.) N.. RHA; Regist. (Paediat. Anaesth.) Liverp. HA; SHO (Paediat.) Leeds E.. HA.

MATTHEWS, Andrew Peter Marston Avenue House Surgery, 109 Saltergate, Chesterfield S40 1LE Tel: 01246 272139 Fax: 01246 556336; Longlands, The Dell, Ashgate, Chesterfield S40 4DL

MATTHEWS

Tel: 01246 200610 — MB ChB 1975 Sheff.; MRCGP 1979; DRCOG 1978.

MATTHEWS, Anna Jozefa Old Cottage Hospital Surgery, Alexandra Road, Epsom KT17 4BL Tel: 01372 724434 Fax: 01372 748171; Spring Cottage, Spring St, Epsom KT17 1UH — MB BS 1984 Lond.; MRCGP 1990; DCH RCP Lond. 1988; DRCOG Lond. 1987.

MATTHEWS, Bridget d'Estouteville (retired) Dale Cottage, Charlcombe Lane, Bath BA1 8DR Tel: 01225 312248 Fax: 01225 312248 — MB BS 1953 Lond.; MRCS Eng. LRCP Lond. 1953.

MATTHEWS, Clare Elizabeth Blackmore Health Centre, Sidmouth EX10 8ET — MB ChB 1987 Bristol; MRCGP 1992; DRCOG 1991.

MATTHEWS, Clare Fiona Dept. Rheumatology, Musgrave Park Hospital, Stockmans Lane, Belfast BT9 7JB Tel: 01247 473730, 028 9066 9501 — MB BCh BAO 1994 Belf.; MRCP (UK) 1997. (QUB) Specialist Regist. Rheum. & Gen. Med. Belf. Socs: BMA; Brit. Soc. Rheum.; Irish Soc. Rheum.

MATTHEWS, Clare Helen Department of Medicine, Level 5, Addenbrooke's Hospital, Cambridge CB2 2QQ Tel: 01223 336862 Fax: 01223 336846; Bardsfield Cottage, Walden Road, Hadstock, Cambridge CB1 6NX Tel: 01223 894053 Fax: 01223 336846 Email: chm@molebio.can.ac.uk — BM BCh 1987 Oxf.; PhD Camb. 1996, MA 1988, BA 1984; MRCP (UK) 1990. Wellcome Advanced Train. Fell. (Med.) Addenbrooke's Hosp. Camb.; Hon. Sen. Regist. (Endocrinol.) Addenbrooke's Hosp. Camb. Socs: BMA; Soc. Endocrinol.

MATTHEWS, Clare Jane 24 Cambridge Road, Sawston, Cambridge CB2 4DG — MB ChB 1987 Sheff.

MATTHEWS, Cynthia Nellie Ann Park House, Itton, Chepstow NP16 6BZ — MB BS 1961 Lond.; FRCP Lond. 1987, M 1966; MRCS Eng. LRCP Lond. 1961; DObst RCOG 1962. (St. Geo.) Cons. Dermat. Gwent AHA. Prev: Sen. Regist. Dermat. United Bristol Hosps.; Res. Med. Off. & Res. Obst. Asst. St. Geo. Hosp. Lond.; Ho. Phys. St. Geo. Hosp. Tooting.

MATTHEWS, David Hamilton 86 Packhorse Road, Gerrards Cross SL9 8JG Tel: 01753 887632 Fax: 01753 892405 — MB BS 1970 Lond.; DOccMed (Faculty of Occupational Medicine, RCP) 1998; AFOM (Faculty of Occupational Medicine, RCP) 2000; MRCS Eng. LRCP Lond. 1970; FRCGP 1987, M 1979; DObst RCOG 1973. (St. Bart.) Asst. Med. Director, BUPA Wellness Occupat.al Health, Lond. Prev: Med. Director of Barbican Health 1996-1999; GP Princip. and VTS Course Organiser, Chalfont St Peter 1973-1996; Trainee GP St. Bart. Hosp. Lond. VTS.

MATTHEWS, David John Giggs Hill Surgery, 14 Raphael Drive, Thames Ditton KT7 0EB Tel: 020 8398 8619 Fax: 020 8398 8874; 75 Thistledene, Thames Ditton KT7 0YW — MB BS 1982 Lond. (St. Geo.) Socs: BMA. Prev: Trainee GP St. Helier & Qu. Mary's Hosps. Carshalton VTS; SHO (Orthop. & ENT) St. Helier Hosp. Carshalton.

MATTHEWS, David Marshall Monklands Hospital, Monkscourt Avenue, Airdrie ML6 0JS Tel: 01236 748748 Fax: 01236 747018; Kennington, 23 Cleghorn Road, Lanark ML11 7QR Tel: 01555 663059 Email: dmmlanark@compuserve.com — MB ChB 1976 Ed.; FRCP Glas. 1992; FRCP Ed. 1990; MRCP (UK) 1979. Cons. Phys. Monklands Hosp. Lanarksh. Acute Hosp.s NHS Trust. Socs: Diabetes UK; Scott. Soc. Phys.; Lanarksh. Diabetes Gp. (Sec.). Prev: Cons. Phys. Hairmyres & StoneHo. Hosps. NHS Trust; Sen. Regist. & Regist. (Med.) Roy. Infirm. Edin.; Regist. Rotat. (Med.) Lothian HB.

MATTHEWS, David Richard Oxford Centre for Diabetes, Endocrinology and Metabolism, Radcliffe Infirmary, Woodstock Road, Oxford OX2 6HE Tel: 01865 224399 Fax: 01865 228403; Tel: 01865 863553 — BM BCh 1975 Oxf.; MA, DPhil Oxf. 1973, BA 1969; FRCP Lond. 1993; MRCP (UK) 1977. (Oxf.) Cons. Phys. & Chairm. Oxf. Centre for Diabetes, Endocrinol. & Metab. Socs: Diabetes UK (Chairm. Research Comm. Mem.); Roy. Coll. Phys.; CME Com. for Diabetes & Endocrinol. Prev: Joan & Richard Doll Sen. Research Fell. Green. Coll. Oxf.; Nuffield Research Fell. & Jun. Research Fell. Balliol Coll. Oxf.

MATTHEWS, David Thomas Quantock Medical Centre, Banneson Road, Nether Stowey, Bridgwater TA5 1NW Tel: 01278 732696 Fax: 01278 733381; The Health Centre, Nether Stowey, Bridgwater — MB BS 1966 Lond.; BSc, MB BS Lond. 1966; DObst RCOG 1970. (Univ. Coll. Hosp.)

***MATTHEWS, David William** 4 Mill Road, Cottingham, Market Harborough LE16 8XP — MB ChB 1998 Liverp.; MB ChB Liverp 1998.

MATTHEWS, Deborah Sheila Frances 23 Manor Court, Beech Road, Headington, Oxford OX3 7SD — MB BS 1983 Lond.

MATTHEWS, Dino Constantine The Annexe, 43 Pearce Avenue, Poole BH14 8EG — MB BS 1993 Lond.

MATTHEWS, Edna (retired) 4 Squirrels Heath Avenue, Gidea Park, Romford RM2 6AH Tel: 01708 74634 — MB BS Lond. 1956; FRCR 1975; FFR 1967; DMRT Eng. 1961. Prev: Cons. Radiother. & Oncol. N. Middlx., P. of Wales, St. Anne's & St. Bart. Hosps. Lond./Recognised Teach. Lond. Univ.

***MATTHEWS, Elaine Elizabeth** 174 Lochee Road, Dundee DD2 2NG — MB ChB 1997 Dund.

MATTHEWS, Eurem Eleri Penfro, Oakridge, Middle Aston, Bicester OX25 5PX — MB BCh 1977 Wales; MRCP (UK) 1982; DCH Eng. 1980. Cons. (Paediat.) Oxf. Radcliffe Hosps, Horton Hosp. Banbury, John Radcliffe Hosp. Oxf. Socs: FRCP; FRCPCH. Prev: Cons. Paediat. P.ss Roy. Hosp. Telford.; Lect. (Child Health) Sultanate of Oman & Inst. Child Health Lond.

MATTHEWS, Fiona Jane Penylan Road Surgery, 100 Penylan Road, Cardiff CF2 5HY Tel: 029 2046 1100 Fax: 029 2045 1623 — MB ChB 1986 Leic. Med. Off. Univ. Wales.

***MATTHEWS, Frances Ruth** 8 Ornsby Hill, Lanchester, Durham DH7 0QL — MB ChB 1998 Sheff.; MB ChB Sheff 1998.

MATTHEWS, Gail Veronica 11 Eaton Road, St Albans AL1 4UD — MB ChB 1991 Bristol.

MATTHEWS, Gary Anthony 22 Grange Avenue, Kenilworth CV8 1DD — MB ChB 1992 Bristol.

MATTHEWS, Gillian Gibson 14 Kingsdown Avenue, South Croydon CR2 6QF Tel: 020 8688 2376 Fax: 020 8688 2376 — MB BChir Camb. 1952; MRCS Eng. LRCP Lond. 1953; FFPHM 1983, M 1978; FRCOG 1984, M 1958, DObst 1956. (King's Coll. Hosp.) Cons. Pub. Health Med. S. Croydon. Socs: BMA & Mem. Med. Wom. Federat.; Fell. RSM. Prev: Dep. Dir. Pub. Health Med. SE Thames RHA; Specialist (Community Med. Health Serv. Plann. & Informat.) Kent AHA; Sen. Regist. (Community Med.) SE Thames RHA.

MATTHEWS, Guy Anthony (retired) 4 Bury Hill Close, Hemel Hempstead HP1 1SS Tel: 01442 252485 — MRCS Eng. LRCP Lond. 1940; FRCPath 1964. Prev: Clin. Path. Hemel Hempstead Gen. Hosp.

MATTHEWS, Helen Claire Department of Anaesthesia, North Devon District Hospital, Barnstaple EX31 4JB — MB BS 1988 Lond.; MRCS Eng. LRCP Lond. 1987; DA (UK) 1995.

MATTHEWS, Helen Pinkerton Western Community Hospital, Walnut Grove, Southampton SO16 4XE Tel: 02380 475400 Fax: 02380 475482; 25 Velmore Road, Eastleigh SO53 3HD Tel: 02380 266476 — MB ChB 1978 Glas.; MRCPsych 1986; MRCGP 1982; DRCOG 1980. Cons. Old Age Psychiat. W.. Hosp. Soton. Prev: Cons. Old Age Psychiat. Moorgreen Hosp. Soton.

MATTHEWS, Herbert Lumley 22 Farley Road, Derby DE23 6BX Tel: 01332 342627 — MB ChB 1947 Manch.; MD Manch. 1963; FRCP Lond. 1972, M 1951. (Manch.) Emerit. Cons. Phys. Derbysh. Roy. Infirm. Socs: Hon. Mem. Derby Med. Soc.; Thyroid Club. Prev: Sen. Regist. (Med.) Roy. Infirm. Sheff.; Regist. (Med.) Addenbrooke's Hosp. Camb. & United Birm. Hosps.

MATTHEWS, Ian William Chapel Street Health Centre, 10 Chapel Street, Spondon, Derby DE21 7RJ Tel: 01332 674173 Fax: 01332 280387; 2 Rectory Farm, Rectory Lane, Breadsall Village, Derby DE21 5LL Tel: 01332 830047 — MB ChB 1985 Ed.; DRCOG 1988.

MATTHEWS, Jack, OBE (retired) 6 Marionville Gardens, Fairwater Road, Llandaff, Cardiff CF5 2LR Tel: 01222 565550 — MB BCh 1945 Wales; BSc Wales 1942. Prev: GP Cardiff.

***MATTHEWS, James Lewis** Hill Cottage, Erstone Road, Middle Barton, Chipping Norton OX7 7BN — MB ChB 1995 Manch.

MATTHEWS, James McIntyre (retired) Windward, Bayswater Road, Headington, Oxford OX3 9RZ Tel: 01865 351245 — MB ChB 1956 St. And. Prev: Assoc. Specialist Oxf. Haemophilia Centre.

MATTHEWS, Jillian Isabel 87 Hazelwood Road, Duffield, Derby DE56 4AA — MB ChB 1989 Manch.

MATTHEWS, John David Park Road Surgery, 93 Park Road, Wallsend NE28 7LP Tel: 0191 262 5680 Fax: 0191 262 3646 —

BM BCh 1984 Oxf.; MA Oxf. 1985, BM BCh 1984; MRCGP 1990. (Oxf.)

MATTHEWS, John Duncan, CVO (retired) 3 Succoth Gardens, Edinburgh EH12 6BR Tel: 0131 337 2636 — MB ChB Ed. 1945; BA Camb. 1942; FRCP Ed. 1958. Prev: Cons. Phys. Roy. Infirm. Edin.

MATTHEWS, Mr John Gilbert Wynne Currysiskan House, Ballymoney BT53 6QY Tel: 0126 56 63273 — MB BCh BAO 1968 Belf.; MCh (Hons.) Belf. 1972, MB BCh BAO 1968; FRCS Eng. 1973. Cons. Surg. Coleraine & Route Hosps. Prev: Sen. Surg. Regist. Belf. City Hosp.; Sen. Surg. Regist. Harari Centr. Hosp. Salisbury Rhodesia; Sen. Regist. Craigavon Area Hosp.

MATTHEWS, Mr John Graham 15 Thornhill Avenue, Wheatley Hills, Doncaster DN2 5SE — MB ChB 1964 Manch.; FRCS Ed. 1973. Cons. Orthop. Surg. Doncaster Roy. Infirm.

MATTHEWS, John Graham 72 Fentiman Road, London SW8 1LA Tel: 020 7582 3185 Email: j.matthews@ic.ac.uk; 1 Dale Close, Ascot SL5 0LZ — MB BS 1993 Lond.; BSc (Hons.) Physiol. Lond. 1990; MRCP 1997. Clin. Fell. Imperial Coll. Sch. ofMed.at Nat. Heart & Lung Inst. & Roy. Brompton Hosp. Prev: Regist. (Toxicology) Guy's & St. Thos. Hosp. Lond.; SHO (Renal & ITU) Guy's & St. Thos. NHS Trust; SHO (Respirat.) Roy. Brompton Hosp.

MATTHEWS, John Jason 15 Kingston Avenue, South Shore, Blackpool FY4 2QB — MB ChB 1992 Manch.; BSc (Hons.) Manch. 1990, MB ChB 1992.

***MATTHEWS, John Paul** 4 Mill Road, Cottingham, Market Harborough LE16 8XP — MB ChB 1998 Liverp.; MB ChB Liverp 1998.

MATTHEWS, Mr John Phillips West Glamorgan Consultants Group (cons. rooms), St David's House, 1 Uplands Terrace, Uplands, Swansea SA2 0GU Tel: 01792 472922 Fax: 01792 466803; Swyny-Don, Aberfelin, Trefin, Haverfordwest SA62 5BA Tel: 01348 831630 Fax: 01348 831630 — MRCS Eng. LRCP Lond. 1961; FRCS Eng. 1968; FRCS Ed. 1967. (Sheff.) Cons. Traum. & Orthop. Surg. Morriston Hosp. Swansea; Hon. Clin. Tutor Welsh Nat. Sch. Med. Socs: Swansea Medico Legal Soc.; Brit. Orthop. Research Soc.; Brit. Soc. Surg. Hand. Prev: Sen. Lect. Dept. Traum. & Orthop. Surg. Welsh Nat. Sch. Med.; Hon. Cons. S. Glam. AHA (T); Vis. Surg. Nat. Referral Hosp. Thimphu, Bhutan.

MATTHEWS, Jonathan James, Surg. Lt. RN HMS Endurance BFPO 279; 48 Station Road, Horrabridge, Yelverton PL20 7SS Tel: 01822 855773 — MB BCh 1995 Wales. (University of Wales College of Medicine) Med. Off. RN; SHO (A & E) Derriford Hosp Plymouth. Socs: MPS; BMA. Prev: Med. Off. HMS Drake; Med. Off. HMS Chatham; SHO (A & E) Derriford Hosp. Plymouth.

MATTHEWS, Joyce Winstanley 31 Ash Close, Wells BA5 2QR — MB ChB 1950 Leeds.

MATTHEWS, Karen Tracy Ann Alpine House Surgery, 86 Rothley Road, Mountsorrel, Loughborough LE12 7JU Tel: 0116 230 3062 Fax: 0116 237 4218 — MB ChB 1983 Leic. Bd. Mem. S. Charnwood PCG.

MATTHEWS, Professor Keith Department of Psychiatry, Dundee University, Ninewells Hospital & Medical School, Dundee DD1 9SY Tel: 01382 632121 Fax: 01382 633923 Email: k.matthews@dundee.ac.uk — MB ChB 1984 Aberd.; MRCPsych 1990; MD (Aberd.) 1997; PhD (CANTAB) 1998. Prof. (Psychiat.) Dundee Univ. & Hon. Cons. Psychiat. Prev: Prof. (Psychiat. & Behavioral Scs. Wolverhampton Univ.; Wellcome Trust Clin. Fell (Experim. Psychol.) Camb. Univ.; Lect. (Ment. Health) Univ. Aberd.

***MATTHEWS, Lisa Jane** 57 Purnells Way, Knowle, Solihull B93 9JP — MB ChB 1998 Sheff.; MB ChB Sheff 1998.

MATTHEWS, Margaret Patricia Pembury Hospital, Tonbridge Rd, Tunbridge Wells TN2 4QJ Tel: 01892 823535; Tel: 01892 669032 — MB BS 1986 Lond.; BSc Lond. 1983; MRCOG 1995. Cons. Obst. & Gyn., Tunbridge Wells Kent. Prev: Specialist Regist. (Flexible).

MATTHEWS, Mary Anne The Surgery, Southview Lodge, South View, Bromley BR1 3DR Tel: 020 8460 1932 Fax: 020 8323 1423 — MB BS 1977 Lond.; DRCOG 1979.

MATTHEWS, Michael Barry Graylingwell Hospital, Chichester PO19 4PQ Tel: 01243 787970 Ext: 4209; Blakedene, Lyminster, Littlehampton BN17 7QF Tel: 01903 882026 — MB BS 1964 (Hons.) Lond.; MRCP (UK) 1971; MRCS Eng. LRCP Lond. 1964; FRCPsych 1995, M 1972; DPM Eng. 1968. (Char. Cross) Cons. Adult Psychiat. (Special Responsibil. Forens. Psychiat.) Sussex Weald and Downs NHS Trust. Socs: BMA (Ex-Chairm. W. Sussex Div.). Prev: Sen. Regist. (Psychiat.) Graylingwell Hosp.; Specialist (Psychiat.) Roy. Vict. Hosp. Netley; Ho. Phys. Char. Cross. Hosp. Lond.

MATTHEWS, Michael Bernard (retired) Colonsay, Winton House Drive, Pencaitland, Tranent EH34 5AS — MD 1954 Camb.; MB BChir 1944; FRCP Ed. 1961, M 1959; FRCP Lond. 1966, M 1946; MRCS Eng. LRCP Lond. 1944. Prev: Phys. & Cardiol. W.. Gen. Hosp. Edin.

MATTHEWS, Mr Michael Gordon Loakes Park Orthopaedic Unit, Wycombe General Hospital, Queen Alexandra Road, High Wycombe HP11 2TT Tel: 01494 426419 Fax: 01494 526418 Email: mgm@dctors.org.uk; Fax: 01494 890772 Email: mgm@doctors.org.uk — MB BS 1980 Lond.; MA (Engin.) Camb. 1970; FRCS Eng. 1985; MRCS Eng. LRCP Lond. 1980. (St. Bart.) Cons. Orthop. Trauma Surg. S. Bucks. NHS Trust. Socs: Brit. Orthopaedic Assn.; Brit. Trauma Soc. Prev: Sen. Regist. St. Geo. Orthop. Train. Scheme; Regist. Rotat. (Orthop.) Qu. Med. Centre Nottm. & Harlow Wood Orthop. Hosp. Mansfield; Regist. (Orthop.) Newham Gen. Hosp. Lond.

MATTHEWS, Michael John (retired) Woodlands Surgery, 24 Woodlands, Meeting House Lane, Balsall Common, Coventry CV7 7FX Tel: 01676 532587 Fax: 01676 535154 — MB ChB 1964 Birm.; DObst RCOG 1967. Prev: Ho. Surg. & Ho. Phys., Ho. Surg. (O & G) & Cas. Off. Selly Oak Hosp. Birm.

MATTHEWS, Michael Weston Bertie 37 Manor Road, Dorchester DT1 2AY — MB BS 1980 Lond.; MRCS Eng. LRCP Lond. 1979. (St. Mary's) SHO (Cas. & Trauma) Poole Gen. Hosp. Prev: Ho. Phys. Amersham Gen. Hosp.; Ho. Surg. King Edwd. VII Hosp. Windsor.

MATTHEWS, Nancy Elizabeth Valentine (retired) 12 Whyke Close, Chichester PO19 2BB — MB BS Lond. 1957; MRCS Eng. LRCP Lond. 1957. Prev: 1st Ho. Surg. Roy. Free Hosp. Lond.

MATTHEWS, Nicola Kate Burnham Medical Centre, Love Lane, Burnham-on-Sea TA8 1EU Tel: 01278 795445 Fax: 01278 793024 — MB ChB 1985 Leeds; BSc (Hons.) Physiol. Leeds 1983; DRCOG 1990. Prev: Trainee GP Huddersfield Roy. Infirm. VTS; Ho. Off. Wharfedale Gen. Hosp.

MATTHEWS, Nicolas William Hazle Cottage, Rodley, Newnham GL14 1RD — MB ChB 1992 Leeds.

MATTHEWS, Nigel Colin 193 Longton Road, Stoke-on-Trent ST4 8BT — MB ChB 1980 Manch.; FFA RCS Eng. 1987. Cons. N. Staffs. HA.

MATTHEWS, Nigel Graham — MB BS 1988 Lond.; MRCGP 1995; DRCOG 1992. (Lond. Hosp. Med. Sch.) Locum GP Chesh. Prev: Regist. (A & E) & SHO (Psychiat.) ChristCh. NZ; SHO (O & G) Bedford.

MATTHEWS, Nigel Rowden Garforth Medical Centre, Church Lane, Garforth, Leeds LS25 1ER Tel: 0113 286 5311 Fax: 0113 281 2679 — MB ChB 1967 Leeds.

MATTHEWS, Norunn Iren Lindbak 42 Georgian View, Bath BA2 2LZ — MB ChB 1992 Manch.

MATTHEWS, Patrick John Moorfield House Surgery, 35 Edgar Street, Hereford HR4 9JP Tel: 01432 272175 Fax: 01432 341942 — MB BChir 1974 Camb.; DRCOG 1977.

MATTHEWS, Paul 3 Cedar Road, Loughborough LE11 2AB — MB BS 1991 Lond.

MATTHEWS, Peter Canton Health Centre, Wessex Street, Cardiff CF5 1XU Tel: 029 2022 6016 Fax: 029 2039 4846; Danescourt Surgery, 4 Rachel Close, Danescourt, Cardiff CF5 2SH Tel: 029 2057 8686 Fax: 01222 555001 — MRCS Eng. LRCP Lond. 1971.

MATTHEWS, Professor Peter Bryan Conrad (retired) 3 Dean Court Road, Cumnor Hill, Oxford OX2 9JL Tel: 01865 862326 Email: pbm@physiol.ox.ac.uk — MB BChir Camb. 1954; FRS; DSc Oxf. 1966; MD Camb. 1959. Emerit. Prof. Sensorimotor Physiol. Oxf. & Stud. of Christ Ch. Prev: Reader Physiol. Motor Control Oxf.

MATTHEWS, Peter Charles Intensive Therapy Unit, Morriston Hospital, Swansea SA6 6NL Tel: 01792 703468 Fax: 01792 703470 Email: petermatthews@swansea_tr.wales.nhs.uk; Tel: 01792 551283 Email: peter.matthews4@virgin.net — MB BS 1990 Lond.; FRCA 1995; DA (UK) 1992. (St. Bart.) Cons. Intens. Care & Anaesth., Morriston hosp. Swansea. Socs: Intens. Care Soc. Prev: Sen. Regist.Intens. care, Alfred Hosp. Melborne, Australia; Locum

MATTHEWS

Cons. Anaesth., Morriston Hosp.; Specialist Regist. Anaesth., Cardiff Rotat.

MATTHEWS, Peter Jeffrey Department of Anaesthesia, Rotherham General Hospital, Morgate Road, Oakwood, Rotherham S60 2UD — MB BS 1979 Newc.; FFA RCS Eng. 1984. Cons., Rotherham Gen. Hosp. Prev: Sen. Regist. (Anaesth.) Nottm. HA.; Regist. (Anaesth.) Sheff. HA; SHO (Aneath.) Nottm. HA.

MATTHEWS, Philip James Mario 4 Parc Des Frais Vents, Bagatelle Road, St Saviour, Jersey JE2 7TL — MB BS 1992 Lond.

MATTHEWS, Philip Lyndon Gower Medical Practice, Scurlage Surgery, Monksland Road, Scurlage, Swansea SA3 1AY Tel: 01792 390413 Fax: 01792 390093; Murton Lodge, Murton, Swansea SA3 3AT Tel: 01792 233782 — MB BS 1984 Lond.; MRCGP 1988; DRCOG 1988; MSc (Med. Educ.) Wales 1998. (St Mary's Hospital London) Course Organizer Swansea VTS.

MATTHEWS, Mr Philip Nevill Dept. of Urol., Univ. Hosp. of Wales, Heath Park, Cardiff Tel: 02920 743318 Fax: 02920 744179 Email: philip.mathews@uhw-tr.wales.nhs.uk; The Old Rectory, St. Mary Church, Cowbridge CF71 7LT Tel: 01446 773334 Fax: 01446 771404 Email: philmathews@doctors.org.uk — MB BS 1971 Lond.; FRCS Eng. 1977; FRCS Ed. 1976. Cons. Urol. Univ. Hosp. Wales. Socs: Brit. Assn. of Neurol. Surg. (Hon Sec); Amer. Unlogy Assn.; Europ. Assn. of Unlogy.

MATTHEWS, Philip Richard ACORNS Primary Care Act Pilot, Grays Health Centre, Brooke Road, Grays RM17 5BY Tel: 01375 397470 — MB BS 1988 Newc.; BMedSc. (Hons.) Newc. 1987; MRC Psych 1996; MRCGP 1992; T(GP) 1992; DRCOG 1992. (Newcastle upon Tyne) p/t GP 'Acorns' Primary Care Act Pilot Scheme, Thurrock Primary Care Trust. Socs: BMA; Med. Practitioner Union; Anglo-French Med. Soc. Prev: GP Facilitator (Primary Care for Homeless People) Camden & Islington; Regist. (Psychiat.) Darlington Memor. Hosp.; Regist. (PsychoGeriat.) Newc. Gen. Hosp.

MATTHEWS, Philippa Margaret Lee Bank Group Practice, Colston Health Centre, 10 Bath Row, Lee Bank, Birmingham B15 1LZ Tel: 0121 622 4846 Fax: 0121 622 7105; 34 Grove Avenue, Moseley, Birmingham B13 9RY — MB BS 1985 Newc.; BMed Sci 1982; MRCGP 1989; DRCOG 1987.

MATTHEWS, Richard Mark Stuart (retired) 2 Repton Avenue, Gidea Park, Romford RM2 5LR Tel: 01708 741603 — MB BChir 1942 Camb.; MRCGP 1968. Prev: RAF Med. Serv. 1943-47.

MATTHEWS, Mr Richard Napier Dept. cosmetic and Reconstructive Surgery, Warwickshire Nuffield Hospital, Old Milverton Lane, Leamington Spa CV32 6RW Tel: 01926 436341 Fax: 01926 422659; The Rooms, The Old Hall, Lilbourne Road, Clifton-upon-Dunsmore, Rugby CV23 0BD Tel: 01788 561057 Fax: 01926 422659 — MB BS 1972 Lond.; FRCS Eng. 1978; FRCS Ed. 1977. (St. Thos.) Cons. Plastic, Reconstruc. & Hand Surg. Geo. Eliot Hosp. Nuneaton, Coventry & Warks. Hosp. Coventry & Hosp. of St. Cross Rugby; Clin. Dir. Specialist Serv. Geo. Eliot NHS Trust; Dep. Med. Director Geo. Eliot NHS Trust; Chairm. W. Midl.s Specialty Advisery Comm. in Burns and Plastic Surg.; W. Midl.s Regional Specialty Adviser in Burns and Plastic Surg. to the Roy. Coll. of Surg.s of Eng. Socs: Brit. Assn. Plastic Surg.; Brit. Assn. Aesthetic Plastic Surgs.; (Ex-Pres.) Warks. Medico-Legal Soc. Prev: Sen. Regist. (Plastic Surg.) W. Middlx. Univ. Hosp. Isleworth & Mt. Vernon Hosp. N.wood; Regist. (Burns & Plastic Surg.) Odstock Hosp.; Research Fell. (Burns) Qu. Vict. Hosp. E. Grinstead.

MATTHEWS, Robert John 2 Sand Close, Bradford-on-Avon BA15 1BJ — MB BS 1985 Lond.; BSc Lond. 1982; MRCGP 1990.

MATTHEWS, Robin Frederic John 12 McAdam Drive, Enfield EN2 8PS Tel: 020 8367 5828 — MRCS Eng. LRCP Lond. 1967; FFA RCS Eng. 1972; DA Eng. 1969. (Guy's) Cons. Anaesth. Chase Farm Hosps. NHS Trust Enfield. Prev: Sen. Regist. & Regist. (Anaesth.) St. Bart. Hosp. Lond.; SHO (Anaesth.) N. Middlx. Hosp. Lond.

MATTHEWS, Roderic Stephen Innisfree, 10 Gortycavan Road, Macosquin, Coleraine BT51 4LT Tel: 01265 2466 — MB BCh BAO 1964 Belf.; FRCPI 1984, M 1967. Cons. Dermat. N. Area Health Bd. Socs: Brit. Assn. Dermat. & Irish Assn. Dermat. Prev: Tutor Microbiol. Qu. Univ. Belf.; Sen. Regist. (Dermat.) Roy. Vict. Hosp. Belf.

MATTHEWS, Roger Stuart James, Wing Cdr. RAF Med. Br. RAF Centre of Aviation Medicine, RAF Henlow, Henlow SG16 6DN Tel: 01462 851515 Ext: 8052 Fax: 01462 851274 Email: rmatthews@rafcam.org.uk; 1 Young's Orchard, Brimscombe, Strand GL5 2RU Tel: 01453 731960 Email: youngsorchard@btinternet.com — MB BS 1984 Lond.; BSc 1981 Lond.; MRCGP 1989; AFOM RCP Lond. 1992; DAvMed. FOM RCP Lond. 1992. (Guy's) SpROM RAF Centre of Aviat. Med., Henlow, Beds. Socs: Assn. Fac. of Occupat.al Med.; Soc. of Occupat.al Med.; Aerospace Med. Assn. Prev: Med. Staff Off., MOD Lond.; Exchange Off. (USAF) Brooks AFB San Antonio Tx.; Sen Med. Off. RAF Learning.

MATTHEWS, Roy Alan Wych Hazel House, Cumberland Gardens, Castle Bytham, Grantham NG33 4SQ Tel: 01780 410554 — MB BS 1952 Lond.; MRCS Eng. LRCP Lond. 1952; MFPHM 1989; MFCM 1972; DPH Eng. 1962. (Middlx.) Emerit. Community Phys. Leics. DHA. Socs: FRSH; FRIPHH. Prev: SCM P'boro. HA; Dist. Community Phys. Leics. HA & Med. Off. (Environm. Health) Rutland HarBoro. & Melton Dists; Co. Med. Off. & Princip. Sch. Med. Off. Rutland CC Apptd. Fact. Doctor.

MATTHEWS, Professor Ruth Christine Department of Medical Microbiology, Clinical Sciences Building, MRI Oxford Road, Manchester M13 9WL — MB BS 1980 Lond.; MRCS Eng. LRCP Lond. 1980; BSc (1st cl Hons.) Lond. 1977, Msc (Distinc.) 1983, MD 1986; PhD Lond. 1989; FRCPath 1996. (Univ. Coll. Hosp. & St. Thos.) Reader (Med. Microbiol.) & Hon. Cons. Manch. Univ.; Dir. UK Pertussis Refer. Laborat. Prev: Wellcome Trust Sen. Research Fell.

MATTHEWS, Sara Helen Margaret 107 Sutton Court, Sutton Court Road, London W4 3EE — MB BCh 1982 Wales.

MATTHEWS, Sara Jacqueline Nottinghill House, 118 Malone Road, Belfast BT9 5HR — MB BCh BAO 1991 Belf.

MATTHEWS, Sarah Ann Sussex House, 1 St Johns Road, Loughton IG10 1RZ Tel: 020 8502 1942 Fax: 020 8508 0954 — MB BS 1971 Lond.; MRCP (UK) 1974; MRCS Eng. LRCP Lond. 1971. (St. Bart.) p/t Cons. Dermat. Havering Hosps. Trust; Cons. Dermat. Mid Essex Hosp. Trust. Socs: Fell. Roy. Soc. Med.; Brit. Assn. Dermat. Prev: Staff Dermat. OldCh. & Harold Wood Hosp. Romford; Regist. (Dermat.) OldCh. Hosp. Romford; SHO (Med.) St. Leonards Hosp. Nuttall St. Lond.

MATTHEWS, Sarah Judith 3 Cedar Road, Loughborough LE11 2AB Tel: 01509 234313 — MB BS 1991 Lond.; MRCGP 1995. Assoc. Mem. Leicester GP Fac. Bd.

MATTHEWS, Sharon Lynn Beverley Ann 344 Foxhill Road, Carlton, Nottingham NG4 1QD — MB ChB 1991 Manch.

MATTHEWS, Sheila Rosemary Childrens Services Directorate, St Mary's Hospital, London Road, Kettering NN15 7PW Tel: 01536 410099 Fax: 01536 417076 — MB ChB 1981 Glas.; DRCOG 1983. Staff Grade (Child Health & Family Plann.) Rockingham Forest NHS Trust. Prev: GP Corby; Trainee GP Kettering Dist. VTS; SHO (Anaesth.) Kettering Gen. Hosp.

MATTHEWS, Stephanie Beatrix 14 Maillards Haven, Penarth CF64 5RF — MB BCh 1978 Wales; PhD Wales 1983, MB BCh 1978; FRCPath. (Wales)

MATTHEWS, Stephen Low Hill Cottage, Low Hill, Baildon, Shipley BD17 6BD — MB ChB 1988 Leic.; BSc Leic. 1982, MB ChB 1988; T(GP) 1992. Trainee GP Leics. VTS.

MATTHEWS, Stephen James 27 Cardiff Road, Dinas Powys CF64 4DH — MB BCh 1986 Wales.

MATTHEWS, Mr Stuart John Elson Chancellor Wing, St. James's University Hospital, Leeds LS9 7TF Tel: 0113 206 4795 Fax: 0113 206 5156 Email: trauma@matthaus85.fabusiness.co.uk — MB BS 1980 Lond.; FRCS Ed. 1987; FRCS Eng. 1987; MRCS Eng. LRCP Lond. 1980; T(S) 1993. (Guy's) Cons. Trauma Surg. St. Jas. Univ. Hosp. Leeds; Hon. Clin. Sen. Lect. St. Jas. Univ. Hosp. Leeds. Socs: Fell. BOA; AO Alumni; Brit. Limb Reconstruct. Soc. Prev: AO Fell. (Pelvis/Acetabulum) Carolinas Med. Centre N. Carolina, USA; Sen. Regist. (Trauma) John Radcliffe Hosp. Oxf.; Sen. Regist. Profess. Unit Nuffield Orthop. Centre Oxf.

MATTHEWS, Susan Margaret 6 Glebe Close, Ambrosden, Bicester OX25 2LH — MB BCh BAO 1984 NUI.

MATTHEWS, Suzanne (Ward) Radiology Department, Northern General Hospital, Herries Road, Sheffield S5 7AU; Tel: 0114 255 2863 — MB BS 1989 Lond.; BSc Lond. 1986; MRCP (UK) 1992; FRCR 1997. (Guys Hosp.) Cons. (Radiol.), N.ern Gen. Hosp., Sheff. Socs: Roy. Coll. Radiol.; Radiological Soc. of N. America. Prev: Regist. (Radiol.) Roy. Hallamsh. Hosp. Sheff.; Fell.Thoracic Imaging Vancouver GH Canada; Regist. (Respirat. Med.) Guy's Hosp. Lond.

MATTHEWS, Mrs Sylvia Mavis (retired) 60 Loughborough Road, West Bridgford, Nottingham NG2 7JJ Tel: 0115 988221 — MB BS

1940 Madras; DGO 1942. Prev: Asst. MOH City Health Dept. Nottm.

MATTHEWS, Terence Haydn John Sussex House, 1 St Johns Road, Loughton IG10 1RZ Tel: 020 8502 1942 Fax: 020 8508 0954 Email: terry.matthews@lineone.net — MB BS 1969 Lond.; BSc (Hons.) Physiol. Lond. 1966; MRCP (U.K.) 1972; MRCS Eng. LRCP Lond. 1969; DCH Eng. 1972; LLM 1999; FRCP 1998; FRCPCH 1998. (Lond. Hosp.) Cons. Clin. Risk Adviser BHB Community Healthcare Trust St Geo.'s Hosp. HornCh. Essex; Hon. Cons. Paediat. Hosp. Sick Childr. Gt. Ormond St. Socs: BMA. Prev: Cons. Paediat. Havering Hosp.s Trust; Sen. Regist. Qu. Eliz. Hosp. Childr. Hackney; Lect. (Child Health) St. Bart. & Lond. Hosp. Med. Colls.

MATTHEWS, Terence Keith South Humber Health Authority, Health Place, Wrawby Road, Brigg DN20 8GS Tel: 01652 601133 Fax: 01652 601126 Email: terry.matthews@shumber_ha.trent.nhs.uk; 5 Herrington Avenue, Nettleham, Lincoln LN2 2XU Tel: 01522 807637 — MB ChB 1975 MB ChB Liverp. 1975; 1991 MCommH Liverp. Sch. Trop. Med.; 1983 MRCGP; 1979 DTM & H Liverp.; 1998 MFPHM. Cons. In Pub. Hlth. & commun. Dis. Control Sth. Humber Hlth Auth. Brigg. Prev: Regist. (Pub. Health Med.) S. Lincs. HA.

MATTHEWS, Mr Timothy David Academic Unit of Neuroscience, Charing Cross Hospital, Fulham Palace Road, London W6 8RF Tel: 020 8846 7712 Fax: 020 8846 7715; Spring Cottage, Spring St, Epsom KT17 1UH — MB BS 1985 Lond.; BSc (Hons.) Lond. 1982, MB BS 1985; FRCS Eng. 1989; FRCOphth 1989, M 1989; DO RCS Eng. 1989. Research Fell. (Neuro Ophth.) Char. Cross & W.m. Med. Sch. Lond. Socs: Fell. Roy. Soc. Med. Prev: Regist. (Ophth.) Moorfields Eye Hosp. Lond.; SHO (Ophth.) Char. Cross Hosp. Lond.; SHO (Neurosurg.) St. Bart. Hosp. Lond.

MATTHEWS, Timothy Paul Mossley Hill Hospital, Park Avenue, Liverpool L18 4PZ Tel: 0151 250 3000; 3 Lampton Close, Wool, Wareham BH20 6EW Tel: 01929 462128 — MB ChB 1995 Bristol. (Bristol) SHO Rotat. (Psychiat.) Liverp. Socs: Med. Defence Union; BMA.

MATTHEWS, Tina Jane Department of Histopathology, Epsom General Hospital, Dorking Road, Epsom KT18 7EG Tel: 01372 735185 Email: tmatthew@sthelier.sghm.ac uk — BM 1983 Soton.; MRCPath 1991; DHMSA Soc. Apoth. Lond. 1996. Cons. Histopath. Epsom Gen. Hosp. Socs: Fell.Roy. Soc. of Med. Counc. Mem. Hist. of Med. Sect. Prev: Sen. Regist. (Histopath.) Roy. Berks. Hosp. Reading & Brompton Hosps. Lond.; Regist. (Histopath.) Mt. Vernon Hosp. N.wood; Regist. (Histopath.) Soton. Gen. Hosp.

MATTHEWS, Trevor Stacey Overtown Farm, Cowan Bridge, Carnforth LA6 2HT Tel: 015242 71443 — MB BChir 1959 Camb.; MB Camb. 1959, BChir 1958; FRCP Lond. 1978, M 1962; MRCS Eng. LRCP Lond. 1958. (St. Bart.) Prev: Cons. Paediat. Roy. Lancaster Infirm. & W.morland Co. Hosp. Kendal; MRC Clin. Research Fell. Dept. Immunol. Inst. Child Health Lond.; Clin. Lect. (Paediat.) Makerere Univ. Coll. Kampala, Uganda.

MATTHEWS, Professor Walter Bryan Sandford House, Sandford-on-Thames, Oxford OX4 4YN Tel: 01865 771704 — BM BCh Oxf. 1943; DM Oxf. 1949; FRCP Lond. 1963, M 1948. (Oxf.) Emerit. Prof. Clin. Neurol. Oxf. Socs: Fell. Derby Med. Soc. Prev: Cons. Neurol. Derby Roy. Infirm., Manch. Roy. Infirm. & Crumpsall Hosp.

MATTHEWS, Wendy Carol Whipps Cross Hospital, Whipps Cross Road, Leytonstone, London E11 1NR Tel: 020 8539 5522; 8 Ascot House, Redhill St, London NW1 4DB Tel: 020 7383 5630 — MB BS 1994 Lond.; BSc (Hons.) Lond. 1986. SHO Dept. Med. Elderly People Whipps Cross Hosp. Lond. Prev: SHO HIV Med. N. Middlx. Hosp. Lond.; SHO Med. Rotat. Whittington Hosp. Lond.; SHO (A & E) UCLH Lond.

***MATTHEWS, Wendy Louise** Woodlea, Ludlow Rd, Church Stretton SY6 6AD — MB ChB 1997 Sheff.

MATTHEWSON, David Iain 119 Deveron Road, Troon KA10 7JH — MB ChB 1990 Ed.; MRCGP 1994. Trainee GP/SHO (Obst.) Ayrsh. & Aran HB.

MATTHEWSON, Kenneth Tel: 0191 282 4610 Fax: 0191 282 0135 Email: ken.matthewson@nuth.northy.nhs.uk; 10 Woodside, Hexham NE46 1HU Tel: 01434 605860 — MB BS 1979 Newc.; MD Newc. 1991; FRCP Lond. 1996; MRCP (UK) 1982. (Newc. u. Tyne) Cons. Phys. and Gastroenterologist, Roy. Vict. Infirm., Newc. upon Tyne. Socs: Brit. Soc. Gastroenterol. Prev: Cons. Phys. Hexham Gen.

Hosp.; Sen. Regist. (Med.) Soton. Gen. Hosp.; Research Sen. Regist. (Gastroenterol.) St. Jas. Hosp. Balham & Univ. Coll. Hosp. Lond.

MATTHEWSON, Mr Murray Hugh 18 Queens Ediths Way, Cambridge CB1 7PN Tel: 01223 244040 — MB ChB 1967 Otago; MA Camb. 1985; FRCS Eng. 1973. (Otago) Cons. Orthop. & Hand Surg. Addenbrooke's Hosp. Camb.; Assoc. Lect. Univ. Camb; Fell. Hughes Hall Camb.; Examr. Intercollegiate Bd. Trauma & Orthop. Surg. Socs: Fell. BOA; Mem. Brit. Soc. Surg. Hand - Vice Pres. 2002. Prev: Sen. Regist. (Orthop.) Addenbrooke's Hosp. Camb.; Spinal Fell. Robt. Jones & Agnes Hunt Hosp. OsW.ry; Vis. Prof. Univ. Texas Health Sci. Center, San Antonio, USA.

MATTHEY, Francis East Surrey Hospital, Canada Avenue, Redhill RH1 5RH Tel: 01737 768551 Fax: 01737 780396; 9 Greville Park Avenue, Ashtead KT21 2QS — MB BS 1980 Lond.; BSc Bristol 1973; FRCP Lond. 1995; MRCP (UK) 1983; MRCPath 1989; FRCPath 1998. Cons. Haemat. E. Surrey Hosp. Redhill. Socs: Brit. Soc. Haematol. Prev: Clin. Lect. & Hon. Sen. Regist. (Haemat.) Univ. Coll. & Middlx. Hosp. Med. Sch. Lond.; Regist. (Haemat.) Roy. Free Hosp. Lond.; Regist. (Med.) Univ. Coll. Hosp. Lond.

MATTHIAS, John Evan Albert Road Medical Centre, Harlescott, Shrewsbury SY1 4HY Tel: 01743 281950 Fax: 01743 233198 Email: andrew.pattison@gp-m82032.nhs.uk; 245 Wenlock Road, Shrewsbury SY2 6SA Tel: 01743 245930 Email: jm.matthias@virgin.net — MB ChB 1968 Birm.; BSc (Hons.) (Anat.) Birm. 1965. Gen. Practitioner Princip. Prev: SHO (Paediat.) E. Birm. Hosp.; Ho. Surg., Ho. Phys. & Ho. Off. (O & G) Dudley Rd. Hosp. Birm.

MATTHIAS, Sheila 2 Llwynderi Road, Newport NP20 4LW Tel: 01633 262748 — MB BCh 1966 Wales; DRCOG 1968.

MATTHIENSEN, Ulrike Room 19 Main Doctors' Residence, Newcastle General Hospital, Westgate Road, Newcastle upon Tyne NE4 6BE — State Exam Med 1992 Frankfurt.

MATTHIES, Frank Alexander Karl Salisbury District Hospital, 47D Victoria Drive E., Salisbury SP2 8BJ — State Exam Med. Gottingen 1992.

MATTHOLIE, Kevin Mark St James Road Surgery, 22 St. James Road, Torpoint PL11 2BH Tel: 01752 812404 Fax: 01752 816436 — MB 1974 Camb.; BA Camb. 1970, MB 1974, BChir 1973; MRCGP Lond. 1981; DCH Eng. 1980. (Camb. & Lond. Hosp.) GP Cornw..

MATTI, Mr Basim Azer 30 Harley Street, Flat 2, London W1G 9PW Tel: 020 7637 9595 Fax: 020 7636 1639 — MB ChB 1973 Mosul; FRCS Ed. 1981. Indep. Cons. Plastic Surg. Socs: Brit. Assn. Aesthetic Plastic Surgs.; Internat. Soc. Aesthetic Plastic Surg.; Brit. Assn. Plastic Surg. Prev: Sen. Regist. (Plastic Surg.) W. Middlx. Hosp. Isleworth, Hammersmith Hosp. & St. Mary's Hosp. Lond.; Sen. Regist. (Plastic Surg.) Fulwood Hosp. Sheff.; Regist. (Plastic Surg.) Basildon & Thurrock HA.

MATTICK, Mr Anthony Peter Royal Infirmary of Edinburgh, 1 Lauriston Place, Edinburgh EH3 9YW Tel: 0131 536 4000; Tel: 0131 661 8658 — MB ChB 1989 Aberd.; FFAEM 2000; FRCS Ed. 1996; DA (UK) 1992. (Aberd.) Specialist Regist. (A & E) Edin. Roy. Infirm. Socs: Fac. A & E Med.; Brit. Assn. Accid. & Emerg. Med.; BMA.

MATTICK, James Alexander 17 Pateley Road, Woodthorpe, Nottingham NG3 5QF — MB ChB 1993 Leeds; MB ChB Leeds. 1993.

MATTINGLY, Professor David Tel: 01392 254754 — MB BS; MB BS Lond. 1953; FRCP Lond. 1969, M 1958; FRCGP (Hon.) 1988. (St. Thos.) Emerit. Prof. Postgrad. Med. Studies Univ. Exeter. Socs: Assn. Phys. Prev: Phys. Roy. Devon & Exeter Hosp.; Regist. (Metab. Dis.) & Ho. Phys. St. Thos. Hosp. Lond.; Sen. Regist. (Med.) Hammersmith Hosp.

MATTINGLY, Peter Croston Rheumatology Department, Kettering General Hospitals NHS Trust, Rothwell Road, Kettering NN16 8UZ Tel: 01536 492384; 3 Pine Court, Little Brington, Northampton NN7 4EZ Tel: 01604 770405 — MB BS 1971 Lond.; FRCP Lond. 1993; MRCP (UK) 1974. (Middlx.) Cons. Rheumatologist Rheum. Dept. Kettering Gen. Hosp. NHS Trust Kettering. Socs: Brit. Soc. Rheum. Prev: Sen. Regist. (Rheum. & Rehabil.) Nuffield Orthop. Centre Oxf.; Regist. (Gen. Med.) Poole Gen. Hosp.; Ho. Phys. Middlx. Hosp.

MATTINGLY, Stephen, TD Highfield House, Steeple Lane, Little Brington, Northampton NN7 4HN Tel: 01604 770271 — MB BS

MATTINSON

Lond. 1946; FRCP Lond. 1970, M 1955; DPhysMed. Eng. 1953. (Univ. Coll. Hosp.) Emerit. Cons. Phys. The Middlx. Hosp. Socs: Sen. Companion Fell. BOA; Life Mem. Brit. Soc. Rheum. Prev: Cons. Phys. Middlx. Hosp. Lond.; Med. Dir. Garston Manor Rehabil. Centre; Hon. Cons. Rheum. & Rehabil. to Army.

MATTINSON, Alison Beverley Westfield House, Westfield Drive, Gosforth, Newcastle upon Tyne NE3 4XY — MB BS 1984 Newc.; MRCGP 1988; DCH RCP Lond. 1987; DRCOG 1986.

MATTINSON, Peter Jonathan Brian Westfield House, Westfield Drive, Gosforth, Newcastle upon Tyne NE3 4XY; Chastleton, Newton Drive, Framwellgate Moor, Durham DH1 5BH Tel: 384 6171 — MB BS 1984 Newc.; MRCGP 1988; DRCOG 1986; DCH RCP Lond. 1988.

MATTISON, Adrian Edward (retired) Springwood, 40 New Platt Lane, Crewe CW4 8NJ — MB ChB Liverp. 1963; DMRD Eng. 1968. Prev: Cons. Radiol. Wythenshawe & N. Chesh. Gp. Hosps.

MATTISON, Avril Felice Collegiate Medical Centre, Brideoak Street, Manchester M8 0AT Tel: 0161 205 4364 Fax: 0161 203 5511; 38 Holden Road, Salford M7 4LR — MB ChB 1972 Liverp.; MRCGP 1988. Prev: SHO (Gen. Med.) & Ho. Off. (Gen. Surg.) Walton Hosp. Liverp.; Clin. Asst. (Cas.) Manch. Roy. Infirm.

MATTISON, Harry 1 Reservoir Road, Liverpool L25 6HR Tel: 0151 428 5245 — M.B., Ch.B. Leeds 1931. (Leeds)

MATTISON, Michael Lewis Unsworth Medical Centre, Parr Lane, Unsworth, Bury BL9 8JR; 38 Holden Road, Salford M7 4LR — MB ChB 1971 Liverp.; MRCP (UK) 1974; MRCGP 1980; DIH Eng. 1981; AFOM RCP Lond. 1981. Prev: Tutor Med. Manch. Roy. Infirm.

MATTOCK, Christopher Haematology Department, The General Hospital, St Helier, Jersey Tel: 01534 622597 Fax: 01534 622883 — MB BS 1981 Lond.; BSc Lond. 1978; MRCP (UK) 1985; MRCPath 1992; T(M) 1992; T(Path.) 1992; FRCP 2000 Edinburgh; FRCPath 2000; FRCP 1999 London. (Univ. Coll. Hosp.) Cons. Clin. Haemat. & Blood Transfus. Gen. Hosp. St. Helier Jersey; Director of Path. Socs: Brit. Blood Trasfusion Soc.; Brit. Soc. Thrombosis & Haemostasis. Prev: Sen. Regist. (Haemat.) NE Thames RHA; Clin. Lect. (Haemat.) Univ. Coll. & Middlx. Sch. Med. Lond.; Bernard Sunley Fell. Roy. Coll. Surg. Eng.

MATTOCK, Elizabeth Jane York District Hospital, Wigginton Road, York YO31 8HE Tel: 01904 631313; 44 The Village, Haxby, York YO32 3HX — MB ChB 1973 Manch.; BSc (Hons.) Manch. 1970, MB ChB (Hons.) 1973; FRCS Eng. 1978; MRCOG 1982. Cons. O & G York Dist. Hosp.

MATTOCK, Robert Pickard 1 Eastcourt Mansions, Limekin Lane, Bridlington YO15 2LU — MB ChB 1941 Leeds. (Leeds)

MATTOCKS, Alison Nicola Brackenfield, 50C Smith House Lane, Brighouse HD6 2LF — MB BS 1988 Lond.; DRCOG 1993. GP Bradford.

MATTS, Suzy Jane Flavell 31 Snellsnook Lane, Nanpantan, Loughborough LE11 3YA Tel: 01509 239258 — MB ChB 1991 Birm.; DFFP 1995; MRCOG 1997. Cons. (Obs. And Gynae) and Lead Obst., Geo. Eliot Hosp., Nuneaton, Warks. Socs: Brit. Soc. of Colposcopy and Cervical Path. (BSCCP); Birm. and Midl.s Obst. and Gyn. Soc. (BMOGS). Prev: Regist. (O & G) Solihull Hosp.; Sen. Regist. (O&G), Walsgrave Hosp., Coventry; Regist. (O&G), Birm. Wom.'s Hosp.

MATTS, Sydney Geoffrey Flavell Alton Lodge, 31 Snells Nook Lane, Nanpantan, Loughborough LE11, 3YA Tel: 01509 239258 Fax: 01509 239258 — MB ChB 1951 Birm.; FRCP Ed. 1971, M 1958; MRCS Eng. LRCP Lond. 1951. (Birm.) Cons. Phys. Leicester & LoughBoro. Hosps.; Lord of Mt.sorrel; Phys. i/c Cardiorespiral. Clin. Physiol. Unit Glenfield Gen. Hosp. Leics.; Clin. Teach. (Med.) Univ. Leics. Med. Sch. Socs: Fell. Europ. Assn. Internal Med.; Brit. Soc. Gastroenterol.; ACP USA 1994. Prev: Sen. Regist. (Med.) Roy. Marsden Hosp., Roy. Cancer Hosp., Chester Beatty Research Inst. & Inst. Dis. Chest Lond.; Sen. Regist. Cardiothoracic Centre Frenchay Hosp. Bristol.

MATTU, Gurdial Singh 240 Bristol Road, Edgbaston, Birmingham B5 7SL — MB BCh 1993 Wales.

MATUK, Mohammad Daoud The Surgery, 4 Old Mill Lane, Barnsley S70 2LA Tel: 01226 284641; 2 Carlton Croft, Sandal, Wakefield WF2 6DA — MB ChB 1953 Birm.; DObst RCOG 1954. (Birm.) Mem. Med. Bd. Dept. Health & Social Security. Socs: BMA. Prev: Ho. Surg. Kidderminster Gen. Hosp.; Sen. Ho. Off. O & G

Dudley Rd. Hosp. Birm.; Regist. O & G Marston Green Matern. Hosp. Birm.

MATUSIEWICZ, Simon Paul Lincoln County Hospital, Greetwell Road, Lincoln LN2 4AX — MB ChB 1983 Leeds; MRCP UK 1987. Cons. Phys. (Gen. & Respirat. Med.) Lincoln Co. Hosp.

MATUTES JUAN, Maria De La Estrella Haematology Department, Royal Marsden Hospital, Fulham Road, London SW3 6JJ Tel: 020 7808 2876 Fax: 020 7351 6420 Email: estella@icr.ac.uk; Flat 11, Cavaye Place, London SW10 9PT Tel: 0207 3735745 — LMS 1976 Barcelona; PhD Lond. 1988; MRCPath 1989; FRCPath 1999. Reader & Hon. Cons. Haemat. Roy. Marsden Hosp. Lond. Socs: Brit. Soc. Haematol. & Amer. Soc. Haemat.; Brit. Task ce; NEQVAS. Prev: Sen. Lect. & Hon. Sen. Regist. Roy. Marsden Hosp. Lond.

MATYKA, Krystyna Anna Birmingham Heartlands Hospital NHS Trust, Bordesley Green East, Birmingham B9 5SS — MB BS 1984 Lond.; MRCP (UK) 1989. Sen. Lect., Paediatric Diabetes, Birm. Heatlands Hosp.. Prev: Research Fell. (Paediat.) John Radcliffe Hosp. Oxf.; Regist. Rotat. (Paediat.) Mayday Hosp. Croydon & St. Geo. Hosp. Tooting; Research Fell. (Metab. Med.) Guy's Hosp. Lond.

***MATZER VAN BLOOIS, Mechteld Suzanna** The Shieling, Violet Way, Loudwater, Rickmansworth WD3 4JP — MB BS 1994 Lond.

MAUCHLINE, Rosalyn Mary 100 Bankton Park W., Murieston, Livingston EH54 9BS — MB ChB 1977 Aberd.

MAUD, Mr George John Haley (retired) Abbeyfield House, South Road, Alnwick NE66 2NZ Tel: 01665 602625 — MRCS Eng. LRCP Lond. 1933; MB BChir Camb. 1936; MA Camb. 1936; FRCS Ed. 1938. Prev: Sen. Surg. Regist. S. Devon & E. Cornw. Hosp. Plymouth.

MAUDAR, Joseph Andre 133 Manchester Old Road, Middleton, Manchester M24 4DZ Tel: 0161 643 5005 Fax: 0161 654 7264 — MB BCh BAO 1959 NUI; FRCP Ed. 1994, M 1963. (Univ.Coll.Dublin)

***MAUDE, Karen Michele** 62 South Park Av, Middlesbrough TS6 0PA — MB ChB 1997 Leeds.

MAUDGAL, Dharam P Day Surgery/ Endoscopic Unit, Barnet General Hospital, Wellhouse Lane, Barnet EN5 3DJ Tel: 07885 196237; 107 Harrowes Meade, Edgware HA8 8RS Tel: 020 8958 5964 Fax: 020 8931 9721 Email: d.maudgal@lineone.net — MB BS Punjabi 1967; PhD (Med.) Lond. 1981; FRCP Lond. 1995; MRCP (UK) 1975. (Med. Coll. Patiala) Cons. Phys. (Gastroenterol.) Barnet & Chase farm Hosp. Trust. Socs: Fell. Roy. Soc. Med.; Brit. Soc. Gastroenterol.; Assur. Med. Soc. Prev: Cons. Gastroenterol. N.wick Pk. Hosp. Harrow; Sen. Regist. (Med. & Gastroenterol.) St. Geo. Hosp. & Med. Sch. Lond.; Cons. Phys. (Gastroenterol.) Manor Ho. Hosp. Lond.

MAUDGIL, Mr Bhagwan Dass Maudgil, Doctors Surgery, 1 Cordwallis Road, Maidenhead SL6 7DQ Tel: 01628 27284 Fax: 01628 32432 — MB BS 1959 Punjab; FRCS Eng. 1972.

MAUDGIL, Deepinder Redfern, Lock Avenue, Maidenhead SL6 8JW — MB BS 1991 Lond.

MAUDSLEY, Gillian Department of Public Health, Whelan Building, The Quadrangle, The University of Liverpool, PO Box 147, Liverpool L69 3BX; 31 Rossmore Road W., Overpool, Ellesmere Port, South Wirral CH66 1LW — MB ChB 1984 Liverp.; MPH (Distinc.) Liverp. 1991; MFPHM RCP (UK) 1995; MRCPath 1990. (Univ. Liverp.) Sen. Lect. & Hon. Cons. Pub. Health Med. Univ. Liverp. Prev: Clin. Lect. & Hon. Sen Regist. (Pub. Health Med.) Univ. Liverp.; Sen. Regist. & Regist. (Pub. Health Med.) Mersey RHA; Regist. (Histopath.) BRd.green Hosp. Liverp. & Arrowe Pk. Hosp. Wirral.

***MAUDSLEY, Iain Mark** 21 Barony Street, Edinburgh EH3 6PD — MB ChB 1994 Ed.

MAUDSLEY, Ian Stewart Unsworth Medical Centre, Park Lane, Bury BL0 9YN; 23 Palmerston Close, Ramsbottom, Bury BL0 9YN — MB ChB 1991 Manch. Prev: Trainee GP Bury VTS.

MAUDSLEY, Mr Roy Homer (retired) 4 Ascot Court, London Road, Ascot SL5 8DW Tel: 01344 882142 Email: rmaudsley@clara.net — MB ChB 1942 Liverp.; FRCS Eng. 1950; MRCS.Eng. LRCP Lond. 1943. Prev: RAF Med. Serv.

MAUGER, Jeremy Stuart West Suffolk Hospital NHS Trust, Hardwick Lane, Bury St Edmunds IP33 2QZ Tel: 01284 713330 Fax: 01284 713100 Email: jeremy.mauger@wsh-tr.anglox.nhs.uk; Email: jmauger@btinternet.com — MB BS 1991 Lond.; BSc Lond. 1988;

FRCA 1995. (St. Geo. Hosp. Lond.) Cons. (Anaesth.) W. Suff. Hosp. Socs: BASICS; Assn. Anaesth. Prev: Clin. Fell. (Anaesth.) St Geo. Hosp. Lond.; Spec. Reg. St Geo. Hosp. Lond.; Spec. Reg. Gt. Ormond St. Hosp. Lond.

MAUGHAN, E Hilary 314 Burton Road, Lincoln LN1 3UW — MB BS 1964 Lond.

MAUGHAN, Elizabeth Olive — BM BCh 1991 Oxf.; BA (Hons.) Oxf. 1989; MRCGP 1996; DFFP 1997; MRCP (UK) 1998. (Oxford) p/t Specialist Regist. - W. Midl. Region Rotat.- Haemalotogy.

MAUGHAN, John Harry 33 Linden Avenue, Darlington DL3 8PS Tel: 01325 481104 — MB BS 1942 Durh.; MFCM 1972; DPH Eng. 1948. (Durh.) Prev: Dist. Community Phys. Darlington Health Dist.; Dist. MOH & Div. Med. Off. E. Riding CC; Dep. MOH & Dep. Princip. Sch. Med. Off. Co. Boro. Bournemouth.

***MAUGHAN, Nicola Joanne** Meadowbank, Great Urswick, Ulverston LA12 0ST — MB ChB 1998 Ed.; MB ChB Ed 1998.

MAUGHAN, Philippe Daniel Avenue De L'universite 75, Bruxelles 1050, Belgium; 38 Gosberton Road, London SW12 8LF — MB ChB 1984 Manch.

MAUGHAN, Timothy Stanley Velindre Hospital, Whitchurch, Cardiff CF14 2TL Tel: 029 2061 5888 Fax: 029 2069 4182 Email: tim.maughan@velindre-tr.nhs.wales.uk; Llwyn Celyn House, Pantmawr Road, Whitchurch, Cardiff CF14 7TB Tel: 029 2069 2685 Email: t.maughan@btinternet.com — MB BS 1978 Lond.; MA Camb. 1980, MD 1991; MRCP (UK) 1980; FRCR 1987; FRCP 1997. (University College Hospital London) Cons. Clin. Oncol. Velindre Hosp. Cardiff; Hon. Sen. Lect. Univ. of Wales Coll. of Med.; Director Welsh Cancer Trust Network. Prev: Clin. Lect. Radiother. & Oncol. Addenbrooke's Hosp. Camb.; Regist. (Radiother.) Velindre Hosp. Cardiff; Lect. Coll. Med. Univ. of Juba, Sudan.

MAULE, Brian Henry 5 Broomvale Drive, Newton Mearns, Glasgow G77 5NN Tel: 0141 639 2748 — MB ChB 1969 Glas.; DObst RCOG 1971; FFA RCS Eng. 1974. Cons. (Anaesth.) Roy. Infirm. Glas. Socs: Scott. Soc. Anaesth. & Assn. Anaesths. Gt. Brit. Prev: Sen. Regist. (Anaesth.) Roy. Infirm. Glas.; Regist. (Anaesth.) Vict. Infirm. Glas.

MAULE, Colette Mary — MB ChB 1981 Glas.

MAULE, Evelyn Janette Weir (retired) Aviemore, 49B Hawton Road, Newark NG24 4QA — MB ChB 1950 Glas. Prev: Clin. Med. Off. Centr. Notts. HA.

MAULE, James Harvey 7 Glen Derry, E. Kilbride, Glasgow G74 2JD Tel: 01355 238717 Email: maule@supanet.com — MB ChB 1963 Glas.; FFA RCS Eng. 1969. Hon. Cons. Pain Relief.Prine & P.ss of Wales Hospice Glas. Socs: Brit. Med. Acupunct. Assn.; N. Brit. Pain Assn.

MAULE, Lawrence Carteret Webb Peploe House Surgery, 45 Church Lane, Lymington SO41 3RA Tel: 01590 674118 — MB BS 1983 Lond.

MAULE, Margaret Montieth 1 Relugas Road, Edinburgh EH9 2NE — MB ChB 1943 Ed.; DPM Ed. & Glas. 1963. (Ed.)

MAUNDER, Robert Francis The Health Centre, Laindon, Basildon SS15 5TR Tel: 01268 546411 Fax: 01268 491248 — MB BS 1988 Lond.

MAUNDERS, David Paul The Surgery, 3 Caskgate St., Gainsborough DN21 2DJ — MB BS 1988 Lond.

MAUNG, Dr 62/62 Church Street, Bilston, Wolverhampton Tel: 01902 496065 Fax: 01902 496384 — MB BS 1956 Rangoon.

MAUNG, Maung (retired) St Nicholas Health Centre, Saunder Bank, Burnley BB11 2EN Tel: 01282 423677 Fax: 01282 832945 — MB BS 1976 Med Inst (I) Rangoon.

MAUNG, Swe Win 5 Milldale Road, Farnsfield, Newark NG22 8DQ — MB BS 1984 Rangoon; MB BS Medical Institute (I) Rangoon 1984.

MAUNG, Swe Win Patel and Partners, Thornley Road Surgery, Thornley Road, Wheatley Hill, Durham DH6 3NR Tel: 01429 820233 Fax: 01429 823667 — MB BS 1984 Med Inst (I) Rangoon. (Med Inst (I) Rangoon) GP Durh.

MAUNG CHO, Mr 2 Woodville, Marathon Road, Douglas IM2 4HL — MB BS 1971 Rangoon; FRCS Glas. 1983; FRCS Eng. 1983; FCOphth. 1989; DO RCS Eng. 1981.

MAUNG MAUNG TUN, Nicholas 14 Ploughfield Close, Littleover, Derby DE23 7UT — MB BS 1967 Mandalay. Staff Grade in Psychogeriat. S.ern Derbysh. Ment. HealthTrust, Kingsway Hosp., Derby. Prev: Clin. Asst. in Psychiat. & Ment. Handicap, S.ern

Derbysh. Ment. Health Trust; Trainee in Gen. Pract., Alness & Invergordon Med. Gp., Alness, Scotl.

MAUNG YAY, Dr c/o Dr S. Sann, 10 Corone Close, Folkestone CT19 5LJ — MB BS 1968 Med. Inst. (II) Mingaladon; MB BS Med Inst (II) Mingaladon 1968.

MAURI SOLE, Inmaculada Escobeck, 127 Wells Road, Bath BA2 3AN Tel: 01225 329183 Fax: 01225 319180 Email: inma.mauri_sole@unforgettable.com — LMS 1993 Barcelona; DRCOG 1995; DFFP 1998. (Barcelona) Asist. GP. Prev: GP Regist. Vire Surg. St.; SHO (Elderly Care) Dorset Co. Hosp.; SHO (Paediat.) Yeovil Dist. Hosp.

***MAURICE, Andrew Richard** 12 Linington Avenue, Chesham HP5 1XP — MB ChB 1996 Birm.

MAURICE, Mr Brian Armstead (retired) Churchside, Langton Road, Tunbridge Wells TN4 8XD Tel: 01892 537919 Fax: 01892 510054 Email: brian.maurice@dial.pipex.com — MB BChir 1953; 1958 FRCS Eng. 1958; 1955 MA Camb.; 1961 MChir 1961. Hon. Cons. MPC Healthcare Ltd. Prev: Cons. Surg. Tunbridge Wells Hosp. Gp.

MAURICE, Charles David Jacques Riverside Medical Practice, Roushill, Shrewsbury SY1 1PQ Tel: 01743 352371 Fax: 01743 340269 — MB ChB 1979 Manch.; BSc Med. Sci. Manch. 1976; MRCGP 1989; DA (UK) 1981.

MAURICE, Mr David Greatrex (retired) 7 Norfolk Road, Lytham St Annes FY8 4JG Tel: 01253 733016 — MB BS 1945 Lond.; FRCS Eng. 1952; MRCS Eng. LRCP Lond. 1943. Prev: Cons. Plastic Surg. Sharoe Green Hosp. Preston.

MAURICE, David Pierce Marlborough Medical Practice, The Surgery, George Lane, Marlborough SN8 4BY Tel: 01672 512187 Fax: 01672 516809; Isbury House, Kingsbury St, Marlborough SN8 1JA Tel: 01672 514119 Email: 73503.3270@compuserve.com — MB BChir 1976 Camb.; MA Camb. 1976; DRCOG 1980. Clin. Asst. (Psychogeriat.) Farmer Memor. Unit Savernake Hosp. Wilts. Socs: BMA.

MAURICE, Nicholas David Marlborough Medical Practice, The Surgery, George Lane, Marlborough SN8 4BY Tel: 01672 512187 Fax: 01672 516809; (Surgery) 41 High Street, Marlborough SN8 — MB BChir 1970 Camb.; MA, MB Camb. 1970, BChir 1969; DCH Eng. 1972; DObst RCOG 1972. (St. Mary's) Radio Doctor Wilts. Radio. Prev: Ho. Surg. Surgic. & Thoracic Unit St. Mary's Hosp. Lond.; Med. Off. (Nutrit.ist) Oxfam Team Kampuchea; Ldr. Britain Nepal Med. Trust E. Nepal.

MAURICE, Paul David Lawrence St. Albans City Hospital, Waverley Road, St Albans AL3 5PN — MB BChir 1978 Camb; MD Camb. 1989, MA 1978; FRCP Lond. 1994. Cons. Dermat. W. Herts. Hosps. NHS Trust. Socs: Fell. Brit. Assn. Dermat. Prev: Sen. Regist. (Dermat.) Char. Cross Hosp. & Centr. Middlx. Hosps. Lond.; Regist. (Dermat.) Qu. Med. Centre Nottm.

MAURICE, Miss Susan Caroline Accident & Emergency Department, south Manchester Hospitals NHS Trust, Wythenshawe, Manchester M23 9LT Tel: 0161 291 6046 Fax: 0161 291 6044 Email: sue.maurice@smuht.nwest.nhs.uk; Tel: 01925 756804 — MB BS Lond. 1985; FRCS Eng. 1991. (Middlx. Hosp. Lond.) p/t Cons. in Emerg. Med. Wythenshawe Hosp. S. Machester Univ. Hosp.s NHS Trust. Prev: Sen. Regist. (A & E) Manch. Roy. Infirm.; Sen. Regist. (A & E) W. Yorks.; Regist. (A & E) Roy. Infirm. Edin.

MAURICE, Timothy Kindersley, OBE (retired) Grasmere, Back Lane, Marlborough SN8 1JJ Tel: 01672 512314 — MB BChir 1939 Camb.; MRCS Eng. LRCP Lond. 1937; DObst RCOG 1947. DL. Prev: Resid. Obst. Off. & Ho. Phys. St. Mary's Hosp.

MAURICE-SMITH, Joan Margaret (retired) Chantry House, 11B Barton Road, Ely CB7 4HZ Tel: 01353 663209 — MB BChir 1958 Camb.; BA Camb. 1958.

MAURICE-SMITH, Norman John Gardeners Cottage, Whilton Lodge, Watling St., Norton, Daventry NN11 5LZ — MB 1960 Camb.; BChir 1959.

MAURICE-WILLIAMS, Mr Robert Stephen Neurosurgical Unit, Wellington Hospital, Wellington Place, London NW8 9LE Tel: 020 7722 1224 Fax: 020 7722 3141 — MB BChir 1968 Camb.; MA Camb. 1968, BA (1st cl. Hons. Nat. Sc. Trip.) 1964; FRCP Lond. 1990; FRCS Eng. 1971; MRCP (UK) 1972; MRCS Eng. LRCP Lond. 1967. (Camb. & St. Thos.) Cons. Neurosurg. Roy. Free Hosp. Lond.; Mem. Ct. Examrs. RCS Eng.; Edr. Brit. Jl. Neurosurg.; Chairm. Specialist Train. Comm. in Neurosurg. N. Thames Region. Socs:

MAURY

(Counc.) Hunt. Soc.; (Counc.) Soc. Brit. Neurol. Surgs. Prev: Cons. Neurosurg. SE Thames Regional NeuroSurgic. Unit; Sen. Regist. (Neurosurg.) St. Bart. Hosp. Lond.; Regist. (Neurosurg.) Maudsley Hosp. & Nat. Hosps. Nerv. Dis. Lond.

*MAURY, Anthony Campbell 16 Cromwell Court, Drighlington, Bradford BD11 1DG — MB ChB 1995 Sheff.

MAVALANKAR, Ashutosh Purushottam c/o Mr J. D. F. Martyn, 9 Cherrywood Drive, London SW15 6DS — MB BS 1984 Gujarat.

MAVI, Balwinder Singh 465 Sutton Road, Walsall WS5 3AU — MB ChB 1985 Birm.; ChB Birm. 1985.

MAVOR, Mr Andrew Innes Deane 5 Birkdale Rise, Alwoodley, Leeds LS17 7SU — MB ChB 1980 Leeds; FRCS Ed. 1985.

MAVOR, Christel Joyce Aire Court Community Unit, Lingwell Grove, Middleton, Leeds LS10 4BS — MB ChB 1981 Leeds; MRCPsych 1988. Staff Grade (Psychiat. of Old Age) Aire Ct. Community Unit Leeds. Prev: Clin. Med. Off. (Psychiat. of Old Age) Seacroft Hosp. Leeds.

MAVOR, William Owen The Little House, Chapel Lane, Burley, Ringwood BH24 4DH — MB BChir 1956 Camb.; MB Camb. 1956, BChir 1955; MA Camb. 1956; FRCP Ed. 1982, M. 1965; FRCPath 1977, M 1965. (Camb. & St. Thos.) Cons. Haemat. Winchester & E.leigh Healthcare Trust. Prev: Cons. Haemat. Centr. Hants. Health Dist.; Anglo-Amer. Research Fell. Witwatersrand Univ. Med. Sch. Johannesburg, S. Afr.; Univ. Asst. Path. & Jun. Asst. Path. Univ. Camb.

*MAVRIDES, Andreas 65 Burfold Gardens, London N13 4LR — MB BS 1996 Lond.

*MAVRIDOU, Despina Flat 12, Minstead Court, 21 Westwood Road, Southampton SO17 1DL — BM 1998 Soton.; BM Soton 1998.

MAVRIKIOS, Antonios c/o Mr Nicolas Katsaras, 61 Leatherhead Road, Ashtead KT21 2TP — Ptychio Iatrikes 1990 Patras.

MAVROLEON, Georgios University Medicine, Level D, Centre Block, Southampton General Hospital, Tremona Road, Southampton SO16 6YD Tel: 02380 794155 Fax: 02380 798492 Email: gm2@soton.ac.uk; 93 Cowley Close, Maxbush, Southampton SO16 9WE Tel: 02380 512784 — Ptychio Iatrikes 1991 Patras. Specialist Regist. (Allergy & Clin. Immunol.).

MAVROUDIS, Leonidas Flat 7, Leonard Court, 68 Westbourne Terrace, London W2 3UF — Ptychio Iatrikes 1991 Thessalonika.

MAW, Anne Elizabeth Ailsa Craig Medical Group, 270 Dickenson Road, Longsight, Manchester M13 0YL Tel: 0161 224 5555 Fax: 0161 248 9112 — MB ChB 1982 Manch.; DCH RCP Lond. 1987; DRCOG 1987. GP Longsight Manch.

MAW, Mr Arthur Richard (cons. rooms) Litfield House, Litfield Place, Clifton, Bristol BS8 3LS Tel: 0117 973 1323 Fax: 0117 973 3303 Email: armaw@doctors.org.uk — MB BS Lond. 1963; MS Lond. 1986; FRCS Ed. 1997; FRCS Eng. 1969. (St. Bart.) Cons. Surg. (ENT) St. Michaels Hosp., Bristol Roy. Infirm. & Bristol Roy. Hosp. Sick Childr.; Sen. Clin. Lect. (Otolaryngol.) Univ. Bristol. Socs: Fell Roy. Soc. Med.; Brit. Assn. Otol.; Hon. Mem. Danish Soc. of Otolaryngologists. Prev: Sen. Regist.(ENT) St. Bart. Hosp. Lond.; Lect. (Anat.) Med. Coll. St. Bart. Hosp. Lond.; Wellcome Trust Trav. Research Fell.sh. Univ. Uppsala, Sweden.

MAW, Dane Stephen Jonathan Chasedale, 53 Madeira Park, Tunbridge Wells TN2 5SY Tel: 01892 534815 — MB BS 1962 Lond.; FRCP Lond. 1980, M 1967. (St. Mary's) Indep. Cons. Phys., Tunbridge Wells; Diabetes Centre, E.bourne Dist. Hosp. Socs: Diabetes UK; Eur. Assn. Study Diabetes. Prev: Cons. Phys. (Gen., Diabetes & Endocrinology) Kent & Sussex Weald NHS Trust; Princip. Med. Off., NPI.

*MAW, Graeme 9 Wilden Court, Sunderland SR3 1NL — BM BS 1995 Nottm.

MAW, Khin Phone 36 Elizabeth Road, Walsall WS5 3PF — MB BS 1972 Mingaladon.

MAW, Michael Crompton (retired) Lower Clerk Hill, Whalley, Clitheroe BB7 9DR Tel: 01254 823136 Fax: 01254 823136 — MB ChB 1950 Ed. Prev: Surg. Lt. RNVR.

MAW, Raymond Douglas 5 Cranmore Park, Belfast BT9 6JF — MB BCh BAO 1973 Belf.; FRCP Lond. 1992; FRCPI 1997. Cons. Phys. Genitourin. Med. Roy. Vict. Hosp. Belf.

MAW, Theodore Stafford 3 Hall Farm Close, Sheffield S26 3XW Tel: 0114 287 3700 — MB ChB 1942 St. And.; FRCOphth 1988; DOMS Eng. 1948. (St. And.) Socs: Life Mem. (Ex-Pres.) N. Eng.

Ophth. Soc. Prev: Emerit. Fell. Roy. Coll. Ophth.; Ophth. Surg. Rotherham & Worksop Dist. Gen. Hosp.s.

MAWBY, Irene Mary Mullett 17 Trematon Place, Teddington TW11 9RH — MB ChB 1975 Birm.; MRCGP 1985.

MAWBY, Nicholas Colin Moorland Medical Centre, Dyson House, Regent Street, Leek ST13 6AU Tel: 01538 399008 Fax: 01538 398228 — MB ChB 1976 Ed.; FRCGP 1996, M 1983. (Ed.)

MAWBY, Norman Earl 23 Bertram Drive, Great Meols, Wirral CH47 0LG Tel: 0151 632 2203 Fax: 0151 632 2203 — MRCS Eng. LRCP Lond. 1936. (Liverp.) Med. Cons. S.B. Caldwell & Co.; Dep. Chief Med. Off. Roy. Liver Friendly Soc. Socs: Fell. Roy. Soc. Med.; Fac. Hist. Med. & Pharmacy Soc. Apoth. Lond. Prev: Clin. Asst. (Anaesth.) & Ho. Surg. Liverp. Roy. Infirm.; Staff Surg. Command HQ Malta.

MAWDESLEY-THOMAS, Jonathan The Manor House, Honington, Grantham NG32 2PG — MB BS 1992 Lond.

MAWDSLEY, Eve Muriel (retired) Westfield House, Winchburgh, Broxburn EH52 6QJ Tel: 0131 331 1013 — MB ChB 1953 Manch.; DCH Eng. 1957. Prev: Clin. Med. Off. W. Lothian Unit Community Child Health Serv. Bangour Gen. Hosp. Broxburn.

MAWDSLEY, Jane Victoria Park Health Centre, Bedford Avenue, Birkenhead CH42 4QJ Tel: 0151 645 8384 Fax: 0151 644 9561; Virginia, 28 Mount Road, Upton, Wirral CH49 6JB Tel: 0151 677 1471 — MB ChB 1983 Liverp.; DRCOG 1986. Prev: Trainee GP Arrow Pk. Hosp. Upton Wirral VTS; Ho. Off. (Med. & Surg.) Clatterbridge Hosp. Wirral.

MAWDSLEY, John Howard Hamilton Medical Group, 4 Queens Road, Aberdeen AB15 4ZT Tel: 01224 622345 Fax: 01224 627426 — MB ChB 1974 Aberd.; MRCGP 1980.

*MAWDSLEY, Michael David 16 Shawclough Dr, Rochdale OL12 7HG — MB ChB 1997 Liverp.

MAWDSLEY, Mr Roger (retired) The Thicket, Mountwood Road, Prenton, Birkenhead CH42 8NQ Tel: 0151 608 5126 — MD 1962 Liverp.; BSc (Hons.) Liverp. 1956, MD 1962, MB ChB 1959; FRCS Eng. 1965. Cons. Surg. Mersey RHA.

*MAWDSLEY, Suzannah Kate Victoria 4 Crispin Way, High Wycombe HP11 1PP — MB ChB 1994 Manch.; MB ChB (Hons.) Manch. 1994.

MAWDSLEY, Thomas Gorsey Lane Surgery, 93 Gorsey Lane, Ford, Liverpool L21 0DF Tel: 0151 928 7757 Fax: 0151 928 9125; 31 Far Moss Road, Blundellsands, Liverpool L23 8TG Tel: 0151 924 7783 Email: tmawd2103@aol.com — LM 1959 Rotunda; MA, MB BCh BAO Dub. 1956; DObst RCOG 1960. (T.C.Dub.) Hon. Lect. Dept. Child Health Univ. Liverp. Prev: Regist. Cas. & Admissions Alder Hey Childr. Hosp. Liverp.; Clin. Clerk Rotunda Hosp. Dub.; Ho. Phys. & Ho. Surg. Sir P. Dun's Hosp. Dub.

MAWE, John Frederick Alderley, 36 Church St., Thriplow, Royston SG8 7RE Tel: 01763 208362 Fax: 01763 208062 — MRCS Eng. LRCP Lond. 1942. (St. Bart.) Ho. Surg. (Orthop.) Hill End Hosp. (St. Bart.).

MAWER, Barbara Jane Maureen Lowestoft Hospital, James Papet Health Care Trust, Tennyson Road, Lowestoft NR32 1PT Tel: 01502 587311 Fax: 01502 589112; Lynton House, 5 Church Plain, Loddon, Norwich NR14 6LX Tel: 01502 677284 — MB BS 1967 Lond.; MRCS Eng. LRCP Lond. 1967; DCH Eng. 1975. (Roy. Free) Cons. Community Paediat. James Paget Healthcare Trust. Socs: RCCPCH; BAACH; BACCDA.

MAWER, Caroline Lambeth, Southwark and Lewisham HA, 1 Lower Marsh, London SE1 7NT — MB BS 1987 Lond.; BSc Lond. 1984, MB BS 1987, MSc (Pub. Health) 1994; MFPHM 1997; DRCOG 1992. Cons. (Pub. Health Med.).

MAWER, George Edward 15 Wingate Drive, Didsbury, Manchester M20 2RT Tel: 0161 445 9397 — MB ChB 1960 Ed.; MB ChB (Hons., Leslie Gold Medal) Ed. 1960; PhD Ed. 1963, BSc (1st Hons. Pharmacol.) 1958; FRCP Ed. 1976, M 1965. (Univ. Ed.) Prof. Emerit. Clin. Pharmacol. Univ. Manch.; Hon. Cons. Phys. Manch. Centr. Dist.; Cons. David Lewis Centre for Epilepsy (Chesh.). Socs: Brit. Pharm. Soc.; Internat. League Against Epilepsy. Prev: Lect. (Therap.) Univ. Edin.; Asst. Lect. (Pharmacol.) Univ. Edin.

MAWER, Samantha Ann Justine 15 West End, Long Clawson, Melton Mowbray LE14 4PE — MB ChB 1993 Sheff.; MRCP 1997. Specialist Regist. (Geriat. & Gen. Med.) Walsgrave Hosp. Coventry. Prev: Specialist Regist. (Geriat. & Gen. Med.) Qu.'s Hosp. Burton-on-Trent; SHO (Gen. Med.) Norf. & Norwich Hosp.; SHO (Oncol. & Radiother.) W.on Pk. Hosp. Sheff.

MAWER, Stewart Lancaster Hull Public Health Laboratory, Hull Royal Infirmary, Hull HU3 2JZ Tel: 01482 323046 Fax: 01482 212655 Email: hulsmae@north.phls.nhs.uk — MB BS 1969 Newc.; MSc (Med. Microbiol.) Lond. 1976; FRCPath 1988, M 1976. Cons. Microbiol. Dir. Pub. Health Laborat. Hull Roy. Infirm. Prev: Asst. Bact. Pub. Health Laborat. City & Sherwood Hosps. Nottm.; Regist. (Microbiol.) Roy. Vict. Infirm. Newc.; Asst. Microbiol. Pub. Health Laborat. N.. Gen. Hosp. Sheff.

MAWHINNEY, Claire 66 Chinauley Park, Banbridge BT32 4JL — MB BCh BAO 1993 Belf.

MAWHINNEY, Elizabeth Orr Wood Close, 90 Flixborough Road, Burton-upon-Stather, Scunthorpe DN15 9HE — MB BCh BAO Belf. 1939. (Belf.)

MAWHINNEY, Mr Hugh John Dennis Royal Victoria Hospital, Grosvenor Road, Belfast BT12 6BA Tel: 02890 240503 Email: orthodox@ukgateway.net; 3 Kathleen Drive, Helen's Bay, Bangor BT19 1NE Tel: 02891 853433 Fax: 02891 852950 — MB BCh BAO 1974 Belf.; BSc Belf. 1971; MD Belf. 1991; FRCS Ed. (Orth.) 1986; FRCS Ed. 1979. (Belf.) Cons. Orthop. Surg. Roy. Vict. & Musgrave Pk. Hosp. Belf. Prev: Sen. Regist. (Orthop. Surg.) Musgrave Pk. Hosp.; Lord Nuffield Schol. Nuffield Orthop. Centre Oxf.

MAWHINNEY, Mr Ian Nicholas 25 Richmond Court, Lisburn BT27 4QU Tel: 01846 607402 Fax: 01846 607402 Email: ian.mawhinney@btinternet.com — MB BCh BAO 1982 Belf.; MD Belf. 1989; FRCS Ed. 1986. Cons. Hand & Orthop. Surg. Musgrave Pk. Hosp. Belf. Socs: Brit. Orthop. Assn.; Brit. Soc. Surg. Hand. Prev: Sen. Regist. Belf. City Hosps.; Hand Fell. Wrightington Hosp. Wigan; Sen. Regist. Musgrave Pk. Hosp. Belf.

MAWHINNEY, Roderick Robert 2 Station Road, Knaresborough HG5 9AA — MB ChB 1977 Bristol; FRCR 1984. Cons. Radiol. Harrogate Health Care Trust.

MAWHINNEY, Sandra Ulster Hospital Dundonald, Belfast BT16 1RH Tel: 02890 484511 Email: dr.s.mawhinney@bt.internet.com; Tel: 02890 769337 Email: dr.s.mawhinney@btinternet.com — MB ChB 1990 Dundee; MRCOG Lond. 2001; DFFP 1994; MRCGP 1994; DCH RCP Lond. 1993; DRCOG 1992. (University of Dundee Scotland) Spec. Reg. O & G Ulster Hosp. Dundonald. Prev: Trainee GP/SHO Rotat. Ulster Hosp. Dundonald.; GP Partner.

***MAWJI, Huseinali Anwarali Rajabali** 37 Kingsley Road, Hainault, Ilford IG6 2LL — MB BS 1998 Lond.; MB BS Lond. 1998.

MAWSON, Andrew Church View Surgery, School La, Collingham, Wetherby LS22 5BQ Tel: 01937 573848 Fax: 01937 574754; The Surgery, Main St, Thorner, Leeds LS14 3DX Tel: 0113 289 2407 — MB ChB 1974 Leeds.

MAWSON, Antony Charles The Healthcare Centre, Flintoff Way, Preston PR1 5AF Tel: 01772 655533 Fax: 01772 653414; Tel: 655533 — MB ChB Leeds 1983; DRCOG 1986; AFOM 1997 RCP Lond. GP Gen. Pract.; Occupat. Phys. United Utilities; Occupat. Phys. Brit. Aerospace. Socs: Soc. Occupat. Med.

MAWSON, Henry Nicholas Christopher Claremont Surgery, Wilderness Medical Centre, 2 Cookham Road, Maidenhead SL6 8AN Tel: 01628 673033 — MB 1972 Camb.; BA Camb. 1968, MB 1972, BChir 1971; MRCGP 1986; DCH Eng. 1979; DObst RCOG 1973. (Camb. & Lond. Hosp.)

MAWSON, Sara Louise Liverpool Women's Hospital, Crown St., Liverpool L8 7SS; Flat 5, 10 Ivanhoe Road, Liverpool L17 8XG Tel: 0151 726 9512 — MB ChB 1996 Liverp. SHO (O & G) Liverp. Woms. Hosp. Liverp. Prev: Pre-registration Ho. Off. Whiston Hosp. Merseyside.

MAWSON, Mr Stuart Radcliffe (retired) Whinbeck, Knodishall, Saxmundham IP17 1UF Tel: 01728 830384 — MB BChir 1946 Camb.; FRCS Eng. 1947; MRCS Eng. LRCP Lond. 1943; DLO Eng. 1949. Hon. Cons. Otolaryngol. King's Coll. Hosp. Lond. Prev: Sen. Surg. (ENT) King's Coll. Hosp. Lond.

MAXA, Dennis Wenceslas (retired) Lavender House, 15 The Drive, Henleaze, Bristol BS9 4LD Tel: 0117 962 4583 — MB ChB 1951 Ed.; DPH Bristol 1969. Prev: Med. Off. DHSS.

MAXEY, Anna Margaret Department of Psychiatry for The Elderly, The Pines, Peterborough District Hospital, Thorpe Road, Peterborough PE3 6SA Tel: 01733 318131 — MRCS Eng. LRCP Lond. 1965. (Roy. Free Hosp. Sch. Med.) Clin. Med. Off. (Psychiat. for Elderly) P'boro. Dist. Hosp. Prev: Regist. & SHO (Psychiat.) P'boro Dist. Hosp.

MAXEY, John Marshall Bel Val Cave, Rue De Flicquet, St Martin, Jersey JE3 6BP Tel: 01534 22381 — MB BS 1986 Lond.; BSc (Hons.) Lond. 1980; DRCOG 1995.

MAXFIELD, Helen Sylvia The Abbey Practice, The Family Health Centre, Stepgates, Chertsey KT16 8HZ Tel: 01932 561199 Fax: 01932 571842 — MB BS 1987 Lond.; MRCGP 1992; DRCOG 1991. Prev: Trainee GP St. Peter's Hosp. Chertsey VTS; Ho. Off. (Med.) Battle Hosp. Reading; Ho. Surg. St. Thos. Hosp. Lond.

MAXFIELD, John Bailey (retired) Ardlair, Crowgate, South Anston, Sheffield S25 5AL Tel: 01909 562207 — MB ChB 1945 Sheff. RAFVR. Prev: Asst. Cas. Off. & Ho. Surg. (Orthop.) Sheff. Roy. Hosp.

MAXIM, Oliver Vivian Windhovers, Gretton, Corby Tel: 01536 459 — MB BS 1953 Lond.; DObst RCOG 1955. (Lond. Hosp.) Prev: ENT Ho. Surg. Lond. Hosp.; Midw. & Gyn. Ho. Surg. Birch Hill Hosp.

MAXIM, Richard Edward Geoffrey Orchard Surgery, New Road, Melbourn, Royston SG8 6BX — MB BS 1971 Lond.; DObst RCOG 1973. (Lond. Hosp.) Prev: Ho. Surg. (Obst.) Lond. Hosp.; Ho. Phys. King Geo. Hosp. Ilford; Emerg. & Accid. Off. Lond. Hosp.

MAXIMOUS, Joseph Sarkis Jacksons Solicitors, 1-15 Queens Square, Middlesbrough TS2 1AL — MB BCh 1974 Ain Shams; MRCOG 1985.

MAXMIN, Jacqueline Susan Highfield Surgery, Highfield Way, Hazlemere, High Wycombe HP15 7UW Tel: 01949 813396 Fax: 01949 814107 — MB BS Lond. 1968; MRCS Eng. LRCP Lond. 1968; MRCGP 1978; DCH Eng. 1970. (Roy. Free) GP; Course Organiser Wycombe VTS. Wycombe Gen. Hosp. High Wycombe, Buck. Prev: Ho. Phys. (Child Psychiat.) Guy's Hosp. Lond.; Ho. Surg. Hampstead Gen. Hosp.; Ho. Phys. Eliz. G. Anderson Hosp. Lond.

MAXTED, David Fleming Steinhardt and Partners, The Surgery, 5A Brookfield Road, Hucclecote, Gloucester GL3 3HB Tel: 01452 617295 Fax: 01452 617296 — MB BS 1979 Lond.; MRCP (UK) 1983; MRCS Eng. LRCP Lond. 1979; MRCGP 1986; DRCOG 1984. Prev: Regist. (Med.) Worcester Roy. Infirm.

MAXTED, Mr Malcolm James Downs House, Yetminster, Sherborne DT9 6NJ Tel: 01935 872929 Fax: 01935 872929 — MB ChB 1971 Liverp.; MChOrth 1978; FRCS Ed. 1976. Cons. Orthop. Surg. Yeovil Dist. Gen. Hosp. Prev: Sen. Regist. (Orthop. Surg.) Soton. Gen. Hosp. Qu. Alex. Hosp. Cosham; Lord Mayor Treloar Hosp., Alton.

MAXTED, Sarah Helen The Green Medical Centre, 65 Leicester Road, Narborough, Leicester Tel: 0116 284 1347; 15 Grange Lane, Mountsorrel, Loughborough LE12 7HY Tel: 0116 237 4794 — MB ChB 1996 Leic.; DRCOG 2000; MRCGP 2000; DFFP 2000. (Leicester) GP Princip.; Family Plann. Off., Coalville; Clin. Asst. in Fertil. Control, Leicester.

MAXTON, David Grant Laurel Bank, 27 New Road, Lymm WA13 9DX Tel: 0192575 3131 — MD 1986 Lond.; MB BS 1977; MRCP (UK) 1980. Lect. & Hon. Sen. Regist. Withington Hosp. Didsbury Manch. Prev: Research Regist. St. Thos. Hosp. Lond.

MAXWELL, Professor Alexander Peter Regional Nephrology Unit, 11 South Office, Belfast City Office, Lisburn Road, Belfast BT9 7AB Tel: 028 9032 9241 Fax: 028 9026 3535 Email: a.p.maxwell@qub.ac.uk — MB BCh BAO 1983 Belf.; PhD Belf. 1994; MD Belf. 1989; FRCP Ed. 1996; FRCPC 1992; MRCP Ed. 1986; FRCP 1998 London. Cons. & Prof. (Renal Med.) Belf.

MAXWELL, Angela Joan 118 Union Grove, Aberdeen AB10 6SB — MB ChB 1984 Aberd. Trainee GP/SHO Aberd. VTS.

MAXWELL, Anthony James Royal Bolton Hospital, Minerva Road, Farnworth, Bolton BL4 0JR Tel: 01204 390010 Email: anthony.maxwell@boltonh-tr.nwest.nhs.uk; 39 Lostock Junction Lane, Lostock, Bolton BL6 4JW Fax: 01204 843691 Email: anthony@themaxwells.freeserve.co.uk — MB ChB 1980 Manch.; FRCS Ed. 1984; FRCR 1987. Cons. Radiol. Bolton Hosps. NHS Trust.

MAXWELL, Camilla Ann 1 Chapel Row, St Mellons, Cardiff CF3 5UB — MB ChB 1968 Liverp. GP Cardiff. Prev: Clin. Asst. (Dermat.) Liverp. AHA (T).

MAXWELL, Celia Margaret 7A Windmill Road, St Andrews KY16 9JJ Tel: 01334 78014; Grove House, Mealsgate, Carlisle CA5 6LQ — MB ChB 1959 St. And. (St. And.) Med. Off. Marks & Spencer Nottm.; Clin. Asst. (Geriat. Med.) Nottm.

MAXWELL

MAXWELL, Christine Mary (retired) 6 Gerrans Hill, Portscatho, Truro TR2 5EE Tel: 0187 258668 — MA, MB BChir Camb. 1952. Prev: Sen. Med. Off. N. Devon Health Dist.

MAXWELL, Christopher John Moore (retired) Boscobel, Brightling Road, Robertsbridge TN32 5EJ Tel: 01580 880475 Email: nosmax1000@netscapeonline.co.uk — MRCS Eng. LRCP Lond. 1959; MA Camb.; DTM & H Eng. 1970. Prev: Med. Off. (Paediat.) Temuco Hosp., Chile (S. Amer. Miss. Soc.).

MAXWELL, Craig William Red House Surgery, 124 Watling Street, Radlett WD7 7JQ Tel: 01923 855606 Fax: 01923 853577; 11 Upper Station Road, Radlett WD7.8BY Tel: 01923 856997 Fax: 01923 853577 Email: craigmaxwell@msn.com — MB ChB 1971 Ed.; DObst RCOG 1973. Socs: Counc. Mem. Med. Off. Sch.s Assn.; Hon. Sec. W. Herts. & Watford Med. Soc.

MAXWELL, David Gordon 118 Union Grove, Aberdeen AB10 6SB — MB ChB 1982 Aberd.

MAXWELL, David Lindsay Eastbourne Hospital NHS Trust, King's Drive, Eastbourne BN21 2UD Tel: 01323 435802 Fax: 01323 435797 — MB BS 1978 Lond.; MA Camb. 1978, MD 1990; MRCP (UK) 1981. Cons. Phys. With an interest in Resp. Med. E.bourne Hosps. NHS Trust E.bourne. Prev: Cons. Phys. King Edwd. VII Hosp. Midhurst; Hon. Sen. Lect. (Med.) UMDS Guy's & St. Thos. Hosps.; Cons. Phys. Dartford & Gravesham NHS Trust.

MAXWELL, David McIntosh (retired) Gernant, Blaenau Ffestiniog LL41 4LL Tel: 01766 762618 — MB ChB 1946 Birm.; MRCS Eng. LRCP Lond. 1946; DObst RCOG 1950. Prev: Ho. Surg. (Obst.) Hallam Hosp. W. Bromwich & Gulson Hosp. Coventry.

MAXWELL, Deborah Ann Bollington Medical Centre, Wellington Road, Bollington, Macclesfield SK10 5JL Tel: 01625 572481; Ollerenshaw Hall, Eccles Road, Whaley Bridge, High Peak SK23 7EW — MB ChB 1983 Manch.; BSc (Med. Sci.) St. And. 1980. Prev: Trainee GP Macclesfield Dist. Gen. Hosp. VTS.

***MAXWELL, Gary John** 55 Lisnevanagh Road, Cromkill, Ballymena BT42 2LJ — MB BCh BAO 1997 Belf.

MAXWELL, Haldane Lindsay Church Street Surgery, 7 Church Street, Ballantrae, Girvan KA26 0NF Tel: 01465 831302 Fax: 01465 831583; The Mount, Church St, Ballantrae, Girvan KA26 0NF Tel: 01465 831326 — MB ChB 1981 Dundee; BMSc (Hons.) Dund 1978; MRCGP 1985; DRCOG 1983. GP Ballantrae.

MAXWELL, Harold (retired) 5 Upper Wimpole Street, London W1G 6BP — MD 1965 Bristol; FRCPsych 1976; MB ChB 1951 Bristol. Prev: Cons. Psychiat. and Sen. Lect. Char. Cross and W.minster Hosps.

MAXWELL, Heather Renal Day Unit, Royal Hospital for Sick Children, Yorkhill NHS Trust, Glasgow G3 8SJ Tel: 0141 201 0122 Fax: 0141 201 0859 Email: heather.maxwell@yorkhill.scot.nhs.uk — MB ChB 1986 Ed.; MD (Edin.) 2001; FRCP (UK) 1998; MRCP (UK) 1990. (Edinburgh) Cons. Paediatric Nephrologist, Roy. Hosp. for Sick Childr., Yorkhill NHS Trust Glas. Prev: Lect. (Paediat. Nephrol.) Inst. of Child Health, Lond.; Clin. Fell. in Paediat. Nephrol. Sick Childr.'s Hosp., Toronto, Canada; Lect. (Paediat. Nephrol.) Roy. Free Med. Sch.

MAXWELL, Mr Henry Adolphus Hope Hospital, Eccles Old Road, Salford M6 8HD Tel: 0161 787 5118 Fax: 0161 787 1196 Email: hamaxwell@msn.com; Cross Bank, Bamford Road, Ramsbottom, Bury BL0 0RT Tel: 01706 828989 Fax: 01706 821002 — MB ChB 1983 Manch.; ChM Manch. 1994; FRCS (Orth.) 1995; FRCS Ed. 1988; FRCS Eng. 1988. Cons. Orthop. Surg. Hope Hosp. Salford. Prev: Sen. Regist. (Orthop. Surg.) Hope Hosp. Salford.

MAXWELL, James Douglas St. Georges Hospital Medical School, Cranmer Terrace, London SW17 0RE Tel: 020 8725 1541 Fax: 020 8725 3520 Email: maxwell@sghms.ac.uk — MB ChB Glas. 1964; BSc Glas. 1961, MD 1978; FRCP Lond. 1981, M 1967; FRCP Glas. 1978; M 1968. (Glas.) Clin. Sub Dean & Reader (Med.) St. Geo. Hosp. Med. Sch. Lond.; Phys. St. Geo. Hosp. Lond. Socs: Brit. Soc. Gastroenterol.; Brit. Assn. Study Liver. Prev: Research Fell. (Clin. Pharmacol.) Univ. Calif. Med. Center, San Francisco; Research Fell. (Hon. Lect.) Liver Unit King's Coll. Hosp.; Regist. (Med.) Roy. Infirm. Glas.

***MAXWELL, James Richard** 4 Church Close, Chedgrave, Norwich NR14 6NH — MB ChB 1998 Liverp.; MB ChB Liverp 1998.

MAXWELL, Janet Mary 17 Church Green, Witney OX28 4AZ — BM Soton. 1977; MRCGP 1983; DRCOG 1983; DCH RCP Lond. 1983.

MAXWELL, Jean Frances Farleigh Hospice, 212 New London Rd, Chelmsford CM2 9AE Tel: 01245 358130 — MB BS 1977 Lond.; MRCGP 1981; DRCOG 1980. Cons. Palliat. Med. & Med. Dir.Farleigh Hospice. Socs: Assn. Palliat. Med. Prev: GP Basildon.; Dep. Med. Director S & Francis Hospice.

MAXWELL, John Roslyn Oakleigh Road Health Centre, Oakleigh Road North, Whetstone, London N20 0DH Tel: 020 8361 1996 — MB BS 1965 Adelaide; MB BS 1965 Adelaide.

MAXWELL, Judith Claire 12 Rushes Lane, Lubenham, Market Harborough LE16 9TN — MB ChB 1986 Manch.; BSc (Hons. Biochem. & Chem.) St. And. 1981; Dip. Occ. Med. RCP Lond. 1996. GP Partner at Husbands Bosworth Surg. Socs: BMA. Prev: Regist. Rotat. Kings. Cross Hosp. Dundee; SHO (Infec. Dis.) City Hosp. Edin.; SHO Rotat. Leeds Gen. Infirm.

MAXWELL, Julie Michelle Nash Cottage, Fownhope, Hereford HR1 4PS — MB BCh 1995 Wales.

MAXWELL, Katharine Neil (retired) Aysgarth, 32 Aberford Road, Wakefield WF1 4AJ Tel: 01924 373796 — MB ChB Glas. 1945; Cert Av Med MoD (Air) & CAA 1976. Hon. Cons. Child & Adolesc. Psychiat. Yorks. RHA. Prev: Cons. Psychiat. Yorks. RHA.

MAXWELL, Kennedy John AME - Medical, BAFC, Booker, Marlow SL7 3DP Tel: 01494 529262 Email: baflyingclub@cs.com — BM 1980 Soton.; Cert. Av. Med. 1991; DA (UK) 1987. GP / AME, AME Med., BAFC, Booker, Bucks, SL7 3DP. Socs: Soc. Advancem. Anaesth. in Dent.; Assn. Dent. Anaesths.; Assn. of authorised medcial Examr.s (AAME). Prev: Trainee GP Gerrard's Cross; SHO (Anaesth.) St. Bart. Hosp. Lond.; SHO (Med.) Roy. Lond. Hosp.

***MAXWELL, Lorraine Elizabeth** 47 Highfield Avenue, Harpenden AL5 5UB — MB ChB 1998 Glas.; MB ChB Glas 1998.

MAXWELL, Melanie 12 Beverley Crescent, Newtownards BT23 7UN Tel: 01247 814460 — MB BCh BAO 1981 Belf.; FRCSI 1986; Dip. Palliat. Med. Wales 1995. Staff Oncol. N. Irel. Centre Clin. Oncol. Belvoir Pk. Hosp. Green Pk. Unit Trust; Doctor Hosp. Support (Palliat. Care.) Team. Socs: Assn. Palliat. Med.; (Sec.) Ulster Soc. Palliat. Med. Prev: Regist. (Gen. Surg.) Waveney Hosp.; SHO Roy. Vict. Hosp.; Ho. Off. Belf. City Hosp.

MAXWELL, Melanie Jayne C.P.R.U. Arrowe Park Hospital, Arrowe Park Road, Upton, Wirral CH49 5PE Tel: 0151 604 7221 Fax: 0151 604 7191 Email: melanie.maxwell@ccmail.wirralh-tr.nwest.nhs.uk; 84 Cambridge Road, Blundellsands, Liverpool L23 7UA Email: thompmel@cs.com — MB BS 1985 Lond.; MRCPI 1991; MFPHM 1997. (University of London) Cons. (Pub. Health Med.) & Head of Clin. Pract. Research Unit Wirral Hosp. Trust; Hon. Researcher in Dept. of Primary Care, Liverp. Univ. Socs: BMA; Fac. Pub. Health Med.; Roy. Coll. Phys. Irel. Prev: Sen. Regist. (Pub. Health Med.) N. W. Rotat.; Regist. (Pub. Health Med.) W. Midl. RHA; Regist. (Paediat.) New Cross Hosp. Wolverhampton.

***MAXWELL, Melanie Jayne** 7 The Ridings, Surbiton KT5 8HG — BM BS 1998 Nottm.; BM BS Nottm 1998.

MAXWELL, Nicola Jane 90B Hackford Road, London SW9 0RD — MB ChB 1991 Bristol; MRCOG 1997. IVF Research Fell. Homerton Hosp. Lond. Prev: Specialist Regist. (O & G) Soton.

MAXWELL, Patrick Henry 110 Old Road, Oxford OX3 8SX — MB BS 1986 (Hons) Lond.; BA Oxf. 1983, DPhil 1994; MRCP (UK) 1989. Univ.Reader & Hon. Cons. Nephrol. Oxf.; Med. Research Fell., Corpus Christi, Coll., Oxf. Socs: Fell. Of Roy. Coll. Of Phys.s, Lond.; Mem. UK Renal Assn. Prev: Clin. Lect. Nuffield Dept. Med. Oxf.; MRC Train. Fell. Inst. Molecular Med. Oxf.; Regist. (Med.) Lewisham Hosp. Lond.

MAXWELL, Paul Robert Whisperwood Cottage, Trout Rise, Loudwater, Rickmansworth WD3 4JU — MB BS 1990 Lond.; BSc (Hons.) Lond. 1987; MRCP (UK) 1994.

MAXWELL, Richard Bruce Hamilton Lodgeside Surgery, 22 Lodgeside Avenue, Kingswood, Bristol BS15 1WW Tel: 0117 961 5666 Fax: 0117 947 6854; 15 York Gardens, Clifton, Bristol BS8 4LL Tel: 0117 974 4658 Fax: 0117 974 4658 — BM BCh 1972 Oxf.; MA Oxf. 1972; FRCGP 1990, M 1980. (Oxf.) GP Princip. Kingswood Bristol; Vis. Lect. Health Serv. Managem. Centre Univ. Birm. Socs: Oxf. Grad. Med. Soc. Prev: Jt. RCGP/DoH GP Stress Fell.

MAXWELL, Robert (retired) 73 Tomswood Road, Chigwell IG7 5QR Tel: 020 8504 4592 — MB ChB 1931 Glas. Prev: Med. Ref. DHSS.

MAXWELL, Mr Robert John Royal Victoria Hospital, Grosvenor Road, Belfast BT12 6BA Tel: 028 9089 4751 Fax: 028 9026 3290;

3 Bristow Park, Upper Malone Road, Belfast BT9 6TF Tel: 028 9066 6361 Fax: 028 9066 0646 Email: maxwell@bristow.dnet.co.uk — MD 1984 Belf.; MB BCh BAO 1974; FRCS Eng. 1980; FRCS Ed. 1979; DRCOG 1978; DCH RCPSI 1977; MA 1999 Belfast. Cons. Surg. Roy. Vict. Hosp. Belf.

MAXWELL, Robert Terence Y Wenallt, Llandegfan, Menai Bridge LL59 5PG Tel: 01248 713249 Fax: 01248 713249 — MD Liverp. 1971, MB ChB 1963; FRCP Lond. 1979, M 1967. (Liverp.) Cons. Phys. Cardiol. Gwynedd Hosp. Bangor. Socs: BMA & Brit. Cardiac. Soc. Prev: Research Fell. (Haemat.) Nuffield Unit Dept. Med. Univ. Liverp.; Regist. Roy. S.. Hosp. Liverp.; Ho. Phys. & Ho. Surg. BRd.green Hosp. Liverp.

MAXWELL, Sarah Department of Microbiology, Stepping Hill Hospital, Stockport SK2 7JE Tel: 0161 419 5603 Fax: 0161 419 5668; St Johns Rectory, Priestnall Road, Heaton Mersey, Stockport SK4 3HR — MB ChB 1978 Liverp.; FRCPath 1997; Dip. Bact. Manch. 1985. Cons. Microbiol. Stockport Acute Servs. Trust; Hon. Lect. Med. Microbiolog. Manch. Univ.

MAXWELL, Sarah Louise 29 Burton Road, London NW6 7LL — MB BS 1994 Lond.

MAXWELL, Sheila Margaret Young (retired) Moorside Cottage, 154 Syke Road, Rochdale OL12 9TE Tel: 01706 642222 — MB ChB 1952 Glas. Prev: Clin. Asst. Renal Unit Manch. Roy. Infirm.

MAXWELL, Sonia Elizabeth Louise Y Wenallt, Llandegfan, Menai Bridge LL59 5PG — MB BS 1988 Lond.; DRCOG 1993; DCH RCP Lond. 1992.

MAXWELL, Stephen Robert Kenmore Medical Centre, 60-62 Alderley Road, Wilmslow SK9 1PA — MB ChB 1983 Manch.; MRCP (UK) 1988; MRCGP 1988; DRCOG 1988; DCH RCPS Glas. 1987; MRCP & CH 1998. (Manchester) Princip. (Gen. Pract.); Hosp. Practitioner Paediat. Roy. Manch. Childr. Hosp.; Examr. DCH RCP; Trainer (Gen. Pract.) Wilmslow. Prev: Trainee GP Rotat Roy. Preston Hosp.; SHO (Paediat.) Roy. Manch. Childr. Hosp. Pendlebury, Salford; Ho. Surg. Wythenshawe Hosp. Manch.

MAXWELL, Therese Mary The Surgery, Mill St., Market Rasen LN8 3BP Tel: 01673 843556; c/o The Old Bakery, Enmore, Bridgwater TA5 2DP — MB ChB 1993 Leic.; DRCOG 1996; MRCGP 1997. GP Market Rasen, Lincs. Prev: CMO Psychiat.; CMO G.U. Med.

MAXWELL, Thomas Gray Sitwell and Partners, Little Common Surgery, 82 Cooden Sea Road, Bexhill-on-Sea TN39 4SP Tel: 01424 845477 Fax: 01424 848225; The Old Watermill, Watermill Lane, Bexhill-on-Sea TN39 5JB — MB ChB 1984 Bristol; MA Camb. 1984; MRCGP 1988; DGM RCP Lond. 1987. Vis. Research Fell. Univ. Sussex; GP Family Plann. Clin. E. Sussex. Prev: Trainee GP Bristol & W.on HA; SHO (Obst.) Bristol Matern. Hosp.; SHO (Gen. & Geriat. Med.) W.on Gen. Hosp.

MAXWELL, Victor Benjamin 21 Sherwood Road, Hendon, London NW4 1AE Tel: 020 8203 7225 Fax: 020 8203 0320 Email: victormaxwell@compuserve.com — MB ChB Manch. 1953; MRCGP 1963. p/t Cons. Adviser Aviat. Med. Global Flying Insur. Servs. Socs: Fell. Aerospace Med. Assn.; Assoc. Fell. Roy. Aeronautical Soc.; Hon. Vice Pres. Assn. Of Aviat. Med. Examr.s. Prev: Hon. Res. Asst. RNID Research Unit Lond.; Auth. Med. Examin. UK CAA; GP Gatley.

MAXWELL, Wayne Ollyn Edwards and Maxwell, The School House Surgery, Buxton Old Road, Disley, Stockport SK12 2BB Tel: 01663 764488 Fax: 01663 766028; Ollerenshaw Hall, Eccles Road, Whaley Bridge, Stockport SK23 7EW — MB ChB 1981 Manch.; DPD 2001; BSc (Med. Sci) St. And. 1978; MRCGP 1988; Cert. Family Plann. JCC 1984; DRCOG 1983. Sch. Med. Off. Stockport Grammar Sch.; Trainer (Gen. Pract.) Mersey; Clin. Asst. Dermat. 2000. Prev: Trainee GP Bollington & Stepping Hill Hosp. Stockport VTS; Ho. Off. Stepping Hill Hosp. Stockport.

MAXWELL, Mr William Angus Department of Surgery, Withybush Hospital, Fishguard Road, Haverfordwest SA61 2PZ Tel: 01437 764545 — MB BS 1975 Lond.; FRCS Ed. 1982; MRCS Eng. LRCP Lond. 1975. Cons. Gen. Surg. Withybush Hosp. HaverfordW.. Prev: Cons. Surg. TPM Hosp. RAF Akrotiri, Cyprus.

MAXWELL, William George Aubrey Innisfree, Friend Lane, Edwinstone, Mansfield NG21 9QZ Tel: 01623 822741; 25 Hiag Crescent, Bunbury WA 6230, Australia Tel: 00 61 0972 18088 — LRCPI & LM, LRCSI & LM 1960; FRACOG 1980; MRCOG 1976.

MAXWELL, William George Smith (retired) Burrishoole, 2 Hemingfield Road, Wombwell, Barnsley S73 0LX — MB BCh BAO 1925 Dub. Prev: Ho. Surg. Sussex Matern. & Wom. Hosp. Brighton.

MAXWELL-ARMSTRONG, Mr Charles Alan 3 The Barns, Wolds Farm, Kinoulton Lane, Kinoulton, Nottingham NG12 3EQ Tel: 01949 81822 Email: chrles.maxwell.armstrong@talk21.com — MB ChB 1991 Bristol; FRCS Eng. 1995; DM Nottm. 1998. (Bristol) Resid. Surgic. Off., St. Marks Hosp., Lond. Prev: Research Regist. Qu. Med. Centre Nottm.; SHO Rotat. (Orthop., Gen. Surg. & Paediat. Surg.) Qu. Med. Centre Nottm.; SHO (A & E) S.mead Hosp. Bristol & Qu. Med. Centre Nottm.

MAY, Alan John 37A St. Johns Road, Watford WD17 1LS; St. Michael's End, Leverstock Green Road, Hemel Hempstead HP3 8LR Tel: 01442 69721 — MB ChB 1967 Liverp.; DObst RCOG 1970. (Liverp.) Mem. Med. Advis. Panel. Socs: Soc. Apoth.; Nat. Eczema Soc.; W Herts. & Watford Med. Soc. Prev: Sessional Doctor BUPA Med. Centres; Clin. Asst. (Dermat.) Peace Mem. Hosp. Watford; Ho. Off. (Obst.) & Ho. Phys. Chester City Hosp.

MAY, Andrew James Lemon Street Surgery, 18 Lemon Street, Truro TR1 2LZ Tel: 01872 73133 Fax: 01872 260900; Lower Croft W., Tregavethan, Truro TR4 9EN Tel: 01872 560149 — MB BS 1990 Lond.; DRCOG 1994. GP Regist. Truro.

MAY, Mr Andrew Rayner Luxmoore, TD Turner Rise Consulting Rooms, 55 Turner Road, Colchester CO4 5JY Tel: 01206 752444 Fax: 01206 752116 — MB BS Lond. 1968; FRCS Eng. 1973; FRCS Ed. 1972. (St. Thos.) Cons. Gen. & Vasc. Surg. Essex Rivers Health Care NHS Trust; Lt.-Col RAMC(V); Hon. Med. Adviser SSAFA (Essex). Socs: Fell. Roy. Soc. Med.; BMA; Vasc. Surg. Soc. GB & Irel. Prev: Sen. Regist. (Surg.) St. Thos. Hosp. Lond.; Research Fell. Mass. Gen. Hosp. & Harvard Med. Sch. Boston, USA; Lect. (Surg.) St. Thos. Hosp. Med. Sch. Lond.

MAY, Annabel Jane Horseleas, Bradfield, Reading RG7 6JA Tel: 0118 974 4220 Fax: 0118 974 4442 — MB BS Lond. 1971; MRCS Eng. LRCP Lond. 1971; FFA RCS Eng. 1976; DObst RCOG 1973. (St. Mary's) Cons. Anaesth. Wexham Pk. Hosp. Slough & Heatherwood Hosp, Ascot. Prev: Sen. Regist. (Anaesth.) Roy. Berks. Hosp. Reading; Sen. Regist. (Anaesth.) St. Mary's Hosp. Lond.

MAY, Anne Elizabeth Department of Anaesthesia, Leicester Royal Infirmary, Infirmary Square, Leicester LE1 5WW Tel: 0116 254 1414; Ringwood, Forest Drive, Kirby Muxloe, Leicester LE9 2EA Tel: 0116 239 3222 — MB BS 1970 Newc.; FFA RCS Eng. 1975. Cons. Anaesth. (Obst. Anaesth.) Leic. Roy. Infirm.; Hon. Sen. Lect. Dept. Anaesth. Leic. Socs: Pres. Obstetric Anaesth. Assn. Prev: Sen. Regist. (Anaesth.) Leicester Roy. Infirm.; Regist. (Anaesth.) Roy. Vict. Infirm. Newc.; Ho. Phys. & Ho. Surg. Cumbld. Infirm. Carlisle.

MAY, Anne-Marie East Barn Surgery, Lychpit, Basingstoke RG24 8TF Tel: 01256 841654; Pitt Hall Farm House, Ramsdell, Basingstoke RG26 5RJ Tel: 01256 850057 — MB BCh BAO 1971 Dub.; BA, MB BCh BAO Dub. 1971; DObst RCOG 1975.

MAY, Bryony Jane c/o Neonatal Unit, Glasgow Royal Maternity Hospital, 147 - 163 Rottenrow, Glasgow G4 0NA — MB ChB 1992 Cape Town.

MAY, Christine Margaret Isabel The Stennack Surgery, The Old Stennack School, St Ives TR26 1RU Tel: 01736 796413 Fax: 01736 796245; The Ship House, Church Road, Lelant, St Ives TR26 3LB Tel: 01736 756337 — MB BS 1979 Lond.; DRCOG 1983. (St. Bart.)

MAY, Christopher David Wideopen Medical Centre, Great North Road, Wideopen, Newcastle upon Tyne NE13 6LN Tel: 0191 236 2115 Fax: 0191 236 2116; Albury House, 28 Runnymede Road, Darras Hall, Ponteland, Newcastle upon Tyne NE20 9HE Tel: 01661 21664 Email: chrismay@beeb.net — MB BS 1982 Newc.; MRCGP 1986; DRCOG 1985. Socs: Assn. Of Police Surg.s. Prev: SHO (Paediat.) N. Tyneside Dist. Gen. Hosp.; Ho. Off. (Gen. Surg.) Hexham Gen. Hosp.; Ho. Off. (Gen. Med.) Dryburn Hosp. Durh.

MAY, Colin John Haldon House Surgery, 37-39 Imperial Road, Exmouth EX8 1DH Tel: 01395 222777/222888 Fax: 01395 269769 — MB ChB 1975 Dundee.

MAY, Mr David Paul Luxmoore 184 Coobe Lane W., Kingston upon Thames KT2 7EG Tel: 020 8336 0000 — MB BS Lond. 1962; FRCS Ed. 1967; FRCOG 1983, M (Gold Medal) 1970, DObst. 1964. (St. Thos.) Cons. O & G Kingston & Esher HA. Prev: Sen. Regist. (O & G) W.m. Hosp. Lond.

MAY

MAY, David Richard The Malthouse Surgery, The Charter, Abingdon OX14 3JY Tel: 01235 524001 Fax: 01235 532197 Email: practice@malthouse.oxongps.co.uk; Tel: 01235 532037 — BM BCh 1984 Oxf.; MA Camb. 1985; MRCGP 1988; DRCOG 1987. Med. Off. Abingdon Sch. Socs: Fell. Roy. Soc. Med. Prev: Trainee GP Oxf. HA VTS; Ho. Surg. & Ho. Phys. Roy. United Hosp. Bath.

MAY, Mr David Robert London Road Medical Centre, 2 London Road, Uppingham, Oakham LE15 9TJ Tel: 01572 823531; An Cala, Church St, Brooke, Oakham LE15 8DE Tel: 01572 770282 Fax: 01572 821145 — MB ChB 1972 St. And.; BMSc (Hons.) Dund 1969; FRCS Glas. 1977. (St. And.) Hosp. Pract. (Gen. Surg.) Oakham.

MAY, Donald William Francis Park Drive Health Centre, 2A Park Drive, Leicester Forest East, Leicester LE3 3FN Tel: 0116 289 8111 — MB BS 1970 Newc.; MRCGP 1974; DObst RCOG 1972; Cert. Family Plann. JCC 1975. Prev: Trainee GP Newc. VTS; SHO (Obst.) Hull Matern. Hosp.; Ho. Surg. & Ho. Phys. Cumbld. Infirm. Carlisle.

MAY, Helen Anne Department of Anaesthetics, Queen Elizabeth Hospital, Sheriff Hill, Gateshead NE9 6SX Tel: 0191 403 2176 Fax: 0191 403 2827 Email: helen.may@exchange.gatesh-tr.northy.nhs.uk — BM BS 1985 Nottm.; BMedSci Nottm. 1983; FRCA 1991. (Nottm.) Cons. (Anaesth.) Qu. Eliz. Hosp. Gateshead. Prev: Sen. Regist. Nuffield Dept. Anaesth. Oxf.

MAY, Helen Margaret Norfolk & Norwich Health Care NHS Trust, Brunswick Road, Norwich NR1 3SR Tel: 01493 425425; Longfield House, 78 London Road, Wymondham NR18 9BP — MB ChB 1986 Birm.; MRCP (UK) 1991. Cons. c/o the Elderly Norf. & Norwich Health Care NHS Trust Norwich. Prev: Research Regist. (Clin. Gerontol.) Addenbrooke's Hosp. Camb.; Sen. Regist. (Med.) Jas. Paget Hosp. Gorleston.

***MAY, James Matthew** 41 Westridge Road, Southampton SO17 2HP — MB ChB 1997 Sheff.

***MAY, Jennifer Alison** Flat 2/L, 39 Ripon Drive, Glasgow G12 0DU — MB ChB 1994 Glas.

MAY, Joan Hannah 25 Lime Grove, New Malden KT3 3TW — MB BCh BAO 1994 Belf. SHO (Gen. Pract.) Roy. Vict. Hosp. Belf.

MAY, Mr John Colm Scarborough Hospital, Woodlands Drive, Scarborough YO12 6QL — MB BCh BAO 1988 NUI; FRCS Ed. 1993.

MAY, Mr John Michael Beveridge Old Station House, Thankerton, Biggar ML12 6NZ — MB ChB 1958 Glas.; FRCS Glas. 1964; FRCS Ed. 1964. (Glas.) Cons. Orthop. Surg. Law Hosp. Carluke. Socs: Fell. Brit. Orthop. Assn. Prev: Sen. Regist. (Orthop.), Regist. (Orthop.) & Regist. (Gen. Surg.); W.. Infirm. Glas.

MAY, John Robertson Raigmore Hospital NHS Trust, Old Perth Road, Inverness IV2 3UJ Tel: 01463 704000; Pinewood, Daviot Muir, Inverness IV2 5ER Tel: 01463 772307 — MB BS 1976 Lond.; BSc Aberd. 1969; MRCS Eng. LRCP Lond. 1976; FFA RCS Eng. 1982. (Roy. Free) Cons. Anaesth. Raigmore Hosp. NHS Trust. Socs: Hon. Mem. (Ex-Hon. Sec.) Lincoln Med. Soc.; Ed. & E. Scot. Soc. Anaesth.; Scot. Soc. Anaesth. Prev: Cons. Anaesth. Lincoln Co. Hosp.; Sen. Regist. (Anaesth.) Nottm.; Regist. (Anaesth.) Edin. Roy. Infirm.

MAY, Joyce Barbara Ballochmyle Medical Practice, Institute Avenue, Catrine, Mauchline KA5 6RU Tel: 01290 551237 Fax: 01290 552784 — MB ChB 1977 Glas.

MAY, Julia Elizabeth The Firs, Itton, Chepstow NP16 6BX Tel: 01291 641652 — MB BCh 1995 Wales. (Univ. Coll. Med. Cardiff) SHO (Paediat.) Llandough Hosp. Cardiff. Prev: Ho. Off. Singleton & Morriston Hosps. Swansea.

***MAY, Kenneth John** 46 Mullentine Road, Portadown, Craigavon BT62 4EJ — MB ChB 1998 Glas.; MB ChB Glas 1998.

***MAY, Kristina Jane** York District General Hospital, Wigginton Road, York YO31 8HE; Hill Farm House, Ilketonhall, St Margarets Road, Bungay NR35 1PL Tel: 01986 781450 — MB ChB 1994 Manch.; BA (Hons.) Camb. 1991.

***MAY, Lavinia Frances** Priors Lea, Priorsfield Rd, Godalming GU7 2RQ — MB BS 1996 Lond.

MAY, Malvern Stewart — BM 1988 Soton.; FRCA 1997; MRCP (UK) 1992; FRCA 1996. Cons. in Anaesth. and Pain Managem., Basildon Hosp., Basildon, Essex. Prev: Specialist Regist. N.E. Thames Rotat.

MAY, Margaret Stedman (retired) Strathyre, Welbeck Road, Bolsover, Chesterfield S44 6DH Tel: 01246 822347 — MB ChB Aberd. 1947; BA Lond. 1975.

MAY, Mr Michael Walter 61 Wimpole Street, London W1M 7DE — MB BS 1973 Lond.; FRCS Eng. 1980; MRCS Eng. LRCP Lond. 1973. (St. Bart.)

MAY, Olive Sibley 219 Cranmer Court, Sloane Avenue, London SW3 3HG Tel: 020 7584 2857 — MRCS Eng. LRCP Lond. 1928. (King's Coll. & King's Coll. Hosp.) CStJ; Med. Off. Civil Serv. Dept.

MAY, Patricia Anne 61 The Butts, Frome BA11 4AE — MB BS 1986 Lond.

MAY, Mr Paul Laurence Royal Liverpool Childrens Hospital, Alderhey, Liverpool L12 2AP Tel: 0151 252 5018 Email: paul.may@rlla-tr.nwest.nhs.uk — MB BS 1981 Lond.; 1981 MB BS Lond.; 1985 FRCS Ed.; 1998 FRCPCH. (St Thomas') Cons. (Paediat. Neurosurg.) Roy. Liverp. Childr.s Hosp.; Cons. (Neurosurg.) Walton Neurocentre Liverp. Socs: Eur. Soc. Paediat. Neurosurg.; Sec. Elect. Brit. Paediatric Neurosurg. Gp.; Internat. Soc. Paediatric Neurosurg. Prev: Fell. (Paediat. Neurosurg.) Hosp. for Sick Childr. Toronto, Canada; Sen. Regist. (Neurosurg.) Walton Hosp. Liverp.; Regist. (Neurosurg.) Roy. Hallamsh. Hosp. Sheff.

MAY, Mr Peter Cameron Princess Royal Hospital, Apley Castle, Telford TF1 6TF Tel: 01952 641222 Fax: 01952 242218; Orchard House, Longford Road, Newport TF10 8LP — MB BS 1971 Lond.; FRCS Eng. 1976; MRCS Eng. LRCP Lond. 1971. Cons. Orthop. & Trauma Surg. & Childr. Orthops. P.ss Roy. Hosp. Telford. Socs; Fell. BOA.

MAY, Peter George Robin Grove Medical Practice, Shirley Health Centre, Grove Road, Shirley, Southampton SO15 3UA Tel: 023 8078 3611 Fax: 023 8078 3156; 41 Westridge Road, Southampton SO17 2HP Tel: 02380 558931 — MRCS Eng. LRCP Lond. 1973; MRCGP 1981. (Roy. Free) Princip. GP Gr. Med. Pract. Prev: Trainee GP Soton. VTS; Ho. Phys. & Ho. Surg. Friarage Hosp. N.allerton.

MAY, Richard Garth Sheringham Health Centre, Cromer Road, Sheringham NR26 8RT Tel: 01263 822066 Fax: 01263 823890; Jesiam, Britons Lane, Sheringham NR26 8TR — MB BS 1963 Lond.; MRCS Eng. LRCP Lond. 1963; DObst RCOG 1965. (Guy's) Clin. Asst. (ENT & Urol.) Cromer & Dist. Hosp. Prev: Clin. Asst. (ENT) Gt. Yarmouth Gen. Hosp.; Ho. Surg. & Ho. Phys. N.ampton Gen. Hosp.

MAY, Rodney Wanderings, Speen Lane, Newbury RG14 1RN — LMSSA 1949 Lond.; FACP 1980; FRCP (Canada) 1976; FFOM RCP 1984, M 1978; MFCM 1974; DIH Soc. Apoth. 1958 Cert. Pub. Health RCP (Canada) 1976; Specialist Accredit. (Occupat. Med.) RCP Lond. 1978. (St. Mary's & Dalhousie) Asst. Prof. Fac. Med. Univ. Alberta, Canada. Socs: Fell. Amer. Coll. Occupat. Med.; Fell. Alberta Occupat. Health Assn.; Soc. Occupat. Med. Prev: Dir. Indust. Health Govt. Alberta Canada; Dir. Occupat. Health Govt. Nova Scotia Canada; Asst. Dep. Minister Occupat. Health & Safety Govt. Ontario, Canada.

MAY, Rosalind Diana The Surgery, 1a Richmond Avenue, Bedfont, Feltham TW14 9SG Tel: 020 8890 2245; 54 Petersfield Road, Staines TW18 1DL Tel: 01784 442332 — MB ChB St. And. 1959; Cert. Family Plann. JCC 1987. Asst. GP Bedfont. Prev: GP Hanworth, Middlx.; Clin. Med. Off. (Community Child Health) Hounslow & Spelthorne HA; GP Ashford, Middlx.

MAY, Mr Roy Edward (retired) Tiburon Lodge, 28 Parrys Lane, Stoke Bishop, Bristol BS9 1AA Tel: 0117 962 3204 Fax: 0117 962 3204 — MS Lond. 1970, MB BS (Hnrs.) 1959; FRCS Eng. 1963; MRCS Eng. LRCP Lond. 1960; DObst RCOG 1960. Prev: Cons. Surg. N. Bristol Healthcare Trust.

MAY, Sally Anne Guildhall Surgery, Bury St Edmunds IP33 2QZ; 6 Beech Rise, Bury St Edmunds IP33 2QE — MB BS 1992 Lond. p/t GP Regist. in Pract. Prev: SHO Elderly Care; SHO Paediat. W. Suff. Hosp.; SHO O & G W. Suff. Hosp.

MAY, Simon Richard Thorpewood Surgery, Woodside Road, Thorpe St Andrew, Norwich NR7 9 Tel: 01603 701477 — MB BS 1991 Lond.; DCH RCP Lond. 1994.

MAY, Stephanie Diana Stockwell Group Practice, 107 Stockwell Road, London SW9 9TJ Tel: 020 7274 3225 Fax: 020 7738 3005 — MB BS 1986 Lond.; BSc Lond. 1983; MRCGP 1990; DRCOG 1988. p/t Gen. Practitioner.

***MAY, Stephen George** 31 Portessie, Erskine PA8 6DR — MB ChB 1998 Glas.; MB ChB Glas 1998.

MAY, Susan Amanda Oakham Medical Practice, Cold Overton Road, Oakham LE15 6NT Tel: 01572 722621/2; Brooke House, 16 Church St, Braunston, Oakham LE15 8QT Tel: 01572 757147 Fax: 01572 757147 — BM BS 1983 Nottm.; BMedSci Nottm. 1981, BM BS 1983; MRCGP 1990; DRCOG 1987.

MAY, Tania 14 Nell Gwyn Crescent, Bestwood Lodge, Arnold, Nottingham NG5 8NQ — MB ChB 1989 Manch.

MAY, Timothy Francis Somerset Occupational Health, Taunton & Somerset Hospital, Musgrove Park, Taunton TA1 5DA Tel: 01823 342477 — MB BS 1982 Nottm.; BMedSci Nottm. 1980; MFOM RCP Lond. 1996, AFOM 1993; MRCGP 1987; DRCOG 1986. Cons. Occupat. Phys. Som. Occupat. Health Taunton & Som. Hosp. Socs: Soc. Occupat. Med.; Fac. Occupat. Med. Prev: Employm. Med. Adviser Health & Safety Exec. Nottm.; GP LoughBoro.; Employm. Med. Adviser Health & Safety Exec. Sussex.

MAY, Vivienne Elisabeth Tel: 0151 342 2557 Fax: 0151 342 9384 — MB BChir 1979 Camb.; MA Camb. 1977; FRCS Eng. 1983; MRCGP 1986; DRCOG 1986. (Camb. & Lond. Hosp.) Princip. GP Heswall; Mem. of Exec. Comm. Badminton and W. Wirral PCT.

MAY, Mr William (retired) 94A Sherwood Avenue, Whitecliff, Poole BH14 8DL Tel: 01202 749467 Fax: 01202 749467 Email: billmay@lineone.net — MB BS 1951 Lond.; FRCS Canada 1972; MRCS Eng. LRCP Lond. 1951; FRCOphth 1989; DO Eng. 1954; LMCC 1957. Ophth. Med. Pract. Dorset. Prev: Assoc. Specialist (Ophth.) Roy. Vict. Hosp. W.bourne & Poole Gen. Hosp.

MAY, William Dixon 170 Victoria Road, Swindon SN1 3DF Tel: 01793 36541; 37 Okebourne Park, Swindon SN3 6AH — BM BCh 1951 Oxf.; BM BCh Oxon. 1951.

MAY, William Jolly The Bourne Surgery, 41 Frensham Road, Lower Bourne, Farnham GU10 3PZ Tel: 01252 793141 — MB BS 1963 Lond.; DObst RCOG 1965. (Char. Cross) Prev: Med. Adviser Bencard Ltd.; GP Camberley; SHO (O & G & Gen. Med.) Cuckfield Hosp.

MAY BA MAUNG, Dr Ansford, 1 Park Road, Dinas Powys CF64 4HJ — MB BS Med. Inst. (I) Rangoon 1976; DRCOG 1983. Clin. Med. Off. (Paediat. & Family Plann.) S. Glam. AHA. Socs: Foundat. Mem. Fac. Family Plann. & Reproduc. Health.

MAY MYA NWE, Dr 36 The Willows, Waterlooville PO7 6YA — MB BS 1984 Rangoon; MB BS Med. Inst. (I) Rangoon, Burma 1984.

MAYAHI, Lila 235 Markfield, Courtwood Lane, Forestdale, Croydon CR0 9HW — MB BS 1996 Lond. (University College London) SHO (Med.).

MAYALL, Elizabeth Marion Tod (retired) Osmond House, Stoke Canon, Exeter EX5 4AA Tel: 01392 841219 — MB BS 1957 Lond.; MFFP 1993; DA Eng. 1959. Prev: SCMO Exeter Community Trust.

MAYALL, Frederick George Department of Histopathology, Withington Hospital, Withington, Manchester M20 8LE Tel: 0161 445 8111; 25 Gillbrook Road, Didsbury, Manchester M20 6WH Tel: 0161 445 8161 — MD 1993 Bristol; MB ChB 1987. Sen. Regist. (Histopath.) Manch. Hosp. Prev: Regist. (Histopath.) Univ. Wales Coll. Med.; SHO (Histopath.) Roy. Liverp. Hosp.

MAYALL, Gordon Francis (retired) Osmond House, Stoke Canon, Exeter EX5 4AA Tel: 01392 841219 — MB BChir 1954 Camb.; MB Camb. 1954, MA, BChir 1953; MRCS Eng. LRCP Lond. 1953; FRCR 1975; FFR 1962; DMRD Eng. 1959. Prev: Cons. Diag. Radiol. Roy. Devon & Exeter Hosp.

MAYALL, Mr Kenneth Miles (retired) 26 Grosvenor Avenue, Park Lane, Pontefract WF8 4QU Tel: 01977 702913 — MB BChir 1937 Camb.; MA Camb. 1935; FRFPS Glas. 1948; MRCS Eng. LRCP Lond. 1934; DLO Eng. 1938. Prev: Cons. Otolaryngol. Pontefract, Castleford & Goole Hosps.

MAYALL, Mark Nicholas Alexander 9 Hillcrest Road, Camberley GU15 1LF — MB BS 1983 Lond.; BSc Lond. 1980, MB BS 1983; MRCGP 1990; MRCPsych 1989.

MAYALL, Martin Francis — MB BS 1986 Lond.; FRCA 1994. (St. George's Hosp. Lond.) Cons. (Anaesth. & Int. Care) Kent & Canterbury Hosp. Prev: Regist. (Anaesth.) Roy. Brompton Hosp.; Regist. (Anaesth.) Gt. Ormond St. Childr.'s Hosp.; Sen. Regist. (Intens. Care) W.mead Hosp. Sydney.

MAYALL, Ruth Margaret Department of Anaesthetics, North Manchester Health Care Trust, Delaunays Road, Crumpsall, Manchester M8 5RB Tel: 0161 720 2280 Fax: 0161 720 2460; 18 Cherington Road, Cheadle SK8 1LN Tel: 0161 428 2188 Email: ruth.mayall@virgin.net — MB ChB 1978 Manch.; BSc (Med. Sci.) St. And. 1976; MRCP (UK) 1982; FANZCA 1989; FRCA 1985. Cons. Anaesth. N. Manch. Health Care Trust. Prev: Cons. Cardiothoracic Anaesth. Cardiothoracic Centre & BRd.green Hosp. Liverp.

MAYBAUM, Simon Walter 9 Hillside Drive, Edgware HA8 7PF — MB BS 1987 Lond.

MAYBERRY, John Francis Leicester General Hospital, Gwendolen Road, Leicester LE5 4PW Tel: 0116 249 0490 Fax: 0116 258 4666; Cariad House, The Spinney, Thurnby, Leicester LE7 9QS Email: jmaybe@globalnet.co.uk — MB BCh 1976 Wales; MPhil Nottm. 1988; BSc Wales 1973, DSc 1995, LLM 1991, MD 1981; FRCP Lond. & Glas. 1993; FRCPI 1990; MRCPI 1987; MRCP (UK) 1981; FBiol. 1989. (Welsh National School of Medicine) Cons. Phys. & Gastroenterol. Leicester Gen. Hosp.; Edr. Postgrad. Med. Jl. (1998); Sen. Lect. (Med.) Univ. of Leicester 1996; Assoc. PostGrad. Dean 2000. Socs: Brit. Soc. Gastroenterol.; Soc. Community Med.; Brit. Soc. Paediat. Gastroenterol. Prev: Sen. Regist. (Med.) Nottm.; Research Fell. (Gastroenterol.) Cardiff; Vis. Prof. LoughBoro. Business Sch. Univ. LoughBoro.

MAYBIN, Agnes Jane Adams (retired) 20 Tower View Avenue, Bangor BT19 6BB Tel: 01247 62745 — MD 1947 Belf.; MD (Commend.) Belf. 1947, MB BCh BAO 1938. Prev: Cons. Geriat. Phys. Belf. City Hosp. & Crawfordsburn Hosp. Bangor.

MAYBIN, Keith Joseph 20 Lyndhurst Avenue, London N12 0LU — MB BS 1993 Lond.

MAYBIN, Maureen Elisabeth (retired) 2 Delph Court, 27A Taptonville Road, Sheffield S10 5BQ Tel: 0114 267 0223 — MD 1948 Belf.; MA Camb. 1972, BA 1941; MB BCh BAO 1944. Prev: Clin. Med. Off. Hants. HA.

MAYBIN, Susanna Marjorie — BM 1977 Soton.; MSc (Pub. Health Develop. Countries) Lond. 1993; MRCP (UK) 1982; MRCGP 1984; DRCOG 1983; DCH RCP Lond. 1982. Sen. Med. Adviser Volun. Serv. Overseas Lond. Prev: Project Co-ordinator Save the Childr. Fund Chautara, Nepal; Med. Off. Save The Childr. Fund Ban Napho Refugee Camp N.E. Thailand; SCMO (Community Health) Plymouth HA.

*MAYBURY, Helena Joanne** 13 Riddings Road, Hale, Altrincham WA15 9DS — MB ChB 1996 Liverp.

MAYBURY, James Wilson (retired) 14 Balmoral Road, Chorley PR7 1LQ Tel: 01257 270696 — MB ChB 1943 Liverp. Prev: Med. Supt. Gillibrand Hall Inst. for Ment. Subn.

MAYBURY, Mr Nigel Keith 18 Crofters Green, Euxton, Chorley PR7 6LQ Tel: 012572 268837 Fax: 012572 268837 — BM BCh 1968 Oxf.; DM Oxf. 1980, MA 1968; FRCS Eng. 1973. (Oxf. & St. Thos.) Cons. Gen. & Vasc. Surg. Roy. Albert Edwd. Infirm. Wigan & Leigh NHS Trust. Socs: BSG; Vasc. Surgic. Soc. GB & Irel.; Assn. Surg. Prev: Lect. (Surg.) Univ. Leic.; Wellcome Research Fell. Middlx. Hosp. Lond.; Prosector (Anat.) St. Thos. Hosp. Med. Sch. Lond.

MAYBURY, Peter Lawrence, Air Commodore (retired) Puddledock Gdn, Clayhall Lane, Acton, Sudbury CO10 0AQ Tel: 01787 377092 — MB BChir 1952 Camb.; MA Camb. 1969; FFPHM 1982, M 1974; MFOM RCP Lond. 1982. Prev: Dir. Health & Research (RAF) Min. Defence (Air).

MAYCOCK, Alison Jane The Surgery, 1 Manor Place, London SE17 3BD Tel: 020 7703 3988 Fax: 020 7252 4002; 47 Mordaunt Street, Brixton, London SW9 9RD Tel: 020 7652 0204 — MB BChir 1990 Camb.; MA Camb. 1995; MA Leeds 1992; DRCOG 1995; MRCGP 1996. (Cambridge and Royal London)

MAYCOCK, Christopher Hugh Chiddenbrook Surgery, Threshers, Crediton EX17 3JJ Tel: 01363 772227 Fax: 01363 901363775528; The Court, Neopardy, Crediton EX17 5EP — MB BChir 1962 Camb.; MA Camb. 1972, BA 1958; DObst RCOG 1964; MRCGP 1973. (Camb. & St. Thos.) Clin. Asst. (Geriat.) Crediton Hosp. Socs: Devon & Exeter Med. Soc. Prev: SHO (Paediat.) Odstock Hosp. Salisbury; Ho. Surg. (Obst.) Kent & Canterbury Hosp.; Ho. Phys. & Ho. Surg. Watford Peace Memor. Hosp.

*MAYCOCK, Linsey Anne** 162 Mid Stocket Road, Aberdeen AB15 5HT — MB ChB 1998 Ed.; MB ChB Ed 1998.

MAYCOCK, Rosalind Ruth Evergreen Oak Surgery, 43 Commercial Road, Parkstone, Poole BH14 0HU Tel: 01202 747496 Fax: 01202 743624 — BM 1979 Soton. Exec. Comm. Mem. Poole Bay Primary Care Trust; Trustee Forest Ho. Hospice.

MAYCOCK, Timothy Peter Pocklington Group Practice, 7 Barmby Road, Pocklington, York YO42 2DL — MB ChB 1994 Leeds; MRCGP 1998; DRCOG 1997; (T)GP 1998.

MAYE

MAYE, Angeli Janet 6 Foster Close, Kettering NN15 7NY — MB ChB 1992 Leic.

MAYE, Matthew James 6 Foster Close, Kettering NN15 7NY — MB ChB 1992 Leics.

MAYELL, Margaret Joyes (retired) Hillside, Private Road, Woodborough, Nottingham NG14 6DW Tel: 0115 965 5214 — MB ChB 1961 Ed.; FRCS Ed. 1964. Prev: Cons. Paediat. Surg. Nottm. City Hosp.

MAYER, Mr Anthony David The Liver Unit, 3rd Floor Nuffield House, Queen Elizabeth Hospital, Birmingham B15 2TH Tel: 0121 627 2393 Fax: 0121 414 1833; 7 Debden Close, Dorridge, Solihull B93 8RL — MB BS 1976 Lond.; 1976 MB BS Lond.; 1971 BSc Sussex; 1986 MS Lond.; 1980 FRCS Eng.; 1976 MRCS Eng. LRCP Lond. (Guy's Hosp. Lond.) Cons. Surg. Hepatobiliary Surg. & Transpl. Liver Unit Qu. Eliz. Hosp. Birm.; Hon. Cons. Surg. Liver Unit Childr. Hosp. Birm.; Hon. Sen. Lect. Univ. Birm. Socs: Transpl. Soc.; Eur. Soc. Organ Transpl.; Brit. Trans. Soc. Prev: Surgic. Fell. Univ. Calif. San Diego Med. Centre, USA; Sen. Regist. Rotat. (Surg.) Qu. Eliz. Hosp. Birm.; Research Fell. Leeds Gen. Infirm.

MAYER, Anton-Paul Thomas The Thatch Cottage, Bury Lane, Epping CM16 5JA Tel: 01992 573378 Fax: 01279 871340 — MB BS 1991 Lond.; BSc (1st. cl. Hons.) Immunol. Univ. Lond. 1988.

MAYER, Arthur Crawford, MBE (retired) Dalhirach, Tarbert PA29 6UF Tel: 01880 820217 — MB ChB Glas. 1935; MRCGP 1953. Prev: Sen. Resid. Med. Off. Falkirk Infirm.

MAYER, Christopher Norman West Suffolk Hospital, Bury St Edmunds IP33 2QZ Tel: 01284 713592 — MB BCh 1977 Wales; FRCPsych 1997; MRCPsych 1983. Cons. Psychiat. W. Suff. Hosp. Bury St. Edmunds. Prev: Sen. Regist. (Psychiat.) St. Geo. Hosp. Med. Sch. Lond.

MAYER, Mr Eric Department of Ophthalmology, St Thomas' Hospital, Lembeth Palace Road, London SE1 7EH; 73 Victor Road, Windsor SL4 3JS — BM BCh 1994 Oxf.; PhD Camb. 1992; BSc Lond. 1988; FRCOphth 1998.

MAYER, Helen Margaret (retired) 19 Moss Close, Pinner HA5 3AY — MRCS Eng. LRCP Lond. 1942; FRCOG 1962, M 1948. Prev: Cons. Gynaecol. Metrop., Harrow & Mt. Vernon Hosps.

MAYER, Jeanette Heidi 37 Grove Lane, Barrow Upon Soar, Loughborough LE12 8NP Tel: 01509 413788 — BM BS 1985 Nottm.; PhD Nottm. 1983.

MAYER, Max (retired) 10 Cloudesley Place, London N1 0JA Tel: 020 7278 5086 — MD 1938 Rome; LAH Dub. 1955; MRCGP 1965; DTM & H Lond. 1955.

***MAYER, Nicholas John** 1 Glenisla Gardens Lane, Edinburgh EH9 2HP — MB ChB 1996 Ed.

MAYER, Peter Paul Department of Geriatric Medicine, Selly Oak Hospital, Selly Oak, Birmingham B29 6JD Tel: 0121 627 8482 Fax: 0121 627 8282; 16 Bryony Road, Selly Oak, Birmingham B29 4BU Tel: 0121 475 2435 Fax: 0121 475 2435 Email: petermayer@btinternet.com — BM BCh Oxf. 1968; MA Oxf. 1968; FRCP Lond. 1987; MRCP (UK) 1971. (Oxf.) Cons. Phys. (Geriat. Med.) Birm. Specialist and Univ. Hosp. Community Trust; Dir. Research & Developm. SBCHT-Chief Exec. Gp.; Hon. Sen. Clin. Lect. Birm. Univ.; Dir. Inst. of Ageing & Health W. Midl.; Chairm. Regional Med. Advis. Comm.; Regional Higher Awards Comm.; BMA Genreal Body of Cons.s Represen. Socs: Brit. Geriat. Soc. (Treas. s/i Gp. in Health Promotion); (Exec. Bd.) CrossRd.s Assn. Prev: Lect. (Geriat. Med.) Birm. Univ.; Sen. Regist. (Geriat. Med.) & Regist. (Renal Med.) E. Birm. Hosp.

MAYER, Robert David Highgate Group Practice, 44 North Hill, London N6 4QA Tel: 020 8340 6628 Fax: 020 8342 8428; 36 Park Avenue S., London N8 8LT Email: rdmayer@compuserve.com — MB ChB 1983 Bristol; MSc Lond. 1994; MRCGP 1991; MRCPsych 1989. (Bristol)

MAYER, Rudolf Raymund 45 Sydney Road, Sheffield S6 3GG Tel: 0114 268 0112 — State Exam Med. Munich 1988.

MAYER, Thomas Charles (Surgery), 150 Longwood Gardens, Ilford IG5 0BE Tel: 020 8550 6362; Elm House, The Green, Wanstead, London E11 2NT — MB ChB Liverp. 1960; BA Open 1973; BSc Lond. 1955; MRCS Eng. LRCP Lond. 1960; MRCGP 1968; DObst RCOG 1961. Private Family Doctor. Socs: BMA. Prev: Ho. Surg. & Ho. Off. (O & G) Gen. Hosp. Burton-on-Trent; Ho. Phys. Joyce Green Hosp. Dartford.

MAYER-JONES, Louis Michael (retired) Merlindene, Longhope GL17 0PD Tel: 01452 830450 Email: lmmj@ukonline.co.uk — MRCS Eng. LRCP Lond. 1962; MFCM 1972; DPH Manch. 1970. Prev: SCM Glos. HA.

MAYER-JONES, Rosemary Ann Merlindene, Longhope GL17 0PD Tel: 01452 830450 — MB ChB 1961 Manch.; DObst RCOG 1963.

MAYERS, Alan James Botley Health Care Centre, Mortimer Road, Botley, Southampton SO32 2UG Tel: 01489 783422 Fax: 01489 781919 — BM 1992 Soton.

MAYERS, Christopher Paul (retired) Corona, The Quay, Instow, Bideford EX39 4HX — MB ChB 1960 Ed.; MRCGP 1981; MRCPath 1971; DGM RCP Lond. 1988. Prev: GP Holsworthy.

***MAYERS, Geoffrey Philip** 56 Blakeney Road, Sheffield S10 1FE — MB ChB 1997 Sheff.

***MAYERS, Graham John** 7 Ashlea Road, Pensby, Wirral CH61 5UG — MB ChB 1998 Manch.; MB ChB Manch 1998.

MAYERS, Jonathan Nigel David Burley Park Doctors, Burley Park Medical Centre, 273 Burley Road, Leeds LS4 2EL Tel: 0113 230 4111; Red Stacks, 32 Foxhill Crescent, Weetwood, Leeds LS16 5PO — MB ChB 1987 Leeds; MRCGP 1994. (Leeds) GP Burley Pk. Med. Centre Leeds; Occupat. Phys. to Carlsberg-Tetley.

MAYERS, Mavis McKenzie Histopathology, Milton Keynes General NHS Trust, Standing Way, Eaglestone, Milton Keynes MK6 5LD Tel: 01908 243156 Fax: 01908 243176 Email: mavis.mayers@mkg-tr.anglox.nhs.uk — MB BCh BAO 1984 NUI; MRCPath 1993; FRCPA 1998. Cons. Histocytopath. Milton Keynes Gen. NHS Trust; Hon. Cons. Histocytopath. Stoke Mandeville NHS Trust Aylesbury. Prev: Sen. Med. Off. (Anat. Path.) Rockhampton Base Hosp. Qu.sland Australia; Sen. Regist. (Histopath.) Roy. Surrey Co. Hosp. & St. Geo. Hosp. Lond.; Regist. (Histopath.) Flinders Med. Centre, Austral.

MAYES, Arnold John Horfield Health Centre, Lockleaze Road, Bristol BS7 9RR Tel: 0117 969 5391 Fax: 0117 931 5879; 19 Hartington Park, Redland, Bristol BS6 7ES Tel: 0117 924 7990 — MB BS 1967 Lond.; FRCGP 1981, M 1974; Cert. FPA JCC 1974; DObst RCOG 1969. (Lond. Hosp.) Teach. (Gen. Pract.) Bristol Univ. Socs: BMA. Prev: Trainer (Gen. Pract.) Bristol. Univ.; Chairm. Severn Fac. RCGP; Clin. Tutor (Gen. Pract.) S.mead Hosp. Bristol.

MAYES, Clifford Bertram Donald 133 Killowen Grange, Lisburn BT28 3JE — MB BCh BAO 1991 Belf.

MAYES, David Eric 69 St Mary's Avenue, Whitley Bay NE26 1TB — MB BS 1972 Newc.

MAYES, Maj-Gen Frederick Brian, CB, Maj.-Gen. late RAMC (retired) 9 Searle Road, Farnham GU9 8LJ Tel: 01252 715453 Email: fbmayes@tinyonline.co.uk — MB BS 1958 Lond.; FRCS Eng. 1968. Prev: Dir. Gen. Army Med. Serv.

MAYES, Nicola Jacqueline 215 Smedley St. W., Matlock DE4 3JD — MB BS 1988 Lond.

MAYES, Philip John Kingswood Surgery, Kingswood Avenue, Swindon SN3 2RJ Tel: 01793 534699 — MB BS 1985 Lond.; Cert. Prescribed Equiv. Exp. JCPTGP 1990; DRCOG 1989; Cert. Family Plann. JCC 1989.

MAYES, Robert William (retired) 8 North Albert Road, Norton, Stockton-on-Tees TS20 1NU Tel: 01642 553486 — MB BS 1949 Durh.; FFOM RCP Lond. 1994, MFOM 1980; DIH Soc. Apoth. Lond. 1978.

***MAYES, Rory Conn Dougan** 20 Limavady Road, Londonderry BT47 1JD — MB BCh BAO 1994 Belf.

***MAYET, Ahmed** 96 Adelaide Avenue, London SE4 1YR — MB BS 1997 Lond.

MAYET, Jamil Department of Cardiology, St Mary's Hospital, Paddington, London W2 1NY Tel: 020 7886 1250 Fax: 020 7886 1763 Email: j.mayet@ic.ac.uk; 43 Rosslyn Hill, London NW3 5UH Tel: 020 7431 6438 — MB ChB 1989 Dundee; MD Dundee 1996; MBA Heriot-Watt 1997; MRCP (UK) 1992. Cons: Cardiol. St Mary's Hosp. Lond. Socs: Brit. Cardiac Soc.; Brit. Hypertens. Soc.; Eur. Soc. Cardiol. (Working Gp. on Echocardiography). Prev: Sen. Regist. (Cardiol.) St Mary's Hosp. Lond.; Regist. (Cardiol.) Roy. Brompton Hosp. Lond.; Regist. (Cardiol. & Gen. Med.) Hillingdon Hosp. & St. Mary's Hosp. Lond.

MAYFIELD, Mr Martin Paul Dept of Obstetrics and Gynaecology, Bradford Royal Infirmary, Bradford — MB ChB 1989 Leeds; BSc (Hons.) Leeds 1986; FRCS Ed. 1994; MPhil. (Clin. Oncol.) Bradford 1997. Specialist Regist. (Urol.) Yorks. Deanery. Prev: SHO Rotat.

(Surg.) Merseyside RHA; Demonst. (Anat.) Univ. Leeds; Ho. Off. (Gen. Surg. & Urol.) Leeds Gen. Infirm.

***MAYHEW, Claire Alexandra** 3 Jutland Rise, Eaton Ford, St Neots, Huntingdon PE19 7NF — MB ChB 1995 Leic.

MAYHEW, Jeremy Colyer 35 Old Town, Brackley NN13 7BZ — MB ChB 1991 Birm.

MAYHEW, John Anthony Lockhart (retired) 24 Bellfield Road, North Kessock, Inverness IV1 3XU Tel: 01463 731445 — MB ChB 1959 Ed.

MAYHEW, Stephen Richard (retired) 3 Jutland Rise, Eaton Ford, St Neots, Huntingdon PE19 7NF Tel: 01480 474623 Email: stevemayhew@intecc.co.uk — MB ChB 1965 Leeds; DCH RCPS Glas. 1968; DObst RCOG 1968. Prev: GP Huntingdon.

MAYHO, Grant Vincent Juniper House, 5A Woodland Way, Canterbury CT2 7LS Tel: 01227 787964 Email: mayho@tesco.net — MB BS 1982 Lond.; FFOM (RCP) 2000; MFOM RCP Lond. 1992, AFOM 1988; T(OM) 1992. (St. Thos.) Director Occupat.al Health, Pfizer Ltd, Sandwich, Kent. Prev: Chief Med. Off., Brit. Energy plc. Gloucestershire; Lect. (Occupat. Med.) St. Mary's Hosp. Med. Sch. Lond. & Lucas Aerospace Ltd.; Occupat. Phys. Centr. Electric Generating Bd. Lond.

***MAYLAND, Catriona Rachel** 11 Sandeman Place, Luncarty, Perth PH1 3RJ — MB ChB 1995 Glas.

MAYLAND, Frederick Anthony Beechland Medical Centre, 60a Keighley Road, Ovenden, Halifax HX2 8AL Tel: 01422 345798; Gate House Farm Cottage, Thorney Lane, Luddendenfoot, Halifax HX2 6UX Tel: 01422 349196 — MB ChB 1988 Birm.; MRCGP 1992. Prev: Ho. Off. (Gen. Med.) Walsall; Ho. Off. (Gen. Surg.) Stafford Dist. Gen. Hosp.

MAYLAND, Paul Anthony Milton Surgery, Millrise Road, Milton, Stoke-on-Trent ST2 7BN Tel: 01782 545444 Fax: 01782 570135; Ubberley Health Centre, Bargrave St., Bentilee, Stoke-on-Trent ST2 0HG Tel: 01782 536600 Fax: 01782 289853 — MB ChB 1966 Liverp. (Liverp.) Hon. Treas. N. Staffs. Med. Inst.

***MAYLEN, Gregory Simon** Flat 11, Phoenix Court, 122 Langney Road, Eastbourne BN22 8AJ; King Edward VII, Midhurst CU29 OBL Tel: 01730 812341 — MB BS 1998 Lond.; MB BS Lond 1998.

MAYNARD, Alan Henry 127 Prince Regent Lane, London E13 8RY Tel: 020 7476 3182 — MB BS 1954 Lond.; MRCS Eng. LRCP Lond. 1952; MRCGP 1964. (St. Thos.) GP Tutor Acad. Centre Newham Gen. Hosp. Prev: Ho. Surg. St. Thos. Hosp.; Res. Med. Off. St. Mary's Hosp. Colchester; Squadron Ldr. RAF Med. Br.

MAYNARD, Mr Christopher Austin Department of Otolaryngology, Level 4, Lauriston Building, 39 Lauriston Place, Edinburgh EH3 9YW — MB BS 1985 West Indies; FRCS Ed. 1991.

MAYNARD, David Gordon Orchard Croft Medical Centre, 2A Westfield Road, Horbury, Wakefield WF4 6LL Tel: 01924 271016 Fax: 01924 279459 — MB ChB 1975 Leeds.

MAYNARD, Deborah Diane Department of General Practice & Primary Care, King's College Hospital Medical School, Bessemer Road, London SE5 9PJ Tel: 020 7312 5683; 50 Margate Road, London SW2 5DT Tel: 020 7274 0170 — MB BChir 1989 Camb.; DRCOG 1996; DFFP 1996. (St. Thos. Hosp. Med. Sch.) Research Fell. (Gen. Pract. & Primary Care) King's Coll. Hosp. Med. Sch. Prev: GP Regist. Wolworth Lond.; GP Regist. Kings Coll. Hosp. Innovative VTA; Regist. (c/o the Elderly) Newham Gen. Hosp. Lond.

MAYNARD, Jeremy Roy 14 Lamont Close, Wickford SS12 9QS — MB BS 1993 Lond.

MAYNARD, Mr John David 97 Harley Street, London W1N 1DF Tel: 020 7935 4988 Fax: 020 7935 6617; 14 Blackheath Park, Blackheath, London SE3 9RP Tel: 020 8852 6766 Fax: 020 7935 6617 — MB BS Lond. 1954; MS Lond. 1966; FRCS Eng. 1961. (Char. Cross) Cons. Surg. Guy's Hosp. Lond.; Dir. of Guy's & St Thos. Path. Museums; Chairm. Salivary Gland Tumour Panel. Socs: Fell. Roy. Soc. Med.; Hunt. Soc. Prev: Regist. & Lect. (Surg.) Guy's Hosp. Lond.; Demonst. (Anat.) Lond. Hosp. Med. Coll.; Ho. Surg. Char. Cross Hosp.

MAYNARD, John Patrick 18 Beeches Walk, Carshalton Beeches, Carshalton SM5 4JT — MB BS 1971 Lond.; MRCS Eng. LRCP Lond. 1971; FFA RCS Eng. 1976. Ho. Surg. (Surg.) Bromley Hosp.; Ho. Phys. (Med.) Char. Cross Hosp.; SHO (Obst.) FarnBoro. Hosp. Kent.

MAYNARD, Mr Nicholas David 23 Banbury Road, Oxford OX2 6NN Tel: 01865 220280 Fax: 01865 220659 Email: nick.maynard@orh.anglox.nhs.uk; New Barn, Stanton Road, Oxford OX2 9AY — MB BS 1986 Lond.; BA Oxf. 1983; MS Lond. 1994; FRCS Eng. 1990; FRCS (Gen.) 1997. Cons. (Gen. Surg.) John Radcliffe Hosp. Oxf. Prev: Sen. Regist. (Gen. Surg.) Guy's & St. Thos. Hosps. Trust Lond.; Sen. Regist. (Gen. Surg.) Austin & Repatriation Med. Campus Melbourne, Austral.; Regist. (Gen. Surg.) E.bourne Dist. Gen. Hosp.

***MAYNARD, Nicola Anne** High Trees, Ashreigney, Chulmleigh EX18 7NB — MB ChB 1998 Bristol.

MAYNARD, Robert Lewis Department of Health, Skipton House, Elephant & Castle, London SE1 6LH Tel: 020 7972 5118 Fax: 020 7972 5167 — MB BCh 1975 Wales; BSc (1st cl. Hons.) Wales 1972; MRCP (UK) 1996; FFOM 1996; FRCPath. 1999; FIBiol 1990, M 1979. (Welsh Nat. Sch. of Med.) Sen. Med. Off. DOH Lond. Socs: Physiol. Soc.; Anat. Soc.; Brit. Thorac. Soc. Prev: Sen. Med. Off. (Research) Chem. Defence Estab. Porton; Ho. Surg. Llandough Hosp. Penarth; Ho. Phys. Neville Hall Hosp. Abergavenny.

MAYNARD, Stephen Michael Langley Group Surgery, Wood Street, Middleton, Manchester M24 5QL Tel: 0161 643 5385 Fax: 0161 653 6430 — MB BS 1982 Lond.

MAYNARD, Suzanne Juliette 19 Upper Malvern Drive, Belfast BT8 6TN — MB BCh BAO Belf.; MB BCh BAO Belf. 1995. SHO (Med.) Roy. Vict. Hosp. Belf.

MAYNE, Andrea Jean 12 Mellish Road, Walsall WS4 2ED — MB BS 1974 Lond.; FRCP Lond. 1995; MRCP (UK) 1979; MRCS Eng. LRCP Lond. 1974. (Roy. Free) Cons. Paediat. Sandwell Dist. Gen. Hosp.

MAYNE, Christopher John Leicester General Hospital, Gwendolen Road, Leicester LE5 4PW Tel: 0116 258 4861 — MB BS 1980 Lond.; FRCOG 1997; MRCOG 1985; T(OG) 1991. Cons. O & G Leicester Gen. Hosp. Socs: N. Eng. Obst. Soc. & Internat. Continence Soc.

MAYNE, David Gregory 25 Aghory Road, Armagh BT61 9LY — MB BCh BAO 1956 Belf.; FRCPI 1990, M 1965; MRCPsych 1971; DPM RCPSI 1961. (Belf.) Prev: Cons. SHSSB & St. Lukes Hosp. Armagh.

MAYNE, David John 70 Woodbine Road, Newcastle upon Tyne NE3 1DE — MB BS 1986 Newc. SHO (Anaesth.) S. Shields Gen. Hosp. Prev: Ho. Off. (Med & Surg.) Hull Roy. Infirm.; SHO Palmerston N. Hosp. Bd. New Zealand; SHO Canterbury Hosp. Bd. ChristCh., New Zealand.

MAYNE, Elizabeth Emily (retired) Department of Haematology, Royal Victoria Hospital, Belfast BT12 6BA Tel: 01232 240503 — MD 1968 Belf.; MB BCh BAO 1962; FRCP Glas. 1986, M 1984; FRCPath 1982, M 1970. Cons. Haemat. Roy. Vict. Hosp. Belf.; Hon. Reader Fac. of Med. Qu. Univ. Belf. Prev: Dir. of N. Irel. Haemophilia Refer. Centre.

MAYNE, Karen Margaret 29 Islip Road, Oxford OX2 7SP — MB ChB 1980 Ed.; BSc (Hons.) Ed. 1977, MB ChB 1980; MRCP (UK) 1983; FRCPath 1997, M 1989. (Edinburgh) Sen. Med. Adviser (Oncol./Haemat.) Roche UK Welwyn Garden City Herts. Socs: Fell. Roy. Coll. Of Pathologists; Roy. Coll. Phys.s; Brit. Soc. of Haematol. Prev: Med. Adviser Zeneca Alderley Pk. Macclesfield, Chesh.; Clin. Research Phys. (Oncol.) Wellcome Beckenham, Kent; Sen. Regist. (Haemat. And Oncol.) Oxon HA.

MAYNE, Michael George (retired) 28 Church Road, Beverley HU17 7EN — MB ChB 1957 Leeds; MRCGP 1966. Prev: Ho. Surg. & Ho. Phys. St. Jas. Hosp. Leeds.

MAYNE, Nicholas Mannering Cuthbert (retired) Glengariff, 119 Leckhampton Road, Cheltenham GL53 0DQ Tel: 01242 521797 Email: nickmayne@glengariff54.freeserve.co.uk — MB BS 1956 Birm.; MB ChB Birm. 1956; MD Birm. 1964; FRCP Lond. 1976, M 1960; MRCS Eng. LRCP Lond. 1956. Prev: Ho. Phys. Gen. Hosp. Birm.

MAYNE, Stewart Derby City General Hospital, Uttoxeter Road, Derby DE22 3NE Tel: 01332 625851 Fax: 01332 625672 Email: stewart.mayne@sdah-tr.trent.nhs.uk; Bentley Fold Farm, Main Road, Ellastone, Ashbourne DE6 2GZ Tel: 01335 324151 Fax: 01335 324152 Email: stewartmayne@ellastone.freeserve.co.uk — MB BCh 1971 Wales; BSc (Hons.) Wales 1968; FRCPath 1989. (Cardiff) Cons. Haemat. S. Derby. Acute Hosps. NHS Trust.

MAYNER, Peter Edward Cherry Orchard, Guarlford, Malvern WR13 6NT — MB ChB 1968 Birm.; DObst RCOG 1970. (Birm.) Sen. Surg. Peninsular & Oriental Steam Navigation Co.; Hon. Mem. US S.W. Obst. & Gyn. Soc. Socs: BMA; Soc. Occupat. Med. Prev:

MAYO

Ho. Phys. Stratford-upon-Avon Hosp.; Ho. Off. (Surg. & Orthop.) Hereford Co. & Gen. Hosps.; Obst. Ho. Surg. Worcester Roy. Infirm.

MAYO, Haydn Guy North Cardiff Medical Centre, Excalibur Drive, Thornhill, Cardiff CF14 9BB Tel: 029 2075 0322 Fax: 029 2075 7705; 10 Pontymason Close, Rogerstone, Newport NP10 9HG Tel: 01633 896369 Email: hgmayo@ad.com — MB BCh 1986 Wales; MRCGP 1990; DRCOG 1990.

MAYO, Katrina Mary Norm Wealdon Elderly Mental Health Team, Framfield Road, Uckfield Tel: 01825 745016 — MB BS 1986 Lond.; MRCPSych 1992. Cons. Old Age Psychiat. (P/T).

MAYO, Lesley Katherine Waterfront Garden Surgery, Jones Lane, Hythe, Southampton SO45 6AW Tel: 02380 841841; 47 Roman Way, Dibden Purlieu, Southampton SO45 4RP Tel: 02380 849339 — MB BS 1982 Lond.; MA Camb. 1985; DCH RCP Lond. 1986; DRCOG 1985. Clin. Med. Off. Soton. & SW Hants. HA.

MAYO, Robert Edmund Peter Blandford House Surgery, 7 London Road, Braintree CM7 2LD Tel: 01376 347100 Fax: 01376 349934 — MB BS 1984 Lond.; MRCGP 1988; DA (UK) 1990; DCH RCP Lond. 1987; DRCOG 1986; MD Lond. 1999. (Middlx.) Prev: Princip. Med. Off. Mseleni Hosp. Kwazulu Dept. Health, Rep. S. Afr.; SHO (Anaesth.) Old Ch. Hosp. Romford; Clin. Med. Off. Barking, Havering & Brentwood HA.

MAYON-WHITE, Richard Timothy Richard Building, Old Road, Oxford OX3 7LG Tel: 01865 226858 Fax: 01865 222999 — MB BS Lond. 1966; FRCP Lond. 1991; MRCP (UK) 1971; FFCM 1986, M 1977. (St. Thos.) Cons. Pub. Health Med. Oxf. HA. Socs: Fell. Roy. Coll. Phys.; Fell.Fac. of Pub. Health Med.; Brit. Infec. Soc. Prev: Pub. Health Laborat. Serv.

MAYON-WHITE, Valerie Ann Diabetes Centre, Stoke Mandeville Hospital, Mandeville Road, Aylesbury HP21 8AL Tel: 01296 315534; 40A Blandford Avenue, Oxford OX2 8DZ Tel: 01865 552986 — MB BS 1966 Lond. (St. Thos.) Staff Phys. Diabetic Centre Stoke Mandeville Hosp. Aylesbury.

MAYOR, Alexander Hearnshaw Vale House, Love's Hill, Timsbury, Bath BA2 0EU — MB BS 1986 Lond.; BSc Lond. 1983; MRCP (UK) 1989; FRCA 1991. Cons. Anaesth. Roy. United Hosp. Bath. Prev: Sen. Regist. (Anaesth.) S. W. Region; Research Fell. (Anaesth.) Bristol; Asst. Anaesth. (Paediat. Anaesth. with Critical Care Med.) Johns Hopkins Hosp. BBaltimore, USA.

MAYOR, Andrew Colin New Hall Lane Practice, The Health Centre, Geoffrey Street, Preston PR1 5NE Tel: 01772 401730 Fax: 01772 401731; 6 The Handbridge, Fulwood, Preston PR2 8LE — MB ChB 1975 Manch.; MRCGP 1979; DRCOG 1978.

MAYOR, Peter Edward Dorfold Cottage, Swanley Lane, Acton, Nantwich CW5 8LP — BM BS 1977 Nottm.; BMedSci Nottm. 1975; MRCP (UK) 1981; FRCR 1988. Cons. Radiol. Leighton Hosp. Crewe.

MAYOR, Sunil Kumar Bath Road Surgery, 169 Bath Road, Hounslow TW3 3BU Tel: 020 8577 9035 Fax: 020 8577 9200; Inglewood House, 21 Ince Road, Burwood Park, Walton-on-Thames KT12 5BJ Tel: 01932 220731 Fax: 01932 228918 — MB ChB 1979 Nairobi. (Univ. Nairobi, Kenya)

MAYOR, Vidhu The Lane Medical Centre, 52 Chesterton Road, Sparkbrook, Birmingham B12 8HE Tel: 0121 442 4555 Fax: 0121 449 1907; 151 Wheelers Lane, Kings Heath, Birmingham B13 0SU Tel: 0121 444 1655 Email: vidhumayor@aol.com — MB ChB 1984 Bristol; MRCGP 1990; DRCOG 1987. (Bristol) Chairm. of Gt.er SPk.brook PCG. Socs: Sec. Small Pract.s Assoc. W. Midl. Prev: Trainee GP/SHO W. Bromwich VTS.

MAYOU, Mr Bryan Jonathan The Lister Hospital, Chelsea Bridge Road, London SW1W 8RH Tel: 020 7824 8080 Fax: 020 7259 9887 Email: bjmayou@uk-consultants.co.uk; 16 Margaretta Terrace, London SW3 5NU Tel: 020 7351 2634 — MB ChB 1969 Birm.; FRCS Eng. 1974. (Birmingham) p/t Hon. Cons. Plastic Surg.Guys & St. Thos. Hosp. Lond. Socs: Brit. Assn. Plastic Surg. & Brit. Soc. Surg. Hand; Brit. Assn. of Aesthetic Plastic Surg.s; Roy. Soc. Med. Prev: Cons. Plastic Surg.Guys & St. Thos. Hosp. Lond.; Sen. Regist. (Plastic Surg.) St. Thos. Hosp. & Hosp. Sick Childr. Gt. Ormond St. Lond.; Regist. (Plastic Surg.) Mt. Vernon Hosp. N.wood.

MAYOU, Professor Richard Anthony University Department of Psychiatry, Warneford Hospital, Oxford OX3 7JX Tel: 01865 226477 Fax: 01865 793101 Email: richard.mayou@psych.ox.ac.uk; Hill House, Shabbington, Aylesbury HP18 9HQ Tel: 01844 201885 — BM BCh 1965 Oxf.; MPhil Lond. 1971; MA Oxf. 1965, MSc 1963, BA 1961; FRCP Lond. 1985, M 1969; FRCPsych 1979, M 1973;

DPM Eng. 1971. (Oxf. & Birm.) Prof. (Psychiat.) Oxf. Univ.; Hon. Cons. Psychiat. Warneford Hosp. & John Radcliffe Hosp. Oxf.; Fell. Nuffield Coll. Oxf. Prev: Sen. Regist. Bethlem Roy. & Maudsley Hosps. Lond.; Ho. Phys. Hammersmith & Brompton Hosps. Lond.

MAYOU, Susan Catherine Dept of Dermatology, Queen Mary's University Hospital, Roehampton, London SW15 5PN Tel: 020 8355 2774 Fax: 020 8355 2317; 16 Margaretta Terrace, London SW3 5NU Tel: 020 7351 2634 Fax: 020 7351 6564 — MB BS 1977 Lond.; BSc (Hons.) Lond. 1974; MRCP (UK) 1980; FRCP 1998. (St. Thomas's Hosp. Med. Sch.) Cons. Dermat. Qu. Mary's Univ. Hosp. & Chelsea & W.minster Hosp. Lond. Socs: Roy. Soc. Med.; Fell. Roy. Coll. Of Phys.s. Prev: Sen. Regist. (Dermat.) St. Bart. Hosp. Lond.; Regist. (Dermat.) St. Thos. Hosp. Lond.; Regist. (Med.) St. Thos. Hosp. Lond.

MAYR, Denis Charles (retired) 11 Drummond Road, Swanage BH19 2DX — MB BS Lond. 1952. Prev: Med. Off. Harrow Sch. & Orley Farm Sch.

MAYS, Christopher Sean Nyali, Epping Road, Roydon, Harlow CM19 5JE — MB BS 1989 Lond.; MRCGP 1993.

*****MAYS, Joseph Lewis** 39 Barton Road, Cambridge CB3 9LG — MB ChB 1998 Bristol.

MAYSON, Robert Lewis The Health Centre, Ash Meadow, High Street, Much Hadham SG10 6DE Tel: 01279 842242 Fax: 01279 843973; Foley Cottage, 3 Station Road, Sawbridgeworth CM21 9AY Tel: 01279 831879 Email: robmayson@freeserve.co.uk — MB BS 1993 Lond.; DFFP 1996; DRCOG 1995. (UCL)

MAYTUM, Catherine Mary 27 Mortimer Road, Bournemouth BH8 9HP Tel: 01202 514016 — MB ChB 1992 Bristol.

MAZ, Stefan Stanislaw Department of Anaesthetics, St. James' University Hospital, Beckett St., Leeds LS9 7TF — MB BS 1984 Lond.; BSc Lond. 1981, MB BS 1984; FRCA. 1990; DA (UK) 1986. (St. Bart.) Staff Anaesth. St. Jas. Univ. Hosp. Leeds. Socs: MDU. Prev: Regist. (Anaesth.) St. Jas. Univ. Hosp. Leeds; SHO (Anaesth.) Soton. Gp. W. Hants. HA; SHO (Anaesth.) Chelmsford Gp. Mid Essex HA.

MAZARELO, Joseph Orlando Victoria Road Health Centre, Victoria Road, Washington NE37 2PU Tel: 0191 417 3557 — MB BS 1983 Bangalore. (Bangalore) GP Washington, Tyne & Wear.

MAZARELO, Juvencio Antonio Xavier Lord Lister Health Centre, 121 Woodgrange Road, Forest Gate, London E7 0EP Fax: 020 8250 7553 — MB BS Bombay 1961; FRCS Eng. 1977. (Topiwala Nat. Med. Coll.) GP Surg. Lond. Lister Health Centre, Lond. E7 0EP. Prev: Med. Off. (Family Plann.) Newham HA.

MAZEIKA, Peter Karl 18 Alma Road, Sale M33 4HB — MB ChB 1982 Manch.; MSc 2001 Lond.; MD Manch. 1994; MRCP (UK) 1985. (Manchester) Prev: Sen. Regist. & Clin. Research Fell. (Clin. Cardiol.) Hammersmith Hosp. & Roy. Postgrad. Med. Sch.

MAZEY, Glyn Hainstock (retired) 16 Avonbank Paddocks, Southern Lane, Stratford-upon-Avon CV37 6BH Tel: 01789 262422 Email: gandwmazey@ukonline.co.uk — MB ChB Manch. 1951. Prev: GP Solihull.

MAZEY, Kathleen Ann Lesley (retired) Upper Turner Top, Rishworth, Sowerby Bridge HX6 4QS Tel: 01422 823441 — MB ChB Manch. 1962; MSc Salford 1983; Dip. Audiol. Manch. 1980. Cons. Paediat. Audiol. Rochdale NHS Trust. Prev: SCMO (Audiol.) Rochdale NHS Trust.

MAZEY, Nicola Suzanne 25 Church Road, Oldswinford, Stourbridge DY8 2HQ; 18 Rangemore Road, Liverpool L18 4PW Tel: 0151 724 2475 — MB ChB 1992 Liverp.; BSc (Hons.) Lond. 1995; DA (UK) 1994. SHO (Anaesth.) City Hosp. NHS Trust Birm. Prev: SHO (Anaesth.) Wolverhampton New Cross Hosp. NHS Trust.

MAZHAR, Mohammad 71 Atkins Road, Clapham Park, London SW12 0AH Tel: 020 8675 0083 — MB BS 1965 Punjab; DO RCPSI 1972.

MAZHAR, Nusrat Ara 71 Atkins Road, London SW12 0AH Tel: 020 8675 0083 — MB BS 1966 Punjab.

MAZHAR, Rasheed Woodhall Health Centre, Valley Green, Off Shenley Road, Hemel Hempstead HP2 7RJ Tel: 01442 61805 Fax: 01442 261750.

MAZHARI, Hasan Khurshid Mazhari, Clayton Health Centre, 89 North Road, Clayton, Manchester M11 4EJ Tel: 0161 223 1658 Fax: 0161 231 6977 — MB BS 1967 Bihar; DTM & H Liverp. 1975; DCH Dub. 1977. (Darbhanga Med. Coll.) GP Clayton. Prev: Trainee Gen. Pract. I. of Wight Vocational Train. Scheme.

*MAZRANI, Waseem 2 Beresford Road, Canonbury, London N5 2HU — MB BS 1997 Lond.

MAZUMDAR, Ranjit Kumar Eye Road Surgery, 144 Eye Road, Off Welland Estate, Peterborough PE1 4SG Tel: 01733 563515; 170 Fulbridge Road, Peterborough PE4 6SP Tel: 01733 67033 — MB BS 1974 Delhi. (Maulana Azad Med. Coll.) Prev: SHO (Psychiat./Ment. Handicap) Llanfrechfa Grange Hosp.; SHO (Anaesth.) Withybush Gen. Hosp. HaverfordW.; SHO (Gen. Surg.) Pilgrim Hosp. Boston.

MAZUMDAR, Shanti 36 Collier Row Lane, Collier Row, Romford RM5 3BJ.

MAZUMDER, Jagat Kumar Bickwell Lodge, Norford Way, Bamford, Rochdale OL11 5QS — MB BS 1969 Calcutta; FFA RCS Eng. 1977; DA Eng. 1973. (R.G. Kar Med. Coll.) Cons. (Anaesth.) & Dir. of ITU Tameside Gen. Hosp. Socs: Fell.of Mcgill Univ. Montreal Canada 1979; Vas. Anaesth. Soc. Prev: Cons. & Chairm. (Anaesth.) Birch Hill Hosp.

MAZUMDER, Mr Rajkumar Freezywater Primary Care Centre, 2B Aylands Rd, Enfield EN3 6PN Tel: 01992 763794 Fax: 01992 764570; 31 Wynchgate, Southgate, London N14 6RP Tel: 0208 882 8419 Fax: 0208 372 9170 Email: rajkumar@mazumder.com — MBBS 1972 R.G.KAR Med. Coll., Calcutta, India; 1978 LRCP; MRCS (Lond.); 1978 DRCOG (Lond.). Prev: Vocational Trainer for Gen. Pract., Chase Farm & The Middlx. Hosp., Lond., 1975-1978; G.P. Tutor, Chase Farm Hosp., Enfield, Middlx., 1994-1997; Med. SHO, N. Middlx. Hosp., Lond. 1974.

MAZZA, David John Howden Health Centre, Howden West, Livingston EH54 6TP Tel: 01506 423800 Fax: 01506 460757 — MB ChB 1988 Ed. GP Livingston, W. Lothian.

MAZZON, Silvano 126 Clonmell Road, London N17 6JU — State Exam Bologna 1983.

***MBAMALI, John Obiozo** 33 Wiltshire Close, London SW3 2NS — MB ChB 1992 Leeds.

MBAMALU, David Paul Flat 1, 235 Lavender Hill, London SW11 1JW — BM BCh 1985 Univ. Nigeria.

MBANU, Alfred London Road Surgery, 79 London Road, Peterborough PE2 9BS Tel: 01733 343139 Fax: 01733 341945 — MB BCh BAO 1967 NUI; MRCS Eng. LRCP Lond. 1968; DRCOG 1979. Regist. (Radiol.) PeterBoro. Dist. Hosp. Socs: BMA. Prev: SHO (O & G) Moyle Hosp. Larne; SHO Orthop. Surg. Co. Hosp. York.

MBAYA, Patrick Samuel 17 Woodthorpe Grange, Prestwich, Manchester M25 0GU — MB ChB 1980 Manch.

MBIZENI, Johannes Manene 35 Iveson Drive, Leeds LS16 6NG — MB ChB 1993 Leeds.

MBONU, Grace Obo 15 Alder Grove, Stretford, Manchester M32 8PG — MB ChB 1978 Manch. SHO (Anaesth.) Salford AHA (T).

MBUBAEGBU, Mr Chima Eric 187 Dumbreck Road, London SE9 1RH — MB BS 1981 Ibadan; FRCS Ed. 1988.

MCALLISTER-WILLIAMS, Richard Hamish Department of Psychiatry, Leazes Wing, Royal Victoria Infirmary, Newcastle upon Tyne NE1 4LP Tel: 0191 232 5131 Ext: 24034 Fax: 0191 227 5108 Email: r.h.mcallister-williams@ncl.ac.uk — MB ChB 1987 Ed.; BSc 1985; MRCPsych 1995. MRC Clin. Sci. Sen. Lect. Level & Hon. Cons. Psychiat. Status Univ. Newc. Socs: Brit. Assn. for Psychopharmacol.; Brit. Neurosci. Assn. Prev: Regist. Rotat. (Psychiat.) SE Scotl., Clin. Lect. (Gen. Adult Psychiat.) Univ. Newc.; Wellcome Clin. Research Fell. (Pharmacol.) Univ. Edin.; Ho. Phys. Roy. Infirm. Edin.

MCARDLE, Carol-Ann Stepping Hill Hospital, Poplar Grove, Stockport SK2 7JE — MB ChB 1990 Manch.; MRCPsych 1996. Clin. Med. Off. (Old Age Psychiat.). Socs: BMA; Roy. Coll. Psychiats. Prev: Regist. Rotat. (Psychiat.) Gtr. Manch.

MCCALL-SMITH, Elizabeth Dorothy Anne, MBE Bruntsfield Medical Practice, 11 Forbes Road, Edinburgh EH10 4EY Tel: 0131 228 6081 Fax: 0131 229 4330; 16A Napier Road, Edinburgh EH10 5AY Tel: 0131 229 6083 — MB ChB 1974 Ed.; FRCGP 2000; MRCGP 1979; Cert. JCC Lond. 1978; DRCOG 1977. GP Partner, Bruntsfield Med. Pract. Edin. Socs: Medico-chirurgical Soc. Edin. (Jun. Sec.). Prev: Regist. (Psychiat.) Roy. Edin. Hosp.; SHO (O & G) W.. Gen. Hosp. Edin.; SHO (Med. & A & E) Auckland Hosp. Bd., NZ.

MCCREADY-HALL, Lisa Penelope 16 Crewdson Road, London SW9 0LJ — MB BS 1993 Lond.

MCDERMOTT, Miss Ann-Louise 12 St Bernards Road, Olton, Solihull B92 7BB — MB ChB 1996 Birm.; BDS Wales 1991; FDS RCS Eng. 1995. SHO (ENT) Birm. Heartlands Hosp. Socs: Fell. RCS. Prev: Ho. Off. (Gen. Surg.) Worcester Roy. Infirm.; Ho. Off. (Gen. Med.) Birm. Heartlands Hosp.; SHO (Maxillofacial Surg.) Selly Oak Hosp. Birm. & Redditch.

MCELWAINE-JOHNN, Hilary Anne Cranmere Cottage, Newbridge, Cadnam, Southampton SO40 2NW — MB BS 1992 Lond.; BSc Lond. 1989.

MCEWAN, M. Shirley Ramsay, MBE University Department of Medicine, Ninewells Hospital & Medical School, Ninewells Avenue, Dundee DD1 9SY Tel: 01382 660111 Ext: 33124 Fax: 01382 660675 Email: s.r.mcewan@dundee.ac.uk; Craig Duich, Golspie Terrace, Broughty Ferry, Dundee DD5 2PW Tel: 01382 775510 Email: srmcewan@altavista.com — MB ChB 1960 St. And.; FRCP 1999 Edin. (St. And.) p/t Sen. Res. Fell./Hon. Lect. (Med.) Univ. Dundee; Hon. Sec. SHARP (Scot. Heart And Arterial Dis. Risk Preven.); MRC Trial Adviser, Dept. of Vas. Med., Ninewells Hosp. Med. Sch. Dundee. Socs: Past Pres. Forfarshire Med. Assn.; Dundee Med. Soc.; FRSM. Prev: GP Dundee; Ho. Phys. King's Cross Hosp. Dundee; Ho. Surg. (Orthop.) Dundee Roy. Infirm.

MCGHEE, Anne-Marie Borders General Hospital, Melrose TD6 9BS; The Knowe, 24 High Cross Avenue, Melrose TD6 9SU — MB ChB 1985 Ed.; MRCGP 1990; DCCH RCP Ed. 1989. (Edinburgh University Medical School) Staff Grade Community Padiatrician. Prev: Regist. (Psychiat.) Roy. Edin. Hosp.; Trainee GP Edin. VTS.

MCGREGOR-NABERBAEUMER, Christiane 15 De Roos Road, Eastbourne BN21 2QA — State Exam Med Munster 1989; MRCGP 1994; DCH RCP Lond. 1994. GP. Prev: Trainee GP/SHO (Gen. Paediat.) King's Coll. Hosp. Lond.; Trainee GP Hastings VTS.

MCGREGOR-ROBERTSON, Gordon Seath (retired) Garry Villa, Abbey Road, Auchterarder PH3 1DN Tel: 01764 662955 — MB ChB 1948 Glas. Prev: Regist. (Gen. Med.) W.. Infirm. Glas.

MCGREGOR-SMITH, Fiona Ann Danebridge Medical Centre, 29 London Road, Northwich CW9 5HR Tel: 01606 45786 Fax: 01606 331977; Gorstage Hall Mews E., Weaverham Road, Gorstage, Northwich CW8 2SG — MB ChB 1986 Manch.; MRCGP 1990. GP N.wich. Prev: Trainee GP Leighton Hosp. VTS.

MCGREGOR-WOOD, Piers Niel Paton 6 Elwell Street, Upwey, Weymouth DT3 5QF; The Glade, Pk Road, Haslemere GU27 Tel: 01428 658612 — MB BS Lond. 1981; MRCGP 1986. (CXHMS) GP Princip.

MCHARDY-YOUNG, Stuart 106 Harley Street, London W1N 1AF Tel: 0207 935 2797 Fax: 0208 453 2415 Email: drsmchy@aol.com; 20 Belmont Road, Twickenham TW2 5DA Tel: 0208 894 3116 Fax: 0208 408 2930 Email: drsmchy@aol.com — MB BS 1960 London; MD 1973 London; FRCP 1978 London; MRCS 1960 London; MRCS Eng. LRCP Lond. 1960 London; MRCP 1964 London. (Guy's) p/t Cons. Phys. Jefferson Kelson Centre, Diabetes & Endocrin. Centr. Middlx. Hosp. Lond.; Con. Phys. Char. Cross Hosp. & Hammersmith Hosp. Lond. Socs: Fell. Roy. Soc. Med.; Brit. Diabetic Assn.; Brit. Thyroid Assn. Prev: Cons. Phys. Dept. Med. & Endocrinol. Centr. Middlx. Hosp. Lond.; Clin. Tutor & Sen. Lect. Dept. Med. Guy's Hosp. Med. Sch. Lond.; Post-Doctoral Fell. Stanford Univ. Sch. Med. Palo Alto, U.S.A.

MCKAY-FERGUSON, Andrew 57 Cambridge Road, Middlesbrough TS5 5NL Tel: 01642 826715; Queen Elizabeth Hospital, Gayton Road, King's Lynn PE30 4ET — BChir 1997 Camb.; MB Camb. 1997; BA Camb. 1994; MA Camb. 1998. (Camb.) Ho. phys., gen. med. & c/o the elderly, Qu. Eliz. Hosp. Kings Lynn. Socs: BMA; MPA. Prev: Ho. surg., gen. surg. & trauma & orthop. The Ipswich Hosp. Ipswich.

MCKENZIE-GRAY, Barry Princess Royal Hospital, Lewes Road, Haywards Heath RH16 4EX Tel: 01444 441881; Gatwick Park Hospital, Povey Cross Road, Horley RH6 0BB Tel: 01293 785511 — MB BS 1975 Lond.; MRCOG 1982; MRCGP 1980. (St. Geo.) Cons. O & G P.ss Roy. Hosp. Haywards Heath; Hon. Sen. Lect. St. Bart. Hosp. Lond. Socs: Fell. Roy. Soc. Med. Prev: Lect. & Hon. Sen. Regist. (O & G) St. Bart. Hosp. Lond.; Sen. Regist. (Gyn. & Oncol.) Roy. Marsden Hosp. Lond.; Regist. (O & G) Ascot & Windsor Gp. Hosps.

MCKENZIE-NEWTON, Elizabeth (retired) Pavings, The Avenue, Sherborne DT9 3AJ Tel: 01935 812840 — MB ChB Ed. 1942; DA Eng. 1946. Prev: Cons. Anaesth. Sch. Dent. Servs. Bolton.

MCKIERNAN-KRIEG

MCKIERNAN-KRIEG, Wilma Susanne 41 Alma Road, Windsor SL4 3HN — State Exam Med 1991 Berlin.

MCLAUGHLIN, Anne-Marie 40 Greenwood Road, Clarkston, Glasgow G76 7AN — MB ChB 1998 Glas.; MB ChB Glas 1998.

MCLAUGHLIN, Mairi-Jean 4 Galloway Road, Airdrie ML6 9RX — MB ChB 1998 Glas.; MB ChB Glas 1998.

MCLEOD-BAIKIE, Sylvia Rosemary (retired) The Forge, Landshipping, Narberth SA67 8BG Tel: 01834 891279 — MB ChB 1947 Ed.

MCMILLAN, Anna-Marie 12 Ormond Rise, Buckhurst Hill IG9 5QQ Tel: 020 8504 3847 — MB ChB 1991 Liverp.; BSc (Hons.) Liverp. 1987. Assoc. Dir. (Clin. Developm.) SmithKline Beecham Pharmaceut. Prev: Regist. Maudsley Hosp. Lond.

MCQUEEN, Marise-Anne Pamela 2 Lochend Road, Bearsden, Glasgow G61 1DU Tel: 0141 942 5909 — MB ChB 1975 Glas.; MRCGP UK 1982; DRCOG Ed. 1982; FFA RCS Eng. 1979. Med. Off. Glas., DRUG PROBLEM Serv., Callander St., Glas. Socs: BMA. Prev: Prison Med. Off. HMP Lowmoss, Glas.; Gen. Practitioner, Anniesland, Glas.

MDINGI, Mr Godfrey Vukile Sandringham Practice, The Medical Centre, 1 Madinah Road, London E8 1PG Tel: 020 7275 0022 Fax: 020 7923 2622; 1 Park Avenue S., London N8 8LU Tel: 020 8348 3304 — MB 1976 Camb.; BChir 1975; FRCS Eng. 1982.

MEACHER, Roseanne Lenore 34 Wheat Close, Sandridge, St Albans AL4 9NN — MB BS 1989 Lond.; BSc (Hons.) Lond. 1986; MRCP (UK) 1992; FRCA 1997. (Univ. Coll. Hosp.) Specialist Regist. (Anaesth.) Char. Cross Hosp. Prev: Specialist Regist. (Anaesth.) Barnet Gen. Hosp.; SHO (Anaesth.) Middlx. Hosp. & Whittington Hosp. Lond.; Regist. (Med.) Chelsea & W.m. Hosp. Lond. & Roy. Bournemouth Hosp.

MEACHIM, George (retired) 5 The Royal, Hoylake, Wirral CH47 1HS — MD Camb. 1958, MB BChir 1953; FRCPath 1978, M 1970. Prev: Reader in Path. Univ. Liverp.

MEACHIM, Ruth Mary (retired) 5 The Royal, Hoylake, Wirral CH47 1HS Tel: 0151 632 4627 — LRCP LRCS Ed. LRFPS Glas. 1950. Prev: Clin. Med. Off. Wirral AHA.

MEACHIM, Susan Mary Garden Lane Medical Centre, 19 Garden Lane, Chester CH1 4EN Tel: 01244 346677 Fax: 01244 310094 — MB ChB 1986 Ed.; DFFP 2001; DRCOG 1990. (Edinburgh) Prev: Trainee GP Nantwich; SHO (Psychiat.) Countess of Chester Hosp.; SHO (O & G & Paediat.) Leighton Hosp. Crewe.

MEACOCK, David John Pilgrim Hospital, Sibsey Road, Boston PE21 9QS Tel: 01205 364801 Fax: 01205 363823 — MB BChir 1974 Camb.; MA, MB Camb. 1974, BChir 1973; FRCP 1993; MRCP (UK) 1978. Cons. (Geriat. Med.) Pilgrim Hosp. Boston. Prev: Sen. Regist. (Gen. & Geriat. Med.) Roy. Hallamsh. & Nether Edge Hosps.Sheff.; Regist. (Med.) S.mead Hosp. Bristol; Regist. (Neurol.) Frenchay Hosp. Bristol.

MEACOCK, Hazel Ruth (retired) 5 Sid Vale Close, Sidford, Sidmouth EX10 9PH Tel: 01395 577990 — MB ChB 1953 Birm.; MFCM 1974; T(PHM) 1991; DPH Manch. 1964; DCH Eng. 1956. Mem. Fac. Pub. Health Med. Prev: Schs. Med. Off. MoD Hohne W. Germany.

MEACOCK, William Ralph 66B Mallinson Road, London SW11 1BP — MB BS 1993 Lond.

***MEAD, Adam Joseph** The Barn House, Old Church Rd, Colwall, Malvern WR13 6EZ — BM BCh 1997 Oxf.

MEAD, Andrew Guy The Mission Practice, 208 Cambridge Heath Road, London E2 9LS Tel: 020 8983 7300 Fax: 020 8983 6800; 13 Merriman Road, Blackheath, London SE3 8RX — MB BS 1986 Lond.; DCH RCP Lond. 1992. (Guy's) Prev: SHO (Paediat.) Greenwich Dist. Hosp.

MEAD, Andrew James Forest Holt, Forest Road, Effingham, Leatherhead KT24 5HL — MB BS 1991 Lond.; DFFP 1997. (Guy's Hospital)

***MEAD, Anna Louise** Rose Corner, 9 Alford Close, Guildford GU4 7YL — BChir 1995 Camb.

MEAD, Bernard John (retired) Moor Croft, 31A Corfe View Road, Corfe Mullen, Wimborne BH21 3LY Tel: 01202 601779 — MRCS Eng. LRCP Lond. 1954; MRCGP 1962. Prev: GP BRd.stone.

MEAD, Brenda Margaret 4 Tenby House, Bishop Close, Whitchurch, Cardiff CF14 1NG Tel: 029 206 6963 — MB BCh 1940 Wales; DPH 1956; DCH Eng. 1949. (Cardiff) Asst. Med. Off. City Cardiff Pub. Health Dept. Socs: BMA & Med. Wom. Federat.

Prev: Ho. Surg. Roy. Liverp. Childr. Hosp.; Capt. RAMC 1943-6; Asst. Med. Off. Glam. CC.

MEAD, David Edwin Briar Cottage, 196 Findhorn, Forres IV36 3YN — MD 1975 Canada; LMCC 1976.

MEAD, Geoffrey Stewart 7 Rowan Lane, Skelmersdale WN8 6UL Tel: 01695 733412; Manchester Blood Centre, Plymouth Grove, Manchester M13 9LL Tel: 0161 251 4331 — MRCS Eng. LRCP Lond. 1969. (Lond. Hosp.) Staff Grade Practitioner Manch. Blood Centre. Prev: Trainee GP Corby.; SHO (A & E) & (O & G) P'boro Dist. Hosp.

MEAD, Gillian Elizabeth 11 Tomkinson Street, Chester CH2 3BX — MB BChir 1987 Camb.

MEAD, Graham Michael Department of Medical Oncology, Royal South Hampshire Hospital, Brinton's Terrace, off St Mary's Road, Southampton SO14 0YG Tel: 02380 825973 Fax: 02380 825441 — MB BS 1972 Lond.; DM Soton. 1980; FRCP Lond. 1992. Cons. Med. Oncol. Soton. Univ. Hosp. & States of Guernsey Hosps.; Hon. Cons. RN. Socs: Fell. Roy. Coll. Phys.; Assn. Cancer Phys. & Amer. Soc. Clin. Oncol. Prev: Sen. Regist. (Med. Oncol.) Roy. S. Hants. Hosp.; Fell. (Oncol.) Stanford Univ., Calif., USA.

MEAD, Helen Margaret Bernadette 206 Hawthorn Drive, Ipswich IP2 0QQ Tel: 01473 685070 Fax: 01473 688707; Home Farm, Valley Farm Drive, Sproughton, Ipswich IP8 3EL Tel: 01473 652622 — MB ChB 1984 Leic.; MRCGP 1988; DRCOG 1987. (Leicester)

MEAD, Janet Lesley Department of Psychotherapy, Campbell Centre, Milton Keynes CMHT, Milton Keynes MK6 5NG Tel: 01908 243134 Fax: 01908 231948 — BM BS 1983 Nottm.; BA York 1976; BMedSci Nottm. 1981; MRCPsych 1990. (Nottm.) Cons. Psychotherapist Milton Keynes CMHT. Prev: Sen. Regist. (Psychother.) Warneford Hosp. Oxf.; Regist. St. John's Hosp. Stone.

MEAD, John Alistair, OStJ, RD (retired) 55 Langstone Road, Langstone, Havant PO9 1RB Tel: 023 9247 1100 — MRCS Eng. LRCP Lond. 1952; MRCGP 1967; DObst RCOG 1961. Trainer GP; Clin. Teach. (Primary Med. Care) Soton Univ.; Med. Ref. Health & Social Security. Prev: Surg. Capt. QHP RNR.

MEAD, Julian Dudley Sandford Princess Royal Hospital, Lewes Road, Haywards Heath RH16 4EX Email: jdsm@jdsm.freeserve.co.uk; 43 Jubilee Close, Haywards Heath RH16 3PJ — MB BS 1996 Lond.; DRCOG 1998. (St. George's Hosp. Med. Sch. Lond.) GP Regist. Mid. Sussex V.T.S., P.ss Roy. Hosp. Haywards Heath.

MEAD, Kevin Ian 24 Coleridge Walk, Hutton, Brentwood CM13 2RT — MB BCh 1992 Wales.

MEAD, Mark Kingsley 41 Dovedale Road, Leicester LE2 2DN — MB BS 1989 Lond.

MEAD, Michael Gordon Park Drive Health Centre, 2A Park Drive, Leicester Forest East, Leicester LE3 3FN Tel: 0116 289 8111 — MB BS 1978 (Distinct. Path.) Lond.; BSc (1st cl. Hons. Microbiol.) Lond.; FRCGP 2000; DRCOG 1982; MRCGP 1982; DCH Eng. 1981. (Univ. Coll. Hosp.)

MEAD, Paul Arthur Cumberland Infirmary, Carlisle CA2 7HY Tel: 01228 523444; Chalk Bridge Cottage, Welton, Carlisle CA5 7HG — MB BS 1989 Newc.; BMedSc (Hons.) Newc. 1986; MRCP (UK) 1992. Cons. (Gen. Med. Nephrol.). Socs: Renal Assn.; Scott. Renal Assn. Prev: Research Regist. (Med.) Univ. of Newc.; Regist. (Nephrol.) Roy. Vict. Infirm. Newc. u. Tyne; Regist. (Gen. Med. & Nephrol.) Sunderland Roy. Infirm.

MEAD, Simon Harvey The Barn House, Old Church Lane, Colwall, Malvern WR13 6EZ Email: shmead@msn.com — BM BCh 1994 Oxf.; MRCP (Lond.) 1997. SHO (Neurol.) NHNN. Prev: SHO (Med.) Rotat. Newc.; Jun. Ho. Off. (Surg.) Falkirk Roy. Infirm.; Jun. Ho. Off. (Med.) Oxf. Radcliffe Infirm.

MEADE, Alan Morgan Europa House, West Street, Bassett Road, Leighton Buzzard LU7 1DD Tel: 01525 851888 Fax: 01525 853319; 267 Heath Road, Leighton Buzzard LU7 3AG Tel: 01525 852772 — MB BS 1973 Lond.; DObst RCOG 1975. (Middlx.)

MEADE, Bernard William (retired) Withers House, Gateley, Dereham NR20 5EF Tel: 01328 829356 — MD Lond. 1952, MB BS 1947; MRCS Eng. LRCP Lond. 1947; FRCPath 1966. Prev: Dist. Gen. Manager & Cons. Path. Kingston & Esher HA.

MEADE, Peter Frank The Seven Dials Medical Centre, 24 Montpelier Crescent, Brighton BN1 3JJ Tel: 01273 773089 Fax: 01273 207098; 24 Newlands Road, Rottingdean, Brighton

BN2 7GD Tel: 01273 304722 Email: pfmeade@aol.com — MRCS 1978 Lond; MRCS Eng. LRCP Lond. 1978. (St Barts) Tutor (Gen. Pract.) Brighton & Lewes Dist. Prev: Trainee GP Crawley; SHO Crawley Hosp.; Med Advis.Brighton & Hove HA.

MEADE, Professor Thomas Wilson, CBE Dept. Epidemiology and Population Health, London School of Hygiene and Tropical Medicine, Keppel St., Gower St., London WC1E 7HT Tel: 020 7927 2182 Fax: 020 7580 6897 Email: tom.meade@lshtm.ac.uk; 28 Cholmeley Crescent, Highgate, London N6 5HA Tel: 020 8340 6260 Fax: 020 8340 6260 — BM BCh 1960 Oxf.; DM Oxf. 1980; FRCP Lond. 1979, M 1964; FFPHM RCP (UK) 1974; FRS 1996. (Oxf. & St. Bart.) Prev: Sen. Lect. (Pub. Health) Lond. Sch. Hyg. & Trop. Med.; Ho. Phys. & Ho. Surg. St. Bart. Hosp. Lond.; Director, MRC Epidemiol. and Med. Care Unit.

MEADE-KING, Michael Liddon (retired) 7 Codenham Lodge, 27 St Stephens Road, Cheltenham GL51 3AB Tel: 01242 5142 — MRCS Eng. LRCP Lond. 1934; DPM Eng. 1937.

MEADEN, John David Norfolk & Norwich Health Care NHS Trust, Brunswick Road, Norwich NR1 3SR Tel: 01603 286307 Fax: 016030 287528; 12 Norwich Road, Brooke, Norwich NR15 1AB — MB BCh 1973 Wales; FRCOG 1996, M 1978; MFFP RCOG 1975; Dip. Ven. Soc. Apoth. Lond. 1979; DObst RCOG 1976. Cons. Genitourin. Med. Norf. & Norwich Hosp.; Hon. Lect. - Sch. Biological Scis. Univ. of E. Anglia.

MEADEN, Richard William Cape Road Surgery, 3 Cape Road, Warwick CV34 4JP Tel: 01926 499988 Fax: 01926 498956; Woodlane Farm, Church Lane, Bearley, Stratford-upon-Avon CV37 0SL — MB ChB 1978 Birm.; MRCGP 1982; DRCOG 1981.

MEADER, Harriet Louise The Old Orchard Surgery, South Street, Wilton, Salisbury SP2 0JU Tel: 01722 744775 Fax: 01722 746616; Flint Cottage, Netherhampton, Salisbury SP2 8PU — MB BS 1989 Lond.; MRCGP 1993; DRCOG 1993; DGM RCP Lond. 1992.

MEADES, David Charles North Road Medical Practice, 182 North Road, Cardiff CF14 3XQ Tel: 029 2061 9188 Fax: 029 2061 3484 — MB BS 1985 Lond.

MEADOW, Professor Sir Samuel Roy Department of Paediatrics & Child Health, St James's University Hospital, Leeds LS9 7TF Tel: 0113 243 3144 Fax: 0113 283 6811; Weeton Grange, Woodgate Lane, Weeton, Leeds LS17 0AP Tel: 01423 734234 Fax: 01423 734726 — LMSSA 1960 Lond.; MA, BM BCh Oxf. 1960; FRCP Lond. 1974, M 1965; DCH Eng. 1963; DObst RCOG 1963. (Oxf. & Guy's) Prof. & Head Dept. Paediat. & Child Health (St. Jas.) Univ. Leeds; Cons. Paediat. Leeds E. HA. Socs: (Ex-Chairm.) Assn. Child Psychol. & Psychiat.; Pres. Brit. Paediat. Assn. (Paterson Prize 1968). Prev: Sen. Regist. (Paediat.) Guy's Hosp. Lond.; Sen. Research Fell. Inst. Child Health Birm.; Ho. Phys. Hosp. Sick Childr. Gt. Ormond St.

MEADOWS, Alfred Jeremy 4 Chessel Avenue, Bitterne, Southampton SO19 4AA Tel: 023 8044 7777; 28 Strawberry Fields, Hedge End, Southampton SO30 4QY — BM 1986 Soton.; MRCGP 1991; T(GP) 1991. (Soton.) Princip. (Gen. Pract.) Chessel Surg. Bitterne, Soton. Prev: Trainee GP Bournemouth; SHO (O & G & A & E) Poole Gen. Hosp.

MEADOWS, Miss Alison Edna Ruth Southampton Eye Unit, Southampton General Hospital, Tremona Road, Southampton SO16 6YD; 28 Strawberry Fields, Hedge End, Southampton SO30 4QY — BM 1985 Soton.; FRCOphth 1996, M 1991. (Univ. Soton.) Staff Grade (Ophth.) Soton. Gen. Hosp. Prev: Clin. Asst. (Ophth.) Soton. Gen. Hosp. & Salisbury Dist. Hosp.; SHO (Ophth.) Roy. Vict. Hosp. W.bourne, Qu. Eliz. Hosp. King's Lynn & W. Norwich Hosp.

MEADOWS, Caroline Anne 5 Talbot Road, London N6 4QS — BM BS 1992 Nottm.

MEADOWS, Christopher Ian Sutherland Whipps Cross Hospital, London E11 1NR; 38 Queens Drive, Prenton CH43 0RP — MB BS 1997 Lond.; BSc (Hons) Lond. 1994. (The Lond. Hosp. Med. Sch.)

MEADOWS, Diana Pearson Brooklet Cottage, Shrigley Road, Stockport SK12 1TF — MB BCh 1978 Wales; MRCP (UK) 1981; FFA RCS Eng. 1985. Cons. Anaesth. & Intens. Care Stepping Hill Hosp. Stockport.

MEADOWS, Grahame Alan (retired) 40 Carlow Road, Prenton, Birkenhead L42 8QR Tel: 0151 608 1288 — MB ChB 1960 Liverp.; FFA RCS Eng. 1966. Clin. Lect. Dept. Anaesth. Univ. Liverp. Prev: Sen. Regist. Liverp. RHB & United Liverp. Hosps.

MEADOWS, Henry Hastings House, Kineton Road, Wellesbourne, Warwick CV35 9NF Tel: 01789 840245 Fax: 01789 470993; Hill Cottage, Combrook, Warwick CV35 9HP Tel: 01926 640375 — MB BChir 1967 Camb.; MA, MB Camb. 1967, BChir 1966; MRCGP 1974; DObst RCOG 1972; DCH Eng. 1970. (Univ. Coll. Hosp.) Socs: BMA. Prev: Ho. Phys. Paediat. Dept. & Ho. Surg. Obst. Unit Univ. Coll. Hosp. Lond.; Ho. Phys. & Ho. Surg. W. Middlx. Hosp. Isleworth.

MEADOWS, Hilary Gaye Market Street Health Group, 52 Market Street, East Ham, London E6 2RA Tel: 020 8548 2200 Fax: 020 8548 2288; 42 Gloucester Circus, Greenwich, London SE10 8RY — MB BS 1975 Lond.

MEADOWS, Isobel Jane Tanner (retired) 47 Swan Street, Seagrave, Loughborough LE12 7NL Tel: 0150 981 2557 — MB BS 1957 Lond.; MRCS Eng. LRCP Lond. 1957. Prev: Clin. Med. Off. Leicester AHA.

MEADOWS, John Christopher 143 Harley Street, London W1G 6BH Tel: 020 7935 1802; The Coach House, 44 Church Road, Wimbledon Village, London SW19 5AN Tel: 020 8946 2707 — MB BChir 1965 Camb.; BA (Nat. Sc. Trip. Pt. I 1st cl., Pt. II 1st cl.) Camb. 1961, MD 1969; FRCP Lond. 1978, M 1966. (Camb. & St. Thos.) Murchison Schol. RCP Lond. 1966; Cons. Neurol. King Edwd. VII Hosp. Offs. Lond.; Hon. Sen. Lect. St. Geo. Hosp. Med. Sch. Lond.; Hon. Neurol. Newspaper Press Fund. Prev: Cons. Neurol. St. Geo. Hosp. Lond. Med. Regist. St. Thos. Hosp. Lond.; Sen. Regist. Nat. Hosp. Nerv. Dis. Qu. Sq. Lond.

MEADOWS, Nigel John Royal Hospitals Trust, Department of Paediatric Gastroenterology, Lucas Block, St Bartholomew's Hospital, London WC1 Tel: 020 7601 7850; 10 Magenta Close, Billericay CM12 0LF Tel: 01277 655633 — MB BS 1975 Lond.; MD Lond. 1989; FRCP (UK) 1995; FRCPCH 1998. (Char. Cross) Cons. Paediat. Gastroenterol. Roy. Hosps. Trust, Hon. Sen. Lect. Prev: Cons. Paediat. Whipps Cross Hosp. Lond.; Lect. (Child Health) Combined Med. Colls. Lond. & St. Bart. Hosp. & Qu. Eliz. Hosp. Lond.

MEADOWS, Paul Sharman The Priory Surgery, 326 Wells Road, Bristol BS4 2QJ Tel: 0117 949 3988 Fax: 0117 778250 — MB ChB 1987 Bristol; MSc Sussex 1977, BSc 1973; MRCGP 1992; DRCOG 1990.

MEADOWS, Mr Timothy Habberley Brooklet Cottage, Shrigley Road, Stockport SK12 1TF — MB ChB 1977 Manch.; FRCS Eng. 1982; FRCS Glas. 1981. Cons. Orthop. Surg. Booth Hall Child. Hosp. Manch.

MEADS, Adele Elizabeth 10 Eugene Flats, Eugene St., St James, Bristol BS2 8EX — MB ChB 1990 Auckland.

MEADS, Jonathan Ernest Dane Lobwood, Blagdon Hill, Taunton TA3 7SN Tel: 0182342 680206 — MB ChB 1965 Bristol; MRCGP 1972; DObst RCOG 1969.

MEADWAY, Rev. Jeanette Valerie Mildmay Mission Hospital, Hackney Road, London E2 7NA Tel: 020 7613 6300 Fax: 020 7729 1898 Email: meadj@dial.pipex.com; 4 Glebe Avenue, Woodford Green IG8 9HB Tel: 020 8504 1958 Fax: 020 8491 6040 Email: meadwayj@dial.pipex.com — MB ChB 1969 Ed.; FRCP Lond. 1987; FRCP Ed. 1987; MRCP (UK) 1972. (Ed.) Cons. Phys. (HIV Med.) & Med. Dir. Mildmay Mission Hosp. Lond.; Hon. Sen. Lect. Lond. Hosp. Med. Coll. Socs: Brit. HIV Assn.; Christ. Med. Fell.sh.; Assn. for Palliat. Med. Prev: Cons. Phys. (Gen. & Respirat. Med.) Newham Healthcare Trust; Clin. Tutor Newham HA; Sen. Regist. (Thoracic Med.) Stoke Mandeville Hosp. Aylesbury.

MEAGER, Philip William David Rickmansworth Road Surgery, 35 Rickmansworth Road, Watford WD1 7HL Tel: 01923 222436 Fax: 01923 243397 — MB ChB 1973 Liverp.; FRCGP 2001; MRCGP 1978; DObst RCOG 1976. (Liverp.) Mem. LMC. Socs: Sec., W. Herts & Watford Med. Soc. Prev: Course Organiser Watford VTS.

MEAGHER, Ethel Mary Sheringham, Great North Road, Milford Haven SA73 2LE — MB BCh BAO 1979 NUI; LRCPI & LM, LRCSI & LM 1979.

MEAGHER, John Columbus (retired) 2 Carolyn Way, Whitley Bay NE26 3EB Tel: 0191 252 4270 — LAH Dub. 1949.

MEAGHER, Michael Augustine Mount Medical Centre, 7 Market Parade, Hampton Road West, Hanworth, Feltham TW13 6AJ Tel: 020 8893 8699 Fax: 020 8893 8680 — MB BCh BAO 1966 NUI; BDS NUI 1962; FDS RCPS Glas. 1970; MRCGP 1985.

MEAGHER

MEAGHER, Thomas Maol Muire Tudor Cottage, 38 Weir Road, Kibworth Beauchamp, Leicester LE8 0LP — MB BCh BAO 1983 NUI.

MEAGHER, Vincent Martin Christopher Yorkshire Street Surgery, 190 Yorkshire Street, Rochdale OL16 2DN Tel: 01706 644973/5; 190 Yorkshire Street, Rochdale Tel: 44975 — MB ChB 1977 Manch. Prev: Ho. Off. (Med./Surg.) Birch Hill Hosp. Rochdale.

MEAKIN, Alan Henry Jessop Medical Practice, 24 Pennine Avenue, Riddings, Alfreton DE55 4AE Tel: 01773 602707 Fax: 01773 513502; 223 Derby Road, Denby, Derby DE5 8NP — MB ChB 1972 Bristol; FRCGP 1991, M 1977; DObst RCOG 1976; DA Eng. 1974. (Bristol)

MEAKIN, Christopher Julian Bradgate Mental Health Unit, Groby Road, Leicester LE3 9EJ — MB ChB 1983 Leeds.

MEAKIN, David Richard Westgate Bay Avenue Surgery, 60 Westgate Bay Avenue, Westgate-on-Sea CT8 8SN Tel: 01843 831335 Fax: 01843 835279; 20 Carlton Road W., Westgate-on-Sea CT8 8PL Tel: 01843 831783 — MB BS 1980 Lond.; MRCGP 1984. (St. Mary's)

MEAKIN, George Harold Department of Anaesthesia, Royal Manchester Childrens Hospital, Pendlebury, Manchester M27 4HA Tel: 0161 727 2291 Fax: 0161 727 2291 Email: george.meakin@man.ac.uk — MB ChB; LMCC 1980; DA 1974; MD 1993 Manch.; FRCA 1976. Sen. Lect. in Paediatric Anaesth., Univ. of Manch.; Hon. Cons. Anaesthethist, Centr. Manch. and Manch. Childr.'s Univ. Hosps. Socs: Sec. of Assn. of Paediat. Anaesth.s of Gt. Britain & Irel.; Assn. of Anaesth.s GB & I; Anaesthetic Research Soc. Prev: Lect. in Paediatric Anaesth., Univ. of Manch.; Cons. Paediatric Anaesth. Roy. Manch. Childr.s Hosp.; Asst. Prof. Univ. Mcgill, Montreal.

MEAKIN, Kathryn Ann Windward, Lillyfield, Gayton, Wirral CH60 8NT — MB 1983 Camb.; BChir 1982.

MEAKIN, Lesley Catherine 6 Dyas Road, Great Barr, Birmingham B43 — MB ChB 1983 Leeds; MRCGP 1987.

MEAKIN, Lucy Henrietta Alban Manor House, Betsham, Southfleet, Gravesend DA13 9LZ — BChir 1996 Camb.; BA Camb. 1994; MB Camb. 1997; MA Camb. 1998. (Camb.) Med. SHO Rotat. Roy. Lond. Hosps. Trust.

MEAKIN, Richard Peter Freshwell Health Centre, Wethersfield Road, Finchingfield, Braintree CM7 4BQ; Birchbrook House, Water Lane, Helions Bumpstead, Haverhill CB9 7AL Tel: 01440 730351 — MB BS 1979 Lond.; MD 2001; MSc (Gen. Pract.) Lond. 1992; DCH RCP Lond. 1984; DRCOG 1983. (St. Mary's) Sen. Lect. (Gen. Pract.) Roy. Free & Univ. Coll. Med. Sch. Lond.

MEAKINS, Philip Gareth Wheyman Old Fire Station Surgery, 68A Portsmouth Road, Woolston, Southampton SO19 9AN Tel: 023 8044 8558/8901 Fax: 023 8043 5569 — MB BS 1974 Lond.; MRCS Eng. LRCP Lond. 1974. (Guy's)

MEAKINS, Sally Joan Priory Medical Group, Cornlands Road, Acomb, York YO24 3WX Tel: 01904 781423 Fax: 01904 784886; 18 Bootham Terrace, Bootham, York YO30 7DH Tel: 01904 639483 — MB BChir 1979 Camb.; MB BChir (Distinc. Surg.) Camb. 1978; MA Camb. 1979; MRCGP 1986; MRCOG 1983; T(GP) 1991; DCH RCP Lond. 1982. (Camb. & King's Coll. Hosp.) GP. Prev: Regist. (O & G) Edgware Gen. Hosp.; Sen. Med. Off. (O & G) Papua New Guinea; Trainee GP Skipton.

***MEAL, Andrew Guy** Department of Nusing Studies, Medical School, Queen's Medical Centre, Nottingham NG7 2UH Tel: 0115 970 9265; Knapthorpe House, Knapthorpe, Caunton, Newark NG23 6AZ Tel: 01636 636764 — BM BS 1988 Nottm.; BMedSci (Hons.) 1986.

MEALY, Kenneth Department of Surgery, Western General Hospital, Crewe Road S., Edinburgh EH4 2XU Tel: 0131 537 1567 Fax: 0131 537 1767 Email: kmealy@srv.o.med.ed.ac.uk — MB BCh BAO 1981 Dub.; MD Dublin 1989; FRCSI Ed. 1985. Sen. Lect. (Surg.) Univ. of Ed. & W.ern Gen. Hosp. Ed.

MEALYEA, Mary Thomson Mackie Bargeddie Manse, Manse Road, Bargeddie, Baillieston, Glasgow G69 6UB Tel: 0141 771 1322 — MB ChB 1976 Dundee. (Dundee) Clin. Asst. (Gen. Med.) Glas.

MEANEY, James Francis Martin CT Unit, Jubilee Building, The General Infirmary at Leeds, Great George St., Leeds LS1 3EX Tel: 0113 392 6495 Fax: 0113 392 5620 — MB BCh BAO 1985 NUI; MRCPI 1987; FRCR 1992; DMRD Liverp. 1990. Cons. Radiol. The Gen. Infirm. at Leeds. Socs: MRCRadiol.; Internat. Soc. Magnetic Resonance in Med.; Eur. Assn. of Radiol. Prev: Regist. (Radiol.) Roy. Liverp. Hosp.

MEANEY, Thomas Paul Ophthalmology Department, N.Staffordshire General Infirmary, Princes Rd, Stoke-on-Trent ST4 7LN — MB BCh BAO 1987 NUI.

MEANLEY, Deborah Ann Child & Family Unit, Westwood Hospital, Beverley Tel: 01482 886675; The Old Orchard, Tunnel Road, Wrawby, Brigg DN20 8SF Tel: 01652 652072 — MB BS 1965 Lond.; MRCS Eng. LRCP Lond. 1965. (Roy. Free) Research Assoc. & Clin. Asst. Child & Family Unit De La. Pole Hosp. Willerby. Prev: Regist. (Psychiat.) De La Pole Hosp. & BRd.gate Hosp.; Clin. Med. Off. Scunthorpe Health Dist.; Ho. Surg. Roy. Free Hosp. Lond.

MEANLEY, Janis Ann The Surgery, 32 Kingsland Road, West Mersea, Colchester CO5 8RA Tel: 01206 382015 Fax: 01206 385593 — MRCS Eng. LRCP Lond. 1967; DObst RCOG 1969.

MEANLEY, Jeremy John (retired) Highfields, Briston, Melton Constable NR24 2LX Tel: 01263 860531 Fax: 01263 860621 Email: jjmean@paston.co.uk — MB Camb. 1962, BChir 1961; DObst RCOG 1964. Locum GP. Prev: Princip. in Gen. Pract., Holt.

MEANLEY, Terence Hugh 59 Victoria Esplanade, West Mersea, Colchester CO5 8BP — MRCS Eng. LRCP Lond. 1970; MFOM RCP Lond. 1986; DIH Eng. 1981. Cons. Occupat. Health Essex Rivers Health Care Trust. Socs: Roy. Soc. Med.; Soc. Occupat. Med. Prev: Sen. Regional Med. Off. BT; Squadron Ldr RAF Med. Br. Med. Off. Dept. of Transport.

MEANOCK, Colin Ian Chapmans Farm, Kirdford, Billingshurst RH14 0JR — MB BS 1976 Lond.; MD Lond. 1982; FRCR 1987. Cons. Radiol. Roy. Berks. Hosp. Reading.

MEANOCK, Ronald Ian 13 Bath Road, Reading Tel: 01734 584711 — MRCS Eng. LRCP Lond. 1944; MD Lond. 1948, MB BS 1944; FRCP Lond. 1969, M 1949. (Middlx.) Socs: Heberden Soc. (Ex-Hon. Sec.); Fell. Roy. Soc. Med. Prev: Cons. Phys. (Rheum). W. Berks. Health Dist.; Area Postgrad. Tutor Univ. Oxf.; Sen. Med. Regist. Middlx. Hosp. & Postgrad. Med. Sch. Lond.

MEARA, Jill Renée Northamptonshire Health Anthority, Highfield, Cliftonville Road, Northampton NN1 5ON Tel: 01604 615225 Fax: 01604 615140 Email: jill.meara@northants-na.anglox.nns.uk; 15 Church Lane, Middleton Cheney, Banbury OX17 2NR Tel: 01295 712065 Fax: 01295 712698 — BM BCh 1981 Oxf.; MSc Lond. 1985; MA Camb. 1981; FFPHM RCP (UK) 1995; DRCOG 1983. (Oxf.) Dir. Pub. Health N.ants. HA; Oxf. Regional Represen. Bd. Fac. Pub. Health. Prev: Cons. Community Med. N.ampton HA; Sen. Regist. (Community Med.) Oxf. RHA.

MEARA, Robert Jolyon Lissadell, Rocklands Lane, Thornton Hough, Wirral CH63 4JX — MD 1990 Camb.; MA Camb. 1981, MD 1990, MB BChir (Distinc.) 1980; FRCP (Lond.) 1997; MRCP (UK) 1984. (Middlx. Hosp.) Sen. Lect. (Geriat. Med.) Univ. Wales Coll. Med.; Hon. Cons. Phys. Glan Clwyd Hosp. Bodelwyddan. Prev: Lect. (Geriat. Med.) Hope Hosp. Univ. Manch.; Regist. (Neurol.) Manch. Roy. Infirm.; Research Regist. Pk.inson's Dis. Soc. Research Fell. Manch. Roy. Infirm.

MEARDON, Neil Harry — BM 1994 Soton.; MRCGP 2000; Dip IMC RCS Ed. 1998. p/t GP Princip., Amesbury (Wilts.); Chairm. Of BASICS Scheme inWilts. (Brit. Assoc. For Immediate Care). Socs: Brit. Assoc. Immediate Care (BASICS) - Individual Mem.; Mem. Of Roy. Coll. of GPs.

MEARES, Denis Edmund Rosellea, Dixter Road, Northiam, Rye TN31 6PE — MB BCh BAO 1938 Dub.; BA Dub. 1934, MB BCh BAO 1938. (T.C. Dub.) Socs: Fell. Hunt. Soc. Prev: Ho. Surg. Obst. & Gynaecol. Dept. & Res. Anaesth. Roy. United Hosp.; Bath.; Surg. Lt. R.N.V.R.

MEARES, Hamish Douglas Devenish 114 Kelmscott Road, London SW11 6PT — MB BS 1996 Sydney.

MEARES, Tanuja Millie 52 Ruskin Walk, Herne Hill, London SE24 9LZ — MB BS 1996 Lond.

MEARING-SMITH, Teresa Mary Elmfield, Portsmouth Road, Esher KT10 9JB Tel: 01372 464234 — MB ChB 1974 Bristol; BSc Bristol 1971, MB ChB 1974; MRCGP 1978; Dip. Pract. Dermat. 1993; DCH Eng. 1977. St. Peter's Hosp. Chertsey, Roy. Surrey Co. Hosp. Guildford & Frimley Pk. Hosp. Socs: Brit. Assn. Dermat. Prev: Clin. Asst. (Rehabil. & Haemat.) St Peter's Hosp. Chertsey.

MEARNS, Mr Alan James 5 Mornington Villas, Manningham Lane, Bradford BD8 7 Tel: 01274 543976 — MB ChB 1963 Liverp.;

FRCS Eng. 1970; FRCS Ed. 1969. (Liverp.) Cons. (Cardiothoracic Surg.) Bradford Roy. Infirm.

MEARNS, Elizabeth Anne Hawthorn Medical Centre, May Close, Swindon SN2 1UU Tel: 01793 536541 Fax: 01793 421049; 1 Mayfield, Wanborough, Swindon SN4 0ED Tel: 01793 791323 — MB ChB 1983 Dundee; MFFP 1993; MRCGP 1988; DRCOG 1985; DA 1988; DPD 1994. (Dundee) Prev: GP Lechlade.

MEARNS, Garry Stuart 15 Croyland Way, Crowland, Peterborough PE6 0NA — MB ChB 1974 Glas.

MEARNS, Margaret Bryce (retired) 70 Manor Avenue, Brockley, London SE4 1TE Tel: 020 8692 2963 — MB BS Lond. 1951; FRCP Ed. 1976, M 1963; MRCS Eng. LRCP Lond. 1951; Hon. FRCPCH 1996; DCH Eng. 1953. Prev: Cons. Paediat. Qu. Eliz. Hosp. Childr. Lond.

MEARS, Clare Swarland Avenue Surgery, 2 Swarland Avenue, Benton, Newcastle upon Tyne NE7 7SP — MB BS 1993 Newc.; MRCGP 1997; DRCOG 1997; DFFP 1997; DCH RCP Lond. 1996. (Newc.) GP (Partner) Swarland Avenue Surg., Newc. Prev: Trainee GP Bellingham; SHO (O & G) Dryburn Hosp. Durh.; GP (Asst.) Ashington.

MEARS, Elspeth Mary Loudon 14 Bramley Orchard, Bushby, Leicester LE7 9RU — MB ChB 1966 Ed.; DObst RCOG 1969.

MEARS, Helen Joan St. Christopher's Hospital, Wickham Road, Fareham PO16 7JD Tel: 01329 286321 Fax: 01329 823912; Tel: 023 8055 1300 Fax: 02380 266448 — BM 1983 Soton.; MRCPsych 1989. Cons. Old Age Psychiat. St. Christopher's Hosp. Fareham. Socs: BMA. Prev: Sen. Regist. (Psychiat.) Wessex; Regist. (Psychiat.) Roy. Hants. Hosp. Soton.

***MEARS, Jane Elin** The Quarry, Roundsnest, Yealmpton, Plymouth PL8 2ND — MB ChB 1997 Bristol.

MEARS, Lisa Hants and the Royal London NHS Trust, Royal London Hospital, Whitechapel, London Tel: 020 7377 7000 Ext: 2689 — MB BS 1994 Lond. (Univ. Coll. Lond. and Middlx. Sch. Med.) Specialist Regist. (Histopath.) Roy. Lond. Hosps. Trust Lond.

MEARS, Michael Paul 5 Newton Hall Barn, High Newton, Grange-over-Sands LA11 6JJ; Round House, Noss Mayo, Plymouth PL8 1ED Tel: 01752 872172 — MB BS 1985 Lond.; BSc (Hons. Biochem) Lond. 1982, MB BS 1985; MRCGP 1993; DRCOG 1992; DA (UK) 1988. Socs: BMA. Prev: SHO (Obst.) Ayrsh. Centr. Hosp. Irvine Scotl.; Regist. (Gen. Med.) Launceston Gen. Hosp. Tasmania, Austral.; SHO (Anaesth.) Roy. United Hosp. Bath.

MEARS, Timothy Paul Plot 10, Arrowsmith Avenue, Bartestree, Hereford HR1 4DW — MB BS 1989 Lond. SHO (Ophth.) Vict. Eye Hosp. Hereford. Prev: Regist. Rotat. (Histopath.) SW Thames Region; SHO (A & E) Wycombe Gen. Hosp.; SHO (Histopath.) Centr. Middlx. Hosp.

***MEARZA, Ali Abdulwahid** 90 Airedale Avenue, London W4 2NN Tel: 020 8994 4159 — MB BS 1996 Lond.; MRCOphth 1998.

***MEARZA, Talib Abdulwahid** 90 Airedale Avenue, London W4 2NN — MB BS 1998 Lond.; MB BS Lond 1998.

MEASDAY, Imogen Frances Mill Hill Surgery, 111 Avenue Road, Acton, London W3 8QH Tel: 020 8992 9955 — MB BS 1985 Lond.; DRCOG Lond. 1988. Princip.

MEASEY, Laurence George Nine Hills Cottage, Offchurch, Leamington Spa CV33 9AQ Email: lg@measey.demon.co.uk; The Caludon Centre, Clifford Bridge Road, Walsgrave, Coventry CV2 2TE Tel: 01703 602020 — MB BS Lond. 1964; MRCS Eng. LRCP Lond. 1964; FRCPsych. 1989, M 1972; DPM Eng. 1968. (Char. Cross) Cons. Psychiat.Coventry Healthcare NHS Trust; Hon. Sen. Clin. Lect. Univ. Birm.; Civil Adviser (Psychiat.) RN.; Chairm. Rehabil. & Social Psychiat. Sect. Roy. Coll. Psych. Socs: Chairm. Postgrad. Psychiat. Train. Comm. W. Midl. Deaney. Prev: Sen. Regist. Glenside Hosp. Bristol; Surg. Lt.-Cdr. RN.

MEASURES, Jennifer Lucy Tel: 01733 874901 Fax: 01733 562187 Email: jmeasures@nwahc-tr.anglox.nhs.uk; Rosecourt Farm, Conington Fen, Conington, Peterborough PE7 3QQ — MB BChir 1977 Camb.; MB Camb. 1976, BChir 1976; MA Camb. 1976; MRCP (UK) 1980; FRCPCH 1998; MRCGP 1982. (Cambridge) Cons. Community Paediat. Cambs. Prev: SCMO NW Anglia HA; Trainee GP Yaxley P'boro. & Stamford.

MEATON, Michael Loraine 17 Geneva Drive, Stoke-on-Trent ST1 6UW — MB BChir 1984 Camb.; MB Camb. 1984, BChir 1983; MA Camb. 1984. (Camb.)

MEATS, Philip Stephen Millbrook, Kings Mill, Sutton-in-Ashfield NG17 4JT Tel: 01623 784709 Email: dr.mears@mhp.cnhc-tr.trent.nhs.uk — MB ChB 1981 Sheff.; MSc (Psychiat.) Manch. 1987; MA Oxf. 1983; MRCPsych 1985. Cons. Psychiat. Centr. Notts. Hlthcare. Trust.

MEBAN, Cowan 5 Sepon Park, Lisburn BT28 3BQ — MB BCh BAO 1969 Belf.; PhD Belf. 1976, BSc 1966, MD 1973, MB BCh BAO 1969. Prof. Anat. Qu. Univ. Belf. Socs: Anat. Soc. & Ulster Med. Soc.

MECCI, Z H Elm Road Surgery, 2 Elm Road, Bedfont, Feltham TW14 8EW Tel: 020 8890 7397 Fax: 020 8890 7397 — MB BS 1974 Bangalore; MB BS 1974 Bangalore.

MECHIE, David Gibb (retired) 67 Owen Road, Lancaster LA1 2LG Tel: 01524 64420 — MB ChB 1954 Ed.

MECHIE, Graeme Lawrence Mechie and Partners, 67 Owen Road, Lancaster LA1 2LG Tel: 01524 846999 Fax: 01524 845174 — MB ChB 1980 Manch.

MECHIE, Kaye Ampleforth Surgery, Back Lane, Ampleforth, York YO62 4EF Tel: 01439 788215 Fax: 01439 788002; Mount Pleasant Farm, Cold Kirby, Thirsk YO7 2HL Tel: 01845 597543 — MB ChB 1979 Glas.; DA Eng. 1984; Cert. Family Plann. JCC 1986. (Glasgow University) GP Princip.

MECHIE, Susan Margaret (retired) Elm Tree Cottage, Ochil Tower School, Auchterarder PH3 18A Tel: 0176 462363 — MB ChB 1957 Glas.; DCH 1965; DObst RCOG 1959.

MECKLENBURGH, Paul Edward Harewood Crescent Surgery, Harewood Crescent, Bournemouth BH7 7BU Tel: 01202 309500 Fax: 01202 309565; 30 Littledown Drive, Bournemouth BH7 7AQ Tel: 01202 395270 — MB BS 1976 Lond.; MRCS Eng. LRCP Lond. 1975; DRCOG 1979. (St. Geo.)

MECROW, Ian Kelvin 96 Altrincham Road, Wilmslow SK9 5NG — BM BS 1983 Nottm.; DM Nottm. 1993, BM BS 1983; MRCP (UK) 1986. Cons. Paediat. Stepping Hill Hosp. Stockport. Prev: Sen. Regist. Rotat. (Paediat.) Manch. Hosp.; Research Fell. & Regist. (Paediat.) Booth Hall Childr. Hosp. Manch.; Regist. (Paediat.) MusGr. Pk. Hosp. Taunton.

MEDBAK, Sami Hanna Department of Chemical Pathology, Queen Alexandra Hospital, Cosham, Portsmouth PO6 3LY Tel: 023 92 286397 Email: sami. medback@qmailoi.porthosp.swest.nhs.uk; 10 Regal Close, Portwmouth, Portsmouth PO6 2EE Tel: 02392 373776 — MB ChB 1974 Basrah; PhD Lond. 1984. Staff Grade (Chem. Path.). Socs: Brit. Soc. Endocrinol.; Assn. Clin. Biochem. Prev: Sen. Lect. (Chem. Endocrinol.) St. Bart. Hosp. Med. Coll. Lond.; Regist. (Chem. Path.) Soton. Gen. Hosp.

MEDCALF, James Frederick 14B Bromley Grove, Bromley BR2 0LN — BM BS 1992 Nottm.

MEDCALF, Jennifer Mary 14B Bromley Grove, Bromley BR2 0LN — MB ChB 1995 Birm.; ChB Birm. 1995. SHO (A&E) Leicester Roy. Infirm.

MEDCALF, Kathryn Ruth 16 Russell Close, Hereford HR1 1DJ — MB ChB 1989 Liverp.

MEDCALF, Mark Steven 157 Lopers Cope Road, Beckenham BR3 1NZ — MB BS 1989 Lond.

MEDCALF, Peter Bertwistle 4 Lindisfarne Drive, Kettering NN15 5JD — MB 1983 Camb.; MA Camb. 1983, MB 1983, BChir 1982. Trainee GP Kettering VTS.

MEDCALF, Philippa Royal Hospital, Chesterfield S44 5BL — MB BS 1982 Lond.; FRCP 1996. Cons. Phys. (Gen. Med.) Roy. Hosp. Chesterfield; Hon. Clin. Lect. Centre for Ageing & Rehabil. Studies Sheff. Prev: Cons. Phys. (Med. for Elderly) Roy. Bournemouth Hosp.; Sen. Regist. (Gen. & Geriat. Med.) Roy. Cornw. Hosps.; Regist. (Geriat.) Bristol Roy. Infirm.

MEDD, Wilfrid Evelyn (retired) Abbey Cottage, Pyrford Road, Pyrford, Woking GU22 8UT Tel: 01932 342584 — MB BS Lond.1948; MD Lond. 1953; FRCP Lond. 1971; MRCP (UK) 1952. Prev: Cons. Phys. Kingston Hosp. Gp.

MEDDINGS, Mr Robert Nash 41 Carrick Road, Ayr KA7 2RD — MB ChB 1983 Manch.; BSc (Med. Sci.) St. And. 1980; MD Manch. 1993; FRCS (Urol.) 1994; FRCS Ed. l988. Cons. Urol. Ayr. Socs: Brit. Assn. Urol. Surgs. Prev: Sen. Regist. Urol. W. of Scotl. Train.

MEDFORD, Nicholas Charles 68 The Furlongs, Ingatestone CM4 0AJ — MB BS 1994 Lond.; MB BS Lond. 1993; MRCP (UK) 1997. (Charling Cross & Westm.) SHO (Neurol.) Roy. Free Hosp.

MEDFORTH

Lond. Socs: BMA. Prev: SHO (Med.) N.wick Pk. Hosp.; SHO (Neurol.) OldCh. Hosp.; SHO (Med.) Lewisham Hosp.

*MEDFORTH, Louise Jane Lypiatt House, Lypiatt Road, Cheltenham GL50 2QW — MB ChB 1994 Manch.

MEDHI, Anil Chandra 1 Denewood, West Lane, Forest Hall, Newcastle upon Tyne NE12 7FA Tel: 0191 268 6812 — MB BS 1967 Gauhati. (Gauhati)

MEDHURST, Allen William John 24/26 Priory Avenue, The Priory Surgery, High Wycombe HP13 6SH Tel: 01494 448132 Fax: 01494 686407; Overshaw, 27 Amersham Road, High Wycombe HP13 6QS Tel: 01494 436377 — MB BS 1965 Lond.; MRCS Eng. LRCP Lond. 1965; DObst RCOG 1967. (Guy's) Hosp. Practitioner (Paediat.) Wycomb Gen. Hosp. Socs: Pres Chiltern Med. Soc. 1998-1999. Prev: Med. Regist. Hither Green Hosp.; Res. Obstetr. & Childr. Ho. Phys. Guy's Hosp. Lond.

MEDHURST, Geoffrey Arkill (retired) Church Hill, Orton, Kettering NN14 1LJ Tel: 01536 711002 — MRCS Eng. LRCP Lond. 1950; DMRD Lond 1953. Prev: Cons. Radiol. Kettering & N.ampton Hosps.

MEDHURST, Joanne 11 Rebecca Court, Highview Road, Sidcup DA14 4EQ — MB BS 1989 Lond.

MEDHURST, Mary Rose Orchards, 39 St Paul's Road, Chichester PO19 3BJ Tel: 01243 785532 — MB ChB 1951 Aberd.

MEDILL, Ernest Victor (retired) Worships Cottage, Worships Hill, Riverhead, Sevenoaks TN13 2AS Tel: 01732 453880 — MB BS 1946 Lond.; MRCS Eng. LRCP Lond. 1944; DMRD Eng. 1950. Prev: Cons. Radiol. FarnBoro. Hosp. Kent.

MEDINA GALERA, Juan Loreto 34 Overbury Road, Gloucester GL1 4EA — LMS 1992 Granada.

MEDINA RUIZ DE ALARCON, Roberto UTS Oxford Centre, Wolsey Hall, 66 Banbury Road, Oxford OX2 6PR — LMS 1983 Cordoba.

MEDIRATTA, Mr Neeraj Kumar The Little Chine, 80 Bell Barn Road, Stoke-Bishop, Bristol BS9 2DG Tel: 0117 968 4360 — MB ChB 1984 Bristol; BSc Bristol 1981, MB ChB 1984; FRCS Eng. 1989. Regist. (Surg.) John Radcliffe Hosp. Oxf. Prev: SHO (Surg.) Taunton & Som. Hosp.; SHO (Orthop. & Accid & Emerg.) Addenbrooke's Hosp. Camb.; Demonst. (Anat.) Univ. Oxf.

MEDIWAKE, Rapti Galahetiyawe 34 Glover Road, Pinner HA5 1LG — BM 1993 Soton.

MEDLAND, Linda Frances Stow on the Wold Surgery, Well Lane, Cheltenham GL54 1EQ Tel: 01451 830625; 40 Greenway Lane, Charlton Kings, Cheltenham GL52 6LB Tel: 01242 526164 Email: ronmedland@hotmail.com — MB BS 1973 Lond.; BSc (Hons.) Lond.; MRCGP 1978; DCH Eng. 1977; DObst RCOG 1975. (Univ. Coll. Hosp.) p/t Gen. Practitioner; Dep. Police Surg. Gloucester Police. Socs: BMA; MWF.

MEDLEY, David Robin Kimball (retired) 4 Harpers Court, North Bar Without, Beverley HU17 7AB Tel: 01482 865201 — BM BCh 1955 Oxf.; MA Oxf. 1956, DM 1964, BM BCh 1955; FRCP Lond. 1974, M 1959. Examr. RCP Lond. Prev: Phys. W. Essex Hosps.

MEDLEY, Ian Ronald Mandala Centre, Gregory Boulevard, Nottingham NG7 6LB Tel: 0115 960 6082 Fax: 0115 924 5627 Email: medley@prima.net — MB BS 1978 Lond.; MRCPsych 1985; DRCOG 1982. Cons. Gen. Psychiat. Nottm. Mapperley Hosp. Prev: Lect. (Psychiat.) Univ. Hosp. Nottm.

MEDLEY, Joyce Margaret (retired) 4 Harpers Court, North Bar Without, Beverley HU17 7AD Tel: 01482 865 6201 — MB ChB 1957 Manch. Prev: Clin. Med. Off. Herts.

*MEDLEY, Louise Clare 32 Dukes Way, Tewkesbury GL20 5FG — MB ChB 1997 Birm.

MEDLEY, Steven Neil Halifax Road Surgery, 9 Halifax Road, Dewsbury WF13 2JH Tel: 01924 463934 Fax: 01924 485800 — MB ChB 1980 Leeds; DRCOG 1984. (Leeds)

*MEDLICOTT, Sarah Anne 12 Bryn Terrace, Ystrad, Pentre CF41 7RX — MB BCh 1995 Wales.

MEDLOCK, John Mervyn (retired) The Lodge, Warley Road, Great Warley, Brentwood CM13 3HX — MB BS 1951 Lond. Cons. Phys. Communicable Dis. Rush Green Hosp. Romford & St. Ann's Hosp. Lond. Gen. Hosp. Tottenham; Lect. in Communicable Dis. Lond. Hosp. Prev: Sen. Regist. St. Ann's Hosp. Tottenham.

MEDLOCK, Karen Elaine 115 Nutley Lane, Reigate RH2 9EF — MB BS 1992 Lond.; BSc Lond. 1989; FRCA 1998. (St. Bartholomew's) Specialist Regist. (Anaesth.) Gt. Osmond St. Hosp.

Lond. Socs: Assn. Anaesth.s of GB & Irel.; BMA; Difficult Avuray Soc. Prev: SPR P.ss Roy. Hosp., Haywards Health; SPR E. Surrey Hosp. Redhill; SPR St Geo.s Hosp. Tootup Lond.

MEDLYCOTT, Brian Randolph (retired) 102 Copse Avenue, West Wickham BR4 9NP — MB BS 1930 Lond.; MRCS Eng. LRCP Lond. 1930; DOMS Eng. 1936. Prev: Ophth. Specialist Med. Eye Centres Bromley AHA.

MEDVEI, Victor Cornelius, CBE (retired) 38 Westmoreland Terrace, London SW1V 3HL Tel: 020 7834 8282 — MD 1930 Vienna; FRCP Lond. 1965, M 1943; MRCS Eng. LRCP Lond. 1941. Exam. Phys. (Lond.) United Nations. Prev: Princip. Med. Off. i/c Med. Servs. HM Foreign Servs.

MEDWAY, Dorothy Grace, MBE (retired) 34 West End Avenue, Pinner HA5 1BJ Tel: 020 8866 2808 — MB BS 1926 Lond.

MEDWAY, Thomas Alan (retired) Greenbanks, Raleigh Hill, Bideford EX39 3PB — MB ChB 1959 Bristol; MRCGP 1977; DObst RCOG 1964. Prev: GP Bideford.

MEDWORTH, Samuel Number 18 Surgery, 18 Upper Oldfield Park, Bath BA2 3JZ Tel: 01225 427402 Fax: 01225 484627; 45 Milton Avenue, Bath BA2 4QZ — MB BS 1980 Lond.; MA Camb. 1981; MRCGP 1994; Cert. Family Plann. JCC 1984; DRCOG 1983. (Westm.) Mem. CMF. Socs: Clin. Soc. Bath; Regius Soc. Prev: SHO (Family Pract. Train. Scheme) Watford Gen. Hosp.; Ho. Phys. Watford Gen. Hosp.; Ho. Surg. Herts. & Essex Gen. Hosp. Bishops Stortford.

MEE, Mr Aeneas David Northwick Park and St Mark's Hospitals, Watford Road, Harrow HA1 3UJ Tel: 020 88869 2616 Fax: 020 88869 2577 — MB ChB Otago 1964; FRCS Eng. 1971. (Univ. Otago) Cons. Urol. Surg. N.wick Pk. & St Mark's Hosps. Harrow. Socs: Brit. Assn. Urol. Surgs.; Brit. Assn. Urol. Surg.; Urolog. Soc. of Australasia. Prev: Cons. Urol. Surg. Char. Cross. Hosp. Lond.; Sen. Lect. (Urol. & Transpl.) Roy. Postgrad. Med. Sch. Lond.; Hon. Cons. Surg. Hammersmith Hosp. Lond.

MEE, Anthony Simon Royal Berkshire Hospital, London Road, Reading RG1 5AN Tel: 0118 987 7523 Fax: 0118 987 8736 — MB BS 1972 Lond.; MD Lond. 1980; MRCP (UK) 1974; MRCS Eng. LRCP Lond. 1972; FRCP Lond. 1989. (Char. Cross) Cons. Phys. & Gastroenterol. Roy. Berks. & Battle Hosp. NHS Trust. Socs: Brit. Soc. Gastroenterol. (BSG); Amer. Soc. Gastroint. Endoscopy (ASGE). Prev: Sen. Regist. (Gen. Med. & Gastroenterol.) Middlx. & Centr. Middlx. Hosp. Lond.; Regist. (Med.) Whipps Cross Hosp.; Research Fell. Roy. Free Hosp. Lond.

MEE, Beverley 94 Montgomery Street, Hillside, Edinburgh EH7 5HE Tel: 0131 478 2155 — MB ChB 1990 Ed.; DRCOG; MRCGP; DFFP; DCCH. (Edinburgh) Sessional Doctor Lothian Brook Advis. Serv. Edin. Prev: GP Locum Charters Towers Med. Centre Qu.sland, Australia.

MEE, John Diarmuid 163 Andersonstown Road, Belfast BT11 9EA — MB BCh BAO 1981 NUI; MRCGP 1986; DObst RCPI 1984; DCH NUI 1983. Socs: MICGP.

MEE, Mary Siobhan Hunters Lodge, Cooks Lane, Banwell BS29 6DS Tel: 01934 824135 — MB BS 1985 Lond.; T(GP) 1993; DA (UK) 1988. Prev: Med. Off. Bethesda Hosp. Kwazulu, RSA; SHO (Paediat.) Gloucester Roy. Hosp.; Trainee GP Gloucester & Rugby.

MEE, Richard Andrew Whittington Moor Surgery, Scarsdale Road, Chesterfield S41 8NA Tel: 01246 542549 Fax: 01246 454669; 6 Hollens Way, Linacre Woods, Chesterfield S40 4XR Tel: 01246 272677 Email: rikmee@aol.com — MB ChB 1972 Sheff.; FRCGP 1988, M 1976.

MEE, Sarah Jane Flat 12, Ash Lodge, Eternit Walk, London SW6 6NN — MB BS 1996 Lond.

MEE, Susan Elizabeth St Marys Surgery, 37 St. Mary's Street, Ely CB7 4HF Tel: 01353 665511 Fax: 01353 669532 — MB BS 1983 Lond.; BSc Lond. 1980, MB BS 1983; MRCGP 1989; DRCOG 1987. (London Hospital Medical College)

MEE, Mr William Michael (retired) Old Vicarage, School Lane, Husborne Crawley, Bedford MK43 0UY — MB BS Lond. 1954; FRCS Eng. 1961; MRCS Eng. LRCP Lond. 1954. Prev: Cons. Surg. Luton & Dunstable Hosp.

MEECH, Stephen Hilary The Mote Medical Practice, St Saviours Road, Maidstone ME15 9FL Tel: 01622 756888 Fax: 01622 672573; The Firs, Spring Grove, Goudhurst Road, Marden, Tonbridge TN12 9NW Tel: 01622 831593 Email: stephen.meech@virgin.net — MB BS 1984 Lond. Unit Med.

Represen. Maidstone Dist. Hosp. Acute Unit. Bd. Prev: Trainee GP Hastings HA VTS.

MEECHAM, John Wirral Hospital NHS Trust, Upton, Wirral CH49 5PE Tel: 0151 678 5111; The White House, Mill Lane, Heswall, Wirral CH60 2TF Tel: 0151 342 5050 — MD 1964 Liverp.; MB ChB 1955; FRCP Lond. 1974, M 1962; DCH Eng. 1957; DObst RCOG 1957. (Liverp.) Med. Dir. & Cons. Phys. Wirral Hosp. NHS Trust. Socs: BMA & Liverp. Med. Inst. Prev: Sen. Regist. (Med.) Liverp. Roy. Infirm. & Walton Hosp. Liverp.; Fell. (Med.) Johns Hopkins Hosp. Baltimore, U.S.A.

MEECHAM JONES, David Jeffrey Department of Thoracic Medicine, Gloucestershire Royal Hospital, Great Western Road, Gloucester GL1 3NN Tel: 01452 394564; Tyrcanol House, Sway Road, Morriston, Swansea SA6 6JD — MB BCh 1986 Wales; MRCP (UK) 1989. Cons. Phys. (Respirat. Med.) Gloucester Roy. NHS Trust.

MEECHAM JONES, Sally Mary Tyrcanol House, Sway Road, Morriston, Swansea SA6 6JD — MB BChir 1984 Camb.; MB BChir Camb. 1983; MA Camb. 1983; MRCP (UK) 1986; FRCR 1991. Cons. Radiol. Maelor Hosp. Wrexham. Prev: Fell. (Paediat. Radiol.) Roy. Liverp. Childr. Hosp.; Regist. & Sen. Regist. (Radiol.) Univ. Hosp. Wales Cardiff; Regist. (Gen. Med.) Roy. Gwent Hosp. Newport.

MEECHAN, Hugh Thomas MMR International, 32 Station Approach, West Byfleet KT14 6NF Tel: 01932 351733 Fax: 01932 341472 Email: hueh.meechan@mmr-international.com; 133 Clomore Street, London SW18 5HD — MB ChB 1986 Manch.; BSc St. And. 1983; MBA Cranfield 1994. Research Dir. MMR Internat. W. Byfleet; Lect. TPI courses 1998; Trials Adviser MSPI. Prev: Regional Customer Marketing Co-ordinator Merck, Sharp & Dohme (UK) Ltd; SHO (Med.) Glenfield Gen. Hosp. Leic.; SHO (Cas. & Intens. Care) Roy. Preston Hosp.

MEECHAN, P O Walton Health Centre, Rodney Road, Walton-on-Thames KT12 3LB Tel: 01932 228999 Fax: 01932 225586 — MB ChB 1971 Edinburgh; MB ChB 1971 Edinburgh.

MEEHAN, Christopher The Surgery, 3 Glasgow Road, Paisley PA1 3QS Tel: 0141 889 2604 Fax: 0141 887 9039; 15 Stonefield Avenue, Paisley PA2 7RN Tel: 0141 884 2516 — MB ChB 1961 Glas. (Glas.) JP.

MEEHAN, Christopher James Pathology Department, Royal United Hospital, Combe Park, Bath BA1 3NG Tel: 01225 824706 Fax: 01225 461044 Email: chris.meehan@ruh-bath.swest.nhs.uk; 21 Forester Road, Bath BA2 6QE Tel: 01225 337054 Fax: 01225 337054 Email: meehan.biddlestone@btopenworld.com — MB ChB 1987 Glas.; BSc (Hons.) Glas. 1985; MRCPath 1994. (Glasgow) Cons. Histopath. Roy. United Hosp. Bath. Prev: Lect. (Path.) Univ. Soton. & Univ. Edin.

MEEHAN, Daniel Desmond Carrickmore Health Centre, Termon Road, Carrickmore, Omagh BT79 9JR Tel: 028 8076 1242 — MB BCh 1955 N U Irel. (N U Irel) GP Omagh, Co. Tyrone.

MEEHAN, Diane Maureen The Health Centre, Garden Terrace Road, Old Harlow, Harlow CM17 0AX Tel: 01279 418136 Fax: 01279 429650; Wynchlows, High St, Hundson, Ware SG12 8NJ Tel: 01279 842841 — MB BS 1970 Lond.; MRCS Eng. LRCP Lond. 1970; FRCGP 1996, M 1976; DRCOG 1972. (Roy. Free Hosp. Sch. Med., Univ. Lond.)

MEEHAN, John Patrick South Kensington & Chelsea Mental Health Centre, Chelsea & Westminster Hospital, 1 Nightingale Place, London SW10 9NG Tel: 020 8846 6055 Fax: 020 8846 6119 — MB BCh BAO 1975 NUI; MRCPsych 1979. Cons. Psychiat. Chelsea & W.m. Hosp. Lond.; Clin. Tutor Univ. Lond.; Cons. Psychiat. Imperial Coll. Health Serv. Lond. Prev: Cons. Psychiat. St. Mary Abbots Hosp. & W.m. Hosp. Lond.; Cons. Psychiat. Waltham Forest HA.

MEEHAN, Louise Christina 11 Seapark Avenue, Holywood BT18 0LL — MB BCh BAO 1992 Belf. (Belfast)

MEEHAN, Rose Ann 46 Hodder Drive, Greenford UB6 8LL — MB BS 1993 Lond.

MEEHAN, Shaun Grange Road Surgery, Bishopsworth, Bristol BS13 8LD Tel: 0117 964 4343 Fax: 0117 9934 5822; 48 Coronation Road, Southville, Bristol BS3 1AR Tel: 0117 966 1645 — MB ChB 1986 Bristol; MRCGP 1991.

MEEHAN, Mr Stewart Edward Ormskirk and District General Hospital, Wigan Road, Ormskirk L39 1AZ Tel: 01695 577111 Ext: 6155 Email: semeehan@mail.soh-tr.nhs.nwest.uk; 23 Harding Road, Burscough, Ormskirk L40 7UJ — MB ChB 1972 Ed.; BSc Ed. 1969; ChM Ed. 1992; FRCS Ed. 1977; FICA 1980. (Edinburgh) Cons. Surg. S.port & Ormskirk Hosp.s NHS Trust; Cons. Surg. Renacres Hall Hosp. Halsall nr. Ormskirk Lancs. Socs: Fell., Counc. Mbr & Mbr of Prof. Pract. Comm., Assn. of Surg. Of GB & Irel.; W. Lancs. Med. Soc. (past Pres.); BMA. Prev: Sen. Regist. (Surg.) & Regist. (Gen. Surg.) Dundee Teach. Hosps.; Ho. Off. (Surg.) E.. Gen. Hosp. Edin.

MEEHAN, Thomasina University of Manchester, Audiology Department, Manchester M13 9PL; 44 Calderbrook Drive, Cheadle Hulme, Stockport SK8 5RT Tel: 0161 485 4358 — MB BCh BAO 1985 NUI; MSc 1998 Univ. Of Manch.; FRCS (Oto) Ed. 1996. Specialist Regist. (Audiol.) Manch. Cardiff notat. Socs: BMA & Med. Protec. Soc. Prev: SHO (Cas.) Middlesbrough Gen. Hosp.; SHO (Orthop.) Ancoats Hosp. Manch.; SHO (ENT) Darlington.

MEEK, Alexander Edwin (retired) 4 Norfolk Street, Beverley HU17 7DN Tel: 01482 882454 — MB ChB 1951 Ed. Prev: GP Beverley.

MEEK, David Burnside 193 High Street, Ponders End, Enfield EN3 4EA Tel: 020 8804 1060 — MB ChB 1947 Glas. (Univ. Glas.) Prev: Orthop. Ho. Surg. & Ho. Surg. Roy. Infirm. Glas.; Capt. RAMC.

MEEK, David Robert Department of Radiology, Whiston Hospital, Dragon Lane, Prescot L35 5DR Tel: 0151 430 1265; 10 Hillfoot Green, Woolton, Liverpool L25 7UH — MB ChB 1972 Glas.; FFR RCSI 1983; DMRD Eng. 1981. (Glas.) Cons. Radiol. Whiston Hosp.; Clin. Lect. Radiodiag. Univ. Liverp. Socs: BMA. Prev: Cons. Cardiac Radiol. Cardiothoracic Centre Liverp.; Sen. Regist. & Regist. (Radiol.) Glas. Roy. Infirm.; Regist. (Med.) Hull Roy. Infirm.

MEEK, Diane Southbank Road Surgery, 17-19 Southbank Road, Kirkintilloch, Glasgow G66 1NH Tel: 0141 776 2183 Fax: 0141 777 8321 — MB ChB 1982 Glas.; MRCGP 1986; DRCOG 1984; DGM 1998. Clin. Asst. (Geriat.) Assessm. and Rehabil. Day Hosp. Stobmill NHS Trust, Balarnock Rd., Glas. Prev: Ho. Off. (Surg.) Glas. Roy. Infirm.

MEEK, James Carrick Radiology Department, Sully Hospital, Sully, Penarth CF64 2YA — MB ChB 1941 Glas.; DMR Lond 1947. (Univ. Glas.) Cons. Radiol. S. Glam. AHA (T). Prev: Cons. Radiol. Roy. Gwent Hosp.; Sen. Regist. Vict. Infirm. Glas.; Regist. Brit. Post-grad. Med. Sch. Lond.

MEEK, Jenifer Louisa Ann Department of Anaesthesia, Victoria Hospital, Kirkcaldy KY2 5AH Tel: 01592 643355 Fax: 01592 647090 Email: jenifermeek@aol.com; 58 Pettycur Road, Kinghorn, Burntisland KY3 9RL — MB ChB 1972 Ed.; 1969 BSc (Med. Sci.) Ed.; 1978 FFA RCS Eng. (Edin.) Cons. Anaesth. Vict. Hosp. Kirkcaldy.; Hon. Sec. Roy. Coll. Of Anaesth.s Scot. Bd. Prev: Sen. Regist. (Anaesth.) Sheff. AHA (T); Regist. (Anaesth.) Roy. Infirm. Edin.

MEEK, Judith Helen 4 Palace Road, London N8 8QJ Fax: 020 7209 6103 Email: j.meek@ucl.ac.uk — MB BS 1987 Lond.; PhD Lond. 1982, MSc 1979; MA (Hons.) Camb. 1978; MRCP (UK) Paediat. 1991. Clin. Lect. & Hon. Sen. Regist. (Paediat.) Univ. Coll. Hosp. Lond.; Specialist Regist. (Neonat.) UCHC. Socs: BMA & RCPCH; Neonat. Soc. Prev: Hon. SR Univ. Coll. Hosp.; SHO (Paediat.) W.m. Childr., Univ. Coll. & Guy's Hosps. Lond.; SHO (Gen. Med.) Whittington Hosp. Lond.

MEEK, Mr Robert Marshall Dominic 12A Sydenham Road, Dowanhill, Glasgow G12 9NP — MB ChB 1990 Glas.; BSc (Hons.) Glas. 1987; FRCS Glas. 1994; FRCS Ed. 1994.

MEEK, Ronald Dunedin, 19 Robertson Avenue, Dumfries DG1 4EY — MB ChB 1971 Ed.; BSc Ed. 1968, MB ChB 1971; FFA RCS Eng. 1979; DObst RCOG 1973. Cons. Anaesth. Dumfries & Galloway Roy. Infirm. Prev: Sen. Regist. (Anaesth.) Roy. Infirm. Edin.

MEEK, Stephen John 27 Upper Belmont Road, Bristol BS7 9DG — MB BS 1985 Lond.

MEEK, Timothy 70 Glenthorn Road, Newcastle upon Tyne NE2 3HN — MB BS 1992 Newc.

MEEKE, Angela Mary Severn NHS Trust, Rikenel, Montpellier, Gloucester GL1 1LY Tel: 01452 891000; Llancraugh Cottage, Marstow, Ross-on-Wye HR9 6EH — MB ChB Liverp. 1965; T(M) (Paediat.) 1991; DCH Eng. 1977. SCMO Severn NHS Trust. Socs: Fac. Fam. Plann. & Reproduc. Health Care; Brit. Paediat. Assn. & BAAF Med. Gp. Prev: SHO (Paediat.) & Ho. Off. (Obst.) St. David's Hosp. Bangor; Ho. Off. Clatterbridge Hosp. Bebington.

MEEKE, Phyllis Avril Elizabeth (retired) 128 Nab Lane, Mirfield WF14 9QJ Tel: 01924 494331 — MB BCh BAO 1948 Belf.

MEEKING

MEEKING, Darryl Richard 28 Raynsford Road, Northampton NN5 7HP — MB ChB 1989 Bristol.

MEEKINGS, Emma Lucia 3 Chestnut Road, Ashford TW15 1DD — BChir 1991 Camb.

***MEEKINGS, Tim Charles** Silver Ridge, 10 Wallings Lane, Silverdale, Carnforth LA5 0RZ — BM BS 1998 Nottm.; BM BS Nottm 1998.

MEEKINS, Mr Jeremy William Stapleford Cottage, Burton Road, Stapleford, Tarporley CW6 0ET — MB BS 1984 Lond.; FRCS Glas. 1988; MRCOG 1990. (Roy. Free) Cons. O & G Leighton Hosp. Chesh. Prev: Sen. Regist. (O & G) Liverp. & Chester; Regist. Rotat. (O & G) Countess of Chester Hosp.; SHO (Gen. Surg.) Countess of Chester Hosp.

MEEKISON, Lynne Anne 11 Dundas Street, Edinburgh EH3 6QG Tel: 0131 558 9263 Fax: 0131 536 2197 — MB ChB 1990 Ed. (Ed.) Staff Grade (Gastroenterol.) Roy. Infirm. Edin. Prev: SHO III (Gen. Med.) E. Gen. Hosp. Edin.; SHO III (Gen. Med. & Endocrinol.) Roy. Infirm. Edin.; SHO Rotat. (Gen. Med.) Ysbyty Glan Clwyd HA.

MEEKS, Andrew Christopher George Selah, Clayton Hill, Clayton, Hassocks BN6 9PQ — MB ChB 1978 Manch.; MRCPI 1984. Lect. in Child Health Univ. Leic.; Hon. Regist. Leics. HA.

MEEKS, Margaret Grace Dept. of Paeds., The Rayne Institute, 5 University St., London WC1E 6JJ Email: m.meeks@ucl.ac.uk; Email: maggie.meeks2@virgin.net — MB ChB 1990 Birm.; 2001 MD; ChB Birm. 1990; MRCP (UK) 1994. Specialist Regist. Paediat.

MEEN, Trevor Fountain (retired) 1 Berkeley Cottages, Plymouth PL1 5QT — MB BS 1957 Lond.; MRCS Eng. LRCP Lond. 1957; DObst RCOG 1962. Prev: Ho. Surg. & Ho. Phys. Roy. Devon & Exeter Hosp.

MEENAGH, Ciaran Patrick 16 Beechill Park N., Saintfield Road, Belfast BT8 6NZ — MB BCh BAO 1985 Belf.

***MEENAGH, Gary Kevin** 35 Dorchester Drive, Ballyhenry Road, Newtownabbey BT36 5WP — MB BCh BAO 1995 Belf.

MEENAN, Gerard William 75 Bingnian Drive, Glen Road, Belfast BT11 8JD — MB BCh BAO 1983 Belf.

MEENAN, John Kieran Patrick 11 Bronsart Road, London SW6 6AJ — MB BCh BAO 1986 NUI; LRCPSI 1986.

***MEENAN, Karen Anne** 7 Northland Parade, Londonderry BT48 7JT — MB ChB 1998 Dund.; MB ChB Dund 1998.

MEER, Hajra 11 Audley Road, Ealing, London W5 3ES — LRCPI & LM, LRCSI & LM 1970 - Roy. Coll. Surgeons Dublin; MFCM 1984; Faculty of PH Med. London. (Royal College of Surgeons) Specialist (Community Med.) Ealing HA.; Cons. Pub. Health Med. (PHM). Socs: Fac. PH Med.; BMA. Prev: Cons. PHM N. Middlx. Health; Cons. PH Med. Enfield & Haringey Health Auth.; Cons. Pub. Health Med. Ealing, Hammersmith & Hounslow HA.

MEER, Mr Jameel Ahmad 173 Wisden Road, Stevenage SG1 5NP — MB BS 1976 Punjab; FRCSI 1985.

MEER, Lorna Catherine 56 Middle Park Road, Birmingham B29 4BJ — MB ChB 1986 Sheff.

MEER, Soraya 2 Lambolle Place, London NW3 4PD — MB BS 1991 Lond.

***MEERAN, Hanif** 27 Bicknell Road, London SE5 9AU — MB BS 1994 Lond.

MEERAN, Mohamed Haniffa Munsif 32 Lismore Road, South Croydon CR2 7QA Tel: 020 8680 0774 Fax: 020 8667 9522; 293 London Road, Croydon CR0 2RN Tel: 020 8680 0774 Fax: 020 8667 9522 — MB BS 1959 Ceylon; LicAc 1980; DRCOG 1970. GP Croydon; Dir. Marina Acad. & Supplies Internat. Socs: Founder Mem. Brit. Med. Acupunc. Soc.; Dir. & Founder Mem. Lond. Med. Acupunc. & AuriculoTher. Soc.; Fell. Roy. Soc. Med. Prev: Dir. Zambia Flying Dr. Serv.; Pres. Zambia Red Cross Soc.

MEERAN, Mohammed Karim ICSM Endocrine Unit, Hammersmith Hospital, Du Cane Road, London W12 0NN Tel: 020 8383 3242 Fax: 020 8383 3142 Email: kmeeran@ic.ac.uk; 2 Rushmore House, 73 Russell Road, Kensington, London W14 8HW Tel: 020 8680 0774 Fax: 020 8680 0774 — MB BS 1988 Lond.; MB BS (Hons.) Lond. 1988; BSc (Biochem.) 1st cl. Lond. 1985; MD 1997; MRCP (UK) 1991. (Roy. Free Hosp. Lond. Univ.) Sen. Lect. & Cons. Endocrinol. Hammersmith Hosp. Lond. Prev: Sen. Regist. (Endocrinol.) St. Bart. Hosp. Lond.; Regist. Rotat. (Med.) Ealing & Hammersmith Lond.; SHO (Renal Med.) St. Thos. Hosp. Lond.

MEERS, Peter Dennis (retired) Dial Cottage, Ebbesbourne Wake, Salisbury SP5 5JF Tel: 01722 780352 Fax: 01722 780352 — MB BS Lond. 1952; MD Lond. 1961; MRCS Eng. LRCP Lond. 1952; FRCPath 1972; Dip. Bact. Lond 1960. Prev: Assoc. Prof. Microbiol. Nat. Univ. Singapore.

MEERSTADT, Peter William Dierck 146 Cloudesley Road, London N1 0EA Tel: 020 7278 1862 — MB BS 1972 Lond.; FRCPCH (UK) 1997; MRCS Eng. LRCP Lond. 1972; FRCP Lond. 1996; MRCP (UK) 1978; DCH Eng. 1975. (St. Mary's) Cons. Paediat. Greenwich.

MEES, Graham Peter Pinfold Lane Surgery, 40 Pinfold Lane, Butterknowle, Bishop Auckland DL13 5NU; Belleisle, Garlieshon, Newton Stewart, Dumfries DG8 8AF Tel: 01988 600768 Email: graham@gpmees.com — MB BS 1971 Lond.; MRCS Eng. LRCP Lond. 1971; MRCGP 1977; DCH Eng. 1977; DObst RCOG 1976. (St. Bart.)

MEESE, John David (retired) 17 York Road, Selsdon, South Croydon CR2 8NR Tel: 020 8657 4024 — MB BS Lond. 1966; MRCS Eng. LRCP Lond. 1966. Prev: GP Selsdon, Surrey.

MEESON, Andrew 260 Finchley Road, London NW3 7AA Tel: 020 7794 4421 Fax: 020 7431 8921; 6 Frognal Lane, London NW3 7DU Tel: 020 7435 9464 Fax: 020 7431 8921 — MA Dub. 1961, MB BCh BAO 1960. Gen. Phys. Charter Nightingale Hosp. Socs: Soc. of Apoth. Prev: Cas. Off. St. Mary's Hosp. Lond.; Sen. Cas. Off. Roy. Free Hosp. Lond.; Ho. Surg. City of Lond. Matern. Hosp.

MEESON, Bohdan 260 Finchley Road, London NW3 7AA Tel: 020 7794 4421 Fax: 020 7431 8921; 6 Frognal Lane, London NW3 7DU Tel: 020 7435 9464 — MA Dub. 1961, MB BCh BAO 1960. Gen. Phys. Charter Nightingale Hosp. Prev: Dep. Med. Supt. P & O Lines; Ho. Phys. Dreadnought Seamen's Hosp.

MEESON, Marion Doris Prospect Surgery, Hungate Lane, Hunmanby, Filey YO14 0NN Tel: 01723 890280 Fax: 01723 890124; Manor Farm House, Main St, Wold Newton, Driffield YO25 3YQ — MB BCh 1980 Wales.

MEESTERS, Henricus Joseph Raphael St Lawrence Medical Centre, 4 Bocking End, Braintree CM7 9AA Tel: 01376 552474 Fax: 01376 552417; Silver End Surgery, Broadway, Silver End, Witham CM8 3RQ Tel: 01376 583387 Fax: 01376 584936 — Artsexamen 1974 Amsterdam. Prev: Med. Off. (Leprosy & Tuberc.) Mansakonko, The Gambia; Med. Off. (Leprosy & Tuberc.) Makeni, Sierra Leone.

MEGAHY, Fiona Roselynne Catriona The Lodge, Lauder TD2 6SU Tel: 01578 722582; The Health Centre, Currie Road, Galashiels TD1 2UA Tel: 01896 754833 Fax: 01896 751389 — MB ChB 1988 Glas. Socs: M-C Soc. Glas. Prev: Trainee GP Earlston; SHO (A & E & Orthop.) S.. Gen. Hosp. Glas.; SHO (O & G) Border Gen. Hosp. Melrose.

MEGARRY, Simon Graham York Dist. Hosp., Wiggington Road, York — MB ChB 1988 Bristol; PhD 2000; MRCP (UK) 1991. (Bristol) Cons. Cardiol. Prev: H.O. Bristol Roy. Infirm.; Regist. (Med.) N. Manch. Gen. Hosp.; SHO (Med.) N.. Gen. Hosp. Sheff.

MEGGITT, Mr Bernard Francis Addenbrooke's Hospital NHS Trust, Orthopaedic Department, Clinic 1, Hills Road, Cambridge CB2 2QQ Tel: 01223 245151 Fax: 01223 216549; 4 Templemore, Cambridge CB1 7TH Tel: 01223 413851, 01233 413851 Fax: 01223 413851 — MB BS 1961 Lond.; MA Camb. 1977; FRCS Eng. 1966; MRCS Eng. LRCP Lond. 1961. (Univ. Coll. Hosp.) p/t Cons. Orthop. & Trauma Addenbrooke's Univ. Hosp. Camb.; Assoc. Lect. Med. Fac. Univ. Camb. Socs: (Past Pres.)Founder Mem. Brit. Orthop. Foot Surg. Soc.; Brit. Hip Soc.; (Past Pres. and Hon. Sec.) Rheumatoid Arthritis Surgic. Soc. Prev: Sen. Regist. (Orthop.) St. Bart. Hosp. Lond.; Regist. (Orthop.) Roy. Nat. Orthop. Hosp. Lond.; Brit. Orthop. Fell. Univ. S. Calif. Los Angeles, USA.

MEGGITT, Simon Jon 14 Cherryburn Gardens, Newcastle upon Tyne NE4 9UQ — BM BS 1992 Nottm.

MEGGS, Anne Marie Alison Lea Medical Centre, Calderwood, East Kilbride, Glasgow G74 3BE Tel: 01355 233981; 15 Field Road, Busby, Glasgow G76 8SE — MB ChB 1981 Aberd. GP E. Kilbride.

MEGGY, Miss Janet Mary The Summerhouse, Grey Green Lane, Bewdley DY12 1LZ Tel: 01299 400511 Fax: 01299 400511 Email: j.meggy@bigfoott.com — MB BS 1973 Lond.; FRCOG 1991, M 1979. (Roy. Free) Cons. O & G Worcester Acute Hosp. Trust. Socs: Birm. and Midl. Obstetirc and Gyn. Soc.; Brit. Menopause Soc.; Brit. Soc. for Colposcopy and Clin. Path. Prev: Sen. Regist. (O & G) Roy Free Hosp. Lond.; Regist. (O & G) Ealing Gen. Hosp. & Roy. Free Hosp. Lond.

MEGHANI, Dhanjibhi K Butetown Health Centre, Loudoun Square, Cardiff CF10 5UZ Tel: 029 2048 8027 Fax: 029 2034 3839.

MEGHANI, Shelina 60C Ferme Park Road, Stroud Grove, London N4 4ED — MB BCh 1986 Wales. Trainee GP Lond.

MEGHARAJ, Patel Duddappa Muppane The Dowlais Medical Practice, Ivor Street, Dowlais, Merthyr Tydfil CF48 3LU Tel: 01685 721400 Fax: 01685 375287.

MEGHJEE, Salim Pyarali Ladha 7B Market Place, London NW11 6LB — MB ChB 1991 Glas.

MEGIAS MARTIN, Eugenia Maria Luisa 63 Humber Road, London SE3 7LR — LMS 1988 La Laguna.

MEGSON, Kenneth 3 Front Street, Tynemouth, North Shields NE30 4RG — MB BS 1979 Newc.; MRCGP 1983; DCH RCP Lond. 1983; DRCOG 1982.

MEGYESI-SCHWARTZ, Francis Coloman Wordsley Hospital, Wordsley, Stream Road, Stourbridge DY8 5QX Tel: 01384 401401 Fax: 01384 244395; 45 Melrose Avenue, Stourbridge DY8 2LE Tel: 01324 394285 — MB BS 1966 Lond.; FRCP Lond. 1985; MRCP (UK) 1970; MRCS Eng. LRCP Lond. 1966; DCH Eng. 1969. (Univ. Coll. Hosp.) Cons. Paediat. W. Midl. RHA. Socs: Brit. Paediat. Assn. & BMA. Prev: Sen. Regist. (Paediat.) Childr. Hosp. Birm.; Regist. (Paediat.) Hillingdon Hosp. Uxbridge; Ho. Surg. Univ. Coll. Hosp. Lond.

MEHAN, Rakesh 22 Sandringham Road, Penn, Wolverhampton WV4 5TG — MB ChB 1991 Manch.

***MEHANNA, Hesham Mohamed Hassan** Flat 8, 25 Western Court, 100 University Place, Glasgow G12 8SQ Tel: 0141 357 2732 — MB ChB 1994 Glas.

MEHARG, William Willowfield, Castlerock, Coleraine — MB BCh BAO 1941 Belf. (Qu. Univ. Belf.) Prev: Ho. Surg. City & Co. Hosp. Lond.derry & City Hosp. Belf.; Squadron Ldr. R.A.F.V.R.

MEHAT, Balvinder Singh The Surgery, 30 Beeston Fields Drive, Beeston, Nottingham NG9 3DB — MB ChB 1984 Bristol.

MEHAY, Ramesh Whinmoor Nook Cottage, York Road, Leeds LS15 4NQ Tel: 0976724533 Fax: 0113 273 1597; 482 Walsall Road, Great Barr, Birmingham B42 2LU — MB ChB 1993 Leeds; DFFP Lond. 1997; MRCGP (Dist.) Edin. 1998. (Univ. Leeds) GP Non-Princip.; MRCGP Tutor. Socs: Diplomate of Fam. Plg. Assoc.; Roy. Coll. Gen. Pract. Prev: SHO (Paediat.) Booth Hall Childr. Hosp. Manch.; SHO (Cardiol.) Ards Hosp. & Bangor Hosp. Newtownards; SHO (A & E) Lond.derry, N. Irel.

***MEHDI ZADEH KASHANI, Shahram** 1 Elmete Mount, Leeds LS8 2NU — MB BS 1998 Lond.; MB BS Lond 1998.

MEHDIAN, Mohammad Hosein Department of Orthopaedics, Centre for Spinal Studies & Surgery, University Hospital, Queen's Medical Centre, Nottingham NG7 2UH Tel: 0115 970 9013 Fax: 0115 970 9013 Email: mehdianspine@hotmail.com; Stoney Gate, 566 Adams Hill, Woollaton, Nottingham NG1 2GZ — MD 1975 Tehran; MS 1982 Tehran; FRCS 2000 Edinburgh. Cons. Orthop. Spinal Surg. Qu. Med. Centre Nottm. Socs: Internat. Soc. Study Lumbar Spine; CSRS; SRS. Prev: Clin. Specialist (Spinal Disorders) Exeter HA; Asst. Prof. Orthop. Nat. Univ., Iran; Assoc. Prof. Orthop., Dir. & Head Orthop. Hosp. Nat. Univ., Iran.

MEHIGAN, Cormac 11 Scotland Street Lane W., Edinburgh EH3 6PT — MB BCh BAO 1990 Dub.

MEHMET, Serife 16E Upwood Road, London SE12 8AA — MB BS 1992 Lond.

***MEHMI, Manjeet** 215 Merridale Street W., Wolverhampton WV3 0RP — MB ChB 1998 Sheff.; MB ChB Sheff 1998.

MEHRA, Arun Premchand 3 Ochil Road, Bearsden, Glasgow G61 4JZ — MB BS 1980 Gujarat.

MEHRA, Manu 35 The Avenue, Cheam, Sutton SM2 7QA — MB BS Lond. 1993; BSc (Hons.) Lond. 1990. (Univ. Coll. Hosp. & Middlx. Hosp.) SHO (ENT) St. Geo. & Mayday Hosps. Lond. Socs: Roy. Soc. Med. Prev: SHO (Audiol. Med. & Developm. Paediat.) Roy. Nat. Throat, Nose & Ear Hosp. Lond.; SHO (Orthop.) Chase Farm. Hosp.; SHO (A & E) Newham Gen. Hosp.

***MEHRA, Pratima** 20 Wentworth Court, Ponteland, Newcastle upon Tyne NE20 9PR — MB BS 1998 Newc.; MB BS Newc 1998.

MEHRA, Rakesh Chand 12 St Martin's Close, Sandwell Valley, West Bromwich B70 6TE — BSc (Hons.) Birm. 1974, MB ChB 1977; DCH RCP Lond. 1985. (Birm) Prev: SHO (Neonat. Pediat.) Birm. Matern. Hosp.; SHO (Paediat.) Birm. Childr. Hosp.; Regist. (Med.) Bristol & W.on Health Dist. (T).

MEHRA, Mr Ram Lal (retired) 25 Carlisle Mansions, Carlisle Place, London SW1P 1EZ Tel: 020 7834 8910 — MB BS 1932 Punjab; MB BS Punjab (Pakistan) 1932; FRCS Eng. 1936; MRCS Eng. LRCP Lond. 1935. Prev: Med. Dir. Internat. Planned Parenthood Federat. Lond.

MEHRA, Ranjeev Kumar 6 Blaking Drive, Prescot L34 0JE — MB ChB 1992 Liverp.

MEHRA, Surendra Kumar Marjory Lees Health Centre, Egerton Street, Oldham OL1 3SF Tel: 0161 652 1221 Fax: 0161 628 6705; 56 Tandlehill Road, Royton, Oldham OL2 5UX Tel: 0161 624 8775 — MB BS 1954 Patna. (Patna Med. Coll.) Socs: BMA & Oldham Med. Soc. Prev: Regist. (Orthop.) Oldham Hosp.; Asst. MoH (Pub. Health) Oldham.

MEHRAJ, Qashif Rizwan 51 Richmond Avenue, Prestwich, Manchester M25 0LW — MB ChB 1993 Manch.

MEHRBAKHSH, Ali 77 Swanton Road, Erith DA8 1LR — MB ChB 1994 Manch. Prev: SHO (Cas.) Stockport Infirm.

MEHRBOD, Kazem 45 Archdale Place, New Malden KT3 3RW — MD 1970 Meshad; DMRD Eng. 1977. Socs: Roy. Coll. Radiol.

MEHREZ, Ismail Abdel-Latif 23 Osmund Drive, Goldings, Northampton NN3 8XB — MB ChB 1972 Ain Shams.

MEHROTRA, Ajit Pratap Windsor Medical Centre, 2 William Street, Leeds Road, Dewsbury WF12 7BD Tel: 01924 465699 Fax: 01924 456232 — MB BS 1964 Agra.

MEHROTRA, Madhup The Surgery, 185 Woodside, Duffryn, Newport NP10 8XF Tel: 01633 815161/817005 — MB BS Indore 1973; Cert. Family Plann. JCC 1979; DCH RCPSI 1979; DCH Dub. 1978. (M.G.M. Med. Coll.) Prev: Regist. (Paediat.) Qu. Pk. Hosp. Blackburn; Trainee GP Bolton; SHO Lewisham Hosp. Lond.

***MEHROTRA, Pallavi** 29 Hallamshire Road, Fulwood, Sheffield S10 4FN — BM BS 1998 Nottm.; MB BS Nottm 1998.

MEHROTRA, Prakash Narain Gildersome Health Centre, Finkle Lane, Gildersome, Morley, Leeds LS27 7HL — MB BS 1960 Lucknow. (Lucknow) GP Leeds.

***MEHROTRA, Ravi** 10 Riverdale Road, Sheffield S10 3FA Tel: 0114 268 5683; 12 Knot House, 3 Brewery Square, London SE1 2LF Tel: 020 7357 6071 — MB BS 1995 Lond.

MEHROTRA, Rina Flat 1, 53 Mablethorpe Road, London SW6 6AQ — MB ChB 1987 Otago.

MEHROTRA, V B Richmond Road Surgery, 400 Richmond Road, Sheffield S13 8LZ Tel: 0114 239 9803.

MEHROTRA, Vishwa Nath Richmond Road Surgery, 400 Richmond Road, Sheffield S13 8LZ Tel: 0114 239 9803; 400 Richmond Road, Sheffield S13 8LZ Tel: 0114 239 9803 Fax: 0114 264 0604 — MB BS 1966 Agra. (S.N. Med. Coll.) Socs: BMA. Prev: Regist. (Geriat. & Med.) St. Luke's Hosp. Huddersfield; SHO (Gen. Med.) Wimbledon Hosp. & Co. Hosp. Louth.

MEHRZAD, Abdul Ali Bishop Auckland General Hospital, Bishop Auckland DL14 6AD Tel: 01388 454000 Fax: 01388 454114; 12 Coniscliffe Mews, Coniscliffe Road, Darlington DL3 8UZ — MD 1971 Kabul; FRCP Lond. 1993; FRCP Ed. 1991; MRCP (UK) 1979. Cons. Phys. Bishop Auckland Gen. Hosp. Socs: Brit. Geriat. Soc; Soc. Echocardiography; BMA. Prev: Sen. Regist. (Geriat.s Med.) Sunderland Dist. Gen. Hosp.; Regist. (Med.) Falkirk & Dist. Roy. Infirm.; Hon. SHO (Med. Cardiol.) S. Gen. Hosp. Glas.

MEHTA, Ajay 60 West Drayton Road, Uxbridge UB8 3LA — BSc Physiol. (Hons.) Wales 1985, MB BCh 1988; MRCGP 1993; DRCOG 1992; DCH RCP Lond. 1991; Cert. Family Plann. JCC 1991.

***MEHTA, Alka** 59 Eton Place, Eton College Rd, London NW3 2BU — MB BS 1997 Lond.

MEHTA, Ameeta Kishor 64 Aberford Road, Wakefield WF1 4AL — MB BS 1991 Bombay.

MEHTA, Amisha Llandough Hospital, Penlaw Road, Penarth CF64 2XX — MB BCh 1988 Wales; FRCA 1994. Cons. Anaesth. Llandough Hosp. Cardiff. Prev: Sen. Regist. (Anaesth.) Univ. Hosp. Wales Cardiff.

MEHTA, Amrish Raj 37 Grove Court, Grove End Road, London NW8 9EP — MB BS 1994 Lond.

MEHTA, Anand Jayant Mayday Healthcare NHS Trust, Thornton Heath CR7 7YE; 27 Seymour Road, London SW19 5JL — MB BS

MEHTA

1983 Bombay; MRCP (UK) 1987. Cons., c/o the Elderly, Mayday Healthcare NHS Trust.

MEHTA, Anantray Bhimjibhai Northern General Hospital, Herries Road, Sheffield S5 7AU Tel: 0114 243 4343; 32 Riverdale Road, Sheffield S10 3FB Tel: 0114 266 1390 — MB BS Bombay 1956; DA Bombay 1960; DA Eng. 1963. (Topiwala Nat. Med. Coll.) Assoc. Specialist (Anaesth.) N. Gen. Hosp. Sheff. Prev: Regist. N.. Gen. Hosp. Sheff., Mansfield Hosp. Gp. & SE N.d. Hosp. Gp.

MEHTA, Anil Tel: 01382 320300 — MB BS 1980 Lond.; MSc (Distinc.) Lond. 1989; MRCP (UK) (Paediat.) 1983; FRCP (Ed.) 1998. (UCH) Sen. Lect. & Hon. Cons. Univ. Dundee. Socs: Physiol. Soc. Prev: Wellcome Fell. Dundee; MRC Train. Fell. Univ. Coll. Lond.

MEHTA, Anil 38 Dudley Road, Ilford IG1 1ES — MB BCh 1992 Wales.

MEHTA, Mr Ardeshir Malden Road Surgery, 118 Malden Road, London NW5 4BY Tel: 020 7813 1600; 43 Victoria Road, London N22 7XA Tel: 020 8889 7895 — MB BS 1964 Vikram; FRCS Ed. 1972; T(GP) 1990. (Gwalior) Clin. Asst. St Bart. & Homerton Hosps. Socs: BMA; Brit. Assn. Urol. Surgs. Prev: Regist. (Cardio-Thoracic Surg.) Lond. Chest. Hosp.; Regist. (Urol.) Roy. N.. & St. Thos. Hosp. Lond.; Cons. Surg. & Hon. Lect. (Surg.) Tata Main Hosp. Bihar, India.

MEHTA, Arjun Dev (retired) — MB BS 1967 All India Inst. Med. Scs.; MRCP (UK) 1973; FRCP Lond. 1990; DCH RCP Lond. 1970. Cons. Phys. Torbay Hosp. Torquay.; Involved in Screening the pop. In Osteoporosis.

MEHTA, Atul The Surgery, 299 Long Lane, Hillingdon, Uxbridge UB10 9JY Tel: 01895 234440 Fax: 01895 272885 Email: atul.mehta@gp-e86036.nhs.uk — MB ChB 1985 Bristol; F.P.cert 1989; BSc (Hons.) Bristol 1982; MRCGP 1989; Lic Ac 1995; DRCOG 1990.

MEHTA, Atul Bhanu Department of Haematology, Royal Free Hospital, London NW3 2QG Tel: 020 7794 0500 Fax: 020 7830 2313 Email: atul.mehta@rfh.nthames.nhs.uk; 6 Dunstan Road, London NW11 8AA Tel: 020 8458 6796 — MB BChir 1979 Camb.; MD Camb. 1987, MA, MB 1979, BChir 1978; MRCP (UK) 1980; MRCPath 1984; FRCP 1995; FRCPath 1996; Dip. Managem. (Keele) 1993. (Cambridge/King's College Hospital London) Hon. Sen. Lect. Roy. Free and Univ. Coll. Sch. of Med. Lond.; Cons. Haemat. Hosp. Of St. John's & St. Eliz., Lond. Socs: Brit. Soc. for Haematol.; Amer. Soc. For Haematol.; Indian Soc. For Haematol. Prev: Sen. Regist. (Haemat.) Roy. Postgrad. Med. Sch. Lond.; MRC Train. Fell. (Haemat.) Roy. Postgrad. Med. Sch. Lond.; Sen. Regist. (Haemat.) N. Middlx. Hosp. Lond.

MEHTA, Bhavinkumar Sammukhlal 264 Walstead Road, Walsall WS5 4DR — MB ChB 1992 Glas.

MEHTA, Brij Mohan Barnsley Community and Priority Services NHS Trust, Department of Substance Misuse, Kendray Hospital, Doncaster Road, Barnsley S70 3RD Tel: 01226 777951 Fax: 01226 298422; 40 Bents Road, Sheffield S11 9RJ Tel: 0114 235 1022 — MB BS 1967 Madras; MRCPsych. 1982; Dip. Psychother. Sheff. 1983; DPM Eng. 1974. (Stanley Med. Coll.) Cons. Psychiat. Subst. Misuse, Kendray Hosp., Barnsley; Hon. Clin. Lect. Psychiat. Univ. Sheff. Prev: Cons. Psychiat. & Clin. Tutor (Psychiat.) Rotherham Dist. Gen. Hosp.; Cons. Psychiat. Stud. Health, Univ. Sheff.; Sen. Regist. (Psychiat.) Univ. Dept. Whiteley Wood Clinic Sheff.

MEHTA, Chandni Praful 7 Murvagh Close, Cheltenham GL53 7QX Tel: 01242 513596 — MB BS 1970 Gujarat; DCH RCP Lond. 1976.

MEHTA, Devinder Kumar 114 Carisbrooke Way, Cyncoed, Cardiff CF23 9HX — MB BS 1980 Ranchi; T(GP) 1992.

MEHTA, Dheeraj Department of Cardiac Surgery, Bristol Royal Infirmary, Bristol BS2 8HW Tel: 0117 928 3145; Flat 1, 14 Manilla Road, Clifton, Bristol BS8 4ED Tel: 0117 974 3183 — MB BS 1990 Lond.; BSc (Hons.) Physiol. Lond. 1987; FRCS Eng. 1995. (Guy's Hospital London') Specialist Regist. (Cardiothoracic Surg.) Bristol Roy. Infirm. Bristol. Prev: Research Regist. Bristol Heart Inst.

MEHTA, Gyan Ugamraj Admiltary House, Northgate Hospital, Northgate Street, Great Yarmouth NR30 1BU Tel: 01603 421557 Fax: 01603 421342 — MB BS Poona 1969; MRCPsych 1976; DPM Eng. 1974. (Armed Forces Med. Coll. Poona, India) Cons. Psychiat. Hellesdon Hosp. Norwich and Nothgate Hosp. Gt. Yarmouth. Prev: Sen. Regist. (Psychiat.) Cricton Roy. Hosp. Dumfries; Regist. (Psychiat.) Runwell Hosp.; SHO (Psychiat.) Bexley Hosp.

MEHTA, Mr Hemchandra Kanji Derwen Deg, Hwfa Road, Bangor LL57 2BN Tel: 01248 353200; Sant Tysilio Nursing Home, Llanfairpwllgwyngyll LL61 5YR Tel: 01248 716400 Fax: 01248 716800 — MB BS 1957 Bombay; FRCS Eng. (Ophth.) 1967; DO Eng. 1962. (Grant Med. Coll.) Cons. Surg. Ophth. Gwynedd Dist. Gen. Hosp. Bangor. Socs: Fell. Coll. Ophth.; Internat. Intraocular Implant Club. Prev: Sen. Regist. Cardiff Roy. Infirm.; Regist. Birm. & Midl. Eye Hosp. & Midl. Centre for Neurosurg.; Ho. Surg. & Resid. Surg. Off. Roy. Eye Hosp. Lond.

MEHTA, James Romesh The Medical Centre, Hodnet, Market Drayton TF9 3NF; 15 Drayton Road, Hodnet, Market Drayton TF9 3NF — MB BS 1993 Lond.

MEHTA, Kamlesh 59 St Mary's Avenue, Norwood Green, Southall UB2 4LU Tel: 020 8574 2818 — MB BS 1970 Rajasthan; DA Eng. 1973. (S.P. Med. Coll. Bikaner) Clin. Med. Off. (Community Med.) Hillingdon Health Auth.; GP Hillingdon FPC.

MEHTA, Mr Khushru Mancherji, OBE (retired) 52 Greenfield Avenue, Carpenders Park, Watford WD19 5DN Tel: 020 8428 5269 — MB BS Bombay 1944; FRCS Ed. 1948. Prev: Sen. Surg. Specialist Qu. Eliz. Hosp. Kota Kinabalu, Sabah, Malaysia.

MEHTA, Kirti Kantilal Hanford Health Clinic, New Inn Lane, Hanford, Stoke-on-Trent ST4 8EX Tel: 01782 642992 Fax: 01782 869489 — MB BS 1974 Saurashtra; MB BS 1974 Saurashtra.

MEHTA, Kishor Jechand 48 Padnall Road, Chadwell Heath, Romford RM6 5BJ — MD (Paediat.) Bombay 1969, MB BS 1966; DCH CPS Bombay 1967. (Topiwala Nat. Med. Coll.) Prev: SHO (Paediat.) Rushgreen Hosp. & Old Ch. Hosp.

MEHTA, Kokila Atul Greenfield Medical Centre, 143-145 Cricklewood Lane, London NW2 1HS Tel: 020 8450 5454; 6 Dunstan Road, London NW11 8AA — MRCS Eng. LRCP Lond. 1983. GP. Prev: Trainee GP Enfield; SHO (O & G) N. Middlx. Hosp. Lond.; SHO (Geriat. Med.) St. Michael's Hosp. Enfield.

MEHTA, Kusum Himatlal Bell Lane Surgery, 22 Bell Lane, Kesgrave, Ipswich IP5 1JF Tel: 01473 624800 Fax: 01473 612269; 53 Edmonton Road, Kesgrave, Ipswich IP5 1EQ Tel: 01473 621980 — MB BS 1974 Bangalore; DCH Dub. 1983. Prev: Trainee GP Tamworth VTS.; Regist. (Paediat.) Bedford Gen. Hosp.; SHO (Anaesth.) Harrogate Gen. Hosp.

MEHTA, M N Langbank Medical Centre, Broad lane, Norris Green, Liverpool L11 1AD Tel: 0151 226 1976 Fax: 0151 270 2873.

MEHTA, Maneck Sorabji Maneckji 96 Hervey Road, London SE3 8BU Tel: 020 8856 1951 — MB BS 1931 Bombay; MRCS Eng. LRCP Lond. 1935.

MEHTA, Mani 2 Grange Crescent, Marton, Middlesbrough TS7 8EA Tel: 01642 284598 — MB BS Bombay 1960; FFA RCS Eng. 1965. Cons. Anaesth. S. Tees Acute Hosp. Trust.

MEHTA, Manijeh Hoshang 50 Denton Road, Twickenham TW1 2HQ Tel: 020 8892 1519 — MB BS 1951 Calcutta; FRCS Eng. 1959; FRCS Ed. 1959. (Calcutta Med. Coll.) Sen. Lect. Clin. Research Inst. Orthop. Univ. Lond. & Hon. Cons. Roy. Nat. Orthop. Hosp. Lond. Socs: (Pres.) Brit. Scoliosis Soc. Prev: Regist. Roy. Nat. Orthop. Hosp.; Research Fell. Inst. Orthop. & Roy. Nat. Orthop. Hosp. Lond.; Asst. Prof. Orthop. All India Inst. Med. Scs. New Delhi.

MEHTA, Mrinalini Hemchandra Derwen Deg, Bangor LL57 2BN Tel: 01248 353200 — MB BS 1956 Baroda; MRCOphth 1990; MRCOG 1964; DO RCS Eng. 1990.

MEHTA, Mukul Karanram Minley Nursery, Spoil Lane, Tongham, Farnham GU10 1BP Tel: 01252 20540 — MB BS 1955 Bombay. (G.S. Med. Coll.)

MEHTA, Mukund Jayavadan Paston Health Centre, Chadburn, Peterborough PE4 7DH Tel: 01733 572584 Fax: 01733 328131; 182 Thorpe Road, Peterborough PE3 6JJ Tel: 01733 62627 — MB BS 1969 Gujarat; DA Eng. 1973. (B.J. Med. Coll. Ahmedabad) Clin. Asst. (Haemat.) P'boro.

MEHTA, Mukundrai Mulshanker Albion Surgery, Pincott Road, Bexleyheath DA6 7LP Tel: 020 8304 8334 Fax: 020 8298 0408 — MB BS 1974 Karnatak; DRCOG 1980; Cert. Family Plann. JCC 1980. (Karnatak Med. Coll. & India) Socs: BMA. Prev: Trainee GP I. of Thanet VTS; Clin. Asst. (Obst.) W.hill Hosp. Dartford; Clin. Asst. Fallowfield Convalesc. Home Chislehurst.

MEHTA, Paresh Suryaprasad Donnington Health Centre, 1 Henley Avenue, Oxford OX4 4DH Tel: 01865 771207 Fax: 01865 770781; Karibu, 22 Cedar Close, Iver Heath SL0 0QX Tel: 01753 631050 Fax: 01753 631051 — MBBS 1973 Gujarat; MD 1973

Gujarat; MRCP (UK) 1979. (N.H.L. Municip. Med. Coll.) GP Princip.; Clin. Asst., Diabetes Centre, Oxf.

MEHTA, Prafulchandra 19 North Circular Road, Finchley, London N3 2TB — MRCS Eng. LRCP Lond. 1977.

MEHTA, Pratibha Ajay Hollington Surgery, 355 Battle Road, St Leonards-on-Sea TN37 7BE Tel: 01424 851706 Fax: 01424 853210; 43 Fern Road, St Leonards-on-Sea TN38 0UJ Tel: 01424 722531 Fax: 01424 722532 — LMSSA 1992 Lond.; MB BS Gujarat, India 1980; MD Gujarat, India 1986; MRCGP 1994; T(GP) 1994.

MEHTA, Pravin Chandulal Lanfranc Medical Practice, 2 Lanfranc Court, Greenford Road, Harrow HA1 3QE Tel: 020 8422 1813 — MB BS 1969 Gujarat.

MEHTA, Mr Prem Prakash Kumar and Mehta, 12 Queens Road, London SE15 2PT Tel: 020 7639 1133; 68 St. George's Road W., Bromley BR1 2NP Tel: 020 8467 3294 — MB BS 1960 Vikram; MS (Gen. Surg.) Vikram 1964, MB BS 1960. (Gandhi Med. Coll. Bhopal) GP Peckham; Med. Off. Family Plann. Community Health Servs. Camberwell.

***MEHTA, Rajesh Chunilal** 60 Sunnyside Road, Ilford IG1 1HX — MB BS 1997 Lond.

MEHTA, Rajeshkumar Lalji 5 Dalemeadow Close, Balsall Common, Coventry CV7 7QB — MB ChB 1978 Manch.; DRCOG 1983; DCH Lond. 1982. GP Coventry.

MEHTA, Rajni Suryakant Stockport NHS Trust, Stockport SK2 7JE Tel: 01614 748404; Tel: 01614 748404 — MB BS 1974 Bombay; DCCH 1994 Univ. of Sheffield; Dip Community Child Health Sheff 1993. (Grant Med. Coll.) Clin. Med. Off. (Community & Child Health) Stockport AHA. Prev: SHO (Anaesth.) Neath Gen. Hosp.

MEHTA, Ramesh Dulichandbhai Bedford Hospital, South Wing, Kempston Road, Bedford MK42 9DJ Tel: 01234 792256 Fax: 01234 795820; 43 Hookhams Lane, Renhold, Bedford MK41 0JU — MB BS 1972 Nagpur; MD Nagpur 1977; MRCPI 1989; FRCPCH 1977; DCH RCP Lond. 1988; DCH Dub. 1983; FRCP 2000 London. (Nagpur) Cons. Paediat. Bedford Hosp. Bedford; Clin. Tutor; Coll. Tutor. Socs: Brit. Assn. Perinatal Med.; RCPCH (Rheum. Gp.); Chairm. BMA N. Bed Div.

MEHTA, Rameshchandra Lalji 143 St Saviours Road, Leicester LE5 3HX Tel: 0116 253 6163 — MB BS 1974 Bombay.

MEHTA, Ramnik Motilal 221 Straight Road, Romford RM3 Tel: 01708 346212 Fax: 01708 378160 — MB BS 1966 Bombay; FFA RCSI 1975; DA Eng. 1969; DCH Bombay 1967. (T.N. Med. Coll.) Private Pract.; Cons. Anaesth.Essex Nuffield Hosp.; BUPA, Hartswood Hosp., Brentwood. Socs: BMA; Hosp. Cons. Assn.

***MEHTA, Ranvir** 46 Raymond Road, Slough SL3 8LW — MB ChB 1994 Leeds.

MEHTA, Rashmi Rohit The Southgate Surgery, 11 Bournbrook Road, Selly Oak, Birmingham B29 7BL Tel: 0121 415 5237 — MB BS 1980 Baroda; MRCS Eng. LRCP Lond. 1988.

MEHTA, Rohaj Kant 17 Burns Close, Liverpool L16 3GQ — MB BS 1992 Lond.

MEHTA, Rohan South Tyneside District Hospital, Harton Lane, South Shields NE34 0PL Tel: 0191 454 8888; 131 Harton Lane, South Shields NE34 0PW Tel: 0191 454 8888 — MB ChB 1992 Ed. SHO (Gen. Med.) S. Tyneside Dist. Hosp.

MEHTA, Rohitkumar Kalidas Neasden Medical Centre, 21 Tanfield Avenue, London NW2 7SA Tel: 020 8450 2834 Fax: 020 8452 4324; 6 Chapman Crescent, Kenton, Harrow HA3 0TE Tel: 020 8206 1411 Fax: 020 8206 1411 — MB BS 1972 Gujarat.

MEHTA, Romesh Bhairavnath The Medical Centre, Hodnet, Market Drayton TF9 3NF Tel: 01630 685230 Fax: 01630 685770 — MB BS 1961 Nagpur; Cert. Family Plann. JCC 1971. (Nagpur Med. Coll.) GP Hodnet; CMO Family Plann. Shropsh. HA. Socs: Assoc. Mem. Roy. Coll. Gen. Pract.

***MEHTA, Roopa** 2 Heritage View, Sudbury Court Drive, Harrow HA1 3TN — MB BS 1996 Lond.

***MEHTA, Rutesh Abhaykant** 1 Drummond Drive, Stanmore HA7 3PF — MB BS 1994 Lond.

***MEHTA, Samir Pravin** 2 Heritage View, Harrow HA1 3TN — BM BCh 1998 Oxf.; BM BCh Oxf 1998.

MEHTA, Sandhya P Lanfranc Medical Practice, 2 Lanfranc Court, Greenford Road, Harrow HA1 3QE Tel: 020 8422 1813 Fax: 020 8423 7698 — MB BS 1970 Gujarat; DA 1976 Lond.; DRCOG 1977 Lond. Prev: Clin. Asst. in Anaesthetics Newport IOW.

***MEHTA, Sanjeev Rasiklal** 22 Albert Road, Heaton, Bolton BL1 5HF — MB BS 1996 Lond.

MEHTA, Sarah Brown 2 Snowdon Place, Stirling FK8 2NH Tel: 01786 450753 Fax: 01786 450753; Department of Community Child Health, Sterling Royal Infirmary, Livilands, Stirling FK8 2AU Tel: 01786 434000 Fax: 01786 434479 — MB ChB Glas. 1968; DTM & H Lond. 1970. Staff Grade (Community Paediat.) Centr. Scotl. Healthcare Trust Larbert.

MEHTA, Sarju Gyan North West Regional Genetics, Service (sm2), St. Marys Hospital, Hathersage Road, Manchester M13 0JH Email: sarju@bigfoot.com; 3 Eaton Road, Norwich NR4 6PY — MB BS 1996 Lond.; MRCP 2000 UK; BSc Lond. 1993. (St. Barth. and the Roy. Lond. Hosp. Med. Coll.) Specialist Regist. in Clin. genetics, ST.Marys Hosp. Manch.

MEHTA, Satish Chander, MBE Park View Group Practice, 2 Longford Road West, Stockport SK5 6ET Tel: 0161 431 9339 Fax: 0161 431 5140; Email: gmartin@cadouxfsnet.co.uk — MB ChB 1962 Birm. (Birmingham) p/t Sen. Partner G.P. Reddish, Stockport.; Memb. Of Bd. Of Trustees., Beechwood Cancer Care. Stockport.; Exec. Comm. Memb. MIND., Stockport. Prev: Stockport N. PCG - Ment. Health LEAD 1998-2001; Chairm., Stockport FHSA 1995-1996; Stockport Drs Co-op. Founder Memb.1996.

MEHTA, Mr Satya Bhushan 28 Chevet Lane, Sandal, Wakefield WF2 6HR Tel: 01924 250223 Fax: 01924 249961 Email: sbmehta007@aol.com — MB BS Punjab (India) 1964; FRCS Ed. 1972. (Amritsar Med. Coll.) Cons. Surg. ENT Barnsley AHA. Socs: Roy. Soc. Med.; Brit. Soc. Utology and Head and Neck Surg.; N. of Engl. ENT Soc. Prev: Rotating Sen. Regist. (ENT) Birm. AHA (T); Regist. (ENT) & SHO (Gen. Surg.) N. Staffs. Med.; -on-Trent.

MEHTA, Sharadchandra Mansukhlal The Surgery, 267 Ealing Road, Wembley HA0 1EZ Tel: 020 8997 3486; 228 Watford Road, Harrow HA1 3TZ Tel: 020 8904 6404 Fax: 020 8908 6414 — MB BS 1972 Bombay. GP.

MEHTA, Sheila 40 Bents Road, Sheffield S11 9RJ — MB BS 1969 Madras; DA Eng. 1972. (Stanley Med. Coll.) Regist. (Psychiat.) Dist. Gen. Hosp. Rotherham. Prev: Regist. (Psychiat.) Ment. Illness Unit, N.. Gen. Hosp. Sheff.; Med. Off. Regional Blood Transfus. Centre Sheff.

MEHTA, Sudarshan Singh (retired) 53 Courtland Road, Torquay TQ2 6JU — MB BS 1951 Panjab; MB BS Panjab (India) 1951; DOMS 1957. Prev: Assoc. Specialist (Ophth.) Torbay Hosp. Torquay.

MEHTA, Sunil 9 Park Avenue, Stockport SK7 1BN — MB ChB 1982 Manch.; BSc (Hons.) Manch. 1979, MB ChB 1982; MRCP (UK) 1987.

MEHTA, Tej Bahadur Singh Newland Health Centre, 34 Newland, Lincoln LN1 1XP Tel: 01522 543573 Fax: 01522 569699; 36 Ripon Street, Lincoln LN5 7NL Tel: 01522 512170 — MB BS 1976 Kashmir. Prev: Regist. (A & E) Lincoln Co. Hosp.

MEHTA, Tripuri 10 Brook Lane, Haywards Heath RH16 1SG Tel: 01444 414300 — MB BS 1948 Bombay; MS Bombay 1952, MB BS 1948; FRCR 1975; DMRD Eng. 1973. Cons. Radiol. Crawley Hosp. & Gatwick Pk. Hosp. Horley.

MEHTA-NIKHAR, Bindi Ramesh 43 Yew Tree Lane, Tettenhall, Wolverhampton WV6 8UG Tel: 01902 752785 — MB BS 1988 Bombay; MRCS Eng. LRCP Lond. 1991.

MEHTAR, Shaheen Department of Microbiology, North Middlesex Hospital Trust, London N18 1QX Tel: 020 8807 1748 Fax: 020 8887 2893; Woodlawn, 8 The Avenue, Finchley, London N3 2LB Tel: 020 8346 5468 — MB BS 1970 Punjab; MB BS Punjab (Pakistan) 1970; FRCPath 1990, M 1978. (Fatima Jinnah Med. Coll. Lahore) Cons. Microbiol. N. Middlx. Hosp. Lond.; Cons. Microbiol. Manor Hse. Hosp. Lond.; Vis. Prof. (Postgrad.) Philippines; Hon. Sen. Lect. Roy. Free Hosp.; Scientif. Sec. Hosp. Infec. Soc.

MEI YUK LUK, Dr 3 Deansbrook Cottages, Deansbrook Road, Edgware HA8 0AD — LRCP LRCS 1984 Ed.; LRCP LRCS Ed. LRCPS Glas. 1984.

MEICHEN, Francis William 267 Church Street, Blackpool FY1 3PB Tel: 01253 628142 Fax: 01253 628142 Email: f.meichem@aol.com; 40 Abercorn Place, Squires Gate, Blackpool FY4 1RZ Tel: 01253 345173 Fax: 01253 628142 — MB ChB 1948 Glas.; FFOM RCP Lond. 1985, MFOM 1979. (Glas.) Occupat. Health Adviser to Local Authorities & Maj. Indust. Companies, Police & Educat.al Authorities; Cons. Specialist Prods. PLC, Wastechem Ltd. & Bachi Gp. etc. Socs: Fell. Roy. Soc. Med.; BMA (Hon. Treas. Blackpool

MEIDLINGER

Div.); Soc. Occupat. Med. Prev: Chief Med. Off. Lancs. Constab. Police HQ Hutton Lancs.; Med. Dir. E. Merck Clin. Research Div.; Chief Med. Off. Cooks OM Gp. Plc.

MEIDLINGER, Joseph Graham 7 Lower Manor Road, Godalming GU7 3EG — MB BCh 1951 Witwatersrand. (Witwatersrand) Prev: State Med. Off. for Tuberc. S. Afr.

MEIER, Valentijn Olivier Kerridge House, Market Rasen Road, Holton-le-Moor, Market Rasen LN7 6AE — Artsexamen 1984 Amsterdam; T(GP) 1994.

MEIGH, Jacqueline Ann 20 Brabant Road, Cheadle Hulme, Cheadle SK8 7AU — MB ChB 1980 Manch.; MRCPath 1987; Dip. Bact. Manch. 1986. Sen. Regist. (Med. Microbiol.) NW RHA.

MEIGH, Rolf Eric Erling Public Health Laboratory, Hull Royal Infirmary, Anlaby Road, Hull HU3 2JZ Tel: 01482 323046 Fax: 01482 848811 Email: hulrmeig@north.phls.nhs.uk — MB ChB 1980 Manch.; FRCPath 1997. Cons. Med. Microbiol. Pub. Health Laborat. Serv. Bd. Cottingham; Hon. Cons. Microbiol. Yorks. RHA; Hon. Clin. Lect. Univ. Leeds. Socs: Brit. Soc. Study of Infec.; Eur. Soc. Clin. Microbiol.; Hosp. Infec. Soc. Prev: Clin. Lect. (Med. Microbiol.) Univ. Liverp.; Ho. Off. Manch. Roy. Infirm.

MEIGHAN, Mr Andrew Alistair Spence 45 Southbrae Drive, Jordanhill, Glasgow G13 1PU Tel: 0141 959 7946 — MB ChB 1987 Glas.; FRCS Glas. 1993. Specialist Regist. (Orthop.) Glas. Roy. Infirm. Prev: Specialist Regist. Law Hosp. Carluke; SHO (Orthop. & A & E) Ayr Co. Hosp.; SHO (Surg.) Monklands Dist. Gen. Hosp.

MEIGHAN, David Patrick 31 Dumbreck Square, Glasgow G41 5SY — MB ChB 1991 Glas.

MEIJER, Eduardus Carolus Maria The Arches, Crewkerne Road, Axminster EX13 5TE — Artsexamen 1991 Leiden.

***MEIKLE, Alistair** 142 Gisburn Road, Barrowford, Nelson BB9 6JD — MB ChB 1996 Ed.

MEIKLE, Mr Anthony Graham (retired) 5 Crichton Mains Steading, Pathhead EH37 5UY — MB ChB 1957 Ed.; FRCS Eng. 1965; FRCS Ed. 1962. Prev: Cons. Gen. Surg. Roodlands Hosp. Haddington.

MEIKLE, Christopher John Philip Bird-In-Eye Surgery, Uckfield Community Hospital, Framfield Road, Uckfield TN22 5AW Tel: 01825 763196 Fax: 01825 760039; Brambledown, Whitehill Avenue, Bexhill-on-Sea TN39 3RX — MB BS 1984 Lond.; MRCGP 1992; DCH RCP Lond. 1991; DRCOG 1991; DA (UK) 1987. (St. Thomas' Hospital)

MEIKLE, Mr David 208 Osborne Road, Jesmond, Newcastle upon Tyne NE2 3LD — MB BS 1978 Newc.; BMedSc Newc. 1975, MB BS 1978; FRCS Eng. 1983. Cons. ENT Surg. Freeman Hosp. Newc. u. Tyne. Prev: Sen. Regist. (ENT) Guy's Hosp. Lond.; Chief Resid. (Otolaryngol.) Univ. Washington.

MEIKLE, Mr Douglas David Linch Close, Charminster, Dorchester DT2 9RR — MB BS 1961 Western Australia; MSc Oxf. 1974; FRCS Eng. 1967. Cons. Surg. Dorset Co. Hosp. Dorchester & Weymouth & Dist. Hosp. Prev: Surg. Regist. & Lect. Radcliffe Infirm. Oxf.; Sen. Surg. Regist. St. Mary's Hosp. Lond.

***MEIKLE, Fiona Sandra** 2/R, 6 Napiershall St., Glasgow G20 6HQ — MB ChB 1995 Glas.

MEIKLE, Joan Tinning (retired) The Knowe, Gretna Green, Gretna DG16 5HF Email: jogorsch@aol.com — LRCP LRCS Ed. LRFPS Glas. 1951; DObst RCOG 1956; FRCGP 1988, M 1974; DCH RCP Lond. 1959. JP.

MEIKLE, John Archibald King (retired) 5 Upper Woodlands, Perth PH1 1DJ — MB ChB Ed. 1952; FRCP Ed. 1971, M 1962; FRCR 1975; FFR 1962; DMRD 1958. Prev: Clin. Dir. Radiol. Perth Roy. Infirm.

MEIKLE, Joyce Nicoll Downfield Medical Practice, 325 Strathmartine Road, Dundee DD3 8NE Tel: 01382 812111 Fax: 01382 858315; 325 Strathmartine Road, Dundee DD3 Tel: 01382 812111 — MB ChB 1979 Dundee; DRCOG 1984.

MEIKLE, Robert James Rintoul Department of Anaesthetics, The James Cook University Hospital, Marton Road, Middlesbrough TS4 3BW Tel: 01642 854600 — MB ChB 1981 Ed.; BSc (Med. Sci) Ed. 1979; FFA RCSI 1987. (Edinburgh) Cons. Anaesth.The James Cook Univ. Hosp. Middlesbrough. Socs: Ordinary Mem. Assn. Of Cardiothoracic Anaesth.s. Prev: Sen. Regist. (Anaesth.) Roy. Lond. Hosp.; Lect. (Anaesth.) Roy. Lond. Hosp.; Regist. (Anaesth.) Roy. Infirm. Edin. & Roy. Lond. Hosp.

MEIKLE, Virginia Mary Antwich Cottage, Shortwood, Nailsworth, Stroud GL6 0SH — MB BS 1984 Lond.; BSc Lond. 1981; DRCOG 1986. Retainer GP Nailsworth. Prev: CMO & Trainee GP Nailsworth; GP Rotat. Swindon VTS.

MEIKLEJOHN, Boyd Hope 1 Benston Crescent, Hollybush, Ayr KA6 6RA Tel: 01292 560434 Email: meikljn@globatnet.co.uk; Ayr Hospital, Dalmellington Road, Ayr KA6 6DX Tel: 01292 610555 — MB ChB 1980 Ed.; BSc Ed. 1977, MB ChB 1980; FFA RCS Eng. 1985. Cons. Anaesth. S. Ayrsh. Hosps. NHS Trust. Socs: Pain Soc. Prev: Sen. Regist. (Anaesth.) Trent RHA; Lect. Leicester Univ.; Regist. (Anaesth.) & Ho. Surg. Roy. Infirm. Edin.

MEIKLEJOHN, David James 15 Ryat Linn, Linburn, Erskine PA8 6HL — MB ChB 1990 Glas.; BSc (Hons.) Physiol. Glas. 1987, MB ChB 1990; MRCP (UK) 1993. Career Regist. (Haemat.) Aberd. Roy. Infirm.

MEILAK, Andrew Antonio 30 Joydens Wood Road, Bexley DA5 2HT — MB BS 1990 Lond.

MEIN, Bruce Gordon (retired) Stride House, Parbrook, Glastonbury BA6 8PB Tel: 01458 851128 — MB ChB 1961 Birm.

MEIN, Douglas Craig 62 North Street, Wilton, Salisbury SP2 0HP — MB ChB 1995 Bristol.

MEINHARD, Elizabeth Ann The Surgery, Clifton Hampden, Abingdon OX14 3EJ; 22 St John Street, Oxford OX1 2LQ Tel: 01865 57615 — MD 1976 Newc.; MB BS Durh. 1962; FRCPath 1982, M 1970, D 1968; DCP Lond 1969. Prev: Lect. in Histopath. Roy. Free Hosp. Lond.; Sen. Regist. Roy. Marsden Hosp. Lond.; Regist. (Pathol.) Hammersmith Hosp. Lond.

***MEINTJES EFSKIND, Kirstin Ingrid** 24 Wallfield Crescent, Aberdeen AB25 2JX — MB ChB 1997 Aberd.

MEIR, Adam Russell 2 Newham Close, Sutton Lane Ends, Macclesfield SK11 0EW — BM BCh 1994 Oxf.; BA Oxf. 1991. SHO (Orthop.) Ashford Hosp. NHS Trust.

MEIR, Nigel Simon 7 Ashworth Road, London W9 1JW Tel: 01865 59926 — BM BCh 1981 Oxf. Resid. Med. Off. AMI Chiltern Hosp. Gt. Missenden Bucks.

MEIRE, Hylton Bruce 30 Durham Avenue, Bromley BR2 0QB Tel: 020 8460 5241 Fax: 020 7346 3061 — MB BS 1967 Lond.; MRCS Eng. LRCP Lond. 1967; FFR 1973; DObst RCOG 1972; DMRD Eng. 1971. (Char. Cross) Cons. Radiol. (Ultrasound) King's Coll. Hosp. Lond.; Dir. Ultrasound Portland Hosp. Lond.; Hon. Sec. Europ. Federat. Socs. for Ultrasound in Med. & Biol. Socs: (Ex-Hon. Sec.) Brit. Inst. Radiol. Prev: Dir. Div. Radiol. Clin. Research Centre N.wick Pk. Hosp. Harrow.

MEIRING, John Keighley (retired) 11 Plantation Grove, Arnside, Carnforth LA5 0HY Tel: 01524 761912 — MB ChB 1944 Liverp.

MEISNER, Peter (retired) 3 College Gardens, London SE21 7BE Tel: 020 8693 6588 Fax: 07733 016865 — MB BS 1960 Durh.; MRCP Lond. 1967. Locum Cons. N. Tyneside Gen. Hosp. Prev: Cons. Phys. St. Thos. Hosp. Lond. & Lewisham Hosp. Gp.

MEISNER, Sarah Julia Department of Microbiology, John Radcliffe Hospital, Oxford OX3 Tel: 01865 741166 Email: sarh@well.ox.ac.uk; 43 Pitts Road, Headington Quarry, Oxford OX3 8BA Tel: 01865 761246 — MB BS 1988 Lond.; MRCP (UK) 1992; DTM & H Lond. 1993. Specialist Regist. (Clin. MicroBiol.). Socs: Harveian Soc. & Roy. Soc. Trop. Med. Prev: MRC research fell.sh. Oxf.; Regist. (Gen. Med.) Soton. & Salisbury; SHO (Infec. Dis. & Paediat.) St. Geo. Hosp. Lond.

MEIWALD, Jutta Margareta 54 Prospect Park, Scarborough YO12 6ET — State Exam Med 1993 Mainz; MD Mainz 1993.

MEJZNER, Richard Hugh Budleigh Salterton Medical Centre, 1 The Lawn, Budleigh Salterton EX9 6LS Tel: 01395 441212 Fax: 01395 441244; 1 Barns Road, Budleigh Salterton EX9 6HJ — MB BS 1987 Lond.; MRCGP 1994; DCH RCP Lond. 1994; DRCOG 1993. Prev: Trainee GP Axminster; SHO (O & G) Torbay & (Paediat.) Freedom Fields Hosp. Plymouth; SHO Rotat. (Med.) Roy. Devon & Exeter Hosp.

MEJZNER, Stefan (retired) 10 James Street, Eastgate, Lincoln LN2 1QE Tel: 01522 528375 — MRCS Eng. LRCP 1977 Lond. Cons. Geriat. Emerit. Lincoln Co. Hosp., Lincoln.

MEKAWI, Laila Mohamed Fakhry Flat 30, Regency Court, 5 Chicheley St., London SE1 7JP — MB ChB 1985 Cairo; MB BCh Cairo 1985.

***MEKWAN, Jayanand** 3A Dennis Avenue, Wembley HA9 8AZ — MB BS 1998 Lond.; MB BS Lond 1998.

MELAMED, Roy 5 Woodlands, Chelmsford CM1 7ES — State Exam Med 1990 Munich.

MELCHER, Alan Alfred Molecular Medicene Program, Guggenheim 1836, Mayo Foundation, 200 First Street SW, Rochester MN 55905, USA Tel: 507 538 0724 Fax: 507 266 4797 Email: melcher.alan@mayo.edu; 75 Durban Road, Beckenham BR3 4EY Tel: 020 8 658 3508 — BM BCh 1989 Oxf.; BA Oxf. 1986; MRCP (UK) 1992; FRCR 1995. Special Project Assoc. Molecular Medicene Program, Mayo Foundat. Prev: MRC Clin. Train. Fell. ICRF Hammersmith Hosp. Lond.; Regist. (Clin. Oncol.) Velindre Hosp. Cardiff; SHO (Gen. Med.) Stoke-on-Trent.

MELCHER, David Henry Manor Laboratory for Clinical Pathology, 13 New Church Road, Hove BN3 4AA Tel: 01273 327363; 69 Shirley Drive, Hove BN3 6UB — MB ChB 1958 Cape Town; FIAC 1976; MA Camb. 1964; FRCPath 1979, M 1967. (Cape Town) Cons. Pathologist; Vis. Fell. Univ. Sussex. Socs: Brit. Soc. Clin. Cytol.; Assn. Clin. Path. Prev: Sen. Regist. (Morbid Anat.) St. Thos. Hosp. Lond. & Wessex RHB; Univ. Asst. (Pathol.) Addenbrooke's Hosp. Camb.

MELCHOR FERRER, Cristina 11 Lock Chase, London SE3 9HB — LMS 1983 La Laguna.

MELDRUM, Brian Stuart Department of Clinical Neurosciences, Institute of Psychiatry, De Crespigny Park, London SE5 8AF Tel: 020 7701 2506 Fax: 020 7740 5272 Email: b.meldrum@iop.bpmf.ac.uk; 128 Croxted Road, London SE21 8NR — MB BChir 1959 Camb.; PhD Lond. 1964; DSc Paris 1994. Prof. Experim. Neurol. Inst. Psychiat. King's Coll. Hosp. Prev: Ho. Off. Guy's Hosp.; Hon. Research Asst. (Physiol.) Univ. Coll. Lond.; Mem. Scientif. Staff MRC Neuropsychiat. Unit Carshalton.

MELDRUM, C Helen (retired) 1 Millgate, Lisvane, Cardiff CF14 0TY Tel: 029 2075 8809 Fax: 029 2075 8809 — MB ChB Birm. 1957; DObst RCOG 1959. Prev: Ho. Surg. Childr. Hosp. Birm. & Birm. Matern. Hosp.

MELDRUM, David Meldrum, Vitty and Pfeiffer, 40-42 Kingsway, Waterloo, Liverpool L22 4RQ Tel: 0151 928 2415 Fax: 0151 928 3775; 6 Linden Avenue, Blundellsands, Liverpool L23 8UL Tel: 0151 924 3962 — MB ChB 1976 Ed.; MRCGP 1980; DRCOG 1979. (Ed.) Med. Off. Merchant Taylor's Schs. Crosby Liverp.

MELDRUM, David Stephen (retired) 34 Graham Road, Ipswich IP1 3QF Tel: 01473 258552 — MB BS 1957 Lond.; DObst RCOG 1961. Prev: Ho. Surg. Ipswich & E. Suff. Hosp.

MELDRUM, Deborah Janet 34 Ashmead Drive, Hardwick, Cambridge CB3 7XT Tel: 01954 211264 — MB ChB 1976 Liverp.; FRCA 1999; DA Eng. 1979; DA Lond. 1997. (Liverpool) Specialist Regist. (Anaesth.) Norf. & Norwich NHS Trust, Norwich. Prev: SHO (Anaesth.) PeterBoro. Hosp. NHS Trust; SHO (Anaesth.) Hinchingbrooke Hosp. NHS Trust Huntingdon; Specialist Regist. (Anaesth.) Addenbrookes NHS Trust, Camb.

MELDRUM, Hamish Robin Peter The Medical Centre, Station Avenue, Bridlington YO16 4LZ Tel: 01262 401385 Fax: 01262 401685; Holly Farm, 9 St. John's Close, Bridlington YO16 4SQ Tel: 01262 400019 Fax: 01262 403147 Email: hamishmeldrum@compuserve.com — MB ChB 1972 Ed.; FRCGP 2001; BSc 1969; MRCGP 1979; DRCOG 1977. (Edinburgh) p/t GP. Princip. Bridlington E. Yorks.; Jt. Dep. Chairm., GP Comm., BMA. Socs: LMC E. Yorks.; Jt. Comm. On Postgrad. Train. for GP; Observer, Counc. of RCGP. Prev: Regist. (Gen. Med.) Torbay Hosp. Torquay; Trainee GP Harrogate VTS; Hon. Phys. Edin. Roy. Infirm.

MELDRUM, Ivy Mary (retired) Nantlais, 52 Troserch Road, Llangennech, Llanelli SA14 8AX — MRCS Eng. LRCP Lond. 1943; BSc 1940, MB BCh Wales 1943; MRCGP 1965; DObst RCOG 1947. Prev: Ho. Phys. (Paediat.) Cardiff Roy. Infirm.

MELDRUM, John Alexander Kenneth (retired) 1 Millgate, Lisvane, Cardiff CF14 0TY Tel: 029 20 758809 Fax: 01222 758809 — MB BCh BAO Dub. 1951; MA Dub. 1952; FRCA 1994; T(Anaesth.) 1991; DA Eng. 1954. Cons. Anaesth. W.. Birm. HA. Prev: Regist. (Anaesth.) United Birm. Hosps.

MELDRUM, John MacGregor Nutrition Associates, Galtres House, Lysander Close, Clifton Moorgate, York YO30 4XB Tel: 01904 691591 Fax: 01904 690588; 29 Bellevue Road (1F1), Edinburgh EH7 4DL Tel: 0131 556 2765 — MB ChB 1968 Ed.; MRCGP 1982; DObst RCOG 1973; DA (UK) 1973; DCH RCPS Glas. 1972; Dip. Zimbabwe. 1988. (Univ. Ed.) Doctor Nutrit. Environm. Med., Nutrit. Assoc. Edin. & York. Socs: (Comm.) Brit. Soc. Allergy Environm. And Nutrit Med..; (Comm.) McCarrison Soc. for Nutrit. & Health Scott. Gp.; Norwegian Holistic Med. Soc. Prev: Regional Adviser (Primary Health Care) Equatorial Region, S. Sudan; Med Off./ Project Lect, Save the Childr. fund. Dhankuta, Nepal; med. Dir. Dede Hosp., Horarge Province Ethiopia.

MELDRUM, Robert (retired) 16B Borestone Place, St. Ninians, Stirling FK7 0PP Tel: 01786 64254 — MB ChB 1944 Glas.; BSc, MB ChB Glas. 1944. Prev: Capt. RAMC.

MELEAGROS, Mr Loukis 126 Harley Street, London W1N 1AH Tel: 020 7935 2030; 24 Landra Gardens, Winchmore Hill, London N21 1RT Tel: 020 8360 5463 — MB BS 1978 Lond.; BSc (Hons.) Lond. 1975, MD 1989; FRCS Eng. 1984; T(S) 1993. Cons. Surg. Homerton Hosp. NHS Trust; Hon. Sen. Lect. St. Bart. Hosp. Med. Coll. Lond. Socs: Brit. Soc. Gastroenterol.; Surgic. Research Soc.; BASO. Prev: Lect. & Hon. Sen. Regist. (Surg.) UCL Med. Sch. Lond.; Regist. (Surg.) Whipps Cross Hosp. Lond.; Research Fell. Roy. Postgrad. Med. Sch. Hammersmith Hosp. Lond.

MELFI, Neville Arthur 24 Weppons, Ravens Road, Shoreham-by-Sea BN43 5AW — MB ChB 1968 Sheff. Regist. (Histopath.) N. Middlx. Hosp. Lond.

MELHUISH, Andrew Henry (retired) The Well House, Upper Culham, Wargrave, Reading RG10 8NS Tel: 01491 576181 Fax: 01491 574701 — MB BS 1961 Lond.; MSc (Physiol.) Lond. 1958; FRCGP 1982, M 1970; DObst RCOG 1964. Med. Adviser to several companies. Prev: GP Oxon.

MELHUISH, Harold Frederic 22 Tempsford Court, Sheepcote Road, Harrow HA1 2JJ Tel: 020 8427 6250 — MRCS Eng. LRCP Lond. 1942; MRCS Eng., LRCP Lond. 1942; DOMS Eng. 1944. (Univ. Coll. Hosp. Med. Sch.) Prev: Ophth. Harefield Hosp. & St. Bernard's Hosp.; Out-pat. Off. Roy. Lond. Ophth. Hosp.

MELHUISH, Jane Elisabeth Glenside Medical Centre, Glenside Rise, Plympton, Plymouth PL7 4DR Tel: 01752 341340 Fax: 01752 348913; 6 Thorn Park, Mannamead, Plymouth PL3 4TG Tel: 01752 229881 — MB ChB 1966 Bristol; FFA RCS Eng. 1973; DA Eng. 1969; DObst RCOG 1969. (Bristol) Princip. GP. Prev: Regist. (Anaesth.) Brit. Roy. Infirm.

MELHUISH, Lisa Margaret 5 Summerhow Cottages, Shap Road, Kendal LA9 6NY Tel: 01539 735339 — MB BS 1989 Lond.; MRCGP (UK) 1998. Locum GP, Morecambe Bay Area, Non-Princip. Prev: GP Regist. Stoneleigh Surg. Milnthorpe; GP Regist. Station Hse. Surg. Kendal; SHO (O & G) Roy. Lancaster Infirm.

MELHUISH, Robert John (retired) Carmel Cottage, Bay Hill, St Margaret's Bay, Dover CT15 6DU Tel: 01304 852142 — MRCS Eng. LRCP Lond. 1941.

MELHUISH, Roger Owen The Paddock, Mount Pleasant, Newburgh, Cupar KY14 6AD Tel: 01337 840595 Fax: 01337 840595 — MB ChB 1971 St. And. (St. And.) Specialist in Complementary Med. Socs: Brit. Holistic Med. Assn.; Brit. Inst. Musculoskel. Med.; Brit. Med. Acupunct. Soc.

MELIA, Charlotte Veronica 142 Hemingford Road, London N1 1DE — MB ChB 1976 Bristol. Non Princip. Gen. Practitioner.

MELIA, Edward William 55 Acton Gate, Wrexham LL11 2PW — MB BS 1949 Lond.; LMSSA Lond. 1949. (Guy's) Prev: Ho. Surg. Maelor Gen. Hosp. Wrexham.

MELIA, Helen Clover 29 Roy Road, Northwood HA6 1EQ — MB ChB 1993 Birm.; ChB Birm. 1993.

MELIA, Norman Peter 1 Treetops Close, Northwood HA6 2PL — MB BS 1965 Newc.; MSc (Social Med.) Lond. 1971; MRCP Lond. 1969. (Newc.)

MELIA, Walter Martin Darent Valley Hospital, Darenth Wood Road, Dartford DA2 8DA Tel: 01322 428424 Fax: 01322 428415; 84 Kidbrooke Grove, Blackheath, London SE3 0LG Tel: 020 8805 1210 — MB BCh BAO 1975 NUI; FRCP Lond. 1995; MRCP (UK) 1977; MRCPI 1977. (Galway) Cons. Phys. (Gastroenterol.) Dartford & Gravesham NHS Trust. Socs: Brit. Soc. Gastroenterol.; Brit. Assn. Study Liver; Amer. Assn. Study Liver Dis. Prev: Cons. Phys. (Gastroenterol.) Roy. Naval Hosp. Haslar; Cons. Phys. (Gastroenterol.) Qu. Eliz. Milit. Hosp. Woolwich; Research Fell. Liver Unit. Dept. Med. King's Coll. Hosp. Med. Sch.

MELICHAR, Jan Krzysztof Psychopharmacology Unit, School of Medical Sciences, University Walk, Bristol BS8 1TD Tel: 0117 925 3066 Fax: 0117 927 7057; 82 Maple Road, Bristol BS7 8RG — MB BS 1992 Lond.; BSc Lond 1989. (Middlesex Hosp. Med. Sch.) SHO (Psychiat.) Avon & W. Wilt. Ment. Helathcare Trust, Bris.; Hon.

MELICHAR

Fell. (Psychopharmacol.) Univ. of Bris.; Hon. Fell. (Psychiat.) MRC Cyclotrum Unit, Hammersmith Hosp. Prev: Clin. Fell. (Psychopharmacolgy) Univ. of Bris. & Bris. Roy. Infirm.; SHO (Psychiat.) St. Lawrence's Hosp. Cornw.; SHO (A&E) MusGr. Pk. Hosp, Taunton.

MELICHAR, Krystyna Barbara (Surgery), 60 Broad Walk, Heston, Hounslow TW5 9AB Tel: 020 8572 2324 Fax: 020 8570 2512 Email: doctor@melichar.com; 131 Popes Lane, London W5 4ND Tel: 020 8810 0475 — MB BCh BAO NUI 1965. (Galw.) Socs: RSM; MBA; SPA.

MELIKIAN, Florence Ruth 8 Pebble Mill Road, Edgbaston, Birmingham B5 7SA — MB ChB 1956 Sheff. Prev: SHO (Med.) & Regist. (Anaesth.) Gen. Hosp. Nottm.; Regist. (Anaesth.) United Sheff. Hosps.

MELIKIAN, Narbeh 4 Helena Court, Eaton Rise, London W5 2RE — MB BS 1996 Lond.; BSc (Hons.) Lond. 1993, MB BS 1996. (UMDS Guy's & St. Thos. Hosp.) SHO (Med.) Hammersmith Hosp. Lond. Prev: SHO (Cardiol.) Roy. Brompton Hosp. Lond.

MELIKIAN, Varazdad (retired) 8 Pebble Mill Road, Edgbaston, Birmingham B5 7SA — MB BS 1959 Lond.; FRCP Ed. 1975, M 1966; FRCP Lond. 1981, M 1968; MRCS Eng. LRCP Lond. 1959. p/t Cons. Phys. Dudley Rd. Hosp. Birm. Prev: Ho. Phys. & Ho. Surg., Sen. Ho. Off. in Path. & Med. Regist. Gen.

MELISSARI, Efthimia King's College Hospital, Thrombosis Research Unit, Denmark Hill, London SE5 8RX; King's College Hospital, Thrombosis Research Inst., Chelsea, London SW3 6LR Tel: 020 7351 8306 — Ptychio Iatrikes 1972 Athens. Hon. Sen. Lect. Head Clin. Coagulation Fibrinolysis Sect. Thrombosis Research Inst. Socs: Fell. BMA; Assoc. Mem. RCPath.

MELL, Alison Kay 28 Great Bolas, Telford TF6 6PQ — MB ChB 1986 Aberd.

MELLADO CALVO, Nuria 44 Jenner House, Hunter St., London WC1N 1BL — LMS 1983 Barcelona.

MELLANBY, Alexander Robert Okehampton Health Centre, Okehampton EX20 1AY; Perrymans, Belstone, Okehampton EX20 1RD — MB BS 1976 Lond.; MRCP (UK) 1979; MRCGP 1980.

MELLANBY, Helen Neilson (retired) Cumnor Place, Cumnor, Oxford OX2 9QN Tel: 01865 862665 — BSc (Hons. Zool.) Lond. 1933, PhD (Entomol.) 1937; MD Sheff. 1949, MB ChB 1944. Prev: on Scientif. Staff Nutrit. Building Nat. Inst. Med. Research, Mill Hill.

MELLER, Kathleen Elizabeth Booth Caecady House, High St., Cowbridge CF71 7AH Tel: 01446 773878; Caecady House, High St, Cowbridge CF71 7AH — MB ChB 1951 Manch. (Manch.) Prev: Ho. Off. (Med.) Nat. Blood Transfus. Serv.; Ho. Phys. (Paediat.) Hope Hosp. Salford; Ho. Phys. Withington Hosp. Manch.

***MELLER, Mark Temple** 52 Park Hill Road, Wallington SM6 0SB — MB BS 1997 Newc.

MELLER, Robert Harry Charles Department of Child Psychiatry, Southmead Hospital, Bristol BS10 5NB — MB BS 1974 Lond.; MRCS Eng. LRCP Lond. 1972; MRCPsych 1979.

MELLER, Simon Temple Children's Department, Royal Marsden Hospital, Downs Road, Sutton SM2 5PT Tel: 020 8642 6011 Fax: 020 8770 7168; 1 Little Flanchford Cottages, Flanchford Road, Leigh, Reigate RH2 8RD Email: stmell@aol.com — MB BS 1968 Lond.; MRCS Eng. LRCP Lond. 1968; FRCP Lond. 1989; MRCP (UK) 1971; FRCPCH 1997; DCH Eng. 1970. (Lond. Hosp.) Cons. Paediat. Roy. Marsden Hosp. Sutton & St. Helier Hosp. Carshalton; Hon. Sen. Lect. St. Geo. Hosp. Med. Sch. Prev: Sen. Regist. (Nuclear Med. & Ultrasound) Roy. Marsden Hosp. Sutton; Sen. Regist. (Paediat.) Qu. Mary's Hosp. Childr. & W.m. Hosp. Lond.; Regist. (Child Health) Univ. Hosp. Wales Cardiff.

MELLERIO, Jemima Elizabeth St John's Institute Of Dermatology, St Thomas Hospital, London SE1 7EH Tel: 020 7928 9292 — MB BS 1991 Lond.; MD Lond. 2000; BSc (Hons.) Lond. 1988; MRCP (UK) 1994. (Lond. Hosp. Med. Sch.) p/t Specialist Regist. Dermat. - Lond.

MELLETT, Peter George 7 Wimpole Street, London W1M 7AB Tel: 020 7580 1584; The Ashtead Hospital, The Warren, Ashtead KT21 2SB Tel: 01372 276161 Fax: 01372 278704 — MB BS 1953 Lond.; FRCPsych 1977, M 1971; DPM Eng. 1963. (Middlx.) p/t Cons. Psychiat. Ashtead Hosp. & Vis. Cons. Psychiat. Priory Sturt Hosp. Walton-on-the-Hill. Socs: Fell. (Ex-Vice Pres.) Roy. Soc. Med. (Ex-Pres. Sect. Hypn. & Psychosomatic Med.); (Ex-Pres.) Soc. Psychosomatic Res.; Fell. Internat. Coll. Psychosomatic Med. Prev:

Cons. Psychiat. Horton Hosp., Epsom & Middlx. Hosp. Outpats. Lond.; Dep. Resid. Med. Off., Sen. Cas. Off. & Ho. Phys. Middlx. Hosp. Lond.

MELLEY, Edwin Thomas Smallwood Health Centre, Church Green West, Redditch B97 4DJ; 31 Crumpfields Lane, Redditch B97 5PN — MB ChB 1954 Birm. Prev: Capt. RAMC, Regtl. Med. Off. 4th Regt. R.H.A.; Ho. Surg. Gyn. Dept. Gen. Hosp. Birm.; Ho. Phys. Manor Hosp. Walsall.

***MELLING, Paul Ronald** 7 Davids Lane, Springhead, Oldham OL4 4RZ — BChir 1995 Camb.

***MELLINGTON, Andrew James** 4 Hilton Drive, Sutton Coldfield B72 1EQ — BM BCh 1998 Oxf.; BM BCh Oxf 1998.

MELLINS, Derek Henry (retired) 45 Midholm, London NW11 6LL — MRCS Eng. LRCP Lond. 1950; MRCGP 1965. Prev: Chairm. Med. Bds. DHSS.

MELLINS, Rachel Anne Heathfield Medical Centre, Lyttelton Road, Hampstead Garden Suburb, London N2 0EE Tel: 020 8458 9262 Fax: 020 8458 0300 — MB ChB 1986 Liverp.

***MELLIS, Andrew James** Lincoln Hospitals N H S Trust, Lincoln County Hospital, Greetwell Road, Lincoln LN2 5QY — BM BS 1997 Nottm.

MELLIS, Colin Alexander Queens Park Medical Centre, Farrer Street, Stockton-on-Tees TS18 2AW Tel: 01642 679681 Fax: 01642 677124; Leven Bank Boarding Kennels, High Leven, Yarm — MB ChB 1970 Ed. (Ed.) Socs: Brit. Soc. Med. & Dent. Hypn.

MELLISH, Robert William Elliot Ancrum Road Medical Centre, 12-14 Ancrum Road, Dundee DD2 2HZ — MB ChB 1995 Dundee.

MELLODY, Joanne 74 Hollingreave Road, Burnley BB11 2HT — MB ChB 1995 Manch.; MRCP UK 1999. SHO Renal Med., Hope Hosp. Salford. Prev: SHO IC, Hope Hosp., Salford; SHO Med. Rotat., Hope Hosp. Salford; SHO A & E, Roy. Bolton Hosp. Bolton.

MELLON, Andrew Farquharson Department of Paediatrics, Swinderland Royal Hospital, Kayel Road, Sunderland SR 4 7TP Tel: 0191 565 6256 Ext: 42899 Fax: 0191 569 9219 Email: andrew.mellon@chs.northy.nhs.uk — MB BS 1984 Lond.; Cert. in Med. Educat.; FRCPCH; BSc Lond. 1981; MRCP (UK) 1988. (St. Mary's Hosp. Med. Sch.) Regist. (Paediat.) Roy. Vict. Infirm. Newc. u Tyne., Cons. Paediat., Sunderland Roy. Hosp.; UnderGrad. Educat. Coordinator Sunderland Roy. Hosp. Prev: Regist. (Paediat.) Roy. Childr. Hosp. Brisbane, Austral.; Regist. (Paediat.) Newc. u Tyne HA; SHO (Paediat.) St. Jas. Univ. Hosp. Leeds.

MELLON, Anne 1A Sherbrooke Drive, Glasgow G41 5AA — MB ChB 1963 Glas.; FFA RCS Eng. 1972; DA Eng. 1966.

MELLON, Claire Frances Mary 18 Pembridge Villas, London W11 2SU — MB ChB 1988 Glas. (Glas.) Regist. (O & G) Univ. Coll. Hosp. Lond. Prev: SHO (O & G & Genitourin. Med.) St. Bart. Hosp. Lond.; Ho. Off. Wittington Hosp. Lond.

MELLON, Mr John Kilian Department of Urology, Freeman Hospital, Newcastle upon Tyne NE7 7DN Tel: 0191 284 3111 Fax: 0191 213 0205 Email: j.k.mellon@ncl.ac.uk; 230 Jesmond Dene Road, Jesmond, Newcastle upon Tyne NE2 2JU Tel: 0191 281 2691 — MB BCh BAO 1983 Belf.; MD (Newc.) 1993; FRCS Ed. 1987; FRCSI 1987; FRCS (Urol.) 1994. (Qu. Univ. Belf.) Sen. Lect. (Urol. Surg.) Newc. Univ. & Freeman Hosp. NHS Trust. Socs: Brit. Assn. Urol. Surgs.; Brit. Assn. Cancer Research; Corr. Mem. Amer. Urol. Assn. Prev: 1st Asst. (Urol. Surg.) Newc. Univ.

MELLOR, Adrian John St Georges University Hospital, Tooting, London SW17 Email: dramellor@aol.com; 16 Chatham Drive, Southsea, Portsmouth PO1 2TF Tel: 01705 345679 Fax: 01705 345697 — MB ChB 1990 Leeds; FRCA 1996. Specialist Regist. (Anaesth.) St. Geo. Hosp. Lond.

MELLOR, Andrew David The Woodgrove Surgery, Doncaster Road, Wath-on-Dearne, Rotherham S63 7AL Tel: 01709 877649 — MB ChB 1985 Leeds; MRCGP 1994; DRCOG 1988.

***MELLOR, Anne** Flat 3A, Tay Square, Dundee DD1 1PB — MB ChB 1997 Dundee.

***MELLOR, Anthony Stuart** 2 Keats Road, Greenmount, Bury BL8 4EP — MB ChB 1998 Manch.; MB ChB Manch 1998.

MELLOR, Christopher Huw Sketty Surgery, De la Beche Road, Sketty, Swansea SA2 9EA Tel: 01792 206862 — MB BS 1988 Lond.; BSc Lond. 1985; MRCGP 1994; DRCOG 1994; DFFP 1994; DGM RCP Lond. 1991. Prev: Trainee GP/SHO (O & G) Swansea.

MELLOWS

MELLOR, Craig Stanley Seaford Health Centre, Dane Road, Seaford BN25 1DH Tel: 01323 490022 Fax: 01323 492156 — MB ChB 1973 Bristol. (Bristol) GP Seaford, E. Sussex.

MELLOR, David Heppenstall (retired) 2 Bromley Road, West Bridgford, Nottingham NG2 7AP Tel: 0115 914 1838 Email: mellor2@ntlworld.com — MB ChB Leeds 1959; MD Leeds 1977; FRCP Lond. 1979, M 1964; FRCPCH 1997, M. 1996; DCH RCPS Glas. 1971. Prev: Cons. Paediat. Neurol. Nottm. Univ. Hosp. NHS Trust.

MELLOR, David Joseph Dept., Of Anaesth., Leeds General Infirmery, Leeds LS1 3EX Tel: 0113 292 6672; 19 The Turnways, Leeds LS6 3DT Tel: 0113 275 8850 Email: 101671.1225@compuserve.com, joemellor@btinternet.com — MB BS 1989 Lond.; BSc (Hons.) Clin. Pharmacol. Lond. 1986; FRCA 1994. (St. Geo. Hosp. Lond.) Cons. Paediat. Anaesth., Leeds Gen. Infirm., Leeds

MELLOR, David Victor 6 Hawthorn Close, Keyworth, Nottingham NG12 5JP — MB ChB 1991 Leeds.

MELLOR, Ellen Gwenddolen (retired) 6 Clifton Terrace, Ingatestone CM4 9EB Tel: 01268 9972354615 — MB ChB 1951 Liverp. Prev: Assoc. Specialist Nat. Blood Transfus. Serv. Brentwood.

MELLOR, Mr Ian 20 Admiralty Wood, Almondbank, Perth PH1 3XW — MB ChB 1990 Dundee; FRCS Ed. 1995. SHO (Anaesth.) Ninewells Hosp. Dundee.

MELLOR, James Philip York House Medical Centre, Heathside Road, Woking GU22 7XL Tel: 01483 761100 Fax: 01483 751185; 120 York Road, Woking GU22 7XS Tel: 01483 715810 — MB 1978 Camb.; BChir 1977; DRCOG 1980.

MELLOR, Jerome 269 The Circle, Queen Elizabeth St., London SE1 2JW — BM 1980 Soton.; MRCGP 1993. SHO (Psychiat.) Friern Hosp. Lond.

MELLOR, John Albert Department of Medicine, Southend Hospital, Prittlewell Chase, Westcliff on Sea SS0 0RY Tel: 01702 435555; Tel: 01702 711246 Email: johnmellor@doctors.org.uk — MB ChB 1973 Leeds; FRCP Lond. 1994; MRCP (UK) 1976. (Leeds) Cons. Phys. S.end. Socs: Brit. Geriat. Soc. Prev: Sen. Regist. Kingston Gen. Hosp. Hull; Lect. (Clin. Med.) Trinity Coll. Dub.; Regist. (Med.) Chapel Allerton Hosp. Leeds.

MELLOR, John Gregory Lakeside Surgery, Cottingham Road, Corby NN17 2UR Tel: 01536 204154 Fax: 01536 748286; Oakley Barn, Little Oakley, Corby NN18 8HA Tel: 01536 744567 — MB BChir 1983 Camb.; MA Camb. 1983; MRCP (UK) 1986; MRCGP 1986; DCH RCP Lond. 1985. Hosp. Pract. (Paediat.) Kettering Gen. Hosp.

MELLOR, Linda Jayne 43 Drummond Drive, Nuthall, Nottingham NG16 1BJ — MB ChB 1992 Manch.

MELLOR, Margaret Elizabeth (retired) Ty Meddyg, 80 Pentrepoeth Road, Morriston, Swansea SA6 6AQ Tel: 01792 771499 — MRCS Eng. LRCP Lond. 1952.

MELLOR, Michael 15 Manor Park, Ruddington, Nottingham NG11 6DS — MB BS 1963 Lond. (Univ. Coll. Hosp.)

MELLOR, Michael James (retired) 30 St Luke's Road, Bournemouth BH3 7LT Tel: 01202 515461 — MB ChB Ed. 1959; DObst RCOG 1961.

MELLOR, Michael John (retired) Swanlands, Arbury, Nuneaton CV10 7PT Tel: 02476 344842 — MB ChB 1964 Leeds. Clin. Asst. (Gen. Surg.) Hinckley & Dist. Hosp.; Clin. Teach. Leic. Univ. Med. Sch.; Clin. Asst. (Dermat.) Leicester Roy. Infirm. Prev: Ho. Surg. (Orthop.) Gen. Infirm. Leeds.

MELLOR, Moira Sutherland 38 Winifred Lane, Aughton, Ormskirk L39 5DJ — MB ChB 1958 Aberd.; DCH Eng. 1961.

***MELLOR, Neil William Meldrum** 38 Winifred Lane, Ormskirk L39 5DJ — MB ChB 1995 Manch.

MELLOR, Paul (retired) Ty Meddyg, 80 Pentrepoeth Road, Morriston, Swansea SA6 6AQ Tel: 01792 771499 — MB ChB Leeds 1950; DObst RCOG 1951.

MELLOR, Peter John (retired) 126 Boothroyden Road, Blackley, Manchester M9 0SH Tel: 0161 653 7101 Fax: 0161 654 8095 Email: pjmellor@compuserve.com — MB ChB Manch. 1966.

MELLOR, Russell John Pendeen Surgery, Kent Avenue, Ross-on-Wye HR9 5AL Tel: 01989 763535 Fax: 01989 768288 — MB ChB 1977 Leeds.

MELLOR, Simon James 3 Moor Park Road, Northwood HA6 2DL — MB ChB 1992 Manch.

MELLOR, Stephen Clifford 11 Southlands Avenue, Standish, Wigan WN6 0TT Tel: 01257 400830 — MB ChB 1991 (Dist. Psych.) Leeds; MRCGP 2001. Ship's Doctor - P&O Cruises. Prev: GP Locum Edin.; GP Train. in E. Cumbria & Edin.; Obs & Gynae SHO at Roy. Infirm. of Edin.

MELLOR, Mr Stephen John 47 Clare Avenue, Porthill, Newcastle ST5 8PY — MB ChB 1991 Birm.; ChB Birm. 1991; FRCS Ed. 1995.

MELLOR, Stuart Kelvingrove Medical Centre, 28 Hands Road, Heanor DE75 7HA Tel: 01773 713201 Fax: 01773 534380 — MB BS 1985 Lond.; MRCGP 1991.

MELLOR, Stuart Latimer, London Road, Prestbury, Macclesfield SK10 4EA Tel: 01625 829156 — MB ChB 1971 Liverp.; MRCOG 1976. Cons. (Obst.) Macclesfield Gen. Hosp. Prev: Sen. Regist. (Obst.) Newc. Gen. Hosp.; Regist. (Obst.) St. Mary's Hosp. Manch.; Regist. O & G Wythenshawe Hosp. Manch.

MELLOR, Mr Timothy Kenneth Maxillofacial Unit, Queen Alexandra Hospital, Cosham, Portsmouth PO6 3LY Tel: 023 9228 6631 Fax: 023 9228 6089 Email: tim.mellor@qmail01.porthosp.swest.nhs.uk — MB BCh 1991 Wales; 2001 FDSRCS; BDS Liverp. 1978; FRCS Ed. 1995; FDS RCPS Glas. 1983. (Univ. Wales) Cons. Maxillofacial Surg. Qu. Alexandra Hosp. Portsmouth; Cons. Maxillofacial Surg. St Mary's Hosp. Isle of Wight. Socs: Fell. Brit. Assn. Oral & Maxillofacial Surg.; Brit. Assn. Head & Neck Oncol.; Eur. Acad. of Facial Plastic Surg. Prev: Cons. Maxillofacial Surg. Roy. Air Force Roy. Hosp. Haslar Gosport; Sen. Regist. W. Midl. HST Rotat. Stoke, Wolverhampton, Dudley & Birm.; Sen. Regist. (Oral & Maxillofacial Surg.) P.ss Alexandra Hosp. Wroughton.

MELLOR, William Eric (retired) 196 Park Road, Guiseley, Leeds LS20 8EN Tel: 01943 870224 — MB ChB 1954 Leeds; MRCGP 1980. Prev: GP Leeds.

MELLOR, William Hezekiah (retired) The Elms Surgery, 5 Derby St., Ormskirk L39 2BJ Tel: 01695 573123 Fax: 01695 578300 — MB ChB Manch. 1957; DObst RCOG 1962.

MELLORS, Arthur Stephen Moreton Medical Centre, 27 Upton Road, Wirral CH46 0PE Tel: 0151 677 2327 Fax: 0151 604 0419; 4 Airlie Road, Hoylake, Wirral CH47 4AB Tel: 0151 632 1192 — MB BS 1975 Newc.; MRCGP 1980.

MELLORS, Branwen Elizabeth Brylls, West End, Walthar St Lawrence, Reading RG10 0NT; Department Community Paediatrics, 3 Craven Road, Reading RG1 5LF Tel: 0118 986 2277 Fax: 0118 975 0297 — MA Oxf. 1969, BM BCh 1969; DObst RCOG 1971; MSc Community Paediatrics 1997. Assoc. Specialist Community Paediat. Roy. Berks. & Battle Hosp. NHS Trust Reading. Prev: Ho. Phys. (Gen. Med.) & Ho. Surg. (Obst.) Whittington Hosp. Lond.; SHO Paediat. Centr. Middlx. Hosp. Lond.

MELLORS, Karen Denise Bristol-Meyers Squibb, 141-149 Staines Road, Hounslow TW3 3JA Tel: 020 8754 3729; 14 Heatherside Gardens, Farnham Common, Slough SL2 3RR — MB BS 1984 Lond.; MRCGP 1989; DCH RCP Lond. 1987; DRCOG 1987. Assoc. Clin. Research Dir. Bristol Myers Squibb Hounslow.

MELLORS, Pamela Ann Department of Occupational Medicine, Horton Wing, St Luke's Hospital, Bradford BD5 0NA Tel: 01274 365217; 5 Hornbeam Crescent, Harrogate HG2 8QA — MB BS 1980 Newc.; MRCGP 1984; AFOM 1999. Sen. Regist. (Occupat. Med.) St. Luke's Hosp. Bradford. Socs: Soc. Occupat. Med.; Assn. Health Care Occu./ Phys. (ANHOPS). Prev: Trainee GP Oxf. VTS.

MELLOTTE, Mary Elizabeth (retired) 28 Downview Avenue, Belfast BT15 4FB Tel: 02890 778945 — MB BCh BAO 1941 NUI.

MELLOTTE, Michele The Surgery, Eene Drive, Ederney, Enniskillen BT93 0AR Tel: 028 6863 1234 Fax: 028 6863 1721 — MB BCh BAO 1978 Belf.; MRCGP 1984; Cert. Family Plann. JCC 1983; DRCOG 1982. (Qu. Univ. Belf.)

MELLOWS, Heather Jean Department of Obstetrics & Gynaecology, Bassetlaw District General Hospital, Worksop S25 1YA Tel: 01909 500990; Brook House Hall, Brookhouse, Laughton, Sheffield S25 1YA Tel: 01909 562399 Fax: 01909 568423 — MB BS 1974 Lond.; MRCS Eng. LRCP Lond. 1974; FRCOG 1993, M 1980. (Roy. Free) Cons. O & G Bassetlaw HA. Socs: Jun. Vice Pres., Roy. Coll. of Obst.s and Gynaecologists 2001. Prev: SCMO (Med. Gyn.) Sheff. HA; Sen. Regist. The Jessop Hosp. for Wom. Sheff.; Sen. Regist. Qu. Charlottes Matern. Hosp.

MELLOWS, Robin John Tel: 0118 973 2678 Fax: 0118 973 3689 Email: robin.mellows@gp-k81025.nhs.uk; Keepers Cottage, Wick

MELLUISH

Hill Lane, Finchampstead, Wokingham RG40 3PY Tel: 01734 734949 Email: rmellows@4ol.com — MB BS 1980 Lond.; MRCGP 1984; DRCOG 1983; AKC. (Westm.) Clin. Asst. in Haemat., Roy. Berks. and Battle NHS Trust, Reading. Prev: GP Wokingham; SHO (Obst., Paediat. & Psychiat.) Qu. Mary's Hosp. Roehampton.

MELLUISH, Philip George Channel View Surgery, 3 Courtenay Place, Teignmouth TQ14 8AY Tel: 01626 774656 Fax: 01626 772743 Email: philip.melluish@gp-l83120.nhs.uk; Tel: 01626 352042 — MB ChB 1988 Bristol; MRCGP 1994; DFFP 1993; DCH RCP Lond. 1992. Bd. Mem. Teignbridge PCT; Presribing Lead, Teignbridge PCT. Prev: Trainee GP Cirencester; SHO (O & G) St. Paul's Hosp. Cheltenham; SHO (Med.) Cirencester Hosp.

MELLUISH, Victoria Sarah-Anne 15 Humber Lane, Kingsteignton, Newton Abbot TQ12 3DJ — MB ChB 1988 Bristol; MRCGP 1994. Assoc. GP Albany Surg. Newton Abbot. Prev: SHO Cirencester Hosp. E. Glos. NHS Trust.

MELNIK, Ludmyla Princess Louise Day Hospital, St. Quintins Avenue, London W10 6DL — MB BS 1985 Lond.; DCH 1988. Staff Grade Pract. (Med. Elderly) P.ss Louise Day Hosp. for Elderly Lond. Prev: Trainee GP St. Albans Herts. VTS; SHO (Paediat.) Paddington & N. Kensington HA.

MELNYK, Anna Patricia 49 Eaton Hill, Cookridge, Leeds LS16 6SE — MB BS 1986 Lond.

MELROSE, Diane Lincluden Surgery, 53 Bellshill Road, Uddingston, Glasgow G71 7PA Tel: 01698 813873; 34 Farm Court, Bothwell, Glasgow G71 8BU — MB ChB 1991 Glas.; Dip. Pract. Dermat. Wales 1997; DFFP 1995; Dip. Forens. Med. Glas 1994; DRCOG 1993. Prev: Trainee GP Monklands Dist. Gen. Hosp. Airdrie; Ho. Off. (Surg. & Med.) Hairmyres Hosp.

MELROSE, Dorothy Margaret The Conifers, Winston, Darlington DL2 3RH Tel: 01325 730695 — MB BS Newc. 1967. Community Med. Off. Darlington HA. Prev: Ho. Surg. & Ho. Phys. Bishop Auckland Gen. Hosp.; Ho. Surg. (Gyn.) Stoke Mandeville Hosp.

MELROSE, Elaine Beaton Meldon House, 103 Bentinck Drive, Troon KA10 6HZ Tel: 01292 314339 Email: elaine.melrose@hotmail.com; Maternity Section, Ayrshire Central Hospital, Kilwinning Road, Irvine KA12 8SS Tel: 01294 323387 Fax: 01294 314397 — MB ChB 1975 Ed.; MRCOG 1980; FRCOG 1993. (University of Edinburgh) Cons. O & G Ayrsh. & Arran Acute NHS Trust; Hon. Clin. Sen. Lect. Univ. Glas.; Train. Progr. Dir. (Obst. & Gyn.) W. of Scotl. Deanery. Socs: Glas. Obst. & Gyn. Soc.; Brit. Menopause Soc.; BSCCP. Prev: Sen. Regist. (O & G) Gtr. Glas. Teachg. Hosps.; Regist. (O & G) Gtr. Glas Health Bd.

MELROSE, George Alexander Glover Street Medical Centre, 133 Glover Street, Perth PH2 0JB Tel: 01738 621844 Fax: 01738 636070 — MB ChB 1972 Ed.

MELROSE, Hilary Gregg Union Street Surgery, 12 Union Street, Kirkintilloch, Glasgow G71 7AP Tel: 0141 776 2468 Fax: 0141 775 3341; York Place, 12 Union St, Kirkintilloch, Glasgow G66 1DG Tel: 0141 776 2468 — MB ChB Glas. 1982; MRCGP 1986; DRCOG 1984. GP Partner Glas. Job-Share. Socs: BMA; Roy. Coll. Gen. Pract. Prev: GP Hong Kong; GP Glas.; Trainee GP Paisley.

***MELROSE, Ian Craig** Brindles, Great Corby, Carlisle CA4 8LL — MB ChB 1995 Leic.

MELROSE, John Robert Church Lane Medical Centre, Orchid Rise, Off Church Lane, Scunthorpe DN15 7AN Tel: 01724 864341 Fax: 01724 876441; 90 Oswald Road, Scunthorpe DN15 7PA Tel: 01724 864341 — MB ChB 1977 Manch.; DRCOG 1982.

MELROSE, Philip Andrew St Margarets Surgery, 8 St. Margarets Road, Solihull B92 7JS Tel: 0121 706 0307 Fax: 0121 765 0161; 21 Charterhouse Drive, Solihull B91 3FH — MB ChB 1988 Sheff.; MRCGP 1993.

MELROSE, Thomas Malcolm Shawwell House, Stagshaw Road, Corbridge NE45 5PE Tel: 01434 632066 — MB BS 1965 Lond.; DObst RCOG 1967; MLCOM 1980. (St. Mary's) Socs: Fell. Roy. Soc. Med. Prev: Ho. Surg. (O & G) Paddington Gen. Hosp.; Ho. Surg. (Orthop.) St. Mary's Hosp. Lond.

MELROSE, William (retired) 11 Yew Tree Road, Liverpool L18 3JL Tel: 0151 428 4143 — MB ChB 1950 Liverp. Prev: GP Yardumian & Melrose Liverp.

MELROSE, William Maxwell (retired) The Conifers, Winston, Darlington DL2 3RH Tel: 01325 730695 — MB BS Newc. 1967. Prev: GP Barnard Castle.

MELSOM, Richard Douglas St. Luke's Hospital, Little Horton Lane, Bradford BD5 0NA Tel: 01274 365399 — MB BChir 1975 Camb.; MA Camb. 1972, MD 1985; MRCP (UK) 1977; FRCP 1998. (Camb. & Lond. Hosp.) Cons. Rheum. St. Luke's Hosp. Bradford. Prev: Sen. Regist. (Rheum.) Lond. Hosp.; Regist. (Rheum.) Char. Cross Hosp. Lond.

***MELSON, Louise Charlotte** 51 Queens Road, Buckhurst Hill IG9 5BU — MB BS 1996 Lond.

***MELTON, Andrew** Carnach, Balnfoich, Inverarnie, Farr, Inverness IV1 2XG — MB ChB 1994 Ed.

MELTON, George (retired) Hurst Grange, 19 Parkfield Road, Worthing BN13 1EN — MRCS Eng. LRCP Lond. 1928; MD Lond. 1933, MB BS 1931; FRCP Lond. 1969, M 1932. Hon. Cons. Phys. Enfield Gp. Hosps. Prev: Cons. Phys. Highlands Hosp. Winchmore Hill.

MELTON, Peter John The Old Rectory, Hatcliffe Road, Hatcliffe, Grimsby DN37 0TH — MB BS 1987 Lond.

MELTON, Richard Philip Kineton Surgery, The Old School, Market Square, Kineton, Warwick CV35 0LP Tel: 01926 640471 Fax: 01926 640390; Beechen Tree House, Main St, Tysoe, Warwick CV35 0SE Tel: 01295 680667 — MB ChB 1980 Birm.; MRCGP 1984; DRCOG 1983. (Birm.) Socs: BMA (Treas. S. Warks. Div.); Soc. Occupat. Med.; Disp. Doctors Assn. Prev: Chairm. W. Midl. Regional Gen. Pract. Trainee's Comm.; Trainee GP/SHO E. Birm. Hosp. VTS; Vice_Chairm. of Dispansiing Doctors Assn.

MELTZER, Edwin Stanley Redford Lodge, 15 Church St., Edmonton, London N9 9DY Tel: 020 8956 1234 Fax: 020 8956 1233 — MB BS 1974 Lond.; FRCPsych 1994, M 1978. (St. Mary's) Cons. Psychiat. Redford Lodge Psychiat. Hosp. Edmonton. Prev: Cons. Psychiat. Warley Hosp. Brentwood; Sen. Regist. (Psychiat.) Maudsley & Bethlem Roy. Hosps.; Sen. Regist. & Regist. (Psychiat.) St. Geo. Hosp. Tooting.

MELTZER, Jean Eileadh Esplanade Surgery, 19 Esplanade, Ryde PO33 2EH Tel: 01983 611444 Fax: 01983 811548; 19 The Esplanade, Ryde PO33 2EH Tel: 01983 813600 Fax: 01983 813609 — MB ChB Birm. 1966; DCH RCP Lond. 1969. (Birm.) Prev: Clin. Asst. (Child Psychiat.) Ryde.

MELTZER, Margaret Leah 24 Finchley Way, London N3 1AG Tel: 020 8346 4022 — MB ChB 1971 Cape Town; MRCPath. 1980. Prev: Lect. (Cytol.) St. Mary's Med. Sch. Lond.; Regist. (Histopath.) Hammersmith Hosp. & Roy. Postgrad. Med. Sch.Lond.

MELVILLE, Alan William Thomas The Health Centre, 80 Main Street, Kelty KY4 0AE Tel: 01383 831281 Fax: 01383 831825; Lochanmeg, 38 Knowehead Road, Crossford, Dunfermline KY12 8QF Tel: 01383 729321 — MB ChB 1968 St. And.; FRCGP 1991, M 1974; DObst RCOG 1971; Assoc. Fac. Occupat. Med. RCP Lond. 1980. (St. And.) Socs: Assn. for Med. Educat. in Europe; Brit. Med. Acupunc. Soc.; BMA. Prev: Dep. Head, Med. Br. Inst. Occupat. Med. Edin.; Ho. Phys. Raigmore Hosp. Inverness; Ho. Surg. Roy. N.. Infirm. Inverness.

MELVILLE, Amanda Jane Faith House Surgery, 723 Beverley Road, Hull HU6 7ER Tel: 01482 853296 Fax: 01482 855235 — MB ChB 1985 Sheff.; DCH 1988; DRCOG 1991. GP.

MELVILLE, Catriona Roberta Stuart (Gordon) — MB ChB 1995 Glas.; MRCOG 1999 (RCOG) London; DFFP; MRCOG 1999 (PCOG) London; DFFP 1998 (faculty family planning & RHC). (Glas.) Specialist Regist., Obst. & Gyn. Socs: Glas. Obs. and Gyn. Soc. Prev: SHO Dept. of Genitourin. Med. & Sexual Health, Glas. Roy. Infirm. NHS Trust.

MELVILLE, Christine Sarah Ann Raymede Clinic, St Charles Hospital, Exmoor St., London W10 6DZ Tel: 020 8960 0942; 18 Caroline Place, London W2 4AN Tel: 020 7229 3398 Fax: 020 7221 4781 Email: melville_family@msn.com — MB BS 1985 Lond.; MA Oxf. 1989, BA 1982; MFFP 1993. (Univ. Coll. Hosp. Lond.) Community Med. Off. Pk.side Lond. HA. Socs: Roy. Soc. Med.

MELVILLE, Colin Alistair Stuart 62 Salisbury Park, Woolton, Liverpool L16 0JT Tel: 0151 722 1913 — MB ChB 1983 Aberd.; MRCP (UK) 1988. Regist. Rotat. (Paediat.) Roy. Liverp. Childr. Hosp. Alder Hey. Socs: Liverp. Med. Inst. Prev: Resid. Med. Off. (Gen. Med. & Gen. Surg.) Aberd. Roy. Infirm.; SHO (Paediat.) Hosp. Sick Childr. Birm.; SHO (Paediat.) Hosp. Sick Childr. Gt. Ormond St. Lond.

MELVILLE, Colin Randolph Hull Royal Infirmary, Anlaby Road, Hull HU3 2JZ Tel: 01482 674052 Fax: 01482 228453 Email:

colinm@rhht_tr.northy.nhs.uk; Briar Croft, St. Michaels Mount, Swanland, North Ferriby HU14 3NR Email: colinmelville@bigfoot.com — MB ChB 1983 Sheff.; FRCA 1992. Cons. (A & E & IC) Hull Roy. Infirm. Socs: BMA; Assn. Anaesth.; Intens. Care Soc. Prev: Sen. Regist. (Anaesth.) NE Thames RHA; Sen. Regist. Helicopter Emerg. Med. Serv. Roy. Lond. Hosp.; Regist. (Anaesth.) Roy. Lond. Hosp. & St. Thos. Hosp. Lond.

MELVILLE, Craig Andrew 41 Bowfield Road, West Kilbride KA23 9LD — MB ChB 1993 Glas.

MELVILLE, David Harcourt Bosmere Medical Practice, PO Box 41, Civic Centre Road, Havant PO9 2AJ Tel: 023 9245 1300 Fax: 023 9249 2524 Email: bosmeremedical@ac.com; Little Buckden, Milberry lane, Stoughton, Chichester PO18 9JJ Tel: 023 9263 1386 Fax: 023 9263 1386 Email: david.melville@bigfoot.com — MB BS 1982 Lond.; FPCert. 1986 (Family Planning Certificate); MRCGP 1987; DRCOG 1986. (King's Coll. Hosp.) GP Princip. Bosmere Med. Pract., Havant; GP Ultrasonography for E. hants PCT/St. Marys Hosp. Portsmouth. Prev: Med. Adviser Servier, WI; GP Barbados; SHO (Ophth.) Soton. Eye Hosp.

MELVILLE, Mr David Murray St George's Hospital, Blackshaw Road, London SW17 0QT Tel: 020 8725 0121 Fax: 020 8725 0115; 18 Caroline Place, London W2 4AN Tel: 020 7229 3398 — MB BS 1979 Lond.; MA Oxf. 1976, DM 1989; FRCS Eng. 1985; FRCS Ed. 1984. (St. Thos.) Cons. Gen. Surg. St Geroge's Hosp. Lond. Socs: Assn. Coloproctol.; Brit. Soc. Gastroenterol.; BMA & Roy. Soc. Med. Prev: Cons. Gen. Surg. N. Middlx. Hosp. Lond.; Sen. Regist. (Gen. Surg.) N. Middlx. & St. Bart. Hosps. Lond.; Resid. Surg. Off. St. Mark's Hosp. Lond.

MELVILLE, Elizabeth Doreen 29 Gorham Avenue, Rottingdean, Brighton BN2 7DP Tel: 01273 303362 — MB BCh Wales 1954; BSc Wales 1954; MFFP 1993. (Cardiff) Regional Assessor Jt. Comm. Contracep. Socs: Soc. Occupat. Med.; Sussex M-C Soc. Prev: Regional Assessor Jt. Comm. Contracep.; Store Med. Off. Marks & Spencer Brighton; Clin. Asst. (Family Plann.) Roy. Sussex Co. Hosp. Brighton.

MELVILLE, Elizabeth Mary Athernase, Lathrisk, by Freuchie, Cupar KY15 7HX Tel: 01337 857124 Email: marella@globalnet.co.uk — MB ChB Ed. 1952; BA Open 1993; MRCGP 1978. (Ed.) Benefits Agency Med. Ref. Socs: BMA. Prev: GP W. Calder.

MELVILLE, Mr Herbert Augustine Harcourt (retired) 29 Gorham Avenue, Rottingdean, Brighton BN2 7DP Tel: 01273 303362 Fax: 01273 303362 Email: herbertmelville@netscapeonline.co.uk — MB BCh 1954 Wales; BSc Wales 1954; FRCS Ed. 1962; FRCOG 1974, M 1961, DObst 1956. Hon. Cons. O & G Brighton & Lewes. Prev: Sen. Regist. (O & G) United Leeds Hosps.

MELVILLE, Hugh Miller (retired) 40 Woodmere, Barton Hills, Luton LU3 4DN Tel: 01582 579654 — MB BChir 1957 Camb.; MB BChir Camb. 1956; MA Camb. 1957. Prev: Ho. Surg. & Resid. Obst. Luton & Dunstable Hosp.

MELVILLE, Ian Dunlop (retired) 9 Mirlees Drive, Glasgow G12 0SH — MB ChB Glas. 1950; FRCP Lond. 1978, M 1957; FRCP Glas. 1966, M 1962; FRFPS Glas. 1956. Prev: Cons. Neurol. Inst. Neurol. Sci. S. Gen. Hosp. Glas.

MELVILLE, James Elliott Moncreiff (retired) 9/11 Christ Church Road, Winchester SO23 9SR — MB BChir 1940 Camb.; MB BChir. Camb. 1940; MRCS Eng. LRCP Lond. 1939. Prev: Clin. Med. Off. Hants. AHA.

MELVILLE, Janet Adrienne 2 Dibbinview Grove, Spital, Wirral CH63 9FW; 214 Park Road N., Birkenhead CH41 8BU Tel: 0151 652 1955 — MB ChB 1981 Liverp.; DRCOG 1983.

MELVILLE, Rex Lindsay Department of Sexual Health, Whipps Cross Hospital, Whipps Cross Road, London E11 1NR Tel: 020 8535 6523 Fax: 020 8535 6524 — MB BS 1971 Monash; Dip. Med. Venereal Sci. Univ. Sydney 1993. Cons. Genitourin. Med. Whipps Cross Hosp. Lond. Socs: Soc. Study VD & Assn. Genitourin. Med.; Fell. Austral. Coll - Sexual Health Phys.; Brit. HIV Assn. Prev: Head Med. Unit Albion St. (AIDS) Centre Sydney, NSW, Austral.

MELVILLE, Mr Richard Henry Duncan The Old Manse, Greenbank Road, Glenfarg, Perth PH2 9NW — MB ChB 1974 Dundee; FRCS Ed. 1979. Cons. (A & E) Qu. Margt. Hosp. Dunfermline.

MELVILLE, Robert Murray, OBE (retired) Athernase, Lathrisk, by Freuchie, Cupar KY15 7HX Tel: 01337 857124 Email: marella@globalnet.co.uk — MB ChB Ed. 1951; FFCM 1981, M 1972; DPH Ed. 1963. Prev: Sen. Med. Off. Scott. Home & Health Dept.

MELVILLE THOMAS, David Graham (retired) Tal-y-Coed Court, Monmouth NP25 5HR Tel: 01600 85272 — MB BChir 1952 Camb.; FRCPsych 1983; DPM Eng. 1960. Prev: Cons. Child Psychiat. Univ. Hosp. Wales.

MELVIN, Catherine Ann Department of Radiology, Stoke Mandeville Hospital, Aylesbury Tel: 01296 316917; Contino, Whisper Wood, Loudwater, Rickmansworth WD3 4JU Tel: 01923 775285 Fax: 01923 711490 — MB BS 1981 Lond.; FRCR 1987. (Roy. Free) Cons. Radiol. Stoke Mandeville Hosp. NHS Trust. Socs: Fell. Roy. Coll. Radiol. Prev: Sen. Regist. Rotat. (Diagn. Radiol.) Nottm. & Derby Hosps.; Vis. Foreign Doctor Ramon y Caval Hosp. Madrid.

MELVIN, Wallace Dewar Blackhall Medical Centre, 51 Hillhouse Road, Edinburgh EH4 3TH Tel: 0131 332 7696 Fax: 0131 315 2884; 51 Hillhouse Road, Edinburgh EH4 — MB ChB 1964 Ed.; DObst RCOG 1966. (Edin.) Prev: Regist. O & G Dumfries & Galloway Roy. Infirm.; Ho. Surg. Vict. Hosp. Kirkcaldy; Ho. Phys. Bangour Hosp. W. Lothian.

MELZER, Mark 17 Brook Road, Heaton Chapel, Stockport SK4 5BZ — MB ChB 1991 Manch.

MEMBREY, Anthony John, MBE The Surgery, Kingswood Road, Tunbridge Wells TN2 4UJ Tel: 01892 511833 Fax: 01892 517597; Shirley Lodge, Leggs Lane, Langton Green, Tunbridge Wells TN3 0RQ Tel: 01892 862228 — MB BS 1955 Lond.; FRCGP 1984; DObst RCOG 1961. (Guy's)

MEMBREY, William Luke Shirley Lodge, Leggs Lane, Langton Green, Tunbridge Wells TN3 0RQ — MB BS 1991 Lond.

MEMEL, David Stephen Air Balloon Surgery, Kenn Road, St George, Bristol BS5 7PD Tel: 0117 909 9914 Fax: 0117 908 6660 — MB ChB 1977 Birm.; BSc Birm. 1974, MMedSc 1995; MRCGP 1982; DCH Eng 1979. Teachg. & Research Assoc. (Primary Health Care) Univ. Bristol. Prev: Trainee GP Charlotte Keel Health Centre Bristol.

MEMON, Aamir Aziz Southport & Formby District General Hospital, Town Lane, Southport PR8 6PN Tel: 01704 704530 Fax: 01704 548229 Email: gillian.greenbank@mail.soh-tr.nwest.nhs.uk; 2 Millburn, Well Road, Moffat DG10 9BP — MB BS 1986 Pakistan; T(M) 1994; MD Liverpool 1996; DDSc Cardiff 1988. (Liaquat Med. Coll.) Cons. Dermat. S.port and Ormskirk NHS Trust. Socs: Brit. Assn. Dermat.; Brit. Soc. Investig. Dermat.; Brit. Assn. Dermatol.

MEMON, Manzoor Ahmed 29 Chigwell Rise, Chigwell IG7 6AQ Tel: 020 8500 2626 — MB BS 1961 Sind; DO Eng. 1968. (Sind)

MEMON, Mohammad Siddique 14 Hill School Road, St Helens WA10 3BH — MB BS 1971 Pakistan.

MEMON, Muhammad Anwar Bridlington & District Hospital, Bessingby Road, Bridlington YO16 4QP Tel: 01262 606666 Fax: 01262 423168 Email: amemon5839@aol.com; 3 Mordacks Close, Martonfields, Bridlington YO16 6ZF Tel: 01262 674895 Email: amemon5839@aol.com — MB BS 1973 Sind; FRCPI 2000; LMSSA Lond. 1984; MRCPI 1987. (Liaquat Med. Coll. Jamshoro, sindh, Pakistan) Cons. (Phys. & Cardiol.) Bridlington. Socs: Brit. Cardiac Soc.; Brit. Heart Failure Soc. Prev: Assoc. Specialist Med. (Cardiol.) Bridlington & Dist. Hosp. Bridlington, E. Yorks.

MEMON, Muhammad Iqbal Oakwood, Whitehall Road, Darwen BB3 2LH — LRCP LRCS Ed. LRCPS Glas. 1983 Glas.; BSc, MB BS Sind 1974; MPH Leeds 1991; DCCH RCP Ed. 1984; DCH NUI 1977; DCH RCP Lond. 1977; DTM & H Liverp. 1977. SCMO Wirral HA.

MEMON, Mumtaz Alam Flat 6A, McRobert House, Hartlepool General Hospital, Hartlepool TS24 9AH Tel: 01429 266654 — MB BS 1982 Karachi; MRCP (UK) 1991.

MEMON, Wali Mohammad Kingswood Medical Centre, Clayhill Road, Basildon SS16 5AD Tel: 01268 533727/280514 Fax: 01268 520513 — MB BS 1963 Sind.

MEMON, Yahya Burnett Edgar Medical Centre, Central Drive, Walney Island, Barrow-in-Furness LA14 3HY Tel: 01229 474526 Fax: 01229 475282 — MB BS Sind Pakistan 1969. (Liaquat Med. Coll.) Socs: Local Med. Comm.; RCGP Assoc. Mem.

MENACHEM, Siegfried 65 Gilling Court, Belsize Grove, London NW3 4XB — MD 1965 Hebrew Univ. Israel; Approbation Berlin 1978.

MENAGE

MENAGE, Catherine Mary Orchard House, Kirkwhelpington, Newcastle upon Tyne NE19 2RT — MB BS 1983 Lond.

MENAGE, Janet Bulkington Surgery, School Road, Bedworth CV12 9JB Tel: 024 7673 3020 — MB ChB 1979 Sheff.; MA 1994 Warwick Univ. (Counsilling). Gen. Practitioner.

MENAGE, Jeremy Leo Narrowboat, Hatton Boat Club, Dark Lane, Hatton, Warwick CV35 8XB — MB BChir 1982 Camb.; MB Camb. 1982, BChir 1981; MA Camb. 1982; MRCP London 1997.

MENAGÉ, Marie Joseph Albert 10 Village Road, Enfield EN1 2DH Tel: 020 8363 5562 — BM BCh 1952 Oxf.; MA Oxf. 1958; DObst RCOG 1959.

MENAGE, Mr Mitchel J Bristol Eye Hospital, Lower Maudlin St., Bristol BS1 2LX Tel: 0117 923 0060 — MB BS 1982 Lond.; FRCS Eng. 1988; MRCP (UK) 1986; FCOphth 1989; DO RCS Eng. 1988. (St. Thos.) Sen. Regist. Bristol Eye Hosp. Prev: Sen. Regist. W. Eng. Eye Infirm. Exeter; Hon. Fell. Glaucoma Studies Univ. Wisconsin, USA; SHO & Regist. Rotat. Bristol Eye Hosp.

MENCE, Alan Eric Harold (retired) 10 Arden Road, Dorridge, Solihull B93 8LQ Tel: 01564 770942 — MB BChir 1957 Camb.; DObst RCOG 1958. Prev: GP Birm.

MENDALL, Michael Anthony Mayday University Hospital, London Road, Thornton Heath, Croydon CR7 7YE — MB BS 1985 Lond.; FRCP London 2000; MA Cantab 1995; MRCP Lond. 1988; MD Lond. 1995. (Cambridge University and Middlesex) Cons. Gastroenterol & Phys. Mayday; Sr Lect. St Geo. Med. Sch. Socs: RCP; Brit. Soc. of Gastroenterol.

MENDALL, Richard Charles Tel: 020 7624 9853 Fax: 020 7372 3660 — MB BS 1986 Lond.; MBA 1999 Durham Univ.; MRCGP 1990; DRCOG 1990; DCH RCP Lond. 1989.

MENDEL, David (retired) Gilhams Cottage, Eastling, Faversham ME13 0BP Tel: 01795 890464 — MB BS 1948 Lond.; FRCP Lond. 1973, M 1952; MRCS Eng. LRCP Lond. 1948. Prev: Cons. Phys. St. Thos. Hosp. Lond.

MENDEL, David Jonathan 44 Castlebar Park, London W5 1BU — MB BS 1979 Lond.; MRCGP 1983.

MENDEL, Dennis 1 Crosslands Avenue, Norwood Green, Southall UB2 5QY Tel: 020 8574 1906 — MRCS Eng. LRCP Lond. 1949; MD Lond. 1955, MB BS 1949; MRCP Lond. 1953. (St. Bart.) Socs: New York Acad. Sci. & Physiol. Soc. Prev: Reader in Physiol. King's Coll. Lond.; Sen. Lect. Physiol. Univ. Coll. Ibadan.

MENDEL, Leslie Department of Anaesthetics, Lincoln County Hospital, Greetwell Road, Lincoln LN2 5QY — MB BS 1967 Melbourne; FRCA (ad eundem) 1994; FFA RACS 1980; DA Eng. 1977. (Univ. of Melbourne) Cons. Anaesth. Lincoln Co. Hosp. Socs: Austral. Soc. Anaesth.; Assn. Anaesth. GB & Irel. Prev: Cons. Anaesth. Louth Co. Hosp.; Research Fell. (Anaesth. & Med.) Addenbrooke's Hosp. Camb.; Asst. Anaesth. Roy. Melbourne Hosp. Melbourne, Austral.

MENDEL, Paul Roger 220 Wheatlands, Hounslow TW5 0SQ — MB ChB 1983 Manch.; BSc St. And. 1980; FRCA 1989. Cons. Anaesth. King's Coll. Hosp. Lond. Prev: Sen. Regist. (Anaesth.) King's Coll. Hosp. Lond.; Vis. Asst. Prof. Anesthesiol. Univ. Texas S. W.. Med. Centre, Dallas, Texas.

MENDELOW, Professor Alexander David Department of Neurosurgery, Newcastle General Hospital, Westgate Road, Newcastle upon Tyne NE4 6BE Tel: 0191 273 8811 Fax: 0191 256 3267; Department Surgery, University of Newcastle upon Tyne, Newcastle upon Tyne — MB BCh Witwatersrand 1969; PhD Witwatersrand 1978; FRCS Ed. (SN) 1979; FRCS Ed. 1974. Prof. Regional Neurosci. Centre Newc. Gen. Hosp. Newc. u. Tyne; Hon. Cons. Neurosurg. Newc. HA & N.. RHA. Socs: Soc. Brit. Neurosurg. & Surg. Research Soc.; Treas. Euroacademia Multidisciplinaria Neurotraumatologica; MRC Neurosci.s and Ment. Health Bd. Prev: Reader (Neurosurg.) Univ. Newc.; Sen. Lect. (Neurosurg.) Univ. Glas. & Hon. Cons. Neurosurg.S.. Gen. Hosp Glas.; Clin. Dir. Neurosci.s 1994-98.

MENDELSOHN, Richard Alan 104 Weoly Park Road, Selly Oak, Birmingham B29 5HA — MB ChB 1987 Birm.

MENDELSOHN, Shevaun Shelagh Countess of Chester Hospital, Liverpool Road, Chester CH2 1UL — MB BS 1972 Lond.; FRCP Lond. 1993; MRCP (UK) 1978; DCH Eng. 1974. (Kings Coll. Hosp.) Cons. Dermat. Countess of Chester Hosp. Socs: BMA; Dowling Club; Brit. Assn. Dermat. Prev: Sen. Regist. (Dermat.) Roy. Liverp. Hosp.; Regist. (Med.) Stoke Mandeville Hosp. Aylesbury; SHO (Med. & Dermat.) High Wycombe Hosp.

MENDELSON, Eric Francis Wathwood Hospital, Gipsy Green Lane, Wath-upon-Dearne, Rotherham S63 7TQ Tel: 01709 870800 Fax: 01709 879976 — MB BS 1978 Lond.; MRCPsych 1983. Clin. Dir. & Cons. Forens. Psychiat. N. Trent Regional Forens. Psychiat. Servs. Prev: Med. Dir. & Cons. Forens. Psychiat. Ravenswood Ho. Wessex.

MENDES, Lionel Xavier Park House Surgery, Cavendish Road, Highams Park, London E11; 621 Patience Road, Clapham, London SW11 2PY — MB BS 1987 Lond. Prev: Trainee GP/SHO (Paediat., Cas., c/o Elderly & O & G) WhippsCross Hosp. Lond.

MENDES, Ruheena Luisa 31 Vaughan Gardens, Ilford IG1 3PA — MB BS 1994 Lond.

MENDES DA COSTA, Baron The Church Street Practice, David Corbet House, 2 Callows Lane, Kidderminster DY10 2JG Tel: 01562 822051 Fax: 01562 827251 — MB BS 1977 Lond.; Dip. Pall. Med. Wales 2000; MA Oxf. 1991, BA 1973; MRCS Eng. LRCP Lond. 1977; FRCGP 1995, M 1984; DRCOG 1981; Dip. Med. Ed. Wales 1994. (Guy's) Prev: SHO Rotat. (Med.) N.wick Pk. Hosp. Harrow; Trainee GP Hastings VTS.

MENDES DA COSTA, Charlotte Jane 4 Chesterfield Road, London W4 3HG — MB BS 1991 Lond.; MRCGP 1995; DFFP 1994; DCH RCP Lond. 1994. (St. Bart.) GP Lond. Retainer Scheme. Socs: Roy. Soc. Med. Prev: Trainee GP Lond.; SHO (O & G) Ealing Hosp. Middlx.

MENDES RIBEIRO, Helen Kathryn John Radcliffe Hospital, Headington, Oxford OX3 9DU; Church Farm House, Church Lane, Horton-cum-Studley, Oxford OX33 1AW — BM BCh 1990 Oxf.; MA Cantab. 1991; MRCP (UK) 1993; FRCR 1996. (Oxford) Cons. in Gastrintestinal Radiol. Oxf. Hosp. Socs: Esgar; Siggar. Prev: SHO Rotat. (Med.) Oxf. Hosps.; Ho. Off. (Med.) John Radcliffe Hosp. Oxf.; Ho. Off. (Surg.) Milton Keynes Dist. Gen. Hosp.

MENDHAN, Janine Elizabeth 12A Osborne Road, Clifton, Bristol BS8 2HB — MB ChB 1981 Bristol.

MENDICK, Manuel 3 Sunningdale Drive, Liverpool L23 7XA — MB ChB 1943 Ed. (Ed.)

MENDIS, Nalaka Campbell Centre, Milton Keynes Community NHS Trust, Standing Way, Eaglestone, Milton Keynes MK6 5NG — MB BS 1971 Ceylon; FRCPsych 1987.

MENDIS, Rajendranath Duleep (retired) 53 Dylan Road, Killay, Swansea SA2 7BN Tel: 01792 208934 — MB BS 1958 Ceylon; DA Eng. 1976. Prev: Regist. (Anaesth.) Gen. Hosp. LLa.lli & Singleton Hosp. Swansea.

MENDIS, Warnakulasuriya Wadumestrige G P 40 Chepstow Road, Croydon CR0 5JA — MB BS 1980 Colombo; MD Colombo 1987; MRCP (UK) 1987.

***MENDONCA, Corinna Olinda** 7 Greenhurst Road, London SE27 0LH — MB ChB 1997 Bristol.

MENDONCA, Mr Dennis Raymond Ear-Nose-Throat Department, Queen Mary's Hospital, Roehampton Lande, London SW15 5JU Tel: 020 8789 5124 Fax: 020 8355 2862; 2 Roedean Crescent, Roehampton, London SW15 5JU Tel: 020 8878 7271 Fax: 020 8878 7271 Email: mendonca@uk.packardbell.org — MB BS 1962 Bombay; MS Bombay 1965; FRCS (ENT) Eng. 1970; FCPS Bombay 1967, Dip. Otorhinolaryng. 1963. (Seth G.S. Med. Coll.) p/t Cons. ENT Surg. Qu. Mary's Univ. Hosp. Roehampton & Kingston Hosp., Surrey. Socs: Brit. Assn. Otol.; BMA; Brit. Voice Assn. Prev: Sen. Regist. (ENT) Leicester Roy. Infirm. & United Sheff. Hosps.; Clin. Fell. (Otolaryngol.) Univ. Toronto; Regist. (ENT) SE Kent Hosp. Gp.

MENDONCA, Lorna Maria Holly Bush House, 30 Ferncroft Avenue, Hampstead, London NW3 7PH Tel: 020 7435 2035 — MB BS 1966 Bombay; FFA RCS Eng. 1971; DA Bombay 1967. (Seth G.S. Med. Coll.) Cons. (Anaesth.) Chase Farm Hosp. Enfield, & Highlands Hosp. Lond. Prev: Sen. Regist. Anaesth. Char. Cross Hosp. Lond.; Sen. Res. Anaesth. Toronto Gen. Hosp. Canada; Regist. United Sheff. Hosps.

MENDONCA, Morel Jose Tome 109 St George's Road, Brighton BN2 1EA Tel: 01273 692444 — MB BS 1979 Lond.; BDS (Hons.) Lond. 1975; LDS RCS Eng. 1976. (Roy. Free) Gen. Dent. Pract.; Hon. Tutor Gen. Pract. Univ. Lond. Prev: BPMF Trainer Gen. Dent. Pract.; SHO (Oral Surg.) Roy. Sussex Co. Hosp.

MENDONCA, Shanti 'Shaneil', 64 Parkhurst Road, Bexley DA5 1AS — MB BS 1978 Bombay; MRCS Eng. LRCP Lond. 1978.

MENDOZA, Mr Nigel Duncan West London Neuroscience Centre, Department of Neurosurgery, Charing Cross Hospital, Fulham Palace Road, London W6 8RF Tel: 020 8846 1186 Fax: 020 8846 7787 Email: n.mendoza@ic.ac.uk; 59 Eastbury Grove, Chiswick, London W4 2JT Tel: 020 8995 6587 — MB BS 1983 Lond.; FRCS (SN) 1993; FRCS Eng. 1987. Cons. Neurosurg. Char. Cross Hosp. Lond. Socs: Soc. Brit. Neurol. Surgs.; Cervical Spine Soc.; Eur. Skull Base Soc. Prev: Sen. Regist. (Neurosurg.) Nat. Hosp. Neurol. & Neurosurg. Lond.

MENDS, David Robert Bowen (retired) 11 Eyre Crescent, Edinburgh EH3 5ET Tel: 0131 557 0335 — MSc Ed. 1980, MB ChB 1953; DTM & H Eng. 1962. Prev: Surg. Cdr. RN.

MENDUS-EDWARDS, Elwyn (retired) The Forge, Park Court, East St., Farnham GU9 7TB Tel: 01252 715835 — MRCS Eng. LRCP Lond. 1943; FFA RCS Eng. 1954; DA Eng. 1947. Prev: Cons. Anaesth. King Edwd. VII Hosp. Midhurst & Roy. Surrey Co. Hosp. Guildford.

MENE, Aruna Ravindra Blackburn Royal Infirmary, Blackburn BB2 3LR Tel: 01254 63555; Ashiana, 12 Hillside, Heaton, Bolton BL1 5DT Tel: 01204 46652 — MD 1975 Nagpur; MD (Path. & Bacteriol.) Nagpur 1975, MB BS 1972, DCH 1981; MRCPath 1986. Cons. Histopath. Blackburn Gp. Hosps. Socs: (Brit. Div.) Internat. Acad. Path.

MENE, Ravindra Chester Road Surgery, 872 Chester Road, Stretford, Manchester M32 0PA Tel: 0161 865 5556 Fax: 0161 866 8688.

MENEZES, Armando Rodolfo Ashville Medical Centre, 430 Doncaster Road, Barnsley S70 3RJ Tel: 01226 282280; 18 Westville Road, Barnsley S75 2TR — MB ChB 1963 Leeds; MRCS Eng. LRCP Lond. 1963; MCOphth 1990; DO RCS Eng. 1967. (Leeds) Ophth. Med. Pract. Barnsley. Prev: SHO Newc. Gen. Hosp.; Ho. Phys. St. Jas. Hosp. Leeds; Clin. Asst. (Ophth.) Barnsley Dist. Gen. Hosp.

MENEZES, George Robert 69 Manister Road, Abbey Wood, London SE2 9PL Tel: 020 8310 9389 — MB BS 1954 Calcutta. (Calcutta) Prev: Ho. Surg. (ENT & Ophth.) Ipswich & E. Suff. Hosp. (Anglesea Rd. Wing); Ho. Surg. (Gen. Surg.) St. Helen's Hosp. Hastings.

***MENEZES, Leon Jonathan Xavier** 7 Polworth Road, London SW16 2ET — BM BCh 1998 Oxf.; BM BCh Oxf 1998.

***MENGHER, Lakhbir Singh** 21 Kirkland Road, Leicester LE3 2JQ — MB BS 1994 West Indies.

MENIN, Paul Terence Waterfront Garden Surgery, Jones Lane, Hythe SO45 6AT Tel: 023 8084 1841/8061 2451 Fax: 023 8084 8084; The Narrows, Lower Mullins Lane, Hythe, Southampton SO45 5AF — MB BS 1981 Lond.; BSc 1978 Lond.; MRCGP 1987; DRCOG 1985. GP Princip. Prev: Trainee GP Hythe Med. Centre; SHO (Paediat., Rheum. & Obst.) W. Middlx. Hosp. Isleworth.

MENKE, Thomas Department of Neurology, Frenchay Hospital, Frenchay Park Road, Bristol BS16 1LE — State Exam Med. Berlin 1992.

MENNELLA, Maurizio Flat 176 Newtown Road, Ronkswood Branch, Worcester WR5 1JB — State Exam 1988 Rome.

MENNIE, George Hardie Banchory Group Practice, The Surgery, Bellfield, Banchory AB31 5XS Tel: 01330 822121 Fax: 01330 825265 — MB ChB 1965 Aberd.; MRCGP 1975; DObst RCOG 1967. (Aberd.) Prev: S. Pacific Health Serv.

MENNIE, Graham Shields 2 Cambustay Gardens, Broughty Ferry, Dundee DD5 2SR — MB ChB 1990 Dundee; MRCGP 1994; DCH RCP Lond. 1993.

MENNIE, Robert Harold Allington Park Surgery, 1C Newbury Avenue, Allington, Maidstone ME16 0RB Tel: 01622 683257 Fax: 01622 677365; (branch Surgery), 54-56 Towbridge Road, Maidstone — MB BS 1980 Lond.; MRCGP 1986; DRCOG 1985; Cert. Family Plann. JCC 1985. Clin. Asst. (Diabetes) Maidstone Hosp.

MENNIM, Peter Gary The Residencies, Leighton Hospital, Middlewich Road, Crewe CW1 4QJ; 38 Merlin Way, Crewe CW1 3RZ — MB ChB 1990 Manch.

MENON, Ambalaparambil Gopalakrishna 6 Maes-yr-Helyg, Llwydcoed, Aberdare CF44 0YW — MB BS 1963 Karnatak; DTCD Wales 1970. (Kasturba Med. Coll. Mangalore) Socs: BMA & Cardiff Med. Soc.

MENON, Professor David Krishna Box 93, Addenbrokes Hospital, Cambridge CB2 2QQ — FRCA 1988 UK; FRCP 1999 London; MRCP 1984 UK; MBBS 1977 University of Madras; MBBS 1977 Madras; PhD 1996 London Univ; MD 1982 Madras. (Jawaharlal Institute, University of Madras) Prof. of Anaesth., Univ. of Camb., Addenbrookes Hosp.; Director of Neurocritical Care & Hon. Cons. Anaesth., Addenbrooke's Hosp. Socs: Roy. Soc. of Med.; Soc. of NeuroAnaesth. and Critical CAre; Assn. of Anaesth.s. Prev: Lect. in Anaesth., Univ. of Camb.; Clin. Lect. in Anaesth., Univ. of Camb.; MRC Research Fell., Hammersmith Hosp.

MENON, Gita Mayday University Hospital, Croydon, London — MB BS 1981; FRCA 1991. Cons. Anaesth.; Coll. Tutor, Dept. of Anaesth. Socs: BMA Roy. Coll. Anaesth. RSM.

MENON, Gopikumar Neonatal Unit, Simpson Memorial Maternity Pavillian, Camriston Place, Edinburgh EH3 9EF Tel: 0131 546 1000 Fax: 0131 536 4297 Email: gopi.menon@ed.ac.uk — MB BChir 1979 Camb.; BA (Hons.) Camb. 1976, MB BChir 1979; MRCP (UK) 1984; FRCPCH 1997. (Cambridge) Cons. (Neonatology) Simpson Matern. Pavil.; Hon. Sen. Lect. Univ. of Edin. Socs: Fell. Roy. Coll. Paediat. Child Health; Brit. Assn. Prenatal Med. Prev: Lect. & Hon. Sen. Regist. (Child Life & Health) Edin. Univ.; Regist. (Paediat.) P'boro & Leic. Gen. Hosp. & Leic. Roy. Infirm.

MENON, John Asoka (retired) Blaencrai, Crai, Brecon LD3 8YR Tel: 018746 36484 — MB BS 1949 Lond.; MRCS Eng. LRCP Lond. 1949; DO Eng. 1962. Prev: Assoc. Specialist N. Middlx. Hosp.

MENON, Kollaikkal Vijaya Kumar Carfin Road Surgery, 15 Carfin Road, Motherwell ML1 5AG Tel: 01698 732501 — MB BS 1974 Madras. (Stanley Medical College Madras)

MENON, Leela (retired) Penwood, The Avenue, Ross-on-Wye HR9 5AW — MB BS 1948 Lond.; MRCS Eng. LRCP Lond. 1948; DObst RCOG 1952. Prev: Ho. Phys. Roy. Free Hosp. & Manch. Childr. Hosp.

MENON, Leela Hollies Health Centre, Merthyr Tydfil CF47 1UA Tel: 01685 722436 Fax: 01685 384286 — MB BS 1948 London; MB BS l948 Lond.; LRCP Lond. 1948; MRCS Eng. (London) GP Merthyr Tydfil.

MENON, Mr Madhav 44 Waltham Court, Beverley HU17 9JF Tel: 0410 502262 Email: m.menon@hotmail.com — MB BS 1988 Madras; FRCS Glas. 1993. Regist. (Gen. Surg.) Castle Hill Hosp. Cottingham.

MENON, Mattacaud Ramakrishna Gopala 25 Orchard Way, Stretton-on-Dunsmore, Rugby CV23 9HP — MB BS 1963 Karnatak; MRCGP 1978; DTM & H Liverp. 1972; DTCD Wales 1974. (Kasturba Med. Coll. Mangalore) GP Princip. Stretton-on-Dunsmore. Socs: FRSH. Prev: SHO (Orthop. & Cas.) & SHO (Surg.) W. Cumbld. Hosp. Gp.; SHO (Neurosurg.) Preston Roy. Infirm.

MENON, Neil Padman 97 Marlborough Gardens, Upminster RM14 1SR — MB ChB 1991 Liverp.

MENON, Mr Nimal Kenneth The Ongar Surgery, High Street, Ongar CM5 9AA Tel: 01277 363976 Fax: 01277 365115; Patonie, Hook End Road, Brentwood CM15 0HA Tel: 01277 822083 Email: kenmenon@compuserve.com — MB BS 1971 Ceylon; MA Wales 1989; FRCS Eng. 1978; MRCS Eng. LRCP Lond. 1980; FRCGP 1995, M 1982; MFFP 1993; DCH RCP Lond. 1981. Prev: Regist. (Surg.) St. Margt. Hosp. Epping; SHO Chelmsford Hosp. Gp.; SHO (Thoracic Surg.) City Hosp. Nottm.

MENON, Peter (retired) Brook House, 59 Bailey St, Ton Pentre, Pentre CF41 7EN Tel: 01443 423758 — MB BS 1957 Madras; BSc Madras 1951, MB BS 1957; DTM & H Ed. 1959.

MENON, Prem Kumar Arrowe Park Hospital, Arrowe Park Road, Upton, Wirral CH49 5PE — MB BS 1976 Karnatak; MRCPsych 1982; DPM Eng. 1980. Cons. Psychiat. Mersey RHA.

MENON, Rajeev The Surgery, Sydenham House, Mill Court, Ashford TN24 8DN Tel: 01233 645851 Fax: 01233 638281 — MB BS 1984 Lond.

MENON, Rajgopalan Arthington Medical Centre, 5 Moor Road, Hunslet, Leeds LS10 2JJ Tel: 0113 270 5645 Fax: 0113 270 0927 — MB BS 1974 Andhra; LMSSA Lond. 1977; DFFP 1994; DCH NUI 1980; DRCOG 1978. (Andhra Med. Coll. Visakhapatnam) Princip. Gen. Pract.; Tutor Gen. Pract. Leeds Univ. Socs: Leeds & W. Riding M-C Soc.; BMA. Prev: Trainee GP Halifax VTS; Ho. Off. (Gen. Surg. & ENT) Staincliffe Gen. Hosp. Dewsbury; Ho. off. Gerontology St James Univ. Hosp.

MENON, Raji Jayaram 48 Granville Park W., Aughton, Ormskirk L39 5DX — MB BS 1971 Madras; DA Eng. 1975. (Jawaharlal Inst. Pondicherry) Clin. Med. Off. Lancs. HA. Prev: SHO (Anaesth.) St. Jas.

MENON

Univ. Hosp. Leeds & Pontefract Gen. Infirm.; Clin. Asst. (Anaesth.) Whipps Cross Hosp. Lond.

MENON, Ram Rajiv Mental Health Centre, Chelsea & Westminster Hospital, Fulham Road, London SW10 9NG Tel: 020 8846 6056 Fax: 020 8846 6060 Email: rajivrmenon@hotmail.com — MB BS 1981 Delhi; MPhil Lond. 1994; MRCPI 1987; MRCPsych 1991. Cons. Psychiat. Chelsea & W.m. Hosp. Lond.; Sen. Research Fell. (Psychiat.) Imperial Coll. Sch. Med.; Hon. Cons. Psychiat. to the Roy. Hosp. Lond. Prev: Sen. Regist. & Regist. Maudsley Hosp. Lond.; Research Fell. (Psychiat.) John Hopkins Univ., USA.

MENON, Ramanpillai Gopinath Ynysybwl Surgery, The Square, Robert Street, Pontypridd CF37 3DU Tel: 01443 790360 Fax: 01443 791309 — MB BS 1970 Utkal. (S.C.B. Med. Coll. Cuttack) Socs: BMA. Prev: SHO (Med.) Minehead & W. Som. Hosp. & Llwynypia Hosp.

MENON, Sanjeev 104 Cardington Square, Hounslow TW4 6AJ — MB BS 1987 Lond.

MENON, Shobha 16 Cholmondeley Avenue, Timperley, Altrincham WA14 5BB Tel: 0161 976 2043 — MB BS 1982 Madras; DCH RCPSI 1987. Staff Grade Med. Pract. (Community Child Health) Mancunian Community NHS Trust. Socs: BMA; Brit. Paediat. Assn.; Brit. Soc. Audiol. Prev: Regist. (Paediat.) Wythenshawe Hosp. & St. Mary's Hosp. Manch.; Regist. (Paediat.) Roy. Manch. Childr. Hosp.

MENON, Mr Thottapilli Jayaram 48 Granville Park W., Aughton, Ormskirk L39 5DX — MB BS 1971 Madras; FRCS Ed. (Orth.) 1983; FRCS Glas. 1976. Cons. Orthop. Surg. S.port and Ormskirk Hosp. NHS Trust. Socs: Brit. Orthopaedic Assn.; Brit. Soc. for Childr.s' Orthopaed. Surg.; Manch. Med. Soc. Prev: Sen. Regist. (Orthop.) N.W. RHA.

MENON, Vengalil Narayani 7 Oakhill Road, Orpington BR6 0AE Tel: 01689 28732 — MB BS 1956 Madras; DCH Eng. 1959. (Madras) Deptm. Med. Off. Lond. Boro. Bromley. Prev: Ho. Surg. Lambeth Hosp. Lond.; Ho. Physs. W. Middlx. Hosp. Isleworth; Med. Off. i/c Families Hosp. Bangalore, India.

MENOWN, Ian Brian Alexander Regional Medical Cardiology Centre, Wards 5 & 6, Royal Victoria Hospital, Grosvenor Road, Belfast BT12 6BA Tel: 01232 240503 Fax: 01232 312907 — MB BCh BAO 1992 Belf.; MRCP (UK) 1995; MD Belf. 1999. (Qu. Univ. Belf.) Specialist Regist. (Cardiol.) Regional Med. Cardiol. Centre Roy. Vict. Hosp. Belf. Socs: RCP Ed.; Ulster Med. Soc. Prev: Specialist Regist. (Cardiol.) Antrim Hosp. Antrim; Specialist Regist. (Cardiol.) Roy. Vict. Hosp. Belf.; Res. Regist. (Cardiol.) Roy. Vict. Hosp. Belf.

MENSAH, Evelyn 11 Boundary Gardens, Newcastle upon Tyne NE7 7AA — MB BS 1991 Lond.

MENSAH, John Amoafo Scarborough Hospital, Woodlands Drive, Scarborough YO12 6QL Tel: 01723 368111 Email: john.mensah@virgin.net; Sunset, Mill Lane, Cloughton, Scarborough YO13 0AB — BM BS 1989 Nottm.; DA (UK) 1992; FRCA 1996; B.Med Sci. (Hons) 1987 Nottm. (Nottm.) Cons. Anaesth., ScarBoro. Hosp.

MENSAH, Paul Kwamina Anfam Department of Obstetrics & Gynaecology, Dumfries & Galloway Royal Infirmary, Bankend Road, Dumfries DG1 4AP Tel: 01387 246246 Fax: 01387 421298; Manoa, 38 Dalbeattie Road, Dumfries DG2 7PL Email: paul.mensah@virgin.net — MB ChB 1983 Ghana; MB ChB U Ghana 1983; MRCOG 1992. (Univ. Of Ghana) Cons. (O & G) Dumfries & Galloway Roy. Infirm. Scotl.; RCOG Dist. Tutor. Socs: Brit. Menopause Soc.; Brit. Matern. & Fetal Med. Soc. Prev: Regist. (O & G) S.lands Hosp. W. Sussex.; Regist. Newc. Gen. Hosp, Dryburn Hosp.

MENSING, Claire Natalie Department of Accident and Emergency, Royal Sussex County Hospital, Eastern Road, Brighton BN2 5BE — MB BS 1997 Lond.

***MENSON, Essie Natasha** 67 York Road, Montpelier, Bristol BS6 5QD — MB ChB 1994 Bristol.

MENT, Jerome Lionel 200 Station Road, Knowle, Solihull B93 0ER — MB ChB 1991 Stellenbosch.

MENTON, John Peter Manor Farm Medical Centre, Manor Farm Road, Huyton, Liverpool L36 0UB Tel: 0151 480 1244 Fax: 0151 480 6047 — MB BCh BAO 1983 NUI; LRCPI & LM LRCSI & LM 1983.

MENTOR, Johan Marthinus 12 Redwood Croft, Nuneaton CV10 7HY — MB ChB 1983 Stellenbosch.

MENZIES, Angus Robert, Maj. RAMC Clare Cottage, Neacroft, Bransgore, Christchurch BH23 8JS — MB BS 1983 Lond.; BA Oxf. 1976. Socs: Medico-Legal Soc. Prev: Ho. Phys. & Ho. Surg. Rochford Hosp.

MENZIES, Colin Benreary Surgery, Seaview Place, Buckie AB56 1JT Tel: 01542 831555 Fax: 01542 835799 — MB ChB 1975 Glas.; MRCGP 1979; MRCPsych. 1982; DRCOG 1979.

MENZIES, Colin James Grant (retired) High Meadow, 55 Oakley Road, Dovercourt, Harwich CO12 4QT Tel: 01255 502804 — MB BS Lond. 1949; FRCGP 1987, M 1962; DObst RCOG 1954; LMSSA Lond. 1949. Prev: Med. Off. Harwich & Dist. Hosp.

MENZIES, David Alexander Block Lane Surgery, 158 Block Lane, Chadderton, Oldham OL9 7SG Tel: 0161 620 2321 Fax: 0161 628 5604 — MB ChB 1974 Aberd.

MENZIES, Diana Elizabeth Fax: 020 7622 9164 Email: dmenzies@swlstg-tr.nhs.uk — MB BS 1988 Lond.; Mem. Inst. Of Group Analysis 2001; BSc Lond. 1978; MRCPsych 1992; CCST Psychother 1997. (St. George's Hospital MS London) Cons. Psychotherapist Henderson Outreach Serv. Team Sutton. Socs: BMA; MWF; Soc. for Psychothapy Research (SPR). Prev: Sen. Regist. (Psychother.) Warneford Hosp. Oxf.; Sen. Regist. (Psychiat.) St. Geo. Hosp. Lond.

MENZIES, Mr Donald Colchester General Hospital, Turner Road, Colchester CO4 5JL Tel: 01206 853535 Email: donald.menzies@tinyworld.co.uk — MB BS 1983 Lond.; MS Lond. 1991, MB BS 1983; FRCS Eng. 1987. Cons. Surg. Colchester Gen. Hosp. Socs: Roy. Soc. Med.; Assn. Endoscopic Surgs.; Assn. Upper G.I. Surg. Prev: Sen. Regist. (Gen. Surg.) Addenbrooke's Hosp. Camb.; Regist. (Gen. Surg.) Colchester Gen. Hosp, & Roy. Lond. Hosp.

MENZIES, Donald Graham Department of Occupational Health and Medicine, Stepping Hill Hospital, Poplar Grove, Stockport SK2 7JE Tel: 0161 419 5492 Fax: 0161 419 4953; 76 Glossop Road, Marple Bridge, Stockport SK6 5EL — MB ChB 1983 Ed.; BSc (Hons.) Physiol. Ed. 1980; FRCP Ed 1997; MRCP (UK) 1986; MFOM RCP Lond. 1994, AFOM 1991. (Ed.) Dir. Occupat. Health Servs. & Cons. Occupat. Med. Stockport NHS Trust. Socs: Soc. Occupat. Med.; Assn. Nat. Health Occupat. Phys.; Assn. Local Auth. Med. Advisors. Prev: Sen. Regist. (Occupat. Med.) N. W.. RHA; Regist. (Med.) Roy. Infirm. Edin.

MENZIES, Mr Donald Norwood (retired) 39 Cherry Vale, Gateacre, Liverpool L25 5PX Tel: 0151 428 7575 Fax: 0151 421 0600 — MB ChB Liverp. 1948; FRCS Ed. 1958; FRCOG 1968, M 1953. Prev: Cons. Gyn. Lourdes Hosp. Liverp.

MENZIES, Euan Ashby Dickson 4 Morley Court, 40 Sydney Road, London N10 2RJ — MB BS 1977 Lond.; MRCP (UK) 1982. (Roy. Free)

MENZIES, Evelyn Mary Perth Royal Infirmary, Taymount Terrace, Perth PH1 1NX; Croit Oran, Carnbo, Kinross KY13 ONX — MB ChB 1984 Ed.; DRCOG 1987; MRCP 1997. (Ed.) Staff Grade Paediat. Perth Roy. Infirm.

MENZIES, Gillian Fiona Flat 311, 123 Tantallon Road, Shawlands, Glasgow G41 3EQ — MB ChB 1995 Glas.; ARCOG; FFP. (Glas.) GP Locum W. of Scotl. Socs: BMA; MDDUS. Prev: GP Regist. E. Kilbridge Lanarksh. Feb 2000-2001; Geriat. Med. Gartnaval Hosp. Aug 1999-Feb 2000; O +G S.. Gen. Hosp. Feb. 1999-Aug 1999.

MENZIES, Ian Crerar (retired) 7 Douglas Terrace, Broughty Ferry, Dundee DD5 1EA Tel: 01382 77183 — MB ChB 1954 Ed.; FRCPsych 1975, M 1972; DPM Ed. & Glas. 1966; DObst RCOG 1959. Prev: Cons. Child Psychiat. Tayside HB.

MENZIES, Ian Stuart Ignatius Villiers Lodge, 1 Cranes Park, Surbiton KT5 8AB Tel: 020 8339 6000 — MB BS 1955 Lond.; DPath. Eng. 1963; FRCPath 1980, M 1967. (St. Bart.) Sen. Lect. & Hon. Cons. (Chem. Path.) St. Thos. Hosp. Lond. Prev: Regist. (Chem. Path.) Hosp. Sick Childr. Gt. Ormond St.; Regist. (Med.) Ashford Hosp. Middlx.; Regist. (Clin. Path.) St. Helier Hosp. Carshalton.

MENZIES, Lisa Julie Quay House Medical Centre, 100 Westfaling Street, Bobblestock, Hereford HR4 0JF Tel: 01432 352600; 22 Redcar Avenue, Bobblestock, Hereford HR4 9TJ Tel: 01432 275309 — BM 1982 Soton.; MRCGP 1989; DCH RCP Lond. 1987; DRCOG 1985. (Soton.)

MENZIES, Lynn Janet 47 Old Park Road S., Enfield EN2 7DD — MB BS 1982 Lond.

MENZIES, Lieutenant General Robert Clark, OBE, QHS, OStJ, Lt.-Gen. late RAMC Surgeon General, Ministry of Defence, Room 6360, Main Building, Whitehall, London SW1A 2HB Fax: 020 7807 8805 — MB ChB Glas. 1967; FRCPath 1992, M 1980; DMJ (Path.) Soc. Apoth. Lond. 1976; FFPHM 1999; FRCP 2000 Edinburgh. (Glas.) Surg. Gen. Defence Med. Serv.s Min. of Defence. Socs: Fell. Roy. Soc. Med.; Brit. Assn. Forens. Med.; Brit. Acad. Forens. Sci. Prev: Director Gen. Army Med. Serv.s; Cdr. Med. HQ Land Command.

MENZIES, Robert Dickson, Lt.-Col. RAMC Retd. Lane End, Deepdene Park Road, Dorking RH5 4AW — MB ChB 1935 Glas. Prev: Clin. Asst. Dermat. Dept. Roy. Infirm. Edin.; Phys. i/c. Skin Dept. Singapore Gen. Hosp.; Lect. in Skin Dis. (p/t) Univ. Singapore.

***MENZIES, Robert William** The Tile House, 19 Arbour Close, The Mount, Fetcham, Leatherhead KT22 9DZ; The Conservatory, Pembury, Lansdown Crescen,, Cheltenham GL50 2JX Tel: 07771 528345 Email: drr_menzies@hotmail.com — MB BS 1998 Lond.; MB BS Lond 1998; BSc Anat 1995.

MENZIES, Rosemary Jane 36 Lodore Road, High West Jesmond, Newcastle upon Tyne NE2 3NN — MB ChB 1977 Ed.; ChB Ed. 1977; MRCP 1982.

MENZIES, Stewart James Rookswood, Chestnut Close, Peakirk, Peterborough PE6 7NW Tel: 01733 252086 — MB BS 1972 Lond.; MRCS Eng. LRCP Lond. 1972; MFHom 1995; DCH Eng. 1976; DObst RCOG 1975. (Westm.) Indep. Pract. (Homoeop. & Acupunc.) P'boro. Socs: Brit. Med. Acupunct. Soc. Prev: Trainee GP Bury St. Edmunds VTS; Ho. Surg. W.m. Hosp. Lond.; Ho. Phys. Roy. Devon & Exeter Hosp.

MENZIES, Susan Elizabeth Health Centre, Avenue Road, Cockenzie, Prestonpans EH32 0JU Tel: 01875 811501 Fax: 01875 814421 Email: administrator@gp76052lothian.hb.scot.nhs.uk; 35 Gilmour Road, Edinburgh EH16 5NS Tel: 0131 667 5086 — MB ChB 1986 Aberd.; MRCGP 1991; DRCOG 1990. Princip. GP.

MENZIES, Sydney William Stuart Appleby Surgery, Hawkeys Lane, North Shields NE29 0SF Tel: 0191 296 1770 Fax: 0191 296 1770; Kirkwall, 32 King Edward Road, Tynemouth, North Shields NE30 2RP Tel: 0191 257 2768 Email: smenzies@epulse.net — MB BS Durh. 1962; MRCGP 1969; Dip. Ther. Newc. 1994; DFFP 1993; Cert. Family Plann. JCC 1979; DObst RCOG 1964. (Newc.) Socs: Fell. Roy. Soc. Med.; BMA; (Hon. Treas.) Pybus Soc. Prev: SHO Doncaster Roy. Infirm. & Craigtoun Matern. Hosp. St. And.; Ho. Surg. Roy. Vict. Infirm. Newc.

***MENZIES-GOW, Andrew Neil** The Corner House, 2 Staines Road, Staines TW18 2TE — MB BS 1994 Lond.; BSc Lond. 1991, MB BS 1994.

MENZIES-GOW, Lynn Christine Weybridge Health Centre, Minorca Road, Weybridge KT13 8DU Tel: 01932 853366 Fax: 01932 844902; The Corner House, 2 Staines Road, Laleham, Staines TW18 2TE Tel: 01784 455830 — MB BS 1969 Lond.; MRCS Eng. LRCP Lond. 1969. (Middlx) GP Asst. Weybridge. Prev: Ho. Surg. (O & G) Centr. Middlx. Hosp. Lond.; Ho. Surg. & Ho. Phys. Harefield Hosp.

MENZIES-GOW, Mr Neil The Princess Grace Hospital, Consulting Rooms, 42/52 Nottingham Place, London W1U 5NY Tel: 020 7486 1234; The Corner House, 2 Staines Road, Laleham, Staines TW18 2TE Tel: 01784 55830 — MB BS 1969 Lond.; FRCS Eng. 1974; MRCS Eng. LRCP Lond. 1969. (Middlx.) Cons. Surg. Centr. Middlx. Hosp. Prev: Sen. Regist. (Surg.) Middlx. Hosp. Lond.; Regist. (Surg.) Centr. Middlx. Hosp. Lond.; Surg. Regist. Middlx. Hosp. Lond.

MEPHAM, Stephen Owen 53 Caiystane Terrace, Edinburgh EH10 6SU — MB ChB 1993 Aberd.; BSc (Hons.) Aberd. 1991; MRCP (UK) 1996. SHO (Infec. Dis.) City Hosp. Edin. Prev: SHO Rotat. (Med.) Aberd. Roy. Infirm.

MERALI, Nizar Roshanali GP Direct, 5/7 Welback Road, West Harrow, Harrow HA2 0RH Tel: 020 8515 9300 Fax: 020 8515 9300 — MB ChB 1976 Manch.; 2000 DDAM; MB ChB (Hons.) Manch. 1976; MBA Lond. 1997; MRCGP 1982; DGM RCP Lond. 1986. (University of Manchester) Hosp. Pract. (Geriat.) Denham Unit, Harrow. Socs: Director, Harmoni (Harrow Medics Out of Hours Network Inc.). Prev: Clin. Asst. (Geriat.) Anmer Lodge Nursing Home.

MERALI, Nizarali Abdulla The High Ridge Surgery, 224 Weston Road, Meir, Stoke-on-Trent ST3 6EE Tel: 01782 598350.

MERCER, Ann Claire Mary (retired) Castor House, Castor, Peterborough PE5 7AX Tel: 01733 380216 Fax: 01733 380843 Email: info@fridgemagic.com — MB ChB 1985 Leic.; MRCGP 1989; Dip. Palliat. Med. Wales 1992; DRCOG 1988. Prev: GP P'boro. retainer scheme.

MERCER, Barbara Elizabeth Agnes (retired) The Surgery, 76 Main St., Broughshane, Ballymena BT42 4JP Tel: 01266 861214 Fax: 01266 862281 — MB BCh BAO 1960 Belf. Prev: GP Broughshane.

MERCER, Colin Ian Holywood Arches Health Centre, Westminster Avenue, Belfast BT4 1NS Tel: 028 9056 3354 Fax: 028 9065 3846; 5 Holland Park, Belfast BT5 6HB Tel: 01232 471429 Email: colin@holland1.onet.co.uk — MB BCh BAO 1988 Belf.; MRCGP 1992; DRCOG 1991; DCH Dub. 1991. Prev: SHO (Gen. Med. & Paediat.) Ulster Hosp. Dundonald NI.

MERCER, Colin Peter Mandalay Medical Centre, 933 Blackburn Road, Bolton BL1 7LR Tel: 01204 302228 Fax: 01204 597949 — MB ChB 1983 Manch.; MRCGP 1987; DCH RCP Lond. 1987; DRCOG 1987. Princip. GP Bolton FPC. Prev: Trainee GP Salford VTS.

MERCER, David (retired) Somercotes, 93 Fore St., Plympton, Plymouth PL7 1NB Tel: 01752 337123 — MB ChB Sheff. 1958; FRCP Lond. 1986, M 1965; MRCS Eng. LRCP Lond. 1958. Prev: Hons. Cons. Phys. Health Care Elderly Derriford Hosp. Plymouth.

MERCER, David Raymond Vaudrey Lower Road, Cookham Rise, Maidenhead SL6 9HX; Back of Beyond, Winter Hill, Cookham, Maidenhead SL6 9TW Tel: 01628 524646 — MB BS 1967 Lond.; MRCS Eng. LRCP Lond. 1967; MRCGP 1984; DObst RCOG 1969. (Char. Cross) PCG Chair, Windsor, Ascot and Maidenhead. Socs: BMA; Brit. Acupunc. Soc. Prev: SHO (Obst.) Canad. Red Cross Memor. Hosp. Taplow; Ho. Phys. Char. Cross Hosp. Lond.; Ho. Surg. (Gyn.) W. Lond. Hosp.

MERCER, Deirdre Susan Brockton House, Brockton, Newport TF10 9EP — MB ChB 1980 Bristol; FFA RCS Eng. 1985.

MERCER, Mr Derek McDonald The Sloane Hospital, 125 Albemarle Road, Beckenham BR3 5HS Tel: 020 8466 6911; No. 11 County Hall, North Black, London SE1 7PJ Tel: 020 7928 5050 Fax: 020 7207 7572 — MB ChB 1974 Dundee; FRCS Eng. 1980; T(S) 1991. Cons. Plastic Surg. St Thos. Hosp. Lond. & Bromley Hosp. Socs: Brit. Assn. Aesthetic Plastic Surgs.; Brit. Assn. Plastic Surg. Prev: Cons. Plastic Surg. King's Coll. Hosp. Lond.; Sen. Regist. Qu. Vict. Hosp. E. Grinstead; Associé CHU Hosp. Henri-Mondor, Paris, France.

MERCER, Gavin William Herdmanflat Hospital, Haddington EH41 3BU Tel: 0131 536 5300 — MB ChB 1984 Ed.; MRCPsych 1990. Cons. Psychiat. Lothian Primary Care NHS. Prev: Sen. Lect. (Psychiat.) Univ. Newc.-u-Tyne; Cons Psychiat Perth & kinross NHS Trust.

MERCER, Ian Hector, Group Capt. RAF Med. Br. Retd. 52 Casterton Road, Stamford PE9 2UA Tel: 01780 764960 Fax: 01780 764960 — LMSSA Lond. 1945; MFPHM 1974; DPH Lond. 1962. (Lond. Hosp.) Prev: PMO HQ Train. Command; OC RAF Hosp. Nocton Hall; Ho. Surg. Neurosurgic. Unit Lond. Hosp.

MERCER, James Campbell Gibson, OBE (retired) 44 Church Street, Ladybank, Cupar KY15 7LE — MB ChB 1941 Ed.; FFCM 1974; FRCGP 1978, M 1953; DCH Eng. 1948. Prev: Chief Admin. Med. Off. Fife HB.

MERCER, Jane 8 Barne Close, Whitestone, Nuneaton CV11 4TP — MB ChB 1979 Leeds; BSc Leeds 1976; MRCPath 1992. Cons. Histopath. Geo. Eliot Hosp. Nuneaton. Socs: Assn. Clin. Paths.; Brit. Soc. Clin. Cytol.; Path. Soc. Prev: Sen. Regist. (Histopath.) Leicester & Kettering.

***MERCER, Joanna Dawn** 6 Bicknor Road, Orpington BR6 0TS — MB BS 1998 Lond.; MB BS Lond 1998.

MERCER, John Dallas The Spinney, 180 Middlewich Road, Sandbach CW11 1JD Tel: 01270 760842 — MB BChir 1970 Camb.; MB Camb. 1970, MA, BChir 1969; MRCS Eng. LRCP Lond. 1960. (Camb. & St. Bart.) GP Half-day Release Course Organiser S. Chesh.

MERCER, John Humphrey Michael 43 Jubilee Road, Wrexham LL13 7NN — MB BS 1980 Med. Inst. (II) Rangoon.

MERCER, Jonathan Henry Victoria House Surgery, 33 Victoria Road, Swindon SN1 3AW Tel: 01793 536515; 38 North Wall,

MERCER

Cricklade, Swindon SN6 6DU — BM BCh 1987 Oxf.; MRCGP 1991. Prev: Trainee GP Swindon/Cirencester VTS.

MERCER, Josephine Mary Kilkeel Health Centre, Knockchree Avenue, Kilkeel, Newry BT34 4BS Tel: 028 4176 2601 Fax: 028 4176 5485 — MB BCh BAO 1978 NUI; LRCPI & LM, LRCSI & LM 1978.

MERCER, Julia Compton Lower Road Medical Health Centre, Lower Road, Cookham Rise, Maidenhead SL6 9HX Tel: 01628 524646 Fax: 01628 810201; Back of Beyond, Winter Hill, Cookham Dean, Maidenhead SL6 9TW Tel: 0162 85 24646 — MB BS 1967 Lond.; MRCS Eng. LRCP Lond. 1967; MRCGP 1982. (Char. Cross) Trainer (Gen. Pract.) Maidenhead. Prev: Ho. Phys. Fulham Hosp. Lond.; Ho. Surg. Fulham Hosp. Lond.; Family Plann. Instruc. Doctor.

MERCER, Katherine Alice (retired) Highfield, Silverdale, Carnforth LA5 0SQ Tel: 01524 701234 Fax: 01524 701234 — MB ChB 1946 Ed. Prev: Clin. Asst. (Psychiat.) Lancaster.

MERCER, Keith John 3/R 42 Belwood Street, Glasgow G41 3ES — MB ChB 1993 Glas.

MERCER, Mr Kevin Graham 58 The Drive, Roundhay, Leeds LS8 1HJ Email: k.g.mercer@leeds.ac.uk — BM BS 1991 Nottm.; FRCS Ed. 1996. Specialist Regist. Gen. Surg. Yorks. Region Rot. Ledds. Prev: SHO Surg. Rotat. St. Jas. & Seacroft NHS Trust Leeds; Research Fell. Vasc. Surg. St Jas. & Seacroft NHS Trust Leeds.

MERCER, Louise Ann Station Road Health Centre, Station Road, Haydock, St Helens NA11 0JN Tel: 01744 22272; 1 Seftonfold Gardens, Billinge, Wigan WN5 7QS — MB ChB 1990 Liverp. GP Princip.

MERCER, Mary Daubeny (retired) 7A Recreation Road, Sydenham, London SE26 4ST Tel: 020 8676 9639 — MB BS Lond. 1938; MRCS Eng. LRCP Lond. 1936; DObst RCOG 1939. Prev: Asst. Med. Off. Middlx. CC.

MERCER, Michael Hopton 5 Greenway House, Redland Park, Redland, Bristol BS6 6SD — MB BChir 1990 Camb.; MB ChB Camb. 1990; MA Camb. 1990; MRCP (UK) 1993; FRCA 1996. (Univ. Camb.) Specialist Regist. (Anaesth.) Bristol & SW Region.

MERCER, Neil Pickford 8 Hoghton Road, Hale, Liverpool L24 4BW — MB ChB 1978 Liverp.; FFA RCS Eng. 1984. Cons. Anaesth. & Intens. Care Walton & Fazakerley Hosps. Liverp. Prev: Sen. Regist. (Anaesth.) Merseyside Regional Rotat.

MERCER, Mr Nigel Stuart George 2 Clifton Park, Clifton, Bristol BS8 3BS Tel: 0117 906 4204 Fax: 0117 973 0887 — MB ChB 1980 Bristol; ChM Bristol 1994; FRCS Eng. 1984; FRCPCH 1997. (Bristol) Cons. Plastic Surg. Frenchay Hosp. Bristol.; Cons. Plastic Surg. Bristol. Roy. Hosp. Sick Child.; Cons. Plastic Surg. Roy. Unitd. Hosp. Bath. Socs: Craniofacial Soc.; Brit. Assn. Plastic Surg.; Brit. Assn. Aesthetic Plastic Surgs. Prev: Sen. Regist. (Plastic Surg.) Char. Cross Hosp. & Mt. Vernon Hosp. N.wood; Regist. (Plastic Surg.) Frenchay Hosp. Bristol.

MERCER, Robert Ferguson c/o P.G.F. Mercer, 123 St Stephens Road, Saltash PL12 4NQ — MB BS 1976 Lond.; MRCS Eng. LRCP Lond. 1975.

MERCER, Roy 11 Marine Crescent, Great Yarmouth NR30 4ER — MB ChB 1960 Aberd.; DA Eng. 1964.

MERCER, Rudolph Emmanuel Orchard Medical Practice, Orchard Street, Ipswich IP4 2PU Tel: 01473 213261 — MB BS 1962 Lond.; MRCS Eng. LRCP Lond. 1962; DObst RCOG 1965; FRCGP 1981, M 1969. (King's Coll. Hosp.) Sec. Suff. LMC. Socs: BMA. Prev: Occupat. Phys. Ipswich; Princip. GP Taunton.

MERCER, Stewart William Department of Psychiatry, St Johns' Hospital, Howden, Livingston EH54 6PP — MB ChB 1992 Bristol; MSc Aberd. 1980, BSc 1979; PhD Camb. 1985. SHO (Psychiat.) St. John's Hosp. Livingston. Prev: SHO (Rehabil. Med.) Astley Ainslie Hosp. Edin.; SHO (O & G) Ayrsh. Centr. Hosp. Irvine; Post-Doctoral Research Asst. MRC Metab. Research Laborat. Radcliffe Infirm. Oxf.

MERCER-JONES, Mr Mark Andrew 7 Ashfield Court, High Spen, Rowlands Gill NE39 2DY Email: mesorectum@hotmail.com — MB BS 1989 Newc.; FRCS Ed. 1994; FRCS Glas. 1994. Specialist Regist. Roy. Vict. Infirm. Newc. Upon Tyne. Socs: ASGBI. Prev: Research Fell. (Surg.) Univ. Louisville, Kentucky, USA.

MERCER-SMITH, Nigel 26 Josephine Avenue, Limavady BT49 9BA — MB BCh BAO 1971 Belf.

MERCEY, Danielle Elizabeth Department of Sexually Transmitted Diseases, Royal Free and University College Medical School, London WC1E 6AU Tel: 020 7380 9946 Fax: 020 7380 9669; Tel: 020

8427 0173 — MB ChB 1982 Leic.; MRCP (UK) 1985; FRCP 1997. Cons. Genitourin. Med. Dept. of Sexually Transm. Dis.s Roy. Free and Univ. Coll. Med. Sch.; Hon. Cons. (Genitourin. Med.) Camden & Islington NHS Trust.

MERCHANT, Eileen Sheila (retired) Ayrshire Central General Hospital, Irvine KA12 8SS Tel: 01294 274191 Fax: 01294 323445 Email: nem@surfaid.org — MB ChB 1963 Liverp.; DObst RCOG 1966; MFFP 1993. Prev: Cons. Family Plann. & Reproduc. Health Care Ayrsh. & Arran Primary Care NHS Trust.

MERCHANT, Elian Blaize Nicholas (retired) 32 Gretton Court, Girton, Cambridge CB3 0QN Tel: 01223 277279 — MB ChB Manch. 1943.

***MERCHANT, Irfan Leonard** 23 Park Circus, Ayr KA7 2DJ — MB ChB 1997 Ed.

MERCHANT, Reshma 129 Elmstead Avenue, Wembley HA9 8NT — MB ChB 1995 Ed.; MRCP (UK) 1999. (Univ. Ed.) SHO (A & E) Barnet Gen. Hosp.; SHO (COE) Hemel Hempstead Hosp. Socs: Med. Defence Union; BMA. Prev: Ho. Off. (Orthop. & Trauma) Roy. Infirm. Edin.

MERCHANT, Stuart Douglas George Street Surgery, 16 George Street, Alderley Edge SK9 7EP Tel: 01625 584545/6; 9 Marlborough Avenue, Alderley Edge SK9 7HS Tel: 01625 584303 — MB ChB 1978 Liverp.; MRCGP 1984; DRCOG 1981. Prev: Trainee GP Chesterfield VTS; Ho. Surg. & Phys. Birkenhead Gen. Hosp.

MERCHANT, William James Histopathology Department, Leeds General Infirmary, Leeds LS1 3EX — MB ChB 1987 Manch.; MRCPath 1994. Cons. Histopath. Leeds Gen. Infirm. Prev: Sen. Regist. (Histopath.) St. Thos. Hosp. Lond.; Regist. (Histopath.) St. Geo. Hosp. Lond.

MERCIECA, Jane Elizabeth St Helier Hospital, Wrythe Lane, Carshalton SM5 1AA Tel: 020 8296 2972 Fax: 020 8461 6450 Email: jmerciec@sthelier.sghms.ac.uk; 37 Dunmore Road, London SW20 8TN Tel: 020 8947 0829 Fax: 020 8641 6450 — MB BS 1981 Lond.; MRCP (UK) 1984; MRCPath 1991; FRCP 1998. Cons. Haemat. St. Helier Hosp. Carshalton. Socs: Fell.Roy. Coll. of Pathologists. Prev: Sen. Regist. (Haemat.) St. Geo. Hosp. Lond.

MERCKEL, Jacqueline Claire Upper Eden Medical Practice, The Health Centre, Silver Street, Kirkby Stephen CA17 4RB Tel: 01228 71369 Fax: 017683 72385; Town Head Farm House, Ravenstonedale, Kirkby Stephen CA17 4NQ Tel: 015396 23358 — MB ChB 1986 Leeds; BSc (Hons.) Leeds 1983; MRCGP 1992; DCH RCP Lond. 1991; DRCOG 1990; Dip. Pract. Dermat. Wales 1997; Dip. Therapeut UWCM Cardiff 1998.

MERCURIO, Gerald Gary 33C Chester Way, London SE11 4UR — MB ChB 1991 Birm.; BSc (Pharm.) Birm. 1988. (Birm.)

MERCURIUS-TAYLOR, Mr Lennox Arlington The Department of Surgery, Neath General Hospital, Neath SA11 2LQ Tel: 01639 641161 Fax: 01639 620150 Email: len@ngh-ub.demon.co.uk; 1 Clifton Place, Skewen, Neath SA10 6BH Tel: 01792 427686 Email: taylor@cableol.co.uk — BM BCh 1975 Oxf.; BSc (1st cl. Hons.) St. And. 1972; FRCS Eng. 1978. (Univ. St. And. & Balliol Coll. Oxf.) Cons. Surg. Neath Gen. Hosp.; PostGrad. Organiser NGH 1996.

MERCY, Linda Catherine 1 Parkway Close, Welwyn Garden City AL8 6HJ — MB ChB 1993 Birm.

MEREDITH, Mr Andrew Peter d'Esterre ENT Department, Conquest Hospital, The Ridge, Hastings TN34 2 Tel: 01424 755255 Fax: 01424 758120; Flowers Green House, Church Road, Herstmonceux, Hailsham BN27 1RL Tel: 01323 833511 — MB BS 1977 Lond.; MA Oxf. 1978; FRCS Glas. 1983; DLO RCS Eng. 1980. Cons. ENT Conquest Hosp. Hastings.; Hon. Cons. ENT E.borne DGH, Chairm. Bd. of Trustees, Link Centre. Prev: Cons. ENT W. Wales Gen. Hosp. Carmarthen & Bronglis Hosp.; Cons. ENT RNH Haslar; Sen. Regist. Head & Neck Unit Roy. Marsden Hosp.

MEREDITH, Andrew Scott 29 Knoll Road, Abergavenny NP7 7AN — MB BS 1974 Lond.; MRCS Eng. LRCP Lond. 1974; DCH Eng. 1977; DObst RCOG 1976. (St. Mary's)

MEREDITH, Mr Ashton David Bronglais General Hospital, Aberystwyth SY23 1ER — BM BCh 1971 Oxf.; FRCS Eng. 1977; FRCS Ed. 1977. Cons. Orthop. Surg. Bronglais Gen. Hosp. Aberystwyth.

***MEREDITH, Emma Louise** 4 Edan Avenue, Uplands, Swansea SA2 0PS — MB BS 1994 Lond.

MEREDITH, Helen Elizabeth Parkfield Medical Centre, 255 Parkfield Road, Wolverhampton WV4 6EG Tel: 01902 342152 Fax:

01902 620868 — MB ChB 1991 Birm.; ChB Birm. 1991; DRCOG 1993; MRCGP 1996. (Birm.)

***MEREDITH, Jonathan Graham** c/o 31 Hillpark Cr, Edinburgh EH4 7BG — MB ChB 1997 Manch.

MEREDITH, Martin John Pinhoe Surgery, Pinn Lane, Exeter EX1 3SY Tel: 01392 469666 Fax: 01392 464178; 2 Riversmeet House, Riversmeet, Topsham, Exeter EX3 0BE — MB BS 1978 Lond.; MRCGP 1983; DRCOG 1980.

MEREDITH, Sheena Gail Tudor House, Horton, Devizes SN10 3NB — MB BS 1981 Lond.; MRCS Eng. LRCP Lond. 1981. (St. Bart.)

MEREDITH-SMITH, Alison New Surgery, Victoria Street, Pontycymer, Bridgend CF32 8NW Tel: 01656 870237 Fax: 01656 870354 — MB BCh 1984 Wales; BA (Hons.) Camb. 1981; DCH RCP Lond. 1993; DRCOG 1987. Socs: BMA.

MERIFIELD, William Kerry High Hill, Top Lane, Beech, Stoke-on-Trent ST4 8SJ — MB ChB 1954 Birm.; MRCS Eng. LRCP Lond. 1954; FFA RCS Eng. 1964; DObst RCOG 1958.

MERINO, Sylvia Victoria Southfield Medical Practice, 14 Southfield Loan, Edinburgh EN6 4NL Tel: 0131 669 0686 Fax: 0131 669 2929; 189 Ferry Road, Edinburgh EH6 4NL Tel: 0131 553 5325 Email: sylviavmerino@hotmail.com — LMS 1990 Universidad Autonoma of Madrid; DFFPA 1995 Lond.; MBCUB 1990; LMS MB ChB 1990; DFFP Lond. 1995. (Edin.) GP S.field, Edin. Socs: BMA; MDDUS. Prev: Clin. Asst. (Community Drug Problem Serv.) Edin. Healthcare Trust; SHO (O & G) Kirkcaldy; Trainee GP WhinPk. Med. Centre Edin.

MERLIN, Mr Michael John (retired) Wharfedale, 1 Clarry Drive, Sutton Coldfield B74 2RA Tel: 0121 308 2826 — MB ChB 1962 Leeds; FRCS Eng. 1969; DObst RCOG 1964. Prev: Cons. Surg. A & E Dept. Walsall Hosps. Gp.

MEROTRA, Mr Sunil Kumar (Surgery), 30 Sandringham Way, Qunicy Rise, Amblecote, Stourbridge Tel: 01384 422698 — MB BS 1970 Aghra; FRCS Ed. 1979.

***MERRETT, Katherine Dawn** 9 Greystoke Close, Berkhamsted HP4 3JJ — MB ChB 1994 Bristol.

MERRIAM, Mr William Frank Tel: 024 7656 1900 Fax: 024 7656 1901 Email: e.info@oakmedics.com; Fowgay Hall, Dingle Lane, Solihull B91 3PB Tel: 0121 704 4870 — MB ChB 1973 Birm.; FRCS Eng. 1979. Cons. Orthop. & Traum. Surg. Coventry & Warks. Hosp. Coventry. Prev: Sen. Regist. (Orthop.) Roy. Orthop. Hosp. Birm.; Profess. Regist. (Orthop.) Roy. N. Shore Hosp. Sydney, Austral.; Sen. Regist. (Spinal Research) Harlow Wood Hosp.

MERRICK, Ms Anna Frances — MB ChB 1990 Manch.; FRCS Glas. 1995; MD Manch. 1996; Dip Paediat. Cardiol. Univ. Lond. 1997. (Manch.) Specialist Regist. (Cardiothoracic Surg.) W. Lond. Rotat. Flexible Trainee. Socs: Wom. in Surg. Train.; Med. Wom. Federat.; Brit. Paediatric Cardiac Assn. Prev: Research Fell. Inst. Child Health Lond.; SHO Cardiothoracic) Wythenshawe Hosp. S. Manch. Univ. Hosps. NHS Trust; SHO Rotat. (Surg. & Cardiothoracic Surg.) Manch. Roy. Infirm.

MERRICK, Augustus Warren (retired) 7 Rosebarn Avenue, Exeter EX4 6DY Tel: 01392 255724 — MB ChB Liverp. 1943. Prev: Treas. Med. Off.

MERRICK, Brian Malcolm Graeme Medical Centre, 1 Western Avenue, Falkirk FK2 7HR Tel: 01324 624437 Fax: 01324 633737 — MB ChB 1977 Dundee. (Dundee) GP Falkirk.

MERRICK, Mr Colin David 2 St Mary's Gardens, Battle Hill, Battle TN33 0DB — BM 1979 Soton.; MRCP (UK) 1982; FRCS Ed. 1986; FCOphth 1988; DO RCS Eng. 1984. Cons. Ophth. Hastings & Rother NHS Trust.

***MERRICK, Graham David** 22 High Street, Great Cheverell, Devizes SN10 5TH — MB ChB 1997 Sheff.

MERRICK, Harry Patrick Oxford Mews, 39A Broad St., Wokingham RG40 1AU Tel: 01734 783599 — MRCS Eng. LRCP Lond. 1943. (Guy's) Socs: Windsor & Dist. Med. Soc. Prev: Ho. Surg. Lewisham Hosp.; O & G Ho. Surg. Co. Hosp. Pembury; Res. Anaesth. Roy. Berks. Hosp. Reading.

MERRICK, John Vine Surgery, Hindhayes Lane, Street BA16 0ET Tel: 01458 841122 Fax: 01458 840044; 68 Leigh Road, Street BA16 0HD Tel: 01458 443361 Fax: 01458 840734 Email: john@68leigh.freeserve.co.uk — BM BCh 1968 Oxf.; MA Oxf. 1968; MRCP (UK) 1972; MRCGP 1982; D.Occ.Med. RCP (UK) 1996; DObst RCOG 1970. (Magdalen Coll. Oxf. & Lond. Hosp. Med. Coll.) Sen. Med. Off. Clarks Internat. St., Som.

MERRICK, John Maurice 4 Court House Road, Llanvair Discoed, Chepstow NP16 6LW — MB BCh 1966 Wales; DObst RCOG 1968. Specialist (Orthop. Med.) Roy. Gwent Hosp. Newport.

MERRICK, Malcolm Vivian (retired) — BM BCh 1964 Oxf.; MSc Lond. 1971; FRCP Ed. 1987, M 1984; FRCR 1972; DMRD Eng. 1970. Prev: Cons. (Nuclear Med.) W.. Gen. Hosp. Edin.

MERRICK, Mark Maurice Cumberland Infirmary, Carlisle CA2 7AY Tel: 01228 523444; 3 Greenwood Garth, Thursby Tel: 01228 711964 — BM 1993 Soton.; DRCOphth. 1997. E. Cumb. Voc. Train. Schm. F/T. Prev: Obs+Gyna; Elderly Core; ENT.

MERRICK, Ronald Herbert Stanley Health Centre, Lake Lock Road, Stanley, Wakefield WF3 4HS Tel: 01924 822328; Hadfield, 158 Rooks Nest Road, Stanley, Wakefield WF3 4DP — MB ChB 1944 Leeds. (Leeds) Socs: BMA. Prev: Ho. Surg. Leeds Gen. Infirm.; Orthop. Off. Clayton Hosp. Wakefield; Capt. RAMC.

MERRICKS, Eleanor Kathleen 146/7 Whitehouse Loan, Edinburgh EH9 2AN — LRCP LRCS 1950 Ed.; LRCP LRCS Ed. LRFPS Glas. 1950; DTM & H Liverp. 1953; DA Eng. 1957. (Roy. Colls. Ed.) Prev: Med. Regist. Bruntsfield Hosp. Edin.; Med. Miss. Zaire.; GP. Ladywell Med. Centre, Edin.

MERRICKS, Melanie Jane 119 York Street, Cambridge CB1 2PZ — MB BS 1991 Lond.

MERRIFIELD, Anthony John, Air Commodore RAF Med. Retd. (retired) 2 Barton Square, Ely CB7 4DF Tel: 01353 664850 Email: tmerrifield@totalise.co.uk — MB BS 1951 Lond.; MRCS Eng. LRCP Lond. 1950; FFA RCS Eng. 1956; DA Eng. 1954. Prev: Cons. Adviser Anaesth. RAF.

MERRIFIELD, Stephanie Patricia 22 Eastfield Close, Tadcaster LS24 8JX — MB BS 1990 Lond.

MERRILEES, Hugh Forbes Health Clinic, Ashgrove, Blackburn, Bathgate EH47 7LL Tel: 01506 652956 Fax: 01506 634790 — MB ChB 1978 Aberd.; MRCGP 1982. (Aberd.) GP Blackburn W. Lothian; Clin. Tutor (Gen. Pract.) Univ. Ed. Prev: Trainee GP (Paediat.) Dalkeith & Trainee GP Fife HB VTS; Ho. Off. (Gen. Med. & Surg.) Inverclyde Roy. Hosp. Greenock.

MERRILL, Charles Richard 33 Dunstan Crescent, Worksop S80 1AE — BM 1978 Soton.; FRCR 1985. Cons. Radiol. Bassetlaw Dist. Gen. Hosp. Worksop.

MERRILL, John Frederick The Surgery, 54 High Street, Somerby, Melton Mowbray LE14 2PZ Tel: 01664 454204 Fax: 01664 454879; Brickyard Farm, Owston, Oakham LE15 8DH Tel: 01664 454458 — MB BS 1968 Lond.; MRCS Eng. LRCP Lond. 1966. (St. Bart.) Socs: Rutland Med. Pract. Assn.; The Pacific Is. Soc. of the UK & Irel. Prev: Ho. Surg. Gen. Hosp. Jersey, C.I.; Med. Off. Zambia Flying Doctor Serv.; Dist. Med. Off. (Santa Cruz Is.s) Brit. Solomon Is.s Protec.

MERRILL, Kenneth John Drugs North West, Mental Health Services of Salford, Bury New Road, Prestwich, Manchester M25 3BL Tel: 0161 772 3527 Fax: 0161 772 3595 Email: jmerrill@man.ac.uk — MB ChB 1979 Birm.; MRCPsych 1984; FRCPsych 2000. Lead Cons. Drug Depend. Drugs NW Ment. Health Serv. Salford; Hon. Lect. (Psychiat.) Univ. Manch. Prev: Sen. Regist. W. Midl. Regional Addict. Treatm. Unit. All St.'s Hosp. Manch.; Research Sen. Regist. W. Midl. Poisons Unit Dudley Rd. Hosp. Birm.

MERRILL, Stephen Bliss, Surg. Cdr. RN Retd. Edith Cavell Hospital, Department of Anaesthesia, Bretton Gate, Peterborough PE3 6GZ Tel: 01733 330777; 40 Exeter Gardens, Stamford PE9 2RN — MB BS 1968 Lond.; MRCS Eng. LRCP Lond. 1967; FFA RCS Eng. 1977; DObst RCOG 1972; DA Eng. 1975. (Westm.) Cons. Anaesth. P'boro. Socs: Assn. Anaesths. & Soc. Naval Anaesth. Prev: Cons. Adviser Anaesth RN; Chairm. Triserv. Anaesth. Comm.

MERRIMAN, Honor Mary Osler Road, Headington, Oxford OX3 9BP; 62 Osler Road, Headington, Oxford OX3 9BN — MB BS 1971 Lond.; DRCOG 1983; FRCGP 1999; MFFP 1993; 1976 Eng.; FFA RCS 1976 Eng.; MRCGP 1982; FFA RCS Eng. 1976; MFFP 1993; DRCOG 1983. (Westm.) Prev: Trainee GP E. Oxf. Health Centre; Sen. Regist. (Anaesth.) Nuffield Dept. Radcliffe Infirm. Oxf.; Regist. (Anaesth.) Soton. Gen. Hosp.

MERRIMAN, Louise Anne 1 Morton Grove, Worksop S81 7QS — MB BS 1987 Lond.

***MERRIMAN, Michael Gerrard** 12 Ince Road, Thornton, Liverpool L23 4UF — MB ChB 1994 Birm.; ChB Birm. 1994.

MERRIN, Denis Hubert (retired) Oaklands, 72 Ford Road, Upton, Wirral CH49 0TG Tel: 0151 677 4193 — LRCPI & LM, LRSCI & LM

MERRIN

1948; LRCPI & LM, LRCSI & LM 1948; FRCPI 1978, M 1955. Prev: Cons. Chest Phys. Clatterbridge Hosp. Bebington & Arrowe Pk. Hosp. Birkenhead.

MERRIN, Peter Kieran The Perranporth Surgery, Perranporth TR6 0PS Tel: 01872 572255; Penbrea, Carnebo Hill, Goonhavern, Truro TR4 9QH — MB BS 1985 Lond.; MRCP (UK) 1988; MRCGP 1995; DFFP 1996. (Westminster Med. Sch.) GP Perranporth.; Princip. Police Surg. Socs: BMA; RCGP; Assn. Police Surg. Prev: Research Fell. St. Mary's Hosp. Lond.; Regist. (Med.) St. Thos. Hosp. Lond.; SHO Rotat. Qu. Mary's Hosp. Sidcup.

MERRINGTON, John Cedric (retired) The Health Centre, Central St., Ludgershall, Andover SP11 9RA Tel: 01264 790356 Fax: 01980 846824 — MB BS 1958 Lond.; MRCS Eng. LRCP Lond. 1958; DObst RCOG 1960. Prev: Ho. Surg. (Gyn.) W.m. Hosp. Gp.

MERRIOTT, David Edward The Surgery, Hazeldene House, Great Haywood, Stafford ST18 0SU Tel: 01889 881206 Fax: 01889 883083 — MB ChB 1975 Birm.; MA Camb. 1976.

MERRITT, Claire Louisa Rose Cottage, Muddles Green, Chiddingly, Lewes BN8 6HS — BM 1990 Soton.

MERRITT, Joanna Louise 11 Carnation Close, Springfield, Chelmsford CM1 6XR — MB ChB 1984 Zimbabwe; LRCP LRCS Ed. LRCPS Glas. 1986; MRCP (UK) 1993; DCH RCP Lond. 1990. Prev: Regist. (Paediat.) Chelmsford.

MERRITT, John Charles c/o 10 Castleton Court, Marlow SL7 3HW — MB BS 1973 Lond.; AFOM RCP Lond. 1992; MRCGP 1978; DObst RCOG 1975; DAvMed. FOM RCP Lond. 1982. (Charing Cross Hosp.) Princip. Med. Off., Cathay Pacific Airlines, Hong Kong. Socs: Aerospace Med. Assoc.; Amer. Coll. Occupat. & Environm. Med.; Pres. Airline Med. Dir. Assn.

MERRITT, John Keith (retired) Longmynd, Main Road, Salcombe TQ8 8JW — MB ChB 1961 Leeds; MRCGP 1977; DObst RCOG 1963. Prev: Med. Pract. (Geriat.) E. Surrey Hosp.

MERRITT, Lorna Gertrude 20 Knockholt Close, Belmont Heights, Sutton SM2 6ED Tel: 020 8643 6008 Fax: 020 8643 6008 Email: lorna@easynet.co.uk; c/o Anaesthetaetic Department, St. George's Hospital, Blackshaw Road, Tooting, London SW17 0QT Tel: 020 8672 1255 — MB BS 1988 West Indies; FRCA (UK) 1996; DA (UK) 1993. (West Indies) Specialist Regist. (Anaesth.) St. Geo.'s Hosp. Socs: BMA; AAGPH; AATT. Prev: Specialist Regist. St. Geo.'s Hosp. Qu. Mary's Univ. Hosp.; Specialist Regist. Mayday Univ. Hosp. & St. Geo. Hosp. Lond.; Regist. (Anaesth.) Atkinson Morley Hosp., Qu. Mary's Univ. Hosp. Lond. & Roy. Surrey Co. Hosp. Guildford.

MERRITT, Richard Andrew 90 Ashington Lane, Ashington, Wimborne BH21 3DG — BM 1989 Soton.; MRCGP 1996; DRCOG 1995.

MERRITT, Sian Mary 3 Keepers Close, Easingwold, York YO61 4TY — BM BCh 1984 Oxf.; MA Camb. 1984; MRCGP 1988.

MERRITT, Thomas James Kitson (retired) 272 Colchester Road, Ipswich IP4 4QX Tel: 01473 413445 — MB BS Lond. 1952; MRCPsych 1971; DPM Eng. 1956. Prev: Cons. Psychiat. E. Anglian RHA Inst. Family Psychiat. Ipswich.

MERRIWEATHER, Fiona Jean 419 Tantallon Road, Glasgow G41 3HS — MB ChB 1988 Glas.; MRCGP 1992; DRCOG 1991. Socs: BMA.

***MERRON, Stephen** Flat 7, St Johns Court, 101 Wentworth Road, Birmingham B17 9ST — MB ChB 1997 Birm.

MERRY, Alexander Johnstone, ERD, TD (retired) Kelmscott, Burrough On The Hill, Melton Mowbray LE14 2JQ Tel: 0166477 709 — MB BS 1946 Lond.; FFA RCS Eng. 1954; DA Eng. 1948. Prev: Cons. Anaesth. Brook, Greenwich & Lewisham Hosps.

MERRY, Allan John South Beach Practice, 17 South Crescent, Ardrossan KA22 8EA Tel: 01294 463011 Fax: 01294 462790 Email: allanmerry@aapct.scot.nhs.uk; 73 Eglington Road, Ardrossan KA22 8NG Tel: 01294 601964 — MB ChB 1978 Ed.; MRCGP 1982; DRCOG 1981. GP Prescriber Methadome Substitutia Clinic Alconn & Subst. Above Serv. Virnol Campus Saltwat.

MERRY, Elisabeth Catriona High Street Surgery, 1st Floor, 97-101 High Street, Fort William PH33 6DG Tel: 01397 703773 Fax: 01397 701068; 3 Seafield Gardens, Fort William PH33 6RJ — MB ChB 1984 Aberd.; MRCGP 1989; DRCOG 1988.

MERRY, Emma Jane 14 Brutasche Terrace, Street BA16 0BD — MB BS 1992 Lond.; DA. 1996. Med. Regist. - N.Shore Hosp. Auckland, NZ.

MERRY, Graham Philip 21 Partridge Close, Thurston, Bury St Edmunds IP31 3QL — MB BS 1987 Lond.

***MERRY, Jason** 98 Weston Road, Runcorn WA7 4LL — MB BS 1994 Lond.

MERRY, John Richard 8 Springbank, Bollington, Macclesfield SK10 5LQ — BM BS 1986 Nottm.

MERRY, Julius Department of Biochemistry, University of Surrey, Guildford GU2 7XH Tel: 01483 571281 — MD 1953 Lond.; MD (Psych. Med.) Lond. 1953, MB BS 1946, DPM 1949; FRCPsych 1972. (Univ. Coll. Hosp.) Hon. Vis. Prof. in Clin. Psychiat. Univ. Surrey; Hon. Cons. Psychiat. St. Thos. Hosp, Lond. Prev: Cons. Psychiat. St. Thos. & St Geo. Hosps., Lond.

MERRY, Peter Woodhurst, 82 Newmarket Road, Norwich NR2 2LA — MD 1990 Lond.; MB BS 1981; MRCP (UK) 1984. Cons. Rheum. Norf. & Norwich Hosps. Prev: Sen. Regist. (Rheum. & Gen. Med.) Char. Cross, St. Mary's & W.m. Hosps. Lond.; ARC Research Fell. Bone & Jt. Research Unit Lond. Hosp.; Regist. (Med.) St. Jas. & St. Geo. Hosps. Lond.

MERRY, Peter Henry (retired) 29 Borrowdale Drive, Burnley BB10 2SG — BM BCh Oxf. 1954; FRCP Ed. 1974, M 1962; MRCS Eng. LRCP Lond. 1955; DPhysMed. Eng. 1962; DObst RCOG 1960. Sessional Cons. Burnley Gen. Hosp. Prev: Cons. Rheum. & Rehabil. Burnley, Pendle & Rossendale & E. Lancs. HAs.

MERRY, Robert Thomas George, OStJ, Air Commodore RAF Med. Br. National Hospital for Neurology & Neurosurgery, Queen Square, London WC1N 3BG Tel: 020 7837 3611 — MB BS Lond. 1962; FRCP Lond. 1986, M 1968; MRCPsych 1974; DRCOG 1964. (St. Bart.) Cons. Adviser Neurol. RAF & Cons. Neurol. Civil Aviat. Auth.; Cons. Neurol & Specialist Advis. Defence Secondary Care Agency. Socs: Fell. Roy. Soc. Med.; Assn. Brit. Neurol. Prev: Cons. Neuropsychiat. Ment. Health Servs. W. Austral.; Regist. (Neurol.) Wessex Neurol. Centre; Regist. (Med.) St. Bart. Hosp. Lond.

MERRY, Tina Louise Frome Medical Practice, Health Centre, Park Road, Frome BA11 1EZ Tel: 01373 301300 Fax: 01373 301313; Stonelilands, Bath Road, Frome BA11 2HJ Tel: 01373 462789 — MB ChB 1982 Sheff. Prev: Trainee GP Sheff. VTS; Fell. (Paediat. Oncol.) Leukaemia Research Fund.

MERRYLEES, Neil 3 Royal Buildings, Newport-on-Tay DD6 8BR — MB ChB 1990 Dundee.

MERRYWEATHER, Mr Reginald (retired) Eden Cottage, Cheltenham Road, Painswick, Stroud GL6 6SJ Tel: 01452 812251 — MB BS 1944 Lond.; FRCS Eng. 1950. Prev: Prof. Orthop. Med. Fac. Addis Ababa Univ.

MERSON, Alan Thomas, TD 151 Rein Road, Tingley, Wakefield WF3 1JJ; 86 Castle Mount, Thornhill, Dewsbury WF12 0DW Tel: 01924 463099 — MB ChB 1948 Leeds. (Leeds)

MERSON, Peter James Ferryhill Medical Practice, Durham Road, Ferryhill DL17 8JJ Tel: 01740 651238 Fax: 01740 656291 — MB ChB 1979 Dundee; MRCGP 1988.

MERSON, Ronald David (retired) Wendover, 18 Fir Tree Close, Hilton, Yarm TS15 9JZ Tel: 01642 591500 — MB ChB 1949 Ed.; MRCGP 1968. Prev: Med. Off. Local Civil Serv. Stockton-on-Tees.

MERSON, Rosemary Daphne Constance Tel: 01278 662221; Dobins Barton, North Petherton, Bridgwater TA6 6PH Tel: 01278 662221 — MB BS 1979 Lond. (Guy's Hosp.) Prev: GP Congresbury.

MERSON, Stephen Ronald Hadrian Clinic, Newcastle General Hospital, Westgate Road, Newcastle upon Tyne NE4 6BE Tel: 0191 273 6666 Email: liz.harris@ncht.northy.nhs.uk — MB 1983 Camb.; BChir 1982; MRCPsych. 1988. Prev: Cons. Psychiat. St. Chas. Hosp. Lond.; Sen. Regist. (Psychiat.) St. Mary's Hosp. Lond.

MERTON, William Louis Department of Clinical Neurophysiology, Portsmouth Hospital NHS Trust, St Mary's Hospital, Milton Road, Portsmouth PO4 0QS Tel: 02392 866786 Fax: 02392 866785; 80 Whitwell Road, Southsea PO4 0QS — MB BS 1982 Lond.; BSc (Hons. Physiol.) Lond. 1977; MRCP (UK) 1987; FRCP London. (University College Hospital London) Cons. (Clin, Neurophysiol.) Portsmouth Hosps. NHS Trust. Socs: Fell. Roy. Coll. Phys. Lond.; Brit. Soc. Clin. Neurophysiol. Prev: Sen. Regist. (Clin. Neurophysiol.) Hosp. Sick Childr. Gt. Ormond St. Lond.; Nat. Hosp. Nerv. Dis. Lond.

MERVIN, Lucy Alice Oakhurst, Byfield Road, Priors Marston, Rugby CV47 7RP — MB ChB 1991 Manch.

***MERVYN-THOMAS, John William** 26 Learmouth Terrace, Edinburgh EH4 1NZ Tel: 0131 332 3139 — MB ChB 1997 Ed.

MERWAHA, Nilam Church Street Surgery, St. Mary's Courtyard, Church St., Ware SG12 9EF Tel: 01920 468941; 13 Wentworth Road, Hertford SG13 8JP — MB ChB 1981 Liverp.; MRCGP 1988. Socs: BMA & Herts. Local Med. Comm. Prev: Trainee Gp Kingslangley.

MERWAHA, Rina Department of Child Life and Health, All Saints' Hospital, Magpie Hall Road, Chatham ME4 5NG Tel: 01634 407311 Email: rina@karm.demon.co.uk; 6 Downs Side, Cheam, Sutton SM2 7EQ Tel: 020 8770 7172 Fax: 020 8770 7173 — BM 1984 Soton.; MRCP (UK) 1987; DCH RCP Lond. 1987; MSc Kingston 1997. (Southampton) Cons. Paediatritian. Prev: Sen. Regist. (Respirat. Med.) Roy. Brompton Hosp. Lond.; Sen. Regist. (Respirat. Med.) Hosp. Sick Childr. Gt. Ormond St. Lond.; Regist. (Intens. Care) Dept. Respirat. Med. Hosp. for Sick Childr. Gt. Ormond St. Lond.

MERZ, Leo Hermann Tarbert, Craighouse PA60 7XH Tel: 01496 820287; Karl-Stirner Str 36, Rosenberg 73494, Germany Tel: 00 49 7967335 — State Exam Med 1989 Erlangen; FMGEMS 1991; DRCOG 1995; DFFP 1996; VTS Trained GP 1996. GP & A&E for Frontier Med. Servs. (Curr.ly in Astrakhan, Russia). Prev: Assoc. GP Isles of Islay & Jura; GP Regist. Lochgilphead; SHO, OMS Baku, Azerbaijan.

MERZER, Roza (retired) 41 East View, Barnet EN5 5TW Tel: 020 8440 2493 — MD 1938 Bologna; LRCP LRCS Ed. LRFPS Glas. 1943. Prev: Clin. Med. Off. Enfield & Haringey AHA.

MESHIKHES, Mr Abdul-Wahed Nasir University Department of Surgery, Manchester Royal Infirmary, Manchester Tel: 0161 276 1234; 31 Brookfield Drive, Littleborough OL15 8RH Tel: 01706 73303 — MB BCh BAO 1984 NUI; FRCS Ed. 1989; LRCPI & LM, LRCSI & LM 1984. Regist. (Gen. Surg.) Manch. Roy. Infirm. Prev: Regist. (Gen. Surg.) Roy. Oldham Hosp.; SHO (Gen. Surg.) Birch Hill Hosp. Rochdale & N. Tees Gen. Hosp. Stockton; SHO (Orthop.) Rotherham Dist. Gen. Hosp.

MESSAGE, Simon David Flat 10, Horatio Place, 118 Kingston Road, London SW19 1LY — MB BS 1991 Lond.; BSc (1st cl. Hons.) Biochem. Lond. 1988; MRCP (UK) 1994. Specialist Regist. (Respirat. Med.) St. Mary's Hosp. Lond.

***MESSAHEL, Bothayna** Flat 3, Mapleton Court, 4 University Road, Leicester LE1 7RB — MB ChB 1995 Leic.

MESSAHEL, Faouk Mahmoud Ahmed 33 Wolseley Avenue, Birmingham B27 6SZ — MB ChB 1963 Alexandria; FFA RCS Eng. 1979.

MESSENGER, Andrew Guy Glenview, Foldrings, Oughtibridge, Sheffield S35 0GE Tel: 0114 286 2662 — MD 1986 Sheff.; MB BS Newc. 1973; MRCP (UK) 1977. Cons. Dermat. Roy. Hallamsh. Hosp. Sheff. Prev: Lect. (Dermat.) Univ. Sheff.

***MESSENGER, Jenny** 24 Wayland Road, Sheffield S11 8YE — MB ChB 1997 Sheff.

MESSENT, Mr Derrick Orry Hunt (retired) Iona, Teignmouth Road, Bishopsteignton, Teignmouth TQ14 9PL Tel: 01626 775474 — MB 1946 Sydney; FRCS Eng. 1964.

MESSENT, John Jeffery 90 Wyndham Road, London SE5 0UD — MRCS Eng. LRCP Lond. 1940; MRCGP 1953. (St. Bart.) Prev: Venereol. W. Middlx. Hosp. & Hillingdon Hosp.; Venereol. St. Thos. Hosp. Lond.; Mem. Nurses Bd. Ghana & Private Hosps. & Matern. Homes Bd. Ghana.

MESSENT, Mark 172 Camberwell Grove, London SE5 8RH Tel: 020 7274 4017 — MB BS 1985 Lond. Regist. (Anaesth.) St. Mary's Hosp. Lond.

MESSER, Basil (retired) 26 Sandmoor Green, Alwoodley, Leeds LS17 7SB Tel: 0113 266 1481 — MB BS Lond. 1942; MRCS Eng. LRCP Lond. 1942. Prev: Capt. RAMC, Graded Anaesth. 1944.

MESSER, Cheryl Patricia Kytes, Loudwater Lane, Rickmansworth WD3 4AL — MB BChir 1979 Camb.; FFA RCS Eng. 1983. (Camb. & St. Thos.) Cons. Anaesth. & Chronic Pain Managem. Hillingdon Hosp. Uxbridge, Middlx. Prev: Sen. Regist. (Anaesth.) NW Thames RHA; Regist. (Anaesth.) Harefield Hosp. Middlx.; Med. Off. (Anaesth.) Qu. Mary Hosp., Hong Kong.

MESSER, Dorothy Elspeth Denburn Health Centre, Rosemount Viaduct, Aberdeen AB25 1QB; 183 Countess Wells Road, Aberdeen AB15 7RA Tel: 01224 312625 — MB ChB 1980 Dundee.

MESSIH, Morad Nasr Abd El Good Hope General Hospita, Rectory Road, Sutton Coldfield B75 7RR Tel: 0121 378 2211; 23 Seal Close, Homewood, Sutton Coldfield B76 1FJ — MB ChB Alexandria 1965; FFA RCS Eng. 1977; FFA RCSI 1976. Cons. Anaesth. Good Hope Gen. Hosp. Sutton Coldfield. Socs: Assn. Anaesth. & BMA.; RCA Eng.; RCA Ire. Prev: Sen. Regist. Rotat. W. Midl.; Regist. Stoke-on-Trent.

MESSINEZY, Maria Demetrius 7 Kildare Gardens, London W2 5JS — BM BCh 1965 Oxf.; MRCP Lond. 1968; FRCP 1997; FRCPath. 1989, M 1977. (St. Thos.)

MESSING, Hubert Janusz Chippenham Surgery, Mouth Street, Monmouth NP25 3EQ Tel: 01600 713811 Fax: 01600 772652 — BM BCh 1970 Oxf.; DCH Eng. 1973; DObst RCOG 1973.

MESSING, Mr Zvi Ram Princess Drive Surgery, 485 Princess Drive, Huyton, Liverpool L14 8XF Tel: 0151 228 2036 — LRCPI & LM, LRSCI & LM 1977; LRCPI & LM, LRCSI & LM; FRCS Ed. 1981; DMJ 1987; DLO Lond. 1979; Soc. Apoth. Lond. (Dublin)

MESSIOS, Nicholas 2 Birkdale Avenue, Stoneygate, Leicester LE2 3HA Tel: 0116 270 5507 — Ptychio latrikes 1973 Athens; DMRO 1980; FRCR 1980. (Univ. Athens) Cons. Gen. & Neuroradiol.) Leicester Roy. Infirm.; Hon. Clin. Teach. Fac. Med. Univ. Leicester. Socs: Fell. Roy. Coll. Radiol. & Brit. Inst. Radiol.; Brit. Soc. Neuro-Radiolog. Prev: SHO (Gen. Med.) Mid-Staffs. (Stafford) Health Dist.; Ho. Surg. (Gen. Surg.) & Ho. Phys. (Gen. Med.) Gulson Rd. Hosp. Coventry.

MESSIOU, Christina Royal Infirmary, Princes Road, Hartshill, Stoke-on-Trent ST1 6PX Tel: 01782 554400 Fax: 01782 745703; 2 Birkdale Avenue, Stoneygate, Leicester LE2 3HA Tel: 0116 270 5507 — BM BS 1998 Nottm.; BM BS BMedSci Nottm 1998. (Nottm) SHO (Med) N Staffs Hosp. Trust.

MESTEL, Anne Leonora 51 Windsor Avenue, Belfast BT9 — MB BS 1981 Newc.

MESTEL, Jessica 58 Mount Pleasant Road, Chigwell IG7 5ER Tel: 020 8500 8542 — MB BS 1943 Lond.; MRCS Eng. LRCP Lond. 1943. (Lond. Sch. Med. Wom.) Prev: Sessional Med. Off. Newham Health Dist.; Med. Off. Family Plann. Assn.; Sessional Med. Off. Marks & Spencer.

MESTON, Nicola Nuffield Department Of Clinical Lab. Sciences, Univ. Of Oxford, John Radcliffe...etc., Oxford Tel: 01865 220466 Fax: 01865 220348 Email: niki.meston@ndcls.ox.ac.uk — BM 1992 Soton.; MRCPI 2000 (Part 1); MSc (Clin. Biochem.) Lond. 1997; Dip. RCPath 1998. Clin. Lect. In Clin. Biochem.ry, Univ. Of Oxf.; (On call) Specialist Regist. in Chem. Pathol. John Radcliffe Hosp. Oxf. Socs: Assn. Clin. Biochem.s; Soc. Endocrinol.; Assoc. Of Clin. Biochem.s of Irel.

MESURE, Joanna Grace 10 Gorphwysfa Avenue, Prestatyn LL19 7SL — BMed 1994 Newc., NSW.

METAXAS, Niki 5 The Hermitgae, Barnes, London SW13 9RF Tel: 020 8748 5377 — Ptychio latrikes 1955 Athens. (Univ. Athens) Assoc. Specialist (Cytol.) Char. Cross Hosp. Lond.

***METCALF, Elizabeth Penelope** Middle Field, Chollacott La, Tavistock PL19 9DD — MB BCh 1997 Wales.

METCALF, Helen Mary Lowedges Surgery, 127a Lowedges Road, Sheffield S8 7LE Tel: 0114 283 9839 — MB ChB 1977 Sheff.; MA Bristol 1969, BA (Hons.) 1967.

METCALF, Jacqueline Leith Walk Surgery, 60 Leith Walk, Edinburgh EH6 5HB Tel: 0131 554 6471 Fax: 0131 555 4964 — MB ChB 1989 Ed.

METCALF, Jane Anne Wellington Road Surgery, Wellington Road, Newport TF10 7HG Tel: 01952 811677; Nutty Hills Farm, Heath Hill, Shifnal TF11 8PR — MB ChB 1972 Aberd.; DA Eng. 1975.

METCALF, Jane Valerie Bristol Royal Infirmary, Bristol BS2 SMW Tel: 01452 528555; 6 St Andrews Road, Montpelier, Bristol BS6 5EH Email: jane.metcalf@virginnet — MB BS 1988 Newc.; MRCP (UK) 1992; Dip. Epidemiol. RCP Lond. 1996; PhD Newcastle 1999. (Newcastle) Sen. Regist. (Gastroenterol. & Gen. Med.) SW Rotat.; Lect. Bristol Univ. Socs: Brit. Soc. Gastroenterol.; Brit. Assn. Study Liver Dis. Prev: Research Regist. (Gastroenterol.) Med. Sch. Newc.; Regist. (Gen. Med. & Gastroenterol.) Roy. Vict. Infirm. Sunderland, Roy. Infirm. Dryburn Hosp. & Roy. Vict. Infirm. Newc.; SHO (Gen. Med.) Newc. Gen. & Freeman Rd. Hosp.

METCALF, John Ayton Sewell (retired) 21 Church Lane, Acklam, Middlesbrough TS5 7EF Tel: 01642 818423 — MB BS Durh. 1946. Prev: Ho. Surg. & Resid. Anaesth. Roy. Infirm. Sunderland.

METCALF, Mr Kenneth Stephen Princess Anne Hospital, Coxford Road, Southampton SO16 5YA Tel: 02380 796042 Fax: 02380 798712; Pond House, Dunbridge Lane, Awbridge, Romsey

METCALF

SO51 0GQ Tel: 01794 341152 Email: ksmetcalf@doctors.org.uk — MB ChB 1984 Leeds; FRCS Ed. 1989; MRCOG 1990; MD 1996 Leeds. (Leeds) Cons. Gyn. & Gynaecologic Oncol., P.ss Anne Hosp. COxf. Rd. Soton. SO16 5YA. Prev: Sen. Regist. (O & G) Leeds Gen. Infirm.; Fell. in Gyn. Oncol., Qu.sland Centre for Gyn. Cancer; Subspecialty Train. Fell. Gyn. Oncol., Leeds Gen. Infirm.

METCALF, Morris (retired) 68 Whitburn Road, Cleadon, Sunderland SR6 7QY Tel: 0191 536 7111 — MB BS 1942 Durh. Prev: RNVR 1943-46.

METCALF, Stephen Walter Flat 201, The Circle, Queen Elizabeth St., London SE1 2JN Tel: 020 8836 4366 Email: smet777637@aol.com; Tel: 020 7231 8777; MB BS 1990 Lond.; FFAEM 1999; MBBS 1990 Lond.; BSc Lond. 1985; MRCP (UK) 1994. Cons., Accid. & Emerg., Qu. Eliz. Hosp. Prev: Cons., Accid. & Emerg., Greenwich Dist. Hosp.; Regist. (Accid. & Emerg.) Univ. Coll. Lond.; SHO (Cardiol., Gen. Med., Endocrinol. & Metab.) Roy. Lond. Hosp.

METCALF, Yvonne Marie (retired) Greenways, Langham Road, Robertsbridge TN32 5DT — BSc (Hons.) Lond. 1955, MB BS 1958; MRCS Eng. LRCP Lond. 1958; DPM Eng. 1962.

METCALFE, Alison Margaret 4 Brandon Mansions, Queens Club Gardens, London W14 9RE — BM 1993 Soton.; DRCOG 1996. Socs: Med. Protect. Soc. Lond. Prev: GP/Regist. Winchester.

METCALFE, Brian (retired) Wynyard, 4 South St., East Rainton, Houghton-le-Spring DH5 9QP Tel: 01783 844504 — MB BS 1950 Durh. Prev: Ho. Surg. Roy. Vict. Infirm. Newc.

METCALFE, Brian Charles Lawson Road Surgery, 5 Lawson Road, Broomhill, Sheffield S10 5BU Tel: 0114 266 5180 — MB ChB 1985 Sheff.; BMedSc (Hons.) Sheff. 1985; MRCGP 1990; DObst Auckland 1988. Prev: Trainee GP Sheff.; SHO Waikato Hosp., NZ; Ho. Off. N.. Gen. Hosp. Sheff.

METCALFE, Cheryl Angela Roper and Partners, Syston Health Centre, Melton Road, Syston, Leicester LE7 2EQ Tel: 0116 260 9111 Fax: 0116 260 9055 — MB ChB 1984 Liverp.; MRCGP 1990.

***METCALFE, Clare Elizabeth** 5 Tilstock Crescent, Prenton, Birkenhead CH43 0ST — MB ChB 1994 Liverp.

METCALFE, Colette Surrey Hant Borders NHS Trust, Jarvis Centre, Stoughton Road, Guildford GU1 1LJ Tel: 01483 783135 — MB ChB 1973 Bristol. Staff Grade (Child Health) & SCMO (Audiol.) Surrey. Socs: Fac. Community Health; BPA; Brit. Soc. Audiol.

METCALFE, Professor David Henry Harold, OBE Westgate Barn, Milburn, Penrith CA10 1TW — MB Camb. 1957, BChir 1956; FFCM 1987, M 1981; FRCGP 1974, M 1964. (Camb.) Emerit. Prof. Gen. Pract. Univ. Manch. Prev: Prof. of Gen. Pract., Unversity of Manch. of Med.; Sen. Lect. (Gen. Pract.) Dept. Community Health Nottm. Univ. Med. Sch.; Asst. Prof. Internal Med., Pediat. & Preven. Med. Dept. Family Med. Rochester, New York.

METCALFE, E Marion Greenacres, 10 Gleneagles Close, Great Hay, Telford TF7 4BE Tel: 01952 585770 — MB BChir 1945 Camb.; MRCP Lond. 1948; MRCS Eng. LRCP Lond. 1944; DObst RCOG 1947; DCH Eng. 1948. (King's Coll. Hosp.) Indep. Counsellor & Psychother. inc. Marital Ther. Shrops. Prev: GP Telford; Hosp. Pract. (Psychiat.) Shelton Hosp. Salop. DHA; Regist. Belgrave Hosp. Childr.

METCALFE, George Christopher (retired) 29 Sion Hill, Lansdown, Bath BA1 2UW Tel: 01225 314619 — MB BChir Camb. 1952; MA Camb. 1953; FRCP Ed. 1976, M 1967; FRCGP 1981, M 1975; DCH Eng. 1963; DObst RCOG 1957. Prev: Sen. Lect. (Primary Med. Care) Univ. Soton.

METCALFE, Graham John Gilbert Carmel Surgery, Nunnery Lane, Darlington DL3 8SQ Tel: 01325 463149 — MB ChB 1977 Dundee.

METCALFE, Heather 79 Glossop Road, Glossop SK13 6EJ — MB ChB 1992 Liverp.

METCALFE, Ian Richard c/o Department of Anaesthesia, Western Infirmary, Dumbarton Road, Glasgow G11 6NT — MB BS 1983 Adelaide.

***METCALFE, James** 62 Marlborough Road, Shipley BD18 3NX — MB BS 1998 Lond.; MB BS Lond 1998.

METCALFE, Mr James Edward 48 Simeon Way, Stone ST15 8FJ Tel: 01785 819238 — MB ChB 1993 Birm.; FRCS (Ed) 1998. Orthop. Specialist Regist. Stroke & OsW.ry (Orthop. Rot.); Stroke & OsW.ry (Orthopae Rot.); Specialist. Regist. Rot.

METCALFE, Jennie Margaret Princess Royal Hospital, Haywards Heath RH16 4EX Tel: 01444 441881 — MB BChir 1976 Camb.;

MA, MB Camb. 1976, BChir 1975; MRCP (UK) 1979; FRCP (UK). Cons. Phys. Cardiol. P.ss Roy. Hosp. W. Sussex; Cons. Cardiol. Roy. Sussex Co. Hosp. Brighton. Socs: Brit. Cardiac Soc.; BMA; RSM. Prev: Sen. Regist. (Cardiol. & Gen. Med.) King's Coll. Hosp. Lond. & Roy. Sussex Co. Hosp. Brighton; Regist. The Nat. Heart Hosp. Lond.; Regist. & Research Fell. (Cardiol.) King's Coll. Hosp. Lond.

METCALFE, Jennifer Ann Westrop Surgery, Newburgh Place, Highworth, Swindon SN6 7DN Tel: 01793 762218 Fax: 01793 766073 — MB BS 1979 Lond.; MRCGP 1983; DRCOG 1982. (St. Mary's) Prev: Trainee GP Wycombe VTS.

METCALFE, Rev. John Burgess (retired) Hornbeams, The Alley, Little Wenlock, Telford TF6 5BG Tel: 01952 504150 — MB BChir 1946 Camb.; MA Camb. 1948; MRCS Eng. LRCP Lond. 1945. Prev: Indep. Psychother. Telford.

METCALFE, John David (retired) 30 Sutton Road, Tadcaster LS24 9HE — MRCS Eng. LRCP Lond. 1961.

METCALFE, John Sydney (retired) 6 Park Mews, Pool-in-Wharfesdale, Otley LS21 1LE Tel: 01132 842647 — MB ChB Leeds 1951. Prev: Clin. Asst. (Anaesth.) W.. (Leeds) Health Dist. (T).

METCALFE, Mr John William Kimberley, 68 Warren Road, Blundell Sands, Liverpool L23 6UG — MB ChB 1962 Liverp.; MChOrth Liverp. 1971; FRCS Eng. 1970; FRCS Ed. 1969. (University of Liverpool)

METCALFE, Karl Anthony Southend Hospital, Westcliff on Sea SS0 0RY — MB BS 1987 Lond.; BA (Hons.) Camb. 1984; MRCP (UK) 1991. (Camb. & Lond. Hosp. Med. Coll.) Cons. Phys. & Endocrinol. S.end Hosp. Socs: Brit. Diabetic Assn.; Soc. Endocrinol.; Roy. Soc. Med. Prev: Lect. & Hon. Sen. Regist. St. Bart. & Roy. Lond. Hosps.; R.D. Lawrence Research Fell. Roy. Lond. Hosp.; Lect. (Med.) Roy. Lond. Hosp.

METCALFE, Kay Alison 3 Paradise Row, Grange Lane, Gateacre, Liverpool L25 5LE — MB BCh 1987 Wales; MRCP (UK) 1991. Regist. Rotat. (Paediat.) Mersey RHA. Prev: SHO (Paediat., Respirat. Med. & Oncol.) Roy. Liverp. Childr. Hosp. Alder Hey; SHO (Neonat.) Liverp. Matern. Hosp.; SHO (Paediat.) Countess of Chester Hosp.

METCALFE, Malcolm John Cardiology Department, Aberdeen Royal Infirmary, Foresterhill, Aberdeen AB25 2ZN Tel: 01224 681818 — MB ChB 1983 Leeds; MD Leeds 1992; FRCP (Ed.) 1997; MRCP (UK) 1986. Cons. Cardiol. Aberd. Roy. Infirm. Prev: Sen. Regist. (Cardiol.) W.. Infirm. Glas.; Regist. (Cardiol.) W.. Infirm Glas.; Clin. Research Fell. & Hon. Regist. (Cardiol.) Aberd. Roy. Infirm.

METCALFE, Matthew James 3 Merchants Road, Clifton, Bristol BS8 4EP Tel: 0117 946 7237 — MB ChB 1998 Bristol. Neurosurg., Perth Aust. Prev: PRHO Surg. - Bristol Roy. Infirm.; PRHO med. - Frenchay Hosp. Bristol.

METCALFE, Matthew Stephen 33 The Green, Hathern, Loughborough, Loughborough LE12 5LQ — BChir 1994 Camb.

METCALFE, Michael William Cossham Hospital, Lodge Road, Kingswood, Bristol BS15 1LQ — MB ChB 1982 Leic. Cons. Community Psychiat. with Special Responsibil. Rehabil. Cossham Hosp. Bristol.

METCALFE, Nicholas Huntley 115 Northfield Road, Crookes, Sheffield S10 1QP — MRCS Eng. LRCP Lond. 1979; DTM & H Liverp. 1987. Trainee Ophth. Sheff. Prev: Med. Off. i/c Leprosy Serv. Gongola State Nigeria; Trainee GP S. Yorks.; Med. Off. Ngora Hosp. Uganda.

METCALFE, Mr Paul William The Surgery, Egton, Whitby YO21 1TX; Old Bear's Barn, Lealholm, Whitby YO21 2AF Tel: 01947 897433 — MB ChB 1981 Leeds; FRCS Ed. 1985; MRCGP 1990; DRCOG 1989. Prev: Regist. (Cardiac Surg.) Nat. Heart Hosp. Lond.; SHO & Regist. Rotat. (Surg.) Leeds E. HA.

METCALFE, Peter EMI Directorate, Mossley Hill Hospital, Park Avenue, Liverpool L18 8BU Tel: 0151 250 6131 Fax: 0151 729 0227 Email: peter.metcalfe@merseycare.nhs.uk — BM 1979 Soton.; MRCP (UK) 1983; MRCPsych 1990; Cert. Prescribed Equiv. Exp. JCPTGP 1985. (Soton.) Cons. Ment. Health of Elderly Mossley Hill Hosp. Liverp.; Cons. (Psychiat.) Young Onset Dementia Serv. Liverp. HA. Socs: Chairm. Merseyside PsychoGeriat.ians Developm.; Old Age Psychiat. Reg. Rep. For RC Psych. Prev: Sen. Regist. (Psychiat.) Merseyside Train. Scheme; Regist. Rotat. (Psychiat.) Merseyside Train. Scheme; Regist. (Med.) Birm. Gen. Hosp.

METCALFE, Richard Andrew Department of Neurology, Institute of Neurological Sciences, Southern General Hospital, Glasgow

G51 4TF Tel: 0141 201 2466 Fax: 0141 201 2993; 4 Camstradden Drive E., Bearsden, Glasgow G61 4AH Tel: 0141 942 6647 Fax: 0141 942 6647 — MB BChir 1974 Camb.; MA Camb. 1974, MD 1987; FRCPS Glas. 1991; MRCP (UK) 1977. (Univ. Coll. Hosp.) Cons. Neurol. S.. Gen. Hosp. NHS Trust; Hon. Sen. Clin. Lect. Univ. Glas. Prev: Lect. (Neurol.) Univ. Manch.; Regist. (Neurol.) Guy's Hosp. Lond.; Ho. Off. Univ. Coll. Hosp. Lond.

METCALFE, Ruth Elizabeth Tryfan, Betws-y-Coed LL24 0HA — MB ChB 1994 Ed.

METCALFE, Ruth Mary 138 Liverpool Road N., Maghull, Liverpool L31 2HW; 12 Rosehill Drive, Ormskirk L39 5AA — MB ChB 1984 Liverp.; MRCGP 1990; DRCOG 1986. Socs: BMA.

***METCALFE, Sandra** 21B South Park Road, Harrogate HG1 5QU — MB ChB 1997 Sheff.

METCALFE, Mr Stephen Frederick ENT Department, Dumfries and Galloway Royal Infirmary, Bankend Road, Dumfries DG1 4AP — MB ChB 1972 Bristol; FRCS Eng. 1977. Cons. Otolaryngol./PostGrad. Tutor Dumfries and Galloway Roy. Infirm. Prev: Cons. Otolaryngol. Borders Gen. Hosp. Melrose; Cons. Otolaryngol. Waterford Regional Hosp. RePub. of Irel.; Cons. Otolaryngol. Dumfries & Galloway Roy. Infirm. 1982-1991.

METCALFE, Susan Margaret 2 Marlborough Avenue, Newcastle upon Tyne NE3 2HT — MB BS 1992 Newc.

METCALFE, Mr Timothy Walker Apricot House, 50 Kent Road, Harrogate HG1 2ET Tel: 01423 505156 — MB ChB 1981 Manch.; FRCS Ed. 1986; FRCOphth 1989. Cons. Ophth. Harrogate Dist. Hosp. Prev: Sen. Regist. (Ophth.) Leeds Gen. Infirm.

METCALFE, Wendy 80 Kirkbrae, Cults, Aberdeen AB15 9QQ — MB ChB 1992 Glas.; MRCP (UK) 1996.

METCALFE, William Patrick (retired) 263 Colchester Road, Ipswich IP4 4SH Tel: 01473 725457 — BM BCh 1958 Oxf.; MA Oxf. 1958; DObst RCOG 1961. Prev: SHO (Orthop.), Ho. Surg. (O & G) & Ho. Phys. Ipswich & E. Suff. Hosp.

METCALFE-GIBSON, Mr Christopher Lorton Bridge Cottage, Low Lorton, Cockermouth CA13 9TB Tel: 01900 85205 Fax: 01900 85032 — MB 1968 Camb.; MA Camb. 1968, MB 1968, BChir 1967; FRCS Eng. 1972. (St. Thos.) Cons. Surg. W. Cumbld. Hosp. White Haven Cumbria. Prev: Sen. Regist. Manch. AHA; Regist. (Surg.) Stockport AHA; Clin. Tutor (Surg.) & Regist. (Cardiothoracic) Manch. Roy. Infirm.

***METHUEN, Caroline Deborah** The Minster House, Bedern Bank, Ripon HG4 1PE — MB BS 1997 Lond.

METHVEN, Charles Thomas (retired) 34A Heathville Road, Gloucester GL1 3JB — MB ChB 1962 St. And.; MRCPsych 1971; DPM Ed. & Glas. 1965. Prev: Cons. Psychiat. Coney Hill & Horton Rd. Hosps. Gloucester.

***METHVEN, Jane Elizabeth** 23 Butterfield, Wooburn Green, High Wycombe HP10 0PX — BChir 1995 Camb.

METSON, David Easthampstead Practice, Easthampstead Surgery, 23 Rectory Lane, Bracknell RG12 7BB Tel: 01344 457535 Fax: 01344 301862 — MB ChB 1977 Birm.; MRCGP 1983; DRCOG 1980.

METSON, Janice Rosemary Hill Brow Surgery, Long Croft, Staincross, Barnsley S75 6FH Tel: 01226 383131 Fax: 01226 380100; The Golden Cross, Cawthorne, Barnsley S75 4HR Tel: 01226 790477 — MB ChB 1963 Sheff. (Sheff.) Prev: Ho. Off. City Gen. Hosp. Sheff.

METSON, Michael John 164 Harold Road, Hastings TN35 5NG Tel: 01424 720878 Fax: 01424 719525 — MB BS 1969 Lond.; MRCS Eng. LRCP Lond. 1968; DA Eng. 1971; DObst RCOG 1971. (Univ. Coll. Hosp.) Socs: BMA (Pres. Hastings Div.). Prev: SHO (Anaesth.) Hastings Hosp. Gp.; SHO (O & G) Buchannan Hosp. Hastings; Ho. Phys. & Ho. Surg. Newmarket Gen. Hosp.

METTAM, Ian Macrae Shackleton Department of Anaesthesia, Southampton General Hospital, Southampton SO16 6YD — MB BS 1983 Lond.; MA Camb. 1984; FRCA 1989. Cons. Anaesth. Soton. Univ. Hosps. NHS Trust. Prev: Sen. Regist. Rotat. Oxf.; Regist. St. Geo. Hosp. Lond.

METTEN, Anne Cecilia (retired) 8 Fairview Road, Woodthorpe, Nottingham NG5 4GW — MB ChB Sheff. 1956; DCH Eng. 1959. Prev: Regist. (Med.) & Ho. Surg. Roy. Hosp. Sheff.

METTERS, Andrew John Francis William 164 Mackintosh Place, Cathays, Cardiff CF24 4RS — MB BCh 1991 Wales; BSc (Hons.) Biochem. 1988.

METTERS, Jeremy Stanley, CB Department of Health, 79 Whitehall, London SW1 — MB BChir 1964 Camb.; MA Camb. 1964, MB BChir. 1964; FRCOG 1982, M 1970. Dep. Chief Med. Off. Dept. Health Lond.

METWALLY, Ahmed Mahrous c/o Mr K.H.A. Wahab, 81 Reddicap Health Road, Sutton Coldfield B75 7DX — MB BCh 1983 Ain Shams.

METZGER, Ronald Edley Wellfield Surgery, 53-55 Crescent Road, Crumpsall, Manchester M8 9JT Tel: 0161 740 2213 Fax: 0161 720 9311 — MB ChB 1980 Manch.

METZGER, Simone Constance c/o Preston Royal Hospital, Sharoe Green Lane N., Fulwood, Preston PR2 9HT — State Exam Med Saarland 1990; MD Saarland 1991. SHO (A & E) Roy. Preston Hosp.

MEUDELL, Carolyn Mary Countryside, Nettleton Shrub, Nettleton, Chippenham SN14 7NN Tel: 01249 782744 — MB ChB Sheff. 1969. (Sheff.) Staff Grade Paediat. Bath & W. Community NHS Trust. Prev: Clin. Med. Off. Salop. HA & N.ants. AHA; Regist. (Bact. & Immunol.) W.. Infirm. Glas.

MEULENDIJK, Hans Nico Station Lane Medical Centre, Station Lane, Featherstone, Pontefract WF7 6JL Tel: 01977 600381 Fax: 01977 600776 — Artsexamen 1986 Leiden; DPD 2000; MRCGP 1998. (Leiden) GP Pontefract, W. Yorks.; Primary Care Phys. in A&E; GP Specialist in Dermat.

MEULMAN, Johannes Harmannus 4 Bron Y Nant, Croesnewydd Road, Wrexham LL13 7TX — Artsexamen 1985 Nijmegen.

MEURER-LABAN, Mary Milne 8 Kings Avenue, Ealing, London W5 2SH Tel: 020 8997 6147 — MB BS 1966 Sydney; FFA RCS Eng. 1971. (Sydney) Cons. Anaesth. Ealing Hosp. Prev: Sen. Regist. (Anaesth.) Roy. Free Hosp. Lond.; Cons. Anaesth. Sion Switz.; Regist. (Anaesth.) Hammersmith Hosp. Lond.

MEURISSE, Miss Fiona Louise Anne 4 Pony Chase, Cobham KT11 2PF — MB BS 1993 Lond.; FRCSI 1998; FRCS (Eng) 1999.

MEUWISSEN, Karel Jan Albert Maria 2 Hague Court, Horseshoe Road, Spalding PE11 3HT — Artsexamen 1990 Maastricht.

MEUX, Clive Julian Broadmoor Hospital, Crowthorne RG45 7EG Tel: 01344 754079 Fax: 01344 754385; The Institute of Psychiatry, De Crespigny Park, Denmark Hill, London SE5 8AF Tel: 020 7919 3123 Fax: 020 7919 3754 — MB BS 1983 Lond.; MRCPsych 1988. (Westm.) Sen. Lect. (Forens. Psychiat.) Inst. Psychiat. Lond.; Hon. Cons. Forens. Psychiat. BRd.moor Hosp. Crowthorne, Attatched Cons.s Bethlem Roy & Maudsley Hosps. Prev: Sen. Regist. (Forens. Psychiat.) Maudsley & Bethlem Roy. Hosps. Lond.; Regist. (Psychiat.) Univ. Liverp. Train. Scheme; SHO (Psychiat.) Hellingly Hosp. E.bourne.

MEUX, Sheila Carol Steuart Riverbrook Medical Centre, Riverbrook Drive, Stirchley, Birmingham B30 2SH Tel: 0121 451 2525 — MB BS 1950 Lond. (King's Coll. Hosp.) Prev: Ophth. Ho. Surg. King's Coll. Hosp.; Paediat. Ho. Phys. Roy. Hosp. Wolverhampton; Ho. Pathol. Childr. Hosp. Birm.

MEW, Christopher John The Surgery, Barnhay, Bampton, Tiverton EX16 9NB.

***MEW, Ian Phillip** 44 Quinta Road, Torquay TQ1 3RN — MB BS 1998 Lond.; MB BS Lond 1998.

MEWAR, Devesh 3 Fitzroy Avenue, Birmingham B17 8RL — BChir 1994 Camb.; MB Cambridge 1995; MRCP (UK) 1997. SHO (Neurol.) Qu.s Med. Centre Nottm. Prev: SHO Med. Rotat. Leicester.

MEWASINGH, Duvika 19 Lynton Drive, Heaton, Bradford BD9 5JX; 102 Swift Road, Abbeydale, Gloucester GL4 4XJ Tel: 01452 533737 — MB ChB 1992 Leeds; MRCP (UK) 1995. SHO (Paediat.) Qu. Med. Centre Nottm. Socs: Med. Protec. Soc.; Phys. Human Rights; BMA. Prev: SHO Leeds Gen. Infirm.

MEYER, Carl Hugh Alexander Queen Elizabeth Neuroscience Centre, Department of Neurosurgery, Queen Elizabeth Hospital, Birmingham B15 2TH — MB BS 1966 Adelaide; BMedSc Adelaide 1962; FRACS 1974. Cons. Neurosurg. Midl. Centre for Neurosurg. & Neurol. Birm. Socs: Eur. Soc. Sterotactic & Func.al Neurosurg. (Exec. Comm. Mem.); World Soc. Stereotactic & Func.al Neurosurg. Prev: Sen. Lect. (Neurosurg.) Univ. Birm.; Sen. Regist. (Neurosurg.) Guy's, Maudsley & King's Coll. Neurosurgic. Unit. & SE Thames Regional Neurosurgic Unit; Fell. Neurosurgic. Research Foundat. S. Austral.

MEYER, Derek Louis 55 Oakwood Road, London NW11 6RJ — MB BCh 1984 Witwatersrand.

MEYER, Miss Felicity Jane Department of Academic Surgery, St. Thomas' Hospital, Lambeth Palace Road, London SE1 7EH Tel: 020

MEYER

7928 9292 Fax: 020 7928 8742 Email: felicity.meyer@kel.ac.uk; The Old School House, Main Road, Longfield DA3 7PW Tel: 020 7928 9292 — BM BCh 1989 Oxf.; MA Oxf. 1986, BM BCh 1989; FRCS Eng. 1993. Regist. (Gen.Surg.) SE Thames.; Lect. (Surg.) St. Thomas' Hosp.; Research Fell. RCS LEA Thomas.

MEYER, Geffrey Willaston Surgery, Neston Road, Willaston, Neston CH64 2TN Tel: 0151 327 4593 Fax: 0151 327 8618; Efteling, 11 Leighton Road, Neston, South Wirral CH64 3SF Tel: 0151 336 7182 — MB ChB 1977 Liverp.; DRCOG 1979. (Liverp.) Prev: Trainee GP Birkenhead (St. Catherine's) VTS; Resid. Ho. Off. Birkenhead Gen. Hosp.

MEYER, Helmuth Andree Martine 32 Knightsbridge Crescent, Staines TW18 2QR — MB BS 1990 Lond.; BA (Hons.) Sheff. 1980; MRCGP 1994; DRCOG 1993. Cons. in Palliat. Med. Braeside Hosp. Sydney Australia. Socs: Assn. Palliat. Med. Prev: Sen. Regist. (Palliat. Med.) P.ss Alice Hosp. Surrey; Sen. Regist. (Palliat. Med.) St. Thos. Hosp. Lond.; Regist. (Palliat. Med.) Trinity Hospice Lond.

MEYER, Hendrika Carlien Kate 17 St Mary's Road, Harbourne, Birmingham B17 0EY — MB ChB 1992 Birm.; ChB Birm. 1992.

MEYER, Hermann Delfryn, Crundale, Haverfordwest SA62 4DF — State Exam Med. Lubeck 1990.

MEYER, John Sidney Bertram (retired) Sun-Acre, 4 Longdown Road, Lower Bourne, Farnham GU10 3JS Tel: 01252 792577 — MB BS Lond. 1955; MRCS Eng. LRCP Lond. 1955; DObst RCOG 1957. Prev: Resid. Ho. Off. Lewisham Gen. Hosp. Lond.

MEYER, Joseph Edward Medway Maritime Hosp, Gillingham ME7 5NY Tel: 01634 830000; Fairview, Church Road, Goudhurst, Cranbrook TN17 1BH Tel: 01580 211750 Email: jomeyer39@hotmail.com — MB BS Lond. 1962; MRCS Eng. LRCP Lond. 1962; FRCP Lond. 1990; MRCP (UK) 1970; FRCPCH 1997; DObst RCOG 1966; DCH RCP Lond. 1965. (Guy's) Cons. Paediat. Medway NHS Trust. Socs: BMA. Prev: Sen. Lect. Fiji Sch. Med.; Cons. Paediat. Tunbridge Wells HA; Sen. Regist. St. Thos. Hosp. Lond.

MEYER, Mr Maurice Department of Plastic Surgery, West Norwich Hospital, Bowthorpe Road, Norwich NR2 3T Tel: 0603 286286; 9 Parkland Close, Chigwell IG7 6LL — MD 1983 Lond.; MB BS 1980; FRCS (Plast) 1984; FRCS Glas. 1984. Cons. Plastic Surg. W. Norwich Hosp. Socs: Assoc. Mem. Brit. Soc. Surg. Hand; Brit. Assn. Plastic Surg. Prev: Sen. Regist. (Plastic Surg.) St. John's Hosp. Livingston & Roy. Hosp. Sick Childr. Edin.; Regist. (Plastic Surg.) St. And. Hosp. Billericay; Research Fell. (Surg.) Univ. Coll. Univ. Lond.

***MEYER, Michael Johan** Furness General Hospital, Dalton Lane, Barrow-in-Furness LA14 4LF — MB ChB 1995 Cape Town.

MEYER, Nina Amy (retired) 8 Southwood Park, Southwood Lawn Road, Highgate, London N6 5SG Tel: 020 8340 6030 — BM BCh 1949 Oxf.; MA Oxf. 1949; MRCPsych 1972; DPM Lond. 1951. Prev: Clin. Asst. (Psychol. Med.) Lond. Hosp.

MEYER, Paul Arthur Roland Department of Ophthalmology, Addenbrooke's Hospital, Hills Road, Cambridge CB2 2QQ Tel: 01223 245151 — MB BChir 1976 Camb.; MA Camb. 1976; MD Camb. 1993; MRCP (UK) 1979. Cons. Med. Ophth. Addenbrooke's Hosp. Camb. Socs: Fell. of Roy. Coll. of Phys.s; Mem. of Roy. Coll. of Ophth.s.

MEYER, Pedro Carlos (retired) 2 Nightingale Lodge, Cowper Road, Berkhamsted HP4 3ED Tel: 01442 862648 — MB BS Lond. 1945; MD (Path.) Lond. 1951; LMSSA Lond. 1945; DCP Lond 1949. Prev: Cons. Path. (Morbid Anat.) Whittington Hosp.

MEYER, Ruth Elizabeth 66 South Hill Park, London NW3 2SJ — MB 1977 Camb.; BChir 1976; DRCOG 1979.

MEYER, Stefan Flat 1, 3 Elm Road, Manchester M20 6XB — MD 1993 Hamburg; State Exam Med. 1992.

MEYER, Timothy Royal Free Hospital, London — MB BS 1990 Lond.; BSc Lond. 1984; MRCP (UK) 1994; PhD Lond. 1999. (Univ. Coll. Lond.) Specialist Regist. (Med. Oncol.) Roy. Free Hosp.

MEYERHOFF, Andrea 6 Claremont Road, Norwich NR4 6SH — State Exam Med 1991 Hamburg. SHO (Anaesth.) Worthing & S.lands Hosps.

***MEYERS, Jessica Lucy Caroline** Kingsley House, The High St., Robertsbridge TN32 5AP — MB BS 1996 Lond.

MEYERS, Rosemary Matilda 39 St Mary's Drive, Perth PH2 7BY — MB BCh BAO 1962 Belf.; DPH Belf. 1968. Clin. Med. Off. Dundee Healthcare Trust. Socs: Fac. Community Health; BMA. Prev: Ho. Off. Roy. Matern. Hosp. Glas.

MEYNELL, Anne 95 Moresdale Lane, Leeds LS14 6GG Tel: 0113 295 1200 — MB BS 1964 Lond.; MRCGP 1977; DObst RCOG 1967. (St. Mary's) Socs: BMA.

MEYNELL, Elinor Wray (retired) Haven House, Granville Road, St Margarets Bay, Dover CT15 6DR Tel: 01304 853299 — MB BCh BAO 1945 Dub.; MD Dub. 1966; Dip. Bact. Lond 1950. Prev: MRC Microbiol. Genetics Research Unit.

MEYNELL, Geoffrey Guy (retired) Haven House, Granville Road, St Margarets Bay, Dover CT15 6DR Tel: 01304 853299 — MB BS 1949 Lond.; DSc Lond. 1972, MD 1958; MRCS Eng. LRCP Lond. 1949. Prev: Prof. Microbiol. Univ. Kent. Canterbury.

MEYNELL, Joseph Francis, Surg. Capt. RN Retd. (retired) 28 Berkeley Avenue, Cadewell, Torquay TQ2 7LE — MRCS Eng. LRCP Lond. 1936; DA Eng. 1955. Prev: Surg. Capt. RN.

MEYNEN, Frederick Godfried Cornelis The Ashlea Medical Practice, Linden House, 39 Woodfield Road, Leatherhead Tel: 01372 375666 Fax: 01372 360117; 30 Upper Fairfield Road, Leatherhead KT22 7HH Tel: 01372 375666 — MB BS 1964 Lond.; MRCS Eng. LRCP Lond. 1964; FRCGP 1995, M 1973; DObst RCOG 1966. (Roy. Free) Med. Off. St. John's Sch. Leatherhead. Prev: Cas. Off. & Jun. Anaesth. Roy. Free Hosp. Lond.; Ho. Phys. & Ho. Off. (Obst.) St. Helier Hosp. Carshalton.

MEYRICK, Jeremy Stewart (retired) Old Swan House, Great Rissington, Cheltenham GL54 2LH Tel: 01451 820497 — BM BCh 1960 Oxf.; MA Oxf. 1960. Non Princip. GP. Prev: GP Bourton-on-the-Water.

MEYRICK, John (retired) 6 Pynchon Paddocks, Little Hallingbury, Bishop's Stortford CM22 7RJ Tel: 01279 725102 — MRCS Eng. LRCP Lond. 1944; DObst RCOG 1950. Prev: RAMC 1945-48.

MEYRICK, Martin Robert Palmer Station House Surgery, Station Road, Kendal LA9 6SA Tel: 01539 722660 Fax: 01539 734845 — MB ChB 1969 Liverpool. (Liverpool) GP Kendal, Cumbria.

MEYRICK, Patricia Virginia (retired) Garth, Abersoch, Pwllheli LL53 7DU Tel: 01758 712730 — MB BS Lond. 1965; MRCS Eng. LRCP Lond. 1965; DCH Eng. 1969. Prev: GP Abersoch Nth. Wales.

MEYRICK, Richard Simon 1 Baber Close, Penylan, Cardiff CF23 9BX — MB BCh 1981 Wales; MRCP (UK) 1986.

MEYRICK, Roger Llewellyn (retired) Boulter's Tor, Smeardon Down, Peter Tavy, Tavistock PL19 9NX Tel: 01822 810525 Email: roger.meyrick@dial.pipex.com — MB BS 1954 Lond.; MRCS Eng. LRCP Lond. 1953; FRCGP 1972, M 1960. JP. Prev: GP Catford.

MEYRICK THOMAS, Mr John Watford General Hospital, Vicarage Road, Watford WD18 0HB Tel: 01923 217692 Fax: 01923 217962; 10 Manor Cottages, Heronsgate Road, Chorleywood, Rickmansworth WD3 5BJ Tel: 01923 282656 — MB BChir 1975 Camb.; MA Camb. 1975, MChir 1991; FRCS Eng. 1978. (Camb. & St. Bart.) Cons. Gen. Surg. & Gastroenterol. Watford Gen. Hosp. Socs: Fell. Roy. Soc. Med. (Mem. Sects. Surg. Colo-Proctol. & Urol.); Brit. Soc. Gastroenterol. (Mem. Surg. Oesoph. & Endoscopy Sects.); Fell. Assn. Surgs. Prev: Sen. Regist. (Surg.) Roy. Free, Whittington & Roy. N.. Hosps. Lond.; Research Fell. & Hon. Regist. (Gastroenterol.) Centr. Middlx. Hosp. Lond.; Ho. Surg. Profess. Unit St. Bart. Hosp. Lond.

MEYRICK THOMAS, Richard Hugh Tilhayes, Church Hill, Iwerne Munster, Blandford Forum DT11 8LS Tel: 01747 811658 — MB BS 1976 Lond.; MA Oxf. 1979; FRCP Lond. 1994; MRCP (UK) 1980. Cons. Dermat. Salisbury Health Care NHS Trust. Socs: Fell. Roy. Soc. Med.; Brit. Assn. Dermat. Prev: Sen. Regist. (Dermat.) St. Bart. Hosp. Lond.; Regist. (Dermat.) St. Thos. Hosp. Lond.; SHO (Med.) & Ho. Phys. St. Bart. Hosp. Lond.

MEYSTRE, Chantal Julie Nicole George Eliot Hospital, Lewes House, College St., Nuneaton CV10 7DJ Tel: 01203 865488; 4 The Courtyard, 81 Glasshouse Lane, Kenilworth CV8 2AH Tel: 01926 512988 — MB ChB 1980 Leeds; FRCP 2001; MRCP (UK) 1983. Clin. Director Palliat. Care ISD Warks.; Hon. Sen. Clin. Lect. Warwick Univ. Socs: Assoc. for Palliat. Med.; BMA; Christian Med. Fell.ship. Prev: Cons. in Palliat. Care Loros Leicester; Sen. Regist. (Palliat. Care) Loros Leicester.

MEZAS, Laura Helen Flat 2, 11 Hanover Square, Leeds LS3 1AP Tel: 0113 243 5296 — Artsexamen 1994 Free U Amsterdam; Artsexamen Free Univ Amsterdam 1994.

MEZEY, Alexander Goldfeder 152 Harley Street, London W1 Tel: 020 7935 3834; 20 Snakes Lane, Woodford Green IG8 Tel: 020 8505 6431 — MD 1946 Geneva; MSc, MB 1945; FRCP Ed. 1968,

M 1954; LAH Dub. 1953; FRCPsych 1977, M 1971; DPM Eng. 1957. (Geneva, Zurich & Paris) Prev: Sen. Cons. Psychiat. Haringey Dist. Gen. Hosp. Lond.; Asst. Univ. Clinics, Geneva & Paris; Sen. Regist. Profess. Unit Maudsley Hosp. Lond.

MEZEY, Gillian Clare Section of Forensic Psychiatry, St. Georges Hospital Medical School, Cranmer Terrace, London SW17 0RE Tel: 020 8725 5568 Fax: 020 8725 2475 Email: gmezey@sghus.ac.uk — MB BS 1980 Lond.; MRCP Psych 1985; FRCP Psych 1999.

MEZILIS, Nikolaos Cardiology Department, Northern General Hospital, Herries Road, Sheffield S5 7AU Tel: 0114 243 7650 — Ptychio latrikes 1987 Thessalonika. Vis. Regist. (Cardiol.) N. Gen. Hosp. Sheff.

MG MG LAT, Dr 283 Queslett Road, Birmingham B43 7HB — MB BS 1968 Mandalay; DTCD Wales 1974.

MIA, Mahomed Shabir 11 Simonburn Avenue, Stoke-on-Trent ST4 5JR — MB ChB 1988 Natal.

***MIAH, Aisha Begum** 34 Edgar Road, Hounslow TW4 5QW — MB BS 1998 Lond.; MB BS Lond 1998.

***MIAH, Sayful Islam** 232 Bowes Road, London N11 2JH — MB BS 1996 Lond.

MIALL, Charles Humfrey Ian (retired) Hill House, Winterfield Road, Paulton, Bristol BS39 7QR Tel: 01761 412051 — MB BCh BAO 1964 Dub.; BA Dub. 1963, MB BCh BAO 1964; DObst RCOG 1967.

***MIALL, Fiona Mary** The Mount, Vicarage Lane, Helsby, Warrington WA6 9AE — BM BS 1994 Nottm.

MIALL, William Einar (retired) Sidegarth, Crook Road, Staveley, Kendal LA8 9NN Tel: 01539 821852 — MRCS Eng. LRCP Lond. 1950; MD Lond. 1962, MB BS (Hons.) 1950; FRCP Lond. 1977, M 1976. Prev: Dir. MRC Epidemiol. Unit, Jamaica.

MIALL-ALLEN, Vivienne Mary GlaxoWellcome Research & Development, Greenford Road, Greenford UB6 0HE; Oakshott, 7 Highlands Road, Leatherhead KT22 8NB — MA Camb. 1983, MB BChir 1982; MRCP 1989; MD (University of Cambridge) 1989. Sen. Phys. Socs: Brit. Cardiac Soc. Prev: Lect./Hon. Sen. Regist. Inst. of Child Health Lond. John Radcliffe Hosp. Oxf.; Regist. Hosp. for Sick Childr., Gt. Ormond St.; SHO Hammersmith Hosp., Brompton Hosp. & W.m. Hosp. Lond.

MIAN, Abdul Hameed The Chalet, Didderhowe Lane, Castleton, Whitby YO21 2DD — MB BS 1955 Punjab; PhD Open Univ. (Pakistan) 1977; MSc (Nuclear Med.) Lond. 1972; BSc Punjab (Pakistan) 1949, MB BS 1955; FRCR 1975; FFR 1967; DMRD Eng. 1965. (King Ed. Med. Coll. Lahore) Prof. Radiol. & Nuclear Med. F.J. Coll. Lahore Pakistan. Socs: BMA & Brit. Nuclear Med. Soc. Prev: Cons. Radiol. & Nuclear Med. S. Tees Health Dist.; Sen. Regist. St. Mary's Hosp. Lond.& Roy. Marsden Hosp. Lond.

MIAN, Fazal Ur Rahman Otterfield Medical Centre, 25 Otterfield Road, West Drayton UB7 8PE Tel: 01895 422611 — MB BS 1994 Lond.; BSc Infec. & Immunity (Hons.) Lond. 1991; MRCGP 1998; DCH 1997. (Imperial College, London) GP Princip. (Partner). Socs: Med. Protec. Soc. Prev: GP Regist. Hillingdon Hosp. VTS; Ho. Off. (Gen. Surg., Med. & Urol.) Hillingdon Hosp. Uxbridge.

MIAN, Ihsanul Haq 33 Shipley Road, Westbury-on-Trym, Bristol BS9 3HR — MB BS 1965 Punjab; FRCPsych 1986, M 1973; DPM Newcastle upon Tyne 1971. Emerit. Cons. Psychiat. S.mead Gen. Hosp. Bristol; Hon. Cons. Psychiat. Priory Hosp. Bristol. Socs: Mem. Ment. Health Review Tribunal; Vice-Pres., Alzheimer Soc., Bristol; Vice-Pres., Dementia Care Trust, Bristol. Prev: Sen. Regist. Exe Vale Hosp. Digby; Sen. Regist. (Psychiat.) Roy. S.. Hosp. & Sefton Gen. Hosp. Liverp.

MIAN, Irfan 8 Chinbrook Road, Grove Park, London SE12 9TH Tel: 020 8857 4249 Fax: 020 8857 9041; 176 Burnt Ash Lane, Bromley BR1 5BU — MRCS Eng. LRCP Lond. 1976; MB BS Lond. 1976, BDS 1972; LDS RCS Eng. 1973; MFGDP 1992 (UK). (Char. Cross) Hon. Research Fell. (Neurol.) Char. Cross Hosp. Lond.; Lect. Kings Coll. Hosp. Dent. Sch. Socs: Fell.Roy. Soc. Med.; (Chairm.) Exec. Comm. Federat. Lond. LDC; (Chairm. & Director) Federat. Lond. LDC.

MIAN, Mohammed Shah-Nawaz 124 Hesleden Avenue, Acklam, Middlesbrough TS5 8RX — MB BS 1991 Newc.

MIAN, Muna Rafi 52 Cedar Road, East Croydon, Croydon CR0 6UD Tel: 020 8680 4213 — MB ChB 1994 Liverp. SHO (Gen. Med.) Qu. Mary's Hosp. Sidcup, Kent. Socs: BMA; Liverp. Med. Soc. Prev: Ho. Off. Roy. Liverp. Univ. Hosp.

MIAN, Rafi Saleem The Health Centre, Rose Tree Avenue, Cudworth, Barnsley S72 8UA Tel: 01226 710326 Fax: 01226 780627 — MB BS 1965 Punjab. (Punjab) GP Barnsley, S. Yorks.

MIAN, T A The Armthorpe Surgery, Church Street, Armthorpe, Doncaster DN3 3AH Tel: 01302 831437 Fax: 01302 300623 — MB BS 1978 Punjab; MB BS 1978 Punjab.

MIAN, Tanwir Muhammed Anaesthetic Department, Royal Gwent Hospital, Cardiff Road, Newport NP20 2UR; 14 Bala Drive, Rogerstowe, Newport NP10 9HN — MB BCh 1983 Wales; FRCA 1989. Cons. Anaesth. Roy. Gwent Hosp. Newport Gwent.

MIAO, Yin Mei Chelsea & Westminster Hospital, 369 Fulham Road, London SW10 9NH Email: ymiao@ic.ac.uk; Flat 42, Jemmett Close, Kingston upon Thames KT2 7AJ Tel: 020 8404 1145 — MB BS 1989 Lond.; MRCP (UK) 1994. (St Geo. Hosp.) Specialist Regist. (Gastroenterol.) Chelsea & W.minster Hosp. Lond.

MIARKOWSKI, Ryszard Feliks 19 Farm Grove, Rugby CV22 5NQ — BM 1992 Soton.

MICALLEF, Alphonse Michaele (retired) The Cottage, Lower Stonehurst Farm, East Grinstead RH19 3PX Tel: 01342 850783 Fax: 01342 850783 — MD 1946 Malta; BSc Malta 1943. Prev: Med. Off. Centr. Hosp. Floriana Malta, & Leicester Roy. Infirm.

MICALLEF, Carmel Highfield Health Centre, 2 Proctor Street, off Tong Street, Bradford BD4 9QA Tel: 01274 227700 Fax: 01274 227900 — MRCS Eng. LRCP Lond. 1977. (University of Malta)

MICALLEF-EYNAUD, Paul David Department of Haematology, Crosshouse Hospital, Kilmarnock KA2 0BE Tel: 01563 572407 Email: dreynaud@aaaht.scot.nhs.uk; Springbank, 21 Doonholm Road, Alloway, Ayr KA7 4QQ Tel: 01292 442455 Email: pmeynaud@aol.com — MRCS Eng. LRCP Lond. 1981; MRCP (UK) 1987; MRCPath 1996; FRCP 1999 Glas. Cons. Haemat. Prev: Sen. Regist. (Haemat.) Roy. Infirm. Edin. NHS Trust; LRF Clin. Research Fell. Roy. Hosp. Sick Childr. Edin.; Regist. (Haemat.) Roy. Infirm. Edin.

MICHAEL, Brenda St Marys Surgery, St. Marys Close, Timsbury, Bath BA2 0HX Tel: 01761 470880 Fax: 01761 472492; Amesbury Hill House, Amesbury Hamlet, Timsbury, Bath BA2 0HF Tel: 01761 472450 Fax: 01761 472038 — MB ChB 1970 Sheff.; Cert. Family Plann. JCC 1984. (Sheff.) GP Princip. Socs: Clin. Soc. Bath. Prev: Med. Off. Johannesburg Gen. Hosp., S. Afr.; Company Doctor Mission Medic-Air, Zambia.

MICHAEL, Catherine Elizabeth 45 High Street, Markinch, Glenrothes KY7 6DQ — MB ChB 1982 Manch.; MRCGP 1986.

MICHAEL, Mr Dean 24B Lonsdale Square, London N1 1EN — MB BS 1994 Lond.; FRCS 1998. (St. Bart's Lond.) Specialist Regist. (Trauma & Orthop.) UCH & Middx Rotat. Prev: Clin. Fell. (Orthop.) the Whittington Hosp. Lond.; SHO (Surg.) The N.wick Pk. & St Mark's Rotat.; Demonst. (Anat.) Guy's & St. Thomas's Hosp.

MICHAEL, Miss Enid Mary 12 Kingswood Avenue, Newcastle upon Tyne NE2 3NS — BM BCh 1980 Oxf.; MA, DPhil Oxf. 1982, BM BCh 1980; MRCOG 1986; T(OG) 1991; FRCOG 1998. Cons. Sen. Lect. O & G Roy. Vict. Infirm. Newc. u. Tyne. Socs: Amer. Fertil. Soc. & Brit. Menopause Soc. Prev: Clin. Lect. & Hon. Sen. Regist. (Human Reprod. & Obst.) P.ss Anne Hosp. Soton.; Vis. Fell. Johns Hopkins Univ. Sch. Med. USA 1986-87; Regist. (O & G) Birm. Matern. Hosp. & Birm & Midl. Hosp. Wom.

MICHAEL, Gerald Maurice 42 London Road, Stanmore HA7 4NU Tel: 020 8958 4237 Fax: 020 8905 4809 Email: 10061.754@compuserve.com — MB BS 1960 Lond.; MRCS Eng. LRCP Lond. 1960; MRCGP 1971; DObst RCOG 1963. (Middlx.) GP Tutor Edgware Community. Hosp. Prev: Ho. Phys. Selly Oak Hosp. Birm.; Ho. Surg. Hillingdon Hosp.; Ho. Surg. (O & G) Chase Farm Hosp. Enfield.

MICHAEL, Gwilym 29 Epsom Road, Ilford IG3 8QP — MRCS Eng. LRCP Lond. 1962.

MICHAEL, Jonathan University Hospital Birmingham NHS Trust, Selly Oak, Birmingham B29 6JF Tel: 0121 627 8934; 26 Moor Green Lane, Moseley, Birmingham B13 8ND Tel: 0121 449 8814 Fax: 0121 449 9393 — MB BS 1970 (St Thos.) Lond; MRCP 1973 UK; MRCS 1970 Eng; FRCP 1985 Lond. (St. Thos.) Chief Exec. Univ. Hosp. Birm. NHS Trust; Cons. Nephrologist Qu. Eliz. Hosp. Birm.; Hon. Sen. Clin. Lect. Univ. Birm. Socs: Fell. Roy. Soc. Med.; Renal Assn.

MICHAEL, Lionel Abraham, SBStJ 599 Wilmslow Road, Didsbury, Manchester M20 3QD Tel: 0161 445 1952 Fax: 0161

MICHAEL

448 1764; 10 Dene Park, Didsbury, Manchester M20 2GF Tel: 0161 445 4930 — MB ChB 1960 Manch.; FRCGP 1976, M 1967; T(GP) 1991; DCH Eng. 1969; DObst RCOG 1962. (Univ. Manch.) Lect. Univ. Coll. Salford. Socs: Fell. Manch. Med. Soc. Prev: Area Commr. St. John Ambul. Brig.; Ho. Off. (Obst.) Pk. Hosp. Davyhulme; Ho. Surg. & Ho. Phys. Withington Hosp. Manch.

*MICHAEL, Natasha Gertrude 99 Brudenell Road, Leeds LS6 1JD — MB ChB 1997 Leeds.

MICHAEL, Raouf Fawzi Royal Gwent Hospital, Cardiff Road, Newport NP20 2UB Tel: 01633 252244; 4 Springfield Lane, Rhiwderin Village, Newport NP10 8QZ Tel: 01633 892429 — MB ChB 1967 Cairo; FFARCSI 1983. Cons. Anaesth. Gwent HA.

MICHAEL, Sandra Ann 197 Brox Road, Ottershaw, Chertsey KT16 0RD — MB BCh BAO 1981 Belf.; MRCGP 1986; DRCOG 1984. Clin. Med. Off. Mid. Surrey HA.

MICHAEL, Stelios Department of Anaesthesia, Northern General Hospital, Herries Road, Sheffield S5 7AU Tel: 0114 271 4818 Fax: 0114 256 0394 Email: s.michael@sheffield.ac.uk; 7 Taptonville Road, Broomhill, Sheffield S10 5BQ — MB ChB 1982 Sheff.; FFA RCSI 1988. Cons. Anaesth. & Intens. Care N. Gen. Hosp. Sheff. Socs: BMA; ICS & AAGBI.

MICHAEL, Terence Thomas Erskine 2 St Quintin Avenue, Kensington, London W10 6NU Tel: 020 8960 0122 — MB BCh BAO 1949 Dub. Socs: Fell. Roy. Soc. Med.

MICHAEL, Wevitavidanalage Don Ambrose 232 Hall Lane, Chingford, London E4 8EY Tel: 020 8529 1463 — MB BS 1971 Ceylon; FFA RCSI 1985; DA (UK) 1982.

MICHAEL, William Francis 19 Durham Avenue, Bromley BR2 0QE Tel: 020 8464 7685 — BM BCh Oxf. 1962; DM Oxf. 1971; FRCP Lond. 1982, M 1966. (Oxf. & St. Thos.) Hon. Cons. Neurol. (Neurosci.) King's Coll. Hosp. Lond. Socs: Osler Soc. & Assn. Brit. Neurol.; Fell. Roy. Soc. of Med. Prev: Sen. Regist. (Neurol.) St. Bart. Hosp. Lond.; Ho. Phys. St. Thos. Hosp. Lond. & Nat. Hosp. Nerv. Dis. Qu. Sq. Lond.

MICHAELIS, Christian c/o Anaesthetic Department, Kings College Hospital, Denmark Hill, London SE5 9RS — State Exam Med 1988 Berlin.

MICHAELIS, Janet Rebecca Durrington Health Centre, Durrington Lane, Worthing BN13 2RX Tel: 01903 843800 — BM 1990 Soton. (Soton.) CMO in Sexual Health.

MICHAELIS, Louise Jane Great Ormond Street Hospital for Children, Great Ormond St., London WC1N 3 Tel: 020 7405 9200; 63 Beaufort Mansions, Beaufort St, Chelsea, London SW3 5AF Tel: 020 7352 3714 Fax: 020 7352 3714 — MB ChB 1994 Ed.; BSc (Hons.) St. And. 1989. (Edin.) Med. Unit Gt. Ormond St. Hosp. Lond.; HO Off. (Paediat.) Roy. Hosp. Childr.; SHO (Paediat.) Roy. Hosp. Childr.; SHO (Neonatol.) Roy. Infirm. Edin. Prev: SHO (I.D. & Immunol.) Gt. Ormond St. Hosp. Lond.; SHO (Paediat. ITU) Newc. Gen. Hosp.; SHO (Cardio. Paediat.) Freeman NHS Trust.

MICHAELS, Achilles Archiebald PO Box 1819, Poole BH14 0YR — BM 1981 Soton.

MICHAELS, Gillian Patricia Royal South Hampshire Hospital, Brinton's Terrace, Southampton Tel: 023 8082 5411 — MB BChir 1981 Camb.; MA Camb. 1981; FRCR 1988. Cons. Radiol.S.ampton Univ. Hosp. Trust. Prev: Con. Radiol. Qu.s Hosp., Buton on Trent.

MICHAELS, Mr Jonathan Anthony Northern General Hospital, Herries Road, Sheffield S5 7AU — MB BChir 1980 Camb.; MA Camb. 1981; MChir Camb. 1991; FRCS Ed. 1985. Cons. Vasc. Surg. N. Gen. Hosp. Sheff. Prev: Clin. Lect. Nuffield Dept. Surg. Oxf.; Clin. Lect. (Surg.) Univ. Coll. Lond.

MICHAELS, Professor Leslie Department of Histopathology, Royal Free & UCL Medical School, University St., London WC1E 6JJ Tel: 020 7679 6038 Fax: 020 7387 3674 Email: l.michaels@ucl.ac.uk; Romany Ridge, Hillbrow Road, Bromley BR1 4JL Tel: 020 8460 5737 — MB BS Lond. 1949; MD Lond. 1960; LMCC 1961; FRCPath 1974, M 1963; FRCPC 1973; Dip. Clin. Path. 1964; Dip. Path. Anat. Amer. Bd. Path. 1962; DPath Eng. 1955. (Westm.) Hon. Cons. Path. Roy. Nat. Throat, Nose & Ear Hosp.; Emerit. Prof. Path. Roy. Free + UCL Med. Sch. Socs: Path. Soc.; Assn. Clin. Path.; BMA. Prev: Asst. Prof. Albert Einstein Coll. Med. New York, USA; Lect. (Morbid Anat.) St. Mary's Hosp. Med. Sch. Lond.; Prof. Path. Univ. Coll. & Middlx. Sch. Med. Lond.

MICHAELS, Michael Skidbrooke House, Staple Fitzpaine, Taunton TA3 5SP — MB BS 1992 Lond.

MICHAELS, Ronald 238 Botwell Lane, Hayes UB3 2AP — MB ChB 1956 Manch.

MICHAELS, Sadie Bessie (retired) 103 New Church Road, Hove BN3 4BD Tel: 01273 732856 — MB BS 1947 Lond.

MICHAELS, Thomas Maurice 3 Elwick Road, Ashford TN23 1 — MRCS Eng. LRCP Lond. 1966.

MICHAELSON, Harry c/o 111 Union Street, Glasgow G1 3SS Tel: 0141 204 1031 — LRCP LRCS Ed. LRFPS Glas. 1931; LDS 1926. (Univ. Glas.) Prev: Dent. Surg. Glas. Roy. Infirm.; Lect. in Bact. Glas. Dent. Hosp.

MICHAELSON, Simon Department of Psychiatry, Northwick Park Hospital, Watford Road, Harrow HA1 3UJ — MB BS 1981 Lond.; MRCPsych 1985. (Roy. Free) Cons. Psychiat. - N.wick Pk. Hosp. Prev: Sen. Regist. Rotat. (Psychiat.) Roy. Free Hosp. Train. Scheme.; Clin. Research Fell. Dept. Psychiat. Univ. Manch.; SHO & Regist. Rotat. (Psychiat.) Sheff.

MICHAIL, Mr Medhat Wadie Azer 4 Sutton Walk, Reading RG1 5HF — MB BS 1980 Garyounis, Libya; FRCS Ed 1994.

MICHAIL, Milad Ibrahim 15 Warwick Road, Derwen Fawr, Swansea SA2 8DZ Tel: 01792 208496 — MB ChB 1972 Alexandria; Dip. Psychiat. Lond. 1985.

MICHALOS, Milton 3 Mill Lane, Bentley Heath, Solihull B93 8PA — MRCS Eng. LRCP Lond. 1972.

MICHALSKI, Antony Julian Department of Haematology and Oncology, Great Ormond St. Hospital for Children NHS Trust, Great Ormond St., London WC1N 3JH Tel: 020 7829 8832 Fax: 020 7813 8588 Email: michaa@gosh.nhs.uk — MB ChB 1982 Birm.; PhD Lond. 1994; MRCP (UK) 1985. Cons. Paediat. Oncol. Gt. Ormond St. Hosp. Lond. Prev: Clin. Research Fell. & Hon. Sen. Regist. (Paediat. Oncol.) Inst. Child Health Lond.

MICHAUD, Mr Roland Jean Charing Cross Hospital, Fulham Palace Road, London W6 8RF Tel: 020 8846 1236; Flat 5, Dunraven House, 230 Kew Road, Kew, Richmond TW9 3LG Tel: 020 8940 7465 — MB ChB 1983 Manch.; MB ChB (Hons.) Manch. 1983; FRCS Eng. 1988; FRCS Orth. 1997. (Manchester) Specialist Regist. (Orthop.) Char. Cross Hosp. Fulham. Socs: Fell. Roy. Coll. Surgs. Eng.; BMA & BOA. Prev: Regist. (Orthop.) W. Middlx. Univ. Hosp. & Hammersmith Hosp. Lond.; Sir John Charnley Research Fell. Redhill; SHO (Orthop.) Profess. Unit Hope Hosp.

MICHEL, Adele Behnam Tutankhamun, Stockton Avenue, Fleet GU51 4NP — MB BCh 1969 Cairo. Clin. Med. Off. SW Thames RHA.

MICHEL, Carol Ann Aspley Medical Centre, 511 Aspley Lane, Aspley, Nottingham NG8 5RW Tel: 0115 929 2700 Fax: 0115 929 8276; April Cottage, 103 Hillston, Beeston, Nottingham NG9 — MB BCh 1977 Wales. GP.

MICHEL, Christopher Charles Department of Biomedical Sciences, Imperial College School of Medicine, South Kensington, London SW7 2AZ Tel: 020 7594 3113 Fax: 020 7594 3114 — BM BCh Oxf. 1966; MA, DPhil. Oxf. 1963; FRCP Lond. 1996; MRCP (UK) 1986. Prof. Physiol. Imperial Coll. Sch. of Med. Lond. Socs: (Ex-Sec.) Physiol. Soc.; (Ex-Pres.) Brit. MicroCirc. Soc.; Hon. Mem. Amer. Physiol. Soc. Prev: Fell. & Praelector (Physiol.) Qu. Coll. Oxf.; Lect. (Physiol.) Univ. Oxf.

MICHEL, Judith Mary Congham House, Moss Lane E., Leyland, Preston PR25 4SE Tel: 01772 621015 — MRCS Eng. LRCP Lond. 1974; BSc (Hons.) Lond. 1971, MB BS 1974; DRCOG 1978. (St. Mary's) Clin. Asst. (O & G, Family Plann. & Genitourin. Med.) Preston.

MICHEL, Magdy Zaky Bassetlaw District General Hospital, Worksop S81 0BD Tel: 01909 500990 — MB BCh 1978 Ain Shams; MRCOG 1985. Cons. O & G Bassetlaw Dist. Gen. Hosp. Prev: Sen. Regist. (O & G) St. Mary's Hosp. Lond. W2.

MICHEL, Maher Zaky Habbib Department of Anaesthesia, Royal Bournemouth Hospital, Castle Lane E., Bournemouth BH7 7DW Tel: 01202 303626 — MB ChB 1981 Ain Shams; FCAnaesth. 1989. Cons. Anaesth. Roy. Bournemouth Hosp. Prev: Sen. Regist. Soton. & Poole.

MICHEL, Mary-Christine Andrea David Rice Hospital, Drayton Road, Norwich NR8 6BH Tel: 01603 421421; 72 Christchurch Road, Norwich NR2 3NG Tel: 01603 56527 — LRCPI & LM, LRSCI & LM 1975; LRCPI & LM, LRCSI & LM 1975. Staff Grade (Psychiat.) David Rice Hosp. Norwich. Prev: Clin. Asst. (Psychiat.) St. Andrews Hosp.

Norwich; Regist. (Geriat.) W. Norwich Hosp.; SHO (Gen. Med. & Chest & Geriat. Med.) Gt. Yarmouth.

MICHEL, Vivian Jean-Marc Rockingham Forest NHS Trust, Child Health Dept., St Mary's Hospital, London Road, Kettering NN15 7PW Tel: 01536 410099; 1 Museum Cottages, Main St, Southwick, Peterborough PE8 5BL Tel: 01832 274024 — MB BCh 1977 Wales; BA Oxf. 1974; MRCP (UK) 1981; DTCH Liverp. 1985. (Univ. Of Oxford / Welsh Nat. Sch. Of Med,Card.) Cons. (Comm. Paediat); Postgrad. Course (Community Child Health) Nottm. Prev: Sen. Regist. (Community Paediat.) Sheff. HA; Lect. (Primary Health) Univ. Centr. Africa, Rwanda; Med. Dir. AHS Rural Health Progr., Nigeria.

MICHELAGNOLI, Maria Pia Paediatric and Adolescent Oncology, Paediatric Unit, Middlesex Hospital, Mortimer St., London W1T 3AA Tel: 020 7380 9950 Fax: 020 7636 2144 Email: maria.mechelagnoli@uclh.org; Flat A, 223 Archway Rd, Highgate, London N6 5BN Tel: 020 8348 7583 — MB ChB 1988 Aberd.; MRCPI 1993. Cons. Paediat. & Adolesc. Oncol. UCLH; Hon. Cons. Paediat. Oncol, Gt. Ormond St, Childr. Hospl. Socs: BMA; UK CCSG. Prev: Regist. (Paediat.) Clarendon Wing Leeds Gen. Infirm.; Sen. Regist. (Paediat. Oncol.) St. Jas. Univ. Hosp. Leeds.

MICHELL, Andrew William Church House, Church La, Yapton, Arundel BN18 0EH — BM BCh 1997 Oxf. (Cambridge & Oxford) SHO Med. Rotat. (Cntral) Newc. Prev: Ho. Off. Oxf.- Bath; SHO Palmerstan N. - New Zealand.

MICHELL, Mr David Robert (retired) Church House, Church Lane, Yapton, Arundel BN18 0EH Tel: 01243 551308 Fax: 01243 555386 — MB BChir 1965 Camb.; MA Camb. 1965; FRCS Eng. 1976; FCOphth 1989; DO Eng. 1972. Prev: Cons. Ophth. Chichester and Worthing Health Dist.s.

MICHELL, Edward Philip Guy 29 Layters Close, Chalfont St Peter, Gerrards Cross SL9 9HS Tel: 01753 884244 — MB BCh 1946 Camb.; BA Camb. 1942, MB BCh 1946; MRCP Lond. 1947; MRCPsych 1973; DCH Eng. 1951. Psychiat. Chalfont St. Peter. Socs: Brit. Psychoanal. Soc. Prev: Phys. i/c Dept. Psychol. Med. Hosp. Sick Childr. Gt Ormond St. Lond.; Cons. Psychiat. Tavistock Clin. Lond.; Vis. Research Prof. Yale Univ. Child Study Centre.

MICHELL, Michael James Department of Radiology, King's College Hospital, Denmark Hill, London SE5 Tel: 020 7346 3380 Fax: 020 7346 4258; 40 Alleyn Road, Dulwich, London SE21 8AL Tel: 020 8516 9897 Fax: 020 8516 9897 — MB 1979 Camb.; BChir 1978; FRCR 1983; DMRD Lond. 1982. Cons. Radiol. King's Coll. Hosp. Lond. Socs: FRCR; Brit. Inst. Radiol.; Brit. BrE. Gp.

MICHELL, Nicholas Paul 92 Hamilton Avenue, Halesowen B62 8SJ — MB ChB 1989 Birm.

MICHELL, Rodney Charles (retired) King's Acre, Courtenay Road, Winchester SO23 7ER Tel: 01962 3899 — MB BS 1950 Lond.; DMRD 1957; FRCP Lond. 1976, M 1954; FFR 1959. Prev: Cons. Radiol. Roy. Hants. Co. Hosp. Winchester.

MICHELMORE, Henry Richard Aubrey (retired) Quest, Fortescue, Sidmouth EX10 9QF Tel: 01395 513112 Fax: 01395 577423 — MB BChir Camb. 1943; DCH Eng. 1948. Prev: Maj. RAMC.

MICHELMORE, Katherine Frances Corbridge Health Centre, Corbridge NE45 5JW — MB BS 1994 Newc. GP Regist. Prev: D. Phil. Stud. Oxf. Univ.

MICHELMORE, Susan Kay The Surgery, 16 Windsor Road, Chobham, Woking GU24 8NA Tel: 01276 857117 Fax: 01276 855668; 25 The Avenue, Chobham, Woking GU24 8RU — MB BS 1984 Newc.; DRCOG 1988.

MICHELS, Aloysius Marinus Josephus Topps Park, Fintry Road, Denny FK6 5JF Tel: 01324 826221 Email: lamichels@yahoo.com — Artsexamen 1987 Utrecht; FRCA 1992. Cons. Anaesth. Stirling Roy. Infirm. Prev: Sen. Regist. (Anaesth.) Yorks.

MICHELS, Gerd Anton 141 Onslow Drive, Glasgow G31 2QA — State Exam Med 1992 Cologne.

MICHIE, Alastair Ross Old Distillery Surgery, Ardronie Park, Kingussie PH21 1ET Tel: 01540 661233 Fax: 01540 661277 — MB ChB 1980 Dundee.

MICHIE, Alistair Brian The Group Practice, Health Centre, Springfield Road, Stornoway HS1 2PS Tel: 01851 703145 Fax: 01851 706138 — MB BS 1982 Lond.; Dip. IMC RCS Ed. 1988.

MICHIE, Alistair Davidson (retired) Braeside, Lostwithiel PL22 0DR Tel: 01208 872430 — MB ChB Aberd. 1956; MRCGP 1968.

MICHIE, Andrew Forbes Netherlaw Surgery, 28 Stanhope Road, Darlington DL3 7SQ Tel: 01325 380640 Fax: 01325 350938; Alwent Mill, Winston, Darlington DL2 3QH — MB BS 1979 Lond.

MICHIE, Bruce Alexander Department of Pathology, Perth Royal Infirmary, Perth PH1 1NX Tel: 01738 623311; Department of Pathology, Ninewells Hospital, Dundee DD1 9SY Tel: 01382 660111 — MB ChB 1987 Glas.; BSc (Hons.) Glas. 1984; MRCPath 1996, D 1993. Cons. Path. Dundee Teachg. Hosps. Univ. NHS Trust. Prev: Regist. (Path.) W.. Infirm. Glas.

MICHIE, Charles (retired) Greenlands, Town St., Swanton Moreley, Dereham NR20 4PB Tel: 01362 637419 — MB ChB 1940 Aberd.; DTM & H Eng. 1942; TDD Wales 1953. Prev: Med. Off. Pneumoconiosis Med. Panel DHSS.

MICHIE, Charles Andrew Harrower Paternoster Lane Surgery, 11 Paternoster Lane, Bradford BD7 3DS Tel: 01274 573696/572573 Fax: 01274 521605; 11 Paternoster Lane, Bradford BD7 3DS — MB ChB 1976 Leeds. Clin. Asst. W.wood Hosp. Bradford.

MICHIE, Colin Alexander Department of Paediatrics, Ealing Hospital NHS Trust, Uxbridge Road, Southall UB1 3HW Tel: 020 8967 5567 Fax: 020 8967 5339 Email: colinm@easynet.co.uk; 34 Union Street, Oxford OX4 1JP — BM BCh 1983 Oxf.; MA BM BCh Oxf. 1983; MRCP Lond. 1987; FRCPCH 1997; FLS 1986. (Camb. & Oxf.) Cons. Sen. Lect. Ealing Hosp. NHS Trust Lond.; Hon. Cons. (Immunol.) Guy's Hosp. Lond.; Hon. Sen. Lect. (Paediat. & Neonat. Med.) Hammersmith Hosp. Imperial Coll. Lond.; Hon. Cons. Chelsea & W.m. Hosp. Lond. Socs: Eur. Paediat. Research soc.; Brit. Paediat. Infec. Dis. & Immunol. Gp.; Brit. Cytokine Gp. Prev: Clin. Research Fell. Imperial Cancer Research Fund; Regist. (Paediat.) Trop. Metab. Research Unit Kingston, Jamaica & Hon. Lect. Paediat. Univ. W. Indies.

MICHIE, Elizabeth Woodrow 92 Hull Road, Cottingham HU16 4PU Tel: 01482 842931 — MB ChB 1955 Aberd. Prev: Ho. Phys. Roy. Aberd. Hosp. Sick Childr. Ho. Surg. Aberd. Matern.; Hosp.

MICHIE, Mr Hamish Robertson 92 Hull Road, Cottingham HU16 4PU — BChir 1981 Camb.; MB 1982; FRCS Ed. 1985. Research Fell. Harvard Univ. USA.

MICHIE, Ian Forbes (retired) Troytown House, Brook, Ashford TN25 5PQ Tel: 01233 812562 — MB BS 1947 Lond.; MRCS Eng. LRCP Lond. 1947. Prev: Regist. (Med.) Lambeth Hosp. & Luton Childr. Hosp.

MICHIE, Marian Helen Newlands Clinic, 41 Kirkleatham St., Redcar TS10 1QH Tel: 01642 490881; 12 High Green, Great Ayton, Middlesbrough TS9 6BJ Tel: 01642 724851 — MB ChB 1982 Aberd.; MRCPsych 1988. Cons. Psychiat. Tees and N. Easst Yorks. NHS Trust. Prev: Sen. Regist. (Psychiat.) N.. RHA; Regist. (Psychiat.) St. Mary's Hosp. Stannington & Roy. Cornhill Hosp. Aberd.

MICHIE, Robin Wilson Sunnyside, Wilton Dean, Hawick TD9 7HY — MB ChB 1992 Manch.

MICHIE, Vera Constance Anne Callan Lodge, 31 Forest Road, Aberdeen AB15 4BZ Tel: 01224 647176 — M.B., Ch.B. Aberd. 1945. (Aberd.) Clin. Asst. A & E Dept. & Asthma Clinic Dept.; Thoracic Med. Aberd. Roy. Infirm. Prev: Obst. Resid. Aberd. Matern. Hosp.; Ho. Surg. Roy. Aberd. Hosp. Sick Childr.

MICIAK, Janina The Grange Practice, Allerton Clinic, Wanstead Crescent, Allerton, Bradford BD15 7PA Tel: 01274 541696 — MB ChB 1990 Manch.

MICKEL, David Robert 43 Deanburn Park, Linlithgow EH49 6HA — MB ChB 1992 Aberd.

MICKHAEL, Nagy Fouad Rancho Nimajah, La Vallee de St Pierre, St Lawrence, Jersey JE3 1EZ — MB BCh 1975 Cairo.

MICKIEWCZ, Adam Jakub 8 Burlington Avenue, Slough SL1 2LD Tel: 01753 731595 — Lekarz 1965 Poznan. GP S. Bucks. NHS Trust High Wycombe. Socs: BMA & Soc. Rheum. Prev: 980.

MICKLEM, John Niel (retired) 4 Egbert House, 54 Hyde St., Winchester SO23 7DY Tel: 01962 868216 — BM BCh 1948 Oxf.; MRCS Eng. LRCP Lond. 1945; Dip. Analyt. Psychol. Zurich 1968. Prev: Clin. Asst. Klinik am Zurichberg Zurich.

MICKLER, Gertrude Rita (retired) 17 Queen's Terrace, Jesmond, Newcastle upon Tyne NE2 Tel: 01632 810156 — B.Sc. 1920, M.B., B.S. Durh. 1943.

MICKLETHWAITE, Glen Milestone Surgery, 208 Farnborough Road, Farnborough GU14 7JN Tel: 01252 545078 Fax: 01252

MICKLEWRIGHT

370751 — MB ChB 1987 Leic.; MRCGP 1992; DCH RCP Lond. 1991; DRCOG 1991. (Leicester)

MICKLEWRIGHT, Rebecca Jane 17 Primrose Gardens, Codsall, Wolverhampton WV8 1PA — BM 1983 Soton.; FRCA 1990. Cons. Anaesth. New Cross Hosp. Wolverhampton. Prev: Regist. (Intens. Care) Waikato Hosp. Hamilton, NZ; SHO (Anaesth.) Newc. HA.

MIDDLE, Geoffrey Bryan (retired) The Granary, Vale Road, Chesham HP5 3HW Tel: 01494 782375 — MB BS 1956 Lond.; LMSSA Lond. 1955. Prev: Ho. Surg. (Obst.), Ho. Phys. And Ho. Surg. Amersham Gen. Hosp.

MIDDLEFELL, Robert (retired) Brook Lodge, 44 Raby Drive, Raby Mere, Wirral CH63 0NL Tel: 0151 334 3893 — MB ChB Liverp. 1953; MD Liverp. 1964; FRCPsych 1972; DPM Eng. 1958. Prev: Cons. Psychiat. Clatterbridge Hosp. Bebington.

MIDDLEHURST, Mr Richard John University Dental Hospital of Manchester, Unit of Oral & Maxillofacial Surgery, Higher Cambridge St., Manchester M15 6PH Tel: 0161 275 6650 Fax: 0161 275 6741 — MB BCh 1980 Wales; BDS (Hons.) Lond. 1975; FRCS Ed. 1987; FDS RCS Eng. 1983; LDS 1975. Lect. & Hon. Cons. Oral & Maxillofacial Surg. Univ. Dent. Hosp. Manch.

MIDDLEMAN, Mark John 27 Rodney Street, Liverpool L1 9EH Tel: 0151 708 0532 Fax: 0151 932 1708 Email: mark.middleman@tesco.net; Friesland, Blundellsands Road E., Liverpool L23 8SG Fax: 0151 932 1708 Email: mark.middleman@tesco.net — MB ChB 1980 Manch.; BSc (Hons. Anat.) Manch. 1977, MB ChB 1980; MRCGP 1984. (Manchester) Medico-Legal Pract. Liverp. Prev: GP Liverp.; Trainee GP Nottm. VTS; Ho. Off. (Gen. Surg., Urol., Gen. Med. & Haemat.) Univ. Hosp. S. Manch.

MIDDLEMISS, John Lionel (retired) 25 West Street, Godmanchester, Huntingdon PE29 2HG Tel: 01480 52905 — MRCS Eng, LRCP Lond. 1944; MRCGP 1952; DObst RCOG 1948. Prev: R.A.M.C. (Capt) Pract. at Bellingham, N.umberland, GodManch. & Huntingdon.

MIDDLEMISS, Susan Anne Meadowbank Health Centre, 3 Salmon Inn Road, Falkirk FK2 0XF Tel: 01324 715753 Fax: 01324 717565 — MD ChB 1977 Edinburgh; MB ChB Edin 1977. (Edinburgh) GP Falkirk.

MIDDLETON, Alan Fowey Health Centre, Rawlings Lane, Fowey PL23 1DT Tel: 01726 832451 — MB ChB 1971 Ed.; BSc (Med. Sci.) Ed. 1969, MB ChB 1971. Prev: Ho. Surg. & Ho. Phys. Roy. Cornw. Hosp. (Treliske) Truro; SHO (Anaesth.) Roy. Cornw. Hosp. Treliske; Flight Lt. RAF Med. Br.

***MIDDLETON, Alan Lloyd** Staff Residences, Weston General Hospital, Grange Road, Weston Super Mare BS23 4TQ — MB ChB 1996 Cape Town.

***MIDDLETON, Alison Jane** 16 March Road, Edinburgh EH4 3TB — MB ChB 1994 Aberd.

MIDDLETON, Alison Margaret Noelle 5 Rosevale Gardens, Dunmurry, Belfast BT17 9LH — MB BS 1994 Lond.

MIDDLETON, Basil Ross 6A Palace Gate, London W8 5NF Tel: 020 7589 2478 Fax: 020 7584 4595; 17 Edenhurst Avenue, London SW6 3PD Tel: 020 7736 1371 — MB BChir 1961 Camb.; MA Camb. 1961; LMSSA Lond. 1960. (Camb. & St. Bart.) Med. Off. W.m. Sch. & W.m. Abbey Choir Sch.; Med. Adviser Inner Lond. Probation Serv.; Med. Mem. Disabil. Appeal Tribunal (Indep. Tribunal Serv.). Prev: Regist. (Med.), Ho. Surg. (ENT) & Ho. Phys. St. Bart. Hosp. Lond.

MIDDLETON, Carol Lesley Chaldon Road Surgery, Chaldon Road, Caterham CR3 5PG Tel: 01883 345466 Fax: 01883 330942; 3 Cornwallis Close, Yorke Gate, Caterham on the Hill, Caterham CR3 5BX Tel: 01883 331054 — MB BS 1983 Lond.; MRCGP 1987; DRCOG 1987. (St. Bart. Hosp. Lond.)

MIDDLETON, Catherine Helen 41 Crofthouse Drive, Otley LS21 2ER — MB ChB 1993 Ed.

MIDDLETON, Catherine Mary Black Moss Barn, Black Moss Road, Barley, Nelson BB9 6LE — MB ChB 1980 Birm.; FFA RCS Eng. 1984. Sen. Regist. (Anaesth.) N. W.. RHA.

MIDDLETON, Christopher Stephen Hugh Middleton and Partners, Sele Gate Surgery, Hencotes, Hexham NE46 2EG Tel: 01434 602237 Fax: 01434 609496; 5 Oakwood, Hexham NE46 4LF Tel: 01434 602018 — MB BS 1971 Lond.; MRCS Eng. LRCP Lond. 1971; DObst RCOG 1975. (King's Coll. Hosp.) GP. Socs: BMA; BMAS. Prev: Med. Off. Dargaville Med. Centre, NZ; Trainee GP Tunbridge Wells VTS; Ho. Phys. Kent & Sussex Hosp. Tunbridge Wells.

MIDDLETON, Frances Heather Huddersfield Road Surgery, 6 Huddersfield Road, Barnsley S70 2LT Tel: 01226 287589 Fax: 01226 731245; 2 Orchard Mews, Cockerham Lane, Barnsley S75 1AY Tel: 01226 771604 — MB ChB 1988 Sheff.; MRCGP 1992; DRCOG 1991. Prev: Trainee GP Sheff. FPC VTS.

MIDDLETON, Frederick Riach Ironside 90 Valley Road, Rickmansworth WD3 4BJ — MB BCh BAO 1967 Dub.; MRCP (UK) 1980; DPhysMed Eng. 1972. Cons. Spinal Unit Roy. Nat. Orthop. Hosp. Stanmore; Med. Dir. Cons. Med. Rehabil. Centre Camden Lond.; Cons. (Rehabil.) Univ. Coll. Hosp. Lond. Prev: Sen. Regist. Rehabil. Med. Unit P.ss Margt. Rose Orthop. Hosp.; Edin.; Clin. Tutor Rehabil. Studies Unit Dept. Orthop. Surg. Edin. Univ.

MIDDLETON, Gary William 65 Blackborough Road, Reigate RH2 7BU — MB BS 1985 Lond.; MRCP (UK) 1989.

MIDDLETON, George Watson, MBE (retired) 52 Bryn Road, St. Davids, Haverfordwest SA62 6QU Tel: 01437 721659 — MRCS Eng. LRCP Lond. 1952; MRCGP 1956. Prev: Ho. Surg. St. Bart. Hosp.

MIDDLETON, Gordon George Alexander, Maj. RAMC Retd. (retired) Chimneys, 42 Aylesbury Road, Aston Clinton, Aylesbury HP22 5AH Tel: 01296 630327 Fax: 01296 630327 — MB ChB 1958 Aberd. Prev: GP Aylesbury.

MIDDLETON, Horace Nelson 2 Summershades Lane, Grasscroft, Oldham OL4 4ED — MRCS Eng. LRCP Lond. 1954. (Leeds)

MIDDLETON, Hugh Crampton University of Nottingham Department of Psychiatry, Duncan Macmillan House, Porchester Road, Nottingham NG3 6AA Tel: 0115 969 1300 Fax: 0115 950 5352 Email: hugh.middleton@nottingham.ac.uk — MB BChir 1975 Camb.; MD Camb. 1981, MA, MB 1974, BChir 1975; MRCP (UK) 1976; MRCPsych 1986. (Camb. & St. Geos.) Hon. Cons. & Sen. Lect. Psychiat. Univ. Nottm. & Centr. Notts. Health Care Trust. Socs: Brit. Assn. Psychopharmacol. & Brain Research Assn. Prev: Clin. Lect. & Hon. Sen. Regist. (Psychiat.) Addenbrooke's Hosp. Camb.; Research & Hon. Sen. Regist. (Psychiat.) Oxf. Univ.; Clin. Lect. (Med.) Camb. Univ. Clin. Sch.

MIDDLETON, Hugh Oliver (retired) Gordon House, 30 Parsons Heath, Colchester CO4 3HX Tel: 01206 862779 — MB BS 1954 Lond.; MRCGP 1965; DObst RCOG 1962. Prev: SHO (Med.) Nottm. Childr. Hosp.

MIDDLETON, Isla Anderson Dept. of Disability, St. Georges Hospital Medical School, Cranmer Terrace, London SW17 0RE Tel: 020 8725 5501 Fax: 020 8672 1070; Ivy Cottage, 62 London Road, Ewell, Epsom KT17 2BW Tel: 020 8393 8708 Email: isla.m@virgin.net — MB ChB 1989 Liverp.; MRCPsych 1998. Specialist Regist. (Psychiat. Of Learning Disab.) SW Lond. Comm. NHS Trust. Socs: Roy. Coll. Psychiat. Prev: Regist. (Psychiat. of Deaf People) Nat. Deaf Servs. Pathfinder Ment. Health Servs. NHS Trust Lond.; Regist. (Rehabil. Psychiat.) Pathfinder NHS Trust; Regist. (Forens. Psychiat.) Pathfinder NHS Trus.

MIDDLETON, John B Windle Villa, Crank Road, Windle, St Helens WA11 7RB — LMSSA Lond. 1956. (Liverp.)

MIDDLETON, John Duncan 80 Lightwoods Hill, Smethwick B67 5EB — BM 1979 Soton.; FFPHM RCP (UK) 1995; DTM & H Liverp. 1982. Dir. Pub. Health Sandwell HA; Hon. Sen. Lect. (Community Med.) Univ. Warwick. Prev: Sen. Regist. (Community Med.) W. Midl. RHA; Regist. Community Med. W. Midl. RHA.

MIDDLETON, John Ellis 8 Blenheim Avenue, Southampton SO17 1DU Tel: 02380 556524 — BM BCh 1948 Oxf.; MA Oxf. 1960, BA 1945; FRCP Lond. 1983, M 1954; FRCPath 1974, M 1963. (Oxf. & St. Thos.) Socs: BMA. Prev: Med.Reg.N..Gen.Hosps.heffield; Lect. (Clin. & Chem. Path.) St. Thos. Hosp. Med. Sch. Lond.; Cons. Chem.Path.&Emerit.Soton.Unbiv.Hosp.

MIDDLETON, John Francis Storer Road Medical Centre, 2A Storer Road, Loughborough LE11 5EQ Tel: 01509 212120 — MB ChB 1973 Manch.; BA Open 1983; FRCGP 1993, M 1978; MD Leicester 1998. Assoc. Adviser Univ. Leicester; Sen. Research Fell. Univ. Leicester. Prev: Course Organiser Leicester VTS.

MIDDLETON, Julia Karen Princess Marina Hospital, Upton, Northampton NN5 6UH Tel: 01604 752323 — MB BS 1984 Lond.; MRCGP 1989; MRCPsych. 1988.

MIDDLETON, Kenneth (retired) Moorlea, Long Lane, Dobcross, Oldham OL3 5QH Tel: 01457 872353 — MB ChB Birm. 1954;

MFPHM 1989; AFOM RCP Lond. 1979; MFCM 1974. Prev: Gp. Med. Adviser Gallaher Ltd.

MIDDLETON, Kevin Gerard 24 Wesley Close, Horley RH6 8JB — MB BS 1990 Lond.; BDS Lond. 1981; MRCGP 1994; DRCOG 1993.

MIDDLETON, Lawrence Grahame 10 Cheltenham Avenue, Marton-in-Cleveland, Middlesbrough TS7 8LR — MB BCh BAO 1952 NUI. (Univ. Coll. Dub.) Clin. Asst. (Gyn.) N. Tees Gen. Hosp. Stockton-on-Tees; Police Surg. Socs: Assn. Police Surgs. Prev: SHO Roy. Infirm. Sunderland & Ryhope Gen. Hosp.; Cas. Off. Roy. Infirm. Sunderland.

MIDDLETON, Margaret Audrey (retired) Rosemary Gate, Chestall Road, Cannock Wood, Rugeley WS15 4RB Tel: 01543 682558 — MB ChB 1952 Birm.; DObst RCOG 1955. Prev: Med. Off. (Path.) Walsall Manor Hosp.

MIDDLETON, Margaret Isobel Broomfield Road Surgery, 252 Broomfield Road, Chelmsford CM1 4DY Tel: 01245 355460 Fax: 01245 344659; 7 Church Green, Roxwell, Chelmsford CM1 4NZ Tel: 01245 248297 — MRCS Eng. LRCP Lond. 1971; MA Camb. 1967; MRCGP 1978; DA Eng. 1974. (Lond. Hosp.) Socs: BMA. Prev: SHO (Anaesth.) St. Bart. Hosp. Lond.; Ho. Surg. Roy. Sussex Co. Hosp. Brighton; Ho. Phys. Poole Gen. Hosp.

MIDDLETON, Mark Ross 7 Walkergate, Otley LS21 1HB — BM BCh 1991 Oxf.; BA Camb. 1988, MA 1992. SHO Rotat. (Gen. Med.) St. Jas. Univ. Hosp. Trust Leeds.

MIDDLETON, Mr Michael David Great Hytall, 97 Lovelace Avenue, Solihull B91 3JR Tel: 0121 704 4018 — MB ChB 1956 Ed.; MSc (Surg.) Univ. Washington, Seattle 1964; FRCS Ed. 1960; FRCS Eng. 1961; DObst RCOG 1958. (Ed.) Cons. Gen. Surg. E. Birm. Hosp. & Solihull Hosp.; Sen. Clin. Lect. (Surg.) Birm. Univ.; Surg. Adviser W. Midl. & Edin. Coll. Surg.; Examr. in Surg. RCS Ed. Socs: Fell. Assn. Surg. Gt. Brit. & Assn. Vasc. Surgs. Prev: Sen. Surg. Regist. Roy. Infirm. Edin.; Surg. Regist. Radcliffe Infirm. Oxf.; Vis. Scientist Dept. of Surg. Univ. Washington, Seattle, U.S.A.

MIDDLETON, Nicholas McKinley The Medical Centre, 2 Francis Street, Doncaster DN1 1JS Tel: 01302 349431 Fax: 01302 364558; 210 Bawtry Road, Bessacarr, Doncaster DN4 7BZ Tel: 01302 530468 — MB ChB 1980 Leic.; MRCGP 1984. (Leic.) Prev: SHO Doncaster Roy. Infirm.; Ho. Phys. Leicester Roy. Infirm.; Ho. Surg. Leicester Gen. Hosp.

MIDDLETON, Paul Ian, Squadron Ldr. RAF Med. Br. The Caxton Surgery, Oswald Road, Oswestry SY11 1RD Tel: 01691 654646 Fax: 01691 670994; Llwynderw, Morda Road, Oswestry SY11 2AU Tel: 01691 653576 Email: middl123@aol.com — BM 1980 Soton.; BM (Hons) Soton. 1980; MRCGP 1985; DRCOG 1987. (Southampton) GP Princip.; MRCGP Examr. 1994; GP Trainer 1989. Prev: RAF Med. Off.

MIDDLETON, Paul MacConachie 137 Shortridge Terrace, Newcastle upon Tyne NE2 2JH — MB BS 1992 Newc.

MIDDLETON, Peter Howard Church Street Medical Centre, Church Street, Byfield, Daventry NN11 6XN Tel: 01327 260230 Fax: 01327 262243 — MB BS 1970 Lond.; BSc (Anat.) Lond. 1967, MB BS 1970. (Oxf.) Prev: Trainee GP Oxf. VTS; SHO Accid. Serv. Unit. Oxf. Hosps.; Ho. Surg. & Ho. Phys. United Oxf. Hosps.

MIDDLETON, Rachel Joanne 7 Hospital Road, Riddlesden, Keighley BD20 5EP — MB ChB 1994 Leeds.

MIDDLETON, Mr Robert Gordon 4 Ventry Close, Poole BH13 6AW Tel: 01202 759521 — BChir 1989 Camb.; FRCS Eng. 1993; FRCS (Orth) 1996. Cons. Orthop. Surg., Bonrnetiouth. Socs: Fell. BOA. Prev: Sen. Regist. (orthp.) Middlx. Hosp.; Regist. (Orthop.) Roy. Nat. Orthop. Hosp. Stanmore.

MIDDLETON, Ronald Alderson Health Centre, Chapel St., Willington, Crook DL15 0EQ; 96 High Street, Willington, Crook DL15 0PE — MB BS 1952 Durh.

MIDDLETON, Sally 7 Tabor Gardens, Cheam, Sutton SM3 8RU — BM BCh 1990 Oxf.; MRCGP 1994; DRCOG 1992; DCH RCP Lond. 1993.

MIDDLETON, Sally Joy Pound House Surgery, Wooburn Green, High Wycombe HP10 0EE Tel: 01628 529633; Lynton, New Road, Cookham, Maidenhead SL6 9HB Tel: 01628 850737 — MB BS 1985 Lond.; BA Oxf. 1980; MRCGP 1989; DRCOG 1988.

MIDDLETON, Sallyann 8/8 Sienna Gardens, Edinburgh EH9 1PG — MB BS 1984 Monash; DRACOG 1987.

MIDDLETON, Mr Simon Bentley, Squadron Ldr. RAF Med. Br. Retd. St. Mark's Hospital, Northwick Park, Watford Road, Harrow HA1 3UJ Tel: 020 8235 4269 Email: s.middleton@icrf.icnet.uk; Ivy Cottage, 62 London Road, Ewell, Epsom KT17 2BW Tel: 020 8393 8708 — MB ChB 1989 Liverp.; FRCS Ed. 1994. Career Regist. (Gen. Surg.) S. Thames (W.); ICRF Clin. Research Fell. Colorectal Cancer Unit St. Marks Lond. Socs: Assn. Surg. Train.; Assn. Surg. Prev: Regist. St. Peters Hosp. Chertsey; Regist. St. Geo. Hosp. Tooting, Lond.

MIDDLETON, Stephen John Addenbrooke's NHS Trust, Hills Road, Cambridge CB2 2QQ Tel: 01223 217467 Fax: 01233 216451 — MB BS 1984 Lond.; FRCP 2000 (UK); MD Lond. 1993; MRCP (UK) 1987. Cons. Gastroenterol. & Gen. Phys. Addenbrooke's NHS Trust Camb. Socs: Harveian Soc.; Brit. Soc. of Gastroenterol. Prev: Sen. Regist. (Gastroenterol. & Gen. Med.) & Research Regist. Addenbrooke's Hosp. Camb.

*****MIDDLETON, Victoria Courtney** 94 Tadcaster Road, Dringhouses, York YO24 1LT — MB ChB 1998 Leeds.

MIDDLETON, Wilson Graham 16 March Road, Edinburgh EH4 3TB Tel: 0131 332 3802 — MB ChB 1968 Ed.; BSc (Hons) Ed. 1965, MB ChB 1968; FRCP Ed. 1981, M 1972. (Ed.) Cons. Phys. St. Johns Hosp. Howden Livingston W. Lothian. Prev: Sen. Regist. (Respirat. Dis.) City Hosp. Edin.

MIDFORTH, Jane Elizabeth The Surgery, The Street, Holbrook, Ipswich IP9 2PZ Tel: 01473 328263 Fax: 01473 327185 — BM BS 1983 Nottm.; MRCGP 1988; DCH RCP Lond. 1987; DRCOG 1986.

MIDGLEY, Adrian Keith Homefield Surgery, 6 Homefield Road, Exeter EX1 2QS Tel: 01392 214151 — MB BS 1980 Lond.; T(GP) 1991.

MIDGLEY, Corinna Judith The Residences, Mildmay Mission Hospital, 2 Hackney Road, London E2 7NA; 80 Kyverdale Road, London N16 6PL — MB BS 1988 Lond.

MIDGLEY, Deborah Yolande St Thomas' Hospital, Lambeth Palace Road, London SE1 7EH; 190 Canbury Park Road, Kingston upon Thames KT2 6LF Tel: 020 8241 6793 — MB ChB 1994 Leic.; DFFP 1997; MRCOG 1996. (Leicester) SHO (O & G) (Acting Regist.) St Thomas' Hosp. Lond. Prev: SHO (Paediat.) Sunderland; SHO (O & G) RVI Newc.; GP Trainee Felling Gateshead.

MIDGLEY, James Michael Overton Studios Trust Ltd., 7 Bevan Avenue, Colwyn Bay LL28 5AD Tel: 01492 546879 Fax: 01492 546879 Email: ostrust@bigfoot.com — MB ChB 1950 Manch.; MRCGP 1959. (Manch.) Founder & Chairm. Overton Studios Trust Ltd. Colwyn Bay; Proprietor Overton Studios Press Colwyn Bay. Prev: Princip. GP & GP Trainer Clwyd FPC; Regtl. Med. Off. 2nd Bn. Durh. Light Infantry; Cas. Off. Pk. Hosp. Davyhulme.

MIDGLEY, Marguerite 49 South Parade, Bramhall, Stockport SK7 3BJ — MB ChB 1949 Manch.; DA Eng. 1955. (Manch.) Cons. Anaesth. Stockport & Buxton Hosp. Gp. Socs: Fell. Manch. Med. Soc. Prev: SHO (Anaesth.) Pk. Hosp. Davyhulme; Anaesth. Regist. W. Manch. & Stockport & Buxton Hosp. Gps.

MIDGLEY, Norman Mitchell 15 Kelvinside Terrace, Glasgow G20 6DW — MRCS Eng. LRCP Lond. 1951; LMSSA Lond. 1951; FDS RCS Eng. 1956.

MIDGLEY, Paula Caroline 15 Kelvinside Terrace, Glasgow G20 6DW — MB ChB 1981 Aberd.; MRCP (UK) 1986.

MIDGLEY, Rachel Susannah-Jane 3 Craven Close, Gomersal, Cleckheaton BD19 4QZ Tel: 01274 870281 — MB ChB 1994 Birm.; ChB Birm. 1994; MRCP (UK) 1997. (Birm.) MRC Research Fell. CRC Inst. Cancer Studies Birm.

MIDGLEY, Roy Lee (retired) The Dell, Hesketh Crescent, Torquay TQ1 2LJ Tel: 01803 23043 — MRCS Eng. LRCP Lond. 1927; MD Lond. 1929, MB BS 1927; MRCP Lond. 1932. Prev: Sen. Chest Phys. Exeter Clin. Area.

MIDGLEY, Stephen Nicholas Department of Mental Health Sciences, Jenner Wing, St Georges Hospital, Tooting, London SW17 0QT Tel: 020 8672 1255; Ground Floor Flat, 242 Worple Road, London SW20 8RH — MB BS 1986 Lond.; MA Camb. 1986; MRCPsych 1992; MRCGP 1990. Regist. Rotat. (Psychiat.) SW Thames Train. Scheme. Prev: Trainee GP/SHO Qu. Mary's Hosp. Roehampton VTS.

MIDGLEY, Susan Department of Anaesthesia, Western General Hospital, Edinburgh EH4 2XU Tel: 0131 537 1652 Fax: 0131 537 1025; Craigievar, 71 Kirk Brae, Edinburgh EH16 6JN — MB ChB 1983 Ed.; FFA RCSI 1989. (Ed.) Cons. Anaesth. W.. Gen. Hosp. Edin. Prev: Sen. Regist. (Anaesth.) Vict. Infirm. Glas.

MIDHA

MIDHA, Ravindra Edward Gwynfa, 15 Glanmor Park Road, Sketty, Swansea SA2 0QG — MB BCh 1993 Wales; BSc Lond. 1982.

***MIDWINTER, Katherine Isobel** 13 St Peter's Road, Abingdon OX14 3SJ — BM BCh 1994 Oxf.

MIDWINTER, Mr Mark John, Surg. Lt.-Cdr. RN Freeman Hospital, Newcastle upon Tyne NE7 7DN Tel: 0191 284 3111 Fax: 0191 213 1968; 2 Queens Court, Gosforth, Newcastle upon Tyne NE3 5NQ — MB BS 1984 Newc.; BMedSc (Hons.) Newc. 1981; FRCS Eng. 1990; Dip. Appl. Stats (Med.) Oxf. 1986. (Newc. u. Tyne) Research Fell. Freeman Hosp. Newc. u. Tyne. Socs: RN Med. Club; Assn. Surg.; Assn. Upper G.I. Surg. Prev: Sen. Regist. (Gen. Surg.) Derriford Hosp. Plymouth; Specialist (Surg.) RN Hosp. Haslar; Med. Off. Brit. Antarctic Survey.

MIDWOOD, Miss Caroline Judith Bromley Hospital, Cromwell Avenue, Bromley BR2 9AJ Tel: 01689 814322; Norsted Manor, Norsted Lane, Pratt's Bottom, Orpington BR6 7PB Tel: 01959 534426 Fax: 01959 534426 — MB BS 1979 Lond.; MS Lond. 1991; FRCS (Gen.) 1993; FRCS Eng. 1984. p/t Cons. Gen. Surg. Bromley Hosps. Trust. Prev: Sen. Regist. King's Coll. Hosp.

MIDYA, Tara Sonkar 114 Westbourne Road, Handsworth, Birmingham B21 8AT — MB BS 1958 Calcutta. (Nat. Med. Coll. Calcutta)

MIEDZYBRODZKA, Zofia Helena Medical Genetics, Medical School, Foresterhill, Aberdeen AB25 2ZD Tel: 01224 681818 Fax: 01224 685157; 2 Postcliffe House, Peterculter AB14 0UY — MB ChB 1988 Aberd.; MRCOG Lond. 1996; PhD Aber. 1995. Lect. (Clin. Genetics) Med. Sch. Aberd. Socs: Clin. Genetics Soc. Prev: SHO (Obst.) Aberd. Matern. Hosp.

MIELI VERGANI, Professor Giorgina Department of Child Health, King's College Hospital, Denmark Hill, London SE5 9RS Tel: 020 7346 4643 Fax: 020 7346 4224 Email: giorgina.vergani@kcl.ac.uk; 14 Crab Hill, Beckenham BR3 5HE Tel: 020 8658 6003 Fax: 020 8658 6211 Email: giorgina@vergani.demon.co.uk — MD 1971 Milan; PhD Lond. 1985; State Exam Milan 1972; Specialist Accredit Paediat. JCHMT 1985; Dip. Clin. Immunol. Milan 1977; Dip. Pediat. Milan 1974. Prof. Paediat. Hepatol. & Hon. Cons. Paediat. King's Coll. Hosp. Lond. Socs: Fell. Roy. Coll. Phys.; Brit. Soc. Paediat. Gastroenterol. & Nutrit; Fell. Coll. Paediat. & Child Health. Prev: Sen. Lect. (Paediat. Hepatol.) King's Coll. Hosp. Lond.

MIELL, Stephen James 3 Bramston Road, Shirley, Southampton SO15 5GH — MB ChB 1986 Bristol.

MIER JEDRZEJOWICZ, Anne Katherine Barnet and Chase Farm Hospitals (NHS) Trust, The Ridgeway, Enfield EN2 8SD Tel: 020 8366 6600 — MB BS 1978 Lond.; MD Lond. 1986; MRCP (UK) 1980; FRCP (UK) 1999. (Middlx.) Cons. Phys. Chase Farm Hosps. NHS Trust. Prev: Lect. (Med.) & Hon. Sen. Regist. Char. Cross Hosp. Lond.; Regist. Brompton Hosp. Lond.; Regist. (Med.) Roy. Free Hosp. Lond.

MIESZKOWSKI, Jozef HMP Wakefield, 5 Love Lane, Wakefield WF2 9AG; 3 Meadow Close, Broadmeadows, Outwood, Wakefield WF1 3TB — MDip Lodz 1956; Cert. Gen. Surg. Lodz 1964. (Med. Acad. Lodz, Poland) Sen. Med. Off. Home Offices Lond. Socs: Devon & Exeter Med. Soc. Prev: Sen. Asst. (Surg.) Dr. K. Jonscher Hosp. Lodz Poland; Cons. Gen. Surg. Dr. Pirogow Hosp. Lodz, Poland; Sen. Regist. (Thoracic Surg.) Thoracic Centre Killingbeck Hosp. & St. Jas. Univ. Hosp. Leeds.

MIFLIN, Gail Kathryn 214 Liverpool Road, London N1 1LE — BChir 1991 Camb.

MIFSUD, Albert John PHLS Collaborating Centre, Department of Microbiology, Royal London Hospital, 37 Ashfield Steet, London E1 1BB Tel: 020 7377 7644 Fax: 020 7247 6750 Email: amifsud@phes.nhs.uk — MB BS 1983 Lond.; MSc (Clin. Microbiol.) Lond. 1988; MBA Westm. 1992; MRCPath 1989; FRCPath 1998; MD. (Royal Free Hospital School of Medicine) Cons. Clin. Microbiologist. Prev: Dir. PHLS PeterBoro.; Regist. (Clin. Microbiol.) St. Mary's Hosp. Lond.; SHO (Med. Microbiol.) Lond. Hosp.

MIFSUD, Mr Ronald Southbank, Brake Lane, West Hagley, Stourbridge DY8 2XW — MD 1969 Malta; FRCS Eng. 1976; FRCS Ed. 1975; T(S) 1991.

MIGDAL, Mr Clive Stephen 149 Harley Street, London W1G 6DE Tel: 020 7935 4444 Fax: 020 7486 3782; 80 Grafton Way, London W1T 6JG Tel: 020 7387 4676 — MB ChB 1971 Cape Town; MD

Cape Town 1990; FRCS Eng. 1979; FRCOphth 1989; DO Eng. 1978. (Cape Town) Cons. Ophth. W. Eye Hosp. & St. Mary's Hosp. Lond.; Vis. Ophth. Moorfields Eye Hosp. Lond. Socs: Fell. Roy. Soc. Med.; Amer. Acad. Ophth.; (Sec.) Europ. Glaucoma Soc. Prev: Sen. Regist. (Ophth.) St. Bart. Hosp. Lond.; Sen. Regist. Moorfields Eye Hosp. (High Holborn Br.) Lond.

***MIGHELL, Alan James** Tel: 0113 206 4717 Fax: 0113 244 4475 Email: a.j.mighell@leeds.ac.uk — MB ChB 1998 Leeds; PhD Leeds 1996; FDS RCS Lond. 1994; BChD Leeds 1990; BSc Leeds 1989.

MIHAI, Alissa Mary 279c Shirland Road, London W9 3JW Tel: 020 8960 6859 Email: avminai@hotmail.com — MB BS 1996 Lond. (St. Marys) Anaesth. SHO Rotat. From Char. Cross Hosp. Socs: BMA; RCA. Prev: SHO (Cardiol.) Harefield Hosp.; SHO (Gastroenterol.) Hillingdon.

MIHAIMEED, Mr Faisal Mohamed Ali Newham General Hospital, Glen Road, Plaistow, London E13 8SL Tel: 020 7363 8128; 10 Crawley Road, Bush Hill Park, Enfield EN1 2ND Tel: 020 7363 8128 Email: fmihaimeed@hotmail.com — MB BCh 1980 Ain Shams; MSc (Lond.) 1997; FRCS (Gen) 1999; CCST; FRCPS Glas. 1990. Cons. Surg., Newham Gen. Hosp.; Hon. Cons. Surg., St Bartholomew's Hosp. Socs: Assoc of Surg.s UK & Irel.; Brit. Assoc. of Sugical Oncol.; Brit. BrE. Gp. Prev: Sen. Regist., Hillingdon; Sen. Regist., Roy. Free; Sen. Regist., Ashford Middx.

MIHAJLOVIC, Slobodan 24 Higher Downs, Chellow Dene, Bradford BD8 0NA — MB ChB 1988 Manch.

MIHSSIN, Mr Numan Kathem Torbay Hospital, Laws Bridge, Torquay TQ2 7AA Tel: 01803 614567; 5 Whitebeam Close, Paignton TQ3 3GA — MB ChB 1974 Mosul, Iraq; FRCS Ed. 1985; FRCS Glas. 1985. Assoc. Specialist (Gen. Surg.). Prev: Staff Grade (Gen. Surg.) Torbay Hosp.; Regist. (Gen. Surg.) Torbay Hosp.; Regist. (Gen. Surg.) Wrexham Maelor Hosp.

MIKE, Nigel Niall Hamlyn 53 Belle Vue Road, Shrewsbury SY3 7LN — MB ChB 1975 Birm.; MD Birm. 1988; MRCP (UK) 1979. Cons. Phys. P.ss Roy. Hosp. Telford.

MIKEL, John Judd Department of Cytology, Michael Darmady Laborat., Queen Alexandra Hospital, Cosham, Portsmouth PO6 3LY Tel: 023 92 379451 — MB ChB 1976 Glas.; MRCPath 1990. Dir. Cytopath. Portsmouth & SE Hants., Portsmouth Hosps. Trust. Socs: Assn. Clin. Path. & Brit. Soc. Clin. Cytol. Prev: Cons. Cytopath. & Histopath. Wessex RHA Portsmouth; Sen. Regist. (Histopath.) Yorks. RHA; Regist. (Histopath.) Manch. HA.

MIKHAEL, Magdi Salama Hanna Department of Anaesthetics, Oldchurch Hospital, Oldchurch Road, Romford RM7 0BE Tel: 01708 708443 Fax: 01708 708040; Karema, Beehive Chase, Hookend, Brentwood CM15 0PG Tel: 01277 821780 Fax: 01277 824880 Email: magdimikhael@hotmail.com — MB BS 1972 Cairo; FFA RCS Eng. 1981; DEAA Oslo 1990. Cons. Pain Relief & Anaesth. Havering NHS Trust. Prev: Cons. (Anaesth.) Greenwich Health Care; Cons. Anaesth. Thanet Health Care; Cons. Anaesth. RAMC.

MIKHAEL MATTA, Wassim Helmy Academic Department of Obstetrics & Gynaecology, Royal Free Hospital, Pond St., London NW3 2QG; 32 Park Mount, Harpenden AL5 3AR — MB ChB 1973 Alexandria; MRCOG 1982.

MIKHAIL, Ashraf Sourour Ishak Sourour Renal Unit, Kent & Canterbury Hospital, Ethelbert Road, Canterbury CT1 3NG — MB BCh 1983 Ain Shams, Egypt; MRCP (UK) 1995.

MIKHAIL, Ghada Wagdy Ibrahim 124 Greenhill, Prince Arthur Road, Hampstead, London NW3 5TY Tel: 020 7433 3411 — MB BS 1990 Lond.; BSc (Immunopath.) Lond. 1987. Regist. (Cardiol. & Transpl. Med.) Harefield Hosp. Prev: Research Fell. (Cardiol. & Transpl. Med.) Harefield Hosp.; SHO (Transpl. Med.) Harefield Hosp.; SHO Rotat. (Med.) Roy. Free Hosp. & Barking Hosps. Lond.

MIKHAIL, Mr Hany Mina Tadros Accident & Emergency Department, Chase Farm Hospital, The Ridgeway, Enfield EN2 Tel: 020 8366 6600; 29 Hampton Gardens, Sawbridgeworth CM21 0AN Tel: 01279 445020 — MRCS Eng. LRCP Lond. 1979; FRCS Glas. 1982; FRCS Ed. 1981; FFAEM 1993. Cons. A & E Med. Chase Farm Hosps. NHS Trust Enfield.

MIKHAIL, John Raymond (retired) 42 Anthony's Avenue, Parkstone, Poole BH14 8JH Tel: 01202 700122 — MRCS Eng. LRCP Lond. 1946. Hon. Cons. Phys. E. Dorset HA. Prev: Cons. Chest Phys. Roy. Nat. Hosp. & Roy. Vict. Hosp. Bournemouth.

MIKHAIL, Karam Helmy Tewfic Eccleston Medical Centre, Broadway, St Helens WA10 5PJ Tel: 01744 454454 Fax: 01744

454622; 8 Bobbies Lane, Eccleston, St Helens WA10 5AL — MB ChB 1967 Alexandria; DPM Eng. 1979. (Alexandria)

MIKHAIL, Medhat Maurice Shehata Parkside Family Practice, Green Road Surgery, 224 Wokingham Road, Reading RG6 1JT Tel: 0118 966 3366 Fax: 0118 926 3269 — MB BCh 1979 Cairo; MRCOG 1988.

MIKHAIL, Sherine Wagdy Ibrahim John Howard Centre, 2 Crozier Terrace, Hackney, London E9 6AT Tel: 0161 499 3777, 020 8919 5657 Fax: 0161 493 9119, 020 8985 0278 — MB BS 1994 Lond.; BSc Lond. 1991; MRC Psych 1998. N. Thames E. Specialist Regist. Train. in Forens. Psychiat.

MIKHAIL, Mr Tarek Moris Shehata 86 Bootham Court, Clarence St., York YO31 8JT — MB BCh 1984 Cairo; FRCSI 1992.

MIKHAIL, Wagdy Ibrahim 12 Parkgate, Blackheath, London SE3 9XB Tel: 020 8852 1438 Fax: 020 8297 8161 — MB BCh Cairo 1958; DM Cairo 1970; FRCPsych 1986, M 1973; DPM & N Cairo 1962. (Kasr El Aini Fac. Med. Cairo) p/t Cons. Psychiat. The Priory Hosp. Hayes Gr., Hayes, Kent. Socs: Fell. Roy. Soc. Med.; Brit. Assn. Psychopharmacol.; The World Federat. of Societies of Biological Psychiat. Prev: Hon. Sen. Lect. UMDS Guy's Campus; Tutor (Psychiat.) Thames Postgrad. Med. & Dent. Educat. Univ. Lond.; Dep. Director Underwater Med. Research Centre Gen. Naval Hosp. Alexandria.

MIKHAIL, Wageeh Maurice Fawzy 38 Simpson Street, Crosshouse Hospital, Kilmarnock KA2 0BD — MB BCh 1982 Cairo, Egypt; MRCOG 1995.

MIKHAILIDIS, Alice Maria 3 Stanhope Road, Highgate, London N6 5NE — Ptychio latrikes 1978 Athens.

MIKHAILIDIS, Dimitri Department of Chemical Pathology & Human Metabolism, Royal Free Hospital, Pond St., London NW3 2QG Tel: 020 7794 0500 Fax: 020 7830 2235; 3 Stanhope Road, London N6 5NE — MB BS 1976 Lond.; MSc (Distinc.) Lond. 1981, BSc (1st cl. Hons.) 1971, MD 1989; MRCS Eng. LRCP Lond. 1976; FRCPath 1997, M 1990; Fell. Amer. Coll. Angiol; FACA 1998. (Roy. Free) Reader & Hon. Cons. Chem. Path. & Human Metab. Roy. Free Hosp. Lond.; Vis. Prof. Kingston Univ. UK & Univ. Ioannina Med. Sch. Greece. Socs: Fell. Roy. Soc. Med. (Vice-Pres. & Edit. Represent. Sect. Path.); BMA; Assn. Clin. Biochem. Prev: Sen. Lect. & Hon. Cons. Chem. Path. & Human Metab. Roy. Free Hosp. Lond.; Lect. & Hon. Sen. Reg. (Chem. Path. & Human Metab.) Roy. Free Hosp. Sch. Med. Lond.; Wellcome Research Fell. & Hon. Lect. Roy. Free Hosp. Sch. Med. Lond.

MIKOU, Panagiota Astor House, 26-30 Craven Hill Gardens, London W2 3EA — Ptychio latrikes 1989 Athens.

MILAN, Paul Anton 31 Wherretts Well Lane, Solihull B91 2SD Tel: 0121 704 3439 Email: pavlo@pavjo.demon.co.uk — MB BS 1991 Lond.; MRCP (Lond.) March 1995; FRCR (Pt I) 1996. (St. Geos.) Specialist Regist. (Radiol.) W. Midl. Rotat. Train. Scheme. Prev: Med. SHO Rotat. Mayday Hosp. Croydon.

MILASZKIEWICZ, Regina Department of Anaesthetics, Barnet Hospital, Wellhouse Lane, Barnet EN5 3DJ; 38 Avenue Rise, Bushey WD23 3AS Tel: 020 8950 5820 Fax: 020 8386 3037 — MB BS 1981 Lond.; FRCA 1990; FFA RCSI 1989. (St. George's Hosp. Lond.) Cons. Anaesth. Barnet & Chase Farm Hosps. NHS Trust.

MILBOURN, Matthew Robert Fontana and Partners, Silsden Health Centre, Elliott Street, Silsden, Keighley BD20 0DG Tel: 01535 652447 Fax: 01535 657296; Box Tree Farm, 5 Main St, Bradley, Keighley BD20 9DG — MB BS 1987 Newc.; DRCOG 1992; DCH RCP Lond. 1991. Prev: Trainee GP Airedale VTS.

MILBURN, Christopher John Holburn Medical Group, 7 Albyn Place, Aberdeen AB10 1YE Tel: 01224 400800 Fax: 01224 407777 — MB ChB 1972 Aberd.; BSc Aberd. 1967; MRCGP 1978; DRCOG 1977. (Aberd.) Prev: Ho. Phys. & Ho. Surg. Aberd. Roy. Infirm.; Lect. (Pathol.) Univ. Aberd.; RAF Med. Br.

MILBURN, David William The Wooda Surgery, Clarence Wharf, Barnstaple Street, Bideford EX39 4AU Tel: 01237 471071 Fax: 01237 471059; 4 Shepherds Meadow, Abbotsham, Bideford EX39 5BP — MB ChB 1987 Leeds; MRCGP 1992. Clin. Asst. (c/o the Elderly). Socs: Med. Protec. Soc.

MILBURN, Diane Kingsteignton Surgery, Whiteway Road, Kingsteignton, Newton Abbot TQ12 3HN Tel: 01626 883312 Fax: 01626 336406 — MB BS 1984 Newc. (Newc. u. Tyne) Socs: Med. Defence Union; BMA. Prev: Trainee GP Torbay VTS.

MILBURN, Heather June Chest Clinic, Guy's Hospital, St Thomas St., London SE1 9RT — MB BS 1979 Lond.; MSc Lond. 1973, MD 1991; BSc Soton 1972; MRCP (UK) 1981; FRCP 2000 UK. (Guy's) p/t Cons. Thoracic Med. Guy's & St. Thos. Hosps. Lond.; Hon. Sen. Lect. (Med.) 1992, Kings Coll. Lond. Socs: Internat. Union Against Tuiberculosis and Lung Dis.; Brit. Thorac. Soc.; Eur. Thoracic Soc. Prev: Sen. Regist. (Thoracic Med.) Guy's Hosp. Lond.; Regist. (Thoracic Med.) Roy. Brompton Hosp. Lond.; Research Fell. (Thoracic Med.) Roy. Free Hosp. Lond.

MILBURN, Jane Black and Partners, Sherwood Health Centre, Elmswood Gardens, Sherwood, Nottingham NG5 4AD Tel: 0115 960 7127 Fax: 0115 985 7899 — MB ChB 1986 Leic.; MRCGP 1990; DCH RCP Lond. 1989; DGM RCP Lond. 1988. GP Nottm. Prev: SHO VTS Nottm.; SHO (O & G) City Hosp. Nottm.

MILBURN, Richard Andrew 14 Windsor Crescent, Elderslie, Johnstone PA5 9QU — MB ChB 1988 Glas.

***MILBURN, Simon** The Old School House, East Rounton, Northallerton DL6 2LA — MB ChB 1997 Liverp.

MILDMAY-WHITE, Abigail Anne Derriford Hospital, Plymouth PL6 8DH Tel: 01752 777111 Fax: 01752 768976; Mothecombe, Holbeton, Plymouth PL8 1LA — MB BS 1976 Lond.; MRCP (UK) 1980. Clin. Asst. (Nuclear Med.) Derriford Hosp. Plymouth. Prev: Regist. (Diag. Radiol.) Guy's Hosp. Lond.; SHO (Med. & Anaesth.) N.ampton Gen. Hosp.

MILE, David Jonathan The Surgery, 50 Barnbygate, Newark NG24 1QD Tel: 01636 704225; Sunnyside House, Doddington Lane, Claypole, Newark NG23 5BE — MB ChB 1983 Birm.; MRCGP 1988; DRCOG 1987. Socs: BMA; GP in Asthma Gp.; Director Condor CoOperat. Newark. Prev: Partner, 1 The Tything, Worcester; SHO (O & G) Dudley Rd. Hosp. Birm.

MILEHAM, Penelope Ann, Maj. RAMC Taylors Copse Farm, Steep Marsh, Petersfield GU32 2BS Tel: 01730 262014 — MB BCh 1987 Wales; MRCGP 1993; DRCOG 1992. Prev: Med. Off. RAMC.

MILES, Mr Andrew James Granville Royal Hampshire County Hospital, Romsey Road, Winchester SO22 5DG Tel: 01962 825924 Email: andrew.miles@weht.swest.nhs.uk — MB BS 1984 Lond.; MS 1991 Lond.; FRCS 1987 Lond.; EBSQ 1998 Malmo, Sweden. (St Thomas's London) Cons. Surg., Roy. Hants. Co. Hosp. Winches.; Dir. Anal Physiol. Unit & Hon. Cons. Surg. S.ham. Univ. Hosp.; Chairm. Centr. S. Coast Colorectal Cancer Network.

MILES, Arnold Ian 95 Eyre Court, Finchley Road, London NW8 9TX Tel: 020 7586 4777 Fax: 020 7586 4777 — MRCS Eng. LRCP Lond. 1965; BChD, LDS Leeds 1955; Dip. Amer. Bd. Internal Med. 1973 & Pulm. Dis. 1976. (Roy. Free) Asst. Dean, Sch. Grad.-Med. Educat. Seton Hall Univ. NJ, USA. Socs: Fell. Amer. Coll. Chest Phys.; FACP. Prev: Chief Pulm. Med. St. Joseph's Hosp. Med. Centre Paterson, New Jersey, USA; Assoc. Prof. Fairlie Dickinson Univ. (Dent. Sch.) New Jersey, USA; Med. Dir. Research & Developm. Johnson & Johnson BPC New Jersey.

MILES, Barbara Joan The Surgery, Tunbridge Lane, Bottisham, Cambridge CB5 9DU; 9 Alwyne Road, Cambridge CB1 8RR Tel: 01233 244676 — MB BS 1961 Lond.; MRCS Eng. LRCP Lond. 1961; DObst RCOG 1964. (King's Coll. Hosp.)

MILES, Barbara Maire Craigmore Cottage, Blanefield, Glasgow G63 9AU — MB ChB 1992 Glas.

MILES, Christine Margaret Claughton Street Surgery, 66 Claughton Street, St Helens WA10 1SN Tel: 01744 734128 Fax: 01744 759978; 18 Headingley Close, St Helens WA9 3YA Tel: 01744 815493 — BSc Manch. 1976, MB ChB (Hons.) 1979; DCH RCP Lond. 1983; Cert. Family Plann. JCC 1983; DRCOG 1982. Prev: Fact. Dr. Remploy Fact. St. Helens; Clin. Med. Off. St. Helens & Knowsley HA.

MILES, Clare Stella 31 Burdiehouse Road, Edinburgh EH17 8AE — MB ChB 1993 Ed.

MILES, David Nicholas 31 Burdiehouse Road, Edinburgh EH17 8AE — MB ChB 1992 Ed.

MILES, David Peter Braddock Cornwall & Isles of Scilly Health Authority, John Keay House, St Austell PL25 4NQ Tel: 01726 77777 Fax: 01726 71777 Email: davidmiles@ciosha.cornwall.nhs.uk; Higher Tregullas, Kea, Truro TR3 6AJ Tel: 01872 862311 — MB BS Lond. 1967; MRCS Eng. LRCP Lond. 1967; FFPHM 1989; FFCM 1984, M 1974; DPH Eng. 1971; DObst RCOG 1969. (St. Bart.) Dir. of Pub. Health Med. Cornw. & I. of Scilly HA. Prev: Dist. Med. Off.

MILES

Cornw. & I. of Scilly HA; Dist. Med. Off. Milton Keynes HA; Dist. Community Phys. Aylesbury & Milton Keynes Health Dist.

MILES, David William (retired) The Grange, Meadowcroft, Draughton, Skipton BD23 6EG Tel: 01756 710300 Fax: 01756 710200 Email: dwmiles@btinternet.com — MB ChB 1960 Leeds; MD Leeds 1969, BSc (Hons. Physiol.) 1958; FRCP Lond. 1979, M 1965. Prev: Cons. Phys. Airedale Gen. Hosp.

MILES, David William 10 Briston Grove, London N8 9EX — MB BS 1981 Lond.; BSc Lond. 1978, MD 1995; MRCP (UK) 1985; FRCP 1998. (Univ. Coll. Lond. & Univ. Coll. Hosp.) Sen. Lect. & Hon. Cons. Med. Oncol. Guy's Hosp. Lond. Socs: Assn. Cancer Phys. Prev: Sen. Regist. Guy's Hosp. Lond.; Regist. Univ. Coll. Hosp. Lond. & Kings Coll. Hosp.

MILES, Edward Herbert Stewart (retired) 91 Western Road, Billericay CM12 9DT Tel: 01277 630123 — MB BS 1960 Lond. Med. Mem. Appeals Serv.

MILES, Gregory Apples Medical Centre, East Mill Lane, Sherborne DT9 3DG Tel: 01935 812633 Fax: 01935 817484 — MB BChir 1981 Camb.; MA Camb. 1981; MRCGP 1985; DA Eng. 1984; DRCOG 1983. (Cambridge University & St. Thomas')

MILES, Harriet Louise Top Flat, 9 Spottiswoode Road, Edinburgh EH9 1BH — BM BS 1994 Nottm. SHO (Paediat.) Newc. Gen. Hosp. Prev: SHO (O & G) Simpson Memor. Matern. Pavil. Edin.

MILES, Helen Clare 6 Wasdale Close, Edwalton Park, Nottingham NG2 6RG — MB ChB 1996 Birm. SHO (O & G) Co. Hosp. Hereford. Prev: SHO (A & E) Sunderland Roy. Hosp. Tyne & Wear.

MILES, James Forsythe (retired) Cobweb Grange, Row Head, Ousby, Penrith CA10 1QB Tel: 01768 881146 — MRCS Eng. LRCP Lond. 1962; DObst RCOG 1964.

MILES, Jane Catherine Spring Lodge, Stonehills, Fawley, Southampton SO45 1DU — MB BS 1993 Lond.

MILES, Mr John Ballard Daymer, Gayton Road, Heswall, Wirral L60 Tel: 0151 342 4101 — MB BCh 1960 Wales; FRCS Eng. 1964. (Cardiff) Hunt. Prof. Roy. Coll. Surg. Eng.; Head Dept. Neurol. Scis. Univ. Liverp.; Cons. Neurosurg. Mersey RHA & Welsh Health Auths. Prev: Regist. Dept. Neurosurg. Radcliffe Infirm. Oxf.; Sen. Regist. Neurosurg. Midl. Centre for Neurosurg. Smethwick & Qu.; Eliz. Hosp. Birm.

MILES, John Patrick Bedale Centre, Glencathara Rd, Bognor Regis; Email: johnmiles41@hotmail.com — BM 1988 Soton.; BSc 1982 (Hons Physiology) London; FRANZCP 2000 Australia; MRCPsych 1997 UK. Cons. Psychiat., Graylingwell Hosp., Chichester. Prev: Cons. Psychiat., Sunshine Coast, Qu.sland, Australia; Psychiatric Regist., Qu.sland, Australia; Psychiatric Regist., St. Geo.s, Lond.

MILES, Jolyon Peter Wye Surgery, 67 Oxenturn Road, Wye, Ashford TN25 5AY Tel: 01233 812414/812419 Fax: 01233 813236 — MB BS 1983 Lond.; Cert. Family Plann. JCC 1988. GP Wye Kent.; Clin. Endoscopist, Kent & Canterbury Hosp.

*****MILES, Jonathan** Honey Bourne, Oak Dene Cl, Claverdon, Warwick CV35 8PZ — MB ChB 1997 Leic.

MILES, Jonathan Francis Department of Respiratory Medicine, North Manchester General Hospital, Crumpsall, Manchester M8 5RB Tel: 0161 720 2122 Fax: 0161 720 2043; 15 Ashfield Road, Cheadle SK8 1BB Tel: 0161 428 7729 — MB BS 1986 Lond.; BSc (Hons.) Lond. 1983; MD Lond. 1997; MRCP (UK) 1989. (St. Mary's Hosp. Med. Sch.) Cons. Phys. (Gen. & Thoracic Med.) N. Manch. Gen. Hosp. Socs: Brit. Thorac. Soc.; Amer. Thoracic Soc.; Brit. Soc. Allergy & Clin. Immunol. Prev: Sen. Research Fell. Wellington Asthma Research Gp. Wellington Sch. Med. NZ; Research Fell. (Respirat. Med.) & Regist. (Gen. & Respirat. Med.) E. Birm. Hosp.

MILES, Laurence Claughton Street Surgery, 66 Claughton Street, St Helens WA10 1SN Tel: 01744 734128 Fax: 01744 759978; 18 Headingley Close, St Helens WA9 3YA Tel: 01744 815493 — MB ChB 1979 Manch.; Cert. Family Plann. JCC 1983. Prev: SHO (O & G & A & E) Whiston Hosp.

MILES, Lyndon Brondevw Surgery, Garth Road, Bangor LL57 2RT Tel: 01248 370900; Bryn Goleu, Pentir, Bangor LL57 4UU Tel: 01248 353889 Email: lyndonmiles@clara.net — MB ChB 1983 Sheff.; 2000 (DFPHM) RCP London; MA 1999 (Health Sci. Public Health & Health Promotion) Univ. of Manchester; MRCGP 1987; AFOM RCP Lond. 1993; Cert. Family Plann. 1987. (Sheff.) GP, Bangor, Gwynedd; SpR in Pub. Health Med. Prev: GP Llangefni & Benllech Anglesey; SCMO (Occupat. Health) St. Woolos Hosp.

Newport; SHO (Paediat., Med. & O & G), P. Chas. Hosp. Merthyr Tydfil.

MILES, Margaret Mary The Medical Centre, 7E Woodfield Road, London W9 3YZ Tel: 020 8451 8119; 31 Ashchurch Grove, London W12 9BU Tel: 020 8743 4114 Fax: 020 8743 9237 — MB BS Lond. 1968; MRCS Eng. LRCP Lond. 1967; DCH Eng. 1970; MSc Audiological Med. 1997. (Roy. Free) Sen. Clin. Med. Off. Pk.side HA. Socs: MRCPCH & Brit. Assn.Community Doctors in Audiol. Prev: Ho. Phys. Roy. Free Hosp. Lond.; Ho. Surg. King Edwd. VII Hosp. Windsor; Ho. Phys. (Paediat.) St. Jas. Hosp. Balham.

MILES, Marion Violet Medical Centre, 7E Woodfield Road, London W9 3XZ Tel: 020 8451 8119 Fax: 020 8451 8215; 28 Blenheim Road, London NW8 0LX Tel: 020 7624 0667 Fax: 020 7328 5708 — MB BS Lond. 1955; FRCP Lond. 1987; FRCP Ed. 1985, M 1963; MRCS Eng. LRCP Lond. 1955; DCH Eng. 1957; FRCPCH 1996. (Univ. Coll. Hosp.) Cons. Community Paediat. Pk.side Health Trust. Socs: Fell. Roy. Soc. Med.; Fell. Roy. Coll. Paediat. and Child Health. Prev: SCMO Bloomsbury HA; Ho. Off. Hosp. Sick Childr. Gt. Ormond St; Regist. (Paediat.) Hammersmith Hosp.

MILES, Norman Alfred (retired) The Old House, Old Lincoln Road, Caythorpe, Grantham NG32 3EJ Tel: 01400 272540 — MB BChir Camb. 1952; MA Camb. 1952; FFPHM 1981, M 1977; DObst RCOG 1953. Prev: Assoc. Postgrad. Dean Fac. of Med. Univ. Nottm.

*****MILES, Owain Hywel** 10 Forest Hill, The Bryn, Pontllanfraith, Blackwood NP12 2PW — MB ChB 1998 Birm.; ChB Birm. 1998.

MILES, Peter David Stony Stratford Surgery, Market Square, Stony Stratford, Milton Keynes MK11 1YA Tel: 01908 565555; 6 Mansel Close, Cosgrove, Milton Keynes MK19 7JQ Tel: 01908 564479 — MB BS 1984 Lond.; MA Camb. 1985; DRCOG 1988.

MILES, Rex Stafford Department of Medical Microbiology, Edinburgh Medical School, Teviot Place, Edinburgh EH8 9AG — MB ChB 1967 Ed.; MB ChB Ed.1967; FRCPath 1986, M 1974. Sen. Lect. (Bact.) Univ. Edin. & Hon Cons. Lothian Health Bd. Socs: Brit. Soc. Study of Infec. & farsh. Med. Assn. Prev: Lect. (Bact.) Univ. Dundee; Ho. Phys. Roy. Infirm. Edin.; Ho. Surg. Peel Hosp. Galashiels.

MILES, Richard Spring Lodge, Stonehills, Fawley, Southampton SO45 1DU — MB BS 1990 Lond.

MILES, Richard Norman Hinchingbrooke Hospital, Huntingdon PE29 6NT Tel: 01480 416224 Fax: 01480 416698; The Coneygarths, 51 High St, Buckden, Huntingdon PE19 5TA Tel: 01480 810836 Fax: 01480 810836 — MB BS 1972 Lond.; FRCP Lond. 1995; MRCP (UK) 1978. (Lond. Hosp.) Cons. Paediat. Hinchingbrooke Hosp. Huntingdon. Socs: Brit. Paediat. Neurol. Assn.; Brit. Paediat. Assn.; Brit. Assn. Perinatal Med. Prev: Sen. Regist. (Paediat.) Sheff. Childr. Hosp.; Regist. (Paediat.) Jessop Hosp. Sheff.; Specialist (Paediat.) Brit. Milit. Hosp. Rinteln.

MILES, Sandra Catherine 2 Oakwood Drive, Southampton SO16 8EN — MB BS 1993 Lond.

MILES, Sarah Margaret Department of Rheumatology, Dewsbury & District Hospital, Healds Road, Dewsbury WF13 4HS Tel: 0113 243 3144; 17 Swan Road, Harrogate HG1 2SS — MB BS 1987 Lond.; BA Oxf. 1984; MRCP (UK) 1990. Sen. Regist. (Rheum.) St. Jas. Hosp. Leeds. Prev: Regist. (Rheum.) Regional Rheum. Centre Chapel Allerton Hosp. Leeds.

MILES, Simon John East Barnet Road Surgery, 113 East Barnet Road, New Barnet, Barnet EN4 8RF Tel: 020 8449 6443 Fax: 020 8441 5760; 19 Quakers Lane, Potters Bar EN6 1RL Tel: 01707 656549 Fax: 01707 665813 — MB BS 1986 Lond.; PhD West. Austral. 1975, BSc (Hons.) 1968; MRCGP 1991; T(GP) 1991. Prev: MRC Research Fell. Lond. Sch. Hyg. & Trop. Med.

MILES, Mr Stephen Antony David Accident & Emergency Department, Royal London Hospital, Whitechapel Road, London E1 1BB Tel: 020 7377 7161 Fax: 020 7377 7014; 36B Earlsfield Road, London SW18 3DN Tel: 020 8874 2797 — MB BCh 1970 Witwatersrand; FRCS Ed. 1976; FFAEM 1994. (Univ. Witwatersrand) Cons. A & E Barts & Lond. NHS Trust; Clin. Dir. Surg. Anaes. A & E Homerton Hosps. Socs: Roy. Soc. Med. (Mem. Ex-Pres. Accid. & Emerg. Sect.); (Hon. Sec.) Brit. Assn. Accid. & Emerg. Med. Prev: Cons. i/c A & E St. Bart. & Homerton Hosps.; Sen. Regist. (A & E) St. Bart. Hosp. Lond.; Med Adviser Lond. Ambul. Serv. (Past).

MILES, Mr William Frederick Anthony 23 Winton Terrace, Fairmile Head, Edinburgh EH10 7AP — MB ChB 1984 Ed.; FRCS

Ed. 1989. Regist. (Gen. Surg.) Lothian HB. Socs: BMA & Internat. Hepato-Biliary Pancreatic Assn. Prev: Regist. (Surg.) & Research Fell. Roy. Infirm. Edin. & Univ. Edin.

*MILESTONE, Andrew Neil Lysways Hall, Lysways Lane, Longdon Green, Rugeley WS15 4QB — MB BS 1998 Lond.; MB BS Lond 1998.

MILEWCZYK, Stefan 83 Arundel Road, Kingston upon Thames KT1 3RY Tel: 020 8287 Ext: 3844 Email: steff@dochawk.freeserve.co.uk — MRCS Eng. LRCP Lond. 1990.

MILEWSKI, Mr Peter Jan Pembrokeshire NHS Trust, Withybush Hospital, Haverfordwest SA61 2PZ Tel: 01437 773330 Fax: 01437 773413 Email: pjm@pookah.demon.co.uk — MB BChir 1971 Camb.; MChir Camb. 1981; FRCS Eng. 1975; DObst RCOG 1972. (Cambridge) Cons. Gen. Surg. Pembrokesh. HA; Lead Clinician, Colo Rectal Cancer Serv.; Hon. Clin. Tutor Univ. Hosp. Wales; RCSE Surg. Tutor Pembrokesh.. Socs: Assn. Surg.; Brit. Soc. Gastroenterol.; Assn. Coloproctol. Prev: Sen. Regist. (Gen. Surg.) NW RHA; Tutor (Surg.) Hope Hosp. Salford; Regist. (Surg.) Glos. AHA.

MILFORD, Christine Denise 1 Almacs Close, Liverpool L23 6XT — MRCS Eng. LRCP Lond. 1981.

MILFORD, Mr Christopher Andrew 4 Rimmer Close, Old Marston, Oxford OX3 0PB — MB BS 1979 Lond.; BSc (Hons.) Lond. 1976; FRCS Eng. 1985; FRCS Glas. 1984; MRCS Eng. LRCP Lond. 1979. (St. Bart.) Cons. ENT Radcliffe Infirm. Oxf. Socs: Roy. Soc. Med. (Ex-Sec. Laryngol. & Rhinol. Sect.). Prev: Sen. Regist. (ENT) Char. Cross Hosp. Lond.; Regist. (ENT) Roy. Nat. Throat, Nose & Ear Hosp. Lond.

MILFORD, David Vernon Department of Nephrology, The Children's Hospital, Steelhouse Lane, Birmingham B4 6NH Tel: 0121 333 9232 Fax: 0121 333 9231 Email: david.milford@bhamchildrens.wmids.nhs.uk — BM 1982 Soton.; DM Soton. 1994; FRCP 1997; MRCP (UK) 1985. (Southampton) Cons. Paediat. Nephrol. Childr.'s Hosp. Birm.; Hon. Sen. Lect. Univ. Birm. Socs: MRCPCH; Brit. Assn. Paediat. Nephrol.; Eur. Soc. Paediat. Nephrol. Prev: Sen. Regist. (Paediat.) Childr.'s Hosp. Birm.

MILHENCH, Myles Robert 8 Orchard Way, Strangford Road, Downpatrick BT30 6LD Tel: 01396 616977 — MB BCh BAO 1976 Belf.; FFA RCSI 1980. Cons. Anaesth. Downe Hosp. Downpatrick. Prev: Cons. Anaesth. Peel Hosp. Galashiels & Borders Gen. Hosp.; Sen. Regist. Belf. City Hosp.

MILIK, Mr Nagy Shafik 15 The Dene, Wembley HA9 7QS — MB BCh 1971 Assiut; FRCS Eng. 1983; FRCS Glas. 1983. (Assiut, Egypt) Regist. (Surg. & Orthop.) Brent DHA.

MILKINS, Steven Royston Department of Pathology, Kettering General Hospital, Rothwell Road, Kettering NN16 8UZ Tel: 01536 492696 Fax: 01536 492704 — MB BS 1981 Lond.; BSc Lond. 1978, MB BS Lond. 1981; FRCPath 1997. Cons. Path. Kettering Gen. Hosp.

MILLA, Professor Peter John Gastroenterology Unit, Institute of Child Health, 30 Guilford St., London WC1N 1EM Tel: 020 7242 9789 Fax: 020 7404 6181 Email: p.milla@ich.ucl.ac.uk — FRCPCH 1996; MSc Lond. 1977, MB BS 1964; FRCP Lond. 1985; MRCP (UK) 1970. (St. Bart.) Prof. of Paediatric Gastroenterol. and Nutrit. Inst of Child Health Univ. Coll. Lond.; Hon. Cons. Paediat. Gastroenterol. Hosp. Sick Childr Gt. Ormond St. Lond; Paediat. Gastroenterol. Inst. of Child Health Lond. Socs: Pres. Europ. Soc. of Paediatrive Gastroenterol., HePath. and Nutrit.; Chairm. United Europ. Gastroenterol. Educat.; Mem. Amer. Gastroenterol. Ass. Prev: Ho. Phys. Hosp. Sick Childr. Gt. Ormond St. Lond. & (Child Health) St.Bart. Hosp. Lond.

MILLAC, Judith Mary (retired) Cradock, Gumley, Market Harborough LE16 7RU — MB BS 1958 Lond.; MRCS Eng. LRCP Lond. 1958; FRCGP 1982, M 1975; DCH Eng. 1961; DObst RCOG 1960. Prev: Assoc. Adviser (Gen. Pract.) Univ. Leic.

MILLAN SERRANO, Rosa 107 T/L Queen Margaret Drive, Glasgow G20 8PB — LMS 1994 Cordoba.

MILLAR, Alan Blair Skellern and Partners, Bridport Medical Centre, North Allington, Bridport DT6 5DU Tel: 01308 421109 Fax: 01308 420869 — MB BS 1990 Lond.

MILLAR, Alan James Arran, 40 Admiral Street, Glasgow G41 1HU Tel: 0141 429 2626 Fax: 0141 429 2331; 90 Blairbeth Road, Rutherglen, Glasgow G73 4JA Tel: 0141 631 3706 Fax: 0141 429 2331 — MB ChB 1981 Aberd.; MRCGP 1990; DCH RCPS Glas.

1988. (Aberd.) Prev: Trainee GP Kilmacolm VTS; Regist. (Paediat.) Roy. Hosp. Sick Childr. Glas.

MILLAR, Alan Young Dept. of Anaesth., Walton Building, Glasgow Royal Infirmary, 84 Castle St., Glasgow G4 0SF Tel: 0141 211 4000 Email: alan@amillar.demon.co.uk — MB ChB 1987 Ed.; FFARCSI 1987. (Glas.) Cons. (Anaesth.) Glas. Roy. Infirm.

MILLAR, Mr Alastair John Ward 28 Victoria Park, Cambridge CB4 3EL Tel: 01223 65082 — MB ChB 1972 Cape Town; FRCS Eng. 1979; FRCS Ed. 1978; FRACS 1984; DCH RCP Lond. 1979. Assoc. Prof. & Princip. Specialist Red Cross War Memor. Childr. Hosp. Capetown S. Africa. Prev: Regist. (Surg.) Univ. Coll. Hosp. Lond.; Sen. Regist. (Paediat. Surg.) Red Cross War Memor. Childr. Hosp. S. Africa; Regist. (Surg.) Roy. Childr. Hosp. Melbourne, Austral.

MILLAR, Alexander McCallum Polwarth Surgery, 72 Polwarth Gardens, Edinburgh EH11 1LL Tel: 0131 229 5914 Fax: 0131 221 9897; 86 Polwarth Terrace, Edinburgh EH11 1NN Tel: 0131 337 4257 — MB ChB 1975 Ed. (Ed.)

MILLAR, Andrew David Department Gastroenterology, North Middlesex Hospital, Sterling Way, London N18 1QS Tel: 020 8887 2251 Fax: 020 8887 2850; Tel: 020 8444 9319 Fax: 020 8444 9319 — MB BS 1986 Lond.; BSc 1983 Lond.; MRCP (UK) 1989; MD Lond. 1996. Cons. Phys. Gastroenterol. The N. Middlx. Hosp. Lond.; Sen. Lect. (Med.) Roy. Free Hosp. Lond. Socs: BMA & Roy. Soc. Med.; Brit. Soc. Gastroenterol. Prev: Research Fell. Gastrointestinal Sc. Research Inst. Roy. Lond. Hosp. Med. Coll. Lond.; Regist. Rotat. (Gen. Med. & Gastroenterol.) N. Middlx. Hosp. & Roy. Free Hosp. Lond.

MILLAR, Andrew John Dundee Erne Health Centre, Erne Hospital, Cornagrade Road, Enniskillen BT74 6AY Tel: 028 6632 5638 — MB ChB 1975 Bristol; MRCGP 1982; DRCOG 1980.

MILLAR, Ann Brigid Lung Research Group, Medical School Unit, Southmead Hospital, Bristol BS10 5NB Tel: 020 7959 5347 Fax: 020 7959 5018 Email: ann.miller@bristol.ac.uk — MD 1987 Liverp.; MB ChB 1979; FRCP 1996. Sen. Lect. Univ. of Bristol. Prev: Lect. & Hon. Sen. Regist. Univ. Coll. & Middlx. Sch. Med. Lond.; Research Regist. Brompton Hosp. Lond.; Regist. Roy. Free Hosp. Lond.

MILLAR, Anne Elizabeth (retired) 8 Mill Lane, Benson, Wallingford OX10 6SA Tel: 01491 838116 — MB BS 1951 Lond.; MRCS Eng. LRCP Lond. 1951.

MILLAR, Barbara-Ann McLellan Misty Law, Manse-Brae, Lochgilphead PA31 8QZ — MB ChB 1992 Sheff.

MILLAR, Barbara Anne Parkhead Health Centre, 101 Salamanca Street, Glasgow G31 5BA Tel: 0141 531 9070 Fax: 0141 531 9020; 12 Oakhill Avenue, Baillieston, Glasgow G69 7ES Tel: 0141 771 1791 — MB BCh BAO 1968 Belf. (Queens Belfast)

MILLAR, Beverley Anne 40 Cranmoor Green, Pilning, Bristol BS35 4QF — MB ChB 1993 Bristol.

MILLAR, Mr Brian Ginn New Cross Hospital, Wednesfield Road, Wolverhampton WV10 0QP Tel: 01902 644906 — MB BS 1980 Lond.; BDS Birm. 1972; FRCS Ed. 1987; FDS RCPS Glas. 1982. Cons. Oral & Maxillofacial Surg. New Cross Hosp., Wolverhampton & Russells Hall Hosp. Dudley.

MILLAR, Carol Louise Department of Anaesthesia, Birmingham Children's Hospital, Steelhouse Lane, Birmingham B4 8NH Tel: 0121 333 9623 Fax: 0121 333 9621; 15 Pembridge Road, Dorridge, Solihull B93 8SA Tel: 01564 739305 — MB BS 1983 Lond.; FRCA 1989; DCH RCP Lond. 1988; DA (UK) 1985. (Char. Cross) p/t Cons. (Anaesth.) Paediatric. Socs: Roy. Coll. Anaesth.; BMA; Assn. Anaesth. Prev: Sen. Regist. (Anaesth.) John Radcliffe Hosp. Oxf.; Sen. Regist. (Paediat. Anaesth.) P.ss Margt. Hosp. for Childr. Perth, W.. Austral.; Clin. Research Fell. (Paediat. Anaesth.) Hosp. for Sick Childr. Toronto, Canada.

MILLAR, Christopher George 23 Newmills Road, Balerno EH14 5SU Tel: 0131 449 6231 — MB ChB 1994 Ed.; BSc Ed. 1992, MB ChB 1994; MRCP (UK) 1997. (Ed.) Specialist Regist. (Immunol.) Dept. Immunol. Leicester Roy. Infirm. Leicester. Socs: (Ordinary) Brit. Soc. Immunol.; BMA. Prev: SHO (Med.) Qu. Med. Centre, Nottm.

MILLAR, Clive William, Surg. Capt. RN 35 Monckton Road, Alverstoke, Gosport PO12 2BG Tel: 02392 580410 — MB BS 1955 Lond.; MRCS Eng. LRCP Lond. 1956; FRCGP 1989, M 1972; DObst RCOG 1964. (St. Geo.) Civil. Med. Pract. RN Sick Quarters HMS

MILLAR

Nelson Portsmouth. Socs: Fell. Roy. Soc. Med. Prev: Pres. Admiralty Med. Bd. & Head (Gen. Pract.) RN Hosp. Haslar; Princip. Med. Off. HMS Seahawk; Med. Off. Med. Dir.-Gen. (Naval) MoD.

MILLAR, Colin Gordon Macgregor 16 Spoutwells Avenue, Scone, Perth PH2 6RP — MB ChB 1985 Ed.

***MILLAR, David** 71 Greenmount Road, Coleraine BT51 3QF — MB BCh BAO 1994 Belf.

MILLAR, David Gavin Peterculter Health Service, Coronation Road, Peterculter AB14 0RQ Tel: 01224 733535 Fax: 01224 735662; Ravelston, 3 St. Devenick Terrace, Cults, Aberdeen AB15 9LX Tel: 01224 861193 — MB ChB Aberd. 1967; FRCGP 1991, M 1974. MacMillan GP Adviser/Hon. Sen. Lect. Univ. Aberd.; Macmillan GP Adviser/Hon. Sen. Lect. Univ. Aberd. Socs: Aberd. M-C Soc.; BMA; (Provost NE Scot. Fac.) Roy. Coll. GPs (Ex-sec.). Prev: Hosp. Pract. Roxburghe Ho. Aberd.

***MILLAR, David Richard** 6 The Paddock, Gullane EH31 2BW — MB ChB 1994 Glas.

MILLAR, Mr David Russell (retired) Stumperlowe Cottage, Stumperlowe Hall Road, Sheffield S10 3QS Tel: 0114 230 1737 — MB ChB Ed. 1956; FRCS Ed. 1962; FRCOG 1977, M 1965. Prev: Lect. (O & G) Univ. Liverp.

MILLAR, Diane Fraser Dow Rhapsody, Oxshott Road, Leatherhead KT22 0EG — MB ChB 1969 Glas. (Glas.)

MILLAR, Donald Edward St Clements Surgery, 39 Temple Street, Oxford OX4 1JS Tel: 01865 248550 — MB ChB 1970 Glas.; DRCOG 1977.

MILLAR, Mr Douglas Malcolm The Oaks Hospital Colchester, Oaks Place, Mile End Road, Colchester CO4 5XR Tel: 01206 752121 Fax: 01206 852701; Cresseners, Church Lane, Lexden, Colchester CO3 4AA Tel: 01206 570852 Fax: 01206 570852 — MB BS 1951 Lond.; FRCS Eng. 1958; FRCS Ed. 1958; MRCS Eng. LRCP Lond. 1951. (St. Geo.) p/t Surg. Colchester Oaks Hosp. & Hon. Cons. Surg. Essex Rivers Trust; Mem. Med. Appeals Tribunal. Socs: (Ex. Pres.) St. Mark's Hosp. Assn. Lond.; Fell. Roy. Soc. Med. (Mem. Counc. Ex-Pres. Coloproctol. Sect.); Fell. Assn. Surgs. Prev: Sen. Lect. St. Geo. Hosp. Med. Sch. Lond.; Hon. Tutor (Surg.) Char. Cross & W.m. Hosps. Lond.; Sen. Regist. St. Marks Hosp. Lond.

MILLAR, Edward (retired) Southcroft, Brookside, Bakewell DE45 1DY Tel: 01629 815679 — MB ChB 1941 Glas.; BSc MB ChB Glas. 1941; MRCGP 1953. Prev: Med. Off. Batchelor Peas Ltd. Sheff.

MILLAR, Edward Leslie 95 Back Lane, Whittington, Lichfield WS14 9SA Tel: 01543 433189 — MB ChB 1980 Birm.; FRCR 1986. Cons. Radiol. Good Hope Hosp. Sutton Coldfield.

MILLAR, Eleanor Isabel (retired) 41 Kensington Park, Bangor BT20 3RF Tel: 01247 454626 — MB BCh BAO Belf. 1941. Prev: Clin. Doctor E. Health & Social Servs. Bd.

MILLAR, Elizabeth 14 Mackintosh Place, Lionthorn, Falkirk FK1 5UL — MB ChB 1988 Ed.; MRCP (UK) 1993. Sen. Regist. City Hosp. Nottm. Prev: Regist. Rotat. Roy. Vict. Hosp. Edin.

MILLAR, Elizabeth Miller Wakefield & Pontefract Community Health NHS Trust, Aberford Centre, Fieldhead, Ouchthorpe Lane, Wakefield WF1 3SP Tel: 01924 327499 Fax: 01924 327459 Email: elizabeth.millar@wpek-tr.morthy.nhs.uk — MB ChB 1971 Ed.; BSc (Hons.) Ed. 1968; MPsy Leeds 1995; MRCPsych 1980; Dip. Soc. Med. Ed. 1974. (Ed.) Cons. Psychiat. Wakefield & Pontefract Community Health NHS Trust. Socs: BMA; Interest Mem. Yorks. Assn. Psychoanal. Psychother.; Reg. with UK Counc. for Psychother. Prev: Sen. Regist. (Psychiat.) Yorks. RHA.

MILLAR, Evangeline Joy Campbell Surgery, 10 Quarry Road, Dungannon BT70 1QR Tel: 01762 391360, 028 8772 2751 — MB BCh BAO 1991 Belf.; MRCGP 1996; DCH RCP Dub. 1995; DRCOG 1995. p/t GP.

MILLAR, Evelyn Ann 8 Crown Terrace, Glasgow G12 9EZ Tel: 0141 357 0685 — MB ChB 1988 Glas.; MD 1996; BSc (Hons.) Glas. 1985; MRCP (UK) 1991. (Glas.) Cons. Phys. Repiratory Med., S.ern Gen. Hosp., Glas. Socs: BMA; Eur. Respirat. Soc.; Brit. Thoracic Soc.

MILLAR, Ewan David Millar Pharmaceutical Consultancy, 48 Kettilstoun Mains, Linlithgow EH49 6SL Tel: 01506 846215 Fax: 01506 203435 Email: e.millar@docc.demon.co.uk — MB ChB 1978 Aberd.; MFPM RCP (UK) 1990. Cons. (Pharmaceut. Med.). Prev: Med. Dir. Scotia Pharmaceut. Ltd Guildford & Stirling; Sen. Med. Adviser Abbott Laboratories Berks. & Lederle Laboratories Hants.

MILLAR, Fergus Allan Intensive Therapy Unit, Aberdeen Royal Infirmary, Foresterhill, Aberdeen AB25 Tel: 01224 552970 Fax: 01224 840724 — MB ChB 1985 Glas.; FFA RCSI 1992. Cons. Anaesth. Ninewells Hosp. Dundee. Socs: Assn. Anaesth.; Anaesth. & Critical Care Soc.

***MILLAR, Gavin John** 3 Horndean Court, Bishopbriggs, Glasgow G64 3NB — MB ChB 1994 Glas.

MILLAR, Mr Geoffrey Thomas (retired) 28 Drummond Place, Edinburgh EH3 6PN Tel: 0131 557 3319 — MB ChB 1959 Ed.; FRCS Ed. 1966; FRCOphth 1993; DObst RCOG 1961. Prev: Tutor Univ. Leeds.

MILLAR, Gerard Patrick Whiteabbey Health Centre, 93-95 Doagh Road, Newtownabbey BT36 6TZ Tel: 01232 864341; 29 Waterloo Park, Antrim Road, Belfast BT15 5HU Tel: 01232 779416 — MB BCh BAO 1983 Belf.; MRCGP (Distinc.) 1987; DRCOG 1987; DGM RCP Lond. 1986; DCH RCPSI 1986. Hon. Treas. N. Local Med. Comm.; Mem. Gen. Med. Servs. Comm. N. Irel.; Dir. Medilife Ltd. Prev: Trainee GP Skegoneil Health Centre VTS; SHO Rotat. (Med.) Roy. Vict. Hosp. Belf.; Ho. Off. Whiteabbey Hosp. Newtownabbey.

MILLAR, Gillian (Scott) 27 Forest View, Kildrum, Cumbernauld, Glasgow G67 2DB Tel: 0141 722683; 7 Sandford Avenue, Belfast BT5 5NW Tel: 01232 672174 — MB ChB 1995 Dundee; DCH 1999; MRCGP 2000; DRCOG 1999; BMSc (Hons.) Dund 1992. (Univ. Dundee) GP Retainer, Bangor Health Centre, Bangor. Prev: SHO (Psychiat.) Mater Hosp. Belf.; SHO (O & G) Laganvalley Hosp., Lisburn Co Down, N. Irel.; SHO (A & E) Caboolture Hosp. Qu.sland, Austral.

MILLAR, Helen Louise Tel: 01382 423112 — MB ChB 1989 Dundee; MRCPsych 1994. Cons. Psychiat. Socs: RCPsych.

MILLAR, Henry Rankin Royal Cornhill Hospital, Cornhill Road, Aberdeen AB25 2ZH Tel: 01224 663131 — MB ChB 1972 Aberd.; BMedBiol Aberd. 1969; FRCPsych 1990, M 1976. (Aberd.) Cons. Psychiat. Roy. Cornhill Hosp. Aberd. Prev: Cons. Psychiat. S.. Gen. Hosp. Glas.; Lect. & Sen. Regist. (Psychiat.) Dundee.

MILLAR, Ian Stuart The Surgery, 30 Old Road West, Gravesend DA11 0LL Tel: 01474 352075/567799 Fax: 01474 333952; Little Gables, Wrotham Road, Meopham, Gravesend DA13 0HX Tel: 01474 813148 — MB BS 1977 Lond.; BSc Lond. 1974; DRCOG 1981.

MILLAR, James Alastair McCallum (retired) 1 Beechmount Park, Edinburgh EH12 5YT Tel: 0131 337 2345 — MB ChB 1947 Ed.

MILLAR, James Anderson Kelso Medical Group Practice, Health Centre, Inch Road, Kelso TD5 7JP Tel: 01573 224424 Fax: 01573 226388 — MB ChB 1990 Ed.; MRCGP 1995; DRCOG 1993. Socs: (Chairm.) Borders G Pass Users Gp.

MILLAR, James Gavin Burnett (retired) 2 Slipper Mill, Slipper Road, Emsworth PO10 8XD Tel: 01243 377071 — MB BChir 1965 Camb.; MSc (Nuclear Med.) Lond. 1972; FRCP Lond. 1980, M 1968; DObst RCOG 1966. Sen. Lect. (Endocrinol.) Univ. Soton.

MILLAR, James Thomas (retired) 19 Abercorn Terrace, Edinburgh EH15 2DE Tel: 0131 657 4527 — MB ChB 1940 Ed.; DTM & H 1960. Prev: Med. Off. Sierra Leone Developm. Co.

***MILLAR, Jane** 18 Matthew Drive, Peterhead AB42 2GA — MB ChB 1995 Aberd.

MILLAR, Janet Mary The Thickett, Gaer Hill, Frome BA11 5EY Tel: 01985 844319 — MB ChB 1977 Bristol; MFHom 1984; MRCGP 1981; DRCOG 1979. (Bristol) Assoc. GP Lindsay, Som. Prev: GP Hackney, Lond.

MILLAR, Jean Marion Bottom Barn, Manor Farm, E. Hagbourne, Didcot OX11 9ND Tel: 01235 813847 — MB ChB 1969 Glas.; FFA RCS Eng. 1979; DA Eng. 1975. Cons. (Anaesth.) Nuffield Dept. of Anaesth. Oxf. Prev: Sen. Regist. (Anaesth.) Roy. Berks. Hosp. Reading; Anaesth. Karolinska Hosp. Stockholm.

MILLAR, Jill Patricia Buckland Surgery, 1 Raleigh Road, Buckland, Newton Abbot TQ12 4HG Tel: 01626 332813 Fax: 01626 332814; 1 College Road, Newton Abbot TQ12 1EF Tel: 01626 333269 Email: jill@millshaw.demon.co.uk — MB BS 1977 Lond.; MA Camb. 1977; FRCGP 1995, MRCGP 1984; DCH RCP Lond. 1983; DRCOG 1981.

***MILLAR, Joanne Ruth** 35 Chapeltown Road, Antrim BT41 2LF — MB BCh BAO 1996 Belf.

MILLAR, John (retired) 14 Thurcaston Lane, Rothley, Leicester LE7 7LF Tel: 0116 230 2532 — MB ChB St. And. 1942; MRCPsych

MILLAR

1971; DPM RCPSI 1952. Prev: Cons. Psychiat. Carlton Hayes Hosp. NarBoro..

MILLAR, John David Craig (retired) 63 Ashgate Avenue, Chesterfield S40 1JD Tel: 01246 234029 — MB ChB 1946 Ed. Prev: Capt. RAMC.

MILLAR, John Grant (retired) 16 Reinette, Avalon Park, St Clement, Jersey JE2 6FJ Tel: 01534 739744 — BM BCh 1950 Oxf.; MA, BM BCh Oxon. 1950; DObst RCOG 1957. Prev: Ho. Surg. Middlx. Hosp.

MILLAR, John Harold Derek, MBE, Maj. (retired) Garden Cottage, 1A Low St., Winterton, Scunthorpe DN15 9RT Tel: 01724 732371 — MD Ed. 1939, MB ChB 1936; FRCP Ed. 1954, M 1946. Hon. Cons. Phys. Scunthorpe Gen. Hosp. Prev: DL Co. Lincs.

MILLAR, John Keith (retired) 1 Deramore Park, Belfast BT9 5JW — MB BCh BAO 1955 Belf.; FRCP Canada 1972; DR McGill 1962; LMCC 1958; FFR 1967; DMRD Eng. 1962; Cert. Radiol. RCPS Canada 1961; DObst RCOG 1957. Prev: Cons. Radiol. Craigavon & S. Down Hosps. N. Irel.

MILLAR, John Knox Waterside Health Centre, Glendermott Road, Londonderry BT47 6AU Tel: 01504 45191; 14 Dunhugh Park, Londonderry BT47 2NL Tel: 01504 311059 — MB BCh BAO 1973 Belf. Hosp. Pract. (Gernitourin. Med.) Altnagelvin Hosp. Lond.derry. Socs: Fell. Roy. Irish Soc. Med.

MILLAR, John Simpson Ferry Road Health Centre, Ferry Road, Dingwall IV15 9QS Tel: 01349 863034 Fax: 01349 862022; The Red House, Strathpeffer IV14 9DH — MB BS 1986 Lond.; BSc (Hons.) Glas. 1978; DPhil Oxf. 1981; MRCGP 1991. Prev: Trainee GP Raigmore Hosp. Inverness VTS.

MILLAR, John Stewart Department of Radiology, Wessex Neurological Centre, Southampton General Hospital, Tremona Road, Southampton SO16 6YD Tel: 02380 777222; Winton Cottage, Whiteshoot, Redlynch, Salisbury SP5 2PR Tel: 01725 513318 — BM BS 1984 Nottm.; MRCP (UK) 1987; FRCR 1991. Cons. Neuroradiol. Wessex Neurol. Centre Soton. Gen. Hosp. Socs: Mem. Brit. Soc of Neuroradiol.; Sec. UK NeuroInterven.al Gp. (1999). Prev: Sen. Regist. (Neuroradiol.) Nat. Hosp. Neurol. & Neurosurg. Qu. Sq. Lond.; Sen. Regist. (Radiol.) Roy. Lond. Hosp.; Sen. Regist. & Regist. (Radiol.) W. Midl.

MILLAR, John Stewart (retired) 24 Gartcows Drive, Falkirk FK1 5QQ Tel: 01324 21713 — MB ChB 1955 Glas.; FRCP Glas. 1971, M 1962; FRCP Ed. 1970, M 1962; FRFPS Glas. 1962. Prev: Cons. Phys. Falkirk & Dist. Roy. Infirm.

MILLAR, John Wilson Poole Hospital Trust, Poole Tel: 01202 665511 Fax: 01202 442997; Manor View House, Salisbury St, Cranbourne BH21 5PU Tel: 01725 517658 Fax: 01725 517712 — MB ChB 1971 Ed.; BSc (Hons.) Ed. 1968; FRCP Lond. 1991; FRCP Ed. 1985. Cons. Phys. (Gen. Med. & Respirat. Dis.) Poole Gen. Hosp. Socs: Eur. Respirat. Soc.; Brit. Thorac. Soc. Prev: Sen. Regist. (Respirat. Dis.) City Hosp. Edin.

MILLAR, Jonathan Michael Western Elms Surgery, 317 Oxford Road, Reading RG30 1AT Tel: 0118 959 0257 Fax: 0118 959 7950 — BM BCh 1990 Oxf.; MA Oxf. 1987; DCH RCP Lond. 1993; DRCOG 1993. (Oxf.) GP Princip. Reading. Prev: Trainee GP Newton Ct. Med. Centre Old Windsor VTS; Trainee GP St. Mary's & St. Chas. Hosp. Lond.; Ho. Off. (Gen. Med.) Heatherwood Hosp. Ascot.

***MILLAR, Jonathan Patrick** Ground Left, 260 Blackness Road, Dundee DD2 1RU — MB ChB 1995 Dundee.

MILLAR, Joyce Margaret 116 Harley Street, London W1N 1AG Tel: 020 7935 1331 — MB ChB 1951 Aberd.; MRO 1990; FLCOM 1955; MFHom Lond. 1960. Socs: BMA; Brit. Inst. Musculoskeletal Med.; BlMM. Prev: Clin. Asst. Roy. Lond. Homoeop. Hosp.; on Teach. Staff Lond. Coll. Osteop. Med.

MILLAR, Kenneth John 49 Newry Road, Armagh BT60 1ER — MB ChB 1986 Ed.

MILLAR, Kenneth Norman Ainslie, Col. Medical Staff Division, HQ Land Command, Weskin Barracks, Wilton, Salisbury SP2 0AG Tel: 01722 433770 Fax: 01722 433169; 3 Highmount, Shady Bower, Salisbury SP1 2RE Tel: 01722 329425 — MB ChB 1971 Glas. Dep. Asst. Chief of Staff (Med.) HQ Land Command. Prev: Ad. Med. Ops. & Plans Min. of Defence Comd. HQ AMS TA; Comm. Med. 3rd Armd. Div.; Staff Off. Army Med. Directorate Min. of Defence.

MILLAR, Kevin Neil Cosgrove Flat 2, 46 Wimpole St., London W1M 7DG — MB ChB 1979 Cape Town.

MILLAR, Lenox Jardine Health Centre, Newgate Street, Worksop S80 1HP Tel: 01909 500266 Fax: 01909 478014; Sherwood House, Sparken Hill, Worksop S80 1AX Tel: 01909 476430 — MB BS 1971 Lond.; MRCS Eng. LRCP Lond. 1971; DRCOG 1973. (St. Barts. Hosp. Lond.) Med. Off. Worksop Coll.; Trainer (Gen. Pract.) VTS. Socs: BMA.

***MILLAR, Louise** 34 Lockharton Avenue, Edinburgh EH14 1AZ — MB ChB 1998 Ed.; MB ChB Ed 1998.

MILLAR, Martin Alexander 29 Akenside Terrace, Newcastle upon Tyne NE2 1TN — MB ChB 1991 Glas.

MILLAR, Mary Bertram (retired) 320 Hill Lane, Southampton SO15 7NW Tel: 023 8077 1709 — MB ChB 1949 Ed. Supervisor for Counselling Dept. of Psychother. Prev: Assoc. Specialist (Psychogeriat. & Psychother.) Moorgreen Hosp. Soton.

MILLAR, Mary Young Inglis (retired) 2 Beechmount Park, Edinburgh EH12 5YT Tel: 0131 313 4936 — MB ChB 1945 Ed.

MILLAR, Michael Ronald Department of Microbiology, Great Ormond St., London WC1N 3JH Tel: 020 7405 9200 Email: mike.millar@gosh-tr.nthames.nhs.uk — MD 1986 Bristol; MB ChB 1976; MRCPath 1986. Cons., Gt. Ormond St. Trust; Hon. Sen. Lect. Inst. Child Health. Prev: Sen. Lect. (Microbiological Path.) Univ. of Bristol; Cons. Microbiological Communication Dis. Control Winchester HA; Sen. Lect. (Hon. Cons.) (Med. MicroBiol.) Univ. of Leeds.

MILLAR, Pauline Mary (retired) 301 Wroxham Road, Sprowston, Norwich NR7 8RN Tel: 01603 412708 — MB BS 1947 Lond.; DCH Eng. 1950. Prev: Paediat. Regist. Qu. Eliz. Hosp. Childr. Hackney Rd., United Bristol.

MILLAR, Mr Robert 17 Ballymenoch Park, Holywood BT18 0LP Tel: 01232 424340 — MB BCh BAO 1967 Belf.; BSc (Hons.) Belf. 1964, MB BCh BAO 1967; FRCS Ed. 1971. (Belf.) Cons. Plastic Surg. Roy. Vict. Hosp. Belf. Socs: Brit. Assn. Plastic Surg. Prev: Sen. Regist. (Plastic Surg.) Ulster Hosp. Dondonald; Res. Ho. Off. & SHO (Surg.) Roy. Vict. Hosp. Belf.; Sen. Regist. (Gen. Surg.) N. Irel. Hosps. Auth.

MILLAR, Sam Porter (retired) 41 Kensington Park, Bangor BT20 3RF Tel: 01247 454626 — MRCS Eng. LRCP Lond. 1940. Prev: GP Newtownards.

MILLAR, Samuel 7 McClaren Grove, Glasgow G74 4SR — MB ChB 1978 Glas.

MILLAR, Sheena Agnes Dept. of Anaesthetics, Royal Infirmary of Edinburgh, 1 Lauriston Place, Edinburgh EH3 9YW Tel: 0131 536 1000; 138/5 Nicolson Street, Edinburgh EH8 9EH Tel: 0131 667 0974 Email: eoas32@holyrood.ed.ac.uk — MB ChB 1990 Ed.; FRCA 1997. (Edin.) Specialist Regist. (Anaesth.) Roy. Infirm. Edin. Socs: Train. Assn. Anaesth. & Scott. Soc. Anaesth.; Ed. & E. Scot. Soc. Anaesth.

MILLAR, Simon 24 Summervale Avenue, Annan DG12 6EP — MB ChB 1993 Ed.

MILLAR, Stephen Westgarth Queen's Hospital, Belvedere Road, Burton-on-Trent DE13 0RB Tel: 01283 566333 Fax: 01283 593084; Caernarvon House, Hall Grounds, Rolleston-on-Dove, Burton-on-Trent DE13 9BS Tel: 01283 813921 — MB BS 1975 Lond.; BSc Lond. 1974; FFA RCS Eng. 1980; DA Eng. 1978. (Lond. Hosp.) Cons. Anaesth. Burton Hosps. NHS Trust; Assoc. Med. Director (Med. Staffing) Burton Hosp.s NHS Trust Burton upon Trent. Socs: BMA (Hon. Sec.Burton & Dist. Div. Chairm. W. Midl.s Regional Cons.s and Specialists Comm., Chairm. W. Midl.s Regional Counc., Dep. Chairm. Centr. Cons.s and Specialists Comm. Anaesthetics Sub-Comm.; Assn. Anaesth. GB & Irel.; Midl. Soc. Anaesth. (Counc. Mem.). Prev: Sen. Regist. (Anaesth.) W.m. Hosp., St. Geo. Hosp. Lond. & Qu. Mary's Hosp. Roehampton.

MILLAR, Stuart William Sinclair, Surg. Lt. RN RNH Haslar, Alverstoke, Gosport PO12 2AA Tel: 01705 584255; 35 Monckton Road, Alverstoke, Gosport PO12 2BG Tel: 01705 580410 — MB BS 1990 Lond. SHO (Gen. Med.) RNH Haslar, Gosport. Prev: Med. Off. HMS York RN.

MILLAR, Vivien Ann (retired) — MB BS 1971 Lond.; MRCS Eng. LRCP Lond. 1971; MRCPsych 1977; DPM Eng. 1976; DObst RCOG 1973. Prev: Sen. Regist. (Psychiat.) Liverp. Roy. Infirm.

MILLAR, William James Raymond 11 Bryansburn Road, Bangor BT20 3RZ — MB BCh BAO 1991 Belf.; MB BCh Belf. 1991.

MILLAR, William Semple, Brigadier late RAMC Retd. 20 Valroy Close, Camberley GU15 3TL Tel: 01276 62449 — LRCP LRCS Ed.

MILLAR CRAIG

LRFPS Glas. 1945; FFCM 1976, M 1972; DTM & H Eng. 1954, DIH 1954; DPH Lond. 1954. Pres. Standing Med. Bd. Aldershot. Prev: Hon. Phys. to HM the Qu.; Surg. Ho. Off. Vict. Infirm. Glas.

MILLAR CRAIG, Janet Alexis Lister House Surgery, Lister House, 53 Harrington Street, Pear Tree, Derby DE23 8PF Tel: 01332 271212 Fax: 01332 271939; Lister House, Harrington St, Derby DE23 8PE — MRCS Eng. LRCP Lond. 1977; BSc (Hons.) Lond. 1974, MB BS 1977; FRCP Glas. 1994; MRCP (UK) 1980; MRCGP 1985. (St. Bart.) Prev: SHO (Med.) N.wick Pk. Hosp. Harrow & Hammersmith Hosp. Lond.; Ho. Surg. St. Bart. Hosp. Lond.

MILLAR-CRAIG, Michael Walker The Laurels, 28 Moorway Lane, Littleover, Derby DE23 7FR Tel: 01332 767963 — MRCS Eng. LRCP Lond. 1971; MD Lond. 1980, MB BS (Hons.) 1971; FRCP Lond. 1994; FRCP Glas. 1990; MRCP (UK) 1975. (St. Bart.) Cons. Phys. & Cardiol. Derbysh. Roy. Infirm. Derby & Hon. Clin. Teach Nottm. Univ.; Brit. Heart Foundat. Fell.sh. Hallstrom Inst. Cardiol. Roy. P. Alfred Hosp. Sydney 1982. Socs: Brit. Cardiac Soc. & Med. Research Soc. Prev: Sen. Regist. (Cardiol.) Roy. Infirm. Glas.; Regist. (Gen. Med. & Cardiol.) N.wick Pk. Hosp. Harrow; SHO (Gen. Med.) Roy. Free Hosp. Lond.

MILLAR-DANKS, Sheila Prospect House, Eyke Road, Bromeswell, Woodbridge IP12 2PW — MB BS 1941 Durh.; FFA RCS Eng. 1969.

MILLAR-JONES, David John 5 Jonquil Close, Willowbrook Vill., St Mellons, Cardiff CF3 0JE — MB BCh 1988 Wales.

MILLAR-JONES, Lynne Royal Glamorgan Hospital, Ynysmaerdy, Llantrisant, Pontyclun CF72 8XR Tel: 01443 443535 — MB BCh 1988 Wales; BSc (Hons.) 1985; MRCP (UK) 1992. (University of Wales College of Medicine) Cons. (Paediat.) Dept. of Child Health Roy. Glam. Hosp. Mid Glam.

***MILLARD, Caroline Dagmar** 26 Orchard Way, Flitwick, Bedford MK45 1LF — MB BS 1998 Newc.; MB BS Newc 1998.

***MILLARD, Christopher Leonard** The Manor House, 2 Middle St., Beeston, Nottingham NG9 1FX — MB ChB 1998 Liverp.; MB ChB Liverp 1998.

MILLARD, David Walter 78 Cumnor Hill, Oxford OX2 9HU Tel: 01865 862224 — MB ChB Birm. 1955; MD Birm. 1995; MA Oxf. 1979; FRCPsych 1981, M 1971; DPM Eng. 1962. Emerit. Fell Green Coll. Prev: Cons. Old Age Psychiat. Oxf.; Lect. (Applied Social Studies) Univ. Oxf.; Cons. Psychiat. Rubery Hill Hosp.

MILLARD, Elizabeth Mary Barnard Medical Centre, 43 Granville Road, Sidcup DA14 4TA Tel: 020 8302 7721 Fax: 020 8309 6579 — MB BS 1976 Lond.; MRCS Eng. LRCP Lond. 1976; MRCGP 1983; Cert. JCC Lond. 1979; DRCOG 1978. (Char. Cross)

MILLARD, Ernest Russell Wick Medical Centre, Martha Terrace, Wick KW1 5EL Tel: 01955 602595 Fax: 01955 602434 — MB ChB 1981 Dundee; BSc 1975 (Hons.) Dundee; MRCGP 1985; Dip. IMC RCS Ed. 1989; DRCOG 1984. Socs: Brit. Soc. Med. & Dent. Hypn. Prev: Med. Off. Turks & Caicos I. BWI; Trainee GP VTS Borders HB; Ho. Phys. Ninewells Hosp. Dundee.

MILLARD, Mr Fraser Charles X-Ray Department, Warwick Hospital, Lakin Road, Warwick CV34 5BW Tel: 01926 495321 — MB BS 1982 Lond.; MA Camb. 1983, BA 1979; FRCS Eng. 1987; FRCS Ed. 1986; FRCR 1990. (King's Coll. Hosp.) p/t Cons. Diagn. Radiol. Warwick Hosp. Prev: Sen. Regist. (Diagn. Radiol.) Roy. Hallamsh. Hosp.; Regist. Rotat. (Surg.) N.ampton Gen. Hosp.; SHO (Surg. & A & E) St. Geo. Hosp. Lond.

MILLARD, Frederick John Clayton 4 Vineyard Hill Road, London SW19 7JH Tel: 0208 946 9693 Fax: 0208 946 9693 — MB BS 1956 Lond.; MD Lond. 1965; FRCP Lond. 1974; MRCP (UK) 1961; MRCS Eng. LRCP Lond. 1956. Socs: Thoracic Soc. Prev: Med. Specialist Jane Furse Memor. Hosp., S. Afr.; Cons. Phys. Roy. Nat. Orthop. Hosp. & St. Geo. Hosp. Lond.; Sen. Lect. St. Geo. Hosp. Med. Sch. Lond.

MILLARD, Frederick William, OBE (retired) 33A Carisbrooke Road, Hucclecote, Gloucester GL3 3QR Tel: 01452 616879 — MB ChB 1947 Birm.; MRCS Eng. LRCP Lond. 1947; FRCGP 1976, M 1960. Prev: Assoc. Adviser (Gen. Pract.) Univ. Bristol.

***MILLARD, Jonathan** 26 Welton Grove, Leeds LS6 1ES — MB ChB 1996 Leeds.

MILLARD, Kathryn Herefordshire Health Authority, Victoria House, Eign St., Hereford HR4 0AN — MB BS 1983; MFPHM RCP (UK) 1992; DCH RCP Lond. 1987; MB BS 1983; BSc 1980 Lond. (Univ. Coll. Hosp.) p/t Cons. (Pub. Health Med.) Heref. HA; Vis. Sen. Clin. Lect., Pub. Health, Sch. of PostGrad. Med. Educat., Univ. of

Warwick. Prev: Sen. Regist. (Pub. Health Med.) W. Midl. RHA.; Sen. Regist. & Regist. (Pub. Health Med.) Trent RHA; SHO Rotat. (Path.) Lewisham Hosp. Lond.

MILLARD, Leslie Graham Dermatology Department, Queens Medical Centre, Nottingham NG7 2UH Tel: 0115 970 9734 Fax: 0115 970 9752 — MB ChB Sheff. 1968; MD Sheff. 1980; FRCP Lond. 1986; FRCP Ed. 1986; MRCP (UK) 1971. (Sheff.) Cons. Dermat. Qu. Med. Centre Nottm.; Hon. Sen. Lect. Univ. Nottm. Prev: Tutor (Dermat.) Univ. Leeds.

MILLARD, Mrs Marie-Louise Greenfields, East St., Hambledon, Waterlooville PO7 4RX Tel: 01705 632485 — MB BS 1990 Lond.; MRCP (UK) 1996. (St. Mary's Hosp.) Regist. (Paediat.) St. Mary's Hosp. Portsmouth.

MILLARD, Nicholas Richard Humber Avenue Road Surgery, 28A Avenue Road, Malvern WR14 3BG Tel: 01684 561333 Fax: 01684 893664 — MB BS 1974 Lond.; DCH Eng. 1977.

MILLARD, Paul Malcolm Ronald St Marys Road Surgery, St. Marys Road, Newbury RG14 1EQ Tel: 01635 31444 Fax: 01635 551316; 74 Enborne Road, Newbury RG14 6AJ — MB BS 1972 Lond.; BSc (Hons.) Lond. 1967; MRCS Eng. LRCP Lond. 1972; FRCGP 1993, M 1978; DRCOG 1978. (St. Bart.) Hosp. Pract. (Continuing Care) Newbury; Trainer Newbury VTS. Socs: Palliat. Med. Assn. Prev: Surg. Lt.-Cdr. RN; Med. Off. HMS Endurance (Antarctic); Ho. Surg. St. Bart. Hosp. Lond.

MILLARD, Paul William Child and Adolescent Mental Health Service, Newtown Centre, Nursery Road, Huntingdon PE29 3RJ Tel: 01480 415280 Fax: 01480 415393 Email: paul.millard@hbhc-tr.anglox.nhs.uk — MB BS 1988 Lond.; MRCPsych 1993. (University College London) Cons. (Child & Adolesc. Psychiat.) Hinchingbrooke Health Care NHS Trust Huntingdon. Prev: Sen. Regist. Rotat. (Child & Adolesc. Psychiat.) Brookside Unit Camb.; Regist. Rotat. (Psychiat.) Roy. Lond. Hosp.

MILLARD, Peter Henry Department of Geriatric Medicine, St. George's Hospital Medical School, Cranmer Terrace, Tooting, London SW17 Tel: 020 8767 5536 Email: p.millard@sghms.ac.uk; 12 Cornwall Road, Cheam, Surrey, Sutton SM2 6DR Tel: 020 8642 0040 — MRCS Eng. LRCP Lond. 1960; PhD Lond. 1993, MD 1989, MB BS (Hons.) 1960; FRCP Lond. 1976, M 1966. (Univ. Coll. Hosp.) Eleanor Peel Prof. Geriat. Med. St. Geo. Hosp. Med. Sch. Lond. Socs: Brit. Geriat. Soc. & Soc. Research on Ageing.; Past Pres. Brit. Geriat. Soc.; Past Pres. Sect. of Geriat. & Gerontol. Roy. Soc. Med. Prev: Sen. Regist. Geriat. Univ. Coll. Hosp. Lond.; Cons. Phys. (Geriat.) St. Geo. Hosp. Tooting; Sen. Lect. St. Geo. Hosp. Med. Sch. Lond.

MILLARD, Peter Richard The Manor House, Mill Lane, Iffley, Oxford OX4 4EJ — MRCS Eng. LRCP Lond. 1963; MD Lond. 1973, MB BS 1963; FRCPath 1987, M 1974; DObst RCOG 1966. (St. Geo.) Cons. Histopath. John Radcliffe Hosp. Oxf. Socs: Path. Soc., Assn. Clin. Pathol. & Pancreatic Soc. GB & Irel. Prev: Ho. Off. St. Geo. Hosp. Lond.; Demonst. & Lect. (Path.) Univ. Camb.; Fell. (Immunopath.) Univ. Pittsburgh, USA.

MILLARD, Rebecca Claire The Croft, Tipping's Hill, Hunt End, Redditch B97 5QJ — MB ChB 1986 Birm.; MRCGP 1990. Prev: Trainee GP/SHO N. Warks. VTS.

***MILLARD, Richard Steven** 10d Dalmeny Road, London N7 0HH — MB BS 1996 Lond.

MILLARD, Richard Vivian Denmead Health Centre, Hambledon Road, Denmead, Waterlooville PO7 6NR Tel: 023 9225 7112 Fax: 023 9225 7113 — MB BS 1987 Lond.; MRCGP 1991. (St. Mary's Hosp. Lond.)

MILLARD, Rosemary Evelyn (retired) 4 Vineyard Hill Road, Wimbledon, London SW19 7JH Tel: 020 8946 9693 — BM BCh 1956 Oxf.; DM Oxf. 1966, BM BCh 1956. Lect. (Haemat.) St. Geo. Hosp. Med. Sch.

MILLARD, Stephen Paul Upwell Health Centre, Townley Close, Upwell, Wisbech PE14 9BT Tel: 01945 773671 Fax: 01945 773152; Lee House, Town St, Upwell, Wisbech PE14 9DF — MB ChB 1978 Leeds; MRCGP 1982; DRCOG 1981; DCH RCPS Glas. 1981.

MILLARD, Steven William Plympton Health Centre, Mudge Way, Plymouth PL7 1AD Tel: 01752 348884 Fax: 01752 345443 Email: steve.millard@gp-83133.nhs.uk; Fax: 01752 894835 Email: bearmillard@btinternet.com — MB BS 1974 Lond.; MRCS Eng. LRCP Lond. 1974; DRCOG 1978. (Roy. Free) Socs: Plymouth Med.

Soc. Prev: Trainee GP Plymouth VTS; SHO Plymouth Gen. Hosp. (Freedom Fields); Ho. Off. Roy. Free Hosp. Hampstead.

MILLARD, Thomas Paul Dept. of Photobiology, St. Thomas's Hospital, London SE1 7EH Tel: 020 7928 9292 Fax: 020 7928 1650 Email: thomas.millard@kcl.ac.uk; 57 Westfield Road, Benson OX10 6NT — MB BS 1994 Lond.; PhD (Lond.) 2002; MRCP. (St. Bart's Hosp.) Spec. Reg. (Dermatol.) Oxf. Deanery; Clin. Research Fell., St. John's Inst. of Dermat.). Socs: Fell. St. John's Dermat. Soc.; Mem. Brit. Assn. Dermat.

MILLARES MARTIN, Pablo The Surgery, 58 Butt Lane, Leeds LS12 5AZ — LMS 1991 La Laguna. GP Leeds.

MILLEDGE, David Thomas Hazelwood, 27 Parkfield Road, Coleshill, Birmingham B46 3LD Tel: 01675 463165 Fax: 01675 466253 — MB ChB 1967 Birm.; MRCGP 1973; DObst RCOG 1969.

MILLEDGE, James Sibree (retired) 137 Highfield Way, Chorleywood, Rickmansworth WD3 7PL Tel: 01923 774010 Fax: 01923 496656 Email: jmilledge@cix.compulink.co.uk — MB ChB 1954 Birm.; MD Birm. 1968; FRCP Lond. 1982; FRCP Ed. 1969, M 1960. Prev; Cons. Phys. & Staff Mem. Med. Research Counc. N.wick Pk. Hosp. Harrow.

MILLEDGE, John Thomas 119 Uxbridge Road, Rickmansworth WD3 7DN Tel: 01923 775588 — MB ChB 1990 Sheff.

MILLEN, James Simon 11 Peterborough Road, Upper Flat, London SW6 3BT — MB BS 1994 Lond.

MILLEN, Nicola Jane Doctors Surgery, 2 Padnell Road, Waterlooville PO8 8DZ Tel: 023 9226 3138 Fax: 023 9261 8100 — MB ChB 1985 Bristol; MRCGP 1990; DCH RCP Lond. 1988. Trainee GP Overton. Prev: SHO (O & G) Roy. United. Hosp. Bath; SHO (Neonat. & Gen. Paediat.) Roy. Berks. Hosp. Reading; SHO (Med. Rotat.) Gloucester HA.

MILLEN, Samuel Archibald Moira, 3 Clooney Park E., Londonderry BT47 6JZ Tel: 01504 43381 — MB BCh BAO 1949 Belf. (Qu. Univ. Belf.) Staff Med. Off. Lond.derry Chest Hosp. Prev: Ho. Surg. City & Co. Hosp. Lond.derry.

MILLER, Aileen Joan Barnsley Health Authority, 49/51 Gawber Road, Barnsley S75 2PY Tel: 01226 777054 Fax: 01226 733978 Email: joan.miller@barnsley_ha.nhs.uk; 36 Woodbank Crescent, Meersbrook, Sheffield S8 9EF Tel: 0114 249 8613 Email: joan.miller@amserve.net — MB ChB 1979 Bristol; MPH Nottm. 1995; DTM & H RCP Lond. 1981; MFPHM 1997. Cons. Pub. Hlth Barnsley Hlth. Auth. Barnsley.

MILLER, Alan McLean Somerton House Surgery, 79A North Road, Midsomer Norton, Bath BA3 2QE Tel: 01761 412141 Fax: 01761 410944; Ivy Cottage, Clapton, Bath BA3 4EB Tel: 01761 416854 — MB ChB 1977 Glas.; DRCOG 1979.

MILLER, Alastair Robert Ogilvie Department of Medicine, Kidderminster Hospital, Bewdley Road, Kidderminster DY11 6RJ Tel: 01562 823424 Fax: 01562 513016 Email: alastair.miller@khct.thenhs.com; Callow Cottage, Sneads Green, Droitwich WR9 0PZ Tel: 01299 851570 Email: alandang.miller@btinternet.com — MB BChir 1978 Camb.; MB Camb. 1978, BChir 1977; MA Camb. 1978; FRCP Lond. 1994; FRCP Ed. 1994; MRCP (UK) 1982; MRCS Eng. LRCP Lond. 1977; DTM & H RCP Lond. 1987. (Camb. & Westm.) Cons. Phys. (Gen. Med. & Infec. Dis.) Worcs. Acute Hosp.s Trust; Hon. Sen. Lect. Birm. Univ. Med. Sch.; Lead Clinician Worcs. HIV Clinic; Clin. Director of Med. Worcs. Socs: Fell. Roy. Soc. Trop. Med. & Hyg.; Brit. Soc. Antimicrob. Chemother.; Brit. Infec. Soc. (Counc. Mem.). Prev: Prof. Med. RN Hosp. Haslar; Cons. Phys. RN Hosp. Plymouth; Hon. Sen. Regist. (Comm. Dis.) St. Geo. Hosp. Med. Sch. Lond.

MILLER, Alexandra Scott Cunningham Wedderburn House, Edward St., Dundee DD1 5NS Tel: 01382 346055; A'chomaraich, 8 South Kingennie Steadings, Kingennie, By Broughty Ferry DO5 3PA — MB ChB 1985 Dundee; MRCGP 1989. (Univ. Dundee & Ninewells Hosp. Med. Sch.) p/t Clin. Asst. (Adult Psychiat.) Dundee Healthcare Trust. Socs: BMA. Prev: Clin. Asst. (Genito-Urin. Med.) Dundee Roy. Infirm.; Clin. Asst. (Ment. Handicap) Birch Ave. Day Hosp. Scone; Regist. (Psychiat.) Roy. Dundee Liff Hosp.

MILLER, Alison Jane Castle Place Surgery, 9 Park Hill, Tiverton EX16 6RR Tel: 01884 252333 Fax: 01884 252152; The Old Rectory, Cadeleigh, Tiverton EX16 8HW — MB ChB 1984 Birm.; DRCOG 1989. GP Devon.

MILLER, Alistair Hamish (retired) 9 Melfort Avenue, Clydebank G81 2HX Tel: 0141 952 4218 — MB ChB 1941 Glas. Prev: Jun. Res. Med. Off. Ballochmyle Hosp. Mauchline, Ayrsh.

MILLER, Alistair Robert 3 Gladstone Terrace, Lerwick ZE1 0EG — MB ChB 1985 Ed.

MILLER, Allan John 1 Weston Park, Weston Green, Thames Ditton KT7 0HW Tel: 020 8224 6098 — MB BS 1961 Lond.; FRCP Lond. 1993; MRCP Lond. 1968; FFPM RCP (UK) 1994; FRSH 1991. (St. Bart.) Head Clin. Research Roche Products Ltd. Welwyn Gdn. City. Socs: Fell. Roy. Soc. Med. Prev: Med. Dir. Napp Laborat. Ltd.; Head Clin. Research Roche Products Ltd.

MILLER, Andrea Lesley Town Farm Cottage, Shirwell, Barnstaple EX31 4JU Tel: 01271 850376 — MB ChB 1969 Birm.; DA Eng. 1972. (Birm.) Occupat. Health Phys. Marks & Spencer, Barnstaple. Socs: Fac. Anaesth. Prev: Regist. (Med. & Paediat.) Palmerston N. Hosp. NZ; SHO (Anaesth.) N. Devon Infirm. Barnstaple; Ho. Phys. E. Birm. Hosp.

MILLER, Andrew Christian Chest Clinic, Mayday University Hospital, London Road, Croydon CR7 7YE Tel: 020 8401 3136 Fax: 020 8401 3460 Email: andrew.miller@mayday.nhs.uk — BM BCh 1973 Oxf.; DPhil. Oxf. 1972, MA, DM 1981; FRCP Lond. 1991; FCCP (USA) 1997. (Oxf.) Cons. Phys. (Respirat. Med.) Mayday Hosp. Croydon. Socs: Dep. Chairm., Educat. & Train. Comm., Brit. Thoracic Soc.; Chairm., Pulm. Embolism Working Party, Brit. Thoracic.

MILLER, Andrew Graeme Blakely (retired) 12 Kenmure Avenue, Bishopsbriggs, Glasgow G64 2RG Tel: 0141 772 1611 — MB ChB 1941 Glas. JP.; Exam. Med. Off. DHSS. Prev: Capt. RAMC.

MILLER, Mr Andrew Stephen Flat 5, 29 Knowsley Road, Cressington Park, Liverpool L19 0PF — MB ChB 1989 Liverp.; FRCS Ed. 1993.

MILLER, Angela Margaret 162 Wentworth Road, Birmingham B17 9BX — MB ChB 1988 Birm.; MRCGP 1994.

MILLER, Angela Mary Hallinan (retired) — MB BS Lond. 1961; FFA RCS Eng. 1968; T(Anaesth.) 1991; DObst RCOG 1963. Prev: Cons. Anaesth. S. Manch. Univ. Hosps. NHS Trust.

***MILLER, Anna Clare** 36 Brookland Hill, London NW11 6DX Tel: 020 8201 9847 — MB BS 1994 Lond.; DCH RCP Lond. 1996; DFFP 1999.

MILLER, Anna Susan 15 Castlemilk Dr, Glasgow G45 9TL — MB ChB 1997 Dundee; BSMC Dund 1994; DCH Roy Coll Paed & Child Health, 1999. SHO (A&E) A&e Dyburn Hosp., Duham. Socs: BMA Mem.

MILLER, Anne 9 Summerfield Close, Emmbrook, Wokingham RG41 1PH — MB ChB 1990 Birm.; MRCGP 1996; DRCOG 1992. (Birm.)

MILLER, Anne Ferriby Department of Community Child Health, Ayrshire Central Hospital, Irvine Tel: 01294 274191; High Smithstown, Kilwinning KA13 6PG Tel: 01294 552756 Email: kjetscom.cuk@pipex.uk — MB BCh BAO 1973 Dub. Clin. Med. Off. Ayrsh. & Arran NHS Community Trust.

MILLER, Anne Louise Catherine 133 Coleraine Road, Blackheath, London SE3 7NT — MB BS 1978 Lond.; BSc Lond. 1975, MB BS 1978; MRCP (UK) 1980; MRCPath 1985. Cons. Haemat. St. Peter's Hosp. Chertsey. Prev: Sen. Regist. & Hon. Regist. Dept. Haemat. St. Bart. Hosp. Lond.

MILLER, Anthony Alexander McCutcheon, MBE (retired) The Lodge, Snainton, Scarborough Tel: 01723 85420 — MB BCh BAO 1942 Belf.; FFA RCS Eng. 1954; DA Eng. 1948. Prev: Cons. Anaesth. ScarBoro. Health Dist.

MILLER, Anthony Richard Priory Surgery, 26 High Street, Holywood BT18 9AD Tel: 028 9042 6991 Fax: 028 9042 3643 — MB BCh BAO 1983 Belf.; MRCGP 1989; DRCOG 1991.

MILLER, Antonia 23 Eversholt Court, 44 Lyonsdown Road, New Barnet, Barnet EN5 2AB Tel: 020 8441 7986 — LMS 1982 Granada.

MILLER, Antony Mark The Petersgate Medical Centre, 99 Amersall Road, Scawthorpe, Doncaster DN5 9PQ Tel: 01302 390490 — MB ChB 1984 Glas. Prev: Regist. (A & E) Roy. Alexandra Hosp. Paisley; SHO (O & G) Stobhill Gen. Hosp.; SHO (Paediat. Med.) Yorkhill Hosp.

MILLER, Arthur Leslie 25 Bradstock Road, Stoneleigh, Epsom KT17 2LD Tel: 020 8393 5310 — MD Lond. 1973, MB BS 1950; FRCP Lond. 1980, M 1965; FRCPath 1968, M 1964. (Middlx.) Socs: Fell. Roy. Soc. Med.; Emerit. Mem. Assn. Clin. Biochem. Prev:

MILLER

Emerit. Reader in Chem. Path. Univ. Coll. Middlx. Sch. Med. & Hon. Cons. Chem. Path. UCLH Trust; Civil Cons. RAF.

MILLER, Mr Ashley John The North Downs Hospital, 46 Tupwood Lane, Caterham CR3 6DP Tel: 01883 78981; Little Court, Badgers Lane, Warlingham CR6 9JX Tel: 01883 624148 — MB BS 1963 Lond.; FRCS Ed. 1969; MRCS Eng. LRCP Lond. 1963. (St. Bart.) Cons. Orthop. Surg. Croydon AHA. Socs: BOA; Eur. Hip Soc.; SICOT. Prev: Regist. Rotat. (Surg.) Wessex RHB; Regist. (Orthop.) Treloar Hosp. Alton & Portsmouth Roy. Infirm.; Sen. Regist. (Orthop.) St. Mary's Hosp. Padd.

MILLER, Barry Mark 4 Baroncroft Road, Liverpool L25 6EH — MB ChB 1990 Manch.

***MILLER, Barry Peter** 8 Haling Park Gardens, South Croydon CR2 6NP — MB BS 1998 Lond.; MB BS Lond 1998.

MILLER, Benjamin James 51 Kennedy Road, Bicester OX26 2BE Tel: 01869 252250 Email: millerbenj@hotmail.com — MB ChB 1996 Brim.; MRCP 2001 UK; BSc 1993 (Hons). (Birm.Uk) Regist. (Radiol.) Univ. Hosp. Trust Biham. Prev: SHO (Med) Worthing Hosp., Sussex; SHO (Med) Univ. Hosp. NHSTrust. Birm.

MILLER, Caroline Scott X-Ray Department, c/o West Middlesex, University Hospital NHS Trust, Twickenham Road, Isleworth TW7 6AF — MB ChB 1978 Glas.; FRCR 1984; T(R) (CR) 1991; DMRD 1983; DRCOG 1980. Cons. Diagn. Radiol. W. Middlx. Univ. Hosp. Isleworth. Prev: Sen. Regist. (Diag. Radiol.) Guy's Hosp. Lond.

MILLER, Catherine Jane Flat 4, 9 Brighton Street, Edinburgh EH1 1HD — MB ChB 1993 Ed.

MILLER, Christine Lavender 23 Downshire Hill, London NW3 1NT — BM BCh 1948 Oxf.; MRCS Eng. LRCP Lond. 1947; MFCM 1986. (Oxf. & W. Lond.) Sen. Epidemiologist CDSE (Immunisation & Research) Pub. Health Laborat Serv. Lond. Prev: Med. Off. Tuberc. Research Unit Med. Research Counc. Lond.

MILLER, Claire Louise 29 Kingston Avenue, Stafford ST16 3RX — MB BS 1998 Lond.; MB BS Lond 1998; BSc Lond 1995. Surgic. Ho. Off. Roy. Sussex Co. Hosp. Brighton. Prev: Med. Ho. Off. Guys Hosp. Lond.

MILLER, Clarence Montague 6 Downham Close, Liverpool L25 4TY — MRCS Eng. LRCP Lond. 1938; MD Lond. 1943, MB BS (Hons.) 1938; FRCP Lond. 1969, M 1942. (Leeds) Clin. Lect. (Med.) Liverp. Univ. Socs: BMA. & Liverp. Med. Inst. Prev: Cons. Phys. Roy. Liverp. Hosp. & P.s Pk. Hosp.; Sen. Ho. Phys. Roy. Infirm. Bradford; Squadron Ldr. R.A.F.V.R. Med. Br.

MILLER, Clive Henry Central Surgery, Bell St., Sawbridgeworth CM21 9AQ — MB BS 1963 Lond.; MRCS Eng. LRCP Lond. 1963; DObst RCOG 1966. (St. Mary's) Prev: Med. Regist. St. Margt.'s Hosp. Epping; Ho. Surg. & Ho. Phys. Chelmsford & Essex Hosp.; SHO (Paediat.) City Gen. Hosp. Stoke-on-Trent.

MILLER, Colin David Stobhill Hospital, Balorneck Road, Glasgow G21 3UW; 15 Hamilton Drive, Glasgow G12 8DN — MB ChB 1976 Glas.; FFA RCS Eng. 1983. Cons. Anaesth. Stobhill Gen. Hosp. Glas. Prev: Sen. Regist. W.. Infirm. Glas.; Sen. Med. Off. Grantham Hosp., Hong Kong; Regist. Glas. Roy. Infirm.

MILLER, Colin George (retired) 15 Heathfield Park, Grappenhall, Warrington WA4 2LA Tel: 01925 66507 — MB BS Lond. 1956; FRCP Lond. 1974, M 1962; FRCP Ed. 1974, M 1962; FRCPCH 1997; DCH Eng. 1961. Clin. Lect. (Paediat.) Univ. Liverp. Prev: Cons. Paediat. Warrington Gen. Hosp.

MILLER, Dan Gordon (retired) 6 St Mary's Close, Appleton, Warrington WA4 5DD — MB BChir 1947 Camb.; BA Camb. 1944, MB BChir 1947; MRCPath 1963. Cons. Path. Warrington Dist. Gen. Hosp. Prev: Jun. Specialist Path. RAMC.

MILLER, Daniel Barry (retired) 1 Dale Close, Mears Ashby, Northampton NN6 0EH Tel: 01604 810906 — MB ChB 1951 Glas. Prev: Hosp. Pract. (Dermat.) N.ampton Gen. Hosp. & Kettering Gen. Hosp.

MILLER, Mr Daniel Ferguson (retired) 20 Crosshill Road, Strathaven ML10 6DS Tel: 01357 20377 — MB ChB Glas. 1961; FRCS Glas. 1982; FRCSEd. 1965; DObst RCOG 1963. Cons. Surg. Hairmyres Hosp. E. Kilbride Glas. Prev: Sen. Regist. Surg. Vict. Infirm. Glas.

MILLER, David George Trescobeas Surgery, Trescobeas Road, Falmouth TR11 2UN Tel: 01326 434888 Fax: 01326 434899 — MB ChB 1977 Leeds; MRCP (UK) 1983; MRCGP 1994; DRACOG 1991. (Univ. Leeds) Prev: Trainee GP Redruth; Regist. (Emerg. Med.) Fremantle Hosp. W.. Austral.; Surg. P & O Lines Ltd. Soton.

MILLER, Mr David Huw Thomas Rook House, Skutterskelfe, Hutton Rudby, Yarm TS15 0JP Tel: 01642 701323 Fax: 01642 701944 Email: dht.miller@virgin.net — MB BS 1974 Lond.; LLM 1994; MCh (Orthop.) Liverp. 1986; FRCS Eng. 1980; MRCS Eng. LRCP Lond. 1974; AKC. (St. Geo.) Cons. Traum. & Orthop. Surg. N. Tees & Hartlepool NHS Trust; Hon. Clin. Lect. Newc. & Teeside Univs.

MILLER, David James Kilwinning Medical Practice, 15 Almswall Road, Kilwinning KA13 6BO Tel: 01294 554591 Fax: 01294 557300 — MB BCh BAO 1973 Dub.; DMRD Ed. 1977. GP Kilwinning Ayrsh.

MILLER, Professor David Louis 83 Rowlands Avenue, Hatch End, Pinner HA5 4BX Tel: 020 8428 1155 Email: miller.dl@virgin.net — MB BChir Camb. 1956; MD Camb. 1965, MA 1956; FRCP Lond. 1978, M 1973; FFPHM RCP (UK) 1989; DPH Eng. 1964; FFCM 1972. (St. Thos.) Emerit. Prof. Pub. Health Med. Univ. Lond.; Hon. Sen. Research Fell. (Pub. Health Med.) Guy's, King's & St Thos. Sch. of Med. Kings Coll. Univ Lond. Socs: Fell. Roy. Soc. Med. (Ex-Pres. Sect. Epidemiol. & Pub. Health); Internat. Epidemiol. Assn.; Fell. Fac. Pub. Health Med. (Ex-Acad. Regist.). Prev: Prof. Pub. Health Med. St. Mary's Hosp. Med. Sch. Lond.; Prof. Community Med. Middlx. Hosp. Med. Sch.; U.S. Pub. Health Serv. Internat. Research Fell. Johns Hopkins Sch.

***MILLER, David Robert** Hull Royal Infirmary, Anlaby Road, Hull HU3 2JZ — BM BS 1998 Nottm.; BM BS Nottm 1998.

MILLER, David Shaw 36 Latimer Road, Oxford OX3 7PF — MB BS 1961 Lond.; MSc Lond. 1977, MB BS 1961; MRCP Lond. 1967. (King's Coll. Hosp.) Sen. Regist. Oxon. HA. Prev: Med. Regist. & Ho. Phys. King's Coll. Hosp. Lond.

MILLER, David William Joseph Levitts Surgery, Levitts Road, Bugbrooke, Northampton NN7 3QN Tel: 01604 830348 Fax: 01604 832785; 17 Dunlop Avenue, Lenton, Nottingham NG7 2BW — BM BCh 1987 Oxf.; MRCGP 1992.

***MILLER, Deborah Marcelle** 25 Middleton Road, London NW11 7NR — MB ChB 1994 Leic.

MILLER, Deborah Mary c/o Major A C B Whitelaw, 1 RHF BFPO 38 — MB BCh BAO 1988 NUI.

MILLER, Delphine Cynthia 268A Baldwins Lane, Croxley Green, Rickmansworth WD3 3LG Tel: 01923 774732; 45 Hagden Lane, Watford WD18 7UJ Tel: 01923 34712 — MB ChB 1961 Ed.; DObst RCOG 1963. (Ed.)

MILLER, Dennis Charles Ardler Surgery, Turnberry Avenue, Dundee DD2 3TP Tel: 01382 833399 Fax: 01382 832484 — MB ChB 1983 Dundee; MRCGP 1988.

MILLER, Dennis Harold 4 Baroncroft Road, Liverpool L25 6EH — MB ChB 1951 Leeds; FRCPsych 1987, M 1971; DPM Eng. 1960, DCH 1955. (Leeds) Cons. Psychiat. Arrowe Pk. Hosp. & Birkenhead & N. Wirral Hosp. Gp.; Clin Lect. (Psychol. Med.) Univ. Liverp. Socs: Liverp. Psychiat. Soc. (Ex-Pres.). Prev: Clin. Dir. (Psychiat.) Arrowe Pk. Hosp.; Lect. (Psychol. Med.) Univ. Liverp.; Flight Lt. RAF Med. Br.

MILLER, Derek John Guisachan, Arndilly, Craigellachie, Aberlour AB38 9QJ — MB ChB 1982 Glas.

MILLER, Diana Evelyn 52 Upper Cheyne Row, London SW3 5JJ Tel: 020 7352 6380 Fax: 01454 238171 Email: emiller@capsticks.co.uk; Sopworth Manor, Sopworth, Chippenham SN14 6PS Tel: 01454 238231 Fax: 01454 238171 Email: miller@sopworth.demon.co.uk — MB BS Lond. 1967; LLM Cardiff 1992; MRCS Eng. LRCP Lond. 1967; FRCA Eng. 1971; DA Eng. 1969. (Char. Cross) p/t Cons. Anaesth. Avon and AW Ment. Health Partnership NHS Trust; Med. Adviser Capsticks Solicitors; Indep. Cons. Anaesth. Lond.; Professional Conduct Comm.; Professional Performance Comm., non exec. Bd. Mem. Prev: Cons. Anaesth. Gwent Community & Maudsley Hosp. Lond.; Clin. Asst. (Anaesth.) St. Geo. Hosp. Lond.; Nat. Blood Transfus. Serv.

MILLER, Diane Mary 9 Golfinch View, Loggerheads, Market Drayton TF9 2QH Tel: 01630 672726 — MB BS 1968 Lond.

MILLER, Donald Cameron 129 Mugdock Road, Milngavie, Glasgow G62 8NW Tel: 0141 956 3354 — MB ChB 1964 Glas.; FFA RCS Eng. 1969. Cons. Anaesth. Roy. Hosp. Sick Childr. & Glas. Roy. Infirm.

MILLER, Doreen Elizabeth Portland Road Surgery, 31 Portland Road, Kilmarnock KA1 2DJ Tel: 01563 522118 Fax: 01563 573562; 25 Ottoline Drive, Troon KA10 7AN — MB BCh BAO 1968 Belf.;

DCH RCPS Glas. 1971; DObst RCOG 1970; Cert. Contracep. & Family Plann. RCOG, RCGP &; Cert FPA 1974. GP Kilmarnock. Prev: Trainee GP Health Centre Dundonald; Clin. Med. Off. (Child Health) Fife HB; SHO (Paediat.) Ulster Hosp. Dundonald.

MILLER, Doreen Margaret Miller Health Management, Worton Park, Cassington, Oxford OX29 4SX Tel: 01865 883349 Fax: 01865 881040 Email: doreen.miller@millerhealth.com — MB BS Lond. 1961; FRCP Lond. 1991; MRCS Eng. LRCP Lond. 1961; FFOM RCP Lond. 1984, MFOM 1980; DIH Eng. 1979. (Guy's) Managing Partner Miller Health Managem. Oxf.; Vis. Fell. Cranfield Univ. Sch. of Managem. Prev: Chief Med. Off. Marks & Spencer plc; Regist. (Fac. Occupat. Med.) RCP Lond.; Vis. Prof. Univ. Dept. Pub. Health Roy. Free Hosp. Sch. Med. Lond.

MILLER, Edmund John (retired) (Surgery), 38 Downpatrick St., Rathfriland, Newry BT34 5DQ Tel: 018206 30300 — MB BCh BAO Belf. 1946.

MILLER, Eileen Cathcart (retired) 6 Bemersyde Drive, Newcastle upon Tyne NE2 2HJ Tel: 0191 281 3021 — MB BS 1941 Durh.; MB BS (Hons.) Durh. 1941; MRCOG 1947. Prev: Ho. Surg. (Obst.) Brit. Postgrad. Med. Sch. Lond.

MILLER, Elizabeth Jane Department of Haematology, Milton Keynes General Hospital, Standing Way, Eaglestone, Milton Keynes MK6 5LD — MRCS Eng. LRCP Lond. 1976; BSc (Biochem.) Lond. 1973, MB BS 1976; MRCP (UK) 1979; MRCPath 1983. Cons. Haemat. Milton Keynes Gen. Hosp., Oxf. RHA. Prev: Sen. Regist. (Haemat.) Roy. Free Hosp. Lond.

MILLER, Elizabeth Sinclair 17 Broadwalk House, Hyde Park Gate, Kensington, London SW7 5DZ Tel: 020 7589 0898 — MB BS 1980 Lond.; FRCS Ed. 1983; MRCGP 1994; T(GP) 1994; AKC. (King's Coll. Hosp.) Indep. Med. Pract. Lond. Socs: Fell. Roy. Soc. Med.; BMA. Prev: Regist. Guy's Hosp. Lond.; Regist. Edin. Roy. Infirm.

MILLER, Emma Christina Belford Medical Practice, The Belford Health Centre, Croftfield, Belford NE70 7ER Tel: 01668 213738 Fax: 01668 213072; The Old Byre, Home Farm, Belford NE70 7EY — MB BCh 1990 Wales; MRCGP 1995; DRCOG 1993; DCH 1995. GP Princip. Belford Med. Pract. N.d. Socs: BMA.

MILLER, Evelyn Margaret (retired) Westend Cottage, Back Dykes, Forfar DD8 1RG — MB ChB 1938 Ed. Prev: Med. Off. Lothian Health Bd.

***MILLER, Fairoz Banu** 1A Talton Crescent, Bryn Newydd, Prestatyn LL19 9HD — MB BCh 1994 Wales.

MILLER, Fiona Natalia Adelaide Campbell Department of Radiology, King's College Hospital, Denmark Hill, London SE15 Tel: 020 7737 4000 Ext: 3331; 12 Hollingbourne Road, London SE24 9ND — MB BS 1992 Lond.; BA Camb. 1983. (UMDS of Guy's and St. Thomas's) Specialist Regist. (Radiol.). Socs: RCP.

MILLER, Mr Geoffrey Francis 15 The Green, Woughton on the Green, Milton Keynes MK6 3BE Tel: 01908 667901 — MB BS 1969 Lond.; FRCS Eng. 1974; MRCS Eng. LRCP Lond. 1969. (St. Thos.) Cons. Orthop. Surg. Milton Keynes Gen. Hosp.

MILLER, Mr George Alan Balmer 12 Birchwood, St. Julian's Road, Omagh BT79 7RA — MB BCh BAO 1974 Dub.; FRCSI 1982.

MILLER, Professor George James MRC Epidemiology and Medical Care Unit, Wolfson Institute of Preventive Medicine, Charterhouse Square, London EC1M 6BQ Tel: 020 7982 6249 Fax: 020 7982 6252 Email: g.miller@mds.qmw.ac.uk — MB ChB 1963 Manch.; MD Manch. 1972; FRCP Lond. 1981, M 1966. Sen. Clin. Scientist (Epidemiol.) Med. Research Counc. Lond.; Vis. Prof. Epidemiol. & Social Med. Albert Einstein Coll. Med. NY, USA; Hon. Cons. Epidemiol. N.wick Pk. & St. Mark's NHS Trust & City & Hackney HA Provider Unit Lond; Prof. Epidemiol. Univ. Lond. Qu. Mary W.hill. Socs: Corr. Fell. Amer. Heart Assn.; Brit. Soc. Thrombosis & Haemostasis; Overseas Fell. Amer. Coll .Epidemiol.

MILLER, George Lindsay (retired) 77 Dundonald Road, Kilmarnock KA1 1TQ Tel: 01563 523031 — MB ChB 1960 Glas.

MILLER, Gerald 8 Sunningdale Close, Gordon Avenue, Stanmore HA7 3QL Tel: 020 8954 5330 — MRCS Eng. LRCP Lond. 1950. (Middlx.) Regional Med. Off. Dept. Health Adjudicating Med. Off. Dept. Social Security. Prev: Recep. Off. Rochford Gen. Hosp.; Squadron Ldr. RAF.

MILLER, Geraldine Ann 6 St James Road, Hereford HR1 2QS — BM BS 1991 Flinders.

MILLER, Glenn Vincent 21 Park Copse, Horsforth, Leeds LS18 5UN — MB ChB 1987 Leeds.

MILLER, Graeme Dunsmore Portlethen Group Practice, Portlethen Health Centre, Bruntland Road, Portlethen, Aberdeen AB12 4QL Tel: 01224 780223 Fax: 01224 781317 — MB ChB 1983 Aberd.; MRCGP 1987.

***MILLER, Graeme Scott** 16 Crossburn Avenue, Milngavie, Glasgow G62 6DR — MB ChB 1996 Glas.

MILLER, Graham Austin Herrock (retired) Mill Farm, Teffont, Salisbury SP3 5RP Tel: 01722 716429 — DM Oxf. 1965, MA, BSc, BM BCh 1955; FRCP Lond. 1973, M 1960. Dir. Cardiac Laborat. Brompton Hosp. Lond. Prev: Dir. Cardiac Laborat. Brompton Hosp. Lond.

MILLER, Hamish Bruce The Surgery, 16 Windsor Road, Chobham, Woking GU24 8NA Tel: 01276 857117 Fax: 01276 855668; Steep Hill Cottage, Steep Hill, Chobham, Woking GU24 8SZ — MB BS Lond. 1970; Dip. IMC RCS Ed 1991; DObst RCOG 1974; Cert. Av. Med. 1987. (St. Geo.) Authorised Med. Examr. Civil Aviat. Auth. Socs: Brit. Aeromed.Pract. Assn. & Med. Off. Sch. Assn. Prev: Res. Med. Off. King Edwd. VII Memor. Hosp. Bermuda; SHO (Obst & Gyn.) St. Geo. Hosp. Lond.; SHO (Paediat.) St. Geo. Hosp. Lond.

MILLER, Heidi 114 Edgwarebury Lane, Edgware HA8 8NB Tel: 020 8958 3255 Fax: 020 8958 7915; 85 Edgwarebury Lane, Edgware HA8 8LZ Tel: 020 8458 7915 Email: kh@rosenfeld.freeserve.co.uk — MB ChB 1991 Cape Town; MRCGP 1995; DRCOG 1994. (Univ. Cape Town, S. Afr.) Asst. GP Wembley & Cricklewood.

MILLER, Helen Clare 117 Milson Road, London W14 0LA — MB ChB 1993 Ed.; DRCOG 1997.

MILLER, Helen Elizabeth Jane 65 Atwood Road, Manchester M20 6TB; Central Manchester Health Care Trust, Oxford Road, Manchester M13 — MB ChB 1986 Glas.; MRCPsych 1990. Cons. Psychiat.

MILLER, Helen Joy Miller and Mann, The College Yard Surgery, Mount Street, Westgate, Gloucester GL1 2RE Tel: 01452 412888 Fax: 01452 387874; 65 Upton Close, Barnwood, Gloucester GL4 3EX Tel: 01452615956 — MB BS 1984 Lond.; T(GP) 1991; DFFP 1993; DRCOG 1986. (St. Geo.) GP.

MILLER, Helen Rachel (retired) Lonsdale Medical Centre, 24 Lonsdale Road, London NW6 6RR Tel: 020 7328 8331 Fax: 020 7328 8630 — MB BS 1961 Lond.; MSC Health Plann. & Financing Lond. Sch. Economics 1992; MRCS Eng. LRCP Lond. 1961; MRCGP 1981; DCH Eng. 1965. Research Assoc. Judge Inst. Managem. Studies Camb. Prev: GP Kentish Town Lond.

MILLER, Helen Stewart Victoria Hospital, Whinney Heys Road, Blackpool FY3 8NP Tel: 01253 300000 Email: helen>miller@btinternet.com; Hillcrest, 268 Newton Drive, Blackpool FY3 8PZ Tel: 01253 393381 — MB ChB 1968 St. And.; MFFP 1994. (St. And.) Specialist (Obst. Ultrasound) (Ultrasound) Vict. Hosp. Blackpool; Clin. Med. Off. (Family Plann.) Poulton-le-Fylde; Clin. Asst. (Genitourin. Med.) Blackpool. Socs: Brit. Med. Ultrasound Soc.; Assn. Genitourin. Med.; Internat. Ultrasound Obs. & Gyn.

MILLER, Henry James Brawn (retired) 11 Victoria Park, Ayr KA7 2TR Tel: 01292 265280 — MB ChB 1939 Glas.; BSc Glas. 1936, MB ChB 1939; FRCPsych 1972; DPM Manch. 1949. Prev: Phys. Supt. Ailsa Hosp. Ayr.

MILLER, Hugh Craig 12 Dick Place, Edinburgh EH9 2JL Tel: 0131 667 4235 — MB ChB 1966 Ed.; BSc (Hons.) Ed. 1964, MB ChB 1966; FRCP Ed. 1979; MRCP (UK) 1970. Cons. (Cardiol.) Roy. Infirm. Edin. Socs: Brit. Cardiac Soc. & Assn. Phys. GB & Irel. Prev: Research Fell. Duke Univ. Med. Center Durh., U.S.A.; Sen. Regist. (Cardiol.) Brompton Hosp. Lond.; MRC Research Fell. Univ. Edin.

MILLER, Mr Ian Arnot Red Roofs, 16 South Drive, Woolsington, Newcastle upon Tyne NE13 8AN — MB BS 1959 Durh.; FRCS Ed. 1967; FRCS Eng. 1967. (Durh.) Cons. Surg. Gateshead HA. Prev: Research Fell. Dept. Surg. Roy. Vict. Infirm. Newc.; Sen. Surg. Regist. Roy. Vict. Infirm. Newc.; Sen. Surg. Regist. (Urol.) Newc. Gen. Hosp.

MILLER, Ian Dougal Craig c/o Anaesthetic Department, William Harvey Hospital, Kennington Road, Willesborough, Ashford TN24 0LZ — MB BS 1992 Queensland.

MILLER, Mr Ian McKenzie Good Hope Hospital NHS Trust, Rectory Road, Sutton Coldfield B75 7RR Tel: 0121 378 2211 Ext: 2381 Fax: 0121 311 1712; 14 Edge Hill Road, Sutton Coldfield B74 4NU Tel: 0121 353 3800 Fax: 0121 580 9351 Email: ian.miller@virgin.net — MB BS Lond. 1967; FRCS Eng. 1972; FRCS

MILLER

Ed. 1971; MRCS Eng. LRCP Lond. 1967. (Lond. Hosp.) Cons. Orthop. Good Hope Hosp. NHS Trust. Socs: Fell. BOA. Prev: Sen. Regist. (Orthop.) Lond. Hosp.; SHO Rotat. United Bristol Hosps.; Ho. Phys. & Ho. Surg. Lond. Hosp.

MILLER, Ian Stuart Clevedon Medical, Old Street, Clevedon BS21 6DG Tel: 01275 335534 — MB ChB 1982 Leeds; MRCGP 1988; Dip Sports Med. . Lond. & Scotl.; DCH RCP Lond. 1987; DRCOG 1987. (Leeds) Gen. Practitioner, Clevedon; Clin. Asst. (Orthop. & Sports Med.) Avon Orthop. Centre Bristol; Governing body Med. Off., Eng. Karate. Prev: Trainee GP Frimley Pk. Hosp. VTS; SHO (Paediat.) Kingston Hosp.; SHO (Cas. & Orthop.) Luton & Dunstable Hosp. Beds.

MILLER, Mr Ian Thornley (retired) Garden End, 94 Queen Alexandra Road, Sunderland SR2 9AH Tel: 0191 522 7859 — MB BS Durh., 1956; FRCS Eng. 1965. Cons. Surg. Sunderland Roy. Infirm.; Regist. Adviser RCS. Prev: Ho. Off. & Sen. Regist. Roy. Vict. Infirm. Newc.

MILLER, Ida Isolda Astwood Stagehall Farm, Stow, Galashiels TD1 2SS Tel: 01578 730241 — MB BS 1943 Lond. (Univ. Coll. Lond.)

MILLER, Ita Mary Compass House, Northgate Hospital, Northgate St., Great Yarmouth NR30 1BU Tel: 01493 337614 Fax: 01493 852753; 19 Mill Lane, Wrentham, Beccles NR34 7JQ Tel: 01502 675353 — MB BCh BAO NUI 1969; DObst RCOG 1970. (Univ. Coll. Dub.) Community Clin. Med. Off. (Paediat.) James Paget Healthcare NHS Trust Gt Yarmouth. Socs: BMA; BACCH. Prev: GP LoW.oft.

MILLER, Jack Elius, OBE, OStJ (retired) 38 Fruin Court, Fruin Avenue, Newton Mearns, Glasgow G77 6HJ Tel: 0141 639 7869 — LRCP LRCS Ed. LRFPS Glas. 1943; FRCGP 1979, M 1953. JP. Prev: Ho. Surg. Kilmarnock Infirm.

MILLER, James Aleck Lee University Hospital, Birmingham Trust, Edgbaston, Birmingham B15 2TT; 115 gordon Road, Harbourne, Birmingham B17 9EX Tel: 0121 684 4404 Email: j.a.l.miller@bham.ac.uk — MB ChB 1990 Glas.; BSc Physiol. Grad. (Hons.) Glas. 1987; MRCP (UK) 1993. Regist. (Neurol.) Birm. Prev: SHO (Neurol.) Edin.; SHO (Med.) Glas.

MILLER, James Brawn Cathcart Practice, 8 Cathcart Street, Ayr KA7 1BJ Tel: 01292 264051 Fax: 01292 293803 — MB ChB 1973 Glas.; BSc Glas. 1970, MB ChB 1973; MRCP (U.K.) 1976. GP Princip. Ayr; Hosp. Pract. (Dermat.) Heathfield Gen. Hosp. Ayr. Prev: Regist. (Med.) W.. Infirm. Glas.

MILLER, James Craig Clydebank Health Centre, Kilbavie Road, Clydebank, Glasgow; 28 Thorn Drive, Bearsden, Glasgow G61 4LU — MB ChB 1981 Glas.; MRCGP 1985; DRCOG 1983.

MILLER, James Edward, TD St Peter's Road Surgery, 1 St. Peters Road, Cirencester GL7 1RF Tel: 01285 653184 Fax: 01285 655795; Littledown, Baunton Lane, Cirencester GL7 2LN Tel: 01285 656457 Fax: 01285 656457 — MB ChB 1982 Manch.; BSc St. And. 1979; MRCGP 1987; DFFP 1993; DTM & H RCP Lond. 1991; DA (UK) 1991; DRCOG 1987. (St Andrews and Manchester) Clin. Asst. (Anaesth. & Gyn.) Gloucester & Swindon Gen. Hosps.; Med. Adviser Cirencester Friendly Soc.; GP Assoc. Tutor. Socs: Brit. Assn. Immed. Care Schemes; Christian Med. Fell.sh.; Brit. Soc. Colpos. & Cerv. Path. Prev: Maj. RAMC (V) 243 Field Hosp.; Ho. Phys. & Ho. Surg. N. Lonsdale Hosp. Barrow in Furness; Med. Off. Howard Hosp., Glendale, Zimbabwe.

MILLER, James Gordon Tel: 01771 623522 Fax: 01771 624349; Kinchoil, Station Terrace, Longside, Peterhead AB42 4UE Tel: 01779 821409 — MB ChB 1970 Aberd.; MRCGP 1975. (Aberd.) Prev: SHO (Paediat.) Hull Roy. Infirm.; SHO (Med.) Aberd. Roy. Infirm.

MILLER, James McCulloch Lanarkshire Health Board, 14 Beckford St., Hamilton ML3 0TA Tel: 01698 281313 Fax: 01698 424316 — MB ChB 1986 Glas.; BSc (Hons.) Glas. 1984; MFPHM RCP (UK) 1996; MRCGP 1991; DRCOG 1990. (Glas.) Cons. (Pub. Health Med.) (CD & EH) NHS Lanarksh. Prev: Sen. Regist. (Pub. Health Med.) Rotherham HA.

MILLER, Miss Janet Marie 47 Methuen Street, Southampton SO14 6FR — MB BS 1990 Lond.

MILLER, Janine 11 Sharman Dale, Bangor BT19 1XG — MB BCh BAO 1994 Belf.; Dip. Ment Health Belfast 1997; Dip. Roy. Coll. Obst. & Gyn. 1998.

MILLER, Janine Moyra (retired) 5 The Borough, Yealmpton, Plymouth PL8 2LR Tel: 01752 880165 — MB ChB Liverp. 1961; MRCS Eng. LRCP Lond. 1961; FRCOG 1980, M 1967; DObst RCOG 1963. Prev: Cons. O & G St. Helens & Knowsley AHA.

MILLER, Jennifer Mary The Loddon Vale Practice, Hurricane Way, Woodley, Reading RG5 4UX Tel: 0118 969 0160 Fax: 0118 969 9103; 8 Pitts Lane, Earley, Reading RG6 1BT Tel: 0118 966 2375 — MB BS 1966 Lond.; MRCP (U.K.) 1972; MRCS Eng. LRCP Lond. 1966; MRCGP 1978. (St. Bart.) Prev: Regist. (Geriat. & Gen. Med.) Battle Hosp. Reading; SHO Neurol & Gen. Med. Roy. United Hosp. Bath. Ho. Phys. Paediat.; Ho. Phys. & Ho. Surg. Roy. United Hosp. Bath.

MILLER, Mrs Jessie Sinclair (retired) Innerwick, Ferntower Road, Crieff PH7 3DH Tel: 01764 2176 — MB BS 1926 Durh.; BHyg. & DPH 1930. Prev: Ho. Surg. Roy. Vict. Infirm. Newc.

MILLER, Joan Donaghadee Health Centre, 3 Killaughey Road, Donaghadee BT21 0BU; 72 Warren Road, Donaghadee BT21 0PD Tel: 883479 — MB BCh BAO 1970 Belf.

MILLER, Joan Mairi (retired) 80 Prestonfield, Milngavie, Glasgow G62 7PZ Tel: 0141 956 1967 Fax: 0141 956 7630 — MB ChB 1963 Glas.; Cert. Family Plann. JCC 1968. Prev: Med. Off. Strathclyde Regional Off. Hamilton.

***MILLER, Joanne Clare** 10 Western Hill, Durham DH1 4RL — MB ChB 1997 Manch.

MILLER, John Lytham Road Surgery, 352 Lytham Road, Blackpool FY4 1DW Tel: 01253 402546 Fax: 01253 349637 — MB ChB 1968 St. And. (St. And.)

MILLER, John The Oaks Medical Centre, Council Avenue, Hull HU4 6RF Tel: 01482 354251; 6 Palmer Avenue, Kingston Road, Willerby, Hull HU10 6LJ Tel: 01482 656031 — MB BS 1981 Lond.; BSc Lond. 1977. (St. Mary's) Prev: Trainee GP N. Humberside; SHO (Geriat. Med.) Castle Hill Hosp. Cottingham; SHO (O & G) Hull Matern. Hosp. & P.ss Roy. Hosp. Hull.

MILLER, John (surg), 306 Blandford Road, Hamworthy, Poole BH15 4JQ Tel: 01202 679234 — MB 1968 Camb.; BChir 1967. (Camb.) Prev: Ho. Surg. Joyce Green Hosp. Dartford; Ho. Phys. Friarage Hosp. N.allerton; SHO (O & G) PeterBoro. Dist. Hosp.

MILLER, Mr John Campbell 19 Granby Gardens, Granby Road, Harrogate HG1 4SR Tel: 01423 560566 — MB ChB 1943 Birm.; FRCS Ed. 1949; FRCOG 1965, M 1951. (Birm.) Prev: Emerit. Cons. O & G Croydon.

MILLER, John Desmond (retired) 101 Lingfield Crescent, Eltham, London SE9 2RQ Tel: 020 8859 1739 — MB BS 1955 Lond.; MRCS Eng. LRCP Lond. 1955; MRCGP 1964; DObst RCOG 1959; DCH Eng. 1960.

MILLER, Mr John Dow Booth Doctor Grays Hospital, Elgin IV30 1SN Tel: 01343 543131; Findrassie House, Elgin IV30 5PS Tel: 01343 547292 — MB ChB 1968 Aberd.; ChM Aberd. 1978; FRCS Ed. 1974; FIBiol 1985. Cons. Surg. Doctors Grays Hosp. Elgin; Hon. Sen. Lect. (Surg.) Aberd. Univ. Socs: Surg. Research Soc.; Assn. Surg. Prev: Sen. Lect. (Surg.) Aberd. Univ.; Research Fell. (Surg.) Harvard Univ., Boston, USA.

MILLER, John Edward Bridgehouse Medical Centre, 11 Ladybridge Road, Cheadle Hulme, Stockport SK8 5LL Tel: 0161 488 4124 — MB ChB 1975 Manch.; MRCGP 1982; DCH RCP Lond. 1985; DRCOG 1983; MFFP 1995. Trainer Gen. Pract. & Trainer Family Plann. Cheadle Hulme Health.

MILLER, John Edward 172 Newmarket Street, Norwich NR2 2DS Tel: 01603 610408 — MB BS 1970 Lond.

MILLER, John Ellis Litchdon Medical Centre, Landkey Road, Barnstaple EX32 9LL Tel: 01271 23443 Fax: 01271 25979 — MB ChB 1969 Birm.; DObst RCOG 1971. (Birm.) Socs: BMA. Prev: SHO Accid. Unit. E. Birm. Hosp.; SHO N. Devon Dist. Hosp. Barnstaple; Regist. (Med. & Paediat.) Palmerston N. Hosp., N.Z.

MILLER, John Eric (retired) The Lodge Medical Centre, Grange Park Avenue, Leeds LS8 3BA Tel: 0113 265 6454 — MB ChB 1949 Leeds. Prev: GP Seacroft Leeds.

MILLER, John Franklin Princess Anne Hospital, Coxford Road, Southampton SO16 5YA Tel: 023 8079 6041; Brocket Green, Rhinefield Road, Brockenhurst SO42 7SR Tel: 01590 622168 — MB BS 1965 Durh.; DM Soton. 1977; FRCOG 1983, M 1969. (Newc.) Cons. O & G S.ampton Univ. NHS Trust; Hon. Clin. Teach. Univ. Soton. Socs: BMA & Blair Bell Research Soc. Prev: Lect. (Human Reproduc. & Obst.) Univ. Soton; Regist. (O & G) Newc. Gen. Hosp.; Ho. Surg. & Ho. Phys. Roy. Vict. Infirm. Newc.

MILLER, John Galbraith (retired) 38 Cromer Road, Mundesley, Norwich NR11 8DB Tel: 01263 721347 — MB Camb. 1958, BChir 1957; LMSSA Lond. 1957; DObst RCOG 1959. Prev: GP Mundesley.

MILLER, John Gavin Department of Plastic Surgery, Northern General Hospital, Sheffield S5 7AU Tel: 0114 261 9651 Fax: 0114 261 9651 Email: gavin.miller@northngh-tr.trent.nhs.uk; 14 The Pines, Lodge Moor, Sheffield S10 4LZ Tel: 0114 230 4493 Email: j.g.miller@sheffield.ac.uk — MB BS 1984 Newc.; FRCS (Plast.) Eng. 1996; Dip. Hand Surgery 1998. Cons. Plastic & Reconstruc. Hand Surg. N. Gen. Hosp. Sheff. Socs: Br. Soc. Surg. of the Hand & BAPS.

MILLER, John Lindsay (retired) 21 Crouch Hall Lane, Redbourn, St Albans AL3 7EQ Tel: 01582 792724 — MB ChB 1949 Ed.; DCH Eng. 1953; DObst RCOG 1952. Prev: Hosp. Pract. (Geriat. & ENT) St. Albans City Hosp.

MILLER, John Meadowcroft Bridge Surgery, St. Peters Street, Stapenhill, Burton-on-Trent DE15 9AW Tel: 01283 563451 Fax: 01283 500896; 7 The Moorings, Aldrewas, Burton-on-Trent DE13 7BG — MB BCh BAO 1962 Belf.; MB BCh BAO Belf. 1962.; FRCGP 1978, M 1975; DObst RCOG 1965. Assoc. Adviser Gen. Pract.

MILLER, John Norman Newbattle Medical Practice, Blackcot, Mayfield, Dalkeith EH22 4AA Tel: 0131 663 1051 Fax: 0131 654 0665; 161A Colinton Road, Edinburgh EH14 1BE — MB ChB 1972 Ed.; BSc (Hons.) Ed. 1970, MB ChB 1972; MRCGP 1982; DObst RCOG 1974; DCH Eng. 1976; DA Eng. 1976. Prev: Ho. Phys. (Infec. Dis.) City Hosp. Edin.; SHO (Paediat.) Perth Roy. Infirm.; SHO Dept. Anaesth. Dundee Teachg. Hosps.

MILLER, John Paul Department of Medicine, South Manchester University Hospitals NHS Trust, Wythenshawe Hospital, Manchester M23 9LT Tel: 0161 291 2400 Fax: 0161 291 2635 — BM BCh 1968 Oxf.; MSc Lond. 1972; DPhil, MA Oxf. 1967; FRCP Lond. 1982, M 1970. (Guy's) Cons. Gastroenterol. S. Manch. Univ. Hosp. NHS Trust; Chairm. of Counc., The Med. Protec. Soc.; Chairm., Bd. of Fac. of Med., Dent., Nursing and Pharmacy, Univ. of Manch. Socs: Fell. Amer. Heart Assn.; Brit. Soc. Gastroenterol.; Brit. Atherosclerosis Soc. (Hon. Treasuerer). Prev: Sen. Lect. (Med.) Univ. Manch. & Hon. Cons. Phys. Univ. Hosp. S. Manch.; MRC Trav. Fell. & Vis. Prof. Baylor Coll. Med. Houston, Texas.

MILLER, John Robin The Surgery, Cheriton Bishop, Exeter EX6 6JA Tel: 01647 24272 — MB ChB 1969 Ed.; DObst RCOG 1971. (Ed.)

MILLER, John Simon Gilbert Department of Child Health, Royal Victoria Infirmary, Newcastle upon Tyne NE1 4LP Tel: 0191 202 3015 Email: j.s.g.miller@ncl.ac.uk — BM BCh Oxf. 1966; DPhil, MA Oxf. 1964, BA (Physiol.) 1960. (Oxf.) Emerit. Prof. Socs: (Ex-Pres.) Soc. Research Rehabil.; Anat. Soc. Physiol. Soc.; (Ex-Pres.) Europ. Federat. for Research in Rehabil. Prev: Reader (Anat.) Erasmus Univ. Rotterdam, Holland; Sen. Lect. (Anat.) Bristol Univ. Med. Sch.; Prof. Of Anatnomy Newc. Univ.

MILLER, John Stuart (retired) 10 Stratford Road, Middleton, Manchester M24 1PT — MA Camb. 1954, MB 1955, BChir 1954.

MILLER, John Stuart (retired) Delfryn, Maudlam, Bridgend CF33 4PH Tel: 01656 740072 — MB BCh 1952 Wales.

MILLER, John Whyte (retired) 111 Middle Drive, Ponteland, Newcastle upon Tyne NE20 9DS — MB ChB 1942 Aberd. Prev: Sch. Med. Off. Metrop. Boro. N. Tyneside.

MILLER, Jonathan Anthony The House By The Green, Bagshot Road, Worplesdon, Woking GU22 0QY Tel: 01483 472481 — MB ChB 1973 Sheff.; FRCP 1997; MRCP (UK) 1976. Cons. Dermat. St. Peter's Hosp. Chertsey. Socs: Fell. Roy. Soc. Med.; St. John's Hosp. Dermat. Soc. Prev: Cons. Dermat. St. Bart. Hosp. Rochester & W. Hill Hosp. Dartford; Sen. Regist. (Dermat.) Middlx. Hosp. Lond.; Regist. (Dermat.) St. Bart. Hosp. Lond.

***MILLER, Jonathan David** 13 Downham Mead, Chippenham SN15 3LN — MB BS 1998 Lond.; MB BS Lond 1998.

MILLER, Jonathan David Temple Market Lavington Surgery, 15 Church Street, Market Lavington, Devizes SN10 4DT Tel: 01380 812500 — MB BS 1969 Lond.; DObst RCOG 1972; DCH Eng. 1971. (Middlx.) Prev: Med. Off. Springdale Hosp. Newfld.

MILLER, Jonathan Wolfe 63 Gloucester Crescent, London NW1 7EG Tel: 020 7485 6973 — MB 1960 Camb.; BChir 1959.

MILLER, Joyce (retired) 112 Knowle Lane, Eccelsall, Sheffield S11 9SJ Tel: 0114 236 2042 — MB ChB 1951 Sheff. Prev: GP Sheff.

MILLER, Julie Shilton Cottage, Shilton Lane, Bishopton PA7 5PR Tel: 01505 862191 — MB ChB 1994 Aberd.; MRCP UK. Staff Grade (Paediat.) York NHS Trust York. Socs: Collegiate Mem. RCP Edin.

***MILLER, Katherine Ann** 16 House O'Hill Avenue, Edinburgh EH4 5DL — MB ChB 1998 Ed.; MB ChB Ed 1998.

MILLER, Katherine Anne Selsey Health Centre, St Peters Crescent, Selsey, Chichester PO20 0NN Tel: 01243604 321; 29 Mosse Gardens, Fishbourne, Chichester PO19 3PQ — MB ChB 1988 Manch.; MRCGP 1996; DRCOG 1994. (Mans.) Hosp. Pract. (Genitourin. Med.) St. Richards Hosp. Chichester. Socs: BMA; MSSUD; AGUM. Prev: GP Asst. Clin. Ast. Gum.

MILLER, Katherine Murray (retired) 71 Campbell Street, Wishaw ML2 8HU — MB ChB 1954 Glas.; FRCPath 1977, M 1965. Prev: Cons. Pathol. (Haemat.) Law Hosp. Carluke & StoneHo. Hosp.

***MILLER, Kathryn Anne** 163 Moor Green Lane, Birmingham B13 8NT — MB BS 1997 Lond.

MILLER, Kevin George Tel: 0114 269 1012 — MB BS 1987 Lond.; MA Camb. 1988, BA 1984; MRCGP 1991; DRCOG 1991.

MILLER, Kirsteen Jane Top Flat Left, 62 White St., Glasgow G11 5EB — MB ChB 1992 Aberd.; DRCOG 1995; MRCGP 1996.

MILLER, Kirsti Elaine 21 Park Copse, Horsforth, Leeds LS18 5UN — MB ChB 1990 Leeds. Regist. (Histopath.) Yorks. Regional Train. Scheme. Prev: SHO (Histopath.) Leeds Gen. Infirm. & N. Manch. HA; SHO (Med. for Elderly) Leeds W.. HA.

MILLER, Lawrence Francis Sherwood House Medical Practice, 9 Sandon Road, Edgbaston, Birmingham B67 8DP Tel: 0121 420 0100 Fax: 0121 420 0107 — MB BS 1989 Lond.; MRCGP 1994; DRCOG 1993. (St Mary's London) GP Princip.

MILLER, Leonard Featherstone (retired) The Cottage, Salt Cellar Hill, Porthleven, Helston TR13 9DP — MB BS Lond. 1942; MRCS Eng. LRCP Lond. 1942. Prev: Maj. RAMC Dermatol.

MILLER, Leslie Lewis (retired) 8 Lynton Drive, Burnage, Manchester M19 2LQ Tel: 0161 224 6190 — MB ChB 1942 Leeds.

MILLER, Linda — BM 1990 Soton.; BSc (Physiol. & Pharmacol.) Jt. Hons. Lond. 1986; DFFP 1997; AKC 1986. (Southampton) p/t GP Lond. Socs: Mem. Nat. Assn. of Non-Princip.s; Mem. Fac. of Family Plann. Prev: SHO Paediatric Kings 1996; SHO Obst. & Gyn. 1995, Kings, Lond.; SHO Oncol., The Middlx., Lond., 1995.

***MILLER, Lindsay Ross** 77 Dundonald Road, Kilmarnock KA1 1TQ; 77 Dundonald Road, Kilmarnock KA1 1TQ — MB ChB 1995 Glas.; BSc (Hons.) Glas. 1992.

MILLER, Lisa Jane 86 Old Landsdowne Road, Manchester M20 8WX — MB ChB 1989 Manch.

MILLER, Louise Barbara 10 Regents Park Terrace, London NW1 7EE Tel: 020 7485 4855 — MB BChir 1979 Camb.; DOMS 2000; MA Camb. 1988; MRCGP 1983; DRCOG 1982. (Cambridge) p/t Doct. Finsbury Circus Med. Centre; Sch. Doct. Godpolhin Thatyther Sch. Lond. Socs: Roy. Soc. of Med.

***MILLER, Louise Frances** 1 Albert Mansions, Luxborough St., London W1U 5BQ — MB BS 1996 Lond.

MILLER, Lyn Marie Eskbridge Medical Centre, 8A Bridge Street, Musselburgh EH21 6AG Tel: 0131 665 6821 Fax: 0131 665 5488; 29 Clayknowes Place, Musselburgh EH21 6UG — MB ChB 1982 Ed.; MRCGP 1987.

MILLER, Mabel Emma 23 Six Acres, Shrewsbury SY3 6AF Tel: 01743 55440 — MB ChB 1940 Ed. (Ed.) Hosp. Pract. (Psychiat.) Shelton Hosp. Shrewsbury. Prev: Asst. Anaesth. Ballochmyle Emerg. Hosp. Mauchline, Ayrsh.; Jun. Res. Med. Off. Hove Gen. Hosp.; Ho. Surg. Corbett Hosp. Stourbridge.

MILLER, Mr Marek Antoni Witold Department of Urology, Northampton General Hospital NHS Trust, Cliftonville, Northampton NN1 5BD Tel: 01604 634700 Email: mmiller@marekmillerngh.demon.co.uk; The Old Plume of Feathers, Stubbs Road, Everdon, Daventry NN11 3BN Tel: 01327 361315 — MB BS 1987 Lond.; BSc Bristol 1981; FRCS Eng. 1992; FRCS (Urol.) 1997; MD Lond. 1997. (UCLH) Cons. Urol. N.ampton Gen. Hosp.; Hon. Research Fell. (Surg.) Roy. Free Hosp. Lond. Socs: BAUS; BMA. Prev: Sen. Regist. (Urol.) St Geo.'s Hospial Lond.; Regist. Inst. Urol. Lond.; Research Regist. (Urol.) Roy. Free Hosp. Lond.

MILLER, Margaret Diane Delfryn Maudlam, Bridgend CF33 4PH Tel: 01656 740072 — MB BCh 1955 Wales. (Cardiff) SCMO Mid. Glam. HA.

MILLER

*MILLER, Margaret Elizabeth 146 East Street, Olney MK46 4BT — MB BS 1996 Lond.

MILLER, Margaret Mary (retired) 24 Midton Road, Prestwick KA9 1PL Tel: 01292 78576 — MB ChB 1957 Glas. Prev: Med. Off. (Child Health) Ayrsh. & Arran HB.

MILLER, Marion 36 Church Field Drive, Wickersley, Rotherham S66 1DS — MB ChB 1976 Glas.; FFA RCS Eng. 1980. Cons. Anaesth. Rotherham HA.

MILLER, Marion Conway (retired) 62 West Road, Newport-on-Tay DD6 8HP — MB ChB 1950 St. And.; FRCS Ed. 1962; FRCOG 1969, M 1956, DObst 1952. Prev: Cons. O & G Edin. Wom. Hosps. & Cons. Elsie Inglis & Bruntsfield Hosp. Edin.

MILLER, Mark William 2 Henshall Drive, Sandbach CW11 1YN — MB ChB 1990 Manch. SHO (A & E) Manch.

MILLER, Martin Raymond Department of Medicine, University of Birmingham, University Hospital Trust, Selly Oak, Birmingham B29 6JD Tel: 0121 627 8479 Fax: 0121 627 8292 Email: m.r.miller@bham.ac.uk; 163 Moor Green Lane, Moseley, Birmingham B13 8NT — MB BS Lond. 1975; BSc (Hons.) Lond. 1972, MD 1983; FRCP Lond. 1994; MRCP (UK) 1978. (St. Bart.) Sen. Lect. (Respirat. Med.) Univ. Birm & Hon. Cons. Phys. Univ. Hosp. Trust. Birm. Socs: Brit. Europ. & Amer. Thoracic Soc. Prev: Sen. Lect. (Respirat. Med.) Univ. Birm. & Hon. Cons. Phys. Good Hope Hosp. Sutton Coldfield; Sen. Regist. (Med.) Papworth & Addenbrooke's Hosp. Camb.

MILLER, Mary Frances Moneymore Medical Centre, Fairhill, Moneymore, Magherafelt BT45 6BL Tel: 0288 674 8350 Fax: 0288 674 8684; 20 Mullan Road, Coagh, Cookstown BT80 0DD — MB BCh BAO 1981 Belf.; MRCGP 1987. (Qu. Univ. Belf.)

MILLER, Mary Hastings (retired) Wall Park, Angle, Pembroke SA71 5AT Tel: 01646 641462 — BM BCh 1951 Oxf.; BM BCh Oxon. 1951; DCH RCPS Glas. 1966.

MILLER, Mary Patricia The Blofield Surgery, Plantation Road, Blofield, Norwich NR13 4PL Tel: 01603 712337 Fax: 01603 712899 — MB BS 1983 Lond.; DRCOG 1986. Gen. Practitioner Princip.

MILLER, Mary Ramsay (retired) 111 Middle Drive, Ponteland, Newcastle upon Tyne NE20 9DS Tel: 01661 72734 — MB ChB 1942 Aberd. Prev: Sen. Med. Off. Child Health N. Tyneside HA.

MILLER, Mary Swan (retired) 69 Eglinton Street, Portrush BT56 8DZ Tel: 01265 823400 — BA, MB BCh BAO Dub. 1926; DPH Dub. 1937. Prev: Asst. Co. MOH Herts. CC.

MILLER, Matthew Thomas Vivian Laurel Hill, Main St., Repton, Derby DE65 6FB Tel: 01283 703132 — MB BS 1993 Lond.

MILLER, Rev. Michael Daukes Miller and Partners, The Health Centre, Albert Street, Lydney GL15 5NQ Tel: 01594 842167 Fax: 01594 845550; Highmead House, Blakeney GL15 4DY Tel: 01594 516668 — MB BChir 1971 Camb.; MA Camb. 1971; MRCGP 1974; DCH Eng. 1973; DObst RCOG 1973. (St. Thos.) Clin. Asst. (Cas.) Lydney Hosp. Gloucester; Clergyman (Curate to Parish of Lydney). Prev: Trainee GP Reading & Bristol VTS.; Ho. Surg. St. Thomas Hosp. Lond.; Ho. Phys. Roy. Berks. Hosp. Reading.

MILLER, Michael George Royal Infirmary, Acre Street, Huddersfield HD3 3EA Tel: 01484 342681 Fax: 01484 342121 Email: mmiller@hudderfd-tr.northy.nhs.uk; 11 Oakes Road South, Huddersfield HD3 4XT Tel: 01484 646378 Email: mmille7102@aol.com — MB BS 1978 Lond.; FRCPCH 1997; BA Camb. 1975; MRCP (UK) 1982; FRCP 1996 UK. (Cambridge University College Hospital) Cons. Paediat., Calderdale & Huddersfield Trust. Prev: Clin. Research Fell. (Cystic Fibrosis) St. Jas. Univ. Hosp. Leeds.; Sen. Regist. (Paediat.) Bloomsbury & Islington HA.

MILLER, Mr Michael Hamilton 73 Harley Street, London W1N 1DE Tel: 020 7224 1664 Fax: 020 7224 1744 Email: millermh@doctors.net.uk — MRCS Eng. LRCP Lond. 1979; MB BS Lond. 1980; MD Lond. 1988; FRCS Glas. 1987; FRCOphth 1989; DO RCS Eng. 1984. (Guy's) Cons. Ophth. And Chairm. Med. Advisery Comm. Moorfields Eye Hosp. Lond.; Hon. Cons. Ophth. N.wick Pk. Hosp. Harrow. Socs: Fell. Roy. Soc. Med.; Liveryman Soc. Apoth.; Chairm. Internat. Glaucoma Assoc. Prev: Fell. (Glaucoma) Eye Care Centre Vancouver, Canada; Sen. Regist. & Regist. Moorfields Eye Hosp. Lond.

MILLER, Michael James Raeburn (retired) Wallacetown Health Centre, Lyon St., Dundee DD4 6RD Tel: 01382 457629 — MB ChB 1956 St. And. Prev: Ho. Phys. Dundee Roy. Infirm.

MILLER, Michael Richard David Fitzalan Medical Centre, Fitzalan Road, Littlehampton BN17 5JR Tel: 01903 733277 Fax: 01903 733773; Ash Lane Surgery, 26 Ash Lane, Rustington, Littlehampton BN16 3BT — MB BS 1989 Lond.

MILLER, Nicola Boswell Teeside Hospice, 1 Northgate Road, Middlesbrough TS5 5NW; 4 Hill Close, Skelton-in-Cleveland, Saltburn-by-the-Sea TS12 2NE — MB BS 1986 Lond. Clin. Asst. (Palliat. Care) Teeside Hospice Middlesbrough. Prev: Trainee GP Cleveland VTS.

*MILLER, Nicola Mary Flat 4, 9 South East Circus Place, Edinburgh EH3 6TJ — MB ChB 1998 Ed.; MB ChB Ed 1998.

MILLER, Professor Norman Eric Department of Cardiovascular Biochemistry, Medical College of St Bartholomews Hospital, London EC1M 6BQ Tel: 020 7982 6185 Fax: 020 7982 6169 Email: n.e.miller@mds.qmw.ac.uk; Flat 28, Lexington Appartments, 40 City Road, London EC1Y 2AN Tel: 020 7938 3172 — MB ChB 1977 Manch.; MB ChB (Hons.) Manch. 1968; PhD Austral. Nat. Univ. 1974; MSc Manch. 1971, BSc (Hons.) Manch. 1965, DSc 1983; MD (Gold Medal) Manch. 1977; FRCP Lond. 1994; MRCP (UK) 1985; FACP 1991; FRCPath 1991, M 1980. (Manch.) Brit. Heart Foundat. Prof. Cardiovasc. Biochem. St. Bart. Hosp. Med. Coll. Lond. Socs: (Ex-Sec.) Europ. Soc. Clin. Invest.; Amer. Heart Assn. (Counc. on Arteriosclerosis.); Amer. Heart Assn. (Counc. on Epidemiol. & Prevent.). Prev: Prof. Med. & Head Sect. Endocrinol. & Metab. Bowman Gray Sch. Med., N. Carolina, USA; Sen. Clin. Research Fell. Baker Med. Research Inst. Melbourne, Austral.; Reader (Metab. Dis.) St. Thos. Hosp. Med. Sch. Lond.

MILLER, Patricia Anne Raeburn (retired) Kilburn, 11 Camelon Road, Falkirk FK1 5RU Tel: 01324 623495 — MB ChB 1957 St. And.; MA Ed. 1951; FRCOG 1979, M 1966, DObst 1960. Cons. (O & G) Falkirk & Dist. Roy. Infirm. Prev: Ho. Surg. (Obst.) Dundee Roy. Infirm.

MILLER, Patrick Francis William Stepping Hill Hospital, Stockport SK2 7SE Tel: 0161 419 5053; Chimes Cottage, Taxal, Whaley Bridge, High Peak SK23 7DY Tel: 01663 732076 — BM 1977 Soton.; MRCP (UK) 1980; T(M)(Paediat.) 1991. (Southampton) Cons. Paediat. Stepping Hill Hosp. Stockport; Undergrad. Tutor. Prev: Cons. Paediat. Macclesfield Dist. Gen. Hosp.

MILLER, Patrick Graeme (retired) Moness, Orchard Lane, Itchenor, Chichester PO20 7AD Tel: 01243 513044 — LRCP LRCS Ed. LRFPS Glas. 1940. Prev: Capt. RAMC 1940-46.

MILLER, Patrick McCutcheon Castle Place Surgery, 9 Park Hill, Tiverton EX16 6RR Tel: 01884 252333 Fax: 01884 252152 — MB ChB 1983 Birm.; MRCOG 1989. Obst. & Gyn. Tiverton & Dist. Hosp. Devon. Prev: Sen. Regist. (O & G) RAF Hosp. Ely; Regist. (O & G) RAF Hosp. Wegberg; SHO (O & G) Selly Oak Hosp. Birm.

MILLER, Paul Anthony Birmingham Childrens Hospital, Steelhouse Lane, Birmingham B4 6NH Tel: 0121 333 9999; Daleswood Farm Cottage, Shut Mill Lane, Romsley, Halesowen B62 0LY Tel: 01562 711053 Email: paul.m@dial.pipex.com — MB ChB 1989 Birm.; ChB Birm. 1989; MB ChB Birm 1989; MRCP 1992; DCH 1993. (Univ. of Birmingham) Specialist Regist. (V) Paediat. Cardiol. Birm. Childr.s Hosp.

MILLER, Paul Christopher Abbey Medical Centre, 42 Station Road, Kenilworth CV8 1JD Tel: 01926 52576; Lawnside, 29 Birches Lane, Kenilworth CV8 2AB Tel: 01926 852576 Fax: 01926 851746 — MB ChB 1969 Ed.; BSc Ed. 1966, MB ChB 1969; DObst RCOG 1973. (Ed.) GP Princip.; Police Surg. S. Warks. Police. Socs: Assn. of Police Surg.

MILLER, Mr Paul David Department of Urology, Surrey & Sussex NHS Trust, Canada Avenue, Redhill RH1 5RH Tel: 01737 231756 Fax: 01737 231803; Collins Farm, Sparks Lane, Brook St, Cuckfield, Haywards Heath RH17 5JP Tel: 01444 415849 Fax: 01444 455007 Email: millerpd99@cs.com — MB BS 1982 Lond.; BSc Lond. 1979, MD 1992; FRCS (Urol.) 1992; FRCS Eng. 1986. (Middlx.) Cons. Urol. Surg. Surrey & Sussex NHS Trust & Dir. Surrey Urol. Research Unit. Socs: Fell. Roy. Soc. Med.; Brit. Assn. Urol. Surg.; Amer. Urological Soc. Prev: Sen. Regist. Bristol Urol. Inst. & Roy. United Hosp. Bath; Research Fell. St. Bart. Hosp. Lond.; Regist. (Surg.) Bristol.

MILLER, Paul David Cherry Knowle Hospital, Ryhope, Sunderland SR2 0NB — MB BS 1986 Newc.; MRCPsych 1990; MBA Durh. 2000. Cons. Pyschiatrist - Priority Heathcare - Wearside - Sunderland. Prev: Regist. Rotat. Barnet Psychiat.; Lect . Men. Sen Regist Univ. Liverp.

MILLER, Paul Giles The Surgery, Edward St., Earby, Colne BB18 6QT Tel: 01282 843407 Fax: 01282 844886; Grange Farm, Earby, Colne BB18 6JJ Tel: 01282 843844 — MRCS Eng. LRCP Lond. 1975. Med. Dir. St. And. Hse. Barnoldswick (Chairm. Oakfoil Ltd.); Dir. Chester-Bowes Ltd.

MILLER, Pauline Ann Blackburn Road Medical Centre, Blackburn Road, Birstall, Batley WF17 9PL Tel: 01924 478265; Little Selborne, Bracken Road, Brighouse HD6 4BQ Tel: 01484 714960 — MB ChB 1974 Birm.; MB ChB (Hons.) Birm. 1974; FRCGP 1993, M (Distinc.) 1978; DRCOG 1977.

MILLER, Pauline Elizabeth 69 Alexandra Road E., Spital, Chesterfield S41 0HF Tel: 01246 233843 — MB BS 1987 Newc.

MILLER, Peter Barrie (retired) The Old Vicarage, Wardle, Rochdale OL12 9NX — MB ChB 1967 Manch.; DObst RCOG 1970.

MILLER, Peter Ian Shaw Health Medical Centre, Gilmore St., Stockport SK3 8DN Tel: 0161 480 2270; Berwyn, 13 Broadway, Bramhall, Stockport SK7 3BT Tel: 0161 440 0041 — MB ChB Manch. 1964; MRCGP 1972. Socs: Fell. Manch. Med. Soc.

MILLER, Peter James Thorneywood Unit, Porchester Road, Nottingham NG3 6LF; 89 Ella Road, West Bridgford, Nottingham NG2 5GZ — MB ChB 1987 Sheff.; MRCPsych 1991. Cons. Child & Adolesc. Psychiat. Nottm.

MILLER, Peter John, CStJ (retired) 38 Clifton Road, Rugby CV21 3QF Tel: 01788 543950 — MRCS Eng. LRCP Lond. 1941. Prev: Co. Surg. St. John Ambul. Brig.

MILLER, Rachael Grace Tel: 01721 720380 Fax: 01721 723430; Tel: 01896 830863 — MB ChB 1985 Ed.; BSc (Social Sci. with Nursing) Ed. 1980; MRCGP 1989; DRCOG 1988. GP Hay Lodge Health Centre, Peebles. Socs: Tweeddale Med. Soc. Prev: Trainee GP Edin. VTS; SHO (Med.) Roy. Infirm. Edin.; SHO (O & G) Simpsons Memor. Matern. Pavil. Edin.

MILLER, Rebecca Joy Willow Thatch, Main Road, Chillerton, Newport PO30 3ER — MB BS 1989 Lond.; BSc Lond. 1986; MRCP (UK) 1992; FRCR 1996; DMRD Ed. 1994. (King's Coll.) Cons. (Radiol.) St. Mary's NHS Trust Newport I. of Wight. Prev: Sen. Regist. (Radiol.) Soton. Gen. Hosp.; Regist. (Radiol.) Roy. Infirm. Edin.

MILLER, Mr Richard Addenbrooke's Hospital, Hill Road, Cambridge CB2 2QQ Tel: 01223 216262 Fax: 01223 216015; Email: richard.miller@consultant .com — MRCS Eng. LRCP Lond. 1978; MS Lond. 1990, MB BS (Hons.) Surg. 1978; FRCS Eng. 1984. (St. Bart.) Cons. Surg. Addenbrooke's Hosp. Camb. Socs: Brit. Soc. Gastroenterol. & Assn. Coloproctol.; Roy. Soc. Med.; BMA. Prev: Resid. Med. Off. St. Mark's Hosp.; Sen. Regist. (Surg.) Bristol Roy. Infirm.; Research Fell. Bristol Roy. Infirm.

MILLER, Richard George (retired) Old Court Cottage, Rectory Road, Hampton Bishop, Hereford HR1 4JU Tel: 01432 870612 — MB BS 1962 Lond.; MRCS Eng. LRCP Lond. 1962; DObst RCOG 1964. Prev: GP Hereford.

MILLER, Richard Ignatius Anaesthetic Department, George Eliot Hospital, College St., Nuneaton CV10 7DJ Tel: 02476 865094; 11 Station Road, Elmesthorpe, Leicester LE9 7SG Tel: 01455 846249 Fax: 01455 846247 Email: 106221.3702@compuserve.com — MD 1971 Malta; T(Anaes.) 1991. Cons. Anaesth. & Intens. Care Geo. Eliot Hosp. Nuneaton. Socs: BMA; Assn. Anaesth.; Intens. Care Soc.

MILLER, Richard John 100 Newington Road, Ramsgate CT12 6EW Tel: 01843 595951 Fax: 01843 853387; 11 Parkwood Close, Broadstairs CT10 2XN — MB BS 1983 Lond. (UCH London)

MILLER, Robert Riverside Medical Centre, Ballifeary Lane, Inverness IV3 5PN Tel: 01463 715999; 26 Grigor Drive, Inverness IV2 4LP Tel: 01463 231528 — MB ChB 1960 Aberd. (Aberd.) Socs: BMA. Prev: SHO (Paediat.) Roy. N.. Infirm. Inverness; Ho. Surg. Roy. Infirm. Edin.; Ho. Phys. Woodend Hosp. Aberd.

MILLER, Robert Alexander (retired) Stagehall Farm, Stow, Galashiels TD1 2SS — MB ChB Ed. 1935; PhD Ed. 1949, MD (High Commend.) 1939; MA Camb. 1933; FRCP Ed. 1945, M 1939. Prev: Phys. Roy. Hosp. Sick Childr. Edin.

MILLER, Robert Ferguson Windeyer Institute of Medical Sciences, RFUCMS, Mortimer Market Centre, Mortimer Market,, Off Capper St., London WC1E 6AU Tel: 020 7380 9945 Fax: 020 7380 9669 Email: rmiller@gum.ucl.ac.uk; 115 Endlesham Road, London SW12 8JP Tel: 020 8675 9728 Fax: 020 8675 3879 — MB BS 1980 Lond.; MB BS (Hons.) Lond. 1980; MRCP (UK) 1983; FRCP 1996. (St. Geo.) Reader (Clin. Infec.) Foyal Freeand Univ. Coll. Med. Sch., Lond.; Hon. Cons. Camden & Islington Community Health Serv. Trust and Univ. Coll. Hosp. Trust Lond. Socs: Brit. Thorac. Soc.; Brit. Infect. Soc.; Med. Soc. Study VD. Prev: Sen. Lect. (Med. & Genitourin. Med.) UCL Med. Sch. Lond.

MILLER, Robert George Allen Brownlow Health Centre, Legahory Centre, Craigavon BT65 5BE; 55A Clare Road, Gilford, Craigavon BT63 6AG Tel: 01762 832645 — MB BCh BAO 1971 Dub.; DObst. RCOG 1974. (Dub.)

MILLER, Robert Glendinning (retired) 5B De Parys Lodge, De Parys Avenue, Bedford MK40 2TZ Tel: 01234 352545 — MB BChir Camb. 1942; MA Camb. 1944, MD 1962; FRCP Lond. 1969, M 1948. Hon. Cons. Geriat. Med. Bedford Gen. Hosp.; Barrister Gray's Inn 1972. Prev: Cons. Phys. Bedford Gen. Hosp.

MILLER, Robert Lewis Woodstock Medical Centre, 222 Woodstock Road, Belfast BT6 9DL — MB BCh BAO 1965 Belf.; MD Belf. 1969; FRCGP 1986, M 1971.

MILLER, Mr Robert Matthew 1 Heyford Road, Radlett WD7 8PP — MB BS 1975 Lond.; FRCS Eng. 1980; MRCS Eng. LRCP Lond. 1975; Dip. Pharm. Med. RCP (UK) 1991. (Lond. Hosp.) Med. Adviser ICI Pharmaceuts. Alderley. Socs: Brit. Assn. of Pharmaceut. Phys.; Fac. Pharmaceut. Med. Prev: Med. Adviser ICI Pharmaceut. (UK); Regist. (Cardiothoracic Surg.) St. Geo. Hosp. & Middlx. Hosp. Lond.

MILLER, Robert Stanley 14 Whinfield Drive, Kinross KY13 8UB Tel: 01577 863074 — MB ChB Glas. 1950.

MILLER, Roland John Learning Disability Service, Flatts Lane Centre, Flatts Lane, Normanby, Middlesbrough TS6 0SZ Tel: 01642 283434 — MB BS 1986 Lond.; BA Camb. 1983; MRCGP 1990. (The Royal London) p/t Staff Grade (Psychiat. of Adults with Learning Disabil.) St. Lukes Hosp. Middlesbrough; Occupat.al Phys., AON Occupat.al Health, Witton Centre, Redcar. Socs: Christian Med. Fell.sh.; BMA. Prev: GP Cleveland; Trainee GP Cleveland VTS.

MILLER, Ronald The Surgery, Angel Lane, Great Dunmow, Dunmow CM6 1AQ Tel: 01371 872105 Fax: 01371 873679; Churchview, High St, Stebbing, Dunmow CM6 3SE — MB BS 1967 Lond.; MRCS Eng. LRCP Lond. 1967. (St. Bart.)

MILLER, Mr Ronald Alan The Whittington Hospital, St Mary's Wing, Department of Urology, Highgate Hill, London N19 5NF Tel: 020 7288 5221 Fax: 020 7288 5565; 39 Shepherds Hill, London N6 5QJ Tel: 020 8341 3422 Email: 340 1376 — MRCS Eng. LRCP Lond. 1974; MS Lond. 1986, MB BS 1974; FRCS Eng. 1979. (St Bartholomews) Cons. Dir. Urol. Whittington; Hon. Cons. Urol. Hosp. John & Eliz.; Hon. Sen. Lect. (Urol.) Inst. Urol. Lond. Socs: Fell. Roy. Soc. Med.; Brit. Assn. Urol. Surgs.; Amer. Urol. Assn. Prev: Sen. Lect. & Lect. (Urol.) Inst. Urol. Lond.; Sen. Regist. (Urol.) St. Bart. Hosp. Lond.

MILLER, Ronald Brown 28 Park Avenue N., Harpenden AL5 2ED — MB ChB Birm. 1955; MRCS Eng. LRCP Lond. 1956; DObst RCOG 1961. Socs: BMA.

MILLER, Mr Roy (retired) 27 Rodger Drive, Rutherglen, Glasgow G73 3QY — MB ChB 1957 Glas.; FRCS Glas. 1968. Prev: Cons. ENT Surg. Monklands Dist. Gen. Hosp. Coatbridge.

MILLER, Roy Gordon 46 Shirley Avenue, Redhill RH1 5AJ — MB BS 1994 Lond.

MILLER, Sara Elizabeth Woman to Woman, 12 Chapel Hill, Farleigh, Bristol BS48 3PP Tel: 01275 464149 — MB BS Lond. 1969; MRCS Eng. LRCP Lond. 1969; DCH Eng. 1971. (Roy. Free) Holistic Phys. Bristol Cancer Help Centre Bristol. Socs: Brit. Holistic Med. Assn.; Med. & Scientif. Network.

MILLER, Sarah 38 Ophir Road, Bournemouth BH8 8LT — BM BCh 1989 Oxf.; BA Oxf. 1986; MRCGP 1993; DRCOG 1993. Clin. Asst. (Palliat. Care) Macmillan Unit ChristCh. Hosp. Prev: Asst. GP Swanage Gp. Pract.; Trainee GP Bournemouth VTS.

MILLER, Sarah Jane 9 The Green, Milcombe, Banbury OX15 4RX — MB ChB 1992 Manch. SHO (Histopath.) John Radcliffe Hosp. Oxf.

MILLER, Sarah Margaret Mortimer Surgery, Victoria Road, Mortimer Common, Reading RG7 1HG Tel: 0118 933 2436 Fax: 0118 933 3801; The Corner House, Calcot Park, Reading

MILLER

RG31 7RW — BM (Hons.) Soton 1983; DCH RCP Lond. 1986; DRCOG 1985. (Soton.) GP Mortimer Surg. Reading.

MILLER, Saul Nicholas The Belford Medical Practice, Croftfield, Belford NE70 7ER Tel: 01668 213738 Fax: 01668 213072 — MB BCh 1990 Wales; MPhil 1999 Glas.; MRCGP 1995; DCH RCP Lond. 1994. (Uni. Wales Coll. Med. Cardiff) Princip. GP, Belford Med Prac. Belford, Nrthhumber. Socs: Roy. Soc. Med.; BMA; Med. Protec. Soc. Prev: Scott. Higher Professional Train. Fell. in Gen. Pract.

***MILLER, Scott Alexander David** Flat 4/L, 7 Garth St., Merchant City, Glasgow G1 1UT — MB ChB 1995 Glas.

MILLER, Sheila Maud Scar Brow, Elmbank Road, Wylam NE41 8HS Tel: 01661 853766 — MB BS 1935 Lond.; MRCS Eng. LRCP Lond. 1935; DCH Eng. 1937. (Lond. Sch. Med. Wom.) Prev: Res. Med. Off. Qu. Hosp. Childr. Hackney Rd.; Ho. Phys. Roy. Free Hosp.; Ho. Surg. S. Lond. Hosp. Wom.

***MILLER, Shona Catriona** 14 Chatelherault Avenue, Cambuslang, Glasgow G72 8BJ — MB ChB 1997 Aberd.

MILLER, Simon Aubrey St Jermain Surgeon General's Department, Ministry of Defence, Whitehall, London SW1A 2HW — MB BChir 1976 Camb.; FFPHM RCP (UK) 1997; MRCGP 1981; DRCOG 1980. Specialist Regist. N. Thames Rot. (Rhemat. & Gen. Med.) Lond. Prev: Regist. (Rhemat. & Gen. Med.) Centr. Middlx. Hosp. Lond.; Reg. (Gen. Med.)Kingston Hosp.

MILLER, Mr Stanley Erle Pitt Westbourne, 4 Agates Lane, Ashtead KT21 2NF — MB ChB 1961 Glas.; FRCS Ed. 1967; FRCS Glas. 1967.

MILLER, Stephen Charles Paxton Green Health Centre, 1 Alleyn Park, London SE21 8AU Tel: 020 8670 6878 Fax: 020 8766 7057; 56A Church Road, London SE19 2EZ Tel: 020 8768 0062 Fax: 020 8768 0478 Email: 100666.2735@compuserve.com — MB BS 1989 Lond.; BSc (Hons.) Lond. 1986; MRCGP 1996; DRCOG 1995; T(GP) 1994. (Char. Cross & Westm.) Hon. Clin. Asst. (Urol.) KCH Lond. Prev: Trainee GP Pk. Surg. Horsham.

MILLER, Stephen Geoffrey Imeary Street Surgery, 78 Imeary Street, South Shields NE33 4EG Tel: 0191 456 3824 Fax: 0191 427 5145 — MB BS 1977 Newc.

MILLER, Stephen John Ilkeston Health Centre, South Street, Ilkeston DE7 5PZ Tel: 0115 932 2968; 85 Toton Lane, Nottingham NG9 7HB — MB BS 1980 Newc.; MRCGP 1984; DCCH RCGP & FCM 1984. Prev: Trainee GP N.umbria VTS.

MILLER, Sir Stephen William Macdonald, Bt Beech House Surgery, Beech House, Shebbear, Beaworthy EX21 5RU Tel: 01409 281221 — MB BS 1977 Lond.; FRCS Eng. 1981; LMSSA Lond. 1976; FRCGP 1995, M 1986. (St. Bart.) Prev: Trainee GP Norwich VTS; Regist. (Surg.) Sheff. HA; Regist. (Orthop.) Newc. HA.

MILLER, Steven Andrew Ashdown Forest Health Centre, Lewes Road, Forest Row RH18 5AQ Tel: 01342 822131 Fax: 01342 826015; Perryhill Oast, Edenbridge Road, Hartfield TN7 4JP — MB BS 1981 Lond.; MRCGP 1986; DFFP 1993; DRCOG 1984. GP Princip., Ashdown Forest Health Centre, Forest Row, Sussex; Mem. GP Staff Qu. Vict. Hosp. E. Grinstead. Prev: Trainee GP Tunbridge Wells VTS; Ho. Phys. St. Richard's Hosp. Chichester; Ho. Surg. St. Mary's Hosp. Lond.

MILLER, Stuart The Surgery, 143A Uxbridge Road, London W12 9RD Tel: 020 8743 1511 Fax: 020 8740 0310; 175 Hendon Way, London NW2 2NB Tel: 020 8209 1016 — MB ChB 1966 Sheff.; MB ChB (Hnrs.) Sheff. 1966. (Sheff.) Dir. (Occupat. Med.) Hammersmith Hosps. NHS Trust; Med. Adviser Occupat. Health Centr. Middlx. Hosp. Lond. & Roy Verw. Coll. Univ Lond. Prev: Clin. Asst. King Edwd. Memor. Hosp. Ealing; Ho. Surg. & Ho. Phys. Roy. Infirm. Sheff.

MILLER, Stuart Ross 6 St James Road, Hereford HR1 2QS — MB BS 1986 Adelaide.

MILLER, Susan Mary Dykebar Hospital, Grahamston Road, Paisley PA2 7DE Tel: 0141 884 5122 — MB ChB 1979 Glas.; MRCPsych 1986; DRCOG 1982. Cons. Psychiat. Renfrewsh. Healthcare NHS Trust. Prev: Cons. Psychiat. Gt.er Glas. HB.

MILLER, Terence David 25 Ottoline Drive, Troon KA10 7AN — MB BCh BAO 1967 Belf.; LMCC 1976; FFA RCS Eng. 1972. Cons. Anaesth. Ayrsh. & Arran HB. Socs: Assn. Anaesth. GB & Irel. Prev: Anaesth. Toronto W.. Hosp. Canada; Fell. (Anaesth.) Baylor Coll. Med. Houston Texas; Ho. Off. Roy. Vict. Hosp. Belf.

MILLER, Tessa Caroline Wright and Partners, Heald Green Medical Centre, Finney Lane, Heald Green, Cheadle SK8 3JD Tel: 0161 436 8448 Fax: 0161 493 9268; Parvey Lodge, Parvey Lane, Sutton, Macclesfield SK11 0HX — MB BS 1979 Lond.; DCH RCP Lond. 1981. (Lond. Hosp.) Prev: Trainee GP Cheadle Hulme VTS; SHO (O & G) N. Manch. Gen. Hosp.; SHO (A & E) Stockport Infirm.

MILLER, Thomas Parkside Cottage, Spoor St., Durston, Gateshead NE11 9BD — LRCP LRCS 1935 Ed.; LRCP LRCS Ed. LRFPS Glas. 1935. (Durh.)

***MILLER, Thomas George Dryden** 77 Dundonald Road, Kilmarnock KA1 1TQ — MB ChB 1998 Glas.; MB ChB Glas 1998.

MILLER, Thomas Marchbank West Wing, Esk Medical Centre, Musselburgh EH21 6A; 5 Seaview Terrace, Edinburgh EH15 2HD — MB ChB 1949 Glas. (Prev: Ho. Surg. W.. Infirm. Glas.; Ho. Off. Glas. Roy. Matern. Hosp.

MILLER, Thomas Nigel Romans Halt, Church Lane, Mildenhall, Marlborough SN8 2LX Tel: 01672 511253 Fax: 01672 512516 Email: nigel.miller@lycos.com — BM BCh 1960 Oxf.; MA, BM BCh Oxf. 1960; FRCP Lond. 1979, M 1964. (St. Thos.) Hon. Cons. Phys. Gastroenterologist Qu.'s Hosp. Burton Hosp.s NHS Trust Burton upon Trent. Socs: Fell. Med. Soc. Lond.; Brit. Soc. Gastroenterol.; FRSM. Prev: Sen. Med. Regist. W.m. Hosp. Lond.; Regist. (Med.) & Sen. Med. Cas. Off. St. Thos. Hosp. Lond.

MILLER, Thomas Robert 3 Chapel Street, Watlington OX49 5QT — BM BS 1992 Nottm.

***MILLER, Timothy Ellis** Town Farm Cottage, Shirwell, Barnstaple EX31 4JU Tel: 01271 850376 — MB ChB 1997 Birm.

MILLER, Veronica Anne 62 Kilmore Road, Lurgan, Craigavon BT67 9LW — MB ChB 1987 Birm.; ChB Birm. 1987.

MILLER, Victor BUPA Hospital, Manchester M16 8AJ Tel: 0161 232 2278; Summer Trees, Hawley Drive, Hale Barns, Altrincham WA15 0DP Tel: 0161 980 2573 Fax: 0161 980 5991 Email: victor_miller@lineone.net — MB ChB 1961 Glas.; FRCP Lond. 1994; FRCP Glas. 1979, M 1965; FRCPCH 1996; DCH RCPS Glas. 1963. (Glas.) p/t Hon. Cons. Paediat. Gastroenterol. Manch. Childr. Hosps. NHS Trust. Prev: Sen. Regist. (Med.) Manch. RHB; Regist. Hosp. Sick Childr. Gt. Ormond St.; Asst. Chief Resid. Phys. Childr. Hosp. Philadelphia, USA.

MILLER, Mr William (retired) 7 Altonhead Drive, Cunninghamhead, Kilmarnock KA3 2PB — MB ChB 1966 Glas.; FRCS Eng. 1972; FRCS Ed. 1971. Prev: Cons. Surg. CrossHo. Hosp. Kilmarnock.

MILLER, William 11 Lodge Avenue, Mortlake, London SW14 8PQ Tel: 020 8876 7888 Fax: 020 8876 7888 — MB ChB 1956 Glas. (Glas.) Chairm. Med. Advis. Comm. (Serv. Comm. & Tribunal Regs 1972) Lond.; Med. Assessor Indep. Tribunal Serv. Lond. Socs: BMA (Chairm. Richmond, Twickenham & Roehampton Div., Ex-Chairm. Leeds Div.). Prev: GP W. Yorks.; Sen. Med. Off. DoH Lond.

MILLER, William David Waters Health Clinic, Brightons, Falkirk FK2 0RH Tel: 01324 715540; 19 Cranshaws Drive, Redding, Falkirk FK2 9UY Tel: 01324 713689 — MB ChB 1953 Ed. (Ed.) Prev: Ho. Surg. Roy. Infirm. Perth; Ho. Phys. Bridge of Earn Hosp. Perth.

MILLER, William George The Surgery, 5 Enys Road, Eastbourne BN21 2DQ Tel: 01323 410088 Fax: 01323 644638 — MB BS 1980 Lond.

MILLER, William Gordon Dennis and Partners, The Medical Centre, Folly Lane, Bewsey, Warrington WA5 0LU Tel: 01925 417247 Fax: 01925 444319; Touraine, West Lane, Broomedge, Lymm WA13 0TW — MB ChB 1981 Manch.; DRCOG 1987.

MILLER, William Leslie Bruce (retired) 62 Kilmore Road, Craigavon BT67 9LW Tel: 02838 323977 Fax: 02838 323977 — MB BCh BAO 1958 Dub.

MILLER - JONES, Carl Michael Hugh East Kent Hospitals NHS trust, William Harvey Hospital, Willesborough, Ashford TN24 0LZ Tel: 01233 616041 Fax: 01233 616043; 7 Fairlight Road, Hythe CT21 4AD Tel: 01303 265787 Email: carl.miller-jones@which.net — MB BS 1971 Lond.; BSc (Biochem.) Lond. 1968; MRCS Eng. LRCP Lond. 1971; FFA RCS Eng. 1977. (Char. Cross) Cons. Anaesth. E. Kent Hosps. NHS Trust William Harvey Hosp. Ashford. Socs: Fell.Roy. Coll. Anaesth.s.; Assn. Anaesth. & Obst. Anaesthetics Assoc.; Difficult Airway Soc. Prev: Sen. Regist. Rotat. King's Coll. Hosp. Lond., Brighton, The Brook & Qu. Victora Hosp. E. Grinstead; Regist. (Anaesth.) Magill Dept. Anaesths. W.minster Hosp. Lond.; Sen. Ho. Off. (Anaesth.) Middlx. Hosp. Lond.

MILLERCHIP, Rachel 132 London Road, Stockton Health, Warrington WA4 6LE — MB ChB 1991 Liverp.

MILLERSHIP, Sally Elizabeth North Essex Health Authority, Collingwood Road, Witham CM8 2TT Tel: 01376 302283 Fax: 01376 302278 Email: neha_ccdci@compuserve.com — MB BChir 1978 Camb.; MSc Lond. 1985, 1995; MA Camb. 1979, MD 1987; MSSA Lond. 1978; FRCPath 1996; MFPHM 1996. (Camb. & St. Thos.) Cons. Communicable Dis. Control. N. Essex HA; Hon. Cons. Microbiol. P.ss Alexandra Hosp. Trust Harlow; Cons. Communicable Dis. Control S. Essex Health Auth.

MILLES, John Jennings 58 Anchorage Road, Sutton Coldfield B74 2PL Tel: 0121 354 6918 — MB BChir 1974 Camb.; MB Camb. 1974, MA, BChir 1973; MRCP (UK) 1976; FRCP 1991. (Cambs/Kings College) Cons. Phys. Gen. Med. Diabetes. Endocrinol. Good Hope.Hosps.alford. Socs: BMA; BDA. Prev: Research Fell. Qu. Eliz. Hosp. & Gen. Hosp. Birm.; Regist. (Med.) & SHO (Med.) N. Staffs. Roy. Infirm.; Ho. Off. (Med. & Surg.) Kings Coll. Hosp. Lond.

***MILLIAMS, Sarah Lucie** Dawn Cottage, 25 The Dell, Bredon, Tewkesbury GL20 7QP — MB BS 1998 Lond.; MB BS Lond 1998.

MILLICAN, Dean Linton James Paget Healthcare NHS Trust, Lowestoft Road, Gorleston, Great Yarmouth NR31 6LA Tel: 01493 452475; Millbeck, Priory Road, St. Olaves NR319HQ Tel: 01493 488528 Email: docdeano@hotmail.com — MB ChB 1983 Leeds; FRCA 1991. (Univ. Leeds) Cons. Anaesth. James Paget NHS Healthcare Trust.

MILLIGAN, David Wyndham Alexander Newcastle Neonatal Service, Ward 35, Leazes Wing, Royal Victoria Infirmary, Newcastle upon Tyne NE1 4LP Tel: 0191 282 5034 Fax: 0191 282 5038 Email: d.w.a.milligan@net.ac.uk — MB BS Lond. 1969; BA Open 1992; LMCC (Canada) 1979; FRCP Lond. 1988, M 1973; DCH Eng. 1971; FRCPCH 1997. (St. Thos.) Cons. Neonat. Paediat. Newc. Hosps. Trust. Socs: Brit. Assn. Perinatal Med.; (Ex. Hon. Asst. Sec.) Roy. Coll. Paediat. & Child Health; Neonat. Soc. Prev: Sen. Regist. (Paediat.) Univ. Coll. Hosp. Lond.; Fell. Hosp. Sick Childr. Toronto; Lect. Lond. Hosp. Med. Coll. 1976-7.

MILLIGAN, Deborah Dawn The Loddon Vale Practice, Hurricane Way, Woodley, Reading RG5 4UX Tel: 0118 969 0160 Fax: 0118 969 9103 — MB BS 1991 Lond.

MILLIGAN, Donald William Department of Haematology, Birmingham Heartlands Hospital, Birmingham B9 5SS Tel: 0121 424 2000 Fax: 0121 766 7530 Email: d.w.milligan@bham.ac.uk — MB ChB 1984 Leeds; MB ChB Leeds 1975; MD Leeds 1984, BSc 1972; FRCP Lond. 1993; MRCP (UK) 1979; FRCPath 1995, M 1985. Cons. Haemat. Birm. Heartlands & Solihull Hosps. Socs: Brit. Soc. Haematol. & BMA; Amer. Soc. Haemat.; Treas. BSBMT 1996. Prev: Sen. Regist. (Haemat.) Leeds Gen. Infirm.; Regist. (Haemat.) Manch. Roy. Infirm.; Tutor (Med.) Leeds Gen. Infirm.

MILLIGAN, Gail Mercedes 3 The Dell, Farnham GU9 0ND — MB ChB 1998 Manch.; MB ChB Manch 1998.

MILLIGAN, Gavin John Hartlepool Health Centre, Victoria Road, Hartlepool TS26 8PB Tel: 01429 278179; 28 Clifton Avenue, Hartlepool TS26 9QN Tel: 01429 273871 — MB ChB 1990 Ed.; MRCGP 1994; DRCOG 1993. (Ed.)

MILLIGAN, Mr George Findlay (retired) 34 Regent Street, Nottingham NG1 5BT Tel: 0115 956 1306 — MB ChB 1965 Glas.; FRCS Ed. 1970. Indep. Cons. Orthopaedic Surg. in Medico-legal Pract. Prev: Cons. Orthopaedic Surg. Qu.'s Med. Centre Nottm.

MILLIGAN, Graeme Robert University Health Service, University of Edinburgh, Richard Verney Health Centre, 6 Bristo Square, Edinburgh EH8 9AL Tel: 0131 650 2777 Fax: 0131 662 1813; 17 Cluny Terrace, Edinburgh EH10 4SW — MB ChB 1974 Ed.; BSc Ed. 1971, MB ChB 1974; MRCGP 1979; DRCOG 1981. GP Lothian HB.

MILLIGAN, Henry Ewan (retired) Birches, Brookside Close, Runcton, Chichester PO20 6PY Tel: 01243 784302 — BM BCh 1950 Oxf.; MA, BM BCh Oxf. 1950. Prev: Ho. Phys. St. Bart. Hosp. & Brompton Hosp.

MILLIGAN, Howard Scott 1 Warwick Road, Worsley, Manchester M28 7BW — MB ChB 1990 Sheff.; DGM RCP Lond. 1994. Med. Off. Bolton Hospice. Socs: Brit. Geriat. Soc.

MILLIGAN, Hugh Peter Cumberland House, 58 Scarisbrick New Road, Southport PR8 6PG Tel: 01704 501500 Fax: 01704 549382; 20 Roe Lane, Southport PR9 9DX — MB ChB 1969 St. And.; MRCP (U.K.) 1974. Prev: Regist. (Med.) United Liverp. Hosps.

MILLIGAN, James Adam Avenue Medical Centre, Adam Avenue, Airdrie ML6 6DN Tel: 0123 64 763581; Dalmagarry, Victoria Place, Airdrie ML6 9BX — MB ChB 1960 Glas.

***MILLIGAN, James Conrad** 30 Granby Road, Cheadle Hulme, Cheadle SK8 6LS — BM BS 1995 Nottm.

MILLIGAN, James Harper (retired) 49 The Broadway, Thorpe Bay, Southend-on-Sea SS1 3HG Tel: 01702 588050 — M.B., Ch.B. Ed. 1937.

***MILLIGAN, James Patrick** 25 Heathfield Place, Cardiff CF14 3JZ — MB BCh 1995 Wales.

MILLIGAN, John Alexander Central Health Centre, Town Centre, Cumbernauld, Glasgow G67 1BJ Tel: 0141 737214 Fax: 0141 781699; Craigmarloch Medical Centre, 17 Auchinbee Way, Cumbernauld, Glasgow G68 0EZ Tel: 01236 780700 — MB ChB 1955 Ed.

MILLIGAN, Julia Mary Purvis and Partners, The Hart Surgery, York Road, Henley-on-Thames RG9 2DR Tel: 01491 843204 Fax: 01491 411296; Brigand House, 41 Kennylands Road, Sonning Common, Reading RG4 9JR Tel: 0118 972 3898 — MB ChB Leeds 1975; MRCGP 1978; DRCOG 1978; Cert. Family Plann. JCC 1978. (Leeds) Med. Off. Young Disabled Unit & Cas. Off. Townlands Hosp. Henley-on-Thames. Socs: Reading Path. Soc.

MILLIGAN, Keith Alastair 44A Church Lane, Middlesbrough TS7 9AU Tel: 01642 320163 — MB BS 1982 Lond.; FFA RCSI 1988. (St. Bart.) Cons. Anaesth. & Pain Relief S. Tees Acute NHS Trust Middlesbrough. Socs: Anaesth. Res. Soc.; Internat. Assn. Study of Pain. Prev: Sen. Regist. (Anaesth.) Newc. Hosps.; Lect. (Anaesth.) Sheff. Univ.; Regist. (Anaesth.) Nottm. Hosps.

MILLIGAN, Kerry Elizabeth Flat 26, 72 St Vincent Crescent, Glasgow G3 8NQ — MB ChB 1994 Glas.

MILLIGAN, Kevin Robert 7 Marlborough Park, Cross Avenue, Belfast BT9 6HQ — MD 1988 Belf.; MB BCh BAO 1980; FFA RCSI 1984; DA Eng. 1982. Cons. Anaesth. Belf. City, Musgrave Pk. & Roy. Vict. Hosps. Socs: Assn. Anaesth. Gt. Brit. & N. Irel.; N. Irel. Soc. Anaesth. Prev: Regist. (Anaesth.) E. Health & Social Servs. Bd. (N.Irel.).

***MILLIGAN, Lisa Jane** Mountside House, 23 Lucknow Drive, Mapperley Park, Nottingham NG3 5EU — MB ChB 1994 Manch.

MILLIGAN, Michael Peter Ratling Court, Ratling, Canterbury CT3 3HN; Ratling Court, Ratling, Canterbury CT3 3HN Tel: 01304 840227 Fax: 01304 842479 Email: spikemilligan@ukgateway.net — MB BS 1969 Lond.; DM Soton. 1982; FRCOG 1995, M 1976; DObst RCOG 1971. Cons. O & G Kent & Canterbury Hosp.; Assoc. Prof. St. Geo. Univ., Grenada; Prof., Kigezi Internat. Sch. Of Med.; Chairm. Of STR, Roy. Coll. Of (O&G). Socs: Becket Med. Soc. Canterbury; RCOG; Pelvic Floor Soc, Cape Town, SA. Prev: Lect. (O & G) St. Thos. Hosp. Lond.; Lect. Soton. Univ. & P.ss Anne Hosp.; Regist. (O & G) Groote Schuur Hosp., Capetown.

MILLIGAN, Nicholas Stephen Department Anaesthetics, Poole General Hospital, Longfleet Road, Poole BH15 2 Tel: 01202 695100; The Knoll, 9 Upper Golf Links Road, Broadstone BH18 8BT — MB ChB 1973 Bristol; FFA RCS Eng. 1979; FFA RCSI 1979. Cons. (Anaesth.) E. Dorset HA.

MILLIGAN, Norman Michael Department of Neurology, Poole General Hospital, Longfleet Road, Poole BH15 2JB; 232 Sandbanks Road, Lilliput, Poole BH14 8HA — MB ChB Birm. 1974; MD Birm. 1982; MRCP (UK) 1978. Cons. Neurol. Poole Gen. Hosp. & Wessex Neurol. Centre Soton. Prev: Sen. Regist. (Neurol.) Univ. Hosp. Wales Cardiff; Research Fell. Inst. Neurol. Qu. Sq. Lond. & Chalfont Centre for Epilepsy Chalfont St. Peter.

MILLIGAN, Patricia Mary Ratling Court, Ratling, Canterbury CT3 3HN — MB ChB 1973 Ed.; DCH Eng. 1976. Princip. In Gen. Pract., Sandwich, Kent; Bd. Mem., Channel PCG.

MILLIGAN, Shelagh Millicent (retired) 19 Maison Belleville, Wellington Road, St Saviour, Jersey JE2 7LZ Tel: 01534 727672 — MB BCh BAO 1953 Belf.

MILLIGAN, Simon David Windy Nook Surgery, Cartmel, Grange-over-Sands LA11 6PJ Tel: 015395 36366 Fax: 015395 36766; Braban House, Burneside, Kendal LA8 9AE Tel: 01539 722020 Fax: 01539 722020 — MB BS 1984 Lond.; MRCGP 1991; DCH RCP Lond. 1991; DRACOG 1989. (Lond. Hosp.)

MILLIGAN, Suzanne Ulster Hospital, Dundonald, Belfast BT16 1RH; 7 Thornhill Mews, Belfast BT5 7AF — MB BCh BAO 1997 Belf. SHO (Gen. Pract.) Rotat.

***MILLIGAN, Trevor Sean** 54 Litherland Park, Liverpool L21 9HR — MB ChB 1997 Leeds.

MILLIGAN

MILLIGAN, Wendy Margaret Northbrook Health Centre, 93 Northbrook Road, Solihull B90 3LX Tel: 0121 746 5000 Fax: 0121 746 5020 — MB ChB 1975 Leeds; BSc Leeds 1971, MB ChB 1975; DRCOG 1978.

MILLIGAN, William Liddell 39 Ebery Grove, Copnor, Portsmouth PO3 6HG Tel: 023 92 22428 — LRCP LRCS 1941 Ed.; BSc Glas. 1938, MD 1944, MB ChB 1941; LRCP LRCS Ed. LRFPS Glas. 1941; MRCPsych 1971. (Glas.) Hon. Cons. Psychiat. Portsmouth & S.E. Hants. Health Dist. Socs: Brit. Med. Assn. Prev: Phys. Supt. St. Jas. Hosp. Portsmouth; Cons. Psychiat. St. Geo. Hosp. Morpeth; Med. Off. RAF.

MILLIKEN, Colin Roy 7 Magheralave Park E., Lisburn BT28 3BT — MB BCh BAO 1991 Belf.

***MILLIKEN, Irene Margaret** 14 Ballylenaghan Park, Primrose Hill, Belfast BT8 6WS — MB BCh 1998 Belf.; MB BCh Belf. 1998.

MILLIKEN, Julie Ann Hilda 3 Glendale Court, Connsbrook Avenue, Belfast BT4 1TS — MB ChB 1984 Sheff.

MILLIKEN, Neil Kenneth Charles Kippen Surgery, Kippen FK8 3D2 Tel: 01786 870369 — MB ChB 1985 Ed.; FDS RCPS (Glas); BDS Ed. 1977; LDS RCS Ed. 1977. (St Andrews/ Edinburgh) Partner Kippen Surg. Kippen, Stirling FK8 3DZ. Socs: Roy. Med. Soc. Edin.; Roy. Odonto-Chir. Soc. Scotl. Prev: Trainee GP Bonnyrigg Midlothian; SHO (Geriat.) Ravenscraig Hosp. Greenock; SHO (Obst.) Rankin Hosp. Greenock.

MILLIKEN, Shaun William George Shotts Health Centre, 36 Station Road, Shotts ML7 5DS Tel: 01501 822099 Fax: 01501 826622; 21 Danes Drive, Scotstown, Glasgow G14 9HZ Tel: 0141 959 4770 — MB ChB 1979 Dundee; MRCGP Ed. 1984; DRCOG 1981; DA Glas. 1987. (Dundee) GP Princip.

MILLIKEN, Thomas David Andrew Room 233, Imperial Cancer Reseach Fund, 44 Lincolns Inn Fields, London WC2A 3PX Tel: 020 7269 3212 Email: d.milliken@ircf.icnet.uk; 6 Fingal Street, Greenwich, London SE10 0JJ Tel: 020 8853 1693 — MB BCh BAO 1991 Belf.; MB BCh Belf. 1991. Specialist Regist. Rotat. Obst. Gyn. S.E. Thames Region.; Research Regist. UMDS & ICRF.

MILLING, Mr Anthony Walter Francis 548 New Hey Road, Huddersfield Royal Infirmary, Huddersfield HD3 3XH Tel: 01484 342000 Fax: 01484 342888; 548 New Hey Road, Mount, Huddersfield HD3 3XH — LRCPI & LM, LRCSI & LM 1969; FRCS Eng. 1976. Cons. Orthop. Surg. Huddersfield Roy. Infirm.; Med. Dir.

MILLING, Mr Martin Ambrose Peter Morriston Hospital, Swansea SA6 6NL Tel: 01792 702222; The Old Rectory, Shirenewton, Chepstow NP16 6RQ Tel: 01291 641503 — MB BChir 1970 Camb.; MA Camb. 1970; FRCS Ed. 1974; FRCS Eng. 1974. (St. Thos.) Cons. Plastic Surg. Morriston Hosp. Swansea. Socs: (Counc.) Brit. Assn. Plastic Surgs.; (Treas.) Craniofacial Soc. GB; Brit. Soc. Surg. Hand. Prev: Cons. Plastic Surg. & Sen. Regist. (Plastic Surg.) St. Lawrence Hosp. Chepstow; Regist. (Plastic Surg.) Leicester Gen. Hosp.

MILLING, Mr Peter Francis (retired) Abbotswood House, Crossag Road, Ballasalla IM9 3DZ — MB BChir Camb. 1941; BA (Hons.) Camb. 1937, MA 1941; FRCS Eng. 1946; MRCS Eng. LRCP Lond. 1940. Prev: Cons. Surg. ENT Univ. Coll. Hosp.

MILLINGTON, Clare 3 Upper Church Street, Bath BA1 2PT — MB ChB 1990 Liverp.; BSc (Hons.) Liverp. 1984, MB ChB 1990. Prev: Trainee GP Bath VTS.

MILLINGTON, Douglas 278 Rocky Lane, Birmingham B42 1NQ Tel: 0121 357 5453 — MB ChB 1952 Manch.; MRCGP 1962; DO Eng. 1967. Ophth. Med. Pract. W. Midl. Prev: Ho. Phys. & SHO Manch. Roy. Infirm; Surg. Lt. RNVR.

MILLINGTON, George William Mark 33A Brocklebank Road, London SW18 3AT — MB BS 1993 Lond.; BSc (1st cl. Hons.) Lond. 1990, MB BS 1993. SHO Rotat. (Med.) Addenbrooke's Hosp. Camb. Prev: SHO (Med.) Hammersmith Hosp. Lond.

MILLINGTON, Gordon William Heyes (retired) 12 Lakeside Road, Lymm WA13 0QE — MB ChB 1939 Liverp.; FRCOG 1965, M 1948. Cons. O & G Warrington & Dist. Hosp. Gp.; Dep. Cons. Obst. & Gyn. Runcorn Memor. Hosp. Prev: Sen. Regist. (O & G) S.port Gp. Hosps.

MILLINGTON, Mr Hugh Trevor Charing Cross Hospital, Fulham Palace Road, London W6 8RF Tel: 020 8846 1007 Fax: 020 8846 1208; 66 Queens Road, Wimbledon, London SW19 8LR Tel: 020 8947 7806 Fax: 020 8947 6041 — MB BS Lond. 1968; FRCS Eng. 1974; MRCS Eng. LRCP Lond. 1968; FFAEM 1993. (Westm.) Cons.

A & E Char. Cross Hosp. Lond.; Postgrad. Sud-Dean Imperial Coll. Sch. of Med. Lond. Prev: Sen Regist. (A & E) Univ. Coll. Hosp. Lond.; Lect. (Surg.) Char. Cross. Hosp. Lond.; SHO St. Jas. Hosp. Lond.

MILLINGTON, Ian Michael Fforestfach Medical Centre, 118 Ravenhill Road, Fforestfach, Swansea SA5 5AA Tel: 01792 581666 Fax: 01792 585332; 586 Pentregethin Road, Ravenhill, Swansea SA5 5ET — MB BCh 1969 Wales; DFFP 1994; Cert. JCC Lond. 1977. Sec. Morgannwg LMC. Socs: Inst. Psychosexual Med.; Gen. Pract. Comm. (Whales); Morganning Local Med. Comm. Prev: Ho. Phys. Cardiff Roy. Infirm.; Cas. Off. & Ho. Surg. Roy. Gwent Hosp. Newport.

MILLINGTON, Malcolm Uxbridge Child Guidance Clinic, Bennett's Yard, Lancaster Road, Uxbridge UB8 1JH Tel: 01895 256521 — MB BS 1961 Lond.; MRCPsych 1972; DPM Eng. 1971; DObst RCOG 1964; DA Eng. 1964. (St. Bart.) Cons. Child Psychiat. Child Guid. Clinics Lond. Boro. Hillingdon & Bowden Hse. Clinic Harrow; Cons. Psychiat. Inst. Marital Studies, Tavistock Clinic Lond.; Mem. UK Counc. for Psychother. Socs: Assoc. Mem. Brit. Psychoanalyt. Soc.; Soc. PsychoAnalyt. & Marital Psychotherapists. Prev: Sen. Regist. (Childr. & Parents) Tavistock Clinic Lond.; Regist. (Psychol. Med.) King's Coll. Hosp. Lond.; Asst. Med. Dir. Hudson Bay Mining & Smelting Company Snow Lake.

***MILLINGTON, Steven Andrew** 65 Cecil Avenue, Sale M33 5BG — BM BS 1998 Nottm.; BM BS Nottm 1998.

MILLINS, Sheena Department of Dermatology, Basildon Hospital, Nether Mayne, Basildon SS16 5NL Tel: 01268 533911; 15 Corona Road, Langdon Hills, Basildon SS16 6HH Tel: 01268 544296 — MB ChB 1975 Aberd.; MRCGP 1981; BMedBiol. 1972; Dip. Pract. Dermat. Wales 1994. Assoc. Specialist (Dermat.) Basildon & Thurrock Hosps. Prev: GP.

MILLINSHIP, Julia 54 The Avenue, Harpfields, Stoke-on-Trent ST4 6DA — MB BS 1979 Lond.; DRCOG 1987.

MILLION, Raymond Oaklands Hospital, Lancaster Road, Salford M6 8AQ Tel: 0161 787 7700 Fax: 0161 787 8097 Email: ray@drmillion.freeserve.co.uk; 1 The Spinney, Ringley Road, Whitefield, Manchester M45 7LZ Tel: 0161 766 1742 Fax: 0161 796 1767 — MB ChB 1956 Manch.; MRCP (UK) 1996; FRCGP 1981, M 1964; DCH Eng. 1960. (Manch.) Cons. Rheum. Univ. Manch. Hope Hosp. Salford & Manch. & Salford Back Pain Centre Ladywell Hosp. Salford; Mem. Med. Appeal Tribunals Indep. Tribunal Serv. Socs: Brit. Soc. Rheum.; Primary Care Rheum. Soc.; Expert Witness Inst. Prev: Mem. (Pres. & Chairm.) Primary Care Soc. for Rheum.; Edr. Jl. Musculoskeletal Med.

MILLIS, Elisabeth Ann Willmott 78 Harley Street, London W1N 1AE Tel: 020 7637 7871 Fax: 020 7580 5671; Linden House, 28B Risborough Road, Stoke Mandeville, Aylesbury HP22 5UT Tel: 01296 614778 — MB BS 1964 Lond.; MD Lond. 1989; MRCOphth 1988; DO Eng. 1967. Socs: (Ex-Pres). Med. Contact Lens Assn.; (Ex-Pres.) Brit. Contact Lens Assn. Prev: Assoc. Specialist W.. Ophth. Hosp. & Paddington Green Childr. Unit St. Mary's Hosp. Lond.; Dir. Contact Lens Unit W.. Ophth. Hosp.

MILLIS, Joanna Louise 2 Sewell Cottages, Low St., Sloley, Norwich NR12 9HB — MB BS 1990 Lond.

MILLIS, Rosalind Ann Hampton Medical Centre, Lansdowne, 49a Priory Road, Hampton TW12 2PB Tel: 020 8979 5150 Fax: 020 8941 9068; Lansdowne, Priory Road, Hampton TW12 2PB Tel: 020 8979 5150 — MB BS 1962 Lond.; MRCS Eng. LRCP Lond. 1962; DObst RCOG 1964. (Guy's) Prev: Med. Regist. Croydon Gen. Hosp.; Res. Med. Off. (Nuffield Ho.) Guy's Hosp. Lond; Paediat. Ho. Phys. FarnBoro. Hosp., Kent.

MILLIS, Rosemary Ruth (retired) Hedley Atkins/ICRF Breast Pathology Laboratory, Guy's Hospital, St Thomas St., London SE1 9RT Tel: 020 7955 4539 Fax: 020 7955 8746 — MB BS Lond. 1962; MRCS Eng. LRCP Lond. 1962; FRCPath 1982, M 1970. Hon. Cons. Histopath. Hedley Atkins/ICRF BrE. Path. Laborat. Guy's Hosp. Lond. Prev: Vis. Asst. Prof. Stanford Univ., USA.

MILLMAN, Adrian Mark 10 Elliot Rise, Hedge End, Southampton SO30 2RU — MB BS 1988 Lond.; MRCGP 1996; DRCOG 1995; DA (UK) 1994. (Guy's Hosp. Lond.)

MILLMAN, Andrew Gareth Occupational Health Department, Nestle UK Ltd, Haxby Road, York YO91 1XY Tel: 01904 602343 Fax: 01904 604531 Email: andrew.millman@uk.nestle.com; 14 Meadow Way, Heworth, York YO31 1EQ Tel: 01904 422427 Email:

andrew.millman@btinternet.com — MB BS 1982 Lond.; AFOM RCP Lond. 1997; D.Occ.Med. RCP Lond. 1995. (Guy's Hosp. Lond.) Sen. Occupat. Phys. Nestle UK Ltd York. Socs: Soc. Occupat. Med. Prev: Occupat. Phys. Nestle UK Ltd. York; Occupat. Phys. Glos. Roy. NHS Trust.

*****MILLMAN, Guy Cameron** 5 Cranmer Gardens, Meltham, Huddersfield HD9 4BS — MB BS 1994 Lond.

MILLN, Janet Elizabeth McFarlane West End Road Surgery, 62 West End Road, Bitterne, Southampton SO18 6TG Tel: 023 8044 9162 Fax: 023 8039 9742; Draycott, Chilworth Road, Chilworth, Southampton SO16 7LA Tel: 02380 768411 Fax: 01703 769798 Email: pmilln@tcp.co.uk — MB BCh 1975 Wales; DRCOG 1978. (Welsh Nat. Sch. Med.)

MILLN, Philip Temple Scott Marchwood Priory Hospital, Hythe Road, Marchwood, Southampton SO40 4WU Tel: 02380 840044 Fax: 02380 207554; Draycott, Chilworth Road, Chilworth, Southampton SO16 7LA Tel: 02380 768411 Fax: 01703 769798 Email: pmillin@tcp.co.uk — MB BS 1973 Lond.; MRCPsych 1980; FRCPsych 1997. (St. Thos. Med. Sch.) Cons. Psychiat. Marchwood Priory Hosp. Soton.; Vis. Fell. (Psychiat.) Univ. Soton. Prev: Cons. Psychiat. Soton. & SW Hants. HA.

MILLNER, Christopher Brian Edwin Prince of Wales Road Surgery, 6 Prince of Wales Road, Dorchester DT1 1PW Tel: 01305 251762 Fax: 01305 251366; 102 Monmouth Road, Dorchester DT1 2DQ — MB BS 1982 Lond.; MRCGP (Distinc.) 1985; Cert. Family Plann. JCC 1985. (Lond. Hosp. Med. Coll.) Prev: Clin. Asst. (Learning Disabil.) Dorchester.

MILLNER, Mr Peter Alan Orthopaedic Office Suite, Ward 23, Level 2, Chancelor Wing, St James's University Hospital, Leeds LS9 7TF Tel: 0113 206 4732 Fax: 0113 206 5156 — MB ChB 1984 (Hons.) Leeds; BSc (Hons.) Leeds 1981; FRCS (Orth.) 1994; FRCS Eng. 1988. Cons. & Sen. Lect. Orthop. Surg. St. Jas. Univ. Hosp. Leeds. Socs: Brit. Orthop. Assn.; Brit. Orthop. Research Soc.; Brit. Scoliosis Soc. Prev: Lect. & Nat. Spinal Fell. (Orthop.) Yorks. Postgrad. Higher Surgic. Train. Scheme; Research Fell. & Hon. Regist. Univ. Dept. Orthop. Surg. St. Jas. Univ. Hosp. Leeds.; Postgrad. Train. Scheme Surg. St. Jas. Univ. Hosp. Leeds.

MILLNER, Veronica Anne Garforth Medical Centre, Main St., Garforth, Leeds LS25 1ER; 11 Lakeland Drive, Alwoodley, Leeds LS17 7PJ — MB ChB 1984 Leeds; Cert. Family Plann. JCC 1987; DRCOG 1987. GP Leeds.

MILLNER, Mr William Frank 15 Harley Street, London W1N 1DA Tel: 020 7580 6833; 3 Seven Roe's Malting, Park Street, Baldock SG7 6YJ Tel: 01462 491979 Fax: 01462 686958 — MB BS 1956 Lond.; FRCS Eng. 1967; FRCS Ed. 1966; DObst RCOG 1957. (St. Thos.) Hon.Cons. Orthop. & Traum. Surg. Lister Hosp. Stevenage. Socs: Fell. BOA; Fell. Roy. Soc. Med. Prev: Sen. Regist. (Orthop. Surg.) Bath & Wessex Orthop. Hosp. & Roy.; United Hosp. Bath; Regist. Rowley Bristow Orthop. Hosp. Pyrford.

MILLNS, Carol Penelope Child Adolescent & Family Service, Moore House, 10-11 Lindum Terrace, Lincoln LN2 5RT Tel: 01522 513875 Fax: 01522 513405; 75 Longdales Road, Lincoln LN2 2JS Tel: 01522 544346 — MB ChB 1968 Ed.; FRCP Lond. 1989; FRCP Ed. 1988; MRCP (UK) 1973; DCH Eng. 1972; FRCPCH 1998. (Ed.) Cons. Paediat. Lincoln Dist. Healthcare Trust. Socs: Roy. Coll. Paediat. & Child Health (Fell.); Brit. Assoc. of Community child health. Prev: Cons. Paediat. S. Lincs. Health Dist. Sen. Med. Off. (Paediat.) Hereford & Worcester AHA; Regist. (Paediat.) Selly Oak Hosp. Birm.

MILLNS, Doreen The Health Centre, Geoffrey St., Preston PR1 5NE Tel: 01772 794227; 34 Croftgate, Fulwood, Preston PR2 8LS Tel: 01772 774250 — MB ChB 1959 Manch.; MRCGP 1975; DCH Eng. 1963. Clin. Asst. (Med.) Roy. Preston Hosp.; Sec. Preston Medico-Ethical Soc. Socs: BMA (Ex-Chairm. Preston, Chorley & S. Ribble Div.). Prev: Regist. (Paediat.) Roy. Infirm. Preston; Ho. Surg. (Neurosurg.) Nat. Hosp. Nerv. Dis. Lond.; Regist. (Neurosurg.) Hosp. Sick Childr. Gt. Ormond St. Lond.

MILLNS, Jonathan Peter Birmingham Womens Hospital, Queen Elizabeth Medical Centre, Birmingham B15 2TG Tel: 0121 472 1377 — MB BS 1979 Lond.; FFARCS Eng. 1984. Cons. Anaesth. Univ. Hosp. Birm. NHS Trust. Prev: Sen. Regist. (Anaesth.) W. Midl. Region; Regist. (Anaesth.) Qu. Eliz. Hosp. Birm.; SHO (Anaesth.) N.ampton Gen. Hosp.

***MILLNS SIZER, Shaun Anthony** 19 Hickman Crescent, Morton, Gainsborough DN21 3BX — MB ChB 1994 Sheff.

MILLO, Julian Leonard Bradford Dorley Cottage, 66 Churchway, Haddenham, Aylesbury HP17 8HA — MB BS 1990 Lond.; BSc Lond. 1987, MB BS 1990; MRCP (UK) 1994; FRCA 1998.

MILLOY, Susan Hamilton Flat 1/1 Camphill House, Queens Park, Pollokshaws Road, Glasgow G41 2DX — MB ChB 1997 Glas.

MILLROY, Miss Sheila Joan Eye Department, Queen Alexandra Hospital, Cosham, Portsmouth PO6 3LY Tel: 023 92 379451; 13 Residence, Royal Hospital Haslar, Gosport PO12 2AA — MB BChir 1976 Camb.; MA Camb. 1976; FRCS Eng. 1982; FRCOphth 1989. (Cambridge and St. Thomas) Assoc. Specialist (Ophth.) Qu. Alexandra Hosp. Portsmouth. Prev: Civil. Assoc. Specialist (Ophth.) RNH Haslar, Gosport; SCMO (Ophth.) Plymouth.

MILLS, Agnes Mary Central Clinic, Cross St., Burton-on-Trent DE14 1EG Tel: 01283 505800; 14 Brizlincote Lane, Burton-on-Trent DE15 0PR Tel: 01283 565929 — MB ChB Birm. 1957; DCH Eng. 1961. Clin. Med. Off. (Child Health) Burton-on-Trent.

MILLS, Alan James David Green End Surgery, 58 Green End, Comberton, Cambridge CB3 7DY Tel: 01223 262500 Fax: 01223 264401; 7 The Elms, Haslingfield, Cambridge CB3 7ND — MB BCh BAO 1984 Belf.; MRCGP 1988; DRCOG 1987.

MILLS, Alan Patrick Graham Clarence Medical Centre, Vansittart Road, Windsor SL4 5AS Tel: 01753 865773 Fax: 01753 833694 — MB ChB 1974 Birm.; MRCGP 1981; DObst RCOG 1976.

MILLS, Alexander Wilson (Surgery), 50 Conisborough Crescent, Catford, London SE6 2SS Tel: 020 8698 8921 Fax: 020 8695 0945; 127 Venner Road, Sydenham, London SE26 5HU Tel: 020 8659 0600 Fax: 020 8695 0945 — MB ChB 1975 Ed.; MRCGP 1981. Prev: Surg. Lt.-Cdr. RN.

MILLS, Alfred Raymond (retired) 23 Inverleith Place, Edinburgh EH3 5QD Tel: 0131 552 4861 — MRCS Eng. LRCP Lond. 1942; PhD Ed. 1962; FRCP Ed. 1979, M 1974; FFCM 1982, M 1976; DPH Ed. 1956; DTM & H Eng. 1949. Prev: WHO Represen. Kathmandu, Nepal.

MILLS, Andrew Frederick Worcestershire Community and Mental Health NHS Trust, Isaac Maddox House, Shrub Hill Road, Worcester WR4 9RW Tel: 01905 681584 Fax: 01905 681596 Email: andy.f.mills@worcsh-tr.wmids.nhs.uk; 24 Britannia Square, Worcester WR1 3DH — MB BS 1978 Lond.; MSc (Community Paediat.) Lond. 1990; MRCP (UK) 1985; FRCPCH 1997; DCH RCP Lond. 1981. (Char. Cross Hosp. Med. Sch.) Clin. Director & Cons. Community Paediat. Worcs. Community Healthcare NHS Trust. Prev: SCMO & Sen. Regist. Bloomsbury & Islington HA.

MILLS, Angela Margaret The United Elizabeth Garrett Anderson Hospital, & Hospital for Women (Soho), 144 Euston Road, London NW1 2AP Tel: 020 7387 2501; 80 Harley Street, London W1N 1AE Tel: 020 7637 0584 Fax: 020 7637 0242 — BM BCh 1972 Oxf.; FRCOG 1993, M 1978; MFPHM RCP (UK) 1996; MFFP 1993. (Somerville Coll. Oxf. & St. Thos. Hosp. Med. Sch. Lond.) Cons. Gyn. Eliz. Garrett Anderson Hosp. Lond.; Hon. Lect. (Obst. & Gyn.) Jt. Med. Sch. UCH & Middlx. Hosp.; Hon. Cons to Margt. Pyke. Socs: Fell. Roy. Soc. Med. Prev: Nat. Med. Off. Family Plann. Assn.; Chair.Clin & Scientif.Community of Fac.Family Plann. & Reproduc.Health.

MILLS, Ann Elizabeth 2 Marton Avenue, Didsbury, Manchester M20 5LN Tel: 0161 445 6780 Email: wyn.price@lineone.net — MB BChir 1990 Camb.; MA Camb. 1991; MRCP (UK) 1993; FRCR Lond. 1997. (Camb. & St. Thomas's Hosp. Lond.) Specialist Regist. (Diagn. Radiol.) Univ. Manch. Prev: SHO (Med.) Roy. Free Hosp. & Coppetts Wood Hosp. Lond.

MILLS, Ann Margaret 7 Henley Road, Ipswich IP1 3SE — MB BS 1958 Lond.; DA Eng. 1961. (Char. Cross) Assoc. Specialist (Anaesth.) Ipswich Hosp.

MILLS, Mr Anthony 79 Belgrave Road, Darwen BB3 2SF Tel: 01254 773194 — MB ChB 1967 St. And.; FRCS Ed. 1974.

MILLS, Mr Asa (retired) 9 Bassett Row, Southampton SO16 7FT Tel: 01703 767844 — MB ChB 1939 Manch.; FRCS Ed. 1948. Prev: GP Soton.

MILLS, Bernard Elms Medical Centre, 31 Hoole Road, Chester CH2 3NH Tel: 01244 351000 — MB ChB 1979 Manch.; DRCOG 1983. Socs: Guild Catholic Doctors.

MILLS

MILLS, Mrs Carole Ann 9 Martins Lane, Witcham, Ely CB6 2LB — BM BS 1987 Nottm.; T(GP) 1992. Trainee GP P'boro. Dist. Hosp.

MILLS, Caroline Ann Burncross Surgery, 1 Bevan Way, Chapeltown, Sheffield S35 1RN Tel: 0114 246 6052 Fax: 0114 245 0276 — MB ChB 1990 Sheff.

MILLS, Caroline Margaret Department of Dermatology, Royal Gwent Hospital, Cardiff Road, Newport NP9 4EZ Tel: 01633 234438; 313 Cyncoed Road, Cyncoed, Cardiff CF23 6PB — MB BCh 1985 Wales; MRCP (UK) 1988; MD 2000; FRCP 2000. Cons. Dermat. Roy. Gwent Hosp. Newport. Prev: Sen. Regist. & Regist. Univ. Hosp. Wales.

MILLS, Catherine Tel: 0141 531 8250 Fax: 0141 531 8248; 12 Berry Hill Drive, Giffnock, Glasgow G46 7AS — MB ChB 1983 Glas.; MRCGP 1987; Cert. Family Plann. JCC 1987; DRCOG 1986. (Glas.)

MILLS, Christian Richard 49 Templegate Crescent, Whitkirk, Leeds LS15 0EZ; 19 Cameron Drive, Ivybridge PL21 9TS Tel: 01752 690058 Email: crmills@qualcon.win-uk.net — MB BS 1996 Lond. (St. Mary's Hospital Medical School) SHO (Surg. Rotat.), Derriford Hosp. Plymouth.

***MILLS, Christopher Alexander** Lintwood, Osmaston, Ashbourne DE6 1LR — MB ChB 1997 Sheff.

MILLS, Christopher David Knowle Green Surgery, Staines Health Centre, Knowle Green, Staines TW18 1XD Tel: 01784 883654 Fax: 01784 441244; 5 Craigwell Close, Staines TW18 3NP Tel: 01784 883650 — MB BS 1977 Lond.; DRCOG 1982. (St. Geo.) Prev: Trainee GP Epsom VTS; Ho. Phys. Dorset Co. Hosp. Dorchester; Ho. Surg. St. Geo. Hosp. Lond.

MILLS, Christopher Herbert (retired) Rose Cottage, Portloe, Truro TR2 5RA Tel: 01872 501128 — MB 1961 Camb.; MA Camb. 1963, MB 1961, BChir 1960; DObst RCOG 1962. Prev: Med. Off. BA MS.

MILLS, Mr Christopher Leslie North Devon District Hospital, Raleigh Park, Barnstaple EX31 4JB Tel: 01271 322489 Fax: 0271 311696; Prixford House, Prixford, Barnstaple EX31 4DX Tel: 01271 329979 — MB ChB Birm. 1974; FRCS Eng. 1981. Cons. Surg. (Orthop. & Trauma) Barnstaple.

MILLS, Clement Aubrey 29 Tyning Road, Saltford, Bristol BS31 3HL Tel: 01225 872459 — MB ChB 1947 Bristol; MB ChB (Hnrs.) Bristol 1947. (Bristol) Prev: Capt. RAMC; Ho. Phys. Profess. Unit Bristol Roy. Infirm.

MILLS, Cyrus Selvajeyan Ticehurst House Hospital, Ticehurst, Wadhurst TN5 7HU Tel: 01580 200391 — MB BS 1986 Madras. Specialist (Psychosexual Med.) Ticehurst Ho. Hosp. E. Sussex; Clin. Dir. Dept. of Marital & Sexual Ther. Ticehurst Hosp. E. Sussex. Socs: Fell. Roy. Soc. Med. Prev: Specialist Psychosexual Med. Ticehurst Ho. Hosp. E. Sussex.

MILLS, David Cameron Cherry Brook Medical Centre, Hookhills Road, Paignton Tel: 01803 844566; Orley Gate, Ipplepen, Newton Abbot TQ12 5SA Tel: 01803 812110 — BM BCh 1973 Oxf.; MA. GP Paignton. Prev: Trainee Gen. Pract. Torbay Vocational Train. Scheme; SHO (Orthop. & Trauma) Torbay Hosp. Torquay.

MILLS, David Charles Department of Anaesthesia, Mount Vernon Hospital, Rickmansworth Road, Northwood HA6 2RN; 92 Lower Road, Gerrards Cross SL9 8LB Tel: 01753 890423 — MB ChB 1983 Manch.; FFA RCS Eng. 1988. Cons. Anaesth. Mt. Vernon Hosp. N.wood Middlx. Prev: Sen. Regist. (Anaesth.) N. W.. RHA.

MILLS, David Michael John Nics Occupational Health Service, Lincoln Buildings, Great Victoria Street, Belfast BT2 7SH — MB BCh BAO 1984 Belf.; 2000 Masters Degree in Business Admin.; MRCGP 1992; DRCOG 1991; DMH Belf. 1991; DCH NUI 1990. Med. Off. Occupat.al Health. Socs: Brit. Med. Assn. Ulster Med. Soc.

MILLS, Douglas John Owen (retired) 23 Churchfield Court, Girton, Cambridge CB3 0XA — MB BS Lond. 1959; MRCS Eng. LRCP Lond. 1958. Prev: Jun. Lect. Inst. Path. Lond. Hosp.

MILLS, Eileen Elspeth Dept. of Anaesthetics, Monklands District General Hospital, Monkscourt Avenue, Airdrie ML6 0JS — MB ChB 1966 St. And.; DA Eng. 1970.

MILLS, Eleanor Mary (retired) The Coachman's House, Moseley Hall, Knutsford WA16 8RB Tel: 01565 653428 — MB ChB 1936 Manch.; FRCS Eng. 1940; MRCS Eng. LRCP Lond. 1937; FRCOG 1958, M 1942. Prev: Cons. O & G N. Manch. Hosp., Stretford Memor. Hosp. & Manch. N.ernHosp.

***MILLS, Elizabeth Jane** 24 Hammerton Street, Pudsey LS28 7DD — MB ChB 1998 Leeds.

MILLS, Elizabeth Jayne Flat 11, Norfolk Mews, 140A South St., Dorking RH4 2EX — MB BS 1990 Lond.; MRCGP 1995; DRCOG 1993.

MILLS, Elizabeth Mary 42 Kinedale Park, Ballynahinch BT24 8YS Tel: 01238 561197 — MB BCh BAO 1940 Belf. (Belf.)

MILLS, Francis 136 Manor Road N., Thames Ditton KT7 0BH Tel: 020 8398 2633 — MB ChB 1955 St. And.; BA Open Univ. 1989; MRCP (UK) 1971; DTM & H Eng. 1959. (St. And.) Cons. Phys. Roy. Surrey Co. Hosp. Guildford. Socs: BMA. Prev: Regist. (Neurol.) Wessex Neurol. Centre Soton. Gen. Hosp.

MILLS, Francis Charles Andrew The Surgery, 2 Church Lane, Merton Park, London SW19 3NY Tel: 020 8542 1174 Fax: 020 8544 1583 — MB BS 1982 Lond.; MRCGP 1986; DRCOG 1985.

MILLS, Gary Hylton Department of Surgical & Anaesthesia Sciences, K Floor, Royal Hallamshire Hospital, Glossop Road, Sheffield S10 Tel: 0114 271 2510 Fax: 0114 271377 Email: g.h.mills@sheffild.ac.uk — MB ChB 1985 Sheff.; BMedSci 1984; FRCA 1992. Sen. Lect. (Anaesth. & IC) Univ. of Sheff. Socs; Fell. Roy. Coll. Anaesth.; Intens. Care Soc. (Treas. Trainee Subcomm.). Prev: Hon. Regist. & Research Fell. (Thoracic Med. & Anaesth.) Roy. Brompton & King's Coll. Hosps. Lond.

MILLS, Geoffrey Arthur Highfield Health Centre, 2 Proctor Street, off Tong Street, Bradford BD4 9QA Tel: 01274 227700 Fax: 01274 227900; Upton Cottage, 46 Glen Road, Bingley BD16 3ET — BSc Lond. 1974, MB BS 1977; MRCP (UK) 1982; DRCOG 1984; DCH RCP Lond. 1985. GP Bradford.

MILLS, Geoffrey Frederick (retired) 49 Glebelands Road, Prestwich, Manchester M25 1WF Tel: 0161 773 8791 — MB ChB 1959 Manch. Prev: Assoc. Specialist (Psychiat.) Ment. Health Servs. Salford NHS Trust.

MILLS, George William, MBE Wayside, 40 High St., Elie, Leven KY9 1DB — MB ChB 1943 St. And.; MB ChB (Commend.) St. And. 1943; FRCGP 1975; DObst RCOG 1945. (St. And.) Prev: R.A.M.C.; Cas. Off. & Ho. Surg. Med. Wards Infirm. Perth.

MILLS, Gordon Newman Lakeside Surgery, Lakeside Road, Lymm, Warrington WA13 0QE Tel: 01925 755050 — MB ChB 1982 Manch.; MRCGP 1987; DGM RCP Lond. 1986. GP Lymm.

MILLS, Hazel Leela Queens Park and Moredon Surgeries, 146 Drove Road, Swindon SN1 3AG Tel: 01793 487394 Fax: 01793 342011 — MB BCh 1982 Wales; BSc (Physiol. & Biochem.) Soton. 1977; MRCGP 1986; DCH RCP Lond. 1984.

MILLS, Heather Margaret 29 Tobermore Road, Magherafelt BT45 5HB — MB ChB 1990 Dundee.

MILLS, Helen The Health Centre, 2 Duke Street, Hoyland, Barnsley S74 9QS Tel: 01226 748719 Fax: 01226 360162 — MB ChB 1984 Sheff.; MRCGP 1988; DRCOG 1986. Socs: BMA. Prev: Trainee GP Barnsley VTS; Ho. Off. (Gen. Surg.) Rotherham Dist. Gen. Hosp.; Ho. Off. (Med.) W.on Pk. & Roy. Hallamsh. Hosps. Sheff.

MILLS, Mr Ian William University Department of Pharmacology, Mansfield Road, Oxford OX1 3QT Tel: 01865 271878 Email: ian.mills@pharm.ox.ac.uk — BM BCh 1991 Oxf.; MA Camb. 1992; FRCS Eng. 1995. Research Fell. (Urol.) Univ. Dept. Pharmacol. Oxf. Prev: SHO (Gen. Surg. & Urol.) N.ampton Gen. Hosp.; Demonst. (Anat.) Guy's Hosp. Lond.; SHO (A & E) St. Thos. Hosp. Lond.

MILLS, Ivor Henry 6 Spinney Drive, Great Shelford, Cambridge CB2 5LY — MB BChir 1951 Camb.; BSc Lond. 1942, PhD 1946, BA Camb. 1948, MA 1963, MD 1956; FRCP Lond. 1964, M 1953; Hon. FACP 1975. (St. Thos.) Emerit. Prof. Med. Univ. Camb.; Hon. Cons. Addenbrooke's Hosp. Camb. Socs: Assn. Phys.; Research Soc.; Med. Research Soc. & Renal Assn. Prev: Censor Roy. Coll. Phys.; Reader in Med. St. Thos. Hosp. Med. Sch.; Med. Research Counc. (Eli Lilly) Trav. Fell. (1956-7).

MILLS, James Edward Orchard Medical Practice, Innisdoon, Crow Hill Drive, Mansfield NG19 7AE Tel: 01623 400100 Fax: 01623 400101; The Brew House, 9 New Road, Oxton, Southwell NG25 0SL — MB ChB 1991 Birm.

MILLS, James Kenyon Culcheth Surgery, Thompson Avenue, Culcheth, Warrington WA3 4EB Tel: 01925 765101 Fax: 01925 765102; 32 Deniston Road, Heaton Moor, Stockport SK4 4RF — MRCS Eng. LRCP Lond. 1956; MRCGP 1968; AFOM RCP Lond. 1982; DObst RCOG 1958. (Manch.) Occupat. Phys. Warrington HA. Socs: Fell. Manch. Med. Soc.; Soc. Occupat. Med.

MILLS, Janet Hart The Health Centre, 68 Pipeland Road, St Andrews KY16 8JZ Tel: 01334 477477 Fax: 01334 466512; Westcroft, Wardlaw Gardens, St Andrews KY16 9DW Tel: 01334 73156 — MB ChB 1966 St. And. GP Princip. St. And.

MILLS, John Arthur Westcroft, Wardlaw Gardens, St Andrews KY16 9DW Tel: 01334 73156 — MD 1974 Dundee; MB ChB St. And. 1966; FRCOG 1985, M 1971. Cons. O & G Ninewells Hosp. Dundee. Socs: Edin. Obst. Soc. & Soc. Study Fertil.. Prev: Sen. Regist. (O & G) Simpson Memor. Matern. Pavil. & Roy.; Infirm. Edin.; Ford Foundat. Research Fell. Dept. O & G Univ. Penna.

MILLS, Mr John Nkrumah 50 Beechwood Gardens, Rainham RM13 9HU — MB ChB 1975 Ghana; FRCS Ed. 1987.

MILLS, John Samuel 314 Wigan Road, Standish, Wigan WN6 0AD Tel: 01257 421078 — LRCPI & LM, LRSCI & LM 1955; LRCPI & LM, LRCSI & LM 1955. (RCSI) Prev: Cas. Off., Ho. Phys. & Sen. Ho. Off. (Orthop.) Roy. Albert Edwd.; Infirm. Wigan.

MILLS, John Warwick X-Ray Department, Ipswich Hospital, Heath Road, Ipswich IP4 5PD Tel: 01473 712233 — MB BS 1958 Lond.; MRCP Lond. 1963; FFR 1968; DMRD Eng. 1965. (Middlx.) Cons. Radiol. Ipswich Hosps. Prev: Sen. Regist. Middlx. Hosp. Lond. & Harefield Hosp.; Instruc. in Radiol. Yale Univ. Sch. Med. New Haven, U.S.A.; Sen. Regist. (Radiol.) Middlx. & Roy. N.. Hosps.

***MILLS, Joseph David** 85 Steel Road, Birmingham B31 2RQ — BChir 1994 Camb.

MILLS, Jude Forty Willows Surgery, 46 Forty Lane, Wembley HA9 9HA Tel: 020 8385 0011 Fax: 020 8385 0411; 141 Salmon Street, Kingsbury, London NW9 8NG Tel: 020 8205 9139 Email: jude.mills@virgin.net — MB BS 1979 Lond.; MRCS Eng. LRCP Lond. 1979; MRCGP 1985; DRCOG 1984. (Char. Cross)

***MILLS, Julia Katherine** 45 Loftus Road, London W12 7EH — MB ChB 1997 Aberd.

MILLS, Julian Charles Kew (retired) Bramble Way, Tremorvah Crescent, Truro TR1 1NL — MB BChir 1964 Camb.; MA, MB Camb. 1964, BChir 1963; Dip. Bact. Lond. 1969. Prev: Truro.

MILLS, June Doreen (retired) 34 Padbrook, Detillens Lane, Limpsfield, Oxted RH8 0DZ — BSc, MB BCh Wales 1949; MRCS Eng. LRCP Lond. 1949; DPH Eng. 1967. Prev: SCMO Croydon HA.

MILLS, Kathryn Frances 60 Celandine Way, Cepan Park N., Chippenham SN14 6XQ Tel: 01249 651639 Email: kathryn.mills@virgin.net; 60 Celandine Way, Cepan Park N., Chippenham SN14 6XQ Tel: 01249 651639 — BM 1997 Soton. Prev: SHO (A & E) Swindon; PRHO (Surg.) Basingstoke; PRHO (Med.) Swindon.

MILLS, Katie Elizabeth 164 Station Road, Harpenden AL5 4RH — MB BS 1994 Lond.

MILLS, Mr Keith Barry Manchester Royal Eye Hospital, Manchester M13 9WH — MB ChB 1972 Leeds; BSc Leeds 1969, MB ChB 1972; FRCS Ed. 1979; DO Eng. 1977. (Leeds) Cons. (Ophth.) Manch. Roy. Eye Hosp.

MILLS, Keith Gordon 25 Sefton Park Road, Liverpool L8 3SL — MB ChB 1983 Liverp.

MILLS, Mr Kenneth Leslie George (retired) 29 Craigiebuckler Avenue, Aberdeen AB15 8SE Tel: 01224 314077 — MB BChir 1954 Camb.; BSc (Anat.) Lond. 1953; MA Camb. 1955, MB BChir 1954; FRCS Eng. 1971; FRCS Ed. 1961; FRCS Canada 1972. Prev: Cons. Orthop. Surg. Grampian HB.

MILLS, Kenneth Lyndon Montague (retired) Beynhurst House, White Waltham, Maidenhead SL6 3RU Tel: 01628 822856 — MB BS Lond. 1957; FFA RCS Eng. 1966; DA Eng. 1960. Prev: Cons. Anaesth. S. (W.m.) Health Dist.

MILLS, Professor Kerry Raphael Academic Neuroscience Centre, King's College Hospital, Denmark Hill, London SE5 9RS Tel: 020 7346 5151 Fax: 020 7346 5152 Email: k.mills@iop.kcl.ac.uk — MB BS 1975 Lond.; PhD Lond. 1971, BSc (Physiol.) 1968; MA Oxf. 1987; FRCP Lond. 1994; MRCP (UK) 1978. (King's Coll. Hosp.) King's Coll. Univ. of Lond.; Hon. Cons. Clin. Neurophysiol. KCH; Hon. Cons. Clin. Neurophysiol. Guy's Hosp. Socs: Fell. Green Coll. Oxf.; Physiol. Soc. & Brit. Soc. Clin. Neurophys. Prev: Prof. (Clin. Neurophysiol.) Univ. of Oxf.; Univ. Lect. (Clin. Neurophysiol.) Univ. of Oxf.; Sen. Regist. (Clin. Neurophysiol.) Nat. Hosp. Nerv. Dis. Qu. Sq. Lond.

MILLS, Linda Margaret Welsh Blood Service, Pontyclun CF72 9WB Tel: 01443 622000 Fax: 01443 622199; 10 Cyncoed Crescent, Cyncoed, Cardiff CF23 6SW — MB BChir Camb. 1968; BA Camb. 1965. (St. Thos. & Camb.) Assoc. Specialist Welsh Blood Serv. Socs: BMA; BBTS; MWF. Prev: Clin. Asst. (Paediat. Oncol.) Llandough Hosp.; Community Med. Off. M. Glam. HA.

MILLS, Mabel Gwendoline (retired) 6 Thorney Road, Capel St Mary, Ipswich IP9 2HL — MB ChB 1936 Ed.; DObst RCOG 1939.

MILLS, Mallika Green Villa, Cripps Corner, Staple Cross, Robertsbridge TN32 5QR — MB BS 1982 Colombo.

MILLS, Margaret Jane (retired) Key Cottage, Dodford, Bromsgrove B61 9BG Tel: 01527 833614 — MB ChB 1938 Birm.; MRCS Eng. LRCP Lond. 1938; FFA RCS Eng. 1955; DA Eng. 1941. Prev: Cons. Anaesth. United Birm. Hosps.

MILLS, Marie Christine (retired) Moorlea, Long Lane, Dobcross, Saddleworth, Oldham OL3 5QH Tel: 01457 872353 — MB ChB Liverp. 1961; MFOM RCP Lond. 1986. Prev: Indep. Cons. Occupat. Health Oldham.

MILLS, Martin Stuart 6 Ninetree Hill, Kingsdown, Bristol BS1 3SG — MB ChB 1982 Bristol; MRCOG Lond. 1988. Clin. Research Fell. (O & G) Bristol Univ.

MILLS, Mary (retired) 20 Nizells Avenue, Hove BN3 1PL — MB BS 1937 Lond.; BA Lond. 1985; MD Lond. 1941; MRCS Eng. LRCP Lond. 1937; DRCOG 1940.

MILLS, Michael John 49 Oakwood Avenue, Leigh-on-Sea SS9 4JX — MB BS 1968 Lond.; MRCS Eng. LRCP Lond. 1968; FRCPath 1989, M 1978. (St. Mary's) Cons. Haemat. S.end Gen. Hosp. Socs: Brit. Soc. Haematol. Prev: Lect. (Haemat.) Lond. Hosp.; Unit Med. Off. RAF Kai Tak, Hong Kong; Ho. Surg. & Ho. Phys. Roy. Devon & Exeter Hosp.

MILLS, Michael Ward (retired) 322 Kingstanding Road, Birmingham B44 8JY Tel: 0121 373 0381 Fax: 0121 350 5610 Email: michael.w.mills@btinternet.com — MB ChB 1948 Ed.; MRCGP 1954; DObst RCOG 1950. Prev: Resid. Ho. Phys. Roy. Infirm. Edin.

MILLS, Norman Henri Neville (retired) Holmby House, 62 Greenhill Road, Sebastopol, Pontypool NP4 5BG Tel: 01495 758178 Fax: 01495 763201 — MB BCh 1962 Wales; MRCPsych 1972; FFPHM RCP (UK) 1985, M 1974; DPH Bristol 1970; DPM Eng. 1968; LIHSM 1986. Prev: Chief Exec. & Hon. Cons. Pub. Health Med. Llandough Hosp. NHS Trust & Glam HA.

MILLS, Patricia Mary 9 Bassett Crescent W., Bassett, Southampton SO16 7EB — MB ChB 1991 Leic.; MRCP (UK) 1994; FRCA 1998. Specialist Regist. (Anaesth.) Wessex.

MILLS, Patricia Mary Mathieson Invicta Community NHS Trust, Homeopathic Hospital, 21 Church Road, Tunbridge Wells TN1 2JU Tel: 01892 539144 Fax: 01892 535522; 19 Grecian Road, Tunbridge Wells TN1 1TG — MB ChB 1975 Ed.; MRCPsych 1981; DCH Eng. 1978; DRCOG 1977. Staff Grade (Community Child Health) Tunbridge Wells. Prev: Regist. Child Guid. Train. Centre Lond.

MILLS, Mr Paul Vincent (retired) Harwin, 50 Ty Gwyn Road, PenylaN, Cardiff CF23 5JG Tel: 029 2048 5349 — MB BS 1958 Lond.; BSc Lond. 1955; FRCS Eng. 1963; MRCS Eng. LRCP Lond. 1958; FCOphth. 1989; DO Eng. 1962. Prev: Cons. Ophth. Univ. Hosp. of Wales Cardiff.

MILLS, Peter George 18 Upper Wimpole Street, London W1G 6LX Tel: 020 7935 2977 Fax: 020 7935 2740 Email: mills158@globalnet.co.uk; 158 Tachbrook St, London SW1V 2NE — BM BCh 1970 Oxf.; MA, BSc, BM BCh Oxf. 1970; FRCP Lond. 1984, M 1973; FACC; FESC. (St. Geo., Oxf) p/t Cons. (Cardiol.) & Sen. Lect. Lond. Hosp. & Med. Coll. Lond; Series Edr. Educat. in Heart. Socs: Brit. Cardiac Soc.; Sec. Specialist Advisory Comm. Cardiol. Roy. Coll. Phys.s; Chairm.Specialty Train. Div. Comm. Cardiol. N. Thames E. Prev: SHO Nat. Hosp. for Nerv. Dis.; Ho. Phys. Brompton Hosp. Lond.; Ho. Phys. & Ho. Surg. St. Geo. Hosp. Lond.

MILLS, Peter Jonathan c/o Anaesthetic Department, The Ipswich Hospital, Ipswich IP4 5PD Tel: 01473 702016 — MB BS 1981 Lond.; FFA RCS Eng. 1987. Cons. Anaesth. Ipswich Hosp. Prev: Sen. Regist. (Anaesth.) Bristol & Exeter.

MILLS, Peter Richard Whittington Hospital, Dept. Respiratory Medicine, Clinic 3A, London N19 5NF Tel: 07958 215431 Email: prmills@nildram.co.uk — MB BS 1990 Lond.; 2000 MD Univ. Lond.; 2001 CCST- Respiratory Med.; MSc Lond. 1993; MRCP (UK) 1994. (Roy. Free Hosp. Sch. Med.) p/t Specialist Regist. (Respir. & Gen. Internal Med.) Whittington Hosp. Lond. Socs: Soc. of

MILLS

Occupat.al Med.; Bristish Sleep Soc.; Roy. Soc. of Med. (Fell.). Prev: Regist. (Respirat. Med.) Roy. Hosps. NHS Trust Lond.

MILLS, Peter Rodney Floor 8, Gartnavel General Hospital, 1053 Great Western Road, Glasgow G12 0YN Tel: 0141 211 3000 Fax: 0141 211 1006 Email: gqna14@udcf.gla.ac.uk; 19 Kirklee Road, Glasgow G12 0RQ Tel: 0141 339 8206 — MB ChB 1972 St. And.; BSc St. And. 1969; MD Dundee 1982; FRCP Glas. 1986; MRCP (UK) 1975; FACP 1988. Cons. Phys. (Gastroenterol.) W.. Infirm. & Gartnavel Gen. Hosp. Glas.; Hon. Sen. Clin. Lect. (Med.) Univ. Glas. Socs: Brit. Soc. Gastroenterol.; Amer. Gastroenterol. Assn.; Assn. Phys. Prev: Assoc. Prof. Dept. Internal Med. Med. Coll. Virginia, USA; Vis. Asst. Prof. Yale Univ., USA; Sen. Regist. Roy. Infirm. Glas.

MILLS, Philippa 7 Royal Chase, Tunbridge Wells TN4 8AX — BM 1982 Soton.; MRCP (UK) 1985; FRCR 1989. Cons. Radiol. Medway HA.

MILLS, Richard Dickson 51 London Road, Kilmarnock KA3 7AG — MB ChB 1947 St. And.

MILLS, Richard Godfrey Hythe Medical Centre, Beaulieu Road, Hythe, Southampton SO45 4ZD Tel: 02380 845955 Fax: 02380 841124 — BM 1990 Soton.; BSc (Hons.) Birm. 1985; MRCGP 1994. GP Soton.

MILLS, Mr Richard Graham Stead 10 Cyncoed Crescent, Cyncoed, Cardiff CF23 6SW — MB 1969 Camb.; BA Camb. 1965, MB 1969, BChir 1968; FRCS Eng. 1973. (Camb. & St. Thos.) Sen. Lect. Welsh Nat. Sch. Med. Cardiff. Prev: Sen, Regist. Roy. Free Hosp. Lond.

MILLS, Robert David Brockleigh, School Lane, Park Gate, South Wirral CH64 6SR — MB ChB 1988 Liverp.

MILLS, Mr Robert Peter Dept. of Otolaryngology, Edinburgh Royal Infirmary, Lauriston Place, Edinburgh EH3 9YW Tel: 0131 536 3743 Email: r.mills@ed.ac.uk; Tel: 0131 668 1828 — MB BS 1973 Lond.; MPhil Lond. 1986, MS 1994; FRCS Eng. 1980; DObst RCOG 1975; FRCS 1999 Ed. (London Hospital Medical College) Cons. ENT Roy. Infirm. of Edin.; p/t Sen. Lect. Univ. of Edin. Socs: BAO - HNS; SOS; BAPO. Prev: Hon. Sen. Lect. Univ. Dundee; Sen. Regist. (ENT) King's Coll. Hosp. Lond.; Cons. ENT Ninewells Hosp. Dundee.

MILLS, Rosalind Jane Ground Floor Flat, 72 Gayville Road, London SW11 6JP — MB BChir 1990 Camb.; MA Camb. 1990, MB BChir 1990. Regist. (Anaesth.) St. Geo. Hosp, Lond.

MILLS, Sarah Blanche 158 Tachbrook Street, London SW1V 2NE — BM BCh Oxf. 1970; MA Oxf. 1970; DFFP 1995; Instructing Doctor Family Planning 1998. Clin. Asst. (Rheum.) St. Mary's Hosp. Lond.; Community Med. Off. (Family Plann.) Riverside Community NHS Trust; Mem. Med. Woms. Federat. Socs: Brit. Soc. Rheum.; Roy. Soc. Med. Prev: Clin. Asst. (Rheum) St. Thos. Hosp. Lond.; Research Regist. (Rheum.) St. Geo. Hosp. Lond.

***MILLS, Sarah Catherine** The Pines, 116 Victoria Road, Formby, Liverpool L37 1LP — BM BCh 1998 Oxf.; BM BCh Oxf 1998.

MILLS, Miss Sarah Jane — BM BS 1987 Nottm.; FRCS Eng. 1991; FRCS (Gen. Surg.) 1998. (Nottingham) Cons. (Surg.) Wansbeck Hosp. N.umberland. Socs: Assn. of Surg.s; Assn. of Coloproctologists of Gt. Britain & N.ern Irel. Prev: Sen. Regist. Rotat. (Gen. Surg.) N.. Region. Roy. Vict. Infirm. Newc.

MILLS, Sarah Louise The Surgery, Cottage Hospital, Alston, Penrith CA9 3QY Tel: 01434 381214 Fax: 01434 382210 — MB ChB 1982 Leic.

MILLS, Sheila Inglis (retired) Gruinard, Carslogie Road, Cupar KY15 4HY Tel: 01334 652518 — MB ChB 1946 Ed.

MILLS, Simon Anthony 31 Brackendale Way, Stourbridge DY9 7HG; 23a Canfield Gardens, South Hampstead, London NW6 3JP Tel: 020 7813 0752 Fax: 020 7813 0752 Email: drsamills@aol.com — MB BCh 1992 Wales; MRCGP 1996; DRCOG 1994. Prev: Ship's Phys. Carnival Cruise Lines Miami Florida USA.

MILLS, Simon Jeremy 6 Swine Hill, Harlaxton, Grantham NG32 1HP — MB ChB 1992 Manch.

MILLS, Simon John Brockleigh, School Lane, Parkgate, South Wirral CH64 6SR — MRCS Eng. LRCP Lond. 1987; FRCA 1994. Assoc. Specialist (Anaesth.) King Edwd. VII Memor. Hosp., Bermuda. Socs: Assn. Anaesth. & BMA. Prev: Regist. (Anaesth.) St. Bart. Hosp. Lond.

MILLS, Stella Margaret The Doctors Group Practice, 19 Batchelor St., London N1 0EG Tel: 020 7837 1663; Finsbury Health Centre, Pine St, London EC1 Tel: 020 7837 9837 — MB BS 1981 Lond.; BSc (Hons.) Anat. Lond. 1978; FRCS Eng. 1986; DRCOG 1991. Clin. Asst. (Gyn.) Roy. Free Hosp. Lond.

MILLS, Stephen Scott 1 Surrey Street, Accrington BB5 6QJ — MB ChB 1987 Manch.

MILLS, Susan Jane Hove Medical Centre, West Way, Hove BN3 8LD Tel: 01273 430088 Fax: 01273 430172 — BM 1987 Soton.

MILLS, Susan Judith 18 Rodborough Avenue, Stroud GL5 3RS — MB BS 1983 Lond.; BSc (Hons.) Lond. 1980, MB BS 1983; MRCGP 1987; DRCOG 1986. (Kings Coll. Hosp.) GP Stroud Retainer Scheme. Prev: TEAR Fund Med. Worker, Zaire.

MILLS, Thomas Daniel Brockleigh, School Lane, Parkgate, South Wirral CH64 6SR — MB BS 1991 Lond.

MILLS, Trevor Anthony The Health Centre, Bailey Street, Old Basford, Nottingham NG6 0HD Tel: 0115 978 1231 Fax: 0115 979 0419; 4 Willerby Road, Woodthorpe, Nottingham NG5 4PB — BM BS 1981 Nottm.; BMedSci (Hons.) Nottm. 1979; MRCGP 1985; DRCOG 1984. (Nottingham) Trainer (GP) Nottm.; Hosp. Pract. (Psychiat.) Nottm. Healthcare Trust. Prev: SHO Mapperly Hosp. Nottm.; SHO W. Midl. RHA; Ho. Off. Univ. Hosp. Nottm.

MILLSON, Charles Edward St James's University Hospital, Beckett St, Leeds LS7 9TF Email: charles.millson@gw.sjsuh.northy.nhs.uk; Northolme, 8 Church View, Thorner, Leeds LS14 3ED — MB BS 1986 Lond.; MD Lond. 1995; MRCP (UK) 1991. (King;s College Hospital) Cons. Hepatologist St Jas. Univ. Hosp. Beckett St Leeds. Prev: Sen. Regist. (Gastroenterol.) St. Jas. & Seacroft Univ. Hosps. NHS Trust.

MILLSON, Professor David Steven Department of Medicines Management, Keele University, Newcastle ST5 5BG Tel: 01782 584200 Fax: 01782 713586 Email: d.millson@keele.ac.uk; 17 Buckingham Drive, off Chelford Road, Knutsford WA16 8LH — MB BChir 1984 Camb.; FFPM RCP (UK) 1999; MB Camb. 1984, BChir 1983; PhD Clin. Pharmacol. 1982; BSc (Hons.) Pharmacol. CNAA 1976; MD Liverp. 1992; MFPM RCP (UK) 1995. (Camb.) Chair in Meds. Managem. Keele Univ.; Prof. (Meds. Managem.) Keele Univ.; Hon. Clin. Pharmo. Newc. Gen. Hosp. N. Staffs. Socs: Brit. Pharm. Soc.; Amer. Acad. Neurol.; Amer. Assn. for Study of Headache. Prev: Drug Team Ldr. (Med. Research) Zeneca Pharmaceuts.; Sen. Research Phys. (Clin. Pharmacol.) Glaxo Gp. Research Greenford; Clin. Pharmacol. Research Assoc. (Clin. Pharmacol. & Therap.) Univ. Liverp.

MILLWARD, Beverley Ann Department of Medicine, Kings College of Medicine & Dentistry, Camberwell, London SE5 Tel: 020 7274 6272; 30 Gaynesford Road, Forest Hill, London SE23 2UQ Tel: 020 8699 4428 — MD 1988 Camb.; MA Camb. 1981, MD 1988, MB BChir 1980; MSc Immunol. Lond. 1987; MRCP (UK) 1983. (Camb. & King's Coll. Hosp.) Lect. Med., King's Coll. Hosp. Prev: MRC Research Fell. Kings Coll. Hosp.; Med. Regist. Kent & Sussex Hosp. Tunbridge Wells.

MILLWARD, David (retired) 182 Cyncoed Road, Cardiff CF23 6BQ Tel: 01222 756039 — MB BCh 1955 Wales; BSc Wales 1952.

MILLWARD, Eleanor Lucy 37 Kilburn Lane, Belper DE56 0SF; 7 Hunts Row, Manor Road, South Wingfield, Alfreton DE55 7NH Tel: 01773 830564 — MB ChB 1994 Manch. SHO (Gen. Med.) Derbysh. Roy. Infirm. Prev: Regist. (Cardiol.) Liverp. Dist. Gen. Sydney; SHO (A & E) Withington & Wythenshawe Hosp. Manch.; Ho. Off. (Gen. Med.) Macclesfield Dist. Gen. Hosp.

***MILLWARD, Esther Joanna** 4 Radcliffe Road, West Bridgford, Nottingham NG2 5FW — MB ChB 1997 Leeds.

MILLWARD, John (Surgery), 102 Southbourne Road, Bournemouth BH6 3QQ Tel: 01202 424833; 5 Byron Road, Bournemouth BH5 1JD Tel: 01202 399711 — BM BCh 1960 Oxf.; BA Oxf. 1960. (Oxf. & St. Bart.) Prev: Ho. Phys. St. Bart. Hosp.; Ho. Surg. Wom. Hosp. Wolverhampton.

MILLWARD, Ralph Peter 146 Nuthurst Road, New Moston, Manchester M40 3WG — MB ChB 1976 Sheff.

MILLWARD, Russell Geoffrey Eaton House, Eaton St., Crewe CW2 7EG Tel: 01270 506702 Fax: 01270 214744 — MB ChB 1972 Birm.; FRCPsych 1997; MRCPsych 1976. Cons. Psychiat. Leighton Hosp. Crewe, Mid Chesh. Hosps. NHS Trust. Prev: Sen. Regist. (Psychiat.) Uffculme Clinic Birm.

MILLWARD-SADLER, George Harry Department of Pathology, General Hospital, Southampton Tel: 02380 796446 Fax: 02380 705580; 75 Shirley Avenue, Shirley, Southampton SO15 5NH Tel:

02380 772607 — MB ChB 1965 Birm.; BSc Birm. 1962, MB ChB 1965; FRCPath 1984, M 1972; LIHSM 1988. Cons. Path. Gen. Hosp. Soton. Univ. Hosp. Trust; Chairm. Clin. Managem. Bd. Soton. Univ. Hosps.; Med. Dir. Soton. Univ. Hosps. Trust. Socs: Assn. Clin. Path. (Ex-Chairm. Histopath. Sub Comm.) (Ex-Counc.; Brit. Soc. Gastroenterol. Prev: Nuffield Lect. (Path.) Radcliffe Infirm. Oxf.; Regist. & SHO (Path.) & SHO (Med.) St. Mary's Hosp. Portsmouth.

MILLWARD-SADLER, Hilary 75 Shirley Avenue, Southampton SO15 5NH Tel: 02380 772607; 75 Shirley Avenue, Southampton SO15 5NH Tel: 02380 772607 — MB ChB 1965 Birm.; DPM Eng. 1979. (Birm.)

MILLWATER, Christopher James CRC Laboratories, Department of Pathology, Edinburgh University Medical School, Edinburgh EH8 9AG Tel: 0131 650 1000 Fax: 0131 540 6528; 97 Dudley Avenue, Trinity, Edinburgh EH6 4PP — MB BS 1985 Lond.; MSc Ed. 1993; MA Camb. 1986, BA (Med. Sci.) 1982; MRCP (UK) 1988. Research Fell. CRC Laborats. Edin. Prev: Regist. (Clin. Oncol.) W.. Gen. & Roy. Infirm. Edin.; Research Fell. (Renal) Leicester; Regist. (Renal) St. Phillips & St. Paul's Hosp. Lond.

MILLWOOD, Anthony John Ernest (retired) The Health Centre, Laindon, Basildon SS15 5TR Tel: 01268 546411 Fax: 01268 491248 — MB BS 1958 Lond. Prev: Ho. Surg. & Ho. Phys. Luton & Dunstable Hosp.

MILNE, Agnes Macfarlane Duncan (retired) Semmering, Arkley, Barnet EN5 3HB — MB BS Lond. 1938; MRCS Eng. LRCP Lond. 1938; FRCOG 1959, M 1945. Prev: Obstetr. & Gynaecol. Barnet Gen. Hosp.

MILNE, Alan Ducat, TD Elm Bank Group, Foresterhill Health Centre, Westburn Road, Aberdeen AB25 2AY Tel: 01224 696949 Fax: 01224 691650; The Briars, 3 Golfview Road, Bieldside, Aberdeen AB15 9AA Tel: 01224 867816 — MB ChB 1964 Aberd.; FRCGP 1988, M 1971; DA Eng. 1968. (Aberd.) Lt. Col. RAMC (V). Prev: Regist. (Anaesth.) Aberd. Gen. Hosp. Gp.; Ho. Phys. Woodend Gen. Hosp. Aberd.; Ho. Surg. (Cas.) Aberd. Roy. Infirm.

MILNE, Alan Henry, Surg. Lt.-Cdr. RN North Cookney Cottage, Muchalls, Stonehaven AB39 3SL Tel: 01569 30613 — MB ChB 1967 Aberd.; MRCGP 1975. Hon. Cons. Nat. Hyperbaric Centre Aberd.; Sen. Med. Off. Antarctic Survey Centre for Offshore Health Aberd.

MILNE, Alan John Morven, Union St., Coupar Angus, Blairgowrie PH13 9AE — MB ChB 1979 Aberd.

MILNE, Alan Ramsay (retired) 5A Inverleith Avenue S., Edinburgh EH3 5QA — MB ChB 1958 Ed.; FRCP Ed. 1975; DObst RCOG 1960. Prev: GP Edin.

MILNE, Alastair Weir 32 Wemyss Crescent, Monifieth, Dundee DD5 4RA — MB ChB 1992 Glas.

MILNE, Alexander John 4 Birkfield Loan, Carluke ML8 4PY — MB ChB 1979 Glas.; MRCGP 1983; DRCOG 1982; Dip. Forens. Med. Glas. 1987.

MILNE, Alison Elizabeth North Hampshire NHS Trust, Aldermaston Rd, Basingstoke RG24 9NA Tel: 01256 766515 Email: alison.milne@bas.swest.nhs.uk — MB BS 1980 Lond.; MRCP (UK) 1983; FRCP Lond. 1995; FRCPath 1997, M 1987. Cons. Haemat. N. Hants. Hosps. NHS Trust. Socs: Brit. Soc. Haematol. Prev: Research Sen. Regist. (Haemat.) St. Geo. Hosp. Lond.; Sen. Regist. (Haemat.) St. Geo. Hosp. Lond.

MILNE, Alistair Bruce (retired) 67 Priest Hill, Caversham, Reading RG4 7RY — MB BS 1957 Lond.; DObst RCOG 1959. Prev: Ho. Phys. Harefield Hosp. Middlx.

MILNE, Andrew Gavin 32C Aynhoe Road, Brook Green, West Kensington, London W14 0QD — MB BS 1994 Lond.; BEng. Soton. 1989. RMO King's Oak Private Hosp. Enfield. Prev: Ho. Off. (Gen. Med.) Qu. Mary Hosp. Roehampton.

MILNE, Andrew Noble 12 Roundway, Grimsby DN34 5AS — MB ChB 1953 Aberd.

MILNE, Anne Dorothy T Childrens Centre, St. Marks Hospital, St Marks Road, Maidenhead SL6 6DU Tel: 01753 638371 Fax: 01753 638536; Glenthorne, One Pin Lane, Farnham Common, Slough SL2 3QY Tel: 01753 642149 — MB BCh BAO Belf. 1966; DCH RCPS Glas. 1968. (Belf.) SCMO E. Berks. HA; Clin. Asst. (Paediat.) St. Mark's Hosp. Maidenhead.

MILNE, Archibald Cousland (retired) 61 Braid Road, Edinburgh EH10 6AR Tel: 0131 447 1302 — MB ChB 1946 Aberd.; FFA RCS Eng. 1954; DA Eng. 1952. Prev: Cons. Anaesth. Edin. Roy. Infirm.

MILNE, Barbara Elizabeth Park House Cottage, Station Road, Lanchester, Durham DH7 0PE Tel: 01207 520877 — MB BS 1976 London. (London) GP Durh.

MILNE, Brian Maternity Unit, Raigmore Hospital, Inverness IV2 3UJ Tel: 01463 704000; Muirfield House, 28 Muirfield Road, Inverness IV2 4AY Tel: 01463 222134 — MB ChB 1966 Aberd.; FRCOG 1984, M 1972; DObst RCOG 1968. Cons. O & G Raigmore Hosp. Inverness; Clin. Sen. Lect. Univ. Aberd.; Clin. Director Wom. and Child Health Directorate. Socs: Brit. Soc. Colpos. & Cerv. Path.; NINES Obst. & Gyn. Soc. Prev: Sen. Regist. (O & G) Leicester Roy. Infirm. & Matern. Hosp.

MILNE, Brian Reid 33 The Hollows, Bessacarr, Doncaster DN4 7PR Tel: 01302 539060 & profess. 366666 — MB ChB 1972 Ed.; BSc (Med. Sci.) Ed. 1969, MB ChB 1972; FFA RCS Eng. 1976. Cons. Anaesth. Doncaster Roy. Infirm. Mem. BMA & Assn. Anaesth. Prev: Sen. Regist. (Anaesth.) Sheff. AHA (T); Regist. (Anaesth.) Bristol Health Dist. (T).

MILNE, Catherine Borough Lane Surgery, 2 Borough Lane, Saffron Walden CB11 4AF Tel: 01799 524224 Fax: 01799 524830 — MB BS 1985 Lond.; MRCGP 1989. (St. Bart.) GP. Prev: GP Milton Keynes; Clin. Med. Off. (Family Plann. Servs.) Milton Keynes.

MILNE, Catherine Hannah Coutts (retired) Red Garth, 84 Middle Bourne Lane, Farnham GU10 3NJ Tel: 01252 714466 — MB ChB 1925 Aberd.; DPH 1927. Prev: Asst. MOH Norf. CC.

MILNE, Clare Anne 3 Belgrave Road, Edinburgh EH12 6NG — MB ChB 1997 Glas.

MILNE, David Sidcup Health Centre, 43 Granville Road, Sidcup DA14 4TA Tel: 020 8302 7721 — MB BS 1977 Newc.; DRCOG 1979.

MILNE, Mr David Dean 28 Newlands Avenue, Melton Park, Newcastle upon Tyne NE3 5PU Tel: 0191 236 3290 — MB ChB 1955 Aberd.; FRCS Ed. 1963. (Aberd.) Cons. Surg. Newc. Gen. Hosp. Prev: Surg. Oil Industry Med. Soc. Tripoli, Libya; Surg. Specialist, Sandakan, N. Borneo.

MILNE, David Robert Marmion North Hill Surgery, 18 North Hill, Colchester CO1 1DZ Tel: 01206 578070 Fax: 01206 769880; Spicers, Old House Road, Great Horkesley, Colchester CO6 4EQ Tel: 01206 271661 Fax: 01206 272107 Email: david.milne1@virgin.net — MB 1983 Camb.; MA Camb. 1983, MB 1983, BChir 1982; MRCP (UK) 1986; DRCOG 1988. (Lond. Hosp.) Prev: Research Fell. (Cardiol.) Flinder Med. Centre Adelaide S. Australia; Regist. (Thoracic Med.) Lond. Hosp. Whitechapel; Regist. (Gen. Med.) Dist. Gen. Hosp. Colchester.

MILNE, Debra Susan Department of Pathology, Sunderland Royal Hospital, Kayll Road, Sunderland SR4 7TP — MB BS 1986 Newc.; MB BS (Hons.) Newc. 1986; MD Newc. 1995, BMedSci (Hons.) 1985; MRCPath 1995. Cons. Histopath. & Cytopath. Prev: Sen. Regist. (Histopath.) Newc.; Lect. (Histopath.) & Hon. Sen. Regist. Univ. Newc.

MILNE, Duncan (retired) Kirklea, Hillside Road, Forfar DD8 — MB ChB 1951 Aberd.; DPH Dundee 1969.

MILNE, Elisabeth Anne Kenneth Day (Medium Secure) Unit, Northgate Hospital, Morpeth NE61 3BP — MB BS 1985 Newc.; MRCPsych 1993; MRCGP 1990. (Newcastle upon Tyne) Cons. Forens. Psychiat. for People with Learning Disabilities N.gate Hosp. Morpeth.

MILNE, Elizabeth Jane Bannatyne Lag an Tairbh, North Connel, Oban PA37 1RF — MB ChB 1954 Glas.; DObst RCOG 1955.

MILNE, Eugene Michael Gerard Newcastle & North Tyneside Health Authority, Benfield Road, Walkergate, Newcastle upon Tyne NE6 4PF Tel: 0191 219 6012 Fax: 0191 219 6066 Email: eugene.milne@nant-ha.northy.nhs.uk — MB BS 1985 Newc.; MSc Newc. 1992, BMedSci (Hons.) 1982; MRCP (UK) 1989; MFPHM RCP (UK) 1993. (Newcastle) Cons. Pub. Health Med. Newc. & N. Tyneside HA; Hon. Lect. in Epidemiol. and Pub. Health Med. Univeristy of Newc.; Chair of Newc. Health City Project Ltd. Prev: Trainee (Pub. Health Med.) N.. RHA.

MILNE, Gordon Graeme The Health Centre, Maryhill, Elgin IV30 3AT Tel: 01343 542225 Fax: 01343 541604; Mill Cottage, Pluscarden, Elgin IV30 8TZ Tel: 01343 890281 — MB ChB 1968 Aberd.; DA Eng. 1971. Hosp. Pract. (Anaesth.) Dr. Gray's Hosp. Elgin. Prev: Regist. (Anaesth.) Aberd. Gen. Hosps.; Ho. Phys. & Ho. Surg. Aberd. Gen. Hosp.

MILNE

MILNE, Graham John c/o The Surgery, 17 Rowe Avenue, Peacehaven, Newhaven BN10 7PE — MB ChB 1980 Sheff.; MRCGP 1986; DRCOG 1986.

MILNE, Graham McNee (retired) Lilac Cottage, 33 Parkgate Road, Neston, South Wirral CH64 6QE Tel: 0151 336 1047 — MB ChB 1956 Glas.; MRCGP 1975; DObst RCOG 1960.

MILNE, Henry Alfred (retired) Four Winds, 68 Downs Wood, Epsom Downs, Epsom KT18 5UL Tel: 01737 210734 — MB BS 1952 Lond.; FRCOG 1971, M 1957. Prev: Cons. O & G Epsom Hosp. Gp.

MILNE, Hugo Buist 9 Eldon Place, Bradford BD1 3AZ — MB ChB 1950 St. And.; DPsych. Ed. 1955; FRCPsych 1974. Prev: Cons. i/c Forens./ psychiat. Unit Waddiloves Hosp. Bradford; Cons. Psychiat. Lynfield Mt. Hosps., Bradford Roy. Infirm. & St.; Luke's Hosp. Bradford.

MILNE, Ian Lewis Padiham Group Practice, Padiham Medical Centre, Burnley Road, Padiham, Burnley BB12 8BP Tel: 01282 771298 Fax: 01282 777720 — MB ChB 1977 Aberd.

MILNE, Ian Sutherland 6 Hamilton Avenue, Harrogate HG2 8JB Tel: 01423 562160 — MB BChir 1967 Camb.; MB Camb. 1968, MA, BChir 1967; FFA RCS Eng. 1971; DObst RCOG 1971. Cons. Anaesth. Harrogate Health Dist. Socs: BMA. Prev: Sen. Regist. (Anaesth.) St. Bart. Hosp. Lond.

MILNE, James Alastair Royal Infirmary, Lauriston Place, Edinburgh EH3 9YW Tel: 0131 536 4123; 2 Crookston Court, Crookston Road, Inveresk, Musselburgh EH21 7TR — MB ChB 1971 Glas.; MA Camb. 1978; FRCS (Ed.) 1997; FRCOG 1989, M 1976. Cons. O & G Roy. Infirm. & Simpson Matern. Pavilion Edin.

MILNE, Jane Elizabeth Coutts Department of Obstetrics & Gynaecology, Royal Victoria Infirmary, Newcastle upon Tyne NE1 4LP Tel: 0191 232 5131 Fax: 0191 222 5066; 61 Whinfell Road, Darras Hall, Ponteland NE20 9EW — MB ChB 1988 Dundee; MRCOG 1993. SpR. (O&G) Roy. Vict. Infirm., Newc. upon Tyne. Prev: Regist. (O & G) P.ss Mary Matern. Hosp. & Roy. Vict. Infirm. Newc.; Regist. (O & G) Sunderland Dist. Gen. Hosp.; SHO (O & G) Bishop Auckland Gen. Hosp. Co. Durh.

MILNE, Janet Dorothy 16 Greenway Road, Redland, Bristol BS6 6SG Tel: 0117 974 1312 — MB ChB 1954 Bristol; MB ChB Aberd. 1954; MD Bristol 1981. (Aberd.) Prev: Assoc. Specialist (Genitourin. Med.) Bristol Roy. Infirm.

MILNE, Jennifer Mary (Surgery), 15 Portland Road, Aldridge, Walsall WS9 8NS Tel: 01922 52139 — MB ChB 1963 Birm.; DObst RCOG 1965. (Birm.) Prev: Ho. Phys. & Ho. Surg. Birm. Gen. Hosp.; Ho. Surg. (O & G) Marston Green, Matern. Hosp. Birm.

MILNE, John Alexander The Surgery, Anderson Drive, Leslie, Glenrothes KY6 3LQ Tel: 01592 620222 Fax: 01592 620553; 27 Westgate, Leslie, Glenrothes KY6 3LP Tel: 01592 742221 Email: jmilne1601@cs.com — MB ChB 1974 Aberd.; DObst RCOG 1976.

MILNE, John Brebner Morrison, OBE, Brigadier late RAMC Retd. (retired) 9 East Saville Road, Edinburgh EH16 5ND Tel: 0131 667 3082 — MB ChB 1938 Ed.; DPhysMed Eng. 1948.

MILNE, John Bruce Billaney (retired) 36 Barningham Close, Elstob Farm, Sunderland SR3 1PX Tel: 0191 520 0989 — MB BChir 1957 Camb.; MB Camb. 1957, BChir 1956; LMSSA Lond. 1956; MA Camb. 1957. JP.; Clin. Asst. (A & E) Sunderland Dist. Gen. Hosp. Prev: GP Sunderland.

MILNE, John Rodney 2 Laureldene, Hadham Cross, Much Hadham SG10 6AP — MB BS 1968 Newc.; FRCP Lond. 1989; MRCP (UK) 1971. Cons. Phys. & Cardiol. W. Essex HA; Hon. Cardiol. Roy. Free Hosp. Trust. Prev: Sen. Regist. (Gen. Med. Cardiol.) St. Bart. Hosp. Lond.; Regist. (Cardiol.) Univ. Coll. Hosp. & Nat. Heart Hosp.

MILNE, John Ross (retired) 424 Devonshire Road, Blackpool FY2 0RE Tel: 01253 351110 — MB ChB Glas. 1946.

MILNE, John Stewart (retired) 8 Macnair Avenue, North Berwick EH39 4QY — MB ChB 1944 Ed.; DSc Ed. 1982, BSc 1952, MD 1973; FRCP Ed. 1979, M 1977. Prev: Cons. Phys. (Geriat. Med.) E. Fortune Hosp. N. Berwick.

***MILNE, Kate Louise** 24 Lyndhurst Avenue, Jesmond, Newcastle upon Tyne NE2 3LJ — MB BS 1998 Newc.; MB BS Newc 1998.

MILNE, Keith (retired) 1 Crosskeys Court, The Green, Cottenham, Cambridge CB4 8UW Tel: 01954 51288 — MB ChB 1944 St. And.

MILNE, Kenneth Grant Sim (retired) 77 Telford Road, Edinburgh EH4 2SB — MB ChB 1951 Aberd.

MILNE, Leslie Allan Hawkslee House, Minn End Lane, Bosley, Macclesfield SK11 0NZ — MB ChB 1973 Dundee; FFA RCS Eng. 1977.

MILNE, Leslie Gordon Llanfair Caereinion Health Centre, Llanfair Caereinion, Welshpool SY21 0RT Tel: 01938 810279 Fax: 01938 810955; Windsor House, Bridge St, Llanfair Caereinion, Welshpool SY21 0RZ Tel: 01938 810914 — MB BCh Wales 1988; MRCGP 1993; DRCOG 1991; DGM RCP Lond. 1991; Cert. Family Plann. JCC 1990. (Cardiff)

MILNE, Mary Jean (retired) 24 Kirk Wynd, Kirriemuir DD8 4BH — MB ChB St. And. 1959; DA Eng. 1963. Prev: Regist. (Anaesth.) Chase Farm Hosp. Enfield, OldCh. Hosp. Romford & Harefield Hosp. Middlx.

MILNE, Mearns Mackenzie (retired) 15 Portland Road, Aldridge, Walsall WS9 8NS Tel: 01922 52139 — MB ChB 1948 Ed. Prev: Ho. Phys. Ipswich Boro. Gen. Hosp.

MILNE, Melville Kermack 71 Elie Avenue, Broughty Ferry, Dundee DD5 3SJ — MB ChB 1965 Aberd.; FFA RCS Eng. 1971. (Aberd.) Cons. Anaesth. Dundee Teach. Hosps. Socs: BMA & Assn. Anaesth.

MILNE, Michael Roger Department of Anaesthetics, Frenchay Hospital, North Bristol NHS Trust, Beckspool Road, Frenchay, Bristol BS16 1ND Tel: 0117 970 2020 Fax: 0117 984 4414; 12 Bramble Drive, Sneyd Park, Bristol BS9 1RE Tel: 0117 968 8067 Email: michael.milne@tesco.net — MB BChir 1984 Camb.; MB Camb. 1984, BChir 1983; BA Camb. 1981; MRCP (UK) 1986; FRCA 1989. (Camb. Univ. Sch. Med.) Cons. Anaesth. Frenchay Healthcare NHS Trust. Prev: Sen. Regist. (Anaesth.) S. W.. RHA; Vis. Instruc. (Anaesthesiol.) Univ. Michigan, Ann Arbor, USA; Wessex Regional Regist. (Anaesth.) Soton. Gen. & Poole Gen. Hosps.

MILNE, Moira Rosalind Portlethen Group Practice, Portlethen Health Centre, Bruntland Road, Portlethen, Aberdeen AB12 4QL Tel: 01224 780223 Fax: 01224 781317; North Cookney Croft, Netherley, Stonehaven AB39 3SB Tel: 01569 730613 — MB ChB 1970 Aberd. Princip. in Gen. Pract.

MILNE, Monica Helen Norwood, Ardmiddle, Turriff AB53 4HJ Email: monica.milne@btinternet.com — MB ChB 1989 Aberd.; MRCGP 1995. Higher Professional Train. Fell. in Gen. Pract. Socs: RCGP; BMA; NANP.

MILNE, Paul Park House Cottage, Station Road, Lanchester, Durham DH7 0PE Tel: 01207 520877; Tel: 01207 520397 — MB BS 1976 Lond.; MRCS Eng. LRCP Lond. 1976; FRCGP 1998; Dip. Clin. Hypn. Sheff. 1991. (Roy. Free) GP Trainer Durh.; GP Tutor Derwentside. Socs: Exam. Panel Roy. Coll. Gen. Pract.; Chairm. RCGP N. of Eng. Fac. Prev: GP Douglas, I. of Man; SHO (Anaesth.) N.ampton Gen. Hosp.; SHO (O & G & A & E) N.ampton Gen. Hosp.

MILNE, Peter (retired) 60 Smitham Bottom Lane, Purley CR8 3DD Tel: 020 8660 6556 — MB ChB 1941 Aberd.; DPH 1948; FFA RCS Eng. 1962; DA Eng. 1955. Prev: Cons. Anaesth. Greenwich Dist. Hosp.

MILNE, Peter Stephen 17 Salet Way, Waterlooville PO7 8QS Tel: 01705 261587 — MB ChB 1984 Bristol; AFOM RCP Lond. 1996; MRCGP 1988; DRCOG 1987. (Univ. Bristol) Occupat. Phys. (f/t) Sedgwick Noble Lowndes Occupat. Health Ltd. Redditch. Socs: Soc. Occupat. Med.; Soc. Occupat. Med., Sec. Centr. S.ern Eng. Gp. Prev: GP Havant Hants.; Trainee GP Portsmouth & SE Hants. HA; Ho. Surg. & Ho. Phys. Bristol Roy. Infirm.

MILNE, Robert Blantyre Health Centre, Victoria St., Blantyre, Glasgow Tel: 0141 828868 Fax: 0141 823678; 36 Wellesley Crescent, East Kilbride, Glasgow G75 8TS — MB ChB 1970 Glas.

MILNE, Mr Robert MacGregor Health Centre, The Glebe, Kirkliston EH29 9AS Tel: 0131 333 3215; Craigbinning, Dechmont, Broxburn EH52 6NB — MB ChB 1965 Ed.; FRCS Ed. 1970; MRCGP 1981; Cert FPA 1973; Cert Av Med MoD (Air) & CAA; Aviat. Auth. 1977.

MILNE, Robert Marshall (retired) 37 Kincarrathie Crescent, Perth PH2 7HH Tel: 01738 623885 — MB ChB 1944 St. And. Prev: Capt. RAMC.

MILNE, Roderick Kerr 31 Newlands Avenue, Melton Park, Gosforth, Newcastle upon Tyne NE3 5PU — MB ChB 1990 Manch.; FFAGM 2001; FRCS (A&E) Ed. 1997. Specialist Regist. (A & E) N.ern Regional Train. Progr.

MILNE, Rosalind Margaret Paul (retired) 38 Rosehill Drive, Aberdeen AB24 4JQ Tel: 01224 483642 — MB ChB 1934 Aberd.;

FFA RCS Eng. 1953; DA Eng. 1936. Prev: Cons. Anaesth. N. E. Regional Hosp. Bd. Scotl.

MILNE, Ruairidh Iain Gordon 1 Rufus Close, Rownhams, Southampton SO16 8LR — MB BS 1984 Lond. Cons. Pub. Health Med. Oxon. HA; Vis. Sen. Clin. Lect. Soton. Univ.

MILNE, Sheena Margaret Health Centre, 73 Main Street, Stoneyburn, Bathgate EH47 8BY Tel: 01501 762515 Fax: 01501 763174; 39 Queen's Crescent, Edinburgh EH9 2BA Tel: 0131 620 0310 — MB ChB 1976 Manch.; MRCGP 1986; DRCOG 1982; DCH Eng. 1978. GP Stoneyburn W. Lothian.

MILNE, Sheila Johnstone Dedman (retired) 37 Kincarrathie Crescent, Perth PH2 7HH Tel: 01738 623885 — MB ChB 1953 Glas.; FRCP Glas. 1978, M 1968 LMCC 1958; MRCPsych 1971; DPM Ed. & Glas. 1965. Prev: Cons. (Psychiat.) Murray Roy. Hosp. Perth.

MILNE, Shelagh Elizabeth (retired) Bow Cottage, The Green, Great Bentley, Colchester CO7 8LX Tel: 01206 250103 — MB 1951 Camb.; MB BChir Camb. 1951; BA Camb. 1951. Prev: Cons. Microbiol. NE Essex HA.

MILNE, Steven The Hutton Centre, St Luke's Hospital, Morton Road, Middlesbrough — MB ChB 1985 Aberd.; MRCPsych 1991. Cons. Forens. Psychiat. St. Lukes Hosp. Middlesbrough.

MILNE, Stewart Edwardson 45 Regent Park Square, Glasgow G41 2AF — MB ChB 1991 Glas.; BSc (Hons.) Glas. 1988; FRCA 1996. (Glas.) Clin. Lect. (Anaesth.) Glas. Roy. Infirm. Glas. Socs: Assn. Anaesth.; Scott. Soc. Anaesth. Prev: SHO (Anaesth.) Glas. Roy. Infirm.; SHO (Anaesth.) Aberd. Roy. Infirm.

MILNE, Victor Gordon (retired) 332 Skip Lane, Walsall WS5 3RA Tel: 01922 25450 — MB ChB 1949 Ed.; DObst RCOG 1954. Prev: Ho. Surg. Deaconess Hosp. Edin. & Roy. Infirm. Edin.

MILNE, William Shireffs (retired) 10 Westhill Grange, Westhill, Westhill AB32 6QJ Tel: 01224 741582 — MB ChB 1939 Aberd.; DO Oxf. 1947; DOMS Eng. 1947. Prev: Cons. Ophth. Surg. N.E. Regional Hosp. Bd.

MILNE, Williamina Hay (retired) Adams Cottage, Marykirk, Laurencekirk AB30 1UT — MB ChB 1938 Aberd. Prev: GP Roy. Cornhill Hosp. Aberd.

MILNE-REDHEAD, Brian The Health Centre, Victoria Road, Ulverston LA12 0EW Tel: 01229 52223; Bowland Park, Stockbridge Lane, Ulverston LA12 7NN Tel: 01229 55057 — MRCS Eng. LRCP Lond. 1966; DObst RCOG 1968. (Manch.) Prev: Med. Off. Botswana Govt.

MILNER, Anthony Charles The Surgery, 29 High Stile, Leven, Beverley HU17 5NL Tel: 01964 542155 Fax: 01964 543954; 62 Hambling Drive, Beverley HU17 9GD — MB ChB 1990 Leeds; MRCGP 1996; DFFP 1995. (Leeds) Prev: Trainee GP York.; Resid. Med. Off. Katoomba Austral.; SHO (Paediat.) Pinderfields Wakefield.

MILNER, Anthony David Department of Paediatrics, St. Thomas Hospital, London SE1 7EH — MRCS Eng. LRCP Lond. 1963; MD Camb. 1972, MB 1964, BChir 1963; FRCP Lond. 1978, M 1967; DCH Eng. 1966. (Camb. & Guy's) Prof. Neonat. St. Thos. Hosp. Lond. Socs: Brit. Paediat. Assn. Prev: Prof. Dept. Paediat. Respirat. Med.; Regist. Guy's Hosp.; Ho. Phys. Hosp. Sick Childr. Gt. Ormond St.

MILNER, Anthony Roger 205 Knighton Church Road, Leicester LE2 3JP — MB BS 1985 Newc.; FRCA 1992. Regist. (Anaesth.) Leicester Roy. Infirm. Prev: Fell. (Intens. Care) Univ. Hosp. Groningen, The Netherlands; SHO (Intens. Care & Neonates) Hope Hosp. Salford; SHO (Anaesth.) Nottm. HA.

MILNER, Astrid Ann Park Hospital, Old Road, Headington, Oxford OX3 7LQ Tel: 01865 226327 — MB BS 1986 Lond.; MA Oxf. 1983; MRCPsych 1993; MRCGP 1990; T(GP) 1991. Cons. Child & Adolesc. Psychiat. Vale of the White Horse. Prev: Sen. Regist. (Child & Adolesc. Psychiat.) W.cotes Hse. Leicester.

MILNER, Brian Briggs The Manor, 125A Denby Dale Road, Wakefield WF2 8EB Tel: 01924 362634 — MRCS Eng. LRCP Lond. 1962; BSc Leeds 1956. (Leeds) Assoc. Specialist (Anaesth.) Pinderfields Gen. Hosp. Wakefield.

MILNER, Brian Stanley Edenbridge Medical Practice, West View, Station Road, Edenbridge TN8 5ND Tel: 01732 864442 Fax: 01732 862376; Bannisters Barn, Mark Beech, Edenbridge TN8 5NS Tel: 01342 850468 — MB ChB Bristol 1958; DA Eng. 1962; DObst RCOG 1962.

MILNER, Catriona 34 Conningsby Drive, Pershore WR10 1QX — BM 1988 Soton.; MRCGP 1993. Prev: GP Abergavenny; SHO (Psychogeriat.) Pen-y-Fal Hosp. Abergavenny.

MILNER, Dawn Gillian Grenville Wellington House, 133-155 Waterloo Road, London SE1 8UG Tel: 020 7972 4026 Fax: 020 7972 4218 Email: dmilner@doh.gov.uk; 27b Pearman Street, London SE1 7RB Tel: 020 726 1076 — MB BS 1965 Lond.; MRCS Eng. LRCP Lond. 1965; MRCGP 1978. (Guy's) Sen. Med. Off. DoH. Socs: BMA; SRNT. Prev: GP Sandy; Ho. Surg. & Ho. Phys. Bedford Gen. Hosp.

MILNER, Dennis (retired) 4 Sandpiper Close, Dukinfield SK16 5QF Tel: 0161 338 2443 — MB ChB 1952 Manch.; DObst RCOG 1958. Prev: Ho. Surg., Ho. Phys. & Ho. Surg. (Obst.) Hope Hosp. Salford.

MILNER, Erik Charles Risteigen 23 Drayton Court, Woodloes Park, Warwick CV34 5RG — MB ChB 1989 Birm.

MILNER, Gabrielle Louise Mental Health Services, 51 Grove Road, Solihull B91 2AQ — MB ChB 1983 Birm.; MRCPsych 1987. Cons. Psychiat. Solihull HA. Prev: SHO (Psychiat.) Hollymoor Hosp. Birm.

MILNER, George (retired) Acrefield, 13 Norton Close, Worcester WR5 3EY Tel: 01905 353552 — MB BCh BAO NUI 1957; FRCPsych 1979, M 1971; DPM Eng. 1960. Mem. Ment. Health Tribunals. Prev: Cons. Psychiat. Worcester Health Dist.

MILNER, Gillian Ruth (retired) 51 Endcliffe Hall Avenue, Sheffield S10 3EL Tel: 0114 268 6861 — BM BCh 1960 Oxf.; PhD Camb. 1970; FRCPath 1984, M 1972; FRCR 1984. Prev: Cons. Radiol. Barnsley Dist. Gen. Hosp. NHS Trust & Rotherham Dist. Gen. Hosp.

MILNER, Ian G 47 Central drive, Lytham St Annes FY8 4DF; 47 Central Drive, Ansdell, Lytham St Annes FY8 4DF — MB ChB Liverp. 1970; DObst RCOG 1973. (Liverp.) p/t Med. Adviser, War Pens. Agency, Norcross, Blackpool; Clin. Asst. (Cardiac Rehabil.) Vict. Hosp. Blackpool. Prev: SHO Roy. Liverp. Childr. Hosp.; SHO (Psychiat.) Sefton Gen. Hosp. Liverp.; Ho. Off. (O & G) BRd.green Hosp. Liverp.

MILNER, John Christopher Geoffrey Merstow Green Medical Practice, Merstow Green, Evesham WR11 4BS Tel: 01386 765600 Fax: 01386 446807 — MB BS 1966 Newc.; BSc Durham. 1963. (Newc.) Hosp. Pract. (Anaesth.) Worcester Health Auth. Socs: Assn. Anaesths. Prev: Regist. Anaesth. United Sheff. Hosps.; SHO Anaesth. United Sheff. Hosps.; Ho. Off. (Gen. Med. & Gen. Surg.) Roy. Vict. Infirm. Newc.

MILNER, Mr John Clifford 50 Duchy Road, Harrogate HG1 2EY Tel: 01423 63240 — MB ChB 1959 Manch.; FRCS Eng. 1966. (Manch.) Cons. Surg. (Orthop. & Trauma) Harrogate Health Dist.

MILNER, Mark Andrew c/o 2 Woodbine Cottages, Wedgenock, Warwick CV35 7PX — MB ChB 1990 Otago.

MILNER, Michael Lloyd Dundas Street West Surgery, 6 Dundas Street West, Saltburn-by-the-Sea TS12 1BL Tel: 01287 622207 Fax: 01287 623803; Beechwood, Victoria Tce, Saltburn-by-the-Sea TS12 1HN Tel: 01287 622023 — MB ChB 1983 Leic.; BSc Med.Sci. Leic. 1980. (Leic.) Clin. Gover. Lead LPCG. Prev: Clin. Ass. Neur. Midd'Brgh.

MILNER, Neil Andrew Tramways Medical Centre, 54a Holme Lane, Sheffield S6 4JQ Tel: 0114 233 9462 — MB ChB 1986 Sheff.; MRCGP 1990; T(GP) 1991. (Sheffield) GP; Primary Care Head Cancer Clinician, Sheff. (W.); Med. Assessor & Adviser Appeals Serv. Socs: BMA; MRCGP. Prev: SHO N. Gen. Hosp. Sheff.; SHO Matern. Hosp. Hull; Ho. Off. RN Hosp. Haslar.

MILNER, Penelope Jane The Surgery, 20 Lee Road, Blackheath, London NW7 1LJ Tel: 020 8852 1235 Fax: 020 8297 2193; 26 Westcombe Park Road, London SE3 7RB — MB BS 1988 Lond.; DRCOG 1991. Trainee GP Vanburgh Hill Health Centre Lond. Prev: SHO (Geriat.) Roy. Lond. Trust; SHO (O & G & Paediat.) Greenwich Dist. Gen. Hosp.

MILNER, Philip Charles Clarendon House, Prospect Place, Beechen Cliff, Bath BA2 4QP — MB ChB 1981 Sheff.; MSc Lond. 1972; BA Camb. 1970; MRCP (UK) 1984; FFPHM RCP (UK) 1996.

MILNER, Philip Michael Rookery Surgery, Chester Road, Tattenhall, Chester CH3 9AH; 2 Brockway W., Tattenhall, Chester CH3 9EZ Tel: 01829 770855 — MB ChB 1978 Liverp.; MRCS Eng. LRCP Lond. 1978; MRCGP 1986; DRCOG 1981. (Liverp.) Prev: SHO (Med.) Whiston Hosp. Prescot; Ho. Off. Roy. Liverp. Hosp.

MILNER, Quentin James Whitmore 2 Grange Grove, London N1 2NP — MB ChB 1988 Bristol.

MILNER

MILNER, Mr Richard Henderson Department of Plastic Surgery, Royal Victoria Infirmary, Newcastle upon Tyne NE1 4LP Tel: 0191 232 5131 Fax: 0191 227 5229; Old Prior Manor, Stagshaw Road, Corbridge NE45 5HR — MB ChB 1977 Manch.; BSc Morbid Anat. Manch. 1976, MD 1990; FRCS (Plast) 1991; FRCS Eng. 1983; DCH Eng. 1979. Cons. Plastic Surg. Roy. Vict. Infirm. W. Cumbld. Hosp. Whitehaven & Cumbld. Infirm. Carlisle; Sen. Lect. (Plastic & Reconstruc. Surg.) Univ. Newc.; Dep. Edr. Brit. Jl. of Plastic Surg.s. Socs: Brit. Assn. of Plastic Surgs.; Brit. Assn. Aesthetic Plastic Surgs.; Brit. Soc. Surg. Hand. Prev: Sen. Regist. (Plastic Surg.) Roy. Vict. Infirm. & Newc. Gen. Hosp.; Regist. Welsh Regional Plastic Surg. Unit; Microvasc. Research Fell. Roy. Adelaide Hosp. Adelaide, Austral.

MILNER, Ronald Stuart 327 Upper Richmond Road, Putney, London SW15 Tel: 020 8788 6002; 121 East Sheen Avenue, London SW14 8AX Tel: 020 8876 9485 — MB BS 1975 Lond.; MRCS Eng. LRCP Lond. 1975; LMSSA Lond. 1975; DRCOG 1977; Cert. JCC Lond. 1977; MPS 1953; MPS NZ 1953. (St. Thos.)

MILNER, Sarah Louise Princess Margaret Hospital, Okus Rd, Swindon SN1 4JU — BM BS 1993 Nottm.; MRCGP 2000; BMedSci (Hons.) 1991; DRCOG 1997; DFFP 1999. (Nottm.) p/t Gen. Practitioner, Ripley Med. Centre; Family Plann. Doctor (CMO), S.. Derbysh. Family Plann. Serv. Prev: GP Regist. Chesterfield Roy. Hosp. VTS; Retainee GP, Littlewick Med. Centre, Ilkeston, Derbysh.

MILNER, Mr Stephen Alexander Department of Orthopaedic Surgery, Queens Medical Centre, Nottingham NG7 2UH Tel: 0115 9249924; Email: stephen.milner@clara.net — MB ChB (Hons.) Sheff. 1990; 2001 DM Nottg Univ.; 2002 FRCS (Tr &Orth); FRCS Eng. 1995. (Sheffield) Specialist Regist. Rotat. (Orthop. Surg.) Mid. Trent. Socs: Assoc. Mem. BOA; Mem. BOTA, (Brit. Orthopaedic Trainees Assn.). Prev: Research Fell. (Orthop. Surg.) Qu. Med. Centre Nottm.; SHO Rotat. (Surg.) Derbysh. Roy. Infirm.

MILNER, Sylvia Margaret Highbury House, Rue Des Potirons, St Martin, Jersey JE3 6HS Tel: 01534 851060 Fax: 01534 856684 — MB BS 1967 Lond.; DObst RCOG 1969. (Middlx.) Med. Adviser Jersey Adoption Panel; Mem. of Attendance Allowance Bd. Prev: Med. Off. Child Developm. Jersey; Ho. Off. (Ophth. & Dermat.) Middlx. Hosp.; Ho. Off. (O & G) & Ho. Surg. Centr. Middlx. Hosp. Lond.

MILNES, David Clive 19 Cromwell Road, York YO1 6DU — MB ChB 1993 Leeds.

MILNES, Ian Saddleworth Medical Practice, The Clinic, Smithy Lane, Uppermill, Oldham OL3 6AH Tel: 01457 872228 Fax: 01457 876520 — MB ChB 1988 Manch.; MRCGP 1992; Cert. Family Plann. JCC 1991; DRCOG 1991. Prev: Trainee GP/SHO (Med.) Roy. Albert Edwd. Infirm. Wigan VTS.

MILNES, Jane Elizabeth Beech House Group Practice, Beech House, Beech Avenue Hazel Grove, Stockport SK7 4QR Tel: 0161 483 6222 Fax: 0161 419 9244; 20 Alwinton Avenue, Heaton Mersery, Stockport SK4 3PU — MB ChB 1991 Manch.; MRCGP 1996. Prev: Trainee GP Marple Cottage S. Reddish Stockport; SHO (O & G & A & E) Withington & Wythenshawe Hosps. Manch.; SHO (Paediat.) Stepping Hill Hosp. Stockport.

MILNES, John Norman (retired) Raymonds Cottage, Withypool, Minehead TA24 7QP Tel: 01643 831457 — MB BChir Camb. 1942; MD Camb. 1948; FRCP Lond. 1970, M 1947. Hon. Cons. Neurol. Roy. Free Hosp. Lond. Prev: Med. Off. Sun Life Assur. Soc.

MILNES, John Paul 5 Nesfield View, Ilkley LS29 9DD Tel: 01943 600584 — MB ChB 1977 Ed.; FRCP Lond. 1996; FRCP Ed. 1997; MRCP (UK) 1980. (Ed.) Cons. Med. for Elderly Airedale Gen. Hosp. Steeton.

MILNES, Robert Sven William The James Cochrane Practice, Maude Street, Kendal LA9 4QE Tel: 01539 722124 Fax: 01539 734995 — MB ChB 1987 Manch.; MRCGP 1992. (Manchester) Gen. Med. Practitioner, Princip.; Hosp Practitioner, OBS & Gynae., Kendal, Cumbria; Clin. Asst. (A & E & Psychiat.) Cumbria. Prev: Trainee GP Kendal; SHO (Gen. Med.) Roy. Albert Edwd. Infirm. Wigan.

MILNES, Stephen David, Wing Cdr. RAF Med. Br. (retired) 19 Buckingham Road, Oakham LE15 6RX Tel: 01572 723165 Fax: 01572 770361 Email: dr_sdmilnes@yahoo.co.uk — MB BS 1974; 2000 FIMC RCS Ed; 1994 MSc Lond.; MRCS Eng. LRCP Lond. 1974; MRCGP 1979; AFOM RCP Lond. 1981; MRAeS 1981; DAvMed Eng. 1980; Dip. IMC RCS Ed. 1990; MFPHC RCS Edin. 1996. Examr. RCS (Edin.); Sen. Ships' Phys. Carnival Cruise Lines (HQ Miami, FL, USA). Prev: Fleet Med. Off. To the Roy. Saudi Golden Fleet.

MILNTHORPE, Joy Clare Derwent Crescent Surgery, 20 Derwent Crescent, Whetstone, London N20 0QQ Tel: 020 8446 0171 Fax: 020 8446 0073; 72 Lincoln Road, London N2 9DL — MB BChir 1971 Camb.; MRCP (UK) 1974; MRCGP 1981; DRCOG 1977.

MILNTHORPE, Peter Derek Graham Road Surgery, 22 Graham Road, Weston Super Mare BS23 1YA Tel: 01934 62811 Fax: 01934 645842 — MB ChB 1974 Birm.

MILO-TURNER, Gilbert Knowle House, Hill Lane, Great Barr, Birmingham B43 6NA Tel: 0121 358 6080 — MB ChB Birm. 1946; DObst RCOG 1948; MRCS LRCP (Lond.) 1945. GP Birm.; Med. Asst. DHSS; Clin. Med. Off. Sandwell DHA; Ltd. Wolverhampton & Delta Extrusions W. Bromwich; Phys. (Occupat. Health) Delta Tubes Ltd. Birm., Delta Rods. Socs: Fell. Roy. Soc. Med. Prev: Sen. Ho. Surg. & Ho. Phys. Chesterfield & N. Derbys. Roy. Hosp.; Res. Obst. Off. Sorrento Matern. Hosp. Birm.; Clin. Asst. St. Margt. Hosp. Ment. Sub-N.

MILOFSKY, Ruth 63B Church Road, London NW4 4DU — MB BCh BAO 1988 Dub.; MB BCh Dub. 1988.

***MILOJEVIC, Nicholas** Deva House, 129 Silverdale Avenue, Ashley Park, Walton-on-Thames KT12 1EH — MB BS 1995 Lond.

MILOJKOVIC, Dragana 16 Netheravon Road, Chiswick, London W4 2NA Tel: 020 8995 6538 — MB BS 1989 Lond. SHO (Med.) OldCh. Hosp. Romford. Prev: Ho. Phys. (Metabol., Endocrinol. & Gen. Med) Lond. Hosp.; Ho. Surg. (Gen. Surg. & Orthop.) Lond. Hosp.

MILOSZEWSKI, Krzysztof J A Academic Unit of Medicine, St. James's University Hospital, Beckett St., Leeds LS9 7TF Tel: 0113 243 3144 Fax: 0113 242 9722 Email: msjkm@stjames.leeds.ac.uk; 7 leeds Road, Barwick in Elmet, Leeds LS15 4JE — MB ChB Leeds 1963; BSc (Physiol.) Leeds 1961, MD 1980; FRCP Lond. 1979, M 1967. Locum Cons. Endoscopist St. Jas. Hosp.; Sen. Clin. Teachg. Fell. Med. Sch. Socs: Brit. Soc. Gastroenterol.; BMA; N. Eng. Gastroenterol. Soc. Prev: Sen. Lect. & Hon. Cons. Phys. (Med. & Gastroenterol.) St. Jas. Univ. Hosp. Leeds.

MILROY, Alison Jane The Surgery, Yeoman Lane, Bearsted, Maidstone ME14 4DS Tel: 01622 737326/738344 Fax: 01622 730745 — MB ChB 1990 Bristol; MRCGP 1995; DFFP 1995; DRCOG 1995; DCH RCP Lond. 1994. Prev: Trainee GP Maidstone; SHO (O & G & Paediat.) Maidstone Hosp.

MILROY, Ms Catherine Flat G, 49 Beaumont St., London W1N 1RE Email: catymilroy@aol.com — BM BCh 1992 Oxf.; FRCS 1995.

MILROY, Professor Christopher Mark The Medico-Legal Centre, Watery St., Sheffield S3 7ES Tel: 0114 273 8721 Fax: 0114 279 8942 Email: cm.milroy@sheffield.ac.uk — MD 1994 Liverp.; MB ChB 1983; MRCPath 1990; DMJ(Path) 1991; FRCPath 1998. Prof. & Hon. Cons. Forens. Path. Univ. Sheff.; Home Office Path. Socs: Fell. Brit. Assn. Forens. Med.; Hon. Sec. Brit. Assn. In Forens. Med. Prev: Lect. (Path). Univ. Coll. & Middlx. Sch. Med.; Regist. (Histopath.) Bristol Roy. Infirm.

MILROY, Mr Euan James Gavin Private Consulting Rooms, King Edward VII Hospital, 37a Devonshire St., London W1G 6AA Tel: 020 7486 6886 Fax: 020 7467 4376; Chestnut Corner, 6 Monroe Drive, London SW14 7AR Tel: 020 8876 9797 — MB BS Lond. 1963; FRCS Eng. 1967; MRCS Eng. LRCP Lond. 1963. (St. Mary's) Cons. Urol. Middlx. Hosp. & King Edwd. VII Hosp. for Off. Lond. Socs: Fell. Roy. Soc. Med.; Brit. Assn. Urol. Surgs. Prev: Sen. Regist. (Urol.) St. Mary's Hosp. Lond.; Sen. Regist. Univ. Hosp. W. Indies, Jamaica; Research Fell. (Urol.) Univ. Rochester, NY, USA.

MILROY, Patrick John Murray The Knoll Surgery Partnership, 46 High Street, Frodsham, Warrington WA6 7HF Tel: 01928 733249 Fax: 01928 739367 Email: patrick-milroy@gp-n81030.nhs.uk; The Old Farm House, Newton Lane, Daresbury, Warrington WA4 4BQ Tel: 01925 740623 Fax: 01928 739367 — MB ChB 1971 Manch.; DObst RCOG 1974. (Manchester) Med. Adviser Amateur Athletics Assoc. Engl.; Lead Police Surg. Chesh. Constab.; Med. Adviser Runners World; Chair. Sports Med. Comm., March. 2002 Commonw. Games. Socs: Brit. Assn. Sports Med. (Asst. & Mem. Sec.); Assoc. Police Surg.s; Roy. Soc. Med. Prev: Trainee GP Chester VTS; Ho. Phys. & Ho. Surg. Pk. Hosp. Davyhulme.

MILROY, Robert Department of Respiratory Medicine, Stobhill Hospital, Glasgow G21 3UW Tel: 0141 201 3715 Fax: 0141 201

3888 — MB ChB Glas. 1990; MD Glas. 1990; FRCP Glas. 1993; MRCP (UK) 1982. Cons. Respirat. & Gen. Med. Stobhill Hosp. Glas. Socs: Scott. Thoracic Soc.; Brit. Thorac. Soc.; (Counc.) Roy. M-C Soc. Prev: Sen. Regist. (Respirat. & Gen. Med.) Glas. Roy. Infirm.; CRC Research Fell. (Med. Oncol.) Glas. Univ.; Regist. (Respirat. & Gen. Med.) Glas. Roy. Infirm.

MILROY, Sarah Elizabeth Constance Flat 8, 4 Ashford Court, Cheltenham GL50 2QZ Tel: 01242 250133 — MB ChB 1988 Bristol. GP. Socs: Fac. Fam. Plann. Prev: CMO (Psychiat.) Cheltenham; GP Trainee Halts Health Centre Gloucestershire; SHO (O & G) Derriford Hosp. Plymouth.

MILROY, Susan Joanna Flat D, 7 Medina Villas, Hove BN3 2RJ — MB BS 1987 Lond.; FRCA 1993; DA (UK) 1991. (Charing Cross and Westminster) Sen. Regist. (Anaesth.) King's Coll. Hosp. Lond. Prev: Regist. (Anaesth.) King's Coll. Hosp. & St. Geo. Hosp. Lond.; SHO (Anaesth.) Roy. Free Hosp. & Worthing Gen. Hosp.; SHO (A & E) Char. Cross Hosp.

MILSOM, John William 24 Lydgate Hall Crescent, Sheffield S10 5NE — MB ChB 1972 Sheff.; Cert JCC Lond. 1979.

***MILSOM, Penny** 55 King Charles Road, Halesowen B62 0DP — MB BS 1997 Newc.

MILSON, Arthur Ralph (retired) Hollybrook, Abbeystead Road, Dolphinholme, Lancaster LA2 9AY Tel: 01524 791021 — MB ChB 1943 Ed. Prev: Capt. RAMC 1943-6.

MILSON, Francis Edwin (retired) Valley View, 5 Spirewood Gardens, Romiley, Stockport SK6 3DT Tel: 0161 430 6944 — MB ChB 1940 Ed. Prev: Ho. Phys. & Obstetr. W. Gen. Hosp. Edin.

MILSON, James Arthur Pfizer Central Research, Sandwich CT13 9NJ Tel: 01304 618633 Fax: 01304 618749 — MB BChir 1975 Camb.; PhD Bristol 1978; MA, MB Camb. 1975, BChir 1974. Gp. Dir. Pfizer Centr. Research Sandwich. Prev: Lect. (Physiol.) Univ. Birm.; Lect. (Physiol.) Guy's Hosp. Med. Sch. Lond.; MRC Train. Fell. (Pharmacol.) Univ. Bristol.

MILSON, Jane Elizabeth Morecambe Bay Hospitals NHS Trust, Royal Lancaster Infirmary, Ashton Road, Lancaster LA1 4RP Tel: 01524 65944 Fax: 01524 846346; 6 Brookside Drive, Dolphinholme, Lancaster LA2 9AZ — MB ChB 1975 Manch.; BA (Hons.) Lond. 1967; BSc (Hons.) Manch. 1972, MB ChB 1975; FRCS Ed. 1980; FRCOphth. Cons. Ophth. Surg. Lancaster Moor Hosp.

MILSON, John Edwin Alvanley Surgery, 1 Auburn Avenue, Bredbury, Stockport SK6 2AH Tel: 0161 430 2727 Fax: 0161 406 7999; 37 Marina Drive, Marple, Stockport SK6 6JL Tel: 0161 427 1424 — MB ChB 1967 Manch.; MRCGP 1981.

MILSON, Olive Broad (retired) Valley View, 5 Spirewood Gardens, Romiley, Stockport SK6 3DT — MB ChB 1940 Ed.

MILSTED, Robert Andrew Victor 64 West Way, Holmes Chapel, Crewe CW4 7DH — MD 1979 Lond.; MSc Lond. 1978, MD 1979, MB BS 1971; MRCP (U.K.) 1975; FRCPM 1995. (St Georges) Regulatory Strategy Dir. Zeneca Pharmaceut. Prev: Sen. Regist. (Oncol.) Glas.

MILSTEIN, Mr Benjamin Bethel (retired) 25 Barrow Road, Cambridge CB2 2AP Tel: 01223 354777 Email: bb.istein@cwcom.net — MA Camb. 1977; MB BS Lond. 1942; FRCS Eng. 1947; MRCS Eng. LRCP Lond. 1942. Prev: Cons. Thoracic & Cardiovasc. Surg. E. Anglian RHA.

MILSTEIN, Penelope Anne Lakeside Health Centre, Tavy Bridge, Thamesmead, London SE2 9UQ Tel: 020 8310 3281; 10 St. Margarets Road, Brockley, London SE4 1YU — BSc (Psych.) Lond. 1981, MB BS 1985; MRCGP 1991; DCH RCP Lond. 1988; DRCOG 1987. Prev: SHO (Psychiat.) Guys Hosp. Lond.

MILTER, Margaret Elizabeth (retired) Southcliff, 27 Bon Accord Road, Swanage BH19 2DW — BSc 1940, MB BCh Wales 1943; MRCS Eng. LRCP Lond. 1943.

MILTON, Ailsa Margaret Scotstown Medical Centre, Cairnfold Road, Bridge of Don, Aberdeen AB22 8LD Tel: 01224 702149 Fax: 01224 706688; 74 Beaconsfield Place, Aberdeen AB15 4AJ Tel: 01224 641743 — MB ChB Aberd. 1969; DRCOG 1982.

MILTON, Ben Campbell 4 Corn Market Hill, Howden, Goole DN14 7BU Tel: 01430 452587 — MB BS 1996 Newc. (Newcastle upon Tyne) SHO (Orthop.) Pinderfields Hosp. Wakefield; SHO (ENT) Pinderfields Gen. Hosp.; SHO (A & E) Pinderfields Gen. Hosp. Prev: SHO (Urol.) TPRH Hull; PRHO (Surg.) HRI Hull; PRHO (Med.) HRI Hull.

MILTON, Catherine Maureen 2 Kingswood Close, Tunbridge Wells TN2 4XA Tel: 01892 537430; Stream Farm, Wenbans Lane, Wadhurst TN5 6NR Tel: 01892 782345 — MB BS 1978 Lond.; FRCS Eng. 1982; MRCS Eng. LRCP Lond. 1977.

MILTON, Jane Crystyan (retired) Linstock House, Linstock, Carlisle CA6 4PY Tel: 01228 524259 — MB BS 1944 Durh. Prev: GP N.shields.

MILTON, Jane Elizabeth Adult Department, The Tavistock Clinic, 120 Belsize Lane, London NW3 5BA Tel: 020 7435 7111 Fax: 020 7435 7111 — MB BS 1978 Lond.; MA Camb. 1978. (Camb. & The Lond. Hosp.) Cons. Psychother. Tavistock Clinic Lond. Socs: (Counc.) Assn. Psychanalyt. Psychother.; Brit. Psychoanal. Soc.; Fell. Roy. Coll. Psychiat. Prev: Edr. Psychoanalystic Psychother.; Cons. Psychother. King's Coll. Hosp. Lond.; Sen. Regist. (Psychother.) Maudsley Hosp. Lond.

MILTON, John Nottingham Healthcare NHS Trust, East Midlands Centre for Forensic Mental Health, Arnold Lodge, Corbelia Close, Leicester LE5 0LE Tel: 0116 225 6060 Fax: 0116 225 6061 Email: john.milton@arnold.cnhc-tr.trent.nhs.uk — MB ChB 1989 Birm.; BSc (Hons.) Birm. 1986; MMedSc Univ. Leeds 1996; MRCPsych 1993. (Birm.) Lect. In Forens. Ment. Health Univ. of Leicester, Leicester. Socs: BMA. Prev: Sen. Regist. (Psychiat.) Mid Trent.

MILTON, Julie Claire Conquest Hospital, The Ridge, St Leonards-on-Sea TN37 7RD — MB ChB 1992 Orange Free State.

MILTON, Matthew Henry Springfield House Medical Centre, 275 Huddersfield Road, Oldham OL4 2RJ Tel: 0161 633 2333 Fax: 0161 628 6682 — MB ChB 1976 Manch.

MILTON, Peter James Denis Kings Head House, Duxford, Cambridge CB2 4RP Tel: 01223 832238 Fax: 01223 832999; Department Gynaecology, Addenbrookes Hospital, Hills Road, Cambridge CB2 2QQ Tel: 01223 45151 — MRCS Eng. LRCP Lond. 1963; MA Camb. 1977; MD Lond. 1978, MB BS 1964; FRCOG 1983, MRCOG 1970; DA Eng. 1969; DObst RCOG 1965. (St. Geo.) Cons. (O & G) Cambs. AHA (T) Adden Brookes Hosp. Camb.; Assoc. Lect. Univ. Camb. Med. Sch. Prev: Lect. & Sen. Regist. O & G St. Thos. Hosp. Lond.; Res. Obst. Asst. & Ho. Phys. St. Geo. Hosp. Lond.

MILTON, Richard Stephen 3 Grosvenor House Mews, Holland Road, Manchester M8 8WW — MB ChB 1993 Sheff.; FRCS Ed 1998. Cardioalexacic Reasearch Fell. - Dept of Cardiovasc. Med.- N.ern Gen. Hosp. - Suesfiels.

MILTON, Robert James Stuart (retired) Farthings, Peterborough Road, Harrow HA1 3DX Tel: 020 8864 2419 — MRCS Eng. LRCP Lond. 1954; MRCGP 1965.

MILTON, Ruth Stephanie Kingston & Richmond Health Authority, 22 Hollyfiel Road, Surbiton UT5 9AC; Maalesh, Millbridge, Frensham, Farnham GU10 3AA — MB BS 1988 Lond.; MSc Lond. 1984; MA Camb. 1986. Specialist Regis., Pub. Health Med., Kingston & Richmond H.A.; Trainee Mem. Fac. Pub. Health Med. Socs: Fell. Roy. Soc. Med.; Soc. Social Med. Prev: SHO (Pub. Health Med.) Croydon HA; Regist. (Med. & Rheum.) W. Middlx. Univ. Hosp.; Regist. (Med.) Watford Gen. Hosp.

MILTON-THOMPSON, David Gerald, OBE (retired) Rochdale House, Rochdale Road, Sevenoaks TN13 1JJ Tel: 01732 462977 — MB BChir 1949 Camb.; MRCS Eng. LRCP Lond. 1942.

MILTON-THOMPSON, Sir Godfrey James, KBE, KStJ, Surg. Vice-Admiral (retired) Pool Hall, Menheniot, Liskeard PL14 3QT Tel: 01579 342321 — MB Camb. 1955, BChir 1954; FRCP Lond. 1974, M 1961; DCH Eng. 1963. Prev: Warden St. Katharine's Hse. Wantage.

MILVERTON, Rose Anne (retired) Cherry Trees, 6 Beverley Gardens, Wargrave, Reading RG10 8ED Tel: 0118 940 2591 — MB BCh BAO NUI 1963; MPH (Epidemiol.) Tulane Sch. Pub. Health USA 1969; DTM & H Liverp. 1968. Prev: GP Warks.

MILWARD, David Victor (retired) Kirklands, Green Lane, Farnham Common, Slough SL2 3SP Tel: 01753 644501 — MRCS Eng. LRCP Lond. 1941; MA, MB BChir Camb. 1946. Med. Adviser to Licensed Victuallers' Nat. Homes. Prev: Surg. Lt. RNVR.

MILWARD, Mr Timothy Michael BUPA Hospital Leicester, Gartree Road, Leicester LE2 2FF Tel: 0116 265 3678 Fax: 0116 265 3679; Pine House, Gaddesby, Leicester LE7 4XE Tel: 01664 840213 Fax: 01664 840660 — MB BChir Camb. 1964; MA Camb. 1964; FRCS Eng. 1967. (St. Thos.) Cons. Plastic Surg. Leicester Roy. Infirm., Lincoln Co. Hosp. & Pilgrim Hosp. Boston. Socs: (Ex-Pres.)

MIMNAGH

Brit. Assn. Plastic Surgs.; (Ex-Pres.) Brit. Assn. Aesthetic Plastic Surgs.; Brit. Soc. Surg. Hand. Prev: Sen. Regist. (Plastic Surg.) Qu. Mary's Hosp. Lond.; Regist. (Plastic Surg.) Canniesburn Hosp. Glas.; Regist. (Surg.) St. Thos. Hosp. Lond.

MIMNAGH, Andrew Patrick Eastview Surgery, 81-83 Crosby Road North, Liverpool L22 4QD Tel: 0151 928 8849 Fax: 0151 92 2090; 6 Manor Drive, Liverpool L23 7YQ Tel: 0151 924 3116 — MB ChB 1988 Liverp.; BSc (Hons.) Physiol. Liverp. 1985; T(GP) 1993.

MIMNAGH, Christopher James Longton Medical Centre, 451 Warrington Road, Rainhill, Prescot L35 4LL; Stoney Croft, 13 Knowsley Road, Rainhill, Prescot L35 0PA — MB ChB 1988 Liverp.

MIMPRISS, Timothy John (retired) — MB BChir 1965 Camb.; BA Camb. 1961, MA 1965; FFA RCS Eng. 1968. Prev: Cons. Anaesth. Gwynedd HA.

MIMS, Cedric Arthur Sherriff House, Hammingden Lane, Ardingly, Haywards Heath RH17 6SR Tel: 01444 892243 Fax: 01444 891043 — MB BS 1952 Lond.; BSc (Zool.) Lond. 1947, MD 1963; FRCPath 1976. (Middlx.) Emerit. Prof. Dept. Microbiol. Guy's Hosp. Med. Sch. UMDS Lond. Prev: Med. Research Off. E. Afr. Virus Research Inst. Entebbe, Uganda; Profess. Fell. Dept. Microbiol. John Curtin Sch. Med. Research Canberra, Austral.

MIN, Aung Dorothy Pattison Hospital, Alumwell Close, Walsall WS2 9XH Tel: 01922 858000 Fax: 01922 858085; 11C Mellish Road, Walsall WS4 2DQ — MB BS 1981 Rangoon; Dip. Psychiat. Keele 1993. SCMO (Rehabil. Psychiat.) Walsall Community Health Trust. Prev: SHO (Psychiat.) St. Matthew's Hosp. Walsall; Regist. (Geriat. Med.) Mid Glam. HA.

MINA, Mr Amal Girgis 289 Spies Lane, Halesowen B62 9BN — LMSSA 1969 Lond.; FRCSI 1990; FRCS Ed. 1967.

MINA, Fathi Shafiq 32 Rutland Gate, London SW7 1PG — MB BCh 1960 Cairo; LMSSA Lond. 1969; MRCOG 1969. (Kasr El Aini) Regist. (O & G) Qu. Eliz. II Hosp. Welwyn Gdn. City.

MINA, Magid Aziz Yacoub The Regency Hospital, West St., Macclesfield SK11 8DW — MB BCh 1979 Ain Shams; MB BCh Ain Shams, Egypt 1979; DRCOG Lond. 1993; DO RCPSI 1990.

MINA, Mary Talaat The Surgery, 25 Cranes Park Road, Sheldon, Birmingham B26 3SE Tel: 0121 743 2018; 96 Hampton Lane, Solihull B91 2RS Tel: 0121 704 3257 — LRCP LRCS 1983 Ed.; MB BCh Egypt 1973; LRFPS Glas. 1983.

MINA, Mokhlis Mina Mikhail The Surgery, 25 Cranes Park Road, Sheldon, Birmingham B26 3SE Tel: 0121 743 2018 — MB BCh 1965 Cairo; DS (Orthop.) Tanta 1973; DS Cairo 1969; LMSSA Lond. 1979. Prev: Regist. (Orthop.) Solihull Hosp.; Regist. (Orthop.) E. Birm. Hosp.

MINAS, Harilaos Petrou St. Martin's Hospital, Midford Road, Coombe Down, Bath BA2 5RP Tel: 01225 832383 Fax: 01225 840754; 8 Moravian Road, Bristol BS15 8LY — MB BS 1988 Serres, Greece; MB BS Serres, Greece 1981; Ptychio Iatrikes Thessalonika 1988. SHO Rotat. (Med.) Roy. United Hosp. NHS Trust. Socs: BMA; MDU. Prev: SHO Rotat. (Med.) Bath; SHO (Med. for Elderly) Ealing Hosp. Lond. & Rochford Hosp. S.end.

MINASIAN, Mr Harvey Cromwell Hospital, Cromwell Road, London SW5 0TU Tel: 020 7460 2000 Fax: 020 7460 5555; 52 Denbigh Road, London W13 8NH Tel: 020 8997 5026 Fax: 020 8810 4783 Email: hminasian@aol.com — MB BS Lond. 1969; MS Lond. 1983; FRCS Eng. 1974. (Roy. Lond. Hosp.) Cons. Gen. Surg. (BrE. & Gastroenterol.) Cromwell Hosp. Lond. Socs: Fell. Roy. Soc. Med.; Brit. Assn. Surg. Oncol. Prev: Sen. Regist. (Surg.) Newham Gen. Hosp. Lond.; Research Asst. BrE. Unit Roy. Marsden Hosp. Lond.; Regist. (Surg.) & SHO Roy. Lond. Hosp.

MINASIAN, Margaret 81 Saxon Drive, London W3 0NY — MB BS 1993 Lond.

MINASSIAN, Mr Darwin The Chestnuts, South Park, Gerrards Cross SL9 8HH — MB BS 1965 Lond.; FRCS Eng. (Ophth.) 1974. Clin. Lect. Inst. Ophth. & Moorfields Eye Hosp. Lond. Prev: Regist. (Ophth.) Oxf. Eye Hosp.

MINATTUR, Daisy Joseph G32 Ducane Court, Balham High Road, London SW17 7JP — Artsexamen 1969 Nijmegen; BSc Madras 1960; DGO 1974; MRCOG 1981; DO RCPSI 1974.

MINAUR, Nicola Jane Tel: 0208 846 1732 Fax: 0208 846 1603 — MB ChB 1989 Ed.; PhD 1999 Bath; BSc Ed. 1987; MRCP (UK) 1992. (Edinburgh) Socs: Brit. Soc. for Rheum.

MINAY, Ian Frederick 5 Witley Road, Lovedean, Waterlooville PO8 9TZ — MB ChB 1988 Manch.; MRCP (UK) 1991; MRCGP 1995; DRCOG 1994; DCH RCP Lond. 1992. Prev: SHO (O & G) York Dist. Hosp.

MINCHIN, Alan John 6 Coombehurst Close, Hadley Wood, Barnet EN4 0JU Tel: 020 8441 8885 — MB BS 1963 Lond.; FRCOG 1981, M 1968. (Char. Cross) p/t Cons. O & G Chase Farm Hosp. NHS Trust. Socs: Hunt. Soc.; (Treas.) Nuffield Vis. Soc. Prev: Ho. Phys. Char. Cross Hosp. Fulham; Regist. (O & G) St. Mary's Hosp. Portsmouth; Sen. Regist. (O & G) N.ampton Gen. Hosp. & Hammersmith Hosp.

MINCHIN, Alison Hilary 18 Burnside Road, Newcastle upon Tyne NE3 2DU Tel: 0191 285 5574 — MB BS 1977 Newc.; MRCGP 1982; DRCOG 1980.

MINCHOM, Alan Martin 33 Charnock, Skelmersdale WN8 9DZ — MB ChB 1992 Manch.

MINCHOM, Philip Ellis Cherry Tree House, Wern, Bersham, Wrexham LL14 4LT — MB ChB 1974 Birm.; MRCP (UK) 1978. Cons. (Paediat.) Maelor Gen. Hosp. Wrexham.

MINCHOM, Sarah Elizabeth North East Wales Trust, Wrexham Child Health Centre, PO Box No 2073, Croesnewydd Road, Wrexham LL13 7ZA Tel: 01978 727006 Email: sally.minchom@newtr.nhs.wales.uk; Cherry Tree house, Wern, Bernam, Wrexham LL14 4LT — MB ChB 1976 Dundee; FRCPCH; MSc (Audiol. Med.) Manch. 1995. Cons. Paediat. (Audiol.) Wrexham.

MINDELL, Jennifer Susan Kings Fund, 11-13 Cavendish Square, London W1G 0AN Email: jmindell@iho.org.uk; Tel: 01923 842141 — MB BS 1980 Lond.; MB BS (Hons.) Lond. 1980; BSc (Hons.) Lond. 1977; MFPHM RCP (UK) 1996; MRCGP 1986; DRCOG 1984. (St. Mary's) p/t Dep. Director Lond.Health Observatory Lond.; Hon. Sen. Clin. Lect., dept Epidemiol. of Pub. health, imperial Coll., Lond. Socs: Soc. for Social Med.; Med. Wom.'s Federat.; Action on Smoking and health (Bd. Mem.). Prev: Specialist Regist. (Pub. health med.) Kensington & Chelsea, & W.minster health Auth.; Sen. Regist. (Pub. Health Med.) Nottm. HA; Regist. (Pub. Health Med.) S.. Derbysh. HA.

MINDHAM, Michael Robert Landseer Road Surgery, 478 Landseer Road, Ipswich IP3 9LU Tel: 01473 274495 Fax: 01473 727642 — MB ChB 1990 Dundee; MRCGP 1994; DCH RCP Lond. 1993; DRCOG 1992.

MINDHAM, Professor Richard Hugh Shiels Division of Psychiatry & Behavioural Sciences, 15 Hyde Terrace, Leeds LS2 9LT Email: r.h.s.mindham@leeds.a.c.uk — MRCS Eng. LRCP 1959 MB BS Lond. 1959; MD Lond. 1974; FRCP Ed. 1978, M 1964; MRCS Eng. LRCP Lond. 1959; FRCPsych 1977, M 1971; DPM Lond. Univ. 1968; DCH Eng. 1962; FRCP Lond 2000. (Guy's) Emerit. Prof. Psychiat. Leeds Univ. Socs: Life Fell. RSM. Prev: Dean Fac. Med., Dent. & Health Univ. Leeds; Chief Examr. Roy. Coll. Psychiat.; Vis. Prof. Johns Hopkins Univ. USA.

MINDLIN, Miranda Juliet c/o 22 Shepherds Close, Highgate, London N6 5AG — BM BCh 1988 Oxf.; MA York 1990; BA Camb. 1985; MRCP (UK) 1995; DCH RCP Lond. 1992. Specialist Regist. (Community Paediat.) Community Health S. Lond. NHS Trust. Prev: SHO (Paediat.) Hosp. Childr. Gt. Ormond St. Lond., Qu. Eliz. Hosp. for Childr. Hackney & Roy. Free Hosp. Lond.

MINER, Mr Elijah Nanpak Selcan Flat 118, Oakwood Court, Abbotsbury Road, London W14 8LA Tel: 020 7603 8390; 25 Norcott Road, London N16 7EJ Tel: 020 8806 9838 — MB BS 1983 Ahmadu Bello Univ. Nigeria; MB BS Ahmadu Bello U. Nigeria 1983; FRCS Ed. 1992. Staff Surg. (Gen. Surg.) Dartford & Gravesham NHS Trust. Socs: BMA.

MINES, Gillian Pamela Cumberland House, Jordangate, Macclesfield SK10 1EG — MB ChB 1981 Birm.; MRCGP 1986; DRCOG 1985. (Birmingham) p/t G.P.

MINETT, Andrew Robert c/o 17 Justicia Way, Up Hatherley, Cheltenham GL51 3YH — MB ChB 1988 Bristol; DRCOG 1991.

MINETT, Nigel Paul Marden Medical Centre, Church Green, Marden, Tonbridge TN12 9HP Tel: 01622 831257 Fax: 01622 832840; Connaught, Headcorn Road, Staplehurst, Tonbridge TN12 0BU Tel: 01580 891936 — MB BS 1981 Lond.; MRCGP 1986; DRCOG 1985. (Kings) Prev: Clin. Asst. (Diabetes) Kent & Sussex Hosp. Tunbridge Wells.

MINFORD, Adrian Marcus Bolton Briarfield, St. John's Park, Menston, Ilkley LS29 6ES — MB BCh BAO 1972 Belf.; FRCP Lond.

1993; MRCP (UK) 1975; DObst RCOG 1974; DCH RCPSI 1974; FRCPCH 1998. Cons. Paediat. St. Lukes Hosp. Bradford & Bradford Roy. Infirm. Prev: Regist. Roy. Hosp. Sick Childr. Edin.; Regist. Roy. Belf. Hosp. Sick Childr.

MINFORD, Eunice Jane Bentra House, 16 Ballybentragh Road, Templepatrick, Ballyclare BT39 0DE; Flat 15, 212 Whitechapel Rd, London E1 1BJ Email: euni.min@btinternet.com — MB ChB 1989 Aberd.; Intercollegiate Exams in General Surgery June 2001; CCST 2001; FRCS Ed. 1993. Specialist Regist. Newc./ Cons. Roy. Lond. Hosp. Prev: Lect. & Sen. Regist. (Transpl.) Newc.; Specialist Regist. Liver Unit Birm.

MINFORD, Hugh Donaldson Ferguson Skegoneill Health Centre, 195 Skegoneill Avenue, Belfast BT15 3LL Tel: 028 9077 2471 Fax: 028 9077 2449 — MB BCh BAO 1975 Belf.; MRCGP 1982.

MINFORD, Jill Elizabeth 10 Birkdale Close, Mickleover, Derby DE3 5YG — MB BCh BAO 1977 Belf.; FRCR 1983; DRCOG 1979. Cons. Radiol. S.. Derbysh. HA.

MING, Hui Ying 8 Cissbury Ring S., London N12 7BE — MB BS 1997 Lond.

***MINGINS, Clare** 119 Stainbank Road, Kendal LA9 5BG — MB ChB 1996 Aberd.

***MINGO, Olivia Helen** Fairholme, Lawn Road, Guildford GU2 4DE — MB ChB 1998 Birm.; ChB Birm. 1998.

MINGO, Rebecca Margaret Fairholme, Lawn Road, Guildford GU2 4DE — MB ChB 1996 Birm.; ChB Birm. 1996.

***MINHAS, Asgher Khan** 82 Runswick Drive, Nottingham NG8 1JB — MB ChB 1994 Manch.

MINHAS, Emad-ul-Mulk The Gables, 231 Swinnow Road, Pudsey LS28 9AP Tel: 0113 257 4730 Fax: 0113 255 8644; Willow Nook Farm, Scholebrook Lane, Bank House Lane, Pudsey LS28 8DZ Tel: 0113 257 9974 — MB BS Peshawar 1968. (Khyber Med. Coll.) Socs: BMA & Brit. Soc. Med. & Dent. Hypn.

MINHAS, Hanna Bagh 53 Mansewood Road, Glasgow G43 1TL — MB ChB 1992 Glas.; MRCP 1997. (Glasgow University)

MINHAS, Harjit Singh 59 Kedleston Road, Leicester LE5 5BN — MB ChB 1990 Manch.

MINHAS, Honeyia Liza 231 Swinnow Road, Pudsey LS28 9AP Tel: 0113 257 9974 — MB BCh 1993 Wales; MRCP 1997 London; MRCP. (VWCM) Specialist Regist. (A & E) Oxf. Regional Train. Scheme. Socs: BMA; Full Mem. BAEM.

MINHAS, Hussan Ara The Gables, 231 Swinnow Road, Pudsey LS28 9AP Tel: 0113 257 4730 Fax: 0113 255 8644 — MB BS 1965 Peshawar; M Medsci (Gen. Pract.) Leeds 1984. (Khyber Med. Coll.) Socs: BMA & Brit. Soc. Med. & Dent. Hypn.; Fell. Roy. Med.

MINHAS, Pawanjit Singh 11 Limes Road, Hardwick, Cambridge CB3 7QR — BM BS 1991 Nottm.

MINHAS, Rahat Butul 131 Wellington Garth, Leeds LS13 4HL — MB BS 1968 Punjab.

MINHAS, Ramanjit Singh 5 Rouen Way, Ashby-de-la-Zouch LE65 2QX — BM BS 1994 Nottm.

MINHAS, Rubin 10 Parkfields, Rochester ME2 2TD — MB ChB 1993 Leeds.

MINHAS, Mr Satvir Singh 8 Cricket Close, Walsall WS5 3PU — MB ChB 1991 Manch.; FRCS (Otolaryngol.) Ed. 1996. (Manchester)

MINHAS, Sukhbinder 16 Albert Place, Horsforth, Leeds LS18 5AE — MB ChB 1989 Sheff.

MINHAS, Mr Tahaw-War Hasnat Ahmad 6 Allington Gardens, Boston PE21 9DP — MB BS 1983 Punjab; FRCSI 1990.

MINIHANE, Nigel Anthony The Laurels Medical Practice, 28 Clarendon Road, St Helier, Jersey JE2 3YS Tel: 01534 733866 Fax: 01534 769597; Clos Du Val, La Ruette Gabard, St Martin, Jersey JE3 6UH Tel: 01534 858396 — BM 1983 Soton.; MRCP (UK) 1986; DRCOG 1987. GP St. Helier, Jersey.

***MINKOFF, Simon** 10 Canons Drive, Edgware HA8 7QP — MB ChB 1998 Manch.; MB ChB Manch 1998.

MINN DIN, Zaw 23 Beacon Road, Rolleston, Burton-on-Trent DE13 9EF Tel: 01283 812787; 5 Wingaba Road, Tangon, Myanmar Tel: 1 542774 — MB BS 1982 Rangoon; MB BS Med. Inst. (I) Rangoon 1982; FCOphth 1992. Prev: Regist. Rotat. Glas.

MINN LWIN, Mr Department Surgery, 5th Floor, UCD Building, Royal Liverpool University Hospital, Prescot St., Liverpool L69 3BX — MB BS 1971 Med. Inst. (I) Rangoon; MB BS Med. Inst. (I) Rangoon; FRCS Glas. 1982; FRCS Ed. 1982.

MINNAAR, Gregory Norfolk & Norwich Hospital, Flat 68 Room 3, Doctor's Residence, St Steven's Road, Norwich NR1 3RE — MB ChB 1996 Pretoria.

MINNE, Carine Clotilde Marie Broadmoor Hospital, Crowthorne RG45 7EG; Portman Clinic, 8 Fitzjohn's Avenue, London NW3 5NA Tel: 020 7794 8262. — MB BCh BAO 1985 NUI; MRCPsych 1991; DRCOG 1988; Dip. Foren. Psychoth. 1997. Cons. Psychia. (Feren. Psychoth.) BRd.moor Hosp. & Portman NHS Clinic. Prev: Sen. Regist. (Forens. Psychiat.) St. Geo. Hosp. Lond., Sen. Regist. (Psychother.) Portman Clinic Lond.; Regist. (Psychiat.) Maudsley Hosp. Lond.; Ho. Off. S. Tyrone Hosp. Dungannon.

MINNEY, Paul Conrad 155B High St. N., Stewkley, Leighton Buzzard LU7 0EX; Pollicot Manor, Lower Pollicot, Ashendon, Aylesbury HP18 0HQ — MB BCh 1988 Wales; MRCGP 1993; T(GP) 1993.

MINNIS, Helen Jennifer Department Child & Family Psychiatry, Yorkhill NHS Trust, Yorkhill, Glasgow G3 8SJ Tel: 0141 201 9237; 72 Duncruin Street, Maryhill, Glasgow G20 0EZ Tel: 020 7738 4090 — MB ChB 1988 Glas.; BSc Biochem. Glas. 1985; MRCPsych 1995; Dip. Obst. Dunedin 1990; MSc (Epidemiol.) Lond. 1996; PLD London 1999. Specialist Regist. Child Pyschiatry, Yorkhill NHS Trust. Prev: Welcome Train. Fell. in Health Servs. Research; Sen. Health Off. Regist., Psychiat. Bethlem & Maudsley; Med. Off., Casa Guatemala Orphanage, Guatemala.

MINNIS, John (retired) 16 Coach Place, Newton Abbot TQ12 1ES Tel: 01626 335018 — MB BS Lond. 1950. Prev: Med. Off. Metrop. Police Train. Sch. Lond.

MINNS, John Patrick The Surgery, Reeth, Richmond DL11 6ST Tel: 01748 884396 Fax: 01748 884250; 116 Dunnocksfold Road, Alsager, Stoke-on-Trent ST7 2TW Tel: 01270 873893 — MB BS 1966 Lond.; MRCS Eng. LRCP Lond. 1966; DObst RCOG 1971. (King's Coll. Hosp.) p/t Assoc. GP N. Yorks. Prev: GP Alsager, Stoke-on-Trent; SHO (O & G) City Hosp. Nottm.; SHO (Paediat.) Copthorne Hosp. Shrewsbury.

MINNS, Robert Thomas The Park Surgery, 4 Alexandra Road, Great Yarmouth NR30 2HW Tel: 01493 855672 — MB BS 1989 Lond.; MRCGP 1993; DCH RCP Lond. 1993; DRCOG 1992.

***MINNS, Sarah Lucy** 116 Dunnocksfold Road, Alsager, Stoke-on-Trent ST7 2TW — MB ChB 1994 Manch.; BSc (Hons. Experim. Immunol. & Oncol.) Manch. 1991.

MINOCHA, Debika Elizabeth Court Surgery, Elizabeth Drive, Airedale, Castleford WF10 3TG Tel: 01977 552574 Fax: 01977 519652; Samarkand, Wentbridge Lane, Thorpe Audlin, Pontefract WF8 3EH Tel: 01977 620362 — MB BS 1957 Calcutta; DA Eng. 1969. (Calcutta) Prev: Med. Asst. (Anaesth.) Pontefract Gen. Infirm.

MINOCHA, Kuldeep 80 Otley Drive, Ilford IG2 6QN — BM 1991 Soton. Trainee GP N.wick Pk. VTS.

MINOCHA, Suniel 26 Langtons Wharf, The Calls, Leeds LS2 7EF Tel: 0113 234 1863 — MB BS Calcutta 1954. (R.G. Kar Med. Coll.)

MINOGUE, Martin Jeffrey O'Brien Penn Hill Surgery, St. Nicholas Close, Yeovil BA20 1SB Tel: 01935 74005 Fax: 01935 421841; Littlemoor, High St, West Coker, Yeovil BA22 9AG — MB BChir 1977 Camb.; MA Camb. 1977; MRCGP 1981; DRCOG 1981; Cert FPA. 1981. Course Organiser Yeovil. Prev: GP Trainer Yeovil.

MINORS, John Duncan (retired) Fishponds Health Centre, Beechwood Road, Fishponds, Bristol BS16 3TD Tel: 0117 965 6281 — MB ChB 1966 Bristol; DObst RCOG 1970.

MINORS, Norma Avonwood, Sea Walls Road, Sneyd Park, Bristol BS9 1PH Tel: 0117 968 6635 — MB ChB 1966 Bristol.

MINSHALL, Christine 120 Chapel Road, Hesketh Bank, Preston PR4 6RU — MB ChB 1985 Liverp.

MINSHALL, Ian Roland Northgate Village Surgery, Northgate Avenue, Chester CH2 2DX Tel: 01244 390396 Fax: 01244 370762; Northgate Village Surgery, Northgate Avenue, Chester CH2 2DX Tel: 01244 390396 Fax: 01244 370762 Email: ianminstall@dial.pipex.com — MB ChB 1987 Bristol; MRCGP 1993; DRCOG 1991; DCH RCP Lond. 1989. GP Tutor Chester & Ellesmere Port. Socs: Med. Audit Advis. Gp. (Chester Represen.). Prev: Clin. Asst. (Dermat. & Cardiol.) Chester.

MINSHULL-BEECH, Catherine Susan 107 King Street, Cambridge CB1 1LD — MB ChB 1981 Birm.

MINTER, Sarah Jane Rose Street, Todmorden OL14 5AT Tel: 01706 815126 Fax: 01706 812693; Tel: 01706 818900 — MB

MINTO

ChB 1979 Leeds; MRCGP 1985. (Leeds) Gen. Practitioner, Todmorden.

MINTO, Alfred 76 Walsingham Road, Woodthorpe, Nottingham NG5 4NR Tel: 0115 926 0221 — MB ChB 1951 Aberd.; MA Nottm. 1996; FRCPsych 1975, M 1972; DPM Eng. 1961. (Aberd.) Emerit. Cons. Psychiat. Rehabil. Pastures Hosp. Derby. Prev: Assoc. Prof. Psychiat. Univ. Calgary, Canada; Clin. Dir. (Forens. Med.) Calgary Gen. Hosp.; Med. Dir. Rampton Hosp. Retford.

MINTO, Catherine Louise York House, 10 Chaucer Road, Cambridge CB2 2EB — MB ChB 1993 Bristol.

MINTO, Gary William 24 Station Road, Whalley, Blackburn BB7 9RH — MB ChB 1992 Cape Town.

MINTO, Stephen Taylor (retired) Greenside Cottage, 33A Queen St., Geddington, Kettering NN14 1AZ Tel: 01536 743719 — MB BS 1961 Lond.; MRCS Eng. LRCP Lond. 1961. Prev: GP Kettering.

MINTON, David Keith 75 Alfred Street, Cardiff CF24 4TZ — MB ChB 1994 Liverp.

MINTON, Derek Bernard (retired) 68 Haven Road, Canford Cliffs, Poole BH13 7LY Tel: 01202 706457 Fax: 01202 706457 — MB ChB 1953 Birm.; MRCPsych 1974; DPM Eng. 1969; DObst RCOG 1954. Prev: GP Coventry.

MINTON, Elizabeth Jane Department Infectious Diseases, Royal Hallamshire Hospital, Glossop Road, Sheffield S10 2JF — MB ChB 1984 Ed.; MRCP (UK) 1987; PhD 1992; DTM & H 1998. Sen. Regist. (Infec. Dis.s) Roy. Hallamshire Hosp. Sheff.

MINTON, Michael John 27 Chalfont Road, Oxford OX2 6TL Tel: 01865 552820 Email: michael.minton@orh.nhs.net — MB BS 1970 Lond.; MRCP 1973 UK; FRCR 1984; FRCP 1993 Lond.; BSc (Hons.) Anat. Lond. 1967, MB BS 1970; FRCP Lond. 1993; MRCP (UK) 1973; FRCR 1984. Cons. Palliat. Med. Sir Michael Sobell Hse. Ch.ill Hosp. Oxf. Prev: Sen. Regist. (Radiother.) Char. Cross Hosp. Lond.; Clin. Research Fell. ICRF BrE. Unit Guy's Hosp. Lond.

MINTON, Nathaniel David 44 Westmoreland Road, Barnes, London SW13 9RY Tel: 020 8748 3758 — MRCS Eng. LRCP Lond. 1960; MA Camb.; MRCPsych 1972; FRCPsych 1994; T(Psychiat.) 1991; DPM Eng. 1965. (Char. Cross) Cons. Privat Pract. Barnes Lond. Socs: Fell. Roy. Soc. Med.; BMA. Prev: Cons. Psychiat. St. Peters Hosp. Chertsey & Bouvenwood NHS Trust; Cons. Psychiat. Roy. Holloway Univ. Lond. Health Centre; Brit. Postgrad. Med. Fed & Roy. Coll. Psychiat. Tutor in Psychiat.

MINTON, Neil Andrew Medical Department, Zeneca Pharma International, Southbank, Alderley Park, Macclesfield SK10 4TF Tel: 01625 515607 Fax: 01625 586296; 28 Priory Road, Wilmslow SK9 5PR Tel: 01625 528506 Fax: 01625 528506 — MB ChB 1979 Birm.; BSc (Hons. Physiol.) Birm. 1976, MD 1993; MRCP (UK) 1985; MFPM RCP (UK) 1992; Dip. Pharm. Med. RCP (UK) 1991. Med. Manager Therap. Area Zeneca Pharma Internat. Macclesfield; Hon. Regist. (Med.) Guy's Hosp. Lond. Socs: Brit. Pharm. Soc.; Brit. Toxicol. Soc. Prev: Lect. (Clin. Pharmacol.) Guy's Hosp. Lond.; Clin. Research Fell. Poisons Unit Guy's Hosp. Lond.; Clin. Research Phys. Glaxo.

***MINTON, Oliver James** 27 Chalfont Road, Oxford OX2 6TL — MB BS 1998 Lond.; MB BS Lond 1998.

MINTOWT-CZYZ, Mr Witold Józef St Josephs Private Hospital, Harding Avenue, Malpas, Newport NP20 6ZE Tel: 01633 820338 Fax: 01633 821487 Email: w.mintowt-czyz@uk.consultants.co.uk; Malbec Fach, Pontymason Lane, Rogerstone, Newport NP10 9GR — MB BS 1971 Lond.; FRCS Eng. 1979; FRCS Ed. 1978. (Lond. Hosp.) Cons. Orthop. Surg. Roy. Gwent Hosp. Socs: BORS; PCL Study Gp.; BMA. Prev: Emmeritus Dir. Train.; Sen. Lect. (Orthop.) Welsh Nat. Sch. Med.; Sen. Regist. (Orthop.) Cardiff Roy. Infirm.

MINTY, Clare Alison 13 Golf Road, Bromley BR1 2JA — MB ChB 1983 Bristol; MRCPysch 1988.

MINTY, Ian Louden South Tyneside District Hospital, Harton Lane, South Shields NE34 0PL Tel: 0191 202 4113 — MB BS 1981 Lond.; MRCP (UK) 1986; MRCS Eng. LRCP Lond. 1981; FRCR 1992. Cons. Radiol. S. Tyneside Dist. Hosp. S. Shields. Prev: Sen. Regist. Rotat. (Radiol.) St. Geo. Hosp. Lond.; Regist. Rotat. (Radiol.) Newc.

MINTY, Sarah Jane Eastgate Surgery, 31B York Place, Knaresborough HG5 0AD Tel: 01423 557200; Home Cottage, Old Scriven, Knaresborough HG5 9DZ Tel: 01423 866935 — MB ChB 1984 Birm.; MRCGP 1989; T(GP) 1991; DRCOG 1987. Prev: SHO (Palliat. Med.) St Gemmas Hospice Leeds.

MINTZ, Barry Jack Eaton Road Surgery, 276 Eaton Road, West Derby, Liverpool L12 2AW Tel: 0151 228 3768 Fax: 0151 259 7008; (Surgery), 122 Deysbrook Lane, Liverpool L12 8RQ — MB ChB Liverp. 1963. Prev: Ho. Phys. & Ho. Surg. S.port Gen. Infirm.

MINTZ, Henry Gilbert Lisson Grove Health Centre, Gateforth St, London NW8 8EG Tel: 020 7262 1366 Fax: 020 7258 1943; 6 Beversbrook Road, London N19 4QF — MB BS 1979 Lond.; BSc Lond. 1976; MRCP (UK) 1984; Dip. Pract. Dermat. Wales 1998. (Univ. Coll Hosp.) Clin. Asst. (Dermat.) Whittington Hosp. Lond.; GP (A & E) St Mary's Hosp. Lond. Prev: Regist. (Med.) Hackney Hosp. Lond.

MINWALLA, Mr Feramerz The Surgery, 22 Shenley Green, Birmingham B29 4HH Tel: 0121 475 7997; 47 Selwyn Road, Edgbaston, Birmingham B16 0SJ Tel: 0121 455 9188 — MB BS 1961 Karachi; FRCS Ed. 1968; MRCGP 1980.

MIODRAG, Aleksandar 6 Midway Road, Leicester LE5 5TP — MB ChB 1978 Leeds; BSc Leeds 1975; FRCP Lond. 1995; MRCP (UK) 1982.

MIOTTI, Antonio Maria 17 Bevan House, Boswell St., London WC1N 3BT Tel: 0207242 8545; 16 Via A. Gabelli, 35100 Padova, Italy — MD 1977 Padua; MSc Lond. 1981; DMD Padua 1980. (Univ. Padua) Cons. Maxillofacial Surg. Regional Trust Hosp. Udine. Socs: Fell. Roy. Soc. Med.; Europ Assn. Cranio Maxillofacial Surg. Prev: Cons. Maxillofacial Surg. USL 19 Veneto; Cons. MaxillofacialSurg. Milit. Hosp. Padua; Maxillofacial Surg. Univ. Milan 1990.

MIOTTI, Francesca Ada 17 Bevan House, Boswell St., London WC1N 3BT Tel: 020 7242 8545; Via Gabelli 16, Padova 35121, Italy Tel: 00 39 49 8757411 Fax: 00 39 49 8761210 — MD 1976 Padua; MSc Lond. 1979; State Exam 1977, DMD 1980. (Padua) Assoc. Prof. Orthodont. Univ. Padua.

MIR, Mohammad Afzal University Hospital of Wales, Heath Park, Cardiff CF4 4XN Tel: 029 2074 2305 Fax: 029 2074 7896 Email: miram@cardiff.ac.uk; Iscoed, Old Mill Road, Lisvane, Cardiff CF14 OXP Tel: 029 2075 5620 Fax: 01222 747896 — MB BS 1961 Vikram; FRCP Lond. 1985; MRCP (UK) 1972; DCH Eng. 1965. (G. R. Med. Coll. Gwalior) Sen. Lect. & Cons. Phys. Dept. Med. Univ. Hosp. Wales Cardiff. Socs: Med. Res. Soc. & Brit. Diabetic Assn.; Brit. Hyperlipid. Assn. Prev: Sen. Regist. (Cardiol.) Manch. Roy. Infirm.; Regist. (Med.) N. Ormesby Hosp. Middlesbrough.; SHO Alder Hey Childr. Hosp. Liverp.

MIR, Naheed 57 Tierney Road, Streatham Hill, London SW2 4QH — MB BS 1978 Lond.

***MIR, Naheed** 28 Culverhouse Road, Luton LU3 1PX — MB BS 1998 Lond.; MB BS Uni. Coll. Lond 1998.

***MIR, Nusrat Ullah** 57 Ancaster Drive, Glasgow G13 1NA — MB ChB 1995 Manch.; BSc (Hons.) Psychol. Manch. 1993.

MIR, Razia Sultana Prestwick Road Surgery, 259 Prestwick Road, Oxhey, Watford WD19 6XU Tel: 020 8428 2432 Fax: 020 8386 2488.

MIR, Saboor Ahmed Prestwick Road Surgery, 259 Prestwick Road, Oxhey, Watford WD19 6XU Tel: 020 8428 2432 Fax: 020 8386 2488.

MIRA, Sirag Abdulghani 9 Neville Court, Abbey Road, St John's Wood, London NW8 9DD — MB BS 1975 Lond.; MRCS Eng. LRCP Lond. 1974; MRCP (UK) 1980.

MIRACLE ECHEGOYEN, Josep Xavier Ham House 119, Hammersmith Hospital, Du Cane Road, London W12 0HS — LMS 1988 Barcelona.

***MIRAKHUR, Anju** 13 Viewfort Park, Dunmurry, Belfast BT17 9JY — BChir 1994 Camb.

MIRAKHUR, Meenakshi Department of Pathology, Royal Victoria Hospital, Belfast BT12 6BA Tel: 01232 240503; 13 Viewfort Park, Belfast BT17 9JY Tel: 01232 626658 — MB BS 1968 Lucknow; MD (Path.) Postgrad. Inst. Chandigarh (India) 1974; MRCPath 1978. (King Geo. Med. Coll. Lucknow) Cons. Path. Roy. Vict. Hosp. Belf. Socs: Path. Soc. & Brit. Soc. Neuropath. Prev: Sen. Regist. (Histopath. & Neuropath.) Roy. Vict. Hosp. Belf.

MIRAKHUR, Professor Rajinder Kumar Department of Anaesthetics, The Queen's University Belfast, 97 Lisburn Road, Belfast BT9 7BL Tel: 02890335785 Fax: 02890 329605 Email: r.mirakhur@queens-belfast.ac.uk — MB BS Jammu & Kashmir 1967; PhD Belf. 1977; MD (Anaesth.) Delhi 1971; FFA RCS Eng. 1976; FFA RCSI 1984. (Govt. Med. Coll. Srinagar) Cons. Anaesth.

Roy. Vict. & Belf. City Hosps.; Prof. (Anaesth.) The Qu.s Univ. Belf. Socs: Assn. Anaesth. GB & Irel. & Anaesth. Research Soc.; Amer. Soc. Anesthesiols. Prev: Sen. Tutor (Anaesth.) Qu. Univ. Belf.; Sen. Regist. (Anaesth.) N. & W. Belf. Health Dist.; Asst. Prof. Postgrad. Inst. Chandigarh, India.

MIRAKIAN, Rita Margherita Immunology Department, St. Barts and Royal London School of Medicine, 38 Little Britian, London EC1A YBE Tel: 020 7601 7431 Fax: 020 7606 0845 Email: rmmirakian@mds.qmw.ac.uk; 141 Mallinson Road, Battersea, London SW11 1BH Tel: 020 7228 3623 — State DMS 1971 Padua. Clin. Sen. Lect. (Immunol.) St. Bart. & Roy. Lond. Sch. Med. & Dent. (Immunol.) Lond.; Hon. Cons. (Immunol.). Socs: Brit. Soc. Immunol.; Brit. Soc. Allergy & Clin. Immunol. Prev: Univ. Contract (Internal Med.) Univ. Verona, Italy.; Research Asst. (St Barts' & Roy. Lond. Hosp. Sch. Of Med.).

MIRALLES, Robin Emmanuel 6 Derby Hills Farm Court, Melbourne, Derby DE73 1EE — MB BChir 1992 Camb. (Camb.) Specialist Regist. (Paediat.) Sheff. Childrs. Hosp. Sheff.

MIRANDA, Sanjay Michael The Convent Hospital, 748 Mansfield Road, Woodthorpe, Nottingham NG5 3FZ; 94 Beech Avenue, Mapperley, Nottingham NG3 5JW — MB BS 1993 Newc.

*MIRANDA, Sumeet Michele 59 Nottingham Road, Trowell, Nottingham NG9 3PJ — MB BS 1998 Newc.; MB BS Newc 1998.

MIRANDA CARABALLO, Jose Ildefonso 18 Norfolk Drive, Chelmsford CM1 4AG Tel: 01245 353487 — LMS 1989 Cadiz; DA (UK) 1995. SHO (Anaesth.) Whittington Hosp. Lond. Prev: SHO (Anaesth. & A & E) Broomfield Hosp. Chelmsford; Resid. (Emerg. Med.) La Linea Hosp., Spain.

MIRANDA FERNANDEZ, Francisco Javier Flat 1, 128 Mansfield Road, London NW3 2JB — LMS 1994 Granada.

MIRANDA PALOMINO, Jose Francisco 52 Steep Hill, Croydon CR0 5QT — LMS 1990 Cadiz.

MIRCHANDANI, Miss Meenu Vasdev 18 Cadogan Gardens, London E18 1LU — BM BS 1988 Nottm.; BMedSci (1st cl. Hons.) Nottm. 1986. Trainee GP Roy. Free Hosp. Lond. VTS. Prev: Ho. Off. City Hosp. Nottm. & Derbysh. Roy. Infirm.

MIRES, Gary John Balgonie, 38 Albert St., Tayport DD6 9AT — MD 1994 Dundee; MB ChB 1983; MRCOG 1988. Sen. Lect. (O & G) Ninewells Hosp. & Med. Sch. Dundee.

MIRES, Joy-Elizabeth 23 Donford Avenue, Mount Vernon, Glasgow G32 9NN — MB ChB 1983 Dundee; DRCOG 1986.

MIRESKANDARI, Kamiar King's College Hospital, Denmark Hill, London SE6 9RS Tel: 020 7737 4000; 3 Harvard House, Manorfields, Putney Hill, London SW15 3NB Tel: 020 8785 1433 — MB ChB 1994 Leeds.

MIRESKANDARI, Maziar 3 Harvard House, Manor Fields., London SW15 3NB — MB ChB 1992 Leeds.

MIRFATTAHI, Mir Mohammad Bagher Burton Hospitals NHS Trust, Belvedere Road, Burton-on-Trent DE13 0RB Tel: 01283 566333 Fax: 01283 593031 Email: mohammad.mirfattahi@btinternet.com; 51 Fallowfield Drive, Barton-under-Needwood, Burton-on-Trent DE13 8DH Tel: 01283 713916 Email: mohammad.mirfattahi@btinternet.com — MD 1967; MSc Human Nutrit. Lond. 1987; DCH RCP Lond. 1975; Dip. Board Paediat. 1976. Cons. Paediat. Qu.'s Hosp. Burton-on-Trent.

*MIRNEZAMI, Alexander Hooman Faghir 4 Effingham Close, Sutton SM2 6AG — BM 1995 Soton.

*MIRPURI, Mohan Gul 7 Brick Street, Sheffield S10 1WR — MB ChB 1998 Sheff.; MB ChB Sheff 1998; BriedSci 1995.

*MIRPURI, Nisha Gul 78 Bickenhall Mansions, Bickenhall St., London W1U 6BS Tel: 020 7935 9622 Email: nisha_mirpuri@yahoo.com — MB BS 1998 Lond.; MB BS Lond 1998.

MIRSADGADY, Seid Yahya The Health Centre, Horse Fair, Rugeley WS15 2EL Tel: 01889 582244; 8 Jones Lane, Slitting Mill, Rugeley WS15 2UJ Tel: 01889 578754 — MB ChB 1965 Birm.; MRCGP 1975; AFOM RCP Lond. 1990; DA Eng. 1967. (Birm.) Med. Pract. Local Civil Serv. Prev: Clin. Asst. (Anaesth.) Horncastle Hosp.; Nat. Iran Oil Co. Med. & Health Off. Kharg Is., Iran.

MIRSKI, Elizabeth Barbara Clifflands, 9 Whitbarrow Road, Lymm WA13 9AG Tel: 01925 752532 — MB ChB 1980 Manch. GP Retainer Scheme Lymm. Prev: GP Stalybridge.

MIRSKI, Teresa Isabel Maria Cheadle Hulme Medical Centre, Smithy Green, Hulme Hall Road, Cheadle Hulme, Cheadle SK8 6LU Tel: 0161 485 7272; 30 High Grove Road, Cheadle SK8 1NR — MB ChB 1982 Manch.; Cert Family Plann. JCC 1985; DRCOG 1985. Prev: SHO. (O & G) Withington Hosp. Manch.; SHO (A & E) Stockport Infirm.; SHO (Geriat. Med.) N. Manch. Gen. Hosp.

MIRVIS, Leonard Michael Clifden House Surgery, 24 Vauxhall Street, St Helier, Jersey JE2 4TJ Tel: 01534 732824 Fax: 01534 735082 — MB BCh 1976 Witwatersrand; MRCGP 1982; MFHom 1986.

*MIRZA, Amatul-Subooh 21 Knoll Road, London SW18 2DF — MB BS 1998 Lond.; MB BS Lond 1998.

*MIRZA, Ashraful Haque 37 Woodbourne Avenue, London SW16 1UP — MB BS 1998 Lond.; MB BS Lond 1998.

MIRZA, Bedar Bakht 19 Shoreham Drive, Moorgate Road, Rotherham S60 3DT Tel: 01709 371139 — MB BS 1965 Dacca; DO RCS Eng. 1978.

*MIRZA, Deena 37 Woodbourne Avenue, London SW16 1UP — MB BS 1996 Lond.

*MIRZA, Fatima 653 Davidson Road, Croydon CR0 6DW — MB BS 1998 Lond.; MB BS Lond 1998.

MIRZA, Ghaffar Hassan, Surg. Lt.-Cdr. RN Retd. Mcdermott Medical Centre, 149 Kingsnorth Road, Ashford TN23 6NE Tel: 01233 622474 Fax: 01233 611664; The Sheiling, Malvern Road, Ashford TN24 8JA Tel: 01233 630995 Fax: 01233 611664 — MB BS 1970 Sind; BSc Karachi 1964; MRCS 1978; LRCP LRCS Ed. LRCPS Glas. 1983. Clin. Asst. Rehabil. Centre Ashford Hosp. Kent; Med. Off. Millbank Pl. Ashford Kent; Port Med. Insp. TML. Cheriton. Kent.; Div. Surg. St. John's Ambul. Kent. Prev: RSO (Cardiothoracic Surg.) Guy's Hosp. Lond.; Resid. Med. Off. (A & E & Chest Pain Project) W.m. Hosp. Lond.

MIRZA, Halima 12 Longfield Avenue, Mill Hill, London NW7 2EG — MB BS 1987 Karachi; LRCP LRCS Ed. LRCPS Glas. 1994.

MIRZA, Intisar Hussain 79 Tonbridge Road, Maidstone ME16 8JN — BM 1991 Soton.; BSc (1st. cl. Hons.) Birm. 1984; PhD Soton. 1987.

MIRZA, Irfan Fyyaz Accident Service, Burnley General Hospital, Burnley BB10 2PQ Tel: 01282 425071; 2 Fairfield Drive, Burnley BB10 2PU Tel: 01282 429197 — MB BS Karachi 1967; FFAEM 1993. (Dow Med. Coll.) Assoc. Specialist (A & E) Burnley Healthcare NHS Trust. Socs: Brit. Trauma Soc. Prev: Regist. Vict. Hosp. Burnley; SHO Rotat. (Surg.) Oldham Roy. Infirm.; SHO Nuffield Orthop. Centre Oxf.

MIRZA, Irshad Ali The Surgery, 30 The Green, Hockwell Ring, Luton LU4 9PG Tel: 01582 505355 Fax: 01582 443126 — MB BS 1972 Marathwada; LMSSA Lond. 1977. (Aurangabad Med. Coll.) SHO (A & E) Mayday Hosp. Thornton Heath. Prev: Ho. Off. (Gen. Surg.) Greenock Roy. Infirm.; SHO (Cas. & Orthop.) Brook Gen. Hosp. Lond.; SHO (Orthop.) St. Nicholas' Hosp. Plumstead.

*MIRZA, Maliha Flat 40, Room 2, Block 3, 5 Beech Hill Road, Sheffield S10 2RA — MB ChB 1997 Sheff.

MIRZA, Mr Mehboob Flat 103, Block 3, Good Hope Hospital NHS Trust, Rectory Road, Sutton Coldfield B75 7RR; 53-1-B Mohammed Ali, Society, Karachi, Pakistan Tel: 00 92 446242 — MB BS 1987 Karachi; FRCS Eng. 1993; FRCS Ed. 1993.

*MIRZA, Mohamed Arif 79 Randal Street, Bolton BL3 4AG — MB ChB 1994 Manch.

MIRZA, Mohammad Rafiq Heatherfield, Shirley Place, Knaphill, Woking GU21 2PL — MB BS 1948 Punjab; MRCPsych 1972; DPM Eng. 1966.

MIRZA, Mumtaz Burnley General Hospital, Burnley BB10 2PQ — MB BS 1967 Karachi. (Dow Med. Coll.) Clin. Asst. Burnley, Pendle & Rossendale HA.

*MIRZA, Nazzia Nosheen 12 Ketley Croft, Highgate, Birmingham B12 0XG — MB ChB 1998 Sheff.; MB ChB Sheff 1998.

MIRZA, Sadiq Raza 239 Parr Lane, Bury BL9 8LX — MB BS 1963 Lucknow; MRCPsych 1973.

MIRZA, Shahzad Mohammed 33 Sage Close, Stoke-on-Trent ST1 3SF — MB ChB 1993 Liverp.

MIRZA, Showkat 7 Cemetery Road, Royton, Oldham OL2 5SP — BM BS 1993 Nottm.; BMedSci Nottm. 1991; FRCS (Otol) Ed.

MIRZA, William Jeffrey Prospect Medical Practice, 95 Aylsham Road, Norwich NR3 2HW Tel: 01603 488477 Fax: 01603 485989 — MB BS 1977 Lond.; MRCGP 1984; DRCOG 1980.

MIRZA

MIRZA, Zulfiquar Ali 127 De Montfort Way, Cannon Park, Coventry CV4 7DU — MB ChB 1990 Liverp.

MISBAH, Siraj Ahmed Department of Immunology, Level 7, John Radcliffe Hospital, Oxford OX3 9DU — MB BS 1981 Colombo; MRCPath 1993; FRCPath 2001; MSc (Immunol.) Lond. 1986; MRCP (UK) 1987, FRCP Lond. 1998; LRCP LRCS Ed. LRCPS Glas. 1985; MRCPath 1993. Cons. Clin. Immunol. John Radcliffe Hosp. Oxf. Socs: Brit. Soc. Immunol.; Clin. Immunol. Soc. Prev: Cons. Clin. Immunol. Leeds Gen. Infirm.; Sen. Regist. (Clin. Immunol.) John Radcliffe Hosp. Oxf.; Regist. (Clin. Immunol.) John Radcliffe & Ch.ill Hosp. Oxf.

MISBAHUDDIN, Anjum 105 St Helens Road, Westcliff on Sea SS0 7LF — MB BS 1996 Lond.; BSc (Hons.) Lond. 1993. (United Medical and Dental Schools)

MISCAMPBELL, Nigel Thomas Miscambell, Four Winds, Main Street, Glenluce, Newton Stewart DG8 0PU Tel: 01581 300315 Fax: 01581 300502 Email: nmiscampbell@dg-primarycare.scot.nhs.uk — MB BCh BAO 1983 Belf.; MRCGP 1989; T(GP) 1991; DMH Belf. 1991; DCH Dub. 1990. (Qu. Univ. Belf.) Prev: Trainee GP Sandhead VTS; SHO (Med. Specialities) Belf. City Hosp.; Ho. Off. Belf. City Hosp.

MISCH, Klaus Joseph 27 Mospey Crescent, Epsom Downs, Epsom KT17 4NA — MB BS 1973 Lond.; BSc Lond. 1970; FRCP Lond. 1994; MRCP (UK) 1976. (Char. Cross) Cons. Dermat. Kingston Hosp. Surrey. Prev: Sen. Regist. (Dermat.) St. Helier Hosp. Carshalton, St. Geo. Hosp. Lond. & Kingston Hosp.; Regist. (Clin. Research) Inst. Dermat. Lond.

MISCH, Peter Abraham Department of Forensic Psychiatry, Institute of Psychiatry, De Crespigny Park, London SE5 8AZ Tel: 020 7740 5266 Email: p.misch@iop.kcl.ac.uk — MB BS 1978 Lond.; MRCPsych 1991; MRCS Eng. LRCP Lond. 1978; Cert. JCC Lond. 1980. (Char. Cross) Cons. Adolesc. Forens. Psychiat. Feltham Young Offenders Inst. & Lect. (Adolesc. Forens. Psychiat.) Inst. Psychiat. Lond. Prev: Regist. (Psychiat.) Maudsley & Bethlem Hosps. Lond.

MISCHEL, Emma Lucy 38 Heol Waun-y-Nant, Cardiff CF14 1JZ Tel: 029 2061 4287 — BM 1995 Soton. GP Regist. (Gen. Pract.) Roy. United Hosp. Bath VTS.

MISCONY, Zuhair Yusuf Manor House Hospital, North End Road, London NW11; 16 Montrose Court, Temple Fortune, Finchley Road, London NW11 6AG Tel: 020 8209 1374 — MB ChB 1962 Baghdad; Dip. Sports Med. Lond 1985. (Baghdad Univ.) Assoc. Specialist (Orthop. Surg.) Manor Hse. Hosp. Lond. Socs: Brit. Assn. Sports Med. & Injury; Internat. Arthroscopy Assn.; Assoc. Mem. Orthop. Assn. Prev: Regist. (Orthop.) Durh. AHA.

MISHRA, Akhileshwar Datta 16 Birkdale Drive, Walton, Chesterfield S40 3JL Tel: 01246 207138 Email: ad@mishra.clara.co.uk — MB BS 1965 Agra; MD (Gen. Med.) Agra 1970; FRSH 1980; FCCP 1976. (S.N. Med. Coll. Agra, India) staff grade, old age pysch, Rotherham Dist.Gen.Hosp. Socs: Fell.Roy. Soc. Med.; Fell. Int. Coll. Angiology. Prev: Clin. Med. Off., Old Age Psychiat.; Staff Grade Adult Gen. Psychiat.; SCMO, Old Age Pysch.

MISHRA, Amar N Orchard Medical Centre, 41 Ladywell Road, Motherwell ML1 3JX Tel: 01698 264187 Fax: 01698 267717 — MB BS 1973 Patna; MB BS 1973 Patna.

MISHRA, Amarendra Mohan South Reddish Medical Centre, The Surgery, Reddish Road, Stockport SK5 7QU — MB BS 1974 Bihar.

MISHRA, Mr Arun Kumar (retired) 214 Woodlands Road, Batley WF17 0QS Tel: 01924 441882 Fax: 01924 441882 — MB BS 1968 Patna; FRCSI 1978; FRCOphth 1989; DO RCPSI 1976; DO Patna 1970. Cons. Ophth.; JP. Prev: Sen. Regist. Nottm. Eye & Univ. Hosps.

MISHRA, Kali Prasanna Bronglais General Hospital, Caradog Road, Aberystwyth SY23 1ER Tel: 01970 623131 Fax: 01970 635923 — MB BS 1971 Utkal; FFA RCSI 1981; DA Dub. 1978. Cons. Anaesth. Bronglais Gen. Hosp. Aberystwyth & Gen. Hosp. Hartlepool. Socs: BMA; Med. Defence Union; Assn. Anaesth. Prev: Cons. Anaesth. MoH Buyaydah Gen. Hosp., Saudi Arabia.

MISHRA, Kiran 434 Wilmslow Road, Heald Green, Cheadle SK8 3NP — MB BS 1982 Patna.

MISHRA, Krishna Mohan Highfield Surgery, The Heights, Jupiter Drive, Hemel Hempstead HP2 5NT Tel: 01442 65322 Fax: 01442 256641; 17 The Copse, Fields End, Hemel Hempstead HP1 2TA Tel: 01442 212447 — MB BS 1970 Banaras Hindu; MD Banaras Hindu 1973; FRCP Ed. 1993; MRCP (UK) 1978; MRCPI 1976; T(GP) 1991.

(Banaras Hindu) Clin. Asst. (Nephrol.) Lister Hosp. Stevenage. Socs: Assn. Roy. Coll. of Gen. Pract.; BMA & Med. Protec. Soc.; Brit. Epilepsy Soc. Prev: Cons. Phys. Univ. Hosp. Banares; Regist. (Gen. Med.) Bethnal Green Hosp.; Reader (Med.) Banares Hindu Univ.

MISHRA, Kumkum Queen Mary's Road Surgery, 2 Queen Mary's Road, Coventry CV6 5LL Tel: 024 7668 5918 — LRCP LRCS 1986 Ed.; LRCP LRCS Ed. LRCPS Glas. 1986.

MISHRA, Maheshwar Dutt Hambleton, 151 Risca Road, Newport NP20 3PP Tel: 01633 263729 — MB BS 1954 Patna; BSc Banaras 1949. (P. of Wales Med. Coll.) Cons. Dermat. S. Gwent Health Dist. (Newport). Socs: Fell. Roy. Soc. Med.; Brit. Assn. Dermat. & BMA. Prev: Asst. Dermat. Glantawe Gp. Hosps.; Med. Regist. Roy. Gwent Hosp. Newport; Regist. Dept. Dermat. Roy. Infirm. Cardiff.

MISHRA, Mamata Department of Cardiology, Hunt's House, Guy's Hospital, St Thomas St., London SE1 9RT Tel: 020 7955 5000; 83 Dacre Park, London SE13 5BX — MB BS 1987 Lond.; MRCP (UK) 1990.

MISHRA, Murari Nand The Surgery, 28 Church Road, Aston, Birmingham B6 5UP Tel: 0121 327 2348 Fax: 0121 328 3618; 91 Springfield Road, Sutton Coldfield B76 2SN Tel: 0121 240 5270 Fax: 0121 328 3618 — MB BS Ranchi 1966; Dobst RCOG (Lond.). (Frjendra Med. Coll, Ranchi (Bihar) India) Socs: Med. Profeetion Soc.; Indian Med. Assn.; Bihan Med. Union.

MISHRA, Padmini Scottish Executive Health Department, Primary Care Unit, St. Andrews House, Regent Road, Edinburgh EH1 3DG Tel: 01255 423075 Fax: 01255 426215; 21 Barclay Place, Laighills Gait, Dunblane FK15 0FB — MB BS 1976 Delhi; MRCGP 1994; MFFP 1994; MRCOG 1981; MNAMS 1981; FRCOG 1998. Med. Adviser (Primary Care) to Scott. Exec. Edin. Socs: Brit. Soc. Colpos. & Cerv. Path.; Brit. Med. Ultrasound Soc.

MISHRA, Pitabas Nuffield Department of Anaesthetics, John Radcliffe Hospital, headington, Oxford OX3 9DU — MB BS 1971 Utkal.

MISHRA, Pradeep Kumar 53 Upton Road, Chester CH2 1JH — MB BS 1977 Patna.

***MISHRA, Rajnish Chandra** 16 Birkdale Dr, Chesterfield S40 3JL — MB ChB 1997 Leic.

***MISHRA, Shashank** 218 Quinton Road, Birmingham B17 0RP — MB BCh 1998 Wales.

MISHRA, Subhash 29 Dunnottar Street, Bishopbriggs, Glasgow G64 1PR — MB ChB 1990 Glas.

MISHRA, Sudhir Kumar 26 Highgrove Meadows, Priorslee, Telford TF2 9RJ — MB BS 1974 Bihar.

MISHREKI, Sameh Kameel Houghton Health Centre, Church Street, Houghton-le-Spring DH4 4DN Tel: 0191 584 2106 Fax: 0191 584 9493; Samsara, 61 Priors Grange, Pittington, Durham DH6 1DA Tel: 0191 372 1749 — MB ChB 1974 Assiut; MRCS Eng. LRCP Lond. 1982; MRCGP 1983; DRCOG 1983. Princip. GP Houghton-Le-Spring.

MISHRIKI, Mr Said Fadel Aberdeen Royal Hospital, Westburn Road, Aberdeen AB25 2ZN Tel: 01224 559434 Fax: 01224 550726 Email: sf.mishriki@arh.grampian.scot.nhs.uk; 35 Denwood, Aberdeen AB15 6JE — MB BCh 1975 Cairo; FRCS 1998 (Urol); 2001 FEBU; MD Bristol 1994; FRCS Eng. 1986; FRCS Ed. 1984; MRCS Eng. LRCP Lond. 1984. (Univ. Cairo Sch. Med.) Cons. Urol. Surg. Aberd. Roy. Hosp.; Hon. Sen. Lect. Univ. of Aberd. Prev: Sen. Regist. (Urol.) Urol. Wessex RHA; Research Fell. Lithotriptor Unit Urol. Dept. S.mead Hosp. Bristol; Tutor (Urol.) Univ. Bristol.

MISIEWICZ, Jerzy Jacek (cons. rooms), Princess Grace Hospital, 42-52 Nottingham Place, London W1U 5NY Tel: 020 7486 1234 Fax: 020 7908 2168 Email: misiewicz@dial.pipex.com — MB BS Lond. 1956; BSc (Hons.) Lond. 1952; FRCP Lond. 1986; FRCP Ed. 1974, M 1967. (St. Bart.) p/t Hon. Cons. Gastroenterol. & Jt. Dir. (Gastroenterol.) Centr. Middlx. Hosp. Lond.; Edr. Europ. Jl. Gastroenterol. & Hepatol. Socs: Brit. Soc. Gastroenterol. & Assn. Phys.; Governing Counc. Europ. Assn. Gastroenterol. & Endoscopy.; Amer. Gastroenterol. Assn. Prev: Regist. St. Bart. Hosp. Lond.; Ho. Phys. Brompton Hosp. & Hammersmith Hosp. & Postgrad. Med. Sch.

MISIR, Anirude Occupational Health Department, Gwent Health NHS Trust, St Woolos Hospital, Newport NP9 4ZS Tel: 01633 238340 Fax: 01633 238341; 16 Springfield Lane, Rhiwderin, Newport NP10 8QZ Tel: 01633 892135 Fax: 01633 892135 — MB BS 1968 Agra; FFOM RCP Lond. 1984; DIH Eng. 1978; DPH Bristol 1975; DTM & H Liverp. 1974. Cons. Occupat. Gwent Healthcare

NHS Trust. Socs: Soc. Occupat. Med.; Assn. NHS Occupat. Health Phys.; Assn. Local Auth. Med. Advisors. Prev: SCMO Kidderminster HA; SHO Manor Pk. Hosp. Bristol; MO Guayana Sugar Est.s Guayana, S. America.

MISIR, Sunil Mahendranath 7 Beaford Grove, London SW20 9LB Tel: 020 542 8869 Email: drs@mcmail.com; 33 Finlayson Street, Lane Cove, Sydney 2066, Australia Tel: +61 2 94270405 — MB ChB 1988 Aberd.; T(GP) 1993. Prev: Indep. GP Lond.; Assoc. GP Sutherland; Trainee GP Thornbury VTS.

MISKELLY, Edel Helen 24 Darragh Road, Crossgar, Downpatrick BT30 9NP Tel: 01238 510209 — MB BCh BAO 1993 Belf.; DRCOG 1998. (Queen's Univ. Belf.) GP Regist.

MISKELLY, Francis Gerald 102 Inglethorpe Street, London SW6 6NX — MB BCh BAO Belf. 1977; PhD Cardiff 1990; MSc Ed. 1982; MD Belf. 1991; MRCP (UK) 1979; DCH RCP Glas. 1982. Sen. Lect. Char. Cross Hosp. Lond.

MISKIN, Nicola 61 Roman Way, Edgbaston, Birmingham B15 2SL — MB ChB 1998 Birm.; ChB Birm. 1998.

MISKIN, Stephen John Wythall Health Centre, May Lane, Hollywood, Birmingham B47 5PD Tel: 01564 822642 Fax: 01564 829319; 75 Rednal Road, Kings Norton, Birmingham B38 8DT — MB ChB 1976 Birm.

MISKRY, Tariq Simon 67 Klea Avenue, Clapham, London SW4 9HZ — MB BS 1990 Lond.; MRCOCT 1995. (Charing Cross and Westminster) Clin. Research Fell. (Gyn.). Socs: RSM.

MISRA, Basanta Kumar Roe Valley Hospital, Limavady BT49 9EU Tel: 0150 472 2281 — MB BS 1953 Utkal; DA Eng. 1965. Med. Asst. Roe Valley Hosp. Limavady.

MISRA, Mr Devesh Chandra Department of Paediatric Surgery, II Floor, David Hughe Building, Royal London Hospital, Whitechapel, London E1 1BB Tel: 020 7375 1861 Fax: 020 7377 7759 Email: dmisra@doctors.org.uk — MB BS 1983 All India Inst. of Med. Sci.; RCS (Paediat. Surg.) 1994. Cons. Paediat. Surg. Roy. Lond. Hosp.; Cons. Paediat. Surg. Bupa Roding Hosp.; Cons. Paediat. Surg. Crosswell Hosp. Prev: Sen. Regist. Roy. Childr. Hosp. Belf.

MISRA, G K 41 Moss Lane, Bootle L20 0EB.

MISRA, Girija Sankar 58 Bell Road, Walsall WS5 3JW — MB BS 1975 Berhampur, India; MRCP (UK) 1987.

MISRA, Hitendra Nath 57 Eskdale Avenue, Bramhall, Stockport SK7 1DX Tel: 0161 440 0808 — MB BS 1958 Calcutta; FRCP (Lond.) 1988; MRCP (U.K.) 1970; DPhysMed Eng 1972; Dip. Cardiol. Calcutta 1964. Cons. (Rheum. & Rehabil.) Wythenshawe Hosp. Manch. & Roy. Devonshire Hosp. Buxton. Prev: Sen. Regist. Dept. Rheum. Coventry & Warks Hosp.; Regist. & Ho. Off. (Gen. Med.) Manch. AHA (T).

MISRA, Kalpana 15 High Street, Cheshunt, Waltham Cross EN8 0BX — MBBS 1968 Utkal University, Orissa India. (S. C. B. Medical College, Cuttack, Orissa, India) Gen. Practitioner, High St. Surg., 15 High St., Cheshunt, Herts. Socs: Med. Protec. Soc.; Brit. Med. Assn.; Vice Chairm. Indian Med. Assn. of UK. Prev: SHO, Barnsley & GH, Reg. Rotherhorn Gen. Hosp., Register (Med.) Eliz. Garrett Anderson Hosp. Lond.; Med. Off., Family Plann. Clinic from 1989 - 2000, 150 Fortis Green, Muswell Hill, Lond. (Haringey Health Auth.).

MISRA, Kaushal Kishore Borough Medical Centre, 1-5 Newington Causeway, London SE1 6ED Tel: 020 7407 4248 Fax: 020 7234 0849 — MB BS 1972 Kanpur; MRCPI 1979.

MISRA, Mridula 88 Vauxhall Bridge Road, London SW1V — MB BS 1967 Lucknow.

MISRA, Neelakantha Pritchard Street Surgery, 1A Pritchard Street, Blackburn BB2 3PF Tel: 01254 56262 Fax: 01254 662835 — MB BS 1967 Utkal; MB BS 1967 Utkal.

MISRA, Nityananda (retired) 22 Burbo Bank Road N., Liverpool L23 8TA — MB BS 1958 Utkal; MSc 1983 Med Sci Glas.; Dip Clin Hypn 1993 Sheff.; Advan. Cert. Acupunc., 1995; MRCGP 1981.

MISRA, Pramod Kumar Newtown Health Centre, 171 Melbourne Avenue, Newtown, Birmingham B19 2JA; 68 Fitzroy Avenue, Harborne, Birmingham B17 8RQ — MB BS 1968 Lucknow; DCH Eng. 1972. (King Geo. Med. Coll.) Prev: Regist. (Psychiat.) Hollymoor Hosp. Birm.; SHO (Paediat.) Roy. Albert Edwd. Infirm. Wigan.

MISRA, Prem Chandra Parkhead Hospital, 81 Salamanca St., Glasgow G31 5ES Tel: 0141 211 8300 Fax: 0141 211 8380 — MB BS 1967 Lucknow; MRC Psych. 2001; BSc Lucknow 1961; DPM Ed.

& Glas. 1972. (King Geo. Med. Coll.) Cons. Psychiat. Glas. Roy. Infirm. & Pk.head Hosp.; Clin. Sen. Lect. (Psychol. Med.) Univ. Glas. Socs: (Exec. Bd.) Europ. Soc. Hypn.; Amer. Psychiat. Assn.; Brit. Soc. Med. & Dent. Hypn. (Scotl.) (Chairm. Acad. Comm.). Prev: Sen. Regist. (Psychiat.) Hollymoor Hosp. Birm.; Sen. Regist. Demonst. (Human Physiol.) King Geo. Med. Coll. Lucknow, India; Regist. & SHO (Psychiat.) Bolton Dist. Gen. Hosp.

MISRA, Rakesh Rinto Ground Floor Flat, 19 Parfrey St., London W6 9EW — MB BS 1992 Lond.

MISRA, Sandhya Department of Psychiatry, Carswell House, 5 Oakley Terrace, Glasgow G31 2HX Tel: 0141 554 6267 Fax: 0141 211 8380 — MBBS DCH 1967; MBBS 1965. (Medical College, Indore, India) Assoc. Specialist Gen. Psychiat. Pk.head Hosp., Glas. (1984 - date). Socs: Fell. Brit. Indian Psychiatric Soc. UK. Prev: Regist. Psychiat. John Conlly Hosp. Birm.; SHO (Obst. & Gyn.) Billinge Hosp. Nr. Inigan Lancs.; SHO (Paediat.) Kendray Hosp. Barnsley Yorks.

MISRA, Saradindu Narayan 6 Laurel Grove, Ashton-in-Makerfield, Wigan WN4 8LJ Tel: 01942 715667 — MB BS 1966 Calcutta.

MISRA, Surendra Charan Green Hill Rise Medical Centre, 2A Harrogate Court, Corby NN18 0PD Tel: 01536 401223 Fax: 01536 407215; Garden House, Pipewell, Kettering NN14 1QZ Tel: 01536 762600 — MB BS 1970 Allahabad; MS Allahabad 1975. (MLN Med. Coll. Allahabad) Prev: Trainee GP Windermere VTS; SHO (Cardiothoracic Surg. & Orthop.) N. Staffs. Roy. Infirm. Stoke-on-Trent.

MISRA, Mrs Unnati Sundri Misra, Soho Health Centre, Louise Road, Handsworth, Birmingham B21 0RY Tel: 0121 554 9929 Fax: 0121 507 1527 — MB BS 1956 Lucknow; DA Eng. 1961. (King Geo. Med. Coll.) Prev: Ho. Surg. King Geo Med. Coll. Lucknow, India; Anaesth. Regist. Centr. Middlx. Hosp. Lond.; Sen. Anaesth. Regist. Univ. Coll. Hosp. Ibadan, Nigeria.

MISRA, Upma Flat c-3 Doctors Residence, 52 Grainger Park Road, Newcastle upon Tyne NE4 8RQ Tel: 0191 273 8811; 24 Larkspur Terrace, Newcastle upon Tyne NE2 2DU — MB BS 1983 Delhi; FFA RCS 1988.

MISRA, Vijay Kant Queen Mary's Road Surgery, 2 Queen Mary's Road, Coventry CV6 5LL Tel: 024 7668 5918 — MB BS 1971 Aligarh.

MISRA, Vijay Peter Ellis The National hospital for Neurology and Neurosurgery, Queen Square, London WC1N 3BG Tel: 020 7829 8752 Fax: 020 7713 7743 Email: v.p.misra@mds.qmw.ac.uk — MB BS 1981 Bombay; MD Bombay 1985; MRCP (UK) 1993; FRCP 2000 UK. Cons. Clin. NeuroPhysiol. The Nat. Hosp. for Neurol. and Neurosurg. Lond.; Cons. Clin. NeuroPhysiol. St Mary's Hosp. Lond.; Hon. Sen. Lect. Univeristy Coll. Hosp. Lond. Socs: Assoc. Mem. Assn. Brit. Neurol.; Assoc. Mem. Assn. Brit. Soc. Clin. Neurophysiol. Prev: Cons. Clin. NeuroPhysiol. St Bart's and the Roy. Lond. Hosp.s.

MISSAKIAN, Seta Khatchick 11 Claydon House, Holders Hill Road, Hendon, London NW4 1LS — MB ChB 1968 Baghdad; FRCOG 1994; MRCOG 1979.

MISSELBROOK, David Paul Bellingham Green Surgery, 24 Bellingham Green, London SE6 3JB Tel: 020 8697 7285 Fax: 020 8695 6094 — MB BS 1979 Lond.; FRCGP 2000; MSc Lond. 1997; MRCGP 1983; DFFP 1996; DRCOG 1986. (Guy's) GP Lond.; Course Organiser, Lewisham GPVTS, Lond. Socs: Christ. Med. Fell.sh.; Christians in Caring Professions; Lewisham Primary Care Research Consrotium. Prev: Ho. Surg. & Ho. Phys. Guy's Hosp. Lond.; Trainee GP Qu. Mary's Hosp. Sidcup VTS.

MISSEN, Mr Anthony John Bartley (retired) Aldingbourne Lodge, Aldingbourne, Chichester PO20 6TT Tel: 01243 542356 — MB BChir 1962 Camb.; MD Camb. 1981; FRCS Eng. 1967. JP. City of Lond. Prev: Medico-Legal Adviser Med. Defence Union.

MISSEN, George Anthony Knight Histopathology Unit, Imperial Cancer Research Fund, 44 Lincolns Inn Fields, London WC2A 3PX Tel: 020 7269 3087; 2 Ingleside Grove, Blackheath, London SE3 7PH — BM BCh 1946 Oxf.; MA Oxf. 1948, DM 1963; FRCPath 1975, M 1963; DCP Lond 1952. (Oxf. & Guy's) Hon. Cons. Histopath. ICRF Lond.; Hon. Cons. Histopath. Guy's Hosp. Lond. Socs: Fell. Roy. Soc. Med. (Ex-Vice Pres. Sects. Path. & Comparative Med.); Path. Soc. Prev: Cons. Morbid Anat. & Clin. Microscopist Guy's Hosp. Lond.; Regist. (Morbid Anat.) Postgrad. Med. Sch. Lond.; Hon. Vis. Path. Johns Hopkins Hosp. Baltimore, USA.

MISSEN

MISSEN, Hedley James (retired) Walnut Tree Cottage, 50 Third Avenue, Frinton-on-Sea CO13 9EE Tel: 01255 670968 Email: hmissen@aol.com — MB BS Lond. 1959; MRCS Eng. LRCP Lond. 1959; MRCGP 1976. Prev: Force Med. Off. Essex Police.

MISSEN, Janet Christine Aldingbourne Lodge, Aldingbourne, Chichester PO20 6TT Tel: 01243 542356 — BM BCh 1961 Oxf.; MA Oxf. 1961; FFA RCS Eng. 1967; DA Eng. 1964. (Oxf. & St. Bart.) Cons. Anaesth. CEGA Aviat.; Vis. Cons. King Edwd. VII Hosp. Midhurst. Socs: Fell. Roy. Soc. Med.; Assn. Anaesth. Prev: Cons. Anaesth. Chichester Health Dist.; Sen. Regist. (Anaesth.) St. Bart. Hosp. Lond.; Regist. (Anaesth.) & Ho. Surg. (O & G) St. Bart. Hosp. Lond.

MISSEN, Marcus Ridley Cross Lane Hospital, Newby, Scarborough YO12 6DN Tel: 01723 343527; Granary Cottage, Nettledale Lane, Snainton, Scarborough YO13 9PW Tel: 01723 859183 — MB ChB 1977 Leeds; MMed Sc 1985 Leeds; MRCPsych. 1983. Cons. Psychiat. Tees & N. E. Yorksh. NHS Trust, Cross La. Hosp., ScarBoro. Prev: Cons. Psychiat. Cheltenham HA; Sen. Regist. (Psychiat.) Exminster Hosp. Exeter; Regist. (Psychiat.) Scalebor Pk. Hosp. Burley-in-Wharfedale.

MISSULA, Anjaneya Sharma 55 Belsize Road, Harrow Weald, Harrow HA3 6JL — MB BS 1972 Andhra; DO RCPSI 1981; DO Andhra 1974. (Andhra Med. Coll. Visakhapatnam) SHO (Ophth.) Eye & Cottage Hosp. Caernarfon. Prev: SHO (Ophth.) Glas. Ophth. Inst. & Canniesburn Hosp. Glas.

MISTRY, Ajay 40 Fairbank Road, Bradford BD8 9JX — MB ChB 1983 Manch.

MISTRY, Anilchandra Dullabhbhai 30 Sefton Avenue, Harrow HA3 5JS Tel: 020 8933 8756 — MB BS 1974 Bombay. (Topiwala Nat. Med. Coll.) SHO (Anaesth.) The Maidstone Hosp. Kent. Prev: SHO (Anaesth.) Qu. Mary's Hosp. Sidcup.

MISTRY, Arun 14 Ledbury Close, Oadby, Leicester LE2 4SR; 26 Waverly Avenue, Appleton, Warrington WA4 3BN — MB ChB 1990 Dundee.

MISTRY, Arvind Khandubhai 92 Newington Street, Leicester LE4 5DH — BSc (Hons.) Path. Lond. 1986, MB BS 1988; DCH RCP Lond. 1994.

MISTRY, Arvindkumar Dahyabhai Spinney Hill Medical Centre, 143 St. Saviours Road, Leicester LE5 3HX Tel: 0116 251 7870 Fax: 0116 262 9816 — MB BS 1978 Bombay; LMSSA Lond. 1983. GP Leicester.

MISTRY, Babubhai The Surgery, 2-4 Halsbury Street, Leicester LE2 1QA; 32 Loughborough Road, Leicester LE4 5LD Tel: 01162 682727 Fax: 01162 611783 — MB BS 1973 Banaras Hindu. (Institute Medical Sciences Varanasi) Socs: Med. Protec. Soc.

MISTRY, Balubhai Pragjibhai 123 Maida Vale Crescent, Styvechale, Coventry CV3 6GE — MB BS 1975 Baroda; MB BS Baroda, India 1975.

MISTRY, Chandrakant Dahyabhai Peterborough District Hospital, Thorpe Road, Peterborough PE3 6DA Tel: 01733 874000 Fax: 01733 874001; 10 Millfield Road, Market Deeping, Peterborough PE6 8AD Tel: 01778 344495 — MB BS 1976 Lond.; MD Lond. 1989; MRCS Eng. LRCP Lond. 1976; MRCP (UK) 1980. (St. Mary's) Cons. Phys. & Nephrol. P'boro. Hosp. NHS Trust. Socs: Renal Assn. Prev: Cons. Phys. P. Chas. Hosp. M. Glam. HA; Lect. & Hon. Sen. Regist. Univ. Manch.; Regist. Manch. Roy. Infirm.

MISTRY, Chandrakant Rambhai 12 Sutherland Road, Edmonton, London N9 7QD — MB BS 1983 Lond. (St. Bart.) SHO (A & E) St. Bart. Hosp. Lond. Prev: Ho. Surg. Yeovil Dist. Hosp.; Ho. Phys. New E. Surrey Hosp. Redhill.

MISTRY, Chhotalal Uttambhai The Health Centre, Wallsgreen Road, Cardenden, Lochgelly KY5 0JE Tel: 01592 722440; 16 Hopetoun Place, Kirkcaldy KY2 6TY — MB BS 1978 Baroda; MRCS Eng. LRCP Lond. 1981. (Baroda Med. Coll.)

MISTRY, Dahyu Dullabhbhai Lytham Road Surgery, 352 Lytham Road, Blackpool FY4 1DW Tel: 01253 402800 Fax: 01253 402994; 35 Tudor Close, Carleton, Blackpool — MB ChB 1982 Manch.; MRCGP 1988; DCH RCPS Glas. 1986. Clin. Asst. (Diabetic Serv.) Blackpool.

MISTRY, Dalpatram Karsan Paradise Medical Centre, Broad Street, Coventry CV6 5BG Tel: 024 7668 9343 Fax: 024 7663 8733; 7 Fairlands Park, Cannon Hill, Coventry CV4 7DS Tel: 024 76 418523 — MB ChB 1973 Glas.; MFFP 1993.

MISTRY, Dhirubhai B K The Surgery, 69 Stockingate, South Kirkby, Pontefract WF9 3PE Tel: 01977 642251 Fax: 01977 645515 — MB ChB 1974 Manch. Socs: Amer. Family Phys. Prev: Trainee GP Barnsley VTS.

MISTRY, Dinesh Kumar 89 King Edward Road, Rugby CV21 2TE — MB BS 1990 Newc.

MISTRY, Mr Firoz Dara 41 Willmore End, London SW19 3DE Tel: 020 8540 1671 — MB BS 1964 Bombay; MS (Gen. Surg.) Bombay 1967, MB BS 1964; FRCS Eng. 1971; FRCS Ed. 1970. (G.S. Med. Coll.) Sen. Regist. Thrombosis Research Unit King's Coll. Hosp. Med. Sch. Prev: Rotating Sen. Regist. (Surg.) King's Coll. Hosp. Lond.; Regist. (Gen. Surg.) S.E. Kent Gp. Hosps. & King Edwd. VII Memor.; Hosp. Bombay, India.

MISTRY, Hamant Kumar Market Harborough Medical Centre, 67 Coventry Road, Market Harborough LE16 9BX Tel: 01858 464242 Fax: 01858 462929 — MB BS 1989 Lond.; BSc (Hons.) Lond. 1985; MRCGP 1993; DCH RCP Lond. 1993; T(GP) 1993; Cert. Family Plann. JCC 1992; DRCOG 1992. (St. Geo. Hosp. Med. Sch.) Tutor (Gen. Pract.) Univ. Leicester. Socs: St Geo. Alumni Assn. Prev: Trainee GP Oxf. VTS.

MISTRY, Harish Ranchhod Spinney Hill Medical Centre, 143 St. Saviours Road, Leicester LE5 3HX Tel: 0116 251 7870 Fax: 0116 262 9816 — MB ChB 1987 Leic.

MISTRY, Harishchandra Gandhabhai The Surgery, 1 Streatfield Road, Harrow HA3 9BP Tel: 020 8907 0381 Fax: 020 8909 2134; 94 Norman Crescent, Pinner HA5 3QL Tel: 020 8909 2134 — MB BS 1981 Lond.; MRCGP 1987; DRCOG 1986. (Univ. Coll. Hosp.) Course Organiser VTS Brent & Harrow; GP Trainer Imperial Coll. LP Foundat.

MISTRY, Harshad Govindbhai Jivan Lincoln Road Surgery, 62 Lincoln Road, Peterborough PE1 2SN Tel: 01733 551008 Fax: 01733 345399 — MB ChB 1985 Manch. Tutor (Gen. Pract.) P'boro. Socs: Camb. LMC. Prev: SHO (Otolaryngol.) Manch. Roy. Infirm.; Trainee GP Solihull & W. Midl. VTS.

MISTRY, Kalavatihen 70B Palermo Road, Harlesden, London NW10 5YP Tel: 020 8961 9621 — BM BS 1990 Nottm.

MISTRY, Karmvir 63 Mount Pleasant Street, Ashton-under-Lyne OL6 9HX — MB ChB 1991 Manch.

MISTRY, Kirtida 183 Joel Street, Pinner HA5 2PD — MB BCh 1991 Witwatersrand.

MISTRY, Mahendra Kumar 6 St Georges Road, Stowlangtoft, Bury St Edmunds IP31 3JP — MB ChB 1987 Manch.

MISTRY, Motilal Ramsunder 20 Glenwood Road, Stoneleigh, Epsom KT17 2LZ Tel: 020 8393 6051 — MRCS Eng. LRCP Lond. 1964; DObst RCOG 1968; Cert FPA 1968. (Univ. Coll. Lond. & W. Lond.) Epsom & Ewell Cott. Hosp. Socs: Vasectomy Advancem. Soc. & Nat. Assn. Family Plann. Doctors. Prev: Ho. Surg. O & G Unit & Ho. Phys. Epsom Dist. Hosp.; Ho. Surg. Brighton Gen. Hosp.

MISTRY, Mukesh 109 Rochester Road, Earlsdon, Coventry CV5 6AF Tel: 024 76 711741 — BM 1981 Soton.; MFFP 1995; MRCGP 1986; DRCOG 1984; DCH RCP Lond. 1985. Sen. Med. Off. (Well Woms. Servs.) Coventry.

MISTRY, Narendra Hirabhai Weavers Medical Centre, 50 School Lane, Kettering NN16 0DH Tel: 01536 513494 Fax: 01536 416521 — MB ChB 1986 Leic. Trainee GP Nottm. VTS; SHO (Obst. & Gyn.) Qu. Med. Centre Nottm. Prev: SHO (Psychiat., Gen. Med. & Dermat.) Walsgrave Hosp. Coventry.

MISTRY, Naresh Thakorbhai Lees Road Surgery, 284 Lees Road, Oldham OL4 1PA Tel: 0161 652 1285 Fax: 0161 628 6843; Jonovans, Thurston Clough Road, Scouthead, Oldham OL4 3RX Tel: 01457 871781 — MB ChB 1982 Manch. Dep. Police Surg. Gtr. Manch. Police; Clin. Asst. (Psychiat.) Community Drug Team Oldham.

MISTRY, Navinchandra Uttambhai Mill Street Surgery, 439 Mill Street, Bradford, Manchester M11 2BL Tel: 0161 223 0637 Fax: 0161 220 7220; 9 Lapwing Close, Stalybridge SK15 1HP Tel: 0161 338 8160 — MB BS 1978 Bangalore; LRCP LRCS Ed. LRCPS Glas. 1982. (Bangalore Med. Coll.)

MISTRY, Pravin Gulabbhai Furnace House Surgery, St. Andrews Road, Carmarthen SA31 1EX Tel: 01267 236616 Fax: 01267 222673; Gwernllwyn, 60 Penymorfa, Llangynnwr, Carmarthen SA31 2NP — MB BCh 1986 Wales; MRCGP 1996; DGM RCP Lond. 1991. (Univ. Wales Coll. Med.)

MISTRY, Pushpaben Lister Medical Centre, Lister House, Staple Tye, Harlow CM18 7LU Tel: 01279 414882 Fax: 01279 439600 — MB ChB 1986 Manch.; DRCOG 1994; DFFP 1993; DCH RCP Lond. 1993. Prev: Trainee GP/SHO (Med. & Cas.) P.ss of Wales Hosp. Bridgend; SHO (O & G) P.ss of Wales Hosp.; SHO (Paediat.) Lister Hosp. Stevenage.

***MISTRY, Sanjaykumar Hasmukhlal** 30 Okehampton Road, Coventry CV3 5AU — MB ChB 1998 Ed.; MB ChB Ed 1998.

MISTRY, Shila Childrens Services, Leicestershire & Rutland Healthcare Trust, Bridge Park Plaza, Bridge Park Road, Thurmaston, Leicester LE4 8PQ Tel: 0116 225 2525 Fax: 0116 225 3850; 15 Dovedale Road, Leicester LE2 2DN Tel: 0116 221 7355 — MB ChB 1990 Manch.; MRCPCH 1998; BSc Manch. 1987; MRCP (UK) 1996. (Univ. Manch.) Specialist Regist. (Paediat.) Leicester Roy. Infirm. NHS Trust. Prev: Trainee GP Nottm. & Turbury; SHO (O & G) Nottm.

MISTRY, Thakorbhai Paragji All Saints Hospital, Lodge Road, Birmingham B18 5SD Tel: 0121 685 6167 Fax: 0121 685 6220 — MB BS 1979 Baroda; MRCPsych 1985. Cons. Psychiat. (Gen. Adult Psychiat.) Black Country Ment. Health NHS Trust (Sandwell).

MISTRY, Vinodbhai Khushalbhai Gold Street Medical Centre, 106 Gold Street, Wellingborough NN8 4BT Tel: 01933 223429 Fax: 01933 229240 — MB ChB 1987 Glas.; T(GP) 1993.

MITAL, Dushyant 13 King's Road, North Chingford, London E4 7HP Tel: 020 8524 7047 Email: d.mital@virgin.net — MB BS 1993 Lond.; MRCP (UK) 1997. (St. Geo. Hosp.) Specialist Regist. GUM/HIV heartlands hosp.Birm. Socs: Mem. BMA; MDU; Coll.Mem.roy.Coll.Phys.Surg. Prev: SHO (Clin. Oncol.) Roy. Marsden Hosp. Lond.; SHO HIV, Genitourin, Neurol. Cent. Midd. Hosp.; SHO (Gastroenterol.) St. Peter's Hosp. Chertsey.

MITAL, Ram Kishan 5 Ridge Lane, Watford WD17 4TQ — MB BS 1955 Agra.

MITCHARD, John Robert 3 Malfort Road, London SE5 8DQ — MB BS 1996 Lond.

MITCHARD, Kathryn Lesley Bridge Cottage, Longley Green, Suckley, Worcester WR6 5DU — MB ChB 1969 Sheff.; DA Eng. 1972.

MITCHEL, Bernadette Mary 4 Station Road, Donaghmore, Dungannon BT71 4JD — MB BCh BAO 1986 Belf.

MITCHELL, Jean (retired) 9 Danecourt Road, Parkstone, Poole BH14 0PG Tel: 01202 742012 — MB BS 1941 Durh.; MRCGP.

MITCHELL, Adam William Michael Flat 6, 112 Clarendon Road, London W11 1SA — MB BS 1987 Lond.; FRCS Eng. 1991; FRCR 1994. Cons. Radiol. Hammersmith Hosp. Trust Char. Cross Hosp. Prev: Regist. (Radiol.) Roy. Free Hosp. Lond.; Regist. (Radiol.) Gt. Ormond St. Hosp.; Lect./Hon. Specialist Regist. (Radiol.) Hammersmith Hosp. Lond.

MITCHELL, Alan Barbara Castle Health Centre, BRoadley Road, Harlow CM19 5SJ — MB BS 1984 Lond. (St. Bart.) Trainee GP Stansted VTS. Prev: SHO (O & G & Paediat.) P.ss Alexandra Hosp. Harlow; SHO (Med. & Cas. & Orthop.) Herts. & Essex Hosp. Bishops Stortford; SHO (Cas. & Orthop.) Hertford Co. Hosp.

MITCHELL, Alan Scottish Prison Service, Calton House, 5 Redheughs Rigg, Edinburgh EH12 9HW Tel: 0131 244 6998 Fax: 0131 244 6995 Email: alan.mitchell@sps.gor.uk; 4 Imlach Place, Motherwell ML1 3FD Tel: 01698 260561 Fax: 01698 260561 — MB ChB 1991 Glas.; MRCGP 1995; DRCOG 1994; DFFP 1994. (Glasgow) Head of Health Cre, Scott. Prison serv. Edin.; Clin. Asst. Dermat. Wishaw Gen. Hosp. Socs: Sec., BMA (Lanarksh. Div.).

MITCHELL, Alan James 5 The Rushes, Bray on Thames, Berks SL6 1UW Tel: 01628 782610; 5 The Rushes, Bray on Thames, Berks SL6 1UW Email: caritas@totalise.co.uk — MB BCh BAO 1959 Belf.; MFOM RCP Lond. 1978; DIH Eng. 1963; DPH Belf. 1962. (Queens University, Belfast) Socs: Fac. Occupat. Med.; Soc. Occupat. Med. Prev: Chief Med. Off. Burtons Gp. plc Lond.; Med. Off. Stewarts & Lloyds Corby; SHO Roy. Vict. Hosp. Belf.

MITCHELL, Alastair John Westminster And Pimlico General Practice, 15 Denbigh Street, London SW1V 2HF Tel: 020 7834 6969 Fax: 020 7931 7747 — MB BS 1980 Lond.; DCH RCP Lond. 1985; DRCOG 1985.

MITCHELL, Alexander Joel PGME, Fulbourn Hospital, Cambridge CB1 5EF Tel: 01223 218673 Fax: 01223 218708 Email: alex.mitchell@dial.pipex.com; 260 Wollaton Road, Nottingham NG8 1GN — MB BS 1993 Newc.; MB BS (2nd cl Hons.) Newc. 1993; BMedSc (Hons.) Newc. 1992. (Univ. Newc. u. Tyne) Research Regist. (Psychiat.) Addenbrooke's Hosp. Camb.; HDBA Family Study Newc. 1987. Socs: Brit. Neuropsychiat. Assn.; Brit. Assn. Psychopharmacol.; Roy. Coll. Psychiats. Prev: SHO (Psychiat. & Old Age Psychiat.) Fulbourn Hosp. Camb.; Ho. Off. (Neurol.) Roy. Vict. Infirm. Newc.

MITCHELL, Alexander John Ballards Walk Surgery, 49 Ballards Walk, Basildon SS15 5HL Tel: 01268 542901 Fax: 01268 491246; Highlands Farm, Highlands Hill, Mayland, Chelmsford CM3 6 EF Tel: 01621 774885 — MB ChB 1982 Manch.; BSc St. And. 1979; DRCOG 1984. Gen. Practitioner, Basildon; Police Surg. Brentwood. Prev: Trainee GP Ormskirk VTS; Ho. Off. (Phys. & Surg.) Ormskirk Dist. Gen. Hosp.

MITCHELL, Alexander Peter Beaton (retired) 68 Gerrard Road, Whitley Bay NE26 4NL Tel: 0191 252 1491 — MB BS Durh. 1943; FRCOG 1966, M 1952. Hon. Cons. (O & G) N. Tyneside HA. Prev: Sen. Cons. (O & G) N. Tyneside AHA.

MITCHELL, Alexander Ross Kerr (retired) 40 Topcliffe Way, Cambridge CB1 8SH Tel: 01223 247733 — MB ChB Ed. 1958; MA Camb. 1978; FRCP Ed. 1982, M 1963; FRCPsych 1976, M 1971; DPM Eng. 1962. Temp. Adviser WHO. Prev: Cons. Psychiat. Fulbourn and Addenbrooks hosp.,Camb.

MITCHELL, Mrs Alice Louise 14 High Street, Knapwell, Cambridge CB3 8NR — MB BCh 1988 Wales; FRCS (ENT) Eng. 1994. Clin. Fell. (ENT) Addenbrooke's Hosp. Camb. Prev: SHO (ENT) P'boro. & Camb.

MITCHELL, Alison Cameron Community & Mental Health Services NHS Trust, Gartnavel Royal Hospital, 1055 Great Western Road, Glasgow G12 0XH; 15 North Erskine Park, Bearsden, Glasgow G61 4LZ — MB ChB 1990 Glas.; MRCPsych 1995.

MITCHELL, Alison Catriona 19 Kessington Road, Bearsden, Glasgow G61 2HL — MB ChB 1986 Dundee; MRCGP 1994; FFA RCSI 1992. Sen. Regist. (Palliat. Med.) Hunters Hill Marie Curie Centre Glas. Prev: Trainee GP Dumfries & Galloway HB.

MITCHELL, Alistair Forbes St Ronans, Canisbray, Wick KW1 4YH — MB ChB 1984 Aberd.

MITCHELL, Mr Andrew Milton Keynes Hospital, Standing Way, Milton Keynes MK6 5LD Tel: 01908 243168 Fax: 01908 243168; Half Acre House, Lower Weald, Calverton, Milton Keynes MK19 6EQ Tel: 01908 560715 — BM BCh 1973 Oxf.; MA Oxf. 1973, MCh 1984; FRCS Eng. 1978. Cons. Gen. Surg. Milton Keynes Hosp. & Saxon Clinic Milton Keynes. Prev: Clin. Lect. (Surg.) Oxf. Univ. & Hon. Sen. Regist. Oxf. RHA; Regist. (Surg.) Norf. & Norwich Hosp.; SHO W. Suff. Hosp.

MITCHELL, Andrew Charles John Stone Cottage, Back Lane, Burrough Green, Newmarket CB8 9NB Tel: 01638 508366 Email: ha@drsmitch.freeserve.co.uk — MB ChB 1994 Birm.; DRCOG 1996; DFFP 1998. (Univ. Birm.) GP Asst. Eagle Ho. Surg. Enfield. Socs: MRCGP. Prev: GP Regist. White Lodge Surg. Enfield.; SHO (Paediat) N. Middlx. Hosp. Lond.; SHO (Psychiat. Old Age) E. Ham Memor. Hosp. Lond.

MITCHELL, Mr Andrew Duncan 11 Brookshaw Way, Coventry CV2 2NJ — MB BS 1988 Newc.; FRCS Eng. 1993. SHO (Orthop.) Good Hope Hosp. Sutton Coldfield. Prev: SHO (Orthop.) Roy. Orthop. Hosp. Birm.; SHO Rotat. (Surg.) Coventry.

MITCHELL, Andrew George Department of Cardiology, Harefield Hospital, Harefield, Uxbridge Tel: 01895 823737; Gordale, 7 Bayhurst Drive, Northwood HA6 3SA Tel: 01923 823166 — BM BCh 1969 Oxf.; BA Oxf. 1966; FRCP Lond. 1991; MRCP (UK) 1972. (Oxf. & Manch.) Cons. Cardiol. Harefield Hosp. Socs: Brit. Cardiac Soc.; Internat. Soc. Heart & Lung Transpl. Prev: Sen. Regist. (Cardiac) Roy. Free Hosp. Lond. & Harefield Hosp.

MITCHELL, Andrew Gordon 12 Blairston Avenue, Bothwell, Glasgow G71 8RZ — MB ChB 1987 Glas.; DCH RCPS Glas. 1993; Dip. Obst. Dunedin 1992; FCA 1998. (Glasgow)

MITCHELL, Andrew Robert John Belwood Farm, Rue Du Hurel, Trinity, Jersey JE3 5JR — BM 1992 Soton.; MRCP (UK) 1996. (Soton) Specialist Regist. (Cariology), John Radcliffe Hosp., Oxf. Socs: Brit. Soc. of Echocardiography; Brit. Soc. of Heart Failure. Prev: SHO (Med.) Torbay Hosp.; SHO (Cas.) Maidstone Hosp.; Regist. (Cardiol), Roy. Cornw. Hosp.

MITCHELL, Andrew Thomas Department of Child Health, Loddon NHS Trust, North Hampshire Hospital, Basingstoke Tel: 01256 314925; Bramley Corner House, Bramley, Tadley RG26 5DJ — MB BS 1980 Lond.; MRCP (UK) 1985; MRCS Eng. LRCP Lond. 1980;

MITCHELL

FRCPCH 1997; DCH RCP Lond. 1984. (Guy's Hosp.) Clin. Dir. & Cons. Paediat. Loddon NHS Trust N. Hants. Hosp. Basingstoke.

MITCHELL, Andrew Victor (retired) Aran Lodge, Ilsham Marine Drive, Torquay TQ1 2PN — MB BCh BAO Belf. 1958; FRCR 1975; FFR 1968; DMRD Eng. 1967; DObst RCOG 1960. Cons. Radiol. Torbay Hosp. Torquay. Prev: Ho. Phys. & Ho. Surg. Roy. Vict. Hosp. Belf.

MITCHELL, Anja Ulrike 204 Cambridge Road, Great Shelford, Cambridge CB2 5JU — BChir 1995 Camb.; MB Camb. 1996. (Cambridge) SHO (Anaesth.) W. Suff. Hosp. Bury St Edmunds.

MITCHELL, Ann Veronica 18 Waid Terrace, Anstruther KY10 3EZ — MB ChB 1984 Aberd.

MITCHELL, Anne Tel: 0117 949 7774 Fax: 0117 949 7730; Tel: 0117 968 3153 — MB BS 1984 Lond.; MRCGP 1991; DCH RCP Lond. 1990. (Westm. Med. Sch.) p/t Princip. in Gen. Pract.

MITCHELL, Anne Clemency Sarah The Binfield Surgery, Terrace Road N., Binfield, Bracknell RG42 5JG Tel: 01344 425434 Fax: 01344 301843; 57 Knox Green, Binfield, Bracknell RG42 4NZ Tel: 01344 459787 Fax: 01344 459787 — MB ChB Aberd. 1961; MRCGP 1986. (Aberd.) Trainer (Gen. Pract.) Bracknell.

MITCHELL, Anne Elizabeth 57 Manor Road, Dorchester DT1 2AZ — MB ChB 1986 Dundee; BMSc Dund 1983, MB ChB 1986.

***MITCHELL, Annemarie Margaret** 23 Coronation Road, Selly Oak, Birmingham B29 7DE — MB ChB 1997 Birm.

MITCHELL, Anthony Bernard Snell North Middlesex Hospital, Sterling Way, London N18 1QX Tel: 020 8887 2000 — MB ChB 1960 Cape Town; FRCP Lond. 1980, M 1966. (Cape Town) Cons. Phys. & Gastroenterol. N. Middlx. Hosp. Edmonton & St. Ann's Hosp. Tottenham; Clin. Tutor N. Lond. Postgrad. Med. Centre; Hon. Lect. Roy. Free Hosp. Med. Sch. Lond. Socs: Fell. Roy. Soc. Med.; Brit. Soc. Gastroenterol. Prev: Hon. Phys. Groote Schuur Hosp. Cape Town, S. Africa; Regist. & Sen. Regist. (Med.) Char. Cross Hosp. Lond.; Cons. Phys. P. of Wales' Gen. Hosp. Lond.

MITCHELL, Anthony Dixon 9 Chatham Street, Colne BB8 9LT Tel: 01282 866314 Fax: 01282 866314 Email: tony@adiem.fsnet.co.uk — MB BS 1976 Lond.; BSc (Hons.) Lond., BA 1987; MBA Open University; MRCS Eng. LRCP Lond. 1976; MFPM RCP Lond. 1989; Dip. Pharm. Med. 1985; AKC Lond. 1976; MSC Applied Statistics 1999. (Westm. Med. Sch. Lond.) Cons. Pharm. Med.; GP Colne; Specialist GP Drug Misuse Burnley Blackburn. Socs: Fac. of Pharmaceutical Med. Prev: Direct Core Technologies Ltd; Direct. Clin. Scientif.. Serv. Hammersmith Med. Research; Cons. in Pharmaceutical Med.

MITCHELL, Anthony Michael Drake 2-3 Victoria Street, Luton LU1 2UA Tel: 01582 434000 Fax: 01582 434003; 179 Old Bedford Road, Luton LU2 7EH Tel: 01582 731754 Email: docmitch@nildram.co.uk — MB BChir 1960 Camb.; DObst RCOG 1962. (Camb. & Middlx.) Hosp. Pract. (Ophth.) Luton & Dunstable Hosp. Prev: Ho. Surg. Addenbrooke's Hosp. Camb.; Ho. Phys. Whittington Hosp.; Ho. Surg. (Obst.) Whittington Hosp. Lond.

MITCHELL, Antony Peter Lynwood House, 6 Lynwood Avenue, Clayton Le Moors, Accrington BB5 5RR — MB ChB 1984 Leeds.

MITCHELL, Arthur William (retired) Sandyacre, 18 Ballyardle Road, Kilkeel, Newry BT34 4JX Tel: 028 4176 2644 — MB BCh BAO Belf. 1963; DObst RCOG 1966. Prev: SHO Ards Gen. Hosp. Newtownards.

MITCHELL, Audrey Helen The Surgery, 63 Rowley Road, Orsett, Grays RM16 3ET Tel: 01375 892082 Fax: 01375 892487 — MB BS 1986 Lond.

MITCHELL, Barry 23 Harris Street, Millfield, Peterborough PE1 2LY Tel: 01733 68403 — MB ChB 1970 Leeds; BSc (Hons.) Leeds 1968. Socs: Assoc. Mem. RCGP; Fell. Roy. Soc. Med.; Brit. Med. & Dent. Hypn. Soc.

MITCHELL, Barry William Lodge Health, 20 Lodge Manor, Coleraine BT52 1JX Tel: 028 7034 4494 Fax: 028 7032 1759; 12 Carnralla Park, Coleraine BT51 3NH Tel: 024 764 2460 — MB BCh BAO 1980 Belf.; MRCGP (Distinc.) 1984; DRCOG 1982. p/t Med. Off. (Dermat. Unit) Coleraine Hosp. GP Audit Facilitator, NHSSB; Locality Team Doctor, N.ern Target; Mem. Causeway HSST GP Forum. Socs: Soc. Orthop. Med.

MITCHELL, Brian David Osborne Practice Surgery, 25 Osborne Road, Southsea PO5 3ND Tel: 023 9282 1371 — BM 1982 Soton.; MRCGP 1986; DRCOG 1985; Cert. Family Plann. JCC 1985; MIBiol 1973; DFFP. (Southampton) Socs: Fell. Roy. Soc. Med. & Linnean

Soc.; Brit. Assn. Sport & Med.; Brit. Soc. of Med. & Dent. Hypn. Prev: Trainee GP Portsmouth & SE Hants. HA VTS; Ho. Surg. Frimley Pk. Hosp. Frimley; Ho. Phys. Roy. Hants. Co. Hosp. Winchester.

MITCHELL, Carole 54 Lynton Avenue, London W13 0EB — MB ChB 1986 Aberd.; MRCPsych 1991.

MITCHELL, Caroline Anne Woodhouse Medical Centre, 7 Skelton Lane, Woodhouse, Sheffield S13 7LY Tel: 0114 269 0025 — MB ChB 1986 Manch.

MITCHELL, Caroline Mary Hairmyres Hospital, East Kilbride, Glasgow G75 8RG; 39 West Port, Lanark ML11 9HD — MB ChB 1981 Ed.; MPhil Glas. 1994; MSc Manch. 1988; MRCPsych 1985. Cons. Psychiat. Hairmyers Hosp. Glas.

MITCHELL, Carolyn Alcohol Problems Clinic, 35 Morningside Park, Morningside, Edinburgh EH10 5HD — MB BS 1985 Newc. Sen. Clin. Research Fell. Prev: Clin. Research Fell. Univ. Edin.; Regist. (Psychiat.) Leicester.

MITCHELL, Catherine Ann The Gloucester Centre, Morpeth Close, Orton Longueville, Peterborough PE2 7JU Tel: 01733 232321 — MB ChB 1968 Ed.; DA Eng. 1970. Assoc. Specialist (Ment. Handicap) Gloucester Centre P'boro. Prev: Clin. Asst. (Psychiat. Ment. Handicap) Gloucester Centre P'boro.; Research Asst. (Gyn.) P'boro. Dist. Hosp.; Anaesth. Portsmouth Gp. Hosps.

***MITCHELL, Catherine Sarah** 9 Zetland Walk, Cambridge CB1 3TY — BChir 1996 Camb.

MITCHELL, Charles James Department of Gastroenterology, Scarborough Hospital, Woodlands Drive, Scarborough YO12 PQL; The Old Rectory, Ebberston, Scarborough YO13 9PA Fax: 01723 342471 — MB ChB 1970 Ed.; BSc Ed. 1967; FRCP Ed. 1987; FRCP Lond. 1988; MRCP (U.K.) 1974. Cons. Phys. ScarBoro. Hosp.; Sec. SAC G(I)M. Socs: Brit. Soc. Gastroenterol.; (EX-Pres.) Pancreatic Soc.; Europ. Pancreatic Club. Prev: Regional Adviser RCP; Lect. (Med.) St. Jas. Univ. Hosp. Leeds; Regist. (Med.) Roy. Free Hosp. Lond.

MITCHELL, Christopher Donald Department of Paediatrics, John Radcliffe Hospital, Oxford OX3 9DU Tel: 01865 221066 Fax: 01865 221083 Email: chris.mitchell@paediatrics.ox.ac.uk; 26 Fernham Road, Faringdon SN7 7LB — MB BS 1977 Lond.; PhD Lond. 1989; FRCP Lond. 1996. (Middlesex Hospital) Cons. Paediat. Oncol. John Radcliffe Hosp. Oxf. Prev: Clin. Research Fell. Imperial Cancer Research Fund Lond.; Fell. (Paediat. Oncol.) Childr. Hosp. Philadelphia; Sen. Lect. & Hon. Cons. Paediat. Oncol. Hosp. Sick Childr. Lond.

MITCHELL, Christopher John Four Gables, 54 Desford Road, Kirby Muxloe, Leicester LE9 2BD Tel: 0116 239 5112 Fax: 0116 255 1949 — MRCS Eng. LRCP Lond. 1967; BSc Lond. 1964, MB BS 1967; FRCPath 1986, M 1974. (Univ. Coll. Hosp.) Dir. Pub. Health Laborat. Leicester; Hon. Cons. Microbiol. Leicester HA. Prev: Sen. Bacteriol. Pub. Health Laborat. Serv. Radcliffe Infirm. Oxf.; Sen. Regist. (Microbiol.) Radcliffe Infirm. Oxf.; Ho. Surg. Univ. Coll. Hosp. Lond.

MITCHELL, Christopher John Haldane The Health Centre, Mountjoy Road, Omagh BT79 7BA Tel: 01662 243521 Fax: 01662 251202; Kevlin Lodge, 40 Ballynahatty Road, Omagh BT78 1PW Tel: 01662 242874 — MB BCh BAO 1960 Belf.; MICGP 1985. Socs: BMA; Irish Soc. Clin. & Experim. Hypn. Prev: Resid. Ho. Surg. & Ho. Phys. Roy. Vict. Hosp. Belf.

MITCHELL, Clyde Paul Britton and Partners, 10 Spencer Street, Carlisle CA1 1BP Tel: 01228 29171; Old Rectory, Great Orton, Carlisle CA5 6NB Tel: 01228 710423 — BA Oxf. 1967, BM BCh 1970; FRCGP 1992, M 1975; DObst RCOG 1974. (Lond. Hosp.) GP Tutor E. Cumbria. Prev: Course Organiser E. Cumbria VTS; Trainee GP Hackney VTS; Ho. Phys. & Ho. Surg. (O & G) Lond. Hosp.

MITCHELL, Darren Mark 1 Tanners Court, Moira, Craigavon BT67 0BJ — MB ChB 1995 Dundee.

MITCHELL, David Poplar House, Scawthorpe, Doncaster DN5 7UL Tel: 01302 49967 — MB ChB 1942 Glas. (Glas.)

MITCHELL, Mr David Andrew Department Oral & Maxillofacial Surgery, Pinderfields Hospital, Aberford Road, Wakefield WF1 4DG Tel: 01924 212923 Fax: 01924 212410 — MB BS 1989 Newc.; FDS RCS Eng. 2000; BDS Dundee 1981; FRCS (Max-Fac.) 1996; FRCS Ed. 1992; FDS RCPS Glas. 1984. Cons. Maxillofacial Surg. Pinderfields Hosp. Wakefield; Hon. Cons. Maxillofacial Surg. Leeds Gen. Infirm. & Yorks. Cancer Centre Cookridge Hosp.; Hon. Sen. Clin. Lect. Leeds Dent. Inst.; Raven Dept. Of Educat., Tutor in Oral

MITCHELL

& Maxillofacial Surg., Roy. Coll. of Surg.s of Eng. Socs: Eur. Assn. for Cranio-Maxillo. Surg.; Fell. Brit. Assn. Oral & Maxillofacial Surg.; Brit. Assn. Head & Neck Oncol. Prev: Sen. Regist. Rotat. (Oral & Maxillofacial) Yorks.; Career Regist. Rotat. (Oral. & Maxillofacial Surg.) Aberd. Roy. Infirm. & Yorks.; Lect. & Regist. (Oral & Maxillofacial Surg.) Newc.

MITCHELL, Mr David Bradford Department of Otolayngology, Kent & Canterbury Hospital, Ethelbert Road, Canterbury CT1 3NG — MB BCh BAO 1977 Dub.; BA Dub. 1975, MB BCh BAO 1977; FRCS (Otol.) Eng. 1985; FRCS Eng. 1983; FRCSI 1983. (TC Dub.) Cons. Surg. ENT Dept. Kent & Canterbury Hosp. & William Harvey Hosp. Ashford; Progr. Director Otolaryn. Train. Scheme SE Thames Region. Prev: Sen. Regist. Hosp. for Sick Childr. Gt. Ormond St. Lond.; Regist. St. Thos. Hosp. Lond.; SHO Hosp. Sick Childr. Lond.

MITCHELL, Mr David Charles Southmead Hospital, North Bristol NHS Trust, Westbury-on-Trym, Bristol BS10 5NB Tel: 0117 959 5166 Fax: 0117 959 5168 Email: mitchell_d@southmead.swest.nhs.uk — MB BS 1982 Lond.; FRCS Eng. 1987; MS Lond. 1992; MA (Hons.) Camb. 1982. Cons. Vasc. and Renal Transpl. Surg., N. Bristol NHS Trust. Socs: Vasc. Surgic. Soc. of GB and Irel.; Assn. of Surg.s of GB and Irel.; Venous Forum. Prev: Lect. (Surg.) Med. Coll. St Bart. Hosp. Lond.; Sen. Ho. Off., Roy. Hants. Co. Hosp., Winchester.; Regist., Bournemouth & Soton. Hosp.s.

MITCHELL, David Colin Mitchell and Partners, The Park Surgery, Old Tetbury Road, Cirencester GL7 1US Tel: 01285 654733 Fax: 01285 641408; 2 Downs Way, Baunton, Cirencester GL7 7DH Tel: 01285 651044 Fax: 01285 651044 — MB BS 1972 Lond.; MRCGP 1979; DObst RCOG 1974. (Middlx.) Sen. Partner; Hosp. Pract. (Orthop.) Cirencester Hosp.; Apoth. to the Roy. Ho.hold. Prev: Ho. Off. (Cardiol.) Middlx. Hosp. Lond.; Ho. Off. (Gen. Surg.) Ipswich Hosp.; Trainee GP Cirencester VTS.

MITCHELL, David Gordon Crieff Health Centre, King Street, Crieff PH7 3SA Tel: 01764 652456 Fax: 01764 655756 — MB ChB 1981 Aberd.; MRCGP 1985; DRCOG 1985. (Aberd.) Hon. Med. Off. Crieff Dist. Hosp.; Hon. Med. Off. Morrisons Acad. Crieff & Glenalmond Coll.; Police Surg. Perthsh.

MITCHELL, David John 2 Laganvalle Court, Stranmillis, Belfast BT9 5BH — MB BCh BAO 1989 Belf.

MITCHELL, David Livingstone The Surgery, Duns Road, Greenlaw, Duns TD10 6XJ Tel: 01361 810216 Fax: 01361 810799 — MB BS 1979 Lond.; BSc Lond., MB BS 1979; MRCGP 1983. (Roy. Free)

MITCHELL, David McKenzie St. Mary's Hospital, Praed St., London W2 1NY Tel: 020 7886 1082 Fax: 020 7886 1613 — MB BChir 1974 Camb.; MD Camb. 1983, MA 1974; FRCP Lond. 1991; BA Lond. 1983; MRCP (UK) 1975; MBA 1998. (Cambridge University/Middlesex Hospital Lndon) Cons. Phys. (Gen. & Respirat. Med.) St. Mary's Hosp. Lond. Socs: Brit. Thorac. Soc.; Amer. Thoracic Soc.; Eur. Respirat. Soc. Prev: Sen. Regist. (Med.) Lond. Chest Hosp. & Univ. Coll. Hosp. Lond.; Regist. (Med.) Univ. Coll. Hosp. Lond.; Regist. (Med.) Brompton Hosp. Lond.

MITCHELL, David Patrick Beeston Hill Health Centre, Beeston Hill, Beeston, Leeds LS11 8BS Tel: 0113 270 5131 Fax: 0113 272 0722 — MB ChB 1984 Leeds; DRCOG 1988.

MITCHELL, David Wright Gordon and Partners, 1 North Street, Peterborough PE1 2RA Tel: 01733 312731 Fax: 01733 311447 — MB ChB 1968 Ed.

MITCHELL, Deborah Mary Salisbury District Hospital, Salisbury SP2 8BJ Tel: 01722 336262; Pavings, The Avenue, Sherborne DT9 3AJ — MB BS 1979 Lond.; MA Oxf. 1982, BA 1974; MRCP (UK) 1981; Spec. Accredit. Dermat. 1989; FRCP 1998. (Guy's) Cons. Dermat. Salisbury HA. Prev: Sen. Regist. (Dermat.) Skin Hosp. Manch.; Regist. (Gen. Med.) W.m. Hosp. Lond.; Ho. Phys. Guy's Hosp. Lond.

MITCHELL, Deirdre Christine Southern Derbyshire Acute Hospital NHS Trust, Dri Site, London Road, Derby DE1 2QY Tel: 01332 254770 Fax: 01332 254924; 22 Arlington Road, Littleover, Derby DE23 6NY Tel: 01332 344399 Email: amitchell@clara.net — MB BCh BAO 1974 Belf.; FRCPath 1981. (Queen's Belf.) Cons. (Haemat.) & Head of Serv. for Haemat.; Clin. Dir. Cancer Servs. Socs: BSH; BAMM; ACP. Prev: Med. Dir.

MITCHELL, Denis Eckersley (retired) Robin Hill, Park Lane, Upper Cumbernorth, Huddersfield HD8 8NP Tel: 01484 606505 — MB ChB 1939 Leeds. Prev: GP Huddersfield.

MITCHELL, Donald Norton 84 Millway, Mill Hill, London NW7 3JJ — MRCS Eng. LRCP Lond. 1947; MD Lond. 1962, MB BS 1952; FRCP Lond. 1986; MRCP (UK) 1981. (St. Geo.) MRC Extern. Clin. Scientif. Staff; Hon. Sen. Lect. Nat. Heart & Lung Inst. & Roy. Postgrad. Med. Sch.; Hon. Cons. Phys. Brompton, Centr. Middx., Univ. Coll., Hammersmith and St Mary's Hosps. Lond. Prev: Regist. Harrow Chest Clinic; Act. Squadron Ldr. Mass Radiog. RAF; Ho. Surg. St. Geo. Hosp.

MITCHELL, Doreen Helen East Wing, Ladywell Medical Centre, 26 Featherhall Avenue, Edinburgh EH12 7UN Tel: 0131 334 5000 Fax: 0131 316 4816; Lymphoy House, Currie EH14 6AJ Tel: 0131 449 3818 — MB ChB 1975 Ed.; BSc Ed. 1972, MB ChB 1975; MRCGP 1988. (Ed.) GP Edin. Socs: BMA; RCGP. Prev: GP Peebles; Trainee Community Paediat. Bruntsfield Health Centre Edin.; Trainee GP Sighthill Health Centre Edin. VTS.

MITCHELL, Elaine Isabella Wallace and Partners, Blue Wing, Clydebank Health Centre, Kilbowie Road, Clydebank G81 2TQ Tel: 0141 531 6410 Fax: 0141 531 6413 — MB ChB 1988 Glas.; BSc (Hons.) Glas. 1986, MB ChB 1988; MRCGP 1992.

MITCHELL, Elizabeth Department of Health & Social Services, Stormont, Belfast BT4 3PP Tel: 01232 520716 Fax: 01232 520718 Email: elizabeth.mitchell2@dhssni.gov.uk; 5 Schomberg Avenue, Belfast BT4 2JR — MB BCh BAO 1980 Belf.; MB BCh BAO (Hons.) Belf. 1980; FRCP Ed 1997, MRCP (UK) 1983; MFCM 1989. (Queen's University Belfast) Sen. Med. Off. DHSS. Prev: Cons. Communicable Dis. Control EHSSB.

MITCHELL, Elizabeth Barclay (retired) 131 Homefield Park, Sutton SM1 2DY — MB BS Lond. 1950. Assoc. Specialist (Cytopath.) St. Helier Hosp. Carshalton.

MITCHELL, Elizabeth Burchell (retired) The Hill House, Wychbold, Droitwich WR9 0BT Tel: 01527 861211 — MB BS Lond. 1955; BDS Birm. 1967. Prev: Community Dent. Off. BromsGr. & Redditch HA.

MITCHELL, Erica Anne Stone House Surgery, Winchcombe, Cheltenham GL54 5LL Tel: 01242 602307; Mill Cottage, 33 Winchcombe Road, Sedgeberrow, Evesham WR11 6UA Tel: 01386 881898 — MB BS Lond. 1988; MRCGP 1992; DRCOG 1991; DCH RCP Lond. 1990. (Guy's Hosp. Lond.) GP Asst. Prev: GP Evesham; Trainee GP Banbury VTS.

MITCHELL, Evelyn Joan (retired) Flat 4, 15 St Germans Place, Blackheath, London SE3 0NN Tel: 020 8858 4002 — MB BChir 1953 Camb.; BSc Lond. 1945; MRCS Eng. LRCP Lond. 1953. Prev: Ho. Surg. & (ENT & Neurosurg.) Lond. Hosp.

MITCHELL, Florence Lucille 11 Station Road, Loughton IG10 4NX; 38 Courtland Drive, Chigwell IG7 6PW Tel: 020 8500 2880 — MB ChB 1944 Liverp.; DCH Eng. 1946. Socs: Harveian Soc. Lond. Prev: Med. Off. Child Welf. Pub. Health Dept. Durh. CC.

MITCHELL, Frances Louisa Blackburn Cottage, Muirs of Milton Duff, Elgin IV30 8TG Tel: 01343 541966 — MB ChB 1984 Aberd.; MB ChB (Commend.) Aberd. 1984; Cert. Family Plann. JCC 1987. Med. Off. (Psychogeriat.) Bilbohall Hosp. Elgin Moray; Med. Off. Pub. Health Med. Grampian HB. Prev: Asst. GP Elgin; SHO (Geriat., ENT & Ophth.) Raigmore Hosp. Inverness; Trainee GP Ardersier VTS.

MITCHELL, Geoffrey (retired) 10 Longcroft Park, Beverley HU17 7DY — MB ChB 1963 Ed.; MRCPsych 1973; DPM Ed. 1968; DCH RCPS Glas. 1966. Hon. Lect. & Clin. Tutor Leeds Univ. Prev: Cons. Psychiat. New Bridges Acute Community Unit Hull.

MITCHELL, Geoffrey Princess Grace Hospital, 42/52 Nottingham Place, London W1U 5NY Tel: 020 7935 2230 Fax: 020 7224 3836; 19 Ravenscourt Road, London W6 0UH Tel: 020 8748 7425 — MB ChB Leeds 1955; FRCP Ed. 1985; MRCP (UK) 1965. (Leeds) Indep. Phys. Lond.; Med. Adviser Gulbenkian Foundat., Hanover Acceptances Ltd., United Dutch (UK) Ltd & Olympus Optical Co. (UK) Ltd. Socs: Fell. Roy. Soc. Med.; Eur. Dialysis & Transpl. Assn.; BMA. Prev: Hon. Regist. Artific. Kidney Unit Roy. Infirm. Edin.; Sen. Specialist in Med. RAF; Ho. Phys. Med. Profess. Unit St. Jas. Hosp. Leeds.

MITCHELL, George Fallas Blair Group Medical Centre, Aysgarth Drive, Lupset, Wakefield WF2 8JE Tel: 01924 376828 Fax: 01924 201649; 5 Woodthorpe Gardens, Woodthorpe Lane, Sandal, Wakefield WF2 6RA Tel: 01924 257088 — MB ChB 1963 Ed.

MITCHELL

MITCHELL, Mr George Grant 16 St John Street, Manchester M3 4EA Tel: 0161 834 4282 — MB ChB Manch. 1962; FRCS Ed. 1973; FRCOG 1984, M 1971. (Manch.) Cons. O & G Hope Hosp. Salford; Clin. Dir. (Obst. & Gyn.) Hope Hosp. Salford. Socs: N. Eng. Obst. & Gyn. Soc.; Brit. Assn. Perinatal Med.; Fell. Roy. Soc. Med. Prev: Lect. (O & G) Univ. Manch.

MITCHELL, George Mutch, OBE, KStJ (retired) 149 King George V Drive E., Heath, Cardiff CF14 4EN Tel: 01222 753363 — MB ChB 1951 Aberd. Stud. Counsellor Univ. Wales Coll. Med. Cardiff. Prev: Dir. Cardiff Poisons Informat. Centre.

MITCHELL, Gina Elizabeth 6 Highwood Close, Marlow SL7 3PG — MB BCh 1985 Wales; BSc (Hons) Wales 1982.

MITCHELL, Grahame Alistair Medical Centre, 16 Seafield Terrace, Portsoy, Banff AB45 2QB Tel: 01261 842336 Fax: 01261 863959 — MB ChB 1985 Aberd.; MSc (Sports Med.) Dub. 1992; MRCGP 1990; Dip. Sports Med. Dub. 1991. (Aberd.) Med. Off. Chalmers Hosp. Banff & Med. Dir. Campbell Hosp. Purbut. Socs: BMA.

***MITCHELL, Guy** 88c Walterton Road, London W9 3PQ — MB BS 1998 Lond.; MB BS Lond 1998.

MITCHELL, Harriet Jennifer Stamford Hill Group Practice, 2 Egerton Rd, London N16 6UA — MB ChB 1994 Birm.; MRCGP 1998; DFFP 1998; ChB Birm. 1994; DCH 1996. (Birmingham) p/t GP Principle Stamford Hill Gp. Pract. Lond. Prev: SHO (A & E) Roy. Lond. Hosp./Homerton Hosp.; SHO (O & G) Homerton Hosp. Lond.; SHO (Psychiat.) Homerton Hosp.

MITCHELL, Heather Department of Paediatric Endocrinology, Cobbold Laboratories, The Middlesex Hospital, Mortimer St., London W1A 8AA Tel: 020 7380 9450 Fax: 020 7636 9941 Email: hd283@aol.com; 21C Milton Avenue, Highgate, London N6 5QF Tel: 020 8374 5034 Email: h.w.mitchell@cablenet.co.uk — BM BCh 1989 Oxf.; MA Camb. 1990, BA 1986; MRCGP 1993; DRCOG 1993; DCH RCP Lond. 1992; MRCP Lond. 1995; MRCPCH 1996. (Univ oxford) Clin. Research Fell. (Paediat. Endocrinol.) Lond. Centre for Paediat. Endocrinol. & Metab. Middlx. & Gt. Ormond St. Hosps. Lond.; Hon. Specialist Regist. (Paediat. Endocrinol.). Prev: SHO (Neonates) Univ. Coll. Lond. Hosp.; SHO Gt. Ormond St. Hosp. Lond.; Trainee/SHO GP Bridgend Mid. Glam. HA VTS.

MITCHELL, Helen Elsie Postgraduate Medical Office, Ninewells Hospital & Medical School, Dundee DD1 9SY Tel: 01382 660111 Fax: 01382 645748; 85 Princes Street, Perth PH2 8LH Tel: 01738 630556 — MB ChB 1989 Aberd.; MRCGP 1993; DFFP 1993; DRCOG 1991. Clin. Research Fell. Postgrad. Med. Educat. Univ. Dundee. Prev: Trainee GP/SHO Dumfries & Galloway Roy. Infirm. VTS.

MITCHELL, Helen Sarah Mortimer MarketCentre, Off Capper St., London WC1E 6AU Tel: 020 7530 5077 Fax: 020 7530 5044 — MB BS 1982 Lond.; MRCOG 1988; Dip. GUM 1998; DFFP 1996; FRCOG 2000. (St. Barts Hosp. London) Cons. in Sexual Health, Camden & Islington NHS Trust; Hon. Cons. (Obst & Gyn.) UCL Hosp. NHS Trust, UCL. Socs: BSCCP; Soc. Cons. Reproduc. Health. Prev: Sen. Regist., Hammersmith Hosp. Lond.

MITCHELL, Henry Atkinson Westholme, 2 Glenfield Road, Heaton Norris, Stockport SK4 2QP Tel: 0161 432 2307; Westholme, 2 Glenfield Road, Heaton Norris SK4 2QP Tel: 0161 432 2307 — MB ChB Manch. 1949; MRCS Eng. LRCP Lond. 1950. (Manch.)

MITCHELL, Hilary Jean Dullshot House Surgery, 12 The Parade, Epsom KT18 5DW Tel: 01372 726361 — MB BS 1985 Lond.

MITCHELL, Hilary Roseann Flat 2, Bishops Mill Court, 210 Old Dumbarton Road, Glasgow G3 8QB — MB ChB 1996 Glas.

***MITCHELL, Iain Joseph** 12 Blairston Avenue, Bothwell, Glasgow G71 8RZ — MB ChB 1995 Glas.

MITCHELL, Mr Ian Charles 2 The Warren, Harpenden AL5 2NH — MB BS 1980 Lond.; MS 1992 Lond.; FRCS Eng. 1986. Cons. Gen. & Gastrointestinal Surg. Barnet & Chase Farm Hosps. Socs: Assn. of Surg.s; Assn. of Upper GI Surg.s; Assn. of ColoProctol. Prev: Sen. Regist. (Surg.) Char. Cross. Hosp. Lond.

MITCHELL, Mr Ian David Cumming 55 Dublin Street, Edinburgh EH3 6NL — MB ChB 1989 Glas.; FRCS Ed. 1995; FRCS Ed (UROL) 1999. Specialist LRegist., E. of Scotl. Urollgy Train. scheme.

MITCHELL, Ian Duncan, Group Capt. RAF Med. Br. Clanna, Popes Hill, Kingsclere, Newbury RG20 5SJ Tel: 01635 297725 — MB BS 1972 Lond.; BSc Lond. 1969, MB BS 1972; MRCGP 1978; AFOM RCP Lond. 1983; DAvMed Eng. 1980; DObst RCOG 1976. RAF Exchange Off. Washington DC, USA. Socs: Aerospace Med. Assn. Prev: OP16 DMSD MoD; Sen. Med. Off. RAF Wildenrath & RAF Brize Norton.

MITCHELL, Mr Ian Moorhouse Tel: 0115 969 1169 Email: imitchel@ncht.trent.nhs.uk — MB ChB 1981 Leeds; BSc (Hons.) Leeds 1978, MD 1994; FRCS (Cth.) 1993; FRCS Glas. 1986. Cons. Cardiac. Surg. Nottm. City Hosp. Socs: Soc. Cardiothoracic Surg.; Brit. Cardiac Soc. Prev: Sen. Regist. Yorks. RHA; Regist. (Cardiothoracic Surg.) Roy. Hosp. Sick Childr. Glas. & Walsgrave Hosp. Coventry; Regist & SHO (Surg.) St. Jas. Hosp. Leeds.

MITCHELL, Ian Robert 60 Hungate Street, Aylsham, Norwich NR11 6AA Tel: 01263 733693 — MB BS 1984 Lond.; MRCGP 1997; DRCOG 1991; DA (UK) 1986.

MITCHELL, Ian William Tel: 01768 245219 Fax: 01768 891052 — MB BS 1981 Newc.; MRCGP 1985.

MITCHELL, Imogen Ann 5 Usborne Mews, London SW8 1LR — MB BS 1989 Lond.; BSc (Hons.) Lond. 1986; MRCP (UK) 1992. Sen. Regist. (ICU) Roy. P. Alfred Hosp. Sydney. Socs: Fell. Roy. Soc. Med. Prev: Research Fell. (ICU) St. Geo. Hosp. Lond.; Regist. (Liver Failure) King's Coll. Hosp. Lond.; SHO (ICU) Guy's Hosp. Lond.

MITCHELL, Isobel Frances Angela (retired) 20 Kimberley Terrace, Llanishen, Cardiff CF14 5EA Tel: 029 2075 8826 — MB BCh 1946 Wales; BSc Wales 1942. Prev: Ho. Phys. Llandough Hosp. & St. David's Hosp. Cardiff.

MITCHELL, James Duncan 20 Clovelly Road, Emsworth PO10 7HL — BM Soton 1984; MRCGP 1990; DCH RCP Lond. 1989. Prev: Resid. Med. Off. Palmerston N. Hosp. NZ; Ho. Surg. Weymouth & Dist. Hosp. Weymouth; Ho. Phys. Roy. S. Hants. Hosp. Soton.

MITCHELL, Mr James Edward (retired) Whitefloods, St. Mary Bourne, Andover SP11 6EF Tel: 01264 738006 Fax: 01264 738359 — MB BCh 1948 Wales; FRCS Eng. 1955. Cons. Surg. Singleton & Morriston Hosps.; Mem. Ct. Examrs. RCS Eng. Prev: Sen. Regist. (Surg.) & Tutor W.m. Hosp. Lond.

MITCHELL, Mr James Farquhar Ogilvie (retired) 19 Rockfield Crescent, Dundee DD2 1JD Tel: 01382 566092 Email: jfomitchell-dundee@talk21.com — MB ChB 1944 Ed.; MD Ed. 1945; FRCS Ed. 1949; DLO Eng. 1946. Hon. Sen. Lect. (Otolaryngol.) Univ. Dundee; Sen. Cons. ENT Surg. Tayside HB Dundee Roy. Infirm. Ninewells Hosp; Stracathro Hosp. Brechin, Forfar & Brechin Infirms. & Montrose Roy Infirm. Prev: Maj. RAMC, Specialist Otol.

MITCHELL, James Hunter Endrigg, Paxton, Berwick-upon-Tweed TD15 1TE Tel: 01289 86608 — MB ChB 1948 Ed. (Ed.) Socs: BMA. Prev: Obst. Ho. Surg. Dunfermline Matern. Hosp.; Ho. Surg. Surgic. Out-pats. Dept. & ENT Leith Gen. Hosp. Edin.

MITCHELL, Jane (retired) Kingfishers, Hall Road, Barton Turf, Norwich NR12 8AR Tel: 01692 630992 — MB ChB 1954 Leeds.

MITCHELL, Jane Kirkliston HC, The Glebe, Kirkliston EH29 9AS Tel: 0131 333 3215; Pilladilly House, 17 Pilladilly, Slotforth, Lancaster LA1 4PX — MB ChB 1991 Ed.; MRCP Ed. 1995; DRCOG 1996; MRGGP 1998. (Edinburgh) p/t GP Retainer. Kirkliston Health Centre Kirkliston. Socs: BMA. Prev: SHO (Psychiat.) St. John's Hosp. Livingston, SHO (O & G) St. John's Hosp. Livingston; SHO (Oncol.) Beatson Oncol. Centre W.ern Infirm. Glas.; GP Regist.Broxburn HC, Broxburn, W. Lothian, GP Regist. Kirkliston HC.,Kirklinston, W. Lothian.

MITCHELL, Jane Alison 12 Fishpond Drive, Nottingham NG7 1DG — MB ChB 1988 Dundee; FRCS Ed. 1994.

MITCHELL, Jean (retired) c/o 14 Talbot Road, Isleworth TW7 7HH — MB BS 1945 Lond.; DCH Eng. 1949. Prev: Med. Regist. Hull 'A' Gp. Hosps.

MITCHELL, Jean Elaine (retired) 68 Gerrard Road, Whitley Bay NE26 4NL Tel: 0191 252 1491 — MB BS Durh. 1945. Prev: Ho. Surg. P.ss Mary Matern. Hosp. Newc. & Accid. Room & Orthop.

***MITCHELL, Jennie Elizabeth** 1 Coverdale Avenue, Heaton, Bolton BL1 5HX — MB BS 1988 Lond.

MITCHELL, Jeremy Bruce 3 Turners Drive, Totteridge Common, High Wycombe HP13 7PA — MB BS 1986 Lond.; FRCA. 1992. Cons. Anaesth. Harefield Hosp. Middlx. Prev: Sen. Regist. (Anaesth.) Roy. Free Hosp. Lond.; Regist. (Anaesth.) St. Mary's Hosp. Lond.; SHO (Anaesth.) St. Bart. Hosp. Lond.

MITCHELL, John Arthur (retired) Tarratt House, East Coker Road, Yeovil BA20 2LS Tel: 01935 24734 — BM BCh 1954 Oxf.; DObst RCOG 1958. Prev: Obst. Ho. Surg. Forest Gate Hosp. Lond.

MITCHELL

MITCHELL, John Bell (retired) 28 Ayloffs Walk, Hornchurch RM11 2RJ — M.R.C.S. Eng., L.R.C.P. Lond. 1943.

MITCHELL, John Charles Flat 2, 26/30 Orchard Street, Manchester M20 2LP — MB ChB 1991 Bristol.

MITCHELL, Professor John Douglas Department of Neurology, Royal Preston Hospital, Sharoe Green Lane N., Fulwood, Preston PR2 9HT Tel: 01772 522 423 Fax: 01772 718746 Email: douglas.mitchell@patr.nhs.uk; (cons. rooms), 11 Moor Pk Avenue, Preston PR1 6AS Tel: 01772 251507 Fax: 01772 558761 Email: j.d.mitchell@dial.pipex.com — MB ChB 1975 Aberd.; FRCP 1989 glas; MRCP 1978 uk; FRCP 1993 Lond; MD 1991 Aberd; FRCP 1992 Ed. (Aberdeen) p/t Cons. Neurol. Roy. Preston Hosp.; Hon. Prof. Clin. Neurol. Univ. Centr. Lancs. Socs: Assn. Brit. Neurols.; Soc. Free Radical Research. Prev: Sen. Regist. (Neurol.) N.. Gen. Hosp. & Roy. Infirm. Edin.; Regist. (Neurol.) Addenbrooke's Hosp. Camb.; Sen. Lect. (Med. Neurol.) Univ. Edin. 1984-5.

MITCHELL, John Lamont 3rd Floor E., Bedford Chambers, London WC2E 8HA Tel: 020 7240 3663 Fax: 020 7240 3297; Flat 9, Newinnsq., 8-13 New Inn St, London EC2A 3PY Tel: 020 7729 5364 Fax: 020 7729 5394 — MB BS 1971 Lond.; FRCP Lond. 1991. Partner Mitchell Damon Organisational Cons. Socs: Roy. Soc. Med.; Soc. Social Med.; BGS. Prev: Cons. Phys. Waltham Forest HA; Fell. King's. Fund Coll. Lond.

MITCHELL, John Neville 204 Cambridge Road, Great Shelford, Cambridge CB2 5JU — MRCS Eng. LRCP Lond. 1968. Trust Specialist Anaesth. Addenbrooke's Hosp. Camb.

MITCHELL, John Noel Sladdin (retired) 6a Burn Road, Inverness IV2 4NG Tel: 01463 221760 Email: usere@mitchel.hi-net.co.uk — MB ChB 1949 Glas.; MB ChB (Commend.) Glas. 1949; FRCP Lond. 1973, M 1954; DCH Eng. 1958. Hon. Clin. Lect. (Dermat.) Univ. Glas. Prev: Cons. (Dermat.) W.. Infirm. Glas.

MITCHELL, Professor John Phillimore, CBE, TD Abbey Cottage, Parry's Close, Stoke Bishop, Bristol BS9 1AW Tel: 01179 968 2673 — MB BS Lond. 1942; MS Lond. 1955; FRCS Eng. 1949; FRCS Ed. 1948; MRCS Eng. LRCP Lond. 1942. (Middlx.) Hon. Prof. Surg. (Urol.) Univ. Bristol; Emerit. Cons. Urol. Surg. United Bristol Hosp. Trust & S.mead Gen. Hosp.; Mem. Ct. Examrs. RCS Eng.; Hon. Col. RAMC. Socs: (Ex-Pres.) Brit. Assn. Urol. Surgs.; (Ex-Pres.) Internat. Soc. Urol. Endoscopy.; (Ex-Pres.) Sect. of Urol. Roy. Soc. Med. Prev: Sen. Regist. (Urol.) Salford Roy. Hosp.; Regist. (Surg.) Profess. Surg. Unit Roy. Infirm. Manch.; Maj. RAMC 1942-47 (Col. TA).

MITCHELL, John Rodney The Surgery, Manlake Avenue, Winterton, Scunthorpe DN15 9TA Tel: 01724 732202 Fax: 01724 734992; The Red House, Burton Upon Stather DN15 9EZ Tel: 01724 720332 Fax: 01724 720726 Email: badger@stather.demon.co.uk — MB ChB 1963 Sheff.; FRCGP 1999. (Sheffield) Sen. Partner; JP. Socs: BMA. Prev: Ho. Phys. & Ho. Surg. Roy. Infirm. Sheff.; Cas. Off. Roy. Hosp. Sheff.

MITCHELL, John Ruthven Springpark Centre, 101Denmark St., Glasgow G22 5EU Tel: 0141 531 9300 Fax: 0141 531 9304; 15C Ledcameroch Road, Beardsden, Glasgow G61 4AB Tel: 0141 931 5182 Fax: 0141 931 5182 — MB ChB Glas. 1989; BSc (Hons) Glas. 1986; MRCP (UK) 1992; MRCPsych 1994; Mphil Edin. 1998. (Glasgow) Cons. (Psychiat.). Socs: BMA. Prev: Sen. Regist. (Psychiat.) Roy. Edin. Hosp.

MITCHELL, John Vincent New Sheepmarket Surgery, Ryhall Road, Stamford PE9 1YA Tel: 01780 758123 Fax: 01780 758102; 84 Tinwell Road, Stamford PE9 2SD Tel: 01780 755538 — MB BS 1973 Lond.; MRCP (UK) 1976; FRCGP 1991, M 1978; DRCOG 1978. (Middlx.)

***MITCHELL, Jonathan** 4 Edgefield Road, Sheffield S7 2BT Tel: 01142 215636 — MB ChB 1998 Sheff.; MB ChB Sheff 1998.

MITCHELL, Jonathan Daniel 17 Gonnerston, Mount Pleasant, St Albans AL3 4SY — BM 1992 Soton.

MITCHELL, Joseph Alexander Stewart The Gardens House, Lindertis, Craigton of Airlie, Kirriemuir DD8 5NT Tel: 01575 574752 — MRCS Eng. LRCP Lond. 1952; DMJ Soc. Apoth Lond. 1979; CIH Dund 1979; Cert. Gen. Av. Med. 1974. (Westm.) Hon. Lect. (Forens. Med.) Univ. Dundee. Socs: Fell. Roy. Soc. Med. (Sect. Clin. Forens. Med.); Assn. Police Surg. Prev: Med. Off. (Occupat. Health) Tayside HB; Med. Adviser Michelin Tyre plc Dundee.

MITCHELL, Josiah Nicholson, Group Capt. RAF Med. Br. Retd. (retired) 10 Earlswood, Orton Brimbles, Peterborough PE2 5UG Tel: 01733 239127 — MB BS 1960 Durh.; 1960 MB BS Durh.; 1980 MSc (Distinc.) Lond.; 1971 DAvMed Eng.; 1982 MFOM. Prev: RAF Med. Directorate Lond.

MITCHELL, Karen Elizabeth 7 Park Chase, Godalming GU7 1TL Tel: 01483 428292 — MB BS 1982 Lond.; DRCOG 1986. p/t Sen. Clin. Med. Off. (BrE. Screening) Jarvis Centre Guildford and BrE. Phys., Roy. Surrey Co. Hosp., Guildford. Socs: Assn. of BrE. Clinicians.

***MITCHELL, Karen Louise** Brigstock Cottage, Eastbury, Hungerford RG17 7JN — MB BS 1998 Lond.; MB BS Lond 1998.

MITCHELL, Karen Natalia Hill Cottage, Harlow Road, Roydon, Harlow CM19 5HH — MB BS 1991 Lond.; DRCOG 1994.

MITCHELL, Kathleen Isabel Paton (retired) 14 Palmer Close, Storrington, Pulborough RH20 3HN Tel: 01903 742263 Email: Kathleen.mitchell@totalise.co.uk — MB ChB St. And. 1961. Prev: Asst. GP.

MITCHELL, Kathryn Jane Appletree Cottage, High St., Dinton, Aylesbury HP17 8UN — MB ChB 1993 Manch.

MITCHELL, Keith Ian Email: helen.mitchell@virgin.net; 18 Punchbowl Lane, Dorking RH5 4BW — MB BChir 1991 Camb.; BA 1991 (Hons.) Camb.; FRCA. (Camb.) SpR (Anaesth.) St. Geo.'s Hosp. Lond. Prev: SHO (Anaesth.) Derriford Hosp. Plymouth; SHO (Anaesth.) Treliske Hosp., Truro.

***MITCHELL, Kenneth Francis** 12 Blairston Avenue, Bothwell, Glasgow G71 8RZ — MB ChB 1995 Glas.

MITCHELL, Mr Kenneth Gordon Royal Alexandra Hospital, Corsebar Road, Paisley PA2 Tel: 0141 887 9111 Email: kenmitch33@hotmail.com; 33 Windsor Avenue, Newton Mearns, Glasgow G77 5NU Tel: 0141 639 3356 — MB ChB 1974 Glas.; FRCS Ed. 1979; FRCS Glas. 1979. Cons. Gen. Surg. Roy. Alexandra Hosp. Paisley.; Hon. Clin. Sen. Lect. Univ. Glas. Socs: Assn. of Surg.s of Gt. Britain & Irel.; W Scotl. Surg. Assn. Prev: Sen. Regist. (Surg.) Gartnavel Gen. Hosp. & W.. Infirm. Glas.; Research Regist. (Gastroenterol.) W.. Infirm. Glas.; Regist. (Surg.) W. Scotl. Surg. Train. Scheme.

MITCHELL, Kenneth Mackinnon R & D Department, Gartnavel Royal Hospital, 1055 Great Western Road, Glasgow G12 0XH — MB ChB 1990 Glas.; MRCPsych. (Lond.) 2000; BDS Glas. 1981; FDS RCPS Glas. 1985. (Glas.) Specialist Regist. (Psychiat.), R & D Dept, Gartnavel Roy. Hosp., Glas. G12 OXH. Prev: Staff Grade (Psychiat.), ShawPk. Centre, Glas.; SHO (Psychiat.) Ravenscraig Hosp., Greenock; Sen. Ho. Off. (Histopath.) W.ern Infirm. Glas. & N. Manch. Gen. Hosp.

MITCHELL, Lara Esther 8 Claremont Street, Spittal Tounges, Newcastle upon Tyne NE2 4AH; 6 Windsor Place, Stirling FK8 2HY Email: laramitch@aol.com — MB ChB 1993 Ed.; MRCP 1997. Regist. (Geriats.) RSI. Prev: SHO (Oncol.) Gen. Hosp. Newc.; SHO Rotat. (Med.) Dryburn.

MITCHELL, Lawrence Hood Tigh-na-Coille, Monikie, Broughty Ferry, Dundee DD5 3QA — MB ChB 1963 St. And.

MITCHELL, Leslie Freeman Hospital, Freeman Road, High Heaton, Newcastle upon Tyne NE7 7DN — MB ChB 1977 Aberd.; FRCR 1986. Cons. Cardiothoracic Radiol. Newc. HA; Hon. Lect. Newc. Univ. Prev: Sen. Regist. (Cardiol./Radiol.) N. W.. RHA; Sen. Regist. & Regist. (Diag. Radiol.) N. W.. RHA.

MITCHELL, Lindsay Dawn Nicol Addenda, Braehead Road, Letham, Forfar DD8 2PG — MB ChB 1990 Ed.

MITCHELL, Louise Isobel Scoular (retired) Woodville, Gavinton, Duns TD11 3QS — MB ChB 1945 St. And. JP. Prev: SCMO Borders Health Bd.

MITCHELL, Malcolm Ian 41 Thyme Close, Chineham, Basingstoke RG24 8XG — MB BS 1973 Newc.

MITCHELL, Margaret Mackinnon Riverview Medical Practice, 6/8 George St., Johnstone PA5 8SL Tel: 01505 331101; Ground Right, 98 Wilton St, Glasgow G20 6QZ — MB ChB 1991 Glas.; DRCOG 1997; MRCGP July 1998. GP Riverview Med. Pract. Johnstone; Clin. Asst. Neurol. S.ern Gen. Hosp. Socs: BMA; RCGP.

MITCHELL, Marilyn Margaret Alexandra House, 52 Alexandra Rd, St Austell PL25 4QN; 25 Penhaligon Way, St Austell PL25 3AR — MB BS 1970 Lond.; MRCS Eng. LRCP Lond. 1969; MRCPsych. 1978.; DCH RCP Lond. 1971. Cons. Psychiat. Cornw. Healthcare Trust, Adult Ment. Health; Roy. Coll. Assessor; CPD Coordinator CHT. Socs: Regional CPD Comm.

MITCHELL, Martin Dominic Pepperpot, Tredington, Tewkesbury GL20 7BS — MB ChB 1988 Birm.; ChB Birm. 1988.

MITCHELL

MITCHELL, Martin Leigh Abbey Mead Surgery, Abbey Mead, Romsey SO51 8EN Tel: 01794 512218 Fax: 01794 514224; 4 Woodley Lane, Romsey SO51 7JN — MB BS 1972 Lond. Clin. Asst. (Dermat.) Winchester.

MITCHELL, Mary Alice 74 Bessbrook Road, Loughgilly, Armagh BT60 2DB — MB BCh BAO 1990 Belf.; MRCGP 1994; DCH RCPS Glas. 1994; DGM RCPS Glas. 1993; DMH Belf. 1992. Staff Grade (Paediat.) Roy. Belf. Hosp. Sick Childr.

MITCHELL, Mary Brigeen The Health Centre, 203 Main Street, Barrhead G78 1HG Tel: 0141 880 6161 Fax: 0141 881 7036 — MB ChB 1971 Glas.

MITCHELL, Mary Catherine Leigh House Hospital, Adolescent Psychiatric Unit, Alresford Road, Winchester SO21 1HD — BM 1983 Soton.; MRCPsych 1996; DCH RCP Lond. 1988. (Soton.) Cons. Child and Adolesc. Psychiat., Leigh Ho. Hosp., Winchester. Prev: Cons. Child and Adolesc. Psychiat., Loddon NHS Trust, Bsingstoke 1999-2000.

MITCHELL, Mary Jane The Surgery, 3 Chequers Drive, Prestwood, Great Missenden HP16 9DU Tel: 01494 862858; Hollygarth, 7 Over Hampden, Prestwood, Great Missenden HP16 9DZ Tel: 01494 866190 — MB BS 1982 Lond.; MRCP (UK) 1987; DCH RCP Lond. 1985. PCG Bd. Mem.

MITCHELL, Michael Collins The Health Centre, Whyteman's Brae, Kirkcaldy KY1 2NA Tel: 01592 641203 — MB ChB 1989 Ed.; BSc (Hons.) Ed. 1987, MB ChB 1989.

MITCHELL, Michael Douglas Department of Anaesthesia, Royal Cornwall Hospital (Treliske), Truro TR1 3LJ Tel: 01872 74242 — MB BS 1978 Lond.; MA Camb. 1979; FFA RCS Eng. 1985. (Westm.) Cons. Anaesth. Roy. Cornw. Hosps. Prev: Sen. Regist. Univ. Hosp. Nottm.; Med. off. King Edwd. VIII Hosp. Durban, SA; Regist. Univ. Hosp. Nottm.

MITCHELL, Michael Henry 19 Mill Place, Kingston upon Thames KT1 2RS — MB BS 1981 Lond.

MITCHELL, Michael Piers Boon The Briars, St. Anne's Road, Tankerton, Whitstable CT5 2DW — LMSSA Lond. 1962. (King's Coll. Lond. & W. Lond.)

MITCHELL, Nicola Anne 5 New Lane, Nun Monkton, York YO26 8EP — MB ChB 1994 Ed.

MITCHELL, Norman John (retired) The Old Farmhouse, Plealey, Pontesbury, Shrewsbury SY5 0UY Tel: 01743 790643 — MB BS Lond. 1962; MRCS Eng. LRCP Lond. 1962; FRCPath 1983, M 1971; Dip. Bact. Lond. 1970. Prev: Cons. Microbiol. PHLS P.ss Roy. Hosp. Telford.

MITCHELL, Mr Oswald Henry Anderson Milecross, Newtownards Tel: 01247 813700 — MB BCh BAO 1949 Belf.; FRCS Ed. 1961. (Belf.) Cons. Surg. N. Down Hosp. Gp. Socs: Fell. Roy. Soc. Trop. Med. & Hyg.

MITCHELL, Patrick Bernard 57 Knox Green, Binfield, Bracknell RG42 4NZ — MB BChir 1989 Camb.

MITCHELL, Colonel Patrick Charles, MC, TD, Col. late RAMC Retd. (retired) Greenhaugh, Rannes St., Insch AB52 6JJ Tel: 01464 820276 — MB ChB 1937 Aberd.; FRCP Ed. 1958, M 1949. Prev: Cons. Dermat. Cumbld. & N. W.morland Special Area.

MITCHELL, Paul Charles Church Street Surgery, 2 Church Street, Sutton, Hull HU7 4TT Tel: 01482 826457 Fax: 01482 824182 — MB BS 1973 Newc.; MRCGP 1978; DObst RCOG 1976.

MITCHELL, Pauline Angela 9 Coronation Terrace, Truro TR1 3HJ — MB BS 1973 Lond.; FFA RCS Eng. 1978; DA Eng. 1975. (King's Coll. Hosp.) Anaesth. Roy. Cornw. Hosp. Treliske Truro. Prev: Regist. (Anaesth.) Stoke Mandeville Hosp. Aylesbury & John Radcliffe Hosp. Oxf.; SHO (Anaesth.) Stoke Mandeville Hosp. Aylesbury; SHO (Anaesth.) Portsmouth & SE Hants. Health Dist.

MITCHELL, Peter Edward Gordon, TD Department of Biochemical Medicine, Ninewells Hospital & Medical School, Dundee DD1 9SY — MD 1960 Aberd.; MB ChB 1953; FRCPath 1976, M 1964 Aberd.; MRCP Ed. 1991. Cons. Clin. Chem. E. RHB (Scotl.). Socs: Assoc. Clin. Biochem. & Assn. Clin. Paths. (Educat. Comm.). Prev: Lt.-Col. RAMC (T & AVR); Clin. Asst. Aberd. Roy. Ment. Hosp.; Ho. Off. Roy. Infirm. Aberd.

MITCHELL, Peter James (retired) Mulberry Cottage, Hook Green, Meopham, Gravesend DA13 0JB Tel: 01474 812230 Email: orestes@doctors.net.uk — BM BCh 1954 Oxf.; MA, BM BCh Oxf. 1954; DObst RCOG 1956.

MITCHELL, Peter Jonathan The Square Surgery, 16A The Square, Comber, Newtownards BT23 5AP Tel: 028 9187 8159; 40A Killinchy Road, Comber, Newtownards BT23 5LU — MB BCh BAO 1989 Belf. Socs: MRCGP; DRCOG.

MITCHELL, Mr Philip Andrew 64 Ruden Way, Epsom KT17 3LN Tel: 01737 373429 Email: phil.angie@btinternet.com — MB BS 1991 Lond.; FRCS Lond. 1995. (St Mary's Hosp.)

MITCHELL, Philip David Vincent Algitha Lodge Surgery, 4 Algitha Road, Skegness PE25 2AQ Tel: 01754 766766 Fax: 01754 760632; 54 Laythorpe Avenue, Skegness PE25 3BX Tel: 01754898494 — MB BS 1992 Lond.; MRCGP 1996.

MITCHELL, Philip Henry (retired) 30 Gordon Avenue, Donnington, Chichester PO19 2QY Tel: 01243 781626 — MB BChir 1954 Camb.; MB BChir Camb. 1943; MA 1944, MD 1954; Hon. MA Kent 1978; FRCPsych 1971; DPM Eng. 1949. Prev: Cons. Psychiat. St. Augustines Hosp. Chartham Down, Canterbury & Thanet Dist.

MITCHELL, Philippa Mary (retired) Whitefloods, St Mary Bourne, Andover SP11 6EF — MB BS Lond. 1952; BSc (Hons. Physiol.) Lond. 1949; MRCS Eng. LRCP Lond. 1952. Prev: GP Gower Pract. Swansea.

MITCHELL, Prudence Jennifer Frederick Place Surgery, 11 Frederick Place, Weymouth DT4 8HQ Tel: 01305 774411 Fax: 01305 760417 — MB ChB 1972 Manch.; MRCGP 1977; DObst RCOG 1975. GP Weymouth. Prev: SHO (Psychiat.) Birch Hill Hosp. Rochdale; SHO (Paediat. & O & G) Bolton Dist. Gen. Hosp.

MITCHELL, Prudence Octavia 21 Prospero Road, London N19 3QX Tel: 020 7272 7656 Fax: 020 7272 7656 — MB ChB 1993 Manch.; BSc St. And. 1990. GP Regist. Roy. Devon & Exeter Hosp. Prev: Med. Coordinator Emerg. Relief Unit Jalalabad, Afghanistan; SHO (Psychiat.) Garlands Hosp. Carlisle; SHO (A & E) Leighton Hosp. Crewe.

***MITCHELL, Rebecca Martha** 59 Kent Avenue, Yate, Bristol BS37 7RZ — MB ChB 1998 Leeds.

MITCHELL, Rhiannon 7 Bayhurst Drive, Northwood HA6 3SA — MB BCh 1966 Wales; FRCS 1975.

MITCHELL, Richard Thomas Carlyle East One Health, 14 Deancross Street, London E1 2QA Tel: 020 7790 2978 — MRCS Eng. LRCP Lond. 1981; MA Oxf. 1981; MB BS Lond. 1981; MRCGP 1985; DRCOG 1984; DCH RCP Lond. 1984.

MITCHELL, Richard William Station House Surgery, Station Road, Kendal LA9 6SA Tel: 01539 722660 Fax: 01539 734845; Thorn Rigg, Garth Row, Kendal LA8 9AT Tel: 01539 83698 — MB ChB 1972 Manch.; MRCGP 1979; DObst RCOG 1975; DCH Eng. 1974.

MITCHELL, Robert Cumming (retired) Whiteman's Surgery, Whitefriar's Street, Perth PH1 1PP Tel: 01738 627912 Fax: 01738 643969 — MB ChB 1963 Glas. Med. Off. CGU Insur. Prev: Ho. Surg. & Ho. Phys, SHO (Surg. & Laborat. Med.) W.. Infirm. Glas.

MITCHELL, Robert Daniel Clifton Lodge Surgery, 7 Clifton Lane, Meltham, Huddersfield HD9 4AH Tel: 01484 852073 Fax: 01484 854760 — MB ChB 1982 Leeds; MRCGP 1986; DRCOG 1986. Prev: Trainee GP Bradford VTS.

MITCHELL, Robert George (retired) 36 Blandford Avenue, Oxford OX2 8DZ Tel: 01865 58931 — BM BCh 1950 Oxf.; DM Oxf. 1969, BM BCh 1950; FRCP Ed. 1975, M 1959; FRCPath 1977, M 1965. Prev: Clin. Pathol. Ch.ill Hosp. Oxf.

MITCHELL, Robert Gordon McKenzie (retired) 7 Cedar Court, Langley Park, Durham DH7 9FG Tel: 0191 373 4070 Fax: 0191 373 4070 Email: gordon.mitchell@which.uk — MB ChB Glas. 1956. Prev: SMO HMP Durh.

MITCHELL, Robert Graham Great Lever Health Centre, Rupert St., Bolton BL3 6RN Tel: 01204 525429 Fax: 01204 380221; 1 Pool Fold Close, Bolton BL1 5SA — MB ChB 1979 Manch.

MITCHELL, Robert Grieg The Surgery, 15 School Lane, North Ferriby HU14 3DB Tel: 01482 634004 Fax: 01482 634004 — MB BS 1973 Lond.; MRCS Eng. LRCP Lond. 1973; DObst RCOG 1975. (Guy's)

MITCHELL, Robert Michael Stephen 4 Windermere Avenue, Belfast BT8 6SZ — MB BCh BAO 1992 Belf.

MITCHELL, Mr Robert Morton (retired) Tideways, Skelbo, Dornoch IV25 3QQ Tel: 01862 810838 — MB ChB 1943 Glas.; FRCS Glas. 1962; FRFPS Glas. 1948. Prev: Cons. Surg. Highland HB.

MITCHELL, Robert Wallace (retired) 40A Killinchy Road, Comber, Newtownards BT23 5LU Tel: 01247 872454 — MB BCh BAO 1952 Dub.

MITCHELL

MITCHELL, Robin Gordon 57 Manor Road, Dorchester DT1 2AZ — MB ChB 1987 Ed.

MITCHELL, Robin William Doig Department of Anaesthetics, Dryburn Hospital, Durham DH1 5TW Tel: 0191 333 2333 Fax: 0191 333 2699; 19 Blaidwood Drive, Durham DH1 3TD Tel: 0191 384 1450 — MB ChB 1980 Ed.; BSc (Med. Sci.) Ed. 1977, MB ChB 1980; FFA RCS Eng. 1984. Cons. Anaesth. Dryburn Hosp. Durh. Socs: Fell. Roy. Med. Soc. Edin.; Obst. Anaesth. Assoc.; Assoc. Anaesth. Gt. Brit. & Irel. Prev: Sen. Regist. (Anaesth.) Leic. Hosps.; Regist. (Anaesth.) Roy. Infirm. Edin.; Research Fell. (Anaesth.) Roy. Infirm. Edin.

MITCHELL, Mr Roger John (retired) Belwood Farm, Rue du Hurel, Trinity, Jersey JE3 5JR Tel: 01534 863679 — MB BChir 1959 Camb.; MChir Camb. 1966, MA, MB 1959, BChir 1958; FRCS Eng. 1964. Prev: Cons. Gen. Surg. & Urol. Gen. Hosp. Jersey.

MITCHELL, Mrs Rosalind Diana Queen Elizabeth Neuroscience Centre, Queen Elizabeth Hospital, Birmingham B15 2TH Tel: 0121 472 1311 — MB BS 1981 Lond.; MD Lond. 1990; FRCS (SN) 1993; FRCS Eng. 1986. (King's) Cons. Neurosurg. Qu. Eliz. Neurosci. Centre Qu. Eliz. Hosp. Birm. Prev: Sen. Regist. Walton Centre Neurol. & Neurosurg. Liverp.; Regist. Manch. Roy. Infirm.

MITCHELL, Rosemary Angela (retired) 12 Chester Grove, Darlington DL3 9DY Tel: 01325 462906 — MB BS 1957 Durh.; Cert Developm. Paediat. Univ. Leeds 1980. Prev: SCMO Durh. HA.

MITCHELL, Rosemary Grant (retired) 51 Mellington Avenue, East Didsbury, Manchester M20 5WE Tel: 0161 445 3197 — MB ChB Manch. 1959; DA Eng. 1963; FFA RCS Eng. 1969. Prev: Cons. Anaesth. Stockport & Buxton Hosp. Gp.

MITCHELL, Ross Galbraith Craigard, Abertay Gardens, Broughty Ferry, Dundee DD5 2RR Tel: 01382 776983 — MB ChB 1944 Ed.; MD (High Commend.) Ed. 1953; FRCP Ed. 1956, M 1949; DCH Eng. 1948; Hon. FRCPCH 1996. (Ed.) Prof. Emerit. Univ. Dundee. Socs: Assn. Phys.; Amer. Acad. Cerebral Palsy & Developm. Med.; (Ex-Chairm.) Brit. Assn. Community Child Health. Prev: Chairm. Edit. Bd. Mac Keith Press Lond.; Prof. Child Health Univ. Dundee & Aberd.; Rockefeller Research Fell. Mayo Clinic, USA.

MITCHELL, Ross James The Health Centre, Queen Street, Jedburgh TD8 6EN Tel: 01835 863361 Fax: 01835 864273; Birkhill, Sharplan Road, Jedburgh TD8 6SF — MB ChB 1987 Ed.; MRCGP 1992; DRCOG 1992. (Edinburgh) Prev: Trainee GP/SHO (Med.) Melrose VTS.

MITCHELL, Mr Roy St John's Hospital, Howden, Livingston EH54 6PP Tel: 01506 419666; Lymphoy House, Currie EH14 6AJ Tel: 0131 449 3818 — MB ChB 1975 Ed.; ChM Ed. 1985; BDS Sheff. 1969; FRCS Ed. 1982; FDS RCS Ed. 1979. Cons. (Oral & Maxillofacial Surg.) St John's Hosp. Howden Livingston W. Lothian; Hon. Sen. Lect. (Oral & Maxillofacial Surg.) Univ. Edin. Prev: Sen. Lect. (Oral & Maxillofacial Surg.) Univ. Edin.

MITCHELL, Ruth Royal Oldham Hospital, Rochdale Road, Oldham OL1 2JH Tel: 0161 624 0420; 34 Stamford Drive, Wood Houses, Failsworth, Manchester M35 9WS Tel: 0161 681 6228 — MB ChB 1960 Cairo; DPM RCPSI 1993. Cons. Psychiat. Roy. Oldham Hosp. Prev: Cons. Psychiat. N. Tyneside & SW Durh.; Assoc. Specialist (Psychiat.) Rotherham Gen. Hosp.; Staff Grade Psychiat. Torbay Hosp. Torquay.

MITCHELL, Ruthven (retired) 2 Byron Court, Bothwell, Glasgow G71 8TW Tel: 01698 853255 Email: ruthveneleanor@talk21.co — MB ChB 1977 Glas.; MB ChB Glas. 1961; BSc (Hons.) Glas. 1958, MD 1977; FRCP Ed. 1989; FRCP Glas. 1982; FRCPS Glas. 1982; FRCPath 1981, M 1969. Hon. Clin. Sen. Lect. Univ. Glas.; Hon. Cons. Haemat. Gtr. Glas., Argyll & Clyde, Lanarksh., Ayrsh. & Arran, Dumfries & Galloway & Forth Valley HBs. Prev: Regional Dir., Glas. & W. Scot. Regional Transfus. Serv.

MITCHELL, Sarah Ryder Road Surgery, 46 Ryder Road, Stoke, Plymouth PL2 1JA Tel: 01752 561973 — BM BS 1985 Nottm.

MITCHELL, Sarah Jane c/o The Whittington Hospital, Department of Paediatrics, Highgate Hill, London N19 5NF — MB BS 1991 Lond.; BSc (Hons.) Psychol. Lond. 1988; MRCP UK 1996. (The London Hospital Medical College)

MITCHELL, Sarah Louise Alder Key Hospital, Eaton Road, Liverpool L12 2AP Tel: 01757 229070 — MB ChB 1988 Leeds; FRCA 1997. Lect. (Paediat. Anaesth.). Socs: Train. Mem. Assn. Anaesth.; Fell. Roy. Coll. Anaesth.; OAA. Prev: Specialist Regist.

(Anaesth.) Yorks. Region; SHO (Anaesth.) Groby Rd. Hosp. Leicester; SHO (Anaesth.) Rotherham Dist. Gen. Hosp.

*****MITCHELL, Sarah Louise Martin** 7 Stoneygate Avenue, Leicester LE2 3HE — MB ChB 1995 Sheff.

MITCHELL, Sheena Catherine Macrae 41 Collingwood Avenue, London N10 3EE — MB ChB 1980 Sheff.

MITCHELL, Shonagh Helen Margaret Llwynbedw Medical Centre, 82/86 Caerphilly Road, Birchgrove, Cardiff CF14 4AG Tel: 029 2052 1222 Fax: 029 2052 2873; 149 King George V Drive, Heath, Cardiff CF14 4EN Tel: 029 2075 3363 — MB BCh 1989 Wales; BSc (Psychol.) Wales 1983; DFFP 1995. Socs: Fell. Roy. Soc. Med. Prev: SHO Rotat. (Paediat.) Newc.

MITCHELL, Simon John Neonatal Intensive Care Unit, Hope Hospital, Stott Lane, Salford M6 8HD Tel: 0161 787 5784 Fax: 0161 787 5786 Email: mitchell.simon@virgin.netsmitchel@fs1.no.man.ac.uk — MB ChB 1985 Dundee; MRCP (UK) 1991; DCH RCP Lond. 1990; DRCOG 1988; MD 1998 Dundee. (Univ. of Dundee) Cons. Neonat. Paeditrician, Hope Hosp., Salford. Socs: Brit. Assoc. for Perinatal med. - Mem.; Paediat. Res. Soc. Prev: Clin. Fell. Neonatology, Univ. of Toronto Neonat. - Perinatol Fell.sh.ip Progr.; Sen. Regist. Neonat. Paediat., Birm. Wom.'s Hosp.; Research Fell., Univ. of Birm. Dept. Paediat. & Child Health.

MITCHELL, Simon Ward The Surgery, 134 Baffins Road, Portsmouth PO3 6BH Tel: 023 9282 7132 Fax: 023 9282 7025; 48 Carmarthen Avenue, Cosham, Portsmouth PO6 2AQ — MB ChB 1975 Dundee; BSc (Med. Sci.) St. And. 1972; DRCOG 1977.

MITCHELL, Stephen Andrew Department of Gastroenterology, Level 2, John Radcliffe Hospital, Headley Way, Headington, Oxford OX3 9DU Tel: 01865 220618 Fax: 01865 308147 Email: stephen.mitchell@clara.net; 50A Quarry Road, Headington, Oxford OX3 8NX — BM BCh 1988 Oxf.; MA Oxf. 1990, BA 1985; MRCP (UK) 1991. Hon. Regist. (Gastroenterol.) John Radcliffe Hosp. Oxf. Prev: Hon. Regist. (Gastroenterol.) Guy's Hosp. Lond.; Regist. (Gastroenterol.) St. Mary's Hosp. Lond.; Regist. (Gen. Med. & Gastroenterol.) N.wich Pk. Hosp. Harrow.

MITCHELL, Stephen Ernest Henry 39 Goodyers Av., Radlett WD7 8AZ — BChir 1991 Camb.; MB BChir 1991; FRCS (Eng.) 1996. Clin. Research Fell. Depts. Surg. & Histopath. Imperial Coll. Sci. Technol. of Med. Hammersmith Hosp. Campus Du Cane Rd. Lond.; Hon. Regist. Urol. Ealing Hosp. NHS Trust S.all Middlx. Socs: Med. Protec. Soc.

MITCHELL, Stephen John 1A St Leonards Road, Exeter EX2 4LA — MB BS 1988 Lond.

MITCHELL, Stephen Robert 10 Abrose Gardens, West Didsbury, Manchester M20 2YF — MB ChB 1995 Manch.

MITCHELL, Stuart John 2 Wayside, Lower Swanwick, Southampton SO31 7JS; Southampton University Hospitals Trust, Tremona Road, Southampton SO16 6YD Tel: 01703 794156 — MB BS 1990 Lond.; BSc Lond. 1989. (Royal Free Hospital School of Medicine) Specialist Regist. (Occupat. Med.) Soton. Univ. Hosps. NHS Trust. Socs: Aerospace Med. Assn.; Soc. Occupat. Med.; BMA. Prev: Sen. Med. Off. Defence Eval. & Research Agency, Centre for Human Sci.s+FarnBoro.

MITCHELL, Susan Carolyn Integrated Care Partnership, Fitznell Manor Surgery, Chessington Road, Ewell, Epsom KT17 1TF Tel: 020 8394 1471 Fax: 020 8393 9753; 7 Links Road, Epsom KT17 3PP Tel: 01372 721018 Fax: 01372 749153 — MB BS 1967 Lond.; MB BS Lond. 1967 MRCS Eng. LRCP Lond. 1967. (Char. Cross) GP Ewell.

MITCHELL, Susan Frances The Retreat, Heslington Rd, York YO1D 5BN Tel: 01904 412551 Fax: 01904 430828 Email: smitchell@retreat-hospital.org; 5 Hopgrove Lane North, Malton Rd, York TO32 9TF — MB BCh BAO 1970 Dub.; FRC Psch 1999; MRCPsych 1977. Cons. Psychiat., The Retreat, York. Prev: Sen. Regist. (Psychiat.) Roy. Dundee Liff Hosp.; Research Asst. Inst. Psychiat. Lond.; Cons. Psychiat. Stratheden Hosp. Cupar Fife.

MITCHELL, Miss Susan Nicola — MB BS 1981 Lond.; MRCOG 1988; DRCOG 1983. Cons. O & G York Dist. Hosp. Socs: Brit. Menopause Soc.; Brit. Matern. & Fetal Med. Soc. Prev: Sen. Regist. Rotat. (O & G) St. Peters Hosp. Chertsey & St. Geo. Hosp. Lond.; Regist. (O & G) Addenbrooke's Hosp. Camb.; SHO (O & G) The Lond. Hosp. & St. Mary's Hosp. & Samarit. Hosp. Lond.

MITCHELL

MITCHELL, Suzanne Margaret Chelsea and Westminster Hospital, Fulham Road, London SW10 9NH Tel: 020 8746 8000 Fax: 020 8846 6198 Email: suzanne.mitchell@chelwest.nhs.uk — MB BS 1984 Lond.; FRCS Ed. 1990; FRCOphth 1991; DO RCPSI 1990. Cons. Ophth. Chelsea & W.m. Hosp.; Cons. Ophtalmologist W.ern Eye Hosp. Marylebone Rd. Lond. Socs: Fell. Mem. Roy. Soc. Med.; BMA; Internat. Mem. of the Amer. Acad. of Ophthalmol. Prev: Sen. Regist. (Ophth.) Moorfields Eye Hosp. Lond.; Wellcome Trust Vision Research Fell. Inst. of Ophth. Lond.

MITCHELL, Tejaln Navin 2 Milton Mansions, Queens Club Gardens, London W14 9RP — MB BS 1994 Lond.

MITCHELL, Terence Reginald James Paget Hospital NHS Trust, Lowestoft Road, Great Yarmouth NR31 6LA Tel: 01493 452444; East Wood, 132 Corton Long Lane, Lowestoft NR32 5HD Tel: 01502 731646 — MB BS 1965 Lond.; MA Camb. 1988; MD Lond. 1981; FRCPath 1983, M 1971; MRCS Eng. LRCP Lond. 1965. (Char. Cross) Cons. Haemat. Gt. Yarmouth & Waveney Health Dist. Prev: Assoc. Dean. Univ. Camb.; Sen. Lect. & Hon. Cons. (Haemat.) Char. Cross Hosp. Fulham; Sen. Regist. & Lect. (Haemat.) Char. Cross Hosp. Med. Sch. & Fulham Hosp.

MITCHELL, Teresa Anne Ladywell Convent, Ashtead Lane, Godalming GU7 1ST Tel: 01483 425775 Fax: 01483 426244 Email: teresamitchell@ladywell.org.uk — MB ChB Birm. 1968; MRCS Eng. LRCP Lond. 1968; DTM & H Lond. 1980; DObst. RCOG 1970. (Birmingham)

MITCHELL, Teresa Jane Thorkhill Road Surgery, 115A Thorkhill Road, Thames Ditton KT7 0UW Tel: 020 8398 3141 Fax: 020 8398 7836 — MB BS 1978 Lond.; MSc (Addic. Behaviour) Lond. 1995; MA (Physiol.) Oxf. 1979; Dip. Addic. Behaviour Lond. 1994; DRCOG 1989. (St. Thos. Hosp. Med. Sch.)

MITCHELL, Timothy David Thame Health Centre, East St., Thame OX9 3JZ — MB BS 1973 Lond.; MRCS Eng. LRCP Lond. 1973.

***MITCHELL, Timothy David** 14 The Woodlands, Stourbridge DY8 2RA — MB BCh 1995 Wales.

MITCHELL, Mr Timothy Edward ENT Department, Royal South Hants Hospital, Bruntons Terrace, off St Mary's Road, Southampton Tel: 023 8082 5635 Fax: 023 8082 5688 — BM BCh 1989 Oxf.; FRCS 1999 (ORL-HNS); FRCS Eng. 1994. Cons. Otolaryngologist, S.ampton Univ. Hosp.s NHS Trust. Socs: Mem. of Brit. Assoc. Of OtoLaryngol., Head and Neck Surg.; Mem. of Brit. Assoc. Of Day Surg.

MITCHELL, Timothy John Fitzmaurice Montpelier Health Centre, Bath Buildings, Bristol BS6 5PT Tel: 0117 942 6811 Fax: 0117 944 4182 Email: tim.mitchelleyp-l81012.nhs.uk — MB ChB 1980 Bristol; MRCGP 1986; Dip. Pract. Dermat. Wales 1991; DRCOG 1982. Exec. Partner, Montpelier Health Centre,Bristol. Socs: Founder Mem. and Hon. Sec. of the Primary Care Dermat. Soc.; Med. Adviser to the Assoc. Parliamentary Gp. on skin.

MITCHELL, Victoria Susan Department Anaesthetics, The Middlesex Hospital, Mordmer Street, London W1N 8AA Tel: 0207 380 9013 Fax: 0207 380 9604; 'Dunida', Lurgan Road, Banbridge BT32 4LU Tel: 0207 402 3003 Email: ben.moran@btinternet.com, vim.sd@virgin.net — MB BS 1987 Lond.; FRCA. 1992. Cons. Anaesth., Univ. Coll. Lond. Hosps. NHS Trust, Lond.

MITCHELL, Vivian Eric Department of Haematology, Leicester Royal Infirmary, Leicester LE1 5WW Tel: 0116 258 6616 Fax: 0116 258 5093; The Larches, Stamford Road, Kirby Muxloe, Leicester LE9 2ER Tel: 0116 239 4383 — MB ChB 1969 Sheff.; FRCP Lond. 1992; MRCP (UK) 1972; FRCPath 1988, M 1977. Cons. Haemat. & Dir. Haemophilia Centre Roy. Infirm. Leic. Socs: Brit. Soc. Haemostasis & Thrombosis; Brit. Soc. Haematol.; UK Haemophilia Centre Doc. Org. Prev: Sen. Regist. (Haemat.) Hallamsh. Hosp. Sheff. & Univ. Hosp. Wales Cardiff; Regist. (Med.) Roy. Infirm. Sheff.

MITCHELL, Wendy Barbara Hartcliffe Health Centre, Hareclive Road, Hartcliffe, Bristol BS13 0JP Tel: 0117 9645588/9647925 Fax: 0117 964 9055; 27 Southfield Road, Westbury on Trym, Bristol BS9 3BG Tel: 0117 962 4580 — MB ChB 1980 Bristol; BSc (Hons. (Zool.) Swansea 1975; MRCGP 1985; DRCOG 1982.

MITCHELL, William Alan Larne Health Centre, Gloucester Avenue, Larne BT40 1PB Tel: 028 2826 1925 Fax: 028 2827 9560; 89 Glenarm Road, Larne BT40 1DY — MB BCh BAO 1980 Belf.; DRCOG 1983.

MITCHELL, William Alexander Laurie Wychwood, The Ridgway, Cranleigh GU6 7HR — MB ChB 1975 Aberd.; FFA RCS Eng. 1982. Prev: Cons. Noble's Hosp. I. of Man.

MITCHELL, Willie Philip (retired) Kingfishers, Hall Road, Barton Turf, Norwich NR12 8AR Tel: 01692 630992 — MB ChB 1954 Leeds.

MITCHELL-FOX, Thomas Maxwell Mensana Medical, 1 The Crescent, Maidenhead SL6 6AA Tel: 01628 631177 Fax: 01628 631140; Swan Upping, Fishery Road, Bray, Maidenhead SL6 1UP Tel: 01628 777727 — MA, MB BChir Camb. 1959. (St. Thos.) Indep. GP Maidenhead. Prev: Med. Dir. Bucks. FHSA Aylesbury; Regional Med. Off. DHSS; Cas. Off. & Ho. Phys. (Neurol. & Thoracic Med.) St. Thos. Hosp. Lond.

MITCHELL-HEGGS, Caroline Anne Winsome 71 Broad Lane, Hampton TW12 3AX Tel: 020 8979 5406 — MB BS 1987 Lond.; MA Camb. 1988; MRCGP 1994; DFFP 1993; DRCOG 1993; DCH RCP Lond. 1991. Asst. GP Hampton & E. Molesey. Prev: SHO (Psychogeriat.) W.Pk. & Epsom Hosps. Epsom; Trainee GP Claygate; SHO (Gen., Neonat.. & Paediat.) N.wick Pk. Hosp. Harrow.

MITCHELL-HEGGS, Nita Ann Occupational Health Department, St. George's Hospital, Tooting, London SW17 0QT Tel: 020 8725 1662 Fax: 020 8725 3087; Pendreath House, 6 Clifton Road, Wimbledon, London SW19 4QT Tel: 020 8947 5500 — MB BS (Hons.) Lond. 1966; FRCP Lond. 1994; MRCP (UK) 1974; MRCS Eng. LRCP Lond. 1966; FFOM RCP Lond. 1994, MFOM 1987; DCH Eng. 1968. (Lond. Hosp.) Cons. Phys. Occupat. Med. St. Geo. Healthcare Trust; Hon. Sen. Lect. (Pub. Health Med.) St. Geo. Hosp. & Med. Sch. Lond. Socs: Soc. Occupat. Med.; Affil. RCPsych. Prev: Sen. Regist. (Research) Psychiat. Dept. St. Geo. Hosp. Lond.; Research Regist. (Psychol. Med.) St. Thos. Hosp. Lond.; Psychiat. Stud. Health Centre Chelsea Coll. Lond.

MITCHELL-HEGGS, Peter Francis Ashtead Hospital, The Warren, Ashtead KT21 2SB Tel: 01372 276161; Pendreath House, 6 Clifton Road, Wimbledon, London SW19 4QT Tel: 020 8947 5500 — MB BChir 1967 Camb.; MA Camb. 1967; PhD Lond. 1974; FRCP Lond. 1988; MRCP (UK) 1970; MRCS Eng. LRCP Lond. 1966. (Camb. & St. Mary's) Cons. Phys. Gen. & Thoracic Med. Epsom Health Care NHS Trust; Med. Dir. Epsom & St Helier NHS Trust.; Hon. Sen. Lect. (Med.) Char. Cross & W.m. Med. Sch. Lond.; Hon. Vis. Cardiol. St. Bart. Hosp. Lond. Socs: Fell. Roy. Soc. Med. (Sec. Hist. Med. Counc.); Amer. Thoracic Soc.; Haiveian Soc. Lond. (Counc). Prev: Lect. (Med.) Char. Cross Hosp. Lond.; Res. Med. Off. Brompton Hosp.; 1st Asst. (Med.) St. Geo. Hosp. Lond.

MITCHELMORE, Andrew Edward Hollybush Cottage, Acton Turville, Badminton GL9 1HL Tel: 0145 218454 — MB ChB 1976 Liverp.; FRCR 1984; DMRD Eng. 1981. Cons. Radiol. S.mead Hosp.

MITCHELMORE, Gordon Edward (retired) Elmhurst, Castle St., Wallingford OX10 8DW Tel: 01491 836370 — MB ChB 1947 Bristol. Prev: Anaesth. Newbury & Dist. Hosp. & Fairmile Hosp. Wallingford.

MITCHELMORE, Una Pearce (retired) Elmhurst, Castle St., Wallingford OX10 8DW Tel: 01491 836370 — MB ChB 1949 Bristol. Prev: Ho. Surg. & Sen. Cas. Off. S.mead Hosp. Bristol.

MITCHELSON, Anne Vass Dumbarton Health Centre, Station Road, Dumbarton G82 1PW Tel: 01389 602611 Fax: 01389 602621; Claremont, 11 West Montrose St, Helensburgh G84 9PF Tel: 01436 673625 — MB ChB 1972 Aberd.; MFHom 2001 Lond. p/t Princip. in Gen. Med.

MITCHELSON, Philippa Anne 7 Warren Drive, Deganwy, Conwy LL31 9ST; Bethmeon, Farnham Lane, Haslemere GU27 1HD — MB ChB 1986 Liverp.

MITCHENERE, Mr Peter Northwood Consulting Rooms, 7 Greenhill Court, 25B Green Lane, Northwood HA6 2UZ Tel: 092 74 26948; 29 Eastbury Avenue, Northwood HA6 3LL — MB BS 1965 Lond.; MS Lond. 1983; FRCS Eng. 1974. (St. Bart.) Cons. Mt. Vernon & Hillingdon Hosps.; Mem. Ct. Examrs. RCS Eng. Prev: Sen. Regist. (Surg.) Roy. Free Hosp. Lond.; Lect. (Anat.) St. Mary's Hosp. Med. Sch. Lond.; Ho. Off. (Surg. & Neuosurg.) St. Bart. Hosp. Lond.

MITCHESON, Jeremy Ian Halcro Health Centre, Victoria Sq, Portishead, Bristol BS20 6AQ Tel: 01275 847474 Fax: 01275 817516; Portishead Health Centre, Portishead, Bristol BS20 6AQ Tel: 01275 847474 Email: yas13@dial.pipex.com — MB BS Lond. 1968; MRCP (U.K.) 1972; DCH Eng. 1971; DObst RCOG 1971. (St. Geo.) Socs: BMA. Prev: SHO (Psych.) Barrow Hosp. Bristol; SHO

Med. S.mead Hosp. Bristol; Jun. Ho. Off. St. Geo. Hosp. Lond. & Roy. Hants. Co. Hosp.

MITCHESON, Martin Christopher, OBE Royal Liverpool University Hospital, Prescot Street, Liverpool L7 8XP Email: mitch@eggconnectinet, richard.azurdia@rlbuh-tr.nwest.nhs.uk — MB BChir 1960 Camb.; B Chir 1959; FRCPsych 1985, M 1971; DPM Lond. 1966. (St. Thos.) p/t Cons. Psychiat. Robt. Smith Unit Bristol United Healthcare Trust. Prev: Clin. Dir. Avon Drug Problem Team & SW Region Drug Advis. Serv.; Regist. Maudsley Hosp. Lond.; Cons. Drug & Alcohol Serv. Univ. Coll. Hosp. Lond.

MITCHINER, Michael Bernard Ravenhill, Rectory Park, Sanderstead, South Croydon CR2 9JR Tel: 020 8657 1813 — MRCS Eng. LRCP Lond. 1964; PhD Lond. 1969, BSc (Hnrs.) 1961, MB BS 1964. (Guy's) Socs: Fell. Roy. Soc. Med.; BMA. Prev: Ho. Phys, & Ho. Surg. Roy. Surrey Co. Hosp. Guildford; Lect. in Path. Guy's Hosp. Med. Sch. Lond.; Hosp. Pract. (Path.) Mayday Hosp. Thornton Heath.

MITCHINSON, Francis John Newtons, The Health Centre, Heath Road, Haywards Heath RH16 3BB Tel: 01444 412280 Fax: 01444 416943 — MB BS 1989 Lond.; MRCGP 1993.

MITCHINSON, James Stephen 12 Hawkhurst Way, New Malden KT3 5BS — MB BS 1987 Lond.

MITCHINSON, Malcolm James University of Cambridge, Department of Pathology, Tennis Court Road, Cambridge CB2 1QP Tel: 01223 333719 Fax: 01223 333872 Email: mjm1002@bio.cam.ac.uk; Abington Lodge, Great Abington, Cambridge CB1 6AB Tel: 01223 892459 — MB BChir Camb. 1961; MD Camb. 1969, MA 1961; FRCPath 1978, M 1966. (Camb. & Manch.) Reader in Cellular Path. (Path.) Univ. Camb.; Fell. Clare Coll. Camb.; Hon. Cons. Addenbrooke's Hosp. Camb. Socs: Path. Soc. Oxygen Soc. Prev: Asst. Pathol. (Path.) Univ. Camb.; Resid. Clin. Path. Manch. Roy. Infirm.; Vis. Asst. Prof. Path. Stanford Univ. Calif., USA.

MITCHISON, Professor Denis Anthony, CMG Department of Medical Microbiology, St. George's Hospital Medical School, Cranmer Terrace, London SW17 0RE Tel: 020 8725 5704 Fax: 020 8682 1320 Email: dmitchis@sghms.ac.uk; 14 Marlborough Road, Richmond TW10 6JR Tel: 020 8940 4751 Fax: 020 8940 4751 — MB BChir 1943 Camb.; FRCP Lond. 1970, M 1965; FRCPath 1977, M 1965. (Univ. Coll. Hosp.) Emerit. Prof. Bact. St. Geo. Hosp. Med. Sch. Lond.; Mem. of Scientif. Advisoy Comm. Global Alliance for TB Drug Developm.; Mem. of Scientif. Advisoy Comm. Epivax. Prev: Dir. MRC Unit for Laborat. Studies in Tuberc.; Dir. (Bact.) Roy. Postgrad. Med. Sch. Lond.

MITCHISON, Harriet Caroline Gastroenterology Department, Sunderland Royal Hospital, Kayll Road, Sunderland SR4 7TP Tel: 0191 565 6256 Fax: 0191 569 9204; 78 Fenham Hall Drive, Newcastle upon Tyne NE4 9XA — MB BS 1980 Newc.; MA Oxf. 1982, BA 1977; MD Newc. 1990; FRCP Lond. 1996; MRCP (UK) 1983. Cons. Phys. & Gastroenterol. Sunderland Roy. Hosp. Sunderland. Socs: Brit. Soc. Gastroenterol.; Brit. Assn. for Study of Liver. Prev: Sen. Regist. (Gastroenterol. & Gen. Med.) Freeman Hosp. Newc.

MITCHISON, Sally Upper Poplars, Cherry Knowle Hospital, Ryhope, Sunderland SR2 0NB Tel: 0191 569 9477 — MB BS 1978 Lond.; BA York 1971; MMedSci Leeds 1991; MRCPsych 1989; Dip. Gp. Anal. 1995. (Roy. Free) Cons. Psychiat. (Psychother.) Sunderland. Socs: Assoc. Mem. Inst. Psychosexual Med. Prev: Sen. Regist. (Psychother.) Leeds; Sen. Regist. (Psychiat.) Leeds Rd. Hosp. Bradford; Sen. Regist. (Psychiat.) Stanley Royds Hosp. Wakefield & St. Jas. Hosp. Leeds.

MITCHLEY, Susan Elizabeth Windmill Medical Practice, 65 Shoot Up Hill, London NW2 3PS Tel: 020 8452 7646 Fax: 020 8450 2319; 194B Fordwych Road, London NW2 3NX Tel: 020 8452 2757 — MB BS Lond. 1967; PhD Lond. 1972; MRCS Eng. LRCP Lond. 1967; Dip Ther. 1997 Wales. (Roy. Free) Lect. (Gen. Pract.) Univ. Coll. Lond. Med. Sch. Prev: Lect. (Pharmacol.) Roy. Free Hosp. Sch. Med. Lond.

MITCHYN, Mark Delamere Street Health Centre, 45 Delamere Street, Crewe CW1 2ER Tel: 01270 214046 — MB ChB 1987 Manch.; T(GP) 1995; DRCOG 1995; DA (UK) 1992. (Manch.) GP. Prev: Staff Grade Community Paeds Chester; Trainee GP N.gate Village Surg. Chester; GP/Regist. Tattenhall.

MITFORD, Emma Green Batt House, The Pinfold, Alnwick NE66 1TZ Tel: 01665 602429 — MB BS 1983 Lond.; MRCGP 1989; DRCOG 1987. Staff Grade N.d. Ment. Health NHS Trust; Clin. Med. Off. N.d. Community Health NHS Trust. Prev: Clin. Med. Off. & Clin. Asst. N.d. HA; Trainee GP Brighton & N.umbria VTS.

MITFORD, Peter Northumberland Health Authority, Merley Croft, Loansdene, Morpeth NE61 2DL Tel: 01670 394400 Fax: 01670 394501; 2 River View, Morpeth NE61 1JU Tel: 01670 514164 — MB BS Durh. 1966; FRCGP 1987, M 1976; DObst RCOG 1968. Cons. Primary Care N.umberland Health Auth. Prev: GP Trainer N.umbria VTS; Roy. Coll. Gen. Pract. Examr.; Mem. Gen. Med. Servs. Comm. BMA.

MITFORD-BARBERTON, Gareth de Bohun (retired) 1 Dolphin Court, Powderham Terrace, Teignmouth TQ14 8BL — BM BCh Oxf. 1949; FRCOG 1975, M 1962; DTM & H Eng. 1951. Prev: Cons. O & G Kettering Dist.

MITFORD-SLADE, Fiona Dawn 6 The Inner Court, 48 Old Church St., London SW3 5BY — BM 1995 Soton.

MITHAL, Avinash (retired) 44 Nettleham Road, Lincoln LN2 1RE Tel: 01522 521855 — MB BS 1954 Rajputana; FRCP Lond. 1982; FRCP Ed. 1977, M 1966; MRCP (UK) 1970; DCH Eng. 1958. Prev: Cons. Allergy Clinic Lincoln.

MITHAL, Natasha Parveen Department of Clinical Oncology, Kent & Canterbury Hospital, Ethelbert Road, Canterbury CT1 3NG Tel: 01227 766877 Email: natasha@rpiper.demon.co.uk; 45 Castle Street, Canterbury CT1 2PY Tel: 01227 761529 — MB BS 1986 Lond.; MRCP (UK) 1990; FRCR 1994. (Lond. Hosp. Med. Coll.) Cons. Clin. Oncol. Dept. of Clin.Oncol.Kent & Canterbury Hosp. Socs: Brit. Oncol. Assn.; Roy. Coll. Radiol. (Clin. Oncol. Sect.); Eur. Soc. Therap. Radiat. & Oncol. Prev: Sen. Regist. (Clin. Oncol.) Roy. Marsden Hosp.; Clin. Sci., Hon. Sen. Regist. & Lect. (Radiat. Oncol.) Roy. Marsden Hosp.; Regist. (Radiother. & Oncol.) Roy. Lond. Hosp.

MITHAN, William John Victoria Place Surgery, 11 Victoria Place, Bethesda, Bangor LL57 3AG Tel: 01248 600212 Fax: 01248 602790; Hafod Wen, Bangor Road, Bethesda, Bangor LL57 3LU Tel: 01248 601587 — MRCS Eng. LRCP Lond. 1974. (Bristol) Clin. Asst. (Dermat.) Ysbyty Gwynedd, Bangor; Med. Off. Penrhyn Quarry, Bethesda. Socs: BMA; Assn. Aviat. Med. Examrs.

MITHILESH, Shubhada c/o Gynaecology Secretaries, Department of Obstetrics & Gynaecology, Dryburn Hospital, North Road, Durham DH1 5TW — MB BS 1980 Delhi; MRCOG 1993.

MITHRA, Sujit Daya Queen Elizabeth II Hospital, East Hertfordshire NHS Trust, Howlands, Welwyn Garden City AL7 4HQ; 5 Woodman Close, Wing, Leighton Buzzard LU7 0RE Tel: 01296 688646 Email: sujit_mithra@yahoo.com — MB BS 1984 Madras; DO Madras 1988; FRCS (Ophth) Glas. 1997. Staff Grade (Ophth.) Qu. Eliz. II Hosp. Welwyn Garden City. Prev: Staff Grade Luton & Dunstable Hosp.; SHO Luton & Dunstable Hosp.

MITKO, Anna Zofia 2 Hart Grove, London W5 3NB Tel: 020 8992 3545 — MB BCh BAO 1960 Dub.; MB BCh Dub. 1960. (Trinity Coll. Dub.) Assoc. Specialist Hillingdon Hosp. Socs: Assn. Clin. Path.; Brit. Soc. Clin. Cytol.

MITRA, Andrew David 20 St Boswells Place, Perth PH1 1SA — MB BS 1991 Lond.; MRCP (UK) 1996; MRCGP 1995; DCCH RCP Ed. 1994; DRCOG 1994. (Roy. Lond. Hosp. Med. Coll.)

MITRA, Mr Anthony Nath Consulting Suite, Humana Hospital, Wellington Place, London NW8 9LE Tel: 020 7935 0032; E.N.T. Department, Highgate Private Hospital, 17 View Road, London N6 4DJ — MB ChB 1956 Birm.; FRCS (Otolaryng.) Eng. 1967; FRCS (Gen. Surg.) Ed. 1965. (Birm.) Cons. ENT Surg. OldCh. Hosp. Romford. Prev: Ho. Surg. Surgic. Profess. Unit, Qu. Eliz. Hosp. Birm.; Sen. Regist. Profess. Unit Roy. Nat. Throat, Nose & Ear Hosp. Lond.; Capt. RAMC.

MITRA, Asit Kumar 35 Maplestead Road, Dagenham RM9 4XH Tel: 020 8595 0018 Fax: 020 8595 7741; 28 Melford Avenue, Barking IG11 9HT Tel: 020 8594 6249 Fax: 020 8595 7741 — MB BS 1957 Lucknow. (K.G. Med. Coll.)

***MITRA, Rajive Kumar** 29 Maple Road, Grays RM17 6LB — MB ChB 1988 Dundee; MRCGP 1996.

MITRA, Sakuntala 39 Arklow Road Intake, Doncaster DN2 5LB Tel: 01302 730869 — MB BS 1982 Calcutta; MRCOG 1991; DObst RCPI 1986.

MITRA, Salil Waldron Health Centre, Stanley Street, London SE8 4BG Tel: 020 8692 2314; 113 Old Woolwich Road, Greenwich,

MITRA

London SE10 9PP — MB BS 1963 Calcutta; DA Eng. 1972. (R.G. Kar Med. Coll.) Mem. Fac. Anaesth. Prev: Ho. Off. (O & G) & Regist. (Anaesth.) Greenwich Dist. Hosp.

MITRA, Samarendranath Tiddington Fields, Tiddington Main Road, Stratford-upon-Avon CV37 7AY Tel: 01789 261455; 122 Shottery Road, Stratford-upon-Avon CV37 9QA Tel: 01789 298552 — MB BS 1959 Calcutta; Dip. Cardiol. Calcutta 1968. Asst. Psychiat. (Psychiat. for Old Age) Tiddington Fields Stratford-upon-Avon.

MITRA, Samir (retired) Redtiles, 165 Pelham Avenue, Scartho, Grimsby DN33 3NE Tel: 01472 328753 Fax: 01472 589435 Email: smitra@ntlworld.co.uk — MB BS 1949 Calcutta; MRCOG 1965; DObst 1962. Prev: Regist. (O & G) Welsh Hosp. Bd.

MITRA, Mr Samit A+E Dept, Middlesbrough General Hospital, Ayresome Green Lane, Middlesbrough TS5 5AZ Tel: 01642 854374 Fax: 01642 854251 Email: samitmitra@email.stahnhst.northy.nhs.uk — MB ChB 1990 Liverp.; FRCS A&E Ed. 1995; FFAEM 1998. (Liverpool) Cons. (Acci.+Emerg.) Middbrgh. Gen. Hosp. Prev: Sen. Reg.(A+E) S. Lond.; Helicopter Med. Serv. Roy, Lond. Hosp.

MITRA, Satyendu Gold Street Surgery, 1A Gold Street, Barnsley S70 1TT Tel: 01226 205339 Fax: 01226 247932 — MB BS 1969 Calcutta. (Calcutta)

MITRA, Smriti Lal (retired) 6 Leys Gardens, Newbury RG14 1HX — MB ChB 1942 Ed.; DMR Eng. 1945. Prev: Cons. Radiol. W. Suff. Gen. Hosp.

MITRA, Surajit 45 Fern Road, Whitby, South Wirral CH65 6PA — MB BS 1980 Calcutta; MRCOG 1990. Prev: Regist. Rotat. NW RHA.

MITRA THAKUR, Gopendra Gopal Reading Road Surgery, 34 Reading Road, Wokingham RG41 1EH Tel: 0118 978 2299 Fax: 0118 977 0284 — MB BS 1962 Calcutta; LRCP 1970; Dip. Venereol. Calcutta 1965; DCH Calcutta 1964. (R.G. Kar Med. Coll.)

MITSIDES, Chrystal Margaret Priors Lodge, Blagdon Hill, Taunton TA3 7SH Tel: 01823 421588 Fax: 01823 421588 — MB BS 1975 Lond.; MRCS Eng. LRCP Lond. 1975; MRCGP 1980; DCH Eng. 1979; DRCOG 1977. (St. Mary's) Clin. Asst. (Genitourin. Med.) Taunton & Som. NHS Trust.

MITTAL, Alok Kumar The Surgery, 50 Markyate Road, Dagenham RM8 2LD Tel: 020 8592 2983 Fax: 020 8984 8500 — MB BS 1970 Agra.

MITTAL, Deepak 8 Wilbraham Road, Walsall WS2 9PT — MB BS 1984 Delhi, India; MRCP (UK) 1995.

MITTAL, Rabinder Kumar Milman Road Health Centre, Milman Road, Reading RG2 0AR Tel: 0118 968 2285 Fax: 0118 975 5033; 11 Hafod, Caversham, Reading RG4 8LZ — MB BS 1990 Lond.; DCH Lond. 1993; DRCOG 1993; MRCGP 1994. (St. George's Hosp. Med. Sch.) GP Princip. Socs: Brit. Med. Acupunct. Soc.

MITTAL, Sanjay 23 Ednam Road, Goldthorn Park, Wolverhampton WV4 5BW — MB ChB 1992 Leeds.

MITTAL, Satish Chandra Golf View Medical Practice, 344 Walton Road, West Molesey KT8 0JP Tel: 020 8979 1605 Fax: 020 8979 1605; Clarewood, 1 Copsem Drive, Esher KT10 9HD Tel: 01372 462483 Fax: 01372 462483 — MB BS 1967 Agra. (Sarojini Naidu Med. Coll. Agra) Gen. Med. Pract. E. Molesey & Hampton Ct. Surrey.; Med. Exam. Various Insur. Cos; Bd. Mem. & Clin. Governance Lead E. Elmbridge PCG. Socs: Assur. Med. Soc. Prev: Regist. (Med.) S.lands Hosp. Shoreham-by-Sea; Regist. (Chest Dis. & Cardiol.) Preston Hall Hosp. Maidstone.; SHO (Neurol.) Claremont St. Hosp. Belf.

MITTAL, Sudha 3 Digby Road, Kingswinford DY6 7RP Tel: 01384 293609 — MB BS 1976 Delhi; FFA RCSI 1985.

MITTAL, Vipin Kumar Russells Hall Hospital, Dudley DY1 2HR Tel: 01384 456111 — MB BS 1970 Rajasthan. (S.M.S. Med. Coll. Jaipur) Clin. Asst. (A & E) Corbett Hosp. Stourbridge.

MITTON, David James 146 Elvaston Road, North Wingfield, Chesterfield S42 5GA — MB ChB 1993 Dundee.

MITTON, Sally Gay Department of Child Health, St. George's Hospital Medical School, Cranmer Terrace, London SW17 0RE Tel: 020 8725 5975 Fax: 020 8725 2858 Email: s.mitton@sghms.ac.uk; 40 Groveway, London SW9 0AR — MB BS 1977 Lond.; MD Lond. 1993; MRCP Lond. 1980; MRCS Eng. LRCP Lond. 1977. Cons. & Sen. Lect. (Paediat.) St. Geo. Hosp. Med. Sch. Lond. Socs: Eur. & Brit. Soc. Paediat. Gastroenterol. & Nutrit.; Paediat. Research Soc. Prev: Research Fell. & Hon. Sen. Regist. (Child Health) W.m. Childr. Hosp.; Regist. (Paediat.) Hosp. Sick Childr. Gt. Ormond St. & Qu.

Eliz. Hosp.Hackney (Paediat. Gastrogenterol.); Research Fell. (AIDS) Jas. Pringle Hse. Middlx. Hosp.

MITTRA, Braj (retired) 3 The Glen, Sunderland SR2 7TX Tel: 0191 567 9637 — MB BS 1956 Agra; PhD Belf. 1966; FRCP Lond. 1985; FRCP Ed. 1971, M 1960; DTM & H Ed. 1959. Prev: Cons. Phys. Sunderland Hosp. Gp.

MIXER, Philip Rowland, OStJ, TD Old Fire Station, Albert Terrace, Beverley HU17 8JW Tel: 01482 862236 Fax: 01482 861863 — MB BS 1977 Lond.; MRCGP 1981; DCH Eng. 1981; DRCOG 1979. (Lond. Hosp.) Trainer (Gen. Pract.) Beverley. Socs: Soc. Occupat. Med. Prev: Trainee GP Harrogate VTS; Ho. Surg. Lond. Hosp.; Ho. Phys. St. Margt. Hosp. Epping.

MIZAN, Jacques Highview Surgery, 20 Southgate Road, Potters Bar EN6 5DZ Tel: 01707 653866; 33 Thornton Road, Little Heath, Potters Bar EN6 1JJ Tel: 01707 652484 — MB ChB 1988 Cape Town; MRCGP 1995; DRCOG 1994.

MIZEN, Caroline Susan Charing Cross Hospital, Fulham Palace Road, Fulham, London W6 8RF Tel: 020 8846 1340; 46 Castlebar Road, Ealing, London W5 2DD Tel: 020 8997 9180 Fax: 020 8997 9180 — MB BS 1986 Lond.; MRCPsych 1991. Cons. Psychother. Char. Cross Hosp. Fulham. Prev: Sen. Regist. (Psychother.) Cassel Hosp. Richmond; SHO (Psychiat.) Gordon Hosp. Lond.

MIZEN, Kelvin David 2 Haggwood Cottages, Broad Highway, Wheldrake, York YO19 6BE — MB ChB 1995 Leic.; BDS Birm. 1985.

***MIZEN, Martin John** Arrowe Park Hospital, Arrowe Park Road, Upton, Wirral L63 5PE — MB ChB 1996 Liverp.

MKANDAWIRE, Ellmann Anicet The Surgery, 4 Collinge St., Shaw, Oldham OL2 8AA Tel: 01706 881028 Fax: 01706 290511; Bank House, Rochdale Road, Shaw, Oldham OL2 7JA — MB ChB 1976 Manch.; ECFMG Cert. 1976; MRCGP 1982; DRCOG 1980; Cert. Family Plann. Assn 1980. (Manch.) County Doctor Oldham Athletic Assoc. Football Club. Prev: Trainee GP Oldham; Trainee GP Essex VTS; SHO (Rheum. & Rehabil.) Mundelsley Hosp.

MLELE, Thomas Joseph Johnson Heath Lane Hospital, Heath Lane, West Bromwich BT1 2BQ Tel: 0121 553 1831 Fax: 0121 607 3229; 13 Dale Close, Great Barr, Birmingham B43 6AS Tel: 0121 358 6514 — MD 1974 Dar-Es-Salaam; MRCPsych 1980; DPM Eng. 1979. Cons. Psychiat. Heath La. Hosp. W. Bromwich W. Midl. Prev: Sen. Regist. Stoke Pk. Hosp. Bristol; Regist. (Psychiat.) Maudsley Hosp. Lond.

MLYNEK, Christine Regina Iona, 12 Cannock Road, Aylesbury HP20 2AN — MB ChB 1978 Leeds; BSc Leeds 1978; MFPHM RCP (UK) 1990; MFCM 1986; FFCM 2000. Cons. Pub. Health Med. Bucks. HA.

MLYNIK, Anna Leicestershire & Rutland Healthcare Trust, Leicester LE3 9DY Tel: 0116 225 2638 — Lekarz 1980 Gdansk, Poland; MRCPsych 1994. Cons. Psychiat. Leics. & Rutland Healthcare Trust. Prev: Sen. Regist. (Psychiat.) Leicester Gen. Hosp.; Regist. (Psychiat.) Leicester Gen. Hosp.

MMONO, Xavier Mmono Keboinee Dept. of Obstetrics & Gynaecology, Nottingham City Hospital, Hucknall Road, Nottingham NG5 1PB Tel: 07775 707 7777 Email: xmkm@aol.com — MB ChB 1988 Manch.; LL.M (Legal Aspects of Medical Practice); MRCOG 1995; DFFP 1995. (Manchester) Cons. (O & G) Nottm. City Hosp. Prev: Regist. (O & G) Wythenshawe Hosp. Manch.

MO, Chi-Ning Cardiology Department, Royal Manchester Childrens Hospital, Hospital Road, Manchester M27 4HA Tel: 0161 794 4696 — MB ChB 1991 Ed.; BSc (Hons.) Ed. 1989; MRCP (UK) 1994. Regist. (Paediat. Cardiol.) Roy. Manch. Childr. Hosp. Prev: Regist. (Paediat.) Roy. Wolverhampton Hosp. NHS Trust; SHO (Paediat.) Salford HA.

MO-SZU-TI, Mo Sam Yan The Surgery, Wood Houses, Little London, Walsall WS1 3EP Tel: 01922 28280 Fax: 01922 23023; 8 Tetley Avenue, Walsall WS4 2HE — MB ChB 1980 Dundee; MB ChB Dundee (Commend.) 1980; MRCGP 1984; DRCOG 1983.

MOABY, Nigel Malcolm 1 Charles Close, Osbaston, Monmouth NP25 3JD — MB ChB 1969 Bristol.

MOAKES, Hilary Townhead Surgeries, Townhead, Settle BD24 9JA Tel: 01729 822611 Fax: 01729 892916; Lincoln House, Greenhead Lane, Settle BD24 9HG Tel: 01729 825309 — MB BS 1987 Lond.; BA Oxf. 1984; MRCGP 1991; DRCOG 1990; DCH RCP Lond. 1989. Prev: SHO (Psychiat.) Hill End Hosp. St. Albans; SHO (A & E) St. Albans City Hosp.; SHO (O & G) Guy's Hosp. Lond.

MOALYPOUR, Mr Seyed-Mahmood Accident & Emergency Department, Kingston Hospital, Kingston upon Thames KT2 7QB Tel: 020 8546 7711 — MB BS 1968 Delhi; FRCS Eng. 1977; FFAEM 1993. Cons. Surg. (A & E) Kingston Hosp. Kingston u. Thames. Prev: Cons. Surg. & Asst. Prof. Shiraz Univ. Med. Sch. Iran.

MOAR, Anoopam Kaur 24 Breydon Close, Shelton Lock, Derby DE24 9DT Tel: 01332 700835 — BM BS 1991 Nottm.; BMedSci. Nottm. 1989; MRCGP 1996; DCH 1995. GP. Prev: SHO (Paediat.) Burnley Gen. Hosp.; SHO (A & E) Roy. United Hosp. Bath; SHO (Gen. Med.) St. Bernard's Hosp., Gibraltar.

MOAR, Robina Williamson (retired) 437 Kilmarnock Road, Newlands, Glasgow G43 2NT — MB ChB St. And. 1957; DPH Glas. 1962; DObst RCOG 1959. Prev: Sch. Med. Off. Educat. Health Serv. Glas.

MOAT, Mr Neil Eric Royal Brompton Hospital, Sydney St., London SW3 6NP Tel: 020 7352 8121; Gatehampton, Mill Lane, Gerrards Cross SL9 8AY Tel: 01753 892779 — MB BS 1981 Lond.; MS Lond. 1993; FRCS Eng. 1985. Cons. Cardiac Surg. Roy. Brompton Hosp. & Hon. Sen. Lect. Nat. Heart & Lung Inst. Socs: Fell. Roy. Soc. Med.; Soc. Cardiothoracic Surgs. GB & Irel. Prev: Sen. Lect. & Hon. Cons. Cardiac Surg. Univ. Sheff.; Sen. Regist. (Cardioac Surg.) Roy. Brompton Nat. Heart & Lond. Chest Hosps.; SHO (Surg.) St. Mary's Hosp. Lond.

MOATE, Mr Benjamin John Richard Royal Victoria Infirmary, Queen Victoria Road, Newcastle upon Tyne NE1 4LP Tel: 0191 232 5131 Fax: 0191 227 5246; Lansdown House, 90 Newgate St, Morpeth NE61 1BU — MB BS 1987 Lond.; FRCS Glas. 1996; FRCOphth 1995. (St. Bart. Hosp. Med. Coll.) Specialist Regist. (Ophth.) Roy. Vict. Infirm. Newc. Prev: Regist. (Ophth.) Roy. Liverp. Univ. Hosp.; Regist. (Ophth.) Sussex Eye Hosp. Brighton; SHO (Ophth.) St. Geo.'s Healthcare NHS Trust Lond.

MOATE, Robin Daniel Christopher Portsdown Group Practice, Cosham Park House, Cosham Park Avenue, Portsmouth PO6 3BG Tel: 02392 210200 Fax: 02392 214342 — MB ChB 1985 Bristol; MRCGP 1992; DRCOG 1990. Clin. Asst., Rheum., Qu. Alexandra Hosp., Cosham; GP Trainer. Prev: Ho. Off., Taunton; SHO A & E, Worthing; GP Army.

MOATE, Toby Jonathan Rilett Charlton Lane Centre, Charlton Lane, Cheltenham GL53 9DZ Tel: 01242 272158; 76 Keynsham Road, Cheltenham GL53 7PX Tel: 01242 254142 — MB BS 1989 Lond.

MOAZZAM, Mr Ahmed 67 Croftfield Road, Godmanchester, Huntingdon PE29 2ED — MB BS 1965 Karachi; FRCS Ed. 1978.

MOAZZEZ, Khalil Barking Hospital, Barking IG11 9LX Tel: 020 8594 3898 — MD 1956 Tehran; MSc Lond. 1964; FRCR 1984; DMRD Eng. 1971; DMR Tehran 1969. (Univ. Tehran) Cons. (Radiol.) Barking Hosp. Prev: Sen. Regist. Oxf. HA.

MOBARAK, Ahmed Nabil Mohamady (retired) — MB BCh Ain Shams Univ. Cairo 1957; LMSSA Lond. 1965; FRCP Ed. 1983, M 1967; FRCP Glas. 1980, M 1966; DCH Eng. 1965; DCH RCPS Glas. 1963; FRCPCH 1998. Prev: Cons. Paediat. Alexandra Hosp. Walderslade.

***MOBASHERI, Reza** Ground Floor Flat, 205 North End Road, London W14 9NP — MB BS 1998 Lond.; MB BS Lond 1998.

MOBB, Gillian Eugenie Department of Urology, Royal Bolton Hospital, Farnworth, Bolton BL4 0JR Tel: 01204 390428 Fax: 01204 390496 Email: gillian.mobb@boltonh-tr.nwest.nhs.uk; 7 Brookland Crescent, Northampton NN1 4SS — MB BS 1979 Lond.; BSc (1st cl. Hons.) Lond.1976; MD Leic. 1991; FRCS (Urol.) 1993; FRCS Ed. 1985. (Middlx.) Cons. Urol. Bolton Hosps NHS Trust. Socs: Brit. Assn. Urol. Surgs. Prev: Lect. & Sen. Regist. (Urol. Surg.) Univ. Hosp. Manch.; Research Fell. (Surg.) Leicester Gen. Hosp.

MOBBS, Charles Noel Arkless Pyle Street Health Centre, 27 Pyle Street, Newport PO30 1JW Tel: 01243 670707 Fax: 01243 672808 — MB BS Lond. 1968; MRCGP 1976; DObst RCOG 1973. (St. Geo.) Asst. Dep. Coroner I. of Wight. Socs: Treas. Wessex Fac. RCGP; Assoc. Police Surg. Prev: Ho. Surg. (ENT & Ophth.) & Cas. Off. St. Geo. Hosp. Lond.

***MOBBS, Christopher John** 17 Menotti Street, London E2 6JH — MB BS 1996 Lond.

MOBBS, Jacquelyn Mary Maryhill Practice, Elgin Health Centre, Maryhill, Elgin IV30 1AT Tel: 01343 543788 Fax: 01343 551604; 109 Duncan Drive, Bishopmill, Elgin IV30 4NH Tel: 01343 541951 — MB ChB 1970 Dundee; MRCGP 1981; FRCOG 1991, M 1975; DFFP 1996; DCH Eng. 1973. (Dundee)

***MOBBS, Joanne** Top Floor Flat, 7 Gloucester Row, Bristol BS8 4AW — MB ChB 1997 Bristol.

MOBERLY, Patience (retired) 35 Pymers Mead, Croxted Road, Dulwich, London SE21 8NH Tel: 020 8670 2680 — BM BCh 1950 Oxf.; MRCP Lond. 1954; MRCS Eng. LRCP Lond. 1950. Prev: Clin. Asst. (Paediat.) St. Thos. Hosp. Lond.

***MOBEY, Jonathan Lee** Stoneyhurst, Milestone Avenue, Charvil, Reading RG10 9TN Tel: 0118 969 2841; 47 Arlington Drive, Old Marston, Oxford OX3 0SJ Tel: 01865 468044 — BM BCh 1998 Oxf.; BM BCh Oxf 1998; MA Camb. 1995.

MOBEY, Louise Jane Stoneyhurst, Milestone Avenue, Charvil, Reading RG10 9TN — MB BS 1996 Lond.

MOBLEY, Katharine Anne Anaesthetic Department, Glenfield Hospital, Groby Road, Leicester LE3 9QP — MB BS 1978 Lond.; FFA RCS Eng. 1982. Cons. Anaesth. Glenfield Hosp. Univ. Hosp.s of Leicester NHS Trust.

MOBLEY, Richard John Wallace House Surgery, 5-11 St. Andrew Street, Hertford SG14 1HZ Tel: 01992 550541 — MB BS 1975 Lond.

MOCKETT, Robert John 39 Walsingham Road, Hove BN3 4FE Tel: 01273 325672; 24 Eaton Place, Brighton BN2 1EH Tel: 01273 686863 Fax: 01273 623402 — MB BS 1984 Newc.; MRCGP 1988. (Newcastle upon Tyne) Sch. Doctor St. Guinydeen Schoo for Deaf & St. Johns Sch. Walpole Rd. Brighton.

MOCKFORD, Brian James 45 Waringfield Avenue, Moira, Craigavon BT67 0FA Tel: 01846 613482 Email: bmockjmock@aol.com — MB BCh BAO 1997 Belf. (Queens University Belfast)

MOCKING, Theodora Petronella Dorothe Maria Maidstone Hospital Psychiatric Wing, Farm Villa, Hermitage Lane, Maidstone ME16 9QQ — Artsexamen 1992 Utrecht.

MOCKLER, Elizabeth Mary 124 High Street, Broadway WR12 7AJ — MB BCh BAO 1943 NUI; LM Nat. Matern. Hosp. Dub. 1943. Socs: BMA. Prev: Med. Regist. Windsor Chest Clinic & Clare Hall Hosp.; Asst. MOH Matern. & Child Welf. Lindsey CC; Princip. GP Birm.

MOCROFT, Andrew Paul White Haven, Lower Frith Common, Eardiston, Tenbury Wells WR15 8JU — MB ChB 1981 Birm.; MD Birm. 1993. Cons. Clin. Neurophysiol. Qu. Eliz. Neurosci. Centre Birm.

***MODARAI, Bijan** 44 Mount Avenue, London W5 2QJ — MB BS 1998 Lond.; MB BS Lond 1998.

MODARRES SADEGHI, Hamid Reza 140 Clarence Avenue, New Malden KT3 3DY — MD 1977 Pahlavi; MRCPI 1985.

MODDER, Joanna Valentina Jeanne 56A Knollys Road, Streatham, London SW16 2JX — MB BS 1987 Ibadan.

MODEL, Douglas Gerald (retired) 54 Chelsea Gate, 93 Ebury Bridge Road, London SW1W 8RB Tel: 020 7730 7353 — BSc Lond. 1961, MB BS 1965; FRCP Lond. 1986; MRCP (UK) 1971. Prev: Cons. Phys. E.bourne Health Dist.

MODELL, Professor Clare Bernadette (retired) Department of Primary Care & Population Sciences, UCLMS, 2nd floor Holborn Union Building, Whittington Campus Highgate Hill, London N19 5LW Tel: 020 7288 5733 Fax: 020 7281 8004 Email: b.modell@pcps.ucl.ac.uk — MB BChir 1964 Camb.; MA Oxf. 1955; PhD Camb. 1959; FRCP Lond. 1991; FRCOG 1994. Emer. Prof. of Community Genetics & Retd. Wellcome Princip. Reasearch Fell.; Hon. Prof. Dept. of Pub. Health & Policy Lond. Sch.. Of Hyg. & Trop. Med. Prev: Ho. Phys. (Paediat.) Univ. Coll. Hosp.

MODELL, Professor Michael (retired) Royal Free and University College London Medical School UCL, Department of Primary Care and Population Sciences, Level 2, Holborn Union Building, Highgate Hill, London N19 5LW Tel: 020 7288 3247 Fax: 020 7281 8004 Email: m.modell@pcps.ucl.ac.uk — MB BS Lond. 1960; FRCP Lond. 1986; MRCP (UK) 1970; MRCS Eng. LRCP Lond. 1960; FRCGP 1976, M 1966; DCH Eng. 1962; DObst RCOG 1961. Prof. of Primary Health Care, Dept. of Primary Care & Populat. Sci.s Univ. Coll. Lond.; Prof. of Primary Health Care; Dir. Archway Site Dept. Primary Care & Populat. Scis. Prev: GP Lond.

MODERN, Gillian Margaret 120 Arngask Road, Catford, London SE6 1XX — MB BS 1980 Lond.

MODERN

MODERN, Nigel 120 Arngask Road, London SE6 1XX — MB BS 1980 Lond.

MODGILL, Mr Vijay Kumar BUPA Hospital Elland; Elland Lane, Elland HX5 9EB; Linden Lea, Cecil Avenue, Light Cliffe, Halifax HX3 8SN Tel: 01422 202182 — MB ChB Leeds 1967; FRCS Ed. 1972; FRCS Eng. 1972. Cons. Gen. Surg. Halifax Hosps.; Regional Adviser in Surg. RCS Lond. Prev: Sen. Regist. Yorks. RHA; Regist. (Rotat.) Gen. Infirm. Leeds; Ho. Surg. St. Jas. Univ. Hosp. Leeds.

MODHA, Deborah Elaine 13 Parkway Court, Drakes Drive, St Albans AL1 5AA — MB ChB 1992 Leic.; BSc (Hons.) Surrey 1986.

MODHA, Jaisukh Shamjibhai Sandy Lane Health Centre, Sandy Lane, Skelmersdale WN8 8LA Tel: 01695 559558 Fax: 01695 726691 — MB BS 1967 Ranchi; MB BS 1967 Ranchi.

MODHA, Jitendra Dayaram Thistlemoor Road Medical Centre, 6-8 Thistlemoor Road, Peterborough PE1 3HP Tel: 01733 551988 Fax: 01733 707702; 21 Cherryfields, Orton Waterville, Peterborough PE2 5XD — LRCP LRCS Ed. LRCPS Glas. 1982.

MODHA, Nalini Jitendra Thistlemoor Road Medical Centre, 6-8 Thistlemoor Road, Peterborough PE1 3HP Tel: 01733 551988 Fax: 01733 707702; 21 Cherryfields, Orton Waterville, Peterborough PE2 5XD — MB BS 1978 Gujarat; LRCP LRCS Ed. LRCPS Glas. 1984. Police Surg. Camb. Constab. Socs: BMA; Police Surgs. Assn.

MODHA, Priyavadan Girdharlal The Medical Centre, 29 Bryant Street, Chatham ME4 5QS Tel: 01634 848913; 12 Lambourn Way, Lordswood, Chatham ME5 8PU Tel: 01634 865600 Fax: 01634 671945 — MB BS 1973 Gujarat; DFFP 1996. (B.J. Med. Coll. Ahmedabad)

MODHWADIA, Malde Mepabhai 245 Goodwood Road, Leicester LE5 6TR — MB BS 1986 Gujarat.

MODI, Amritlal Jinabhai Stag Lane Medical Centre, 245 Stag Lane, London NW9 0EF Tel: 020 8204 0777; 69 Carpenders Avenue, Watford WD19 5BP Tel: 020 8428 7234 — MB BS Poona 1966.

MODI, Bhupendra Vanravan Canon Street Medical Centre, 122 Canon Street, Leicester LE4 6NL Tel: 0116 266 1247 — MB ChB 1986 Dundee; BMSc (Hons.) (Anat.) Dund 1984, MB ChB 1986; MRCGP 1993; DRCOG 1992; DCH RCP Lond. 1991; Cert Family Plann. JCC 1991. Trainer Leicester. Prev: Trainee GP Leicester; SHO Leicester VTS; SHO & Regist. Rotat. (Gen. Med.) Tayside.

MODI, Dasharathlal Sankalchand Woodhead Road Surgery, 157 Woodhead Road, Bradford BD7 2BL Tel: 01274 502050 Fax: 01274 414308; Three Gables, 30A Bartle Close, Bradford BD7 4QU Tel: 01274 503128 — MB BS 1973 Baroda. (Med. Coll. Baroda) Prev: Trainee GP Batley; SHO (Gen. Med.) Dewsbury Gen. Hosp.; SHO (Paediat.) Staincliffe Gen. Hosp. Dewsbury.

MODI, Dipa Cripps Medical Centre, Northampton General Hospital, Cliftonville, Northampton NN1 5BD; 30 Eden Road, Oadby, Leicester LE2 4JP — MB ChB 1987 Leic. Trainee GP N.ampton Gen. Hosp. VTS. Prev: Ho. Off. (Gen. Surg.) Leicester Roy. Infirm.; Ho. Off. (Gen. Med.) Pilgrim Hosp. Boston; SHO (A & E) Pboro. Dist. Hosp.

MODI, Jaswant Kumar (retired) 40 Fitzroy Avenue, Birmingham B17 8RJ Tel: 0121 427 1825 Fax: 0121 681 2507 — BSc, MB BS Calcutta 1964. Prev: GP.

MODI, Kiran Whitley Villa Surgery, 1 Christchurch Road, Reading RG2 7AB Tel: 0118 987 1645 Fax: 0118 931 4046 — MB BS 1968 Delhi. (Lady Hardinge Med. Coll.)

MODI, Mr Mahesh Chandra 44 Farley Road, Catford, London SE6 2AB Tel: 020 8698 0334 — MB BS 1960 Nagpur; FRCS Ed. 1971.

MODI, Nand Kishore 155 Manchester Road, Swinton, Manchester M27 4FH Tel: 0161 794 6901 Fax: 0161 728 4977 — MB BS 1956 Lucknow; DLO Eng. 1963, DA 1960. (King Geo. Med. Lucknow) Socs: Fell. Manch. Med. Soc. Prev: Regist. (Otolaryngol.) N. Manch., Booth Hall & Monsall Gp. Hosp.

MODI, Neena Department of Paediatrics & Neonatal Medicine Imperial, + College Faculty of Medicine, Hammersmith Hospital, Du Cane Road, London W12 0HS Tel: 020 8383 1000 Fax: 020 8740 8281 — MB ChB 1976 Ed.; MD Ed. 1991; FRCP Lond. 1994; MRCP (UK) 1979; FRCPCH 1997. (Edinburgh) Sen. Lect. (Neonat. Paediat.) Imperial Coll. Sch. of Med. Hammersmith Hosp. Lond. Socs: Hon. Sec. Neonat. Soc. 1995-99.

***MODI, Neha** 27 Ladygate La, Ruislip HA4 7QT — MB ChB 1997 Leeds.

MODI, Sunil Kumar Whitley Villa Surgery, 1 Christchurch Road, Reading RG2 7AB Tel: 0118 987 1645 Fax: 0118 931 4046 — MB BS 1969 Bombay. (Grant Med. Coll.)

MODI, Suresh Paul 11 Quayside Close, The Moorings, Worsley, Manchester M28 1YB — MB ChB 1994 Leeds. SHO (Gen. Surg.) N.ern Gen. Hosp. Sheff.

MODI, Vinodini 3 Tenlands Road, Halesowen B63 4JJ Tel: 0121 550 7171; 40 Fitzroy Avenue, Harborne, Birmingham B17 8RJ Tel: 0121 427 1825 — MB BS 1963 Delhi. (Lady Hardinge Med. Coll.)

MODLE, William John (retired) 5 Dacre Gardens, Chigwell IG7 5HH Tel: 020 8500 6558 — MB BS Lond. 1962; MRCS Eng. LRCP Lond. 1961; FRCOG 1988, M 1966. Prev: Sen. Med. Off. DoH.

MODY, Arunkumar Sakerlal 99 Wentworth Drive, Mowsbury Park, Bedford MK41 8QE Tel: 01234 210513 — MD 1969 Gujarat; MD (Anaesth.) Gujarat 1969, MB BS 1966; DA Gujarat 1967. (B.J. Med. Coll. Ahmedabad) Assoc. Specialist (Anaesth.) Bedford Gen Hosp. (S. Wing). Prev: Clin. Asst. (Anaesth.) Bedford Gen. Hosp. (S. Wing); Regist. (Anaesth.) Ipswich Hosp.

MODY, Ashish 5 Francis Road, Hounslow TW4 7JU — MB BChir 1987 Camb.

MODY, Ramesh The Surgery, 62 Waltham Road, Carshalton SM5 1PW Tel: 020 8644 8989 Fax: 020 8661 9348; 34 Holland Avenue, Cheam, Sutton SM2 6HU Tel: 020 8643 0402 Fax: 020 8661 9348 — MB BS Bombay 1969; DObst RCOG 1972. (T.N. Med. Coll.)

MOEDERLE-LUMB, Douglas Andrew Peasholm Surgery, 98 Tennyson Avenue, Scarborough YO12 7RE Tel: 01723 361268 Fax: 01723 501335 Email: douglumb@epulse.net; Wesley House, 11 Castlegate, Old Town, Scarborough YO11 1QY — MB ChB 1987 Sheff.; MRCGP 1991; Cert. Prescribed Equiv. Exp. JCPTGP 1992. (Sheff.)

MOEN, Carl Rikard Langlands, Alfred St., Dunoon PA23 7BG — MB ChB 1991 Ed.

MOENS, Veronique Romanie Therese University Health Centre, 9 Northcourt Avenue, Reading RG2 7HE Tel: 01189 874551; 11 Allcroft Road, Reading RG1 5HJ Tel: 01734 312251 Email: vmoens@doctors.org.uk — MD 1976 Ghent. Med. Off., The Brandon Centre, 26 P. of Wales Rd, Lond. NW5 3LG. Socs: BMA; Assoc. Mem. Inst. Psycho-Sexual Med. Prev: Hon. Treas. BMA W. Berks. Div.

MOESEN, Joan Rayfield (retired) Bwthyn Cynidr, 1 Forge Road, Llangyndir, Crickhowell NP8 1LU — MRCS Eng. LRCP Lond. 1949; DCH Eng. 1951. Prev: Asst. Med. Off. Div. 7, LCC.

MOFEEZ, Mehrdad Ali 33 Vicarage Road, London SW14 8RZ — MB BS 1994 Lond.

MOFFAT, Brian Kemsley Division, St. Andrews Hospital, Billing Road, Northampton NN1 5DG — MB ChB 1973 Aberd.; FRCP Lond. 1992; MRCP (UK) 1976. Sen. Lect. (Neurol.) Guy's Hosp. & Lewisham Hosp. Lond.

MOFFAT, Christopher John Cameron Department of Histopathology, Eastbourne District General Hospital, Kings Drive, Eastbourne BN21 2UD Tel: 01323 417400 — MB BS 1986 Lond.; BA Camb. 1982; MRCPath 1993. Cons. Histopath. & Cytopath. E.bourne Dist. Gen. Hosp. Prev: Cons. (Histopath. & Cytopath.) Glenfield Hosp. Leicester Roy. Infirm.; Sen. Regist. (Histopath.) Leicester Roy. Infirm.; Regist. (Histopath.) Univ. & City Hosps. Nottm.

***MOFFAT, David** 127 Glencoats Drive, Paisley PA3 1RP — MB ChB 1994 Glas.; BSc Glas. 1991, MB ChB 1994.

MOFFAT, Mr David Andrew Department of Otolaryngology, Addenbrooke's Hospital, Hills Road, Cambridge CB2 2QQ Tel: 01223 586638 Fax: 01223 217559 Email: dam26@cam.ac.uk; Millington Lodge, 3 Millington Road, Newnham, Cambridge CB3 9HW Tel: 01223 364114 Fax: 01223 364114 — MRCS Eng. LRCP Lond. 1971; MA Camb. 1984; BSc Lond. 1969, MB BS 1971(1st Class Hons); FRCS Eng. 1976. (Royal London Hospital) Cons. Ear, Nose & Throat Surg. Addenbrooke's Hosp. Camb. & Newmarket Hosp.; Assoc. Lect. Univ. Camb.; Chairm. Intercollegiate Fac. Bd.; Cons. in Otoneurol. & Skull Base Surg.; Mem. of S.A.C. in Otolaryniology. Socs: Treas. Sect. Otol. Roy. Soc. Med.; Politzer Soc.; Founding Mem. Europ. Acad. Otol. and Neuro-otol. Prev: Cons. Ear, Nose & Throat Surg. W.minster Hosp. & Metrop. Ear, Nose & Throat

Hosp. Lond.; Sen. Regist. Lond. Hosp.; Hon. Sen. Regist. Roy. Postgrad. Med. Sch. Hammersmith Hosp.

MOFFAT, Professor David Burns, VRD 12 Wenallt Road, Rhiwbina, Cardiff CF14 6SD Tel: 029 2062 0417 — MB BS Lond. 1953; MD Lond. 1960; FRCS Eng. 1953; MRCS Eng. LRCP Lond. 1943. (St. Bart.) Prof. Emerit. Anat. Univ. Coll. Cardiff. Socs: Life Mem. Anat. Soc. Prev: Examr. Anat. RCS Eng. & Edin.; Edr. Jl. Anat.; Surg. Capt. RNR.

MOFFAT, Elizabeth Helen Department of Haematology, Royal Gwent Hospital, Newport — MB ChB 1977 Glas.; FRCPS Glas. 1992; MRCP (UK) 1982; MRCPath 1983. Clin. Research Off. Univ. Hosp. Wales Cardiff. Prev: Sen. Regist. & Regist. (Haemat.) Univ. Hosp. Wales Cardiff.

MOFFAT, Glenn Macgregor Clarkson Surgery, De-Havilland Road, Wisbech PE13 3AN Tel: 01945 583133 Fax: 01945 464465 — MB ChB 1986 Aberd.; MRCGP 1994.

MOFFAT, Graeme Lee The Medical Centre, 7 Hill Place, Arbroath DD11 1AE Tel: 01241 431144 Fax: 01241 430764; 60 High Street, Arbroath DD11 1AW — MB ChB 1981 Dundee; MRCGP 1985. GP Arbroath.

MOFFAT, Ian Angus Leith Walk Surgery, 60 Leith Walk, Edinburgh EH6 5HB Tel: 0131 554 6471 Fax: 0131 555 4964 — MB ChB 1968 Ed. (Ed.)

MOFFAT, Mr James Roxburgh Willow House, Rede, Bury St Edmunds IP29 4BE — MRCS Eng. LRCP Lond. 1943; MA Camb. 1944, MB BChir 1945; FRCS Eng. 1950; FRCS Ed. 1950. (Camb. & St. Bart.) Prev: Cons. Surg. Nuneaton & N. Warks. Health Dist.; Sen. Surg. Regist. Dudley Rd. Hosp. Birm.; Surg. Regist. Qu. Eliz. Hosp. Birm.

MOFFAT, John (retired) 53 Margaret Street, Greenock PA16 8EB Tel: 01475 720975 — MB ChB Glas. 1958; FRCPsych 1979, M 1971; DPM Eng. 1961. Prev: Phys. Supt. & Cons. Psychiat. Ravenscraig Hosp. Greenock.

MOFFAT, John Stewart, CStJ, Maj. RAMC 2 Hodgson's Court, Scotch St., Carlisle CA3 8PL Tel: 01228 531188; Seaward, Toward Point, Dunoon PA23 7UA Tel: 01369 870256 — MB ChB Glas. 1947; FRCGP 1997, M 1953. (Glas.) Adviser (Occupat. Health) John Lewis Partnership; Occupat. Health Adviser BHS; Pastoral Adviser Ch. of Scotl. Prev: Vice-Chairm. Argyll & Bute NHS Trust; RMO MoH; Ship's Surg. Anchor Line Ltd.

MOFFAT, Katrina Jean Clydebank Health Centre, Kilbowie Road, Glasgow Tel: 0141 531 6440 Fax: 0141 531 6442 Email: kjm6y@clinmed.gla.ac.uk — MB ChB 1989 Glas.; BSc (Hons.) Glas. 1986, MB ChB 1989; MRCGP 1993. GP Clydebank, Glas.; Research Lect. (Gen. Pract.) Univ. Glas.

MOFFAT, Mr Leslie Ernest Fraser Department of Urology, Ward 44, Aberdeen Royal Infirmary, Foresterhill, Aberdeen AB25 2ZN Tel: 01224 840517 Fax: 01224 840726; Tillery House, Udny, Ellon AB41 6SE Tel: 01651 842898 Fax: 01651 842019 — MB ChB 1974 Ed.; BSc Ed. 1971; FRCS Ed. 1979; FRCS 2000 Glasgow. (Edinburgh) Cons. Aberd. Roy. Infirm.; Clin. Sen. Lect. (Urol.) Univ. of Aberd.; Chairm. Working Party Urol. Cancer Serv. in Scotl. Socs: Brit. Assn. Urol. Surgs.; EAU; AUA. Prev: Chairm. MRC Working Party on Prostatic Cancer; Sen. Regist. (Urol.) W.. Infirm. Glas.; SHO & Regist. (Surg.) Roy. Infirm. Edin.

MOFFAT, Maire 70 Petersfield Avenue, Harold Hill, Romford RM3 9PD Tel: 014023 43113; 16 Fieldhouse Close, South Woodford, London E18 2RJ Tel: 020 8504 2514 — MB BCh BAO 1966 NUI. Prev: Ho. Phys. (Paediat.) & Ho. Phys. (Med.) Regional Hosp. Galway.

MOFFAT, Mary Drummond 332A Old Ford Road, Bow, London E3 5TA — MB ChB 1989 Ed.; MA Camb. 1983. Regist. (Infec. Dis. & Med. Microbiol.) Roy. Lond. Hosp. Prev: SHO (Med.) Romford, Barking, Havering & Brentwood HA; Ho. Phys. Vict. Hosp. Kirkcaldy; Ho. Off. (Surg.) Falkirk Infirm. W. Lothian.

MOFFAT, Peter Leigh, MBE (retired) Prospect House, Corvisel Road, Newton Stewart DG8 6LN — MB ChB Ed. 1969; DCH RCPS Glas. 1972. Prev: Med. Off. Penninghame Open Prison Newton Stewart.

MOFFAT, Robert Cuthbert Easton 5 Mayfield Gardens, Edinburgh EH9 2AX Tel: 01795 1289 — MB ChB 1941 Ed.; DOMS Eng. 1946. (Univ. Ed.)

MOFFAT, Robin John Russell G.Wilson, Informa Health Care, 69-77 Paul Street, London EC2A 4LQ — MRCS Eng. LRCP Lond. 1954;

FRCGP 1991, M 1962; DObst RCOG 1958. (Guy's) Sen. Forens. Med. Examr. Metrop. Police Serv. Lond. (ZD. H.Q.); Sen. Hon. Sec. Roy. Soc. Med.; Med. Examr. Securicor Custodial Servs.; Mem. Internat. Bd. Jl. Clin. Forens. Med.; Mem. Croydon Community Police Cons. Comm. Socs: Fell. (Ex-Pres.) & Hon. Trustee Med. Offs. Schs. Assn.; Roy. Soc. Med. (Ex-Pres. Clin. Forens. Med. Sect.); Assn. Police Surg. (Ex-Mem. Counc. + Medico-Legal Soc.). Prev: Princip. GP Obst. Croydon; Ho. Surg. Guy's Hosp. Lond.; Ho. Phys. & Resid. (Obst.) Croydon Hosp. Gp.

MOFFAT, Sir William Cameron, KBE, CStJ, Lt.-Gen. late RAMC Retd. Kippax, Pound Green, Freshwater PO40 9HH — MB ChB 1952 Glas.; DSc Glas. 1991; FRCS Eng. 1963; DTM & H Eng. 1960. (Glas.) Socs: Fell. Assn. Surgs. & Roy. Soc. Med. Prev: Chief Med. Advisor Brit. Red Cross Soc.; Dir. Gen. Army Med. Servs. & Surg. Gen. MoD; Jt. Prof. Milit. Surg. RCS Eng. & RAM Coll. Millbank.

MOFFAT, William James Singleton Medical Centre, 10 Singleton Court, Ashford TN23 5GR Tel: 01233 646036/646037 Fax: 01233 663150; 102 Sandyhurst Lane, Ashford TN25 4NT — MB BS 1980 Lond.; MRCGP 1987. (Char. Cross) Prev: Trainee GP St. Helier VTS Carshalton; Ho. Surg. King Edwd. VII Hosp. Midhurst; Ho. Phys. Kent & Canterbury Hosp. Canterbury.

MOFFAT, William Malcolm Unwin (retired) 16 Ferguson Drive, Musselburgh EH21 6XA Tel: 0131 665 3834 Email: wmumoffat@onetel.net.uk — MB ChB Ed. 1956; MD Ed. 1976; FRCP Lond. 1979, M 1966; FRCPCH 1997. Volun. Med. Adviser Chengelo Sch. & Educat. Trust Zambia. Prev: Cons. Paediat. Lothian HB & E. & Midlothian NHS Trust.

MOFFATT, Christopher David Sherbourne Medical Centre, 40 Oxford Street, Leamington Spa CV32 4RA Tel: 01926 424736 Fax: 01926 470884; Wootton Lodge, 10A Lillington Avenue, Leamington Spa CV32 5UJ Tel: 01926 312355 Email: drmoffatt@drkiffy.demon.co.uk — MB BS 1972 Newc.; MRCGP 1977; DRCOG 1977; Cert JCC Lond. 1977. (Newc.) Clin. Asst. (Genitourin. Med.) Warwick Hosp.

MOFFATT, John Logan (retired) 5 Millington Road, Cambridge CB3 9HW Tel: 01223 359380 — MB BChir 1947 Camb. Prev: Hosp. Pract. (Dermat.) W. Suff. Gen. Hosp. Bury St. Edmunds.

MOFFATT, Robert John Doctors Surgery, Pembroke Road, Framlingham, Woodbridge IP13 9HA Tel: 01728 723627 Fax: 01728 621064 — MB BS 1984 Lond.; BSc Norwich 1977; DRCOG 1986. (Westm.)

MOFFATT, William Henry, OBE (retired) Woodvale, School Lane, Greenisland, Carrickfergus BT38 8RF Tel: 01232 863253 — MB BCh BAO 1948 Belf.; FRCPI 1968, M 1956. Prev: Dir. N.. Irel. Hosp. Advis. Serv.

MOFFATT, William Raymond Ards Hospital, Newtownards BT23 4AS — MB BCh BAO 1949 Belf.; MRCPsych 1971; DPM RCPSI 1954. Cons. (Foren. Psychiat.) Dept. Health & Social Servs. Belf.; Cons. Psychiatr. Downshire Hosp. Downpatrick.

MOFFETT, Alan William George Hunter Health Centre, Andrew Street, East Kilbride, Glasgow G74 1AD Tel: 01355 906676 Fax: 01355 906679; Parklea, 44 Monreith Road, Newlands, Glasgow G43 2NZ Tel: 0141 632 6701 — MB ChB 1978 Glas.; MRCGP 1989; MRCOG 1987.

MOFFETT, Gale Samuel John Newtownards Health Centre, Frederick Street, Newtownards BT23 4LS Tel: 028 9181 7239; 43 Manse Road, Newtownards BT23 4TP — MB BCh BAO 1976 Belf.; DRCOG 1978.

MOFFETT, John Cuming (retired) 5 Woodford Green, Belfast BT8 6GP — MB BCh BAO 1975 Belf.; FRCA 1980. Prev: Cons. Anaesth. Belf. City Hosp.

MOFFETT, Mary (retired) Silverwood, Uplawmoor, Glasgow G78 4AG — MB ChB 1933 Ed.; DPH Ed. & Glas. 1935. Prev: Cons. Venereol. W.. RHB Scotl.

MOFFETT, Sandra Patricia Anaesthetic Department, Newcastle General Hospital, Westgate Road, Newcastle upon Tyne NE4 6BE Tel: 0191 273 8811 — MB BChir 1973 Camb.; MA, MB Camb. 1973, BChir 1972; LMSSA Lond. 1972; FFA RCS Eng. 1977. (Camb. & King's Coll. Hosp.) Cons. Anaesth. Newc. Gen. Hosp.

MOFFITT, Deborah Louise 13 Velmore Road, Eastleigh SO53 3HD — MB BS 1992 Lond.; BSc Lond. 1989; MRCP (UK) 1996. (Univ. Coll. & Middlx. Hosp. Lond.) Specialist Regist. (Dermat.) Bristol Roy. Infirm. Prev: SHO (Gen. Med.) Cheltenham

MOFFITT

Gen. Hosp.; SHO (Gen. Med.) Glos. Roy. Hosp.; SHO (Cas.) W.on Gen. Hosp.

MOFFITT, John Andrew 119 Rowe Court, Reading RG30 2HZ Tel: 01734 393538 — LRCPI & LM, LRSCI & LM 1952; LRCPI & LM, LRSCI & LM 1952; DPH Eng. 1960. (RCSI) Prev: Maj. RCAMC; Regist. Holloway Sanat. Virginia Water; Assoc. Specialist Fair Mile Hosp. Oxon.

MOFFITT, Peter Ernest (retired) Honeysuckle House, 24 Church Lane, Bitton, Bristol BS30 6LH Tel: 0117 932 2392 — BM BCh Oxf. 1957; DObst RCOG 1959. Prev: GP Bristol.

MOFFITT, Phillip Andrew 32 St Bedes, East Boldon NE36 0LF — MB BS 1980 Lond. (St. Mary's) GP Sunderland.

MOFFITT, Robert Malcolm (retired) Cuckoo Hill, The Rise, Haverbreaks, Lancaster LA1 5XD Tel: 01524 63977 — MB BS 1956 Lond.; MA Camb. 1952; MRCP (UK) 1977; FRCGP 1983, M 1964; DO Eng. 1964; DObst RCOG 1959. Sen. Med. Off. Univ. Lancaster. Prev: Ho. Phys. Dept. Nerv. Dis. & Ho. Phys. St. Mary's Hosp. Lond.

MOFFITT, Sandra Jane The Old Inn, Flush House Lane, Holmbridge, Holmfirth, Huddersfield HD7 1QD — MB ChB 1983 Birm.; MRCGP (Distinc.) 1987; DRCOG 1986.

MOFFITT, Sandra Jane Health Centre, Iveldale Drive, Shefford SG17 5AU Tel: 01462 814899; Southlands, Mill Lane, St. Ippollitts, Hitchin SG4 7NN Tel: 01462 450182 — MB BS 1984 Newc.; MRCP (UK) 1988. (Newc. u. Tyne)

MOFFITT, Virginia Kerry St Richard's Hospital, Spitalfield Lane, Chichester PO19 4SE Tel: 01243 788122 — BSc (Physiol with Basic Med. Sci) Lond. 1986, MB BS 1989; MRCP (UK) 1995. (Char. Cross & Westm.) Staff Grade Phsy. (Elderly Care & Neurol.). Prev: SHO (Med.) N. Hants. Hosp. Basingstoke.; Research SHO (Neurosci.s) Wessex Neurol. Centre Soton. Gen. Hosp.; SHO (Geriat. Med.) Soton. Gen. Hosp.

MOFFOOT, Anthony Pelham Robertson 14 Cambridge Gardens, Edinburgh EH6 5DJ — MB ChB 1982 Ed.; MRCPsych 1987. Hon. Sen. Regist. Roy. Edin. Hosp.; Cons. Psychiat. Rosscynlee Hosp. Roslin Midlothian.

MOFTAH, Mr Farid Samir 13 The Old Yews, Longfield DA3 7JS Tel: 01474 709919 Fax: 01474 709919 — MB BCh 1976 Cairo; FRCS Glas. 1986. Cons (Orthop. Surg.) Joyce Green Hosp. Dartford, Kent. Socs: BMA.

MOGAN, John Edward Martins Oak Surgery, 36 High Street, Battle TN33 0EA Tel: 01424 772263/772060 — MB ChB 1975 Manch.; DRCOG 1981; Cert. JCC Lond. 1981. Prev: Regist. (Med.) P.ss Margt. Hosp. Swindon; SHO (Neurol.) N. Manch. Gen. Hosp.; SHO (Paediat.) Booth Hall Childr. Hosp. Manch.

MOGANASUNDRAM, Shyamala Guy's Hospital, Department of Anaesthetics, St Thomas St., London E1 9RT Tel: 020 7955 4051; 131 Marsham Court, Marsham St, London SW1P 4LB Tel: 020 7828 4556 — MB ChB 1991 Bristol; BSc (Hons.) 1988; FRCA 1996. (University of Bristol) Specialist Regist. (Anaesth.) Guy's Hosp. Lond. Socs: BMA; Assn. Anaesth. GB & Irel.; Fell. Roy. Soc. Med. Prev: SHO (Anaesth.) Univ. Hosp. Lewisham Lond.; Med. Off. (Anaesth.) Ipok Hosp. Malaysia; Ho. Off. (Med.) Bristol Roy. Infirm.

MOGER, Philip William The Health Centre, The Green, Upper Poppleton, York YO26 6EQ Tel: 01904 794322 Fax: 01904 788084; Glen Hyrst, 75 Millfield Lane, Nether Poppleton, York YO26 6NA — MB ChB 1972 Leeds; BSc (Hons. Physiol.) Leeds 1969.

MOGEY, George Alexander (retired) Whitecroft, Tweeddale Avenue, Gifford, Haddington EH41 4QN Tel: 01620 810803 Email: mogey@tesco.net — MD 1957 Belf.; MD (Commend.) Belf. 1957, MB BCh BAO 1940. Prev: Sec. Counc. Postgrad. Med. Educat. Eng. & Wales.

MOGFORD, Nicola Jayne 25 Coed y Brenin, Maesycoed, Pontypridd CF37 1QE — BM 1993 Soton.

***MOGG, Andrew James** 35 Barnhill Road, Marlow SL7 3EY — MB BS 1994 Lond.

MOGG, Elizabeth Jane 35 Barnhill Road, Marlow SL7 3EY — MB ChB 1995 Birm.; ChB Birm. 1995.

MOGHAL, Arif Mahmood 37 Morlais Street, Cardiff CF23 5HQ — BM 1993 Soton.; FRCA 1998; Exam. Bd. RCA 1998. (Southamp.) Spcialist Regist. Anaesth. Mersey Deanary. Socs: MRCAnaesth.

MOGHAL, Asma 33 Nelmes Way, Emerson Park, Hornchurch RM11 2QY — MB BS 1972 Karachi; MRCS Eng. LRCP Lond. 1979; DA Eng. 1976. (Dow Med. Coll.) Prev: Ho. Surg. & SHO (Anaesth.) Gt. Yarmouth & Gorleston Gen. Hosp.; SHO (O & G) Rochford Gen. Hosp.

MOGHAL, Israr Ahmed The Surgery, 188 Ripple Road, Barking IG11 7PR Tel: 020 8594 0212 Fax: 020 8594 2438 — MB BS 1968 Karachi.

MOGHISSI, Alexander James Holborn Medical Centre, 64 Lambs Conduit Street, London WC1N 3NA Tel: 020 7405 3541 Fax: 02 7404 8198; 13 Princess Court, 105 Hornsey Lane, London N6 5XD — MB BS 1982 Lond.; MRCGP 1988. (Middlx.) GP Tutor UCH & Middlx. Hosp. Sch. Med.; FHSA Clin. Asst. Camden Refugee Project. Prev: Trainee GP Middlx. Hosp. VTS; Trainee GP Covent Gdn. Med. Centre.

MOGHISSI, Professor Keyvan The Yorkshire Laser Centre, Goole & District Hospital, Woodland Avenue, Goole DN14 6RX Tel: 01724 290456 Email: k.moghissi@breathemail.net; Lime Tree House, 3 West Leys Park, Swanland, North Ferriby HU14 3LS Tel: 01482 632197 — MD Geneva 1954, MB 1950, Med. Specialist in Surg 1958; FRCS Eng. 1983; FRCS Ed. 1968; LAH Dub. 1959. (Geneva) Cons. Cardiothoracic Surg. Dir. Yorks. Laser Centre; Hon. Cons. Cardiothoracic Surg. Scunthorpe & Goole Hosps. Trust; Hon. Prof. Physics & Laser Univ. Hull. Socs: (Ex-Pres.) Europ. Assn. Cardiothoracic Surg.; Soc. of Cardiothoracic Surgs. GB & Irel.; Sen. Mem. Brit. Thoracic Soc. Prev: Cons. Thoracic Surg. BUPA Hosp. Hull & E. Riding; Cons. Cardio-Thoracic Surg. Castle Hill Hosp. Cottingham; Sen. Regist. (Cardiothoracic) Hammersmith & Roy. Post. Grad. Med. Sch.

***MOGHUL, Shehram** 89 Montrose Avenue, Luton LU3 1HP — BM 1994 Soton.

MOHABIR, Nigel Ashok Bridge Medical Centre, Wassand Close, Three Bridges Nam, Crawley RH10 1LL Tel: 01293 526025 — MB ChB 1989 Aberd.; DRCOG 1994. GP Princip.

MOHAJER, Ceri Jane 9 Crossfield Avenue, Porthcawl CF36 3LA — MB BCh 1982 Wales.

MOHAJER, Michele Parvaneh Meir Health Centre, Saracen Way, Meir, Stoke-on-Trent ST3 7DS — BM BS 1983 Nottm.; BMedSci Nottm. 1981, BM BS 1983; MRCOG 1988. Prev: Regist. (Obsts. & Gyn.) City Hosp. Nottm. Regist. (Obsts. & Gyn.) City Hosp. Nottm.; SHO (Orthop.) Qu.'s Med. Centre Nottm.

MOHAJER, Seyed Kim Parviz Heol Fach Surgery, Heol Fach, North Cornelly, Bridgend CF33 4LD Tel: 01656 740345 Fax: 01656 740872; 9 Crossfield Avenue, Porthcawl CF36 3LA Tel: 01656 784717 — MB BCh 1981 Wales; DCH RCP Lond. 1986; DRCOG 1985. (Welsh Nat. Sch. Med.) Director - Bridgend Gen. Practitioner out of Hours Co-op., Bridgend. Socs: (Ex-Chairm.) Ogwr Med. Soc.

MOHAJERIN, Hedyeh 108 Queenshill Avenue, Leeds LS17 6BP Tel: 0113 268 6075 — MB ChB 1994 Leeds. Socs: BMA.

MOHAMAD, Jamal Azmi 25 Tolchurch, Dartmouth Close, London W11 1DT — MB BS 1985 Malaya.

MOHAMAD, Mr Kuttaiba Kassim Fakry St Margaret's Doctors Consulting Rooms, Chesterfield S40 4SY Tel: 01246 232511 Fax: 01246 232511 Email: k.mohamad@bigfoot.com; 191 Old Road, Brampton, Chesterfield S40 3QH — MB ChB Baghdad 1964; FRCS Ed. 1978; FRCOphth 1991; FRCPS Glas. 1978; DO RCS Eng. 1971. Cons. Ophth. Surg. Chesterfield & N. Derbysh. Roy. Hosp. Socs: Midl. Ophthalm. Soc.; Amer. Acad. Ophth.

MOHAMED, Abd Halim 46 Rose Lane, Liverpool L18 5ED — MB ChB 1993 Liverp.

MOHAMED, Mr Abdel Rahman Abdel Aziz 34 Webster Avenue, Scunthorpe DN15 7DU Tel: 01724 282282 — MB BS 1974 Khartoum; PhD Glas. 1990; FRCS Glas. 1989. Sen. Regist. (A & E) Chase Farm Hosp. Enfield Middlx.

MOHAMED, Abdul Hassanali Bridge Medical Centre, Wassand Close, Three Bridges Road, Crawley RH10 1LL Tel: 01293 526025 — LRCPI & LM, LRSCI & LM 1967; LRCPI & LM, LRSCI & LM 1967. (RCSI) Socs: BMA. Prev: SHO (Obst.) Derby City Hosp.; SHO (Gen. Surg.) Lymington Hosp.; Cas. Off. Mercer's Hosp. Dub.

MOHAMED, Adam Omer 5 Rowallan Way, Priorslee, Telford TF2 9RX — MB BS 1979 Khartoum; MRCP (UK) 1992.

MOHAMED, Ali Moses Saleh 17 Conduit Road, London SE18 7AJ — Ptychio Iatrikes 1977 Athens.

MOHAMED, Anissa Woodways, Balcombe Road, Crawley RH10 7SY Email: anissa@am14.freeserve.co.uk — MB BS 1994 Lond.; MRCGP 1998; DFFP 1997; MA Camb. 1994.

MOHAMMED

*MOHAMED, Faheez 1F2, 67 Warrender Park Road, Marchmont, Edinburgh EH8 9EZ — MB ChB 1996 Ed.

MOHAMED, Galal Eldin Yousif 18 Rowan Close, Almond Avenue, London W5 4YJ — MB BS 1975 Khartoum.

MOHAMED, Helmy Ezzat Abdel Moty Department of Anaesthetics, Royal Gwent Hospital, Cardiff Road, Newport NP20 2UB — MB BCh 1979 Ain Shams.

MOHAMED, Huda Hassan Department of Public Health, Warwickshire Health Authority, Market Street, Westgate House, Warwick CV34 4DE Tel: 01926 493491 Fax: 01926 478123 Email: huda.mohamed@warwick-ha.wmids.nhs.uk; 7 Appleby Grove, Solihull B90 4SG Tel: 0121 745 5091 — MB BCh 1979 Ain Shams; MFPHM; MCM. (Ain Shams, Egypt) Cons. in Communicable Dis. Control, Warks.; Master Community Med. Khartoum Univ. 1991; Mem.ship of the Fac. of Pub. Health Med. Prev: Regist. (Pub. Health) Khartoum Univ.; SpR in Shoihull Health Auth.

MOHAMED, Merghani Salman Cottage 27, Inverclyde Royal Hospital, Greenock PA16 0XN Tel: 01475 633777 — MB ChB 1982 Alexandria; MRCOG 1993.

MOHAMED, Mohamed Abdul Mohssin 56 Princes Avenue, Woodford Green IG8 0LP Tel: 020 8504 7619 Fax: 020 8556 0372 — MB ChB 1972 Baghdad; MSc (Nuclear Med.) Lond. 1994; Dip. Thoracic Med. Lond 1986. Socs: BMA Memer; Small Pract.s Assn.

MOHAMED, Mr Mohamed Sadrudin Hasham 84 Watson Avenue, Chatham ME5 9SN — MB BS 1986 Lond.; FRCS Ed. 1991; MS (Lond.) 1997; FRCS (Gen.) 1999. (Middlx. Hosp. Med. Sch.) Specialist Regist. (Gen. Surg.) William Harvey Hosp. Ashford. Socs: Affil. Mem. Assn. Surg. GB & Irel.; Affil. Mem. Vasc. Surg. Soc. GB & Irel. Prev: Specialist Regist. (Gen. Surg.) Kent & Sussex Hosp. Tunbridge Wells; Specialist Regist. St Thomas' Hosp., Lond.; Specialist Regist. (Gen. Surg.) Maidstone Hosp. Kent.

MOHAMED, Moinuddin 41 Chatsworth Street, Leicester LE2 0FR Email: m.d.mohamed@leeds.ac.uk — MB ChB 1991 Sheff.; FRCOphth 1996. Specialist Regist. (Opthalmol.) Yorks. Regional Rotat. Train. Scheme St. James Univ. Hosp. Leeds; Wellcome Trust Clin. Research Fell., Vision Research Gp., Molecular Med., Univ. of Leeds. Prev: SHO (Ophth.) Roy. Hallamshire Hosp. Sheff.; SHO (Neurolsurg.) Roy. Hallamshire Hosp. Sheff.; Demonst. (Anat. & Physiol.) Univ. Sheff.

MOHAMED, Munira Sultan 5 Heathfield, Martlesham Heath, Ipswich IP5 3UB — MB BS 1982 Karachi.

MOHAMED, Mustafa Yousif 133 Heritage Park, St. Mellons, Cardiff CF3 0DS — MB BS 1973 Khartoum, Sudan; MRCPI 1982.

*MOHAMED, Quresh Amir 8 St Andrews Road, Heaton Moor, Stockport SK4 4BD Email: qureshm@yahoo.com — BM 1995 Soton.; BSc (1st cl. Hons) Biomed. Sci. Soton 1994; MRCOPHTH Pt I 1997.

MOHAMED, Ramzan 16 Waverley Grove, London N3 3PX — MB ChB 1980 Aberd.

MOHAMED, Wael Nouh Abd El-Rahim Linden Unit, Hospital of St Cross, Barby Road, Rugby CV22 5PX Tel: 01788 545253 Fax: 01788 545277; 2 Birchmoor Close, Olton, Birmingham B28 9NS Tel: 0121 777 7785 — MB ChB 1975 Ain Shams; MB ChB Ain Shams Egypt 1975; MRCS Eng. LRCP Lond. 1982; MRCPsych 1991. Cons. Old Age Psychiat. Hosp. St. Cross Rugby.

*MOHAMED HAFLAH, Nor Hazla 480 Rochdale Road, Oldham OL1 2JN — MB ChB 1997 Manch.

*MOHAMED KHALIL, Mas Rina Yasmin 70 Llanishen Street, Cardiff CF14 3QD — MB BCh 1997 Wales.

MOHAMED RELA, Mr Shamsudin 7 Bavent Road, Camberwell, London SE5 9RY Tel: 020 7326 3575 — MB BS 1982 Madras; MS Madras 1987; FRCS Ed. 1988.

MOHAMEDAIN, Mr Hamid Mohamed 2 Blackthorne, Brambleside, Kettering NN16 9BH — MB BS 1981 Khartoum; FRCS Ed. 1992.

MOHAMEDALI, Akber Grove Medical Centre, Windlass Place, London SE8 3QH Tel: 020 8692 1882 Fax: 020 8691 1703; 7 Liphook Crescent, London SE23 3BN — MB ChB 1976 Manch.; MSc Lond. 1994; MRCP (UK) 1979.

MOHAMMAD, Dost Copson Street Surgery, 6 Copson Street, Withington, Manchester M20 9BU Tel: 0161 445 2181 — MB BS 1969 Calcutta; DTCD Wales 1973. (Nilratan Sircar Med. Coll.) GP Manch. FPC; Clin. Asst. (Rheum. & Rehabil. Med.) Manch. Roy.

Infirm. Prev: Clin. Asst. (Haemat.) Manch. Roy. Infirm.; Trainee GP Manch.; Regist. (Thoracic Med.) Manch. AHA (T).

MOHAMMED, Mr Saeed 37 Briardene Crescent, Newcastle upon Tyne NE3 4RX — MB ChB 1988 Glas.; FRCS Glas. 1992. Specialist Regist. (N.ern Rotat.) (Orthop.).

MOHAMMED, Tahira Saleem 88 The Heights, Northolt UB5 4BS — MB ChB 1991 Glas.; MRCGP Lond. 1996; DCH Lond. 1995; DFFP Lond. 1996; DRCOG Lond. 1996.

MOHAMMED, Warid Alfeshan Medical Centre, 3 Shirley Road, Cheetham, Manchester M8 0WB Tel: 0161 795 0200 Fax: 0161 795 4908; 24 Fairway, Prestwich, Manchester M25 0JH — MB BS 1964 Peshawar. (Khyber Med. Coll., Peshawar, Pakistan) Prev: Med. Off. i/c Civil Hosp. Shakardara; SHO Seafield Childr. Hosp. Ayr; Ho. Off. Aberd. Roy. Infirm.

*MOHAMMAD ISA, Hazlita Flat 39, 1 Stewart St., London E14 3EX — MB ChB 1997 Glas.

MOHAMMED, Abdullah Ali 67 Hartington Road, West Derby, Liverpool L12 8QN — MB ChB 1995 Glas.

MOHAMMED, Amjid 53 Springdale Avenue, Huddersfield HD1 3NE — MB ChB 1993 Liverp.

MOHAMMED, Mr Aslam Chorley & South Ribble District General Hospital, Chorley PR7 1PP Tel: 01257 245269 Fax: 01257 247119; The Hip Centre, Wrightington Hospital for Joint Disease, Hall Lane, Appley Bridge, Wigan WN6 9EP Tel: 01257 256304 Fax: 01257 256291 — MB BCh Wales 1984; FRCS (Orth.) 1995; FRCS Lond. 1990. (Welsh Nat. Coll. Med.) Cons. Orthop. Surg. Hip Centre Wrightington Hosp. Wigan. Socs: BMA (Old OsW.rians); Brit. Orthop. Assn. Prev: Sen. Regist. Rotat. Stoke & OsW.ry.

MOHAMMED, Emile Pedro 28 Firth Road, Troon KA10 6TF — MB ChB 1993 Aberd.

MOHAMMED, Hanif South Grange Medical Centre, Trunk Road, Eston, Middlesbrough TS6 9QG Tel: 01642 467001 Fax: 01642 463334; 2(B) Cargo Fleet Lane, Ormsby, Middlesbrough TS3 0LW Tel: 01642 318644 — MB ChB 1977 Manch. Clin. Asst. (Learning Disabil.) Middlesbrough.

MOHAMMED, Hashim Yousif St Lukes Hospital, Marton Road, Middlesbrough TS4 3AF Tel: 01642 850850 Fax: 01642 595430 — MB BS 1978 Khartoum; MSc Clin. Trop. Med. Lond. 1986; DPM RCPSI 1991; DTM & H RCP Lond. 1986. (Univ. of Khartoum) Cons. (Psychiat.) St. Lukes Hosp. Middlesbrough; Asst. Prof. St. Geo. Univ. Grenada, W. Indies. Prev: Assoc. Specialist (Gen. Psychiat.) St. Ann's Hosp. Poole; Regist. (Child & Adult Psychiat.) Highcroft Winchester Hants; Regist. (Child Psychiat.) Darlington Memor. Hosp.

MOHAMMED, Idris 34 Townshend Road, London NW8 6LE Tel: 020 7722 3564 — MRCS Eng. LRCP Lond. 1974; MD Ibadan 1977, MB BS 1969; MRCPI 1975; DTM & H Eng. 1975. (Ibadan) Research Fell. MRC Immunol. Gp. Bone & Jt. Research Unit Lond.; Hosp. Med. Coll.; Hon. Clin. Asst. Lond. Hosp. Socs: BMA. Prev: SHO (Gen. Med.) Univ. Coll. Hosp. Ibadan, Nigeria; Regist. (Gen. Med.) Ahmadu Bello Univ. Hosp. Zaria, Nigeria; Research Fell. (Immunol.) MRC Rheum. Research Unit Canad. Red Cross.

MOHAMMED, Imtiyaz 166 Anthony Road, Alum Rock, Birmingham B8 3AN — MB BS 1993 Lond.; BSc Hons. 1991; MRCE UK 1997. (Univ. Coll. Of Lond. & Middlesex School of Med.) Specialist Regist. Gastroentrol. W. Midl. Socs: BSG; Midl. Gastroentrol. Soc.

MOHAMMED, Khali Ibrahim 8 The Spinney, Bradwell, Milton Keynes MK13 9BX — MB ChB 1976 Baghdad.

MOHAMMED, Mohammed Abd El-Moneim Ground Floor, The Poplar, St. Matthews Road, Burntwood, Walsall WS7 9ES; 23 California Grove, Chase Terrace, Walsall WS7 8BG — MB BCh 1975 Ain Shams; LMSSA 1988.

MOHAMMED, Nazia 27 Clincarthill Road, Rutherglen, Glasgow G73 2LF — MB ChB 1992 Glas. Specialist Regist. (Oncol.) DeatsonOncol.Centre Glas.

MOHAMMED, Osman El Nur Hartington Street Surgery, 26 Hartington Street, Barrow-in-Furness LA14 5SL Tel: 01229 820250 Fax: 01229 871468.

MOHAMMED, Mr Paul Desiderius Department of Plastic Surgery, Royal Victoria Infirmary, Queen Victoria Road, Newcastle upon Tyne NE1 4LP — MB BS 1989 W. Indies; FRCS Ed. 1995. (Univ. W. Indies) Specialist Regist. Plastic & Reconstruc. Surg. Newcaste-upon-Tyne. Prev: Vis. Specialist Regist. (Plastic Surg.) Lister Hosp. Stevenage.

MOHAMMED

MOHAMMED, Rasheed Azard 40 Craven Avenue, Silsden, Keighley BD20 0HH Tel: 01535 657984 Email: chancamohammed@freeserve.co.uk — MB BS 1989 West Indies. (Univ. West Indies) Staff Grade (Eld. Med.) Airedale Gen. Hosp. Socs: Trinidad & Tobago Med. Assn. Prev: Sen. SHO (Gen. Med. & Cardiol.) Ipswich Dist. Hosp.; SHO (Gen. Med.) Thanet Dist. Gen. Hosp.; Regist., SHO & Ho. Off. Port of Spain Hosp., Trinidad.

MOHAMMED, Mr Riaz Dept. of Surg., The Victoria Infirmary, Langside Road, Langside, Glasgow G42 9TY Tel: 0141 201 6000 Fax: 0141 201 5206 — MB ChB 1974 Glas.; MD Glas. 1982; FRCS Ed. 1994; FRCS Glas. 1978. Cons. Gen. Surg. Fife Health Bd. Dunfermline, Cons. Gen. and Upper Gastro-Intestimal Surg., S. Glas. NHS Trust, Gtr. Glas. Health Bd., Glas. Socs: Assn. Upper Gastro-intestinal Surg. UK & Irel.; Assn. of Surg.s of Gt. Britain and Irel.; Assn. of Endoscopic Surg.s of Gt. Britain and Irel. Prev: Cons. Gen. Surg. and Clin. Director for Surg., Fife Heath Bd., Dumfermline.

MOHAMMED, Shezara Adeline 36 Oakcroft Road, Lewisham, London SE13 7ED — MB BS 1987 Lond.

MOHAMMED, Soraya Department of Radiology, Royal Cornwall Hospital Trust, Treliske Hospital, Truro TR1 3LJ Tel: 01872 274242; Mill Farm, Scawswater, Idless, Truro TR4 9QS Email: sorayamohammed@rcht.swest.nhs.uk — MB ChB 1990 Glas.; MRCP (UK) 1993; FRCR 1996. (Glas.) Cons. Radiologist Roy. Cornw. Hosp.s Trust Treliske Hosp. Truro Cornw. Prev: Sen. Regist. (Radiol.) Treliske Hosp. Cornw.; Career Regist. (Radiol.) W. Glas. Hosps. Univ. NHS Trust; Sen. Regist. (Radiol.) Roy. Infirm. Edin.

MOHAMMED, Tariq Hillside, 4 Billinge End Road, Blackburn BB2 6PY — MB ChB 1982 Manch.; MRCP Ed. 1986. Research Regist. St. Mary's Hosp. Manch. Socs: Med. Protec. Soc. Prev: SHO & Regist. Roy. Manch. Childr. Hosp. Salford; Regist. Bolton Dist. Gen. Hosp.; SHO Booth Hall Childr. Hosp. Manch.

MOHAMMED, Yahaya Isah 50 Donaldson Road, London SE18 3JY — MB BS 1986 Ahmadu Bello Univ. Nigeria.

MOHAMMED, Yasin Westmuir Medical Centre, 109 Crail Street, Glasgow G31 5RA Tel: 0141 554 4253 Fax: 0141 550 0177 — MB ChB 1979 Manch.; BSc (Med. Sci.) St. And. 1975; MRCGP 1985. (Manch.) GP Glas.; Research Asst. (Med.) Vict. Hosp. Glas. HB. Prev: Regist. (Surg.) St. Helens & Whiston Hosps. Merseyside.

MOHAMMED FAUZI, Abdul Rani 256 Stainforth Road, Sheffield S9 3FS — MB ChB 1992 Sheff.

MOHAMMED ISMAIL KADAR SHA, Shahul Hameed The Surgery, Doncaster Road, Goldthorpe, Rotherham S63 9JB Tel: 01709 893678 — MB BS 1969 Madras.

MOHAN, Mr Amitabh Jagadish Saran The Surgery, Bennett Way, Darenth, Dartford DA2 7JU Tel: 01474 707662 Fax: 01474 708940; 3 Wyvern Close, Dartford DA1 2NA — MB BS 1973 Poona; MS Allahabad 1975; MB BS Poora 1973; DLO RCS Eng. 1978. (Armed Forces Med. Coll. Prona, India)

MOHAN, Bose Vattathara Hughenden, 1 Henry Smiths Terrace, Headland, Hartlepool TS24 0PD — MB BS 1986 Bombay. Specialist Regist. Med.

MOHAN, Chandra Balakrishnan John Black Day Hospital, 4 Maple Leaf Drive, Marston Green, Birmingham B37 7JB Tel: 0121 788 0038 Fax: 0121 788 2231; 9 Chadstone Close, Monkspath, Solihull B90 4YX Tel: 0121 733 8621 — MB BS 1977 Kerala, India; MD Kerala, India 1982; DPM RCPSI 1991. SCMO (Elderly Ment. Illness) John Black day Hosp. Solihull Healthcare NHS Trust. Prev: Regist. (Psychiat.) Severalls Hosp. Colchester.

MOHAN, Damian James Broadmoor Hospital, Crowthorne RG45 7EG Tel: 01344 7731 111 Email: d.mohan@bmth.online — MB BCh BAO 1985 Dub.; MRCPsych 1993; DPM RCPSI 1992; DObstRCPI 1990; MICGP 1989; DCH Dub. 1986. (Trinity Coll. Dub.) Cons. Forens. Psychiat. Prev: Lect. (Forens. Psych) BRd.moor Hosp. + Univ. of Soton; Regist. (Forens. Psychiat.) Centr. Ment. Hosp. Dub.; Regist. Rotat. St. Patricks Hosp. Dub.

***MOHAN, Diviya** 66 Farndon Way, Oxton, Birkenhead CH43 2NP — MB BCh 1998 Wales.

MOHAN, Govindaraj Victoria Road Surgery, 82 Victoria Road, Oulton Broad, Lowestoft NR33 9LU Tel: 01502 572368 Fax: 01502 537035 — MB BS 1969 Madras; MB BS 1969 Madras.

MOHAN, Harry Bonthala Christmas Maltings Surgery, Camps Road, Haverhill CB9 8HF Tel: 01440 702010 Fax: 01440 714761 — MB BS 1972 Osmania.

MOHAN, Indira Chandra BHB Community Trust, Willows, 117 Suttons Lane, Hornchurch RM12 6RS Tel: 01708 465462 Fax: 01708 465158; Chinaarkee, 33B Woodlands Avenue, Emerson Park, Hornchurch RM11 2QT — MB BS 1971 Madras; DRCOG Lond. 1978; MSc (Audiological Medicine) Manchester University. SCMO, Stockport Community Drug Team. Socs: BMA; Brit. Soc. Audiol.; Assoc. Mem. Roy. Coll. Paediat. Child Health. Prev: SCMO, Bolton Community Drug Team; Assoc. Specialist (Paediat. Audiol.) Audiol. BHB Community Trust HornCh.

MOHAN, Kumaran Kondath 27 Purley Vale, Purley CR8 2DU — LRCP LRCS Ed. LRCPS Glas. 1985; MB BS Calicut 1979. SHO Med. for Elderly Leeds W.. HA, (Teachg.) Middleton & WharfedaleGen. Hosp. W. Yorks. Prev: SHO (A & E Med.) & Ho. Phys. James Paget Hosp. Gt. Yarmouth; Ho. Surg. Cumbld. Infirm. Carlisle.

MOHAN, Meyyammai 56/4 Orchard Brae Avenue, Edinburgh EH4 2HN — MB BS 1986 Madras; FRCS Ed. 1992.

MOHAN, Neesha 36 Purfield Drive, Wargrave, Reading RG10 8AR — MB BS 1989 Lond.; DRCOG 1993. Trainee GP Henley on Thames.

MOHAN, Shruti 3 Wyvern Close, Dartford DA1 2NA — MB ChB 1998 Bristol. (Bristol Univ) SHO (O & G) Chelsea & W.minster Hosp. Lond. Prev: Ho. Off. Med. S.mead Hosp. Bristol; Ho. Off. Surg. Bristol Roy. Infirm.

MOHAN, Thilagavathy Chandra Sunray Surgery, 97 Warren Drive South, Surbiton KT5 9QD Tel: 020 8330 4056 Fax: 020 8335 4080; 48 Blakes Avenue, New Malden KT3 6RF Tel: 020 8942 1801 — MB BS 1973 Ceylon; MRCS Eng. LRCP Lond. 1977; LRCP LRCS Ed. LRCPS Glas. 1977; MRCGP 1983; DObst. RCOG 1980. (Colombo) Prev: Med. Off. Kingston & Esher HA; SHO (Obst.) S. Lond. Hosp. Wom.; SHO (Geriat. Med.) Tolworth Hosp. & Kingston & Richmond AHA.

MOHAN, Thota Chandra The Surgery, 35 Maplestead Road, Dagenham RM9 4XH Tel: 020 8595 0017 Fax: 020 8595 7741 — MB BS 1975 Madras.

***MOHAN, Vikas** 28 Francis Way, Slough SL1 5PJ — BM BCh 1994 Oxf.; MA Camb. 1995, BA 1991.

MOHAN ADYANTHAYA, Kedembadi Raja Ram Grange Medical Group, 21a Kersiebank Avenue, Grangemouth FK3 9EL Tel: 01324 665533 Fax: 01324 665693 — MB BS 1965 Mysore. (Mysore) GP Grangemouth.

MOHAN KRISHNA, Nama 90 Parkstone Road, Hastings TN34 2NU — MB BS 1975 Madras. Staff. Anaesth. Hastings Health Unit.

MOHANAN, Koratty Swaroopam Sandringham Medical Centre, 1A Aigburth Road, Liverpool L17 4JP Tel: 0151 727 1352 — MB BS 1973 Kerala; MRCGP 1999; Dip. Prescribing Sci. 1999.

MOHANARUBAN, Kanthaya Withybush General Hospital, Haverfordwest SA61 2PZ Tel: 01437 773328; 104 Cardigan Road, Haverfordwest SA61 2QS — MB BS 1975 Sri Lanka; MRCS Eng. LRCP Lond. 1979; FRCP 2000 UK. Cons. Phys. with an interest in Elderly Med. Socs: BMA; Brit. Geriat. Soc. Prev: Sen. Regist. (Geriat. Med.) Cardiff Roy. Infirm.; Regist. (Haemat.) Whipps Cross Hosp. Lond.

MOHANKUMAR, Srirangam 10 Argyll Road, Cheltenham GL53 7PZ — MB BS 1985 Madras.

MOHANNA, Kay Spires Practice, St Chads Health Centre, Lichfield DE14 1SL Tel: 01283 564848 Fax: 01283 569416; 19 Windham Wood Close, Fradley, Lichfield NS13 8UZ Tel: 01543 415764 Email: kaymohanna@aol.com — MB ChB 1988 Birm.; Posgraduate Cert. Redical Educat. 1999 Dund.; MA (Med. Ethics) Keele Univ. 1992; MRCGP 1994; DCH RCP Lond. 1992. (Birm.) GP; Sen. Lect. Redical Educat. Staffs. Univ.

***MOHANNA, Pari-Naz** Royal Free Hospital, Pond St., Hampstead, London NW3 Tel: 020 7794 0500; 36 Falmouth House, Clarendon Place, London W2 2NT Tel: 020 7262 7444 — MB BS 1994 Lond.; MB BS (Hons.) Lond. 1994.

MOHANRAJ, Mallika 29 Timothy Lane, Batley WF17 0BA — MD 1974 Madras; MD (Microbiol.) Madras 1974, MB BS 1968; MRCPath 1979; DGO Madras 1970. (Stanley Med. Coll.) Sen. Regist. St. Geo. Hosp. Lond.

MOHANTY, Artatran Hollins Road Surgery, 796 Hollins Road, Oldham OL8 4SA Tel: 0161 682 2512 — LRCP LRCS Ed. LRCPS Glas. 1981; MB BS Utkal 1971.

MOHAPATRA, Jyoti Ranjan 6 Coppetts Close, London N12 0AG — MB BS 1984 Univ. Sambalpur; MRCP (UK) 1992.

***MOHD MUSLIM, Ida Mumtaz** Flat 2/1, 22 Ashley St., Glasgow G3 6DR — MB ChB 1998 Glas.; MB ChB Glas 1998.

***MOHD SANI, Abdul Khalid** 56 Church Street, Hyde SK14 1JJ — MB ChB 1997 Manch.

MOHER, Michael Gary Inst. Of Health Sciences, University of Oxford, Headington, Oxford OX3 7LF — MB BCh BAO 1981 NUI; LRCPI & LM, LRCSI & LM 1981. Res. Train. Fell. Inst. Of Health Sci. Oxf.

***MOHIDDIN, Abdulrahman Ahmed** 18 Craigie Street, Aberdeen AB25 1EL — MB ChB 1994 Aberd.

***MOHIL, Randeep Singh** 3 The Warke, Worsley, Manchester M28 2WX — MB BCh 1997 Wales.

MOHILE, Rajan Vishwanath Chadwell Medical Centre, 1 Brentwood Road, Chadwell St. Mary, Grays RM16 4JD Tel: 01375 842289 Fax: 01375 840357 — MB BS 1982 Lond.; MRCS Eng. LRCP Lond. 1983. Princip. GP Chadwell-St-Mary. Prev: SHO (ENT & Obst.) Orsett Hosp. Orsett; SHO (A & E) Basildon Hosp.

MOHILE, Vishwanath Vaman 1 Brentwood Road, Chadwell St Mary, Grays RM16 4JD Tel: 013752 2289; 33 Balfour Road, Grays RM17 5NS Tel: 01375 370681 — MB BS 1941 Bombay; DObst RCOG 1946. Mem. Essex Local Med. Comm. Socs: BMA & Indian Med. Assn.

MOHINDRA, Arun 66 Gatley Road, Gatley, Cheadle SK8 4AA — MB ChB 1992 Manch.; MRCGP 1996; DRCOG 1994; DGM RCP Lond. 1995. (Univ. Manch.)

MOHINDRA, Raj Kumar 89 Albion Road, Hounslow TW3 3RS Email: rajm@dial.pipex.com — BM BCh 1994 Oxf.; MRCP (UK) 1997. (Oxf.) Specialist Regist. (Gen. Internal Med.) Oxf. Prev: SHO Qu. Med. Centre Nott.

MOHINDRA, Suman 11 Eaton Drive, Alderley Edge SK9 7RA — MB 1978 Camb.; BChir 1977.

MOHINDRU, Avinash Chander CWM Health Centre, CWM, Ebbw Vale NP23 7RW Tel: 01495 370209, 01495 371697; 1 Cued Melyn View, Risca Road, Newport NP20 3PP Tel: 01633 251203 Fax: 01633 251203 — MBBS 1970 Punjab, India; DCCH 1995 Univ. of Warwick, Coventry; DFFP 1993 Fac. Of Family Plan. London; MSc 2000 Univ. of Warwick, Coventry; DPD 1993 Univ. of Wales, Cardiff; DTCD 1974 GNU Univ. Punjab, India. (Medical College Amritsar, Punjab, India) Princip., Gen. Med. Practitioner, CWM Health Centre, CWM, Ebbw Vale, Gwent NP23 7RW; Clin. Asst. Psycho Geriat., Aberbeeg Hosp., Aberbeeg, Gwent.

MOHIT MAFI, Nasser 17 Cock Pit Close, Anlaby, Hull HU10 7LG Tel: 01482 656326; De La Pole Hospital, Willerby, Hull — MD 1947 Teheran; MRCPsych 1973; DPM Eng. 1967. (Teheran Med. Sch.) Cons. (Psychiat.) De La Pole Hosp. Willerby.

MOHITE, Anand Shankarrao Dudley Group of Hospitals NHS Trust, Wordsley Hospital, Stream Road, Stourbridge DY8 5QX Tel: 01384 456111 Fax: 01384 244367 Email: amand.mohite@dudleygoh-tr.wmids.nhs.uk — MB BS 1982 Bombay; MD (Paediat.) Bombay 1984; MRCP (UK) 1990; FRCPCH 1995. (T.N. Medical College, Bombay, India) Cons. Paediat. & Neonatologist, Wordsley Hosp., Stourbridge, W. Midl.; Hon. Sen. Lect. Univ. Birm. Socs: BMA; Indian Acad. Paediats.; Fell.Roy. Coll. of Paediat.s & Child Health.

MOHITH, Anil Bhushan Department of Medical Oncology, Charing Cross Hospital, Fulham Palace Road, London W6 8RF Tel: 020 8846 1234 Fax: 020 8748 5665; 13 Culmstock Close, Milton Keynes MK4 2BH — MB ChB 1987 Leeds; MRCP (UK) 1993. Specialist Regist. (Med. Oncol.) Char. Cross Hosp. Lond.

MOHIUD-DIN, Fouzia The Surgery, 30 Acre Lane, Carshalton SM5 3AB Tel: 020 8647 2433 — MB BS 1972 Osmania. (Osmania Med. Coll. Hyderabad) Prev: SHO (Med.) & Regist. (Psychiat.) Wilson Hosp. Mitcham.

MOHIUD-DIN, Syed Mustafa The Surgery, 30 Acre Lane, Carshalton SM5 3AB Tel: 020 8647 2433 — MB BS 1971 Osmania. (Gandhi Med. Coll. Hyderabad) GP Surrey.

MOHIUDDIN, Rabia Joan Woodburn, Wood Lane, Parkgate, South Wirral CH64 6QZ — LRCP LRCS 1969 Ed.; MRCP (UK) 1976; LRCP LRCS Ed. LRCPS Glas. 1969; DPH Liverp. 1973; DCH RCPS Glas. 1971.

MOHIUDDIN, Syed Ahmed Anaesthetic Department, Castle Hill Hospital, Castle Road, Cottingham HU16 5JQ Tel: 01482 875875; Faizan, Beech Hill Road, Swanland, North Ferriby HU14 3QY Tel: 01482 631060 — MB BS Osmania 1961; DA Osmania 1965. (Osmania Med. Coll. Hyderabad) Assoc. Specialist (Anaesth.) Castle Hill Hosp. Cottingham.

MOHLA, Mr Dushyant Jaigopal 6 School Lane, Kirkella, Hull HU10 7NR Tel: 01482 654969 — MB BS 1968 Bombay; MS Bombay 1973, MB BS 1968; FICS 1985. Staff Grade (Paediat. Surg.) Roy. Hull Hosps. NHS Trust. Socs: Brit. Assn. Paediat. Surg. & BMA.

MOHLER, Thomas c/o Anaesthetic Department, Good Hope Hospital, Rectory Road, Sutton Coldfield B75 7RR — MB BS 1989 Tasmania.

MOHR, Adrian Richard Sun Lane Surgery, Sun Lane, Hythe CT21 5JX Tel: 01303 267131 Fax: 01303 265861; 68 North Road, Hythe CT21 5DU Tel: 01303 260908 — MB BS 1969 Lond.; MRCS Eng. LRCP Lond. 1969. (St. Geo.) Socs: BMA. Prev: Sen. Ho. Phys. WillesBoro. Hosp. Ashford & King Edwd. VII Memor. Hosp. Warwick.

MOHR, Peter Dean 16 Westminster Road, Eccles, Manchester M30 9EB — MB ChB 1969 Manch.; PhD Manch. 1995; MSc Manch. 1991, BSc (Hons.) 1967; FRCP Lond. 1990; MRCP (UK) 1972. (Manch.) Cons. Neurol. Hope Hosp. Salford. Prev: Regist. (Neurol.) Qu. Eliz. Hosp. Birm.; Sen. Regist. (Neurol.) Manch. Roy. Infirm.

MOHR, St John James Roman Ditteridge House, Ditteridge, Box, Corsham SN13 8QF — MB ChB 1991 Birm.; MRCGP 1997.

MOHSEN, Mr Amr Mohamed Mohamed Abdel Castle Hill Hospital, Castle Road, Cottingham HU16 5JQ Tel: 01482 875875 Fax: 01482 674121 Email: 106052.1352@compuserv.com; Hull Royal Infirmary, Analby Road, Hull HU3 2JZ Tel: 01482 328541 Fax: 01482 674121 — MB BCh 1984 Cairo; PhD Hull 1995; FRCS (Orth.) 1996; FRCS Ed. 1991. Cons. (Orthop. & Traumatology); Hon. Prof. Sch. Engin. & Computing Univ. Hull. Socs: Fell.Brit. Orthopaedic Assoc.; Brit. Orth. Spinal Soc.; Brit. Cervical Spine Soc. Prev: Sen. Regist. (Orthop. & Traumatology) Yorks.; Regist. Rotat. (Orthop. & Traumat.) E. Yorks.

MOHSEN, Mr Yasser Mohamed Abdel Hillingdon Hospital, Pield Heath Road, Uxbridge UB8 3NN Tel: 01895 238282 Fax: 01895 238891; Tel: 020 7262 5197 Email: ynohsen@doctorsnet.co.uk — MB BCh 1984 Cairo; FRCS Ed. 1991; MS Lond. 1998; FRCS Ed. (Gen. Surg.) 1998. Cons. Surg. in Gen. and Colorectal Surg. Hillingdon and Mt. Vernon Hosp.s Middlx. Lond.; Hon. Lect. St Mary's Hosp. Paddington Lond. Socs: RSM; Brit. Assn. of Surgic. Oncol.; Assn. of Colorectologists of GB & N.ern Irel.

MOHSINI, Abid Aziz 64 Hallam Road, Moorgate, Rotherham S60 3EB — MD 1977 Aligarh; MD (Gen. Med.) Aligarh 1977, MB BS 1974; MRCPI 1986.

MOHTESHAMZADEH, Mobin 35 Blevedere Gardens, Benton, Newcastle upon Tyne NE12 9PE Email: mobin@doctors.org.uk — MB ChB 1995 Sheff.; MRCP (UK) 1998; Roy. Col. Phys. Lond. Specialist Regist. Nephrol./Gen. Med.

MOHUN, Sarah Caroline Green Acres, Golden Bank, Plymouth Road, Liskeard PL14 3PB — MB 1976 Camb.; BA Camb. 1972, MB 1976, BChir 1975.

MOIEMEN, Mr Naiem Shokry Mohamed St. Andrew's Hospital, Billericay CM12 0BL Tel: 01277 622611 — MB BCh 1980 Cairo; FRCS Ed. 1988.

MOIN UDDIN, Sheikh Muhammad 40 Heronsforde, St. Stephens Road, Ealing, London W5 — MB BS 1956 Dacca; LAH Dub. 1962; DCH Eng. 1967. (Med. Coll. Dacca) Hosp. Pract. S.all-Norwood Hosp. Prev: Res. Med. Off. (Paediat. & Gen. Med.) City Gen. Hosp. Gloucester; Regist. (Paediat.) St. Helen Hosp. Barnsley; Regist. (Paediat.) W. Middlx. Hosp. Isleworth.

MOIR, Alexander Thomas Boyd 23 Murrayfield Gardens, Edinburgh EH12 6DG Tel: 0131 337 3937 — MB ChB 1963 Ed.; PhD Ed. 1967, BSc (Hons. Pharmacol.) 1964; FRCP Glas. 1985; FRCP Ed. 1979; MRCP (UK) 1972; FRCPath 1988, M 1976; FFPHM 1993 M 1986; MFOM RCP Lond. 1984; FIBiol 1979. (Ed.) Dir. & Dep. Chief Sci. Scott. Home & Health Dept. Edin. Socs: Brit. Assn. Med. Managers; Internat. Soc. Health Technol. Assessm. Prev: on Clin. Scientif. Staff MRC Brain Metab. Unit Dept. Pharmacol. Edin. Univ.; Hon. Sen. Regist. Poisoning Treatm. Centre & Dept. Therap. Edin. Roy.

MOIR

MOIR, Mr Andrew Anthony The Willows, 27 Barrow Road, Sileby, Loughborough LE12 7LW Tel: 01509 814405 Fax: 01509 816350 Email: gandamoir@hotmail.com — MB BS 1976 Lond.; FRCS Eng. 1981; MRCS Eng. LRCP Lond. 1975. (St. Mary's) Cons. (ENT Surg.) Leicester Roy. Infirm. Prev: Sen. Regist. (ENT) Roy. Hallamsh./N. Gen. Hosp. Sheff.; Regist. ENT St. Mary's Hosp. Lond.

MOIR, Charles Cameron 204 Garstang Road, Fulwood, Preston PR2 8RD Tel: 01772 717413 — MB ChB 1951 Ed. (Ed)

***MOIR, Claire Louise** Errochty, Old Whisky Rd, Auchterhouse, Dundee DD3 0RD — MB ChB 1997 Manch.

MOIR, Dorothy Carnegie Lanarkshire Health Board, 14 Beckford St., Hamilton ML3 0TA Tel: 01698 206322 Fax: 01698 424316 Email: dorothymoin@lanarkshirehb.scot.nhs.uk — MB ChB 1965 Aberd.; MD Aberd. 1970; FRCP Ed. 1996; Dip. Mgt. 1995; FFPHM RCP (UK) 1990; FFCM 1988, M 1974. (Aberdeen) Chief Admin. Med. Off. & Dir. of Pub. Health Lanarksh. HB; Sen. Clin. Lect. (Pub. Health Med.) Glas. Univ. Socs: Fell. Soc. Social Med. Prev: Dir. Pub. Health Forth Valley HB; Community Med. Specialist Grampian HB; Lect. (Community Med.) Univ. Aberd.

MOIR, Fiona Margaret c/o Dr A T B Moir, 23 Murrayfield Gardens, Edinburgh EH12 6DG Tel: 0131 337 3937 — MB ChB 1989 Sheff.; MRCGP 1994.

MOIR, Mr Graeme Christopher 18 Hillview Road, Orpington BR6 0SF Tel: 01689 870058 — MB ChB 1982 Aberd.; FRCS 1998. Cons. (Plastic Surg.) Roy. Lond. Hosp. Whitechapel. Socs: Brit. Assn. Plastic Surg.; RSM.

MOIR, Jeremy Gordon Bedsit 10, 45 Matheson Road, London W14 8SN — MB BS 1972 Western Australia.

MOIR, Mr John Stuart Western Infirmary, Dumbarton Road, Glasgow G11 6NT Tel: 0141 211 2422; Woodlands, 5 Craigmarloch View, Blanefield, Glasgow G63 9JH Tel: 01360 770698 Fax: 01360 770698 — MB ChB 1980 Aberd.; ChM (Commend.) Aberd. 1997; FRCS Ed. 1989; FRCS (Orth) Ed. 1996; MRCGP 1984. (Aberd.) Cons. (Orthop. Surg.) N Glas. Univ. NHS Trust. Socs: Brit. Orthop. Assn.; Brit. Orthop. Foot Surg. Soc. Prev: Sen. Regist. (Orthop.) Grampian & N. Scotl. Train. Scheme; Surg. Fell. Orthop. & Arthritic Hosp. Toronto; Regist. (Orthop.) Grampian HB.

MOIR, Morag Elizabeth 17/10 Roseburn Maltings, Edinburgh EH12 5LJ Tel: 0131 313 3940 — MB ChB 1996 Ed. GP Train. Edin. S/E Scot. GP Voc. Train. Schm.

MOIR, Susan Barbara The Long House, 73-75 East Trinity Road, Edinburgh EH5 3EL Tel: 0131 552 4919 — MB ChB 1989 Ed.; MRCGP 1993; DCCH RCP Ed. 1994.

MOISEY, Mr Clifford Urwin 7 Combe Park, Bath BA1 3NP Tel: 01225 332996 Email: cliff.moisey@ruh-bath.swest.nhs.uk — MB ChB 1964 Leeds; MB ChB Leeds. 1964; FRCS Eng. 1970. Cons. Urol. Surg. Roy. United Hosp. Bath; Hon. Sen. Lect. Inst. Urol. Lond. Prev: Sen. Regist. (Urol.) S. Glam. AHA; Regist. Gen. Surg. & Urol. Roy. Hosp. Sheff.; Rotating Surg. Regist. United Leeds Hosps.

MOITRA, Rupak Kumar 14 Gathorne Road, London N22 5ND Tel: 020 8888 9871 — MB BS 1994 Lond.; MB BS Lond. 11994; BSc (Anat. & Path.) Lond. 1991; MRCP (UK) 1997. (Char. Cross & Westm.) SHO (Oncol.) Roy. Marsden Hosp. (Sutton). Socs: MPS. Prev: SHO (Med.) Mayday Hosp. Croydon; Ho. Off. (Cardiol. & Rheum.) Char. Cross Hosp. Lond.; Ho. Off. (Gen. Surg. & Orthop.) Qu. Mary's Hosp. Lond.

MOIZ, Mr Malik 14 Dorchester Court, Buckingham Road, London E18 2NG — MB BS 1980 Nigeria; FRCS Ed. 1988. Staff Grade Orthop. Surg. Ipswich Hosp. Prev: Regist. (Gen. Surg. & Orthop.) Qu. Eliz. Hosp. King's Lynn.

MOJIMINIYI, Olusegun Ademola Department of Chemical Pathology & Metabolism, St. Helier Hospital, Wrythe Lane, Carshalton SM5 1AA Tel: 020 8644 4343 Fax: 020 8641 2633; Wolfson College, Oxford OX2 6UD — MB BS 1981 Lagos; DPhil Oxf. 1991; MRCPath 1996. Sen. Regist. (Chem. Path.) St. Helier Hosp. Carshalton. Socs: Assn. Clin. Path.; Amer. Assn. Clin. Chems.; Brit. Nuclear Med. Soc. Prev: Hon. Regist. (Nuclear Med.) Univ. Dept. Radiol. Radcliffe Infirm. Oxf.; Sen. Regist. (Chem. Path.) Univ. Coll. Hosp. Ibadan, Nigeria.

MOK, Andrew Wing-Fung Carlton House Surgery, 28 Tenniswood Road, Enfield EN1 3LL Tel: 020 8363 7575 Fax: 020 8366 8228 — MB BS 1992 Lond.

MOK, Catherine Ann Kit Yee Pettifer and Mok, Colville Health Centre, 51 Kensington Park Road, London W11 1PA Tel: 020 7727 4592 Fax: 020 7221 4613; 16 Claremont Road, Ealing, London W13 0DQ Tel: 020 8998 1720 Fax: 020 8998 1720 Email: kitmok@aol.com — MB BS 1981 Lond.; MRCGP 1986; DRCOG 1984. (King's Coll. Hosp.) Socs: MRCOG. Prev: SHO (Paediat.) Wexham Pk. Hosp.; SHO (Rheum.) Canad. Red Cross Memor. Hosp. Slough; Trainee GP Burnham Health Centre VTS.

MOK, Mr Daniel Wah Hong Epsom General Hospital, Dorking Road, Epsom KT18 7EG — MB BS 1980 Lond.; FRCS Ed. 1985; FRCS Glas. 1984; MRCS Eng. LRCP Lond. 1980. (St. Bart.) Cons. Orthop. Epsom Gen. Hosp. Socs: Fell. BOA; BESS. Prev: Sen. Regist. (Orthop.) St. Bart. Hosp. Lond.; Regist. (Orthop.) St. Geo. Hosp. Lond.

MOK, Hiram Lai-Hong 15 Sylvan Court, 102 Holden Road, London N12 7ED — MB BCh BAO 1992 Dub.; MB BCh Dub. 1992.

MOK, Jacqueline Yek Quen Craigesk House, Lothianbridge, Dalkeith EH22 4TP Tel: 0131 660 3281 Fax: 0131 660 4227 Email: jmok@ed.ac.uk — MD 1983 Ed.; MB ChB 1974; FRCP Ed. 1989; MRCP (UK) 1977; DCH RCPS Glas. 1976; FRCPCH 1997. (Edin.) Cons. Paediat. Roy. Hosp. for Sick Childr. Edin.; Sen. Lect. Dept. Child Life & Health Univ. Edin.

***MOK, Louis Kuan Yong** 101A Rosemount Place, Aberdeen AB25 2YG — MB ChB 1995 Aberd.

MOK, Michael Hing Hung 16 Cambridge Square, London W2 2QE — MB BS 1974 Lond.; MRCS Eng. LRCP Lond. 1974; MRCP (UK) 1981. (Guy's)

MOK, Quen Quen Paediatric Intensive Care Unit, Great Ormond Street Hospital for Children NHS Trust, London WC1N 3JH Tel: 020 7405 9200 Fax: 020 7813 8206 Email: qmok@ich.ucl.ac.uk; 33 Copley Park, London SW16 3DD Tel: 020 8764 1406 Fax: 020 8764 1406 — MB BS 1980 Malaya; MRCP (UK) 1985; MRCPI 1985; DCH RCP Lond. 1983. Cons. Paediat. Intens. Care Gt. Ormond St. Hosp. Childr. NHS Trust Lond. Socs: Fell. Roy. Coll. Paediat. & Child Health; Eur. Soc. Paediat. Intens. Care; Paediat. Intens. Care Soc. Prev: Sen. Regist. (Paediat.) Qu. Mary's Hosp. Childr. Carshalton & St. Geo.Hosp. Lond.; Lect. & Hon. Regist. (Paediat.) Brompton Hosp. Lond.; Lect. & Hon. Regist. (Neonat.) St. Geo. Hosp. Lond.

***MOK, Un Sam** Flat 6, 125 Wilton St., Glasgow G20 6RD — MB ChB 1998 Glas.; MB ChB Glas 1998.

MOK, Victoria Susan 16 East Burnside, Dollar FK14 7AX Tel: 01259 742766 — MB ChB 1995 Aberd.

MOK YUN WING, Thomas Southampton General Hospital, Tremona Road, Shirley, Southampton SO16 6YD — MB BS 1983 Hong Kong.

MOKASHI, A V Clayton Health Centre, 89 North Road, Clayton, Manchester M11 4EJ Tel: 0161 223 8388 Fax: 0161 202 3700 — MB BS 1971 Gujarat; MB BS 1971 Gujarat.

MOKATE, Tefo Royal Oldham Hospital, 1 Rochdale Road, Oldham OL1 2JH Tel: 0161 624 0420; 12 Birchwood Close, Stockport SK4 2BS Tel: 0161 432 4205 — MB BS 1975 Ibadan; MRCOG 1993. Staff Grade (O & G) Roy. Oldham Hosp.

MOKBEL, Kefah Department Academic Surgery, The Royal Marsden Hospital, Fulham Road, London SW3 6JJ; 2A Guthrie Street, London SW3 Tel: 020 7352 0081 — MB BS 1990 Lond. SHO (Gen. Surg. & Oncol.) Roy. Marsden Hosp. Lond. Prev: SHO (A & E) Roy. Lond. Hosp.

MOKETE, Bataung 63 Newchurch Road, Slough SL2 1UE — MB ChB 1992 Bristol; BSc Lesotho 1987. SHO (Ophth.) Kent & Canterbury Hosp. Prev: SHO (Ophth.) York Dist. Hosp.; Ho. Off. Bristol Roy. Infirm.; Ho. Off. W.on Gen. Hosp. Avon.

***MOKETE, Moeketsi** Top Floor Flat, 24 West Park, Bristol BS8 2LT — MB ChB 1994 Bristol.

MOKHTAR, Mr Hussain Hassan 24 Sandhurst Avenue, Mansfield NG18 4BG Tel: 01623 31255 — MB BCh 1966 Cairo; FRCS (Ophth.) Ed. 1980.

MOLAJO, Adeniyi Olufemi Leigh Infirmary, The Avenue, Leigh WN7 1HS Tel: 01942 264311 Fax: 01942 264394; Cornerstone, 10 Albert Road, Heaton, Bolton BL1 5HE Tel: 01204 492415 Fax: 01204 412932 — MD 1986 Manch.; MB ChB 1976; BSc (Hons.) St. And. 1973; FRCP Ed. & Lond. 1998. (St. And. & Manch.) Cons. Cardiol. Phys. Wigan & Leigh NHS Trust.

MOLAN, Christopher Joseph The Medical Centre, The Medical Centre, Fore Street, St Marychurch, Torquay TQ1 4QX Tel: 01803

MOLLOY

325123 Fax: 01803 322136 — MB ChB 1971 Bristol. Clin. Asst. (Diabetes) Torbay Hosp.

MOLAVE, Elmer Ramos 33 Cotswold Drive, Gonerby Hill Foot, Grantham NG31 8GE — LMSSA 1992 Lond.

MOLD, Ernest Thomas (retired) 10 Longmead, Lynton EX35 6DQ Tel: 01598 752205 — MB BS Lond. 1952. Prev: Ho. Surg. Lond. Hosp.

***MOLE, Damian James** 44 Half Moon Lane, London SE24 9HU — MB ChB 1998 Birm.; ChB Birm. 1998.

MOLE, David Robert Flat 4, 293 Winchester Road, Southampton SO16 6TS — BM 1991 Soton.

MOLE, Jonathan Roger 1 Frenchs Road, Cambridge CB4 3JZ — MB BS 1994 Lond. SHO PeterBoro.; SHO (Med.) Hinchingbrooke; SHO Addenbrookes Hosp.

MOLE, Kenneth Fawcett The School, Buckhorn Weston, Gillingham SP8 5HS Tel: 01963 371006 — MB BS 1954 Lond.; MA Oxf. 1946; MRCS Eng. LRCP Lond. 1954; MRCGP 1976; LM Nat. Matern. Hosp. 1955. (St. Mary's) Prev: Hon. Phys. Horsham Hosp.; Med. Off. Hydroforce Ltd.; Ho. Phys. St. Mary's Hosp.

MOLE, Maria Teresa (retired) — State Exam 1986 Cantania; FRCS Ed. 1994. Prev: Transpl. Regist. (Cardiothoracic Surg.) N.. Gen. Hosp. Sheff.

MOLE, Michael Richard Pinhoe Surgery, Pinn Lane, Exeter EX1 3SY Tel: 01392 469666 Fax: 01392 464178 — BM BCh 1968 Oxf.; MA; DA Eng. 1973. (Middlx.) Prev: Ho. Surg. Middlx. Hosp. Lond.; Ho. Phys. Centr. Middlx. Hosp. Lond.; SHO ENT Rush Green Hosp. Romford.

MOLEELE, Gontle Tjedza Queens Medical Centre, Clifton Boulevard, Nottingham NG7 2; 15 Greenford Close, Nuthall, Nottingham NG16 1RH — MB ChB 1991 Glas.; MRCP (UK) 1995. Specialist Regist. Diabetes/Endocrinol. QMC, Nottm.

***MOLEFI, Wendy** 10 Icarus House, British St., London E3 4LZ — BM 1997 Soton.

MOLES, Doreen Jane 42 Knowe Park Avenue, Carlisle CA3 9EL — MB BCh BAO 1979 Belf.; MRCGP 1986; DRCOG 1985; DCH RCPS Glas. 1982. Prev: Clin. Med. Off. Coleraine Co. Lond.derry.

MOLES, George (retired) 16 Lisbarnet Road, Lisbane, Comber, Newtownards BT23 6AW Tel: 01238 541466 — MB BCh BAO 1950 Belf.; MRCGP 1972; DObst RCOG 1964; DTM & H Liverp. 1953. GP Newtownards. Prev: Med. Supt. Vom Christian Hosp. N. Nigeria.

MOLES, George Iain David Lisbarnet Road Surgery, 24 Lisbarnet Road, Lisbane, Newtownards BT23 6AW Tel: 028 9754 1466 Fax: 028 9754 1734; 46 Ballygoskin Road, Crossgar, Downpatrick BT30 9LW Tel: 01238 542063 — MB BCh BAO 1982 Belf.; MB BCh Belf. 1982; MRCGP 1987. Socs: Soc. Orthop. Med.; Brit. Assn. Sport & Med.

MOLES, Kenneth William Altnagelvin Area Hospital, Londonderry BT47 6SB; 146 Windyhill Road, Stradreagh, Limavady BT49 0QY — MD 1988 Belf.; MB BCh BAO Belf. 1974; FRCP Lond. 1994; MRCP (UK) 1980; DObst RCOG 1976. Cons. Phys. Altnagelvin Area Hosp. & Tyrone Co. Hosp.

MOLES, Muriel Rosemary Cherryville, 39 Coleraine Road, Ballymoney BT53 6BS — MB BCh BAO 1983 Belf.; MRCGP 1988; DRCOG 1987.

MOLESWORTH, Trudy Hillside, Bridgwater Road, Weston Super Mare BS23 4TY Tel: 01934 812814 — MB ChB Sheff. 1973. (Sheff.)

MOLEY, Frances Mary Boundary House, 462 Northenden Road, Sale M33 2RH Tel: 0161 972 9999 Fax: 0161 972 9995 — MB ChB 1976 Manch.; DRCOG 1978. (Manch.)

***MOLIFE, Lulama Rhoda** 6 Longship Way, Maldon CM9 6UG — BM BS 1995 Nottm.

MOLINA NAVARRO, Carlos 16 Barrow View, Ferndown BH22 9SY Tel: 01202 890299 Email: carlosm@globalnet.co.uk — LMS 1990 Malaga; FRCS Ed, 1996. Specialist Regist. Gen. Surg., Roy. Bournemouth Hosp. Socs: BMA; Affil. Fell.. ASGBI; ASIT.

MOLINA SANCHEZ, Beatriz 6 Bella View Gardens, Glastonbury BA6 9HQ — LMS 1993 Malaga.

MOLITOR, Mr Peter John Alexander Scunthorpe General Hospital, Cliff Gardens, Scunthorpe DN15 7BH Tel: 01724 282282; Chartwell House, Church St, Amcotts, Scunthorpe DN17 4AL Tel: 01724 783247 Fax: 01724 782492 — MB BS Lond. 1979; MS Lond. 1991; FRCS Ed. 1984; MRCS Eng. LRCP Lond. 1979. (Roy. Free) Cons. Orthop. Surg. Scunthorpe & Goole Hosps. Socs: Fell. BOA; BMA. Prev: Regist. (Orthop.) Addenbrooke's Hosp. Camb.; Research Fell. Univ. Orthop. Research Unit Addenbrooke's Hosp. Camb.

MOLIVER, Adam Aron Charlton Lane Unit, Cheltenham GL53 Tel: 01242 272008 — MB BS 1982 Lond.; MRCPsych 1987. Cons. Psychiat. E. Glos. NHS Trust. Prev: Sen. Regist. (Psychiat.) Roy. Free Hosp. Lond.

MOLIVER, Sarah Overton Park Surgery, Overton Park Road, Cheltenham GL50 3BP Tel: 01242 580511 — MB ChB 1980 Bristol; MRCGP 1988; DRCOG 1985; DCH RCP Lond. 1984; DA Eng. 1983. (Bristol) GP Partner.

MOLL, Edward Francis Henderson (retired) St Johns Lodge, 35 Barmby Road, Pocklington, York YO42 2DW Tel: 01759 302192 — MB ChB Leeds 1961; DObst RCOG 1964. Prev: SHO (Ophth. Surg.) Leeds Gen. Infirm.

MOLL, Edward Leslie (retired) 97 Tufton Road, Rainham, Gillingham ME8 7LQ Tel: 01634 230901 — LMSSA 1939 Lond.; MRCS Eng. LRCP Lond. 1939; MRCGP 1953; LDS RCS Eng. 1935. Prev: Med. Examr. Army & RAF Careers Office Canterbury.

MOLL, John Michael Henderson Nether Edge Hospital, Sheffield S11 9EL Tel: 0114 271 1941 Fax: 0114 271 1844 — BM BCh 1962 Oxf.; PhD Leeds 1981, BSc (Hons.) 1960; DM Oxf. 1971; FRCP Lond. 1980, M 1969. (Leeds & Oxf.) Cons. Rheum. & Head Sheff. Centre Rheum. Dis. Nether Edge Hosp. Sheff.; Hon. Clin. Lect. (Rheum. Dis.) Univ. Sheff.; Founder & Edr.-in-Chief Jl. Orthop. Rheum.; Founder & Edr. Jl. Med. Biogr. Socs: Fell. & Sen. Hon. Edr. Roy. Soc. Med. (Mem., Vice-Pres. & Ex-Pres. Sect. Rheum.& Rehabil.); Fell. Internat. Biogr. Assn.; Life Fell. Amer. Biogr. Inst. Res. Assn. Prev: Founder & Edr.-in-Chief Rheum. Rev. & Gen. Edr. Arthritis & Rheum. Counc. Literature; Sen. Regist. (Rheum. & Physical Med.) Oxf. RHB.

MOLLA, Abu Layes Weston Favell Health Centre, Weston Favell Centre, Northampton NN3 8DW Tel: 01604 409631 Fax: 01604 786738 — MB BS 1966 Dacca. (Dacca) Prev: Ho. Surg. St. Mary's Hosp. Plaistow; Ho. Phys. Gen. Hosp. Rochford; Asst. Res. Med. Off. (Gen. Med.) Salford Roy. Hosp.

***MOLLAN, Ian Alexander** Orchard Hill, 167 Bangor Rd, Holywood BT18 0ET — MB ChB 1997 Dundee.

MOLLAN, Mr Raymond Alexander Boyce Orchard Hill, 167 Bangor Road, Craigavad, Holywood BT18 0ET — MB BCh BAO (Hons.) Belf. 1969; MD Belf. 1981; FRCSI 1985; FRCS Ed. 1974; DObst RCOG 1971. (Belf.) Prof Dept. Orthop. Surg. Qu. Univ. Belf.; Cons. Orthop. Surg. Musgrave Pk. Hosp., Roy. Vict. Hosp. Belf. & Belf. City Hosp. Prev: Sen. Lect. Dept. Orthop. Surg. Qu. Univ. Belf.

MOLLART, Joanne Elizabeth 72 Lansdowne Road, Bayston Hill, Shrewsbury SY3 0JG — MB ChB 1979 Manch. Prev: Princip. Gen. Pract. Ashley Nr Market Drayton.

MOLLER, Cea-Cea Barbara c/o Musgrove Park Hospital, Taunton TA1 5DA — MB BS 1991 Adelaide.

MOLLER, Hans Kaltoft (retired) 215 Maidstone Road, Rochester ME1 3BU Tel: 01634 844721 — MB BS 1956 Lond.

MOLLISON, Margaret Doreen 29 Burford Lodge, Pegasus Grange, Whitehouse Road, Oxford OX1 4QG Tel: 01865 791843 — MB ChB 1937 Cape Town; MFCM 1974; DPH Eng. 1966. (Cape Town)

MOLLISON, Patrick Loudon, CBE 60 King Henry's Road, London NW3 3RR Tel: 020 7722 1947 Fax: 020 7813 9257 — MB BChir 1938 Camb.; FRS; BA (Nat. Sc. Trip.) Camb. 1935, MD 1944; FRCP Lond. 1957, M 1940; MRCS Eng. LRCP Lond. 1938; FRCOG 1980; FRCPath 1964. (Camb. & St. Thos.) Hon. Cons. Immunohaemat. N. Lond. Blood Transfus. Centre Lond.; Prof. Emerit. Haemat. (Univ. Lond.) St. Mary's Hosp. Lond. Socs: Hon. Mem. Amer. Soc. Haematol. Prev: Med. Cas. Off. & Ho. Phys. St. Thos. Hosp.; Sen. Lect. (Med.) Postgrad. Med. Sch. Lond.; Dir. MRC Experim. Haemat. Unit & Cons. Haemat. St. Mary's Hosp.

MOLLOY, Bernard (retired) 134 Thorkhill Road, Thames Ditton KT7 0UN Tel: 020 8398 4530 — MB ChB 1920 Birm.; MRCS Eng. LRCP Lond. 1920.

MOLLOY, Catherine Frances (retired) Old Orchard Lodge, Park Lane, Harefield, Uxbridge UB9 6HJ Tel: 01895 822162 — MB BCh BAO NUI 1949; LM Coombe 1954. Prev: Med. Asst. Harefield Hosp.

MOLLOY

MOLLOY, Cornelius Christopher, OBE, KStJ (retired) 49 Torbay Road, London NW6 7DX Tel: 020 7625 4103 — MB BS 1950 Lond.; BSc Lond. 1938, MB BS 1950; FFOM RCP Lond. 1982, M 1979; DIH Soc. Apoth. Lond. 1956. Prev: SMO. Civil Med. Servs. M.O.D.

MOLLOY, Ita Doncaster & South Humber Healthcare NHS Trust, Brumby Hospital, East Common Lane, Scunthorpe DN16 1QQ Tel: 01724 290062 Fax: 01724 279704; 74/76 Ealand Outgate, Crowle, Scunthorpe DN17 4JD Tel: 01724 711283 — MB BCh BAO 1971 NUI; DCH NUI 1975; Dip Developm Paed Leeds 1990; Cert. Counselling, Ripon & York St John 1996. Cons. Rehabil. Med. Doncaster & S. Humber Healthcare NHS Trust. Socs: Fac. Family Plann. & Reproduc. Health Care RCOG; BMA; Brit. Soc. Rehabil. Med.

MOLLOY, Jane Elizabeth Talwrn Farm, Talwrn Road, Rhostyllen, Wrexham LL14 4ER — MB ChB 1992 Ed.; MRCP (UK) 1995. (Ed.) Specialist Regist. (Clin. Pharmacol. & Therap.) W.ern Infirm. Glas. Prev: Clin. Research Fell./Hon. Regist. (Neurol.) King's Coll. Sch. of Med. & Dent. Lond.

MOLLOY, Joan Sunday (retired) Glen Gerrack, Menie, Balmedie, Aberdeen AB23 8YD — MB BS Lond. 1942; MRCS Eng. LRCP Lond. 1941.

***MOLLOY, Kevin John** 5 Lavender Row, Darley Abbey, Derby DE22 1DF — MB ChB 1997 Leic.

MOLLOY, Maria Brigid 215 Titwood Road, Glasgow G41 4BH — MB ChB 1994 Ed.; BA Oxf. 1991; DRCOG 1998. (Oxford/Edinburgh) GP Regist., W. Kilbride.

MOLLOY, Mary Elizabeth 71 Galwally Avenue, Belfast BT8 7AJ — MB BCh BAO 1991 Belf.

MOLLOY, Patrick Christopher (retired) Learings Hall, Heptonstall, Hebden Bridge HX7 7PD Tel: 01422 843341 — MB BCh BAO 1951 NUI. Prev: SHO (Orthop. & Cas.) Chester Roy. Infirm.

***MOLLOY, Paul Gerard** 59 Gleneagles, Gulmore Rd, Londonderry BT48 7TE — MB BCh BAO 1997 Belf.

***MOLLOY, Rachel Helen** Haddon House, 38 West End, Grat Eccleston, Preston PR3 0YL — MB ChB 1995 Manch.

MOLLOY, Mr Richard Gerard Department of Surgery, Gartnavel General Hospital, 1053 Great Western Road, Glasgow G12 0YN Tel: 0141 211 3000 Fax: 0141 311 3211; 215 Titwood Road, Crossmyloof, Glasgow G41 4BH Tel: 0141 424 0351 — MB BCh BAO 1986 NUI; MD NUI 1993, MB BCh BAO 1986; FRCSI 1990; FRCS (Gen) 1993; Intercollegiate Fellshp. In Gen. Surgery. (Univ. Coll. Cork Irel.) Cons. (Gen. Surg. s/i Colon-Rectal Surg.) Gartnavavel Gen. Hosp. & W Glas. Hosps. Univ NHS Trust; Hon. Sen. Lect. (Surg.) Univ. Glas. Socs: Amer. Soc. Colon & Rectal Surg.; Assn. ColoProctol.; Assn. Surg.

MOLLOY, Robert Edward (retired) Penlee, Perranwell Station, Truro TR3 7JS Tel: 01872 864421 — MB BS Lond. 1950; MRCS Eng. LRCP Lond. 1950; FFA RCS Eng. 1956; DA Eng. 1953. Cons. Anaesth. Whittington Hosp. Lond. & Roy. Free Hosp. Lond. Prev: Vis. Fell. Anaesth. Univ. Pittsburgh.

MOLODECKA, Jolanta Maria Avril, Racecourse Lane, Shrewsbury SY3 5BJ Tel: 01743 358755 — Lekarz 1983 Warsaw; FFA RCSI 1991; DA (UK) 1989.

MOLODECKI, Czeslaw Andrzej Avril, Racecourse Lane, Bicton Heath, Shrewsbury SY3 5BJ Tel: 01743 358755 — Lekarz 1982 Warsaw; DA (UK) 1989. Clin. Asst. (Anaesth.) Roy. Shrewsbury Hosp. Prev: Regist. (Anaesth.) Roy. Shrewsbury Hosp.; SHO (Anaesth.) Bolton Dist. Gen. Hosp. & Bolton Roy. Infirm.

***MOLODYNSKI, Andrew Carl** 6 Balmoral Road, St Annes on Sea, Lytham St Annes FY8 1ER — MB ChB 1996 Ed.

MOLODYNSKI, Carl John Blackpool Victoria Hospital, Blackpool FY3 8PW — MB ChB 1967 Liverp.; MRCPsych 1972; DPM Eng. 1970. Cons. Psychiat. Blackpool Health Dist.

MOLOKHIA, Mariam 5A Fulwood Park, Liverpool L17 5AA — MB ChB 1990 Manch.; BSc (Med Sci) St And. 1987. SHO (A & E) Roy. Oldham Hosp.

MOLONEY, Anna Mary Department of Public Health, West Pennine Health Authority, Westhulme Avenue, Oldham OL1 2PL — MB ChB 1985 Leeds; MSc (Pub. Health & Epidemiol.) Manch. Univ. 1993; MFPHM RCP (UK) 1994.

MOLONEY, Anne 12 Leigh Road, West Kirby, Wirral CH48 5DY — MB BS 1973 Lond.; BSc St. And. 1970; FRCP Lond. 1995; MRCP (UK) 1977. Cons. Geriat. Halton Hosp. Runcorn.

MOLONEY, Cornelius Mark 51 Gresham Road, London SW9 7NU — MB BCh BAO 1985 NUI.

MOLONEY, Dermot Thomas 64 Heathfield Road, Wavertree, Liverpool L15 9HA — MB ChB 1991 Liverp.

MOLONEY, Dominique Martine 17 Hornby Park, Liverpool L18 3LL — BM BCh 1990 Oxf.

MOLONEY, Eamonn Francis 28 Denmark Road, London SW19 4PG — MB BCh BAO 1984 NUI.

MOLONEY, Mr John Richard (retired) Meadowside, 31 Manor Road, Oadby, Leicester LE2 2LL — BM BCh 1969 Oxf.; MA 1969 Oxf.; FRCS Eng. 1974. Cons. ENT Surg. Leic. Roy. Infirm. Prev: Ho. Surg. St. Thos. Hosp. Lond.

MOLONEY, Maresa-Clare 15 Kensington Court Gardens, London W8 5QF Tel: 020 7937 0447 Fax: 020 7938 3766 — BChir 1992 Camb.; MB (CANTAB) 1992; MA OXON 1989. (Camb.)

MOLONEY, Michael Desmond Good Hope General Hospital, Rectory Road, Sutton Coldfield B75 7RR — MB BCh BAO 1977 NUI; FRCOG 1997; MRCOG 1985. Cons. O & G W. Midl. RHA.

MOLONEY, Patrick Gerard 202 Ashby Road, Burton-on-Trent DE15 0LB — MB BCh BAO 1960 NUI.

MOLONEY, Stephen John 14 Chantry Close, Windsor SL4 5EP — MB ChB 1990 Bristol.

MOLONY, Joseph Paul Sturry Surgery, 53 Island Road, Sturry CT2 7JU Tel: 01227 711203 Fax: 01227 713060 Email: paul.molony@gp-g82082.nhu.uk; Old St. Stephen's School, St. Stephen's Green, Canterbury CT2 7JU Tel: 01227 762835 Email: jo.molony@btinternet.com — MB BS 1982 Lond.; MA Kent 1992; DCH RCP Lond. 1986; DA (UK) 1985; Dip. Occ. Med. (King's Coll. Hosp.) Police Surg.; Occupat. Health Adviser to Christ Ch. Univ. Coll.; Bd. Mem., PCG.

MOLONY, Marcus (retired) Winterfold House, Westbere Lane, Westbere, Canterbury CT2 0HH Tel: 01227 710390 — LM 1957 Dub.; LRCPI & LM, LRCSI & LM 1955; LM Nat. Matern. Hosp. Dub. 1957. Prev: Intern. Mercy Hosp. Canton, Ohio.

MOLONY, Pauline Edna Winterfold House, Westbere Lane, Westbere, Canterbury CT2 0HH; 26 St. Mary's Gardens, London SE11 4UD Tel: 020 7735 5517 — LRCPI & LM, LRSCI & LM 1960; LRCPI & LM, LRCSI & LM 1960; MA (Med. Ethics & Law) Lond. 1988. (Dub.)

MOLTO, Alberto 92 Low Lane, Horsforth, Leeds LS18 5PX — LMS 1992 Navarre.

MOLTU, Andrew Peter The Limes Medical Centre, 65 Leicester Road, Narborough, Leicester LE9 5DU Tel: 0116 284 1347 Fax: 0116 275 2447; Brooklands, Narborough Road, Cosby, Leicester LE9 1TB — MB ChB 1987 Leic. Prev: Trainee GP Nuneaton; SHO (Paediat. & O & G) Geo. Eliot Hosp. Nuneaton; SHO (A & E) Manor Hosp. Nuneaton.

MOLYNEAUX, Alison Morag (retired) 10 Oakwell Drive, Unsworth, Bury BL9 8LB Tel: 0161 280 5358 — MB ChB Manch. 1954; DObst RCOG 1960. Prev: Ho. Phys. Bury Gen. Hosp.

MOLYNEAUX, Brian (retired) 84 Nipper Lane, Whitefield, Manchester M45 7RF Tel: 0161 796 5166 — MB ChB 1954 Manch. Prev: Med. Adviser Bury FHSA.

MOLYNEAUX, Pamela Jean Fax: 01224 840632 Email: p.molyneaux@arh.grampian.scot.nhs.uk — MB ChB 1978 Bristol; FRCPath 2000; BSc (Hons.) Bristol 1975; FRCP Ed. 1996; MRCPath 1992. Cons. Virol. Dept. Med. Microbiol. Aberd. Roy. Infirm. Prev: Sen. Regist. & Regist. (Virol.) City Hosp. Edin.; Regist. Microbiol. Centr. Microbiol. Laborat. W.. Gen. Hosp. Edin.; Regist. (Med.) E.. Gen. Hosp. Edin.

MOLYNEUX, Andrew James Wootton End, Sandy Lane, Boars Hill, Oxford OX1 5HN — MB 1972 Camb.; BChir 1971; FRCR 1977; DObst RCOG 1974. Cons. (Neuroradiol.) Radcliffe Infirm. Oxf.

MOLYNEUX, Andrew William Pradit 11 Mill Lane, Cropwell Bishop, Nottingham NG12 3BT — BM BS 1992 Nottm.

MOLYNEUX, Angus James Department of Cellular Pathology, Northampton General Hospital NHS Trust, Billing Road, Northampton NN1 5BD Tel: 01604 235596 Fax: 01604 235575; 44 Banbury Lane, Cold Higham, Towcester NN12 8LR Tel: 01327 831057 Email: angus@ajm-path.demon.co.uk — MB ChB 1987 Sheff.; MRCPath 1993. Cons. Histopath. & Cytopath. N.ampton Gen. Hosp.

MOLYNEUX, Anne Heather Staploe Medical Centre, Brewhouse Lane, Soham, Ely CB7 5JD Tel: 01353 624121 Fax: 01353 624203;

MONARD

The Grove, Carte St, Fordham, Ely CB7 5JU — MB 1988 Camb.; BChir 1987. Instruc. Doctor (Family Plann.) Cambs. Socs: Fac. Fam. Plann. & Reproduc. Health Care.

MOLYNEUX, Anthony Robert 12 Taunton Road, Bridgwater TA6 3LD Tel: 01278 444400; 31 Durleigh Road, Bridgwater TA6 7HX — MB BS 1958 Lond.; MRCS Eng. LRCP Lond. 1958; DObst RCOG 1962. (Lond. Hosp.) Socs: BMA. Prev: Sen. Ho. Off. (O & G) MusGr. Pk. Hosp. Taunton; Ho. Phys. Chelmsford & Essex Hosp.; Ho. Surg. St. John's Hosp. Chelmsford. .

MOLYNEUX, David Harvey 99 Carholme Avenue, Burnley BB10 4PT Tel: 01282 54393 — MB BS 1979 Lond.; MA Oxf. 1982, BA 1976; MRCGP 1984; DRCOG 1982. Dept. Gen. Pract. Leeds Univ.

MOLYNEUX, Mrs Helen Mary 26 Nairn Road, Canford Cliffs, Poole BH13 7NH — MB BS 1991 Lond.; BSc (Physiol.) Lond. 1988.

***MOLYNEUX, Matthew Keith** Flat 1, Cap Martin, The Serpentine, Crosby, Liverpool L23 6TD — MB BS 1998 Lond.; MB BS Lond 1998.

MOLYNEUX, Neil Richard Parkenwise, Penny's Lane, Par PL24 2SH — MB BS 1991 Lond.; BSc Lond. 1988; MRCP (UK) 1995.

MOLYNEUX, Paul David Cover Drive, Hosey Hill, Westerham TN16 1TA — MB BS 1991 Lond.

MOM, Mr Jaswant Singh 1 Canterbury Avenue, Bowerham, Lancaster LA1 4AU Tel: 01524 60268; 161 Balden Road, Harborne, Birmingham B32 2EL Tel: 0121 681 2876 — MB BS 1980 New Delhi; MS New Delhi 1984; MRCS Eng. LRCP Lond. 1986; FRCS Glas. 1989; Dip. Urol. Lond 1992. Founder Mem. Brit. Erectile DysFunc. Gp. Socs: BMA; W Scotl. Urol. Gp.; (Ex.-Pres.) Doctor's Mess St. Chad's Hosp. Birm. Prev: Regist. (Surg.) NW Region; SHO (Urol. & Surg.) Roy. Lancaster Infirm.; SHO Rotat. Sunderland Roy. Infirm. VTS.

MOMAN, Roshanali Bhanji Station Road Surgery, 33b Station Road, New Barnet, Barnet EN5 1PH Tel: 020 8440 2912 Fax: 020 8441 8711 — MB BS 1963 Lond. (Univ. Coll. Hosp.)

MOMEN, A Avenue Medical Centre, 51-53 Victoria Avenue, Blackley, Manchester M9 6BA Tel: 0161 720 8282 Fax: 0161 740 7991 — MB BS 1968 Dacca; MB BS 1968 Dacca.

MOMEN, Moojan Sandy Health Centre Medical Practice, Northcroft, Sandy SG19 1JQ Tel: 01767 682525 Fax: 01767 681600 — MB BChir 1975 Camb.; MA Camb. 1975; MRCS Eng. LRCP Lond. 1974. (Camb. & Guy's) Prev: SHO (Gen. Med.) Plymouth Gen. Hosp.; Ho. Off. (Gen. Surg.) St. Olave's Hosp. Lond.; Ho. Off. (Gen. Med.) Guy's Hosp. Lond.

***MOMEN, Sedrhat Attar** Wixamtree, Sand Lane, Northill, Biggleswade SG18 9AD — MB ChB 1998 Liverp.; MB ChB Liverp 1998.

MOMJIAN, Lena Leon Baghdasar 10 Romanby Court, 31-33 Mill St., Redhill RH1 6PA Tel: 01737 213885; 10 Romanby Court, 31-33 Mill St., Redhill RH1 6PA Tel: 01737 213885 — MB ChB 1982 Basrah. Prev: Regist. (O & G) Redhill Hosp. & Hillingdon Hosp.; SHO (O & G) Ealing Hosp.

MOMOH, John Aidenomo 31 Ingel Way, London N12 0QP — State Exam Med 1983 Cologne.

MON MON, Gale Paediatric Department, Southport & Formby NHS Trust, Town Lane Kew, Southport PR8 2NE — MB BS 1985 Rangoon; MRCP (UK) 1992. Staff Grade (Paediat.) S.port & Formby NHS Trust. Prev: Clin. Med. Off. Clwyd HA.

MONAGHAN, Andrew Martin 45 Kingscote Road, Birmingham B15 3LA — MB ChB 1996 Birm.; ChB Birm. 1996.

MONAGHAN, Carl Armstrong 40 Carmel Street, Belfast BT7 1QE — MB BCh BAO 1993 Belf.

MONAGHAN, Caroline Anne 30 Highgrove, Lisburn BT27 5AX — MB BCh BAO 1991 Belf.

***MONAGHAN, Catherine Mary** 401 Thornaby Road, Thornaby, Stockton-on-Tees TS17 8QN — MB ChB 1997 Leeds.

MONAGHAN, Clare Elizabeth Tel: 02887 722821 — MB BCh BAO 1981 Belf.; MRCPsych 1988. Cons. Gen. Adult & Psychiat. of Old Age.

***MONAGHAN, Darren Andrew Thomas** 19 Wandsworth Park, Bangor BT19 1BD — MB ChB 1998 Glas.; MB ChB Glas 1998.

MONAGHAN, David 30 Spring Grove Gardens, Wharncliffe Side, Sheffield S35 0EL — MB ChB 1981 Liverp.; MRCP (UK) 1984; FRCR 1990. Cons. Radiol. Doncaster. Prev: Sen. Regist. (Radiol.) Sheff.

***MONAGHAN, Deborah Ann** 19 Portland Street, Coatbridge ML5 3LH — MB ChB 1997 Glas.

MONAGHAN, Hannah 22 Dundas Street, Edinburgh EH3 6JN Tel: 0131 566 7177 Email: hannah.m@demon.ac.uk — MB BS 1994 Lond.; BSC (Hons.) 1991; MRCP (Ed.) 1997. (St. Marys Hosp.) Regist. (Path) RIE Edin. Prev: SHO (Path.) RVI Newc.; SHO Med. Rotat.

MONAGHAN, Mr John Michael Red Lodge, 6 Montagu Avenue, Gosforth, Newcastle upon Tyne NE3 4HY — MB ChB 1966 Ed.; FRCS Ed. 1971; FRCOG 1984, M 1972. Dir. Gyn. Oncol. Servs. Qu. Eliz. Hosp. Gateshead; Hon. Cons. Newc. Hosps.; Hon. Sen. Lect. (Gyn. Oncol.) Univ. Newc. u Tyne; Hon. Vis. Cons. Dumfries & Galloway Hosps.; Dep. Edr. in Chief Internat. Jl. Gyn. Cancer.

MONAGHAN, Kim Nina Park Green Surgery, Sunderland Street, Macclesfield SK11 6HW Tel: 01625 429555 Fax: 01625 502950 — MB BS 1983 Newc.; MRCGP 1989; DRCOG 1986. Prev: Trainee GP Stockport VTS; Ho. Phys. Sunderland Gen. Hosp.; Ho. Surg. Hosp. N. Shields.

MONAGHAN, Kyran Francis Fintona Medical Centre, 33 Dromore Road, Fintona, Omagh BT78 2BB Tel: 028 8284 1203 Fax: 028 8284 0545; 5 Killyliss Road, Fintona, Omagh BT78 2DL — MB BCh BAO 1982 Belf.; MRCGP 1988; DCH RCP Dub. 1987; DRCOG 1985. Prev: SHO (Paediat.) Waveney Hosp. Ballymena; SHO (Med.) Coleraine Hosp.; SHO (Surg.) & (A & E) S. Tyrone Hosp. Dungannon.

MONAGHAN, Mary Teresa 9 Drumgelloch Street, Airdrie ML6 7EW — MB ChB 1975 Glas.; MRCPsych 1987; DRCOG 1977.

MONAGHAN, Paul Bernard Flat 1, 101 Maryhill Road, Glasgow G20 7XN — MB ChB 1994 Aberd.

MONAGHAN, Stephen Paul Department of Public Health and Policy, Bro Taf HA, Temple of Peace and Health, Cathays Park, Cardiff CF10 3NW Tel: 029 2040 2514 Fax: 029 2040 2526; 12 Archer Road, Penarth CF64 3LS Tel: 029 2065 3312 — MB ChB 1987 Leic.; MFPHM 1997; MRCGP 1996; MPH Wales 1995; Dip. Epidemiol. RCP 1992. Research Fell. Univ. of Wales. Prev: Sen. Regist. (Pub. Health Med.) Morgannwg HA; Regist. (Gen. Pract.) Swansea; Regist. (Pub. Health Med.) E. Dyfed & Pembrokesh. HA.

MONAGHAN, Steven Cunningham 52 Thornley Park Avenue, Paisley PA2 7SF — MB ChB 1991 Glas.

MONAGHAN, Suna Dawn 141 Crewe Road, Nantwich CW5 6NB — MB BChir 1990 Camb.; DRCOG 1993; DCH RCP Lond. 1992; FRCA 1997.

MONAGHAN, Susan Jane Failsworth Health Centre, Ashton Road W., Failsworth, Manchester M35 0HN Tel: 0161 681 1818 — MB ChB 1980 Manch.

MONAGHAN ADDY, David John Erme House, Mount Gould Hospital, Mount Gould Road, Plymouth PL7 2AU — MB BS 1971 Lond.; MRCS Eng. LRCP Lond. 1969; MRCPsych 1975; DPM Eng. 1974. (St. Bart.) Cons. Child & Family Psychiat. Mt. Gold Hosp. Plymouth.

MONAHAN, Ann Maria 46 Kingsley Street, London SW11 5LE — MB BS 1980 Lond.

MONAHAN, Elaine Catherine 34 Dupont Road, London SW20 8EQ — MB BS 1994 Lond.; MB BS (Hons.) Lond. 1994; BSc Lond. 1991; FRCA 1998. SHO (Anaesth.) Frimley Pk. Hosp. Specialist Regist. - St. Geo.s Hosp. Rotat., Lond. Specialist Regist. - Epsam Hosp. Prev: Specialist Regist. Kingston Hosp.

MONAHAN, Eoin Bernard 43 Ventress Farm Court, Cambridge CB1 8HD — MB BCh BAO 1990 NUI.

MONAHAN, Jacqueline Quarryfield, Bakers Hill, Tiverton EX16 5NE Tel: 0188 425 3774 — MB ChB Manch. 1967.

MONAHAN, Mr Patrick Robert Wallworth (retired) Parklands, 19 Lime Trees Avenue, Llangattock, Crickhowell NP8 1LB — MB BS 1960 Lond.; FRCS Ed. 1966. Prev: Cons. Surg. Ridgeway Hosp. Swindon.

MONAHAN, Peter Brian (retired) Quarryfield Bakers Hill, Tiverton EX16 5NE Tel: 01884 253774 — MB BChir Camb. 1964; BA Camb. 1964; FRCOG 1989, M 1971; DObst RCOG 1968. Prev: Hosp. Pract. (O & G) Tiverton & Dist. Hosp.

MONARD, Patrick Terence (retired) Abbotts, The St, Brockdish, Diss IP21 4JB Tel: 01379 668667 — MB ChB 1950 Ed.; MSc (Occupat. Med.) Lond. 1971; MFOM RCP Lond. 1979. Prev: Med. Off. Occupat. Health W. Suff. Health Auth.

MONCASTER

*MONCASTER, Michael Gareth 2 Saracens Row, High St., Measham, Swadlincote DE12 7HZ Tel: 01530 271663 — MB ChB 1998 Manch.; MB ChB Manch 1998.

MONCK-MASON, Julia Margaret 3 Hayside Walk, Malpas SY14 8PE — MB ChB 1977 Leeds; MFFP 1993; BSc (Hons) 1994. Clin. Med. Off. (Family Plann. & Wom. Health) Conway & Derbysh. Trust; Clin. Med. Off. (Family Plann. & Wom. Health) Chester & Halton Comm. Trust; Staff Grade (Paediat.) Chester & Halton Comm. Trust.

MONCKTON, John (retired) Highbury Cottage, 40 College St., Bury St Edmunds IP33 1NL Tel: 01284 754409 Email: burymonk@aol.com — MRCS Eng. LRCP Lond. 1948; FCOphth. 1989; DO Eng. 1951. Prev: Cons. Ophth. Surg. W. Suff. Hosp. Gp. & Newmarket Gen. Hosp.

MONCRIEF, Andrew Charles West Walk Surgery, 21 West Walk, Yate, Bristol BS37 4AX Tel: 01454 272200 — MB ChB 1986 Sheff.; MRCGP 1993; Cert. Family Plann. JCC 1989. Socs: Dip. Obst. RNZCOG.

MONCRIEFF, Anne Brunton 'Manor Croft', Manor Heath Road, Halifax HX3 0EE — MB ChB 1977 Glas.; MRCGP 1982; DRCOG 1979.

MONCRIEFF, Colin James Heath Lane Surgery, Earl Shilton, Leicester LE9 7PB Tel: 01455 844431 Fax: 01455 442297 — MB ChB 1981 Glas.; MRCGP 1986; DA (UK) 1987; DRCOG 1983.

MONCRIEFF, Evelyn Margaret Cherryvalley Health Centre, Kings Square, Belfast BT5 7AR — MB BCh BAO 1989 Belf.; MRCGP 1993; DCH Dub. 1992; DRCOG 1992; DFFP 1992. (Qu. Univ. Belf.) Prev: Clin. Med. Off. Sch. Health (Family Plann. & Pub. Health Med.) Belf.; SHO (Med.) Belf. City Hosp.

MONCRIEFF, George Craven Bicester Health Centre, Coker Close, Bicester OX26 6AT Tel: 01869 249333 Fax: 01869 320314; Lime Hollow, Middleton Stoney, Bicester OX25 4AP Tel: 01869 343242 — MB BS 1979 Lond.; MRCP (UK) 1985; MRCGP 1985; DRCOG 1984; DCH RCP Lond. 1984. Prev: Trainee GP Banbury VTS; SHO (Gen. Med.) Kingston Gen. Hosp. Surrey; SHO (Renal Med.) St. Thos. Hosp. Lond.

MONCRIEFF, Joanna Margaret Moors End, North St., Islip, Kidlington OX5 2SQ — MB BS 1989 Newc.

*MONCRIEFF, Joanne 5 Lampson Lane, Killearn, Glasgow G63 9PF — MB ChB 1995 Glas.

MONCRIEFF, Marc Dominic Spence Mere Cottage, Church Lane, Semer, Ipswich IP7 6JB — MB BS 1995 Lond. (UMDS) SHO Rotat. (Plastic Surg.) W. Norwich Hosp.

MONCRIEFF, Martin Wedmore John Radcliffe Hospital, Oxford OX3 9DU — BM BCh 1958 Oxf.; FRCP Lond. 1977, M 1965; DObst RCOG 1960. Cons. Paediat. John Radcliffe Hosp. Oxf. Socs: Brit. Paediat. Assn. & Renal Assn. Prev: Cons. Paediat. Derbysh. Childr. Hosp.; Lect. Dept. Child Health Univ. Birm.; Ho. Phys. Hosp. Sick Childr. Gt. Ormond St. Lond.

MONCRIEFF, Robert Health Centre, Victoria Road, Hartlepool TS26 8DB Tel: 01429 273191; 4 Newlands Avenue, Hartlepool TS26 9NU Tel: 01429 272614 — MB ChB 1952 St. And.; DObst RCOG 1953. Prev: Ho. Surg. Hartlepools Hosp. & Plaistow Matern. Hosp.; Ho. Phys. (Paediat.) Middlesbrough Gen. Hosp.

MONCRIEFF, Zina Eveline (retired) 129 Harley Street, London W1G 6BA Tel: 020 7935 1777 — MB ChB 1938 Aberd.; FRCP Lond. 1970, M 1944; DCH Eng. 1942.

MONCUR, Peter Harrigan 3 The Croft, Strensall, York YO32 5WU Tel: 01904 492517 — MB ChB 1992 Dundee; MRCP 1996. (Dund.) Research Fell. (Gastroenterol.) St. Jas. Univ. Hosp., Leeds. Prev: Specialist Regist. (Gastroenterol.) Yorks. Rotat.

MOND, Carmel Tessa 10 Meadway Close, London NW11 7BH — MB BS 1983 Lond.

MOND, Nathaniel Cohen (retired) Mannings, Bull Hill, Chadlington, Oxford OX7 3ND — MRCS Eng. LRCP Lond. 1939; FRCGP 1971. Prev: Maj. RAMC.

MONDAL, Ansar Ali 12 Haworth Crescent, Moorgate, Rotherham S60 3BW Tel: 01709 362752 — MB BS 1967 Calcutta; MRCOG 1980.

MONDAL, Bijoy Krishna Rotherham General Hospital, Rotherham S60 2UD Tel: 01709 304162 Fax: 01709 304419; Shanti-Niketan, Sitwell Grove, Moorgate, Rotherham S60 3AY Tel: 01709 373985 — MB BS Dacca 1964; FRCP Lond. 1987; FRCP Ed. 1986; FRCP Glas. 1984; MRCP (UK) 1973; DTM & H Liverp. 1967. (Dacca) Clin. Dir. & Cons. Phys. Geriat. Rotherham HA.; Hon. Clin. Lect. Sheff. Univ. Socs: BMA & Geriat. Soc. Prev: Sen. Regist. (Geriat. Med.) Birm. RHB & United Birm. Hosps.; Regist. (Med.) Grange Hosp. Weaverham & Salford Hosps.

*MONDAL, Debjani 7 Bryncoed, Radyr, Cardiff CF15 8RH — MB BS 1998 Lond.; MB BS Lond 1998.

MONDAL, Kamalendra Nath District General Hospital, Gawber Road, Barnsley S75 3EP Tel: 012226 286122 — LRCP LRCS 1982 Ed.; MB BS APS Univ. Rewa 1980; LRCP LRCS Ed. LRCPS Glas. 1982.

MONE, Arthur Denis Ferrybridge Medical Centre, 8-10 High Street, Ferrybridge, Wakefield WF11 8NQ Tel: 01977 672109 Fax: 01977 671107; Rowardennan, Well Farm, Lumby, Leeds LS25 5JA Tel: 01977 682149 Fax: 01977 680291 Email: amonex2@aol.com — MB ChB 1982 Glas.; MRCGP 1986; Dip. Sports Med Lond. 1992. GP Ferrybridge.

MONE, Arthur Joseph 11 Muirhill Avenue, Glasgow G44 3HP Tel: 0141 637 9695 — LRCP LRCS 1948 Ed.; LRCP LRCS Ed. LRFPS Glas. 1948.

MONE, James Gerrard 6 Quadrant Road, Newlands, Glasgow G43 2QJ — MB ChB 1950 Glas.; MRCP (UK) 1981; FRCPS Glas. 1991; FFA RCS Eng. 1964; DA Eng. 1961. (Glas.) Cons. Anaesth. W.. Infirm. Glas. Prev: Sen. Regist. W.. Infirm. Glas.

MONEDERO ISORNA, Miguel Cottage 36, Residential Complex, Inverclyde Royal Hospital, Larkfield Road, Greenock PA16 0XH — LMS 1988 Basque Provinces.

MONELLA, Salvatore Christopher Medwyn Surgery, Moores Road, Dorking RH4 2BG Tel: 01306 882422 Fax: 01306 742280; 1-4 Marley Rise, 2 Ridgeway Road, Dorking RH4 3BP — MB BS 1991 Lond.; BSc (Hons.) 1996; MRCGP 1995.

MONELLE, Tessa Jag Kent County Ophthalmic & Aural Hospital, Church St., Maidstone ME14 1DT; 82 Roseholme, Maidstone ME16 8DS — MB BS 1991 Newc.

MONELLE, Timothy John Sun-Lea, 26 Ifton Road, Rogiet, Newport NP26 3SS — MB BS 1990 Lond.

MONEY, Brian Ironside Maryport Group Practice, Alneburgh House, Ewanrigg Road, Maryport CA15 8EL Tel: 01900 815544 Fax: 01900 816626; The Mount, Camp Road, Maryport CA15 6JN Tel: 01900 812244 — MB BS 1978 Lond.; MRCGP 1983; DRCOG 1982. (St. Mary's) Clin. Dir., Maryport Health Servs. (Primary Care Act Pilot Site).

MONEY, Patricia Jean (retired) 5 Rowlands Close, Bathford, Bath BA1 7TZ Tel: 01225 859454 — MB BS Lond. 1961; MRCS Eng. LRCP Lond. 1962; MRCGP 1974; DObst RCOG 1964. Prev: Ho. Surg. & Ho. Phys. St. Alfege's Hosp. Lond.

MONEY, Mr Richard Peter Station Road Surgery, 69 Station Road, Sidcup DA15 7DS Tel: 020 8309 0201 Fax: 020 8309 9040 — MB BChir 1978 Camb.; FRCS Eng. 1982; MRCGP 1989. Prev: Regist. (Gen. Surg.) Orpington Hosp.; SHO (Gen. Surg.) Lewisham Hosp.; Ho. Surg. Guy's Hosp. Lond.

MONEY, Theodore David Fountain (retired) Walnut Tree Farm, Bunwell, Norwich NR16 1NA Tel: 01953 789358 — MB BChir 1937 Camb.; MRCS Eng. LRCP Lond. 1932; MA Camb. (Nat. Sc. Trip. Pt. I. cl. I, Pt. II, cl; III); DObst RCOG 1947. Prev: Ho. Phys. Roy. Infirm. Bristol.

MONEY-KYRLE, Andrew Richard William Redbridge NHS Trust, Department Cardiology, King George Hospital, Ilford, London SW1 Tel: 020 8983 8000; 22 Kerrison Road, London SW11 2QE Tel: 020 7228 0352 Email: amkyrle@globalnet.co.uk — MB BS 1991 Lond.; MA Oxf. 1988; MRCP (UK) 1994. (St Bartholomews) Specialist Regist. (Cardiol.). Prev: Research Fell. Roy. Brompton Hosp.

MONEY-KYRLE, Julian Francis Radiotherapy Department, Royal Marsden Hospital, Fulham Road, London SW3 6JJ Tel: 020 7352 8171; 8 Burnaby Gardens, London W4 3DT Tel: 020 8995 6795 Fax: 020 8995 3611 Email: 101757.3154@compuserve.com — MB BS 1986 Lond.; MA Camb. 1992, BA 1983; MRCP (UK) 1992; FRCR 1997. (Westm.) Specialist Trainee Regist. (Clin. Oncol.) Roy. Marsden Hosp. Lond. Prev: Specialist Trainee Regist. (Clin. Oncol.) Guildford; Jun. Research Fell. (HIV & Oncol.) W.m. Hosp. Lond.; SHO (Med.) Watford Gen. Hosp. & St. Geo. Hosp. Lond.

MONEY-KYRLE, Roger Spencer (retired) Whetham Farm House, Calne SN11 0PU Tel: 01380 850270 — MB BS 1964 Lond.; MA Camb. 1953; MRCS Eng. LRCP Lond. 1964; DObst RCOG 1966. Prev: GP Wallingford.

MONGA, Ashwani Kumar 96 Mantilla Road, London SW17 8DU — BM BS 1986 Nottm.; MRCOG 1992.

MONGALEE, Mehmood-El-Rashid Medical Centre, 36 Engineer Regiment, Invicta Park, Maidstone ME14 2NA Tel: 01622 767280; 41 Curzon Road, Maidstone ME14 5BB Tel: 01622 754055 — LRCPI & LM, LRSCI & LM 1972; LRCPI & LM, LRCSI & LM 1972.

MONGER, John David (retired) Arnsdorf, Walden Avenue, Arborfield, Reading RG2 9HR Tel: 01189 760603 — MB BS 1959 Lond.; MRCS Eng. LRCP Lond. 1959. Prev: GP Reading.

MONGWA, Shathani Leonora c/o Dr Segwagwe, Residence 13, Medway Hospital, Windmill Road, Gillingham ME7 5NY — MB ChB 1986 Glas.

MONIE, Robert David Hugh The Chest Clinic, Southern General Hospital, 1451 Govan Road, Glasgow G51 4TF; 15 Colquhoun Drive, Bearsden, Glasgow G61 4NQ — MB ChB 1970 Ed.; FRCPS Glas. 1992; FRCP Ed. 1989; MRCP (UK) 1976; DRCOG 1972. Cons. Phys. i/c Respirat. Med. S.. Gen. Hosp. Glas.

MONIER-WILLIAMS, Peter Lawrence Crawford (retired) Downsview, Duncton, Petworth GU28 0JY — BM BCh 1954 Oxf.

MONIZ, Cajetan Francis Clinical Biochemistry, King's College Hospital, London SE5 9RS Tel: 020 7346 3728 Fax: 020 7737 7434; 31 Sandilands, Croydon CR0 5DF — MB BS 1975 Lond.; BSc Sussex 1970; MSc Lond. 1979; MRCS Eng. LRCP Lond. 1975; FRCPath 1994, M 1982. (Westm.) Cons. Chem. Path. Kings Coll. Hosp. Lond.; Hon. Sen. Lect. KCSMD. Socs: Bone & Tooth Soc.; (Edit. Comm.) ACP; ACB. Prev: Sen. Regist. King's Coll. Hosp. Lond.; Sen. Regist. (Clin. Chem.) Lewisham Hosp. Lond.; Asst. Lect. Middlx. Hosp. Med. Sch.

MONK, Barry Edward Manor Hospital, Biddenham, Bedford MK40 4AW Tel: 01234 792262 Fax: 01234 792223 Email: barry.monk@bedhos.anglox.nhs.uk; Manor Hospital, Biddenham, Bedford MK40 4AW Tel: 01234 792262 Fax: 01234 792223 — MB BChir 1976 Camb.; MA Camb. 1976; FRCP Lond. 1994; MRCP (UK) 1977. (Westm.) Cons. Dermat. Bedford Gen. Hosp.; Cons. i/c Tunable Dye Laser Unit Bedford Hosp.; Mem. Med. Panel, Brit. Boxing Bd. Control. Socs: Fell. Roy. Soc. Med. (Mem. Sect. Dermat.); Brit. Skin Laser Study Gp.; Pres. Elect, Dowling Club. Prev: Sen. Regist. (Dermat.) King's Coll. Hosp. Lond.; Regist. (Dermat.) Roy. Free Hosp. Lond.; Regist. (Med.) W.m. Hosp. Lond.

MONK, Christopher Richard Directorate of Anaesthesia, Bristol Royal Infirmary, Marlborough St., Bristol BS2 8HW Tel: 0117 928 2163 Fax: 0117 928 2098; Litfield House, Litfield Place, Clifton, Bristol Tel: 0117 923 8541 — MB ChB 1978 Manch.; FRCA 1983. Cons. Anaesth. Bristol Roy. Infirm. Socs: Med. Soc. Assn. Anaesths.

MONK, Mr Cyril John Elmes 88 Rodney Street, Liverpool L1 9AR Tel: 0151 709 5469 Fax: 0151 709 7279; 16 St Anthonys Road, Liverpool L23 8TP — MChOrth Liverp. 1966; MB BCh Witwatersrand 1954; FRCS Ed. 1959; FRCS Eng. 1962. (Witwatersrand) Emerit. Cons. Surg. Orthop. Roy. Liverp. Univ. Hosp. Trust; Emerit. Cons. Orthop. Surg. Roy. Liverp. Childrs. Hosp. Alder Hey. Socs: Fell. BOA; Liverp. Med. Inst. Prev: Sen. Lect. (Orthop. Surg.) Univ. Liverp.; Regist. Robt. Jones & Agnes Hunt Orthop. Hosp. OsW.ry.

MONK, Mr David Nigel Countess of Chester NHS Trust, Liverpool Road, Chester CH2 1UL Tel: 01244 365000 Fax: 01244 365252 Email: davidmonk@compuserve.com — MB ChB 1986 Liverp.; FRCS Eng. 1990; FRCS 1998. Cons. (Surg.) Countess of Chester NHS Trust, Chester. Prev: Sen. Regist. (Gen. Surg.) NW RHA.

MONK, Dorothy Anne 16 St Anthony's Road, Blundellsands, Liverpool L23 8TP — MB ChB 1965 Liverp.; Dip. Occ. Med. 1997. Occupat. Health Liverp. Socs: Liverp. Med. Inst.; Soc. Occup. Med. Prev: JP Co. of Merseyside S., Sefton Petty Sessional Div.

***MONK, Fleur Louise** 5 Hawks Road, Hailsham BN27 3BL — MB BS 1998 Lond.; MB BS Lond 1998.

MONK, James Francis (retired) Bridge Cottage, Goring, Reading RG8 9AN Tel: 01491 872500 Email: j.monk@talk21.com — BM BCh 1941 Oxf.; DM Oxf. 1950, BM BCh 1941. Prev: GP Goring-on-Thames.

***MONK, Jonathan Peter** 16 St Anthonys Road, Liverpool L23 8TP — MB ChB 1994 Sheff.

MONK, Michael Charles Brewers Cottage, 35 London Rd, Copford, Colchester CO6 1LG Tel: 01206 211370 — MB BS 1970 Lond.; MRCS Eng. LRCP Lond. 1970; MLCOM 1979; DMRD Eng. 1978. (St. Mary's) Tutor (Radiodiag.) Lond. Coll. Osteop. Med. Socs: Brit. Osteop. Assn. & Brit. Assn. Manip. Med. Prev: Surg. Lt.-Cdr. RN, Dep. Base Med. Off. HMS Tamar, Hong Kong; Trainee Radiol. RN Hosp. Haslar; Regist. (Radiol.) St. Thos. Hosp. Lond.

MONK, Penelope Elizabeth Middleway Surgery, Middleway, St. Blazey, Par PL24 2JL Tel: 01726 812019 Fax: 01726 816464 — MB ChB 1986 Bristol.

MONK, Philip Nigel Leicestershire Health, Gwendolen Road, Leicester LE5 4QF Tel: 0116 258 8572 Fax: 0116 258 8569; 18 Hill Field, Oadby, Leicester LE2 4RW Tel: 0116 271 6687 — MB ChB 1979 Birm.; FFPHM RCP (UK) 1990; MRCGP 1983. Cons. Communicable Dis. Control. Leics. HA. Socs: BMA. Prev: GP Leic.

***MONK, Rachel Elizabeth** 43a Earls Av, Folkestone CT20 2HB — MB ChB 1997 Sheff.

MONKHOUSE, Christopher Richard Queens Road Medical Practice, The Grange, St. Peter Port, Guernsey GY1 1RH Tel: 01481 724184 Fax: 01481 716431; 28 Saumarez Street, St. Peter Port, Guernsey GY1 2PU — MB BS 1977 Lond.; BSc (Hons.) Lond. 1974; MRCGP 1982; DRCOG 1982. (Middlx.) Mem. Med. Staff P.ss Eliz. Hosp. Guernsey.

MONKHOUSE, Diane 11 The Lane, Sedgefield, Stockton-on-Tees TS21 3BE — MB BS 1993 Newc.

MONKHOUSE, Marilyn Shackleton Department of Anaesthesia, Southampton Gen. Hospital, Tremona Road, Southampton SO16 6YD Tel: 02380 777222; Apartment 7f, St Mary's Court, Rohais De Haut, Castel, Guernsey GY5 7AA Tel: 0481 52935 — MB BS 1977 Lond.; FFA RCS Eng. 1981. (Middlx. Hosp. Med. Sch.) Staff Grade Anaesth. - Soton Gen Hosp.; Clin. Asst. (Anaesth.) Soton. Gen. Hosp. Socs: BMA. Prev: GP Guernsey.

MONKHOUSE, Mr Ray 3 Bankfield Drive, Holmbridge, Huddersfield HD9 2PH — MB ChB 1991 Ed.; FRCS Ed. 1996. SHO (Gen. Surg.) Huddersfield NHS Trust; Specialsit Regist. - Orthops. - Yorks. Train. Scheme. Prev: SHO (Surg.) Aintree Hosps. Liverp.

MONKLEY, Clive Ronald The Bull Ring Surgery, 5 The Bull Ring, St. John's, Worcester WR2 5AA Tel: 01905 422883 Fax: 01905 423639; Ridgeway House, Ridgeway Cross, Cradley, Malvern WR13 5JJ Tel: 01886 880158 — MB BS 1981 Lond.; MSc (Sports Med.) Nottm. 1994; MRCGP 1985; DRCOG 1983. (Lond. Hosp.) Sports Phys. - BUPA S. Bank Hosp., Worcester; Lect. Worcester Coll. Higher Educat. Sports Scis. Socs: Brit. Assn. Sport & Med.; Soc. Orthop. Med.

MONKMAN, David Simon East Barnet Health Centre, 149 East Barnet Road, Barnet EN4 8QZ Tel: 020 8440 7417 Fax: 020 8447 0126 — MB BS 1981 Lond.; MRCP (UK) 1985; Cert. Family Plann. JCC 1988; DRCOG 1988. Prev: Regist. (Haemat.) Lond. Hosp. & N. Middlx. Hosp.; Ho. Phys. Roy. Free Hosp. Lond.; SHO (Med.) Roy. N.ern & Whittington Hosp. Lond.

***MONKS, Allan William** 51 Gig La, Woolston, Warrington WA1 4EE — MB ChB 1997 Dundee.

MONKS, Charles John 31 Kensington Road, Oldham OL8 4BZ Tel: 0161 633 3957 — MB ChB 1967 Manch. Socs: BMA.

MONKS, David Clayson Pemberley Avenue Surgery, 32 Pemberley Avenue, Bedford MK40 2LA Tel: 01234 351051 Fax: 01234 349246 — MB BS 1963 Lond.; MRCS Eng. LRCP Lond. 1962. (St. Geo.) Socs: BMA. Prev: Ho. Phys. Kingston Gen. Hosp.; Ho. Surg. Salisbury Gen. Infirm.; Ho. Off. (Obst.) Beckenham Matern. Hosp.

MONKS, Mrs Ishbel Margaret (retired) 38 Taylors Field, Kingsmill Road, Driffield YO25 6FQ Tel: 01377 256174 — MB ChB Aberd. 1943; FRCOG 1984, M 1950; DRCOG 1948. Prev: Sen. Regist. (O & G) W. Middlx. Hosp.

MONKS, Marjorie 93 Whitefield Road, Stockton Heath, Warrington WA4 6ND Tel: 01925 263073; 29 Wilson Patten Street, Warrington WA1 1PG Tel: 01925 50705 — MB BS 1963 Lond.; DObst RCOG 1965. (Roy. Free)

***MONKS, Paul James** Lister Hospital, Coveys Mill Lane, Stevenage SG1 4RT — BChir 1995 Camb.

MONKS, Paul Saville 90 Chichester Road, Park Hill, Croydon CR0 5NB Tel: 020 8681 3645 Fax: 020 8688 9877 Email: pands.monks@btinternet.com — BM BCh 1964 Oxf.; MA, BM BCh Oxf. 1964; FFA RCS Eng. 1969. (St. Thos.) Cons. Anaesth. Lond. Hosp.; Cons. Anaesths. Barts 1995; Teach. Univ. Lond. 1974. Socs: Soc. for Minimally Invasive Ther.; Soc. Francaise D'Anesth. & Reanimation; Assn. Anaesth. Prev: Sen. Regist. (Anaesth.) Roy. Postgrad. Med. Sch. Lond.; Regist. (Anaesth.) St. Thomas's Hosp. Lond.

MONKS

MONKS, Mr Peter Joseph Wilkinson (retired) Ashton Court, Holne, Newton Abbot TQ13 7SR Tel: 01364 631264 — MB BS 1944 Lond.; FRCS Eng. 1951. Prev: Cons. Surg. Torbay, Paignton, Dartmouth, Brixham & Newton Abbott Hosps.

MONKSFIELD, Peter Andrew 9 Myra Street, London SE2 0HA Tel: 0976 626521 Email: pmonksfield@hotmail.com — MB ChB 1997 Manch. (Manchester) SHO A+E - Preston 1999; SHO Ortha. Barnsley 1999.

MONNERY, Lisa 9 Sandringham Close, Chandlers Ford, Eastleigh SO53 4LE — MB BS 1994 Lond.; BSc (Biomed. Sci.) Lond. 1991. SHO (Anaesth.) P.ss Margt. Hosp. Swindon. Prev: Ho. Off. (Gen. Med.) St. Heliers Hosp. Carshalton; Ho. Off. (Gen. Surg.) S. Warks. Hosp. Warwick.

MONNERY, Philip Michael, Squadron Ldr. RAF Med. Br. Officers Mess, Royal Hospital, Haslar, Gosport PO12 2AA Tel: 01705 584255 — MB BS 1991 Lond. SHO (ENT) Roy. Hosp. Haslar Gosport.

MONNINGTON HOWE, Marie-Anne Alexia 7 Croft House, Paddock Lane, Chuckery, Walsall WS1 2HP — MB ChB 1993 Sheff.

MONRO, Alexander James Vine Surgery, Hindhayes Lane, Street BA16 0ET Tel: 01458 841122; 6 South Street, Walton, Street BA16 9RY — MB BS 1980 Lond.; BA Oxf. 1977; MRCP (UK) 1986; MRCGP 1988; DRCOG 1988; DCH RCP Lond. 1987.

MONRO, Andrew Donald 6 The Lays, Goose St., Beckington, Bath BA11 6RS Tel: 01373 831166 — MB ChB 1993 Sheff.; DRCOG 1996. (Sheff.)

MONRO, James Armour (retired) Mander Hill, Andrew Hill Lane, Hedgerley, Slough SL2 3UL Tel: 01753 644407 Fax: 01753 645911 — MB ChB 1954 New Zealand; BSc New Zealand 1948; FFA RCS Eng. 1961; DA Eng. 1959. Prev: Cons. Anaesth. Hillingdon Hosp. Uxbridge.

MONRO, Mr James Lawrence Wessex Cardiac & Thoracic Centre, Level E, East Wing, General Hospital, Southampton SO16 6YD Tel: 02380 777222 — MB BS 1964 Lond.; FRCS Eng. 1969; MRCS Eng. LRCP Lond. 1964. (Lond. Hosp.) Cons. Cardiac Surg. Soton. Univ. Hosps. Socs: Soc. Thoracic & Cardiovasc. Surg. GB & Irel.; Brit. Cardiac Soc.; Eur. Assn. Cardiothoracic Surg. Prev: Sen. Regist. (Thoracic Surg.) Lond. Hosp.; Sen. Regist. (Cardiothoracic Surg.) Green La. Hosp. Auckland; Resid. Surg. Off. Brompton Hosp. Lond.

MONRO, James Scott Campbell 89 Woodland Road, Darlington DL3 7UA Tel: 01325 3398 — MB ChB 1940 Aberd.; DLO Eng. 1941.

MONRO, Jean Anne Breakspear Hospital, Hertfordshire House, Wood Lane, Paradise Estate, Hemel Hempstead HP2 4FD Tel: 01442 261333 Fax: 01442 266388 Email: jmonro@breakspear.org; 36 North Common, Redbourn, St Albans AL3 7BU Email: jmonro@breakspear.org — MB BS 1960 Lond.; MRCS Eng. LRCP Lond. 1960. (Lond. Hosp.) Med. Dir. (Allergy & Environm. Med.) Breakspear Hosp. Hemel Hempstead; Cons. Phys. Fachkrankenhaus Nordfriesland Bredstedt, Germany; Dip. Internat. Bd. Environm. Med. Socs: Fell. Amer. Acad. Environm. Med.; Amer. Acad. Occupat. & Environm. Med.

MONRO, John Bentley The Courtyard Surgery, London Road, Horsham RH12 1AT; Rock House, Copsale Rd, Maplehurst, Horsham RH13 6QY Tel: 01403 864341 — MB BS 1959 Lond.; DTM & H Eng. 1963. (St. Thos.) Socs: BMA.

MONRO, Pauline Sylvia (retired) 106 Westbury Road, New Malden KT3 5AL Tel: 020 8942 8510 — MB BS 1958 Lond.; BSc (1st cl. Hons.) Lond. 1955, MD 1968, MB BS (Hons.) 1958; FRCP Lond. 1974, M 1962; MRCS Eng. LRCP Lond. 1958. Prev: Cons. Neurol St. Geo. Hosp. & Atkinson Morley's Hosp. Lond.

MONRO, Peter Alexander George 7 Wigmore Close, Godmanchester, Huntingdon PE29 2JX — MRCS Eng. LRCP Lond. 1943; BA Camb. 1940, MA 1950, MD 1954, MB BChir 1943; MSc Lond. 1951. (Camb. & Lond. Hosp.) Socs: Hon. Mem. Brit. (Ex-Pres.) Brit. Microcirculat. Soc.; Hon. Mem. (Ex-Treas.) Europ. Soc. MicroCirc.; Anat. Soc. & Brit. Soc. Clin. Anat. Prev: Univ. Lect. (Anat.) Sch. Univ. Camb.; Fell, & Lect. & Dir. Studies Anat. St. John's Coll. Camb.

MONSELL, Mr Fergal Patrick 4 Tower Close, Berkhamsted HP4 3NF Tel: 01442 863123 Email: fergal.monsell@virgin.net — MB BCh 1984 Wales; MSc Wales 1995; FRCS (Orth.) 1995; FRCS Ed. 1990. (Univ. Coll. Wales) Cons. Orthop. Surg. Gt. Ormond St. Hosp. Lond.; Cons. Orthop. Surg. Roy. Nat. Orthop. Hosp. Stanmore; Hon. Sen. Lect. Inst. Child Health Lond. Prev: Lect. (Orthop. Surg.) Univ. Manch.; Research Fell. (Med. Biophysics) Univ. Manch.

MONSELL, Neil John Whitley House Surgery, Moulsham Street, Chelmsford CM2 0JJ Tel: 01245 352194 Fax: 01245 344478 — MB BS 1987 Lond.; MRCGP 1992; DRCOG 1992.

MONSELL, Raymond Michael Thomas 27 Woodview Rise, Strood, Rochester ME2 3RP — MB BCh 1984 Wales.

MONSON, Professor John Patrick Department of Endocrinology, Medical Unit, St. Bart's Hospital, London EC1A 7BE Tel: 020 7601 8346 Fax: 020 7601 8505 Email: j.p.monson@qmul.ac.uk; 13 Buckstone Close, Forest Hill, London SE23 3QT Tel: 020 8699 8562 — MB BS 1973 Lond.; MRCS Eng. LRCP Lond. 1973; FRCP 1989 Lond; MD 1983 Lond; MRCP 1975 UK. (Guy's) Prof. Of Clin. Endocrin. St Bart's & The Roy. Lond. Sch. Of Med. & Dent Qu. Mary Univ. of Lond.; Hon. Cons. Phys. & Endocrinol. St. Bart. & Roy. Lond. Hosp.; Head of Div. of Gen. and Developm. Med., Barts & The Lond. QMUL. Socs: Soc. Endocrinol.; Growth Hormone Res. Soc.; Brit. Thysoid Assn. Prev: Reader & Hon. Cons. Phys. (Endocrinol.) Lond. Hosp.; Sen. Lect. (Med., Metab. & Endocrinol.) Lond. Hosp. Med. Coll. OldCh. Hosp.; Regist. (Med.) St. Geo. Hosp. Lond.

MONSON, Professor John Rowat Telford Academic Surgical Unit, Castle Hill Hospital, Castle Road, Cottingham HU16 5JQ Tel: 01482 623225 Fax: 01482 623274 Email: j.r.monson@medschool.hull.ac.uk — MB BCh BAO Dub.; MB BCh BAO Dub. 1979; MD Dub. 1987; FRCS Eng. 1987; FRCSI 1983; FACS 1992. Prof. Surg. Castle Hill Hosp. Cottingham; Acad. Surgic. Unit Univ. Hull. Socs: (Hon. Sec.) Surg. Research Soc.; Assn. Surg.; (Vice-Pres.) Brit. Assn. Surgic. Oncol. Prev: Assoc. Dir. & Sen. Lect. Acad. Surg. Unit St. Mary's Hosp. Lond.; Surg. Fell. Mayo Clinic USA; Sen. Regist. (Surg.) Meath Hosp. Dub.

MONTAGNON, Sarah Ann Jackson and Partners, Glastonbury Surgery, Feversham Lane, Glastonbury BA6 9LP Tel: 01458 833666 Fax: 01458 834536; Freehill Villa, Westbury-sub-Mendip, Wells BA5 1HR Tel: 01749 870218 Email: sarah@freehill.demon.co.uk — MB BS 1980 Lond.; DRCOG 1984. (St. Geo.) Prev: GP Retainer Scheme Wells; GP Croydon; Trainee GP St. Helier Hosp. Carshalton VTS.

MONTAGUE, Mr Alan Peter Accident & Emergency Department, Frenchay & Southmead Hospitals, Bristol Tel: 0117 959 5112 Fax: 0117 959 5090; Box Bush Farm, Chaingate Lane, Iron Acton, Bristol BS37 9XJ Tel: 01454 228576 Email: a.montague@cwcon.net — MB BS 1979 Lond.; FRCS Ed. 1983. (St. Thos.) Cons. A & E Med. N. Bristol NHS Trust (Frenchay & S.mead Hosps.); Hon. Sen. Lect. University of Bristol. Socs: Med. Leg. Soc.; Milit. Surg. Soc.; Bristol M-C Soc. Prev: Sen. Regist. (A & E Med.) Guy's Hosp. Lond.

MONTAGUE, Celia Claire The Surgery, Newbury St., Kintbury, Hungerford RG17 9UX Tel: 01488 658294 Fax: 01488 658745 — MB BS 1985 Lond.; MA Camb. 1986. (Camb. Univ. & St. Thos. Hosp. Med. Sch.) Prev: Trainee GP Salisbury VTS; SHO (Psychiat.) Pk. Prewett Hosp. & Basingstoke Dist. Hosp.; SHO (Spinal Injuries) Odstock Hosp. Salisbury.

MONTAGUE, Gillian Rosemary Foxleigh Grange, Ascot Road, Holyport, Maidenhead SL6 3LD — MB BS 1958 Lond.; MRCS Eng. LRCP Lond. 1958. (St. Mary's)

MONTAGUE, Imogen Aletheia The Royal Oak, Fore St., Thorncombe, Chard TA20 4PD — MB ChB 1989 Sheff.

MONTAGUE, James Joseph Ederney, Enniskillen BT93 0DH Tel: 013656 31237 — MB BCh BAO 1946 NUI.

MONTAGUE, Joan Mary (retired) Elsinore, Mount Pleasant Drive, Bearsted, Maidstone ME14 4LA — MB BS 1954 Lond.; DCH Eng. 1957.

MONTAGUE, Linda Rose Trafford Healthcare NHS Trust, Trafford General Hospital, 3 Moorside Road, Urmston, Manchester M41 5SL Tel: 0161 748 4022 Fax: 0161 746 2676; Plas Brain, Llanbedreoch LL76 8SJ Tel: 01248 450847, 0161 881 6715 Email: lindamontague@doctors.org.uk — BM BS 1981 Nottm.; BMedSci Nottm. 1979; MRCPsych 1986. (Nottm.) Cons. Psychiat. Trafford Healthcare NHS Trust. Socs: Manch. Med. Soc. Prev: Sen. Regist. (Psychiat.) S. Wales Scheme; Clin. Research Fell. Univ. Manch.; Regist. (Psychiat.) Burton Rd. Hosp. Dudley.

MONTAGUE, Ray Ferguson Hartcliffe Health Centre, Hareclive Road, Hartcliffe, Bristol BS13 0JP Tel: 0117 9645588/9647925 Fax:

0117 964 9055 — MB BS 1986 Lond.; BA Oxf. 1983. Trainee GP Exeter VTS.

MONTAGUE, Richard Julian 74 Brooklands Crescent, Fulwood, Sheffield S10 4QQ Tel: 0144 230 1865 — MB ChB 1994 Sheff.

MONTAGUE-BROWN, Mr Herbert James The William Fisher Medical Centre, High Street, Southminster CM0 7AY Tel: 01621 772360 Fax: 01621 773880; 4 Cherry Orchard, Southminster CM0 7HE Tel: 01621 772207 — MB ChB 1974 Otago; FRCS Eng. 1980; MRCGP 1984. (Otago) Socs: Fell. Roy. Soc. Med.; BMA. Prev: Trainee GP Gt. Eccleston Health Centre; Regist. (Cardiothoracic Surg.) Vict. Hosp. Blackpool; SHO (O & G) Preston HA.

MONTANDON, Penelope Elizabeth (Stanley) Bewdley Medical Centre, Dog Lane, Bewdley DY12 2EG — MB ChB 1994 Birm.; DRCOG 1996; MRCGP 1998. (Birmingham) GP Partner. Prev: Locum.

MONTANEZ, Antonio 33 Redington Road, London NW3 7QY Tel: 020 7435 8500 — LMS 1960 Madrid; DPM Eng. 1970. (Univ. Madrid) Prev: Cons. Psychiat. Barnet Gen. Hosp. & Napsbury Hosp. St. Albans; Hon. Med. Asst. Univ. Coll. Hosp. Lond.; Sen. Regist. & Regist. Napsbury Hosp.

MONTANINO OLIVA, Mario Via Rubicone 8, Rome 00198, Italy; 49 Barkston Gardens, London SW5 Tel: 020 7370 4462 — State Exam Rome 1990. Socs: Amer. Assn. Gyn. Laparoscopists. Prev: Researcher (Reproduc. Endocrinol. & Infertil.) Univ. Connecticut Sch. Med., USA.

MONTE, Sarah Louise Woodcroft, Burras Lane, Otley LS21 3ET — MB BS 1993 Lond.

MONTEFIORE, David Goldsmid, OBE (retired) Hopedene, Sparrow Hill Way, Upper Weare, Axbridge BS26 2LN Tel: 01934 732182 Fax: 01934 732182 — MB BChir 1953 Camb.; MD Camb. 1960; FRCPath 1972; Dip. Bact. Lond 1960. Prev: Prof. Dept. Med. Microbiol. Univ., Ibadan.

MONTEFIORE, Madeleine Rose 75 Woolton Hill Road, Liverpool L25 4RD — MB BS 1987 Lond.; BSc Lond. 1984; MRCGP 1991; DCH RCP Lond. 1990.

MONTEGRIFFO, Victor Manuel Esteban Parkfield Medical Centre, Potters Bar EN6 1QH Tel: 01707 651234 Fax: 01707 660452; 4 Blunesfield, Potters Bar EN6 5DG Tel: 01707 653047 — MB BS 1959 Lond. (St. Mary's) Socs: Fell. Roy. Soc. Med. Prev: Regist. (Med.) Kingston & Dorking Hosps.; Ho. Phys. & Ho. Surg. St. Mary's Hosp. Lond.

MONTEIL, Michele Anne Department of Pathology, Faculty of Medical Sciences, University of the West Indies, Eric Williams Medical Sciences Complex, Champs Fleur, Trinidad & Tobago; 81 Addiscombe Court Road, Croydon CR0 6TT — MB BS 1984 W. Indies; MB BS (Hons.) W. Indies 1984; PhD (Immunol.) Univ. Lond. 1990, MSc (Clin. Immunol.) 1992; BSc Biochem. (1st. cl. Hons.) Lond. 1977; MRCPath (Immunol.) 1993. Clin. Sen. Lect. & Hon. Cons. Immunol. Char. Cross & W.m. Med. Sch. Socs: BMA.

MONTEIRO, Brendan Thomas National Centre for Mental Health Services, John Denmark Unit, Bury New Road, Manchester M25 3BL Tel: 0161 772 3437 Fax: 0161 798 5853 Email: smcateer@jdu.mhss-tr.nwest.nhs.uk — MB BS 1978 Bombay; MRCS Eng. LRCP Lond. 1981; MRCPsych Lond. 1983. (Grant Med. Coll.) Cons. Psychiat. Nat. Centre for Ment. Health & Deafness John Denmark Unit Ment. Health Servs. Salford NHS Trust; Hon. Cons. Psychiat. Brit. Deaf Assn.; Cons. Psychiat. Altrincham Priory Hosp.; Cons. Psychiat. Mayflower Hosp.- Special Forens. Servs. for Deaf people. Socs: Manch. Med. Soc. Prev: Cons. Psychiat. Ment. Health Centre for Deaf People Whittingham Hosp.; Sen. Regist. (Psychiat. for The Deaf) Whittingham Hosp. Preston & (Adult Psychiat.) Manch. Roy. Infirm.; Regist. (Psychiat.) Fife HB.

MONTEIRO, Eric Francis Fax: 0113 292 6387 Email: e.f.monteiro@leeds.ac.uk; Silverdale, 50 Leeds Road, Rawdon, Leeds LS19 6JG — MB ChB 1978 Liverp.; FRCP Lond. 1995; MRCP (UK) 1983. Cons. Phys. (Genitourin. Med.) Gen. Infirm. Leeds; Hon. Sen. Lect. (Genitourin. Med.) Leeds Univ.

MONTEIRO, Joao Leonardo Village Surgery, 233 Village Street, Derby DE23 8DD Tel: 01332 766762 Fax: 01332 272084 — MB ChB 1981 Sheff.; MRCGP 1986; DRCOG 1986. (Sheffield) GP Derby. Prev: Trainee GP Derby VTS.

MONTEIRO, Robert Flage Central Surgery, 8 Corbett Road, Walthamstow, London E17 3LA Tel: 020 8503 6700 — LRCPI & LM, LRSCI & LM 1973; LRCPI & LM, LRCSI & LM 1973.

MONTEITH, Helen Elfrida (retired) Beckside, Casthorpe Road, Barrowby, Grantham NG32 1DP Tel: 01476 565230 — MB ChB Glas. 1956. Prev: Cas. Off. Kilmarnock Infirm.

MONTEITH, Peter Gregory, Surg. Lt.-Cdr. RN 111 Worsborough Avenue, Great Sankey, Warrington WA5 1UZ — MRCS Eng. LRCP Lond. 1978. Sen. Med. Off. HMS Gloucester 5th Destroyer Squadron.

MONTEMAGNO, Rodolfo 48 Ockendon Road, London N1 3NW — State Exam Naples 1982.

MONTEOLIVA MURGA, Virginia 7 Milton Road, Eastbourne BN21 1SG — LMS 1983 Santander; MSc London 1996. Staff Grade S. Downs Health Auth. Socs: MRCPCH; BMA. Prev: Regist. (Paediat.) E.bourne.

MONTERO GARCIA, Jose Miguel A & E Department, Chorley & South Ribble District General Hospital, Preston Road, Chorley PR7 1PP; 117 Ighten Road, Burnley BB12 0LJ — LMS 1991 Granada. SHO (A & E) Chorley & S. Ribble Dist. Gen. Hosp. Socs: BMA. Prev: SHO (Orthop. & Urol.) Burnley Gen. Hosp.

*****MONTFORD, Donna Louise** 15 Middlemarch, Woodfield, Northampton NN3 8QY — MB ChB 1998 Birm.; ChB Birm. 1998.

MONTFORD, Heather 25 Sydney Road, Richmond TW9 1UB Tel: 020 8948 0907 — MB BS Lond. 1956; DObst RCOG 1958. (St. Mary's) SCMO Richmond, Twickenham & Roehampton HA. Socs: Inst. Psychosexual Med.; Fac. Fam. Plann. & Reproduc. Health Care.

MONTGOMERIE, George Alastair (retired) Riverview, Oxnam Road, Jedburgh TD8 6JJ Tel: 01835 862249 — MB ChB 1960 Glas.; DObst RCOG 1962. Prev: Regist. (ENT) Roy. Infirm. Glas.

MONTGOMERIE, James Coach House, Upper Swainswick, Bath BA1 8BU — MB BS 1991 Lond.

*****MONTGOMERIE, Roderick Alexander** Morven, Stockton Avenue, Fleet GU51 4NY — BM BS 1998 Nottm.; BM BS Nottm 1998.

*****MONTGOMERIE, Shora Daisy** 93 Lenton Boulevard, Lenton, Nottingham NG7 2FQ — BM BS 1998 Nottm.; BM BS Nottm 1998.

MONTGOMERY, Alexander John 19 Camps Crescent, Renfrew PA4 0YR — MB ChB 1961 Glas.

MONTGOMERY, Alexander Rentoul (retired) 10 Holden Road, Beeston, Nottingham NG9 1AP Tel: 0115 925 1945 — MB BCh BAO 1927 Belf. Prev: Ho. Surg. Roy. Vict. Hosp. Belf.

MONTGOMERY, Alistair John Tay Court Surgery, 50 South Tay Street, Dundee DD1 1PF — MB ChB 1978 Dundee; MRCGP 1988; DRCOG 1984. Socs: BMA (Treas. Exec. Comm. Dundee Br.).

MONTGOMERY, Mr Andrew Charles Victor (cons. rooms), Blackheath Hospital, 40-42 Lee Terrace, Blackheath, London SE3 9UD Tel: 020 8318 7722; Department Colorectal & Breast Surgery, Queen Elizabeth 2 hospital, Stadium Road, Woolwich, London SE18 4QH Tel: 020 8836 6000 — MB BS Lond. 1969; MS Lond. 1986; FRCS Eng. 1974; MRCS Eng. LRCP Lond. 1969. (Lond. Hosp.) Cons. Gen. Surg. Qu. Eliz. 2 Hosp. Socs: Assn. Coloproctol.; Brit. Assn. Surg. Oncol.; Fell.Roy. Soc. Med. Prev: Sen. Regist. (Surg.) Roy. Marsden & King's Coll. Hosp. Lond.; Resid. Surg. Off. & Sen. Regist. St. Mark's Hosp. Lond.; Sen. Regist. (Surg.) Univ. Hosp. Wales Cardiff.

MONTGOMERY, Andrew James 57 Avonmore Road, London W14 8RT — MB BChir 1993 Camb.; MRCP (UK) 1995. Prev: SHO (Neurol.) Morriston Hosp. Swansea; SHO (Med.) Wexham Pk. Hosp. Slough.

MONTGOMERY, Angela Tower Hill, Church Lane, Middleton St George, Darlington DL2 1DU — MB BS 1982 Newc.; MRCGP 1987; DRCOG 1985.

MONTGOMERY, Brian William The Health Centre, 147 Main St., East Calder, Livingston EH53 0EW Tel: 01506 882882 Fax: 01506 883630; Orchardbank, 12 Pumpherston Road, Mid Calder, Livingston EH53 0AY Tel: 01506 881358 — MB ChB 1982 Ed.; BSc MedSci Ed. 1979, MB ChB 1982. (Ed.) Med. Dir. (P/T) W. Lothian Healthcare NHS Trust, St John's Hosp., Livingston, W. Lothian. Socs: Fell. Roy. Med. Soc.

MONTGOMERY, Mr Bruce Stuart Irlam Farnham Part NHS Trust, Portsmouth Road, Rimley, Camberley GU16 5UJ Tel: 01276 604604 Ext: 4227 Fax: 01276 604829; Chaundlers Farm, Dippenhall St., Crondall, Farnham GU10 5NX Tel: 01252 851106 Fax: 01252 851830 Email: bmontgo@attglobal.net — MB BS 1981 Lond.; BSc (Hons.) Physiol. Lond. 1978, MS 1992; FRCS (Urol.) 1993; FRCS Eng. 1986. (Univ. Coll. Lond.) Cons. Urol. Frimley Pk. &

MONTGOMERY

Basingstoke Dist. Hosps. Socs: Roy. Soc. Med.; Brit. Assn. Urol. Surg.; Physiol. Soc. Prev: Sen. Regist. (Urol.) Battle Hosp. Reading & St. Thos. Hosp. Lond.

MONTGOMERY, Charles Darragh Wonford House Hospital, Dryden Rd, Exeter EX2 5AF — MB ChB 1985 Bristol; MRCPsych. 1991. Cons. (Psychiat.) Wonford Hse. Hosp. Exeter; Research Fell. Dept. of Ment. Health Univ. of Exeter. Socs: Asso. Mem. Brit. PsychOncol. Soc.; Stud. Mem. Inst. Gp. Anal. Prev: Regist. (Psychiat.) N. Devon Dist. Hosp. & Glenside Hosp. Bristol; SHO Rotat. (Psychiat.) Glenside Hosp. Bristol.; Sen. Regist. (Psychiat.) Wonford Hse. Hosp. Exeter.

MONTGOMERY, Colin Edward Alexander Dingleton Hospital, Melrose TD6 9HN Tel: 01896 822727; Rowchester Cottage, Kippilaw, Melrose TD6 9HF Tel: 01835 23393 — MB ChB 1984 Ed.

MONTGOMERY, David Aitken (retired) 11 Highcroft, Cherry Burton, Beverley HU17 7SG Tel: 01964 550818 — MB BS 1956 Lond.; MRCS Eng. LRCP Lond. 1956; FRCPath 1982, M 1970; DCP Lond 1967. Cons. Haemat. Kingston Gen. Hosp. Hull. Prev: Cons. Pathol. RAF Med. Br.

MONTGOMERY, David Pirrie Victoria Hospital, Whinney Heys Road, Blackpool FY3 8NR — MB ChB 1973 Dundee; FRCP Glas. 1989; FRCR 1980; DMRD Eng. 1978. Cons. (Radiol.) Vict. Hosp. Blackpool.

***MONTGOMERY, Deborah Anne** 27 Reahill Road, Newtownabbey BT36 5SF — MB ChB 1995 Dundee.

MONTGOMERY, Desmond Alan Dill, CBE (retired) 59 Church Road, Newtownbreda, Belfast BT8 7AN Tel: 01232 648326 — DSc NUI 1980; MD (Gold Medal) Belf. 1946, MB BCh BAO (Hnrs.); FRCPI 1975, M 1974; FRCP Lond. 1964, M 1948; FRCOG 1981. Prev: Temp. Maj. RAMC 1941-5.

MONTGOMERY, Donald (retired) 15 Enbrook Road, Folkestone CT20 3BL — MB ChB Glas. 1952; FRCP Ed. 1982 M 1958. Prev: Hosp. Pract. (Rheum.) SE Kent HA.

MONTGOMERY, Donald Hugh Gender Identity Clinic, Department of Psychiatry, Charing Cross Hospital, Fulham Palace Road, London W6 8RF Tel: 020 8846 1516 Fax: 020 8846 1133; Tolworth Hospital, Red Lion Road, Tolworth, Surbiton KT6 7QU Tel: 020 8390 0102 Fax: 020 8390 3877 — MB ChB 1966 Otago; FRCPsych 1994, M 1990; FRANZCP 1983, M 1973. Cons. Psychiat. Gender Identity Clinic Char. Cross Hosp. Lond.; Cons. Psycother. Tolworth Hosp. Surrey, St. Geo. Hosp. & Kingston Hosp. Socs: Gp. Analyt. Soc.; Internat. Assn. Forens. Psychother.; Inst. Gp. Anal. Prev: Commonw. Sen. Regist. (Psychother.) Cassel Hosp. Richmond; Cons. Psychiat. Roy. P. Alfred Hosp. Sydney, Austral.; Cons. Psychiat. Parramatta Psychiat. Centre Sydney, Austral.

MONTGOMERY, Elizabeth Anne 41 Derryvolgie Avenue, Belfast BT9 6FP — MB BCh BAO 1974 Belf.; FRCPsych 1997; MRCPsych 1978. Cons. Psychiat. of Old Age Belf.

MONTGOMERY, Helen Rosalind 9 Stanhope Street, Hereford HR4 0HA — MB BS 1985 Lond.; MRCGP 1989; DRCOG 1987.

MONTGOMERY, Mr Hugh Dyson 10 Throstle Nest Close, Otley LS21 2RR Email: hugh@hmtnc.demon.co.uk — MB ChB 1972 Ed.; FRCS Glas. 1980; DMRD Ed. 1983. Cons. Radiol. Halifax Gen. Hosp. W. Yorks. Socs: BSIR.

MONTGOMERY, Hugh Edward Centre for Cardiovascular Genetics, 3rd Floor, Rayne Institute, University St., London WC1E 6JT Tel: 020 7209 6965 Fax: 020 7209 6212; 45 Sharon Gardens, South Hackney, London E9 7RX Tel: 020 7679 6965 Email: h.montgomery@ucl.ac.uk — MB BS 1987 Lond.; BSc Lond. 1984; MRCP (UK) 1990; MD 1997. (Middlesex) Sen. Lect. in Cardiovasc. Genetics; Hon. Cons. in Intens. Care Med. Socs: Roy. Coll. Phys.; Intens. Care Soc.; Europ. Soc. of Intens. Care Med. Prev: Sen. Regist., UCL Intens. Care; SPR Cardiol., UCL Hopitals.

MONTGOMERY, James Ardgowan Medical Practice, 2 Finnart Street, Greenock PA16 8HW Tel: 01475 888155 Fax: 01475 785060 — MB ChB 1966 Glas.; MRCGP 1972; DObst RCOG 1968; Cert. Family Plann. JCC 1982. (Glas.) GP Greenock, Renrewshire. Socs: BMA. Prev: SHO (O & G) Thornhill Hosp. Paisley; Ho. Off. S.. Gen. Hosp. Glas.; Ho. Off. (Surg.) W.. Infirm. Glas.

MONTGOMERY, James Nelson (retired) Arundel, Higher Churchway, Plymstock, Plymouth PL9 8LA Tel: 01752 402386 — MB BCh BAO 1945 Belf.; MD Belf. 1950; FRCP Lond. 1970, M 1950; DCH Eng. 1948. Prev: Resid. Asst. Phys. Gt. Ormond St. Hosp. for Childr. Lond.

MONTGOMERY, Jane Emma Dept. of Anaesthesia, Torbay Hospital, Lawes Bridge, Torquay TQ2 7AA Tel: 01803654311 Email: jane.montgomery@sdevonhc-tr.swest.nhs.uk — MB BS 1989 Lond.; BSc 1986 Lond.; FRCA 1994. (University College London) Cons. Anaesth. (Interest in Day Surg.) Torbay Hosp. Torquay; Cons. (Anaesth.) Torbay Hosp. Prev: Specialist Regist. (Anaesth.) Derriford Hosp. Plymouth; Regist. (Anaesth.) Univ. Hosp. Wales, Specialist Regist. - Anaesth- Deffiford Hosp. - Plymouth.

MONTGOMERY, Jane Neilson Borders General Hospital, Melrose TD6 9BS; Shaws, Shawpark Road, Selkirk TD7 4PR — MB ChB 1979 Glas.; T(Anaesth.) 1991; FFA RCS Eng. 1984. Cons. Anaesth. Borders Gen. Hosp. Melrose. Prev: Cons. Anaesth. BMH Hannover.

MONTGOMERY, Jennifer Susan Stuart Road Surgery, Stuart Road, Pontefract WF8 4PQ Tel: 01977 703437 Fax: 01977 602334; 37 Highfield Road, Pontefract WF8 4LL — MB BCh BAO 1977 Belf.; DRCOG 1980. (Queen's University Belfast) Clin. Asst. (Gyn.) Pinderfields Hosp. Trust; Med. Off. (Family Plann.) Wakefield & Pontefract Community Health NHS Trust.

MONTGOMERY, Joanne Edyth 34 Butterfield Drive, Eaglescliffe, Stockton-on-Tees TS16 0EX — BChir 1989 Camb.

MONTGOMERY, Johanna Victoria Road Surgery, 50 Victoria Road, Worthing BN11 1XB Tel: 01903 230656 Fax: 01903 520094 — BM 1983 Soton.

MONTGOMERY, Joseph The Medical Centre, 6 The Green, West Drayton UB7 7PJ Tel: 01895 442026 Fax: 01895 430753; 27 Coopers Row, Iver SL0 0HP Tel: 01753 710637 — MB BS 1980 Lond.

MONTGOMERY, Julia Caroline Royal Sussex County Hospital, Eastern Road, Brighton BN2 5BE Tel: 01273 696955 — MRCS Eng. LRCP Lond. 1981; MB BS Lond. 1981; MRCOG 1989. Cons. Obstetrician & Gyn., Roy. Sussex Co. Hosp., E.ern Rd., Brighton.

MONTGOMERY, Mr Richard John Middlesbrough General Hospital, Middlesbrough TS5 5AZ Tel: 01642 854215 — MB BS 1978 Newc.; FRCS Ed. 1983. Cons. Orthop. Middlesbrough Gen. Hosp. & S. Cleveland Hosp.; Hon. Clin. Lect. Univ. Teeside & Univ. Newc. Socs: Fell. BOA; Brit. Soc. Childr. Orthop. Surg.; Brit. Limb Reconstruc. Soc. Prev: Cons. Orthop. Surg. N. Tees Gen. Hosp. Stockton on Tees & Middlesbrough Gen. Hosp.; Sen. Regist. (Orthop.) N.. Region; Research Fell. (Orthop.) Mayo Clinic Rochester, Minnesota.

MONTGOMERY, Richard William St Lukes Medical Centre, 17 New Road, Brixham TQ5 8NA Tel: 01803 852731 Fax: 01803 852637; Furzeacre, Higher Furzeham Road, Brixham TQ5 8QZ — MB BS 1980 Lond.; BA Camb. 1977; MRCGP 1985; DTM & H RCP Lond. 1990; DRCOG 1984; DCH RCP Lond. 1983. (Roy. Lond.) Prev: Med. Supt. Kiwoko Hosp., Uganda; GP Nottm.

MONTGOMERY, Robert Cassels 17 Circular Road, Castlerock, Coleraine BT51 4XA — MB BCh BAO Belf. 1967; DMH Belf. 1990; DHMSA 1981. Staff Grade (Psychiat.) Hollywell Hosp. Antrim. Socs: Fell. Ulster Med. Soc.; Fell. Roy. Soc. Med.; Fell. Fac. Philosophy, Hist. Med. & Pharmacy Worshipful Soc. Apoth. Lond. Prev: Research Fell. Dept. Therap. Qu.. Univ. Belf.; Apoth. Lond. 1982.

MONTGOMERY, Robert Darragh (retired) 5 Riverbank Gardens, Tiddington Road, Stratford-upon-Avon CV37 7BW — MB BChir Camb. 1950; MA Camb. 1951, MD 1962; FRCP Lond. 1974; FRCP Ed. 1967. Prev: Cons. Phys. E. Birm. Hosp. & Solihull Hosp.

MONTGOMERY, Sarah Ann 6 Katrine Park, Belfast BT10 0HT — MB ChB 1997 Dundee.

MONTGOMERY, Sheila Mary Fishponds Health Centre, Beechwood Road, Fishponds, Bristol BS16 3TD Tel: 0117 965 6281; 292 Ashley Down Road, Horfield, Bristol BS7 9BQ — MB ChB 1978 Bristol; MRCGP 1989; DCCH RCP Ed. 1989. Med Off. Stud. Health Univ. Bristol.

MONTGOMERY, Mr Stephen Charles Fazakerley Hospital, Longmoor Lane, Liverpool L9 7AL Tel: 0151 529 2548 Fax: 0151 529 2549 — BM BS 1981 Nottm.; MChOrth Liverp. 1989; FRCS (Orth.) Ed. 1993; FRCS Ed. 1986. (Nottm.) Cons. Orthop. Surg. Aintree Hosps. NHS Trust. Prev: Sen. Regist. (Orthop. Surg.) Aberd. Roy. Infirm.; Regist. (Orthop. Surg.) Walton Hosp., Roy. Liverp. Hosp. & Roy. Liverp. Childr. Hosp.

MONTGOMERY, Professor Stuart Anthony Imperial College School of Medicine, Norfolk Place, London W2 1NY — MB BS

MOODY

1963 Lond.; MD Stockholm 1978; BSc (Hons.); FRCPsych 1982, M 1975; DPM Eng. 1973. Emerit. Prof. Imperial Coll. of Med.; Edr. Internat. Clin. Psychopharmacol. & Europ. Neuropsychoparmacol. Prev: Sen. Lect. & Hon. Cons. Guy's Hosp. Med. Sch. Lond. & Oakwood Hosp. Maidstone; Lect. (Psychiat.) St. Bart. Hosp. Med. Sch.

MONTGOMERY, Mr Stuart James 2 Dykes Court, Darvel KA17 0NH — MB ChB 1995 Glas.; BSc (Hons.) Glas. 1992; MRCS Glas. 1999. Prev: W. Scotl. Basic Surgic. Train. Scheme 1997-1999.

MONTGOMERY, Susan Harrower (retired) 23 Forefield Lane, Crosby, Liverpool L23 9TG — MB ChB 1921 Liverp. Prev: Dep. MOH Boro. Crosby.

MONTGOMERY, Tara Louise — BM BS 1991 Nottm.; MRCP (UK) 1994. (Nottingham) p/t Locum Cons., Clin. Genetics, Dept. of Clin. Genetics, Newc. Upon Tyne. Socs: Brit. Soc. Human Genetics; Eur. Soc. Human Genet. Prev: Specialist Regist. (Clin. Genetics) Newc.; Nat. Geneticist in Train. Represen.

MONTGOMERY, Veronica Josephine 37 Wandle Road, Hackbridge, Wallington SM6 7ET — MB BS 1990 Lond.

MONTROSE, Michael Kenneth Medical Centre, Holme House, Holme House Road, Stockton-on-Tees TS18 2QU — MB ChB 1974 Manch.; BSc (Hons. 1st cl. Morbid Anat.) Manch. 1972. Forens. Phys. Gtr. Manch. Police. Socs: Forens. Soc.; FBIM; Roy. Coll. Radiol. Prev: Edr. Manch. Med.; Regist. (Radiother. & Oncol.) Christie Hosp. & Holt Radium Inst. Manch.; SHO Rotat. Mater Miser. Hosps. Brisbane, Austral.

MONTY, Mr Cyril Philip (retired) 20 Kingsley Lodge, 23 New Cavendish St., London W1G 9UG Tel: 020 7487 4996 — MB BS Lond. 1957; MD Lond. 1968; FRCS Eng. 1961; MRCS Eng. LRCP Lond. 1957. Prev: Cons. Orthop. Surg. Lewisham & N. S.wark HA.

MONYPENNY, Mr Ian James Southra Green, The Common, Dinas Powys CF64 4DL Tel: 01222 515065 — MB 1975 Camb.; MA Camb. 1975, MChir 1986, MB 1975, BChir 1974; FRCS Eng. 1978. (St. Thos.) Cons. Surg. Welsh BrE. Screening Centre Cardiff; Cons. Gen. Surg. Llandough Hosp. Cardiff S. Glam. HA. Prev: Sen. Surg. Regist. W. Midl. RHA.

MONYPENNY, Isabelle Guthrie (retired) The Fairways, 22A Windyridge, Dinas Powys CF64 4AW Tel: 01222 514789 — MRCS Eng. LRCP Lond. 1941; FCAnaesth. 1989; FFA RCS Eng. 1953; DA Eng. 1942. Prev: Cons. Anaesth. Sheff. Roy. Hosp. & N. Staffs. Hosp. Centre Stoke-on-Trent.

MOOCHHALA, Hatim Shaikhadam The Parklands Medical Practice, Park Road, Bradford BD5 0SG Tel: 01274 227575 Fax: 01274 693558; 18 Northcroft Rise, Crowtrees Park, Bradford BD8 0BW Tel: 01274 487750 — MB BS 1967 Nagpur; DTM & H RCP Lond. 1969. (Nagpur)

***MOOCHHALA, Shabbir Hatim** 18 Northcroft Rise, Crow Trees Park, Bradford BD8 0BW — MB ChB 1998 Ed.; MB ChB Ed 1998.

MOODALEY, Devi Woodcroft Medical Centre, Gervase Road, Burnt Oak, Edgware HA8 0NR Tel: 020 8906 8700 Fax: 020 8959 0718; 17 Holland Walk, Stanmore HA7 3AL Tel: 020 8954 3502 — MB BS 1980 Lond.; DCH RCP Lond. 1986; DRCOG 1984. (Char. Cross)

MOODALEY, Lalitha Caroline Maria Moorfields Eye Hospital, City Road, London EC1V 2PD Tel: 020 7253 3411 Fax: 020 7253 4696; 5 Rockhampton Close, London SE27 0NG — MB BS 1981 Lond.; DO RCS Eng. 1985. (Char. Cross) Assoc. Specialist (Cornea & Extern. Dis. Serv.) Moorfields Eye Hosp. Lond.; Clin. Asst. Contact Lens Clinic Univ. Coll. Hosp. Lond.; Vis. Lect. City Univ. Lond. Socs: (Past Pres. & UK Nat. Represen.) Med. Contact Lens & Ocular Surface Assn.; (Counc.) Brit. Contact Lens Assn.

MOODALEY, Veerapatharen Krishnasamy (retired) 17 Holland Walk, Stanmore HA7 3AL Tel: 020 8954 3502 — LRCP LRCS 1949 Ed.; LRCP LRCS Ed. LRFPS Glas. 1949.

MOODIE, Gordon Robert James (retired) Bardwell, Sparken Hill, Worksop S80 1AX Tel: 01909 475299 Email: gordon.moodie@ukgateway.net — MB BS 1948 Lond.; MRCS Eng. LRCP Lond. 1948; FRCGP 1976. Prev: Regist. Maryfield Hosp. Dundee.

MOODIE, Ian James Montague Health Centre, Oakenhurst Road, Blackburn BB2 1PP Tel: 01254 268436 Fax: 01254 268440; 8 Charnwood Close, Blackburn BB2 7BT — MB ChB 1981 Manch.; MRCGP 1987; DRCOG 1985. (Manchester) GP Facilitator Blackburn Post Grad. Prev: SHO/Trainee GP Blackburn Gp. Hosps. VTS.

MOODIE, James Sharp Deerness Park Medical Centre, Suffolk St., Hendon, Sunderland SR2 8AD Tel: 0191 567 0961 Fax: 0191 565 0075; 2 Bainbridge Holme Close, Sunderland SR3 1YX — MRCS Eng. LRCP Lond. 1961.

MOODIE, John (retired) 14 Woodhurst N., Ray Mead Road, Maidenhead SL6 8PH — MB ChB (Commend.) Glas. 1949. Prev: Med. Dir. (U.K. & Scand.) Bristol-Myers Co. Internat. Ltd.

MOODIE, Simon James 5 Elmbridge Gardens, Exeter EX4 4AE — MB BS 1993 Lond.

***MOODIE, Stewart Faulkner** Brimps House, Upton St Leonards, Gloucester GL4 8DE — MB ChB 1995 Leeds.

MOODY, Alan Rowland 42 Main Street, Great Glen, Leicester LE8 9GG — MB BS 1983 Lond.; FRCR Eng. 1989; MRCP (UK) 1986. Sen. Lect. (Radiol.) Leicester Roy. Infirm. Prev: Sen. Regist. (Radiol.) St. Geo. Hosp. Lond.

MOODY, Mr Andrew Paul Warrington Hospital NHS Trust, Lovely Lane, Warrington WA5 1QG Tel: 01925 662075 Fax: 01925 662042 — MB ChB 1980 Liverp.; MD Liverp. 1994; FRCS (Gen.) 1995; FRCS Eng. 1985. (Liverpool) Cons. Gen. & Vasc. Surg. Warrington Hosp. Socs: Vasc. Surgic. Soc. GB & Irel.; Eur. Soc. Vasc. Surg.; Soc. of Vasc. Technologies. Prev: Sen. Regist. Rotat. (Surg.) Roy. Liverp. Univ. Hosp.

MOODY, Anne Margaret Oncology Unit, G1, West Suffolk Hospital, Bury St Edmunds IP33 Tel: 01284 713571 Fax: 01284 713571 — MB BChir 1987 Camb.; MRCP (UK) 1990; FRCR 1994. Cons. Clin. Oncol., W. Suff. Hosp. & Addenbrookes Hosp. Camb. Prev: Regist. (Radiother.) Roy. Marsden Hosp. Surrey.; Sen. Regist. (Clin. Oncol.) Addenbrooke's Hosp. Camb.

***MOODY, Caroline Mary Elizabeth** 1 Shirley Av, Leicester LE2 3NB — MB ChB 1997 Birm.

MOODY, Dorothy Rae (retired) 29 Covertside, West Kirby, Wirral CH48 9UD Tel: 0151 625 2452 — LRCPI & LM, LRCSI & LM 1957; MFCM 1974; DCH RFPS Glas. 1961; DPH Belf. 1964; Dip. Audiol. Manch. 1969. Prev: Sen. Sch. Med. Off. Chesh. CC.

MOODY, Ellen Margaret 23 Southway, Manor Park, Burley in Wharfedale, Ilkley LS29 7HJ Tel: 01943 864382 — MB ChB 1948 Leeds; MRCS Eng. LRCP Lond. 1948. (Leeds)

MOODY, James Eric 42 Winchester Road, Sheffield S10 4EE Tel: 0114 230 1746 — MB ChB 1997 Liverp.; BSc Cell Bio. (Hons) Liver. 1994. (Liverpool) Basic Surg. Train. Rota. - Barnsley DGH + Roy. Hallamshire Hosp. Sheff.

MOODY, Julia Marion The Lawson Practice, St. Leonards Hospital, Nuttall St., London N1 5HZ Tel: 020 7739 9701 — MB BS 1990 Lond.; MRCGP 1944; DRCOG 1993; DCH RCP Lond. 1992.

MOODY, Michael Ernest Arthur Main Street Surgery, 45 Main Street, Willerby, Hull HU10 6BP Tel: 01482 652652 — MB ChB 1974 Liverp.; BDS Liverp. 1967.

MOODY, Nicola Jane Huddersfield Roy. Infirm., Acre Street, Lindley, Huddersfield HD3 3EA Tel: 0114 230 1646, 01484 342965 Fax: 01484 347068 Email: jemoody@dial.pipex.com — MB ChB 1997 Liverp. (Liverpool) Salaried Gen. Practitioner. Prev: SHO Gen. Med., Sheff.

MOODY, Richard Anthony Anaesthetic Deperatment, Kettering General Hospital, Kettering NN16 8UZ Tel: 01536 492000; The Manor House, Irthlingborough, Wellingborough NN9 5SP — MB BS 1972 Lond.; FFA RCS Eng. 1980; DA Eng. 1977. (St. Bart.) Cons. Anaesth. Kettering Gen. Hosp. Socs: Assn. Anaesth. GB & Irel. Prev: Cons. Anaesth. RNH Plymouth; Ho. Phys. Plymouth Gen. Hosp. (Devonport Br.); Ho. Surg. Profess. Surg. Unit St. Bart. Hosp. Lond.

MOODY, Richard George The Health Centre, Victoria Road, Hartlepool TS26 8DB Tel: 01429 272000/274899 Fax: 01429 863877; 9 Wilton Avenue, Hartlepool TS26 9PT — MB ChB 1977 Dundee; DA Eng. 1982.

MOODY, Robert Henry Heavitree Health Centre, South Lawn Terrace, Heavitree, Exeter EX1 2RX Tel: 01392 211511 Fax: 01392 499451 — MRCS Eng. LRCP Lond. 1971; BSc (Pharmacol.) Lond. 1968, MB BS 1971; MRCGP 1977; DObst RCOG 1974. (St. Geo.)

MOODY, Thomas Edwin (retired) Chesterhill, 62 Forest Lane, Kirklevington, Yarm TS15 9ND Tel: 01642 782886 — MB BCh BAO 1939 Belf. Prev: Ho. Phys. N. Lonsdale Hosp. Barrow-in-Furness.

MOODY, Thomas Laurence (retired) Kingsway Medical Centre, 23 Kingsway, Narborough Road South, Leicester LE3 2JN Tel: 0116 289 5081 Fax: 0116 263 0145 — MB BS 1967 Newc.; FFA RCS Eng. 1974; DA Eng. 1971. Prev: Surg. Lt.-Cdr. RN.

MOODY-JONES

MOODY-JONES, Mr Wyndham David Thomas Royal Glamorgan Hospital, Ynysmaerdy, Llantrisant, Pontyclun CF72 8XR Tel: 01443 443443 Email: david.moody-jones@pr-tr.wales.nhs.uk; Email: moodyjones@tesco.net — MB BS 1975 Lond.; FRCS Eng. 1980; FFAEM 1993. (St. Bart.) Cons. A & E Med. Pontypridd & Rhondda NHS Trust; Dir. N. Glam. Advanced Life Support Course Merthyr Tydfil. Socs: Fell. (Counc. Mem.) Roy. Soc. Med. (Founder Mem. Sect. Accid. & Emerg.); Brit. Assn. Accid. & Emerg. Med.; Eur. Resusc. Counc. Prev: Regist. (A & E) W. Glam. HA; Research Fell. Univ. Soton.; Ho. Surg. St. Bart. Hosp. Lond.

MOOHAN, James Martin Dept Of Obstetrics & Gynaecology, Altnagelvin Hospital, Londonderry BT47 6SB Tel: 028 7134 5171 Fax: 028 7134 8071 Email: jmoohan@alt.n.i.nhs.uk; 8 Marlborough Gardens, Belfast BT9 6SQ Tel: 028 9068 3993 Email: jmoohan99@yahoo.com — MB BCh BAO 1986 Belf.; BSc (Hons.) Belf. 1984; MRCOG 1991; DRCOG 1989; MD Belf. 1998. (Queen's Univ. Belf.) Cons. (O & G) Altnagelvin Area Hosp., Lond.derry. Socs: Ulster Obs. & Gynae. Soc.; ESHRE; ESGE. Prev: Sen. Regist. (Reprod. Med.) Rotunda Hosp. Dub.

MOOHAN, Vincent Paul 6 Cardigan Drive, Belfast BT14 6LX — MB BCh BAO 1988 Belf.

MOOKERJEE, Rajeshwar Prosad 33 Candytuft Road, Chelmsford CM1 6YS — MB BS 1994 Lond.

MOOLA, Mahomed Ismail Heaton Moor Medical Centre, 32 Heaton Moor Road, Stockport SK4 4NX Tel: 0161 432 0671 — LRCPI & LM, LRSCI & LM 1964; LRCPI & LM, LRCSI & LM 1964. (RCSI)

MOOLGAOKER, Mr Arvind Sumant (retired) Kymore, 128 Cliddesden Road, Basingstoke RG21 3HH Tel: 01256 355677 Fax: 01256 355677 Email: moolgaoker@aol.com — MB BS Bombay 1958; MD Bombay 1961; FRCOG 1979, M 1964. Prev: Cons. O & G Basingstoke & Dist. Hosps.

MOOLLAN, Oomar Cassam 32 Howards Lane, Rowtown, Addlestone, Weybridge — MB ChB 1981 Manch.; MRCOG 1987. Regist. (O & G) St. Peter's Hosp. Chertsey.

***MOON, Andrew Peter** 1 Mistletoe Street, Crossgate, Durham DH1 4EP — MB BS 1996 Newc.

MOON, Anna Rebecca (retired) Flat 10, Kerrington Court, 119 Marlborough Park S., Belfast BT9 6JB Tel: 02890 682627 — MB BCh BAO 1926 Belf.; DPH Belf. 1930. Prev: Asst. MOH Surrey CC & Fulham Boro.

MOON, Anthony James Eastglade, London Road, Rickmansworth WD3 1JR Tel: 01923 772367 Fax: 01923 77660 — MB BS Lond. 1943; FRCP Lond. 1970, M 1947; MRCS Eng. LRCP Lond. 1943. (St. Bart.) Phys. Harefield Hosp., Hillingdon Hosp., Mt. Vernon Hosp. & S.all-Norwood Hosp. Socs: BMA; Thoracic Soc. Prev: Phys. Supt. Pinewood Hosp. Wokingham; Sen. Regist. (Med.) Lond. Chest Hosp.; Resid. Surg. Off. Brompton Hosp.

MOON, Bertram Gerrard (retired) 12 Norman Court, 36 Crameswater Park, Southsea PO4 0LY Tel: 01705 819448 — MB ChB 1951 Birm.

MOON, Charles Arthur Leslie Mile House, Mile Hill, Porthtowan, Truro TR4 8TY Tel: 01209 890600 Fax: 01209 890600 — MB BS 1960 Lond.; MRCS Eng. LRCP Lond. 1960. (Lond. Hosp.) Hosp. Pract. (Geriats.) Barncoose Hosp. Redruth; Managing Dir. Cornw. & Devon Clin. Research. Prev: Ho. Phys. & Ho. Surg. (O & G) Camborne-Redruth Gen. Hosp.; Ho. Surg. Roy. Sussex Co. Hosp. Brighton.

MOON, Charles James Bevern Bridge House, South Chailey, Lewes BN8 4QH Tel: 01273 400395 Fax: 01273 401 966 Email: c.j.moon@btinternet.com — MB BS 1982 Lond.; FFA 1970 RCS Eng.; DA 1969 Eng; Dobst RCOG 1966. (Lond. Hosp.) p/t Late Cons. Anaesth. Crawley Hosp. Socs: Assn. Anaesth. Prev: Ho. Surg. Lond. Hosp.; Med. Off. RN; Sen. Regist. (Anaesth.) Char. Cross Hosp. Lond.

MOON, David John St. Johns Lane, Bristol BS3 5AS Tel: 0117 966 7681 Fax: 0117 977 9676 — MB ChB 1966 Bristol. William Budd Health Centre, Downton Rd, Knowle, Bristol, BS4 1WH, Tel: 0117 944 9700.

MOON, David Nigel Lee Hamilton Road Surgery, 201 Hamilton Road, Felixstowe IP11 7DT Tel: 01394 283197 Fax: 01394 270304; Quintons, 53 Links Avenue, Felixstowe IP11 9HE Tel: 01394 283647 — MB BS 1981 Lond.

MOON, Elizabeth Ann Christine 1 Beeching Drive, Lowestoft NR32 4TB — MB BS 1982 Lond.; MRCGP 1989; DRCOG 1989. GP Retainer Kineton.

MOON, Jacqueline Anne 163 Longedge Lane, Wingerworth, Chesterfield S42 6PR — MB ChB 1990 Manch.

***MOON, James Kenneth** Tattenhall Post Office, High St., Tattenhall, Chester CH3 9PX — BM BCh 1996 Oxf.

MOON, Jean Voase (retired) Eastglade, London Road, Rickmansworth WD3 1JR Tel: 01923 772367 Fax: 01923 777660 — MB BS Lond. 1945; MRCS Eng. LRCP Lond. 1945.

MOON, Jennifer Ann (retired) 14 Alum Way, Downend, Fareham PO16 8RJ Tel: 01329 310133 Email: jmoon@doctors.org.uk — BM BCh Oxf. 1966; MA Oxf. 1966; DObst RCOG 1968. Prev: SCMO (Child Health) Portsmouth Healthcare NHS Trust.

MOON, John Richard Arthur (retired) 14 Alum Way, Downend, Fareham PO16 8RJ Tel: 01329 310133 Email: jmoon@doctors.org.uk — BM BCh Oxf. 1966; MA Oxf. 1966; FFA RCS Eng. 1971. Prev: Cons. Anaesth. Portsmouth Hosps. NHS Trust.

MOON, Philip Vincent 1 Ash Close, Redhill RH1 3HJ — MB ChB 1983 Sheff.

MOON, Ruth Celia 21 Biddulph Way, Ledbury HR8 2HP — MB BS 1989 Lond.; BSc (Hons.) Cell Path. Lond. 1986, MB BS 1989; MRCP (UK) 1993. Prev: SHO (Med.) N. Devon Dist. Hosp. Barnstaple; SHO (Med.) Basingstoke Dist. Hosp.; SHO (A & E) Salisbury.

MOONCEY, Sophia 71 Long Lane, Finchley Central, London N3 2HY Tel: 020 8346 2213 — MB BS 1987 Delhi; MRCP (UK) 1991.

***MOONDI, Parvez Pal Singh** 333 Sopwith Crescent, Wimborne BH21 1XQ — MB ChB 1994 Leeds.

MOONEY, Andrew Francis Renal Unit, St. James's University Hospital, Leeds LS9 7TF; 51 Sutherland Avenue, Roundhay, Leeds LS8 1BY — BM BS 1988 Nottm.; BMedSci (Hons.) 1986 Nottm.; BM BS 1988; PhD 1998 (Nottm.); BMedSci (Hons.) Nottm. 1986; MRCP (UK) 1991. Cons. Nephrologist, St Jas. Univ. Hosp., Leeds.

MOONEY, Angela Abbey Mead Surgery, Abbey Mead, Romsey SO51 8EN Tel: 01794 512218 Fax: 01794 514224 — BM 1986 Soton.; MRCGP 1992.

MOONEY, Daniel James Wapping Health Centre, 22 Wapping Lane, London E1W 2RL Tel: 020 7481 9376; 32 Oswell House, Farthing Fields, London E1W 3RU Tel: 020 7481 8295 Fax: 020 7481 8295 Email: danny@32-oswell.freeserve.co.uk — MB BS 1989 Lond.; MRCGP 1996; MCOphth. 1993. (Bart's.) GP Lond.

MOONEY, Eamon Martin Longford Street Surgery, Longford Street, Heywood OL10 4NH Tel: 01706 621417 Fax: 01706 622915 — MB BCh BAO 1978 NUI; DCH RCPSI 1982; DRCOG 1982. (Cork)

MOONEY, Grant Kelso Medical Group Practice, Health Centre, Inch Road, Kelso TD5 7JP Tel: 01573 224424 Fax: 01573 226388 — MB ChB 1964 Ed.; DObst RCOG 1966. Prev: SHO Obst. P.ss Mary Matern. Hosp. Newc.

MOONEY, John Kristian Weavers Lane Surgery, 1 Weavers Lane, Whitburn, Bathgate EH47 0QU Tel: 01501 740297 Fax: 01501 744302 — MB BCh BAO 1989 NUI; DCL NUI 1991; DOLs College of Physicians Ire. 1995; MRCGP@ RCGP 1997. GP Princip., Whithern Health Centre, Whithern, f/t.

MOONEY, Patricia 28 Ledger Road, Haydock, St Helens WA11 0DZ — MB ChB 1986 Leeds; BSc (Hons.) Leeds 1983, MB ChB 1986. SHO (Renal Med.) Roy. Vict. Infirm. Newc. Prev: Ho. Off. (Surg.) Leeds Gen. Infirm.; Ho. Phys. St. Jas. Hosp. Leeds.

MOONEY, Patrick Joseph 2 Childwall Park Avenue, Liverpool L16 0JG — LRCPI & LM, LRCSI & LM 1949. (RCSI) Prev: Ho. Surg. Mercer's Hosp. Dub.; RAMC 1954-5.

MOONEY, Mr Paul The Ipswich Hospital NHS Trust, Heath Road, Ipswich IP4 5PD Tel: 01473 703009 Fax: 01473 703015 Email: paulmooney@doctors.org.uk — MB ChB 1981 Liverp.; MD Liverp. 1993; MRCOG 1987. Cons. O & G Ipswich Hosp. NHS Trust. Socs: Brit. Soc. Gyn. Endoscopy.; E. Anglia Obst. & Gyn. Soc.

MOONEY, Peter Nicholas Burngreave Road Surgery, 5 Burngreave Road, Sheffield S3 9DA Tel: 0114 272 2858 — MB ChB 1978 Sheff.

MOONEY, Sandra Elizabeth British Airways Health Services, Waterside (HMAG), PO Box 365, Harmondsworth UB7 0GB Tel: 020 8738 7700 Fax: 020 8738 9784 Email:

sandra.e.mooney@britishairways.com — MB ChB 1967 Bristol; FFOM RCP Lond. 1993, MFOM 1984, AFOM 1980; DAvMed. FOM RCP Lond. 1984; DIH Soc. Apoth. Lond. 1980; DObst RCOG 1971.

MOONEY, Sylvester Joseph Mary 27 Derby Road, Portsmouth PO2 8HP — MB BCh BAO 1985 NUI; LRCPI & LM, LRCSI & LM 1985.

MOONEY, Vanessa Mary Bridget Cromwell Hospital, GP Department, Cromwell Road, Kensington, London SW5 0TU Tel: 020 7460 2000 Fax: 020 7460 5555; 3 Bath Road, London W4 1LL Tel: 020 8995 1044 — LRCPI & LM, LRSCI & LM 1977; LRCPI & LM, LRCSI & LM 1977; DCH RCPSI 1979. (Dub.) Indep. GP Lond. Socs: MICGP. Prev: SHO (Med.) Baggot St. Hosp. & St. Jas. Hosp. Dub.; SHO (Paediat.) Brompton Hosp. Lond.

MOONGA, Paramjit Singh Moonga, 726 Coventry Road, Small Heath, Birmingham B10 0TU Tel: 0121 773 2094 Fax: 0121 753 0334; 3 Belgrove Close, Edgbaston, Birmingham B15 3RQ — MB BS 1974 Punjab; MB BS Punjabi 1974; MMediaSci (Gen. Pract.) Birm. 1994.

***MOONIE, Alasdair** 149 Raeberry Street, Glasgow G20 6EE — MB ChB 1998 Glas.; MB ChB Glas 1998.

MOONIE, Lewis George 85 Sauchenbush Road, Kirkcaldy KY2 5RN Tel: 0592 201873 — MB ChB 1970 St. And.; MSc Ed. 1981; MFCM RCP (UK) 1984; MRCPsych 1979; DPM Ed. & Glas. 1975. (St. And.) Community Med. Specialist Fife Health Bd.; Labour MP for Kirkcaldy. Prev: Sen. Regist. (Community Med.) Fife Health Bd.; Clin. Pharmacol. Syntex; Research Centre Heriot-Watt Univ. Edin.; Psychiat. Ciba-Geigy AG; Basel, Switz. & Organon Internat. BV Oss, Netherlands.

MOONIE, William Cathcart (retired) 119 Junction Road, Norton, Stockton-on-Tees TS20 1PX Tel: 01642 553307 — MB BS Durh. 1941; FRCGP 1981. Prev: Ho. Phys. Roy. Vict. Infirm. Newc.-on-Tyne.

MOONSAWMY, Stanley Augustine Dick Place Surgery, 15 Dick Place, Loanhead EH9 2JU — MB ChB 1965 Ed. (Ed.) GP Princip. Edin. Socs: BMA. Prev: Regist. Med. & Chest Unit Bangour Gen. Hosp.; Regist. Periph. Vasc. Clinic Roy. Infirm. Edin.

***MOOR, James William** 11 Breary Ter, Horsforth, Leeds LS18 5QJ Tel: 0113 293 4672 — MB ChB 1997 Leeds.

MOOR, John Frewen Church Farm House, East Meon, Petersfield GU32 1QE — MB BChir 1951 Camb.; DTM & H Eng. 1964; DObst RCOG 1956. (St. Geo.) Prev: Sen. Med. Off. RePub. of Botswana; Ho. Surg. & Cas. Off. St. Geo. Hosp. Lond.

MOOR, Michael John Eaton Socon Health Centre, 274 North Road, Eaton Socon, St. Neots, Huntingdon PE19 8BB Tel: 01480 477111 Fax: 01480 403524; Hedgerow, Spring Hill, Little Staughton, Bedford MK44 2BS — MB ChB 1982 Leic.; MRCGP 1986; DCH RCP Lond. 1985; DRCOG 1985.

***MOOR, Paul Steven** 54 Julie Avenue, Heanor DE75 7HW — BM BS 1997 Nottm.

MOOR, Stephanie Young Peoples Unit, Royal Edinburgh Hospital, Edinburgh EH10 5HF Tel: 0131 537 6000 — MB ChB 1983 Auckland; MRCPsych 1989. Sen. Regist. (Adolesc. Psychiat.) Young People's Unit Roy. Edin. Hosp. Prev: Sen. Regist. (Child & Adolesc. Psychiat.) Auckland Pub. Hosp., NZ; Sen. Regist. (Child & Adolesc. Psychiat.) Addenbrooke's Hosp. Camb.; Regist. (Psychiat.) St. Geo. Hosp. Lond.

MOORBY, Allyson Mary 14 Alcroft Close, Abbeygrange, North Walbottle, Newcastle upon Tyne NE5 1QX — MB BS 1989 Newc.

MOORBY, Arthur Leslie, Surg. Cdr. RN Retd. The Red House Retirement Home, Clonway, Yelverton PL20 6EF — MRCS Eng. LRCP Lond. 1925. (King's Coll. Lond.) Socs: BMA. Prev: Jun. Hon. Anaesth. King's Coll. Hosp.; Hon. Anaesth. P. of Wales Gen. Hosp. Tottenham; Final Exam. Med. Off. RN & RM S. W..

MOORBY, Timothy John Department of Haematology, Nottingham City Hospital, Nottingham NG7; Email: moorby@doctors.org.uk — MB ChB 1994 Leeds; BSc (Genetics) Leeds 1991; MRCP 1997. (Leeds) Specialist Regist. Rotat. (Haemat.) Mid Trent Region.

MOORCRAFT, James Royal glamorgan Hospital, Ynysmaerdy, Llantrisant, Pontyclun CF72 8XR Tel: 01443 443536 Fax: 01443 443223 Email: james.moorcroft@pr-tr.wales.nhs.uk — BM 1982 Soton.; DM Soton. 1991; FRCP 1997; FRCPCH 1997. Cons. Neonat. Paediat. Roy. Glam. Hosp. Llantrisant; Hon. Clin. Lect. Univ. of Wales Coll. of Med. Socs: Brit. Assn. Perinatal Med.; Neonat. Soc.;

Eur. Soc. Paediat. Res. Prev: Cons. Paediat. Taunton & Som. NHS Trust; Sen. Regist. (Paediat.) S. & Mid Glam. HA; Research Fell. (Neonatology) Univ. of Oxf.

MOORCROFT, Alexander James Chest Medicine, North Tyneside General Hospital, Rake Lane, North Shields NE29 8HH — MB ChB 1988 Leeds; BSc (Hons.) Leeds 1985; MRCP (UK) 1991; MD 2000 Leeds. Cons. Phys., N. Tyneside Gen. Hosp. Socs: BTS, BMA. Prev: Sen. Regist. Respirat. & Gen. Med. Roy. Vic. Infirm. Newc.; CF Clin. Fell. Wythenshawe Hosp. Mans.

MOORCROFT, Jacqueline Vera Churchview Surgery, 30 Holland Road, Plymstock, Plymouth PL9 9BW — MB BS 1986 Lond.

***MOORCROFT, Sally Elizabeth** 12 Leopold Road, Leicester LE2 1YB — MB ChB 1998 Leic.; MB ChB Leic 1998.

MOORE, Alan (retired) Richmond Villa, New St., Ledbury HR8 2EB Tel: 01531 635536 Fax: 01531 638910 Email: amoore@infosafe.co.uk — MB ChB Bristol 1952; MRCGP 1974; MFPHM RCP (UK) 1989; MFCM RCP (UK) 1981; DPH Bristol 1974; DObst RCOG 1957. Prev: Dir. of Pub. Health & Informat. Servs. Chichester HA.

MOORE, Alan Graham Blackberry Hill Hospital, Manor Road, Fishponds, Bristol BS16 2EW — MB BCh BAO 1981 Dub.

MOORE, Albert Roland (retired) 117 Burnham Green Road, Welwyn AL6 0NH Tel: 01438 798644 — 1948 LRCPSI; FRCPath 1975, M 1964; DTM & H Liverp. 1952. Prev: Cons. Haemat. Qu. Eliz. II Hosp. Welwyn Gdn. City.

MOORE, Alison Elizabeth Jennifer Churchward and Partners, Croft Medical Centre, 2 Glen Road, Oadby, Leicester LE2 4PE Tel: 0116 271 2564 Fax: 0116 272 9000; White House, North Avenue, Leicester LE2 1TL Tel: 0116 270 6336 Fax: 0116 212 4834 — MB BS 1968 Lond.; MRCS Eng. LRCP Lond. 1968; DA Eng. 1971. (Guy's) Female Force Med. Off., Leics. Constable; Princip. Police Suirgeon, Leics. Constable. Socs: Leic. Med. Soc.; Leic. Medico Legal Soc.; Roy. Soc. Med. Prev: Prison Med. Off., Leicester & Rutland; Regist. (Anaesth.) Guy's Hosp. Lond.; Clin. Asst. Anaesth. Leicester Gp. Hosps.

MOORE, Alistair Charles Park View Surgery, 26/28 Leicester Road, Loughborough LE11 2AG; Whips Cottage, 21 Quorn Road, Paudy Lane, Barrow-upon-Soar, Leicester LE12 8HL Tel: 01509 842386 Fax: 01509 815038 — MB ChB 1983 Ed.; DLO RCS Eng. 1986. (Ed.) Socs: Brit. Med. Acupunct. Soc. Prev: Trainee GP Fort William Inverness-sh.; SHO (Neonat. Paediat.) Marston Green Hosp. Solihull; SHO (ENT Surg. & Cas.) Gwent HA.

MOORE, Andrew Harland Hassocks Health Centre, Windmill Avenue, Hassocks BN6 8LY Tel: 01273 844242 Fax: 01273 842709; The Halfpennies, 65 East End Lane, Ditchling, Hassocks BN6 8UR Tel: 01273 844242 Fax: 01273 842709 — MB ChB 1972 Bristol. Socs: Dep. Chair Mid Sussex Shadow PCG. Prev: SHO (Obst.) Treliske Hosp. Truro; SHO (Paediat.) S.lands Hosp. Shoreham; Ho. Phys. & Ho. Surg. W. Cornw. Hosp. Penzance.

MOORE, Andrew Patrick — MB ChB 1987 Sheff.; MRCGP 1991; DRCOG 1991. (Sheffield) SHO Psychiat., Leighton Hosp., Crewe. Socs: Christians in Caring Professions; Christ. Med. Fell.sh. Prev: Trainee GP Cleveland VTS.; SHO (Anaesth.) N. Devon Dist. Hosp. Barnstaple; GP Locum.

MOORE, Andrew William 19 Chiltern Drive, Stockport SK2 7BE — MB ChB 1976 Manch.; DRCOG 1979.

MOORE, Ann Lavinia Ulster Hospital, Dundonald, Belfast BT16 1RH Tel: 01232 484511 Fax: 01232 481166; 11 Highgrove Drive, Doagh Road, Ballyclare BT39 9XH — MB BCh BAO 1989 Belf.; MD Belf. 1997; MRCP (UK) 1992. Staff Grade (Gen. Med.) Ulster Hosp. Dundonald. Socs: Ulster Med. Soc.; Collegiate Mem. Roy. Coll. Phys. & Surgs. (Glas.).

MOORE, Annabel Fiona Katherine Mary 25 Streatfield Road, Harrow HA3 9BP — MB BS 1991 Lond.; BSc (Anat.) Lond. 1988. SHO Rotat. (Surg.) St. Bart. Hosp. Lond.

MOORE, Miss Anne Josephine Atkinson Morley's Hospital, 31 Copse Hill, London SW20 0NE Tel: 020 8946 7711 Fax: 020 8947 8389; 54 Eland Road, London SW11 5JY — MB BS 1982 Lond.; BSc Lond. 1979; FRCS Eng. 1987. Cons. Neurosurg. Atkinson Morley's Hosp. Lond.

MOORE, Anthony Northam Surgery, Bayview Road, Northam, Bideford EX39 1AZ Tel: 01237 474994; Penhir, Cornborough Road, Westward Ho!, Bideford EX39 1AA Tel: 01237 471936 — MB BCh 1980 Wales; MRCGP 1988; DRCOG 1984.

MOORE

MOORE, Antonia Louise Churchill COttage, Castle St., Portchester, Fareham PO16 9QW — MB ChB 1993 Bristol.

MOORE, Antony Richard Osborne Road Surgery, 17 Osborne Road, Newcastle upon Tyne NE2 2AH Tel: 0191 281 4588 Fax: 0191 212 0379; 9 The Grove, Benton, Newcastle upon Tyne NE12 9PE Tel: 0191 215 0803 — MB BS 1988 Newc.; MRCGP 1993.

MOORE, Arthur Timothy Eastern Regional Executive, Capital Park, Fulbourn, Cambridge CB1 5XB Tel: 01223 597 655 Email: tim.moore@doh.gsi.gov.uk; 67 Queen Ediths Way, Cambridge CB1 8P2 Tel: 01223 575 218 Email: moore@flexnet.co.uk — MB BCh BAO 1977 Dub.; MSc Lond. 1982; BA MOD Hons. (Physiol.) Dub. 1972, MB BCh BAO 1977; FFPHM 1992; MFCM 1986; DCH NUI 1979. (Trinity College Dublin) Cons. Rotat. Pub. Health Med. Anglia & Oxf.; Cons. Pub. Health Med. E.. Regional Offices NHS Exec. Prev: Sen. Regist. (Community Med.) Camb. HA.; Anglia Clin. Effectiveness Team Instit. Pub. Health Camb.

MOORE, Austen Joseph 38 Prince's Avenue, Walsall WS1 2DG Tel: 01922 623603 — MB ChB 1950 Sheff. (Sheff.) Socs: Roy. Coll. Gen. Pract. Prev: Army Civil. Med. Pract.; Squadron Ldr. RAF Med. Br.; Asst. Cas. Off. & Ho. Surg. Roy. Hosp. Sheff.

MOORE, Austen Peter Walton Centre for Neurology & Neurosurgery, Fazakerley Hospital, Lower Lane, Liverpool L9 7LJ Tel: 0151 525 3611 Fax: 0151 529 5512; Ridgewood, 5 Links Hey Road, Caldy, Wirral CH48 1NA Tel: 0151 625 7112 — MB ChB 1975 Birm.; MD Birm. 1987; MRCP (UK) 1980. Sen. Lect. (Neurol.) Liverp. Univ. & Hons. Cons. Neurol. Walton Centre for Neurol. & Neurosurg. NHS Trust Liverp. Socs: Assn. Brit. Neurol.; Movem. Disorder Soc.; Cochrane Collaboration. Prev: Lect. (Neurol.) Liverp.; Regist. (Neurol.) Inst. Neurol. Scs. Glas. & Qu. Eliz. Hosp. Birm.; Regist. (Gen. Med.) Hallamsh. Hosp. Sheff.

MOORE, Benjamin TPMH, RAF Akrotiri BFPO 57 Tel: 00 357 5265562 Fax: 00 357 5265623; Greentrees, 15 St. Margaret's Road, Hereford HR1 1TS Tel: 01432 271855 — MB BChir 1970 Camb.; MD Camb. 1981; MRCS Eng. LRCP Lond. 1969; FRCOG 1987, M 1974; LM Rotunda Nat. Matern. Hosp. Coombe 1972. (St. Bart.) Cons. Obst. & Gyn. The P.ss Mary's Hosp. RAF Akrotiri, Cyprus; Assoc. Prof. RCSI NWAFH Tabuk, KSA. Socs: BMA; Internat. Menopause Soc. Prev: Cons. Obst. & Gyn. Hereford Co. Hosp. Hereford HA; Sen. Regist. (Obst. & Gyn.) Dudley Rd. Hosp. Birm. AHA; Sen. Regist. (Obst.) Harare Hosp. Salisbury, Zimbabwe.

MOORE, Brenda Kingshill House, Kingshill Road, Old Town, Swindon SN1 4LG Tel: 01793 491917 Fax: 01793 491047 — MB ChB Bristol 1965; FRCPsych 1994, M 1974. Cons. Psychiat. Swindon.

MOORE, Bruce Jonathan 53 Ash Grove, Wavertree, Liverpool L15 1ES — MB ChB 1993 Liverp.

MOORE, Bryan William Reginald Saltash Road Surgery, 218 Saltash Road, Keyham, Plymouth PL2 2BB Tel: 01752 562843 Fax: 01752 607024; 2 Warleigh Villas, Culver Road, Saltash PL12 4EP Tel: 01752 843875 — MRCS Eng. LRCP Lond. 1968; MA Camb. 1969, MB 1968, BChir 1967. (Camb. & Guy's) Prev: Ho. Phys. & Jun. Regist. (Med.) Guy's Hosp. Lond.; SHO (Paediat.) Lewisham Hosp. Lond.

MOORE, Caroline Mary Flat 15, 33 Elsynge Road, London SW18 2HR Tel: 020 8870 7621 — MB BS 1997 Lond. (St. George's Hosp. Med. Sch.)

MOORE, Catherine Angela Wolverhampton Healthcare NHS Trust, Community Child Health, Redhill St. Health Centre, Redhill St., Wolverhampton WV1 1NR Tel: 01902 444325 Fax: 01902 444442 Email: angela.moore@whc-tr.nhs.uk — MB BS Lond. 1972; MRCP (UK) 1975; DCH Eng. 1975; FRCP, 1996; FRCPCH. (St. Geo.) Cons. Community Paediat. Wolverhampton Healthcare NHS Trust, Wolverhampton. Cons. Paediat. (Community Child Health); Hon. Sen. Lect. Univ. Birm.; Child Health. Socs: Brit. Assn. Community Child Health; Fell. Roy. Coll. Paediat. & Child Health; Brit. Paediatric Neurol. Assn. (Mem.). Prev: Research Fell. (Paediat.) Char. Cross Hosp. Lond.; Cons. (Community Paediat.) Birm. Childr. Hosp., Birm.; Cons. Community Paediat. & Med. Dir. 1st Community Health Mid Staffs. Stafford.

MOORE, Catherine Dawn Henrietta Street Health Centre, 109A Henrietta Street, Girvan KA26 9AN Tel: 01465 713343 Fax: 01465 714591 — MB BCh BAO 1985 Belf.; MRCGP 1990; DRCOG 1989.

MOORE, Charles Alexander Department of Anaesthetics, Northern General Hospital, Herries Rd, Sheffield S5 7AU Tel: 0114 271 4818 Fax: 0114 271 4818 Email: c.a.moore@sheffield.ac.uk — MB BS 1976 Lond.; MRCS Eng. LRCP Lond. 1976; DCH RCP Lond. 1979; FFA RCS Eng. 1981. Cons. Anaesth. N.ern Gen. Hosp. NHS Trust. Socs: Internat. Assn. for Study of Pain; Europ. Soc. of Anaesthesiologists. Prev: Cons. Anaesth. Scunthorpe & Goole NHS Trust; Vis. Asst. Prof. Univ. Oklahoma, USA.

MOORE, Mr Charles John (retired) Bracondale House, Parsonage Lane, Little Baddow, Chelmsford CM3 4SU Tel: 01245 222324 Fax: 01245 227375 — MB BChir 1955 Camb.; FRCS Eng. 1961. Hon. Cons. Orthop. & Traum. Surg. Mid. Essex NHS Trust. Prev: Sen. Regist. Lond. Hosp.

MOORE, Cheryl Ann, Capt. Garrison Medical Centre, Episkopi BFPO 53 Tel: 00357 521 1355 Fax: 00357 5 211 355 Email: candy@spidernet.com.cy; Garrison Medical Centre, Episkopi BFPO 53 Tel: 00357 521 1355 Fax: 00357 5 211 355 — MB BS 1996 Lond.; BSc Lond. 1984. (University College London) GP VTS Cyprus. Prev: SHO (A & E) Roy. Hosp. Haslar; PRHO Whittington Hosp.; PRHO Ipswich.

MOORE, Christine Pendorlau, Pendwill Road, Moss, Wrexham LL11 6EU — MB ChB 1973 Liverp.; DCH Eng. 1975. Clin. Med. Off. Liverp. AHA.

MOORE, Christopher Edward Gareth Department of Clinical Neurophysiology, Manchester Royal Infirmary, Oxford Road, Manchester M13 9WL Email: chris.moore@man.ac.uk — MB BS 1989 Lond.; BSc (Hons.) Lond. 1986; MRCP (UK) 1992; PhD 1999. Cons.(Clin. Neurophysiol.) Manch. Roy. Infirm.; Cons.(clin.Neurophysiol) hope hosp.Salford. Socs: Brit. Soc. Clin. Neurophysiol.; Assoc. Mem. Asso. Brit. NeUrol.s, .Brit. Neurosci. Asso. Prev: Specialist Regist. (Clin. Neurophysiol.) Soton, MRC Train. Fell. & Hon. Sen. Regist. (Clin. Neurol.) Manch. Roy. Infirm. & Univ. Manch.; Regist. (Neurophyyriol.) N. Manch. Gen. & Manch. Roy. Infirm.

MOORE, Christopher John Frost Wootton Medical Centre, 36-38 High Street, Wootton, Northampton NN4 6LW Tel: 01604 709933 Fax: 01604 709944; Harlestone House Lodge, Church Lane, Lower Halestone, Northampton NN7 4EN — MB ChB 1986 Sheff.; MRCGP 1991; DRCOG 1989.

MOORE, Colin Scott The Anchorage, Chambers Terrace, Peebles EH45 9DZ — MB ChB 1994 Aberd. SHO (Infec. Dis.) King's Cross Hosp. Dundee.

MOORE, Cyril Gordon (Surgery) 129 St George's Road, Cheltenham GL50 3ER Tel: 01242 580468 — MB ChB 1960 Sheff.; DObst RCOG 1962.

MOORE, Daniel Jeffery Faversham Health Centre, Bank Street, Faversham ME13 8QR Tel: 01795 536621/533987/534150; 112 The St, Boughton-under-Blean, Faversham ME13 9AP — MB ChB 1990 Manch.; MB BS Manch. 1990; MRCGP Lond. 1996. (Manch.) GP Princip. Faversham. Socs: BMA; MDU.

MOORE, Mr David Accident & Emergency Department, Morriston Hospital, Swansea SA6 6NL — BM BCh 1986 Oxf.; FRCS Ed. 1994.

MOORE, David Alexander James c/o Wellcome Trust, 183 Euston Rd, London NW1 2W; 26 Wycliffe Road, London SW11 5QR Tel: 020 7924 6814 Email: davidajmoore@email.msn.com — MB ChB 1989 Birm.; MD 2000; DTM & H 2000; MRCP (UK) 1992. (Birm.) Wellcome Trust Research Fell. in Clin. Trop. Med.; Hon. Cons./Sen. Lect.(Infec. Dis.s), Imperial Coll. at Hammersmith Hosp., Lond.. Socs: Roy. Soc. Trop. Med. & Hyg.; BMA. Prev: Specialist Regist., Hosp. For Trop. Dis.s, Lond.

MOORE, David Arthur (retired) The Green, Priory Road, Blythburgh, Halesworth IP19 9LR Tel: 01502 478278 — MB BS 1964 Durh.; DTM & H Eng. 1973; DPH Bristol 1974; DIH Eng. 1975; MFOM RCP Lond. 1982; FFom RCP Lond. 1993. Hon. Clin. Teach. Univ. Edin. Prev: Dir. Gp. Med. Servs. Scott. & Newc. Plc.

MOORE, David Charles Fosse Acre, Dunkerton, Bath BA2 8BR Tel: 01761 434698 Fax: 0161 434698 — MSc Occupat. Med. Lond. 1983, MB BS 1964; MFOM RCP Lond. 1985, AFOM 1983; MRCS Eng. LRCP Lond. 1964. (King's Coll Hosp.) Occupat. Phys., various companies; Clin. Asst. Occupat. Med. Roy. United Hosp. Bath; Med. Adviser Benefits Agency. Socs: Fell. Roy. Inst. Pub. Health & Hyg.; Soc. Occupat. Med.; Clin. Soc. Bath. Prev: Regional Med. Adviser Brit. Gas S. W..; Chief Med. Off. Brit. Gas. N. Thames.

MOORE, David Gerald Caen Health Centre, Braunton EX33 1LR Tel: 01271 812005 Fax: 01271 814768; Park Cottage, Higher Pk Road, Braunton EX33 2LG Tel: 01271 812005 — MB ChB 1979 Birm.; DRCOG 1984.

MOORE, David Gerrard The Medical Centre, 143 Rookwood Avenue, Leeds LS9 ONL Tel: 0113 249 3011 Fax: 0113 240 1958 — MB ChB 1983 Leeds. GP Leeds. Prev: SHO (O & G) St. Jas. Hosp. Leeds; SHO (A & E) Pinderfields Gen. Hosp. Wakefield; Ho. Off. (Gen. Surg.) St. Jas. Hosp. Leeds.

MOORE, David James Northern General Hospital, Herries Road, Sheffield S5 7AY Tel: 0114 271 4045; 632 Fulwood, Sheffield S10 3EJ — MB ChB 1976 Sheff.; FRCR 1985. Cons. Radiol. N. Gen. Hosp. Sheff. Socs: Brit.Soc. Skeletal Radiol.; Europ. Soc. Skeletal Radiol.; Mem. Brit. Med. Ultrasound Soc.

MOORE, Mr David John Colchester General Hospital, Turner Road, Colchester CO4 5JL Tel: 01206 742813 Fax: 01206 742814; 247 Berechurch Hall Road, Colchester CO2 9NP Tel: 01206 548568 Email: david@coldoc.demon.co.uk — MB BS 1986 Lond.; BSc Lond. 1983; FRCS (Orth.) 1996; FRCS Eng. 1990. Cons. (Orthop.) Colchester Gen. Hosp. Colchester. Prev: Sen. Regist. (Orthop.) Roy. Lond. Hosp.; Regist. (Orthop.) Roy. Lond. Hosp.; SHO Whipps Cross Hosp. Lond.

MOORE, David Robert 51 Station Road, Bamber Bridge, Preston PR5 6PE Tel: 01772 335128 Fax: 01772 492248 — MB ChB 1990 Manch.; MRCGP 1994; T(GP) 1994; DFFP 1993; DRCOG 1993. (Manch.) Hosp. Practitioner (Dermat.) Chorley Dist. Hosp.

MOORE, Deborah Anne c/o Alison Moore, 46 Churchdown, Bromley BR1 5PT — State Exam Med 1991 Leipzig.

MOORE, Deirdre Irene 2 Pinehill Green, Ballycrochan Road, Bangor BT19 6SQ Tel: 01247 2840 — MB BCh BAO 1973 Belf. GP Bangor Co. Down. Prev: Regist. (Psychiat.) E. HSSB N. Irel.; Ho. Off. Ulster Hosp. Dundonald.

MOORE, Derek Alan (retired) Tanronen, Hawson Court, Buckfastleigh TQ11 0HP Tel: 01364 643544 — MB BS 1957 Lond. Prev: GP Buckfastleigh.

MOORE, Donna Rachel The Coatham Surgery, 18 Coatham Road, Redcar TS10 1RJ Tel: 01642 483495 Fax: 01642 487520; 153 High Street, Marske, Redcar TS11 7LN Tel: 01642 476817 Email: drm@elfland.demon.co.uk — MB ChB 1986 Manch.

MOORE, Dorothy Margaret Medway Maritime Hospital, Windmill Road, Gillingham ME7 5NY Tel: 01634 830000 Ext: 5149 Fax: 01634 811250 — MB ChB Ed. 1966; FRCOG 1985, M 1973. Cons. O & G Medway Maritime Hosp. Gillingham Kent. Socs: BMA. Prev: Lect. (Human Reproduct. & Obst.) Univ. Soton.; SHO (Obst.) Hammersmith Hosp. Lond.; SHO (O & G) Simpson Memor. Matern. Pavil. & Roy. Infirm. Edin.

MOORE, Duncan 4 York Road, Torpoint PL11 2LG Tel: 01752 812152; Glendale, Wilcove, Torpoint PL11 2PH Tel: 01752 812289 — MB BS 1967 Lond.; MRCS Eng. LRCP Lond. 1967. (King's Coll. Hosp.) Prev: SHO (Obst. & Gen. Surg.) Luton & Dunstable Hosp.; Orthop. Regist. Odstock Hosp.; Ho. Off. (Gen. Surg. & Med.) & SHO (Accid. & Emer.) King's Coll.

MOORE, E Jane Blackbird Leys Health Centre, 63 Blackbird Leys Road, Oxford OX4 6HL Tel: 01865 778244; Stonecross House, Southend, Garsington, Oxford OX44 9DD Tel: 01865 361497 — MB BS 1973 Lond.; MRCGP 1979. (Middlesex)

MOORE, Eamonn Joseph Flat 15, Apsley Mews, Little High St., Worthing BN11 1DH — MB BCh BAO 1991 NUI.

MOORE, Edward Charles 27 Cedar Gardens, Kinver, Stourbridge DY7 6BW — MB ChB 1961 Liverp.; DObst RCOG 1963. (Liverp.) Prev: Med. Off. RAF.

MOORE, Edward James Howlett, OStJ (retired) Hillhead Cottage, Inverfarigaig, Inverness IV2 6XR Tel: 01456 486255 — MB ChB St. And. 1961; MFCM 1977; MFHom 1972; Dip. Soc. Med. Ed. 1974. Prev: Cons. Pub. Health Med. Tayside HB Ninewells Hosp. Dundee.

MOORE, Edward Lewis, MC, Lt.-Col. RAMC Retd. Homestead, Thanet Road, Westgate-on-Sea CT8 8PB — MB ChB 1941 Liverp.; DOMS Eng. 1950. (Liverp.) Prev: Sen. Regist. Ophth. Kent Co. Ophth. Hosp.; Sen. Specialist in Ophth. R.A.M.C., D.A.D.M.S. Commando Gp.; Sen. Ho. Off. Sussex Eye Hosp. Brighton.

MOORE, Mrs Eileen Elizabeth Mackenzie (retired) 6 Drummond Street, Dundee DD3 6LL Tel: 01382 224299 — MB BCh BAO 1945 Belf. Prev: SCMO Tayside HB.

MOORE, Elinor The Moat, Rectory Lane, Carriers Road, Cranbrook TN17 3JY Tel: 01580 712151 — MB BS 1996 Lond.; DTM & H Liverpool 1998. (Royal Free Hospital) Kala-azar Team S. Sudan "Med. Sans Frontiers". Socs: BMA; Fell. Roy. Soc. Trop. Med. and Hyg. Prev: SHO (A & E) Kent & Sussex Hosp.; Ho. Off. (Phys.) Brighton Health Care; Ho. Off. (Surgic.) Plymouth.

MOORE, Elizabeth Jane Linden House, Mynyddbach, Shirenewton, Chepstow NP16 6RP — MB ChB 1986 Bristol; DRCOG 1989.

MOORE, Elizabeth Mary Morrison (retired) Blakeney Downs, Morston Road, Blakeney, Holt NR25 7BG Tel: 01263 740895 Fax: 01263 740895 — BM BCh 1958 Oxf.; MA Oxf. 1958. Prev: GP Harrow.

MOORE, Emily Madge St. Nectans, Welcombe, Bideford EX39 6HF Tel: 01288 331205 — MRCS Eng. LRCP Lond. 1947. (Roy. Free) Indep. Cons. Bideford Area. Prev: Clin. Asst. (Psychosexual Problems) Psychiat. Dept. N. Devon & Dist. Hosp. Barnstaple; Med. Off. Marital Difficulties Clinic Woking & Weybridge; Cons. Stud.s' Problem Clinic Univ. Surrey Health Dept.

MOORE, Evan William 17 Druids Cross Road, Liverpool L18 3EA — MB BCh BAO 1994 Belf.; DA (UK) 1996; FRCA 1998. (Belfast) Lect. (Anaesth.) Dept. of Anaesth., Univ. Liverp. Prev: SHO (Anaesth.) Aintree Hosps.; SHO (Anaesth.) Roy. Liverp. Univ. Hosp.; Specialist Regist. Merseyside.

MOORE, Fiona Cameron (retired) 25 Woodbury Hill, Loughton IG10 1JF Tel: 020 8508 1782 — MB ChB 1962 St. And.; DMedRehab RCP Lond. 1979. Prev: Cons. Rehabil. Heenan Hse. Rehabil. Centre St. Joseph's Hospice Hackney.

MOORE, Fiona Catherine Leicester Terrace Health Care Centre, 8 Leicester Terrace, Northampton NN2 6AL Tel: 01604 33682 Fax: 01604 233408; 35 Booth Lane N., Northampton NN3 6JQ Tel: 01604 499957 — MB BS 1988 Lond.; MRCGP 1993; DRCOG 1992. Prev: Trainee GP Milton Keynes VTS.

MOORE, Fionna Patricia 10 Penrhyn Crescent, E. Sheen, London SW14 7PF — MB BS 1974 Lond.; BSc Lond. 1971; FRCS Eng. 1979; FRCS Ed. 1979. (Univ. Coll. Hosp.) Cons. A & E Char. Cross & Hammersmith Hosps.; Med. Dir. Lond. Ambul. Serv. NHS Trust. Socs: Fell. Fac. A & E Med. Prev: Cons. A & E Univ. Coll. Hosp., Middlx. Hosp. Lond. & Oxf. Radcliffe Hosp.; Sen. Regist. (Accid & Emerg.) Ealing & Hammersmith Hosp.; Bayer Research Fell. Surgic. Unit Univ. Coll. Hosp. Lond.

MOORE, Geoffrey John The Croft Surgery, Penny Bridge, Ulverston LA12 7TD Tel: 01229 861249 — MB BS 1972 Lond.; MRCS Eng. LRCP Lond. 1972; DRCOG 1977. (St. Geo.) Prev: Ho. Phys. & Ho. Surg. Salisbury Gen. Infirm.

MOORE, George Leslie (retired) 58 Main Street, Kirby Muxlow, Leicester LE9 2AL Tel: 0116 239 3240 — LRCPI & LM, LRSCI & LM 1942; LRCPI & LM, LRCSI & LM 1942. Prev: Cons. Chest Phys. Leics. AHA (T).

MOORE, George William (retired) 4 Westville Road, Bexhill-on-Sea TN39 3QB Tel: 01424 210513 — MRCS Eng. LRCP Lond. 1949. Prev: Sen. WHO Adviser E. Pakistan.

MOORE, Gerald Ernest (retired) Tordown House, Swimbridge, Barnstaple EX32 0QY — LAH 1954 Dub.; MSc (Med.) Surrey 1970; MGDS RCS Eng. 1980, LDS 1949. Prev: Ho. Surg. St. Nicholas's Hosp. Plumstead.

MOORE, Gillian Fenella 10 Norfolk Court, Holdgate Road, Middle Park, Northfield, Birmingham B29 4PT — MB ChB 1977 Birm.

MOORE, Graeme John Dundas (retired) Twitten Cottage, Ropewalk, Alfriston, Polegate BN26 5SU Tel: 01323 871236 — MB BS Lond. 1965; MRCS Eng. LRCP Lond. 1965; DObst RCOG 1969. Prev: Lingfield Surg., Surrey 1970-1998.

MOORE, Graeme Robert Whiston Hospital, Warrington Road, Prescot L35 5DR Tel: 0151 426 1600; Flat 4, 164 Bedford Street S., Liverpool L7 7DD Tel: 0151 709 9381 — MB ChB 1996 Liverp. (Liverp.) SHO (A&E) Whiston Hosp. Prev: Ho. Off. (Med.); Ho. Off. (Surg.).

MOORE, Graham David Carleton (retired) St. Michael's Surgery, Walwyn Close, Twerton on Avon, Bath BA2 1ER Tel: 01225 832659 Fax: 01225 832659 Email: familymoore@supanet.com — MB BS 1964 Lond. Prev: Mem. BMA.

MOORE, Graham Stephen Caradoc Surgery, Station Approach, Frinton-on-Sea CO13 9JT Tel: 01255 850101 Fax: 01255 851004

MOORE

— MB BS 1979 Lond.; MA Oxf. 1980, BA 1976; MRCGP 1983; Dip. Med. Educat. Dund 1994; DRCOG 1982.

MOORE, Greville John Matthes Badgers Rest, Clyst St Mary, Topsham, Exeter EX5 1AJ — MB BS 1950 Lond. (St. Bart.) Local Treasury Med. Off.; Bd.ing Med. Off. DHSS. Prev: Asst. Res. Med. Off. Gen. Hosp. Birm.; Squadron Ldr. RAF Med. Br., Med. Specialist & Pathol.; Jun. Regist. Path. Qu. Eliz. Hosp. Birm.

MOORE, Harold Stewart, OStJ, MBE(Mil), QHP, Maj.-Gen. late RAMC Retd. (retired) 22 Curzon Drive, Church Crookham, Fleet GU52 6JL Tel: 01252 624141 — MB BS Lond. 1948; FRCP Ed. 1970, M 1956; FRCP Lond. 1975, M 1956; MRCS Eng. LRCP Lond. 1948; DTM & H Eng. 1955. Prev: Hon. Phys. to HM the Qu./Dir. Army Med.

***MOORE, Harriet Louise** 6 Abbotts Road, Winchester SO23 7EX — MB BS 1996 Lond.

MOORE, Helen Elisabeth Ferryhill Medical Practice, Durham Road, Ferryhill DL17 8JJ Tel: 01740 651238; 49 Blackwell, Darlington DL3 8QT Tel: 01325 464291 — MB BS 1987 Newc.; FRCS Glas. 1992. (Newcastle) p/t Gen. Practitioner; Clin. Asst. Endoscopy, Dermat. Bishop Auckland Gen. Hosp.

***MOORE, Helen Louise** 31 Hurst Lea Road, New Mills, High Peak SK22 3HP — MB BS 1996 Newc.

MOORE, Hugh Samuel Cooper (retired) FLat 12 Radlyn Oval, 20 Park Avenue, Harrogate HG2 9BQ — MB ChB 1954 Leeds; MB ChB (Distinc. Surg.) Leeds 1954; DObst RCOG 1958. Prev: Ho. Phys. York Co. Hosp.

MOORE, Jack Edghill (retired) Meilen, 21 Ospringe Place, Faversham ME13 8TB Tel: 01480 300881 — MRCS Eng. LRCP Lond. 1941. Prev: Med. Off. W.. Hse. Ware.

MOORE, James 11 Ingledene, Temple Patrick, Ballyclare BT39 0JN Tel: 01232 779092 Fax: 028 94 433932 — MB ChB BAO 1952; PhD Belf. 1974, MD (Hons.) 1961; FFA RCS Eng. 1957. (Belf.) Cons. Anaesth. Belf. City & Musgrave Pk. Hosp. Socs: Assn. Anaesths. Gt. Brit. Prev: Sen. Regist. Roy. Vict. Hosp. Belf.; Sen. Tutor Dept. Anaesth. Qu. Univ. Belf.; Research Fell. Mercy Hosp. Pittsburgh, U.S.A.

***MOORE, Mr James Ashley** 46 The High Street, Burford OX18 4QA — MB BCh 1995 Wales; MRCS (Eng.).

MOORE, James Brown The Surgery, 4 Stoke Road, Bishops Cleeve, Cheltenham GL52 8RP Tel: 01242 672007; Langton Leys, Butts Lane, Woodmancote, Cheltenham GL52 9QH Tel: 01242 675690 — MB ChB 1981 Ed.

MOORE, Mr James Macadam (retired) Marchmont, 11 Bellevue Road, Ayr KA7 2SA Tel: 01292 263808 — LRCP LRCS 1945 Ed.; FRCS Ed. 1953; FRFPS Glas. 1951; LRCP LRCS Ed. LRFPS Glas. 1945. Prev: Cons. Surg. S. Ayrsh. Hosp. Gp.

MOORE, James MacIntyre (retired) Swan House, Misson, Doncaster DN10 6ED — MB ChB Glas. 1943; MD Glas. 1965; MRCPath 1965.

MOORE, James Richard (Surgery), Rush View, Holme on Spalding Moor, York YO43 4BJ Tel: 01430 860221 Fax: 01430 861389; Chain Bar House, 39 Main St., Bubwith, Selby YO8 6LT Tel: 01757 288616 — MB ChB 1971 Leeds; MB ChB Leeds. 1971; DObst RCOG 1973. (Leeds) Princip. (Gen. Pract.).

MOORE, James Richard Armstrong Quay Lane Surgery, Old Quay Lane, St Germans, Saltash PL12 5LH Tel: 01503 230088 Fax: 01503 230713 Email: james.moore@guaylane.cornwall.nhs.uk; Penewin, Trerulefoot, Saltash PL12 5DA Tel: 01752 851365 — MB BS 1980 Lond.; FRCGP 1995, M 1985; DCH RCPS Glas. 1984; DRCOG 1982. (Lond. Hosp.) GP Princip. Prev: Trainee GP Plymouth VTS; SHO (A & E) & SHO (O & G) Lond. Hosp. Whitechapel; Ho. Off. P.ss Alexandra Hosp. Harlow.

MOORE, Jane 6 Clifton Park Road, Reading RG4 7PD Tel: 01734 474056 — MB BS 1987 Lond.; BA Camb. 1984; MRCOG 1994. Regist. (O & G) Roy. Berks. Hosp. Reading. Prev: Research Regist. (O & G) Whipps Cross Hosp. Lond.; SHO (O & G) S.mead Hosp. Bristol.

MOORE, Jane Elizabeth Anne Chadwell Medical Centre, 1 Brentwood Road, Chadwell St. Mary, Grays RM16 4JD Tel: 01375 842289 Fax: 01375 840357; 9 The Knowle, Vange, Basildon SS16 4BP Tel: 01268 287173 — MB BS 1982 Lond.

MOORE, Jane Rosamund Molebridge Practice, 3 Cannon Side, Fetcham, Leatherhead KT22 9LE Tel: 01372 379941 Fax: 01372 361178 — MB ChB 1974 Bristol; MRCGP 1981; DCH Eng. 1980.

MOORE, Janette Mary — MB BCh BAO 1990 Belf.; MRCPsych 1995.

***MOORE, Janice Karena** 29 Forsyth Road, Newcastle upon Tyne NE2 3DB — MB BS 1997 Newc.

***MOORE, Jason Cresswell** 37 Linthorpe Road, Buckley CH7 3HF — BM BS 1997 Nottm.

MOORE, Jayne Karen Allen, Moore, Jackson and Ferrer, Wellside Medical Centre, 3 Burton Road, Derby DE1 1TH Tel: 01332 737777 Fax: 01332 737778 — MB ChB 1982 Leeds; DRCOG 1986. (Leeds)

MOORE, Jeanette Elizabeth Maureen 21 Malone Hill Park, Belfast BT9 6RE — MB BCh BAO 1968 Belf.

MOORE, Jennifer Susan Linden Medical Group, Linden Medical Centre, Linden Avenue, Kettering NN15 7NX Tel: 01536 512104 Fax: 01536 415930 — MB BS 1973 Lond.; MRCP (UK) 1977. Partner Gen. Pract.

***MOORE, Jessica Mary** 8 Balmoral Terrace, Heaton, Newcastle upon Tyne NE6 5YA — MB BS 1996 Newc.

***MOORE, John Andrew** 9 Ellieslea Road, Broughty Ferry, Dundee DD5 1JH — MB ChB 1996 Manch.

MOORE, Mr John Charles Gibson (retired) 12 Farmer Street, London W8 7SN Tel: 020 7221 6227 — MB BCh BAO 1939 Dub.; BA Open 1992; BA Dub. 1937, MB BCh BAO 1939; FRCS Ed. (Ophth.) 1947; DOMS Eng. 1946. Prev: Ophth. Surg. Barnet & Edgware Gen. Hosps.

MOORE, John Edmund Keir (retired) Glebe End, Sulham Lane, Pangbourne, Reading RG8 7LJ Tel: 0118 984 2381 Email: jemoor@waitrose.com — BM BCh 1951 Oxf.; LMSSA Lond. 1951. Prev: Med. Off. DHSS (LSRO).

MOORE, John McEwan Gardner Street Surgery, 11 Gardner Street, Glasgow G11 5NR Tel: 0141 334 2215 Fax: 0141 338 8197 — MB ChB 1968 Glas.

***MOORE, John Michael Francis** 3 The Maltings, Pound St., Warminster BA12 8JR — MB BS 1997 Lond.

MOORE, John Philip Warders Medical Centre, 47 East Street, Tonbridge TN9 1LA Tel: 01732 770088 Fax: 01732 770033; Maple House, Claremont Gardens, Tunbridge Wells TN2 5DD Tel: 01892 539593 — MB BS 1989 Lond.; MRCGP Lond. 1996; DRCOG Lond. 1996; DCH RCP Lond. 1994; DA (UK) 1992. (St George's) GP Princip. Warders Med. Centre E. St. Tunbridge Kent. Socs: RCGP.

MOORE, John Richard (retired) 11 Sycamore Close, Oadby, Leicester LE2 2RN Tel: 0116 270 0034 Fax: 0709 202 7278 Email: johnmoorell@doctors.org.uk — MB ChB 1961 Birm.; BSc (Hons.) Birm. 1958; FRCP Lond. 1980, M 1967; FRCPCH 1997; DCH Eng. 1965. Hon. Vis. Clin. Fell. Univ. Leics.; Hon. Cons. Leics & Rutland NHS Health Trust. Prev: Cons. Community Paediat. Community Unit Leicester.

MOORE, Mr John Rowsell MacRae 107 Wentworth Road, Harborne, Birmingham B17 9SU — MB ChB 1970 Sheff.; BSc (Hons.) (Anat.) Sheff. 1967; FRCS Ed. 1976. Cons. Surg. (ENT) Birm. Univ. Trust, Alexandra Healthcare Trust & Childr. Hosp. Birm. Trust; Hon. Clin. Lect. (Surg.) Univ. Birm. Socs: Roy. Soc. Med. & Brit. Assn. Otolaryngol. Prev: Sen. Regist. (ENT) Bristol Health Dist. (T); Ho. Surg. Sheff. Roy. Infirm.; Ho. Phys. Sheff. Roy. Hosp.

MOORE, John York (retired) Stella, 10 Laregan Hill, Penzance TR18 4NY Tel: 01736 362474 — MB BS Lond. 1945. Prev: GP Camb.

MOORE, Jonathan Edward 75 Palmerston Road, Belfast BT4 1QD — MB BCh BAO 1991 Belf.

MOORE, Jonathan Graeme Walton and Partners, West Street Surgery, 12 West Street, Chipping Norton OX7 5AA Tel: 01608 642529 Fax: 01608 645066 — MB BS 1991 Lond.; LLM 1999 (Legal aspects of medical practice); DFFP 1993; DRCOG 1993; MRCGP 1996. GP Partner; N. Oxf. Addicts Project (Co-ordinator for PCT of project). Socs: Comm. Mem. of the Oxf. Medico-Legal Soc.; Comm. Mem. Lawrence Home Nursing Team; Comm. Based Palliat. care nursing team, Chipping Norton area. Prev: Ent. Clin. Assist. ('97-'00) under Mr. Castle, Warwick Hosp.; PCT Ment. health Lead ('98-'00).

MOORE, Jonathan Wentworth Anthony Bentley Village Surgery, Hole Lane, Bentley, Farnham GU10 5LP Tel: 01420 22106 Fax: 01420 520024 Email: jwam2@yahoo!.co.uk; West End Cottage, Upper Froyle, Alton GU34 4JT Tel: 01420 522843 Fax: 01420 522543 — MB BS 1979 Lond.; DRCOG 1982. (Guy's Hosp. Lond.)

Hosp. Pract. (Dermat.) & Clin. Asst. (Obst. & Gyn.) N. Hants. Hosp. Basingstoke; Lt. Col. RAMC (V) SOI Med. HQ 3 (UK) Div.

MOORE, Joy Alison (retired) 72 Newtonwood Road, Ashtead KT21 1NP Tel: 01372 813999 — MB ChB St. And. 1963. Community Paediat. (Sessional). Prev: Cons. Community Paediat. Bournewood Community & Ment. Health NHS Trust Woking.

MOORE, Judith Ann 24 Birchwood Road, Utley, Keighley BD20 6BX — MB BS 1989 Newc.

MOORE, Judith Carole Community Child Health, Taunton & Somerset NHS Trust, Musgrove Park Hospital, Taunton TA1 5DA Tel: 01823 342690; 21 Northfield, Bridgwater TA6 7HA Tel: 01278 423405 — MB ChB 1991 Leic.; BSc Leic. 1988; MRCGP 1995; DRCOG 1993. (Leic.) Staff Grade (Community Child Health) Taunton & Som. NHS Trust; Asst. GP Creech Med. Centre Taunton; Clin. Asst. Family Plann. Bridgwater & Taunton. Socs: MRCGP; Diplomates of Fac. Family Plann. & Reproduc. Health; Brit. Assn. Community Child Health. Prev: Med. Off. Gaol St. FPC; GP/Regist. Wargrave Hse. Hereford; SHO (O & G, Paediat., Age Care & A & E) Hereford Acute Hosp.

MOORE, Judith Sarah Whitehouse Farm, Lower Road, Adgerstone, Sandown PO36 0HN — BM 1985 Soton. Prev: SHO (Psychiat.) Whitecroft Hosp. I. of Wight; SHO (Cas. & Orthop.) Roy. I. of Wight Co. Hosp. Ryde; Ho. Surg. St. Mary's Hosp. Newport, I. of Wight.

MOORE, Julia Kay Department of Anaesthesia, Arrowe Park Hospital, Arrowe Park Road, Wirral CH49 5PE Tel: 0151 678 5111; Tel: 0151 625 7112 — MB ChB 1979 Sheff.; FRCA 1984; MBA Keele 1997. (Sheffield) Cons. Anaesth. Arrowe Pk. Hosp. Wirral; Sen. Med. Off. NHS. Prev: Sen. Regist. (Anaesth) Mersey RHA; Sen. Regist. (Anaesth.) Roy. Infirm. Glas.; Regist. (Anaesth.) W.ern. Infirm. Glas. & Centr. Birm. HA.

***MOORE, Julian James** 7 Aragon Place, Kimbolton, Huntingdon PE28 0JD — MB BS 1998 Lond.; MB BS Lond 1998.

MOORE, Julian Nigel Blinkhorn Long Furlong Medical Centre, 45 Loyd Close, Abingdon OX14 1XR Tel: 01235 522379; 39 Eason Drive, Abingdon OX14 3YD — MB BS 1989 Lond.; BSc Lond. 1986; MRCGP 1994; DFFP 1994; DRCOG 1993. Prev: Trainee GP Oxf. VTS; SHO (Geriat. & Cas.) Lister Hosp. Stevenage.

MOORE, Katherine Joan 22 Craneford Way, Twickenham TW2 7SE — MB BS 1992 Lond.

***MOORE, Katherine Margaret Heath** Goatscliff Farm, Grindleford, Hope Valley S32 2HW — MB BS 1998 Lond.; MB BS Lond 1998.

MOORE, Kathryn Sylvia Park Road Group Practice, The Elms Medical Centre, 3 The Elms, Dingle, Liverpool L8 3SS Tel: 0151 727 5555 Fax: 0151 288 5016 — MB ChB 1988 Liverp.; DRCOG 1992; MRCGP. GP Princip.; GP Tutor; Clin. Asst. (Gyn.). Prev: Mem. Liverp. Med. Instit.

MOORE, Mr Keith Arthur (retired) The Old Mill, Lower Road, Bratton, Westbury BA13 4RQ Tel: 01380 830773 — MB BS Sydney 1936; FRCS Eng. 1940. Prev: Cons. Surg. N. Middlx. Hosp. Lond.

MOORE, Mr Kenneth Thomas Heath Thornbury Hospital, Fulwood Road, Sheffield S10 3BR Tel: 0114 266 4455 Fax: 0114 268 6913; Pippin Cottage, Church St., Eyam, Hope Valley S32 5QH Tel: 01433 631945 Fax: 01433 631830 Email: kthm@bigwig.net — MB BS Lond. 1964; FRCS Eng. 1969; MRCS Eng. LRCP Lond. 1964. (Univ. Coll. Hosp.) Cons. Urol. Surg. Roy. Thornbury Hosp. Sheff. Socs: Fell. Roy. Soc. Med. (Counc. Mem. Sect. Urol.); Brit. Assn. Urol. Surgs.; BMA. Prev: Cons. Urol. Surg. Centr. Sheff. Univ. Hosp.; Sen. Regist. (Surg.) United Sheff. Hosps.; Ho. Off. (Surg.) Univ. Coll. Hosp. Lond.

MOORE, Kevin Charles Hutch Royd Farm, Parrock Nook, Rishworth, Sowerby Bridge HX6 4RF Tel: 01422 823498 Fax: 01422 824556 — MB ChB 1965 Manch.; MRCS Eng. LRCP Lond. 1966; FFA RCS Eng. 1972; DA Eng. 1968. (Manch.) Cons. Anaesth. Roy. Oldham Hosp.; Med. Dir. Dr. Kershaws Hospice Oldham. Socs: (Hon. Treas.) Brit. Med. Laser Assn.; (Hon. Treas.) World Assn. Laser Ther. Prev: Sen. Regist. (Anaesth.) S. W.. RHB; Regist. (Anaesth.) United Bristol Hosps. & Rush Green Hosp. Romford.

MOORE, Kevin Peter Department of Medicine, Royal Free Hospital, Pond St., London NW3 1QG — MB BS 1983 Lond.; PhD Lond. 1993, BSc 1980, MB BS 1983; FRCP 1997. MRC Sen. Clin. Fell. (Hepat.). Socs: Fell. Roy. Soc. Med.; EASL. Prev: Sen. Regist. (Clin. Pharmacol.) Hammersmith Hosp. Lond.; MRC Train. Fell. Liver Unit King's Coll. Hosp. Lond.; Regist. Liver Unit King's Coll. Hosp. Lond.

***MOORE, Kirk Andrew** 228 Queens Road, Leicester LE2 3FT — MB ChB 1994 Leic.

***MOORE, Kirsty** 53 Barleyway, Stanway, Colchester CO3 5YD — MB BS 1996 Lond.

MOORE, Margaret Mina (retired) Farnham House, Broadway WR12 7AE Tel: 01386 853212 — MRCS Eng. LRCP Lond. 1922; BSc (Hons.) (Human Anat. & Morphol.) Lond. 1919. Prev: Clin. Asst. (ENT) P.ss Louise Hosp. Childr. N. Kensington & Nat. Temperance Hosp. Lond.

MOORE, Martin Edward (retired) 5 Otterbourne House, Otterbourne, Winchester SO21 2EQ Tel: 01962 713796 — MD 1951 Camb.; MA Camb. 1939, MD 1951, MB BChir 1939. Prev: Med. Dir. & Cons. Chest Phys. Regional Chest Radiogr. Centre.

MOORE, Mary Christine North London Blood Centre, Colindale Avenue, London NW9 5BG Tel: 020 8258 2700 Fax: 020 8258 2970; 12 Audley Close, Borehamwood WD6 1UF Tel: 020 8953 4292 — MB BS Lond. 1966; BSc (Anat.) Lond. 1963; MRCS Eng. LRCP Lond. 1966. (Roy. Free) Assoc. Specialist (Blood Transfus.) N. Lond. Blood Transfus. Lond.

MOORE, Maureen Cynthia 4 Maxwell Park, Bangor BT20 3SH — MB BCh BAO 1956 Belf.; DObst RCOG 1958.

MOORE, Michael Allan Windward Group Practice, 68 Worsley Road, Worsley, Manchester M28 2SN Tel: 0161 794 1603 Fax: 0161 794 2371; The Paddock, Worsley, Manchester M28 2QR Tel: 0161 703 8634 Fax: 0161 794 2371 — MB ChB 1969 Liverp.; DObst RCOG 1971. (Liverp.) Orthop. Phys. Hope Hosp. Salford. Socs: Brit. Assn. Sport & Med. & Soc. Orthop. Med. Prev: Ho. Off. (Med., Surg. & O & G) Whiston Hosp. Prescot.

MOORE, Michael David (retired) 11 Apley Close, Harrogate HG2 8PS Tel: 01423 884455 Email: drmdmoore@aol.com — MB ChB 1961 Leeds; DObst RCOG 1964. Prev: GP Harrogate.

MOORE, Michael David 44 Grange Road, Bangor BT20 3QQ — MB BCh BAO 1980 Belf.; DRCOG 1983.

MOORE, Michael George St Paul's Practice, Oram's Mount, Winchester SO22 5DD Tel: 01962 853599 Fax: 01962 849982; 6 Abbotts Road, Winchester SO23 7EX — MB BCh BAO 1972 Dub.; MRCS Eng. LRCP Lond. 1970; MRCGP 1976. (Trinity College, Dublin) Gen. Pract.; Sch. Med. Off., Winchester Coll.

MOORE, Michael Henry Parsons Heath Medical Practice, 35A Parsons Heath, Colchester CO4 3HS Tel: 01206 864395 Fax: 01206 869047; Arboretum, 59A Parsons Heath, Colchester CO4 3HX Tel: 01206 862416 — MB ChB 1969 Birm.; DObst RCOG 1972.

MOORE, Michael Robert Reginald Weybridge Health Centre, Weybridge KT13 8DU Tel: 01932 853366; Dorincourt East Road, St. Georges Hill, Weybridge KT13 0LD — MB BS 1959 Lond.; MRCS Eng. LRCP Lond. 1959; DObst RCOG 1961. (Westm.) Princip. Police Surg. Addlestone Area Surrey; Med. Off. Weybridge Hosp. Weybridge. Socs: BMA; Assn. Police Surgs. Prev: Forens. Med. Examr. Metrop. Police.

MOORE, Michael Taylor Church House, Grittleton, Chippenham SN14 6AP Tel: 01249 782562 Fax: 01249 782546 — MB BChir 1955 Camb.; MA Camb. 1950, BA 1947; MRCS Eng. LRCP Lond. 1954; LMCC 1957; DTM & H Eng. 1958. (Camb. & Lond. Hosp.) Cons. Aviat. Med. Wilts.; Authorised Examr. Civil Aviat. Auth. Socs: Fell. Roy. Soc. Med.; Assoc. Mem: Fac. Occupat. Med; Roy. Soc. Trop. Med. & Hyg. Prev: Med. Off. (Research) RAF Inst. Aviat. Med. FarnBoro., Hants.; Dir. Lesotho Flying Doctor Serv.; Sen. Lect. (Anat.) Univ. Coll. Cork.

MOORE, Michael Vivian The Three Swans Surgery, Rollestone Street, Salisbury SP1 1DX Tel: 01722 333548 Fax: 01722 503626 — MB BS 1982 Nottm.; FRCGP 2000; BMedSci Nottm. 1980; MRCP (UK) 1985; MRCGP 1988; DRCOG 1987. GP (Gen. Pract.) S. & W. Regional Research.

MOORE, Natalie Lisa Brixton Hill Group Practice, 22 Raleigh Gardens, London SW2 1AE Tel: 020 8674 6376 Fax: 020 8671 0283; 26 Wycliffe Road, Battersea, London SW11 5QR Tel: 020 7924 6814 — MB ChB 1989 Birm.; MRCGP 1995; DCH RCP Lond. 1992. (Birm.)

MOORE, Niall James Avon & Wiltshire Partnership Mental Health Care NHS Trust, Barrow Hospital, Barrow Gurney, Bristol BS48 3SG Tel: 0117 928 6606 Fax: 0117 928 6606 Email: jeanette.bennet@awast.swest.nhs.uk — FRCPsych; BA, MB BCh

MOORE

BAO Dub. 1977; MRCPI 1980; MRCPsych 1985; DCH NUI 1979; FRCP 2000. (TC Dub.) Cons.(Phys. Psychiat). Avon & Wilts. Partnership Ment. Healthcare NHS Trust. Socs: Bristol Medico Chirurgical Soc.- Hon. Sec. Prev: Cons. Phys. Psychiat. Old Age. & Div. Dir. Psychiat. Hackney Hosp. Lond.; Sen. Regist. & Regist. Maudsley Hosp. Lond.; Sen. Regist. Kings Coll. Hosp. Lond.

MOORE, Niall Richard The Oxford MRI Centre, John Radcliffe Hospital, Headley Way, Headington, Oxford OX3 9DU Tel: 01865 222966 Fax: 01865 221932 — MB BChir 1982 Camb.; MA Camb. 1982; MRCP (UK) 1984; FRCR 1987; FRCP 1998. (Camb. & King's College Hosp.) Univ. Lect. (Radiol.) Oxf. Univ.; Hon. Cons. Radiol. Oxf. HA.; Hon. Cons. Radiol., Heatherwood & Wexham Pk. NHS Trust. Socs: Fell.Green Coll. Oxf. Univ. Prev: Clin. Lect. (Radiol.) Camb. Univ.; Regist. & Sen. Regist. (Radiol.) Addenbrookes & Papworth Hosps. Camb.; SHO (Neurol.) Derby Roy. Infirmaray.

MOORE, Nicholas Andrew 20 Beaumaris Road, Mountsorrel, Loughborough LE12 7DY Tel: 0116 287 1471 Ext: 3056 Email: nickmoore@webtribe.net — MB ChB 1982 Sheff.; FCAnaesth. 1989; FFA RCSI 1988; DA (UK) 1986. Cons. Cardiothoracic Anaesth. Paediatric and Adult. Socs: Provin. Fell. Roy. Soc. of Med.; Paediatric Intens. Care Soc.; Assn. of Paediatric Anaesth.s. Prev: Sen. Regist. (Anaesth.) Mersey RHA.; Regist. Anaesth. Sheff.; Lect. (Anaesth.) Liverp.

***MOORE, Nicholas Hedley** 37 Orchard Road, Southsea PO4 0AA — MB BS 1997 Lond.

MOORE, Nicola 47 Stakesby Road, Whitby YO21 1JF Tel: 01947 825003 — MB BChir 1992 Camb.; MRCP (Lond.) 1995. (Camb.) SHO (Anaesth.) Countess of Chester Hosp.

MOORE, Norma Ada (retired) Bramcote, Lyth Hill, Shrewsbury SY3 0BS Tel: 01743 873132 — MB BCh 1952 Wales; BSc, MB BCh Wales 1952; DCH Eng. 1954. Clin. Med. Off. Shrops. DHA. Prev: Assoc. Specialist (Neonat.) Copthorne Matern. Hosp. Shrewsbury.

MOORE, Pathma, Flight Lt. RAF Med. Br. c/o Department of Obst. & Gyn., Christchurch Womens Hospital, Christchurch, Canterbury, New Zealand; 2 Hazelmere Close, Feltham TW14 9PX Tel: 020 8384 3617 — MB BS 1985 Lond. Regist. (Obst. & Gyn.) ChristCh. Woms. Hosp. Canterbury, NZ. Prev: Chief Med. Off. Roy. Flying Doctors Austral.

MOORE, Patricia Eveline Ingleside, 11 Chapel Road, Alderley Edge SK9 7DX — MB BS 1978 Lond.; MRCS Eng. LRCP Lond. 1977; DRCOG 1980. (Roy. Free) Prev: Clin. Med. Off. (Family Plann.) City & Hackney HA.

MOORE, Patricia Lynn 1 Western Drive, Hanslope, Milton Keynes MK19 7LA Tel: 01908 510914; 1C Berry Lane, Wootton, Northampton NN4 6JU Tel: 01604 762901 — BM 1978 Soton.; MRCP (UK) 1982; MRCGP 1985; DRCOG 1983.

MOORE, Patricia Theresa 38 Princes Avenue, Walsall WS1 2DG Tel: 01922 623603 — MB ChB 1950 Sheff. (Sheff.) Socs: Birm. Br. Med. & Dent. Hypn. Soc. & Brit. Soc. Med. & Experim. Prev: Asst. Cas. Off., Ho. Surg. & Ho. Phys. Roy. Hosp. Sheff.

MOORE, Patrick Christopher Henry Boutport Street Surgery, 110 Boutport Street, Barnstaple EX31 1TD Tel: 01271 324106 Fax: 01271 347150; Thynnes, Guineaford, Barnstaple EX31 4EA — MB BS 1976 Lond. (Univ. Coll. Hosp.) Prev: Trainee GP P.s RisBoro.; SHO Stoke Mandeville Hosp. Aylesbury.

MOORE, Patrick Richard Joseph Pound Lane Health Centre, Pound Lane, Downpatrick BT30 6HY Tel: 028 4461 3016; Ballygallum, Downpatrick BT30 7DA Tel: 01396 614084 Email: paddy.m@which.net — MB BCh BAO 1977 Belf.; MRCGP 1981 RCGP Lond.; D.Occ.Med. RCP Lond. 1996; DRCOG 1980 RCOG Lond. (Qu. Univ. Belf.) Med. Off. (Occupat. Health) Downshire Hosp. Downpatrick. Socs: (Hon. Treas.) Downpatrick & Dist. Med. Soc.

MOORE, Paul Nicholas 26 Sadlers Way, Ringmer, Lewes BN8 5HG Tel: 01273 813664 Fax: 01273 611527 — MB ChB 1988 Birm.; DFFP 1994; T(GP) 1994. SHO Rotat. (Med.) Brighton; SHO (Cardiol.) Roy. Sussex Co. Hosp. Prev: SHO (Gen. Med.) E.bourne Dist. Gen. Hosp.; Ho. Surg. Sandwell Dist. Gen Hosp.; Ho. Phys. Stafford Dist. Gen. Hosp. & Staffsh. Gen. Infirm.

MOORE, Paula Judith Market Square Health Centre, Bishop's Stortford CM23 3UU Tel: 01279 652745; 1 Northfield, Braughing, Ware SG11 2QQ Tel: 01920 821824 Fax: 01920 822748 — MB BS 1979 Lond.; DRCOG 1982. (Lond. Hosp.) Community Med. Off. (Child Health) E. Herts. HA; Community Med. Off. (Family Plann.) &

Instruc. W. Essex HA. Socs: Fac. Fam. Plann. & BMA. Prev: GP Hertford.

MOORE, Penelope Jane Victoria House Surgery, Victoria Road, Bicester OX26 6PB Tel: 01869 248585; 3 Wytham Street, Oxford OX1 4SU Tel: 01865 728122 — MB BS 1987 Melbourne; MRCGP 1993; DRCOG 1992; DCH RCP Lond. 1991. Prev: Trainee GP E. Oxf. Health Centre.

MOORE, Peter Brian 12 Springsyde Close, Whickham, Newcastle upon Tyne NE16 5UP — MB BS 1985 Newc.

MOORE, Peter Francis Rickmansworth Road Surgery, 35 Rickmansworth Road, Watford WD1 7HL Tel: 01923 223232 Fax: 01923 243397; 2 Harford Drive, Watford WD17 3DG Tel: 01923 223043 — MB BChir 1977 Camb.; MA 1977, BChir 1976; MRCGP 1981; DRCOG 1980. (Camb.) Clin. Asst. (Dermat.) Hemel Hempstead Hosps. Prev: Trainee GP Watford VTS; Ho. Surg. Univ. Coll. Hosp. Lond.; Ho. Phys. St. Chas. Hosp. Lond.

MOORE, Peter John Kingswood Health Centre, Alma Road, Kingswood, Bristol BS15 4EJ Tel: 0117 961 1774 Fax: 0117 947 8969 — MB BCh 1975 Wales; MRCGP 1980; DRCOG 1977.

MOORE, Mr Peter John Scunthorpe General Hospital, Cliff Gardens, Scunthorpe DN15 7BY Tel: 01724 290001 — MB BS Lond. 1971; MD Sheff. 1986; FRCS Eng. 1976. (St. Geo.) Cons. Gen. Surg. N.Lincs. & Goole, NHS Trust; Mem. Edit. Bd. Progress in Med. Managem.; Clin. Lead for Cancer in the Trust. Socs: BMA; Assn. Surg.; Brit. Assn. Endocrin. Surgs. Prev: Sen. Regist. Sheff. HA; Regist. United Norwich Hosps.

MOORE, Peter Lionel Chatto Road Surgery, 104 Chatto Road, Torquay TQ1 4HY Tel: 01803 314277 Fax: 01803 323967; Haytor, Higher Westerlands, Marldon, Paignton TQ3 1RR Tel: 01803 526638 Email: su1364@eclipse.co.uk — MB BS 1975 Lond.; BSc (Biochem.) Lond. 1972; FRCGP 1997; DRCOG 1979; DMJ (Clin) 1999. (St. Bart.) GP Princip. Torbay; Trainer & Course Organiser (Gen. Pract.) Torbay VTS; Police Surg.; Regular weekly columnist in Torbay Herald Express. Socs: Assn. Police Surg.; BMA; Assn. Course Organisers. Prev: GP Plymouth; Trainee GP Plymouth VTS; Ho. Surg. & Ho. Phys. Roy. Berks. Hosp. Reading.

MOORE, Philip Andrew Somers 331 Rotten Park Road, Edgbaston, Birmingham B16 0LB — MB ChB 1991 Birm.; ChB Birm. 1991.

MOORE, Philip Conway (retired) Bramcote, Lyth Hill, Shrewsbury SY3 0BS Tel: 01743 873132 — MB BCh 1954 Wales; BSc Wales 1951, MB BCh 1954, DPH 1960; FFCM 1974; DObst RCOG 1956. Prev: Regional Med. Off. W. Midl. RHA.

MOORE, Philip Daniel Oak Hill Health Centre, Oak Hill Road, Surbiton KT6 6EN Tel: 020 8399 6622 Fax: 020 8390 4470; 42 Thistledene, Thames Ditton KT7 0YJ Tel: 020 8398 2416 Fax: 020 8398 6770 Email: philmoore2@compuserve.com — MB ChB 1975 Ed.; DA Eng. 1979; DRCOG 1978. (Ed.) Chairm. Kingston PCG.

MOORE, Philip Raymond The Maltings Surgery, 2 Victoria Street, St Albans AL1 3JB Tel: 01727 855500; 3 Lansdowne Road, Cambridge CB3 0EU — MB ChB 1989 Manch.; PHD 1999 (Manchester University); MRCP (UK) 1993. Gen. Practitioner, The Maltings Surg., St Albans. Prev: Research Regist. (Renal) Manch. Roy. Infirm.

MOORE, Philippa Claire Lucinda Flat 5, 9 Gwendolen Avenue, Putney, London SW15 6ET Tel: 020 8788 7649; St. George's Healthcare NHS Trust, St. George's Hospital, Blackshaw Road, Tooting, London SW17 0QT Tel: 020 8672 1255 Email: pmoore@sghms.ac.uk — MB BS 1991 Lond.; MA Oxf. 1988; MRCPI 1995; DTM & H RCP Lond. 1994; DRCPath 1998. (Qu. Coll. Oxf., UMDS & St. Thos. Hosps.) Specialist Regist. (Microbiol. & Communicable Dis.) St. Geo. Hosp. Lond.

MOORE, Philippa Mary 15 Binswood Avenue, Headington, Oxford OX3 8NY — MB BS 1981 Lond.; MRCGP 1989; DCH RCP Lond. 1985; DRCOG 1985. Teach. Residency Progr. for Family Med. Univ. Chile, Santiago.

MOORE, Ralph (retired) Thornton Medical Centre, Church Road, Thornton-Cleveleys, Blackpool FY5 2TZ Tel: 01253 854321 Fax: 01253 862854 — MB ChB 1969 Liverp. Prev: Ho. Off. & SHO Regional Urol. Unit Sefton Gen. Hosp. Liverp.

***MOORE, Rebecca Jan** 9 Lime Avenue, Duffield, Belper DE56 4DX — MB BS 1997 Liverp.

MOORE, Richard George Waldron 50 Church Road, Ashford TW15 2TU Tel: 01784 420700 Fax: 01784 424503 — FRCGP

1999; BSc Lond. 1977, MB BS 1980; MRCGP 1985; Dip. Pract. Dermat. Wales 1991; DCH RCP Lond. 1989; DRCOG 1986; DFFP RCOG 1985. GP Princip. and Trainer; St. Peters Hosp. VTS Gp. Convenor. Socs: Primary Care Dermat. Soc. Prev: SHO (Paediat. & Obst.) N.wick Pk. Hosp. Harrow; SHO (Med.) Oxf. RHA.; GP Regist. Calcot, Chalfont St Peter.

MOORE, Richard Graham Wylie 66 Shenfield Road, Shenfield, Brentwood CM15 8EW — MB BS 1943 Lond.; MRCS Eng. LRCP Lond. 1939. (St. Mary's) Prev: Regist. (Med.) Harold Wood Hosp.; Cas. Off. St. Mary's Hosp. Padd.; Resid. Surg. Off. King Edwd. Memor. Hosp. Ealing.

MOORE, Richard Hugh University Hospital of Wales, Heath Park, Cardiff CF14 4XW Tel: 029 2074 6646 Fax: 029 2074 6661 Email: richard.moore@uhw-tr.nhs.wales.uk — MRCS Eng. LRCP Lond. 1977; BSc (Hons.) Lond. 1974, MD 1989, MB BS 1977; FRCP Lond. 1993; MRCP (UK) 1980; MBA 1996. (Guy's) Cons. Nephrol. & Clin. Dir. Nephrol. & Transpl.ation. Prev: Lect. & Hon. Sen. Regist. Roy. Lond. Hosp.; Regist. (Med.) St. Thos. Hosp. Lond.

MOORE, Mr Richard Hugh 63 Mountsandel Road, Coleraine BT52 1JF Tel: 01265 55660 — MB BChir 1989 Camb.; MA Camb. 1989; FRCS Eng. 1993. (Camb.) Specialist Regist. (Gen. Surg.) P.ss Alexandra Hosp. Harlow, NE Thames Region. Prev: Regist. (Cardiothoracic Surg.) Aberd.; SHO Rotat. (Gen. Surg.) Addenbrooke's Hosp. Camb. & Hinchingbrooke Hosp. Huntingdon; SHO (Cardiothoracic Surg.) Roy. Bromton & Nat. Heart Hosp. Lond. & Harefield Hosp. Middlx.

MOORE, Richard Maurice Armstrong (retired) 6 Mayfield Park, Shrewsbury SY2 6PD Tel: 01743 362731 Fax: 01743 362731 Email: ramoore@enta.net — MB BChir Camb. 1954; FRCGP 1981, M 1961; DObst RCOG 1957. Prev: GP Shrewsbury.

MOORE, Mr Robert Clive Greenford Road Medical Centre, 591 Greenford Road, Greenford UB6 8QH Tel: 020 8578 1764 Fax: 020 8578 8347; 5 Rodney Gardens, Pinner HA5 2RS Tel: 020 8866 4370 — MB BS 1971 Lond.; FRCS Eng. 1976; MRCGP 1982; MRCOG 1979.

MOORE, Mr Robert Stephen Accident and Emergency Department, Northampton General Hospital, Cliftonville, Northampton NN1 5BD Tel: 01604 634700 Fax: 01604 545615 Email: steve.moore@ngh-tr.anglox.nhs.uk — MB ChB 1979 Manch.; FRCS Ed. 1985; FFAEM 1993; DA (UK) 1991. Cons. A & E N.ampton Gen. Hosp. NHS Trust. Socs: Eur. Resusc. Counc.; Brit. Assn. Accid. & Emerg. Med. Prev: Sen. Regist. (A & E) N.ampton; Regist. (Accid & Emerg.) Withington Manch.; Regist. (A & E) Chester & Liverp.

MOORE, Roderick Peter 112 West Park Drive, Nottage, Porthcawl CF36 3RN — MB ChB 1981 Leic.

***MOORE, Roger Kevin Geoffrey** 7 Onslow Drive, Ascot SL5 7UL — MB ChB 1994 Manch.

MOORE, Mr Roger Spencer (retired) 90 Elm Road, March PE15 8PG Tel: 01354 655464 — MB BChir Camb. 1961; FRCS Ed. 1972; DTM & H Liverp. 1965; DObst RCOG 1963. Prev: GP Cambs.

MOORE, Roland Ian Lower Cottage, Pitt Plain, Higher Odcombe, Yeovil BA22 8UA — MB ChB 1969 Ed.

MOORE, Rosa May Glebe End, Sulham Lane, Pangbourne, Reading RG8 7LJ Tel: 0118 984 2381 — MRCS Eng. LRCP Lond. 1941; DCH Eng. 1947. (King's Coll. Hosp.) Prev: Asst. MOH Reading; Sen. Regist. Paddington Hosp. Lond.; Asst. Med. Off. Qu. Mary's Hosp. Childr. Carshalton.

MOORE, Rosemary 3 Fields Park Road, Newport NP20 5BA — MB ChB 1982 Glas.; MRCPsych 1989.

***MOORE, Sacha Pierre** 34 Clarry Drive, Sutton Coldfield B74 2QT — BM BCh 1998 Oxf.; BM BCh Oxf 1998.

MOORE, Samuel Lisburn Health Centre, Linenhall Street, Lisburn BT28 1LU; 12 Abercorn Park, Culcavey Road, Hillsborough BT26 6HA Tel: 02892) 682982 Email: docsam@hillsborough99.freeserve.co.uk — MB BCh BAO Belf. 1969; FRCGP 1987, M 1973; MICGP 1987; Cert. Family Plann. N. Irel. 1974; DCH RCPSI 1972; DObst RCOG 1971. (Belf.) GP Trainer N. Irel. VTS; Med. Off. Down Lisburn Trust; Asst. Med. Off. Lisburn Boro. Counc.; Vis. Med. Off. Drumlough Hse. & Ballymacoss Hostel Lisburn; Med. Off. Nat. Transcommunications Ltd. Socs: Fell. Ulster Med. Soc. Prev: Med. Off. Grundig Works N. Irel.; Ho. Off. & SHO Belf. City Hosp.; Hon. Sec. N. Irel. Fac. RCGP.

MOORE, Samuel Robert William (retired) Green Mantle, Church Lane, Skelton, York YO30 1XT Tel: 01904 470223 — MB BCh BAO 1953 Belf.; MD Belf. 1967; FFPHM 1989; FFCM 1977, M 1972; DPH Liverp. 1959. Prev: Dir. (Pub. Health) & Dist. Med. Off. Leeds W.. HA.

MOORE, Sarah Jo Wythall Health Centre, May Lane, Hollywood, Birmingham B47 5PD Tel: 01564 822642 Fax: 01564 829319; 34 Carless Avenue, Harborne, Birmingham B17 9EL Tel: 01455 822996 — MB BS 1989 Lond.; MRCGP 1995; DRCOG 1993; DCH RCP Lond. 1992.

MOORE, Seamus Patrick (retired) Duntally, 7 Somerton Close, Somerton Road, Belfast BT15 4DF Tel: 01232 805910 — MB BCh BAO Belf. 1942; FRCGP 1980, M 1953. Prev: GP Belf.

MOORE, Sheila Mary Louise (retired) 12 Belgrave Crescent, Harrogate HG2 8HZ — MB ChB 1954 Ed.; BSc Ed. 1949, MB ChB 1954; DObst RCOG 1957.

MOORE, Sian Anita Llinos 22 Arlington Drive, Stockport SK2 7EB — MB ChB 1992 Liverp.; Dip Family Plann. (Liverpool)

MOORE, Simon James 72 Chesterfield Road, Barnet EN5 2RF — MB BS 1993 Lond.; BSc (Hons.) Immunol. Lond. 1989; FRCA June 1999. Specialist Regist. Annsthtetis S. Thames.

MOORE, Simon Johnathon 6 Westbrook Green, Blewbury, Didcot OX11 9QD — MB BS 1991 Lond.

MOORE, Simon Patrick Giles 10 Pennant Mews, London W8 5JN Tel: 020 7460 5980 Fax: 020 7460 5981; 29 Blenheim Road, Chiswick, London W4 1ET Tel: 020 8994 3024 Fax: 020 8994 3312 — MB BS Lond. 1981; MRCS Eng. LRCP Lond. 1981; MRCGP 1987; DRCOG 1986. (Guy's) Socs: Indep. Doctors Forum; Chelsea Clin. Soc.; Sloane Soc. Prev: Med. Off. RAMC.

MOORE, Stephen Christopher The Orchard Surgery, Commercial Road, Dereham NR19 1AE Tel: 01362 692916 Fax: 01362 698347 — MB 1974 Camb.; BChir 1973; MRCGP 1978.

MOORE, Stephen James 7 Hadley Close, Cheadle Hulme, Cheadle SK8 6SH — MB BS 1990 Lond.

MOORE, Stephen John 31 The Nook, Whissendine, Oakham LE15 7EZ Tel: 01664 474744 Fax: 01664 474744 Email: sjmoore@lineonc.net; 31 The Nook, Whissendine, Oakham LE15 7EZ Tel: 01664 474744 Fax: 01664 474744 — MB BS 1979 Lond.; AFOM RCP Lond. 1995; D.Occ.Med. RCP Lond. 1995; DRCOG 1982. (Roy. Free) Occupat. Phys. (Community Hosps. Gp.); Occupat. Phys. & Indep. Med. Adviser; Apptd. Doctor Ionising Radiat. Regulat. & Lead at Work Regulat.s. Socs: Soc. Occupat. Med.; Assn. NHS Occupat.al Phys.

MOORE, Stephen Mark Email: sm.moore@virgin.net — MB ChB 1988 Sheff.; MSc 1999 (Sports Medicine); MRCGP 1996; DRCOG 1994.

MOORE, Susan Jean 12 Ashfield Road, Cults, Aberdeen AB15 9NQ — MB ChB 1993 Ed.

MOORE, Susan Jones 13 Anglers Reach, Grove Rd, Surbiton KT6 4EU Tel: 020 8390 7621 Fax: 020 8390 7621 — MB BS 1973 Lond.; DMJ Clin. Soc. Apoth. Lond. 1996; DObst RCOG 1975; Cert. JCC Lond. 1975. (St. Bart.) Princip. Forens. Med. Examr. Metrop. Police Force; Sen. Police Surg. Surrey Police. Socs: Assn. Police Surg.; Medico-Legal Soc.; BMA. Prev: GP Weybridge, Surrey; Trainee GP Wessex VTS; Clin. Med. Off. Winchester & Centr. Hants. Health Dist.

MOORE, Suzanne Tattenham Health Centre, Tattenham Crescent, Epsom KT18 5NU Tel: 01737 371011 Fax: 01737 359641; 39 Glebe Road, Ashtead KT21 2NT — MB ChB 1991 Leic.; Cert. Family Plann. JCC 1995; DCH RCP Lond. 1994. Socs: BMA; Med. Protec. Soc. Prev: SHO (O & G & Paediat.) Epsom Gen. Hosp.

MOORE, Mr Terence Morthen Road Surgery, 2 Morthen Road, Wickersley, Rotherham S66 1EU Tel: 01709 549711; Pear Tree Farm, Brook House, Laughton en le Morthen, Sheffield S25 1YA Tel: 01909 562188 — MB ChB 1972 Sheff.; FRCS Eng. 1977; FRCS Ed. 1976; DMJ (Clin.) 1988. Police Surg. S. Yorks. Police; Fact. Med. Off. Laporte Industs., & Aven Tools. Socs: Assn. Police Surg.

MOORE, Mr Thomas Malcolm Colles Franklin's Way Surgery, Franklins Way, Wickford SS11 8AT Tel: 01268 733020 Fax: 01268 570855 — MB BS 1965 Lond.; FRCS Eng. 1971; MRCS Eng. LRCP Lond. 1965. (Middlx.) Prev: Surg. Regist. St. And. Hosp. Billericay; Ho. Surg. (Orthop.) Middlx. Hosp. Lond.; Cas. Off. Kettering Gen. Hosp.

MOORE

MOORE, Thomas William St. Helens, Ludwells Lane, Waltham Chase, Southampton SO32 2NP Tel: 01489 896850 — MB BS 1973 Lond.; MRCS Eng. LRCP Lond. 1973; Dip. IMC RCS Ed. 1991; DA Eng. 1978. (St. Bart.)

MOORE, Timothy Richard Guildhall Surgery, High Street, Clare, Sudbury CO10 8NY Tel: 01787 277523 Fax: 01787 278628 Email: timothy.moore@gp-d83076.nhs.uk; Tel: 01787 310993 Email: mulberry.moore@virgin.net — MB BS 1981 Lond.; MPH Leeds 1991; T(GP) 1985; DRCOG 1984. (St. Geo. Hosp. Med. Sch.) GP Clare. Prev: Dep. Chief Med. Off. Falkland Is. Govt.; Postgrad. Stud. (MPH) Leeds Univ.; Princip. Med. Off. W.. Province Solomon Is.

MOORE, Tracy Altnagelvin Area Hospital, Londonderry BT47 1NB Tel: 01504 45171; 13 Moyra Drive, Saintfield, Ballynahinch BT24 7AF Tel: 01238 511078 — MB BCh BAO 1994 Belf.

MOORE, Victor Chestnutt 3 Royal Oaks, Belfast BT8 6YX — MD 1988 Belf.; MB BCh BAO 1977; MRCOG 1983; DRCOG 1980. Cons. O & G Dewsbury HA.

MOORE, Victoria Jane 23 Wadleys Road, Solihull B91 1JJ — MB ChB 1981 Birm.

MOORE, Victoria Jane 25 Avon Road, Birchley, Billinge, Wigan WN5 7QU — MB ChB 1993 Liverp.

MOORE, Wentworth Patrick Nikolai (retired) Watersmeet, Water Lane, Bishops Sutton, Alresford SO24 9SW Tel: 01962 735087 — MRCS Eng. LRCP Lond. 1955; DA Eng. 1968; DTM & H Eng. 1965; LMSSA Lond. 1953. Regional Med. Cons. Amer. Life Insur. Company. Prev: Ho. Surg. (ENT) & Ho. Phys. (Dermat.) Guy's Hosp. Lond.

MOORE, Wieland John Shire Glatt Farm, Canon Pyon, Hereford HR4 8PD; Department of Anaesthetics, County Hospital, Union Walk, Hereford HR1 2ER Tel: 01432 364080 — MB ChB 1983 Leics.; MRCGP 1987; FRCA. 1992; DA (UK) 1987; DRCOG 1985; Cert. Family Plann. JCC 1985. Cons. Anaesth. Hereford Hosp. Trust. Socs: Fell. Roy. Soc. Med.; Assn. Anaesth. GB & Irel.; S.W. Soc. Anaesth. Prev: Sen. Regist. Rotat. (Anaesth.) SW Region.

MOORE, William Edmonds Dodwell (retired) Hillsborough, 7 Weald Way, Caterham CR3 6EL — MRCS Eng. LRCP Lond. 1938; MA, MB BChir Camb. 1938. Prev: Asst. Chest Phys. Croydon.

MOORE, William Peter Francis The Medical Centre, Hall Close, Marske-by-the-Sea, Redcar TS11 6BW Tel: 01642 482725 Fax: 01642 483334 — MB BCh BAO 1979 NUI.

MOORE-EDE, Martin Christopher 2 Springs Road, Keswick CA12 4AQ; 2 Springs Road, Keswick CA12 4AQ — MB BS 1970 Lond.; PhD Harvard Med. Sch. 1974; BSc (1st cl. Hons.) Physiol. Lond. 1967; MRCS Eng. LRCP Lond. 1970. (Guy's Hosp. Med. Sch.) Chief Exec.off & Pres. Circadian technologies Inc; Managing Dir. Circadian Technologies (UK); Assoc. Prof. Physiol. Harvard. Med. Sch. Boston USA. Prev: Dir. Inst. Circadian Physiol; Assoc. Prof. Physiol. Harvard Med. Sch.

MOORE-GILLON, John Christopher Department of Respiratory Medicine, St Bartholomew's Hospital, London EC1A 7BE Tel: 020 7601 8441 Fax: 020 7601 8437; 5 Alleyn Park, London SE21 8AU — MB BChir 1976 Camb.; MA Camb. 1977, MD 1987; FRCP Lond. 1992; MRCP (UK) 1978. (Camb. & St. Thos.) Cons. Phys. St. Bart. Hosp. & Roy. Lond. Hosp.s.; Hon. Sen. Lect. Respirat. Med. Socs: (Counc.) Brit. Thoracic Soc.; (Pres.) Brit. Lung Foundat. Prev: Hon. Lect. (Med.) UMDS Sch. Guy's & St. Thos. Hosps. Lond.; Sen. Regist. Lond. Chest Hosp.

MOORE-GILLON, Ms Victoria Linder 55 Harley Street, London W1N 1BB Fax: 020 7637 4254 — MRCS Eng. LRCP Lond. 1976; BSc (Hons.) Lond. 1972, MB BS 1976; FRCS Eng. (Orl.) 1983; FRCS Ed. (Gen.) 1981. (St. Thos.) Cons. ENT Surg. St. Geo. Hosp. Lond. Prev: Sen. Regist. Roy. Nat. ENT & St. Geo. Hosps. Lond.; Research Fell. Smell & Taste Research Centre Univ. Pennsylvania, USA; Regist. (Gen. Surg.) Brook Hosp. Lond.

MOORE-SMITH, Bryan (retired) Wolmers, Stonham Aspal, Stowmarket IP14 6AS Tel: 01449 711261 — BM BCh Oxf. 1955; MA Oxf. 1955; FRCP Lond. 1978, M 1964. Cons. Mem. Occup. Therap. Bd. CPSM; Mem. E. Sukkolf Community Health Counc. Prev: Clin. Dir. Servs. for Elderly Ipswich Hosp.

MOORE-SMITH, James Patrick Wolmers, East End Road, Stonham Aspal, Stowmarket IP14 6AS Tel: 01449 711261 — MB BS 1996 Lond.; MPhil Cranfield 1992; BSc (Hons) Warwick 1988. (St Bartholomews Hospital)

MOOREHEAD, Christopher Noel Summerville 3B Mornington, Annadale Avenue, Belfast BT7 3JS — MB BCh BAO 1956 Belf.; MRCPI 1966; MRCPsych 1971; DPM RCPSI 1963. (Qu. Univ. Belf.) Cons. Purdysburn Psychiat. Hosp. & Shaftesbury Sq. Hosp. Belf.

MOOREHEAD, Mr Robert John Ulster Hospital, Dundonald, Belfast BT16 1RH Tel: 02890 561358 Fax: 02890 561374; 2 Teal Park, Portaferry Road, Newtownards BT23 8GH Email: john.moorehead@lineone.net — MB BCh BAO 1978 Belf.; MD Belf. 1986; FRCS Ed. 1982. Cons. Surg. Ulster Community & Hosps. Trust. Socs: Fell. Ulster Med. Soc.; Irish Soc. Gastroenterol.; Brit. Soc. Gastroenterol. Prev: Lect. Roy. Vict. Hosp. Belf.; Research Assoc. Univ. Hong Kong; Sen. Lect. (Surg.) Qu. Univ. Belf.

MOOREHEAD, Rosemary Ann 2 Teal Park, Portaferry Road, Newtownards BT23 8GH Tel: 01247 818493 — MB BCh BAO 1978 Belf.

MOORES, Anthony Hugh 1 FR 47 Spottiswoode Street, Edinburgh EH9 1DQ — MB ChB 1991 Ed.

MOORES, Carl Richard 54 Rankeillor Street, Edinburgh EH8 9HZ — MB ChB 1990 Ed.

MOORES, Caron Department of Anaesthesia, Royal Liverpool Childrens NHS Trust, Alderhey, Eaton Road, Liverpool L12 2AP; c/o 119 Worsley Avenue, Worsley, Manchester M28 0HZ — MB ChB 1983 Liverp.; FCAnaesth 1990; DCH RCP Lond. 1986; DRCOG 1985. Cons. Anaesth. Roy. Liverp. Childr. Hosp. NHS Trust. Prev: Sen. Regist. (Anaesth.) BRd.green Hosp. Liverp.; Regist. (Anaesth.) Addenbrooke's Hosp. Camb.

MOORES, Mr Noel Sidney (retired) Knoll House, Westacres, Esher KT10 9JE Tel: 01372 465232 — MB ChB Manch. 1946; FRCS Eng. 1952; MRCS Eng. LRCP Lond. 1946; FCROphth 1989; DOMS Eng. 1950. Prev: Cons. Ophth. Surg. Roy. Eye Hosp., Kingston & Putney Hosps.

MOORES, Mr William Keith Doncaster Royal Infirmary, Armthorpe Road, Doncaster DN2 5LD Tel: 01302 366666; Shelton House, 4 Bennet Thorpe, Doncaster DN2 6AD Tel: 01302 323489 — MRCS Eng. LRCP Lond. 1968; FRCS Ed. 1973; FRCS Glas. 1974; FRCS Eng. 1974; FRCOG 1994, M 1981. (Char. Cross) Cons O & G Doncaster & BassetLaw Hosp.s NHS Trust. Socs: Assoc. Mem. BAUS; BMA. Prev: Regist. (O & G) Mill Rd. Matern. Hosp. Liverp. & Shrodells Hosp. Watford; Regist. (Surg.) Liverp. Regional Urol. Centre.

MOOREY, Helen Claire Top Floor Flat, 1 Wolseley Road, London N8 8RR — MB ChB 1992 Manch.

MOOREY, Stirling South London And Mandsley Trust, Department Of Psychotherapy, Mandsley Hospital, Denmark Hill, London SE5 8A2 Tel: 020 7919 2383 Fax: 020 7919 2514 Email: stirling.moorey@slam_tr.nhs.uk — MB BS 1980 Lond.; BSc Lond. 1977; FRCPsych 1998. (Middlesex Hospital Medical School 1974-80) Cons. Psychiat.S. Lond. And Mandsley. Trust; Hon. Sen. Lect. Inst. Of Psychiat. Socs: Founding Mem. Acad. Of Cognitive Ther.

MOORGHEN, Moganaden 36 Westbourne Avenue, Gosforth, Newcastle upon Tyne NE3 2HN — MB ChB 1981 Manch.

MOORHEAD, Ann 6 Craigleath Hill Row, Edinburgh EH4 2JX — MB ChB 1983 Ed.; MFFP 1994; DRCOG 1989. Clin. Asst. Edin. BrE. Unit; Clin. Med. Off. Family Plann. & Well Wom. Servs. Lothian HB.

MOORHEAD, John Francis 15 Ashworth Road, London W9 1JW Tel: 020 7286 7610 Email: jmoorhead@ashworth.u-net.com — MB ChB Liverp. 1957; FRCP Lond. 1973, M 1963. (Liverp.) Hon. Cons. Nephrol. Hosp. St. John & Eliz. Lond.; Hon. Cons. Roy. Free Hosp.; Emerit. Prof. Renal Med. Roy. Free & Univ. Coll. Sch. of Med.; Trustee of Moorhead Trust. Socs: BMA; Roy. Soc. Med.; Med. Soc. Lond. Prev: Examr. Univ. Lond.; Mem. N.E. Thames RHA; Edr. Proc. Europ. Dial. & Transpl. Assn.

MOORHEAD, Pandora Mary Argyl House, 2 Carpenter's Lane, Cirencester GL7 1EE Tel: 01285 656047 — LRCPI & LM, LRSCI & LM 1959; LRCPI & LM, LRCSI & LM 1959.

MOORHEAD, Peter James Northern General Hospital NHS Trust, Sheffield S5 7AU; Gunthwaite House, Gunthwaite, Penistone, Sheffield S36 7GE Tel: 01484 863377 — MB ChB 1958 Liverp.; FRCP Lond. 1978, M 1964. Cons. Phys. N. Gen. Hosp. & Roy. Hosp. Sheff.

MOORHEAD, Philippa Jean 56 Norfolk Road, Sheffield S2 2SY — MB ChB 1988 Sheff.

MOORHEAD, Stephen Peter Gunthwaite House, Gunthwaite Lane, Penistone, Sheffield S36 7GE — MB ChB 1993 Sheff.

MOORHEAD, Stephen Ronald James Department of Psychiatry, A Floor, South Block, Queens Medical Centre, Nottingham NG7 2UH Tel: 0115 924 9924 — MB ChB 1986 Ed.; MRCPsych 1991. Regist. (Psychiat.) Qu. Med. Centre Nottm. Prev: SHO (Gen. Med.) Ulster Hosp. Belf.

MOORHEAD, Timothy 19 Pimmcroft Way, Sale M33 2LA — MB ChB 1988 Sheff.

***MOORHOUSE, Catherine Victoria** 40 Gledholt Road, Huddersfield HD1 4HR — MB BS 1997 Newc.

MOORHOUSE, Joseph (retired) Sherwood, 41 Vyner Road S., Noctorum, Birkenhead CH43 7PN Tel: 0151 653 9951 — MB ChB Liverp. 1941. Prev: Med. Off. Birkenhead Gen. Hosp.

MOORHOUSE, Peter Ronald 57A Shrewbridge Road, Nantwich CW5 7AD — MB BCh 1970 Wales; FRCR 1985; DMRD Eng. 1977. Cons. Radiol. Crewe HA. Prev: Sen. Regist. Mersey RHA; Regist. Sheff. HA.

MOORHOUSE, Philip John 300 Clifton Drive S., Lytham St Annes Tel: 01253 723194; 7 Queen Road, St Annes-on-Sea, Lytham St Annes FY8 1HR Tel: 01253 728739 — MB ChB 1979 Manch.; MRCGP 1984. (Manchester)

***MOORHOUSE, Sally Anne Rosser** Flat 2, 254 Newport Road, Cardiff CF24 1RR — MB BCh 1994 Wales.

MOORJANI, Mr Narain 72 Streetly Crescent, Sutton Coldfield B74 4PU Tel: 0121 353 9636 — MB ChB 1995 Bristol; MRCS 1999. SHO (Gen. Surg. & Urol.) Horton Hospial, Banbury; Surg. Rotat. (Cardiothoracic Surg. John Radcliffe Hosp. Oxf.; SHO (Trauma & Orth) John Radcliffe Hosp Oxf. Socs: BMA; Med. Protec. Soc. Prev: SHO (A & E) John Radcliffe Hosp. Oxf.

MOORJANI, Ramsingh 72 Streetley Crescent, Sutton Coldfield B74 4PU — MB BS 1954 Calcutta; FRCR 1979; DMRD Eng. 1972; DTM & H Ed. 1963. (Nat. Med. Coll. Calcutta) Cons. Radiol. Gen. & Manor Hosps. Walsall. Prev: Sen. Regist. Lond. Hosp.; Regist. W. Suff. Gen. Hosp. Bury St. Edmunds; Regist. Addenbrooke's Hosp. Camb.

MOORMAN, Ms Consuela Marie Stoke Mandeville Hospital, Mandeville Rd, Aylesbury HP21 8AL Tel: 01296 315961 Email: cmoorman@compuserve.com; 125 Dore Road, Dore, Sheffield S17 3NF Tel: 01865 513851 — MB BS 1982 Lond.; MSc (Epid.) 1999; FRCS Ed. 1986; FRCOphth 1991. Cons. Opthamologist SMH. Prev: Sen. Regist. Oxf. Eye Hosp.

***MOORMAN, David John Everard** 12 Borrowdale Cl, Plymouth PL6 5BN Tel: 01752 781422 — MB ChB 1997 Bristol.

MOORMAN, Nina Elizabeth Whiteladies Medical Group, Whatley Road, Clifton, Bristol BS7 2GL Tel: 0117 973 1201 — MB ChB 1970 Sheff.; MSc Bristol 1997; DA Eng. 1984. (Sheff.) Princip. Gen. Pract.; PCG Bd. Mem.; Clin. Governance Lead.

MOORS, Mr Adam Princess Anne Hospital, Coxford Rd, Southampton SO16 5YA Tel: 023 8079 6041 Fax: 023 8079 4243 Email: adam.moors@suht.swest.nhs.uk — MB BS 1987 Lond.; MRCOG 1993; DM 2001. Cons. (O&G) P.ss Anne Hosp. S.ampton. Socs: Brit. Soc. for Gyn. Endoscopy; World Endometriosis Soc. Prev: Clin. Research Fell. P.ss Anne Hosp. Soton.; Regist. (O & G) Chelsea & W.m. Hosp. & Basingstoke; Sen. Regist. (O & G) Winchester & P.ss Anne Hosp. Soton.

MOORS, Anthony Hamilton Department of Anaesthesia, Russels Hall Hospital, Dudley DY1 2HQ Tel: 01384 244076 Fax: 01384 244044 Email: ah.moors@dulleygoh-tr.wmids.nhs.uk — MB ChB 1984 Sheff.; MA Camb. 1985; FRCA 1992; DA (UK) 1987. (Sheffield) Cons. Anaesth. Dudley Gp. Hosps. NHS Trust. Prev: Sen. Regist. (Anaesth.) W. Midl. RHA; Clin. Fell. (Cardiothoracic Anaesth.) Papworth Hosp. NHS Trust.

MOORSHEAD, John Courtney (retired) Les Prés, St. Pierre du Bois, Guernsey GY7 9DH Tel: 01481 63581 — MB BS 1955 Lond.; FRCP Lond. 1997; MRCP (UK) 1972; DTM & H Eng. 1968; DCH Eng. 1968.

MOORTHIE, Gomathy Anandan Victoria Road Surgery, 82 Victoria Road, Oulton Broad, Lowestoft NR33 9LU Tel: 01502 572368 Fax: 01502 537035; 6 Colsterdale, Carlton Colville, Lowestoft NR33 8TN — MB BS 1975 Sri Lanka; LMSSA Lond. 1992; MRCGP 1994; DFFP 1992; DCH RCP Lond. 1992; DGM RCP Lond. 1990. (Fac. Med. Colombo) Clin. Asst. (Rheum.) Jas. Paget Hosp. Prev: GP Norwich.

MOORTHY, Bagavatheswaran, Col. Department of Paediatrics, Frimley Park Hospital, Camberley GU16 5UJ Tel: 01276 604604 Fax: 01276 604307 Email: bmoorthy@aol.com — MB BS Kerala 1972; MD (Paediat.) Panjab (India) 1976; MRCP (Paediat.) (UK) 1984; FLEX Lic (USA) 1977; ECFMG Cert. 1976; FRCP 1997; FRCPCH 1996. Cons. Paediat. Frimley Pk. Hosp. Frimley Surrey; Hon. Cons. Paediat. S.ampton Gen. Hosp. S.ampton. Socs: Roy. Coll. Paediat. & Child Health. Prev: Cons. Paediat. Roy. Hosp. Haslar; Cons. Paediat. Camb. Milit. Hosp. Aldershot & Brit. Milit. Hosp. Rinteln, Germany; Sen. Regist. (Paediat.) P.ss Alexandra RAF Hosp. Wroughton.

MOORTHY, Imayavalli Thedchana 95 Russell Road, London SW19 1LN — MB BS 1988 Madras; MRCP (UK) 1993.

***MOORTHY, Sutharshini Shankari** 21 Osborn Gardens, Mill Hill, London NW7 1DY — MB BS 1996 Lond.

MOORTHY, Vanita 36 New Park Avenue, London N13 5NB — MB BS 1997 Lond. VTS Barnet Gen. Hosp. Lond. Socs: MDU. Prev: A & E, Paeds, Obs. & Gynae., Pall. Med.

MOORTHY, Vasee 4 Walnut Drive, Kingswood, Tadworth KT20 6QX — BM BCh 1995 Oxf.

MOOS, Professor Khursheed Francis, OBE (retired) Oral & Maxillofacial Surgical Department, Glasgow Dental Hospital & School, 378 Sauchiehall St., Glasgow G2 3JZ Tel: 0141 211 9824 Fax: 0141 211 9824 Email: kmoos@udcf.gla.ac.uk — MB BS Lond. 1964; BDS Lond. 1957; FRCS Ed. 1986; MRCS Eng. LRCP Lond. 1964; FDS RCPS Glas. 1982; FDS RCS Ed. 1981; FDS RCS Eng. 1961. Hon. Cons. in Oral and Maxillofacial Surg. Glas. Dent. Hosp. and Sch. Glas.; Hon. Prof. Univ. Glas.; Hon. Sen. Research Fell.; Hon. Cons. Adviser RN. Prev: Cons. Oral & Maxillofacial Surg. Plastic Surg. Unit Canniesburn Hosp. & Glas. Dent. Hosp.

MOOSA, A S Balfour Surgery, 41-42 Balfour, Riverside, Tamworth B79 7BH Tel: 01827 66676 Fax: 01827 313095 — MB BS 1968 Patna; MB BS 1968 Patna.

MOOSA, Akeel Hadi Department of Haematology, Dorset County Hospital, William Avenue, Dorchester DT1 2JY Tel: 01305 254361 Fax: 01305 254319; 40 Rothesay Road, Dorchester DT1 2DX Tel: 01305 263887 — MB ChB 1982 Basrah; MB ChB Basrah, Iraq 1982; PhD Sheffield 1992; MCPath Haematology 1994. Cons. (Haemat.). Prev: Sen. Regist. & Lect. United Med. & Dent. Sch. St Thomas's Hosp. Lond.

***MOOSA, Haroon Ahmed Umerji** 326 Preston New Road, Beardwood, Blackburn BB2 7AQ Tel: 01254 671895 Email: haroon.hmoosa@freeserve.co.uk — MB ChB 1994 Manch.; MRC Psyc. 1998.

MOOSSUN, Mr Hassam 38 St Margarets Road, London N17 6TY — MB BCh BAO 1965 Belf.; MB BCh Belf. 1965; FRCS Glas. 1969.

MOOSVI, R S The Surgery, 340 High Street, Ponders End, Enfield EN3 4DE Tel: 020 8805 5972 Fax: 020 8292 3772 — MB BS 1958 Punjab; MB BS 1958 Punjab.

MOOSVI, Syed Kazim The Surgery, Main Road, Knockholt, Sevenoaks TN14 7LG Tel: 01959 533466; 2B Tile Farm Road, Orpington BR6 9RZ Tel: 01689 855022 — MB BS 1965 Karachi. (Dow Med. Coll.) Socs: Assoc. Mem. RCGP. Prev: Regist. (Anaesth.) Hemel Hempstead Gen. Hosp.; SHO (A & E) St. Peter's Hosp. Chertsey; Ho. Off. (Gen. Surg.) Crumpsall Hosp. Manch.

***MOOSVI, Syed Raza** 104 Tubbenden Lane, Orpington BR6 9PR — MB BS 1998 Lond.; MB BS Lond 1998.

MOOTOO, Ramesh Vivec The Homerton Hospital NHS Trust, Homerton Row, Hackney, London E9 6SR Tel: 020 8510 7612 Fax: 020 8510 7574 Email: ramesh.mootoo@homerton-hospital.thenhs.com — MB BCh BAO 1986 NUI; MRCP (UK) 1991; LRCPSI 1986. (Royal Coll. Of Surg. Dubl.) Cons. (Phys. & Rheumat.) Homerton Hosp. Lond. Prev: Sen. Regist., N. Middx Hosp., Whipps Cross Hosp., Roy. Lond. Hosp.

MOOTOOSAMY, Indira Mathi 2 Linden Road, Muswell Hill, London N10 3DH — MB BS 1975 Lond.; FRCR 1983. Cons. Radiol. Whipps Cross Hosp. Lond. Prev: Sen. Regist. (Radiol.) St. Bart. Hosp. & Gt. Ormond St. Hosp. Sick; Childr. Lond.; SHO (Med. Rotat.) St. Bart. Hosp. Lond.; SHO (A & E) Whipps Cross Hosp. Lond.

MOOTS, Robert John Department Rheumatology, University Clinical Depts, University Hospital Aintree, Longmoor Lane, Liverpool L9 7AL Tel: 0151 529 2091 Fax: 0151 529 2420 Email: rjmoots@liverpool.ac.uk; 6 Pear Tree Close, Wirral CH60 1YD — MB BS 1985 Lond.; MB BS (Hons.) Lond. 1985; PhD CNAA Oxf. 1992; BSc (Hons.) (Infec. & Immunol.) Lond. 1982; MRCP (UK)

MOPPETT

1988. (St. Mary's Hospital London University) Sen. Lect. (Rheum.) Liverp. Univ.; Hon. Cons. Rheum. Univ. Hosp. Aintree; Hon. Cons. Rheum. Roy. Liverp. Univ. Hosp. Socs: Christ. Med. Fell.sh. & Brit. Soc. Rheum.; Assn. Phys. Prev: Wellcome Trust Advanced Train. Fell. Harvard Univ., USA; Clin. Lect. (Rheum.) Birm.; MRC Train. Fell. Inst. Molecular Med. Oxf.

MOPPETT, Iain Keith 5 Ariel Close, Basford, Nottingham NG6 0EH Tel: 0115 978 2578 Email: imoppett@surfaid.org — MB BChir 1994 Camb.; MA 1995; BA Camb. 1991; MRCP 1996. (Camb.) Specialist Regist. Anaesth. - Nottm. Rotat. Socs: BMA; Christ. Med. Fell.sh.; Intens Care Soc. Prev: SHO Anaesth. - Nottm.; SHO Med. - Qu. Med. Centre, Nottm.

MOPPETT, John Paul 45 Woodfield Road, Solihull B91 2DN — MB BChir 1993 Camb.; MA Camb. 1993, MB Chir 1993; MRCP (UK) 1995; MRCPCH 1997.

MORAFA, Olawale Adetayo 70 Church Drive, London NW9 8DS — MB BS 1986 Ibadan; MRCOG 1993.

MORAITOU, Eleni Antimicrobial Agents Research Group, Department of Infection, The Medical School, Vincent Drive, Edgbaston, Birmingham B15 2TJ — Ptychio latrikes 1991 Athens.

MORALEE, Petrina Student Health Service, 25 Belgrave Road, Bristol BS8 2AA Tel: 0117 973 7716 Fax: 0117 970 6804 — BM BCh 1987 Oxf.; MA Oxf. 1990; MRCGP 1993; DCH RCP Lond. 1992; DRCOG 1990. (Oxf.) GP Partner. Prev: GP & Hon. Fell. (Gen. Pract.) Edin. Univ.; Trainee GP/SHO Nottm. VTS; Hosp. Med. Off. Roy. Childr. Hosp. Melbourne, Austral.

MORALEE, Mr Stephen John Murrayfield Hospital, Corstorphine Rd, Edinburgh Scotland — BM BCh 1987 Oxf.; MA Camb. 1988; FRCS Ed. 1993; Cert. Med. Educat. 1999; FRCS 1997 ORL. Cons. (OtoLaryngol.) Borders Gen. Hosp. Melrose. Prev: Sen. Resid. (Otolary., Head & Neck Surg.) Toronto Hosp. Canada; Sen. Regist. (Otolary.) Bristol Roy. Infirm.; Regist. (Otolary.) Edin. Roy. Infirm.

MORAN, Alexander Department of Medicine, North Devon District General Hospital, Raleigh Park, Barnstaple EX31 4JB Tel: 01271 322734 — MB ChB 1984 Bristol; MRCP (UK) 1989; MD Bristol 1995. (Bristol) Cons. Gastroenterologist N. Devon Dist. Hosp. Socs: Brit. Soc. Gastroenterol.; BMA; FRCP Lond. Prev: Sen. Regist. & Lect. (Med. & Gastroenterol.) Bristol Roy. Infirm.; Regist. (Med. & Gastroenterol.) & Research Fell. Birm. Heartlands Hosp. & Univ. Birm.

MORAN, Anthony 23 Cranmer Road, Manchester M20 6AW — MB BCh BAO 1977 NUI; MFCM 1988; MPH NUI 1984; DCH NUI 1985. (Cork) Lect. (Epidemiol.) Manch. Univ.; Cons. (Pub. Health Med.) N. W.. RHA. Prev: Sen. Regist. Community Med. N. W.. RHA; Regist. (Community Med.) N. W.. RHA. Regist. (Community Med.) N. W.. RHA; Jun. Ho. Off. Centr. Hosp. Bantry.

MORAN, Anthony Gerard The Health Centre, Manor Road, Beverley HU17 7BZ Tel: 01482 862733 Fax: 01482 864958 — MB ChB 1987 Sheff. SHO (Gen. Med.) N. Gen. Hosp. Sheff.

MORAN, Mr Brendan John The Hampshire Clinic, Basing Road, Basingstoke RG24 7AL Tel: 01256 354747; Church Farm House, Church Lane, Cliddesden, Basingstoke RG25 2JQ — MB BCh BAO 1980 NUI; MCh NUI 1989; FRCSI (Gen.) 1995; FRCSI 1984. (Univ. Coll. Cork, Irel.) Cons. Surg. N. Hants. Hosp. Trust Basingstoke. Socs: Assn. Coloproctol.; Roy. Soc. Med.; Assn. Surg. Prev: Director NSCAG Pseudomyxoma Paeritonei Centre, Basingstoke.

MORAN, Brendan Patrick The Health Centre Surgery, 60 Roseheath Drive, Halewood, Liverpool L26 9UH Tel: 0151 486 3780 — MB ChB 1983 Liverp.; MRCGP 1988. (Liverp.)

*MORAN, Catherine Helen Royal Lancaster Infirmary, Ashton Road, Lancaster LA1 4RP — MB ChB 1998 Manch.; MB ChB Manch 1998.

MORAN, Mr Christopher Gerrard Queens Medical Centre, Nottingham NG7 2UH Tel: 0115 924 9924 — BM BCh 1982 Wales; MD Wales 1993; FRCS Ed. 1986. Cons. Orthop. Surg. Qu.s Med. Centre Nottm. Prev: Cons. Orthop. Surg. Freeman Hosp. Newc.

MORAN, Christopher John 20 Rowlands Hill, Wimborne BH21 1AW — BSc, MB ChB Bristol 1965; FRCP Lond. 1988; MRCP (UK) 1970. (Bristol) Honary Cons. Phys. Roy. Bournemoth and Christ Ch. Hosp. Trust. Prev: Sen. Regist. (Med.) Univ. Coll. Hosp. Lond.; MRC Research Fell. RCS Lond.; Regist. (Med.) S.mead Hosp. Bristol.

MORAN, Damian Gerard Wincobank Medical Centre, 16 Chapman Street, Sheffield S9 1NG Tel: 0114 242 6411; 29 Ivy Park Road, Sheffield S10 3LA Tel: 0114 230 1644 Fax: 0114 263 0059 — MB ChB 1972 Sheff.; Dip. Occ. Med. RCP Lond. 1997. (Sheff.) Med. Dir. Occupat. Med. Serv. Sheff. Ltd.; Med. Dir. Occupat. Med. Serv. Ltd.; Med. Dir. Occupat. Nursing Serv. Ltd. Socs: Soc. Occupat. Med.; Assur. Med. Soc. Prev: Clin. Asst. (Cardiol. & Haemat.) N. Gen. Hosp. Sheff.; Clin. Tutor (Gen. Pract.) Univ. Sheff.

MORAN, Donal Gerard Mary Harrowby Lane Surgery, Harrowby Lane, Grantham NG31 9NS Tel: 01476 579494 Fax: 01476 579694; Woolfox Cottage, 87 Village St, Oasby, Grantham NG32 3NB — MB BCh BAO 1984 NUI; BSc (Hons.) NUI 1979; Cert. Family Plann. JCC 1989; DObst Otago 1988. (Univ. Coll. Dub.) GP Brisbane, Austral. & Grantham Lincs. Socs: BMA; Med. Protec. Soc. Prev: Trainee GP Preston; SHO. (Paediat. & Obst.) Rotorua Hosp, NZ; SHO (A & E) Ancoats Hosp. Manch.

MORAN, Emanuel 7 Longleat Road, Bush Hill Park, Enfield EN1 2QJ Tel: 020 8360 1323 — MB 1954 Camb.; MA Camb. 1954, BA 1950; MB 1954, BChir 1953; MRCP Lond. 1959; MRCPsych 1971; DPM Lond. 1962. (Camb. & Guy's) Cons. Psychiat. & Chairm. Med. Exec. Comm. Claybury Hosp. Woodford Bridge; Cons. Psychiat. Chase Farm Hosp. Enfield. Socs: Fell. Roy. Soc. Med. Prev: Neurol. Ho. Phys. Guy's Hosp.; Regist. & Sen. Regist. Maudsley Hosp. Lond.

MORAN, Frances Mary Family Doctor Unit Surgery, 92 Bath Road, Hounslow TW3 3LN Tel: 020 8570 6271 Fax: 020 8570 3243; 34 College Road, Isleworth TW7 5DW Tel: 020 8847 2211 — MB BS 1980 Lond.; DRCOG 1983. (Charing Cross Hospital)

MORAN, Francis 106 Strathblane Road, Milngavie, Glasgow G62 8HD Tel: 0141 956 2232 — MB ChB 1954 Glas.; MSc N. West. Univ. Chicago 1964; BSc (Hons. Physiol.) Glas. 1951; MB ChB (Commend.) 1954; FRCP Ed. 1970, M 1960; FRCP Glas. 1968, M 1963. (Glas.) Phys. i/c Centre Respirat. Investig. Roy. Infirm. Glas. Socs: Amer. Thoracic Soc. & Scott. Thoracic Soc. Prev: Research Fell. in Cardiopulm. Dis. N.W.ern Univ. Med. Sch.

MORAN, Gregory Daniel 69 Glenthorn Road, Newcastle upon Tyne NE2 3HL — MB BS 1989 Lond.; MRCP (UK) 1993.

*MORAN, Helen Victoria 54 Grace Road, Leicester LE2 8AE — MB ChB 1995 Leic.

MORAN, Ignatius Bernard (retired) Banbridge Medical Group Centre, Linenhall Street, Banbridge BT32 3EG — MD 1965 Belf.; MICGP; MB BCh BAO 1956; FRCGP 1982, M 1965; DCH RCPS Glas. 1963. Prev: Adviser (Gen. Pract.) N. Irel. Counc. Postgrad. Med. Educat.

MORAN, John Denton, RD HMCHolistic Medical Clinics Ltd, 30A Wimpole St., London W1G 8GR Tel: 020 7935 4870 Fax: 020 7486 9156 Email: doctor@hmc-holistic.demon.co.uk — MB BS Lond. 1970; LDS RCS Eng. 1964; DFFP 1994. (St. Geo.) Med. Off. Marie Stopes Clinic. Socs: Fell. Roy. Soc. Med.; Brit. Menopause Soc.; Brit. Erectile DysFunc. Soc. Prev: Ho. Surg. (ENT) St. Geo. Hosp. Lond.; Ho. Phys. ChristCh. Hosp. & Roy. Vict. Hosp. Boscombe.

MORAN, John Ronan 26 Pentelow Gardens, Feltham TW14 9EF — MB BCh BAO 1975 NUI. (Univ. Coll. Dub.) Prev: SHO (O & G) Basingstoke Dist. Hosp.

MORAN, Mr Manus Francis, CStJ, Air Vice-Marshal RAF Med. Br. Retd. (retired) Nuffield Hospital, Scraptoft Lane, Leicester LE5 1HY Tel: 0116 276 9401 Fax: 0116 246 1076 — MB BCh BAO NUI 1952; MCh NUI 1964; Hon. FRCSI 1991; DLO Eng. 1963. Sessional Cons. Metrop. Police Lond.; Special Trustee Roy. Nat. Throat, Nose & Ear Hosp. Lond. Prev: Vis. Cons. Otorhinolaryng. Nuffield Hosp. Leicester.

MORAN, Martin Bernard c/o Dunida, Lurgan Road, Banbridge BT32 4LU — MB BCh BAO 1985 Belf.

*MORAN, Matthew 27 Glen Court, Compton, Wolverhampton WV3 9JW — BM BCh 1996 Oxf.

MORAN, Michael Morrison 27 Croftdown Road, Parliament Hill Fields, London NW5 1EL Tel: 020 7485 7189; 62 East 21st. Avenue, Vancouver BC V5V 1P5, Canada Tel: 604 879 9485 — MB BS 1987 Lond.; BA (Hons.) Oxf. 1980; BSc Brit. Columbia 1976. Orthop. Res. Univ. Brit. Columbia, Vancouver, Canada.

MORAN, Neil The Surgery, Southfields Road, Strensall, York YO32 5UA Tel: 01904 490532 — MB ChB 1971 Leeds.

MORAN, Neil Francis 398 Albert Drive, Glasgow G41 4JP — BM BCh 1993 Oxf.

MORAN, Nicholas Frederick Epilepsy Research Group, The National Hospital for Neurology & Neurosurgery, London

MORELAND

WC1N 3BG Tel: 020 7837 3611 Email: nmoran@erg.ion.bpmf.ac.uk — MB ChB 1989 Liverp.; MSc Neurosci. (Distinc.) Lond. 1993; MRCP (UK) 1994. (Liverp.) Research Fell. (Epilepsy) Nat. Hosp. for Neurol. & Neurosurg. Lond.

MORAN, Paul 12 Southside, Shadforth, Durham DH6 1LL — BM BS 1989 Nottm.

MORAN, Paul Andrew Buntings, Hunters Lodge, High St., Shipton-under-Wychwood, Chipping Norton OX7 6DG — BM BS 1990 Nottm.

MORAN, Paul Anthony 7 Longleat Road, Bush Hill Park, Enfield EN1 2QJ — MB BS 1991 Lond.; BSc (Hons.) 1987; MRCPsych 1996. (St. Bartholomew's Hospital) Hon. Specialist Regist. (Psychiat.) Maudsley Hosp. Prev: Regist. Bethlem & Maudsley Hosp.

MORAN, Peter Forster, TD (retired) The Poplars, 2 Calderwood Crescent, Low Fell, Gateshead NE9 6PH Tel: 0191 487 7348 — MB BS Durh. 1958; FRCGP 1981, M 1974; DObst RCOG 1962.

MORAN, Peter James The Social Cottage, Chibbyr Pherric, Lonan, Laxey IM4 7QA — MRCS Eng. LRCP Lond. 1975.

MORAN, Sally Anne Inchcolm, Church Road, Lelant, St Ives TR26 3LE — MB ChB 1981 Bristol.

MORAN, Simon Gavin Rao and Partners, 90 Darnley Road, Gravesend DA11 0SW Tel: 01474 355331 Fax: 01474 324407 — MB BS 1986 Lond.

MORAN, Stephen Francis 37 Deene Close, Adderbury, Banbury OX17 3LD — MB BCh 1992 Wales.

MORANDO, Sarah Joy 34 Buxton Avenue, Caversham Heights, Reading RG4 7BU — MB ChB 1993 Leic.

MORAR, Kaushik Kumar 71 Asfordby Street, Leicester LE5 3QL — MB ChB 1990 Manch.

MORAR, Mr Pradeep 5 Teal Close, Aughton, Ormskirk L39 5QQ — MB ChB 1985 Manch.; FRCS Ed. 1993. Regist. Rotat. Mersey RHA. Prev: SHO Rotat. (Surg. & A & E) Chesterfield & N. Derbysh. Roy. Hosp.

MORAR, Shaheen Flat G/R, 10 Lawrence St., Glasgow G11 5HQ — MB ChB 1994 Glas.

MORCH-SIDDALL, Julia 11 Beech Close, Low Gosforth, Newcastle upon Tyne NE3 5PH — MB ChB 1991 Manc.; FRCS. Specialist Regist. (Anaesth.) N.ern Sch. Anaesth. Prev: SHO (O & G) St. Mary's Hosp. Manch.; Ho. Off. (Med. & Surg.) Stepping Hill Hosp. Stockport.

MORCOM, Alexandra Mary 24 Lawn Crescent, Kew, Richmond TW9 3NS — MB BChir 1991 Camb.; MB BChir Camb.1991.

MORCOM, R C Grange Medical Centre, West Cliff Road, Ramsgate CT11 9LJ Tel: 01843 595051 Fax: 01843 591999 — MB BCh 1981 Witwatersrand; MB BCh 1981 Witwatersrand.

MORCOS, Maged Ibrahim 18 Heron Way, Blackpool FY3 8FB — MB BCh 1979 Ains Shams.

MORCOS, Michel Youssef Chase Farm Hospitals NHS Trust, The Ridgeway, Enfield EN2 8JL Tel: 020 8366 6688 — MB BCh 1978 Ain Shams; FRCOG 2000. Cons. O & G Chase Farm Hosps. NHS Trust Enfield. Socs: BMA. Prev: Sen. Regist. (O & G) BMH Rinteln BFPO 29; Regist. (O & G) Chase Farm Hosp. Enfield & Univ. Coll. Hosp. Lond.

***MORCOS, Samy Awad Ghebrial** 2 Walker Cl, Hampton, Hampton TW12 3XT — LRCP LRCS Ed. LRCPS Glas. 1997.

MORCOS, Selim Naguib (retired) Balaton, Bickley Park Road, Bickley, Bromley BR1 2AT Tel: 020 8467 8700 — MRCS Eng. LRCP Lond. 1963; FRCOG 1980, M 1967, DObst 1963. Prev: Cons. (O & G) Qu. Mary's Hosp. Sidcup.

MORCOS, Wafik Edward Queen Elizabeth Queen Mother Hospital, St. Peter's Road, Margate CT9 4AN Tel: 01843 225544 Fax: 01843 234446 — MB BCh 1973 Mansourah; FRCA 1982. (Mansourah Fac. Med.) Cons. Anaesth. E. Kent NHS Trust. Socs: Hon. Sec. E. Kent Div. of BMA. Prev: Cons. Anaesth. Gwent HA.

MORCOS HANNA, Mounir Youssef 9 Church View, Coatbridge ML5 3BE — MB BCh 1977 Ain Shams; MRCOG 1992.

MORDEY, Patricia Lilian St Johns Street Health Centre, St Johns Street, Wirksworth, Derby DE4 4DR Tel: 01629 822434; Pingle End, Carsington, Matlock DE4 4DD — MB BS 1971 Newc.

MORDUCH, Marina Ida Whittington Hospital, Highgate Hill, London N19 — MB BS 1963 Lond. Clin. Asst. Whittington Hosp. Lond. & Roy. N. Hosp. Lond. Prev: Clin. Asst. Goodmayes Hosp. Ilford; Clin. Asst. Friern Hosp. Lond.

MORDUE, Alan Netherraw Farmhouse, Lilliesleaf, Melrose TD6 9EP — MB ChB 1979 Bristol; MFCM 1988; MFPHM 1989. Cons. Pub. Health Med. Borders HB. Prev: Cons. Pub. Health Med. N.. RHA & Newc. HA; GP Co. Durh.

MORE, Eleanor Janet (retired) Morven Bank, Maxwellbank Road, Lochmaben, Lockerbie DG11 1RJ Tel: 01387 810057 — MB ChB 1949 Ed.; MFCM 1972; DPH Ed. 1953. Prev: SCM (Child Health) Notts. HA.

MORE, Ian Aitken Ross University Department of Pathology, Western Infirmary, Glasgow G11 6NT Tel: 0141 211 2205 Fax: 0141 337 2494 Email: iam1j@clin.med.gla.uk; 13 Hawthorn Way, Milton-of-Campsie, Glasgow G66 8DX Tel: 01360 312227 — MB ChB 1967 Glas.; MB ChB (Commend.) Glas. 1967; PhD Glas. 1971, BSc (Hons. Biochem.) 1964, MD (Hons.) 1980; FRCP Lond. 1996; MRCP (UK) 1994; FRCPath 1987, M 1976. (Glas.) Sen. Lect. (Path.) & Hon. Cons. Univ. Glas. Dept. Path. W.. Infirm.; Mem. Brit. Ultrastructural Path. Panel. Socs: W Scotl. Renal Club. Prev: Beit Med. Research Fell. Beatson Inst. Cancer Research Univ. Lond.

MORE, Iqbal Singh 15 The Russells, Moseley, Birmingham B13 8RT — MB ChB 1993 Manch.

MORE, John Ronald Spence (retired) Rockcliffe, Castle Road, Wemyss Bay PA18 6AN Tel: 01475 520488 Fax: 01475 522566 — MB ChB 1959 Manch.; FRCPath 1980, M 1968. Cons. Forens. Med. & Sci. Univ. Glas. Prev: Cons. Pathol. Inverclyde Roy. Hosp. Greenock.

MORE, Marion 4 Saxe Coburg Street, Edinburgh EH3 5BN — MRCS Eng. LRCP Lond. 1958; BSc Lond. 1953, MB BS 1958. (St. Geo.) SCMO Family Plann. Centre Edin. Prev: Res. Anaesthesiol. Mass. Gen. Hosp. Boston, Mass.

MORE, Mary Brown (retired) Abbeyfield House, 262 Nithsdale Road, Glasgow G41 5AN Tel: 0141 427 6193 — MB ChB 1939 Glas.

MORE, Ranjit Singh Department of Cardiology, St. Mary's Hospital, Milton Road, Portsmouth PO3 6AD Tel: 023 92 866065 Fax: 023 92 866067 — MB ChB 1986 Manch.; BSc (Hons.) Anat. Manch 1983; MRCP (UK) 1989. Cons. (Cardiol.) St. Mary's Hosp. Portsmouth; Hon. Cons. (Cardiol.) St. Mary's Hosp. Lond. Socs: Med. Guidelines Comm. Brit. Cardiac Soc.; Jt. Cardiol. Comm, Clin. Affairs Comm. & New Cons. Comm. Roy. Coll. Phys. Prev: Lect. & Hon. Sen. Regist. (Cardiol.) St. Mary's Hosp. Lond.; Regist. (Cardiol.) King's Coll. Hosp. Lond.; Regist. (Cardiol. & Gen. Med.) Roy. Sussex Co. Hosp. Brighton.

MORE, Richard Edward Alexander Hendford Lodge Medical Centre, 74 Hendford, Yeovil BA20 1UJ Tel: 01935 470200 Fax: 01935 470202 — BM 1985 Soton.; BM Soton 1985; Dip. IMC RCS Ed. 1995; DRCOG 1991; DCH RCP Lond. 1990; DA (UK) 1988.

MOREAU, Alexander Piers Merlin Rowley Cottage, Rowley Lane, Wrexham, Slough SL3 6DT — BChir 1991 Camb.

MOREBODI-MASUPE, Tiny Kelebogile 4 Oakfield Crescent, Tonteg, Pontypridd CF38 1NG Tel: 01443 208709 — MB BCh Wales 1997. (University of Wales, College of Medicine) SHO Med. P. Chas. Hosp. Methyr Tydfill. Socs: BMA; MPS; MSS. Prev: Ho. Off. Surg. Nevill Hall Hosp. Abergavenny; Ho. Off. Med. Roy. Gwent Hosp. Newport.

MORECROFT, Mr James Alexander Sheffield Childrens Hospital, Western Bank, Sheffield S10 2TH Tel: 0114 271 7000 Fax: 0114 276 8419 Email: j.a.morecroft@sheffield.ac.uk; 17 Sandygate Park Crescent, Sheffield S10 5TW — MB BChir 1983 Camb.; MB Camb. 1983, BChir 1982; MA Camb. 1983; FRCS (Paediat.) 1996; FRCS Ed. 1986. (Camb. & Char. Cross) Sen. Regist. (Paediat. Surg.) Sheff. Childr. Hosp. Prev: Clin. Lect. (Paediat. Surg.) King's Coll. Hosp. Lond.; Clin. Research Fell. (Paediat. Surg.) Inst. Child Health Lond.; Regist. (Paediat. Surg.) Qu. Mary's Hosp. Childr. Carshalton & St. Geo. Hosp. Lond.

MOREEA, Mr Sulleman Mamode Bradford Royal Infirmary, Duckworth Lane, Bradford BD9; Spen House, 241 Spen Lane, Leeds LS16 5EL Tel: 0208 254 1101 — MB ChB 1991 (Hons.) Leeds; MRCP (UK) 1996; FRCS (Glas.) 1998. (Univ. Of Leeds) Specialist Regist. (Gast.) Yorks. Deanery, Seacroft Hosp. Leeds. Socs: Roy. Coll. of Phys.s; Roy. Coll. of Surg.s, Glas.; Brit. Soc. of Gastroenterologist. Prev: SHO Rotat. Bradford Roy. Infirm.; SHO Rotat. (Surg.) Hanogate Dist. Hosp.

MORELAND, Brian Omar Crescent Surgery, 3 The Crescent, Boscombe, Bournemouth BH1 4EX Tel: 01202 393755 Fax: 01202

MORELAND

303511 — MB BCh BAO 1979 NUI; MB BCh NUI 1979; LRCPI & LM, LRCSI & LM 1979.

MORELAND, Helen Elizabeth 19 Crowlees Road, Mirfield WF14 9PJ Tel: 01924 493950 — MRCS Eng. LRCP Lond. 1963. (Manch.) Clin. Med. Off. (Family Plann.) Clin. Asst. (Gyn.) Dewsbury Health Care Trust; Clin. Med. Off. Family Plann. & Clin. Asst. (Gyn.) Dewsbury HA. Socs: Brit. Soc. Colpos. & Cerv. Path.; Med. Wom. Federat.; BMA. Prev: Clin. Asst. (Ophth.) Huddersfield HA; Regist. & Resid. Surg. Off. Manch. Roy. Eye. Hosp.; Ho. Off. (Phys.) Hope Hosp. Salford.

***MORELAND, Neil John** 65 Ashburton Road, Blackpool FY1 2PF — MB BS 1998 Lond.; MB BS Lond 1998.

MORENO BETETA, Aurelia 24 Crutchley Road, Wokingham RG40 1XA — LMS 1989 U Complutense Madrid.

MORENO GARCIA, Jose 13 Matchells Close, St Annes Park, Bristol BS4 4AD — LMS 1992 Cadiz.

MORETON, Carol Ann Gurney Surgery, 101-103 Magdalen Street, Norwich NR3 1LN Tel: 01603 448800; 43 Harvey Lane, Norwich NR7 0BZ — BM 1984 Soton.; MRCGP 1994; DO RCS Eng. 1988. (Soton.) Prev: SHO (Geriat.) St. Michael's Hosp. Aylsham; SHO (Paediat.) Norf. & Norwich Hosp.; SHO (Ophth.) St. Paul's Eye Hosp. Liverp.

MORETON, Earl Ivor John Sutton Park Surgery, 34 Chester Road North, Sutton Coldfield B73 6SP Tel: 0121 353 2586 Fax: 0121 353 5289 — MB BCh 1978 Wales.

MORETON, Paul Flat 6, 3 Bramhall Road, Crosby, Liverpool L22 3XA — MB ChB 1993 Liverp.

MORETON, Philippa Wren The Health Centre, Aylesbury Road, Wendover, Aylesbury HP22 6LD Tel: 01296 623452; Little Hundridge Farm, Little Hundridge Lane, Great Missenden HP16 0RP Tel: 01494 866363 Fax: 01494 866364 Email: pmoreton@oxford-pgmde.co.uk — MB BS 1976 Lond.; FRCGP 1995, M 1981; DRCOG 1979. Assoc. Adviser, Oxf. PGMDE. Socs: Chairm. Thames Valley Fac. RCGP. Prev: Course Organiser, Aylesbury.

MORETTO, June Christine Straight Bit Surgery, 17 Straight Bit, Flackwell Heath, High Wycombe HP10 9LS Tel: 01628 522838 Fax: 01628 529255; Ledgewood, 220 Marlow Bottom Road, Marlow SL7 3PR — MB ChB 1974 Liverp.

MOREWOOD, Mr Geoffrey Arthur 32 Broadway, Cheadle SK8 1LD — MB ChB 1962 Manch.; FRCS Ed. 1969; FRCOG 1980. (Manch.) Cons. (O & G) Wythenshawe Hosp. Manch. Socs: Fell. Manch. Med. Soc.; N. Eng. Obst. & Gyn. Soc. Prev: Lect. (O & G) Univ. W. Indies Kingston, Jamaica; Sen. Regist. (O & G) St. Mary's Hosp. Manch.; Lect. (O & G) Univ. Manch.

MOREWOOD, John Howard Michael The Surgery, 20-22 Westdale Lane, Carlton, Nottingham NG4 3JA Tel: 0115 961 9401; 22 Westdale Lane, Gedling, Nottingham NG4 3JA Tel: 0115 961 9401 — MB ChB 1965 Sheff.; MRCGP 1976; DObst RCOG 1967. (Sheff.) Gen. Med. Pract. Socs: Assur. Med. Soc.; Brit. Med. Assoc.; Guild Catholic Doctors. Prev: Hon. Phys. & Hon. Surg. Sheff. Roy. Infirm.; Hon. Surg. Jessop Hosp. Wom. Sheff.

MOREWOOD, Sally Ann 6 Redclyffe Road, West Didsbury, Manchester M20 3JR Tel: 0161 445 2275 — MB ChB 1989 Manch.; BSc St. And. 1986. SHO (Orthop.) Bolton Roy. Infirm.

MOREY, Adrienne Louise Nuffield Department of Pathology, John Radcliffe Hospital, Headington, Oxford OX3 9DU Tel: 01865 220540 Fax: 01865 220524; 35 Castle Mill House, Juxon St, Oxford OX2 6DR — MB BS 1987 Med.; BSc (Med.) Sydney 1984, MB BS 1987. Nuffield Med. Research Fell. Univ. Oxf & Research Fell. New Coll. Oxf. Prev: Intern. Roy. N. Shore Hosp. Sydney.

MOREY, Paula-Jane 11 Newlands Avenue, Southampton SO15 5EP Email: pjmorey@doctors.org.uk — BM 1991 Soton.; MRCP (UK) 1996. Specialist Regist. S. Thames Region.

MOREY, Richard George The Surgery, Main Road, Sellindge, Ashford TN25 6JX Tel: 01303 812180 Fax: 01303 814069 — MB BS 1971 Lond.; MRCS Eng. LRCP Lond. 1971; FRCGP 1999.

MOREY, Richard James Frederick Middlesex Hospital, London W1; 44 Eastbrook Road, London SE3 8BT — MB BS 1987 Lond.; FRCA. 1994; DA (UK) 1991. Regist. (Anaesth.) Middlx. Hosp. Lond.

MOREY CANELLAS, Jaime Whitchurch Hospital, Whitchurch, Cardiff CF14 7XB — LMS 1994 Saragossa. SHO (Psychiat. of Old Age) WhitCh. Hosp. Cardiff; Inceptor Roy. Coll. Psychiat. Socs: BMA; Med. Defence Union.

MORFEY, Dorothea Harriet 2 Royston Close, Southampton SO17 1TB — MB BS 1996 Lond.

MORGAN, Alastair Hamilton Stonehaven Medical Group, Stonehaven Medical Centre, 32 Robert Street, Stonehaven AB39 2EL Tel: 01569 762945 Fax: 01569 766552; Laurel Bank, Woodcot Lane, Stonehaven AB39 2GJ Tel: 01569 764039 — MB ChB 1975 Aberd. (Aberd.) Med. Dir. Kincardine Community Hosp. Stonehaven.

MORGAN, Mr Alexandre Aloysius 7 Westacott Close, London N19 3LE — MB ChB 1964 Ed.; FRCS Ed. 1975.

MORGAN, Alison York Road Surgery, Southwold IP18 6AN; 112 High Street, Aldeburgh IP15 5AB — MB BS 1991 Lond.; BSc (Hons.) Lond. 1989. GP.

MORGAN, Allan Thomas Kings Court, The Broadway, Winchester SO23 9BE Tel: 01962 826000 Fax: 01962 826001 Email: morgana@iconuk.com — MB BCh 1978 Wales; BSc (Hons.) Wales 1975, MB BCh 1978. Chief Med. Off. - ICON Clin. Research UK. Prev: Dir. Clin. Research Ayerst Laborat.; Med. Dir. Clin. Research Europe, Abbott Laborats.

MORGAN, Andrew Duncan Department of Medicine, Queen Elizabeth the Queen Mother's Hospital, Margate CT9 4AN Fax: 01843 291980 Email: worthct@aol.com — MB ChB 1974 Ed.; BSc Ed. 1971, MD 1986; FRCP Lond. 1994; FRCP Ed. 1992, M 1977. Cons. Phys. Cardiol. and Gen. Med. E. Kent Hosp.s Trust; Hon. Cons. Cardiol. Guy's and St Thomas's Hosp.s Trust Lond. Socs: Thoracic Soc.; Med. Res. Soc.; Brit. Cardiac Soc. Prev: Sen. Regist. W.m. & Brompton Hosps.; Research Fell. and Regist. Dept. of Med. Univ. of Edin.

MORGAN, Andrew George Lloyd Manselton Surgery, Elgin Street, Manselton, Swansea SA5 8QQ Tel: 01792 653643 / 642459 Fax: 01792 645257; 17 Clos Tymawr, Penllergaer, Swansea SA4 1DA Tel: 01792 893441 — MB BCh 1975 Wales; MRCGP 1979; DA Eng. 1978; DRCOG 1978.

MORGAN, Andrew Howard Granby Place Surgery, Granby Place, 1 High Street, Northfleet, Gravesend DA11 9EY Tel: 01474 352447/362252; 17 New Road, Meopham, Gravesend DA13 0LS Tel: 01474 815064 Fax: 01474 815064 Email: amorgan@gping-asthma.org — BM 1985 Soton. (Univ. Soton.) GP N.fleet.

MORGAN, Andrew James High Dyon Side, Distington, Workington CA14 4QQ — MB BS 1993 Lond.

MORGAN, Andrew James Anthony 169 Banbury Road, Stratford-upon-Avon CV37 7HT — BM 1991 Soton.

MORGAN, Mr Andrew Roger 31 Southward Lane, Langland, Swansea SA3 4QE — MB BCh 1985 Wales; BSc (2/1) Wales 1977; FRCS Ed. 1990. Cons. Surg. (Colrectal Surg.) Singleton Hosp. Swansea. Prev: Lect. (Surg.) W.m. Med. Sch. Lond.; Sen. Regist. Univ. Hosp. Wales; Regist. Rotat. (Surg.) Cardiff.

MORGAN, Andrew Timothy Balham Park Surgery, 92 Balham Park Road, London SW12 8EA Tel: 020 8767 8828 Fax: 020 8682 1736; 8 Effra Road, Wimbledon, London SW19 8PP Tel: 020 8543 2325 — MB BS 1980 Lond.; BA Camb. 1975, MA 1976; MRCGP 1984; DCH 1983; DRCOG 1982. (Guy's)

***MORGAN, Angela Jane** 41 Lower Packington Road, Ashby-de-la-Zouch LE65 1GE — BChir 1996 Camb.

MORGAN, Ann Tel: 01656 733262 Fax: 01656 735239; 22 Yr Ysfa, Maesteg CF34 9AG — MB BCh 1975 Wales.

MORGAN, Ann Griffith (retired) 127 Old Bath Road, Cheltenham GL53 7DH Tel: 01242 528411 — MB BS 1952 Lond.; MRCS Eng. LRCP Lond. 1951; DCH Eng. 1955; DObst RCOG 1953. Sen. Med. Off. (Family Plann.) Cheltenham DHA. Prev: Resid. Med. Off. Vict. Hosp. Childr. Lond.

MORGAN, Ann Wendy Leeds General Infirmary, St. James's University Hospital, Leeds L59 Tel: 0113 206 6215 Fax: 0113 244 4475 Email: mrpawm@leeds.ac.uk; 14 Studleigh Terrace, Brighouse HD6 2PG Tel: 01484 710001 — MB ChB 1990 Leeds; BSc (Hons.) Leeds 1987; MRCP (UK) 1993. (Leeds) Specialist Regist. (Rheum.) Yorks. Deanery; Clin. Research Fell. Molecular Med. Unit, SJUH. Socs: BSI; BSR.

MORGAN, Anne Helen Drumchapel Health Centre, 80-90 Kinfauns Drive, Glasgow G15 7TS; 60 Cleveden Drive, Glasgow G12 0NX Tel: 0141 334 5295 — MB ChB 1984 Glas.; DRCOG 1988; MRCGP 1989; MRCGP 1989; DRCOG 1988. Prev: Trainee GP Alexandria Med. Centre; SHO (O & G & Geriat.) S.. Gen. Hosp.; SHO (Infec. Dis.) Monklands Dist. Gen. Hosp.

MORGAN

MORGAN, Anthony George Nottingham City Hospital, Hucknall Road, Nottingham NG5 1PB Tel: 0115 969 1169 Fax: 0115 962 7678 Email: amorgan@ncht.trent.nhs.uk; Fairham House, Clifton Lane, Ruddington, Nottingham NG11 6AA — MB BS 1968 Lond.; BSc Lond. 1965, MD 1977; FRCP Lond. 1986; MRCP (UK) 1971. (Lond. Hosp.) Cons. Phys. & Med. Dir. Nottm. City Hosp. NHS Trust. Socs: Renal Assn.; Internat. Soc. Nephrol.; Brit. Assoc. Med. Managers. Prev: Sen. Lect. Univ. Hosp. W. Indies, Jamaica; Lect. (Med.) Lond. Hosp. Med. Coll.; Research Fell. (Immunol.) Inst. Child Health Lond.

MORGAN, Anthony Gwyn (retired) 18 Grassington Road, Skipton BD23 1LL Tel: 01756 792286 — MB ChB 1961 Bristol; MB ChB (2nd cl. Hons.) 1961; MD Bristol 1969; FRCP Lond. 1982, M 1967. Prev: Med. Dir. & Cons. Gastroenterol. Airedale NHS Trust Steeton Keighley W. Yorks.

MORGAN, Mr Anthony Maxwell Froize Lodge, 25 Lode Way, Haddenham, Ely CB6 3UL — MB BChir 1956 Camb.; FRCS Ed. 1973.

MORGAN, Barbara Hilary Milch Hill, Great Leighs, Chelmsford CM3 1QE Tel: 01245 361222 — MB BS Durh. 1953. Med. Off. BTS E. Anglian RHA.

MORGAN, Barbara Lisca Paddocks, Plowden Park, Aston Rowant, Oxford OX1 5JD — MB BS 1966 Lond.; MRCS Eng. LRCP Lond. 1966; Dip. Ven. Soc. Apoth. Lond. 1974. (St. Bart.) Assoc. Specialist (Venereol.) Radcliffe Infirm. Oxf. Socs: Med. Soc. Study VD; BMA; Assn. Genitourin. Med. Prev: Sen. Regist. & Regist. (Venereol.) Radcliffe Infirm. Oxf.; Clin. Asst. (Dermat. & Venereol.) & SHO (ENT) High Wycombe Gen. Hosp.

MORGAN, Barbara Mary (retired) 56 Curzon St. Apt 49, London W1Y 7PF Tel: 020 7629 0399 — MB ChB 1964 Pretoria; FFA RCS Eng. 1969. Prev: Cons. Anaesth. & Sen. Lect. Inst. O & G Q. Charlotte's Hosp. Lond.

***MORGAN, Barry John** 2 The Ridgeway, Sutton SM2 5JY — MB BS 1998 Lond.; MB BS Lond 1998.

MORGAN, Bassem The Thatch, Cambridge Road, Ugley, Bishop's Stortford CM22 6HZ — BChir 1994 Camb.

MORGAN, Bernard Allan Robert Jones & Agnes Hunt Orthopaedic & District Hospital Trust, Oswestry SY10 7AG Tel: 01691 404246; Bachie Ganol, Llanfyllin SY22 5NF — MB BS 1976 Lond.; MRCS Eng. LRCP Lond. 1976; DA Eng. 1979; FFA RCS Eng. 1982. (St. Geo.) Cons. Anaesth. Robt. Jones & Agnes Hunt Orthop. & Dist. Hosp. OsW.ry; Dir. Chronic Pain Managem. Clinic Robt Jones & Agnes Hunt Orthop. & Dist. Hosp. OsW.ry. Socs: Age Anaesth. Assn.; Assn. Anaesth.; Difficult Airway Soc. Prev: Sen. Regist. (Anaesth.) Roy. Vict. Infirm. Newc.; Regist. Soton. Gen. Hosp.

MORGAN, Bethan Uplands Surgery, 48 Sketty Road, Uplands, Swansea SA2 0LJ Tel: 01792 298554 / 298555 Fax: 01792 280416 — MB BS 1991 Lond.

MORGAN, Mr Brian David Gwynne (retired) Stockers House, Stockers Farm Road, Rickmansworth WD3 1NZ Tel: 01923 773922 Fax: 01923 773754 Email: bmorgan@mailbox.xo.uk — MB BS Lond. 1959; FRCS Eng. 1963; MRCS Eng. LRCP Lond. 1959; FRCOphth 1995. King Edwd. VII Hosp. for Offs. Lond. Prev: Cons. Plastic Surg. Univ. Coll. Hosp. Lond., Plastic Surg. Unit Mt. Vernon Hosp. N.wood &. King Edwd. VII Hosp. for Offs. Lond.

MORGAN, Brian John Francis 9 Malone View Park, Belfast BT9 5PN — MB BCh BAO 1967 Belf.; MFPHMI 1979; DPH Belf. 1970. (Belf.) Cons. Pub. Health Med. E. Health & Social Servs. Bd.

MORGAN, Bruno Academic Department of Radiology, Leicester Royal Infirmary, Leicester LE1 5WW Tel: 0116 258 6719 Fax: 0116 258 6721 Email: bmorgan@lri.org.uk — BM BCh 1989 Oxf.; BA Oxf. 1986; MRCP (UK) 1992; FRCR 1995. (Oxford Univ.) Sen. Lect. (Radiol.), Leic. Univ.; Hon. Cons. Leic. Roy. Infirm.

MORGAN, Bryan Paul 68 Lake Road E., Cardiff CF5 5NN — MB BCh 1980 Wales; PhD Wales 1984, BSc (Hons. Med. Biochem.) 1977; MRCPath 1987. Sen. Lect. (Med. Biochem.) Univ. Wales Coll. Med. Cardiff.

***MORGAN, Camilla Rebecca** Lower Letton, Bucknell SY7 0DS — MB BS 1996 Lond.

MORGAN, Caroline Jane 30 Colebrook Avenue, Shirley, Southampton SO15 5NR Email: cjmi@soton.ac.uk — BM 1994 Soton.; BM (Hons.) Soton. 1994; MRCP (UK) 1997. Clin. Res. Fell. (Dermat.) Soton. Gen. Hosp.; SHO (Dermat.) Roy. S. Hants. Hosp.

Soton. Prev: SHO (Med.) Poole Gen.Hosp.; SHO (Med.) Roy. Bournemouth Hosp.; SHO (Cas.) Qu. Alexandra Hosp. Cosham.

MORGAN, Caryl Neil 31 Crassington Drive, Nuneaton CV11 6WP — MB BS 1987 Lond.; MRCGP 1991; DCH RCP Lond. 1990.

***MORGAN, Carys Angharad** 77 Conway Road, Cardiff CF11 9NW — MB ChB 1997 Birm.

MORGAN, Catharine Elizabeth 3 Northmoor Place, Northmoor Road, Oxford OX2 6XB — BChir 1994 Camb.; BA Camb. 1992.

MORGAN, Cecil Irwel (retired) 3 Pine Tree Close, Burry Port SA16 0TF — MRCS Eng. LRCP Lond. 1954. Prev: Sen. Med. Off. Dyfed HA.

MORGAN, Cecil Rowland (retired) Easthorpe Manor, Bottesford, Nottingham NG13 0DU — MRCS Eng. LRCP Lond. 1939; LMSSA Lond. 1938. Prev: Regional Med. Off. Min. of Health.

***MORGAN, Ceri Elizabeth Townsend** Cottage, Randwick, Stroud GL6 6EU — MB ChB 1996 Birm.; ChB Birm. 1996.

***MORGAN, Ceridwen Jane** Hillside House, Prisk, Cowbridge CF71 7TJ — MB BS 1998 Lond.; MB BS Lond 1998.

MORGAN, Mr Cerys Ashton The New Surgery, Coychurch Road, Pencoed, Bridgend CF35 5LP Tel: 01656 860343 Fax: 01656 864451 — MB BCh 1970 Wales; FRCS Eng. 1976. Socs: Ogwr Med. Soc.

MORGAN, Charles Terence (retired) 11 Greenfield Way, Porthcawl CF36 3SH — MRCS Eng. LRCP Lond. 1947. Prev: Ho. Surg. W.m. Hosp.

MORGAN, Christine Cardiff Road Medical Centre, Cardiff Road, Taffs Well, Cardiff CF15 7YG Tel: 029 2081 0260 Fax: 029 2081 3002; 85 Church Road, Tonteg, Pontypridd CF38 1EW Tel: 01443 208255 — MB BCh 1977 Wales; DRCOG 1979.

MORGAN, Christopher James Lewis Old School Surgery, School Street, Pontyclun CF72 9AA Tel: 01443 222567 Fax: 01443 229205; Hillside House, Prisk, Cowbridge CF71 7TJ — MB BCh 1967 Wales; MFFP 1992 RCOG; MRCGP 1976; DObst RCOG 1970. (Cardiff) Hosp. Pract. (A & E) Roy. Glam. Hosp. Prev: SHO (O & G) (A & E) United Cardiff Hosps.

MORGAN, Colin 6 Rossett Way, Harrogate HG2 0EE — BM BS 1989 Nottm.; MRCP (UK) 1992.

MORGAN, Cyril Richard The Gowerton Medical Centre, Mill Street, Gowerton, Swansea SA4 3ED Tel: 01792 872404 Fax: 01792 875170; Gowerton Surgery, Gowerton Medical Centre, Mill Street, Gowerton, Swansea SA4 3ED Tel: 01792 872404 Fax: 01792 875170 — MB BCh Wales. 1969. Prev: SHO (O & G) Morriston Hosp. Swansea; SHO (Paediat.) Nevill Hall Hosp. Abergavenny.; Ho. Off. (Surg. & Med.) Singleton Hosp. Swansea.

MORGAN, Daniel Richard 16 Elmslie Court, North Road, Maidenhead SL6 1PL — MRCS Eng. LRCP Lond. 1957.

MORGAN, David 3 Devonshire Place, London W1G 6HE — MB ChB 1975 Bristol; MRCGP 1981; DRCOG 1984. Med. Secretariat MDU Lond. Prev: GP S.sea & Yeovil; Surg. Lt. Cdr. RN (Retd.).

MORGAN, David Alun Lloyd Department of Clinical Oncology, Nottingham City Hospital NHS Trust, Nottingham NG5 1PB Tel: 0115 969 1169 Fax: 0115 962 8027 Email: david.morgan@nottingham.ac.uk; 17 Beaulieu Gardens, West Bridgford, Nottingham NG2 7TL Tel: 0115 981 8291 — MB ChB 1972 Bristol; FRCR 1981. (Bristol) Cons. Clin. Oncol. City Hosp. Nottm. Prev: EORTC Fell. Inst. Gustave Roussy, Villejuif, France.

MORGAN, David Christopher Marine Medical, Blyth Health Centre, Thoroton Street, Blyth NE24 1DX Tel: 01670 396520 Fax: 01670 396537 — MB ChB 1983 Leeds; MRCGP 1988. GP Blyth, N.d.

MORGAN, David Frederick Spring Cottage, Brog St., Corfe Mullen, Wimborne BH21 3HB Tel: 01202 676111 Fax: 01202 667126 — MB BChir 1969 Camb.; MA Camb. 1969; DObst RCOG 1971; DCH Eng. 1971. (St. Geo.)

MORGAN, David Gwilym Email: doctormorgan@hotmail.com; P.O. Box 65236, Tueson A2, 85728, USA — MRCS Eng. LRCP Lond. 1978. (Cardiff)

***MORGAN, David James** 8 Handel Terrace, Southampton SO15 2FG Tel: 02380 631347; Queen Alexandra Hospital, Southwick Hill Road, Cosham, Portsmouth PO6 3LY Tel: 01705 286000 — BM 1997 Soton.

MORGAN, David John Northwick Park Hospital & Clinical Research Centre, Watford Road, Harrow HA1 3UJ Tel: 020 8864

MORGAN

3232; Golden Grove, Trem Dyffryn, Red Bank, Welshpool SY21 7PT Tel: 01938 553788 — MB BS 1988 Lond. Research Fell. (O & G) N.wick Pk. Hosp. Harrow. Prev: SHO (Gyn.) N.wick Pk: Hosp. & Qu. Charlotte's & Chelsea Hosp.; SHO (Obst.) St. Mary's Hosp. Lond.

MORGAN, David John Richard Department of Medicine & Therapeutics, Imperial Coll. School of Medicine, Chelsea & Westminster Hospital, 369 Fulham Road, London SW10 9NH Tel: 020 8746 8146 Fax: 020 8746 8887 Email: richard.morgan@ic.ac.uk; Links Cottage, Holders Hill Crescent, Hendon, London NW4 1NE Tel: 020 8203 2217 Email: rm06444599@aol.com — MB BS 1975 Lond.; FRCP Lond. 1993; MRCP (UK) 1980; MRCS Eng. LRCP Lond. 1975. (St. Bart.) Cons. Phys. Chelsea & W.m. Hlthcare NHS Trust Lond.; Hon. Sen. Lect. (Clin. Pharmacol. & Therap.) Imperial Coll. Sch. Med. Socs: Brit. Geriat. Soc.; BMA; Soc. Research into Hydrocephalus and Spina Bifida. Prev: Lect. (Therap.) & Sen. Regist. (Med.) Char. Cross & W.m. Med. Sch. Lond. Univ.; Research Fell. (Chest) St. Bart. Hosp. Lond.; Ho. Phys. Med. Profess. Unit & Neurol. Dept. St. Bart. Hosp. Lond.

***MORGAN, David Kenneth** 17 Briarwood Cl, Neath SA10 7UH — MB BCh 1997 Wales.

MORGAN, David Laurence Silverstrand, Pwllmelin Road, Llandaff, Cardiff CF5 Tel: 029 2056 3022 — MB BS 1965 Lond.; MRCS Eng. LRCP Lond. 1965. (King's Coll. Hosp.) Prev: Ho. Phys. Addenbrooke's Hosp. Camb.; Ho. Surg. King's Coll. Hosp.

MORGAN, David Lewis McLaughlin and Partners, 27-29 Derby Road, North End, Portsmouth PO2 8HW Tel: 023 9266 3024 Fax: 023 9265 4991 — MRCS Eng. LRCP Lond. 1960. (Guy's) Med. Off. Smiths Food Gp. Prev: Ho. Surg. & Ho. Phys. Qu. Alexandra Hosp. Portsmouth; Ho. Surg. (Obst.) St. Mary's Hosp. Portsmouth.

MORGAN, David Michael Trevor Rheola Street Medical Centre, 50 Rheola Street, Penrhiwceiber, Mountain Ash CF45 3TB Tel: 01443 473328 Fax: 01443 473796; Clyne Moor, 76 Owl's Lodge Lane, Mayals, Swansea SA3 5DP Tel: 01792 403307 — MB BCh BAO 1989 NUI; LRCPSI 1989; MRCGP 1993.

MORGAN, David Ronald Lee Bank Group Practice, Colston Health Centre, 10 Bath Row, Lee Bank, Birmingham B15 1LZ Tel: 0121 622 4846 Fax: 0121 622 7105 — MD 1991 Glas.; MB ChB 1974; FRCP Glas. 1988; MRCP (UK) 1977; FRCGP 1991, M 1981; DRCOG 1979; DCH Eng. 1978. (Glas.) Princip. (Gen. Pract.); Hon. Sen. Lect. (Gen. Pract.) Birm. Univ. Prev: Sen. Lect. (Gen. Pract.) Birm. Univ.; Regist. Roy. Hosp. Sick Childr. Glas.; Regist. (Med.) Roy. Infirm. Glas.

MORGAN, David Russell Department of Pathology, Scarborough Hospital, Scarborough Tel: 01723 368111 Ext: 2326; 109 Stepney Road, Scarborough YO12 5BT — MB ChB 1981 Leeds; FRCPath 1988. Cons. Histopath. ScarBoro. Trust.

MORGAN, Mr David Ward Woodrow House, 165 Woodrow Lane, Lydiate Ash, Bromsgrove B61 0PL Tel: 0121 453 8589 — MB ChB 1981 Birm.; BSc (Hons) Birm. 1978, MB ChB 1981; FRCS Ed. 1986; FRCS Otol. Eng. 1987. Cons. ENT Birm. Heartlands, Good Hope Hosp., Univ. Hosp. Birm. Prev: Sen. Regist. (ENT) Roy. Nat. Throat, Nose & Ear Hosp., Gt. Ormond St.,Roy. Berks. Hosp., Roy. Brompton Hosp. & Nat. Hosp. Nerv. Dis. Lond.; Fell. Paediat. Laryngol. R.A.H.C. Sydney, Austral.; Fell. H & N Reconstruc. Surg. Tata Hosp. Bombay.

***MORGAN, David William** Heddfan, Derllwyn Road, Tondu, Bridgend CF32 9HD — MB BCh 1998 Wales.

MORGAN, Deborah Leah The Medical Centre, Badgers Crescent, Shipston-on-Stour CV36 4BQ — MB ChB 1993 Leic.; MRCGP 1997; DCH 1996; DRCOG 1995. (Leic.)

MORGAN, Debra Sian 38 Heather Road, Lee, London SE12 0UQ — MB ChB 1981 Manch.; MRCGP 1986; DRCOG 1983.

MORGAN, Denis Mervyn Richmond Clinic, 172 Caerleon Road, Newport NP19 7FY Tel: 01633 259970 Fax: 01633 221210; Brookhurst, Ton Road, Llangybi, Usk NP15 1PA Tel: 01633 450311 — MB BCh 1971 Wales; DObst RCOG 1974; Cert Family Plann. 1976. (Welsh Nat. Sch. of Med. Cardiff) Gen. Med. Practitioner; Clin. Asst. Dept. Genitourin. Med. Roy. Gwent Hosp. Newport; Clin. Asst. Dept. Urol. Roy. Gwent Hosp. Newport. Socs: Assn. Genitourin. Med.; Assoc. Mem. Inst. Psychosexual Med.; Diplomate Fac. Fam. Plann.

MORGAN, Dewi James Rosser (retired) Merrylands, Thrupps Lane, Hersham, Walton-on-Thames KT12 4NF Tel: 01932 224662 — MB BS 1951 Lond.; MRCS Eng. LRCP Lond. 1948; DObst RCOG 1952.

MORGAN, Dewi Randall Silver Birches, West Grimstead, Salisbury SP5 3RE Tel: 01722 710225 Fax: 01722 710559; Little Tithe, Seale, Farnham GU10 1JA Tel: 01252 752194 — MB BCh Wales 1964; MFOM RCP Lond. 1981; DAvMed Eng. 1968. (Cardiff) Indep. Occupat. Health Pract. (Aviat. Med.) Wilts. Socs: Roy. Aeronaut. Soc. Prev: SHO (Anaesth.) Singleton Hosp. Swansea; Ho. Phys. (Child Health) United Cardiff Hosps.; Ho. Surg. Llandough Hosp. Penarth.

MORGAN, Elizabeth Joan 12 Lordwood Square, Lordswood Road, Birmingham B17 9BS — MB BS 1976 Newc.; Cert. Prescribed Equiv. Exp. JCPTGP 1989; DA Eng. 1980; Family Plann. Cert 1979. (Newc.) Prev: Regist. (Anaesth.) Dumfries & Galloway Roy. Infirm.; Cas. Off. Cheltenham Gen. Hosp.; Trainee GP Camb.

MORGAN, Elizabeth Rae McFarlane (retired) 19 Parliament Hill, London NW3 2TA Tel: 020 7435 7539 — MB ChB 1942 N.Z.; DCH Eng. 1949.

MORGAN, Eric John Rowland (retired) 74 Eaton Crescent, Swansea SA1 4QN Tel: 01792 463408 — MB ChB 1954 Bristol; MPhil Wales 1992; BDS 1946; FDS RCS Eng. 1957. Cons. Dent. Surg. W. Glam., E. Dyfed & Pembrokesh. HAs. Prev: Cons. Dent. Surg. Tees-side, Darlington, S.W. Durh. & N.allerton Hosp. Gps.

MORGAN, Esther Irene Kyle Penderyn, 18 Wentwood View, Caldicot, Newport NP18 2AD — MB BCh 1967 Wales.

MORGAN, Francis Brendan Aylmer Lodge Surgery, Broomfield Road, Kidderminster DY11 5PA Tel: 01562 822015 Fax: 01562 827137 — MB ChB 1978 Birm.; MRCP (UK) 1980; MRCGP 1982; DRCOG 1981. GP Kidderminster. Prev: SHO (Paediat.) Good Hope Hosp. Sutton Coldfield; SHO (Gen. Med.) Selly Oak Hosp. Birm.; Ho. Phys. Qu. Eliz. Hosp. Birm.

MORGAN, Frederick (retired) Four Stacks, 23 Kingsweston Road, Henbury, Bristol BS10 7QT Tel: 0117 950 4659 — MD 1936 Brno; AFOM RCP Lond. 1983. Prev: Regist. (Dermat.) Manch. Skin Hosp.

MORGAN, Gareth Department Paediatrics and Department Microbiology, Faculty of Medicine, University of Kuwait, PO Box 24923, Safat 13110, Kuwait Tel: 00 965 531 9486 Fax: 00 965 531 9486 Email: gmorgan@hsc.kuniv.edu.kw; 8 John Street, Bargoed CF81 8PG Tel: 01443 831019 — MB ChB 1977 Manch.; MD Manch. 1988; FRCP Lond. 1994; MRCP (UK) 1980; FRCPCH 1997. (Manchester) Prof. Immunol.; Hon. Cons. Paediat. Immunol. Mubarak Al-Kabeer Hosp., Kuwait. Prev: Sen. Lect. (Paediat. Immunol.) Inst. Child Health Univ. Lond.; Hon. Cons. Hosp. Sick Childr. Gt. Ormond St. Lond.; Wellcome Lect. (Trop. Dis.) MRC Laborats. The Gambia, W. Africa.

MORGAN, Professor Gareth John Department of Haematology, University of Leeds Teaching Hospital NHS Trust, General Infirmary at Leeds, Great George St., Leeds LS2 Tel: 01532 243 2799 Fax: 01532 233 3404 Email: garethm@pathology.leeds.ac.uk; 18 Gledhow Wood Grove, Roundhay, Leeds LS8 1NZ Tel: 0113 294 7314 — MB BCh 1981 Wales; PhD Lond. 1991; BSc Wales 1978; MRCP (UK) 1985; FRCP 1998. (University of Wales College of Medicine) Hon. Cons. Haematol. Gen. Infirm. Leeds; Prof. (Haemat.). Socs: Brit. Soc. Haematol. (Scientif. Sec.); Eur. Blood & Marrow Transpl.; UKCCR (Lymphoma Gp.). Prev: Sen. Regist. (Haemat.) Hammersmith Hosp. Lond.; LRF Research Fell. Chester Beatty Research Laborats. & Roy. Marsden Hosp. Lond.

MORGAN, Gareth John Murdishaw Health Centre, Gorsewood Road, Murdishaw, Runcorn WA7 6ES Tel: 01928 712061 Fax: 01928 791988; Trinity House, High St, Frodsham, Warrington WA6 7HE — MB BS 1976 Lond.; MRCS Eng. LRCP Lond. 1976; MRCGP 1982. (Westm.)

MORGAN, Gareth Lewis Harmans Meadow, Bury, Dulverton TA22 9NE Tel: 01398 323054 Fax: 01398 323054 Email: glmexmoor@aol.com; 6 Woodstock Road, Taunton TA1 1EJ Tel: 01823 333973 — MB ChB 1958 Birm.; MFHOM 1983; DObst RCOG 1960. (Birm.)

MORGAN, Gaynor Nicola Grenways, Dorchester Road, Hook RG27 9DW — MB BS 1995 Lond.

MORGAN, Geoffrey Frank Ely Bridge Surgery, 23 Mill Road, Ely, Cardiff CF5 4AD Tel: 029 2056 1808 Fax: 029 2057 8871; 22 Hardwicke Court, Llandaff, Cardiff CF5 2LB — MB BCh 1968 Wales; FRCGP 1985, M 1974; DObst RCOG 1970. (Cardiff) Course Organiser S. Glam VTS; Hon. Med. Off. Glam. Wanderers RFC. Socs:

Cardiff Med. Old Studs. Assn.; SE Wales Fac RCGP; Chairm. Welsh Counc. RCGP.

MORGAN, Gerallt Wyn Pentre Farm, Cwmystwyth, Aberystwyth SY23 4AD — MB BCh 1991 Wales.

MORGAN, Giles Anthony Rowland Royal Cornwall Hospital, Treliske, Truro TR1 3LJ Tel: 01872 274242 Fax: 01872 252480 Email: giles.morgan@rcht.swest.nhs.uk; South Penarth, St. Clements Hill, Truro TR1 1NX Tel: 01872 41144 — MB BS 1973 Lond.; FFA RCS Eng. 1978. (St. Thos.) Cons. Anaesth. & Co-Dir. Intens. Therap. Unit Roy. Hosp. Treliske Truro. Socs: IC Soc. UK; Eur. Soc. IC Med.; Hon. Sec. Intens. Care Soc. Prev: Clin. Fell. (Anaesth.) Hosp. For Sick Childr. Toronto, Canada; Sen. Regist. Humphrey Davy Dept. Anaesth. Bristol Roy. Infirm.

MORGAN, Gillian Margaret North & East Devon Health Authority, Dean Clarke House, Southernhay East, Exeter EX1 1PQ Tel: 01392 207313 Email: gill.morgan@nedevon ha.swest.nhs.uk; 1 Betony Rise, Exeter EX2 5RR — MB BS 1976 Lond.; MRCP (UK) 1979; FFPHM 1996, M 1987; DRCOG 1981; Cert FPA. 1981; FRCP 1999. (Univ. Coll. Hosp.) Chief. Exec. N. & E. Devon Heath Auth. Prev: Dir. & Cons. Pub. Health Med. Leics. HA.

MORGAN, Graham Robert 201 Wells Road, Knowle, Bristol BS4 2DB Tel: 0117 971 4365 Fax: 0117 971 4365 — MB ChB 1971 Leeds; LMCC 1985; MF Hom 1988.

MORGAN, Gwylfa Wyn Coed y Glyn Surgery, Coed y Glyn, Church Street, Llangefni LL77 7DU Tel: 01248 722229; Hedd yr Ynys, Lon yr Fron, Llangefni LL77 7HB Tel: 01248 723791 Email: wyu.morgan@lineone.net — MB ChB 1975 Liverp.; MRCGP 1985; Dip. Pract. Dermat. Wales 1989; DRCOG 1977. (Liverp.)

MORGAN, Gwyn (retired) 12 Collwall Gardens, Woodford Green IG8 0HS Tel: 020 8504 9810 — PhD Lond. 1969, MD 1967, MB BS 1956; MRCS Eng. LRCP Lond. 1948; FRCPath 1974, M 1963. Consg. Path. Moorfields Eye Hosp. Lond. Prev: Univ. Reader & Cons. Path. Moorfields Eye Hosp.

MORGAN, Harriet Marie 32 Chestnut Grove, New Malden KT3 3JN; 32 Chestnut Grove, New Malden KT3 3JN — MB BS 1998 Lond.; MB BS Lond 1998. Ho. Off. (Gen. Surg.) Qu. Eliz. II Hosp. Herts. Socs: BMA; MDU. Prev: Ho. Off. (Gen. Med.) N. Hants. Hosp. Basingstoke.

MORGAN, Harry McIntosh (retired) Suil Na Mara, Forres IV36 1DJ Tel: 01309 72361 — MB ChB 1953 Glas.; DObst RCOG 1955. Med. Off. Leanchoil Hosp. Forres. Prev: Ho. Surg. Glas. Roy. Infirm.; Perth Roy. Infirm. & Lennox Castle.

MORGAN, Henry Edwin George 10 Bridge Avenue, Otley LS21 2AA — MB ChB 1993 Birm.; MRCP (Paeds) 1997. (Birm.) Specialist Regist. (Paediat.) Yorks., Deanery.

MORGAN, Professor Henry Gemmell (retired) Firwood House, 8 Eaglesham Road, Newton Mearns, Glasgow G77 5BG Tel: 0141 639 4404 Email: profmorgan@gem9.demon.co.uk — MB ChB 1946 St. And.; MB ChB (Commend.) St. And. 1946; FRSE 1971; BSc St. And. 1943; FRCP Glas. 1968, M 1965; FRCP Ed. 1962, M 1952; FRCPath 1970, M 1963. Prev: Prof. Path. Biochem. Univ. Glas. & Hon. Cons. Biochem. Roy. Infirm. Glas.

MORGAN, Heulwen Gynaecology Office, St. Mary's Wing, Whittington Hospital, Highgate Hill, London N19 5NF — MB BCh 1973 Wales; FRCOG 1990, M 1978. Cons. & Sen. Clin. Lect. (O & G) Whittington Hosp., Roy. Free & Univ. Coll., Lond. Med. Sch. Socs: Roayl Soc. of Med.; Brit. Fertil. Soc.; Brit. Fetal and Matern. Med. Soc.

MORGAN, Hilda (retired) 48 Barham Road, West Wimbledon, London SW20 0ET Tel: 020 8946 0899 — MB ChB 1940 Liverp. Prev: GP Lond.

MORGAN, Howard Gethin Department of Mental Health, University of Bristol, 41 St Michael's Hill, Bristol BS2 8DZ — MB BChir 1958 Camb.; MD Camb. 1973; FRCP Lond. 1976, M 1962; MRCS Eng. LRCP Lond. 1958; FRCPsych 1977, M 1971; DPM (Distinc.) Lond. 1966. (Lond. Hosp.) Prof. Emerit. Univ. Bristol; Dir. (Continuing Professional Developm.) Roy. Coll. Psychiats. Prev: Norah Cooke Hurle Prof. Ment. Health Univ. Bristol; Cons. & Sen. Lect. Dept. Ment. Health Univ. Bristol; Sen. Regist. Maudsley Hosp.

MORGAN, Huw Castle Surgery, 1 Prince of Wales Drive, Neath SA11 3EW Tel: 01639 641444 Fax: 01639 636288; 82 Gnoll Park Road, Neath SA11 3DD — MB BCh 1980 Wales; DRCOG 1984.

MORGAN, Ian David Paul Grove Road Surgery, 3 Grove Road, Solihull B91 2AG Tel: 0121 705 1105 Fax: 0121 711 4098; Warren Pearl Marie Curie Centre, 911 Warwick Road, Solihull B91 3ER Tel: 0121 705 4607 — MB ChB 1981 Birm.; MRCGP 1987; Dip. Palliat. Med. Wales 1994. Dep. Med. Dir. Marie Curie Warren Pearl Hospice Solihull.

MORGAN, Ian Donald Frank Romiley Health Centre, Chichester Road, Romiley, Stockport SK6 4QR Tel: 0161 494 1234 Fax: 0161 406 8932 — MB ChB 1971 Liverp.; DObst RCOG 1974.

MORGAN, Ian George The Ashgrove Surgery, Morgan Street, Pontypridd CF37 2DR Tel: 01443 404444 Fax: 01443 480917 — MB BS 1977 Lond.

MORGAN, Ian Lyn Princess Street Surgery, Princess Street, Gorseinon, Swansea SA4 4US Tel: 01792 895681 Fax: 01792 893051 — MB BCh 1985 Wales; MRCGP 1993. (Cardiff) Gen. Med. Practitioner; Hosp. Practitioner in Elderly Care & Rehabil. Med., Swansea NHS Trust, Swansea.; Clin. Teach. to Univ. of Wales Coll. of Med., Cardiff. Socs: BMA & Med. Protec. Soc.

MORGAN, Mr Ian Stewart Department of Cardiothorscic Surgery, St. Mary's Hospital, Paddington, London W2 1NY Tel: 020 7886 6666 Email: ian.morgan@ed.ac.uk; 2 Dundee Wharf, 100 Three Colt Street, Canary Riverside, London E14 8AX — MB ChB 1988 Ed.; BSc (Hons) 1986; FRCS Ed. 1993; Dip. IMC RCS Ed. 1994. (Ed.) SpR (Cardiothoracic Surg.) Lond.

MORGAN, Mrs Irene Central Clinic, 15 Margaret St., Wakefield WF1 2NJ Tel: 01924327601; Sycamore Cottage, Half Moon Lane, Kirkthorpe, Wakefield WF1 5SY — MB BS 1961 Geneva; BSc Geneva 1957; LRCP LRCS Ed. LRCPS Glas. 1967; MFFP 1993; Dip. Psychosexual Med. 1995; DCP Sheff. 1989; MFCH 1990. (Geneva/Leeds) Cons. Fac. Family Plann. & Reproduc. Healthcare Wakefield & Pontefract Community Health NHS Trust. Socs: Fac. Fam. Plann. & Reproduc. Health Care; Med. Protec. Soc.; Soc. Cons. Family Plann. & Reproductive Health. Prev: SCMO & Med. Co-ordinator for Wom. & Young People Servs. Wakefield & Pontefract Community NHS Trust.

MORGAN, Ivor Bowen The Nook, Brynawel Close, Crynant, Neath SA10 8TG Tel: 01639 750204 — MB BCh 1952 Wales; BSc, MB BCh Wales 1952.

MORGAN, Jacinta Cornwall Stroke and Rehabilitation Unit, Royal Cornwall Hospitals Trust, Treliske Hospital, Truro TR1 Tel: 01872 253548 Email: jacinta.morgan@rcht.swest.nhs.uk; 1 The Courtyard, David Penhaligon Way, Truro TR1 2EN — MB BCh BAO 1985 NUI; MRCP (UK) 1994, MRCPI 1988. (Univ. Coll. Galway, Irel.) Cons. (Rehabil. Med.) Roy. Cornw. Hosps. Trust. Prev: Sen. Regist. (Rehabil. Med.) RNRU Homerton Hosp. & Roy. Nat. Orthop. Hosp. Lond.; Advanced Trainee (Haemat. & Oncol.) Qu. Eliz. Hosp. Adelaide, Austral.; Med. Regist. Roy. Lancaster Infirm.

MORGAN, Jacqueline Winchester and Eastleigh Health Care Trust, Child Health Department, Highcroft, Romsey Road, Winchester SO22 5DH Tel: 01962 863511 Fax: 01962 856726; 37A Springvale Road, Kingsworthy, Winchester SO23 7ND Tel: 01962 882019 Fax: 01962 889394 Email: morgana@interalpha.co.uk — MB BCh 1977 Wales; MA Lond. 1999. (Welsh National School of Medicine) Staff Grade (Commun. Paediat.). Socs: BACCH; Assoc. Mem. MRCPCH; BACDA. Prev: Clin. Med. Off. Wessex HA.; Clin. Med. Off. W. Surrey DHA.

MORGAN, Jacqueline Mary Department of Dermatology, South Cleveland Hospital, Marton Road, Middlesbrough TS4 3BW Tel: 01642 850850 Fax: 01642 854763; Kirby House, Kirby-in-Cleveland, Middlesbrough TS9 7AN — MB Camb. 1968, BChir 1967; MA Camb. 1968; DCH Eng. 1971; DObst RCOG 1969. (Camb. & St. Thos.) Assoc. Specialist (Dermat.) S. Cleveland Hosp. Middlesbrough. Socs: N. Eng. Dermat. Soc.; Brit. Assn. Dermat.; Med. Wom. Federat. Prev: Staff Grade Dermatol., S. Cleveland Hosp., Middlesbrough; GP Nottm.; SHO (Paediat.) Dorset Co. Hosp. Dorchester.

MORGAN, James Edwards Eye Unit, University Hospital of Wales, Heath Park, Cardiff CF14 4XW Tel: 029 2074 4970 Email: morganje3@cardiff.ac.uk — BM BCh 1988 Oxf.; DPhil Oxf. 1986; BA Camb. 1982; FRCOphth. 1992. (Oxf.) Hon.Cons. Sen. Lect. Ophth. Univ. Hosp. Wales, Cardiff. Socs: ARVO; BMA. Prev: Sen. Regist. (Ophth.) Bristol Eye Hosp.; MRC Trav. Fell. Yale Univ. Sch. Med U.S.A.; Glaucoma Fell.

MORGAN, James Horace Sidney (retired) 9 Lands Road, Brixham TQ5 9AS Tel: 01803 853934 — MRCS Eng. LRCP Lond. 1949; MRCGP 1954. Prev: GP Devon.

MORGAN

MORGAN, James Huw Cole 67 Cavms Road, Westbury Park, Bristol BS6 7TT Tel: 0117 9249320 Email: huwmorganuk@yehoo.co.uk — MB ChB 1976 Birm.; MRCGP 1980; Cert. Med. Educat. Dund. 1998. (Birmingham) p/t Cons. in Internat. Primary Health Care Developm. & Educat., with PRIME (Partnership in Internat. Med. Educat.) and IHSD (Internat. Health Sector Developm.); Vis. Cons. Primary Health Care Reform Project Almaty, Kazakstan; GP Clin. Tutor, Bristol. Socs: BMA; Christ. Med. Fell. Prev: Trainee GP Abergavenny VTS; Chief Med. Cons. ECWA Community Health Prog., Nigeria; Course Organiser Univ. Bristol (Avon VTS).

MORGAN, James Paterson Ballantine (retired) Mallards, Balbuthie Road, Kilconquhar, Leven KY9 1LE — MB ChB 1951 Glas.

MORGAN, James Roderick 28 Hawthorn Road, Hale, Altrincham WA15 9RG Email: doctorjrm@aol.com — BM 1989 Soton.; MRCP (UK) 1993; FRCA 1996. Specialist Regist. (Anaesth.) Manch. Univ. Hosps. Socs: Intens. Care Soc.; Assn. Cardiothoracic Anaesths. Prev: Regist. (Anaesth.) Sheff. Univ. Hosps.

MORGAN, Jamey Stuart Ipswich Hospital NHS Trust, Heath Road, Ipswich IP4 5PD — MB BS 1982 Lond.; BSc Lond. 1979; MRCP (UK) 1986; FRCR 1992. Cons. Clin. Oncol., Ipswich Hosp., NHS Trust. Prev: Sen. Regist. (Oncol.) Velindre Hosp. Cardiff; Regist. (Radiol. & Oncol.) Char. Cross Hosp. Lond.

MORGAN, Janet Elspeth 3 Beech Holt, Leatherhead KT22 8RE Tel: 01372 378447 — MB BS 1954 Lond.; MRCS Eng. LRCP Lond. 1954. Clin. Med. Off. Mid Surrey HA.

MORGAN, Janet Myfanwy Woodmead, Bishops Hull Road, Taunton TA1 5EP Tel: 018230 282000 — MB BS 1965 Lond.; MRCS Eng. LRCP Lond. 1965. (Lond. Hosp.) GP Taunton. Prev: Clin. Asst. Alfred Morris Ho. Young Phys. Handicap. Unit Taunton; Clin. Asst. Trinity Hosp. Taunton.

MORGAN, Jean (retired) 19 Gorsewood Drive, Milford Haven SA73 3EP Tel: 01646 692775 — MB BCh Wales 1958; DCH Eng. 1961. Prev: Assoc. Specialist (Paediat.) Withybush Gen. Hosp. HaverfordW.

MORGAN, Jean Elisabeth 74 Eaton Crescent, Swansea SA1 4QN Tel: 01792 463408 — MB ChB 1948 Bristol. (Bristol) Prev: Ho. Surg. Bristol Roy. Hosp.; SHO Path. Frenchay Hosp. Bristol; Regist. Path. Bath Hosp. Gp.

MORGAN, Jeffery Richard Bronturnor Uchaf, Maentwrog, Blaenau Ffestiniog LL41 3YU — MB ChB 1969 Ed.; BSc, MB ChB Ed. 1969; MFOM RCP Lond. 1990, A 1983; DHMSA 1982; DObst RCOG 1971. Sec. & Treas. UK Forum for Organisational Health. Prev: Dep. Head. Med. Scs. Atomic Energy Research Estab. Harwell; Med. Off. Univ. Hull.

MORGAN, Jennifer Ann Bournewood Community & Mental Health NHS Trust, Goldsworth Park Health Centre, Woking GU21 3LQ Tel: 01483 728201; Wild Wood, Heather Close, Horsell, Woking GU21 4JR Tel: 01483 761033 — MB ChB 1972 Liverp.; DObst RCOG 1974. Staff Grade (Community Paediat.) Bournewood Community & Ment. Health NHS Trust.

***MORGAN, Jennifer Claire** 8 Rosebank, Lymm WA13 0JH — MB BS 1997 Newc.

MORGAN, Jennifer Gillian Fairmile Hospital, Cholsey, Wallingford OX10 9HH Tel: 01491 651281 — MB ChB 1981 Bristol. Clin. Asst. (Psychiat.) Fairmile Hosp. Wallingford. Prev: SHO (Psychiat.) Fairmile Hosp. Wallingford & Warneford Hosp. Oxf.; SHO (A & E) W.on Gen. Hosp.

MORGAN, Jessica Patrice Holme Wood, Manor Park S., Knutsford WA16 8AG — MB ChB 1990 Manch.

MORGAN, Joanna Louise 7 Nine Mile Ride, Finchampstead, Wokingham RG40 4QA — BM 1992 Soton.

MORGAN, Joanna Penelope Mount Devon House, Dollar FK14 7PT — MB ChB 1993 Aberd.

MORGAN, John Hilmorie, Heath Road, Woodham Road, Woking GU21 4DU Tel: 01483 773760 — MD 1937 Brno. (Masaryk Univ. Brno) Prev: Emerit. Cons. (Dermat.) E. Berks. Health Dist. & N.W. Surrey HA.

MORGAN, John Erfyl The New Surgery, 35 High St., Colerne, Chippenham SN14 8DD Tel: 01225 742028 Fax: 01225 743694; Home Farm, Lucknam Park, Colerne, Chippenham SN14 8AZ — MB ChB Leeds 1977; BSc (Hons.) Leeds 1972; MRCGP 1981.

MORGAN, John Farnill 45c Onslow Road, Richmond TW10 6QH Email: jmorgan@sgyms.ac.uk — BChir 1991 Camb.; MB Camb, B Chir 1991; MA (Experim. Psychol.) Camb. 1988; MRCPsych 1995. Sen. Regist. & Clin. Research Fell. Psychosamtic Med. St. Geo.'s Hosp. Lond.

MORGAN, John Howard White Chimneys, The Street, Felthorpe, Norwich NR10 4AB — MB ChB 1948 Birm.

MORGAN, John Huw The Health Centre, Canning St., Cwm, Ebbw Vale NP3 6AU Tel: 01495 370230 Fax: 01495 371115; 23 Meyricks, Coed Eva, Cwmbran NP44 6TU Tel: 01633 864648 — BM BS 1985 Nottm.; BMedSci Nottm. 1983, BM BS 1985; MRCGP 1989.

MORGAN, John Leslie Radiol. Department, Sheikh Khalifa Med. Centre, Abu Dhabi POBox 51900, United Arab Emirates; 20 The Badgers, Mearse Lane, Barnt Green, Birmingham B45 8QR Tel: 0121 447 7675 — MB BS 1976 Lond.; 1976 MB BS Lond.; 1972 BSc (Hons.) (Biochem.) Lond.; 1976 MRCS Eng. LRCP Lond.; 1984 FRCR; 1982 DMRD Eng. (St. Bart.) Cons. (Radiol.) Sheikh Khalifa Med. Centre. Abu Dhabi UAE. Socs: Roy. Coll. Radiol. Prev: Cons. Neuroradiol. Riyadh, Saudi Arabia; Dir. (Imaging Servs.) Allied Diagn. Centre Dubai, UAE; Cons. (Radiol.) Wellcare Hosp. Dubai UAE.

MORGAN, John Mansel (retired) 21 Redwood Close, Lymington SO41 9LT Tel: 01590 673462 — MRCS Eng. LRCP Lond. 1942; MA (Hons.) Camb. 1942, MB BChir 1945. Prev: Dir. SE Lond. Mass. Radiog. Serv. SE Metrop. Regional Hosp. Bd.

MORGAN, John Mark Southampton General Hospital, Tremona Rd, Southampton SO16 6YD Tel: 02380 796240 Fax: 02380 798693; Chalybeate Hospital, Tremona Road, Southampton SO16 6UY Tel: 02380 764333 Fax: 01703 511551 — MD 1992 Camb.; MA Camb. 1983, BA (Nat.Sci.Tripos) 1979, MD 1992, MB BChir 1982. (Camb. & Westm.) Cons. Cardiol. Wessex Regional Cardiothoracic Unit.; Hon. Cons. Cardiol. Tri-Serv. Milit. Hosp. Haslar. Prev: Sen. Regist. Roy. Brompton Hosp.

MORGAN, John Mitchell Landrick House, 124 Crewe Road, Nantwich CW5 6JS — MB ChB 1969 St. And.; MB ChB (Commend.) St. And. 1969; FRCPath 1992, M 1980. (St. And.) Cons. Histopath. Leighton Hosp. Crewe. Prev: Flying Doctor Zambian Flying Doctor Serv.; Staff Phys. Fundy Hosp. Black's Harbour, Canada.

MORGAN, John Roy Slade Hospital Resource Centre, Horspath Driftway, Headington, Oxford OX3 7JH Tel: 01865 228101 Fax: 01865 228140 Email: john.morgan@oldt.anglox.nhs.uk — MB ChB 1980 Sheff.; FRCPsych 2000; BSc (Hons.) Bangor 1973; MBA 1994. Cons. Psychiat. Learning Disabil. Slade Hosp. Resource Centre Oxf.; Med. Director. Socs: FRCPsych.

MORGAN, Jonathan Edward Francis 129 Walkley Bank Road, Sheffield S6 5AN — MB ChB 1990 Sheff.

MORGAN, Jonathan Paul 24 King Ecgbert Road, Totley Rise, Sheffield S17 3QQ — MB BS 1996 Lond.; MSc Warwick 1989; BSc Birm. 1988. (Guy's & St. Thomas's Hosp.)

MORGAN, Jonathan William 48 St Kenya Avenue, Hove BN3 4PP — MRCS Eng. LRCP Lond. 1974; DRCOG 1978.

MORGAN, Joyce (retired) Tyddyn Llangybi, Chwilog, Pwllheli, Caernarfon Tel: 0176 688 810342 — MB BS 1929 Lond.; BSc (Hons.) Lond., MD 1931, MB BS 1929; DA Eng. 1936; FRCOG 1950. Prev: Cons. Obstetr. Hillingdon Hosp.

MORGAN, Judith Elizabeth MSS Pneumoconiosis Medical Panel, Grove House, Grove Place, Swansea SA1 5DF; 13 Marine Walk, Maritime Quarter, Swansea SA1 1YQ — MB BCh 1979 Wales; DRCOG 1984. SEMA Med. Adviser.

***MORGAN, Judith Margaret** 32 Aldred Road, Sheffield S10 1PD — MB ChB 1994 Sheff.

MORGAN, Judith Rosemary Dual Team, 151 Blackfriars Road, London SE1 8EL Tel: 020 7620 1888 Fax: 020 7620 0540 Email: judith.morgan@slam-tr.nhs.uk — MB ChB 1969 Leeds; MRCP (UK) 1973; MRCPsych 1975. Cons. Psychiat. Subst. Misuse S. Lond. & Maudsley NHS Trust. Prev: Cons. Psychiat. Drug Depend. King's Coll. Hosp. Lond. & Bexley Hosp.

MORGAN, Julia Patricia Hedd yr Ynys, Lon Fron, Llangefni LL77 7HB — MB BS 1975 Melbourne; DObst 1979; Dip. FPA. (Austral.) 1979. (Roy. Melbourne Hosp.)

MORGAN

MORGAN, Julie Elizabeth 3 Meades Close, Marden, Tonbridge TN12 9QG Tel: 01622 831620 Email: julie@djmorgan.dircon.co.uk — BM 1990 Soton.; MRCGP 1996. (Soton.)

MORGAN, June (retired) 2 Saxonbury Close, Crowborough TN6 1EA Tel: 01892 668341 — MB ChB Bristol 1949.

MORGAN, Mr Justin David Toriel 1 Newlyn Avenue, Stoke Bishop, Bristol BS9 1BP — MB BCh 1986 Wales; MD Leic. 1995; FRCS Eng. 1990. (Univ. Wales Coll. Med.) Cons. Gen. & Transpl. Surg. S.end Hosp., Bristol. Socs: BMA; Brit. Transpl. Soc.

MORGAN, Kate Gale Department of Pathology, Stepping Hill Hospital, Poplar Grove, Stockport SK2 7JE — MB BS 1976 Lond.; BSc Lond. 1973; MRCP (UK) 1979; MRCPath 1993. (King's Coll. Hosp.) p/t Cons. Histopath. Stepping Hill Hosp. Stockport. Prev: Sen. Regist. (Histopath.) N.. W.. RHA.; Sen. Regist. (Histopath.) Yorks. RHA.

MORGAN, Kathleen Beryl (retired) Tanygraig, Llangefni LL77 7HR — MRCS Eng. LRCP Lond. 1943. Prev: Cas. Off., Ho. Surg. (Gen. & ENT) & Ho. Phys. Coventry & Warw. Hosp.

MORGAN, Kathryn Lillian Hilton House Surgery, 77 Swan Street, Sible Hedingham, Halstead CO9 3HT Tel: 01787 460612 Fax: 01787 462754; Coram Lodge Barn, Coram St, Hadleigh, Ipswich IP7 5NR — MB ChB 1982 Leeds; B.Tech (Pharmacol.) Bradford 1973. (Leeds)

MORGAN, Kathryn Patricia 91 Higher Lane, Lymm WA13 0BZ — MB ChB 1987 Manch.

MORGAN, Kenneth Peter 1/3F3 Spittalfield Crescent, Edinburgh EH8 9QZ — MB ChB 1996 Ed.

MORGAN, Kieran Francis Holdway Beach Wood Cottage, Lansdown, Bath BA1 9DB — MB BS 1971 Newc.; MFCM 1984; DCH RCPS Glas. 1973.

MORGAN, Kim 10 St Catherines Road, Winchester SO23 0PP — BM 1995 Soton.

MORGAN, Laleh Flat 121, South Block, County Hall, 1B Belvedere Road, London SE1 7GD Tel: 020 7787 2501 Email: finlal@dircon.co.uk — MB BS 1996 Lond.; BSc Lond. 1993. (St. Bart. Med. Coll.) SHO (Orthop.) St Mary's Hosp. Paddington. Socs: MDU. Prev: SHO (A & E) St. Mary's Hosp. Paddington; SHO (Orthop.) Stanmore Orthop. Hosp. Middlx.; Surg. HS The Roy. Lond. Hosp.

MORGAN, Mr Laurence Hugh 7 Bunkers Hill, Romiley, Stockport SK6 3DS — MB ChB 1977 Liverp.; FRCS Ed. 1983; MRCS Eng. LRCP Lond. 1977; FRCOphth 1993. (Liverpool) Cons. Ophth. Surg. Stepping Hill Hosp. Stockport. Prev: Sen. Regist. Manch. Roy. Eye Hosp.

MORGAN, Lelia Catherine Mary McCann and Morgan, Rathfriland Health Centre, John Street, Rathfriland, Newry BT34 5QH Tel: 028 4063 0666 Fax: 028 4063 1198 — MB BCh BAO 1987 NUI.

MORGAN, Leonard Jones (retired) Tanygraig, Llangefni LL77 7HR Tel: 01248 722211 — MB BS 1943 Lond.; MRCS Eng. LRCP Lond. 1943. Prev: Ho. Surg. Caern. & Anglesey Infirm. & Coventry & Warw. Hosp.

MORGAN, Lewis Bamford Kingsway Surgery, 37 The Kingsway, Swansea SA1 5LF Tel: 01792 650716 Fax: 01792 456902 — MB BCh 1975 Wales; DCH Eng. 1977; DRCOG 1979.

MORGAN, Lilian Margaret (retired) 5 St Arvans Close, Chepstow Rise, Croydon CR0 5UR Tel: 020 8681 2178 — BSc Wales 1945, MB BCh 1948; MFCM 1974; DPH Lond. 1960. Prev: Sen. Med. Off. Croydon AHA.

MORGAN, Linda Jean Southacre, Nottingham Road, Thurgarton, Nottingham NG14 7GZ — MB ChB Sheff. 1969; MRCPath 1992. Sen. Lect./Hon. Cons. Univ. Hosp. Nottm.

MORGAN, Linda Vivien King Street Surgery, 84 King Street, Maidstone ME14 1DZ Tel: 01622 756721/756722/3 — MB BS 1987 Lond.; DCH RCP Lond. 1991; DRCOG 1991.

MORGAN, Lindsay Gwynne, CStJ Glynteg, Park Road, Ynystawe, Swansea SA6 5AP Tel: 01792 843510 Fax: 01792 844866 — MB BS 1954 Lond.; DIH Soc. Apoth. Lond. 1961; FFOM RCP Lond. 1984, MFOM 1969. (Univ. Coll. Hosp.) Cons. Occupat. Health Swansea; JP. Socs: Fell. Roy. Soc. Med.; Soc. Occupat. Med. Prev: Chief Med. Off. INCO (Europe) Ltd. Clydach; Med. Off. i/c Radiolog. Servs. S. W.. Div. Nat. Coal Bd.; Med. Off. Richard Thomas & Baldwins Ltd.

MORGAN, Louise Gwendolen Gwyndy Farm, Bethel, Caernarfon LL55 1YD — MB ChB 1992 Leic.

MORGAN, Luke Conrad 112 High Street, Aldeburgh IP15 5AB — BM BS 1992 Nottm.

MORGAN, Lyndon Rees (retired) Sandymears, Tonkenfig, Pyle, Bridgend CF33 4PT Tel: 01656 745481 — MB ChB 1960 Ed. Clin. Asst. (Geriat. Med.) Cymla Hosp. Neath; Med. Off. BSC Port Talbot. Prev: Police Surg. Port Talbot.

MORGAN, Lynne Mary Belvoir Road Surgery, 99 Belvoir Road, Coalville LE67 3PH Tel: 01530 831331 Fax: 01530 833985; 30 Shepherds Close, Loughborough LE11 3LA Tel: 01509 214305 — MB ChB 1981 Leeds; MRCGP 1996.

MORGAN, Maher Guirguis Guindy Spring Gardens Health Centre, Providence Street, Worcester WR1 2BS Tel: 01905 681681 Fax: 01905 681699 — LRCP LRCS 1985 Ed.; MB BCh Ain-Shams 1977; LRCP LRCS Ed. LRCPS Glas. 1985.

MORGAN, Maldwyn 39 Gurney Drive, Hampstead Garden Suburb, London N2 0DF Tel: 020 8455 8682 Fax: 020 8209 0625 — MB BS Lond. 1961; FFA RCS Eng. 1966; DA Eng. 1963. (Middlx.) Reader in Clin. Anaesth. Roy. Postgrad. Med. Sch.; Hon. Cons. Anaesth. Hammersmith Hosp. Lond. Socs: Assn. Anaesths. Gt. Brit & Irel. & Anaesth. Research Soc. Prev: Sen. Regist. & Regist. Dept. Anaesth. Hammersmith Hosp. & Roy.; Postgrad. Med. Sch. Lond.; Regist. P. of Wales' Hosp. Tottenham.

MORGAN, Margaret (retired) Firwood House, 8 Eaglesham Road, Newton Mearns, Glasgow G77 5BG — MB ChB 1946 St. And.; BSc St. And. 1943. Prev: Assoc. Specialist W. of Scotl. Blood Transfus. Serv. Glas.

MORGAN, Margaret Eleanor Imogen Birmingham Women's Hospital, Edgbaston, Birmingham B15 2TG Tel: 0121 627 2749 Fax: 0121 627 2646; 26 Kingsley Road, Northampton NN2 7BL — MB ChB 1976 Glas.; FRCP Lond. 1993; FRCP Ch 1998; FRCP Glas. 1988; MRCP (UK) 1978; DCH Eng. 1979. Cons. Neonat. Paediat. Birm. Wom.'s Hosp.; Hon. Clin. Lect. Univ. Birm. Prev: Lect. (Child Health) Univ. Liverp.; Regist. (Paediat.) Roy. Hosp. Sick Childr. Edin.

MORGAN, Margaret Hilary (retired) 3 Downleaze, Stoke Bishop, Bristol BS9 1NB Tel: 0117 968 1143 — MB BChir 1959 Camb.; MD Bristol 1973; MA Camb. 1959; FRCP Lond. 1983, M 1967; MRCS Eng. LRCP Lond. 1959. Prev: Cons. EEG & Clin. Neurophysiol. Frenchay Healthcare Trust.

MORGAN, Margaret Joyce (retired) 5 Hill Park, Tenby SA70 8HX — MRCS Eng. LRCP Lond. 1939.

MORGAN, Margaret Mary 6 Malone Park, Londonderry BT47 5PE — MB BCh BAO 1986 NUI.

MORGAN, Margery Department Obstetrics & Gynaecology, Singleton Hospital, Sketty, Swansea SA2 8QA; Green Lane Farm, Pennard, Gower, Swansea SA3 2AD — MB ChB 1977 Sheff.; DM Nottm. 1990; MRCOG 1984. Cons. O & G Singleton Hosp. Swansea.

MORGAN, Marina Sian Department of Medical Microbiology, Public Health Laboratory, Church Lane, Exeter EX2 5AD Tel: 01392 402970 Fax: 01392 412835 — MB ChB 1985 Liverp. Cons. MicroBiol. (Med. MicroBiol.) Exeter Pub. Health Laborat.; Clin. Tutor Roy. Devon & Exeter Healthcare NHS Trust; Hon. Sen. Lect. Univ. Plymouth Postgrad. Med. Sch. Socs: Fell. Roy. Soc. Med.; Welsh Microbiol. Assn.; Assn. Clin. Pathol. (MicroBiol. Comm.). Prev: Lect. Univ. of Plymouth; Sen. Regist. (Med. MicroBiol.) Exeter Pub. Health Laborat.; Regist. (Med. MicroBiol.) Walton Hosp. Liverp.

MORGAN, Mark Andrew John 12 Fullers Field, Great Milton, Oxford OX44 7PJ — BM BCh 1993 Oxf.; DRCOG 1996. (Camb. & Oxf.) GP Regist. Oxf.

MORGAN, Mark Blond Fraser Avalon, Whitemore Road, Guildford GU1 1QT — MB BS 1989 Lond.

MORGAN, Mark Christopher Dean Lane Surgery, Dean Lane, Sixpenny Handley, Salisbury SP5 5PA Tel: 01725 552500; Doves Meadow Surgery, Broad Chalke, Salisbury SP5 5EL Tel: 01722 780282 — MB BS 1987 Lond.; FRCGP 1993. Prev: GP New St. Surg. Salisbury; Trainee GP Windsor VTS; SHO (ENT) Norf. & Norwich Hosp.

MORGAN, Marsha Yvonne Centre for Hepatology, Royal Free and University College Medical School, Pond St., London NW3 2QG Tel: 020 7433 2873 Fax: 020 7433 2870 — MB ChB 1969 Manch.; MB ChB (Distinc.) Manch. 1969; MRCP (UK) 1973; FRCP Lond. 1991. (Manchester University Medical School) Reader (Med.)

MORGAN

& Hon. Cons. Phys. Centre for Hepat. Roy. Free Campus, Lond. Socs: Brit. Soc. of Gastroenterol.; Med. Res. Soc.; Europ. Assn. for Study of the Liver. Prev: Hon. Sen. Lect. & Cons. Phys. Profess. Unit Roy. Free Hosp. Lond.; Lect. Med. Profess. Unit Roy. Free Hosp. Lond.; SHO (Haemat.) Hammersmith Hosp. Lond.

MORGAN, Mary Catherine (retired) Ty-Mawr, Aberffrwd Road, Mountain Ash CF45 4DD Tel: 01443 473438 — LRCPI & LM, LRCSI & LM 1958.

MORGAN, Mary Ruth c/o The Coach House, Kings Heanton, Barnstaple EX31 4ED — MB ChB 1992 Auckland.

***MORGAN, Mary Saleh** The Thatch, Cambridge Road, Ugley, Bishop's Stortford CM22 6HZ — MB BS 1998 Lond.; MB BS Lond. 1998.

***MORGAN, Matthew David** 76 Trevor Drive, Allington, Maidstone ME16 0QR — MB ChB 1995 Birm.; ChB Birm. 1995.

MORGAN, Maurice Tony (retired) Brookhurst, Winkfield Road, Ascot SL5 7LT Tel: 01344 883462 Email: mtmorgan@doctors.org.uk — MB BS Lond. 1956; DObst RCOG 1957. Prev: Ho. Phys. Univ. Coll. Hosp. Lond.

MORGAN, Michael Cottingham Medical Centre, 17-19 South Street, Cottingham HU16 4AJ Tel: 01482 845078 Fax: 01482 845078; 42 Riplingham Road, Kirk Ella, Hull HU10 7TP — MB ChB 1982 Dundee; MRCGP 1986.

MORGAN, Michael David Lane Glenfield Hospital, Groby Road, Leicester LE3 9QP Tel: 0116 287 1471; 14 Woodland Avenue, Stoneygate, Leicester LE2 3HG — MB BChir 1976 Camb.; MD Camb. 1984; FRCP Lond. 1992. Cons. Phys. (Respirat. Med.) Glenfield Gen. Hosp. Leicester; Hon. Sen. Lect. Univ. Leicester.

MORGAN, Michael George Microbiology Department, QEQMH, St Peter's Road, Margate CT9 4AN Tel: 01843 225544 Fax: 01843 234531 Email: mmorgan@bizonline.co.uk — MB BCh 1975 Ain Shams; FRCPske. 1999; MD Aberd. 1995; MRCPath 1991. Cons. Microbiol. Infec. Control Office, E. Kent Acute Trust. Socs: Hosp. Infec. Soc. & Brit. Soc. Study Infec. Prev: Sen. Regist. & Hon. Lect. (Microbiol.) Aberd. Hosps.(Univ. Aberd.); Regist. (Microbiol.) Roy. Free Hosp. Lond.; Cons (Microbiol.) Lanarksh. Acute Trust.

***MORGAN, Michael John** 24 West Mount, Wigan WN1 3PA — MB ChB 1998 Sheff.; MB ChB Sheff 1998.

MORGAN, Mr Michael Naunton 149 Harley Street, London W1 Tel: 020 8788 4913 — MRCS Eng. LRCP Lond. 1957; MChir Camb. 1966, MB 1958, BChir 1957; FRCS Eng. 1962. (Guy's) Cons. Surg. W.m. Hosp. Lond. Socs: Fell. Roy. Soc. Med. & Assn. Surgs. Gt. Brit. & N. Irel. Prev: Lect. (Surg.) & Sen. Regist. W.m. Hosp. Lond.; Clin. Asst. St. Mark's Hosp.

MORGAN, Michael Stanley The Surgery, Bull Yard, Simpson St., Spilsby PE23 — MB BS 1969 Lond. (Middlx.)

MORGAN, Mr Michael Watkin Edwards Little Acre, Back Lane, Sheering, Bishop's Stortford CM22 7NF Tel: 01279 725164 Fax: 01279 724346 Email: mikemorgan@btinternet.com — MB BCh Wales 1965; MD New York 1978; FRCS Eng. 1972. Cons. Surg. St. Margt. Hosp. Epping & P.ss Alexandra Hosp. Harlow. Prev: Surg. Fell. Memor. Sloane-Kettering Inst. NY USA; Sen. Regist. Roy. Marsden & St. Geo. Hosp. Lond.; Lect. Ludwig Inst. Lond.

MORGAN, Michael William Musgrave Burdwood Surgery, Wheelers Green Way, Thatcham RG19 4YF Tel: 01635 868006 Fax: 01635 867484 — MB ChB 1979 Bristol; BSc (Hons.) Bristol, 1979; DFFP 1994; DCH RCP Lond. 1986; DGM RCP Lond. 1986. (Bristol) GP; Sch. Med. Off. Downe Hse. Sch. Prev: Trainee GP Huntingdon VTS.

MORGAN, Myles Finnegan Flat 121, South Block, County Hall, 1B Belvedere Road, London SE1 7GD Tel: 020 7787 2501 Fax: 020 7787 2501 Email: finlal@dircon.co.uk — MB BS 1994 Lond.; BSc Lond. 1991; FRCS (Eng.) 1998. (St. Bart.) Research Fell. Dept. of Urol., Hammersmith Hosp. Socs: Fell. Roy. Soc. Med. Prev: SHO hammersmith Hosp. (Urol.); SHO Barnet Gen. Hosp. (Gen. Surg.); SHO (Gen. Surg.), IC, & Orthop.) Char. Cross Hosp. Lond.

MORGAN, Nader Khalil Westgate Surgery, 60 Westgate, Peterborough PE1 1RG Tel: 01733 562420 Fax: 01733 564081; 14 Thorpe Avenue, Longthorpe, Peterborough PE3 6LA — MB ChB 1966 Alexandria. Clin. Asst. (Psychiat.) P'Boro.

MORGAN, Natalie Jane Wycombe Child Mental Health Clinic, 2 Hamilton Road, High Wycombe HP13 5BW Tel: 01494 535727; Woodstock, Reade Ave, Abingdon OX14 3YE — MB ChB 1993 Manch.; MRC Psych 1999. SHO (Psychiat.) Wycombe child Ment.

health Clinic, Bucks. Prev: SHO Adult Psychiat. Littlemore Hosp. Oxf..; SHO Psychother. Warneford Hosp., Oxf.; SHO Psychiat. community alcohol Serv., Reading.

MORGAN, Natalie Rebecca Glynis Flat 78 Gloucester Green, Oxford OX1 2BU — BM BCh 1990 Oxf.

MORGAN, Natalie Sian 35 Fox Street, Treharris CF46 5HE — MB BCh 1994 Wales.

***MORGAN, Neal Anthony** 9 Malone View Park, Belfast BT9 5PN Tel: 01232 615391; 9 Malone View Park, Belfast BT9 5PN Tel: 01232 615391 — MB BCh BAO 1997 Belf.

MORGAN, Neil Davies Tavistock Clinic, 120 Belsize Lane, London NW3 5BA Tel: 020 7435 7111 Fax: 020 7447 3709 — MB ChB 1991 Bristol; PhD Lond. 1982, MSc 1978, BSc (Hons.) 1976; MRCPsych 1996. (Bristol) Specialist Regist. (Psychother.) Tavistock Clinic Lond. Socs: Eur. Assn. Hist. of Psychiat. Prev: Specialist Regist. (Psychiat.) Bristol; Ho. Phys. Bristol. Roy. Infirm.; Ho. Surg. S.mead Hosp.

MORGAN, Nicholas Hywel Flat 3 Trinity Grange, 319 Trinity Road, Wandsworth, London SW18 3SL — MB BS 1986 Lond.; BSc (Hons.) Wales 1980; FRCS Ed. 1991. (Char. Cross) Sen. Regist. St Geos. Hosp. Orthop. Rotat. Lond.

MORGAN, Mr Nicholas James West Wales General Hospital, Glangwili, Carmarthen SA31 2AF; Castell Mal, Llangynin, St Clears, Carmarthen SA33 4JU — MB BS 1980 Lond.; MSc Soton. 1986; FRCS (Orl) 1994; FRCS Ed. 1988. Cons. ENT Surg.

MORGAN, Mr Nicholas Vaughan, Surg. Cdr. RN 138 Wingfield Road, Stoke, Plymouth PL3 4ER — MB BS 1976 Lond.; FRCS Ed. 1985; Dip. Sports Med. Lond 1988.

MORGAN, Nicola Anne 12 Fuller's Field, Great Milton, Oxford OX44 7PJ Tel: 01844 279036 — BM BCh 1993 Oxf. Trainee GP/SHO Oxf. VTS.

MORGAN, Nicola Anne New Chapel Street Surgery, Harold Street, Pontnewydd, Cwmbran NP44 1DU Tel: 01633 485155 Fax: 01633 484133 — MB BCh 1990 Wales.

MORGAN, Nicola Jane 5 Bosworth Gardens, Woodley, Reading RG5 3RS — MB ChB 1988 Birm.; ChB Birm. 1988.

MORGAN, Nicola Katherine 88 Hoole Road, Hoole, Chester CH2 3NT Tel: 01244 351075; Flat 7, Acton House, Suffolk Square, Cheltenham GL50 2DT Tel: 01242 255632 — BM BS 1995 Nottm.; BMedSci. Nottm. 1993; MCPP Part 1 1997; FRCA Prim. 1999. SHO (Anaesth.) Cheltnm. Gen. Hosp.

MORGAN, Nicolette Mary Jean 101 Britannia Avenue, Nottingham NG6 0EA — BM BS 1993 Nottm.

MORGAN, Nigel Francis Anthony Dickson 11 Knivet Road, London SW6 1JR — MB BS 1981 Lond.

***MORGAN, Olivia Mary** 78 Fergort Road, Derrynoose, Armagh BT60 3DW — MB BCh 1998 Belf.; MB BCh Belf 1998.

***MORGAN, Patrick Gower** Enborne House, Bonemill Lane, Enborne, Newbury RG20 0EU — MB ChB 1998 Leic.; MB ChB Leic. 1998.

MORGAN, Patrick Reginald Felix, MBE Communicable Disease Control/Environmental Health Section, Directorate of Public Health Medicine, Northamptonshire HA, Highfield, Cliftonville Road, Northampton NN1 5DN Tel: 01604 615289 Fax: 01604 615295; The Old Rectory, Warmington, Peterborough PE8 6TQ Tel: 01832 280277 Fax: 01832 280165 — MB BS 1969 Lond.; MSc Lond. 1979; MRCS Eng. LRCP Lond. 1969; MFFP 1993; FFPHM RCP (UK) 1990; MFCM 1984. (King's Coll. Hosp. Lond.) Cons. Communicable Dis. Control. N.ants. HA; Med. Lead Family Plann. Socs: Pub. Health Med. Environm. Health Gp. Prev: Cons. Pub. Health Med. Kettering HA; Sen. Med. Off. (Pub. Health), Malawi Afr.; Med. Off. Health, Turks & Caicos Is.s, W. Indies.

MORGAN, Paul 21 Ffordd Cwellyn, Cardiff CF23 5NB Tel: 029 2049 7621 Email: paul@drmorgan.force9.net — MB BCh 1985 Wales; FRCA 1991. Cons. Anaesth. Univ. Hosp. Wales Cardiff. Socs: Assn. Anaesth.; Intens. Care Soc. Prev: Sen. Regist. (Anaesth.) Stoke Sch. of Anaesth.; Regist. (Anaesth.) Univ. Hosp. Wales Cardiff; Resid. Med. Off. BUPA Hosp. Cardiff & Research Fell. Univ. Hosp. Wales.

MORGAN, Paul Gregory 344 Cwmbach Road, Fforestfach, Swansea SA5 4QA — MB BS 1977 Lond.

MORGAN, Peter 15 Jesmond Park W., Newcastle upon Tyne NE7 7BU Tel: 0191 281 2968 Fax: 01661 825253 Email: jenninicholson.domain@quista.net — MB BS 1955 Durh.; BSc

MORGAN

Durham. 1950; FRCPsych 1976; DPM Durham. 1959. (Durh.) Cons. Psychiat. Socs: BMA; Fell.Roy. Coll. Psychiat. Prev: Med. Dir. & Cons. Psychiat. Lindisfarne Unit Newc. Nuffield Hosp.; Cons. Psychiat. Newc. Univ. Hosps.; SHO (Psychol. Med.) Newc. Gen. Hosp.

MORGAN, Peter John Patrick Church Road Surgery, Church Road, Kyle IV40 8DD Tel: 01599 534257 Fax: 01599 534107; Cooper Street, Plockton IV52 8TJ — MB ChB Bristol 1970; MRCGP 1988; DRCOG 1976. (Bristol)

MORGAN, Peter Woodnoth St. James University Hosp., Beckett Street, Leeds LS9 7TF — MB ChB 1990 Leeds; FRCA 1996. Cons. Anaesth.

MORGAN, Philip Arthur Peter 11 Gleneagle Drive, Blackwell, Bromsgrove B60 1BD — MB ChB 1985 Leic.

MORGAN, Philip David 171 Prestbury Road, Cheltenham GL52 2DU — MB ChB 1971 Birm.

MORGAN, Philip Denzil 27 Sunningdale, Caerphilly CF83 1BB — MB BCh 1990 Wales.

MORGAN, Philip Robert Porthdafach, Rhos Lane, Bethel, Caernarfon — MB ChB 1984 Liverp.

MORGAN, Rhiannon (retired) Lyndale, Alexandra Road, Abergavenny NP7 5RL — MB BS Lond. 1949; MRCS Eng. LRCP Lond. 1944; MFCM 1973; DPH Wales 1958.

***MORGAN, Rhiannon Meleri Llinos** 23 Greenfield Avenue, Canton, Cardiff CF11 9PT — MB BS 1996 Lond.

MORGAN, Rhodrey Nigel Wynne Department of Anaesthesia, Singleton Hospital, Sketty Lane, Swansea SA2 8QA Tel: 01792 285427 Fax: 01792 285427 Email: cars.morgan@cableol.co.uk — MB BS 1973 Lond.; MRCS Eng. LRCP Lond. 1973; FFA RCS Eng. 1977; DA Eng. 1975. (Char. Cross) Cons. Anaesth. Singleton Hosp. Swansea. Prev: Clin. Dir. & Cons. Anaesth. Neath Gen. Hosp.; Cons. (Anaesth.) Groote Schuur Hosp. Capetown, S. Afr.; Sen. Regist. (Anaesth.) Char. Cross Hosp. Lond.

MORGAN, Richard The Surgery, Grove St., Petworth GU28 0LP Tel: 01798 42248 — MB BS 1971 Lond.; MRCGP 1976; DObst RCOG 1973; DCH Eng. 1974. (St. Geo.)

MORGAN, Richard Hugh Blythe Practice, 1500 Warwick Road, Knowle, Solihull B93 9LE Tel: 01564 779280 Fax: 01564 771224; 5 Leam Terrace, Leamington Spa CV31 1BB Tel: 01926 421210 — MB BS 1978 Lond.; MRCGP 1983. Clin. Asst. (Ophth.) Birm. & Midl. Eye Hosp. Socs: Brit. Ophth. Photogr. Assn. Prev: SHO (O & G) Solihull Hosp.; SHO (Gastroenterol. & Paediat.) E. Birm. Hosp.

MORGAN, Mr Richard Hywel City General Hospital, Newcastle Road, Stoke-on-Trent ST4 6QG Tel: 01782 715444 — MB BCh 1979 Wales; MD Wales 1989; FRCS Eng. 1985; FRCS Ed. 1985. Hon. Sen. Lect. (Surg.) City Gen. Hosp. Stoke-on-Trent.

MORGAN, Richard John Hope Hospital, Salford M6 8HD Tel: 0161 789 7373; 72 Leigh Road, Hale, Altrincham WA15 9BD — MB ChB 1982 Leeds; FCAnaesth 1990; DA (UK) 1987; DRCOG 1985. Cons. Anaesth. Hope Hosp. Salford. Socs: Anaesth. Res. Soc.; Manch. Med. Soc. Prev: Regist. (Anaesth.) Manch. Roy. Infirm.; SHO (O & G) & Ho. Off. (Gen. Surg.) St. Luke's Hosp. Bradford.

MORGAN, Richard John Hugh Children's Centre, Royal Glamorgan Hospital, Llantrisant, Pontyclun CF72 8XR Tel: 01443 443534 Fax: 01443 443223 Email: john.morgan@pr-tr.wales.nhs.uk; 10 Y Parc, Groesfaew, Pontyclun CF72 8NP — MB BCh 1971 Wales; FRCP Lond. 1992; MRCP (UK) 1977; DCH RCP Lond. 1974; DObst RCOG 1973. (Welsh National School of Medicine) Cons. Paediat. Roy. Glamrogan Hosp. Pontypridd and Rhondda NHS Trust. Socs: Pres. Welsh Paediat. Soc.; Rhondda Med. Soc.; Off. to Wales Roy. Coll. Paediatr. and Child Health. Prev: Sen. Regist. (Paediat.) Univ. Hosp. Wales Cardiff; Regist. (Neonat. Med.) St. Mary's Hosp. Manch.; Regist. (Paediat.) Duchess York Hosp. for Babies Manch.

MORGAN, Richard John Metcalf Department of Anaesthesia and Intensive Care, Blackpool Victoria Hospital NHS Trust, Whinney Heyes Road, Blackpool FY3 8NR Tel: 01253 303499 Email: dr.morgan@bvh-tr.nwest.nhs.uk — MB BS 1976 Lond.; MRCS Eng. LRCP Lond. 1976; FFA RCS Eng. 1982. (St. Mary's) p/t Cons. Anaesth. (ICU) Blackpool Vict. Hosp. Blackpool. Socs: BMA; ICS; AAGBI. Prev: Cons. Anaesth.James Paget Hosp. Gorleston on Sea.

MORGAN, Richard Julian 91 Higher Lane, Lymm WA13 0BZ — MB ChB 1988 Manch.; MRCP (UK) 1992.

MORGAN, Richard Neil 25 Oxford Way, Wellesbourne, Warwick CV35 9LN — MB BS 1974 Melbourne.

MORGAN, Robert Anthony Department of Radiology, St George's Hospital, Blackshaw Road, London SW17 0QT Tel: 020 8725 1481 Fax: 020 8725 2936 Email: robert.morgan@ndstgh-tr.sthomas.nhs.uk; 3 Spencer Road, Chiswick, London W4 3SS — MB ChB 1983 Bristol; MRCP (UK) 1987; FRCR 1991. (Bristol) Cons. Radiolgist St. Geo.'s Hosp. Lond. Prev: Cons. Radiol. St Mary's Hosp. Lond.; Lect. (Interven. Radiol.) Guy's & St Thomas' Hosp. Lond.; Clin. Instructer (Radiol.) Univ. Texas Galveston, USA.

MORGAN, Robert David Bryn-y-Wawr, Pentre CF41 7DZ; Vaynor, High St, New Quay SA45 9NY Tel: 01545 560203 — MB BS 1989 Lond.; MRCGP 1993; DRCOG 1992.

MORGAN, Mr Robert John 147 Harley Street, London W1G 6BL Tel: 020 7935 4444 Fax: 020 7486 3782; 36 Highgate West Hill, London N6 6LS Tel: 020 8340 8769 Fax: 020 8342 9847 — BM BCh 1966 Oxf.; MA Oxf. 1966; FRCS Eng. 1972. (Oxf. & Guy's) Cons. Urol. Surg. Roy. Free Hosp. Lond.; Hon. Cons. Urol St. Luke's Hosp. for Clergy & Hosp. St. John & St. Eliz. Lond. & King Edwd. VII Hosp. for Offs.; Hon. Sen. Lect. (Surg.) Roy. Free and Univ. Coll. Sch. of Med. Socs: Brit. Assn. Urol. Surgs. (Ex-Hon. Sec. & Ex-Counc. Mem.); Fell. Roy. Soc. Med. (Mem. Counc. Sect. Urol. and Pres. Elect.). Prev: Cons. Urol. Whittington Hosp. Lond.; Hon. Cons. Urol. St. Peter's Hosps. Lond.; Sen. Lect. (Urol.) Inst. Urol. Univ. Lond.

MORGAN, Robert Owen Tyn-y-Coed Surgery, 20 Merfield Close, Bryncethin, Bridgend CF32 9SW Tel: 01656 720334 Fax: 01656 721998; 13 Newborough Avenue, Llanishen, Cardiff CF14 5BY Tel: 01222 764105 — MB ChB 1992 Birm.; B ChB Birm. 1992; PhD Cardiff 1987, BSc 1984; MRCGP 1996; DRCOG 1996; DFFP 1995. SHO (Geriat.) Univ. Hosp. Wales Cardiff.

MORGAN, Roger 84 Greyhound Farm Road, Liverpool L24 3TR — MB ChB 1992 Sheff.

MORGAN, Roger Harold (retired) 33 Wingate Way, Cambridge CB2 2HD Tel: 01223 840166 — LMSSA 1953 Lond.; MD Camb. 1966, MB BChir 1953. Prev: Regist. Off. Nursing Homes Camb. HA.

MORGAN, Roger James 25 Holme Park Avenue, Upper Newbold, Chesterfield S41 8XB; Department of Obstetrics, Jessop Hospital For Women, Sheffield S3 7RE Tel: 0114 276 6333 — MB ChB Leeds 1969. Assoc. Specialist (O & G) Centr. Sheff. Univ. Hosps. Jessop Hosp. for Wom.

MORGAN, Roger John Northampton General Hospital, Billring Road, Northampton NN1 5RB Tel: 01604 634700 Fax: 01604 235556 — MB ChB 1971 Leeds; MD Leeds 1985; FRCP Lond. 1996; MRCP (UK) 1977; DA Eng. 1973. (Leeds) Cons. Phys. & Geriat. N.ampton Gen. Hosp. Socs: Brit. Soc. Gastroenterol.; Brit. Geriat. Soc.; BMA. Prev: Sen. Regist. (Gen. Med. & Geriat.) Roy. Devon & Exeter Hosp.; Regist. (Gen. Med. & Gastroenterol.) Glas. Roy. Infirm.

MORGAN, Ronald Frank 98 Pye Corner, Gilston, Harlow CM20 2RD — MB ChB Sheff. 1970; FRCP Lond. 1994; MRCP (UK) 1982; Dip Palliat Med 2000 University of Wales. (Univ. Sheff.) Cons. Phys. (Med. for Elderly) P.ss Alexandra Hosp. NHS Trust. Socs: Brit. Geriat. Soc.; Tissue Viability Soc.; RSM. Prev: Med. Dir. Essex & Herts. Community NHS Trust; Lect. (Geriat. Med.) St. Bart. Hosp. Lond.; Regist. (Med.) Barnet Gen. Hosp. Lond.

MORGAN, Rosemary — MB BCh 1989 Wales; BSc (Hons.) Med. Biol. St. And. 1985; MRCP (UK) 1992. Cons. Phys. (Geriat. Med.) Arrow Pk. Hosp. Wirral. Socs: Brit. Geriat. Soc.; Brit. Soc. for Gastroenterol. Prev: Sen. Regist. (Gen. Med.) Stepping Hill Hosp. Stockport; Sen. Regist. (Geriat. Med.) Withington Hosp. Manch.; Regist. (Med.) BRd.green Hosp. Liverp.

MORGAN, Rowland Jones (retired) 5 High Lea, Cheadle SK8 1NY Tel: 0161 428 7262 Fax: 0161 428 7262 Email: row@onetel.net.uk — MB BS 1953 Lond.; MRCS Eng. LRCP Lond. 1953; MRCGP 1965; DObst RCOG 1955. Prev: Princip. GP Cheadle.

MORGAN, Ruth Esther Eisai Limited, 3 Shortlands, London W6 8EE Tel: 020 8600 1450 Fax: 020 8600 1401; Flat 1, Coleraine House, 21-22 Nassau St, London W1W 7AB Tel: 020 7323 4988 — MB BS 1993 Lond.; BPharm (Hons.) Lond. 1987; DRCOG 1996; DCH RCP Lond. 1995; MRCGP 1998. (St. Geo. Hosp. Med. Sch.) Med. Adviser Eisai Ltd. Lond.; Hon. Clin. Asst. Old Age Psychiat., Whiltington Hosp. Prev: GP/Regist. Lond.; Trainee GP/SHO Whittington Hosp. Lond.

MORGAN

MORGAN, Mr Salathiel Penrhyn, Penllwyn Park, Carmarthen SA31 3BU Tel: 01267 7148 — MB BCh 1943 Wales; BSc, MB BCh Wales 1943; FRCS Ed. 1948. (Cardiff) Cons. ENT Surg. Mid. & W. Wales. Socs: Fell. Roy. Soc. Med. (Mem. Laryng. & Otol. Sects.). Prev: Ho. Surg. Ophth. Dept. & Regist. ENT Dept. Roy. Infirm. Cardiff; Maj. RAMC, ENT Specialist 1944-7.

MORGAN, Sally Ann Department of Oncology, City Hospital, Hucknall Road, Nottingham NG5 1PB Tel: 0115 969 1169 Ext: 46053 Fax: 0115 840 2616 Email: smorgan@ncht.trent.nhs.uk — MB BS 1979 Lond.; MA Camb. 1979; MRCP (UK) 1982; FRCR 1985. (Middlx.) Cons. Clin. Oncol. City Hosp. Nottm.

***MORGAN, Sally Anne** 34 Westbourne Road, Sheffield S10 2QQ — MB ChB 1993 Sheff.

MORGAN, Sally Anne Community Child Health Unit, Livingstone Hospital, East Hill, Dartford DA1 1SA Tel: 01322 622343; 17 New Road, Meopham, Gravesend DA13 0LS Tel: 01474 815064 Email: mogandbints@msn.com — BM 1985 Soton.; DCH RCP Lond. 1988; DCCH RCP Ed. 1988. (Univ. Soton.) Staff Grade (Community Paediat.) Kent. Socs: Assoc. Mem. BPA.

MORGAN, Sarah Louise Hampstead Group Practice, 75 Fleet Road, London NW3 2QU Tel: 020 7435 4000 Fax: 020 7435 9000 — MB ChB 1990 Manch.

MORGAN, Sarah Margaret Central Health Clinic, Mulberry St., Sheffield S1 2PJ; Beech Dene, Brookhouse Hill, Sheffield S10 3TE — MRCS Eng. LRCP Lond. 1979. Clin. Med. Off. Centr. Health Clinic Sheff.

MORGAN, Sarah Mary Four Elms Medical Centres, 103 Newport Road, Cardiff CF24 0AF Tel: 029 2048 5526 Fax: 029 2048 2871 — MB BCh 1976 Wales; LLM.

MORGAN, Sharon Ann 67C Station Road, Greeisland, Carrickfergus BT38 8UP — MB BCh BAO 1990 Belf.; MRCGP 1994; DRCOG 1993; DGM RCP Lond. 1992.

MORGAN, Sian Cathryn 1 Shropshire Road, Pembroke Dock SA72 6EF — MB ChB 1991 Bristol.

MORGAN, Simon James Scott Dept. of Ophthalmology, Univ. Hospital, Heath Park, Cardiff CF14 4XN — MB BCh 1992 Wales; BSc (Physiol.) Wales 1989; MRCP (UK) 1995; FRCS Ed 1999; FRCOphth 1999. (Univ. Wales Coll. Med.) Specialist Regist. Prev: SHO (Opthop.) St. James Univ. Hosp. Leeds; Resid. Med. Off. Greymouth, NZ; SHO (Neurol. & Med.) Qu. Med. Centre Nottm.

MORGAN, Stephen Aldermoor Health Centre, Aldermoor Close, Southampton SO16 5ST Tel: 02380 797700 — MB BChir 1989 Camb.; MRCGP 1994. Research Fell. Soton. Prev: GP Soton.; Trainee GP Soton.

MORGAN, Stephen Hugh Department of Renal Medicine, Basildon Hospital, Nether Mayne, Basildon SS16 5NL Tel: 01268 533911 Fax: 01268 593196 — MB BS 1977 Lond.; MD Lond. 1991; MRCS Eng. LRCP Lond. 1977; FRCP Lond. 1996; MRCP (UK) 1981; T(M) 1991. (St. Mary's) Cons. Renal Phys. Basildon & S.end Hosps. Essex; Hon. Sen. Lect. Inst. Urol. & Nephrol. Middlx. Hosp. Lond. Socs: Roy. Soc. Med.; Intens. Care Soc.; Eur. Dialysis & Transpl. Assn. Prev: Cons. Renal Phys. & Dir. (IC) Mayday Hosp. Croydon; Sen. Regist. (Med. & Nephrol.) St. Geo.'s Hosp. Lond.; Hon. Sen. Regist. (Med.) N.wick Pk. Hosp. Harrow.

MORGAN, Mr Stephen John Sunderland Eye Infirmary, Queen Alexandra Road, Sunderland SR2 9HP Tel: 0191 569 9279 Fax: 0191 5699060 Email: stephen.morgan@chs.northy.nhs.uk — MB 1982 Camb.; MB BChir Camb. 1982; MA Camb. 1982; FRCS (Ophth.) Ed. 1987; FRCOphth. 1988; DO RCS Eng. 1985. (Camb. & St.Thos. Lond.) Cons. Ophth. Sunderland Eye Infirm. & Univ. Hopsital of N. Durh. Socs: Brit. Soc. of Refractive Surg.; Med. Contact Lens and Ocular Surface Assn.; The Bowman Club. Prev: Sen. Regist. Soton. Eye Hosp. & Qu. Alexandra Hosp. Portsmouth; Regist. (Ophth.) Newc. Gen. Hosp.; SHO (Ophth.) Croydon Eye Unit.

MORGAN, Stephen Vincent St Georges Hospital, Blackshaw Road, Tooting, London SW17 0QT Tel: 020 8672 1255; 21 Foresters Crescent, Bexleyheath DA7 4JW Email: sumorgan@aol.com — MB BS 1990 Lond.; BSc (1st cl. Hons.) Pharmacol. Lond. 1987, MB BS 1990; MRCP (UK) 1994; FRCR 1998. (Charing Cross & Westminster) Regist. (Diag. Radiol.) St. Geo. Healthcare Trust Lond.

MORGAN, Steven John Heath Lane Surgery, Earl Shilton, Leicester LE9 7PB Tel: 01455 844431 — MB BS 1982 Lond.; MRCGP 1986.

MORGAN, Stuart Robert Ewing The Surgery, 1 Rowner Road, Gosport PO13 9UA Tel: 023 9258 0093 Fax: 023 92 504060; Glebe House, 26 Goldfinch Lane, Lee-on-the-Solent PO13 8LN — BM 1986 Soton.; MRCGP 1990; DRCOG 1988.

MORGAN, Susan Constance Rock Dale, Mount Pleasant Road, Weald, Sevenoaks TN14 6PS — MB BS 1980 Lond.; MRCP (UK) 1985.

MORGAN, Susan Deborah 79 Clarence Road, Moseley, Birmingham B13 9UH — MB ChB 1993 Birm.

MORGAN, Susan Jane Clifton Surgery, 151-153 Newport Road, Roath, Cardiff CF24 1AG Tel: 029 2049 4539 Fax: 029 2049 4657 Email: susan.morgan@gp-w97060.wales.nhs.uk; 22 Ty Draw Road, Roath, Cardiff CF23 5HB Tel: 029 2046 3608 Fax: 01222 494657 — MB BCh Wales 1974. Socs: Cardiff Med. Soc.; Rhondda Med. Soc.

MORGAN, Susan Lara Compton House, High St., Compton, Newbury RG20 6NJ Tel: 01635 578328 — BM 1993 Soton.; BSc Soton. 1992. SHO (Histopath.) Centr. Path. Laborat. Stoke-on-Trent.

MORGAN, Susan Mary TY Olwen, Morriston Hospital, Swansea NHST, Swansea SA6 6NL Tel: 01792 703412 Fax: 01792 703695; 17 Gwerneinon Road, Drerwen Fawr, Swansea SA2 8EN — MB BCh 1993 Wales; BMedSci (Hons.) Wales 1993. (University of Wales) Staff Grade Palliat. Med. Tyolwen, Morriston Hosp. Swansea NHST; Staff Grade Radiother. Singleton Hosp. Prev: SHO med. P. Philip Hosp. LLa.lli; SHO Oncol. Clatterbridge Centre for Oncol., Bebington Wirrail; SHO med. W. Wales gen. Hospl Carmerthen.

MORGAN, Sydney Donald (retired) 15 Colcot Road, Barry CF62 8HJ Tel: 01446 737260 — MB BS Lond. 1953.

MORGAN, Thomas Keith Dan-y-Coed, Brynaman, Ammanford SA18 1SH Tel: 01269 822222 — MB BS 1942 Lond.; MRCS Eng. LRCP Lond. 1941; DMRT Eng. 1947. (Middlx.) Prev: Cons. Radiotherap. Roy. S. Hants Hosp. Soton.; Surg. Regist. Cas. Surg. Off. & Demonst. Anat. Middlx. Hosp.

MORGAN, Thomas William Lewis Greenways, Dorchester Road, Hook RG27 9DW Tel: 01256 762795 Email: tom.morgy@demon.co.uk — MB BS 1992 Lond.; DRCOG 1997; MRCGP 1997. (Charing Cross and Westminster) GP. Prev: SHO O & G Frimley Pk.. Hosp; SHO med.Oncol. Char. Cross.Hosp.Lond; SHO Neurol.Char. Cross hosp.Lond.

MORGAN, Mr Timothy Richard Martyn Teesside Hospice Care Foundation, 1 Northgate Road, Linthorpe, Middlesbrough TS5 5NW Tel: 01642 819819 Fax: 01642 823034 — MB ChB 1983 Ed.; BSc (Med. Sci.) (Hons.) St. And. 1980; FRCS Glas. 1993. Med. Dir. & Cons. Palliat. Med. Teesside Hospice Care Foundat.; Hon. Cons. S. Tees Acute NHS Trust. Prev: Acting Med. Dir. Highland Hospice Inverness; Regist. Rotat. (Gen. Surg.) Raigmore Hosp. Inverness; Regist. (Surg.) Aberd. Roy. Infirm.

MORGAN, Trevor Anthony 39 Monastery Drive, Solihull B91 1DW — BM 1986 Soton.; BDS (Hons.) Lond. 1980; MRCP (UK) 1992.

MORGAN, Valerie Glynteg, Park Road, Ynystawe, Swansea SA6 5AP — MB BCh 1953 Wales; BSc Wales 1950, MB BCh 1953; DPM Eng. 1960. Assoc. Specialist (Psychogeriat.) Cefn Coed Hosp. Swansea.

MORGAN, Vera Ellen (retired) 58 Mount Pleasant Street, Trecynon, Aberdare CF44 8NG Tel: 01685 871712 — MB BS 1945 Lond.; DObst RCOG 1948. Prev: Med. Off. Baptist Miss. Hosps. Palwal, & Bhiwani, India.

MORGAN, Wayne Fitzalan Medical Centre, Fitzalan Road, Littlehampton BN17 5JR Tel: 01903 733288 Fax: 01903 733773; Tegleaze, 18 Torton Hill Road, Arundel BN18 9HE Tel: 01903 882010 — MB BCh 1975 Wales; MRCGP 1983. Prev: Regist. (Geriat. Med.) Univ. Hosp. Wales Cardiff; SHO (A & E) Roy. Hants. Co. Hosp. Winchester.

MORGAN, Wilfred Stewart Ramsey House, The Street, Bessingham, Norwich NR11 7JR Tel: 0126 377226 — MB BS 1944 Lond.; DPM Eng. 1966. (Guy's) Prev: Assoc. Specialist (Psychiat.) Old Manor Hosp. Salisbury; GP Princip. Hockley Essex; Capt. RAMC.

MORGAN, William David Glanrhyd Surgery, Riverside, Beaufort, Ebbw Vale NP23 5NU Tel: 01495 301210 Fax: 01633 350684; Llangattock Park House, Llangattock, Crickhowell NP8 1LD Tel: 01873 811242 Fax: 01873 812254 Email: w.d.morgan@virgin.net — MB BCh 1972 Wales. (Cardiff) Prev: Regtl. Med. Off. 49 Field Regt. RA Hohne.

MORGAN, Mr William Ellis Southacre, Thurgarton, Nottingham NG14 7GZ — MB ChB 1969 Sheff.; FRCS Eng. 1976; FRCS Ed. 1976. Cons. Thoracic Surg. City Hosp. Nottm. Prev: Sen. Regist. (Cardiothoracic Surg.) St. Thos. Hosp., Brook Hosp. & St. Geo. Hosp. Lond.; Regist. (Cardiothoracic Surg.) N.. Gen. Hosp. Sheff.

MORGAN, William Howell 68 Longlands Road, Carlisle CA3 9AE Tel: 01228 387728 — MB ChB 1952 Ed.

MORGAN, William Iain Craig St. Thomas Health Centre, Cowick St., Exeter EX4 1HJ Tel: 01392 278031 Fax: 01392 495114; The Butler's Lodge, Dry Lane, Christow, Exeter EX6 7PE — MB BChir 1971 Camb.; MA Camb. 1971; DObst RCOG 1972. (Camb. & Kings Coll. Hosp. Lond.) Chief Med. Advisor Exeter Friendly Soc. Socs: Assur. Med. Soc.; Assn. BRd.casting Doctors. Prev: Med. Off. Mowbray Matern. Hosp. Exeter; SHO (Respirat. Med.) Tehidy Hosp. Camborne; Ho. Off. & SHO (O & G) King's Coll. Hosp. Lond.

MORGAN, Mr William John 11 Court Crescent, Bassaleg, Newport NP10 8NJ — MB ChB 1970 Ed.; FRCS Ed. 1975. Cons. (A & E) Roy. Gwent Hosp. Newport.

MORGAN, Mr Wyn Price Royal Lancaster Infirmary, Ashton Road, Lancaster LA1 4RP — MB ChB 1971 Ed.; BSc Ed. 1969, ChM 1985, MB ChB 1971; FRCS Eng. 1977. Cons. Gen. Surg. Lancaster & S. Cumbria HA. Prev: Sen. Lect. & Cons. Roy. Hallamsh. Hosp. Sheff.; Sen. Regist. S. & W. Glam. HAs.; Sen. Regist. P. of Wales Hosp. Sydney, Australia.

MORGAN-CAPNER, Kay Crow Trees, Melling, Carnforth LA6 2QZ — MB BS 1971 Lond.; MRCS Eng. LRCP Lond. 1970.

MORGAN-CAPNER, Professor Peter Trust Headquarters, Chorley & South Ribble District Hospital, Preston Road, Chorley PR7 1PP Tel: 01257 248304 Fax: 01257 245309 Email: peter.morgan-capner@csrtr.nhs.uk; Crow Trees, Melling, Carnforth LA6 2QZ Tel: 01524 221241 Fax: 01524 221632 Email: pete.m-c@virgin.net — MRCS Eng. LRCP Lond. 1971; MB BS (Hons.) Lond. 1971; BSc (Hons.) Lond. 1968; 2000 Hon. FFPHM; FRCPath 1992, M 1980; FRCP 2000. (St. Mary's) Med. Dir., Preston Acute Hosp.s NHS Trust, Charley & S. Ribble NHS Trust Presteon and Charley; Cons. Virol. Preston Hosp.; Hon. Prof. Clin. Virol. Prev: Gp. Dir. Pub. Health Laborat. Servs. NW; Sen. Lect. (Virol.) King's Coll. Hosp. Lond.

MORGAN-GRAY, Karen Jennifer 60 Shefford Road, Clifton, Shefford SG17 5RQ — MB BS 1983 Lond.; LMSSA Lond. 1981; MRCPsych 1989.

MORGAN-HOUGH, Mrs Clare Vanessa June 82 Old Penkridge Road, Cannock WS11 1HY — MB BS 1994 Lond.; BSc 1991 London; FRCS 1998 England. (Kings College London) p/t Specialist Regist. (Trauma & Orthop.) OsW.ry & Stoke; N. Staffs Infirm./City Gen. Stoke-on-Trent. Socs: BOA. Prev: Rjah Hosp., OsW.ry; Kent & Sussex Hosp., Tunbridge Weus; Maidstone Hosp., Maidstone Kent.

MORGAN-HUGHES, Gareth James 18 Colney Lane, Cringleford, Norwich NR4 7RE — BM BS 1991 Nottm.

MORGAN-HUGHES, John Alun Private Consulting Room, The National Hospital, 23 Queen Sqaure, London Tel: 020 7833 8658; 14 Ibis Lane, Hartington Road, Chiswick, London W4 3UP Tel: 020 8995 6691 — MD 1966 Camb.; BA Camb. 1954, MD 1966, MB 1958, BChir 1957; FRCP Lond. 1975 M 1961. (St. Bart.) Cons. Emerit. Nat. Hosp. For Neurol. & NeroSurg. Qu. Sq. Lond. WCIN 3BG; Hon. Sen. Res. Fell. Inst. Neurol. Qu. Sq.; Hon. Phys. Bedford Gen. Hosp. Socs: Fell. Roy. Soc. Med.; Assn. Brit. Neurols. Prev: Lect. Univ. Dept. of Clin. Neurol. Nat. Hosp. Qu. Sq.; Postdoctoral Research Fell. Nat. Insts. of Health, Bethesda, USA; Resid. Med. Off. Nat. Hosp. Nerv. Dis. Qu. Sq.

MORGAN-HUGHES, John Oakely (retired) 18 Colney Lane, Cringleford, Norwich NR4 7RE Tel: 01603 451514 Fax: 01603 451514 Email: jmorganhughes@hotmail.com — MB BChir 1962 Camb.; BA Camb. 1962; FFA RCS Eng. 1965; DA Eng. 1963. Prev: Cons. Anaesth. Norf. & Norwich Hosp.

MORGAN-HUGHES, Nicholas John 1 Croft Top, New Hey Road, Outland, Huddersfield HD3 3FA — MB ChB 1986 Leeds; MRCP (UK) 1989.

MORGAN-JONES, David John, MBE, Lt.-Col. RAMC The Defence Medical Services Training Centre, Keogh Barracks, Mychett, Aldershot Tel: 01252 340251; 69 Wakefords Park, Church Crookham, Fleet GU52 8EZ — MB BS 1984 Lond.; MRCGP 1990; DMCC 1996. (St Mary's Hospital Medical School) Chief Instruc. The Defence Med. Servs. Train. Centre Aldershot.

MORGAN-JONES, David Vincent (retired) 15 Kings End, Ruislip HA4 7DE — MRCS Eng. LRCP Lond. 1942; MRCP Lond. 1949; DCH Eng. 1950; MSc 1999 London; BSc 1997 O.U. Asst. Phys. Colindale Hosp; Treasury Med. Off.; Apptd. Fact. Doctor; Med. Ref. Pruden. Assur. Co. Prev: Hon. Phys. & Hon. Surg. Port Talbot Gen. & Dist. Hosp.

MORGAN-JONES, Mr Rhidian Lyn Laurel House, Tetchill, Ellesmere SY12 9AP — MB BCh 1989 Wales; FRCS Ed. 1993. Regist. Rotat. (Orthop.) OsW.ry.

MORGANS, Mr Brian Thomas, QHP, Air Commodore RAF Med. Br. House 12, Royal Hospital Haslar, Haslar Road, Gosport PO12 2AA Tel: 02392 762962 Fax: 02392 762962; Quantock House, 12 Greens Lane, Wroughton, Swindon SN4 0RJ — MB BCh Wales 1965; FRCS Ed. 1994; FRCS Glas. 1972; FRCS 1997. Cons. Surg. Roy. Hosp. Haslar; Cade Prof. Surg. RCS. Socs: Fell. Roy. Soc. Med.; Brit. Assn. Urol. Prev: Cons. Surg. RAF Hosp. Wroughton.

***MORGANS, Clare Louise** 8 Cliffside Gardens, Leeds LS6 2HA Tel: 0113 278 9692 — MB ChB 1997 Leeds.

MORGANS, Colin Maurice (retired) 13 Spencer Road, Southsea PO4 9RN Tel: 01705 828347 — MB BChir 1963 Camb.; MB Camb. 1963, BChir 1962; MA Camb. 1963; FRCP Lond. 1979; M 1967; DObst RCOG 1964. Prev: Cons. Phys. Portsmouth Gp. Hosps.

***MORGANS, Donna Louise** 137 Kenny Street, Tonypandy CF40 1DD — MB BCh 1993 Wales.

MORGANS, Gerald Palmer Silverdale Medical Centre, Vale Pleasant, Silverdale, Newcastle ST5 6PS Tel: 01782 612375 Fax: 01782 714036 — MB ChB 1977 Birm.; MRCGP 1983; DRCOG 1982.

MORGANS, Julian Palmer Prestwood Road West Surgery, 81 Prestwood Road West, Wednesfield, Wolverhampton WV11 1HT Tel: 01902 721021 Fax: 01902 306225; 3 Wincote Drive, Wolverhampton WV6 8LR — MB ChB 1979 Birm.

MORGANS, Margaret Eleanor 50 Noel Road, London N1 8HA Tel: 020 7226 7600 — MB BS 1940 Lond.; FRCP Lond. 1966, M 1942; MRCS Eng. LRCP Lond. 1939. (Univ. Coll. Hosp.) Emerit. Cons. Bloomsbury HA. Socs: Thyroid Club; Diabetic Assn. Prev: Hon. Cons. Phys. & Hon. Sen. Lect. (Endocrinol.) Univ. Coll. Hosp. & Med. Sch. Lond.; Cons. Phys. S Lond. Hosp. Wom. & Eliz. Garrett Anderson Hosp.; Ho. Phys Qu. Eliz. Hosp Childr. Lond.

***MORGANSTEIN, Daniel** Flat 5, Defoe House, Barbican, London EC2Y 8DN — MB BS 1998 Lond.; MB BS Lond 1998.

MORGANTI, Kirsa Marie 39 Gladbeck Way, Enfield EN2 7EL — MB ChB 1989 Aberd.; MRCGP 1996; Dip. Pharm. Med. RCP (UK) 1994; DCH RCP Lond. 1992. GP Asst. Enfield. Prev: Clin. Research Phys. Roche Products Welwyn Garden City Herts.

MORGENSTERN, Franz-Stephan (retired) 65 Court Lane, London SE21 7EF Tel: 020 8693 5550 — BM BCh 1955 Oxf.; DM Oxf. 1968, BM BCh 1955; MRCPsych 1972; DPM Eng. 1960. Prev: Cons. Psychiat. (AMI) Langton Hse. Langton Matravers, Dorset.

MORGENSTERN, Godfrey Roger 261 Ashley Road, Hale, Altrincham WA15 9NF — MB BChir 1971 Camb.; MA Camb. 1972, MB BChir 1971; FRCPath 1993, M 1977. Cons. Haemat. Christie Hosp. NHS Trust. Prev: Sen. Regist. Leukaemia Unit Roy. Marsden Hosp. Sutton; Sen. Regist. (Haemat.) Oxon. AHA (T); Sen. Regist. (Haemat.) Roy. Berks. Hosp. Reading.

MORI, Katharine 1 Wyatt House, Wemyss Road, Blackheath, London SE3 OTE Tel: 0410 415364 Fax: 020 8318 4201 Email: katmori@compuserve.com — MB BS 1996 Lond.; BSc St And 1989; MA Oxon 1965. (UCLMS) GP Regist., Lond. Prev: SHO (O & G) Luton & Dunstable Hosp.; SHO (Paediat.) VTS/GP, Hereford Co. Hosp. Hereford; SHO (Psychiat.) Forest Healthcare.

MORIARTY, Andrew Joseph 1 Carrigart, Tullygally, Lurgan, Craigavon BT65 5BU — MB BCh BAO 1981 Belf. Research Fell. (Cardiol.) Craigavon Area Hosp.

MORIARTY, Anthony John 66 Vincent Close, Studlands Park, Newmarket CB8 7AW Tel: 01638 668088 — MB BS 1985 Lond.; FCAnaesth. 1991; DA (UK) 1989. Regist. (Anaesth.) Gt. Ormond St. Hosp. Lond. Prev: Regist. (Anaesth.) Addenbrookes Hosp. Camb. & Norf. & Norwich Hosp.; SHO (Anaesth.) St. Thos. Hosp. Lond.; SHO (Med.) Worthing Gen. Hosp. Sussex.

MORIARTY, Mr Anthony Peter Highfield House, 442 Buxton Road, Stockport SK2 7JB Tel: 0161 483 9512 Fax: 0161 487 3492 Email: julia@highfieldmedical.freeserve.co.uk — MB BChir 1983 Camb.; MA Camb. 1984; FRCS Glas. 1989; FRCOphth 1989.

MORIARTY

(Camb.) Cons. (Ophthmol.) Stepping Hill Hosp. Stockport; Vis. Sen. Lect. Dept. Optometry UMIST. Socs: Amer. Acad. Ophth.; Eur. Soc. Cataract & Refractive Surgs.; Amer. Soc. Of Cataract and Refractive Surg. Prev: Sen. Regist. (Ophth.) Roy. Liverp. Univ. Hosp.; Sen. Regist. Roy. Perth Hosp., W. Austral.; Regist. (Ophth.) St. Thos. Hosp. Lond. & Moorfields Eye Hosp.

MORIARTY, Mr Brendan Joseph Department of Ophthalmology, Leighton Hospital, Crewe CW1 4QJ Tel: 01270 612102 Fax: 01270 612398; 81 New Street, Altrincham WA14 2QP Tel: 0161 928 1314 Fax: 01270 612398 — MB BChir 1979 Camb.; MA; MD Camb. 1989; FRCS Eng. 1984; FCOphth 1989. (Cambridge) Cons. (Ophth.) Mid Chesh. Hosps. Trust; Moderator & Guest Lect. New Orleans Acad. Ophth. Socs: Internat. Soc. Geogr. Ophth.; Internat. Mem. Amer. Acad. Prev: Lect. (Ophth.) St. Pauls Eye Hosp. Liverp.; Frost Fell. (Glaucoma) Moorfields Eye Hosp. Lond.; Fell. Med. Research Counc. Sickle Cell Unit, Jamaica.

MORIARTY, Gillian Kathleen 99 Offington Avenue, Worthing BN14 9PR — MB BS 1992 Lond.

MORIARTY, Johanna Mary Angela Ringmead Medical Practice, Great Hollands Health Centre, Great Hollands Square, Bracknell RG12 8WY Tel: 01344 454338 Fax: 01344 861050; Stoke End, West End Lane, Stoke Poges, Slough SL2 4NA — MB BCh BAO 1976 NUI; MRCGP 1982. (Univ. Coll. Cork) Socs: BMA; Windsor Med. Soc. Prev: GP New Milton.

MORIARTY, John Gordon Hospital, Bloomburg St., London SW1V 2RH Tel: 020 8746 8000 — MB BCh BAO 1985 Dub.; MRCPI 1988; MRCPsych 1991; MD Dub. 1998. (Trinity Coll. Dub.) Cons. Psychiat. Gordon Hosp. Lond.; Hon. Lect. (Neuropsychiat.) Inst. Neurol. Qu. Sq. Lond. Prev: Sen. Regist. (Adult Gen. Psychiat.) Maudsley Hosp. Lond.

MORIARTY, Kieran John Royal Bolton Hospital, Farnworth, Bolton BL4 0JR Tel: 01204 390938 Fax: 01204 390141 Email: kieran.moriarty@bolton-tr.nwest.nhs.uk; 20 Bramhall Park Road, Bramhall, Stockport SK7 3DQ Tel: 0161 439 7556 — MB BChir 1976 Camb.; MA Camb. 1978, MD 1984; MRCP (UK) 1977; FRCP Lond. 1994. (Camb. & Roy. Lond. Hosp.) Cons. Gen. Med. & Gastroenterol. Roy. Bolton Hosp. Trust; Chief Med. Off., Salford Diocesan Lourdes Pilgrimage. Socs: Brit. Soc. Gastroenterol.; Inter. Med. Assoc. of Lourdes; Manch. Med. Soc. (Counc. Mem. Med. Soc.). Prev: Clin. Tutor & Sen. Regist. (Med.) Univ. Manch. Med. Sch. & Hope Hosp. Salford; MRC Train. Fell. & Hon. Lect. (Gastroenterol.) St. Bart. Hosp. Lond.; Ho. Off. (Gen. & Respirat. Med. & Neurol.) Lond. Hosp.

MORIARTY, Kieron Timothy Medical Department, Pfizer Ltd., Sandwich CT13 9NJ Tel: 01304 625241 Fax: 01304 625547; 3 China Farm Barn, Plough Lane, Upper Marbledown, Canterbury CT2 9AR Tel: 01227 457133 Fax: 01304 508001 Email: moriat1@pfizer.com — BM BCh 1985 Oxf.; MA Camb. 1986, BA 1982; DM Nottm. 1994; MRCP (UK) 1988. Med. Adviser Pfizer Ltd. Sandwich; Hon. Clin. Asst. Kent & Canterbury Hosp. Socs: Brit. Diabetic Assn. (Med. & Scientif. Sect.); Eur. Assn. Study Diabetes. Prev: Clin. Research Fell. Univ. Nottm.; Regist. (Med.) Sheff. Dist. HA; SHO (Med.) Newc. HA.

MORIARTY, Margaret Anne The Medical Centre, 45 Enderley Road, Harrow Weald, Harrow HA3 5HF Tel: 020 8863 3333; 24 Maricas Avenue, Harrow HA3 6JA — MB BS 1985 Lond.; BSc (Hons.) Lond. 1982; MRCGP 1990. GP Retainer Scheme Harrow. Socs: BMA & Christian Med. Fell.sh. Prev: Trainee GP N.wick Pk. VTS; SHO (O & G) Qu. Eliz. II Hosp. Welwyn Gdn. City; SHO (Paediat.) & Cas. Off. Qu. Eliz. II Hosp. Welwyn Gdn. City.

MORIARTY, Nora (retired) 59 Hesketh Road, Southport PR9 9PA — MB BCh BAO 1959 NUI.

MORIARTY, Richard John The East Leicester Medical Practice, 131 Uppingham Road, Leicester LE5 4BP Tel: 0116 276 7145 Fax: 0116 246 1637 — BM BS 1986 Nottm.; PhD Wales 1977, BSc 1973; MRCGP 1991; DCH RCP Lond. 1989.

MORICE, Professor Alyn Hugh Academic Department of Medicine, Castle Hill Hospital, Castle Road, Cottingham HU16 5JQ Tel: 01482 624067 Fax: 01482 624068 Email: a.h.morice@medschool.hull.ac.uk; Elstronwick Hall, Elstronwick, Hull HU12 9BP Tel: 01964 670220 Fax: 01964 671623 — MB BChir 1978 Camb.; MA Camb. 1979, BA (Hons.) 1975, MD 1987; FRCP Lond. 1993; MRCP (UK) 1980. Prof. (Respirat. Med.) Acad. Dept. of Med. Univ. of Hull. Socs: Brit. Thorac. Soc.; Brit. Pharm. Soc.; Amer.

Thoracic Soc. Prev: Reader (Med.) & Hon. Cons. Phys. Roy. Hallamsh. Hosp.; Clin. Lect. (Med.) Addenbrooke's Hosp. Camb.

MORICE, Robert Owen Launceston Medical Centre, Landlake Road, Launceston PL15 9HH Tel: 01566 772131 Fax: 01566 772223; Park Cottage, 1 Tavistock Road, Launceston PL15 9HA — MB BS 1975 Lond.; MRCGP 1980; DRCOG 1979; Cert. JCC Lond. 1979; DCH Eng. 1978.

MORING, Clair Fiona The Old School House, London Road, Bourne End, Hemel Hempstead HP1 2RH — MB BChir 1991 Camb.; MA Camb. 1991; MRCGP 1995; DFFP 1995; DCH RCP Lond. 1994; DGM RCP Lond. 1993.

MORISON, Colin John Child & Adolescent, Mental Health Service, Gaol St., Hereford HR1 2HU Tel: 01432 357351 — MB BS Lond. 1970; MRCPsych 1976. (Univ. Coll. Hosp.) Cons. Child Psychiat. C.A.M.H.S. Hereford & Hazel Clinic Llandrindod Wells, Powys. Prev: Cons. Child Psychiat. Haringey Child Guid. & N. Middlx. Hosp.; Sen. Regist. (Child. Psychiat.) Tavistock Clinic Lond.; Regist. Psychiat. Roy. Edin. Hosp.

MORISON, John Edgar, OBE (retired) 22 Shrewsbury Gardens, Belfast BT9 6PJ Tel: 028 9066 6175 — MB BCh BAO 1935 Belf.; DSc Belf. 1952, BSc (Hons.) 1932, MD (Gold Medal); FRCPath 1964; FRCOG (ad eund.) 1975. Hon. Cons. Histol. Belf. City Hosp. Prev: Hon. Prof. Histopath. Qu. Univ. Belf.

MORISON, Mary (retired) 14 Glenmore House, Richmond Hill, Richmond TW10 6BQ Tel: 020 8940 8809 — MB ChB 1943 St. And.; MRCPsych 1973; DPM Eng. 1968. Prev: Cons. Psychiat. Horton Hosp. Epsom.

MORISON, Neil James Sixways Clinic, London Road, Charlton Kings, Cheltenham GL52 6HS Tel: 01242 583520 — MB BS 1978 Lond.; MRCGP 1982; DRCOG 1980; DCH RCP Lond. 1981. GP Glos. FPC; Hosp. Pract. (Genitourin. Med.) Glos. HA; GP Trainer Glos.; GP Clin. Tutor Cheltenham. Prev: Trainee GP Dudley VTS.

MORISON, Niel (retired) Flat 19, Carrick Gardens, Ayr KA7 2RT Tel: 01292 282145 — MB ChB 1934 Glas.

MORISON, Stewart Rutherford 4 Orchard Close, Horndean, Waterlooville PO8 9LL Tel: 023 9259 3529 Fax: 023 9259 3529 Email: stewart.morison@lineone.net; 4 Orchard Close, Horndean, Waterlooville PO8 9LL Tel: 023 9259 3529 Fax: 023 9259 3529 — MRCS Eng. LRCP Lond. 1967; MA Camb. 1965. (Camb. & St. Bart.) Specialist (Allergy & Environm.) Horndean; Edr. Brit. Soc. for Allergy & Environm. & Nutrit. Med. Newsletters. Socs: BMA; (Comm.) Brit. Soc. for Allergy, Environm. & Nutrit. Med.; (Comm.) RSM Food & Health Forum. Prev: GP Jersey, CI; Sen. Med. Off. Govt. of Fiji; SHO (Surg.) N. Devon Infirm. Barnstaple.

MORISON, William Bruce The Birches, Oak Lane, Llanellen, Abergavenny NP7 9LD — MRCS Eng. LRCP Lond. 1968; DA Eng. 1972.

MORKS, Thelma Henriette Willy (retired) Abbey View, North Row, Darley Abbey, Derby DE22 1DP — MB BCh BAO 1949 Dub. Prev: Clin. Med. Off. Derbysh. AHA.

MORLAND, Bruce Jonathan Birmingham Childrens Hospital NHS Trust, Steelhouse Lane, Birmingham B4 6NH Tel: 0121 333 8233 Fax: 0121 333 8241 Email: bruce.morland@bhamchildrens.wmids.nhs.uk; 2 Cherry Hill Drive, Barnt Green, Birmingham B45 8JY — MB ChB 1983 Birm.; DM Soton. 1994; MRCP (UK) 1988; FRCPCH 1997. (Birmingham) Cons. Paediat. Oncol. Birm. Childr. Hosp.

***MORLAND, Bryan David** 21 Parkside, Spennymoor DL16 6SA — MB ChB 1998 Ed.; MB ChB Ed 1998.

MORLE, Iain Jeremy Forgan Hurworth Burn House, Hurworth Burn, Wingate TS28 5NS — MB ChB 1967 Liverp.; FRCR 1975; FFR 1973. Cons. Radiol. Hartlepool Gen. Hosp. Prev: Cons. Radiol. Walton Hosp. Liverp. & St. Mary's Hosp. Newport I. of Wight; Chief Radiol. Sultanate of Oman.

MORLESE, John Fitzgerald 6 Aintree Drive, Lower Darwen, Darwen BB3 0QW — MB BS 1993 Lond.

MORLEY, Adrian Roberts (retired) Garden House, Aydon Road, Corbridge NE45 5DT Tel: 01434 632507 Email: adrianmorley@csi.com — MD Newc. 1970; MB BS Durh. 1962; FRCPath 1984, M 1972. Prev: Clin. Dir. of Path. Freeman Hosp.

MORLEY, Alan Frederick Tramways Medical Centre, 54 Holme Lane, Sheffield S6 4JQ Tel: 0114 234 3418 Fax: 0114 285 5958; 514 Loxley Road, Loxley, Sheffield S6 6RT — MB ChB 1972 Sheff.; DObst RCOG 1974. (Sheffield University)

***MORLEY, Andrew Robert Ure** 62 Africa Gardens, Cardiff CF14 3BU — MB BCh 1995 Wales.

MORLEY, Anne Deborah 11 Beechwood, Linlithgow EH49 6SD — MB ChB 1989 Ed.; BSc Ed. 1987; FRCA 1994. p/t Cons. Anaesth. W.. Gen. Hosp., Edin. Prev: SHO (Anaesth.) St. John's Hosp. Livingston; SHO & SHO 3 (Anaesth.) Roy. Infirm. Edin.; Sen. Regist. (Anaesth.) Roy. Infirm. Edin.

MORLEY, Avisa Jeanne Mary Cleve Cross, Selborne Road, Croydon CR0 5JQ Tel: 020 8686 1591 — MB BS 1951 Lond.; MRCS Eng. LRCP Lond. 1951; DCH Eng. 1955. (King's Coll. Hosp.) Prev: Ho. Off. Belgrave Hosp. Lond. & S. Lond. Hosp. Wom. Clapham; Clin. Asst. Roy. Nat. Orthop. Hosp. Lond.

MORLEY, Caroline Elizabeth Jubilee Fields, c/o How Keyell Surgery, Chippenham SN14 7EJ Tel: 01249 782204 — MB ChB 1983 Bristol; Cert. Family Plann. JCC 1987. Prev: SHO (O & G) S.mead Hosp. Bristol; SHO (Renal Med.) S.mead Hosp. Bristol; Ho. Phys. Bristol Roy. Infirm.

MORLEY, Catherine Flat 2, 42 Howard Road, Leicester LE2 1XH — MB ChB 1993 Leic.

MORLEY, Christine 13 Gordon Close, Billericay CM12 0HX Tel: 01277 625582 — MB BS 1983 Newc.; FRCOphth 1996; DO RCPSI 1986. Clin. Asst. Ophth. S.end Gen. Hosp. Prev: Med. Off. (Ophth.) St. Geo. Hosp. Lond.; SHO (Ophth.) S.end Gen. Hosp.; Ho. Off. (Med. & Surg.) Middlesbrough Gen. Hosp.

MORLEY, Christopher Anthony Dept. of Cardiology, Bradford Royal Infirmary, Ductworth Lane, Bradford — BM BCh 1977 Oxf.; MRCP (UK) 1979; FRCP 1998 UK. Cons. Cardiol. Bradford. Socs: BPEG; Brit. ht failure Soc.; Brit. Cardiac Soc.

MORLEY, David C, CBE 51 Eastmoor Park, Harpenden AL5 1BN Tel: 01582 712199 Fax: 01582 712199 — MB BChir 1947 Camb.; MD (hon. causa) Uppsala 1986; MA 1955, BA 1947; MD Camb. 1955; FRCP Lond. 1977, M 1972; DCH Eng. 1955. (Camb. & St. Thos.) Prof. Emerit. Trop. Child Health Univ. Lond.; Hon. Dir. Teachg. Aid at Low Cost; Developm. of People's Centre for Culture & Technol. Genoa 1986. Socs: Fell. Roy. Soc. Med.; Fell. Trop. Med. & Hyg.; Brit. Paediat. Assn. Prev: Sen. Lect. (Human Nutrit.) Lond. Sch. Hyg. & Trop. Med.; Paediat. Wesley Guild Hosp., Ilesha; Assoc. Lect. (Paediat.) Univ. Coll., Ibadan.

MORLEY, David Frederick (retired) 396 Woodgrange Drive, Southend-on-Sea SS1 3DZ Tel: 01702 464963 — MB BS Lond. 1949; MRCS Eng. LRCP Lond. 1949; DObst RCOG 1953. Prev: Sen. Surg. SS Orion, Orient Line.

MORLEY, George Edwin 24 Courtenay Road, Winchester SO23 7ER Tel: 01962 864778 Fax: 01962 864778 — MB ChB Birm. 1951; FFOM RCP Lond. 1985, MFOM 1979; DIH Eng. 1969. (Birm.) Indep. Cons. Occupat. Med. Winchester; Doctor HSE Asbestos, Lead, Radiat. REGS. Socs: Soc. Occupat. Med. Prev: Sen. Regional Med. Off. Civil Serv. Occupat. Health Serv. Roy. Aerospace Estabs., Meteorolog. Office, & Hants. & Wilts. Regions; Sen. Med. Off. RAF Changi, Singapore & Army of S. Arabian Emirates; Med. Off. i/c Aeromed. & Safety Train. Sch. Boscombe Down.

MORLEY, Gregory John Eggleton North Cumbria Mental Health & Learning Disabilities NHS Trust, West Cumberland Hospital, Whitehaven CA28 8JG Tel: 01946 693181 Fax: 01946 523521 — MB ChB 1972 Ed.; MRCPsych 1985. (Edinburgh) Cons. Psych. W. Cumbld. Hosp. Whitehaven.

MORLEY, Harriet Lucy 11 Marius Mansions, Marius Road, London SW17 7QG — MB BS 1995 Lond.

MORLEY, Howard Stanton 322 Gilmerton Road, Edinburgh EH17 7PR; 10 Minto Street, Edinburgh EH9 1RG Tel: 0131 667 1628 — MB ChB 1978 Manch.; MRCGP 1985. Prev: Regist. (Med.) Vale of Leven Hosp. Alexandria; Sen. Ho. Phys. W.. Infirm. Glas.

MORLEY, Jean Marion (retired) Garden House, Aydon Road, Corbridge NE45 5DT Tel: 01434 632507 — MB ChB Leeds 1962. Prev: SCMO N. Tyneside HA.

MORLEY, John, CStJ 86 College Street, Long Eaton, Nottingham NG10 4NP Tel: 0115 973 4502; 149 Wilsthorpe Road, Breaston, Derby DE72 3AF Tel: 01332 873911 — MB ChB 1960 Birm.; AFOM 1980. (Birm.) Socs: Soc. Occupat. Med.; Nottm. M-C Soc.

***MORLEY, John Russell** 57 Mosshead Road, Bearsden, Glasgow G61 3EY — MB ChB 1994 Glas.

MORLEY, Joseph 8 Bartley Road, Northenden, Manchester M22 4BG — LAH Dub. 1957.

MORLEY, Keith David 6 Esk Road, Lowry Hill, Carlisle CA3 0HN — MB ChB 1990 Glas.; FRCA 1994. Regist. (Anaesth.) Glas. Roy. Infirm. Prev: SHO (Anaesth.) W.. Infirm. Glas.

MORLEY, Kenneth Donald Tel: 01382 660111 Fax: 01382 425509 Email: ken.morley@tuht.scot.nhs.uk; Tel: 01382 562673 — MB ChB 1974 Aberd.; BMedBiol (Hons.) Aberd. 1971; FRCP Ed. 1985; MRCP (UK) 1980; FRACP 1980. (Aberdeen) Gen. Phys. & Rheum. Dundee Teachg. Hosps. Trust; Hon. Sen. Lect. (Med.) Univ. Dundee. Socs: Counc. Mbr. Brit. Soc. For Rheum.; Counc. Memb. Scottisch Soc. for Rheum. Prev: ARC Copeman Research Fell. & Hon. Sen. Regist. Roy. Postgrad. Med. Sch. & Hammersmith Hosp. Lond.; Regist. (Med.) ChristCh. Hosps. & Clin. Sch. NZ; Lect. (Med.) Univ. Aberd.

MORLEY, Mary (retired) 96 West Kensington Court, West Cromwell Road, London W14 9AB Tel: 020 7603 7117 — MB BCh BAO 1944 NUI; MB BCh BAO (Hons.) NUI 1944.

***MORLEY, Michael Edward** 49B South View Road, East Bierley, Bradford BD4 6PP — BM BCh 1997 Oxf.

MORLEY, Nicholas John 38 High Street, Horsell, Woking GU21 4UD — MB BS 1996 Lond.; BA Camb. 1993. (Cambridge and London Hospital Medical College) SHO (Med.) Greenwich Dist. Gen. Hosp.

MORLEY, Nora Sivewright 226 Stockton Lane, York YO31 1EY Tel: 01904 423028 — MRCS Eng. LRCP Lond. 1945. (Leeds) Sen. Med. Off. N. Yorks. AHA.

MORLEY, Patricia (retired) Parkhall, Balfron, Glasgow G63 0LQ Tel: 01360 440124 Fax: 01360 440124 — MB BS Lond. 1953; FRCP Glas. 1985, M 1983; FRCR 1980; DMRD Ed. 1960. Prev: Cons. Radiol. W.ern Infirm. Glas.

MORLEY, Peter Keith The Health Centre, 10 Gresham Road, Oxted RH8 0BQ Tel: 01883 714361 Fax: 01883 722679; St. Denys, The Walk, Tandridge, Oxted RH8 9NY — MB BS 1982 Lond.; MRCGP 1986; DRCOG 1986. (St. Mary's)

MORLEY, Robert Luigi Erdington Medical Centre, 103 Wood End Road, Erdington, Birmingham B24 8NT Tel: 0121 373 0085 Fax: 0121 386 1768 — MB ChB 1983 Birm.; MRCGP 1990; DFFP 1993; DRCOG 1987. (Univ. Birm.) GP Princip. Erdington Birm.; Exec. Comm. Chairm. Birm. N.E. Primary Care Trust. Socs: BMA; Birm. Med. Inst. Prev: Trainee GP Birm. & BromsGr.; SHO (A & E) E. Birm. Hosp.; SHO (ENT) Roy. Hosp. Wolverhampton.

MORLEY, Mr Roland, Surg. Lt.-Cdr. RN Retd. Kingston Hospital, Galsworthy Road, Kingston upon Thames KT2 7QB Tel: 020 8546 7711; Hunters Moon, Blundel Lane, Stoke D'Abernon, Cobham KT11 2SF Email: rolyrat@compuserve.com — MB BS 1982 Lond.; FRCS Eng. 1989. (St. Georges) Cons. (Urol.); Sen. Regist. (Urol.) Wessex Train. Scheme. Prev: Research Regist. (Urol.) Soton. Gen. Hosp.

MORLEY, Sarah Louise 15 Tenterfield Road, Maldon CM9 5EN — MB BS 1992 Lond.

MORLEY, Simon John 1 Digby Mansions, Hammersmith Bridge Road, London W6 9DE Tel: 020 8748 9883 Fax: 020 8746 3602 — BM BCh 1996 Oxf.

MORLEY, Stuart William (retired) Orchard Surgery, Blackhorse Way, Horsham RH12 1SG Tel: 01403 253966/7 — MB BS 1970 Lond.; MRCGP 1974; DObst RCOG 1973.

MORLEY, Susan Margaret Department of Dermatology, Ninewells Hospital, Ninewells, Dundee DD1 9SY Tel: 01382 660111 Fax: 01382 633916; 9 Burnside Road, Invergowrie, Dundee DD2 5JL Tel: 01382 562673 Email: smmorley@bad.dundee.ac.uk — MB ChB 1973 Aberd.; MD (Commend.) Aberd. 1988; FRCP Ed. 1996; MRCP (UK) 1980; FRACP 1987. (Univ. Aberd.) Cons. Dermat. Ninewells Hosp. Dundee; Clin. Research Fell. Cancer Research Laborat. Univ. Dundee. Socs: Brit. Assn. Dermat.; Eur. Soc. Dermat. Res.; Assn. Phys. Prev: Sen. Regist. (Dermat.) Ninewells Hosp. Dundee & Roy. Free Hosp. Lond.; Regist. (Dermat.) ChristCh. Hosp., NZ.

MORLEY, Tania Louise Healey Surgery, Whitworth Road, Rochdale OL12 0SN — MB ChB 1989 Liverp.

MORLEY, Terence (retired) 3 The Grange, Long Acres Close, Coombe Dingle, Bristol BS9 2RD Tel: 0117 968 1797 — MB ChB 1956 Bristol; MRCGP 1968; DPM Eng. 1976; DObst RCOG 1958. Prev: Assoc. Specialist (Psychiat.) Barrow Hosp. Bristol & W.on HA.

MORLEY, Thomas Selwyn (retired) Grianagh, Ballacurry Road, Greeba, Douglas IM4 3LE — MB BS Lond. 1960; MRCS Eng. LRCP Lond. 1960; FACA 1966; Dip. Amer. Bd. Anaesth. 1969. Prev:

MORLEY

Anaesth. Willliam Beaumont Hosp., Roy. Oak Michigan, Grace Hosp., Detroit Michigan & St. Mary's Hosp. Richmond, Virginia, USA.

MORLEY, Mr Timothy Rowland 148 Harley Street, London W1A 1AH Tel: 020 7487 5020 Fax: 020 7224 1528; Fife House, Heath Drive, Walton on the Hill, Tadworth KT20 7QQ Tel: 01737 812538 Fax: 01737 819770 — MB BChir 1965 Camb.; MA, MB Camb. 1965, BChir 1964; FRCS Eng. 1969; MRCS Eng. LRCP Lond. 1964. (Univ. Coll. Hosp.) Cons. Orthop. Roy. Nat. Orthop. Hosp. Lond. Socs: Fell. Roy. Soc. Med. (Ex.-Sec.) & Pres. Orthop. Sect.; Fell. Brit. Orthop. Soc. Prev: Sen. Surgic. Off. & Sen. Regist. Roy. Nat. Orthop. Hosp. Lond.

***MORLEY, Wendy Linda** 12 Eaton Close, Hulland Ward, Ashbourne DE6 3EX — MB ChB 1998 Ed.; MB ChB Ed 1998.

MORLEY, William Neil, RD (retired) Parkhall, Balfron, Glasgow G63 0LQ Tel: 01360 440124 Fax: 01360 440124 — MB ChB Ed. 1954; FRCP Glas. 1975, M 1972; FRCP Ed. 1970, M 1961. Dermat. HCI Hosp. Clydebank. Prev: Mem. Med. Appeal Tribunal DSS.

MORLEY-DAVIES, Adrian John 30 Aytoun Road, Glasgow G41 5HP — MB Ch 1987 Wales; BSc (1st. cl. Hons.) Biochem. Wales 1984; MRCP (UK) 1990. Regist. (Cardiol.) Roy. Infirm. Edin.

MORLEY-DAVIES, Royden Barry (retired) Bryngoleu, Penrhys Road, Ystrad, Pentre CF41 Tel: 01443 434042 — MB BCh 1949 Wales; BSc Wales 1946, MB BCh 1949, DPH 1954; FFCM 1980, M 1974. Prev: Sen. Med. Off. Welsh Office.

MORLEY-JACOB, Catherine Ann Red House, Cooksmill Green, Chelmsford CM1 3SJ Tel: 01245 248689 Fax: 01245 248689; 9 Coton Road, Grantchester, Cambridge CB3 9NH Tel: 01223 841108 Email: cam49@mole.bio.cam.ac.uk — MB BS 1989 Lond.; MRCP (UK) 1996; DFFP 1994; DCH RCP Lond. 1993. (Char. Cross & Westm.) Clin. Research Asst. Univ. of Camb.; Regist. (Paediat.) Addenbrooke's Hosp. Camb..

MORMESH, Nabil Mokhtar Rheumatology Unit, Stonehouse Hospital, Strathaven Road, Stonehouse, Larkhall ML9 3NT — MB BS 1977 Garyounis; MB BS Garyounis, Libya 1977; MSc Glas. 1985.

MORONEY, John Daniel Minster Health, 35 Monkgate, York YO31 7WE Tel: 01904 626234 — MB BS 1979 Newc.

MORONEY, John Francis 33 Chatsworth Road, Eccles, Manchester M30 9DZ — MB BCh BAO 1946 NUI. (Galw.) Prev: Ho. Surg. & Sen. Res. Obst. Off. Centr. Hosp. Galw.; Ho. Phys. Conskea Fev. Hosp. Dub.

MORONEY, Lucy Helen Emily Braeside, Clayhead Road, Baldrine, Douglas IM4 6DL Tel: 01624 781390 — MB ChB 1938 Liverp.; DPH 1940. (Liverp.) Prev: Asst. M.O.H. & Asst. Sch. Med. Off. Co. Boro. Wallasey; Asst. Sch. Med. Off. Liverp. Educat. Comm.; Ho. Surg. Liverp. Roy. Infirm.

MORONEY, Margaret Mary Tamworth Health Centre, Upper Gungate, Tamworth — MB BCh BAO 1984 NUI.

MORONEY, Patrick Joseph (retired) 3 Harley Road, Sheffield S11 9SD Tel: 0114 236 4993 — MB BCh BAO 1941 NUI; DPH 1945; LM Coombe 1945. Prev: Cons. Phys. Lodge Moor Hosp. Sheff.

MOROSS, Tessa 51 Northway, London NW11 6PB Tel: 020 8455 4616 Fax: 020 8455 4616 — MB BCh 1978 Witwatersrand.

MORPETH, Georges 261 Normanby Road, South Bank, Middlesbrough TS6 6TB — MB BS 1952 Durh.

MORPETH, Simon Jonathan Cwm Llywi Isaf, Abercegir, Machynlleth SY20 8NP — MB BS 1978 Newc.

***MORPHEW, John Anthony** The Cottage, Penrose, Wadebridge PL27 7TB — MB BS 1988 Lond.

MORPHEW, John Anthony (retired) 31 Perry Orchard, Upton St Leonards, Gloucester GL4 8EH — MB ChB 1961 Bristol; MB ChB (2nd Cl. Hons.) Bristol 1961; MRCPsych 1971; DPM Eng. 1964. Prev: Cons. Psychiat. Coney Hill Hosp., Gloucester & Forest of Dean Resource Centre Coleford.

MORPHEW, Kenneth John St George's Surgery, St Pauls Medical Centre, 121 Swindon Road, Cheltenham GL50 4DP Tel: 01242 707755 Fax: 01242 707749; Arosa, 15 Sandy Lane, Cheltenham GL53 9BS — MB ChB 1965 Leeds; MRCGP 1975; DObst Auckland 1969. GP Trainer. Prev: SHO & Regist. (ENT) Auckland Pub. Hosp.; Ho. Surg. & Ho. Phys. Leeds Gen. Infirm.

***MORPHY, Hannah Faith** Yew Tree House, Church St., Bloxham, Banbury OX15 4ET — MB ChB 1998 Dund.; MB ChB Dund 1998; BMSc 1996.

MORRA, Mauro Carlo Via Biasioli 321, Genova 16167, Italy Tel: 00 39 10 3727551 Email: maurofs@tin-it; 53 Highfield Avenue, London NW11 9EU Tel: 020 8455 1953 — State DMS 1948 Milan. (Milan) Socs: Ordine die Medici, Italy. Prev: Vis. Prof. Adolesc. Psychiat. & Child & Adolesc. Psychiat. Genova Univ.; Cons. Child Psychiat. Burnt Oak Child Guid. & Hammersmith Child Guid.; Cons. Child Psychiat. Stevenage Social Servs.

MORRALL, John Thomas Fowler (retired) 8 Dumfries Park, Ayr KA6 6DA Tel: 01292 442427 — MB ChB Birm. 1952; FRCGP 1991, M 1965; DObst RCOG 1956. Prev: Hon. Lect. Postgrad. Med. Univ. Glas.

MORRAN, Mr Christopher George 15 Ottoline Drive, Troon KA10 7AN — MB ChB 1973 Glas.; FRCS Eng. 1979; FRCS Glas. 1979. Cons. Surg. Ayrsh.

MORRANT, Barbara Lois Weston Favell Health Centre, Weston Favell Centre, Northampton NN3 8DW Tel: 01604 409002 Fax: 01604 407034; 3 Hardingstone Lane, Hardingstone, Northampton NN4 6DF — MB BS 1974 Lond.; MRCS Eng. LRCP Lond. 1974; MRCGP 1979; DRCOG 1976. (Middlx.)

MORRANT, John Denning Queens Medical Centre, Nottingham NG2 7UH Tel: 0115 924 9924 Email: john.morrant@mail.qmcuh-tr.trent.nhs.uk; 29 Mapperley Hall Drive, Mapperley Park, Nottingham NG3 5EY — MB BS 1980 Lond.; BSc (Hons.) Lond. 1977, MB BS 1980; FRCP Lond. 1994. (Middlx.) Cons. Geriat. Med. Univ. & Highbury Hosps. Nottm.; Cons. Phys. Geriat. Med. Qu.s Med. Centre, Univ. Hosp. and Highbury Rehabil. Hosp. Prev: Sen. Regist. (Health c/o Elderly) Nottm. Hosps.

MORREAU, Philip Neil Department of Paediatric Surgery, Birmingham Childrens Hospital, Ladywood Middleway, Birmingham B16 8ET — MB ChB 1985 Otago.

MORRELL, Mr Andrew Jonathan St. James University Hospital, Beckett St., Leeds LS9 7TF Tel: 0113 243 3144 — MB ChB 1981 Birm.; BSc Birm. 1978; FRCS Ed. 1987; FRCS Lond. 1987; FCOphth 1989. Cons. Ophth. St. Jas. Univ. Hosp. Prev: Sen. Regist. (Ophth.) Birm. & Midl. Eye Hosp.

MORRELL, Professor David Cameron, OBE 14 Higher Green, Epsom KT17 3BA Tel: 020 8224 5781 — MB BS Lond. 1952; FRCP Lond 1976, M 1955; MRCS Eng. LRCP Lond. 1952; FFPHM 1986; FRCGP 1972; DObst RCOG 1958; MD 1999 Plymouth. (St. Mary's) Emerit. Prof. Gen. Pract. Univ. Lond. Socs: (EX-Pres.) BMA. Prev: Prof. of Gen. Pract. (MUDS); Lect. (Gen. Pract.) Univ. Edin.; Phys. RAF Med. Br.

MORRELL, Helen Bernadette Glenmay, Muddy Lane, Linton, Wetherby LS22 4HW — MB ChB 1982 Birm.

MORRELL, Ian Richard Shiphay Manor, 37 Shiphay Lane, Torquay TQ2 7DU Tel: 01803 615059 Fax: 01803 614545 — MB BS 1979 Lond.; MRCS Eng. LRCP Lond. 1978. GP Torquay. Prev: GP Brimington; Med. Adviser Devon FHSA.

MORRELL, Jacqueline Elizabeth 12 Cecil Road, London W3 0DA — MB BS 1983 Lond.; MRCPsych 1987. Cons. Child & Adolesc. Psychiat. N. W. Thames Ment. Health Trust.

MORRELL, John Richard David (retired) Bridge End Surgery, Chester-le-Street DH3 3SL Tel: 0191 388 3236 — MB BS 1970 Newc.

MORRELL, Jonathan Mark Fitznells Manor Surgery, Chessington Road, Epsom KT17 1TF Tel: 020 8394 2365 Fax: 020 8393 9753 — MB BChir 1978 Camb.; MRCGP 1983; DRCOG 1981; DCH Eng. 1980; FRCGP 1997. GP Ewell. Socs: Brit. Hyperlipid. Assn. (Chair. Health Care Sect.); Mem. of Primary Care Cardiovasc. Soc.

MORRELL, Julian Michael Bedford 28 The Terrace, Northwick Park Hospital, Harrow — MB BS 1986 Lond.; MA Camb. 1983; MB ChB (2nd Cl. Hons.) Bristol 1961; MRCPsych 1971; DPM Eng. 1964. BS (Hons. Surg.) Lond. 1986. SHO (A & E) Whipps Cross Hosp. Lond.

MORRELL, Miss Margaret Tessa Tameside General Hospital, Ashton-under-Lyne OL6 9RW — MB BChir Camb. 1962; MA Camb. 1962; FRCS Eng. 1965. (Camb. & Oxf.) Cons. Surg. Thameside Gen. Hosp. Ashton-under-Lyne. Prev: Lect. (Surg.) Nuffield Dept. Surg. Radcliffe Infirm. Oxf.; Regist. (Urol.) Gen. Infirm. Leeds.

MORRELL, Nicholas Wayne 13 Main Street, Scarcliffe, Chesterfield S44 6SZ — MB BS 1987 Lond.

MORRELL, Mr Richard Robert James 15 Hunters Close, Oakley, Basingstoke RG23 7BG — MB ChB 1987 Birm.; FRCS Ed. 1993.

MORRELL, Rosemary Ann 7 Orchard Rise, Richmond TW10 5BX — MB BS 1952 Lond.; MRCS Eng. LRCP Lond. 1952; DA Eng.

MORRIS

1954. (Univ. Coll. Hosp.) Dep. Coroner W.. Dist. Gtr. Lond. Socs: Coroners Soc. Prev: Ho. Surg. Surgic. Unit Univ. Coll. Hosp.; Resid. Anaesth. Luton & Dunstable Hosp.

***MORREY, Ian Andrew** 33 Briar Close, Lickey Eng, Bromsgrove B60 1GE; 122 Mayfield Close, Catshill, Bromsgrove B61 0NP — MB ChB 1998 Birm.; ChB Birm. 1998.

MORRHALL, Graham Edward Deryck (retired) Bank Flat Abbey Close, 95 High St., Newport TF10 7AZ Tel: 01952 815718 — BM BCh 1950 Oxf.; MA, BM BCh Oxf. 1950.

MORRICE, Amanda Elaine Medway Hospital NHS Trust, Windmill Road, Gillingham ME7 5NY Tel: 01634 833911 Fax: 01634 828542; The Anchorage, The St, Stockbury, Sittingbourne ME9 7UE — MB BCh BAO 1984 Belf.; MB BCh Belf. 1984; FFAEM 1995; FRCS Ed. 1989. (Queen's University Belfast) Cons. (A & E Med.) Medway NHS Trust, Gillingham, Kent. Socs: Brit. Assn. Emerg. Med. Prev: Regist. (A & E Med.) Mersey.

MORRICE, Andrew Alexander George St Chads Surgery, Gullock Tyning, Midsomer Norton, Bath BA3 2UH Tel: 01761 413334 Fax: 01761 411176 — MB BS 1991 Lond.; MD (Lond.) 1999; MRCGP 2000; BSc (Hons.) Lond. 1988; T(GP) 1996. (St. Mary's Hosp. Med. Sch.) Socs: BHMA. Prev: Research Fell. Wellcome Inst. Hist. Med. Univ. Coll. Lond.; Clin. Asst. (Otolaryngol.) Roy. United Hosp. Bath.

MORRICE, David John 39 Snowdon Place, Stirling FK8 2JP — MB ChB 1991 Ed.

MORRICE, George Mitchell Insch Health Centre 1, Rannes Street, Insch AB52 6JJ Tel: 01464 20707 Fax: 01464 820395 — MB ChB 1973 Aberd.; DPhil Aberd. 1983, MB ChB 1973.

MORRICE, Mr Graham Durward 39 Snowdon Place, Stirling FK8 2JP — MB ChB Aberd. 1959; FRCS (Ophth.) Ed. 1980; DObst RCOG 1967; DO Eng. 1977. Cons. Ophth. Stirling Roy. Infirm. Prev: Sen. Regist. Ophth. Woodend Gen. Hosp. Aberd.; Med. Off. Quarrier's Homes, Bridge of Weir; Med. Off. Charteris Hosp. Kalimpong, India.

MORRICE, Graham Taylor The Medical Centre, 12 East King Street, Helensburgh G84 7QL Tel: 01436 672277 Fax: 01436 674526; 26 Edward Drive, Helensburgh G84 9QP — MB ChB Aberd. 1967.

MORRICE, James Kenneth Watt (retired) 30 Carnegie Crescent, Aberdeen AB15 4AE Tel: 01224 310136 — MB ChB 1946 Aberd.; MD Aberd. 1954; FRCPsych 1972; DPM Lond. 1951. Hon. Cons. Psychiat. Grampian HB; Hon. Fell. (Ment. Health) Univ. Aberd. Prev: Cons. Psychiat. Ross Clinic & Roy. Cornhill Hosp. Aberd.

MORRICE, Mr John James Coruisk, Lochwinnoch Road, Kilmacolm PA13 4DZ Tel: 0150 587 3806 Email: morrice@coruisk.u-net.com — MPhil (Law & Ethics Med.) Glas. 1994, MB ChB 1968; FRCS Glas. 1973; DObst RCOG 1970; FCS Bangladesh (Hon) 1997. (Glasgow) Cons. Gen. & Vasc. Surg. Inverclyde Roy. Hosp. Greenock; Hon. Sen. Lect. (Surg.) Univ. Glas. Socs: Vasc. Surg. Soc. GB & Irel.; Surg. Research Soc.; Assn. Surg.

***MORRICE, John Samuel** Doctors' Residence, Borders General Hospital, Melrose — MB ChB 1994 Aberd.

MORRICE, Kenneth Findlay 22 Meadow Lane, Hamble, Southampton SO31 4RD; 1 Sedgemead Court, Victoria Road, Netley Abbey, Southampton SO31 5QB Tel: 01703 453979 — LMSSA 1952 Lond.; MA Camb. 1954, MB BChir 1952; LLCO 1969. (Camb. & Lond. Hosp.) Occupat. Phys. Philips Components Ltd, Standard Telephones &Cables Soton. Socs: Soc. Occupat. Med. & Brit. Assn. Manip. Med; Assoc. Fac. Occupat. Med.

MORRICE, Michael Sutherland Busby Road Surgery, 75 Busby Road, Clarkston, Glasgow G76 7BW Tel: 0141 644 2666 Fax: 0141 644 5171; Strathallan, 5 Eglinton Drive, Giffnock, Glasgow G46 7NQ — MB ChB 1983 Aberd.; MRCGP 1987; DRCOG 1986. Prev: Trainee GP Dumfries VTS.

MORRILL, Peter Oliver 1 Ashen Close, Sedgley, Dudley DY3 3UZ — MB ChB 1961 St. And. (St. And.)

MORRIS, Adrian James Ryder William Harvey Hospital, Kennington Road, Ashford TN24 0LZ Tel: 01233 616265 Fax: 01233 616441; Downfield House, Wye Downs, Hastingleigh, Ashford TN25 5HE Tel: 01233 750244 Fax: 01233 750514 Email: wyedowns@clara.co.uk — MB BCh 1972 Witwatersrand; FRCP Lond. 1994; MRCP (UK) 1976. Cons. Gen. & Chest Med. William Harvey Hosp. Ashford, Buckland Hosp. Dover & Roy. Vict. Hosp. Folkestone. Prev: Sen. Regist. (Chest Med.) Brompton Hosp. & St.

Jas. Hosp. Lond.; Clin. Lect. Cardiothoracic Inst. Lond.; Clin. Tutor William Harvey Hosp. Ashford.

***MORRIS, Adrian John** 59A Norton Road, Letchworth SG6 1AD — MB BS 1996 Lond.

MORRIS, Alan Edward Aureole House Surgery, Market Square, 9 Church Street, Chesham HP5 1HS Tel: 01494 792558; 3 Woodland Court, Long Park, Chesham Bois, Amersham HP6 5LG Tel: 01494 722385 — MB BS 1960 Lond.; MRCS Eng. LRCP Lond. 1960; MRCGP 1975; DCH Eng. 1965; DObst RCOG 1963. (Univ. Coll. Hosp.) Phys. Chesham Hosp. Socs: Fell. Roy. Soc. Med. Prev: Regist. (Med.) Char. Cross Hosp. Lond.; SHO Qu. Eliz. Hosp. Childr. Lond.; Ho. Phys. (Geriat.) Univ. Coll. Hosp. Lond.

MORRIS, Alan Paul The Medical Centre, Market St., Whitworth, Rochdale OL12 8JZ Tel: 0170 685 2238 Fax: 01706 853877; 47 Longacres Drive, Whitworth, Rochdale OL12 8QX Tel: 01706 852804 Fax: 01706 853877 — MB ChB 1980 Manch.; Cert. Family Plann. JCC 1985. Police Surg. Rochdale Div. Gtr. Manch. Police; Prison Med. Off. Buckley Hall Prison Rochdale; Company Med. Off. Palmers (Textlite) Whitworth Lancs.

MORRIS, Alastair Richard 1 Deanwood Avenue, Glasgow G44 3RL — MB ChB 1990 Glas.; MRCOG 1998.

MORRIS, Alexander James Craignure, 24 Main St., Craigie, Kilmarnock KA1 5LY — MB ChB 1974 Aberd.; FFA RCS Eng. 1978; DA Eng. 1977.

MORRIS, Alexander Russell Kelso Medical Group Practice, Health Centre, Inch Road, Kelso TD5 7JP Tel: 01573 224424 Fax: 01573 226388 — MB ChB 1981 Ed.; MRCGP 1985; DRCOG 1984.

MORRIS, Mr Alfred David 5 Eaton Road, West Kirby, Wirral CH48 3HE — MB ChB 1991 Sheff.; FRCS Eng. 1995. (Sheff.) Specialist Regist. (Orthop. Surg.) Roy. Liverp. Univ. Hosp. Prev: SHO (Renal Transpl. Surg.) Roy. Liverp. Univ. Hosp.; SHO (A & E) Roy. Liverp. Univ. Hosp.

***MORRIS, Alistair Paul** Flat 29, Monkmoor Road, Shrewsbury SY2 5AH — MB BS 1998 Lond.; MB BS Lond 1998.

MORRIS, Allan John Gastroenterogy Unit, Glasgow Royal Infirmary, Castle St., Glasgow G4 0SF Tel: 0141 211 4470 Fax: 0141 211 1120 Email: ajmorrisl@ibn.net — MB ChB 1984 Aberd.; MRCP (UK) 1988. Cons. Gastroenterol. & Med. Glas. Roy. Infirm.; Vis. Assoc. Prof. Med., Med. Univ. S. Carolina, USA. Socs: Caledonian Soc. Gastroenterol.; Brit. Soc. Gastroenterol. Prev: Sen. Regist. (Gastroenterol. & Med.) Glas. Roy. Infirm.; Regist. & SHO (Med.) Grampian HB; Regist. (Gastroenterol. & Med.) Glas. Roy. Infirm.

MORRIS, Alun Richard Maelog, 4 Belmont Drive, Bangor LL57 2HS Tel: 01248 364258 — MB ChB 1960 Liverp.; DObst RCOG 1964; DCH Eng. 1966. (Liverp.) Med. Asst. (Paediat.) & Assoc. Specialist St. David's Hosp. Bangor; Paediat. Ysbyty Gwynedd Dist. Gen. Hosp. Bangor. Prev: SHO (Paediat.) Alder Hey Childr. Hosp. Liverp.; Regist. (Paediat.) St. David's Hosp. Bangor; Asst. MOH Caerns. CC.

***MORRIS, Andrea Lorraine** Flat 14A, Wellington Mansions, Queens Club Gardens, London W14 9TF — MB BS 1997 Lond.

MORRIS, Andrew Alan Myles Department of Child Health, Royal Victoria Infirmary, Queen Victoria Road, Newcastle upon Tyne NE1 4LP Tel: 0191 202 3012 Fax: 0191 202 3022 Email: a.a.m.morris@ncl.ac.uk — BM BCh 1984 Oxf.; PhD Newc. 1995; MA Camb. 1985; MRCP (UK) 1987; FRCPCH 1997. Sen. Lect. (Paediat. Metab. Med.) & Hon. Cons. Paediat. Dept. Child Health Roy. Vict. Infirm. Newc. u. Tyne. Socs: Soc. Study Inborn Errors of Metabol. Prev: Lect. (Paediat. Metab. Dis.) Gt. Ormond St. Hosp. & Inst. Child Health Lond.; Action Research Fell. (Clin. Neurosci. & Child Health) Med. Sch. Newc. u. Tyne; Regist. Childr. Hosp. Birm.

MORRIS, Andrew David Erochy, Heughfield Road, Bridge of Earn, Perth PH2 9BH — MB ChB 1987 Glas.; Msc Glas. 1992; MD Glas. 1994; MRCP (UK) 1990. (Glas.) Sen. Lect. (Med.) Univ. Dundee Ninewells Hosp. & Med. Sch. Socs: Brit. Diabetic Assn.; MRC.; Amer. Diabetic. Assn.

MORRIS, Andrew David 15 Gellifawr Road, Morriston, Swansea SA6 7PN — MB BCh 1993 Wales.

MORRIS, Andrew David Philip Beechwood House, Bouverie Close, Salisbury SP2 8DY Tel: 01722 331333 — MB ChB 1971 Liverp.; FRCR 1978; DMRD Liverp. 1976. Cons. Radiol. Salisbury Healthcare NHS Trust. Prev: Sen. Regist. (Radiol.) Liverp. AHA (T); Ho. Off. Walton Hosp. Liverp.

MORRIS

MORRIS, Andrew Duncan 10 Worcester Grove, Shirebrook Park, Glossop SK13 8SJ — MB ChB 1986 Leeds.

MORRIS, Andrew Gareth 16 Osprey Road, Off Farthindale Lane, Waltham Abbey EN9 — MB BS 1988 Lond.; MRCP (UK) 1992. Regist. Rotat. (Anaesth.) St. Barts. Hosp.; Regist. (Anaesth.) Havering Hosps. Trust. Prev: Regist. (Med.) OldCh. Hosp. Romford; SHO (Anaesth.) Whipps Cross Hosp. Lond. & Roy. Free Hosp. Lond.

MORRIS, Mr Andrew Harold Clarence Royal Bournemouth Hospital, Castle Lane East (Eye Unit), Bournemouth BH7 7DW Email: morrisandy@hotmail.com; 26 Finches Gardens, Haywards Heath RH16 2PA — MB BS 1990 Lond.; BSc Lond. 1989; FRCOphth 1995. (Roy. Free Hosp.) Specialist Regist. (Ophth.) Soton. Cons. Roy. Bournemouth Hosp. (Locum). Prev: Vitreoretinal Fell. Addenbrooke's Camb. July '99-June '00; Vitreoretinal Fell. Vancouver Canada Jul '00-June '01.

MORRIS, Andrew James 20 Stanhopes, Limpsfield, Oxted RH8 0TY — MB BS 1971 Lond.; MRCS Eng. LRCP Lond. 1971; MFOM RCP Lond. 1996; DIH Soc. Apoth. Lond. 1990. Employm. Med. Adviser Health & Safety Exec. Lond.

MORRIS, Angela Eileen 9 Steeple Close, West Canford Heath, Poole BH17 9BJ — MB BS 1972 Lond.; MRCS Eng. LRCP Lond. 1971. Med. Off. Dorset AHA. Prev: SHO (O & G) Roy. Vict. Hosp. Boscombe; Ho. Phys. Roy. Vict. Hosp. Boscombe.

MORRIS, Ann Dorothy 44 Lindeth Road, Silverdale, Carnforth LA5 0TX — MB ChB 1974 Manch. Clin. Asst. (Psychother.) Kendal & Indep. (Psychother.) Carnforth.

MORRIS, Ann Helen Margaret The Group Practice, Green St., Forfar DD8 3AR Tel: 01307 426316 Fax: 01307 463623; Inchley, Alyth, Blairgowrie PH11 8HJ Tel: 01828 632548 Fax: 01828 633081 — MB ChB 1973 Glas.; MRCGP 1983. Hon. Lect. Univ. of Dundee.

MORRIS, Ann Kathleen Flat 3, 47 Cathcart Road, London SW10 9JE — MB ChB 1971 Leeds.

MORRIS, Ann Phyllis Caesar's Camp, Sandy SG19 2AD Tel: 01767 680388 Fax: 01767 692099 — MB BS 1961 Lond.; MRCS Eng. LRCP Lond. 1961; T(GP) 1991. (St. Thos.) Socs: Retd. FRSM.

MORRIS, Anna Claire 1 Badgers Cross, Gulval, Penzance TR20 8XE Email: smorris@cwcom.net — MB BS 1991 Lond.; DCH RCP Lond. 1996; DRCOG 1995; MRCGP 1998. (Guy's) GP Retainee, Cornw.

***MORRIS, Anna Katherine** Green Pastures, Battenhall Avenue, Worcester WR5 2HW — MB BS 1998 Lond.; MB BS Lond 1998.

MORRIS, Anthony Harcourt Ladysmith Avenue Surgery, 1 Ladysmith Avenue, Brightlingsea, Colchester CO7 0JB Tel: 01206 305577 Fax: 01206 304866; 21 Church Road, Brightlingsea, Colchester CO7 0JE Tel: 0120630 3875 — MB BS Lond. 1965; MRCS Eng. LRCP Lond. 1965; DA Eng. 1968. (St. Geo.) Med. Off. (Anaesth.) Colchester Hosps.; Local Med. Dir. Health Call Serv. Clacton-on-Sea. Socs: Assn. Anaesth. Prev: Regist. (Anaesth.) Roy. N.. Hosp. Lond.; Resid. (Anaesth.) Guy's Hosp. Lond.; Surg. Lt. CDR RNR Retd.

MORRIS, Anthony Isaac 7 Cromptons Lane, Calderstones, Liverpool L18 3EU Tel: 0151 722 5530 Fax: 0151 722 5530 Email: morris@l18.u-net.com — MSc Manch. 1967, BSc (Hons. Physiol.) 1966, MD 1981; MB ChB Manch. 1969; FRCP Lond. 1985; MRCP (UK) 1972. (Manchester) Cons. Phys. & Gastroenterol. Roy. Liverp. Univ. Hosp. Socs: Assn. Phys.; Brit. Soc. Gastroenterol. Prev: Sen. Lect. (Med.) & Cons. Phys. Walton Hosp. Liverp.; Lect. (Med.) Univ. Manch. Hope Hosp. Salford; Regist. Univ. Coll. Hosp. & Whittington Hosp. Lond.

MORRIS, Mr Arthur Leyland Robinson 19 Salisbury Road, Cressington Park, Liverpool L19 0PH — MB ChB 1957 Liverp.; MChOrth Liverp. 1966, MB ChB 1957; FRCS Ed. 1965.

MORRIS, Mr Arthur MacGregor, OBE Tayside University Hospital Trust, Nine Wells Hospital, Dundee DD1 9SY Tel: 01382 660111; Tel: 01334 477741 — MB BChir 1965 Camb.; MA Camb. 1966; FRCS Ed. 1981; FRCS Eng. 1970; MRCS Eng. LRCP Lond. 1965. (Camb. & Guy's) Cons. Plastic Surg. Ninewells Hosp. Dundee; Hon. Sen. Lect. Univ. Dundee; Clin. Gp. Director Tayside Univ. Hosp. Trust. Socs: Brit. Assn. Plastic Surg. & Brit. Assn. Aesthetic Plastic Surgs.; BMA (Past Chairm. Scott. Counc.). Prev: Sen. Regist. (Plastic Surg.) Bangour Gen. Hosp. Broxburn; Regist. (Plastic Surg.) Canniesburn Hosp. Glas.; Regist. (Accid. & Orthop. Surg.) Guy's Hosp. Lond.

MORRIS, Arthur Oliver Nixon (retired) 106 Molesworth Road, Stoke, Plymouth PL3 4AQ Tel: 01752 51170 — MB BS 1954 Lond. Ho. Phys. Staincliffe Hosp. Dewsbury. Prev: Ho. Surg. Gen. Hosp. Soton. & Alexandra Matern. Hosp. Devonport.

MORRIS, Brenda (retired) 12 Bassett Crescent East, Southampton SO16 7PB Tel: 02380 27258 — LRCP LRCS 1952 Ed.; LRCP LRCS Ed. LRFPS Glas. 1952; FRCPsych 1983, M 1973; DPM Eng. 1970. Prev: Cons. Psychiat. Knowle Hosp. Fareham & Roy. S. Hants. Hosp. Soton.

MORRIS, Mr Bruce Daniel Alexander The Priory, Prestbury, Cheltenham GL52 3AP Tel: 01242 516894 Fax: 01242 514874; The Priory, Prestbury, Cheltenham GL52 3AP Tel: 01242 516894 Fax: 01242 514894 — MB BS Lond. 1965; FRCS Eng. 1970; MRCS Eng. LRCP Lond. 1965. (Char. Cross) Cons. Orthop. Surg. Glos. Roy. Hosp. Socs: Fell. BOA; Brit. Elbow & Shoulder Soc. Prev: Sen. Regist. (Orthop.) Wessex RHB; Regist. (Orthop.) St. Geo. Hosp. S.W. Metrop. RHB; Ho. Surg. (Orthop.) Dept. Hosp. Sick Childr. Lond.

MORRIS, Carey Boynes Phyllis Tuckwell Hospice, Waverley Lane, Farnham GU9 8BL; Westgate, 6 Burnt Hill Road, Farnham GU10 4RZ Tel: 01252 715590 Email: gs24@dial.pipex.com — MB BS 1973 Lond.; MRCS Eng. LRCP Lond. 1973; DObst RCOG 1976. (Guy's) Med. Dir. Phyllis Tuckwell Hospice Farnham; Hon. Cons. Palliat. Med. Roy. Surrey Co. Hosp. Trust & Frimley Pk. Hosp. Trust. Socs: Assn. Palliat. Med.; Fell. RSM. Prev: GP Farnham.

MORRIS, Carmel Mary Castle Surgery, 5 Darwin Street, Castle, Northwich CW8 1BU Tel: 01606 74863 Fax: 01606 784847; 7 Granby Road, Stockton Heath, Warrington WA4 6PH — MB ChB 1989 Liverp.; MRCGP 1994; DRCOG 1992; Cert. Family Plann. JCC 1992. GP Princip. Prev: Trainee GP Frodsham; SHO (Cas.) Alder Hey Childr. Hosp. & Roy. Liverp. Hosp.

MORRIS, Catherine Margaret Radiology Dept., St James Wing, St Georges Hospital, Blackshaw Rd, London SW17 0QT Tel: 020 8725 1481; 162 Wimbledon Park Road, London SW18 SUG Tel: 020 8874 2170 — MB ChB 1988 Liverp.; BSc (Hons.) 1985; MRCP (UK) 1991; FRCR 1996; DTM & H RCP Lond. 1992. (Liverp.) Cons.Radiol. St. Geo. Hosp. Lond. Prev: Specialist Regist. (Radiol.) St. Geo. Hosp. Lond.; Regist. (Radiol.) John Radcliffe Hosp. Oxf.; Regist. (Med.) Hillingdon Hosp. Uxbridge.

MORRIS, Charles Henry St. Andrews Lodge, Julian Hospital, Norwich NR2 3TD Tel: 01603 421839 Fax: 01603 421839 Email: charles.morris@narfmhc-tr.anglox.nhs.uk — MB BChir 1981 Camb.; MRCPsych. 1987. (Camb. & King's) Cons. Old Age Psychiat. Norf. Healthcare NHS Trust. Prev: Regist. & Sen. Regist. (Psychiat.) Warneford Hosp. Oxf.; Cons. Old Age Psychiat. St. And. Hosp. Norwich.

MORRIS, Charles John (retired) 1 Manor Farm House, Lime Avenue, Leamington Spa CV32 7DB Tel: 01926 425561 — MB ChB 1960 Ed.; DObst RCOG 1964.

MORRIS, Charles Quentin Zeneca Pharmaceuticals, Mereside, Alderly Park, Macclesfield SK10 4TG Tel: 01625 512749 Fax: 01625 582901; 8 Westminster Close, Sale M33 5WZ Tel: 0161 969 0892 — MB ChB 1989 Sheff.; BMedSci (Hons.) Sheff. 1988; MRCP (UK) 1992. (Sheff.) Med. Adviser (Oncol.) Zeneca Pharmaceut. Macclesfield. Prev: Lect. & Regist. (Med. Oncol.) Christie Hosp. Manch.; SHO (Med.) Manch. Roy. Infirm.

MORRIS, Christopher Abrahall (retired) 16 Mayfield Drive, Shrewsbury SY2 6PB Tel: 01743 236120 — MB BS 1959 Lond.; BSc Lond. 1953, MD 1971; Dip. Ven. Soc. Apoth. Lond. 1983; Dip. Bact. Lond 1963. Prev: Cons. Microbiol. & Dir. Pub. Health Laborat. Roy. Shrewsbury Hosp.

MORRIS, Christopher Brian, Group Capt. RAF Med. Br. Ministry of Defence Surgeon General's Department, Room 755, St. Giles Court, 1-13 St Giles High Street, London WC2H 8LD Tel: 020 7807 8761 — MB BS 1975 Lond.; MMedSci Birm. 1995; AFOM 1996 MFOM 1996; DAvMed FOM RCP Lond. 1986; DRCOG 1978.

MORRIS, Christopher David Eaton Oakeswell Health Centre, Wednesbury WS10 9HP Tel: 0121 556 2114 Fax: 0121 505 1843; 48 Brookhouse Road, Walsall WS5 3AD Tel: 01922 612296 — MB ChB 1969 St. And.; MRCGP 1974; DObst RCOG 1972. (St. And.) Socs: BMA. Prev: SHO (Obst.) RAF Hosp. Wegberg; Ho. Surg. Roy. Salop. Infirm. Shrewsbury; Flight Lt. RAF Med. Br.

***MORRIS, Christopher Richard** Tresco, St. Marys Road, Osbaston, Monmouth NP25 3JE — MB ChB 1995 Manch.

MORRIS, Clive Dylan Tyddyn Bach, Malltraeth, Bodorgan LL62 5AG — MB ChB 1995 Manch.

MORRIS, Connor Edward Nuffield Health Centre, Welch Way, Witney OX28 6JQ Tel: 01993 703641; The Priory, 3 Church Green, Witney OX28 4AZ Tel: 01993 776445 Email: edmorris@moggie23.freeserve.co.uk — MB BS 1977 Lond.; BSc (Anthropol.) Lond. 1974; MRCGP 1982. (St. Bart.) GP; Trainer Oxf. VTS. Socs: Oxf. Med. Soc.; BMA. Prev: Med. Off. Maua Methodist Hosp. Kenya & Madadeni Hosp. Zululand S. Afr.; Trainee GP Roy. Free VTS & Kentish Town Health Centre; Ho. Phys. Addenbrooke's Hosp. Camb.

MORRIS, Craig Andrew 27 James Grove, Kirkcaldy KY1 1TN — MB ChB 1992 Ed.

MORRIS, Cyril Harold 7 Sandmoor Green, Sandmoor Lane, Leeds LS17 7SB — MB ChB Leeds 1948.

MORRIS, Danielle Louise — MB BS 1990 Lond.; BSc (Hons.) Lond. 1987; MRCP (UK) 1994. (Middlx. Hosp.) p/t Specialist Regist. Gastroenterol.; Gastroenterol. Regist. (Calman Trainee). Socs: BMA & Roy. Soc. Med. Prev: Regist. (Med.) Middlx. Hosp. Lond., Roy Free Hosp Lond. & King Geo. Hosp. Ilford; SHO (Med.) N.wick Pk. Hosp. Harrow; Ho. Off. (Med.) Middlx. & Univ. Coll. Hosp. Lond.

MORRIS, David (retired) 43 Collingwood Crescent, Ponteland, Newcastle upon Tyne NE20 9DZ Tel: 01661 824708 — MD Ed. 1968, MB ChB 1961; FFPHM 1989; FFCM 1982, M 1974; DPH Ed. 1965. Sen. Lect. (Pub. Health) Univ. Newc. Upon Tyne.; Cons. Pub. Health Med. N.. RHA. Prev: PMO N.Z. Dept. Health.

MORRIS, David 7 Merlay Drive, Dinnington, Newcastle upon Tyne NE13 7LT Tel: 01661 825362 Email: david.morris@ncl.ac.uk — MB ChB 1989 Sheff.; MRCP (UK) 1992; Dip. Med. Sci. Newc. 1997. (Univ. of Sheff.) Research Regist. (Cardiol.) Freeman Hosp. Newc. u. Tyne. Socs: Brit. Soc. of Echocardiography. Prev: Regist. (Cardiol.) Newc. Gen. Hosp.; Regist. (Cardiol.) Freeman Hosp. Newc.

MORRIS, David Evan St Mark's Dee View Surgery, Church Street, Connah's Quay, Deeside CH5 4AD Tel: 01244 812003 — MB BCh 1980 Wales; MA Camb. 1981; MRCP (UK) 1985; MRCGP 1987; DRCOG 1987; DCH RCP Lond. 1983. Med. Director, Deeside out-of-hours GP Co-op. Socs: Y Gymdeithas Feddygol.; Clwyd Med. Audit. Advis. Gp. Prev: Regist. (Med.) Glan Clwyd Hosp. Bodelwyddan; SHO (Radiol. & Oncol.) Roy. Beatson Mem. Hosp. Glas.; Ho. Surg. Caernarvonsh. & Anglesey Hosp. Bangor.

MORRIS, David John Michael Batt Foundation, 4 Creykes Court, Craigie Drive, Millfields, Stonehouse, Plymouth PL1 3JB Tel: 01752 310531 — MB ChB Bristol 1968; MRCPsych 1972; DPM Eng. 1971. (Bristol) Cons. Psychiatrist Michael Batt Foundat. Prev: Cons. Psychiat. (Learning Disabil.) Plymouth Community Servs. NHS Trust; Med. Dir. Plymouth Community Serv. NHS Trust; Cons. Child Adolesc. Psychiat. Bristol Hosp. for Sick Childr. & Ment. Handicap Bristol & W.on HA.

***MORRIS, David Michael** 33 Sefton Road, Birmingham B16 9DR — MB ChB 1994 Birm.; ChB Birm. 1994.

MORRIS, Mr David Peter Flat 1, 23 Whitworth Street, Manchester M1 5ND Email: dp_morris@yahoo.co.uk; Flat 1, 23 Whitworth Street, Manchester M1 5ND Email: dp_morris@yahoo.co.uk — MB BS 1991 Lond.; FRCS (ORL-HNS) 2001; BSc (Hons.) Lond. 1987; FRCS Eng. 1995; FRCS (Oto.) 1996. (St. Barts.) Specialist Regist. Rotat. (Otorhinolaryng.) N W Eng.; Fell. in Otol./NeurOtol., Dalmousie Univ., Halifax, Nova Scotia, Canada (from Jan. 2002). Socs: Assn. Otolaryng. in Train.; Brit. Assn. Paediat. Otol.; Brit. Assn. Otorhinol. Head & Neck Surg. Prev: SHO (Otorhinolaryng.) Addenbrooke's Camb., Gt. Ormond St. Hosp. Lond. & RNTNEH Lond.

MORRIS, David Robert Park Green Surgery, Sunderland Street, Macclesfield SK11 6HW Tel: 01625 429555 Fax: 01625 502950; 14 Harrington Drive, Gawsworth, Macclesfield SK11 9RD — MB ChB 1990 Bristol; MRCGP 1995; Dip. IMC RCS Ed. 1994. Prev: Trainee GP Plymouth.

MORRIS, David Stuart 6 Earlston Park, The Mount, Shrewsbury SY3 8BE — MB BChir 1990 Camb.; PhD Camb. 1981, MA 1981; MRCGP 1995; DRCOG 1994; DFFP 1994; DCH RCP Lond. 1993; MRCP (Lond.) 1997. (Cambridge)

MORRIS, Deborah East Street Surgery, East Street, South Molton EX36 3BU Tel: 01769 573811; Forest View, North St, South Molton EX36 3AW — MB ChB 1979 Birm. GP S. Molton.

MORRIS, Delia Florence (retired) 16 Mayfield Drive, Shrewsbury SY2 6PB Tel: 01743 236120 — MB BS 1956 Lond.; MFPHM 1974; Dip. Ven. Soc. Apoth. Lond. 1975; DPH Bristol 1965. Prev: Cons. Genitourin Med. Walsall & Burton Dist. Hosp.

MORRIS, Donald Ridgway (retired) Lower Deck, 1 Queens Park, Pipers Lane, Heswall, Wirral CH60 9HP Tel: 0151 342 8472 — MB ChB Liverp. 1953; DPH Liverp. 1959; FFCM 1981, M 1974. Prev: Cons. Occupat. Health Phys. Clwyd HA.

MORRIS, Dorothy Cecilia 52 Eton Court, Eton Avenue, London NW3 3HJ Tel: 020 7722 0216 — MB BS 1935 Durh. (Newc.upon Tyne) Prev: Ho. Surg. (ENT) Qu. Eliz. Hosp. Childr. Hackney Rd.; Clin. Asst. Hosp. Sick Childr. Gt. Ormond St.; Asst. MOH Wembley.

MORRIS, Edith Wendy The Surgery, Madams Paddock, Chew Magna, Bristol BS40 8PP Tel: 01275 332420 Fax: 01275 333860 — MB BS 1987 Lond.; MRCGP 1991.

MORRIS, Edmund Arthur John 2 Fraley Road, Bristol BS9 3BS — MB BS 1992 Lond.; BSc (Hons.) Human Genetics Lond. 1989; FRCA Lond. 1997. Specialist Regist. (Anaesth.) Bristol & SW Regions. Socs: Assn. Anaesth.; Soc. Anaesth. SW Region; Europ. Soc. Of Anaesthesiology. Prev: Med. SHO Frenchay Hosp. Bristol Anaesth. SHO Bristol & SW Region; Vis. Instruc. in anaesthesiology, Univ. of Michigan, USA.

MORRIS, Edmund Noel Blackmore Health Centre, Blackmore Drive, Sidmouth EX10 8ET Tel: 01395 512601 Fax: 01395 578408; Trenoweth, Elmway, Coreway, Sidford, Sidmouth EX10 9SE Tel: 01395 577574 — MB BS 1973 Lond.; MRCGP 1978; DA Eng. 1980; DCH Eng. 1978; DObst RCOG 1975. (King's Coll. Hosp.) SHO (Anaesth.) Roy. Devon & Exeter Hosp. (Wonford Br.). Prev: Trainee GP Exeter VTS.

MORRIS, Edward Patrick Norfolk & Norwich University, Hospital NHS Trust, Branswick Road, Norwich NR1 3SR Tel: 01603 286829 Email: edward.morris@norfolk-norwich.thenhs.com — MB BS 1989 Lond.; BSc (Hons.) Lond. 1986; MRCOG 1995. Cons. Norf. & Norwich Univ. Hosp., Dept. of Obst. & Gyn., Norwich. Socs: BMA; Brit. Menopause Soc.

***MORRIS, Edward Stephen** Delamore Lodge, Long Sutton, Spalding PE12 9DP — BM BS 1995 Nottm.

MORRIS, Mr Edwin David 22 Sheen Common Drive, Richmond TW10 5BN Tel: 020 8876 4023 — MD Wales 1969, MB BCh (Distinc. Anat. & Obst. &; Gyn.) 1950; FRCS Eng. 1958; FRCOG 1972, M 1960, DObst 1951. (Cardiff) Cons. Emerit. O & G Surg. Qu. Charlotte's & Chelsea Hosp. Wom.Lond; Cons. Emerit. O & G Surg. Guy's Hosp. Lond. Prev: Hon. Cons. Advisor to the Army; Examr. Centr. Midw. Bd., Univ. Lond., RCOG & RCS Eng.; Fell. Roy. Soc. Med. (Ex-Pres. Sect. O & G).

MORRIS, Elizabeth Helene Mulberry Tree House, Devonshire Avenue, Amersham HP6 5JF — BM 1992 Soton.

MORRIS, Elizabeth Jane West Lodge, Oaklands Manor, Thorner Lane, Scarcroft, Leeds LS14 3AH — MB BS 1991 Lond.

MORRIS, Elizabeth Jane Brenda The Cullen Centre, 29 Morningside Park, Edinburgh EH10 5HD Tel: 0131 537 6797 Email: janemorris@talk21.com — BChir 1980 Camb.; MRCPsych 1990. Specialist Regist. Edin. Prev: Vis. Psychiat. Cons. Gen. Pract. Edin.; Regist. (Psychiat.) Roy. Edin. Hosp.

MORRIS, Elizabeth Margaret Longsight Health Centre, Stockport Road, Longsight, Manchester M13 0RR Tel: 0161 248 1203; Spring Meadow, Coppice Lane, Disley, Stockport SK12 2LT Tel: 01663 762182 — MB ChB 1971 Manch.; DCH Eng. 1973. (Manchester) Assoc. Specialist (Community Child Health) Manch. Community NHS Trust. Socs: Manch. Med. Soc.; Fell. Roy. Soc. Med.; Manch. Paed. Club. Prev: SHO (Obst.) Univ. Hosp. S. Manch.; SHO Booth Hall Childr. Hosp. Manch.; Ho. Phys. Manch. Roy. Infirm.

MORRIS, Eluned Department of Radiology, Torbay Hospital, Lawes Bridge, Torquay TQ2 7AA Tel: 01803 655620 Fax: 01803 655638; Summerhill Cottage, Broadhempston, Totnes TQ9 6BD Tel: 01803 813791 — MB BCh 1980 Wales; FRCR 1988. (Welsh National School Medicine, Cardiff) Cons. Radiol. Torbay Hosp. Prev: Cons. Radiol. Vict. Hosp. NHS Trust Blackpool; Sen. Regist. (Radiol.) Birm. Hosps.; Regist. (Radiol.) Leic. Roy. Infirm.

MORRIS, Emma Catherine 10 Sydney Terrace, Bishop's Stortford CM23 3TU — MB BChir 1993 Camb.; MRCP (UK) 1995.

MORRIS, Mr Emyr Wynne Lincoln County Hospital, Greetwell Road, Lincoln LN2 4AX — MB BCh 1969 Wales; FRCS Ed. 1977. (Cardiff) Cons. Orthop. Surg. Lincoln Co. Hosp. Socs: Fell. BOA; Brit.

MORRIS

Cervical Spine Soc. Prev: Sen. Regist. (Orthop.) Glas. Roy. Infirm.; MRC Clin. Research Fell. (Spinal Surg.) Univ. Dept. Orthop. W.. Infirm. Glas.; Spinal Fell. Robt. Jones & Agnes Hunt Orthop. Hosp. OsW.ry.

MORRIS, Mr Francis Paul Accident & Emergency Department, Northern General Hospital, Herries Road, Sheffield S5 7AU — MB BS 1982 Lond.; FRCS Ed. 1987; MRCP (UK) 1985. Cons. A & E N. Gen. Hosp. Sheff.

MORRIS, Mr Gareth Edward Department of Vascular Surgery, Southampton General Hospital, Tremona Road, Southampton SO16 6YD Tel: 02380 798803 Fax: 02380 798827 — BM BCh 1977 Oxf.; DM 1988; BA Oxf. 1974, MCh 1988; FRCS Ed. 1982; FRCS Eng. 1982; T(S) 1992. Cons. Surg. Soton Gen. Hosp.

MORRIS, George Charles Ransom (retired) Terrysfield, Downe, Orpington BR6 7JT Tel: 01959 572454 — DM Oxf. 1964, MA, BM BCh 1950; MRCP Lond. 1956. Prev: Sen. Lect. (Applied Physiol.) Inst. Basic Med. Scs.

MORRIS, George Dimond Earngey (retired) The Cedars, 85 Lethame Road, Strathaven ML10 6EF Tel: 01357 521397 Email: gmorris4@compuserve.com — MB ChB Ed. 1951; DTM & H Liverp. 1959. Prev: Dep. Gp. Med. Supt. Edin. N.. Hosp. Gp.

MORRIS, George Keith Dept of Cardiology, City Hospital, Hucknall Road, Nottingham NG5 1PJ Tel: 01159 691169 Fax: 01159 627691; Rivermead, Gibsmere, Bleasby, Nottingham NG14 7FS Fax: 01636 830626 — MD 1975 (Commend.) Dundee; MB ChB St. And. 1965; FRCP Lond. 1982, M 1970. Cons. Phys. & Cardiol. City & Univ. Hosp. Nottm. Socs: Brit. Cardiac Soc.; Brit. Atherosclerosis Soc. Prev: Sen. Lect. (Med.) Univ. Nottm; Regist. (Cardiol.) Dundee Roy. Infirm; Lect. (Path.) Univ. Dundee.

MORRIS, Geraint 22 Forest Road, Victoria Park, Cardiff CF5 1HR — MB BCh 1990 Wales.

MORRIS, Gillian Jane 69 Lindley Street, York YO24 4JG — MB ChB 1985 Ed.; DCH RCPS Glas. 1987. Regist. (Med. Paediat.) Roy. Aberd. Childr. Hosp. Prev: Research Fell. (Cystic Fibrosis) Roy. Hosp. Sick Childr. Yorkhill Glas.; SHO (Med. Paediat.) S.. Gen. Hosp. Glas.; SHO (Surg. Paediat.) RHSC Yorkhill.

MORRIS, Gordon James Agnew The Riverbank Practice, Janet Street, Thurso KW14 7AR Tel: 01847 892027 Fax: 01847 892690; 23 Duncan Street, Thurso KW14 7HU Tel: 01847 894533 Email: gomogjam@aol.com — MB ChB 1976 Glas.; AFOM RCP Lond. 1989; MRCGP 1984; DRCOG 1978. (Glascow University) p/t Gen. Practitioner Princip.; Occupat.al Phys. Socs: BMA; Soc. Occupat. Med.; Basics Scotl. Prev: UK AEA Govt. Div. Med. Adviser, Dounreay; Squadron Ldr. RAF Med. Br.; Ho. Off. Greenock Hosps.

MORRIS, Grace Elizabeth Dorema Surgery, Dorema, Bridge of Weir Road, Kilmacolm PA13 4AP Tel: 01505 872155 Fax: 01505 874191; Knapps, Kilmacolm PA13 Tel: 01505 872774 — MB ChB 1976 Glas.; BSc Strathclyde 1971.

MORRIS, Granville Craig Prince Philip Hospital, Dafen, Llanelli SA14 8QF Tel: 01554 756567 Fax: 01554 749527 — MB BCh 1983 Wales; MRCP (UK) 1988; MD UWCM 1998; FRCP (UK) 1998. Cons. Phys. P. Philip Hosp. LLa.lli. Socs: BMA; Brit. Geriat. Soc.

MORRIS, Harold Flat 8, Hadleigh Court, Shadwell Lane, Leeds LS17 6DP — LRCPI & LM, LRSCI.& LM 1960; LRCPI & LM, LRCSI & LM 1960.

MORRIS, Heather Margaret Agnes 27 Euston Avenue, Watford WD18 7SZ Tel: 01923 233065 Fax: 01923 233065 — MB BS 1994 Lond.; BSc (Nutrit. & Basic Scis.) Lond. 1991. (St. Mary's Hosp. Med. Sch. of IC of Sci., Technol. & Med.) SHO (Anaesth.) St Geo.s Hosp. - Tooting. Socs: Assoc. of St. Mary's. Prev: SHO (Anaesth.) Watford Gen. Hosp.; SHO (O & G) Hemel Hempstead; SHO (A & E) Wexham Pk.

MORRIS, Helen Diane Margaret Street Surgery, Margaret Street, Ammanford SA18 2PJ Tel: 01269 592477 Fax: 01269 597326 — MB BCh Wales 1979; DRCOG 1984. (Cardiff)

MORRIS, Helen Diane Penistone Group Practice, The Surgery, 19 High St., Penistone, Sheffield S36 6BR Tel: 01226 762257 — MB ChB 1992 Sheff.; MRCGP 1996; DCH RCP Lond. 1996; DRCOG 1995; DFFP 1995. (Sheff.) GP. Socs: Med. Defence Union; BMA. Prev: Trainee GP/SHO (O & G) Chesterfield & N. Derbysh. Roy. Hosp.

MORRIS, Hermon Tuscan, Hall Lane, Mobberley, Knutsford WA16 7AE Tel: 0156 587 3380 — MB ChB 1961 Manch.; LMSSA Lond. 1961. (Manch.) Prev: Regist. Psychiat. Mary Dendy Hosp. Alderley Edge, Qu.'s Pk. Hosp.; Blackburn & Mendip Hosp. Wells.

MORRIS, Howard Jeffrey 82 Southgrove Road, Sheffield S10 2NQ — MB BS 1970 Lond.

MORRIS, Hubert Charles Talwin The Health Centre, 68 Pipeland Road, St Andrews KY16 8JZ Tel: 01334 477477 Fax: 01334 466512 — MB 1972 Camb.; BChir 1971; MRCGP 1975; DObst RCOG 1975. (Camb. & St. Thos.)

MORRIS, Huw Lloyd 5 Dynevor Avenue, Neath SA10 7AG — MB BCh 1990 Wales.

MORRIS, Huw Rees Institute of Clinical Neurology, Department of Neurology, University of London, Queen Square, London WC1N 3BR Tel: 020 7337 3611 Email: h.morris@ion.ucl.ac.uk — MB BS 1992 Lond.; BSc (Neurosc.) Lond. 1989; MRCP (UK) 1995. (Guy's) Res. Fell. (Neurogenetics) Inst. Neurol. Univ. Lond. Prev: Regist. Neuro. Middlx. UC & Nat. Hosps.

MORRIS, Hywel John Lloyd Fordingbridge Surgery, Bartons Road, Fordingbridge SP6 1RS Tel: 01425 652123 Fax: 01425 654393 — MB BS 1978 Lond.; MRCS Eng. LRCP Lond. 1978; MRCGP 1984; DRCOG 1982. (St. Bart.)

***MORRIS, Ian David** 6 The Orchard, Aberthin, Cowbridge CF71 7HU — MB BCh 1995 Wales.

MORRIS, Ian Hugh 6 Bridge Street, Warwick CV34 5PD — BM BS 1984 Nottm.

MORRIS, Ian Martin Meadowcourt, 42 Desborough Road, Rothwell, Kettering NN14 6JG — MB Camb. 1970, BChir 1969; MA Camb. 1970; FRCP Lond. 1991; MRCP (UK) 1973; DCH Eng. 1971. (Camb. & Guy's) Cons. Rheum. Kettering & N.ampton Hosps. Prev: Sen. Regist. (Rheum.) Coventry Hosps.; Ho. Phys. Guy's Hosp. Lond.; Ho. Surg. Hereford Hosps.

MORRIS, Mr Ian Raymond Barnsley District General Hospital, Gawber Road, Barnsley S75 2EP — MB BChir 1974 Camb.; MA, MChir Camb. 1985, MB 1974, BChir 1973; FRCS Eng. 1978; MRCS Eng. LRCP Lond. 1973. (King's Coll. Hosp.) Cons Vasc. & Gen. Surg. Barnsley Gen. Hosp. Socs: Vasc. Surg. Soc. Prev: Sen. Regist. (Gen. Surg.) N. RHA; Regist. (Paediat. Surg.) Soton. Gen. Hosp.; Sen. Research Asst. (Surg.) Liverp. Univ.

MORRIS, Ivor Joseph Lionel (retired) Imperial Suite, The Grand, The Leas, Folkestone CT20 2LR — MB BCh BAO 1943 NUI; DLO Eng. 1947. Prev: Regist. (ENT & Eye) Gen. Hosp. S.end-on-Sea.

MORRIS, Iwan Bebb Ty Isaf Miskin, Pontyclun CF7 9EA — MB ChB 1991 Bristol.

MORRIS, Iwan Machreth Morris and Partners, Ty Bryn Surgery, The Bryn, Trethomas, Newport CF83 8GL Tel: 029 2086 8011 Fax: 029 2086 9463; Maesyrhaf, Machen, Newport CF83 8QQ Tel: 01633 440196 Fax: 01633 440196 — MB BCh 1965 Wales. (Cardiff) Prev: SHO (Anaesth. & Cas.) Roy. Gwent Hosp. Newport.

MORRIS, Jacqueline Evelyn 23 Balcombe Street, Dorset Square, London NW1 6HE Tel: 020 7258 3548 Fax: 020 7258 3548 — MB BS 1971 Lond.; FRCP Lond. 1990; MRCP (UK) 1974. (St. Mary's) Cons. Phys. (Geriat. Med.) & Hon. Sen. Lect. (Med.) Roy. Free Hosp. Lond.; Vice Chairm. Acad. Bd. RSR. Socs: Brit. Geriat. Soc. (Mem. Counc. & Sec.); Past Hon. Sec. Brit. Geriat.s Soc. Prev: Past Pres. Sec. (Geriat.s & Gerontology) RSR; Cons. Phys. (Geriat. Med.) St. Mary's Hosp. Lond.; Frohlich Vis. Prof. (UCLA).

MORRIS, Professor James Alfred The Gables, 44 Lindeth Road, Silverdale, Carnforth LA5 0TX Tel: 01524 701533 — MB 1973 Camb.; MA Camb. 1977, MB 1973, BChir 1972; FRCPath 1990, M 1978. Cons. Histopath. Lancaster Acute Trust; Hon. Prof. (Biological Scis.) Lancaster Univ. Socs: Sec. Manch. Med. Soc. Prev: Regist. & SHO Bristol Roy. Infirm.; Sen. Regist. Leeds Gen. Infirm.; Lect. Univ. Leeds.

MORRIS, James Anthony Charles Fressingfield Medical Centre, New St., Fressingfield, Eye IP21 5PJ Tel: 01379 586227; Brookside, Grove Road, Brockdish, Diss IP21 4JP Tel: 01379 668748 Email: jacm238@aol.com — MB BS 1990 Lond.; DCH RCP Lond. 1995; MRCGP 1995; DFFP 1997. (St. Mary's)

MORRIS, James Edward (retired) 9 Penlee Gardens, Stoke, Plymouth PL3 4AN Tel: 01752 561776 — MB BS 1958 Lond.; Mem. BMA.

MORRIS, James Henry (retired) Green Pastures, Battenhall Avenue, Worcester WR5 2HW Tel: 01905 354986 — MB ChB 1959 Birm.; MRCPsych 1971; DPM Eng. 1969. Sen. Clin. Lect. (Psychiat.) Univ. Birm. Prev: Cons. Psychiat. S. Birm. HA.

MORRIS, James Martin Eryl Surgery, Eryl, Station Road, Llantwit Major CF61 1ST Tel: 01446 793444 Fax: 01446 793115; Penwyllt, Llanmaes, Llantwit Major CF61 2XR Tel: 01446 794590 — MB BCh 1981 Wales.

MORRIS, Jane Elizabeth Banbury Road Surgery, 172 Banbury Road, Oxford OX2 7BT Tel: 01865 515731 Fax: 01865 510711; Pettiwell House, Pettiwell, Garsington, Oxford OX44 9BD Tel: 01865 361426 — MB BS 1975 Lond.; MRCS Eng. LRCP Lond. 1975; DRCOG 1986; DA Eng. 1980. (Roy. Free Hosp. Med. Sch.)

MORRIS, Jane Marjorie 7 Canonbury, Shrewsbury SY3 7AH Tel: 01743 232406 Fax: 01743 232406 — MB BS 1971 Lond.; DObst RCOG 1974. Prev: Ho. Phys. Med. Unit Roy. Free Hosp. Lond.; Ho. Surg. Copthorne Hosp. Shrewsbury; Ho. Off. (Obst.) Whittington Hosp. Lond.

MORRIS, Jean (retired) 16 Nascot Wood Road, Watford WD17 4SA Tel: 01923 221724 — MB BS 1959 Lond. Prev: Ho. Phys. Char. Cross Hosp.

MORRIS, Jean Ebsworth 79 Lavernock Road, Penarth CF64 3NY Tel: 01222 702238 — MB BCh 1952 Wales; BSc, MB BCh Wales 1952; DCH Eng. 1956. (Cardiff) SCMO S. Glam. HA (T).

MORRIS, Jeffrey Ivan John Pencester Surgery, 10/12 Pencester Road, Dover CT16 1BW Tel: 01304 240553 Fax: 01304 201773 — MB ChB 1974 Liverp.; MRCOG 1982. Prev: Clin. Tutor (O & G) Liverp. Univ.

MORRIS, Jennifer Alice 20 Lennox Street, Edinburgh EH4 1QA — MB ChB 1992 Bristol; FRCA 1997. (Bristol)

MORRIS, Jennifer Elizabeth (retired) — MB ChB 1963 Manch.

MORRIS, Professor Jeremy Noah, CBE Health Promotion Research Unit, London School of Hygiene & Tropical Medicine, Keppel St., London WC1E 7HT Tel: 020 7927 2451 Fax: 020 7637 3238 Email: j.gardner@lshtm.ac.uk; 3 Briardale Gardens, London NW3 7PN Tel: 020 7435 5024 — MRCS Eng. LRCP Lond. 1934; DSc Lond. 1961; Hon. DSc Hull 1982; MA Glas. 1930; Hon. MD Ed. 1974; FRCP Lond. 1957, M 1939; FFCM 1974, Hon. 1977; DPH Lond. 1947; Hon. Fell. LSHTM 1978. (Glas. & Univ. Coll. Hosp.) p/t Chairm. Fitness & Health Advis. Gp. Sports Counc. & Health Educat. Auth.; Cons. Cardiovas. Dis. WHO; Hon. Sen. Research Fell. Lond. Sch. Hyg. & Trop. Med. Socs: Hon. Fell. Roy. Soc. Med.; Hon. Fell. Soc. Social Med.; Hon. Fell. Brit. Card. Soc. Prev: Prof. Pub. Health Univ. Lond. at Lond. Sch. Hyg. & Trop. Med.; Dir. MRC Social Med. Unit; Lt.-Col. RAMC.

***MORRIS, Jill** 60 Hareside, Cramlington NE23 6BL — MB ChB 1994 Leic.

MORRIS, John 2 Boyes Brow, Tower Hill, Kirkby, Liverpool L33 2DZ — MB BS 1990 Newc.

MORRIS, John Brown (retired) 11 Cruickshank Park, Hillside, Montrose DD10 9NA Tel: 01674 830008 — MB ChB 1954 Glas.; FFCM 1981, M 1974; DPH Glas. 1958. Prev: Med. Off. Angus Unit, Tayside HB.

MORRIS, John Derrick (retired) 17 Bourne Way, Midhurst GU29 9HZ — MRCS Eng. LRCP Lond. 1943.

MORRIS, John Edward (retired) 71 Oxford Road, St Annes-on-Sea, Lytham St Annes FY8 2DY Tel: 01253 727338 — BSc Wales 1950, MD 1971, MB BCh 1953; FFPHM 1981, M 1974; DPH Manch. 1958; DCH Eng. 1956, DIH 1959. Prev: Cons. Pub. Health Med. Blackpool, Wyre & Fylde HA.

MORRIS, John Edward Critical Carg., The William Harvey Hospital, Ashford TN24 0LZ Tel: 01233 616041 Fax: 01233 616043 Email: johnmorris@hosphill.demon.co.uk — MB ChB 1974 Ed.; FRCA 1980. (Ed.) Cons. Anaesth. & Intens. Care E. Kent Hosps. Trust William Harvey Hosp. Ashford; Lead Clinician, Critical Care, E. Kent Hosp., NHS Trust. Socs: Intens. Care Soc.; Assn. Anaesth.; Roy. Soc. Med.

MORRIS, John Frank (retired) 13 Springfield Road, Hinckley LE10 1AN Email: john.morris@tinyonline.co.uk — MB ChB Birm. 1959; DObst RCOG 1960. Prev: Sen. Med. Off. DSS.

MORRIS, Professor John Frederick Department of Human Anatomy, South Parks Road, Oxford OX1 3QX Tel: 01865 272164 Fax: 01865 272420; 57 The Moors, Kidlington OX5 2AQ Tel: 01865 375922 Fax: 01865 375922 — BSc (Anat., 1st cl. Hons.) Bristol 1964, MD 1974, MB ChB 1967. (Bristol) Prof. Human Anat. Univ. Oxf.; Wellcome-Franks Tutor (Med. Studies) St. Hugh's Coll. Oxf.; Edit. Bd. Cell & Tissue Research, Neurosci., Jl. Endocrinol. Socs: (Jl. Sec. Counc.) Brit. Neuroendocrine Gp.; (Counc.) Anat. Soc.; Edit. Bd. Soc. for Endocrinol. Prev: Ho. Surg. & Ho. Phys. United Bristol Hosps.

MORRIS, John Llewellyn 109 Nutgrove Hall Drive, Thatto Heath, St Helens WA9 5NW — MB BS 1986 Lond.; MRCP (UK) 1990. (The Med. Coll. of St. Barts. Hosp. Lond.) Sen. Regist. (Cardiol.) The Cardiothoracic Centre, Liverp. Prev: Regist. (Cardiol.) CTC Liverpl.; Research Fell. (Cardiol.) Univ. Leeds; SHO Rotat. (Med.) Brighton.

MORRIS, John Rhidian Morris, Harker, Bleiker and Partners, Ivybridge Health Centre, Station Road, Ivybridge PL21 0AJ Tel: 01752 690777 Fax: 01752 690252 Email: postmaster@gp-I83100.nhs.uk — MB BS 1968 Lond.; MRCS Eng. LRCP Lond. 1968; DObst RCOG 1972. Vice Chairm. S.hams, W. Devon PCT.

MORRIS, John Simon 18 Kingfisher Way, Horsham RH12 2LT — MB BS 1991 Lond.

MORRIS, John Stuart 84 Park Street, Bridgend CF31 4BB Tel: 01656 59155 — MD 1973 Bristol; MB BCh Wales 1963; FRCP Lond. 1979, M 1968. (Cardiff) Phys. Bridgend Gen. Hosp. Socs: Med. Research Soc.; Brit. Soc. Gastroenterol. Prev: Prof. Med. Univ. Riyadh, Saudi Arabia; Lect. Med. Roy. Free Hosp. Lond.; Research Regist. Profess. Med. Unit Bristol Roy. Infirm.

MORRIS, Jonathan Charles Willow Cottage, Warnford, Southampton SO32 3LE — BSc (Intercalated) Anthropol. Lond. 1979, MB BS 1982; MRCGP 1990; Dip. Sports Med. Dub. 1991; DRCOG 1987; DCH RCP Lond. 1986. (St. Bart.) Prev: Trainee GP Winchester VTS.

MORRIS, Mr Joseph Chappell Ranpura, 6 Church Lane, Freshford, Bath BA2 7WD — BSc, MB ChB Manch. 1933; FRCS Ed. 1946. (Manch.) Prev: Cons. Surg. W. Hill & Joyce Green Hosps. Dartford.

MORRIS, Julian Rupert Laurence Ivel Medical Centre, 35/39 The Baulk, Biggleswade, Sandy SG19 0NX Tel: 01767 312441 Fax: 01767 601272; Caesar's Lodge, Caesar's Camp, Sandy SG19 2AD Tel: 01767 681935 — MB ChB 1985 Birm.; ChB Birm. 1985; Dip. IMC RCS Ed. 1992.

MORRIS, Juliet Clare Stoney Stanton Medical Centre, 475 Stoney Stanton Road, Coventry CV6 5EA Tel: 024 7688 8484 Fax: 024 7658 1247; 20 Elmdene Close, Wolston, Coventry CV8 3JN Tel: 024 76 543703 — MB ChB 1972 Bristol; MRCS Eng. LRCP Lond. 1972; DFFP 1993; MRCGP 1977; Cert. Family Plann. JCC 1977; DA Eng. 1974. (St. And. & Bristol) GP Princip. Prev: Regist. (Anaesth.) Coventry Gp. Hosps.; Ho. Phys. Walsgrave Hosp. Coventry; Ho. Surg. Good Hope Hosp. Sutton Coldfield.

MORRIS, June 23 College Fields, Marlborough SN8 1UA — MB ChB 1983 Glas.; MRCGP 1987; DCH RCP Lond. 1987; DRCOG 1986.

MORRIS, Justin Vivian Beacon Surgery, Beacon Road, Crowborough TN6 1AF Tel: 01892 652233 Fax: 01892 668840 — MB BS 1985 Lond.

MORRIS, Kathryn Elizabeth Anne Department of Anaesthesia, Royal Hampshire County Hospital, Romsey Road, Winchester SO22 5DG Tel: 01962 825042; Drove Cottage, Compton, Winchester SO21 2AR — MB BS 1986 Lond.; FRCA 1992; DA (UK) 1990. Cons. Anaesth. Roy. Hants. Co. Hosp. Winchester. Prev: Sen. Regist. (Anaesth.) Soton. Univ. Hosp.; Sen. Regist. & Regist. (Anaesth.) Addenbrooke's Hosp. Camb.; Regist. (Anaesth.) Roy. Adelaide Hosp. S. Austral.

***MORRIS, Katy Laura** 14 Bryn Aber, Holywell CH8 7NZ — MB ChB 1998 Manch.; MB ChB Manch 1998.

MORRIS, Kelly Anne 71B Nightingale Lane, London SW12 8LY — MB BChir 1993 Camb.; BA Camb. (Camb. Univ. & King's Coll.)

MORRIS, Mr Kevin Mark Department of Neurosurgery, Hull Royal Infirmary, Anlaby Road, Hull HU3 2JZ Tel: 01482 675242 Fax: 01482 674636 Email: kevinmorris@btinternet.com — MB ChB Manch. 1984; 1981 BSc Physiol. Hons. Manch.; 1992 FRCS (SN); 1988 FRCS Eng.; 1994 MD. (Univ. Manch.) Cons. Neurosurg. Hull Roy. Infirm. Socs: Soc. Brit. Neurosurgs. Prev: Sen. Regist. (Neurosurg.) Hope Hosp. Salford, Manch. Roy. Infirm. & Roy. Manch. Childr. Hosp.; Regist. (Neurosurg.) Walton Hosp. Liverp. & Manch. Roy. Infirm.

MORRIS, Kieran 21 Laurel Grove, Ballymaconaghy Road, Belfast BT8 — MB BCh BAO 1985 NUI; MRCP (UK) 1990.

MORRIS, Lenore (retired) 3 Lanfranc Court, Greenford Road, Harrow HA1 3QE Tel: 020 8864 0022 — MB BS 1963 Lond.; DPM Eng. 1975. Prev: Clin. Asst. Shenley Hosp. Herts.

MORRIS

MORRIS, Leonard Gwyn Parkside Surgery, 40 Algitha Road, Skegness PE25 2AN Tel: 01754 762108; The Villa, 7 Seacroft Drive, Skegness PE25 3AH Tel: 01754 763968 Fax: 01754 761024 — MB BS 1966 Lond.; MRCS Eng. LRCP Lond. 1966; MRCGP 1976; DObst RCOG 1970. (Char. Cross)

MORRIS, Louise Jennifer 21 headingham Close, Macclesfield SK10 3LZ Tel: 01625 617062 — MB ChB 1998 Manch.; MB ChB Manch 1998. (Manchester) SHO (O & G) Leighton Hosp. Crewe. Prev: Ho. Off. Gen. Med. Stepping Hill Hosp. Stockport; Ho. Off. Surg. Macclesfield DGM.

MORRIS, Lucy Margaret 84 Park Street, Bridgend CF31 4BB — MB BCh 1963 Wales. (Cardiff) Assoc. Specialist Blood Transfus. Serv. Wales.

MORRIS, Madeleine Brenda (retired) Fearnach, 11 Woodland Road, Ulverston LA12 0DX Tel: 01229 52507 — MRCS Eng. LRCP Lond. 1941; MD Lond. 1950, MB BS 1941; FRCP Lond. 1974, M 1954; FRCP Ed. 1974, M 1955; DCH Eng. 1948. Prev: Cons. Paediat. Barrow & Furness Hosp. Gp.

MORRIS, Malcolm David Roy (retired) 42 Hollywood Way, Woodford Green IG8 9LQ — MB BS 1960 Lond.; 1960 MB BS Lond.; 1968 MRCP Lond.; 1960 MRCS Eng. LRCP Lond.; 1991 T(M); 1963 DObst RCOG. Prev: Cons. Phys. Gen. Med. Forest Healthcare Trust Lond.

MORRIS, Marcelle Wendy 10 Haredon Close, Forest Hill, London SE23 3TG — MB BS 1978 Lond.; BSc Lond. 1975, MB BS 1978; DRCOG 1982. (Lond. Hosp.) Community Med. Off. Kings Health Dist. Camberwell.

MORRIS, Margaret (retired) The Cedars, 85 Lethame Road, Strathaven ML10 6EF Tel: 01357 521397 — MB ChB Ed. 1950. Prev: Med. Off. Beihan Miss. Clinic, W. Aden Federat.

MORRIS, Margaret-Ann Martin The Hall, High St., Upton, Gainsborough DN21 5NQ Tel: 01427 838535 — MB ChB Glas. 1974; DRCOG 1978.

MORRIS, Margaret Ruth Harcourt Medical Centre, Crane Bridge Road, Salisbury SP2 7TD Tel: 01722 333214 Fax: 01722 421643 — MB ChB 1971 Liverp.; DObst RCOG 1974. Prev: SHO Alder Hey Childr. Hosp. Liverp.; Ho. Off. Walton Hosp. Liverp.

MORRIS, Maria Teresa Crossgoats, Beacon Road, Ditchling, Hassocks BN6 8XB Tel: 01273 846353 — BM 1977 Soton.; DO RCS Eng. 1981. Assoc. Specialist Sussex Eye Hosp. Brighton.

MORRIS, Marion Algarth House, 12 Algarth Road, Stockton Lane, York YO31 1HA Tel: 01904 59712 — MB ChB 1957 Leeds; DPM 1963. (Leeds) Affil. RCPsych. Prev: Clin. Asst. (Psychiat.) & Regist. Clifton Hosp. York; Jun. Hosp. Med. Off. St. Jas. Hosp. Leeds.

MORRIS, Mark 19 Grovehill Drive, Falmouth TR11 3HS Tel: 01326 314273; 25 Farriers Reach, Bishops Cleeve, Cheltenham GL52 7UZ Tel: 01242 679147 — BM 1994 Soton. SHO (Psychiat.) Charlton La. Centre Cheltenham. Prev: SHO (Psychiat.) Wotton Lawn Gloucester; SHO (Psychiat.) Charlton La. Centre Cheltenham; SHO (A & E) Cheltenham Gen. Hosp.

MORRIS, Mark George Andrew 1 Lynton Road, London NW6 6BD — MB ChB 1986 Glas.

MORRIS, Martha Bronwen 16 Lon Tyllwyd, Llanfarian, Aberystwyth SY23 4UH; 25 St. Francis Road, Whitchurch, Cardiff CF14 1AW — MB BCh 1988 Wales. Clin. Med. Off. (Child & Adolesc. Psychiat.) Brynffynnon Child & Family Serv. Pontypridd Rhondda Health Trust. Prev: Regist. (Gen. Psychiat.) Mid Glam. HA.

MORRIS, Martin Samuel Dominic 5 Brockwell Park Gardens, London SE24 9BL — MB BS 1984 Lond.

MORRIS, Mary-Anne Christine Norfolk & Norwich University Hospital Trust, Bransurck Road, Norwich NR1 3SR Tel: 01603 289936; Fax: 01722 321789 — MB BS 1989 Lond.; MD 2000; MRCP (UK) 1992. Cons., Paediat., Norf. & Norwich Univ. Hosp., Norwich. Socs: Roy. Coll. Paediat. & Child Health - Fell.

MORRIS, Mary Gibb (retired) 11 Cruickshank Park, Hillside, Montrose DD10 9NA Tel: 01674 830008 — MB ChB 1954 Ed. Prev: SCMO Angus Unit, Tayside Health Bd.

MORRIS, Mary Jacinta Raphael, 36 Headland Avenue, Seaford BN25 4PZ Tel: 01323 893899 Fax: 01323 893899 Email: maghee@fastnet.co.uk — MB BS 1976 Lond.; Cert. JCC Lond. 1981. (King's Coll. Hosp.) Clin. Med. Off. (Child Health) Brighton HA; Pract. (Family Plann.) E.bourne FPC & Seaford FPC & GU Med. E.bourne; Forens. Med. Examr. Sussex Constab. Socs: Foundat. Diplomate Fac. Family Plann. & Reproduc. Health Care RCOG; BMA

& Assn. Police Surgs. Prev: SHO (A & E) Roy. Sussex Co. Hosp. Brighton; Ho. Surg. King's Coll. Hosp. Lond.; Ho. Phys. Kent & Sussex Hosp. Tunbridge Wells.

MORRIS, Mary Jocelyn Osler Chest Unit, Churchill Hospital, Oxford OX3 7LJ Tel: 01865 225252 Fax: 01865 225221; 19 Lucerne Road, Oxford OX2 7QB — MB BS 1957 Melbourne; MD Melbourne 1975; MRCP (UK) 1982. Assoc. Specialist (Chest Dis.) Ch.ill Hosp. Oxf. Socs: Brit. Thorac. Soc. & Europ. Respirat. Soc. Prev: Research Fell. (Anaesth.) Harvard Univ.

***MORRIS, Matthew Wiliam John** Vale House Farm, Tintwistle, Glossop SK13 1HT — MB ChB 1998 Sheff.; MB ChB Sheff 1998.

MORRIS, Maya Mary 21 Wood Lane, Bearwood, Bournemouth BH11 9NG Tel: 01202 572820; 112 Chipperfield Road, Kings Langley WD4 9JD Tel: 01923 265565 — MB BS 1987 Lond.; Dip. Pharm. Med. RCP (UK) 1996; FRCA 1993. (Middlx. Hosp. Lond.) Sen. Med. Adviser Merck & Lipha Pharmacuet. Prev: Regist. (Anaesth.) Hammersmith Hosp. Lond.; SHO (Anaesth.) Leeds Gen. Infirm.

MORRIS, Michael The Whitfield Practice, Hunslet Health Centre, 24 Church Street, Leeds LS10 2PT — MB ChB 1977 Ed.

MORRIS, Mr Michael Andrew Spring Meadow, Coppice Lane, Disley, Stockport SK12 2LT Tel: 01663 762182 — MB ChB Manch. 1968; FRCS Eng. 1973. p/t Cons. Orthop. Surg. Stockport NHS Trust. Socs: Brit. Soc. Surg. of Hand; BMA; Rheumatoid Arthritis Surgic. Soc. Prev: Sen. Regist. (Orthop.) Manch. AHA (T); Research Fell. Mayo Clinic, USA; Regist. (Orthop.) Salford AHA (T).

MORRIS, Michael David (retired) York Private Clinic, 16 Priory St., York YO1 6EX Tel: 01904 30411 — MB ChB 1957 Leeds. Prev: Hon. Dir. Research York Clinic.

MORRIS, Michael John Inchley, Alyth, Blairgowrie PH11 8HJ Tel: 0182 832548 — MB ChB 1973 Glas.; MRCGP 1977.

MORRIS, Michael John Warders Medical Centre, 47 East Street, Tonbridge TN9 1LA Tel: 01732 770088 Fax: 01732 770033 — MB BS 1990 Lond.; MRCGP 1995; DRCOG 1994; DCH RCP Lond. 1993.

MORRIS, Michael Sydney The Accident & Emergency Dept, Warwick Hospital, Laiken Road, Warwick CV34 5BW — MB BCh 1961 Witwatersrand; DA RCP London; RCS (England); FFAEM (UK). Cons. A & E Entabeni Hosp. Durban. Socs: BMA; BASICS; BAEM. Prev: Trauma Unit Johannesburg Hosp.; Cons. A & E N. Staffs. Roy. Infirm.

MORRIS, Neil Anthony 1 Oxford Terrace, Bensham, Gateshead NE8 1RQ Tel: 0191 477 2169 Fax: 0191 477 5633; 6 Carlton Terrace, Low Fell, Gateshead NE9 6DE — MB ChB 1985 Dundee; MRCGP 1990; Dip. Ther. Newc. 1996.

MORRIS, Neil Anthony 61 Kedleston Road, Roundhay, Leeds LS8 2BJ Tel: 0113 266 5201 — MB ChB 1977 Birm.; DA Eng. 1979.

MORRIS, Neville Grantham IMI Medical Department, IMI plc, PO Box 216, Birmingham B6 7BA Tel: 0121 356 4848 Fax: 0121 344 4632; 26 Holsworthy Close, Horeston Grange, Nuneaton CV11 6YH Tel: 01203 373179 — MB ChB 1982 Birm.; FFOM RCP Lond. 1997; MFOM 1991, AFOM 1988; MRCGP 1986. IMI Med Adviser Birm. Prev: Med. Off. Nat. Grid. Co.; Dep. Med. Off. Brit. Coal Corp.

***MORRIS, Nichola Claire** 156 MacDonald Road, Lightwater GU18 5YB Tel: 01276 474473; 156 MacDonald Road, Lightwater GU18 5YB — MB BS 1998 Lond.; MB BS Lond 1998; BSc London 1995.

MORRIS, Nicholas Humphrey 15 Dollis Park, London N3 1HJ — MB BS 1984 Lond.; MRCOG 1991. Birthright Train Fell. Acad. Dept. Obst. & Gyn. Chelsea & W.m. Hosp. Prev: Sen. Regist. (O & G) John Radcliffe Hosp.; Regist. (O & G) Roy. Free Hosp. & Edgware Gen. Hosp.; Resid. Med. Off. Samarit. Hosp. for Wom. Lond.

MORRIS, Nicola Mary Hethersett Surgery, Great Melton Road, Hethersett, Norwich NR9 3AB Tel: 01603 810250 Fax: 01603 812402 Email: nicky.morris@gp-d82064.nhs.uk; Pear Tree Farm House, Wymondham Road, Wreningham, Norwich NR16 1AT Tel: 01508 488318 — MB ChB 1985 Leic.; MRCGP 1994; DFFP 1995; DCH RCP Lond. 1989. (Univ. Leicester) GP Partner, Humbleyard Pract. Prev: Trainee GP Norwich VTS.

MORRIS, Professor Norman Frederick Cromwell Hospital, Cromwell Road, London SW5 0TU Tel: 020 7460 5758 Fax: 020 7460 5644; Flat 3, The Etons, 13 Eton Avenue, London NW3 3EL Tel: 020 7431 4626 Fax: 020 7431 4626 — MB BS Lond. 1943;

MD Lond. 1949; MRCS Eng. LRCP Lond. 1943; FFFP 1994; FRCOG 1959, M 1949. (St. Mary's) Emerit. Prof. O & G Univ. Lond.; Hon. Cons. Obst. & Gyn. Char. Cross Hosp. Lond.; Dir. Postgrad. Educat. Cromwell Hosp. Lond.; Chairm. Steering Gp. Commonw. Health Developm. Progr. Commonw. Secretariat Lond.; Sec. Gen. Comomwealth Health Foundat.; Chairm. Scientif. Comm. Little Foundat. Socs: Fell. Roy. Soc. Med. (Ex-Pres. Sect. Obst. & Gyn.); Med. Soc. Lond.; (Ex-Pres.) W. Lond. M-C Soc. Prev: Dep. Vice-Chancellor Univ. Lond.; Dean Fac. Med. Univ. Lond.; Pres. Internat. Soc. Psychosomatic O & G.

MORRIS, Onsy Kerollos Kingston Hospital NHS Trust, Galsworthy Road, Kingston upon Thames KT2 7QB Tel: 020 8546 7711 Fax: 01372 818418 Email: onsymorris@aol.com; New Victoria Hospital, 184 Coombs Lane W., Kingston upon Thames KT2 7EG Tel: 020 8949 9000 Fax: 020 8949 9099 — MB BCh 1976 Assiut; LRCP LRCS Ed. LRCPS Glas. 1983; MRCOG 1987; T(OG) 1991; DObst RCPI 1981. Cons. O & G Kingston Hosp. Socs: Eur. Soc. Hysteroscopy; Victor Bonny Soc. Prev: Sen. Regist. (O & G) Guy's Hosp. Lond.; Sen. Regist. Camb. Milit. Hosp. Aldershot; Regist. (O & G) W.m. Hosp. Lond.

MORRIS, Osmond Denis 24 Cairn Hill, Crieve Road, Newry BT34 2ST — MB BCh BAO 1983 NUI; MRCGP 1988.

MORRIS, Owen Gwyn 26 Frondeg, Llandegfan, Menai Bridge LL59 5TN — MB BCh 1994 Wales.

MORRIS, Patricia Anne (retired) Westgate Lodge, Ruskington, Sleaford NG34 9EN Tel: 01526 832249 — MB ChB 1955 Liverp. Prev: Princip. Clin. Med. Off. S. Lincs. HA.

MORRIS, Patrick Little Belmore, Ratlinghope, Shrewsbury SY5 0SR Tel: 0158 861203 — MRCS Eng. LRCP Lond. 1934; DPM Eng. 1942. (Westm.) Socs: BMA. Prev: Res. Med. Off. W.m. Hosp.; Ho. Phys. Bethlem Roy. Hosp. Asst. Med. Off. Ipswich Ment. Hosp.

MORRIS, Patrick Neville The Surgery, 2 Oxford Street, Southampton SO14 3DJ Tel: 023 8033 5158/1366 Fax: 023 8033 5158; Oak Cottage, The Crescent, Woodlands, Southampton SO40 7AQ Tel: 02380 293300 — MB BS 1976 Lond.

MORRIS, Paul Margaret Street Surgery, Margaret Street, Ammanford SA18 2PJ Tel: 01269 592477 Fax: 01269 597326 — MB BCh 1983 Wales; MRCGP 1987; DRCOG 1986. Prev: Trainee GP Newport VTS; Ho. Phys. Univ. Hosp. Wales Cardiff; Ho. Surg. Morriston Hosp. Swansea.

MORRIS, Paul Michael (retired) Broom Knolls, Lawford, Manningtree CO11 2LP Tel: 01206 230512 — MB BS Lond. 1958; MRCS Eng. LRCP Lond. 1958; DObst RCOG 1962; DA Eng. 1960. Prev: Clin. Fell. (Anaesth.) Hinchingbrooke Hosp. Huntingdon.

MORRIS, Paul Neville 76 Station Road, Wigston LE18 2DJ — MB ChB 1993 Leic.

MORRIS, Paul Robert 18 Elm Drive, Billinge, Wigan WN5 7PU — MB ChB 1986 Liverp.

MORRIS, Paul Thomas Woodlands Park Health Centre, Canterbury Way, Wideopen, Newcastle upon Tyne NE13 6JL Tel: 0191 236 2366 Fax: 0191 236 7619; 21 Falconhill, Kirkhill, Morpeth NE61 2YG — MB BS 1983 Newc.; MRCGP 1987; DRCOG 1986.

MORRIS, Pauline 274 Gorticashel Road, Mountfield, Omagh BT79 8HN — MB BCh BAO 1993 Belf.

MORRIS, Penelope Jane Darwen Health Centre, Union Street, Darwen BB3 0DA Tel: 01254 778366 Fax: 01254 778367 — MB ChB 1986 Manch.; BSc (Hons.) Manch. 1983; MRCGP 1990; DRCOG 1989. (Manchester)

MORRIS, Peter (retired) Gledholt Cottage, 1 Church Lane, Barsby, Leicester LE7 4RF Tel: 01664 840087 Fax: 01664 840791 Email: morrishawoth@anaes88.freeserve.co.uk — MB ChB 1956 Manch.; DObst RCOG 1958; FFA RCS Eng. 1965; DCH Eng. 1960, DA 1961. Prev: Cons. Paediatric Anaestheshetist, Roy. Manch. Childr.s Hosp.

MORRIS, Peter Whitehall Medical Practice, 11 Whitehall Road, Rugby CV21 3AQ Tel: 01788 544264 Fax: 01788 575783; 7 Westwood Road, Hillmorton, Rugby CV22 5QL Tel: 01788 572800 — MB BS 1971 Lond.; DObst RCOG 1973. (Char. Cross)

MORRIS, Peter David Fairfax Road Surgery, 25 Fairfax Road, London NW6 4ET — MB ChB 1962 Ed. Prev: Clin. Asst. Roy. Nat. Throat Nose & Ear Hosp. Lond.

MORRIS, Peter Edward (retired) Godolphin House, Wheal Venture Road, Carbis Bay, St Ives TR26 2PQ Tel: 01736 794807 — MB ChB Birm. 1937.

MORRIS, Peter Gwyn Princess of Wales Hospital, Coity Road, Bridgend CF31 1RQ Tel: 01656 752752 — MB BCh 1970 Wales; FRCOG 1991, M 1976; DObst RCOG 1972. Cons. O & G BroMorgannwg NHS Trust. Prev: Cons. O & G Canterbury & Thanet HA; Sen. Regist. (O & G) Univ. Hosp. Wales, Cardiff & Roy. Gwent Hosp. Newport; Regist. (O & G) Plymouth Gen. Hosp. Freedom Fields.

MORRIS, Professor Sir Peter John, KBE Royal College of Surgeons, 35-43 Lincoln's Inn Fields, London WC2A 3PE Tel: 020 7405 3474 Fax: 020 7869 6005; Fax: 01865 515442 — FRS 1994; MB BS 1957 Melbourne; MA 1974 Oxf.; Hon. DSc 1999 U. Hong Kong; FRCP 2001; PhD 1972; FRCS 1962 Eng.; Hon. FRCS Ed. 1994; FACS 1969, Hon. FACS 1986; FRACS 1968, Hon. FRACS 1995. Pres. Roy. Coll. of Surg. of Eng.; Nuffield Prof. Surg. Emerit. Univ. Oxf. John Radcliffe Hosp. Headington; Edr. Transpl.ation & Transpl.ation Reviews; Emerit. Fell. Balliol Coll. Socs: BMA; Transpl. Soc.; (Counc.) Acad. of Med. Sci. Prev: Cons. Surg. Cancer Inst. Melb., Austral.; Research Fell. (Surg.) Harvard Med. Sch. Mass. Gen. Hosp. Boston; Reader (Surg.) Univ. Melb. Roy. Melb. Hosp., Austral.

MORRIS, Peter Jonathan 9 Figham Springs Way, Beverley HU17 8WB — MB BS 1976 Newc. Staff Grade (Anaesth.) E. Yorks. Hosps. Trust.

MORRIS, Peter Timothy 45 Pikemere Road, Alsager, Stoke-on-Trent ST7 2SE — MB ChB 1971 Manch.

MORRIS, Philip Ashton (retired) 278 Duffield Road, Derby DE22 1EP Tel: 01332 558247 — MRCS Eng. LRCP Lond. 1959; MPhil Nottm. 1974; FRCPsych 1974, M 1971; LAH Dub. 1952; LM Nat. Matern. Hosp. Dub. 1952; DPM Eng. 1957; DMJ (Clin.) Soc. Apoth. Lond. 1966. Prev: Cons. Psychiat. Kingsway Hosp. Derby & Derbysh. Roy. Infirm.

MORRIS, Philip John 29 Church Street, Great Shelford, Cambridge CB2 5EL — MB ChB 1971 Bristol; MA Camb. 1989; FFA RCS Eng. 1975; DObst RCOG 1972. (Bristol) Cons. Anaesth. Addenbrooke's Hosp. Camb.; Assoc. Lect. Univ. Camb. Socs: Assn. Anaesth. Prev: Staff Anaesth. Massachussets Gen. Hosp. Boston, U.S.A.; Clin. Research Fell. Hosp. Sick Childr. Toronto; Regist. Nuffield Dept. Anaesth. Radcliffe Infirm. Oxf.

***MORRIS, Rachel Katherine** 12 Beaumont Green, Colerton, Coalville LE67 8FU — MB ChB 1998 Liverp.; MB ChB Liverp 1998.

MORRIS, Renu 24 Wotton Green Lane, Balsall Common, Coventry CV7 7EZ — MB BS 1964 Lond.; MRCS Eng. LRCP Lond. 1963; DA Eng. 1966. (Roy. Free) Clin. Asst. King Edwd. VII Memor. Chest Hosp. Warwick. Socs: BMA. Prev: Med. Off. Anaesth. Dept. Singapore Gen. Hosp.; SHO Anaesth. Dept. Paddington Gen. Hosp.; SHO Anaesth. Dept. St. Mary's Hosp. Lond.

MORRIS, Robert Hywel Creamore Villa, Whitchurch Road, Wem, Shrewsbury SY4 5QR — MB ChB 1979 Liverp. Cons. in Clin. Audit and Effectiveness; Indep. Practitioner. Socs: Y Gymdeithas Feddygol. Prev: Cons. Clin. Audit Shrops. Health Shrewsbury; GP Holywell.

MORRIS, Mr Robert James Department Plastic and Reconstructive Surgery, Level 05, Derriford Hospital, Derriford Road, Plymouth PL6 8DH Tel: 01752 792628 Fax: 01752 763185 Email: rob.morris@phnt.swest.nhs.uk — MB BS 1985 Lond.; FRCS Eng. 1990; FRCS (Plast.) Eng. 1997. (St. Thomas' Hospital Medical School) Lead Clinician Cons. Reconstruc. & Plast. Surg. Derriford Hosp. Plymouth. Socs: Brit. Assn. Plastic Surg.; Brit. Assn. of Aesthetic Plastic Surg.s; BMA. Prev: Sen. Regist. (Plastic Surg.) Canniesburn Hosp. Glas.; Regist. (Plastic Surg.) Canniesburn Hosp. Glas.; Regist. (Plastic & Craniofacial Surg.) Roy. Adelaide Hosp. Australia.

MORRIS, Mr Robert John Southampton Eye Unit, Southampton SO16 6YD Tel: 02380 794485 Fax: 02380 794120 Email: rob.morris@suht.swest.nhs.uk; Tel: 01962 620600 Fax: 01962 620601 — MB BS 1979 Lond.; BSc (Hons.) Lond. 1976; FRCS Eng. 1986; MRCP (UK) 1983; FRCOphth 1989. (St. Bart.) Cons. Ophth. Soton. Eye Hosp. & Roy. Hants. Co. Hosp. Winchester. Prev: Sen. Regist. Moorfields Eye. Hosp. Lond.; Fell. (Paediat. Ophth.) Univ. Iowa, USA; Regist. Oxf. Eye Hosp.

MORRIS, Robert Joseph Charles 26 Holly Grove, London SE15 5DF — MB BS 1967 Lond.; MRCS Eng. LRCP Lond. 1967; MFCM 1981. (St. Thos.) Med. Specialist (Community Health) Hosp. Good Samarit. Los Angeles. Prev: Dist. Med. Off. W. Lambeth HA; Community Med. Specialist (Informat. & Plann.) Lambeth, S.wark & Lewisham HA.

MORRIS

MORRIS, Robert Owen City Hospitla, Hucknall Road, Nottingham NG5 1PB Tel: 0115 969 1169 Ext: 45630 Fax: 0115 960 8409 Email: drbob@innotts.co.uk; Glen Mount, 285 Trowell Road, Nottingham NG8 2FE Tel: 0115 928 6168 Fax: 0115 913 0826 — BM BS 1988 Nottm.; MRCP (UK) 1996. (Nottm.) Cons. Phys. Gen. Med./Health c/o the Elderly City Hosp. Nottm. Socs: Roy. Coll. Phys. Edin.; Brit. Geriat. Soc. Prev: GP/Regist. Nottm. VTS; Clin. Asst. (A & E) Gdn. City Clinic Johannesburg; SHO & Ho. Off. City Hosp. Nottm.

MORRIS, Robert Philip Dumbledore Surgery, High Street, Handcross, Haywards Heath RH17 6BN Tel: 01444 400243 Fax: 01444 401461; Greenbanks, Horsham Road, Handcross, Haywards Heath RH17 6DH Tel: 01444 400413 Fax: 01444 401461 Email: robandjen@compuserve.com — MB BS 1974 Lond.; MRCGP 1978; DRCOG 1977; DTM & H RCP Lond. 1982; Dip. IMC RCS Ed. 1998. (King's Coll.) GP; Med. Adviser S. E. Water Co. & Anchor Seafoods Ltd.; Staff Mem. Interhealth; Port Med. Office Gatwick Airport; Bd. Mem. Mid Sussex PCG; Accredit. Mem. SIMCAS & BASICS. Prev: Med. Supt. Kagando Hosp. & Project Dir. Rural Developm. Centre Kasese, Uganda.

MORRIS, Robert Walter Epping Place, High Road, Epping CM16 4DD — MB BS 1960 Lond.; FFPM RCP (UK) 1989.

MORRIS, Roger Lloyd Llanedeyrn Health Centre, Maelfa, Llanedeyrn, Cardiff CF23 9PN Tel: 029 2073 1671 Fax: 029 2054 0129 — MB BS 1988 Lond.; MRCGP 1991; DGM RCP Lond. 1990. Prev: Lect. (Gen. Pract.) Univ. Wales; Regist. Rockhampton Hosp., Austral.; Trainee GP S. Glam. VTS.

MORRIS, Roland Howard Morris and Partners, 93 Queens Drive, Bedford MK41 9JE — MB BS 1967 Lond.; MRCS Eng. LRCP Lond. 1967; DObst RCOG 1969. (St. Bart.) Hosp. Pract. (Rheum.) Bedford Hosp.; Bd. Mem. Bedford PCT. Prev: Ho. Phys. & Ho. Surg. Redhill Gen. Hosp.; Ho. Surg. (Obst.) N. Middlx. Hosp.; Police Surg. Bedford.

MORRIS, Rosemary Clara (retired) Broom Knolls, Lawford, Manningtree CO11 2LP Tel: 01206 230265 — MB BS 1960 Lond.; MRCS Eng. LRCP Lond. 1960. Prev: SCMO Huntingdon HA.

MORRIS, Rupa Maxine Jane 24 Wootton Green Lane, Balsall Common, Coventry CV7 7EZ Tel: 01676 533060 Email: 106412.430@compuserve.com — MB BS 1993 Lond.; MA Camb. 1989. (Roy. Lond. Hosp.) Prev: SHO (Psychiat.) Roy. Edin. Hosps.; SHO (O & G) E.. Gen. Hosp. Edin.; SHO (Anaesth.) Edgware & Barnet.

MORRIS, Russell Wilton 71 Park Street, Bridgend CF31 4AZ — MB BCh 1971 Wales; FFA RCS Eng. 1976.

MORRIS, Ruth Rose Cottage, Church End, Stebbing, Dunmow CM6 3SW — MB BChir 1996 Camb.

MORRIS, Ruth Louise Health Centre, Whyteman's Brae, Kirkcaldy KY1 2NA Tel: 01592 642902 Fax: 01592 644814 — MB ChB 1990 Ed.; DRCOG 1994. (Edinburgh) GP Partner.

MORRIS, Ruth Olivia The Grove Surgery, Church Road, Egham TW20 9QJ Tel: 01784 433159 — MB BS 1987 Lond.; MRCGP 1996; Dip. Sports Med. RCS Ed. 1995; DRCOG 1992. (St. Mary's Hosp. Med. Sch.) Princip. GP Egham; Clin. Asst. (A & E) St. Peters Hosp. NHS Trust Chertsey. Socs: RCGP; Brit. Assn. Sports Med. Prev: GP Aldershot; Trainee GP Epsom Dist. Hosp. VTS.

MORRIS, Sally Lapstone, The Leys, Atwick Road, Hornsea HU18 1ET Tel: 01964 532630 Fax: 01964 535548 — MB BS 1957 Lond.; MRCS Eng. LRCP Lond. 1957; DObst RCOG 1959. (Univ. Coll. Hosp.)

MORRIS, Sarah Anne 6 Brewers Close, Longstanton, Cambridge CB4 5BY — MB ChB 1994 Leics.; MB ChB (Hons.) Leics. 1994; BSc (Hons.) Leic. 1992.

MORRIS, Sarah Caroline 20 Durnsford Avenue, London SW19 8BH — MB BS 1986 Lond.; BSc Lond. 1983, MB BS 1986; MRCP (UK) 1990. Regist. (Paediat.) St Geo. Hosp. Lond.

MORRIS, Sarah Jane Top Farm, Croydon, Royston SG8 0EG — MB ChB 1982 Leeds; MRCGP 1989; DCH RCP Lond. 1988; DRCOG 1987. GP Royston.

MORRIS, Sarah Jean 19 Lucerne Road, Oxford OX2 7QB — MB BS 1988 Lond.

MORRIS, Sasha Ruth (retired) 19 Chessington Lodge, Regents Park Road, London N3 3AA Tel: 020 8343 0551 Fax: 020 8343 0551 — MB ChB Glas. 1952; MSc (Nuclear Med.) Lond. 1980; MD Glas. 1973; DMRT Eng. 1968. Prev: Assoc. Specialist (Nuclear Med.) Kings Coll. Hosp. Lond.

MORRIS, Scott Thomas William Renal Unit, Western Infirmary, Dumbarton Road, Glasgow G11 6NT Tel: 0141 211 1851; Flat 6/3, 79 Candleriggs, Glasgow G1 1NP Tel: 0141 552 3670 Email: stwmorris@aol.com — MB ChB 1993 Glas.; MB ChB (Hons.) Glas. 1993; BSc (Hons.) Glas. 1990; MRCP (UK) 1996. (Glas.) Specialist Regist., Renal Unit, W.ern Infirm., Glas. Prev: SHO Rotat. (Med.) W.ern Infirm. Glas.; Research Fell., W.ern Infirm., Glas.

MORRIS, Mr Sean Bryan Birmingham Heartland Hospital, Bordesley Green E., Birmingham B9 5SS Tel: 0121 424 2000 — MB BS 1985 Lond.; FRCS Eng. 1990; FRCS 1997. (St. George's London) Cons. (Urol.) Birm. Heartlands and Solihull Hosps.

***MORRIS, Sharon Rachel** 2 Shelley Road, High Wycombe HP11 2UP — BM 1997 Soton.

MORRIS, Siencyn Evans Lloyd 79 Lavernock Road, Penarth CF64 3NY Tel: 01222 702238 & 702467 — MB BCh 1951 Wales; BSc, MB BCh Wales 1951; DCH Eng. 1956; MRCGP 1970. (Cardiff) Socs: Rhondda Med. Soc. Prev: Ho. Surg. Cardiff Roy. Infirm.; RAMC.

MORRIS, Simon Alexander Roger Chancellor House Surgery, 6 Shinfield Road, Reading RG2 7BW Tel: 0118 931 0006 Fax: 0118 975 7194 — MB ChB 1989 Birm.; MRCGP 1995; DRCOG 1994. (Birm.) LMC Mem.

***MORRIS, Simon John** 7 Willow Road, Liss GU33 7EE — MB ChB 1995 Bristol.

MORRIS, Simon Jonathan Steps Cottage, Penoleton Road, Wisswell, Clitheroe BB7 9BZ Email: drsjmorris@hotmail.com — MB ChB 1992 Liverp. (Liverpool) Doctors to Ford World Rally Team; Gen. Practitioner Locum, Lancs.

MORRIS, Stella Margaret — MB ChB 1988 Manch.; PhD (Psych.) 1999 Manch.; BDS Manch. 1982; MSc (Psych.) Manch. 1994; MRCPsych 1992. Sen. Regist. Rotat. (Psychiat.) NW RHA. Prev: Regist. Rotat. (Psychiat.) Gtr. Manch.; SHO Rotat. (Psychiat.) S. Manch.

MORRIS, Stephen Clayton and Partners, 45 Castle Street, Dumfries DG1 1DU Tel: 01387 252848 Fax: 01387 248096 — MB ChB 1985 Glas.; MRCGP 1993.

MORRIS, Stephen Anaesthetic Department, Llandough Hospital, Penlan Road, Penarth CF64 2XX Tel: 01222 702435 Email: stephen.morris@lineone.net; 17 Cefn Onn Meadows, Lisvane, Cardiff CF14 0FL Tel: 01222 762520 — MB 1984 Camb.; MA Camb. 1984, MB 1984, BChir 1983; FRCA 1990; DA (UK) 1986. Cons. (Anaesth.) Llandough Hosp. Cardiff. Prev: Lect. (Anaesth.) Univ. Hosp. Wales Cardiff.

MORRIS, Stephen Reynolds Seymour Apples Medical Centre, East Mill Lane, Sherborne DT9 3DG; Middle Farm House, Charlton Horethorne, Sherborne DT9 4NL — MB BS 1987 Lond.; DRCOG Lond. 1991. (Lond.) Princip. GP. Prev: Trainee GP Som.

MORRIS, Steven Heatherview Medical Centre, 2 Alder Park, Alder Road, Parkstone, Poole BH12 4AY Tel: 01202 743678 Fax: 01202 739960; 2A Hennings Park Road, Oakdale, Poole BH15 3QU Tel: 01202 673520 Fax: 01202 671095 — MB ChB 1975 Bristol; MRCGP 1980; DRCOG 1979. (Bristol)

MORRIS, Susan Catherine Torbay Hospital, Lawesbridge, Torquay TQ2 7AA Tel: 01803 614567; 1 Decoy Road, Newton Abbot TQ12 1DY — MB BS 1982 Lond.; DRCOG 1984. Clin. Asst. (ENT) Torbay HA.

MORRIS, Susan Debra 14 Ormonde Court, 10-14 Belsize Grove, London NW3 4UP Tel: 020 7681 9217 Email: susie_d_morris@compuserve.com — MB BS 1989 Lond.; BSc Lond. 1986, MB BS 1989; MRCP (UK) 1992; MD Lond. 1998. Jun. Research Fell. Brit. Heart. Foundat. Prev: Regist. (Med. & Cardiol.) Univ. Coll. Lond. Hosps.; Ho. Phys. Univ. Coll. Lond. Hosps.; SHO (Intens. Ther.) Whittington Hosp. Lond.

MORRIS, Susan Jane 17 Cefn Onn Meadows, Lisvane, Cardiff CF14 0FL — MB BS Lond. 1985; MRCP (UK) 1989; FRCR 1993; DCH RCP Lond. 1987. Cons. Paediat. Radiol.

MORRIS, Terence John 3 Windsor Close, Radyr, Cardiff CF15 8BZ — MB BCh 1971 Wales; BSc (Hons.) Wales 1968, MB BCh 1971; FRCP Lond. 1991; MRCP (UK) 1974. Cons. Phys. P. Chas. Hosp. Merthyr Tydfil; Hon. Clin. Teach., Welsh Nat. Sch. Med. Socs: BMA, Brit. Soc. Gastroenterol. & Soc. Phys. Wales. Prev: Sen. Regist. Univ.

Hosp. Wales Cardiff; Ho. Phys. Med. Unit & Ho. Surg. Surg. Unit Cardiff Roy. Infirm.

MORRIS, Thomas Arthur Bayer Hall Clinic, Coseley, Bilston WV14 9DS Tel: 01902 673899; 129 Wolverhampton Road, Sedgley, Dudley DY3 1QT Tel: 01902 674419 — BM BCh 1963 Oxf.; MA; DObst RCOG 1965. (Univ. Coll. Hosp.)

MORRIS, Thomas Arthur Watkin Cricketfield Surgery, Cricketfield Road, Newton Abbot TQ12 2AS Tel: 01626 208020 Fax: 01626 333356; 1 Decoy Road, Newton Abbot TQ12 1DY — MB BS 1982 Lond.; DCH RCP Lond. 1986; DRCOG 1985. (Westm.) GP Newton Abbot.

MORRIS, Thomas Meredydd Medeval Ltd., University of Manchester, Lloyd St. North, Manchester M15 4SH Tel: 0161 226 6525; 15 Woodlands Road, Wilmslow SK9 5QB — MB BCh 1987 Wales; BSc Wales 1984, MB BCh 1987; MRCP (UK) 1992.

MORRIS, Timothy Widnes Child Mental Health Team, Chapel Street Clinic, Chapel Street, Widnes WA8 7RE Tel: 0151 257 8108 Email: tim.morris@cahc-tr.nwest.nhs.uk; Email: tcammorris@btinternet.com — MB ChB 1988 Liverp.; MRCPsych 1994. Cons. Chester & Halton Community NHS Trust. Prev: Sen. Regist. Alder Hey Hosp.

MORRIS, Timothy John The Medico-Legal Consultancy, The Old Docks Office, Commercial Road, Gloucester GL1 2EB Tel: 01452 386242 Fax: 01452 304436; Ulwell Lodge, Redcliffe Road, Swanage BH19 1ND Tel: 01929 423359 Fax: 01929 423359 Email: tim.morris@doctors.org.uk — MB BS 1972 Lond. (Middlx.) Sen. Assoc. Medico-Legal Consultancy Gloucester. Socs: BMA & BMAS; Expert Witness Inst. Prev: Sen. Partner Swanage Grp. Med. Pract.; Clin. Dir. Swanage Hosp.; Squadron Ldr. RAF Med. Br.

MORRIS, Treen Carson Michael Haematology Department, Belfast City Hospital, Lisburn Road, Belfast BT9 4AD Tel: 0289 026 3733 Fax: 0289 026 3870 Email: curly.morris@bll.n-i.nhs.uk; The Cliff, Waterloo Road, Larne BT40 1NP Tel: 028 2827 4588 Fax: 028 2827 2766 Email: drcurly@the-cliff.demon.co.uk — MB BCh BAO 1967 Belf.; FRCP 1998 Lond.; MD Belf. 1975; FRCPI 1990, M 1989; FRCPath 1987, M 1975. (Belf.) Cons. Haemat. Belf. City Hosp.; Hon. Sen. Lect. Haemat. Qu. Univ. of Belf; Dep. Director Belf. Link Laborat. Socs: Brit. Soc. Haematol.; Internat. Soc. Experim. Haematol.; Eur. Blood & Marrow Transpl. Gp. Prev: Research Fell. Med. Research Dept. Kanematsu Memor. Inst. Sydney Hosp., Austral.; Sen. Regist. Roy. Vict. Hosp. Belf.

MORRIS, Mrs Ursula Violet Lindley (retired) The Coppice, 29 Pine Bank, Hindhead GU26 6SS Tel: 01428 605049 Email: rhulmorris@aol.com — MB BS Lond. 1960; MRCS Eng. LRCP Lond. 1960. Community Paediat. Surrey Hants Border NHS Trust.

MORRIS, Valerie Jean Stonehaven Medical Centre, Robert St., Stonehaven AB39; 36 Bernham Avenue, Stonehaven AB39 2WD — MB ChB 1987 Aberd.; MRCGP 1991. Retainer.

MORRIS, Vanessa Henrietta University College London Hospitals (Dept. of Rheumatology), Arthur Stanley House, 50 Tottenham St., London W1P 9PG Tel: 020 7380 9035 — MB BS 1987 Lond.; MRCP (UK) 1990. p/t Cons. (Rheumat.) Lond. Socs: Brit. Soc. Rheum.; Roy. Soc. Med.; Roy. Coll. Phys.s. Prev: Sen. Regist. (Rheum.) Lond.; Hon. Clin. Lect. (Rheum.) Roy. Lond. Hosp.; Regist. (Rheum.) Hammersmith Hosp. Lond.

MORRIS, Vernon Charles (retired) Courtyard Cottage, 10 Calcot Park, Calcot, Reading RG31 7RN Tel: 0118 945 2553 Fax: 0118 945 2553 Email: drvem.mm@virgin.net — MB BS Lond. 1949; MRCS Eng. LRCP Lond. 1950; MRCGP 1978. Prev: GP Reading.

MORRIS, Wendy Patrina Robertson Department of Psychiatry, Roundhay Wing, St James University Hospital, Leeds; 7 Nursery Grove, Alwoodley, Leeds LS17 7AL — MB BCh 1983 Wales; DCH RCP Lond. 1986. SHO (Psychiat.) St. Jas. Univ. Hosp. Leeds.

MORRIS, William Brychan (retired) 21 Llwyn-y-Grant Road, Penylan, Cardiff CF23 9HL Tel: 0290 470395 — MRCS Eng. LRCP Lond. 1961. Prev: GP Newport.

MORRIS, William Rex PO Box 15122, London NW11 7ZF Tel: 020 8458 2863 — MB ChB New Zealand 1951; MD New Zealand 1958; DPhysMed RCP Lond. 1971. (Univ. New Zealand) Socs: FAFRM RACP 1984; Fell. Roy. Soc. Med.; BMA. Prev: Regist. (Neurol.) Guy's Hosp. Lond.; Regist. (Physical Med.) Roy. N.. Hosp.; Phys. i/c Med. Rehabil. Unit Palmerston N., NZ.

MORRIS, Yvonne Susan Southpark Surgery, 250 Park Lane, Macclesfield SK11 8AD Tel: 01625 422249; Cherry Trees, 15 Woodlands Road, Pownall Park, Wilmslow SK9 5QB Tel: 01625 525186 — MB BCh 1987 Wales; DFFP. (University of Wales College of Medicine)

***MORRIS, Zoe Susan Clare** 34 Lilburn Gardens, Newcastle upon Tyne NE3 1SU — MB BS 1998 Lond.; MB BS Lond 1998.

***MORRIS-JONES, Rachael** St John's Institute of Dermatology, St Thomas' Hospital, Bel, London SE1 7EH — MB BCh 1994 Wales; MRCP 1997 UK; BSc 1988.

MORRIS-JONES, Stephen David Immunology Department, MRC Laboratories, Fajara, Gambia; 15C Manor Mount, Forest Hill, London SE23 3PY Tel: 020 8291 3958 — MB BS 1985 Lond.; MA Camb. 1986; MSc Lond. 1990, MB BS 1985; MRCP (UK) 1988; DTM & H Lond. 1989. Immunol. MRC Laborats., Gambia.

MORRIS-MANCOR, Charles John (retired) 6A Ravelston Park, Edinburgh EH4 3DX Tel: 0131 332 3777 — MB ChB 1949 Ed. Prev: SHO Chelsea Hosp. Wom. & Qu. Charlotte's Hosp. Lond.

MORRIS-STIFF, Mr Gareth John Dringfa, Darren Ddu Road, Pontypridd CF37 2AH Tel: 01443 491829 Fax: 01443 493486 Email: morrisstiff@compuserve.com; Department of Surgery, University of Wales College of Medicine, Heath Park, Cardiff CF14 4XN Tel: 01222 746536 Fax: 01222 761023 Email: stiffgj@cf.ac.uk — MB BCh 1992 Wales; FRCS Eng. 1997. (University of Wales College of Medicine) Roy. Coll. Surgs. Transpl.ation Research Fell. Socs: Brit. Transpl. Soc.; Assn. Surg.; Assn. Surg. Train.

MORRISH, Caragh 8 Springhill Road, Peebles EH45 9EW Tel: 01721 720543 — MB ChB 1978 Ed.; MFHom 1993. Indep. Homoeopp. Pract. Peebles.

MORRISH, Claude Hugh Francis Hollybank Surgery, 31 London Road, Sittingbourne ME10 1NQ Tel: 01795 472534/425439 Fax: 01795 473886 — MB BS 1963 Lond.; MRCS Eng. LRCP Lond. 1963; DObst RCOG 1965. (St. Geo.) AKC. Socs: Medway PGMS. Prev: Ho. Off. (Anaesth.) Manor Hosp. Nuneaton; Ho. Off. (Med.) Mayday Hosp. Thornton Heath; Ho. Off. (Orthop.) St. Geo. Hosp. Lond.

MORRISH, Leslie William Cardinal Clinic, Oakley Green, Windsor SL4 5UL — MB BS 1959 Lond.; MRCS Eng. LRCP Lond. 1959; FRCPsych 1995, M 1971; DPM Eng. 1965. (Char. Cross) Med. Dir. Cardinal Clinic Windsor. Prev: Fell. (Psychiat.) Univ. Oklahoma, USA; Cons. Psychiat. Bowden Ho. Clinic & St. Bernards Hosp.; Hon. Sen. Lect. Univ. Lond.

MORRISH, Lorna Hollywood Bunton Woodlands, Church Lane, South Elkington, Louth LN11 0SA — MB ChB 1976 Glas.; FFARCS Eng. 1981. Prev: Regist. (Anaesth.) Vict. Infirm. Glas.; Ho. Off. (Med.) Vict. Infirm. Glas.; Ho. Off. (Surg.) Glas. Roy. Infirm.

MORRISH, Nicholas John Bedford Hospital, Kempston Road, Bedford MK42 9DJ Tel: 01234 355122 Fax: 01234 792180 Email: nick.morrish@ledhos.anglox.nhs.uk; 38 Day's Lane, Biddenham, Bedford MK40 4AE — MB BChir 1979 Camb.; MD Camb. 1990; MRCP (UK) 1981; FRCP Lond. 1996. Cons. Phys. Bedford Gen. Hosp. Prev: Research Fell. & Hon. Sen. Regist. Unit for Metab. Med. Guy's Hosp.Lond.; Regist. (Gen. Med.) St. Thos. Hosp. Lond.; SHO (Gen. Med.) Soton. Gen. Hosp.

MORRISH, Paul Kevin Consultant in Neurology, Hurstwood Park Neurology Centre, Princess Royal Hospital, Haywards Heath RH16 4EX Tel: 01444 441881; High Gables, 52 Houndean Rise, Lewes BN7 1EH — BM BCh 1983 Oxf.; MRCP (UK) 1990; MRCGP 1988; DRCOG 1988; DM 1997. (Oxford) Cons. Neurol., Sussex Co. Hosp., Brighton.

MORRISON, Agnes Windyridge, Thornton-in-Craven, Skipton BD23 3TU — MB BCh BAO 1942 NUI.

MORRISON, Aideen Mary 24 Culmore Road, Londonderry BT48 7RS — MB BCh BAO 1984 NUI; MRCPSych 1993.

MORRISON, Alan Gordon 3 Ravelston House Loan, Edinburgh EH4 3LY — MB ChB 1986 Ed.

MORRISON, Alan John St James Surgery, 89 Wash Lane, Clacton-on-Sea CO15 1DA Tel: 01255 222121 — MB ChB 1982 Glas.

MORRISON, Alasdair Duncan Templehill Surgery, 23 Templehill, Troon KA10 6BQ Tel: 01292 312012 Fax: 01292 317594; 9 Harling Drive, Troon KA10 6NF — MB ChB 1974 Aberd.; DRCOG 1977. Socs: Fell. Christian Med. Soc.

MORRISON, Mr Alastair (retired) Torran, 26 Inshes View, Westhill, Inverness IV2 5DS Tel: 01463 790178 — MB ChB Ed.

MORRISON

1948; FRCS Glas. 1963. Prev: Cons. Orthop. Surg. Raigmore Hosp. Inverness.

MORRISON, Alastair Crieff Health Centre, King Street, Crieff PH7 3SA Tel: 01764 652456 Fax: 01764 655756 — MB ChB 1965 Aberd.; MRCGP 1977; DObst RCOG 1967. (Aberd.) Socs: BMA. Prev: SHO (Paediat.) & (Anaesth.) Perth Roy. Infirm.

MORRISON, Alexander Reid, OBE (retired) Lynalder, 42 Brockfield, Culloden Moor, Inverness IV2 5GL Tel: 01443 792030 — MB ChB Glas. 1949; FRCP Glas. 1977, M 1974; FFCM 1979, M 1974. Prev: Chief Admin. Med. Off. Highland HB.

MORRISON, Alison Melville Ardgowan Hospice, Nelson St., Greenock PA15 1TS Tel: 01475 726830 Fax: 01475 888770 Email: alison.m@ardhosp.co.uk — MB ChB 1982 Ed.; MRCGP 1987; Dip. Palliat. Med. Wales 1995; DRCOG 1985; MSc Med.Sci. 1998 Glas. Uni. Med. Dir. Ardgowan Hospice; Hon. Cons. Inverclyde Roy. Hosp. Greenock; Hon. Clin. Lect. Univ. Glas.; Hon. Clin. Lect. Univ. Pais. Prev: GP Greenock.

MORRISON, Andrew Liberton Medical Group, 55 Liberton Gardens, Edinburgh EH16 6JT Tel: 0131 664 3050 Fax: 0131 692 1952; 9 Braid Avenue, Edinburgh EH10 4SL Tel: 0131 447 3875 — MB ChB 1978 Glas.; MRCGP 1985; Dip. Pract. Dermat. Wales 1990; DRCOG 1983; DCH RCPS Glas. 1983. (Glas.) Clin. Asst. (Dermat.) Roy. Infirm. Edin.

MORRISON, Andrew Bruce 18 Park Terrace, Stirling FK8 2JT — MB ChB 1991 Aberd.

MORRISON, Andrew Paul 9 The Pastures, Stocksfield NE43 7NG — MB ChB 1989 Birm.

MORRISON, Mr Andrew William (retired) Dyers, Marden Ash, Chipping Ongar, Ongar CM5 9BT Tel: 01277 365931 Fax: 01277 365931 Email: a.morrison@which.net — MB ChB 1948 Glas.; FRCS Eng. 1957; DLO Eng. 1953. Hon. Cons. ENT Surg. Roy. Lond. Hosp.; Mem. Ct. Examrs. RCS Eng. Prev: Cons. Surg. ENT Lond. Hosp.

MORRISON, Ann Catherine Morven Northcote Surgery, 2 Victoria Circus, Glasgow G12 9LD Tel: 0141 339 3211 Fax: 0141 357 4480 — MB ChB 1969 Glas. (Glas.) Socs: BMA. Prev: Jun. Ho. Off. (O & G) Stobhill Hosp. Glas.

MORRISON, Anna 13 Cawder Road, Bridge of Allan, Stirling FK9 4JJ Tel: 01786 834270 — MB ChB 1992 Ed.; BSc (Hons.) Anat. Ed. 1989; DRCOG 1995; DCH RCPS Glas. 1995; MRCGP 1997. GP Retainee, Stirling. Prev: Trainee GP Forth Valley VTS.

MORRISON, Anne Elizabeth Department of Haematology, Southern General Hospital, 1345 Govan Road, Glasgow G41 5HW Tel: 0141 201 1595 Fax: 0141 201 1608 Email: gcl23@clinmed.gla.ac.uk — MB ChB 1982 Dundee; FRCP 2000; FRCPath 1999; MD Dundee 1993; MRCPath 1993; FRCP 1998. (Dundee) Cons. (Haemat.) S.ern Gen. Hosp. Glas.

MORRISON, Miss Anne Macintosh Department of Ophthalmology, Royal Bolton Hospital, Minerva Road, Farnworth, Bolton BL4 0JR Tel: 01204 390390 — MB ChB 1975 Liverp.; FRCOphth; FRCS Ed. 1980; DO Eng. 1979. p/t Cons. Ophth. Surg. Roy. Bolton NHS Trust. Socs: Manch. Med. Soc. (Mem. Counc.); Bolton Med. Soc.; N. Eng. Ophth. Soc. Prev: Cons. Ophth. Surg. Birch Hill Hosp. Rochdale & Bury Gen. Hosp.; Sen. Regist. (Ophth.) Manch. Roy. Eye Hosp.; Regist. St. Paul's Eye Hosp. Liverp. SHO St. Paul's Eye Hosp. Liverp.

MORRISON, Anne Robertson 78 Scarisbrick New Road, Southport PR8 6PJ Tel: 01704 538299 — MB ChB 1940 Glas. Prev: Asst. Med. Off. Stobhill Hosp. Glas. & Robroyston Hosp. Glas.

MORRISON, Audrey Teaching & Research division, Royal Dundee Liill Hospital, Dundee DD2 5NF — MB ChB 1983 Aberd.; MRCGP 1987; MRCPsych 1991; DRCOG 1987. Sen. Regist. (Psychiat.) Dundee. Prev: Clin. Asst. (Psychiat.) Stirling; Staff Grade Psychiat. Knowle Hosp. Fareham; Regist. (Psychiat.) Gtr. Glas. HB.

MORRISON, Audrey Butler (retired) 4 Roselands, Sidmouth EX10 8PB Tel: 01395 513058 — MB ChB Ed. 1943; DPH St. And. 1949. Prev: SCMO E. Sussex AHA.

MORRISON, Brenda Findon, Minster Drive, Minster, Isle of Sheppey, Sheerness ME12 2NG Tel: 01795 876043 — MB BS 1939 Durh.; MD Durh. 1942. (Durh.) Socs: Brit. Psychoanal Soc.

MORRISON, Calum Alexander 13 Cawder Road, Bridge of Allan, Stirling FK9 4JJ Tel: 01786 834270 — MB ChB 1992 Ed.; MRCP (UK) 1995. Specialist Regist. (Paediat.) Roy. Hosp. For Sick Childr., Glas.

MORRISON, Carole Diane (retired) The Surgery, St. Meddard Road, Wedmore BS28 4AN Tel: 01934 712774 Fax: 01934 713799 — MB BS 1969 Lond.; MRCS Eng. LRCP Lond. 1968; DObst RCOG 1970; Cert FPA 1973, (IUD 1974). Prev: Ho. Surg. New End. Hosp. Lond.

MORRISON, Caroline Elizabeth Greater Glasgow Health Board, Dalian House, 350 St. Vincent Street, Glasgow G3 8YZ Tel: 0141 201 4722 Fax: 0141 201 4733 Email: carolinemorrison@gghb.scot.nhs.uk — MB ChB 1968 Glas.; MPH Glas. 1991; MFPHM RCP (UK) 1993; FFA RCS Eng. 1975; DA Eng. 1970. (Glasgow) Cons. Pub. Health Gtr. Glas. HB; Hon. Sen. Lect. (Pub. Health & Cardiol.) Univ. Glas. Prev: Sen. Regist. (Anaesth.) Vict. Infirm. Glas.

MORRISON, Carolyn Ann Worcester Royal Infirmary, Newtown Branch, Newtown Road, Worcester WR5 1JG Tel: 01905 763333 — MB BS 1968 Lond.; MRCS Eng. LRCP Lond. 1968. (St. Bart.)

***MORRISON, Catherine Jane** King's Healthcare NHS Trust, King's College Hospital, Denmark Hill, London SE5 9RS Tel: 020 7737 4000; Washwell House, Cheltenham Road, Painswick, Stroud GL6 6SJ Tel: 01452 813556 — MB BS 1998 Lond.; MB BS Lond 1998; BSc Pharm. Lond. 1995.

***MORRISON, Catriona Mary** Thyme House, Rattlesden Rd, Drinkstone, Bury St Edmunds IP30 9TL — MB ChB 1997 Leic.

MORRISON, Charles Melvin Charlton House Medical Centre, 581 High Road, Tottenham, London N17 6SB Tel: 020 8808 2837 Fax: 020 8801 4179; 14 Brook Avenue, Edgware HA8 9XF Tel: 020 8958 7737 — MB BS 1975 Lond.; BSc (Hons.) Lond. 1971. (Lond. Hosp. Med. Coll.)

***MORRISON, Charles Paul** 4 Cwm Carn, Caversham, Reading RG4 8LE — MB ChB 1997 Leic.

MORRISON, Clare Elizabeth Suite E, Havant Health Centre, Civic Centre Road, Havant PO9 2AG; 26 Lincoln Green, Chichester PO19 4DN — MB ChB 1990 Leic.; MRCGP 1995; T(GP) 1995; DCH RCP Lond. 1993; DRCOG 1993. GP Princip. Prev: Trainee GP Havant & Gosport.

MORRISON, Clive Leonard The Maryland Centre, 8 Maryland Street, Liverpool L1 9DE Tel: 0151 709 2231 Fax: 0151 707 2721; 6 Steventon, Sandymoor, Runcorn WA7 1UB Tel: 01928 579463 — MB ChB 1985 Liverp. Prev: Trainee GP Wirral VTS; Ho. Off. (Gen. Surg., Orthop. & ENT) Ormskirk Hosp.; Ho. Off. (Gen. & Geriat. Med.) Fazakerley Hosp. Liverp.

MORRISON, Cora Mary Health Centre, Great James Street, Londonderry BT48 7DH Tel: 028 7137 8500 — MB BCh BAO 1982 Dub.; MB BCh Dub. 1982.

MORRISON, Cyril Charles Mitchell 111 Strand Road, Portstewart BT55 7LZ — MB BCh BAO 1967 Dub.; FFR 1994; FRCR 1976; DMRD Eng. 1974; DCH RCPSI 1970. (T.C. Dub.) Cons. Radiol. Altnagelvin Hosp. Lond.derry. Prev: Cons. Radiol. Roy. Vict. & Roy. Belf. Hosp. Sick Childr.; Ho. Off. Nat. Childr. Hosp. Dub.; SHO (Paediat.) Dundonald Hosp. Belf.

MORRISON, David (retired) Welcome House, North Bank, Belford NE70 7LY Tel: 01668 213758 — MB ChB 1958 Manch. Prev: Cons. Clin. Measurem. & Dir. Intens. Care, Coronary Care & Renal Units N. Manch. Gen. Hosp.

MORRISON, David Allan Naismith 1 Bulloch Avenue, Giffnock, Glasgow G46 6NF; 19 Evershot Road, Finsbury Park, London N4 3DG Tel: 020 7281 4421 — MB ChB 1988 Ed.; MRCGP 1994. Prev: SHO Timaru Hosp. NZ.

MORRISON, David Stewart Greater Glasgow Health Board, Dawan House, PO Box 8327, 350 St Vincents St., Glasgow G3 8YU Tel: 0141 201 4926 Email: david.morrison@glasgow-hb.scct.nhs; 3 Hamilton Drive, Glasgow G12 8DW Tel: 0141 334 4715 — MB ChB 1990 Glas.; MB ChB Glasgow 1990; MRCPI 1995; MPH, Glasgow 1997. (Univ. Glas.) Specialist Regist. Rotat. W.ern Scotl. Pub. Health. Socs: Soc. of Social Med.

MORRISON, Diana Patricia Cambridge Street Day Unit, 5 Cambridge St., Edinburgh EH1 2DY Tel: 0131 229 9581 Fax: 0131 228 9075; 3 Eglinton Crescent, Edinburgh EH12 6DH Tel: 0131 225 4439 — MD 1988 Glas.; MB ChB 1978; MRCPsych 1982; Dip. Pharm. Med. RCP (UK) 1992. Cons. Psychiat. Gen. Adult Psychiat. Roy. Edin. Hosp.; Hon. Sen. Lect. (Psychiat.) Edin. Prev: Cons. Psychiat. (Gen. Adult with Special Responsibil. for Rehabil.) Roy. Cornhill Hosp. Aberd.; Dep. Dir. Astra Clin. Research Unit Edin.;

MORRISON

Sen. Med. Adviser CNS Astra Clin. Research Centre Södertalje, Sweden.

MORRISON, Mr Donald Leslie (retired) Crouch House, Langenhoe, Colchester CO5 7LT Tel: 01206 735220 Fax: 01206 735220 — MB ChB Glas. 1956; FRCS Ed. 1968; FRCOG 1978, M 1963. Cons. O & G Colchester & Dist. Hosp. Gp. Prev: Lect. Nuffield Dept. O & G Oxf.

MORRISON, Dorothy Josephine Walnut Tree Health Centre, Blackberry Court, Walnut Tree, Milton Keynes MK7 7NR Tel: 01908 691123 — MB ChB 1986 Liverp.; Cert. Family Plann. JCC 1990.

MORRISON, Douglas Department of Medicine, Falkirk & District Royal Infirmary, Major's Loan, Falkirk FK1 5QE Tel: 01324 624000 Fax: 01324 616000 Email: dougie.morrison@fuah.scot.nhs.uk — MB ChB 1985 Ed.; FRCP (Ed) 1997; BSc (Hons.) Pharmacol. Ed. 1982; MD 1997; MRCP (UK) 1988. (Ed.) Cons. Gen. & Respirat. Med. Falkirk & Dist. Roy. Infirm. Socs: Brit. Thorac. Soc.; Scott. Thoracic Soc.; Scott. Soc. Phys. Prev: Sen. Regist. (Gen. & Respirat. Med.) Frenchay Hosp. & Bristol Roy. Infirm.; Research Fell. Brit. Lung Foundat. & Research Fell. Brit. Heart Foundat. Rayne Laborat. Edin.; Regist. (Respirat. Med.) City Hosp. Edin.

MORRISON, Duart Murray 2 Robsland Avenue, Ayr KA7 2RW — MB ChB 1993 Dundee.

MORRISON, Eileen Elizabeth Sidinish, Ferntower Road, Crieff PH7 3DH — MB ChB 1964 Ed.; DCH RCPS Glas. 1967. (Ed.) Socs: BMA. Prev: SHO Paediat. Raigmore Hosp. Inverness; SHO Paediat. Perth Roy. Infirm.

MORRISON, Elspeth Anne (retired) Calcot Farmhouse, Horsham Road, Steyning BN44 3AA Tel: 01903 813281 — MB BS Lond. 1961; MRCS Eng. LRCP Lond. 1961; MRCPath 1983; FRCPath 1995. Prev: Cons. Histopath. Roy. Sussex Co. Hosp. Brighton.

MORRISON, Mr Ernest (retired) 5 Sandringham Court, Hillsborough BT26 6RB — MB BCh BAO 1942 Belf.; MB BCh BAO (2nd Cl. Hnrs.) Belf. 1942; FRCSI 1969; FRCS Ed. 1948. Prev: Cons. Urol. Roy. Vict. Hosp. Belf. & Belf. City Hosp.

MORRISON, Fiona Kathleen Stirling Royal Infirmary, Livilands, Stirling FK8 2AU Tel: 01786 434000 — MB ChB 1983 Ed.; MRCOG 1990; DRCOG 1985. (Univ. Ed.) p/t Cons. O & G Stirling Roy. Infirm.

MORRISON, Fiona Margaret Milton Surgery, 132 Mountcastle Drive South, Edinburgh EH15 3LL; 7 Kilgraston Road, Edinburgh EH9 2DR — MB ChB 1981 Ed.; MRCGP 1986; DCH Glas. 1985; DRCOG 1984. (Ed.) GP.

MORRISON, Fiona Soutar Royal Cornhill Hospital, Cornhill Road, Aberdeen AB25 2ZH; 143 Clifton Road, Aberdeen AB24 4RH — MB ChB 1992 Dundee; MRCPsych 1997. (Dundee) Specialist Regist. (Psychiat.) Roy. Cornhill Hosp. Aberd. Prev: Regist. (Psychiat.) Roy. Cornhill Hosp. Aberd.; SHO (Psychiat.) Sunnyside Roy. Hosp. Hillside Montrose.

***MORRISON, Garfield Roland** 53 Kingsfort Park, Londonderry BT48 7SY — MB BS 1998 Lond.; MB BS Lond 1998.

MORRISON, Gary Hugh 11 Caulfield Park, Cradlehall, Inverness IV2 5GB — MB ChB 1990 Ed.

MORRISON, Mr Gavin Andrew John 73 Harley Street, London W1G 8QJ Tel: 020 74874446 Email: GAJMorrison@aol.com — MB BS 1983 Lond.; MA Camb. 1983, BA 1980; FRCS (Orl.) Eng. 1988. p/t Cons. ENT Surg. St. Thos., Guy's & King's Coll. Hosps. Lond. Socs: Fell. RSM. Prev: Sen. Regist. St. Thos. Hosp. Lond.; Regist. (ENT Surg.) Lond. Hosp.; Ho. Surg. Middlx. Hosp. Lond.

MORRISON, Gavin Comgall 22 Invergourie Road, Braemere Heights, Holywood BT18 0NL — MB BCh BAO 1987 Belf.

MORRISON, Geoffrey Wilson Bradford Royal Infirmary, Bradford BD9 6RJ Tel: 01274 542200 Fax: 01274 364741 — MB BS 1971 Newc.; PhD Leeds 1982; FRCP Lond. 1990; MRCP (UK) 1973. Cons. Cardiol. Bradford Roy. Infirm. Prev: Sen. Regist. (Cardiol.) St. Jas. Univ. Hosp. Leeds; Brit. Heart Foundat. Jun. Research Fell. Cardiovasc. Unit Leeds Univ.; Regist. Roy. Lancaster Infirm.

MORRISON, George Breton Central Health Centre, North Carbrain Road, Cumbernauld, Glasgow G67 1BJ Tel: 01236 731738; Ancasteil, Dullatur, Cumbernauld, Glasgow G68 0AN — MB ChB 1971 Glas.; MRCP (UK) 1975; MRCGP 1982.

MORRISON, George Duncan West Thorpe, 9 Church Road, Plymstock, Plymouth PL9 9AJ Tel: 01752 482305 — MB BS Lond. 1964; FRCP Lond. 1992; FRCP Ed. 1984; MRCP (UK) 1971. (St. Mary's) Cons. Genitourin. Med.Plymouth Hosp.s NHS Trust; Hon.

Sen. Lect. (Genitourin. Med.) Univ. Plymouth. Socs: Med. Soc. Study VD; Sec. Brit. Soc. for the Study of Vulval Dis.s. Prev: Sen. Regist. (Venereol.) Bristol Roy. Infirm. & S. W.. RHB; Asst. Edr. Brit. Jl. of Ven. Dis.; Ho. Phys. St. Mary's Hosp. Lond.

MORRISON, George Will, MBE (retired) Iverna, 9A Institution Road, Elgin IV30 1QU Tel: 01343 546830 — MB ChB Aberd. 1945; FRCGP 1979, M 1957; DObst RCOG 1950. Prev: Ho. Surg. Aberd. Roy. Infirm.

MORRISON, Gillian Elizabeth (retired) 28 Sheridan Drive, Helens Bay, Bangor BT19 1LB Tel: 01247 852857 — MB BCh BAO 1982 Belf.; MB BCh Belf. 1982; MRCGP 1986; DRCOG 1985; DCH RCPSI 1984.

MORRISON, Graham Edwin Tel: 0141 956 1005 Fax: 0141 955 0342 — MB BCh BAO 1989 Belf.; MRCGP 1994; DRCOG 1993; DCH RCPI 1992. (Qu. Univ. Belf.)

MORRISON, Heather Margaret Selly Oak Hospital, Selly Oak, Birmingham B29 6JD Tel: 0121 627 1627 Fax: 0121 627 8439; 53 Country Park Avenue, Halesowen B62 8SX Tel: 0121 503 0147 — MB BChir 1980 Camb.; MA Camb. 1980, MD 1986; MRCP (UK) 1982; T(M) 1991; FRCP 1997. (Camb.) Cons. Gen. & Thoracic Med. Univ. Hosp. Birm. NHS Trust. Socs: Brit. Thorac. & Amer. Thoracic Soc.; Assn. Palliat. Med.

***MORRISON, Helen Patricia** 4 Cwmcarn, Caversham, Reading RG4 8LE — MB ChB 1997 Bristol.

MORRISON, Hilary Elizabeth 21 Balfour Road, Highbury, London N5 2HB — MB BS 1982 Nottm.; BMedSci. Nottm. 1979, MB BS 1982; DRCOG 1984. Trainee GP John Scott Health Centre Lond. Prev: SHO (Hosp. & Community Paediat.) Lond. Hosp.; SHO (Cas.) Roy. Cornw. Hosp. Truro; SHO (O & G) Nottm. City Hosp.

MORRISON, Hugh Hunter (retired) Shield Row House, Stanley DH9 8AW Tel: 01207 232926 — MB ChB Glas. 1943; BSc Glas. 1940. Prev: Ho. Surg. (Gyn.) W.. Infirm. Glas.

MORRISON, Iain David Kent and Canterbury Hospital, Ethelbert Road, Canterbury CT1 3NG Tel: 01227 766877; Email: iainm@publiconline.co.uk — MB BS 1986 Lond.; MRCP (UK) 1989; FRCR 1993. (St. Thos. Hosp. Med. Sch.) Cons. Radiol. E. Kent Hosp.s NHS Trust Canterbury. Prev: Sen. Regist. & Regist. (Radiol.) St. Bart. Hosp. Lond.; SHO (Neurol.) Addenbrooke's Hosp. Camb.

MORRISON, Iain Martin St. Richard's Hospital, Chichester PO19 4SE Tel: 01243 788122 — MB BS 1963 Lond.; FRCP Lond. 1989. (St. Thos.) Phys. St. Richard's Hosp. Chichester & King Edwd. VII Hosp. Midhurst; Hon. Sen. Lect. Char. Cross Hosp. Lond. Socs: Fell. Roy. Soc. Med. Prev: Sen. Regist. (Med.) Brompton Hosp. & St. Jas. Hosp. Lond.; Regist. (Med.) St. Jas. Hosp. Balham; Regist. (Med.) St. Thos. Hosp. Lond.

MORRISON, Ian Alexander Ardmorn, Culbokie, Dingwall IV7 8JS Tel: 01349 87531 — MB ChB 1948 Ed. (Ed.)

MORRISON, Ian Alexander Neston Surgery, Mellock Lane, Little Neston, South Wirral CH64 4BN Tel: 0151 336 3951 Fax: 0151 353 0173; Lynhurst, Neston Road, Ness, South Wirral CH64 4AP — MB ChB 1964 Glas.; MRCGP 1979; DObst. RCOG 1968. Prev: SHO (Med) Vict. Infirm & W.. Infirm. Glas.; Ho. Off. (O & G) S.port Gen. Infirm.

MORRISON, Ian Donald 125 Worlds End Lane, Quinton, Birmingham B32 1JX Tel: 0121 559 1631 Fax: 0121 240 7661 — MB ChB Birm. 1962; LMSSA Lond. 1961. (Birm.) Med. & Surgic. Hair Treatm. Birm.; GP Birm.; Hon. Sec. Brit. Assn. of Hair Transpl. Surgs. Prev: Resid. Clin. Pathol. Qu. Eliz. Hosp. Birm.; Regist. (Venereol.) Gen. Hosp. Birm.; Asst. Med. Off. Lionel Town Hosp. Jamaica.

MORRISON, Mr Ian Middleton (retired) Morven, 14 Rockbourne Avenue, Liverpool L25 4TW Tel: 0151 428 3755 — MB ChB 1944 Aberd.; FRCS Eng. 1952. Prev: Cons. Cardiothoracic Surg. Mersey RHA.

MORRISON, Ian Ross Garden Flat, 125 Mountview Road, London N4 4JH Tel: 020 8347 9058 — MB BCh BAO 1993 Belf.; MRCP Lond. 1997. (Queen's Belfast) Specialist Regist. (Paediat.) Barnet Gen. Hosp. Barnet. Prev: Specialist Regist. (Paediat.) Roy. Lond. Hosp. Lond.; SHO (Paediat.) Roy. Brompton Hosp. Lond. & Chelsea & W.minster Hosp. Lond.

MORRISON, James Tranent Medical Practice, Loch Road, Tranent EH33 2JX; Cuileann, 7 Kings Road, Longniddry EH32 0NN Tel: 01875 853123 — MB ChB 1969 Glas. Prev: SHO (Path. & Anaesth.) & Ho. Off. (Surg.) Vict. Infirm. Glas.

MORRISON

MORRISON, Mr James Dougall Prosthetic Service, Mary Marlborough Centre, Nuffield Orthopaedic Centre, Windmill Road, Headington, Oxford OX3 7LD Tel: 01865 227291 Fax: 01865 227463; 22 Abberbury Road, Iffley, Oxford OX4 4ES — BM BCh 1972 Oxf.; MA Oxf. 1972; FRCS Eng. 1978; FRCS Ed. 1978; LMSSA Lond. 1972. (St. Thos.) Cons. Rehabil. Nuffield Orthop. Centre Oxf. Socs: Internat. Soc. Prosth.s & Orthotics; Liveryman Soc. Apoth. Lond.; Brit. Soc. of Rehabil. Med. Prev: Sen. Med. Off. Disablem. Serv. Centre (ALAC) Oxf.; Research Fell. (Surg.) Brighton Health Dist.; Regist. (Surg.) S. Lothian (Edin.) Health Dist.

MORRISON, Jane Duncan Department of Anaesthetics, Royal Infirmary, Glasgow G31 2FR Tel: 0141 211 4000 — MB ChB 1990 Glas.; FFA RCS1 1995. (Univ. Of Glasgow) Specialist Regist. (Anasth.) Glas. Roy. Infirm. Socs: Obstetric Anaestretists Assn.; W. of Scotl. Intens. Care Soc.; Assn. of Anaestretists.

MORRISON, Jayne McIntyre Parkhead Health Centre, 101 Salamanca Street, Glasgow G31 5BA Tel: 0141 531 9060 Fax: 0141 531 9042 — MB ChB Glas. 1992; DRCOG 1993; MrCGP 1997. (Glasgow) GP Locums; Family Plann. Locums; Healthcall. Socs: MRCGP.

MORRISON, Jennifer Mary Victoria Road Surgery, 82 Victoria Road, Oulton Broad, Lowestoft NR33 9LU Tel: 01502 572368 Fax: 01502 537035 — MB ChB 1982 Liverp.; MRCGP 1987.

MORRISON, Professor Jillian Margaret Department of General Practice, University of Glasgow, 4 Lancaster Crescent, Glasgow G12 0RR Tel: 0141 211 1666 Fax: 0141 211 1667 Email: jmm4y@clinmed.gla.ac.uk; 38 Grange Knowe, Linlithgow EH49 7HX Tel: 01506 846246 — MB ChB 1982 Glas.; MRCGP 1986; MSc 1988 (Med. Sci.) Glas.; FRCGP 1997; DCH 1986 RCPS, Glas.; DRCOG 1984; PhD 1995 Glas. (Glas.) Prof. (Gen. Pract.) Univ. Glas. Prev: GP Bathgate.

MORRISON, John 199 Acomb Road, Acomb, York YO24 4HD Tel: 01904 342999 Fax: 01904 342990; 3 Nursery Road, Nether Poppleton, York YO26 6NN Tel: 01904 783755 — MB ChB 1980 Aberd. Socs: BMA & Soc. Occupat. Med.

MORRISON, John Booth (retired) Glade House, 2 Archery Fields, Odiham, Hook RG29 1AE Tel: 01256 702348 — MB BS 1947 Lond.; MD Lond. 1958; DPhysMed. Eng. 1955. Prev: Cons. Rheum. & Rehabil. Lord May. Treloar Orthop. Hosp. Alton, Basingstoke Dist. Hosp. & Roy. Hants. Co. Hosp. Winchester.

MORRISON, John Cochrane (retired) — MB BS 1968 Lond.

MORRISON, John David Richmond, Maj. RAMC Retd. 22 Machan Avenue, Larkhall ML9 2HE — MB ChB 1975 Glas.; MRCGP 1981; DRCOG 1980; DGM 1998. GP Motherwell Health Centre; GP Modyrvale Med. Centre, Motherwell; Clin. Asst., Dept. of Geriat. Med., Law Hosp., Carluke. Prev: Regtl. Med. Off. 10th Gurkha Rifles Sek Kong; GP Trainee Brit. Milit. Hosp. Munster; Med. Off. Krefeld, BAOR.

MORRISON, John Douglas (retired) Lime Kilns Farm, Elton, Ludlow SY8 2HQ Tel: 01568 770683 — MB BS Lond. 1960.

MORRISON, John Duncan Riverbank Surgery, Riverbank, Janet Street, Thurso KW14 7AR Tel: 01847 892027/892009 Fax: 01847 892690; 1 College Court, Thurso KW14 7QQ Tel: 01847 895714 — MB ChB 1979 Aberd.; DRCOG 1981. GP Thurso.; Clin. Asst. A & E, Dunbar Hosp., Thurso. Prev: Trainee GP Highland VTS.

MORRISON, Professor John Finlay Benzie Dalesmoor, Reeth, Richmond DL11 6SG — MB ChB 1966 Ed.; PhD Ed. 1970, BSc (Hons.) 1963; FRCS Ed. 1992; FIBiol 1996. (Ed.) Prof. Physiol. Univ. Leeds. Socs: Physiol. Soc.; BMA; Brit. Neurosci. Assn. Prev: Reader (Physiol.) Univ. Leeds; Sen. Lect (Physiol.) Univ. Leeds; Lect. (Physiol.) Univ. Leeds.

MORRISON, John Francis Joseph West Riding Medical Research Trust, Molecula Medicine Unit, Level 6, Clinical Sciences Building, St James's University Hospital, Leeds LS9 7TF — MD 1988 Leeds; MB ChB Leeds 1979; MRCP (UK) 1984; MRCGP 1985; DRCOG 1982; DCH Eng. 1981. Sen. Lect. Clin. Pharmacol. Univ. Leeds. Socs: Brit. Thorac. Soc. & Yorks. Thoracic Soc. Prev: Tutor Respirat. Med. Killingbeck Hosp. Leeds; Sen. Regist. (Chest & Gen. Med.) Camb.; MRC Train. Fell. Camb.

MORRISON, John Lang (retired) Birnie Acre, Balmore, Torrance, Glasgow G64 4AF Tel: 01360 620707 — MB ChB 1956 Glas.; DObst RCOG 1960.

MORRISON, John Lang Birnie Acre, Balmore, Torrance, Glasgow G64 4AF — MB ChB 1991 Ed.

MORRISON, John Mackinnon (retired) 1a Sutton Court, Fauconberg Road, Chiswick, London W4 3JG — MB ChB 1961 Ed. Prev: Late Maj., RAMC.

MORRISON, Mr John Michael 34 Chantry Road, Moseley, Birmingham B13 8DJ Tel: 0121 449 0669 Fax: 0121 449 0669 — MB BS 1958 Durh.; FRCS Eng. 1964. (Newc.) Indep. Cons. Birm.; Hon. Cons. Surg. S. Birm. HA. Socs: Assn. Surg.; Brit. Assn. Surg. Oncol.; Brit. BrE. Gp. Prev: Cons. Surg. Selly Oak Hosp. Birm.; Sen. Clin. Lect. & Tutor (Surg.) Birm. Univ.; Capt. RAMC, Surg. Specialist.

MORRISON, Julia Elizabeth 6 Clifton Drive, Marple, Stockport SK6 6PP — MB ChB 1978 Leeds.

MORRISON, Katharine Mary Ballochmyle Medical Practice, Institute Avenue, Catrine, Mauchline KA5 6RU Tel: 01290 551237 Fax: 01290 552784; 2 Netherwalk, Mauchline KA5 5BL Tel: 01290 552740 Fax: 01290 550747 — MB ChB 1982 Glas.; MRCGP 1986; DMJ(Clin) Soc. Apoth. Lond. 1991; DCCH RCP Ed. 1987; DRCOG 1984; Cert. Family Plann. JCC 1985. (Glas.) Princip. Police Surg. Kilmarnock. Socs: Assn. Police Surg.; Expert Witness Inst.; Scoth. Medicolegal Soc. Prev: Chin. Med. Off. Psychiat. CrossHo. Hosp. Kilmarnock; Trainee GP Irvine VTS; Sessional Clin. Med. Off. Well Wom. Irvine.

MORRISON, Katriona Agnes West Balbithan, Kintore, Inverurie AB51 0UR — MB ChB 1976 Aberd.

MORRISON, Lachlan MacInnes Mackinnon Department of Anaesthetics, St. John's Hospital, Howden, Livingston Tel: 01506 419666; 38 Grange Knowe, Linlithgow EH49 7HX Tel: 01506 846246 Fax: 01506 416182 — MB ChB 1981 Glas.; BSc Glas. 1978; FFA RCSI 1987. (Glas.) Cons. Anaesth. St. John's Hosp. Livingston. Socs: BMA. Prev: Sen. Regist. & Regist. (Anaesth.) Roy. Infirm. Edin.; Research Fell. Roy. Infirm. Edin.

MORRISON, Mr Lindsay MacKinnon Department of Urology, Southern General Hospital NHS Trust, Govan Road, Glasgow G51 4TF — MB ChB 1976 Glas.; BSc (Hons.) Glas. 1974; FRCS Glas. 1981. Assoc. Specialist (Urol.) S.. Gen. Hosp. Glas.

MORRISON, Mr Malcolm Cameron Tatham 15 Prospect Hill, Swindon SN1 3JU Tel: 01793 644610 Fax: 01793 644610 — MB BS 1951 Lond.; FRCS Eng. 1960. (St. Thos.) Cons. Orthop. Surg. Swindon. Socs: Fell. BOA; Soc. Back Pain Research; Past Pres. Brit. Inst. Musculoskeletal Med. Prev: Cons. Accid. & Orthop. Surg. P.ss Margt. Hosp. Swindon; Sen. Regist. (Orthop.) St. Thos. Hosp. Lond.; Regist. (Orthop.) St. Geo. Hosp. Tooting.

MORRISON, Malcolm Macleod Tel: 0131 669 0686 Fax: 0131 669 2929; 137 Gilberstoun, Edinburgh EH15 2RA Tel: 0131 669 9135 — MB ChB 1970 Glas.; MSc (Community Med.) Ed. 1980; DObst RCOG 1973. (Glas.)

MORRISON, Margaret Douglas Inch Centre, 2 Woodside Terrace, Glasgow G3 7UY Tel: 0141 211 8000 Fax: 0141 211 8005 — MB ChB 1979 Glas.; MRCPsych 1985. Cons. Forens. Psychiat. Douglas Inch Centre Glas.

MORRISON, Margaret Elizabeth Evans Medical Centre, 12 East King Street, Helensburgh G84 7QL Tel: 01436 673366 Fax: 01436 679715 — MB ChB 1973 Aberd.

MORRISON, Margaret Linda Malpas Medical Centre, 535 Malpas Road, Newport NP20 6NA Tel: 01633 850049; 165 Highfields, Brackla, Bridgend CF31 2PE Tel: 01656 669856 — MB BCh 1976 Wales; BSc (Hons.) (Med. Biochem.) Birm. 1971; DFFP 1993; DRCOG 1978. Socs: Brit. Assn. Sports Med. (Welsh Br.). Prev: Community Clin. Med. Off. Mid Glam. HA; GP Anglesey.

MORRISON, Mary Catherine St Lukes Surgery, Warren Road, Guildford GU1 3JH Tel: 01483 572364 Fax: 01483 304379; 19 Ennismore Avenue, Guildford GU1 1SP — MB BCh BAO 1983 Dub.; MRCGP 1988; DCH NUI 1984.

MORRISON, Michael c/o Dr Philip Jones, St James Surgery, 8-9 Northampton Buildings, Bath BA1 2SR — MB ChB 1994 Glas.; BSc (Hons.) Immunol. Glas. 1991. (Glasgow) Socs: Med. & Dent. Defence Union Scotl.; BMA. Prev: GP Regist. St James Surg. Bath; SHO (A & E) R.A.H. Paisley Renfrewsh. Scotl.; SHO (O & G) S.ern & Gen. Hosp. Glas. Scotl.

MORRISON, Patrick John Department of Medical Genetics, Belfast City Hospital, Belfast BT9 7AB Tel: 02890 263872 Fax: 02890 236911 Email: patrick.morrison@bch.n-i.nhs.uk; 4 Osborne Gardens, Belfast BT9 6LE — MB BCh BAO 1986 Belf.; FRCPCH 2000; MD Belf. 1993; MRCPCH 1996; MFPHMI 1994; DPH Belf. 1993; DCH Dub. 1989. Cons. (Med. Genetics) Belf. City Hosp.;

Postgrad. Tutor, Belf. Postgrad. Centre. Socs: Fell.Roy.Acad.Med.Irec.; Fell. Roy. Coll. Phys. Molecular Biol. Irel. Prev: Ho. Off. Roy. Vict. Hosp. Belf.

MORRISON, Paul Albert Anaesthetics Department, Hammersmith Hospital, Du Cane Road, London W12 0NN Tel: 020 8383 3143; 2 Glentham Cottage, Glentham Road, Barnes, London SW13 9JH — MB BS 1985 Lond.; FRCA 1994.

MORRISON, Paul Anthony 125 Bishops Road, Bishopston, Bristol BS7 8LX — MB ChB 1976 Ed.

***MORRISON, Paul Dugald** 33G Herbert Street, Glasgow G20 6NB — MB ChB 1994 Glas.; BSc (Hons.) Glas. 1991.

MORRISON, Paul James Directorate of Anaesthesia and Intensive Care Medicine, City General Hospital, Newcastle Road, Stoke-on-Trent ST4 6QG Tel: 01782 552732 — BM BS 1981 Nottm.; BMedSci Nottm. 1979; FFA RCS Eng. 1986. Cons. Anaesth. (Intens. Care & Trauma) N. Staffs. HA. Prev: Clin. Fell. (Intens. Care) Hosp. Sick Childr. Toronto, Canada; Sen. Regist. (Anaesth.) W. Midl. VTS.

MORRISON, Mr Peter John Murray (retired) Longwood House, The Bath Clinic, Claverton Down Road, Bath BA2 7BR Tel: 01225 835555 — MB BChir 1963 Camb.; MB Camb. 1963, BChir 1962; MA Camb. 1963; FRCS Eng. 1969; MRCS Eng. LRCP Lond. 1962. Cons. Surg. (Orthop.) Bath Health Clinic. Prev: Regist. (Orthop.) Nuffield Orthop. Cenrre Oxf.

MORRISON, Reginald Joseph Gordon, CB, CBE, Maj.-Gen. late RAMC Retd. 1 Hollington Court, High St., Chislehurst BR7 5AJ Tel: 020 8467 3633 — MRCS Eng. LRCP Lond. 1933; MD Lond. 1935, MB BS 1933; FRCP Lond. 1954, M 1944. (St. Bart.) Fitzpatrick Lect. RCP Lond. 1973. Prev: Cas. Ho. Phys. & Ho. Phys. St. Bart. Hosp.; Examr. (Trop. Med.) RCP Lond. & Univ. Lond.; Dir. of Med. Min. of Defence (Army).

MORRISON, Rhona Anne Dunrowan Resource Centre, Maggiewoods Loan, Falkirk Tel: 01324 639009; 3 Carnoustie Way, Cumbernauld, Glasgow G68 0JS — MB ChB 1985 Glas.; MRCPsych Lond. 1989; Dip. Forens. Med. Glas 1992. Cons. Psychiat. (Forens. Psychiat.) Dunrowan Resource Centre Falkirk. Prev: Sen. Regist. (Forens. Psychiat.) Douglas Inch Centre Gtr. Glas. HB.

MORRISON, Richard Clive Marylebone Health Centre, 17a Marylebone Road, London NW1 5LT Tel: 0207 9356 328 Fax: 0207 2242 924 — MB BChir 1973 Camb.; MA Camb. 1973; MRCGP 1998. (Camb. Univ. & St. Thos. Hosp. Lond.) GP Princip. Prev: Psychother. Spectrum (Centre for Humanistic Psychother.) Lond.; Clin. Asst. (Psychiat.) Haringey Day Hosp. Lond.; GP Highgate & Crouch End Lond.

MORRISON, Roanna Pamela 2 Stanfield Court, Newcastle upon Tyne NE7 7FN — MB BS 1993 Newc.

MORRISON, Robert David Thorneloe Lodge Surgery, 29 Barbourne Road, Worcester WR1 1RU Tel: 01905 22445 Fax: 01905 610963 — MB ChB 1970 Birm.; DObst RCOG 1972.

MORRISON, Robert Douglas McDougall (retired) 32 Chapel Street, Warwick CV34 4HL Tel: 01926 492735 — MB ChB 1936 Glas.

MORRISON, Robert Hugh Heaton Road Surgery, 41 Heaton Road, Heaton, Newcastle upon Tyne NE6 1TP Tel: 0191 265 5509 Fax: 0191 224 1824 — MB ChB 1982 Ed.; MRCGP 1986; DRCOG 1985. Med. Off. Newc. Racecourse. Socs: Brit. Soc. Med. & Dent. Hypn.; Racecourse Med. Offs. Assn.

MORRISON, Mr Robert Leonard Cherryvalley Health Centre, Kings Square, Belfast BT5 7AR; Cherry Valley Health Centre, Belfast BT4 — MB BCh BAO 1973 Belf.; FRCS Ed. 1977. (Belf.) Prev: Regist. (Surg.) Roy. Vict. Hosp. Belf., Waveney Hosp. Ballymena & Craigavon Hosp.

MORRISON, Robert Spence British Broadcasting Corporation, White City, 201 Wood Lane, London W12 7TS Tel: 020 8752 4887 Fax: 020 8752 4707 Email: oh@bbc.co.uk — MB ChB 1971 Glas.; MBA Strathclyde 1991; MFOM RCP Lond. 1993, AFOM 1990; T(OM) 1993; DIH Lond. 1990. Chief Med. Off.,BBC. Prev: Regional Med. Off. Gen. Counc. Brit. Shipping Lond.; Med. Dir. N.rop Corp. Taif KSA; Occupat. Phys. & Sen. Med. Off. Ct.aulds plc Coventry.

MORRISON, Roderick Murray Medical Centre, 1 Reidhaven Street, Cullen, Buckie AB56 4SZ Tel: 01542 840272 Fax: 01542 840799; 9 Seafield Place, Cullen, Buckie AB56 4TE Tel: 01542 841172 Fax: 01542 840799 — MB ChB 1970 Aberd.; DObst RCOG 1972.

MORRISON, Ruth 22 Wolfgill Road, Dumfries DG1 4XU — MB ChB 1991 Aberd. Staff Grade (Rehabil. Med.); Med. Off. Palliat. Care.

MORRISON, Mrs Ruth Elizabeth 3 Nursery Road, Nether Poppleton, York YO26 6NN Tel: 01904 783755 — MB ChB 1979 Aberd.; DRCOG 1983.

MORRISON, Samuel Stirling Bonnybridge Health Clinic, 8 South Broomage Avenue, Larbert FK5 3LF; 10 Albert Road, Falkirk FK1 5LS — MB ChB 1978 Ed.

MORRISON, Shionagh Livingstone Denview, 92 Glengate, Kirriemuir DD8 4JG — MB ChB 1996 Dundee; BSc Glas. 1987.

MORRISON, Shona 66 White Street, Flat Top 1 Left, Glasgow G11 5ED — MB ChB 1992 Glas.

MORRISON, Simon John Edenbridge Medical Practice, West View, Station Road, Edenbridge TN8 5ND Tel: 01732 864442 Fax: 01732 862376 — MB BS 1985 Lond.; MA Oxf. (Literate Humaniores) 1979; MRCGP 1991. (St Barts. Hosp. Lond.) GP Princip.

MORRISON, Stuart Gordon 10 Findlater Drive, Cullen, Buckie AB56 4RW — MB ChB 1984 Ed.

MORRISON, Stuart Love (retired) 4 Roselands, Sidmouth EX10 8PB Tel: 01395 513058 — MB ChB St. And. 1951; FRCP Ed. 1968, M 1966; FFCM 1974; DPH (Distinc.) Lond. 1954. Prev: Prof. Community Med. Univ. Edin.

MORRISON, Susan Christine Marylebone Health Centre, 17a Marylebone Road, London NW1 5LT Tel: 020 7935 6328 Fax: 020 7224 2924 Email: smorriso@rpms.ac.uk — MB BS 1974 Lond.; MRCGP 1980; Cert. Family Plann. (Univ. Coll. Hosp.) Assoc. Dean Dept. Postgrad. Gen. Pract. (N. Thames W.). Socs: Brit. Holistic Med. Assn.; RCGP. Prev: Dir. Stud. & Ocupat. Health Serv. Univ. W.m.; Partner Goodince Health Centre Lond.; GP Trainee Kentish Town.

MORRISON, Susan Diana Oxfordshire Learning Disability NHS Trust, Slade House, Headington, Oxford OX3 7JH; 22 Abberbury Road, Iffley, Oxford OX4 4ES Tel: 01865 774810 — MB BS 1972 Lond.; MRCS Eng. LRCP Lond. 1972; MRCPsych 1989. (Char. Cross) Staff Grade (Psychiat. of Ment. Handicap.) Slade Hosp. Resource Centr. Oxf.

MORRISON, Susan Janet Ferguson 1 Reidhaven Street, Cullen, Buckie AB56 4SZ Tel: 01542 840272 Fax: 01542 840799; 9 Seafield Place, Cullen, Buckie AB56 4TE Tel: 01542 841172 — MB ChB 1970 Aberd. Asst. GP Seafield Med. Ctr.

MORRISON, William David 117 Blackpool Road, Poulton-le-Fylde FY6 7QH — MB ChB 1984 Liverp.

MORRISON, William George Dundee Teaching Hospitals, Ninewells Hospital, Dundee — MB ChB 1980 Aberd.; FRCP 1999; FFAEM 1993; MRCGP 1988; FFA RCS Eng. 1987; DRCOG 1984. Cons. A & E Ninewells Hosp., Dundee. Socs: Brit. Assn. Accid. & Emerg. Med. Prev: Cons. A & E Stirling Roy. Infirm.; Sen. Regist. (A & E) Qu. Alexandria Hosp. Portsmouth; Regist. (A & E) Glas. Roy. Infirm.

MORRISON, William James The Health Centre, Wellpark, Ellon AB41 9AH Tel: 01358 720333; Drumgarth, Ogston Road, Ellon AB41 9DG Tel: 01358 720532 — MB ChB 1959 Aberd.; DObst. RCOG 1962.

MORRISON, William James South Cleveland Hospital, Marton Road, Middlesbrough TS4 3BW Tel: 01642 854600 Fax: 01642 854636; 16 Harley Terrace, Gosforth, Newcastle upon Tyne NE3 1UL Email: morrison@publiconline.co.uk — MB ChB 1989 Glas.; DA (UK) 1993; FRCA 1999. Staff Grade (Anaesth.) S Tees NHS Trust. Socs: BMA; Assn. Anaesth.; Soc. Computing & Technol. Anaesth. Prev: SHO (Anaesth.) Newc. & Gateshead Hosps.; SHO (ITU) Birm. Heartlands Hosp. & Solihull Hosp.; SHO (Anaesth.) Memor. Hosp. Darlington.

MORRISON, William John (retired) Poolfield Farm, Charfield, Wotton-under-Edge GL12 8HY — MB BCh BAO 1921 Belf.

MORRISON, William Lindsay Cardiothoracic Centre, Thomas Drive, Liverpool L14 3PE Tel: 0151 228 1616; Four Oaks, 9 Telegraph Road, Heswall, Wirral CH60 8NA — MB ChB 1980 Dundee; MD Dundee 1987; FRCP Lond. 1996; MRCP (UK) 1983. Cons. Cardiol. Cardiothoracic Centre Liverp. Socs: Brit. Cardiac Soc.; Brit. Cardiovasc. Interven. Soc. Prev: Sen. Regist. (Cardiol.) BRd.green Hosp. Liverp.; Research Fell. (Cardiol.) Papworth Hosp. Camb.

MORRISON

MORRISON, William Macaskill Elgin Medical Centre, 10 Victoria Crescent, Elgin IV30 1RQ Tel: 01343 547512 Fax: 01343 546781 — MB ChB 1967 Glas.; DObst RCOG 1968. (Glas.)

MORRISON, William Melvin Keith Medical Group, Health Centre, Turner St, Keith AB55 5DJ Tel: 01542 882244 Fax: 01542 882317; Haughs Bungalow, Keith AB55 6QN Tel: 01542 882940 Fax: 01542 888023 Email: melvinmorr@aol.com — MB ChB 1972 Aberd.; FRCGP 1996, M 1979; DObst RCOG 1975; DA Eng. 1976. GP Princip. Keith Med. Gp. Prev: Regist. (Anaesth.) Dumfries & Galloway Roy. Infirm.; SHO (O & G) ScarBoro. Hosp.; Resid. Med. Off. Woodend Gen. Hosp. Aberd.

MORRISON, Yvonne Ann Craigentore, Seafield St., Elgin IV30 1QZ Tel: 01343 543683 — MB ChB 1968 Glas. (Glas.) Staff grade Psychiat. de greys Hosp. Elgin. Prev: Quality Assur. Manager Moray Health Servs.; Clin. Asst. (Psychiat.) Bilbohall Hosp. Elgin; Clin.Audit.Co-ordin. Moray Health Servs.

MORRISS, Geoffrey William, TD (retired) Gellilednais, Upland Arms, Carmarthen SA32 8DZ Tel: 01267 237002 — MRCS Eng. LRCP Lond. 1961; FFA RCS Eng. 1969; DTM & H RCP Lond. 1965; DA Eng. 1963. Prev: Cons. Anaesth. Carmarthen & Dist. NHS Trust.

MORRISS, Richard Keith University of Liverpool, Department of Psychiatry, Royal Liverpool Hospital, Prescott St., Liverpool L7 8XP Tel: 0151 706 4147 — MB ChB 1984 Leeds; MD Leeds 1994, MMedSci (Clin. Psychiat.) 1990; MRCPsych 1989. Prof. (Psychiat.) Liverp. Univ. Prev: Sen. Lect. (Psychiat.) Manch. Univ.; Lect. (Psychiat.) Manch. Univ.; Sen. Regist. Rotat. (Psychiat.) Oxf. RHA.

MORRISSEY, Alison Frances Boghall, Gateside By Beith, Beith KA15 2LQ Tel: 01505 502679 — MB ChB 1982 Bristol. Regist. (Psychiat. Rotat.) Oxf. HA. Prev: SHO (Geriat.) Dudley Rd. Hosp. Birm.; SHO (Psychiat.) Glenside Hosp. Bristol; SHO (A & E) Frenchay Hosp. Bristol.

MORRISSEY, James John 2 Green Lane, Belper, Derby DE56 1BZ Tel: 01773 823521 — BM BCh 1972 Oxf.

MORRISSEY, John Robert 13 Shetland Drive, Glendale, Nuneaton CV10 7LA — MB ChB 1974 Birm.; MA Camb. 1974; MRCP (UK) 1979. Hosp. Pract. (Gen. Med.) Geo. Eliot Hosp. Nuneaton.

MORRISSEY, Mr Michael Simon Champlain Boghall, Gateside, Beith KA15 2LQ Tel: 01505 502679 Fax: 01505 504988 Email: simon.morrissey@which.net — MB ChB 1978 Birm.; FRCS (Otol.) Eng. 1987; FRCS (Gen. Surg.) Eng. 1982. Cons. Otolaryngol. Roy. Hosp. Sick Childr. Glas. & W.. Infirm. Gartnavel Glas. Socs: Birm. Med. Res. Expeditionary Soc.; Brit. Assn. Otol. Prev: Sen. Regist. (Otolaryngol.) Hosp. for Sick Childr. Gt. Ormond St., St.Thos. Hosp. & Norf. & Norwich Hosps.; Clin. Fell. Universitatspital Zurich, CH; Regist. (Otalaryngol.) Radcliffe Infirm. Oxf.

MORRISSEY, Patrick Matthew 9 Gloucester Walk, London W8 4HZ Tel: 020 7937 9290 — MB BCh BAO 1950 NUI. (Univ. Coll. Dub.) Prev: Ho. Surg. Montagu Hosp. MexBoro.; SHO (O & G) Rossendale Hosp.; Ships Surg. P & O Lines Lond.

MORRISSEY, Thomas Declan Greenore, Horn St., Snodland ME6 Tel: 01634 240422 — MB BCh BAO 1944 NUI. (Univ. Coll. Dub.) Prev: Ho. Surg. St. Vincent's Hosp. Dub.

MORRISSEY, William Joseph (retired) Ravensworth, 71 Mount Pleasant Drive, Belper, Derby — MB BCh BAO 1940 NUI; MFCM 1974; DPH Manch. 1947. Prev: Med. Off. Derbysh. AHA.

MORRITT, Mr Graham Nathaniel Cardiac Department, South Cleveland Hospital, Marton Road, Middlesbrough TS4 3BW Tel: 01642 854612 Fax: 01642 854618 — MB BS 1969 Madras; FRCS Ed. 1975; FRCP Ed 1998; FETCS 1998; FRCS Eng 1999. (Christian Med. Coll. Vellore) Cons. Cardiothoracic Surg. S. Cleveland Hosp. Middlesbrough; Cons. Cardiothoracic Surg. at BUPA Washington Hosp. Socs: N. Engl. Thoracic Soc. (Former Pres.); BMA; Soc. of Cardiothoracic Surgs. of FB & I (Exec. Comm.). Prev: Cons. Cardiothoracic Surg. Freeman Hosp. Newc.

MORRITT, Jennifer Audrey West Lane Hospital, Acklam Road, Middlesbrough TS5 4EE Tel: 01642 813144 Fax: 01642 822717 — MB BS 1969 Madras; MSc (Community Child Health) Newc. 1994. (Christian Med. Coll. Vellore) Assoc. Specialist (Community Child Health) W. La. Hosp. Middlesbrough. Socs: Brit. Assn. Community Child Health; MRCPCH; NE Paediat. Assn. Prev: Clin. Med. Off. Newbiggin Hall Clinic Newc.

MORROD, Deirdre Ann 68 Leigh Road, Hale, Altrincham WA15 9BD — MB ChB 1968 Birm.

MORROW, Barbara Anne Banbridge Medical Group Centre, Linenhall Street, Banbridge BT32 3EG — MB BCh BAO 1981 Belf.

MORROW, Brian Christopher c/o Anaesthesia Department, Altnage lvin Hospital, Londonderry B747 1SB Tel: 028 7134 5171 — MB BCh BAO 1985 Dub.; MA Med. Ethics & Law, QUB; FFA RCSI Dub. 1989; Dip. ICM Dub. 1998. (Trinity Coll, Dub. Univ.) Cons. (Anaesth.) Altnage Lvin Hosp. Socs: BMA & Med. Defence Union; Irish Intens. Care Soc. Prev: Sen. Regist. & Sen. Tutor (Anaesth.) Qu. Univ. Belf.; SHO (Anaesth.) Belf. City Hosp.; SHO (Anaesth.) Altnagelvin Hosp. Lond.derry & Roy. Vict. Hosp. Belf.

MORROW, Mr Darren Robert 12 Birch Road, Hethersett, Norwich NR9 3QH Email: mail@darrenmorrow.com — MB BS 1993 Lond.; MSc 2001 Lond; BSc Lond. 1990, MB BS 1993; FRCS (Eng) 1997. (St. Bart's Lond.) Specialist Regist. (Gen. Surg.) E.. Deanery; Guest Lect. Medic. Informatics, City Univ. Lond. Socs: Affil. Mem. Assoc. of Surg. Of GB & Ire.; Assn. Surg. Train.; Jun. Mem. Europ. Soc. For Vasc. Surg.

MORROW, Dorothy (retired) 1 Killuney Park, Portadown Road, Armagh BT61 9HG Tel: 028 3752 8435 — MB BCh BAO 1952 Belf. Prev: GP Armagh.

MORROW, Gerald Allendale Health Centre, Shilburl Road, Allendale, Hexham NE47 9SW Tel: 01434 683280 Fax: 01434 683884 Email: gerrymorrow@hotmail.com — MB ChB 1987 Glas.; MRCGP 1994. (Glas.) Prev: GP Advisor Acute Unit Trust Worcs.

MORROW, Helen Mary 6 Methven Avenue, Bearsden, Glasgow G61 2AY — MB ChB 1983 Glas.; DGM RCPS Glas. 1992. Clin. Asst. (Geriat.) Drumchapel Hosp.; Clin. Asst. (Endocrnology) - W.ern Infirmary.

MORROW, James (retired) 1 Killuney Park, Portadown Road, Armagh BT61 9HG Tel: 028 3752 8435 — MB BCh BAO 1951 Dub. Prev: Ho. Surg. Waveney Hosp. Ballymena.

MORROW, James Irvine Department of Neurology, Royal Victoria Hospital, Belfast BT12 6BA Tel: 01232 240503 Fax: 01232 235258; Cullintraw House, 38 Ballydrain Road, Comber, Newtownards BT23 5SS — MD 1993 Belf.; MB BCh BAO (Hons.) 1980; FRCP Lond 1993; MRCP (UK) 1983; BA (Hons.) (OU) 1999. Cons. Neurol. Roy. Vict. Hosp. Belf. Socs: Assn. Brit. Neurol.; Irish Neurol. Assn.. Prev: Clin. Lect. Epilepsy Unit Univ. Hosp. Wales Coll. Med. Cardiff; Regist. (Neurol.) Roy. Vict. Hosp. Belf.

MORROW, John Joseph (retired) 12 Glenpark Place, Ayr KA7 4SQ Tel: 01292 41995 — MB ChB 1956 Glas.; FRCP Lond. 1982, M 1963; FRCP Glas. 1971, M 1961. Prev: Cons. Phys. CrossHo. Hosp. Kilmarnock Ayrsh.

MORROW, Lesley Anne 140 Belfast Road, Newtownards BT23 4TY — MB BCh BAO 1990 Belf.; MB BCh Belf. 1990.

MORROW, Margaret Pantiles, Tower Hill, Dorking RH4 2AP Tel: 01306 884529 — MB BCh BAO 1961 Belf.; DObst RCOG 1963. (Belf.) Clin. Med. Pract. Army Blood Supply Depot. Prev: Capt. RAMC Families Med. Off.; Clin. Med. Off. Surrey AHA; Clin. Med. Pract. Wom. Roy. Army Corps.

MORROW, Pauline Carrol delancey Assessment & Rehabilitation Hospital, Charlton Lane, Leckhampton, Cheltenham GL53 9DU Tel: 01453 272044 — MB BS 1987 Monash; BMedSci Monash 1985; MRCP (UK) 1993. Staff Grade Phys. Delancey Hosp. Cheltenham. Socs: BMA; BGS (Respirat. Sect.); MPS. Prev: Staff Grade Phys. (Med. for Elderly) St. Margt. Hosp. Swindon; Assoc. Specialist (Med. for Elderly) P.ss Margt. Hosp. Swindon.

MORROW, Mr Robert Joseph, Surg. Capt. RN Retd. (retired) Connemara, 65 Crescent Road, Alverstoke, Gosport PO12 2DN Tel: 023 9258 1130 — MB BCh BAO NUI 1955; FRCS Eng. 1966.

MORROW, Thomas James The Doctors House, Victoria Road, Marlow SL7 1DN Tel: 01628 484666 Fax: 01628 891206 — BM BCh 1990 Oxf.; MA Camb. 1991; MRCGP 1994; T(GP) 1994. (Oxf.) GP Partner Private Gen. Pract. Bon Secours Hosp. Beaconsfield.

MORROW, Valerie Susanna Chapman and Partners, 370-372 Cregagh Road, Belfast BT6 9EY Tel: 028 9049 2214 Fax: 028 9049 2214; Rockhaven, 2 Rocky Road, Gilnahirk, Belfast BT5 7QJ — MB BCh BAO 1982 Belf.; MRCGP 1988; DCH Dub. 1987; DRCOG 1986. Socs: Med. Protec. Soc.

MORSE, Gordon Ridding Bechers Brook Surgery, High Street, Fovant, Salisbury SP3 5JL Tel: 01722 714789 Fax: 01722 714702; Becher's Brook, High St, Fovant, Salisbury SP3 5JL Tel: 01722 714496 — MB ChB 1976 Dundee; MRCGP 1984; DRCOG 1983. (Dundee) Med. Off. Clouds Hse. Drugs & Alcohol Rehabil. Unit E.

Knoyle; Hon. Lect. (Gen. Pract.) Univ. Soton. Prev: Trainee GP Cirencester VTS; Specialist (Traumatol.) Dept. Family Pract. MoD, Saudi Arabia; SHO (O & G) P.ss Margt. Hosp. Swindon.

MORSE, Joanne Catherine Buckley Hill House, Buckley Hill Lane, Milnrow, Rochdale OL16 4BU — MB ChB 1993 Sheff.

MORSE, Martin Hill 58 Woodstock Road, Redland, Bristol BS6 7EP — MB ChB 1981 Bristol; BDS Bristol 1970, MB ChB Bristol 1981; FDS 1976; MRCP (UK) 1984; FRCR 1988. Cons. Radiol. Frenchay Hosp. Bristol.

MORSE, Rhian Elizabeth Level B6, University Hospital of Wales, Health Park, Cardiff CF4 4XW Tel: 029 2074 3142 Email: rhian.morse@uhw-tr.wales.nhs.uk; 77 Plasturton Ave, Pontcanna, Cardiff CF11 9HN Tel: 029 2037 3821 Email: rhian.morse@btinternet.com — MB BS 1985 Lond.; BA Camb. 1982; MRCP (UK) 1988; FRCP 2000. (Trinity College Cambridge & The Royal London Hosp.) Cons. Phys. Geriat. & Gen. Med. Univ. Hosp. of Wales Cardiff and Vale NHS Trust; Clin. Director Rehabil. Cardiff and Vale NHS Trust. Prev: Sen. Regist. - Gen. Med. & Geriat. Med. John Radcliffe Hosp. Oxf.; Regist. (Gen. Med.) Univ. Hosp. Wales, Cadiff; SHO Neuology Radcliffe Infirm. Oxf..

MORSMAN, Mr John Murray Nuffield Hospital, Derriford Road, Plymouth PL6 8BG Tel: 01752 790482 Fax: 01752 778421; Kilmuir, 78 Yealm Road, Newton Ferrers, Plymouth PL8 1BL — MB BS Lond. 1970; FRCS (Gen. Surg.) Ed. 1975; FRCS Eng. 1975; MRCS Eng. LRCP Lond. 1970; LMSSA Lond. 1970; FRCOG 1990, M 1978, DObst 1972; Hon. MIBiol 1978; CBiol 1985. (Guys) Cons. O & G Plymouth Gen. Hosp. Socs: Chelsea Clin. Soc.; Liveryman Worshipful Soc. Apoth. Lond. Prev: Sen. Regist. & Med. Research Counc. Fell. King's Coll. Hosp. Lond.; Resid. Med. & Surg. Off. Qu. Charlotte's & Chelsea Hosp. for Wom. Lond.; Regist. (Gen. Surg.) Qu. Mary's Hosp. Sidcup.

MORSON, Basil Clifford, CBE, VRD 14 Crossways Park, West Chiltington, Pulborough RH20 2QZ Tel: 01798 813528 — BM BCh 1953 Oxf.; MA, DM Oxf. 1955; FRCP Lond. 1979, M 1973; FRCS Eng. 1972; MRCS Eng. LRCP Lond. 1949; Hon. FRACS 1990; FRCPath 1968, M 1964. (Middlx.) Emerit. Cons. Path. N.wick Pk. & St. Marks Hosp. Trust Lond. & The Lond. Clinic; Emerit. Cons. Path. RN (Civil.). Socs: Hon. Fell. Roy. Soc. Med.; Fell. (Ex- Vice Pres. & Ex-Treas.) Roy. Coll. Paths.; Hon. Fell. Brit. Soc. Gastroenterol. Prev: Pres. Sect. Proctol. Roy. Soc. Med.; Pres. Brit. Div. Internat. Acad. Path.; Pres. Brit. Soc. Gastroenterol.

MORSY, Mostafa Kamel Heckington Manor, Heckington, Sleaford NG34 9RJ — MB BCh Al Azhar 1970. Med. Dir. Ferdowse Clinic Heckington Manor Heckington Lincs.; Dir. Med. Recruitment Internat. Socs: Soc. Study of Addic.; Alcohol Concern; EATA.

MORT, Dominic Julian 151 Westfields, St Albans AL3 4JU Tel: 01727 863667 — MB BS 1993 Lond.; MB BS (Hons.) Lond. 1993; BA (Hons.) Physiol. Oxf. 1990, BM 1989; MRCP (UK) 1997. PhD Stud. Univ. Coll. Lond. Prev: SHO High Dependency Med. St. Thos. Hosp. Lond.; SHO Neurol. St. Thos. Hosp. Lond.; SHO Renal, St Mary's Hosp. Paddington.

MORT, Lonw Elizabeth Stable Cottage, Linfield Road, Ardingley, Haywards Heath RH17 6TS — MB BCh 1965 Wales. (Cardiff) SCMO Dept. Pub. Health Med. N. Staffs. HA. Prev: Clin. Med. Off. Guy's Health Dist.; Regist. (Community Med.) N.E. Thames RHA; Asst. MOH Caerns. CC.

MORT, Michael John Lightbody Mort, Ann Burrow Thomas Health Centre, South William Street, Workington CA14 2EW Tel: 01900 605258 Fax: 01900 605258; 22 Brayton Street, Workington CA14 2NP — MB ChB 1968 St. And.; MRCGP 1975.

MORT, Stephen John Anthony The Surgery, 4A Church Road, Cowley, Uxbridge UB8 3NA Tel: 01895 233736 Fax: 01895 256881 — MB BS 1979 Lond.; Dip Occ. Med. RCP Lond. 1995; T(GP) 1991; Cert. Family Plann. JCC 1983; DRCOG 1982; DCH Eng. 1981; AFOM 1997; Dip. Med. Acupunc. 1997. (St. Geo.) Princip. in Gen. Pract. (Mort. W. Stapleton); Occupat. Health Phys. to various Cos.; Examr. & Adviser for various Ins. Cos.; Lect. & Examr. Brit. Red Cross; Vice-Chairm. Hillingdon LMC; Mem. Uxbridge, Yievsley & W. Drayton PCG Bd. Socs: Fell.Med. Soc. Lond.; Soc. Occup. Med.; Assur. Med. Soc. Prev: SHO. Isle of Thanet Gp. Hosps.; Hosp. Surg., Roy. Cornw. Gp. Hosps.; Hosp. Phys. Prof. Unit St. Geo.s Gp.. Hosps.

MORTENSEN, Jane Alison Beaumont Street Surgery, 27 Beaumont Street, Oxford City, Oxford OX1 2NR Tel: 01865 311500

Fax: 01865 311720 — MB ChB 1973 Birm.; MRCGP 1977. Prev: Trainee Gen. Pract. Bristol Vocational Train. Scheme; Ho. Phys. Hereford Co. Hosp.; Ho. Surg. Gen. Hosp. Birm.

MORTENSEN, Professor Neil James McCready Department of Colorectal Surgery, John Radcliffe Hospital, Oxford OX3 9DU Tel: 01865 220926 Fax: 01865 760390 — MB ChB Birm. 1973; MD Bristol 1977; FRCS Eng. 1978. Prof. of Colorectal Surg. and Cons. Colorectal Surg. Oxf. Univ.; Treas. & Dir. Brit. Jl. Surg. Soc. Socs: Fell. Roy. Soc. Med. (Counc. Mem. And Sec. Proctol. Sect.); Assn. Surg.; (Counc.) Assn. Coloproctol. Gt. Britain and Irel. Prev: Clin. Reader (Surg.) Univ. Oxf.; Cons. & Sen. Lect. (Surg.) Univ. Bristol & Bristol Roy. Infirm.; Sen. Regist. (Surg.) St. Marks Hosp. Lond.

MORTIBOY, Deborah Elizabeth 51 Moor Green Lane, Birmingham B13 8NE — MB ChB 1986 Birm.; MRCP (UK) 1989; MRCPath 1993. Cons. Microbiol. Good Hope Hosp. Sutton Coldfield. Prev: Regist. (Med.) Dudley Rd. Hosp. Birm.

MORTIMER, Andrew Joseph Tel: 0161 291 5710 Fax: 0161 291 5709 — MB BS 1973 Newc.; BSc (Hons.) Newc. 1970, MD (Commend.) 1986; FRCA. 1980; FFA RCS Eng. 1980; DObst RCOG 1975. (Univ. Newc. u. Tyne) Cons. Anaesth. Univ. Hosp. S. Manch.; Hon. Clin. Lect. Vict. Univ. Manch.; Examr. Final FRCA Roy. Coll. Anaesth. Socs: Assn. Anaesth.; Europ. Acad. Anaesth.; Manch. Med. Soc. Prev: MRC Research Train. Fell. Nuffield Dept. Anaesth. Radcliffe Infirm. Oxf.; Hon. Sen. Regist. Oxf. AHA; Regist. Nuffield Dept. Anaesth. Radcliffe Infirm. Oxf.

MORTIMER, Andrew Reginald 119 Bower Street, Maidstone ME16 8BB — MB BS 1994 Lond.

MORTIMER, Angela Teresa 31 Hindon Square, Vicarage Road, Edgbaston, Birmingham B15 3HA — MB ChB 1988 Leeds; FRCR 1995; FFR RCSI 1995. (LEEDS) Cons., Trafford Gen. Hosp., Moorside Rd., Daryhulme, Manch.,M41 55L. Prev: Sen. Regist. (Clin. Radiol.) W.

MORTIMER, Professor Ann Margaret Department of Psychiatry, Coniston House, East Riding Campus, University of Hull, Beverley Road, Willerby, Hull HU10 6NS Tel: 01482 466756 Fax: 01482 466966 Email: a.m.mortime@hull.ac.uk; The Old Vicarage, North Frodingham, Driffield YO25 8JT Tel: 01262 488591 — MB ChB 1981 Leic.; BSc Leic. 1978, MB ChB 1981; MMedSc Leeds 1987; MRCPsych 1985; FRCPsych 1999. (Leicester) Foundat. Chair Psychiat. Univ. Hull. Prev: Sen. Lect. (Psychiat.) Char. Cross & W.minster Med. Sch. Univ. Lond.; Cons. Psychiat. Yorks. RHA; Lect. & Hon. Sen. Regist. (Psychiat.) Univ. Leeds.

MORTIMER, Arthur Hamilton (retired) 4 New Inn Lane, Easingwold, York YO61 3PH Tel: 01347 821851 — MRCS Eng. LRCP Lond. 1950. Prev: GP Hull.

MORTIMER, Caroline Jane Denise 33 Spring Lane, Watlington, Oxford OX4 6LF — MB BS 1984 Lond.; FRCS Eng. 1989.

MORTIMER, Clive Bennett 67 Spa Hill, London SE19 3TW — MD 1961 Camb.; MB BChir 1955.

***MORTIMER, Heather Jane** 41 Somerville Road, Sutton Coldfield B73 6HH — MB BCh 1997 Wales.

MORTIMER, Jeffrey Stuart Springfield Surgery, 24-28 Commercial Road, Hazel Grove, Stockport SK7 4AA Tel: 0161 487 1200 Fax: 0161 483 6183 — MB ChB 1966 Manch.; DCH Eng. 1970. (Manch.) Clin. Asst. (Gastroenterol.) Stepping Hill Hosp. Stockport (Stockport Acute Servs.). Prev: Capt. RAMC; Trainee Paediat. Brit. Milit. Hosp. Hong Kong; Specialist Paediat. Milit. Hosp. Tidworth.

MORTIMER, Joan Alexandra Doctors Surgery, Glanfa, Orme Road, Bangor LL57 1AY Tel: 01248 370540 Fax: 01248 370637 — MB BCh 1974 Wales.

MORTIMER, John Gardner McLean (retired) Oakapple Cottage, Phillips Acre, Yarpole, Leominster HR6 0DA Tel: 01568 780788 Fax: 01568 780788 Email: mortimer@globalnet.co.uk — MB ChB Glas. 1955; MFCM 1974; DPH Lond. 1967; DObst RCOG 1959. Prev: Dist. Community Phys. NW Herts. Health Dist.

MORTIMER, Jonathan Mark Patrick The Surgery, 13 Camberwell Green, London SE5 7AF Tel: 020 7703 3788; 41 Pickwick Road, London SE21 7JN Tel: 020 7733 1916 — MB BS 1986 Lond.; BA Camb. 1982. Prev: Trainee GP St. Thos. Hosp. Lond. VTS.

MORTIMER, Keith Edwin Cherry Tree Cottage, Arundell Road, Tangmere, Chichester PO18 0DU Tel: 01243 784535 — MRCS Eng. LRCP Lond. 1949. (King's Coll. Hosp.)

MORTIMER, Marek Jerzy 9 Sandon Road, Edgbaston, Birmingham B67 8DP Tel: 0121 420 0100 Fax: 0121 420 0107; 74

MORTIMER

Westfield Road, Edgbaston, Birmingham B15 3QQ Tel: 0121 455 6192 — MB ChB 1976 Birm.; BSc (Hons.) Wales 1971; MD Birm. 1994; MRCGP 1984; DFFP 1993; Dip. Pract. Dermat. Wales 1991. (Birm.) Trainer Gen. Pract. Birm.; Adviser (Occupat. Med.) Birm.; Mem. Steering Comm. Advanced Project; Franchise Med. Off. DVLA; Mem. Research Ethics Comm. City. Hosp. Trust Birm.; Hon. Sen. Clin. Lect. Primary Care Sch. Health Sc. Wolverhampton Univ.; Mem. Steering Comm. Ascot Project. Socs: W Midl. Dermat. Soc.; Birm. Medico-Legal Soc.; BMAS. Prev: GP Advisor Unit Managem. W. Birm. HA; Clin. & Research Asst. Birm. Migraine Clinic.; Mem. Comm. Reshaping Traditional Parterns of Care Sandwell HA.

*MORTIMER, Neil James 22 Kingston Road, Leicester LE2 1QB — MB ChB 1997 Leic.

MORTIMER, Patricia Eva (retired) 9 Lancaster Avenue, Hadley Wood, Barnet EN4 0EP Tel: 020 8440 9213 Fax: 020 8440 9213 — MB BS Lond. 1953; FRCP Lond. 1976, M 1960; MRCS Eng. LRCP Lond. 1953; DCH Eng. 1955. Prev: Cons. Paediat. Enfield Hosp. Gp.

MORTIMER, Professor Peter Sydney Division Physiological Medicine (Dermatology), St. George's Hospital Medical School, Room 57 - Ground Floor - Jenner Wing, Cranmer Terrace, London SW17 0RE Tel: 020 8725 1784 Fax: 020 8725 5955 Email: p.mortimer@sghms.ac.uk; 85 Pine Walk, Carshalton SM5 4HL Tel: 020 8643 1523 — MB BS 1975 London; MD Lond. 1990, MB BS 1975; FRCP Lond. 1992; MRCP (UK) 1978; MRCS Eng. LRCP Lond. 1975. (St. Bart.) Cons. Dermat. St. Geo. Hosp. Lond. & Roy. Marsden Hosp. Lond.; Prof. of Dermatological Med. Prev: Sen. Regist. (Dermat.) John Radcliffe & Slade Hosps. Oxf.; Regist. (Dermat.) Roy. Hallamsh. Hosp. Sheff.; Regist. (Med.) Groby Rd. Hosp. Leicester.

MORTIMER, Philip Paul Central Public Health Laboratory, London NW9 5HT Tel: 020 8200 4400 Fax: 020 8200 1569; 5 Birkbeck Road, London NW7 4BP Tel: 020 8959 0022 — MB BS 1969 Lond.; MD Lond. 1976; MRCPath 1976; Dip. Bact. Lond 1973. (St. Thos.) Chairm. Virus Ref. Div. Centr. Pub. Health Laborat. Lond. Socs: Fell. Roy. Coll. Path.

MORTIMER, Philip Randall (retired) Starlings, 9 Almond Avenue, Leamington Spa CV32 6QD — MB BS Lond. 1961; FRCPath 1980, M 1968. Prev: Dir. Coventry Pub. Health Laborat.

MORTIMER, Phyllis Marjorie (retired) Kingsmead Lodge, 28 Carlton Road, Seaford BN25 2LJ Tel: 01323 898267 — MB BS Lond. 1957; DObst RCOG 1960; MFFP 1992. p/t Med. Off. S. Downs Health NHS Trust Brighton. Prev: SCMO & Med. Dir. Croydon Community (NHS) Trust.

MORTIMER, Robert John Kingsway Surgery, 37 The Kingsway, Swansea SA1 5LF Tel: 01792 650716 Fax: 01792 456902; 2 Heol Pant-y-Lliw, Pontlliw, Swansea SA4 1DG — MB BCh 1983 Wales; MRCGP 1992; DRCOG 1987. GP Tutor (Continuing Med. Educat.) Swansea.

*MORTIMER, Virginia 48 Queens Park Court, Ilbert St, London W10 4QB Tel: 020 8969 8169 — MB BS 1994 Lond.; BSc History of medicine 1992.

MORTIMORE, Andrew John Southampton & South West Hampshire HA, Oakley Road, Southampton SO16 4GX — MB BS 1978 Lond.; MA Camb. 1979; MSc Lond. 1993; MFPHM RCP (UK) 1995; MRCGP 1986; DRCOG 1981; DCH Eng. 1981; DTM & H Liverp. 1980. (Westm.) Cons. Pub. Health Med. Soton. & SW Hants. HA. Prev: Regional Health Off. Lilongwe, Malawi; Healthcare Co-Ordinator Tonj Dist. S. Sudan.

MORTIMORE, Christopher Holly Court, Summerland's Hospital, Preston Road, Yeovil BA20 2BX Tel: 01935 428420 — MB BChir 1991 Camb.; MA (Hons.) Camb. 1991; MRCPsych 1995. (Cambridge) Cons. (Psychiat.). Prev: Sen. Regist. Rotat. (Adult Gen. Psychiat.) Manch.; Regist. Rotat. (Psychiat.) Cornw. & Plymouth; SHO Rotat. (Psychiat.) Cornw.

MORTIMORE, Ian Lind Chetenham General Hospital, Cheltenham GL53 7AN Tel: 01242 274346 — MB BS 1987 Lond.; BSc. Newc. 1979; MRCP (UK) 1990; PhD. Newc. 1982. (St. Marys') Cons. Phys. Chelt. Gen. Hosp. Socs: Brit. Thoracic Soc.; Roy. Coll. of Phys.s, Lond. Prev: Regist. (Med.) St. Thos. Hosp. Lond.; Research Fell. Roy. Infirm. Edin.; Sen. Regist. Roy. Infirm., Edin.

MORTLOCK, Alison Jayne 8 Rowan Way, Boston PE21 9DH — MB ChB 1993 Birm.

MORTON, Alan Keith 6 Danebank Road, Lymm WA13 9DH — MB ChB 1969 Manch.; FFA RCS Eng. 1976. Cons. (Anaesth.) Centr. (Manch.) Health Dist.

MORTON, Alex David 7 Eastbank, London N16 5RG — MB BS 1989 Lond.; BSc (Psychol.) Lond. 1986; DRCOG 1994. (Univ. Coll. Lond.) GP Lond.

*MORTON, Allison Claire 310 Sharrow Vale Road, Sheffield S11 8ZL — MB ChB 1998 Sheff.; MB ChB Sheff 1998.

MORTON, Andrew David Norton Medical Centre, Stockton on Tees TS20 2UZ Tel: 01642 360111; 7 Locomotion Court, Eaglescliffe, Stockton-on-Tees TS16 0RP Tel: 01642 788445 Email: andrewvictoria@hotmail.com — MB BS 1991 Newc.; MRCGP.

MORTON, Ann Marie Ashdown House, 24 Park Road, Winslow, Buckingham MK18 3DL Tel: 01296 712667 — MRCS Eng. LRCP Lond. 1969; DA (UK) 1972. (Guy's Hosp. Lond.) Socs: Soc. Pub. Health. Prev: Clin. Med. Off. (Community Child Health) Milton Keynes Community NHS Trust.

MORTON, Mr Archibald Lawrie 4 Collylinn Road, Bearsden, Glasgow G61 4PN — MB ChB 1983 Glas.; MD Glas. 1993; FRCS (Urol) 1994; FRCS Glas. 1987. Cons. Urol. Roy. Alexandria Hosp. Paisley.

MORTON, Catriona Margaret Craigmillar Medical Group, 106 Niddrie Mains Road, Edinburgh EH16 4DT; 127 Warrender Park Road, Edinburgh EH9 1DS Tel: 0131 228 1594 — MB ChB 1986 Manch.; BMedSci St. And. 1983; MRCGP 1991; DRCOG 1994; DTM & H Liverp. 1991. (Manch.) GP. Socs: LMC; SGPC. Prev: GP (Princip.) Nottm.; Clin. Assoc. (Gen. Pract.) Univ. Manch.

MORTON, Charles Murray 432 Liverpool Road, Southport PR8 3BA Tel: 0170477395 — MB ChB 1952 Glas. (Glas.) Prev: Ho. Surg. S.port Infirm.

MORTON, Charles Patrick John c/o Department Anaesthetics, Royal Infirmary of Edinburgh, Lauriston Place, Edinburgh EH3 9YW Tel: 0131 536 3651 Fax: 0131 536 3672 Email: c.morton@ed.ac.uk; 103 Craigleith Road, Edinburgh EH4 2EH Tel: 0131 332 1118 — MB BS 1983 Lond.; FRCA 1990. (Char. Cross Hosp. Med. Sch. Univ. Lond.) Cons. Anaesth. Roy. Infirm. Edin. NHS Trust. Socs: Anaesth. Res. Soc. Prev: Regist. (Anaesth.) Auckland Hosp., NZ; Astra Clin. Research Fell. (Anaesth.) Roy. Infirm. Edin.

MORTON, Christina Cochrane (retired) 8 Barshaw House, Blairmore Avenue, Paisley PA1 3JH Tel: 0141 889 6600 — MB ChB 1949 Glas. Prev: Cytol. Roy. Alexandra Infirm. Paisley.

MORTON, Christopher Charles White House Surgery, High Street, Moreton-in-Marsh GL56 0AT Tel: 01608 650317 Fax: 01608 650071; Phillips Farm House, Todenham, Moreton-in-Marsh GL56 9NY Tel: 01608 51654 — MB BS 1981 Lond. Socs: Fell. Internat. Soc. for Paraplegia; BMA. Prev: SHO (Internat. Med.) Riyadh Milit. Hosp., Saudi Arabia.

MORTON, Claire Elizabeth HM Stanley Hospital, St Asaph LL17 0RS Tel: 01745 583910; 49 The Rock, Helsby, Warrington WA6 9AS — MB ChB 1982 Bristol; FRCS Glas. 1988. Cons. Ophth. HM Stanley Hosp. St. Asaph. Prev: Sen. Regist. (Ophth.) Roy. Liverp. Univ. Hosp.; Regist. (Ophth.) Manch. Roy. Eye Hosp.; SHO (Ophth.) St. Pauls Eye Hosp.

MORTON, Colin Andrew Braeside, Montrose Road, Auchterarder PH3 1BZ — MB ChB 1986 Glas.; MRCP (UK) 1991; MD Glas. 1999. (Glas. Univ.) Cons. (Dermat.) Falkirk Roy. Infirm. Falkirk. Prev: Sen. Regist. (Dermat.) Glas. Roy. Infirm.

MORTON, David Edward Lomond & Argyu Primary Care Trust, Hartfield Clinic, Latia Street, Dumbarton G82 2DD Tel: 01389 604510 Email: david.morton@aandb.scot.nhs.uk; The Old Coach House, 22 Queen St, Helensburgh G84 9LG Tel: 01436 673179 Fax: 01436 674947 — MB ChB 1969 Glas. Med. Dir. Lomond & Argyll Primary Care NHS Trust. Prev: GP Greenlaw Med. Centre, Paisley.

MORTON, David Nigel 6 Dryden Place, Edinburgh EH9 1RP — MB BS 1970 Lond.; MRCS Eng. LRCP Lond. 1970. (Guy's)

MORTON, Mr Dion Gregory Department of Surgery, Queen Elizabeth Hospital, Queen Elizabeth Medical Centre, Edgbaston, Birmingham B15 2TH; 4 Albert Road, Harborne, Birmingham B17 0AN — MB ChB 1985 Bristol; FRCS Eng. 1989. Lect. (Surg.) Qu. Eliz. Hosp. Birm. Prev: Career Regist. (Surg.) W. Midl. RHA; Research Regist. (Surg.) Birm.

MORTON

MORTON, Donald (retired) 82A The Grove, Marton, Middlesbrough TS7 8AP Tel: 01642 316097 — MB ChB 1956 Ed.; FRCGP 1991, M 1972. Prev: GP Middlesbrough.

MORTON, Doris Euphemia (retired) 31 Whiteley Wood Road, Sheffield S11 7FF — MB BCh BAO 1934 Dub.

MORTON, Edward (retired) Mellowmead Cottage, Bundys Way, Staines TW18 3LD Tel: 01784 463871 Email: morton.tedwood@aol.com — MB ChB 1951 Leeds. Prev: Sen. Hosp. Med. Off. (A & E) Roy. S. Hants. Hosp. Soton.

MORTON, Elizabeth Ann Riley House Farm, Riley Back Lane, Eyam, Hope Valley S32 5QZ — MB BS 1967 Lond.; MRCS Eng. LRCP Lond. 1967.

MORTON, Elizabeth Wendy Fraser Leith Mount Surgery, 46 Ferry Road, Edinburgh EH6 4AE; 103 Craigleith Road, Edinburgh EH4 2EH Tel: 0131 332 1118 Email: libby@morton.abel.co.uk — MB BS 1983 Lond.; DRCOG 1988. GP Retainer Leith Maint Surg. Edin. Prev: GP Leith Mt. Surg. Edin.; Trainee GP Addenbrooke's Hosp. Camb. & Hinchingbrooke Hosp. Huntingdon; SHO (Hospice Care) Arthur Rank Hse. Camb.

MORTON, Eric Vodden Bradshaw, VRD (retired) Tredorne, St. Clement, Truro TR1 1TA Tel: 01872 273548 — MD Ed. 1958, MB ChB 1942; FRCP Ed. 1966, M 1948. Prev: Cons. Phys. Barncoose Hosp. Redruth.

MORTON, Ernest Dickson (retired) 139 Balshagray Avenue, Glasgow G11 7DL Tel: 0141 959 5595 — MB ChB Glas. 1948. Prev: Ho. Phys. S.. Gen. Hosp. Glas.

MORTON, Esther Elisabeth Heath House, Headley, Epsom KT18 6NJ — MB ChB 1964 Bristol. (Bristol) Prev: Ho. Off. Obst. Bath Hosp. Gp.

MORTON, Hugh Gloag (retired) 5A Balgove Road, Gauldry, Newport-on-Tay DD6 8SH Tel: 01382 330477 — MB ChB 1967 St. And.; FRCPsych 1986, M 1972; DPM Ed. & Glas. 1970. Prev: Cons. Childr. & Young People Psychiat. Tayside HB.

MORTON, Iain Chalmers The Health Centre, 203 Main Street, Barrhead G78 1HG Tel: 0141 880 6161 Fax: 0141 881 7063; Stuart Rais, Darnley Road, Barrhead, Glasgow G78 1TA Tel: 0141 881 3950 — MB ChB 1964 Glas.; MRCGP 1971; DObst RCOG 1966.

MORTON, Ian Nicholas Trinity and Bowthorpe Medical Practice, 1 Trinity Street, Norwich NR2 2BG Tel: 01603 624844 Fax: 01603 766829 Email: nick.morton@D82017.nhs.uk — MB BS 1983 Lond.; MRCGP 1989; DFFP 1993. (Westm.) p/t Med. Director, Norwich GP out of hours Co-op. - Mem. of Notfolk Local Med. Comm. Socs: BMA; BASICS. Prev: Sen. Med. Off. Detmold Garrison BAOR; Med. Off. Armoured Field Ambul. Gulf War; SHO (Paediat. & O & G) Camb. Milit. Hosp. Aldershot.

MORTON, Irena Maria Mental Welfare Commission, 25 Drumsheugh Gardens, Edinburgh EH3 7RB; St Marys Tower, Birnam, Dunkeld PH8 0BJ — MB ChB 1973 Dundee; MRCPsych 1987. Med. Off. Ment. Welf. Commiss. Edin. Prev: Regist. (Psychiat.) Roy. Dundee Liff Hosp.

MORTON, Isobel Patricia Blair 7 Viewmount Road, Wormit, Newport-on-Tay DD6 8NJ — MB ChB 1967 Glas.; DObst RCOG 1969. (Glas.) Med. Off. (Family Plann.) (A & E) Dundee Roy. Infirm. Prev: Ho. Appts. Glas. Roy. Infirm.; SHO Matern. Hosp. Glas.; Regist. (Gen. Med.) Perth Roy. Infirm.

MORTON, James Alexander 107 Highfield Lane, Highfield, Southampton SO17 1NN Tel: 02380 557062 — MB ChB 1994 Ed.; MRCP (UK) 1997. (Ed.)

***MORTON, James Alexander Burn,** Senior Surgical Trainee 95 The Martlets, Rustington, Littlehampton BN16 2UQ Tel: 01903 786179 Email: baccus@hotmail.com; PO Box1998, 1 Marine Parade, Marine Drive, Brighton BN1 1UQ — MB BS 1996 Lond.; UMDS Sethra.

MORTON, James Robert Fairhurst, 2 Magdalen Lane, Christchurch BH23 1PH Tel: 01202 259256 — MB BS 1966 Lond.; DA Eng. 1970; DObst RCOG 1969. (Univ. Coll. Hosp.) Prev: SHO (A & E & O & G) Epsom Dist. Hosp.

MORTON, James Roderick Campbell Friarsgate Practice, Friarsgate Medical Centre, Friarsgate, Winchester SO23 8EF Tel: 01962 853599 Fax: 01962 849982; Orchard House, Morestead, Winchester SO21 1LZ Tel: 01962 714553 — MB 1971 Camb.; MA Camb. 1972, MB 1971, BChir 1970; DObst RCOG 1972. (Camb.) Sen. Med. Off. Winchester Coll.

MORTON, Jane Elizabeth Victoria Clinical Genetics Unit, Birmingham Women's Hospital, Edgbaston, Birmingham B15 2TG Tel: 0121 627 2630 Fax: 0121 627 2618 Email: jenny.morton@bham-womens.thenhs.com — MB ChB 1984 Bristol; MRCP (UK) 1987. (Univ. Bristol) p/t Cons. Clin. Genetics Birm. Wom. Hosp.; Hon. Sen. Lect. Dept. Paediat. Birm. Univer. Prev: Sen. Regist. (Clin. Genetics) Birm. Matern. Hosp.; Hon. Research Regist. (Haemat.) E. Birm. Hosp.; Sheldon Research Fell. E. Birm. Hosp.

MORTON, Jeannette Margaret Health Centre, St. Marys Place, Townend, Kirkcudbright DG6 4BJ Tel: 01557 330755 Fax: 01557 330917 — MB ChB 1979 Ed.; DRCOG 1982.

***MORTON, Jeremy James Craig** TFM 9, South East Circus Place, Edinburgh EH3 6TJ — MB ChB 1994 Ed.

MORTON, John Stewart Rothesay Health Centre, Townhead, Rothesay PA20 9JL Tel: 01700 502290 Fax: 01700 505692 — MB ChB 1989 Glas. GP Rothesay, Isle of Bute.

MORTON, Mr Jonathan David 49 The Rock, Helsby, Warrington WA6 9AS — MB ChB 1983 Liverp.; BSc (Hons.) Liverp. 1980; FRCS Ed. 1988; MRCGP 1991. Clin. Asst. (Plastic Surg.) Whiston Hosp. Prev: Trainee GP Leighton Hosp. Crewe VTS; Regist. (Gen. Surg.) Warrington Dist. Gen. Hosp.; Regist. (Plastic & Gen. Surg.) Whiston Hosp.

MORTON, Karen Elizabeth 21 Rusholme Road, London SW15 3JX Tel: 020 8789 5863 — MB 1979 Camb.; MA Camb. 1980, MB 1979, BChir 1978; MRCP (UK) 1981; MRCOG 1984. Cons. O & G Roy. Surrey Co. Hosp. Guildford.

MORTON, Kathleen Muriel (retired) 70 Tavistock Drive, Mapperley Park, Nottingham NG3 5DW Tel: 0115 962 1368 — MB ChB 1939 Ed. Prev: Sen. Med. Off. Nottm. HA.

MORTON, Kathryn Davidson Dept. of Pathology, Stirling Royal Infirmary, Livilands, Stirling FK8 2AU Tel: 01786 434000; The Orchard, Doune Road, Dunblane FK15 9AR Tel: 01786 822964 Email: kathrynmorton@netscapeonline.co.uk — MB ChB 1978 Glas.; MRCPath 1987. Cons. Histopath. Stirling Roy. Infirm. Prev: Clin. Lect. Dept. Path. Ninewells Hosp. & Med. Sch.

MORTON, Katrina Mary Banchory Group Practice, The Surgery, Bellfield, Banchory AB31 5XS Tel: 01330 822121 Fax: 01330 825265; Larkview, Woodside Road, Banchory AB31 4EN Tel: 01330 823541 — MB ChB 1980 Glas.; DRCOG 1983. (Glasgow Univ.) Med. Dir., Gleo Dee Hosp., Barchory (Community Hosp.).

MORTON, Lisa Anne 44 St Quentin Drive, Sheffield S17 4PP — MB ChB 1988 Sheff.

MORTON, Lynda Jane Carnoustie Medical Group, The Health Centre, Dundee Street, Carnoustie DD7 7RB Tel: 01241 859888 Fax: 01241 852080; 40 Carlogie Road, Carnoustie DD7 6EY — MB ChB 1982 Aberd.

MORTON, Margaret Alice Stuart Sheldon Child Development Centre, St. Giles Hospital, St Giles Road, London SE3 9SJ; 50 Blackheath Park, London SE3 9SJ Tel: 020 8852 7430 — MB ChB 1968 Bristol; DCH Lond. 1972; MSc. Lond. 1997. Staff Grade, Community Paediat., Optimum Health Servs., NHS Trust, Lond. (p/t).

MORTON, Margo Louise 14 Primrose Street, Dumfries DG2 7AU — MB ChB 1994 Aberd. (Univ. Aberd.) GP Regist Dumfries & Galloway Acute & Matern. Hosps. NHS Trust VTS. Socs: BMA.

MORTON, Mary Roberta Joan Adams and Partners, The Health Centre, Tavanagh Avenue, Portadown, Craigavon BT62 3BU Tel: 028 3835 1393 — MB BCh BAO 1975 Belf.; MRCGP 1979; DCH Dub. 1978; DRCOG 1977.

MORTON, Michael John Stuart Child & Family Psychiatry, Royal Hospital for Sick Children, Yorkhill, Glasgow G3 8SJ Tel: 0141 201 0000 Fax: 0141 201 9261 — MB ChB 1982 Ed.; MPhil Ed. 1988; MA Camb. 1983. Cons. Child Psychiat. Roy. Hosp. Sick Childr. Glas. Socs: Roy. Coll. Psychiat.; Fell. Roy. Coll. Paediat. & Child Health. Prev: Cons. Child Psychiat. (Family Psychiat.) Ladyfield, Dumfries; Sen. Regist. (Child & Adolesc. Psychiat.) Manch.; Regist. (Psychiat.) Roy. Edin. Hosp. & Dingleton Hosp.

MORTON, Michael Robert (retired) 39 Brockington Road, Hereford HR1 3LP Tel: 01568 797291 — MB BS 1955 Lond.; MRCPsych 1972; DPM Eng. 1963. Prev: Cons. Psychiat. Burton Rd. Hosp. Dudley & Lea Castle Hosp. Kidderminster.

MORTON, Moira Anne 5 Hill Farm, Contlaw Road, Milltimber AB13 0DR — MB ChB 1991 Aberd.

MORTON, Neil Stuart c/o Department of Anaesthesia, Royal Hospital for Sick Children, Yorkhill, Glasgow G3 8SJ Tel: 0141 201

MORTON

0186 Fax: 0141 201 0821 — MB ChB 1978 Aberd.; FRCA 1983; FFA RCSI 1982. Cons. Paediat. Anaesth. Intens. Care Roy. Hosp. for Sick Childr. Yorkhill Glas.; Sen. Lect. Univ. of Glas. Socs: Assn. Paediat. Anaesth.; Paediat. Intens. Care Soc. Prev: Asst. Prof. Montreal Childr. Hosp., Canada; Sen. Regist. (Anaesth.) Ninewells Hosp. & Med. Sch. Dundee.; IC Soc. Trav. Fell. 1988.

MORTON, Nuala Brigid Mary Tudor House Surgery, 43 Broad Street, Wokingham RG40 1BE Tel: 0118 978 3544 Fax: 0118 977 0420; Keepers Cottage, Wick Hill Lane, Wokingham RG40 3PY Tel: 01734 734949 — MB BS 1979 Lond.; MRCS Eng. LRCP Lond. 1979; DCH RCP Lond. 1984. (Char. Cross) Prev: SHO (Paediat.) Char. Cross Hosp. Lond.; Sen. Ho. Off. (Neurol.) Roy. Surrey Co. Hosp. Guildford; SHO (Obst.) W. Lond. Hosp.

MORTON, Oswald 5 St Hilda's Close, Christchurch Avenue, London NW6 7NY Tel: 020 8459 7333 Fax: 020 8451 4617 Email: ossiemorton@aol.com — MB BS 1954 Lond.; MRCS Eng. LRCP Lond. 1954; FFPM RCP (UK) 1989; MRCGP 1963; Dip Pharm Med RCP (UK) 1976. (Guy's) Cons. Pharmaceutical Phys. Socs: Fell. Roy. Soc. Med.; Liveryman Soc. Apoth.; Brit. Assn. Pharmaceut. Phys. Prev: Director of Commercial Developm. Reckitt Pharmaceut. Ltd; Director of Research Lloyds Pharmaceut. Ltd; World Med. Director and Jt. Research Director BDH Ltd.

MORTON, Patricia (retired) 12 Old Quay Court, Marino, Holywood BT18 0HT Tel: 01232 423514 — MD Belf. 1963, MB BCh BAO 1958; FRCP Ed. 1974, M 1963; FRCP (Lond.) 1990. Prev: Cons. (Cardiol.) Cardiac Unit Belf. City Hosp.

MORTON, Paul Philip Vauxhall Surgery, Vauxhall Lane, Chepstow NP16 5PZ Tel: 01291 623246 Fax: 01291 627975; Moynes Cottage, Mathern, Chepstow NP16 6HZ — MB BS 1967 Lond.; DObst RCOG 1970; DA Eng. 1971.

MORTON, Peter Richard 87 Douglas Road, Stafford ST16 3QD — MB ChB 1990 Auckland.

MORTON, Richard Pathology Department, Southern General Hospital NHS Trust, Glasgow G51 4TF Tel: 0141 201 1833 Fax: 0141 201 1838; 25 Airyligg Drive, Eaglesham, Glasgow G76 0LJ Tel: 01355 303266 — MB ChB 1970 Glas.; FRCPath 1990, M 1977. (Glasgow University) Cons. Histopath. S. Gen. Hosp. Glas; Hon. Clin. Sen. Lect. Glas. Univ. Prev: Sen. Regist. (Path.) & Ho. Phys. & Surg. W.. Infirm. Glas.

MORTON, Richard Emile 10 Broadway, Duffield, Derby DE56 4BT — BM BCh 1974 Oxf.; BA Oxf. 1971, BM BCh 1974; MRCP (UK) 1979; FRCPCH 1989. (Oxford/UCH London) Cons. Paediat. Derbysh. Childr. Hosp. Derby.

MORTON, Robert Steel, MBE (retired) Flat 6, Montrose Court, Hill Turrets Close, Sheffield S11 9RF Tel: 0114 236 5420 — MD 1982 Sheff.; FRCP Ed. 1962, M 1953; LRCP LRCS Ed. LRFPS Glas. 1939; DHMSA 1983. Hon. Lect. (Hist. Med.) Univ. Sheff. Prev: Cons. Venereol. Sheff.

MORTON, Roger Nicholas Falsgrave Surgery, 33 Falsgrave Road, Scarborough YO12 5EA Tel: 01723 360835 Fax: 01723 503220 — MB ChB 1973 Dundee.

MORTON, Rosemary Jane Accident & Emergency Department, Manchester Royal Infirmary, Oxford Road, Manchester M13 9WL Tel: 0161 276 8539 Fax: 0161 276 8538 — MB ChB 1979 Manch.; FRCP Lond. 1995; FRCS Ed. 1984; FRCPCH 1997; FFAEM 1995; MRCP Lond. 1982; DCH Eng. 1981. (Manch.) Cons. A & E Manch. Roy. Infirm. Socs: Brit. Assn. Accid. & Emerg. Med.; (Comm.) BPAEG.

MORTON, Sally Victoria St. Johns Mental Health Centre, St. Johns Road, Sevenoaks TN13 3LR Tel: 01732 743222 Fax: 01732 742909; 174 Chesterfield Drive, Riverhead, Sevenoaks TN13 2EH Tel: 01732 456309 Email: sa.morton@virgin.net — BM BS 1981 Nottm. Staff Grade (Psychiat.) St. John's Community Ment. Health Centre Sevenoaks; Hon. Staff. Grade (Psychiat.) Maudsley Hosp. Lond. Prev: Clin. Research Worker Inst. of Psychiat. Lond.; Clin. Asst. (Psychiat.) Tunbridge Wells Health Auth.; Regist. (Psychiat.) St Thomas' Hosp. Lond.

MORTON, Sarah Helen 11 Canning Street, Toxteth, Liverpool L8 7NN Tel: 0151 709 9119 — MB ChB 1994 Dundee. SHO (Gen. Surg.) Countess of Chester Hosp. Prev: SHO (Orthop.) Countess of Chester Hosp.; SHO (Renal Transpl. Surg.) Roy. Liverp. Univ. Hosp.; SHO (Orthop.) Warrington Gen. Hosp.

MORTON, Sharon Leanne The Respiratory Unit, Western General Hospital, Crewe Road S., Edinburgh EH4 2XU — BM BS 1988 Flinders; FRACP 1994.

MORTON, Sheena Jane 15 Hunters Way, Chichester PO19 4RB Tel: 01243 527007 — BM BS 1993 Nottm.; MRCP 1997. (Nottingham) Research Fell. (Clin. Immunol.) Univ. Hosp. Nottm. Socs: Med. Protec. Soc. & MSS. Prev: SHO (Neurol.) Nottm.; SHO (Med.) Lincoln; SHO (HCE) Nottm.

MORTON, Stuart Thomas 13 The Glebe, Stannington, Morpeth NE61 6HW — MB ChB 1955 Ed.; FRCPsych 1976; DCH RCPS Glas. 1967; DPM Eng. 1966. Cons. (Child & Adolesc. Psychiat.) Hosp. Sick Childr. Newc. Socs: Fell. Roy. Soc. Med.; Roy. Med. Soc. Edin. Prev: Sen. Regist. Dept. Psychol. Med. Roy. Hosp. for Sick Childr. Edin.; Asst. Resid. Med. Off. Roy. Manch. Childr. Hosp.; Sen. Resid. med. Roy. Hosp. Sick Childr. Edin.

MORTON, Thomas Craig (retired) 33 Mount Stuart Road, Rothesay PA20 9EB Tel: 01700 503366 — MB ChB Glas. 1951.

MORTON, Timothy John The Health Centre, St. Marys Road, Beccles NR34 9NQ Tel: 01502 712662 Fax: 01502 712906 — MB BS 1983 Lond.; MRCGP 1987; DFFP 1996; DCH RCP Lond. 1986; DRCOG 1985. (Westm.) Med. Off. Beccles & Dist. War Memor. Hosp. Prev: Regist. (Psychiat.) Dunedin Univ. Hosp., NZ; SHO (Paediat.) William Harvey Hosp. Ashford Kent.

MORTON, Valerie Jeanne Kings Family Practice, 30-34 Magpie Hall Road, Chatham ME4 5JY Tel: 01634 404632 Fax: 01634 842370; 29 Hill Road, Borstal, Rochester ME1 3NJ — MB BS 1988 Lond.; MA Oxf. 1979. Prev: Trainee GP Macclesfield; SHO (Paediat., Community & Hosp., O & G & Psychiat.) Macclesfield Dist. Gen. Hosp.

MORTON, Valerie Louise Melanie 11 Cumin Place, Edinburgh EH9 2JX — LRCPI & LM, LRSCI & LM 1972; LRCPI & LM, LRCSI & LM 1972. Princip GP Whitburn.

MORTON, Walter Hugill (retired) 4 Llyswen Road, Cycoed, Cardiff CF23 6NG Tel: 01222 756150 — MRCS Eng. LRCP Lond. 1957; FFA RCS Eng. 1967. Prev: Cons. Anaesth. Univ. Hosp. Wales & Llandough Hosp. Cardiff.

MORTON, William Stephen 1 Anshaw Close, Belmont Village, Bolton BL7 8BS — MB BCh BAO 1978 Belf.; MSc Manch. 1985; BSc (Hons.) Belf. 1975; FFPHM 1997; MFPHM 1989; MCFM 1986; FRSH 1995. (Qus. Univ. Belf.) Dir. (Pub. Health) E. Lancs. HA.

MORTON, Winifred Alice 194 Croydon Road, Beckenham BR3 4DQ Tel: 020 8650 1274 — MB ChB 1949 Ed.; DObst RCOG 1953. (Ed.) Socs: BMA. Prev: Asst. Med. Off. African Health Centres, Nairobi; Med. Off. Kaloleni Hosp. Kenya; Sen. Ho. Off. St. Mary's Matern. Hosp. Croydon.

***MORTON-KILI, Caron May** Grosvenor Cottage, 25 Culross St., London W1K 7HF — MB ChB 1996 Stellenbosch.

MORUS, Lowri Clwyd Hiraethog, Caemelyn, Aberystwyth SY23 2HA — MB BCh 1985 Wales.

MORWOOD, Mr Charles Ian Stratton Medical Centre, Hospital Road, Stratton, Bude EX23 9BP Tel: 01288 352133 — MB ChB 1974 Bristol; FRCS Eng. 1979.

MOSA, Mohamed Ali Mohamed 9 Lon Glyn, Denbigh LL16 5YG — MB BCh 1982 Ain Shams; MRCOG 1986.

MOSAHEBI-MOHAMMADI, Afshin 34 Ruskin Way, London SW19 2UP — MB BS 1994 Lond.; FRCS Ed. (UMDS) Plastic Surg.; Research Fell.

***MOSCHAT, Petros** 1st Floor, Fernbank, 134 Lavender Hill, London SW11 5RB Tel: 020 7228 7234 — MB BS 1994 Lond.

MOSCUZZA, Franco 70A Shooters Hill Road, London SE3 7BG — MB BS 1988 Lond.; FRCA 1994.

MOSEDALE, Brenda Mary Bates Green Health Centre, Bates Green, Norwich NR5 8YT Tel: 01603 749921 — MB ChB 1975 Bristol; MSc (Univ. Lond.) 2000. p/t Gen. Practitioner.

MOSELEY, David John Evelyn Medical Centre, Marsh Avenue, Hope, Sheffield S30 2RJ Tel: 01433 621557 — MB ChB 1979 Sheff.; BSc Manch. 1968; MRCP (UK) 1982; DRCOG 1983. GP Peak Dist. Prev: Phys. Abu Dhabi Nat. Oil Co. United Arab Emirates.

MOSELEY, Glynn Edward 5 Harrow Close, Hagley, Stourbridge DY9 0PP — MB BS 1987 Lond.; MRCGP 1991; DRCOG 1989; T(GP) 1992.

MOSELEY, Ivan Frederick 65 St Mary's Grove, London W4 3LW Tel: 020 8995 5668 Fax: 020 8747 0833 — MB BS 1965 Lond.; PhD Wales 1995; BSc (Physiol.) Lond. 1962, MD 1978; FRCP Lond.

1985, M 1968; MRCS Eng. LRCP Lond. 1965; FRCR 1975; FFR 1972; DMRD Eng. 1970. (St. Mary's) Socs: Assoc. Mem. Soc. Française Neuroradiol.; Eur. Soc. Neuroradiol. (Chair,Nat. Delegate); Assoc. Mem. Soc. Française Neuroradiol.(Past Pres.). Prev: Clin. Affil. Fell. (Radiol.) Mt. Zion Hosp. San Francisco, USA; Sen. Regist. (Radiol.) St. Bart. Hosp. Lond.; Ho. Phys. (Neurosurg.) Whittington Hosp. Lond.

MOSELEY, Robin Peter Department of Histopathology, Box 235, Addenbrooke's Hospital, Hills Road, Cambridge CB2 2QQ Tel: 01223 216857; 71 Cottenham Road, Histon, Cambridge CB4 9ET — MB BS 1978 Lond.; PhD Bristol 1990; BSc (Hons.) Lond. 1975, MD 1991; FRCS Eng. 1984; FRCS Ed. 1983; MRCP (UK) 1980; MRCPath 1996. (Univ. Coll. Hosp. Lond. Med. Sch.) Cons. Histopath. and Cytopathologist, Addenbrooke's Hosp., Camb. Prev: Sen. Regist. (Histopath.) Univ. Coll. Lond. Med. Sch.

MOSELHI, Mr Marsham Flat 40, Caswell House, The Crescent, Cardiff Road, Cardiff CF5 2DL — MB BS 1986 Lond.; FRCS Ed. 1990. Regist. Rotat. (Surg.) St. Geo. Hosp. Lond. Prev: SHO (Surg.) Harold Wood Hosp. & Hammersmith Hosp. Lond.; SHO (Orthop.) St. Geo. Hosp. Lond.

MOSELING, Denise Margaret Austwick, 14 Paddockhall Road, Haywards Heath RH16 1HH Tel: 01444 452330 — MB BS 1971 Lond.; BSc Lond. 1968, MB BS 1971; MFCM 1990; DCCH RCP Ed. 1987. (Middlx.) Clin. Med. Off. (Child Health) Surrey & Sussex Healthcare Trust. Prev: Clin. Med. Off. (Child Health) E. Sussex HA.

MOSER, Mr Eric Steven Bethel, 54 Deben Valley Drive, Grange Farm, Kesgrave, Ipswich IP5 2FB — MB BS 1963 Madras; FRCS Ed. 1976.

MOSER, John Branthwaite 19 School Street, Daventry NN11 5ET Tel: 01327 871933 — MRCS Eng. LRCP Lond. 1948. (St. Bart.) Prev: Ho. Surg. St. Bart Hosp. & N.ampton Gen. Hosp.

MOSER, Steven Gerald Bethel, 54 Deben Valley Drive, Kesgrave, Ipswich IP5 2FB — MB ChB 1991 Aberd.

MOSER, Susan 83 Schreiber Road, Ipswich IP4 4NJ — MB BS 1963 Madras.

MOSER, Susan Charlotte 7 Whitehouse Road, Grandpont, Oxford OX1 4PA — MB ChB 1978 Bristol; DRCOG 1981.

MOSES, Mr Alastair Gordon William 56 Craigleith View, Edinburgh EH4 3JY — MB ChB 1992 Glas.; BSc (Hons.) Glas. 1989; FRCS Ed. 1996. Surgic. Research Fell. (Gen. Surg.) Univ. Dept. of Surg. Edin.

MOSES, D V K The Surgery, 34 Rotherhithe New Road, London SE16 2PS Tel: 020 7237 4091 Fax: 020 7231 8944 — MB BS 1969 Osmania; MB BS 1969 Osmania.

MOSES, George The Surgery, 143A Uxbridge Road, London W12 9RD Tel: 020 8743 1511 Fax: 020 8740 0310; Tel: 020 8997 6321 — MB BS 1958 Lond.; MRCS Eng. LRCP Lond. 1958; FRCGP 1992; MRCGP 1965; AFOM 1982. (Univ. Coll. Hosp.) Clin. Asst. Hammersmith & Qu. Charlotte's Hosps. Lond. Prev: Hosp. Pract. Ealing Hosp. Lond.; Clin. Asst. W. Middlx. Hosp.; Cas. Off. Roy. Bucks. Hosp. Aylesbury.

MOSES, Karin Wilhelmina St. Cadocs Hospital, Lodge Road, Caerleon, Newport NP18 3XQ Tel: 01633 436700 — MB BCh 1975 Wales; MA Oxf. 1977; FRCPCH 1997, M 1996; MRCPsych 1980. Cons. Child & Adolesc. Psychiat. Gwent Healthcare NHS Trust. Prev: Cons. Child & Adolesc. Psychiat. Bury HA & Crewe HA; Sen. Regist. (Child & Adolesc. Psychiat.) Manch. HA.

MOSES, Michael Alan 88 Kitswell Way, Radlett WD7 7HN Tel: 01923 469294 Fax: 01923 469294 — BM BCh 1997 Oxf.; BSc (Hons) 1995 Uni. Mans. BST Rot. Derriford Hosp. Plymth.

MOSES, Mr Paul Christin 6 Alder Park Road, Solihull B91 1NU Tel: 0121 711 1069 Fax: 0121 711 1069 — MB BS 1966 Kerala; FRCS Ed. 1975. (Trivandrum Med. Coll.) Indep. Orthop. Surg. W. Midl. Socs: Indep. Doctors Forum.

MOSES, Mr Peter Chellappa 6 Thomson Crescent, Falkirk FK1 5PZ; 6 Thomson Crescent, Falkirk FK1 5PZ — MB BS 1985 Madras; D. Orth. Madras 1987; MCh. ORTH Dundee 1994; FRCS Glas. 1999. (Madras Med. Sch.) Staff grade (Orthop. Surg.) Forth Valley Acute Servs. NHS Trust, Falkirk.

MOSES, Robert George Alloa Health Centre, Alloa FK10 1AB Tel: 01259 212088 Fax: 01259 724788; Craig Na Ard, 37 Claremont, Alloa FK10 2DG — MB ChB 1959 Ed.; DObst RCOG 1964.

***MOSES, Sharon Hema** Flat 4, 12 Oakfield Grove, Bristol BS8 2BN — MB ChB 1998 Bristol.

MOSHAKIS, Mr Vidianos George Eliot Hospital NHS Trust, College St., Nuneaton CV10 7DJ Tel: 01203 865103 Fax: 01203 865395; Heath Park, Forde Hall Lane, Ullenhall, Henley-in-Arden, Stratford on Avon B95 5RR — MB BS Lond. 1972; MS Lond. 1981; FRCS Eng. 1977; MRCS Eng. LRCP Lond. 1972. (Roy. Lond. Hosp.) Cons. Surg. Gen. Surg. NE Warks. HA; Clin. Tutor Univ. Leics. Med. Sch. Socs: Assn. Coloproctol. & Brit. Soc. Gastroenterol. Prev: Sen. Regist. Rotat. (Gen. Surg.) St. Geo. & Roy. Marsden Scheme; Sen. Regist. (Gen. Surg.) Frimley Pk. Hosp. & Roy. Marsden Hosp.

MOSHARAF, Ali The Health Centre, Magna Lane, Dalton, Rotherham S65 4HH Tel: 01709 850229 — MB BS 1968 Peshawar. (Khyber Med. Coll.)

MOSHEGOV, Con Nicholas Flat 7, Coverdale Court, London Road, East Grinstead RH19 1QB.

MOSHY, Roger Ezra X Ray Department, Peterborough District Hospital, Peterborough PE3 6DA Tel: 01733 874426 Fax: 01733 875690; 23 Dry Leys, Peterborough PE2 7HP Tel: 01733 238835 Fax: 01733 238835 — MB ChB 1977 Manch.; BSc (Med. Sci.) (Hons.) St. And. 1974; FRCR 1983; DMRD Eng. 1983. Cons. Radiol. P'boro. Hosps. NHS Trust; Clin. Teach. Univ. Camb. & Leics. Socs: Chairm. Assn. of Early Pregn. Units. Prev: Sen. Regist. (Radiol.) N. W. RHA; Regist. Rotat. (Radiol.) Manch.; SHO (Gen. Med.) Selly Oak Hosp. Birm.

MOSIERI, Chizoba Nkeiruka Alexandra Hospital NHS Trust, Woodrow Drive, Redditch B98 7UB; 35 Moorcroft Close, Callow Hill, Redditch B97 5WB Tel: 01527 404998 Fax: 01527 455319 Email: cmosieri@hotmail.com — MB BS 1978 Ibadan; DA Lond. 1982; FFARCS Irel. 1982. (Ibadan, Nigeria) Cons. Anaesth. Alexandra Hosp. NHS Trust Redditch Worcs. Socs: IC Soc.; AAGBI; Vasc. Anaesth. Soc. (UK). Prev: Cons. Anaesth.NWAFH Tabuk Saudi Arabia.

MOSKOVIC, Eleanor Carmel Royal Marsden Hospital, Fulham Rd, London SW3 6JJ; 42 Shawfield Street, London SW3 4BD Tel: 020 7352 7545 Fax: 020 7376 7665 — MB BS 1981 Lond.; MRCP (UK) 1984; FRCR 1987. (Roy. Free) Cons. Radiol. Roy. Marsden Hosp. Lond. Prev: Sen. Lect. (Diag. Radiol.) Roy. Marsden Hosp. & W.m. Hosp. Lond.; Regist. (Diagn. Radiol.) The Lond. Hosp.; SHO (Med.) St. Mary's Hosp. Lond.

MOSKOVITS, Paul Emeric Department of Anaesthetics, Kent & Canterbury NHS Trust, Ethelbert Road, Canterbury CT1 3NU Tel: 01227 766877; Pine Cottage, 51 New Doner Rd, Canterbury CT1 3DP Tel: 01227 462434 — MB BS 1975 Adelaide; FFA RCS 1980 Eng.; DA 1980 Eng.; DRCOG 1979; FFA RCS Eng. 1982; DA Eng. 1980; DRCOG 1979. Cons. Anaesth. & Pain Specialist Kent & Canterbury NHS Trust. Socs: Assn. Anaesth.; Pain Soc. Prev: Sen. Regist. W.m. Hosp. & S.end-on-Sea; Sen. Regist. W.mead, Sydney.

MOSLEY, Angela Macrae 15 Staneholm Road, Strathaven ML10 6JH — MB ChB 1990 Aberd.; MRCGP 1995; DFFP 1995. Socs: BMA & MDDUS.

MOSQUERA, Mr Damien Anthony Birmingham Heartlands and Solihull NHS Trust, Bordesley Green E., Birmingham B9 5SS Tel: 0121 424 2000 — MB ChB 1983 Liverp.; BSc (Hons.) Liverp. 1980; MD Birm. 1993; FRCS Eng. 1988. (Liverpool) Cons. Vasc. Surg.; Hon. Clin. Sen. Lect. Univ. Birm. Socs: Surg. Research Soc.; Vasc. Surg. Soc. GB & Irel. Prev: Regist. (Surg.) W. Midl. Higher Train. Scheme.; Regist. (Surg.) Roy. Liverp. Hosp.; Temp. Lect. (Anat.) Univ. Manch.

MOSQUERA LOPEZ DE LARRINZAR, Aurora Flat 2, 63 Oxford Road, Moseley, Birmingham B13 9ES — LMS 1985 Bilbao; FRCA (UK) 1996. Specialist Regist. (Anaesth.).

***MOSS, Adrian Christopher** 220 Minster Court, Liverpool L7 3QH — MB ChB 1997 Liverp.

MOSS, Andrew York Dobson Stratton Medical Centre, Hospital Road, Stratton, Bude EX23 9BP Tel: 01288 352133; Lymsworthy Old Farm House, Kilkhampton, Bude EX23 9RY Tel: 01288 321454 — MB BS 1983 Lond.; MRCGP 1989; DRCOG 1990. (Char. Cross) Prev: Regt.. Med. Off. The Ho.hold Cavalry; Trainee GP Cornw. VTS.

MOSS, Mr Anthony Leslie Hugh St. George's Hospital, Blackshaw Road, Tooting, London SW17 0QT Tel: 020 8672 1255 Fax: 020 8725 2416 Email: amoss@sghms.ac.uk — MB BS 1971 Lond.; MRCS Eng. LRCP Lond. 1971; FRACS (Plast Surg.) 1981; T(S) 1991; FRCS; DA RCSI 1974; Dip. Obs. Auckland 1976. (Kings Coll. Hosp.) Cons. Reconstruction Plastic Surg. St. Geo.'s Hosp., Tooting; Paedeatric Plastic Surg. Kingston, Qu. Mary's, Roehampton, Mayday.

MOSS

Socs: Brit. Assn. Plast. Surgs.; Craniofacial Soc.; Brit. Soc. Surg. Hand. Prev: Sen. Regist. (Plas. Surg.) Frenchay Hosp., Bristol; Sen. Regist. (Plas. Surg.) Glas.; Sen. Regist. (Plas. Surg.) Middlemore Hosp. Auck. NZ.

MOSS, Brian (Surgery) 3 Catherine Street, Whitehaven CA28 7PD Tel: 01946 693094; Overdale, 26 Standings Rise, Whitehaven CA28 6SY — MB BS 1966 Durh. (Durh.) Prev: Vis. Phys. Chronic Sick & Geriat. Units Whitehaven Hosp.; SHO (Obst.) & Ho. Surg. W. Cumbld. Hosp.; Ho. Paediat. Walker Gate Hosp. Newc. e.

MOSS, Catherine Margaret Grazeley ICU, Fair Mile Hospital, Wallingford OX10 9HH Tel: 01491 651281 Fax: 01491 652863 — BM BCh 1984 Oxf.; MRCPsych 1992. Cons. (Forens. Psychiat.) Fair Mile Hosp. Wallingford. Prev: Sen. Regist. (Forens. Psychiat.) Fair Mile Hosp. Wallingford.; Regist. (Psychiat.) Oxf. & Warwick; SHO (Psychiat.) Centr. Hosp. Warwick.

MOSS, Catherine Mary Guilsborough Surgery, High Street, Guilsborough, Northampton NN6 8PU Tel: 01604 740210/740142 Fax: 01604 740869 — MB BS 1978 Lond.; MA Camb. 1979, BA 1975; MRCGP 1982; DRCOG 1982. (Univ. Coll. Hosp.)

MOSS, Mr Cecil Isidore (retired) 48 Rodney Street, Liverpool L1 9AA Tel: 0151 709 3022 — MB ChB Manch. 1947; FRCOG 1975, M 1962; DObst 1958. Prev: Cons. Gyn. Liverp. Wom.'s Hosp.

MOSS, Celia The Children's Hospital, Steelhouse Lane, Birmingham B4 6NH Tel: 0121 3338228 Fax: 0212 333 8231 Email: celia.moss@bhamchildrens.wmids.nhs.uk — MB BS 1975 Lond.; DM Oxf. 1983, MA 1976; FRCP 1997; MRCP (UK) 1978; MRCPH 1997. (Univ. Coll. Hosp.) Cons. Dermat. Childr. Hosp. Birm.; Hon. Sen. Clin. Lect. (Paediat. & Child Health) Univ. Birm.; Cons. Dermatol. Sandwell Gen. Hosp. Socs: Brit. Assn. Dermat.; Brit. Soc. Paediat. Dermat.(past Chairm.); Roy. Soc. of Med., Sect. of Dermat., (Counc. Mem.). Prev: Sen. Regist. (Dermat.) Roy. Vict. Hosp. Newc.; Regist. Rotat. (Med.) Whittington Hosp. Lond.; SHO Rotat. (Med.) N. Staffs. Hosp. Centre Stoke-on-Trent.

***MOSS, Charlotte Hannah** 31 Hollycroft Avenue, London NW3 7QJ — MB BS 1997 Lond.

MOSS, Christine Elizabeth River Surgery, 16 Rous Road, Buckhurst Hill IG9 6BN Tel: 020 8504 7364 Fax: 020 8559 0269; 17 Church Road, Buckhurst Hill IG9 5RU Tel: 020 8506 0868 — MB ChB 1980 Otago; MRCGP 1988; DRCOG 1987.

MOSS, Mr Clive Edward Peterborough Hospitals NHS Trust, Thorpe Rd, Peterborough PE3 6DA Tel: 01733 873729 — MB BS 1993 Lond.; FRCS 2000 OMFS; BDS Lond. 1984; FDS RCS Eng. 1992; FRCS Lond. 1996. (St. Thos.) Cons. Oral & Maxillofacial Surg., PeterBoro. Dist. Hosp. Prev: Regist. (Maxillofacial Surg.) Qu. Eliz. Hosp. Edgbaston; SHO (Gen. Surg.) OldCh. Hosp. Romford; Sen. Regist. (Maxillofacial Surg.) Univ. Hosp.s, NHS Trust Birm.

MOSS, Mr David The North Hampshire Hospital, Aldermaston Road, Basingstoke RG24 9NA Tel: 01256 314719 Fax: 01256 313264; Amberwood, 66 Roman Road, Basingstoke RG23 8HA Tel: 01256 468923 — MB BChir 1964 Camb.; MA Camb. 1964; FRCS Ed. 1970; FRCOphth 1988; DO Eng. 1968. (Camb. & Univ. Coll. Hosp.) Cons. Ophth. N. Hants. Hosps. Trust. Prev: Sen. Regist. Birm. & Midl. Eye Hosp.; Regist. & SHO (Ophth.) Roy. Vict. Infirm. Newc.

MOSS, David 119 Clayhall Avenue, Ilford IG5 0PN Tel: 020 8550 4786 — MRCS Eng. LRCP Lond. 1937; BSc (Engin. Hons.) Lond. 1926. (Lond. Hosp.) Prev: Ho. Phys. & Ho. Surg. Roy. Berks. Hosp. Reading; Ho. Surg. Taunton & Dist. Hosp. & Beckett Hosp. Barnsley.

MOSS, David Paul Tudor Surgery, 139 Bushey Mill Lane, Watford WD2 4PD Tel: 01923 223724 Fax: 01923 237327 — MB BS 1983 Lond.; MRCGP 1987; DRCOG 1986; DCH RCP Lond. 1985. GP Watford.

MOSS, Douglas Britton (Surgery), 42 Tudor Way, Petts Wood, Orpington BR5 1LH Tel: 01689 820268; Flat 1, 9 Church Row, Chislehurst BR7 5PG Tel: 020 8295 1517 — MB BS 1961 Lond.; MRCS Eng. LRCP Lond. 1961. (King's Coll. Hosp.) Prev: SHO Neurosurg. Unit Brook Gen. Hosp. Lond.; Ho. Surg. King's Coll. Hosp. Lond.

MOSS, Dudley Arthur Prestwich Health Centre, Fairfax Road, Prestwich, Manchester M25 1BT Tel: 0161 773 0525 Fax: 0161 773 9218 — MB ChB 1972 Manch.

MOSS, Edward Department of Anaesthetics, Leeds General Infirmary, Great George St., Leeds LS1 3EX Tel: 0113 392 6672 Fax: 0113 392 2645 Email: edward.moss@leedsth.nhs.uk; 10 Dunstarn Lane, Leeds LS16 8EL Tel: 0113 3922 645 — MB ChB 1972; MD Ed. 1983; FFA RCS Eng. 1976. (Ed.) Cons. Anaesth. Gen. Infirm. Leeds; Sen. Clin. Lect. Univ. Leeds. Socs: BMA & Assn. Anaesth.; Neuroanaesth. Soc.; Roy. Soc. Med. Prev: Sen. Regist. (Anaesth.) Yorks. RHA; Lect. (Anaesth.) Univ. Leeds; Regist. (Anaesth.) Leeds W.. Health Dist.

***MOSS, Esther Louise** 10 Hunter Street, Northampton NN1 3QD — MB ChB 1998 Birm.; ChB Birm. 1998.

MOSS, Fiona Mary London Postgraduate Medical & Dental Education, 20 Guilford Street, London WC1N 1D2 Tel: 020 7692 3381 Fax: 020 7692 3396 — MD 1989 Lond.; MB BS Lond. 1976; MRCP (UK) 1979; FRCP 1994. (University College London) p/t Cons. Respirat. Phys. Centr. Middlx. NHS Trust; Assoc. Postgrad. Dean Lond.; Edr. in Chief Quality and Safety in Healthcare. Prev: Edr. Quality in Health Care.

***MOSS, Fiona Sheila** 10 Camcross Cl, Portsmouth PO6 4DX — MB BCh 1997 Wales.

MOSS, Francis Leigh Strickland BMI Three Shires Hospital, The Avenue, Northampton NN1 5DR Tel: 01604 231568; Braeside, Brafield Rd, Horton, Northampton NN7 2AZ Tel: 01604 870439 Email: leighmoss@btinternet.com — MB BS 1977 Lond.; MRCS Eng. LRCP Lond. 1977; FRCR Eng. 1983; DMRD Eng. 1982. (Westm.) Cons. (Radiol.) N.ampton Gen. Hosp. NHS Trust; Chairm. of Med. Staff 1990-2001. Socs: Brit. Inst. Radiol.; RCR BrE. Gr. Prev: Sen. Regist. (Radiol.) W.m. Hosp. Lond.; Regist. (Renal Med.) Kent & Canterbury Hosp.

MOSS, Gail Denise 37 Chelsea Road, Brincliffe, Sheffield S11 9BQ — MB ChB 1981 Sheff.; MRCP (UK) 1986. Cons. Paediat. Childr. Hosp. Sheff.

MOSS, Gillian Elizabeth Mental Health Services of Salford, Department of Psychiatry of Later Life, Meadowbrook, Salford M6 8DD Tel: 0161 772 3765 Fax: 0161 772 3772 — MB ChB 1980 Manch.; MSc Manch. 1989, MB ChB 1980; MRCPsych 1985. Cons. Old Age Psychiat. Ment. Health Servs. Salford; Hon. Clin. Lect.

MOSS, Hadrian Dryland Surgery, 1 Field Street, Kettering NN16 8JZ Tel: 01536 518951 Fax: 01536 486200; 17 Warkton Lane, Kettering NN15 5AB Email: hadrian@wlane.demon.co.uk — MB BS 1982 Lond.; MRCGP 1986; DRCOG 1986. (Middlx. Hosp.) Socs: Brit. Med. Acupunct. Soc.

MOSS, Hilary Ann 11 Park Drive, Harrogate HG2 9AY — BM BS 1990 Nottm.; MRCP (UK) 1993.

MOSS, Ivor Sydney 2 Meadowbanks, Barnet Road, Arkley, Barnet EN5 3LY Tel: 020 8449 2535 — MB BS Lond. 1949. (Guy's) Med. Asst. (Pain Clinic) Centr. Middlx. Hosp. Socs: Fell. Roy. Soc. Med.; Med. Acupunct. Soc. Prev: Regist. (Venereol.) Guy's Hosp. Lond.; Clin. Asst. St. Thos. Hosp. Lond.; Hosp. Pract. St. Geo. Hosp. Lond.

MOSS, John 4 Wharfedale Road, Reddish, Stockport SK5 6HE — MB BCh 1973 Wales; FFA RCS Eng. 1980; DA Eng. 1979; DFFP 1998; Cert. Av Med 1998 : CAA/RAF.

MOSS, John Allington (retired) 400 Wells Road, Knowle, Bristol BS14 9AA Tel: 0117 977 0817 — MB BS Lond. 1955.

MOSS, John Edward Antrim Health Centre, Station Road, Antrim BT41 4BS Tel: 028 9446 4937 Fax: 028 9446 4930; 34 Ballynoe Road, Antrim BT41 2QX Tel: 0184 94 69903 — MB BCh BAO 1979 Belf. (Queens University Belfast) Socs: Roy. Coll. Gen. Pract.; BMA.

MOSS, John Wallis (retired) Beechcroft, Cromer Road, High Kelling, Holt NR25 6QZ Tel: 01263 711276 — MB ChB 1953 Birm. Prev: Med. Off. RAF.

MOSS, Jonathan George North Glasgow Hospitals University NHS Trust, Dunbarton Road, Glasgow G11 6NT Tel: 0141 211 3113 Fax: 0141 211 3471 Email: j.moss@climed.gla.ac.uk; 21 Ledameroch Crescent, Bearsden, Glasgow G61 4AD Tel: 0141 942 3404 Email: j.moss@clinmed.gla.ac.uk — MB ChB 1979 Ed.; FRCS Ed. 1984; FRCR 1989; DMRD Ed. 1987. (Edinburgh) Cons. Radiologist, N. Glas. Hosp.s Univ. NHS Trust; Ross Hall Hosp., Glas. Socs: SCUIR; CVIR; BSIR. Prev: Fell. Radiol. Univ. of Texas.

MOSS, Julia Louise Maria 6 Hawkins Close, Edgbaston, Birmingham B5 7NW — MB ChB 1988 Birm.; ChB Birm. 1988.

MOSS, Katie Emily Royal National Orthopaedic Hospital, Brockley Hill, Stanmore HA7 4LP Tel: 020 8954 2300 Fax: 020 8420 7487 Email: kayteemoss@hotmail.com; Flat 5, 101 Ridgway, Wimbledon, London SW19 4SX Tel: 020 8879 7486 Email: kayteemoss@hotmail.com — MB ChB 1992 Bristol; MRCP (UK)

MOSS

1997. Regist. (Rheumatol./Gen. Med.) Roy. Nat. Orthopaedic Hosp., Stanmore, Middlx. Socs: BSR. Prev: SPR Rheum. / Gen. Med. Whittington Hosp. Lond.; SPR Rheumatol. / Gen. Med. N. Middlx. Hosp. Lond.; Clin. Research Fell. Rheumatol. - UCL / Middlx. Hosp. Lond.

MOSS, Katrina Helen 192 Upper Road, Kennington, Oxford OX1 5LR — MB ChB 1993 Birm.

MOSS, Laura Jane Velindre Hospital, Whitchurch, Cardiff CF14 2TL Tel: 029 2061 5888 — MB BCh 1993 Wales; FRCP 2001; MRCP 1996; 1996 MRCP Lond. (Cardiff) Specialist Regist. (Clin. Oncol.).

MOSS, Leonard Hargreaves (retired) Beckwith Cottages, Beckwith, Harrogate HG3 1QQ Tel: 01423 563323 — MB ChB 1939 Leeds. Prev: Cas. Off. Leeds Pub. Disp.

MOSS, Mrs Lilian Gwendolyn Noelle (retired) The Paddock, Broseley Avenue, Culcheth, Warrington WA3 4HL — MB BCh BAO 1953 Dub.; BA Dub. 1950, MA 1960, MB BCh BAO 1953. Prev: Ho. Surg. Roy. City of Dub. Hosp.

MOSS, Louise Sarah Moss Valley Medical Practice, Gosber Road, Eckington, Sheffield S21 4BZ Tel: 01246 432131 — MB ChB 1990 Birm.; MRCGP 1994; Dip. Pract. Demat. Wales 1997; DRCOG 1992. (Birm.) GP, Eckington; Hosp. Practitioner in Dermat. Chesterfield Roy. Hosp. Socs: BMA; Med. Protec. Soc. Prev: Trainee GP Kidderminster VTS.

MOSS, Mark Stephen Department of Radiology, City Hospital, Dudley Road, Birmingham B18 7QH Tel: 0121 507 4727 Fax: 0121 523 5041 — MB BS 1984 Lond.; MRCP (UK) 1988; FRCR 1992. Cons. Radiol. City Hosp. Birm.

MOSS, Martin Leslie The Surgery, Yeoman Lane, Bearsted, Maidstone ME14 4DS Tel: 01622 737326/738344 Fax: 01622 730745; Old Forge House, Busbridge Road, Loose, Maidstone ME15 0ER Tel: 01622 745175 — MB BS 1977 Lond.; MRCS Eng. LRCP Lond. 1977. (Guy's) GP Princip.; Bd. Mem. Maidstone PCG. Socs: Fell.Roy. Soc. Med.; Fell. Roy. Soc. Med.; BMA. Prev: Hosp. Pract. (Cardiol.) Maidstone Hosp.; Ho. Phys. (Gen. Med.) St. Nicholas' Hosp. Lond.; Ho. Surg. (Urol.) Guy's Hosp. Lond.

MOSS, Mary Lynette Marlowe House, Popley 1, Basingstoke RG24 9DD; 66 Roman Road, Basingstoke RG23 8HA Tel: 01256 468923 — BM BCh 1965 Oxf.; MA Oxf. 1965. (Oxf. & St. Thos.) Prev: Ho. Phys. Preston Hosp. N. Shields; Ho. Surg. E. Glam. Hosp. Pontypridd.

MOSS, Mr Michael Charles 30 Thornton Road, London SW19 4NG — MB BS 1983 Lond.; FRCS Eng. 1988; T(S) 1993.

MOSS, Nathan Hammond Middle Park Medical Centre, 15 Middle Park Way, Leigh Park, Havant PO9 4AB Tel: 023 9261 1055 Fax: 023 9278 2389 — MB ChB 1970 Baghdad; MRCGP 1995. (Bagdad) Prev: Trainee GP N. Devon VTS; SHO Regist. Psychiat. Swindon.

MOSS, Norman Arthur (retired) The Roserie, Westhorpe, Sibbertoft, Market Harborough LE16 9UL — LRCPI & LM, LRSCI & LM 1954; LRCPI & LM, LRCSI & LM 1954. Prev: Assoc. Specialist (A & E) Roy. Infirm. Leicester.

MOSS, Nuala Margaret 7 Letham Drive, Newlands, Glasgow G43 2SL — MB BCh BAO 1981 NUI; FRCSI 1985; FRCR 1990.

MOSS, Patricia (retired) 3 Laurel Mount, Richmond Road, Bowdon, Altrincham WA14 2TU Tel: 0161 928 4139 — MB ChB 1948 Manch. Clin. Med. Off. Trafford HA.

MOSS, Professor Paul Austin Henry C.R.C. Institute for cancer studies, University of Birmingham, Edgbaston, Birmingham B15 2TA Email: p.moss@bham.ac.uk; 5 Ascot Road, Moseley, Birmingham B13 9EN — BM BS 1986 Oxf.; BA Camb. 1983; MRCP (UK) 1989; MRCPath 1996; Ph.D. 1993. Prof. of Haemat. Uni. Of Birm. Prev: Clin. Scientist Univ. Oxf.

MOSS, Paul Nicholas Bolton North Shoebury Surgery, Frobisher Way, Shoeburyness, Southend-on-Sea SS3 8UT Tel: 01702 297976 Fax: 01702 290131; 22 Dungannon Chase, Thorpe Bay, Southend-on-Sea SS1 3NJ Tel: 01702 584422 Fax: 01702 290131 — BM 1979 Soton.; MRCGP 1989.

MOSS, Peter Derrick (retired) 6 Brookes Lane, Whalley, Blackburn BB7 9RG Tel: 01254 823931 — MB ChB 1942 Liverp.; FRCP Lond. 1972, M 1948; DCH Eng. 1947. Prev: Cons. Paediatr. Blackburn Dist. Hosp.

MOSS, Peter John Lister House Surgery, Lister House, 53 Harrington Street, Pear Tree, Derby DE23 8PF Tel: 01332 271212

Fax: 01332 271939; The Old School, King Street, Duffield, Belper DE56 4EU — MB BS 1982 Nottm. Clin. Gov. Lead Centr. Derby PCT.

MOSS, Peter Jonathan 12 Carr Bank Lane, Sheffield S11 7FB — MB ChB 1987 Birm.; MRCP (UK) 1991; DTM & H 1992.

MOSS, Peter Michael (retired) Amalrie, Franklin Road, North Fambridge, Chelmsford CM3 6NF — MB ChB Birm. 1955; DObst RCOG 1959.

MOSS, Philip John York District Hospital, Wigginton Road, York YO31 8HE Tel: 01904 631313 — MB BS 1975 Lond.; FFA RCS Eng. 1981. (Charing Cross, University of London) Cons. Anaesth. York Dist. Hosp.

MOSS, Philip Simon 47 Salterford Road, London SW17 9TE — MB BS 1993 Lond.

MOSS, Roger Charles Sarra (retired) 3 Earl Richard's Road N., Exeter EX2 6AQ Tel: 01392 274302 Fax: 01392 495264 Email: 106116.3404@compuserve.com — MRCS Eng. LRCP Lond. 1964; MRCPsych 1972; DPM Eng. 1969. Psychiat. Adviser Centre for Ment. Health Serv. Developm. King's Coll. Lond. Prev: Cons. Psychiat. Torbay HA.

MOSS, Roger Michael Halden High Halden, Wilmslow Park, Wilmslow SK9 2BD; 27 Myrtle Road, Brentwood CM14 5EG Tel: 01277 214541 — MB BS 1980 Lond.; MRCGP 1993; DCH RCP Lond. 1991; DRCOG 1987; FRCA 1997. (St. George's Hosp., Univ. of Lond.) Specialist Regist. (Anaesth.).

***MOSS, Samantha Jane** 12 Cromwell Drive, Shavington, Crewe CW2 5EJ — MB BS 1998 Lond.; MB BS Lond 1998.

MOSS, Samuel David The Longton Health Centre, Longton, Preston PR4 5HA; Crosland House, Orchard Lane, Loughton, Preston PR4 5AX Tel: 01772 614219 — MB ChB 1967 Ed.; DObst RCOG 1967.

MOSS, Sarah Louise North House Surgery, North St., Ripon HG4 1HL Tel: 01765 690666 Fax: 01765 690249 — MB BS 1986 Lond.; MRCGP 1992. (Middlesex Hospital Medical School) p/t GP Princip. N. Ho. Surg., Ripon.

MOSS, Sebastian 25 Cherryborn Gardens, Fenham, Newcastle upon Tyne NE4 9UQ — MB BS 1994 Newc.

MOSS, Sheila Peasley Suite, St. Helens Hospital, Marshalls Cross Road, St Helens LA9 3EA; 3 Lawton Road, Rainhill, Prescot L35 0PL — MB ChB 1983 Sheff.; MRCP 1996 (UK); Dip Ven 1992; MRCPsych 1990 (I); BMedSci 1981. Cons. Phys. GU Med. Prev: Sp. Reg. Mersey Rotat.; SP. Reg. Respirat. Med. Roy. Liverp.

MOSS, Stephanie Ann 353 Station Road, Dorridge, Solihull B93 8EY Tel: 01564 773973 — MB BS 1979 Lond.; DRCOG 1982. GP Retainer Scheme Gr. Rd. Surg. Solihull. Prev: GP Partnership Crossbrook Surg. Cheshunt, Herts.

MOSS, Stephen The Old Rectory, Church Lane, Scartho, Grimsby DN33 2EX Tel: 01472 750698 Fax: 01472 751991 — MB BChir Camb. 1966; MD Camb. 1979; FRCP Lond. 1989; MRCP (UK) 1970. (Camb. & St. Thos.) Cons. Phys. & Gastroenterol. NE Lincs. Health Trust. Socs: Brit. Soc. Gastroenterol.; Med. Res. Soc. Prev: Sen. Regist. (Med.) St. Mary's Hosp. Lond.; Tutor (Med.) & Hon. Sen. Regist. Manch. Roy. Infirm.

MOSS, Susan Jane Little Oaks, Rhinefield Close, Brockenhurst SO42 7SQ — BM 1986 Soton.; BM (Clin. Hons.) Soton. 1986; MRCGP 1990; DRCOG 1988. Clin. Asst. (Rheum.) Bournemouth & ChristCh. Hosp. Trust. Prev: GP Brockenhurst Retainer VTS; Trainee GP Hants. VTS.

***MOSS, Susan Joan** 18 The Copse, Marple Bridge, Stockport SK6 5QQ — MB ChB 1998 Dund.; MB ChB Dund 1998.

MOSS, Susan Marie Hemingford, 56 Epsom Road, Guildford GU1 3LG Tel: 01483 572364 — MB BS 1983 Camb.; MA Camb. 1981, MB BS 1983; MRCGP (Distinc.) 1987; DRCOG 1987.

MOSS, Sylvia Anne (retired) Green Rising, Quarry Heads Lane, Durham DH1 3DY Tel: 0191 384 2510 — MB BS Durh. 1949. Prev: GP Durh.

MOSS, Timothy Hugh Department of Neuropathology, Frenchay Hospital, Bristol BS16 1LE Tel: 0117 970 1700 Fax: 0117 975 3760 Email: tim.moss@dial.pipex.com — MB ChB 1977 Bristol; PhD 1980 Bristol; FRCPath 1996; MRCPath 1986. (Bristol) Cons. Neuropath. Frenchay Hosp. Bristol; Sen. Clin. Lect. Bristol Univ. Socs: Hon. Sec. Brit. Neuropath. Soc. Prev: Sen. Regist. (Neuropath.) Frenchay Hosp. Bristol; SHO (Path.) S.mead Hosp. Bristol; Research Stud. (Experim. Neuropath.) Dept. Physiol. Univ. Bristol.

MOSS

MOSS, Timothy Roger Clinical Director, Doncaster Royal & Doncaster and Bassettaw NHS Trust, Armthorpe Road, Doncaster DN2 5LT Tel: 01302 553111 Fax: 01302 553202; Crooked Oak Cottage, Cusworth Village, Doncaster DN5 7TR Tel: 01302 787657 Fax: 01302 553202 — MB ChB 1974 Leeds; BSc (Hons.) Leeds 1971; FRCGP 1997; MRCGP (Distinc.) 1978; DRCOG 1977. (Leeds) Clin. Dir. (Genitourin. Med. & AIDS) Doncaster Roy. Infirm.; Hon. Clin. Lect. (Genitourin. Med.) Univ. Sheff.; Nat. Cervical Screen. Prog. Nat. Co-ord. Network Policy Maker; Chairm. Trent Regional Colposcopy Quality Assur. Gp.; Founder Mem. Nat. Colposcopy Quality Assur. Gp.l. Socs: Med. Soc. Study VD; Founder Mem. UK Genitourin. Colposcopy Soc.; BSCCP. Prev: Sen. Regist. (Sexually Transm. Dis.) Newc. Gen. Hosp.

MOSS-MORRIS, Sheila Beryl 31 West Heath Drive, London NW11 7QG Tel: 020 8455 8077 — MB BCh 1945 Witwatersrand; DCH Eng. 1948. (Witwatersrand) Prev: Sen. Med. Off. Camden & Islington AHA (T).

MOSSA, Federico 4 Blaen Y Wawr, Bangor LL57 4TR — State Exam Bari 1993.

MOSSAD, Makram Gabra Whinmoor Surgery, White Laithe Approach, Whinmoor, Leeds LS14 2EH Tel: 0113 295 3295 Fax: 0113 295 3291; 31 High Ash Avenue, Alwoodley, Leeds LS17 8RS Tel: 0113 295 3299 — MB BCh 1972 Assiut; T(GP) 1992. Occupat. Med. Off. Agfa Leeds. Socs: Soc. Occupat. Health. Prev: Regist. (Orthop.) Harrogate; Trainee GP Harrogate VTS.

MOSSCROP, Lewis Edwin (retired) 5 Middlewood Road, Aughton, Ormskirk L39 6RG Tel: 01695 423972 — LRCP 1942 Ed.; LRCP, LRCS Ed. LRFPS Glas. 1942; FFA RCS Eng. 1954; DA Eng. 1948. Prev: Anaesth. Ormskirk & S.port Hosp. Gps.

MOSSMAN, Andrew Donald The Health Centre, Elm Grove, Mengham, Hayling Island PO11 9AP Tel: 023 9246 6224 Fax: 023 9246 6079; 30 Brooklyn Close, Waltham Chase, Southampton SO32 2RY — MB ChB 1979 Liverp.; MRCP (UK) 1984; DRCOG 1989.

***MOSSOP, David James** A & E Department, Royal Bournemouth Hospital, Castle La E., Bournemouth BH7 7DW — BM 1997 Soton.

MOSSOP, Gwyrie Wendy Elizabeth Julian Exeter & District Hospice, Dryden Road, Exeter EX2 5JJ Tel: 01392 402555 Fax: 01392 495981; Barnhayes, Huxham, Exeter EX5 4EW Tel: 01392 841249 — MRCS Eng. LRCP Lond. 1967. (St. Bart.) Clin. Asst. (Palliat. Med.) Exeter & Dist. Hospice. Prev: Ho. Surg. & Ho. Phys. Weymouth & Dist. Hosp.

MOSSOP, Helen Elizabeth Jane St Helena Hospice, Barncroft Road, Colchester CO4 4SF Tel: 01206 845566 Fax: 01206 842445; 14 Deben Heath, Parsons Heath, Colchester CO4 3UZ Tel: 01206 791227 Email: patm@essex.ac.uk — MB ChB 1972 Birm.; DObst RCOG 1974; Dip Palliat Med. (Dip. Pall Med.) 1998 Univ. South Wales. Asst. Med. Dir. (Pallliat. Med.) St. Helena Hospice Colchester.

MOSTAD, Hege The Surgery, 141-143 Lupus Street, London SW1V 3HQ Tel: 020 7828 9252 — State Exam 1984 Florence. Clin. Asst. (Cardiol.). Prev: GP Lond.

MOSTAFA, Mostafa Awad Alla, Maj. RAMC 31 Malmains Drive, Frenchay, Bristol BS16 1PQ Tel: 0117 956 9336 — MB BCh 1963 Cairo; FFA RCS Eng. 1980; DA Cairo 1969. (Kasr El Aini Med. Coll.) Cons. Anaesth. Al Salama Hosp. Jeddah, Saudi Arabia. Prev: Specialist (Anaesth.) Polde Inst. Cairo; Regist. Grimsby Gp. Hosps. & Leics. AHA.

MOSTAFA, Sobhy Morsy Royal Liverpool University Hospital, Prescot St., Liverpool L7 8XP Tel: 0151 706 2000; Greenwood, 3 Cottage Drive W., Gayton, Wirral CH60 8NX Tel: 0151 342 2471 — MB ChB 1966 Cairo; MRCS Eng. LRCP Lond. 1976; FFA RCS Eng. 1973. Cons. Anaesth. & Dir. ITU Roy. Liverp. Hosp.; Clin. Lect. (Anaesth.) Univ. Liverp. Socs: Life Mem. Midl. Soc. Anaesth. (Past Hon. Sec. & Treas.); Assn. Anaesth.; BMA & Intens. Care Soc., Anaesth. Research Soc. - Anaesth. Res. Soc. AMICU (ex-chairm.). Prev: Cons. Anaesth. Selly Hosp. Birm.; Fac. Tutor S. Birm. Health Dist.; Regist. & Sen. Regist. (Anaesth.) Liverp. Hosp.

MOSTAFID, Mr Amir Hossein The North Hampshire Hospital, Aldermaston Road, Basingstoke RG27 9NA Tel: 01256 314701 Fax: 01256 313512; Email: mostafid@hotmail.com — MB BS 1989 Lond.; FEBU 2000; MSc Lond. 1996; FRCS Eng. 1993; FRCS (Urol.) 1999. Cons. Urological Surg., N. Hants. Hosp., Basingstoke. Prev: SHO (Surg.) W. Suff. Hosp.

MOSTON, Roger Hyde The Doctors House, Victoria Road, Marlow SL7 1DN Tel: 01628 484666 Fax: 01628 891206 — MB BS 1972 Lond.; MRCGP 1976; DRCOG 1976.

MOSTYN, Penelope Ann Caldest Centre, King's Healthcare, 15-22 Caldecot Road, London SE5 9RS Tel: 020 7346 3478 Fax: 020 7346 3486 — MB BS 1986 Lond.; BA Camb. 1977; DRCOG 1993; Dip. Human Sex 1993. Assoc. Specialist (Psy. Med. Dept. Sex. Health) King's Coll. Hosp. Lond. (P/T).

MOTABHOY, Banoo Rusi 3 Stanhope Heath, Stanwell, Staines TW19 7PH Tel: 01784 55156 — MB BS 1950 Bombay.

MOTAHAR, Mohammed Moti 10 The Heights, Foxgrove Road, Beckenham BR3 5BY Tel: 020 8650 4481 — MB BS 1960 Dacca; DCH Eng. 1965; DTM & H Eng. 1964. Sen. Med. Off. (Child Health) Greenwich & Bexley AHA & Devonport Annexe Lond. Prev: Paediatr. i/c Inas Hosp. Tripoli, Libya; Regist. Sydenham Childr. Hosp.; Med. Off. (Child Health) King's Coll. Hosp. Lond.

MOTAMED, Mehdi 25 Embassy House, West End Lane, London NW6 2NA — MB BS 1992 Lond.

MOTASHAW, Rusi Darashaw Jer-Daw, Herga Hyll, Orsett, Grays RM16 3JA Tel: 01375 891044 — MB BS 1941 Bombay; MD Bombay 1945. (Bombay) Prev: Resid. Accouch. & Demonst. (Obst.) NW Matern. Hosp.; Regist. King Edwd. VII Memor. Hosp. Bombay; Assoc. Dir. Clin. Developm. Lederle Laborat. India.

***MOTAZED, Reza** 120 Oakwood Court, Abbotsbury Road, London W14 8LB — MB BS 1996 Lond.

MOTHA, Mr Joseph Thambiah 73 Horringer Road, Bury St Edmunds IP33 2DQ Tel: 01284 706218 — MB BS 1972 Kerala; FRCS Eng. 1984. (Trivandrum Med. Coll.) SHO (Orthop.) Manfield Hosp. N.ampton. Prev: SHO (Gen. Surg.) Bronglais Hosp. Aberystwyth; SHO (A & E) King Geo. Hosp. Ilford.

MOTHA, Mr Sivakumar Conquest Hospital, The Ridge, St Leonards-on-Sea TN37 7RD Tel: 01424 755255 Fax: 01424 758115; 41 The Suttons, St Leonards-on-Sea TN38 9RA Tel: 01424 852543 Email: mothas@hotmail.com — MB BS 1972 Andhra; FRCS Glas. 1984. (Andhra Med. Coll. Visakhapatnam) Assoc. Specialist (Surg.) Conquest Hosp. St. Leonards-on-Sea.

***MOTHERWELL, Duncan Wylie** Invercarron, Watt Road, Bridge of Weir PA11 3DN Tel: 01505 612353 Fax: 01505 612352 — MB ChB 1998 Glas.; MB ChB Glas 1998; BSc Glasgow 1996.

MOTIWALA, Hanif Gaffarbhai Department of Urology, Mayday University Hospital, London Road, Croydon CR7 7YE — MB BS 1984 Gujarat; MB BS Gujarat, India 1984.

MOTLEY, Brenda Mary (retired) Last House, Crescent Drive, Brentwood CM15 8DS Tel: 01277 216489 — MB BS 1959 Lond.; MRCPsych 1978. Cons. Psychiat. Speciality Rehabil. Warley Hosp. Brentwood; Sen. Regist. (Psych.) Warley Hosp. Brentwood. Prev: SHO (Paediat.) St. John's Hosp. Chelmsford.

MOTLEY, Richard John Welsch Institute of Dermatology, University Hospital of Wales, Heath Park, Cardiff CF14 4XW Tel: 029 2074 4629 Fax: 029 2074 5161 Email: richard.motley@uhw-tr.wales.nhs.uk — MB BChir 1983 Camb.; MA Camb. 1983, MD 1993, BA 1979, MB 1983, BChir 1982; MRCP (UK) 1985; FRCP 2000. (Cambridge and St. Thomas) p/t Cons. Dermatol. Univ. Hosp. of Wales S. Glam. HA. Prev: Ho. Phys. St. Thomas Hosp. Lond.

MOTSON, Mr Roger Wingfield (cons. rooms), Oaks Hospital, Oaks Place, Colchester CO4 5XR Tel: 01206 753209 Fax: 01206 852701 Email: motson@doctors.org.uk; Mulberry Green Farm House, Copford Green, Colchester CO6 1DJ Tel: 01206 210231 Fax: 01206 210231 Email: rwmotson@aol.com — MB BS 1970 Lond.; MB BS Lond. 1971; MS Lond. 1981; FRCS Eng. 1975; MRCS Eng. LRCP Lond. 1970. (Char. Cross) Cons. Surg. (Laparoscopic & Colorectal) Colchester Dist. Gen. Hosp.; Vis. Prof. Armed Forces Hosp. Alexandria, Egypt. Socs: Fell. Roy. Soc. Med. (Vice-Pres. Counc. Coloproctol. Sect.); Hon. Mem. S. African Soc. of Endoscopic Surgs.; Fell. (Pres.) Assn. Endoscopic Surgs. GB & Irel. Prev: Sen. Regist. (Surg.) Lond. Hosp.; Research Fell. Univ. Calif. San Francisco, USA; Regist. (Surg.) Norf. & Norwich Hosp.

MOTT, Alison Mary Department Community Child Health, Lansdowne Hospital, Cardiff CF11 8PL Tel: 029 2037 2451 Fax: 029 2023 7378 Email: alison.mott@uhw-tr.wales.nhs.uk — BM 1981 Soton.; MRCP (UK) 1985; DRCOG 1984; DTCH Liverp. 1988; FRCPCH. (Southampton University) p/t Cons. Paediat. in Community Child Health. Socs: Fell. Roy. Coll. Of Paeds. & Child Health. Prev: Sen. Regist. (Paediat. & Community Child Health) S. Glam. HA.;

Clin. Med. Off. (Community Child Health) Bristol; Paediat. Mendi Hosp. Papua New Guinea.

MOTT, Andrew Norman The Surgery, Torton Hill Road, Arundel BN18 9HG — MB BS 1972 Lond.; BSc (Hons. Physiol.) Lond. 1969; MRCGP 1980; DObst RCOG 1976; DCH Eng. 1975. (Lond. Hosp.) Tutor (Gen. Pract.) St. Geo. Hosp. Med. Sch. Lond.; Bd. Mem. & Clin. Governance Lead Regis PCG. Socs: BMA; Christian Med. Fell.sh. Prev: Ho. Surg. (Thoracic Dept.) Lond. Hosp.; Ho. Phys. Roy. United Hosp. Bath.

MOTT, Emily Rose Red House Farm, Burgh, Woodbridge IP13 6SR Tel: 0143 735727 — MB ChB 1998 Bristol.

MOTT, Frederick William Martin (retired) 7 Greaves Close, Walsall WS5 3QT Tel: 01922 634525 — MB BCh BAO NUI 1950.

MOTT, Heiltje Wilhelmina Essex Way Surgery, 34 Essex Way, Benfleet SS7 1LT Tel: 01268 792203 Fax: 01268 759495 — Artsexamen 1970 Leiden. (Leiden) GP Benfleet.

MOTT, Sir John Harmar, Bt (retired) Staniford, Brookside, Kingsley, Warrington WA6 8BG Tel: 01928 88123 — BM BCh 1951 Oxf.; MA Oxf. 1948, BM BCh 1951; MRCGP 1958. Med. Ref. DHSS. Prev: Regional Med. Off. DHSS (Manch.).

MOTT, Professor Martin Gerard (retired) Email: m.g.mott@bris.ac.uk — MB ChB 1966 Bristol; DSc Bristol 1991, BSc 1963; FRCP Lond. 1983; MRCP (UK) 1969; FRCPCH 1997; DCH Eng. 1971. Prev: Prof. Paediat. Oncol. Univ. Bristol & Dept. Child Health Roy. Hosp. Sick Childr. Bristol.

MOTT, Paul Anthony Evelyn Belvidere Medical Practice, 23 Belvidere Road, Shrewsbury SY2 5LS Tel: 01743 363640 Fax: 01743 357400; 156 Longden Road, Shrewsbury SY3 9ED Tel: 01743 246893 — MB ChB 1977 Birm.; DRCOG 1980. Hosp. Practitioner (Learning Disabil.) Shrewsbury. Prev: SHO (Obst.) Birm. Matern. Hosp.; SHO (Gyn.) Birm. & Midl. Wom.'s Hosp.; SHO (Paediat.) Wolverhampton, New Cross & Roy. Hosps.

MOTT, Mr Terence John The Suffolk Nuffield Hopital, Foxhall Road, Ipswich IP4 5SW Tel: 01473 276100 Fax: 01473 279101; Red House Farm, Burgh, Woodbridge IP13 6SR Tel: 01473 735727 — MB BS 1959 Lond.; FRCS Eng. 1964; MRCS Eng. LRCP Lond. 1959; FFR 1972; DMRT Eng. 1970. (Westm.) Clin. Oncologist. Prev: Cons. Radiotherapist Ipswich Hosp. & Hon. Cons. Radiotherapist Addenbrooke's Hosp. Camb.; Sen. Regist. (Radiother.) W.m. Hosp. Lond.; Ho. Surg. W.m. Hosp. Lond.

MOTTAHEDEH, Mina Department of General Surgery, Southampton General Hospital, Tremona Road, Southampton SO16 6YD; 25 Constantine Avenue, Chandlers Ford, Eastleigh SO53 2BR — BM 1993 Soton.; BSc (Hons. Chem.) Soton. 1985; PhD (Organic Chem.) Soton. 1988. SHO Rotat. (Surg.) Soton. Gen. Hosp. Prev: Demonst. (Anat.) Soton. Univ. & RMO Sarum Rd. Hosp. Winchester; SHO (A & E) Qu. Alexandra Hosp. Portsmouth; Ho. Off. (Med.) Roy. Hants. Co. Hosp.

MOTTALIB, Esmat Abdel 18 Ruskin Court, Winchmore Hill Road, London N21 1QJ — MB BCh 1961 Cairo; DS Cairo 1965, MB BCh 1961; MRCOG 1978. (Kasv Al-Aini) Cons. O & G MoH Saudi Arabia.

MOTTERSHEAD, Anthony Charles Pencester Surgery, 10/12 Pencester Road, Dover CT16 1BW Tel: 01304 240553 Fax: 01304 201773 — MB BS 1983 Lond.; DRCOG 1987. GP Dover.

MOTTERSHEAD, Brian 12 Chatterton, Stubbins, Ramsbottom, Bury BL0 0PG — MB ChB 1981 Liverp.

MOTTERSHEAD, John Philip 310 Upton Lane, Widnes WA8 9AG Email: j.mottershead@araucaria.u_net.com — BM BCh 1990 Oxf.; MRCP (UK) 1994. (Oxford) Specialist Regist. (Neurol.) Frenchay Hosp. Bristol. Prev: Research Fell. (Clin. Neurol.) Inst. Neurol. Qu. Sq. Lond.; SHO (Med.) Stoke-on-Trent.

MOTTERSHEAD, Linda Mary The Surgery, 991 Bristol Road South, Northfield, Birmingham B31 2QT Tel: 0121 476 9191 — MB ChB 1974 Birm.; DObst RCOG 1976.

MOTTERSHEAD, Marcus Robert John Lord 5 Clifton Cres., Wigan WN1 2LB Tel: 01942 244000 — MB ChB 1997 Ed. (Edin.)

MOTTERSHEAD, Mark Stephen 8 Brackenwood Drive, Cheadle SK8 1JX — MB ChB 1987 Manch.; DCH; DRCOG; MRCGP. Ship's Phys. Carnival Cruise Lines Miami Florida; GP Non Princip. Prev: Manch. Gen. Hosp.

MOTTERSHEAD, Naomi Jayne 82 Gravelly Bank, Stoke-on-Trent ST3 7EF — MB ChB 1990 Leeds. Prev: GP Retainer Scheme; Trainee GP N. Staffs. VTS.

*****MOTTIAR, Nasima Shireen** 17 Hampton Place, Belfast BT7 3BZ — MB BCh BAO 1995 Belf.

MOTTO, Judith Elizabeth 26 The Drive, Orpington BR6 9AP — MB BS 1980 Lond.; DRCOG 1983. Prev: GP Norwich.

MOTTO, Stephen Giuseppe Anthony London Bridge Hospital, Emblem House, 27 Tooley St., London SE1 2PR Tel: 020 7403 0330 Fax: 020 7815 2930 Email: info@smsportmed.co.uk; Fax: 01689 873981 Email: info@smsportmed.co.uk — BM 1984 Soton.; Dip. Sports Med. Lond. Hosp. 1989; DMS Med. Soc. Apoth. Lond. 1993; Dip. Med. Acupunc. 1995. (Soton) Cons. Sports & Musculoskeletal Med. Lond. Bridge Hosp.; Med. Off. Brit. Olympic Med. Centre N.wick Pk. Hosp.; Lect. & Tutor (Sports Med.) Lond. Hosp.; Musculoskeletal Phys. Roy. Lond. Homoeop. Hosp.; Sports Phys. Crystal Palace Sports Injury Centre. Socs: Brit. Assn. Sport & Exc. Med.; Brit. Inst. Musculoskel. Med.; Amer. Col. Sports Med. Prev: Specialist (Sports & Musculoskeletal Med.) Lond. Bridge Hosp.; Specialist (Sports Med.) Lond. Bridge Clinic Lond.; Regist. Sports Injuries Clinic Addenbrooke's Hosp. Camb.

MOTTRAM, Nicholas Peter John 67 Chestnut Drive S., Pennington, Leigh WN7 3JX — MB ChB 1983 Manch.

MOTTRAM, Simon Nicholas New Land Surgery, Grove Medical Centre, Wooton Grove, Sherborne DT9 4DL Tel: 01935 813438 Fax: 01935 817470; Silver Heys, Priestlands, Sherborne DT9 4HN Tel: 01935 812003 — MB ChB 1979 Birm.; MRCGP 1986; DCH RCP Lond. 1984; DRCOG 1985. Clin. Asst. (Gyn. Urol. & Cas.) Yeatman Hosp. Sherborne.

MOTTRAM, Susan Andrea Murdishaw Health Centre, Gorsewood Road, Runcorn WA7 6ES Tel: 01928 712061 Fax: 01928 791988; 20 Crowley Road, Timperley, Altrincham WA15 7ST Tel: 0161 980 8529 — MB ChB 1991 Liverp.; MRCGP 1996. (Liverp.) GP Princip.; Mem. Runcorn Young Princip. GP. Prev: GP/Regist. Brookfield Surg. Lymm; GP/Regist. Weavervale Pract. Runcorn; SHO (O & G & Paediat.) Warrington NHS Trust Hosp.

MOTWANI, Catherine Anne Sunderland Royal Hospital, Kayll Road, Sunderland SR4 7TP Tel: 0191 565 6256; 7 Portland Mews, Sandyford, Newcastle upon Tyne NE2 1RW Tel: 0191 261 0069 — MB ChB 1993 Dundee. (Dundee) Staff Grade (A & E) Sunderland; ALS Instruc. (UK Resusc. Counc.).

MOTWANI, Joseph Gerard Derriford Hospital, Plymouth PL6 8DH — MB ChB 1986 Dundee; BMSc (Hons.) Dund 1983; MRCP (UK) 1989. Cons. Cardiologist, Derriford Hosp. Plymouth. Prev: Clin. Research Fell. Dept. Clin. Pharmacol. Ninewells Hosp. Dundee.

MOTWANI, Mr Nandlal Sitaldas 19 Inchcolm Drive, Balmossie, Broughty Ferry, Dundee DD5 2LF; 1 St. Mary's Road, Downfield, Dundee DD3 9DH Tel: 816816 — MB BS 1957 Agra; FRCS Ed. 1965. (Agra Med. Coll.) Prev: SHO (Orthop.) Killearn Hosp. Glas.; Regist. Surgic. Neurol. Roy. Infirm. Dundee; Surg. Regist. Bangour Gen. Hosp. Broxburn.

MOUAT, Patricia 10 Oan Ha, Dysart, Kirkcaldy KY1 2TL — MB ChB 1966 Aberd. (Aberd.)

MOUCHIZADEH, Joseph 2 Linden Lea, London N2 0RG — MB BS 1979 Lond.

MOUDGIL, Harmesh Princess Royal Hospital, Telford TF1 6TF Tel: 01952 641222 Fax: 01952 277785 Email: h.moudgil@thedoctor.co.uk; 9 Goldcrest Avenue, Apley Castle, Telford TR1 6TA Tel: 01952 250080 Email: h.moudgil@thedoctor.co.uk — MB ChB 1986 Glas.; MRCP (UK) 1989. Cons. Ohysician in Gen. (Internal) and Respirat. Med. P.ss Roy. Hosp. NHS Trust Telford Shrops. Socs: Roy. Coll. Phys.s; Midl.s Thoracic Soc.; Scott. Thoracic Soc. Prev: SPR Respirat. Med. (W. Midl.s) City Hosp. Birm., Heartlands Hosp. Birm.; Research Fell./Hon. Clin. Lectuere Univ. of Birm.; Regist. (Respirat. & Gen. Med.) Edin. Roy. Infirm. & City Hosp. Edin.

MOUDIOTIS, Christopher Robert 172 Nine Mile Ride, Finchampstead, Wokingham RG40 4JB Tel: 01734 732706 — BM 1993 Soton. SHO (Paediat. & Neonat.Care) Roy. Devon & Exeter Hosp. Prev: SHO (Cas.) Qu. Alexandra Hosp. Portsmouth.

MOUL, Dennis Jonathan Dalkeith, 116 Worrin Road, Shenfield, Brentwood CM15 8JN Tel: 01277 230008 — BM BCh 1964 Oxf.; FRCP Lond. 1990; MRCP (UK) 1972; DObst RCOG 1967. (Oxf. & St. Thos.) Cons. Phys. Harold Wood Hosp. Socs: Fell. Roy. Soc. Med.; Brit. Diabetic Assn. Prev: Sen. Regist. (Med.) St. Bart. Hosp. Lond.; Regist. (Med.) Whipps Cross Hosp. Lond.; Ho. Surg. & Ho. Off. (Obst.) St. Thos. Hosp. Lond.

MOUL

MOUL, Patricia Elizabeth (retired) 340A Upper Richmond Road, London SW15 6TL Tel: 020 8788 6435 — MB BS Lond. 1954; MRCS Eng. LRCP Lond. 1954. Prev: GP.

MOULANA, Nasser Victoria House, Holloway Road, Runcorn WA7 4TH Tel: 01928 740404 Email: nmoulana@hotmail.com; 18 Spring Field Drive, Wilmslow SK9 6EN Tel: 01625 525299 Fax: 01625 525299 Email: nassermoulana@aol.com — MD 1972 Pahlavi, Iran; Dip. Spec Paediat.; Nat. Board of Paediat. Iran 1978. Staff Grade (Community Paediat.) Chester & Halton Community NHS Trust Runcorn; Sen. Clin. Med. Off. (Community Phys.) Warrington Community Health Care. Socs: BMA; Fac. Child Health; ODA. Prev: Sen. SHO (Paediat.) Warrington Gen. Hosp.

MOULD, Grace Mari Stewart (retired) Appin, 2 Rectory Lane, Harlaxton, Grantham NG32 1HD — MB ChB 1951 St. And.; DA Eng. 1955. Prev: Med. Asst. (Anaesth.) Grantham & Kesteven Gen. Hosp.

MOULD, John (retired) Woodlands Cottage, Bussage, Stroud GL6 8BB Tel: 01453 885274 — BM BCh 1953 Oxf. Local Treasury Med. Off. Prev: GP Stroud.

MOULD, John Joseph (retired) 38 Clifton Road, Lower Parkstone, Poole BH14 9PP Tel: 01202 745976 — MB BS 1969 Lond.; MRCS Eng. LRCP Lond. 1969; FRCOG 1988; FRCR 1981. Prev: Sen. Regist. (Radiother.) Christie Hosp. Manch.

MOULD, Jonathan Taverham Surgery, Sandy Lane, Taverham, Norwich NR8 6JR Tel: 01603 867481 Fax: 01603 261781 — MB BS 1977 Melbourne; MB BS 1977 Melbourne.

MOULD, Tiffany Lalor 4A Charles Street, Oxford OX4 3AS — MB BS 1983 Adelaide.

MOULD, Timothy Andrew James 2 Netherford Road, London SW4 6AE — MB BS 1988 Lond.

MOULDING, Fenella Jane Flat 2 Albert Court, 7 Elm Grove, Didsbury, Manchester M20 6PQ Tel: 0161 448 7654 Fax: 0161 448 7654 Email: fenellam@hotmail.com — MB ChB 1993 Dundee; MRCP (UK) 1996. Specialist Regist. (Radiol.) Manch.

MOULDING, Kenneth William (retired) 10 Sid Vale Close, Sidford, Sidmouth EX10 9PH — MB ChB 1954 Bristol. Prev: Ho. Surg., Cas. Off. & Ho. Phys. Bristol Roy. Hosp.

MOULDS, Alistair John Laindon Health Centre, Laindon, Basildon SS15 5TR Tel: 01268 546411 Fax: 01268 491248; 8 Caterwood, Billericay CM12 0AP Tel: 01277 653935 — MB ChB 1971 St. And.; MB ChB (Commend.) St. And. 1971; FRCGP 1985, M (Distinc.) 1976; DObst RCOG 1974; FRCGP 1998. (St Andrews) Course Organiser Basildon VTS; Edit. Adviser Update. Prev: Assoc. Regional Adviser NETHRA; Squadron Ldr. RAF Med. Br.; Asst. Tutor (Gen. Pract.) RAM Coll. Millbank.

MOULDS, Judy Rivergreen Medical Centre, 106 Southchurch Drive, Clifton, Nottingham NG11 8AD.

MOULE, Brian Larachmhor, Drymen, Glasgow G63 0HX — MB BCh 1957 Wales; MB BCh (Commend.) Wales 1957; FRCP Glas. 1988, M 1986; FRCR 1964; DMRD Eng. 1962. Clin. Dir. (Imaging) Glas. Roy. Infirm. Prev: Cons. Radiol. Glas. Roy. Infirm.; Ho. Surg. & Ho. Phys. Cardiff Roy. Infirm.

MOULE, Mr Ivan Maxillofacial Unit, Hospital of St Cross, Barby Road, Rugby CV22 5PX Tel: 01788 572831 Fax: 01788 545205; The Hawthorns, Swinford, Lutterworth LE17 6AU Tel: 01788 860348 Fax: 01788 860348 — MB BS 1980 Lond.; BDS Lond. 1971; FRCS Ed. 1986; MRCS Eng. LRCP Lond. 1980; FDS RCS Eng. 1983. (Charing Cross Hospital) Cons. Oral & Maxillofacial Surg. Univ. Hosp.s Coventry and Warks. NHS Trust. Socs: BMA; BDA; Fell. BAOMS. Prev: Sen. Regist. (Oral Surg.) SW & SE Thames RHA; Regist. (Oral Surg.) W.m. & Qu. Mary's Hosps. Lond.

MOULSDALE, Martin Thomas 67 The Avenue, Watford WD17 4NU — BM BCh 1974 Oxf.; MSc (Microbiol.) Lond. 1981; BA (Hons.) Oxf. 1970, MA 1974; FRCPath 1993, M 1981. Cons. Med. Microbiol. Mt. Vernon & Watford Hosps. NHS Trust. Socs: Assn. Med. Microbiol.; BMA. Prev: Lect. (Path.) St. Thos. Hosp. Med. Sch. Lond.; Regist. (Microbiol.) Roy. Perth Hosp., W.. Austral.; Asst. Lect. (Path.) Middlx. Hosp. Med. Sch. Lond.

MOULSDALE, Patricia Anne Blackwall Peter Hodgkinson Centre, Lincoln County Hospital, Lincoln LN2 5UA — MB BS 1966 Lond.; MRCS Eng. LRCP Lond. 1966; MRCPsych 1974; DPM Eng. 1972. Assoc. Specialist (Psychiat.) Day Hosp. Peter Hodgkinson Centre Co. Hosp. Lincoln.

MOULSHER, Peter John 9 Millfield Road, Market Deeping, Peterborough PE6 8AD Email: moulsher@aol.com — MB ChB 1994 Sheff.; DCH 1997.

MOULSON, Andrew Michael The Kirkbymoorside Surgery, Tinley Garth, Kirkbymoorside, York YO62 6AR Tel: 01751 431254 Fax: 01751 432980 — MB BS 1976 Lond.; FRCS Eng. 1980; MRCGP 1986; Dip IMC RCS Ed. 1990; DGM RCP Lond. 1986. (Middlx.) Prev: Demonst. (Anat.) Nottm. Univ.; Med. Off. St. Francis Hosp. Katete, Zambia.

MOULSON, Angela Jane Highfield Health Centre, 2 Proctor Street, off Tong Street, Bradford BD4 9QA Tel: 01274 227700 Fax: 01274 227900; Tel: 01274 690045 — MB ChB 1983 Liverp.; DRCOG 1986. GP Specialist in Psychiat.. Bradford Community Health Trust, Bradford.

MOULSON, Felicity Jane 8 Mount Crescent, Stone ST15 8LR Tel: 01785 816272; 2 Railway Terrace, Coulsdon CR5 2NR Tel: 020 8645 0535 — MB ChB 1994 Birm.; ChB Birm. 1994; DRCOG; Dip. Family Plann. GP Regist. Merstham Surrey. Prev: SHO (A & E) Norf. & Norwich Healthcare Trust; SHO (O & G) Norf. & Norwich Health Care Trust; Ho. Off. (Gen. Surg.) Stafford Dist. Gen. Hosp.

MOULT, Emanuel Michael Park Surgery, Albion Way, Horsham RH12 1BG Tel: 01403 217100; 70 Worthing Road, Horsham RH12 1TD Tel: 01403 218000 — MB BS Lond. 1969; MRCS Eng. LRCP Lond. 1969; MRCGP 1975; DA Eng. 1971; Cert. Av Med. MoD (Air) & CAA 1978; Cert. Family Plann. JCC 1975. (King's Coll. Hosp.) Socs: Assn. Anaesth. & Soc. Occupat. Therapists; Med. Off. Sch. Assn.; Assn. Police Surg. Prev: Ho. Phys. (Med.) King's Coll. Hosp. Lond.; SHO (Obst. & Anaesth.) Roy. Sussex Co. Hosp. Brighton.

MOULT, Peter John Allestree 144 Castelnau, London SW13 9ET — MRCS Eng. LRCP Lond. 1969; MD Lond. 1978, MB BS 1969; FRCP 1988; MRCP (U.K.) 1972. (Westm.) Sen. Lect. (Med.) Fac. Clin. Sc. Univ. Coll. Lond. Cons. Endocrinol.; Cons. Endocrinol. Whittington Hosp. Lond.

MOULTON, Mr Alan Pine Lodge, 8 Kirkby Road, Ravenshead, Nottingham NG15 9HF Tel: 01623 793308 Fax: 01623 490831 — MRCS Eng. LRCP Lond. 1964; FRCS Ed. 1971. (Liverp.) Cons. Orthop. Surg. King's Mill Centre Health Care Servs.; Hon. Clin. Teach. (Orthop. Surg.) Univ. Nottm. Socs: Fell. BOA; BMA. Prev: Sen. Regist. (Orthop.) Sheff. AHA (T); Regist. (Orthop.) Robt. Jones & Agnes Hunt Orthop. Hosp. OsW.ry; SHO (Orthop. & Neurosurg.) Walton Hosp. Liverp.

MOULTON, Christopher Department of Accident & Emergency Medicine, The Royal Bolton Hospital, Minerva Road, Bolton BL4 0JR Tel: 01204 390381 Fax: 01204 390652 Email: chris.moulton@boltonh-tr.nwest.nhs.uk — MB ChB 1981 Manch.; FFAEM 1994; FFA RCS Eng. 1988; MRCGP 1985; DFFP 1994; DRCOG 1987. (Manch.) Bolton Cons. A & E Med. Roy. Bolton Hosp.

MOULTON, Elizabeth Alison The Bungalow, Grove Lane, Badsworth, Pontefract WF9 1AN — MB ChB 1979 Leeds.

MOULTON, Lisa Caroline 2 Cormorant Court, Wallasey CH45 3QL — MB ChB Sheff. 1995.

MOULTRIE, Patricia Anne Ardgowan Medical Practice, 2 Finnart Street, Greenock PA16 8HW Tel: 01475 888155 Fax: 01475 785060 — MB ChB 1983 Glas.; MRCGP 1987; DRCOG 1986; Cert. Family Plann. JCC 1986.

MOULTRIE, Samantha Jane Royal Infirmary of Edinburgh, Lauriston Place, Edinburgh EH3 9 Tel: 0131 536 1000; 3 Inzievar House, Oakley, Dunfermline KY12 8HB — MB ChB 1990 Ed.; MRCP (UK) 1993; FRCA 1998. (Edin.) Specialist Regist. (Anaesth.).

***MOUMOULIDIS, Ioannis** 9 Wingate Place, Aberdeen AB24 2TD — MB ChB 1998 Aberd.; MB ChB Aberd 1998.

MOUNFIELD, Philip Arnold The White House, 1A Westlands Avenue, Grimsby DN34 4SP Tel: 01472 356573 — MB BS 1956 Lond.; FRCOG 1980, M 1967. (St. Thos.) Cons. O & G Grimsby Hosp. Gp. Prev: Cons. O & G RAF Hosp. Nocton Hall.

MOUNSEY, James Allen Boyed, MBE (retired) c/o Barclays Bank Plc, 21 High St., Lymington SO41 9YJ — MRCS Eng. LRCP Lond. 1945. Prev: Med. Off. Civil Serv. (Soc. Secur.).

MOUNSEY, Nicola Lesley 142 Outgang Lane, Bramley, Leeds LS13 2QY — MB ChB 1996 Leeds.

MOUNSEY, Rachel Mary Castle Place Surgery, 9 Park Hill, Tiverton EX16 6RR Tel: 01884 252333 Fax: 01884 252152; Yarde

Down Barne, Silverton EX5 4DG — MB BS 1978 Newc.; BSc (Psychol.) 1972; MRCGP 1982; DCH RCP Eng. 1980.

MOUNSTEPHEN, Andrew Hugh Health & Safety Executive, Belford House, 59 Belford Road, Edinburgh EH4 3UE Tel: 0131 247 2014 Fax: 0131 247 2055 Email: andrew.mounstephen@hse.gov.uk; 14 Cramond Glebe Gardens, Edinburgh EH4 6NZ — BM BCh 1982 Oxf.; MA Oxf. 1987; AFOM RCP Lond. 1991, MFOM 1994; MRCGP 1986; T(OM) 1994; T(GP) 1991; DRCOG 1986. (Oxf.) Med. Insp. Health & Safety Exec. Edin. Socs: BMA; Soc. Occupat. Med.; Fac. Occupat. Med. Prev: GP Oxf.; Occupat. Phys. BT, DuPont & ICI.

MOUNT, Janice Hawthorne 21 Pittville Lawn, Cheltenham GL52 2BE Tel: 01242 580668; 12 Carlton Street, Cheltenham GL52 6AQ — MB BS 1956 Lond.; MRCS Eng. LRCP Lond. 1956; DCH Eng. 1958; DObst RCOG 1959. (St. Mary's)

***MOUNT, Susanna Jane** Derriford Hospital, Derriford Road, Plymouth PL6 8DH Tel: 01752 777111; 2 Coney Court, Haven Road, Exeter EX2 8DA Tel: 01392 272394 — MB BS 1998 Lond.; MB BS Lond 1998; BSc (Hons) Animal Phys.Lond. 1992.

MOUNTAIN, Alistair John Cameron 18 St James Avenue, Southend-on-Sea SS1 3LH Tel: 01702 588071 — MB ChB 1994 Birm.; ChB Birm. 1994. (Birmingham) SHO (Orthop.) Roy. Hosp. Haslar Gosport. Prev: SHO (ITU) Roy. Hosp. Haslar Regl.. Med. Off. 1st Bn. Roy. Regt. of Fusiliers Ebrington Barracks.

MOUNTAIN, Bernadette Ann Quince Cottage, Henfield Road, Cowfold, Horsham RH13 8DR — MB BS 1982 Lond.; MB BS (Hons. Path.) Lond. 1982; DRCOG 1987.

MOUNTAIN, David 169 Ashlands Road, Northallerton DL6 1HB — MB BS 1987 Newc. SHO (A & E) Wigan Roy. Infirm. Prev: SHO (Rheum.) & (ENT) City Gen. Hosp. Carlise.

MOUNTAIN, Deborah Ann 22 Learmouth Terrace, Edinburgh EH4 1PG — MB ChB 1990 Cape Town.

MOUNTAIN, Jeanine Stella 248 Park Lane, Keighley BD21 4RL — MB BS 1993 Lond.

MOUNTER, Norman Alexander Mid-Kent Healthcare Trust, Maidstone Hospital, Hermitage Lane, Maidstone ME14 1OT Tel: 01622 729000; The Willows, 32 Fairfax Drive, Beltinge, Herne Bay CT6 6QZ Tel: 01227 371580 — MB ChB 1995 Manch. SHO (Histopath.), Mid-Kent Healthcare Trust Maidstone. & St. Thomas' Hosp. Lond. Socs: BMA. Prev: SHO (Paediat.) Qu. Eliz. The Qu. Mother Hosp. Margate; SHO (A & E) QEQM Margate; SHO (O & G): WEQM, Margate.

MOUNTER, Philip John Department of Haematology, Royal Victoria Infirmary, Newcastle upon Tyne NE1 4LP Tel: 0191 232 5131 Fax: 0191 222 7632; 35a Leazes Terrace, Newcastle upon Tyne NE1 4LZ Tel: 0191 232 5461 — MB BS 1990 Newc.; MRCP (UK) 1993; DRCPath. (Newc.) Regist. (Haemat.) Roy. Vict. Infirm. Newc. upon Tyne. Prev: Regist. (Haemat.) Sunderland Roy. Infirm.

MOUNTFIELD, Sarah Joanna Princess Anne Hospital, Coxford Rd, Southampton SO16 5YA Tel: 02380 796980 Fax: 02380 796207 Email: joanna.mountfield@suht.swest.nhs.uk — MB ChB 1987 Bristol; MA (Education) King Alfred's Winchester 2001; MRCOG 1993. (Bristol) Cons. Obst. P.ss Anne Hosp. Soton. & Course Director Wessex Unit Soton. Gen. Hosp. Soton.; Flexible Train. Coordinator Wessex Deanery Winchester. Socs: Brit. Maturnal & Fetal Med. Soc. Prev: Specialist Regist. (O & G) P.ss Anne Hosp. Soton.; Regist. (O & G) Jessop Hosp. for Wom. Sheff.; Specialist Regist. (O & G) Roy. Hants. Co. Hosp. Winchester.

***MOUNTFORD, James John** 69 Glen Eyre Road, Southampton SO16 3NP — BM BCh 1998 Oxf.; BM BCh Oxf 1998.

MOUNTFORD, Judith Ann Consett Medical Centre, Station Yard, Consett DH8 5YA Tel: 01207 216116 Fax: 01207 216119 — MB BS 1987 Newc.

MOUNTFORD, Laurence Oliver (retired) 19A King Street, Emsworth PO10 7AX Tel: 01243 376581 — MB BChir 1937 Camb.; MA Camb. 1937; MRCS Eng. LRCP Lond. 1934; FFA RCS Eng. 1953; DA Eng. 1937. Hon. Cons. Anaesth. Lond. Chest Hosp. & Hosp. St. John & Eliz. Lond. Prev: Cons. Anaesth. Harefield Thoracic Unit & Poplar Hosp.

MOUNTFORD, Lesley 2 Larchmore Court, Kingsdown Road, London N19 4LE — MB BS 1992 Newc.

MOUNTFORD, Richard Andrew University Department of Medicine, Bristol Royal Infirmary, Bristol BS2 8HW Tel: 0117 923 0000; 1 Hurle Crescent, Clifton, Bristol BS8 2SX Tel: 0117 973

5246 — MB ChB 1968 Bristol; BSc (Physiol.) Bristol 1965, MD 1973, MB ChB 1968; FRCP Lond. 1989; MRCP (UK) 1975; FRCR 1976. (Bristol) Cons. Phys., WBHT; Hon. Sen. Lect. Univ. Bristol. Socs: Brit. Soc. Gastroenterol. Prev: Sen. Lect. (Med.) Univ. of Bristol & Hon. Cons. Phys. Bristol Roy. Infirm.; Lect. (Med.) Univ. of Bristol; Regist. & Sen. Regist. (Radio Diagnostics) Bristol Roy. Infirm.

MOUNTFORD, Tracy Hilary The Lanes Medical Practice, Plough Lane, Slough SL2 4JW — MB BS 1985 Lond. Cosmetic Med. Practitioner (Non-Surgic. cosmetic) The La.s Med. Pract., Stoke Poges, Bucks. Socs: GMC; Cosmetic Doctors Assn. Prev: Gen. Med. (Health Screening & Preventative Med.) Heritage Healthcare Pavil. Clinic Stoke Poges Bucks.

MOUNTJOY, Christopher Quentin (retired) St. Andrews Hospital, Northampton NN1 5DG Tel: 01604 29696 Fax: 01604 232325 Email: mountjo@skynet.co.uk — MB BS Lond. 1966; MRCS Eng. LRCP Lond. 1966; FRCPsych 1985, M 1972; DPM Eng. 1971. Research Co-ordinator St And. Hosp. N.ampton NN1 5DG. Prev: Cons. Psychiat. St. And. Hosp. N.ampton.

MOUNTNEY, Mr John 84 Havendale, Hedge End, Southampton SO30 0FF — MB ChB 1991 Sheff.; FRCS Eng. 1996.

MOUNTROSE, Joseph David B, OBE 75 Harley Street, London W1 Tel: 020 7935 4808; Flat 3, 66 Wimpole St, London W1G 8AW — MD 1936 Warsaw; MD Bale 1935. (Bale) Phys. St. Theresa's Hosp. Wimbledon. Socs: Fell. Roy. Soc. Med. Prev: Clin. Asst. Rheum. Unit St. Stephen's Hosp. Fulham.

MOUNTY, Elizabeth Jane South London and Maudsley NHS Trust, Ladywell Unit, Lewisham Hospital, London SE13 6LH Tel: 020 8333 3030 Ext: 8445 — MB BS 1979 Lond.; BSc (Hons.) (Anat.) Lond. 1976, MB BS 1979; VQE 1979; FLEX Lic. (USA) 1982; MRCPsych 1984. (Univ. Coll. Lond. & St. Geo.) Gen. Adult & Rehabil. Psychiat. Lewisham Sth. Lond. & NHS Trust. Socs: Med. Wom. Fed.; BMA; Treas., Wom.'s Spec. Int. Grp. Psych., Roy. Soc. Psychs. Prev: Cons. Psychiat. specialising in Rehabil. S. Bucks. NHS Trust; Cons. Psychiat. Greenwich; Sen. Regist. (Psychiat.) Guy's Hosp. Lond.

MOUNTY, Jonathan Paul Meopham Medical Centre, Wrotham Road, Meopham, Gravesend DA13 0AH Tel: 01474 814811/814068 Fax: 01474 814699 — MB ChB 1982 Birm.; MRCGP 1986; DRCOG 1986. Community Med. Off. (Paediat. Developm.) Dartford & Gravesham HA.

MOURANT, Anthony John Royal Cornwall Hospital, Truro TR1 3LJ Tel: 01872 274242 Fax: 01872 252877; 74 Highertown, Truro TR1 3QD Tel: 01872 277269 — BSc Lond. 1965, MB BS 1970; FRCP Lond. 1990; MRCP (UK) 1972; MRCS Eng. LRCP Lond. 1970. (Westm.) Cons. Cardiol. Roy. Cornw. Hosp. Truro.

MOURANT, Philippa Noel White Lodge Practices, 21 Grosvenor Street, St Helier, Jersey JE1 4HA Tel: 01534 873633 Fax: 01534 878938 — MB ChB 1958 Birm.; DObst RCOG 1961. Prev: Ho. Surg. Birm. & Midl. Hosp. Wom. & Marston Green Matern. Hosp.; Birm.; Ho. Phys. Childr. Hosp. Birm.

MOURIN, Kenneth Arthur Ayres (retired) Lynwood, Quebec Road, Dereham NR19 2DR Tel: 01362 692989 — MRCS Eng. LRCP Lond. 1957; MA, MB BChir Camb. 1957; FRCGP 1979, M 1965; DObst RCOG 1960. Prev: Med. Adviser Norf. Family Health Serv. Auth.

MOURMOURIS, Nicolaos New Wortley Health Centre, 15 Green Lane, Tong Road, Leeds LS12 1JE Tel: 0113 231 0626 Fax: 0113 231 9428; 41 High Ash Drive, Alwoodley, Leeds LS17 8QZ Tel: 0113 268 1394 — State DMS 1982 Rome.

MOUSA, Mohamed Abdel Aziz 31 Gillow Road, Kirkham, Preston PR4 2JS Tel: 01772 686877 — MB BS 1969 Khartoum; DPM Eng. 1979; DTCD Wales 1975.

MOUSDALE, Stephen 5 Beardwood Meadow, Blackburn BB2 7BH Tel: 01254 698952 — MB ChB 1979 Manch.; FFA RCS Eng. 1984. Cons. Anaesth. Blackburn Roy. Infirm. Socs: IC Soc. Prev: Sen. Regist. (Anaesth.) Univ. Hosp. Wales.

MOUSLEY, Alan Arthur (retired) North Nottingham Health Authority, Ransom Hospital, Rainworth, Mansfield NG21 0ER Tel: 01623 22515 Fax: 01623 653527 — MB ChB Sheff. 1957; MRCGP 1974; FFPHM RCP (UK) 1989; FFCM 1989, M 1982. Occupat. Health Phys. Newark & Sherwood DC; Med. Adviser Bassetlaw, Mansfield & Newark & Sherwood DC; Cons. Infec. Control Doctor Rampton Hosp. Retford Nottm. Prev: Dir. of Pub. Health N. Nottm. HA.

MOUSLEY

MOUSLEY, Mr James Silvester (retired) 5 St Michaels Gardens, Winchester SO23 9JD Tel: 01962 862774 — MB BS 1951 Lond.; FRCS Eng. 1956; MRCS Eng. LRCP Lond. 1951. Cons. Surg. Roy. Hants. Co. Hosp. Winchester & Andover War Memor. Hosp.; Clin. Teach. in Surg. Soton. Univ. Med. Sch.; Examr. in Surg. Univ. Khartoum; Examr. in Surg. Univ. Singapore. Prev: Surgic. 1st Asst. St. Geo. Hosp. Lond.

MOUSLEY, Nigel Castletown Road, Port Erin IM9 6B — MB ChB 1975 Bristol. (Bristol) GP The Surg. Port Erin Isle of Man. Socs: Isle of Man Med. Soc.

MOUSSA, Kamal Tawfik Stetchford Health Centre, 393 Station Road, Stechford, Birmingham B33 8PL Tel: 0121-783 2109 — MB BCh 1957 Cairo; DS Cairo 1962; MCh Cairo 1964. (Kasr El Aini Fac. Med. Univ. Cairo) Prev: Locum Cons. Orthop. Surg. UK; Cons. Orthop. Surg. Egypt.

MOUSSA, Mr Mahmoud Mokhtar Habib 106 Claremont Road, London E7 0PX — MB ChB 1964 Cairo; FRCS Eng. 1979; DGS 1966; Dip Orthopaed. 1967; MSc. Orthopaed. (Cairo University, Egypt) Sen. Lect. W.. Med. Internat. Coll. Oriental Med. E. Grinstead.; Cons. (A & E/Orthop.) Vict. Hosp. Kirkcaldy. Socs: Brit. Orthop. Assn.; Brit. Assn. Accid. & Emerg. Med. Prev: Prof. of Orthop., AL ARAB Univ., Fac. of Med., Bon-Ghazi, Libya; Lect. of W.ern Med., Sch. of Oriental Med., E. Grinstead; Clin. Asst. (Orthop.) Albert Dock Hosp. & E. Ham. Memor. Hosp.

MOUSSA, Rizkallah Chiswick Health Centre, 1 Fisher's Lane, Chiswick, London W4 1RX Tel: 020 8994 4482 — MD 1974 Damascus; MD Damascus 1959; MRCP (UK) 1974.

MOUSSA, Mr Sami Ahmed Scottish Lithotriptor Centre, Western General Hospital, Crewe Road S., Edinburgh EH4 2XU Tel: 0131 537 1600 Fax: 0131 537 1020 — MB BCh 1971 Alexandria; FRCS Ed. 1977; FRACS 1982; FRCR 1987; DMRD Ed. 1985. Cons. Radiol. W.. Gen. Hosp. Edin. Prev: Sen. Regist. (Radiol.) N.wick Pk. Hosp. Harrow.

MOUSSA, Wageeh Abdel-Ghaffar Mohamed Aly 6 Dale Road, Shirley, Southampton SO16 6QG Tel: 02380 781021 — MB BCh 1977 Ain Shams.

MOUSTAFA, Abd El-Fatah Mahmoud Manchester Road Health Centre, 27 Manchester Road, Haslingden, Rossendale BB4 5SL Tel: 01706 214281 — MB BCh 1967 Cairo; MB BCh 1967 Cairo.

MOUSTAFA, Mr Alaa Abbass Sabry Staff Village, Royal Preston Hospital, Sharoe Green Lane, Preston PR2 9HT Tel: 01772 716841 — MB BCh 1984 Ain Shams; FRCS Eng. 1990; FRCS Ed. 1990.

MOUSTAFA, Wafik Mohamed The Village Surgery, Long Lane, Carlton-in-Lindrick, Worksop S81 9AR; Ambleside, Churchfield Close, Carlton-in-Lindrick, Worksop S81 9EZ Tel: 01909 730308 — MB BCh 1972 Cairo; LRCP LRCS Ed. LRCPS Glas. 1980. Hon. Teach. (Gen. Pract.) Univ. Sheff. Socs: Assoc. Mem. RCGP.

MOUYEN, Guy Jean Marcel Afan Valley Group Practice, Medical Centre, Blaengwynfi, Port Talbot SA13 3TH Tel: 01639 850345 — MD 1984 Toulouse.

MOUZAS, Mr George Lucas 5 Wedderburn House, Wedderburn Road, London NW3 5QR Tel: 020 7431 3488 — LAH 1958 Dub.; MD Athens 1960; FRCS Eng. 1986; FICS 1962; Dip. Med. 1948. Socs: Fell. Hunt. Soc. & Med. Soc. Lond. Prev: Research Asst. (Surg.) W.m. Hosp. Lond.; Cons. Surg. A & E Chase Farm Hosp. Enfield; Research Prof. Yale Univ. New Haven, Conn.

MOWAT, Alastair Graham (retired) Honeoye, South Green, Kidlington OX5 3HJ Tel: 01869 350525 Fax: 01869 351544 — MB ChB Ed. 1962; FRCP Lond. 1985; FRCP Ed. 1975, M 1967. Mem. Edit. Comm. Jl. Rheum.; Pres. Brit. League Against Rheumatism. Prev: Instruc. (Med.) Univ. Rochester New York, USA.

MOWAT, Allan McIntosh Department of Immunology, University of Glasgow, Western Infirmary, Glasgow G11 6NT Tel: 0141 211 2728 Fax: 0141 337 3217 Email: a.m.mowat@clinmed.gla.ac.uk — MB ChB 1977 Glas.; PhD Ed. 1982; BSc (Hons.) Glas. 1975, MB ChB 1977; FRCPath 1997, MRCPath 1989. Reader & Hon. Cons. Immunol. Univ. Glas. W.. Infirm. Socs: Comm. Mem. Brit. Soc. Immunol.; Brit. Soc. Gastroenterol. Prev: Lect. & Hon. Clin. Immunol. W.. Infirm. & Univ. Glas.; MRC Sen. Clin. Fell. & Hon. Sen. Regist. (Bact. & Immunol.) W.. Infirm. Glas.; Hon. Regist. (Med.) & Research Fell. Wolfson Gastrointest. Unit Hosp. Edin.

MOWAT, Andrew John James Street Family Practice, 49 James Street, Louth LN11 0JN Tel: 01507 611122 Fax: 01507 610435; Franklin House, Raithby Road, Hundleby, Spilsby PE23 5NH Tel: 01790 754734 Fax: 01790 754733 Email: andmowat@aol.uk — MB ChB 1982 Aberd.; MRCGP 1986; Dip. IMC RCS Ed. 1990; DRCOG 1986. Co. Surg. St. John Ambul. Lincs.; CHMN BASICS Educat. Socs: (Exec Counc.) Brit. Assn. Immediate Care; Fac. PreHosp. Care RCS Ed. Prev: GP Heckington, Lincs.; Trainee GP/SHO Grampian HB; Chairm. Lincs. Subfac. RCGP.

MOWAT, Anthea Mary Franklin House, Raithby Road, Hundleby, Spilsby PE23 5NH Tel: 01790 754734 Fax: 01790 754733 — MB ChB 1982 Aberd. Staff Grade (Anaesth.) Pilgrim Hosp. Boston; Div. Surg. St. John Ambul. Lincs. Prev: Regist. (Anaesth.) Grampian HB; SHO (Anaesth.) & Ho. Off. (Gen. Med.) Highland HB Inverness; Ho. Off. (Neurosurg.) Grampian HB Aberd.

MOWAT, Craig Flat G/1, 149 Raeberry St., Glasgow G20 6EE — MB ChB 1992 Glas.

MOWAT, Donald Arthur Edward, OStJ (retired) 2 Warrack Terrace, Montrose DD10 8RX Tel: 01674 673456 — MB ChB 1953 Aberd.; FRCGP 1989, M 1965; AFOM RCP Lond. 1983; CIH Dund 1980. Prev: Occupat. Health Phys. Glaxochem Ltd. Montrose.

MOWAT, Donald Hugh Ross Tameside Centre for General Practice, Kirsty Semple Way, Ninewells, Dundee DD2 4AD Tel: 01382 632771 Fax: 01382 633839; 28 Rose Crescent, Perth PH1 1NT Tel: 01738 637418 — MB ChB 1978 Aberd.; MRCP (UK) 1980; MRCGP (Distinc.) 1983; DRCOG 1984. Hon. Lect. (Gen. Pract.) Univ. Dundee; Assoc. Adviser (Gen. Pract.) E. Scotl. Socs: BMA. Prev: Lect. (Med.) Aberd. Univ.; Hon. Regist. (Med.) Aberd. Hosps.; SHO Aberd. Matern. Hosp.

MOWAT, Esther Marjory 137 Terregles Avenue, Glasgow G41 4DG — MB ChB 1991 Aberd. GP Regist. Gen. Pract. Glas.

MOWAT, Ian Gordon, MBE (retired) 1 Exeter Court, Stamford PE9 2PF Tel: 01780 57091 — MB BS 1952 Lond.; BA Open 1992; MRCS Eng. LRCP Lond. 1952; FRCGP 1979, M 1968; DObst RCOG 1958. Prev: Chief Med. Off. Guadalcanal Province, Solomon Is.s.

MOWAT, Mr James, RD 8 High Street, Keiss, Wick KW1 4XB — MB ChB 1961 Ed.; FRCS Glas. 1968; FRCS Ed. 1968; FRCOG 1981, M 1968, DObst. 1963.

MOWAT, John Stuart Simpson, Surg. Cdr. RN Meeting House Cottage, Faulkland, Bath BA3 5XD — MB ChB 1958 Aberd.

MOWAT, Katharine Jean The Surgery, Gladstone Road, Chesham HP5 3AD Tel: 01494 722063; 24 Woodfield Park, Amersham HP6 5QQ Tel: 01494 782884 — MB ChB 1977 Glas.; MRCOG 1983. Prev: Regist. (O & G) N.wick Pk. Hosp. Harrow & Rutherglen; Matern. Hosp. Glas.; SHO (O & G) E.. Gen. Hosp. Edin.

MOWAT, Norman Ashley George, QHP Gastrointestinal Unit, Aberdeen Royal Hospitals, Aberdeen Tel: 01224 681818 Fax: 01224 840711; 13 Kings Cross Road, Aberdeen AB15 6BE Tel: 01224 319223 — MB ChB 1966 Aberd.; FRCP Ed. 1991; FRCP Lond. 1984; MRCP (UK) 1971. Cons. Phys. Gastroenterol. Gastrointestinal Unit Aberd. Roy. Hosp.; Clin. Sen. Lect. (Med.) Univ. Aberd. Socs: Brit. Gastroenterol. Soc. & Assn. Phys. Prev: Cons. Phys. Gastroenterol. Woodend Gen. Hosp. Aberd.; Regist. (Med.) Aberd. Teach. Hosps.; Lect. (Med.) Aberd. Univ.

MOWAT, William 137 Terregles Avenue, Glasgow G41 4DG — MB ChB 1961 Aberd.; FRCR 1979; DMRD Eng. 1965. Cons. Radiol. Monklands Dist. Gen. Hosp. Coatbridge. Prev: Cons. Radiol. Hairmyres Hosp. E. Kilbride & Law Hosp. Carluke.

*MOWATT, Peter 75 Woodend Cr, Aberdeen AB15 6YQ — MB ChB 1997 Aberd.

MOWBRAY, Aidan Giles Howard 19 Locks Road, Locks Heath, Southampton SO31 6NS Tel: 01489 575383 — MB BS 1993 Lond.; BSc Lond. 1991. (St. Geo.) SHO (O & G) Roy. Bournemouth Hosp. Prev: Med. Off. Bethesda Hosp. Ubomb & S. Afr.; SHO (Gen. & Geriat. Med.) Roy. Bournemouth Hosp.; SHO (A & E) Soton.

MOWBRAY, Alexander 13 Kilcruik Road, Kinghorn, Burntisland KY3 9XH Tel: 01592 890031 — MB ChB 1978 Ed.; BSc. (Med. Sci.) Ed. 1975; FFA RCS Eng. 1983. (Edin.) Cons. Anaesth. Vict. Hosp. Kirkcaldy. Prev: Sen. Regist. (Anaesth.) Roy. Infirm. Edin.; Vis. Lect. (Anaesth.) Chinese Univ. Hong Kong.

MOWBRAY, Anthony Howard (retired) 233A Brook Lane, Sarisbury Green, Southampton SO31 7DQ — MB BS 1965 Lond.; MRCS Eng. LRCP Lond. 1965; DCH Eng. 1972; DObst RCOG 1969.

MOWBRAY, Carolyn Jane 51 Locks Road, Locks Heath, Southampton SO31 7ZL Tel: 01489 583777 Fax: 01489 571374; 19 Locks Road, Locks Heath, Southampton SO31 6NS Tel: 01489 575383 Email: cmowbray@lineone.net — MB BS Lond. 1966;

MRCS Eng. LRCP Lond. 1966; DFFP 1994. (Guy's) Prev: Community Med. Off. (Family Plann.) SE Hants.

*MOWBRAY, Christine Knox 247 Baldwins La, Croxley Green, Rickmansworth WD3 3LH — MB ChB 1997 Birm.

MOWBRAY, Christopher Henry Little Harwood Health Centre, Plane Tree Road, Blackburn BB1 6PH Tel: 01254 580931 Fax: 01254 695794 — MB ChB 1977 Manch.; MRCGP 1982.

MOWBRAY, Edith Susan Milada Jaroslava Ivana King Edward VII Hospital, Castel GY5 7NU Tel: 01481 53111; La Fontennelle, Rue des Fontenelles Forest, Guernsey GY8 0BL Tel: 01481 64931 — MD 1975 Dub.; MB BCh BAO 1967. Assoc. Specialist (Geriat.) King Edwd. VII. Hosp. Guernsey, CI. Prev: Ho. Off. Sir Patrick Duns Hosp. Dub.; Ho. Path. Hosp. Sick Childr. Gt. Ormond St. Lond.

MOWBRAY, Ivrene Violet (retired) Raymond Cottage, Kemerton, Tewkesbury GL20 7HZ Tel: 01386 725274 — MB BS Durh. 1936.

MOWBRAY, Professor James Frederick St. Mary's Hospital Medical School, Norfolk Place, London W2 1PG Tel: 020 7725 1592; 4 Branksome Way, New Malden KT3 3AX Tel: 020 8942 8109 — MB 1955 Camb.; BChir 1954; FRCP Lond. 1980, M 1957. (St. Mary's & Camb.) Prof. Immunopath. St. Mary's Hosp. Med. Sch. Socs: Transpl. Soc. & Brit. Soc. Immunol. Prev: Reader in Immunopath. St. Mary's Hosp. Med. Sch. Lond.; Sen. Lect. & Regist. (Med. Unit) St. Mary's Hosp. Lond.

MOWBRAY, Margaret Bridge House Surgery, Aldbrough St John, Richmond DL11 7SU Tel: 01325 374332; Lennox House, Maison Dieu, Richmond DL10 7AU Tel: 01748 826170 — MB BS Newc. 1967. (Newc.) Clin. Ass. Prev: SHO (Paediat.) Qu. Eliz. Hosp. Gateshead; Ho. Off. (Med. & Surg.) Roy. Vict. Infirm. Newc.

MOWBRAY, Martin John Bridge House Surgery, Aldbrough St John, Richmond DL11 7SU Tel: 01325 374332; Lennox House, Maison Dieu, Richmond DL10 7AU Tel: 01748 826170 — MB BS Newc. 1967; DObst RCOG 1970. (Newc.) Prev: SHO, Ho. Phys. & Ho. Surg. (O & G) Gen. Hosp. Hexham.

MOWBRAY, Michael The Queens Road Medical Practice, The Queens Road, St Peter Port, Guernsey GY8 0BL Tel: 01481 25121; La Fontenelle, Rue des Fontenelles Forest, Guernsey GY1 5RH Tel: 01481 64931 — MB BCh BAO Dub. 1967; BA Dub. 1965; MICGP 1986; DObst RCOG 1971; DCH RCPSI 1970. (TC Dub.) Princip. Prev: Ho. Off. Adelaide Hosp. Dub.; SHO Qu. Eliz. Hosp. Childr. Lond.; Regist. Accid. Dept. King's Coll. Hosp. Lond.

MOWBRAY, Mr Michael Antony Sydee Orthopaedic Dept, Mayday Uni Hosp, London, Rd, Croydon CR7 7YE Tel: 0208 401 3194 Fax: 0208 401 3100; 67 Chartfield Ave, Putney, London SW15 6HN — MB BS Lond. 1969; MSc (Bioeng.) Lond. 1986; MS Lond. 1996; FRCS Ed. 1975; MRCS Eng. LRCP Lond. 1969; FRCS Eng 1998. (St. Mary's) Cons. Orthop. Surg. Mayday Hosp. Croydon. Socs: Fell. BOA; Brit. Orthop. Research Soc.; Brit. Assn. Surg. of the Knee. Prev: Clin. Fell. (Orthop. Surg.) Toronto Univ. Canada; Sen. Regist. (Orthop. Surg.) St. Mary's Hosp. Lond.; Sen. Regist. Roy. Nat. Orthop. Hosp. Lond.

MOWBRAY, Michael James Department Anaesthesia, King's Mill Hospital, Mansfield Road, Sutton-in-Ashfield NG17 4JL Tel: 01623 22515 Fax: 01623 21770; The Old School, Kirklington Road, Southwell NG25 0AY — MB BS 1981 Lond.; FFA RCS Eng. 1986; T(Anaes.) 1991. Cons. Anaesth. King's Mill Hosp. Sutton-in-Ashfield. Socs: Assn. Anaesth. & Hist. Anaesth. Soc. Prev: Sen. Regist. Rotat. (Anaesth.), Nottm. Hosp.; Sen. Clin. Fell. Rotat. (Anaesth.) Adelaide Hosp., Austral.; Regist. (Anaesth.) Mansfield & Nottm.

MOWBRAY, Paul 82 Eden Crest, Gainford, Darlington DL2 3DE — MB ChB 1993 Dundee.

MOWER, Isabel M Lee House Surgery, 84 Osborne Road, Windsor SL4 3EW Tel: 01753 861612 Fax: 01753 833695 — MB BS 1979 London; MB BS 1979 London.

*MOWER, Johanna 11C The Cathedral Green, Llandaff, Cardiff CF5 2EB — MB BCh 1995 Wales.

MOWER, Michael Thomas Charles Lee House Surgery, 84 Osborne Road, Windsor SL4 3EW Tel: 01753 861612 Fax: 01753 833695; 16 Bolton Crescent, Windsor SL4 3JQ Tel: 01753 865259 — MB BChir 1967 Camb.; MRCS Eng. LRCP Lond. 1954; MRCGP 1967; MMSA Lond. 1959; Dip. Palliat. Med. Wales 1991. (Westm.) Dir. Thames Valley Hospice. Socs: Brit. Med. Acupunct. Soc. Prev: Ho. Surg. W.m. Hosp.; Squadron Ldr. RAF Med. Br.; Ho. Surg. Roy. Eye Hosp. Lond.

*MOWLA, Bibi Nasreen 16 Fortrose Avenue, Sunderland SR3 1UT Tel: 0191 528 2792 — MB BS 1998 Newc.; MB BS Newc 1998.

MOWLE, Mr David Huang Dept. of Neurosurgery, Ninewells Hospital and Medical School, Dundee DD1 9SY Tel: 01382 660111; 34 Eatock Way, Westhoughton, Bolton BL5 2RR Tel: 01942 840212 — MB ChB Dundee 1988; BMSc (Hons.) Dund 1984; FRCS Eng. 1992; FRCS (Neurosurg.) (Eng.) 1998. Cons. Neurosurg. Tayside Univeristy Hosp.s NHS Trust; Hon. Sen. Clin. Teach. Dundee Univ. Prev: Specialist Regist. (Neurosurg.) N. W. Regional Rotat.; Regist. (Neurosurg.) S. Wales Rotat.

MOWLE, Stephen Huang Dept. of General Practice, University of Wales College of Medicine, Llomedeym, Cardiff CF3 7PN Email: movlesh@colf.ac.uk; 9 Archery Fields, Clacton-on-Sea CO15 6RB Tel: 01255 436939 — MB BCh 1993 Wales; MRCGP 1997; DFFP 1997. Clin. Fell., Dept of Gen. Pract.; Univ. Wales Coll. Med. Cardiff. Socs: Chairm. Welsh Assn. GP Trainees; WGMSC; BroTaf LREC. Prev: Asst. Ships Phys., P&O Cruise Ltd.; Sen. Resid. Med. Oficer, Emerg. Med.- Toual N. Sore Hosp., Sydney; GP Regist., Lla.neyrn Health Centre, Cardiff.

MOWLES, Adam John Norwich Road Surgery, 199 Norwich Road, Ipswich IP1 4BX Tel: 01473 289777 Fax: 01473 289545 — BM BS 1992 Nottm.

MOWLL, Richard Finch (retired) Tanners, Turners Green Road, Wadhurst TN5 6EA — MB BS 1935 Lond.; MRCS Eng. LRCP Lond. 1934. Prev: Ho. Phys. Miller Gen. Hosp. Greenwich.

MOWNAH, Abdoolla Summer House, 8 Hall Farm Close, Stanmore HA7 4JT Tel: 0208 954 6708 — Vrach 1974 Rostov Med. Inst.; Vrach Rostov Med Inst 1974; FRCS Ed. 1981. (Rostou-on-Don State Med. Inst.) Trust Surg. Gen. Surg. King's Lynn & Wisbech Hosps. Nat. Health Serv. Trust. Socs: Med. Defence Union Ltd. Prev: Staff Surg. Norf. & Norwich Health Care NHS Trust Norwich, Norf.

MOXEY, Joanne Elizabeth Rosyth Surgery, Medical Practice, 195 Queensferry Road, Rosyth, Dunfermline KY11 2LQ Tel: 01383 414874 Fax: 01383 410616 — MB BS 1989 Lond.; MRCGP 1994; DRCOG 1993.

MOXHAM, Professor John Department of Respiratory Medicine, Kings College Hospital, Denmark Hill, London SE5 9PJ Tel: 020 7346 3165 Fax: 020 7346 3589; 17 Maude Road, Camberwell, London SE5 8NY Tel: 020 7703 4396 — MB BS 1973 Lond.; MD Lond. 1982, BSc 1967; FRCP Lond. 1987; MRCP (UK) 1975. (Univ. Coll. Hosp.) Dean Kings Denmark Hill Campus, Guys, Kings & st Thomas' Sch. of Med.; Prof. Respirat. Med.Guy's, Kings & St. Thos. Sch. Med.; Cons. Phys. Kings Coll. Hosp. Lond. Prev: Sen. Regist. Brompton Hosp. Lond.; Lect. (Med.) Univ. Coll. Hosp. Lond.; Ho. Phys. Med. Unit Univ. Coll. Hosp. Lond.

*MOXHAM, Victoria Frances 85 Station Road, Redhill RH1 1DL — MB BS 1998 Lond.; MB BS Lond 1998.

MOXON, Charles Philip (retired) 19 Euan Close, Gillhurst Road, Birmingham B17 8PL Tel: 0121 420 1441 Email: philkit@hotmail.com — MRCS Eng. LRCP Lond. 1944; 1944 MRCS Eng., LRCP Lond.; 1979 FRCR; 1950 DMRD Eng. Prev: Cons. Radiol. Birm. AHA (T) & W. Midl. RHA.

MOXON, Christine 38 Queens Drive, Cottingham HU16 4EL — MB BS 1971 Newc.

MOXON, David 47 Hillcrest Road, Deepcar, Sheffield S36 2QL — MB BS 1992 Lond.

MOXON, Professor Edward Richard Department of Paediatrics, John Radcliffe Hospital, Headington, Oxford OX3 9DU Tel: 01865 221075 Fax: 01865 220479; 17 Moreton Road, Oxford OX2 7AX Tel: 01865 515344 — MB 1967 Camb.; BChir 1966; FRCP Lond. 1984, M 1968. Prof. (Paediat.) Oxf. Univ. Socs: Brit. Paediat. Assn.; Soc. Paediat. Research USA. Prev: Assoc. Prof. Paediat. & Chief Endowood Div. Paediat. Infec. Dis. John Hopkins Univ., USA.

MOXON, Gordon William The Surgery, Thorverton, Exeter EX5 5NT Tel: 01392 860273; The Surgery, Silverton, Exeter EX5 4HZ Tel: 01392 860176 — MB BS 1959 Lond.; MRCS Eng. LRCP Lond. 1959; DObst RCOG 1962. (Univ. Coll. Hosp.) GP Exeter. Socs: Devon & Exeter Med. Soc.

MOXON, James William Alexander Wharfe View, Chapel Hill, Kearby, Wetherby LS22 4BU — MB ChB 1957 Leeds. (Leeds) Prev: Ho. Off. Leeds Matern. Hosp.; SHO. & Ho. Phys. Leeds Gen. Infirm.

MOXON

MOXON, James William David Burton Croft Surgery, 5 Burton Crescent, Leeds LS6 4DN Tel: 0113 274 4777 Fax: 0113 230 4219; 457 Otley Road, Adel, Leeds LS16 6AJ Email: jmox@argonet.co.uk — MB BS 1986 Lond.; BA Camb. 1983; MRCGP 1990. (St Mary's Hosp. Lond.) Socs: BASM.

MOXON, Jennifer 35 Paddock Close, Radcliffe on Trent, Nottingham NG12 2BX — BM BS 1986 Nottm.

MOXON, John Ernest Unsworth, MBE (retired) West Lodge, Frome BA11 1EH Tel: 01373 464343 — MRCS Eng. LRCP Lond. 1955. Prev: Ho. Surg. & Ho. Phys. Roy. W. Sussex Hosp. Chichester.

MOXON, Mary Ann 38 Fulmead Road, Reading RG30 1JX — MB ChB 1971 Ed.; DA Eng. 1975. Prev: Regist. (Anaesth.) & SHO (Anaesth.) Roy. Berks. Hosp. Reading.

MOXON, Paul Kirkstall Lane Medical Centre, 216B Kirkstall Lane, Leeds LS6 3DS Tel: 0113 295 3666 Fax: 0113 295 3650; 99 Alwoodley Lane, Leeds LS17 1PN Tel: 0113 295 3666 Fax: 0113 295 3650 — MB BS Lond. 1963; MRCGP 1972; LLB Leeds 1954; DCH Eng. 1965; DObst RCOG 1965. (St. Mary's) City Counc.lor Leeds. Socs: Brit. Med. Acupunct. Soc.

MOXON, Philip John Larwood Health Centre, 56 Larwood, Worksop S81 0HH Tel: 01909 500233 Fax: 01909 479722 — MB ChB 1989 Leic.; MRCGP 1993; DFFP 1994; DRCOG 1993. GP Princip.; VTS Course Tutor N. Notts; Police Surg. Prev: Trainee GP/SHO Bassetlaw VTS.; Ho. Off. (Med. & Surg.) Pilgrim Hosp. Boston.

MOXON, Mr Richard Andrew Radiology Department, Bedford Hospital NHS Trust, Kempston Road, Bedford MK42 9DJ Tel: 01234 792243 Fax: 01234 792106 Email: richard@moxon2.freeserve.co.uk; 2 Nodders Way, Biddenham, Bedford MK40 4BJ Tel: 01234 217685 Email: ricradiol@aol.com — BM BCh 1974 Oxf.; FRCS Eng. 1982; FRCR 1987. (Univ. Oxf. & Lond. Hosp.) Cons. Radiol. Bedford Gen. Hosp. Prev: Sen. Regist. (Radiol.) Lond. Hosp.

MOY, John Richard The Surgery, 195 Queensferry Road, Rosyth, Dunfermline KY11 2LQ Tel: 01383 414874 Fax: 01383 410616; 7 Ferryhills Road, North Queensferry, Inverkeithing KY11 1HE Tel: 01383 413507 — MB ChB 1978 Ed.; FRCGP 2000; DCCH RCP Ed. 1983. (Edinburgh) Assoc. Adviser (Gen. Pract.) S. E. Scotl.

MOY, Robert John David 26 Knightlow Road, Harborne, Birmingham B17 8QB Tel: 0121 429 5871 Email: r.j.d.moy@bham.ac.uk — MB BChir 1977 Camb.; MSc Warwick 1996; MD Camb. 1994; MRCP (UK) 1983; FRCPCH 1997. Sen. Lect. (Community Child Health) Inst. Child Health Univ. Birm. Prev: Sen. Regist. (Community Child Health) N. Birm. Community Health NHS Trust; Med. Off. MoH, Zimbabwe; Research Fell. Inst. Child Health Univ. Birm.

MOY-THOMAS, Jonathan Melville Longfleet House Surgery, 56 Longfleet Road, Poole BH15 2JD Tel: 01202 666677 Fax: 01202 660319 — MB BS 1967 Lond.; DA Eng. 1970; DObst RCOG 1969. (St. Geo.)

MOYCE, Andrew Charles Michael (retired) Moat House, Station Road, Whissendine, Oakham LE15 7HA Tel: 01664 474406 — MB BS 1964 Lond.; MRCS Eng. LRCP Lond. 1964; DObst RCOG 1966. GP Oakham, Leics. Prev: SHO (Obst.) WillesBoro. Hosp.

MOYE, Alastair Roderick Queen Elizabeth II Hospital, 28 Docklands Avenue, Welwyn Garden City, Welwyn AL7 4HQ; Ash House, 33 Park Lane, Knebworth SG3 6PH — BM BCh 1990 Oxf.; BA Oxf. 1987; FRCA Lond. 1997. (Oxf.) Cons. Anaesth., Qu. Eliz. II Hosp., Welwyn Garden City, Herts. Socs: Assn. Anaesth.; BMA; Obst. Anaesth. Assn. Prev: SHO (Gen. Med.) Addenbrooke's Hosp. Camb.; SHO (Anaesth.) W. Suff. Hosp. Bury St. Edmunds; Specialist Regist. (Anaesth.) Mid. Essex Hosps. Chelmsford.

MOYES, Barbara Alison 3 Regency Lawn, Croftdown Road, London NW5 1HF Tel: 020 7485 2531 — MRCS Eng. LRCP Lond. 1961; MFFP 1994; DCH Eng. 1965; DObst RCOG 1964. (Manch.) SCMO Roy. Free Hampstead NHS Trust Wom. & Childr. Servs. Socs: BMA; Lond. Soc. Family Plann. Doctors. Prev: Regist. Paediat. Whittington Hosp. Lond.

***MOYES, Denise Anne** 31 Kelvin Parade, Belfast BT14 6NB — MB BCh BAO 1995 Belf.

MOYES, Donald George c/o Douche, Lodsworth, Bringhurst, Market Harborough — MB ChB 1962 Birm.; MRCS Eng. LRCP Lond. 1962; FFA RCS Eng. 1968.

MOYES, Elizabeth Cecilia 53 St Kilda Drive, Jordanhill, Glasgow G14 9LT — MB ChB 1982 Glas.

MOYES, Frances Wilson (retired) 968 Anlaby Road, Hull HU4 6AH Tel: 01482 52937 — MB ChB 1927 Glas.

MOYES, Ronald William (retired) The Lodge, Holm Hill, Village Road, West Kirby, Wirral CH48 7HF Tel: 0151 625 6139 — MB BS Lond. 1956; MFCM 1974; DIH Dund 1968; DPH Liverp. 1964; DTM & H Liverp. 1961; LM Rotunda 1966. Prev: Cons. Communicable Dis. Control Liverp. HA.

MOYES, Mr Simon Tobias 25 Sunderland Terrace, Bayswater, London W2 5PA; 86 Harley Street, London W1N Tel: 020 7323 0040 Fax: 020 7323 0080 — MB BS 1982 Lond.; FRCS (Orth.) 1991; FRCS Ed. 1987; Dip. Sports Med. Soc. Apoth. Lond. 1995. Cons. Orthop., Wellington Hosp., Lond. Socs: Fell.BDA; BDSTA; BESS.

MOYLAN, Tricia Louise Top Left Flat, 89 Novar Drive, Glasgow G12 9SS — MB ChB 1994 Glas.

MOYLE, John Trelawny Brooks Milton Keynes General Hospital, Standing Way, Milton Keynes MK6 5LD Tel: 01908 660033 Fax: 01908 243159; Oakley Cottage, 9 Main Road, Astwood, Newport Pagnell MK16 9JS Tel: 01234 391154 Fax: 0870 056 8458 Email: john@moyle.demon.co.uk — MB BS 1976 Lond.; Dip. Palliat. Med. Wales 1994; T(Anaesth) 1991; FRCA Eng. 1981. (St. Bart.) Cons. Anaesth. & Intens. Care Milton Keynes Gen. Hosp.; Med. Dir. Willen Hospice; Vis. Prof. Human Factors, Coll. Aeronaut. Cranfield Univ. Socs: Assn. Palliat.. Med.; Christian Med. Fell.ship; Inst. of Measurem. and Control. Prev: Sen. Regist., Regist & SHO (Anaesth.) Kings Coll. Hosp. Lond.

***MOYLE, Penelope Laura** Grassmere, 140 Balcombe Rd, Horley RH6 9DS — MB ChB 1997 Leic.

MOYLE, Peter Newton 19 The Glebe, Stannington, Morpeth NE61 6HW Tel: 0167 089480 — MB BS 1964 Durh. Prev: Ho. Off. Walker Gate Hosp. Newc. & Ingham Infirm. S. Shields.

MOYLETT, Elizabeth Margaret Irvine House, Bank Top, Crawcrook, Ryton NE40 4EF — MB BS 1991 Newc.; MRCGP 1995.

MOYNAGH, David Kenneth Silver Springs Medical Practice, Beaufort Road, St Leonards-on-Sea TN37 6PP Tel: 01424 422300/426464 Fax: 01424 436400; Stalkhurst Farm, Ivy House Lane, Hastings TN35 4NN Tel: 01424 751314 — MB BS 1970 Lond.; MRCS Eng. LRCP Lond. 1970; MRCGP 1976. (St. Bart.)

MOYNAGH, Mr Paul Digby (retired) — MB BS 1962 Lond.; FRCS Eng. 1967; Specialist Accredit. (Orthop.) RCS Eng. 1975. Prev: Sen. Regist. Rotat. (Orthop.) St. Barts Hosp. Lond.

MOYNIHAN, Fergus David Ashwell Surgery, Gardiners Lane, Ashwell, Baldock SG7 5PY Tel: 01462 742230 Fax: 01462 742764 Email: ashwellsurgery@compuserve.co — MB BS Lond. 1963; MRCS Eng. LRCP Lond. 1963; DObst RCOG 1965. (Char. Cross.) Prev: Ho. Phys. & Cas. Off. W. Lond. Hosp.; Res. Obst. Off. Kingsbury Matern. Hosp.

MOYNIHAN, Mr Francis John (retired) Minstead House, Minstead, Lyndhurst SO43 7GL Tel: 028 8081 2232 Fax: 028 8081 4388 — MB BS 1951 Lond.; FRCS Eng. 1958; MRCS Eng. LRCP Lond. 1951. Prev: Cons. Orthop. Surg. Roy. Hants. Co. Hosp. Winchester.

MOYNIHAN, Patricia 27 North Parade, Belfast BT7 2GF — MB BCh BAO 1993 Belf.

MOYO, Charles 8 Queens Road, Hale, Altrincham WA15 9HF — BM 1982 Soton.; DRCOG 1992; DTM & H Liverp. 1991.

MOYO, Parmjit Kaur Greenbrow Medical Practice, 379 Greenbrow Road, Newall Green, Manchester M23 2XW Tel: 0161 493 9030 Fax: 0161 436 6217; 8 Queens Road, Hale, Altrincham WA15 9HF — BM 1985 Soton. (Southampton)

MOYSE, Barry Colin Creech Medical Centre, Creech St Michael, Taunton TA3 5QQ Tel: 01823 442357 — MB BS 1985 Lond.; MRCGP 1991; DRCOG 1991; AKC 1985. Racecourse Med. Off., Taunton, Racecourse. Taunton, Som.; Occupat.al Health Cons., Bridgwater Coll., Bridgwater, Som. Socs: W Som. Med. Club.

MOYSE, Graham Alan Adam Practice, 306 Blandford Road, Poole BH15 4JQ Tel: 01202 679234 Fax: 01202 667127 — MRCGP 1987; MB ChB 1982 Manchester; MB ChB 1982 Manchester. GP Princip., The Adam Pract., Poole, Dorset.

MOYSE, Marilyn Bodnant Surgery, Menai Avenue, Bangor LL57 2HH Tel: 01248 364567 Fax: 01248 370654; 1 Glanrafon,

Talwrn, Llangefni LL77 7SY — MB BS 1978 Lond.; BSc Lond. 1975; MRCGP 1982; DRCOG 1982.

MOYSES, Christopher Oxford Glycosciences, Abingdon Science Park, Abingdon OX14 1RG Tel: 01235 543200 Fax: 01235 543258 Email: chris.moyses@ogs.co.uk — MB BChir 1979 Camb.; BA Oxf. 1977, DM 1987; MRCP (UK) 1983; DPM Eng. 1987. Dir. Developm. Oxf. Glyco Sci.s plc. Prev: Vice-Pres. Clin. & Regulat. Affairs Amylin Europe Ltd.; Cardiovasc. Drug Team Ldr. ICI Pharmaceut. Alderley Pk. Chesh.; Lect. (Clin. Med.) St. Mary's Hosp. Med. Sch. Lond.

MOYSEY, Jeffery Osmer Donnybrook House Group Practice, Clarendon Street, Hyde SK14 2AH Tel: 0161 368 3838 Fax: 0161 368 2210 — MB BS 1976 Newc. Socs: Vice-Chairm. W. Pennine Local Med. Comm.

MOYSEY, Joanne Caroline 3 Bucknall Court, Wake Green Park, Moseley, Birmingham B13 9XR — MB ChB 1990 Birm.; DA (UK) 1993.

MOZDZIERZ, Wladyslaw Janusz (retired) Leopolis, 10 Birchwood Court, Bessacarr, Doncaster DN4 6SX Tel: 01302 868802 — MD 1936 Lwow. Prev: Princip. GP Bessacarr.

MOZLEY, Charles Richard 19 Ashmere Avenue, Beckenham BR3 6PQ — LMSSA 1976 Lond.

MOZUMDAR, S K High Street Medical Centre, High St, Winsford CW7 2AS Tel: 01606 862767 Fax: 01606 550876 — MB BS 1969 Patna; MB BS 1969 Patna.

MPANGA, Lydia Ann Zawedde 25 Beacon Hill, London N7 9LY — BM BCh 1992 Oxf.

MRIDHA, Elizabeth Una 3 Churchwood Drive, Chestfield, Whitstable CT5 3PG — MB BS 1990 Lond.; MSc (Clin. Microbiol.) Lond. 1996. (Lond. Hosp. Med. Coll.) Clin. Submissions Manager, Centr. Research Pfizer Ltd, Sandwich, Kent. Prev: Specialist Regist. (Med. Microbiol.) Hammersmith Hosps. NHS Trust; SHO (Med.) Stafford Dist. Gen. Hosp., Staffs. Gen. Infirm. & Horton Gen. Hosp.

MRIDHA, K B The Surgery, 97 Browning Road, Manor Park, London E12 6RB Tel: 020 8472 0744 Fax: 020 8550 7957 — MB BS 1963 Dacca; MB BS 1963 Dacca.

MRIDHA, Khurshid Alam Pfizer Limited, Sandwich CT13 9NJ Tel: 01304 648670; 3 Churchwood Drive, Chestfield, Whitstable CT5 3PG — MB BS 1990 Lond.; BSc (Hons) Lond. 1987; MRCP (UK) 1994; Dip. Pharm. Med. RCP (UK) 1997; AFPM (Asso. Facul. Pharmaceut. Med. - Roy. Coll. Phys. UK 1998. (Lond. Hosp. Med. Coll.) Director, Clin. Regulatory Submissions, Pfizer Ltd., Sandwich, Kent; Qu. Eliz. Hosp., Woolwich, Lond.; Hon. Clin. Asst. (Med. & Gastroenterol.). Prev: Regist. (Med.) Brook Gen. & Greenwich Dist. Hosps. Lond.; SHO (Med.) Colchester Gen. Hosp.; SHO (Geriat. Med. & Rheum.) Roy. Lond. Hosp.

MRIDHA, M S A The Surgery, 97 Browning Road, Manor Park, London E12 6RB Tel: 020 8472 0744 Fax: 020 8550 7957 — MB BS 1962 Dacca; MB BS 1962 Dacca.

MROZINSKI, Richard Alexander Ashfield, Hale Road, Hale, Altrincham WA15 9HP — MB ChB Manch. 1974.

MROZINSKI, Waldemar Josef Paul c/o Mrs J. Crisp, 39 Swallowmead, Salisbury SP2 8JD — MB 1979 Camb.; BChir 1978.

***MTANDABARI, Thomas Martin Richard** 34 Whitchurch Gardens, Edgware HA8 6PD — MB BS 1997 Lond.

***MUAMMAR, Muna** 4 Avenue Mansions, Finchley Road, London NW3 7AU — BM 1995 Soton.

MUAYED, Mr Raouf Mohammed Hossain 55 Knightlow Road, Birmingham B17 8PX — MB ChB 1968 Baghdad; FICS 1989; FRCS Eng. 1977; FRCS Ed. 1976; MRCS Eng. LRCP Lond. 1980. Prev: Asst. Prof. Surg. Univ.,Isfahan; Surg. (Paediat.) Sina Gen. Hosp., Isfahan.

MUCCI, Brian 8 Reelick Quadrant, Glasgow G13 4ND — MB ChB 1980 Glas.

MUCHALL, Arthur James Marsden Road Surgery, The Health Centre, Marsden Road, South Shields NE34 6RE Tel: 0191 454 0457 Fax: 0191 427 1793; 31 Brandling Court, South Shields NE34 8PA Tel: 0191 454 4307 — MB BS 1977 Newc.; MRCGP 1985.

***MUCHATUTA, Neil Alexander** 342 Knighton Lane E., Leicester LE2 6FS — MB BS 1998 Lond.; MB BS Lond 1998.

MUCKLE, Mr David Sutherland Park View Medical Clinic, 276 Markton Road, Middlesbrough TS4 2NS Tel: 01642 242357 Fax: 01642 325693 — MB BS Durh. 1963; MD Newc. 1981, MS 1972; FRCS Ed. 1989; FRCS Eng. 1969. (Durh.) Cons. Orthop. & Accid.

Surg. Cleveland AHA; Hon. Cons. Football Assn. Eng. (Dep. Chairm. Med. Comm.); Med. Adviser Federat. Internat. Football Assns. & Union des Assn. Europ de Football. Socs: Fell. BOA. Prev: Sen. Regist. Nuffield Orthop. Centre & Radcliffe Infirm. Oxf.

MUCKLE-JONES, Daniel Edmund Pendre Surgery, Clayton Road, Mold CH7 1SS Tel: 01352 759163 Fax: 01352 758255 — MB BChir 1984 Camb.; MRCGP 1992; MA Camb. Univ. 1985; DRCOG 1987.

MUCKLOW, Edward Stuart (retired) Keep Cottage, 5 Castle Lane, Carisbrooke, Newport PO30 1PH Tel: 01983 522096 Fax: 01983 822569 — BM BCh 1957 Oxf.; MA Oxf. 1957; FRCP Lond. 1989; FRCP Ed. 1986, M 1966; FRCPCH 1997; DTM RCP & SI 1995; DCH Eng. 1963; DObst RCOG 1960. Hon. Clin. Lect. (Child Health) Univ. Soton.; Med. Off. to Roy. and SunAlliance PLC. Prev: Cons. Paediat. I. of Wight & SE Hants. Dist. (T).

MUCKLOW, Gillian Kathleen Macgregor The Covey, Church Avenue, Clent, Stourbridge DY9 9QT Tel: 01562 883618 — MB ChB 1959 Birm.; DObst RCOG 1961. (Birm.)

MUCKLOW, John Christopher North Staffordshire Hospital, Stoke-on-Trent ST4 6QG Tel: 01782 552917 Fax: 01782 552918 Email: john.mucklow@nstaffs.wmids.nhs.uk — MB ChB Birm. 1970; MD Birm. 1980; FRCP Lond. 1987; MRCP (UK) 1974. Cons. Phys. Clin. Pharmacol. N. Staffs. Hosp. NHS Trust S. on Trent; Sen. Lect. (Clin. Pharmacol. Therap.) Dept. Meds. Managem, Univ. Keele. Socs: Fell. Roy. Soc. Med.; Brit. Pharm. Soc. (Clin. Sect.). Prev: Lect. (Clin. Pharmacol.) Univ. Newc.; Wellcome Research Fell. (Clin. Pharmacol.) Roy. Postgrad. Med. Sch. Hammersmith Hosp. Lond.

MUCKLOW, John Trevor Wychbury Medical Centre, 121 Oakfield Road, Wollescote, Stourbridge DY9 9DS — MB ChB 1959 Birm.; MRCS Eng. LRCP Lond. 1959; DObst RCOG 1961. (Birm.)

***MUCKLOW, Stuart Fernie** Keep Cottage, 5 Castle La, Newport PO30 1PH — BM BCh 1997 Oxf.

MUDALIAR, Ramalingam Kuppuramaswamy Princess Marina Hospital, Northampton NN5 6UH Tel: 01604 752323 Fax: 01604 595306 — MB BS 1975 Bombay; MD (Psychol. Med.) Bombay 1978; MRCPsych. 1981; Dip. Psychother. Liverp. 1984. (Topiwala National Medical School Bombay) Cons. Psychogeriat. N.ampton Healthcare NHS Trust; Clin. Direcotr Elderly Ment. Health Trust N.ampton Healthcare NHS Trust.

***MUDALIAR, Vivek** Doctors Residences, Doncaster Royal Infirmary, Armthorpe Rd, Doncaster DN2 5 — MB ChB 1997 Sheff.

MUDAN, Mr Satvinder Singh Tel: 020 87253594 Fax: 020 8672 8114 Email: mudans@sghms.ac.uk; 50 Bond Road, Surbiton KT6 7SH — MB BS 1986 Lond.; BSc (Hons.) Lond. 1983, MB BS 1986; FRCS Lond. 1990, FRCS (gen) 1997; MD Lond. 1997. Cons. Surg. Surgic. Oncol. Dept, of Surg. St Geo.'s Hosp Med Sch. Socs: Assn Upper Gastrointestinal Surg. Coun. Mem 1997-2000; Brit Assoc of Surgic. Oncologists. Prev: Fell. (surg. Oncol.) Nat. Cancer Centre, Tokyo, Japan, 1999; Fell.(Surg,oncol) Memor. Sloan-Kettering cancer Centre, New York, USA 1995-1996.

MUDANNAYAKA, Therese Savitri Swarnamalie 175 Knolton Way, Wexham, Slough SL2 5SP Tel: 01753 23285 — MB BS 1979 Colombo; DA (UK) 1982; FFA RCSI 1986.

MUDAWI, Mr Ahmed Mohamed Department of General Surgery, Frenchay Hospital, Bristol Road, Bristol BS16 1LE — MB BS 1980 Khartoum; FRCS Ed. 1987.

MUDAWI, Hatim Mohamed Yousif Endoscopy Unit, St Marys Hospital, Parkhurst Road, Newport PO30 5TQ — MB BS 1987 Khartoum, Sudan; MRCP (UK) 1995.

MUDD, Mr David Geoffrey Farthings, 14 Brocklamont Park, Old Galgorm Road, Ballymena BT42 1AS — MB BCh BAO 1970 Belf.; BSc Belf. 1967, MD 1979; FRCS Ed. 1974. Cons. Surg. (Gen. Surg. & Urol.) Antrim Hosp.

***MUDD, Paul David** 14 Brocklamont Park, Ballymena BT42 1AS — MB BS 1996 Newc.

***MUDD, Sarah Jane** 28 Celtic Road, Whitchurch, Cardiff CF14 1EG — MB BCh 1997 Wales.

MUDDAPPA, Y N The Health Centre, 20 Cleveland Square, Middlesbrough TS1 2NX Tel: 01642 242746 Fax: 01642 220766 — MB BS 1968 Mysore; MB BS 1968 Mysore.

MUDDIMAN, Margaret Joy Number 18 Surgery, 18 Upper Oldfield Park, Bath BA2 3JZ Tel: 01225 427402 Fax: 01225 484627; 19 Entry Hill, Bath BA2 5LZ — MB BS 1973 Lond.; MRCP (UK) 1977; MRCS Eng. LRCP Lond. 1973; DCH Eng. 1977. (Roy.

MUDDLE

Free) GP. Socs: Internat. League Against Epilepsy; (Local Rep.) Christian Med. Fell.sh. Prev: Regist. (Paediat.) S.mead Hosp. Bristol; Research Regist. Soton. Gen. Hosp.; Paediat. United Mission to Nepal, Tansen, Nepal.

*MUDDLE, Sarah Louise Birch Coppice, Heath End Road, Baughurst, Tadley RG26 5ND — MB BS 1998 Lond.; MB BS Lond 1998.

MUDDU, Vijayalakshmi 10 Pownall Avenue, Bramhall, Stockport SK7 2HE — MB BS 1971 Bangalore.

MUDGAL, Rakesh DUDLEY Group of Hospitals NHS Trust, c/o Paediatric Secretary, Wordsley Hospital, Stream Road, Stourbridge DY8 5QX Tel: 01384 244437 Fax: 01384 244367 Email: r.mudgal@virgin.net; 20 Osmaston Road, Stourbridge DY8 2AL — MB BS 1979 Rajasthan; MRCP (UK) 1992. Cons. Paediat.; Hon. Sen. Clin. Lect., Dept. of Child Health, Univ. of Birm. Socs: RCPCH; BMA; MPS.

MUDGE, Marjorie 6 Fairwater Road, Llandaff, Cardiff CF5 2LD — MB ChB 1960 Leeds. (Leeds) Stud. Counsellor Univ. Wales Coll. Med. Prev: Clin. Asst. (Dermat.) Bro-Morgannwg Gp. Hosps.; Research Asst. (Surg.) Univ. Wales Coll. Med.; Hon. Clin. Asst. (Gen. Surg.) S. Glam. HA.

*MUDHAR, Hardeep Singh 256 Caxton Street, Sunnyhill, Derby DE23 7RB — BChir 1995 Camb.

MUDIE, Leslie Laurence Department of Anaesthetics, Wolverhampton Health Authority, New Cross Hospital, Wolverhampton WV10 0QP Tel: 01902 307999; 3 Coalway Avenue, Penn, Wolverhampton WV3 7LT Tel: 01902 686567 Fax: 01902 644914 Email: lessheena@netscapeonline.co.uk — MB ChB 1977 Dundee; FFA RCS Eng. 1984. Cons. Anaesth. Wolverhampton HA.; Clin. Director Intesive Care. Prev: Sen. Regist. (Anaesth.) W. Midl. RHA; Regist. (Anaesth.) Manch. & Wolverhampton HA.

MUDREWICZ, Julian (retired) 23A Bracknell Gardens, London NW3 7EE — MB ChB 1943 Polish Sch. of Med. Prev: Regist. (O & G) Boston Gen. Hosp. Lincs., St. Albans City Hosp.& Welwyn Gdn. Matern. Hosp.

MUEHLBAYER, Simone Department of Chemical Pathology, Leicester Royal Infirmary, Leicester LE1 5WW — State Exam Med 1994 Aachen.

MUELLER, Kamala-Maria Thorneywood Unit, Porchester Road, Nottingham NG3 6LF Tel: 0115 844 0506; 62 County Road, Gedling, Nottingham NG4 4JC Tel: 0115 953 7580 Email: marktmroberts@compuserve.com — State Exam Med 1982 Aachen; MRCPsych 1993. (Child & Adolesc. Psychiat.) Cons.

MUELLER, Martin Franz Florian 6 Western Road, Tunbridge Wells TN1 2JJ — State Exam Med 1991 Munster; MD Munster 1992; MRCGP 1996; DFFP 1996; Dip. IMC RCS Ed. 1996; DRCOG 1995; DCH RCP Lond. 1994.

MUELLER, Professor Robert Frederick Department of Clinical Genetics, Ashley Wing, St James' Hospital, Beckett St., Leeds LS9 7TF Tel: 0113 283 2072 Fax: 0113 246 7090; The Lodge, Adel Croft, 12 Long Causeway, Leeds LS16 8EF Tel: 0113 267 0053 Fax: 0113 246 7090 — MB BS 1976 Lond.; BSc Lond. 1973; FRCP Lond. 1993; MRCP (UK) 1980; MRCS Eng. LRCP Lond. 1976. Cons. Clin. Geneticist (Genetic Counselling) St. Jas. Hosp. Leeds; Prof. Clin. Genetics Univ. Leeds. Socs: Brit. Soc. Human Genetics; Amer. Soc. Human Genetics. Prev: MRC Train. Fell. MRC Laborat. Molecular Biol. Camb.; Hon. Sen. Regist. (Genetic Counselling) Addenbrooke's Hosp. Camb.

*MUEN, Wisam Jasim University of Wales Hospital, Cardiff CF4 4XW Tel: 029 2071 1711 — MB ChB 1997 Manch.

MUERS, Martin Faraday Dept. of Resp.Med., Gen. Infirm. Leeds, Great George St., Leeds LS1 3EX Tel: 0113 392 5299 Fax: 0113 392 5299 Email: amandajones@leedsth.nhs.uk; 1 Wedgewood Grove, Roundhay, Leeds LS8 1EG Tel: 0113 266 3154 Email: mfmuers@aol.com — BM BCh 1971 Oxf.; 1972 DPhil Oxf.; 1985 FRCP Lond.; 1970 MA; 1971 BM BCh. (St. Thos.) p/t Cons. Phys. Respirat. Unit Leeds Gen. Inf.; Sen. Clin. Lect. (Med.) Univ. Leeds. Socs: Brit. Thorac. Soc.; Eur. Respirat. Soc.; Amer. Thoracic. Soc. Prev: Sen. Regist. John Radcliffe Hosp. Oxf.; Regist. (Med.) Radcliffe Infirm. Oxf.; Ho. Phys. St. Thos. Hosp. Lond.

*MUFTI, Arjmand Rasool Littleton, Queens Road, Maidstone ME16 0HX — MB BS 1998 Lond.; MB BS Lond 1998.

MUFTI, Faiza Hassan South London and Maudsley NHS Trust, Tamworth Resource Centre, 37 Tamworth Road, Croydon CR0 1XU Tel: 0208 700 8700 Fax: 0208 686 4308 — MB BS 1985 Kashmir, India; MRCPsych 1995. (Srinagar, India) Cons. Psychiat. (Gen. Adult Psychiat. and Perinatal Psychiat.) S. Lond. and Maudsley NHS Trust. Socs: Roy. Coll. of Psychiat.s; Brit. Med. Assn. Prev: Sen. Regist. (Gen. Adult Psychiat.) Maudsley & Bethlehem NHS Trust.

MUFTI, Mr Ghulam Rasool Medway Hospital, Windmill Road, Gillingham ME7 5NY Tel: 01634 830000; Littleton, Queens Road, Maidstone ME16 0HX Tel: 01622 755446 Email: grmufti@aol.com — MB BS Jammu & Kashmir 1965; MS (Univ. of Gufarat, India) 1969; MCh (Urology) 1977; FRCS Ed. 1984; T(S) 1991. (Srinagar Medical College, Kashmir) Cons. Urol. Medway NHS Trust; Hon. Lect. King's, Guy's & St. Thos. Med. Sch. Socs: Brit. Assn. Urol. Surgs.; Brit. Soc. Endocrinol.; Brit. Soc. Androl. Prev: Locum Cons. Urol. Glas. Roy. Infirm.; Clin. Lect. Inst. Urol. Lond.; Regist. (Surg. & Urol.) Whipps Cross Hosp. Lond.

MUFTI, Muhammad Muzammil (retired) 4 Somerville Drive, Crawley RH10 3TF — MB BS 1957 Punjab; MB BS Punjab (Pakistan) 1957; DMRD Punjab (Pakistan) 1963. Prev: Cons. Radiol. Gravesend & N. Kent Hosp.

MUFTI, Mr Samir Tawfik Zenith House, 53 Brook Lane, Warsash, Southampton SO31 9FF Tel: 0148 95 84343 — MB ChB 1960 Baghdad; FRCS Eng. 1967; FRCS Ed. 1967. (Baghdad Univ.) Cons. i/c A & E Dept. St. Helier Hosp. Carshalton.

MUFTI, Ward-i-Samin Department of Cardiology, John Radcliffe Hospital, Headley Way, Headington, Oxford OX3 9DU Tel: 01865 741166; 200 London Road, Headington, Oxford OX3 9EE Tel: 01865 767244 Fax: 01865 455543 Email: drmufti@compuserve.com — MB BS 1984 Punjab, Pakistan; MRCP (UK) 1992. (King Edwd. Med. Coll. Lahore, Pakistan) Staff Cardiol. John Radcliffe Hosp. Oxf.; Inter. Fell. Dept. Inter. Card. UAB Univ. Alabama Birm. Alabama USA 1998. Socs: Brit. Soc. Echocard.; Brit. Soc. Nucl. Card.; BMA. Prev: Regist. (Cardiol.) John Radcliffe Hosp. Oxf.; Regist. (Med.) Seacroft Hosp. Leeds & St. Luke's Hosp. Bradford.

MUGGE, Laura Estelle Anderson 35 Cardy Road, Hemel Hempstead HP1 1RL; Dr L. Mugge, 63 Tylney Rd, Sheffield S2 2RX — MB ChB 1997 Sheff. VTS, Sheff., Curr.ly SHO (O & G).

MUGGLESTONE, Christopher John CJM Medical Ltd., Salatin House, 19 Cedar Road, Sutton SM2 5JG Tel: 020 8770 1110 Fax: 020 8770 1166 Email: cjmmedical@compuserve.com; 233 Banstead Road, Banstead SM7 1RB Tel: 020 8393 9990 Fax: 020 8393 6164 — MB ChB 1962 Birm.; FFPM RCP (UK) 1989; Dip Pharm Med RCP (UK) 1977. Chairm. CJM Med. Ltd. Lond.; Dir. Dermatechnol. Ltd.; Director MediSite Managem. Ltd. Socs: Fell. Roy. Soc. Med.; Brit. Assn. Psychopharmacol. Prev: Hon. Cons. Androl Cuckfield Hosp.; Med. Dir. Brocades (GB) Ltd.; Head Clin. Research Schering Chem. Ltd.

MUGGLESTONE, Sophie Jane Rutherford Medical Centre, 1 Rutherford Road, Mossley Hill, Liverpool L18 0HL Tel: 0151 722 1803 Fax: 0151 738 0083 — MB ChB 1992 Liverp.

MUGGLETON, Dafne Elizabeth MacGillycuddy Curvalion House, Creech St Michael, Taunton TA3 5QF Tel: 01823 443842 — MB BCh BAO Belf. 1951; DCH Eng. 1953. (Queens University Belfast) Prev: Regist. Roy. Manch. Childr. Hosp.; Paediat. Regist. Oldham & Dist. Gen. Hosp.; Research Asst. Dept. Child Health Manch.

MUGGLETON, Robert John Stonecroft Medical Centre, 871 Gleadless Road, Sheffield S12 2LJ Tel: 0114 398575 Fax: 0114 265 0001 — MB ChB 1986 Sheff.; BMedSci 1984; MRCGP 1990; DRCOG 1990.

MUGHAL, Abdul Halim 6 Kevin Close, Hounslow TW4 7RX Tel: 020 8572 5647 Fax: 020 8230 5811 Email: ah.mughal@btinternet.com — MB BS 1980 Mysore. Staff Grade (Psychiat.) Pk. Roy. Centre for Ment. Health Lond. Prev: Regist. (Psychiat.) FarnBoro. Hosp. Orpington; SHO (Geriat.) Rotherham Dist. Gen. Hosp.

MUGHAL, M. Tariq Imdadali Royal Preston Hospital, Preston PR7 1PP Tel: 01772 710916 Fax: 01772 710963 Email: tmughal@freenet.co.uk; 25 Park Lodge Close, Cheadle SK8 1HU Tel: 0161 446 3269 Email: tmughal@freenet.co.uk — MRCS Eng. LRCP Lond. 1976; MD (Haemat.) Lond. 1986, MB BS 1976; MRCP 1999; FACP 1986; Dip Amer. Bd. Intern Med. 1984; Dip Amer. Bd. Med. Oncol. 1993; Dip Amer. Bd. Haemat. 1985. (St. George's Hospital Medical School London) Cons. Haemat. & Med. Oncol.,

Roy. Preston NHS Trust Hosps.; Cons. Haemat. & Med. Oncol., Christie Hosp., Manch., M20 4BX. Socs: Amer. Soc. Haemat. & Amer. Soc. Oncol.; Eur. Soc. Oncol.; Eur. Blood & Marrow Transpl. Prev: Sen. Regist. Hammersmith Hosp. & Roy. Postgrad. Med. Sch. Lond.; Head Div. Haemat. & Oncol. King Fahad Hosp., Riyadh; Fell. Univ. Colorado Sch. Med. Denver, USA.

MUGHAL, Mahera Shaheen The Surgery, 127 Trinity Road, Tooting, London SW17 7HJ Tel: 020 8672 3331 — MB BS 1992 Lond.

***MUGHAL, Mehmood Sadiq** 5 Wynyard Close, Sale M33 3JT — MB BS 1997 Lond.

MUGHAL, Mohamed Shariff 87 Balham Park Road, London SW12 8EB — LRCP LRCS 1977 Ed.; LRCP LRCS Ed. LRCPS Glas. 1977.

MUGHAL, Mohamed Zulficar Department of Paediatrics, St Mary's Hospital, Hatersage Road, Manchester M13 0JH Tel: 0161 276 6501 Fax: 0161 276 6907 Email: mmughal@fs1.cmht.nwest.nhs.uk — MB ChB 1978 Liverp.; FRCP Lond. 1996; MRCP (UK) 1980; MRCS Eng. LRCP Lond. 1978; DCH Eng. 1980; FRCPCH 1997. (Liverp.) Cons. Paediat. & Hon. Sen. Lect. (Child Health) St. Mary's Hosp. Manch. Prev: Perinatal Research Fell. Univ. Cincinnati, USA; Lect. (Child Health) Univ. Manch.; Regist. Rotat. (Paediat.) Bolton Gen. Hosp., Roy. Manch. Childr. Hosp. & Hope Hosp. Salford.

MUGHAL, Mr Mohammed Muntzer Chorley & District Hospital, Preston Road, Chorley PR7 1PP Tel: 01257 245267 Fax: 01257 245280 Email: muntzer@delhi.demon.co.uk; 22A Windsor Road, Chorley PR7 1LN — MB ChB 1977 Manch.; ChM Manch. 1985, MB ChB 1977; FRCS Eng. 1981. Cons. Surg. Chorley & Dist. Hosp. Prev: Cons. Surg. Roy. Preston Hosp.; Sen. Lect. & Hon. Cons. Surg. Hope Hosp. Salford; Lect. & Hon. Sen. Regist. (Surg.) Manch. Roy. Infirm.

***MUGHAL, Mohammed Shakeel** 16 Byron Street, Bradford BD3 0AD — MB BS 1997 Lond.

MUGHAL, N J The Surgery, 127 Trinity Road, Tooting, London SW17 7HJ Tel: 020 8672 3331 — MB BS 1969 Dacca; MB BS 1969 Dacca.

MUGHAL, Naveed Ahmed 60 Cressex Road, High Wycombe HP12 4TY — MB ChB 1986 Leeds.

MUGHAL, Ramzan Mohamed Ethelbert Gardens Surgery, 63-65 Ethelbert Gardens, Ilford IG2 6UW Tel: 020 8550 3740 Fax: 020 8550 4300 — MB ChB 1981 Sheff.

MUGHAL, Sajjad 31 Hazelmere Road, Birmingham B28 8HZ — MB ChB 1992 Dundee.

MUGHAL, Salma Dicconson Terrace Surgery, Dicconson Terrace, Wigan WN1 2AF Tel: 01942 239525 Fax: 01942 826552 — MRCS Eng. LRCP Lond. 1975; MRCGP 1981; DRCOG 1977. (King's Coll. Hosp.) Socs: Local Med. Comm.

MUGHAL, Zahir Ahmed Great Horton Road Surgery, 462 Great Horton Road, Bradford BD7 3HS Tel: 01274 504425 Fax: 01274 414282 — MB ChB 1978 Manch. Clin. Asst. (Rheum. & Psychiat.) Barnsley HA.

MUGHRABI, Mahmoud Arafa Mahmoud Ward 16, Victoria Hospital, Kirkcaldy KY2 5AH Tel: 01592 643355; 1 Longcraigs Terrace, Kinghorn, Burntisland KY3 9TA — MB BCh 1971 Ain Shams; MRCPI 1986; Dip. Thoracic Med. Lond 1985. Staff Phys. (Chest Med.) Vict. Hosp. Kirkcaldy.

MUGLISTON, Mr Terence Anthony Howard 6A Peterborough Villas, London SW6 — MB BS 1976 Lond.; BA Oxf. 1971; FRCS Eng. 1983; MRCP (UK) 1980; MRCS Eng. LRCP Lond. 1976.

MUGRIDGE, Mr Anthony Robert, Surg. Capt. RN Department of Surgery, Royal Hospital Haslar, Gosport PO12 2AA; 63 St. Stephen's Road, Saltash PL12 4BQ — MB ChB 1971 Bristol; FRCS Ed. 1981. Socs: Fell. Assn. Surgs.; Assoc. Mem. BAUS; Anglo-French Med. Soc. Prev: Princip. Med. Off. HMS Invincible; Clin. Fell. Inst. Urol. Bristol.

MUHAIREZ, Muhammad Abdul-Qader 28 Copperfield Avenue, Hillingdon, Uxbridge UB8 3NU — LRCPI & LM, LRSCI & LM 1958; LRCPI & LM, LRCSI & LM 1958.

MUHAMMAD, Faisal Abdul 128 Knight Manor Way, Dartford DA1 5SL — MB BS 1987 Karachi.

MUHAMMAD, Haroon Ali The Surgery, 455 Wandsworth Road, London SW8 4NX Tel: 020 7622 2808 Fax: 020 7498 1073; 13 Kirkdale, London SE26 4NB Tel: 020 8699 4176 Fax: 020 7498 1073 — MB BS 1967 Karachi. (Dow Med. Coll.) Med. Off. Brit. Boxing Bd.; Clin. Tutor (Gen. Prac.) St. Thos. Hosp. Lond. Socs: Pres. Overseas Doctors Assn. (S.N. Lond. Div.). Prev: SHO (A & E Neurosurg., Orthop. & Gen. Surg.) N. Staff. Roy. Infirm. Stoke-on-Trent; SHO (Orthop.) Putney Hosp. Lond.; SHO (A & E & Orthop.) Leicester Roy. Infirm.

MUHAMMAD, Joseph Kamal 26 Higher Darcy Street, Bolton BL2 1NG — MB BS 1994 Lond.; BDS Lond. 1986; LDS Lond. 1985; FDE RCS Ed. 1989; FDS RCS Eng. 1989; FRCS Ed. 1997; FRCS Eng. 1997. (Roy. Dental Hosp. UMDS) Specialist Regist. Oral & Maxillofacial Surg. Morriston Hosp. Swansea Wales. Socs: BMA; Brit. Assn. Oral & Maxillofacial Surg.; Craniofacial Soc.

MUHAMMAD, Liman Mahamoud The Surgery, 11-13 Charlton Road, Blackheath, London SE3 7HB Tel: 020 8858 2632; 1 Danehill Walk, Hatherley Road, Sidcup DA14 4AL — MB BS 1978 Ahmadu Bello; FRSM; FRSH. GP Princip. Blackheath Standrd Surg. Socs: Fell. Roy. Soc. Health; Fell. Roy. Soc. Med. Prev: Trainee GP Hatfield Peverel & Colchester VTS; Regist. (O & G) Bromley AHA.

MUHAMMAD, Shehla Nilofer Genetics Centre, Division of Medical & Molecular Genetics, 7th Floor, New Guy's House, St Thomas' St., London SE1 9RT Tel: 020 7955 4648/9 Fax: 020 7955 2550 Email: shehla.mohammed@gstt.sthames.nhs.uk — MB BS 1983 Punjab; MRCP (UK) 1989; DCH RCP Lond. 1987; MD Lond. 1998. (University of London) Cons. Clin. Genetics & Hon. Sen. Lect. (Div. of Med. & Molecular Genetics) Guys Hosp. Lond.; Head of Serv. (Clin. Genetics) Guys Hosp. Lond. Socs: Clin. Genetics Soc. Prev: Sen. Regist. (Clin. Genetics) & Research Fell. (Cancer Genetics) Paediat. Research Unit Guy's Hosp. Lond.; Regist. (Paediat.) Qu. Mary's Hosp. for Childr. Carshalton; SHO (Paediat.) Guy's Hosp. & Whittington Hosp. Lond.

MUHAMMAD TAIB, Rohayati Haji Flat 1/L, 314 St George's Road, Glasgow G3 6JR — MB ChB 1995 Glas.

MUHAMMED, Sadia Priory Medical Group, Cornlands Road, Acomb, York YO24 3WX Tel: 01904 781423 Fax: 01904 784886; 4 Post Office Row, Bilton-in-Ainsty, York YO26 7NW — MB ChB 1983 Manch.

MUHIDDIN, Khulood Abdul Latif Derby City General Hospital, Uttoxeter Road, Derby DE22 3NE Tel: 01332 340131 Fax: 01332 625735 Email: khulood.muhiddin@sdah-tr.trent.nhs.uk — MB ChB 1977; PhD Lond. 1984; MRCP (UK) 1989; FRCP 2000 UK. Cons. Med. for Elderly Derby City Gen. Hosp. Socs: Brit. Geriat. Soc.; Roy. Coll. Phys.; Brit. Geriat. Soc. Cardiol. Sect. Prev: Sen. Regist. (Geriat. & Gen. Med.) Roy. Devon & Exeter Hosp.; Regist. (Geriat.) Bristol Roy. Infirm.; Regist. (Respirat.) W.. Infirm. Glas.

MUHIUDEEN, Helen Armena 20 Barons Court Mansions, Gledstanes Road, London W14 9HZ — MB BCh 1989 Wales; PhD Bristol 1979, BSc 1975.

MUHLEMANN, Mark Frederick Jersey General Hospital, Gloucester St., St Helier, Jersey JE2 3 — MB BS 1977 Lond.; FRCP 1989 UK; BSc (Hons.) Lond. 1974; FRCP Lond. 1994; MRCP (UK) 1979. Cons. Dermat. Jersey Gp. Hosps.

MUHUNDHAKUMAR, Sabaretnam 46 Shamrock Way, Southgate, London N14 5RY — MB BS 1978 Sri Lanka.

MUHUNTHAKUMAR, Puvaneswary 46 Shamrock Way, London N14 5RY — MB BS 1976 Sri Lanka.

MUIESAN, Paolo Liver Transplant Surgical Service, King's College Hospital, Denmark Hill, London SE5 9RS Tel: 020 7346 3575 Fax: 020 7346 3575 Email: p.muiesan@virgin.net — State Exam Brescia 1985; Spec. Train. Cert. Gen. Surg. Brescia 1990; Spec. Train. Cert. Vasc. Surg. Brescia 1995. (Brescia) Cons. Surg. Liver Trans. Hepatobiliary Surg. Liver Trans.Serv. KCHosp. Lond. Socs: Internat. Hepato Pancreato Biliary Assn.; BMA; Brit Transpl.. Soc. Prev: Sen. Regist. (Liver Transpl. Surgic. Serv.) King's Coll. Hosp. Lond.; Regist. (Liver Transpl. Surgic. Serv.) King's Coll. Hosp. Lond.; Research Fell., Gen. Surg., Univ. of Brescia.

MUIR, Alan (retired) 9 Gidea Close, Romford RM2 5NP Tel: 01708 740816 — MB BS 1951 Lond. Prev: Sen. Cas. Off. Char. Cross Hosp.

MUIR, Alan Morton Hunters Ride, The Maltings, West Ilsley, Newbury RG20 7AX Tel: 01635 281647 Fax: 01635 281138 Email: alan.muir@rg207ax.freeserve.co.uk — MB BS 1977 Lond.; MRCS Eng. LRCP Lond. 1977; MFOM RCP Lond. 1985; DAvMed. FOM RCP Lond. 1982. (Westm.) Socs: BMA.

MUIR

MUIR, Alan Roderic Department of Public Health Medicine, Forth Valley Health Board, Stirling FK8 1DX Tel: 01786 457281 Fax: 01786 451474 Email: rod_muir@hotmail.com; 102 Findhorn Place, Edinburgh EH9 2NZ Tel: 0131 668 3440 — MB ChB 1972 Ed.; MSc Ed. 1991, BSc 1970; MFPHM RCP (UK) 1994; MRCGP 1989; DA (UK) 1982. (Ed.) Cons. Pub. Health Med. Forth Valley HB. Prev: GP Dalkeith & Thurso; Lect. (Gen. Pract.) Univ. Edin.

MUIR, Alastair John Woodside Health Centre, Barr Street, Glasgow G20 7LR Tel: 0141 531 9510 Fax: 0141 531 9515 — MB ChB 1985 Glas.; BSc (Hons.) Immunol. Glas. 1982, MB ChB 1985; MRCGP 1989; DRCOG 1987.

MUIR, Professor Alexander Laird (retired) 31/9 Hermitage Drive, Edinburgh EH10 6BY Tel: 0131 447 2652 — MB ChB 1961 Ed.; MD Ed. 1970; FRCS Ed. 1994; FRCP Ed. 1975, M 1967; FRCR 1986; FRCP 1998. Postgrad. Dean Univ. Edin.; Hon. Cons. Phys. Roy. Infirm. Edin.; Hon. Phys. to Army in Scotl. Prev: Phys. to HM the Qu. in Scotl.

MUIR, Alexander Peter John Bognor Medical Practice, West St., Bognor Regis PO21 1; Pool House, Lock Lane, Birdham, Chichester PO20 7BB — MB BS 1989 Lond.; BSc 1986; DRCOG 1995; DFFP 1997. (Royal Free Hospital, London) GP.

***MUIR, Andrew Duncan** 6 Alexander Road, Carrickfergus BT38 7LY — MB BCh BAO 1997 Belf.

MUIR, Andrew Herd Wards 3 & 4, Ninewells Hospital, Dundee DD1 9SY Tel: 01382 660111 Fax: 01382 660675; Forgan House, Newport-on-Tay DD6 8RB Tel: 01382 542894 Email: 106013.3273@compuserve.com — MB ChB 1977 Dundee. Staff Grade (Med.) Ninewells Hosp. Dundee. Socs: BMA; BSR.

MUIR, Andrew Menzies Briton Ferry Health Centre, Hunter Street, Briton Ferry, Neath SA11 5SF Tel: 01639 812270 Fax: 01639 813019 — MB BCh 1976 Wales; MRCGP 1983; DRCOG 1979. Prev: Ho. Phys. Neath Gen. Hosp.; Ho. Surg. Belford Hosp. Fort William; Trainee Gen. Pract. S. Glam. Vocational Train. Scheme.

MUIR, Anne St. George's Hospital, Corporation St., Stafford ST16 3AG — MB ChB 1971 Glas.; MRCPsych. 1982. Cons. Psychiat. St. Geo. Hosp. Stafford.

MUIR, Archie (retired) 31 Southdown Drive, Thornton-Cleveleys FY5 5BL Tel: 01253 855405 — LRCP LRCS Ed. LRFPS Glas. 1948. Local Med. Off. Civil Serv. Lancs.

MUIR, Berenice Barker NHSBSP S.E. Scottish Division, Ardmillan House, 42 Ardmillan Terrace, Edinburgh EH11 2JL Tel: 0131 537 7410 Fax: 0131 537 7420; 31/9 Hermitage Drive, Edinburgh EH10 6BY Email: muir.etal@btinternet.co — MB ChB Ed. 1966; FRCR 1977; DMRD Ed. 1971. Cons. Radiol. (Dep. Dir.) SE Scotl. BrE. Screening Prog. Prev: Simpson memor. Matern. Pavil. Ed.

MUIR, Celeste Una (retired) The Parsonage, Westwell, Ashford TN25 4JH — MB BS 1954 Lond. Prev: GP Ashford.

MUIR, Donald William Walter (retired) Riverside Medical Practice, Roushill, Shrewsbury SY1 1PQ Tel: 01743 52371 — MB ChB 1962 Sheff.; DObst RCOG 1964. Mem. Assn. Police Surgs. & BMA.

MUIR, Douglas Findlay 199 Wilton Street, Glasgow G20 6DF Email: d.f.muir@clinmed.gla.ac.uk — MB ChB 1992 Glas.; MRCP (UK) 1995. Clin. Research Fell. (Cardiol.) W.. Infirm. Glas.

MUIR, Duncan Peter Rennie Mitchell Road Surgery, 9 Mitchell Road, Canferd Heath, Poole BH17 8UE Tel: 01202 672474 Fax: 01202 660926; Sundial Lodge, 126 Canford Cliffs Road, Poole BH13 7ER Tel: 01202 701882 — MB BS 1981 Lond.; MRCGP 1986; DRCOG 1984. (King's Coll. Hosp.) Mem. Wessex GP Educat. Trust. Socs: BMA; Wessex Asthma Club; Med. Defence Union. Prev: Trainee GP Norf. & Norwich Hosp. VTS; Regist. (Paediat.) Norf. & Norwich Hosp. Norwich; SHO (A & E) Hackney Hosp. Lond.

MUIR, Edward Antony (retired) Dunmore, Pulpit Hill, Oban PA34 4LU Tel: 01631 565339 — MB ChB 1960 Glas. Prev: GP Argyll.

MUIR, Edward Summerfield The Health Centre, Queen Street, Jedburgh TD8 6EN Tel: 01835 863361 Fax: 01835 864273; 46 Dounehill, Jedburgh TD8 6LJ Tel: 01835 863608 — MB ChB 1970 Glas.; MRCGP 1974; DObst RCOG 1972.

MUIR, Elizabeth Hilary (retired) 9 Chiltern Road, Wendover, Aylesbury HP22 6DB Tel: 01296 625231 — MB BS 1980 Lond.; BSc 1977 Lond.; MRCP (UK) 1983; MRCGP 1987; AKC. Clin. Asst. Florence Nightingale Hospice Stoke Mandeville Hosp. Prev: SHO (Med.) Whittington Hosp. Lond.

MUIR, Fergus Hyslop The Surgery, New Hayes Bank, Bybrook, Kennington, Ashford TN24 9JZ Tel: 01233 624624 Fax: 01233 637304; The Parsonage, Westwell, Ashford TN25 4JH Tel: 01233 630606 — MB BS 1957 Lond.; MRCS Eng LRCP Lond. 1956; DObst RCOG 1961; Cert Av Med MoD (Air) & CAA; Aviat. Auth. 1975. (Guy's) Socs: Roy. Coll. Gen Pract.; BMA. Prev: Ho. Surg. (ENT) Guy's Hosp.

MUIR, Fiona 45 Glenview, Glasgow G66 1PG — MB ChB 1992 Glas.

***MUIR, Fiona Mary** Lark Rise, 110 Harmer Green Lane, Welwyn AL6 0ET — MB ChB 1994 Bristol.

MUIR, Gillian Lorraine Anniston House, Inverkeilor, Arbroath DD11 5SW — MB ChB 1985 Dundee; DA (UK) 1987.

MUIR, Mr Iain Murray Dumfries & Galloway Royal Infirmary, Bankend Road, Dumfries DG1 4AP Tel: 01387 246246 Fax: 01387 241088 Email: i.muir@dgri.scot.nhs.uk — MB ChB 1977 Dundee; MD Melbourne 1989; FRCS Ed. 1983. Cons. Surg. Dumfries & Galloway Acute & Matern. NHS Trust. Prev: Sen. Regist. (Surg.) Nottm. & Derby Hosps.; Research Fell. (Surg.) St. Vincent's Hosp. Melbourne, Austral.

MUIR, Iain William Selden Medical Centre, 6 Selden Road, Worthing BN11 2LL Tel: 01903 234962 Fax: 01903 214531 Email: iain.muir@gp-h82061.nhs.uk; Dunelm, 59 West Avenue, Worthing BN11 5NA Tel: 01903 502510 — MB ChB 1977 Dundee; Cert. Family Plann. JCC 1980. (Dundee) GP. Prev: SHO (Paediat. & O & G) S.lands Hosp. Shoreham-by-Sea; SHO (Med.) Worthing Hosp.; SHO (A & E) Dist. Gen. Hosp. Sunderland.

MUIR, Mr Ian Fraser Kerr, MBE, VRD (retired) 98 Sports Road, Glenfield, Leicester LE3 8AJ Tel: 0116 232 1490 — MB BS Lond. 1943; MS Lond. 1960; FRCS Ed. 1973; FRCS Eng. 1948; MRCS Eng. LRCP Lond. 1943. Hon. Cons. Plastic Surg. Aberd. Roy. Infirm. & Roy. Aberd. Childr. Hosp. Prev: Hon. Research Fell. (Surg.) Univ. Aberd.

MUIR, Ian Gordon 24 Gerrard Road, Whitley Bay NE26 4NL — MB BS 1973 Newc.; DObst RCOG 1975.

MUIR, Ian Stirling (retired) Feliz, Ginns Road, Stocking Pelham, Buntingford SG9 0JD Tel: 01279 777178 — MB BChir Camb. 1959; MRCS Eng. LRCP Lond. 1958; DMJ (Clin.) 1982; DObst RCOG 1960.

MUIR, Jacqueline Merchiston Hospital, Brookfield, Johnstone PA5 8TY — MB ChB 1985 Ed.; MRCGP 1989; MRCPsych 1993; DCCH RCP Ed. 1990. Cons. Psychiat.

MUIR, Jacqueline Elizabeth Combs Ford Surgery, Combs Lane, Stowmarket IP14 2SY Tel: 01449 678333 Fax: 01449 614535; Hawthorn Cottage, Green Road, Haughley, Stowmarket IP14 3RA Tel: 01449 774274 Email: jackieem.c@aol.com — MB ChB 1985 Ed.; MRCGP 1992; DRCOG 1991; DCCH RCP Ed. 1991. (Edinburgh) Prev: Trainee GP St. And.

MUIR, James Allan Howie The Surgery, 41-43 Great Peter Street, London SW1P 3LT Tel: 020 7222 1040 Fax: 020 7222 0520; 801 Hood House, Dophin Square, London SW1V 3NL Tel: 020 7828 3264 — MB ChB 1964 St. And.; MB ChB (Hons.) St. And. 1964; LM Rotunda 1966; AFOM RCP Lond. 1972 MFOM 1975. (St. And.) Primary Healthcare Phys. Chelsea & W.m. Hosp. Lond.; Med. Adviser Kala Ltd., Chem. Industries Assn., Environm. Agency, Monsanto plc; Water Auth. Assn., Bank of Boston & Various Other Companies; Hon. Staff Cromwell Hosp. & Lister Hosp. Socs: BMA; Roy. Soc. Med. Prev: Regist. (Gyn.) & Ho. Off. (Phys.) Profess. Univ. St. And.; Clin. Asst. (Surg.) St. Thos. Hosp. Lond.

MUIR, James Guthrie 201 Newton Drive, Blackpool FY3 8NU Tel: 01253 32471 — MB ChB 1942 Glas. (Glas.)

MUIR, James Morton, DSO, OBE (retired) 1 Queens Lane, Eynsham, Witney OX29 4HL — MB ChB 1939 Ed.; MFOM RCP Lond. 1978; MRCGP 1953; DIH Eng. 1949. Prev: Chief Med. Off. BL Cars Ltd.

MUIR, Mr James Nicholas The Links Medical Practice, 27 Brook Lane, Bromley BR1 4PX Tel: 020 8461 3333 Fax: 020 8695 5567; Gerizim, 7 Oak Tree Gardens, Bromley BR1 5BQ Tel: 0208 461 3333 Email: jmuir@doctors.org.uk — MB BS 1986 Lond.; FRCS Ed. 1991; MRCGP 1998. (King's College Hospital) Princip. of The Links Med. Pract.; Clin. Asst. in Dermatological Surg., Orpington Hosp. Socs: Christians in Caring Professions.

MUKERJEA

MUIR, Jean (retired) 5 Hill Park, Inverness IV2 4AL Tel: 01463 230264 Email: muirbield@ouvip.com — MB ChB Glas. 1961. Prev: Med. Asst. (Path.) S.. Highland (Inverness) Health Dist.

MUIR, John Robert Flat 1, 21 Devonshire Place, London W1G 6HZ Tel: 020 7486 8738 Fax: 020 7580 9988 — BM BCh 1961 Oxf.; DM Oxf. 1969; FRCP Lond. 1975, M 1963. (Middlx.) Socs: Brit. Cardiac Soc.; Assn. Phys. Prev: Prof. Cardiol. Welsh Nat. Sch. Med.; Sen. Regist. Nat. Heart Hosp. Lond.; US PHS Research Fell. Dept. Biochem. St. Louis Univ. Missouri, USA.

MUIR, John William The Surgery, Eleanor Close, Woburn, Milton Keynes MK17 9QU Tel: 01525 290214 Fax: 01525 290197; Segenhoe Cottages, Ridgmont, Bedford MK43 0XW Tel: 01525 280788 Email: drjohnmuir@compuserve.com — MB BS 1973 Lond.; MD Lond. 1980; MRCP (UK) 1976; MRCS Eng. LRCP Lond. 1973; MRCGP 1984; FRCP Lond. 1997; FRCGP 1998. (St. Bart.) Socs: BMA. Prev: Med. Co-ordinator Ox-Check Trial; Sen. Research Fell. ICRF Gen. Pract. Research Gps. (Pub. Health & Primary Care) Univ. Oxf.; Lect. (Med.) Radcliffe Infirm. Oxf. 1985.

MUIR, Julian Main Hamilton 1A Cadogan Street, London SW3 2PP Tel: 020 7589 9966 — MB BS 1971 Lond.; MRCS Eng. LRCP Lond. 1971.

MUIR, Keith William Department of Neurology, Insititute of Neurological Sciences, Southern General Hospital, Glasgow G51 4TF Tel: 0141 201 1100 Fax: 0141 201 2993 Email: k.muir@clinmed.gla.ac.uk; 58 Dowanside Road, Dowanhill, Glasgow G12 9DL — MB ChB 1989 Aberd.; MSc (Med. Sci.) Glas. 1994; MRCP (UK) 1992; MD 1997. (Aberdeen) Cons. (Neurol.) S.. Gen. Hosp. Glas.; Hon. Clin. Teach. Univ. of Glas. Prev: Regist. (Neurol.) S.. Gen. Hosp. Glas.; Clin. Research Fell. Gtr. Glas. HB.

MUIR, Mr Lindsay Thomas Stewart Walker Hope Hospital, Stott Lane, Salford M6 8HD — MB ChB 1981 Glas.; MChOrth Liverp. 1990; FRCS (Orth.) 1994; FRCS Glas. 1987. (Univ. Glas.) Cons. Orthop. Surg. (Upper Limb & Trauma) Hope Hosp. Salford.

MUIR, Marjorie Gray 30 Heather Avenue, Bearsden, Glasgow G61 3JE — MB ChB 1994 Aberd. SHO (Anaesth.) Roy. Alexandra Infirm. Paisley.

MUIR, Mary Scott Royal Cornhill Hospital, Clerkseat Building, 26 Cornhill Road, Aberdeen AB25 2ZH Tel: 01224 557598 — MB ChB 1978 Aberd. Cons. Psychiat.

MUIR, Robert Flynn 27 Springbank Road, Ayr KA8 9BP — MB ChB 1993 Aberd.

MUIR, Robert Francis Lodge Surgery, Lodge Road, Chippenham SN15 3SY Tel: 01249 660667 Fax: 01249 447350; Charlbrook, Bremhill, Calne SN11 9HN — MB BS 1976 Lond.; MRCGP 1986; MRCPsych 1982. (St. Bart.) Prev: Dep. Police Surg. Chippenham; Sen. Regist. (Child Adolesc. Psychiat.) BoroCt. Hosp. Reading; SHO Regist. Rotat. (Psychiat.) Oxf.

MUIR, Ruth Margaret Charlotte Keel Health Center, Seymour Road, Easton, Bristol BS5 0UA Tel: 0117 951 2244; 10 Henleaze Road, Henleaze, Bristol BS9 4EX Tel: 0117 962 9761 — MB ChB 1984 Bristol; DRCOG 1988; DFFP 1997. (Bristol) p/t Three quarter time GP Partner. Prev: Trainee GP E.on; SHO (O & G & A & E) S.mead Hosp.

***MUIR, Scott William** 21 Caledonia Road, Shotts ML7 4DU — MB ChB 1998 Glas.; MB ChB Glas 1998.

MUIR, Victoria Robin-Jane Belgrave Medical Centre, 13 Pimlico Road, London SW1W 8NA Tel: 020 7730 5171 Fax: 020 7823 5062 Email: victoria.muir@gp-e87753.nhs.uk — MB BS 1975 Lond.; BSc (Hons. Physiol.) Lond. 1972; MRCP (UK) 1978; MRCGP 1982.

MUIR, Willa Jane Coronation Cottage, Stickleball Lane, Sticklynch, West Pennard, Glastonbury BA6 8NA — MB BS 1982 Lond.; MRCGP 1988; DRCOG 1987.

MUIR, William John The Surgery, John St., Bellshill ML4 1RJ Tel: 01698 747195 — MB ChB 1962 Glas. (Glas.)

MUIR, William Whitelaw (retired) Cornerstones, 97 Main St., Swannington, Coalville LE67 1AH Tel: 01530 812274 — LRCP LRCS Ed. LRFPS Glas. 1948.

MUIR-COCHRANE, Robin Richard Armley Ridge Road Surgery, 43 Armley Ridge Road, Leeds LS12 3NP Tel: 0113 263 8603 Fax: 0113 231 9839 — LRCPI & LM, LRSCI & LM 1957; LRCPI & LM, LRCSI & LM 1957; LM Rotunda 1959. (RCSI) Med. Ref. City of Leeds Corp.; Div. Surg. St. John's Ambul. Brig. Socs: BMA; Leeds &

W. Riding M-C Soc. Prev: Ho. Surg. & Ho. Phys. Roy. Gwent Hosp. Newport; Clin. Clerk Rotunda Hosp. Dub.

MUIR-TAYLOR, Douglas James The Shieling, 24 Spratt Hall Road, London E11 2RQ Tel: 020 8989 0585 Fax: 020 8518 8977; The Shieling, Spratt Hall Road, London E11 2RQ Tel: 020 8989 0585 — MB BS 1960 Lond.; MRCS Eng. LRCP Lond. 1960; DO Eng. 1964; FBOA Ed. 1954; MCOphth 1988. (King's Coll. Hosp.) Dir. Contact Lens Dept. Roy. Lond. Hosp.; Med. Off. Telephone Cables Co. Ltd. Dagenham; Mem. Amer. Soc. of Cateract & Refractive Surg.; Mem. Amer. Soc. Refractive & Corneal Surg. Prev: Med. Off. Outpats. Moorfields Eye Hosp. Lond.

MUIR-TAYLOR, Jane Helen The Shieling, 24 Spratt Hall Road, London E11 2RQ Tel: 020 8989 0585 Fax: 020 8518 8977; 15 Westminster Gardens, Chingford, London E4 6ER Tel: 020 8559 4410 — MB BS 1985 Lond.; BSc Lond. 1979. Socs: Fell. Roy. Soc. Med.

***MUIRCROFT, Wendy Margaret** 30 Herondale Crescent, Wollaston, Stourbridge DY8 3LH — MB ChB 1995 Glas.

MUIRHEAD, Mr Andrew Gordon The Ayr Hospital, Dalmellington Road, Ayr KA6 6DX Tel: 01292 610555; 33 Bellevue Road, Ayr KA7 2SA Tel: 01292 262110 — MB ChB 1977 Manch.; FRCS Ed. (Orth.) 1987; FRCS Eng. 1981; MRCP (UK) 1982. Cons. Orthop. Surg. Ayr Hosp.; Hon. Sen. Lect. Univ. Glas. Prev: Cons. Orthop. Surg. Ayr Co. Hosp.

MUIRHEAD, Christina Susan McClure The Ayrshire Hospice, 35 Racecourse Road, Ayr KA7 2TG Tel: 01292 269200; 33 Bellevue Road, Ayr KA7 2SA — MB ChB 1977 Glas.; MRCP (UK) 1981; MRCPath 1985. Dep. Dir. Ayrsh. Hospice. Prev: Sen. Regist. (Haemat.) W.. Infirm. Glas.

MUIRHEAD, David Gilbertson (retired) Rockhead Cottage, Latheronwheel, Caithness KW5 6DW — MB ChB Glas. 1957.

MUIRHEAD, Richard John Dept of anaesthesia, Rotherham district Hospital, Moongate Round, Rotherham S65 2UD Tel: 01709 304550 Email: rmuirhead@compuserve.com — MB BS 1977 Lond.; MSc York 1991; MRCS Eng. LRCP Lond. 1977; FFA RCS Eng. 1983; DA Eng. 1982. (Middlx.) Assoc. Specialist (Anaesth.) Rotherham Dist. Gen. Hosp. Socs: Soc. Computing & Tech. Anaesth. Prev: Regist. (Anaesth.) York Dist. Hosp.; Regist. (A & E) Centr. Middlx. Hosp. Lond.; Regist. (Anaesth.) Roy. Free Hosp. Lond.

MUIRHEAD, Russell Northgate Medical Centre, 10 Upper Northgate St., Chester CH1 4EE — MB ChB 1982 Glas.; DA (UK) 1986.

MUIRHEAD-ALLWOOD, Miss Sarah Kathryn (cons. rooms), 19 Wimpole St., London W1M 7AD Tel: 020 7935 8488 Fax: 020 7636 5758; 194 Wymering Mansions, Wymering Road, London W9 2NQ Tel: 020 7286 2822 — MB BS 1971 Lond.; BSc (Hons.) Lond. 1968; FRCS Eng. 1976; MRCS Eng. LRCP Lond. 1971. (St. Thos.) Cons. Orthop. Surg. The Whittington Hosp., Roy. Nat. Orthop. Hosp. Trust & St. Luke's Hosp. for the Clergy Lond.; Cons. Orthop. Surg. King Edwd. VII's Hosp. for Off. St. John & St. Eliz. Hosp.; Hon. Sen. Clin. Lect. Univ. Lond. Socs: Fell. BOA; Fell. Brit. Hip Soc.; Fell. Europ. Hip Soc. Prev: Sen. Regist. (Orthop.) W.m. & Univ. Coll. Hosps. Lond.; Sen. Regist. Roy. Nat. Orthop. Hosp.; Regist. (Orthop.) Char. Cross Hosp. Lond.

MUJAHED, Muhammed Azeemuddin Ann Burrow Thomas Health Centre, South William Street, Workington CA14 2ED Tel: 01900 603985 Fax: 01900 871131 — MB BS 1962 Karachi.

MUJEEB-UR-RAHMAN, Mr 25 Angram Close, Clifton, York YO30 5ZN — MB BS 1967 Karachi; FRCS Eng. 1975. Assoc. Specialist (Gen. Surg.) York Dist. Hosp. York. Prev: Cons. Gen. Surg. Kulsum Bai Valika Hosp. Karachi, Pakistan.

MUKADAM, Ghalib Amir 10 Woodhayes, Willow Grove, Chislehurst BR7 5EX — MB ChB 1993 Dundee.

MUKADAM, Hafiz 26 Jacklin Drive, Leicester LE4 7SU — MB ChB 1993 Leeds.

MUKEMBO, Shadrach Mukwana 35 Mossdale Drive, Rainhill, Prescot L35 4NF — MB ChB 1973 Makerere; MRCOG 1982; Dip Ven 1990. (Makerere Univ. Kampala) Regist. (O & G) Whiston Hosp. Liverp.; Staff Grade GUM Roy. Liverp. Hosp.

MUKERJEA, Mr Shyamal Kumar Scunthorpe General Hospital, Cliff Gardens, Scunthorpe DN15 7BH Tel: 01724 282282 — MB BS 1960 Calcutta; FRCS Ed. 1971. (R.G. Kar Med. Coll.) Cons. Orthop. & Trauma Surg. Scunthorpe Gen. Hosp. Socs: Fell. Europ. Hip Soc.; Fell. Roy. Soc. Med.; Brit. Orthop. Assn. Prev: Sen. Regist. (Rheum.)

MUKERJEE

Stoke Mandeville Hosp. Aylesbury; Regist. (Orthop.) Mt. Gould Hosp. Plymouth & Char. Cross Hosp. Fulham.

MUKERJEE, Kamala The Surgery, 141 Leybridge Court, Eltham Road, London SE12 8TL Tel: 020 8852 5158 — MB BS 1956 Calcutta.

MUKERJI, Mr Arun Kumar 143 Lexden Road, Colchester CO3 3RN — MB BS 1971 Jammu & Kashmir; BSc, MB BS Jammu & Kashmir 1971; FRCS Ed. 1980. (Govt. Med. Coll. Srinagar) SHO (A & E) Basildon Hosp.

MUKERJI, Baman Das, TD (retired) 25 Sandhills Road, Barnt Green, Birmingham B45 8NP Tel: 0121 447 7207 — MB BS 1957 Calcutta; BSc Allahabad 1951; FRCS Eng. 1971; DA Eng. 1964. Prev: Cons. Anaesth. BromsGr. & Redditch Health Dist.

MUKERJI, Dev Mill Farm, Westerfield, Ipswich IP6 9AA Tel: 01473 257011 Fax: 01473 211376 Email: dev@muker.demon.co.uk — MB BS 1959 Calcutta. (Nat. Med. Coll.) Dermat. Hosp. Practitioner Ipswich Hosp. Socs: BMA. Prev: Regist. Accid. Unit Ipswich & E. Suff. Hosp.; SHO (Gen. Surg.) Macclesfield Hosp.; SHO Orthop. Dept. Preston Roy. Infirm.

MUKERJI, Shyamoli 143 Lexden Road, Colchester CO3 3RN Tel: 01206 43039; No. 2 Motilal Nehru Road, Calcutta 700029, India Tel: 00913 346 2223 — MB BS 1972 Calcutta; FRCPCH; MRCP (UK) 1987; DCH RCP Lond. 1976. Cons. Paediat. Colchester. Socs: Indian Paediat. Assn.

MUKHERJEE, A Central Park Medical Centre, 132-134 Liscard Road, Wallasey CH44 0AB Tel: 0151 638 8833 Fax: 0151 637 0208.

MUKHERJEE, Ajit Kumar (retired) 2 The Paddock, Sudbrooke, Lincoln LN2 2QS Tel: 01522 752402 — MB BS 1957 Calcutta; DO Eng. 1961. Prev: Assoc. Specialist in Ophth.

MUKHERJEE, Anandamoy Wigan Road Medicentre, 185 Wigan Road, Ashton-in-Makerfield, Wigan WN4 9SL Tel: 01942 726325 Fax: 01942 272137; 6 Houghwood Grange, Ashton-in-Makerfield, Wigan WN4 9LT — MB BS 1966 Calcutta; BSc Calcutta 1959; DA Delhi 1968. (R.G. Kar Med. Coll. Calcutta)

MUKHERJEE, Annice Lewisham Hospital, High St., Lewisham, London SE13 6LH; 3 Klea Avenue, London SW4 9HG — MB ChB 1992 Manch.; MRCP (UK) 1995. Regist. (Gen. Med.) Margate Hosp. Kent. Prev: Regist. (Gen. Med.) King's Hosp. Lond.

MUKHERJEE, Aradhana The Surgery, Groom Road, Turnford, Broxbourne EN10 6BW Tel: 01992 444203.

MUKHERJEE, Mr Baidya Nath (retired) Cann Hall Road Surgery, 135 Cann Hall Road, Leytonstone, London E11 3NJ Tel: 020 8534 1882 Fax: 020 8555 7109 — MRCS Eng. LRCP Lond. 1976; BSc Calcutta 1949, MB BS 1958; FRCS Ed. 1966. Redbridge & Waltham Forest, City & E. Lond. FPC. Prev: Regist. (Surg.) Wanstead Hosp. Lond.

MUKHERJEE, Chinmoyee Bastwell House, 89 Whalley New Road, Blackburn BB1 6LA Tel: 01254 56500 — MB BS 1960 Calcutta; BSc Calcutta 1954, MB BS 1960; DA Calcutta 1964. (Nilratan Sircar Med. Coll.)

MUKHERJEE, Debesh Princess Margaret Hospital, Okus Road, Swindon SN1 4JU Tel: 01793 536231 Fax: 01793 425113 Email: debeshmukherjee@yahoo.com; 3 The Whiteway, Cirencester GL7 2ER Tel: 01285 643220 — MB BS 1984 Lond.; MRCP (UK) 1988; FRCP Lond. 1999. Cons. Phys. (Geriat. & Gen. Med.) Swindon & MarlBoro. NHS Trust; Clin. Dir. Dept. of Med. for the Elderly & Rehabil. Socs: Brit. Geriat. Soc.; Fell. Roy. Coll. Phys. Lond.; Pk.insons Dis. Soc. Prev: Sen. Regist. Rotat. (Geriat. Med.) SW Thames; Lect. (Geriat. Med.) St. Geo. Hosp. Lond.; Regist. Rotat. Leciester Roy. Infirm.

MUKHERJEE, Dipak Kumar 99 Delaunays Road, Manchester M8 4RE — MB BS 1987 Magadh; MRCP (UK) 1994.

MUKHERJEE, Dipankar 87 Albert Road W., Bolton BL1 5ED — MB BS 1973 Gauhati; DCH RCP Lond. 1983; DCCH RCP Ed. 1983. Socs: Fac. Community Health.

MUKHERJEE, Emma Finchley Road Surgery, 999 Finchley Road, London NW11 7HB Tel: 020 8458 5708; 47 Ludlow Way, London N2 0JZ Tel: 020 8883 2409 — MB BS 1953 Calcutta; BSc Calcutta 1947, MB BS 1953; FRCR 1969; FFR 1966; DMRT Eng. 1959; DGO Calcutta 1956. (Calcutta Med. Coll.) Socs: Brit. Inst. Radiol.; BMA. Prev: Regist. Roy. Marsden Hosp. Lond.; Research Asst. & Sen. Regist. Guy's Hosp. Lond.; Asst. Prof. Radiother. Calcutta Med. Coll., India.

***MUKHERJEE, Jayanta** 18 Mount Drive, North Harrow, Harrow HA2 7RP — MB ChB 1995 Bristol.

MUKHERJEE, Kirtida Department of Anaesthesia, Medway Maritime Hospital, Windmill Rd, Gillingham ME7 Tel: 01634 830000 (Hosp.), 01634 833722 (Sec.); Email: kirtimuk@hotmail.com — LRCP (Edin.) LRCS (Edin.) LRCRS (Glas.) 1994; 1998 FRCA; 1998 FFA RCSI; MBBS 1981 Calcutta Univ. India. (Med. Coll. Hosps. Calcutta, India) Cons. Anaesth., Medway Maritime Hosp., Gillingham, Kent, BUPA Alexandra Hosp. Chatham, Kent. Socs: Assn. of Anaesthetics of Gt. Britain and Irel.; Obst. Anaesth.s Assn.; Amer. Assn. of Anaesthesiologists. Prev: Specialist Regist. in Anaesthetics, S. W.. Deanery, Plymouth Sch. of Anaesth., 1997-2001.

***MUKHERJEE, Mousumi Rumpa** 39 Meadowburn, Bishopbriggs, Glasgow G64 3HA — MB ChB 1998 Glas.; MB ChB Glas 1998.

MUKHERJEE, Raja Anindya Sekhar Department of Pychiatry of Disability, St. Georges Hospital Medical School, Tooting, London SW17 0RE — MB BS 1996 Lond.; MRCPoych 2001. (St George's Hosp. Med. Sch.) Specialist Regist. Learing Disabil. Psychiaty, St. Geo.s Hosp. Med. Sch. Socs: MDU; BMA; Mem. Nat. Jun. Doctor Committiee. Prev: SHO (Psych Old Age) Epson; SHO (Psych Gen. Adult) Epson; SHO (Psych Gen. Adult Pychoth) Epson.

MUKHERJEE, Mr Ranjit Kumar 38 East End Road, London N3 3QU — MB BS 1959 Calcutta; MSc (Physiol.) Calcutta 1955, MB BS 1959; FRCS Ed. 1970; T(S) 1991. (Calcutta Med. Coll.) Cons. i/c Accid. Dept. & Cons. Surg. (Orthop. Div.) Vict. Hosp. Kirkaldy. Socs: Fell. Brit. Orthop. Assn.

***MUKHERJEE, Rono** Level 10, Professional Surgical Unit, Western Infirmary, Glasgow G11 6NT; 41 2/2 Caird Dr, Glasgow G11 5DX Tel: 0141 334 1333 — MB ChB 1997 Glas.; BSc (Hons.) (Experim. Path.) 1994.

MUKHERJEE, S K Central Park Medical Centre, 132-134 Liscard Road, Wallasey CH44 0AB Tel: 0151 638 8833 Fax: 0151 637 0208.

MUKHERJEE, Mr Sadhan Kumar Glasgow Nuffield Hospital, 25 Beaconsfield Road, Glasgow G12 0PJ Tel: 0141 334 9441 Fax: 0141 339 1352; 27 Myrtle Avenue, Lenzie, Glasgow G66 4HW Tel: 0141 776 1732 Fax: 0141 339 1352 Email: mayandboo@aol.com — MB BS Calcutta 1957; FRCS Eng. 1966; FRCS Glas. 1989; FICS 1995. (Calcutta) Cons. Orthop. Surg. Glas. Nuffield Hosp. & Ross Hall Hosp. Glas.; Hon. Clin. Sen. Lect. Univ. Glas.; Hon. Orthop. Surg. Hamilton Acc. Football Club. Socs: Fell. BOA & Brit. Assn. Trauma in Sports; Fell. Europ. Soc. Knee Surg. Arthroscopy; Internat. Federat. Sports Med. Prev: Cons. Orthop. Surg. Monklands Dist. Gen. Hosp. Airdrie; Hon. Clin. Sen. Lect. Univ. Glas.; Cons. Orthop. Surg. Peel Hosp. Galashiels.

MUKHERJEE, Samar Newtown Health Centre, 171 Melbourne Avenue, Newtown, Birmingham B19 2JA Tel: 0121 554 7541 Fax: 0121 515 4447; 94 Handsworth Wood Road, Handworth Wood, Birmingham B20 2PN Tel: 0121 551 1586 Email: samarmuk@aol.com — MB BS 1981 Calcutta; LRCP LRCS Ed. LRCPS Glas. 1984; MRCGP 1988. Hon. Clin. Lect. Univ. Birm. Med. Sch.

MUKHERJEE, Sarbani Royal Albert Edward Infirmary, Wigan Lane, Wigan WN1 2NN Tel: 01942 44000; 6 Houghwood Grange, Ashton in Makerfield, Wigan WN4 9LT Tel: 01942 715078 — MB BS 1973 Calcutta; FRCR 1979; DMRD Eng. 1976. (Nilratan Sarkar Med. Coll.) Cons. Radiol. N. W.. RHA. Prev: Sen. Regist. (Radiol.) Manch. & Salford AHAs (T); Trainee Regist. (Radiol.) Manch. Roy. Infirm.

MUKHERJEE, Satya Prokash Pallion Health Centre, Hylton Road, Sunderland SR4 7XF Tel: 0191 657 1319 — MB BS 1959 Calcutta. (Calcutta) GP Sunderland.

***MUKHERJEE, Shraeosee** 86 Inveroran Drive, Bearsden, Glasgow G61 2AT — MB ChB 1994 Glas.

MUKHERJEE, Sisir Kumar Bastwell House, 89 Whalley New Road, Blackburn BB1 6LA Tel: 01254 56500 — MB BS 1960 Calcutta; MRCP (UK) 1972. (Calcutta Med. Coll.)

MUKHERJEE, Sonali 57 Avondale Gardens, Hounslow TW4 5EU — MB BS 1994 Lond.

MUKHERJEE, Subir Kumar Queen Elizabeth The Queen Mother Hospital, St. Peter's Road, Margate CT9 4AN Tel: 01843 225544 Fax: 01843 220048 — MB BS 1981 Calcutta; FRCP 2001; MD Calcutta 1988; MRCP (UK) 1992; DGM RCPS Glas. 1992. (Medical College Hospital, Calcutta) Cons. Phys. Qu. Eliz. the Qu. Mother

Hosp. Margate. Socs: Brit. Thorac. Soc.; Brit. Geriat. Soc.; Amer. Gastroenterological Assn. Prev: Hon. Sen. Regist. & Sen. Clin. Fell. Addenbrooke's Hosp. Camb.; Regist. (Gen. Med.) W. Midl. RHA.

MUKHERJEE, Sulekha 38 East End Road, Finchley, London N3 3QU Tel: 020 8346 1490 — MB BS 1959 Calcutta; DA Eng. 1967. (Calcutta Med. Coll.) Cons. Anaesth. (long term locum) Roy. Free Hosp. Lond. Prev: Cons. Anaesth. Barrow-in-Furness; Regist. Roy. Albert Edwd. Infirm. Wigan; SHO (Surg.) Gen. Hosp. Middlesbrough.

MUKHERJEE, Sumitra Kumar Davenport Surgery, 200 Buxton Road, Stockport SK2 7AE Tel: 0161 483 8833 Fax: 0161 456 5444 — MB BS 1965 Calcutta; DCH RCPS Glas. 1974. (Calcutta Nat. Med. Coll.) GP Davenport. Prev: Regist. (Paediat.) Birch Hill Hosp. Rochdale.

MUKHERJEE, Sunil Kumar Department of Health Care of the Elderly, City Hospital, Hucknall Road, Nottingham NG5 1PD Tel: 0115 969 1169 — MB BS 1959 Calcutta; FRCP Lond. 1985, M 1967; FRCP Ed. 1984, M 1967. (RG Kar Med. Coll.) Cons. Phys. (Gen. Med. with interest in healthc/o the elderly) Nottm. Socs: BMA. Prev: Sen. Regist. (Geriat. Med.) Crumpsall Hosp. Manch.; SHO & Regist. (Med.) Newsham Gen. Hosp. Liverp.

MUKHERJEE, Swapan Muiredge Surgery, Merlin Crescent, Buckhaven, Leven KY8 1HJ Tel: 01592 713299 Fax: 01592 715728 — MB BS 1980 Calcutta; LRCP LRCS Ed. LRCPS Glas. 1983; DRCOG 1985.

MUKHERJEE, Swarnali 15 Somerby Drive, Solihull B91 3YY — MB BS 1994 Lond.; DRCOG Lond. 1996; DCH Lond. 1998. (United Medical and Dental Schools of Guy's & Thomas's Hosp.)

MUKHERJEE, Tapati 31 School Lane, Silk Willoughby, Sleaford NG34 8PG — MB BS 1979 Calcutta; MRCPsych 1986.

MUKHERJEE, Vaskar Flat 32, Tealby Court, Wilbraham Road, Manchester M21 0XB — MB ChB 1982 Manch.

MUKHERJI, Chandra Shekhar 2 Elysium Terrace, Kingsthorpe Road, Northampton NN2 6EN — MB BS 1982 Poona; MRCPsych 1986; DHMSA 1985; DNB 1986. Cons. Psychiat. S.end HA; Vis. Cons. Psychiat. Hayes Gr. Priory Hosp.

MUKHERJI, Dibya Jyoti Glenross, 10 Whalley Road, Wilpshire, Blackburn BB1 9PJ — MB BS Patna 1953.

MUKHERJI, Dilip Kumar (retired) Bury General Hospital, Walmersley Road, Bury BL9 6PG Tel: 0161 764 6081 — MB BS Calcutta 1955; FFA RCS Eng. 1966; DA Eng. 1956. Cons. Anaesth. Bury Gen. Hosp. Prev: Cons. Anaesth. Bolton Gp. Hosps.

MUKHERJI, Melanie Jayne Lovat Cottage, Endmoor, Kendal LA8 0UE — MB ChB 1986 Ed.

MUKHERJI, Purnendu Samaddar 66 Pentland Terrace, Braids, Edinburgh EH10 6HE Tel: 0131 445 5668 Fax: 0131 445 5668 Email: p.s.mukherji@btinternet.com — MB BS 1951 Calcutta; FRCP Ed. 1977, M 1957; MFHom 1993; FRCGP 1978, M 1969; DCH Eng. 1956. (R.G. Kar Med. Coll.) Indep. Pract. Homoeop., Allergy & Acupunc. Edin. Socs: BMAS; BMA; Fac. Homoeop. Prev: Lect. (Gen. Pract.) Edin. Univ.; PMO Jokai Centr. Hosp. Panitola, India; Assoc. Prof. Paediat. All India Inst. Hyg. & Pub. Health Calcutta.

MUKHERJI, Mr Santanu The Health Centre, Bartholomew Road, Goole DN14 6AW Tel: 01405 767711; 42 Woodland Avenue, Goole DN14 6QT — MB BS 1956 Calcutta; FRCS Eng. 1968; FRCS Ed. 1968. (N.R. Sircar Med. Coll.) Prev: Regist. (Surg.) Hull Roy. Infirm.

MUKHOPADHYAY, Mr Arun Kumar 12 Heol Iscoed, Efail Isaf, Pontypridd CF38 1BP — MSc (Community Med.) Manch. 1988; PhD Patna 1973, MS 1962; MB BS Calcutta 1958; FRCOG 1977; FFPHM 1996. (R.G. Kar Med. Coll. Calcutta) Cons. Bro Taf Health Auth. Temple of Peace Cardiff; Sen. Clin. Med. Off. Dept. Family Plann. & Community Health Staffs. AHA. Prev: Assoc. Prof. Dept. O & G P. of Wales Med. Coll. Patna, India.

MUKHOPADHYAY, Dipendra Nath Aarogya Medical Centre, 270-274 West Green Road, Tottenham, London N15 3QR Tel: 020 8365 7282 Fax: 020 8374 7770 — MB BS 1970 Calcutta; BSc 1965 Calcutta; DGO Galway 1972. Gen. Practitioner; Clin. Asst. (Subst. Misuse) St. Thos. Hosp. & DASH at St. Ann's Hosp. Lond. Socs: Med. Protec. Soc.

***MUKHOPADHYAY, Nandini** 20 Lathkill Cl, Enfield EN1 1HA — MB BS 1997 Lond.

MUKHOPADHYAY, Mr Partha Sarathi 20 West Cliffe Gardens, Appleton, Warrington WA4 5FQ — MB BS 1977 Calcutta; FRCS Ed.

1991; LMSSA Lond. 1989; Dip Urol.1998. Staff Grade Surg. (Gen. Surg.) Halton Gen. Hosp. Runcorn. Prev: Regist. (Gen. Surg.) Tameside Gen. Hosp. Ashton u. Lyne.

MUKHOPADHYAY, Sambit 7 Earlswood Drive, Mickleover, Derby DE3 5LN — MB BS 1987 Calcutta; MRCOG 1994.

MUKHOPADHYAY, Tapan Kumar The Surgery, Sough Hall Road, Thorpe Hesley, Rotherham S61 2QP — MB BS 1968 Calcutta.

MUKHOPADHYAY, Tapan Kumar 7 Beckford Close, Barrows Green, Crewe CW1 3PT — MB BS 1974 Calcutta.

MUKHOPADHYAY, Tilottama Kettering General Hospital NHS Trust, Rothwell Road, Kettering NN16 8UZ Tel: 01536 492000; Little Acre, 6 Cross Lane, Aldwincle, Kettering NN14 3EG — MB BS 1972 Calcutta; MD Calcutta 1977; MRCP (Paediat.) (UK) 1984. Cons. Paediat. Kettering Gen. Hosp. NHS Trust. Socs: Brit. Paediat. Assn.

MUKHOPADHYAYA, Pranab Kumar (retired) The Park Surgery, 60 Ilkeston Road, Heanor DE75 7DX Tel: 01773 531011 — MB BS 1960 Calcutta; BSc Calcutta 1954; FRCOG 1987, M 1966; DGO 1962. Hosp. Pract. (Obst. & Gyn.) Kilton & Vict. Hosps. Worksop. Prev: Regist. (O & G) Kilton & Vict. Hosps. Worksop.

MUKOYOGO, Mr James Muganyizi Kidderminster HC NHS Trust, Bewdley Road, Kidderminster DY11 6RJ Tel: 01562 823424 Fax: 01562 887304; 51 Middlefield Lane, Hagley, Stourbridge DY9 0PY Tel: 01562 884864 Fax: 01562 887304 — MB ChB 1972 Makerere; FRCS Glas. 1986; MFFP 1993; MRCOG 1982, D 1980; FRCOG 1996. (Makerere Med. Sch. Kampala) Cons. O & G Kidderminster HC NHS Trust; Cons. O & G Worcs. Acute Hosp.s NHS Trust Worcester. Socs: BMA; Brit. Fertil. Soc.; EAGO. Prev: Sen. Regist. Rotat. W. Midl.; Regist. (O & G) Qu. Eliz. Matern. Hosp., Midl. Hosp. for Wom. & Dudley Rd. Hosp. Birm.

MULATERO, Clive Warren Far Horizon, West Ashling Road, Hambrook, Chichester PO18 8UF — MB BChir 1993 Camb.; MRCP (UK) 1995. (Camb.) Specialist Regist. (Med. Oncol.) St. Bart. Hosp. Lond.

MULCAHY, Alastair James Basement Flat, 5 Barclay Road, London SW6 1EJ Email: ajmulcahy@hotmail.com; 22 Withdean Road, Brighton BN1 5BL Tel: 01956 268480 — MB BS 1990 Lond.; FRCA 1995; Dip. IMC Ed. 1997; DA (UK) 1992. (St Georges Hospital London) Specialist Regist. (Anaesth.) Roy. Lond. Hosp.; Hon. Specialist Regist. (Anaesth.) Roy. Lond. Hosp. Socs: BMA; Brit. Assn. Immed. Care Schemes; Assn. Anaesth. Prev: Specialist Regist. Helicopter Emerg. Med. Serv. Lond.; SHO Rotat. (Anaesth.) St. Geo. Hosp. Lond., St. Helier Hosp. Carshalton & Qu. Mary's Hosp. Lond.; Lect. (Human Dis.) Univ. Lond. 1997-1998.

MULCAHY, Brian Dominic Department of Rheumatology, Whipps Cross Hospital, London E11 1NR — MB BCh BAO 1986 NUI.

MULCAHY, Edmond Francis (retired) Oaklea, Harborough Gorse, Harborough Hill, West Chiltington, Pulborough RH20 2RU Tel: 01798 812989 — MB BCh BAO NUI 1938. Prev: GP Guildford Surrey 1947-1982.

MULCAHY, Hugh Digestive Diseases Research Centre, St. Bartholomew's & Royal London School of Medicine, and Dentistry, Turner St., London E1 2AD Tel: 020 7295 7191 Fax: 020 7295 7192 Email: h.e.mulcahy@mds.qmw.ac.uk — MB BCh BAO 1987 NUI; MD Dub. 1994; MRCPI 1991; LRCPSI 1987. Hon. Sen. Regist. (Gastroenterol. & Gen. Med.) St. Bart. Hosp. Lond. Socs: Brit. Soc. Gastroenterol.; Irish Soc. Gastroenterol.

MULCAHY, Kevin Anthony 2A Southland Road, South Knighton, Leicester LE2 3RJ — BM BS 1986 Nottm.; BMedSci Nottm. 1984; FRCR 1995. Cons. Radiol. Leicester Gen. Hosp. Socs: Fell. Roy. Coll. Radiol.; Brit. Inst. Radiol.; BMA. Prev: Trainee Radiol. Leicester Train. Scheme; Regist. & SHO (Gen. Med.) P.ss Margt. Hosp. Swindon.

MULCAHY, Michael Padraig Edward Flat 705, Block 7, Friars Field, Royal Gwent Hospital, Newport NP20 4EZ — MB BCh BAO 1989 NUI.

MULCAHY, Patrick Declan Laurencekirk Medical Group, Blackiemuir Avenue, Laurencekirk AB30 1GX Tel: 01561 377258 Fax: 01561 378270 — MB BCh BAO 1984 NUI; MRCGP 1989; DObst RCPI 1988; DCH RCPSI 1987. Prev: Med. Off. Sacred Heart Mission Jamaica, W. Indies; Clin. Asst. Strathcarron Hosp. Denny, Stirlingsh.

MULCAHY, Patrick Desmond (retired) 15 Thorn Park, Mannamead, Plymouth PL3 4TG Tel: 01752 662525 Fax: 01752

MULCAHY

662921 — MB BChir 1957 Camb.; MA Camb. 1957, MD 1963; FRCP Lond. 1975, M 1958. Prev: Cons. Phys. Plymouth Health Dist.

*MULCAHY, Rachel Eileen 13 Durham Road, London SW20 0QH — MB ChB 1997 Bristol.

MULCAHY, Robin Philip Colm The Surgery, 35A High Street, Wimbledon, London SW19 5BY Tel: 020 8946 4820 Fax: 020 8944 9794; Tel: 020 8947 4323 — MB BS 1975 Lond.; MA Oxf. 1970; MB BS, LMSSA Lond. 1975; MRCGP 1979; DRCOG 1978. (St. Thomas') Med. Off. Kings Coll. Sch. Wimbledon.

MULCAHY, Timothy Marcus 26 Valentine Road, Birmingham B14 7AJ — MB ChB 1992 Birm.

*MULCHANDANI, Haresh 23 Hoylake Road, London W3 7NP — MB ChB 1997 Birm.

MULCOCK, Heidi 8 Grovelands Road, Teg Down, Winchester SO22 5JU — MB BS 1996 Lond.

*MULCRONE, Paul Simon Ground Floor Flat, 5 Fyffe St., Dundee DD1 5QN — MB ChB 1998 Dund.; MB ChB Dund 1998.

MULDER, F A Park Attwood Clinic, Trimpley, Bewdley DY12 1RE Tel: 01299 861444 Fax: 01299 861375 — Artsexamen 1984 Utrecht; Artsexamen 1984 Utrecht.

MULDER, Margriet The Calderdal Royal Hospital, Salterhebble, Halifax HX3 0PW Tel: 01270 874381, 01422 224077 — Artsexamen 1986 Free U Amsterdam. Staff Grade (Anaesth.) The Calderdale Roy. Hosp., Halifax. Prev: Regist. (Anaesth.) Univ. Hosp. Wales Cardiff; Regist. (Anaesth.) St. James Univ. Hosp. Leeds.

MULDOON, Christopher Gerald Great Stone Cottage, Great Stone, Cuddington, Aylesbury HP18 0AZ — MB ChB 1981 Glas.; MRCGP 1988.

MULDOON, Dominic Gerald 8 Whittingehame Drive, Glasgow G12 0XX Tel: 0141 339 7388 — LRCP LRCS 1950 Ed.; LRCP LRCS Ed. LRFPS Glas. 1950.

MULDOON, John Gerard (retired) Gortin, Omagh BT79 8NL Tel: 0166 264 8170 — LRCPI & LM, LRCSI & LM 1952.

MULDOON, Michael Joseph (retired) The Firs, Chuch Lane, Saltfleetby All Saints, Louth LN11 7TU Tel: 01507 338746 — MB ChB Glas. 1961; FRCOG 1981, M 1967. Prev: Cons. O & G Grimsby Gp. Hosps.

MULDOON, Owen Terence 123 Marlborough Park Central, Belfast BT9 6HP Tel: 01232 664987 — MB BCh BAO 1988 Belf.; FRCA 1994. Regist. (Anaesth.) Belf. City Hosp. Prev: Regist. (Anaesth.) Valley Hosp. Lisburn; SHO (Anaesth.) Belf. City Hosp. & Roy. Vict. Hosp. Belf.

MULDOON, Richard John (retired) 39 Ditton Reach, Thames Ditton KT7 0XB Tel: 020 8398 3357 — MB BCh BAO 1952 NUI; LM Nat. Matern. Hosp. Dub. 1954. Prev: Regist. (Surg.) Roscommon Co. Hosp.

MULENGA, Henry Proby Stokes 39 Hollymead Close, Colchester CO4 5JU Tel: 01206 845944 — MB ChB Zambia 1979; MRCP (UK) 1989; DCH RCP Lond. 1989.

MULES, Arthur Benjamin Stephen (retired) Matchbox, Freshwater East, Pembroke SA71 5LG — MRCS Eng. LRCP Lond. 1941. Prev: Med. Regist. Ashford Co. Hosp.

MULES, Frances Mary (retired) CromlixLodge, Summer Hill, Chislehurst BR7 5NZ Tel: 020 8325 5058 — MRCS Eng. LRCP Lond. 1951. Prev: Cas. Off. & Ho. Surg. Bromley Hosp.

MULES, Roger John (retired) Manaton Gate, Manaton, Newton Abbot TQ13 9UJ Tel: 01647 221352 — MB BS Lond. 1953. Prev: Affil. RCPsych.

MULFORD, Sheila Diane 27 Oak Place, Meir, Stoke-on-Trent ST3 5PN — BM 1982 Soton.; DRCOG 1990.

MULGIRIGAMA, Lokuhuruluge Douglas Mental Health Resource Centre, Clarendon House, 28 West St., Dorking RH4 1UJ Tel: 01306 502506 Fax: 01306 502608; 10 The Ridge, Purley CR8 3PE Tel: 020 8660 6228 Fax: 020 8296 8050 Email: douglas.mulgirigama@virgin.net — MB BS 1968 Sri Lanka; MRCPsych 1977; DPM ENG. 1975; FRCPsych 1999. Cons. Psychiat. Surrey Oaklands NHS Trust. Prev: Sen. Regist. Rotat. Qu. Mary's Hosp. Roehampton & Netherne Hosp.; Research Regist. St. Bart. Hosp. Lond; Ho. Off. (Psychiat.) Univ. Sri Lanka, Colombo.

*MULGREW, Christopher James 39 Butterfield Drive, Eaglescliffe, Stockton-on-Tees TS16 0EX — MB BS 1996 Lond.

MULGREW, John Anthony 46 Greystown Avenue, Upper Malone Road, Belfast BT9 6UL — MB BCh BAO 1988 Belf.

MULHALL, Margaret Mary The Green Surgery, 12 The Green, Irish Street, Downpatrick BT30 6BE — MB BCh BAO 1984 NUI; MRCGP 1988; DRCOG 1987. Socs: Downe Med. Soc.

MULHALL, Patrick Plunkett (retired) Ty-Usk, Llanspyddid, Brecon LD3 8PB — MB BCh BAO 1945 NUI; DCH RCPSI 1957; LM Coombe 1947. Cons. Chest Phys. Powys AHA. Prev: Jun. Specialist Med. RAMC.

MULHALL, Rosamund Mary Saintbridge Surgery, Askwith Road, Saintbridge, Gloucester GL4 4SH Tel: 01452 500252; Nut Cottage, Scar Hill, Box, Stroud GL6 9AH Tel: 01453 833781 — MB BCh 1978 Wales; MRCGP 1997. (Welsh National School Medicine) GP St.bridge Surg.; Clin. Asst. (Osteoporosis) Gloucester Roy. Hosp. Socs: Roy. Coll. Gen. Pract.; BMA. Prev: GP Newport Gwent.

MULHEARN, John Francis, TD Woodside Health Centre, Barr Street, Glasgow G20 7LR Tel: 0141 531 9521 Fax: 0141 531 9545; 27 Hillside Road, Glasgow G43 1DB Tel: 0141 649 5298 — MB ChB 1966 Glas.; LMCC 1969. (Toronto) Socs: BMA. Prev: Resid. (Surg.) S.. Gen. Hosp. Glas.; Resid. (Obst.) Ayrsh. Centr. Hosp. Irvine; Resid. (Med.) Ruchill Hosp. Glas.

*MULHEARN, Nicola Margaret 27 Hillside Road, Glasgow G43 1DB — MB ChB 1997 Glas.

MULHERN, Felix Joseph (retired) Erne Health Centre, Erne Hospital, Cornagrade Road, Enniskillen BT74 6AY Fax: 028 6632 8686 — MB BCh BAO 1969 NUI; BA NUI 1962, MB BCh BAO 1969.

*MULHERN, Michael Felix 27 Riverview Street, Belfast BT9 5FD — MB BCh BAO 1997 Belf.

MULHOLLAND, Adrian Oliver Newtownhamilton Health Centre, 2A Markethill Road, Newtownhamilton, Newry BT35 0BE Tel: 028 3087 8202/8223 Fax: 028 3087 9043; Sevaghan, 4 Ninemile Road, Newtownhamilton, Newry BT35 0HN — MB BCh BAO 1979 Belf.; MRCGP 1983; DRCOG 1983; DCH RCPSI 1981. Gen. Med. Servs. Adviser Newry & Mourne H & SS Trust.

MULHOLLAND, Bridget Moorfield Eye Hospital, City Road, London EC1V 2PD; 22B Islington Green, London N1 8DU — MB ChB 1988 Sheff.; FRCOphth. 1993. Regist. (Ophth.) Moorfields Eye Hosp. Lond. Socs: Fell. Roy. Soc. Med. Prev: SHO (Ophth.) W.. Ophth. Hosp. Lond.

MULHOLLAND, Bridget Anne 82 Ballronan Road, Magherafelt BT45 6EW — MB BCh BAO 1978 Belf.; MRCGP 1982.

MULHOLLAND, Mr Colin Kennedy 23 Alt-Min Avenue, Belfast BT8 6NJ — MB BCh BAO 1982 Belf.; FRCSI 1986.

MULHOLLAND, David Alan Altnagelvin Hospital, Londonderry BT47 6SB — MB BCh BAO 1989 Belf.; MRCP (UK) 1992; FRCOphth 1995. Cons. Opthalmologist, Altnagelvin Hosp. Lond.derry. Socs: BMA; Ulster Med. Soc.

MULHOLLAND, Gerald Vincent (retired) 25 Harbour View Road, Poole BH14 0PD Tel: 01202 737996 — MB BS 1949 Lond.; MRCS Eng. LRCP Lond. 1949; DA Sydney 1953. Prev: Regist. (Anaesth.) Chelmsford & Essex Hosp. & St. John's Hosp.

*MULHOLLAND, Gillian Margaret 14 Glen Falloch, St Leonards, East Kilbride, Glasgow G74 2JL — MB ChB 1994 Glas.

MULHOLLAND, Hugh Connor Royal Victoria Hospital, Grosvenor Road, Belfast BT12 6BA Tel: 01232 894703 Fax: 01232 31297; 31 Deramore Drive, Belfast BT9 5JR — MB BCh BAO 1962 Belf.; BSc Belf. 1959; FRCP Ed. 1979, M 1967. (Belf.) Cons. Paediat. Cardiol. Roy. Hosps. Trust N. Irel.; Assoc. Med. Director Roy. Hosps. Trust. Socs: Brit. Cardiac Soc. & Irish Cardiac Soc.; Coun. Mem. Brit. Paediatric Cardiol. Assn.; Assn. for Europ. Paediatric Oncol. Prev: Asst. Prof. Dept. Med. Christian Med. Coll. Ludhiana, India; Clin. Research Fell. Ont. Heart Foundat. Hosp. Sick Childr. Toronto, Canada.

MULHOLLAND, James Kieran 82 Ballyrowan Road, Magherafelt BT45 6EW — MB BCh BAO 1979 NUI.

MULHOLLAND, Joan Margaret (retired) 12 Parkside, Mill Hill, London NW7 2LH Tel: 020 8959 5483 — MB ChB 1950 Liverp.; MFCM 1972; DPH Lond. 1965; DCH Eng. 1955. Prev: SCM Barnet HA.

MULHOLLAND, John Edmund Terence (retired) 9 Killynure Wood, Enniskillen BT74 6FR Tel: 02866 329383 Email: terrymulholland@talk21.com — MB BCh BAO 1967 Belf.; Dobst RCOG 1970; FRCOG 1987, M 1974. Cons. O & G Erne Hosp. Enniskillen.

MULHOLLAND, K Elizabeth Hill View, 39 Private Road, Sherwood, Nottingham NG5 4DD Tel: 0115 960 8389 — MB BCh BAO 1956 NUI; LAH Dub. 1955; DA Eng. 1958. (Univ. Coll. Dub.)

MULHOLLAND, Kathleen Mary 1 Stonehouse Green, Clayton-Le-Woods, Chorley PR6 7JT — MB BCh BAO 1985 Belf.

***MULHOLLAND, Keith Charles** 8 The Willows, Bangor BT19 7XZ — MB BCh 1998 Belf.; MB BCh Belf 1998.

MULHOLLAND, Kieran Columba 61 South Parade, Ormeau Road, Belfast BT7 2GN — MB BCh BAO 1987 Belf.; MRCPsych 1993; DMH Belf. 1992.

MULHOLLAND, Margaret Ita 31 Greenwood Glen, Purdysburn Road, Belfast BT8 7WE — MB BCh BAO 1994 Belf.

MULHOLLAND, Margaret Letitia Elizabeth April Cottage, 24 Blackwood Crescent, Helens Bay, Bangor BT19 1TJ — MB BCh BAO Belf. 1969; DObst RCOG 1971. SCMO (Family Plann. & Colposcopy) N. & W. Community Trust. Socs: Ulster Obst. & Gyn. Soc.; Fac. Fam. Plann.; N. Irel. Family Plann. Doctors Assn.

MULHOLLAND, Michael George Hillsborough Health Centre, Ballynahinch Street, Hillsborough BT26 6AW Tel: 028 9268 2216 Fax: 028 9268 9721 — MB BCh BAO 1989 Belf.

MULHOLLAND, Michael Gerard Stewartstown Health Centre, 212 Stewartstown Road, Dunmurry, Belfast BT17 0FB Tel: 028 9060 2931 Fax: 028 9060 5728 — MB BCh BAO 1985 Belf.; MRCGP 1991; DRCOG 1991. (Qu. Univ. Belf.) Gen. Pract. Princip. Woodbrooke Med. Pract. Stewartstown Rd, Dunmurry BT17 0FB.

MULHOLLAND, Michael Nial Connor 5 Poplars Close, Stone, Aylesbury HP17 8PQ — MB ChB 1994 Bristol; BSc (Hons. Physiol.) Bristol 1991; DRCOG 1997. GP Regist. Thame Health Centre Oxf.

MULHOLLAND, Paul James 6 Fern Close, Coventry CV2 1LD — MB BS 1992 Lond.

***MULHOLLAND, Paula Karen** 40 Glendale, Belfast BT10 0NX — MB BCh BAO 1997 Belf.

MULHOLLAND, Professor Robert Charles (retired) 34 Regent Street, Nottingham NG1 5BT Tel: 0115 956 1303 Fax: 0151 956 1314 — MB BS 1957 Lond.; FRCS Eng. 1963; MRCS Eng. LRCP Lond. 1957; DObst RCOG 1959. Cons. Orthop. & Accid. Surg. Spinal Disorders Unit Nottm. Univ. Hosp. Prev: Sen. Regist. (Orthop.) Robt. Jones & Agnes Hunt Orthop. Hosp. OsW.ry.

MULHOLLAND, Seamus Niall Paul 39 Private Road, Sherwood, Nottingham NG5 4DD — MB ChB 1993 Birm.; DA 1996. (Birmingham) SHO (O & G/GPVTS) - Tebsko Hosp. - Truro. Prev: SHO (Med.) Wanganui Hosp., New Zealand; SHO (Anaesth. & A & E) Treliske Hosp., Truro.

MULIK, Roopa Baburao Paediatric Department, Heartlands Hospital, Birmingham B9 5SS Tel: 0121 424 2000 Fax: 0121 424 0827; 7 Alder Park Road, Solihull B91 1NU Tel: 0121 680 1420 Fax: 0121 680 1307 — MB BS 1979 Shivaji, India; FRCPCH 1996; MD (Paed.) Shivaji India 1982; MRCP (UK) 1986; DCH RCP Lond. 1985. (V.M. Med. Coll. Solapur, India) Cons. Paediat. Heartlands Solihull NHS Trust. Socs: BMA. Prev: Cons. Paediat. & Neonat. King Abdul Aziz Hosp. Jeddah, Saudi Arbaia.

MULINGA, John Dickson 28 Back Lane, Appleybridge, Wigan WN6 9LH; 28 Back Lane, Appleybridge, Wigan WN6 9LH — MB ChB 1984 Manch.

MULIRA, Mr Apollo John Enoch Lubambula Worcester Royal Infirmary, Ronkswood Branch, Worcester WR5 1HN Tel: 01905 763333 Fax: 01905 350922; 31 Ashleigh Road, Solihull B91 1AF Tel: 0121 704 4380 — MB BChir 1975 Camb.; FFAEM 1994; MA, MB Camb. 1975, BChir 1974; FRCS Eng. 1978. (St. George's Hospital, London) Cons. A & E Surg. Worcester Roy. Infirm. Socs: Brit. Assn. of Emerg. Med.; Founder Fell. of Fac. of Accid. & Emerg.; Brit. Med. Assn. Prev: Sen. Regist. (A & E Med.) W. Midl. RHA Rotat.; Regist. (Surg.) Worcester Roy. Infirm.; Ho. Surg. St. Geo. Hosp. Lond.

MULKERN, Edward Michael 8 Welland Road, Wittering, Peterborough PE8 6BN — BM BS 1991 Nottm.

MULKERN, Philip Dudley (retired) Briar Cottage, Horseman Side, Navestock, Brentwood CM14 5SS Tel: 01277 372564 — MRCS Eng. LRCP Lond. 1933.

MULKIS, Howard Brian Colney Hatch Lane Surgery, 192 Colney Hatch Lane, Muswell Hill, London N10 1ET Tel: 020 8883 5877/5555 — MB BS 1982 Lond.; Cert Family Planning 1986; DRCOG 1986; JJC 1986; DRCOG 1986; Cert. Family Plann. JCC 1986. (Lond.)

MULL, Ajaiya Anaesthetic Department, Royal Sussex County Hospital, Eastern Road, Brighton BN2 5BE — State Exam Med 1990 Frankfurt.

MULL, Parasmull Jaswant Southend Road Surgery, 271A Southend Road, Stanford-le-Hope SS17 8HD Tel: 01375 679316 Fax: 01375 679335 — MB BS 1959 Osmania; MRCP Glas. 1965; DCH Eng. 1962; DCH Osmania 1961. (Osmania Med. Coll. Hyderabad)

MULLA, Hilal Mohammed 4 Frenchwood Knoll, Frenchwood, Preston PR1 4LE — MB ChB 1991 Dundee.

MULLA, Mohammedmustafa Moulasaheb 26 Summer Fields, Abingdon OX14 2PG — MB BS 1971 Karnatak.

MULLA, Najeeba Abdulla Flat 22, 33 Prince Albert Road, London NW8 7LU — MRCS Eng. LRCP Lond. 1966.

MULLA, Simon Christopher 253 Leicester Road, Markfield, Leicester LE67 9RH — MRCS Eng. LRCP Lond. 1986. SHO (Anaesth.) P'boro. Dist. Gen. Hosp.

***MULLA, Zubair** 14 Eldon Street, Preston PR1 7YE — MB BS 1994 Lond.

MULLALLY, Brian 2 Malone Court Mews, Balmoral Avenue, Belfast BT9 6PQ — MD 1950 Belf.; MB BCh BAO 1945; FRCP Lond. 1972, M 1949; FRCPI 1979, M 1977. (Qu. Univ. Belf.) Clin. Lect. Qu. Univ. Belf.; Hon. Cons. Phys. Mater Infirm. Hosp. Belf. Prev: Ho. Phys. Connaught Hosp. Lond. Mater Infirm. Hosp. Belf. & WellHo. Hosp. Barnet.

MULLALLY, John Joseph Larkfield, Hillbrow, Bromley BR1 2PQ — MB BCh BAO 1945 NUI.

MULLAN, Bernard Alan 71 Killygullib Road, Maghera BT46 5QR — MB BCh BAO 1993 Belf.

***MULLAN, Carol Marie** 112 Kevlin Road, Omagh BT78 1PL — MB ChB 1998 Glas.; MB ChB Glas 1998.

***MULLAN, Charles Patrick** 71 Killygullib Road, Maghera BT46 5QR — MB BS 1998 Lond.; MB BS Lond 1998.

MULLAN, Ciaran Hugh 22 Pellipar Park, Dungiven, Londonderry BT47 4PB; Site 66, Sevenoaks, Crescent Link, Londonderry BT47 6BO Tel: 01504 329013 — MB BCh BAO 1997 Belf.

MULLAN, Dermot Patrick Old Manor House, Winterslow, Salisbury SP5 1RY Tel: 01980 862308 — MB 1957 Camb.; MA Camb. 1964, MB 1957, BChir 1956; FRCP Lond. 1977, M 1960. (Middlx.) Cons. Phys. Salisbury Hosp. Gp.; Hon. Clin. Teach. Soton. Univ. Med. Sch. Socs: Fell. Roy. Soc. Med. Prev: Sen. Med. Regist. & Med. Regist. Profess. Med. Unit Roy. Hosp. Sheff.; Ho. Phys. & Dep. Res. Med. Off. Middlx. Hosp. Lond.

MULLAN, Eleanor Mary Amyand House, Strafford Road, Twickenham TW1 3HQ Tel: 020 8744 9943 Fax: 020 8744 9945 — MB BCh BAO 1983 Dub.; MRCPsych 1988; MMsc Galway 1992. (Trinity College Dublin Ireland) Cons. (Old Age Psychiat.); Hon. Sen. Lect. UCL.

MULLAN, Mr Frederick John Tel: 02870 327032 Fax: 02870 346273 — MB BCh BAO 1982 Belf.; FRCS Ed. 1986. (Queens University Belfast) Cons. Surg. (Gen. Surg.) Causeway Trust Coleraine; Cons. Surg. (BrE. Clinic) Antrim Area Hosp.; Lead Clinician (Oncol.) Causeway Trust Coleraine. Socs: Fell.Assn. of Surg.s; Brit. Assn. Surg. Oncol.; Fell. Ulster Med. Soc. Prev: Sen. Regist. (Surg.) N.ern Irel. Rotat.; Research Fell. Ulster Hosp. Belf.

MULLAN, Helen Margaret Dept. GU Medicine, Watford General Hospital, Uicarace Road, Watford WD18 0HB Tel: 01923 217207; 1 Somerset Road, Harrow HA1 4NF Tel: 020 8863 4343 — MB BCh BAO 1985 NUI; DFFP 1997; Dip. GU Med. Soc. Apoth. Lond. 1993. (Univ. Coll. Dublin, Irel.) Staff Grade, Assoc. Specialist, (Genitourin. Med.) Watford. Socs: Full Mem. Med. Soc. Study VDs; Full Mem. Assn. Genitourin. Med.; Diplomate Fac. Family Plann.

***MULLAN, James Maurice** 305 Ballymoney Road, Ballymena BT43 5JE — MB BCh BAO 1997 Belf.

MULLAN, James Richard Aberfoyle Medical Practice, 120 Strand Road, Derry City, Londonderry BT48 7PB Tel: 01504 264868; 44 Prehen Road, Derry City, Londonderry BT47 2NS Tel: 01504 348121 — MB BCh BAO 1993 Belf.; DCH Dub. 1996; DRCOG 1996. (Qu. Univ. Belf.) GP Regist. Derry City. Socs: BMA. Prev: SHO Altnagelvin Area Hosp. Derry; Ho. Off. Mater Hosp. Belf.

***MULLAN, Karen Rotsin** 51 Glen Road, Garvagh, Coleraine BT51 5DD — BChir 1995 Camb.

MULLAN, Miss Michelle Helene Ballarye, off Ramsey Road, Laxey IM4 7PS Tel: 01624 862197 Fax: 01624 862013; 2 Elton

MULLAN

House, Rodney Place, Clifton, Bristol BS8 4HZ Tel: 0117 923 8691 Email: michelle@laxey.demon.co.uk — MB ChB 1995 Bristol; Mem. Royal College of Surgeons (MRCS) 1998. (Bristol)

*MULLAN, Robert Niall 71 Killygullib Road, Swatragh, Maghera BT46 5QR — MB BCh BAO 1995 Belf.

MULLAN, Roisin Philomena 28 Fairhill Grove, Cookstown BT80 8TG — MB BCh BAO 1980 Belf.

MULLANE, Deidre Mary 14 Victoria Court, Tower Court Mews, Westcliff on Sea SS0 7QJ — MB BCh BAO 1988 NUI.

MULLANE, Michelle Colette 86 Priory Road, Sutton SM3 8LN — MB BS 1994 Lond. (St. Geo. Hosp. Med. Sch.) SHO (Paediat.) Univ. Hosp. Wales Cardiff. Prev: SHO (Paediat.) N. Hants. Hosp.; SHO (A & E) N. Hants. Hosp.; Ho. Off. (Med.) Haywards Heath Hosp.

MULLARD, Mr Kenneth Stanley (retired) 2 Aynhoe Park, Aynho, Banbury OX17 3BQ Tel: 01869 811203 — MB BChir 1938 Camb.; MA Camb. 1938; FRCS Eng. (ad eund.) 1964; FRCS Ed. 1940; MRCS Eng. LRCP Lond. 1937. Prev: Cons. & Dir. Cardiothoracic Surg. Serv. Wessex RHB.

MULLEA, Mohinder Singh Health Centre, Flagg Court, South Shields NE33 2LS — MB BS 1965 Panjab; MB BS Panjab (India) 1965. (Glancy Med. Coll. Amritsar)

MULLEN, Charles Clarke Orchard House Health Centre, Union Street, Stirling FK8 1PH Tel: 01786 50394 Fax: 01786 448284; The Smiddy, 35 Birkhill Road, Cambusbarron, Stirling FK7 9LA — MB ChB 1978 Ed.; DRCOG 1983; MRCGP 1983. (Ed.) Club Med. Off. Alloa Athletic Football Club.

MULLEN, Daryl James The Surgery, The Green, Parbold, Wigan WN8 7DN Tel: 01257 463126 Fax: 01257 464021 Email: 101445.2153@compuserve.com — MB ChB 1988 Liverp.; MRCGP 1995; DCCH RCP Ed. 1994. (Liverp.) TA Capt. Socs: BMA. Prev: Trainee GP Wirral; SHO (Paediat.) Ormskirk Hosp.

*MULLEN, Donna Marie 86 Gorestown Road, Dungannon BT71 7EX — MB BCh 1998 Belf.; MB BCh Belf 1998.

MULLEN, Henry Andrew, TD 25 Brompton Drive, Pinkneys Green, Maidenhead SL6 6SP Tel: 01628 74137 — MB ChB 1935 Glas. (Univ. Glas.) Hon. Phys. to H.M. The Qu.; Col. RAMC, TA. Prev: Regional Med. Off. Welsh Office; ADMS 53(W) Inf. Div. TA.

MULLEN, Michael John Flat A, 49 Beresford, London N5 2HR — MB BS 1988 Newc.; MRCP (UK) 1992. Research Fell. (Cardiol.) Inst. Child Health Lond.

MULLEN, Nicholas Brian 45 Thrale Road, London SW16 — MB BCh BAO 1952 NUI. (Univ. Coll. Dub.)

MULLEN, Patrick Michael Fax: 0151 706 5646 Email: patrickmullen@csi.com; 43 Mount Road, West Kirby, Wirral CH48 2HH Tel: 0151 625 0820 Fax: 0151 625 4787 — MB BCh BAO 1985 Dub.; FFA RCSI 1994; DA (UK) 1993. (Dub.) Cons. (Anaesth. & Intens. Ther.) Roy. Liverp. Univ. Hosp. Prev: Sen. Regist. (Anaesth.) Mersey Region; Regist. Rotat. (Anaesth.) Mersey Regional Train. Scheme; SHO (Anaesth.) Qu. Med. Centre Nottm. & Worcester Roy. Infirm.

MULLEN, Paul Francis Penny Lane Surgery, 7 Smithdown Place, Liverpool L15 9EH Tel: 0151 733 2800 — MB ChB 1983 Liverp.

MULLEN, Peter John Philip c/o The Medical Specialist Group, PO Box 113, Alexandra House, Les Frieteaux, St Martin's, Guernsey GY1 3EX Tel: 01481 239914 Fax: 01481 237782; Chateau Lierre, Clos Des Isles, St. Sampson's, Guernsey GY2 4AP Tel: 01481 720256 Email: chateau@guernsey.net — MB ChB 1980 Liverp.; MRCP (UK) 1985; FRCP Wet 1999. Cons. Phys. (Gastroenterol.) Guernsey. Socs: Brit. Soc. Gastroenterol. Prev: Cons. Gen. Med. & Gastroenterol. TPMH Akrotiri; Cons. Gen. Med. & Gastroenterol. P.ss Mary's RAF Hosp. Halton Aylesbury.

MULLEN, Richard James 24 Lintwhite Court, Bridge of Weir PA11 3NW — MB BCh BAO 1987 NUI.

*MULLEN, Stephanie Marie 5 Carrick Strand, Bradley Way, Strabane BT82 9RN — MB BCh BAO 1996 Belf.

MULLENS, Edwina Lynette 2 Stratford Drive, Porthcawl CF36 3LG — MB BS 1987 Lond.

MULLER, Andrew Frank The Kent & Canterbury Hospital, Ethelbert Road, Canterbury CT1 3NG Tel: 01227 766877; Woodside, Nackington Road, Canterbury CT4 7AY — MB BS 1983 Lond.; DM Nottm. 1992; MRCP (UK) 1986; FRCP 1999. (St. Mary's) Cons. Phys. & Gastroenterol. Kent & Canterbury Hosp. Socs: Brit. Soc. Gastroenterol.; Amer. Gastroenterol. Assn. Prev: Sen. Regist. (Med.) Univ. & City Hosps. Nottm.; Regist. (Med.) Univ. Hosp. Nottm.; Clin. Research Fell. Univ. Hosp. Nottm.

MULLER, David John Rectory Farm House, Longstowe, Cambridge CB3 7UU — LMSSA 1950 Lond.; MA Camb. 1976; MA (Hons.) Oxf. 1947, BM BCh 1951; MRCPsych 1971; DPM Eng. 1960. (Oxf. & Guy's) Cons. Psychiat. Home Office; Mem. Ment. Health Review Tribunal. Socs: Past Pres. Camb. Med. Soc. Prev: Cons. Psychiat. Cambs. DHA.; Adviser HM Sec. of State (Scotl.) on Drug Addic.; Lect. Fac. of Med. Univ. of Camb.

MULLER, Elizabeth Jean Westgate Practice, Greenhill Health Centre, Church Street, Lichfield WS13 6JL Tel: 01543 414311 Fax: 01543 256364; 170 Main Street, Alrewas, Burton-on-Trent DE13 7ED Tel: 01283 790379 — MB ChB 1975 Cape Town; MRCGP 1990; Dip. Dermat. Wales 1994.

MULLER, Graham Stephen Ramsbury Surgery, High Street, Ramsbury, Marlborough SN8 2QT Tel: 01672 520366 Fax: 01672 520180; 6 Union Street, Ramsbury, Marlborough SN8 2PR — MB BCh 1988 Witwatersrand; MRCGP 1994. Clin. Asst. (Rheum.) P.ss Margt. Hosp. Swindon.

MULLER, Guy William 71B Holly Hill, Bassett, Southampton SO16 7ES Tel: 02380 760495 — MB ChB 1991 Leic. SHO (Gen. Surg.) Soton. Univ. Hosp. Socs: BMA. Prev: SHO (ENT Surg.) Qu. Alexandra Hosp. Portsmouth.

MULLER, Klaus Gottlob Section of Molecular & Paediatric Rheumatology Unit, Northwick Park Hospital, Watford Road, Harrow HA1 3UJ — MD 1984 Copenhagen.

MULLER, Margaret Anne Pud's Meadow, Marley Lane, Kingston, Canterbury CT4 6JH — MB ChB 1964 Ed.; MRCP (U.K.) 1970; DCH Eng. 1967.

MULLER, Mr Paul Wilhelm Stephen (retired) 4 Woodthorpe Gardens, Sandal Magna, Wakefield WF2 6RA — MB ChB 1961 Sheff.; FRCS Eng. 1968. Cons. Gen. Surg. Barnsley Dist. Gen. Hosp.

MULLER, Reinhold Karl Gerhard Ceredigion & Mid Wales NHS Trust, Bronglais Hospital, Caradoc Road, Aberystwyth SY23 1ER — State Exam Med 1990 Giessen.

MULLER, Salli 41 Cliffe Road, Birstall, Leicester LE4 3AE — MB BS 1978 Newc.; FRCPath 1995. Cons. Histopath. Leicester Roy. Infirm. & Glenfield Gen. Hosp. Leicester.

MULLER, Wolfgang Gerhard 14 Museum Mansions, 63A Great Russell St., London WC1B 3BJ Tel: 020 7405 0237 Fax: 020 7405 0237; Hillingdon Hospital, Pield Heath Road, Uxbridge UB8 3NN Tel: 01895 238232 Fax: 01895 279901 — State Exam Med. Saarland 1992; MRCP (UK) 1996. Specialist Regist. Paediat. Socs: RCPCH; RCP. Prev: Specialist Regist. Neonat. Hammersmith Hosp.; Specialist Regist. (Neonat. Neurol.) Hammersmith Hosp.

*MULLER-POLLARD, Christopher Sutherland 6 Trinity Street, London SE1 1DB — MB BS 1996 Lond.

MULLERAT, Jose 6 Blawith Road, Harrow HA1 1TN — LMS 1988 Barcelona; LMS Barcelona 1999. SHO (Gen. Surg.) Birm. Heartlands Hosp. Socs: BMA & Med. Protec. Soc. Prev: SHO (A & E) Birm. Heartlands Hosp.; SHO (Cardiothoracic Surg.) N.. Gen. Hosp. Sheff.; SHO (Orthop.) Airedale NHS Trust.

MULLETT, Helen Susan MTL Medical Services, 24 Hatton Gardens, Liverpool L3 2AN Tel: 0151 227 1875 Fax: 0151 236 5857; 9 Salisbury Park, Woolton, Liverpool L16 0JT Tel: 0151 722 1864 — MB ChB 1979 Liverp.; A.F.O.M. 1999. Occupat. Phys., MTL Med. Servs., Liverp.

MULLETT, Shaun Steven Penny Lane Surgery, 7 Smithdown Place, Liverpool L15 9EH Tel: 0151 733 2800; 9 Salisbury Park, Woolton Road, Liverpool L16 0JT Tel: 0151 722 1864 — MRCS Eng. LRCP Lond. 1980.

MULLETT, Mr Simon Thomas Howard 12 The Green, Compton, Chichester PO18 9HD Tel: 01705 631799 — MB BS 1986 Lond.; FRCS Ed. 1991. Cons. A & E Qu. Alexandra Hosp. Cosham. Prev: Sen. Regist. (A & E) Char. Cross Hosp. Lond.

MULLEY, Professor Graham Peter 7 Woodlea, Boston Spa, Wetherby LS23 6SB Tel: 01937 844023 Email: gpmulley@aol.com — MB ChB Leeds 1970; DM Nottm. 1983; FRCP Lond. 1987; MRCP (UK) 1973. (Leeds) Developm. Prof. Med. for Elderly St. Jas. Univ. Hosp. Leeds. Socs: Brit. Geriat. Soc.; Roy. Soc. Med.; Brit. Stroke Research Gp. Prev: Sen. Regist. (Health c/o Elderly) Nottm.; MRC Research Fell. Nottm.

MULLEY, Joanna Oclanis 10 Sutcliffe Drive, Harbury, Leamington Spa CV33 9LT — BM BS 1988 Nottm.; BMedSci Nottm. 1986; MRCGP 1994; Dip. Obst. NZ 1991. Prev: GP Rugby.

MULLHI, Damanjeet 15 Battenhall Road, Harborne, Birmingham B17 9UD Tel: 0121 426 1559 Fax: 0121 426 1847; 275 Woodlands Road, Upper Batley, Batley WF17 0QJ — MB ChB 1994 Birm.; ChB Birm. 1994. (Univ. of Birm.) SHO (Anaesth.) New Cross Hosp. Wolverhampton. Prev: SHO (A & E) Birm. Heartlands Hosp.; Ho. Off. (Surg.) Sandwell Dist. Gen. Hosp.; Ho. Off. (Med.) Qu. Eliz. Hosp. Birm.

MULLHI, Paul Singh Grove House Surgery, Soothill, Batley WF17 5SS Tel: 01924 476363 Fax: 01924 474119; 275 Woodlands Road, Batley WF17 0QJ Tel: 01924 479599 — MB BS 1966 Punjab; MB BS Punjabi 1966; MRCOphth. 1991; Cert. JCC Lond. 1977; DO RCPSI 1970; DOMS Agra 1967. (Govt. Med. Coll. Patiala) Hosp. Med. Pract. (Ophth.) W. Yorks. HA.

MULLIGAN, Geoffrey Robert Erne Health Centre, Erne Hospital, Cornagrade Road, Enniskillen BT74 6AY Tel: 028 6632 5638; Rosemary Cottage, Derryinch, Enniskillen BT74 4HZ — MB BS 1990 Lond.; MRCGP 1995; DRCOG 1994; DCH RCPI 1993.

MULLIGAN, Ian Patrick 11 Chalfont Road, Oxford OX2 6TL — MB BS 1979 Lond.; BSc (1st cl. Hons. Physiol.) Lond. 1976, MB BS 1979; MRCP (UK) 1982. (St. Thos.) Sen. Regist. John Radcliffe Hosp. Oxf.

MULLIGAN, Michael John Christopher 73 Princes Avenue, Woodford Green IG8 0LW — MB BS 1984 Lond.; BSc Lond. 1983, MB BS 1984.

MULLIGAN, Mr Patrick Joseph 81 Harborne Road, Edgbaston, Birmingham B15 3HG Tel: 0121 455 9496 Fax: 0121 455 0288; 21 Hamilton Avenue, Harborne, Birmingham B17 8AH Tel: 0121 429 2188 Fax: 0121 434 5711 — MB ChB 1964 Glas.; FRCS Eng. 1980; FRCS Glas. 1969. (Glas.) Cons. Orthop. Surg. & Dir. Studies Roy. Orthop. Hosp. Birm.; Hon. Sen. Clin. Lect. Tutor (Orthop.) Univ. Birm. Socs: (Ex-Pres.) Midl. Med. Soc.; (Ex-Pres.) Brit. Soc. Surg. Hand.; Fell. (Ex-Pres.) BOA. Prev: Sen. Regist. (Orthop.) W.. Infirm. Glas.; Ho. Off. Glas. Roy. Infirm.

MULLIGAN, Pauline Mary 4 Corraghy, Corranny Roslea, Enniskillen BT92 7DZ Tel: 03657 51534 — MB ChB 1990 Manch.; MRCGP 1994; DCH RCP Lond. 1993; DRCOG 1992.

MULLIGAN, Robert Angus Craig (retired) 238 Coast Road, Ballygally, Larne BT40 2QQ Tel: 01574 583632 — MB BCh BAO 1953 Belf.; DObst RCOG 1955; DCH Eng. 1956.

MULLIGAN, Rosemary Anne (retired) Cliff Barn, Cliff Farm, Old Hunstanton Road, Hunstanton PE36 6HX Tel: 01485 600256 — MB BS 1962 Lond.; MD Lond. 1973, BSc, MB BS 1962; FRCP Lond. 1978, M 1965. Prev: Cons. Phys. Qu. Eliz. Hosp. King's Lynn.

MULLIGAN, Terence Joseph Ravenscourt Road Surgery, 34 Ravenscourt Road, London W6 0UG Tel: 020 8748 4842 Fax: 020 8563 2779; 53 Netheravon Road, Cheswick, London W4 2NA — MB BS 1981 Lond. Prev: SHO (O & G) Ascot; SHO (Paediat.) Redhill; SHO (A & E) Slough.

MULLIGAN, Terence Shaun A&E Department, City Hospital, Dudley Road, Birmingham B18 7QH Tel: 0121 554 3801 Fax: 0121 507 5182; 30 St. Matthews Road, Burntwood WS7 9DR — MB BCh 1992 Witwatersrand.

MULLIGAN, Mr Thomas Osmond (retired) Koala Lodge, 144 Gilford Road, Portadown, Craigavon BT63 5LD Tel: 02838 335801 Email: osmond@omulligan.freeserve.co.uk — MB ChB 1959 Ed.; FRCS Ed. 1964; FMC Nigeria 1971. Prev: Cons. Gen. Surg. Craigavon Area Hosp.

MULLIN, Anne McKinlay Govan Health Centre, 5 Drumoyne Road, Glasgow G51 4BJ Tel: 0141 531 8400 Fax: 0141 531 8404 — MB ChB 1988 Glas.

MULLIN, Mrs Libuse Ayrshire Central Hospital, Kilwiniry Road, Irvine KA12 8SS; 19 Lothian Road, Ayr KA7 3BU Tel: 012192 283287 — MUDr 1971 Charles Univ. Prague; MUDR Charles U Prague 1971. Clin. Med. Off. Ayrsh. & Arran Health Bd. Staff Grade Paediat. Com. Child Health Dept. -Ayeshire cent. Socs: BAAF. Prev: Regist. (Haematol.) Ballochmyle Hosp. Mauchline; SHO (Anaesth.) Kilmarnock Infirm.

MULLIN, Michael Scott 116 Chelwood Avenue, Childwall, Liverpool L16 3NW Tel: 0151 722 0857 — MB ChB 1992 Liverp.

MULLIN, Michelle Myra Greyswood Practice, 238 Mitcham Lane, London SW16 6NT Tel: 020 8769 0845/8363 Fax: 020 8677 2960 — MB BS 1984 Lond.

MULLIN, Nicola Hayley 19 Kingsbury, Grange, West Kirby, Wirral CH48 6ES — MB ChB 1991 Manch.; DFFP 1997; BSc (Hons.) Path. Manch. 1989; MRCOG 1998. (Manch.) Specialist Regist. (O & G) Whiston Hosp. Prescot. Socs: Bristish Soc. for colposcopy & cervical Path. Prev: Specialist Regist. (O & G) Liverp. Wom.s Hosp.; Specialist Regist. (O & G) Fazakeley Hosp. Liverp.; SHO (O & G) Arrowe Pk. Hosp. Wirral.

MULLIN, Patrick (retired) 17 Wansbeck Road S., Gosforth, Newcastle upon Tyne NE3 3PE — MB BS Lond. 1961; MRCS Eng. LRCP Lond. 1959; FRCPsych 1983, M 1972; DPM Eng. 1964. Prev: Cons. Psychiat. S.. Gen. Hosp. & Char. Cross Clinic Glas.

*****MULLIN, Siobhan** 54 Ralston Dr, Glasgow G52 3LU — MB ChB 1997 Glas.

MULLIN, Terence Stockbridge Village Health Centre, Leachcroft, Waterpark Drive, Stockbridge Village, Liverpool L28 1ST Tel: 0151 489 9924 Fax: 0151 489 8298 Email: terrymullin@bigfoot.com; Email: terrymullin@bigfoot.com — MB ChB 1983 Liverp.

MULLINGER, Anne Victoria Primrose Lane, Huntingdon PE29 1WG Tel: 01480 415200; Brambles, 37 Upwood Road, Bury, Huntingdon PE26 2PA Tel: 01487 813004 — MB ChB 1970 Ed.; BSc Ed. 1968; DObst RCOG 1973. (Ed.) Clin. Med. Off. Community Child Health. Prev: Civil. Med. Pract. MoD; Clin. Asst. Drug Dependancy Unit Cambs.; Resource Managem. Hinchingbrooke Hosp. Huntingdon.

MULLINS, David Francis (retired) The Drays, Court Lane, Hadlow, Tonbridge TN11 0JU — BM BCh 1948 Oxf.; MA Oxf. 1948. Prev: GP Oxf. and Lymington.

MULLINS, Margaret Rosemary The Well House, Upper Culham, Wargrave, Reading RG10 8NS Tel: 01491 576181 — MB BS 1973 Lond. (Char. Cross Hosp.) Clin. Asst. (Ophth.) Townlands Hosp. & Roy. Berks. Hosp. Reading; Clin. Asst. (Ophth.) Townlands Hosp. & Roy. Berks. Hosp. Reading. Prev: GP Henley on Thames.

MULLINS, Mark Meyrick Flat 38, Cranfield Court, 21 Homer St., London W1H 4NF — MB BS 1995 Lond.; MA Camb. 1992; MRCA Eng. 1999. (Camb. St Mary's Lond.)

MULLINS, Megan Kate 38 Cranfield Court, 21 Homer St., London W1H 4NF — MB BS 1996 Lond. GP Trainee.

MULLINS, Paul Anthony Link 7Z, Royal Liverpool University Hospital, Prescot St., Liverpool L7 8XP Tel: 0151 706 2662 Fax: 0151 706 5833; 32 Beryl Road, Upton, Birkenhead CH43 9RT Tel: 0151 677 1142 Email: dr.pmullins@lineone.net — MB BS Lond. 1983; MD Lond. 1993; MRCP (UK) 1988; FRCP 1997. Cons. Phys. & Cardiol. Roy. Liverp. Univ. Hosp.; Hon. Cons. Cardiol. BRd.green Hosp. Liverp. Socs: Brit. Cardiac Soc. & Brit. Cardiovasc. Interven. Soc. Prev: Hon. Sen. Regist. & Regist. (Cardiol.) Papworth Hosp. Camb.

MULLINS, Paul Dominic 82 Edge Lane, Stretford, Manchester M32 8PX — MB BS 1987 Lond.; MRCP (UK) 1992; DM Soton. 1999. (The Lond. Hosp. Med. Sch.) Locum Cons. Gastroenterologist; Roy. United Hosp., Bath. Socs: Brit. Soc. of Gastroenterol. Prev: Specialist Regist. (Gastro) Qu. Alexandra Hosp. Portsmouth; Specialist Regist. (Gastro) Roy. Hosp. Haslar; Regist. (Med. & Gastroenterol.) NW RHA.

*****MULLINS, Simon David** 12 Elmsfield Close, Liverpool L25 4SF — MB ChB 1995 Sheff.

MULNIER, Charlotte Ellen Sternfield House IP17 1RS Tel: 01728 605788 Fax: 020 8347 8837; Sternfield House IP17 1RS Tel: 01728 605788 — MB BS 1988 Lond.; MA Oxf. 1985; MRCP Lond. 1992; FRCA Lond. 1994. Specialist Regist., Anaesth. Roy. Nat. Trust, Nose & Ear Hosp. Lond.; Specialist Regist., Anaesth. W. Suff. Hosp. Bury St. Edmunds Suff. Prev: Lect. (Anaesth., Qu. Mary Hosp. Hong Kong; Regist. (Anaesth.) Middlx. Hosp. Lond.; Med. Off. (Anaesth.) Duchess of Kent Childr.'s Hosp. Hong Kong.

MULRENAN, Michael John Church Street Surgery, 77 Church Street, Tewkesbury GL20 5RY Tel: 01684 292343 Fax: 01684 274305 — MB BS 1974 Lond.; DRCOG 1981. (Middlx.)

MULRENNAN, Siobhan 1 St Marys Avenue, Carlton Grange, Batley WF17 7AP — MB ChB 1996 Glas.; MRCP (uk) 1999. (Glasgow) SHO (Gen. Med.), Wansbeck Gen. Hosp. Ashington. Socs: BMA; MDU. Prev: SHO (A & E) Monklands Hosp. Airdrie; Jun. Ho.

MULRINE

Off. (Surg.) RAH Hosp. Paisley; Jun. Ho. Off. (Med.) Stobhill NHS Trust Glas.

MULRINE, Anne Therese North Berwick Health Centre, 54 St. Baldreds Road, North Berwick EH39 4PU Tel: 01620 892169 Fax: 01620 897005 — MB BCh BAO 1987 NUI; LRCPSI 1987; DObst RCPI 1990; DCH NUI 1989.

MULRINE, Catriona Helen 66 Lond Hey, Whiston, Prescot L35 3JW — MB ChB 1988 Liverp.

MULROONEY, Leo 18 North Park, Mansfield NG18 4PB Tel: 01623 20388 — MB BCh BAO 1950 NUI; FFA RCS Eng. 1967; DA Eng. 1963. (Galway) Cons. Anaesth. Mansfield Hosp. Gp. Prev: Wing Cdr. RAF Med. Br., Cons. Anaesth.; JHMO (Anaesth.) Wakefield Hosp. Gps.; Regist. (Anaesth.) Guy's Hosp.

MULROONEY, Peter, Squadron Ldr. RAF Med. Br. Retd. Department of Anaesthesia, Walsgrave Hospital NHS Trust, Clifford Bridge Road, Walsgrave, Coventry CV2 2DX Tel: 024 76 538952 Fax: 024 76 538767; 24 Drovers Way, Southam, Leamington Spa CV47 1FW Tel: 01926 815268 — MB ChB 1982 Sheff.; FRCA 1990. Cons. Anaesth. Cardiothoracic Walsgrave Hosp. NHS Trust Coventry. Socs: Assn. Cardiothoracic Anaesth. & Assn. Anaesth.; Brit. Assn. of Med. Managers. Prev: Sen. Regist. Univ. Coll. Hosp. Lond.; Sen. Specialist RAF.

MULROY, Julie Mary Old Vicarage, Chapelthorpe, Wakefield WF4 3JB Tel: 01924 250466 — MB ChB Ed. 1960. SCMO Pontefract HA. Prev: Ho. Phys. & Ho. Surg. Providence Hosp. St. Helens.

MULROY, Ronald (retired) Old Vicarage, Chapelthorpe, Wakefield WF4 3JB Tel: 01924 250466 — MB ChB 1959 Ed.; FRCGP 1978, M 1970; DObst RCOG 1961. Prev: GP Wakefield.

MULROY, Sharon Elizabeth 27 Histon Road, Cambridge CB4 3JB — BChir 1994 Camb.

MULTANI, Satwant Singh Meadowbank Health Centre, 3 Salmon Inn Road, Falkirk FK2 OXF Tel: 01324 714157 — MB BS 1966 Panjab; MB BS Panjab (India) 1966. (Glancy Med. Coll. Amritsar)

MULUGETA, Yemisrach 9 Simpson Street, Crosshouse, Kilmarnock KA2 0BD — MD 1989 Addis Ababa; LRCP LRCS Ed. LRCPS Glas. 1994.

MULUKUTLA, Raghava Dutt 222 Minster Court, Liverpool L7 3QH — MB BS 1980 Osmania.

MULVANEY, Declan George 1 Upper Kiln Street, Newry BT35 8TT — MB BCh BAO 1995 Belf. (Belf.) SHO (Gen. Med.) Good Hope Hosp. Sutton Coldfield. Socs: BMA. Prev: SHO (c/o Elderly) Belf. City Hosp.; Ho. Off. Belf. City Hosp.

***MULVANEY, Gabriel Paul** 1 Upper Kiln Street, Newry BT35 8TT — MB BCh BAO 1994 Belf.

MULVANEY, Gerard Aidan Cornmarket Surgery, 6 Newry Health Village, Monaghan Street, Newry BT35 6BW Tel: 028 3026 5838 Fax: 028 3026 6727; Glencairn, Rathfriland Road, Newry BT34 Tel: 01693 64254 — MB BCh BAO 1981 Belf.; MRCGP 1986; DRCOG 1985; DCH RCPSI 1984. Prev: SHO Daisy Hill Hosp. Newry; SHO & Ho. Off. Belf. City Hosp.

MULVANEY, Jane Kathleen 42 Southend Close, London SE9 2SF — MB ChB 1993 Dundee.

MULVANY, Silvia Ruth 15 Cromwell Avenue, London N6 5HN — MB ChB 1972 Cape Town; FFPsych S.I.Afr. 1978; MRCPsych 1978. Sen. Regist. Adult Dept. Tavistock Clinic. Prev: Clin. Asst. Paddington Centre of Psychother.

***MULVANY, Stephen Anthony** 20 Belfast Road, Lisburn BT27 4AS — MB BCh 1998 Belf.; MB BCh Belf 1998.

MULVEIN, James Tweedily (retired) Brook Farm, Lower Tockington Road, Tockington, Bristol BS32 4LE Tel: 01454 616346 Fax: 01454 616346 — MA, MB Camb. 1964, BChir 1963; FFA RCS Eng 1966; DA Eng. 1965. Prev: Cons. Anaesth. S.mead Hosp. Bristol.

MULVENNA, Bernadete Attracta 29 Waterloo Park, Belfast BT15 5HU Tel: 01232 779416 — MB BCh BAO 1984 Belf.; MRCGP 1989; DRCOG 1991; DGM RCP Lond. 1986. Trainee GP Newtownabbey VTS; Med. Asst. Whiteabbey Hosp. Belf.

MULVENNA, Paula Mary Northern Centre for Cancer Treatment, Newcastle General Hosptial, Westgate Road, Newcastle upon Tyne NE4 6BE Tel: 0191 219 4366 Fax: 0191 272 4236 — MB BS 1985 Newc.; FRCR (1998); BMedSc (Hons.) Newc. 1984; MRCP (Ed.) 1988. Cons. Clin. Oncol. N.. Centre for Cancer Treatm., Newc.-upon-Tyne. Socs: Assn. Palliat. Med.; Roy. Coll. Radiologists (Fac. of Clin. Oncol.); Europ. Organisation of Research & Treatm. of Cancer. Prev: Sen. Regist. (Palliat. Med.) N.. RHA; Clin. Research Fell. (AIDS) Roy. Free Hosp. Lond.; Sen. Regist. (Oncol.) Newc. Gen. Hosp.

MULVEY, David Anthony Department of Anaesthesia, Derbyshire Royal Infirmary NHS Trust, London Road, Derby DE1 2QY Tel: 01332 254828 — MB BS 1982 Lond.; BSc Pharm. Lond. 1979; MD Lond. 1992; FRCA 1987; DA (UK) 1985. (St. Bart.) Cons. Anaesth. & Intens. Care Derbysh. Roy. Infirm. Socs: BMA & Assn. Anaesth.; Intens. Care Soc. Prev: Sen. Regist. & Regist. (Anaesth.) Roy. Free Hosp. Lond.; Clin. Research Fell. Brompton Hosp. Lond.

MULVEY, Joyce Marie Park Surgery, Albion Way, Horsham RH12 1BG Tel: 01403 217100 — MB ChB 1984 Bristol; MA Oxf. 1978; MRCGP 1990; DCH RCP Lond. 1990; Cert. Family Plann. JCC 1988; DRCOG 1988. Prev: SHO (Paediat.) St. Chas. Hosp. Lond.; SHO (O & G) Univ. Coll. Hosp. Lond.

MULVEY, Mary Joanna Department of Psychiatry, Guy's Hospital, London SE1 9RT Tel: 020 7955 5000 — MB BCh BAO 1980 NUI; BSc (Path.) NUI 1982; MRCPsych 1987. Sen. Regist. (Psychiat. Ment. Handicap) Guy's Hosp. Lond. Socs: BMA. Prev: Research Asst.; Maudsley & Middlx. Hosps.; Regist. & SHO Bloomsbury Psychiat. Train. Scheme.

MULVEY, Paul (retired) 14 Goodison Close, Bury BL9 8JY Tel: 0161 766 6788 — MB ChB Manch. 1953.

MULVIHILL, Hilary Eileen The Health Centre, Claremont Grove, Exmouth EX8 2JF — MB BCh BAO 1989 Dub.

MULVIN, Mr David William Department of Urology, Kings College Hospital, Denmark Hill, London SE5 9RS; 149 Court Lane, Dulwich, London SE21 7EE — MB BCh BAO 1981 NUI; FRCSI 1985; MCh 1992; FRCS (Urol.) 1994. Cons. (Urol.) Kings Coll. Hosp. Lond.

MUMBY, Philip Stewart Norwood House Surgery, Belle Vue Street, Scarborough YO12 7EJ Tel: 01723 374485 Fax: 01723 501517 — MB ChB 1977 Manch.; BSc St. And. 1974; MRCOG 1982, D 1979; DCH RCPS Glas. 1980; FRCOG 1998. GP. Socs: BMA. Prev: SHO (O & G) Wythenshawe Hosp. Manch. & Addenbrookes Camb.; SHO (Paediat. & A & E) Leeds Gen. Infirm.

MUMFORD, Andrew David Tree Tops, Downhall Drive, Wembdon, Bridgwater TA6 7RT — MB ChB 1991 Bristol.

MUMFORD, Colin John Department Clinical Neurosciences, Western General Hospital, Crewe Road, Edinburgh EH4 2XU Tel: 0131 537 1169 Fax: 0131 537 1106 Email: cm@skull.dcn.ed.ac.uk; 46A Inverleith Place, Edinburgh EH3 5QB Tel: 0131 552 4244 — BM BS 1983 Nottm.; FRCP 2000; DM Nottm. 1993, BMedSci (Hons.) 1981; MRCP (UK) 1986; Dip. IMC RCS Ed. 1989; FRCP Ed. 1998. (Nottingham) Cons. Neurol. W.. Gen. Hosp. Edin. & Vic. Hosp. Kirkcaldy; Hon. Sen. Lect. Univ. Edin. Socs: Assn. Brit. Neurols.; Scott. Neurol. Assn.; Brit. Assn. for the Study of Headache. Prev: Sen. Regist. (Neurol.) Lothian HB Edin.; Regist. (Neurol.) Nat. Hosp. Qu. Sq. Lond. & Univ. Hosp. Qu. Med. Centre Nottm.; Research Assoc. (Neurol.) Univ. Camb. Addenbrooke's Hosp.

MUMFORD, David Bardwell Division of Psychiatry, University of Bristol, 41 St Michael's Hill, Bristol BS2 8DZ Tel: 0117 928 7773 Fax: 0117 925 9709 Email: david.mumford@bris.ac.uk; 14 Clifton Vale, Clifton, Bristol BS8 4PT Tel: 0117 927 2221 — MB ChB 1981 Bristol; MPhil Ed. 1989; MA Camb. 1975; MD Bristol 1992; MRCPsych 1986. (Bristol) Cons. Sen. Lect. Psychiat. Univ. Bristol; Hon. Cons. United Bristol Healthcare Trust; Dir. Med. Educat. Univ. Bristol. Socs: Fell. Roy. Soc. Med. Prev: Cons. Psychiat. United Bristol Healthcare Trust; Sen. Regist. Yorks. Regional Scheme; Regist. (Psychiat.) Roy. Edin Hosp.

MUMFORD, James Walter The Gables, Station Road, Mildenhall, Bury St Edmunds IP28 7DR Tel: 01638 717766 — BM BCh 1987 Oxf.; MRCGP 1991; DRCOG 1991; DCH RCP Lond. 1990. GP Trainee W. Suff. HA. Prev: Ho. Phys. Dorset Co. Hosp.; Ho. Surg. Hereford Co. Hosp.

MUMFORD, John Percival (retired) The Old School, Oakham Lane, Staverton, Daventry NN11 6JQ Tel: 01327 312153 Fax: 01327 706565 Email: mumpharm@msn.com — MB ChB 1957 Manch.; MRCGP 1965; FFPM RCP (UK) 1989; DObst RCOG 1960. Prev: Internat. Therap. Area Dir. Marion Merrell.

MUMFORD, Jonathan Derry Harrogate Clinic, 23 Ripon Road, Harrogate HG1 2JL Tel: 01423 500599 Fax: 01609 748028 Email: fleetham@msn.com — MB ChB 1976 Liverp.; MRCPsych 1982;

FRCPsych 1998. (Liverp.) Cons. Psychiat. Harrogate Clinic N. Yorks. Socs: Acad. of Experts; Expert Witness Inst.; Leeds Medico Legal Soc. Prev: Cons. Psychiat. Stockton Hall Hosp. York - Medium Secure Unit; Cons. Psychiat. & Dir. Ment. Health Servs. Friarage Hosp. N.allerton; Cons. Psychiat. Brit. Milit. Hosp. Hannover & Hong Kong.

MUMFORD, Nicholas Gordon The Health Centre, Chapel St., Ely CB6 1BJ Tel: 01353 663434; Crown Cottage, 12 Main St, Coveney, Ely CB6 2DJ — MB BS 1969 Lond.; MRCS Eng. LRCP Lond. 1969; DObst RCOG 1976; Cert FPA 1976. (Middlx.) Clin. Teach. Univ. Camb.; Med. Off. Kings Sch. Ely; Treas. Cambs. LMC. Socs: BMA, Camb. Med. Soc. & Med. Off. Schs. Assn. Prev: Squadron Ldr. RAF Med. Br.; Ho. Surg. Middlx. Hosp. Lond.; Ho. Phys. St. And. Hosp. Billericay.

MUMFORD, Patricia Anne Granville House Medical Centre, Granville Street, Adlington, Chorley PR6 9PY Tel: 01257 481966 Fax: 01257 474655; 55A Chorley Road, Blackrod, Bolton BL6 5JU Tel: 01257 480919 — MB ChB 1976 Liverp.; DRCOG 1978. Prev: Clin. Med. Off. Preston HA.

MUMMERY, Catherine Jane 70 Pinehurst Court, 1-3 Colville Gardens, London W11 2BJ — MB BS 1990 Lond.; BSc (Hons.) Lond. 1987, MB BS 1990; MRCP (UK) 1993. SHO (Gen. Med.) Roy. Sussex Co. Hosp. Brighton.

***MUMMERY, David Frank** 5 Canonbury Grove, London N1 2HP — MB ChB 1998 Bristol.

MUMMERY, Jacqueline 1 Upton Avenue, St Albans AL3 5ER; 26 Beaumont Avenue, St Albans AL1 4TJ Tel: 01727 51326 — MB ChB 1963 Bristol; DObst RCOG 1965. (Bristol)

MUMMERY, Raymond Victor (retired) Microbiology Department, Chase Farm Hospitals (NHS) Trust, The Ridgeway, Enfield EN2 8JL Tel: 020 8366 6600 — MB BS Lond. 1964; MRCS Eng. LRCP Lond. 1963; MRCPath 1970. Cons. Microbiol. Roy. Nat. Orthop. Hosp. Stanmore; Hon. Lect. (Microbiol.) Roy. Free Hosp. Med. Sch. Lond. Prev: Cons. Microbiol. Armed Forces Hosp. Riyadh, Saudi Arabia.

MUMTAZ, Mr Faizul Hassan 65 Howcroft Crescent, London N3 1PA Tel: 020 8343 4650; 65 Howcroft Crescent, London N3 1PA Tel: 020 8343 4650 Email: fmumtaz@ukgateway.net — MB BS 1985 Nigeria; FRCSI 1992; FRCS Eng. 1992; Dip. Urol. Lond 1993. Specialist Regist. (Urol.) Roy. Free Hosp. Lond.

MUMTAZ, Mr Hamid Department of Surgery, 67-73 Riding House St., London W1P 7LD — MB BS 1986 Nigeria; FRCS Ed. 1991.

***MUMTAZ, Haroon Mohammed** 2 Balliol Street, Manchester M8 0WS — MB ChB 1997 Liverp.

MUMTAZ, Talat 65 Howcroft Crescent, London N3 1PA Tel: 020 8343 4650; 65 Howcroft Crescent, London N3 1PA Tel: 020 8343 4650 Email: tmumtaz@ukgateway.net — MB BS 1983 Ibadan; FRCA 1994; DA (UK) 1991. Cons. Anaesthet. Chase Farm Hosp. Enfield, Lond. Socs: OAA; SOAP; ESA.

MUNASINGHE, D W S The Medical Centre, Gun Lane, Strood, Rochester ME2 4UW Tel: 01634 720220 — MB BS 1967 Ceylon; MB BS 1967 Ceylon.

MUNASINGHE, Don Ranjith (retired) Gilda, Gresham Avenue, Hartley, Longfield DA3 7BT — MD 1965 Ceylon; MB BS 1959; FRCP Lond. 1989, M 1968; FRCP Ed. 1984, M 1968; T(M) 1991. Prev: Sen. Regist. (Geriat. Med.) St. Thos. Hosp. Lond.

MUNASINGHE, Srimathi Beatrice Gilda, Gresham Avenue, Hartley, Longfield DA3 7BT; Oxleas NHS Trust, Pinewood House, Bexley Hospital, Old Bexley Lane, Bexley DA5 2BF Tel: 01322 526282 — MB BS Ceylon 1965. Clin. Med. Off. Oxleas NHS Trust.

MUNBY, Jean Suzanne Brunswick Surgery, Oakhill Health Centre, Oakhill Road, Surbiton KT6 6EN Tel: 020 8399 2161; 11 Wool Road, Wimbledon, London SW20 0HN Tel: 020 8946 5873 — MB BS 1951 Lond. (Roy. Free)

MUNBY, Judy Caroline Ann Brunswick Surgery, Oak Hill Health Centre, Oak Hill Road, Surbiton KT6 6EN Tel: 020 8390 5321 Fax: 020 8390 5321; 97 Kings Road, Long Ditton, Surbiton KT6 5JE Tel: 020 8398 0307 — MB BS 1978 Lond.; MRCGP 1982; DRCOG 1980; DCH Eng. 1980. (Char. Cross) GP Surbiton.

MUNCASTER, Anna Elizabeth 22 North Avenue, South Shields NE34 6BB — MB ChB 1990 Sheff. SHO (Gen. Med.) St. Geo. Hosp. Lincoln. Prev: Ho. Off. (Surg.) Barnsley Dist. Gen. Hosp.; Ho. Off. (Med.) Sheff. HA.

MUNCASTER, John Wallace, TD Stanhope Parade Health Centre, Gordon Street, South Shields NE33 4HX Tel: 0191 455 4621 Fax: 0191 427 3180 — MB BS 1960 Durh.; DObst RCOG 1962. Staff Phys. S. Tyneside HA. Socs: BMA. Prev: Ho. Off. (Obst.) Dryburn Hosp. Durh.; Ho. Phys. Chester-le-St. Gen. Hosp.; Ho. Off. (Paediat.) Dryburn Hosp. Durh.

MUNCER, Zelia Karen Dib Lane Practice, 112A Dib Lane, Leeds LS8 3AY Tel: 0113 295 4650 Fax: 0113 295 4663; Rosedene, 14 Shaftesbury Avenue, Leeds LS8 1DT Tel: 0113 664392 — MB ChB 1979 Leeds; MRCGP 1983; DRCOG 1982. Clin. Asst. (Gyn.) St. Jas. NHS Trust Hosp. Leeds.

MUNCEY, Felicity Anne Breast Screening, Charing Cross Hospital, Fulham Palace Road, London W6; 5 Somerset Square, Holland Park, London W14 8EE — MB BS 1980 Lond.; MRCP (UK) 1983; T(R) (CR) 1991; FRCR 1987. (King's Coll. Hosp.) Cons. BrE. Imaging Radiol. Hammersmith Hosp. NHS Trust Lond. Socs: FRCR. Prev: Cons. Radiol. W. Essex; Sen. Regist. King's Coll. Hosp. Lond.; Regist. St. Thos. Hosp. Lond.

MUNDASAD, Mr Mohan Veerabhadrappa — MB BS 1975 Karnatak; FRCS Ed. 1988; FRCOphth 1989; DO RCPSI 1988; DOMS Karnatak 1977; ERSC 1998. (Karnatak Med. Coll. India) p/t Assoc. Specialist (Ophth.) Bristol Eye Hosp.; Mem. Non. Cons. Career Grade Comms.; Mem. Local Negot. Comm. Socs: BMA; Oversea's Doc's Assoc.; Brit. Soc. of Ref. Surg. Prev: Research Cons. Simbec Research Ltd.; Locum Cons. Bridgend Gen. Hosp.; Res. Fell. Univ. of Bristol.

MUNDASAD, Sarvamangala Mohan Cefn Coed Hospital, Cockett, Swansea SA2 0GH — LMSSA 1984 Lond.

***MUNDAY, Anna Natasha** 77 Calmont Road, Bromley BR1 4BY — MB BS 1998 Lond.; MB BS Lond 1998.

MUNDAY, Christine Anne 2 Cecil Road, Clifton, Bristol BS8 3HR — MB BS 1984 Lond.

MUNDAY, Daniel Frederick 7 Guy's Close, Warwick CV34 5JH Tel: 01926 402227 — MB BS 1982 Lond.; MRCGP 1996; Cert. Family Plann. JCC 1993; DRCOG 1992; FFA RCSI 1987; Dip Palliat. Med. 1998. (Roy. Free) Specialist Regist. (Palliat. Med.) Walsgrave Hosp. NHS Trust Coventry; Vis. Clin. Sen. Lect. Primary Care Unit, Univ. Warwick. Prev: GP Aberd.; Cons. Anaesth. United Mission, Nepal; Regist. (Anaesth.) Roy. Shrewsbury Hosp.

MUNDAY, Derek Charles Brookside Group Practice, Brookside Close, Gipsy Lane, Earley, Reading RG6 7HG; 375 Wokingham Road, Earley, Reading RG6 7EH Tel: 0118 926 4398 — MB BS 1971 Lond.; MRCGP 1975; DCH Eng. 1975; DObst RCOG 1973; FRCGP 1998. (Roy. Free) Exec. Chair Wokingham PCT. Prev: Chair Wokingham PCG.

MUNDAY, Jeremy Nigel Roderick Swanage Health Centre, Railway Station Approach, Station Road, Swanage BH19 1HB Tel: 01929 422231; 26 Moor Road, Swanage BH19 1RG Tel: 01929 422791 — MB BS 1985 Lond. (Lond.) Socs: Roy. Coll. Gen. Pract.

MUNDAY, Jonathan Eric Lewis Westminster And Pimlico General Practice, 15 Denbigh Street, London SW1V 2HF Tel: 020 7834 6969 Fax: 020 7931 7747 Email: wpmc@hotmail.com; 59 Abingdon Road, London W8 6AN Tel: 020 7937 2203 Email: jonathan.muday@btinternet.com — MB BChir 1982 Camb.; BA (Hons.) Oxf. 1980, MA 1984; MRCGP 1987. (Camb.) Prev: Trainee GP/SHO W. Middlx. Hosp. Isleworth VTS; Trainee GP Lond.

MUNDAY, Mary Joy Rigden 375 Wokingham Road, Earley, Reading RG6 7EH Tel: 0118 926 4398 — MB BS 1972 Lond.; DO RCS Eng. 1987. (Roy. Free) Clin. Asst. (Ophth.) Roy. Berks. Hosp. Reading.

MUNDAY, Patricia Eileen Department of Genitourinary Medicine, Watford General Hospital, Vicarage Road, Watford WD18 0HB Tel: 01923 217206 Fax: 01923 217131 Email: patmunday@watfordgum.freeserve.co.uk — MFFP 1993; MB ChB Liverp. 1970; MD Liverp. 1982; FRCOG 1989, M 1975; DObst RCOG 1972; FRCP 2000 Edinburgh. Cons. Genitourin. Phys. Watford Gen. Hosp.; Clin. Director W. Herts. Sexual Health Directorate. Prev: Cons. Genitourin. Phys. St. Mary's Hosp. Lond.; Mem. Sci. Staff MRC Clin. Research Centre.

***MUNDAY, Rachel Joy** 375 Wokingham Road, Earley, Reading RG6 7EH — BM BS 1998 Nottm.; BM BS Nottm 1998.

MUNDAY, Stephen John Birmingham HA, St. Chad's Court, Hagley Road, Birmingham B16 9RG Tel: 0121 695 2378 Fax: 0121 695 2233 Email: stephen.munday@hq.birminghamha.wmids.nhs.uk; 1 Barton Drive, Knowle, Solihull B93 0PE Tel: 01564 775723 Email: stephen@munday57.freeserve.co.uk — MB BCh 1980 Wales;

MUNDAY

MFPHM 1990; MRCGP 1984; FFPHM 1998. Cons. Pub. Health Med. Birm. HA.

MUNDAY, Stewart Anthony Primrose Cottage, Waterloo Road, Caythorpe, Grantham NG32 3DX Tel: 01400 272262 Fax: 01400 272262 — MB BS 1966 Lond.; MRCS Eng. LRCP Lond. 1966; MRCGP 1979. (King's Coll. Lond. & King's Coll. Hosp.) Freelance Cons. on Disabil. Policy; Asst. Dep. Coroner Boston & Spalding Dist. Socs: Coroners Soc. Eng. & Wales; BMA (Ex-Chairm. Lincoln Div.); Brit. Soc. Rehabil. Med. Prev: Sen. Govt. Med. Off. DoH; GP Willingham by Stow, Lincs.; Regist. (Path.) Lincoln Co. Hosp.

MUNDELL, Elaine Balfour McNair 48 Bank Street, Glasgow G12 8LZ — MB ChB 1990 Glas.

MUNDELL, Mr Robert Henderson 52 Mayfield Close, Great Sankey, Warrington WA5 3PL — MB ChB 1995 Aberd.; AFRCS (End.) Apr 1999. SHO Neurosurg. S.ern Gen. Hosp. Glas. Prev: SHO Cardiothor. Surg. W.ern Infirm. Glas.; SHO Plastic Surg., Canmesburn Hosp. Glas.; SHO Gen. Surg. Ayr Hosp.

MUNDEN, Alison Clare The Oaklands Centre, raddlebown Road, Sally Oak, Birmingham B29 6JB Tel: 0121 627 8231 Fax: 0121 627 8684 — MB ChB 1988 Birm.; ChB Birm. 1988; MRCGP 1992; DRCOG 1992; MRCPsych 1995. (Birmingham) Sen. Regist. (Child & Adolesc. Psychiat.) W. Midl. Rotat.al & Train. Scheme. Socs: ACPP. Prev: Regist. Rotat. (Psychiat.) All Birm. Train. Scheme.; Trainee GP Henley-in-Arden.

MUNDEN, Amanda Jane Westlands Medical Centre, 20b Westlands Grove, Portchester, Fareham PO16 9AD Tel: 02392 377514 Fax: 023 92 214236 — MB BS 1979 Lond.; DRCOG 1981. (Middlx.) Gen. Practitioner, W.lands Med. Centre, Portcheser. Prev: Asst. (Gen. Pract.) Stubbington.

MUNDEN, Angela Clapham Family Practice, 51 Clapham High Street, London SW4 7TL Tel: 020 7622 4455 Fax: 020 7622 4466 — BM 1983 Soton.; DCCH RCGP 1990; DRCOG 1989.

MUNDEN, Joanna Elizabeth Shotfield Health Centre, Shotfield, Wallington SM6 0HY — MB BS 1987 Lond.; MRCGP (Distinction) 2001 Roy. Coll. GP; Summative Assessm. 2001 Roy. Coll. GP; BSc (Physiol.) 1984; DFFP 1995 Faculty family planning; DRCOG 1996. (King's College London) Gen. Practitioner; Clin. Med. Off. (Family Plann.). Prev: Gyn. (Gen. Pract.).

***MUNDRAY, Sunita** 30 Brackenbury Road, East Finchley, London N2 0ST — MB BS 1997 Lond.

MUNDY, Alison Jane Cozens House, 122a Warley St., London W1N 1AF; 4 Lakeside Grange, Weybridge KT13 9ZE Tel: 01932 821362 — MB BS 1982 Lond.; MD Lond. 1993; MRCOG 1988. Cons. Gyn. Prev: Sen. Regist. (O & G) St. Heliers Hosp. Carshalton; Research Fell. (Reproduct. Med.) Qu. Charlotte's & Chelsea Hosp. Lond.; Lect. & Hon. Regist. (O & G) St. Thos. Hosp. Lond.

MUNDY, Mr Anthony Richard Emblem House, London Bridge Hospital, Tooley St., London SE1 2PR Tel: 020 7403 1221 Fax: 020 7403 1664 Email: mundyurol@aol.com; The Fleete House, Smarden, Ashford TN27 8QF Email: tonymundy@aol.com — MB BS 1971 Lond.; MB BS (Hons. Surg.) Lond. 1971; MS Lond. 1982; FRCP Lond. 1996; FRCS Eng. 1975; MRCP (UK) 1974; MRCS Eng. LRCP Lond. 1971. (St. Mary's) Prof. Urol. Guy's Hosp. UMDS & Inst. Urol. UCL Lond.; Cons. Urol. Surg. Guys & St. Peter's Hosps. Lond.; Vis. Cons. Urol. St. Lukes Hosp. Malta; Dir. Inst. Urol. & Nephrol. UCL Lond.; Hon. Cons. (Urol.) Nat. Hosp. Neurol. & Neurosurg. Socs: (Counc.) Brit. Assn. Urol. Surgs.; Autralasian Urol. Assn.; Hon. Mem. S. Africa, Singapore & Malaysian Urol. Assn. Prev: Cons. Urol. Surg. Lewisham Hosp. Lond.; Sen. Regist. (Urol. & Surg.) Guy's Hosp. Lond.; CO & Cons. Surg. Force Base Hosp. Muscat, Oman.

MUNDY, Elizabeth Mary The Herries, London Road, Retford DN22 7HY — MB ChB 1983 Liverp.

MUNDY, Fiona Helen Hillview Lodge, Royal United Hospital, Combe Park, Bath BA1 3NG — BM 1985 Soton.

MUNDY, Janitha Victoria Briscoe Royal Hallamshire Hospital, Glossop Road, Sheffield S10 2JF Tel: 0114 271 1900 — MB ChB 1977 Sheff.; BSc (Hons. Physiol.) Sheff. 1972; FFA RCS Eng. 1981. Cons. Neuroanaesth. Roy. Hallamsh. Hosp. Prev: Sen. Regist. (Anaesth.) Sheff. HA; Regist. (Anaesth.) Derbysh. AHA; SHO (Anaesth.) Derbysh. AHA.

MUNDY, John Douglas, DFC (retired) Catfoss Grange House, Catfoss Lane, Sigglesthorne, Kingston upon Thames HU11 5QN — LRCPI & LM, LRCSI & LM 1965; MFPHM 1989; MFCM 1974; DPH Liverp. 1970; DCH RCPSI 1968. Prev: SCMO (Child Health) Beverley Health Dist.

MUNDY, Keith Ian Frimley Park Hospital, Portsmouth Road, Frimley, Camberley GU16 7UJ Tel: 01276 604085 Fax: 01276 604862; The Shrubbery, 75 Kings Road, Fleet GU51 3AS Tel: 01252 616524 — MB BChir 1978 Camb.; MRCP (UK) 1980; FRCP LOND.1996. (Camb. & St. Geo.) Cons. Phys. & Geriat. Frimley Pk. Hosp. NHS Trust; Lead Cons. Stroke Serv. Socs: BMA; BGS. Prev: Sen. Regist. (Geriat+Gen. Med.) Univ. Hosp. S. Manch. & Bolton Gen. Hosp.; Regist. (Med.) Roy. Hallamsh. Hosp. Sheff.

MUNDY, Max (retired) 75 Bedford Gardens, London W8 7EF Tel: 020 7229 2825 — MRCS Eng. LRCP Lond. 1926. Prev: Hon. Med. Staff Wembley Hosp.

MUNDY, Pamela Joy Ley Mill Surgery, 228 Lichfield Road, Sutton Coldfield B74 2UE Tel: 0121 308 0359 Fax: 0121 323 2682; 5 Bennett Road, Sutton Coldfield B74 4TJ — MB ChB 1974 Manch.; MRCGP 1979; MFFP 1994; DRCOG 1977; DA Eng. 1977. (Manchester)

MUNDY, Peter The Medical Centre, Station Avenue, Bridlington YO16 4LZ Tel: 01262 670686 Fax: 01262 401685 — MB BChir 1972 Camb.; DObst RCOG 1974. (St. Thos.) Prev: Trainee Gen. Pract. I. of Wight Vocational Train. Scheme; Ho. Surg. ENT Dept. St. Thos. Hosp. Lond.; Ho. Phys. St. Jas. Hosp. Balham.

MUNDY, Peter Gordon 70 Bedford Ct Mansions, Bedford Avenue, London WC1B 3AD Tel: 020 7637 3986 — MRCS Eng. LRCP Lond. 1943. (St. Mary's) Prev: Capt. RAMC; Ho. Surg. Orthop. Unit, Pk. Prewett Hosp. Basingstoke.

MUNEER, Asif 10 St Pauls Avenue, Slough SL2 5ES — MB ChB 1994 Manch.; BSc (Hons.) Physiol. Manch. 1991. SHO (Otolaryngol.) Qu. Med. Centre Nottm.; Demonst. (Anat.) Univ. Oxf. Prev: Ho. Off. (Gen. & Cardiothoracic Surg.) Manch. Roy. Infirm.; Ho. Off. (Gastroenterol.) Hope Hosp. Salford.

MUNGALL, Donald Forbes (retired) The Dormer House, 19A Shipton Road, York YO30 5RE Tel: 01904 26016 — MB ChB 1939 Ed. Prev: Med. Off. Bootham Sch. York & Colls. Ripon & York St. John.

MUNGALL, Iain James The Surgery, Bellingham, Hexham NE48 2HE Tel: 01434 220203 Fax: 01434 220798 Email: iain.mungall@ongxnet.co.uk; Thorneyburn Lodge, Tarset, Hexham NE48 1NA Tel: 01434 240240 — MBBS 1968 Newc.; FRCGP 1993, M 1972; DObst RCOG 1971. Edr. Country Matters (RCGP Newsletter); Chair. Rural Pract. Standing Comm. of RCGP. Prev: Scheme Organizer N.umbria VTS 1996-2000.

MUNGALL, Ian Paul Forbes April Cottage, 4 Church St., Alwalton, Peterborough PE7 3UU — MB BChir 1971 Camb.; MD Camb. 1977, MA, MB 1971, BChir 1970; FRCP Lond. 1993; MRCP (UK) 1973. (Camb. & St. Thos.) Cons. Phys. P'boro. Dist. & Stamford Hosps. Prev: Sen. Regist. Leeds & Bradford AHAs; Regist. Roy. Hosp. Sheff.

***MUNGALL, Sarah Bethan** April Cottage, 4 Church St., Alwalton, Peterborough PE7 3UU — BM BS 1997 Nottm.

MUNGLANI, Rajesh Department of Anaesthesia and Pain Relief, Box 93, Addenbrooke's Hospital, Cambridge CB2 2QQ Tel: 01223 217890 Fax: 01223 217890 Email: rajesh@munglani.ms — MB BS 1985 Lond.; FRCA 1990; DCH RCP Lond. 1989; DA (UK) 1987. (St. Geo.) Lect. (Anaesth.) Univ. Camb. & Hon. Cons. Anaesth. & Pain Relief Addenbrooke's Hosp. Camb. + Lifespan NHS Trust; John Farman Prof. Roy. Coll. Anaesth.; Dir. Pain Relief Serv. Prev: Clin. Lect. (Anaesth.) Univ. Camb.; Research Fell. & Regist. Rotat. (Anaesth.) Addenbrooke's Hosp. Camb.

MUNIM, Farid Mohammad Saleh Abdul Doctors Mess, Queen Elizabeth Hospital, Gayton Road, King's Lynn PE30 4ET — MB ChB 1984 Baghdad, Iraq; MRCP (UK) 1996. (Univ. Baghdad) SHO (Gen. Med.) Bromley Hosps. NHS Trust. Prev: SHO (Paediat.) St. Helier Hosp. Carshalton; SHO (Paediat.) Sunderland Dist. Gen. Hosp.; SHO (ENT) Doncaster Roy. Infirm.

MUNIR, Aamir 106 Holly Avenue, Jesmond, Newcastle upon Tyne NE2 2QB; 25 Oakland Road, West Jesmond, Newcastle upon Tyne NE2 3DR Tel: 0191 212 1676 — MB BS 1996 Newc. SHO (A & E) RVI Newc. Prev: SHO (Cardiothoracic Surg.) Newc.

***MUNIR, Alia** 17 Fieldfare, Abbeydale, Gloucester GL4 4WH — MB BCh 1998 Wales.

MUNIR, Mohammad 17 Fieldfare, Abbeydale, Gloucester GL4 4WH — MB BS 1966 Karachi.

*MUNIR, Mohammad 61 Parkmills Road, Bury BL9 9AR — MB ChB 1994 Leeds; BSc (Hons. Physiol.) Leeds 1992.

MUNIR, Mohammad 96 Blakemere Close, Winyate East, Redditch B98 0LZ — MB BS 1978 Peshawar.

*MUNIR, Shahzad Mahmood 285 Dawlish Road, Selly Oak, Birmingham B29 7AU — MB ChB 1997 Birm.

MUNJAL, Mr Rameshkumar Shantilal Hope Hospital, Stott Lane, Salford M6 8HD Tel: 0161 789 7373 — MB BS 1976 Gujarat; MS Gujarat 1980, MB BS 1976; FRCSI 1987. Sen. Regist. (Neurol.). Socs: Manch. Med. Soc.; Brit. Soc. of Rehabil. Med.; BMA.

MUNJAL, Sandeep c/o Dr R. Kapoor, 36 The Drive, London E18 2BL — MB BS 1986 Devi Ahilya.

MUNK, Mauveen Ethel Vera Blue Haze, Beckaford, Manaton, Newton Abbot TQ13 9XH — MB ChB 1954 Leeds. (Leeds)

MUNKLEY, Rita May 17 Bush Grove, Birmingham B21 8PH — MB ChB 1965 St. And.

MUNKS, Arthur William (retired) Whincroft, 2 Holnicote Road, Bude EX23 8EJ Tel: 01288 352503 — MB BS 1954 Lond.; FRCGP 1966. Prev: Hosp. Pract. (Surg.) Stratton Hosp. Bude.

MUNKS, Jane (retired) Whincroft, 2 Holnicote Road, Bude EX23 8EJ Tel: 01288 352503 — MB BS 1954 Lond.; MRCS Eng. LRCP Lond. 1954; MFFP 1993; Cert Family Plann 1965. Prev: SCMO Cornw. AHA.

MUNN, Adrian David 133 Butler Road, Harrow HA1 4DX — MB BS 1994 Lond.

MUNN, Alexander The Cottage, 9 Crown Lane, Benson, Wallingford OX10 6LP Tel: 01491 838545 — MB ChB Glas. 1947; DIH Soc. Apoth. Lond. 1952; FFOM RCP Lond. 1983, MFOM 1982. (Univ. Glas.) Socs: Fell. Roy. Soc. Med.; (Ex-Pres.) Brit. Occupat. Hyg. Soc.; Soc. Occupat. Med. Prev: Med. Dir. Monsanto Europe S.A. Brussels; Div. Med. Off. ICI Ltd. Organics Div. Blackley, Manch.; Flight Lt. RAF.

MUNN, Eileen Mungall (retired) Wednesday Cottage, Main St., Buchlyvie, Stirling FK8 3LR Tel: 01360 850408 — MB ChB 1945 Ed.; Cert Family Plann JCC 1965. Prev: Princip. GP Edin.

MUNN, Julia Royal Devon & Exeter Hospital (Wonford), Barrack Road, Exeter EX6 8NH — MB BCh 1980 Wales; BSc Wales, 1977; MRCP (UK) 1984; FFA RCS Eng. 1987. Cons. Anaesth. (Intens. Care) Roy. Devon & Exeter Hosp.

MUNN, Olivia Michela Anna 4 Greenwood Road, Thames Ditton KT7 0DY Tel: 020 8398 7329 Email: oliviamunn@hotmail.com — MB ChB 1997 Birm.; ChB Birm. 1997. GP VTS Cheltenham.

MUNN, Stephanie Elizabeth 307A Greenford Road, Greenford UB6 8RE Tel: 020 8575 7702 — MB BS 1988 Lond.; BSc (Hons.) Lond. 1985; MRCP (UK) 1992. Research Fell. & Hon. Sen. Regist. (Dermat.) Hammersmith Hosps. RPMS Lond. Socs: BMA; BAD. Prev: Regist. (Dermat.) Ealing Hosp. Lond.

*MUNNEKE, Graham John 17 Katherine Gardens, Ilford IG6 2LF — MB BS 1996 Lond.

*MUNNEKE, Robert 17 Katherine Gardens, Ilford IG6 2LF — MB BS 1998 Lond.; MB BS Lond 1998.

MUNNELLY, Joan Teresa Esher Green Surgery, Esher Green Drive, Esher KT10 8BX Tel: 01372 462726 Fax: 01372 471050; 6 Heathside, Hinchley Wood, Esher KT10 9TB — MB BCh BAO 1983 NUI; LRCPI & LRCSI 1983; Cert. Family Plann. JCC 1989; DObst RCPI 1986; DCH NUI 1986. (RCSI) GP Princip. Esher; Clin. Med. Off. (Child Health) Kingston & Esher HA. Prev: Clin. Med. Off. (Child Health) W. Surrey & NE Hants. HA; Trainee GP Fetcham Leatherhead VTS; SHO (Paediat.) Childr. Hosp. Dub.

MUNNELLY, Niall Hillcrest, Keldholme, Kirkbymoorside, York YO62 6ND — MB BCh BAO 1990 NUI.

MUNNELLY, Sonia Mary Flat 2, 30 West End Lane, London NW6 4PA — MB BS 1994 Lond.

MUNNO, Antonio Bedford Road Surgery, 273 Bedford Road, Kempston, Bedford MK42 8QD Tel: 01234 852222 — MB BS 1990 Lond.; BSc 1987; MRCGP 1995; DRCOG 1994; DCH RCP Lond. 1994; DGM RCP Lond. 1993. (university college and Middlesex Hospital University, London)

MUNNOCH, Mr David Alexander 33 Malmesbury Park, Runcorn WA7 1XD Tel: 01928 571595 Fax: 01928 571596 Email: alex.munnoch@talk21.com — MB ChB 1988 Dundee; FRCS Ed. 1994. (Dund. Univ.) Specialist Regist. (Plastic Surg.)Whiston Hosp. Liverp. Prev: SHO (Plastic Surg.) Dundee Roy. Infirm.

MUNNOCH, Norma Agnes Mary 33 Malmesbury Park, Runcorn WA7 1XD Tel: 01928 571595 — MB ChB 1989 Dundee; FRCA 1996. Specialist Regist. (Anaesth.) Liverp. Roy. Infirm., (merseyside Rotat.), Part - time Train. Prev: Specialist Regist. (Anaesth.) Ninewells Hosp. Dundee.

*MUNNS, Jacqui 79 Sirdar Road, London W11 4EQ — MB BS 1998 Lond.; MB BS Lond 1998.

MUNRO, Alan Henry Girvin Guisachan, Black Isle Road, Muir of Ord IV6 7RR — MB ChB 1968 Ed.; FRCP Ed. 1984; FRCP Ed. 1974; FRCGP 1989, M 1976.

MUNRO, Alastair John Blaich Cottage, Locheilside, Fort William, Inverness IV3 6LA — MB ChB 1975 Dundee; BSc St. And. 1972; MRCP (UK) 1978. Lect. (Clin. Oncol.) Univ. Edin.

MUNRO, Mr Alexander 23 Eriskay Road, Inverness IV2 3LX Tel: 01463 223804 — MB ChB 1967 Aberd.; ChM Aberd. 1978; FRCS Glas. 1993; FRCS Ed. 1972. (Aberd.) Cons. Gen. Surg. Raigmore Hosp. Inverness. Socs: Fell. Assn Surgs. GB & Irel.; (Colo-Proctol. Sect.) Roy. Soc. Med. Prev: Sen. Regist. Grampian HB & St. Mark's Hosp. Lond.; SHO Hosp. Sick Childr. Lond.

MUNRO, Alexander James Cranford Medical Centre, 24 High Street, Cranford, Hounslow West, Hounslow TW5 9RG Tel: 020 8564 8696 Fax: 020 8564 7891; 16 Aquarius, Eel Pie Island, Twickenham TW1 3EA Tel: 020 8892 6033 Fax: 020 8891 1735 — MB ChB 1972 Ed.; MRCP (UK) 1975. Chairm. Hounslow PCG. Socs: Roy. Soc. Med.; Coun. GP Sect. Prev: Sen. Regist. (Chem. Path.) Kings Coll. Hosp. Lond.

MUNRO, Alexandra Janet 45 Deeview Road S., Cults, Aberdeen AB15 9NA — MB ChB 1988 Aberd.; MRCGP 1993.

MUNRO, Alison Margaret Conival, 4 dene Park, Biggar ML12 6DD — MB ChB 1989 Aberd.; MRCGP 1994. Staff Grade (Gen. Psychiat.) Govan Resource Centre Glas.

MUNRO, Alistair John Clinical Biochemistry Department, Worcester Royal Infirmary, Ronkswood Branch, Newtown Road, Worcester WR5 1HN Tel: 01905 760630 Fax: 01905 760781 Email: alistair.munro@wri-tr.wmids.nhs.uk — MB BS 1975 Lond.; BSc (Hons.) Lond. 1972, MD 1984; FRCPath 1996, M 1984. (St. Bart.) Cons. Chem. Path. Worcs. Acute Hosp.s NHS Trust.

MUNRO, Angela Elizabeth Brazell Almondsbury Surgery, Sundays Hill, Almondsbury BS32 4DS Tel: 01454 613161 — MB ChB 1989 Birm.; DRCOG 1991. GP Retainer, Almondsbury, Bristol. Prev: GP Asst. Stoke-on-Trent; GP f/t Partner; Trainee GP Walsall VTS.

MUNRO, Anita Rumpha 1 Arlington Gardens, London W4 4EZ — MB ChB 1993 Manch.

MUNRO, Anne Lyle (retired) 6/19 Succoth Court, Succoth Park, Edinburgh EH12 6BY Tel: 0131 337 3167 — MB ChB Ed. 1955; 1959 DA Eng.; 1958 DObst RCOG. Prev: Sen. Community/Clin. Med. Off. (Family Plann.) Lothian HB.

MUNRO, Bernard Francis Chase Farm Hospital, The Ridgeway, Enfield EN2 8JL Tel: 020 8366 9152 Fax: 020 8366 6586; 34 Ravenscroft Park, Barnet EN5 4NH — BM 1980 Soton.; FRCA 1989. Cons. Anaesth. Chase Farm Hosp. Middlx. Prev: Sen. Regist. (Anaesth.) Univ. Coll. Hosp. Lond.

MUNRO, Cameron Holburn Medical Group, 7 Albyn Place, Aberdeen AB10 1YE Tel: 01224 400800 Fax: 01224 407777; 22 Cairncry Avenue, Aberdeen AB16 5DS Tel: 01224 484471 — MB ChB 1983 Aberd.; DRCOG 1990.

MUNRO, Catherine Mary Highview Surgery, 20 Southgate Road, Potters Bar EN6 5DZ Tel: 01707 871980 Fax: 01707 871995; 34 Ravenscroft Park, Barnet EN5 4NH — BM 1980 Soton.; MRCGP 1984; DRCOG 1982. (Soton.)

MUNRO, Catriona Jane Fallon and Partners, 1 Houghton Lane, Shevington, Wigan WN6 8ET Tel: 01257 253311 Fax: 01257 251081 — MB ChB 1980 Manch.; MRCGP 1988; DCH RCP Lond. 1983; Cert. Family Plann. JCC 1983; DRCOG 1982. Gen. Practitioner.

MUNRO, Charles Keith Clarendon Medical, 35 Northland Avenue, Londonderry BT48 7JW Tel: 028 7126 5391 Fax: 028 7126 5932 — MB BCh BAO 1967 Belf. (Qu. Univ. Belf.) Sen. Foren. Med. Off. Lond.derry. Prev: Regist. (Psychiat.) Gransha Hosp. Lond.derry; Ho. Off. Altnagelvin Hosp. Lond.derry.

MUNRO, Colin Scott Department Dermatology, Southern General Hospital NHS Trust, 1345 Govan Road, Glasgow G51 4TF Tel: 0141 201 1567 Fax: 0141 201 2989 — MB BChir 1977 Camb.; MA

MUNRO

Camb. 1977, MD 1987; FRCP Glas. 1995; MRCP (UK) 1978. (Univ. Coll. Hosp.) Cons. Dermat. S.. Gen. Hosp. & Vict. Infirm. Glas.; Hon. Clin. Sen. Lect. Univ. Glas. Prev: Sen. Regist. (Dermat.) Roy. Vict. Infirm. Newc.

MUNRO, David Ernest 21 West End, Walcott, Lincoln LN4 3ST Tel: 01526 861375 — MD 1959 Glas.; MB ChB 1943; DPM RCPSI 1953. (Univ. Glas.) Prev: Phys. Supt. & Cons. Psychiat. Bilbohall Hosp. Elgin.

MUNRO, David George Matheson Old Distillery Surgery, Ardronie Park, Kingussie PH21 1ET Tel: 01540 661233 Fax: 01540 661277 — MB ChB 1970 Glasgow; MB ChB Glas. 1970. (Glasgow) GP Kingussie, Inverness-sh.

MUNRO, David Sutherland (retired) 11B Sunnymead, Keynsham, Bristol BS31 1JD — MB ChB 1948 St. And.

MUNRO, Denise Irene 49 Ladysmith Road, Ashton-under-Lyne OL6 9BZ — MRCS Eng. LRCP Lond. 1975.

MUNRO, Donald Oaklands House, 163 Netherton Lane, Netherton, Wakefield WF4 4HL Tel: 01924 274234 — MB ChB Ed. 1943; FRCP Ed. 1972, M 1949; FFA RCS Eng. 1954; DA Eng. 1948. (Ed.) Cons. Emerit. Nottm. Hosps. Socs: Fell. Roy. Soc. Med.; Assn. Anaesths.; IC Soc. Prev: Cons. Admin. Charge Intens: Care Unit City Hosp. Nottm.; Resid. Ho. Surg. Edin. Roy. Infirm.; Flight Lt. RAFVR.

MUNRO, Donald Forrest Saqqajja House, Coombehurst Drive, Basingstoke RG21 3HE Tel: 01256 473337 Fax: 01256 329909; Saqqajja House, Coombehurst Drive, Basingstoke RG21 3HE Tel: 01256 473337 Fax: 21256 329909 — MB BS 1958 Lond.; MRCS Eng. LRCP Lond. 1958; DObst. RCOG 1960. (Westm.) Med. Ref. Basingstoke Crematorium Basingstoke RG25 2BA. Socs: BMA; RSM. Prev: Resid. Obst. Asst. W.m. Hosp. Lond.; Sen. Partner Ch. Grange Partnership Basingstoke Hants.; Capt. RAMC (O & G) Brit. Milit. Hosp., Benghazi.

MUNRO, Professor Donald Sinclair (retired) 26 Endcliffe Grove Avenue, Sheffield S10 3EJ Tel: 0114 266 2837 — MB ChB 1947 Aberd.; MD Aberd. 1957; FRCP Lond. 1967, M 1949. Prev: Sir Arthur Hall Prof. Med. Univ. Sheff.

MUNRO, Dorothy Jane Tweeddale Medical Practice, High Street, Fort William PH33 6EU Tel: 01397 703136 Fax: 01397 700139; 6 Lady Margaret Drive, Corpach, Fort William PH33 7LQ — MB ChB 1983 Dundee; MRCGP 1996.

MUNRO, Dowling Donald 18 Upper Hollis, Great Missenden HP16 9HP Tel: 01494 864683 — MB BS Lond. 1954; MD Lond. 1975; FRCP Lond. 1974, M 1960; MRCS Eng. LRCP Lond. 1954; DObst RCOG 1955. (Roy. Free) Civil Cons. Dermat. RN; Med. Off. St John's Ambul. Bucks. Socs: Fell. Roy. Soc. Med.; BMA. Prev: Cons. Dermat. St. Bart. Hosp. Lond. & Roy. Masonic Hsop. Lond.; US Pub. Health Research Fell. W.. Reserve Univ. Cleveland, USA.

MUNRO, Duncan Sutherland, OStJ, RD, Surg. Capt. RNR (retired) 10 Sandifield Avenue, Milngavie, Glasgow G62 8NR Tel: 0141 956 3776 — MB ChB 1956 Glas.; MRCGP 1970; DCH Eng. 1960; DObst RCOG 1958. Surg. Capt. RNR. Prev: GP Glas.

MUNRO, Elaine 61 Millar Street, Glassford, Strathaven ML10 6TD — MB ChB 1993 Dundee.

MUNRO, Ernest Wilfrid Bedlington Medical Group, Glebe Road, Bedlington NE22 6JX Tel: 01670 822695 Fax: 01670 531860; 3 Shadfon Farm Mews, Hepscott, Morpeth NE61 6NP — MB BS 1975 Newc.; MRCGP 1979; DRCOG 1978.

MUNRO, Mr Euan Nicholas Department of Surgery, Frenchay Hospital, Beckspool Road, Bristol BS16 1JE Tel: 01785 813673 — MB ChB 1986 Dundee; MD Dundee 1994, BMSc (Hons.) 1983; FRCS (Gen.) 1996; FRCS Ed. 1990. Cons. (Vasc. Gen. Surg.) Frenchay Hosp., Bristol. Socs: Surgic. Research Soc.; Assn. Surg.; Vasc. Surg. Soc. Prev: Sen. Regist. (Gen. & Vasc. Surg.) N. Trent Region; Career Regist. (Gen. Surg.) N. Trent Region; Regist. (Surg.) Centr. Birm. HA & N. Trent Region.

MUNRO, Fiona Jean Inverclyde Royal NHS Trust, Larkfield Road, Greenock PA16 0XN Fax: 01475 631700; The Storr, Langbank Drive, Kilmacolm PA13 4PL Fax: 01475 631700 — MB ChB 1989 Glas.; FRCA 1994. (Glasgow) Cons. Anaesth. Prev: Specialist Regist. (Anaesth.) Glas.; Career Regist. (Anaesth.) Glas.

MUNRO, Fiona Marie Eileen Appletree Cottage, Church Lane, Pirbright, Woking GU24 0JJ Tel: 01483 474308 Fax: 01483 474308 — MB ChB 1998 Dund.; BMSc (1st cl Hons) Dund. 1996. (Uni.

Dund.) SHO (Psych.) Unit. Med.& Dent. Sch's Guy's, St Thomas, & Kings Coll. Lond.

MUNRO, Mr Fraser Donald Royal Hospital For Sick Children, Sciennes Road, Edinburgh EH9 1LF Tel: 0131 536 0649 Fax: 0131 536 0685 Email: fdmunro@rcsed.ac.uk — MB ChB 1983 Ed.; FRCS Ed. 1988; FRCS (Paed.) 1996. (Ed.) Cons. (Paediat. Surg.) Roy. Hosp. Sick Child. Edin.

MUNRO, George Cheveley Park Medical Centre, Cheveley Park Shopping Centre, Belmont, Durham DH1 2UW Tel: 0191 386 4285 Fax: 0191 386 5934; Elpha Green, Farnley Hey Road, Durham DH1 4EA Tel: 0191 386 2808 — MB ChB 1970 Ed.; MRCGP 1974; DObst RCOG 1973. Fact. Med. Off. Kerry Foods Durh. City; Trainer (Gen. Pract.) N.umbria VTS; Med. Off. Frankland Prison Durh. Prev: Trainee GP Aberd. VTS.

MUNRO, Gertrude Heather Macarthur (retired) Barnbarroch House, Dalbeattie DG5 4QS — MB ChB 1951 Glas. Asst. Med. Off. Richmond, Twickenham & Roehampton HA. Prev: Ho. Phys. & Ho. Surg. Glas. Roy. Infirm.

MUNRO, Hamish Cameron 11C Skinnergate., Perth PH1 5JH — MB ChB 1992 Ed.

MUNRO, Helen Reid (retired) 26 Endcliffe Grove Avenue, Sheffield S10 3EJ — MB ChB 1949 Aberd.; DMRT Eng. 1973. Prev: Regist. (Radiother.) W.on Pk. Hosp. Sheff.

MUNRO, Hugh David Ross (retired) 4 Barnton Loan, Edinburgh EH4 6JQ Tel: 0131 312 7574 Fax: 0131 312 7574 — MB ChB 1955 Aberd.; 1955 MB ChB Aberd.; 1975 FRCGP; 1972 MRCOG; 1960 DObst RCOG; 1975 MRCGP. Prev: GP Kirkleston Edin.

MUNRO, Mr Ian Pinkerton (retired) Glencairn, Ranfurly Place, Bridge of Weir PA11 3DF Tel: 01505 612068 — MB ChB Glas. 1940; FRCS Glas. 1962; FRCS Ed. 1949; FRFPS Glas. 1948. Prev: Cons. ENT Surg. Glas. & Greenock.

MUNRO, James Farquharson Medical Care Research Unit, University of Sheffield, Regent Court, 30 Regent St., Sheffield S1 4DA Tel: 0114 222 5202 Fax: 0114 272 4095 Email: j.f.munro@sheffield.ac.uk — MB BS 1984 Lond.; BA (Hons.) Camb. 1981; MRCP (UK) 1989; MFPHM RCP (UK) 1995. Sen. Lect. (Health Serv. Research); Edr. Health Matters Magazine. Prev: Sen. Regist. (Pub. Health) Trent RHA; Regist. (Pub. Health) N. Derbysh. HA; Regist. (Gen. Med.) Rotherham Dist. Gen. Hosp.

MUNRO, Janet Christine The Maudsley Hospital, Denmark Hill, London SE5 8AZ Tel: 020 7919 3189 Fax: 020 7919 2418 Email: j.munro@iop.kcl.ac.uk — MB BS 1989 Lond. (Royal Free Hospital School of Medicine) Clin. research Worker (psychiat.), Inst. of Psychiat. Lond.; Hon. Sen. Regist. (Psychiat) Maudsley Hosp. Lond. Prev: Clin. Research Fell. Roy. Free Hosp.; SHO (Neurosurg.) Lond. Hosp.; Ho. Phys. Roy. Free Hosp.

MUNRO, John Forbes, OBE (retired) Dower House, Backhill, Carberry, Musselburgh EH21 8QD Tel: 0131 663 4935 Fax: 0131 663 4935 — MB ChB (Hons.) Ed. 1960; FRCP Ed. 1971, M 1963; FRCP Glas 1996; FRCP Lond. 1997. Hon. Fell. (Med.) W. Gen. Hosp. Edin. Prev: Sen. Lect. (Med.) W.. Gen. Hosp. Edin./p/tCons. Phys. E.. Gen. & Edenhall Hosp. Edin.

MUNRO, John Graham 6 Du Pre Walk, Wooburn Green, High Wycombe HP10 0QJ Tel: 01628 810584 — MB BCh Wales 1968. Socs: Fell. Roy. Soc. Med. Prev: Ho. Phys. Roy. Gwent Hosp.; Ho. Surg. Caerphilly & Dist. Miners Hosp.

MUNRO, John Hector MacLeven 22 Old Station Way, Woodburn Green, High Wycombe HP10 0HZ — MRCS Eng. LRCP Lond. 1941. (Lond. Hosp.)

MUNRO, John MacGregor (retired) Barnbarroch House, Dalbeattie DG5 4QS Tel: 01556 620208 — MB ChB 1952 Glas. Prev: Ho. Phys. Glas. Roy. Infirm.

MUNRO, John Michael 10 Hurst Lodge, Coolhurst Road, London N8 8ES — MB BS 1980 Lond.

MUNRO, John Stewart (retired) 2 The Manor Close, Shincliffe Village, Durham DH1 2NS Tel: 0191 386 5818 — MB ChB 1955 Ed.; DObst RCOG 1961. Prev: Hosp. Pract. (Psychol. Med.) Dryburn Hosp. Durh.

MUNRO, Julia Ashcroft 2 Greenlawns, Penylan, Cardiff CF23 6AW — MB BS 1961 Lond.; MRCS Eng. LRCP Lond. 1961.

MUNRO, Karen Anne Flat 4, Foulkes House, Opal Ct., Moseley Road, Fallowfield, Manchester M14 6ZZ Tel: 0161 225 4395 — MB ChB 1995 Manch. SHO Paediat. Wythenshawe Hosp. Manch.

MUNRO-FAURE

*MUNRO, Laura Helen Dreva Cottages, Broughton, Biggar ML12 6HH — MB ChB 1995 Aberd.

MUNRO, Laura Rachel Department Haematology, Aberdeen Royal Infirmary, Forrester Hill, Aberdeen AB25 2 Tel: 01224 588834; 29 Devanha Gardens S., Aberdeen AB11 7UG — MB ChB 1991 Manch.; MRCP (Glas.) 1994. Specialist Regist. Haemat. Aberd. Roy. Infirm.

MUNRO, Lilias Margaret Agnes (retired) Maplehurst, 22 Ratcliffe Road, Leicester LE2 3TB Tel: 0116 270 8485 — MB BS 1953 Lond.; MRCS Eng., LRCP Lond. 1953. Prev: Ho. Surg. Roy. Free Hosp.

MUNRO, Lillie Lund (retired) Glan-y-Don A., Bay View, Windsor Mount, Ramsey IM8 3EQ Tel: 01624 812714 — MB ChB Liverp. 1941; DPH Liverp. 1952; MFCM 1972. Prev: Sen. Med. Off. (Sch. Health) & Dep. MOH I. of Man.

MUNRO, Lucy Margaret 1 Laggan Road, Bishopbriggs, Glasgow G64 1BS — MB ChB 1993 Glas.

MUNRO, Malcolm Ross Totton Health Centre, Testwood Lane, Totton, Southampton SO40 3ZN Tel: 02380 865051; 32 Lyndhurst Road, Ashurst, Southampton SO40 7DU Tel: 02380 865051 — MB BS 1957 Lond.; DObst RCOG 1963. (Char. Cross) Prev: Ho. Surg., Ho. Phys. & Cas. Off. Char. Cross Hosp. Lond.

MUNRO, Margaret 42 Blackheath Park, Blackheath, London SE3 9SJ Tel: 020 8852 8435 — MB ChB 1945 Ed.; BSc (Physiol.), MB ChB Ed. 1945; FRCP Ed. 1973, M 1954; FRCPsych 1991, M 1971; DCH Eng. 1946, DPM 1957. Hon. Cons. Child Psychiat. Greenwich Dist. Hosp. Prev: Cons. Bexley Clinic Child & Family Psychiat.; Acad. Regist. Nat. Hosp. Qu. Sq.; Regist. (Neurol. & Neurosurg.) Hosp. Sick Childr. Gt. Ormond St.

MUNRO, Margaret Anne Park Lodge, Orphan Drive, Liverpool L6 7UN Tel: 0151 287 6918 Fax: 0151 287 0372 — MB ChB 1976 Dundee; MRCPsych 1981. Cons. Acute & Community Psychiat. N. Mersey Community NHS Trust. Prev: Cons. Forens. Psychiat. Ashworth Hosp. Maghull; Sen. Regist. (Forens. Psychiat.) Yorks. RHA; Med. Off. (Ment. Health) Govt. of Lesotho.

MUNRO, Margaret Evelyn The Gables, Steeple Ashton, Trowbridge BA14 6EU Tel: 01380 870393 — MB ChB Glas. 1943; DPH Lond. 1948. (Glas.) Prev: Ho. Phys. Roy. Hosp. Sick Childr. Glas. & Stobhill Hosp. Glas.; Capt. RAMC.

MUNRO, Mark Hugh William 80 Woodgrange Road, Forest Gate, London E7 0EW Tel: 020 8555 3336 Fax: 020 8502 1963 — MB BS 1980 Lond.; BDS (Hons.) 1973; FDS RCS Eng. 1979. (London Hospital) Socs: RSM. Prev: Lect. Oral Surg. Roy. Lond. Hosp.

MUNRO, Melanie Fiona Rowley Rectory, Old Village Road, Little Weighton, Cottingham HU16 — BM 1981 Soton.; MRCGP 1986; DRCOG 1986.

MUNRO, Michael John Whinnybrae, 45 Deeview Road S., Cults, Aberdeen AB15 9NA — MB ChB 1989 Aberd.

MUNRO, Neil Allan Robertson Harville House, Harville Road, Wye, Ashford TN25 5EU; Wye Mill House, Bridge St, Wye, Ashford TN25 5EB Tel: 01233 813867 Fax: 01233 813830 — MB BS 1984 Lond.; MA Oxf. 1976; MRCP (UK) 1988; Dphil 1995. Cons. (Neurol.) King's Coll. Lond. & William Harvey Hosp. Ashford. Prev: Sen. Regist. Nat. Hosp. For Neurol. & Neurosurg., Lond.

MUNRO, Neil Cameron University Hospital of North Durham, North Road, Durham DH1 5TW Tel: 0191 333 2333 — MB ChB 1982 Dundee; MRCP (UK) 1985; Cert Med Educat 2000 University of Newcastle; FRCP 1999 London. Cons. in Gen. & Respirat. Med. N. Durh. Health Care NHS Trust; Caldicott Guardian N. Durh. Healthcare NHS Trust. Socs: Brit. Thoracic Soc.; Europ. Respirat. Soc. Prev: Cons. Gen. & Respirat. Med. N. Durh. Acute Hosp. Trust Dryburn Hosp. Durh. & Shotley Bridge Hosp.; Sen. Regist. & Regist. N.ern RHA; Regist. (Med.) Hexham Gen. Hosp.

MUNRO, Neil Macarthur Capelfield Surgery, Elm Road, Claygate, Esher KT10 0EH Tel: 01372 462501 Fax: 01372 470258; Email: neil@nmunro.demon.co.uk — MRCS Eng. LRCP Lond. 1978; FRCGP 1997, M 1985; MICGP 1987; MRCGP 1985; Dip. Med. Educat. Dund 1995; MMed. Dundee 1997. (RCSI) GP Claygate; Ass. Spec. (Diabetes) Diabetes Centre Chelsea & W.minster Hosp.; MRGGP Examr. Socs: BMA. Prev: Med. Off. HMS Endurance; SHO (A & E) RN Hosp. Haslar; SHO (Obst.) St. Peters Hosp. Chertsey.

*MUNRO, Niall Alasdair 23 Eriskay Road, Inverness IV2 3LX — MB ChB 1994 Aberd.

MUNRO, Nicholas Pitt 50 Whitworth Crescent, Southampton SO18 1GD — MB BS 1994 Lond. (St Bartholomews) SHO Rotat. (Surg.) Brighton NHS Trust.

MUNRO, Nicola Ruth 9 School End, Aynho, Banbury OX17 3BS Tel: 01869 810885 — MB ChB 1993 Auckland; DRCOG 1995. Trainee GP/SHO (A & E) Horton Gen. Hosp. Banbury. Prev: Trainee GP/SHO (O & G) P.ss Margt. Hosp. Swindon VTS & (Psychiat.) St. Crispin's Hosp. N.ampton; SHO (c/o the Elderly) Bristol Hosp.

MUNRO, Nigel Hastings The Health Centre, 35 High St., Bonnyrigg EH19 2DA; 12 Maryfield Place, Bonnyrigg EH19 3BQ — MB ChB 1958 Ed.; MRCGP 1966. Socs: BMA.

MUNRO, Olive Isabel (retired) Oakwood, Bayleys Hill, Sevenoaks TN14 6HS Tel: 01732 454993 — MRCS Eng. LRCP Lond. 1949. Prev: SCMO Tunbridge Wells HA.

MUNRO, Peter Ian Ballyclare Group Practice, Ballyclare Health Centre, George Avenue, Ballyclare BT39 9HL Tel: 028 9332 2575 Fax: 028 9334 9897; Talisker Lodge, 54B Templepatrick Road, Ballyclare BT39 9TX Tel: 01960 323421 — MB BCh BAO 1970 Belf.; FRCGP 1993, M 1974; DObst RCOG 1972. Authorised Med. Examr. Civil Aviat. Auth.

MUNRO, Philip Thomas Tel: 0141 201 1864 Email: phil.munro@sgh.scot.nhs.uk — MB ChB 1989 Glas.; MRCP (UK) 1993; FFAEM 1999. (University Of Glasgow) Cons. In A&E Med. S. Gen. Hosp., Glas.. Socs: Brit. Assn. Accid. & Emerg. Med.; Fell.Fac. Accid. & Emerg. Med.; Amer. Coll. Emerg. Phys.s. Prev: Specialist Regist. (A & E) Vict. Infirm., Glas.; Specialist Regist. (A & E) CrossHo. Hosp. Kilmarnock; Regist. (A & E Med.) Cork Univeristy Hosp. & Roy. Infirm. Edin.

MUNRO, Robert Duncan Great Bansons Surgery, Bansons Lane, Ongar CM5 9AR Tel: 01277 363028 Fax: 01277 365264; The Bays, The St, Ongar CM5 9NH Tel: 01277 362257 — MB BS 1990 Lond. (St. Bart. Hosp.)

MUNRO, Robin Alexander Leslie Law Hospital, Carluke ML8 5 Tel: 01698 361100 — MB ChB 1989 Aberd.; MRCP (UK) 1992. Cons. Rhewmatologist, Law Hosp. Prev: Sen. Regist. (Rhem. Gen. Med.) Glas. Roy. Infirm.

MUNRO, Ronald Mackenzie (retired) 19 Allesley Hall Drive, Allesley Park, Coventry CV5 9NS Tel: 01203 672518 — MB ChB 1943 St. And. Prev: Ho. Surg. ENT Dept. & Jun. Cas. Off. Roy. Infirm. Dundee.

MUNRO, Thomas Norman (retired) Arlington, Arlington Drive, Poynton, Stockport SK12 1JB Tel: 01625 873589 — MB BS 1953 Lond.; FFA RCS Eng. 1960; DA Eng. 1955. Hon. Cons. Anaesth. Wythenshawe Hosp. Manch.

*MUNRO, Wendy Alicia 43 Grosvenor Avenue, Carshalton SM5 3EJ Tel: 0956 840035 — MB BS 1997 Lond.

MUNRO, William Pitt St. Mary's Surgery, James St., Southampton SO14 1PJ Tel: 02380 333778 — MB BS 1965 Lond.; MRCS Eng. LRCP Lond. 1965; DObst RCOG 1967. (Univ. Coll. Hosp.) Clin. Asst. Gr. Ho. Hostel for Ment. Handicap. Adults; Clin. Asst. Soton. Drugs Advis. Centre. Socs: BMA & Brit. Med. Acupunc. Soc. Prev: Regist. (Obst.) Qu. Eliz. Hosp., Barbados; Hon. Vis. Med. Off. Newc. W.. Suburbs Matern. Hosp., Austral.; Clin. Asst. Wallsend Dist. Hosp., Austral.

MUNRO, William Sim SALT (Stress and Life Trust), The Istana, Freezeland Lane, Bexhill-on-Sea TN39 5JD Tel: 01424 219133 Fax: 01424 219133 Email: saltmunro@compuserve.com — MB ChB Ed. 1952; MFOM RCP Lond. 1981; MFCH RCP (UK) 1989; FRIPHH 1998; DPH Ed. 1962; DIH Eng. 1962; DTM & H Liverp. 1958. (Ed.) Stress Cons. Bexhill-on-Sea; Chief Exec. Stress & Life Trust; Ref. DSS. Socs: Fell. Roy. Soc. Med.; Soc. Occupat. Med.; Fell. Roy. Soc. Trop. Med. & Hye. Prev: Regional Med. Off. The Post Office SE; Med. Dir. Armour Pharmaceut.; Head Med. Operats. Fisons Pharmaceut. Ltd.

MUNRO-DAVIES, Mrs Lisa Edana Wessex Neurological Centre, Southampton General Hospital, Tremona Road, Southampton Tel: 02380 777222; 25 Barn Piece, Chandlers Ford, Eastleigh SO53 4HP Email: lisa.davies@physiol.ox.ac.uk — MB BS Lond. 1991; FRCS Eng. 1996. (Roy. Free) Specialist Regis. In Neurosurg., Wessex Newrological Centre, Soton.

MUNRO-FAURE, Arthur Douglas (retired) Moorings, Butlers Dene Road, Woldingham, Caterham CR3 7HH Tel: 01883 652373 — BM BCh 1949 Oxf.; MA Oxf. 1949; FRCP Lond. 1978, M 1956; FRCP

MUNSADIA

Canada 1958. Prev: Dir. Clin. Applied Research Wellcome Foundat. Ltd.

MUNSADIA, Ishwarlal Dahyabhai Samuel Falic Centre, Birch Hill Hospital, Union Road, Rochdale OL12 9QB; Ross Moyne, 401 Rochdale Road, Walsden, Todmorden OL14 6RH — MB ChB 1963 Aberd.; MRCPsych 1974; DPM Ed. & Glas. 1968. (Aberd.) Cons. Psychiat. Birch Hill Hosp. Rochdale. Prev: Sen. Regist. (Psychiat.) St. Luke's Hosp. Middlesbrough; Med. & Surg. Ho. Off. Aberd. Roy. Infirm.; Psychiat. Regist. Ross Clinic Aberd. & Kingseat Hosp. Newmachar.

MUNSCH, Mr Christopher Mark Yorkshire Heart Centre, Leeds General Infirmary, Gt George St., Leeds LS1 3EX Tel: 0113 292 3436 Fax: 0113 292 6657 Email: chrismunch@lineone.net; 1 Wellbank Cottages, Dacre Bank, Harrogate HG3 4EP Tel: 01423 781382 — MB ChB 1978 Manch.; ChM Manch. 1990; FRCS Ed. 1983; FRCS Eng. 1983; T(S) 1991. (Manchester) Cons. Cardiothoracic Surg. Gen. Infirm. Leeds.; Hon. Sen. Clin. Lect. Univ. Leeds; Train. Progr. Dir. Yorks. Regional Specialty Adviser Cardiothoracic Surg.; Tutor in Cardiothoracic Surg.-Roy. Coll. of Surg.s of Eng.. Socs: BMA; Soc. Cardiothoracic Surg. GB & Irel. (Exofficio Mem. Exec 2000); Australasian Soc. Cardiothoracic Surg.s. Prev: Sen. Regist. (Surg.) Hammersmith Hosp. Lond. & St. Geo.'s Hosp. Lond.; Research Fell. Baker Instititute Melbourne.

MUNSHI, Firoze Ratanshah 254 Watford Road, Harrow HA1 3TX Tel: 020 8922 5750 — MB BS 1963 Vikram; DA Bombay 1966. (M.G.M. Med. Coll. Indore) Cons., ManorHo. Hosp., Golders Green, Lond.

MUNSHI, Mr Nurul Islam 27 Fordwich Road, Welwyn Garden City AL8 6EX Tel: 01707 376698 Fax: 01707 896345 — MB BS Rajshahi 1968; FRCS Glas. 1988. Assoc. Specialist Orthop. Socs: BOA; BMA.

MUNSHI, Shahabuddin Castlebeck Care, 1a Enterprise House, Valley Street North, Darlington DL1 1PY Tel: 01325 252001 Fax: 01325 252004 Email: munshi@castlebeck-care.co.uk; Parkdale, 20 High Green, Woodham Village, Newton Aycliffe DL5 4RZ Tel: 01325 320646 Email: munshi@castlebeck-care.com — MB BS 1971 Calcutta; DPM 1978. (Calcutta Nat. Med. Coll.) Cons. Psychiat. Castlebeck Care Darlington; Cons. (Psychiat.) N. Tees NHS Trust. Socs: Fell. RSM; Founder Mem. Brit. Assoc. of Ment. Health and Law Lond. Prev: Cons. (Psychiat.) S. Durh. NHS Trust.

MUNSHI, Shahid Ahmed Bashir Kearsley Medical Centre, Jackson St., Kearsley, Bolton BL4 8EP Tel: 01204 573164 Fax: 01204 792161; Tel: 01204 497428 — MB ChB 1984 Manch.; MRCGP 1995; DRCOG 1995. (Manch.) Tutor (Gen. Pract.) Undergrad. Med. Studs. Bolton.

MUNSHI, Sohail Bashir Collegiate Medical Centre, Brideoak Street, Manchester M8 0AT Tel: 0161 205 4364 Fax: 0161 203 5511 — MB ChB 1991 Manch.; MRCGP 1995; DRCOG 1993. (Manch.) GP Princip.

MUNSIE, Andrew James Flat 1, 26 Pelham Road, London SW19 1SX — MB ChB 1991 Cape Town.

MUNSLOW, Debra Jane Logan, Harper and Munslow, Castlefield Surgery, Castle Way, Stafford ST16 1BS Tel: 01785 223012; 24 St Johns Road, Stafford ST17 9AS — MB BS 1983 Lond.; MRCGP 1987; DRCOG 1987. Prev: Trainee GP Stafford VTS.

MUNSON, David John Cringleford Surgery, Cantley Lane, Norwich NR4 6TA Tel: 01603 54678 Fax: 01603 58287; The Coach House, 2 Colney Lane, Cringleford, Norwich NR4 7RE — MB BS 1978 Lond.

MUNSON, Mr Kenneth William (retired) The Old Farm, Rectory Lane, Breadsall, Derby DE21 5LL Tel: 01332 831659 — MB BS 1965 Lond.; FRCS Eng. 1971. Cons. Urol. S. Derbysh. Health Dist. Prev: Sen. Regist. (Urol.) Kings Coll. Hosp. Lond.

MUNT, David Francis (retired) 56 Kassassin Street, Southsea PO4 9PT Tel: 01705 734951 — MB BS Lond. 1959; DObst RCOG 1963. Prev: GP S.sea.

MUNTARBHORN, Mr Smarn 6 Atherton Road, Barnes, London SW13 9NH Tel: 020 8748 8152 — MB BS 1941 Lond.; FRCS Eng. 1945; MRCS Eng. LRCP Lond. 1941 FICS 1950; Hon. MD Univ. Sonkla, Thailand 1980. (Guy's) Emerit. Prof. (Surg.) Chulalongkorn Univ. Bangkok, Thailand. Socs: Fell. Amer. Coll. Chest Phys.

MUNTON, Mr Charles Gregory Francis (cons. rooms), 36 Marsham St., Maidstone ME14 1HG Tel: 01622 756038 Fax: 01622 756038; 86 Amsbury Road, Hunton, Maidstone ME15 0QH Tel: 01622 745831 Fax: 01622 756038 — MB ChB Birm 1960; FRCS (Ophth.) Eng. 1966; FRCOphth 1989; DO RCS Eng. 1962. Cons. Ophth. Surg. (Private Pract.) Maidstone Kent. Socs: Fell. Roy. Soc. Med. Prev: Cons. Ophth. Surg. Kent Co. Ophth. & Aural Hosp. Maidstone & Medway Hosp.; Sen. Regist. (Ophth.) Shrewsbury Eye & Ear Hosp.; Regist. Wolverhampton & Midl. Cos. Eye Infirm.

MUNTONI, Mr Francesco Department of Paediatrics & Neonatal Medicine, Hammersmith Hospital, Du Cane Road, London W12 0NN Tel: 020 8743 2030 Fax: 020 8740 8281 Email: fmuntoni@rpms.ac.uk; 166 Gloucester Terrace, London W2 6QR Tel: 020 7262 8953 — State Exam 1984 Cagliari; Child Neurol. & Psychiat. Specialisation 1985; SASSARI. Prof. & Cons. (Paediat. Neurol.) Hammersmith Hosp. Lond. Socs: Brit. Paediat. Neurol. Assn.; World Muscle Soc.; Eur. Soc. Paediat. Neurol.

MUNYARD, Paul Frederick Royal Cornwall Hospital, Treliske, Truro TR1 3LJ Tel: 01872 274242 Email: paul.munyard@rcht.swest.nhs.uk; St Petroc, The Avenue, Truro TR1 1HR Tel: 01872 272382 — BM 1980 Soton.; MRCP (UK) 1988; FRCPCH 1997; DCH RCP Lond. 1985. Cons. Paedia Treliske Hosp. Cornw. Socs: BMA; Brit. Assn. Perinatal Med. Prev: Sen. Regist. (Neonat.) Univ. Coll. Hosp. Lond.; Sen. Regist. (Paediat.) Whittington Hosp. Lond.; Research Regist. (Paediat. Respirat. Med.) Roy. Brompton Nat. Heart & Lung Hosp.Lond.

MUOGBO, Joseph Chidi St Joseph's Medical Centre, 350 Upper Parliament Street, Liverpool L8 7QL Tel: 0151 709 3985 Fax: 0151 708 5367; 276 Upper Parliament Street, Liverpool L8 7QE Tel: 0151 709 3985 — MB BS 1965 Calcutta; DA Ibadan 1971. (Calcutta Med. Coll.) Princip. GP Liverp. FPC. Prev: Trainee GP Liverp. VTS; Regist. (Anaesth.) St. Helens & Knowsley HA.

MUOTUNE, Andrew Peter 94 Ashburton Road, Kelvindale, Glasgow G12 0LZ — MB ChB 1991 Manc.

MUOTUNE, Hannah 94 Ashburton Road, Glasgow G12 0LZ Tel: 0141 334 1606 — MB ChB 1994 Manch.; MRCOG (Pt. 1); BSc (Med. Sci.) St. And. 1991. SHO (Urol.) Glas. Roy. Infirm. Prev: SHO (Obst.) St. Mary's Paddington; SHO (Gyn. & Obst.) Roy. Free Hosp. Hampstead.

MUPANEMUNDA, Richard Henry Neonatal Unit Princess of Wales Womens Unit, Birmingham Heartlands Hospital, Bordesley Green East, Birmingham B9 5SS Tel: 0121 424 3728 Fax: 0121 424 2718 Email: rhmunda@aol.com — BM 1983 Soton.; BSc (Hons.) Med. Cell Biol. & Biochem. Liverp. 1979; MRCP (UK) 1989; LMCC 1991; FRCPCH (1997). (Soton.) Cons. (Neonat. Med. & Paediat.) Birm. Heartlands Hosp. Socs: Roy. Coll. Phys. Lond.; Brit. Assn. Perinatal Med.; Fell. Roy. Coll. Paediat. & Child Health. Prev: Sen. Regist. (Paediat. Med.) Roy. Postgrad. Med. Sch. Hammersmith Hosp. Lond.; Sen. Fell. (Perinatal-Neonat. Med.) Univ. W.. Ontario St. Joseph's Health Centre Lond., Ontario, Canada; Sen. Fell. (Neonat. Med.) Univ. Toronto Hosp. for Sick Childr. Toronto, Ontario, Canada.

***MUQIT, Miratul Mohamid Khan** Flat 3, 7 Sienna Gardens, Edinburgh EH9 1PG — MB ChB 1997 Ed.

MUR LAFFON, Dionisio 126 Iffley Road, London W6 0PE Tel: 020 8748 8701 — LMS 1986 Madrid.

MURAD, Amnah Sabri (retired) Flat 6, 20 Hyde Park Place, Bayswater Road, London W2 2LP Tel: 020 7262 1741 — MB ChB Baghdad 1945; MS Baghdad 196; LMSSA Lond. 1949; LRCS Ed. 1948; DObst RCOG 1949; DGO & LM Dub. 1949. Prev: Dir. Qu. Alia Hosp. Wom. Baghdad, Iraq.

MURAD, Jane 6A Lawrence Gardens, Mill Hill, London NW7 4JT — MB BS 1988 Lond.; MRCGP 1993.

MURAD, Jwan Suad Suite 280, 28 Old Brompton Road, London SW7 3SS — MB ChB 1972 Mosul; MRCOG 1983; DObst RCPI 1982.

MURAD, Muhammad Jamal Rasheed 5 Farthing Court, Long Eaton, Nottingham NG10 3QU — MB BS 1984 Karachi.

MURALEEDARAN, Rajan 135 Welbeck Road, Harrow HA2 0RY — MB BS 1975 Madras.

MURALI KRISHNAN, Manian 22 The Spinney, Hartlepool TS26 0AW — MB BS 1984 Madras; DA (UK) 1990.

MURALITHARAN, Velaitham 50 Alston Road, Tooting, London SW17 0TP Tel: 020 8767 9112 — MB BS 1983 Peradeniya; FFA RCSI 1992. Regist. (Anaesth.) St. Mary's Hosp. Lond.

MURCH, Clifford Rowan Dept. of Radiol.., Hairmyres Hospital, Eaglesham Road, East Kilbride, Glasgow G75 8 Tel: 01355 220292;

MURDOCH

3 Barnes Crescent, Ayr KA7 2BW Tel: 01292 266351 — MB BS 1977 Lond.; MRCS Eng. LRCP Lond. 1977; MRCP (UK) 1982; FRCR 1987. (Guy's) Cons. Radiol. Lanarksh. Acute Hosp.s NHS Trust. Prev: Cons. Radiol. S. Ayrsh. Hosp. NHS Trust.

MURCH, Simon Harry University Department of Paediatric Gastroenterology, Royal Free Hospital, Pond St., London NW3 2QG Tel: 020 7830 2779 Fax: 020 7830 2146 Email: smurch@rfhsm.ac.uk; 149 Elms Crescent, London SW4 8QQ — MB BS 1980 Lond.; PhD Lond. 1995, BSc 1977; MRCP (UK) 1984; MRCS Eng. LRCP Lond. 1980; FRCP Lond. 1998; FRCPCH 1997. Sen. Lect. & Hon. Cons. Paediat. Gastroenterol. Roy. Free Hosp. Lond. Socs: Fell. Roy. Soc. Med.; Eur. Soc. Paediat. Gastroenterol. & Nutrit.; Brit. Soc. Immunol. Prev: Sen. Lect. (Paediat. Gastroenterol.), Lect. & Action Research Fell. (Child Health) St. Bart. Hosp. Lond.

MURCHIE, Peter 69 Macaulay Drive, Craigiebucker, Aberdeen AB15 8FL Tel: 01224 312386 — MB ChB 1994 Aberd.; BSc (Med. Sci.) 1992; MRCGP 1998.

MURCHISON, Angus Gordon Lorn Medical Centre, Soroba Road, Oban PA34 4HE Tel: 01631 563175 Fax: 01631 562708; Orasaig, Pulpit Hill, Oban PA34 — MB ChB 1970 Glas.

MURCHISON, John Tallach Royal Infirmary of Edinburgh, Lauriston Place, Edinburgh EH3 9YW Tel: 0131 536 2900 Fax: 0131 536 2920 Email: john.murchison@luht.scot.nhs.uk; 81 Woodfield Park, Edinburgh EH13 0RA — MB ChB 1984 Ed.; BSc (Hons.) Pharmacol. Ed. 1982; MRCP (UK) 1987; FRCR 1992; DMRD Ed. 1990; FRCP 1998. (Edinburgh) Cons. Radiol. Edin. Roy. Infirm. NHS Trust.; Hon Sen. Lect. Ed. Univ. Med. Sch. Prev: Sen. Regist. (Diag. Radiol.) Edin. Roy. Infirm. & W.. Gen. Hosp. Edin.; Regist. (Gen. Med.) Raigmore Hosp. Inverness; SHO (Gen. Med. & Gastroenterol.) W.. Gen. Hosp. Edin.

MURCHISON, Lilian Elizabeth (retired) 35 Lynedoch Road, Scone, Perth PH2 6RJ Tel: 01738 553651 — MB ChB 1959 Ed.; PhD Glas. 1969; FRCP Lond. 1987; FRCP Ed. 1981; MRCP (UK) 1970. Cons. Phys. Diabetes & Endocrinol. Aberd. Roy. Hosps. NHS Trust; Clin. Sen. Lect. Univ. Aberd. Prev: Lect. (Therap. & Clin. Pharmacol.) Univ. Aberd.

MURCHISON, Murdoch (retired) Ord House, Strathpeffer IV14 9AX Tel: 01997 421117 — MB ChB 1957 Ed.; FFCM RCP (UK) 1979, M 1974; DIH RCPS Glas. 1968; DPH Eng. 1963; DObst RCOG 1960. Prev: Chief Admin. Med. Off. & Dir. Pub. Health Grampian HB.

MURCHNER, Marion Patricia 19 The Crossway, Kenton, Newcastle upon Tyne NE3 4LB — State Exam Med 1992 Berlin.

MURCOTT, Christopher Adrian Madeira Road Surgery, 1A Madeira Road, Parkstone, Poole BH14 9ET Tel: 01202 741345; Woodside, 54 Anthonys Avenue, Lilliput, Poole BH14 8JH Email: chris.murcott@virgin.net — MB BS 1983 Lond.; MRCGP 1988; DRCOG 1987; Cert. Family Plann. JCC 1987; LFHom 1997 Royal Homeopathic Hosp.

MURDAY, Mr Andrew James 11 Consort Road, London SE15 2PH Tel: 020 7277 9969; St George's Hospital, Blackshaw Road, London SW17 0QT Tel: 020 8725 3565 Fax: 020 8725 2049 Email: ajmurday@sghms.ac.uk — MB BS 1977 Lond.; MA Camb. 1978; MS Lond. 1984, MB BS 1977; FRCS Eng. 1982. Cons. Cardiothoracic Surg. St. Geo. Hosp. Lond. Prev: Cons. Cardiothoracic Surg. Leeds Gen. Infirm.

MURDAY, Victoria Alice 11 Consort Road, London SE15 2PH Tel: 020 7277 9969; St George's Hospital Medical School, Department of Clinical Genetics, Cranmer Terrace, London SW17 0RE Tel: 020 8725 5331 Fax: 020 8767 8150 — MB BS 1977 Lond.; BSc Lond. 1974, MB BS 1977; MRCP (UK) 1980; FRCP Lond. 1994. Cons. Geneticist.

MURDESHWAR, Shalini Shankar Merthyr Tydfil Health Centre, Merthyr Tydfil CF47 0AY Tel: 01685 722884 Fax: 01685 370920 — MB BS 1960 Vikram. (Vikram) GP Merthyr Tydfil.

MURDIE, Mr William (retired) Cornerways, Church End, Biddenham, Bedford MK43 7JB Tel: 01234 51805 — MB ChB 1943 Ed.; FRCS Ed. 1947. Prev: Sen. Surg. Regist. Bedford Hosp. Gp.

***MURDIN, Louisa Jane** 32 Belvoir Road, Cambridge CB4 1JJ Tel: 01223 312843 Email: murdin@doctors.net.uk — BM BCh 1998 Oxf.; BM BCh Oxf 1998.

MURDIN, Philip Graham Tudor Lodge Health Centre, 3 Nithsdale Road, Weston Super Mare BS23 4JP Tel: 01934 622665 Fax:

01934 644332; Ranscombe House, Worlebury Hill Road, Weston Super Mare BS22 9TG — MB ChB 1969 Bristol; DObst RCOG 1972. GP Trainer Avon; Chairm. W.on Med. Assn. Socs: Med. Audit & Advis. Gp.

MURDOCH, Alastair John Macdonald Woodlands Surgery, Woodlands, Shadsworth Road, Blackburn BB1 2HR Tel: 01254 665664 Fax: 01254 695883 — MB ChB 1981 Manch.; BSc Manch. 1979, MB ChB 1981; MRCP (UK) 1984; MRCGP 1987.

MURDOCH, Alison Elizabeth 8 Heatherfield Court, Wilmslow SK9 2QE Tel: 01625 532430 Fax: 01625 532430 Email: alison@heatherfield.freeserve.co.uk — MB ChB Bristol 1988; MRCGP 1994; DRCOG 1994; DFFP 1994. (Bristol) Clin. Asst. Ophth. (p/t) Macclesfield Dist. Gen. Hosp. Socs: BMA. Prev: SHO Ophth. (p/t) N. Hamps. Hosp.; SHO Ophth.; Regtl. Med. Off. RAMC.

MURDOCH, Alison Pamela Reproductive Medicine, International Centre for Life, Times Square, Newcastle upon Tyne NE1 4EP Tel: 0191 219 4740 Fax: 0191 219 4747 — MD 1987 Ed.; BSc Ed. 1972, MD 1987, MB ChB 1975; MRCOG 1982. (Edinburgh) Cons. Gynaecologist and Sen. Lect. in Reproductive Med. Newc. Univ. Prev: Sen. Regist. (O & G) N.. RHA.

MURDOCH, Carol Jane 4 Penrith Avenue, Giffnock, Glasgow G46 6LU Tel: 0141 638 1790 — MB ChB 1989 Glas.; FRCA Lond. 1995. Specialist Regist. (Anaesth.). Socs: Assn. Anaesth.; Intens. Care Soc.

***MURDOCH, Clarissa Helen** Brickhill, Oxdrove, Burghclere, Newbury RG20 9HJ — MB ChB 1995 Sheff.

MURDOCH, David Alexander Flat 4, 5 Eaton Crescent, Bristol BS8 2EJ Tel: 0117 973 1435 Email: danmurdoch@hotmail.com — MB BS 1982 Lond.; MSc Lond. 1986, MD 1991; MA Oxf. 1984, BA 1979. (Guy's) Socs: Fell. Roy. Soc. Trop. Med. & Hyg.

MURDOCH, David Laird 42 Dunellan Road, Milngavie, Glasgow G62 7RE — MB ChB 1984 Ed.; FRCP 2001 Glasg.; BSc (Hons.) Ed. 1981; MRCP (UK) 1987. Cons. Cardiol. S.. Gen. Hosp. Glas.; Hon. Sen. Clin. Lect., Univ. of Glas. Socs: Brit. Cardiac Soc.; Scott. Cardiac Soc.; Brit. Soc. of Echocardiography. Prev: Cons. Phys. & Cardiol. Inverclyde Roy. Hosp. Greenock; Sen. Regist. (Cardiol.) S.. Gen. Hosp. Glas.; Career Regist. (Cardiol.) W.. Infirm. Glas.

MURDOCH, David Ronald Department of Cardiology, Western Infirmary, Dumbarton Road, Glasgow G11 6NT Tel: 0141 211 2000 Fax: 0141 557 0227 Email: drm2x@udcf.gla.ac.uk; 99 Saughs Drive, Glasgow G33 1BN Tel: 0141 557 0227 Fax: 0141 557 0227 — MB ChB 1992 Dundee; BMSc (Hons.) Dund 1990; MRCP (UK) 1995. Specialist Regist. Cardiol. W.. Infirm. Glas.; Hon. Clin. Teach., Dept. of Med., Univ. of Glas. Prev: Clin. Research Fell. Clin. Research Initiative in Heart Failure. Univ. Glas.; SHO Rotat. (Med.) Glas. W.. Infirm.; Ho. Off. Profess. Med. & Surg. Units Ninewells Hosp. Dundee.

MURDOCH, Edile 6 Pratt Walk, Lambeth Road, London SE11 6AR — BM 1990 Soton.

MURDOCH, Elizabeth Anne Hutton Community Division Headquarters, Cornhill Hospital, Berryden Road, Aberdeen AB25 3HG; 10 Bellswood Crescent, Banchory AB31 5TE Tel: 01330 822049 — MB ChB 1971 Ed.; DObst RCOG 1973. Staff Grade (Community Child Health) Grampian Univ. Hosps. Trust - Aberd.

MURDOCH, Ewart Gladstone (retired) 29 Park Place, Elie, Leven KY9 1DH Tel: 01333 330677 — MB ChB St. And. 1954. Prev: GP Elie Fife.

MURDOCH, Fiona Department of Pathology, Glasgow Royal Infirmary, Castle Street, Glasgow G4 0SF Tel: 01382 660111; 14 Battlefield Gardens, Langside, Glasgow G42 9JW — MB ChB 1990 Dundee; BMSc Dund 1987; DRCOG 1993. Trainee (Path.) Glas. Roy. Infirm., Glas. Socs: BMA; ACP.

MURDOCH, Fiona Ann The Health Centre, 20 Duncan Street, Greenock PA15 4LY Tel: 01475 724477 Fax: 01475 723450; Hebrides, Bullwood Road, Dunoon PA23 7QN — MB ChB 1989 Glas.; BSc (Hons.) Pharmacol. Glas. 1986; MRCGP 1993; DFFP 1995.

MURDOCH, Gail Elizabeth 163 Robertson Road, Dunfermline KY12 0BL Tel: 01383 629200 Fax: 01383 629203 — MB ChB 1988 Dundee; MRCGP 1992; DCH RCPS Glas. 1991. Socs: BMA. Prev: SHO (Radiother. & Oncol.) Ninewells Hosp. Dundee; SHO (O & G) Perth Roy. Inirm.; SHO (Cas.) Dundee Roy. Infirm.

MURDOCH, Professor George 439 King Street, Broughty Ferry, Dundee DD5 2HA Tel: 01382 770792 Fax: 01738 445772; 439

MURDOCH

Kiing Street, Broughty Ferry, Dundee DD5 2HA Tel: 01382 770792 — MB ChB (Commend.) St. And. 1943; DSc (hon. causa) Strathclyde 1989; FRCS Ed. 1947. (St. And.) Prof. Emerit. Orthop. Surg. & Trauma Univ. Dundee. Socs: Hon. Fell. (Ex-Pres.) Internat. Soc. Prosth.s & Orthotics; Fell. BOA; Hon. Fell. Internat. Soc. Prosth.s & Orthotics. Prev: Prof. Orthop. Surg. Univ. Dundee; Vis. Prof. Nat. Centre. TEPO Univ. Strathclyde; Specialist (Orthop.) RAF.

MURDOCH, Gregor John Airthrey Park Medical Centre, Hermitage Road, Stirling University, Stirling FK9 4NJ Tel: 01786 463831 Fax: 01786 447482 — MB ChB 1989 Aberd.; BMedBiol Aberd. 1986; DRCOG 1991.

MURDOCH, Helen Buchan Community Division HQ, Upper Hospital, Berryden Road, Aberdeen AB25 3HG Tel: 01224 663131 Fax: 01224 840969; 20 Bede Way, Tarves, Ellon AB41 7WE Tel: 01651 851546 — MB ChB 1980 Aberd. Assoc. Specialist (Community Child Health) Aberd. Socs: Roy. Coll. Paediat. & Child Health; BMA. Prev: SCMO Aberd.

MURDOCH, Ian Alexander 23 Homefield Road, Chiswick, London W4 2LW — MB BS 1982 Lond.; BSc Lond. 1979; MRCP (UK) 1986. (Univ. Coll. Hosp.) Cons. Paediat. Intens. Care Guy's Hosp. Lond. Socs: Fell. (Intens. Care) Childr. Hosp. Melbourne, Austral. Prev: Sen. Regist. (Paediat.) Guy's Hosp. Lond.

MURDOCH, Ian Brown Bo'ness Road Medical Practice, 31-33 Bo'ness Road, Grangemouth FK3 8AN Tel: 01324 482653 — MB ChB 1979 Glas.; AFOM RCP Lond. 1992; MRCGP 1984; DRCOG 1983.

MURDOCH, Mr Ian Elliot Moorfields Eye Hospital, City Road, London EC1V 2PD Tel: 020 7253 3411 Fax: 020 7253 4696; The Brow, Chalfont St Giles HP8 4JD — MB BS 1981 Lond.; MSc (Epidemiol.) Lond. 1995; BSc Lond. 1978, MD 1993; FRCS (Ophth.) Lond. 1987; FRCOphth 1989; Spec. Accredit. Ophth. RCS Eng. 1993. Cons. Ophth. Moorfields Eye Hosp. Lond.

MURDOCH, James McCash (retired) 16 Braehead Drive, Edinburgh EH4 6QL Tel: 0131 339 4041 — LRCP LRCS Ed. LRFPS Glas. 1944; FRCP Glas. 1964; FRCP Ed. 1961, M 1950; FRFPS Glas. 1950. Prev: Cons. Phys. City Hosp. Edin. & Sen. Lect. Univ. Edin.

MURDOCH, James Rennie Mundie (retired) Gilmorehill, Northfield, Tomich, Invergordon IV18 0LF Tel: 01349 854085 — MB ChB 1959 Glas.; DPH 1964. Prev: MOH Chesterton & S. Cambs. RDs.

MURDOCH, James William (retired) 17 Onslow Road, Hove BN3 6TA Tel: 01273 506828 — MRCS Eng. LRCP Lond. 1951; DIH Eng. 1955; MRCGP 1968. Prev: GP Hove.

MURDOCH, Jane Margaret 2 Riverside Park, Port Elphinstone, Inverurie AB51 3SB — MB ChB 1994 Ed.

MURDOCH, Janet Muriel 2 Ewenfield Road, Ayr KA7 2QB — MB ChB 1961 Ed.; DO Eng. 1965; DCH RCPS Glas. 1963. (Ed.) Prev: SHO (Med.) Belvidere Hosp. Glas.; Jun. Ho. Off. (Paediat.) Roy. Hosp. Sick Childr. Glas.; Jun. Ho. Off. (Med.) Dumfries & Galloway Roy. Infirm.

MURDOCH, Joan Margaret (retired) 20 Farfield Road, Shipley BD18 4QP Tel: 01274 581211 — L.M.S.S.A. Lond. 1947. Prev: SCMO (Child Heath) Bradford HA.

MURDOCH, Mr John Bannatyne 2 Clifton Park, Bristol BS8 3BS Tel: 0117 906 4210 Fax: 0117 946 6875; 8 Leigh Road, Bristol BS8 2DA Tel: 0117 973 1373 Fax: 0117 946 6875 Email: annejohnmurdoch@lineone.net — MD 1989 Glas.; MB ChB 1978; MRCOG 1988. (Glasgow) Cons. Gyn. & Gyn. Oncologist St Michaels Hosp. Bristol; Cons. Gyn. & Gyn. Oncologist S.mead Hosp. Bristol. Socs: Brit. Gyn. Cancer Soc.; Internat. Gyn. Cancer Soc.; The Gyn. Club. Prev: Sen. Lect. (O & G) Univ. Sheff.; Seniior Regist. (O & G) N.ern RHA.

MURDOCH, Mr John Robert Stobhill NHS Trust, 133 Balornock Road, Glasgow G21 3UW Tel: 0141 201 3000 Fax: 0141 201 3887; 27 Victoria Road, Rutherglen, Glasgow G73 3QF Tel: 0141 647 3464 Fax: 0141 647 3464 — MB ChB 1984 Dundee; FRCS (Ophth.) Glas. 1990; FRCOphth. 1990; DO RCPSI 1988. (Univ. Dundee) Cons. Ophth. Stobhill NHS Trust. Prev: Sen. Regist. (Ophth.) Manch. Roy. Eye Hosp.; Regist. (Ophth.) Gartnavel Gen. Hosp. Glas.; SHO (Ophth.) Ninewells Hosp. Dundee.

MURDOCH, Karen Alison Perranporth Surgery, Beach Road, Perranporth TR6 0PS Tel: 01872 572255 — MB BS 1987 Lond.; MRCGP 1991; DRCOG 1991. Prev: GP Taunton.

MURDOCH, Linda Jane Anaesthetic Department, St. George's Hospital, Blackshaw Road, Tooting, London SW17 0QT Tel: 020 8672 1255 — MB BS 1983 Lond.; FFA RCS Eng. 1988. Cons. Anaesth. St. Geo. Hosp. Lond.

MURDOCH, Michele Esther West Hertfordshire Hospitals NHS Trust, Dermatology Department, Watford General Hospital, Vicarage Road, Watford WD18 0HB Tel: 01923 217375 Fax: 01923 217945; 7 The Brow, Chalfont St Giles HP8 4JD — MB BS 1981 Lond.; BSc Lond. 1978; MRCP (UK) 1984. (Univ. Coll. Hosp.) Cons. (Dermat.) Mt. Vernon & Watford Hosp. NHS Trust. Prev: Wellcome Clin. Research Fell. (Biol.) Imperial Coll. Lond. & Hon. Sen. Regist. St. John's Dermat. Centre St. Thos. Hosp. Lond.; Regist. (Dermat.) Lond. Hosp.; Regist. Acad. Dept. Med. Roy. Free Hosp. Lond.

MURDOCH, Nicola Jane Longroyde Surgery, 38 Castle Avenue, Rastrick HO6 3HT Tel: 01484 721102 — MB ChB 1991 Glas.; DRCOG 1994. Socs: Med. & Dent. Defence Union Scotl.; BMA. Prev: Trainee GP Kilmcolm; SHO (Paediat.) Stirling Roy. Infirm.; SHO (Psychiat.) Dykebar Hosp. Glas.

MURDOCH, Peter Stevenson Falkirk & District Royal Infirmary, Falkirk FK1 5QE Tel: 01324 24000 Fax: 01324 616149, pmurdoch@sri.scot.nhs.uk; 4 Abercromby Place, Stirling FK8 2QP — MB BS 1973 Lond.; MRCS Eng. LRCP Lond. 1973; FRCP Glas. 1993; FRCP Ed. 1987; MRCP (UK) 1977; DObst RCOG 1974. (Guy's) Cons. Phys. (Geriat. Med.) Falkirk Roy. Infirm.; Chairm., intermediate care and Rehabil. Clin. unit. Forth Valley Acute Hosp. Trust. Socs: (Vice-Chairm. Scott. Br.) Brit. Geriat. Soc. (Mem. Exec. Comm.). Prev: Sen. Regist. Roy. Vict. Hosp. Edin.; Med. Supt. Presbyt. Jt. Hosp. Uburu, Nigeria; Ho. Phys. Guy's Hosp. Lond.

MURDOCH, Robert Olive Branch, Mill Lane, Faceby, Middlesbrough TS9 7BN — MB ChB 1970 Manch.; BSc (Hons.) Physiol. Manch. 1970, MB ChB (Hons.) 1973; MRCP (UK) 1977; DCH Eng. 1977. Cons. Phys. (Geriat.) S. Cleveland Hosp. Middlesbrough.

MURDOCH, Mr Robert William Gordon Perth Royal Infirmary, Perth PH1 1NX; Millbeck Cottage, Muckhart Mill, Dollar FK14 7PH Tel: 01259 743798 — MB BS 1971 Lond.; MB BS 1971 Lond.; FRCS Glas. 1976. Cons. Surg. Perth Roy. Infirm. Prev: Cons. Surg. W. Cumbld. Hosp. Whitehaven; Sen. Regist. (Surg.) Vict. Infirm. Glas.; Ho. Off. Middlx. Hosp. Lond.

MURDOCH, Roger Alexander Fleming, MBE 24 Inverleith Row, Edinburgh EH3 5QH Tel: 0131 552 2121 — LRCP LRCS 1933 Ed.; LRCP LRCS Ed. LRFPS Glas. 1933; FDS RCS Ed. 1970, LDS 1932. (Ed.)

MURDOCH, Ronald MacDonald Occupationl Health, DHPO, George Square, Glasgow G2 — MB ChB 1979 Manch.; BSc St. And. 1976; AFOM RCP Lond. 1986; DObst 1981. Area Med. Adviser Scotl. Post Office. Prev: Sen. Med. Off. Brit. Steel plc Ravenscraig Works.

MURDOCH, Sandra, Col. late RAMC Retd. (retired) The Windsor Court Hotel, 34 Bodorgan Road, Bournemouth BH2 6NJ — MB ChB Birm. 1954; MA Wales 1988; FFA RCS Eng. 1961; T(Anaesth.) 1991; DA Eng. 1956, DTM & H 1963; BSc Open Univ 1998. Prev: Med. Off. DHSS.

MURDOCH, Stephen Richard Dermatology Department, Royal South Hants. Hospital, Britons Terrace, Southampton SO14 0YG Tel: 02380 634288; 10 Springford Crescent, Southampton SO16 5LE Tel: 02380 782323 Email: dr.murdoch@dial.pipex.com — MB ChB 1988 Bristol; MRCP (UK) 1994. Specialist Regist. (Dermat.) Soton. Univ. Hosps. NHS Trust. Socs: BMA; Train. Mem. Brit. Assn. Dermat.; Fell. Roy. Soc. Med. Prev: SHO Dermat. Soton. Univ. Hosp. NHS Trust; Med. Off. RAMC.

MURDOCH, Stuart Donald Mount Pleasant, St. Giles Road, Skelton, York YO30 1XR — MB ChB 1992 Leeds.

MURDOCH, William Child & Family Unit, Diana Princess of Wales Hospital, Grimsby DN33 2BA Tel: 01472 875205 Fax: 01472 875328; 27 Bradford Avenue, Cleethorpes DN35 0BG — MB BS 1958 Lond.; FRCPsych 1992, M 1972; DPM Eng. 1971; DObst RCOG 1961; DA Eng. 1961. Cons. Psychiat. (Child & Adolesc. Psychiat.) Dist. Gen. Hosp. Grimsby. Socs: Assn. Child Psychol. & Psychiat.; Assn. Prof. in Serv. of Adolesc. Prev: Sen. Regist. St. John's Hosp. Stone, Aylesbury, Bucks.; Hon. Lect. Univ. Zimbabwe; Govt. Psychiat. Harare.

*****MURDOCH, William** 66 Daffodil Court, Ty Canol, Cwmbran NP44 6JG Tel: 01633 679864 Email: drbox@hotmail.com — MB ChB 1998 Birm.; ChB Birm. 1998.

MURDOCH, William Ian, Lt.-Col. RAMC Retd. Gorwel Deg, Caer Gog, Aberystwyth SY23 1ET — MB ChB 1945 Birm.; MRCS Eng. LRCP Lond. 1946. (Birm.)

MURDOCH, William Ronald (retired) 2 Ewenfield Road, Ayr KA7 2QB Tel: 01292 268360 — MB ChB 1951 Glas.; MRCP Lond. 1959; FRCP Lond.; FRCP Ed. 1972, M 1957; FRCP Glas. 1971, M 1962; FRFPS Glas. 1956. Cons. Phys. Ayr Hosp. Prev: Sen. Regist., W.ern Infirm., Glas.

MURDOCH EATON, Deborah Gail Division of Paediatrics, D Floor, Clarendon Wing, Leeds General Infirmary, Belmont Grove, Leeds LS2 9NS Tel: 0113 392 3903 Fax: 0113 329 3902 — MB BS 1983 Lond.; MD Lond. 1996; MRCP (UK) 1987; Dip. Med. Educat. Dund 1996. Sen. Lect. (Paediat. & Med. Educat.) Leeds Gen. Infirm. & Hon. Cons. Leeds Gen. Infirm. Prev: Hon. Sen. Regist. & Tutor (Child Health) Univ. Dept. Paediat. Gen. Infirm. Leeds; Hon. Regist. Hammersmith Hosp. Lond. & Research Fell. (Neonat. Neurol.) Roy. Postgrad. Med. Sch. Lond.; Ho. Off. Hosp. Sick Childr. Gt. Ormond St. Lond.

*****MURDOCK, Andrew Marshall** 7 Ballyhannon Gr, Portadown, Craigavon BT63 5SD — MB BCh BAO 1997 Belf.

MURDOCK, Elaine Marie 147 Cregagh Road, Belfast BT5 Tel: 02890 457947; 306 Gilnahirk Road, Belfast BT5 7SJ Tel: 02890 704185 — MB ChB 1988 Dundee; MB ChB (Hons.) Dundee 1988; MRCP (UK) 1991; DFFP 1993; MRCGP (Distinc.) 1993; DRCOG 1992. (Univ. Dundee & Ninewells Hosp. and Med. Sch.) Socs: BMA; Roy. Coll. Phys. & Surg. of Glas.; Ulster Med. Soc. Prev: Trainee GP Belf.; SHO (Haemat. & Gen. Med.) Belf. City Hosp.; SHO (Paediat.) Ulster Hosp. Dundonald.

MURDOCK, James Ronald, TD Devon Area Health Authority, Renslade House, Bonhay Road, Exeter EX4 3DE Tel: 01392 52181 — BA (Mod.) Dub. 1937, MD 1944, MB BCh BAO 1938; DPH (Hnrs.) NUI 1942; DCH Eng. 1950. (T.C. Dub.) Specialist Community Med. (Social Servs. Liaison) Devon AHA; Lt.-Col. RARO Specialist Army Health. Socs: FRSH; Fell. Roy. Soc. Med. Prev: MOH & Princip. Sch. Med. Off. City & Co. Norwich; MOH & Princip. Sch. Med. Off. Huddersfield Co. Boro.; Ho. Surg. Derbysh. Roy. Infirm.

*****MURDOCK, Joanne** 7 Ballyhannon Grove, Portadown, Craigavon BT63 5SD — MB BCh BAO 1994 Belf.

MURDOCK, Nicola Kim Feddinch Mansion House, Feddinch, St Andrews KY16 8NG — BM 1983 Soton.; MRCP (UK) 1996; DCP Sheff. 1990; DRCOG 1987. (Sen. Regist. (Paediat.) Dundee)

MURDOCK, Oral Windsor Nelson Ballymoney Health Centre, Robinson Memorial Hospital, 21 Newal Road, Ballymoney BT53 6HB Tel: 028 2766 0300 Fax: 028 2766 0321 — MB BCh BAO 1983 NUI.

MURFIN, David Edward Brynteg Surgery, Brynmawr Avenue, Ammanford SA18 2DA — MB BS 1970 Lond.; MPhil Wales 1997; FRCGP 1985, M 1976; DObst RCOG 1972. (St. Geo.) Socs: Former (Vice-Chairm.) Counc. RCGP. Prev: SHO (Paediat.) Qu. Eliz. Hosp. Barbados.; Ho. Phys. P'boro. Dist. & Gen. Hosp.; Ho. Surg. St. Geo. Hosp. Lond.

MURFITT, Janet Barbara The Royal London Hospital, Whitechapel Road, London E1 1BB Tel: 020 7377 7000; 2 Warwick Road, Bishop's Stortford CM23 5NN Tel: 01279 654201 — MB BS 1972 Lond.; MRCP (U.K.) 1975; MRCS Eng. LRCP Lond. 1972; FRCR 1979; DMRD Eng. 1977. (Lond. Hosp.) Cons. Radiol. Roy. Lond. Hosp. Prev: Sen. Regist. (Radiol.) St. Mary's Hosp. Lond.; SHO W.m. Childr. Hosp. Lond.; SHO (Paediat.).

MURGATROYD, Anthony Bruce Royal Lancaster Infirmary, Lancaster LA1 4RP — BM BCh 1971 Oxf.; MA Oxf. 1972, BM BCh 1971; FRCP Lond. 1991; MRCP (UK) 1974. (Oxf. & Guy's) Cons. Phys. (Geriat. Med.) Morecambe Bay Hosps. NHS Trust.

MURGATROYD, Damon 4 Hulse Road, Banister Park, Southampton SO15 2LJ Tel: 02380 232721; 69 Queens Park Avenue, Queens Park, Bournemouth BH8 9LJ — MB ChB 1984 Leic.; MLCOM 1992; MRO 1992. Indep. Osteop. Phys. Dorset. Socs: Brit. Osteop. Assn.

MURGATROYD, Helen Katherine Wood Corner, Brookledge Lane, Adlington, Macclesfield SK10 4JX — BM BS 1991 Nottm.

MURGATROYD, Jack (retired) 28 Osbaldeston Gardens, Newcastle upon Tyne NE3 4JE Tel: 0191 285 1367 — MB ChB 1958 Glas.; FDS RCS Eng. 1963; BChD Leeds 1952, LDS 1952. Cons. Oral Surg. Newc. HA; Head (Oral Surg.) Newc. Univ.

MURGATROYD, Morna Janet Meadowside Medical Practice, 1 and 3 Meadowside, Lancaster LA1 3AQ Tel: 01524 32622 Fax: 01524 846353 Email: msidesurg@aol.com; 11 Hatlex Hill, Hest Bank, Lancaster LA2 6ET Tel: 01524 822332 — MB BS 1971 Lond.; MRCGP 1986; MRCS Eng. LRCP Lond. 1971; MFFP 1995; T(GP) 1984. (Guy's) Clin. Asst. (Med. for Elderly) Roy. Lancaster Infirm. Socs: Fac. of Family Plann. and Reproductive Health Care; Brit. Med. Acupunc. Soc. Prev: Ho. Surg. Guy's Hosp. Lond.; Ho. Off. (Obst.) Roy. Free Hosp. Lond.; Ho. Phys. Evelina Childr. Hosp. of Guy's Hosp. Lond.

MURGATROYD, Peter Whiteley (retired) 162 Pemberton Road, Winstanley, Wigan WN3 6DB Tel: 01942 222702 — MB ChB 1962 Liverp. Mem. DHSS Med. Bd. Prev: Flight Lt. RAF Med. Br.

MURGATROYD, Ruth Elizabeth Derriford Hospital, Plymouth PL6 8DH; Park Cottage, 1 Tavistock Road, Launceston PL15 9HA — MB BS 1974 Lond.; BSc Lond. 1971; MRCP (UK) 1977; MRCS Eng. LRCP Lond. 1974. (St. Mary's)

MURIE, Jill Lanark Doctors, Health Centre, South Vennel, Lanark ML11 7JT Tel: 01555 665522 Fax: 01555 666857; Birkwood, 33 Albany Drive, Lanark ML11 9AG Tel: 01555 665522 Email: jillmurie@aol.com — MB ChB 1981 Dundee; MPH Glas. 1997; MRCGP 1985; Dip. Forens Med. Glas. 1990; DRCOG 1983. Med. Off. Lockhart Hosp. Lanark; Police Surg.

MURIE, Mr John Andrew Department of Surgery, Royal Infirmary, Edinburgh EH3 9YW Tel: 0131 536 1000 Fax: 0131 536 1513 Email: jamurie@compuserve.com; MA Oxf. 1984; BSc (1st cl. Hons.) 1971, MB ChB (Hons.) 1975; FRCS Ed. 1993; FRCS Glas. 1979; MD Glas. 1984. (Glas.) Cons. Surg. Edin. Roy. Infirm.; Hon. Sen. Lect. (Surg.) Univ. Edin.; Ed. Brit. Jl. Surg.; Lead Clinician Vasc. Surg. Serv. Lothian Univ. Hosps. NHS Trust. Socs: Counc. Mem. Roy. Coll. Phys. & Surg. Glas.; Counc. Mem. Vasc. Surg. Soc. GB & Irel. Prev: Reader (Surg.) Univ. Oxf.; Hon. Cons. Surg. John Radcliffe Hosp. Oxf.; Univ. Glas. Hall. Fell. (Surg.) W.. Infirm. Glas.

MURILLO, Rosa Maria 26 Homewood Drive, Whitehaven CA28 8JX — LMS 1989 Saragossa.

MURIS, Eric 7 Tudor Close, Summersdale, Chichester PO19 4QZ Tel: 01243 779183 — MB BS Durh. 1953. (Durh.)

MURIS, Jane Elizabeth Community Mental Health Team (North Wrekin), Bridge Road, Wellington, Telford TF1 1RY Tel: 01952 222725; 32 Mount Street, Shrewsbury SY3 8QH Tel: 01743 367968 — MB ChB 1977 Liverp. Clin. Asst. Shrops. Ment. Health Trust.

MURISON, Ian Campbell Canal Farmhouse, Bathampton, Bath BA2 6TH Tel: 01225 460874 — MB ChB 1952 Bristol; DObst RCOG 1956. (Bristol)

MURISON, Mr Maxwell Samuel Cabot Welsh Regional Centre for Burns & Plastic Surgery, Morriston Hospital/Ysbyty Treforys NHS Trust, Morriston, Swansea SA6 6NL Tel: 01792 703869 Fax: 01792 703875; Forge Mill, Bronwydd Arms, Carmarthen SA33 6JG Tel: 01267 281795 Email: murison@plastic-surgery.demon.co.uk — MB BCh 1984 Wales; FRCS (Plast) 1995; FRCS Ed. 1988. (Cardiff) Cons. Plastic Surg. Morriston Hosp. Swansea; Clin. Prog. Dir. Socs: Brit. Assn. Plastic Surg.; Brit. Assn. Soc. Surg. Hand; Brit. Assn. Aesth. Plastic Surg. Prev: Sen. Regist. (Plastic Surg.) The Ulster Hosp. Belf.; Career Regist. (Plastic Surg.) Frenchay Hosp. Bristol; SHO (Plastic Surg.) Frenchay Hosp. Bristol.

MURJAN, Aldo Rahim Peter Hodgkinson Centre, Department of Psychiatry, County Hospital, Greetwell Road, Lincoln LN2 5QY Tel: 01522 512512; 2 Lindrick Close, Heighington, Lincoln LN4 1TN — State DMS 1975 Bologna; MB CHB Bologna Italy 1975; State Exam. 1976. (Bologna, Italy) Staff Grade Practitioner (Psychiat.). Prev: Hosp. Med. & Gen. Pract. Italy.

MURJAN, Sarah Mary 2 Lindrick Close, Heighington, Lincoln LN4 1TN — BM BS 1992 Nottm. SHO (Psychiat.) Mid. Trent Rotat. Train. Scheme Nottm.

*****MURNAGHAN, Claire** Flat 1/1, 79 Lumsden St., Yorkhill, Glasgow G3 8RH — MB ChB 1996 Glas.

MURNAGHAN, Mary Elizabeth 16 Elaine Street, Belfast BT9 5AR — MB BCh BAO 1989 Belf.; DCH Dub. 1992; DGM RCPS Glas. 1991.

MURNAL, Samuel Bhaskar Biggleswade Health Centre, Saffron Road, Biggleswade SG18 8DJ Tel: 01767 313647 Fax: 01767

MURNAN

312568; White House, School Lane, Southill, Biggleswade SG18 9JA — MB BS 1965 Karnatak; DA (UK) 1971.

MURNAN, Amanda 16 Grasmere Avenue, Hindley, Wigan WN2 3QA — MB ChB 1992 Liverp.; BSc (Hons.) Liverp. 1990; MRCP (UK) 1995.

MURPHIE, Robert William Wigtown Medical Practice, High Vennel, Wigtown, Newton Stewart DG8 9JQ Tel: 01988 402210 Fax: 01988 403482; Milldriggan House, Braehead, Kirkinner, Newton Stewart DG8 9AH — MB ChB 1985 Glas.; MRCGP 1989.

MURPHY, Aine Maria Armadale Surgery, 18 North St., Armadale, Bathgate EH48 3QB Tel: 01501 730432; 64 South Loch Park, Bathgate EH48 2QZ Tel: 01506 634932 — MB BCh BAO 1989 NUI; MRCGP 1994.

MURPHY, Alan, MBE, Lt.-Col. RAMC (retired) 19 Ireton Grove, Attenborough, Nottingham NG9 6BJ Tel: 0115 925 6789 — MB ChB 1947 Manch.; FRCGP 1980, M 1972. Prev: Lect. (Gen. Pract.) Nottm. Univ.

MURPHY, Alan Michael Barbican House, 3 White Lyon Court, London EC2Y 8EA; Manor Cottage, Pitt, Winchester SO22 5QW — MB BS 1989 Lond.; BSc (Hons.) Lond. 1986, MB BS 1989. GP Private Pract.

MURPHY, Alistair Eugene Harvey Montgomery House Surgery, Piggy Lane, Bicester OX26 6HT Tel: 01869 249222 — BM BS 1977 Nottm.; BMedSci Nottm. 1975, BM BS 1977; MRCGP 1982.

MURPHY, Andrew The Health Centre, St. Peters Crescent, Selsey, Chichester PO20 0NN Tel: 01243 604321/602261 Fax: 01243 607996; Little Acre, 17 Warner Road, Selsey, Chichester PO20 9DE Tel: 01243 602486 — MB BS 1963 Lond.; DObst RCOG 1967. (Guy's) Hon. Med. Adviser RNLI Selsey. Socs: BMA. Prev: Ho. Surg. Roy. Sussex Co. Hosp. Brighton; Ho. Phys. Hove Gen. Hosp.; Obst. Ho. Surg. Brighton Gen. Hosp.

MURPHY, Mr Andrew James Dept. Trauma & Orthopaedic Surgery, The North Hampshire Hospital, Aldermaston Road, Basingstoke RG24 9NA Tel: 01256 314702 Email: murphyandy@yahoo.com — MB ChB 1992 Bristol; FRCS Ed 1998. (Bristol) Specialist Regist. in Trauma & Orthopaedic Surg., N. Hants Hosp. Prev: Sen. SHO (Ortha. Surg.) Roy. United. Hosp. Bath; SHO (Neuro. Surg., Intens. Care, Plastic Surg., Orthop. Surg. & Gen.Surg.) Derriford Hosp. Plymouth; Orthopaedic Regist., Wessex Region, (portsmouth, Winchester, Dorchester, Bath).

MURPHY, Andrew Lawrence 9 Sandhurst Park, Bangor BT20 5NU — MB BCh BAO 1952 Belf.; DObst RCOG 1952. Socs: BMA. Prev: Surg. Lt.-Cdr. RN.

MURPHY, Anna Maria 120 High Street, Knaresborough HG5 0HN — MB BCh BAO 1980 Dub.; MRCPI 1982; FRCR 1987. Cons. Radiol. York Dist. Hosp. Prev: Sen. Regist. (Radiol.) Leeds HA; Regist. (Radiol.) Plymouth Gen. Hosp.; SHO (Med.) Federated Dub. Volun. Hosps.

MURPHY, Anna Veronica 31 Viewpark Drive, Burnside, Rutherglen, Glasgow G73 3QE — MB ChB 1964 Glas.; MRCP (UK) 1969; FRCP Glas. 1984, M 1969; DCH RCPS Glas. 1966; DObst RCOG 1966. (Glas.) Cons. Roy. Hosp. Sick Childr. Glas.; Lect. (Child Health) Univ. Glas. Socs: BMA. Prev: Ho. Off. Glas. Roy. Infirm., Roy. Hosp. Sick Childr. Glas. & Glas.; Roy. Matern. Hosp.

MURPHY, Anne Louise 69 Layton Road, Brentford TW8 0PU — MB BS 1998 Lond.; MB BS Lond 1998. (Imperial college (CXWMS)) GP Regist./SHO on GP VTS at N.wick Pk. Hosp. Prev: PRHO (med.) W. Middlx. Hosp; PRHO (Surg.) Kingston Hosp. Surrey.

MURPHY, Anne-Marie 17 Hoyle Fold, Sunderland SR3 2TT — MB ChB 1984 Leeds.

MURPHY, Mr Anthony Gabriel 23 Grimescar Meadows, Birkby, Huddersfield HD2 2DZ — MB ChB 1965 Liverp.; FRCS Ed. (Ophth.) 1972; MRCS Eng. LRCP Lond. 1965; FCOphth 1989; DO Eng. 1970. Cons. Ophth. Roy. Infirm. Huddersfield. Prev: Cons. Ophth. HM Forces Qu. Eliz. Hosp. Lond.

MURPHY, Anthony Liam 203 Finchampstead Road, Wokingham RG40 3HS — MB BS 1990 Lond.

MURPHY, Barrie Department of Haematology, Torbay Hospital, Torquay TQ2 7AA Tel: 01803 64567 — MB BS 1956 Lond.; DObst RCOG 1957; FRCPath 1979, M 1967. (Char. Cross) Cons. Haemat. Torbay Gp. Laborat. Torquay. Socs: Brit. Soc. Haematol. & Assn. Clin. Path. Prev: Sen. Regist. & Lect. (Path.) Gp. Laborat. St. Stephen's Hosp. Lond. & Char. Cross Hosp. Lond.

MURPHY, Billie Joanne Mary The Surgery, The Meads, Kington HR5 3DQ Tel: 01544 230302 Fax: 01544 230824; Yew Tree House, Marston, Pembridge, Leominster HR6 9JA — MB ChB 1987 Manch.; DRCOG 1991.

***MURPHY, Breige** 84 Ballyscullion Road, Bellaghy, Magherafelt BT45 8NA — MB BCh BAO 1997 Belf.

MURPHY, Brendan Gerard 1 Ceara Court, 46 Windsor Avenue, Belfast BT9 6EJ — MB BCh BAO 1984 Belf.; MB BCh Belf. 1984; MD Belf. 1991; MRCP (UK) 1988.

MURPHY, Brendan Patrick c/o 3 Falkland Road, Greyotones, Sheffield S11 7PL — MB BS 1989 Lond.; MRCPsych 1994. Cons. Gen. Adult Psychiat. Melbourne, Vict., Aus.

MURPHY, Bridget Anne Marie 54 Westwood Road, Beverley HU17 8EJ — MB BCh BAO 1985 NUI; MRCPI 1988.

MURPHY, Bruno Dominic David Oxford Radcliffe Hospital, Headley Way, Headington, Oxford OX3 9DZ Tel: 0865 741166 Fax: 0865 222614; 53 Amberley Road, Palmes Green, London N13 4BH Tel: 020 8888 1664 — MB BS 1996 Lond.; BSc (Basic Med. Scis. with Anat.) Lond. 1993. (Kings College Hospital School of Medicine) Med. SHO Oxf. Radcliffe Hosp. Prev: SHO (Renal Med.) Kings Coll. Hosp. Lond.; SHO (Med.) The Hammersmith Hosp. Lond.

MURPHY, Carmel Anne Victoria Street Medical Group, 7 Victoria Street, Aberdeen AB10 1QW Tel: 01224 641930 Fax: 01224 644081 — MB BCh BAO 1992 NUI.

MURPHY, Caroline Anne 79 Pelham Road, Londonderry BT47 6FF — MB BCh BAO 1987 Belf.

MURPHY, Catherine Anna The Barn, Hillside Farm, Bovey Tracey, Newton Abbot TQ13 9LZ — MB BS 1991 Lond.

MURPHY, Celia Frances Edgewood House, 151 High St., Chapmanslade, Westbury BA13 4AP — BM BS 1990 Nottm.; BMedSci Nottm. 1988. Socs: BMA & Med. Protec. Soc. Prev: GP Amer. Med. Centre., Moscow, Russia.; Trainee GP Nottm. VTS.

MURPHY, Christine Jill 1 St Michaels Close, Lydbury North SY7 8EA Tel: 01588 680493 — MB ChB 1985 Sheff.

MURPHY, Christopher John Royal Shrewsbury Hospital, Shelton, Bicton Heath, Shrewsbury SY3 8DN; 89 Montrose Avenue, Leamington Spa CV32 7DR — MB BS 1982 Lond.; MRCPsych 1987.

MURPHY, Christopher Luke 108 Sackville Road, Heaton, Newcastle upon Tyne NE6 5TB Tel: 0191 224 4088; 108 Sackville Road, Heaton, Newcastle upon Tyne NE6 5TB Tel: 0191 224 4088 — MB BS 1997 Newc. (Newcastle-upon-Tyne) SHO Med. Rotat. S. Tyneside Dist. Hosp. Tyne & Wear. Socs: Med. Protec. Soc. Prev: PRHO (Surgic.) Freeman Hosp. Newc.-upon-Tyne; PRHO (Med.) S. Tyneside Dist. Hosp.

MURPHY, Miss Claire Eileen 412 Otley Road, Adel, Leeds LS16 8AD — MB BS 1992 Lond.; FRCS Ed. 1997. (Roy. Free Hosp. Lond.) SHO (Surg.) N. Manch. Gen. Hosp. Socs: Med. Wom. Federat. Prev: SHO (A & E) St. Jas. Univ. Hosp. Leeds; Demonst. (Anat.) Univ. Manch.

MURPHY, Clare Elizabeth Tel: 01232 644923; 90b Newtonbreda Road, Belfast BT8 7BP Tel: 02890 644923 — MB BCh BAO 1978 Dub.; MRCGP 1983; DCH RCP Lond. 1983; DRCOG 1980.

MURPHY, Clare Louise Dukes Avenue Practice, 1 Dukes Avenue, Muswell Hill, London N10 2PS — MB BS 1987 Lond.; BSc (Econ.) Lond. 1981, MB BS 1987; DRCOG 1990. GP Muswell Hill Lond. Retainer Scheme.

***MURPHY, Clare Louise** 33 Souillac Drive, Denny FK6 5HE — MB ChB 1998 Glas.; MB ChB Glas 1998.

MURPHY, Clare Margaret Basement Flat, 13 Portland Place, Bath BA1 2RY — BM BS 1992 Nottm.; DRCOG 1996; DGM 1995. Trainee GP/SHO Bath VTS; GP Regist. Socs: Med. Protec. Soc. Prev: SHO (A & E) Treliske Hosp. Cornw.; SHO (Geriat.) Derriford Hosp. Plymouth.

MURPHY, Colette Marta Flat No. 5, 270 Bonnington Road, Edinburgh EH6 5BE — MB BCh BAO 1988 NUI.

MURPHY, Conrad Frederick St Richard's Hospital, Spitalfield Lane, Chichester PO19 4SE Tel: 01243 788122 Email: conrad.murphy@rsw-tr.sthames.nhs.uk; Chelwood house, West Broyle Drive, Chichester PO19 3PP — MB BS 1986 Lond.; MD Lond. 1995; BA (Hons.) Oxf. 1983; MRCP (UK) 1989. (Guy's Hosp. Lond.) Cons. Cardiol. St. Richard Hosp. Cichester. Socs: Brit. Cardiac Soc.; Brit. Pacing & Electrophysiol. Gp. Prev: Regist. (Cardiol.) Soton.

Gen. Hosp.; Research Regist. (Physiol.) Char. Cross & W.m. Hosp. Med. Sch. Lond.; Regist. (Med.) W.m. Hosp. Lond.

MURPHY, Cormac Rowland Coman Shirley Avenue Surgery, 1 Shirley Avenue, Shirley, Southampton SO15 5RP Tel: 023 8077 3258/1356 Fax: 023 8070 3078 — MB BCh BAO 1980 NUI.

MURPHY, Craig Andrew 33 Edwards Lane, Nottingham NG5 3DH.

MURPHY, Damian John 41 Delph Brook Way, Egerton, Bolton BL7 9UB — MB ChB 1983 Leeds.

MURPHY, Daniel Peter 11 Guildford Drive, Chandlersford, Eastleigh SO53 3PR — MB BCh BAO 1977 NUI.

MURPHY, David Alan Sleaford Medical Group, Riverside Surgery, 47 Boston Road, Sleaford NG34 7HD Tel: 01529 303301 Fax: 01529 415401; 2 Clay Hill Road, Sleaford NG34 7TF — MB ChB 1978 Liverp.; MRCGP 1983; DRCOG 1981.

MURPHY, Mr David Hugh, Group Capt. RAF Med. Br. Retd. The Old Carpenters Arms, 32 High St., Little Bytham, Grantham NG33 4QX — MRCS Eng. LRCP Lond. 1956; FRCS Glas. 1969. (Camb. & St. Mary's) Prev: Cons. Orthop. Surg. RAF Med. Bd.; Regist. Harlow Wood Orthop. Hosp. Mansfield; Sen. Regist. Robt. Jones & Agnes Hunt Orthop. Hosp. OsW.ry.

MURPHY, Mr David James Llewellyn Lind House, The Street, Box Grove, Chichester PO18 0EB — MB BS 1950 Lond.; BSc Wales 1942; FRCS Eng. 1954. (Univ. Coll. Hosp.) Emerit. Cons. Surg. (ENT) Leics. HA. Socs: Leicester Med. Soc. Prev: Surg. Regist. Surgic. Unit, Univ. Coll. Hosp.; Sen. Regist. Roy. Ear Hosp. (Univ. Coll. Hosp.).

MURPHY, Denis John S.A.S.S. Unit, Cane Hill Hospital, Coulsdon CR5 3YL Tel: 01737 556619 Fax: 01737 551287 — MB BCh BAO 1975 NUI; MRCPsych 1980. Cons. Forens. Psychiat. Ravensbourne NHS Trust & W. Lambeth Community Care Trust.

MURPHY, Derek Michael George (retired) 3 Summercourt, Harbour Village, Penryn TR10 8GG Tel: 01326 374372 — MB BS 1955 Lond.; MRCS Eng. LRCP Lond. 1955. Prev: Chief Med. Off. Falkland Isls.

MURPHY, Dermot Matthew 12 Stevenage Road, London SW6 6ES — MB BS 1988 Lond.

MURPHY, Mr Dermot Simon Department of Surgery, Western Infirmary, Dumbarton Road, Glasgow G11 6NT — MB BCh BAO 1987 NUI; FRCSI 1992.

MURPHY, Desmond St Mary;s Hospital, Newport PO30 5TG Tel: 01983 524081; Redworth, Appley Rise, Ryde PO33 1LE Tel: 01983 615243 — MB ChB Glas. 1969; FRCP Lond. 1994; FRCP Glas. 1986; MRCP (UK) 1973; DObst RCOG 1971. (Glas.) Cons. Phys. I. of Wight HA. Socs: Scott. & Brit. Thoracic Socs.; BMA; Fell.of Roy. Coll. Phys. Lond. Prev: Sen. Regist. John Radcliffe Hosp. Oxf.; Regist. Glas. Roy. Infirm. & Roy. Alexandra Infirm. Paisley.

MURPHY, Dilys Anne Barbican Health, 13 Queen Anne St., London W1G 9JH Tel: 020 7436 9095 — MB BS 1972 Lond.; MRCS Eng. LRCP Lond. 1972. (Guy's) Dep. Chairm. Barbican Health Lond.; Chairm. Clin. Progr. Barbican Health Lond. Prev: Ho. Surg. Guy's Hosp. Lond.; Ho. Phys. Hither Green Hosp. Lond.

MURPHY, Mr Donal 30 Upper Dickinson Street, Wigan WN1 2AG Tel: 01942 242366; Aspinall House Farm, Aspinall Road, Standish, Wigan WN6 0YP — MB ChB 1959 Liverp.; FRCS Ed. 1968. (Liverp.) Cons. ENT Surg. Roy. Albert Edwd. Infirm. Wigan. Socs: Med. Liverp. Med. Inst. Prev: Regist . ENT Infirm. Liverp.; Ho. Phys. & Ho. Surg. Walton Hosp. Liverp.; Maj. RAMC (T & AVR).

MURPHY, Dorothy Anne 78 Whitburn Road, Cleadon, Sunderland SR6 7QX — MB BCh BAO 1977 Belf.; FFA RCSI 1981.

MURPHY, Douglas James 2/1 38 Edgehill Road, Glasgow G11 7JD — MB ChB 1979 Dundee; MRCGP 1984; DRCOG 1984.

MURPHY, Douglas St John, TD (retired) 32 Alderton Hill, Loughton IG10 3JB — MB BCh BAO NUI 1947. Prev: Ho. Surg. & Ho. Phys. St. Vincent's Hosp. Dub.

MURPHY, Dylan Lloyd 1 Trem y Bedol, Carmarthen SA31 1JL — MB BCh 1997 Wales.

MURPHY, Eamon Michael 35 Glenmanus Road, Portrush BT56 8HU — BM 1991 Soton.; MRCGP (UK) 1998; DME 1994; DCH 1997. GP Regist. High St. Pract. Fort William Scotl. Prev: SHO (Paediat.) Erane Hosp. Enniskillen; Princip. Ho. Off. (A & E) Qu.sland, Australia; SHO (Med.) Co. Down.

MURPHY, Edna La Couse 49 Lee Terrace, Blackheath, London SE3 9TA — MA Dub. 1966, MD 1958, MB BCh BAO 1953; DPH Lond. 1964.

MURPHY, Eileen Larne Health Centre, Gloucester Avenue, Larne BT40 1PB Tel: 028 2826 1924 Fax: 028 2826 1940 — MB BCh BAO 1986 Belf.; MRCGP 1990; DRCOG 1990.

MURPHY, Professor Elaine 382 Lauderdale Tower, Barbican, London EC2Y 8NA Tel: 020 7301 3307 Fax: 020 7588 1432 Email: emjmm@compuserve.com — MD 1979 Manch.; MB ChB 1971; FRCPsych 1985, M 1976. Chairm. City & Hackney Community NHS Trust; Vis. Prof. QMW Coll. Univ. of Lond.; Research Fell. Wellcome Inst. for the Hist. of Med. Prev: Prof. (Psychogeriat. of Old Age) United Med. & Dent. Schs.; Vice-Chairm. Ment. Health Act Commiss.

MURPHY, Eleni 48 Archilles Road, London NW6 1EA — MB BS 1996 Lond.

MURPHY, Elizabeth Dept. of Occupational & Environmental Medicene, Medical School, University of Aberdeen, Foresthill, Aberdeen AB25 2ZD — MB BS 1988 Newc.; MRCP (UK) 1993; AFOM 1997. Clin. Lect. (Occup. Med.).

MURPHY, Elizabeth Ann Underwood Surgery, 139 St. Georges Road, Cheltenham GL50 3EQ Tel: 01242 580644 Fax: 01242 253519 — MB ChB 1985 Bristol; DRCOG 1991. Prev: SHO (A & E) Gloucester Roy. Hosp.; Ho. Phys. Frenchay Hosp. Bristol; Ho. Surg. Cheltenham Gen. Hosp.

MURPHY, Elizabeth Anne Gloucester Avenue Surgery, 158 Gloucester Avenue, Chelmsford CM2 9LQ Tel: 01245 353182 Fax: 01245 344479; Forty Hill, Moulsham Thrift, Chelmsford CM2 8BP — MB BS 1986 Lond.; Dip. Pract. Dermat. Wales 1995. (St. Mary's Hosp. Med. Sch. Lond.)

MURPHY, Elizabeth Anne Wishaw General Hospital, 50 Netherton Street, Wishaw ML2 0DP Tel: 01698 366088 Fax: 01698 366085; 16 Beech Avenue, Dumbreck, Glasgow G41 5BX Tel: 0141 427 7129 Fax: 0141 427 7129 — MB ChB 1985 Glas.; BSc Glas. 1982; MRCP (UK) 1989. Cons. Gen. Med. & Rheum. Wishaw Gen. Hosp. Prev: Lect. (Med. & Rheum.) Univ. Glas.; Regist. Centre for Rheum. Dis. Glas. Roy. Infirm.; SHO (Med.) W.. Infirm. Glas.

MURPHY, Elizabeth Jane 5 Airyligg Drive, Eaglesham, Glasgow G76 0LJ; 5 Airyligg Drive, Eaglesham, Glasgow G76 0LJ — MB ChB 1986 Glas.; MRCGP 2000; DRCOh 1988. Locum Gen. Practitioner Family Plann. Doctor; Hunter Health Centre, E. Kilbride G74. Socs: The Roy. Coll. of Gen. Practitioners; Brit. Med. Assn. Prev: GP Coalbridge Health Centre.; GP Alison Ler Med. Centre, E. Kilbride.

MURPHY, Elizabeth Mary A Luta Continua, 18 Jubilee Road, Bristol BS2 9RS — MB ChB 1977 Ed.; DRCOG 1982.

MURPHY, Emma Florence Weatherhead 29 Tutor Close, Hamble, Southampton SO31 4RU — BM 1992 Soton.; MRCP (I) Nov 1996. Specialist Regist. Rehabil. Med. Soton. Socs: Brit. Soc. Rehabil. Med.

MURPHY, Eugene Frederick Harvey (retired) 6 Mill Lane, Arncot, Bicester OX25 1PB Tel: 01869 246882 — BM BCh Oxf. 1950. Prev: Ho. Phys. Radcliffe Infirm. Oxf.

MURPHY, Finbarre Augustine (retired) Highlands, Lawrence Road, Skircoat Green, Halifax HX3 0LW Tel: 01422 356362 — MB BCh BAO 1952 NUI; FRCP Lond. 1985, M 1965; DCH Eng. 1959; DTM & H Liverp. 1958; FRCPCH. Prev: Cons. Paediat. Halifax Gen. Hosp.

MURPHY, Fiona Margaret Westbourne, Scott Hospital, Beacon Park Road, Plymouth PL2 2PQ Tel: 01752 605940; 14 Torbay Court, Marina Drive, Brixham TQ5 9BD Tel: 01803 859221 Email: fmmurphy@talk21.com — MB BCh BAO 1987 NUI. Specialist Regist. Gen. Adult Psych. Glenbourne Hosp., Plymouth. Socs: Fell. Roy. Soc. Med.; Roy. Coll. Psychiat. Prev: Sen. Regist. (Old Age Psychiat.) Manch. Cmo (Ment. Health) Paignton; Regist. (Gen. Psychiat.) Brentwood; SHO (Psychiat.) Dartford & Gravesham HA.

MURPHY, Fiona Mary Dourado and Partners, Maybush Medical Centre, Belle Isle Health Park, Portobello Road, Wakefield WF1 5PN Tel: 01924 328132 Fax: 01924 328130 — MB BCh BAO 1992 NUI; LRCPSI 1992.

MURPHY, Frances Mary 12 Moira Drive, Bangor BT20 4RN — MB BCh BAO 1952 Belf.

MURPHY, Mr Francis The Grove, Aston-by-Stone, Stone ST15 0BL — MB ChB 1968 Sheff.; FRCS Eng. 1973. (Sheff.) Cons. Stafford

MURPHY

Dist. Gen. Hosp. Prev: Hon. Sen. Regist. & Research Fell. St. Mary's Hosp. Lond.; Sen. Regist. (Surg.) W. Middlx. Hosp. Isleworth & St. Mary's Hosp. Lond.

MURPHY, Francis Bernard 12 Moorgate Park, Retford DN22 6TH — MB BCh BAO 1962 Dub.; MRCPsych 1980.

MURPHY, Francis Robert 8 Fry Close, Hamble, Southampton SO31 4PF — BM 1993 Soton.

MURPHY, Frank 9 Green House Road, Doncaster DN2 5NG — MB ChB 1962 Sheff.; FRCP Glas. 1986, M 1968. (Sheff.)

MURPHY, Frank William (retired) Budd's House, Rosemary Lane, Dulverton TA22 9DP Tel: 01398 323414 Email: fkmur@globalnet.co.uk — MB ChB Manch. 1953; FFCM 1979, M 1974; DTM & H Eng. 1959; DPH Lond. 1963. Prev: Dir. of Pub. Health W. Essex. HA.

***MURPHY, Gavin James** 2 Craigadick Park, Maghera BT46 5DD — MB ChB 1994 Bristol.

MURPHY, Gerald Vincent 35 Parc Gwelfor, Dyserth, Rhyl LL18 6LN — MB ChB 1988 Manch.

MURPHY, Gerard Anthony Bothwell Medical Centre, 3 Uddingston Road, Bothwell, Glasgow G71 8ET Tel: 01698 852299; 12 Homeston Avenue, Bothwell, Glasgow G71 8PL — MB ChB. 1984 Glas.; MRCGP 1988; DRCOG 1986.

MURPHY, Gerard Joachim Halton General Hospital, Runcorn WA7 2DA Tel: 01928 714567; 78 Wood Lane, Timperley, Altrincham WA15 7PJ — MB BS 1977 Lond.; MRCS Eng. LRCP Lond. 1977; BSc (Hons.) Lond. 1974; FRCR 1985; DMRD Eng. 1984. Cons. Radiol. Halton Gen. Hosp. Runcorn.

MURPHY, Gerard John James Stewartstown Health Centre, 212 Stewartstown Road, Dunmurry, Belfast BT17 0FB Tel: 028 9060 2931 Fax: 028 9060 5728; 3 Sequoia Park, Lambeg, Lisburn BT27 4SJ Tel: 01846 667299 Email: 100652.3043@compuserve.com — MB BCh BAO 1981 Belf.; MRCP (UK) 1984; MICGP 1987; MRCGP 1986; FRCP Edin 1998; DPD (Cardiff) 1999. (Belf.) Tutor (Gen. Pract.) Qu. Univ. Belf.; GP Trainer, N.I. VTS. Socs: Fell. Ulster Med. Soc.; Foundat. Mem. Irish Coll. Gen. Pract. Prev: Trainee GP Lond.derry VTS; SHO (Paediat.) Daisy Hill Hosp. Newry; SHO (Psychiat.) St. Luke's Hosp. Armagh.

MURPHY, Helen Catherine 9 Claudia Place, London SW19 6ES — BM BCh 1992 Oxf.

MURPHY, Helen Mary Murphy, Soho Centre for Health and Care, First Floor, 1 Frith Street, London W1D 3QS Tel: 020 7534 6570 Fax: 020 7534 6566 — MB BS 1981 Lond.; PhD Dub. 1964, BSc (Hons.) 1961; DFFP 1993. (Univ. Coll. Lond.) Clin. Asst. (Chest & Allergy Clinic) St. Mary's Hosp. Lond.; Community Med. Off. (Family Plann.) Pk.side Trust.

***MURPHY, Helen Rose** 8 Malibres Road, Chandlers Ford, Eastleigh SO53 5DT — MB ChB 1997 Manch.

MURPHY, Henry Joseph 2 Calthorpe Cottages, The Green, Acle, Norwich NR13 3QX — MB BCh BAO 1941 NUI; BDS 1939.

MURPHY, Ian James Sheffield Occupational Health Service, Northern General Hospital, Herries Rd, Sheffield S5 7AU Tel: 0114 271 4161; 20 Bishops Orchard, East Hagbourne, Didcot OX11 9JS — MB ChB 1986 Bristol; MFOM 2001; MRCGP 1995; DRCOG 1996. Cons. Occupat.al health, Sheff. Teachg. Hosps. NHS Trust Sheff. Prev: Specialist Regist. Occupat. Med. Roy. Berks. & Battle Hosps. NHS Trust Reading.

MURPHY, James Whyteman's Brae Hospital, Whytemans Brae, Kirkcaldy KY1 2ND Tel: 01592 643355 Ext: 2030 Fax: 01592 643790 — MB ChB 1978 Glas.; MRCPsych 1983. Cons. Psychiat. Whyteman's Brae Hosp. Kirkcaldy.

MURPHY, James Hanns Hall, Hanns Hall Road, Willaston, South Wirral CH64 2TQ Tel: 0151 353 1655 — MB ChB 1982 Sheff.; FRCA. 1988. Cons. Anaesth. Cardiothoracic Centre (NHS Trust) Liverp. Socs: Assn. Anaesth. GB & Irel.; Assn. Cardiothoracic Anaesth. Prev: Sen. Regist. (Anaesth.) W. Midl. RHA; Regist. Rotat. (Anaesth.) Riyadh Milt. Hosp. Saudi Arabia & Univ. Hosp. of Wales; SHO (Cardiothoracic Surg.) W.m. Gen. Hosp.

MURPHY, James Barrie, OStJ Greater Glasgow Community & Mental Health Services NHS Trust, Gartnavel Royal Hospital, 1055 Great Western Road, Glasgow G12 0XH Tel: 0141 211 3824; 33 Hawkhead Road, Paisley PA1 3NE Tel: 0141 889 5574 — MB ChB 1965 Glas.; FRCPsych 1989, M 1972; DPM Ed. & Glas. 1968. (Glas.) Assoc. Med. Dir. Gt.er Glas. Community Ment. Health Servs. NHS Trust.

MURPHY, James Malachy Glenside, 86 Bromley Common, Bromley BR2 9PF — MB BCh BAO 1961 NUI. (Univ. Coll. Dub.) Prev: SHO Cromer Hosp., St. Vincent's Hosp. Dub. & St. Michael's Hosp. Dun; Laoghaire.

MURPHY, James Royse Hadwen Medical Practice, Glevum Way Surgery, Abbeydale, Gloucester GL4 4BL Tel: 01452 529933; 52 Lansdown Road, Gloucester GL1 3JD Email: royse.murphy@msn.com — MB ChB 1977 Bristol; MRCGP 1981; Cert. Family Plann. JCC 1980; DRCOG 1980; Cert Av Med 1987. Ordained Anglican Minister (Non Stipendiary). Socs: BMA. Prev: Med. Off. Marks & Spencer PLC.

MURPHY, James Thomson 13 Glebe Road, Kilmarnock KA1 3BA — MB ChB 1960 Glas. (Glas.)

MURPHY, James W Wishaw Health Centre, Kenilworth Avenue, Wishaw ML2 7BQ Tel: 01698 372888 Fax: 01698 376289 — MB ChB 1977 Glasgow; MB ChB 1977 Glasgow.

MURPHY, Jeremiah George The Health Centre, 20 Cleveland Square, Middlesbrough TS1 2NX Tel: 01642 246138 Fax: 01642 222291; 35 Marton Moor Road, Nunthorpe, Middlesbrough TS7 0BH Tel: 01642 314038 — MB BCh BAO 1980 NUI; DRCOG 1984; DCH RCSI 1983. (University College Cork Ireland)

MURPHY, Jeremy James Darlington Memorial Hospital, Hollyhurst Road, Darlington DL3 6HX Tel: 01325 380100 Fax: 01325 743435; 43 Cleveland Avenue, Darlington DL3 7HF Tel: 01325 362537 — MB BS 1980 Lond.; DM Nottm. 1991; MRCP (UK) 1983; FRCP Lond. 1996. Cons. Phys. Cardiol. Darlington Memor. Hosp. Socs: Brit. Cardiac Soc.; Brit. Stroke Research Gp. Prev: Research Regist & Lect. (Med.) Univ. Hosp. Nottm.; Regist. (Med.) Univ. Hosp. S. Manch.; SHO (Med.) Wolverhampton Hosps.

MURPHY, John 29 Brompton Avenue, Liverpool L17 3BT — MD 1953 NUI; MB BCh BAO 1949.

MURPHY, John Aidan Department of Haematology, Monklands Hospital, Airdrie ML6 0JS — MB ChB 1983 Glas.; BSc (Hons.) Glas. 1980; FRCP 2000 Glas.; FRCPath 2000. Cons. Haemat. Monklands Hosp. Airdrie. Prev: Sen. Regist. (Haemat.) Glas. Roy. Infirm.

MURPHY, John Bernard Roselands Resource Centre, 163b Kingston Road, New Malden KT3 3NN Tel: 020 8336 2848 Fax: 020 8336 2839 Email: docjmurphy@mcmail.com; Magna Carta Cottage, Magna Carta Island, Wraysbury, Staines TW19 5AF Tel: 01784 483396 — MB BS 1984 Lond.; MA Camb. 1987. (Camb. & Middlx. Hosp.) Staff Psychiat. Kingston & Community Dist. NHS Trust; Cons. Psychiat. Ascot Nursing Home. Prev: GP Egham; SHO (A & E) Univ. Coll. Hosp. Lond.; Lect. (Psychiat.) Middlx. Hosp. Lond.

MURPHY, Mr John Clifford Michael Blythewood, Lady Alices Drive, Lathorn, Ormskirk L40 5UD — MB ChB 1956 Ed.; FRCS Ed. 1966. Sen. Cons. (Orthop. Surg.) Hip Centre Wrightington.

MURPHY, John Francis Desmond 8 Lyndale Drive, Fleet GU51 3JH Tel: 01252 628641 — MB BCh BAO 1937 NUI; MD NUI 1955; FRCPsych 1971; DPM Eng. 1947; LM Nat. Matern. Hosp. Dub. 1937. (Dub.)

MURPHY, John Humphrey (retired) Rose Cottage, Woore Road, Buerton, Audlem, Crewe CW3 0DA Tel: 01270 811243 — MD 1950 Dub.; MB BCh BAO 1945. Prev: Ho. Phys. Haywood Hosp. Stoke-on-Trent.

MURPHY, John Kevin Department of Pathology, West Wales General Hospital, Carmarthen SA31 2AF Tel: 01267 235151 Fax: 01267 222724 — MB BCh BAO 1982 NUI; FRCPath 2000; MRCPI 1985; MRCPath 1992. Cons. Histopath. W. Wales Gen. Hosp. Carmarthen. Socs: Int. Acad. Of Path.; Assn. Of Clin. Pathologists - Sec. Cambrian Br.; Path. Soc. Gt. Britain & N. Ire.

MURPHY, John Martin 27C Frant Road, Tunbridge Wells TN2 5JT — MB BCh BAO 1990 NUI; MRCGP 1994; DRCOG 1994; DCH RCP Lond. 1993.

MURPHY, John Patrick Roundwood Surgery, Wood Street, Mansfield NG18 1QQ Tel: 01623 648880 Fax: 01623 631761 — BM BS 1982 Nottm.; BMedSci (2nd. cl. Hons.) Nottm. 1980, BM BS 1982; DRCOG 1987.

MURPHY, John Patrick (retired) 59 Osmaston Road, Stourbridge DY8 2AN Tel: 01384 394897 — MB BCh BAO NUI 1943; FFA RCS Eng. 1954; DA Eng. 1947. Cons. Anaesth. Dudley & Stourbridge Hosp. Gp. Prev: Sen. Regist. (Anaesth.) City Gen. Hosp. Stoke-on-Trent.

MURPHY

MURPHY, Mr John Paul 58B Halford Road, Ickenham, Uxbridge UB10 8QA — MB ChB 1984 Glas.; BSc (Hons.) Glas. 1981, MB ChB 1984; FRCS Eng. 1988. Sen. Regist. Chelsea & W.m. Hosp. Lond. Prev: Sen. Regist. Qu. Mary's Univ. Hosp. Leeds; Regist. (Orthop.) Char. Cross Hosp. Lond.

MURPHY, John Philip 24 The Crescent, Wharley End, Cranield, Bedford MK43 0SU — MB BCh BAO 1993 Belf.

MURPHY, Karen Mary Spring Gardens, Town Hall Lane, Swanage BH19 1EX — MB BS 1990 Lond.

MURPHY, Mr Karl William Department of Obstetrics and Gynaecology, St. Mary's Hospital, Praed St., London W2 1NY Tel: 020 7886 1567 Fax: 020 7886 6368 — MB BCh BAO 1981 NUI; FRCOG 1999; MD NUI 1992; MRCPI 1987; MRCOG 1987; DCH NUI 1984; FRCPI 1999. Cons. O & G & Subspecialist Fetal Med./High Risk Obst. St. Mary's Hosp. Lond.; Hon. Sen. Lect. Imperial Coll. Sch. of Med. Lond. Socs: Fell.Roy. Soc. Med.; Lond. Cons. Assoc.; Indep. Doctors Forum. Prev: RCOG Subspecialist Progr. in Fetal Med. Glas.; MRC Perinatal Research Fell. John Radcliffe Hosp. Oxf.; Clin. Dir. of Woms. & Childr. Servs. St Mary's.

MURPHY, Kathryn Alison c/o York District General Hospital, York YO3 7ES; 2 Maghaberry Manor, Moira, Craigavon BT67 0JZ Tel: 01846 619140 — MB ChB 1994 Ed.; BSc (Hons.) Ed. 1993.

MURPHY, Kathryn Gillian c/o Clydesdale Bank, 31-2 St Jame's St., London SW1 — MB BS 1965 Lond.

MURPHY, Kathryn Paula Maria Garden Flat, 86 Cotham Brow, Bristol BS6 6AP — MB BCh BAO 1977 NUI.

MURPHY, Kieran Christopher Institute of Psychiatry, Kings College London, De Crespigny Park, Denmark Hill, London SE5 8AF — MB BCh BAO 1987 NUI; MRCPsych 1992; MRCP(1) 1990; M.Med.Sci 1994. (Uni. Coll. Dublin) Sen. Lect. Behavioural Genetics.

MURPHY, Kieran Edward Moore Street Health Centre, 77 Moore Street, Bootle L20 4SE Tel: 0151 944 1066 Fax: 0151 933 4715 — MB BCh BAO 1983 Belf.; MRCGP 1987; DRCOG 1989; DGM RCP Lond. 1986. (Belf.) GP Bootle. Prev: SHO (O & G) Downe Matern. Hosp. Co. Down; SHO (Geriat. Med.) Sefton Gen. Hosp. Liverp.; Ho. Off. Mater Infirmorium Hosp. Belf.

MURPHY, Laurence John Prince Charles Hospital, Merthyr Tydfil CF47 9DT Tel: 01685 721721; Station Road, Carlow, Republic of Ireland Tel: 01503 31132 — MB BCh BAO 1986 NUI. Trainee GP Pr. Chas. Hosp. Merthyr Tydfil.

MURPHY, Linus Gabriel Belcoo, Enniskillen BT93 5AN — MB BCh BAO 1944 NUI.

MURPHY, Lorraine 2/R, 157 Broomhill Drive, Glasgow G11 7ND — MB ChB 1990 Glas.; MRCP (UK) 1994.

MURPHY, Mairead 400 High Street, West Bromwich B70 9LB — MB BCh BAO 1988 NUI.

MURPHY, Malachy Main Street Surgery, 11 Main Street, Killough, Downpatrick BT30 7QA Tel: 028 4484 1242 — MB BCh BAO 1978 Belf.; MRCGP 1982; MICGP 1987; DObst Dub. 1981; DCH Dub. 1981. Princip. GP Killough. Prev: SHO Internat. Miss. Train. Hosp. Drogheda; SHO & Ho. Off. Roy. Vict. Hosp. Belf.

MURPHY, Margaret Ann Catherine 33 Bramfield Avenue, Derby DE22 3TN — MB ChB 1986 Aberd.

MURPHY, Margaret Jane North Hill Surgery, 18 North Hill, Colchester CO1 1DZ Tel: 01206 578070 Fax: 01206 769880; Honeysuckle Cottage, Perry Lane, Langham, Colchester CO4 5PH — MB BS 1973 Lond.; MRCP (UK) 1978. (Char. Cross) GP Essex FPC; Aviat. Med Examr. (Civil Aviat. Auth.). Socs: Fell. Roy. Soc. Med.

MURPHY, Margaret Kathleen (retired) 63 Gilhams Avenue, Banstead SM7 1QW — MB BS 1962 Lond.; 1962 MRCS Eng. LRCP Lond.; 1968 FFA RCS Eng.; 1964 DA Eng. Prev: Cons. Anaesth. St. Helier Hosp. Gp. Carshalton Surrey.

MURPHY, Margaret Mary Lind House, The Street, Box Grove, Chichester PO18 0EB — MB BS 1948 Lond.; MRCS Eng. LRCP Lond. 1948; FFA RCS Eng. 1956; DA Eng. 1951. (Univ. Coll. Hosp.) Emerit. Cons. Anaesth. Leics. HA. Socs: Assn. Anaesth. Prev: Cons. Anaesth. Lambeth Hosp. Gp.; Sen. Hosp. Med. Off. W. Middlx. Hosp.; Regist. Univ. Coll. Hosp.

MURPHY, Marie Bernadette The London Hospital, London E1 1BB; 30 Trent Court, London E11 2TF — MB BCh BAO 1983 NUI; MRCPsych 1987.

MURPHY, Mark Joseph O'Tierney, Murphy and Ryan, Health Centre, Summerhill, Warrenpoint, Newry BT34 3JD Tel: 028 4175 4100 Fax: 028 4175 4050 — MB BCh BAO 1987 Belf.

MURPHY, Martin Francis 6 Sharman Way, Belfast BT9 5FU — MB BCh BAO 1987 Belf.

MURPHY, Martin Grant Weaver Vale Practice, Hallwood Health Centre, Runcorn WA7 2UT Tel: 01928 711911; Glastonbury, Bradley Lane, Frodsham, Warrington — MB BCh 1981 Wales; MRCGP 1987.

MURPHY, Martin Hugh Chiddenbrook Surgery, Threshers, Crediton EX17 3JJ Tel: 01363 772227 Fax: 01363 775528 — MB BS 1990 Lond.

MURPHY, Mary Clodagh The London Fields Medical Centres, 38-44 Broadway Market, London E8 4QJ Tel: 020 7254 2883 Fax: 020 7254 2066 — MB BChir 1989 Camb.

MURPHY, Mary Deirdre Flat 2, Innescrone House, Queen's Road, Datchet, Slough SL3 9BN — LAH Dub. 1959.

MURPHY, Maura Kingsway Surgery, 20-22 Kingsway, Waterloo, Liverpool L22 4RQ Tel: 0151 920 9000 Fax: 0151 928 2411 — MB ChB 1973 Dundee; MRCGP 1996; Dip. Med. Educat. Dund 1994. p/t Tutor (Gen. Pract.) Liverp. & Clin. Tutor Liverp. Univ.; Mem. Postgrad. GP Tutor. Socs: Liverp. Med. Inst.; Fell. Roy. Soc. Med.; Catholic Doctors Guild. Prev: Primary Care Facilitator Liverp.

MURPHY, Maureen Elizabeth (retired) 67 Moor Drive, Crosby, Liverpool L23 2UT Tel: 0151 924 4531 — MB ChB 1952 Liverp.; DObst RCOG 1954. Prev: Sen. Med. Off. Sefton AHA.

MURPHY, Maurice Edward Nympsfield, Blagden's Lane, Southgate, London N14 6DD — MB BCh BAO 1986 Dub.; MB BCh Dub. 1986; BSc (Hons.) Dub. 1988; DCH Dub. 1989; MRCPI 1989. Sen. Regist. (Genitourin. Med.) Leeds Gen. Infirm. Socs: Soc. Study VD & Internat. Soc. Study Sexually Transm. Dis. Prev: Regist. (Genitourin. Med.) St. Jas. Hosp. Dub.

MURPHY, Michael Department of of Clinical Chemistry, Derriford Hospital, Plymouth PL6 8DH Tel: 01752 792291 Fax: 01752 792400; 36 Tamerton Close, Plymouth PL5 4JX Tel: 01752 780800 — MB BCh BAO 1987 Dub.; BSc 1984 Dub.; MRCPI 1990; MRCPath 1997. Cons. Chem. Pathologist Plymouth Hosp.s NHS Trust. Socs: Assn. Clin. Biochem.; Assn. Clin. Pathologists; Brit. Hyperlipidaemia Assn. Prev: SHO (Haemat., Immunol. & Clin. Biochem.) St. Jas. Hosp. Dub.; Regist. (Path. Biochem.) Glas. Roy. Infirm.; Sen. Regist. (Path. Biochem.) Glas. Roy. Infirm.

MURPHY, Michael Furber National Blood Service - Oxford Centre, The John Radcliffe Hospital, Headington, Oxford OX3 9DU Tel: 01865 447902 Fax: 01865 447915 Email: mike.murphy@nbs.nhs.uk — MB BS 1973 Lond.; MD Lond. 1989; FRCP Lond. 1993; MRCP (UK) 1976; FRCPath 1994, M 1982. (St. Bart. Hosp. Med. Coll.) Cons. Haemat. Nat. Blood Serv. Dept. of Haemat. John Radcliffe Hosp. Oxf.; Hon. Sen. Clin. Lect. (Blood Transfus.) Univ. Oxf. Socs: Blood Transfus. Task Force of Brit. Comm. for Standards in Haematol.; Comm. BioMed. Excellence for Safer Transfus. (BEST); Internat. Soc. Blood Transfus. Prev: Sen. Lect. & Hon. Cons. (Haemat.) St. Bart. Hosp. Lond.; Sen. Regist., Regist. & Ho. Phys. (Haemat.) St. Bart. Hosp. Lond.

MURPHY, Michael Robert Department of Psychological Medicine, King's College Hospital, Denmark Hill, London SE5 Tel: 020 7720 9341; 34 Nightingale Lane, London SW12 8TD Tel: 020 8673 3485 — MB ChB 1978 Cape Town; MRCP (UK) 1982; MRCPsych 1986. Lect. (Psychol. Med.) Kings Coll. Hosp. Sch. Med. & Inst. Psychiat.; Hon. Sen. Regist. KCH Bethlem Roy. & Maudsley Hosp.

MURPHY, Michael Stephen Institute of Child Health, Clinical Research Block, Whittall St, Birmingham B4 6NH Tel: 0121 333 8705 Fax: 0121 333 8701 — MB BCh BAO 1977 NUI; BSc NUI 1979; MRCPI 1982; DCH RCPSI 1980; DCH (RCPSI) 1980; MD 1990; FRCPI 1994; FRCPCH 1996. (Nat. Univ. of Ireland, Univ. Coll. CORR) Cons. Peadiatric Gastroenterol., Birm. Childr.'s Hosp.; Sen. Lect. in Paediat. & Child Health, Dept. of Child Health, Univ. of Birm. Socs: Eur. Soc. Paed. Gast. Hepat. & Nut.; Brit. Soc. Paediat. Gast.; Amer. Gastoenterol. Assn. Prev: Action Research Train. Fell. & Hon. Sen. Regist. Dept. Child Health Univ. Newc.; Fell. Comb. Prog. (Paediat., Gast. &Nut.) Harvard Med. Sch., Boston; Instruc. (Paediat.) Harvard Med. Sch. Boston.

MURPHY, Nicholas Dominic 25 Church Road, Halewood, Liverpool L26 0US — MB BS 1991 Lond.

MURPHY, Noelle Mary Accident & Emergency Department, Raigmore Hospital, Perth Road, Inverness IV2 3UJ Tel: 01463 711322 — MB BCh BAO 1979 NUI; FRCSI 1983. Cons A & E Highland Acute Hosp.s Trust. Socs: BMA & Brit. Assn. Emerg. Med.

MURPHY

Prev: Sen. Regist. (A & E) Middlesbrough Gen. Hosp.; Regist. (A & E) Milton Keynes; Regist. Rotat. (Surg.) N.. Irel.

MURPHY, Olive Mary Microbiology Department, Freeman Hospital, Freeman Road, Newcastle upon Tyne NE7 7DN — MB BCh BAO 1988 NUI.

MURPHY, Padraig Gerard (retired) Teac Muire, 2 Station Road, Killough, Downpatrick BT30 7QA Tel: 01396 841006 — MB BCh BAO Belf. 1940; FRCGP 1970. Prev: Ho. Phys. & Surg. Mater. Infirm. Hosp. Belf.

MURPHY, Patrick 13 Normandy Court, West Parade, Worthing BN11 3QY Tel: 01903 211354 — MB BCh BAO 1938 NUI. (Cork)

MURPHY, Patrick Ashington (retired) Western Lodge, 28 Horn St., Winslow, Buckingham MK18 3AW Tel: 01296 712423 — MB ChB Birm. 1941.

MURPHY, Patrick Desmond Erdington Medical Centre, 103 Wood End Road, Erdington, Birmingham B24 8NT Tel: 0121 373 0085 Fax: 0121 386 1768; 54 Halton Road, Sutton Coldfield B73 6NU Tel: 0121 354 5474 — LRCPI & LM, LRSCI & LM 1969; LRCPI & LM, LRCSI & LM 1969; MRCGP 1976; DCH Eng. 1973; DObst RCOG 1971. (RCSI) Prev: Ho. Off. (Med., Surg., Paediat. & Obst.) Dudley Rd. Hosp. Birm.

MURPHY, Patrick Joseph 10 Blyth Road, Bromley BR1 3R Tel: 020 8460 7182 — MB BCh BAO 1940 NUI. (Univ. Coll. Cork) Prev: Ho. Surg. Roy. S. Hants & Soton. Hosp.; Surg. Lt. RNVR.

MURPHY, Patrick Joseph (retired) The Cedars, 65 Marsh Lane, Nantwich CW5 5HP Tel: 01270 623464 — MB BCh BAO NUI 1957, MAO 1968; FRCOG 1980, M 1967, DObst 1961. Prev: Cons. O & G Leighton Hosp. Crewe.

MURPHY, Patrick Noel 4 Wood Close, Childer Thornton, South Wirral CH66 1QX Tel: 0151 327 7041 — MB BCh BAO 1972 NUI; FRCPCH 1997; FRCP Lond. 1993; MRCP (UK) 1979; MSc Liverp. 1998. (University College Galway, Ireland) Cons. Paediat. Countess of Chester Hosp. Chester; Hon. Clin. Tutor Univ. Liverp. Socs: Fell. Roy. Coll. Paediat. and Child Health; Neonat. Soc.; Brit. Assn. Perinatal Med. Prev: Sen. Regist. Alder Hey Hosp. Liverp.; Resid. Hosp. Sick Childr. Toronto, Canada; Ho. Off. Hosp. Sick Childr. Gt. Ormond St. Lond.

MURPHY, Mr Paul Desmond South Warwickshire Hospitals NHS Trust, Lakin Road, Warwick CV34 5BW Tel: 01926 495321 — MB BS 1976 Lond.; PhD Soton. 1986; FRCS Eng. 1982. Cons. Gen. And GI Surg. S. Warks. Hosp. Warwick. Prev: Sen. Regist. N.. Region; Resid. Surg. Off. St. Mark's Hosp. Lond.; Regist. (Hepatobillary & Paediat. Surg.) King's Coll. Hosp. Lond.

MURPHY, Paul Edward 49 Vale Road, Woolton, Liverpool L25 7RN Tel: 0151 428 6479 — MB ChB 1994 Liverp.

MURPHY, Paul Gerard Kenilworth Lodge, Clifford Road, Boston Spa, Wetherby LS23 6BZ — MB ChB 1984 Bristol; FCAnaesth. 1989. Cons. Anaesth. S.mead Hosp. Bristol. Prev: Sen. Regist. (Anaesth.) Yorksh. RHA.

MURPHY, Paul Michael Woodliffe 17 Burkitt Road, Woodbridge IP12 4JJ — MB BS 1986 Lond.

MURPHY, Peter John 32 Beche Road, Cambridge CB5 8HU — MB BS 1977 Lond.; MRCS Eng. LRCP Lond. 1977; MRCP (UK) 1980.

MURPHY, Peter John Paediatric Intensive Care Unit, Bristol Children's Hospital, Bristol; 23 Henleaze Avenue, Henleaze, Bristol BS9 4EU — MB ChB 1984 Leeds; FCAnaesth 1990; DA (UK) 1986. Cons. Anaesth. Roy. Hosp. Sick Childr. Bristol. Prev: Lect. (Anaesth.) Univ. Leic.

MURPHY, Peter Michael Melrose, The Crescent, Crapstone, Yelverton PL20 7PS Tel: 01822 852847 — MB BS 1983 Lond.; MRCP (UK) 1987; FRCA 1989. (St. Thos. Hosp. Lond.) Cons. Anaesth. Derriford Hosp. Plymouth. Socs: Cardiothoracic Anaesth. Assn.; Assn. Anaesth. Prev: Sen. Regist. (Anaesth.) SW RHA; Regist. (Anaesth.) Hosp. Sick Childr. Gt. Ormond St., St. Thos. Hosp. Lond. & Salisbury HA.

MURPHY, Philip Patrick South Tyrone Hospital, Dungannon BT71 4AU Tel: 01868 722821 — MB BCh BAO 1984 Belf.; MD Belf. 1989; MRCP (UK) 1987. Cons. Phys. S. Tyrone Hosp. Dungannon.

MURPHY, Pilar Anne Ellon Group Practice, Health Centre, Schoolhill, Ellon AB41 9AH Tel: 01358 720333 Fax: 01358 721578 — MB ChB 1990 Dundee.

MURPHY, Rachael Elizabeth Department of Academic Radiology, 8 Floor, Medical School, Queen's Medical Centre, University Hospital, Nottingham NG7 2UU Email: rachael.murphy@nottingham.ac.uk — BM BS 1994 Nottm. (Nottingham) Specialist Regist. Gen. Rotat. (Med. & Geriats.) Nottm. Socs: MPS; BGS.

MURPHY, Rachel Catherine 1 Trem y Bedol, Carmarthen SA31 1JL — MB BCh 1997 Wales.

MURPHY, Richard D Ross Road Surgery, 21 Ross Road, Belfast BT12 4JR; 44 Bladon Drive, Belfast BT9 5JN — MB ChB 1971 Belf.; MRCOG 1978, DObst 1973. Princip. GP Belf. Socs: Ulster Obst. Soc. Prev: Intern Mater Infirm. Hosp. Belf.; SHO Roy. Matern. Hosp. Belf.; Regist. (O & G) City Hosp. Belf.

MURPHY, Richard John Witton Street Surgery, 162 Witton Street, Northwich CW9 5QU Tel: 01606 42007 Fax: 01606 350659; 4 The Coppice, Cuddington, Northwich CW8 2XF Tel: 01606 888490 — MB BCh BAO 1973 NUI; DObst. RCPI 1978; DA RCPSI 1976. Clin. Asst. (Anaesth.) Leighton Hosp. Crewe; Med. Adviser AMEC plc; Pres. N.wick Med. Soc. Prev: SHO (Psych.) St. Vincent's Hosp. Dub.; Intern N. Infirm. Cork; SHO (Anaesth.) Roy. City of Dub. Hosp.

MURPHY, Richard Ronan 53 North Castle Street, Edinburgh EH2 3LJ — MB ChB 1993 Ed.

MURPHY, Richard Stewart 12 Mountstewart, Wynyard Park, Billingham TS22 5QN — MB ChB 1983 Liverp.; MRCGP 1988; DRCOG 1986. GP Middlesbrough.

MURPHY, Robert Alan Blyth Health Centre, Thoroton Street, Blyth NE24 1DX Tel: 01670 396560 Fax: 01670 396579; 11 Holywell Avenue, Whitley Bay NE26 3AH Tel: 0191 252 3831 — MB BS 1975 Newc.; MRCGP 1980; DRCOG 1979. (Newc.) GP & Forens. Med. Examr.; Police Surg. N.umbria; Tutor (Gen. Pract.) N.d.; Trainer (Gen. Pract.) N.umbria VTS; Examr. & Med. Off. Assur. Socs. Socs: Assn. Police Surg.; Assur. Med. Soc.; Expert Witness Inst. Prev: Lect. (Anat.) Univ. Newc.; Ho. Surg. & Phys. Roy. Vict. Infirm. Newc.

MURPHY, Rose Mary 3 Knighton Road, Stoneygate, Leicester LE2 3HL Tel: 0116 270 8536 — MB ChB St. And. 1968. (St. And.) Clin. Asst. (Psychiat.) Acad. Dept. of Psychiat. for the Elderly Leicester Gen. Hosp. Prev: Clin. Asst. (Psychiat.) N. Staffs. Hosp. Centre Stoke-on-Trent; Ho. Off. (Med.) & SHO (Paediat.) Roy. Infirm. Dundee.

MURPHY, Roy Carey Wilson (retired) 25 Strawberry Terrace, Carlisle CA3 9LT — MB BCh BAO 1952 Belf. Prev: Ho. Phys. & Ho. Surg. Belf. City Hosp.

MURPHY, Ruth Sea Mews, Lancaster Road, Knott-End-on-Sea, Poulton-le-Fylde FY6 0DX — MB ChB 1990 Sheff.

MURPHY, Siobhan Marie Dungiven Health Centre, 1 Chapel Road, Dungiven, Londonderry BT47 4RS Tel: 028 7774 1801 Fax: 028 7774 1355; 30 Limavady Road, Londonderry BT47 6JD Tel: 01504 48743 — MB BCh BAO 1983 NUI; Cert. Family Plann. JCC 1990. Prev: Trainee GP Derry VTS; Regist. (Psychiat.) Derry Hosp.; SHO (Obst. & Paediat.) Derry Hosp.

MURPHY, Siobhan Mary Psychotherapy Department, Maudsley Hospital, Denmark Hill, London SE5 8AZ Tel: 0207 919 2384/5 — BM BS 1980 Nottm.; MD Nottm. 1990; BMedSci Nottm. 1978; MRCPsych 1984; T(Psych) 1993. Cons. Psychotherapist, S. Lond. & Maudsley NHS Trust, Lond. Prev: Sen. Lect. (Psychother.) & Hon. Cons. St. Bart. Hosp. Lon.

MURPHY, Stephen Anthony Department of Respiratory Medicine, Leeds General Infirmary, Great George St., Leeds LS1 3EX Tel: 0113 292 3328 Fax: 0113 292 6316; 51 Chaucer Drive, West Derby, Liverpool L12 0LH Email: murphsa@cableinet.co.uk — MB ChB 1986 Liverp.; BSc (Hons.) Liverp. 1984; MRCP (UK) 1989. Sen. Regist. (Gen. & Respirat. Med.) Leeds Gen. Infirm. Socs: BMA; Roy. Coll. Phys. of Edin.; Brit. Thorac. Soc. Prev: Clin. Researcher Oxf. Wellcome Trust Research Unit. Kilifi, Kenya; Regist. (Infec. Dis.) Fazakerley Hosp. Liverp.; SHO (Gen. Med.) Ninewells Hosp. Dundee, Perth Roy. Infirm. & Roy. Liverp. Hosp.

MURPHY, Stephen Denis Pavilion Family Doctors, 153A Stroud Road, Gloucester GL1 5JJ Tel: 01452 385555 Fax: 01452 387905 — MB ChB 1981 Manch.; MRCGP 1993. Princip. GP. Socs: Assoc. Mem. Roy. Coll. Homeop. Prev: Trainee GP ScarBoro. & Exeter VTS; Med. Pract. (Nutrit., Allergies & Homoeop.) Chester; Jun. Hosp. Rotat. (Psychiat.) Univ. S. Manch.

MURPHY, Susan Mary The Surgery, South Hermitage, Belle Vue, Shrewsbury SY3 7JS Tel: 01743 343148 Fax: 01743 357772 — MB ChB 1986 Birm.

MURPHY, Thomas Francis Brian 17 Cooldarragh Park, Belfast BT14 6TH — MB BCh BAO 1960 Belf.; DObst RCOG 1966.

MURPHY, Thomas Joseph 1 Tintern Close, Sutton Coldfield B74 2EL — MB BCh BAO 1936 NUI. (Univ. Coll. Dub.) Act. Asst. Med. Off. Matern. & Child Welf. Birm. Prev: Med. Off. Hollymoor E.M.S. Hosp.

MURPHY, Thomas Joseph Charles Department of Psychotherapy, 40 Colinton Road, Edinburgh EH10 5BT Tel: 0131 537 6926 Fax: 0131 537 6931 — MB BCh BAO 1974 Dub.; MRCPsych 1979. (Trinity College, Dublin) Cons. Psychother. Roy. Edin. Hosp.; Hon. Sen. Lect. Univ. Edin. Socs: Assoc. Mem. Brit. Psychoanalyt. Soc.; Scott. Assn. Psychoanalyt. Psychother. Prev: Cons. Psychother. Roy. Dundee Liff Hosp.; Sen. Regist. (Psychother.) Roy. Edin. Hosp.; Sen. Regist. Qu. Eliz. Hosp. Birm.

MURPHY, Ursula Margaret (retired) Western Lodge, Winslow, Buckingham MK18 3AW Tel: 01296 712423 — MB ChB 1943 Birm.; MB ChB. Birm. 1943; MRCS Eng. LRCP Lond. 1943.

MURPHY, Vincent John (retired) Vange Health Centre, Southview Road, Basildon SS16 4HD Tel: 01268 533151 — MB ChB 1953 Aberd.

MURPHY, William Anthony 22 Longbarn Lane, Reading RG2 7SZ Tel: 01734 871727; Shanzu, 31 West Drive, Sonning, Reading RG4 6GE Tel: 01734 692523 — MB BS 1954 Lond. (St. Mary's)

MURPHY, William Gerrard Department of Transfusion Medicine, Royal Infirmary, Edinburgh EH3 9HB Tel: 0131 229 2585 Fax: 0131 225 2296 — MD 1990 NUI; MB BCh BAO 1976; MRCP (UK) 1982; FRCP Ed. 1994; MRCPath 1989. Sen. Lect. (Med.) Univ. Edin.

MURPHY, William James Crawford Glenside Medical Centre, Glenside Rise, Plympton, Plymouth PL7 4DR Tel: 01752 341340 Fax: 01752 348913 — MB ChB 1984 Bristol; MRCGP 1988.

MURPHY, William John (retired) Millersneuk House Millersneuk Road, Lenzie, Kirkintilloch, Glasgow G66 5JD Tel: 0141 776 3178 — MB ChB Glas. 1942.

MURPHY, William Robert Harnett (retired) 34 Haslam Crescent, Pebsham, Bexhill-on-Sea TN40 2PD Tel: 01424 214031 — LRCPI & LM, LRSCI & LM 1938; LRCPI & LM, LRCSI & LM 1938; FFA RCS Eng. 1954; DA Eng. 1952; DA RCPSI 1942. Prev: Cons. Anaesth. Hastings Health Dist.

MURRANT, Mr Nicholas John Department Otolaryngology, Cumberland Infirmary, Carlisle CA2 7HY Tel: 01228 523444 Fax: 01228 814276 — MB BS 1981 Lond.; FRCS Eng. 1988. Cons. Otolaryngol. City Gen. Hosp. Carlisle & Cumbld. Infirm. Prev: Sen. Regist. (Otolaryngol.) Aberd. Roy. Infirm.; Vis. Fell. (Head & Neck Surg.) Roy. P. Alfred Hosp. Sydney, Austral.; Regist. (Otolaryngol.) St. Bart. Hosp. Lond.

MURRAY, Adrian Duchess of Westminster Wing, Arrowe Park Hospital, Arrowe Park Road, Upton, Wirral CH49 5PE Tel: 0151 604 7059 Fax: 0151 604 1552; Fachddeillog, Llangower, Bala LL23 7BT Tel: 01678 520344 Fax: 01678 521193 Email: dradrianmurray@hotmail.com — MB ChB 1973 Liverp.; MB ChB (Hons.) 1973; MD Liverp. 1988; FRCOG 1990, M 1978. Cons. Obst.& Gyn. Wirral Hosp. Trust; Hon. Lect. (Obst. & Gyn.) Univ. Liverp. Socs: Ospreys Gyn. Soc. & Brit. Fertil. Soc.; Internat. Continence Soc. Prev: Ethel Boyce Research Fell. (O & G) Liverp. Univ.

MURRAY, Agnes Cecilia Coombe Eden, Armathwaite, Carlisle CA4 9PQ Tel: 016974 72234 — MB ChB 1951 St. And. Prev: Clin. Med. Off. E. Cumbria & Essex HAs; GP Essex; Research Assoc. Dept. O & G Univ. Birm.

MURRAY, Mr Aidan Thomas Birmingham & Midland Eye Centre, Dudley Road, Birmingham B18 7QU Tel: 0121 236 4911 — MB BS 1991 Lond.; BSc (Hons.) Ophth. Optics Bradford 1982; FRCOphth 1995. (Roy. Lond. Hosp.) Cons. Ophth.. Birm. & Midl. Eye Centre,Birm.; Cons. Opthalmology, Univ. Hosp.s, NHS Trust, Selly Oak, Birm. Socs: Brit. Coll. Optom.; Roy. Coll. of Opthalmologists; BOS. Prev: Fell. Ophth., Moorfields Eye Hosp.; Regist.(Ophth) Birm & Midl. Eye Hosp.; SHO (Ophth.) Birm. & Midl. Eye Hosp. & Sunderland Eye Infirm.

MURRAY, Mr Alan (retired) 5 Grand Drive, Leigh-on-Sea SS9 1BG Tel: 01702 710294 Fax: 01702 710294 — MB BS 1979 Lond.; MS Lond. 1990; FRCS Eng. 1984; T(S) 1992. Prev: Cons. Gen. Vasc. Surg. S.end Health Care NHS Trust.

MURRAY, Alan Charles Drumullie Mill, Boat of Garten PH24 3BG — MB ChB 1990 Manch.

MURRAY, Alan Edward Department of Medical Microbiology, Pathology Block, Clatterbridge Hospital, Bebington, Wirral CH63 4JY Tel: 0151 482 7694 Fax: 0151 482 7695; 11 Wood Lea, Alder Meadow Est., Liverpool L12 0JF Tel: 0151 546 2439 — BM 1983 Soton.; FRCPath 1998. Cons. Med. Microbiol. Wirral Hosps. NHS Trust; Hon. Lect. (Med. Microbiol.) Univ. Liverp. Socs: Fell. Inst. BioMed. Sci.; FRCPath. & Assn. Clin. Paths. Prev: Cons. Med. Microbiol. Scunthorpe HA; Sen. Regist. & Regist. (Med. Microbiol.) Roy. Liverp. Hosp.

MURRAY, Alan William Huntsmans Cottage, Tinklers Hill, Shotley Bridge, Consett DH8 0NN Tel: 01207 591948 Fax: 01207 591948 Email: a.w.murray@ncl.ac.uk — MB ChB 1981 Glas.; FFA RCS Eng. 1987. Dryburn Hosp. Durh.; Hon. Clin. Lect. (Anaesth.) Univ. Newc. Socs: Neuroanaesth. Trav. Club & Soc. Computing & Technol. Anaesth. Prev: Cons. Anaesth. & Sen. Regist. Rotat. (Anaesth.) Newc. Gen. Hosp.; Regist. (Anaesth.) Roy. Infirm. Glas.

*****MURRAY, Alastair William** 41 Oxgangs Road, Edinburgh EH10 7BE — MB ChB 1995 Aberd.

*****MURRAY, Alexandra Xenia** 95 Highfield Way, Rickmansworth WD3 7PN — MB BS 1996 Lond.

*****MURRAY, Alice Fiona** 22 Stanley Road, Leicester LE2 1RE — MB ChB 1998 Leic.; MB ChB Leic 1998.

MURRAY, Alison Dorothy Department of Diagnostic Radiology, Aberdeen Royal Infirmary, Foresterhill, Aberdeen AB25 2ZN Tel: 01224 681818 Fax: 01224 840778 Email: a.s.murray@abdn.ac.uk; Mill of Findon, Portlethen, Aberdeen AB12 4QQ Tel: 01224 780176 — MB ChB 1985 Aberd.; MB ChB (Hons.) Aberd. 1985; MRCP (UK) 1988; FRCR 1992; FRCP Ed 1999. (University of Aberdeen) Sen. Lect. in Radiol., Univ. of Aberd.; Hon. Cons. Radiol. Grampian Univer. Hosp. NHST, Foresterhill, Aberd. Socs: BMA, Internat. Soc. for Magnetic Resonace in Med. - Mem.; Scott. Radiol. Soc. Prev: Cons. Radiol., Aberd. Roy. Infirm., Aberd..

MURRAY, Allyson May Lorn Medical Centre, Soroba Road, Oban PA34 4HE Tel: 01631 563175 Fax: 01631 562708 — MB ChB 1986 Aberd.

MURRAY, Mr Andrew Department of Otolaryngology, CrossHouse Hospital, Kilmarnour KA2 0BE Tel: 01563 577893 Email: andrew_murray@aaaht.swt.nhs.uk — MB ChB 1988 Glas.; FRCS 1999 (ORL HNS). Cons. Otolaryngologist, CrossHo. Hosp. Kilmarnour. Socs: Brit. Assoc. of Head & Neck Oncologists; Brit. Assoc. of Otolaryngologists, Head & Neck Surg.s; Scott. OtoLaryngol. Soc.

MURRAY, Mr Andrew Fax: 01553 613700; 7 Bernard Crescent, Hunstanton PE36 6ER Tel: 01485 532376 Email: andrew.murray1@virgin.net — MB ChB 1971 Birm.; FRCS Ed. 1976. Cons. Surg. Orthop. & Trauma Qu. Eliz. Hosp. & Sandringham Hosp., King's Lynn Pk.way Hosp. Solihull. Socs: Assoc. Inst. Med. Laborat. Technol. 1966; Fell. BOA; Brit. Soc. Paediat. Orthop. Surg. Prev: Surg. (Orthop. & Trauma) Solihull Hosp.; Surg. (Orthop. & Trauma) Manor Hosp. Nuneaton; Regist. Robt. Jones & Agnes Hunt Orthop. Hosp. OsW.ry.

MURRAY, Andrew Christopher East Parade Medical Practice, 89 East Parade, Heworth, York YO31 7YD Tel: 01904 423666 Fax: 01904 431329 — MB ChB 1980 Ed.; BSc (Med. Sci.) Ed. 1977; MRCGP 1984; DRCOG 1983. GP Princip.; Hosp. Practitioner Upper (GI Endoscopy) York Dist. Hosp.

MURRAY, Andrew James Farquhar 8 Coastguard Cottages, Coastguard Avenue, Helens Bay, Bangor BT19 1JY — MB BCh BAO 1993 Belf.

MURRAY, Angela Mary Basildon Hospital, Nethermayne, Basildon SS16 5NL Tel: 01268 533911; 9 St Johns Avenue, Warley, Brentwood CM14 5DF — MB BS 1977 Lond.; FFA RCS Eng. 1984; DRCOG 1979. Cons. Anaesth. Basildon & Orsett Hosps. Essex. Prev: Sen. Regist. (Anaesth.) Hammersmith Hosp. Lond.; Regist. (Anaesth.) Nottm.

MURRAY, Anne Patricia Veronica Foyle Trust Child and Family Mental Health Team, The Railway Centre, Old Railway Station, Duke Street, Londonderry BT47 1DH Tel: 01504 343501 Fax: 01504 346091 Email: amurray@foylebv.n-i.nhs.uk; 13 Dunhugh Park, Londonderry BT47 2NL — MB BCh BAO 1979 Dub.; MRCPsych

MURRAY

1986; DCH RCPSI 1983. Cons. Child & Adolesc. Psychiat. Foyle Heath & Social Serv. Trust N. Irel. Socs: Roy. Coll. Psychiat.; BMA. Prev: Sen. Regist. Young Peoples Centre Belf.; Sen. Regist. (Child Psychiat.) Roy. Belf. Hosp. Sick Childr.; Regist. (Psychiat. & Child Psychiat.) Forster Green Hosp. Belf.

MURRAY, Anthony Edward West Hoe Surgery, 2 Cliff Road, Plymouth PL1 3BP Tel: 01752 660105 Fax: 01752 268992 — MB BS 1983 London; MB BS 1983 London.

MURRAY, Barbara Castle Gardens Medical Centre, 78 East Hill, Colchester CO1 2QS Tel: 01206 866626 Fax: 01206 869575 — MB BS 1979 Lond.; MA Camb. 1980; MRCP (UK) 1983; MRCGP 1985; DRCOG 1984; DCH RCP Lond. 1983.

MURRAY, Bernard Moyrein, 161 Andersonstown Road, Belfast BT11 9EA Tel: 01232 612452 — MB BCh BAO 1946 Belf.

MURRAY, Bernard John Department of Gynaecology, Sunderland Royal Hospital, Sunderland SR4 7TP; Asphodel Cottage, Broomfarm West, Broompark, Durham DH7 7QS Tel: 0191 386 2484 — MB BS 1964 Durh.; FRCOG 1986, M 1974, DObst 1967. (Newc.) Cons. O & G Sunderland Roy. Hosp. Prev: Regist. (Gyn.) Qu. Eliz. Hosp. Gateshead & Univ. Newc. Hosp. Gp.; Ho. Surg. & Ho. Phys. Roy. Vict. Infirm. Newc.; Med. Off. Brit. Solomon Is.s Govt.

MURRAY, Brian Joseph Sibylla, 14 Addison Road, Steeple Claydon, Buckingham MK18 2NP — BM BCh 1992 Oxf.; BA Oxf. 1993, BM BCh 1992.

MURRAY, Brian Robert Pairman 8 Stanford Close, Hove BN3 6PU — MB BS 1957 Lond.; FFA RCS Eng. 1960; MRCS Eng. LRCP Lond. 1957. (Guy's) Cons. Anaesth. Brighton Health Dist. Socs: Assoc. Mem. Assn. Anaesths. Gt. Brit; BMA. Prev: Ho. Surg. & Sen. Anaesth. Regist. Guy's Hosp. Lond.; Anaesth. Regist. New Cross Hosp. Lond.

MURRAY, Campbell (retired) 10 Oakhill Road, Aberdeen AB15 5ES Tel: 01224 313416 — MB ChB Aberd. 1955; FRCP Ed. 1980, M 1965; FRCGP 1986, M 1966. Prev: Dean Postgrad. Med. Studies & Exec. Dean. Undergrad. Studies Univ. Aberd.

MURRAY, Carolyn Ann Department of Genitourinary Medicine, Queens Hospital, Belvedere Road, Burton-on-Trent DE13 0RB Tel: 01283 566333; 24 Friary Road, Lichfield WS13 6QL — MB ChB 1980 Aberd.; MRCOG 1987. Cons. Genitourin. Med. Qu.s Hosp. Burton-on-Trent. Prev: Sen. Regist. (Genitourin. Med.) Glas. Roy. Infirm.

***MURRAY, Catherine Jean** 4 Chorley Close, Bury BL8 2TB — MB ChB 1998 Leeds.

MURRAY, Catriona 44 Minster's Park, East Kilbride, Glasgow G74 5BX; 31 Davies Acre, Kittochmuir, East Kilbridge, Glasgow G74 5BZ — MB ChB 1991 Glas. SHO (Psychiat.) Lanarksh. Healthcare NHS Trust.

MURRAY, Cecily Rosaleen (retired) 3 Hamilton Road, Glasgow G32 9QD Tel: 0141 778 3343 — LRCP 1952 Ed.; LRCP, LRCS Ed. LRFPS Glas. 1952. Prev: Ho. Phys. Roy. Infirm. Glas.

MURRAY, Mr Charles Mitchell McQuibban, TD (retired) Martha Cottage, 59 Sinah Lane, Hayling Island PO11 0HJ Tel: 01705 464044 — MB ChB 1931 Aberd.; FRCS Ed. 1937. Prev: Sen. Orthop. Surg. Portsmouth Gp. Hosps.

MURRAY, Charles Richard Harrison Cooil Bane, Quarterbridge Road, Douglas IM2 3RJ Tel: 01624 622668 — MB BS 1966 Lond. BSc Lond. 1962, MB BS 1966; FRCP Lond. 1990; MRCP (UK) 1971. (Lond. Hosp.) Cons. Phys. Noble's Hosp. Douglas I. of Man. Socs: Brit. Soc. Gastroenterol.

MURRAY, Charles Thomas Anthony Lennard Road Surgery, 26 Lennard Road, Croydon CR0 2UL Tel: 020 8680 2270 Fax: 020 8649 8763 — LRCPI & LM, LRSCI & LM 1975; LRCPI & LM, LRCSI & LM 1975; DCH RCPSI 1979; MICGP 1987. Prev: Sen. Resid. (Paediat.) Salmaniya Hosp. Mauama, Bahrain.

***MURRAY, Christina Margaret** 100 Rullion Road, Penicuik EH26 9JA — MB ChB 1997 Aberd.

MURRAY, Christine The Priory Hospital, Stump Lane, Springfield Green, Chelmsford CM1 7SJ Tel: 01245 345345 Fax: 01245 346177; 55 Worrin Road, Shenfield, Brentwood CM15 8DH Tel: 01277 212147 Fax: 01277 262739 — MB BS Lond. 1969; MRCS Eng. LRCP Lond. 1969; MRCPsych 1983; DA Eng. 1971. (Lond. Hosp.) Cons. Psychiat. & Med. Dir. Priory Hosp. Chelmsford. Prev: Cons. Psychiat. Hayes Gr. Priory Hosp. Kent; Cons. Psychiat. Mid-Essex HA; Sen. Regist. St. Ann's & St. Bart. Hosps. Lond. & Warley Hosp. Brentwood.

MURRAY, Christine Margaret The Surgery, 15 King Street, Paisley PA1 2PR Tel: 0141 889 3144 Fax: 0141 889 7134 — MB ChB 1977 Glas. Prev: Clin. Asst. (Geriat. Med.) Roy. Alexandra Hosp. Paisley.

MURRAY, Christopher Charles G/L 17 Polwarth Street, Glasgow G12 9UD — MB ChB 1980 Manch.; BSc St. And. 1977; MBA Strathclyde 1996; DRCOG 1987; DA (UK) 1985. Commiss.er for Cancer Servs. Ayrsh. & Arran Health Bd.; Clin. Asst. (Anaesth.) Inverclyde Roy. Hosp. Greenock. Prev: GP Birm.; GP Ruthesay.

MURRAY, Clare Suzanne 8 Church Green, Warburton, Lymm WA13 9SS Tel: 01925 758973 Email: echeetham@compuserve.com — MB ChB 1990 Ed.; MRCP (UK) 1995. (Ed) Specialist Regist. (Paediat.) Roy. Liverp. Childr. Hosp.

MURRAY, Colin William Angless (retired) The Stables, Heytesbury Park, Heytesbury, Warminster BA12 0HG Tel: 01985 840313 — MB ChB 1947 Ed.; DA (UK) 1960; DObst RCOG 1956; DCH Eng. 1953. Prev: Ho. Phys. Birm. Childr. Hosp.

MURRAY, Mr Craig David 128 Essex Drive, Jordanhill, Glasgow G14 9PD — MB ChB 1988 Glas.; FRCS Glas. 1993.

MURRAY, David (retired) Willow Cottage, Tibbermore, Perth PH1 1QJ Tel: 01738 583453 — MB ChB 1951 St. And.; MRCGP 1959; DObst RCOG 1967. Prev: Med. Off. Achimota Sch. & Hosp. Ghana.

MURRAY, David 152 Harley Street, London W1N 1HH Tel: 020 7935 8868 Fax: 020 7224 2574; Mill House, Wistow, Huntingdon PE28 0QD Tel: 01487 822487 Fax: 01487 824080 Email: pdm152@aol.com — MB BS Lond. 1967; FRCP Lond. 1985; Dip. Dermat. Lond 1977. (St. Thos.) Cons. Dermat. Lond.; Hon. Civil. Cons. Adviser RAF. Socs: Fell. Brit. Assn. Dermat.; Fell. (Dermat.) St. John's. Hosp. Dermat. Soc. Prev: Cons. Adviser (Dermat.) RAF Lond.

MURRAY, David Barclay Ferguson Medical Centre, Lochcarron, Strathcarron IV54 8YD Tel: 01520 722215 Fax: 01520 722230; Dalchuirn, Lochcarron, Strathcarron IV54 8YD Tel: 015202 722221 — MB ChB 1979 Dundee.

MURRAY, David Brierley (retired) 6 Pleck Farm Avenue, Blackburn BB1 8PE Tel: 01254 698313 — LRCP LRCS Ed. LRFPS Glas. 1949; DA Eng. 1956. Prev: Cons. Anaesth. Blackburn & Dist. Hosp. Gp.

MURRAY, David Keith 11 Alexandra Road, Harrogate HG1 5JS Tel: 01423 503218 Fax: 01423 505512; 11 Grey Street, Harrogate HG2 8DL Tel: 01423 879771 Fax: 01423 879769 — BM BS 1984 Nottm.; BMedSci (Hons.) Nottm. 1982, BM BS 1984; MRCGP 1988; DRCOG 1987. Socs: BMA. Prev: SHO (O & G) City Gen. Hosp. Carlisle; Ho. Off. (Gen. Med.) Newc. Gen. Hosp.; Trainee GP E. Cumbria VTS.

MURRAY, David Mark 171 Linnet Drive, Chelmsford CM2 8AH — MB BS 1993 Lond.

MURRAY, Professor David W Nuffield Orthopaedic Centre, Headington, Oxford OX3 7LD Tel: 01865 227482 Fax: 01865 742348 Email: david.murray@noc.anglox.nhs.uk; Cuddesdon House, Cuddesdon, Oxford OX44 9HB Tel: 01865 227482 Fax: 01865 742348 — MD 1989 Camb.; MB BChir 1983; FRCS (Orth.) 1993; FRCS Eng. 1987. Cons. Nuffield Dept. Orthop. Surg. Oxf.; Prof.of Orthopaedic Surg. Oxf. Univ. Prev: Sen. Research Fell. Oxf. Univ. Hon.Clin. Sen. Lect. Ox/Uni; Sen. Regist. (Orthop.) Nuffield Orthop. Centre & John Radcliffe Hosp. Oxf.; Regist. (Orthop.) Roy. Berks. Hosp. Reading.

MURRAY, Deirdre Mary c/o 5 Hermitage Terrace, Morningside, Edinburgh EH10 4RP — MB BCh BAO 1990 NUI.

MURRAY, Denis (retired) 3 Rosemary Drive, Lisburn BT28 1LE — LRCP LRCS 1950 Ed.; LRCP LRCS Ed. LRFPS Glas. 1950.

MURRAY, Dermot Patrick, TD, Lt.-Col. RAMC Retd. (retired) Tamaris, Old Vicarage Lane, Quarndon, Derby DE22 5JB Tel: 01332 553238 — MB ChB Liverp. 1962; BA Open 1990; MRCP (UK) 1974; DFFP 1996; Dip. Ven. Soc. Apoth. Lond. 1976. Regt.. med. Off., Army Cadet Force Derbysh. Prev: Cons. Genitourin. Med. Derbysh. Roy. Infirm.

MURRAY, Desiree Cisne Birmingham & Midland Eye Centre, City Hospital NHS Trust, Dudley Road, Birmingham B18 7QH Tel: 0121 507 6700 Fax: 0121 507 6853 Email: desiree@mcmail.com — MB BS 1991 West Indies; FRCS Ed. 1995; FRCOphth 1995. (Univ. W. Indies) Regist. (Ophth.) Birm. & Midl. Eye Centre City Hosp. NHS Trust.

MURRAY

MURRAY, Diane — BM BS 1990 Nottm.; BMedSci (Hons.) 1988; MRCP (UK) 1994; FRCR 1997. Prev: Radiol. Fell., Roy. Perth Hosp., W. Australia; Regist. (Radiol.) Roy. Free Hosp. Lond.

MURRAY, Donald 49 Marine Avenue, Whitley Bay NE26 1NA — MB ChB 1957 Ed. (Ed.) Socs: BMA. Prev: Ho Surg. Hexham Gen. Hosp.; Ho. Phys. & Ho. Surg. Shotley Bridge Gen. Hosp.; Med. Off. RAF.

MURRAY, Donald John 9 Swainbost, Ness, Stornoway HS1 0TA Tel: 01851 810651 — MB ChB 1982 Glas. (Glas.) Regist. (A & E) Sir Chas. Gairdner Hosp. Perth W. Australia. Prev: Staff Grade (Med.) W.. Isles Hosp. I. of Lewis; Attend. Phys. (A & E) Amer. Hosp. Paris, Neuilly, France; Trainee GP Paisley VTS.

MURRAY, Donald Roderick Repose, Crossbost, Isle of Lewis HS2 9NP — MB ChB 1950 Aberd. (Aberd.)

MURRAY, Donald William Harrison 12 Beech Road, Glen Anil, Natal 4051, South Africa Tel: 0131 525301; Wilmar, 12 Burntwood Road, Sevenoaks TN13 1PT Tel: 01732 453739 — MRCS Eng. LRCP Lond. 1971. Sen. Med. Off. Osindisweni Provin. Hosp. Natal, S. Africa. Prev: Regist. (Orthop.) Poole Gen. Hosp.; Regist. (Dept. Surg.) Mypilo Hosp. Bulawayo, Rhodesia; SHO (Accid., Emerg. & Orthop.) Poole Gen. Hosp.

MURRAY, Douglas Graham Surgery, 154 Bispham Road, Blackpool FY2 0NG Tel: 01253 352066 Fax: 01253 596083; 93 Poulton Old Road, Blackpool FY3 7LJ Tel: 01253 392122 — MB ChB 1976 Dundee.

MURRAY, Douglas John (retired) Sunnyknowe, Sanquhar Road, Forres IV36 1DG Tel: 01309 672545 — MB ChB Ed. 1962.

MURRAY, Mr Douglas Stewart Abberley Lodge, Abberley, Worcester WR6 6DB Tel: 01299 896305 Fax: 01299 896954 — MB ChB Ed. 1966; FRCS Eng. 1971; FRCS Ed. 1970. Socs: Past-Pres. Brit. Assn. Plastic Surgs. Prev: Sen. Regist. (Plastic Surg.) Regional Plastic Surg. Unit Wordsley Hosp.; Regist. (Burns & Plastic Surg.) Whiston Hosp. Prescot.

MURRAY, Duncan Roy Grange Medical Group, 21A Kersiebank Avenue, Grangemouth FK3 9EL Tel: 01324 665533 Fax: 01324 665693; 26 Ronaldshay Crescent, Grangemouth FK3 9JH — MB ChB 1988 Dundee; MRCGP 1994.

MURRAY, Edmund Oliver Royal Eye Infirmary, Dorset Country Hospital, Williams Avenue, Dorchester DT1 2JY — MB BS 1983 Lond.; DRCOphth. Lond. Roy Coll. Ophth, 1998. (St. Mary's Lond.) Staff Grade Ophth. Roy. Eye Infirm. Dorchester. Prev: GP Gloucester; Regist. (Haemat.) W. Middlx. Univ. Hosp.; Med. Off. Zambia Airways.

MURRAY, Eileen Mary 26 Main Street, Temple, Gorebridge EH23 4SQ — MB ChB Sheff. 1969; DCH Eng. 1971. Community Med. Off. Midlothian. Prev: Regist. Ninewells Hosp. Dundee & Roy. Vict. Infirm. Newc.

MURRAY, Eleanor Leslie Department of Pathology, Argyll and Clyde Acute Hospitals NHS Trust, Vale of Leven Hospital, Alexandria G83 0UA Tel: 01389 754121 Fax: 01389 603870 Email: lesliemurray@vol.scot.nhs.uk — MB ChB 1966 Glas.; MRCPath 1978 FRCPath 1990; FRCOG 1989, M 1970. Cons. Path. Vale of Leven Dist. Hosp. Alexandria.; Hon. Clin. Sen. Lect. Glas. Univ. Socs: Assn. of Clin. Pathologists; Nines Gynaecol. Soc.; Brit. Med. Assn. Prev: Lect. (Gyn. Path.) W.. Infirm. Glas.

MURRAY, Elizabeth Lonsdale Medical Centre, 24 Lonsdale Road, London NW6 6RR Tel: 020 7328 8331 Fax: 020 7328 8630; Flat 3, 72 Burghley Road, London NW5 1UN Tel: 020 7267 1154 — MB BS 1985 Lond.; MSc Oxf. 1982; MRCGP 1991; DRCOG 1989. Sen. Lect. (Primary Health Care) UCL Med. Sch. Prev: Lect. (Primary Health Care) Univ. Coll. Univ. Coll. Lond. Med. Sch.

MURRAY, Elizabeth Diana Stewart (retired) 97 South Beach, Troon KA10 6EQ Tel: 01292 312438 — MB ChB 1959 Glas.

MURRAY, Elizabeth Ledingham Anderson 4 Fairfield Road, Ayr KA7 2AR — MB ChB 1980 Glas.; MPH Glas. 1992; DCH RCPS Glas. 1987.

MURRAY, Ernest (retired) 306 Blandford Road, Hamworthy, Poole BH15 4JQ Tel: 01202 679234 — MB ChB 1965 Aberd. Prev: Ho. Phys. City Hosp. Aberd.

MURRAY, Fidelma Harris (retired) La Cachette, Haute Vue, Rue Du Carrefour, Trinity, Jersey JE3 5HD Tel: 01534 861619 — MB BCh BAO NUI 1957. Clin. Med. Off. Family Nursing Servs. (Jersey) Inc.

MURRAY, Fiona 53 Bellshill Road, Uddingston, Glasgow G71 7PA; 1 MacNicol Place, Stewartfield, Glasgow G74 4QF — MB ChB 1981 Glas. Company Med. Off. United Distillers; Med. Off. (Occupat. Health) Lanarksh. HB. Socs: Roy. Coll. Gen. Pract.

MURRAY, Fiona Elsie Flat 1/L, 174 Newlands Road, Glasgow G44 4ES — MB ChB 1994 Glas.

MURRAY, Francis Joseph, MBE 18 Merrion Avenue, Newcastle BT33 0BH — MB BCh BAO 1937 Belf. (Belf.) Prev: Ho. Surg. Mater Infirm. Hosp. Belf.; Temp. Maj. RAMC 1939-46.

MURRAY, Geoffrey Holker (retired) 4 Shireburn Road, Formby, Liverpool L37 1LR — MB ChB 1940 Ed.; FRCP Ed. 1971, M 1949. Cons. Phys. Univ. Hosp. Aintree Liverp.

MURRAY, George Sinclair Ashleigh, 66 Finchfield Road W., Wolverhampton — MB ChB 1971 Ed.

MURRAY, Gerald Michael, RD Heatherfield, Ruthin Road, Bwlchgwyn, Wrexham LL11 5UU Tel: 01978 759754 — MB ChB 1969 Liverp.; FFR 1974; DMRD Liverp. 1972. Cons. Radiol. Maelor Gen. Hosp. Wrexham. Socs: Brit. Inst. Radiol.

MURRAY, Gerald Richard Ulverston Health Centre, Victoria ROAd, Ulverston LA12 0EW Tel: 01229 582588; Dalegarth, 31 The Drive, Ulverston LA12 0DY Tel: 01229 581584 — MB BCh BAO 1979 NUI; MRCGP 1983; DObst RCPI 1982; DCH NUI Dub. 1981. GP Tutor Barrow in Furness. Socs: Anglo-French Med. Soc.; GP Asthma Gp. Prev: SHO St. Luke's & St. Canice's Hosps. Kilkenny; SHO & Ho. Off. Waveney Hosp. Ballymena; Ho. Off. Intern. Gen. Hosp. Castleban RePub. of Irel.

MURRAY, Gerard (retired) Strathlene, Rochdale Road E., Heywood OL10 4DY — LRCPI & LM, LRCSI & LM 1942.

MURRAY, Graeme Department of Pathology, University of Aberdeen, Foresterhill, Aberdeen AB25 2ZD Tel: 01224 681818 Fax: 01224 663002 — MB ChB 1983 Aberd.; PhD Aberd. 1989; MRCPath 1990; FRCPath 1998. Reader in Path., Univ. of Aberd.. & Hon. Cons. Path. Grampian Uni. Hosps. Trust. Prev: Lect. (Path.) Univ. Aberd. & Hon. Sen. Regist. (Path.) Grampian HB; Sen. Lect in Path., Uni of Aberd.

MURRAY, Guta Heinrike 15 The Birches, Mannings Heath, Horsham RH13 6JT Tel: 01403 52099 — MB BCh 1983 Witwatersrand; MA (Clin. Psychol.) Natal 1976.

MURRAY, Helen 15 Park Field, Menston, Ilkley LS29 6LP — MB ChB 1986 Leeds. SHO (O & G) Airedale Gen. Hosp. Keighley. Prev: SHO (A & E) Harrogate Dist. Hosp.; SHO (Gen. Med.) Wharfedale Gen. Hosp. Otley.

MURRAY, Helena Geraldine 17 Fairlight Drive, Harefield Road, Uxbridge UB8 1XP — MB BCh BAO 1983 NUI.

MURRAY, Henry Allan 11 Beveridge Road, Kirkcaldy KY1 1UY Tel: 01592 641876 — MB ChB 1984 Aberd.; DRCOG 1989. Socs: MDDUS.

MURRAY, Henry Graham Stanley Bernersmede Cottage, Gaudick Road, Eastbourne BN20 7SP — MB BCh BAO 1951 Belf.; MD Belf. 1964. (Belf.)

MURRAY, Hilary Sarah Fach Ddeiliog, Llangower, Bala LL23 7BT Tel: 01678 520344 Fax: 01678 521193 Email: hilarymum@aol.com — MB ChB 1973 Liverp.; MFFP 1993. (Liverp.) p/t Clin. Asst. Colposcopy, Birkinhead, Locum Clin. Asst. Family Plann., Gwynedd. Socs: BMA; BSCCP; Fac. Fam. Plann. & Reproduc. Health Care. Prev: Clin. Asst. Cleaver Hosp. Heswall; Ho. Off. (Med. & Surg.) W. Cumbld. Hosp. Hensingham; GP Riverside Surg., 525 New Chester Rd., Birkenhead CH42 2AG.

MURRAY, Howard Norman (retired) Highfield, Oakwood, Hexham NE46 4LJ Tel: 01434 602781 — MB BS 1958 Durh.

MURRAY, Hugh Martin 33 Harlington Road, Luton LU3 3PE — MB ChB 1937 Glas. (Glas.)

MURRAY, Hugh Miller Edinburgh University Health Service, Bristo Square, Edinburgh EH8 9AL Tel: 0131 650 2777 Fax: 0131 662 1813; 41 Oxgangs Road, Edinburgh EH10 7BE Tel: 0131 445 1965 Email: murry-hm@virgin.net — MB ChB 1958 Ed. (Ed.) Socs: Counc. Mem. Brit. Soc. Med. & Dent. Hypn. (Scot.). Prev: Med. Off. Regina Community Health Clinic, Canada.

MURRAY, Ian H. F. Coombe Eden, Armathwaite, Carlisle CA4 9PQ Tel: 016974 72234 — MB ChB 1954 St. And.; DMSA Ed. 1961; FFCM 1980, M 1974. Hon. Cons. Community Med. E. Cumbria HA. Prev: Dist. Med. Off. E. Cumbria HA.; Specialist (Community Med.) NE Thames & Birm. RHAs; Med. Supt. Raigmore Hosp. Inverness.

MURRAY

MURRAY, Ianthe Elizabeth Lee Ladywell Medical Centre (West), Ladywell Road, Edinburgh EH12 7TB Tel: 0131 334 3602 Fax: 0131 316 4816 — MB ChB 1988 Ed.

MURRAY, James Alexander (retired) Coull, Insh, Kingussie PH21 1NU Tel: 01540 651250 — MB ChB Aberd. 1957.

MURRAY, James Ambrose Department of Haematology, University Hospital Birmingham NHS Trust, Raddlebarn Road, Birmingham B29 6JD Tel: 0121 627 1627 — MB ChB 1974 Bris.; FRCP Lond. 1993; MRCP (UK) 1978; FRCPath 1994, M 1982. Cons. Haemat. Univ. Hosp. Birm. NHS Trust.

MURRAY, James Antony The Surgery, 2 Great Wood Road, Small Heath, Birmingham B10 9QE Tel: 0121 766 8828 Fax: 0121 773 0091; 10 Pool Meadow Close, Birmingham B13 9YP Tel: 0121 702 2629 — MB BCh BAO 1979 Dub.; MB BCh Dub. 1979; DObst. RCPI 1984.

MURRAY, James Bryan Joseph (retired) Springwood, 16 Kennel Lane, Fetcham, Leatherhead KT22 9PL — BSc NUI 1945, MB BCh BAO 1942; DMRD Eng. 1954; DPH NUI 1945. Hon. Cons. Radiol. St. Theresa's Hosp. Wimbledon; Cons. Radiol. Holy Cross Hosp. Haslemere. Prev: Med. Supt. & Cons. Radiol. St. Anthony's Hosp. Cheam.

MURRAY, James Graeme Sutherland Dean Park, 4 Fairfield Road, Ayr KA7 2AR — MB ChB 1980 Glas.

MURRAY, James John The Surgery, Mount Avenue, Shenfield, Brentwood CM13 2NL Tel: 01277 224612 Fax: 01277 201218; 55 Worrin Road, Shenfield, Brentwood CM15 8DH — MB BS 1963 Lond.; MRCP Lond. 1968; MRCS Eng. LRCP Lond. 1963; DObst RCOG 1965. (Lond. Hosp.) Prev: Lect. (Med.) Lond. Hosp.; Regist. (Med.) Chelmsford & Essex Hosp.

MURRAY, James Joseph Anthony 199 Kensington, Liverpool L7 2RF — LRCPI & LM, LRSCI & LM 1948; LRCPI & LM, LRCSI & LM 1948.

MURRAY, James Michael Andrew Queen's University Belfast, 96 Lisburn Rd, Belfast BT9 7BL Tel: 012890 35785 Fax: 012890 329605; 96 Kings Road, Belfast BT5 7BW Tel: 01232 796580 — MB BCh BAO 1980 Dub.; MD Belf. 1993; FFA RCSI 1984; FRCA 1996. Sen. Lect. Qu.s Univ. Belf.; Cons. AnE.hetist Musgrave Pk. Hosp. Belf. Socs: Intens. Care Soc.; Assn. Anaesth.; BMA. Prev: Cons. Anaesth. & Plastic & Reconstruc. Surg. Ulster Hosp. Belf.

MURRAY, James Robert Hunter Fleming Ltd, Regus House, 1 Friary, Temple Quay, Bristol BS1 6EA Tel: 0117 900 8264; Lamb House, Ludwell, Shaftesbury SP7 9ND Tel: 01747 828313 Fax: 01747 828865 — MB BS Lond. 1967; MRCS Eng. LRCP Lond. 1967; MRCGP 1972; FFPM 1990; DFFP 1993; DObst RCOG 1969. (Char. Cross) Chief Exec., Hunter-Fleming LTD, Bristol: Socs: Fell. Roy. Soc. Med.; Fell. Amer. Acad. Dermatol.; Eur. Renal Assn. Prev: Scientif. Developm. Dir. Shire Pharmaceut. Developm. Ltd. Andover; Licensing Scientif. Affairs Dir. Gist-Brocades Delft, The Netherlands; GP Dereham, Norf.

MURRAY, James Roderick Donald 23 Middle Way, Oxford OX2 7LG — BChir 1996 Camb.; MA MB. SHO (Trauma) John Radcliffe Infirm.; SHO (Plastics) John Radcliffe Infirm.

MURRAY, James William Ian Ralphs Ride Practice, Ralphs Ride Surgery, Ralphs Ride, Bracknell RG12 9LH Tel: 01344 454626 Fax: 01344 303929 — MRCS Eng. LRCP Lond. 1977; BSc Lond. 1974, MB BS 1977; MRCP (UK) 1979; MRCGP 1986. (St. Geo.)

MURRAY, Jane Margaret The Red House, Watling St., Radlett WD7 7JQ; 14 Oakridge Avenue, Radlett WD7 8EP — MB ChB 1972 Glas.; BSc Ed. 1966. Socs: BMA.

MURRAY, Janet Grant Craig Miller Medical Group, 106 Niddrie Mains Road, Edinburgh EH16 4DT Tel: 0131 536 9500; Kirkton Farm, Golspie KW10 6TA — MB ChB 1981 Ed.; MSc Ed. 1990, MB ChB 1981; MRCGP 1989; DRCOG 1989; DCCH RCP Ed. 1987. (Edinburgh) G.P Retainer, Craig Miller Med. Gp. Prev: Sen. Regist. (Pub. Health) Trent RHA.

MURRAY, Janet Lilias The Abingdon Surgery, 65 Stert Street, Abingdon OX14 3LB Tel: 01235 523126 Fax: 01235 550625; 6 The Warren, Abingdon OX14 3XB Tel: 01235 550061 — BM BCh 1985 Oxf.; BA Oxf. 1982, MA 1989; MRCGP 1992; DRCOG 1989. Prev: Trainee GP E. Dorset VTS.

MURRAY, Jean Elizabeth 27 Barnshot Road, Colinton, Edinburgh EH13 0DJ; South East Scotland Breast Screening Centre, 42 Ardmillan Terrace, Edinburgh EH11 2JL — MB ChB 1975 Ed.; DMRD Ed. 1979. Staff Grade (Radiol.) & Clinician SE Scotl. BrE. Screening Centre Edin. Socs: Roy. Coll. Radiol. BrE. Gp. Prev: Clin. Med. Off. (Radiol.) SE Scotl. BrE. Screen Centre Edin.; Med. Off. SE Regional Blood Transfus. Centre Edin.; Regist. (Radiol.) Roy. Infirm. Edin.

MURRAY, John Benedict 16 Cove Place, Cove, Aberdeen AB12 3QP Email: j.b.murray@abdn.ac.uk — MB ChB 1993 Aberd.; FRCS Ed 1997. (Gen. Surg.) Aberd. Roy. Hosps. NHS Trust, Specialist Regist. - Orthop., Grampian Univ. Hosp. Trust., Aberd.

MURRAY, John Francis (retired) 509 Chester Road S., Kidderminster DY10 1XD Tel: 01562 752773 Email: johnfmmurray@msn.com — MB BS 1960 Lond.; MRCS Eng. LRCP Lond. 1960; FFA RCS Eng. 1967; DA Eng. 1966; DObst RCOG 1962. Prev: Cons. Anaesth. Kidderminster Gen. Hosp.

MURRAY, John Hubert 7 Hamilton Square, Birkenhead CH41 6AU — M.B., Ch.B. Liverp. 1948. Prev: Ho. Surg. Bootle Gen. Hosp.; R.A.M.C.

MURRAY, Mr John Leo Accident and Emergency Department, The Ayr Hospital, Ayr KA6 6DX Tel: 01292 610555 Fax: 01292 288105 Email: leo.murray@sayrshire.scot.nhs.uk; High Glengall Farm, Alloway, Ayr KA6 6BJ Tel: 01292 442378 Email: leo.murray@tesco.net — MB ChB 1979 Ed.; BSc (Med. Sci) Ed. 1975; FRCS Ed. 1985; MRCP (UK) 1982; MRCGP 1987; DA (UK) 1988. (Ed.) Cons. A & E Ayr Hosp. Prev: Sen. Regist. (A & E) Cardiff Roy. Infirm.; Phys. & Surg. St. Mary's Mission Hosp., Zululand.

MURRAY, Jonathan Paul Pentargon, Job's Well Road, Carmarthen SA31 3HB — MB ChB 1983 Leeds. Prev: SHO (Cas.) Roy. Liverp. Hosp.; SHO (Urol.) Roy. Liverp. Hosp.; Ho. Off. (Med. & Surg.) Halifax Gen. Hosp.

MURRAY, Mrs Judith Mary Royal Glamorgan Hospital, Ynysmaerdy, Llantrisant, Pontyclun CF72 8XR Tel: 01443 443443 Fax: 01443 443385 — MB BS 1972 Lond.; FRCS 1977 Eng.; LRCP 1972 Lond. (Roy. Free) Cons. (Orthop.) Roy. Glam. Gen. Hosp. Llantrisant. Prev: Sen. Regist. (Orthop.) S. Glam. HA (T); Regist. (Orthop.) Harlow Wood Orthop. Hosp. Mansfield.

MURRAY, Justin Bruce 25 Iain Road, Bearsden, Glasgow G61 4PA — MB ChB 1977 Dundee.

MURRAY, Mr Keith Harold Andrew Kent & Canterbury Hospital, Ethelbert Road, Canterbury CT1 3NG; 12 Beech Hill Bridge, Canterbury CT4 5AU — BM BCh 1974 Oxf.; MCh Oxf. 1985; FRCS Eng. 1979. Cons. Urol. Surg. Kent & Canterbury Hosp. Prev: Sen. Regist. (Urol.) Cardiff Roy. Infirm.; Sen. Regist. (Urol.) Guy's Hosp. Lond.

MURRAY, Keith Sayers (retired) 33 Muirfield, Whitley Bay NE25 9HY Tel: 0191 251 0889 — MB BChir 1947 Camb.; MRCS Eng. LRCP Lond. 1945; DOMS 1949.

MURRAY, Kenneth (retired) 3 Templeland Road, Edinburgh EH12 8RP Tel: 0131 334 2476 — MB ChB 1937 Glas.; FRCP Ed. 1972, M 1956. Prev: Cons. Phys. Bangour Gen. Hosp.

MURRAY, Kenneth Edward (retired) 40A Draycot Road, London E11 2NX — MRCS Eng. LRCP Lond. 1953. Prev: Capt. RAMC.

MURRAY, Kenneth Joseph Flat 2/L, 45 Thornwood Avenue, Glasgow G11 7PU — MB ChB 1992 Glas.

MURRAY, Kenneth Nisbet (retired) 31 Monument Road, Ayr KA7 2QW — MB ChB 1959 Ed.; FRCPsych 1988, M 1976; DPM Eng. 1975; DTM & H Eng. 1967. Prev: Cons. (Psychiat. & Phys. Supt.) Ailsa Hosp. Ayr.

MURRAY, Kevin James West London Mental Health Trust, Broadmoor Hospital, Crowthorne RG45 7EG — MB BS 1979 Lond.; MRCPsych 1985. Cons. Forens. Psychiat. St. Bernards Hosp. Middlx. Prev: Sen. Regist. (Forens. Psychiat.) NW Thames RHA; Sen. Regist. Littlemore Hosp. Oxf.

MURRAY, Lesley Anne Prince Phillip Hospital, Bryngwynmawr, Llanelli SA14 8QF — MB ChB 1977 Aberd.

MURRAY, Liam Joseph 58 Bannview Heights, Banbridge BT32 4NA — MB BCh BAO 1986 Belf.; MRCGP 1992; DRCOG 1992.

MURRAY, Lorna Ann 3/2, 138 Fergus Drive, Glasgow G20 6AT — MB ChB 1995 Glas.; BSc (Hons) Glas. 1992; MRCP (UK) 1998.

MURRAY, Louis Aloysius Ban (retired) Dispensary House, Loughbrickland, Banbridge BT32 4NH — LMSSA 1960 Lond. Prev: Ho. Surg. & Ho. Phys. Coleraine & Portrush Hosps.

MURRAY, Lynn Elizabeth 16 Main Street, Hilltown, Newry BT34 5UH — MB BCh BAO 1990 Belf.; MRCGP 1994; DCH RCPS

MURRAY

Glas. 1993; DGM RCP Lond. 1992. Socs: BMA. Prev: Clin. Med. Off. (Child Health) Ballymena.

MURRAY, Mairi Catrina Woodhall Spa New Surgery, The Broadway, Woodhall Spa LN10 6SQ Tel: 01526 353888 Fax: 01526 354445 — MB BS 1980 Lond.; DRCOG 1988.

MURRAY, Malcolm Springfield Hospital, Lawn Lane, Chelmsford CM1 7GU Tel: 01245 234000 Fax: 01245 234039; 9 Longleat Close, Chelmsford CM1 4DQ Tel: 01245 440867 Fax: 01245 440867 Email: marrersandmalc@lineone.net — MB BS 1961 Lond.; FRCP Lond. 1979, M 1964. (Lond. Hosp.) Cons. Phys. Mid. Essex Hosp. Servs. NHS Trust Chelmsford & Springfield Hosp. Chelmsford. Socs: Brit. Cardiac Soc. Prev: Sen. Regist. (Med.) Lond. Hosp.; Anglo-Amer. Fell. Brit. Heart Foundat. Johns Hopkins Hosp. Baltimore, USA.

MURRAY, Margaret Denise Rickmansworth Road Surgery, 35 Rickmansworth Road, Watford WD18 7HD Tel: 01923 223232 Fax: 01923 243397; 14 Roughwood Close, Watford WD17 3HN Fax: 01923 336042 Email: mgt@mtek.demon.co.uk — MB ChB 1971 St. And.; DFFP 2001; FRCGP 1995, M 1975; DObst RCOG 1974. (St. And.) Mem. Panel Examrs. Roy. Coll. Gen. Pract. Prev: Pres. Watford & W. Herts Med. Soc.

MURRAY, Margaret Helen (retired) 35 Octavia Terrace, Greenock PA16 7SR — MB ChB 1955 Glas.; FRCOG 1973, M 1959. Prev: Cons. O & G Inverclyde Roy. & Rankin Memor. Hosps. Greenock.

MURRAY, Maria Lisa 28 Milcote Road, Solihull B91 1JN — MB BS 1997 Lond.

MURRAY, Marleen 25 Durham Road, Edinburgh EH15 1NY; Milton House, Pencaitland, Tranent EH34 5EP — MB ChB 1980 Ed.; BSc Ed. 1977, MB ChB 1980; MRCGP 1984; DRCOG 1984.

MURRAY, Mary Elizabeth Duncan Dalkeith Medical Centre, St. Andrews St., Dalkeith EH22 1AP Tel: 0131 561 5500 Fax: 0131 561 5555; 15 Wilton Road, Edinburgh EH16 5NX Tel: 0131 667 9625 — MB ChB 1977 Aberd.; MRCGP 1991; DRCOG 1980; DFFP 1997. (Aberd.) Prev: Med. Off. PCEA Chogoria Hosp., Kenya.

MURRAY, Mrs Mary Gartshore Smith (retired) 1 West Avenue, Carluke ML8 5AE Tel: 01555 770516 — MB ChB 1952 Glas. Prev: Sen. Med. Off. (Audiol. & Child Health) Lanarksh. HB.

MURRAY, Mary Hughes (retired) 21 Larch Road, Dumbreck, Glasgow G41 5DA — LRCP LRCS 1950 Ed.; LRCP LRCS Ed. LRFPS Glas. 1950. Prev: Ho. Off. E. Dist. Hosp. Glas.

MURRAY, Marylou Anna Evelyn Scarva Street Surgery, 60 Scarva Street, Loughbrickland, Banbridge BT32 3NH Tel: 028 4062 2278 Fax: 028 4066 9182 — MB BCh BAO 1986 Belf.; MRCGP 1991; DRCOG 1992.

***MURRAY, Matthew Jonathan** 20 Barnfield Road, St Albans AL4 9UP — BChir 1996 Camb.

MURRAY, Maurice (retired) 12 Middlefielde, Clevelands, Ealing, London W13 8BB Tel: 020 8997 6407 Email: mmurray310@aol — MRCS Eng. LRCP Lond. 1938; FRCGP 1980, M 1953; Dip. Ven. Soc. Apoth. Lond. 1977; FRGS 1986. JP. Prev: Capt. RAMC.

MURRAY, Maxine Elizabeth 3 Old Camp Road, Eastbourne BN20 8DH — MB ChB 1985 Bristol; MRCP (UK) 1988; FRCR 1995. Cons. Radiol. Worthing Hosp. Prev: Sen. Regist. (Radiol.) St. Geo. Hosp. Lond.; Regist. (Med.) Kings Coll. Hosp.

MURRAY, Michael David 7 Glenmore Drive, Bonnybridge FK4 1EU Tel: 01324 814491 Fax: 01324 814491; 23 Macnab Place, New Farm Loch, Kilmarnock KA3 7EH Tel: 01563 27328 — MB ChB 1990 Dundee. SHO Anaesth., W.ern Gen. Hosp., Edin. Prev: SHO (Anaesth.) Vict., Kirkcaldy; SHO (Anaesth.) Stirling Roy. Infirm.

MURRAY, Michael John Newbattle Group Practice, Mayfield, Dalkeith EH22 4AD Tel: 0131 663 1051 — MB ChB 1972 Glas.; DCH Eng. 1975; DObst RCOG 1975. GP Dalkeith, Midlothian. Prev: Regist. (Paediat.) Ninewells Hosp. Dundee.

MURRAY, Michael Joseph (retired) 1 Rathview, Sligo Road, Enniskillen BT74 7NU Tel: 01365 322969 — MB BCh BAO 1942 NUI. Prev: Ho. Surg. Mater Hosp. Dub.

MURRAY, Neil Alexander 31 Old Cote Drive, Hounslow TW5 0RW — MB ChB 1983 Aberd. SHO (Paediat.) Coventry HA.

MURRAY, Neil Hamilton The Stables, Balsams Close, Hertford SG13 8BW — MB BS 1980 Lond.; BSc (Hons.) Lond. 1977; MRCP (UK) 1984; Dip. Pharm. Med. RCP (UK) 1991. (Lond. Hosp.) Clin. Research Phys. Roche Products Ltd. Welwyn Gdn. City. Prev: Cardiac

Regist. Regional Cardiac Centre Groby Rd. Hosp. Leicester; Research Regist. (Cardiol.) Lond. Chest Hosp.; Med. Adviser ICI Pharmaceuts.

MURRAY, Neil Scott 26 Dean Park Mews, Edinburgh EH4 1ED — MB ChB 1994 Glas.

***MURRAY, Neil Smith** 61 Braeside Avenue, Milngavie, Glasgow G62 6NN — MB ChB 1995 Glas.

MURRAY, Nicholas Michael Fitzmaurice The National Hospital for Neurology and Neurosurgery, Queen Square, London WC1N 3BG Tel: 020 7829 8752 Fax: 020 7713 7743 Email: nicholas.murray@uclh.org; 14 Oakridge Avenue, Radlett WD7 8EP Tel: 01923 855011 — MB ChB 1972 Glas.; FRCP Lond. 1989; MRCP (UK) 1975. Cons. Clin. Neurophysiol. Nat. Hosp. Qu. Sq. Lond.; Hon. Cons. Roy. Nat. Orthop. Hosp. Lond. Socs: Assn. Brit. Neurols.; Amer. Neurol. Assn.; Brit. Soc. Clin. Neurophysiol. Prev: Sen. Regist. (Clin. Neurophysiol.) Nat. Hosp. Qu. Sq.; Regist. (Neurol.) St. Jas. Hosp. Leeds.

MURRAY, Nina Sergeievna Shtetinin (retired) 14 Swallowfield Park, Swallowfield, Reading RG7 1TG Tel: 0118 988 6156 — MB ChB 1937 Manch.; DOMS Eng. 1947. Prev: Ophth. Camden & Harrow FPC's.

MURRAY, Patrick Francis Anaesthetic Department, Good Hope Hospital, Sutton Coldfield B75 7RR Tel: 0121 378 2211 — MB BCh BAO 1982 NUI; FFA RCSI 1986. (Galway) Cons. Anaesth. Good Hope Hosp. Sutton Coldfield; Med. Dir. Socs: BMA & Assn. Anaesth. Prev: Sen. Regist. (Anaesth.) Midl. Train Scheme; Regist. (Anaesth.) Centr. Birm. & Coventry HAs.

MURRAY, Paul 53 Rustings Road, Sheffield S11 7AA — MB ChB 1985 Ed.

MURRAY, Paul Vincent 13 Salisbury Road, Crawley RH10 5LY — MB BS 1992 Lond.; MRCP Lond. 1995. Specialist Regist. Rotat. (Respirat. Med.) N. E. Thames.

***MURRAY, Peter Darryl** 4 Perry Road, Bangor BT19 6UA — MB BCh BAO 1995 Belf.

MURRAY, Philip Anthony Brook Cottage, London Road, Copford, Colchester CO6 1BL — MB BS 1979 Lond.; MRCP (UK) 1983; FRCR 1987. (Univ. Coll.) Cons. Clin. Oncol. Essex Co. Hosp. Colchester. Prev: Sen. Regist. Meyerstein Inst. Oncol. Middlx. Hosp. Lond.; Lect. Roy. Marsden Hosp. Surrey; Regist. St. Bart. Hosp. Lond.

MURRAY, Professor Philip Ian Birmingham and Midland Eye Centre, City Hospital NHS Trust, Dudley Road, Birmingham B18 7QU Tel: 0121 507 6851 Fax: 0121 507 6853 Email: p.i.murray@bham.ac.uk — MB BS 1978 Lond.; PhD Amsterdam 1990; FRCS Eng. 1985; MRCS Eng. LRCP Lond. 1978; FRCOphth 1993; DO RCS Eng. 1982. (St Geos. Hosp.) Prof. Ophth. Prev: Reader Ophth.; Sen. Lect & Hon. Cons. Birm. & Midl. Eye Centre; Sen. Regist. & Regist. Moorfields Eye Hosp. Lond.

MURRAY, Richard Howard Stewart Conifera, Lawers, Conrie, Crieff PH6 2LT — MB BS 1972 Lond.; MRCS Eng. LRCP Lond. 1972; FRCR 1980. Cons. Radiol. Perth Roy. Infirm. & Bridge of Earn Hosp.; Hon. Sen. Lect. in Diag. Radiol. Univ. Dundee. Socs: Brit. Inst. Radiol.; Scott. Radiol. Soc. Prev: Sen. Regist. Middlx. Hosp. & Roy. Nat. Orthop. Hosp. Lond.; Regist. Middlx. Hosp. Lond.

MURRAY, Richard Hugh Eden Medical Group, Port Road, Carlisle CA2 7AJ Tel: 01228 24477 — MB BS 1970 Newc.; MRCGP 1974; DObst RCOG 1973. Prev: Trainer (Gen. Pract.) Carlisle.

MURRAY, Mr Richard Stanley (retired) Wilmar, 12 Burntwood Road, Sevenoaks TN13 1PT Tel: 01732 453739 — MB BCh BAO Belf. 1942; MD Belf. 1947; FRCSI 1947; FRCR 1982; FFR RCSI 1962; DMR Lond 1945. Prev: Radiol. Roy. Masonic Hosp.

MURRAY, Mr Richard William Cordiner (retired) 14A Culduthel Road, Inverness IV2 4AG Tel: 01463 233209 — MB BChir 1933 Camb.; BA (Nat. Sc. Trip.) Camb. 1928; FRCS Ed. 1957; FRCS Eng. 1935; MRCS Eng. LRCP Lond. 1931. Prev: Cons. Orthop. Surg. N.. RHB (Scotl.).

MURRAY, Robert Blair Deerness Park Medical Centre, Suffolk Street, Sunderland SR2 8AD Tel: 0191 567 0961 Fax: 0191 565 0075; 61 Bolbec Road, Fenham, Newcastle upon Tyne NE4 9EP Tel: 0191 274 7635 — MB ChB 1981 Ed. (Ed.) GP Sunderland. Prev: GP Gateshead.

MURRAY, Robert Douglas 53 Queens Road, Welling DA16 3EA Email: rob.murray@christie-tr.nwest.nhs.uk — MB BS 1990 Lond.; BSc Lond. 1987; MRCP (UK) 1994. Clin. Research Fell., Endocrinol., Christie Hosp., Manch.; Regist. (Diabetes & Endocrinol.) UCL &

MURRAY

Middlx. Hosp. Prev: Regist. (Gen. Med. & Diabetes) Basildon Hosp.; SHO (c/o Elderly) St. Mary's & St. Chas. Hosps. Lond.

MURRAY, Robert Gordon East Birmingham NHS Trust, Bordesley Green E., Birmingham B9 5PU Tel: 0121 766 6611 Fax: 0121 753 0608; 57 Church Hill Road, Solihull B91 3JA — MB ChB 1971 Glas.; FRCP Glas. 1985; FRCP Lond. 1991; MRCP (UK) 1974.

MURRAY, Robert Ian Borders Eye Centre, Borders General Hospital, Melrose TD6 9QU Tel: 01896 826762 Fax: 01896 826773 Email: lynn.field@borders.scot.nhs.uk; 6 Dundas Terrace, Melrose TD6 9QU Tel: 01896 823895 Fax: 01896 823895 Email: robert.eyedoc@tinyworld.co.uk — MB ChB; FRCS 1986 Royal College of Surgeons Edinburgh; FRCOphth 1989 Royal College of Ophthalmologists; FCS 1985 College of Medicine, S. Africa. (University of Cape Town 1975) Cons. Ophth., Borders Gen. Hosp.; Examr., Roy. Coll. of Surg.s of Edin. Socs: Brit. Med. Assn.; S. African Med. Assn.; Oxf. Ophthalmol. Congr. Prev: Cons. Ophth., Frere Hosp., E. Lond., S. Africa.

MURRAY, Robert Samuel Miller Crimond Medical Centre, Crimond, Fraserburgh AB43 8QJ Tel: 01346 532215 Fax: 01346 531808; Johnston Lodge, Crimond, Fraserburgh AB43 8QN Tel: 01346 532710 Fax: 01346 532839 — MB ChB 1975 Aberd. Clin. Asst. (Ophth.) Eye Dept. Aberd. Roy. Infirm.

MURRAY, Robert William Rutherford House, Langley Park, Durham DH7 9XD Tel: 0191 373 1386 Fax: 0191 373 4288; Mackenzie House, Newhouse Road, Esh Winning, Durham DH7 9LA Tel: 01385 734232 — MB ChB 1980 Dundee; MRCGP 1984; DRCOG 1984.

MURRAY, Professor Robin MacGregor Kings College Hospital, Institute of Psychiatry, De Crespigny Park, London SE5 8AF Tel: 020 7703 6091 Fax: 020 8777 1204 — MD 1974 Glas.; DSc Lond. 1988, MPhil 1976; MB ChB 1968; FRCP Glas. 1984; MRCP (UK) 1972; FRCPsych 1986, M 1975. Prof. Psychol. Med. Inst. Psychiat. Kings Coll. Hosp. Med. Sch. Socs: (Pres.) Assn. Europ. Psychiat. Prev: Dean. Inst. Psychiat. Lond.; Sen. Lect. Inst. Psychiat. Lond.; Lilly Internat. Fell. Nat. Inst. Ment. Health Bethesda, Washington, USA.

MURRAY, Rodney Jossart 19 Thornsett Road, Kenwood, Sheffield S7 1NB Tel: 0114 255 5808 Email: rjmurray@compuserve.com; 10 Waterloo Park S., Belfast BT15 5HX — MB ChB 1984 Sheff.; FRCA 1992; Dip. IMC RCS Ed. 1989; DA (UK) 1986. Cons: Anaesth. Chesterfield. Prev: Sen. Regist. (Anaesth.) Cardiff.

***MURRAY, Rosanne Elizabeth** 155 Mid Stocket Road, Aberdeen AB15 5LU — MB ChB 1997 Aberd.

MURRAY, Rose Maria Brenda Ash House, Back Lane, Souldrop, Bedford MK44 1HQ — MB BCh BAO 1974 NUI.

MURRAY, Roy 20 Gorsefield Avenue, Bromborough, Wirral CH62 6BZ Tel: 0151 327 2438 — MB ChB 1967 Aberd.; MRCGP 1979; DObst RCOG 1969. (Aberd.)

MURRAY, Ruth Adrienne 150 Nursery Lane, Alwoodley, Leeds LS17 Tel: 0113 295 3444 — MB ChB 1994 Glas.; MRCGP 2000; DRCOG 1997. (Glas.)

MURRAY, Sarah Judith Peverell Park Surgery, 162 Outlands Road, Peverell, Plymouth PL2 3PR Tel: 01752 791438 Fax: 01752 783623; Sparkatown House, Sparkatown Lane, Dousland, Yelverton PL20 6LY Tel: 01822 852173 — BM 1981 Soton.; DRCOG 1984.

MURRAY, Scott Anderson McKenzie Medical Centre, 20 West Richmond Street, Edinburgh EH8 9DX Tel: 0131 650 8101 Fax: 0131 650 9119 Email: scott.murray@ed.ac.uk; 15 Wilton Road, Edinburgh EH16 5NX Tel: 0131 667 9625 — MB ChB 1977 Aberd.; FRCGP 1999; MD Aberd. 1995; MRCGP 1981; DCH RCPS Glas. 1980; DRCOG 1980. Sen. Lect. (Gen. Pract.) Univ. Edin.; Chairm. Regional Comm. GP Postgrad. Educat. Socs: BMA; Assn. Univ. Teach. Gen. Pract.; WONCA. Prev: Med. Off. PCEA Chogoria Hosp., Kenya.

MURRAY, Mr Scott Thomas Christian Hospital, Manorom, Chainat 17110, Thailand Tel: 00 66 56 411930; 3 Langside Place, Glasgow G41 3DL Tel: 0141 649 7346 — MB ChB 1985 Dundee; FRCS Glas. 1989. Gen. Surg. Christian Hosp. Manorom 17110, Thailand. Prev: Regist. (Surg.) Glas. Roy. Infirm.

MURRAY, Selwyn MacDonald West End Lodge, Ashley Road, St Annes, Lytham St Annes FY8 3EL Tel: 01253 724885 — MD 1963 Durh.; BSc Durham. 1953, MD 1963; MB BS 1957; FRCPath 1977, M 1965. (Durh.) Cons. Pathol. Vict. Hosp. Blackpool. Prev:

Demonst. (Path.) Roy. Vict. Infirm. Newc.; Lect. (Morbid Anat.) Univ. Coll. W. Indies, Kingston, Jamaica.

MURRAY, Shona Archibald Freeman Hospital, High Heaton, Newcastle upon Tyne NE7 7DN Tel: 0191 2813 1287 Fax: 0191 223 1328; 3 The Shires, Great North Road, Clifton, Morpeth NE61 6DQ Fax: 0191 223 1328 — MB ChB 1977 Ed.; BSc (Path.) Ed. 1974; FRCS Ed. 1981. Cons. Orthopaedic Surg. Newc. upon Tyne Hosp.s NHS Trust. Prev: Cons. Orthopaedic Surg. W. Glas. Hosp.s Univ. NHS Trust; Sen. Regist. (Orthop.) Sheff. Teach. Hosps.; MRC Research Fell. (Human Metab. & Clin. Biochem.) Univ. Sheff.

MURRAY, Simon James 1 Poplar Close, Brixham TQ5 0SA — MB ChB 1983 Sheff.; DCH Glas. 1987; DRCOG 1986.

MURRAY, Stannard 27 Gray Street, Aberdeen AB10 6JD — MB ChB 1978 Aberd.

MURRAY, Stephen Dept. of Cardiology, Taunton & Somerset Hospital, Mushrove Park, Taunton TA1 5DA; 14 Suffolk Crescent, Taunton TA1 4JN Email: steve.murray@taunton14.freeserve.co.uk — MB BS 1994 Lond.; BSc Lond. 1991, MB BS 1994; MRCP (UK) 1997. (Lond. Hosp. Whitechapel) Research Fell. (Cardiol.) Musgrave Pk. Hosp. Taunton.

MURRAY, Mr Stephen Bernard 3A Grange Road, Bearsden, Glasgow G61 3PL — MB BCh BAO 1972 Belf.; MB BCh BAO (Hons.) Belf. 1972; FRCS Ed. (Ophth.) 1977; FRCOphth 1989; DO RCPSI 1975. Cons. (Ophth.) Roy. Alexandra Hosp. Paisley; Hon. Clin. Lect. (Ophth.) Univ. Glas. Prev: Sen. Regist. (Ophth.) Tennent Inst. Univ. Glas.; Regist. (Ophth.) Roy. Vict. Hosp. Belf.; Ho. Off. Mater Hosp. Belf.

MURRAY, Steven Avenue House Surgery, 109 Saltergate, Chesterfield S40 1LE Tel: 01246 272139 Fax: 01246 556336 — MB ChB 1978 Sheff.

***MURRAY, Stuart Ian** 13 Heathside Gardens, Woking GU22 7HR — MB ChB 1994 Bristol.

MURRAY, Stuart Raymond Flat 31, Warwick House, Central Avenue, Levenshulme, Manchester M19 2FF — MB ChB 1990 Manch.

MURRAY, Stuart Robert Child Health Department, Newbridge Hill, Bath BA1 3QE Tel: 01225 731500 Fax: 01225 339959 Email: stuart.murray@burc-tr.sw3est.nhs.uk — MB ChB 1980 Ed.; DCCH RCP Ed. 1985; DCH RCP Lond. 1983. Cons. Community Paediat. Bath. Socs: FRCPCH 1996. Prev: SCMO (Child Health) Bath & W. Community NHS Trust; Regist. (Community Paediat.) Roy. United Hosp. Bath; SHO Rotat. (Neonat. Paediat.) St. Mary's Hosp. & W.m. Hosp. Lond.

MURRAY, Susan Ann 21 South Park Road, Hamilton ML3 6PN — MB ChB 1988 Glas.

MURRAY, Thomas Gerald Somerville Flat One, 74 Westgate, Chichester PO19 3HH Tel: 01243 785489 — MRCS Eng. LRCP Lond. 1942; DOMS Eng. 1947. (King's Coll. Hosp.) Socs: S.. Ophth. Soc. Prev: Ophth. Portsmouth Gp. Hosps.; Surg. Lt. RNVR.

MURRAY, Professor Thomas Stuart Woodside Health Centre, Barr Street, Glasgow G20 7LR Tel: 0141 531 9200; 61 Braeside Avenue, Milngavie, Glasgow G62 6NN Tel: 0141 956 1981 — MB ChB 1967 Glas.; PhD Glas. 1977, MD 1995; FRCP Ed. 1993; FRCP Glas. 1981; MRCP (UK) 1971; FRCGP 1981, M 1975; DObst RCOG 1969. (Glas.) Dir. Postgrad. Gen. Pract. Educat. W. Scott.; Prof. Gen. Pract. Univ. Glas. Prev: Sen. Lect. (Gen. Pract.) Univ. Glas.

MURRAY, Valerie Department of Psychiatry, Hairmyers Hospital, E. Kilbride, Glasgow G75 8RG Tel: 0141 20292 — MB ChB 1987 Glas.; BSc (Hons.) Glas. 1981, MB ChB 1987; MRCPsych 1992. Research Regist. (Psychiat.) Hairmyres Hosp. Glas.

MURRAY, Virginia Suzette Gauvain Medical Toxicology Unit, Guy's & St Thomas NHS Trust, Avonley Road, London SE14 5ER Tel: 020 7771 5383 Fax: 020 7771 5363 Email: cirs@cix.co.uk — MB BS 1975 Lond.; MSc Lond. 1979; DIH Eng. 1979; FFOM RCP Lond. 1995, MFOM 1986, AFOM 1981. Cons. Occupat. & Environm. Toxicology, Dir. Chem. Incident Response Serv., Med. Toxicology Unit Guy's & St. Thomas' Hosp. Lond. Socs: Fell. Roy. Soc. Med.; Brit. Toxicol. Soc.; World Assn. Disaster & Emerg. Med. Prev: Regist., SHO & (Homeopathy Phys.) Roy. Free Hosp. Lond.

***MURRAY, Wendy Michele** Flat C, 14 Marischal St., Aberdeen AB11 5AJ Tel: 01224 588560 — MB ChB 1998 Aberd.; MB ChB Aberd 1998 (Commendation).

MURRAY, William La Siala, Sandhurst Lane, Sandhurst, Gloucester GL2 9NP Tel: 01452 731063 — MB ChB 1943 Glas. (Glas.)

MURRAY, William 15 Broadstone Park, Inverness IV2 3JZ — MB ChB 1975 Glas.; FRCP Glas. 1994; MRCP (UK) 1979; MRCPath 1986. Cons. Haemat. Raigmore Hosp. Inverness.

MURRAY, William 36 Boghead Road, Dumbarton G82 2HP — MB ChB 1977 Glas.; MRCGP 1982.

MURRAY, William Douglas (retired) 51 Old Edinburgh Road, Inverness IV2 3PG Tel: 01463 235463 — MB ChB 1956 Ed.; FRCP Ed. 1971, M 1961. Prev: Cons. Phys. Raigmore Hosp. Inverness.

MURRAY, William George Duncan (retired) Blair Lodge, 249 London Road, West Malling, Maidstone ME19 5AD Tel: 01732 842183 — MB ChB 1947 Aberd.; MD Aberd. 1958; MFOM 1979; DIH Eng. 1961. Prev: PMO Distillers Co. Ltd.

MURRAY, Mr William James Greig Perth Royal Infirmary, Perth PH1 1NX; Brunty Mill, Woodside, Blairgowrie PH13 9NH — MB BS 1975 Lond.; MS Lond. 1986, MB BS 1975; FRCS Ed. 1993; FRCS Eng. 1981. Cons. Surg. Perth Roy. Infirm. Prev: Sen. Regist. (Surg.) Univ. Coll. Hosp. Lond.; Regist. (Gen. Surg. & Urol.) Kings Coll. Hosp. Lond.; Research Fell. Thrombosis Research Unit Kings Coll. Hosp. Lond.

MURRAY, Mr William Ritchie The Royal Infirmary, Castle St., Glasgow G4 0SF Fax: 0141 211 4991 Email: endobill@ntlworld.com; 76 Bailie Drive, Bearsden, Glasgow G61 3HU Tel: 0141 563 8635 — MB ChB 1971 Glas.; BSc (Hons.) (Physiol.) 1969; FRCS Glas. 1975; MD Glas. 1982. (Glas.) Cons. Surg. Glas. Roy. Infirm. Socs: Assn. Surg.; Brit. Soc. Gastroenterol. Prev: Sen. Lect. (Surg.) Univ. Glas.

MURRAY-LESLIE, Christian Francis Victor Derbyshire Royal Infirmary, London Road, Derby DE1 2QY Tel: 01332 47141 Fax: 01332 254934 Email: c.murray-leslie@virgin.net; 122 Derby Road, Melbourne, Derby DE73 1FL Tel: 01332 862921 Email: c.murray-leslie@compaqnet.co.net — MB BS 1969 Lond.; FRCP Lond. 1986; MRCP (UK) 1972. (Middlx.) Cons. Rehabil. Med. Derbysh. Roy. Infirm.; Clin. Teach. Univ. Nottm. Socs: Brit. Soc. Rehabil. Med.; Soc. Research in Rehabil. Prev: Sen. Regist. (Rheum. & Rehabil.) Leeds Gen. Infirm.; Research Asst. Univ. Leeds; Regist. (Med.) W.m. Hosp. Lond.

MURRAY-LYON, Iain Malcolm 149 Harley Street, London W1G 6DE Tel: 020 7935 6747 Fax: 020 7935 7017 Email: i.m-lyon@lonclin.co.uk; 12 St. James's Gardens, London W11 4RD Tel: 020 7602 1806 — MB ChB Ed. 1964; BSc (Hons.) Ed. 1962, MD 1973; FRCP Ed. 1980, M 1967; FRCP Lond. 1979, M 1967. Cons. Phys. (Gastroenterol.) Char. Cross Hosp. & Chelsea W.m. Hosp. Lond.; Hon. Cons. Phys. King Edwd. VII Hosp. for Off's Lond. & St. John & Eliz. Hosp. Lond. Socs: Brit. Soc. Gastroenterol.; Brit. Assn. Study Liver; Eur. Assn. Study Liver. Prev: Hon. Sen. Lect. & Cons. Phys. Liver Unit King's Coll. Hosp. Lond.; Regist. (Gen. Med.) Roy. Infirm. Edin.; Ho. Phys. (Gastrointestinal Unit) W.. Gen. Hosp. Edin.

MURRAY-LYON, Robert Niall Gourock Health Centre, 181 Shore Street, Gourock PA19 1AQ Tel: 01475 634617; The Clett, 18 Urquhart Drive, Gourock PA19 1JG Tel: 01475 634447 — MB ChB 1977 Glas.; MRCGP 1981; DRCOG 1980. (Glas.) Socs: Soc. Occupat. Med. Prev: Med. Adviser Compaq Manufacturing Ltd. Erskine; Semiconductor (UK) Ltd Greenoch.

MURRELL, Dorothy Shirley (retired) Rectory Cottage, Newtimber, Hassocks BN6 9BT — MB BS 1954 Lond.; FRCP Lond. 1991; MRCP (UK) 1974; MRCS Eng. LRCP Lond. 1954; FRCR 1975; FFR 1964; DMRT Eng. 1958. Prev: Cons. Clin. Oncol. Roy. Sussex Co. Hosp. Brighton.

MURRELL, Helen Calvert (retired) 8 Lawkland, Farnham Royal, Slough SL2 3AN Tel: 01753 642881 Email: helencm@callnetuk.com — MB BS 1955 Adelaide; 1949 BSc Adelaide; 1993 MFFP; 1985 FRCOG 1985; 1975 DTPH Lond; 1962 DObst; 1963 MRCOG. Prev: SCMO Oxon HA.

MURRELL, Helen Margret Ethel Street Surgery, 88/90 Ethel Street, Benwell, Newcastle upon Tyne NE4 8QA Tel: 0191 219 5456 Fax: 0191 226 0300; 234 Jesmond Dene Road, Newcastle upon Tyne NE2 2JU Tel: 0191 281 1665 — MB ChB 1982 Sheff.; MRCGP 1986; DTM & H Liverp. 1988; DRCOG 1984; DFFP 1997. (Sheffield) GP Newc.; Salaried Princip. Trust Employee Consultatn. Socs: RCGP; BMA. Prev: GP Barnsley; Trainee GP N.umbria VTS; Clin. Med. Off., Mozambique.

MURRELL, John Stanley Lambe Creek House, Old Kea, Truro TR3 6AN — MB BS 1954 Lond.; FRCP Ed. 1979, M 1961; FRCPath 1976, M 1964. (St. Bart.) Cons. Haemat. Cornw. & I. of Scilly HA.

Socs: Brit. Soc. Haemat. Prev: Ho. Phys. & Regist. Dept. Path. St. Bart. Hosp.; Sen. Regist. (Path.) St. Geo. Hosp. Lond.

MURRELL, Sheila Janet Lambe Creek House, Old Kea, Truro TR3 6AN — MB BS 1954 Lond.; DCH Eng. 1956. (St. Bart.) Prev: Ho. Phys. St. Bart. Hosp.

MURRIN, Karen Lisa Lea Castle, Kidderminster DY10 3PP — MB BCh 1991 Wales; MRCPsych 1996; MMedSci Birm. 1998. Specialist Regist. (Pschiat. Of learning disabilities) W. Midl. Rotat.

MURRIN, Keith Robin Department of Anaesthetics, University Hospital of Wales, Heath Park, Cardiff CF14 4WZ Tel: 029 2075 5944; 12 Oyster Bend, Sully, Penarth CF64 5LW Tel: 02920 530474 — MB BCh 1967 Wales; FFA RCS Eng. 1971. Cons. Anaesth. Univ. Hosp. Wales Cardiff.

MURRIN, Richard Julian Antley Walsgrave Hospital, Clifford Bridge Road, Walsgrave, Coventry CV2 2DX Tel: 024 76 602020; 225 Anstey Lane, Leicester LE4 0FJ — MB ChB 1994 Leic.; BSc Leic. 1991; MRCP (UK) 1997. (University of Leicester) Specialist Regist. (Haemat.) Walsgrave Hosp. Coventry. Socs: BMA; Brit. Soc. Haematol.; Roy. Coll. Phys.s of Lond. Prev: Haemat. Regist. (LAS) Stafford Gen. Hosp. Stafford; SHO Haemat. Leicester Roy. Infirm.; SHO (Gen. Med.) Leicester Roy. Infirm.

MURRISON, Andrew William, Surg. Lt. RN 219 Castle Street, Portchester, Fareham PO16 9QW — MB ChB 1984 Bristol. Med. Off. RN. Socs: BMA. Prev: SHO (Med.) RN Hosp. Plymouth; Ho. Phys. RN Hosp. Plymouth; Ho. Surg. S.mead Hosp. Bristol.

MURRISON, Brenda Laing Boynds Farm, Inverurie AB51 0HL Tel: 01467 621944 Fax: 01467 621944; PO Box 243, Kojonup WA 6395, Australia — MB ChB 1994 Aberd.; DRCOG 1997; MRCGP 1998. (Aberdeen) Locum GP. Socs: BMA; MDDUS; RCOGP.

MURROW, Janet Nora (retired) Wintersweet Cottage, 119 Portsmouth Road, Frimley, Camberley GU16 7AA — MB ChB 1948 Ed.; MRCPsych 1972; DPM Lond. 1952. Prev: Cons. Psychiat. Hersham Child Guid. Clinic.

MURTAGH, Eimear Breige 1 Whitehall Mews, Belfast BT7 3GE — MB BCh BAO 1992 Belf.; FRCR 2000; MRCP (UK) 1996. Specialist Regist. Dept. of Radiol., Roy. Vict. Hosp., Belf. Socs: BMA.

MURTAGH, Eoin Gerard 27 Ascot Gardens, Belfast BT5 6LX — MB BCh BAO 1993 Belf. (Queen's University Belfast)

MURTAGH, Felicity Elizabeth Mary Thorndike Health Care Centre, Longley Road, Rochester ME1 2TH Tel: 01634 817217 Fax: 01634 817701; 106 Common Road, Chatham ME5 9RG — MB BS 1986 Lond.; MRCGP 1995; DCH RCP Lond. 1988; Dip. Palliat. Med. Wales 1997.

MURTAGH, Gerald Paul 4 Swanland Way, The Dales, Cottingham HU16 5JP Tel: 01482 847070 — MB BCh BAO 1942 Belf.; FFA RCS Eng. 1954; DA Eng. 1948; DA RCPSI 1948. (Qu. Univ. Belf.) Prev: Anaesth. S. Belf. Hosp. Gp.; Sen. Regist. (Anaesth.) Gen. Infirm. Leeds; Anaesth. N. Antrim Gp. Hosps.

MURTAGH, Hugh Brendan Radiology Department, Belfast City Hospital, Lisburn Road, Belfast BT9 7AB Tel: 01232 665487; Dalgan, 112 Harberton Park, Belfast BT9 6TU Tel: 01232 665487 — MB BCh BAO 1960 Belf.; MRCGP 1968; FRCR 1979; FFR RCSI (ad eundem) 1986; DMRD Eng. 1978. Cons. Radiol. Belf. City Hosp. & Musgrave Hosp. Belf. Socs: Ulster Med. Soc. Prev: Sen. Regist. (Radiol.) Roy. Vict. Hosp. Belf.; Regist. (Diag. Imaging) Mater Miser. Hosp. Dub.; Ho. Surg. & Ho. Phys. Mater Infirm. Hosp. Belf.

MURTAGH, James Gerard Haslemere, 19 Cambourne Park, Belfast BT9 6RL Tel: 01232 665553 — MB BCh BAO 1964 Belf.; FRCPI 1996; FRCP Lond. 1995; FRCP Ed. 1977; MRCP (UK) 1970. (Qu. Univ. Belf.) Cons. Cardiol. (Cardiac) Belf. City Hosp. Socs: Fell. Europ. Soc. Cardiol.; Brit. Cardiac Soc.; Irish Cardiac Soc. Prev: Brit. Heart Foundat. Research Fell. MRC Cardiovasc. Research Unit Roy. Postgrad. Med. Sch. Lond.; Sen. Regist. (Cardiol.) Hammersmith Hosp. Lond.

MURTAGH, Joseph (retired) Ballyowen Health Centre, 179 Andersonstown Road, Belfast BT11 9EA Tel: 028 9061 0611 Fax: 028 9043 1323 — MB BCh BAO 1955 NUI; MRCGP 1953. Prev: Ho. Phys. & Ho. Surg. Kilkenny Co. Hosp.

MURTAGH, Mary Pluscardon Clinic, Dr Gray's Hospital, Elgin IV30 1SN — MB BCh BAO 1978 NUI; MRCPsych 1983. Cons. Psychiat. Dr. Gray's Hosp. Elgin. Prev: SHO (Psychiat.) P.ss Alexandra Hosp. Harlow; Sen. Regist. (Psychiat.) Roy. Dundee Liff Hosp.; Regist. (Psychiat.) Warlingham Pk. Hosp. Warlingham.

MURTAZA

MURTAZA, Lily Nilofar Mid-Essex Community and Mental Health Trust, Atlantic Square, Station Road, Witham CM8 2TL — MB BS 1970 Lond.; FRCP 1997; LRCPI & LM, LRCSI & LM 1970; MRCP (UK) 1973; FRCPCH 1997; DCH Eng. 1972. Cons. Paediat. Mid Essex Community & Ment. Health Trust & Mid Essex Hosps. Trust.

MURTHY, Abhayamba Arya 33 Wembley Gardens, Bramcote Moor, Beeston, Nottingham NG9 3FE Tel: 0115 928 7048 — MB BS Mysore 1956; DCH Eng. 1962; DTM & H (Liverp.) 1975. (Med. Coll. Mysore) Clin. Med. Off. Notts. AHA.

MURTHY, Arepalli Padmaja Heaton Norris Health Centre, Cheviot Close, Heaton Norris, Stockport SK4 1JX Tel: 0161 480 3338.

MURTHY, Buddhavarapu Venkateswara Rajani N Walsgrave Hospitals NHS Trust, Clifford Bridge Road, Coventry CV2 2DX — MB BS 1981 Andhra; FCAnaesth 1992. Cons. (Anaesth. & IC) Walsgrave Hosps. NHS Trust Coventry. Socs: Intens. Care Soc. UK. Prev: Cons. (Anaesth.) Grantham & Dist. Hosp. NHS Trust Grantham.

MURTHY, Kirshna 36 Pandora Street, Belfast BT12 5PR — MB BS 1977 Mysore, India; MB BS Mysore 1977; MRCPI 1994.

MURTHY, Venkatesha Bretton Health Centre, Rightwell, Bretton, Peterborough PE3 8DT Tel: 01733 264506 Fax: 01733 266728 Email: bmp@brettonmedical.co.uk — MB BS 1970 Bangalore; M.BSCH (Lond. Univ.) 2000; M.DCH (Lond. Univ.) 1999. (Bangalore Med. Coll.) NHS GP in P'boro. Socs: Fell. Roy. Soc. Med.; Fell. Roy. Soc. Health; BMA.

MURTOCK, Thomas (retired) 4 West Mount, Sunderland SR4 8PY Tel: 0191 514 1758 — MB ChB 1939 Liverp.

MURTON, Michael Damien 133 Barlborough Road, Clowne, Chesterfield S43 4QT — MB ChB 1975 Sheff.

***MURTUZA, Bari** 1 Mount View, Northwood HA6 3NZ — BChir 1994 Camb.

MURTY, Mr George Edward — MB ChB 1982 Glas.; MD Newc. 1992; FRCS Ed. 1988. Cons. ENT & Head & Neck Surg. Leicester Roy. Infirm. Prev: Sen. Regist. (ENT Surg.) E. Midl.; Regist. (ENT Surg.) Newc. u. Tyne.

MURTY, James Gerard (retired) 1 Helensburgh Drive, Jordanhill, Glasgow G13 1RR Tel: 0141 959 3055 — LRCP LRCS Ed. LRFPS Glas. 1951. Prev: Police Surg. Strathclyde Police.

MURTY, Judith Anne Family Planning Leeds Community Health Trust, Burmantofts Health Centre, Cromwell Mount, Leeds LS9 7TA Tel: 0113 295 3359; 19 Swinsty Court, Clifton, York YO30 5ZP Tel: 01904 692518 Fax: 01904 692518 Email: murty@easynet.co.uk — MB ChB 1973 Manch.; MFFP 1993; DRCOG 1974. (Manchester) p/t SCMO (Community Med.) Leeds Community Health Trust & Cons.; Instruc. Doctor (Family Plann.) Leeds Community Health Trust; Hon. Lec. Bradford Univ.; Regional Adviser for Fac. of Family Plann. Socs: Brit. Menopause Soc.; Fell.Roy. Soc. of Med.; Expert Witness Inst. Prev: Cons. Marie Stopes Internat. Leeds; Clin. Dir. Nat. Audit. Unit Family Plann. & Clin. Research Fell. Postgrad. Med. Sch. (O & G) Univ. Hull; SHO (Obst.) Craigtoun Hosp. St. And.

MURUGAN, Gnanamurthy Gorton Road Family Surgery, 306 Gorton Road, Reddish, Stockport SK5 6RN Tel: 0161 432 1235 Fax: 0161 442 2495 — MB BS 1974 Madras.

MURUGAN, Manickam The Portacabin, Hednesford Health Centre, Eskrett Street, Hednesford, Cannock WS12 5AR Tel: 01543 423777 Fax: 01543 426111; 1 Spode Place, Heath Hayes, Cannock WS11 2YZ — MB BS 1981 Madras; DFFP 1995; DA (UK) 1986. GP. Prev: Regist. (Anaesth.) Watford Gen. Hosp., Mt. Vernon Hosp. N.wood & Maelor Hosp. Wrexham.

MURUGAN, Mr Shanmugam Pillai Department of Surgery, Craigavon Area Hospital, Craigavon BT63 5YQ Tel: 01762 334444; 41 Lynedale Grange, Portadown, Craigavon BT63 5XB Tel: 01702 361567 Email: murugan@cwcom.net — MB BS 1983 Madras; FRCS Ed. 1991. Staff Grade (Surg.).

MURUGANANTHAN, Nagalingam Ferndale Unit, University Hospital Aintree, Longmoor Lane, Liverpool L9 7AL Tel: 0151 529 3206 Fax: 0151 529 3063; Moorlands, North Drive, Sandfield Park, Liverpool L12 1LD Tel: 0151 281 8981 — MB BS 1965 Ceylon; FRCPsych 1996, M 1973; DPM Eng. 1974. (Ceylon) Cons. Univ. Hosp. Aintree Liverp. Socs: Liverp. Psychiat. Soc. Prev: Cons. Psychiat. Whiston Hosp.; Cons. Psychiat. Rainhill Hosp. Prescot; Sen. Regist. (Psychiat.) Rainhill Hosp. Prescot.

MURUGANANTHAN, Nirodhini Moorlands, North Drive, Sandfield Park, Liverpool L12 1LD — MB BS 1996 Lond. SHO S. E. Lond., Ophth. Rotat.

MURUGANINRAJAH, Mr Senathirajah 21 Draycott Road, Wyken, Coventry CV2 3ND Tel: 024 76 683052 — MB BS 1981 Colombo; FRCS Ed. 1991.

MURUGAPPAN, Mr Nachiappan ENT Department, Furness General Hospital, Barrow-in-Furness LA14 1EF Tel: 01229 870870 — MB BS Madras 1976; FRCS Ed. 1989. Staff Grade (ENT) Furness Gen. Hosp. Barrow-in-Furness, Cumbria. Prev: Regist. (ENT) Bolton Roy. Infirm.

MURUGASU, Mr Euan ENT Department, Royal Sussex County Hospital, Brighton BN2 5BE Tel: 01273 696955 Fax: 01273 602730; 27 Ferndale Road, Hove BN3 6EU Tel: 01273 729136 — MB BS 1986 Singapore; FRCS Eng. 1992; FRCS Ed. 1992. Research Regist. (ENT) Roy. Sussex Co. Hosp. Brighton; Lect. (Otolaryngol.) Nat. Univ. Singapore. Socs: Fell. Roy. Soc. Med.; (Region. Co-ordinator) Asian Med. Doctors Assn.; Brit. Assn. Otol. Head & Neck Surg. Prev: Regist. (ENT) Hope Hosp. Manch.

MURUGASU, Murali Dharmapalan Flat 2, 47 Cochrane St., Glasgow G1 1HL Email: murali.m@bigfoot.com — MB ChB 1993 Glas.; MB ChB Glasgow 1993; BGM Glasgow 1998. Socs: BGS (Mem.).

MURUGESH-WARAN, Seethaluxmy Abinesh Luxmi, 30 Watford Road, Northwood HA6 3NT — MRCS Eng. LRCP Lond. 1986; DA 1994. Staff Grade Doctor Centr. Middlx. Hosp. Lond.

MURUGESU, Indrani Mathew, George and Murugesu, 2-4 Buckingham Road, Harlesden, London NW10 4RR Tel: 020 8965 6078 Fax: 020 8961 9315; 72 Norval Road, Wembley HA0 3SZ Tel: 020 8904 6372 Fax: 020 8961 9315 — MB BS 1972 Sri Lanka; LMSSA Lond. 1987; MRCOG 1989. (Univ. Sri Lanka Fac. of Med.) GP Princip.; Clin. Med. Off., Pk.side HA.

MURUGIAH, Subramaniam 7 The Glen, Wembley HA9 7LA — MB BS 1980 Peradeniya; LRCP LRCS Ed. LRCPS Glas. 1986.

MUSA, Mr Benedict Sele Flat 4 Ty-Meddyg, Nevill Hall Hospital, Brecon Road, Abergavenny NP7 7EG — MD 1981 Liberia; FRCS Ed. 1991.

***MUSA, Mark** 7 Clwyd Way, Ledsham Park, Little Sutton, South Wirral CH66 4GH — MB BS 1998 West Indies.

MUSA, Mohamed Osman Hassan 114 Rothwell Road, Kettering NN16 8UP Tel: 01536 514471 — MB BS 1978 Khartoum; MRCP (UK) 1985.

MUSA, Shabir Ahmed Fieldhead Hospital, Ouchthorpe Lane, Wakefield WF1 3SP Tel: 01924 327310 Fax: 01924 327306 Email: shabirm@urpch-tr.northy.nhs.uk — MB ChB 1988 Zambia; MB ChB Univ. Zambia 1988; MRCPsych 1993. Cons. in Old Age Psychiat. Fieldhead Hosp. Wakefield. Prev: Sen. Regist. (Old Age Psychiatr.) High Royds Hosp. Leeds; Sen. Regist. (Psychiat.) Lynfield Mt. Hosp. Bradford; Sen. Regist. (Old Age Psychiat.) Seacroft Hosp. Leeds.

MUSADIQ, Mr Mohammed Walton Hospital, Rice Lane, Liverpool L9 1AE — MB BS 1986 Madras; FRCS Ed. 1992.

MUSAJI, Moshin Akberali 111 Gregories Road, Beaconsfield HP9 1HZ Tel: 01494 674096 — MB ChB 1972 Leeds; FRCR 1981 DMRD Eng. 1979. (Leeds) Cons. (Radiol.) Wycombe Gen. Hosp. High Wycombe. Prev: Sen. Regist. (Radiol.) St. Geo. Hosp. Lond.; Regist. (Radiol.) St. Geo. Hosp. Lond.

MUSAJO, Francesco Giovanni 3 Windsor Court, Moscow Road, London W2 4SN — State DMS 1988 Modena.

MUSAWWIR ALI, Muhammad Harlington Road Practice, 198 Harlington Road, Hillingdon, Uxbridge UB8 3HA Tel: 01895 233881 Fax: 01895 812773 — MB BS 1966 Dacca; MB BS 1966 Dacca.

MUSCAT, Ivan General Hospital, St Helier, Jersey JE2 3QS Tel: 01534 59000 Fax: 01534 888259 — MRCS Eng. LRCP Lond. 1980; MRCPath 1987; FRCPath 1997. (Newcastle) Cons. Med. Microbiol. States of Jersey; GUM Cons. Socs: AMM; MSSVD; BMA. Prev: Sen. Regist. Pub. Health Laborat. Exeter; Regist. & SHO Centr. Microbiol. Laborats. W.. Gen. Hosp. Edin.

MUSCAT, Salvino Stradbrook Ford, Mells, Frome BA11 3QG — MD 1949 Malta; BSc Malta 1946, MD 1949; FRCOG 1974, M 1958; DObst RCOG 1952.

MUSCAT, Stephen Mark Rangar, Muscat and Uccelli, 20 Woods Terrace East, Murton, Seaham SR7 9AB Tel: 0191 517 0170 Fax: 0191 526 4289; 37 Dalton Heights, Dalton-le-Dale, Seaham

SR7 8LB Tel: 0191 581 0297 — MB ChB 1982 Manch. GP Seaham Co. Durh.

MUSCAT-BARON, Joseph 7ower Woodhouse, Woodhouse Lane, Copley, Halifax HX3 0UW Tel: 01422 835882 — BSc, BPharm Malta 1955, MD 1958; FRCP Lond. 1980, M 1967; FRCP Ed. 1980, M 1963. (Malta) Cons. Phys. & Cardiol. Dubai Hosps., UAE; Prof. Med. Dubai Med. Coll. UAE. Socs: Brit. Cardiac Soc. Prev: Cons. Phys. & Cardiol. Halifax Hosp. Gp.; Regist. (Med.) Maryfield Hosp. Dundee; Sen. Regist. (Med.) Roy. Vict. Infirm. Newc.

MUSCROFT, Mr Timothy John The Manor Hospital, Walsall WS2 9PS; 27 Buchanan Road, Walsall WS4 2EW — MB ChB 1972 Birm.; MSc Birm. 1976; FRCS Eng. 1978. Cons. Gen. Surg. and Coloproctologist Manor Hosp. Walsall. Socs: Assn. of ColoprOtol. of Gt. Britain and Irel.

MUSGRAVE, Michael Stuart St Georges Medical Centre, 7 Sunningfields Road, Hendon, London NW4 4QR Tel: 020 8202 6232 Fax: 020 8202 3906 — MB BCh BAO 1974 Dub.; MRCGP 1981; DCH RCPSI 1978; DObst RCOG 1976. (Trinity College Dublin)

MUSGRAVE, Richard James West Malling Group Practice, 116 High Street, Milverton, West Malling ME19 6LX; Hemmings Bank, Oldbury Lane, Ightham, Sevenoaks TN15 9DD Tel: 01732 884215 — MRCS Eng. LRCP Lond. 1973; MB BS Lond. 1973; BSc Lond. 1969; MRCGP 1979. (Guy's)

MUSGRAVE, Simon Richard 17 Grosvenor Square, Sale M33 6QU — MB 1977 Camb.; BChir 1976.

MUSGROVE, Mr Brian Thomas Maxillofacial Unit, Manchester Royal Infirmary, Oxford Road, Manchester M13 9WL Tel: 0161 276 8639 Fax: 0161 276 8639 Email: musgrove@central.cmht.nwest.nhs.uk; Promise Hill, 52 Maulesfield Road, Prestbury SK10 4BH Tel: 01625 824903 Fax: 01625 824904 — MB ChB 1978 Liverp.; FRCS Ed. 1985; FDS RCS Eng. 1974. (Liverpool) Cons. Maxillofacial Surg., Centr. Manch. And Manch. Childr.'s Univ. Hosps. NHS Trust - Christie Hosp. - Cons., Maxillofacial (Head and Neck) Surg.; Hon. Sen. Lect. (Oral & Maxillofacial Surg.) Manch. Univ. Socs: BMA; Brit. Assn. Oral & Maxillofacial Surg.; Eur. Assn. Facial Plast. Surg. Prev: Sen. Regist. (Oral & Maxillofacial Surg.) Edin. Roy. Infirm.

MUSGROVE, Carolyn Whinshiels, Main Road, Wrinehill, Crewe CW3 9BJ — MB ChB 1979 Manch.; BSc (Hons.) Manch. 1976, MB ChB 1979; MRCPath 1987.

MUSGROVE, Elizabeth Ann (retired) — MB BS 1962 Lond.; MRCS Eng. LRCP Lond. 1962; DObst RCOG 1964. Prev: SHO (Paediat.) Warwick Hosp.

MUSGROVE, Helen Elisabeth Mendip Country Practice, Church Street, Colgford, Bath Tel: 01373 812244; 1 Derwon Fawr, Cilfrow, Neath SA10 8NX — MB BS 1994 Lond.; 1999 HRCGP; DRCOG 1996. (Char. Cross & Westm.) p/t GP Retainer, Colesford Bath. Prev: Roy. United Hosp. Bath. Gen. Pract. Vocational Train. Scheme.

MUSGROVE, John Stuart (retired) Rivendell, The Tors, Kingskerswell, Newton Abbot TQ12 5DR — MB BS 1960 Lond.; MRCS Eng. LRCP Lond. 1960.

MUSHAHWAR, Shukri Saliba Shukri 11 Clifton Crescent, Wigan WN1 2LB — MB BS 1987 Newc.

MUSHAMBI, Mary Carmel — MB ChB 1983 Zimbabwe; LRCP LRCS Ed. LRCPS Glas. 1983; FFA RCS Eng. 1988. Cons. Anaesth. Leicester Roy. Infirm. Prev: Sen. Regist. (Anaesth.) Leicester Roy. Infirm.; Regist. & Lect. Univ. Leicester Roy. Infirm.; Regist. (Anaesth.) Guy's Hosp. Lond.

MUSHENS, Elizabeth Judith Gudgeheath Lane Surgery, 187 Gudgeheath Lane, Fareham PO15 6QA Tel: 01329 280887 Fax: 01329 231321 — MB BS 1980 Newc.; MRCGP 1987; DRCOG 1987; DCH RCP Lond. 1983. 1st Prize RCGP/ASTRA Research Award 1983.

MUSHET, Greta Leigh Regional Department of Psychotherapy, Claremont House, Off Framlington Place, Newcastle upon Tyne NE2 4AA Tel: 0191 227 5142 Fax: 0191 227 5142; Netherraw Farm House, Lilliesleaf, Melrose TD6 9EP — MB ChB 1979 Bristol; MRCPsych 1984. Cons. Psychother. Regional Dept. Psychother. Newc. Socs: Scott. Assn. Psychonalyt. Psychother.; APP.

MUSHIN, Mr Alan Spencer 82 Harley Street, London W1G 7HN Tel: 020 7580 3116 Fax: 020 7580 6998; 935 Finchley Road, London NW11 7PE Tel: 020 8455 7212 — MB BS 1960 Lond.; FRCPCH 1996; FRCOphth 1990; FRCS Eng. 1968; FCOphth. 1988; DO Eng. 1964. (Lond. Hosp.) p/t Cons. Ophth. Surg. Roy. Lond.

Hosp. Socs: Fell. Roy. Soc. Med; Internat. Glaucoma Assn.; Amer. Soc. of Ophth. Prev: Sen. Lect. Dept. Clin. Ophth. Inst. Ophth. Univ. Lond.; Cons. Ophth. Dept. Child Health Hammersmith Hosp. Lond.; Sen. Regist. Ophth. Dept. Univ. Coll. Hosp. Lond.

MUSHIN, Anna (retired) 57 Highfield Gardens, London NW11 9HA — MRCS Eng. LRCP Lond. 1947; DCH Eng. 1951. Hon. Sen. Regist. Nuffield Hearing & Speech Centre, Lond. Prev: Princip. Phys. (Child Health) Hampstead Community Health Servs.

MUSHIN, Jonathan Simon 14 Compton Road, London SW19 7QD — MB BS 1986 Monash.

MUSHIN, Susan Esther 41 Moor Green Lane, Moseley, Birmingham B13 8NE Tel: 0121 449 1707 — MB BCh 1967 Wales; BA Open 1994; DObst RCOG 1969. (Cardiff) Sen. Clin. Med. Off. Well Wom. Servs. N. Birm. Community Trust. Socs: BMA; Fac. Family Plann. Prev: Regist. (Venereol.) Birm. Gen. Hosp.; Ho. Surg. (Obst. & Gyn.) St. Mary Abbots Hosp. Lond.; Med. Off. (Family Plann.) Hants. CC.

MUSHTAQ, Mr Imran 3 Magnum Close, Rainham RM13 9PU Tel: 01708 556735 — MB ChB 1989 Glas.; FRCS Glas. 1994.

MUSHTAQ, Majid 22-S Usman Park, Bond Road, Dhozanwal, Lahore 54570, Pakistan; 34 The Limes, New Heath Close, Wednesfield, Wolverhampton WV11 1XX — MB BS 1988 Punjab; MRCP (UK) 1990.

MUSHTAQ, Nadeem 43 Riverdale Avenue, Stanley, Wakefield WF3 4LF Email: mush@general_hospital.com — MB BS 1996 Lond.; BSc Lond. 1995. (St. George's London) Surg. Rotat. United Leeds Teachg. Hosps. Trust. Prev: SHO (Paediat. Surg.); SHO (A & E).

***MUSHTAQ, Saleem Akhtar** 45 Cressey Avenue, Shenley Brook End, Milton Keynes MK5 7EL — MB BS 1997 Lond.

***MUSHTAQ, Talat** 5 Hunting Lodge Gardens, Hamilton ML3 7EB Tel: 01698 422304 — MB ChB 1994 Manch.; BSc Med. Sci. St. And. 1991.

MUSIL, Jan Princes Avenue Surgery, 137 Princes Avenue, Hull HU5 3HH Tel: 01482 342473 Fax: 01482 493382 — MB ChB 1984 Sheff. Trainee GP Henry Moore Clinic Castleford VTS. Prev: SHO (Otorhinolaryngol.) FarnBoro. Hosp.; SHO (Paediat.) FarnBoro. Hosp.

MUSK, Colin Stewart South Hill Cottage, Bathgate EH47 7AE — MB ChB 1984 Ed.; MRCGP 1988; Dip. IMC RCS Ed. 1989. Trainee Paediat. Livingstone. Prev: Trainee GP Borders VTS; Trainee GP Galashiels; SHO (A & E) Glas. Roy. Infirm.

MUSK, David Cowan Alloa Health Centre, West Johnstone St., Alloa FK10 1AQ Tel: 01259 60331 — MB ChB 1980 Ed.; MRCGP 1984; DTM & H Liverp. 1987; DRCOG 1984. Prev: Dist. Med. Off. Nkhotarota, Malawi.

MUSS, David Craig DIRECTOR, Posttraumatic Stress Disorder Unit, Birmingham Nuffield Hospital, 22 Somerset Road, Birmingham B15 2QQ Tel: 0121 456 2000; The School House, Exhall, Alcester B49 6EA — Laurea 1968 Rome; Laurea Med. Chir. Rome 1968; LMSSA Lond. 1977. Dir. PostTraum. Stress Disorder Unit Birm. Nuffield Hosp. Socs: BMA; Brit. Soc. Med. & Dent. Hypn.; Internat. Soc. Traum. Stress Studies. Prev: GP Warley; SHO (Cardiothoracic Surg.) Hosp. Sick Childr. Gt. Ormond St. Lond.; SHO (Gen. Med. & O & G) Solihull Hosp.

MUSSA, Mohamedshafi Yakub 101 Amberley Road, Enfield EN1 2QZ — MB BS 1997 Lond.; MA CANTAB Camb. 1998. SHO (Orthop.), Roy. Nat. Orthop. Hosp., Stanmore Middx.; SHO (Surg.) St. Bart's & Roy. Lond. Rotat. Prev: SHO (Cardiothoracic Surg.) John Radcliffe Hosp. Oxf..

MUSSELL, Felicity Mary Rosalind Top Flat, 9 Connaught Place, Weston Super Mare BS23 2QA Tel: 01934 417363 — MB ChB 1976 Liverp.; MRCOG 1985; DTM & H Liverp. 1997.

MUSSELLWHITE, Amanda Queens Medical Centre, Nottingham NG1 2UH; Picks Barn, The Green, Stonesby, Melton Mowbray LE14 4QE — BM BS 1994 Nottm.; BMedSci.; DRCOG. (Nottingham) SHO (Paediat.).

MUSSELWHITE, Derrick Harvey Firs Farm, Cowgate Lane, Hawkinge, Folkestone CT18 7AT — MRCS Eng. LRCP Lond. 1947. (St. Mary's) Clin. Asst. Skin Dept. Roy. Vict. Hosp. Folkestone. Socs: Folkestone Med. Soc. Prev: Med. Off. RAF; Regist. (Surg.) Lambeth Hosp.; Ho. Surg. Paddington Hosp.

MUSSEN

MUSSEN, Julianne Alexandra 45 Waringfield Avenue, Moira, Craigavon BT67 0FA — MB BCh BAO 1997 Belf. (Queens University Belfast)

MUSSETT, Jennifer Mary 12 Hill Park, Congresbury, Bristol BS49 5BT — BM BS 1985 Nottm.; MRCGP 1991; DRCOG 1991.

MUSSON, Frances Ann (retired) Strand House, Topsham, Exeter EX5 1LZ Tel: 01392 873982 — MRCS Eng. LRCP Lond. 1958; MRCOG 1965; DObst RCOG 1959. Clin. Sen. Lect . N. Nigeria. Prev: Med. Off. N. Region Nigeria.

MUSSON, James Cowtan 13 Woodlands, Ponteland, Newcastle upon Tyne NE20 9EU — MB BS 1991 Newc.

MUSSON, Richard Ian 67 Langwith Gardens, Holbeach, Spalding PE12 7JJ — MB BS 1991 Lond.; MRCGP 1995; Cert. Family Plann. JCC 1995.

***MUSSON, Zoe Caroline** 16 Cherry Tree Avenue, Dan-y-Graig, Porthcawl CF36 5RD — BM 1998 Soton.; BM Soton 1998.

MUSTAFA, Anis 22 Babington Road, Hendon Central, London NW4 4LD Tel: 020 8202 7726 — MB BS 1962 Dacca; MRCP (UK) 1979; DCH RCPS Glas. 1975.

MUSTAFA, Atika Musa 42 Wemyss Crescent, Monifieth, Dundee DD5 4RA — MB ChB 1980 Baghdad.

MUSTAFA, Mahmud Shajahan Department of Paediatrics, St Mary's Hospital, Milton Road, Portsmouth PO3 6AD Tel: 023 92 286000 Fax: 023 92 866101 — MB BS 1989 Lond.; MRCP (UK) 1992; MRCPCH 1995. (Royal London Hospital) Cons. Paediat.. Prev: Sen. Regist. (Paediat.).

MUSTAFA, Marina 99 Hassett Road, London E9 5SL — MB BS 1993 Lond.

MUSTAFA, Mustasim Abu Bakr 18 Bawnmore Road, Belfast BT9 6LA Tel: 01232 201765 — MB BS 1962 Khartoum; PhD Belf. 1970; FRCOG 1980, M 1967. Socs: Ulster Obst. & Gyn. Soc.

***MUSTAFA, Soleman** 74 Goldington Avenue, Oakes, Huddersfield HD3 3QA — MB ChB 1998 Manch.; MB ChB March 1998.

MUSTAFA, Mr Yahya Akram 44 Windsor Road, Swindon SN3 1JX Tel: 01793 486661 Fax: 01793 488896 — MB ChB 1987 Al-Mustansirya Univ. Iraq; FRCS Glas. 1993. Staff Doctor Hexham Gen. Hosp. N.d. Socs: BMA & Med. Defence Union. Prev: Regist. (Gen. Surg.) Univ. Hosp. Wales Cardif.; Regist. (Gen. Surg.) Glan Clwyd Hosp. Rhyl; SHO (Surg. & Orthop.) Pontefract Gen. Infirm.

MUSTAJAB, Asmat Department of Histopathology, Kingston Hospital, Galsworthy Road, Kingston upon Thames KT2 7QB Tel: 020 8546 7711 — MB BS 1976 Peshawar; MRCPath 1990; DCP Lond 1981.

MUSTAPHA, Mr Ademola Adefala 34 Mayday Gardens, Blackheath, London SE3 8NN — MB BS 1976 Ibadan; FRCSI 1990. Med. Off. HM Prisons Belmarsh Lond. Socs: Fell. Roy. Soc. Med.; BMA. Prev: Regist. (Orthop.) Newham Gen. Hosp. Lond.

MUSTAPHA, Mr Nabil Mohammed (retired) Villa Ola, 94 Manor Drive, Esher KT10 0BA Tel: 020 8398 2014 Fax: 020 8398 2014 Email: nabil@alton.com — MB BCh 1956 Ain Shams; FRCS Eng. 1966; MRCS Eng. LRCP Lond. 1966. Prev: Cons. Rehabil. Garston Manor Med. Rehabil. Centre NW Herts. HA.

MUSTCHIN, Charles Peter Carlisle Hospitals, The Cumberland Infirmary, Carlisle CA2 7HY Tel: 01228 814142 Fax: 01228 814840 Email: peter.mustchin@n.cumbria-acte.nhs.uk; 10 Vestaneum, Crosby-on-Eden, Carlisle CA6 4PN — MB BS 1970 (Hons) Newc.; MD Newc. 1977; FRCP Lond. 1987; MRCP (UK) 1973. Cons. Phys. N.Cumbria Acute Hosp. NHS Trust Cumbld. Infirm. Carlisle. Socs: Brit. Thorac. Soc. Prev: Sen. Regist. Wythenshawe Hosp.; Research Fell. Soton. Univ. Hosps.; Hon. Regist. (Med.) Soton. Gen. Hosp.

MUSTFA, Ghulam Spearpoint Gardens Surgery, 1 Spearpoint Gardens, Aldborough Road North, Ilford IG2 7SX Tel: 020 8590 3048 Fax: 020 8983 8241; 20 Devonshire Road, Newbury Park, Ilford IG2 7EN Tel: 020 8599 7249 — MB BS Punjab 1965; MRCGP 1977. Socs: BMA; Med. Protec. Soc.; Ilford Med. Soc.

MUSTFA, Naveed North Staffordshire Royal Infirmary, Stoke-on-Trent ST4 7LN; 3 Dartmouth Avenue, Pattingham, Wolverhampton WV6 7DP Tel: 01902 700972 — MB BS 1991 Lond.; MRCP (UK) 1995. (St Bartholomews HMC) Regist. (Med.) N. Staffs. Roy. Infirm. Stoke. Socs: Brit. Thorac. Soc.; Midl. Thoracic Soc. Prev: Regist. (Med.) P.ss Roy. Hosp. Telford; Regist. (Med.) New Cross Hosp. Wolverhampton; SHO (Med.) Roy. Surrey Co. Hosp. Guildford.

MUSTILL, Anna Louise Department of Accident and Emergency, Royal Sussex County Hospital, Eastern Road, Brighton BN2 5DE; 61 Malden Hill Gardens, New Malden KT3 4HX — MB ChB 1998 Sheff.; MB ChB Sheff 1998.

***MUSTON, Gail Catherine** Bramble Cottage, Boundary Lane, Over Peover, Knutsford WA16 8UJ — MB BCh 1996 Wales.

MUSTON, Gillian Catherine Bramble Cottage, Boundary Lane, Over Peover, Knutsford WA16 8UJ — MB BCh 1968 Wales; DObst RCOG 1970. (Cardiff) Clin. Asst. (Dermat.) Stepping Hill Hosp. Stockport. Prev: Ho. Off. (Gen. Med.) & (Gen. Surg.) & Regist. (Dermat.) Univ. Hosp.; Wales, Cardiff; Clin. Asst. (Dermat.) Newc. AHA (T).

MUSTON, Haydn Lee University Department of Dermatology, Hope Hospital, Stott Lane, Salford M6 8HD Tel: 0161 787 1010; Bramble Cottage, Boundary Lane, Over Peover, Knutsford WA16 8UJ — MB BCh 1971 Wales; FRCP Lond. 1990; FRCP Ed. 1986; MRCP (UK) 1974. Cons. Dermat. Salford, Centr. Manch., S. Manch. & Trafford NHS Trust. Socs: Brit. Assn. Dermat.; Hon. Sec. & Treas. N. Eng. Dermat. Soc.; Exec. Comm. Brit. Assn. Dermat. Prev: Sen. Regist. (Dermat.) N. Staffs. Hosp. Centre Stoke-on-Trent; Regist. (Dermat.) Roy. Vict. Infirm. Newc.; Ho. Phys. Profess. Med. Unit Univ. Hosp. Wales, Cardiff.

MUTALE, Innocent Theodore Raphael Wyvill Cottage, 22B Private Road, Sherwood, Nottingham NG5 4DB — MB ChB 1983 Manch.

***MUTALITHAS, Kugathasan** 3 St Johns Chase, Wakefield WF1 2QY — MB ChB 1997 Sheff.

MUTCH, Alexander James, TD (retired) Chapel View, 1b Bradley Lane, Eccleston, Chorley PR7 5TG Tel: 01257 452509 Fax: 01257 452 0019 — MB ChB 1952 St. And.; DIH Soc. Apoth. Lond. 1970; DTM & H Liverp. 1982. Prev: Med. Off. Abu Dhabi Nat. Oil Company.

MUTCH, Archibald Fraser Cytology Department, Bedford Hospital, Kempston Road, Bedford MK42 9DJ Tel: 01234 792325 Fax: 01234 792325 Email: bedhos.anglox.nhs.uk — MB ChB 1977 Glas.; FRCPath 1996; MIAC 1990. Cons. Cytopath. Bedford Hosp.; Trust Based Co-ordinator Cervical Screening Progr. Socs: Brit. Soc. Clin. Cytol.; Internat. Acad. Cytolpath.; Thames Valley Cytolpathol. Soc. Prev: Cons. Cytopath. Aberd. Roy. Infirm.; Cons. Cytopath. Glas. Roy. Infirm.

***MUTCH, Claire Elaine** 5 Mound Close, Gosport PO12 3QA — MB BS 1998 Lond.; MB BS Lond 1998.

MUTCH, Helen Jane The Lennard Surgery, 1-3 Lewis Road, Bishopsworth, Bristol BS13 7JD Tel: 0117 964 0900 Fax: 0117 987 3227; 54 Kennington Avenue, Bishopston, Bristol BS7 9ET Tel: 0117 942 6803 Email: 101535.356@compuserve.com — MB ChB 1982 Bristol; MRCGP 1986; DCCH RCP Ed. 1989; DRCOG 1984. GP Bristol. Prev: Trainee GP Avon VTS.

MUTCH, Lesley Margaret Mollison (retired) 13 Abbotsford Park, Edinburgh EH10 5DZ Tel: 0131 446 0230 Fax: 0131 446 0230 Email: lesley.mutch@wolfson.ox.ac.uk — MB ChB Aberd. 1956; MD Aberd. 1986; FRCPCH 1996. Prev: Research Fell. Pub. Health Research Unit. Univ. Glas. & Hon. Cons. Community Paediat. Epidemiol. Glas.

MUTCH, Michael Whitlock Dungoyne, Port Glasgow Road, Kilmacolm PA13 4QQ — MB ChB 1976 Dundee.

MUTCH, Olive Ruth (retired) Home Farm, Storeton, Bebington, Wirral CH63 6HG — MB ChB 1945 Liverp.

MUTCH, Susan May Croftfoot Road Surgery, 30 Croftfoot Road, Glasgow G44 5JT Tel: 0141 531 8600 Fax: 0141 531 6202; 1 Novar Drive, Hyndland, Glasgow G12 9PX — MB ChB 1980 Ed.; MRCGP 1986; DRCOG 1983. (Edinburgh)

MUTCH, William John 16 New Park Road, Aberdeen AB16 6UT — MB ChB 1974 Aberd.; MRCP (UK) 1977.

MUTCH, Wilma Mary McArthur Easterhouse Health Centre, 9 Auchinlea Road, Glasgow G34 9HQ Tel: 0141 531 8180 Fax: 0141 531 8186 — MB ChB 1990 Glas.

MUTHAPPAN, Anandamangalam Kunjupillia 31a Main Road, Hextable, Swanley BR8 7RB — MBBS 1970; (DLO) Roy. Coll. Of Surg. London; FRCS (Primary) RCS Dublin; BSc 1970. (Trirandrums, Kerale, India) GP Princip.; Clin. Asst. ENT. Socs: Regist. in OtoLaryngol. Prev: Regist. In ENT, Dartford, Kent.

***MUTHESIUS, Bianca Helena** 8 Perne Avenue, Cambridge CB1 3SA — MB BS 1998 Lond.; MB BS Lond 1998.

MUTHIAH, Mr Christian Yogendradeva Theivendrasena Rugby Road Surgery, 18 Rugby Road, Bulkington, Nuneaton

CV12 9JE Tel: 024 7664 3243 Fax: 024 7664 3918 — MB BS 1973 Sri Lanka; FRCS Glas. 1985; MRCS Eng. LRCP Lond. 1981.

MUTHIAH, Mankaiatkarasi 6 Meadow Close, Wovey, Hinckley LE10 3LW — MB BS 1971 Ceylon.

MUTHIAH, Moses Mahendran Bassetlaw Hospital & Community Services Trust, Blyth Road, Worksop S81 0BD Tel: 01909 500990 Ext: 2954 Fax: 01909 502984 — MB BS 1973 Sri Lanka; FRCP Lond. 1994; MRCP (UK) 1980. (Univ. Ceylon Peradeniya Med. Sch.) Cons. Phys. Bassetlaw Dist. Gen. Hosp. Worksop. Socs: Christian Med. Fell.sh.; Brit. Thorac. Soc.; Brit. Soc. Med. Managers.

MUTHIAH, Ravindrasena Navaratnam The Salisbury Surgery, 178 Dawes Road, Fulham, London SW6 7HS Tel: 020 7381 9195; 178 Dawes Road, Fulham, London SW6 7HS Tel: 020 7381 9195 — MB BS 1971 Ceylon; MSc 1998 (Clinical Parasitology) Univ. of Lond.; MRCOG 1979. (University of Ceylon)

MUTHU, Bala Subramaniam Westbourne Surgery, Kelso Grove, Shiney Row, Houghton-le-Spring DH4 4RW Tel: 0191 385 2512 Fax: 0191 385 6922 — MB BS 1970 Madras. (Madras) GP Houghton-le-Spring, Tyne & Wear.

***MUTHU, Jagadish** 7 Dalby Close, Luton LU4 OXF — MB BS 1998 Lond.; MB BS Lond. 1998.

MUTHU, Mr Sundar Langbank Medical Centre, Broad lane, Norris Green, Liverpool L11 1AD Tel: 0151 226 1976 Fax: 0151 270 2873; 25 St. Michaels Road, Blundellsands, Liverpool L23 7UJ Tel: 0151 931 3721 Email: dr.s.muthu@cableinet.co.uk — MB BS 1967 Delhi; MS Madras 1971; FRCS Ed. 1976; DRCOG 1984. (Maulana Azad Med. Coll, New Delhi) Med. Off. Donald Tod Rehabil. Centre Fazakerley Hosp. & Bedford Clinic Wom Hosp Liverp.; Mem. Disabil. Appeals Tribunal. Socs: BMA; Overseas Doctors Assn. Prev: Med. Off. Disablem. Serv. Centre Liverp.; Med. Off. Artific. Limb & Appliance Centre Bristol; Regist. (Surg.) Buckland Hosp. Dover & Peel Hosp. Galashiels.

***MUTHU, Vivek Sundar** 25 St Michaels Road, Crosby, Liverpool L23 7UJ — BM BCh 1997 Oxf.

MUTHU KRISHNAN, N 108 Rawling Road, Bensham, Gateshead NE8 2PJ Tel: 0191 420 3255 Fax: 0191 478 1288; Bangalore House, 52 Belle Vue Bank, Gateshead NE9 6BS — MB BS 1967 Bangalore. GP Gateshead, Tyne & Wear.

MUTHUKUMAR, Mr Thirumoolanathan 49 Kingscote Road, Dorridge, Solihull B93 8RB — MB BS 1985 Madras; FRCS Ed. 1989.

MUTHULINGAM, Mr Saravanamuthu The Medical Centre, 17-19 Clarence Road, London NW6 7TG Tel: 020 7624 1345 Fax: 020 7624 7292; 10 Kenton Park Road, Kenton, Harrow HA3 8TY Tel: 020 8909 2197 — MB BS 1971 Ceylon; FRCS Ed. 1983. Prev: Trainee GP Airedale VTS; Regist. (Orthop. & Trauma) Grimsby Dist. Hosp. & Airedale Gen. Hosp. Keighley.

MUTHULINGASWAMY, Murugesu Kilnhurst Surgery, Highthorne Road, Kilnhurst, Mexborough S64 5UT Tel: 01709 582206 — MB BS 1970 Mysore.

***MUTHUSAMY, Brinda** 59/6 Cockburn Street, Edinburgh EH1 1BS — MB ChB 1998 Ed.; MB ChB Ed 1998.

MUTHUSAMY, Rangasamy Department of Cardiology, Rotherham District General Hospital, Moorgate Road, Rotherham S60 2UD Tel: 01709 304158 Fax: 01709 304220 — MB BS 1979 Madras; MRCPI 1985; FRCP (Ed.)1996; MRCP (UK) 1985; FRCP (Lon.) 1999. (Madras Medical College, Madras, India) Cons. Cardiol. & Phys. Rotherham Dist. Gen. Hosp. Socs: Assoc. Fell. Amer. Coll. Cardiol.; Brit. Cardiac Soc.; Brit. Soc. Nuclear Cardiol. Prev: Cons. Cardiol. Kovai Med. Centre & Hosp. Ltd. Coimdature, India; Sen. Regist. (Cardiol.) King Faisal Specialist Hosp. & Research Centre Riyadh, Saudi Arabia; Regist. (Gen. Med.) Alexandra Hosp. Redditch.

MUTHUVELOE, Daniel Wijeyaraja Haden Vale Surgery, 50 Barrs Road, Cradley Heath, Cradley Heath B64 7HG Tel: 01384 634511 Fax: 01384 410716; Crawford House, Norton Road, Stourbridge DY8 2AJ Tel: 01384 395165 Email: muthu@ibm.net — MB BS Ceylon 1972; LMSSA Lond. 1982. (Colombo) Clin. Asst. (Respirat. Med.) Dudley Gp. Hosps.

MUTIBOKO, Isaac Kunguru DHME, St Annes Centre, St Leonards-on-Sea TN37 7PT Tel: 01424 754889 Fax: 01424 755630 Email: sussexclinical@btInternet.com; 63 Hawkhurst Way, Cooden, Bexhill-on-Sea TN39 3SN Tel: 01424 846498 Fax: 01424 846658 Email: sussexclinical@btinternet.com — MB ChB 1975 Nairobi; MRCPsych 1982; DPM Eng. 1979. (Nairobi) Cons. Geriat. Psychiat.& Coll.

Tutor Hastings HA; Cons. (Old Age Psychiat.) & Coll. Tutor Hastings & Rother NHS Trust. Prev: Cons. Psychiat. & Clin. Tutor (Ment. Handicap) Kidderminster HA; Sen. Regist. Rotat. (Ment. Handicap) W. Midl. RHA.; Regist. (Psychiat.) Bexley HA.

MUTIMER, Jean Eleanor (retired) Peace, Queens Road, Maidstone ME16 0JD Tel: 01622 761780 — MB BS Lond. 1962; MRCS Eng. LRCP Lond. 1962; MRCGP 1979; DObst RCOG 1966; DCH Eng. 1964. Prev: GP Maidstone.

MUTIMER, Joanne Emma 1 Jacquemart Close, Coalville, Leicester LE67 4PQ — MB ChB 1993 Bristol.

***MUTIMER, Jonathan Nigel** 1 Jacquemart Cl, Coalville LE67 4QP — MB ChB 1997 Bristol.

***MUTLOW, Nigel Jonathan** Cwm-Yr-Adar, Mill-Lay Lane, Llantwit Major CF61 1QE — MB BS 1996 Lond.

MUTSAERTS, Johannes Franciscus Maria 44 Billinton Drive, Maidenbower, Crawley RH10 7UU — Artsexamen 1992 Amsterdam.

MUTTALIB, Mr Masoom 192 Broomwood Road, London SW11 6JY — MB BS 1994 Lond.; MSc. Unvi. Coll. Of Lond.1998; FRCS Ire. 1998. (Univ. Lond. St. Geo. Hosp. Med. Sch.) SHO (Gen. Surg.) Qu. Marys Hosp. Prev: SHO (Gen. Surg.) Epsom Gen. Hosp.; SHO (Urol., Orthop. & Trauma) Epsom Gen. Hosp.; SHO (A & E) St. Helier Hosp.

MUTTON, Adrienne Elizabeth Department of Cellular Pathology, James Cook University Hospital, Marton Road, Middlesbrough TS4 3BW Tel: 01642 854383 Fax: 01642 282636 Email: adrienne.mutton@email.stahnhst.northy.nhs.uk; Email: amutton@btinternet.com — MB ChB 1990 Manch.; MRCPath 2000; BSc Anat. & Cell Biol. Sheff. 1985; DRCPath 1996. (Manch.) p/t Cons. (Histopath.) Dept. of Cellular Path., James Cook Univ. Hosp. Socs: Assn. Clin. Path.; BMA. Prev: Specialist Regist. Rotat. (Histopath.) Roy. Vict. Infirm. Newc.-U-Tyne; Regist. Rotat. (Histopath.) Manch. Region; Regist. Rotat. (Histopath.) Mersey Region.

***MUTTON, Gemma Elizabeth Eve** Home Farm House, Freshford, Bath BA2 7TX — MB ChB 1997 Bristol.

MUTTON, Kenneth James Public Health Laboratory, Fazakerley Hospital, Lower Lane, Liverpool L9 7AL Tel: 0151 529 4940 Email: kmutton@nw.phls.nhs.uk — MB BS 1973 Sydney; MRCPath 1993; FRCPA 1982. Cons. Virol. Pub. Health Laborat. Fazakerley Hosp. Liverp.; Cons. Virologist Pub. Health Laborat. Withington Hosp. Manch. Socs: Austral. Soc. for Microbiol.; Assn. of Med. Microbiologists; Soc. for Gen. Microbiol. Prev: Sen. Regist. (Virol.) City Hosp. Edin.

MUTTUCUMARU, Nimalendran Jayantha Briarwood Medical Centre, 514 Blackpool Road, Ashton-on-Ribble, Preston PR2 1HY Tel: 01772 726186 Fax: 01772 768823 — MB ChB 1984 Leic.

MUTUCUMARANA, Chandawimala de Silva 231 Brandlesholme Road, Bury BL8 1DJ — MD 1959 Ceylon; MB BS 1945; FRCP Ed. 1977, M 1959; MRCP Lond. 1959.

MUZAFER, Mr Mohammad Hussain Hatton Medical Practice, 186 Hatton Road, Bedfont, Feltham TW14 9PY Tel: 020 8893 2993 Fax: 020 8893 2889; 10 Dukes Avenue, Northolt UB5 5DA Tel: 020 8842 2842 Fax: 020 8845 9595 — MB BS 1975 Madras; MS Madras 1980; FRCS Ed. 1984; FICS 1986; FICA 1986; MSc (GPPH) 1998. Socs: Fell. Internat. Coll. Surgs.; Fell. Internat. Coll of Angiologist. Prev: Cons. Surg. MoD & Aviat. KKMC Hosp., Saudia Arabia; Regist. (Surg. & Urol.) Mayday & Croydon Gen. Hosps. Croydon; Surg. Rota. Guy's Hosp. Lond.

MWALE, Ethel M Y Bennetts Road North Surgery, 2 Bennetts Road North, Keresley End, Coventry CV7 8LA Tel: 024 7633 2636 Fax: 024 7633 7353 — MB ChB 1975 Manchester; MB ChB 1975 Manchester.

MWAMBINGU, Faulds Aliko Lydia Tom Bromfield Medical Centre, Reproductive Health, Sealmart House, Bryn Hilyn Lane, Mold CH7 1JY Tel: 01352 700212 Fax: 01352 750721 Email: f.t.mwambingu@talk21.com; 9 Lowerfield Road, Westminster Park, Chester CH4 7QE Tel: 01244 674827 Email: drtom@drtom.demon.co.uk — MB ChB 1976; MFFP (UK) Fac. of Family Plann. and Reproductive Health of Roy. Coll. of Obst. & Gynaecol. 1993; FRCOG (UK) Roy. Coll. of Obstets. & Gynaecol. 1998; DCH (Glas.) Roy. Coll. Of Surgeons & Physicians 1980; MRCOG (UK) Roy. Coll. of Obstets. & Gynaecol. 1983. (Makerere University) Reproductive Health and Sexual Med. Specialist at Mold

MWANSAMBO

Centre and Gen. Practitioner, Bromfield Med. Practive; Marie Stopes Private Pat.s; Med. researcher for MRC (UK); (GPRF) Center; Instruc. Doctor for Diplomates of Fac. of Family Plann. and Reproductive Health c/o Roy. Coll. of Obst. and Gynaecologists. Socs: Brit. Fetal and Matern. Soc.; Soc. of Federat. on Internat.; Assn. of Supporters of Federat. on Gyn. and Obst. (FIGO). Prev: Asst. Prof.e/Sen. Specialist, Univ. of King Saiid, Med. Sch., Riyadh, Saudi Arabia; Specialist Regist. Chester City and Wrexham NHS Hosps., UK.

MWANSAMBO, Charles Chithengo Vazene Milton Keynes General Hospital, 2 Whitegate Court, Eaglestone, Milton Keynes MK6 5LL — MB ChB 1987 Zimbabwe; MRCP (UK) 1995.

MWENDA, Maxon Yesaya 7 Forge Crescent, Rhymney NP22 5PR — MB ChB 1983 Manch. Ho. Phys. Birch Hill Hosp. Rochdale. Prev: Ho. Surg. Bolton Roy. Infirm.

MYA THAUNG, Dr (retired) Mayville, Kilmacolm PA13 4AP Tel: 01505 872112 — MB BS 1956 Rangoon; DA Eng. 1962. Prev: Assoc. Specialist Inverclyde Roy. Hosp.

MYA WIN, Dr 4A Fant Lane, Maidstone ME16 8NL — MB BS 1973 Rangoon; MB BS Med Inst (I) Rangoon 1973.

MYANT, Audrey (retired) 86 Lower Road, Gerrards Cross SL9 8LB — MB BS 1943 Lond.; DPH 1964; MRCP Lond. 1944. Prev: PMO (Child Health) E. Berks. Health Dist.

MYANT, Nicolas Bruce Sheepcote Cottage, Kingsway, Chalfont St Peter, Gerrards Cross SL9 — BM BCh 1943 Oxf.; BSc 1944; DM Oxf. 1950, BA, BM BCh 1943; FRCP Lond. 1971, M 1964. (Univ. Coll. Hosp.) Dir. MRC Lipid Metab. Unit. Hammersmith Hosp. Prev: Maj. RAMC.

MYAT, Jane Mimi Caversham Group Practice, 4 Peckwater St., Kentish Town, London NW5 2UP Tel: 020 7530 6500 Fax: 020 7530 6530; Email: jmyat@netcomuk.co.uk — MB BS 1993 Lond.; MA (CANTAB) 1990; DCH 1995; DRCOG 1996; MRCGP 1997. (Univ. Coll. Lond.) GP.

MYATT, Frances Constance (retired) 47 Mount Road, Tettenhall Wood, Wolverhampton WV6 8HP Tel: 01902 755415 — MB ChB 1937 Birm.; DPH Eng. 1952; DIH Soc. Apoth. Lond. 1951. Prev: Asst. MOH & Sch. Med. Off. Co. Boro. Smethwick.

MYATT, Ivan William Myatt and Rhodes, Hermitage Surgery, Dammas Lane, Old Town, Swindon SN1 3EF Tel: 01793 522492 Fax: 01793 512520; 215 Marlborough Road, Swindon SN3 1NN — MB ChB 1977 Birm.; DRCOG 1982; DA Eng. 1981; Dip. Occ. Med. 1995. (Birmingham) Prev: Regist. (Anaesth.) Plymouth Gen. Hosp.; SHO (Paediat.) Cheltenham Gen. Hosp.; SHO (O & G) Gloucestersh. Roy. Hosp.

MYATT, John Kelvin 12 Dover Road, Poole BH13 6DZ — MD 1990 Lond.; MA Oxon. 1976; MB BS 1979; FFA RCS Eng. 1984.

MYATT, Paul Stephen Hartwoodhill Hospital, Shotts ML7 4LA Tel: 01501 824561 Fax: 01501 824583 — MB BS 1986 Lond.; MRCPsych 1993. Cons. (Foren. Psychiat.) Hartwoodhill Hosp. Shotts.; Vis. Psychiat. HMP Shotts Shott Lanarksh. Prev: Sen. Regist. (Forens. Psychiat.) Murray Roy. Hosp. Perth; Sen. Regist. (Gen. Psychiat.) Roy. Dundee Liff Hosp.; Regist. (Psychiat.) Roy. Edin. Hosp.

MYATT, Tessa Sharon 66 Gatley Road, Gatley, Cheadle SK8 4AA — MB ChB 1992 Birm.; MRCGP 1996; DCH RCP Lond. 1995; DRCOG 1995. (Birm.)

MYCOCK, Heather Dawn Bramblys Grange Health Centre, Bramblys Drive, Basingstoke RG21 8UW Tel: 01256 467778 — BM 1981 Soton.; MRCGP 1986; DRCOG 1984. (Soton.)

MYCOCK, Pearl Patricia (retired) 129 Woodford Road, Woodford, Stockport SK7 1QD Tel: 0161 440 8172 Fax: 0161 440 8172 — MB ChB Manch. 1963; FRCPCH 1997; DObst RCOG 1966. Prev: Head of Clin. Med. Off. Servs. Stockport HA.

MYERS, A Mary 97 Broomspring Lane, Sheffield S10 2FB Tel: 0114 272 7714 Fax: 0114 272 7714 — MRCS Eng. LRCP Lond. 1960; FRCPsych 1985, M 1982; DPM Eng. 1972. (Cardiff) Cons. Psychiat. (Learn. Disabil. Prev: Cons. Psychiat. (Ment. Handicap.) Sheff. HA & Rotherham AHA.

***MYERS, Alistair Francis** 12B Starfield Road, London W12 9SW — BM 1998 Soton.; BM Soton 1998; BSc 1997.

MYERS, Allan Sherwood Rooms, Beardwood Hospital, Preston New Road, Blackburn BB2 7AA Tel: 01254 581311; The Old Vicarage, Whins Lane, Read, Burnley BB12 7RB — MB BS 1968 Newc.; FRCP Lond. 1988; MRCP (UK) 1973. Cons. Phys. Gen. Med. & Cardiol. Blackburn Health Dist. Socs: Brit. Cardiac Soc. Prev: Sen.

Regist. (Gen. Med. & Cardiol.) Roy. Free Hosp. Lond.; Regist. (Med.) Lond. Hosp. & Roy. Berks. Hosp. Reading.

MYERS, Anne Elizabeth 12 Styal Road, Wilmslow SK9 4AE — MB ChB 1960 Leeds. (Leeds)

MYERS, Bethan Queens Medical Centre, University Hospital, Nottingham NG7 2UH Tel: 0115 924 9924 Fax: 0115 970 9186; 148 Edwards Lane, Sherwood, Nottingham NG5 3HZ Tel: 0115 920 3299 Email: bmyers@hospital-doctor.net — MB BCh 1982 Wales; MA Camb. 1979; MRCP (UK) 1986; Cert. Family Plann. JCC 1989; DTM & H RCP Lond. 1987; DRCPath 1994; MRCPath 1998. p/t Locum Cons. Haematologist, Qu.s Med. Centre. Prev: Sen. Regist. Nott. HA; Regist. (Haemat.) Derby & Nottm. HAs; Regist. (Rheum. & Neurol.) Chichester HA.

MYERS, Carol Amanda Fairhill Medical Practice, 81 Kingston Hill, Kingston upon Thames KT2 7PX Tel: 020 8546 1407 Fax: 020 8547 0075; 13 Ennerdale Road, Kew, Richmond TW9 3PG — MB BS 1985 Lond.; MRCGP 1990; DRCOG 1987.

MYERS, Caroline Elizabeth 7 Meadow Valley, Alwoodley, Leeds LS17 7RF — MB ChB 1989 Leic.; DRCOG 1993.

MYERS, Catherine Elizabeth 21 St Johns Grove, Wakefield WF1 3SA — BM BS 1993 Nottm.

MYERS, Christopher Peter Greenside Surgery, Greasbrough, Rotherham S61 4PT Tel: 01709 560773; 7 Main Street, Olley, Sheffield S26 3YD Tel: 0114 287 5219 — MB BS 1982 Lond.; MRCGP 1988; DRCOG 1989; DCCH RCGP & FCM 1989; Cert. Family Plann. JCC 1989. (St George's London) GP Tutor VTS. Socs: Brit. Med. Acupunct. Soc.; Primary Care Rheum. Soc.

MYERS, David Oakenhall Medical Practice, Bolsover Street, Hucknall, Nottingham NG15 7UA Tel: 0115 963 3511 Fax: 0115 968 0947; 148 Edwards Lane, Nottingham NG5 3HZ — BM BCh 1982 Oxf.; MA Camb. 1979; DO RCS Eng. 1986. Trainee GP Pontesbury VTS. Prev: SHO (Med. Ophth.) St. Thos. Hosp. Lond.; SHO (Gen. Med.) Roy. Shrewsbury Hosp.

MYERS, David Herrick Shelton Hospital, Shrewsbury SY3 8DN Tel: 01743 261251 Fax: 01743 261279 — BM BCh Oxf. 1960; MRCP Lond. 1966; FRCP Ed. 1982, M 1966; FRCPsych 1986; DPM Eng. 1964. Cons. Psychiat. Shelton Hosp. Shrewsbury. Prev: 1st Asst. Dept. Psychiat. Univ. Newc.

MYERS, David Michael (retired) Medical Centre, Church Road, Tiptree, Colchester CO5 0HB Tel: 01621 816475 Fax: 01621 819902 — BM BCh 1962 Oxf.; MA Oxf. 1962. Prev: Clin. Tutor (O & G) Fiji Sch. Med.

MYERS, David Stephen Highgate Private Hospital, 17/19 View Road, Highgate, London N6 4DJ Tel: 020 8340 4050 Fax: 020 8340 4060; 31 Church Vale, London N2 9PB Tel: 020 8883 2312 — MB BS Lond. 1969; MRCS Eng. LRCP Lond. 1969; MFFP 1994; DObst RCOG 1974. (Middlx.) Prev: SCMO (Family Plann.) Margt. Pyke Centre Lond.; Occupat. Health Phys. Middlx. Hosp.; Trainee GP Whittington Hosp. VTS.

MYERS, Denis Norman Elsdon (retired) 5 Highview Avenue N., Patcham, Brighton BN1 8WR Tel: 01273 554699 — MRCS Eng. LRCP Lond. 1959; MA Camb., MB BChir 1960.

MYERS, Edward David (retired) St. Davids, 96 Lancaster Road, Newcastle ST5 1DS Tel: 01782 619434 — MB ChB 1948 Cape Town; FRCP Ed. 1971, M 1955; FRCPsych 1985, M 1971; DPM Eng. 1959, DTM & H 1950. Hon. Research Fell. (Psychiat.) Dept. Postgrad. Med. Univ. Keele. Prev: Cons. Psychiat. N. Staffs. Health Dist.

MYERS, Elizabeth Child & Family Centre Trelishe Hospital, Penventinme Lane, Truro Tel: 01872 354350; 9 Glybargfed Close, Treharris CF46 6AJ — BM 1991 Soton.; MRCPsych 1996. (Soton.) Cons. Child and Adolscent Psychiatist, W. Cornw. Prev: Specialist Regist. Rotat. (Child & Adolesc Psychiat.) UMDS S. Thames.

MYERS, Geoffrey Alexander (retired) Timbers, Limekiln Lane, Bishops Waltham, Southampton SO32 1FY — MB ChB 1933 New Zealand; FRCS Eng. 1937; MRCS Eng. LRCP Lond. 1934; FRACS 1945; FACS 1946. Prev: Cons. Surg. United Fruit Company Inc.

MYERS, Graham John Churchill Colchester General Hospital, Turner Road, Colchester CO4 5; Walton Manor, Walton-on-the-Hill, Tadworth KT20 7SA — BM BS 1997 Nottm.

***MYERS, Jenny Elisabeth** 30 Bath Road, Froxfield, Marlborough SN8 1PX — BM BS 1997 Nottm.

***MYERS, Joanne Louise** Flat 4, 11B West Newington Place, Edinburgh EH9 1QT — MB ChB 1997 Ed.

MYERS, John Martin Morpeth Health Centre, Gas House Lane, Morpeth NE61 1SR Tel: 01670 513657 Fax: 01670 511966; 2 Shadfen Farm Mews, Hepscott, Morpeth NE61 6NP — MB BS 1967 Newc. (Newc.) Prev: Ho. Surg. & Ho. Phys. Roy. Vict. Infirm. Newc.

MYERS, Jonathan Daniel Royal Cornwall Hospital, Treliske, Truro TR1 3LJ Tel: 01872 252732 Email: jonathan.myers@rcht.swest.nhs.uk; Allowanshay, Upper Tredrea, Perranarworthal, Truro TR3 7QU — MB BS 1988 Lond.; BSc Lond. 1985; MRCP (UK) 1992. Cons. Phys. Respirat. Dept. Roy. Cornw. Hosp. Truro.

MYERS, Judith Helen Riversgate Practice, Friarsgate Medical Centre, Friarsgate, Winchester SO23 8EF — MB BS 1989 Lond.

MYERS, Kathryn Gwyneth Pembridge Palliative Care Centre, St. Charles Hospital, Exmoor St., London W10 6DZ Tel: 020 8962 4406 Fax: 020 8962 4407; 31 Mowbray Road, London NW6 7QS — MB BS 1986 Lond.; BA Oxf. 1983; MRCP (UK) 1990. (Roy. Lond. Hosp.) Sen. Regist. (Palliat. Med.) Pk.side Health Trust & St. Mary's Hosp. Lond. Prev: Sen. Regist. (Palliat. Med.) UCL Hosps. Lond.; Regist. (Palliat. Med.) Mt. Vernon Hosp. N.wood; Regist. (Haemat.) Roy. Lond. Hosp.

MYERS, Keith Pathology Department, Prince Charles Hospital, Merthyr Tydfil CF47 9DT Tel: 01685 721721 — MB ChB 1976 Bristol; BSc (Hons.) Bristol 1973; FRCP Lond. 1996; MRCP (UK) 1979; FRCPath 1995, M 1983. Cons. Haemat. M. Glam. HA. Prev: Cons. Haemat. Dyfed HA; Lect. (Haemat.) Univ. Wales Coll. Med.; Regist. (Haemat.) W. Midl. RHA.

MYERS, Kenneth 97 Broomspring Lane, Sheffield S10 2FB Tel: 0114 272 7714 — MB BCh 1954 Wales; BSc Wales 1950, MB BCh 1954; DPM Eng. 1961; FRCPsych 1981, M 1971. (Cardiff)

MYERS, Kenneth William Haxby-Wigginton Health Centre, Wigginton, York YO32 2LL Tel: 01904 760125 Fax: 01904 760168; 25 Usher Park Road, Haxby, York YO32 3RX Tel: 01904 760144 — MB ChB 1968 Ed.; FRCGP 1992, M 1976. (Ed.)

MYERS, Michael 99 Eastwood Boulevard, Westcliff on Sea SS0 0BY Tel: 01702 347607 — MB BS Lond. 1958; DObst RCOG 1961. (St. Thos.) JP. Socs: BMA. Prev: Ho. Surg. & Ho. Phys. St. Mary's Hosp. E.bourne; Sen. Ho. Surg. (O & G) St. Mary's Hosp. Newport, I. of Wight.

MYERS, Michael John The Health Centre, 10 Gresham Road, Oxted RH8 0BQ Tel: 01883 714361 Fax: 01883 722679; White Oaks, 33 Chichele Road, Oxted RH8 0AE Tel: 01883 714174 — MB BS 1968 Lond.; MRCS Eng. LRCP Lond. 1967. (St. Thos.) Med. Off. Oxted & Limpsfield Hosp.; Clin. Asst. (Anaesth.) E. Surrey Hosp. Prev: SHO (O & G) Farnboro. Hosp. Kent; Ho. Surg. St. Richard's Hosp. Chichester; Ho. Phys. Orpington Hosp.

MYERS, Nicholas John c/o Foreign and Commonwealth Office (Lagos), King Charles St., London SW1A 2AH; The Old Cottage, Gayhurst, Newport Pagnell MK16 8LG — MB BS 1982 Lond.; BSc Lond. 1979, MB BS 1982; MRCGP 1989; DRCOG 1986; DCH RCP Lond. 1989. (Middlx.) Reg. Med. Off. (W. Africa) Foreign, Commonw. Office. Prev: GP Bentley Alberta Canada; Clin. Med. Off. Barbados; Trainee GP N.ampton VTS.

MYERS, Nigel Andrew 7 Nixon Close, Dewsbury WF12 0JA — MB BS 1986 Lond.

MYERS, Paul Charles Western Road Medical Centre, 99 Western Road, Romford RM1 3LS Tel: 01708 746495 Fax: 01708 737936; 95 Crossways, Gidea Park, Romford RM2 6AS Tel: 01708 25066 — MB BS 1975 Lond.; BSc (Hons.) Lond. 1972; MRCS Eng. LRCP Lond. 1975; FRCGP 1993, M 1980; DRCOG 1978. (St. Mary's) p/t NHS G.P.; Private G.P. Socs: Brit. Assoc. Cosmetic Doctors. Prev: Ho. Phys. Med. Unit & Ho. Surg. St. Mary's Hosp. Lond.; Sen. Lect. (Gen. Pract. & Primary Care) St. Bart. Hosp. Lond.

MYERS, Paulette Pauline Valerie 22 Glena Avenue, Knowle, Bristol BS4 2LB; 8 Deans Close, Llandaff, Cardiff CF5 2BR — MB ChB 1986 Birm.; MRCP (UK) 1992; MFPHM 1997. (Birm.) Cons. (Pub. Health Med.); Hon. Clin. Lect. (Pub. Health & Epidemiol.) Univ. Birm. Prev: Sen. Regist. (Pub. Health Med.) Coventry HA; Sen. Regist (pub. health med.) Sandwell HA; Regist. (pub. health med.) Sandwell HA.

MYERS, Rachael Elizabeth 25 Woodbine Avenue, Gosforth, Newcastle upon Tyne NE3 4EU Tel: 0191 285 1925; 76 Melton Road, Kings Heath, Birmingham B14 7ES Tel: 0121 441 5715 — MB ChB 1991 Birm.; ChB Birm. 1991. (Birm.)

MYERS, Robert Weldon (retired) 17 Barnoldby Road, Waltham, Grimsby DN37 0JR — MB ChB 1959 Birm.; MRCS Eng. LRCP Lond. 1959; FFA RCS Eng. 1964.

MYERS, Samuel Mark Doctors Surgery, 7-8 East Side, Hutton Rudby, Yarm TS15 0DB — MB ChB 1994 Leeds.

MYERS, Sandra Fiona Alton Health Centre, Anstey Road, Alton GU34 2QX Tel: 01420 84676 Fax: 01420 542975; Shalden Park Cottage, Shaldon, Alton GU34 4DS — MB ChB 1976 Cape Town; DRCOG 1980.

MYERS, Mr Simon Richard 26 Dalkeith Road, Dulwich, London SE21 8LS Tel: 020 8670 5909 — MB BS 1988 Lond.; FRCS Eng. 1992. Specialist Regist. (Plastic Surg.) UCLH Trust & Mt. Vernon & Watford NHS Trust. Prev: Research Regist. Restoration of Appearance & Func. Trust. Lond.

MYERS, Stanley (retired) 9 Sandmoor Green, Leeds LS17 7SB Tel: 0113 268 9309 — MB, BS Lond. 1949. Prev: GP Bradford.

MYERS, Stephen Boutport Street Surgery, 110 Boutport Street, Barnstaple EX31 1TD Tel: 01271 324106 Fax: 01271 347150; Homeleigh, Bratton Fleming, Barnstaple EX31 4RT — MB BS 1979 Lond.; MRCGP 1985; Dip. IMC RCS Ed. 1991; DRCOG 1984. (Guy's) Socs: Brit. Assn. Immed. Care Schemes.

MYERS, Tonia Rosalind Health Centre, Handsworth Avenue, Highams Park, London E4 9PD Tel: 020 8527 0913 Fax: 020 8527 6597 — MB BS 1985 Lond.; MRCGP 1989; DCH RCP Lond. 1990; DRCOG 1988. Prev: Trainee GP Whipps Cross VTS.

MYERSCOUGH, Amanda 8 Pensby Walk, Miles Platting, Manchester M40 8EN; 8 Dovecote Mews, Chorlton, Manchester M21 9HN — MB ChB 1990 Manch.; MRCGP 1994.

MYERSCOUGH, Eric Granville 50 Whinfell Road, Sandfield Park, Liverpool L12 2AT Tel: 0151 228 5538 — M.B., Ch.B. Liverp. 1948.

MYERSCOUGH, Nicola 66D Southwood Lane, Highgate, London N6 5DY — MB BS 1989 Lond.

MYERSCOUGH, Philip Roger 11 Wardie Road, Edinburgh EH5 3QE Tel: 0131 552 3093 — MB ChB 1947 Ed.; FRCP Ed. 1986; FRCS Ed. 1957; FRCOG 1965, M 1952. (Ed.) Hon. Fell. (O & G) Univ. Edin. Socs: Hon. Fell. Edin. Obst. Soc. Prev: Cons. O & G Roy. Infirm. & Simpson Memor. Matern. Pavil. Edin.; Sen. Lect. (O & G) Univ. Edin.; Chief Obst. Servs. Sultanate of Oman.

MYERSON, James Stephen Princess Margaret Hospital, Okus Road, Swindon SN1 4JU Tel: 01793 536231 Fax: 01793 480817 Email: james@myerson.swinternet.co.uk; Kerensa, 34 Warnford Road, Tilehurst, Reading RG30 4LA Tel: 0118 941 6924 — MB BS 1997 Lond.; BSc (Int) 1994. (Uni. Coll. Lond.) Med. (Gen.) Sen. Ho.. Off. Prin. Marg. Hosp. Swind. Socs: MPS; CMF; BMA. Prev: Sho Med. Kettering Gen. Hosp. N.ants; Ho. Off. Med. Kettering Gen. Hosp. N.ants; Ho. Off. Surg. Basildon & Orsett Hosp. Essex.

MYERSON, Keith Roger Department of Anaesthetics, District General Hospital, Kings Drive, Eastbourne BN21 2UD; Highlands Farm, Arlington Road W., Hailsham BN27 3RD — MB ChB 1973 Liverp.; FRCA 1981 England. Cons. Anaesth. Dist. Gen. Hosp. E.bourne. Socs: Hon. Treas. Soc. for Educat. in Anaesth. (UK). Prev: Sen. Regist. (Anaesth.) S. W.. RHA & Univ. Flinders Adelaide, S. Austral.; Regist. Soton. Gen. Hosp.

MYERSON, Nicholas Antony Department of Obstetrics & Gynaecology, University Hospital of Wales, Allensbank Road, Heath, Cardiff CF4 4XN Tel: 029 2074 7747 — MB BS 1990 Lond.; BA Oxf. 1986. Regist. (O & G) Univ. Hosp. Wales Cardiff.

MYERSON, Saul Gareth 24C Melina Road, Shepards Bush, London W12 9HZ Tel: 020 8743 8766 Email: smyerson@aol.com — MB ChB 1993 Bristol; MRCP (UK) 1996. Clin. Research Fell., Univ. Coll. & Roy. Brompton Hosp. Lond. Prev: SHO (Cardiol.) Middlx. Hosp. Lond.; SHO Rotat. (Gen. Med.) Roy. Berks. Hosp. Reading.

MYHILL, Michael David Harry Crantock, Guildford Road, Cranleigh GU6 8PP Tel: 01483 273352 — MRCS Eng. LRCP Lond. 1951; MA, BM BCh Oxon. 1951; DPH Eng. 1957. (Univ. Coll. Hosp.) Sen. Med. Off. S. W. Surrey DHA. Socs: Fell. Soc. Community Med.; BMA. Prev: Ho. Surg. Roy. Ear Hosp. Univ. Coll. Hosp.; Res. Med. Off. Hosp. Trop. Dis. Lond.; Sch. Med. Off. Cornw. CC.

MYHILL, Sarah Barbara Upper Weston, Llangunllo, Knighton LD7 1SL Tel: 01547 550331 Fax: 01547 550339 — MB BS 1981 Lond. (Middlx. Hosp.) Indep. GP & Allergist Powys. Socs: Brit. Soc. Allergy, Environm. & Nutrit. Med. (Hon. Sec.).

MYINT

MYINT, Claire Marianne (Griffiths) Salisbury Health Care NHS Trust, Salisbury District Hospital, Salisbury SP2 8BJ; 8 Fell Close, Locks Heath, Southampton SO31 6UT Tel: 01489 583047 — MB BCh 1992 Wales; MRCP (UK) 1995. (Univ. Wales Coll. Med.) Specialist Regist. (Rehabil. Med.) Salisbury Dist. Hosp. Socs: Roy. Coll. Phys. Lond.; Brit. Soc. of Rehabil. Med. Prev: Specialist Regist. (Rehabil. Meds.) St Mary's Hosp. Portsmouth; SHO (Neurol.) Soton. Gen. Hosp. Soton.; Research Phys. (Pharmaceut. Med.) Simbec Merthyr Tydfil.

MYINT, Fiona Pwint-oo St Bartholomews Hospital, West Smithfield, London EC1A 7BE Tel: 020 7601 8888 — MB BS 1987 Lond.; BSc (Hons.) Lond. 1984, MB BS 1987; FRCS Ed. 1992. SHO (Gen. Surg.) St Bart. Hosp. Lond. Prev: SHO (Neurosurg.) Atkinson Morley's Hosp. Wimbledon.; Ho. Phys. Guys Hosp. Lond.; SHO (A & E) Kings Coll. Hosp. Lond. & Demonst. (Anat.) KingsColl. & Lond. Univ.

MYINT, Han Royal Bournemouth Hospital, Castle Lane E., Bournemouth BH7 7DW Tel: 01202 704790 Fax: 01202 300248 Email: hanm.yint@ybch-tr.swest.nhs.uk; 10 Harewood Gardens, Bournemouth BH7 7RH Tel: 01202 399096 Email: h.myint@ybh.org.uk — MB BS 1977 Med. Inst. (I) Rangoon; MRCP (UK) 1989; MRCPath 1994; T(M) 1994; FRCP Ed. 1998; FRCP 2000 Edinburgh. Cons. Haemat. Roy. Bournemouth Hosp. Socs: Brit. Soc. Haematol.; Amer. Blood & Bone Marrow Transpl. Soc.; Amer. Soc. Haemat.

MYINT, Kyaw Princess Alexandra Eye Pavilion, Chalmers Street, Edinburgh EH3 9HA; 4 Hawthorne Crescent, Liverpool L37 4JF — FRCS; DO; MBBS; MBBS; MRCOpth.

MYINT, Professor Steven Hla Department of Microbiology, University of Leicester, Leicester LE1 7EH Tel: 0116 252 2951 Fax: 0116 252 5030; The Croft, Ragdale, Six Hills Lane, Melton Mowbray LE14 3PG — MB BS 1980 Lond.; MD Lond. 1989; MRCP (UK) 1986; MRCS Eng. LRCP Lond. 1981; Dip. Clin. Microbiol. Lond. 1986. (Guy's) Prof. Clin. Microbiol. Univ. Leicester; Hon. Cons. Leicester Roy. Infirm. Prev: Sen. Lect. (Clin. Virol.) Univ. Leicester; New Blood Lect. Univ. Coll. Lond.; Postdoctoral Fell. Univ. of Würzburg, Germany.

MYINT, Thein Thein Myint, Shrubbery House, 13 Prentis Road, London SW16 1QB Tel: 020 8769 2844 — MB BS Rangoon 1956; DObst RCOG 1965; DCH Eng. 1961. (Rangoon)

MYINT, Ye Department of Anaesthetics, Barnsley District General Hospital, Gawber Road, Barnsley S75 2EP Tel: 01226 730000; 2 Buttermere Croft, Walton, Wakefield WF2 6TL Tel: 01924 253705 — MB BS 1984 Rangoon; FRCA 1991; DA (UK) 1989. Cons. Anaesth. Socs: BMA & Assn. Anaesth.; Anaesth. Res. Soc.; Intens. Care Soc. Prev: Clin. Lect. & Hon Sen. Regist. Univ. of Sheff.; Regist. (Anaesth.) Stoke-on-Trent & Sheff.

MYINT MYINT MU, Dr Dewi Sant Hospital, Albert Road, Pontypridd CF37 1LB; 15 Clos Myddlyn, Beddau, Pontypridd CF38 2JS — MB BS 1976 Rangoon.

MYINT THEIN KHINE, Dr 92 Ifield Road, West Green, Crawley RH11 7BQ — MB BS 1973 Med. Inst. (I) Rangoon.

MYLES, Alan Boulton (retired) Boultons, The Fairway, Brooklands Road, Weybridge KT13 0RZ Tel: 01932 346397 — MB BChir Camb. 1953; FRCP Lond. 1976, M 1960. Prev: Cons. Phys. & Rheum. St. Peters Hosp. Chertsey.

MYLES, Barbara (retired) La Blinerie, la Rue de la Blinerie, St Clement, Jersey JE2 6QT Tel: 01534 735861 — MB BCh BAO Dub. 1955; DA Eng. 1960. Med. Off. Jersey Family Nursing Serv.-Infant Welf. & Developm. Clinics. Prev: SHO (Anaest.) St Peter's Hosp.

MYLES, Belinda Jane The Backwater, Paddockfields, Old Basing, Basingstoke — MB BS 1959 Lond.; DObst RCOG 1961.

MYLES, David Macdonald Gollan, OBE, TD, OStJ, Lt.-Col. RAMC (retired) 16 East Acres, Cotgrave, Nottingham NG12 3JP Tel: 0115 989 2172 Fax: 0115 989 2172 Email: davidmyles@cs.com — MB ChB St. And. 1951. Prev: Civil. Trainer (Gen. Pract.) Rheindahlen, W. Germany.

MYLES, John Cruickshank 12 Greenmount Road S., Burntisland — MB ChB 1987 Dundee.

MYLES, Mr John Graeme Boulton (retired) La Blinerie, La Rue de la Blinerie, St Clement, Jersey JE2 6QT Tel: 01534 735861 — BA Camb. 1946, MB BChir 1950; FRCS Ed. 1957; FRCS Eng. 1958; MRCS Eng. LRCP Lond. 1949. Hon. Cons. Orthop. Surg. Jersey Gp.

Hosps. Prev: Regist. & Ho. Surg. (Orthop. & Plastic Surg.) St. Thos. Hosp. Lond.

MYLES, John Malcolm The Moorings, Common Lane, Culcheth, Warrington WA3 4HN — MB ChB 1966 Manch.; DObst RCOG 1969.

MYLES, Mr John Whitson (retired) 17 Audley Gate, Peterborough PE3 9PG Tel: 01733 263216 — MB ChB 1953 Glas.; FRCS Ed. 1965. Prev: Hon. Clin. Teach. Univ. Leicester.

MYLES, Judith Sally Avon & Western Wiltshire mental health Care NHS Trust, Blackberry Hill Hospital, Manor Road, Fishponds, Bristol BS16 2EW Tel: 0117 975 4840 Fax: 0117 958 6569 — MB BCh BAO 1973 Dub.; MRCPsych 1987; T(Psych) 1991. (Trincity Coll., Dublin Univ.) Cons. Psychiat./Specialty Dir.y Subst. Misuse; Bristol Specialist Drug Serv. Regional Drug Advis. Serv.; Sen. Clin. Lect. Bristol Univ. Socs: Fell Roy. Coll. of Psychiat.; Soc. for the Study of Addic. Prev: Cons. Psychiat., Drugs & Alcohol Wonford Hse. Hosp.

MYLES, Miss Lynn Marion 9 Strathfillan Road, Edinburgh EH9 2AG Fax: 0131 447 3805 Email: lynn.myles@ed.ac.uk; 9 Strathfillan Road, Edinburgh EH9 2AG — MB ChB 1986 Ed.; BSc (Hons.) Ed. 1984, MD 1991; FRCS (SN) Ed 1997. (Edin.) Hon. Cons. Neurosurg. & Res. Fell., W.ern Gen. Hosp. Edin.; Hon. Cons. Neurosurg., Roy. Hosp. For Sick childr., Edin. Socs: BAMM; Soc. Of Brit. Neurolog. Surg. Prev: SR (neurosurg.) Soton. Gen. Hosp.; GPR (neurosurg.) Soton. Gen. Hosp.; Vis. Fell., Neurosurg. Hosp. For Sick Childr., Toronto, Canada.

MYLES, Richard William Llwyn, Llanbadarn Road, Aberystwyth SY23 1EY — MB BCh BAO 1974 Dub.; MRCOG 1982.

MYLES, Steven Alexander Robert Auchlea Villa, 237 North Deeside Road, Peterculter, Peterculter AB14 0UJ — MB ChB 1986 Aberd.

MYLES, Terence James Murphy (retired) 100 Carnbane Road, Lisburn BT27 5NG Tel: 02892 689682 — MB BCh BAO Belf. 1947; MD Belf. 1960; FRCOG 1966, M 1953; DObst RCOG 1950. Cons. O & G Craigavon Area Hosp. Prev: Sen. Tutor Roy. Matern. Hosp. Belf.

MYLONOPOULOU, Marianthi Royal London Hospital, Whitechapel, London E1 1BB Tel: 020 7377 700; 180A Basement Flat, Westbourne Pk Road, London W11 1BT Tel: 020 7243 2515 — Ptychio Iatrikes Athens 1991. (Athens) SHO (Paediat.) Roy. Lond. Hosp. Socs: BMA. Prev: Qu. Eliz. Hosp. Lond.; St. Bartholomews Hosp. Lond.; St Mary's Hosp. Lond.

MYLVAGANAM, Arumugam 30 The Meadows, Rainhill, Prescot L35 0PQ Tel: 0151 426 5802 — MB BS 1963 Ceylon; MRCPsych 1983; DPM Eng. 1981. (Colombo) Cons. Child & Adolesc. Psychiat. Mersey RHA. Socs: Liverp. Med. Inst. Prev: Sen. Regist. (Child & Adolesc. Psychiat.) Alder Hey Childr. Hosp.; Liverp.; Regist. St. Francis Hosp. Haywards Heath.

***MYLVAGANAM, Jayanthan** 30 The Meadows, Rainhill, Prescot L35 0PQ — MB ChB 1998 Manch.; MB ChB Manch 1998.

MYLVAGANAM, Kandappu Luton & Dunstable Hospital Trust, Lewsey Road, Luton LU4 0DZ — MB BS 1976 Sri Lanka; MRCP (UK) 1984; LRCP LRCS Ed. LRCPS Glas. 1984; FRCP 1998. Cons. Phys. Geriat. Med. Luton & Dunstable Hosp. Prev: Cons. Phys. Geriat. Med. Pembroksh. HA; Sen. Regist. (Geriat. & Gen. Med.) S. N. Tees HA.

MYLVAGANAM, Rock Rajasothy Xavier 43 Granes End, Great Linford, Milton Keynes MK14 5DY Tel: 01908 605314 — MB BS 1971 Ceylon; MRCPsych 1985. (Colombo) Clin. Asst. Ment. Health Unit Chesterfield & N. Derbysh. Roy. Hosp. Chesterfield. Prev: Regist. (Psychiat.) St. John's Hosp. Aylesbury, Pen-y-fal Hosp.; Abergavenny & Milton Keynes Gen. Hosp.

MYLVAHAN, Natarajan City Hospital, Uttoxeter Road, Derby DE22 3NE Tel: 01332 40131; 54 Ford Lane, Allestree, Derby DE22 2EW Tel: 01332 553370 — MB BS 1972 Sri Lanka; MD Sri Lanka 1976; FRCP Lond. 1993; MRCS Eng. LRCP Lond. 1979; DCH Sri Lanka 1978. (Sri Lanka) Cons. Phys. & Med. for Elderly Derbysh. Roy. Infirm. & Derby City Hosp. Socs: BMA. Prev: Sen. Regist. (Geriat. Med.) St. Mary's Hosp. Lond.; Regist. (Med.) Mansfield Dist. & Gen. Hosp.

MYMIN, Jonathan Selwyn 4 Princes Crescent, Hove BN3 4GS Tel: 01273 720406 — MB ChB 1985 Cape Town.

MYNN HTYN, Dr 9 Barnes House, Residential Village, Bovemoors La, Exeter EX2 5DS Tel: 01392 403208 — MB BS 1982 Med.; MB BS Med. Inst. (I) Rangoon 1982; DA (UK) 1992.

MYNORS-WALLIS, Laurence Mark St. Ann's Hospital, Haven Road, Poole BH13 7LN Tel: 01202 735537 Fax: 01202 492109 Email: lmmw@soton.ac.uk — BM BCh 1984 Oxf.; MA Camb. 1981; DM Oxf. 1995; MRCP (UK) 1987; MRCPsych. 1989. (Oxford and Cambridge) Cons. Psychiat. Dorset Health Care NHS Trust; Sen. Lect Soton. Univ.; Med. Director Dorset Healthcare NHS Trust. Prev: Cons. (Psychiat.) Littlemore Hosp. Oxf.; Wellcome Research Fell. & Hon. Sen. Regist. (Ment. Health) Warneford Hosp. Oxf.; Regist. (Psychiat.) Maudsley Hosp.

MYNOTT, Michael James The Tiled House, Chesterfield Road, Eastbourne BN20 7NT — MB BChir 1953 Camb.; DObst RCOG 1957. (St. Thos.) JP. Prev: Med. Off. E.bourne Coll.; RAF Med. Br.; Clin. Asst. (Orthop.) E.bourne HA.

MYO MINN, Dr 19 Roundway Down, Fulwood, Preston PR2 3NE — MB BS 1975 Med. Inst. (I) Rangoon.

MYO NYUNT, Mr Accident & Emergency Department, Hexham General Hospital, Hexham NE46 1QJ Tel: 01434 606161 — MB BS 1968 Med. Inst. (I) Rangoon; MB BS Rangoon, Burma 1968; MMedSci Rangoon, Burma 1978; FRCS Ed. 1994. Staff Doctor (A & E) Hexham Gen. Hosp.

MYRDDIN-EVANS, Towy Owen Watkin Kerri Cottage, 205 Cooden Sea Road, Cooden, Bexhill-on-Sea TN39 4TR Tel: 01424 843400 — MRCS Eng. LRCP Lond. 1948; MRCGP 1960. (Oxf. & St. Mary's) Socs: Fell. Roy. Soc. Med.; BMA. Prev: Cons. to Numerous Indust. Companies; Surg. Cdr. RNR (Retd.); Regist. (Anaesth.) & SHO (Surg.) Harold Wood Hosp.

MYRES, Miles Paul High Street Surgery, 15 High Street, Overton, Wrexham LL13 0ED Tel: 01978 710666 Fax: 01978 710494 (Call before faxing); Clemhill Cottage, New Marton, Oswestry SY11 3HR — MB ChB 1978 Ed.; MMedSc. Birm. 1994; DRCOG 1982; DTM & H Liverp. 1981. (Edinburgh) GP Princip. & Trainer; Mem. GPC Wales, N. Wales LMC; Professional Off. Clin. Governance Support & Developm. Unit Wales. Prev: C.M.E. Gp. Tutor, Clwyd S.; Indep. Med. Adviser N. Wales Health Auth.; GP Vocational Train. Course Organiser Wrexham.

MYSKOVA, Ivanka Anna 21 Fugelmere Close, Harborne, Birmingham B17 8SE Tel: 0121 429 8968 — MUDR Charles U Prague 1960. Assoc. Specialist (Psychiat.) Qu. Eliz. Psychiat. Hosp. Birm. Socs: BMA; HCSA.

MYSKOW, Lyndsey Morag Whin Park Medical Centre, 6 Saughton Road, Edinburgh EH11 3RA Tel: 0131 455 7999 Fax: 0131 455 8800; 8 Magdala Crescent, Edinburgh EH12 5BE Tel: 0131 337 1043 Email: myskow@cableinet.co.uk — MB ChB 1979 Ed.; BSc Ed. 1976; T(GP) 1991; DCH RCP Lond. 1984. (Edinburgh) Hosp. Pract. (Psychosexual Med.) Roy. Infirm. Edin. & Murrayfield Hosp. Edin.; Sen. Lect. (Gen. Pract.) Edin. Univ. Prev: GP Sighthill Health Centre Edin.

MYSKOW, Michael William Department of Pathology, Countess of Chester Hospital, Liverpool Road, Chester CH2 1UL Tel: 01244 365644 Fax: 01786 449233 Email: dr.myskow@coch-tr.nwest.nhs.uk; 12 Scholars Green Lane, Lymm WA13 0QA Tel: 01925 757171 Email: mmyskow@aol.com — MB ChB 1980 Ed.; BSc (Med. Sci) Hons. (Path.) Ed. 1977; MRCPath 1987; FRCPath 1998. (Edinburgh) Cons. Histopath. Countess of Chester Hosp. Prev: Cons. Histopath., Stirling Roy. Infirm.; Cons. Histopath. BRd.green Hosp. Liverp.; Sen. Regist. (Path.) Roy. Infirm. & Univ. Edin.

MYSZKA, Zbigniew Jerzy Gordon and Partners, 1 North Street, Peterborough PE1 2RA Tel: 01733 312731 Fax: 01733 311447 — MB ChB 1972 Sheff.

MYSZOR, Margaret Francisca Royal Berkshire Hospital, Reading RG1 5AN Tel: 0118 987 7416 — MD 1985 Manch.; BSc (Hons.) Manch. 1975, MB ChB (Hons.) 1978; FRCP 1994. (Manchester) Cons. Gastroenterol. & Phys. Roy. Berks. Hosp. Reading. Socs: Brit. Soc. Gastroenterol. & Brit. Assn. Study Liver. Prev: Lect. (Gastroenterol.) Univ. Newc.; Regist (Gen. Med. & Gastroenterol.) Hammersmith Hosp. Lond.; Research Fell. (Gastroenterol.) Guy's Hosp. Med. Sch. Lond.

MYTHEN, Professor Michael Gerard Centre for Anaesthesia, University College London, Middlesex Hospital, London W1T 3AA Tel: 0207 380 9477 Fax: 0207 580 6423 Email: montymython@compuserve.com; 40 Kent Avenue, London W12 8BH — MB BS 1984 Lond.; MD Lond. 1995; FRCA 1990. (Middlesex) Portex Prof. Anaesth. & Critical Care Univ. Coll. Lond.; Director Centre for Anaesth. Univ. Coll. Lond.; Head of Portex Unit Inst. of Chil Health Univ. Coll. Lond.; Clin. Director Critical Care Univ. Coll. Lond.; Co-Director Surgic. Outcomes Center Univ. Coll. Lond. Prev: Sir Jules Thorn Research Fell. & Regist. (Anaesth.) Middlx. Hosp. Lond.; Sen. Regist. (Anaesth.) Char. Cross Hosp. Lond.; Asst. Prof. (Anaesth. & Critical Care) Duke Univ. Med. Centre, N. Carolina USA.

MYTHILI, Kalathur c/o Barclays Bank, Rose Hill, Carlisle CA1 2RT — MB BS 1968 Dibrugarh; DA Eng. 1979; DObst RCOG 1974. (Assam Med. Coll.) SHO (Anaesth.) Dryburn Hosp. Durh.

MYTON, Tracey Louise 3 Patshull Road, Albrighton, Wolverhampton WV7 3BH — MB ChB 1992 Liverp.

MYTTAS, Nicholas Child and Adoloscent Mental Health Service, Finchley Memorial Hospital, Granville Road, London N12 0JE Tel: 020 8349 6308 Fax: 020 8346 6030 Email: nikos.myttas@bhc-tr.nthames.nhs.uk; 34 Talbot Road, London N6 4QP Tel: 020 8374 9699 Fax: 0870 130 5012 Email: n.myttas@lineone.net — Ptychio Iatrikes 1983 Athens; MRCPsych 1991. Cons. Child & Adolesc. Psychiat. Child and Adolesc. Ment. Health Serv. - Barnet, Enfield, Haringey Ment. Health Trust Lond.; Cons. Child and Adolesc. Psychiat. Finchley Memor. Hosp. Finchley. Socs: Assn. Child Psychol. & Psychiat.; Brit. Juvenile & Family Ct.s Soc.; Roy. Coll. Psychiat. Prev: Sen. Regist. (Child & Adolesc. Psychiat.) St. Geo. Hosp. Lond.; Regist. (Psychiat.) Napsbury Hosp. Lond.

MYTTON, Julie Ann Dept. Of Pub. Health, W. Pennine Health Auth., Westhulme Avenue, Oldham OL1 2PL Tel: 0161 622 6618 Fax: 0161 622 6622; 1A Briarfield Road, Heswall, Wirral CH60 2TH Tel: 0151 342 2168 — MB BS 1990 Lond.; MRCGP 1996; DRCOG 1995; DCH RCP Lond. 1994; MSc Community Paediatrics 1998. (St. Bartholomews Hospital Medical College) Staff Grade Community Paediat., Countess of Chester Hosp. (p/t); Specialist Regist., Pub. Health, W. Pennine Health Auth., Manch.; Research Fell. Inst. Child Health Lond.

MZIMBA, Zola Sipo 41 Paddock Drive, Birmingham B26 1QP — MB ChB 1990 Birm.; ChB Birm. 1990.

N'DOW, Mr James Michael Olu 73 Thorngrove Avenue, Aberdeen AB15 7FG — MB ChB 1990 Aberd.; FRCS Ed. 1994. SHO (Surg.) Kincardinsh.

N'DOW, Kathleen Elizabeth 32 Westfield Park, Stonehaven. AB39 2EF — MB ChB 1991 Aberd. Trainee GP/SHO Kincardinesh. VTS.

NAASAN, Mr Anas Department of Plastic Surgery, Ninewells Hospital and Medical Schools, Dundee DD1 9SY Tel: 01382 425644 Fax: 01382 223136 Email: a.naasan@dundee.ac.uk; Denehurst, Kincarrathie Crescent, Perth PH2 7HH Tel: 01738 621455 Fax: 01738 635255 Email: anaasan@doctors.org.uk — MB BCh 1979 Ain Shams; FRCS Glas. 1987; T(S) 1994. Cons. Plastic Surg. Tayside Univ. Hosp. NHS Trust; Hon. Sen. Lect. Univ. Dundee. Socs: Brit. Assn. Plastic Surg.; Brit. Soc. Surg. Hand. Prev: Sen. Regist. N. Gen. Hosp. Sheff.; Regist. Bangour Gen. Hosp. & Roy. Hosp. Sick Childr. Edin.; SHO St. And. Hosp. Billericay.

NABAR, Mr Bhalchandra Vasudeo (retired) 18 Elias Drive, Bryncoch, Neath SA10 7TG Tel: 01639 642068 — MB BS Bombay 1949; MS Bombay 1953; FRCS Eng. 1959; FRCS Ed. 1954; DLO Eng. 1965. Prev: Cons. Surg. (ENT) Singleton Hosp. Swansea, Neath Gen. Hosp. & Port Talbot Gen. Hosp.

NABAR, Mohan Anant (retired) Southwick Health Centre, The Green, Southwick, Sunderland SR5 2LT Tel: 0191 548 6550 Fax: 0191 548 0867 — MB BS 1955 Bombay.

NABARRO, Joan Margaret (retired) 33 Woodside Avenue, London N12 8AT Tel: 020 8445 7925 — MB BChir 1947 Camb.; MRCP (UK) 1978; DObst RCOG 1953. Prev: Cons. Venereol. Centr. Middlx. Hosp. & Watford Gen. Hosp. (Shrodells Wing).

NABARRO, Ruth Mary Grace Annandale Surgery, 239 Mutton Lane, Potters Bar EN6 2AS Tel: 01707 644451; The Old Jail House, Salisbury Hall Barns, St Albans AL2 1BU — MB BS 1988 Lond.; BSc Lond. 1985, MB BS 1988; MRCGP 1992; DRCOG 1991. Princip. EP Potteb. Boui.

NABI, Dewan Wahedun 17 Church Street, Wales, Sheffield S26 5LQ — MB BS 1967 Rajshahi; MB BS Rajshahi Bangladesh 1967; MRCPsych 1983.

NABI

NABI, Ijaz Mahmood 403 Rochfords Gardens, Slough SL2 5XE — MB BS 1994 Lond. (Charing Cross & Westm. Med. Sch.) Prev: Ho. Phys. Chelsea & W.m. Hosp. Lond.; Ho. Surg. Watford Gen. Hosp.

NABIJEE, Abdul Hussain Asgar Ali Alexandra Surgery, 39 Alexandra Road, London SW19 7JZ Tel: 020 8946 7578 Fax: 020 8944 5650; 235 West Barnes Lane, New Malden KT3 6JD Tel: 020 8395 9292 — MB BS 1974 Rajasthan. (SMS Medical College Jarpur Royaslhan) GP Princip.; Clin. Asst. (A & E). Socs: MDU.

NABILI, Aqdas Tel: 020 8368 0437 Email: aqdas@doctors.org.uk; Tel: 01229 491263 Fax: 01229 491046 — Ptychio latrikes 1989 Ioannina; Specialist Training (SR) in Paediatrics. Cons. (Paediat.) Morecambe Bay PCT NHS Trust; PhD Research Project in Platelet Agrigation Univ. Ioannina Med. Sch., Greece; MSc in Community Paediat. on going; Cons. Paediat. in Acute & Community. Socs: BMA; Autistic Soc.; RCOPCH. Prev: Specialist Regist. (Paediat.) 1998 with Greek Min. of Health; Specialist Regist. (Paediat.) GMC as Specialist Register 1998; Middle Grade (Paediat. & Neonat.) Lincoln Co. Hosp. NHS Trust.

*NABILI, Shahriar Flat 17, The Oaks, Millholm Rd, Glasgow G44 3YQ — MB ChB 1997 Glas.

NABNEY, Samuel Pierce Wesley Knock-na-Knowe, Newtownstewart, Omagh Tel: 0166 26 61333 — LAH 1960 Dub.; MRCGP 1967; MPS Irel. 1960. (TC Dub., RCSI & Qu. Univ. Belf.) Princip. GP Newtownstewart. Socs: BMA; Fell. Ulster Med. Soc. Prev: Chairm. Tyrone & W.. Divs. BMA; Ho. Surg. & Ho. Phys. Tyrone Co. Hosp. Omagh.

*NACHEV, Parashkev Choudomirov 321 Hills Road, Cambridge CB2 2QT — BM BCh 1998 Oxf.; BM BCh Oxf 1998.

NACKASHA, Evelyn Petrous 10 Erin Close, Bromley BR1 4NX — MB ChB 1970 Mosul, Iraq; MRCOG 1978.

NACKASHA, Wajdi Louis Children's Unit, St. Peters Hospital, Guildford Road, Chertsey KT16 0PZ Tel: 01483 728201 Fax: 01483 776957; 23 Cross Acres, Pyrford Woods, Pyrford, Woking GU22 8QS Tel: 01932 341986 Fax: 01483 776957 Email: wajdi@nackasha.freeserve.co.uk — MB ChB 1973 Baghdad; FRCP Lond. 1996; MRCP (UK) 1981. Cons. Paediat. (Community Child Health) Goldsworth Pk. Health Centre Woking & St. Peter's Hosp. Chertsey; Cons. Paediat. Ashford & St Peters NHS Trust. Prev: Sen. Regist. (Community Child Health) St. Leonard's Hosp. Lond.; Clin. Asst. Roy. Lond. Hosp.

NACZK, Antoni The Health Centre, 2 The Tanyard, Cumnock KA18 1BF Tel: 01290 422723 Fax: 01290 425444 — MB ChB 1985 Ed.; DRCOG 1989; MRCGP 1991; DFFP 1993; Dip IMC RCS Ed 1998; Ass. FFAEM 1999. (Edinburgh) Gen. Prac.; Staff Grade Phys. (A & E) CrossHo. Hosp. Kilmarnock. Prev: Med. Adv. Bens. Agen. Med. Serv.; Med. Dir. Blairston Ho. Nursery Home, Bothwell S. Lancs.; Part. Gen. Prac. Isle of Bute.

NADA, Mr Esmael Mokhtar Esmael 239 Wrotham Road, Gravesend DA11 7LL — MB BCh 1975 Mansoura, Egypt; FRCSI 1986.

NADAL, Miguel Jose 22 The Park, London NW11 7SU — MB BS 1982 Lond.

NADARAJAH, Kamalini 3 Martingale Road, Billericay CM11 1SG — MB ChB 1997 Aberd.

*NADARAJAH, Mahendran 17 Longmeade Gardens, Wilmslow SK9 1DA — MB BS 1997 Lond.

NADARAJAH, Ramalingam Frimley Park Hospital, Portsmouth Road, Frimley, Camberley GU16 7UJ Tel: 01276 604544 Fax: 01276 604297; 46 Elvetham Road, Fleet, Aldershot GU12 8HL — MB BS 1978 Colombo; MRCS Eng. LRCP Lond. 1987; MRCP (UK) 1985; FRCP (UK) 1997. Cons. Genitourin. Med. Frimley Pk. Hosp. NHS Trust Camberley. Socs: Assn. Genitourin. Med.; BMA; Med. Soc. Study VD. Prev: Sen. Regist. (Genitourin. Med.) MRI Withington & Hope Hosp. Manch.; Regist. (Genitourin. Med.) St. Helier Hosp. Carshalton.

NADARAJAH, Srimalini Department of Public Health, Camden & Islington HA, 110 Hampstead Road, London NW1 2LJ Tel: 020 7853 5353 Fax: 020 7853 5355; 85 Weirdale Avenue, Whetstone, London N20 0AJ Tel: 020 8368 7500 — MB BS 1974 Sri Lanka; LRCP LRCS Ed. LRCPS Glas. 1984. SCMO (Pub. Health) Camden & Islington HA. Prev: Clin. Med. Off. (Community Med.) Islington HA; SHO (Geriat. Med.) ChristCh. Hosp.; SHO (Geriat. Med.) New Cross Hosp. Wolverhampton.

NADARAJAH, Thambiayah (retired) Flat 23 Elderfield Place, Church Lane, London SW17 6EB Tel: 020 8672 0653 — MB BS 1957 Ceylon; DA Eng. 1975. Prev: GP MexBoro.

NADARAJAN, Mr Periasamy 26 Prospect Road, Lowestoft NR32 3PT — MB BS 1976 Madurai; MS (Orth.) Madras 1979; FRCS (Orth.) 1987. Cons. Orthop. Surg. Jas. Paget Hosp. Gt. Yarmouth.

NADEEM, Faris 222 Stanford Road, Norbury, London SW16 4QW Tel: 020 8764 7161 — MB BS 1976 Punjab; BSc Punjab 1970, MB BS 1976; FFA RCSI 1985; DA Eng. 1984.

NADEEM, Mr Rana Dilawaiz Postgraduate Centre, Falkirk & District Royal Infirmary, Falkirk FK1 5QE — MB BS 1985 Punjab; FRCS Glas. 1993; FRCS Ed. 1992.

NADEL, Simon Department of Paediatrics, St Mary's Hospital, London W2 1NY Tel: 020 7886 6077; 18 Summerfield Road, London W5 1ND Tel: 020 8537 2715 Email: s.nadel@ic.ac.uk — MB BS 1985 Lond.; MRCP (UK) Paediat. 1988. (King's Coll.) Cons. & Paediat. IC & Paediat. Infec. Disc. St. Mary Hosp. Lond. Socs: Fell. Clin. Research Paediat. St. Mary's Hosp. Lond.; MRCPCH; Intens. Care Soc. Prev: Fell. Paediat. Infec. Dis. Childr. Hosp. Philadelphia; SHO Hosp. for Sick Childr. Gt. Ormond St. Lond.; SHO (Paediat.) Whipps Cross Hosp. Lond.

NADERSEPAHI, Ali 6 Beverley Place, 38 Eton Rise, London W5 2ER — MB BS 1991 Lond.

NADIN, John Charles Kenneth Preston Grove Medical Centre, Preston Grove, Yeovil BA20 2BQ Tel: 01935 474353 Fax: 01935 425171 — MB BChir 1976 Camb.; MA Camb. 1977, MB 1976, BChir 1975; MRCGP 1983; DCH Eng. 1980; DRCOG 1979.

NADJAT-SHOKOUHI, Mr Mohammed Ali Abbas c/o Mr. J. Al-Ibrahim FRCS, 55 Knightlow Road, Harborne, Birmingham B17 8PX — MB ChB 1968 Baghdad; FRCS Ed. 1976.

NADKARNI, Sanjay c/o Department of Radiology, Royal Hallamshire Hospital, Glossop Road, Sheffield S10; 9 Fuler Road, Sheffield S11 8UF — MB BS 1992 West. Austral.; MB BS Western Australia 1992; MRCP (UK) 1996; FRCR 1997; DA (UK) 1995. (Univ. of Western Australia) Specialist Regist. (Radiol.). Socs: Austral. Med. Assn.

NADLACAN, Liviu Mircea Flat 112, Room 1, Osler Road, Headington, Oxford OX3 9JW — State Exam Rome 1993.

*NADRA, Aida Mary 6 Westminster Drive, Wrexham LL12 7AU — MB BCh 1994 Wales.

NADRA, Asmat Nadra and Partners, The Surgery, Gardden Road, Rhosllanerchrugog, Wrexham LL14 2EN Tel: 01978 840034 Fax: 01978 845782 — LRCP LRCS Ed. LRCPS Glas. 1982 Edinburgh & Glasgow; MD 1973 Komensky; MD 1973 Komensky.

NADRA, Azmi Baddow Road Surgery, 115 Baddow Road, Chelmsford CM2 7PY Tel: 01245 351351 Fax: 01245 494192 — MD 1969 Warsaw; LRCP LRCS Ed. LRCPS Glas. 1976; DCH Eng. 1973. (Med. Acad. Warsaw) Prev: SHO (Paediat.) Stepping Hill & Cherry Tree Hosps. Stockport & Roy.; Alexandra Hosp. Rhyl; Regist. (Paediat.) Maelor Gen. Hosp. Wrexham.

NAEEM, Abdul The Surgery, 64 Dog Kennel Lane, Oldbury B68 9LZ Tel: 01922 552 1713 Fax: 01922 552 9980 — MRCS Eng. LRCP Lond. 1978. (Khyber Med. Coll.) SHO (Anaesth.) Roy. Gwent Hosp. Newport. Prev: SHO (Gen. Med.) St. Woolos Hosp. Newport; SHO (Gyn. & Obst.) Aberdare Gen. Hosp.; Ho. Off. (Gen. Med.) Merthyr Gen. Hosp. Merthyr Tydfil.

NAEEM, Ajaz Ahmed The Surgery, 8 Shenfield Road, Brentwood CM15 8AB Tel: 01277 218393 Fax: 01277 201017 — MB BCh 1991 Wales; BSc Wales 1988; MRCP (UK) 1994. Prev: Clin. Med. Off. Community Paediat. SE Lond.

NAEEM, Asim 7 Eton Avenue, Westlands, Newcastle ST5 3JL Tel: 01782 613667 — MB BS 1997 Lond. (St Georges University of London) SHO Rotat. (Psychiat.) Univ. of Lond., St Geo.'s Train. Scheme. Socs: Roy. Coll. Psychiatr. Inceptorship. Prev: Ho. Off. (Surg./Orthop.) St. Helier Hosp. Lond.; Ho. Off. (Gen. Med.) Manor Hosp. Walsall.

NAEEM, Muhammed The Surgery, High Street, Talke Pits, Stoke-on-Trent ST7 1QH Tel: 01782 782440 Fax: 01782 763884 — MB BS 1963 Karachi; BSc, MB BS Karachi 1963. (Dow Med. Coll.)

NAEEM, Naushene Sara 241 Kingsway, Cheadle SK8 1LA Tel: 0161 428 9795 — MB ChB 1991 Dundee; MRCGP 1997.

NAEEM, Mr Sardar Mohammad Department of Orthopaedics, Bedford Hospital, South Wing, Kempson Road, Bedford MK42 9DJ — MB BS 1983 Peshawar; FRCSI 1991.

NAERGER, Mr Harry Guy Anthony Motley Bank, Earls Grove, Camberley GU15 2EN Tel: 01276 509600 Fax: 01276 709555 — MB BS 1984 Lond.; FRCS 1988 Eng.; FRCS 1997 Urol; FRCS Eng. 1988; FRCS (Urol.) 1997. (Middlx.) Cons. Urol. Frimley Pk. Hosp. Surrey & the Min. Defence. Prev: Sen. Regist. (Urol.) St. Thos. Hosp. Lond.; Sen. Regist. (Urol.) Battle Hosp. Reading.

NAFIE, Sami Abdel El-Alim Abdo 57 Brunswick Road, Ealing, London W5 1AQ; 47 Ashdown Drive, Stourbridge DY8 5QY — MB BCh 1977 Ain Shams; MChOrth Liverp. 1986; MRCS Eng. LRCP Lond. 1988. Regist. (Orthop. Surg.) Russells Hall/Corbett Hosps. Dudley HA.

NAFTALIN, Adrian Paul Gray's Inn Medical, (surg.) 79 Gray's Inn Road, London WC1X 8TP Tel: 020 7405 9360 Fax: 020 7831 1964; 5 Ardwick Road, London NW2 2BX Tel: 020 7435 5781 Fax: 020 7435 9635 Email: natfalin@mistral.co.uk — MB BChir 1963 Camb.; BA Camb. 1959, MA; FRCS Eng. 1968. (Camb. & Middlx.) Forens. Med. Examr. (Metrop. Police); Med. Off. Legal Educat. Lond.; Med. Off. Jewish Care; Vis. Med. Off. Camden Mens Hostels. Socs: Fell. Hunt. Soc.; BMA; (Counc.) Hampstead Med. Soc. Prev: Cons. Health Screening Wellington Hosp. Lond.; Med. Off. Reader's Digest Assn.; Regist. (Plastic Surg.) Mt. Vernon & Middlx. Hosps.

NAFTALIN, Alan Avrom Newham General Hospital, Glen Road, London E13 8SL Tel: 020 7363 8063 Fax: 020 7363 8314 — MB ChB 1972 Glas.; FRCOG 1991, M 1979. Cons. O & G Newham Gen. Hosp. Lond.; Hon. Sen. Lect. (Obst. and Gyn.) at Roy. Lond. and St Bart. Sch. of Med.; Director Med. Educat., Newham Healthcare Trust. Prev: Lect. & Sen. Regist. (O & G) Roy. Free Hosp. Lond.; Regist. (O & G) Leicester Gen. Hosp.; Clin. Tutor Qu. Vict. Hosp. Melbourne, Austral.

NAFTALIN, Leslie (retired) Woodend, 3c 19 Milverton Road, Giffnock, Glasgow G46 7JN — LRCP LRCS Ed. LRFPS Glas. 1938; MRCGP 1956; LDS RFPS Glas. 1936. Med. Off. Attend. Allowance Bd. & Mem. Med. Bd. Panel Dept. Health & Social Security. Prev: Ho. Surg. Sunderland Roy. Infirm.

NAFTALIN, Lionel 4 Whitegables, 116 Andrews Drive, Glasgow G41 4RB Tel: 0141 427 1395 — LRCP LRCS Ed. LRFPS Glas. 1942; BSc Glas. 1942; FRCPath 1963. Chem. Path. Emerit. Lincoln Gp. Hosps.; Hon. Research Fell. Univ. Strathclyde. Socs: Biochem. Soc. Prev: Capt. RAMC.

NAFTALIN, Mr Nicholas Jonathan, OBE University Hospitals of Leiceister NHS Trust, Leicestershire Royal Infirmary, Infirmary Square, Leicester LE1 5WW Tel: 0116 258 6476 Fax: 0116 258 7560 Email: batkin@uhl.trent.nhs.uk; 15 Knighton grange Road, Oadby, Leicester LE2 2LF Tel: 011602703358 Fax: 0116 270 6513 Email: naftalin@nascr.net — MB ChB 1965 Glas.; FRCOG 1983, M 1970. Cons. Gyn. Leicester Roy. Infirm. Leicester. Prev: Sen. Lect. Dept. O & G Univ. Leicester; Hall Fell. Dept. O & G Univ. Glas.; Research Fell. in Anesth. Harvard Med. Sch. Boston, U.S.A.

NAFTALIN, Professor Richard Julian Department of Physiology, University of London new Hunts House, King's College, Guy's Campus, London SE1 1OL Tel: 02078486216 Fax: 020 7848 6002 Email: richard.naftalin@kcl.ac.uk; 50 Wood Vale, London N10 3DN Tel: 020 8883 5602 — MB ChB 1962 Glas.; PhD Lond. 1969, MSc 1965; DSc Glas. 1990. (Glas.) Prof. Physiol. Kings Coll. Lond. Socs: Biochem. Soc.; Physiol. Soc. Prev: Reader (Physiol.) King's Coll. Lond.; Lect. (Physiol.) Univ. Leicester; Ho. Surg. Glas. Roy. Infirm.

NAG, Shipra 2 Sark Close, Heston, Hounslow TW5 0PZ Tel: 020 8572 3216 — MB BS 1966 Indore; MS Indore 1969.

NAG-CHAUDHURY, Satya Ranjan 121 Harley Street, London W1N 1DH Tel: 020 7224 0130; 11 Bentley Way, Woodford Green IG8 0SE Tel: 020 8504 7920 Fax: 020 8504 3879 — MB BS 1953 Calcutta; FRCOG 1993, M 1978; FFA RCS Eng. 1970. Assoc. Specialist (O & G) N. Middlx. Hosp. Lond. Socs: BMA. Prev: Asst. (O & G) Barking Hosp. & N. Middlx. Hosp. Lond.; Regist. (O & G) Shrewsbury Gp. Hosps. & Groundslow Hosp. Tittensor.

NAGABHYRU, Anita 2 Pethill Close, Plymouth PL6 8NL Tel: 01752 784480 Fax: 01752 309716 Email: anagabhyn@yahoo.com — MB ChB 1994 Dundee. (Dundee University) SHO (ENT) Derriford Hosp. Plymouth. Prev: A & E Derriford Hosp. Plymouth; SHO (Gen. Med.) Derriford Hosp. Plymouth; SHO (Gen. Surg.) Derriford Hosp. Plymouth.

NAGABHYRU, Apparao Trelawny Surgery, 45 Ham Drive, Plymouth PL2 2NJ Tel: 01752 350700 Fax: 01752 784480; 2 Prethill Close, Earlswood, Plymouth PL6 8NL Tel: 01752 784480 Fax: 01752 309716 Email: anagabhyru@mcmail.com — MB BS 1968 Andhra; DLO Eng. 1976. (Rangaraya Med. Coll.) GP. Prev: Trainee GP Exeter VTS; Regist. (ENT) Warrington Gen. Hosp.; Clin. Asst. (ENT) Roy. Devon & Exeter Hosp.

NAGANATHAR, Indira 18 Glenham Drive, Ilford IG2 6SG — MB BS 1971 Ceylon.

NAGAR, Hans Alexis 69 Glendarragh, Belfast BT4 2WB — MB ChB 1993 Birm.

NAGAR, Mahesh Prabhashanker 74 Aberford Road, Wakefield WF1 4AL — MB BS 1983 Jabalpur, India.

NAGARAJ, Channanagowd Basavaraj Om Shakthi, 7 Freemans Walk, Pembroke SA71 4AS — MB BS 1977 Mysore; BSc Mysore 1968; T(GP) 1992; DMedRehab RCP Lond 1988; DGM RCP Lond. 1987. Med. Examr. (Assessor) Benefits Agency Med. Servs. DSS Swansea; Police Surg. HaverfordW.; Assoc. Psychiat. St. David's Hosp. Carmarthen; Deputising GP, Healthcall, Swansea Med. Serv.s; Medico-Legal Report Writer. Socs: BMA; Mem. Of Assoc of Police Surg., APS 5078. Prev: Staff. Phys. (Geriat. Med.) S. Pembrokesh. Hosp. Pembroke Dock.; Trainee GP Porthcawl; Regist. (Geriat. & Gen. Med.) Vict. Hosp. Blackpool.

NAGARAJ, Hutchappa Nandeesh 39 Drummond Way, Macclesfield SK10 4XJ — MB BS 1984 Bangalore.

NAGARAJA, Etagi Gugupadappa Alim and Partners, 151 North Street, Keighley BD21 3AU Tel: 01535 607444 Fax: 01535 691201 — MB BS 1974 Mysore. (Mysore) GP Keighley, W. Yorks.

***NAGARAJAH, Kugan** 247 Clifton Road, Aberdeen AB24 4HJ — MB ChB 1998 Aberd.; MB ChB Aberd 1998.

NAGARAJAN, Srikantiah Department of Histopathology, Middlesbrough General Hospital, Ayresome Green Lane, Middlesbrough TS5 5AZ Tel: 01642 850222 Fax: 01642 825071 — MB BS 1974 Bangalore; MRCPath 1990.

NAGARIA, Ahmed Javaid 24 Jay Close, Lower Earley, Reading RG6 4HE — MB BS 1985 Karachi.

NAGASUBRAMANIAN, Suryanarayanan London Eye Diagnostic Centre, 23 Harley St., London W1G 9QN Tel: 020 7323 5967 Fax: 020 7323 5972 Email: ledc@compuserve.com — PhD Lond. 1974; MB BS Madras 1962; DO Madras 1966. (Madurai Med. Coll.) Ophth. Lond. Eye Diagnostic Centre Lond.; Clin. Asst. Moorfields Eye Hosp. (City Rd. Br.); Sen. Lect. Inst. Ophth. Univ. Lond. Socs: Sec. Glaucoma Soc.; Comm. Mem. Internat. Glaucoma Soc. of Internat. Congr. of Ophth.; Fell. Amer. Acad. of Ophth. Prev: Sen. Lect. Inst. of Ophth.; Dept. of Clin. Ophth.; Lister Research Fell. Moorfields Eye Hosp. Lond.

NAGDEE, Khadija Amiena 6 Newstead Road, St. John's, Wakefield WF1 2DE — MB BCh 1946 Witwatersrand; BSc, MB BCh Witwatersrand 1946; DPM Eng. 1975.

NAGEH, Thuraia 104 Gowan Avenue, Fulham, London SW6 6RG Tel: 020 7731 6132 — MB BS 1993 Lond.; MRCP (UK) 1996. (St. Bart. Hosp. Med. Sch.) Gen. Practitioner Farnisham, Kent.

NAGENDAR, Kopparam Flat 2, Married Accommodation, General Hospital, Ayresome Gree Lane, Middlesbrough TS5 5AZ — MB BS 1983 Bangalore.

NAGENDRA, Kyle Hadley Victor Newtons, The Health Centre, Heath Road, Haywards Heath RH16 3BB Tel: 01444 412280 Fax: 01444 416943; The Magpies, The St, Bolney, Haywards Heath RH17 5PF — MB BS 1990 Lond.; MRCGP 1995; DRCOG 1994; DFFP 1994. (St Georges Hosp. M S Univ. Liver'pl.)

NAGENDRAN, Kulandavelu Department of Clinical Neurosciences, 38 Little Britain, St Bartholomews Hospital, London EC1A 7BE Tel: 020 7601 8859 Fax: 020 7601 7875 — MB BS 1978 Sri Lanka; FRCP Lond. 1996; MRCP (UK) 1983. Cons. Clin. Neurophysiol. St. Bart. Hosp. Lond. & Roy. Lond. Hosp.; Cons. Clin. Neurophysiologist Broomfield Hosp. Chelmsford Essex. Socs: Assn. Brit. Clin. Neurophysiol.; Brit. Soc. Clin. Neurophysiol.

NAGENDRAN, Ravindra Department of Radiology, Queen Elizabeth Hospital, Stadium Road, Woolwich, London SE18 4QH Tel: 0208 836 4766 — MB BS 1971 Ceylon; FRCS Eng. 1979; FRCR 1984. Cons. Radiol.Qu. Eliz. Hosp. Lond.

NAGENDRAN, Mr Sivanandy c/o Drive K. Puvanachandra, Department of Ophthalmology, H. M. Stanley Hospital, St Asaph LL17 0RS Tel: 01745 583910 Fax: 01745 583143; Brindavan, 8

NAGENDRAN

Clos Aberconway, Prestatyn LL19 9HU — MB BS 1985 Peradeniya; FRCS Ed. 1993. Assoc. Specialist in Ophth., HM Stanley Hosp. St Asaph. Prev: Staff Grade HM Stanley Hosp. St Asaph.

NAGENDRAN, Vasantha Regional Department of Clinical Immunology, The Guest Hospital, Tipton Road, Dudley DY1 4SE Tel: 01384 244855 — MB BS 1972 Ceylon; MSc (Med. Immunol.) Lond. 1986; MD Ceylon 1976; MRCP (UK) 1979; MRCS Eng. LRCP Lond. 1978; FRCPath 1997, M 1988; FRCP (Lond.) 1998. Hon. Sen. Lect. In Clin. Immunol., Univ. of Wolverhampton. Socs: Brit. Soc. Allergy & Clin. Immunol.; Brit. Soc. Immunol.; Eur. Acad. Allergol. & Clin. Immunol. Prev: Sen. Regist. (Immunol.) Univ. Hosp. Qu. Med. Centre Nottm.; Clin. Research Fell. (Immunol.) St. Thos. Hosp. Lond. & Char. Cross Hosp. Lond.; Lect. (Med.) Univ. Ceylon.

NAGESH, Kalakonda 7 Hillside Road, Wallasey CH44 2DZ — MB BS 1988 Madras; MRCP (UK) 1992.

NAGESH RAO, Mr Gadiyar East Glamorgan Hospital, Church Village, Pontypridd CF38 1AB Tel: 01443 218218 Fax: 01443 217213; 161 Lascelles Drive, Regents Gate, Pontprennau, Cardiff CF23 8NP Tel: 01222 733193 Fax: 00153 0323 6085 Email: nagesh@tesco.net — MB BS 1981 Madras; FRCS Ed. 1986; FRCS Glas. 1986; MD Hull 1997. Sen. Regist. (Colorectal Surg.) E. Glam. Hosp. Socs: Med. Defence Union; BMA. Prev: Regist. (Gen. Surg.) Sunderland Dist. Gen. Hosp., Aberd. Roy. Infirm., Bradford Roy. Infirm. & St. Lukes Hosp. Bradford.

NAGESWARAN, Ananda Sundram Department of Genitourinary Medicine, St. Anns General Hospital, St Anns Road, London N15 3TH Tel: 020 8442 6536 Fax: 020 8442 6811 Email: ana.nageswaran@haringey.nhs.uk; 47 Merryhills Drive, Enfield EN2 7NY — MB BS 1975 Sri Lanka; FRCP 1999; MRCP (UK) 1983. Cons. Phys. (Genitourin. Med.) St. Anns Gen. Hosp. Lond.; Hon. Cons. Phys. (HIV) N. Middlx. Hosp. Lond; Cons. Phys. (Genitourin. Med.) Roy. Free Hosp. Lond. Socs: Med. Soc. Study VD; Brit. HIV Assn. Prev: Sen. Regist. & Regist. (Genitourin. Med.) Sheff.; Regist. (Infec. Dis.) Manch.

NAGI, Hussein Mostafa Grimsby District Hospital, Grimsby DN33 2BA Tel: 01472 874111 — MSc Pain 2001; FRCA 1980; MB BCh Cairo 1980; FFA RCSI 1988. Cons. Anaesth. Grimsby Dist. Hosp.; Cons. in Chronic Pain Managem. Socs: Pain Soc.; IARS.

NAGI, Sukhwinder Singh Browney House Surgery, Front Street, Langley Park, Durham DH7 9YT Tel: 0191 373 2860; Magadi, Cadger Bank, Lanchester, Durham DH7 0HE Tel: 0191 520774 — MB BS 1974 Calicut; MRCGP 1980; DRCOG 1978. (Med. Sch. Calicut) GP Trainer Durh. Socs: Med. Protec. Soc. Prev: SHO (Obst. & Coronary Care) Dryburn Hosp. Durh.; SHO (Cardiol.) Shotley Bridge Gen. Hosp. Consett.

NAGINGTON, Jack (retired) 20 Gog Magog Way, Stapleford, Cambridge CB2 5BQ — MB ChB 1947 Manch.; MD (Commend.) Manch. 1956; MRCS Eng. LRCP Lond. 1947; Dip. Bact. 1950. Prev: Cons. Virol. Pub. Health Laborat. Serv.

NAGIUBE, Adel Fathy 1 Palace Court, Bayswater Road, London W1 4LP — MB BCh 1982 Assiut.

NAGLE, Christopher James 12 Rotton Park Road, Edgbaston, Birmingham B16 9JJ — MB ChB 1982 Bristol.

NAGLE, Conor James Cliff Road Surgery, 10A Cliff Road, London NW1 9AN Tel: 020 7485 2276 Fax: 020 7428 9602; 13 Carlingford Road, London NW3 1RY — MB BS 1975 Lond.; MRCS Eng. LRCP Lond. 1975; MRCGP 1988; MRCPsych 1980.

NAGLE, Lionel Richard Pall Mall Surgery, 178 Pall Mall, Leigh-on-Sea SS9 1RB Tel: 01702 478338 Fax: 01702 471294 — MB ChB 1987 Bristol; DRCOG 1991.

NAGLE, Paul Joseph Colbrook Surgery, Coleford GL16 8RH Tel: 01594 833496 Fax: 01594 833243; Tel: 01483 505658 — MB ChB 1975 Bristol; MRCGP 1980; DRCOG 1981. Prev: SHO (Neurol.) Tayside Health Bd.; Trainee Gen. Pract. Tayside Vocational Train. Scheme.

NAGLE, Robert Emerson (retired) 12 Rotton Park Road, Birmingham B16 9JJ Tel: 0121 454 2136 — MB BChir 1955 Camb.; FRCP Lond. 1974, M 1963. Cons. Cardiol. Qu. Eliz. & Selly Oak Hosps. Birm. Prev: Research Asst. Univ. Coll. Hosp. Lond.

NAGLE, Robert Sharp 10 Kirk Park, Liberton, Edinburgh EH16 6HZ — MB ChB 1951 Ed.; DTM & H 1957. (Ed.)

NAGMOTI, Vidyashankar Gangadhar Hempstead Family Practice, 146 Hempstead Road, Hempstead, Gillingham ME7 3QE Tel: 01634 363561 Fax: 01634 263768 — MB BS 1973 Bangalor; MB BS Bangalore 1973.

NAGPAL, Inderjeet Singh Flat 103, Doctors' Residences, Alder Hey Children's Hospital, Liverpool L12 2AP — MB BS 1988 Delhi; MRCP (UK) 1994.

NAGPAL, Mr Iqbal Chand Adwick Road Surgery, 24 Adwick Road, Mexborough S64 0DB Tel: 01709 590238 — MB BS 1964 All India Inst. Med. Sci.; FRCS Ed. 1968.

NAGPAL, Kanval Kant Stanhope Surgery, Stanhope Road, Waltham Cross EN8 7DJ Tel: 01992 635300 Fax: 01992 624292; 6 Homewood Avenue, Cuffley, Potters Bar EN6 4QG — MB BS 1974 Dibrugarh; DRCOG 1982. (Assam Med. Coll. Dibrugarh) Prev: Trainee GP Enfield & Haringey VTS; SHO Dartford & Gravesham Health Dist.

NAGPAL, Nirmala William Hopwood Street Surgery, William Hopwood Street, Audley, Blackburn BB1 1LX Tel: 01254 52522 Fax: 01254 696086; Arley Oaks, Wyfordby Avenue, Blackburn BB2 7AR Tel: 01254 582628 Fax: 01254 582646 — MB BS 1973 Rajasthan. (R.N.T. Med. Coll. Udaipur) Socs: BMA; Overseas Doctors Assn.; Med. Protec. Soc. Prev: Trainee GP Preston; SHO (O & G) Qu. Pk. Hosp. Blackburn; SHO (A & E) Roy. Infirm. Blackburn.

NAGPAL, Promilla 110 Sidney Grove, Newcastle upon Tyne NE4 5PE — MB BS 1968 Delhi.

NAGPAL, Satish William Hopwood Street Surgery, William Hopwood Street, Audley, Blackburn BB1 1LX Tel: 01254 52522 Fax: 01254 696086; Arley Oaks, Wyfordby Avenue, Blackburn BB2 7AR Tel: 01254 582628 Fax: 01254 582646 — MB BS 1969 Rajasthan; MS (Ophth.) Rajasthan 1973; MCOphth 1988; DO RCPSI 1979; DO Eng. 1979. (R.N.T. Med. Coll. Udaipur) Sen. Clin. Med. Off. Blackburn. Socs: BMA; Med. Protec. Soc.; Overseas Doctors Assn. Prev: Clin. Asst. (Ophth.) Roy. Infirm. Blackburn; Regist. (Ophth.) Roy. Infirm. Blackburn.

NAGPAL, Suman South Quay Surgery, 35-36 South Quay, Great Yarmouth NR30 2RG Tel: 01493 843196; 94 Victoria Road, Gorleston, Great Yarmouth NR31 6EA Tel: 01493 650772 Email: suman@ncgpcd.idps.co.uk — LMSSA 1985 Lond. Socs: MDU.

NAGPAL, Sunita South Quay Surgery, 35-36 South Quay, Great Yarmouth NR30 2RG Tel: 01493 843196 — MB BS 1977 Delhi; MB BS 1977 Delhi.

NAGPAL, Vidya Sagar 21 The Warren Drive, London E11 2LR Tel: 020 8989 0966 — MB BS 1954 Calcutta; DGO 1956, DCH 1957; MRCOG 1961; MRCGP 1968. (Calcutta Med. Coll.) Socs: BMA. Prev: Ho. Off. & SHO Med. Coll. Calcutta; Regist. O & G St. Chad's Hosp. Birm.

NAGPAUL, Chaand The Surgery, 404 Honeypot Lane, Stanmore HA7 1JP Tel: 020 8204 1363 Fax: 020 8903 0286 — MB BS 1985 Lond.; BSc (Hons.) Lond. 1982; DRCOG 1987; MRCGP 1990. (St. Bart.) Chairm. Harrow E. & Kingsbury PCG. Socs: Exec. Mem. NHS Primary Care Gp. Alliance; GMSC; RCGP Counc. Prev: Trainee GP Char. Cross Hosp. Lond. VTS.

NAGPAUL, Seema Watling Medical Centre, 108 Watling Avenue, Burnt Oak, Edgware HA8 0NR Tel: 020 8906 1711 Fax: 020 8201 1283 — MB BS 1986 Lond.; MRCGP 1990; DCH RCP Lond. 1989; DRCOG 1988. (Guy's) Prev: Trainee GP Barnet; Trainee GP Ilford VTS; Ho. Surg. Guys Hosp. Lond.

NAGRA, Amarjit Singh Oakham Surgery, 213 Regent Road, Tividale, Oldbury B69 1RZ Tel: 01384 252274 Fax: 01384 240088 — BM 1986 Soton.; MRCGP 1990; DRCOG 1990. (Southampton)

NAGRA, Arvind 12 Berkeley Avenue, Cranford, Hounslow TW4 6LA — MB ChB 1988 Leeds.

NAGRA, Indarjit Singh Solihull Hospital, Lode Lane, Solihull B91 2JL Tel: 0121 711 4455; 56 Wells Green Road, Olton, Solihull B92 7PG Tel: 0121 743 8812 — BM BS 1988 Nottm.; BMedSci. Nottm. 1986; DCCH RCP Ed. 1992; DRCOG 1992; Cert. Family Plann. JCC 1991; DFFP 1995; M.Sc. Sports Med 1997. (Nottm.) SHO (Med.) Solihull Hosp.

NAGRANI, P Ince Green Lane Surgery, 238 Ince Green Lane, Ince, Wigan WN3 4RP Tel: 01942 246263 Fax: 01942 824084 — MB BS 1968 Lucknow; MB BS 1968 Lucknow.

NAGRANI, Rani 8 Pavenham Drive, Birmingham B5 7TW — MB BS 1979 Delhi; MRCOG 1993.

NAGRATH, Krishan Dass The Surgery, 21 Brownfield Street, London E14 6ND Tel: 020 7987 2774; The Manor House, Rectory Road, Orsett, Grays RM16 3EH Tel: 01375 891419 Fax: 01375

892825 — MB BS Panjab (India) 1954. (Amritsar Med. Coll.) Princip. Gen. Med. Practitioner Reader NHS. Socs: ODA; BMA; Indian Med. Assn. Prev: Med. Off. Kenya.; Regist. (A & E) Kiddermister Gen. Hosp.

NAGREH, Baljit Kaur 237 London Road, Bedford MK42 0PX — MB ChB 1993 Sheff.

NAGUIB, Magdi Fouad Department of Medicine for Elderly, Norfolk & Norwich University Hospital, Colney Lane, Norwich NR4 7UY Tel: 01603 288011; 385 Unthank Road, Norwich NR4 7QG — MB BCh 1972 Cairo; FRCP Lond. 1994; MRCP (UK) 1976. Cons. Phys. (elderly) Norf. & Nowich Univ. Hosp.; Clin. Teach. Univ. Camb. Prev: Sen. Regist. Roy. Vict. Hosp. Edin.; Regist. (Med.) Roy. Infirm. & Chalmers Hosp. Edin.; SHO (Med.) Hope Hosp. Salford.

NAGUIB, Meena Elshaher Nassef Charing Cross Hospital, Fulham Palace Road, London W6 8RF Tel: 020 8846 1234 — MB BCh 1976 Ain Shams.

NAGUIB, Mr Mohamed Abd El-Aziem Ahmed 98 Preston New Road, Blackpool FY4 4HF Tel: 01253 698313 Fax: 01253 698313 Email: mnaguib@onetel.net.uk — MB BCh 1975 Ain Shams; 1989 DLO (Dip. Laryngo. Otology) Roy. Coll. of Surgeons of Eng.; FRCSI 1990.

NAGVEKAR, Vidyalaxmi Fareham Health Centre, Fareham PO16 7ER; 2 Wightways Mews, Warsash, Southampton SO31 9AF — BM 1981 Soton. GP Retainer.

NAGY, Barbara Maria Carmela 179 Great Cambridge Road, Enfield EN1 1SG Tel: 020 8366 0352 — MB ChB 1990 Glas.; MRCGP 1994; T(GP) 1994; DRCOG 1993. Princip. GP. Socs: MDDS; BMA. Prev: SHO (A & E) Gtr. Glas. HB; SHO (Psychiat.) Woodilee, Stobhill Ruchill Hosps. Glas.

NAHA, Bishwajit 11 Sandbourne Avenue, London SW19 3EW — BM BS 1985 Nottm.

*NAHA-BISWAS, Papiya 2 Pendlefields, Fence, Burnley BB12 9HN — MB ChB 1998 Ed.; MB ChB Ed 1998.

NAHABEDIAN, Arakel M Orthopaedic Department, Mid Cheshire Hospitals Trust, Leighton Hospital, Crewe CW1 7QJ Tel: 01270 255141; High Doon, Moss Lane, Leighton, Crewe CW1 4RN Tel: 01270 522319 — MD 1981 Beirut; BSc (Biol. & Chem.) Amer. Univ. Beirut 1974, MSc (Human Morphol.) 1976. (Amer. Univ. Beirut. Lebanon) Clin. Specialist (Orthop.) Mid Chesh. Hosp. Trust Crewe. Socs: BMA; AMA. Prev: Regist. (Orthop.) Crewe HA.

NAHAI, Simine Chantal Mount Tyndal, Spaniards Road, London NW3 Tel: 020 8458 5543 — MB ChB 1972 Bristol; BSc Bristol 1969, MB ChB 1972. Prev: Ho. Off. (Paediat.) S.mead Hosp. Bristol.

NAHAMI, G R Sheffield Medical Centre, 21 Spital Street, Sheffield S3 9LB Tel: 0114 272 6245.

NAHAR, Prem Nath Kildrum Health Centre, Afton Road, Cumbernauld, Glasgow G67 2EU Tel: 01236 721354 — MB ChB 1974 Glas.

*NAHEED, Yasara 52 Lomeshaye Road, Nelson BB9 7AR — MB ChB 1998 Leeds.

NAHHAS, Aktham Sobhi 110 Larkspur Drive, Langney, Eastbourne BN23 8EH — MD 1983 Aleppo, Syria.

NAHHAS OUBEID, Abdul Gaffar 97 Lime Road, Normanby, Middlesbrough TS6 0BZ — MB BS 1976 Peshawar; MRCPath 1990.

NAHL, Mr Sukhdev Singh Telfer Road, 190 Telfer Road, Coventry CV6 3DJ Tel: 024 7659 6060 Fax: 024 7660 1607 — MB ChB 1979 Birm.; FRCS Glas. 1986; FRCS Ed. 1988. Prev: Regist. (ENT) W. Midl. Scheme.

NAIDOO, Arunavema Sathyadatta The Valley Surgery, 81 Bramcote Lane, Chilwell, Nottingham NG9 4ET Tel: 0115 943 0530 Fax: 0115 943 1958; 360 Musters Road, West Bridgford, Nottingham NG2 7DA — MB ChB 1978 Manch.; BSc (Anat.) (Hons.) St. And. 1975; FRCGP 1982; DCH RCPS 1982; DRCOG 1983. Princip. GP Beeston & Chillwell Nottm.; Course Organiser Nottm. VTS. Socs: Panel Examr. Roy. Coll. Gen. Pract.

NAIDOO, Govindarajaloo Ramamurthie 1 Ludworth Road, Southport PR8 2AS Tel: 01704 77866; 2 Leamington Road, Ainsdale, Southport PR8 5LB — MB BCh 1948 Witwatersrand. Mem. Sefton Med. Servs. Comm. Socs: BMA & S. Afr. Med. Assn. Prev: Clin. Asst. (Dermat.) S.port Infirm.

NAIDOO, Kebalanandha Ramamurthie Liverpool Road Practice, 107 Liverpool Road, Southport PR8 4DB Tel: 01704 566646 Fax: 01704 550858; Hilltop, 13 Selworthy Road, Birkdale, Southport PR8 2NS Tel: 01704 564666 Fax: 01704 550858 — MB BCh BAO 1983 NUI; LRCPI LM, LRCSI & LM 1983; DRCOG 1988; Cert. Family Plann. JCC 1986; Dip. Radiol. RCSI 1983; Dip. Trop. Med. RCSI 1982. (RCS Irel.) GP S.port. Socs: Vice-Chairm. Sefton LMC; (Comm.) S.port Med. Soc.

NAIDOO, Nirmala Kausilya Nuffield Health Centre, Welch Way, Witney OX28 6JQ Tel: 01993 703641; 5 Leys Villas, The Leys, Witney OX28 4DH Tel: 01993 702316 — MB ChB 1975 Manch.; BSc St. And. 1972; MRCGP 1982; DRCOG 1983.

NAIDOO, Padhmanaba (retired) 49 Hillmorton Road, Rugby CV22 5AB Tel: 01788 330470 Email: patnaidoo@ntlworld.com — MB BCh Witwatersrand 1950; DCH Eng. 1956. Prev: Regist. (Paediat.) Whittington Hosp. Lond.

NAIDOO, Rajan Olof Magnus 63 Leicester Road, London N2 9DY — MB BS 1990 Lond.; BSc Psychol. Lond. 1987, MB BS 1990.

NAIDOO, Ramamurthie Surendra Kew Medical Centre, 66 Folkstone Road, Southport PR8 5PH Tel: 01704 546800 Fax: 01704 540486 — MB BCh BAO 1978 NUI; LRCPI & LM, LRCSI & LM 1978. Socs: DRCOG.

NAIDOO, Rani Kristina Anita Warrell Unit, St Mary's Hospital, Manchester M13 0JH Tel: 0161 276 6119 Fax: 0161 276 6140 Email: knaidoo@ugynae.cmht.nwest.nhs.uk; Foden Bank Farm, Byrons Lane, Macclesfield SK11 0HA Tel: 01625 614102 — MB ChB 1985 Sheff.; BMedSci Sheff. 1984; MRCOG 1992. (Sheffield) p/t Cons. Gynaecologist, St. Mary's Hosp., Manch.. Prev: Sen. Regist. St. Mary's Hosp. Manch.

NAIDOO, Tharuna Maya St Anns Hospital, London N15 Tel: 020 8442 6467; Tel: 020 7229 2204 — MB ChB 1972 Dundee; DCH Eng. 1975; MRCPsych 1979. (Lond.) Cons. Child & Adolesc. Psychiat. Haringey Heathcare Trust; Cons.child & Adolesc.Psychiat. N. Middlx. Hosp. Trust, Lond. Socs: Assoc. Mem. Brit. Psychoanal. Soc. Prev: Sen. Regist. (Child Psychiat.) St. Mary's Hosp. Lond.; Regist. (Psychol. Med.) Univ. Coll. Hosp. Lond.

NAIDOO, Vahini Vishnu Wolfson College, Oxford OX2 6UD — MB ChB 1985 Natal.

NAIDU, Govindarajalu Cupswami Perumal General Hospital, St Helier, Jersey JE2 3QS Tel: 01534 59000 Fax: 01534 622880; Fiorano House, Mont Gras D'Eau, St Brelade, Jersey JE3 8ED Tel: 01534 744175 Email: govnaidu@aol.com — MB BS 1981 Lond. (Univ. Coll. Hosp.) Assoc. Specialist (Orthop. & Trauma) Gen. Hosp. Jersey. Socs: BOA; BASK; AAOS. Prev: Regist. (Orthop., A & E & Trauma) Gen. Hosp. Jersey; Regist. (Surg.) Roy. Masonic Hosp. Lond.; SHO (Orthop.) Hammersmith Hosp. Lond.

NAIDU, Sadhana 16 Greystane Road, Invergowrie, Dundee DD2 5JQ — MB BS 1984 Osmania; FRCS Ed. 1992.

*NAIDU, Vasanampalli 4 Beaulieu Close, London SE5 8BA — MB BS 1994 Lond.

NAIK, Caroline Susheila Barrington Medical Centre, 68 Barrington Road, Altrincham WA14 1JB Tel: 0161 928 9621 Fax: 0161 926 9317 — MB ChB 1991 Liverp.

NAIK, Darshana Rupal The Jays, Broadmoor, Kilgetty SA68 0RJ Tel: 01834 814634 — MB BCh 1996 Wales. GP Reg. New Surg. N. Rd. Whitland, Cerms. Socs: MPS; BMA. Prev: SHO O & G Carmarthen; SHO Gen. Med. P.ss of Wales. Bridgend; SHO Neoratol. Uni. Hosp. Wales.

NAIK, Dineshchandra Rameschandra White Lodge, 11 Denbank Avenue, Sheffield S10 5NZ Tel: 0114 230 1254 — MB ChB 1962 Sheff.; FRCR 1975; FFR 1970; DMRD Eng. 1967. (Sheff.) Cons. Radiol. & Hon. Clin. Lect. Univ. Sheff. N. Gen. Hosp. Sheff. Socs: BMA (Chairm. Sheff. Div.); Brit. Inst. Radiol. Prev: Edr. Brit. Med. Ultrasound Bull. BMU Soc.; Sen. Regist. (Radiol.) N.. Gen. Hosp. Sheff. & United Sheff. Hosps.; Regist. Radiol. United Sheff. Hosps.

*NAIK, Jay 17 Carnoustie Close, New Moston, Manchester M40 3NF — MB ChB 1998 Leeds; BSc Leeds 1996.

NAIK, Jayant Narayan Albion Street Surgery, 1 Albion Street, Liverpool L5 3QN Tel: 0151 263 1176 Fax: 0151 261 1295; 5 Cromptons Lane, Liverpool L18 3EU Tel: 0151 722 3101 — MB BS 1961 Karnatak; DA Eng. 1963. Clin. Asst. (Dent. Anaesth.) Liverp.; Clin. Asst. (A & E) Walton Hosp. Liverp. Socs: BMA; Liverp. Med. Inst.; Roy. Coll. Anaesth. Prev: Regist. (Anaesth.) Liverp. Roy. Infirm., Sefton Hosp. Liverp. & Cumbld. Infirm. Carlisle.

NAIK, Katherine Sunita Huddersfield Royal Infirmary, Acre Street, Lindley, Huddersfield HD3 3EA Tel: 01484 342762; 34 The Drive, Roundhay, Leeds LS8 1JH Tel: 0113 293 5042 — MB ChB 1989

NAIK

(Hons.) Leeds; BSc (Hons.) Leeds 1986; MRCP (UK) 1992; FRCR 1995. Cons. Radiol. Huddersfield Roy. Infirm.

NAIK, Purushottam Narayan c/o Drive S. Phadnis, 141 New Park Avenue, Palmers Green, London N13 5NA — MD 1981 Poona; MB BS Ponna 1975; MRCPI 1984.

NAIK, Rajan Northern Gynaecological Oncology Centre, Queen Elizabeth Hospital, Sheriff Hill, Gateshead NE9 6SX Tel: 0191 403 2392; 1 Springfield Avenue, Eighton Banks, Gateshead NE9 7HL Tel: 0191 487 3459 — MB ChB 1986 Manch.; MRCOG 1992; MD Newcastle 1997. Cons. Gyn. Oncologist, N.. Gyn. Oncol. Centre. Prev: Sen. Regist. Rotat. (O & G) Newc. & N. Region.

NAIK, Ramachandra Krishna Beechdrive Surgery, 17-19 Beechdrive, Fulwood, Preston PR2 3NB Tel: 01772 863033 — MB BS 1972 Mysore. (Govt. Med. Coll. Mysore) Prev: GP Wrexham; SHO (Geriat.) Hallam & Heath La. Hosps. W. Bromwich; Clin. Asst. (Psych.) Winwick Hosp. Warrington.

NAIK, Ramesh Bhagwanji The Lawns, Old Bath Road, Sonning-on-Thames, Reading RG4 6TQ — MB ChB 1968 Birm.; MRCP (UK) 1973. (Rhodesia) Cons. Phys. & Nephrol. Roy. Berks. Hosp. Reading. Socs: RCP Comm. Renal Dis. Assoc. Edr. Proc. Europ. Dialysis & Transpl Assn. Prev: Sen. Regist. Wessex Renal Unit Portsmouth & Roy. S. Hants. Hosp.; Soton.; Regist. Renal Unit E. Birm. Hosp.; Hon. Sen. Regist. E. Birm. Hosp. & Hon. Clin. Lect. Univ. Birm.

NAIK, Ravin Wadsley Bridge Medical Centre, 103 Halifax Road, Sheffield S6 1LA; Broom House, 12 Broomgrove Road, Sheffield S10 2LR — MB ChB 1985 Sheff.; MRCGP 1994; DCH RCP Lond. 1990.

NAIK, Sandhia 58 Sancroft Road, Harrow HA3 7NT — MB ChB 1989 Manch.

NAIK, Sandra Valerie Isabella (retired) White Lodge, 11 Denbank Avenue, Sheffield S10 5NZ Tel: 0114 230 1254 — MB ChB 1962 Sheff.; DA RCPSI 1968. Prev: Asst. Specialist (Endocrinol.) Sheff. HA (T).

***NAIK, Sarita** The Lawns, Old Bath Road, Sonning, Reading RG4 6TQ — BM BS 1997 Nottm.

NAIK, Sharatchandra Manohar (retired) The Garth, 93 Oldfield Road, Altrincham WA14 4BL Tel: 0161 928 9621 — MB BS Bombay 1950. Prev: Regist. Orthop. Surg. City Gen. Hosp. Sheff.

NAIM, Tahir 17 Museum Mansion, 63a Great Russell St., London WC1B 3BJ — MB BS 1985 Punjab.

NAIMA, Mr Sabah Jassim 66 Shelford Road, Fulbourn, Cambridge CB1 5HJ — MB ChB 1976 Baghdad; FRCS Glas. 1990.

NAINBY-LUXMOORE, Jonathan Chave The Surgery, Hill Terrace, Middleton-in-Teesdale, Barnard Castle DL12 0QE Tel: 01833 640217; Heather Brae, Snaisgill Road, Middleton-in-Teesdale, Barnard Castle DL12 0RP Tel: 01833 640420 Fax: 01833 640410 — MB BS 1983 Lond.; MA Oxf. 1989, BA 1980; MRCGP 1991; DRCOG 1988. (St. Bartholomew's Hospital) Socs: BMA. Prev: Maj. RAMC GP Roy. Milit. Acad. Sandhurst; Ho. Off. (Surg.) St. Barts Hosp. Lond.

NAINBY-LUXMOORE, Richard Chave (retired) The Old Vicarage, Fareham Road, Southwick Village, Fareham PO17 6DY Tel: 01705 327792 — MRCS Eng. LRCP Lond. 1954; MA Camb. 1956, BA 1950, MB 1955, BChir 1954; FFA RCS Eng. 1961; DA Eng. 1956. Prev: Cons. Anaesth. Portsmouth & S.E. Hants. Health Dist.

NAING, Sao Yan Dunsbury Way Clinic, Dunsbury Way, Leigh Park, Havant PO9 5BG Tel: 01705 482154 Fax: 01705 471892; 36 Breach Avenue, Emsworth PO10 8NB Tel: 01243 373608 — MB BS 1960 Rangoon; DCH RCPS Glas. 1966. Clin. Med. Off. Dunsbury Way Clinic Hants.

NAINTHY, Nalini Margot 38B Wendover Way, Tilehurst, Reading RG30 4RU — MB BCh 1994 Wales.

***NAIR, Amanda Lesley** 17 Harness Close, Springfield, Chelmsford CM1 6UU — BM 1996 Soton.

NAIR, Balgopal 5-A Templebank Flats, Duckworth Lane, Bradford BD9 6RJ — MB BS 1979 Aligarh Muslim U India.

NAIR, Divakaran Vakkappulathu Gopalain 16 Brunel Road, Chigwell IG8 8BE Tel: 0831 614508 — Vrach 1973 Moscow; Vrach Peoples' Friendship U Moscow 1973. Prev: Regist. & SHO (Chest & Gen. Med.) Ipswich Hosp. Suff.

NAIR, Gopal Vasudevan 1 Bridgewater Way, Bushey, Watford WD23 4UA; 7 Hazel Grove, Watford WD25 0RX Tel: 01923 679080 — MB BS 1972 Mysore. (Kasturba Med. Coll.) Regist. (Anaesth.) Ormskirk Health Dist.; Clin. Asst. Watford Gen. Hosp. & N. Lond. Blood Transfus. Serv. Prev: SHO (Anaesth.) Roy. Liverp. Hosp., St. Catherine's Hosp. Birkenhead & Vict. Hosp. Blackpool.

NAIR, Hemant Thankappan 11 Gambier Parry Gardens, Gloucester GL2 9RD — MB BS 1980 Bombay.

NAIR, Indira Havering Hospitals NHS Trust, Waterloo Road, Romford RM7 0BE; 40 The Bowls, Vicarage Lane, Chigwell IG7 6NB — MB BS 1982 Lond.; FFA RCSI 1992; FRCA 1992. Cons. (Anaesth.) Havering Hosp. NHS Trust Romford, Essex. Socs: Assn. Anaesth.; BMA.

NAIR, Karal Venugopalan Chesterfield & North Derbyshire Royal Hospital, Calow, Chesterfield S44 5BL — MB BS 1969 Kerala; FRCR Eng. 1980; DMRD Eng. 1978. (Med. Coll. Calicut) Cons. Radiol. Chesterfield & N. Derbysh. Roy. Hosp. Prev: Sen. Regist. (Diag. Radiol.) Newc. AHA (T).

NAIR, Mr Kunhi Krishnan Humberside Cardiothoracic Surgical Centre, Castle Hill Hospital, Cottingham HU16 5JQ Tel: 01482 875875; 85 Ferriby Road, Hessle HU13 0HU — MB BS 1963 Karnatak; FRCS Eng. 1969; FRCS Ed. 1967; FACS 1989. (Kasturba Med. Coll. Mangalore) Cons. Cardiothoracic Surg. Humberside Cardiothoracic Centre Castle Hill Hosp. Cottingham. Socs: Fell. Internat. Coll. Angiol.; Fell. Roy. Soc. Med.; Intens. Care Soc. Prev: Regist. (Cardiothoracic Surg.) Harefield Hosp.; Regist. (Cardiac Surg.) Nat. Heart Hosp. Lond.; Sen. Regist. (Cardiothoracic Surg.) Guy's Hosp. & Med. Sch. Lond.

NAIR, Prakash Peterborough District Hospital, Thorpe Road, Peterborough PE3 6DA Tel: 01733 875948 Fax: 01733 875967 Email: sunny.nair@pbh-tr.anglox.nhs.uk — MB BCh 1987 Wales; MRCP (UK) 1991. (University of Wales College of Medicine) Cons. Phys. (Gen. Med./Gastroenterol.). Socs: Brit. Soc. Gastroenterol.; Roy. Coll. of Phys.s. Prev: SHO Leicester Med. Rotat.; Regist. E. of Eng. Gastroenterol. Rotat./Leicester/Peterboro; Sen. Reg. S.W. Rotat.

NAIR, Rajasekhararan Ramakrishnan Department of Anaesthetics, Airedale General Hospital, Skipton Road, Steeton, Keighley BD20 6TD Tel: 01535 652511; Rose Tor, 19 View Road, Keighley BD20 6JN Tel: 01535 602260 — MB BS 1974 Kerala; BSc Kerala 1968; DA (UK) 1989; DLO RCS Eng. 1981. Staff Grade (Anaesth.) Airedale Gen. Hosp. Steeton. Prev: Regist. (Anaesth.) King Geo. Hosp. Ilford; Regist. (Anaesth.) St. Margt. Hosp. Epping; Clin. Asst. (ENT) Roy. Devon & Exeter Hosp.

NAIR, Mr Rajeev Gopal 8 Clare Drive, Macclesfield SK10 2TX — MB BS 1986 Bombay; FRCS Glas. 1993.

NAIR, Raveendran Raghavan Pelton Fell Surgery, 21 Gardner Crescent, Pelton Fell, Chester-le-Street DH2 2NJ Tel: 0191 368 0614 Fax: 0191 387 4644 — MB BS 1974 Kerala. (Kerala) GP CHester-le-St., Co. Durh.

NAIR, Mr Salil Baskaran c/o Department of ENT, Leeds Infirmary, Great George St., Leeds LS1 3EX Tel: 0113 292 6247; 70 Harcourt Road, Thornton Heath CR7 6BW Tel: 020 8689 4993 — MB ChB 1991 Dundee; FRCS Glas. 1994; FRCSI 1994. SHO (ENT) Leeds Infirm. Prev: SHO (Neurosurg.) Addenbrooke's Hosp. Camb.; SHO (A & E) Bristol; SHO (Plastic Surg.) Bradford Roy. Infirm.

NAIR, Shanta 11 Gambier Parry Gardens, Gloucester GL2 9RD — MB BS 1985 Bombay.

***NAIR, Sindhu** 96 Bay Horse Lane, Scarcroft, Leeds LS14 3JQ — MB ChB 1998 Leeds.

NAIR, Mr Sunil 73 Evergreen Way, Hayes UB3 2BH — MB BS 1990 All India Inst. Med. Sci.; FRCS Glas. 1994.

NAIR, Mr Unnikrishnan Ramanpillai The Yorkshire Heart Centre, Leeds General Infirmary, Great George St., Leeds LS1 3EX Tel: 0113 392 5792 Fax: 0113 392 5408 Email: knair@ulth.northy.nhs.uk — MB BS Kerala 1970; MS Kerala 1973; FRCS Eng. 1977; FRCS Ed. 1976; FETCS 1998. (Trivandrum Med. Coll.) Cons. Cardiothoracic Surg. Yorks. Heart Centre, Leeds Gen. Infirm.; Hon. Sen. Lect. (Cardiothoracic Surg.) St. James'. Univ. Hosp.Leeds. Socs: Soc. Thoracic & Cardiovasc. Surg. GB & Irel.; Eur. Assn. Cardiothoracic Surg.; Yorks. Thoracic Soc. Prev: Sen. Regist. (Cardiothoracic Surg.) Wythenshawe Hosp. Manch.; Sen. Regist. (Cardiothoracic Surg.) Killingbeck Hosp. Leeds; Cons. Surg. Palghat Polyclinic & Assisi Hosp. Kanjikode.

NAIR, Velayudhan Pillai Raghunadhan 5 Kensington Close, Mansfield Woodhouse, Mansfield NG19 9GZ — MB BS Andhra 1967.

NAIRAC, Bertrand Laurence Orchard House, 17 Church St., St Peters, Broadstairs CT10 2TT Tel: 01843 604777 Fax: 01843 862211; Napier Lodge, Monkton Road, Minster, Ramsgate CT12 4EB — BM BCh 1980 Oxf.; BA (Hons.) Oxf. 1977; MRCPsych 1985. Cons. Psychiat. (Child & Adolesc.) Canterbury & Thanet Community Healthcare NHS Trust. Prev: Sen. Regist. (Child & Adolesc. Psychiat.) Nottm.; Assoc. Research Fell. Univ. Coll. Lond.; Regist. (Psychiat.) Roy. Free, Friern & Whittington Hosps. Lond.

NAIRN, Mr David Sherwood 206 High Street, Roydon, Harlow CM19 5EQ Tel: 01279 793431 Fax: 01279 793431 — MB BChir 1968 Camb.; BA Camb. 1964; FRCS Eng. 1972. Cons. Orthop. & Hand Surg. P.ss Alexandra Hosp. NHS Trust Harlow. Socs: Fell. BOA; (Ex-Counc.) Brit. Soc. Surg. of Hand; Brit. Orthop. Foot Surg. Soc. Prev: Cons. Orthop. Surg. Herts. & Essex Hosp. Bishop's Stortford & St. Margt. Hosp. Epping; Cons. Hand Surg. P.ss Alexandra Hosp. Harlow; Sen. Regist. (Orthop.) King's Coll. Hosp. Lond.

NAIRN, Edwin Robert Department of Histopathology, Crosshouse Hospital, Kilmarnock KA2 0BE Tel: 01563 577426 Fax: 01563 572407 Email: robert.nairn@aacht.scot.nhs.uk; 8 Lady Margaret Drive, Troon KA10 7AL Tel: 01292 311597 Email: rnairn@iname.com — MB ChB 1981 Manch.; BSc St. And. 1978; MRCPath 1988; DFM Glas. 1990. Cons. Path. CrossHo. Hosp. Kilmarnock. Prev: Sen. Regist. (Histopath.) Dept. Histopath. Univ. Birm.; Sen. Regist. Dudley Rd. Hosp.; Sen. Regist. E. Birm. Hosp & Childr. Hosp. Birm.

NAIRN, Lesley May 119 Balshagray Avenue, Glasgow G11 7EG — MB ChB 1990 Glas.; MRCP (UK) 1993.

NAIRN, Robert Martin Clarendon Medical, 35 Northland Avenue, Londonderry BT48 7JW Tel: 028 7126 5391 Fax: 028 7126 5932 — MB BCh BAO 1979 NUI; BSc (Hons.) NUI 1976; MRCGP 1987; DRCOG 1986; Dip. Family Plann. 1986. Chairperson Foyle Young Pract. Gp.

NAIRN, Stuart Angus (retired) Filin, Lochinver, Lairg IV27 4LP Tel: 01571 844439 — MB ChB St. And. 1959. Prev: GP Lochinver.

NAIRNE, Angela Alice Dept. of Neurology, Royal Berkshire Hospital, Reading RG30 1AG — MB BS 1984 Lond.; BSc Lond. 1978, MB BS 1984; MRCP (UK) 1994; DRCOG 1987. (Guy's) Assoc. Specialist. Neurol. Prev: Regist. (Neurol.) Oxf. Region Train Scheme.; SHO (Med.) Roy. Berks. Hosp. Reading; Clin. Asst. (Ophth.) Stoke Manderville Hosp. Aylesbury.

NAISBY, Geoffrey Philip South Cleveland Hospital, Marton Road, Middlesbrough TS4 3BW Tel: 01642 850850 Fax: 01642 700153 Email: geofnaisby@aol.com — MB BS 1981 Newc.; FRCR 1988. Cons. Radiol. S. Cleveland Hosp. N. RHA. Prev: Sen. Regist. (Radiol.) Newc. u Tyne.

NAISBY, Mary Gwendoline Tennatn Street Medical Practice, Stockton-on-Tees TS18 2AT Tel: 01642 613331 — MB BS 1981 Newc.; MRCGP 1985; Dip. Ther. Newc. 1995; DCCH RCGP 1984; DRCOG 1983.

NAISH, Clare Surgery, 65D Midland Road, Royston, Barnsley S71 4QW Tel: 01226 722418 Fax: 01226 700648; 30 Far Croft, Lepton, Huddersfield HD8 0LS Tel: 01484 5552 — MB BS 1972 Lond.; MRCS Eng. LRCP Lond. 1972; MRCGP 1977; DRCOG 1977. (Roy. Free)

NAISH, Mrs Jeannette Chung-Meng Market Street Health Group, 52 Market Street, East Ham, London E6 2RA Tel: 020 8548 2200 Fax: 020 8548 2288 — MRCS Eng. LRCP Lond. 1965; MSc Lond. 1989, MB BS 1966; MRCGP 1981. Sen. Lect. Dept. Gen. Pract. & Primary Care St. Bart. & Lond. Hosp. Prev: Sen. Lect. Dept. Pub. Health & Primary Care Roy. Free Hosp. Lond.; Clin. Asst. Ment. Handicap Unit Enfield Dist. Hosp.; Chairm. N. E. Lond. Fac. Bd.

NAISH, John Michael Algars Manor, Iron Acton, Bristol BS37 9TB Tel: 01454 228372 — MD 1947 Camb.; MA Camb. 1940, MD 1947, MB BChir 1939; FRCP Lond. 1954, M 1945. (King's Coll. Hosp.) Emerit. Cons. Gen. Med. Avon HA (T). Socs: Assn. Phys. Gt. Brit. & Irel. Prev: Cons. Phys. Frenchay Hosp. Bristol; Lect. in Med. Univ. Bristol; Prof. & Head Dept. Med. Univ. Lagos, Nigeria.

NAISH, Nora (retired) 8 River Road, Chipping Sodbury, Bristol BS37 6HQ Tel: 01454 319420 — MB BS Lond. 1938; MRCS Eng. LRCP Lond. 1938; DCH Eng. 1948.

NAISH, Richard Hanwell Health Centre, 20 Church Road, Hanwell, London W7 1DR Tel: 020 8567 5738; Old Coach House, Bray, Maidenhead SL6 2AE — LMSSA 1975 Lond.

*****NAISH, Sonya** Algars Manor, Station Road, Iron Acton, Bristol BS37 9TB — MB ChB 1998 Birm.; ChB Birm. 1998.

NAISMITH, Alastair James William 27 Otterburn Drive, Glasgow G46 6PZ — MB ChB 1972 Glas.; FFA RCSI 1978. Cons. Anaesth. Monklands Dist. Gen. Hosp. Airdrie. Prev: Sen. Anaesth. Qu. Eliz. Centr. Hosp. Blantyre, Malawi; Sen. Regist. (Anaesth.) Stobhill Hosp. Glas.; Regist. (Anaesth.) Glas. Roy. Infirm.

NAISMITH, Alison Jane Dept. Psychiatry, Southern General Hospital, 1345 Gosan Rd, Glasgow G51 4TF Tel: 0141 201 2607 Fax: 0141 201 1920; 12 Wykeham Road, Glasgow G13 3YT Tel: 0141 954 9885 Fax: 0141 954 9885 — MB ChB Dundee 1980; MRCPsych 1987; MRCGP 1985; DObst 1982. Cons. Psychotherapist Dept. Of Psychiat., S.ern Gen. Hosp., Glas.; Hon. Clin. Sen. Lect. Univ. Glas. Socs: Scott. Assn. Psychoan. Psychother. Prev: Sen. Regist. (Psychiat.) Gtr. Glas. HB.

NAISMITH, David Ardrey (retired) 1 Scott Avenue, Polmont, Falkirk FK2 0PN Tel: 01324 715812 — MB ChB 1935 Glas.; DA Eng. 1945. Prev: Anaesth. Falkirk & Dist. Roy. Infirm.

NAISMITH, Douglas Stuart Low Waters Medical Centre, 11 Mill Road, Hamilton ML3 8AA Tel: 01698 283626 Fax: 01698 282839; 2 Gleneagles Park, Castle Park, Bothwell, Glasgow G71 8UT — MB ChB 1973 Glas.; DObst RCOG 1975.

NAISMITH, James Henderson Wishaw Health Centre, Kennilworth Avenue, Wishaw ML2 7BQ Tel: 01698 372201; 119 Old Manse Road, Wishaw ML2 0EW Tel: 01698 372201 — MB ChB 1961 Glas.

NAISMITH, Karen Isobel Department Community Child Health, Strathmartine Hospital, Dundee; 369 Blackness Road, Dundee DD2 1ST — MB ChB 1984 Glas.; DCH RCPS Glas. 1986; FRCP FRCPCH. Cons. Paediat. & Complex Disabil.

NAISMITH, Laurence James Hutton Centre, St Luke's Hospital, Marton Road, Middlesbrough TS4 3AF Tel: 01642 854978 Fax: 01642 829542 — MRCS Eng. LRCP Lond. 1976; MRCPsych 1982; DPM Eng. 1982. Cons. Forens. Psychiat. St Luke's Hosp. Middlesbrough. Prev: Cons. Forens. Psychiat. AMI Stockton Hall, Pk. La. Special Hosp. Merseyside; Sen. Regist. (Forens. Psychiat.) Yorks. RHA.

NAISMITH, Lorna Dorothy (retired) 12A Upper Glenburn Road, Bearsden, Glasgow G61 4BW — MB ChB Ed. 1948; DObst RCOG 1952, Lond. Prev: Assoc. Specialist (Psycho-sexual Disorders & Coronary Rehab.) Gtr. Glas. HB.

NAISMITH, Shelagh Margaret The Surgery, Denmark Street, Darlington DL3 0PD Tel: 01325 460731 Fax: 01325 362183; 119 Old Manse Road, Wishaw ML2 0EW Tel: 01698 375573 — MB ChB 1988 Glas. Resid. (Surg.) Monklands Dist. Gen. Hosp. Airdrie & Law Hosp. Carluke.

NAISMITH, Mr William Cairns McLean Kerr Innesfallen, 146 Mugdock Road, Milngavie, Glasgow G62 8NP Tel: 0141 571 7117 — MB ChB 1964 Glas.; FRCS Glas. 1993; FRCOG 1981, M 1967. (Glas.) Cons. (O & G) S.. Gen. Hosp. Glas.; Hon. Clin. Sen. Lect. Univ. Glas.

NAJADA, Salim Fadel (Surgery), 131 Addison Road, Kings Heath, Birmingham B14 7ER Tel: 0121 444 2729; 12 Manor Park Road, Castle Bromwich, Birmingham B36 0DL — LMS 1968 Madrid. (Madrid) Prev: Regist. (O & G) Preston Hosp.; Regist. (O & G) Grimsby Gen. Hosp.

NAJAK, Bahadurali Gulam Hussein Blakesley Surgery, 39 Blakesley Road, Yardley, Birmingham B25 8XU Tel: 0121 783 4224 Fax: 0121 785 0423; Bahil, 2 The Tyburns, Hutton, Brentwood CM13 2JD — MB BS 1973 Madras. (Madras Med. Coll.) Prev: Ho. Off./SHO (Med.) Newham Gp. Hosps. Lond.; Rotating Res. Ho. Off.; Govt. Gen. Hosp. & Govt. Hosp. Wom. & Childr. Madras India; Regist. (Med.) & SHO (Paediat.) St. Bart. Hosp. Lond.

NAJAM UD DIN, Dr 66 Henniker Point, Stratford, London E15 1LQ — MB BS 1985 Punjab; FRCR 1994.

NAJIB, Riad Ahmad Mahamad Department of Haematology, Singleton Hospital, Swansea SA2 8QA Tel: 01792 205666; c/o Radam, First Floor, 75 Kimberley Gardens, London N4 1LD Email: drnajib@hotmail.com — MB ChB 1985 Basrah; MSc (Haemat.) Lond. 1995; MRCPI 1995. Staff Haemat. Singleton Hosp. Swansea. Socs: Brit. Soc. Haematol. Prev: Regist. (Med.) Hull & York; SHO (Haemat.) Birm.

NAJIM

NAJIM, Hellme Abdullah Runwell Hospital, Runwell Chase, Runwell, Wickford SS11 7XX — MB ChB 1977 Mosul; MRCPsych 1984.

NAJIM, Zahair Nahi The Surgery, 59 Anson Road, London NW2 3UY Tel: 020 8208 4141 Fax: 020 8208 3536 — MB ChB 1974 Basrah; MRCP (UK) 1987; (DPD) Cardiff 1997. GP Princip.; Trial in IDDM & Nephropathy. Prev: Regist. (Acting Sen. Regist.) Edgware Gen. Hosp.

NAJM-TEHRANI, Nasrin 8A Martindale Road, Calderstones, Liverpool L18 3LQ; 26 Kazeroon Av., Zafar, Davoodieh, Tehran 19 199, Iran Tel: 00 98 21 227213 — MB BCh 1987 Wales; FRCS Ed. 1992.

NAJMALDIN, Mr Azad The Leeds Teaching Hospitals, Department of Paediatric Surgery, Gledhow Wing, St. James's University Hospital, Leeds LS9 7TF Tel: 0113 206 4014 Fax: 0113 206 5496 Email: parmjit.jajuha@gw.sjsuh.northy.nhs.uk — MB ChB 1973 Baghdad; MS South Hampton. 1991; FRCS Ed. 1982; FRCS Eng 1998. Socs: Brit. Assn. Paediat. Surg.; Brit. Assn. of Paeuduatric Urologists; Pres, Chairm. Brit. Assn. of Paediatric Endoscopic Surg. Prev: Sen. Regist. Wessex Regional Centre for Paediat. Surg. & Roy. Childr. Hosp. Melbourne.

NAJMI, Syed Muhammad Azizullah Skegness and District Hospital, Dorothy Avenue, Skegness PE25 2BS Tel: 01754 762401 Fax: 01754 760132; 43 Amanda Drive, Louth LN11 0AZ Tel: 01507 604499 Fax: 01507 602005 — MB BS 1962 Sind; MB BS Sind, Pakistan 1962. Assoc. Specialist (A & E & Orthop.) Pilgrim & Assoc. Hosps. NHS Trust. Prev: Regist. (Orthop.) Lonsdale Hosp. Barrow in Furness, Barnsley Dist. Gen. Hosp. & Lancaster Roy. Infirm.

NAKHLA, Labib Shehata (retired) 40 Mount Avenue, Ealing, London W5 2QJ — MB BCh 1957 Ein Shams Univ. Cairo; PhD Lond. 1966; LMSSA Lond. 1969; FRCPath 1986, M 1973; ECFMG Cert 1969; DLO 1959. Prev: Cons. Microbiol. Mt. Vernon Hosp. N.wood & Harefield Hosp.

NAKHLA, Miss Venice 12 Cherrington Way, Solihull B91 3TH Tel: 0121 705 6890 Fax: 0121 705 6890; 40 Mount Avenue, Ealing, London W5 2QJ Tel: 020 8998 5434 Fax: 020 8991 1548 — MB ChB 1990 Liverp. (Liverp.) SHO (ENT) Roy. Liverp. Univ. Hosp.; Specialist Regist. Warwick Hosp. Socs: Brit. Assn. Otorhinolaryngol.; BMA; MDU.

NAKHUDA, Yacoob Ebrahim 41 Gladstone Avenue, Childwall, Liverpool L16 2LG; Flat 27A, Pembroke Court, Pembroke Place, Liverpool L3 5PH Tel: 0151 708 9683 — MB BS 1990 Karachi; MRCP (UK) 1994. Regist. (Radiol.) NWRHA (Mersey) Liverp. Prev: SHO (Med.) Manch. Roy. Infirm. Manch.

NAKIELNY, Edward Antoni Blaennant, Talley, Llandeilo SA19 7YW Tel: 015583 354 — MB 1974 Camb.; BChir 1973. (Univ. Coll. Hosp.) Prev: Ho. Phys. Kingston Gen. Hosp. Hull; Ho. Surg. Hull Roy. Infirm.

NAKIELNY, Edward Antoni (retired) 9 Braids Walk, Kirkella, Hull HU10 7PB Tel: 01482 657963 — MB ChB 1945 Polish Sch. of Med. Prev: Cons. Chest Phys. Chest Clinic Hull, Castle Hill Hosp.

NAKIELNY, Joanna Margaret 9 Braids Walk, Kirk Ella, Hull HU10 7PB — MB ChB 1985 Sheff.

NAKIELNY, Richard Alexander 47 Brooklands Avenue, Sheffield S10 4GB — BM BCh 1977 Oxf.; MA (Camb.) 1975; FRCR 1982. Cons. Radiol. (C.T. Scanning) Roy. Hallamsh. Hosp. Sheff.

NALINASEGAREN, Govindasamy Summerlee Medical Centre, Summerlee Road, Finedon, Wellingborough NN9 5LJ Tel: 01933 682203 Fax: 01933 682205; 136 Rothwell Road, Kettering NN16 8UP Tel: 01536 516828 — MB BS 1976 Madras; MB BS Madras 1973; MRCS Eng. LRCP Lond. 1979; DGM RCP Lond. 1989; DCH RCPS Glas. 1984; DTCH Liverp. 1982. (Christian Med. Coll. Vellore, Madras) Hosp. Pract. (Paediat.) Ketting Gen. Hosp. N.ants. Socs: BMA; (Counc.) Small Pract.s Assn.; Christ. Med. Fell.sh. Prev: Regist. (Paediat.) Kettering Gen. Hosp.; Research Asst. (Paediat. Nephrol.) Alder Hey Hosp. Liverp.; SHO Rotat. (Paediat.) Alder Hey Hosp. Liverp.

NALINI, Chakram Sampath Kumaran 8 Lister Close, Stevenage SG1 4AB — MB BS 1983 Delhi; MRCP (UK) 1991.

NALINI, Velagapudi The Gables, Harold Road, Abergavenny NP7 7DG Tel: 018730 852374 — MB BS 1972 Andhra; DGO Andhra 1974. (Guntur Med. Coll.) Clin. Asst. & Hosp. Specialist (Anaesth.) Gwent HA. Prev: SHO (Anaesth.) New Cross Hosp. Wolverhampton; SHO (Anaesth.) Ipswich Hosp. & Enfield Dist. Hosp.

NALL, Peter Thomas The Surgery, 1493 Stratford Road, Hall Green, Birmingham B28 9HT Tel: 0121 744 1731 — BM BCh 1983 Oxf. GP Birm.

NALLA, Jayasree 7 Hurley Crescent, Marlow Way, Rotherhithe, London SE16 6AL Tel: 020 7231 7387 — MB BS 1973 Andhra; DA (UK) 1983.

NALLA, Mr Ramachandra Rao 5 Dorney Close, Appleton, Warrington WA4 5HY — MB BS 1971 Andhra; FRCS Ed. 1980.

NALLETAMBY, Xavier Philippe Tel: 01273 606006 Fax: 01273 623896; 16 Raphael Road, Hove BN3 5QQ Tel: 01273 729607 — MB BS 1981 Lond.; MRCGP 1987; DRCOG 1986; DCH RCP Lond. 1984. (Lond.) Med. Dir. Brightdocc. Prev: SHO (O & G) Brighton HA; SHO (Paediat.) W.m. Hosp. Lond. & Brighton HA.

NALLIAH, Stanley Jeyaratnam 94 Croydon Road, London SE20 7AB — MB BS 1963 Ceylon.

NALLY, Anthony Patrick Flat 2F1, 30 Craighall Crescent, Edinburgh EH6 4RZ Tel: 0131 552 3819 Email: anthony@hyoid.demon.co.uk; 17 Westwood Street, Accrington BB5 4BW Tel: 01254 383388 — MB ChB 1992 Glas. SHO (Vasc. Surg.) Roy. Infirm. Edin. SHO3 (Plastic Surg.) St John's Livingston; Resid. Med. Off. BUPA Murrayfield Hosp. Edin. Prev: SHO3 (Paediat. Surg.) RHSC Edin.; SHO3 (Vasc. Surg.) Roy. Infirm. Edin.

NALLY, Rhiannon Elise Wansford Surgery, Yarwell Road, Wansford, Peterborough PE8 6PL Tel: 01780 782342 Fax: 01780 783434; 9 Wansford Road, Elton, Peterborough PE8 6RZ Tel: 01832 280361 — MB BCh 1988 Wales; MRCGP 1993; DCH RCP Lond. 1992; DRCOG 1991. (Univ. Coll. Wales) Prev: Trainee GP St. Mary's Med. Centre; SHO (Psychiat. & Paediat.) P'boro. Dist. Hosp.; SHO (ENT) UHW Heath Pk. Cardiff Hosp.

NALPAS, Agnes Claudine 13 Lyttelton Road, Edgbaston, Birmingham B16 9JN — MD 1977 Paris.

***NAM, Helena Patricia** 57/58 The Crescent, Cardiff Road, Llandaff, Cardiff CF5 2DL — MB BCh 1997 Wales.

NAM, Robert Charles Clipstone Health Centre, First Avenue, Clipstone, Mansfield NG21 9DA Tel: 01623 626132 Fax: 01623 420578 — MB BCh 1988 Wales; MRCGP 1993; DCH RCP Lond. 1993. GP Princip. Clipstone Health Centre; Doctor Mansfield Town Football Club. Socs: Christ. Med. Fell. Prev: SHO (Paediat.) P.ss of Wales Hosp. Bridgend; Resid. (Med.) King Edwd. VIII Memor. Hosp., Bermuda; Trainee GP Maesteg Llynfi Surg.

NAM, Sidney 68 Cathedral Road, Cardiff CF11 9LL Tel: 029 2038 8377 Fax: 029 2034 4033 — MB BCh 1960 Wales; MRCPsych 1972; DPM Eng. 1965. Socs: Welsh Psychiat. Soc.; Rhondda Med. Soc. Prev: Self Employed Medico-Legal Psychiat.; Cons. Psychiat. Mid Glam. HA; Resid. Clin. Path. St. Mary's Hosps. Manch.

NAMASIVAYAM, Kumutha South Tanbridge Community Mental Health Team, Church Road, Oxted RH8 9LH; 12 Mountsfield Court, Hither Green Lane, London SE13 6RR Tel: 020 8318 7559 — MB BS 1977 Sri Lanka; LMSSA Lond. 1991.

NAMASIVAYAM, Sivakumar 100 Argyle Street, Cambridge CB1 3LS; 25 Manor Close, Buckden, St Neots, Huntingdon PE19 5XR — BChir 1987 Camb.

NAMBIAR, Suresh Chandroth The Health Centre, Welbeck Street, Castleford WF10 1DP Tel: 01977 465777 Fax: 01977 519342; 51 Shelley Crescent, Oulton, Leeds LS26 8ER — MB BS 1977 Kerala; BSc Kerala 1970; LRCP LRCS Ed. LRCPS Glas. 1987; MRCP (UK) 1990. GP Princip.; Clin. Asst. (Rheum.) W. Yorks. Socs: Roy. Coll. Phys. Prev: Trainee GP Manch.

NAMBISAN, Lakshmanan Sumathy Chapel Street Surgery, 1 Chapel Street, Pelsall, Walsall WS3 4LN Tel: 01922 685858 Fax: 01922 694763 — MB BS 1969 Madras.

NAMDARAN, Mr Farshid 2/6 Craufurdland, Braepark Road, Edinburgh EH4 6DL Tel: 0131 317 8283 — MB ChB 1964 Glas.; MSc Ed. 1983; FRCS Ed. 1968; MFCM RCP (UK) 1985. (Glasgow University) Cons. Pub. Health Med. Lothian HB. Socs: MTh. Ed.2000. Prev: Asst. Prof. Shiraz Univ. Iran; Cons. Surg. Tajrish Med. Centre, Tehran, Iran.

NAMNYAK, Simon Sandett Department of Medical Microbiology, Harold Wood Hospital, Gubbins Lane, Romford RM3 0BE Tel: 01708 345533 Fax: 01708 381486; 30 Sunbury Avenue, Mill Hill, London NW7 3SJ Tel: 020 8906 8493 Fax: 020 8906 8493 Email: 100142.744@compuserve.com — MD 1975 Dar-es-Salaam, Tanzania; PhD Lond. 1981; FRCPath 1994, M 1983; T(Path) 1991. (Univ. Dar-es-Salaam, Tanzania) Cons.Infec. control doctor.

Microbiol. Havering Hosps. NHS Trust Romford Essex. Socs: Assn. Clin. Path.; Assn. Med. Microbiol.; Hosp. Infec. Soc. Prev: Cons. Med. Microbiol. Altnagelvin Area Hosp. Lond.derry; Cons. Med. Microbiol. Regional Laborat. & Blood Bank, Saudi Arabia; Regist. (Med. Microbiol.) St Stephen's Hosp. Lond.

NANA, Ahmed 4 Gipsy Road, Leicester LE4 6QH Tel: 0116 266 5835 — MB ChB 1994 Birm.; MB ChB (Hons.) Birm. 1994.

NANABAWA, Hashim Ismail (branch Surgery) The Mount, 60 High Road, Earlsheaton, Dewsbury WF13 4HR Tel: 01924 465511; Hyrst House, 8 Track Road, Batley WF17 7AA — MB BS 1960 Baroda; DLO Baroda 1962. (Med. Coll. Baroda)

NANAVATI, B T John Amery Drive Surgery, 14 John Amery Drive, Rising Brook, Stafford ST17 9LZ Tel: 01785 252244 — MB BS 1971 Gujarat; MB BS 1971 Gujarat.

NANAVATI, Bharatkumar Anant Ailsa Craig Medical Group, 270 Dickenson Road, Longsight, Manchester M13 0YL Tel: 0161 224 5555 Fax: 0161 248 9112; 60 Hilltop Ave, Cheadle Hulme, Cheadle SK8 7HY Tel: 0161 486 1804 Fax: 0161 486 1804 — MB ChB 1980 Manch.; Dip. Occ. Med. 1998; MRCGP 1984; DRCOG 1983. p/t Clin. Asst. Pheum. - Univ. Hosp. S. Manch.; Hosp. Practitioner Univ. Hosp. S. Manch.

NANAVATI, C B John Amery Drive Surgery, 14 John Amery Drive, Rising Brook, Stafford ST17 9LZ Tel: 01785 252244 — MB BS 1973 Indore; MB BS 1973 Indore.

NANAVATI, Mayur Kumar Glendale Medical Centre, 155 High Street, Harlington, Hayes UB3 5DA Tel: 020 8897 8288 Fax: 020 8754 1539 — MB ChB 1983 Manch.; MRCGP 1989; DA 1985. (Manchester) GP Princip.; Clin. Asst. (Anaesth.) Hillingdon Hosp.

NANAVATI, Nayan Arvindbhai Barmston Medical Centre, Westerhope Road, Washington NE38 8JF Tel: 0191 419 0333 Fax: 0191 419 0444 — MB BS 1971 Gujarat. (B.J. Med. Coll. Ahmedabad)

NANAVATY, S 1 Chambres Road, Southport PR8 6JG.

NANAYAKKARA, Charithananda Surasena Kettering General Hospital, Rothwell Road, Kettering NN16 8UZ Tel: 01536 492112 — MB BS 1965 Ceylon; FRCP Lond. 1994; MRCP (UK) 1980; FRCPCH 1997; DCH RCP Lond.; T(M) 1991. (Fac. Med. Colombo (Univ. Ceylon)) Cons. Paediat. Kettering Gen. Hosp. N.ants. Socs: BMA; MDU. Prev: Cons. Paediat. Grantham & Kesteven Hosps.; Sen. Regist. (Paediat.) Radcliffe Infirm. Oxf.

NANAYAKKARA, Gamini (retired) 4 Elliswick Road, Harpenden AL5 4TP — MB BS 1963 Ceylon; MB BS (2nd Cl. Hons.) Ceylon 1963; MRCPsych 1977; DPM Eng. 1975. Gen. Hosp. Hemel Hempstead. Prev: Cons. Psychiat. Ment. Illness Hill End Hosp. St. Albans & W. Herts Gen. Hosp. Hemel Hempstead.

***NANAYAKKARA, Ishanthi** 4 Elliswick Road, Harpenden AL5 4TP — MB BS 1998 Lond.; MB BS Lond 1998; BSc (Hons) 1993.

NANCARROW, Mr Jeffrey Douglas 81 Harborne Road, Edgbaston, Birmingham B15 3HG Tel: 0121 455 9496 Fax: 0121 455 0288 — MRCS Eng. LRCP Lond. 1969; BSc (Anat.) Lond. 1966, MB BS 1969; FRCS Eng. 1975. (St. Thos.) p/t Cons. Plastic & Reconstruc. & Hand Surg. W. Midl.s Regional Burns & Plastic Surg. Centre Selly Oak Hosp. Raddlebarn Rd, Selly Oak, Birm.; Cons. Plastic & Reconstruc. Surg., Qu.s Hosp., Burton NHS Trust Burton-on-Trent, Staffs. Socs: Brit. Assn. Plastic Surg.; Brit. Soc. Surg. Hand.; Brit. Med. Assn. Prev: Cons. Plastic & Reconstruc. Surg. W. Midl. Regional Plastic Surg. Unit, Wordsley Hosp., Stourbridge.

NANCARROW, Jenny Georgina Ground Floor Flat, 33 Wrentham Avenue, London NW10 3HS — MB ChB 1992 Birm.; MRCGP 1997; DRCOG 1996. (Birm.)

NANCARROW, Julie Accident and Emergency, Warwick HoSPITAL, Lakin Rd, Warwick CV34 5BW Tel: 01926 495321; Rowans, Longworth Road, Billington, Clitheroe BB7 9TS — MB ChB 1986 Manch.; MRCGP 1990; DRCOG 1990; FRCS Ed. 1994; Dip. IMC RCS Ed. 1995; DA 1994. Cons. (A & E) Warwick Hosp. Socs: FFAEM. Prev: Sen. Regist. (A & E) N. W. Region; Cons. (A & E) Blackburn Roy. Infirm.

NANCEKIEVILL, David Guy 50 Ormonde Terrace, Regents Park, London NW8 7LR Tel: 020 7586 5685 Fax: 020 7586 5685; Cintra, Marley Lane, Haslemere GU27 3RG — MB BS 1964 Lond.; MRCS Eng. LRCP Lond. 1964; FFA RCS Eng. 1967; DA Eng. 1966. (Guy's) Cons. Anaesth. Harley St. Lond. Socs: Assn. of Amaesthetists; Assn. of Dent. Anaesth.s; Dent. Soc. of Lond. Prev: Dir. (Anaesth. Servs.), Cons. Anaesth. & Sen. Cons. ITU St. Bart. Hosp. Lond.; Sen. Regist.

& Resid. Anaesth. Guy's Hosp.; Regist. (Anaesth.) Guy's Hosp., St. Bart. Hosp. & Roy. N.. Hosp. Lond.

NANCEKIEVILL, Leslie (retired) Gibbs Corner, Oak Hill, East Budleigh, Budleigh Salterton EX9 7DW Tel: 01395 442101 — MB BS 1939 Lond.; MD Lond. 1947; FRCP Lond. 1969, M 1946; MRCS Eng. LRCP Lond. 1938. Prev: Sen. Regist. (Med.) United Sheff. Hosps.

NANCEKIEVILL, Martin Leslie Fairacre, Fairfield Road, Shawford, Winchester SO21 2DA Tel: 01962 714320 Fax: 01962 714264 — MB BS 1972 Lond.; MRCS Eng. LRCP Lond. 1972; FFA RCS Eng. 1977; DA Eng. 1974. (Guy's) Cons. Anaesth. Winchester Health Dist. Socs: Assn. Anaesths. Gt. Brit. & Irel.; BMA. Prev: Sen. Regist. (Anaesth.) Winchester & Soton. Health Dist. Regist.; (Anaesth.) Guy's Hosp. Lond. & Brighton Health Dist.; Resid. Anaesth. Guy's Hosp. Lond.

NANCHAHAL, Mr Jagdeep Department of Plastic Surgery, Charing Cross Hospital, Fulham Palace Road, London W6 8RF Tel: 020 8846 1790 Fax: 020 8846 1719 Email: j.nanchahal@ic.ac.uk — MB BS 1985 Lond.; PhD Lond. 1982, BSc 1980; FRCS (Plast) 1996; FRCS Ed. 1989; FRCS Eng. 1989. Sen. Lect. And Hon. Cons. (Plastic Surg.) Char. Cross Hosp. Lond. & Chelsea & W.minister Hosp.

NANCOLLAS, Christopher Edward Yorkley Health Centre, Bailey Hill, Yorkley, Lydney GL15 4RS Tel: 01594 562437 — MB BS 1978 Lond.; FFA RCSI 1984.

NANDA, Balbir Sain (retired) Castle Hill Hospital, Cottingham HU16 5JQ Tel: 01482 875875 — MB BS 1959 Agra; BSc Lucknow 1954; FRCP Lond. 1986; MRCP (UK) 1972. Cons. Phys. Castle Hill Hosp. Cottingham.

NANDA, Deepak 51 Ash Grove, Heston, Hounslow TW5 9DU — MB BS 1987 Lond.

NANDA, Mr Kalyan Kumar Department of Radiology, Burton Hospital NHS Trust, Burton-on-Trent Tel: 01283 66333; Redhill House, 5 Redhill Lane, Tutbury, Burton-on-Trent DE13 9JN Tel: 01283 814494 — MB BS 1968 Calcutta; MS Delhi 1972; FRCS Ed. 1976; FRCR 1986. (Med. Coll. Calcutta) Cons. Radiol. Burton Hosp. NHS Trust. Prev: Regist. (Diag. Radiol.) W. Midl. RHA.

NANDA, Nibedita Rickleton Medical Centre, Vigo Lane, Rickleton, Washington NE38 9EJ Tel: 0191 415 0576 — LRCP LRCS Ed. LRCPS Glas. 1982; MB BS Utkal 1979.

NANDA, Umesh Chandra Rickleton Medical Centre, Vigo Lane, Rickleton, Washington NE38 9EJ Tel: 0191 415 0576 — MB BS 1973 Utkal.

NANDADEVA, Mr Pinnawalalage Gedara 562 Green Lanes, London N13 5SA — MB BS 1967 Ceylon; FRCS Eng. 1976.

NANDAGOPAL, Mr Narayanan 20 Kenworthy Gardens, Holt Park, Leeds LS16 7QT Tel: 0113 261 3260 — MB BS 1977 Madras; FRCS Eng. 1983; FRCS Glas. 1983; LMS 1984.

NANDAKUMAR, Calathur Ganapathy c/o Mr. R. Nair, 41 Oakfield Road, Eastham, London E6 1LN Tel: 020 8470 2460 — MB BS 1979 Madras; FFA RCSI 1992.

NANDAKUMAR, Elamana Department of Diagnostic Radiology, Blackburn Royal Infirmary, Bolton Road, Blackburn BB2 Tel: 01254 63555; 95 Rogersfield, Langho, Blackburn BB6 8HD Tel: 01254 240767 — MD 1982 Madras; MB BS Kerala 1978; FRCR 1986. Cons. Radiol. Blackburn Roy. Infirm. Prev: Sen. Regist. (Radiol.) Withington Hosp. Manch.; Regist. (Radiol.) Manch. Gp. Hosps.

NANDAKUMAR, Kalyana Naidu Department of Anaesthesia, Kingston Hospital, Galsworthy Road, Kingston upon Thames KT2 7QB — MB BS 1980 Madras; FFA RCSI 1989.

NANDAKUMAR, Komath Marshall's Road Surgery, 7 Marshall's Road, Raunds, Wellingborough NN9 6ET Tel: 01933 622349 Fax: 01933 625421; Tel: 01933 622654 — MB BS 1972 Mysore; DA Eng. 1979. (Kasturba Med. Coll.) Regist. (Anaesth.) Kettering Dist. Gen. Hosp. Prev: SHO (Anaesth.) St. Chas. Hosp. Lond.; SHO & Regist. (Anaesth.) Kettering & Dist. Gen. Hosp.

NANDANWAR, Chetana 34 Princes Way, London SW19 6QP — MB ChB 1976 Manch.; FFA RCS 1982; DA 1980.

NANDAPALAN, Mr Velanthapillai 6 Pinnington Road, Whiston, Prescot L35 3TY — MRCS Eng. LRCP Lond. 1986; FRCS Ed. 1992.

***NANDASOMA, Udvitha Charatha** 23 Worcester Road, Lodge Moor, Sheffield S10 4JH — BChir 1996 Camb.

NANDHABALAN

NANDHABALAN, Kanagasingham 17 London Road, Stanmore HA7 4PA — MB BS 1972 Sri Lanka; LRCP LRCS Ed. LRCPS Glas. 1983; DLO RCS Eng. 1981.

NANDHRA, Harpal Singh 332 New North Road, Hainault, Ilford IG6 3BZ — MB BS 1998 Lond.; MB BS Lond 1998.

NANDI, Ann Christine Surrey & Sussex Healthcare Trust, Crawley Hospital, Department of Haematology, West Green Drive, Crawley RH11 7DH Tel: 01293 600300 Fax: 01293 525716 Email: ac.nandi@doctors.org.uk — MB BS 1979 Lond.; MRCP (UK) 1982; MRCPath 1987; FRCP 1998; FRCPath 1997. (University College London) Cons. Haemat. Crawley Hosp. Prev: Sen. Regist. (Haemat.) Roy. Marsden Hosp. Sutton & St. Geo. Hosp. Tooting.

NANDI, Bipul Chandra The Ridgeway Surgery, 93 The Ridgeway, Chingford, London E4 7HS Tel: 020 8529 6479 Fax: 020 8523 7341 — MB BS 1972 Calcutta.

NANDI, Debal K Tower Hill Medical Centre, 25 Tower Hill, Great Barr, Birmingham B42 1LG Tel: 0121 357 1077 — MB BS 1967 Calcutta; MB BS 1967 Calcutta.

NANDI, Lisa Reema Sarah Neera Flat 4, 19 Shepherds Hill, London N6 5QJ — MB BS 1992 Lond.

NANDI, Paul Romen Department of Anaesthetics, National Hospital for Neurology & Neurosurgery, Queen Square, London WC1N 3BG; 2 Salehurst Road, Worth, Crawley RH10 7GL — MB BS 1977 Lond.; MRCP (UK) 1982; FFA RCS Eng. 1986. Cons. Anaesth. Nat. Hosp. Neurol. & Neurosurg. Lond. Prev: Sen. Regist. (Anaesth.) Bloomsbury HA.

NANDI, Runa 19 Bittacy Rise, London NW7 2HH — MB BS 1992 Lond.

NANDI, Santi Ranjan Wigan & Leigh Health Services NHS Trust, Wigan Infirmary, Wigan Lane, Wigan WN1 2NN Tel: 01942 244000 — MB BS 1967 Gauhati; FRCPS Glas. 1991; MRCP (UK) 1977; DCH Eng. 1970. Cons. Phys. (Elderly Med.) Wigan Infirm. & Leigh Infirm. Lancs. Socs: Brit. Geriat. Soc.

NANDI, Mr Satyanarayan Kingston Medical Group, 151 Beverley Road, Hull HU3 1TY Tel: 01482 328861 — MB BS 1961 Calcutta; FRCS Ed. 1973. (N.R.S. Med. Coll. Calcutta) Socs: Hull Med. Soc.; BMA. Prev: Clin. Asst. (Gen. Surg.) Kingston Gen. Hosp. Hull; Clin. Asst. (Venereol.) Hull Roy. Infirm.; Regist. (Gen. Surg.) Huddersfield Roy. Infirm.

NANDRA, Hardip Singh Tel: 020 8472 4888 Fax: 020 8472 5777; 14 Alloa Road, Goodmayes, Ilford IG3 9SP — MB ChB 1985 Glas.; MBA Univ. Keele 1996; MRCGP 1989; DFFP 1996; DRCOG 1989. Charges Non-Exec. Dir. ELCHA. Prev: GP Auckland, NZ; GP Ilford; Trainee GP/SHO Newham Hosp. Lond. VTS.

NANDRA, Jasvendar Singh St Albans Medical Centre, 26-28 St. Albans Crescent, Bournemouth BH8 9EW Tel: 01202 517333; 61 Huntly Road, Talbot Woods, Bournemouth BH3 7HQ Tel: 01202 534824 — MB ChB 1981 Manch.; BSc St. And. 1978; LicAc 1995; DA (UK) 1985. Socs: Brit. Acupunc. Assn.

NANDRA, Kanwalpal Singh Bulbanks Medical Centre, 62 Battle Road, Erith DA8 1BJ Tel: 01322 432997 Fax: 01322 442324 — MB BS 1981 Bihar.

NANDRA, Surjit Singh 5 Clive Road, Belvedere DA17 5BJ — BM 1995 Soton.

NANDWANI, Naresh 35 Ravenswood Road, Bristol BS6 6BW — BM BS 1988 Nottm.

NANDWANI, Rak Department of Genitourinary Medicine, The Sandyford Iniative, 6 Sandyford Place, Glasgow G3 7NB Tel: 0141 211 8608, 0141 211 8610 Fax: 0141 211 8609 Email: Rak.Nandwani@glacomen.scot.nhs.uk — MB BS 1985 Lond.; MRCP (UK) 1991; DFFP 1993. (Middlx. Hosp.) Assoc. Director, The Sandyford Initiative, Gt.er Glas. Primary Care NHS Trust; Hon. Clin. Sen. Lect. Univ. Glas. Socs: Med. Soc. Study VD Fell.; Med Soc Stud VD Counc. Mem.; Med Soc Stud VD Scott. Br. Sec. Prev: Cons. HIV & Genitourin. Med. Glas. Roy. Infirm.; Regist. (HIV Med.) St. Stephens Clinic & Chelsea & W.m. Hosp. Lond.; Sen. Regist. (HIV & Genitourin Med.) King's Coll. Hosp. Lond. & Roy. Sussex Co. Hosp. Brighton.

NANDY, Anita Margaret 4 St Johns Close, Welwyn AL6 9RB — BM BS 1993 Nottm.

NANDY, Debanjan 10 Steping Stone, Highfield, Goytre, Usk NP5 0RP — MB BS 1970 Dacca.

NANDY, Mihir Kanti Doctor's Residence, Hexham General Hospital, Hexham NE46 1QJ — MB BS 1963 Dacca. (Dacca) Assoc. Specialist Spinal Injuries Unit Hexham Gen. Hosp. Prev: SHO (Orthop. Surg.) Sanderson (W.J.) Orthop. Hosp. Gosforth; SHO (Orthop. Surg.) St. Hilda's Hosp. Hartlepool; SHO (Orthop. Surg.) Peel Hosp. Galashiels.

NANDY, Sudip Kumar 38A Carnarvon Road, London E18 2NU — MB BS 1991 Lond.; MRCGP 1996; DCH RCP Lond. 1994; Dip. Obst. Auckland 1994. (Lond. Hosp.)

NANGALIA, Mr Ramlal 215 Hinckley Road, Nuneaton CV11 6LL — MB BS 1972 Utkal; MS Utkal 1977; FRCS Ed. 1980.

NANJIANI, Mr Magsoodali Ross Hall Hospital, Crookston Road, Glasgow G52 3NQ Tel: 0141 810 3151; 24 Dunobin Avenue, Elderslie, Johnstone PA5 9NW Tel: 01505 346038 — MB BS 1958 Punjab; MB BS Punjab (Pakistan) 1958; FRCS Ed. 1972; FCOphth 1988; DOMS RCPSI 1964; DO Eng. 1963. (King Edwd. Med. Coll. Lahore) JP.; Cons. Ophth. Surg. Eye Dept. Roy. Ross Hall Hosp. Crookston Rd. Glas. Socs: Fac. Ophthalmol. Prev: Ho. Surg. St. Helen's Hosp. Hastings; Cas. Off. Roy. E. Sussex Hosp. Hastings; Ho. Phys. Gartloch Hosp. Glas.

NANKANI, Angana Jay 6 Ffordd Ystrad, Wrexham LL13 7QQ — MB ChB 1998 Liverp.; MB ChB Liverp 1998.

NANKANI, Mr Jayprakash Navalram Hill Crest Medical Centre, 86 Holt Road, Wrexham LL13 8RG Tel: 01978 262193 Fax: 01978 310193 (Call before faxing); 6 Ffordd Ystrad, Coed-y-Glyn, Wrexham LL13 7QQ Tel: 01978 262893 Fax: 01978 262893 — MB BS 1972 Gujarat; MS Gujarat 1976, MB BS 1972. Clin. Asst. (Orthop.) Maelor Gen. Hosp. Wrexham.

NANKHONYA, Joseph McLagen Stepping Hill Hospital, Poplar Grove, Stockport SK2 7JE Tel: 0161 483 1010 Fax: 0161 419 4356 Email: jnankhonya@aol.com; 3 Holly Grange, Bramhall, Stockport SK7 3PP Tel: 0161 440 7841 Fax: 0161 440 7841 — MB ChB 1981 Manch.; BSc Malawi 1976; MRCP (UK) 1988; FRCP Irel. 1998. (Manchester) Cons. Phys. Gen. & Geriat. Med. Stepping Hill Hosp. & St Thomas Hosp. Stockport. Socs: Fell. Roy. Soc. Med.; BMA; Brit. Geriat. Soc. Prev: Sen. Regist. (Gen. & Geriat. Med.) N. W.. RHA; Regist. Rotat. (Med.) Liverp. & Wirral.

NANKIVELL, Muriel (retired) 77 Pereira Road, Birmingham B17 9JA — MB ChB 1957 Birm.; DObst RCOG 1975. Med. Assessor Benefits Agency. Prev: GP Kingstanding.

NANSON, Eileen Margaret 71 Kingswood Road, Wimbledon, London SW19 3ND Tel: 020 8542 4004 — MB BCh 1962 Camb. (St. Bart.) Med. Advis. DSS Lond. Prev: Clin. Asst. (Chest Med.) St. Geo. Hosp. Lond.; Research Fell. (Med. Ophth.) Roy. Postgrad. Med. Sch. Lond.; Clin. Asst. (Disabil. Support Team) Kingston Hosp. Surrey.

NANSON, Justine Katherine La Playa, Coast Road, St Clement, Jersey JE2 6SB — MB ChB 1990 Bristol; FRCA 1996; DCH RCP Lond. 1995. (Univ. Bristol) Specialist Regist. (Anaesth.) Soton. Gen. Hosp.

NANSON, Patricia 20 Mitchell Avenue, Jesmond, Newcastle upon Tyne NE2 3LA — MB BS 1977 Newc.; MRCGP 1981; DRCOG 1980. GP DSS.

NANU KANDIYIL, Vaniya 5-7 Norcot Road, Tilehurst, Reading RG30 6BP — FRCOG Lond.; MB BS 1971 Kerala; MRCOG Lond.

NAOUM, Hikmat George 5 Hornby Close, London NW3 3JL — MB ChB 1974 Baghdad; MRCOG 1984.

NAOUMOV, Nikolai Vesselinov Institute of Hepatology, University College London Medical School, 69-75 Chenies Mews, London WC1E 6HX Tel: 020 7388 2013 Fax: 020 7380 0405 Email: n.naoumov@ucl.ac.uk; 78 Lavenham Road, Southfields, London SW18 5HE Tel: 020 8870 6086 Fax: 020 8870 6086 — State Exam Med 1978 Sofia; MD Med. Acad. Sofia 1985; DSc Med. Acad. Sofia 1991; MRCPath Lond. 1998. Sen. Lect. (Hepat.) Univ. Coll. Lond. Med. Sch.; Hon. Cons. Phys. UCL. Hosps. NHS Trust. Socs: BASL; EASL; AASLD.

NAOUMOVA, Rossitza Petkova MRC Molecular Medicine, MRC Clinical Sciences Centre, Hammersmith Hospital, Du Cane Road, London W12 0NN Tel: 0208 383 1346 Fax: 0208 383 2028 Email: rossi.naoumova@csc.murc.ac.uk — State Exam Med 1978 Acad. Med. Sofia, Bulgaria; 1998 U.K; Dip Metabol Dis State Exam Med. Academy Sofia, Bulgaria 1981; Dip Internal Med State Exam Bd Sofia, Bulgaria 1985. (Sofia, Bulgaria) MRC Clin. Scientist Lipid Clinic,Hammersmith Hosp. and Hon. Cons. Phys. In Molecular Med. Hammersmith Hosp. Lond. Socs: Comm. Mem. Brit. Hyperlipidaemia Assn.; Amer. Heart Assn.; Brit. Med. Soc.

*NAPIER, Alex James Carmel, Low St., East Markham, Newark NG22 0QQ — MB ChB 1998 Liverp.; MB ChB Liverp 1998.

NAPIER, Alison Madelaine Avondale Unit, Royal Preston Hospital, Preston — MB ChB 1991 Bristol; DRCOG 1994; MRCGP 1995; MRC Psych 1997. (Bristol) Specialist Regist. Psychiat. N. W. Rotat.(Manch.). Socs: RCGP; MRCPsych.

NAPIER, Anne Christine 8 Woodhead Drive, Orpington BR6 9RD — MB ChB 1968 Aberd.

NAPIER, David Charles The Surgery, Marlborough, Seaham SR7 7TS Tel: 0191 581 2866 Fax: 0191 513 0393 — MB ChB 1979 Sheffield; MB ChB Sheff 1979. (Sheffield) GP Seaham, Co. Durh.

NAPIER, Donna Elizabeth The Crescent Medical Practice, 12 Walmer Crescent, Glasgow G51 1AT Tel: 0141 427 0191 Fax: 0141 427 1581; 38 Addison Road, Glasgow G12 0TT — MB ChB 1979 Glas.

NAPIER, Elizabeth Susan 11 Polnoon Street, Eaglesham, Glasgow G76 0BH — MB ChB 1965 Ed.; MB ChB Ed.1965.

*NAPIER, Eoin Dominic 13 St Patricks Road, Saul, Downpatrick BT30 7JG — MB BCh BAO 1995 Belf.

NAPIER, Hilary Barbara Bridge Cottage Surgery, 41 High Street, Welwyn AL6 9EF Tel: 01438 715044 Fax: 01438 714013 — MB BS 1981 Lond.; BSc (Psychol.) Lond. 1978; MRCGP (Distinc.) 1986; DRCOG 1983. (Univ. Coll. Hosp.) Trainee GP Lond. Prev: SHO (Paediat.) & (O & G) Edgware Gen. Hosp.; Ho. Phys. (Cardiol.) Whittington Hosp. Lond.

NAPIER, Ian Gordon Donnybrook House Group Practice, Clarendon Street, Hyde SK14 2AH Tel: 0161 368 3838 Fax: 0161 368 2210; Rye Flatt, Combs, Chapel-en-le-Frith, High Peak SK23 9UY Tel: 01298 812844 — MB ChB 1970 Manch. GP Hyde; Clin. Asst. (Anaesth.) Tameside Gen. Hosp. Prev: SHO (Anaesth.) Manch. Roy. Infirm.; SHO (O & G) Crumpall Hosp.; GP Stockport.

NAPIER, Isabella Ross Rothmar, 43 South Avenue, Thornly Park, Paisley PA2 7SG Tel: 0141 884 3201 — MB ChB 1948 Ed.; DPH 1960; MRCOG 1958. Cons. (Genitourin. Med.) Roy. Infirm. Glas. Prev: Sen. Regist. (O & G) S.. Gen. Hosp. Glas.; Regist. (Obst.) Area Dept. Dumfries; Ho. Phys. & Ho. Surg. Dumfries & Galloway Roy. Infirm.

NAPIER, Jacqueline Claire Schering Health Care Ltd, The Brow, Burgess Hill RH15 9NE — MB ChB 1987 Birm.; MB ChB Hons.) Birm. 1987; BSc (Hons.) Birm. 1984; MRCP (UK) 1990; MFPM RCP Lond. 1997; Dip. Pharm. Med. RCP (UK) 1992. Assoc. Med. Dir. Schering Healthcare Ltd. W. Sussex. Prev: SHO (Gen. Med.) Sandwell Dist. Gen. Hosp.; Ho. Off. (Gen. Surg.) E. Birm. Hosp.; Ho. Off. (Gen. Med. & Neurol.) Qu. Eliz. Hosp. Birm.

NAPIER, James Alexander 86 Ennerdale Road, Richmond TW9 2DL — MB ChB 1993 Ed.

NAPIER, Jane Margaret 11 Polnoon Street, Eaglesham, Glasgow G76 0BH — MB ChB 1992 Ed.

NAPIER, Janet Elizabeth Manchester Road Surgery, 280 Manchester Road, Warrington WA1 3RB Tel: 01925 230022 Fax: 01925 575069; 80 Whitbarrow Road, Lymm WA13 9BA Tel: 01925 754825 — MB BS Lond. 1968; MRCS Eng. LRCP Lond. 1968; DMJ(Clin) Soc. Apoth. Lond. 1993; DCH Eng. 1971; DObst RCOG 1970. (St. Bart.) Police Surg Chesh. & Merseyside; Asst. Dep. Coroner Chesh. Socs: BMA; Assn. Police Surg.; Jun. Sec. Sect. Clin. Forens. & Legal Med. Roy. Soc. Med. Prev: SHO (Obst.) Luton & Dunstable Hosp.; Ho. Phys. (Child Health) St. Bart. Hosp. Lond.; Ho. Surg. (Orthop.) St. Bart. Hosp. Lond.

NAPIER, John Anthony Francis (retired) Rhyd-Y-Gwern Farm, Lower Machen, Newport NP10 8GJ Tel: 01633 441194 Email: napier@which.net — MB BS 1964 Lond.; PhD Camb. 1972; BSc Lond. 1961, MB BS 1964; FRCPath M 1972. Cons. Haematolog. Prev: Wellcome Research Fell. Dept. Pathol. Univ. Camb.

NAPIER, John Francis (retired) Alderslade, 125 Derby Road, Aston-on-Trent, Derby DE72 2AE Tel: 01332 792657 — LRCPI & LM, LRCSI & LM 1949. Vis. Gen. Pract. Aston Hall Hosp. Aston-on-Trent. Prev: Dep. Civil. Med. Off. RAF.

NAPIER, Mr John Gordon (retired) 68 Wragby Road, Lincoln LN2 4PH Tel: 01522 526083 — MB ChB Ed. 1940; FRCS Ed. 1948; FRCOG 1964, M 1950. Prev: Cons. O & G Lincoln Co. Hosp.

NAPIER, Karen Claire The Redcliffe Surgery, 10 Redcliffe Street, London SW10 9DT Tel: 020 7460 2222 Fax: 020 7460 0116 — MB BChir 1988 Camb.; MRCGP 1992.

*NAPIER, Noel Joseph 13 St Patricks Road, Downpatrick BT30 7JG — MB BCh BAO 1997 Belf.

NAPIER, Ramsay Brotchie (retired) 4 Sletts Park, Lerwick ZE1 0LN Tel: 01595 693716 — MB ChB 1960 Glas.; DObst RCOG 1963.

NAPIER, Thomas George (retired) 11 Polnoon Street, Eaglesham, Glasgow G76 0BH — MB ChB 1960 St. And.; MRCGP 1978; MRCOG 1969.

NAPIER-HEMY, Mr Richard Donald Department of Urology, Manchester Royal Infirmary, Oxford Road, Manchester M13 9WL Tel: 0161 276 4312 Fax: 0161 276 4221; 73 Higher Lane, Lymm WA13 0BZ Tel: 01925 753222 Email: nchardnh@hotmail.com — MB ChB 1988 Manch.; BSc (Med. Sci.) St. And. 1985; FRCS Ed. 1994; FRCS (Urol) 1998. (Manchester) Cons. (Urol.Surg.) Mans. Roy. Infirm. Socs: Brit. Assn. Urol. Surg.; Brit. Soc. for Endocrinol. Prev: Specialist Regist. (Urol.) Manch. Roy. Infirm., Specialists Regist. (Urol.) Preston Roy. Hosp.; Regist. (Urol.) Hope Hosp. Salford Roy. Hosp., Specialists Regist. (Urol.) Withington. Hosp.; Regist. (Urol.) Stockport Acute Servs. NHS Trust.

NAPPER, Adrian John Drumhar Health Centre, North Methven Street, Perth PH1 5PD Tel: 01738 621726 — MB ChB 1970 Aberd.; MRCGP 1976. GP Princip., Perth. Prev: SHO Tayside Health Bd.; SHO (Paediat.) Darlington Memor. Hosp.; Med. Off. Ch. of Scotl. Miss. Hosp. Qumbu, S. Africa.

NAPPER, Alexandra Mary Sophia Plenty House, Shipton Lane, Burton Bradstock, Bridport DT6 4NQ Tel: 01308 898259; Joseph Weld Hospice, Herrington Road, Dorchester DT1 2 — BM 1991 Soton.; MRCGP 1995. Med. Off. Joseph Weld Hospice Dorchester.

NAPTHINE, Edith Ellen 76 Private Road, Mapperley, Nottingham NG3 5FQ Tel: 0115 969 1255 — MB ChB 1944 Bristol. (Bristol)

NAQESH-BANDI, Mr Hasan Abdulla University Hospital of Hartlepool, Holforth Road, Hartlepool TS24 9AH; 26 Pinewood Close, Hartlepool TS27 3QU — MB ChB Baghdad 1969; FRCS Ed. 1981; FRCS Glas. 1980. Cons. Gen. Surg. (Surgic. Gastroenterol., Gastrointestinal Endoscopy & Lazerscopic Surg.), Univ. Hosp. of Hartlepool. Socs: Fell. Assn. Surgs.; Assn. Coloproctol.; N. Eng. Surgic. Soc.

NAQUI, Fatima Ahmed Parkside Medical Centre, 187 Northmoor Road, Longsight, Manchester M12 5RU Tel: 0161 257 3338 Fax: 0161 257 3338; 387 Wilbraham Road, Chorlton, Manchester M21 0UT Tel: 0161 881 3969 Fax: 0161 257 0205 — MB BS 1970 Punjab; MB BS (Hons.) Punjab 1970; MRCS Eng. LRCP Lond. 1979; Cert. Prescribed Equiv. Exp. JCPTGP 1982; DRCOG 1981. (Nishtar Med. Coll. Multan, Pakistan) Socs: BMA; Fam. Plann. & Contracep. Assn.; Pakistan Med. Assn. Prev: Wom. Med. Off. Burewala, Multan; SHO (Geriat. & O & G) Tameside Gen. Hosp. Ashton-under-Lyne; SHO (O & G) Pk. Hosp. Davy Hulme.

NAQVI, Ahmad Tunveer Cheshunt Medical Centre, 11 Cromwell Avenue, Cheshunt, Waltham Cross EN7 5DL Tel: 01992 624732 — MB BS 1970 Punjab; MB BS Punjab (Pakistan) 1970; DPH Eng. 1976. (King Edwd. Med. Coll. Lahore) Socs: FRIPHH.

NAQVI, Nayyar Royal Albert Edward Infirmary, Wigan WN1 2NN Tel: 01942 44000 — MB BS 1968 Karachi; FRCP Lond. 1995; FRCP Ed. 1986; MRCP (UK) 1975. (Dow Med. Coll. Karachi) Cons. Phys. & Cardiol. Roy. Albert Edwd. Infirm. Wigan. Socs: Fell. Europ. Soc. of Cardiol.; BMA & Mem. Brit. Cardiac Soc. Prev: Regist. Rotat. (Cardiothoracic Med.) Wythenshawe Hosp. Manch.; Kleinwort Research Fell. Dept. Cardiol. & Sen. Cardiac Research Fell.; (Hon. Sen. Regist.) St. Thos. Hosp. Lond.

NAQVI, Salma Batool 26 Chertsey Street, Tooting Broadway, London SW17 8LG — MB BS 1973 Karachi.

NAQVI, Sarah Doctor's Mess, Leicester General Hospital, Gwendolen Road, Leicester LE5 4PW — MB ChB 1993 Leic.

NAQVI, Syed Mohammad Haider 54 Kilworth Drive, Lostock, Bolton BL6 4RL Tel: 01204 494931; 7 Manchester Road, Walkden, Worsley, Manchester M28 3NS Tel: 0161 790 3132 — MB BS 1979 Aligarh; MB BS Aligarh Muslim 1979; Dip. Orthop. Surg. Aligarh Muslim 1972. Clin. Asst. (Orthop. Surg.) Bolton Roy. Infirm. Prev: Regist. (Orthop. Surg.) Walton Hosp. Liverp.; Regist. (Accid. & Orthop.) Coventry & Warks. Hosp.; SHO (Geriat. Med.) Billinge Hosp.

*NAQVI, Syed Mohammed Asim 8 Taunton Avenue, Hounslow TW3 4AF — MB BS 1996 Lond.

NAQVI

NAQVI, Syed Nasim Hasan 47 Regent Road, Lostock, Bolton BL6 4DG Tel: 01204 47111 — MB BS 1962 Punjab (Pakistan); FFA RCS Eng. 1970; DA Eng. 1967. (Nishtar Med. Coll. Multan) Cons. Anaesth. Bolton Roy. Infirm. Socs: Assn. Anaesths. & Obst. Anaesths. Assn. Prev: Sen. Regist. (Anaesth.) Manch. Roy. Infirm.; Sen. Regist. (Obst. Analgesia & Anaesth.) King's Coll. Hosp. Lond.; Regist. (Anaesth.) Alder Hey Childr. Hosp. Liverp.

*****NARAD, Parveen Kumari** 95 Himley Road, Dudley DY1 2QF — MB BS 1996 Lond.

NARAGHI, Arash Hajabdolazim 13 Dame Elizabeth Court, Puddings Wood Lane, Broomfield, Chelmsford CM1 7WE — MB BS 1996 Lond.

NARAIN, Mr Bipin Garrick Hospital, Edinburgh Road, Stranraer DG9 7HQ Tel: 01776 702323 Fax: 01776 889102; 16 Abington Road, Dunfermline KY12 7XU Tel: 01383 621855 — State DMS 1972 Rome; FRCS Ed. 1987; Dip. Urol. Lond 1992. Assoc. Specialist (Gen. Surg. & Urol.) Garrick Hosp. Stranraer. Prev: Regist. (Gen. Surg.) W. Fife Hosp. Dunfermline.

NARAIN, Ishwar 1 Plas Elwy Orchard, The Roe, St Asaph LL17 0LT Tel: 01745 582048 — MB BS 1956 Calcutta; DLO Eng. 1958. (R.G. Kar Med. Coll.) Clin. Asst. (ENT) Glan Clwyd Hosp. Bodelwyddan. Prev: Ho. Surg. Roy. Nat. Throat, Nose & Ear Hosp. Lond.; Regist (ENT) N. Staffs. Roy. Infirm. Stoke-on-Trent & Qu. Eliz. Hosp.Birm.; H.M. Stanley Hosp. St. Asaph.

NARAIN, Mark Andrew Ceredigion & Mid Wales NHS Trust, Bronglass General Hospital, Aberystwyth SY23 1ER Tel: 01970 635981 Fax: 01970 635955 Email: mark.narain@ceredigiontr.wales.nhs.uk — MB BS 1989 Lond.; MRCP (UK) 1994. (St Mary's Lond.) Cons. Phys. & Gastroenterologist, Bronglass Gen. Hospita, Aberystwyth. Prev: Specialist Regist. Gen. Med. & Gastroenterol., W. Midl.s Rotat.

NARAN, Kishore B Whitley Villa Surgery, 1 Christchurch Road, Reading RG2 7AB Tel: 0118 987 1645 Fax: 0118 931 4046 Email: kbnaran@doctors.org.uk; Cedar Lodge, Elm Lane, Reading RG6 5UH Tel: 0118 987 6084 — MRCGP (UK) 1985; MRCP (UK) 1982; MB ChB 1974 Birmingham. Princip. in Gen. Pract., Reading; Hosp. Practitioner, Genitourin. Med., Roy. Berks. Hosp., Reading. Socs: Reading Path. Soc. - Exec. Comm. Mem.

NARANG, Indra 15 Africa Gardens, Cardiff CF14 3BT Tel: 029 2061 3874 — MB BCh 1993 Wales; BMedSci Cardiff 1993. SHO (Paediat.) Univ. Hosp. Wales, Cardiff. Prev: SHO (A & E) Cardiff; Ho. Off. (Gen. Med.) Cardiff; Ho. Off. (Paediat. Surg.) Edin.

NARANG, Mr Kush Kumar 16 Woodcote Lodge, 32 Woodcote Green Road, Epsom KT1S 7DW Tel: 01372 735735 Email: kushnarang@aol.com; 138 Edge Hill, Darras Hall Est., Ponteland, Newcastle upon Tyne NE20 9JL Tel: 01661 872603 — MB BS 1982 Delhi; MS 1985 Delhi; FRCS Ed. 1990; FRCS Glas. 1990; FRCS Eng. 1990; FRCS (Tr. & Orth.) 1999. (Maulania Azad Med. Coll. N Delhi India) Assoc. Specialist Worthing & S.lands Hosp. NHS Trust Worthing; Specialist Regist. SW Thames Region Rot. St Geo. Hosp. Socs: BMA. Prev: Staff Grade (Orthop.) Worthing & S.lands Hosp. Shoreham-by-Sea; Regist. (Orthop.) W. Hill Dartford; Regist. Rotat. (Orthop.) W. Midl.

NARANG, Radhe Sham 3 Lilian Board Way, Greenford UB6 0SA — MB BS 1951 Madras; FFA RCS Eng. 1972. (Madras Med. Coll.) Cons. Anaesth. Roy. Albert Edwd. Infirm. Wigan.

NARANG, Ram Prakash (Surgery), 111-113 Netherhall Road, Leicester LE5 1DR Tel: 0116 243 2077 — MB BS 1972 Punjabi.

NARANG, Satish Kumar Aberbeeg Medical Centre, The Square, Aberbeeg, Abertillery NP13 2AB Tel: 01495 320520 Fax: 01495 320084 — MB BS 1974 Lucknow.

***NARANG, Satwant Kaur** 30 Moorhead Lane, Shipley BD18 4JW — MB ChB 1995 Manch.

NARANG, Verinder Pal Singh 22 Northleigh, Bradford-on-Avon BA15 2RG — MB BS 1980 Lond.; FFA RCS Eng. 1985. (Char. Cross) Regist. (Anaesth.) Soton Gen. Hosp.

NARASAPUR, Surendra Laxmanrao Nethergate Medical Centre, 2 Tay Square, Dundee DD1 1PB Tel: 01382 21527 Fax: 01382 26772 — Mumbai 1975; MRCGP UK 1987; MBBS. (Grant medical College) GP Dundee; Med. Office, Pens. & DHSS. Socs: Med. & Dent. Defence Union, Scotl.

NARASIMHA MURTHY, Hosaholalu Sanjeevasetty Dewi Sant Hospital, Albert Road, Pontypridd CF37 1LB — MB BS 1974 Mysore; MRCPI 1985. (Mysore Med. Coll.) Regist. (Geriat. Med.) Llandough Hosp. Cardiff.

NARASIMHA RAO, Madhavapeddy Venkata Sesha Barnsley District General Hospital, Barnsley S75 2EP Tel: 01226 730000; 142 Summer Lane, Barnsley S75 2AD Tel: 01226 207418 — MD 1972 Banaras Hindu; MD (Anaesth.) Banaras Hindu 1972; MB BS Andhra 1966; FFA RCSI 1982; DA Andhra 1969. (Guntur Med. Coll.) Cons. Anaesth. Barnsley Dist. Gen. Hosp. Socs: Intens. Care Soc. Prev: Anaesth. Specialist K.O.C. Hosp. Kuwait; Cons. Anaesth. Erne Hosp. Enniskillen.

NARAVI, Maya Krishnanand 154 Lower Fairmead Road, Yeovil BA21 5SS Tel: 01935427452 Email: mnaraavi@yahoo.com — BM 1993 Soton.; MRCPI 1997. (Southampton) Specialist Regist. (A & E) N. Staffs. Roy. Infirm. Stoke on Trent; SHO (A & E) City Hosp. Dudley Rd. Birm.; SHO (Med.) Wolverhampton New Cross Hosp. Wolverhampton. Socs: Assoc. Mem. BAEM; BMA; MPS. Prev: SHO (A & E) Birm. Heartlands Hosp. Birm.

NARAYAN, Mr Badri Singh The Old Mill Surgery, 22 Speedwell Road, Edgbaston, Birmingham B5 7QA Tel: 0121 440 4215 — MB BS Ranchi 1967; FRCS Glas. 1976. (Rajendra Med. Coll. Ranchi) Socs: BMA; ODA.

NARAYAN, Harini Department of Obstetrics & Gynaecology, Princess Margaret Hospital, Okus Road, Swindon SN1 4JU Tel: 01793 426675 Fax: 01793 426069 — MB BS 1980 Bangalore; MRCOG 1989; DGO Mangalore 1983. Cons. (O & G) P.ss Margt. Hosp., Okus Rd., Swindon SN1 4JU. Socs: BMA; Roy. Coll. Obst. & Gyn. Prev: Sen. Lect. Univ. Leic.; Sen. Regist./Lect. Univ. Leic.

NARAYAN, Mrs Kamalini (retired) c/o Lloyds Bank Ltd., Bromley BR1 1LJ — MB BS Lucknow 1952; BSc Lucknow 1947; DCH Eng. 1961; DObst RCOG 1956. Prev: GP Birm.

NARAYAN, Prakash (retired) 52 Beaudesert Road, Handsworth, Birmingham B20 3TG Tel: 0121 554 5966 — MB BS Lucknow 1951; DTM & H Liverp. 1960. Prev: GP Birm.

***NARAYAN, Prasanna Lakshmi** 238 Birmingham Road, Wylde Green, Sutton Coldfield B72 1DH — MB ChB 1996 Birm.; ChB Birm. 1996.

NARAYAN, Ramnath Eldon Square Surgery, 9 Eldon Square, Reading RG1 4DP Tel: 0118 957 4891 — MB BS 1971 Poona; MB BS 1971 Poona.

NARAYAN, Ravindra D Porth Farm Surgery, Porth Street, Porth CF39 9RR Tel: 01443 682579 Fax: 01443 683667 — BSc; MBBS. (Darbhanga Medical College, Bihar, India)

NARAYAN, Shalini 1 Tynycymmer Close, Porth CF39 9DE; 91 Lascelles Drive, Pontprennav, Cardiff CF23 8NZ Tel: 01222 541093 — MB BCh 1993 Wales; MRCP. (University of Wales College of Medicine) SHO (Dermat.) Glas. Roy. Infirm. Socs: BMA; Med. Sickness Soc.; MDU. Prev: SHO (Med. Oncol.) Derby City Gen. Hosp.; SHO (Renal Med.) Derby City Gen. Hosp.; SHO (Respirat. Med.) Derby City Gen. Hosp.

NARAYANA, Previn Lakshmi 63 Hightown Road, Banbury OX16 9BE — MB ChB 1996 Manch.

NARAYANA, Suguna Lakshmi 12 Rosemount Avenue, Kirkcaldy KY2 6SP — MB ChB 1994 Manch.

NARAYANA, Venkataswamy Thursby Surgery, 2 Browhead Road, Burnley BB10 3BF Tel: 01282 422447 Fax: 01282 832575 — MB BS 1971 Bangalor; MB BS Bangalore 1971. (Bangalore Med. Coll.) GP Burnley; Clin. Asst. (Rheum.) Burnley Gen. Hosp. Prev: Regist. (Med.) Burnley Gen. Hosp.; SHO (Gen. Med.) Vict. Hosp. Burnley.

NARAYANA SWAMY, Bole Gowda 15 Poolsbrook Road, Duckmanton, Chesterfield S44 5EL — MB BS 1970 Mysore.

***NARAYANAN, Anushree Noorsaloman** Department of Elderly Medicine, Northern General Hospital N H S Trust, Herries Rd, Sheffield S5 7AU; 32A Parkers Lane, Sheffield S10 1BR — MB ChB 1997 Sheff.

NARAYANAN, Mrs Janaki (retired) 1 St Margaret's Avenue, Leeds LS8 1RY Tel: 0113 686979 — MB BS 1945 Madras; MFCM 1974; DPH Newc. 1966. Prev: SCM (Child Health) Sunderland AHA.

NARAYANAN, Mekkali Narayanan Department of Haematology, George Eliot Hospital, College St., Nuneaton CV10 7DJ Tel: 02476 351351 Email: mekkali.narayanan@geh-tr.wmids.nhs.uk; 15 Poppyfield Court, Gibbet Hill, Coventry CV4 7HW Tel: 02476 697217 — MB BS 1978 Calicut; FRCP 1999; FRCPath (Haemat.) 1997, M 1988; MRCP (UK) 1985; MD Chandigarh 1982. Cons. Haemat. Geo. Eliot Hosp. Nuneaton; Cons. Haematologist,

Walsgrave Hosp., coventry. Socs: Brit. Soc. Haematol. Prev: Sen. Regist. (Haemat.) N. W.. RHA; Tutor (Clin. Haemat.) Univ. Manch. & Manch. Roy. Infirm.

NARAYANAN, Seetha Flat B, 153 Southgate Road, London N1 3LE Tel: 020 7359 2744 Email: nseetha@aol.com — MB ChB 1983 Liverp.; MRCP (UK) 1990; FRCPCH 1997; DCH RCP Lond. 1989; DTCH Liverp. 1990. (Liverp.) Cons. - Community Paediat. Tower Hamlets Healthcare Trust Lond.

NARAYANAN, Shanmuganathan 67 Prince of Wales Drive, Ipswich IP2 9BP Tel: 01473 275306 — MB BS 1987 Malaya; MRCP (UK) 1996. Specialist Regist. (Com. Paed) Loc. Heath Partn'shp, NHS Trust, Ipswich. Socs: BMA. Prev: Locum Lect. Dept. of Paediat. Camb. Uni.; Sen. SHO, P.ss Margeret Hosp. Swind.

NARAYNSINGH, Priya Aan 95 Fawnbrake Avenue, London SE24 0BG — MB BS 1987 West Indies.

NARBOROUGH, Geoffrey Charles The Hawthorne, Cumberhills Road, Duffield DE50 4HA — MB ChB 1980 Manch.; MRCP (UK) 1983; FRCR 1989. Cons. Radiol. Derbysh. Roy. Infirm. Prev: Sen. Regist. (Radiol.) Nottm.

NAREN, Mudigonda 28 Compton Hill Drive, Wolverhampton WV3 9DL — MB BS 1972 Osmania; MRCPsych 1985.

NARENDRAN, Partheepan 110 Deans Lane, Edgware HA8 9NR — MB BS 1992 Lond.; BSc (Basic Med. Sci. & Immunol.) Lond. 1989; MRCP (UK) 1995. Clin. Research Fell. Univ. of Bristol. Socs: Brit. Soc. Endocrinol.; Brit. Soc. Immunol.; Brit. Diabetic Assn. Prev: Med. Regist. W.on Gen. Hosp.; Med. SHO N. Manch. Gen. Hosp.

NARENDRAN, Raghava 36 Wilton Drive, Unsworth, Bury BL9 8BG — MB BS 1970 Madras. (Christian Med. Coll. Vellore) SHO (Psychiat.) Salford AHA (T).

NARENDRAN, Sivaguru Toby Cottage, North Road, Alfriston, Polegate BN26 5XB Tel: 01323 870596 — MB BS 1968 Ceylon. (Ceylon) Assoc. Specialist Orthop., Horder Centre Arthritics, CrowBoro.. Prev: Regist. (Orthop.) Shotley Bridge Gen. Hosp. Consett; Regist. (A & E) E.bourne Gen. Hosp.; SHO (Orthop.) Enfield Dist. Hosp. (Chace Wing).

NARGOL, Mr Antoni Viraf Francis 17 Richmond Way, Barnes Park, Cramlington NE23 7XE — MB BS 1988 Newc.; FRCS Ed. 1993. (Newc.) Specialist Regist. (Orthop.) Sunderland Gen. Hosp.

NARGOLWALA, Mr Viraf Sohrabji Newcastle Clinic, 4 Towers Avenue, Jesmond, Newcastle upon Tyne NE2 3QE Tel: 0191 281 2636 Fax: 0191 239 9922; Coppertop, 16 Holburn Gardens, Ryton NE40 3DZ Tel: 0191 413 2103 — MB BS Osmania 1958; FRCS Eng. 1963; FRCS Ed. 1963. (Osmania Med. Coll. Hyderabad) Hon. Cons. Orthop. Surg. NW Durh. Health Dist.; Spinal Surg. Washington Hosp. Tyne & Wear; Cons. Orthop. Surg. Newc. Nuffield Hosp. Socs: Fell. BOA. Prev: Sen. Regist. Roy. Vict. Infirm. Newc.

NARGUND, Mr Vinod Hanamantrao Department of Urology, Churchill Hospital, Headington, Oxford OX3 7LJ; 38 Ash Grove, Headington, Oxford OX3 9JL Tel: 01865 69758 Fax: 01865 69758 — MB BS 1978 Karnatak; MB BS Karnatak 1981; PhD Bradford 1995; MS Karnatak 1981; FRCS (Urol.) 1996; FRCS Ed. 1985. (Karnatak Med. Coll., Hubli) Clin. Lect. (Urol.) Nuffield Dept. Surg. Univ. Oxf. & Oxf. Radcliffe Hosp.; Mem. Europ. Bd. Urol. Socs: Assoc. Mem. BAUS; Brit. Cancer Res. Prev: Research Fell. Univ. Bradford.

***NARHLYA, Nerinder Kumar** 85 Fountain Road, Edgbaston, Birmingham B17 8NP — MB ChB 1996 Dundee.

NARHLYA, Pawn Kumar 68 Fountain Road, Birmingham B17 8NR — MB ChB 1991 Aberd.

NARNOR, Francis William Dornu 4 Park Avenue, Woodthorpe, Nottingham NG5 4HS — MB BS 1967 Lond.; DO Eng. 1972.

***NARODDEN, Mohamad Noorsalomon** 4 Parsonage Ct, Sheffield S6 5BU — MB ChB 1997 Sheff.

NAROZ, Nabil Awadalla Trinity Medical Centre, New George Street, South Shields NE33 5DU Tel: 0191 455 5958 Fax: 0191 456 5828 — MB BCh 1971 Assiut; DFFP 1993; MFFP 1993; DRCOG 1983; DO RCPSI 1981. Family Plann. Off. & Instruc. S. & NW Durh. HAs & S. Tyneside; Med. Off. (Maj.) Territorial Army; Police Surg. Durh. Constab. Socs: Med. Protec. Soc.; BMA. Prev: Regist. (Oncol. & O & G) Shotley Bridge Gen. Hosp. Consett.

NAROZNY, Ryszard Hubert 38 St James Avenue, London W13 9DJ Tel: 020 8567 6781 — LRCPI & LM, LRSCI & LM 1958; LRCPI & LM, LRCSI & LM 1958. (Dub.)

NARRAINEN, Marreemootoo (retired) 94 Andrew Lane, High Lane, Stockport SK6 8HY — MD 1968 Malta; DCH RCPS Glas. 1981. Barrister-at-Law Lincoln's Inn; Assoc. Specialist (Paediat.) Stepping Hill Hosp. Stockport. Prev: SHO (Obst.) Grimsby Matern. Hosp.

NARULA, Mr Antony Ajay Pall Blaby Hill House, Blaby, Leicester LE8 4FG Tel: 0116 278 0995 Fax: 0116 277 7895 Email: tony.narula@btinternet.com — MB BChir 1980 Camb.; MB Camb. 1980, BChir 1979; MA Camb. 1980; FRCS Eng. 1984. Cons. Otolaryngol. St Mary's Hosp. Lond.; Edr. CME Bull. Socs: Fell. Brit. Soc. Audiol.; Fell. Roy. Soc. Med.; Fell. Amer. Acad. ORL-HNS. Prev: Cons. Otolaryngol. Leicester Roy. Infirm.

NARULA, Harmohan Singh Bryngwyn Surgery, 4 Bryngwyn Road, Newport NP20 4JS Tel: 01633 263463 Fax: 01633 221421 — MB BS 1971 Panjab; MS (Ophth.) Rajasthan, India 1974; DO RCS Eng. 1977; Dip. Ther. Wales. (Amritsar, Panjab) Mem. LMC (Ophth. Comm.). Socs: SW Ophth. Soc.; Overseas Doctors Assn.

NARULA, Kaur Bryngwyn Surgery, 4 Bryngwyn Road, Newport NP20 4JS Tel: 01633 263463 Fax: 01633 221421 — MB BS 1975 Guru Nanak Dev.; MRCOG 1992; DRCOG 1992; DObst RCPI 1978. Clin. Asst. (Gyn.) & GP Obst. Unit. Gwent HA; Mem. LMC.

NARULA, Yash Pall Aveley Hill, 2 Vicarage Hill, Farnham GU9 8HG — MB BS 1959 Bombay. (Seth G.S. Med. Coll.) Prev: Civil Surg. Burma; Dep. Resid. Surg. Off. E. Ham Memor. Hosp.; Regist. (Surg.) Farnham Hosp.

***NARVANI, Amir Ali** 8 Reynolds Close, London NW11 7EA — MB BS 1996 Lond.

NASAH, Tony Feuko Email: tony@nashah.freeserve.co.uk — MB BS 1986 Ibadan; MRCOG 1994.

NASAR, Mohammad Abu Bridlington & Distrct Hospital, Bessingby Road, Bridlington YO16 4QP Tel: 01262 423166 Fax: 01262 400583; 4 Roundhay Road, Bridlington YO15 3JY Tel: 01262 672809 Fax: 01262 672809/400583 — MBBS 1965 Dacca Bangladesh; FRCP Glas. 1994; FRCP Lond. 1993; FRCP Ed. 1993; MRCP (UK) 1977. (Chittagong Med. Coll.) Cons. Phys. Dept. Med. Elderly Bridlington & Dist. Hosp. Socs: Fell. Roy. Soc. Health; Brit. Geriat. Soc.; Fell. Roy. Coll. of Phys.s (Lond. Ed.). Prev: Sen. Regist. (Geriat. Med. & Gen. Med.) St. John's Hosp. & W.m. Hosp. Lond.; Regist. Geriat. Research Unit St. John's Hosp. Lond.; Assoc. Prof. (Med.) Rangpur Med. Coll., Bangladesh.

NASAR, Muhammad Akram Paediatric Department, Conquest Hospital, St Leonards-on-Sea TN37 7RD Tel: 01424 755255 Fax: 01424 758014; 12 Albany Road, St Leonards-on-Sea TN38 0LN Tel: 01424 425279 — MB BS 1974 Karachi; MRCPI 1986; FRCPCH 1997; DTM & H RCP Lond. 1978. (Dow Med. Coll., Karachi) Cons. Paediat. Conquest Hosp. St Leonards on Sea. Socs: Fell. Roy. Soc. Med. Prev: Regist. (Paediat.) Ipswich Hosp.; Community Hosp. Regist. Ipswich.

NASAR, Razia Begum 171 Ferrymead Avenue, Greenford UB6 9TP Tel: 020 8575 0163 — MB BS 1967 Punjab; MRCOG 1977.

NASEEM, Mohammad (retired) 177 Church Hill Road, Birmingham B20 3PX Tel: 0121 515 2459 — MB BS Punjab (Pakistan) 1953. Med. Pract.; Clin. Asst. Birm. & Midl. Eye Hosp. Prev: Clin. Asst. (Cas.) Gen. Hosp. Birm.

***NASEEM, Mohammad Arfan** 27 Talbot Street, Canton, Cardiff CF11 9BW — MB BCh 1996 Wales.

NASEEM, Muhammad Thorpe House Farm, Middleton Lane, Thorpe, Wakefield WF3 3BU — MB BS 1968 Punjab.

NASEEM, Mr Muhammed Saleem Medway Hospital, Windmill Road, Gillingham ME7 5NY Tel: 01634 830000; 4 Smithys Close, St Leonards-on-Sea TN37 7SU Tel: 01424 753487 — MB BS 1985 Punjab; FRCSI 1991; FRCS Eng. 1991; Dip. Urol. Lond 1993. (King Edward Med. Coll. Lahore, Pakistan) Staff Grade (Urol.) Medway Hosp. Gill'ham, Kent. Prev: Regist. (Urol.) St Barts. Hosp. Lond.; Reg. (Urol.) Conquest Hosp. Hastings; Reg. (Urol.) Whipps Cross. Hosp. Lond.

NASH, Andrew Paul The Surgery, 18 Fouracre Road, Bristol BS16 6PG Tel: 0117 970 2033; (branch Surgery), 42 Abbortswood, Yate, Bristol Tel: 01454 313577 — MB ChB 1972 Bristol.

NASH

NASH, Anthony Frances 7 Arlington Crescent, Wilmslow SK9 6BH — MB BCh 1985 Wales.

NASH, Mr Anthony Gordon Hatherleigh, 13 Devonshire Road, Sutton SM2 5HQ — MB ChB 1959 Bristol; FRCS Eng. 1966. Cons. Surg. Roy. Marsden Hosp.; Cons. Surg. St. Helier Hosp. Carshalton; Sen. Lect. (Surg.) St. Geo. Hosp. Lond. Prev: Sen. Regist. Roy. Marsden Hosp. Lond. & St. Geo. Hosp. Lond.; Fell. Surg. Memor. Hosp., New York.

*NASH, Audrey Ann 9 Whirlow Court Road, Sheffield S11 9NS Tel: 0114 236 2296 — MB ChB 1998 Sheff.; MB ChB Sheff 1998.

NASH, Carey Helen Dr. Grays Hospital, Elgin IV30 1SN — BM BS 1980 Nottm. Staff Grade (Psychiat.) Moray Health Servs.

NASH, Catherine Mary The Central Family Planning Clinic, 2/4 Brunswick Road, Norwich NR2 2HA Tel: 01603 287345 Fax: 01603 287358; 22 West Parade, Norwich NR2 3DW Tel: 01603 627802 — MB BS 1972 Lond.; MRCS Eng. LRCP Lond. 1972; MFFP 1993; DRCOG 1977. (Roy. Free Hosp. Med. Sch. Lond.) Cons. Family Plann. Norf. & Norwich Hosp. NHS Health Care Trust. Prev: Clin. Asst. (Psychiat.) St. And. Hosp. Norwich & Hellesdon Hosp.; Trainee GP Norwich VTS.

NASH, Mr Charles John Amersham Health Centre, Chiltern Avenue, Amersham HP6 5AY Tel: 01494 434344; Oakfield, 2 Church Grove, Little Chalfont, Amersham HP6 6SH — MB BS 1982 Lond.; FRCS Eng. 1986; MRCGP 1989; DRCOG 1988. (Middlx. Hosp.) Hosp. Practitioner, Urol., Wycombe Gen. Hosp.

NASH, Mr Desmond Tyrie Llewellyn 34 Victoria Square, Rostrevor, Newry BT34 3EU — MB BCh BAO 1946 Dub.; FRCSI 1951; LMCC 1956. (T.C. Dub.) Socs: BMA. Prev: Cons. Surg. Daisy Hill Hosp. Newry; Sen. Regist. (Surg.) Belf. Hosp. Gp.; Res. Surg. Off. Roy. Devon & Exeter Hosp.

NASH, Dylan Llywelyn The Cripps Health Centre, University Park, Nottingham NG7 2QW Tel: 0115 950 1654 — BM BS 1985 Nottm.

*NASH, Edward Fairbairn 40 More Close, St Paul's Court, London W14 9BN — MB BS 1998 Lond.; MB BS Lond 1998.

*NASH, Elizabeth Jane Lanarth, Lytton Road, Woking GU22 7BH — BM BS 1997 Nottm.

NASH, Guy Fairbairn 40 More Close, London W14 9BN — MB BS 1992 Lond.

NASH, Ian Trevor The Old School Surgery, Bolts Hill, Chartham, Canterbury CT4 7JY Tel: 01227 738282 Fax: 01227 732122; White Ladies, White Hill, Bilting, Ashford TN25 4HB Tel: 01233 812360. Fax: 01233 813852 — MB BS 1969 Lond.; MRCS Eng. LRCP Lond. 1969. (Guy's) Prev: Regist. (Anaesth.) Hastings Gp. Hosp.; Ho. Surg. Roy. E. Sussex Hosp. Hastings.

NASH, Joanna Clare Jeanne House, Dauntsey School, High St., West Lavington, Devizes SN10 4HE — MB ChB 1993 Birm.

NASH, John Martin Western Elms Surgery, 317 Oxford Road, Reading RG30 1AT Tel: 0118 959 0257 Fax: 0118 959 7950 — MB BS 1970 Newc.; DObst RCOG 1974.

NASH, Mr John Roderick East Midlands Nuffield Hospital, Rykneld Road, Littleover, Derby DE23 7SN Tel: 01332 381150 Fax: 01332 865 505; Fax: 01332 865505 — MB BS 1972 Lond.; MD 1979 Leics.; FRCS 1977 Ed; FRCS 1988 Eng. (Middlx.) p/t Cons. Gen. Vasc. & Endocr. Surg.; Med. Director, Nat. Pat.'s Access Team. Socs: Assn. Surg. & Vasc. Soc.; 1921 Surg. Club GB (GB). Prev: Chief Exec. Derbysh. Roy. Infirm. NHS Trust; Med. Director Derbysh. Roy. Infirm. NHS Trust; Cons. Surg. S.. Derbysh. HA.

NASH, John Rupert Gifford Liverpool University Department of Pathology, Duncan Building, Daulby St., Liverpool L69 3GA Tel: 0151 706 4483 Fax: 0151 706 5859 Email: jnash@liv.ac.uk — BM BCh 1975 Oxf.; MA, DPhil Oxf. 1973; FRCPath 1996, M 1983. Sen. Lect. (Path.) Univ. Liverp.; Hon. Cons. Path. Roy. Liverp. Univ. Hosps. Trust. Socs: Fell. Roy. Coll. Pathol.; BMA; Internat. Acad. Path. Prev: Clin. Tutor & Clin. Lect. (Path.) Univ. Oxf.

NASH, Jonathan Robert 22 Birch Polygon, Rusholme, Manchester M14 5HX Tel: 0161 256 2452 — MB ChB 1993 Manch. SHO (Med.) N. Manch. Gen. Hosp.

NASH, Julian Trevor 2 Pen-Deri Cl., Maes-y-Garn EStreet, Oakdale, Blackwood NP12 0NJ — MB BCh 1990 Wales; BSc (Hons.) 1987 Wales; MRCP 1993 UK. Specialist Regist. Rheum. and Gen. Med. Homerton Hosp. Lond. Socs: Med. Protec. Soc.; Brit. Soc. of Rheum.; Roy. Soc. of Med. Prev: Regist. (Med.) Stoke Mandeville

Hosp. Aylesbury.; MRC Clin. Train. Fell. & Hon. Regist. (Rheum.) RPMS Hammersmith Hosp. Lond.

NASH, Julie Ann 7 Acresgate Court, Grange Lane, Liverpool L25 4UF — MB ChB 1982 Liverp. Regist. (Anaesth.) Liverp. HA.

*NASH, Kathryn Louise 14 Fourth Avenue, Denvilles, Havant PO9 2QX — BChir 1995 Camb.

NASH, Michael John Bwlchcilau, Llanafanfawr, Builth Wells LD2 3PG — MB ChB 1973 Dundee. (Dundee)

NASH, Pamela Elaine 47 Owls Lodge Lane, Mayals, Swansea SA3 5DP — MB BS 1980 Lond.; FRCP Lond. 1995; MRCP (UK). 1983; FFAEM 1992. (St. Mary's Hosp. Lond.) Cons. A & E Neath Hosp. W. Glam. Prev: Cons. A & E Hillingdon Hosp. Uxbridge; Sen. Regist. (A & E) Centr. Middlx. Hosp. Lond.

NASH, Peter James, CStJ 1 Rectory Close, Eastbourne BN20 8AQ Tel: 01323 411220 Fax: 01323 411575 — MB ChB 1967 Sheff.; FFA RCS Eng. 1974; DA Eng. 1971. (Sheff.) p/t Cons. Anaesth. & E.bourne Hosps. NHS Trust; Dep. Chief Commiss.er (Operat.s) St. John Ambul. Socs: BMA; Assn. Anaesth. Prev: Sen. Regist. Roy. Sussex Co. Hosp. Brighton; Squadron Ldr. RAF Med. Br.; Direct Med. Servs. E.bourne Hosp. NHS Trust.

NASH, Robert William (retired) Woodside Cottage, Clashmore, Dornoch IV25 3RG Tel: 01862 881307 Fax: 01862 810197 — MB BS Lond. 1950; MRCS Eng. LRCP Lond. 1944; MRCGP 1968; DCH RCP Lond. 1951. Prev: Sch. Doctor MichaelHo. Natal, S. Afr.

NASH, Ruth Mary Dept Histopathology, King's College School of Medicine and Dentistry, Bessemer Road, London SE5 9PJ Tel: 020 7346 3005 Fax: 020 7346 3670; 157 Underhill Road, E. Dulwich, London SE22 0PG — MB BS Lond. 1978; BSc (Hons) Ed. 1975; DRCPath (Cytol.) 1996; MRCPath 1992. (Sen. Lect. (Perinatal/Paediat. Path.)) Socs: MRCPath.; Brit. Soc. Clin. Cytol.; Paediat. Path. Soc.

*NASH, Sally Marion Katherine 44 Pinner Court, Pinner HA5 5RL — MB ChB 1994 Birm.; ChB Birm. 1994.

NASH, Steven Roy Lanescot House, Lanescot, Par PL24 2RS — MB BS 1984 Lond.; MRCGP 1989. Trainee GP Liskeard VTS.

NASH, Mr Thorolf Guy (retired) Westlands, 36 Collington Avenue, Bexhill-on-Sea TN39 3NE Tel: 01424 221886 Fax: 01424 213249 Email: tgnash@aol.com — MB BS 1960 Lond.; FRCS Eng. 1970; FRCS Ed. 1969; MRCS Eng. LRCP Lond. 1959; FRCOG 1979, M 1966, DObst 1961. Gynaecologist in Private Pract.; Authorised Med. Examr. Civil Aviat. Auth. Prev: Regist. (Gen. Surg.) Roy. Vict. Hosp. Bournemouth.

NASH, Timothy Paul The Walton Centre, Lower Lane, Fazakerley, Liverpool L9 7LJ Tel: 0151 529 5749 Fax: 0151 529 5486 Email: nash-t@wcnn-tr.nwest.nhs.uk; Danesfield, 21 Stanley Road, Hoylake, Wirral CH47 1HN Tel: 0151 632 6985 Fax: 0151 632 0307 Email: nashtp@liv.ac.uk ; tim.nash@which.net — MB BS Lond. 1969; FRCA Eng. 1974; DObst RCOG 1971. (Univ. Coll. Hosp.) Cons. Pain Managem. Walton Centre Liverp.; Hon. Sen. Lect., Univ. of Liverp.; Hon. Director of Pain Studie, Univ. of Liverp. Socs: Assn. Anaesths.; (Ex-Pres. & Ex-Hon. Sec.) Pres. Pain Soc.; IASP. Prev: Cons. Anaesth. & Pain Managem. Basingstoke Dist. Hosp.; Sen. Regist. (Anaesth.) Addenbrooke's Hosp. Camb.; Regist. (Anaesth.) Univ. Coll. Hosp. Lond.

NASH, William Norman Cecil The Health Centre, Garden Terrace Road, Old Harlow, Harlow CM17 0AX Tel: 01279 418136 Fax: 01279 429650 — MB BCh BAO 1965 Dub.; MA.

NASHEF, Alexandra Jean Alconbury and Brampton Surgeries, The Surgery, School Lane, Alconbury, Huntingdon PE28 4EQ Tel: 01480 890281 Fax: 01480 891787 — MB ChB 1984 Glas.; MRCGP 1989; DRCOG 1986. Clin. Med. Off. (Genitourin. Med.) Hinchingbrooke Hosp. Huntingdon.

NASHEF, Lina Kent & Canterbury Hospital, Ethelbert Road, Canterbury CT1 3NG; Neurology Department, Mapother House, King's College Hospital, Denmark Hill, London SE5 9RS — MB ChB 1980 Bristol; MD 1995; MRCP 1984 UK; FRCP 2000 UK. (Bristol) Cons. Neurol. Kent & Canterbury Hosp. & King's Coll. Hosp. Lond.; Hon. Sen. Lect. Kings Coll. Sch. Med. & Dent.

NASHEF, Mr Samer Abdel-Malik Papworth Hospital, Cambridge CB3 8RE Tel: 01480 364299 Fax: 01480 364774 Email: samnashef@papworth-tr.anglox.nhs.uk; 16 Allen's Orchard, Brampton, Huntingdon PE28 4NW Tel: 01480 414966 Email: samnashef@aol.com — MB ChB 1980 Bristol; BSc AUB 1976; FRCS Glas. 1984; FRCS Eng. 1984. (Bristol) Cons.(Cardiothoracic

Surg.) Papworth Hosp. Camb.; Hon. Cons.(Cardiothoracic Surg.) Addenbrooke's Hosp. Camb. Socs: Eur. Club, Young Cardiac Surg. (Scientif. Sec.). Prev: Sen. Regist. (Cardiothoracic Surg.) Wythenshawe Hosp. Manch.; Attached Surg. Xavier Arnozan & Haut-Leveque Hosps. Bordeaux France.

NASIB, Asif 12 Glencairn Drive, Glasgow G41 4QN Tel: 0141 423 8179 Email: nasib96@aol.com — MB ChB 1995 Glas. (University of Glasgow) SHO (ENT Surg.).

NASIM, Mr Akhtar South Manchester University Hospitals Trust, Wythenshawe Hospital, Southmoor Road, Wythenshawe, Manchester M23 9LT Tel: 0161 291 6642 — MB ChB 1990 Aberd.; FRCS Ed. 1994; MD Leic. 1998. Cons. Vasc. Surg.; Hon. Lect. Univ. of Manch. Socs: Europ. Soc. Vasc. & Endovasc. Surg.; Vasc. Surg. Soc. GB & Irel.; Assn. Surgs. GB & Irel. Prev: Specialist Regist. (Surg.) Leicester Roy. Infirm.; Clin. Research Fell. (Surg.) Univ. Leicester; SHO Rotat. (Surg.) Leicester.

NASIM, M Marsh Farm Health Centre, Purley Centre, The Moakes, Luton LU3 3SR — MB BS 1965 Karachi; MB BS 1965 Karachi.

NASIR, A North Road Surgery, 60 North Road, St Helens WA10 2TR Tel: 01744 22548.

***NASIR, Nirwan** c/o Rozeyati Nasir, Ground Floor Flat, 2 Forest Garden, London NW11 7EX — MB ChB 1997 Manch.

NASIR, Taqleed Ullah Khan (retired) 8 Highfield Gardens, Heaton, Bradford BD9 6LY Tel: 01274 491573 — MB BS 1963 Sind; MRCPsych 1972; DPM Eng. 1969. Cons. Psychiat. W.wood Hosp. Bradford. Prev: Regist. & Med. Asst. (Psychiat.) Whittingham Hosp. Preston.

NASIRI, Ahmed Zafar Sovereign Medical Centre, Sovereign Drive, Pennyland, Milton Keynes MK15 8AJ Tel: 01908 661166 Fax: 01908 233921; 26 Saddlers Place, Downs Barn, Milton Keynes MK14 7RS Tel: 01908 605265 — MB BChir 1988 Camb.; MRCGP 1992; DCCH RCGP 1992; DRCOG 1992. (Cambridge) GP Partner; Prison Med. Off. HMP Woodhill, Milton Keynes. Prev: SHO Milton Keynes Gen. Hosp. GP VTS; Ho. Off. Ipswich Gen. Hosp.; Ho. Off. (Surg.) P'boro. Dist. Hosp.

***NASIRUDDIN, Ismat Jehan** 40 Kyrle Road, London SW11 6BA — MB BS 1994 Lond.

NASMYTH, Mr David George Department of Surgery, Furness General Hospital, Dalton Lane, Barrow-in-Furness LA14 4LF Tel: 01229 870870; Fellwood Head, Hooks Lane, Little Urswick, Ulverston LA12 0TH — MB BS 1976 Lond.; MS 1988 Lond.; MA Oxf. 1973; FRCS Ed. 1982; FRCS Eng. 1982. (Oxf. & Middlx.) Cons. Gen. Surg. Furness Gen. Hosp.; Clin. Tutor Furness Gen. Hosp.; Lead Clinician Colorectal Cancer Unit (Morecombe Bay NHS Trus).t. Socs: Fell. Roy. Soc. Med.; Assn. Coloproctol.; Assn. Surg.s GB & I. Prev: Sen. Regist. (Surg.) Roy. Liverp. Hosp.; Research Fell. Univ. Dept. Surg. Gen. Infirm. Leeds; Regist. (Surg.) Leicester Roy. Infirm.

NASR, Ehab Fayez 32 Whinney Heys Road, Blackpool FY3 8NP — MB BCh 1984 Ain Shams.

NASR, Ibrahim Sobhy Ibrahim Mohamed Scunthorpe General Hospital, Dermatology Department, Cliff Gardens, Scunthorpe DN15 7BH Tel: 01724 282282 — MRCP (UK) 1995; MA in Dermatology & Venereology 1985; MBChB 1978. (Alexandria University, Egypt) DermpatoloigstScunthorpe Gen Hosp Scunthorpe; Cons Dermatol. The Roy. Hallamshire Hosp The Centr. Sheff. Univ, Hosps Sheff.; Hon Clin.Lec. Sheff. Univ Med Sch. Sheff.; Asst. Med. Director, Scunthorpe Gen. Hosp., Scunthorpe. Socs: Fell.of the Roy. Soc. of Med.; Brit. Assoc. of Dermatol.s; N. Eng. Dermatol. Soc. Prev: Cons. Dermatol., St Mary's Hosp., Newport, Isle of Wight; Cons. Dermatol., Alexandria, Egypt; Cons. Dermato. Wwales Gen Hosp Carmarthen.

NASR, Mr Mohamed Sayed Ahmed Department of Genito-Urinary Medicine, Royal South Hants Hospital, Southampton SO14 0YG; The Pines, Hadrian Way, Chilworth, Southampton SO16 7HZ — MRCS Eng. LRCP Lond. 1978; MRCOG 1977; FRCOG 1998. Cons. Genitourin. Med. Soton. Univ. Hosps. NHS Trust Salisbury NHS Trust.

NASRA, Mr Salim Elias St Mary's Hospital, Newport PO30 5TG Tel: 01983 534724 Fax: 01983 822569 Email: salimnasra@btinternet.com; La Paz, Kite Hill, Wootton, Ryde PO33 4LE Tel: 01983 882545 Fax: 01983 882545 — MD 1977 Damascus; FRCS (Trauma & Orthop.) 1999; MRCS Eng. LRCP Lond. 1988; FRCS Glas. 1986. Cons. Orthop. Surg. St Mary's Hosp Isle of Wight. Socs: Overseas Fell. BOA; Fell. BOA.

NASRALLA, A H K Wordsworth Health Centre, 19 Wordsworth Avenue, Manor Park, London E12 6SU Tel: 020 8548 5960 Fax: 020 8548 5983 — MB BS 1969 Lucknow; MB BS 1969 Lucknow.

NASRALLAH, Fayez Khalil Saleh 4 Underwood Road, Bassett, Southampton SO16 7BU Tel: 02380 767755 — MB BCh 1958 Alexandria; MRCS Eng. LRCP Lond. 1977; DCH Eng. 1974. (Alexandria) SCMO (Child Health) Soton. & S.W. Hants. Health Dist. (T). Socs: BMA; Assoc. Mem. Brit. Paediat. Assn. Prev: Clin. Med. Off. (Child Health) Mid Surrey Health Dist.; SHO (Paediat.) N. Devon Dist. Hosp. Barnstaple.

***NASRUDDIN, Imelda Nasreen** 31 Fore Street, Roche, St Austell PL26 8EP — MB ChB 1997 Manch.

***NASSABEH, Sepideh** 9 Broadview Gardens, Worthing BN13 3DZ — MB ChB 1994 Aberd.

NASSAR, Mr Ahmad Hafez Mohamed Vale of Leven District General Hospital, Alexandria G83 0UA Tel: 01389 754121 Fax: 01389 711150 Email: anassar@vol.scot.nhs.uk; 3 Courthill, Bearsden, Glasgow G61 3SN Tel: 0771 134 6603 Email: anassar@clinmed.gla.ac.uk — MB BCh 1977 Zagazig; FRCS Ed. 1986. Cons. Surg. (Upper Gastrointestinal & Laparoscopic Surg.) Vale of Leven Dist. Gen. Hosp. Alexandria; Tutor (Minimal Access Ther. Train. Unit) RCS Eng.; Hon Clin Sen Lec Univ of Glas. Socs: Soc. Minimally Invasive Ther.; Assn. Endoscopic Surgs.; Eur. Assn. Endoscopic Surgs. Prev: Lect. (Surg.) Univ. Coll. Cork; Cons. (Surg.) Nat. Guard Hosp. Jeddah, Saudi Arabia.

NASSAR, Mr Wadi Yusuf The Beeches Consulting Centre, Mill Lane, Cheadle SK8 2PY Tel: 0161 491 2470 Fax: 0161 428 1692; (rooms), 21 St. John St, Manchester M3 4DT Tel: 0161 834 4242 — MD 1956 Amer. Univ. Beirut; MCh (Orl.) Liverp. 1967; FRCS Eng. 1969; LAH Dub. 1967; DLO Eng. 1964. (Amer. Univ. Beirut) Cons. ENT Surg. S. Manch. Health Dist. (T) S. Manch. Univ. Hosps. NHS Trust; Hon Lect. (Clin. Otolaryngol.) Manch. Univ. Socs: Fell. Roy. Soc. Med.; Brit. Soc. Audiol.; Brit. Med. Assn. Prev: Regist. Warrington Gen. Hosp.; Lect. Univ. Manch.; Sen. Regist. Manch. Roy. Infirm.

NASSER, Jaffar Mansfield District General Hospital, Westhill Drive, Mansfield NG18 1PH Tel: 01623 22515 — MD 1969 Damascus.

NASSER, Syed Muhammad Shuaib Addenbrookes Hospital, Box 40, Chest Clinic 2A, Addenbrooke's Hospital, Cambridge CB2 2QQ Tel: 01223 245151 — MB BS 1985 Lond.; MRCP (UK) 1989; MD London 1999. (Guys Hospital) Sen. Regist. & Clin. Lect. (Allergy Clin. Immunol. & Thoracic Med.) Addenbrooke's NHS Trust Univ. Camb. Socs: Coun. Mem. 2000 Brit. Soc. Allergy & Clin. Immunol.; E. Anglian Thoracic Soc.; SE Thames Thoracic Soc. Prev: Sen. Regist. Papworth Hosp.; Research Regist. & Regist. (Clin. Med.) Guy's Hosp. Lond.

NASSER, Zeinab Abdel-Aziz Ibrahim The Medical Centre, 2 Manor Court Avenue, Nuneaton CV11 5HX — MB BCh 1983 Cairo; MSc Cairo 1989. SCMO Med. Centre Nuneaton. Prev: Staff Grade (Psychiat.) Ashworth Hosp. Liverp.

NASSIM, Michael Arnold The Croft, 10 Chapel Lane, Old Dalby, Melton Mowbray LE14 3LA Tel: 01664 822377 — BM BCh 1968 Oxf.; BSc, MA Oxf. 1968; MRCP (UK) 1971. (St. Geo.) Socs: Collegiate Mem. RCP Lond.; HAPPI. Prev: Sen. Clin. Pharmacol. Astra Charnwood Pharmaceuts. LoughBoro.; Lect. (Nephrol.) Inst. Urol. Lond.; Hon. Sen. Regist. St. Peter's Hosps. Lond.

NATALE, Salvatore Buckleigh House, 127 Devonport Road, Plymouth PL1 5RQ — State Exam 1982 Messina.

NATALI, Colin The London Clinic, 147 Harley St., London W1N 2DE Tel: 020 7616 7693 Email: colin@backquack.demon.co.uk; Old Kiln House, 79 Haymeads Lane, Bishop's Stortford CM23 5JJ Tel: 01279 659287 Fax: 01279 755972 — MB BS 1986 Lond.; BSc (Hons.) Lond. 1983, MB BS 1986; FRCS Eng. 1991; FRCS (Orth.) 1996. (Lond. Hosp. Med. Coll.) Cons. (Orthop. Surg.) Roy. Lond. Hosp.

NATALWALA, Siraj Block 47, Flat 3, Good Hope Hospital, Rectory Road, Sutton Coldfield B75 7RR; 50 West View Road, Sutton Coldfield B75 6AY — MB BS 1983 Devi Ahilya India.

NATARAJ, Vasudevan Bolton Road Surgery, 431-433 Bolton Road, Ewood, Blackburn BB2 4HY Tel: 01254 679781 Fax: 01254 693031; (Surgery) 2 Velvet Street, Ewood, Blackburn — MB BS 1972 Bihar. (Darbhanga Med. Coll.)

NATARAJAN, Dhanapal c/o Dr S Anand, 2 Maindiff Court House, Ross Road, Abergavenny NP7 5LT — MB BS 1984 Madras.

NATARAJAN

NATARAJAN, Sivakumar Royal Hospital, Kayall Road, Sunderland SR4 7TP Tel: 0191 569 0004 Fax: 0191 569 9201; 9 West Farm Road, Cleadon, Sunderland SR6 7UG Tel: 0191 536 6111 Fax: 0191 536 6111 — MB BS 1976 Madras; FRCP 1999; MRCP (UK) 1990; MD (Dermat.) Madras 1980. Cons. Dermat. Roy. Hosp. Sunderland. Socs: BMA; Brit. Assn. Dermat.; Scott. Dermat. Soc. Prev: Regist. (Dermat.) P'boro. Dist. Hosp.; Resid. (Dermat.) Jipmer, Pondicherry, India; Regist. (Dermat.) Stobhill Hosp. Glas.

NATARAJU, Manni Rathna (Surgery), 19 The Grove, London N3 1QN Tel: 020 8346 1242 — MB BS 1973 Bangalore.

***NATAS, Sarah Anne** 38 Kingfisher Drive, Ham, Richmond TW10 7UD — MB BS 1998 Lond.; MB BS Lond 1998.

NATERWALLA, Mr Russi Hormusji Frenesi, 68 Lyndhurst Road, River, Dover CT17 0NH Tel: 01304 825104 — MB BS 1965 Bombay; FRCS Ed. 1975. (Topiwala Nat. Med. Coll.) Assoc. Specialist (A & E) Buckland Hosp. Dover. Prev: Clin. Asst. (Accid. Surg.) Buckland Hosp. Dover; Regist. (Gen. & Thoracic Surg.) B.Y.L. Nair Hosp. Bombay, India; SHO (Gen. Surg.) & SHO (Accid. & Orthop.) Buckland Hosp. Dover.

NATH, Abdulrehman Ramji 1 Hunters Park, Berkhamsted HP4 2PT; Royal Brompton and Harefield NHS Trust, Department Thoracic Medicine, Harefield Hospital, Hill End Road, Uxbridge UB9 6JH Tel: 01895 828692 Fax: 01895 822870 — MD Lond. 1973, MB BS 1962; MRCP Lond. 1968; MRCS Eng. LRCP Lond. 1962. (Guy's) Cons. Phys. (Thoracic Med.) Harefield Hosp. & Hemel Hempstead Gen. Hosp. Socs: Thoracic Soc.; FRCP (Lond.). Prev: Ho. Surg. Guy's Hosp. Lond.; Regist. (Med.) Qu. Mary's Hosp. Sidcup; Sen. Regist. Lond. Chest Hosp.

NATH, Aruna Medicines Control Agency, Department of Health, Market Towers, 1 Nine Elms Lane, Vauxhall, London SW8 5NQ Tel: 020 7273 0360 Fax: 020 7273 0293; Abbotswood, Bridle Way, Shirley Heath, Croydon CR0 5AH Tel: 020 8777 0464 — MB BS 1965 Delhi; FRCOG 1987, M 1970, DObst 1968; MFFP 1992; FFPM RCP (UK) 1990, M 1989. (Lady Hardinge Med. Coll.) Sen. Assessm. Cons. Med. Control Agency DoH; Hon. Outpat. Obst. & Gyn. St. Geo. Hosp. Lond.; Instruc. Med. Off. (Family Plann.). Socs: Fell. Roy. Soc. Med.; Nat. Assn. Family Plann. Doctors; Blair Bell Res. Soc. Prev: Research Fell. & Hon. Sen. Regist. (O & G) St. Bart. Hosp. Lond.; Regist. (O & G) W.m. Gp. Hosps.; Ho. Surg. (O & G) Kings Coll. Hosp. Lond.

NATH, Basdeo Karamchand The Baird Health Centre, Gassiot House, St. Thomas' Hospital, London SE1 7EH Tel: 020 7202 8300; 27 Rosemont Avenue, London N12 0BY Tel: 020 8446 2156 — MB ChB 1967 Glas.; T(GP) 1992. Civil. GP MoD Middlx. Socs: BMA & Med. Defence Union. Prev: Lect. Univ. Guyana S. Amer. Fac. Health Sci.

NATH, Mr Fredrik Prem 18 Bridge Street, Yarm TS15 9BY — MB ChB 1974 Liverp.; FRCS Ed. 1980. (Liverp.) Cons. Neurosurg. Middlesbrough Gen. Hosp. Prev: Sen. Regist. (Neurosurg.) S.. Gen. Hosp. Glas.

NATH, Jaharlal Doctor's Mess, Princess Royal Hospital, Lewes Road, Haywards Heath RH16 4EX; 14 Colwell Gardens, Haywards Heath, Haywards Heath RH16 4HG Tel: 01444 417040 — MB BS 1974 Calcutta; DRCOG 1990; MRCOG 1990. Staff Obst. (O & G) P.ss Roy. Hosp. Haywards Heath.

NATH, Kantimon Maerdy Surgery, North Terrace, Maerdy, Ferndale CF43 4DD Tel: 01443 733202 Fax: 01443 733730.

NATH, Mahendra Aston Hall Hospital, Aston-on-Trent, Derby DE72 2AL; 77 Wollaton Vale, Nottingham NG8 2PD — MB BS 1972 Bangalore; MRCPsych 1989. (Bangalore Medical College, India) Sen. Cons. Psychiat./Clin Dir. Prev: Sen. Regist.N. E. Thames Rotat. Scheme; Cons. Psychiat. Ballamona Hosp. Douglas Isle of Man.

NATH, Margaret Vicki 68 Russell Drive, Bearsden, Glasgow G61 3BB — MB ChB 1974 Liverp. (Liverp.)

NATH, Mohan Lal Treharris Health Centre, Bargoed Terrace, Treharris CF46 5RB Tel: 01443 410242 Fax: 01443 413312; 9 Glybargfed Close, Treharris CF46 6AJ — MB BS 1965 Calcutta. (R.G. Kar Med. Coll.)

NATH, Nirmal Kumar 51 Church Hill, Loughton IG10 1QP Tel: 020 8508 7477 — MB BS 1960 Calcutta; DA Eng. 1965. (R.G. Kar Med. Coll.) Assoc. Specialist (Anaesth.) Moorfields Hosp. Lond. Prev: Regist. (Anaesth.) Moorfields Eye Hosp. (City Rd. Br.) Lond.; Jun.

Ho. Off. (Med.) & SHO (Anaesth.) St. Jas. Hosp. Leeds; Regist. (Anaesth.) Hackney Hosp. Lond.

NATH, Pathikonda Uma 21 Beamish View, East Stanley, Stanley DH9 0XB — MB BS 1991 Newc.; BMedSc Newc. 1989; MRCP (UK) 1994. Regist. (Neurol.) RVI Newc.

NATH, Pathikonda Viswambara, MBE Front Street Surgery, 1 Front Street, Craghead, Stanley DH9 6DS Tel: 01207 232698; Tapaswi, 21 Beamish View, Stanley DH9 0XB Tel: 01207 290606 Fax: 01207 230712 — MB BS Mysore 1965; DLO Eng. 1970. GP. Socs: Acupunc. Soc.

NATH, R Queens Park and Moredon Surgeries, 146 Drove Road, Swindon SN1 3AG Tel: 01793 487394 Fax: 01793 342011 — MB BS 1962 Agra; MB BS 1962 Agra.

NATH, Rahul Abbotswood, Bridle Way, Croydon CR0 5AH — MB BCh 1992 Wales; BSc (Hons.) Pharmacol. Wales 1991, MB BCh 1992.

NATH, Samiran 10 Park Avenue, Grange Park, Gosforth, Newcastle upon Tyne NE3 2HL — MB ChB 1994 Ed.; BSc (Med. Sci.) Ed. 1992. Ho. Off. (Med.) Roy. Infirm. Edin.; Ho. Off. (Surg.) Qu. Margt. Hosp. Trust Dunfermline.

NATHA, Dharmesh Jayanti Bexley Hospital, 21 Heath House, Old Bexley Lane, Bexley DA5 2BW — MB BCh 1993 Witwatersrand.

***NATHA, Liaqat Ali** 67 Swan Lane, Bolton BL3 6TQ; 60 Swan Lane, Bolton BL3 6TQ — MB ChB 1997 Liverp.

***NATHA, Maksood Ibrahim** 2 Victoria Terrace, Hathersage Road, Longsight, Manchester M13 0HY — MB ChB 1995 Leeds.

NATHA, Mr Salim Christopher Home Eye Unit, Royal Albert Edward Infirmary, Wigan Lane, Wigan WN1 2NN Tel: 01942 822503 — MB ChB 1992 Liverp.; FRCOphth 1996. Cons. Opthamologist Roy. Albert Edwd. Infirm. Wigan. Prev: Specialist Regist. Mersey Rotat.

***NATHAN, Anita Rama** 32 Claremont Av, Beeston, Nottingham NG9 3DG — MB ChB 1997 Birm.

NATHAN, Bernard Edward 31 Langland Gardens, London NW3 6QE Tel: 020 7794 7136 — MB BCh 1962 Witwatersrand; FRCR 1975; FFR 1970; DMRD Eng. 1968. (Witwatersrand) Cons. Radiol. Edgware Gen. Hosp. & Hammersmith Hosp. Lond. Socs: Brit. Inst. Radiol. Prev: Sen. Regist. Hammersmith Hosp. Lond.

***NATHAN, James Alexander** 24 Lansdown Road, Redland, Bristol BS6 6NS — MB ChB 1998 Bristol.

NATHAN, Jeremy Charles David Wembley Park Medical Centre, 21 Wembley Park Drive, Wembley HA9 8HD — MB BS 1990 Lond.; BSc (Hons.) Lond. 1987, MB BS 1990; MRCGP 1994; DRCOG 1992.

NATHAN, Joanna Mary 160 Hatfield Road, St Albans AL1 4JD — BM 1996 Soton.

NATHAN, John Joseph The Health Centre, 10 Gresham Road, Oxted RH8 0BQ Tel: 01883 714361 Fax: 01883 722679; Summerhill, 39 Detillens Lane, Limpsfield, Oxted RH8 0DH — MB BS 1967 Lond.; MRCS Eng. LRCP Lond. 1966; DObst RCOG 1973. (King's Coll. Lond. & King's Coll. Hosp.) Prev: Regist. Rotat. (Surg.) Wessex RHB; SHO (Orthop.) Norf. & Norwich Hosp.; Ho. Surg. King's Coll. Hosp. Lond.

NATHAN, Laurence Andrew Longcroft Clinic, 5 Woodmanstene Lane, Banstead SM7 3HH Tel: 01737 359332 Fax: 01737 370835 — MB BS 1973 Lond.; MRCP (UK) 1976; MRCS Eng. LRCP Lond. 1973. (Westm.) Prev: Regist. (Radiother. & Oncol.) Roy. Marsden Hosp. Lond.; Regist. (Gen. Med.) Orpington Hosp.; Ho. Surg. Gordon Hosp. Lond.

NATHAN, Mark Peter Flat 1, 18 The Avenue, London NW6 7YD — MB ChB 1991 Manch.

NATHAN, Mr Nathan Walderslade Village Surgery, 62A Robin Hood Lane, Walderslade, Chatham ME5 9LD Tel: 01634 687250; 6 Meteor Road, Kate Reed Wood, West Malling, Maidstone ME18 6TH — MB BS 1981 Lond.; FRCS 1984; DCH Lond. 1986; DRCOG 1987. Prev: Trainee Bournehall Health Centre Ewell Epsom.; SHO (Cas.) St. Geo.'s Hosp.; SHO (Neurol. & Neuro-surg.) Atkinson Morley's Hosp. Wimbledon.

NATHAN, Nicholas John (Surgery), 3 Bridge St., Otley LS21 1BQ Tel: 01943 464001 Fax: 01943 461465 Email: bridgestreet@doctors.org.net; 45 Alwoodley Lane, Leeds LS17 7PU Tel: 0113 230 0106 Fax: 0113 295 7514 Email: njnathan@fdn.co.uk — MB ChB 1971 Leeds; MRCP (UK) 1976; Dip. Pract. Dermat. 1997. (Leeds) Hosp. Pract. (Genitourin. Med.) Leeds Gen. Infirm.; Med. Assessor Indep. Tribunal Serv. Prev: Regist.

(Gen. Med.) Wharfedale Gen. Hosp. Otley; SHO (Gen. Med.) Bradford Roy. Infirm.; SHO (Neurosurg.) Gen. Infirm. Leeds.

NATHAN, Nicki Lisa 160A High Road, London N2 9AS — MB BS 1990 Lond.

NATHAN, Paul Andrew Meadow House, Church View, Derby Road, Duffield, Belper DE56 4FL — BM BS Nottm. 1986. Chair. Centr. Derby PCG.

***NATHAN, Paul Daniel** 16 Augustus Close, Brentford Dock, Brentford TW8 8QE — MB BS 1996 Lond.

NATHAN, Peter Wilfred (retired) 85 Ladbroke Road, London W11 3PJ Tel: 020 7727 9445 Fax: 020 7229 0635 — MB BS 1939 Lond.; MD (Distinc.) Lond. 1952; FRCP Lond. 1964; MRCP (UK) 1940. Prev: Hon. Cons. Nat. Hosp. for Nerv. Dis.

NATHAN, Rajan Neil 39 The Ridgeway, Tarvin, Chester CH3 8JR — MB BCh 1991 Wales.

NATHAN, Mr Senthil Tel: 0207 636 8333 Fax: 0207 676 7076 Email: senthil.nathan@ucl.ac.uk; 58 Fitzjohn's Avenue, Hampstead, London NW3 5LT Tel: 0207 794 9715 Fax: 0207 431 0600 Email: senthil@snathan.co.uk — BM BS 1983 Madras; MPhil 1997 Lond.; 2000 FEBU European Board of Urology; 1990 FRCS Edin RCS Edin; 1987 MS; 1998 FRCS RCS Edin. (Madras Medical College) Cons Urol. UCL Hosp.s NHS Trust; Hon. Sen. Lec. Inst. Of Urol.; Hon. Cons Urol. Whittington Hosp NHS Trust. Socs: Brit. Soc. Of Urological Surg.; Euro Assoc. of Urol.; Brit. Med. Assoc.

NATHAN, Shirley Evelyn Brown Gables, Barnet Lane, Elstree, Borehamwood WD6 3RQ Tel: 020 8953 2350 Fax: 0208 953 7687 — MB BS 1951 Lond.; FRCGP 1981, M 1965; DObst RCOG 1953. (Univ. Coll. Hosp.) p/t Contract Med. Assessor for Hestor Disabil. Anal.

NATHAN, Thevakunchary 1 Aldridge Rise, New Malden KT3 5RJ — MB BS 1971 Ceylon.

***NATHAN, Yashica** 75 Elmfield Way, Sanderstead, Purley CR2 0EH — MB BS 1998 Lond.; MB BS Lond 1998.

***NATHANSON, Esther Charlotte** Fair Mile Hospital, Cholsey, Wallingford OX10 9HH — MB ChB 1996 Bristol.

NATHANSON, Michael Harvey Department of Anaesthesia, University Hospital, Queen's Medical Centre, Nottingham NG7 2UH Tel: 0115 970 9195 Fax: 0115 978 3891; Yorke Farm House, 130 Loughborough Road, Bradmore, Nottingham NG11 6PA — MB BS 1984 Lond.; MRCP (UK) 1988; FRCA 1991. (Middlesex Hospital Medical School) Cons. Anaesth. Univ. Hosp. Qu. Med. Centre Nottm. Socs: Assn. Anaesth.; Amer. Soc. Anesthesiol.; Anaesth. Res. Soc. Prev: Sen. Regist. (Anaesth.) Univ. Hosp. Qu. Med. Centre Nottm.; Vis. Asst. Prof. Univ. Texas S.W.ern Med. Center, USA; Regist. (Anaesth.) St. Bart. Hosp. Lond.

NATHANSON, Vivienne Hilary BMA House, Tavistock Square, London WC1H 9JP Tel: 020 7387 4499 Fax: 020 7383 6710 Email: vivn@bma.org.uk — MB BS 1978 Lond. Head of Prof. Resources & Research GP BMA. Socs: Scott. Sect. BMA (Ethics & Sci.). Prev: Regist. (Med.) Glan Clwyd Hosp. Bodelwyddan.

NATHAVITHARANA, Chandrika Priyani Geethamala 293 Quinton Road, Harborne, Birmingham B17 0RB — MB BS 1979 Peradeniya; MB BS Peradeniya, Sri Lanka 1979.

NATHAVITHARANA, Kamal Augustine The Nuffield Building, Francis Road, Birmingham B16 8ET Tel: 0121 454 4851 Fax: 0121 454 5383; The Gables, 232 Bristol Road, Edgbaston, Birmingham B5 7TA Tel: 0121 472 1896 — MB BS 1980 Sri Lanka; PhD Birm. 1989; MRCP (UK) 1986; DCH RCP Lond. 1987; FRCPCH, RCPCCH Lond. 1996. (Univ. Peradeniya Sri Lanka) Cons. (Paediat. & Gastroenterol.); Hon. Sen. Lect. Univ. Birm.; Sen. Lect. Univ. Warwick. Prev: Lect. (Paediat. & Child Health) Univ. Birm.; Tutor (Child Health) Univ. Manch.; Lect. (Paediat.).

NATHDWARAWALA, Mr Yogesh Ramdas Flat A, Panteg Hospital, Coedygrig Road, Griffithstown, Pontypool NP4 5YA — MB BS 1986 Baroda; MS (Orthop.) Baroda 1990, MB BS 1986. Regist. (Orthop.) Glan Clwyd Hosp. Rhyl. Prev: Regist. (Orthop.) Roy. Gwent Hosp. Newport.

NATHOO, Vijay 2 Glenholme Road, Bramhall, Stockport SK7 2BR — MB BCh 1982 Wales; LLM 2001 (LAMP) Wales; BSc Salford 1976; MSc Manch. 1977; MRCGP 1989; DRCOG 1986.

NATHOO, Yasmin 50 Grove Farm Park, Northwood HA6 2BQ — MB BS 1979 Newc.

NATHU, Azmeena Pennygate Surgery, 210 Pennygate, Spalding PE11 1LT Tel: 01775 710133.

NATHWANI, Ameet SmithKline Beecham R+D, New Frontiers Science Park (South), Harrow CM19 5AW Tel: 01279 646656 Fax: 01279 644976 Email: ameet_nathwani-1@sbphrd.com; 2 Axen Way, Osbourne Park, Welwyn Garden City AL7 1HR Tel: 01707 323638 Email: ameetnathwani@compuserve.com — MB BS 1987 Lond.; MRCP (UK) 1991. (Middlx. Hosp.) Dir. & Vice-Pres. (Cardio. Therepu.Team). Prev: Sen. Clin. Research Phys. (Cardiopulm. & Anti-infec.) SmithKline Beecham Pharmaceut. Welwyn Garden City.; Cardiovasc. Research Phys. Glaxo Research & Developm.; SHO (Path. & Haemat.) Ashford Hosp. Middlx., Gp. Dir. Cardiovasc. Clin. Developm. SmithKline Beecham Pharmaceut. Harlow.

NATHWANI, Amit Chunilal The Coppice, Kingfisher Lyre, Loudwater, Rickmansworth WD3 4ET — MB ChB 1984 Aberd.; MRCP (UK) 1988; MRCPath 1995. (Univ. Aberd.)

NATHWANI, Deepak Chandrakant 7A High Worple, Rayners Lane, Harrow HA2 9SJ — MB ChB 1987 Dundee; FRCA 1994. Sen. Regist. (Anaesth. & IC) The Roy. Free Hosp. Rotat. Lond. Prev: Sen. Regist. (Anaesth. & IC) The Nat. Hosp. for Nerv. Dis.s & Neurosurg. Lond.; Lect. Hon. Sen. Regist. (Anaesth.) N.wick Pk. & St. Marks Hosp. Harrow.

NATHWANI, Dilip Infection and Immunodeficiency Unit, Dundee Teaching Hospitals, Dundee DD3 8EA Tel: 01382 660111 Fax: 01382 816178; 3 William Street, Carnoustie DD7 6DG Email: nathwani@globalnet.co.uk — MB ChB 1984 Aberd.; FRCP Ed. 1995; MRCP (UK) 1988; DTM & H RCP Lond. 1992. Cons. Phys. (Infec.) & Hon. Sen. Lect. (Med.) Univ. Dundee Med. Sch.; Edr. in Chief CME Bull.-Infec. Dis. & Trop. Med.; Sec. Specialist Advis. Comm. for Train. in Infect Dis. & Trop. Med. Socs: Brit. Soc. Study of Infec.; Brit. Soc. Antimicrob. Chemother. Prev: Edr. Jl. Antimicrobial Chemother.

NATHWANI, Dinesh Kantilal 54 Kingsbridge Crescent, Southall UB1 2DL — MB ChB 1991 Sheff.; FRCS Irel. 1996. Specialist Regist. (Orthop. & Trauma Surg.) Roy. Liverp. Univ. Hosp.

NATHWANI, Nahendra 2 Bayons Avenue, Scartho, Grimsby DN33 3LN Tel: 01472 750143 — MB BS 1975 Calcutta.

NATIN, Daniel Joseph Mary Department of Genitourinary Medicine, Warwick Hospital, Lakin Road, Warwick CV34 5BW Tel: 01926 495321 Email: natingum@globalnet.co.uk — MB BCh BAO 1982 NUI; LRCPI, LRCSI 1982; MRCPI 1988. Cons. Genitourin. Med. S. Warks. Hosp. Prev: Sen. Regist. (Genitourin. Med.) N. Staffs. Hosp. Centre Stoke-on-Trent.

NATION, Caroline Barbara May 63 Shortwood Main Road, Mangotsfield, Bristol BS16 9NQ — MB ChB 1996 Bristol. VTS (Gen. Pract.) Univ. Bristol.

NATKUNARAJAH, Sarathadevi 1 Old Orchard Close, Barnet EN4 0ND — MB BS 1974 Sri Lanka; MRCS Eng. LRCP Lond. 1984; FFA RCSI 1984.

NATKUNARAJAH, Sellathurai 1 Old Orchard Close, Barnet EN4 0ND — MB BS 1973 Sri Lanka; MRCS Eng. LRCP Lond. 1983.

NATORFF, Benona Lillian Pharm-Olam International (UK) Ltd., The Brackens, London Road, Ascot SL5 8BE Tel: 01344 891121 Fax: 01344 890335 Email: dr.natorff@pharm-olam.co.uk; 28 Coworth Close, Sunningdale, Ascot SL5 0NR Tel: 01344 624746 Fax: 01344 875060 — Lekarz 1973 Warsaw. (Warsaw Med. Acad., Poland) Med. Dir. Pharm-Olam Internat. UK Ltd. Ascot; Clin. Research Off. Centr. & E. Europ. Socs: Brit. Assn. Psychopharmacol.; Drug Informat. Assn.; Fac. Pharmaceut. Med. RCP (UK). Prev: Med. Dir. Glaxo E. Europe Glaxo. Gp. Research Stockley Pk.; Clin. Research Phys. CNS Lilly Research Centre Windlesham; Clin. Research Fell. Human Psychopharm. Unit Med. Coll. St. Bart. & Roy. Lond. Med. Coll.

NATRAJAN, Krishnamoorthy 46 Abbotts Walk, Fleetwood FY7 6QG; 57 The Esplanade, Fleetwood FY7 6QE — MB BS 1971 Madras; FFA RCS Eng. 1978. Cons. (Cardiothoracic Anaesth.) S. Cleveland Hosp. Middlesbrough; Clin. Dir. Cardiothoracic IC S. Cleveland Hosp. Middlesbrough. Prev: Cons. Cardiothoracic Anaesth. Vict. Hosp. Blackpool; Sen. Regist. Qu. Eliz. Hosp. Birm. & Birm. Childr. Hosp.; Regist. (Anaesth.) N. Staffs Roy. Infirm. Stoke-on-Trent.

NATT, Antony Leo St Lawrence Road Doctors Surgery, 17-19 St. Lawrence Road, North Wingfield, Chesterfield S42 5LH Tel: 01246 851029 — MB BS 1978 Lond.; MRCP (UK) 1982; MRCS Eng. LRCP Lond. 1978; DCH RCP Lond. 1985; DRCOG 1984; DMedRehab RCP

NATT

Lond. 1983. (St Bartholomew's) Prev: Clin. Asst. (Rheum.) N. Derbysh. Dist. Gen. Hosp.

NATT, Rupinder Singh 11 Adamson Road, London NW3 3HX — BM BCh 1989 Oxf.

***NATTRASS, Anneliese** 27 Beech Hill Road, Wylde Green, Sutton Coldfield B72 1BY — MB ChB 1995 Leeds.

NATTRASS, John James (retired) 20 Landmere Grove, Lincoln LN6 0PD Tel: 01522 684545 — MB ChB 1959 Manch.; DObst. RCOG 1961. Prev: GP Lincoln.

NATTRASS, Malcolm Selly Oak Hospital, Raddlebarn Road, Birmingham B29 6JD Tel: 0121 627 1627 Fax: 0121 627 8758 — MB ChB Leeds 1970; PhD Soton 1982; BSc Leeds 1967; FRCP Lond. 1987; MRCP (UK) 1974; FRCPath 1993. Cons. Phys. Univ. Hosp. Birm. NHS Trust. Prev: Lect. (Chem. Path. & Human Metab.) Soton. Univ.

NATUCCI, Matteo Ovarian Scanning Clinic, 7th Floor, New World Block, Kings Cross Hospital, Denmark Hill, London SE5 9RS — State Exam Pavia 1991.

NATUSCH, Douglas Ian Torbay Hospital, South Devon Healthcare, Torquay TQ2 7AA Tel: 01803 614567 — MB ChB 1990 Manch.; MSc 2001 (Pain Management) University of Wales College of Medicine; BSc (Med. Sci.) St Andrews 1987. Cons. (Anaes & Pain Manag.). Socs: Pain. Soc; Int. Assoc. Study of Pain; Assoc. Anaes.

NATUSCH, Hilary Ann 55 Elms Road, Stockport SK4 4PT — MB ChB 1986 Manch.

NAUDEER, Sarah Fatimah Mariam 18 Carmalt Gardens, London SW15 6NE — MB BS 1993 Lond.

NAUGHTON, Anthony Thornton Practice, Church Road, Thornton-Cleveleys FY5 2TZ Tel: 01253 827231 Fax: 01253 863478 — MB ChB 1989 Manch.

NAUGHTON, Carol Ann The Surgery, Heywood, Lodway Gdns, Pill, Bristol BS20 0DN Tel: 01275 372105 Fax: 01275 373879 — MB ChB 1978 Bristol; MRCP (UK) 1981; MRCGP 1986; DRCOG 1985.

NAUGHTON, Mary Deidre Adcote House, Columbia Road, Oxton, Birkenhead CH43 6TU Tel: 0151 670 0031 Fax: 0151 670 6031 — MB BCh BAO 1985 NUI; MRCPsych 1990. Cons. Child & Adolesc. Psychiat. Prev: Lect. (Child & Adolesc. Psychiat.) Univ. Liverp.; Regist. St. Finans Hosp. Killarney Eire; Regist. Roy. Hosp. Sick Childr. Yorkhill Glas.

NAUGHTON, Michael Anthony Department of Rheumatology, Ealing Hospital, Uxbridge Road, Southall UB1 3HW — MB BCh BAO 1986 NUI; PhD Lond. 1997; MRCPI 1988. (Univ. Coll. Dub. Med. Sch.) Cons. Rheumat. Ealing Hosp.; Hon. Sen. Lect. Imperial Coll. Sc. Med. Hammersmith. Prev: Sen. Regist. (Rheum.) Char. Cross Hosp. Lond.; ARC Research Fell. Roy. Postgrad. Med. Sch. Lond.; Regist. (Rheum.) Univ. Hosp. Wales Cardiff.

NAUGHTON, Pauline Elizabeth Medical Services Examination Centre, Disability Benifit Centre, Fireways Complex, Islington Road, Middleway, Birmingham B15 1UT — MB BS 1981 Lond.; MBA (Pub. Serv.) Birm. 1995; MRCGP 1986; DRCOG 1984. (Char. Cross) Disabil. Analyst. Med. Serv.s Exam. Centre, Fireways Complex. Prev: Med. Off. DSS Edgbaston.; GP BRd.meadow; Police Surg. W. Midl.

NAUGHTON, Sophie Jane 10 Perry Road, Timperley, Altrincham WA15 7SU Tel: 0161 980 1695 — MB ChB 1993 Liverp.; DRCOG; DFFP; JCTPGP. (Liverpool) GP; Family Plann. Off. Socs: MDU. Prev: Gp Regist.; Paediat. SHO; O & G SHO.

NAUGHTON-DOE, Patrick Edward George Health Centre, Marmaduke Street, Hessle Road, Hull HU3 3BH Tel: 01482 327708 Fax: 01482 210250; 44 Wellesley Avenue, Beverley High Road, Hull HU6 7LW — MB ChB 1985 Leic. SHO (Gen. Med.) Leicester HA (T). Prev: Ho. Off. (Gen. Med./Cardiol.) & Ho. Off. (Gen. Surg./Neurosurg.); Hull HA.

NAUNTON, Andrew Peterborough District Hospital, Peterborough PE3 6DA — MB ChB 1974 Manch.; FFA RCS Eng. 1979. Cons. Anaesth. E. Anglian RHA. Prev: Sen. Regist. (Anaesth.) Brompton & W.m. Hosps.; Regist. (Anaesth.) Hosp. Sick Childr. Lond. & Soton. Gen. Hosp.

NAUNTON, William Johnson 182 Newmarket Road, Norwich NR4 6AR Tel: 01603 452035 — MRCS Eng. LRCP Lond. 1943; MA, MB BChir Camb. 1945; DOMS Eng. 1948. (Cambs. & Manch.) Prev: Emerit. Sen. Cons. Ophth. Surg. United Norwich Hosps.; Sen. Regist. Dept. Ophth. Univ. Manch.; Temp. Surg. Lt. RNVR.

NAUNTON MORGAN, Jonathan Clifford Bodnant Surgery, Menai Avenue, Bangor LL57 2HH Tel: 01248 364567 Fax: 01248 370654 — MB BS 1990 Lond.

NAUNTON MORGAN, Thomas Clifford Department of Diagnostic Radiology, West Middlesex University Hospital, Twickenham Road, Isleworth TW7 6AF Tel: 020 8565 5865 Fax: 020 8565 5251; 3 Campion Road, Putney, London SW15 6NN Tel: 020 8789 5211 Email: naunton@ndirect.co.uk — MB BS 1973 Lond.; FRCS Eng. 1979; MRCS Eng. LRCP Lond. 1973; FRCR 1987. (St. Bart.) Cons. Radiol. W. Middlx. Univ. Hosp. Isleworth; Cons. Radiol. Stamford Hosp.; Hon. Cons. Radiol. P.ss Margt. Hosp. Windsor. Socs: BMA; Worshipful Co. Barbers. Prev: Sen. Regist. (Radiol.) Char. Cross Hosp. Lond.; Regist. (Radiol.) W.m. Hosp. Lond.; Regist. (Surg.) Lond. Hosp. & Ipswich Hosp.

NAUTA, Maud Emilie 43 Duchess Road, Crumpsall, Manchester M8 5UP — Artsexamen 1993 Rotterdam.

NAUTH-MISIR, Mr Rohan Ravindra University College London Hospitals NHS Trust, The Institute of Urology, 48 Riding House St., London W1P 7PN Tel: 020 7636 8333 Fax: 020 7637 7076 Email: rohan.nauth@ucl.ac.uk — MB BS 1983 Lond.; BSc (Hons.) (Pharmacol.) Lond. 1980, MB BS 1983; FRCS Eng. 1987; FRCS (Urol.) 1995. (Lond. Hosp.) Cons. (Urol. & Transp. Surg.) Univ. Coll. Lond. Hosp. Trust Lond.; Hon. Sen. Lect. (Urol.) Inst. Urol. Lond. Socs: Brit. Assn. Urol. Surg.; Brit. Transpl. Soc.

NAUTH-MISIR, Tikai Narendra (retired) Owlets, The Glade, Hutton Mount, Brentwood CM13 2JL Tel: 01277 222443 — MB BS Lond. 1941; FRCP Lond. 1973, M 1949; MRCS Eng. LRCP Lond. 1940; DCH Eng. 1947. Prev: Cons. Paediatr. OldCh. Hosp. Romford & Harold Wood Hosp.

NAVA, Gillian Manor Farm House, Stratford Road, Honeybourne, Evesham WR11 5PP — MB ChB 1976 Birm.; MRCOG 1983.

NAVA, Peter Linton The Health Centre, High Street, Bidford-on-Avon, Alcester B50 4BQ Tel: 01789 773372 Fax: 01789 490380 — MB ChB 1981 Birm.; PhD Birm. 1981, BSc (Hons.) 1974, MB ChB 1981; MRCGP 1986.

NAVAMANI, Alexander Sharon Mayfield Surgery, 246 Roehampton Lane, Roehampton, London SW15 4AA Tel: 020 8780 5770; 14 Queen's Court, Queen's Road, Richmond TW10 6LA Tel: 020 8332 6489 — MB BS 1994 Lond.; DRCOG 1997; MRCGP. (St. Bartholomew's Hospital Medical College) GP Regist.

NAVAMANI, Sterlin Bretton Health Centre, Rightwell, Bretton, Peterborough PE3 8DT Tel: 01733 264506 Fax: 01733 266728 — MB BS 1967 Madras; DLO Madurai 1970. (Madurai Med. Coll.)

NAVAN EETHA RAJAH, Prithvia 45 Granville Park W., Aughton, Ormskirk L39 5HS — MB ChB 1992 Liverp.

NAVANEETHARAJA, Nadarajah Ethelbert Gardens Surgery, 63-65 Ethelbert Gardens, Ilford IG2 6UW Tel: 020 8550 3740 Fax: 020 8550 4300 — MB BS 1981 Colombo; MB BS 1981 Colombo.

NAVANEETHARAJAH, Beatrice Mary Jessie 45 Granville Park W., Aughton, Ormskirk L39 5HS — MB BS 1962 Ceylon; DPH Liverp. 1972. (Ceylon)

NAVANEETHARAJAH, Navaratnam Britonside Avenue Surgery, 41 Britonside Avenue, Southdene, Kirkby, Liverpool L32 6RZ Tel: 0151 546 2409 Fax: 0151 548 1941 — MB BS 1963 Ceylon. (Ceylon)

NAVANI, L High Street Surgery, 190 High Street, Feltham TW13 4HY Tel: 020 8751 3404 Fax: 020 8890 4858 — MB BS 1969 Rajasthan; MB BS 1969 Rajasthan.

NAVANI, Sunil Department of Obstetrics & Gynaecology, Doctor Grays Hospital, Elgin IV30 1SN; 44 Smith Drive, Elgin IV30 4NE — MB BS 1983 Bombay; MRCOG 1993.

NAVAPURKAR, Vilas Umesh 7 Russell Road, Moor Park, Northwood HA6 2LJ — MB ChB 1986 Dundee; FRCA 1992; DA (UK) 1988. Sen. Regist. (Anaesth.) Addenbrooke's NHS Trust Camb. Socs: Intens. Care Soc.; Assn. Anaesth. Prev: Research Fell. (Clin. Intens. Care) Camb.; Regist. (Anaesth.) Trent RHA; SHO (Neonat. & Adult Intens. Care) Camb.

NAVARATNAM, Anton Elmo Devanayagam (retired) 28 Chestnut Close, Duffield Hall, Duffield, Derby DE56 4HD — MB BS 1956 Ceylon; FRCP Lond. 1980; MRCP Ed. 1969; MRCP (U.K.) 1969. Mem. Indep. Tribunal. Serv. Prev: Cons. Dermat. Derbysh. Gp. Hosps. Derby.

***NAVARATNAM, Manchula** 8 Valley Park, Hermitage Park, Wrexham LL13 7GW — MB ChB 1997 Ed.

NAVARATNAM, Romesh Marino 28 Chestnut Close, Duffield, Derby DE56 4HD; 66 Nursey Road, Pinner, Harrow HA5 2AR — BM BS 1990 Nottm.; BmedSci (Hons) Nottm 1988; FRCS (Lond) 1994; MSC (Lond) 1998. Specialist Regist. Clin. Research Fell. Roy. Free Hosp. Lond. NW3.

NAVARATNAM, Seeniar 5 Windy Hill, Hutton, Brentwood CM13 2HF Tel: 01277 223981 — MB BS 1964 Ceylon; FRCP Lond. 1971; DPhysMed Eng. 1971; DCH Eng. 1969. (Colombo) Cons. Rheum. & Rehabil. Basildon & Thurrock HA; Cons. Essex Nuffield Hosp Brentwood; BUPA Hartswood Hosp. Brentwood; Chesterfield Pk. Hosp. Orpington Kent. Socs: Fell. Roy. Soc. Med.; Brit. Soc. Rheum. & BMA. Prev: Sen. Regist. Dept. Rheum. & Rehabil. Univ. Coll. Hosp. Lond.; Regist. Dept. Rheum. & Rehabil. Roy. Free Hosp. Lond.; SHO (Gen. Med.) Tottenham Gp. Hosps.

NAVARATNAM, Visvanathan School of Anatomy, University, Downing St., Cambridge CB2 3DZ Tel: 01223 333750 Fax: 01223 333786 Email: vn@mole.bio.cam.ac.uk; 93 Gilbert Road, Cambridge CB4 3NZ — MB BS Ceylon 1957; PhD Camb. 1964. (Colombo) Univ. Lect. (Anat.) & Dir. Med. Studies Christ's Coll. Camb. Socs: Anat. Soc. Prev: Ho. Off. Gen. Hosp. Kandy, Ceylon.

NAVARATNAM, Yogaranjitham 3 Kilmaine Drive, Ladybridge, Bolton BL3 4RU — MB BS 1975 Sri Lanka; LRCP LRCS Ed. LRCPS Glas. 1988.

NAVARATNARAJAH, Grace Chandraranee Park Side Health Authority Medical Centre, Woodfield Road, London W9; 69 Hayes Lane, Kenley CR8 5JR Tel: 020 8668 5461 — MB BS 1967 Ceylon. Clin. Med. Off. (Community Paediat.) Pk. Side AHA. Prev: SHO Rotat. (Psychiat.) St. Bart. Hosp. Lond.

NAVARATNARAJAH, Murugesu Anaesthetic Department, May Day Hospital, Croydon — MB BS 1973 Ceylon; MRCS Eng. LRCP Lond. 1979; FFA RCS Lond. 1980. Cons. (Anaesth.) Croydon Dist. HA; Sen. Regist. (Anaesth.) (Rotat.) Roy. Free Hosp. Lond., N.wick Pk. Hosp. & Clin. Research Centre Harrow. Socs: Croydon Med Soc. Prev: Regist. (Anaesth.) Whittington Hosp. & Whipps Cross Hosp. Lond.

NAVARATNE, Lesley Amy 9 Birch Grove, Pyrford, Woking GU22 8NB — MB BS 1992 Lond.; MRCP Lond. 1998. (The London Hospital Medical College)

NAVARATNE, Mohottalage Flat 7,Rowan House, Oakapple Lane, Maidstone ME16 9QQ — LRCP LRCS 1987 Ed.; LRCP LRCS Ed. LRCPS Glas. 1987.

NAVARRO SERRANO, Oscar Stepping Hill Hospital, Elm House, Poplar Grove, Stockport SK2 7JE — LMS 1989 Saragossa.

NAVARRO-WEITZEL, Ilona Claudia Royal London Hospital, Department of Anaesthetics, Whitechapel, London E1 1BB Tel: 020 7377 7700; 55 Highbury New Park, Basement Flat, London N5 2ET Tel: 020 7226 5415 — State Exam Med 1992 Freiburg. SHO (Cardiothoracic Surg.) Roy. Brompton Hosp. Lond. Prev: SHO (A & E) St Bart. Hosp. Lond.

NAVAS, Frank (retired) Alviento, Gorsewood Drive, Hakin, Milford Haven SA73 3EP Tel: 01646 695804 — MB BCh Wales 1958; DObst RCOG 1963. Prev: SHO (O & G) H.M. Stanley Hosp. St. Asaph.

NAVE, Elmar Ward Medical Centre, Medomsley Road, Consett DH8 5HR Tel: 01207 502266 Fax: 01207 506077; Haining Bank, Strathmore Road, Rowlands Gill NE39 1JA Tel: 01207 542678 — MB BS 1960 Durh.

NAVEIN, John Francis, Maj. RAMC 46 Abercorn Crescent, Harrow HA2 0PT — MB ChB 1979 Liverp.; MRCS Eng. LRCP Lond. 1979; MRCGP 1984; DTM & H Liverp. 1986; DCH RCP Lond. 1985. Sen. Med. Off. Penanjong Garrison Roy. Brunei Armed Forces.

NAVEN, Tom Barrhead Health Centre, 203 Main Street, Barrhead G78 1HG Tel: 0141 880 6161 Fax: 0141 881 7036; The Oaks, Kingston Road, Neilston, Glasgow G78 3HZ — MB BCh BAO 1976 NUI; MRCGP 1991. (Galway, Ireland) GP Glas.

NAVEY, Fleur Louise Tel: 020 8993 8058 Fax: 020 8993 8058 — MB BS 1982 Lond.; MRCGP 1988; Cert. Family Plann. JCC 1988. (Lond. Hosp.) Locum GP (Freelance); Mem. A & E Primary Care Team St. Mary's Hosp. Lond.; Health Screening Doctor Clementine Ch.ill Hosp. (p/t). Socs: BMA; Roy. Coll. Gen. Pract. Prev: Princip. GP The Gr. Health Centre Lond.; SHO (Infec. Dis.) St. Ann's Hosp. Tottenham; Ho. Off. The Lond. Hosp. Mile End.

NAVIN, William Patrick 57 Walsgrave Road, Gosford Green, Coventry CV2 4HF Tel: 024 76 222271 — MB BCh BAO 1940 NUI.

NAWAL, Hari Charan Singh Goldington Road Surgery, 12 Goldington Road, Bedford MK40 3NE Tel: 01234 352493 — DPM 1974 Dublin; DPM 1974 London; MB BS 1962 Vikram.

NAWARI, Elzahawi Omer Mohamed 5D Margham House, St. Mary's Hospital, Newport PO30 5TG — MB ChB 1982 Alexandria; MRCP (UK) 1994.

NAWARSKI, Bernard John 14 Highfield Crescent, Northwood HA6 1EZ — MB BS 1996 Lond.

NAWAZ, Mohamed 34 Rennishaw Way, Links View, Northampton NN2 7NE — MB BS 1964 Ceylon. (Colombo) Clin. Asst. (Psychogeriat.) N.ampton HA. Prev: Med. Off. Gen. Hosp. Kurunagala, Sri Lanka; Ho. Off. Govt. Hosp. Matale, Sri Lanka & Govt. Hosp. Avissawella, Sri; Lanka.

NAWAZ, Mohammad 14 Park Lane, Aberdare CF44 8HN — MB BS 1966 Peshawar.

NAWAZ, Rashad Mehmood 25 Wingfield Mount, Bradford BD3 0AG — MB ChB 1992 Manch.

NAWAZ, Mr Shah Clinical Sciences Centre, Hermes Road, Northern General Hospital, Sheffield S5 7AU Tel: 0114 271 4648 Email: s.nawaz@sheffield.ac.uk; 11 Ferrars Drive, Sheffield S9 1WU Tel: 0114 244 6069 — MB ChB 1991 Aberd.; FRCS 1995. Lect. Univ. of Sheff. Socs: Rouceaux Club; SRS. Prev: SHO (Surg.) York. Dist. Hosp.

NAWAZ, Shahid 1 St Andrews Drive, Alwoodley, Leeds LS17 7TR — MB BS 1972 Punjab; MB BS Punjab (Pakistan) 1972; MRCPI 1977; MRCP (UK) 1977; LMSSA Lond. 1977. (King Edwd. Med. Coll. Lahore)

***NAWAZ, Shokat** 87 St Lawrence Road, Sheffield S9 1SB — MB ChB 1998 Sheff.; MB ChB Sheff 1998.

NAWROCKA, Aleksandra Stefania 1 Sefton Road, Petts Wood, Orpington BR5 1RG Tel: 01689 824716 — MB ChB Wroclaw 1951; DCH 1955; LAH Dub. 1969. (Wroclaw Univ. Poland) Prev: Jun. Regist. Our Lady's Hosp. Dub.

NAWROCKI, Albert Sharmont, Deepdene Avenue, Croydon Tel: 020 8688 3634 — MB ChB 1963 St. And.; MRCGP 1977. Prev: Clin. Adviser (Rhuematol.) S.W. Thames Region; Clin. Asst. Roy. Marsden Hosp. Lond.; Resid. in Med. Mayo Clinic U.S.A.

NAWROCKI, Mr Jan Dominik Princess Royal Hospital, Lewes Road, Haywards Heath RH16 4EX Tel: 01444 441881 Fax: 01444 455895 — MB BS 1985 Lond.; MS Lond. 1995; FRCS Eng. 1989; FRCS (Urol.) 1996. (King's College London) Cons. Urol. P.ss Roy. Heath & Roy. Sussex Co. Hosp. Brighton. Prev: Sen. Regist. Urol., Guy's Hosp. Lond.; Regist. Urol. Inst. Urol., Middlx. Hosp. Lond.; Regist. Gen. Surg., King's Coll. Hosp.

NAWROOZ, Neamat Mohamad Jawad 7 Brookview, Fulwood, Preston PR2 8FG — MB ChB 1979 Basrah, Iraq; DCH Glas. 1985. Staff Grade (Community Child Health) Blackburn Communicare NHS Trust.

NAY WIN, Dr 7 Langley Grove, New Malden KT3 3AL — MB BS 1979 Rangoon; FRCP (UK) 1996; MRCP (UK) 1985; MRCPath 1992. Cons. Haemat. NBS, S. Thames Centre Lond.

NAYAGAM, Andrew Thanaraj Warren Brown Unit, Southlands Hospital, Upper Shoreham Road, Shoreham-by-Sea BN43 6TQ Tel: 01273 461453 Fax: 01273 446049; 93 Woodland Drive, Hove BN3 6DF Tel: 01273 501894 — MB BS 1972 Ceylon; FRCP (UK) 1996; MRCP (UK) 1983; MRCS Eng. LRCP Lond. 1981. Cons. Genitourin. Med. S.lands Hosp. Shoreham. Socs: Med. Soc. Study VD; Brit. Soc. Of Colposcopy & Cervial Path.; BMA. Prev: Sen. Regist. (Genitourin. Med.) Univ. Coll. Hosp. Lond.; Regist. (Genitourin. Med.) Roy. Lond. Hosp.; Regist. (Dermat.) Hull Roy. Infirm.

NAYAGAM, Mr Selvadurai 30 Eshe Road N., Crosby, Liverpool L23 8UF Tel: 0151 924 3019 Fax: 0151 931 5405 Email: s.nayagam@dial.pipex.com — MB ChB 1984 Manch.; BSc St. And. 1981; MCh (Orth.) Liverp. 1995; FRCS (Orth.) 1996; FRCS Ed. 1989. Cons. (Orthop. & Trauma Surg.) Roy. Liverp. Univ. Hosp. Roy. Liverp. Childr. Hosp. Socs: Fell. Roy. Soc. Med.; Brit. Limb Reconstruc. Soc.; Fell. BOA. Prev: Career Regist. (Orthop. Surg.) Mersy RHA; SHO (Orthop. & Gen. Surg.) Roy. Liverp. Hosp.; Sen. Resid. (Orthop. Surg.) Mass. Gen. Hosp. Boston, USA.

NAYAK, Baidya Nath Wigan Infirmary, Wigan Lane, Wigan WN1 Tel: 01942 244000; 71 Ormskirk Road, Knowsley, Prescot L34 8HB Tel: 0151 546 1151 — MB BS 1962 Calcutta; FRCP Lond. 1994; MRCP (UK) 1971. Socs: BMA & Brit. Geriat. Soc. Prev: Cons. Phys.

NAYAK

Med. for Elderly Leigh & Wigan Trust; Cons. Phys. Med. for Elderly St. Helens & Knowsley HA.

NAYAK, Geeta Prashant Roby Medical Centre, 70-72 Pilch Lane East, Roby, Liverpool L36 4NP Tel: 0151 449 1972 Fax: 0151 489 4020; 1 Calderfield Road, Calderstones, Liverpool L18 3HB Tel: 0151 722 8800 — MB BS 1972 Baroda. (M.S. Univ. Med. Coll.) Princip. GP Roby. Prev: Regist. (Chest Med.) Liverp. AHA (T).

*NAYAK, Neena 56 Nairn Street, Crookes, Sheffield S10 1UN — MB ChB 1994 Sheff.

NAYAK, Prashant Raghubhai Claremont Medical Practice, 171-173 Liverpool Road S., Maghull, Liverpool L31 8AA Tel: 0151 520 3060 Fax: 0151 520 3080; 1 Calderfield Road, Calderstones, Liverpool L18 3HB Tel: 0151 722 6700 — MB BS 1970 Delhi; MS (Orthop.) Delhi 1974. (Maulana Azad Med. Coll.) GP Princip. Maghull. Prev: Regist. (Orthop.) Liverp. HA; SHO (Orthop.) Walton Hosp. Liverp.; Sen. Resid. (Orthop.) Centr. Inst. Orthop.

*NAYAK, Shilpa 1 Caderfield Road, Calderstones, Liverpool L18 3HB — MB ChB 1996 Liverp.

NAYANI, Guruprasada Rao 2 Solar Court, Great Linford, Milton Keynes MK14 5HD — MB BS 1969 Bombay.

NAYANI, Salim Bradgate Mental Health Unit, Glenfield Hospital, Groby Road, Leicester LE3 9EJ Tel: 0116 250 2662 Fax: 0116 250 2651 Email: salim_nayani@compuserve.com; 33 The Huntings, Kirby Muxloe, Leicester LE9 2BX — MB BS 1977 Karachi; MMedSc Leeds 1987; MRCPsych 1985. Cons. Psychiat. Leicestersh. Ment. Health, NHS Trust. Prev: Sen. Regist. (Psychiat.) Leicester Gen. Hosp.

NAYANI, Tanveer Husein 6 Colville Terrace, London W11 2BE — MB BS 1986 Lond.

NAYAR, Anoop 10 Bengeworth Road, Harrow HA1 3SE — MB BS 1982 Lond.

NAYAR, Asha Woodley Health Centre, Hyde Road, Woodley, Stockport SK6 1ND Tel: 0161 494 0213 Fax: 0161 406 9231; 43 Winnington Road, Marple, Stockport SK6 6PT Tel: 0161 427 7181 — MB BS 1967 Rajasthan; MSc Audiol. Med. Manch. 1992. (S.M.S. Med. Coll. Jaipur) SCMO Stockport AHA. Socs: Fac. Community Health. Prev: Clin. Med. Off. Stockport & Tameside AHA.

NAYAR, Janaky Kutty Newland Health Centre, 187 Cottingham Road, Hull HU5 2EG Tel: 01482 492219 Fax: 01482 441418 — MB BS 1970 Kerala. GP Sen. Partner.

NAYAR, Manjit Singh Lucie Wedgewood Health Centre, Chapel Lane, Burslem, Stoke-on-Trent ST6 2AD Tel: 01782 834488 Fax: 01782 837738 — MB BS 1959 Panjab.

NAYAR, Omesh Kumar Uttoxeter Road Surgery, 669 Uttoxeter Road, Meir, Stoke-on-Trent ST3 5PZ Tel: 01782 313884; Langdale, 963 Lightwood Road, Lightwood, Stoke-on-Trent ST3 7NE Tel: 01782 392702 — MB BS 1961 Bombay; MRCGP 1976; DCH Eng. 1962. (Grant Med. Coll.) Clin. Asst., Geriat.s, Longton Cottage Hosp., Stoke on Trent.

*NAYAR, Pritibala 14 Sneyd Av, Newcastle ST5 2PP — MB BS 1997 Lond.

NAYAR, Rahul 336 Wilbraham Road, Manchester M21 0UX — MB ChB 1993 Manch.

NAYAR, Rosebind Noreen 49 Highfields, Llandaff, Cardiff CF5 2QB — MB BS 1961 Punjab; DA 1964.

NAYAR, Vijay Krishan Bedford Road Surgery, 273 Bedford Road, Kempston, Bedford MK42 8QD Tel: 01234 852222 Fax: 01234 843558; 126 Putnoe Lane, Bedford MK41 8LA Tel: 01234 402998 — MB BS 1986 Lond.; BSc (Hons.) Lond. 1983; MRCGP 1990; DRCOG 1990; DCH RCP Lond. 1989; Cert. Family Plann. JCC 1989. (Middlx. & Univ. Coll. Hosp.) Course Organiser Bedford GP VTS.

NAYEEM, Mr Nadeem Accident & Emergency Department, Lewisham Hospital, Lewisham High St., London SE13 6LH Tel: 020 8333 3058 Fax: 020 8333 3109 Email: nnayeem2@yahoo.com — MB BS 1980 Karachi; FRCS Ed. 1986. Cons. A & E Lewisham Hosp. Lond. Socs: Brit. Assn. Accid. & Emerg. Med.; Roy. Soc. Med. Lond. Prev: Sen. Regist. (A & E) Guy's Hosp. Lond.; Regist. (A & E) Milton Keynes Gen. Hosp.; Regist. (Gen. Surg.) OldCh. Hosp. Romford.

NAYEEMUDDIN, Farzana Anjum 11 Bromsberrow Way, Stoke-on-Trent ST3 7UE Tel: 01782 388600 — MB ChB 1995 Leeds. SHO (Med.) Stoke-on-Trent.

NAYER, Parvathy Learning Difficulties Service, St Leonards D Block, Nuttall Street, Hackney, London N1 5LZ Tel: 020 7301 3107 Email: parvanayor@yahoo.com; Tel: 020 8926 0462 — MB BS 1972 Kerala; MRCPsych 1984. (Med. Coll. Trivandrum) Cons. Psychiat. E. Lond. and the City Ment. Health Trust. Prev: Sen. Lect. & Hon. Cons. Psychiat. (Learning Difficulties) St. Bart. Med. Coll.

*NAYLER, Lisa 16 Horsa Road, Bournemouth BH6 3AL — MB BS 1998 Lond.; MB BS Lond 1998.

NAYLOR, Andrew Ian The Surgery, Ferry Road, Leverburgh, Isle of Harris HS5 3UA Tel: 01859 520278 Fax: 01859 520202; 18 Ferry Road, Leverburgh, Isle of Harris HS5 3UA Tel: 01859 520200 — MB BS 1985 Newc.; MRCGP 1989; DGM RCP Lond. 1989. Socs: BASICS; Brit. Geriat. Soc. Prev: Trainee GP Cleveland VTS.

NAYLOR, Andrew Mark Antony, Surg. Lt.-Cdr. RN Grove House Surgery, 80 Pryors Lane, Rose Green, Bognor Regis PO21 4JB Tel: 01243 265222/266413 Fax: 01243 268693 — MB BS 1985 Lond. (Guy's)

NAYLOR, Mr Andrew Ross Department of Surgery, Clinical Sciences Building, Leicester Royal Infirmary, Leicester LE1 5WW Tel: 0116 258 6136 Fax: 0116 252 3179; 9 Dalby Avenue, Bushby, Leicester LE7 9RE Tel: 0116 241 7318 — MB ChB 1981 Aberd.; MD Aberd. 1990; FRCS Ed. 1986; FRCS Eng. 1998. (Aberdeen) Cons. Surg. Vasc. Leicester Roy. Infirm.; Hon. Sen. Lect. (Surg.) Leicester Univ. Socs: Vasc. Surgic. Soc.; Eur. Vasc. Soc. Prev: Cons. Surg. Vasc. Unit Aberd. Roy. Infirm.; Lect. (Surg.) Leicester Univ.

NAYLOR, Ann Frances (retired) 4 Huskards, Fryerning, Ingatestone CM4 0HR Tel: 01277 354841 Fax: 01277 355959 — MB BS 1961 Lond.; MRCS Eng. LRCP Lond. 1961; FRCA Eng. 1965; DA Eng. 1963. p/t Clin. Adviser to Health Serv. Ombudsman.

NAYLOR, Arthur (retired) Moat Cottage, Midgley Lane, Goldsborough, Knaresborough HG5 8NN Tel: 01423 865775 — MB ChB 1937 Sheff.; MSc Sheff. 1935, BSc (Hons.) 1934. MD 1989, ChM 1940; FRCS Eng. 1944; FRCS Ed. 1939. Hon. Cons. Surg. Orthop. Roy. Infirm. Bradford, Bradford Hosp., Woodlands Orthop. Hosp. Rawdon & St. Luke's Hosp. Bradford. Prev: Temp. Maj. RAMC.

NAYLOR, Carolyn Ruth Yew Tree Medical Centre, 100 Yew Tree Lane, Solihull B91 2RA Tel: 0121 705 8787 Fax: 0121 709 0240 — MB ChB 1991 Birm.; ChB Birm. 1991.

NAYLOR, Mr Christopher Hardy The Portland Hospital, 212-214 Great Portland Street, London W1W 5QN Tel: 020 7935 6911 Fax: 020 8905 2412 Email: dr@naylor0.demon.co.uk; 35 Chiswick Quay, Hartington Road, London W4 3UR Tel: 020 8995 8701 Fax: 020 8995 1233 Email: dr@naylor0.demon.co.uk — MB BCh 1958 Wales; FRCOG 1981, M 1968, DObst. 1961. (Cardiff) Cons. O & G Centr. Middlx. Hosp. Lond.; Hon. Sen. Lect. Univ. Coll. Hosp., Lond. Socs: Roy. Soc. Med.; Brit. Med. Assn.; Hosp. Cons.s & Specialists Assn. Prev: Sen. Regist. Qu. Charlotte's Hosp. & Chelsea Hosp. Wom. Lond.; Regist. King's Coll. Hosp. Lond.; Ho. Off. Matern. Hosp. Cardiff.

NAYLOR, Doris Helen Ruth 86 Blockley Road, Sudbury Court, Wembley HA0 3LW Tel: 020 8904 3073 — MB ChB 1964 Liverp.; DA Eng. 1973. (Liverp.) Clin. Asst. Anaesth. Centr. Middlx. Hosp. Lond. Prev: Ho. Surg. & Ho. Phys. Roy. S. Hosp. Liverp.; SHO (Anaesth.) Nottm. City Hosp.; Clin. Asst. Anaesth. N.wick Pk. Hosp.

NAYLOR, Edwin Gilderdale (retired) 18 Little Dene Copse, Pennington, Lymington SO41 8EW Tel: 01590 72021 — MB ChB St. And. 1945.

*NAYLOR, Emma Louise 16 The Paddocks, Nuthall, Nottingham NG16 1DR — MB ChB 1998 Sheff.; MB ChB Sheff 1998.

NAYLOR, Frances Louise Pelaw Medical Practice, 7&8 Croxdale Terrace, Pelaw, Gateshead NE10 0RR; 83 St. Marys Field, Morpeth NE61 2QQ — MB BS 1991 Newc.; MRCGP 196; DRCOG 1994; DFFP 1996. GP Princip. 6/9 Time. Socs: MRCGP; Dip. Roy. Coll. Obs & Gyn.; Dip. Fac. Fam. Plan. & Repro. Health c/o RCOG.

NAYLOR, Mr Gerald 222 Norbreck Road, Thornton-Cleveleys FY5 1PD — MB ChB 1981 Leeds; FRCS Ed. 1986; FRCOphth 1989. Cons. Ophth. Blackpool. Vict. Hosp. Prev: Regist. (Ophth.) Birm. & Midl. Eye Hosp.

NAYLOR, Graham John (retired) Little Acres, Baltic Road, Kirk Michael IM6 1EF Tel: 01624 878377 — MB ChB Sheff. 1962; BSc Sheff. 1965, MD 1970; FRCPsych 1976, M 1970; DPM Ed. & Glas. 1967. Prev: Cons. Psychiat. Tayside HB.

NAYLOR, Gregory Michael Plumtree House, Prescot Road, Aughton, Ormskirk L39 6TA — MB ChB 1990 Sheff.

NAYLOR, Heather Ann Doctors Surgery, Hinnings Road, Distington, Workington CA14 5UR Tel: 01946 830207; 35 Broombank, Whitehaven CA28 6SB — MB BS 1989 Newc.; MRCGP

1993; DRCOG 1992. Prev: SHO (Elderly Care) W. Cumbld. Hosp. Whitehaven; SHO (O & G) N. Tyneside Hosp. N. Shields.

NAYLOR, Mr Henry Gordon (retired) Timbers, 63 Ardleigh Green Road, Hornchurch RM11 2JZ Tel: 01708 449524 Fax: 01708 453488 — MB BS Lond. 1960; FRCS Eng. 1967; MRCS Eng. LRCP Lond. 1960. Prev: Cons. Surg. Basildon & Thurrock Gen. Hosps. NHS Trust.

NAYLOR, Howard Christopher 6 Havering Close, Great Wakering, Southend-on-Sea SS3 0AF — MB ChB 1979 Bristol; FFA RCS Eng. 1984. Cons. Anaesth. S.end HA. Prev: Sen. Regist. (Anaesth.) Mersey RHA.

NAYLOR, Jane Mary Pool Health Centre, Station Road, Pool, Redruth TR15 3DU Tel: 01209 717471; 33 Higher Penponds, Camborne TR14 0QG — BM BS 1986 Nottm.; BMedSci (Hons.) Nottm. 1984. Prev: Trainee GP Pool Health Centre Cornw.; SHO (O & G) Redruth & Truro Hosp.; SHO (A & E) Derbysh. Roy. Infirm.

NAYLOR, Janet Sarah 2 Monarch Close, Locks Heath, Southampton SO31 6UG — BM 1992 Soton.

NAYLOR, John Edward (retired) Jays Nest, Welford Road, Chapel Brampton, Northampton NN6 8AF Tel: 01604 843838 — MB BChir 1949 Camb.; MA Camb. 1949; MRCGP 1963.

NAYLOR, John Richard Medicine For The Elderly, St Luke's Hospital, Blackmoorfoot Road, Huddersfield HD4 5RQ — MB ChB 1985 Leeds; MRCP (UK) 1988.

NAYLOR, Jonathan Richard, Flight Lt. RAF Med. Br. MDHU, Peterborough District Hospital, Thorpe Road, Peterborough PE3 6DA Tel: 01733 874000 Email: jonnaylor@bedlam20.freeserve.co.uk; 3 Nene Close, Wittering, Peterborough PE8 6BP — MB ChB 1994 Manch.; MRCP (UK) 1999. Specialist Regist. Gen. Med. P'boro. Dist. Hosp. MOD Unit. Socs: Internat. Soc. Mt.ain Med. Prev: SHO (Inten. Care) Roy. Brompton Hosp.; SHO (Gen. Med.) PeterBoro. dist. Hosp.; Jun. Med. Off. RAF, Cranwell.

NAYLOR, Joyce Parker (retired) Jays Nest, Welford Road, Chapel Brampton, Northampton NN6 8AF — MB ChB 1949 Leeds.

NAYLOR, Karen Jacqueline 32 Mandeville Close, Weymouth DT4 9HP — BM 1989 Soton.

NAYLOR, Kathryn Phyllis Ashworth Hospital, Maghull, Liverpool L31 1HW Tel: 0151 473 0303 — MB ChB 1991 Liverp.

NAYLOR, Kevin Michael Thomas 5 Carlton Road, Worsley, Manchester M28 7TT — MB ChB 1985 Sheff.; MRCGP 1989.

NAYLOR, Professor Paul Francis Dorian Manor Park, Broadway, Sidmouth EX10 8HS Tel: 01395 516131 — MB BChir 1948 Camb.; MD Camb. 1954, MA 1948. (Camb. & St. Thos) Emerit. Prof. Dermat. Univ. Lond.; Hon. Cons. Dermat. St. Thos. Hosp. Lond. Socs: Brit. Assn. Dermat. Prev: Prof. Dermat. St. Thos. Hosp. Med. Sch. Lond.; Hon. Cons. St. Thos. Hosp. Lond.; Adviser (Clin. Studies) St. Thos. Hosp. Med. Sch. Lond.

NAYLOR, Pauline Mary 10 Mole House, Old Esher Road, Hersham, Walton-on-Thames KT12 4LF — MB BS 1961 Lond.; FRCOG 1985, M 1968.

NAYLOR, Peter 7 Snab Wood Close, Little Neston, South Wirral CH64 0UP — MB ChB 1996 Sheff.

NAYLOR, Roger 18 Lakeside, Wickham Road, Beckenham BR3 6LX — MB BS 1956 Lond.; MRCP Lond. 1968. Cons. Phys. (Geriat. Med.) Mayday Healthcare Croydon. Prev: Cons. Phys. Geriat. Med. Bromley HA.; Sen. Regist. (Geriat. Med.) Guy's Hosp. Lond.

NAYLOR, Sally Elizabeth Boughton Medical Group, Boughton Health Centre, Hoole Lane, Chester CH2 3DP Tel: 01244 325421; 12 Kensington Gardens, Hale, Altrincham WA15 9DP Tel: 0161 904 8921 Fax: 0161 904 8921 — MB ChB 1988 Liverp.; MRCGP 1995; DRCOG 1991. (Liverp.)

NAYLOR, Stanley (retired) 99 Windleshaw Road, St Helens WA10 6TR Tel: 01744 26997 — BSc Lond. 1953; MB ChB Liverp. 1953; DPH 1958. Prev: Clin. Med. Off. Wigan AHA.

NAYLOR, Steven Roy Trengweath Hospital, Penryn St., Redruth TR15 2SP — BM BS 1983 Nottm.; BMedSci (Hons.) Nottm. 1981; MRCGP 1987; DRCOG 1987; DGM RCP Lond. 1986; MRCPsych 1998. Specialist Regist. (Psychiat.) Cornw. Healthcare Trust. Prev: GP Camborne Cornw.

NAYLOR, Ursula Veronica Peggy Birchwood, 39 Tranby Lane, Swanland, North Ferriby HU14 3NE — MB ChB 1962 Liverp.; DPM Eng. 1969. (Liverp.) Cons. Psychiat. BRd.gate Hosp. Socs: Roy.

Med.-Psych. Assn. Prev: Sen. Regist. (Psychiat.) & Med. Asst. BRd.gate Hosp.; Regist. Psychiat. United Leeds Hosps.

NAYLOR, William Geoffrey Knowle Surgery, 1500 Warwick Road, Knowle, Solihull B93 9LE Tel: 01564 772010 — MB ChB 1990 Birm.; ChB Birm. 1990; BSc 1989; MRCGP 1995. (Birm.) G P Princ. (F/T). Prev: Med. Asst. Solihull Hosp.

NAYSMITH, Anne Pembridge Palliative Care Centre, St. Charles Hospital, Exmoor St., London W10 6DZ Tel: 020 8962 4405 Fax: 020 8962 4407 — MB ChB 1973 Ed.; FRCP Ed. 1991; MRCP (UK) 1976. Cons. Palliat. Med. St Chas. Hosp.; Med Dir Pk.side Health NHS Trust. Socs: Assn. Palliat. Med. Prev: Lect. (Med. Oncol.) Middlx. Hosp. Lond. & Edin. Roy. Infirm.

NAYSMITH, Cumming 77 Eastgate Street, Cowbridge CF71 7AA — MB ChB 1942 Glas.; BSc Glas. 1939, MB ChB 1942. (Glas.)

NAYSMITH, James Hall (retired) 7 Berrymead Road, Cyncoed, Cardiff CF23 6QA Tel: 01222 751754 — MB BCh 1952 Wales; BSc Wales 1948; MRCGP 1964; DObst RCOG 1956.

NAYSMITH, Lisa 51 Nethervale Avenue, Glasgow G44 3XP — MB ChB 1995 Glas.

NAYSMITH, Margaret Caroline Southmead Health Centre, Ullswater Road, Bristol BS10 6DF Tel: 0117 950 7150 Fax: 0117 959 1110; 9 Belvoir Road, Bristol BS6 5DG Tel: 0117 942 2775 — MB ChB 1983 Brist.; MSc Leic. 1967; BSc Ed. 1965; MRCGP 1987; DRCOG 1987.

NAYYAR, Nadim Ahmed 6 Helensburgh Close, Barnsley S75 2EU Tel: 01226 730000; 51 Green Hey, Much Hoole, Preston PR4 4QH — MB ChB 1991 Leic.

***NAYYAR, Nicholas Sunil** 6 Falaise, Egham TW20 0BB — MB BS 1995 Lond.

NAZ, Evelyn Mary Burley Street Surgery, Burley Street, Elland HX5 0AQ Tel: 01422 372057 Fax: 01422 311563 — MB ChB 1969 Ed.; DObst RCOG 1973.

NAZ, Falak Burley Street Surgery, Burley Street, Elland HX5 0AQ Tel: 01422 372057 Fax: 01422 311563 — MB BS 1965 Peshawar. (Khyber Med. Coll.)

NAZARE, Joao Caetano Felix 46 Arundel Drive, Worcester WR5 2HU — MB BS 1973 Bombay.

NAZARETH, Hubert Anthony Agnelo Waterloo Surgery, 617 Wakefield Road, Waterloo, Huddersfield HD5 9XP Tel: 01484 531461; 6 School Hill, Kirkburton, Huddersfield HD8 0SG Tel: 01484 602814 — MB ChB 1987 Liverp.; MRCGP 1991; DRCOG 1990; DCH RCP Lond. 1990. Socs: BMA; Hudds. Med. Soc. Prev: Trainee GP Kirby Liverp. VTS; SHO (Gen. Med.) Whiston Hosp. Prescot GP VTS.

NAZARETH, Irwin The Keats Group Practice, 1B Downshire Hill, London NW3 1NR Tel: 020 7435 1131 Email: i.nazareth@ucl.ac.uk — MB BS 1984 Bombay; LRCP LRCS Ed. LRCPS Glas. 1986; MRCGP 1989; DRCOG 1988; PhD Lond. 1987. Sen. Lect. (Primary Health Care) Univ. Coll. Lond. Med. Sch.; GP Partner.

NAZEER, Anisa Fatima c/o Eye Clinic, Odstock Hospital, Salisbury SP2 8BJ — MB BS 1985 Peshawar; MB BS Peshawar, Pakistan 1985; FRCSI 1992. Staff Ophth.

NAZEER, Shaukat Mayfair Medical Centre, 3-5 Weighhouse, London W1K 5LS Tel: 020 7493 1647 Fax: 020 7493 3169 — LMSSA 1989 Lond.; MA Oxf. 1990. Socs: BMA. Prev: Ho. Phys. Univ. Coll. & Middlx. Sch. Med. Lond.

NAZEM, Abul Bashar Mohammad Al Shafa Medical Centre, 507 Little Oaks Road, Aston, Birmingham B6 6JY Tel: 0121 328 1977; 97 Hamstead Hall Road, Handsworth Wood, Birmingham B20 1JA Tel: 0121 523 5957 — MB BS 1966 Dacca.

NAZERALI, Gulzar Abdullah 80 The Knoll, London W13 8HY — LRCPI & LM, LRSCI & LM 1958; LRCPI & LM, LRCSI & LM 1958; DObst RCPI 1962. (RCSI)

NAZIR, Masood 88 Nansen Road, Sparkhill, Birmingham B11 4DT Tel: 0121 778 5192; 88 Nansen Road, Sparkhill, Birmingham B11 4DT Tel: 0121 778 5192 — MB ChB 1997 Birm. (Birm. Med. Sch.) SHO Med. Birm. Healthcare Hosp. Socs: BMA. Prev: Boldesley Green E. - B'Ham.

NAZIR, Nargas Harrogate Road Surgery, 355 Harrogate Road, Leeds LS17 6PZ Tel: 0113 268 0066 Fax: 0113 288 8643 — MB ChB 1992 Leeds.

NAZIR, Tallat Yausmine Department of Anaesthesia, Stepping Hill Hospital, Poplar Grove, Stockport SK2 7JE Tel: 0161 419 5869 — MB ChB 1989 Manch.; BSc St. And. 1986. Gen. Cons. Anaesth.,

NAZKI

Stepping Hill Hosp., Stockport. Socs: Fell. of the Roy. Coll. of Anaesth.s; OAA; DAS.

NAZKI, Mohamed Tariq Stockland Green Health Centre, 192 Reservoir Road, Erdington, Birmingham B23 6DJ Tel: 0121 373 5405 Fax: 0121 386 4909; 100 Wake Green Road, Moseley, Birmingham B13 9PX Tel: 0121 449 5211 — MB BS 1967 Patna. Sen. GP, Stockland Green Health Centre, Erdington, Birm. Socs: LMC; MDU.

NAZROO, Jacques Yzet University College London, Department of Epidemiology and Public Health, 1-19 Torrington Place, London WC1E 6BT Tel: 020 7391 1705 Fax: 020 7813 0242 Email: j.nazroo@public-health.ucl.ac.uk — MB BS 1986 Lond.; MSc Lond. 1989, BSc (Hons.) 1983. (St. George's Hospital Medical School) Reader (Sociology) Univ. Coll. Lond.; Hon. Lect. (Psychiat.) Univ. Coll. Prev: Sen. Research Fell. Policy Studies Inst. Lond.

***NCUBE, Fortune Mabensela** The Saplings, 8 Vine Lane, Boundstone, Farnham GU10 4TD — BM BS 1986 Nottm.

NCUBE, William Alexandra Group Medical Practice, Glodwick Health Centre, 137 Glodwick Road, Oldham OL4 1YN Tel: 0161 909 8377 Fax: 0161 909 8414; Tel: 0161 439 4973 — MUDr 1982 Charles Univ. Prague; DFFP 1993; DRCOG 1992. Cosmetic Med. Practitioner, Pioneer Laser Clinic, 19 Buxton Rd, Stockport, Chesh. SK2 6LS. Socs: Assoc. Mem. RCGP; Fell. Roy. Soc. of Med.; Mem. of Brit. Assn. of Cosmetic Doctors.

NDEGWA, David Gituma South London and Maudsley NHS Trust, 108 Landor Road, London SW9 9NT — MB ChB 1979 Ghana; MRCPsych 1985. Cons. Forens. Psychiat. S Lond. and Maudsley NHS Trust Care NHS Trust; Hon. Sen. Lect. King's Coll., Guy's, St Thos Med. Sch. Prev: Cons. Forens. Psychiat. NE Thames RHA; Sen. Lect. (Forens. Psychiat.) St. Bart. Hosp. Med. Coll.

NDIRIKA, Amelia Chinwe Charlotte Keel Health Centre, Seymour Road, Easton, Bristol BS5 — MB BS 1989 Lond.; MA Physiol., BA Oxf. 1984; MRCGP 1993; DRCOG 1991. (St. Geo. Hosp. Lond.) Socs: BMA.

NDOWA, Francis Jim 25 Moat Lane, Solihull B91 2LN; 6 Thames Road, Vainona, Harare, Zimbabwe — MB ChB 1977 Birm; Dip. GU Med. Soc. Apoth. Lond. 1989; Dip. Dermat. Lond 1989.

***NDUKA, Charles Chukwuemeka** 30 Bellew Street, London SW17 0AD — MB BS 1994 Lond.; BA Oxf. 1991.

NDUKA, Stella Aleruchi Maple Ward, Chase Farm Hospital, The Ridgeway, Enfield EN2 8JL Tel: 020 8366 6600; 20 The Larches, Long Lane, Hillingdon, Uxbridge UB10 0DJ Tel: 01895 251093 — MB BS 1982 Nigeria; MB BS U. Nigeria 1982; DGM RCP Lond. 1995.

NDUKWE, George Okechukwu 17 Manor Drive, Long Bennington, Newark NG23 5GZ — MB BS 1978 Ibadan; MRCOG 1985.

NE WIN, Dr 222 Preston Road, Chorley PR6 7BA — MB BS 1976 Med. Inst. (I) Rangoon.

NEADES, Mr Glyn Thomas 2 Hillview Terrace, Edinburgh EH12 8RA — MB ChB 1983 Aberd.; ChM Aberd. 1993; BMedBiol 1983; FRCS Glas. 1988; FRCS Ed. 1988. Cons. Surg. W.. Gen. Hosp. Edin.

NEAGLE, Elaine Heather 73 Kensington Road, Belfast BT5 6NL — MB BCh BAO 1990 Belf.; MB BCh Belf. 1990.

NEAGLE, Glynis Mary 4 Niddrie Square, Glasgow G42 8QE — MB ChB 1992 Glas.

NEAGLE, William Brian Birch Hill House, 26 Mullaghcarton Road, Ballinderry Upper, Lisburn BT28 2NP — MB BCh BAO 1991 Belf.

***NEAL, Alice Julie** 119 Ashurst Road, London N12 9AA Tel: 020 8446 4651 — MB BS 1986 Lond.

NEAL, Alistair John Duncan, Surg. Lt.-Cdr. RN 38 Peninsula Square, Winchester SO23 8GJ — MB ChB 1983 Aberd.

NEAL, Anthony James St Luke's Cancer Centre, Royal Surrey County Hospital, Guildford GU2 7XX Tel: 01483 406767 Fax: 01483 406767 Email: aneal@royalsurrey.nhs.uk — MB BS 1985 Lond.; MD Lond. 1995; MRCP (UK) 1988; FRCR 1992. (St. Thom. Hosp. Med. Sch. Lond.) Cons Clin Oncol. St Luke's Cancer Centre Guildford Surrey. Prev: Sen. Regist. (Clin. Oncol.) Roy. Marsden Hosp. Lond. & Sutton; Clin. Research Fell. Inst. of Cancer Research Roy. Marsden Hosp. Sutton; Lect. (Med. Oncol.) & Regist. (Radiother. & Oncol.) Roy. Lond. Hosp.

NEAL, Beryl Rose 25 Hawthorn Avenue, Wilmslow SK9 5BR — MB ChB 1961 St. And. (St. And.)

NEAL, Brian Ernest Holmes (retired) Penylan House, Wormegay Road, Blackborough End, King's Lynn PE32 1SG Tel: 01553 841573 — MB BS Lond. 1953; DObst RCOG 1957. Prev: Ho. Phys. Bedford Gen. Hosp.

NEAL, Brynmor Lloyd Rectory Meadow Surgery, School Lane, Amersham HP7 0HG Tel: 01494 727711 Fax: 01494 431790; Hawthorn, Weedon Hill, Hyde Heath, Amersham HP6 5RN Tel: 01494 774421 — MB BS 1972 Lond.; DObst RCOG 1975; FRCGP 1994, M 1977; MRCS Eng. LRCP Lond. 1972. (Westm.) GP Tutor Wycombe Dist.; Bd. Mem. PCG; Chairm. Organisation Managem./Educat. Div. TVF RCGP. Socs: Chiltern Med. Soc. Prev: GP Represen. on Community Unit Wycombe HA; Med. Adviser MPS Soc.; Clin. Asst. Psychiat.

NEAL, Christine Mary 65 Shoot-up-Hill, London NW2; 11 Silver Cres., London W4 5SF — MB BS 1984 Lond.; MA Camb. 1986; DRCOG 1987.

NEAL, Christopher John Marlborough Park Avenue Surgery, 82 Marlborough Park Avenue, Sidcup DA15 7DX Tel: 020 8300 1197 Fax: 020 8309 7187 — MB ChB 1979 Manch.

NEAL, David Andrew James 35 Upper High Street, Thame OX9 2DN — BM 1990 Soton.

NEAL, Professor David Edgar University Department of Surgery, The Medical School, The University, Newcastle upon Tyne NE2 4HH Tel: 0191 222 7067 Fax: 0191 222 8514 Email: d.e.neal@ncl.ac.uk — MB BS 1975 Lond.; 1998 Med Sci, Acad. Of Med. Sci.; MS Lond. 1983, BSc (Anat.) 1972, MB BS 1975; FRCS Ed. 1994; FRCS Eng. 1980. Prof. Surg. & Hons. Cons. Urol. Surg. Med. Sch. Univ. Newc. u Tyne. Socs: Amer. Assn.. of Genito-Urin. Surg.s; Austral. Urological Assci.; Amerial Assoc. for Ceudr. Research. Prev: Sen. Lect. & Cons. Urol Surg. Univ. Newc. u Tyne; 1st Asst. Urol. Univ. Newc. upon Tyne & Lect. Surg. The Gen. Infirm. Leeds.

NEAL, David Mark Top Floor Flat, 4 Clifton Park Road, Clifton, Bristol BS8 3HL; Lauriston House, 43 Shepherds Way, Liphook GU30 7HH — MB ChB 1994 Manch. SHO (Cardiac Surg.) Bristol Roy. Infirm. Prev: SHO (Thoracic Surg.) Frenchay Hosp.; SHO (ENT Surg.) S.mead Hosp. Bristol; SHO (A & E) Frenchay Hosp.

NEAL, Frank Edward (retired) Sharon, Doncaster Road, Rotherham S65 1NN Tel: 01709 382300 — MB ChB 1950 Sheff.; FRCR 1976; FFR 1959; DMRT Eng. 1953. Prev: Gen. Manager W.on Pk. Hosp. Sheff.

NEAL, Frank Richard Honor Oak Health Centre, 20-21 Turnham Road, London SE4 2HH Tel: 020 7639 9797 — MB 1983 Camb.; MA Camb. 1984, MB 1983, BChir 1982. Prev: SHO (O & G) Lewisham Hosp. Lond.; SHO (Psychiat.) S. W.. Hosp. Lond.; SHO (ENT) Hither Green Hosp. Lond.

NEAL, Gillian 7 Dykes Terrace, Stanwix, Carlisle CA3 9AS — MB BS 1991 Newc.; DRCOG 1994.

NEAL, James William Department of Histopathology, University Hospital of Wales, Cardiff CF4 4XN — DPhil Oxf. 1988; MB ChB Bristol 1978; FRCS Eng. 1984; FRC Path 2000. Sen. Lect. & Hon. Cons. Neuropath. Univ. Hosp. Wales Cardiff.

NEAL, Janet Christine 4 Kingfisher Way, Romsey SO51 7RY; 4A Fourth Avenue, Denvilles, Havant PO9 2QX Tel: 01705 479301 — MB BS 1988 Lond.; MRCGP 1994; DA (UK) 1996; DRCOG 1992. (UMDS Guy's Hosp. Lond.)

NEAL, Keith Richard Dept. of Public Health & Epidemiology, University of Nottingham, Queens Medical Centre, Nottingham NG7 2UH; 8 Windley Crescent, Darley Abbey, Derby DE22 1BZ — BM 1981 Soton.; MRCP (UK) 1985. Sen. Lect., Dept of Health & Epidemiol., Univ. Nott.

NEAL, Leigh Anthony 52 Haig Road, Catterick Garrison DL9 3AH — MB BCh 1981 Wales; MRCGP 1985; MRCPsych 1990.

NEAL, Lesley Margaret Flash Cottage, Stannington, Sheffield S6 6GR — MB ChB 1976 Bristol.

NEAL, Margaret Mary (retired) Sharon, Doncaster Road, Rotherham S65 1NN Tel: 01709 382300 — MRCS Eng. LRCP Lond. 1950.

NEAL, Matthew Russell 128 High Storrs Road, Sheffield S11 7LF Tel: 01142 685746 Email: mattneal@compuserve.com — BM 1990 Soton.; DA (UK) 1993; FRCA 1997. Specialist Regist. (Anaesth.) N. Trent Rotat. Centr. Sheff. Univ. Hosps. Socs: Train. Mem. Assn. AnE.h.; Brit. Med. Acupunct. Soc.

NEAL, Nicholas Charles 51 Balmoral Crescent, Oswestry SY11 2XQ — MB ChB 1981 Birm.

NEAL, Philip Department of Anaesthesia, Ninewells Hospital & Medical School, Dundee Tel: 01382 660111 Ext: 32175; 29 Lammerton Terrace, Dundee DD4 7BR Tel: 01382 462271 — MB ChB 1991 Ed. SHO (Paediat.) Yorkhill Hosp. Glas. Socs: Life Mem. Roy. Med. Soc.

***NEAL, Rachel Mary** Sharon, Doncaster Road, Rotherham S65 1NN — MB ChB 1994 Manch.

NEAL, Richard David Meanwood Group Practice, 548 Meanwood Road, Leeds LS6 4JN Tel: 0113 295 1737 Fax: 0113 295 1736; Meanwood Group Practice, 548 Meanwood Road, Leeds LS6 4JN Tel: 0113 295 1730 Fax: 0113 295 1736 — MB ChB 1988 Birm.; MRCGP 1994; DFFP 1992; DRCOG 1992. (Birm.) Lect. in Primary Care Research Centre for Research in Primary Care Leeds.; GP Princip. Meanwood Gp. Pract. Prev: Research Train. Fell. Centre for Research in Primary Care; Trainee GP ScarBoro. VTS; SHO (Gen. Med.) S.port & Formby Dist. Gen. Hosp.

NEAL, Roger Charles Toddington Medical Centre, Luton Road, Toddington, Dunstable LU5 6DE Tel: 01525 872222 Fax: 01525 876711 — MB BCh 1985 Wales; MRCGP 1989.

NEAL, Shona McDonald St John's Hospital, Howden EH54 — MB ChB 1991 Ed.; BSc (Hons.) Ed.. 1989. (Ed.) Specialist Regist. (Anaesth.) Dundee Teachg. Hosps.

NEAL, Timothy James Department of Medical Microbiology, Royal Liverpool University Hospital, Prescot St., Liverpool L7 8XP Tel: 0151 706 5849 Email: tjneal@liv.ac.uk; 3 Holkham Gardens, St Helens WA9 5SS — MB ChB 1987 Liverp.; MSc Manch. 1994; MRCPath 1997. Cons. Microbio. Liv'pl.

NEAL-DERKS, Jacinta Anna Maria Byways, Forestside, Rowlands Castle PO9 6EQ Tel: 01705 412355 — MB BS 1980 Adelaide; DRCOG 1983.

NEAL-SMITH, Gillian Ann (retired) The Surgery, 1B The Green, Twickenham TW2 5TU Tel: 020 8894 6870 Fax: 020 8893 8579 — MB BS 1964 Lond.; MRCS Eng. LRCP Lond. 1964; DObst RCOG 1966. Prev: Ho. Phys. (Gen. Med. & Paediat.) & Ho. Surg. Fulham Hosp.

NEALE, Aileen Winifred The Red House, Great Plumstead, Norwich NR13 5ED — MB ChB 1950 Birm.; DPM Eng. 1973. (Birm.) Prev: Clin. Asst. St. Nicholas Hosp. Gt. Yarmouth.

NEALE, Alastair James Brynallt, Polesgate, Pontesbury Hill, Pontesbury, Shrewsbury SY5 0YL — MB ChB 1987 Birm.; MRCPsych 1992. Sen. Regist. (Child & Adolesc. Psychiat.) SW Peninsula.

NEALE, David Vivian Greenways, Main St., Northam, Rye TN31 6ND — BM 1984 Soton.; MRCGP 1989; Dip. Palliat. Med. Wales 1993; DRCOG 1989; DGM RCP Lond. 1988. Socs: BMA; Assoc. Mem. Palliat. Med. Assn. Prev: Med. Dir. St. Michaels Hospice St. Leonards-on-Sea; GP Headcorn Kent; Trainee GP William Harvey Hosp. Ashford VTS.

NEALE, Mr Edmund John Bedford Hospital NHS Trust, Kempston Road, Bedford MK42 9DJ Tel: 01234 792065; Tel: 01234 792065 — MB BS 1982 Lond.; BSc Lond. 1979,; MRCOG 1988. (St. Geo.) Cons. O & G Bedford Hosp. Socs: Foundat. Mem. Hong Kong Coll. Obst. & Gyn.; E. Anglian O&G Soc.; Nuffield Vis. Soc. Prev: Lect. & Hon. Sen. Regist. (O & G) Univ. Leicester; Vis. Lect. (O & G) Chinese Univ. Hong Kong; Regist. Qu. Med. Centre Nottm. & Kings Mill Hosp. Mansfield.

NEALE, Fiona Rosalind 21 St John's Road, Knutsford WA16 0DP — BM BS 1991 Nottm.

NEALE, Graham (retired) Clinical Risk Unit, Dept of Psychology (Torrington Place), UCL. Gower St., London WC1E 6BT Tel: 020 7391 1607 Fax: 020 7391 1647 Email: grahamneate@hotmail.com — MB ChB 1960 Bristol; MA Camb. 1987; BSc Lond. 1950; FRCP Lond. 1971, M 1963; FRCPI 1979. Clin: Reseach Fell. Clin. Risk Unit Univ. Coll. Lond. Prev: Lect. (Med.) Univ. Camb.

***NEALE, Gregory** 16 Cecilia Road, Clarendon Park, Leicester LE2 1TA — MB ChB 1996 Leic.

NEALE, Ian Andrew High Street Surgery, 48 High Street, Chalgrove, Oxford OX44 7SS Tel: 01865 890760 Fax: 01865 400226; Darenth Lodge, 2 High St, Chalgrove, Oxford OX44 7SR Tel: 01865 890803 Fax: 01865 890803 — BM BCh 1977 Oxf.; MA Camb. 1978; DRCOG 1980. (Oxford) Non-Exec. Dir. Oxf. HA; Med. Counsellor Med. Insur. Agency; Performance Assessor GMC; Med. Dir. OXDOC S. GP Out of Hours Coop; Professioinal Conduct Comm. GMC. Prev: Complaints Off. Oxf. LMC; Sec. Oxon. LMC 1987-94.

NEALE, Jacqueline Suzanne Gable House Surgery, High Street, Malmesbury SN16 9AT Tel: 01666 825825; 4 Copperfield Court, New St., Altrincham WA14 2QF Tel: 0161 928 5878, 01666 510353 — MB ChB 1983 Birm.; DRCOG 1991; DA (UK) 1988. (Birm.) GP Princip.

NEALE, Michael Lawrence (retired) 30 Roydscliffe Road, Heaton, Bradford BD9 5PS Tel: 01274 492115 Fax: 01274 492115 Email: neale@legend.co.uk — MB ChB Manch. 1960; DObst RCOG 1962. Prev: Ho. Phys. City Hosp. York.

NEALE, Phyllis Mary (retired) Ground Floor Flat, 3 Miles Road, Bristol BS8 2JN Tel: 0117 973 6317 — MB ChB 1934 Birm.; MB ChB (Hnrs.) Birm. 1934. Prev: Demonst. Anat. Univ. Bristol.

NEALE, Richard John Horace Herschel Medical Centre, 45 Osborne Street, Slough SL1 1TT Tel: 01753 520643 Fax: 01753 554964; Three Hollies, Cherry Tree Road, Farnham Royal, Slough SL2 3EF Tel: 01753 645757 — MB ChB 1966 St. And. (Queen's Coll. Dundee) Socs: BMA. Prev: SHO Upton Hosp. Slough & St. Mary Abbot's Hosp. Lond.; Resid. Med. Off. Fitzroy Nuffield Hosp. Lond.

NEALE, Robert Desmond (retired) 74 Parrys Lane, Stoke Bishop, Bristol BS9 1AQ Tel: 0117 968 2484 — MB ChB 1957 Bristol; DPM Eng. 1962. Prev: Sen. Hosp. Med. Off. Barrow Hosp. Bristol.

NEALE, Ruth (retired) Bridlecroft, 314 Spring Lane, Mapperley Plains, Nottingham NG3 5RQ Tel: 011590 268956 — MB ChB 1954 Leeds.

NEALE, Thomas William Kings Pond Cottage, Chesham Road, Hyde End, Great Missenden HP16 0RD — MB BS 1992 Lond.

NEALES, Kate Elisabeth Kent & Canterbury Hospital, Canterbury CT1 3NG Tel: 01227 766877; 4 The Grove, Barham, Canterbury CT4 6PP Tel: 01227 831363 — MB BS 1980 Melbourne; FRACOG 1992, M 1987; MRCOG 1989. (Univ. Melbourne Vict., Austral.) Cons. O & G Kent & Canterbury Hosp. Socs: Brit. Med. Soc.; Brit. Soc. Colpos. & Cerv. Path. Prev: Sen. Regist. (O & G) NW RHA; Research Regist. (Fetal Med.) Guy's Hosp. Lond.

NEAMAN, Gillian Mary The Surgery, 66 Long Lane, London EC1A 9EJ; 11 Chadwell Street, London EC1R 1XD Tel: 020 7837 4455 Fax: 020 7833 0268 — BM BCh 1958 Oxf.; MA, BM BCh Oxf. 1958. (Guy's) Med. Off. to Reuters (p/t), Lond. Prev: Ho. Surg. New End Hosp. Hampstead; Ho. Phys. Whittington Hosp. Highgate; Resid. Med. Off. Hornsey Centr. Hosp.

NEAME, Mr John Humphrey (retired) Till's End, Stapleford, Salisbury SP3 4LT Tel: 01722 790484 — BA Camb. 1946, MA 1958, MB BChir 1949; FRCS Eng. 1958. Prev: Cons. Otolaryngol. Salisbury Hosp Gp. & Swindon & MarlBoro. Hosps.

NEAME, Kenneth Dell (retired) Marlowe, Hessle Drive, Lower Heswall, Wirral CH60 8PS Tel: 0151 342 2132 — MB BS 1954 Lond.; PhD Sheff. 1959. Prev: Sen. Lect. Univ. Liverp.

***NEAME, Rebecca Louise** 2 Mountbatten Way, Raunds, Wellingborough NN9 6PA — MB ChB 1995 Leic.

NEAME, Mr Robert Lawrence Hollands and Partners, Bridport Medical Centre, North Allington, Bridport DT6 5DU Tel: 01308 421896 Fax: 01308 421109 — MB BS 1986 Lond.; FRCS Eng. 1991; MRCGP 1994; DRCOG 1993. Prev: Trainee GP Salisbury; Regist. (Surg.) Soton. Gen. Hosp.; SHO (Surg.) Bristol & W.on HA.

***NEARY, Bruce Richard** The Wicketts, 9 Dower Park, Escrick, York YO19 6JN — MB ChB 1997 Liverp.

NEARY, Professor David Department of Neurology, Manchester Royal Infirmary, Oxford Road, Manchester M13 9WL Tel: 0161 276 4149 Fax: 0161 276 4681; 8 Bollington Mill, Park Lane, Altrincham WA14 4TJ Tel: 0161 929 4690 — MD Manch. 1977, MB ChB 1967; FRCP UK 1981, M 1971. Cons. Neurol. Manch. Roy. Infirm.; Prof. Neurol. Univ. Manch. Socs: Assn. Brit. Neurol.; Brit. Neurol. Path. Soc.; Assn. Phys.

NEARY, Dermot Mellotte Tramways Medical Centre, Newtownabbey BT36 7XX Tel: 02890 342131 Fax: 02890 839111; 27 Downview Avenue, Belfast BT15 4FB Tel: 02890 777311 — MB BCh BAO 1973 Belf.

NEARY, John Gerard Tramways Medical Centre, Farmley Road, Newtownabbey BT36 7XX Tel: 028 9034 2131 Fax: 028 9083 9111 — MB BCh BAO 1974 Belf. GP Princip. Belf./Newtonabbey; Chairm. of SEAL; S. E. Antrim Locality, Total purchasing project.

NEARY, John Taaffe (retired) 28 Downview Avenue, Belfast BT15 4FB — MB BCh BAO 1941 NUI.

NEARY

NEARY, Joseph Mary Trinity Surgery, Norwich Road, Wisbech PE13 3UZ Tel: 01945 476999 Fax: 01945 476900; 66 North Brink, Wisbech PE13 1LN Tel: 01945 585884 Fax: 01945 474189 — MB BCh BAO 1981 NUI; MRCGP 1983; DCH RCP Lond. 1986; MSc UEA 1998. Princip. Gen. Pract. Trinity Surg. Wisbech. Socs: GP Asthma Gp.; Vice-Chairm. Camb. LMC; Nat. Counc. RCGP. Prev: Surg. Lt. RN; SMO HMS Glam..

*NEARY, Nicola Marguerite Little Cloister, Netherfield Hill, Battle TN33 0LF — BM BCh 1997 Oxf.

NEARY, Peter Joseph Lytham Road Surgery, 352 Lytham Road, Blackpool FY4 1DW Tel: 01253 402800 Fax: 01253 402994; Flat 1, Cyprus Court, Cuprus Avenue, Lytham St Annes FY8 1DZ Tel: 01253 712968 — MB ChB 1964 Manch.

NEARY, Richard Henry 37 Chancery Lane, Alsager, Stoke-on-Trent ST7 2HE — MD 1991 Manch.; MB ChB 1979; MRCPath 1986. Cons. Chem. Path. N. Staffs. Hosp. Centre Stoke-on-Trent.

NEARY, Russell The Keele Centre, Keele, Newcastle ST5 5AR Tel: 01782 204099 Fax: 01782 204099 — MB BS 1985 Lond.; BSc (Psychol. & Basic Med. Sci. II) Lond. 1982. (Royal Free) Indep. Med. Pract. Staffs.; Clin. Asst. Laser Dermat.; Lifestyle Sandy La. Clinic, The Hill, Sandy La., Newc., Staffs. ST5 0LZ. Socs: Assoc. Mem. of Brit. Assn. Of Cosmetic Surg.s.

NEARY, Wanda Janetta Child Health Unit, Guardian House, Guardian St., Warrington WA5 1TP Tel: 01925 405717 Fax: 01925 405725; 36 Brooklands Road, Sale M33 3SJ Tel: 0161 973 5950 — MB ChB 1968 Manch.; MSc (Audiol. Med.) Manch. 1990; MD Manch. 1995. (Manch.) Cons. Community Paediat. (Paediat. Audiol.) Warrington Community Health Care (NHS) Trust. Prev: SCMO Warrington HA; Clin. Med. Off. Manch. HA; Lect. (Path.) Univ. Manch.

*NEARY, William David 36 Brooklands Road, Sale M33 3SJ — MB ChB 1995 Bristol.

NEASHAM, John 26 Carr Bottom Road, Greengates, Bradford BD10 0BB — MB ChB 1968 Leeds; FFA RCS Eng. 1973; DA Eng. 1971. (Leeds) Cons. Anaesth. Gen. Infirm. Leeds. Prev: Cons. Anaesth. S. Tees HA.

NEASHAM, John Percival Ilkley Health Centre, Springs Lane, Ilkley LS29 8TQ Tel: 01943 609255 Fax: 01943 430005; 4 Lakeside Close, Middleton, Ilkley LS29 0AG Tel: 01943 816271 Fax: 01943 816271 — MB ChB 1956 Birm.; MRCGP 1978; DObst RCOG 1961. (Birm.) Clin. Asst. (Orthop.) Ilkley Coronation Hosp.; Med. Adviser Internat. Wool Secretariat, Ilkley; Clin. Asst. (Med.) Wharfedale Gen. Hosp. Prev: Ho. Surg. Worcester Roy. Infirm.; Ho. Phys. St. Mary's Hosp. Portsmouth; Ho. Surg. (O & G) Dudley Rd. Hosp. Birm.

NEATBY, Guy Oliver Miller (retired) 7 Leighwood House, Church Road, Leighwoods, Bristol BS8 3PQ Tel: 0117 973 8398 — BA (1st cl. Classic Trip. Pt. I) Camb. 1932, MA; MRCS Eng. LRCP Lond. 1938; DOMS Eng. 1942. Prev: Ophth. Bath Clin. Area.

NEAVE, Farhad 81 Lynwood Road, Ealing, London W5 1JG Tel: 020 8998 3409 — MD 1973 Iran; MPhil Lond. 1986; FRCR 1992; DMRT Ed. 1980. Cons. Radiother. & Oncol. N. Middlx. Hosp. Lond.

NEAVE, Sandra Margaret The Adan Practice, 306 Blondford Road, Hamworthy, Poole BH15 4JQ Tel: 01202 679234; 85 Catalina Drive, Baiter Park, Poole BH15 1TQ Tel: 01202 673276 — BM 1989 Soton.; MRCGP 1995; DRCOG 1995. Socs: Roy. Coll. Gen. Pract.; BMA.

NEAVES, Christopher Henry (retired) 18 Stepney Drive, Scarborough YO12 5DH Tel: 01723 376650 — MB BS 1949 Lond. Prev: Ho. Surg. ENT Dept. King's Coll. Hosp.

NEAVES, Judith Mary Benbeculla Medical Practice, Griminish, Isle of Benbecula HS7 5QA Tel: 01870 602215; 1 Uiskavagh, Isle of Benbecula HS7 5QL — MB BS 1983 Lond.; MRCGP 1990; DRCOG 1988; DA (UK) 1996. Med. Off. & Ltd. Specialist Anaesth. Daliburgh Hosp. Prev: GP Woking; SHO (Anaesth.) Chesterfield Hosp. Derbysh.

NEBHRAJANI, Jayantee 22 Harley Street, London W1N 1AA Tel: 020 7637 0491; 106 The Ridgeway, London E4 6PU Tel: 020 8529 3719 — MB BS 1961 Gauhati; FFA RCS Eng. 1970; DA Eng. 1963. (Assam Med. Coll.) Cons. Anaesth. Homerton Hosp. Lond. Socs: Assn. Anaesths. Prev: Regist. (Anaesth.) St. Jas. Hosp. Lond. & Hackney Hosp. Lond.; SHO (Anaesth.) N. Middlx. Hosp.

NEBHRAJANI, Mr Vir Tirthdas 22 Harley Street, London W1N 1AA Tel: 020 7637 0491; 106 The Ridgeway, London E4 6PU Tel: 020 8529 3719 — MB BS 1959 Gauhati; FRCS Ed. 1969; DLO Eng. 1961. (Assam Med. Coll.) Cons. ENT Surg. Manor Hse. Hosp.

Lond.; Otol. City & Hackney Health Dist. (T). Socs: BMA. Prev: Regist. (ENT) Dudley Rd. Hosp. Birm. & Whipps Cross Hosp. Lond.; Ho. Surg. (ENT) Metrop. ENT Hosp. Lond.

NECATI, Guner 17 Durham Avenue, Willenhall WV13 1JH — LMSSA 1975 Lond.

NEDEN, Catherine Anne Mildmay Court Surgery, Mildmay Court, Bellevue Road, Ramsgate CT11 8JX Tel: 01843 592576 Fax: 01843 852980 Email: catherie.neden@mildmaysurgery.co.uk — BM BCh 1984 Oxf.; MA Camb. 1985; FRCP 2000; FRCGP 1999; DCH RCP Lond. 1988; DGM RCP Lond. 1988; DRCOG 1987. Prev: SHO (Rheum.) Middlx. Hosp.; SHO (Paediat.) Char. Cross Hosp. Lond.; Trainee GP Bath VTS.

NEDEN, David Arthur John The Surgery, Grange Road, Ramsgate CT11 9NB Tel: 01843 852853; Langham, 33 St. Mildreds Avenue, Ramsgate CT11 0HS Tel: 01843 593836 — MB BS Lond. 1952; FRCGP 1993; DObst RCOG 1956. (Univ. Coll. Hosp.) Local Med. Off. Civil Serv. Dept.; Exam. Med. Off. DSS. Prev: Ho. Surg., Ho. Phys. & Resid. Med. Off. Univ. Coll. Hosp. Lond.

NEDEN, John Wilfred David Mildmay Court Surgery, Mildmay Court, Bellevue Road, Ramsgate CT11 8JX Tel: 01843 592576 Fax: 01843 852980; The Surgery Flat, Grange Road, Ramsgate CT11 9NB Tel: 01843 852853 — MB BS 1984 Lond.; MA Camb. 1985; FRCGP 1999; Dip. Pale 2001 (Med); MRCGP 1988; DCH RCP Lond. 1989; DRCOG 1987. Macriellan GP facilitator. Prev: Trainee GP Soton. & Bath VTS; SHO (Med. Microbiol.) Roy. Free Hosp. Lond.; Ho. Surg. King's Coll. Hosp. Lond.

*NEDJATI, Richard Mehmet Flat 3/3, 83 Magdalen Yard Road, Dundee DD2 1BA — MB ChB 1998 Dund.; MB ChB Dund 1998.

NEE, Mr Patrick Anthony Michael Whiston Hospital, Prescot L35 5DR Tel: 0151 430 1853; 5 Peter's Close, Prestbury, Macclesfield SK10 4JQ Tel: 01625 828988 — MB ChB 1982 Liverp.; FRCP 1998; FFAEM 1994; MRCP (UK) 1987; FRCS Ed. (A&E) 1989. Cons. Emerg. Med. & Critical Care Whiston Hosp. Prescot. Socs: Intens. Care Soc.; Brit. Assn. Accid. & Emerg. Med.; UK Trauma (Audit & Research) Network. Prev: Sen. Regist. (A & E) NW RHA; Regist. (A & E) Univ. Hosp. S. Manch.; Regist. (Gen. Med.) Derbysh. Roy. Infirm.

NEECH, Mrs Sarah Evalyn Kirkman (retired) The Gardens Cottage, 114 The Street, Rockland St Mary, Norwich NR14 7HQ Tel: 01508 538519 — BA Calif. 1931, MD 1935; MRCS Eng. LRCP Lond. 1964. Prev: Med. Off. Mission Hosp. Kachwa, India.

NEED, Rachel Elisabeth (retired) 2 Damer Gardens, Henley-on-Thames RG9 1HX Tel: 01491 572898 — MB BS Lond. 1954; MCOphth 1989; DO RCS Eng. 1967. Prev: Ho. Surg. (Ophth.) St. Bart. Hosp. Lond.

NEEDHAM, Andrew Donald Department of Ophthalmology, Royal Liverpool Hospital, Prescot Road, Liverpool L7 8XP; The Laurels, Burton Road, Little Neston, South Wirral CH64 4AG — MB ChB 1989 Liverp.; BSc Liverp. 1985; FRCOphth 1993. (Liverp.) Glaucoma Fell. Liverp. Socs: BMA. Prev: Specialist Regist. (Ophth.) Dundee.

NEEDHAM, Charles Douglas (retired) Drumgray, Edrom, Duns TD11 3PX Tel: 01890 818525 — MB BS 1939 Lond.; MD Lond. 1942; FRCP Lond. 1957, M 1940; MRCS Eng. LRCP Lond. 1939. Prev: Cons. Phys. Aberd. Gen. Hosps.

NEEDHAM, David Jonathan Tregenna Group Practice, 399 Portway, Woodhouse Park, Manchester M22 0EP Tel: 0161 499 3777 Fax: 0161 493 9119; 23 Grosvenor Square, Sale M33 6QU Tel: 0161 905 2229 — MB ChB 1988 Manch.; MRCGP 1992; DCH 1991; DRCOG 1991; BSc St. And. 1985. Trainee GP Stepping Hosp. Stockport.

NEEDHAM, Elizabeth Richmond Group Medical Centre, 1 Albion Street, Ashton-under-Lyne OL6 6HF Tel: 0161 339 9161 Fax: 0161 343 5131; Broomland, 5 Gallowsclough Road, Stalybridge SK15 3QS Tel: 01457 764505 — MB ChB 1975 Liverp.; MB ChB (Hons.) Liverp. 1975; MRCGP 1979; DCH RCPS Glas. 1978; DRCOG 1977. (Liverpool) Clin. Asst. Diabetes Centre Tameside Gen. Hosp. Socs: Manch. Med. Soc. Prev: SHO (Obst.) Crumpsall Hosp. Manch.; SHO (Gyn.) St. Mary's Hosp. Manch.; SHO (Paediat.) Booth Hall Childr. Hosp, Manch.

NEEDHAM, Geoffrey Derek Keith (retired) 8A Station Road, Kintbury, Hungerford RG17 9UP Tel: 01488 657482 — MRCS Eng. LRCP Lond. 1943; DPH Lond. 1948. Prev: Sen. Med. Off. Swindon DHA.

NEEDHAM, Geoffrey Kenneth Holmside Medical Group, 142 Armstrong Road, Benwell, Newcastle upon Tyne NE4 8QB Tel: 0191 273 4009 Fax: 0191 273 2745; Tel: 0191 281 6566 — MB ChB 1977 Liverp.; MD Newc. 1988; FRCS Eng. 1982; MRCGP 1991. Prev: Regist. (Surg.) S. Cleveland Hosp.; Sen. Research Assoc. (Surg.) Univ. Newc. u. Tyne.

NEEDHAM, Professor Gillian Westbank, 180 Nrthdeeside Road, Milltimber, Aberdeen AB13 0HL — MB ChB 1981 Manch.; FRCP (EDIN) 1999; BSc (Hons.) Anat. Manch. 1978; FRCR 1986. p/t PostGrad. Med. Dean Univ. of Aberd.; Hon. Cons. Radiologist Grampian Univeristy Hosp.s Trust Aberd. Prev: Sen. Regist. (Radiol.) N. W. RHA; Regist. (Radiol.) N. W.. RHA.; Cons. Radiologist Aberd. Roy. Hosp.s.

NEEDHAM, Hazel Joan Woodlands Park Health Centre, Canterbury Way, Wideopen, Newcastle upon Tyne NE13 6JL Tel: 0191 236 2366 Fax: 0191 236 7619; 34 Clayworth Road, Brunton Park, Newcastle upon Tyne NE3 5AB — MB ChB 1981 Dundee; MRCGP 1985.

***NEEDHAM, Hazel Maria** 122 Alfreton Road, Newton, Alfreton DE55 5TR — MB ChB 1997 Dundee.

NEEDHAM, Ian Charles 5 Greenways, Wolsingham, Bishop Auckland DL13 3HN Tel: 01388 527300 — MB ChB 1973 Sheff.

NEEDHAM, John Allan Peter House Surgery, Captain Lees Road, Westhoughton, Bolton BL5 3UB Tel: 01942 812525; 30 Lakelands Drive, Ladybridge, Bolton BL3 4NN Tel: 01204 653691 — MB ChB 1970 Manch.; DObst RCOG 1973.

NEEDHAM, Karen Lesley College Lane Surgery, Barnsley Road, Ackworth, Pontefract WF7 7HZ Tel: 01977 611023 Fax: 01977 612146; Moat Cottage, 76 Sherburn St, Cawood, Selby YO8 3SS Tel: 01757 268893 — BM BS 1982 Nottm.; MRCGP 1989; DCH RCP Lond. 1986. (Nottingham) GP.

NEEDHAM, Morag Jane The Congregational Hall, Town Street, Marple Bridge, Stockport SK6 5AA Tel: 0161 427 2049/1074 Fax: 0161 427 8389 — MB ChB 1990 Sheff.; MRCGP 1995; DFFP 1997. Prev: Trainee GP Chesh.

NEEDHAM, Patricia Ruth Dorothy House Foundation, Winsley, Bradford-on-Avon BA15 Tel: 01225 311335 — MB BS 1986 Lond.; FRCP 2000 UK. (London) p/t Cons. Palliat. Med. Bath. Prev: Sen. Regist. (Palliat Med.) Avon; Regist. (Palliat. Med., Radiother. & Oncol.) Roy. Lond. Hosp.; Regist. (Palliat. Med.) St. Bart. Hosp. Lond.

***NEEDHAM, Paul Jonathan** 26 North Road, Williton, Taunton TA4 4SN — MB ChB 1996 Manch.

NEEDHAM, Mr Peter Grenville Solihull Hospital, Lode Lane, Solihull B91 2JL — MB 1965 Camb.; BChir 1964; FRCS Eng. 1970; FRCOG 1986, M 1974. (St. Bart.) Cons. O & G Solihull Hosp. W. Midl. Prev: Sen. Regist. (O & G) Hammersmith & St. Helier Hosps.; SHO Chelsea Hosp. Wom. Lond.; SHO Qu. Charlottes Matern. Hosp. Lond.

NEEDHAM, Peter Ronald George (retired) Bryn y Gwynt Isaf, Prion, Denbigh LL16 4RW Tel: 01745 812805 — MB BS 1966 Lond.; MRCS Eng. LRCP Lond. 1966; LMSSA Lond. 1964; FRCPath 1984, M 1972. Prev: Cons. Histopath. Ysbyty Glan Clwyd, Bodelwyddan Rhyl Denbighsh.

NEEDHAM, Sravoni Bonny 23 Grosvenor Square, Sale M33 6QU Tel: 0161 905 2229 — MB ChB 1988 Manch.; BSc St. And. 1985. SHO (Paediat.) Withington & Wythenshawe Hosp. S. Manch. Prev: Ho. Off. (Surg.) Withingtron Hosp. Manch.; Ho. Off. (Med.) Stepping Hill Hosp. Stockport HA.

NEEDHAM, Stephanie Jane 1 The Leas, Sedgefield, Stockton-on-Tees TS21 2DS — MB BS 1992 Lond.

NEEDHAM, Vernon Harold Charlton Hill Surgery, Charlton Road, Andover SP10 3JY Tel: 01264 337979 Fax: 01264 334251 — MB BS 1978 Lond.; FRCGP 1999; BSc Lond. 1975; MRCGP 1982; DRCOG 1984. Med. Off. Enham Village Andover; Med. Adviser Coke Hole Trust Andover; Bd. Mem. PCG; GP Trainer. Prev: Regtl. Med. Off. 15/19 Hussars; Regtl. Med. Off. 3rd Regt. Roy. Horse Artillery; Trainee Anaesth. Camb. Milit. Hosp. Aldershot.

NEEDHAM-BENNETT, Humphrey Walter Adrian 85 Boyne Road, London SE13 5AN — MB BS 1987 Lond.

NEEDOFF, Joseph (retired) 52 Middlefield Lane, Hagley, Stourbridge DY9 0PX Tel: 01562 883624 — MB ChB 1946 Manch. Prev: GP & Hosp. Pract. (Dermat.) Dudley & Stourbridge Hosps.

NEEDOFF, Mr Maurice King's Mill Hospital, Mansfield Road, Sutton-in-Ashfield NG17 4JL Tel: 01623 672378 — MB ChB 1981 Birm.; FRCS (Orth.) 1994; FRCS Ed. 1986. Cons. Orthop. & Trauma Surg. King's Mill Hosp. Mansfield. Socs: Brit. Trauma Soc.; Brit. Assn. Surg. Knee. Prev: Sen. Regist. (Orthop.) Derby & Nottm.; Regist. (Orthop.) Nottm. & Mansfield.

NEEDS, John David (retired) The Old Rectory, Little Wenlock, Telford TF6 5BD — MB BS 1970 Lond.; DA Eng. 1974. Prev: Surg. Lt.-Cdr. RN.

NEEHALL, Mr David John 3 Knoll Drive, Southgate, London N14 5LU Tel: 0208 368 7184; 6 Montserrat Avenue, Federation Park, Port-of-Spain, Trinidad, West Indies Tel: 0101 868 628 0635 — MB BS 1991 West Indies; MRCOG 1998. (West Indies)

NEELAMKAVIL, Devassy Paul Sunny 6 Plaxtol Close, Bromley BR1 3AU — State Exam 1973 Padua; BSc (Chem.) Kerala 1964; Dip. Addic. Behaviour Lond. 1996; DFFP 1993; Cert. Occupat. Med. 1992; Cert. Prescribed Equiv. Exp. JCPTGP 1985; DObst RCPSI 1982.

NEELEMAN, Jan The Maudsley Hospital, Denmark Hill, London SE5 8AZ — Artsexamen 1988 Utrecht; MRCPsych 1992. Sen. Regist. (Psychiat.) Maudsley Hosp. Lond.

NEELY, Mr Julian Alexander Cavendish (retired) 27 Springfield Park, North Parade, Horsham RH12 2BF Tel: 01403 248355 — MB BS 1958 Lond.; MS Lond. 1968; FRCS Eng. 1963. Prev: Cons. Surg. Crawley Hosp., Qu. Vict. Hosp. E. Grinstead & Horsham Hosp.

NEELY, Robert Alwyn (retired) 106 Galgorm Road, Ballymena BT42 1AE Tel: 01266 3200 — MD 1949 Belf.; MB BCh BAO 1945; FRCPath 1967. Prev: Cons. Pathol. N.. Irel. Hosps. Auth.

NEELY, Robert Dermot Garmany 52 Albert Street, Durham DH1 4RJ — MB BCh 1983 Belf.; BSc (1st cl. Hons.) (Biochem.) Belf. 1980, MB BCh BAO 1983; MRCP (UK) 1986; MRCPath 1991. Regist. (Chem. Path.) Roy. Vict. Hosp. Belf.

NEEP, Richard James Chatsworth Road Medical Centre, Chatsworth Road, Brampton, Chesterfield S40 3PY Tel: 01246 568065 Fax: 01246 567116 — MB ChB 1981 Manch.; MRCGP 1986; DRCOG 1986.

NEEQUAYE, Alfred Robinson 37 Augustus Close, Brentford TW8 8QE — MB BS 1969 Lond.; FRCP Ed. 1992; MRCP (UK) 1974; MRCS Eng. LRCP Lond. 1969.

NEEQUAYE, Janet Elizabeth 37 Augustus Close, Brentford TW8 8QE — MB BS 1969 Lond.; MRCP (UK) 1974; MRCS Eng. LRCP Lond. 1969.

***NEERKIN, Jane** Flat 4, 61 Fordwych Road, London NW2 3TL; St. Thomas's Hospital, Lambeth Palace Road, London SE1 7EH — MB BS 1997 Lond.; BSc (Hons) Leeds 1992.

NEESON, Conor Clifton Street Surgery, 15-17 Clifton Street, Belfast BT13 1AD Tel: 028 9032 2330 Fax: 028 9043 9812 — MB BCh BAO 1981 Belf.; MRCGP 1985; DRCOG 1983.

NEESON, Lilwen Elonwy The Clears House, Colley Lane, Reigate RH2 9JJ Tel: 0173 72 47277 — MRCS Eng. LRCP Lond. 1945. (Ed.) Clin. Asst. (Cas. Dept.) St. Helier Hosp. Carshalton.

NEEVES, Zofia Wanda 51 Leckie Road, Walsall WS2 8DA Tel: 01922 623755 Fax: 01922 746477 — LRCP LRCS 1969 Ed.; LRCPS Glas. 1969. Socs: BMA.

NEGANDHI, Damodar Bhagwandas Rugelian, 4 Toley Avenue, Wembley HA9 9TB Tel: 020 8908 6690 — MB BS 1952 Bombay; MRCGP 1962; Cert JCC (with IUD) Lond 1978. (G.S. Med. Coll.) Socs: BMA.

***NEGARGAR, Aryan** 219 Burbury Street, Birmingham B19 1TW — MB ChB 1995 Birm.; ChB Birm. 1995.

NEGRETTE, Jacinto Joseph Royal Alexandra Hospital, Corsebar Road, Paisley PA2 9PN Tel: 0141 887 9111 — MB ChB 1976 Manch.; FRCR 1983; DMRD Lond. 1980. Cons. Radiol. Roy. Alexandra Hosp. Paisley.

NEGRETTE, Joseph Louis 2B Church Street, Histon, Cambridge CB4 9JG — MB BS 1992 Lond.

NEGRYCZ, Roslyn Jane Community Paediatrics, 6th Floor, Maternity building, City General, Stoke-on-Trent ST4 6QG Tel: 01782 553352 — MB BCh 1983 Wales; MA 1996 Keele University; MRCGP 1988; DCH RCP Lond. 1987. Assoc. Specialist N. Staffs. Hosps. NHS Trust.

NEGUS, Andrew Graham Whitchurch Health Centre, Armada Road, Bristol BS14 0SU Tel: 01275 832285 Fax: 01275 540035 — MB ChB 1969 Bristol; DRCOG 1971. (Bristol) Socs: BMA; Sec. S.

NEGUS

Bristol Med. Soc. Prev: Ho. Surg. Frenchay Hosp. Bristol; SHO (Paediat.) Bristol Childr. Hosp.; SHO (Obst.) Bristol Matern. Hosp.

NEGUS, Mr David Lister Hospital, Chelsea Bridge Road, London SW1W 8RH Tel: 020 7730 3417 Fax: 020 7824 8867; 10 Deamark Avenue, Wimbledon, London SW19 4HF Tel: 020 8946 9371 Fax: 020 8946 8034 — BM BCh Oxf. 1958; MA Oxf. 1958, DM, MCh 1967; FRCS Eng. 1962; MRCS Eng. LRCP Lond. 1958. (St. Thos.) Emerit. Cons. Surg. Lewisham Hosp. Lond. Socs: Hon. Mem. Soc. Francaise De Phlébologie; Fell. Roy. Soc. Med. (Ex-Mem. Counc. Surg. & Clin. Sects. & Ex-Chairm.Venous Forum); Hon. Mem. Soc. Francaise De Phlébologie. Prev: Edr. Emerit. Phlebol.; Cons. Surg. Lewisham Hosp. Lond.; Sen. Regist. & Lect. (Surg.) St. Thos. Hosp.

NEGUS, Rupert Peter Michael 17 Keyes Road, London NW2 3XB Tel: 020 8450 8327 — MB BS 1986 Lond.; BA Oxf. 1983; MRCP (UK) 1990; PhD (Lond.) 1998. Specialist Regist. (Gastroenterol. & Gen. Med.) N. W. Thames Train. Progr. Socs: Young Fell. Roy. Soc. Med.; Roy. Coll. Phys.; Brit. Cytokine Gp. Prev: Clin. Research Fell. Imperial Cancer Research Fund, Lond.; Regist. (Gen. Med. & Nephrol.) St Mary's & St Chas. Hosps. Lond.; SHO (Neurol.) Roy. Free Hosp. Lond.

NEHAUL, Balbir Ball Greene, OBE 5 Shadwell Park Grove, Leeds LS17 8TU Tel: 0113 266 3474 — MB BS 1937 Lond.; MRCS Eng. LRCP Lond. 1938; FRCPath 1963; DPH Lond. 1952; DTM & H Eng. 1938. (Univ. Coll. Hosp.) Mem. Dept. Microbiol. Univ. Leeds. Socs: Life Mem. BMA; Path. Soc. Prev: WHO Microbiol. Kathmandu, Nepal; Dep. Chief Med. Off. & Hon. Cons. Path. MoH, Guyana; Sen. Govt. Bacteriol. & Path. Centr. Med. Laborat. Geo.town.

NEHAUL, John Jaikaran Harrogate Clinic, 23 Ripon Road, Harrogate HG1 2JL Tel: 01423 500599 — LRCPI & LM, LRSCI & LM 1973; FRCPsych 1995, M 1979; DPM Leeds 1979. (RCSI) Cons. Psychiat. Leeds Community & Ment. Health Trust, St James Univ. Hosp. Leeds; Sen. Clin. Lect. (Psychiat.) Univ. Leeds. Prev: Sen. Regist. Yorks. HA; Regist. (Psychiat.) Leeds AHA; Regist. Rotat. (Med.) St. Jas. Univ. Hosp. Leeds.

NEHAUL, Lika Kevin 5 Romsley Drive, The Farthings, Shrewsbury SY2 6TG — LRCPI & LM, LRSCI & LM 1975; LRCPI & LM, LRCSI & LM 1975; DCH Eng. 1979. Sen. Regist. (Community Med.) W. Midl. RHA. Prev: Regist. (Community Med.) S.E. Thames RHA.

NEHRA, Mr Dhiren 224 Balgores Lane, Gidea Park, Romford RM2 6BS Tel: 01708 455245 Email: dnehra@compuserve.com — MB BS 1983 Bombay; MPhil Cardiff 1996; FRCS Glas. 1990. (Bombay) Regist. Rotat. Higher Surgic. Train. Wales; Specialist Regist. (Upper G.I. Surg.) Roy. Gwent Hosp. Newport. Socs: Soc. Minimal Invasive Ther.; Surgic Research Soc.; BMA. Prev: Regist. (Gen. Surg.) Singleton Hosp.; Regist. (Gen. Surg.) Neath Gen. Hosp.; Regist. (Gen. Surg.) Wrexham Maelor Hosp.

NEHRA, Paul Plot 2, College of Rose Isle, Rose Isle, Elgin IV30 5YF — MB ChB 1972 Liverp.; LMCC 1974; FCFPC 1990; MICGP 1987. Prof. Med. Univ Manitoba, Canada; Dir. Intens. Therap.; Sen. Staff Phys. The Pas Clinic, Canada; Dir. Canad. Coll. of Family Phys.; Mem. (Pres.) Coll. Family Phys. Canada 1990. Socs: Canad. Med. Assn. Prev: Chief Paediat. (Intens. Med.) St. Anthonys Gen. Hosp. The Pas, Canada; Regist. (Med.) Clatterbridge Hosp. Wirral; Regist. (Med.) & Ho. Phys. Roy. S.. Hosp. Liverp.

NEHRING, Julia Valerie Fair Mile Hospital, Wallingford OX10 9HH — MB BS 1985 Lond.; BA Oxf. 1980; MRCPsych 1989. Cons. Psychiat. Berks. Healthcare NHS Trust. Prev: Clin. Research Fell. UMDS; Sen. Regist. (Psychiat.) St. Thos. Hosp. Lond.; Regist. (Psychiat.) Littlemore & Warneford Hosps. Oxf.

NEHRING, Sandra Jane Beighton Health Centre, Queens Road, Beighton, Sheffield S20 1BJ Tel: 0114 269 5061; Cloonmore, 29 Meadowhead, Sheffield S8 7UA — MB BS 1982 Lond.; MRCGP 1986.

NEIGHBOUR, Roger Harvey Vine House Health Centre, 87 High Street, Abbots Langley WD5 0AJ Tel: 01923 262363 Fax: 01923 267374 Email: roger.neighbour@dial.pipex.com; Argowan, Bell Lane, Bedmond, Abbots Langley WD5 0QS Tel: 01923 263961 Fax: 01923 264511 Email: roger.neighbour@dial.pipex.com — MB BChir 1971 Camb.; MA Camb. 1972; FRCGP 1986, M 1975; DObst RCOG 1973. Developm. Convenor Examrs.M RCGP 1997. Socs: Fell. Assn. of Course Organisers 1988. Prev: Couvenor, Panel of MRCGP Examr.s, 1997-2002; Course Organiser Watford VTS.

NEIL, Agnes Emily (retired) 1 Wolseley Gardens, Edinburgh EH8 7DG Tel: 0131 659 6545 — LRCP LRCS 1946 Ed.; LRCP LRCS Ed. LRFPS Glas. 1946. Prev: Cas. Off. Bootle Gen. Hosp.

NEIL, Andrew Fulton 55 Merton Hall Road, Wimbledon, London SW19 3PR — MB BS 1978 Lond.; MRCP (UK) 1981; FRCP 1995. (Middlesex Hospital) Cons. Geriat. Qu. Mary's Hosp. Roehampton.

NEIL, Andrew Jardine (retired) 1 Wolseley Gardens, Edinburgh EH8 7DG Tel: 0131 659 6545 — LRCP LRCS Ed. LRFPS Glas. 1944. Prev: Surg. Lt. RNVR.

NEIL, Mrs Anne Baron (retired) 53 Talbot Road, Highgate, London N6 4QX Tel: 020 8340 0543 — MB ChB 1949 Leeds. Prev: Sen. Community Med. Off. Lond. Boro. Ealing.

NEIL, Christine Anne 55 Bishop Crescent, Shepton Mallet BA4 5XX — MB ChB 1983 Aberd. SHO Roy. Devon & Exeter Hosp. Exeter.

NEIL, Duncan 12 Colletts Green, Powick, Worcester WR2 4SB — MB ChB 1962 Glas.; DObst RCOG 1964. (Glas. & Brit. Columbia) Socs: BMA. Prev: Surg. Resid. Joyce Green Hosp. Dartford; Med. Resid. Ballochmyle Hosp. Mauchline; Obst. Resid. Bellshill Matern. Hosp.

NEIL, Hugh Andrew Wade Division of Public Health & Primary Health Care, Institute of Health Sciences, University of Oxford, Old Road, Oxford OX3 7LF Tel: 01865 226777 Fax: 01865 226777 Email: andrew.neil@dphpc.ox.ac.uk; 40 Beechcroft Road, Summertown, Oxford OX2 7AZ Tel: 01865 513348 — MB BS 1976 Lond.; MSc Lond. 1981; MA Camb. 1974, BA 1970; FRCP Lond. 1995; MRCP (UK) 1979; MRCS Eng. LRCP Lond. 1976; FFPHM RCP (UK) 1995; MFCM 1987. (St. Thos. & Camb.) Univ. Lect. (Clin. Epidemiol.) Univ. Oxf.; Hon. Cons. Phys. Diabetes, Endocrinol. & Metab. Radcliffe Infirm. Oxf. Socs: Fell. Wolfson Coll. Univ. Oxf.; Brit. Hyperlip. Assn.; Chairm. of Epidemiol. Study Gp. of the Europ. Assn. Assn. for the Study of Diabetes (EASD). Prev: Hon. Sen. Regist. & Lect. (Med.) Univ. Newc. Med. Sch.; Hon. Regist. (Med.) & Clin. Lect. (Social & Community Med.) Univ. Oxf.

NEIL, Mr James Fulton (retired) Quaker Cottage, Quaker Lane, Farnsfield, Newark NG22 8EE Tel: 01623 882281 — MA, MB BChir Camb. 1943; FRCS Ed. 1947; MRCS Eng. LRCP Lond. 1942; DLO Eng. 1951. Prev: Cons. ENT Surg. Nottm. Univ. Hosp. & Kings Mill Hosp. Sutton-in-Ashfield.

NEIL, James Morton 4 Mid Brae, Mount Melville, Graigtoun, St Andrews KY16 8NT — MB ChB 1990 Manch.

NEIL, John Robert Knox Glenkens Medical Practice, The Surgery, High Street, New Galloway, Castle Douglas DG7 3RN Tel: 01644 420234 Fax: 01644 920493; The Cottage, New Galloway, Castle Douglas DG7 3RP Tel: 01644 420275 Email: neildocs@globalnet.co.uk — MB ChB 1971 Glasgow; MB ChB Glas 1971; MFHaem 1985; MRCGP 1978; MRCP (UK) 1977. (Glasgow) GP Princip. Socs: BMA; BASICS.

NEIL, Lindsay Douglas (retired) Woodlands, Selkirk TD7 4ND Tel: 01750 20841 Email: neils@inigo.net — MB ChB Ed. 1965; DA Eng. 1972. p/t Freelance GP Selkirk. Prev: Lt.-Col. RAMC, 205 Gen. Hosp. Gulf War.

NEIL, Shelagh Patricia Glenkens Medical Practice, The Surgery, High Street, New Galloway, Castle Douglas DG7 3RN Tel: 01644 420234 Fax: 01644 920493 — MB ChB 1972 Aberdeen; MB ChB Aberd 1972. (Aberdeen) GP Castle Douglas, Kirkcudbrightshire.

NEIL, Mr Thomas Kings Lane Surgery, 100 Kings Lane, Wirral CH63 5LY Tel: 0151 608 4347 Fax: 0151 608 9095 — MB ChB 1984 Leeds; FRCS Ed. 1989; DRCOG 1991. Prev: Trainee GP Wirral VTS; SHO (Paediat.) Chester; SHO (Obst.) Warrington.

NEIL, Vanessa Shena Half Acre House, Lower Weald, Calverton, Milton Keynes MK19 6EQ Tel: 01908 560715 — MB BChir 1974 Camb.; MA, MB Camb. 1974, BChir 1973; MRCP (UK) 1977; MRCPath 1982. Cons. Haemat. Bedford Gen. Hosp. Prev: Sen. Regist. (Haemat.) Oxon AHA (T); Regist. (Med.) Norwich Health Dist.

NEIL, Wendy Jane 41 Chapel Field, Gamlingay, Sandy SG19 3QP — MB ChB 1996 Ed.

NEIL, Mr William Fulton Head and Neck Centre, Royal Shrewsbury Hospital, Mytton Oak Road, Shrewsbury SY3 8XQ Tel: 01743 261499 Fax: 01742 261006 — MB BS Lond. 1969; FRCS Eng. 1975. (Middlx.) Cons. ENT Surg. Roy. Shrewsbury Hosp. NHS Trust. Socs: Roy. Soc. Med. (Sects. Laryngol. & Otol.). Prev: Sen. Regist. (ENT) Roy. Berks. Hosp. Reading; Sen. Regist. Roy. Nat. Throat, Nose & Ear Hosp. Lond.

NEILSON

NEIL-DWYER, Mr Glenn Wessex Neurological Centre, Southampton General Hospital, Southampton SO16 6YD Tel: 02380 277222; Annesley Glade, Bank, Lyndhurst SO43 7FD Tel: 0142 128 3352 — MB BS 1963 Lond.; MS Lond. 1974; FRCS Eng. 1969; FRCS Ed. 1967. (St. Mary's) p/t Cons. Neurosurg. Wessex Neurol. Centre Soton. Gen. Hosp.; Hon. Cons. Neurosurg. Army. Socs: (Counc. Mem.) Brit. Soc. Neurol. Surgs. Prev: Cons. Neurosurg. SE Regional Neurosurg. Unit Brook Gen. Hosp. Lond.; Cons. Neurosurg. Cornw. Regional Hosp., Jamaica; Sen. Regist. (Neurosurg.) Wessex Neurosurg. Unit Soton. Gen. Hosp.

NEIL-DWYER, Jason Glen Annesley Glade, Bank, Lyndhurst, Southampton SO4 7FD — MB BS 1992 Lond.; BSc (Hons. Surg.) Lond. 1989, MB BS 1992. SHO (Plastic Surg.) Qu. Vict. Hosp. E. Grinstead. Socs: BMA. Prev: Ho. Off. (Gen. Med.) Roy. Sussex Co. Hosp.; Ho. Surg. Guy's Hosp. Lond.

NEIL-DWYER, Jennifer Susan Edith Annesley Glade, Bank, Lyndhurst SO43 7FD Tel: 01703 283352 — MB BS 1964 Lond.; MRCS Eng. LRCP Lond. 1964; DO Eng. 1967. (St. Mary's) Clin. Asst. Soton. Eye Hosp. Prev: Clin. Asst. Guy's Hosp. Lond.; SHO Eye Unit Mayday Hosp. Croydon; SHO W.. Ophth. Hosp. Lond.

NEILD, Professor Guy Hume Institute of Urology and Nephrology, University College and Middlesex School of Medicine, Middlesex Hospital, Mortimer Road, London W1T 3AA Tel: 020 7380 9302 Fax: 020 7637 7006 Email: g.neild@ucl.ac.uk — MB BS 1971 Lond.; MD Lond. 1985; FRCP Lond. 1988. (St. Thos.) Prof. Nephrol. UCMSM; Hon. Cons. St. Peter's Renal Unit UCL Hosps. (Middlx Hosp.) Lond. Prev: Sen. Lect. (Nephrol.) Inst. of Urol.

NEILD, Julia Elizabeth Medical Defence Union, 3 Devonshire Place, London W1G 6HE Tel: 020 7486 6181 — MB BS 1977 Lond.; MB BS (Hons.) Lond. 1977; FRCP 1998. (St. Thos.) Head Claims Handling Med. Defence Union.

NEILD, Penelope Jane c/o Mrs P. M. Neild (Matron), Rustington Convalescent Home, Littlehampton BN16 2LZ — MB ChB 1987 Birm.

NEILD, Valerie Susan Royal Victoria Hospital, Folkestone CT19 5HL; Swarling Manor, Petham, Canterbury CT4 5QP Tel: 01227 700377 — MB BS 1973 Lond.; FRCP Lond. 1993; MRCP (UK) 1976. (St. Thos.) Cons. Dermat. SE Kent HA.

***NEILL, Adrian K** Site 3, Orchardvale, Upper Knockbreda Road, Belfast BT6 XXX — MB BCh BAO 1996 Belf.

NEILL, Alexander Edward (retired) South Knoll, South Stoke, Bath BA2 7DN — MB BChir Camb. 1949; BA Camb. 1949. Prev: Med. Ref. BPA.

NEILL, Anne-Marie Grove House, Bury Road, Stapleford, Cambridge CB2 5BP Tel: 01223 846249 — MB ChB 1988 Sheff.; MRCOG 1993. Specialist Regist. E. Anglian Deanery. Prev: Regist. (O & G) Rosie Matern. Hosp. Camb. & W. Suff. Hosp. Bury St. Edmunds; Regist. (O & G) N. Gen. Hosp. Sheff.; SHO (O & G) Jessop Hosp. Sheff.

NEILL, Dilys Jane The Surgery, Well Lane, Stow on the Wold, Cheltenham GL54 1EQ Tel: 01451 30625; Templis, Broadwell, Moreton-in-Marsh GL56 0TU — MB BS 1977 Lond.; MRCP (UK) 1983; MRCS Eng. LRCP Lond. 1977; MRCGP 1986; DRCOG 1986; DA Eng. 1980. Prev: GP Moreton-in-Marsh.

NEILL, Fiona Elizabeth Silver Lodge, 44 Chatsworth Heights, Camberley GU15 1NH — MB BS 1990 Lond.; DCH RCP Lond. 1995. (St. Bart. Hosp. Lond.) Specialist Regist. (Anaesth.) Kettering & Oxf.

NEILL, Hugh Western Infirmary, Glasgow G11 6NT; 15 Raasay Gardens, Newton Mearns, Glasgow G77 6TH Tel: 0141 639 7535 — MB ChB 1992 Glas.; BSc Glas. 1990; FRCA Lond. 1996. SPE(Anaesth.) N. Glas. Univ. Trust. Socs: Glas. & W. Scot. Soc. Anaesth.; Scott. Soc. Anaesth.; Assoc. of Anaesth. Prev: SHO (Anaesth.) W.. Infirm. Trust Hosps. Glas.

NEILL, James Hood (retired) 17 Hayne Park, Tipton St John, Sidmouth EX10 0TA Tel: 01404 811038 — MB ChB Ed. 1949. Prev: GP Eyam Derbysh.

NEILL, Joyce Gibbon (retired) 42A Cadogan Park, Belfast BT9 6HH Tel: 01232 662861 — MB BChir Camb. 1940; MRCS Eng. LRCP Lond. 1940; DObst RCOG 1943. Prev: Med. Off. Family Plann. Clinic Roy. Matern. Hosp. Belf.

NEILL, Leslie Gary Eskdaill Medical Centre, Eskdaill Street, Kettering NN16 8RA Tel: 01536 513053 Fax: 01536 417572;

Beech House, Rectory Hill, Cranford, Kettering NN14 4AH Fax: 01536 417572 — MB ChB 1981 Sheff.; DRCOG 1983.

NEILL, Margaret Philomena 4 Colbern Close, Brook Road, Maghull, Liverpool L31 3EP Tel: 0151 526 3726 — MB BCh BAO 1952 NUI; MRCPsych 1974; DCH Dub. 1958; DPH NUI 1958. Prev: Cons. Psychiat. Moss Side Hosp. Liverp.

NEILL, Rashida 7 Lowerfold Crescent, Rochdale OL12 7HZ Tel: 01706 584671 — MB BS 1957 Punjab; MSc (Pub. Health) Manch. 1974; MB BS Punjab (Pakistan) 1957; DCH Eng. 1964. (Fatima Jinnah Med. Sch. Lahore) Area Specialist (Community Med.) Rochdale AHA. Socs: BMA. Prev: Med. Off. Kenya Min. of Health.

NEILL, Robert Alfred 6 Warren Sr., Donaghadee BT21 0PF — MB BCh BAO 1980 Belf.; MRCGP 1986; DRCOG 1985.

NEILL, Mr Robert Watson Kerr (retired) Grune House, Jarman Lane, Sutton, Macclesfield SK11 0HJ Tel: 01260 253172 — MB ChB 1957 Manch.; FRCS Eng. 1968. Prev: Cons. Surg. Macclesfield Dist. Gen. Hosp.

NEILL, Sarah Mary St. Peters Hospital, Guildford Road, Chertsey KT16 0PZ; Moorlands, Coronation Road, Ascot SL5 9HF — MB ChB 1973 Manch.; MRCP (UK) 1981. Cons. Dermat. St. Peter's Hosp. Chertsey. Prev: Sen. Regist. (Dermat.) W.m. Hosp. Lond.; Regist. (Dermat.) King's Coll. Hosp. Lond.; SHO St. John's Hosp. Dis. Skin.

NEILL, Sarah Valerie 155A High Street, Brentwood CM14 4SD — MB ChB 1991 Glas.

NEILLIE, Darren William Robert Flat 3/1, 8 Stewartville St., Glasgow G11 5PE — MB ChB 1993 Glas.

NEILLIE, Jane Louise Worcester Royal Infirmary NHS Trust, Castle St., Worcester WR1 3AS; Apartment 6, Albemarle, Norton Barracks, Norton, Worcester WR5 2NZ — MB ChB 1993 Glas. Staff Grade (Psychiat.) Worcester Roy. Infirm. NHS Trust. Prev: SHO (Dermat.) Monklands NHS Trust Airdrie; SHO (Dermat.) Stobhill NHS Trust Airdrie; SHO (Geriat.) Stobhill NHS Trust Glas.

NEILLY, Ian Joseph Wansbeck General Hospital, Woodhorn Lane, Ashington NE63 9JJ Tel: 01670 521212; 2 Swinton Close, Morpeth NE61 2XD Tel: 01670 518202 Email: ineilly@aol.com — MB ChB 1982 Aberd.; FRCP 1998; MD Aberdeen 1997; MRCPath 1992; MRCP (UK) 1985; FRCPath 2000. (Aberdeen) Cons. Haemat. Wansbeck Gen. Hosp. Ashington. Prev: Sen. Regist. (Haemat.) Roy. Vict. Infirm. Belf.; Regist. (Haemat.) Aberd. Roy. Infirm.; Regist. (Med.) Roy. Alexandra Infirm. Paisley & W.. & Gartnaval Infirms. Glas.

NEILLY, Paul John David 21 Glenwell Park, Glengormley, Newtownabbey BT36 7TA — MB BCh BAO 1986 Belf.

NEILSON, Angela Brasch — MB ChB 1981 Dundee. (Dundee) p/t GP Regist., Elmbank Gp., Foresterhill Health Centre, Aberd. Prev: SHO Psychiat., Roy. Cornhill Hosp., Aberd.; Clin. Asst., Subst. Misuse, Roy. Cornhill Hosp., Aberd.; GP Assistance, Fyvie/Old Meldrum Med. Gp.

***NEILSON, Anna Marguerite** Craggie, Meikle Richorn Road, Dalbeattie DG5 4QT — MB ChB 1996 Glas.

NEILSON, David Ritchie Stratheden Hospital, Cupar KY15 5RR Tel: 01334 652611 Fax: 01334 653950; 9 Trinity Place, St Andrews KY16 8SG Email: dave@neilson1953.freeserve.co.uk — MB ChB 1978 Ed.; MPhil 1986; MRCPsych 1982. Cons. Gen. Psychiat. Fife Primary Care Trust N. E. Fife; Hon. Sen. Lect. Dept. of Psychiat. Univ. of Dundee; Hon. Lect. Sch. of Divinity Univ. of St Andrews. Prev: Sen. Regist. (Psychiat.) Nottm. & S. Derbysh. HAs; Regist. & SHO Roy. Edin. Hosp.

NEILSON, David William 1/2 72 Novar Drive, Hyndland, Glasgow G12 9TZ Tel: 0141 357 2489 — MB ChB 1983 Glas.

NEILSON, Derek James Currer The Clinic, Mill Isle, Craignair Street, Dalbeattie DG5 4HE Tel: 01556 610331; Craggie, Dalbeattie DG5 4QT Tel: 01556 610455 — MB ChB St. And. 1967; DObst RCOG 1970. (St. And.) Prev: Ho. Off. (Med.) Falkirk & Dist. Roy. Infirm.; Ho. Off. (Obst.) Elsie Inglis Matern. Hosp. Edin.; Ho. Off. (Surg. & Paediat.) Roy. Hosp. Sick Childr. Edin.

NEILSON, Mr Donald Blackburn Royal Infirmary, Bolton Road, Blackburn BB2 3LR Tel: 01254 263555 Fax: 01254 294017 — MB ChB 1981 Liverp.; FRCS (Urol.) 1996; FRCS Ed. 1986; MD 1997. (Liverp.) Cons. Urol. Blackburn Roy. Infirm. Blackburn. Prev: Sen. Regist. (Urol.) Manch. Roy. Infirm.; Sen. Regist. (Urol.) Stepping Hill Hosp. Stockport; Sen. Regist. (Urol.) Withington Hosp. Manch.

***NEILSON, Ewan Graham** 55 Deanwood Avenue, Netherlee, Glasgow G44 3RQ — MB ChB 1996 Glas.

NEILSON

NEILSON, Frances Marguerite Currer The Sycamores, 5 Almoners Barn, Potters Bank, Durham DH1 3TZ — MB ChB 1967 Ed.; DPH Glas. 1971; DObst RCOG 1970. (Ed.) Clin. Med. Off. (Community Child Health) Durh.

NEILSON, Frances Mary 63 Beatty Avenue, Coldean, Brighton BN1 9EP — MB ChB 1976 Aberd.; MRCPsych 1982.

NEILSON, Graham Alexander 27 Turnberry Drive, Newton Mearns, Glasgow G77 5SE — MB ChB 1997 Glas. SHO (Anaesth.) Stobhill Hosp., Glas. Socs: BMA. Prev: SHO A & E SHO Orthop.; Jun. Ho. Off. Med.; Jun. Ho. Off. Surg.

NEILSON, Professor James Purdie Department Obstetrics & Gynaecology, University of Liverpool, Liverpool L69 3BX Tel: 0151 702 4100 Fax: 0151 702 4024 Email: jneilson@liv.ac.uk; 10 Oldfield Road, Heswall, Wirral CH60 6SE Tel: 0151 342 2796 — MB ChB 1975 Ed.; MD Ed. 1985, BSc 1972; MRCOG 1981; FRCOG 1997. Prof. O & G Univ. Liverp.; Hon. Cons. Obst. & Gyn. Liverp. Wom. Hosp. Prev: Sen. Lect. (O & G) Univ. Edin.; Lect. (Obst.) Univ. Glas.; Sen. Regist. Harare Centr. Hosp., Zimbabwe.

NEILSON, Jeffrey Roy Department of Haematology, Leicester Royal Infirmary, Leicester LE1 5WW; 43 Main Street, Snarestone, Swadlincote DE12 7DB — MB ChB 1987 Manch.; MRCP (UK) 1991; MRCPath 1998. Sen. Regist. (Haemat.) Leicester Roy. Infirm. Prev: Research Fell. (Haemat.) Birm. Heartlands Hosp.; Regist. Rot. (Haemat.) W. Midl.; SHO Rotat. (Gen. Med.) Blackburn Roy. Infirm.

NEILSON, Mr John Rosewood, Park St., Dumfries DG2 7PH Tel: 01387 255678 — MB ChB Glas. 1937, DPH 1939; FRFPS Glas. 1947; FRCS Glas. 1962; FRCS Ed. (ad eund.) 1961. (Univ. Glas.) Socs: Fell. Assn. Surgs. Gt. Brit.; BMA. Prev: Sen. Cons. Surg. Dumfries & Galloway Roy. Infirm.; Sen. Clin. Lect. Aberd. Univ.; Med. Off. Hackney LCC Hosp.

NEILSON, Roderick Forsyth Medical and Dental Defence Union of Scotland, MackIntosh House, 120 Blythswood St., Glasgow G2 4EA Tel: 0141 221 5858; 182 Southbrae Drive, Glasgow G13 1TX Tel: 0141 959 2449 Email: roddy@arneilson.demon.co.uk — MB ChB 1985 Glas.; FRCP 1999; MRCPath 1995, D 1992; Dip. Forens. Med. Glas 1994; MRCP (UK) 1988. Med. Adviser Med. & Dent. Defence Union Scotl. Prev: Cons. (Haemat. & Haemophilia Centre) Dir. N. Hants. Hosp. Basingstoke; Sen. Regist. (Haemat.) Glas. Roy. Infirm.

NEILSON, William Robert 15 Mermaid Street, Rye TN31 7ET — MB BS 1975 Lond.; MRCS Eng. LRCP Lond. 1975.

NEININGER, Patrick David Roger Woodbank Surgery, 2 Hunstanton Drive, Bury BL8 1EG Tel: 0161 705 1630 Fax: 0161 763 3221 Email: patrick.neininger@gp-p83017.nhs.uk; 11 Tonbridge Close, Bury BL8 1YH Email: patrick.neininger@virgin.net — MRCS Eng. LRCP Lond. 1972; MRCGP 1978; DObst RCOG 1975. (Birm.) Socs: BMA; Sands Cox Soc. Prev: Trainee GP Bury VTS; Ho. Surg. Dorset Co. Hosp. Dorchester; Ho. Phys. Whiston Hosp. Prescot.

NEITHERCUT, Margaret Stewart (retired) 4 Albany Drive, Burnside, Rutherglen, Glasgow G73 3QN Tel: 0141 647 6823 — MB ChB 1942 Glas.; MD Glas. 1947. Prev: Cytol. Monklands Gen. Hosp. Airdrie.

NEITHERCUT, William Duncan Department of Chemical Pathology, Arrowe Park Hospital, Arrowe Park Road, Upton, Wirral CH49 5LN; Department of Chemical Pathology, Clatterbridge Hospital, Bebington, Wirral CH63 4JY — MB ChB 1980 Glas.

NEJIM, Mr Ali Nejih Airedale General Hospital, Steeton, Keighley BD20 6TD; Shay Croft, Shay Lane, Heaton, Bradford BD9 6SQ — MB ChB 1979 Baghdad; FRCS Eng. 1991. Cons. Gen. Surg. Airedale Gen. Hosp. Keighley; Hon. Lect. Surg. Leeds Univ. Socs: BMA; BASO; VSS. Prev: Sen. Regist. (Gen. Surg.) St. Jas. Univ. Hosp.; Regist. Rotat. W. Yorks.; SHO (Urol.) Wakefield.

NEJO, Tunde Akinwale Surrey Hampshire Borders NHS Trust, Briarwood Rehabilitation Unit, Broadhurst, Cove, Farnborough GU14 9XW — MB BCh BAO 1985 NUI; MRCPsych 1993. Cons. Psychiat. Surrey Hants. Borders NHS Trust Briarwood Rehabil. Unit BRd.hurst Cove FarnBoro. Socs: BMA; Roy. Coll. Psychiat.; Fell. Roy. Soc. Med. Prev: Cons./Sen. Regist. Gen. Psychiat. Norf. Ment. Health Care NHS Trust Norwich; Sen. Regist. (Geriat. Psychiat.) W. Suff. Hosp. Mid-Anglia NHS Trust.

NEL, George Department of Orthopaedic Surgery, Bedford Hospital, South Wing, Kempston Road, Bedford MK42 9DJ Tel: 01234 792201 Fax: 01234 340122; 62 Putnoe Heights, Bedford MK41 8EB Tel: 01234 352966 Fax: 01234 343202 — MB ChB Cape Town 1964; FCS(SA) (Orth) 1981. (Univ. of Cape town, S Africa) Clin Dir Orthop.Dept. Bedford Hosp. Socs: Brit. Orthop. Assn.; Roy. Soc. Med. Prev: Orthop. Cons. Mines Benefit Soc. S. Africa.

NEL, Thomas Pierre Cottney Meadow, Old Park, Bradley, Ashbourne DE6 1PL Tel: 01335 372033 Fax: 01335 372171 Email: huntex@msn.com — MB ChB 1983 Stellenbosch.

NELEMANS, Ian St Albans Medical Centre, 26-28 St. Albans Crescent, Bournemouth BH8 9EW Tel: 01202 517333; 34 Castlemain Avenue, Bournemouth BH6 5EJ — Artsexamen 1980 Nijmegen; FRCGP 1996, M 1987. Clin. Asst. Pacing Dept., Dept. of Cardiol. Roy. Bournemouth Hosp. Prev: Med. Off. i/c Consolata Hosp. Kyeni, Kenya.

NELIGAN, Patrick Hugh Manor Farm, 45 White Gap Road, Little Weighton, Cottingham HU20 3XF; Manor Farm, 45 Whitegap Road, Little Weighton, Cottingham HU20 3XF Tel: 01482 845003 — MB ChB 1972 Birm.; FRCP Lond. 1991; MRCP (UK) 1977. (Birm.) Cons. Geriat. Roy. Hull Hosps. Kingston upon Hull. Socs: Brit. Geriat. Soc. Prev: Lect. (Med.) Univ. Dundee; SHO (Med.) Roy. Hosp. Wolverhampton; Ho. Phys. Childr. Hosp. Birm.

NELKI, Julia Sibyl Seymour House, 43 Seymour Terrace, Liverpool L3 5TE Tel: 0151 707 0101 Fax: 0151 708 9200 — MB ChB 1979 Bristol; MSc 1990; MA Oxf. 1975; MRCPsych 1985; DRCOG 1981. p/t Cons. Child & Adolesc. Psychiat. Roy. Liverp. Child. NHS Trust; Course Dproject Director Family Refugee Support Project; Course Comm. Mem. for MA PsychoAnalyt. Observational Studies. Socs: Assn. Psychoanal. Psychother. & Assn. Family Ther..; Wom. in Med.; Assn. of Child Psychiat. & Psychol. Prev: Sen. Regist. (Child & Adolesc. Psychiat.) Tavistock Clin.; SHO & Regist. (Adult Psychiat.) Lond. Hosp. Whitechapel.

NELKI, Michael Fenner Hermann Yatton Family Practice, 155 Mendip Road, Yatton BS49 4ER Tel: 01934 832277; The Courtyard Flat, 41 Royal York Crescent, Bristol BG8 3JS — MB BS Lond. 1969; MRCS Eng. LRCP Lond. 1970; DObst RCOG 1971. (St. Geo.) Socs: MN.

NELL, Joanna Louise Burton Medical Centre, 123 Salisbury Road, Burton, Christchurch BH23 7JN Tel: 01202 474311 Fax: 01202 484412; The Creamery, Burton Green Farm, Christchurch BH23 7JN Tel: 01202 473533 Email: jospain@aol.com — BM BCh 1991 Oxf.; DCH RCP Lond. 1993; DRCOG 1994 (RCOG); MRCGP 1995 (RCGP). Clin. Asst. (A&E) Lymington Hosp. Prev: Ships Doc. (P&O Cruises) 1995; Staff Grade (A&E) Jersey Gen. Hosp. 1997.

NELLIST, Paul John Wawn Street Surgery, Wawn St., South Shields NE33 4DX Tel: 0191 454 0421; 111 Victoria Road W., Hebburn NE31 1UX — MB BS 1989 Newc.

NELMS, Mark Thomas Carlisle House, 53 Lanegland Street, Poole BH15 1QD Tel: 01202 678484 Fax: 01202 660507; 52 Twemlow Avenue, Parkstone, Poole BH14 8AN — BM 1985 Soton.; DRCOG 1989.

NELSON, Alan Rache Harley House Surgery, 2 Irnham Road, Minehead TA24 5DL Tel: 01643 703441 Fax: 01643 704867 — MB BS 1977 Lond.; MRCS Eng. LRCP Lond. 1977; MRCGP 1981; DRCOG 1981. (St. Thomas' Hospital London) Clin. Governance Lead Som. Coast PCG.

NELSON, Alys Patricia (retired) Newby, 25 The Northern Road, Great Crosby, Liverpool L23 2RA — MB ChB 1943 Glas.; BSc, MB ChB Glas. 1943. Prev: Ho. Phys. Roy. Infirm. Glas.

NELSON, Andrew Moore (retired) Sunny Meed Surgery, 15-17 Heathside Road, Woking GU22 7EY Tel: 01483 772760 — MB BS 1956 Lond. Police Surg. Woking.

NELSON, Brian Lynn Powell (retired) West Haven, Ton Kenfig Pyle, Bridgend CF33 4PT Tel: 01656 742159 — MB BCh 1955 Wales. Prev: GP Port Talbot.

NELSON, Christopher Sinclair 6 Park Lane, Allestree, Derby DE22 2DR Tel: 01332 557675 — MB ChB 1970 Glas.; FRCP Glas. 1986; MRCP (UK) 1975. Cons. Paediat. & Paediat. Nephrol. Derby Childr. Hosp. & Nottm. City. Prev: Lect. in Child Health Univ. Glas. Dept. Child Health Roy. Hosp. Sick; Childr. Glas.; Regist. (Gen. Med.) Roy. Alexandra Infirm. Paisley; Regist. (Med. Paediat.) Roy. Hosp. Sick Childr. Glas.

NELSON, Cyril Anthony 3 Highbridge Road, Sutton Coldfield B73 5QA — MB ChB 1984 Birm.; BSc Birm. 1981; FRCR 1993. Cons. Radiol. Good Hope NHS Trust. Socs: Fell. Roy. Coll. Radiol.

NELSON

NELSON, Cyril Ellis 31 Avondale Road, Southport PR9 0NH — MRCS Eng. LRCP Lond. 1953. (Sheff.) Prev: Med. Regist. & Sen. Ho. Phys. Sharoe Green Hosp. Fulwood; SHO (Obst.) & Ho. Phys. Preston Roy. Infirm.

NELSON, David 101 Gledhow Lane, Roundhay, Leeds LS8 1NE Tel: 0113 266 7948 — MRCS Eng. LRCP Lond. 1961. (Liverp.) Regional Sec. Med. Protec. Soc.

NELSON, Deborah Elizabeth Palmerston House, 44Colinton Road, Edinburgh EH14 1AH Tel: 0131 377 5949 Email: dr_debbie_nelson@yahoo.com — MB ChB 1990 Ed.; MRCPsych 1996; Dip. FMSA 1998. Cons. Psychiat., Falkirk Roy. Infirm., Falkirk. Prev: Specialist Regist. in Forens. Psychiat., Orchard Clinic, Roy. Edin. Hosp.

***NELSON, Deborah Louise** 8 Pembridge Place, London W2 4XB — MB BS 1997 Lond.

NELSON, Doreen Elizabeth Auskaird, 5 Greenwood, Culmore, Londonderry BT48 8NP — MB BCh BAO 1959 Belf.

NELSON, Elizabeth Christina 79 Cloch Road, Gourock PA19 1AU Tel: 01475 32332 — MB ChB 1948 Ed.; DPM Leeds 1963; DPH Ed. 1952; DCH Eng. 1957. (Ed.) Prev: Cons. Child Psychiat. Argyll & Clyde HB; Sen. Regist. Wessex RHB & W.. RHB (Scotl.); Regional Med. & Health Off. Sask., Canada.

NELSON, Fiona Gray Hounsfield Way Surgery, Hounsfield Way, Sutton-on-Trent, Newark NG23 6PX Tel: 01636 821023 Fax: 01636 822308 — MB ChB 1971 Sheff. Asst. GP Sutton-on-Trent, Newark; Clin. Med. Off. Bassetlaw & Centr. Notts. HAs.

NELSON, Fiona Rosalind 22 Gilmour Road, Edinburgh EH16 5NT Tel: 0131 667 1173 Email: fiona.barry@tinyworld.co.uk; 22 Gilmour Road, Edinburgh EH16 5NT — MB ChB 1992 Ed.; DFFP 1999; M.Phil (Law & Med. Eth.) Glas. 1998. (Edin.) Specialist Regist. (O & G) S.E. Scot. Rot. Roy. Infirm. Edin. Hosp. & Simpson Memor. Matern. Pavilion; Sessional Doctor (Sexual Health) Midlothian Young Person Advis. Serv. Dalkeith and Penicuik, Midlothian; Sessional Doctor (Sexual Health) Scot-Pep Edin. Socs: Edin. Obst. Soc.; Scott. Medico-Legal Soc. Prev: Res. Fell. (O & G) Roy. Infirm. Edin.; Sen. SHO (O & G) P.ss Anne Hosp. Soton.; SHO (A & E) Jersey Gen. Hosp.

NELSON, Professor George Stanley Snarlton House, Wingfield, Trowbridge BA14 9LH Tel: 01225 754763 — MB ChB 1948 St. And.; DSc St. And. 1966, MD 1956; FRCP 1981, M 1971; FRCPath 1979; DTM & H Liverp. 1953; Dip. Applied Parasitol. & Entomol. Univ. Lond 1960. (St. And.) Emerit. Prof. Trop. Med. Infec. Dis. Liverp. Sch. Med. Socs: Fell. (Pres.) Roy. Soc. Trop. Med. & Hyg.; Hon. Fell. Amer. Soc. Trop. Med. & Hyg. Prev: Walter Myers Prof. Parasitol. Liverp. Sch. Trop. Med.; Prof. Helminthol. Lond. Sch. Hyg. & Trop. Med.; Sen. Parasitol. Nairobi.

NELSON, Gillian Louise Perrott End, New Yatt Road, North Leigh, Witney OX29 6TT — MB ChB 1991 Leic.

NELSON, Helen Margaret Queen's Hospital, Burton, Belvedere Road, Burton-on-Trent DE13 0RB Tel: 01283 566333 Fax: 01283 593014; 6 Park Lane, Allestree, Derby DE22 2DR — MB ChB 1974 Glas.; FRCP Glas. 1989. Cons. Dermat. Burton Hosp. NHS Trust. Socs: Orindary Mem. Brit. Assn. Dermat.; Brit. Soc. Paediat. Dermatol.; Brit. Contact Dermatitis Gp. Prev: Sen. Regist. (Dermat.) Univ. Hosp. Nottm., Glas. Roy. Infirm. & W.. Infirm. Glas.

NELSON, Hugh Francis John 99 Magheralane Road, Randalstowvn, Antrim BT41 2PA — MB BCh BAO 1991 Belf.

NELSON, Mr Ian Wilkie Department of Orthopaedic Surgery, Frenchay Hospital, Frenchay Park Road, Bristol BS16 1LE Tel: 0117 918 6514 Fax: 0117 975 3759 — MB BS 1979 Lond.; MCh Orth. Liverp. 1990; FRCS Eng. 1984; MRCS Eng. LRCP Lond. 1979. (Westm.) Cons. Orthop. Surg. Frenchay Hosp. & Avon Orthop. Centre S.mead Hosp. Bristol.; Hon. Sen. Lect. Univ. Bristol. Socs: Brit. Scoliosis Soc.; Brit. Assn. Spine Surg.s. Prev: Lect. (Orthop.) Nuffield Orthop. Centre Oxf.; Regist. (Orthop.) Univ. Coll. Hosp. Lond.; Ho. Surg. & Cas. Off. W.m. Hosp. Lond.

NELSON, Ivan Douglas Magill (retired) 8 Leveson Close, Gosport PO12 2QJ Tel: 01705 358363 — MB BCh BAO Belf. 1941, DPH 1947; MFCM 1974. Hon. Clin. Teach. Soton. Univ. Med. Sch. Prev: SCM Hants. AHA (T).

NELSON, Jagbir 2 Aspen Court, Cedar Grove, Castlehill, Ayr KA7 3QS — MB ChB 1991 Glas. Clin. Asst. (Diabetes) CrossHo. Hosp. Kilmarnock.

NELSON, James Prestwich The Nelson Practice, Amersall Road, Scawthorpe, Doncaster DN5 9PQ Tel: 01302 780704 Fax: 01302 390512; Grove Cottage, The Grove, Barnby Dun, Doncaster DN3 1EB — MB ChB 1965 Sheff.

NELSON, James Spiers 19 Trevose Gardens, Sherwood, Nottingham NG5 3FU Tel: 0115 960 9834 — MB BCh BAO 1949 Belf.; LRCP LRCS Ed. LRFPS Glas. 1949; DMJ (Clin.) Soc. Apoth. Lond. 1971. (Belf.) Sen. Police Surg. Notts. Constab.; Phys. i/c BUPA Med. Centre Nottm.. Prev: Ho. Phys. City Hosp. Nottm.; Res. Ho. Off. Childr. Hosp. Nottm.

NELSON, James William 39 Parkside View, Leeds LS6 4NS — MB ChB 1998 Leeds; BSc Leeds 1986; PhD Edinburgh 1990. (University of Leeds Medical School)

NELSON, Jennifer Jane Ashworth St Surgery, 85 Spotland Road, Rochdale; 5 Beaumonds Way, Rochdale OL11 5NL Tel: 01706 646081 — MB ChB 1993 Manch.; BSc St. And. 1990; MRCGP1998. (Mans.)

NELSON, Joanne Katherine Cupar Street Clinic, 91 Cupar St., Belfast BT12 2LJ Tel: 01232 327613; Email: joannenelson@royalhospitalsn-i.nhs.uk — BM BCh 1990 Oxf.; MA Camb. 1991; MRCP (UK) 1994; MD Queens Univ. Belfast 1999. Cons. (Paeds). Socs: Ulster Med. Soc.; RCPCH; Paediat. Res. Soc.

NELSON, John Kenneth The Ulster Hospital, Dundonald, Belfast BT16 1RH Tel: 02890 561384 Fax: 02890 550436 Email: susan.williams@nda.n-i.nhs.uk; 4 Rosepark E., Belfast BT5 7RL Tel: 01232 483221 Fax: 01232 487131 — MB BCh BAO (Hons.) Belf. 1960; MD Belf. 1963; FRCP Lond. 1988; FRCP Ed. 1971, M 1964. (Qu. Univ. Belf.) Cons. Phys. Ulster Hosp. Dundonald, Belf.; Sen. Lect. (Med.) Qu. Univ. Belf.; Regional Adviser N.. Irel. & Adviser RePub. Irel. for Roy. Coll. of Phys. Ed. Socs: Fell. Roy. Soc. Med.; Sen. Mem. Assn. Phys.; Brit. Diabetic Assn. (Med. & Scientif. Sect.). Prev: Sen. Regist. Sir Geo. E. Clark Metab. Unit Roy. Vict. Hosp. Belf.; Research Fell. Johns Hopkins Univ. Hosp. Baltimore, USA; Research Fell. (Med.) Qu. Univ. Belf.

***NELSON, John Kenneth Mackenzie** 3/2, 8 Cowan Street, Hillhead, Glasgow G12 8PF — MB ChB 1995 Glas.

NELSON, John Steven Department of Anaesthetics, Charing Cross Hospital, Gulham Palace Road, London SW1; 18 Manchuria Road, Battersea, London SW11 6AE — MB ChB 1988 Glas.; FRCA (UK). (Glasgow University) Specialist Regist. (Anaesth.) St. Mary's Sch. Anaesth. Lond.

NELSON, Joyce Marjorie (Surgery), 262 Stockport Road, Cheadle Heath, Stockport Tel: 0161 428 6729; 89 Gatley Road, Cheadle SK8 1LX — MB ChB 1959 Liverp.; DObst RCOG 1962.

NELSON, Juliet Deborah 31 Tantallon Road, London SW12 8DF — MB ChB 1988 Bristol; BSc (Hons.) Bristol 1986; MRCP (UK) 1992. SHO (A & E) Bristol Roy. Infirm. Prev: Ho. Surg. Bristol Roy. Infirm.; Ho. Phys. (Cardiol.) Torquay Gen. Hosp.

NELSON, Katherine Wendy 237 Spring Vale Road, Sheffield S10 1LG — MB ChB 1991 Sheff.

NELSON, Kenneth Alexander (retired) Clonvara, 17 Glenarm Road, Larne BT40 1BN — MB BCh BAO 1949 Belf. Prev: Res. Ho. Off. Roy. Vict. Hosp. Belf. & Roy. Hosp. Sick Childr. Belf.

NELSON, Kenneth Andrew Shankill Road Surgery, 136-138 Shankill Road, Belfast BT13 2BD Tel: 028 9032 4524; 5 Locksley Park, Belfast BT10 0AR — MB BCh BAO 1979 Belf.; MRCGP 1984; DCH Dub. 1983.

NELSON, Leslie Digby (retired) Little Gables, Brampton CA8 2HZ Tel: 01502 2375 — MB BS 1927 Durh. Prev: Surg. Cdr. RNVR.

NELSON, Mrs Margaret Elizabeth Kelsey (retired) Ivy House, Castlecaulfield, Dungannon BT70 3NP Tel: 0186 87 61240 — MB BCh BAO 1954 Dub.; BA, MB BCh BAO Dub. 1954. SCMO S.. Health & Social Servs. Bd. Prev: Princip. in Gen. Pract. Fivemiletown Co. Tyrone.

NELSON, Mark Richard Chelsea & Westminster Hospital, 369 Fulham Road, London SW10 — MB BS 1986 Lond.; MA Camb. 1982. Cons. HIV Chelsea & W.m. Hosp. Lond. Socs: Roy. Coll. Phys. Prev: Sen. Regist. (HIV & Genitourin. Med.) Chelsea & W.m. Hosp. Lond.; Regist. (HIV Med., Neurol. & Gastroenterol.) W.m. Hosp. Lond.

NELSON, Mr Martin Andrew Wingfield House, 22 Street Ln., Leeds LS8 2ET Tel: 0113 266 0719 Fax: 0113 237 0336 Email: ortholeeds@aol.com; Carnaby House, 1 Sandmoor Avenue, Leeds LS17 7DW Tel: 0113 269 2921 Fax: 0113 269 2921 Email:

NELSON

ortholeeds@btinternet.com — MB BS Lond. 1956; FRCS Eng. 1960; MRCS Eng. LRCP Lond. 1956; BA 1997 Sheffield; MA 1999 Leeds. (St. Mary's) Emerit. Cons. Orthop. Surg. Gen. Infirm. Leeds. Socs: (Ex-Chairm.) Soc. Back Pain Research; (Ex-Chairm. & Mem. Research Counc.) Nat. Back Pain Assn.; Vice-Pres. Restricted Growth Assn. Prev: Sen. Lect. (Orthop.) Univ. Leeds; Instruc. (Orthop.) Johns Hopkins Hosp. Baltimore, USA; Sen. Regist. (Orthop.) Guy's Hosp. Lond. & St. Bart. Hosp. Rochester.

NELSON, Professor Maurice Gerald (retired) Rosefield, Ballylesson, Belfast BT8 8JX Tel: 0123 126433 — MD 1940 Belf.; MD (Gold Medal) Belf. 1940, MB BCh BAO (Hnrs.); FRCP Lond. 1961, M 1940; FRCPI 1955, M 1946; DTM & H Eng. 1947; FRCPath 1963. Prev: Cons. Clin. Pathol. Belf. Gp. Hosps.

NELSON, Michael Department of Neuroradiology, Clarendon Wing, Leeds General Infirmary, Leeds LS1 3EX Tel: 0113 392 3683 Fax: 0113 392 5196 Email: gillr@with.northy.nhs.uk; 10 West Park Avenue, Leeds LS8 2HG — MB BChir 1974 Camb.; MRCP (UK) 1977; FRCR 1982. Cons. Neuroradiol. Yorks. RHA & ULTH NHS Trust; Clin. Sen. Lect. Univ. Leeds; Founder Mem. UK Neuro-Interven. Gp. Socs: Brit. Soc. Neuroradiol.; N. Eng. Neurol. Assn. Prev: Sen. Regist. (Radiodiagn.) Oxf. HA (T); Hon. Clin. Asst. Nat. Hosp. Nerv. Dis. Lond.

NELSON, Mr Michael Eric Dept. Ophthalmology, Royal Hallamshire Hospital, Glossop Rd, Sheffield S10 2JF Tel: 0114 271 2223 — MB ChB 1980 Liverp.; 2000 Masters in Education; BSc (Hons.) Open 1995; FRCS Eng. 1985; FCOphth 1989. Cons. Ophth. Roy. Hallamsh. Hosp. Sheff.; Hon. Sen. Lect. (Ophth.) Univ. Sheff.

NELSON, Paul David Orchard Cottage, Grahams Road, Cambridge CB2 5JY — MB BChir 1994 Camb.

NELSON, Peter 25 Lime Avenue, Willerby, Hull HU10 6LA — MB ChB 1983 Sheff.

NELSON, Philip David Flat 2, 27 Essendine Road, Maida Vale, London W9 2LT Tel: 020 7286 6282 — MB ChB 1988 Leeds; FRCA 1995. Specialist Regist. (Anaesth.) St. Mary's Hosp. Lond. Socs: BMA; Anaesth. Res. Soc.; Intens. Care Soc. Prev: Specialist Regist. (Anaesth.) Roy. Brompton Hosp. Lond.; Specialist Regist. (Anaesth.) Luton & Dunstable Hosp.; Specialist Regist. (Anaesth.) Qu. Charlotte's Hosp. Lond.

NELSON, Richard Andrew Countess of Chester Hospital, Liverpool Road, Chester CH2 1BQ Tel: 01244 365000 Fax: 01244 365112; 155 Hough Green, Chester CH4 8JR Tel: 01244 680270 Email: 106465.2204@compuserve.com — BM 1982 Soton.; BM (Hons.) Soton. 1982; MRCP (UK) 1985; FCAnaesth 1990; FRCA. Cons. Anaesth. Countess of Chester Hosp. Prev: Sen. Regist. Rotat. (Anaesth.) Mersey RHA.; Research Fell. (Clin. Pharmacol.) Vanderbilt Univ. Nashville, Tennessee, USA; Regist. Rotat. (Anaesth.) Mersey RHA.

NELSON, Robert (retired) 33 Beech Grove, Benton, Newcastle upon Tyne NE12 8LA Tel: 0791 266 6114 — MB ChB 1962 Manch.; FRCP Lond. 1979, M 1967; DCH Eng. 1964. Cons. Paediatr. Roy. Vict. Infirm. Newc. u. Tyne. Prev: Lect. (Paediat.) Univ. Birm.

NELSON, Robert Russell Shanks Flat 114, 67 Lumsden St., Glasgow G3 8RH — MB ChB 1990 Glas.

NELSON, Russell Ravenswood House, Knowle, Fareham PO17 5NA — BM 1985 Soton.; MRCPsych 1997. Socs: Roy. Coll. Psychiat.

NELSON, Sally Judith Wiltshire Health Authority, Southgate House, Pans Lane, Devizes SN10 5EQ Tel: 01380 733777 — MB ChB 1987 Sheff.; MFPHM 1998. Cons. (Pub. Health Med.) Wilts. HA.

NELSON, Samuel David (retired) Haematology Department, Craigavon Area Hospital, Craigavon BT63 5QQ Tel: 01762 334444 Fax: 01762 334582 — MB BCh BAO 1956 Belf.; FRCPI 1970, M 1962; FRCPath 1979, M 1967. Cons. Haemat. Craigavon Area Hosp. Prev: Dep. Dir. Nat. Tissue Typing Ref. Laborat. Bristol.

NELSON, Sarah Ann The Strand Practice, 2 The Strand, Goring-by-Sea, Worthing BN12 6DN Tel: 01903 243351 Fax: 01903 705804 — BM 1987 Soton.; BSc (Biochem.) Lond. 1976; MRCGP 1991; DRCOG 1991. Prev: Trainee GP Kent & Canterbury Hosp. VTS; Community Med. Off. (Community Child Health) Thameslink NHS Trust.

NELSON, Sheila 26 Tunstall Precinct, Sunderland SR2 9DN — MB BS 1960 Durh. Prev: Med. Off. Health Dept. Sunderland.

NELSON, Sir (Sidney) Richard (Carlyle), KCB, OBE Caffyn's Copse, Shappen Hill Lane, Burley, Ringwood BH24 4EP Tel: 01425 403308; Caffyn's Copse, Shappen Hill Lane, Burley, Ringwood BH24 4EP Tel: 01425 403308 — MD 1934 Alta. Socs: BMA; (Counc.) Armed Forces Comm. Prev: Dir.-Gen. Med. Servs. RAF; Dir. Research & Med. Servs. Nicholas Internat. Ltd. Slough.

***NELSON, Simon Charles** Sid House, Sid Rd, Sidmouth, Sidmouth EX10 9AH — MB BS 1997 Lond.

NELSON, Stephen Ralph — MB ChB 1982 Leeds; MB ChB (Hons.) Leeds 1982; MD Leeds 1991; FRCP 1997. (Leeds) Cons. Nephrol. St. Geo. Healthcare NHS Trust Lond. Prev: Cons. Nephrol. King's Coll. Hosp. Lond.

NELSON, Stuart Angus Barrons Overton Park Surgery, Overton Park Road, Cheltenham GL50 3BP Tel: 01242 580511; Bourneside, Bourne Lane, Brimscombe, Stroud GL5 2RQ — MB BS 1983 Lond.; MRCGP 1987; DFFP 1994; DCH 1988; DRCOG 1986. (St. Geo.) Trainer (Gen. Pract.) Cheltenham. Socs: (Treas.) Severn Fac. RCGP. Prev: Trainee GP Suff. VTS.

NELSON, Susan Priory View Medical Centre, 2A Green Lane, Leeds LS12 1HU; 40 Denton Ave, Leeds LS8 1LE — MB ChB 1991 Leeds; DFFP 1994; MRCGP 1998. GP Princip. Prev: Non-Princip. GP Leeds; SHO (A & E) Halifax Roy. Infirm.; SHO (O & G) Leeds Gen. Infirm.

NELSON, Susan Anne c/o Doctors Mess, Tameside General Hospital, Fountain St., Ashton-under-Lyne OL6 9RW — MB ChB 1989 Manch. SHO (O & G) Tameside Gen. Hosp. Ashton-under-Lyne.

NELSON, Susan Elizabeth Tippitiwitchet Cottage, Hall Road, Outwell, Wisbech PE14 8PE — MB BS 1974 Lond.; MRCGP 1979; DCH Eng. 1976. (Univ. Coll. Hosp.)

NELSON, Tanya Rose 3 Rona Road, South End Green, London NW3 2HY — MB BS 1992 Lond.

NELSON, Terence Edward (retired) High Bank House, 46 Main St., Addingham, Ilkley LS29 0PL — MB BS 1959 Durh.; MRCP Lond. 1968; FRCPsych 1983, M 1971; DPM Eng. 1965; FRCP 1999 London. Prev: Med. Dir. Leeds CMH Teach. Hosp.

NELSON, Vivienne Margaret Anaesthetic Department, Whiston Hospital, Warrington Road, Prescot L35 5DS — MB ChB 1981 Leeds; FFA RCS Eng. 1987.

NELSON, William Edward Renal Unit, Belfast City Hospital, Belfast BT9; 2 Rosevale Gardens, Drumbeg, Dunmurry, Belfast BT17 9LH — MD 1983 Belf.; MB BCh BAO 1974; MRCP (UK) 1980; DRCOG 1976; DCH RCPSI 1976. Cons. Nephrol. Belf. City Hosp.

NELSON, William McClure 14 Rosepark, Belfast BT5 7RG Tel: 0123 183889 — MB BCh BAO 1958 Belf.; MRCPI 1965; MRCPsych 1971; DPM Eng. 1965. (Belf.)

NELSON, William Myles Antrim Hospital, 45 Bush Road, Antrim BT41; 137 Whitesides Road, Ballymena BT42 2JG — MB BCh BAO 1992 Belf.; FRCR 2001; BSc (Hons.) Belf. 1989. (Qu. Univ. Belf.) Cons. Radiologist. Socs: Fell. of Roy. Coll. of Radiologist. Prev: Specialist Regist. (Radiol.) Hull Roy. Infirm.; SHO (Gen. Surg.) Ards Hosp.; SHO (Orthop. Surg.) Musgrave Pk. Hosp.

***NELSON-IYE, Ada Comfort** 38 Moray Avenue, Hayes UB3 2AX — MB ChB 1991 Sheff.

NELSON-OWEN, Margot Esther Constance c/o Count & Countess De Lucovich, Llan Farm, Lisvane, Cardiff CF14 0RP — MB BCh 1985 Wales.

NELSON-PIERCY, Catherine Department of Obstetrics, Mary Ward, 7th Floor, N. Wing, St Thomas' Hospital, Lambeth Palace Road, London SE1 7CH Tel: 020 7928 9292 Ext: 3575 Fax: 020 7628 2322; 392 Shakespeare Tower, Barbican, London EC2Y 8NJ — MB BS 1986 Lond.; MA Camb. 1987; MRCP (UK) 1989; FRCP (UK) 2000. (Camb. Univ. & St. Barts. Hosp.) Cons. Obst. Phys. Guy's & St. Hosp. Trust & Whipps Cross Hosp.; Flexible Working Off. RCP. Socs: BMA. Prev: Sen. Regist. (Obst. Med.) NE Thames RHA; Regist. (Obst. Med.) NE Thames RHA; Regist. (Endocrinol.) Hammersmith Hosp. Lond.

NELSTROP, George Anthony West Herts Hospital NHS Trust, Watford General Hospital, Vicarage Road, Watford WD18 0HB — MB ChB 1962 Manch. (Manch.) Assoc. Med. Director Clin. Effectiveness. Prev: Cons. Phys. Watford Gen. Hosp.

NEMETH, Andrea Hilary The Wellcome Trust, Centre for Human Genetics, Windmill Road, Oxford OX3 7BN Tel: 01865 740021 Fax: 01865 742186 Email: hilary.nemeth@well.ox.ac.uk; Department of

Clinical Neurology, The Radcliffe Infirmary, Woodstock Road, Oxford OX2 6HE Tel: 01865 311188 — MB BS 1987 Lond.; DPhil Oxf. 1995; BSc Lond. 1984; MRCP (UK) 1991. MRC Clinician & Scientist Fell. Wellcome Trust Centre for Human Genetics Oxf.; Hon. Sen. Regist. (Neurol.) Radcliffe Infirm. Oxf. Prev: MRC Train. Fell. (Molecular Genetics) John Radcliffe Hosp. Oxf.; Regist. (HIV & AIDS) Roy. Free Hosp. Lond.; SHO (Neurol.) Radcliffe Infirm. Oxf.

NEMETH, Cyril Hubert 10 Harley Street, London W1N 1AH Tel: 020 7636 6504 Fax: 020 7286 2633; 1 Langford Place, London NW8 0LJ Tel: 020 7286 2669 Fax: 020 7286 2633 — MRCS Eng. LRCP Lond. 1951; MA Camb. 1951; MRCGP 1962. (Camb. & Westm.) Phys. N.wood, Pinner & Dist. Hosp.; Lord Mayor City of W.minster; JP; Dep. High Steward W.m. Abbey. Socs: Fell. Roy. Soc. Arts; Med. Soc. Lond. & Hunt. Soc.; Fell. Roy. Geogr. Soc. Prev: Mem. (Chairm.) Hillingdon FPC; Mem. (Chairm.) Hillingdon Med. Advis. Comm.; Mem. (Chairm.) Lond. Boro. Hillingdon Soc. Servs. Comm.

NEMETH, Gabor 34 Derwent Court, District General Hospital, Moorgate Road, Rotherham S60 2UD — MD 1960 Budapest; DA Eng. 1981.

NEMETH, William Department of Anaesthetics, St. George's Hospital, London SW17 0QT; 85 Montholme Road, London SW11 6HX — MB BS 1959 Sydney; FFA RCS Eng. 1967; DA Eng. 1962. (Sydney) Cons. (Anaesth.) St. Geo. Hosp. Lond.; Hon. Sen. Lect. St. Geo. Med. Sch. Univ. Lond.

NENSEY, Minaz Flat 4, Park Court, West Pk., 32 Ring Road, Leeds LS16 6EJ — MB BS 1969 Dacca. (Dacca Med. Coll.)

NEOFYTOU, Stavros Kleopas Talliadoros High Street Surgery, 117 High Street, Clay Cross, Chesterfield S45 9DZ — MB BS 1972 Lond.; DObst RCOG 1974. (Univ. Coll. Lond. & St. Geo.) Prev: Ho. Surg. Salisbury Gen. Infirm.; Ho. Phys. St. Geo. Hosp. Lond.; Res. Obstetr. Guy's Hosp. Lond.

NEOH, Kathleen Hong Peng 16 Greer Park, Heights, Newtownbreda, Belfast BT8 7YG Email: kathleen@sugerll.freeserve.co.uk — MB BCh BAO 1993 Belf.

NEOH, Leng Chuan Brean Down, The Spital, Yarm TS15 9EX — MB BCh BAO 1975 Dub.; MRCGP 1980; DRCOG 1979.

NEOMAN, Isis Fouad Zaki The Surgery, 9 Dollis Hill Lane, London NW2 6JH Tel: 020 8450 4040 Fax: 020 8450 7334; 8 Old Church Lane, London NW9 8TD Tel: 020 8205 2052 Fax: 020 8205 2205 — MB BCh 1972 Cairo; MRCS Eng. LRCP Lond. 1979. Prev: Trainee GP Wembley; Ho. Off., SHO & Regist. (O & G) St. Mary's Hosp. Lond.; Clin. Asst. (Gen. Med. & Geriat. Med.) Whipps Cross Hosp. Lond.

NEOPTOLEMOS, Professor John P Department of Surgery, University of Liverpool, 5th Floor UCD Block, Daulby St., Liverpool L69 3GA Tel: 0151 706 4175 Fax: 0151 706 5798 Email: j.p.neoptolemos@liv.ac.uk — MB BChir 1977 Camb.; MD Leic. 1985; MA Camb. 1977; FRCS Eng. 1981; T(S) 1991. (Uni. Camb. & Guy's) Socs: (Pres.) Pancreatic Soc.; (Treas.) Europ. Digestive Surg. Soc.; (Sec.) Eur. Pancreatic Club. Prev: Hons. Cons. Surg. City Hosp. Birm. 1994; Hon. Cons. Surg. Qu. Eliz. Hosp. Birm. 1996.

NEPALI, Panna Kaji 8 Meadow Lane, E. Herrington, Sunderland SR3 3RQ Tel: 0191 528 0060 — MB BS 1961 Kerala; DA Eng. 1963. (Trivandrum Med. Coll.) Med. Asst. (Anaesth.) Sunderland AHA.

NERELI, Besim Evren Garden Flat, 8 Cowper Road, Bristol BS6 6NY. — MB ChB 1983 Bristol.

NERI, Mauro Suite 675, 2 Old Brompton Road, London SW7 3DQ — State DMS 1987 Turin. Staff Grade Phys., A&E, Barnet Hosp.

NERURKAR, Ian David Janardan Foxhill Medical Centre, 363 Halifax Road, Sheffield S6 1AF Tel: 0114 232 2055 Fax: 0114 285 5963 — MB ChB 1987 Bristol; BSc (Hons.) Bristol 1984.

NERURKAR, Maya Jane 184 Doncaster Road, Newcastle upon Tyne NE2 1RB — MB ChB 1992 Bristol.

NESA, Quamar Un 8 The Crescent, London NW2 6HA Tel: 020 8452 6892 — MB BS 1968 Bangladesh.

NESARATNAM, Sakunthala Department of Anaesthetics, Luton & Dunstable Hospital NHS Trust, Lewsey Road, Luton LU4 0DZ Tel: 01582 491122 Fax: 01582 598990; 10 Simpson Road, Walton Park, Milton Keynes MK7 7HN Tel: 01908 691097 — MB BS 1978 Colombo; MRCS Eng. LRCP Lond. 1987; FFA RCS Eng. 1986. Staff Grade (Anaesth.) Luton & Dunstable Hosp. NHS Trust.

NESBITT, Anne 10 Talisman Square, London SE26 6XY Tel: 020 8778 4960 Fax: 020 8778 4960; Community Health South London, Elizabeth Blackwell House, Avonly Road, London SE14 5ER Tel: 020 7771 5212 Fax: 020 7771 5115 — BM BCh 1971 Oxf.; MSc Lond. 1990; FRCP 1996; DCH Eng. 1975; DObst RCOG 1973; FRCPCH 1997. Cons. Community Paediat.Community health S. Lond.; Med. Dir. Prev: Clin. Med. Off. Camberwell HA; Lect. (Paediat.) Univ. Nairobi, Kenya; Lect. (Paediat.) Ahmadu Bello Univ. Hosp. Kaduna, Nigeria.

NESBITT, Deborah Joanne 72 Tranmere Road, Earlsfield, London SW18 3QW Tel: 020 8947 1389 — MB ChB 1992 Manch.; MRCP 1996. Specialist Regist. (Paeds); Specialist Regist. (Paediat) Kingston Gen. Hosp. Kingston. Surrey. Socs: MRCPCH.

NESBITT, Kenneth Tarras, 21 Tobermore Road, Magherafelt BT45 5HB Tel: 01648 32713 Fax: 01648 32713 — MB ChB 1964 Ed.; FFAEM 1993; DO RCPSI 1976. (Ed.) Assoc. Specialist. (A & E) Mid Ulster Hosp. Magherafelt. Socs: Brit. Assn. Accid. & Emerg. Med. (Hon. Sec. Irish Br.); NI Medico-Legal Soc. Prev: SHO Sunderland Eye Infirm.; SHO & Ho. Surg. Mid-Ulster Hosp.

NESBITT, Mary Elizabeth Tarras, 21 Tobermore Road, Magherafelt BT45 5HB Tel: 028796 32713 Fax: 028796 32713 — MB ChB 1964 Ed.; MFFP; Dip. Med. Acupunc. p/t SCMO Reproduc. Healthcare; Indep. GP Acupunc. & Hypnother. Maagherafelt; EMO DHSS. Socs: Brit. Med. Acupunct. Soc.; Brit. Soc. Med. & Dent. Hypn. Prev: Med. Off. DHSS; GP Magherafelt.

NESBITT, Sharon Fiona 30 Meadow Grove, Crawfordsburn, Bangor BT19 1JL Tel: 01247 852387 — MB BCh BAO 1996 Belf.; DFFP 1999; DRCOG 1999. (QUB) SHO (Gen. Pract.). Socs: Family Plg Assoc.

NESBITT, Sidney James 56 Hargrave Mansions, Hargrave Road, London N19 5SR — MB BCh BAO 1989 Dub.; MRCP (UK) 1994.

NESBITT, Wilhelmina Delilah Norfolk & Norwich General Hospital, Brunswick Road, Norwich NR1 3SR — MB BS 1995 Lond.

NESDALE, Annette Deborah Flat 1, 39 Kyrle Road, London SW11 6BB — MB ChB 1992 Otago.

NESFIELD, John Clive Baird (retired) Cowbeach, Sandhurst, Hawkhurst, Cranbrook TN18 5JU Tel: 01580 850541 — MB BChir 1940 Camb.; MA Camb. 1934; LMSSA Lond. 1938; DPM Lond. 1969. Prev: Med. Off. St. Augustine's Hosp. Chartham.

NESHA, Marium Rotherham District General Hospital, 'B' Level Maternity Unit, Moorgate, Rotherham S60 2UD Tel: 01709 820000; 75 Spinneyfield, Rotherham S60 3HT Tel: 01709 531848 — MB BS 1973 Dacca; MB BS Dacca, Bangladesh 1973. (Dhaka, Bangladesh) Clin. Asst. Rotherham Gen. Hosp.; Rotherham Priority Health Family Plann. Prev: Specialist Gyn. Conisbrough Health Auth.

NESLING, Peter Mark Department of Anaesthetics, Singleton Hospital, Sketty Lane, Swansea SA2 8QA Tel: 01792 285427 Fax: 01792 285427 Email: peter.nesling@swansea_tr.wales.nhs.uk; 356 Gower Road, Killay, Swansea SA2 7AE Fax: 01792 205691 — MB BCh 1983 Wales; FRCA 1991. Cons. Anaesth. Singleton Hosp. Swansea. Socs: Assn. Anaesth.; Obst. Anaesth. Assn. Prev: Sen. Regist. (Anaesth.) Cardiff & Merthyr Tydfil; Regist. (Anaesth.) Swansea; Regist. & SHO (Anaesth.) Birm.

NESS, Andrew Robert Department of Social Medicine, Canynge Hall, Whiteladies Road, Bristol BS8 2PR — BM BS 1986 Nottm.; PhD Camb. 1997; MRCP (UK) 1991; DPH Camb. 1994; DA 1990. (Nottingham) Sen. Lect. Epidemiol.

NESS, Lawrence McKinnon Radiology Department, Royal Lancaster Infirmary, Ashton Road, Lancaster LA1 4RP Tel: 01524 65944; 15 Scotforth Road, Lancaster LA1 4TS — MB ChB 1982 Leeds; T(R) (CR) 1991; FRCR 1989. (Leeds) Cons. Radiol. Roy. Lancaster Infirm. & W.morland Gen. Hosp. Prev: Sen. Regist. (Diag. Radiol.) Yorks. RHA.

NESS, Thomas Mackie 91 Townhill Road, Dunfermline KY12 0BW — MB ChB 1945 Ed.; FFA RCS Eng. 1958; DA Eng. 1954. (Ed.) Cons. Anaesth. E. & W. Fife Hosp. Gps. Prev: Anaesth. Perth & Dist. Hosps.

NESSIM, Amir Adly Hanway Road Surgery, 2 Hanway Road, Buckland, Portsmouth PO1 4ND Tel: 023 9281 5317 Fax: 023 9289 9926; 331 London Road, Clanfield, Waterlooville PO8 0PJ — MB BCh 1972 Ain Shams; Docc Med. Lond. 2000; MRCOG 1987; MRCGP 1982; Spec. Accredit. Community Child Health JCHMT 1990; DCCH RCP Ed. 1987; DCH RCP Lond. 1980. GP Hanway Gp. Pract.; Sessional Occupat.al Med. Med. Adviser for Consignia

NESSIM MORCOS

(Portsmouth and S.ampton); Medico-Legal Work. Socs: Fac. Comm. Health. Prev: SCMO & Assoc. Specialist (Community Paediat.) N. Downs Community Care Unit.; Wide range of Hosp. Med. and Surgic. posts; GP Vocational Train.

NESSIM MORCOS, Isis Bulwell Health Centre, Bulwell, Nottingham NG6 8QJ; 4 Rectory Gardens, Nottingham NG8 2AR — LMSSA 1964 Lond.

NESTORIDIS, Georgios 10C Ashingdon Road, Rochford SS4 1NJ — Ptychio Iatrikes 1985 Thessalonika.

NETHERCLIFFE, Janine Mary-Sue 67 Goldney Road, Camberley GU15 1DW — MB BS 1990 Lond.

NETHERCOTT, Albert Stephen (retired) Caledon House, Marton, Welshpool SY21 8JX Tel: 01743 891340 — MB ChB 1944 Bristol; DIH Dund 1970; DPH Bristol 1966. Prev: Sec. Health & Welf. Kwazulu Govt. Serv. S. Afr.

NETHERCOTT, Raymond Gerard 12 Ardmore Park S., Belfast BT10 0JF — MB BCh BAO 1992 Belf.

NETHERSELL, Anthony Barry Walter North Wales Cancer Treatment Centre, Glan Clwyd Hospital, Rhyl LL18 5UJ Tel: 01745 445156 Fax: 01745 445212; Dilysdale, Gannock Road, Deganwy, Conwy LL31 9HJ Tel: 01492 573447 Email: anthony.nethersell@medix-uk.com — MB BChir 1974 Camb.; MA Camb. 1972, BA (Nat. Sc.) 1968; MRCP (UK) 1978; FRCR 1982; FRCP 1998. (Camb. & St. Bart.) Cons. Clin. Oncol. N. Wales Cancer Treatm. Centre. Socs: Fell. Roy. Soc. Med.; Eur. Sch. Therapeutic Radiol. & Oncol.; Mem. Amer. Soc Clin. Oncol. Prev: Head Sect. Oncol. Wellcome Research Laborat. & Hon. Cons. Radiother. & Oncol. King's Coll. & St. Thos. Hosps. Lond.; Sen. Regist. (Radiother. & Oncol.) Addenbrooke's Hosp. Camb.; Ho. Phys. (Med. Oncol.) St. Bart. Hosp. Lond.

NETHERWOOD, Angela Jane 120 Pintail Court, Lyneham, Chippenham SN15 4QH — MB BS 1996 Lond.

NETHERWOOD, Siobhan Tavistock clinic, 120 Belsize Lane, London NW3 — MB BChir 1993 Camb.; MA (Hons.) Camb. 1989; MRC (Pcych) 1997. Specialist Regist. (Child Psychiat.) Tavistock Clin. Lond. Prev: SHO (Psychiat.)Oxf.; Regist. (Psychiat.) Maudsley Hosp. Lond.

NETHISINGHE, Shelton Wennel Ways, Southam Road, Dunchurch, Rugby CV22 6NW Email: nethisinghe@thefree.net — LMSSA 1978 Lond.; FFA RCSI 1977. Cons. Anaesth. Coventry & Warks. AHA's. Prev: Sen. Regist. (Anaesth.) Newc. AHA (T); SHO (Anaesth.) Leighton Hosp. Crewe; Regist. (Anaesth.) Killingbeck Hosp. Leeds.

NETHISINGHE, Somanathage Kamala Nandani Wennel Ways, Southam Road, Dunchurch, Rugby CV22 6NW — LMSSA 1976 Lond.; MSc (Audiol. Med.) Manch. 1995; Dip. Community Paediat. Warwick 1988. (Friendship Univ. Moscow) SCMO (Audiol. Med.) N.ampton HA. Prev: Ho. Off. (Gen. Med. & Gen. Surg.) Vict. Centr. Hosp. Wallasey; Clin. Med. Off. Barnsley HA.

NETSCHER, Margaret May 30 Braintree Road, Witham CM8 2DD — MB BS 1962 Lond.; MRCS Eng. LRCP Lond. 1962; DObst RCOG 1964. (Char. Cross) Prev: Teachg. Fell. (Family Pract. & Paediat.) McGill Univ. Montreal; Canada; Sen. Ho. Phys. Musgrave Pk. Hosp. Belf.; Ho. Surg. City Hosp. & Jubilee Matern. Hosp. Belf.

NETTLE, Christopher John Harcourt Medical Centre, Crane Bridge Road, Salisbury SP2 7TD Tel: 01722 333214 Fax: 01722 421643 — MB BS 1971 Lond.; BSc Lond. 1968; DObst RCOG 1974; Cert. Family Plann. JCC 1974. (King's Coll. Hosp.) Prev: SHO (Obst.& Gyn. & Paediat.) Nottm. City Hosp.; Ho. Phys. King's Coll. Hosp.; Ho. Surg. Kent & Sussex Hosp. Tunbridge Wells.

NETTLETON, Clare Leslie 19 BRoadhurst Gardens, Ruislip HA4 9JQ Tel: 020 8868 7070; 2 Torrington Place, Kenton, Exeter EX6 8NF Tel: 01626 891674 — MB BS 1992 Lond.; MRCP Lond. 1997. (St Mary's Hosp.) GP Reg. Blackmore H C, Sidmouth.

NETTS, Paul Henry The Medical Centre, 37A Heaton Road, Heaton, Newcastle upon Tyne NE6 1TH Tel: 0191 265 8121 Fax: 0191 276 6085 — MB ChB 1988 Leeds.

NEUBAUER, Kyra Anne Elgar House, South Mead Hospital, Westbury on Trym, Bristol BS10 5NB Tel: 0117 959 5368 — MB BS 1983 Lond.; MRCP (UK) 1986. (Roy. Free Hosp.) Cons. (c/o Elderly & Gen. Med.) Bristol.

NEUBAUER, Stefan Department of Cardiovascular Medicine, John Radcliffe Hospital, Headley Way, Headington, Oxford OX3 9DU — State Exam 1985 Wurzburg.

NEUBER, Miriam 25 Offerton Road, London SW4 0DJ — State Exam Med 1993 Lubeck; Med State Exam Lubeck 1993. Socs: Roy. Coll. Psychiats. (Inceptor). Prev: SHO Rotat. (Gen. Psychiat. & Psychiat. of Old Age) St. Geo.'s Tooting Lond.

NEUBERG, Kim Daniel 9 Barrington Road, Leicester LE2 2RA — MB ChB 1992 Leic. SHO (Geriat.) Leicester Gen. Hosp. Prev: Trainee GP Market HarBoro. Med. Centre Leics.; SHO (A & E Med.) Arrowe Pk. Hosp. Wirral.

NEUBERG, Roger Wolfe 9 Barrington Road, Stoneygate, Leicester LE2 2RA Tel: 0116 255 3933 — MB BS 1965 Lond.; MRCS Eng. LRCP Lond. 1965; FRCOG 1983, M 1970, DObst 1967. (Middlx.) Cons. O & G Leicester Roy. Infirm. Socs: Brit. Fertil. Soc.; BMA; Assn. BRd.casting Doctors. Prev: Sen. Regist. (O & G) John Radcliffe Hosp. Oxf. & Roy. Berks. Hosp. Reading; Regist. (O & G) Middlx. Hosp. & Hosp. for Wom. Lond.

NEUBERGER, Professor James Max Queen Elizabeth Hospital, Edgbaston, Birmingham B15 2TH Tel: 0121 472 1311 Fax: 0121 627 2449 Email: j.m.neuberger@bham.ac.uk; The Moat House, Radford Road, Alvechurch, Birmingham B48 7ST Tel: 0121 445 1773 — BM BCh 1974 Oxf.; DM Oxf. 1982; FRCP Lond. 1991; MRCP (UK) 1977. (Oxford University and University College Hospital London) Cons. Phys. Qu. Eliz. Hosp. Birm. Prev: Sen. Wellcome Clin. Research Fell. Liver Unit King's Coll. Hosp. Lond.

NEUBERT, Frank Reginald (retired) Le Bon, La Corbiere, Forest GY8 0JG Tel: 01481 64269 — MRCS Eng. LRCP Lond. 1940; MD Liverp. 1946, MB ChB 1939; LMSSA Lond. 1935; DOMS Eng. 1944; MFHom. 1944; DO Oxf. 1946. Prev: Regist. Roy. Lond. Ophth. Hosp. (Moorfields).

NEUBERT, Stefanie Elsbeth County Hospital, Longfield House, Hereford HR1 2ER — State Exam Med. Freiburg 1991.

NEUGEBAUER, Mr Mark Andrew Zygmunt Department of Ophthalmology, Leighton Hospital, Middlewich Road, Crewe CW1 4Q Tel: 01270 255141; Church Farm, Willbank Lane, Faddiley, Nantwich CW5 8JG — MB ChB 1977 Manch.; FRCS RCPS Glas. 1984; FCOphth 1988; DO 1983. Cons. Ophth. Crewe & Macclesfield HAs. Prev: Sen. Regist. Univ. Hosp., Nottm.; Regist. Roy. Vic. Infirm. Newc.

NEUKOM, Christopher Ralph City Walls Medical Centre, St. Martin's Way, Chester CH1 2NR Tel: 01244 357800 — MB ChB 1980 Liverp.; MRCS Eng. LRCP Lond. 1980; MRCGP 1984; DRCOG 1985. (Liverp.)

*NEULING, Kim Fiona Susamme 25 Grand Avenue, Muswell Hill, London N10 3BD — MB ChB 1996 Leeds.

NEUMANN, Kai Michael Solva Surgery, Cysgod-Yr-Eglwys, Solva, Haverfordwest SA62 6TW Tel: 01437 721306 Fax: 01437 720046; No Name Cottage, Llanddinog, Solva, Haverfordwest SA62 6NA — State Exam Med 1984 Hamburg; MD Hamburg 1986; T(GP) 1994. GP Princip.

NEUMANN, Mr Lars The Nottingham Shoulder & Elbow Unit, Nottingham City Hospital NHS Trust, Hucknall Road, Nottingham NG5 1PB Tel: 0115 969 1169 Fax: 0115 962 8062 Email: larsneumann@rcsed.ac.uk; Rotherwood, 8 Sefton Drive, Mapperley Park, Nottingham NG3 5ER Tel: 0115 985 8189 Fax: 0115 985 6761 Email: larsneumann@rcsed.ac.uk — MD 1980 Odense; FRCS Ed. 1997. (University of Odense, Denmark) Cons. Orthop. Surg. Nottm. Shoulder & Elbow Unit Nottm. City Hosp. Socs: Fell. BOA; Eur. Soc. Surg. Shoulder & Elbow (Educat. Comm.); Brit. Elbow & Shoulder Soc. (Hon. Treas.). Prev: Sen. Regist. (Orthop.) Univ. Hosp. Odense, Denmark; Cons. Orthop. Surg. & Hon. Sen. Lect. (Orthop. & Trauma Surg.) Qu. Med. Centre Nottm.; Shoulder Fell. to Prof. W. Angus Wallace Qu. Med. Centre Nottm.

NEUMANN, Vera Camilla Margit Chapel Allerton Hospital, Chapeltown Road, Leeds LS7 4SA Tel: 0113 392 4614 Fax: 0113 392 4653 Email: veran@neugold.prestel.co.uk — MD 1990 Lond.; BA (Hons.) Oxf. 1973; MB BS 1976; MRCP (UK) 1979; FRCP. (Westm.) Sen. Lect. & Cons. Rehabil. Med. Univ. Leeds & United Leeds Teach. Hosp. Trust. Socs: Soc. Research in Rehabil.; Internat. Soc. Prosth.s & Orthotics.; Exec. Bd. - Brit. Soc. Rehabil. Med. Prev: Sen. Regist. (Rheum. & Rehabil.) Leeds & Harrogate HAs; Research Fell. Rheum. Research Unit Leeds Univ.; SHO (Med.) Dudley Rd. Hosp. Birm.

NEVARD, Corinne Hazel Frances 22 Wellington Street, Edinburgh EH7 5ED — MB ChB 1988 Leic.

NEVARD, Richard Spencer Charles The Sollershott Surgery, 44 Sollershott East, Letchworth SG6 3JW Tel: 01462 683637 Fax: 01462 481348 — MB BS 1981 Lond. (Univ. Coll. Hosp.) GP Letchworth.

NEVE, Hilary Ann Waterloo Surgery, 191 Devonport Road, Stoke, Plymouth PL1 5RN Tel: 01752 563147 Fax: 01752 563304 — MB ChB 1983 Bristol; M.Ed. Bristol 1993; MRCGP 1991; DA (UK) 1989; DRCOG 1985. (Bristol)

NEVE, Janet Mair 5 Leonard Place, Westerham Road, Keston BR2 6HQ — MB BS 1982 Lond.

NEVILL, Christopher Gerald Newton Surgery, Park Street, Newtown SY16 1EF Tel: 01686 626221/626224 Fax: 01686 622610; Newtown Medical Practice, Park St, Newtown SY16 1EF — MB BChir Camb. 1980; MRCGP 1984; DRCOG 1983. (Univ. Camb. & St. Thos. Hosp.) Socs: Roy. Soc. Trop. Med. & Hyg. Prev: Research Dir. AMREF Nairobi, Kenya.

NEVILLE, Professor Alexander Munro Ludwig Institute for Cancer Research, Glen House, Stag Place, London SW1E 5AG Tel: 020 7828 0202 Fax: 020 7828 5427 Email: munro.neville@lno.licr.org; 6 Woodlands Park, Tadworth KT20 7JL Tel: 01737 844113 Fax: 01737 844287 — MB ChB 1959 Glas.; DSc Lond. 1985; PhD Glas. 1965, MD 1969; FRCPath 1980, M 1969. Assoc. Dir. Ludwig Inst. for Cancer Research Zürich, New York & Lond.; Edr. Tumor Biol. & Biopsy Path. Socs: (Treas.) Roy. Coll. Path.; Roy. Soc. Med. Prev: Prof. Path. Univ. Lond.; Dir. Ludwig Inst. for Cancer Research Lond.; Dean Inst. of Cancer Research.

NEVILLE, Alexander Munro 10 Culverden Square, Tunbridge Wells TN4 9NS — MB BS 1989 Lond. SHO (Phys.) Roy. P. Alfred Hosp., Sydney. Prev: Ho. Off. (Phys.) Redhill Gen. Hosp. Surrey; Ho. Off. (Surg.) Homerton Hosp. Lond.

NEVILLE, Amanda Joyce St. Anns Health Centre, St. Anns, Well Road, Nottingham NG3 3PX — MB BS 1985 Lond. Prev: Trainee GP Nottm. VTS; SHO (O & G) Derby City Hosp.

NEVILLE, Anne Caroline Greatwood, Gainford, Darlington DL2 3EU — MB ChB 1979 Sheff.; MRCGP 1987. Indep. GP Darlington.

NEVILLE, Anne Eleanor Pen y Gadlas, Ffordd Bryniau, Prestatyn LL19 8RD Tel: 01745 571626 — MB ChB Manch. 1980; MRCGP 1984; DRCOG 1983.

NEVILLE, Professor Brian George Richard Institute of Child Health, Wolfson centre, Mechlenburgh Square, London WC1N 2AP Tel: 020 7837 7618 Fax: 020 7833 9469; 10 the Chenies, Petts Wood, Orpington BR6 0ED Tel: 01689 825811 — MB BS 1964 Lond.; FRCP Lond. 1979, M 1966. (Guy's) Prof. Paediat. Neurol. Inst. Child Health Lond.; Hon. Cons. Paediat. Neurol. Hosp. Sick Childr. Gt. Ormond St. Lond. Prev: Cons. Paediat. Neurol. & Dir. Newcomen Centre Guy's Hosp. Lond.; Sen. Regist. (Paediat. Neurol.) Hosp. Sick Childr. Gt. Ormond St. & Nat. Hosp. Nerv. Dis. Qu. Sq. Lond.

***NEVILLE, Catherine Ellen** 44 Langstone Road, Langstone, Havant PO9 1RF — BChir 1996 Camb.

NEVILLE, Edmund St. Mary's Hospital, Portsmouth PO3 6AD Tel: 023 92 866782 Fax: 023 92 866735 — MD Lond. 1979, MB BS 1970; FRCP Lond. 1989; MRCP (UK) 1973; MRCS Eng. LRCP Lond. 1970. (Guy's) Cons. Phys. St. Mary's Hosp. Portsmouth; Dir. of Train. at RCP. Socs: Brit. Thoracic Soc. Prev: Sen. Regist. Newc. AHA; Med. Regist. Roy. N.. Hosp. Lond.

NEVILLE, Edmund Andrew (retired) 7 Heriot Road, Lenzie, Kirkintilloch, Glasgow G66 5AX Tel: 0141 776 2543 — MB ChB 1958 Glas.; FRCP Glas. 1981, M 1962; FRCGP 1984, M 1978; DObst RCOG 1960. GP. Prev: Assoc. Adviser (Gen. Pract.) W. Scotl. Comm. Postgrad. Med. Educat.

NEVILLE, Joseph Godfrey (retired) 2 Mile End Road, Newmarket Road, Norwich NR4 7QY Tel: 01603 452179— MB BS 1948 Lond.; MRCP Lond. 1951; MRCS Eng. LRCP Lond. 1948; MRCPsych 1971; DCH Eng. 1950, DPM 1954. Prev: Cons. Psychiat. (Child & Family Psychiat.) Bethel Hosp. Norwich.

NEVILLE, Kathleen Mary 73 Burdon Lane, Cheam, Sutton SM2 7BY Tel: 020 8642 9744 — MB ChB 1952 Birm.; MRCS Eng. LRCP Lond. 1952.

NEVILLE, Kevin Francis Mill Cottage, Blaina, Ebbw Vale NP13 3HL Tel: 01495 290325 — MB BCh BAO 1950 NUI.

NEVILLE, Lisa Ann 10 The Chenies, Orpington BR6 0ED — MB ChB 1994 Bristol; MRCP (UK) 1998.

NEVILLE, Louise Olwen Department of Medical Microbiology, Kingston NHS Trust, Galsworthy Rd, Kingston upon Thames KT2 — MB BS 1979 Lond.; MA Camb. 1980, BA 1976; MRCP (UK) 1983; MRCPath 1993. (University College Hospital) Cons. (Med. MicroBiol.) Kingston NHST. Socs: Hosp. Infec. Soc.; Assn. Med. Microbiol. Prev: Temp. Sen. Lect. (Med. MicroBiol.) Roy. Hosps. Trust Lond.; Sen. Regist. & Regist. (Med. MicroBiol.) Roy. Free Hosp. Lond.; Research Fell. (Med. MicroBiol.) Roy. Free Hosp. Lond.

NEVILLE, Mary Louise (retired) Elm Court, Wychbold, Droitwich WR9 0DF Tel: 01527 861237 — MB BCh BAO 1940 NUI; FRCOG 1969, M 1947. Prev: Asst. Med. Off. St. Mary's Hospice Selly Oak.

NEVILLE, Michael James High Green Surgery, 16 High Green, Gainford, Darlington DL2 3DL Tel: 01325 730204 — MB ChB 1978 Sheff.; DRCOG 1982.

NEVILLE, Peter George 191 Main St, Thornton LE67 1AU Tel: 01530 230768; Bennion Centre, Glenfield Hospital, Groby Road, Leicester LE3 9DZ Tel: 0116 250 2761 — BM 1977 Soton.; MRCPsych 1981. Cons. Psychiat. Leicester Ment. Health Servs. Trust. Prev: Sen. Regist. (Psychiat.) Leics. Rotat. Scheme.

NEVILLE, Peter Michael 18 Abbeydale Gardens, Kirkstall, Leeds LS5 3RG — MB ChB 1989 Leeds; BSc Leeds 1986, MB ChB 1989; MRCP (UK) 1992. Regist. Rotat. (Gastroenterol.) Hull Roy. Infirm., Bradford Roy. Infirm. & Leeds Gen. Infirm. Prev: SHO Rotat. (Med.) St. Jas. Univ. Hosp. Leeds.

NEVILLE, Philippa Susan Harley House Surgery, 2 Irnham Road, Minehead TA24 5DL Tel: 01643 703441 Fax: 01643 704867; Higher Moor, Moor Road, Minehead TA24 5RY Tel: 01643 706875 — MB ChB 1980 Birm.; MRCGP 1985; DFFP 1996; DRCOG 1982.

NEVILLE, Richard (retired) Rosedene, 4 Stubfield, Horsham RH12 2AJ — MRCS Eng. LRCP Lond. 1956; DPM Eng. 1959; FRCPsych 1979, M 1971; BA (Hons.) Open 1976. Health Rev. Trib. The S. Lond. S. & S. W. Region. Prev: Cons. Psychiat. (Ment. Illness) Mid Downs Health Dist.

NEVILLE, Richard Charles (retired) 7 Mylnbeck Court, Windermere LA23 2JE Tel: 0196 624371 — MB BChir 1937 Camb.; MRCS Eng. LRCP Lond. 1936. Prev: Asst. Ho. Surg. Out-pat. Off. & Ho. Phys. Guy's Hosp.

NEVILLE, Richard James (retired) Garden House, Rockmount, Pimlico, Clitheroe BB7 4PZ Tel: 01200 24129 — MB ChB 1963 St. And.; MRCGP 1972; DObst RCOG 1966. Prev: GP Clitheroe Health Centre Lancs.

NEVILLE, Ronald Gilmour West Gate Health Centre, Charleston Drive, Dundee DD2 4AD Tel: 01382 668189 Fax: 01382 665943 — MB ChB 1980 Dundee; FRCGP 1998; MD 1990; DRCOG 1985; MRCGP (Distinction) 1984. (Dundee) GP Dundee.

NEVILLE, Theresa Patricia 1 Blenheim Close, Bidford on Avon, Alcester B50 4HW — MB ChB 1946 Manch. (Manch.)

NEVILLE, Thomas Eugene Blackley Health Studio, 25 Old Market Street, Blackley, Manchester M9 3DT Tel: 0161 721 4865 Fax: 0161 740 6532 — MB BCh BAO 1978 NUI; LRCPI & LM, LRCSI & LM 1978. (Royal College of Surgeons Ireland)

NEVILLE, William 12 High Row, Gainford, Darlington DL2 3DN Tel: 01325 730073 — MB BCh BAO 1946 NUI. (Cork) Prev: ENT Ho. Surg. Gen. Hosp. N.ampton; Res. Med. Off. Dunston Hill Hosp. Gateshead; Capt. RAMC.

NEVILLE, William Peter 43 Ffordd Ffynnon, Prestatyn LL19 8BD — LMSSA 1954 Lond.

NEVILLE, William Thomas Abbey Road Surgery, 63 Abbey Road, Waltham Cross EN8 7LJ Tel: 01992 762082 Fax: 01992 717746 Email: bill.nevile@gpe.82042.nhs.uk — MB BS 1978 Newc.; MRCGP 1988; T(GP) 1991. (Newc.) Princip. GP Abbey Rd. Surg. Herts. Prev: RAMC 1981-89.

NEVILLE-SMITH, Roger Fairfax The Health Centre, Byland Road, Skelton-in-Cleveland, Saltburn-by-the-Sea TS12 2NN Tel: 01287 650430 Fax: 01287 651268; Linton, 10 Victoria Road, Saltburn-by-the-Sea TS12 1JD Tel: 01287 623001 — MB ChB 1975 Manch.; LFHom RCP Lond. 1996; DRCOG 1978; MFHom 1998. Prev: SHO (Paediat.) Alder Hey Childr. Hosp. Liverp.; SHO (O & G & Psychiat.) Tameside Gen. Hosp.

NEVILLE-TOWLE, Andrew Ship House Surgery, The Square, Liphook GU30 7AQ Tel: 01428 723296 Fax: 01420 724022 — MB BS 1975 Lond.; MRCS Eng. LRCP Lond. 1975; FRACGP 1980;

NÉVIN

DRCOG 1986. (Middlx.) Prev: SHO Portway Hosp. Weymouth; Resid. Med. Off. Ryde Hosp. Sydney, Australia; Ho. Phys. Mt. Vernon Hosp. N.wood.

NÉVIN, Judith Alexandra 20 Ryeland Street, Crosshills, Keighley BD20 8SR — MB BS 1994 Lond. (RFHSM)

NEVIN, Linda Joyce 9 Ballymadigan Road, Castlerock, Coleraine BT51 4RR — MB BCh BAO 1981 Belf.

NEVIN, Michael Gables, Oaklands Way, Bassett, Southampton SO16 7PA — MB BS 1978 Lond.

NEVIN, Professor Norman Cummings 17 Ogles Grove, Hillsborough BT26 6RS Tel: 01846 689126 — MB BCh BAO 1960 Belf.; BSc Belf. 1957, MD 1965; FRCP Lond. 1990; FRCP Ed. 1976, M 1968; FRCPath 1981; FFCM 1981. (Belf.) Prof. Med. Genetics Qu. Univ. Belf.; Cons. Med. Genetics BCH Trust, N. Irel. Socs: Fell. Ulster Med. Soc.; Clin. Genetics Soc. Prev: John Dunville Fell. (Path.) Qu. Univ. Belf.; MRC Fell. Clin. Genetics Research Unit Inst. Child Health Lond.; MRC Fell. Populat. Genetics Research Unit Oxf.

NEVISON, Jennifer 33 Wedon Way, Bygrave, Baldock SG7 5DX Tel: 01462 894743 Fax: 01462 894743 — MB BS 1968 Lond. (King's Coll. Hosp.) Indep. Specialist (Allergy & Environm. Med.) Herts. Prev: Unit Med. Off. RAF; Ho. Surg. (Ophth.) King's Coll. Hosp.; Ho. Phys. Greenbank Hosp. Plymouth.

NEVISON-ANDREWS, David Gordon St. Andrew's Hospital, Billing Road, Northampton NN1 5DG — MB ChB 1975 Ed.; BSc Ed. 1972; MRCPsych. 1981. Cons. Psychiat. St. And. Hosp. N.ampton. Prev: Sen. Regist. (Psychiat.) Guy's Hosp. Lond.

NEVITT, Gerald John Whiteley and Partners, 4 Market Place, Billesdon, Leicester LE7 9AJ Tel: 0116 259 6206 Fax: 0116 259 6388; Hill Rise, Gaulby Road, Gaulby, Leicester LE7 9BB — MB BS 1974 Lond.; FRCS 2001; BSc (Anat.) Lond. 1971; MRCP (UK) 1978. (Roy. Free) Clin. Asst. (Dermat.) Leicester Gen. Hosp.

NEVRKLA, Elizabeth Julia Barnet Healthcare Trust, Children's Services, Edgware Community Hospital, Edgware HA8 0AD Tel: 020 8732 6566 Fax: 020 8732 6474; 5 Bittacy Rise, London NW7 2HH — MB BS Lond. 1967; BSc Lond. 1964; MRCP 1970; FRCPCH 1997. (Univ. Coll. Hosp.) p/t Cons. Community Paediat. Barnet & Chase Farm Hosp. NHS Trust. Socs: (Psychat. Psychol. Gp.); Brit. Assn. Community Child Health. Prev: Sen. Regist. (Paediat.) Centr. Middlx. Hosp.; SCMO (Child Health) Brent HA; Regist. (Developm. Paediat.) Edgware Gen. Hosp.

NEW, Alison Caroline 9 Battenhall Road, Worcester WR5 2BJ — BM BS 1986 Nottm. VTS Worcester.

NEW, David Ian 24 Lee Road, London SE3 9RT — MB BS 1990 Lond.; MA Oxf. 1991; MRCP (UK) 1993. Regist. (Nephrol.) Roy. Lond. Hosp. Prev: Regist. (Med.) Whipps Cross Hosp. Lond.; SHO (Med.) St. Bart. Hosp. Lond.

NEW, Fiona Caroline 41 Colwyn Road, Bramhall, Stockport SK7 2JG — MB ChB 1988 Ed.; DRCOG 1993. Regist. (O & G) St. Jas. Univ. Hosp. Leeds. Prev: SHO (O & G) St. Jas. Univ. Hosp. Leeds.

NEW, Helen Vivien Dept pf Paediatrics, St Mary's Hospital, Praed St, London W2 1NY Email: helen.new@st-marys.nhs.uk — MB BS 1989 Lond.; MRCPath 2000; PhD Lond. 1986, BSc 1983; MRCP (UK) 1995. (University College London) p/t Cons. Paediatric Haematologist, St. Mary's Hosp., Lond. (9 sessions). Socs: Brit. Soc. for Haemat. Prev: Specialist Regist. (Haemat.) Univ. Coll. Lond. Hosp. Lond.; Regist. (Haemat.) Hammersmith Hosp. Lond.; Post-doctoral Research Scientist Nat. Inst. Med. Research Mill Hill Lond.

NEW, John Philip 41 Colwyn Road, Bramhall, Stockport SK7 2JG — MB BS 1987 Newc.; MRCP (UK) 1991. Lect. & Hon. Sen. Regist. (Med. Diabetes & Endocrinol.) Hope Hosp. Salford. Prev: Research Fell. (Med.) Newc. Med. Sch.; Regist. (Med.) Roy. Liverp. Univ. Hosp.

NEW, Mr John Wickham St James Surgery, Gains Lane, Devizes SN10 1QU Tel: 01380 722206 Fax: 01380 734541 — MB BChir 1972 Camb.; MA Camb. 1973; FRCS Eng. 1976; AFOM RCP Lond. 1993. (Lond. Hosp.) Hosp. Pract. P.ss Margt. Hosp. Swindon; Co. Med. Off. Wilts. Red Cross; Force Med. Off. Wilts. Constab. Socs: Assn. Police Surg.; ALAMA; BMA. Prev: Regist. (Surg.) Mt. Vernon Hosp. N.wood; SHO Roy. Nat. Orthop. Hosp. Stanmore; Ho. Phys. & Ho. Surg. Lond. Hosp.

NEW, Linda Carol 48 Durleston Park Drive, Bookham, Leatherhead KT23 4AJ — MB BS 1983 Lond.; MB BS (Distinc.) Lond. 1983; MSc Clin. Microbiol. Lond. 1990, BSc (1st cl. Hons.) 1980; MRCP (UK) 1987. Prev: Asst. Med. Microbiol. & Hon. Sen. Regist. Pub. Health Laborat. Serv. St. Geo. Hosp. Lond.

NEW, Norman Edwin Department of Pathology, Queen Elizabeth Hospital, Gayton Road, King's Lynn PE30 4ET — MB ChB 1983 Ed.; BMedBiol. Aberd. 1980; FRCS Ed. 1988; MRCPath 1993; FRCPath 2001. Cons. Histopath. King's Lynn & Wisbech NHS Trust. Prev: Sen. Regist. Rotat. (Histopath.) NW RHA.

***NEWALL, Islay** 39 Knoweholm, Doonfoot, Ayr KA7 4HB — MB ChB 1998 Glas.; MB ChB Glas 1998.

NEWALL, Nicholas Oak Lodge, Windmill, Bishop Auckland DL14 0PT — MB BS 1992 Newc.

NEWBEGIN, Mr Christopher John Richard Lingards Wood House, Manchester Road, Marsden, Huddersfield HD7 6LR Tel: 01484 846506 Fax: 01484 482147 Email: newbegin@bigfoot.com — MB BS 1976 Lond.; FRCS Eng. 1982. (St. Mary's) Cons. (ENT Surg.) Calderdale + Huddersfield NHS Trust; Regional Speciality Adviser in OtoLaryngol. Prev: Sen. Regist. (ENT Surg.) Yorks. Region; Regist. (ENT Surg.) Char. Cross Hosp. Lond.

NEWBEGIN, Hilary Eileen Lingards Wood House, Manchester Road, Marsden, Huddersfield HD7 6LR — MB BS 1978 Lond.; MSc; BA Oxf. 1975; FFA RCS Eng. 1982. (St. Mary's) Cons. Anaesth. Roy. Halifax Infirm. Prev: Cons. Anaesth. Huddersfield Roy. Infirm.; Sen. Regist. (Anaesth.) Yorks. Region; Lect. (Anaesth.) Leeds Univ.

NEWBERRY, Damian John Craven Terrace, London W2 3QD — MB BS 1992 Adelaide.

NEWBERRY, Douglas John Ashford and St Peter's Hospital, Ashford TW15 3AA Tel: 01784 884246 Fax: 01784 884437; 25 Fordbridge Road, Ashford TW15 2TD Tel: 01399 743650 — MD 1974 McMaster Univ., Canada; MSc Epidemiol. Lond. 1988; MRCP (UK) 1991; CCFP 1980; BSc 1971. Cons. Phys. (Gen., Thoracic & Geriat. Med.) Ashford & St Peter's Hosp. Middlx. Socs: Brit. Geriat. Soc.; Brit. Thorac. Soc.

NEWBERRY, Julian 33 West Dhuhill Drive, Helensburgh G84 9AW Tel: 01436 676572 Fax: 01434 676572 — MB ChB 1996 Glas. SHO (O & G) Ayrsh. Centr. Hosp. Irvine. Prev: SHO (Surg.) Gartnavel Gen. Hosp.; SHO (A & E) Hairmyres Hosp.; SHO (Med.) Ayr Hosp.

NEWBERRY, Roger Garstang (retired) 75 Sheepdown Drive, Petworth GU28 0BX Tel: 01798 343390 — MB BS 1952 Lond.; MFCM 1974; DPH Eng. 1958. Prev: Dist. Community Phys. Gt. Yarmouth & Waveney Health Dist. MOH & Port. Med. Off. Gt. Yarmouth Co. Boro.

NEWBERY, Frederica Erna Failand House, Ox House Lane, Failand, Bristol BS8 3SL — MB ChB 1975 Bristol; DRCOG 1978.

NEWBERY, John Michael (retired) 68 Victoria Place, Carlisle CA1 1LR Tel: 01228 32987 — MB BChir 1964 Camb.; MRCS Eng. LRCP Lond. 1963; FFA RCS Eng. 1971; DA Eng. 1968. Prev: Cons. Anaesth. Cumbld. Infirm. Carlisle & E. Cumbria Hosps.

NEWBERY, Sarah Ruth Medical Centre, 1 Oxford Drive, Eastcote, Ruislip HA4 9EY Tel: 020 8866 6589 Fax: 020 8868 3317 — MB BS 1989 Lond.; MRCGP 1993; DRCOG 1993; DFFP 1993; DCH RCP Lond. 1992.

NEWBOLD, Barbara 60 Cranmere Avenue, The Wergs, Tettenhall, Wolverhampton WV6 8TS Tel: 01902 751015 — MRCS Eng. LRCP Lond. 1939.

NEWBOLD, George Frank (retired) Golden Hill, Windmill Lane, Llantwit Major CF61 2SU Tel: 01446 792480 — MB BS Lond. 1949; MRCS Eng. LRCP Lond. 1945; MMSA Lond. 1948; DCH Eng. 1951; DObst RCOG 1947. Prev: Obst. & Gyn Orsett Lodge Hosp. Essex.

***NEWBOLD, Katie Lindsay** Bowerhouse, Thurlbear, Taunton TA3 5AY — MB ChB 1996 Bristol.

NEWBOLD, Kenneth (retired) 6 Wrights Close, Quorn, Loughborough LE12 8TU Tel: 01509 412786 — MB ChB 1958 Birm.; MRCGP 1970; DObst RCOG 1963. Prev: GP LoughBoro.

NEWBOLD, Kenneth Mark Histology Department, Walsgrave Hospital, Clifford Bridge Road, Coventry CV2 2DX Tel: 024 7653 8855 Fax: 024 7653 8715 Email: mark.newbold@wh-tr.wmids.nhs.uk — MB ChB 1983 Birm.; FRCPath 1998; Dip. BA Warwick 1998; MD Birm. 1991; MRCPath 1989. (Birm.) Cons. (Histopath. & Cytopath.); Hon. Sen. Clin. Lect. Warwick Univ.; Clin. Director of Path., Univ. Hosps. Coventry and Warks. NHS Trust. Socs: Assn. Clin. Path.; Brit. Soc. Clin. Cytol.; Brit. Soc. of Gastroenterol. Prev: Lect. (Clin. Path.) Univ. Birm.; Hon. Sen. Regist.

(Histopath.) Qu. Eliz. Hosp. Birm.; Cons. (Histopath. and CytoPath.) Warwick Hosp. Warwick.

NEWBOLD, Sandra Margaret 22 Engliff Lane, Pyrford, Woking GU22 8SU — MB BS Lond. 1983; MD Lond. 1993; MRCOG 1991. (St. Bart. Lond.) Cons. O & G St. Peter's Hosp. Chertsey, Surrey. Prev: Sen. Regist. (O & G) John Radcliffe Hosp. Oxf.; Sen. Regist. Acad. Dept. Wellington Wom. Hosp., NZ; Regist. (O & G) Gloucester & Bristol Matern. Hosp.

NEWBON, Sarah 90 Ack La W., Cheadle Hulme, Cheadle SK8 7ES — MB BS 1997 Newc.

NEWBOULD, Melanie Joy Department of Pathology, Royal Manchester Children's Hospital, Hospital Road, Pendlebury, Manchester M27 4HA — MB BS 1979 Lond.

NEWBOULD, Ruth Anne 37 Daleside, Pudsey LS28 8HA Tel: 01274 667430 — MB ChB 1963 Leeds. (Leeds) SCMO (Family Plann.) Bradford Community NHS Trust.

NEWBOUND, Andrew David Meanwood Group Practice, 548 Meanwood Road, Leeds LS6 4JN Tel: 0113 295 1741; The Beeches, Allerton Hill, Leeds LS7 3QB Fax: 0113 268 3234 — MB ChB 1979 Leeds; DCH RCP Lond. 1982; MRCGP 1983; DRCOG 1982. GP Princip.; GP Trainee; Medico Legal Reporting.

NEWBURY, Anna Louise Beech Cottage, Raby Drive, Bebington, Wirral CH63 0NL — BM BS 1992 Nottm.; DRCOG 1997.

NEWBURY, Louise The Cottage, Thorns Beach, Beaulieu, Brockenhurst SO42 7XN Email: newburyl@hotmail.com — MB BS 1994 Lond.; MRCP (Lond.) 1997. E. Anglian Specialist Regist. Rotat. (Paediat.) Qu. Eliz. Hosp. Kings Lynn, Norf. Socs: MRCP; MRCPCH.

NEWBURY, Norma Gillian (retired) Cruachan, West Glen Road, Kilmacolm PA13 4PN — MRCS Eng. LRCP Lond. 1957.

***NEWBURY, Richard George Charles** Yew Tree Cottage, Earls Common, Droitwich WR9 7LD — MB ChB 1998 Birm.; ChB Birm. 1998.

NEWBURY-ECOB, Ruth Angela 28 Ox Lane, Harpenden AL5 4HE — MB ChB 1983 Sheff.; MRCP (UK) 1988; FRCPCH 1996; FRCP 2000. (Sheffield) Cons. (Clin. Genetics) Inst. Child Health Bristol. Prev: Sen. Regist. (Clin. Genetics) Leicester.; Clin. Research Fell., Univ. of Nottm.; Sen. Regist. Clin. Genetics, Nottm.

NEWBY, David Ernest Royal Infirmary of Edinburgh, 1 Lauriston Road, Edinburgh EH3 9YW Tel: 0131 536 1000 Fax: 0131 536 2021; Upper Flat, 34 Mansion House Road, Edinburgh EH9 2JD — BM 1991 Soton.; BSc (Hons.) Soton. 1990; MRCP (UK) 1994. Research Fell. Edin. Socs: BMA. Prev: SHO (CCU & Med.) Roy. Infirm. Edin.; SHO (Med.) Borders Gen. Hosp.

NEWBY, David Malcolm Rotherham District General Hospital, Moorgate Road, Rotherham S60 2UD — MB ChB 1971 Leeds; FFA RCS Eng. 1976. Cons. Anaesth. (IC) Rotherham AHA. Prev: Staff Anaesth. Univ. Hosp. Groningen, Netherlands; Sen. Regist. (Anaesth.) Leeds AHA (T); Regist. Anaesth. Sheff. AHA (T).

NEWBY, Elizabeth Ann Brewers Home, 2 Burnside, Addingham, Ilkley LS29 0PJ — MB ChB 1995 Manch. SHO (Paediat.).

NEWBY, Jacqueline Clare Department of Oncology, Royal Free Hospital, Pond St, London NW3 2QG Email: jcnewby@mera-peak.freeserve.co.uk; Tel: 01727 869544 Email: jcnewby@mera-peak.freeserve.net — MB ChB 1988 Manch.; MD Manch 1997; MA Camb. 1990; MRCP (UK) 1991. (Camb./Manch.) p/t Locum Cons., Med. Oncollogy, Roy. Free Hosp., Lond. Prev: Clin. Research Fell. Roy. Marsden Hosp. Lond.; Sen. Reg. N. Lond. Cancer network, Med. Oncol.

NEWBY, Martin Rodney Eaton Socon Health Centre, 274 North Road, Eaton Socon, St. Neots, Huntingdon PE19 8BB Tel: 01480 477111 Fax: 01480 403524; 3 Gordon Road, Little Paxton, Huntingdon PE19 6NU — MB ChB 1970 Sheff.; DObst RCOG 1972. Prev: Ho. Phys. Roy. Hosp. Chesterfield; Ho. Surg. ENT & Cas. Roy. Infirm. Sheff.; SHO (Obst.) N. Gen. Hosp. Sheff.

NEWBY, Michael Paul 15 Jubilee Avenue, Eighton Banks, Gateshead NE9 7HN — MB BS 1994 Newc. (Newcastle) Specialist Regist. (Radiol.) S. Tyneside Health Care Trust.

NEWBY, Robert Thomas 32 Rose Glen, London NW9 0JS — MB BS 1991 Lond.

NEWBY, Vanessa Jane 15 Jubilee Avenue, Eighton Banks, Gateshead NE9 7HN — MB BS 1994 Newc. (Newcastle) Sen. SHO (Psychiat.) S. Tyneside Health Care Trust.

NEWCOMBE, Charles Patrick (cons. rooms), 27 High Petergate, York YO1 7HP Tel: 01904 624007; 7 Thorn Nook, York YO31 9LH Tel: 01904 423163 — MRCS Eng. LRCP Lond. 1946; MD Lond. 1952, MB BS 1946; FRCP Lond. 1972, M 1954. (St. Bart.) Chief Med. Off. Gen. Accid. Life Assur. Co. Socs: Brit. Cardiac. Soc. & Thoracic Soc. Prev: Cons. Phys. York Health Dist.; Cons. Phys. Cardio-Thoracic Centre Killingbeck; Sen. Med. Regist. Leeds Gen. Infirm.

NEWCOMBE, Guy Lister Well Cottage, Bodenham, Hereford HR1 3JT Tel: 01568 797309 Fax: 01568 797309 — MB BS 1973 Lond.; MRCGP 1980. (Char. Cross) Prev: Surg. Lt.-Cdr. RN.

NEWCOMBE, Mr John Fernley (retired) 36 Sandy Lodge Road, Rickmansworth WD3 1LJ Tel: 01923 822370 — MB BChir Camb. 1952; MA Camb. 1955, MChir 1963; FRCS Eng. 1957. Prev: Cons. Surg. Centr. Middlx. Hosp. Lond. & Wembley Hosp.

NEWELL, Antonia Gay Priory Road Surgery, Priory Road, Park South, Swindon SN3 2EZ Tel: 01793 521154 Fax: 01793 512562 — MB BS 1981 Lond.; MRCGP 1985; DRCOG 1984. (Char. Cross)

NEWELL, Antony Maxwell Barrett 66 Norfolk House Road, Streatham, London SW16 1JH; Mayday University Hospital, London Road, Thornton Heath CR7 7YE Tel: 020 8401 5033 Fax: 020 8402 3003 — MB BS 1987 Lond.; MRCOG 1993. Cons. (HIV & Genitorinary Med.) Mayday Univ. Hosp. Prev: Sen. Regist. (HIV & Genitourin. Med.) St. Stephen's Clinic Lond.

NEWELL, Barry Anthony Thomas 50 Carlton Road, Grays RM16 2YA — MB BS 1996 Lond.; BSc (Hons) Lond. 1993; MRCP (UK) 1999. (Roy. Free Hosp. Sch. of Med.)

NEWELL, David Nicholas The Surgery, 24 Albert Road, Bexhill-on-Sea TN40 1DG Tel: 01424 730456/734430 Fax: 01424 225615 — MB ChB 1982 Bristol.

NEWELL, Debra Moorcroft Surgery, 646 King Lane, Leeds LS17 7AN Tel: 0113 295 2750 Fax: 0113 295 2761; Milestones, 5 Creskeld Park, Bramhope, Leeds LS16 9EZ — MB ChB 1980 Leeds; MRCGP 1985; DRCOG 1982. Prev: Princip. GP Birm.; Asst. GP Guiseley.

***NEWELL, Emma Louise** 145 North Road, St Andrews, Bristol BS6 5AH — MB ChB 1998 Manch.; MB ChB Manch 1998.

NEWELL, Janet 30 Sourhill, Dan's Road, Ballymena BT42 2LG — MB BCh BAO Belf. 1990; MRCGP 1995; DRCOG 1994; DGM RCP Ed. 1993.

NEWELL, Jennifer Rachel Dolphins, Rue De St Jean, St Lawrence, Jersey JE3 1ND — MB BS 1962 Lond.; MRCS Eng. LRCP Lond. 1962. (Univ. Coll. Hosp.) Community Health Jersey.

NEWELL, Jennifer Rachel Le Warne Clive House, The Street, Walsham Le Willows, Bury St Edmunds IP31 3AZ — MB BS 1993 Lond.

NEWELL, John Philip 34 Pierce Lane, Fulbourn, Cambridge CB1 5DL — MB ChB 1969 Leeds; MA Camb. 1979; PhD Leeds 1983, BSc (Hons.) 1966; FFA RCS Eng. 1974. Cons. Anaesth. Camb. HA (T). Prev: Clin. Lect. (Anaesth.) Univ. Camb. Sch. Clin. Med.

NEWELL, Kathryn Anne 15 Gransha Close, Comber, Newtownards BT23 5RB Tel: 01232 448174 — MB ChB 1992 Ed.; DRCOG 1994; MRCGP 1996. (Edinburgh) Primary Care Doctor (A & E) GP Geo.town Grand Cayman. Socs: BMA; RCGP; MDU.

NEWELL, Paul Albert Astor House, 8 Astorville Park Road, Chellaston, Derby DE73 1XW — MB BS 1981 Lond.; MRCP (UK) 1984. (St. Mary's)

***NEWELL, Richard Andrew** 25 Belle Vue Gardens, Shrewsbury SY3 7JG — BChir 1996 Camb.

NEWELL, Richard Jonathan West Malling Group Practice, 116 High Street, Milverton, West Malling ME19 6LX Tel: 01732 870212 Fax: 01732 742437; Ladham Oast, Ladham Road, Goudhurst, Cranbrook TN17 1DE — MB ChB 1985 Liverp.

NEWELL, Mr Richard Leonard Martyn (retired) Cardiff School of Biosciences, Cardiff University, Museum Avenue, PO Box 911, Cardiff CF10 3US Tel: 029 2087 4031 Email: newell@cardiff.ac.uk — MB BS 1968 Lond.; BSc Lond. 1965; FRCS Eng. 1973; MRCS Eng. LRCP Lond. 1968. Clin. Anatomist Cardiff Univ., Cardiff; Hon. Cons. Orth. Surg .Roy .Devon & Exeter. NHS.Trust. Prev: Cons. Orthop. Surg. N. Devon Dist. Hosp. Barnstaple & P.ss Eliz. Orthop. Hosp. Exeter.

NEWELL, Simon James St. James's University Hospital, Beckett St., Leeds LS9 7TF Tel: 0113 206 6959 Fax: 0113 206 5405 Email: newells@sjuhnnu.demon.co.uk; Milestones, 5 Creskeld Park, Bramhope, Leeds LS16 9EZ Tel: 0113 230 1170 — MB ChB 1980

NEWELL

Leeds; MRCP (UK) 1983; DTM & H Liverp. 1989; MD Leeds 1996; FRCP Lond. 1996. (Leeds) Cons. Neonat. Med. & Paediat. St. Jas. Univ. Hosp. Leeds; Sen. Clin. Lect. Univ. of Leeds; Acad. Sub-Dean Sch. of Med. Univ. of Leeds. Socs: Paediat. Research Soc.; Fell. Roy. Coll. Paediat. & Child Health; Brit. Soc. Paediat. Gastroenterol. & Nutrit. Prev: Lect. (Paediat.) Univ. Birm.; Clin. Research Fell. Inst. Child Health Univ. Birm.; Regist. (Paediat.) Childr. Hosp. Birm. & York Dist. Hosp.

NEWELL, Stephen John North Street Medical Centre, 274 North Street, Romford RM1 4QJ Tel: 01708 764477 Fax: 01708 757656; 3 Wayside Close, Romford RM1 4ES Tel: 01708 760736 Fax: 01708 760736 Email: doctorsjn@aol.com — MB BS 1980 Lond.; BSc Lond. 1977; MRCGP 1985; DRCOG 1982; Cert. Family Plann. JCC 1982; DFFP 1995. (Roy. Lond. Hosp.) GP Princip.; Course Organiser for Havering VTS; Clin. Asst. Diabetic Clinic OldCh. Hosp. Romford; Mem. (Non-Exec. Dir.) Barking & Havering HA; Univ. Tutor (Gen. Pract.) St. Bart. & The Lond. Med. Schs. Prev: Trainer (Gen. Pract.) Romford; Mem. Barking & Havering LMC.

NEWELL PRICE, John Charles (retired) Dragon Lodge, Millbridge, Fresham, Farnham GU10 3DQ — MB 1954 Camb.; BChir 1953; MRCGP. Clin. Asst. (Rheum.) Frimley Pk. Hosp. Prev: Med. Off. RAMC.

NEWELL-PRICE, John David Charles Department of Endocrinology, 5th Floor, King George V Block, St Bartholomew's Hospital, West Smithfield, London EC1A 7BE Tel: 020 7601 8343 Fax: 020 7601 8505 Email: j.d.c.newellprice@mds.qmu.ac.uk; 77 Lyal Road, Bow, London E3 5QQ — MB BChir 1990 Camb.; MA Camb. 1991, BA (Hons.) 1987; MRCP (UK) 1993. (Cambridge University) Lect. in Endocrinol. Socs: Soc. for Endocrinol.

NEWELL PRICE, Rebecca Jane 26 Withy Close, Romsey SO51 7SA — BM 1990 Soton.; MRCGP 1995. GP Retainer.

NEWELL PRICE, Sarah Ruth Dragon Lodge, Millbridge, Fresham, Farnham GU10 3DQ Tel: 0125125 3317 — MB BS 1980 Lond.

***NEWEY, Charlotte Anne** 8 Northcliffe House, 2 Droitwich Road, Worcester WR3 7LJ — MB BS 1997 Lond.

NEWEY, James Arthur Drs. Beynon, Cottier, Rearon, Frood, Johnson & Newby Weaver Vale Practice, Hallwood Health Centre, Hospital Way, Runcorn WA7 2UT Tel: 01928 711911 Fax: 01928 717368; 61 Beech View Road, Kingsley, Frodsham WA6 8DG Tel: 01928 788132 — MB ChB 1972 Liverp.; MRCGP 1977; DObst RCOG 1975; DCH Eng. 1974.

NEWEY, Mr Martyn Leslie 32 Twmpath Lane, Gobowen, Oswestry SY10 7AQ — MB BS 1986 Lond.; BSc (Hons.) Sussex 1981; FRCS (Orth.) 1996; FRCS Ed. 1990. Sen. Regist. Robt. Jones & Agnes Hunt Orthop. Hosp. OsW.ry. Socs: Sekforde Club; Roy. Soc. Med. Prev: Sen. Regist. (Orthop.) N. Staffs. Roy. Infirm.; Regist. (Orthop.) St. Geo. Hosp. Train. Scheme; SHO (Gen. Surg.) William Harvey Hosp. Ashford Kent.

NEWEY, Sarah Francesca 302 Ombersley Road, Worcester WR3 7HD — MB ChB 1989 Birm.

NEWGROSH, Bernard Stephen Great Lever Health Centre, Rupert St., Bolton — MB BS 1975 Lond.

NEWHAM, Mr John Reginald Turner Health Centre, Old Hall, Cowbridge CF71 7AD Tel: 01446 774008; Caecady House, 58 High St, Cowbridge CF71 7AH Tel: 01446 773878 — MB ChB Cape Town 1946; BSc Cape Town 1946; FRCS Eng. 1952.

NEWHOUSE, Robert Guy (retired) — MB ChB 1964 Bristol; DObst RCOG 1966. Prev: Regist. (Med.) Plymouth Gen. Hosp.

NEWHOUSE, Ruth Elizabeth Handforth Health Centre, The Green, 166 Wilmslow Road, Handforth, Wilmslow SK9 3HL Tel: 01625 529421, 01625 536560 — MB ChB 1980 Manch.; MRCP (UK) 1983; MRCGP 1985; DRCOG 1986.

NEWHOUSE, Shân Margaret The Elizabeth Courtauld Surgery, Factory Lane West, Halstead CO9 1EX Tel: 01787 475944 Fax: 01787 474506; Hare House, Wethersfield Road, Sible Hedingham, Halstead CO9 3LA — BM 1984 (Hons.) Soton.; BA (Social Philosophy) CNAA 1982; MRCGP 1989. GP Princip. Socs: BMA. Prev: Trainee GP Soton. VTS; SHO (O & G) P.ss Anne Hosp. Soton.

NEWILL, Robert George Douglass (retired) Fern Court, 39 Park Road, Aldeburgh IP15 5ET Tel: 01728 453109 — MB BS Lond. 1953; MD Lond. 1966; MRCGP 1963. Prev: Clin. Lect. (Fertil. & Endocrine) Univ. Coll. Hosp. Med. Sch.

NEWINGTON, Mr David Peter 260 Gower Road, Sketty, Swansea SA2 9JL — MB BS 1985 Lond.; FRCS (Orth.) 1993; FRCS Eng.

1989. Cons. Orthop. Surg. Morriston Hosp. Swansea. Socs: Brit. Orthop. Assn.; Brit. Soc. Surg. Hand. Prev: Sen. Regist. (Orthop.) Cardiff; Regist. (Orthop.) Glas. Roy. Infirm.

NEWISS, Louise Patricia Thornton Medical Centre, Church Road, Thornton-Cleveleys, Blackpool FY5 2TZ Tel: 01253 854321 Fax: 01253 862854; 54 St Albans Road, Blackpool FY1 4EQ — MB ChB 1988 Manch.

NEWLAND, Professor Adrian Charles Department of Haematology, Royal London Hospital, Whitechapel, London E1 1BB Tel: 020 7377 7180 Fax: 020 7377 7016; 41 Elmwood Road, London SE24 9NS Tel: 020 7274 3295 — MB BChir 1975 Camb.; MA Camb. 1975; FRCP Lond. 1992; MRCP (UK) 1976; FRCPath 1992, M 1980. (Cambridge and London Hospital) Prof. Haemat. St. Bart. & Roy. Lond. Sch. Med. Dent.; Hon. Cons. Roy. Lond. Hosp. (Roy. Hosps. Trust); Hon. Cons. RAMC.; Dir. for Research & Developm. Roy. Hosp. Trust. Socs: BMA; Brit. Soc. Haematol.; Assn. Phys. Prev: Sen. Regist. (Haemat.) Lond. Hosp.

***NEWLAND, Anthony David** Lydiate Farm, Village Road, Lower Heswall, Wirral L60 8PR Tel: 0151 342 8733; 11 Silverdale Road, Oxton, Wirral CH43 2JS Tel: 0151 652 6566 — MB ChB 1986 Liverp.; FRCS Ed. 1991; ECFMG Cert, FMGEMS 1988.

NEWLAND, Carol Jean X-Ray Department, Leicester General Hospital, Gwendolin Road, Leicester LE5 4PW Tel: 0116 249 0490; 3 Church Lane, Ashby Folville, Melton Mowbray LE14 2TA Tel: 01664 840519 — BM Soton. 1981; MRCP (UK) 1985; FRCR 1989. Cons. (Diag. Radiol.) Leicester Gen. Hosp. Prev: Sen. Regist. (Diag. Radiol.) Leicester Roy. Infirm.

NEWLAND, Lesley Ann 4 Hamilton Road, Golders Green, London NW11 9EJ — MB BS 1978 Lond.

NEWLAND, Lynda Jane Mary 62 Highburgh Road, Glasgow G12 9EJ Tel: 0141 334 0880; Oswald House, 81 Crosshill St, Lennoxtown, Glasgow G66 7HF — MB BS 1979 Lond.; MRCGP 1986; MRCOG 1985.

NEWLAND, Michael Arthur 14 Breakspeare, College Road, London SE21 Tel: 020 8693 7917 — MB BChir 1954 Camb.; DTM & H Liverp. 1959; DA Eng. 1966; DObst RCOG 1967. (St. Thos.) Socs: Fac. Anaesth. RCS Eng. Prev: Cons. Primary Care Phys. Riyadh Al-Kharj Hosp. Progr., Saudi Arabia; Asst. Health Adviser Aden Protectorate Health Serv.; Med. Supt. Govt. Hosp. Dubai.

NEWLAND, Richard David Philip Derbyshire Royal Infirmary, London Road, Derby DE1 2QY — MB BS 1987 Lond.; MA Camb. 1984. Trainee GP/SHO Derby VTS. Prev: Ho. Off. St. Mary's Hosp. Lond.

NEWLAND, Rita Anne London Road Surgery, 501 London Road, Thornton Heath CR7 6AR Tel: 020 8684 1172 Fax: 020 8665 5011; 37 Essendene Road, Caterham CR3 5PB — MB BS 1977 Lond.; MRCGP 1981; DRCOG 1981.

NEWLAND, Tadeusz Michal The Hamlet, Tollerton, York YO61 1QR Tel: 01347 838462 — MB ChB Polish Sch. of Med. 1948 Ed. (Polish Sch. of Med. Ed.) Socs: Past Chairm. BMA - York Div.; Past Pres. York Med. Soc.; Anglo-Amer. Med. Soc. Prev: Regist. City Hosp. York; Hosp. Med. Off. St. Mary's Hosp. York; Cas. Off. & Anaesth. Harrogate Gen. Hosp.

NEWLANDS, Edward Stewart Charing Cross Hospital, Fulham Palace Road, London W6 8RF Tel: 020 8846 1419 Fax: 020 8846 1443 Email: e.newlands@ic.ac.uk; 3 Newington Green Road, London N1 4QP Tel: 020 7226 7211 Fax: 020 7226 7211 — PhD Lond. 1976; BA, BM BCh Oxf. 1966; FRCP Lond. 1984; MRCP (UK) 1970. (Middlx.) Prof. Cancer Med. Char. Imperial Coll. Sch. Med. Lond.; Dir. DoH Chorio Carcinoma Unit; Dir. Supra Regional Tumour Marker Assay Laborat. Socs: Fell. Roy. Soc. Med.; Assn. Cancer Phys.s; Amer. Assn. Cancer Research. Prev: Reader (Med. Oncol.) Char. Cross & W.m. Med. Sch.; Sen. Lect. & Hon. Cons. Med. Oncol. Char. Cross Hosp. Med. Sch. Lond.; Lect. (Med. Oncol.) Char. Cross Hosp. Med. Sch. Lond.

NEWLANDS, Linda Caroline 42 Cranmore Gardens, Belfast BT9 6JL — MB BCh BAO Belf. 1994.

NEWLANDS, Peter William 32 Foxley Lane, Purley CR8 3EE Tel: 020 8660 1304; 140 Chipstead Valley Road, Coulsdon CR5 3BB Tel: 020 8660 1305 — MRCS Eng. LRCP Lond. 1977; DRCOG 1980. (Roy. Free) GP Purley & Coulsdon. Prev: SHO (Gen. Med.) Croydon Gen. Hosp.; Ho. Surg. W. Norf. & Kings Lynn Gen. Hosp.; Ho. Phys. Shrewsbury Hosp.

NEWMAN

NEWLANDS, Mr William Jeffrey Aberdeen Royal Infirmary, Foresterhill, Aberdeen AB25 2ZN Tel: 01224 681818; 43 Westholme Avenue, Aberdeen AB15 6AB Tel: 01224312987 — MB ChB 1952 Ed.; FRCS Ed. 1961. (Ed.) Cons. Otolaryngol. Aberd. Roy. Hosp. (NHS Trust) & Orkney & Shetland HBs; Clin. Sen. Lect. (Otolaryngol.) Univ. Aberd. Prev: Prof. Otolaryngol. King Faisal Univ. Coll. Med. Dammam, Saudi Arabia; Cons. Otolaryngol. Co. Hosp. Uddevalla Sweden; Otolaryngol. Brown Clinic Calgary, Canada.

NEWLEY, Kevin Peter Evington Road Medical Centre, 71 Evington Road, Leicester LE2 1QH Tel: 0116 212 0212 — MB ChB 1982 Leic. GP Leicester.

***NEWLOVE, Russell Martin** 11 Carlton Street, Monton, Eccles, Manchester M30 9QE — MB ChB 1996 Manch.

NEWMAN, Anthony James 36 Parkstone Road, Poole BH15 2PG Tel: 01202 682174 Fax: 01202 660718; 4 Alton Road, Lower Parkstone, Poole BH14 8SJ Tel: 01202 723460 Email: ajn@docs84.freeserve.co.ul — MB BS 1982 Lond.; DRCOG 1986; Cert. Family Plann. JCC 1986. Med. Off. Bombardier Support Servs.; Med. Off. Marconi plc Poole; Med. Off. Siemens plc Poole; Dorset Occupat. Care Servs. Prev: SHO (A & E) St. Geo. Hosp. Lond.; SHO Poole Gen. Hosp.; Trainee GP E. Dorset HA.

NEWMAN, Barbara Joyce (retired) 62 Hazelwood Avenue, Newton Mearns, Glasgow G77 5QS Tel: 0141 639 2986 — MB ChB 1956 Glas.; FFA RCS Eng. 1972. Prev: Cons. Anaesth. Inverclyde Roy. Hosp. Greenock.

NEWMAN, Barbara Mary (retired) Wyevale, 11 Primrose Way, Sandhurst GU47 8PL — MRCS Eng. LRCP Lond. 1947. Prev: Assoc. Specialist W. Middlx. Hosp. Isleworth.

NEWMAN, Mr Brian Maurice Newlands Medical Centre, Chorley New Road, Bolton BL1 5BP Tel: 01204 846909 Fax: 01204 847073 — MB ChB 1968 Manch.; MD Manch. 1977; FRCS Ed. 1973. (Manch.) Indep. Cons. Surg. Bolton; Chairm. Med. Innovations; Dir. Newlands Med. Serv. Prev: Cons. Surg. Bolton Dist. Hosp. HA; Sen. Regist. (Surg.) Manch. Roy. Infirm.; Lect. (Surg.) Dept. Gastroenterol. Manch. Roy. Infirm.

NEWMAN, Carole Ann Park Cottage, Farrington Road, Paulton, Bristol BS39 7LW Tel: 01761 412312 Email: carole.newman@mcmail.com — MB ChB Bristol 1966. (Bristol)

NEWMAN, Christopher John Forest Gate Surgery, Hazel Farm Road, Totton, Southampton SO40 8WU Tel: 023 8066 3839 Fax: 023 8066 7090 — MB BCh 1974 Wales; DRCOG 1978.

NEWMAN, Christopher Leonard Royal Berkshire & Battle Hosps. NHS Trust, Royal Berkshire Hospital, Department of Paediatrics, Reading RG1 5AN Tel: 0118 987 5111 Fax: 0118 987 8383; Kiln House, The Street, Aldermaston Village, Reading RG7 4LN Tel: 0118 971 3525 Email: chris/newman@hotmail.com — MB BS 1966 Lond.; FRCP Lond. 1986; MRCP (UK) 1971; MRCS Eng. LRCP Lond. 1966; DObst RCOG 1968; FRCPCH. (Guy's) Cons. Paediat. Roy. Berks. Hosp. Reading. Socs: Fell of Roy. Coll of Paediat. & Child Health; Fell. & Collegiate Mem. Roy. Coll. Phys. Lond.; Fell. Roy. Soc. Med. Prev: Sen. Regist. (Paediat.) Hosp. Sick Childr. Gt. Ormond St.; Regist. (Paediat.) Roy. Hosp. Sick Childr. Glas.; SHO (Neonat. Paediat.) Hammersmith Hosp. Lond.

NEWMAN, Christopher Mark Howard Clinical Services Centre, Northern General Hospital, Sheffield S5 7AY Tel: 0114 271 4456 Fax: 0114 261 9587 Email: c.newman@sheffield.ac.uk; 58 Devonshire Road, Dore, Sheffield S17 3NW Tel: 0114 236 0219 — MB BS 1983 Lond.; MA Camb. 1984, BA 1980; PhD CNAA 1992; MRCP (UK) 1986; FRCP 1999. Sen. Lect. (Cardiol.) Univ. Sheff. & Hon. Cons. Cardiol. N. Gen. Hosp. Sheff. Prev: MRC Clinician Sci. Fell 1995; Reg. (Cardio) RPMS/Hamm'smth Hosp. 1989.

NEWMAN, Mr Christopher Patrick St John 1 Willow Garth, Ferrensby, Knaresborough HG5 0QD Tel: 01423 340534 — MB BS 1966 Lond.; FRCS Eng. 1972; MRCS Eng. LRCP Lond. 1966.

NEWMAN, Cicely Emmeline 783 Faranseer Park, Macosquin, Coleraine BT51 4NB — MB BCh BAO 1958 Dub. (T.C. Dub.) Prev: Med. Asst. (Anaesth.) Altnagelvin Hosp. Lond.derry; Med. Asst. (Gen. Med.) Roe Valley Hosp. Limavady.

NEWMAN, Claude Gerald Hugh Chelsea & Westminster Hospital, London SW10 9NH; 31 Southwood Lawn Road, Highgate, London N6 5SD Tel: 020 8340 3516 Fax: 020 8340 1457 — MB BS 1953 Lond.; FRCP Lond. 1976, M 1955; FRCPCH 1997; MRCS Eng. LRCP Lond. 1953; DCH Eng. 1957. (Middlx.) Emerit. Cardiol. Paediat. Chelsea & W.m. Hosp. Lond.; Hon. Cons. Paediat. Qu. Mary's Univ. Hosp. Roehampton; Med. Advis. Thalidomide Soc. Socs: Fell. Roy. Soc. Med.; Brit. Soc. Rehabil. Med. Prev: Dir. Leon Gillis Unit & Cons. Paediat. Qu. Mary's Hosp. Roehampton; Sen. Regist. (Paediat.) St. Thos. Hosp. Lond.; Cons. Paed. Cardiol. Chelsea & W.m. Hosp. Lond. SW10.

NEWMAN, Clive George Medical Centre, Cambridge Avenue, Bottesford, Scunthorpe DN16 3LG Tel: 01724 842415 Fax: 01724 271437; Briggate Farm House, Old Brigg Road, Messingham, Scunthorpe DN17 3RJ — MB ChB 1979 Sheff.; MRCGP 1983; Dip. Palliat. Med. Wales. 1995.

NEWMAN, David Anthony King Street Surgery, 84 King Street, Maidstone ME14 1DZ Tel: 01622 756721/756722/3; Durrants House, West St, Hunton, Maidstone ME15 0RY — BM BCh 1984 Oxf.; MA Oxf. 1987, BA 1981; MRCGP 1989; DCH RCP Lond. 1986. (Oxford) GP Maidstone. Prev: SHO (Paediat.) Maidstone Hosp.; Ho. Surg. Dorset Co. Hosp. Dorchester; Ho. Phys. Roy. Cornw. Hosp. Truro.

NEWMAN, David John Forest Road Health Centre, 8 Forest Road, Hugglescote, Coalville LE67 3SH Tel: 01530 832109 — MB ChB 1976 Sheff.

NEWMAN, Douglas Keith Dept. of Ophthalmology (Box 41), Addenbrooke's NHS Trust, Hills Road, Cambridge CB2 2QQ — BM BCh 1990 Oxf.; MA Camb. 1991; FRCOphth 1994. (University of Oxford Medical School) Cons. Ophthalmis Surg., Addenbrooke's NHS Trust, Camb. Socs: Fell. Roy. Coll. of Ophth.s; Mem. Amer. Acad. of Ophth.; Fell. Roy. Soc. of Med. Prev: Fell. (Med. Retina), Moorfield's Eye Hosp.; Fell. (Uitreoretinal Surg.), Manch. Roy. Eye Hosp.; Specialist Regist. (Ophth.), Addenbrooke's Hosp.

NEWMAN, Francesca St Thomas Surgery, Ysyol Street, St. Thomas, Swansea SA1 8LH Tel: 01792 653992 — MB BS 1987 Lond.; MRCGP 1991. (London St. Bartholomews) GP Princip. St. Thos. Surg. Swansea. Socs: Roy. Coll. Gen. Pract.; BMA. Prev: Trainee GP Briton Ferry Health Centre Neath W. Glam.; SHO (Paediat. & O & G) Neath Gen. Hosp.

NEWMAN, Geoffrey Hannell Sussex Oncology Centre, Royal Sussex County Hospital, Eastern Road, Brighton BN2 5BE Tel: 01273 696955 — MB ChB 1976 Bristol; MRCP (UK) 1979; FRCR 1989. Cons. Clin. Oncol. Roy. Sussex Co. Hosp. Brighton. Prev: Sen. Regist. Bristol.

NEWMAN, Gwyneth Margaret (retired) Crwys Road Surgery, 151 Crwys Road, Cathays, Cardiff CF24 4XT Tel: 029 2039 6987 Fax: 029 2064 0523 — MB BCh 1962 Wales; DPH Wales 1966; DObst RCOG 1964.

NEWMAN, Helena Hillview Medical Centre, 3 Heathside Road, Woking GU22 7QP Tel: 01483 760707 — MB BS 1981 Lond.; Cert. Family Plann. JCC 1987; DRCOG 1987.

NEWMAN, Hugh Francis Vernon Bristol Oncology Centre, Bristol BS2 8ED Tel: 0117 928 2412 Email: hugh.newman@ubht.swest.nhs.uk; Trunders, Upper Lansdown Mews, Bath BA1 5HF Tel: 01225 480491 — MB ChB 1977 Sheff.; MD Sheff. 1988; B. Jur. Sheff. 1972; FRCR 1983. Cons. Clin. Oncol. Roy. Infirm. Bristol & Roy. United Hosp. Bath. Socs: Brit. Inst. Radiol. & Brit. Oncol. Assn. Prev: Clin. Sci MRC Clin. Oncol. Unit & Hon. Sen. Regist. (Oncol.) Addenbrooke's Hosp. Camb.; Regist. (Radiother. & Oncol.) Velindre Hosp. Cardiff; Hon. Fell. (Therap. Radiol.) Univ. Minnesota Hosp.

***NEWMAN, Jennifer** 68 Stewarton Drive, Cambuslang, Glasgow G72 8DG — MB ChB 1998 Dund.; MB ChB Dund 1998.

NEWMAN, Jennifer Anne Ave. Cottage, 12 Beech Bank, Ulverston LA12 7EZ — MB ChB 1989 Leic.

NEWMAN, John Henry 10 Harley Street, London W1N 1AA Tel: 020 7636 6504; 6 Johnsons Drive, Hampton TW12 2EQ — MB ChB 1973 Ed.; BSc (Med. Sci.) Ed. 1970, MB ChB 1973; AFOM RCP Lond. 1981. Sen. Phys. (Occupat. Med.) Char. Cross Hosp. Lond. Socs: Assoc. Mem. RCGP; Soc. Occupat. Med. Prev: Sen. Med. Adviser BBC TV Lond.; Phys. (Occupat. Med.) St. Stephens Hosp. Lond.; Phys. (Occupat. Med.) Banstead Psychiat. Hosp.

NEWMAN, John Howard 30 Baroncroft Road, Liverpool L25 6EH Tel: 0151 428 4932 Fax: 0151 428 4932 — MB ChB 1964 Liverp. (Liverp.) Socs: Liverp. Med. Inst.; BMA. Prev: Dep. Police Surg.; SHO Olive Mt. Childr. Hosp. Liverp.; Ho. Phys. Clatterbridge Hosp.

NEWMAN, Mr John Howard 2 Clifton Park, Bristol BS8 1BL Tel: 0117 906 4213 Fax: 0117 973 0887 Email: newman2en@aol.com; Cornerstones, 41 Canynge Road, Bristol BS8 3LH Tel: 0117 973

NEWMAN

6030 Email: newmancorner@doctors.org.uk — MB BChir 1968 Camb.; FRCS Eng. 1972; T(S) 1991. (Guy's) Cons. Orthop. Surg. Bristol Roy. Infirm. & Avon Orthop. Centre; Edr. The Knee. Socs: Brit. Orthop. Assn.; Pres. Brit. Assn. Surg. of Knee. Prev: Sen. Regist. (Orthop.) Harlow Wood Hosp. & Nottm. Gen. Hosp.; Regist. (Surg.) United Oxf. Hosps.

NEWMAN, Joseph Department of Cellular Pathology, Birmingham Heartlands Hospital, Bordesley Green E., Birmingham B9 5SS Tel: 0121 685 5877 Fax: 0121 685 5898 Email: newmanj@heartsol.wmids.nhs.uk — MB ChB Cape Town 1966; MMed (Path.) Cape Town 1971; FRCPath 1986, M 1974. (Cape Town) p/t Cons. Histopath.& Cytopath Birm. Heartlands Hosp. Socs: Brit. Soc. Gastroenterol.; Brit Soc. Cytol.

NEWMAN, Joshua Leslie (retired) Flat 5, Millo Lodge, 17 Derby Road, Bournemouth BH1 3PZ Tel: 01202 316198 — MRCS Eng. LRCP Lond. 1942. Prev: Ho. Surg. Nelson Hosp. Merton.

NEWMAN, Joycelyn Helen Westwood (retired) 2 Makepeace Avenue, Highgate, London N6 6EJ — MB ChB 1948 Ed.; DObst RCOG 1951; DPH Lond. 1954. Prev: Sen. Med. Off. (Child Health) Enfield & Haringey HA.

***NEWMAN, Karen Louise** 9 Woodlea Court, Woodlea Village, Meanwood Park, Leeds LS6 4SL — MB ChB 1997 Leeds.

NEWMAN, Mr Kevin John Hanmer St. Peter's Hospital, Guildford Road, Chertsey KT16 0PZ Tel: 01932 872000 Fax: 01932 874757; 6 Greenside Close, Merrow Park, Guildford GU4 7EU Tel: 01483 574364 Email: kevinnewmanortho@hotmail.com — MB BS Lond. 1984; FRCS (Orth.) 1995; FRCS Eng. 1988. (Char. Cross Hosp. Lond.) Cons. Orthop. & Trauma St. Peter's Hosp. Chertsey. Socs: Fell. BOA; Brit. Assn. Surg. of the Knee. Prev: Sen. Regist. (Orthop.) St. Geo. Hosp. Lond.; Regist. (Orthop.) St. Geo. Hosp. Lond.

NEWMAN, Mr Laurence Department Oral & Maxillofacial Surgery, Univeristy College London Hospitals Maxillofacial Unit, Mortimer Market, London WC1E 6AU Tel: 020 7380 9859 Fax: 020 7380 9855 Email: laurence.newman@uclh.org — MB BS 1990 Lond.; BDS Lond. 1981; FRCS Eng. 1992; FDS RCS Eng. 1988; FFD 1984. (Lond. Hosp. Med. Coll.) Cons. Maxillofacial Surg. UCL Hosps. Lond. & Gt. Ormond St. Hosp for Childr. Lond. Socs: Brit. Assn. Head & Neck Orcol.; Fell. Brit. Assn. Oral & Maxillofacial Surg.; Graisofacial Soc. Gt. Brit. Prev: Sen. Regist. Qu. Vict. Hosp. E. Grinstead.

NEWMAN, Lotte Therese, CBE Medical Advisor, St John's Ambulance National Headquarters, 27 St John's Lane, London EC1M 4BU Tel: 020 7324 4001 Fax: 020 7324 4000 Email: jh44@dial.pipex.com; The White House, 1Ardwick Road, London NW2 2BX Tel: 020 7435 6630 Fax: 020 7435 6672 — MB BS 1957 Lond.; BSc Birm. 1951; MRCS Eng. LRCP Lond. 1957; FRCGP 1977, M 1967. (Westm.) GP Lond.; Chairm. Of Heritage Comm. of Roy. Coll. Of Gen. Pract.; Med. Adviser - St Johns Ambul. Nat. HQ; Memb. Of Bd. Of Deputies Of Brit. Jews & Of Its Defence & Gp. Relations Comm. Socs: Liveryman Worshipful Soc. Apoth. (Mem. Livery Comm.); Fell. Roy. Soc. Med. Prev: Pres. RCGP; Past Chairm. - Registration Comm. Of the Gen. Med. Counc.; Europ. Regional VP & Mem. of Exec. World Organisation of Nat. Coll. Acads. & Acad. Assn. of GPs.

NEWMAN, Lynn Hazel Department of Anaesthesia, Southern General Hospital, 1345 Govan Road, Glasgow G51 4TF Tel: 0141 201 1658 Email: lynnnwm@aol.com — MB ChB 1980 Liverp.; FCAnaesth 1984. Cons. Anaesth. S.. Gen. Hosp. Glas. Prev: Cons. Anaesth. & Dir. of Intens. Care BRd.green Hosp. Liverp.; Sen. Regist. Rotat. (Anaesth.) Merseyside; Research Regist. (Clin. Shock Study Gp.) W.. Infirm. Glas.

NEWMAN, Margaret Joy Community Health Office, Ambulance HQ, Ascots Lane, Welwyn Garden City AL7 4HL Tel: 01707 328111 Fax: 01707 335168 — MB BS 1976 Lond. (UCHMS) p/t Clin. Med. Off. (Community Health) E. Herts. NHS Trust. Prev: GP St. Albans.

NEWMAN, Mrs Marianna (retired) 15 Wickham Way, Park Laugley, Beckenham BR3 3AA — MB BS 1951 Lond.; MRCS Eng. LRCP Lond. 1951; DCH Eng. 1953. Prev: Clin. Med. Off. Bromley HA.

NEWMAN, Martin Charles — MB ChB 1979 Bristol; MRC Psych. 1992. Cons. & Hon. Sen. Lect. (Child & Adol. Psychia) S.&W. Lond. & St Geo.s Ment. Health, NHS Trust, Lond. SW17.

NEWMAN, Maurice 155 Inner Promenade, St Annes-on-Sea, Lytham St Annes FY8 1DW — MB ChB 1921 Liverp.; MB ChB (Hons.) Liverp. 1921; MD Liverp. 1925; MRCP Lond. 1926; MRCS Eng. LRCP Lond. 1921. (Univ. Liverp.) Socs: Fell. Roy. Soc. Med. Prev: Cons. Med. to HM Govt. Whitehall Lond.; PMO Min. Social Security Blackpool; Hon. Asst. Phys. Liverp. & Dist. Hosp. Dis. Heart.

NEWMAN, Michael Roland Blair Eyebrook House, Stoke Dry, Oakham LE15 9JG Tel: 01572 821796 Fax: 01572 821268 Email: michaelnewman1@compuserve.com — MB BChir 1975 Camb.; MA 1975; FRCOG 1994; DA Eng. 1979. Cons. (O & G) Kettering Gen. Hosp. NHS Trust. Socs: BMA; BFS; BSCCP.

NEWMAN, Michelle Julia 6 Sunnyfield, Mill Hill, London NW7 4RG — MB BS 1988 Lond.; DRCOG 1991. GP Winchmore Hill.

NEWMAN, Myra Claremont Surgery, 2 Cookham Road, Maidenhead SL6 8AN Tel: 01628 673033 Fax: 01628 673432 Email: myra.newman@gp-k81020.anglox.nhs.uk; Willow Corner, Poyle Lane, Burnham, Slough SL1 8LA Tel: 01628 602589 Email: myra.newman@btinternet.com — MB BS 1967 Lond.; DObst RCOG 1969. (St. Geo.) Clin. Asst.Obst. Wexham Pk. Hosp. Slough. Socs: Windsor Med. Soc. & BMA. Prev: SHO (Paediat.) Wexham Pk. Hosp. Slough; SHO (O & G) Upton Hosp. Slough; Ho. Phys. & Ho. Surg. (ENT & Eye) St. Geo. Hosp. Tooting.

NEWMAN, Nathan The Wick Clinic, 200 Wick Road, London E9 Tel: 020 8986 6341; 18 Palace Court, Finchley Road, London NW3 Tel: 020 7431 0892 — MB ChB 1926 Leeds. (Univ. Leeds) Prev: Ho. Surg. Centr. Hosp. Plymouth; Sen. Res. Med. Off. Weir Hosp. Balham; Ho. Surg. St. Mark's Hosp. For Rectal Dis.

NEWMAN, Noel (retired) Withdean, Old Midford Road, Southstoke, Bath BA2 7DH Tel: 01225 832392 — MB BCh BAO 1938 NUI; MFCM 1974; DPH Eng. 1950. Prev: Community Med. Off. Wilts. AHA.

NEWMAN, Patrick Fitzgerald Marfleet Group Practice, 350 Preston Road, Hull HU9 5HH Tel: 01482 701834 — MB BS Lond. 1970; MRCGP 1977; DCH Eng. 1977; DObst RCOG 1976. Socs: Fell. Hypnother. Research Soc.

NEWMAN, Paul Leslie 141 Surrenden Road, Brighton BN1 6ZA — MB BS 1983 Lond.

NEWMAN, Paul Mark Barrhead HC, 201 Main St., Barrhead, Glasgow G78 1SD Tel: 0141 880 6161 Email: newmimed@aol.com; 55 Dalziel Drive, Pollokshields, Glasgow G41 4NY — MB ChB 1991 Liverp.; BA 1996; DRCOG 1998; MRCGP 1999; PhD Glas. 1986. GP Princip.; Vocational Studies Tutor, Univ. of Glas.; Prescribing Adviser. Prev: SHO (Anaesth.) Glas. Roy. Infirm.

NEWMAN, Penelope Jane 68B Finsbury Park Road, London N4 2JX Tel: 020 7704 1531 — MB BS 1985 Lond.; MSc Lond. 1991. Cons. Pub. Health Med. Havering Hosp. NHS Trust; Fell. Kings Fund. Prev: Trainee (Pub. Health) N. Thames (W.); Regist. (Paediat.) Wellington, NZ; SHO (O & G) Roehampton.

NEWMAN, Penelope Mary The Health Centre, North Road, Stokesley, Middlesbrough TS9 5DY Tel: 01642 710748 Fax: 01642 713037; Old Farm, Newby, Middlesbrough TS8 0AD Tel: 01642 325999 — MB BS 1974 Lond.

NEWMAN, Percival Peter 16 North Park Grove, Leeds LS8 1JJ Tel: 0113 266 3654 — MD 1952 Liverp.; MB ChB 1941. (Liverp.) Sen. Lect. Neurophysiol. Univ. Leeds. Socs: Fell. Roy. Soc. Med.; Physiol. Soc. Prev: Fulbright Schol. 1959; Vis. Prof. Physiol. Einstein Coll. Med. New York U.S.A.; Asst. Neurosurg. Off. Walton Hosp. Liverp.

NEWMAN, Peter Kevin Department of Neurology, Derriford Hospital, Plymouth PL6 8DH Tel: 01642 854408 Fax: 01642 826852 Email: peter.newman@ phat.swest.nhs.uk; Old Farm, Newby, Middlesbrough TS8 0AD Email: pnewman@lineone.net — MB ChB 1973 Birm.; FRCP Lond. 1989; MRCP (UK) 1977. Cons. Neurol.Derriford Hosp Plymouth. Socs: Assn. Brit. Neurol.

NEWMAN, Philip Jonathon 104 Durlston Road, Kingston upon Thames KT2 5RU — MB BS 1987 Lond.; FRCA. 1991. Cons. Anaesth. & Intens. Care Research Fell. (Anaesth.) St. Geo. Hosp. Lond.

NEWMAN, Philippa Mary North Street House Surgery, 6 North Street, Emsworth PO10 7DD Tel: 0143 373538; 110 Station Road, Liss GU33 7AQ Tel: 01730 895056 — MB BS 1984 Lond.; DRCOG 1995. (Lond. Hosp. Med. Coll.) Prev: Trainee GP Hastings VTS; SHO (A & E) Roy. E. Sussex Hosp.; SHO (O & G) St. Mary's Hosp. Portsmouth.

NEWMAN, Piers Fenton Princess Royal Hospital, Apley Castle, Telford TF1 6TF Tel: 01952 641222 — MB BS 1988 Lond.; MRCP (UK) 1992; BSc 1985. Neurol.

NEWMAN, Rachel Maria Countess Mountbatten House, Moorgreen Hospital, Botley Road, West End, Southampton SO30 3JB Tel: 02380 477414 Fax: 023 8047 5305; Fax: 0870 054 3938 — MB ChB 1985 Ed.; MRCP (UK) 1994. (Ed.) p/t Specialist Regist. (Palliat. Med.) Countess Mt.batten Ho. Socs: Assoc. Palliat. Med.; Palliat. Care Research Soc. Prev: Specialist Regist. (Palliat. Med.) Salisbury Dist. Hosp.; Macmillan Fell. (Oncol., Palliat. Care & Gen. Med.) Roy. Lancaster Infirm.; Regist. (Med.) Birch Hill Hosp. Rochdale.

NEWMAN, Mr Raymond Julian Harrogate District Hospital, Lancaster Park Road, Harrogate HG2 7SX Tel: 01423 885959 Fax: 01423 555443; Wingfield House, 22 Street Lane, Roundhay, Leeds LS8 2ET Tel: 0113 237 0327 Fax: 0113 237 0336 — MB ChB 1975 Leeds; BSc Leeds 1972; DPhil Oxf. 1983; FRCS Ed. 1980; FRCS Eng. 1980; FRSH 1990. (Leeds) Cons. Orthop. Surg. Harrogate Dist. Hosp.; Hon. Lect. (Orthop. Surg.) Univ. Leeds. Socs: Fell. BOA; Brit. Orthop. Research Soc.; Brit. Elbow & Shoulder Soc. Prev: Sen. Lect. (Orthop. Surg.) Univ. Leeds. & Cons. St. Jas. Hosp. Leeds; Lect. (Orthop. Surg.) & Hon. Sen. Regist. Univ. Glas.; MRC Research Fell. & Hon. Sen. Regist. Nuffield Orthop. Centre Oxf.

NEWMAN, Richard Roderick Churchfield Surgery, 14 Iburndale Lane, Sleights, Whitby YO22 5DP Tel: 01947 810466 Fax: 01947 811375; 190 Coach Road, Sleights, Whitby YO22 5EN Tel: 01947 810866 — MB BChir 1979 Camb.

NEWMAN, Roy John The Old Mill Surgery, Stoke Rd NR14 7JL; Church Farm, Wymondham Road, Wramplingham, Wymondham NR18 0RH — MB BS 1978 Lond; BSc Biochem. (1st cl. Hons.) Lond. 1978; MRCP (UK) 1987; MRCGP 1994; DCH RCP Lond. 1986; DRCOG 1985. (Roy. Free)

NEWMAN, Ruth (retired) 19 Hayes End, South Petherton TA13 5AG Tel: 01460 41044 — MB ChB 1932 Liverp.; MA, MB ChB Liverp. 1932.

***NEWMAN, Sarah Victoria** 11 Paultons Street, London SW3 5DR — MB BS 1996 Lond.

NEWMAN, Sian Elizabeth 34 Heol-y-Forlan, Whitchurch, Cardiff CF14 1BA Tel: 029 2052 1917 — MB BCh 1995 Wales; DCH 1998. (Cardiff) SHO (Paediat.).

NEWMAN, Terence Anthony Stanley Road Surgery, 204 Stanley Road, Bootle L20 3EW Tel: 0151 922 5719 — MB ChB 1978 Manch.; DCH RCP Lond. 1985; DRCOG 1983.

NEWMAN, Valerie Jean Crawley Hospital, West Green Drive, Crawley RH11 7DH Tel: 01293 600300; 16 Smithbarn, Horsham RH13 6EB Tel: 01403 211154 — MB BS 1972 Lond.; FFA RCS Eng. 1976. (St. Thos.) Cons. Anaesth. & Lead Clin. Anaesth. Theatres & ITU Surrey & Sussex Healthcare NHS Trusst. Prev: Sen. Regist. (Anaesth.) Guildford Hosp. Surrey.

NEWMAN, Vanessa Ruth 130 Busbridge Lane, Godalming GU7 1QJ — MB BS 1988 Lond.; MRCP (Paediat.) (UK) 1992; FRCR 1997. Regist. (Diagn. Radiol.) King's Coll. Hosp. Lond. Prev: Regist. (Paediat.) Roy. Surrey Co. Hosp. Guildford.

NEWMAN, Mr William David Tennent Institute of Ophthalmology, Western Infirmary, Dumbarton Road, Glasgow G11 6NT; 22 Arthurlie Drive, Uplawmoor, Glasgow G78 4AH Tel: 01505 850584 Email: bill_newman@msn.com — MB BS 1987 Lond.; FRCS Glas. 1995; FRCOphth 1996, M 1993. (Lond. Hosp. Med. Coll.) Specialist Regist. (Ophth.) Tennent Inst. Ophth. Glas. Prev: SHO III (Ophth.) Glas. Roy. Infirm.; SHO (Ophth.) W.bourne Eye Hosp. Bournemouth; SHO Rotat. (Gen. Med.) Roy. Vic. Hosp. Bournemouth.

NEWMAN, William Gerard James St Mary's Hospital, Hathersage Road, Manchester M13 0JH — MB ChB 1992 Manch.; MB ChB (Hons.) Manch. 1992; BSc (Hons.) Manch. 1989; MRCP (UK) 1995; MA Healthcare Ethics & Law. Manch. 1999. (Specialist Regist. (Clin. Genetics) St. Mary's Hosp. Manch.) Wellcome Trust Clin. Train. Fell. Univ. of Manch. Socs: BSHG.

NEWMAN, William James 110 Freehold Street, Lower Heyford, Kidlington OX5 3NT — BM 1990 Soton.

NEWMAN TAYLOR, Professor Anthony John, OBE Royal Brompton Harefield NHS Trust, Sydney St., London SW3 6NP Tel: 020 7351 8328 Fax: 020 7351 8336 Email: a.newmant@ebh.nthames.nhs.uk; 11 Waldegrave Road, Bickley, Bromley BR1 2JP — FRCP (Edin.) 2000; MB BS Lond. 1970; MSc (Occupat. Med.) Lond. 1979; FRCP Lond. 1986; MRCP (UK) 1973; FFOM RCP Lond. 1987, MFOM 1983; F Med Sci 1999. (St. Bart.) Cons. Phys. Roy. Brompton & harefield NHS Trust; Prof. Occupat. & Environm. Med. & Head Dept. Occupat. Environm. Med. Brompton Hosp & Imperial Coll. Sch. Med. Nat. Heart & Lung Inst. Lond.; Scientif. Adviser to Colt Foundat.; Mem. (Chairm.) Injuries Advis. Counc.; Civil. Cons. in Chest Med. RAF; Med. Dir. & Dir. of Research Roy Brompton & Harefield NHS Trust; Chairm. CORDA Charity. Socs: Brit. Thorac. Soc.; Brit. Soc. Allergy & Clin. Immunol.; Amer. Thoracic Soc. Prev: Sen. Regist. (Med.) Brompton & W.m. Hosps. Lond.; Lect. (Clin. Immunol.) Cardiothoracic Inst. Brompton Hosp. Lond.; Regist. (Med.) St. Bart. Hosp. Lond.

NEWMARCH, Bernard Wellington Medical Centre, Bulford, Wellington TA21 8PW Tel: 01823 663551 Fax: 01823 660650 — MB BS 1979 Lond.; MRCS Eng. LRCP Lond. 1978; DRCOG 1981; Cert. Family Plann. 1981. (Guy's) p/t GP Wellington.; NHS Direct W. Country Med. Dir. Prev: GP Trainee Soton. Univ. Hosps. VTS.; Chairm. Som. Local Med. Comm.

NEWMARK, James Christopher Paul Farrow Medical Centre, 177 Otley Road, Bradford BD3 0HX Tel: 01274 637031 — MB ChB 1976 Leeds; MPH Leeds 1996; MRCGP 1988. (Leeds) JP.

NEWMARK, Patricia Ann Farrow Medical Centre, 177 Otley Road, Bradford BD3 0HX Tel: 01274 637031 — MB ChB 1976 Leeds; MRCGP 1989; DRCOG 1978.

NEWMARK, Robert Walter (retired) 85 Woodlands Road, Cleadon, Sunderland SR6 7UB Tel: 0191 536 2066 Email: rownew@compuserve.com — MB BS Durh. 1952.

NEWNAM, Peter Thomas Frank The Grange, Hutton Gate, Guisborough TS14 8EQ Tel: 01287 633928 — MB BS 1960 Durh.; FFA RCS Eng. 1964. (Newc.) p/t Cons. Anaesth. N & S Tees Hosp. Gps. Prev: Asst. Clin. Tutor (Anaesth.) United Birm. Hosps.; Regist. (Anaesth.) Roy. Hosp. Wolverhampton; Regist. (Anaesth.) Newc. Gen. Hosp.

NEWNHAM, Angela Veronica West Sussex Health Authority, 1 The Causeway, Durrington, Worthing BN12 6BT — MB BS 1993 Lond.; MA Camb. 1994.

NEWNHAM, Claude Tristram Mead Cottage, Mackney Lane, Brightwell-cum-Sotwell, Wallingford OX10 0SQ — MRCS Eng. LRCP Lond. 1943; DOMS Eng. 1947. (St. Mary's) CStJ; Mem. Med. Counc. on Alcoholism. Prev: Regional Med. Off. W.. Region Brit. Rly.; Ho. Surg. St. Mary's Hosp. Lond.; Squadron Ldr. RAF, Graded Ophth. & Venereol.

NEWNHAM, Donald Mackenzie 6 Buckie Grove, Bridge of Don, Aberdeen AB22 8DL — MB ChB 1983 Aberd.; MRCP (UK) 1988.

NEWNHAM, John Alan Victoria Road Surgery, 50 Victoria Road, Worthing BN11 1XB Tel: 01903 230656 Fax: 01903 520094; Walton House, 61 Grand Avenue, Worthing BN11 5BA Tel: 01903 247596 — MB ChB 1973 Ed.; BSc (Med. Sci.) Ed. 1970. Prev: Trainee GP Brighton VTS.

NEWNS, George Reginald Thatch Dyke, Whimpwell Green, Happisburgh, Norwich NR12 0QF — MB ChB 1938 Birm.; FRCP Lond 1970, M 1945. (Birm.) Prev: Cons. Phys. Sheff. Centre for Investig. & Treatm. Of Rheum. Dis.; Hon. Clin. Lect. (Rheum. Dis.) Univ. Sheff.; Graded Phys. RAMC.

NEWPORT, Barry Tel: 01276 472248 Fax: 01276 473873 — MB ChB Birm. 1970; DObst RCOG 1973. Prev: SHO Dept. Communicable Dis. & SHO (Paediat.) E. Birm. Hosp.; Ho. Off. (Obst.) Cheltenham Matern. Hosp.

NEWPORT, Melanie Jane Cambridge Institute For Medical Research, Addenbrookes Hospital, Cambridge CB2 2XY Tel: 01223 331153 Email: melanie.newport@cimr.cam.ac.uk; 78 Stanley Road, Cambridge CB5 8LB — MB BS 1986 Lond.; MRCP (UK) 1989; DCH RCP Lond. 1990; PhD Lond. Uni. 1996. (St Marys Hopsital Med School) Research Assoc.(Dept. of Med) Addenbrookes Hosp. Camb.; Hon. Cons. in Infec. Dis.s. Prev: Research Assoc. MRC Labs. The Gambia, W. Africa.

NEWPORT, Nigel Gareth Whitmore Way Surgery, Aegis Medical Centre, Felmores Centre, Basildon SS15 5LE Tel: 01268 520641 Fax: 01268 271057; 10 The Meadoway, Billericay CM11 2HL — MB BS 1983 Lond.; DRCOG 1986. GP Basildon. Prev: SHO (Accid./Orthop.) CrossHo. Hosp. Kilmarnock.

NEWPORT, Sheila Mary Ivy Grove Surgery, 1 Ivy Grove, Ripley DE5 3HN Tel: 01773 742286 Fax: 01773 749812; Redhill Cottage,

NEWRICK

Duffield Bank, Makeney, Derby DE56 0RT Tel: 01332 841304 — BM BS 1980 Nottm.

NEWRICK, Charles William, Group Capt. RAF Med. Br. (retired) 5 Brays Lane, Ely CB7 4QJ Tel: 01353 665202 — MB BChir 1962 Camb.; MA Camb. 1974; FRCPath 1986, M 1975; DCP Lond 1972.

NEWRICK, Paul Gerrard Department of Medicine, Worcestershire Acute Hospitals NHS Trust, Kidderminster DY11 6RJ Tel: 01562 823424 Fax: 01562 515068 Email: drpgn@bigfoot.com — MB ChB 1979 Bristol; MD Bristol 1988; MRCP (UK) 1982; T(M) 1992; FRCP Lond. 1998. Cons. Phys. (Diabetes & Endocrinol.) Kidderminster Gen. Hosp. Prev: Sen. Regist. (Diabetes & Endocrinol.) Bristol Roy. Infirm. & Roy. Devon & Exeter Hosp.; Research Fell. (Diabetes) Roy. Hallamsh. Hosp. Sheff.; Regist. (Med.) Frenchay Hosp. Bristol.

NEWRITH, Christopher Russell Francis Birmingham Therapeutic Community Service, Bridger House, 22 Summer Road, Acocks Green, Birmingham B27 7UT Tel: 0121 678 3244 Fax: 0121 678 3245 — MB ChB 1990 Manch.; BSc St. And. 1987; 2000 MSc Oxford Brookes (Psychodynamic Psychotherapy in NHS settings); MRCPsych 1996. Cons. Psychiat. Birm.Therapeutic Community Serv. Birm. Prev: Regist. Oxf. Rotat. (Psychiat.); Specialist Regist. Oxf. Rotat. (Psychother.).

NEWRITH, Stella Fiona c/o Winterbourne House, 53-55 Argyle Road, Reading RG1 7YL — MB ChB 1990 Manch.; BSc St. And 1987.

***NEWS, Marie Therese** St. Johns Wood, 10 Woodville Avenue, Lurgan, Craigavon BT66 6JP — MB BCh BAO 1995 Belf.

NEWSAM, Avril Gladys, MBE (retired) 14 Comely Bank, Edinburgh EH4 1AN Tel: 0131 332 6307 — MB ChB 1954 Ed.

NEWSAM, Mr John Ernest (retired) 14 Comely Bank, Edinburgh EH4 1AN Tel: 0131 332 6307 — MB ChB 1949 Ed.; FRCS Ed. 1955. Prev: Cons. Urol. Surg. W.. Gen. Hosp. Edin.

NEWSHAM, Julie Ann 17 Grisedale Close, Formby, Liverpool L37 2YE — MB ChB 1984 Leeds; DO RCS Eng. 1987.

NEWSHOLME, George Adam (retired) Yew Tree Cottage, Pentre Lane, Bredwardine, Hereford HR3 6BY Tel: 0198 17 366 — MD 1951 Camb.; MA Camb. 1945, MD 1951, MB BChir 1945; FRCP Lond. 1970, M 1948; FRCR 1975; DMRT Eng. 1957. Prev: Radiotherap. United Birm. Hosps.

NEWSHOLME, Richard George Salters Medical Practice, The Health Centre, Ombersley Street, Droitwich WR9 8RD — MB ChB 1979 Birm.; BA Oxf. 1976.

NEWSHOLME, William Arthur 72 Holmefield Court, Belsize Grove, London NW3 4TU — MB BS 1992 Lond.

NEWSOM, Richard Samuel Babington Ophthalmology Department, St Thomas' Hospital, Lambeth Palace Road, London SE1 Tel: 020 7928 9292; 27 Sutherland Street, London SW1V 4JU — MB BS 1987 Lond.; BSc Lond. 1984, MD 1994; FRCOphth 1994. Regist. (Ophth.) St. Thos. Hosp. Socs: BMA & RSM. Prev: SHO (Ophth.) Char. Cross Hosp. Lond. & King Edwd: VII Hosp. Lond.; Research Fell. Hammersmith Hosp. Lond.

NEWSOM, Rose Aylmer (retired) 11 The Footpath, Coton, Cambridge CB3 7PX Tel: 01954 210228 Fax: 01954 211871 Email: rose@newsom.demon.co.uk — MB BCh BAO Dub. 1957; MA Dub. 1957; MFFP 1993; DObst RCOG 1959. Prev: Sen. Clin. Med. Off. Cambs. HA.

NEWSOM, Samuel William Babington (retired) 11 The Footpath, Coton, Cambridge CB3 7PX Tel: 01954 210228 Fax: 01954 211871 — MB BChir Camb. 1957; MD Camb. 1977, MA 1957; FRCPath 1976, M 1964; T(Path.) 1991; DTM & H Eng. 1964. Pres. Inst. Sterile Serv. Managers; Asst. Edr. Jl. Hosp. Infec. Prev: Cons. Microbiol. Camb. RHA.

NEWSOM-DAVIS, Professor John Michael, CBE Department of Clinical Neurology, University Oxford, Radcliffe Infirmary, Woodstock Road, Oxford OX2 6HE Tel: 01865 224492 Fax: 01865 790493 — MB BChir 1961 Camb.; FRS 1991; MA Camb. 1957, MD 1966; FRCP Lond. 1973, M 1962. (Middlx.) Prof. Clin. Neurol. Univ. Oxf. Socs: Assn. Brit. Neurol.; Eur. Neurol. Soc. Prev: MRC Clin. Research Prof. Neurol.; Hon. Cons. Roy. Free Hosp. & Nat. Hosp. Nerv. Dis. Lond.; Lect. Univ. Dept. Clin. Neurol. Nat. Hosp. Nerv. Dis. Lond.

NEWSON, Christopher Douglas Dept. of Anaesthetics, Walsall Manor Hospital, Moat Rd, Walsall WS2 9PS Tel: 0121 353 5948 Email: newsonc@wht.walsall-tr.wmids.nhs.uk; 10 Thornhill Road, Streetly, Sutton Coldfield B74 3EH Tel: 0121 353 5948 — MB BS 1984 Lond.; MRCS Eng. LRCP Lond. 1984; FRCA 1991. (Guy's) Cons. Anaesth. Walsall Manor Hosp.; Vis. Asst. Prof. Univ. Texas S. W.. Med. Centre, Dallas. Socs: Assn. Anaesth.; Obst. Anaesth. Assn.; Christian Med. Fell.sh. Prev: SHO (Anaesth.) MusGr. Pk. Hosp. Taunton & Frenchay Hosp. Bristol; SHO (Cardiol. & Chest Med.) Harefield Hosp. Middlx.

NEWSON, David Heath 39 Yeldham Road, London W6 8JF Tel: 020 8748 6840 — MB BS 1991 Lond.; BSc (Pharmacol.) Lond. 1988; MRCP (UK) 1995. (Char. Cross & Westm.) Resid. (Paediat. ICU) Guy's Hosp. Lond. Socs: Christian Med. Fell.sh.; Brit. Paediat. Assn. Prev: Regist. (Paediat.) Mater Miser. Childr Hosp. Brisbane, Austral.; Regist. (Paediat.) Lewisham Gen. Hosp. Lond.; SHO (Paediat. Neonates) Univ. Coll. Hosp. Lond.

NEWSON, Diana Charmian Westgate Practice, Greenhill Health Centre, Church St., Lichfield WS13 6JL Tel: 01543 414311 Fax: 01543 256364 — MB BS 1984 Lond.; MRCGP 1988. (Guy's)

***NEWSON, Edward James** 156 Alms Hill, Bourn, Cambridge CB3 7SZ — BM 1998 Soton.; BM Soton 1998.

NEWSON, Mrs Elizabeth Rachel Alberta Hebblethwaite Hall, Cautley, Sedbergh LA10 5LX Tel: 0153 96 21307 — BM BCh 1967 Oxf. (Oxf. & Lond. Hosp.) Prev: Ho. Phys. Childr. Dept. & Receiv. Room Off. Lond. Hosp.; GP & Postgrad. Trainer (Gen. Pract.) Lond.

NEWSON, Louise Rachel 22 Finchley Road, Hale, Hale, Altrincham WA15 9RD Tel: 0161 928 0483 Email: louis.newson@talk21.com — MB ChB 1994 Manch.; MB ChB (Hons.) Manch. 1994; BSc (Hons.) Manch. 1992; MRCP 1996. (Manch.) GP Regist. Socs: Med. Wom. Federat. Prev: SHO (O & G) Chester; SHO (Med.) Mans.

NEWSON, Mary Penelope Valley Medical Centre, 14 Waller Close, Liverpool L4 4QJ Tel: 0151 207 3447 — MB ChB 1986 Liverp.; MRCGP 1990; DRCOG 1990. (Liverpool) GP Liverp.; Clin. Asst. (Dermat.) Roy. Liverp. Univ. Hosp. Prev: SHO (O & G) Wom. Hosp. Liverp.

NEWSON, Timothy Peter Kent & Canterbury Hospitals, NHS Trust, Canterbury CT1 3NG Tel: 01227 766877; 2 The Granary, Limetree Farm, Stone St, Petham, Canterbury CT4 5PW — BM BS 1986 Nottm.; MRCP (UK) 1991. Cons. (Paed) Kent & Cantb. Hosp. Cantab. Kent. Prev: Regist. (Paediat.) Qu. Eliz. Hosp. for Childr. Hackney; Sen. Med. Off. (Paediat.) Jane Furse Memor. Hosp. Transvaal, S. Afr.; Sen. Regist. (Paediat.) Newc. Gen. Hosp.

NEWSON-SMITH, Grevile Robin Farnham Road Surgery, 301 Farnham Road, Slough SL2 1HD Tel: 01753 520917 Fax: 01753 550680; 3 Braybank, Old Mill Lane, Bray, Maidenhead SL6 2BQ Tel: 01628 624085 Fax: 01628 624085 — MB BS 1967 Lond.; DObst RCOG 1973. (St. Geo.) Socs: Brit. Soc. Med. & Dent. Hypn. Prev: Ho. Phys. & Ho. Surg. Wycombe Gen. Hosp. High Wycombe; Resid. Obst. Asst. St. Geo. Hosp. Lond.; Squadron Ldr. RAF Med. Br.

NEWSON-SMITH, Jane Grace Beatrice Newcroft, St. Mary's Hospital, Newport PO30 5TG Tel: 01983 524081 — MB BS 1970 Lond.; MRCS Eng. LRCP Lond. 1970; MRCPsych 1976. (Char. Cross) Cons. Psychiat. St Mary's Hosp. Newport, I. of Wight. Socs: BMA. Prev: Cons. Psychiat. Knowle Hosp. Fareham; Sen. Regist. (Psychiat.) St. Geo. Hosp. Lond.; Regist. (Psychiat.) & Clin. Research Fell. Char. Cross Hosp. Lond.

NEWSTEAD, Charles George Renal Unit, St James' University Hospital, Beckett St., Leeds LS9 7TF Tel: 0113 243 3144 Fax: 0113 244 0499 — MB BS 1981 Lond.; BSc Lond. 1978, MD 1991; MRCP (UK) 1986; FRCP 1997. (Guy's) Cons. Renal Phys. St. Jas. Univ. Hosp. Leeds. Socs: Physiol. Soc. & Internat. Soc. Nephrol.; Renal Assn.; Brit. Transpl. Soc.

NEWSTEAD, Jonathan Simon 9 Ancliff Square, Avoncliff, Bradford-on-Avon BA15 2HD — MB BS 1982 Lond. Med. Off. Cunard Shipping Line.

NEWSTEAD, Mr Mark Roberts Coastal Villages Practice, Pippin Close, Ormesby St. Margaret, Great Yarmouth NR29 3RW Tel: 01493 730205 Fax: 01493 733120; North End Farm, Long Lane, Ingham, Stalham, Norwich NR12 0TJ — MB ChB 1983 Liverp.; FRCS Ed. 1988; FRCS Eng. 1988; MRCGP 1993; T(GP) 1993.

NEWSTEAD, Peter Oakmeadow Surgery, 87 Tatlow Road, Glenfield, Leicester LE3 8NF Tel: 0116 287 7911 — MB BS 1983 Lond.; DRCOG 1988. GP Leicester FPC.

NEWSTEAD, Sheila Mary Setters, Hyde, Fordingbridge SP6 2QB Tel: 01425 52993 — MB BS 1940 Lond.; FRCP Lond. 1973, M 1943; MRCS Eng. LRCP Lond. 1940; FRCPath 1971. (King's Coll.

Hosp.) Socs: Assn. Clin. Pathols. & Brit. Soc. Haemat. Prev: Cons. Pathol. Bromley Gp. Hosps.; Asst. Clin. Pathol. King's Coll. Hosp.

NEWSTONE, Justin 67 Lance Lane, Liverpool L15 6TU — MB ChB 1995 Leic.; MRCP (UK) 1998. (Glasgow)

NEWTH, Jeffrey Bernard 16 Springfield Crescent, Parkstone, Poole BH14 0LL — MB BChir 1961 Camb.; BA Camb. 1958, MB BChir 1961; MRCP Lond. 1965; DTM & H Liverp. 1967. (Camb. & Lond. Hosp.) Med. Adviser Dorset Health Commiss. Socs: BMA. Prev: GP S. Molton; Regist. (Paediat.) Bath Gp. Hosps.; Directeur Centre Nutrit. EAR Kigeme, Rwanda.

NEWTH, Sarah Jane 17 Portland Road, Edgbaston, Birmingham B16 9BN Tel: 0121 454 2217 Fax: 01212423529 Email: newthsj@hotmail.com — MB ChB 1979 Birm.; BSc (Anat.) Birm. 1975, MB ChB 1979; MRCPsych 1984. Child Psychiat. Private Pract., Medico Legal. Socs: Roy. Coll. Psychiat. Prev: Cons. Developm. Psychiat. S. Birm. Health Dist.; Cons. Child Psychiat. Solohull Healthcare NHS Trust.

NEWTON, Adrienne Ashley Tina The Surgery, 4 Hardell Rise, Tulse Hill, London SW2 3DX Tel: 020 8674 6586 — MB BS 1986 Lond.; BSc Manch. 1980; MRCGP 1992. (Uni. Coll. Hosp. (Lond))

NEWTON, Alastair Inglis 29 Munro Road, Glasgow G13 1SQ — MB ChB 1990 Glas.

NEWTON, Andrew Paul Accident and Emergency Department, Weston General Hospital, Grange Road, Uphill, Weston Super Mare BS23 4TQ Tel: 01934 647103; Fair View, Top Road, Shipham, Winscombe BS25 1TB Tel: 0934 843246 — BM BS 1985 Nottm.; 2001 MSc (Child Health) Cardiff; BMedSci Nottm. 1983; MRCGP 1993; DCCH Ed. 1998. (Nottm.) Assoc. Specialist A&E (Paediat.) W.on Gen. Hosp.; On-call Doctor Mendip Rescue Organisation (Cave Rescue); Med. Adviser Dyslexia Assn. N. Som.; Hon. Med. Adviser RNLI W.on; Nat. Chair of BAEM Forum for Assoc. Specs and Staff Grades in A&E. Socs: Brit. Dyslexia Assn.; Roy. Coll. Surg. Ed. (Fac. Immediate Med. Care); Brit. Assn. Community Child Health. Prev: Squadron Med. Off. to Sixth Frigate Squadron RN; Gen. Pract. Avon FHSA.

NEWTON, Angela Francesca Woodbrook Medical Centre, 28 Bridge Street, Loughborough LE11 1NH Tel: 01509 239166 Fax: 01509 238747; Vine Cottage, 69 Brook St, Wymeswold, Loughborough LE12 6TT — MB BS 1973 Lond. (Char. Cross)

NEWTON, Anthony Simon Merchiston Surgery, Highworth Road, Swindon SN3 4BF Tel: 01793 823307 Fax: 01793 820923 — MB BS 1985 Lond.; MA Camb. 1982; MRCGP 1990; DA (UK) 1988. Prev: Trainee GP Winchester VTS; SHO (Anaesth.) Whipps Cross Hosp. Lond.

NEWTON, Anthony Winston Lichfield Street Surgery, 19 Lichfield Street, Walsall WS1 1UG Tel: 01922 20532 Fax: 01922 616605 — MB ChB 1974 Birm.; BSc (Hons.) (Physiol.) Birm. 1971, MB ChB 1974; MRCGP 1979; DRCOG 1978; DCH Eng. 1978.

***NEWTON, Catherine Elizabeth** Lawn House, Main St., Etwall, Derby DE65 4LP — MB ChB 1997 Bristol.

NEWTON, Charmian Rosemary St. George's Hospital, Blackshaw Road, London SW17 0QT Tel: 020 8725 3032 Fax: 020 8725 0830 Email: charmain.newton@stgeorges.nhs.uk — MB BS Lond. 1965; FRCP Lond. 1993; MRCP Lond. 1967; MRCS Eng. LRCP Lond. 1965; DObst RCOG 1967. (Westm.) Cons. Phys. St. Geo. Hosp. & Bolingbroke Hosp. Lond. Socs: Brit. Soc. Gastroenterol.; Brit. Diabetic Assn. Prev: Sen. Regist. (Med.) Middlx. Hosp. Lond. 1975-77; Sen. Regist. (Gastroenterol.) Centr. Middlx. Hosp. Lond. 1973-75; Research Asst. St. Mark's Hosp. Dis. of Rectum Lond. 1969-72.

NEWTON, David John Tel: 023 8087 7900 — MD 1984 Birm.; MB ChB 1972; MRCP (UK) 1976. Socs: BMA; Diabetes U.K. Prev: Regist. (Endocrinol.) Radcliffe Infirm. Oxf.; Regist. (Gen. Med. & Diabetes) John Radcliffe Hosp. Oxf.; Clin. Research Fell. (Therapeut.) Roy. Hallamsh. Hosp. Sheff.

NEWTON, David John Highfield Surgery, Highfield Way, Hazlemere, High Wycombe HP15 7UW Tel: 01949 813396 Fax: 01949 814107; 74 Baring Road, Beaconsfield HP9 2NF Tel: 01494 675359 — BM BCh Oxf. 1965; MRCP (U.K.) 1970. (Univ. Coll. Hosp.) Prev: Research Fell. & Hon. Sen. Regist. MRC Rheum. Research Unit Canad.; Red Cross Memor. Hosp. Taplow; Med. Regist. Hammersmith Hosp. Lond. Ho. Phys. & Ho. Surg. Univ.

NEWTON, Duncan Angus Gray (private rooms), The Yorkshire Clinic, Bradford Road, Bingley BD16 1TW Tel: 01274 560311; Tiverton, Southfield Road, Burley-in-Wharfedale, Ilkley LS29 7PA Tel: 01943 862258 — MB BS 1968 Newc.; FRCP Lond. 1990; MRCP (UK) 1971. (Newc.) Cons. Phys. St. Luke's Hosp. Bradford. & Bradford Roy. Infirm. Prev: Sen. Med. Regist. St. Jas. Hosp. Leeds; Med. Regist. Hammersmith Hosp. Lond.; Res. Med. Off. Nat. Heart Hosp. Lond.

NEWTON, Elizabeth Mary Gray Tiverton, Southfield Road, Burley-in-Wharfedale, Ilkley LS29 7PA Tel: 01943 862258 — MB BS 1967 Newc. (Newc.) Prev: Regist. Roy. Hosp. Sick Childr. Glas.

NEWTON, Ellen Rosemary The David Lewis Centre, Mill Lane, Gt Warford, Alderley Edge SK9 7UD Tel: 01565 640027 Fax: 01565 640100 Email: rosemary@davidlewis.org.uk; The White Cottage, Parkfield Road, Knutsford WA16 8 — MB BS 1976 Lond. Assoc. Specialist in Childh. Epilepsy/ Manager Childr.'s Assessement Serv. Prev: Clin. Med. Off. Child Health Stockport HA; Trainee GP Macclesfield VTS; Princip. GP Knutsford, Chesh.

NEWTON, Mr Eric Joseph (retired) 237 Eccleshall Road, Stafford ST16 1PE Tel: 01785 251841 — MB BS 1942 Madras; FRCS Eng. 1950; MRCS Eng. LRCP Lond. 1949. Prev: Cons. Neurosurg. Stoke-on-Trent Hosp. Gp.

NEWTON, Eric Michael (retired) Netherfield, Round St., Cobham, Gravesend DA13 9BA Tel: 01474 814247 — MRCS Eng. LRCP Lond. 1951; DObst RCOG 1958. Prev: Regtl. Med. Off. 2nd Btn. Black Watch.

NEWTON, Eva Katharina Stoke Mandeville Hospital NHS Trust, Mandeville Road, Aylesbury HP21 8AL; Ribbleton, Foxcombe Lane, Boars Hill, Oxford OX1 5DH Tel: 01865 735307 — MB BS 1982 Lond.; BSc (Physiol.) Lond. 1979; MRCOphth 1995. (Kings Coll.) Staff Grade (Ophth.) Stoke Mandeville Hosp. Aylesbury.

NEWTON, Frank Antony (retired) Grafton Leys, 39 Cattle End, Silverstone, Towcester NN12 8UX Tel: 01327 857415 Fax: 01327 857415 Email: frank@sorebones.freeserve.co.uk — MRCS Eng. LRCP Lond. 1956; MSc (Sports Med.) Nottm. 1994; DA Eng. 1958. Hon. Med. Off. UK: Athletics; Resid. Hon. Med. Off. Silverstone Circuit; Med. Comm. Internat. Sailing Federat. Prev: Regist. (Anaesth.) Dudley Rd. Hosp. Birm.

***NEWTON, Fraser Leigh** 56 Ringstead Cr, Sheffield S10 5SH — MB ChB 1997 Liverp.

NEWTON, Mr Geoffrey (retired) The School House, The Green, Bretby, Burton-on-Trent DE15 0RE Tel: 01283 703721 — MB ChB 1954 Manch.; FRCS Eng. 1965. Prev: Cons. Orthop. Surg. Derbysh. Roy. Infirm.

NEWTON, Helen Princess Margaret Hospital, Swindon SN1 4JU Tel: 01793 437080 Email: careofthe.elderly@smnhs.swest.nhs.uk; Grove Farm House, Bourton, Swindon SN6 8JA Tel: 01793 784413 Email: helen.newton@lineone.net — BM 1982 Soton.; MRCP (UK) 1985. p/t Cons. Phys. Care Elderly P.ss Margt. Hosp. Swindon & Lead Cons. For Stroke Serv.s. Socs: Brit. Geriat. Soc.; Brit. Assn. of Stroke Phys.s. Prev: Hon. Lect. & Sen. Regist. (Geriat. Med.) Portsmouth & Soton.

NEWTON, Helen Agnes (retired) 35 Bay Street, Fairlie, Largs KA29 0AL Tel: 01475 568355 — MB ChB 1954 Glas.

NEWTON, Hilary Skardon 20 Castle Street, Thornbury, Bristol BS35 1HB Tel: 01454 418698 — MB ChB 1957 Bristol. (Bristol) Prev: Ho. Surg. Bristol Roy. Infirm.; Ho. Phys. S.mead Hosp. Bristol.

***NEWTON, James Douglas** 142 Howard Road, Leicester LE2 1XJ — MB ChB 1998 Leic.; MB ChB Leic 1998.

NEWTON, James Evelyn Watton Place Clinic, 60 High Street, Watton-at-Stone, Hertford SG14 3TA Tel: 01920 830232; Garden Cottage, Rectory Lane, Datchworth, Knebworth SG3 6RD — MB BS 1980 Lond.; MRCGP 1986; DRCOG 1984. Socs: BMA. Prev: Ho. Surg. St. Bart. Hosp. Lond.; Ho. Phys. Hackney Hosp. Lond.

NEWTON, Janet Suzanne Red Bank Group Practice, Red Bank Health Centre, Unsworth Street, Radcliffe, Manchester M26 3GH Tel: 0161 724 0777 Fax: 0161 724 8288; 1 Delbooth Avenue, Flixton, Urmston, Manchester M41 8SD — MB ChB 1986 Birm.; MRCGP 1992; DRCOG 1991; DFFP 1990.

NEWTON, Joan Marie 231 Lauderdale Tower, Barbican, London EC2Y 8BY Tel: 020 7628 6781 — MB BS 1952 Lond.; MRCS Eng. LRCP Lond. 1952; DA Eng. 1955. (Guy's) Prev: Ho. Surg. St. John's Hosp. Lewisham; Ho. Phys. St. Nicholas Hosp. Plumstead; Regist. Anaesth. N. Middlx. Hosp.

NEWTON, Joan Victoria (retired) 6 Briar Rigg, Keswick CA12 4NW Tel: 017687 73242 — MB BS 1939 Lond.; MRCS Eng.

NEWTON

LRCP Lond. 1939. Prev: Hon. Clin. Asst. Psychiat. Dept. Bromley Hosp.

NEWTON, John 72 Clober Road, Milngavie, Glasgow G62 7SR — MB ChB 1941 Glas. (Univ. Glas.) Prev: Ho. Surg. Vict. Infirm. Glas.; Squadron Ldr. RAFVR (Ret.).

NEWTON, John (retired) Five Oaks, Nightingale Lane, Storrington, Pulborough RH20 4NU — BM BCh 1941 Oxf.; BM BCh Oxon. 1941. Prev: Ho. Surg. Roy. Berks. Hosp. Reading.

NEWTON, John Henry 8 Days Lane, Biddenham, Bedford MK40 4AD Tel: 01234 363828 — MB BS 1964 Lond.; DMRD 1969 Eng.; MRCS 1964 Eng.; FFR 1971; FRCP 1975; LRCP 1964 Lond.; MRCS Eng. LRCP Lond. 1964; FRCR 1975; FFR 1971; DMRD Eng. 1969. (Char. Cross) Cons. Radiol. Bedford Hosp. Prev: Chairm. NW Thames RHA Radiol. Sub-Comm.; Sen. Regist. (Radiodiag.) Char. Cross Hosp. Lond.; Regist. (Radiodiag.) Bristol United & Kings Coll. Hosps.

NEWTON, John Hotham (retired) The Coach House, Landridge Road, London SW6 4LF Tel: 020 7736 8017 Fax: 020 7731 1801 — MB BChir 1952 Camb.; MRCS Eng. LRCP Lond. 1951; MRCPsych 1974; DPM Eng. 1973. Hon. Vis. Lect. Dept. Psychiat. Nat. Univ. Malaysia, Kuala Lumpur. Prev: Cons. Adolesc. Psychiat. E. Berks.

NEWTON, John Murray Endekiln, Strathblane, Glasgow Tel: 0141 70340 — MB ChB 1954 Glas.

NEWTON, John Norman Unit of Health-Care Epidemiology, University of Oxford, Old Road, Oxford OX3 7LF Tel: 01865 226991 Fax: 01865 226993; Ribbleton, Foxcombe Lane, Boars Hill, Oxford OX1 5DH — MB BS 1982 Lond.; MSc Lond. 1989; MA Oxf. 1979; MRCP (UK) 1985; MFPHM RCP (UK) 1991; FRCP (UK) 1999; FFPHM RCP (UK) 2000. Cons. Epidemiol. Univ. Oxf. Unit of Healthcare Epidemiol.; Director of Research & Developm., S.on Univ. Hosp.; Hon. Cons. Pub. Health Med. Oxf. HA; Univ. Research Lect. Univ. Oxf.; Hon. Sen. Lect. Univ. S.on. Prev: Sen. Regist. (Pub. Health Med.) Oxf. RHA; Regist. (Dermat.) Wycombe Gen. Hosp.

NEWTON, Professor John Richard Department of Obstetrics and Gynaecology, Birmingham Women's Healthcare NHS Trust, Edgbaston, Birmingham B15 2TG Tel: 0121 627 2696 Fax: 0121 414 1576 Email: j.r.newton@bham.ac.uk; 25 Westfield Road, Edgbaston, Birmingham B15 3QF Tel: 0121 455 0263 Fax: 0121 684 2141 Email: johnnewton@hilltrees.freeserve.co.uk — MB BS Lond. 1962; LLM 1994; MD Lond. 1972; MRCS Eng. LRCP Lond. 1962; FRCOG 1980, M 1967, DObst 1964. (St. Bart.) Prof. & Cons. O & G Univ. Birm. Dir. Laser & Endoscopy Train. Centre W. Midl.; Examr. Univs. Birm. Socs: (Comm.) ESGE & ISGE; Foundat. Bd. Mem. Fac. Family Plann.; Chairm. Scienti. Comm. ISGE. Prev: Sen. Lect. (O & G) King's Coll. Hosp. Lond.

NEWTON, John Roland 126 Harley Street, London W1N 1AH Tel: 020 7580 3383; 158 Sheen Lane, East Sheen, London SW14 8LZ Tel: 020 8876 7590 — MB ChB Manch. 1962; MRCS Eng. LRCP Lond. 1962; FRCR 1975; FFR 1972; DMRD Eng. 1969. Cons. Radiol. Char. Cross Hosp. & W.m. Hosp. Lond. Socs: BMA; Fell. Roy. Coll. Radiologists; Brit. Inst. Radiol.

NEWTON, Jonathan Ray 70 Seafield Road, Broughty Ferry, Dundee DD5 3AQ Tel: 01382 776239; 6 Bellefield Avenue, Dundee DD1 4NQ Tel: 01382 642535 — MB ChB 1994 Ed. (Ed.) SHO (Paediat.) Ninewells Hosp. Dundee Teach. Hosps. Prev: Resid. Med. Off. Mater Miser. Hosp. Brisbane, Austral.

NEWTON, Josephine Clare Fairview, Top Road, Shipham, Winscombe BS25 1TB — BM 1989 Soton.; BA (1st cl. Hons. Human Scis.) Oxf. 1983; MRCGP 1994; DRCOG 1993; DCH RCP Lond. 1992.

NEWTON, Joyce Hegglehead, Hutton Roof, Penrith CA11 0XS Tel: 0185 34 566 — MB ChB 1958 Manch.

NEWTON, Julia Lindsey 51 Castledene Court, Newcastle upon Tyne NE3 1NZ Tel: 0191 284 1762 — MB BS 1990 Newc.; MRCP (UK) 1993. Clin. Research Assoc. (Physiol. & Med.) Med. Sch. Newc. u. Tyne. Socs: Brit. Geriat. Soc. Prev: Clin. Regist. (Med. & Geriat.) Qu. Eliz Hosp. Gateshead.

NEWTON, Julia Louise Manchester Royal Infirmary, Manchester M13 9WL; The Willows, Walesby, Market Rasen LN8 3UW — MB ChB 1994 Manch.; MB ChB (Hons.) Manch. 1994.

NEWTON, Julian Charles Barker Ashenfell Surgery, Church Lane, Baslow, Bakewell DE45 1SP Tel: 01246 582216 Fax: 01246 583867 — MB ChB 1972 Manch.; MRCGP 1977; DRCOG 1976; Dip. Palliat. Med. Wales 1991; DCH Eng. 1975. Assoc. Med. Dir. Ashgate Hospice Chesterfield.

NEWTON, Katherine Lucinda 221 Wentworth Avenue, Slough SL2 2AP — MB ChB 1991 Birm.; ChB Birm. 1991; DRCOG 1993; MRC Psych. 1998. (Birmingham) Specialist Regist. (Psychiat.) N. Thames. Prev: Regist. (Psychiat.) Char. Cross Scheme.

NEWTON, Kay Jocelyn Welsby Ralphs Ride Practice, Ralphs Ride Surgery, Ralphs Ride, Bracknell RG12 9LH Tel: 01344 454626 Fax: 01344 303929; 4 Walnut Close, Wokingham RG41 4BG Tel: 0118 978 7962 Fax: 01344 303929 Email: kaykw@lineone.com — MB BS 1968 Lond.; MB BS London 1968 (Honours); MRCS England LRCP London 1968; DCH England 1972. (Char. Cross)

NEWTON, Kenneth Arthur (retired) Tumbling Bay, Underriver, Sevenoaks TN15 0SD Tel: 01732 832016 — MB BS 1945 Lond.; DMR 1952; FRCP Lond. 1967, M 1949; FRCR 1975; FFR 1955; DMRT Eng. 1952. Prev: Hon Civil Cons. Radiother. RAF.

NEWTON, Lisa Jane Ward 7, Bradford Royal Infirmary, Duckworth Road, Bradford BD9 6RJ Tel: 01274 364367 Email: ljnewts@hotmail.com — MB ChB 1991 Sheff.; MRCP (UK) 1994; Dip RCPath 1996; MRCPATH 1999. (Sheffield) Cons. Haematologist, Bradford Roy. Infirm., Bradford. Prev: Specialist Regist. in Haemat. Leeds Region; SHO (Gen. Med.) Roy, Hallamsh. Hosp. Sheff.

NEWTON, Magda St Mark's Hospital, Northwick Park, Watford Road, Harrow HA1 3JU Tel: 020 8235 4160 Fax: 020 8235 4162; 17 Copper Beech Close, Harborne, Birmingham B32 2HT Tel: 0121 426 2302 — MB BS 1987 Lond.; MRCP (UK) 1990. Research Regist. (Gastroenterol.) St. Marks Hosp. Lond. Prev: Regist. (Gastroenterol.) Dudley Rd. Hosp. Birm.; SHO (Gen. Med.) OldCh. Hosp. Romford; Ho. Phys. Crawley Hosp.

NEWTON, Margaret (retired) Tigh-na-Gaoith, Achterneed, Strathpeffer IV14 9AE Tel: 01997 421241 — MB ChB Ed. 1943. Prev: Ho. Phys. Roy. Edin. Hosp. Sick Childr.

NEWTON, Margaret Patricia The Schoolhouse, The Green, Bretby, Burton-on-Trent DE15 0RE Tel: 01283 703721 — MB ChB 1954 Manch.; DObst RCOG 1960.

NEWTON, Marjorie Stella (retired) 30 Silverknowes Hill, Edinburgh EH4 5HD Tel: 0131 336 3785 — MB ChB Ed. 1956; DObst RCOG 1960. Prev: GP Edin.

NEWTON, Mary Constance Department of Anaesthesia, National Hospital for Neurology and Neurosurgery, Queen Square, London WC1N 3BG Tel: 020 7837 3611; 53 Colebrooke Row, Islington, London N1 8AF Tel: 020 7359 5597 — MB BS 1979 Lond.; FFA RCS Eng. 1985. (St. Geos. Hosp. Med. Sch. Lond.) Cons. Neuroanaesth. Nat. Hosp. Neurol. & Neurosurg. Lond. Prev: Cons. Anaesth. St. Bart. Hosp. Lond.; Regist. (Anaesth.) Univ. Coll. Hosp., Hosp. for Sick Childr. Gt. Ormond St. & St. Geo. Hosp. Med. Sch. Lond.

NEWTON, Mathew Laurence 80 Knutsford Road, Wilmslow SK9 6JD Tel: 01625 548534 Fax: 01625 529152 — MB ChB 1981 Manch.; MBA Keele 1995. (Manch.) Dir., Pterion Ltd.; Clin. Asst. Cardiol. Stepping Hill Hosp. Prev: Sen. Assoc. Coopers & Lybrand Manch.

NEWTON, Michael Anthony 138 Harley Street, London W1G 7LA Tel: 020 7935 0554 — MD Camb. 1966, MB 1958, BChir 1957; FRCP Lond. 1977, M 1961. (St. Bart.) Cons. Phys. Private Pract. Socs: Brit. Hypertens. Soc.; Fell. Roy. Soc. Med.; Fell. Med. Soc. Lond. Prev: Gen. Phys. Centr. Middlx. Hosp. Lond.; Recogn. Teach. & Examr. Lond. Univ.; Examr. Roy. Coll. Phys.

NEWTON, Nicholas Ian Department of Anaesthetics, Guy's Hospital, London SE1 9RT Tel: 020 7955 4051 Fax: 020 7955 8844; 41 Grange Grove, London N1 2NP — BM BCh 1969 Oxf.; BA (Hons.) Camb. 1966, MA 1980; FRCA 1976; DA Eng. 1972. (Oxf.) Cons. Anaesth. Guy's & St. Thos. NHS Hosp. Trust. Socs: Assn. Anaesths.; Roy. Soc. Med.; BMA. Prev: Sen. Regist. (Anaesth.) St. Bart. Hosp. Lond.; Regist. (Anaesth.) Nuffield Dept. Anaesth. Radcliffe Infirm. Oxf.; Regist. (Anaesth.) Groote Schuur Hosp. Cape Town, S. Afr.

NEWTON, Paul 68 Wrottesley Road, Wolverhampton WV6 8SF — MB ChB 1974 Ed.; MRCP (UK) 1977; FRCP 1996. Cons. Rheum. Roy. Wolverhampton Hosps. NHS Trust. Prev: Sen. Regist. (Rheum.) Hope Hosp. Salford, Wrightington Hosp. Wigan & Manch. Roy. Infirm.

NEWTON, Paul Gregory 19 Peel Road, Douglas IM1 4LS — MB ChB 1967 Birm.; MSc Columbia Pacific Univ. 1989; MCPS Sask.

1975. Socs: Fell. Inst. for Supervis. & Managem.; World Assn. for Disaster & Emerg. Med. Prev: Employee Health Phys. King Fahd Milit. Hosp. Dhahran, Saudi Arabia; Ships Surg. Roy. Fleet Auxil.; Med. Off. Canad. Forces Base Trenton, Ontario.

NEWTON, Paul Nicholas 90 Crescent Road, Oxford OX4 2PD — BM BCh 1989 Oxf.; MRCP (UK) 1992; DTM & H (Lond.) 1996. (University of Oxford)

NEWTON, Paula Jane Bartlett, Cronk and Newton, Chequers Lane, Papworth Everard, Cambridge CB3 8QQ Tel: 01480 830888 Fax: 01480 830001; 31 Victory Way, Cottenham, Cambridge CB4 8TG Tel: 01954 200667 — MB BChir 1990 Camb.; MRCGP 1994; DCH RCP Lond. 1992. Prev: Trainee GP/SHO Hinchingbrooke Trust Hosp. Camb. VTS.

NEWTON, Peter Michael Carlton House Surgery, 28 Tenniswood Road, Enfield EN1 3LL Tel: 020 8363 7575 Fax: 020 8366 8228 — MB BS 1976 Lond.; MRCGP 1982; DRCOG 1982. GP Enfield.; Trainer Cons. Deaney.

NEWTON, Philippa Jane Clock House, Lea Road, Lea Town, Preston PR4 0RA — MB BS 1992 Lond.

NEWTON, Professor Ray William 70 Seafield Road, Broughty Ferry, Dundee DD5 3AQ Tel: 01385 76239 — MB ChB 1969 Ed.; FRCP 1995 Glasgow; FRCP Ed. 1981; MRCP (UK) 1972. (Ed.) Cons. Phys. Ninewells Hosp.; PostGrad. Dean E. of Scotl. Socs: Brit. Diabetic Assn.; Scott. Soc. Phys.; Brit. Diabetic Assn. Prev: Regist. Roy. Infirm. Edin.

NEWTON, Richard Charles Feakes RCF Newton, St. Peter's Hospital, Guildford Road, Chertsey KT16 0PZ Tel: 01932 87200; Woodhambury, Woodham Lane, Woking GU21 5SR — MB Camb. 1963, BChir 1962; FRCP 1994; FRCPCH 1997; MRCP (UK) 1969; DCH Eng. 1969; DObst RCOG 1964. (Univ. Coll. Hosp.) p/t Cons. Paediat. St. Peters Hosp. Chertsey & Ashford Hosp. Middlx. Prev: Ho. Off. Qu. Eliz. Hosp. Childr. Lond.; Resid. Med. Off. W.m. Childr. Hosp. Lond.; Sen. Regist. (Paediat.) Char. Cross Hosp. Lond.

NEWTON, Richard David Alan Witsend, Hill Hayes Lane, Hullavington, Chippenham SN14 6EB Tel: 01666 838013 — BM 1991 Soton.

NEWTON, Richard Ward Royal Manchester Childrens Hospital, Pendlebury, Manchester M27 4HA Tel: 0161 794 4696 Fax: 0161 727 2555; 7 Oakwood Drive, Heaton, Bolton BL1 5EE Tel: 01204 843303 — MB BS 1973 Lond.; MD Lond. 1982; FRCP Lond. 1990; MRCP (UK) 1977; MRCS Eng. LRCP Lond. 1973; MRCGP 1977; DRCOG 1977; DCH Eng. 1976; FRCPCH 1997. (King's Coll. Hosp.) Cons. Paediat. Neurol. Roy. Manch. Childr. Hosp. & Booth Hall Childr. Hosp. Socs: Paediat. Research Soc.; MAMH Euro Assoc of Intellectual Disabil. med. (Pres.); Brit. Paediat. Neurol. Assn. (Pres.). Prev: Trainee GP Hull VTS; Tutor (Child Health) St. Mary's Hosp. Manch.; Regist. (Paediat.) Hull Roy. Infirm.

NEWTON, Robert Edward ICRF Cancer Epidemiology Unit, Gibson Building, Radcliffe Infirmary, Oxford OX2 6HE — MB BS 1991 Lond. MRC Clin. Research Fell. ICRF Cancer Epidemiol. Unit Oxf. Prev: Ho. Off. (Surg.) Medway Hosp. Kent; Ho. Off. (Med.) Qu. Eliz. Hosp. King's Lynn.

NEWTON, Robert George (retired) 58 Moor Lane, Bramcote, Beeston, Nottingham NG9 3FH Tel: 0115 925 6987 Fax: 0115 925 6987 — MB BS Lond. 1952; AKC. Prev: GP Nottm.

NEWTON, Robin Archibald Houston (retired) 35 Bay Street, Fairlie, Largs KA29 0AL Tel: 01475 568355 — MB ChB 1954 Glas.

NEWTON, Roger John Etwall Surgery, Egginton Road, Etwall, Derby DE65 6NB Tel: 01283 732257 Fax: 01283 734876; 131 Station Road, Mickleover, Derby DE3 5FN Tel: 01332 514176 Email: newton@131station.freeserve.co.uk — MB BS 1974 Newc.; DRCOG 1979; DCH RCPS Glas. 1976. (Newc. u. Tyne) Socs: Derby Med. Soc. Prev: Trainee GP Derby VTS; Ho. Phys. Nottm. City Hosp.; Ho. Surg. Burton-on-Trent Gen. Hosp.

NEWTON, Sally Eelin (retired) 107 Randolph Avenue, London W9 1DL — MB BS 1957 Lond. Prev: Regist. (Med.) Centr. Middlx. Hosp. Lond.

*NEWTON, Sarah Lucy 38 Dibbinsdale Road, Wirral CH63 0HH — MB ChB 1997 Leeds.

NEWTON, Sheelin Jane The Surgery, Trimperley, Ellesmere SY12 0DB Tel: 01691 622798 Fax: 01691 623294 — MB ChB 1983 Bristol; MRCGP 1990.

NEWTON, Tina 80 Grasmere Road, Kennington, Ashford TN24 9BG — MB ChB 1991 Birm.; ChB Birm. 1991.

NEWTON, Professor Emerita Valerie Elizabeth Human Communication and Deafness, Manchester University, Manchester M13 9PL Tel: 0161 275 3370 Fax: 0161 275 3373 Email: valerie.newton@man.ac.uk — MB ChB Sheff. 1960; MSc Manch. 1979; MD Sheff. 1987. Socs: Fell. Roy. Soc. Med.; (Vice-Chairm.) BAAP; BSA. Prev: Hon. Cons. Paediat. Audiol. Univ. Manch.; Prof. (Audiol. Med.) Univ. Manch.

NEWTON, Mr Walter Dick 14 Bonnyton Drive, Eaglesham, Glasgow G76 0LU — MB ChB 1970 Glas.; FRCS Glas. 1975. Cons. Orthop. Surg. StoneHo. Hosp. & Hairmyres Hosp. Lanarksh.

NEWTON, William Boyd (retired) Kilbrennan, Brockham Green, Betchworth RH3 7HJ Tel: 0173 784 3609 — MB ChB 1941 Glas.; MB ChB (Commend.) Glas. 1941.

NEWTON, William Kenneth 79 Harley Street, London W1N 1DE Tel: 020 7935 0871 Fax: 020 7935 3417 — MB BS 1979 Lond.; MB BS Lond. 1949; MRCP Lond. 1954. (Westm.) Socs: Fell. Harv. Soc. & Roy. Soc. Med. Prev: Regist. (Med.) Nat. Hosp. Nerv. Dis. Lond.; Resid. Med. Off. Nat. Heart Hosp. Lond.; Ho. Phys. W.m. Hosp.

NEWTON BISHOP, Julia Ann Department of Dermatology, St. James' University Hospital, Beckett St., Leeds LS9 7TF Tel: 0113 206 5816 Fax: 0113 242 9886 Email: j.newton-bishop@icrf.icnet.uk — MB ChB 1978 Sheff.; MB ChB (Hons.) Sheff. 1978; MD (Commend.) Sheff. 1987; FRCP Lond. 1994; MRCP (UK) 1980. Cons. Dermat. & ICRF Sen. Clin. Scientist St. Jas. Univ. Hosps. Socs: Fell. Roy. Soc. Med.; Brit. Assn. Dermat.; Brit. Assn. Cancer Research. Prev: Sen. Lect. & Hons. Cons. (Dermat.) Roy. Lond. Hosp. Med. Coll.; Regist (Dermat.) St. Thos. Hosp.; Regist. Rotat. (Med.) & SHO The Lond. Hosp.

NEWTON DUNN, Alan Richard A R Newton Dunn and Partners, 61 New Street, Salisbury SP1 2PH — MB BS 1972 Lond.; MRCS Eng. LRCP Lond. 1972; DObst RCOG 1975. (St. Bart.) Socs: BMA. Prev: Ho. Surg. N. Middlx. Hosp. Edmonton; Ho. Phys. Salisbury Gen. Infirm.; SHO (O & G) Soton. Gen. Hosp.

NEYLAN, Catherine Margaret Mary Angela Brennan and Neylan, The GP Centre, 322 Malden Road, North Cheam, Sutton SM3 8EP Tel: 020 8644 0224; 15 Deepdale, Wimbledon, London SW19 5EZ Tel: 020 8946 1327 Email: catherineneylan@hotmail.com — MB BS 1966 Lond.; MRCS Eng. LRCP Lond. 1966; DFFP Lond. 1993; DCH RCP Lond. 1992. (St. Mary's) GP Brennan and Neylan, Nr. Cheam. Socs: Assoc. Mem. Brit. Roy. Coll. Paediat. & Child Health. Prev: Clin. Med. Off. Merton & Sutton HA.

NEYLON, Jonathan James St James Surgery, Harold Street, Dover CT16 1SF Tel: 01304 225559 Fax: 01304 213070; 3 Guthrie Gardens, Common Lane, River, Dover CT17 0PW — MB ChB 1979 Birm. (Birmingham) GP Dover. Prev: Cas. Off. Roy. Vict. Hosp. Folkestone.

*NEYLON, Kerri Louise 28 Ness Bank, Inverness IV2 4SF — MB ChB 1998 Glas.; MB ChB Glas 1998.

NG, Antony Ka Man 82 South View, E. Denton, Newcastle upon Tyne NE5 2BQ — MB BS 1991 Newc.

*NG, Biing Yann Musgrave and Clark House, Royal Victoria Hospital, Grosvenor Road, Belfast BT12 6BA — MB BCh BAO 1995 Belf.

NG, Mr Bobby Kin Wah 16 Park Court, Cardrew Avenue, Friern Park, London N12 9UH — MB ChB 1984 Bristol; FRCS Ed. 1992. Ho. Off. (Gen. Surg.) Dewsbury Gen. Hosp; Ho. Off. (Gen Med.) Frenchay Hosp. Brist.; SHO (Orthop.) St. Ann's Hosp. Lond.; SHO (A & E) N. Middlx. Hosp. Lond.

*NG, Calvin Shin Haw 315 Sir John Henry Biggart House, Broadway, Belfast BT12 6HQ; 31 Cloona Park, Upper Dunmurry Lane, Lisburn BT17 0HQ Tel: 07801 351907 Email: u9310665@hotmail.com — MB BCh 1998 Belf.; MB BCh Belf 1998.

NG, Chaan Soong University of Radiology Box 219, Addenbrookes Hospital, Hills Road, Cambridge CB2 2QQ — MB BS 1989 Lond.; MRCP (UK) 1992; FRCR 1995.

*NG, Chi Hwa 4 Blackwood Avenue, Newton Mearns, Glasgow G77 5BA — MB ChB 1998 Glas.; MB ChB Glas 1998.

NG, Cho Yiu 67 Gordon Mansions, Torrington Place, London WC1E 7HH — BChir 1990 Camb.

NG

NG, Chong Sum HM Stanley Hospital, St Asaph LL17 0RS Tel: 01745 589725 — MB ChB 1987 Leic.; FRCOphth 1993. Cons Ophthamology Conwy & Denbighsh. NHS Trust Bodelwyddan.

NG, Chun Yan Unit 3 Room 1, Opal Court, Wexham Park Hospital, Wexham St., Wexham, Slough SL2 4HL — MB ChB 1991 Aberd. SHO (Radiother. & Clin. Oncol.) United Leeds Teachg. Hosps. NHS Trust. Prev: SHO (O & G) Coventry HA.

***NG, Chung Hong Selwyn** 25 Bradley Street, Sheffield S10 1PA — MB ChB 1998 Sheff.; MB ChB Sheff 1998.

NG, Mr Colin Leong Liong 119 Turnpike Link, Croydon CR0 5NU — MB ChB 1988 Liverp.; FRCS Glas. 1994. Regist. (Surg.) John Radcliffe Hosp. Oxf. Socs: Fell. Roy. Soc. Med.

NG, David Pak-Ken 1 Mooreway, Rainhill, Prescot L35 6PD — MB ChB 1985 Liverp.

***NG, David Palkin** 12 Richmond Way, Ponteland, Newcastle upon Tyne NE20 9HU — MB ChB 1998 Dund.; MB ChB Dund 1998.

NG, Doris Hui Lan 11 The Thistles, Newcastle ST5 2HL — MB BCh BAO 1991 Belf.; MB BCh BAO (Hons.) Belf. 1991; MRCP (UK) 1995. SHO (Gen. Med.) Roy. Vict. Hosp. Belf. Socs: BMA & Med. Protec. Soc. Prev: Ho. Off. Roy. Vict. Hosp. Belf.

***NG, Ernest Wee Oon** 183 Knighton Church Road, Leicester LE2 3JP — MB ChB 1996 Leic.

NG, Geraldine Yin Taeng Department of Paediatrics, St. George's Hospital, Blacksyaw, London Tel: 0208 672 1255; 115 Turnpike Link, Croydon CR0 5NU — MB BS 1994 Lond.; BSc (Hons.) Neurosci. Lond. 1991; MRCP (Lond) 1997; MRCPCH 1997. Specialist Regist. (Paediat.) St. Geo.s Hosp. Lond. Prev: Fell. in Neonazal - Perinatal Med.; The Hosp. For Sick Childr., Toronto, Canada.

NG, Ghulam Andre Division Of Cardiology, Clinical Sciences wing, Glenfield Hospital, Leicester LE3 9QP Tel: 0116 2502438 Fax: 0116 2875792 Email: gan1@le.ac.uk — MB ChB 1989 Glas.; MRCP (UK) 1992; PhD Glas. 1998. (Glas.) Sen. Lect./Cons. Cardiol., Cardiol., univ hosp leic. Socs: BMA; Scott. Cardial Soc.; BPEG. Prev: Research Fell. (Med. Cardiol.) Glas. Roy. Infirm.; SHO (Med. Cardiol.) Glas. Roy. Infirm.; SHO Rotat. (Med.) Stobhill Gen. Hosp. Glas.

NG, Hon Wah Kelvin Kent Elms Health Centre, Rayleigh Road, Leigh-on-Sea SS9 5UU Tel: 01702 522012 Fax: 01702 512375 — MB ChB 1984 Sheff.; MD Liverp. 1994; MRCP (UK) 1987; T(GP) 1995; T(M) 1993; Spec. Accredit. Gen. Med. & Clin. Pharmacol. JCHMT 1993. Socs: Med. Defence Union; BMA. Prev: Lect. & Hon. Sen. Regist. (Gen. Med., Clin. Pharmacol. & Therap.) Univ. Liverp. & Roy. Liverp. Univ. Hosp.; Research Fell. & Hon. Sen. Regist. (Clin. Pharmacol. & Therap.) Univ. Liverp. & Roy. Liverp. Univ. Hosp.; Regist. (Gen. Med., Haemat. & Coronary Care) S.port Dist. Gen. Hosp.

NG, Jonathan Chun Man 81 Hornsey Lane Gardens, Highgate, London N6 5PA — MB ChB 1994 Liverp.

NG, Joo Li 3 Hunters Lodge, The Green, Wallsend NE28 7ES — MB BS 1992 Newc.

***NG, Julia Mae-Zsianne** Calremont House, 51 London Road, Liphook GU30 7SG — MB BS 1996 Lond.

NG, Kai Yiu Leeds General Infirmary, Great George St., Leeds LS1 3EX Tel: 0113 243 2799; 14 Woodsley Road, Leeds LS3 1DT Tel: 0113 246 8613 — MB ChB 1995 Leeds; BSc (Hons.) Leeds 1992. (Leeds) SHO (Med.) Leeds Gen. Infirm.

***NG, Mr Keng Jin** Apartment 45, Bishop Court, 76 Bishops Bridge Road, London W2 6BE — MB BCh 1986 Wales; FRCS Ed. 1990.

***NG, Kerry Shin Lih** 86 Upper Malone Park, Belfast BT9 6PP — MB BCh BAO 1994 Belf.

NG, Lenny Vi-Lynn 63 Cloisters Avenue, Bromley BR2 8AN — MB BCh 1996 Wales.

NG, Professor Leong Loke Department of Pharmacology, Clinical Sciences Building, Leicester Royal Infirmary, Leicester LE2 7LX Tel: 01162 523108 Fax: 01162 523108 — MB BChir 1979 Camb.; MA Camb. 1982, MD 1988; MRCP (UK) 1982; FRCP Lond 1996. (University of Cambridge) Prof. of Med. and Therap. Socs: Brit. Pharmacological Soc. Prev: Lect. Radcliffe Infirm. Oxf.; MRC Train. Fell., Radcliffe Infirm. Oxf.; Regist. (Med.) Addenbrooke's Hosp. Camb.

***NG, Nicola Su-Han** 30 Montagu Mansions, London W1U 6LB — MB BS 1998 Lond.; MB BS Lond 1998.

NG, Pak Cheung 58 Bancroft Avenue, East Finchley, London N2 0AS — MB ChB 1982 Dundee; MRCP (UK) 1987; DCH RCP Lond. 1985. Sen. Regist. & Tutor (Paediat.) St. Jas. Hosp. Leeds; Sen. Lect. & Cons. Neonat. Med. Coll. St. Bart. Hosp. Univ. Lond. Socs: Paediat. Research Soc. & Brit. Paediat. Assn. Prev: Regist. & SHO (Paediat.) Leeds HA; SHO (Paediat.) Ninewells Hosp. Med. Sch. Dundee; SHO (Paediat.) Leics. HA.

***NG, Pang Han** 18 Chandos Avenue, Southgate, London N14 7ET — MB ChB 1996 Sheff.

***NG, Raymond Sai Ho** 12 Halland Way, Northwood HA6 2AG — MB BS 1997 Lond.

NG, Mr Roy Lip Hin Dept of Plastic Surgery, UCL Hospitals, Pond St., London NW3 2QG Tel: 020 7794 0500; 18 Parkgate Mews, 14-16 Stanhope Road, Highgate, London N6 5NB Tel: 020 8347 7853 Email: rlhn@msn.com — BM BCh Oxf. 1989; MA Camb. 1990; FRCS Eng. 1993. Specialist Regist. (Plastic Surg.)Roy. Free Hosps. Lond. Prev: Research Regist. (Plastic Surg.) Blond McIndoe Centre Qu. Vict. Hosp. E. Grinstead; Specialist Regist. Pastic surg.UCH; Specialist Regist. Plastic Surg.Mt. Vernon Hosp.

NG, Siew Teng Apartment 291, Metro Central Heights, 119 Newington Causeway, London SE1 6DB — MB ChB 1996 Aberd.

NG, Sui Yin 2 Kensington Place, Bristol BS8 3AH Email: syng@lineone.net; 9 Gerbang Ampang Hilir 55000, Malaysia — MB ChB 1994 Bristol; MRCP (Lond.) 1998. Paediatric Lect., Univ. Putra Malaysia. Socs: MRCPCH. Prev: SHO (Paediat.) St. Geo.s Hosp. Lond.; SHO (Paediat.) Roy. Lond. Hosp.; SHO (Paediat.) Mayday Univ. Hosp.

NG, Sze Hing (retired) 115 Turnpike Link, Croydon CR0 5NU Tel: 020 8686 5020 — MB BS Malaya 1961; FRCP Lond. 1987, M 1967; DCH Eng. 1963. Prev: Sen. Regist. (Paediat.) King's Coll. Hosp. Lond.

NG, Thomas Siu Fai — MB ChB 1990 Dundee; MRCP 1996; BMSc Dund 1987; MRCPI 1996. (Univ. of Dundee, Scotl.) Med. Advis. Manager, Roche Product Ltd. (UK), Welwyn Garden City, Herts AL7 3AY. Socs: Fell. of Roy. Soc. of Med.; Soc. of Pharmaceutical Med.; Europ. Soc. of Pharmacol. Prev: Regist. (Gen. Med.) Warrington Hosp.; Regist. Rotat. (Haemat.) Pembury Hosp., Kent & Sussex Hosp. & King's Coll. Hosp. Lond.

NG, Tony Tsz Cheong Cell Biophysics Laboratory, Imperial Cancer Research Fund, 44 Lincoln's Inn Fields, London WC2A 3PX Tel: 020 7269 3082 Email: T.Ng@cancer.org.uk — MB ChB 1989 Aberd.; PhD Lond. 1997; MRCP (UK) 1992. Gp. Ldr./ MRC Clin. Scient./ Hon. Sen. Clin. Lect. Kings Coll. Lond. Prev: MRC AIDS Progr. Clin. Fell. Dept. Immunol. St. Bart. Hosp. Lond.; Translational Clin. Research Fell. Imperial Cancer Research Fund Lond.

NG, Virginia Wun Kum Neuroimaging Department, Maudsley Hospital, Denmark Hill, London SE5 8AZ Tel: 020 7919 2470 Fax: 020 7919 2477 Email: v.ng@iop.kcl.ac.uk; 2 Rollscourt Avenue, Herne Hill, London SE24 0EA — MB BS 1987 Lond.; MRCP (UK) 1991; FRCR 1995; MD 2000 Lond. (St. Bart. Med. Sch.) Cons. Neuro. Maudsley Hosp. Lond. 1/2000; Hon. Sen. Lect. Inst. of Psychiat. Lond. Prev: Wellcome Clin. Train. Fell. (Neuroimaging) Inst. of Psychiat. Lond.; Specialist Regist. Nat. Hosp. Neurol. (Neuroradiolo.) Lond.; Sen. Regist. (Radiol.) St. Geo. Hosp. Lond.

NG, Wang Tat 9 Woodvale Avenue, Cardiff CF23 6SP — MB BCh 1984 Wales.

NG, Wei Seng 1B The Green, Twickenham TW2 5TU Tel: 020 8894 6870 Fax: 020 8893 8579; 8 Fairwater House, Twickenham Road, Teddington TW11 8AY Tel: 020 8977 1704 — MB BS 1989 Lond.

NG, Wing Shang 6 Park Road, Radyr, Cardiff CF15 8DG Tel: 029 2084 2318 — MB BCh 1961 Wales; FFA RCS Eng. 1966. (Cardiff) Cons. Anaesth. Univ. Hosp. Wales Cardiff. Prev: Assoc. Prof. Anaesth. Thos. Jefferson Univ. Philadelphia, USA; Sen. Regist. & Research Fell. (Anaesth.) United Cardiff Hosps.

***NG, Yeung Hwa** 4 Blackwood Avenue, Newton Mearns, Glasgow G77 5BA — MB ChB 1998 Glas.; MB ChB Glas 1998.

NG, Yin Khow Dovecote House, 38 Wollaton Road, Beeston, Nottingham NG9 5NR Tel: 0115 925 4281 Fax: 0115 925 3361; Tel: 0115 914 1838 — MB BS 1977 Lond.; BSc (Physiol.) Lond. 1974; MD Leic. 1996; MRCP (UK) 1981; DCH Eng. 1980; DRCOG 1979; FRCPCH 1997. (King's Coll. Hosp.) Cons. Paediat. (Community Child Health) Qu.s Med. Centre Nottm. Univ. Hosp. NHS Trust. Socs: Med. Wom.'s Federat.; Nottm. Med. Chirurgical

Soc.; Brit. Assn. Community Child Health. Prev: Lect. (Community Paediat.) Univ. Nottm.; Clin. Research Fell. Univ. Leic.; Ho. Phys. Hosp. for Sick Childr. Gt. Ormond St. Lond.

NG CHENG HIN, Alan Kenneth Woodside, Kincraig, Invergordon IV18 0PW — MB ChB 1986 Dundee; LMCC 1993 (Canada); FLEX Lic. (Canada) 1992; MRCGP 1992; DFFP 1993; DCH RCP Lond. 1991; Dip. Obst. Otago 1989; DTM & H Liverp. 1996. Family Phys., Lakeside Med. Clinic, Saskatoon, SK, Canada. Prev: Dept. Family Med. Univ. Saskatchewan, Saskatoon, Canada.

NG CHENG HIN, Harold Sinkwee Lehman and Partners, Hightown Surgery, Hightown Gardens, Banbury OX16 9DB Tel: 01295 270722 Fax: 01295 263000; Durrel Cottage, Chapel Lane, Bodicote, Banbury OX15 4DB — MB ChB 1980 Birm.; MRCP (UK) 1983.

NG CHENG HIN, Patrick Yan 12 Sherwood Road, Croydon CR0 7DH — MB ChB 1978 Dundee.

NG CHENG HIN, Mr Philip c/o Drive Ah Kye, 8 Rockwells Gardens, London SE19 1HW — MD 1977 Lyon; MD (Hons.) Lyon 1977; FRCS Ed. 1983; ECFMG Cert. 1975. Cons. Surg. Dallah Hosp. Riyadh. Socs: Fell. Roy. Soc. Med. Prev: Cons. Surg. Tawam Hosp. Al Ain, UAE; Vis. Lect. Chinese Univ. Hong Kong; Regist. Rotat. (Surg.) Guy's Hosp. Lond.

NG CHIENG HIN, Mr Steve Miow Cheong 25 Leybourne Road, Kingsbury, London NW9 9QG — MB ChB 1985 Leeds; FRCS Ed. 1989.

NG HOCK OON, Paul Flat D, 125 Grove Park, London SE5 8LD — MB ChB 1992 Leic.

NG HUANG, Stephen Chee Peng Alvaston Cottage, 66 Ack La W., Cheadle Hulme, Cheadle SK8 7ES — MB BS 1986 Singapore; MRCGP 1992.

NG MAN KWONG, Georges Det. Of Thoracic Medicine, Royal Bolton Hospitals, Minerva Road, Farnworth, Bolton BL2 0JR Tel: 01204 390390 — MB ChB 1990 Manch.; MRCP (UK) 1993. Sp Respirat. & Gen. Internal Med., Roy. Bolton Hosps. NHS Trust. Prev: Regist. (Thoracic Med.) NW Lung Centre Manch.; Clin. Research Fell., Respirat. Med., Univ. of Sheff. 1999-2001.

NG PING CHEUNG, Jean-Pierre Department of Haematology, Barnsley District General Hospital, Gawber Road, Barnsley S75 2EH; 39 Moorbank Road, Sandygate, Sheffield S10 5TQ Email: jeanpierre@lineone.net — MB ChB 1981 Glas.; MRCP (UK) 1984; MRCPath 1989 FRC Path; FRCP Lond.; FRCP Glas. Cons. Haemat. Barnsley Dist. Gen. Hosp. Prev: Sen. Regist. (Haemat.) W. Midl. RHA.

NG SUI HING, Ng You Kwong 51 Cathles Road, London SW12 9LE — MB ChB 1977 Glas.

NGAN, Cheung Yuen 41 The Avenue, Sale M33 4PJ — MB ChB 1982 Manch.

NGAN, Henry 22 Lavington Court, 77 Putney Hill, London SW15 3NU Tel: 020 8789 8417 — MB BS 1962 Lond.; MRCS Eng. LRCP Lond. 1962; MRCP Ed. 1965; MRCP Lond. 1967; FFR 1971; DMRD Eng. 1969. (Westm.) Cons. Radiol. Qu. Mary's Hosp. Roehampton. Socs: Fell. Roy. Soc. Med. Prev: Sen. Regist. Radiol. W.m. Hosp.; Regist. Med. Roy. Marsden Hosp.; Regist. Radiol. Hammersmith Hosp.

***NGAN, Sarah** 3 Coombs Street, London N1 8DJ — MB BS 1998 Lond.; MB BS Lond 1998.

***NGAN-SOO, Eleanor Mei-San** 94 Higher Drive, Banstead SM7 1PQ — MB BS 1998 Lond.; MB BS Lond 1998.

NGO, Thi Cuu 26 Mafeking Road, London N17 9BG — MB BS 1991 Lond.

NGUYEN, Anthony Long 10A Fairview Road, Wednesfield, Wolverhampton WV11 1BY — MB ChB 1993 Leeds.

NGUYEN, Chinh Truong 20B Anson Road, London N7 0RD — MB BS 1993 Lond.

***NGUYEN, Cuong Tuan** 40 Downsview Road, London SE19 3XB — MB BS 1995 Lond.

***NGUYEN, Dai Quoc Anh** 22 Sidcup Road, London SE12 8BW — MB ChB 1998 Bristol.

NGUYEN, Duke Duc Hoang 210 Gurney Close, Barking IG11 8JZ — MB BS 1996 Lond.; BSc 1994.

NGUYEN, Dzung Manh 7 St Andrews Gardens, Cobham KT11 1HG — MRCS Eng. LRCP Lond. 1985; DRCOG 1990.

NGUYEN, Hiep 32 Maran Way, Erith DA18 4BP — MB BS 1993 Lond.

NGUYEN, Hoa Binh 7 St Andrews Gardens, Cobham KT11 1HG — MRCS Eng. LRCP Lond. 1985.

***NGUYEN, Michael Loc** 10A Fairview Road, Wednesfield, Wolverhampton WV11 1BY — MB ChB 1997 Birm.

NGUYEN, Tan Dung The Surgery, 80 Torridon Road, London SE6 1RA Tel: 020 8698 5281 Fax: 020 8695 1841 — MB BS 1991 Lond.

NGUYEN-VAN-TAM, Jonathan Stafford Department of Public Health Medicine & Epidemiology, University of Nottingham Medical School, Queen's Medical Centre, Nottingham NG7 2UH Tel: 0115 970 9320 Fax: 0115 970 9316; 14 Greengate Lane, Birstall, Leicester LE4 3DJ Tel: 0116 267 1004 — BM BS 1987 Nottm.; BMedSci (Hons) 1985. Sen. Lect. (Pub. Health Med.) Univ. Nottm; Hon. Sen. Regist. N. Lincs. HA; Clin. Med. Off. Lincs. Army Cadet Force (TA). Prev: Hon. Regist. (Pub. Health Med.) Nottm. HA; SHO (Pub. Health Med.) Leicester HA; SHO (Anaesth.) Univ. Hosp. Nottm. & Co. Hosp. Lincoln.

NGWU, Mr Uchechukwu Okoronkwo Newbold Verdon Medical Practice, 14 Arnolds Crescent, Newbold Verdon, Leicester LE9 9PZ Tel: 01445 822171 Fax: 01445 824968 — BM BCh 1977 Nigeria; FRCS Ed. 1986. (University of Nigeria, Enugu)

NHEMACHENA, Charles Musena 174 Aberford Road, Stanley, Wakefield WF3 4NP Tel: 01924 828924 — MB ChB 1979 Birm. Assoc. Specialist Anaesth. Fairfield Gen. Hosp. Bury. Socs: Med. Protec. Soc.; BMA.

NI BHROLCHAIN, Cliona Maire Hinchingbrooke Health Care NHS Trust, Primrose Lane, Huntingdon PE29 1WG Tel: 01480 415211 Fax: 01480 415212; 104 Bridgwater Drive, Northampton NN3 3BB — MB BCh BAO 1981 NUI; MRCPI 1985; MRCGP 1986; DObst RCPI 1985; DCH RCPSI 1983. Cons. Community Paediat. Hinchingbrooke Health Care. Socs: Brit. Assn. Community Child Health (Treas.); Fell. Roy. Coll. Paediat.s & Child Health. Prev: Cons. Community Paediat. N.ampton Gen. Hosp.; Sen. Regist. (Community Paediat.) N.ampton; Clin. Med. Off. S. Sefton HA.

NI CHUILEANNAIN, Fiona Maire 2B Tarn House, Abbey Way, Barrow-in-Furness LA14 1BP; 14 Avondale Lawn, Blackrock, County Dublin, Republic of Ireland — MB BCh BAO 1989 NUI; MRCOG 1994. Regist. (O & G) Furness Gen. Hosp. Cumbria.

NI FHLAITHBHEARTAIGH, Eilin Maire Brent House Surgery, King St., Bridgwater TA6 3ND; 16B Chilkwell Street, Glastonbury BA6 8DB — MB BCh BAO 1984 NUI. Trainee GP Bridgwater. Prev: Regist. (Anaesth.) Vict. Hosp. Dub.

NI'MAN, Mufeed Na'eem 79 Hamilton Road, Boscombe, Bournemouth BH1 4EG Tel: 01202 773267 — MD 1985 Aleppo; LMSSA LRCS LRCP Lond. 1998. ENT SHO, Poole Gen. Hosp.

NIALL WALKER, Mrs Norah Margaret Aileen (retired) Bower Cottage, 31 Roseacre Lane, Bearsted, Maidstone ME14 4JE — MRCS Eng. LRCP Lond. 1926. Prev: Ho. Surg. Char. Cross Hosp.

NIAYESH, Mr Mohammad Hossein Homerton Hospital, Homerton Row, London E9 6SR Tel: 020 8510 5555; 40 The Woodlands, High Rd, London N12 0DU Tel: 020 8445 1899 Fax: 020 8445 1899 Email: mhniayesh@hotmail.com — MD Pahlavi 1984; MRCS Eng. LRCP Lond. 1988; FRCS Ed. 1988; FRCS Gen Surg 1999; MRCS Eng. LRCP Lond. 1988. (Pahlavi University) Sen. Regist. Gen.Surg, Horneton Hosp. Prev: Reg.Gen.Surg.Gt.er.Manch.Hosp.

NIAZI, Sultana 3 Ravenstone Road, London N8 0JT — MB ChB 1984 Glas.

NIBLETT, David John Department of Anaesthesia, Bedford Hospital, Kempston Road, Bedford MK42 9DJ Tel: 01234 355122 Fax: 01234 795910 Email: david.niblett@bedhos.anglox.nhs.uk; Alberta, Station Road, Turvey, Bedford MK43 8BH Tel: 01234 881468 Fax: 01234 881468 — MB BS 1977 Lond.; FFA RCS Eng. 1982. (Univ. Coll. Hosp.) Cons. Anaesth. & Intens. Care Bedford Hosp. Prev: Sen. Regist. Nuffield Dept. Anaesth. Oxf.; Lect. (Anat.) Stanford Univ. Med. Sch. Calif., USA.

NIBLOCK, James Logan Barns Street Surgery, 3 Barns Street, Ayr KA7 1XB Tel: 01292 281439 Fax: 01292 288268; 13 Doonholm Road, Alloway, Ayr KA7 4QQ Tel: 01292 443112 — MB ChB 1969 Glas.; DObst RCOG 1973. Med. Off. Marks & Spencer plc & Digital Equip. (Scotl.) Ltd. Socs: Soc. Occupat. Med. Prev: Regist. (O & G)

NIC EOIN

Robroyston Hosp. Glas.; Ho. Phys. Falkirk & Dist. Roy. Infirm.; Ho. Surg. W.. Infirm. Glas.

NIC EOIN, Maire Siobhan 14 St James Court, c/o St James Hospital, Beckett St., Leeds LS9 7TF — MB BCh BAO 1986 NUI.

NICE, Alison Mary The Priory Surgery, 24-26 Priory Avenue, High Wycombe HP13 6SH Tel: 01494 448132 — MB ChB 1988 Leeds; DCH RCPS Glas. 1992. Prev: Trainee GP Wakefield VTS; Ho. Off. (Gen. Med.) Bradford Roy. Infirm.; Ho. Off. (Gen. Surg.) St. Jas. Univ. Hosp.

NICE, Colin Andrew 9 Candelford Close, Newcastle upon Tyne NE7 7FG — MB ChB 1991 Dundee.

NICELL, Donald Thomas 5 Penbrey Path, St. Dial's, Cwmbran NP44 4RR — MB ChB 1982 Cape Town.

NICHANI, Sanjiv Hari Leicester Royal Infirmary, Infirmary Square, Leicester LE1 5WW — MB BS 1986 Univ. Poona; MRCP (UK) 1991.

NICHOL, Frank Edward Department of Rheumatology, Leicester Royal Infirmary, Infirmary Square, Leicester LE1 5WW Tel: 0116 258 6473 — MB ChB 1973 Liverp.; MD Liverp. 1981; FRCP Lond. 1993; FRCP Ed. 1988. Cons. Rheum. Leicester Roy. Infirm. Socs: Brit. Soc. Rheum. Prev: Sen. Regist. Leicester Roy. Infirm.; Research Fell. & Hon. Sen. Regist. (Med.) Univ. Liverp. & Roy. Liverp. Hosp.

NICHOL, Geoffrey Martin 5 Archel Road, London W14 9QJ — MB ChB 1979 Otago; FRACP 1987. Assoc. Dir. Clin. Investig. SmithKline Beecham Pharmaceut. Reigate. Prev: Regist. Brompton Hosp.; Research Regist. Nat. Heart & Lung Inst.; Regist. Repatriation Gen. Hosp. Adelaide, Austral.

NICHOL, Ian Edward 104 Rayleigh Drive, Wideopen, Newcastle upon Tyne NE13 6AJ — MB BS 1992 Newc.

NICHOL, Mr Neil Macpherson A&E Department, Ninewells Hospital, Dundee DD1 9SY — MB ChB 1983 Ed.; BSc (Med. Sci.) Ed. 1980; FRCS Ed. 1994; MRCGP 1987; Cert. Family Plann. JCC 1986; DRCOG 1986; FFAEM 1999. (Edin.) Cons.(A & E Dept) Ninewells Hosp. Dund. Prev: SHO III (A & E) Roy. Infirm. Edin.; Sen. Reg. (A&E) Roy. Infirm. Edin.; Chief Med. Off. St. Helena.

NICHOL, William Dorrien (retired) Chasewood House, 1 Chasewood Avenue, Enfield EN2 8PT Tel: 020 8363 9444 — MB ChB 1941 N.Z.; DMR Lond 1947; FRCR 1975; FFR 1952. Prev: Dir. Diag. Radiol. Dept. St. Bart. Hosp.

NICHOLAOU, Theodorakis Andrew 2 Ulster Gardens, Palmers Green, London N13 5DW — MB BS 1993 Lond.; BSc (Hons.) 1992 (Lond. Hosp. Med. Coll.) Radiother. SHO Roy. Lond. Hosp. Whitechapel Lond. Socs: BMA; Hellenic Med. Soc. Prev: SHO (HIV Med.) St. Barts. Hosp. Lond.; SHO (Cardiol./Gen. Med.) The Homerton Hosp. Lond.; SHO (Gastroenterol./Respirat. Med.) St. Barts. Lond.

NICHOLAS, Angela Patricia 95 Lander Close, Poole BH15 1UL — MB ChB 1992 Manch.; BSc (Hons.) Manch. 1988. (Manchester)

NICHOLAS, Anne Mary 1 Seymour Road, London SW18 5JB — MB BS 1979 Lond.

NICHOLAS, Annette Christaline Shandhini Woodsley Road Surgery, 144 Woodsley Road, Leeds LS2 9LZ Tel: 0113 245 4038 Fax: 0113 244 2084; 170 Cardigan Road, Leeds LS6 1LL Tel: 0113 275 2220 — MB BS 1964 Ceylon; MRCP (UK) 1979; DCH Ceylon 1972. (Ceylon) Socs: BMA.

NICHOLAS, Arthur Stuart 1 Tower Lane, Colehill, Wimborne BH21 2QP Tel: 01202 841505 — MB ChB 1952 Manch.; MRCS Eng. LRCP Lond. 1952. (Manch.)

NICHOLAS, Audrey (retired) 1 Devereux Way, Billericay CM12 0YS Tel: 01277 626295 — MB BS 1960 Durh.

NICHOLAS, Bridget Mary Child & Family Unit, St James University Hospital, Beckett St., Leeds LS9 7TF — MB ChB 1985 Sheff.; MRCGP 1989; MRCPsych 1994; DRCOG 1989; DCH RCP Lond. 1988. Sp. Regist. Rotat. (Child & Adolesc. Psychiat.) Leeds. Prev: Sen. Regist. Rotat. (Child & Adolesc. Psychiat.) Oxf.; Regist. Rotat. (Psychiat.) Oxf.; Sp. Regist. Rotat C & A Psych Bristol.

NICHOLAS, David Stuart Pathology Department, Poole Hospital NHS Trust, Longfleet Road, Poole BH15 2JB Tel: 01202 442211 — MB BS 1979 Lond.; BA Oxf. 1976. Cons. Histopath. Poole Hosp. NHS Trust.

NICHOLAS, Dorothy Joy (retired) 9 Orchard Drive, Durham DH1 1LA Tel: 0191 384 3598 Email: ken@kendor32.freeserve.co.uk — MB ChB 1961 Birm. Prev: Dent. Anaesth. Sunderland HA.

NICHOLAS, Florence Eileen Woodmount, Linden Road, Clevedon BS21 — MB ChB 1946 Bristol. (Bristol) Med. Off. Family Plann. Assn. Socs: BMA. Prev: Ho. Surg. Bristol Roy. Hosp.

NICHOLAS, Ivor Hugh 42 Doddington Road, Wellingborough NN8 2JH — MB BS 1973 Lond.; MRCP (UK) 1977; MRCS Eng. LRCP Lond. 1973.

NICHOLAS, Jacob 6 Castlehill Manor, Belfast BT4 3QH — MB BS 1974 Kerala.

NICHOLAS, Jeffery John, Surg. Cdr. RN (retired) Hope Cottage, Exton, Southampton SO32 3LT Tel: 01489 877347 — MB ChB 1961 Bristol; MFOM RCP Lond. 1980; DIH Eng. 1976. Prev: Late Roy. Naval Med. Serv.

NICHOLAS, Johann Chitranjan Babapulle 113 Dartmouth Avenue, Newcastle ST5 3NS — MB ChB 1989 Dundee; MRCP (UK) 1993.

NICHOLAS, Mr John Leyton (retired) Hull Royal Infirmary, Anlaby Road, Hull HU3 2JZ — BM BCh 1960 Oxf.; MA. 1960; FRCS Eng. 1967. Cons. Paediat. Surg. Hull Roy. Infirm. Prev: Sen. Surg. Regist. Hosp. Sick Childr. Gt. Ormond St. & W.m. Hosp.

NICHOLAS, John Richard Queens Park Medical Centre, Farrer Street, Stockton-on-Tees TS18 2AW Tel: 01642 679681 Fax: 01642 677124 — MB Camb. 1979, BChir 1978; MRCGP 1982; DCH RCP Lond. 1982. GP Qu. Pk. Med. Centre Stockton-on-Tees.

NICHOLAS, Justin Morgan Robin Hill, Castle Court, Llandough, Cowbridge CF71 7LZ — MB ChB 1991 Birm.; ChB Birm. 1991. SHO (A & E) Bedford Hosp. NHS Trust.

NICHOLAS, Keith Stuart Heswall Medical Centre, Telegraph Road, Heswall, Wirral CH60 7SG Tel: 0151 342 2230 — MB ChB 1970 Liverp.; DObst RCOG 1974.

NICHOLAS, Martin Edward Leckhampton Surgery, Lloyd Davies House, 17 Moorend Park Road, Cheltenham GL53 0LA Tel: 01242 515363 Fax: 01242 253512; Home Farm, Foxcote, Cheltenham GL54 4LP Tel: 01242 820252 Fax: 01242 820173 Email: lecksurg@btinternet.com — MB BS 1983 Lond.; MRCGP 1987; Dip. Sports Med. Scotl. 1995; DRCOG 1987. (St. George's Hospital)

NICHOLAS, Martin Paul Queen Margaret Hospital, Whitefield Road, Dunfermline KY12 0SU Tel: 01383 623623 — MB BS 1979 Lond.; FFA RCS Eng. 1984. Cons. Anaesth. Qu. Margt. Hosp. Dunfermline.

NICHOLAS, Michael 14 Hill View, Henleaze, Bristol BS9 4PZ Tel: 0117 962 3180 — MB ChB Brist. 1958 SR; MRCP Lond. 1969; FRCPsych 1986, M 1971; DPM Eng. 1964. (Bristol) Prev: Cons. Psychiat. Glenside Hosp. Bristol.

NICHOLAS, Michelle 13 Castle View, Bridgend CF31 1HL Email: michellenicholas@doctors.org.uk — BM 1992 Soton.; FRCA 1988. (Sth'mptn) Specialist Regist. (Anaes) All Wales Rot. 1997. Socs: Assoc. of Anaes. (GB & Irel.). Prev: SHO (Anaes) Swansea Hosp. 1997; SHO (Acc. & Emerg) Poole Hosp. 1994; SHO (Med. For Eld.) Salisbury Dist. Hosp. 1994.

NICHOLAS, Nicos Sotiriou 41 Main Avenue, Moor Park, Northwood HA6 2LH Tel: 01923 820001 Email: nicholas@obgyn.demon.co.uk — MB BS 1977 Lond.; BSc (Hons.) Lond. 1974, MD 1987; MRCS Eng. LRCP Lond. 1977; FRCOG 1994, M 1981; Cert. Family Plann JCC 1979. (Guy's) Cons. O & G Hillingdon Hosp.; Sen. Regist. (Obst. & Gyn.) Qu. Charlottes Hosp. & Chelsea Wom. Hosp. Lond. Socs: Blair Bell Res. Soc.; Victor Bonney Soc. (Scientif. Sect.) Roy. Soc. Med.; (Pres.) Hellenic Med. Soc. Prev: Wellcome Surg. Research Fell. Guy's Hosp. Lond.; Regist. (O & G) Guy's Hosp. Lond.; Lect. (O & G) Guy's Hosp. Lond.

NICHOLAS, Paul Lindsay The Surgery, 298 Cavendish Road, Balham, London SW12 0PL Tel: 020 8672 3331; 43 Winterbrook Road, London SE24 9HZ Tel: 020 7274 3491 — MB BS 1976 Lond.

NICHOLAS, Peter Thomas (retired) Cedarwood, 105 Highgate Lane, Lepton, Huddersfield HD8 0HQ Tel: 01484 605179 — MRCS Eng. LRCP Lond. 1953; FRCGP 1977, M 1963. Prev: Med. Off. DSS.

NICHOLAS, Philip Owen (retired) 1 Northampton Road, Orlingbury, Kettering NN14 1JF — MB ChB (Distinc. Pub. Health) Bristol 1953; FFPHM 1980, M 1972; DCH Eng. 1958; DPH Leeds 1961. Prev: Community Phys. Wirral & Chester HAs.

NICHOLAS, Mr Reginald John 28 Broom Park, Teddington TW11 9RS Tel: 020 8977 9449 Fax: 020 8977 9449; 28 Broom Park, Teddington TW11 9RS Tel: 020 8977 9449 Fax: 020 8977 9449 — MB BS 1964 Durh.; MD Newc.1969; FRCS Ed. 1976.

NICHOLLS

(King's College, Durham, UK) p/t Locum Cons. Paediat. Surg. John Radcliffe Hosp. Prev: Cons. Paediat. Surg. Roy. Commiss. Med. Centre Yanbu al Sinaiyah, Saudi Arabia; Cons. Paediat. Surg., King Khaled Hosp., Tabuk, Saudi Arabia.

NICHOLAS, Richard Charles Melbourne Street Medical Centre, 56 Melbourne Street, Leicester LE2 0AS Tel: 0116 262 2721; 304 Victoria Park Road, Leicester LE2 1XE — MRCS Eng. LRCP Lond. 1978.

NICHOLAS, Mr Richard Martin 13 Ulsterville Avenue, Belfast BT9 7AS Tel: 01232 665517 Fax: 01232 663328 Email: uss.ortho@virgin.net; 34 Myrtlefield Park, Belfast BT9 6NF — MB BCh BAO 1985 Belf.; MD Belf. 1992; BDS Lond. 1980; FRCS (Orth.) 1995; FRCS Ed. 1989; FRCSI 1989. (Qu. Univ. Belf.) Cons. Orthop. and Trauma Surg. Roy. Vict.l Hosp. Belf. & Musgrave Pk. Hosp. Belf. Socs: Brit. Orthop. Assn.; BMA; Brit. Assn. Sport & Med. Prev: Sen. Regist. Rotat. (Orthop. & Trauma Surg.) N. Irel.; Fell. Brisbane Orthop. & Sports Med. Centre; DHSS Research Fell. (Orthop. Surg.) Qu. Univ. Belf.

NICHOLAS, Richard St John 6 Kilmorey Road, St. Margarets, Twickenham TW1 1PX — MB BS 1991 Lond.

NICHOLAS, Roy Xavier Woodsley Road Surgery, 144 Woodsley Road, Leeds LS2 9LZ Tel: 0113 245 4038 Fax: 0113 244 2084; 144 Woodsley Road, Leeds LS2 9LZ Tel: 0113 245 4038 Fax: 0113 244 2084 — MB BS 1961 Ceylon; MD Ceylon 1972; MRCP (UK) 1974; DCH Ceylon 1970. (Colombo) Socs: Occupat. Med. Soc. Prev: Assoc. Specialist Infect. Dis. Seacroft Hosp. Leeds.

***NICHOLAS, Saran Gwenllian** Plas Maes y Groes, Talybont, Bangor LL57 3YD — MB BCh 1997 Wales.

NICHOLAS, Shirley Pamela Kay (retired) 1 Northampton Road, Orlingbury, Kettering NN14 1JF Tel: 01933 678340 — MB ChB 1955 Liverp.; DObst RCOG 1957.

NICHOLAS, Simon Courtenay 2 Newport Road, Barnes, London SW13 9PE Tel: 020 8748 4845; Greek Court, 14A Old Compton St, London W1D 4TJ Tel: 020 7437 1772 Fax: 020 7437 1782 — MB BChir Camb. 1966; MA Camb. 1966; MRCS Eng. LRCP Lond. 1965. (Camb. & Lond. Hosp.) Clin. Asst. (Anaesth.) Centr. Middlx. Hosp. Lond.

***NICHOLAS, Victor Selvaranjan Babapulle** 30 Whinmoor Gardens, Leeds LS14 1AF Tel: 0113 293 3558 — MB BS 1997 Lond.

NICHOLAS-PILLAI, Anthonipillai Bush Hill Park Surgery, 24 Amberley Road, Enfield EN1 2QY Tel: 020 8360 2477, 020 8364 0787; 24A Amberley Road, Enfield EN1 2QY Tel: 020 8360 2477 — MB BS Bangalore 1970; LMSSA Lond. 1980; DTM & H Lond 1981; DRCOG 1980; Dip.in Primary Care 1997. (St. Johns Medical College India) GP Enfield & Haringey Health Auth. Socs: Hon. Sec. & Treas. Enfield & Haringey BMA div; Roy. Soc. Med.; Hon. Sec. & Treas. & Exec. Mem. LMC Enfield, Haringey & Barnet LMC. Prev: Regist. (A & E) N. Middlx. Hosp. Lond.; SHO (Cardiothoracic Dept. N. Middlx. Hosp. Lond.; SHO (Orthop.) P.ss Alexandra Hosp. Harlow.

NICHOLL, Anthony David Joseph 41 Graham Road, Ipswich IP1 3QE Tel: 01473 430563 — MRCS Eng. LRCP Lond. 1977; FFA RCS Eng. 1984; FFA RCSI 1983. (St. Mary's) Cons. Anaesth. Ipswich Hosps. Socs: Assn. Anaesth. Prev: Sen. Regist. (Anaesth.) E. Anglian RHA.; Regist. Rotat. (Anaesth.) Sheff. HA; Post-Fell.sh. (Anaesth.) Killingbeck Cardiothoracic Unit Leeds.

NICHOLL, Betty, OBE (retired) 19 Runkerry Road, Bushmills BT57 8SZ Tel: 028207 32314 Email: betty.bailie@btinternet.com — MB BCh BAO 1952 Belfast; MD Belf. 1960; FRCPath 1978, M 1967. Prev: Cons. Clin. Pathologist, Belvoir Pk. Hosp. Belf.

NICHOLL, Claire Gilmour Department of Medicine for the Elderly, Box 135 Addenbrooke's Hospital, Hills Road, Cambridge CB2 2QQ Tel: 01223 217784 Fax: 01223 217783 Email: claire.nicholl@rmsexc.addenbrookes.anglox.nhs.uk; Quanea Farm, Quanea Drove, Ely CB7 5TJ Email: nicholl.wood@btinternet.com — MB BS 1979 Lond.; BSc Lond. 1976; FRCP Lond. 1994; MRCP (UK) 1982; DGM RCP Lond. 1986. (St. Mary's) Cons. Phys., Addenbrooke's Hosp. Camb.; Chief of Serv. (Med. for Elderly) Hammersmith Hosps Trust; RCP Dist. Tutor Hammersmith Hosp.; Cons. Phys. P.ss of Wales Hosp. Ely. Socs: Brit. Geriat. Soc.; Nat. Train. Comm. Prev: Sen. Lect. in Med. ICSM & Chief of Serv. for Med. for the Elderly, Hon. Cons. Phys., Hammersmith Hosps. Trust.

NICHOLL, David Joseph 109 Humphrey Middlemore Drive, Harborne, Birmingham B17 0JJ — MB ChB 1989 Birm.; MRCP (UK) 1993. Research Regist. (Neurol.) Qu. Eliz. Hosp. Birm. Prev: Regist. (Med.) Groote Schuur Hosp. Cape Town.

NICHOLL, Geoffrey McKillop Joseph (retired) Pear Tree Cottage, South Carlton, Lincoln LN1 2RH Tel: 01522 730151 — MRCS Eng. LRCP Lond. 1942; MA Camb. 1944; MRCPsych 1971; MRCGP 1956; DPM Eng. 1960. Prev: Cons. Child Psychiat. Gwynedd AHA & Lincoln.

NICHOLL, Hilda Jane McKay 20 Orby Grove, Belfast BT5 6AL Tel: 01232 704801 Email: hildanicholl@hotmail.com — MB ChB 1994 Ed. (Edinburgh) Specialist Regist. (Emerg. Med.) N Irel.

NICHOLL, Mr James Edward Kent & Sussex Hospital, Mount Ephraim, Tunbridge Wells TN4 8AT Tel: 01892 526111; 76 Warwick Park, Tunbridge Wells TN2 5EF — MB BChir 1989 Camb.; MA Camb. 1989; FRCS Eng. 1992; FRCS (Orth.) 1996. Cons. (Orthop.) Kent & Sussex hosp.

***NICHOLL, Joanne Louise** Little Orchard, Franfield Road, Buxted, Uckfield TN22 4LE — MB BS 1996 Lond.

NICHOLL, Keith The General Medical Centre, PO Box 11962, Dubai, United Arab Emirates Tel: 00 971 43495959 Fax: 00 971 43495634 Email: knicholl@associated-clinics.com; The Old Studio, West Green, Crail, Anstruther KY10 3RD Tel: 01333 450574 — MB ChB 1980 Dundee; DCH RCPS Glas. 1986. (Univ. Dundee) Paediat. Specialist Gen. Med. Centre Dubai, UAE/ Med. Director. Socs: Roy. Coll. Paediat. & Child Health; Fell. of Roy. Soc. of Trop. Med. and Hygene.; Emirate Med. Assn. Prev: Regist. (Paediat.) Ninewells Hosp. Med. Sch. Dundee.

NICHOLL, Michael Eakin Lodge Health, 20 Lodge Manor, Coleraine BT52 1JX Tel: 028 7034 4494 Fax: 028 7032 1759; Iniskeel, 7 O'Hara Drive, Portstewart BT55 7PD — MB BCh BAO 1982 Belf.; MB BCh Belf. 1982; MRCGP 1986; DCH Dub. 1985; DRCOG 1984. Socs: BMA.

NICHOLL, Mr Philip Thomas Flat 2, 18 Vernon Road, Birmingham B16 9SH — MB BCh BAO 1987 Belf.; FRCS Ed. 1991. Research Regist. (Vasc. Surg.) Roy. Free Hosp. Lond.

NICHOLL, Raymond Stuart (retired) 27 Throxenby Lane, Newby, Scarborough YO12 5HN Tel: 01723 503449 — MRCS Eng. LRCP Lond. 1957. Prev: Clin. Asst. (Geriat.) St. Mary's Hosp. ScarBoro.

NICHOLL, Richard Martin Northwick Park Hospital, Northwest London Hospitals NHS Trusts, Harrow HA1 3VJ Tel: 020 869 2642 Fax: 020 8889 2927 Email: drnicholl@aol.com — MB ChB 1983 Birm.; MRCP (UK) 1990; MRCPCH 1996; DCH RCP Lond. 1989; FRCPCH 1993. Cons. Neonatologist N.wick Pk. Hosp. Harrow. Socs: Neonat. Soc.; Paediat. Research Soc.; Brit. Assn. of Perinatal Med. Prev: Lect. (Neonat.) & Sen. Regist. King's Coll. Hosp. Lond.

NICHOLL, Robert Martin (retired) 32 Deramore Drive, Malone Road, Belfast BT9 5JR Tel: 028 9066 9684 Email: robertnicholl@ukgateway.net — MD 1965 Belf.; MB BCh BAO 1952; FFA RCSI 1971; FFA RCS Eng. 1958. Prev: Cons. Anaesth. Roy. Vict. Hosp. Belf.

NICHOLL, Stuart 56 Houlgate Way, Axbridge BS26 2BY — MB BS 1995 Lond.

NICHOLLES, Maia — MB BS 1992 Lond.; BSc London 1989; DRCOG 1995; MRCGP 1996. (Royal Free) GP Princip.

NICHOLLS, Agnes Mary Hinshelwood 45 Middle Park Road, Selly Oak, Birmingham B29 4BH — MB ChB 1965 Birm.; DA Eng. 1967. Staff Grade (Anaesth.) Roy. Orthop. Hosp. Birm.

NICHOLLS, Anne West Suffolk Hospital, Hardwick Lane, Bury St Edmunds IP33 2QZ Tel: 01284 713440 Fax: 01284 712519; The Old Rectory, Bradfield St George, Bury St Edmunds IP30 0DH Tel: 01284 386551 — MB BS Lond. 1962; FRCP Lond. 1983, M 1969; MRCS Eng. LRCP Lond. 1962. (St. Mary's) Cons. Rheum. & Rehabil. W. Suff. Hosp. Socs: Fell. Roy. Soc. Med.; Brit. Soc. Rheum. Prev: Sen. Regist. (Rheum. & Gen. Med.) W.m. Hosp., Chelsea & Kensington Hosps. Gp. & Kennedy Inst. Rheum.; Regist. (Med.) Norf. & Norwich Hosp.

NICHOLLS, Anne Patricia (retired) 41 Dry Hill Park Road, Tonbridge TN10 3BU Tel: 01732 354009 — MB BS 1959 Lond.; MRCS Eng. LRCP Lond. 1958. Prev: GP Tonbridge.

NICHOLLS, Anthony Jeffery Stephen Pinn Medical Centre, 8 Eastcote Road, Pinner HA5 1HF Tel: 020 8866 5766 Fax: 020 8429 0251 — MB BS 1968 Lond.; MRCP (UK) 1972; MRCS Eng. LRCP Lond. 1968; MRCGP 1983; DCH Eng. 1971; DObst RCOG 1970.

NICHOLLS

(Westm.) Prev: SHO (Med.) Nottm. City Hosp.; SHO Cardio-Thoracic Unit Hosp. Sick Childr. Gt. Ormond St. Lond.; Paediat. Regist. Roy. Free Hosp. & Edgware Gen. Hosp. Lond.

NICHOLLS, Anthony Julian Royal Devon and Exeter Hospital, Barrack Road, Exeter EX2 5DW Tel: 01392 402535 Fax: 01392 402527; Laurel Cottage, Elmside, Exeter EX4 6LN Tel: 01392 250075 Email: ajnich@eurobell.co.uk — MB BS 1975 Lond.; FRCP Ed. 1999; FRCP Lond. 1992; MRCP (UK) 1977. (Guy's) Cons. Phys. & Nephrol. Roy. Devon & Exeter Healthcare NHS Trust. Socs: Renal Assn.; Eur. Dialysis & Transpl. Assn.; Brit. Transpl. Soc. Prev: Sen. Regist. (Nephrol.) Sheff. AHA; Lect. (Med.) Univ. Aberd.; Ho. Phys. Guy's Hosp. Lond.

NICHOLLS, Barry John Langholm, 10 Church St., Bishops Lydeard, Taunton TA4 3AT — MB ChB 1977 Liverp.; FFA RCS Eng. 1983.

NICHOLLS, Charles Sebastian Rose Cottage, 217 Whitchurch Road, Tavistock PL19 9DQ Tel: 01822 617684 Email: nichollstavistock@compuserve.com — MB BCh 1989 Wales; MRCGP 1997; DFFP 1997.

NICHOLLS, Christopher William Camelot, 8 Tromode Close, Douglas IM2 5PE Tel: 01623 452900, 01624 662644 — MB ChB 1974 Liverpool. (Liverpool) G.P. Locum; M.O. To D.H.S.S. Socs: Isle Of Man Med. Soc. Prev: GP Douglas, Isle of Man.

NICHOLLS, Cicely Ruth Camelot, Tromode Close, Douglas IM2 5PE Tel: 01624 662644 Email: chrisnicholls@im25pe.freeserve.co.uk — MB ChB 1967 Liverp.; BSc Liverp. 1964. (Liverp.) Med. Adviser I. of Man Civil Serv. Commiss.; Adjudicating Off. Manx DHSS. Socs: I. of Man Med. Soc.

NICHOLLS, Dasha Elizabeth Department of Psychological Medicine, Great Ormond Street Hospital, Great Ormond St., London WC1N 3JH Tel: 020 7829 8679 Email: d.nicholls@ich.ucl.ac.uk; 27C Packington Street, London N1 8QB — MB BS 1988 Lond.; MRCPsych 1993.

NICHOLLS, Professor David Paul Royal Victoria Hospital, Belfast BT12 6BA Tel: 028 9089 4951 Fax: 028 9026 3168 Email: dp.nicholls@royal hospitals.n-i.nhs.uk; 2 Printshop Road, Templepatrick, Ballyclare BT39 0HZ Tel: 028 9443 3351 Email: dpnicholls@compuserve.com — MB ChB 1969 Manch; MD Manch. 1984, MB ChB 1969; FRCP Lond. 1991; MRCP (UK) 1974; DSc (QUB) 1999. (manchester) Cons. (Phys.) Roy. Vict. Hosp. Belf.; Hon. Prof. Med. Qu.s Univ.Belf. Prev: Sen. Regist. (Cardiol.) Belf. City Hosp.; Regist. (Med.) Tameside Gen. Hosp. Ashton-under-Lyne; Tutor (Med.) Hope Hosp. Salford.

NICHOLLS, David Ronald The Health Centre, Cakeham Road, East Wittering, Chichester PO20 8BH Tel: 01243 673434 Fax: 01243 672563; The Gables, Tangmere Road, Shopwhyke, Chichester PO20 6BL — BM BCh 1971 Oxf.; MA; DObst RCOG 1975; DCH Eng. 1974. Prev: Trainee GP Chichester VTS; Ho. Off. (Med.) Roy. United Hosp. Bath; Ho. Surg. Radcliffe Infirm. Oxf.

NICHOLLS, Elizabeth Anne St Clement's Surgery, 24 Marshland Street, Terrington St. Clement, King's Lynn PE34 4NE Tel: 01553 828475/827051 Fax: 01553 827594 — MB BCh 1985 Wales; DRCOG 1990.

***NICHOLLS, Emma Lucy** 35 Barnhill, Pinner HA5 2SY — MB BS 1998 Lond.; MB BS Lond 1998.

NICHOLLS, Fiona Michelle Department of Anesthesiology, University of Michigan, Ann Arbor MI 48109, USA Tel: 313 936 4235 Fax: 313 936 9091; 84 Waverley Road, Enfield EN2 7AQ Tel: 020 8367 5581 — MB BS 1989 Lond.; FRCA Lond. 1996. (Lond. Hosp.) Specialist Regist. (Anaesth.) St. Mary's Hosp. Lond.; Vis. Instruct. (Anesth.) Univ. Michigan, USA. Prev: SHO (Anaesth.) Roy. Lond. Hosp. & Harold Wood Hosp.; SHO (Gen. Med.) Maidstone Hosp.

NICHOLLS, Francis Ambrose John Highdown Surgery, 1 Highdown Avenue, Worthing BN13 1PU Tel: 01903 265656 Fax: 01903 830450; 7 Modena Road, Hove BN3 5QF — MB BS 1988 Lond. GP Highdown Surg. Worthing; Clin. Asst. St. Barnabas Hospice Worthing. Socs: BMA & Med. Defence Union. Prev: Trainee GP St. Lawrence Surg.; SHO (c/o the Elderly, O & G, Palliat. Med. & Padiat.) Worthing VTS; SHO (Orthop., A & E) Roy. Sussex Co. Hosp. Brighton.

NICHOLLS, Gail Catherine (Scott) Rosebank Surgery, Pointer Court, Ashton Rd, Lancaster LA1 4JS Tel: 01524 842284 — MB ChB 1997 Manch.; BSc St. And. 1994. (St. And. and Manch.) GP

Regist. Lancaster. Socs: Assoc. of CCGP. Prev: SHO. (Paediat.) New Zealand.; SHO. (A&E.) Lancaster.; SHO in Obst. & Gyn., Lancaster.

NICHOLLS, Mr Guy Department Paediatric Surgery, Bristol Royal Hospital for Sick Children, St. Micheal's Hill, Bristol BS2 8BJ Tel: 0117 921 5411; Flat 2, 13 Dowry Square, Clifton, Bristol B58 4SL — MB ChB 1986 Birm.; BSc Birm. 1983, MB ChB 1986; FRCS Ed. 1990; MD Birm. 1997; FRCS (Paed. Surg.) 1998. Cons. in Paediat. Surg. & Urol., Bristol Childr.'s Hosp.; Hon. Clin. Lect., Univ. of Bristol.

NICHOLLS, Harriet Anne 3 Mount Drive, Park St., St Albans AL2 2NP — MB BChir 1993 Camb.; FRCA 1996. (Camb.) Regist. (Anaesth.) The Middlx. Hosp. Prev: SHO (ITU) Nat. Hosp. Neurol. & Neurosurg.; SHO (Anaesth.) Watford Gen. Hosp.

NICHOLLS, Heather Meddygfa'r Llan, Church Surgery, Portland Street, Aberystwyth SY23 2DX Tel: 01970 624855 Fax: 01970 625824; Llys Terfyn, Taliesin, Machynlleth SY20 8JR Tel: 01970 832251 — MB BCh 1983 Wales; DRCOG 1987. GP Princip. Prev: SCMO E. Dyfed HA Aberystwyth Dyfed.

NICHOLLS, Hedley John Leslie Blackbarrow, Norton-sub-Hamdon, Taunton Tel: 0193 588236 — MB ChB 1955 Bristol; MRCS Eng. LRCP Lond. 1955; DObst RCOG 1957. (Bristol) Prev: Ho. Phys. Frenchay Hosp. Bristol; Ho. Surg. MusGr. Pk. Hosp. Taunton.

NICHOLLS, Ivy (retired) 115 Cowley Lane, Chapeltown, Sheffield S35 1SU Tel: 0114 246 6109 — MB ChB 1941 Birm.; BA Open 1981, BA Hons. 1986.

NICHOLLS, James Eric Woodlands Surgery, 55 Southend Road, Hockley SS5 4PZ Tel: 01702 202514 Fax: 01702 204110; The Myrtles, 215 Hockley Road, Rayleigh SS6 8BH Tel: 01268 777872 Fax: 01268 779333 Email: jamienicholls@compuserve.com — MB BS 1974 Lond.; DRCOG 1976. (Lond. Hosp.) GP Princip.; GP Tutor S.end-on-Sea.

NICHOLLS, Janet Mary Epsom General Hospital, Dorking Road, Epsom KT18 7EG Tel: 01372 735261 — MB BS 1978 Lond.; FRCP Lond. 1996; MRCP (UK) 1982; T(M) (Paed) 1991. Cons. Paediat. Epsom Gen. Hosp. Epsom.

NICHOLLS, Jennifer Burnfield Medical Practice, Harris Road, Inverness IV2 3PF Tel: 01463 220077 Fax: 01463 714588 — MB ChB 1974 Dundee; Dip Palliat Med 1994 Cardiff; MRCGP 1991 UK. Assoc. Adviser in Gen. Pract., N. of Scotl. Inst. for Postgrad. Med. & Dent. Educat., Railmore Hosp., Inverness. Socs: BMA; Assn. for Palliat. Med.

NICHOLLS, Joanna Lyndall Mary Highfield, 20 South Road, Newton Abbot TQ12 1HQ — MB BS 1985 Lond.; MRCGP 1990.

NICHOLLS, John Alastair James Tadcaster Medical Centre, Crab Garth, Tadcaster LS24 8HD Tel: 01937 530082; Manor Close, High St, Bramham, Wetherby LS23 6QQ Tel: 01937 844850 — MB ChB 1976 Leeds; DRCOG 1978. Socs: Brit. Soc. Med. & Dent. Hypn. Prev: Trainee GP Carlisle VTS; SHO (Gyn.) Hosp. Wom. Leeds; SHO (Obst.) Matern. Hosp. Leeds.

NICHOLLS, Mr John Charles Hemel Hempstead Hospital, Hemel Hempstead HP2 4AD Tel: 01442 213141 Fax: 01442 287405 Email: john_nicholls_1@hotmail.com; Tel: 01494 758 369 — MB BS 1963 Lond; FRCS Eng. 1969; MRCS Eng. LRCP Lond. 1963. (Char. Cross) Cons. Surg. Hemel Hempstead Hosp. Socs: Fell. Assn. Surg.; Brit. Assn. Surgic. Oncol.; BMA. Prev: Cons. Surg. Govt. of Seychelles; Med. Dir. St. Albans & Hemel Hempstead NHS Trust.

NICHOLLS, Jonathan Simon David Oxford Radcliffe Hospitals NHS Trust, Horton Hospital, Dept of Obst. & Gyn., Banbury OX16 9AL Email: jonathan.nicholls@orh.nhs.uk; Scotland Mount, Round Close Road, Banbury OX15 5NT Tel: 01608 737348 — MD 2000; MB BS Lond. 1985; MRCOG 1994. (Westm.) Cons. (Obst. & Gyn.) Horton Hosp., Banbury; Cons. (Obs & Gyn) John Radcliffe Hosp., Oxf. Socs: Brit. Soc. of Gyn. Endoscopy; Oxf. Medico-Legal Soc.; Bristol Obst. & Gyn. Soc. Prev: Sen. Regist. (Obst. & Gyn.) St Michaels Hosp. Bristol; Sen. Regist. (Obst. & Gyn.) S.mead Hosp. Bristol; Clin. Research Fell. Dept. Clin. Endocrinol. St. Mary's Hosp. Med. Sch. Lond.

NICHOLLS, Judith Elizabeth Ablewell House, 30 Birmingham Road, Walsall WS1 2LT Tel: 01922 775000 Fax: 01922 775002 — MB ChB 1986 Birm.; MRCPsych 1990. p/t Cons. (Child & Adolesc. Psychiat.) Walsall Community Health Trust. Prev: Sen. Regist. (Child Adolesc. Psychiat.) W. Midl. Rotat.

NICHOLLS, Kate Charlotte Keel Health Centre, Seymour Road, Easton, Bristol BS5 0UA Tel: 0117 951 2244 Fax: 0117 951 2373;

3 Birchall Road, Bristol BS6 7TW — MB ChB 1978 Bristol; MRCGP 1983; DRCOG 1981. Socs: Roy. Coll. Gen. Pract.

NICHOLLS, Kevin Roy Shelton Hospital, Bicton Heath, Shrewsbury SY3 8DN Tel: 01743 261246; Bray's Tenement, Marton, Welshpool SY21 8JY — MB ChB 1988 Birm.; BSc (Hons.) Birm. 1985; MRCPsych 1995. Sen. Regist. Profess. Unit Stoke-on-Trent; Cons. Gen. Psych.

NICHOLLS, Kit-Mei Hebburn Health Centre, Campbell Park Road, Hebburn NE31 2SP Tel: 0191 483 5533 Fax: 0191 428 1826; 7 Townhead, Slaley, Hexham NE47 0AT — MB ChB 1989 Dundee. GP Hebburn, Tyne & Wear.

***NICHOLLS, Marcus John** Heath End Cottage, Heath End, Berkhamsted HP4 3UE — MB ChB 1997 Manch.

NICHOLLS, Margot Jane — MB BS 1990 Lond.; DRCOG 1992; MRCGP 1994. (UCMHMS) Specialist Regist. (Pub. Health.), Croydon Health Auth. Prev: Toxic. Reg. NPIS, Lond.; GP Reg. S. Harrow, N.wick Pk. Hosp. VTS.

NICHOLLS, Martyn John The Surgery, 59 Sevenoaks Road, Orpington BR6 9JN Tel: 01689 820159; 29 Goldfinch Close, Chelsfield, Orpington BR6 6NF Tel: 01689 860639 — MB ChB 1984 Manch.

NICHOLLS, Maxim Daniel William 23 Alan Drive, Barnet EN5 2PP — MB BS 1993 Lond.

NICHOLLS, Michael John (retired) 28 The Hamlet, Leek Wootton, Warwick CV35 7QW — MB BS 1959 Lond.; MRCS Eng. LRCP Lond. 1959; DObst RCOG 1962. Prev: Sen. Part. Or Nicholls and Partners S.ampton.

NICHOLLS, Michael William Newbery (retired) Creekside, 28 Greenacres, Birdham, Chichester PO20 7HL Tel: 01243 512937 Fax: 01243 511087 Email: michael.nicholls@which.net — MB BS Lond. 1957; MRCS Eng. LRCP Lond. 1955; FRCPath 1980, M 1968. Director of Finance Fell.ship of PostGrad. Med. Lond.; Med. Laborat. Techinicians Bd., Counc. of Professions Supplm.ary to Med. (Roy. Coll.'s Nominee); Trustee Tushinskaya Hosp. Trust Lond. Prev: Dean Postgrad. Med. (SE Thames) Univ. Lond. & Asst. Dir. Brit. Postgrad. Med. Federat. Univ. Lond.

NICHOLLS, Peter Eric Department of Histopathology, Royal Shrewsbury Hospital, Shrewsbury SY3 8XQ Tel: 01743 261168 Fax: 01743 355963 Email: pen@rshhis.demon.co.uk; 36 Roman Road, Shrewsbury SY3 9AT Email: pe.nicholls@virgin.net — MB BS 1969 Lond.; MRCS Eng. LRCP Lond. 1969; FRCPath 1989, M 1977. (Guy's) Cons. (Histopath.) Roy. Shrewsbury Hosp. Socs: Acad. Path. & Assn. Clin. Path.; Internat. Acad. Path.; Assn. Clin. Pathol. Prev: Lect. (Histopath.) W.m. Med. Sch. Lond.; SHO (Path.) Miller Gen. Hosp. Greenwich; Regist. (Clin. Path.) Guy's Hosp. Lond.

NICHOLLS, Peter Grahame 16 Woodlands Close, Denby Dale, Huddersfield HD8 8RH — MB BS 1987 Lond.

NICHOLLS, Professor Ralph John 149 Harley Street, London W1N 2DE Tel: 020 7935 4444 Fax: 020 7486 0665; 24 St Marks Crescent, London NW1 7TU — MB BChir Camb. 1968; BA Camb. 1964, MChir 1978; FRCS Eng. 1972; FRCS Glas. 1993. Cons. Surg. St. Marks Hosps. Lond.; Edr. Colorectal Dis.; Clin. Dir. St. Marks Hosp.; Sec Div. of ColoProctol. UEMS. Socs: Brit. Soc. Gastroenterol.; (Exec.) Assn. Coloproctol.; Mem. d'Honneur Assn. Fr. de Chirurgie. Prev: Cons. Surg. St. Thos. Hosp. Lond.; Sen. Lect. (Surg. Oncol.) St. Bart. Hosp. Med. Coll. Lond.; Clin. Asst. Univ. Heidelberg.

***NICHOLLS, Robert David** 31 Weald Way, Reigate RH2 7RG — MB ChB 1998 Manch.; MB ChB Manch 1998.

NICHOLLS, Sarah Department of Sexual Health, Princess Alice Bay Hospital, Carew Road, Eastbourne BN21 2AX; Ave. House, The Avenue, Eastbourne BN21 3XY — MB BS 1991 Lond.

NICHOLLS, Sarah Louise 16 Woodlands Close, Denby Dale, Huddersfield HD8 8RH — MB BS 1990 Lond.

NICHOLLS, Stuart Warren 53 Westbourne Gardens, Hove BN3 5PN; Department of Paediatrics, Worthing Hospital, Lyndhurst Road, Worthing BN11 2DH — MB BCh 1984 Wales; FRCP Edin.; FRCP Edin.; FRCPCH. (Cardiff) Cons. (Paediat.) Worthing Hosp.

NICHOLLS, Susanna Jane Leicester General Hospital NHS Trust, Gwendoline Road, Leicester LE5 4PW; Chinneys, Creeton Road, Little Bytham, Grantham NG33 4SU Tel: 01780 410684 — MB ChB 1993 Sheff.; BA (Hons.) Wales 1982.

NICHOLLS-VAN VLIET, Maria Anna Theresia Winstanley Drive Surgery, 138 Winstanley Drive, Leicester LE3 1PB Tel: 0116 285 8435 Fax: 0116 275 5416; 8 Farley Road, Leicester LE2 3LD Tel: 0116 270 3744 — Artsexamen 1978 Rotterdam; PhD Nijmegen 1985. (Rotterdam) p/t Gen. Pract.

NICHOLS, David Borve Medical Practice, Borve, Isle of Lewis HS2 0RS Tel: 01851 850282 Fax: 01851 860333 Email: davenichols@borvelewis.fsnet.com; 14 Port of Ness, Isle of Lewis HS2 0XA Tel: 01851 810794 — MB ChB 1974 Glas. Prev: GP E. Kilbride; Regist. (Anaesth.) Glas. Roy. Infirm. & Roy. Alexandra Infirm.; SHO Paisley Matern. Hosp.

NICHOLS, David Martin Department Radiodiagnosis, Raigmore Hospital, Inverness IV2 3UJ Tel: 01463 704000 — MB ChB 1974 Aberd.; FRCS Ed. 1997; FRCR 1983; FFR RCSI 1981; MRCP (UK) 1978; FRCP Ed. 1990; FRCP (C) 1982; DMRD Aberd. 1979. (Aberdeen) Cons. Radiol. Raigmore Hosp. Inverness.; Sen. Lect. Radiol. Univ. Aberd. Prev: Radiol. Vancouver Gen. Hosp. & Asst. Prof., Univ. Brit. Columbia; Sen. Regist. (Diag. Radiol.) Aberd. Hosps.

NICHOLS, Elizabeth Anne, Surg. Lt.-Cdr. RN 25 Valletort Road, Plymouth PL1 5PH — MB BS 1990 Lond.; DRCOG; MRCGP. (Guy's Hospital) Roy. Navy.

NICHOLS, Mr Geoffrey James Park Lane Surgery, 2 Park Lane, Allestree, Derby DE22 2DS Tel: 01332 552461 Fax: 01332 541500 — BM 1985 Soton.; FRCS Ed. 1990; T(GP) 1994. Prev: SHO (O & G) Trafford Gen. Hosp.; SHO & Regist. (Gen. Surg.) Trafford & N. Manch. Gen. Hosp.; SHO (A & E & Orthop. Surg.) Hope Hosp. Salford.

***NICHOLS, Jennifer Anne** 64 Holly Avenue, Jesmond, Newcastle upon Tyne NE2 2QA — MB BS 1997 Newc.

NICHOLS, John Anthony Alvan Fairlands Medical Centre, Fairlands Avenue, Worplesdon, Guildford GU3 3NA Tel: 01483 594250 Fax: 01483 598767; 60 Manor Way, Onslow Village, Guildford GU2 7RR Tel: 01483 564967 Email: drjaan.com@aol — MB ChB 1967 Liverp.; MRCGP 1973; DCH Eng. 1972; DObst RCOG 1970. (Liverp.) Socs: Brit. Soc. Allergy & Environm. Med. Prev: Regist. (Gen. Med.) St. Luke's Hosp. Guildford; SHO (O & G & Paediat.) St. Luke's Hosp. Guildford; Ho. Phys. Sefton Gen. Hosp. Liverp.

NICHOLS, John Bowes (retired) Greenways, Moor End, Stibbard, Fakenham NR21 0EJ Tel: 01328 829225 Email: jbnichols@ukonline.co.uk — MB Camb. 1958, BChir 1957; DObst RCOG 1960. Prev: Regist. (Med.), Ho. Surg. & Ho. Phys. St. Bart. Hosp.

NICHOLS, Kathleen Clare The Surgery, 18 Fouracre Road, Bristol BS16 6PG Tel: 0117 970 2033 — MB ChB 1975 Bristol; DRCOG 1979.

NICHOLS, Marion Jane The Parks Surgery, 116 Kings Rd, Herne Bay, Canterbury CT65RE Tel: 01227 771474, 01926 513060 Email: cm.dallaway@talk21.com, marionn@gp-g82119.nhs.uk; 11 Juniper Close, Canterbury CT1 3LL Tel: 01227 455558 Email: marionnichols@btinternet.com — MB ChB 1995 Bristol; BSc (Hons.) Bradford 1985. (Bristol) GP Princip., The Pk. Surg., Herne Bay. Prev: GP Locum Whitstable Med. Pract.

NICHOLS, Mary Elizabeth 4 Caraden Crt., Hawkins Close, Plymouth PL6 6LL — MB ChB 1989 Manch. GP Yelverton. Prev: SHO (A & E) Derriford Hosp. Plymouth.

NICHOLS, Mary Patricia ; 76A Norwich Road, Wymondham NR18 0SZ Email: mary.nichols@bigfoot.com — MB BS 1982 Lond.; MSc 1999 (Dist) Oxf. Brookes Univ.; Cert Med Educat 1999 Dundee Univ.; MRCGP 1986; DFFP 1993; DRCOG 1987; Cert. Family Plann. JCC 1987; DGM RCP Lond. 1985. (Roy. Free) GP Non-Princip.; Educat.al Facilitator Norwich PCT. Socs: BMA; AMEE. Prev: Trainee GP Oxf. VTS.

NICHOLS, Mr Paul Henry 3 Laser Close, Warsash, Southampton SO31 9AZ Tel: 01489 570329 Email: paul_nichols@virgin.net — MB ChB 1989 Leeds; FRCS (Eng.) 1995; MD Leeds 1999. (Leeds) Specialist Regist. (Gen. Surg.) Wessex. Socs: Surgic. Research Soc.; Assn. Coloproct.

NICHOLS, Paul Kenneth Trevor Royal Gwent Hospital, Newport NP20 2UB — MB BCh 1982 Wales; FFA RCS Eng. 1987. Cons. Anaesth. Intens. Ther. Unit. Roy. Gwent Hosp. Prev: Sen. Regist. (Anaesth.) W. Glam. HA.

NICHOLS, Roger William Townsend Station Road Surgery, 69 Station Road, Sidcup DA15 7DS Tel: 020 8309 0201 Fax: 020 8309

NICHOLS

9040; 11 Buckingham Drive, Chislehurst BR7 6TB — MB BS 1975 Lond.; FRCS Eng. 1980; MRCS Eng. LRCP Lond. 1975. (Guy's)

NICHOLS, Roy Reginald William 1 Barrington Close, Earley, Reading RG6 1ET Tel: 0118 966 1386 — MRCS Eng. LRCP Lond. 1945. (Guy's)

NICHOLSBY, Diane 5 Greenbank Road, Radcliffe, Manchester M26 4FR Tel: 0161 723 3791 — MB ChB 1989 Manch.; BSc St. And. 1986; MRCGP 1993; DRCOG 1993; DFFP 1992. Prev: GP Bolton; Trainee GP Radcliffe; SHO (O & G) Hope Hosp. Salford & St. Mary's Hosp. Manch.

NICHOLSON, Agnes Frances Barrhead Health Centre, 203 Main Street, Barrhead G78 1HG Tel: 0141 880 6161 Fax: 0141 881 7036; 11 Letham Drive, Glasgow G43 2SL Tel: 0141 637 2410 — MB ChB 1968 Glas. (Glas.)

NICHOLSON, Alexander Barnes Shropshire & Mid Wales Hospice, Bicton Heath, Shrewsbury SY3 8HS Tel: 01743 236565 Fax: 01743 261512 — MB BS 1993 Newc.; DRCOG 1995; DCH 1997; MRCGP 1998; JCPTGP Cert. Of Equiv. Exp. 1998; Dip Palliat Med 2000. (Newc. upon Tyne) Specialist Regist. in Palliat. Med., W. Midl.s Rotat. Socs: Assn. for Palliat. Med.; Fell. of Roy. Soc. of Med. Prev: GP Princ. Wylam, N.umber. 1999; Locum cons. In Pall. Med, St. Benedicts Hospice, Sunderland 2000.

NICHOLSON, Amanda Claire Dept. of Epidemiology & Public Health, University College London, 1-19 Torrington Place, London WC1E 7HB; 12 Red Lane Cottages, Red Lane, Oxted RH8 0RU — MB BS 1987 Lond.; MB BS (Hons.) (Distinc. Surg.) Lond. 1987; MSc (Epidemiol.) Lond. 1992; MA Camb. 1988. Stud. Cor-ord. (Epidemiol. & Pub. Health) Univ. Coll. & Middlx. Sch. Med. Lond. Prev: Research Asst. (Epidemiol.) Med. Coll. St. Bart. Hosp. Lond.; SHO (Histopath.) St. Bart. Hosp. Lond.

NICHOLSON, Andrew Gordon 8 Strouden Avenue, Bournemouth BH8 9HT — MB BS 1987 Lond.

NICHOLSON, Anthony Andrew 75 Southfield, Hessle HU13 0EX Tel: 01482 645840 Fax: 01482 649938 Email: tonynick@tonynick.demon.co.uk — MB ChB 1983 Sheff.; FRCR 1988. (Sheffield) Cons. Radiol. Hull Roy. Infirm. Socs: Brit. Soc. Interven.al Radiol. (Vice Pres. 1997-1999, Pres. 1999-2001); Soc. Cardiovasc. & Interven.al Radiolog. Soc. of N. Amer.; Fell.Cardiovasc. & Interven.al Soc. Europe. Prev: Sen. Regist. Univ. Hosp. Wales Cardiff; SHO (Gen. Med.) Roy. Hallamsh. Hosp. Sheff.

NICHOLSON, Professor Anthony Norman, OBE Human Physiology and Aerospace Medicine, Kings College, London Tel: 020 7848 6313, 020 7848 6341; Applewood Island, Steep, Petersfield GU32 1AE Tel: 01730 233863 Fax: 01730 260610 — MB ChB 1957 Birm.; PhD Birm. 1964, DSc 1980; FRCP Ed. 1986; FRCP Lond. 1998; FFOM 1997; FRAeS 1992; FRCPath 1978; 1996 MD (hc) Russian Academy of Sci. (Birm.) Prof. Aviat. Med. King's Coll. Lond.; Vis. Prof. Med. Imperial. Coll. Lond; Chairm. of Trustees, UK Confidential Human Factors Incident Reporting Progr.; Trustee, Farnbouough Air Sci. Trust. Socs: Brit. Pharmacol. Soc.; Liveryman Soc. of Apoth.; Freeman Guild of Air Pilots and Air Navigators. Prev: Commandant RAF Inst.and Sch. Aviat. Med., FarnBoro.; Cons. Adviser in Aviat. Med., RAF; Vis. Prof. Physiol. Univ. Lond.

NICHOLSON, Anthony Paul Rosewood House, 200 Abbotswell Crescent, Aberdeen AB12 3DD — MB ChB 1958 Aberd. (Aberd.) Med. Off. Stud. Health Aberd. Univ. Prev: Asst. MOH Aberd.sh. CC.

NICHOLSON, Arthur Robert (retired) Clifton Cross, Asbourne DE6 2DH Tel: 0161 432 7382 — MB ChB 1965 Sheff.; MRCGP 1972; DObst RCOG 1967. Prev: Ho. Phys. Profess. Cardiovasc. Unit & Ho. Surg. Urol. Unit City Gen.

NICHOLSON, Basil Sonoma, Valley, Holyhead LL65 3EY — MB ChB 1944 Manch.; MFCM 1973; DTM & H Eng. 1948; DPH Lond. 1953. (Manch.) Asst. Dir. Med. Dept. Brit. Counc. Prev: Princip. Asst. Sen. Med. Off. (Computer Servs.) Birm. RHB; Sen. Med. Off. Glos. CC; Sen. Leprosy Off. Nigeria (W. Region).

NICHOLSON, Catherine Agnes Grove Road Surgery, 25 Grove Road, Borehamwood WD6 5DX Tel: 020 8953 2444 Fax: 020 8207 4060; 104 Aldenham Road, Bushey, Watford WD23 2EX Tel: 01923 229905 — MB BS 1978 Lond.; MRCGP 1983; DRCOG 1981.

***NICHOLSON, Claire Louise** St Luags, 2 West Munro Drive, Helensburgh G84 9AA — MB ChB 1998 Glas.; MB ChB Glas 1998.

NICHOLSON, David Andrew Ingledene, Richmond Green, Bowdon, Altrincham WA14 2UB — BM BS 1983 Nottm.; BMedSci 1981; BMedSci 1981; FRCR 1990. Cons. Radiol. Hope Hosp.

Manch.; Sen. Research Fell. Hammersmith Hosp. Lond. Prev: Sen. Regist. (Diagn. Radiol.) Manch.; Lect. (Anat.) Univ. Hosp. Nottm.; SHO (Surg.) Addenbrooke's Hosp. Camb.

NICHOLSON, David George Garden Lane Medical Centre, 19 Garden Lane, Chester CH1 4EN Tel: 01244 346677 Fax: 01244 310094 — MB ChB 1989 Sheff.

NICHOLSON, Elizabeth (retired) 48 Commoor Road, Whickham, Newcastle upon Tyne NE16 4PU Tel: 0191 488 7165 — MB BS Durh. 1950. Prev: Ho. Phys. & Ho. Surg. (Accid. Room) Roy. Vict. Infirm. Newc.

NICHOLSON, Elizabeth Mary (retired) abbots Leigh Manor, Manor Rd, Abbots Leigh, Bristol BS8 3RP Tel: 0117 374669 Email: 10664.3657@compuserve.com — MB BS 1952 Lond.; MD Bristol 1982; DA Eng. 1959. Prev: Assoc. Specialist (Thoracic Med.) Bristol.

NICHOLSON, Felicity 13 Tidenham Gardens, Park Hill, Croydon CR0 5UT — MB BS 1984 Lond.; BSc (1st cl. Hons.) Lond. 1981, MB BS 1984; MRCPath 1991; FRCPath 1999. Forens. Med. Examr. for Metrop. Police; Cons. in Travel Med. Trailfinders Immunisation Centre Lond. Socs: BMA; Medico-legal Soc.; Assn. of Police Surg.s. Prev: Sen. Regist. (Virol.) St. Thos. Hosp. Lond.; Regist. (Microbiol.) St. Thos. Hosp. Lond.; SHO Rotat. (Path.) & Ho. Phys. St. Thos. Hosp. Lond.

NICHOLSON, Geoffrey (retired) Ravenscar, 99 Broadbottom Road, Mottram-in-Longdendale, Hyde SK14 6JA Tel: 01457 763653 — MB ChB 1971 Birm.; BSc (Hons.) (Physiol.) Birm. 1968, MD 1978, MB ChB; MRCP (UK) 1974. Prev: Cons. Phys. Roy. Oldham Hosp.

NICHOLSON, George 25 Witbank Road, Darlington DL3 6SB — MB BS 1983 Lond.

NICHOLSON, Gertrude Maggie (retired) 6 Pelham Gardens, Folkestone CT20 2LF — MRCS Eng. LRCP Lond. 1927.

NICHOLSON, Gillian Marilyn 55 Sleepy Valley, Richhill, Armagh BT61 9LH Tel: 01762 871520 — MB BCh BAO 1988 Belf.; MB BCh Belf. 1988; MRCGP 1993; DCCH RCGP 1994; Cert. Adv. Family Plann. JCC 1993; Cert. Family Plann. JCC 1992; Cert. Prescribed Equiv. Exp. 1993; DRCOG 1992. Prev: SHO (Psychiat.) Holyell Antrim; SHO (O & G) S. Tyrone Hosp. Dungannon; SHO (Paediat.) Craigavon Area Hosp. Portadown.

NICHOLSON, Graeme, Surg. Lt.-Cdr. RN c/o Sickbay, HMS Rooke BFPO 52; 23 Connaught Avenue, Plymouth PL4 7BT — MB ChB 1986 Ed.

NICHOLSON, Mr Hamish Oliphant (retired) The Granary, Foss Home Farm, Foss, Pitlochry PH16 5NQ Tel: 01882 634307 Email: hamish@nicholson34.fsnet.co.uk — MB ChB 1957 Ed.; FRCS Ed. 1965; FRCOG 1978, M 1966. Prev: Cons. O & G Centr. Birm. Health Dist.

NICHOLSON, Helen Diana Department of Anatomy, School of Medical Sciences, University of Bristol, Bristol BS8 1TD Tel: 0117 928 8692 Fax: 0117 929 1687 Email: hod.nicholsan@bristol.ac.uk — MB ChB 1979 Bristol; MD Bristol 1986. Sen. Lect. (Anat.) Univ. Bristol.

NICHOLSON, Howard (retired) Chelwood, Laughton, Lewes BN8 6BE — MB BS Lond. 1935; MD Lond. 1938, MB BS 1935; FRCP Lond. 1949, M 1938; MRCS Eng. LRCP Lond. 1935. Fell. Univ. Coll. Lond.; Consg. Phys. Univ. Coll. Hosp. & Brompton Hosp. Prev: Phys. Univ. Coll. Hosp. & Brompton Hosp.

NICHOLSON, Hugh Philip The Surgery, 4 Stone Street, Hastings TN34 1QD Tel: 01424 427015 Fax: 01424 427633 — BM 1983 Soton. Socs: Assoc. Inst. Med. Laborat. Scs.

NICHOLSON, Iain Gordon 8 Strouden Avenue, Bournemouth BH8 9HT Tel: 01202 517250 — MB BS 1976 Lond.; DObst 1982. (Guy's) Prev: SHO (O & G) Middlx. Hosp. Lond.; Cas. Off. Guy's Hosp. Lond.; Resid. Med. Off. (Chest Med. & Tuberc.) Ruttonjee Sanat. Hong Kong.

NICHOLSON, Jacob Alexander 106 East Sheen Avenue, London SW14 8AU — MB BS 1966 Lond.; MRCP Lond. 1969; MRCS Eng. LRCP Lond. 1966.

NICHOLSON, Jacqueline — FRCPCH 1997; MB ChB (Hons.) Sheff. 1966; DCH Eng. 1969; Cert JCC Lond. 1976. (Sheff.) Designated doctor special needs SDHA. Socs: Eur. Acad. Childh. Disabil.; Fell. Roy. coll. Paediat. and Child Health. Prev: SHO Profess. Unit Sheff. Childr. Hosp.; Ho. Off. Profess. Therap. Unit & Ho. Off. Surg. Unit Sheff. Roy. Infirm.; Cons. Community Paediat. Community Child & Family Health S. Derbysh.

NICHOLSON

NICHOLSON, James Alexander Tobias 9 Cleveland Road, Lytham St Annes FY8 5JH Tel: 01253 731021 Email: chokertoby@aol.com — MB BS 1994 Lond.

NICHOLSON, James Christopher Addenbrookes Hospital (Box 181), Hills Road, Cambridge CB2 2QQ Tel: 01223 216878 Fax: 01223 586794 Email: james.nicholson@addenbrookes.nhs.uk — MB BChir 1989 Camb.; DM (Southampton) 1999; MA Camb. 1990; MRCP (UK) 1992. (Camb.) Cons. (Paediat. Oncol.) Addenbrookes NHS Trust Camb. Socs: MRCPCH; UKCCSG. Prev: Clin. Research Fell. (Paediat.) Soton.; Regist. Roy. Childr.'s Hosp. Melbourne, Australia.; Specialist Regist. (Paediat. Oncol.) Soton. & Roy. Marsden Hosp.

NICHOLSON, James Gordon (retired) 8 Strouden Avenue, Bournemouth BH8 9HT Tel: 01202 517250 Fax: 01202 517250 Email: jimmienich@amserve.net — MB BS 1951 Lond.; DObst RCOG 1956. Prev: Ho. Surg. Roy. Ear Hosp. (Univ. Coll. Hosp.).

NICHOLSON, John Antrim Hospital, Bush Road, Antrim BT41 2QB Tel: 018494 64921 — MB BCh BAO 1978 Belf.; MRCP (UK) 1982. Cons. Paediat. N. HSSB. Prev: Cons. Paediat. Worcester HA; Lect. (Paediat.) Univ. Sheff.

NICHOLSON, John Alan Bennett, MBE (retired) Berry House, Mulberry Hill, Chilham, Canterbury CT4 8AH — MB ChB 1941 Liverp.; MRCS Eng. LRCP Lond. 1941; MFPHM 1989; MFCM 1972; DPH Lond. 1952. Prev: Princip. Med. Adviser Overseas Developm. Admin.

NICHOLSON, John Charles Woodland View Surgery, Woodland View, West Rainton, Houghton-le-Spring DH4 6RQ Tel: 0191 584 3809 Fax: 0191 584 9177 — MB ChB 1974 Glas.; DRCOG 1976.

NICHOLSON, John Philip (retired) 64 Dalkeith Road, Harpenden AL5 5PW Tel: 01582 715026 — MB BS 1967 Lond.; PhD Lond. 1957, BSc 1949; BA Camb. 1942; MRCS Eng. LRCP Lond. 1966. Prev: Chief Physicist W.m. Hosp. Lond.

NICHOLSON, John William (retired) 17 MacNair Avenue, North Berwick EH39 4QY Tel: 01620 3747 — MB ChB 1951 Ed. Prev: Obst. Ho. Surg. Amersham Gen. Hosp.

NICHOLSON, Jolyon Anthony Howard The Halliwell Surgery, Lindfield Drive, Bolton BL1 3RG Tel: 01204 523813 Fax: 01204 384204 — MB ChB 1963 St. And. (St andrews)

NICHOLSON, Jonathan Peter 14 Cardigan Street, Newmarket CB8 8HZ — MB BS 1990 New South Wales.

NICHOLSON, Julian 85 Holly Avenue, Breaston, Derby DE72 3BR Tel: 0133 172971; Health Centre, Midland St, Long Eaton, Nottingham NG10 1NY — MB ChB 1970 St. And.; MRCGP 1977; DObst RCOG 1974.

NICHOLSON, Karl Graham 2 Huntsmans Close, Quorn, Loughborough LE12 8AR — MB BS 1973 Lond.; MD Leics. 1990; FRCP Lond. 1988; MRCP (UK) 1975; MRCS Eng. LRCP Lond. 1973; FRCPath 1994, M 1989; FRCP 1988. Sen. Lect. & Hon. Cons. Infec. Dis. Leicester Univ. & Leicester Roy. Infirm. Socs: Assn. Phys.; (Sec.) Europ. Scientif. Working Gp. on Influenza. Prev: Lilly Research Fell. Nat. Centre for Dis. Control Atlanta, USA; Mem. Staff of MRC Div. Communicable Dis. N.wick Pk. Hosp.

NICHOLSON, Katrina Mary St Johns Medical Centre, 62 London Road, Grantham NG31 6HR Tel: 01476 590055 Fax: 01476 400042 — MB ChB 1988 Liverp.; MRCGP 1993; DCH RCP Lond. 1992; DRCOG 1991.

NICHOLSON, Margaret Jean 6 Canton Court, Belfast BT6 9EL — MB BCh BAO 1984 Belf.; MB BCh Belf. 1984.

NICHOLSON, Mark Edward James Imperial Surgery, 49 Imperial Road, Exmouth EX8 1DQ Tel: 01395 224555 Fax: 01395 279282 — MB ChB 1990 Bristol; MRCGP 1994; DGM RCP Lond. 1993. (Southampton) Princip. Gen. Pract., Exmouth. Prev: Locum Clin. Asst. Exeter Hospice; SHO (Palliat. Care) Rowcroft Hospice Torquay; GP VTS Exeter.

NICHOLSON, Matthew Andrew (retired) 33 Kilmorie, Marine Drive, Torquay TQ1 2HU Tel: 01803 27303 — MB ChB 1935 Bristol. Prev: Res. Obst. Off., Cas. Ho. Surg. & 1st Ho. Surg. Bristol Gen. Hosp.

NICHOLSON, Meriel Susan (retired) Ladymead, Huggett's Lane, Willingdon, Eastbourne BN22 0LH Tel: 01323 502793 Fax: 01323 521390 Email: merielnicholson@compuserve.com — MB BS Lond. 1965; MRCP (UK) 1982; DCH Eng. 1979. p/t Project Director Child Friendly Healthcare Initiative Child Advocacy Internat. Prev: Cons. Child Health Dist. Gen. Hosp. E.bourne.

NICHOLSON, Professor Michael Lennard Department of Surgery, Leicester General Hospital, Leicester LE5 4PW Tel: 0116 258 4604 Fax: 0116 249 0064 — BM BS 1982 Nottm.; MD Leic. 1990; BMedSci (Ist cl. Hons.) Nottm. 1980; FRCS Eng. 1986. Prof. (Surg.) Leic. Gen. Hps. Prev: Cons. Surg. & Sen. Lect. Leic. Gen. Hosp.; Sen. Regist. (Surg.) Univ. Hosp. Nottm.; Regist. (Surg.) Leicester Hosps.

NICHOLSON, Michael Robert Craigavon Psychiatric Unit, 68 Lurgan Road, Portadown, Craigavon, Co. Armagh BT63 5QQ, Republic of Ireland; 15 The Rowans, Banbridge BT32 4D4 — MB BCh BAO Belf. 1986; MRCPsych 1993; DCH RCPSI 1989. Cons. (Gen. Adult. Psychiat.) Craigdown Psychiatric Unit, Portadown. Prev: Trainee GP Stranraer.

NICHOLSON, Olwen Patricia 8 Hardwick Court, Hartlepool TS26 0AZ Tel: 01429 263667 — MB BS 1994 Newc.; BMedSc (Hons.) Newc. 1991. (Univ. Newc. u. Tyne) SHO (Psychiat.) Watford Gen. Hosp. Socs: BMA; MPS; MSS. Prev: SHO (Psychiat.) Napsbury Hosp. St. Albans; SHO (Med.) Middlx. Hosp. Lond.; Ho. Off. (Med.) Roy. Vict. Infirm. Newc. u. Tyne.

NICHOLSON, Paul Anthony SmithKline Beecham Pharmaceuticals, New Frontiers Science Park, Third Avenue, Harlow CM19 5AW Tel: 01279 644335 Fax: 01279 644908; Lorton Park, High Lorton, Cockermouth CA13 9UG Tel: 01900 85088 Fax: 01900 85088 — MB BS 1960 Durh.; FFPM RCP (UK) 1989. Sen. Vice-Pres. World Wide Developm. SmithKline Beecham Pharmaceuts. Harlow. Socs: Fell. Roy. Soc. Med. Prev: Regist. (Clin. Path.) United Sheff. Hosps.; Clin. Path. Bristol Roy. Infirm.

NICHOLSON, Paul James Procter & Gamble, Whitehall Lane, Egham TW20 9NW Tel: 01784 474612 Fax: 01784 474547 Email: nicholson.pj@pg.com; 16 North Block, County Hall, London SE1 7PJ — MB BS 1981 Newc.; FRCP 2001 RCP London; MRCGP 1986; MFOM RCP Lond. 1992, AFOM 1986; DAvMed FOM RCP Lond. 1990; FFOM RCP Lond. 1998. Assoc. Med. Director, Procter & Gamble. Socs: BMA (Occupat. Health Comm.); Soc Occupat.med-past hon.asst.edr & past Pres. Prev: Occupat. Phys. ICI Chem. & Polymers Ltd. Teeside; Sqd. Ldr. RAF Med. Br.

NICHOLSON, Mr Richard Arthur Thorpe Grange Farm, Thorpe Audlin, Pontefract WF8 3HG Tel: 01977 620629 Fax: 01977 620062 — MRCS Eng. LRCP 1963 Lond.; FRCS Glas. 1972. (Guy's) Cons. Orthop. in Medico-Legal Pract. Prev: Cons. Orthop. Pontefract Gen. Infirm.; Sen. Regist. Orthop. Middlesbrough Gen. Hosp.; Orthop. Regist. Bradford Roy. Infirm.

NICHOLSON, Richard Hugh 6 Gallia Road, London N5 1LA Tel: 020 7359 8803 — MA, BM BCh Oxf. 1974; DCH RCPS Glas. 1977. (Oxf. & Lond. Hosp.) Edr. Bull. Med. Ethics. Socs: Fell. Roy. Soc. Med. (Pres. Open Sect.); Brit. Paediat. Assn. Prev: Clin. Med. Off. (Child Health) Tower Hamlets Health Dist.; Leverhulme Research Fell. in Med. Ethics; Regist. (Paediat. Audiol.) Roy. Nat. Throat, Nose & Ear Hosp. Lond.

NICHOLSON, Mr Robert Dunning Heale Cottage, Dunster, Minehead TA24 Tel: 0164 382330 — MB BS 1947 Lond.; FRCS Eng. 1956; MRCS Eng. LRCP Lond. 1943. (St. Bart.) Assoc. Specialist (Gen. Surg.) W. Som. Hosp. Gp. Socs: BMA. Prev: Surg. Regist. Vict. Hosp. Swindon; Orthop. Regist. Roy. Hants. Co. Hosp. Winchester; Cas. Regist. St. Bart. Hosp.

NICHOLSON, Robert Gordon (retired) Meadow View, Holt Lane, Holt, Wimborne BH21 7DQ Tel: 01202 884292 — MB BS 1949 Lond.; FRCGP 1979, M 1965; DObst RCOG 1953. Prev: Out-pat. Off., Childr. Ho. Phys. & Res. Obstetr. Guy's Hosp.

NICHOLSON, Robert Stephen Barn Surgery, Hill Road, Watlington, Oxford OX49 5AF Tel: 01491 612444 Fax: 01491 613988 Email: steve.nicholson@watington.oxongps.co.uk; Forelands, 26 Hill Road, Watlington, Oxford OX44 5AD — BM BCh 1976 Oxf.; BA Camb. 1974; MA, BM BCh Oxf. 1976; MRCGP 1981. GP Princip.; Bd. Mem. S.E. Oxf. PCG.

NICHOLSON, Mr Robert William Dept. of General Surgery, Blackburn Royal Infirmary, Bolton Road, Blackburn BB2 3LR; Ellisland, Station Road, Hoghton, Preston PR5 0DD — MB ChB Manch. 1971; MD Manch. 1980; FRCS Eng. 1976. (Manch.) Cons. Surg. Blackburn, Hyndburn & Ribble Valley Health Care NHS Trust. Prev: Sen. Regist. (Surg.) N. W.. RHA; Regist. (Surg.) Bury Gen. Hosp.; C.P. Zochonis Research Schol. Manch. Roy. Infirm.

NICHOLSON, Roger David 72 Longwestgate, Scarborough YO11 1RG — MB ChB 1973 Leeds; MRCPsych 1979.

NICHOLSON

NICHOLSON, Sandra 24 Townfoot Court, Carlisle Road, Brampton CA8 1SP Tel: 016977 3363 — MB ChB 1988 Leic.; MRCGP 1993.

NICHOLSON, Sarah Mary 1 Wharf Hill, Winchester SO23 9NQ — MB BS 1986 Lond.; MRCPsych 1993; DCH RCP Lond. 1994; DGM RCP Lond. 1990; Dip. Obst. Auckland 1989. Staff Grade Child Psychiat. Soton. Prev: Clin. Med. Off. (Child Psychiat.) Centr. Health Clinic Soton.; Regist. Rotat. (Psychiat.) Soton. HA.

NICHOLSON, Simon St. John's Hospital, Livingston, Edinburgh; Richmond, 13 Dreghorn Loan, Edinburgh EH13 0DF — MB BChir 1989 Camb.; MD Camb. 1995; MRCOG 1995. Cons., St. John's Hosp., Livingston. Prev: Regist. (O & G) Simpson Memor. Matern. Pavil. Edin.; Research Fell. Nuffield Dept. O & G John Radcliffe Matern. Hosp. Oxf.; SHO (O & G) John Radcliffe Matern. Hosp. Oxf.

NICHOLSON, Simon Dennis Fairfield Cottage, 8 Barbican Road, Barnstaple EX32 9HW — MB BS 1982 Lond.; BSc (Hons.) Lond. 1978, MB BS 1982; DGM RCP Lond. 1986. Liaison (Psychiat.) Lewisham Hosp. Lond.

NICHOLSON, Sonia Colleen — MB BS 1986 Lond.; MRCP (UK) 1989; FRCA 1993. Sen. Regist. (Anaesth.) John Radcliffe Hosp. Oxf.

NICHOLSON, Stephen 1 Downs Lodge Court, Church St., Epsom KT17 4QG — MB BS 1986 Lond.

NICHOLSON, Mr Stewart 119 Lancaster Drive, Darian Park, Wallsend NE28 9TF — MB BS 1980 Newc.; MB BS (Hons.) Newc. 1980; FRCS Eng. 1985.

NICHOLSON, Teresa Felicity Exmouth Health Centre, Claremont Grove, Exmouth EX8 2JF Tel: 01395 273001 Fax: 01395 273771; 13 Green Close, Exmouth EX8 3QH — MB ChB 1983 Bristol; MRCGP 1987; DRCOG 1987. Clin. Asst. (Learning Disabil.) Exmouth. Socs: BMA. Prev: Trainee GP Exeter VTS; Ho. Phys. N. Devon Dist. Hosp. Barnstaple; Ho. Surg. MusGr. Pk. Hosp. Taunton.

NICHOLSON, Tonia Chrisula 35 Maidwell Way, Laceby Acres, Grimsby DN34 5UP Tel: 01475 752655 — MB BS 1992 Lond.; BSc (Psych.) Lond. 1989; MRCP Ed. 1995. Regist. (ED) Sir Chas. Gairdrer Hosp., Perth, WA. Prev: Regist. (Gen. Med.) Waikato Hosp. Hamilton, NZ; Regist. (Paediat.) ChristCh. Pub. Hosp. ChristCh., NZ; SHO (Med.) Bradford.

NICHOLSON, William Dallas (retired) Brookwood, 3 Brookwood Avenue, Sale M33 5BZ Tel: 0161 962 2172 — MB ChB Aberd. 1949. Prev: Ho. Phys. Aberd. Roy. Infirm.

NICHOLSON, William John Brook Hospital, London SE18 4LW — MB BCh BAO 1954 Belf.; FRCP Lond. 1979, M 1966; FRCP Ed. 1970, M 1961; FRCPsych 1977, M 1971; DPM Eng. 1958; DCH RCP Lond. 1956. (Qu. Univ. Belf.) Cons. Phys. (Geriat.) Brook Hosp. & Greenwich Dist. Hosp. Lond.; Cons. Phys. Memor. Hosp. Woolwich. Socs: Brit. Geriat. Soc.; Brit. Soc. Research in Ageing. Prev: Regist. (Med.) & Ho. Phys. Whittington Hosp. Lond.; SHO Bethlem Roy. & Maudsley Hosps. Lond.

NICHOLSON-LAILEY, Peter John Frederick (retired) Orchard Cottage, Baltonsborough, Glastonbury BA6 8RJ Tel: 01458 50399. — MB BChir 1961 Camb.; MA, MB Camb. 1961, BChir 1960; MRCS Eng. LRCP Lond. 1960; DA Eng. 1963; DObst RCOG 1962. Prev: Res. Surg. Off. Roy. Marsden Hosp. Lond.

NICHOLSON-LAILEY, Thomas John Francis East Oxford Health Centre, Manzil Way, Cowley Road, Cowley, Oxford OX4 1XD Tel: 01865 242109; 52 Aston Street, Oxford OX4 1EP — MB BS 1982 Lond.; MA Camb. 1983; MRCGP 1987; DRCOG 1986.

NICHOLSON ROBERTS, Timothy Charles, Capt. RAMC Church House, Withington, Hereford HR1 3QE Tel: 01432 850260 Email: drarse@msn.com — MB BS 1996 Lond.; BSc Lond. 1994. (Charing Cross and Westminster) RMO 4 Regt. RA. Prev: SHO, A & E, RH. Haslar; Ho. Off. Med, Char. Cross Hosp.; Ho. Off. Surg MDHU Derriford.

NICKALLS, Richard William Dye Department of Anaesthesia, City Hospital, Nottingham NG5 1PB — MB BS 1974 Lond.; PhD Leeds 1989; BSc (1st cl. Hons. Physics in Med.) Lond. 1971; FFA RCS Eng. 1979. (Guy's) Cons. Anaesth. City Hosp. Nottm. Socs: Mathematical Assn.; Soc. Computing & Technol. in Anaesth.; Hist. Anaesth. Soc. Prev: Sen. Lect. (Anaesth.) Univ. Nottm.; Sen. Regist. (Anaesth.) Newc. u. Tyne; MRC Research Fell. (Cardiovasc. Stud.) Leeds Univ.

NICKELLS, James Shaughn Sonamar, East Shalford Lane, Guildford GU4 8AF — MB BS 1990 Lond.

***NICKELS, Robert Charles** 111 Torr Lane, Hartley, Plymouth PL3 5UF — MB ChB 1996 Bristol.

NICKERSON, Mr Christopher Bruce Northenden Health Centre, 489 Palatine Road, Northenden, Manchester M22 4DH Tel: 0161 998 3206 Fax: 0161 945 9173; 16 Palatine Crescent, Didsbury, Manchester M20 3LL — MB ChB 1982 Ed.; FRCS Ed. 1987; FRCS Glas. 1987; MRCGP 1992; DCH RCP Lond. 1991; DRCOG 1990. GP Manch.

NICKERSON, Susan Mary 96 Craiglea Drive, Edinburgh EH10 5PH Tel: 0131 446 0628 — MB ChB 1989 Manch.; MRCOG 1994. (St. And. Manch.) GP Regist. (Locum). Prev: Regist. (O & G) Stepping Hill Hosp.

***NICKFORD, Claire Louise** Tanglewood Piggery, Carlton Road, South Park, Godstone RH9 8LE — MB ChB 1998 Aberd.; MB ChB Aberd 1998.

NICKLESS, Stephen James — MB BS 1976 Lond.; MRCGP 1983; T(GP) 1991; DRCOG 1984; DTM & H RCP Lond. 1983; DA Eng. 1978. (St Marys Hospital London) GP Asst., Brondesbury Med. Centre, Lond. NW6. Prev: SHO (Anaesth. & A & E) St. Richards Hosp. Chichester; SHO (Paediat.) City Gen. Hosp. Stoke-on-Trent.

NICKLIN, Michael John Caskgate Street Surgery, 3 Caskgate Street, Gainsborough DN21 2DJ Tel: 01427 612501 Fax: 01427 615459 — MB BChir Camb. 1966; MRCS Eng. LRCP Lond. 1964; DIH Eng. 1969. (Lond. Hosp.)

NICKLIN, Sean 85 Gorsey Lane, Cannock WS11 1EX — MB ChB 1991 Liverp.

NICKOL, Kenneth Hugh 415 Baddow Road, Great Baddow, Chelmsford CM2 7QL Tel: 01245 471349 Fax: 01245 477759 — MB BS 1946 Lond.; FRCP Lond. 1974; FFOM RCP Lond. 1979; DIH Eng. 1963; FRIPHH 1999. (Lond. Hosp.) Socs: Fell. Roy. Soc. Med.; Soc. Occupat. Med.; fFell.Roy.Inst..Pub.Health & Hyg. Prev: Sen. Med. Off. Ford Motor Company; Sen. Regist. Camb. Chest Clinic; Regist. (Med.) Brompton Hosp.

NICKSON, Harold (retired) 20 Hazlewood Road, Duffield, Derby DE56 4DQ Tel: 01332 841070 — MB ChB 1956 Manch.; MRCGP 1969; DObst RCOG 1959.

NICKSON, Jack Warren Down, Peasemore, Newbury RG20 7JL Tel: 01635 248331 Fax: 01635 248331 — MB BS Lond. 1953; MRCS Eng. LRCP Lond. 1953; DObst RCOG 1955. (King's Coll. Hosp.) Phys. (Orthop.) Newbury. Socs: Brit. Inst. Musculoskel. Med. Prev: Ho. Surg. (Cas.) King's Coll. Hosp. Lond.; Ho. Phys. Sutton & Cheam Gen. Hosp.; Ho. Off. (Obst.) Luton Matern. Hosp.

NICKSON, Paul Jeffrey Victoria Place Surgery, 11 Victoria Place, Bethesda, Bangor LL57 3AG Tel: 01248 600212 Fax: 01248 602790; Tyddyn Alys, Cwm y Glo, Caernarfon LL55 4EA Tel: 01286 871200 Email: jennymts@aol.com — MB BS 1976 Lond.; MSc (Nutrit.) Lond. 1978; MRCS Eng. LRCP Lond. 1976; MRCGP 1983; MFHom 1976; DRCOG 1981; DCH Eng. 1980. (Westminster) Clin. Asst. (Homoeop.) Colwyn Bay; Clin. Asst. (Subst. Misuse) Ysbyty Gwynedd Bangor. Prev: GP Trainee Hayes; SHO (Obst.) S.mead Hosp. Bristol; SHO (Paediat.) Bronglais Gen. Hosp. Aberystwyth.

NICOL, Alan Peter Mayberry, CBE, LVO, Surg. Capt. RN (retired) 11 Churchill Road, Whitchurch, Tavistock PL19 9BU Tel: 01822 614698 — MRCS Eng. LRCP Lond. 1943; BA Camb. 1940; FFA RCSI 1965; FFA RCS Eng. 1966; DA Eng. 1956. Prev: Cons. Anaesth. PeterBoro. Dist. Hosp.

NICOL, Alastair McPherson, Maj. RAMC Penanjong Garrison, RBAF (LS) BFPO 605 Tel: 00 673 4 233094 Fax: 00 673 4 233094 Email: mcpnicol@brcnet.bn; c/o Nicol, 10 Bridge Lane, Barnhill, Dundee DD5 2SZ Tel: 01382 779476 — MB ChB 1988 Dundee; MRCGP 1993; Dip. IMC RCS Ed. 1995; DFFP 1993; DRCOG 1992. (Dundee) HM Forces Med. Off.

NICOL, Alexander (retired) The Glebe House, Badgeworth, Cheltenham GL51 4UL Tel: 01452 712159 — MD 1962 Aberd.; MD (Commend.) Aberd. 1962, MB ChB 1949; FRCPath 1976, M 1964. Prev: Hon. Cons. Path. Glos. Roy. Hosp. & Cheltenham Gen. Hosp.

***NICOL, Alexandra Elizabeth Shona** Oldfield Farm, Over Haddon, Bakewell DE45 1JE — MB BS 1998 Lond.; MB BS Lond 1998.

NICOL, Andrew The Surgery, 61 Wheatway, Abbeydale, Gloucester GL4 5ET Tel: 01452 383323 — MB ChB 1977 Sheff.; MFHom 1989; DRCOG 1980. Clin. Asst. (Geriat. Med.) Glos. HA.

NICOL, Andrew Kingfisher House, Hellesdon Hospital, Norwich NR12 0BL Tel: 01603 421608 — MB ChB 1986 Sheff.; MRCPsych 1990. Cons. Psychiat., Gen. & Community, Norf. Ment. Healthcare

Trust, Norwich; Cons. Psychiat. To Home Treatm. of Crisis Resolution Serv., Norf. Socs: Brit. Assoc. of PsychoPharmacol. Prev: Sen. Regist. (Psychiat.) Roy. Hallamsh. Sheff.; Research Fell., Bristol; Psychiat. Trainee (Sen/Reg.), Glenside Hosp. Bristol.

NICOL, Andrew Edward Leslie 42 Sutherland Avenue, Cuffley, Potters Bar EN6 4EQ — MB BS 1975 Lond.; FFA RCS Eng. 1980.

NICOL, Andrew Graeme, TD OMS Ltd., 12 Sunnybank Road, Aberdeen AB24 3NG Tel: 01224 492884 Fax: 01224 487812 — MB ChB 1958 Aberd.; PhD Aberd. 1968, MB ChB 1958; FRCP Ed. 1982, M 1963; FRCPath 1978, M 1966; MFOM Lond. 1988; DIH Lond. 1985. Med. Dir. OMS Ltd. Aberd. Prev: Sen. Med. Adviser BP Oil Internat.; Head & Sen. Med. Off. Gen. Med. Servs. BP Internat. Lond.; Chief Med. Off. ADCO-ADMA OPCO Combined Med. Serv. Abu Dhabi, UAE.

NICOL, Anne Department of Pathology, Leighton Hospital, Crewe CW1 4QS Tel: 01270 255141 — MB ChB 1977 Dundee; MRCPath. 1984; FRCPath 1995; Dip. Health Mgt. Keele 1994. Cons. Path. Leighton Hosp. Crewe.

NICOL, Professor Arthur Rory WHO Collaborating Centre, Institute of Psychiatry, De Crespigny Park, London SE5 Tel: 020 7919 2546; 27 Springcroft Avenue, London N2 9JH Tel: 020 8883 8691 Fax: 020 8020 8883 8691 Email: rorynicol@lineone.net — M Phil Lond. 1970, BSc 1960, MB BS 1963; FRCPsych. 1981 M 1972; FRCP 1985, M 1967; FRCPCH 1996. (Univ. Coll. Hosp.) Vis. Prof. Inst. Psych. Lond. Prev: Prof. Cild Psychiat. Univ. Leicester.

NICOL, Barbara Jane Lapworth Surgery, Old Warwick Road, Lapworth, Solihull B94 6LH Tel: 01564 783983 — MB ChB 1978 Birm.; MRCGP 1982; DRCOG 1980. (Birm.) Prev: Trainee GP E. Birm. VTS; Ho. Surg. Dudley Rd. Hosp. Birm.; Ho. Phys. E. Birm. Hosp.

NICOL, Barbara Josephine (retired) 194 Kimbolton Road, Bedford MK41 8DP Tel: 01234 353579 — MB ChB Manch. 1949; DCH Eng. 1953.

NICOL, Dennis James Finch Badgers LEa, Hill Green, Ingatestone CM4 0PT — MB BS 1958 Lond. (Middlx.) Regist. Ophth. OldCh. Hosp. Romford. Socs: BMA. Prev: Sen. Ho. Off. Ophth. Sunderland Eye Infirm.; Ho. Surg. (Ophth.) Middlx. Hosp.; Ho. Surg. Mt. Vernon Hosp. N.wood.

NICOL, Denys Bewdley The Swan Medical Centre, 4 Willard Road, Yardley, Birmingham B25 8AA Tel: 0121 706 0216 Fax: 0121 707 3105; Field House, 261 Blossomfield Road, Solihull B91 1TA Tel: 0121 705 3337 — MB BChir 1966 Camb.; MA, MB Camb. 1966, BChir 1965; DCH Eng. 1968; DObst RCOG 1968. (Camb. & Char. Cross) Prev: SHO (Paediat.) Jenny Lind Hosp. Norwich; SHO (O & G) Ipswich & E. Suff. Hosp.; Family Pract. Sen. Resid. Fairview Hosp. Minneapolis, USA.

NICOL, Douglas Robert Hamilton Mintlaw Group Practice, Newlands Road, Mintlaw, Peterhead AB42 5GP Tel: 01771 623522 Fax: 01771 624349; 2 Anderson Drive, Longside, Peterhead AB42 4XG Tel: 01779 821560 Email: nicol01@globalnet.co.uk — MB ChB 1977 Aberd.; DRCOG 1980; BMedBiol 1974; MRCGP 1982. GP Mintlaw, Peterhead.; Hon. Tutor Univ. Aberd. Socs: Peterhead & Dist. Med. Soc. Prev: Trainee Asst. Peterhead Health Centre; Research Fell. (O & G) Univ. Aberd. SHO Aberd. Matern.; Hosp., Kingseat Hosp. & Roy. Aberd. Childr. Hosp.

NICOL, Eben Russell Macmillan (retired) 26 Mytchett Heath, Mytchett, Camberley GU16 6DP Tel: 01252 376571 — LRCP LRCS Ed. LRFPS Glas. 1945. Prev: Ho. Surg. Glas. Roy. Infirm.

NICOL, Edith Fiona Stockbridge Health Centre, 1 India Place, Edinburgh EH3 6EH; 11 West Carnethy Avenue, Edinburgh EH13 0ED Tel: 0131 477 0800 Fax: 0131 536 7469 — MB BS 1976 Lond.; BSc (Hons.) Lond. 1973; MRCP (UK) 1979; MRCS Eng. LRCP Lond. 1976; MRCGP 1982. Sen. Lect. Med. Educat. Univ. Edin. Prev: Assoc. Adviser SE Scotl. Comm. for Postgrad. Med. & Dent. Educat.

*****NICOL, Edward David** Officers Mess, Royal Air Force, Wittering, Peterborough PE8 6HB Email: e.med@which.net; 6 Orchard Green, Alderley Edge SK9 7DT — BM BS 1998 Nottm.; BM BS Nottm 1998; M Med Sci 1996.

*****NICOL, Gavin Lindsay James** 34 Copstone Drive, Dorridge, Solihull B93 8DJ — MB ChB 1994 Birm.; ChB Birm. 1994.

*****NICOL, Gillian Jane Catherine** 30 Victoria Road, Grangemouth FK3 9JN Tel: 01324 486696 — MB ChB 1998 Ed.; MB ChB Ed 1998.

NICOL, John 12 London Road, Kilmarnock KA3 7AE; 49 London Road, Kilmarnock KA3 7AG Tel: 23593 — MB ChB 1961 Glas.

NICOL, John William Maryhill Practice, Elgin Health Centre, Maryhill, Elgin IV30 1AT Tel: 01343 543788 Fax: 01343 551604 — MB ChB 1988 Ed.; MRCGP 1995. (Ed.)

NICOL, Keith Mill Farm, Brigg Road, South Kelsey, Market Rasen LN7 6PH — MB BS 1969 Lond.; St. Geo.).

NICOL, Leslie George (retired) 194 Kimbolton Road, Bedford MK41 8DP Tel: 01234 353579 — MRCS Eng. LRCP Lond. 1947; DPM Manch. 1950, DPH 1956. Prev: Community Phys. (Liaison Social Servs.) Beds. AHA.

*****NICOL, Malcolm John Manning** Field House, 261 Blossom Field Road, Solihull B91 1TA — MB BS 1998 Lond.; MB BS Lond 1998.

NICOL, Margaret Elizabeth 6 Weybridge Walk, Shoeburyness, Southend-on-Sea SS3 8YJ — MB ChB 1982 Aberd.; FFA RCS Eng. 1988; DA (UK) 1985.

NICOL, Mark Fergus c/o Strathmuir, Duchal Road, Kilmacolm PA13 4AS; 30 Hertford Close, Congleton CW12 1TB — MB ChB 1987 Manch.; BSc (Med. Sci.) St. And. 1984. Regist. Rotat. (Anaesth.) Stoke-on-Trent. Prev: SHO (Anaesth.) Wythenshawe Hosp. & Oldham Hosps.; SHO (A & E) Hope Hosp. Manch.

NICOL, Mrs Mary (retired) 8 Rowley Crescent, Stratford-upon-Avon CV37 6UT Tel: 01789 205084 — MB BChir Camb. 1959; MA Camb. 1959. Prev: Cas. Off. Stratford-upon-Avon Gen. Hosp.

NICOL, Norman Thomas, OBE, TD Bracken Rigg, 5 Egton Road, Aislaby, Whitby YO21 1SU — MB ChB 1950 Aberd.; FRCR 1975; FFR 1959; DMRT Eng. 1954. (Aberd.) Emerit. Radiother. Leicester HA. Socs: Fell. Roy. Soc. Med.; BMA. Prev: Radiother. i/c Dept. Radiother. Roy. Infirm. Leic.; Assoc. Cons. Nat. Centre for Radiother.; Clin. Tutor. Fac. of Med. Univ. Leic.

NICOL, Peter Alan Bangor Health Centre, Newtownards Road, Bangor BT20 4LD Tel: 02891 515222 Fax: 02891 515397; 40 Sheridan Drive, Helens Bay, Bangor BT19 1LB Tel: 01247 853528 — MB BCh BAO 1982 Belf.; MRCGP 1986; DCH Dub. 1987; DRCOG 1984. Socs: BMA.

NICOL, Peter James Stewart, Surg. Cdr. RN Medical Centre, HMS Sultan, Military Road, Gosport PO12 3BY; 21 Castle Road, Southsea PO5 3DE — MB BS 1979 Lond.; MRCS Eng. LRCP Lond. 1977. (Roy. Free) Princip. Med. Off. HMS Sultan Gosport; Course Co-Ordinator SHO GPVT Scheme The Roy. Hosp. Haslar Gosport. Prev: Trainee Psychiat. P.ss Alexandra Hosp. RAF Wroughton; Trainee GP Watford Gen. Hosp. Family Pract. VTS; SHO (Paediat.) Edgware Gen. Hosp.

NICOL, Rhoderic Eion Lapworth Surgery, Old Warwick Road, Lapworth, Solihull B94 6LH Tel: 01564 783983 — MB ChB 1978 Birm.; MRCGP 1982; DRCOG 1980. (Birm.) Prev: Trainee GP E. Birm. VTS; Ho. Surg. E. Birm. Hosp.; Ho. Phys. Dudley Rd. Hosp. Birm.

NICOL, Robert John Auld (retired) Mountain Ash, Viewlands Avenue, Off Grays Road, Westerham TN16 2JE Tel: 01959 532893 — MB ChB (Commend.) St. And. 1947. Prev: Regist. (Med.) Roy. Infirm. Perth.

NICOL, Shirley Avril (retired) Abbey Royd, Bridge St., Kelso TD5 7JE Tel: 01573 225052 — MB ChB Ed. 1956; MFFP 1993. Prev: Clin. Med. Off. (Family Plann.) Newc., N. Tyneside & N.d. HAs.

*****NICOL, Stephen Graham** 27 The Gallolee, Edinburgh EH13 9QL — MB ChB 1997 Ed.

NICOL, Sylvester Desmond Willoughby Doctor's Mess, Southend Hospital, Prittlewell Chase, Westcliff on Sea SS0 0RY — MB BChir 1992 Camb.

NICOL, Verna Sturgess (retired) High Bank, Hartlebury, Kidderminster DY11 7TB Tel: 01299 250336 — MB ChB 1953 Birm.; FRCP Lond. 1991; MRCP (UK) 1977; MRCS Eng. LRCP Lond. 1953; DCH Eng. 1956. Prev: Cons. Paediat. Kidderminster Health Dist.

NICOL, William Alan (retired) 24 Abbots Way, Doonfoot, Ayr KA7 4EY — MB ChB 1954 Glas.; MFPHM RCP (UK) 1989; MFCM RCP (UK) 1982; MRCGP 1966. Prev: Cons. Pub. Health Med. Ayrsh. & Arran HB.

NICOL, Mr William James (retired) Abbey Royd, Bridge St., Kelso TD5 7JE Tel: 01573 25052 — MB ChB St. And. 1958; MSc (Afr. Studies) Ed. 1996; BA Open 1987; FRCS Ed. 1968. Cons. Orthop.

NICOLA

Surg. Roy. Halifax Infirm. Prev: Sen. Regist. (Orthop.) Dundee Roy. Infirm.

*NICOLA, Kyriacos Panayioutou 20 Woodland Way, London N21 3QA — MB BS 1998 Lond.; MB BS Lond 1998.

NICOLAIDES, Professor Andreas Nicos Academic Surgical Unit, St Mary's Hospital Medical School, Praed St., London W2 1PG Tel: 020 7725 6243 Fax: 020 7725 6416; 9 North Grove, Highgate, London N6 4SH Tel: 020 8341 4230 — MB BS Lond. 1962; MS Lond. 1976; FRCS Ed. 1967; FRCS Eng. 1967; MRCS Eng. LRCP Lond. 1962. (Guy's) Prof. Vasc. Surg. Hon. Cons. & Dir. Irvine Laborat. For; Cardiovasc. Investig. & Research St. Mary's Hosp. Lond. Socs: Vasc. Soc. GB; (Pres.) Internat. Union of Angiol.; Roy. Soc. Med. (Pres. Sect. Measurem. in Med.). Prev: Reader (Vasc. Surg.) & Hon. Cons. St. Mary's Hosp. Lond.; Sen. Lect. (Cardiovasc. Surg.) & Hon. Cons. St. Mary's Hosp. Lond.; Pfizer Research Fell. & Hon. Sen. Regist. (Surg.) King's Coll. Hosp. Lond.

NICOLAIDES, Professor Kyprianos Herodotou 107 Alleyn Park, London SE21 8AA — MB BS 1978 Lond.; BSc Lond. 1974; MRCOG 1984. Prof. Fetal Med. Univ. Lond. Prev: Lect. Harris Birthright Research Centre for Fetal Med. King's Coll. Hosp. Med. Sch. Lond.

NICOLAIDES, Paulina Child Development Centre, Royal Liverpool Children's NHS Trust, Alder Road, Liverpool L12 2AP; Raby Glen, Blakeley Dell, Raby Mere, Wirral CH63 0NJ Tel: 0151 343 0573 Email: pnicolaides@btinternet.com — MB ChB 1985 Manch.; MRCP (UK) 1991. Cons.. (Paediat. Neurol.) The Roy. Liverp. Childr.'s NHS Trust. Socs: Brit. Paediat. Assn.; Paediat. Neurol. Assn. (BPNA); Europ. Paed. Neurol. Soc. (EPNS). Prev: Sen. Regist. (Paediat. Neurol.) The Roy. Liverp. Childr.'s NHS Trust; Regist. (Paediat. Neurol.) Roy. Manch. Childr. Hosp.; Regist. (Intens. Care) Hosp. for Sick Childr. Gt. Ormond St. Lond.

NICOLAOU, Andrew John Eastwood, Friars Close, Shenfield, Brentwood CM15 8HX Email: dranicolaou@yahoo.com — MB BS 1990 Lond.; BSc (Hons) Lond. 1997; FRCA. (Kings Coll. Hosp.) Cons. (Anaes) St Geo.'s Hosp, Atkinson Morley's Hosp.& Trinity Hospice, Clapham Lond.; Cons. (Path Specialist) St. Geo. Hosp., Atkinson Morley's Hosp.& Trinity Hospice, Clapham Lond. Socs: Assoc. of Anaes; Path. Soc; Inter. Assoc. for the Study of Pain. Prev: Clin. Pain Fell. Guy's & St Thomas' Hosp.; Specialist Regist. (Anaesth.) Guy's Hosp.

NICOLAOU, Anthony Christopher Whaddon Way Surgery, 293 Whaddon Way, Bletchley, Milton Keynes MK3 7LW Tel: 01908 375341 Fax: 01908 374975 — MB BS 1981 Lond.; DRCOG 1988.

*NICOLAOU, Nicolas George Neuadd Meirionnydd School Hall of Residence, Heath Park, Cardiff CF14 4YS — MB BCh 1994 Wales.

*NICOLAU, Marios 5 Hinchin Brook, Lenton, Nottingham NG7 2EF — BM BS 1998 Nottm.; BM BS Nottm 1998.

NICOLE, Thomasina Mary Street Farm, South Brewham, Bruton BA10 0JZ Tel: 01749 850524 Fax: 01749 850876 — MB BS 1975 Lond.; MA Oxf. 1977; MRCPCH 1996. (St. Thos.) Assoc. Specialist (Paediat.) Yeovil Dist. Hosp. Socs: Brit. Assn. Preven. Child Abuse & Neglect. Prev: Clin. Asst. (Paediat. Med.) Yeovil Dist. Hosp.; SHO (Neonat. Paediat.) St. Thos. Hosp. Lond.; SHO (Paediat.) MusGr. Pk. Hosp. Taunton.

NICOLL, Angus Gordon Communicable Disease Surveillance Centre, 61 Colindale Avenue, London NW9 5EQ Tel: 020 8200 6868 Fax: 020 8200 7868 Email: anicoll@phls.co.uk; 2 New House Park, St Albans AL1 1UB — MB 1977 Camb.; BChir 1976; MSc Epidemiol. Lond. 1986; MRCP (Paediat.) (UK) 1980; MFPHM RCP (UK) 1996. (Camb.) Cons. Epidemiol. Communicable Dis. Surveillance Centre Lond.; Sen. Lect. Univ. Lond. Socs: Med. Soc. Study VD; Fell. RCP. Prev: Sen. Lect. Lond. Sch. Hyg. & Trop. Med, Univ. Lond.

NICOLL, Ann Middleton (retired) Westlands, Eyemouth TD14 5BZ Tel: 018907 51040 — MB ChB 1955 Ed. Prev: Gen. Practioner Eyemouth Berwicksh.

NICOLL, Antony Edward Flat 3/1, 57 Airlie St., Hyndland, Glasgow G12 9SP Tel: 0141 334 8664 — MB ChB 1995 Dundee. SHO (Gyn.) Glas. Roy. Infirm. Socs: Glas. Obst. and Gyn. Soc. Prev: SHO (Obst.) Glas. Roy. Matern. Hosp.; SHO (Gyn.) W.ern Infirm. Glas.; SHO (Obst.) Qu. Mother's Hosp, Glas.

*NICOLL, David 2 Nevis Place, Broughty Ferry, Dundee DD5 3EL — MB ChB 1998 Dund.; MB ChB Dund 1998.

NICOLL, David Melville Lister House, 473 Dunstable Road, Luton LU4 8DG Tel: 01582 571565 Fax: 01582 582074 — MB ChB 1958 Birm.; BSc Queensld. 1972. (Birm.) Socs: BMA.

NICOLL, Derek Alan Proctor, Wing Cdr. RAF Med. Br. Retd. Station Medical Centre, Royal Air Force, Menwith Hill, Harrowgate HG3 2RF Tel: 01423 777885; Greenbanks, 5 Westgate, Rillington, Malton YO17 8LN Tel: 01944 758740 — MB ChB 1979 Dundee; 1974 BSc (Hons.) Biochem. Dundee; Cert. Occupat. Health Aberd. 1992. (Dundee) Med. Off. Prev: Sen. Med. Off. RAF Linton-on-Ouse, York.

NICOLL, Frederick James (retired) Westlands, Coldingham Road, Eyemouth TD14 5BZ Tel: 018907 51040 Email: fred.nicoll@exmouth.demon.co.uk — MB ChB Ed. 1956. Prev: GP Eyemouth Berwicksh.

NICOLL, James Alan Ramsay Department of Neuropathology, Institute of Neurological Sciences, Southern General Hospital, Glasgow G51 4TF Tel: 0141 201 2046 Fax: 0141 201 2998 Email: j.nicoll@clinmed.gla.ac.uk — MB ChB 1984 Bristol; BSc (Physiol.) Bristol 1981, MD 1993, MB ChB 1984; MRCPath 1990. Cons. Sen. Lect. Neuropath. Glas. Univ.

NICOLL, Janet Alison 8 Claremont Crescent, Edinburgh EH7 4HX — MB ChB 1988 Ed.

NICOLL, John Martin Vere 2 Manor Park, Hougham, Grantham NG32 2JJ Tel: 0140 025 0508 Fax: 01400 250508 Email: martinnic@btinternet.com; 2 Manor Park, Hougham, Grantham NG32 2JJ Tel: 0140 025 0508 Fax: 01400 250508 — MB BS 1965 Lond.; MCRS Eng. LRCP Lond. 1965; DRCOG 1970. Cons. Anaesth. Univ. Hosp. Nottm. Prev: Cons. Anaesth. King Fahad Nat. Guard Hosp., K. Khaled Eye Specialist Hosp. Riyadh & St. Jas. Univ. Hosp. Leeds; Princip. Anaesth. Johannesburg Hosp., S. Africa.

NICOLL, Jonathan James Bankdale Park, Wreay, Carlisle CA4 0RR — MB BS 1977 Lond.; FRCP 1999; FRCR 1987; MRCP (UK) 1981; BA Camb. 1974, MA 1980. (Westm.) Cons. Radiother. & Oncol. Cumbld. Infirm. Carlisle.

NICOLL, Kirsteen Sheonagh Royal Camhill Hospital, Camhill Hospital, Aberdeen AB25 2RQ Tel: 01224 663131; The Bungalow, Hardhillock, Marycutler, Aberdeen AB12 5GQ Tel: 01224 733545 Email: kirsteen@tmcnamee.freeserve.co.uk — MB ChB 1993 Aberd.; MRC Psych 1999. Specialist Regist. Roy. Cornhill Hosp. Aberd. Prev: Locum GP Brisbane, Austral., SHO (Psychiat.) Roy. Cornhill Hosp. Aberd.; SHO (Surg.) Stirling; SHO (Med.) Inverness.

NICOLL, Lorna May West Gate Health Centre, Charleston Drive, Dundee DD2 4AD Tel: 01382 668189 Fax: 01382 665943 — MB ChB 1981 Dundee; MRCGP 1985.

NICOLL, Stephanie Jane Barnes Eastbourne District General Hospital, Kings Drive, Eastbourne BN21 2UD Tel: 01323 413745 — MB ChB 1984 Glas.; FFA RCS Eng. 1989; DA (UK) 1986. (Univ. Glas.) p/t Cons. (anaesth.), E.bourne Dist. Gen. Hosp. Prev: Sen. Regist. (Anaesth.) Qu. Vict. Hosp. E. Grinstead.; Sen. Regist. (Anaesth.) Gt. Ormond St. Hosp. Sick Childr. Lond.; Sen. Regist. (Anaesth.) Guy's Hosp. Lond.

NICOLL, William Douglas (retired) 8Lochpark, Ayr KA7 4EU Tel: 01292 441657 — MB ChB 1945 Glas.; FRCP Glas. 1975, M 1972; FRCPath 1966, M 1963. Prev: Cons. Haematol. Ayrsh. Area.

NICOLL, William Sim Galston Surgery, 5A Henrietta Street, Galston KA4 8JW Tel: 01563 820424 Fax: 01563 822380 — MB ChB 1982 Ed.; BSc Ed. 1979, MB ChB 1982; MRCGP 1986.

NICOLLE, Annette Louise 6 Market Lane, Dunston, Gateshead NE11 9NY; 204 Surgerys Lane, Arnold, Nottingham NG5 8FY — MB BS 1996 Newc. SHO (Gen. Med.) N. Tees Gen. Hosp. Hardwick Stockton. Socs: BMA.

NICOLLE, Mr Frederick Villeneuve Flat 2, 30 Harley Street, London W1G 9PW Tel: 020 7637 9595 Fax: 020 7636 1639 — MB 1957 Camb.; BA Camb. 1953, MChir 1972, MB 1957, BChir 1956; FRCS Canada 1962; LMCC 1958. (Camb. & Middlx.) Cons. Plastic Surg. Hosp. St. John & Eliz. Lond. Socs: (Pres.) Brit. Assn. Aesthetic Plastic Surgs.; (Treas.) Internat. Soc. Aesthetic Plastic Surgs.; Brit. Assn. Plastic Surg. Prev: Cons. Plastic Surg. Hammersmith Hosp. & Lect. (Surg.) Roy. Postgrad. Med. Sch. Lond.; Sen. Regist. (Plastic Surg.) Hammersmith Hosp. Lond.; Chief Resid. Plastic Surg. & Trauma Unit Montreal Gen. Hosp.

NICOLLE, Penelope Drs Anderson & Ptns, Shop 9116, 109 Repulse Bay Road, Repulse Bay, Hong Kong Tel: 00 852 2812 2392 Fax: 00 852 2812 9593 Email: olipenny@asiaonline.net; Upper

Folds, Little Bognor, Fittleworth, Pulborough RH20 1JT — MB BS 1989 Lond.; MRCGP Lond. 1993; DRCOG Lond. 1993. (St. Geo. Hosp.) Socs: BMA (Ex.-Hon. Sec. Hong Kong Br.).

NICOLLE, Philip Lionel (retired) Barracks Bungalow, 29 Long Park, Modbury, Ivybridge PL21 0RP Tel: 01548 830382 — MRCS Eng. LRCP Lond. 1940. Prev: Surg. Lt. RNVR.

NICOLLS, David Bruce Hilltops Medical Centre, Kensington Drive, Great Holm, Milton Keynes MK8 9HN Tel: 01908 568446 — MB BS 1987 Lond.; MRCGP 1991; T(GP) 1991.

***NICOLSON, Andrew** 1 Morton Carr Lane, Nunthorpe, Middlesbrough TS7 0JU — MB ChB 1995 Manch.; MRCPI 1997.

NICOLSON, Anne West Suffolk Hospital, Hardwick Lane, Bury St Edmunds IP33 2QZ — MB BS 1976 Adelaide; MRCP (UK) 1983.

NICOLSON, Anne Law Skerryvore Practice, Health Centre, New Scapa Road, Kirkwall KW15 1BQ Tel: 01856 885440 Fax: 01856 870043 — MB ChB 1990 Aberd. Trainee GP Kirkwall. Prev: SHO (O & G & A & E) St. Johns Hosp. Livingston; SHO (Psychiat.) Argyll & Bute Hosp. Lochgilphead.

NICOLSON, Bridget Ruth Leckhampton Surgery, Lloyd Davies House, 17 Moorend Park Road, Cheltenham GL53 0LA Tel: 01242 515363 Fax: 01242 253512 — MB ChB 1987 Bristol; DRCOG 1991. GP Glos. VTS.

NICOLSON, Helen Stewart (retired) — MB ChB 1947 St. And.; MRCPsych 1971; Dip. Psychother. Aberd. 1966; DPM Manch. 1960. Prev: Cons. (Child & Adolesc. Psychiat.) Tayside Health Bd.

NICOLSON, Joan MacPherson 32 Netherview Road, Glasgow G44 3XH — MB ChB 1962 Glas.; DObst RCOG 1965; Cert FPA 1971, IUD 1972. Community Paediat. (Community Health) Yorkhill Trust Glas.; Clin. Med. Off. (Family Plann.) Well Wom. Serv. Gt.er Glas. HB. Socs: Assoc. Mem. Fac. Homoeop; BMA. Prev: GP Glas.; Regist. (Dermat.) Vict. Infirm. Glas.; SHO Redlands Hosp. Glas.

NICOLSON, John Andrew Devon Road Surgery, 32 Devon Road, South Darenth, Dartford DA4 9AB Tel: 01322 862121 Fax: 01322 868794; Griffins, Sparepenny Lane, Eynsford, Dartford DA4 0JJ Tel: 01322 862977 Fax: 01322 868794 Email: johnandrewnicolson@lineone.net — MB BS 1972 Lond.; FRCGP 1998; MRCS Eng. LRCP Lond. 1972; MRCGP 1980. (King's Coll. Hosp.) Clin. Governance Lead, Dartford, Gravesend and Swanley PCT.; Exec. Bd. Mem., Dartford, Gravesend and Swanley P.C.T.; Vice Chairm., W. Kent L.M.C. Prev: Course Organiser NW Kent Postgrad. Centre, Dartford & Gravesham VTS; Trainee GP Dartford VTS; Assoc. Adviser (Gen. Pract.) W. Kent.

NICOLSON, Kenneth Thomas (retired) The Old Rectory, West Camel, Yeovil BA22 7QB Tel: 01935 850214 — MB BS 1957 Lond. Prev: GP Qu. Camel.

NICOLSON, Marianne Coutts Anchor Unit, Aberdeen Royal Infirmary, Foresterhill, Aberdeen AB25 2ZN Tel: 01224 681818 Fax: 01224 554183 Email: m.nicholson@arh.grampian.scot.nhs.uk — MB ChB 1982 Ed.; BSc (Med. Biol.) Ed. 1979, MB ChB 1982; BSc 1979 (Med. Biol.) Ed.; MD Edin. 1996; FRCP (Ed.) 1996; MRCP (UK) 1985. (Ed. Univ.) Cons. Med. Oncol. Aberd. Roy. Infirm. Socs: Assn. Cancer Phys.s(Treas.); Scott. Melanoma Gp. (Sec.). Prev: Sen. Regist. (Med. Oncol.) Roy. Marsden Hosp. Sutton.

NICOLSON, Susan Jane Longfield, Clitheroe Road, Knowle Green, Preston PR3 2YQ — MB ChB 1987 Glas.; MRCP (UK) 1990.

NICPON, Mr Krzysztof Jozef 14 Meadowcroft Close, Otterbourne, Winchester SO21 2HD — BM 1984 Soton.; BM (Hons.) Soton. 1984; FRCS Eng. 1988.

***NICUM, Rupal** 22 Alveston Gr, Knowle, Solihull B93 9NX — MB ChB 1997 Leic.

***NICUM, Shibani** 17 Kelton Court, Carpenter Road, Birmingham B15 2JX — MB ChB 1996 Birm.; ChB Birm. 1996.

NIDA, Anne Mary Dunorlan Medical Group, 64 Pembury Road, Tonbridge TN9 2JG Tel: 01732 352907 Fax: 01732 367408; 24 Ridgeway Crescent, Tonbridge TN10 4NP Tel: 01732 362248 — MB BS 1977 Lond. GP Princip. Prev: GP Stansted.

NIEDER, Mary 107 Northfield Road, Crookes, Sheffield S10 1QP — MB ChB 1995 Sheff. (Sheff.) GP Regist. Chesterfield & N. Derbysh. Roy. Hosp.

NIEHUES, Dorothea Maria Princess Royal Hospital, Apley Castle, Telford TF1 6TF — State Exam Med 1992 Munster.

NIELD, Mrs Dalia Virginia 149 Harley Street, London W1N 2DE Tel: 020 7935 4444 Fax: 020 7935 5091; 16 Wellfield Avenue, Muswell Hill, London N10 2EA Tel: 020 8883 1976 Email: dalienield@btinternet.com — Medico-Cirujano Andes Venezuela 1970; FRCS Ed. 1982; CSST(Plastic Surg.) 1991. Cons. Plastic & Reconstruc. Surg. The Lond. Clinic; Cons. Plastic Surg. Lond. Clinic; Recognised Teach. Univ. Lond. Socs: Fell. Roy. Soc. Med. (Plastic Surg. Chapter); Brit. Assn. Plastic Surg.; Internat. Microsurg. Soc. Prev: Cons. Plastic Surg. St. Bart. & Homerton Hosps. Lond.; Sen. Regist. (Head, Neck and BrE. Reconstruc. Surg.) Roy. Marsden Hosp.; Sen. Regist. & Regist. (Plastic Surg.) Wexham Pk. Hosp.

NIELD, Frances Victoria Mary 28 St Michael's Avenue, Bramhall, Stockport SK7 2PW — MB ChB 1978 Manch. GP Stockport.

NIELD, Jonathan 16 High Brigham, Brigham, Cockermouth CA13 0TE — MB BS 1984 Lond.; DTM & H Lond. 1990. Med. Off. (Community & Trop. Med.) Medecins Du Monde Dak Lak Province, Vietnam. Prev: Med. Off. MSF (Belgium), Hong Kong; Med. Off. Ruttonjee Sanat.; Med. Off. Britain-Nepal Med. Trust.

NIELSEN, Ebba 108 Station Road, Hampton TW12 2AS Tel: 020 8898 1696 Fax: 020 8898 1696 Email: nielsen@medical_vision@com.uk; Hans Place Practice, 43 Hans Place, Knightsbridge, London SW1X 0JZ Tel: 020 7584 1642 Fax: 020 7589 5862 — MD 1991 Copenhagen; DRCOG 1997; DFFP 1995. GP Princip. Centr. Lond. Socs: BMA. Prev: Lizei GP Centr. Lond.; GP/Regist. Capelfield Surg. Esher; SHO (O & G) Qu. Mary's Hosp. Sidcup.

NIELSEN, Fiona 247 ThurnCt. Road, Leicester LE5 2NL Tel: 0116 243 2093; 247 Thurncourt Road, Leicester LE5 2NL Tel: 0116 243 2093 — MB ChB 1992 Ed. (Univ. Ed.) SHO (Gen. Psychiat.) Leicester Gen. Hosp. Socs: Inceptor Roy. Coll. Psychiat.; BMA. Prev: SHO (Liaison Psychiat.) Leicester Gen. Hosp.; SHO (Therapeutic comm.) Francis Down Lodge, Leicester.

NIELSEN, Hugh John Village Medical Centre, 20 Quarry Street, Liverpool L25 6HE Tel: 0151 428 4282 Fax: 0151 421 0884; 25 Mount Clair Drive, Mosseley Hill, Liverpool L18 0HA — BM BCh 1979 Oxf.; MA Oxf. 1980, BM BCh 1979; MRCP (UK) 1986; MFHom 1990. Prev: Regist. (Med.) Roy. Liverp. Hosp.; Med. Dir. Outpats. Dept. Curtis Memor. Hosp. Newfld., Canada; SHO Roy. Brisbane Hosp. Austral.

NIELSEN, Jane Winefred 44 High Ash Avenue, Leeds LS17 8RG — MB BS 1991 Lond.

NIELSEN, Karen Chinedu Grove Medical Group, 1 The Grove, Gosforth, Newcastle upon Tyne NE3 1NU Tel: 0191 210 6680 Fax: 0191 210 6682 — MB BS 1987 Newc.; BMedSc Newc. 1984; MRCGP 1992; DRCOG 1992. Prev: Trainee GP Newc VTS.

NIELSEN, Karin Schoubo Ralphs Ride Practice, Ralphs Ride Surgery, Ralphs Ride, Bracknell RG12 9LH Tel: 01344 454626 Fax: 01344 303929 — MD 1994 Aarhus.

NIELSEN, Michael Stewart Intensive Care Unit, Southampton General Hospital, Southampton SO16 6YD Tel: 02380 796117 Fax: 02380 794753; 7 Grosvenor Road, Chandlers Ford, Eastleigh SO53 5BU — MB BS 1971 Lond.; MB BS (Hons., Distinc. Obst. & Gyn.) Lond. 1971; FFA RCS Eng. 1975. (Guy's) Cons. Anaesth. & Intens. Care Soton. Gen. Hosp.

NIELSON, Paul Christian East Street Medical Centre, East Street, Okehampton EX20 1AY Tel: 01837 52233; The Glebe House, Exbourne, Okehampton EX20 3RD — MB BS 1985 Lond.; BSc Lond. 1979, MB BS 1985; DRCOG 1988. (Charing Cross) GP Princip.; Hosp. Specialist (Gen. Med.).

NIEMAN, Eric Arnold The Consulting Rooms, Hospital of St John and St Elizabeth, 60 Grove End Road, London NW8 9NH Tel: 020 7286 5126 Fax: 020 7266 2316; 24 Woodside Avenue, London N6 4SS — MB ChB Liverp. 1950; MD Liverp. 1958; FRCP Lond. 1974, M 1955; DCH Eng. 1952. (Liverp.) Hon. Cons. Neurol. St. Mary's Hosp. Lond. Socs: Assn. Brit. Neurols.; Harveian Soc.; Internat. Soc. Hist. of Neurosci. Prev: Cons. Neurol. St. Mary's, St. Chas. & Roy. Masonic Hosps. Lond.; Sen. Regist. (Neurol.) St. Mary's Hosp. Lond.; Regist. Nat. Hosp. Qu. Sq. Lond.

NIEMCZUK, Peter Smith, Niemczuk, Woolrych and Marcus, 279-281 Mill Road, Cambridge CB1 3DG Tel: 01223 247812 Fax: 01223 214191 — MB ChB 1983 Leic.

NIEMIRO, Lorynda Aleksandra Krystyna Department of Anaesthetics, Frimley Park Hospital, Portsmouth Road, Frimley, Camberley GU16 7UJ Tel: 01276 604161; Oaklawn House, Star Hill Drive, Churt, Farnham GU10 2HP Tel: 01276 712207 — MB BS 1981 Lond.; FRCA 1989; DA (UK) 1986. (St. Bartholomew's) Cons. Anaesth. Frimley Pk. Hosp. Surrey. Prev: Cons. & Sen. Regist.

NIEPEL

(Anaesth.) Camb. Milit. Hosp.; Sen. Regist. (Anaesth.) Bristol & Frenchay Hosps.

***NIEPEL, Graham Gerd** 21 Robinson Drive, Pannal Ash, Harrogate HG2 9DJ — MB ChB 1997 Liverp.

NIESSER, Alison Janet Feddygfa Wen Surgery, Feddygfa Wen, Porthmadog LL49 4NU Tel: 01766 514207 Fax: 01766 514828 — MB BS 1979 Lond.; MRCGP 1984.

NIESSER, Anton Arthur Fron Olau, Mersey St., Borth y Gest, Porthmadog LL49 9UB Tel: 01766 513041 Fax: 01766 514828; Y Feddygfa Wen, Hafod Y Gest, Porthmadog LL49 9NU Tel: 01766 514610 — State Exam Med 1978 Ulm; MD Ulm 1980; T(GP) 1991. (Ulm, Germany) Socs: Balint Soc.

NIETO VELILLAS, Jose Joaquin 6 Carson Road, Barnet EN4 9EX Tel: 020 8441 6962 — LMS 1986 Saragossa; BSc Saragossa 1987; MRCOG 1995.

NIEVEL, John George Mayridge, 8 Brownlow Road, Croydon CR0 5JT Tel: 020 8681 0331 Fax: 020 8681 0331 — MD 1958 Budapest; PhD Lond. 1967; FRCPI 1984, M 1981; FRSC 1980; FRIC 1976; FIBiol. 1976. Co-Dir. Dept. Clin. Pharmacol. & Therap. & The Hypertens. Unit & Sen. Regist. Roy. N. Hosp. Lond; Hon. Lect. (Med.) Acad. Dept. Med. Roy. Free Hosp. Sch. Med. Univ. Lond; Hon. Sen. Regist. Roy. Free Hosp. Lond. Prev: Dir. Med. Research Brit. Indust. Biol. Research Assn.; Sen. Clin. Research Fell. Dept. Med. King's Coll. Hosp. Med. Sch. Univ. Lond.; Prof. Clin. Pharmacol. & Therap. Jeddah Saudi Arabia.

NIEZYWINSKI, Wojciech Aleksander Orthopaedic Department, King's Mill Hospital, Sutton in Ashfield, Nottingham NG17 4JL; 36 Florence Road, West Bridgford, Nottingham NG2 5HR — Lekarz 1984 Gdansk.

NIGAM, Mr Ajay Depart. Of Otolaryngology, Blackpool Victoria Hospital, Whinney Heys Road, Blackpool FY3 8NR Tel: 01253 306838 — MB BS 1979 Kanpur; FRCS 1995 (ORL); FRCS (Otol.) Ed. 1990; FRCS (Otol.) Lond 1990; FRCS (Surg.) Ed. 1985. Sen. Regist. (Otolaryngol.) Freeman Hosp. Newc. upon Tyne; Cons. (OtoLaryngol.), Blackpool Vict. Hosp., Blackpool. Socs: BMA & Otolaryngol. Research Soc. Prev: Regist. Rotat. (ENT) W. Midl.; SHO (ENT) Leicester Roy. Infirm.; Sen. Regist. (ENT), Freeman Hosp., Newc. Upon Tyne.

NIGAM, Mr Anurag Kishore Royal Surrey County Hospital, Department of Urology, Egerton Rd, Guildford GU2 7XX Tel: 01483 464045 Fax: 01483 454871 Email: aknigam@hotmail.com; Tel: 07956 912591 — MB BS 1987 Lond.; FRCS (Urol.) 1997; FRCS Eng. 1991; FEBU. 1998; MD 1999 Lond. (University College London) Cons. Urological Surg., Roy. Surrey Co. Hosp., Guildford. Socs: Fell. Roy. Soc. Med. (Edit. Represent. Clin. Sect.) Pres.-Elect; Jun. Mem. Brit. Assn. Urol. Surgs.; Roy. Coll. Surg. (Edr.ial Rep.of Jl., Mem. of Acad. Bd. & Pres. Clin. Sec.). Prev: Sen. Regist. (Urol.) St. Bart. Hosp. & Roy. Lond. Hosp.; Sen. Regist. (Urol.) S.end Hosp. W.cliff-on-Sea; Regist. (Urol.) St. Mary's Hosp. Lond.

NIGAM, Ashok Kumar Prince Philip Hospital, Bryngwynmawr, Dafen, Llanelli SA14 8QF Tel: 01554 756567; 83 Rhyd-y-Defaid Drive, Derwen Fawr, Swansea SA2 8AN Tel: 01792 296326 — MB BS 1969 Jabalpur; FFA RCS 1978; DA Delhi 1973. Cons. Anaesth. P. Philip Hosp, LLa.lli, Dyfed. Prev: Cons. Anaesth. LLa.lli Gen. Hosp. Dyfed; Regist. (Anaesth.) Singleton Hosp. Swansea & Univ. Hosp. Wales Cardiff.

NIGAM, Bishan Kumar (retired) 6A Bilton Road, Rugby CV22 7AB — MB BS Agra 1958; BSc Lucknow 1953; DTCD Wales 1963; DTD Lucknow 1961. Med. Practioner freelance. Prev: Assoc. Specialist Cardiothoracic Unit Walsgrave Hosp. Coventry.

NIGAM, Mr Keshav Department of Surgery, Torbay Hospital, Torquay TQ2 7AA Tel: 01803 614567; Pytchley, Foxhole Road, Chelston, Torquay TQ2 6RY Tel: 01803 607529 — MB BS 1983 Delhi; MB BS Delhi India 1983; MS (Gen. Surg.) Delhi 1986; FRCS Ed. 1991. (Maulana Azad Med. Coll. Delhi, India) Staff Grade (Gen. Surg.) Torbay Hosp. Socs: Brit. Soc. Gastroenterol.; Torquay Dist. Med. Soc.; BMA. Prev: Regist. & SHO (Gen. Surg.) Torbay Hosp.; Regist. (Gen. Surg.) LNJPN Hosp. New Delhi.

NIGAM, Ragni Wibsey and Queensbury Medical Practice, Fair Road, Wibsey, Bradford BD6 1TB Tel: 01274 677198 Fax: 01274 693389; 61 Hodgson Lane, Drighlington, Bradford BD11 1BW — MB BS 1988 Newc.; DRCOG 1993. (Univ. Newc. u. Tyne) Partner Wibsey Med. Centre, Bradford; Clin. Asst. (Genito - Urin. Med.) St

Lukes Hosp. Bradford. Prev: Trainee GP Bradford Roy. Infirm. VTS.; SHO (Gen. Med., Microbiol. & Infec. Dis.) Hope Hosp. Salford.

NIGAM, Subhash Chandra 129 Straight Road, Harold Hill, Romford RM3 7JD Tel: 01708 342517; 94 Parkstone Avenue, Emerson Park, Hornchurch RM11 3LR Tel: 01708 455574 — MB BS 1967 Lucknow; BSc Agra 1958. (G.S.V.M. Med. Coll. Kanpur)

NIGHTINGALE, Angus Kullervo 12 Springfield Road, Portishead, Bristol BS20 6LH Tel: 01275 814016 Email: nightingale@cardiff.ac.uk — MB BChir 1993 Camb.; MRCP (Lond) 1995.

NIGHTINGALE, Anne Margaret Lansdowne Clinic, 3 Whittingehame Gardens, Great Western Road, Glasgow G12 0AA Tel: 0141 211 3558 Fax: 0141 211 3522 Email: anne.nightingale@glacomen.scot.nhs.uk — MB BChir 1980 Camb.; MA Camb. 1979; MRCPsych 1986. (Cambridge University Addenbrooks Hosp) Cons. Psychotherapist Lansdowne Clinic Glas.

NIGHTINGALE, David Anthony 26 Salisbury Road, Cressington Park, Liverpool L19 0PJ Tel: 0151 427 0766 — MB BChir Camb. 1957; BA Camb. 1954; FRCA 1961; DA Eng. 1960. (Lond. Hosp.) Emerit. Cons. Anaesth. Roy. Liverp. Childr. Hosp. Alder Hey. Socs: Assn. Anaesth.; Assn. Paediat. Anaesth. Prev: Regional Educat. Adviser Coll. of Anaesth.; Dir. of Studies in Paediat. Anaesth. Univ. Liverp.; Sen. Fell. (Anaesth.) Childr. Hosp. Philadelphia, USA.

NIGHTINGALE, Doreen (retired) Flat 158, The White House, Albany St., London NW1 3UP — MRCS Eng. LRCP Lond. 1939; MS Lond. 1945, MB BS 1940; FRCS Eng. 1945. Fell. UCL. Prev: Thoracic Surg. Univ. Coll. Hosp. & Examr. in Surg. Univ. Lond.

NIGHTINGALE, Elizabeth Anne Esslemont Richards and Partners, The Surgery, North Street, Langport TA10 9RH Tel: 01458 250464 Fax: 01458 253246; South Ham Farm, Muchelney Ham, Langport TA10 0DJ Tel: 01458 250816 — MB ChB 1974 Aberd.; DObst RCOG 1976. Prev: SHO (Geriat.) High Carley Hosp. Ulverston; SHO (O & G) Risedale Matern. Hosp. Barrow-in-Furness; Ho. Phys. (Gen. Med.) & Ho. Surg. (Gen. Surg.) Roy. Hosp. Chesterfield.

NIGHTINGALE, Evelyn Agnes (retired) 39 Cranston Avenue, Bexhill-on-Sea TN39 3NN Tel: 01424 216316 — MB BS Lond. 1941; MRCS Eng. LRCP Lond. 1941.

NIGHTINGALE, Jeremy John Email: jeremy.nightingale@porthosp.swest.nhs.uk — MB ChB Bristol 1978; FFA RCS Eng. 1983. Cons. Anaesth. Portsmouth Hosps. Socs: Assn. Anaesth.; Anaesth. Res. Soc.; Obst. Anaesth. Assn. Prev: Cons. Stoke Mandeville Hosp. Aylesbury; Sen. Regist. (Anaesth.) Soton. Gen. Hosp.; Lect. (Anaesth.) Univ. Soton.

NIGHTINGALE, Jeremy Mark Darby Department of Gastroenterology, Leicester Royal Infirmary, Leicester LE1 5WW Tel: 0116 258 6324 Fax: 0116 258 6985 Email: jnight@globalnet.co.uk; 68 Theydon Street, Walthamstow, London E17 8EL Tel: 020 8556 4953 — MB BS 1981 Lond.; MD Lond. 1993; MRCP (UK) 1984. (Lond. Hosp. Med. Coll.) Cons. Gastroenterol. (Gen. Phys.) Leicester Roy. Infirm. Socs: Brit. Soc. Gastroenterol.; Inst. Health Servs. Managem.; Sec. Small Bowel/Nutrit. Sect. Prev: Sen. Regist. (Gen. Med. & Gastroenterol.) Leicester Roy. Infirm. & Leicester Gen. Hosp.; Regist. (Gastroenterol.) St. Mark's Hosp. Lond.; Research Regist. (Gastroenterol.) St. Marks Hosp. Lond. & OldCh. Hosp. Romford.

NIGHTINGALE, John Alexander (retired) 1 Charney Fold, Charney Well Lane, Grange-over-Sands LA11 6DB — MB ChB 1947 Manch.; MRCP Lond. 1949. Prev: Regist. (Cardiol.) & Resid. Clin. Path. Manch. Roy. Infirm.

NIGHTINGALE, John Halkon Grove Medical Practice, Shirley Health Centre, Grove Road, Shirley, Southampton SO15 3UA Tel: 023 8078 3611 Fax: 023 8078 3156 Email: john.nightingale@gp-j82088.nhs.uk; 1 Crofton Close, Oakmount, Highfield, Southampton SO17 1XB Tel: 02380 559274 — MB BS Newc. 1970; MRCGP 1976; DObst RCOG 1973. (Newcastle-upon-Tyne) Indep. Med. Assessor; Clin. Asst. Dermat. Prev: Resid. Hosp. Sick Childr. Toronto, Canada; SHO (O & G) Soton. Univ. Gp. Hosps.; SHO (Psychiat.) Knowle Hosp. Fareham.

NIGHTINGALE, Julia Anne 146 Woodside Road, Huddersfield HD4 5JJ — BM BCh 1991 Oxf.; BA (Hons.) Oxf. 1988; MRCP (UK) 1994. (Oxford University) Specialist Regist., Thoracic Medicene, NW Thames Region. Prev: Research Fell. (Thoracic Med.) Nat. Heart & Lung Inst. Imperial Coll.

NIGHTINGALE, Michael Douglas Bourne Hall Health Centre, Chessington Road, Ewell, Epsom KT17 1TG Tel: 020 8394 1500 — MB BS 1966 Lond.; MRCS Eng. LRCP Lond. 1966; MRCGP 1979; FFA RCS Eng. 1970. (St. Bart.) Socs: Brit. Soc. Allergy, Environm. & Nutrit. Med. Prev: SHO (Anaesth.) Nuffield Dept. Anaesth. Oxf. & Poole Gen. Hosp.; SHO (Cas.) Redhill Gen. Hosp.

NIGHTINGALE, Oswald Draper (retired) 6 Church View, Braddan, Douglas IM4 4TF — MB BCh BAO 1943 Dub. Prev: GP Lond.

NIGHTINGALE, Paul Douglas Lakeside Medical Centre, Church Road, Perton, Wolverhampton WV6 7QL Tel: 01903 755329 Fax: 01902 755224 — MB ChB 1979 Birm.

NIGHTINGALE, Peter Intensive Care Unit, Wythenshawe Hospital, Southmoor Road, Manchester M23 9LT Tel: 0161 291 6420 Fax: 0161 291 6421 Email: pnightingale@compuserve.com; 29 Moorfield Road, West Didsbury, Manchester M20 2UZ Tel: 0161 445 7307 Fax: 0161 438 0574 Email: pnightingale@compuserve.com — MB BS 1975 Lond.; FRCP Lond. 2000; MRCS Eng. LRCP Lond. 1975; FRCA 1980. (Guy's Hosp. Lond.) p/t Cons. Anaesth. and Intens. Care Wythenshawe Hosp. Manch.

NIGHTINGALE, Peter Bryan The Surgery, Grasmere Drive, High Bentham, Lancaster LA2 7JP Tel: 01524 261202 Fax: 01524 262222905; Fieldway, Mount Pleasant, High Bentham, Lancaster LA2 7LA Tel: 01524 262652 — MB BS 1982 Lond.; MRCGP 1986; DRCOG 1986; DTM & H Liverp. 1986; DCH RCP Lond. 1985. Prev: Med. Off. St Francis Hosp. Katete, Zambia.

NIGHTINGALE, Peter John Health Clinic, 407 Main Road, Dovercourt, Harwich CO12 4ET Tel: 01255 201299 Fax: 01255 201270; Terling, Oakley Road, Little Oakley, Harwich CO12 5DR Tel: 01255 508397 — MB BChir 1976 Camb.; BA Camb. 1973, MA, MB BChir 1976; DRCOG 1983; Danish Med. Lic. 1978. Gen. Med. Pract. DoverCt. Essex; Med. Off. Trinity Ho. Lond.; Police Surg. Essex Constab.; Med. Off. Harwich & DoverCt. Hosp.; Aviat. Med. Examr. Prev: Trainee GP Colchester Gp. VTS; Regist. (Anaesth. & IC) Bispebjerg Hosp. & Sundby Hosp. Copenhagen.

NIGHTINGALE, Peter John Richards and Partners, The Surgery, North Street, Langport TA10 9RH Tel: 01458 250464 Fax: 01458 253246; South Ham Farm, Muchelney Ham, Langport TA10 0DJ — MB ChB 1974 Sheff. Prev: SHO (O & G) Risedale Hosp. Barrow-in-Furness. Regist. Gen.; Med. N. Lonsdale Hosp. Barrow-in-Furness; Ho. Off. (Gen. Surg.) & Ho. Off. (Gen. Med.) Roy. Hosp. Chesterfield.

NIGHTINGALE, Robert Charles 5 Thornley Drive, Rushmere Road, Ipswich IP4 3LR Tel: 01473 718854 — MRCS Eng. LRCP Lond. 1973; MB Camb. 1974, BChir 1973; MRCP (UK) 1977; FRCR 1982. (St. Mary's) Cons. Radiol. Ipswich Hosp. Socs: Brit. Med. Ultrasound Soc. Prev: Sen. Regist. (Radiol.) Addenbrookes Hosp. Camb.; SHO (Anaesth.) & (Renal Unit) Addenbrookes Hosp. Camb.; SHO (Chest Unit) Papworth Hosp. Camb.

NIGHTINGALE, Sharon Louise 14 Station Road, Denby, Ripley DE5 8ND — MB ChB 1993 Leeds.

NIGHTINGALE, Simon Robert Severn Lodge, 58 New St., Shrewsbury SY3 8JQ — MD 1987 Lond.; BSc Lond. 1970, MD 1987, MB BS 1973; MRCP (U.K.) 1976; FRCP 1996. (UCHMS London) Cons. Neurol. Roy. Shrewsbury Hosp. Prev: Hon. Sen. Clin. Lect. Univ. of Birm.

NIHAL, Mr Aneel Flat 4, 62 Sinclair Road, London W14 0NH Tel: 020 7603 8194 — MB BS 1986 Karachi, Pakistan; FRCS Ed. 1992; FRCS Glas. 1992. Regist. (Orthop.) Roy. Surrey Co. Hosp. Guildford. Prev: Regist. (Orthop.) Kingston Hosp. Surrey.

NIHOYANNOPOULOS, Petros Hammersmith Hospital, Du Cane Road, London W12 0NN Tel: 020 8383 3948 Fax: 020 8740 8373 Email: petros@ic.ac.uk; 18 Endlesham Road, London SW12 8JU Tel: 020 8673 2095 — MD 1979 Strasbourg. (Louis Pasteur Strasbourg, France) Cons. Cardiol. Hammersmith Hosp. Lond.; Reader, Imp. Coll. Sch. Med. Lond. Socs: Founding Mem. Brit. Soc. Exchocardiogr.; Brit. Cardiac Soc.; Sec. Europ. Working Gp. Echocardiogr. Prev: Sen. Lect., Sen. Regist. & Regist. Hammersmith Hosp. & Roy. Postgrad. Med. Sch. Lond.

NIJHAR, Amarjeet The Surgery, 1 Waynflete Square, London W10 6UX — MB ChB 1980 Liverp.

NIJJAR, Amarjit Singh 255 Nithsdale Road, Glasgow G41 5AQ — MB ChB 1976 Glas.

NIJJAR, Avtar Singh Family Doctor Unit Surgery, 92 Bath Road, Hounslow TW3 3LN Tel: 020 8570 6271 Fax: 020 8570 3243; 378 Jersey Road, Osterley, Isleworth TW7 5PL Tel: 020 8758 2288 — MB BChir 1987 Camb.; MA Camb. 1987; MRCGP 1991; Cert. Family Plann. JCC 1991; DCH RCP Lond. 1991. (Addenbrooke's Hosp. Camb.) Asst. (Cardiol.) Ashford Hosp. Middx.

NIJJAR, Rajwinder Singh 8 Kingscote Grove, Cheltenham GL51 6JX — MB ChB 1994 Birm.; ChB Birm. 1994.

NIK ABDULLAH, Nik Azwar Izani Doctors Residence, Burton General Hospital, Burton-on-Trent DE14 4QH — MB BCh 1986 Wales.

NIKAM, Dattajirao Balkrishnarao c/o The Medical Staffing Officer, West Suffolk Hospital, Hardwick Lane, Bury St Edmunds IP33 2QZ — MB BS 1966 Poona.

NIKAPOTA, Herath Mudiyanselage Vijita L B Barnet General Hospital, Barnet EN5 3DJ Tel: 020 8732 4496 Fax: 020 8732 4499; 90 Abbots Road, Abbots Langley WD5 0BH Tel: 01923 62228 Fax: 020 8732 4499 — MB BS Ceylon 1965; MD Colombo 1982; FRCR 1975; FFR 1974; DMRD Eng. 1972. Cons. Radiol. Barnet Gen. Hosp. Socs: FRCR; Sri Lanka Med. Assn.; Med. Defence Union. Prev: Sen. Regist. Roy. Free Hosp. Lond.; Sen. Regist. Childr. Hosp. Lond.; Regist. N.wick Pk. Hosp.

NIKITAKIS, Nikolaos Nikitas Flat 5, 18 McDowall Road, Myatts Field Ctr., London SE5 9LD — Ptychio latrikes 1986 Athens.

NIKITIK, Constantin (retired) The Dene, Hillside Road, Aldershot GU11 3NB Tel: 01252 314106 — Med. Dipl. State Inst. Med. Lwow 1941; FFA RCS Eng. 1955; DA Eng. 1953. Prev: Cons. Anaesth. S. Shields Hosp. Gp.

NIKLAUS, Lisa Justine Windsor House, Coleford, Crediton EX17 5DE — MB ChB 1993 Manch.

NIKOLAOU, Constantine Marios c/o V. Philips, 243 Hurst Road, Sidcup DA15 9AL — Ptychio latrikes 1964 Athens.

NIKOLAOU, Dimitrios IVF Unit, Hammersmith Hospital, Du Cane Road, London W12 0NN Tel: 020 8383 8160 Email: dnikolaou@talk21.com; 54 Cavendish Road, Ealing, London W13 03Q Tel: 020 8997 2891 — Ptychio latrikes 1993 Athens; DFFP 1996; MD Ptychio latrikes Athens 1993; MRCOG 1997. Clin. Rec. Fell. (Repro. Med.) IVF Unit Ham'smth Hosp. Lond. W12 0NN. Socs: MBA. Prev: Specialist Regist. (O & G) Aber. Mater. Hosp.; Sen. SHO (O & G) Nevill Hall Hosp. Abergoreuas Wales.; SHO (O & G) St Jowes Hosp. Leeds.

NIKOLOPOULOS, John 41 Glasslyn Road, London N8 8RJ — Ptychio latrikes 1981 Athens.

NIMAN, Wilfred 6 Hilton Court, South Promenade, Lytham St Annes FY8 1LZ Tel: 01253 728408 — MRCS Eng. LRCP Lond. 1945. (Leeds) Prev: Ho. Surg. & Ho. Phys. Pinderfields Emerg. Hosp. Wakefield.

NIMBKAR, Vidyadhar Waman (retired) Flat 4A, Harlestones Close, Stourbridge DY8 4JL Tel: 01384 371522 — MB BS 1953 Bombay; MS Bombay 1955; DA Eng. 1970. Prev: Med. Off. Nat. Blood Transfus. Serv. Birm.

NIMENKO, Wasyl John 108 St Albans Avenue, London W4 5JR — MB BS 1979 Lond.; MRCS Eng. LRCP Lond. 1979. (Char. Cross)

NIMMO, Alaister John (retired) The Bungalow, 2A Dovedale Road, London SE22 0NF Tel: 020 8299 2835 — MB BS 1938 Lond.; MRCS Eng. LRCP Lond. 1937.

NIMMO, Alastair Forbes Department of Anaesthesia, Royal Infirmary of Edinburgh, Lauriston Place, Edinburgh EH3 9YW Tel: 0131 536 3651 Fax: 0131 536 3672 Email: a.nimmo@ed.ac.uk; 3 Queens Avenue, Blackhall, Edinburgh EH4 2DG Tel: 0131 539 2130 Fax: 08700 347157 — MB ChB 1983 Aberd.; FFA RCS Eng. 1988. (Aberdeen) Cons. Anaesth. Roy. Infirm. Edin. NHS Trust; Hon. Clin. Sen. Lect. Univ. of Edin. Socs: Assn. Anaesth.; Vasc. Anaesth. Soc.; Soc. Intravenous Anaesth. Prev: Specialist Anaesth. Charité Univ., Berlin; Sen. Regist. (Anaesth.) Lothian HB; Research Fell. (Anaesth.) Roy. Infirm. Edin.

NIMMO, David Henderson (retired) 46 Kelvin Walk, Netherhall, Largs KA30 8SJ Tel: 01475 675415 — MB ChB 1952 Glas.; MRCPsych 1971; DPM Eng. 1957. Prev: Cons. Psychiat. Leverndale Hosp. Glas.

NIMMO, Graham Robert Acute Receiving Unit, Western General Hosp, Lothian University Hospitals NHS Trust, Edinburgh EH4 2XU Tel: 0131 534 1876 Fax: 0131 539 1021 Email: g.nimmo@ed.ac.uk; Kolvir, 79 Belgrave Road, Corstorphine, Edinburgh EH12 6NH Tel: 0131 334 1876 Email: g.nimmo@ed.ac.uk — MB ChB 1982 Ed.; BSc (Med. Sci.) Ed. 1979;

NIMMO

MD Ed. 1996; MRCP (UK) 1985; FFA RCSI 1996; DA (UK) 1993; FRCP Edin 1998. (Univ. Ed.) Cons.INT Med. & Intens. Care W.. Gen. Hosp. Edin.; Hon. Sen. Lec. Univ of Edin. Prev: Career Regist. (Anaesth.) Vict. Infirm.Glas.; Career Regist. (Renal Med.) Glas. Roy. Infirm.; Regist. (Renal Med.) Roy. Infirm. Edin.

NIMMO, Isabelle Gardner Reid (retired) Flat 6, Dunard, 123 Grange Loan, Edinburgh EH9 2EA Tel: 0131 667 0094 — 1949 MB ChB St. And. 1949; BSc 1945.

NIMMO, Jessie Fraser Grieve's Cottage, Duntarvie, Winchburgh, Broxburn EH52 6QA — MB ChB 1944 Ed. (Ed.)

NIMMO, Jill Patricia Grangewood, Church Lane, Thurstaston, Wirral CH61 0HW — MB ChB 1982 Birm.; ChB Birm. 1982; MRCGP 1986; DRCOG 1985. Med. Ref. DSS Liverp.

NIMMO, John Medical Unit, Western General Hospital, Crewe Rd, Edinburgh EH4 2XU Tel: 0131 537 1037 Fax: 0131 537 1728; 5A Wedderburn Terr, Inveresk, Musselburgh EH21 7TJ Tel: 0131 665 5432 — MB ChB 1965 Ed.; FRCP Ed. 1976, M 1969; FFPM RCP (UK) 1995. (Ed.) Cons. Phys. W.ern Gen. Hosp., Edin.; Hon. Sen. Lect. (Med.) W.. Gen. Hosp. Edin. Prev: Cons Phys.E.ern. Gen. Hosp.Edin. 1974-1998.

NIMMO, Malcolm James Ninewells Hospital, Ninewells Avenue, Dundee DD1 9SY Tel: 01382 632651 Email: malcolm@dth.scot.nhs.uk; The Court, 6 Farington St, Dundee DD2 1PJ Tel: 01382 668061 Email: mnimmo7128@aol.com — MB ChB 1981 Ed.; FRCR 1989. (Edinburgh) Cons. Radiol. Ninewells Hosp. Dundee.

NIMMO, Shirin Kingswood Medical Centre, Clayhill Road, Kingswood, Basildon SS16 5AD; 24 Wick Lane, Wickford SS11 8AR Tel: 01268 561047 — MB BCh 1985 Wales. Prev: Trainee GP Cardiff; SHO (Obst.) Merthyr Gen. Hosp.; SHO (Gen. Med.) Carmarthen Hosps.

NIMMO, Steven Brian Barton Surgery, Barton, Horn Lane, Plymouth PL9 9BR Tel: 01752 407129 Fax: 01752 482620 — MB ChB 1988 Leic.; BSc Leic. 1986; DRCOG 1995; DFFP 1995; MRCGP 1996.

NIMMO, Susan Mary Kolvir, 79 Belgrave Road, Corstorphine, Edinburgh EH12 6NH — MB ChB 1985 Ed.; BSc (Hons.) Ed. 1983; MRCP (UK) 1988; FRCA 1992. Cons. Anaesth. Roy. Infirm. Edin. Prev: Sen. Regist. (Anaesth.) Roy. Infirm. Glas.; Regist. (Renal Med.) W.. Infirm. Glas.; SHO (Anaesth.) Roy. Infirm. Edin.

NIMMO, Thomas William Camelon Medical Practice, 3 Baird Street, Camelon, Falkirk FK1 4PP Tel: 01324 622854 Fax: 01324 633858; 40 Majors Loan, Falkirk FK1 5QB Tel: 01324 26955 — BSc (Med. Sci.) Ed. 1975, MB ChB 1978; MRCGP 1982; DRCOG 1980; DCH Glas. 1980.

NIMMO, Walter Sneddon Inveresk Research, Tranent EH33 2NE Tel: 01875 614545 Fax: 01875 614555 Email: walter_nimmo@sgsgroup.com; 26 Stafford Street (IF), Edinburgh EH3 7BD Tel: 0131 225 7715 Email: walter_nimm@msn.com — MD 1982 Ed.; BSc (Med. Sc.) 1968, MB ChB 1971; FRCP Ed. 1984; FRCP Glas. 1984; MRCP (UK) 1975; FRCA 1993; FANZCA 1993; FFA RCS Eng. 1977; FFPM RCP (UK) 1993. Chief Exec. Inveresk Research; Hon. Fell. Univ. (Anaesth.) Roy. Infirm. Edin. Prev: Prof. (Anaesth.) Univ. Sheff.; Sen. Lect. (Anaesth.) W.. Infirm. Glas.; Lect. (Anaesth.) & Lect. (Therap. & Clin. Pharmacol.) Roy. Infirm. Ed.

NINAN, Mr Andrews Chirathalattu Flat 4, Noble's Hospital, Westmoreland Road, Douglas IM1 4QA — MB BS 1983 Kerala; FRCS Ed. 1992.

NINAN, Golda Mary 173 Queens Crescent, Chippenham SN14 0NW Tel: 01249 445003 Email: gninan@hotmail.com — MB BCh 1995 Wales. (University of Wales College of Medicine Cardiff) Med. Regist. Tauranga Hosp. New Zealand. Prev: Med. SHO Rotat. Co. Hosp. Hereford.

NINAN, Mammen c/o Mr V. Harihar, 49 Chapman Road, Coreys Mill Lane, Stevenage SG1 4RJ — MB BS 1992 Kerala, India; MRCP (UK) 1992.

NINAN, Titus Kallupurackal 6 Park Road, Solihull B91 3SU — MD 1982 Bombay; MB BS Bombay 1979; MRCP (UK) 1987; DCH Bombay 1982.

***NIND, Nicholas Robert** 120 Shelford Road, Cambridge CB2 2NF — MB ChB 1995 Sheff.

NINES, Ronald John Nines and Partners, Shoreham Health Centre, Pond Road, Shoreham-by-Sea BN43 5US Tel: 01273 440550 — MB 1976 Camb.; BChir 1975; MRCGP 1979; DRCOG 1977; DCH Eng. 1977.

NINHAM, Mark Charles Royal Manor Health Care, Park Estate Road, Easton, Portland DT5 2BJ Tel: 01305 820422 Fax: 01305 824143 — BM BS 1992 Nottm.; MRCGP 1998.

NINIS, Nelly 3 Monkfrith Way, London N14 5LG — MB BS 1989 Lond.

NINKOVIC, Mary 226 Hills Road, Cambridge CB2 2QE — MB BChir 1987 Camb.; PhD Camb. 1982; BPharm Lond. 1978; Mps 1979. Sen. Regist. (Gastroenterol.) Addenbrooke's Hosp. Camb. Prev: Foulkes Foundat. Fell.sh. 1984-86.; Sen. Regist. (Gastroenterol.) Roy. Free Hosp. Lond.; Teach. Regist. (Gastroenterol.) Roy. Postgrad. Med. Sch. Hammersmith Hosp. Lond.

NINOS, Anestis Room B5, The Oaks, Little Ridge Avenue, St Leonards-on-Sea TN37 7UW — Ptychio Iatrikes 1986 Athens.

NIRANJAN, Kantha Redbridge Heath Trust, King Georges Hospital, Gioudmayes Lane, Ilford IG18 3XJ\ Tel: 020 8924 6224 Fax: 020 8924 6199; 12 Grosvenor Gardens, Oakwood, London N14 4TX Tel: 020 8360 1628 Email: niranjan@easynet.co.uk — MB BS 1981 Sri Lanka; MB BS Sri Lanka 1980; MSc Gerontol. Lond. 1995; MRCS Eng LRCP Lond. 1988; MRCP (UK) 1990. (Univ. Perdeniya, Sri-Lanka) Cons. Physic. Redbridge NHS Healthcare, Essex Trust. Socs: Brit Geriat. Soc.; BMA; RCP. Prev: Sen. Regist. Integrated Med. W. Mid. Rot. Birm.; Research Fell. (Neuro.) Old Ch. Hosp. Romford.

NIRANJAN, Nadarajah 12 Grosvenor Gardens, London N14 4TX — MB BS 1980 Colombo.

NIRANJAN, Mr Nandagudi Shivaiah Broomfield Hospital, St. Andrews Centre for Plastic Surgery, Chelmsford CM1 7ET Tel: 01245 516123 Fax: 01245 516132; Weatherby, Goat Hall Lane, Chelmsford CM2 8PG Tel: 01245 266985 Fax: 01245 263668 — MB BS 1972 Karnatak; MB BS Karnatak Univ. 1972; MS Mysore 1975; FRCS (Plast) 1992; FRCS Eng. 1980; FRCS Ed. 1979; MRCS Eng. LRCP Lond. 1979. (JN Medical College Belgaum, India) Cons. Plastic Surg. Broomfield Hosp.; Hon. Cons. Plastic Surg. Roy. Lond. Hosp. Socs: Brit. Assn. Plastic Surg.; Brit. Assn. Aesthetic Plastic Surgs.; Brit. Soc. Surg. Hand. Prev: Cons. Plastic Surg. Roy. Lond. Hosp.; Sen. Regist. (Plastic Surg.) St. Lawrence Hosp. Chepstow; Regist. (Plastic & Reconstruc. Surg.) St. Lawrence Hosp., Chepstow.

***NIRDOSH, Neetu** 62 Elizabeth Road, Moseley, Birmingham B13 8QJ — MB ChB 1998 Birm.; ChB Birm. 1998.

NIRGUDE, Subhashchandra Vasant Russell Street Surgery, 41 Russell Street, Reading RG1 7XD Tel: 0118 957 3752 Fax: 0118 956 0381; 1 The Chase, Calcot, Reading RG31 7DW Tel: 0118 957 3752 Fax: 0118 956 0381 — MB BS 1969 Nagpur; DFFP 1993. (Govt. Med. Coll. Nagpur) Sen. Police Surg. Thames Valley Police Auth.; Med. Off. i/c Bath Rd. Day Hosp. for Dementia; Med. Adviser (Aviat. Med.) for Air India Lond. Socs: Fell. Roy. Soc. Health; Fell. Roy. Soc. Med.; Roy. Aeronaut. Soc.

NIRMAL, Divyabala Lalitkumar Fairwater Surgery, Fairwater, Cwmbran NP44 Tel: 0163 33 69544; (resid), 86 Glan Ryde, Coed Eva, Cwmbran NP44 6TZ Tel: 0163 33 66233 — MB BS 1970 Saurashtra; DObst RCOG 1972. (M.P. Shah Med. Coll. Jamnagar) Prev: Regist. (O & G) & SHO (O & G) Wordsley Hosp.; Stourbridge.

NIRMALAN, Rajanayagam Roehampton Surgery, 191 Roehampton Lane, London SW15 4HN Tel: 020 8788 1188 Fax: 020 8789 9914; 32 Presburg Road, New Malden KT3 5AH — MB BS 1980 Lond.; MRCS Eng. LRCP Lond. 1979. (Char. Cross)

NIRMALANANTHAN, Mr Sivaguru 50 Marlands Road, Clayhall, Ilford IG5 0JJ Tel: 020 8551 6906 — MB BS 1963 Ceylon; FRCS Ed. 1980; FRCOphth 1989; DO RCS Eng. 1979. Hon. Cons. Ophth. Roy. Free Hosp. Lond.; Assoc. Specialist Moorfields Eye Hosp. Lond. Prev: Cons. Ophth. Govt. Gen. Hosp. Jaffna, Sri Lanka; Clin. Asst. Moorfields Eye Hosp. Lond.; Regist. Chelmsford & Essex Hosp. Chelmsford.

NIRODI, Gajanan Niranjan 31 Derby Street, Beverley Road, Hull HU3 1ST — MB ChB 1994 Manch.

NIRODI, Pratibha 5 Linden Close, Saintfield, Ballynahinch BT24 7BH — MB BCh BAO 1991 Belf.

***NIRODI, Sandya** 5 Linden Close, Saintfield, Ballynahinch BT24 7BH — MB ChB 1996 Ed.

NIRODI, Vinatha Niranjan 5 Linden Close, Saintfield, Ballynahinch BT24 7BH Tel: 01238 510839 — MB BS 1962 Bombay; DGO CPS Bombay 1964; Cert. Family Plann. JCC 1983. (Topiwalla Nat. Med. Coll. Bombay)

NIRULA, Mr Harish Chandra Artificial Limb and Appliance Centre, Wrexham Maelor Hospital, Croesnewydd Rd, Wrexham LL13 7NT Tel: 01978 727288 Fax: 01978 290820; 9 Badgers Rake, Victoria Road, Formby, Liverpool L37 1XU Tel: 01704 870003 — MB BS Nagpur 1960; FRCS Eng. 1964. (Govt. Med. Coll. Nagpur) p/t Cons. Rehabil. Med. Wrexham Maelor Hosp.

NIRULA, Neera H. M. Prison, 2 Ribbleton Lane, Preston PR1 5AB Tel: 01772 57734; 9 Badgers Rake, Victoria Road, Formby, Liverpool L37 1XU Tel: 017048 70003 — MD 1971 Nagpur; MD (Obst. & Gyn.) Nagpur 1971; MB BS Delhi 1966; DA Eng. 1974; DGO Nagpur 1969. (Lady Hardinge Med. Coll.) Sen. Med. Off. H.M Prison Preston. Prev: Med. Off. H.M. Prison Wakefield; SHO (Obst.) & SHO (Anaesth.) Pontefract Gen. Infirm.; SHO (Anaesth.) Nevill Hall Hosp. Abergavenny.

***NIRULA, Radhika Payal** 9 Badgers Rake, Formby, Liverpool L37 1XU — BM BS 1998 Nottm.; BM BS Nottm 1998.

NISBET, Alister Macgregor 32 Rosebery Avenue, Bridlington YO15 3PR Tel: 01262 675003 — MB ChB 1954 Aberd.; MFCH 1989; DObst RCOG 1959; Cert Developm. Paediat. Univ. Leeds 1980. Sen. Clin. Off. (Child Health) Hull HA. Socs: Fac. Community Health.

NISBET, Angus Paul Department of Neurology, Royal Sussex County Hospital, Eastern Road, Brighton BN2 5BG Tel: 01273 676011 Email: angus_nisbet@brighton_healthcare.nhs.uk — BM BS 1986 Nottm.; BMedSci Nottm. 1984; MRCP (UK) 1990. Cons. Neurol. Health Care NHS Trust. Socs: Internat. League Against Epilepsy; Assoc. Mem. Assn. Brit. Neurol.; Movem. Disorder Soc. Prev: Sen. Regist. (Neurol.) Qu.'s Med. Centre, Nottm.; Research Fell. Nat. Hosp. for Neurol. & Neurosurg.; Regist. (Neurol.) Univ. Hosp. Wales.

NISBET, Charlotte (retired) 2 Grey Gables, Southwood, Monkton, Prestwick KA9 1UR — MB ChB 1963 Glas.; FRCPath 1987, M 1973. Prev: Cons. Haemat. Ayrsh. & Arran HB.

NISBET, Ian Gardner Old Brandon Road Surgery, Old Brandon Road, Feltwell, Thetford IP26 4AY Tel: 01842 828481 Fax: 01842 828172; The Old House, Feltwell, Thetford IP26 4DL Tel: 01842 828956 — MB BS Lond. 1968; MRCS Eng. LRCP Lond. 1968; DObst RCOG 1970. (Lond. Hosp.) Prev: SHO (Obst.) & Ho. Phys. Redhill Gen. Hosp.; Ho. Surg. (Accid. & Orthop.) Lond. Hosp.

NISBET, Nanette Hendry (retired) 6 High Street, Pittenweem, Anstruther KY10 2LA — MD (High Commend.) Glas. 1952, MB ChB 1948; FRCP Glas. 1977, M 1964. Prev: Cons. Geriat. Highland Health Bd.

NISBET, Mr Norman Walter (retired) 3 Canberra Court, Richmond Avenue, Bognor Regis PO21 2YH Tel: 01243 863555 — LRCP LRCS Ed. LRFPS Glas. 1934; FRCS Eng. 1966; FRCS Ed. 1936; LDS RCS Ed. 1932. Prev: Dir. Research Robt. Jones & Agnes Hunt Orthop. Hosp. OsW.ry Shrops.

NISBET, Ruby Jean Brodie (retired) White House, Forest Road, E. Horsley, Leatherhead KT24 5BA — MB ChB 1931 Ed.; DPH 1933. Prev: Med. Off. (Social Welf.) Singapore.

NISBET, Ruth Kelso Medical Group Practice, Health Centre, Inch Road, Kelso TD5 7JP Tel: 01573 224424 Fax: 01573 226388; Eden House, Eden Road, Ednam, Kelso TD5 7QG — MB ChB 1981 Ed.; MRCGP 1985; DRCOG 1984.

NISBET, Ruth Margaret 1 Laverockbank Avenue, Edinburgh EH5 3BP — MB ChB 1988 Ed.; MRCGP 1993. (Ed.) SHO ENT. Socs: BMA.

NISBET, William Henry (retired) 294 Ferry Road, Edinburgh EH5 3NP Tel: 0131 552 5390 — MB ChB 1947 Ed.; Dip. Ven. Soc. Apoth. Lond. 1976. Prev: Clin. Asst. Sexually Transm. Dis. Roy. Infirm. Edin.

NISBET-SMITH, Ann Patricia 2 Middleton Buildings, Langham St., London W1W 7SZ Tel: 020 7636 6403 — MB BS Lond. 1959; MRCS Eng. LRCP Lond. 1959. (St. Mary's) Socs: BMA; ACP. Prev: Assoc. Specialist (Histopath.) N.wick Pk. Hosp. Harrow; Med. Off. (Cytol.) Vict. Infirm. Glas.; Med. Off. Barbados Gen. Hosp. & Port of Spain Gen. Hosp., Trinidad.

NISBET-SMITH, Catherine Heathgate Surgery, Poringland, Norwich NR14 7JT Tel: 01508 494343; Whitehouse Farm, 4 Edward Seago Place, Brooke, Norwich NR15 1HL Tel: 01508 558387 — MB BS 1987 Lond.; MA Camb. 1984; BSc (Hons.) St. And. 1982.

NISCHAL, Mr Kanwal Ken Dept. of Ophthalmology, Great Ormond Street Hospital for Children, Great Ormond Street, London WC1N 3JH Tel: 020 7813 8524 Fax: 020 7829 8647; Tel: 01753 889225 Fax: 01753 884877 Email: kkn@btinternet.com — MB BS 1988 Lond.; FRCOphth 1993. p/t Cons., Gt. Ormond St. Hosp.; Hon. Sen. Lect., Inst. of Child Health, Lond.; Mem. of the Standard Med. Advisery Comm. to The Dept. of Health; Mem. of the Scientif. Advisery Bd. of the Cornecia de Lange Soc.; Mem. of the Edr.ial Bd. of the Amer. Orthoptic Jl. Socs: Foundat. of Sci. & Technol.; Brit. Med. Assn.; Roy. Soc. Med. Prev: Clin. Fell., Hosp. for Sick Childr., Toronto; Sen. Regist. Oxf. Eye Hosp. & P. Chas. Eye Unit Windsor; Regist. Birm. & Morland Eye Hosp.

NISCHAL, Vijaya Kumar 20 Blenheim Avenue, Gants Hill, Ilford IG2 6JQ — MB BCh BAO 1980 Belf.; DRCOG 1983.

NISHITH, Shirish 4 College Close, Birkdale, Southport PR8 4DG — MB BS 1983 Madras; FCOphth 1990.

NISSEN, Mr Justin James Flat 3, 20 Montagu Square, London W1H 2LE — BM BS 1989 Nottm.; FRCS Eng. 1993.

NISSENBAUM, Hilary 10 Cheviot Gardens, London NW2 1QN — MB ChB 1978 Liverp.; MA (Med. Law & Ethics, Keys Col. 1997); BSc (Hons.) (Physiol.) Liverp. 1975; MRCPsych 1982. (Liverp.) p/t Cons. (Old Age Psychiat.) Harrow and Hillingdon NHS Trust, N.wick Pk. Hosp.; Second Opinion Doctor Ment. Health Act Commisss.; Ment. Health Review Tribunal. Prev: Cons. Psychogeriat., S. Lond. and Maudsley Trust; Cons. Psychogeriat. Qu. Eliz. Psychiat. Hosp.; Regist. (Psychiat.) Withington Hosp. Manch.

NISSENBAUM, Simon Henry Welbeck Road Surgery, 1A Welbeck Road, Bolsover, Chesterfield S44 6DF Tel: 01246 823742 — MB ChB 1980 Manch.; MRCGP 1984.

***NISTALA, Kiran** 9c Hugerford Road, London N7 9LA — MB BS 1996 Lond.

NITHI, Kannan Athavan 53 The Green, Shustoke, Birmingham B46 2AT Tel: 01675 481349 Email: kannan@globalnet.co.uk; c/o Neurology Unit, Radcliffe Infirmary, Oxford OX2 6HE — MB BS 1992 Lond.; BSc Lond. 1989; MRCP (UK) 1995. Specialist Regist. Neurol. Radcliffe Infirm. Oxf. Socs: Assoc. Mem. Assn. Brit. Neurol.; Brit. Soc. Clin. Neurophysiol. Prev: Research Regist. (Clin. Neurol.) Radcliffe Infirm. Oxf.

NITHIANANDAN, Mr Ponniah Kings Hill Hospital, Sutton-in-Ashfield NG17 4JL — MB BS 1972 Ceylon; FRCS (Ophth.) Ed. 1982; MRCS Eng. LRCP Lond. 1979; DO Eng. 1981. Regist. (Ophth.) Kings Mill Hosp. Notts.

NITHIANANDAN, Sulochana Kings Mill Hospital, Sutton-in-Ashfield NG17 4JL — MB BS 1976 Sri Lanka; MB BS Sri Lanka 1976 MRCS Eng. LRCP Lond. 1979; FFA RCS Eng. 1981 DA Eng. 1980. Regist. (Anaesth.) Qu. Univ. Med. Centre, Notts.

NITHIANANTHAM, Vellore Thiruvengadam 70 Hither Green Lane, Redditch B98 9BW — MB BS 1969 Madras.

NITHIYANANTHAN, Ratnasingam Birmingham Heartlands Hospital, Boardesly Green E., Birmingham B9 5SS Tel: 0121 766 6611; 20 King Henrys Road, Kingston upon Thames KT1 3QA Tel: 020 8241 3469 — MB ChB 1993 Leeds; MRCP (UK) 1997. (Leeds) Specialist Regist. (Diabetes & Endocrinol. with Gen. Med.) Heartland & Solihull NHS Trust Birm. Socs: BMA; Med. Protec. Soc.

NITHYANANDARAJAH, Mr Gnanapragasam Antony Loyala 123 Waverly Road, Harrow HA2 9RQ Email: nithy.g@btinternet.com — MB BS 1982 Peradeniya; FRCS Ed. 1989; FCOphth 1990.

NITHYANANDHAN, Govindasamy The Medical Centre, St. Omer Barracks, Aldershot GU11 2BN — MB BS 1961 Madras.

NITZKE, Franciszek Jerzy (retired) 96 Timberley Lane, Birmingham B34 7EN Tel: 0121 747 2100 — MD Warsaw 1930.

NIVEN, Anne Pullar Tel: 01753 646994 Fax: 01753 646907 Email: anne.niven@dial.pipex.com — MB ChB 1975 Cape Town; MRCGP 1980; DRCOG 1980. (Cape Town)

NIVEN, Christine Frances Fife Primary Care, NHS Trust, * *, Rosyth, Dunfermline KY11 2SE Tel: 01383 416181 — MB ChB 1980 Glas.; BSc (Hons.) (Molecular Biol.) Glas. 1977, MB ChB 1980; MRCGP 1986; DCCH RCGP & FCM 1986; DRCOG 1986. (Univ. Glas.) Staff Grade. Comm. Paediat. Fife Prim. Care NHS Trust. Socs: BMA. Prev: Trainee GP & Community Paediat. Edin. VTS.; SHO (Otorhinolaryngol.) Vict. Infirm. Glas.; GP Dumbarton Health Centre VTS.

NIVEN, Mr Peter Ashley Robertson 2 Clifton Park, Clifton, Bristol BS8 3BS Tel: 0117 9738446 & profess. 238206 — MA, MB Camb. 1963, BChir 1962; FRCS Eng. 1966; FRCOG 1982, M 1969. (Camb. & St. Bart.) Cons. O & G St. Michael's Hosp. Bristol United

NIVEN

Bristol Healthcare Trust. Prev: Eden Trav. Fell.sh. RCOG; Sen. Regist. (O & G) St. Bart. Hosp. Lond.; Cons. O & G Newc. Gen. & Hexham Gen. Hosps.

NIVEN, Robert McLay North West Lung Centre, Wythenshawe Hospital, Southmoor Road, Manchester M23 9LT Tel: 0161 998 7070 Fax: 0161 291 2832; 1 Stour Close, Altrincham WA14 4UE Tel: 0161 929 9448 — MD 1994 Manch.; FRCP 2001 (UK); BSc St. And. 1981; MB ChB 1984; MRCP (UK) 1988; MFOM RCP Lond. 1995. Hon. Cons. (Phys. Respirat. Med.) Wythenshawe Hosp. Prev: Sen. Regist. (Respirat. Med.) Wythenshawe Hosp.; Sen. Regist. Train. Post (Occupat. Med.) Manch. Univ. Wythenshaw Hosp. & Agrevo Ltd; Research Regist. Wythenshawe Hosp.

NIVEN, Sacha David 2 Abbey Court, Woolton, Liverpool L25 5HS Tel: 0151 421 0750 — MB ChB 1993 Liverp.; MRCP 1997. Specialist Regist. (Radiol.) Roy. Liverp. Univ. Hosp.

NIVEN-JENKINS, Nicholas Craig 26 High Street, Erdington, Birmingham B23 6RN Tel: 0121 373 0086; 86 Antrobus Road, Boldmere, Sutton Coldfield B73 5EL Tel: 0121 355 6511 — MB ChB 1978 Birm.; BSc (Hons.) Birm. 1975, MB ChB 1978; MRCGP 1984. Socs: Roy. Coll. Gen. Pract.; Soc. Occupat. Med. Prev: SHO VTS Birm. Dist.; Ho. Off. (Surg.) Qu. Eliz. Hosp. Birm.; Ho. Off. (Med.) Dudley Rd. Hosp. Birm.

***NIWA, Khatim** 85 Dolobran Road, Birmingham B11 1HL — MB BS 1998 Lond.; MB BS Lond 1998.

NIX, Amanda Louise 13 Stanmore Street, Burley, Leeds LS4 2RS — MB ChB 1993 Leeds.

NIX, Anthony John Haunton (retired) 11 Willingale Way, Thorpe Bay, Southend-on-Sea SS1 3SL Tel: 01702 586440 Email: anthonyetwill@aol.com — MB BChir Camb. 1960; BA Camb. 1956; MRCS Eng. LRCP Lond. 1960. Prev: GP S.end-on-Sea.

***NIX, Paul Alan** Carrfield House, 54 Carrfield Road, Barwick in Elmet, Leeds LS15 4JB Tel: 0113 281 2577 — BM BCh 1994 Oxf.; BA (Physiol. Sci.) Oxf. 1991.

NIXON, Alexander Allan Dr McElhone and Partners, Townhead Surgery, 6-8 High St., Irvine KA12 0AY Tel: 01294 273131 Fax: 01294 312832 — MB ChB 1981 Dundee; BMSc 1978.

NIXON, Caroline Meryl The Medical Centre, Badgers Crescent, Shipston-on-Stour CV36 4BQ Tel: 01608 661845 Fax: 01608 663614 — MB ChB 1983 Birm.; MRCP (UK) 1986; MRCGP 1989.

NIXON, Caroline Violet Charlotte 15 Kingfisher Close, Hamble, Southampton SO31 4PE — BM 1990 Soton.

NIXON, Christopher John The Health Centre, Oliver St., Ampthill, Bedford MK45 2SB Tel: 01525 402302 Fax: 01525 840764 — MB BS 1970 Lond.; MRCS Eng. LRCP Lond. 1971; MRCP (UK) 1973; MRCGP 1983; DRCOG 1979. Course Organiser Bedford VTS.

NIXON, Mr David Peter Wychwood Surgery, 62 High Street, Milton-under-Wychwood, Chipping Norton OX7 6LE Tel: 01993 830260 Fax: 01993 831867; Snowdon House, Fiddlers Hill, Shipton under Wychwood, Chipping Norton OX7 6DR — MB ChB 1979 Ed.; FRCS Ed. 1985; FRCS Eng. 1985; MRCGP 1990; DRCOG 1988. (Ed.) Prev: Regist. (Surg.) Roy. Liverp. Hosp.; Trainee GP/SHO Roy. Utd. Hosp. Bath VTS; Princip. Med. Off. Gizo, Solomon Is.

NIXON, Dennis The Medical Centre, Pinkham, Cleobury Mortimer, Kidderminster DY14 8QE Tel: 01299 270209 Fax: 01299 270482 Email: docs@cleoburymedical.freeserve.co.uk; The Old Barns, Tenbury Road, Cleobury Mortimer, Kidderminster DY14 8RB Tel: 01299 270209 Email: dennis@oldbouns.freeserve.co.uk — MB ChB 1973 Birm.; MRCGP 1978; DObst RCOG 1976. Med. Assessor Indep. Tribunal Serv.

***NIXON, Desni Lee** 10B Wester Coates Gardens, Edinburgh EH12 5LT Tel: 0131 337 0331 — MB ChB 1995 Aberd.

NIXON, Helena Katherine BUPA Occupational Health, 7th Floor, 102 New Street, Birmingham B2 4HQ Tel: 0121 695 5472 Fax: 0121 695 5471 Email: nixon@bupa.com; Fax: 0121 447 7107 — MB ChB 1985 Leic.; AFOM RCP Lond. 1996; Cert. Family Plann. JCC 1991; DRCOG 1991; MFOM RCP Lond. 1998. Cons Occupat.al Phys. BUPA Occupat.al Health; Assoc. Specialist Occupat.al Health, Selly Oak Hosp., Birm. Socs: Soc. Occupat. Med.; Roy. Soc. Med.; Diplomates Assn. RCOG. Prev: Med. Off. Lucas Indust. Birm., Post Office & Benefits Agency Birm.

NIXON, Professor James Robert 1 Hamilton Villa, Ballyholme BT9 5DS Tel: 02891 474015 Fax: 02891 474015 Email: james.nixon@dnet.co.uk — MB BCh BAO 1967 MB BCh BAO Dub.; 1975 MChOrth Liverp.; 1972 FRCS Eng.; 1971 FRCSI; 1991 T(S). p/t

Cons. Orthop. Surg. Musgrave Pk. Hosp.; Hon. Prof. Qu. Univ. Belf. Socs: Fell. BOA; Irish Orthop. Assn.; Eur. Hip Soc. Prev: Med. Dir. GreenPk. Health Care Trust.

NIXON, Janet Ruth 15 Purnells Way, Knowle, Solihull B93 9JN — MB BS 1983 Lond.; DRCOG 1988.

NIXON, Jennifer Margaret 8 Cryon View, Gloweth, Truro TR1 3JT Tel: 01872 79207 — MB BCh BAO 1959 NUI; MRCOG 1967. Clin. Asst. (O & G) Roy. Cornw. Hosp. (Treliske) Truro.

NIXON, John 10 Moorlands Avenue., Mill Hill, London NW7 2DF — MB ChB 1962 Bristol. (Bristol) Clin. Asst. (Psychiat.) N. Middlx. Hosp. Lond.; Hosp. Pract. (Gen. Med.) N. Middlx. Hosp. Lond.

NIXON, John Department of Neurology, Royal United Hospital, Bath BA1 3NG — MB ChB 1989 Bristol; BSc (Hons.) Bristol 1983, MB ChB 1989; MRCP (UK) 1992.

NIXON, Mr John Edwin 148 Harley Street, London W1G 7LG Tel: 020 7935 1207 Fax: 020 7224 1528; Department of Orthopaedic Surgery, Charing Cross Hospital, Fulham Palace Road, London W6 8RF Tel: 020 8846 1475 — MB ChB 1972 Ed.; MA Oxf. 1980; ChM Ed. 1987; FRCS Eng. 1978. (Ed.) p/t Cons. Orthop. Surg. Char. Cross Hosp. & Hon. Sen. Lect. Imperial Coll. Sch. of Med. Lond.; Sen. Examr. (Surg.) Univ. Lond.; Hon. Sen. Lect. Imperial Coll. Socs: Fell. Roy. Soc. Med.; Fell. BOA; Brit. Assoication of Spinal Surg.s. Prev: Cons. Orthop. Surg. King's Coll. Hosp. Lond.; Clin. Reader & Hon. Cons. Orthop. Surg. Univ. Oxf. & Nuffield Orthop. Centre Oxf.

NIXON, Mr John Moylett Gerrard (retired) 13 Park Drive, Chilmark, Salisbury SP3 5AW — MB BCh BAO Dub. 1937; FRCS Eng. 1948; DOMS Eng. 1946. Hon. Cons. Ophth. Surg. W. Dorset Gp. Hosps. Prev: Sen. Ho. Surg. Moorfields, W.m. & Centr. Eye Hosp. (Centr. Br.).

NIXON, Jonathan Mark 18 Tay Ter., Newport-on-Tay DD6 8AZ Tel: 01382 542241 Email: jnixon@globalnet.co.uk — MB ChB 1993 Ed.

NIXON, Julian Robert 11 Admirals Court, Hamble, Southampton SO31 4LT — MB BS 1994 Lond.

NIXON, Keith Pinfold Health Centre, Field Road, Bloxwich, Walsall WS3 3JP Fax: 01922 775132; Brook House Farm, Audmore Road, Gnosall, Stafford ST20 0HA — MB ChB 1975 Manch. Prev: Trainee GP N. Staffs. VTS; Ho. Surg. Staffs. Roy. Infirm. Stoke-on-Trent; Ho. Phys. Gen. Hosp. Stoke-on-Trent.

NIXON, Kenneth Harry (retired) Rose Cottage, East St., Westbourne, Emsworth PO10 8SH Tel: 01243 373163 — MB BS 1955 Lond.; DPhysMed Eng. 1958. Prev: Cons. Phys. (Rheum. & Rehabil.) Portsmouth Hosp. Gp.

NIXON, Lesley Margaret Hilda 17 Harling Drive, Troon KA10 6NF — MB ChB 1987 Glas.

NIXON, Marie Clare Department of Anaesthetics, Leicester General Hospital, Gwendolen Road, Leicester LE5 4PW — MB BS 1992 Lond.

***NIXON, Neil Leslie Peter** 14 Rusland Park Road, Harrow HA1 1UT — MB BS 1996 Lond.

NIXON, Paul 6 Barnacre Close, Fulwood, Preston PR2 9WN — MB BS 1994 Newc.

NIXON, Peter George Frederick 43 Weymouth Street, London W1N 3LD Tel: 020 7935 9558 Fax: 020 7935 0617; Evenlode Cottage, Evenlode, Moreton-in-Marsh GL56 0NT Tel: 01608 651337 Fax: 01608 651337 Email: peternixon@edolneve.demon.co.uk — MB BS 1949 Durh.; FRCP Lond. 1970, M 1955. (Durh.) Hon. Cons. Cardiol. Riverside HA. Socs: Brit. Cardiac Soc.; Counc. Fell. Clin. Cardiol. Amer. Heart Assn. Prev: Cons. Cardiol. Dept. Thoracic Surg. Gen. Infirm. Leeds; Guest Scientist Nat. Heart Inst. Bethesda, USA.

NIXON, Robert Giles Ashington House, Ashington Way, Westlea, Swindon SN5 7XY Tel: 01793 614840; 24 Wrde Hill, Highworth, Swindon SN6 7BX Tel: 01793 764233 — MB BS 1978 Lond.

NIXON, Ronald John Church Lane Surgery, Church Lane, Boroughbridge, York YO51 9BD Tel: 01423 322309 Fax: 01423 324458 Email: church.lane@btinternet.com; The Red House, Kirby Hill, Boroughbridge, York YO51 9DR Tel: 01423 322500 Fax: 01423 325388 Email: ronald_nixon@compuserve.com — MB ChB 1967 Ed.; DObst RCOG 1969. (Ed.) Socs: Life Mem. Roy. Med. Soc.

NIXON, Sarah Jane 9 Oakways, Appleton, Warrington WA4 5HD — MB BChir 1992 Camb. Trainee GP/SHO Yeovil Dist. Hosp.

NIXON, Mr Stephen James 78 Greenbank Crescent, Edinburgh EH10 5SW — MB ChB 1973 Ed.; FRCS Ed. 1978.

NIXON, Susan Joanna The Surgery, 1 Manor Place, London SE17 3BD Tel: 020 7703 3988 Fax: 020 7252 4002 — MB ChB 1988 Bristol; MRCGP 1994; DRCOG 1991; MA (Med. Law & Ethics) Lond. 1996. (Bristol) GP Partner; Researcher (Med. Ethics) Kings Coll. Hosp.

NIXON, Susan Margaret 108 Roman Road, Broadstone BH18 9JU — MB ChB 1990 Sheff.

NIXON, Thomas Edward Welford Cottage, Old Coach Road, Kelsall, Tarporley — MB ChB 1979 Liverp.

NIXSEAMAN, Mr David Hugh (retired) River Cottage, Denmark St., Diss IP22 4BE Tel: 01379 643659 — MB BChir 1950 Camb.; FRCS Eng. 1957; MRCS Eng. LRCP Lond. 1949; DO Eng. 1959. Prev: Cons. Ophth. Ayrsh. & Galloway Area.

NIYADURUPOLA, Mr Thisara West Sussex Eye Unit, Worthing Hospital, Lyndhurst Road, Worthing BN11 2DH Tel: 01903 205111 Fax: 01903 285062 Email: thisaraniyadurupola@compuserve.com — MB BS 1974 Sri Lanka; FRCS (Ophth.) Ed. 1985; FRCOphth 1989; DO RCS Eng. 1983. (Peradeniya, Sri Lanka) Cons. Ophth. Worthing Hosp. & St Richards Hosp. Chichester; Cons Ophthamologist Goring Hall Hosp. Goring by Sea W. Sussex; Cons Ophthamologist The Sherburne Hosp Chichester W. Sussex. Socs: S.ern Ophthamol. Soc.; Brighton & Sussex Medico-chirurgical Soc.; Comm. Mem. Sri Lankan Med & Dent. Assoc.

*****NIZAM, Ikram** Flat 10A, Orchard Residence, Kent & Canterbury Hospital, Canterbury CT1 3NG Tel: 01227 766877 Ext: 3447 — MB ChB 1996 Leic.

NIZAM, Mr Mazhar 246 Whitton Avenue E., Greenford UB6 0QA — FRCS Ed. 1989.

NIZAMANI, Saifullah 18 Stammers Road, Mile End, Colchester CO4 5LX — MB BS 1980 Karachi. Clin. Asst. (Psychiat.) Clacton Gen. Hosp.

NJIE, Baba Musa 5 Cranborne Chase, Clifford Park, Walsgrave, Coventry CV2 2JH — MB BS 1979 Lond.; MRCS Eng. LRCP Lond. 1979.

NJOKU, Lucia Ihuoma 127 Long Elms, Harrow Weald, Harrow HA3 5LB — MB BS 1983 Benin; MB BS Benin, Nigeria 1983; MRCGP 1994; MRCOG 1990.

NJOKU, Mr Peter Emeka Islington Independent Clinic, 344-346 Essex Road, Islington, London N1 3PD Tel: 020 7266 4122 Fax: 020 7226 4474; 18 Frays Lea, Uxbridge UB8 2AT Tel: 01895 252394 — MB BS 1981 Lagos; FRCSI 1987. Cons. Surg. & Med. Dir. Islington Indep. Clinic & Day-Surg. Centre Lond. Socs: Fell. Roy. Soc. Med.; Fell. Amer. Coll. Trop. Med. & Hyg. Prev: Sen. Clin. Research Fell. (Urol.) Univ. Toronto Canada; Sen. Regist. (Gen. Surg.) Nassau, Bahamas; Regist. (Gen. Surg.) P.ss Alexandra Hosp. Harlow.

NJOVU, Michael 212 Julian Crossley Court, William Goodenough House, Mecklenburgh Square, London WC1N 2AN — MB ChB Zambia 1980; BSc Zambia 1977; MRCPI 1992; DCH RCP Lond. 1992.

NJUKI, Frederick Ivan 16 Strandgeld Close, Plumstead, London SE18 1LA Email: fred.njuki@zetnet.co.uk — LMSSA 1994 Lond.; LRCS Eng. LRCP Lond. 1994. (Univ. Coll. Lond.) SHO (Med.) Mayday Univ. Hosp. Croydon. Socs: Med. Defence Union. Prev: SHO (Geriat.) S. Manch. Univ. Hosp.

NKANZA, Kamona Margaret East Surrey Hospital, Three Arch Road, Redhill RH1 5RH; 110 Sandcross Lane, Woodhatch, Reigate RH2 8EY — MB BS 1979 Delhi; FRCS Ed. (Ophth.) 1986; DO RCPSI 1982. Assoc. Specialist (Ophth.) Surrey.

NKERE, Udim Uto 64 Halstead Road, London N21 3DS — MB BS 1981 Lond. Cardiac Unit Roy. Infirm. Glas. Prev: SHO (Gen. Surg.) Leicester Gen. Hosp.; SHO (A & E) Crawley Hosp.

NKOLOKOSA, Mbugwile Stewart Flat 10, Handford House, Cavendish Road, Urmston, Manchester M41 0YG — MB ChB 1977 Manch.

NKONDE, Petronella Mwamba 24 Plantation Avenue, Alwoodley, Leeds LS17 8TB Tel: 0113 225 1986 Fax: 0113 225 1986 — MB ChB 1978 Zambia; MRCS Eng. LRCP Lond. 1988. Clin. Med. Off. (Psychiat.) Leeds. Prev: Regist. Rotat. (Psychiat.) Leeds, Wakefield & Pontefract.

NKONGE, Frederick Michael Kiwanuka S 22 Thornton Close, Girton, Cambridge CB3 0NG — MB BChir 1977 Camb.; MA Camb. 1977, MB BChir 1977; MRCP (UK) 1984. Internist Naval Base Hosp. Jubail, Saudi Arabia; Regist. (Med.) Roy. N.. Hosp. Lond. Prev:

Regist. (Chest & Gen. Med.) St. Margt. Hosp. Epping; SHO OldCh. Hosp. Romford; SHO Roy. N.. Hosp. Lond.

NKUO, Kuma Queen Elizabeth Medical Centre, Edgbaston, Birmingham B15 2TH — MB ChB 1982 Bristol.

NNOCHIRI, Mr Cosmas Chiedozi Paschal Old Fletton Surgery, Rectory Gardens, Peterborough PE2 8AY Tel: 01733 343137; Marriotts Way, Ramsey Mereside, Huntingdon PE26 2TY — MB BChir 1980 Camb.; MA Camb. 1982, MB BChir 1980; FRCS Eng. 1987; FRCS Ed. 1985. Bank Surg. PeterBoro. Hosp. NHS Trust, Cambs. Prev: Regist. (Surg.) The Middlx. Hosp. Lond., Regist. Rotat. (Surg.) Bloomsbury HA; Regist. (Surg.) Roy. Liverp. Hosp. & Alder Heys Hosp. Liverp.; Demonst. & Tutor Anat. Dept. Univ. Camb.

NOAH, Professor Norman David London School of Hygiene & Tropical Medicine, Kappol St., London WC1E 7HT Tel: 020 7927 2812 Fax: 020 7436 4230 Email: n.noah@ishtm.ac.uk; Orley Rise, Orley Farm Road, Harrow-on-The-Hill, Harrow HA1 3PE Tel: 020 8422 2649 Fax: 020 8423 8845 — MB BS 1963 Lond.; FRCP Lond. 1988; MRCP Lond. 1968; FFPHM RCP (UK) 1987, M 1981. (St. Thos.) Prof. Epidemiol. & Pub. Health Lond. Sch. Hyg. & Trop. Med.; Cons. Epidemiol. PHLS Communicable Dis. Surveillance Centre Colindale. Socs: Fell. Roy. Soc. Med.; (Sec.) Internat. Epidemiol. Assn. Prev: Prof. Epidemiol. & Pub. Health Kings Healthcare; Research Asst. Inst. Dis. Chest. Brompton Hosp. Lond.; SHO W. End Hosp. Neurol. & Neurosurg. Lond.

NOAH, Sammy Bashir 24 Potters Field, Aberdare CF44 8HX — MB BS 1975 Khartoum, Sudan.

NOAKES, John Edward, OBE Simpson House Medical Centre, 255 Eastcote Lane, Harrow HA2 8RS Tel: 020 8864 3466 Fax: 020 8864 1002 — MB BS 1959 Lond.; FRCGP 1988, M 1977; DObst RCOG 1962. (Char. Cross) Non-Exec. Dir. Health Educat. Auth. Socs: (Vice-Chairm.) Roy. Coll. Gen. Practs.

NOAKES, John Peter Llewelyn Dolwar, High St., Cilgerran, Cardigan SA43 2SL — MB BS 1982 Lond.

NOAKES, Michael John Hollin House, 10 Combe Park, Weston, Bath BA1 3NP — MB BS 1970 Lond.; MRCS Eng. LRCP Lond. 1970; FRCR 1978; DMRD Eng. 1977. (Char. Cross) Cons. (Radiol.) Roy. United Hosp. Bath. Prev: Sen. Regist. (Radiol.) Leeds Gen. Infirm.; SHO (Med. & Paediat.) Plymouth Gen. Hosp.; Ho. Off. Char. Cross Hosp. Lond.

NOAKES, Moragh Jean Little St Marys, Uplyme, Lyme Regis DT7 3XH; Little St. Mary's, St.Mary's Lane, Uplyme, Lyme Regis DT7 3XH — MRCS Eng. LRCP Lond. 1945. (Bristol)

*****NOAKES, Paul Christopher** The Park Surgery, 4 Alexandra Road, Great Yarmouth NR30 2HW Tel: 01493 855672 — MB ChB 1986 Bristol.

NOAMAN, Linda Ann 16 Lammerton Terrace, Dundee DD4 7BW — MB ChB 1972 Aberd.

NOBBS, William Michael Anthony Apartment 3, The Haie, Newnham GL14 1HW — MB BS 1965 Lond.; MRCS Eng. LRCP Lond. 1965.

NOBLE, Alastair Lockington Lodgehill Road Clinic, Lodgehill Road, Nairn IV12 4RF Tel: 01667 452096 Fax: 01667 456785 — MB ChB 1969 Glas.; DObst RCOG 1972.

*****NOBLE, Alison Margaret** Bankfield, 465 Garstang Road, Broughton, Preston PR3 5JA — MB ChB 1998 Bristol.

NOBLE, Andrew David 272 Bannerdale Road, Sheffield S11 9FE — MB ChB 1996 Leeds.

NOBLE, Mr Anthony Douglas Upper Barford Farm, Bramshaw, Lyndhurst SO43 7JN Tel: 01794 390564 Fax: 01794 390592 — MB BS 1958 Lond.; FRCS Ed. 1966; MRCS Eng. LRCP Lond. 1958; FRCOG 1981, M 1968, DObst. 1964; DCH Eng. 1960. (Lond. Hosp.) Medico-legal Expert witness Obst. & Gyn. Socs: BMA. Prev: Cons. (O & G) Winchester & E. Leigh Health Care Trust; Hon. Clin. Teach. Med. Univ. Soton.

NOBLE, Barbara Sylvia Duncan Street Surgery, Duncan Street, Wolverhampton WV2 3AN Tel: 01902 458193 Fax: 01902 458193; 1 Rowley Park Farm House, Worfield, Bridgnorth WV15 5NT Tel: 01746 716584 Fax: 01746 716584 — MB ChB 1977 Liverp.; MMedsci. Birm. 1995; MRCGP 1983; DRCOG 1979. GP Tutor Wolverhampton; Clin. Asst. (Obst. & Gyn.) New Cross Hosp. Wolverhampton.

NOBLE, Mr Bruce Alexander Yorkshire Eye Hospital, Harrogate Road, Apperly Bridge, Bradford Tel: 0113 218 5941 Fax: 0113 266 3717; The Lodge, Kirkby Overblow, Harrogate HG3 1HH Tel: 01423

NOBLE

879355 Email: bruce@overblow.demon.co.uk — MB BS 1972 Lond.; BSc Cape Town 1966; FRCS Eng. 1977; FRCOphth 1988. (St. Bart.) Cons. Ophth. Gen. Infirm. United Leeds Teachg. Hosps. Trust; Hon. Clin. Sen. Lect. Univ. Leeds. Socs: Internat. Ophth. Microsurg. Study Gp. (Sec.). Prev: Chief Asst. (Eye) St. Bart. Hosp. Lond.; Regist. & SHO Bristol Eye Hosp.; Resid. Surg. Off. Moorfields Eye Hosp. Lond.

NOBLE, Christopher James 6 Dukesthorpe Road, Sydenham, London SE26 4PB Tel: 020 8778 1366 Fax: 020 8778 1366 Email: c.j.noble@bizonline.co.uk; 6Dukesthorpe Road, Sydenham, London SE26 4PB Tel: 020 8778 1366 Fax: 020 8778 1366 — MB BS 1970 Lond.; MSc Lond. 1977; MRCS Eng. LRCP Lond. 1970; FRCPath 1994, M 1981. (Guy's) Private Med. Pract. Socs: Assn. Clin. Path; BMA. Prev: Cons. MicroBiol. E.bourne Health Dist.

*NOBLE, Colin** 87 Colthill Circle, Milltimber AB13 0EH — MB ChB 1996 Aberd.

NOBLE, Dawn Louise Dryburn Hospital, North Road, Durham DH1 5TW Tel: 0191 333 2333; 16 The Oval, Hartlepool TS26 9QH Tel: 01429 861250 — MB BS 1997 Newc.

NOBLE, Deborah Clare 6 Sergison Road, Haywards Heath RH16 1HS — BM BS 1995 Nottm.

NOBLE, Dilys Ann Birley Health Centre, 120 Birley Lane, Sheffield S12 3BP Tel: 0114 239 2541 Fax: 0114 264 5814; 92 Ashdell Road, Sheffield S10 3DB Tel: 0114 661372 — MB ChB 1971 Sheff.; DCH Eng. 1976; DRCOG 1973. Prev: Regist. (Cas.) Sheff. Childr. Hosp.; SHO (O & G) Scarsdale Hosp. Chesterfield; Med. Off. St. Joseph's Hosp. Jirapa, Ghana.

NOBLE, Elizabeth Patricia Eastfield Group Practice, 1 Eastway, Eastfield, Scarborough YO11 3LS Tel: 01723 582297 Fax: 01723 582528; 16 Holbeck Avenue, Scarborough YO11 2XQ — MB ChB 1983 Aberd.; DRCOG 1986. GP E.field Surg. ScarBoro. VTS. Prev: Clin. Med. Off. ScarBoro. HA; Trainee GP ScarBoro. Hosp. VTS; Ho. Off. (Surg.) Harrogate Dist. Hosp.

NOBLE, Euan Paul April Cottage, 40 High St., Blunsdon, Swindon SN26 7AE — MB ChB 1994 Ed.

NOBLE, George Edward 6 Schofield Way, Eastbourne BN23 6HQ — MB BS 1983 Lond.; LLM Wales 1995; LLB Lond. 1991; MRCP (UK) 1986; FRACP 1999.

NOBLE, Gillian Margaret White Medical Group, Thornhill Road, Ponteland, Newcastle upon Tyne NE20 9 Tel: 01661 822222 Fax: 01661 821994 — MB BS 1982 Newc. GP Newc.

NOBLE, Hartley Marshall Sutherland (retired) 46 Broadway, Sheerness ME12 Tel: 01795 663481 — MB ChB 1949 Ed.; MRCGP 1963. Div. Surg. St. John Ambul. Brig.; Med. Off. Red Cross I. of Sheppey Br. Prev: GP Sheerness.

NOBLE, Hilary Alison Appt. 1, The Gloster, The Parade, Cowes PO31 7QD Tel: 01983 280865 — BM 1977 Soton.; FRCA 1984 (Eng.); FFA RCS Eng. 1984. Cons. Anaesth. St. Mary's Hosp. Newport I. of Wight.

NOBLE, Iain Samuel Fairhill Health Centre, Fairhill Road, Magherafelt BT45 6BD — MB ChB 1984 Bristol; MRCGP 1988; DRCOG 1986.

NOBLE, Isabel Mary (retired) 17 Glenorchy Terrace, Edinburgh EH9 2DQ — MB ChB 1954 Aberd.; FRCP Ed. 1973, M 1971; MRCP Lond. 1963. Cons. Phys. Roy. Infirm. & Chalmers Hosp. Edin. Prev: Cons. Phys. Bruntsfield, Longmore & Deaconess Hosps. Edin.

NOBLE, James Kelvingrove Medical Centre, 28 Hands Road, Heanor DE75 7HA Tel: 01773 713201 Fax: 01773 534380; Gartocharn House, 51A The Old Road, Heage, Derby DE56 2BN — MB ChB 1974 Glas.; BSc Glas. 1974, MB ChB 1974; MRCGP 1985.

NOBLE, James Gordon 201 Hesketh Lane, Tarleton, Preston PR4 6AT — LRCP LRCS 1953 Ed.; LRCP LRCS Ed. LRFPS Glas. 1953; MRCPsych 1971; DPM Eng. 1962. (Ed.) Prev: Cons. Psychiat. Greaves Hall Hosp.; Dep. Med. Supt. & Cons. Psychiat. Rampton Hosp. Retford & Moss Side Hosp.; Asst. Psychiat. Stoke Pk. Hosp. Bristol.

NOBLE, Jane Elizabeth 30 India Street, Montrose DD10 8PG — MB ChB 1991 Ed.

NOBLE, Jane Mary 6 Hambledon Gardens, High Heaton, Newcastle upon Tyne NE7 7AL — BM BCh 1991 Oxf.

NOBLE, Mr Jeremy Guy Department of Urology, The Churchill Hospital, Headington, Oxford OX3 7LJ Tel: 01865 225942 Fax: 01865 278554 Email: jeremy.noble@nds.ox.ac.uk; Tel: 01869 277968 Email: Jeremygnoble@hotmail.com — MB BS 1984 Lond.; MD Lond. 1994; FRCS (Urol.) 1994; FRCS Ed. 1989; FRCS Eng. 1989. (St. Bart. Hosp. Lond.) Cons. Urol. Surg. Oxf. Radcliffe Hosp. Trust. Socs: Brit. Assn. Urol. Surgs.; Roy. Soc. Med. Prev: Sen. Regist. (Urol.) Guy's Hosp. Lond., St. Peter's Hosp. & Inst. Urol. Lond.; Research Fell. (Urol.) Middlx Hosp. Lond.; Regist. (Surg.) Lond.

NOBLE, Joan Lamont Lodgehill Road Clinic, Lodgehill Road, Nairn IV12 4RF Tel: 01667 452096 Fax: 01667 456785 — MB ChB 1971 Aberd.; FRCP Glas. 1994; MRCP (UK) 1973; FRCP Glas. 1994; BA (Hons.) Open Univ. 1994.

NOBLE, Joan Laura Manchester Royal Eye Hospital, Oxford Road, Manchester M13 9WH Tel: 0161 276 1234 Fax: 0161 272 6618; New Hall, Stocks Lane, Over Peover, Knutsford WA16 9HE Tel: 01565 722871 Fax: 01565 722871 — MB ChB 1971 Ed.; FRCS Ed. 1976; FRCOphth 1989; DO Eng. 1976. Cons. Ophth. Surg. Roy. Manch. Eye Hosp.; Hon. Lect. Manch. Med. Sch. Socs: Fell. Coll. Ophth.s; Fell. Roy. Coll. Surgs. Edin.; Eur. Occuloplastic & Reconstruc. Surgs.

NOBLE, John Robinson Solstrand, Whiterock Bay, Killinchy, Newtownards BT23 6QA — MB BCh BAO 1953 Dub.; MA Dub. 1971, BA 1951; FRCPsych 1985, M 1972; DPM Eng. 1970. (T.C. Dub.) Prev: Cons. Psychiat. Holywell Hosp. Antrim.

NOBLE, John Stephen Cumine Flat 5, 60 Lumsden St., Over Newton Square, Glasgow G3 8RH Tel: 0141 357 3234; 19 Grattan Place, Fraserburgh AB43 9SD Tel: 01346 518115 — MB ChB 1986 Aberd.; MRCP (UK) 1990; FFARCS 1997; FRCA 1997; MRCGP 1993; DRCOG 1990. Specialist Regist. (Anaesth.) Vict. Infirm. Glas.

NOBLE, Mr Jonathan BUPA Hospital, Russell Road, Whalley Range, Manchester M16 8AJ; New Hall, Stocks Lane, Over Peover, Knutsford WA16 9HE Tel: 01565 722871 — MB ChB Ed. 1966; ChM Ed. 1980; FRCS Eng. 1990; FRCS Ed 1972. (Ed.) Cons. Orthop. Surg. Salford HA; Hon. Sen. Lect. (Orthop. Surg.) Univ. Manch. Socs: Fell. BOA; Brit. Soc. Surg. Hand; Past Pres. Brit. Assn. Surg. Knee. Prev: Reader (Orthop. Surg.) Univ. Manch; Sen. Lect. (Orthop. Surg.) Univ. Manch.; Lect. (Orthop. Surg.) Univ. Edin.

NOBLE, Katharine Louise New Sheepmarket Surgery, Ryhall Road, Stamford PE9 1YA Tel: 01780 758123 Fax: 01780 758102 — MB ChB 1988 Leic.

NOBLE, Kerr William 17 Foulis Crescent, Juniper Green EH14 5BN Tel: 0131 453 4041; Braids Medical Practice, 6 Camus Avenue, Edinburgh EH10 6QT Tel: 0131 445 5999 Fax: 0131 445 3553 — MB ChB 1982 Dundee; MRCGP 1986; DRCOG 1985. (University of Dundee)

NOBLE, Margaret Bonney (retired) 10 New Yatt Road, Witney OX28 1NZ Tel: 01993 774836 — MB ChB 1944 St. And.; MB ChB (Commend.) St. And. 1944; BSc St. And. 1941; MRCGP 1963; MRCOG 1952.

NOBLE, Mr Mark Christopher Brian Scarborough Hospital, Scarborough YO12 6QL Tel: 01723 368111; Finistere, Hutton Buscel, Scarborough YO13 9LL — MB ChB 1973 Aberd.; FRCOG 1996, M 1979. Cons. O & G ScarBoro. & N. E. Yorks. Healthcare Trust. Socs: Blair Bell Res. Soc.; Spencer Wells Soc.; Brit. Soc. Colpos. & Cerv. Path. Prev: Sen. Regist. (O & G) P.ss Mary Matern. Hosp. & Roy. Vict. Infirm. Newc.; Regist. (O & G) King's Coll. Hosp. Lond.; SHO (Obst.) St. Mary's Hosp. Lond.

NOBLE, Professor Mark Ian Munro Academic Unit of Cardiovascular Medicine, Charing Cross and Westminster Medical School, Fulham Palace Road, London W6 8RF — MB BS 1960 Lond.; DSc Lond. 1980, PhD 1965, BSc 1957, MD 1969; FRCP Lond. 1979; MRCP (UK) 1969. (St. Bart.) Prof. Cardiovasc. Med. Char. Cross & W.m. Med. Sch. Lond. Socs: Fell. Europ. Soc. Cardiol.; Med. Res. Soc.; (Ex-Sec.) Europ. Soc. Clin. Investig. Prev: Cons. Phys. King Edwd. VII Hosp. Midhurst; Hon. Sen. Lect. (Med.) Char. Cross & W.m. Med. Sch. Lond.; Hon. Cons. Phys. Char. Cross Hosp. Gp. & S.W. Thames RHA.

NOBLE, Matthew Dominic 7 Charnwood Drive, Thurnby, Leicester LE7 9PD — MB BS 1988 Lond.; DRCOG 1993. SHO (Adult Psychiat.) Peter Hodgkinson Centre Lincoln.

NOBLE, Michael John Acle Medical Centre, Bridewell Lane, Acle, Norwich NR13 3RA Tel: 01493 750888 Fax: 01493 751652 — MB BChir 1988 Camb.

NOBLE, Paul David — MB BCh 1987 Wales; FRCA 1993; DA (UK) 1991. Socs: Assoc. Mem. Assn of Cardio-Thoracic Anaesth.

Prev: Sen. Regist. (Anaesth.) King's Coll. Hosp. Lond.; Sen. Regist. (Anaesth.) Roy. Sussex Co. Hosp. Brighton.

NOBLE, Mr Paul John Department Ophthalmology, Stonehouse Hospital, Stonehouse, Larkhall ML9 3NT Tel: 01698 793521; 5 Hartree Square, Biggar ML12 6JJ Tel: 01899 21097 — BM BS 1976 Nottm.; BMedSci 1974; FRCS Ed. 1984; DO RCS Eng. 1982. Cons. Ophth. Lanarksh. Area Health Bd.

NOBLE, Penelope Louise 46 Sunray Avenue, London SE24 9PX — MB BS 1991 Lond.; BSc (Psychol.) Lond. 1988; MRCOG 1997. (King's College Hospital London) Research Fell. (Fetal Med.) King's Coll. Hosp. Lond. Prev: SHO (O & G) Roy. Sussex Co. Hosp. Brighton.

NOBLE, Peter John The Maudsley Hospital, Denmark Hill, London SE5 8AZ Tel: 0207 733 6333 — MB BChir 1962 Camb.; MA Camb. 1971, MD 1971; FRCP Lond. 1981, M 1964; FRCPsych 1979, M 1971; DPM Lond. 1969. Emerit. Cons. Psychiat. Bethlem Roy. & Maudsley Hosps. Lond. Socs: Fell. Roy. Soc. Med.; Fell. Roy. Coll. Phys.; Fell. Roy. Coll. Psychiat. Prev: Cons. Psychiat. Bethlem Roy. & Maudsley Hosps. Lond.; Sen. Lect. Univ. Lond.; Lect. Inst. Psychiat. Lond.

NOBLE, Peter Richard 51 Grosvenor Park, London SE5 0NH — BM BCh 1985 Oxf.

NOBLE, Richard Simon c/o Haematology Department, Treliske Hospital, Truro TR1 3LJ Tel: 01872 74242 — MB ChB 1983 Bristol; MRCP (UK) 1988; MRCPath 1996. Cons. Haemat. Treliske Hosp. Truro. Prev: Sen. Regist. (Haemat.) W. Yorks.; Regist. (Haemat.) Roy. Vict. Infirm. Newc.; Research Regist. (Haemat.) Sunderland Roy. Infirm.

NOBLE, Simon Ian Robert 2 Ladbroke Hurst, Dormansland, Lingfield RH7 6QB — MB BS 1993 Lond.

NOBLE, Stanley Charles The Health Centre, Marmaduke St., Hull HU3 3BH — MB ChB 1954 Leeds.

NOBLE, Susan Grace 8 Blairmore Gardens, Eaglescliffe, Stockton-on-Tees TS16 9HX — MB ChB 1985 Glas.; MRCGP 1990; DCH RCPS Glas. 1989; DRCOG 1988.

NOBLE, Thomas Cyril (retired) 2 Sycamore Close, Sedbergh LA10 5EB Tel: 015396 20100 Email: t.c.noble@talk21.com — MB ChB 1944 Ed.; FRCP Ed. 1970, M 1949; DCH Eng. 1951; FRCPCH 1998. Prev: Cons. Paediat. Newc. AHA (T).

NOBLE, Thomas William Norwood Medical Centre, 360 Herries Road, Sheffield S5 7HD Tel: 0114 426208; 29 Fir Street, Sheffield S6 3TG — MB ChB 1979 Sheff.; MRCGP 1985. Assoc. Specialist in Palliat. Care St. Luke's Nursing Home Sheff. Prev: Trainee GP Sheff. VTS; Ho. Surg. Sheff. Childr. Hosp.; Ho. Phys. Roy. Hallamsh. Hosp.

NOBLE, Timothy Charles University Medical Centre, Giles Lane, Canterbury CT2 7PB Tel: 01227 765682 Fax: 01227 780954 — MB BS 1986 Lond.; MRCGP 1995; DRCOG 1994. Clin. Asst. (Med. Oncol.) Kent & Cantrerbury Hosp. Prev: Regist. Gen. Hosp. St. Helier Jersey; SHO Roy. Marsden Hosp. Sutton & W.m. Hosp. Lond.

NOBLE, Timothy John 42 Walney Road, Heworth, York YO31 1AJ — MB BS 1989 Lond.; MRCP (UK) 1995. Specialist Regist. (Resp.) N.ern Gen. Hosp. Sheff.

NOBLE, Vibert Dukeries Centre, King's Mill Centre for Healthcare Services, Mansfield Road, Sutton-in-Ashfield NG17 4JL Tel: 01623 622515 Ext: 3155 Fax: 01623 672306; 19 Misterton Crescent, Ravenshead, Nottingham NG15 9AX Tel: 01623 797092 Email: vibertnoble@aol.com — MB BS 1980 Lond.; MRCP (UK) 1986. (King's Coll. Hosp.) Cons. Paediat. King's Mill Centre for Healthcare Serv.

NOBLE, Warwick Stanley (retired) 516 Clive Court, Maida Vale, London W9 1SG — MRCS Eng. LRCP Lond. 1934. Prev: Ho. Surg. Gravesend & N. Kent Hosp.

NOBLE, Wendy Lou Oakhouse, 43 North Barr Without, Beverley HU17 7AG Tel: 01482 888099 — MB ChB 1985 Leic.; 2000 CCST; BSc Biol. Chem. Essex 1980; MRCOG 1994. Cons. Obsehician & Gynaecologist; Hull & E. Yorks. Hosp. Trust. Socs: RCOG; BSGE. Prev: Regist. (Genitourin. Med.) & SHO (O & G) St. Richards Hosp. Chichester; Regist. (O & G) St. Mary's Hosp. Portsmouth.; SR (OTG) P.ss Anne Hosp. S.ampton.

NOBLE, William Arthur Bankfiled, Broughton, Preston PR3 5JA — MB BCh BAO 1960 NUI; FFA RCS Eng. 1969.

NOBLE-JAMIESON, Charles MacIntosh West Suffolk Hospital, Bury St Edmunds IP33 2QZ — BM BCh 1973 Oxf.; MA (Physiol.) Oxf. 1974, BM BCh 1973; MRCP (UK) 1978. Cons. Paediat. W. Suff. Hosp. Bury St. Edmunds. Prev: Sen. Regist. (Paediat.) Hammersmith Hosp. Lond.; Lect. Paediat. Char. Cross Hosp. Lond.

NOBLE-MATHEWS, Priscilla Mary, OStJ (retired) Lovehill Cottage, Trotton, Petersfield GU31 5ER Tel: 01730 816583 Fax: 01730 816583 Email: priscillamary.nm@virgin.net — BM 1976 Soton.; FIMC (RCS ed.) 2000; Dip. IMC (RCS Ed.) 1996; Dip. Palliat. Med. Wales 1992; Barrister at Law Middle Temple 1953. Prev: Clin. Asst. (Diabetes) Worthing Hosp.

NOBLETT, Angela Katherine Over Wyre Medical Centre, Pilling Lane, Preesall, Poulton-le-Fylde FY6 0FA Tel: 01253 810722 Fax: 01253 812039 Email: overwyremed.centre@btinternet.com; Brooklyn, Carr Lane, Hambleton, Poulton-le-Fylde FY6 9AZ Tel: 01253 700381 — MB BS 1985 Newc.; MRCGP 1989; DRCOG 1988; Cert. Family Plann. JCC 1987. (Newc.) Socs: Brit. Med. Soc. Prev: Trainee GP Preston VTS; SHO (Paediat.& Gen. Med.) Roy. Preston. Hosp.; SHO (A & E & O & G) Preston HA.

NOBLETT, John Joseph The Croft Surgery, The Croft, Kirkbridge, Carlisle CA7 5JH — MB ChB 1986 Liverp.

NOBLETT, Robert William (retired) 1 Ashfield Court, Ingol, Preston PR2 7HE Tel: 01772 724183 — LRCP LRCS Ed. LRFPS Glas. 1952. Prev: Ho. Surg. Roy. Infirm. Preston.

NOCK, Ian David 6 Widecombe Avenue, Stafford ST17 0HX — BM 1991 Soton.

NOCKLER, Ingeborg Barbara Department of Radiology, St Bartholomews Hospital, West Smithfield, London EC1A Fax: 020 7601 8301; 48 Stanhope Road, Highgate, London N6 5AJ Tel: 020 8348 0026 Fax: 020 8348 0026 Email: ingenockler@hotmail.com — MB ChB 1971 Pretoria; FRCR 1981. Cons. Radiol.St Bart's Hosp W. Smithfield Lond.; Cons Radiologist (BrE. Screening) Char. Cross Hosp Lond. Socs: Roy. Coll. Radiol.; BMA; Roy. Soc. Med. Prev: Cons. Radiol. Centr. Middlx. Hosp Lond.

***NOCKOLDS, Claire Louise** 55 Milton Av, King's Lynn PE30 2QQ — MB ChB 1997 Sheff.

NOCTON, John Marcus (retired) Cobdown, Five Ash Down, Uckfield TN22 3AR Tel: 01825 732175 — MB BS Lond. 1961; DObst RCOG 1963. Prev: Cas. Off., Ho. Surg. (Orthop.) & Ho. Phys. (O & G) St. Thos. Hosp. Lond.

NODDER, Elizabeth Mary Louise Dean Lane Surgery, Dean Lane, Sixpenny Handley, Salisbury SP5 5PA Tel: 01725 552500 Fax: 01725 552029; The White House, High St, Sixpenny Handley, Salisbury SP5 5ND — BM BCh 1983 Oxf.; MRCGP 1988; DCH RCP Lond. 1986; DGM RCP Lond. 1985. (Univ. Camb., John Radcliffe Hosp. Oxf.) Socs: Assn. Med. Advisers Brit. Orchestras.

NODDER, James Henry Bennetts End Surgery, Gatecroft, Hemel Hempstead HP3 9LY Tel: 01442 63511 Fax: 01442 235419 — MB BS 1973 Lond.; DRCOG 1976. Prev: Ho. Surg. (Neurosurg.) & SHO (O & G) Lond. Hosp.; Trainee Gen. Pract. Watford Vocational Train. Scheme.

NODEN, Jayne Belinda 10 Grange Holt, Alwoodley, Leeds LS17 7TY — MB ChB 1987 Leeds.

NOEL, Mr Douglas James Solihull Hospital, Lode Lane, Solihull B91 2JL; 9 Redwood Croft, Nuneaton CV10 7HY — MB BCh BAO 1984 NUI; FRCS Ed. 1992.

NOEL, Isabel Department Pathology, Dryburn Hospital, North Road, Durham DH1 5TW — MB ChB 1978 Dundee; MSc (Med. Microbiol.) Lond. 1983; MD Dundee 1996, BMedSci (Anat.) (Hons.) 1975. (Dundee) Assoc. Specialist (Med. Microbiol) Dryburn Hosp. Durh.

NOEL, Montague Geoffrey Bickersteth High Street Surgery, 137 High Street, Cranfield, Bedford MK43 0HZ Tel: 01234 750234; Monastery House, Little Crawley, Newport Pagnell MK16 9LT Tel: 01230 65228 — MRCS Eng. LRCP Lond. 1956; FFA RCS Eng. 1968; DA Eng. 1967. (Westm.)

NOEL, Peter Roy Butlin (retired) 8 Church Street, Hemingford Grey, Huntingdon PE28 9DF — MB BS 1948 Lond. Prev: Med. & Sci. Dir. Huntingdon Res. Centre.

NOEL-PATON, Mary Kezia Hewlett Park Surgery, Albion Way, Horsham RH12 1BG Tel: 01403 217100 Fax: 01403 214639 Email: admin@gp-h82017.nhs.uk; The South Wing, Holmbrush House, Faygate, Horsham RH12 4SE Tel: 01293 851578 — MB BS 1964 Lond.; DObst RCOG 1968. (St. Thos.) Sch. Med. Off. Christ's Hosp. Horsham. Socs: Brit. Soc. Allergy & Environm. Med.; Med. Off. Sch. Assn. Prev: Regist. (Psychiat.) Brookwood Hosp. Knaphill; Ho. Surg. (Obst.) Weir Hosp. Balham.

NOFAL

NOFAL, Mr Farhat Metwally Chesterfield & North Derbyshire Royal NHS Hospial, ENT Department, Calow, Chesterfield S44 5BL; Rosehill, 57 Chesterfield Road, Deconsfield, Dronfield S18 2XA Tel: 01246 413706 Fax: 01246 413706 Email: thenofals@fnofal.freeserve.co.uk — MB BCh 1972 Cairo; FRCS Ed. 1980; DLO RCS Eng. 1979. (Cairo Uni.) Cons. ENT Chesterfield & N. Derbysh. Roy. Hosp.

NOFAL, Mr Magdy Abd-El Monem Saleh Torbay General Hospital, Lawe's Bridge, Torquay TQ2 7AA; 5 Stadium Drive, Kingskerswell, Newton Abbot TQ12 5HP — MB ChB 1975 Cairo; FRCS (Ophth.) Ed. 1983.

NOGLIK, Anne Marga Willow Bank, 64 Barnston Road, Hewasll, Wirral CH60 2SU — MB ChB 1992 Liverp.; MRCP (UK) 1997. Specialist Regist. (Paediat.) Alder Mey Child. Hosp. Liv'pl.

NOH, Mohamed Bin Md 22 Adelaide Park, Belfast BT9 6FX — MB BCh BAO 1992 Belf.

NOHL-OSER, Mr H Christian (retired) 23 Bracknell Gate, Frognal Lane, London NW3 7EA Tel: 020 7435 3376 — BM BCh 1944 Oxf.; DM Oxf. 1960, MA, BM BCh 1944; FRCS Eng. 1951. Hon. Cons. Thoracic Surg. Harefield Hosp. Prev: Cons. Thoracic Surg. Harefield, Hillingdon & W. Middlx. (Univ.) Hosp.

NOHR, Karine Foxhill Medical Centre, 363 Halifax Road, Sheffield S6 1AF Tel: 0114 232 2055 Fax: 0114 285 5963; Foxhill MC, 363 Halifax Road, Sheffield S6 1AF Tel: 0114 232 2055 — MB ChB 1982 Sheff.; MRCGP 1993; MRCOG 1987. GP Sheff.; Clin. Asst. (Psychosexual Med.); Hon. Lect. Clin. Tutor Dept. Gen. Pract. Univ. of Sheff.

NOKES, Leonard Derek Martin Cardiff School of Engineering, PO Box 917, Newport Road, Cardiff CF24 0XH; 35 Lon Isa, Rhiwbina, Cardiff CF14 6EE — MB BCh 1990 Wales; PhD Wales 1983; MSc Wales 1982; MD Wales 1993; BEng Wales 1980. Dir. Med. Systems Research Unit Univ. Wales Coll. Cardiff; Hon. Lect. (Forens,. Med.) Univ. Wales Coll. Med.

NOKES, Timothy John Charles 32 Wynndale Road, London E18 1DX Tel: 020 8505 9684 Email: louise.nokes@virgin.net; Department of Haematology, UCLH, Grafton Way, London WC1 Tel: 020 7387 9300 — MB BS 1990 Lond.; MRCP (UK) 1993; DRCPath 1995; MRCPath 1997. (Roy. Free Hosp.) Sen. Regist. (Haemat.) UCLH. Socs: Roy. Coll. Path.; Brit. Soc. Haematol. Prev: Sen. Regist. (Haemat.) Centr. Middlx. Hosp. Lond.; Sen. Regist. (Haemat.) Edgware & Barnet Gen. Hosp. Middlx.; Regist. (Haemat.) UCLH & Whipps Cross Hosp. Lond.

NOKTEHDAN, Niloufar 25 Kings College Court, 55 Primrose Hill Road, London NW3 3EA — BM 1995 Soton.

NOLAN, Mr Bernard (retired) Webster Rubislaw, 79/1 Braid Avenue, Edinburgh EH10 6ED Tel: 0131 447 3383 — MB ChB 1949 Ed.; ChM Ed. 1968, MB ChB 1949; FRCS Ed. 1955; FRCS Eng. 1957. Prev: Cons. Surg. Roy. Infirm. Edin.

NOLAN, Catherine Mary Intensive Care Unit, Southampton General Hospital, Southampton SO16 6YD Tel: 02380 796117 Email: kathleen.nolan@suht.swest.nhs.uk — MB BCh BAO 1982 NUI; FFA RCSI 1987. Cons. Intens. Care Soton. Gen. Hosp.

NOLAN, Christopher Paul 47 Sandhurst Gardens, Belfast BT9 5AX Email: paul.nolan@hotmail.com — MB BCh BAO 1987 Belf. Cons., Orthop.

***NOLAN, Claire Elizabeth** 73 Mallard Place, East Kilbride, Glasgow G75 8UE — MB ChB 1997 Glas.; BSc (Hons.) Glas. 1994.

NOLAN, Daniel Joseph (retired) — MB BCh BAO 1965 NUI; MB BCh BAO NUI 1980; MD NUI 1980; MRCP (UK) 1971; FRCR 1972; DMRD Eng. 1970; LM Rotunda. 1966; FRCP 1998. Prev: Cons. Radiol. John Radcliffe Hosp. Oxf.

***NOLAN, David Francis Luke** Horstead House, Mill Road, Horstead, Norwich NR12 7AU — MB BS 1998 Lond.; MB BS Lond 1998.

NOLAN, Deborah Mary 34 Sandhurst Road, Didsbury, Manchester M20 5LR — MB ChB 1978 Manch.; FFA RCS Eng. 1984. Cons. Anaesth. Univ. Hosp. S. Manch. Prev: Sen. Regist. (Anaesth.) Roy. Perth Hosp., Australia.

NOLAN, Eileen Mary Aylestone Road Medical Centre, 705 Aylestone Road, Leicester LE2 8TG Tel: 0116 283 2325; Glennamaddy, 8 Link Road, Leicester LE2 3RA — MB ChB 1972 Glas.

NOLAN, Ellen Mary Oakengates Medical Practice, Limes Walk, Oakengates, Telford TF2 6JJ — MB BCh BAO 1983 NUI; MRCGP 1988; DRCOG 1987; DCH RCP Lond. 1986.

NOLAN, Frances Carmel The Surgery, 939 Green Lanes, Winchmore Hill, London N21 2PB Tel: 020 8360 2228 Fax: 020 9360 5702 — MB BCh BAO 1976 NUI; DRCOG 1980. Princip. in Gen. Pract. Lond. Prev: Trainee GP Brighton; Ho. Surg. St. Geo. Hosp. Lond.; Ho. Phys. S.lands Hosp. Shoreham-by-Sea.

NOLAN, James 31 Enfield Road, Old Swan, Liverpool L13 5TB — MB ChB 1983 Leeds.

NOLAN, Jane Ann Brunswick House Medical Group, 1 Brunswick Street, Carlisle CA1 1ED Tel: 01228 515808 Fax: 01228 593048; 4 The Forge, Dalston, Carlisle CA5 7QL Tel: 01228 711183 — MB ChB 1979 Birm.; MRCGP 1984; DCH RCP Lond. 1983; DRCOG 1981. Prev: GP Birm.

NOLAN, Jane Carmel 9 Clive Court, Maida Vale, London W9 1SE — MB BCh BAO 1985 Dub.

NOLAN, Janet Anne Devonshire Road Surgery, 467 Devonshire Road, Blackpool FY2 0JP Tel: 01253 352233; 467 Devonshire Road, Blackpool FY2 0JP Tel: 01253 52233 — MB ChB 1985 Manch. Socs: Primary Care Rheum. Soc.; Brit. Menopause Soc. Prev: Trainee GP Preston; Trainee GP/SHO Truro VTS; Ho. Off. Blackburn.

NOLAN, Jeremy Paul Department of Anaesthetics, Royal United Hospital, Combe Park, Bath BA1 3NG Tel: 01225 825056 Fax: 01225 825061 — MB ChB 1983 Bristol; FRCA 1989. Cons. Anaesth. Roy. United Hosp. Bath. Socs: Assn. Anaesth.; Intens. Care Soc.; Resusc. Counc. Mem. of Exec. Comm. Prev: Sen. Regist. (Anaesth.) Roy. United Hosp. Bath.; Regist. Rotat. (Anaesth.) Bristol.

NOLAN, Joanne Elizabeth The Old Vicarage, The Street, Hempnall, Norwich NR15 2AD Tel: 01508 499641 Email: jfnolan@enterprise.net — MB BS Lond. 1989; MRCGP 1994.

NOLAN, Johanna Assumpta Cecilia Lochhead Cottage, Forfar DD8 2RL — MB BCh BAO 1975 Dub.

NOLAN, Mr John Francis Orthopaedic Department, Norfolk & Norwich Hospital, Brunswick Road, Norwich NR1 3SR Tel: 01603 287853 Fax: 01603 287498 Email: john.nolan@norfolk-norwich.thehns.com; Email: jfnolan@enterprise.net — MB BS 1984 Lond.; FRCS (Orth.) 1993; FRCS Eng. 1988. Cons. Orthop. & Trauma Norf. & Norwich Hosp. Socs: Brit. Hip Soc. - Mem.; Brit. Orthopaedic Assn. - Fell.; E. Anglian Orthopaedic Club - Sec.

NOLAN, Mary Elizabeth 10 Fairfax Road, Rhiwbina, Cardiff CF14 4SG — MB ChB 1983 Leeds.

NOLAN, Michael Stephen Richard 37 Monteith Court, Boston PE21 9AY — MB ChB 1990 Sheff.

NOLAN, Philip John (retired) Meltham Road Surgery, 9 Meltham Road, Lockwood, Huddersfield HD1 3UP Tel: 01484 432940 Fax: 01484 451423 — MB ChB 1962 Manch.; FRCGP 1980, M 1974.

NOLAN, William Patrick New Caple Street Surgery, Pontnewydd, Cwmbran NP44 1DU — MB BCh BAO 1985 NUI.

NOLAN, Miss Winifred Patricia The Institute of Opthalmology, University of London, Bath St., London EC1V 9EL; 10 Apsley Road, Summertown, Oxford OX2 7QY — MB ChB 1991 Birm.; FRCOphth 1997. (Uni. Birm.) Research Fell. (Ophth.) Inst. Ophth.

NOLAN-HUGHES, Stephanie Ann 12 Main Street, Lyddington, Oakham LE15 9LT — MB ChB 1983 Leic.

NOLAND, Deborah Jane Student Services Centre, 150 Mount Pleasant, Liverpool L69 3BX Tel: 0151 794 4720 — MB ChB 1989 Liverp.; MRCGP 1994; DRCOG 1991.

NOLTIE, Anne Christina Kirsty South Lewisham Health Centre, 50 Conisborough Crescent, London SE6 2SS Tel: 020 8698 8921; 3 Merchiston Road, London SE6 1SH — MB ChB 1981 Manch.; BSc MedSci St. And. 1978; MRCGP 1986. (Manchester)

NOMAN, Latifa Housesteads, Hernes Road, Summertown, Oxford OX2 7PT — MB BS 1967 Punjab. (Fatima Jinnah Med. Coll. Lahore)

NOMPOZOLO, Caroline Nonina (retired) Moonraker, 1 Sandpits Road, Glastonbury BA6 8EH Tel: 01458 834128 — LRCP LRCS Ed. LRFPS Glas. 1943; DA (UK) 1956. Prev: GP HornCh.

NONDY, Bissesswor c/o Lloyds Bank, Southampton Row, London WC1; 15 Saxon Road, South Norwood, Selhurst, London SE25 5EQ — MB BS 1955 Calcutta; DLO Eng. 1966. Socs: BMA; Med. Protec. Soc. Prev: GP Lond.

NORDEN

*****NONHEBEL, Alice Charlotte** Rowleys, Southwood Rd, Shalden, Alton GU34 4EB — MB ChB 1996 Leeds.

NONIS, Chrisanta Nicholas Anthony 51 Gilling Court, Belsize Grove, London NW3 4XA — MB BS 1990 Lond.; BSc Lond. 1989.

NONOO-COHEN, Cinderella Ground Floor Flat, 101 Talbot Road, Highgate, London N6 4QX Tel: 020 8347 7486 Fax: 020 8347 7486 Email: cnonoo@aol.com — MB BS 1993 Lond.; DRCOG 1998. GP Regist. Socs: LJMS. Prev: SHO (c/o Elderly) Univ. Coll. Hosp. Lond.; SHO (A & E) Whittington Hosp. Lond.; SHO Rotat. (Med.) St. Bart. Hosp. Lond.

NOOH, Ahmed Mohamed Mahdy Khaleel 11 Gayton Road, King's Lynn PE30 4EA — MB BCh 1981 Zagazig, Egypt.

NOOHU KANNU, Abdulkhadir The Surgery, 33 Penrose Street, London SE17 3DW Tel: 020 7703 3677; 29 Fermoy Road, Greenford UB6 9HX Tel: 020 8578 3751 — MB BS 1971 Kerala; MICGP 1987; Cert. Prescribed Exp. JCC 1980. (Med. Coll. Trivandrum) Prev: Tutor (Gen. Med.) Coll. Kottayam, India; Med. Off. Mwanza Consulat Hosp. Tanzania; SHO (Geriat. Med.) Linton Hosp. Maidstone.

NOOKARAJU, Kondru Nantyglo Medical Centre, Queen Street, Nantyglo, Brynmawr NP23 4LW Tel: 01495 310381 Fax: 01495 310807; 2 Coed-Cae, Rassau, Ebbw Vale NP23 5TP Tel: 01495 303798 — MB BS 1963 Andhra; Cert FPA 1974. (Guntur Med. Coll.)

***NOON, Adrian James** 10 Church Close, Wythall, Birmingham B47 6JQ — MB ChB 1986 Birm.

NOON, Mr Charles Frederick (retired) 21 Lawrie Park Crescent, London SE26 6HH Tel: 020 8778 5174 Fax: 020 8249 5193 Email: charlesn@msn.com — BA (2nd cl. Nat. Sci. Trip. Pts. 1 & 2) Camb.; FRCS Eng. 1953; MRCS Eng. LRCP Lond. 1947. Prev: Cons. Surg. Redbridge HA.

NOON, Christopher Charles The Surgery, Pleasant Place, Hersham, Walton-on-Thames KT12 4HT Tel: 01932 229033 Fax: 01932 254706; 28 St. Martins Drive, Walton-on-Thames KT12 3BW Email: chris@famnoon.demon.co.uk — MB BS 1976 Lond.; MRCS Eng. LRCP Lond. 1976. (St. Bart.) Clin. Asst. (Cardiol.) St. Peters Hosp. Chertsey. Prev: Trainee GP King's Lynn VTS; SHO (Cas.) Wexham Pk. Slough; Ho. Off. (Gen. Surg.) Norf. & Norwich Hosp.

NOON, John Richard Flat 8, 8 Cranbury Terrace, Southampton SO14 0LH — BM 1989 Soton.

NOONAN, Alex (retired) — MB BS 1966 Lond.; MRCS Eng. LRCP Lond. 1966. Prev: Ho. Phys. St. Bart. Hosp.

NOONAN, Carmel Patricia 12 Bonnington Avenue, Crosby, Liverpool L23 7YJ — MB BCh BAO 1985 NUI.

NOONAN, Walter John The Health Centre, Rikenel, The Park, Gloucester GL1 1XR Tel: 01452 891110 Fax: 01452 891111 — MB BS 1977 Sydney; MRCGP 1986.

NOONE, Bridget Eleanor Mary 5 Nicholl Court, Mumbles, Swansea SA3 4LZ — MB BCh BAO 1977 NUI.

NOONE, Catherine Stoke Mandeville Hospital, Mandeville Road, Aylesbury HP21 8AL Tel: 01296 315159 Fax: 01296 345163; 17 Haglis Drive, Wendover, Aylesbury HP22 6LY — MB BS 1976 Lond.; FRCP Lond. 1995; MRCP (UK) 1979. (King's Coll. Hosp.) Cons. Paediat. Stoke Mandeville Hosp. Aylesbury.

NOONE, John Francis Elms Medical Centre, Green Lane, Whitefield, Manchester M45 7FD Tel: 0161 766 2311 Fax: 0161 767 9544; 15 Longley Drive, Worsley, Manchester M28 2TP — MB ChB 1971 Manch.; MRCGP 1977. (Manchester) Lect. Dept. Gen. Pract. Univ. Manch.; Clin. Governance Lead Bury S. PCG.

NOONE, Martina Ann 12 Chappell Road, Droylsden, Manchester M43 7NA; University College London, 26 Rustat Road, Cambridge CB1 3QT — MB ChB 1992 Manch. Clin. Research. Fell. Uni. Coll. Lond.

NOONE, Oliver Pratap 25 Loddon Bridge Road, Woodley, Reading RG5 4AU — MB BS 1972 Kerala; Dip. Thoracic Med. Lond 1983.

NOONE, Vincent, Col. late RAMC Retd. c/o Williams & Glyn's Bank, 22 Whitehall, London SW1A 2EB — LAH Dub. 1954; DA (Eng.) 1961.

NOOR, Farah 979 Eastern Avenue, Newbury Park, Ilford IG2 7SB — MB BS 1996 Lond. Socs: MDU. Prev: SHO (O & G) Qu.s Hosp. Staffs.; PRHO (Gen. Surg) Roy. Lond. Hosp. Whitechapel; PRHO (Gen. Med.) King Geo. Hosp., Barky La., Goodmeyes.

NOOR, Mr Nadim Bungalow 1, Castle Leazes, Spital Tongues, Newcastle upon Tyne NE2 4NY — MB BS 1985 Pakistan; FRCS Ed. 1992.

NOOR, Rizwana 20 The Orchard, Winchmore Hill, London N21 2DH — MB ChB 1986 Leeds.

NOORAH, Saida Beebee 344A Minster Road, Minster on Sea, Sheerness ME12 3PE — MB ChB 1984 Leeds; MRCGP 1989; DRCOG 1988.

***NOORANI, Farah** 177 Rectory Road, Farnborough GU14 8AJ — MB BS 1998 Lond.; MB BS Lond 1998.

NOORANI, Mr Mohammed Ali (retired) 20 Littlebourne Road, Maidstone ME14 5QP Tel: 01622 209535 Fax: 01622 209535 — MB BS Karachi 1960; FRCS Ed. 1969; DLO RCS Eng. 1967. Prev: Locum Cons. ENT Surg., MiddlesBoro., Basingstoke, Whipps Cross Hosp., Crawley.

NOORDEEN, Mr Mohammed Hamza Hilali 107 Harley Street, London W1G 6AL Tel: 020 7487 2819 Fax: 020 7935 3036 Email: hilali.noordeen@virgin.net — BM BCh 1985 Oxf.; MA Oxf. 1983; MCh (Orth.) 1993; FRCS (Orth.) 1993; FRCS Eng. 1989. Cons. Orthop. Surg. Roy. Nat. Orthop. Hosp. & Hosp. Childr. Gt. Ormond St. Lond.; Hon. Sen. Lect. Inst. of Orthop. Univ. of Lond.; Hon. Sen. Lect. Insititute of Child Health Univ. of Lond. Socs: Brit. Orthop. Assn.; Brit. Scoliosis Soc.; BMA. Prev: Cons. Orthop. Surg. Middlx. & Unit. Coll. Hosp. Lond.; Sen. Regist. Middlx. Hosp.; Regist. Univ. Coll. Hosp. Lond. and RNOH Stanmore.

***NOORI, Muna** 39 Scotts Lane, Shortlands, Bromley BR2 0LT Tel: 020 8658 2860 — MB BS 1998 Lond.; MB BS Lond 1998; BSc (Hons) June 1995.

***NOORI, Sharifah Nuriyah** c/o 166 Devonshire Road, London NW7 1DJ — MB BS 1997 Lond.

NOORPURI, Ranbir Singh PO Box 53, Birkenhead L42 5ET — MB ChB 1993 Liverp. SHO (O & G) Wirral Hosp. NHS Trust.

NOOTT, Gerald Guy Glenside, Scarrowscant Lane, Haverfordwest SA61 — LRCPI & LM, LRSCI & LM 1955; LRCPI & LM, LRCSI & LM 1955.

NOR, Kartini Binti Mohd 46 Laberge Gardens, New Stevenston, Motherwell ML1 4FD — MB BCh BAO 1991 Belf.

NORBROOK, Penelope Jane 12 Amenbury Lane, Harpenden AL5 2DF — MB BS 1974 Lond.; MRCS Eng. LRCP Lond. 1974. (Roy. Free) Clin. Asst. (Dermat.) Hemel Hempstead. Prev: GP Princip. Lond.; SHO (Med.) Whittington Hosp. Lond.; Ho. Phys. Roy. Free Hosp. Lond.

NORBURN, Peter Stuart Department of Radiology, Trafford District General Hospital, Moorside Road, Davyhulme, Manchester M41 5SL — MB ChB 1979 Manch.; MRCP (UK) 1982; FRCR 1987. Cons. Radiol. Trafford Dist. Gen. Hosp. Manch.

NORBURY, Lynn Patricia 62 Whitchurch Road, Withington, Manchester M20 1EB Tel: 0161 445 5907 Fax: 0161 448 0466 — BM 1977 Soton.; M Med. Sci. 1999; MRCGP 1984; DRCOG 1985.

***NORCLIFFE, Pamela Jayne** 17 Beech Road, Glinton, Peterborough PE6 7LA — MB ChB 1997 Bristol.

NORCOTT, Mr Harry Christopher Russells Hall Hospital, Dudley DY1 2HQ; 16 Dingle Road, Stourbridge DY9 0RS Tel: 01562 883239 — MB BS 1969 Lond.; FRCS Eng. 1974; MRCS Eng. LRCP Lond. 1969. (Char. Cross) Cons. (Gen. Surg.) Russells Hall Hosp. Dudley. Prev: Sen. Regist. (Gen. Surg.) Qu. Eliz. Hosp. Birm.; Regist. (Gen. Surg.) N. Staffs. Roy. Infirm. Stoke-on-Trent; Regist. (Gen. Surg.) Roy. Hosp. Wolverhampton.

NORCROSS, Fiona Heather Wrafton House Surgery, Wrafton House, 9-11 Wellfield Road, Hatfield AL10 0BS Tel: 01707 265454 Fax: 01707361286; 1 Whitehill Cottages, Whitehill, Welwyn AL6 9AE Tel: 01438 717924 — MB BS 1983 Lond.; MA Camb. 1984; MRCGP 1987; DRCOG 1985. (Middlx.) Prev: SHO (Paediat. & Psychiat.) Qu. Eliz II Hosp. Welwyn Garden City; SHO (Obst.) Lister Hosp. Stevenage.

NORDEN, Anthony George William Department of Clinical Pathology, Hinchingbrooke Hospital, Hinchingbrooke Park, Huntingdon PE29 6NT Tel: 01480 416266 Fax: 01480 416527 Email: agwn@cam.ac.uk; School Cottage, 10 School Lane, Watton-at-Stone, Hertford SG14 3SF Tel: 01920 830838 Fax: 01920 830838 — MB BS 1979 Lond.; PhD Calif. 1974; BSc Lond. 1971; FRCPath 1996; T(Path) 1991. (Univ. Coll. Hosp.) Cons. Chem. Path. Hinchingbrooke, Addenbrooke's and Papworth Hosp.s: Prev: Sen. Regist. (Chem. Path.) Univ. Coll. Hosp. & Whittington Hosp. Lond.

NORDIN

NORDIN, Andrew John Chelsea & Westminster Hospital, 369 Fulham Road, Chelsea, London SW10 9NH; 38 Cross Gates Close, Marlins Heron, Bracknell RG12 9TY — MB BS 1987 Adelaide; MRCOG 1994. Regist. (O & G) Chelsea & W.m. Hosp. Lond. Prev: Regist. (O & G) N. Hants. Hosp. Basingstoke & MusGr.r Pk. Hosp. Taunton.

NORDSTROM, Monica Evelyn Chest Department, St. Peter's Hospital, Guildford Road, Chertsey KT16 0PZ Tel: 01932 692310 Fax: 01932 873983 Email: monica.nordstrom@btinternet.com; Petra, Linden Road, St. George's Hill, Weybridge KT13 0QW Tel: 01932 842682 Fax: 01932 851353 — MD 1980 Odense; MD (Gen. Med. & Gerontol.) Odense 1980. (Odense, Denmark) Clin. Asst. (Chest) St. Peter's Hosp. Chertsey. Prev: Gen. Med. Univ. Hosp. Malmö, Sweden.

NORELDEEN, Saadia Abdelrhman 25 Dane House, The Alexandra Hospital, Woodrow Drive, Redditch B98 7UB — MB BS 1983 Khartoum.

NORELL, Michael Simon Cadic Department, Hull Royal Infirmary, Anlaby Road, Hull HU3 2JZ Tel: 01482 674224 Fax: 01482 321128; OrchardGreen, 37 East Road, Walkington, Beverley HU17 8RX Tel: 01482 868549 Fax: 01482 868549 Email: norellmike@aol.com — MB BS 1978 Lond.; MD Lond. 1990; FRCP. (University College London) Cons. Cardiol. Hull Roy. Infirm. & Castle Hill Hosp., Cottingham, E. Yorks. Socs: Hon. Sec. Brit. Cardiovasc. Interven. Soc.; Brit. Cardiac Soc.

NOREN, Claes Eric Steyning Health Centre, Tanyard Lane, Steyning BN44 3RJ Tel: 01903 843400 Fax: 01903 843440 — MB BS 1975 Lond.; MRCP (UK) 1978; MRCGP 1984. (St. Bart.) Sch. Doctor Windlesham Hse. Findon, W. Sussex; Trainer (Gen. Pract.) W. Sussex; Hosp. Pract. (Diabetes) Roy. Sussex Co. Hosp. Brighton. Prev: SHO Rotat. (Gen. Med.) & Ho. Phys. (Gen. Med. & Cardiol.) St. Bart. Hosp. Lond.; Ho. Surg. (Gen. Surg.) Roy. Berks. Hosp. Reading.

NORFOLK, Derek Raymond Department of Haematology, The General Infirmary at Leeds, Leeds LS1 3EX Tel: 0113 292 3935 Fax: 0113 242 0881 Email: derekn@pathology.leeds.ac.uk — MB BS 1975 Lond.; FRCP Lond. 1993; MRCP (UK) 1978; MRCS Eng. LRCP Lond. 1975; FRCPath 1994, M 1983. (Guy's) Cons. Haemat. Gen. Infirm. Leeds; Hon. Sen. Clin. Lect. (Med. & Path.) Univ. Leeds; Assoc. Director of Research and Developm. Leeds Teachg. Hosp.s NHS Trust. Socs: BMA; Brit. Soc. Haematol. Prev: Sen. Regist. (Haemat.) Gen. Infirm. Leeds; Regist. & SHO (Gen. Med.) Vict. Hosp. Blackpool.

NORFOLK, Guy Adrian Stockwood Health Clinic, Hollway Road, Bristol BS14 8PT Tel: 01275 833103 Fax: 01275 891637; Whitewood Lodge, Norton Lane, Whitchurch, Bristol BS14 0BU Tel: 01275 834888 — MB ChB 1980 Leeds; MRCGP 1985; LLM Cardiff 1995; DMJ Soc. Apoth. Lond. 1991.

***NORGAIN, Helen Ruth** Rockwood, Sandy Lane, Helsby, Warrington WA6 9BD — BM BS 1994 Nottm.

NORGATE, Dominic Alexander Medical Centre, Second Battalion, The Light Infantry BFPO 806 — MB BS 1992 Lond.

NORGATE, Ian Francis Tristram (retired) 60 Chester Road, Salterswall, Winsford CW7 2NQ Tel: 01606 593387 — LRCP LRCS 1951 Ed.; LRCP LRCS Ed. LRFPS Glas. 1951. Prev: Ho. Surg. Wrexham Memor. Hosp.

NORGREN, Priscilla Marie 47 Westbridge Cottages, Tavistock PL19 8DQ — MB BS 1992 Lond.

NORLEY, Ian White Gables, 4 Clennon Park, Paignton TQ4 5HL — MB BS 1977 Lond.; FFA RCS Eng. 1982. (St ary's Hospital, London) Cons. Anaesth. Torbay Hosp. Torquay.

NORMAN, Abraham Eric (retired) 2 Rockbourne Avenue, Liverpool L25 4TW Tel: 0151 428 1340 — MB ChB Liverp. 1938; FRCGP 1979, M 1954. Hon. Capt. RAMC. Prev: Exam. Med. Off. Dept. Health & Social Security.

NORMAN, Aidan Thomas 7 Elizabeth Court, Collingham, Wetherby LS22 5JL — MB ChB 1992 Manch.

NORMAN, Mr Alan Greaves (retired) Thatched Cottage, Clarks Yard, Cavendish, Sudbury CO10 8AZ Tel: 01787 281437 — MRCS Eng. LRCP Lond. 1947; MA Camb. 1949, MChir 1961, MB BChir 1947; FRCS Eng. 1952. Prev: Cons. Thoracic Surg. Sheff. HA.

NORMAN, Alan Sellers Castle Surgery, 5 Darwin Street, Castle, Northwich CW8 1BU Tel: 01606 74863 Fax: 01606 784847; Findhorn, 10 Sandfield Lane, Hartford, Northwich CW8 1PU Tel: 01606 75208 Email: alan.norman@bigfoot.com — MB ChB 1988 Manch.; BSc St. And. 1985; MRCGP 1992. (Manch. & St. And.)

NORMAN, Aleida Elisabeth Mabel May White Lodge, Heather Close, Kingswood, Tadworth KT20 6NY Tel: 01737 832626 — BM BCh 1946 Oxf.; MA Oxf. 1946; DCH Eng. 1949. (Oxf.) Prev: Ho. Phys. Radcliffe Infirm. Oxf.; Ho. Surg. Qu. Eliz. Hosp. Childr. Hackney Rd. & Hosp. Sick Childr. Gt. Ormond St.

NORMAN, Andrew Michael Clinical Genetics Unit, Birmingham Women's Hospital, Edgbaston, Birmingham B15 2TG Tel: 0121 607 4727 Fax: 0121 627 2618 Email: andrew.norman@bham-womens.thenhs.com — MB BCh 1981 Wales; MA Camb. 1982; MD Wales 1992; MRCP (UK) 1984; FRCP 2000. Cons. Clin. Genetics Birm. Wom.'s Hosp. Prev: Sen. Regist. (Clin. Genetics) Manch.; Clin. Research Off. Inst. Med. Genetics Cardiff; Regist. (Med.) Plymouth Gen. Hosp.

NORMAN, Andrew Richard Francis 121 Ladbroke Grove, London W11 1PN Tel: 020 7792 8060 Fax: 020 7792 3236; 4 Dewhurst Road, London W14 0ET — MB ChB 1972 Bristol. Prev: GP Alderton; GP Trainee Cirencester VTS; Dep. to Chief Med. Adviser Commercial Union Assur. plc.

NORMAN, Andrew Spencer Wells Health Centre, Glastonbury Road, Wells BA5 1XJ Tel: 01749 672137 Fax: 01749 679833 — MB BS 1990 Lond.; MRCGP 1996.

NORMAN, Andrew William Market Deeping Health Centre, 2 Douglas Road, Market Deeping, Peterborough PE6 8PA — MB BS 1975 Lond.; MRCS Eng. LRCP Lond. 1975; MRCGP 1979.

NORMAN, Annabel Le Sauteur Fairfield, Faldouet, Gorey, St Martin, Jersey JE3 6DP — MB BS 1993 Lond.; BSc (Hons.) 1990; DFFP 1997; DRCOG 1997; DCH 1998. (Lond. Hosp. Med. Coll.) GP Regist. Bath. Prev: SHO (Paediat.) Roy. Alexandra Hosp. Brighton; SHO (O & G) Jersey Gen.

NORMAN, Anthea Mary 21 Summerhill Road, Waterlooville PO8 8XD Tel: 01705 256147 Email: danthea@cwcom.net — BM BS 1991 Nottm.; RCGP 1997; DRCOG 1995; T(GP) 1995. Trainee GP Portsmouth VTS; GP Retainee Horndean.

NORMAN, Archibald Percy, MBE (retired) White Lodge, Heather Close, Kingswood, Tadworth KT20 6NY Tel: 01737 832626 — MB BChir Camb. 1938; MA Camb. 1938, MD 1949; FRCPI 1995; FRCP Lond. 1954, M 1947; MRCS Eng. LRCP Lond. 1937; FRCPCH 1996; DCH Eng. 1947. Hon. Phys. Hosp. Sick Childr. Gt. Ormond St.; Hon. Paediat. Qu. Charlotte's Matern. Hosp. Lond. Prev: Resid. Asst. Phys. W.m. Childr. Hosp. Vincent Sq.

***NORMAN, Benjamin Peter** Flat 1F2, 3 West Preston St., Edinburgh EH8 9PX — MB ChB 1998 Ed.; MB ChB Ed 1998.

NORMAN, Bernard John Charing Cross Hospital, Fulham Palace Road, London W6 8RF Tel: 020 8846 1234; 125 St. Albans Avenue, Chiswick, London W4 5JS — MB BS 1990 Lond.; BSc (Hons.) Lond. 1987; FRCA 1994. Specialist Regist. (Anaesth.) Char. Cross Hosp. Lond. Socs: Fell. Roy. Soc. Med.; Assn. Anaesth.; Obst. Anaesth. Assn. Prev: SHO (Anaesth.) St. Geo. Hosp. Lond.

***NORMAN, Charles William** Flat 5, 10 Chester Way, London SE11 4UT — MB BS 1996 Lond.

NORMAN, David Paul Ringmead Medical Practice, Great Hollands Health Centre, Great Hollands Square, Bracknell RG12 8WY Tel: 01344 454338 Fax: 01344 861050; 28 Avebury, Little Foxes, Bracknell RG12 8SQ — MRCS Eng. LRCP Lond. 1975; MA Camb. 1972; DCH Eng. 1978; DRCOG 1978.

NORMAN, Dorothy (retired) 1 Churchgate Mews, Bibby Road, Southport PR9 7PS — MB ChB Leeds 1953. Prev: SHO (O & G) Crewe Memor. Hosp. & Barony Hosp. Nantwich.

***NORMAN, Francesca Florence** Flat 3, Johnston Lodge, Admiral Walk, London W9 3TJ — MB BS 1997 Lond.

NORMAN, George Anthony Hamilton (retired) 92 The Lain, Epping CM16 6TW Tel: 01992 914054 — MB BS 1926 Lond.; MRCS Eng. LRCP Lond. 1925. Prev: Ho. Surg. W.m. Hosp. & Addenbrooke's Hosp. Camb.

NORMAN, Hugh Michael McCormick (retired) Hillside, Vicarage Lane, Barrow Gurney, Bristol BS48 3RT Tel: 01275 462730 — MB BCh BAO 1954 Dub.; DObst RCOG 1963. Prev: SHO (Obst.) Stafford Gen. Infirm.

NORMAN, James Marcus Charlotte Keel Health Centre, Seymour Road, Easton, Bristol BS5 0UA Tel: 0117 951 2244 Fax: 0117 951 2373; 1 Leigh Road, Clifton, Bristol BS8 2DA — MB ChB 1972 Bristol; MRCGP 1978.

NORMAN, Jane Elizabeth Department Obstetrics & Gynaecology, University of Glasgow, Queen Elizabeth Building, Glasgow Royal Infirmary, 10 Alexandra Place, Glasgow G31 2ER Tel: 0141 211 4702 Fax: 0141 553 1367; 33 Southbrae Drive, Glasgow G13 1PU — MB ChB 1986 Ed.; MD Ed.1992; MRCOG 1992. Sen. Lect. (O & G) Glas. Univ. Prev: Lect. (O & G) Univs. Edin. & Glas.; Research Regist. (O & G) Edin.; Regist. (O & G) Borders Gen. Hosp. Melrose.

*****NORMAN, Joanne Louise** 245 Upper Halliford Road, Shepperton TW17 8ST — MB BS 1994 Lond.; BSc (Hons.) Lond. 1991, MB BS 1994.

NORMAN, John (retired) 2 Russell Place, Portswood, Southampton SO17 1NU Tel: 01703 555177 Fax: 01703 794348 Email: jnorman@compuserve.com — MB ChB Leeds 1957; PhD Leeds 1969; FANZCA 1983; FRCA 1963. Hon. Cons. Anaesth. Soton. & SW Hants. Health Dist. (T). Prev: Hon. Cons. Anaesth. Soton. & SW Hants. Health Dist. (T).

NORMAN, Professor John Nelson 39 Morningfield Road, Aberdeen AB15 4AP Tel: 01224 316765 Fax: 01224 316765 Email: gpr169@abdd.ac.uk — MB ChB 1957 Glas.; DSc Aberd. 1976; PhD Glas. 1964, MD 1961; FRCS Glas. 1967; FRCS Ed. 1967; FFOM RCP Lond. 1993, MFOM 1986. (Glas.) Emerit. Prof. Environ. Studies. Univ. Aberd.; Vis. Prof. Communit. Med. UAE. Socs: Underwater Med. Soc. Prev: Med. Dir. Robt. Gordon's Inst. Technol. Survival Centre Ltd., Aberd.; Dir. Inst. Environm. & Offshore Med. Univ. Aberd.; Reader (Surg.) Univ. Aberd.

NORMAN, John Richard Nutwood Surgery, Windermere Road, Grange-over-Sands LA11 6EG Tel: 015395 32108 Fax: 015395 35986; The Old Parsonage, Grange Fell Road, Grange-over-Sands LA11 6BJ Tel: 01539 534428 Fax: 01539 536288 — MB ChB 1975 Leeds; MB ChB (Hons.) Leeds 1975. Med. Off. Cartmel Racecourse.

NORMAN, John Robin Henfield Medical Centre, Deer Park, Henfield BN5 9JQ Tel: 01273 492255 Fax: 01273 495050; Clovelly, Cagefoot Lane, Henfield BN5 9HD Tel: 01273 492612 — MB BChir 1968 Camb.; MA Camb. 1968; MRCP (UK) 1972; DObst RCOG 1974; DCH Eng. 1970. (Camb. & St. Thos.) Gen. Med. Pract. Henfield. Prev: Clin. Asst. (Child Psychiat.) Roy. Alexandra Hosp. Brighton; Regist. (Paediat.) St. Thos. Hosp. Lond.; Ho. Off. (O & G) King's Coll. Hosp. Lond.

NORMAN, Jonathan Barrie 50 Graythwaite, Chester-le-Street DH2 2UH — MB BS 1993 Newc.

NORMAN, Joseph Edward (retired) 55 Spylaw Bank Road, Colinton, Edinburgh EH13 0JB Tel: 0131 441 6643 — MB ChB 1945 Ed.; FFA RCS Eng. 1954; DA Eng. 1951. Prev: Cons. Anaesth. Edin. N.. Gp. Hosps.

NORMAN, Joseph Roger, RD (retired) Glenwood House, 33 Queens Road, Waterlooville PO7 7SB Tel: 01705 251624 — MB BS 1960 Lond.; MRCS Eng. LRCP Lond. 1960; DCH Eng. 1963. Prev: Ho. Phys. & Ho. Surg. Pembury Hosp.

***NORMAN, Justine Clare** Casapeka, Low Road, Harwich CO12 3TS — MB ChB 1994 Leic.

***NORMAN, Lucinda Jane** 49 Woodlands Road, Surbiton KT6 6PR — MB BS 1996 Lond.

NORMAN, Lucinda Kathryn Victoria 19 Arlington Place, Gordon Road, Winchester SO23 7TR — MB BS 1990 Lond.

NORMAN, Madeline Georgina Northcroft Surgery, Northcroft Lane, Newbury RG14 1BU Tel: 01635 31575 Fax: 01635 551857 — MB BS 1988 Lond.; MRCGP 1994; DRCOG 1992. Princip. GP, Berks.

NORMAN, Margaret Ann 4 Old Steine, Brighton BN1 1EJ Tel: 01273 685588 — MB BS 1952 Lond.; MRCS Eng. LRCP Lond. 1952; DObst RCOG 1955; DCH Eng. 1955. (Roy. Free) Prev: Paediat. Regist. Bromley Gp. Hosps.; Ho. Surg. Roy. Free Hosp.

NORMAN, Maria Louise The Briars, Farm Road, Bristol BS16 6DD — MB ChB 1991 Bristol. SHO (O & G) S.mead Hosp. Bristol.

NORMAN, Mark 10 Hivings Park, Chesham HP5 2LG — MB BS 1993 Lond.

NORMAN, Mark Adrian Orchard Medical Centre, Macdonald Walk, Kingswood, Bristol BS15 8NJ Tel: 0117 980 5100 Fax: 0117 980 5104; Greystone Cottage, Bury Lane, Doynton, Bristol BS30 5SW — MB ChB 1983 Birm.; DCH RCP Lond. 1988.

NORMAN, Michael Hayes 88 Humberstone Road, Luton LU4 9SS Tel: 01582 51131 — LMSSA 1951 Lond.; DA Eng. 1956. (St. Bart.)

NORMAN, Michael Hugh University Medical Centre, Giles Lane, Canterbury CT2 7LR Tel: 01227 65682; Monks Hall, School Lane, Fordwich, Canterbury CT2 0DF — MB BChir 1981 Camb.; MA Camb. 1983, MB BChir 1981; DRCOG 1987.

NORMAN, Patricia Mary National Hospital for Neurology & Neurosurgery, Queen Square, London WC1N 3BG Tel: 020 7837 3611; Queen's Lodge, Queen's Club Gardens, West Kensington, London W14 9TA Tel: 020 7385 3122 — MB BCh BAO 1958 Dub.; FRCPath 1980, M 1968. Cons. Path. (Haemat., Microbiol. & Cytol.) Nat. Hosps. Nerv. Dis. Qu. Sq. & Maida Vale.

NORMAN, Paul Public Health Laboratory, Northern General Hospital, Herries Road, Sheffield S5 7AU Tel: 0114 243 7749 Fax: 0114 242 1385 — MB 1975 Camb.; BChir 1974.

NORMAN, Paul Richard Minden Medical Centre, 2 Barlow Street, Bury BL9 0QP Tel: 0161 764 2652 Fax: 0161 761 5967 — MB ChB 1991 Liverp.; MRCGP 1995; DRCOG 1995; DCH RCP Lond. 1993. Prev: Trainee GP/SHO Bury VTS; Ho. Off. (Surg. & Med.) Wirral Hosps.

NORMAN, Peter Frank (retired) Barafundle, Down Park Drive, Tavistock PL19 9AH Tel: 01822 613834 — MB ChB Manch. 1960; FRCR 1975; FFR 1967; DMRD Eng. 1965. Prev: Cons. Neuroradiol. Plymouth Gen. Hosp.

NORMAN, Sarah Ann Medico -Legal Practice, Atlantic Business Centre, Atlantic St, Altrincham WA14 5NQ Tel: 0161 926 3660, 0161 926 3661; 2 The Haven, Hale, Altrincham WA15 8SA — BM BS 1988 Nottm.; MEWI 1998; MRCGP 1992; DRCOG 1991; Cert. Family Plann. JCC 1991. Medio-legal Cons. Socs: Expert Witnen Inst. Mem.; BMA Mem. Prev: Trainee GP Chester VTS; Gen. Practitioner Chester.

NORMAN, Simon Philip The Briars, Farm Road, Bristol BS16 6DD — MB ChB 1995 Bristol.

NORMAN, Stephen George Medway Maritime Hospital, Windmill Road, Gillingham ME7 5NY Tel: 01634 830000 Fax: 01634 811250; Tel: 01634 819370 — BM BS 1984 Nottm.; FRCOG 2001; BMedSci Nottm. 1982; BSc Leeds 1974; PhD Camb. 1978; MRCOG 1989. (Nottingham) Cons. O & G Medway Maritime Hosp. Gillingham. Prev: Cons. O & G All St.s Hosp. Chatham; Sen. Regist. (O & G) King's Coll. Hosp. Lond.

NORMAN, Stephen Grahame 12 Cardiff Road, Luton LU1 1QG Tel: 01582 22143 Fax: 01582 485721 Email: sno1@cableol.co.uk; 65 Stopsley Way, Stopsley, Luton LU2 7UU Tel: 01582 411726 — MB ChB 1980 Sheff.; MRCGP 1988. Socs: Christian Med. Fell.sh. & Caring Professions Concern. Prev: Trainee GP Luton & Dunstable Hosp. VTS; Paediat. N.. Gen. Hosp. Sheff.; Ho. Phys. (Surg.) Rotherham Dist. Gen. Hosp.

NORMAN, Susan 1 Leigh Road, Clifton, Bristol BS8 2DA — MB ChB 1972 Bristol; DObst RCOG 1975. Clin. Asst. (Venereol. & Colposcopy) Bristol Roy. Infirm.

NORMAN, Thomas (retired) The Old Rectory, Winterborne Houghton, Blandford Forum DT11 0PD Tel: 01258 880272 — MB BChir Camb. 1943; MA Camb.; DTM & H Eng. 1951. Prev: PMO Jhanzie Tea Assn. & Amguri Tea Est.s.

NORMAN, Valerie Elizabeth (retired) 3 Princes Road, Clevedon BS21 7SY Tel: 01275 874124 — MB ChB Birm. 1963. Prev: Sen. Med. Off. (Family Plann.) United Bristol Healthcare & W.on Area Health Trusts.

NORMAN, William Anthony Cromer Group Practice, 48 Overstrand Road, Cromer NR27 0AJ Tel: 01263 513148 — MB 1964 Camb.; BChir 1963; DA Eng. 1966; DRCOG 1965; CCFP Canada 1973.

NORMAN, William John The Rope Walk, Lyth Hill, Bayston Hill, Shrewsbury SY3 0BS Tel: 01743 872554; Fullers Cottage, Condover, Shrewsbury SY5 7BT Tel: 01743 872554 — MB BChir 1961 Camb.; MA, MB BChir Camb. 1961; FFR 1972; DMRD Eng. 1969. (Camb. & Guy's) Cons. Radiol. Roy. Shrewsbury Hosp. Prev: Sen. Regist. (Radiol.) United Bristol Hosps.

***NORMAN-NOTT, Arabella Gabriella** The Limberlost, St Giles Hill, Winchester SO23 0HH — MB BS 1996 Lond.

NORMAN-TAYLOR, Mr Fabian Hugh 12 Maida Vale, Norwich NR2 3EP — MB BS 1988 Lond.; FRCS Eng. 1992.

NORMAN-TAYLOR, Mr Julian Quentin The Portland Hospital, Great Portland St., London WC1 — MB ChB 1982 Leic.; MRCOG. Cons. (Gynae.). Socs: Roy. Coll. Obst. & Gyn.; Brit. Fertil. Soc.

NORMAND

NORMAND, Professor Ian Colin Stuart 23 St Thomas' Street, Winchester SO23 9HJ Tel: 01962 852550 — BM BCh 1952 Oxf.; MA Oxf. 1963, DM 1976; FRCP Lond. 1971, M 1956; Hon. FRCPCH 1996. (Oxf. & St. Mary's) Emerit. Prof. Child Health Univ. Soton. Prev: Dean Fac. Med. Univ. Soton.; Cons. Paediat. & Hon. Sen. Lect. (Paediat.) Univ. Coll. Hosp. Lond.; Fell. (Pediat.) Johns Hopkins Hosp., USA.

NORMANDALE, Jeremy Philip Pear Tree Cottage, West Lane, Snainton, Scarborough YO13 9AR — MB BS 1978 Lond.; FFARCS 1983. Cons. (Anaesth.) ScarBoro. & Bridlington Hosps. Socs: Obst. Anaesth. Assn. Prev: Attend. Anaesth. Univ. Washington Seattle, USA; Sen. Regist. Dept. Anaesth. Middlx. Hosp. Lond.; Regist. Hammersmith Hosp. Lond.

NORMINTON, David Roger Harold Kings Corner Surgery, Kings Road, Ascot SL5 0AE Tel: 01344 623181 Fax: 01344 875129 — MB BS 1969 Lond.; MRCGP 1986; DObst RCOG 1971; Cert. FPA 1973.

NORONHA, Mr Derek Thomas 28 Wallace Street, Spital Tongues, Newcastle upon Tyne NE2 4AU — MD 1986 Dar-es-Salaam; FRCS Ed. 1992.

NORONHA, Enid Antoinette Manchester Road Surgery, 39 Manchester Road, Walkden Worsley, Manchester M28 3NS Tel: 0161 702 8595 Fax: 0161 702 8592; 39 Manchester Road, Walkden, Worsley, Manchester M28 3NS Tel: 0161 702 8595 Fax: 0161 702 8592 — MB BS 1964 Poona. (B.J. Med. Coll.) GP Salford & Scaffold SHSA. Prev: SHO (Paediat.) Bradford Roy. Infirm.; Ho. Phys. St. Luke's Hosp. Bradford; Ho. Surg. Bury Gen. Hosp.

NORONHA, Hermes Dulci Santana 10 Bracewood Gardens, Park Hill Rise, Croydon CR0 5JL — MB ChB 1973 Leeds.

NORONHA, Michael Diago 2 Park Close, Shirland, Alfreton DE55 6AZ — MB BS 1988 Bangalore.

NORONHA, Michael Joseph 35 Ellesmere Road, Eccles, Manchester M30 9FE Tel: 0161 789 3761 Fax: 0161 789 3761 — MRCS Eng. LRCP Lond. 1959; MRCPI 1961; LRCPI & LM, LRCSI & LM 1958; FRCP Lond. 1981, M 1967; FRCP Ed. 1976, M 1963. (RCSI) Hon. Cons. Paediat. Neurol. Roy. Manch. Childr. Hosp. & Booth Hall Childr. Hosp.Manch. Socs: Assn. Brit. Neurol. & Assn. Brit. Paediat. Neurol. Prev: Research Regist. (Neurol.) Leeds Gen. Infirm.; Regist. (Med.) Bradford Roy. Infirm.; SHO Edin. Roy. Infirm.

NORRIE, Bruce Garland (retired) Eildonhurst, 500 Perth Road, Dundee DD2 1LS — MB ChB 1962 St. And. Prev: SHO (Paediat.) Inverness Hosp. Gp.

NORRIE, Douglas McKane Moorcroft, 16 Southway Lane, Roborough, Plymouth PL6 7DH Tel: 01752 774464 — MB ChB 1955 St. And.; DA Eng. 1959. (St. And.) Adjudicating Med. Pract. Indust. Injury Benefit Bds.; Examg. Med. Pract. War Pension Med. Bds.; Med. Adviser Incapacity Benefit Bds. Prev: GP Plymouth; Regist. (Anaesth.) S. Devon & E. Cornw. Hosps.

***NORRIE, Glenda Mary** 140A Rosemount Place, Aberdeen AB25 2YU — MB ChB 1996 Aberd.

NORRIE, Iain Alexander The Health Centre, Campbeltown PA28 6AT Tel: 01586 552105 — MB ChB 1993 Leeds.

NORRIE, Mary Stella 8 Abbey Close, Fairfield, Stockton-on-Tees TS19 7SP Tel: 01642 654243 Email: maureen.norrie@onyxnet.co.uk — MB BCh BAO 1972 Belf.; MRCGP Ed. 1977. (Queens University Belfast) Med. Adviser GS Med. Advisers & Teachs. Pens. Agency Darlington & Co. Durh.; Non Princip. (Gen. Pract.); Pract. (Neuro Linguistics & Hypnother.); Pract. (Complementary Med.). Socs: Soc. Occupat. Med.; Brit. Soc. Med. and Dent. Hypn. Prev: Clin. Med. Off. & SCMO (Community Child Health) N. Tees HA & S. Tees HA; Princip. (Gen. Pract.) Teesside.

NORRIE, Muriel Kinnison (retired) Moorcroft, 16 Southway Lane, Roborough, Plymouth PL6 7DH Tel: 01752 774464 — MB ChB St. And. 1955. Med. Ref. DHSS.; Mem. Examr. Incapacity Benefit Bd. Prev: Adjudicating Med. Pract. Indust. Benefit Bds.

NORRIE, Stuart David Leek Health Centre, Fountain St., Leek ST13 6JB Tel: 01538 381022; Pinehurst, Sutherland Road, Longsdon, Stoke-on-Trent ST9 9QD Tel: 01538 399680 — MB ChB 1979 Birm.; DRCOG 1983.

NORRIS, Alan Central Health Centre, North Carbrain Road, Cumbernauld, Glasgow G67 1BJ Tel: 01236 737214 Fax: 01236 781699 — MB ChB 1977 Glas.

NORRIS, Alan 13 Pickletullum Road, Craigie, Perth PH2 0LL — MB ChB 1987 Ed.; BSc (Hons.) Ed. 1985; MRCP (UK) 1992. Assoc. Specialist (Blood Transfus.) Ninewells Hosp. Dundee. Prev: Regist. (Haemat.) Glas. Roy. Infirm. & Stobhill Hosp. Glas.; Regist. (Med.) Raigmore Hosp. Inverness; SHO (Med.) Law Hosp. Carluke.

NORRIS, Alan Michael Mater Hospital, Belfast BT14 6AB Tel: 01232 741211 Fax: 01232 741342; 36 Royal Lodge Avenue, Purdysburn Road, Belfast BT8 7YR — MB BCh BAO 1985 Dub.; MRCP (UK) 1990; MRCPI 1988; FRCR 1993. Cons. Radiol. Mater Hosp. Belf.

NORRIS, Alexander Donald Craig Tel: 01303 265581 Fax: 01303 264940 Email: alexnorris@compuserve.com; Stone Stile Oast, Selling, Faversham ME13 9SD Tel: 01233 714962 Fax: 01233 713340 Email: alex@charing.fsnet.co.uk — MB BChir Camb. 1961; MA Camb. 1961; FRCP Lond. 1978, M 1963. (Camb. & Lond. Hosp.) Cons. Cardiol., Benenden Hosp., Cranbrook, Kent; Cons. Cardiac Guys Hosp. Lond. Socs: BMA & Brit. Cardiac Soc. Prev: Sen. Regist. (Gen. Med.), Regist. (Gen. Med. & Cardiol.) Lond. Hosp.; Cons. Phys. William Harvey Hosp. Ashford, Kent.

NORRIS, Andrea Jane 6 Glenside Drive, Wilmslow SK9 1EH — MB ChB 1994 Leeds.

***NORRIS, Andrew** Ipswich Hospital NHS Trust, Heath Road, Ipswich IP4 5PD — MB BS 1996 Lond.

NORRIS, Andrew Michael Top Hovel, Hockerton Road, Hockerton, Southwell NG25 0PP — MB ChB 1986 Sheff.; FRCA 1993. Cons. (Anaesth.) Qu. Med. Centre Nottm.

NORRIS, Christopher Stewart Park Road Surgery, 3 Park Road, Shepton Mallet BA4 5BP Tel: 01749 342350 Fax: 01749 346845 — MB ChB 1972 Bristol; DObst RCOG 1974; MRCGP 1976.

NORRIS, Clive Denis 1206 Christchurch Road, Boscombe East, Bournemouth BH7 6DZ — MB BS 1970 Lond.; MRCS Eng. LRCP Lond. 1970; MRCGP 1981; DObst RCOG 1973; Cert FPA 1973. (Lond. Hosp.)

NORRIS, Elizabeth Angela (retired) 9 Melton Green, Wath Upon Dearne, Rotherham S63 6AA Tel: 01709 872051 — MB ChB 1978 Sheff.; DA (UK) 1981; DRCOG 1985. Prev: GP Wombwell Barnsley S. Yorks.

NORRIS, Elizabeth Margaret Blandford Group Practice, Whitecliff, Mill St., Blandford Forum DT11 7BH; 60 Falcondale Road, Westbury-on-Trym, Bristol BS9 — MB ChB 1977 Bristol; MRCGP 1981; DRCOG 1980. Prev: GP W.bury on Trym; Clin. Asst. (Cardiol.) Bristol Roy. Infirm.

NORRIS, Elizabeth Mary Freshfield House, Freshfield Lane, Danehill, Haywards Heath RH17 7HE Tel: 01825 791121 Fax: 01825 791460 — MB ChB 1996 Bristol; BSc Bristol 1992. (Bristol Uni.) Sen. SHO (O & G) Guy's & St Thomas' Lond. Socs: BMA. Prev: SHO (O & G) Bristol 1998; SHO (Med.) Bristol 1997.

NORRIS, Geoffrey Francis, MBE GP Office, Medical Education Centre, Whipps Cross Hospital, Whipps Cross Road, London E11 1NR Tel: 020 8535 6417 Fax: 020 8535 6417 Email: sheilagped@aol.com; 21 Falmouth Avenue, Highams Park, London E4 9QL Tel: 020 8527 3544 — MB BChir Camb. 1960; MA Camb. 1960; DObst RCOG 1963; FRCGP 1988, M 1968. (Westm.) Princip. in Gen. Pract.; Course Organiser Whipps Cross Hosp. VTS. Socs: RCGP; Hosp. Convenor N. E. Lond. Fac. Prev: SHO (O & G), Ho. Phys. (Gen. Med. & Paediat.) & Ho. Surg. St. Margt. Hosp. Epping; Assoc. Dean Pan Thames; TPMDE Facilitator Extended VTS.

NORRIS, Joan Gladys Harcourt 16 Norman Avenue, Abingdon OX14 2HH Tel: 01235 520207 — MRCS Eng. LRCP Lond. 1932. (Lond. Sch. Med. Wom.) JP.

NORRIS, Joan Hattersley (retired) 51 Moberly Road, Salisbury SP1 3BX Tel: 01722 322440 — MB ChB 1949 Bristol. Prev: GP Salisbury.

NORRIS, John Phillips, QGM (retired) 51 Moberly Road, Salisbury SP1 3BX Tel: 01722 322440 — MB ChB 1948 Bristol; FRCGP 1978, M 1960; DObst RCOG 1952.

NORRIS, Mr John Samuel Hurstwood Park Neurological Centre, Princess Royal Hospital, Haywards Heath RH16 4EX Tel: 01444 441881 Fax: 01444 417995; Email: jsn@dial.pipex.com — MB ChB 1986 Bristol; FRCS (SN) 1995; FRCS Ed. 1990. (Bristol) Cons. Neuro. Surg.Hurstwood Pk. Neurosci.s Centre P.ss Roy. Hosp. Haywards Heath; Fell. (Neurovasc.) Toronto Hosp. Canad. Socs: BMA; Roy. Soc. Med.; Soc. Brit. Neurol. Surgs. Prev: Regist. (Neurosurg.) Qu. Med. Centre Nottm.; Sen. Regist. (Neurosurg.) Roy. Lond. & OldCh. Hosps. Lond.; Fell. (Neurovasc.) Toronto Hosp., Canada.

NORRIS, Professor John William Department of Neurology, Sunnybrook Medical Centre, 2075 Bayview Avenue, Toronto M4N 3M5, Canada Tel: 416 480 4473 Fax: 416 480 5753; 20 Onslow Square, London SW7 3NP Tel: 0207 225 1329 Fax: 0207 225 1329 — MB ChB 1957 Aberd.; FRCP Ed. 1978, M 1962; FRCP Lond. 1982, M 1964. (Aberd.) Prof. (Neurol.) Univ. Toronto, Canada.; Chairm. Canad. Stroke Consortium. Socs: Assn. Brit. Neurols.; Amer. Neurol. Assn.; Amer. Acad. Neurol.

NORRIS, Jonathan Falcon Woodham Corner, Woodham Road, Woking — MB BS 1979 Lond.

NORRIS, Jonathan Frazer Bate Denbie, Lockerbie DG11 1DU Tel: 01387 840333 — MB ChB 1974 Manch.; FRCP Ed. 1996; MRCP (UK) 1979; DCH Eng. 1977; DRCOG 1977. Cons. Dermat. Dumfries & Galloway Roy. Infirm. Dumfries. Prev: Tutor (Dermat.) Leeds Univ.; Hon. Sen. Regist. (Dermat.) Leeds Gen. Infirm.

NORRIS, Jonathan Scott Fairlands Medical Centre, Fairlands Avenue, Worplesdon, Guildford GU3 3NA Tel: 01483 594250 Fax: 01483 598767; 32 Selbourne Road, Burpham, Guildford GU4 7JP — BM BS 1978 Nottm.; MRCGP 1982. (Nottm.) Trainer (Gen. Pract.) Guildford. Prev: Trainee GP Derbysh. Family Pract. Comm. VTS.

NORRIS, Julia Constance Fircroft, Gladsmuir Road, Barnet EN5 4PJ — MB BCh 1967 Wales; MB BCh Wales, 1967; DA Eng. 1969. (Cardiff)

NORRIS, Kate Louise St. Marys Street Surgery, 47 St Marys St., Ely CB7 4HF Tel: 01353 663434 Fax: 01353 669532; 66 Aldreth Road, Haddenham, Ely CB6 3PW — MB BS 1982 Lond.; DRCOG 1986. (CXHMS) Clin. Asst. in Gen. Pract.; Clin. Asst. in Gyn., P.ss of Wales Hosp., Ely, Cambs. Prev: Asst. GP Cheltenham; Trainee GP Cheltenham VTS.

NORRIS, Katharine Joanne West Timperley Medical Centre, 21 Dawson Road, Altrincham WA14 5PF Tel: 0161 929 1515 Fax: 0161 941 6500; 3 Bankhall Lane, Hale, Altrincham WA15 0LA Tel: 0161 928 8979 — MB ChB 1986 Bristol; MRCGP 1991; T(GP) 1991; DRCOG 1990. (Bristol) Prev: SHO (Paediat. & A & E) S. Manch. Hosp.; SHO (Geriat.) Chester City Hosp.

NORRIS, Margaret Jennifer 7 Endcliffe Grove Avenue, Sheffield S10 3EJ Tel: 0114 666568 — MB ChB 1969 Ed.; BSc (Med. Sci.) Ed. 1966, MB ChB 1969. (Ed.) Prev: Ho. Phys. Leith Hosp. Edin.; Ho. Surg. Roodlands Hosp. Haddington; SHO (O & G) St. Mary's Hosp. Kettering.

***NORRIS, Mark Christopher** 46 The Willows, Newington, Sittingbourne ME9 7LS — MB ChB 1996 Leic.

NORRIS, Mr Michael Graham Hall Farm, Somerford Booths, Congleton CW12 2JR Tel: 01260 224261 — MB ChB 1965 St. And.; FRCS Ed. 1972; DObst RCOG 1967. (St. Andrews) p/t Cons. Orthop. Surg. E. Chesh. NHS Trust. Socs: Fell. BOA; BMA; HCSA. Prev: Regist. (Orthop.) Nuffield Orthop. Centre Oxf.; Sen. Regist. (Orthop.) Harlow Wood Orthop. Hosp. Mansfield.

NORRIS, Patricia Mary The Surgery, 212 Richmond Road, Kingston upon Thames KT2 5HF Tel: 020 8546 0400 Fax: 020 8974 5771; 4 Rosewood, 105 Manor Road N., Thames Ditton KT7 0BH Tel: 020 8398 8226 — MB ChB 1970 Liverp.; MRCS Eng. LRCP Lond. 1970; MRCGP 1991; Cert. Av. Med. 1993; Cert. Occupat. Med. 1988; Cert. Family Plann. JCC 1986; D.Occ. Med. 1997; DObst RCOG 1972. (Liverp.) Med. Adviser Lond. Gen. Holdings Kingston, PPS Europe Worthing & AIM Avionics Byfleet; Gp. Med. Adviser Brit. Aerospace FarnBoro. & Dunsfold; Local Med. Adviser Thames Water. Socs: Soc. Occupat. Med.

NORRIS, Paul Graham Department of Dermatology, Addenbrooke's Hospital, Cambridge CB2 2QQ; 73 Rampton Road, Cottenham, Cambridge CB4 8TH — MB BChir 1981 Camb.; MRCP (UK) 1984. (St George's) Cons. Dermat. Addenbrooke's Hosp. Camb. Socs: FRCP.

***NORRIS, Paul Martin** 43 Carver Road, London SE24 9LS — MB BS 1998 Lond.; MB BS Lond 1998.

NORRIS, Peter Edward Riverside Surgery, Barnard Avenue, Brigg DN20 8AS Tel: 01652 650131 Fax: 01652 651551; 3 St. Helens Road, Brigg DN20 8BX Tel: 01652 653236 — BM BCh 1977 Oxf.; MA Oxf. 1978. Socs: Brit. Assn. Sport & Med.

NORRIS, Philip, Wing Cdr. RAF Med. Br. Retd. Church Park, Rhossili, Gower, Swansea SA3 1PL Tel: 01792 390540 — MB ChB 1952 Bristol. Prev: Flying Personel Med. Off. RAF Inst. Aviat. Med.

FarnBoro.; GP Camberley; Med. Adviser Dept. Transport DVLC Swansea.

NORRIS, Philip Ronald Woodham Corner, Woodham Road, Woking GU21 4EG Tel: 01483 761182 — MD 1962 Lond.; MB BS 1952; FRCOG 1969, M 1957. Emerit. Cons. O & G S.W. Thames RHA; Hon. Clin. Tutor St. Thos. Hosp. Lond. Socs: Fell. Roy. Soc. Med.; Pres. Brit. Sect. World Fed. of Doctors Who Respect Human Life. Prev: Sen. Lect. & Hon. Cons. O & G Roy. Free Hosp. & Med. Sch. Lond.; Sen. Regist. (O & G) St. Thos. Hosp. Lond.

NORRIS, Richard Lansdowne Road Surgery, 6 Lansdowne Road, Bedford MK40 2BU Tel: 01234 270170 Fax: 01234 214033; 3 Turner Way, Bedford MK41 7LY Tel: 01234 307740 Fax: 01234 307740 — BM BS 1978 Nottm.; BMedSci Nottm. 1978; Cert. Family Plann. JCC 1981. (Nottm.) GP Bedford. Prev: Dep. Police Surg. & Prison Med. Off.

NORRIS, Richard Lindley (retired) Francis Close, North Road, South Molton EX36 3AZ Tel: 0176 952903 — MB BS 1941 Lond.

NORRIS, Richard Martin Parkfield Medical Centre, The Walk, Potters Bar EN6 1QH Tel: 01707 651234 Fax: 01707 660452; 21 Mount Grace Road, Potters Bar EN6 1RD — MB BChir 1972 Camb.; BA Camb. 1968; MRCGP 1983. (Univ. Coll. Hosp.) Bd. Mem. Hertsmere PCG. Prev: SHO St. Martin's Hosp. Bath; Cas. Surg. Off. Middlx. Hosp. Lond.; Ho. Surg. Whittington Hosp. Lond.

NORRIS, Mr Richard William BUPA Alexandra Hospital, Impton Lane, Walderslade, Chatham ME5 9PG Tel: 01634 687166; Torridon House, Church Cliff, Kingsdown, Deal CT14 8AT Tel: 01304 380684 — MB BS 1976 Lond.; FRCS Eng. 1980; MRCS Eng. LRCP Lond. 1976; T(S) Lond. 1987. (Lond. Hosp.) Cons. Plastic Surg. Chaucer Hosp Canterbury., BUPA Alexandra Hosp. Walderslade & Chaucer Hosp. Canterbury; Dir. of Surg. The Kent Hand & Plastic Surg. Unit Alexandra Hosp. Walderslade. Socs: Brit. Assn. Plastic Surg.; Brit. Assn. Aesthetic Plastic Surgs.; Brit. Soc. For Surg. of the hand. Prev: Cons. Plastic Surg. Qu. Vict. Hosp. E. Grinstead; Regist. (Surg.) Lond. Hosp.; Demonst. (Anat.) Lond. Hosp. Med. Coll.

NORRIS, Robin John Powderject Pharmaceuticals Plc, 4 Robert Robinson Avenue, Oxford OX4 4GA Tel: 01865 782500 Fax: 01865 782801; 6511 Dumbarton Circle, Fremont CA 94555, USA Tel: 00 1 510 742 9700 Fax: 00 1 510 742 9720 — MB BS 1971 Lond.; MRCGP 1976; Dip. Pharm. Med. RCP (UK) 1981; DObst RCOG 1974. (Westm.) Chief Operating Off. Powderject Pharmaceut. Plc Oxf.; Pres. Powderject Technologies Inc. Fremont Calif., USA. Socs: Fell. Roy. Soc. Med. Prev: Chief Operating Off. Noven Miami, USA; Vice-Pres. Med. Affairs Rorer Internat. Pharmaceut.; Dir. Clin. Research Schering-Plough Internat. Pharmaceut. Div.

NORRIS, Robin MacKenzie (retired) Cardiac Department, The Royal Sussex County Hospital, Brighton BN2 5BE Tel: 01273 696955 Fax: 01273 673106 — MB ChB New Zealand 1955; MD Birm. 1965; FRCP Lond. 1977; MRCP (UK) 1960; FRACP 1972. Hon. Cons. Cardiol. & Sen. Vis. Fell. (Cardiac) Roy. Sussex Co. Hosp. Prev: Hon. Prof. Cardiovasc. Therap. Univ. Auckland Sch. Med., NZ.

NORRIS, Stephanie Claire Denbie, Lockerbie DG11 1DU — MB ChB 1979 Manch.; MB ChB (Hons.) Manch. 1979; BSc (1st cl. Hons. Pharm.) Manch. 1973; MRCP (UK) 1982. Med. Adviser Primary Care Dumfries & Galloway HB. Prev: Med. Adviser ICI Pharmaceut. Div. Alderley Pk.; Clin. Research Fell. ICI Pharmaceut. Div. Alderley Pk.; Regist. (Gen. Med.) Altrincham Gen. Hosp.

NORRIS, Mr Stephen Henley 7 Endcliffe Grove Avenue, Sheffield S10 3EJ Tel: 0114 266 0707 Fax: 0114 267 8600 Email: stephennorris@medix-uk.com — MD 1985 Bristol; MB BS Lond. 1970; FRCS Eng. 1974. (Middlx.) p/t Cons. Orthop. Surg. N. Gen. Hosp. Sheff.; Mem. Ct. of Examr.s Roy. Coll. of Surg.s. Socs: Fell. BOA; Hand Soc.; Ct. Exam. RCS Eng. Prev: Sen. Lect. (Orthop. Surg.) Univ. Sheff.; Lect. (Orthop. & Traum. Surg.) Univ. Bristol; Resid. (Orthop.) Mass. Gen. Hosp., Boston.

NORRIS, Tessa Carolyn Margaret The Surgery, Cordell Rd, Longmelford, Sudbury CD10 9EP — MB BS 1983 Lond.; MA (Hons.) Camb. 1984; MRCGP 1987. Med. Adviser Schering-Plough Ltd. Mildenhall.; GP, The Surg., Sudbury. Prev: GP Richmond; SHO (Paediat., Med. & A & E) Qu. Mary's Hosp. Lond.

NORRIS, Thomas St Martin (retired) 14 Jury Park, South Molton EX36 4DW — MA Camb., MD 1948, MB BChir 1928; FRCP Lond.

NORRIS

1962, M 1930; MRCS Eng. LRCP Lond. 1927; DPH Eng. 1932. Prev: Cons. Phys. Whittington Hosp. Lond.

NORRIS, Virginia Heidi 44 West Drayton Park Avenue, West Drayton UB7 7QB — MB BS 1993 Lond.

***NORRIS, Willam Desmond** 6 Forbes Road, Rosyth, Dunfermline KY11 2AN — MB ChB 1997 Dundee.

NORRIS, William Anderson, OBE (retired) 42 Bawn Hill Road, Ballynahinch. BT24 8LD Tel: 01238 561266 Fax: 01238 561266 — MD 1952 Belf.; MB BCh BAO 1948, DPM 1952; FRCPsych 1982, M 1971; FRCPI 1981, M 1954. Prev: Cons. Psychiat. Purdysburn Hosp., Roy. Vict. Hosp. & Day Hosp. Belf.

NORRISH, Elizabeth Lois 2 Great Eastern Street, Cambridge CB1 3AD Tel: 01223 563635 Email: norish@globalnet.co.uk — MRCP(1) 1998; MB BS Lond. 1996; DRCOG. (Charing Cross and Westminster) SHO 0 & G Addenbrooke's Hosp. Camb.; Gen. Pract. VTS Addenbrooke's Hosp. Camb. Socs: Christ. Med. Fell.sh. Prev: SHO Gen. Med. Addenbrooke's Hosp. Camb.; Ho. Off. Gen. Med. Hinchingbrooke Hosp. Huntingdon; Ho. Off. Gen. Surg. Hinchingbrooke Hosp. Huntington.

NORTCLIFFE, Sally Ann 3 Cobden Terrace, Hipperholme, Halifax HX3 8JH — MB ChB 1991 Leic.

***NORTH, Adrian C** 19 Laithes Drive, Alverthorpe, Wakefield WF2 9TE Email: anorth@compuserve.com — MB ChB 1997 Manch.

NORTH, Mr Andrew David Scarborough Hospital, Woodlands Drive, Scarborough YO12 6QL Tel: 01723 368111; The Old Station, Staintondale, Scarborough YO13 0EZ — BM BS 1980 Nottm.; FRCS Orth. Glas. 1992; FRCS Glas. 1984. Cons. Orthop. Surg. ScarBoro. Hosp. N. Yorks. Prev: Sen. Regist. Guy's Hosp. Lond.; Regist. Qu. Med. Centre Nottm.

NORTH, Andrew Peter Green Acres, Kingswood Road, Penn, High Wycombe HP10 8JL — MB ChB 1991 Leic.

***NORTH, Carolyn Elizabeth** Nidderdale View, Burnt Yates, Harrogate HG3 3EG — MB BS 1998 Lond.; MB BS Lond 1998.

NORTH, Christopher Hill Brow Surgery, Long Croft, Mapplewell, Barnsley S75 6FH Tel: 01226 383131 Fax: 01226 380100; 136 Park Grove, Barnsley S70 1QG — MB ChB 1977 Sheff.

NORTH, Christopher Ivan The Doctors House, Victoria Road, Marlow SL7 1DN Tel: 01628 484666 Fax: 01628 891206 — MB BS 1979 Lond.; DCH RCP Lond. 1983; DRCOG 1981.

NORTH, Claire Elizabeth Orchard Surgery, Cope Road, Banbury OX16 2EJ Tel: 01295 256201 Fax: 01295 277783; Aldsworth, Hook Norton Road, Sibford Ferris, Banbury OX15 5QR — MB ChB 1985 Leic.; MRCGP 1989; DRCOG 1987. Prev: Trainee GP Qu. Eliz. II Hosp. Welwyn Gdn. City VTS.

NORTH, Clive Doyne Child and Family Consultation Service, 25 West Avenue, Clacton-on-Sea CO15 1EU Tel: 01255 207070 Fax: 01255 207088 — MB BS 1987 Lond.; MA Oxf. 1992, BA 1983; MSc Manch. 1992; MD Lond. 1997; MRCPsych 1992. Cons. Child & Adolesc. Psychiat. N. Essex Ment. Health Partnership Trust.

NORTH, Derek The Surgery, 66-68 Stoke Road, Gosport PO12 1PA Tel: 023 9258 1529 Fax: 023 9250 1417; 3 Ellachie Road, Gosport PO12 2DP Tel: 02392 581529 — MB ChB 1975 Sheff.; MRCGP 1980; DRCOG 1979; DCH Eng. 1977. GP Princip. GP Trainer. Socs: BMA.

NORTH, Elizabeth Ann St. Helier NHS Trust, Wrythe Lane, Carshalton SM5 1AA Tel: 020 8296 2655; Cavendish Lodge, 1 Cavendish Rd, Sutton SM2 5ET Tel: 020 8642 8027 Fax: 020 8770 0945 Email: stefantiz@msn.com — MB ChB Liverp. 1970; BA (Hons.) Open 1988; FRCR 1975; DMRD Liverp. 1974; DObst RCOG 1972. Cons. Radiol. St. Heliers Hosp. Carshalton; Hon. Lect. St. Geo. Hosp. Tooting. Socs: (Ex-Pres.) Sutton & Merton Dist. Med. Soc.; Brit. Soc. Interven. Radiol.; Cardiovasc. & Interven. Soc. Europe. Prev: Sen. Regist. (Radiol.) St. Mary's Hosp. Paddington; Ho. Off. David Lewis N.. Hosp. Liverp.

NORTH, Gillian Norma Shiregreen Medical Centre, 492 Bellhouse Road, Sheffield S5 0RG Tel: 0114 245 6123 Fax: 0114 257 0964; 38 Eagleton Drive, High Green, Sheffield S35 4DS Tel: 0114 284 5830 Email: gill@eagleton.demon.co.uk — MB ChB 1978 Leeds; MRCGP 1982; Dip. Palliat. Med. Wales 1991; DCH RCP Lond. 1982. (Leeds) GP Trainer Sheff.; Hosp. Pract. Wheata Day Hospice Sheff. Prev: Trainee GP/SHO Huddersfield Roy. Infirm. VTS; Ho. Phys. & Ho. Surg. St. Jas. Hosp. Leeds.

NORTH, Jennifer Rachel 61 Compton Road, London N21 3NU — MB ChB 1993 Sheff.

NORTH, Joan Lane End Farm, Hightown, Ringwood BH24 3DY Tel: 0142 542036 — MB ChB 1949 St. And.; MRCOG 1958.

NORTH, Mr John Frederick (retired) Boundary Cottage, Kemerton, Tewkesbury GL20 7JD Tel: 01386 725376 — MRCS Eng. LRCP Lond. 1941; BA Camb 1938, MA 1942, MB BChir 1941; FRCS Eng. 1947. Prev: Surg. i/c W. Midl. Regional Plastic Surg. Centre Wordsley Hosp.

NORTH, John Kingsley Rosebank Surgery, Ashton Road, Road, Lancaster LA1 4JS Tel: 01524 842284 Fax: 01524 844839; 5 Pinewood Close, Lancaster LA2 0AD Tel: 01524 68338 — MB BS 1982 Lond.; MRCGP 1988; DRCOG 1987; DCH RCP Lond. 1986. (Guy's Hospital, London) GP Lancaster.

NORTH, Jonathan Paul Immunology Department, City Hospital, Dudley Road, Birmingham B18 7QH Tel: 0121 507 4250 Fax: 0121 507 4567 Email: jpn@immunology.demon.co.uk — MB BCh 1982 Wales; DM Soton. 1993; MRCPath 1992; FRCP 2000 (Path). Cons. Immunol. City Hosp. & NBS Birm.; Hon. Sen. Lect. Immunol. Birm. Med. Sch. Socs: Brit. Soc. Immunol.; Assn. Clin. Path.; Brit. Soc. Allergy and Clin. Immunol. Prev: Sen. Regist. (Immunol.) Leics. Roy. Infirm.; Regist. (Immunol.) Dudley Rd. Hosp. Birm.; Research Regist. Roy. Vict. Hosp. Bournemouth & Tenovus Research Inst. Soton.

NORTH, Michael Alan Maylandsea Medical Centre, Imperial Avenue, Maylandsea, Chelmsford CM3 6AH Tel: 01621 742233 Fax: 01621 742917; Downside Cottage, Summerhill, Althorne, Chelmsford CM3 6BY Email: mikenorth@equip.ac.uk — MB BS 1978 Lond.; FRCGP 1996, M 1986; DRCOG 1981. (Royal Free Hospital)

NORTH, Penelope Claire Moregrove, Perrymead, Bath BA2 5AZ — BM 1991 Soton.; BSc Sheff. 1986.

NORTH, Peter Edwin (retired) Long Meadow, 58 Burnham Road, Epworth, Doncaster DN9 1BY Tel: 01427 872422 — MB ChB 1957 St. And.; FFA RCS Eng. 1964. Prev: Cons. Anaesth. Scunthorpe Health Dist.

NORTH, Peter John 9 Chadderton Drive, Unsworth, Bury BL9 8NL — MRCS Eng. LRCP Lond. 1964; DO Eng. 1970.

***NORTH, Philipa Therese** 1 Maywood Cl, Beckenham Pl Pk, Beckenham BR3 5BW — MB ChB 1997 Ed.

NORTH, Professor Richard Alan Institute of Molecular Physiology, University of Sheffield, Alfred Denny Building, Western Bank, Sheffield S10 2TN Tel: 0114 222 4668 Fax: 0114 222 2360 Email: r.a.north@sheffield.ac.uk; 64 A Dore Road, Sheffield S17 3NE — MB ChB 1969 Aberd.; PhD Aberd. 1973; BSc Aberd. 1969. Prof. Inst. Molecular Physiol. Univ. Sheff. Socs: Fell. Roy. Soc. Lond.; Fell. Roy. Coll. Phys. Prev: Prof. Vollum Inst.; Prof. Mass. Inst. Technol.; Princip. Scientist, Glaxo Wellcome Research and Developm., Geneva.

NORTH, Roger Francis, Lt.-Col. RAMC Beacon Medical Practice, Churchill Avenue, Skegness PE25 2AN Tel: 01754 897000 Fax: 01754 761024; 38 Lebanon Park, Twickenham TW1 3DG Email: rnorth@globalnet.co.uk — MB ChB 1983 Leic.; MRCGP 1987; DRCOG 1987. Princip. Prev: Retd. RAMC Off.

NORTH, Sarah Melody Putneymead Medical Centre, 350 Upper Richmond Road, London SW15 6TL Tel: 020 8788 0686; 9 Ellison Road, Barnes, London SW13 0AD — MB BS 1974 Lond.

NORTH, Serena Laura Peabody The Surgery, 3 Austin Road, Battersea, London SW11 5JP Tel: 020 7498 0232 Fax: 020 7498 0271 — BM BCh 1975 Oxf.; MRCGP 1979. (Oxford) GP Battersea Fields Lond.; Med. Cons. to Christian Action Research & Educat. (CARE).

NORTH-COOMBES, David Paul The Bridges Practice, The Health Centre, Stepgates, Chertsey KT16 8HZ Tel: 01932 561199; Farthings, Brox Lane, Ottershaw, Chertsey KT16 0LL Tel: 01932 872220 — MB BS 1978 Lond.; MRCGP 1984; DRCOG 1982; DCH RCP Lond. 1980. (Middlx.)

NORTH-SMITH, Margaret Holden (retired) 29 Esher Park Avenue, Esher KT10 9NX Tel: 01372 486784 — LRCP LRCS Ed. LRFPS Glas. 1949; DA Eng. 1954. Prev: Anaesth. NW Surrey Hosp. Gp.

NORTHCOTE, Robin John Department of Medicine, The Victoria Infirmary, Langside, Glasgow G42 9TY Tel: 0141 201 5396; Whinmuir, 11 Ewenfield Road, Ayr KA7 2QF — MD 1986 Glas.; MB ChB 1978; FRCPS Glas. 1992; MRCP (UK) 1982; Dip. Sp. Med. 1997. (Glas.) Cons. Phys. & Cardiol. Vict. Infirm. Glas. Socs: Brit.

ardiac Soc. & Med. Research Soc. Prev: Sen. Regist. (Cardiol. & Gen. Med.) & Research Fell. (Cardiol.) Vict. Infirm. Glas.

NORTHEAST, Mr Andrew David Roland Wycombe General Hospital, Queen Alexandra Road, High Wycombe HP11 2TT Tel: 01494 526161 Email: anortheast@compuserve.com — BM BCh 980 Oxf.; MA Oxf. 1981; FRCS Eng. 1987; FRCS Ed. 1986. (Oxf.) Cons. Gen. Surg. S. Bucks. NHS Trust. Socs: Fell. Roy. Soc. Of Med.; Vasc. Scrn. Soc.(GB); Assn. Surg. Prev: Sen. Regist. & Regist. St. hos. Hosp. Lond.; Regist. (Gen. Surg.) St. Thos. Hosp. Lond.; SHO Surg.) MusGr. Pk. Hosp. Taunton.

NORTHEN, Mary Ellen Lingfield Surgery, East Grinstead Road, Lingfield RH7 6ER Tel: 01342 833456 Fax: 01342 836347; Hadlow, k Road, Dormans Park, East Grinstead RH19 2NQ Tel: 01342 870646 — MB ChB 1971 Glas.; MRCP (UK) 1974. GP Lingfield. Prev: GP Hitchin; Regist. (Gen. Med.) W.. Infirm. Glas.

NORTHERN, David Graham Frank Oakengates Medical Practice, Imes Walk, Oakengates, Telford TF2 6JJ Tel: 01952 620077 Fax: 01952 620209; 8 Woodhouse Lane, Priorslee, Telford TF2 9SX Tel: 01952 293775 — MB ChB 1981 Manch.; MRCGP 1985; DCH RCP Lond. 1984; DRCOG 1983.

*NORTHFIELD, John William Hazelwood Farm, Doghurst La, Coulsdon CR5 3PL — MB BS 1997 Lond.

NORTHFIELD, Mark 574 Broadway, Chadderton, Oldham OL9 9NF — MB ChB 1982 Manch.; BSc St. And. 1979.

NORTHFIELD, Rosemary Raymonde (retired) Hazelwood Farm, Doghurst Lane, Chipstead, Coulsdon, Croydon CR5 3PL Tel: 01737 553209 Fax: 01737 551560 — MB BS Lond. 1961; MRCS Eng. RCP Lond. 1961; FFOM RCP Lond. 1997; MFOM 1978; T(OM) 991; DIH Eng. 1970; DA Eng. 1964. Prev: Med. Adviser Brit. Gas Croydon.

NORTHFIELD, Professor Timothy Clive Hazelwood Farm, Doghurst Lane, Chipstead, Coulsdon CR5 3PL Tel: 01737 553209 Fax: 01737 551560 — MB BChir 1963 Camb.; MA Camb. 1959, MD 1970; FRCP Lond. 1977, M 1965; MRCS Eng. LRCP Lond. 962. (Guy's) Cons. Phys. & Prof. Gastroenterol. St. Geo. Hosp. & Med. Sch. Lond. Socs: Fell. Roy. Soc. Med.; Brit. Soc. Gastroenterol. Prev: Regist. (Gastroenterol.) Centr. Middlx. Hosp. Lond.; MRC Trav. Fell. Gastroenterol. Unit Mayo Clinic, USA; Sen. Regist. (Gastroenterol.) Guy's Hosp. Lond.

NORTHMORE-BALL, Mr Martin Dacre The Robert Jones and Agnes Hunt, Orthopaedic Hospital, Ellesmere SY12 9DH; Higher Grange, Ellesmere SY12 9DH — MB BChir 1968 Camb.; MA Camb. 968; FRCS Eng. 1973. (Camb. & St. Thos.) Hon. Cons. Orthop. Surg. Robt. Jones & Agnes Hunt Orthop. Hosp. OsW.ry. Prev: Sen. Regist. (Orthop.) Addenbrooke's Hosp. Camb.; Clin. Fell. (Orthop.) Univ. Toronto, Canada; Regist. (Orthop.) King's Coll. Hosp. Lond.

NORTHOVER, Catherine Sophia Cutlers Hill Surgery, Burgay Road, Halesworth IP19 8HP Tel: 01986 874618, 01986 874908 — MB ChB 1972 Liverp.; DCH Eng. 1976.

NORTHOVER, Mr John Martin Alban St. Mark's Hospital, Northwick Park, Watford Road, Harrow HA1 3JU Tel: 020 8235 1250 Fax: 020 8235 4277 Email: northov@icrf.icnet.uk; 2 Park Avenue N., Priory Park, London N8 7RT Tel: 020 8342 9837 Fax: 20 8348 7605 — MB BS 1970 Lond.; MS Lond. 1980; FRCS Eng. 975; MRCS Eng. LRCP Lond. 1970. (King's Coll. Hosp.) Cons. Surg. St. Marks Hosp. Lond.; Hon. Dir. ICRF Colorectal Cancer Unit.; Sen. Lect. Imp. Coll. Lond.

NORTHOVER, Julian Roy Little Thatches, Hill St., Calmore, Southampton SO40 2RX — BM 1997 Soton.

NORTHOVER, Ruth Patricia St Thomas Health Centre, Cowick Street, St. Thomas, Exeter EX4 1HJ Tel: 01392 676677 Fax: 01392 876677; Home Farm, Oxton, Exeter EX6 8EX Tel: 01626 891162 — MB BS 1985 Lond.; MRCGP 1989; DRCOG 1989. (St Bart.) GP Exeter. Prev: Clin. Asst. (Diabetes) Exeter; Trainee GP Dartmouth; HO (O & G & Med.) Harold Wood Hosp. Romford.

NORTHOVER, Susan Carolyn 17 Kyle Close, Bracknell RG12 7DF — BM 1998 Soton.

NORTHOVER, Tracy Heidi Royal Bolton Hospital, Minerva Road, Farnworth, Bolton BL4 0JR Tel: 01204 390390 Email: eidi.northover@boltonh-tr.nwest.nhs.uk — MB ChB 1986 Manch.; MRCP (UK) 1992; DCH RCP Lond. 1989; DRCOG 1988; FRCPCH 996. Cons. Paediat. Roy. Bolton Hosp. Prev: Sen. Regist. (Paediat.) Roy. Manch. Childr. Hosp.; Regist. (Paediat.) Roy. Manch. Childr. Hosp.; Regist. (Paediat.) Roy. Childr. Hosp. Melbourne, Austral.

NORTHRIDGE, Cecil Samuel Colne Health Centre, Market Street, Colne BB8 0LJ Tel: 01282 862451 — MB BCh BAO 1976 Dub. (TC Dub.) GP Princip.; Bd. Mem., Pendle P.C.G. 1998; E. La.s L.M.C. Mem. 1995.

NORTHRIDGE, David Bourke Department Cardiology, Western General Hospital, Edinburgh EH4 2XU Tel: 0131 537 1849 Fax: 0131 537 1849 — MB ChB 1983 Ed.; MRCP (UK) 1986. Cons. Cardiol. W.ern Gen. Hosp. Edin.; Hon. Sen. Lect. Univ. of Edin. Socs: Coun. Mem. Brit. Soc. Echocardigraphy. Prev: Sen. Regist. (Cardiol.) Univ. Hosp. Wales Cardiff.; Regist. (Cardiol.) W.. Infirm. Glas.

NORTHRIDGE, Guy Hamilton 3 Basil Street, London SW3 1AU Tel: 020 7235 6642 Fax: 020 7235 6052 — BM BCh 1978 Oxf.; MA Oxf. 1978; MRCP (UK) 1981; MRCS Eng. LRCP Lond. 1977; MRCGP 1982; DCH Eng. 1981. Prev: Regist. (Med.) St. Bart. Hosp. Lond.; SHO (Paediat.) & Ho. Phys. St. Thos. Hosp. Lond.

*NORTHROP, Michelle Marie 300A Victoria Drive, Eastbourne BN20 8XS — BM 1998 Soton.; BM Soton 1998.

NORTHWAY, Mr Jonathan Ross Berega Hospital, Morogoro PO BOX 320, Tanzania Email: elct_box@maf.org; c/o 97 Shelvers Way, Tadworth KT20 5QQ Tel: 01737 354674 — BM 1988 Soton.; FRCS Eng. 1993; DTM + H Liv'pl Sch. Trop. Med. 1996. (Liverpool Uni.) Med. Miss. Prev: SHO (Gen. Surg.) Horton Gen. Hosp. Banbury; SHO (Accid. & Emerg., Gen. Surg. & Orthop.) Wycombe Gen. Hosp.; SHO (Paediat. Surg.) John Radcliffe Hosp. Oxf.

NORTHWOOD, David 8 The Paddocks, Cusworth, Doncaster DN5 7TW — LMSSA 1980 Lond.; BSc Lond. 1977, MB BS 1981; FFA RCS Eng. 1985. Cons. (Anaesth.) Doncaster Roy. Infirm. & Montago Hosp. NHS Trust Doncaster.

NORTLEY, Ernest Richmond Wulck The Merton Surgery, 156-8 Merton High Street, London SW19 1AZ Tel: 020 8540 1109 Fax: 020 8543 3353 — MB ChB 1978 Ghana; LRCP LRCS Ed. LRCPS Glas. 1985; DObst RCPI 1985. Socs: MDU. Prev: Vis. Med. Off. Sticklan Lodge Lond.; Clin. Med. Off. (Family Plann.) St. Geo. Hosp. Lond.

*NORTON, Alice Elizabeth 26 St Leodegars Way, Hunston, Chichester PO20 6PF — MB ChB 1997 Bristol.

NORTON, Andrew Carey The Barn, At Stickford Grange, Stickford, Boston PE22 8EU Email: 1001032434@compuserve.com — MB BS 1981 Lond.; BSc Lond. 1977; FFA RCS Eng. 1985. Cons. Anaesth. Pilgrim Hosp. Boston. Socs: Soc. Computing & Technol. in Anaesth.; Obst. Anaesth. Assn. Prev: Lect. & Hon. Sen. Regist. (Anaesth.) Aberd. Univ. & Aberd. Roy. Infirm.; Regist. (Anaesth.) S.. Gen. Hosp. Glas.

NORTON, Andrew John Department of Histopathology, St Bartholomew's Medical School, London EC1A 7BE Tel: 020 7601 8539 — MB BS 1981 Lond.; MRCPath 1987. (Char Cross) Sen. Lect. & Hon. Cons. (Histopath.) St. Bart. Med. Sch. Prev: Lect. Univ. Coll. & Inst. Laryng. & Otol.; Graham Schol. Univ. Coll. Lond.

NORTON, Andrew McNeill Bonnyrigg Health Centre, High Street, Bonnyrigg EH19 2DA Tel: 0131 663 7272 Fax: 0131 660 5636; 81 Woodfield Avenue, Colinton, Edinburgh EH13 0QR — MB ChB 1974 Ed.; BSc Ed. 1971, MB ChB 1974. Socs: Life Mem. Roy. Med. Soc. Prev: SHO (Gen. Surg.) Roodlands Gen. Hosp. Haddington; SHO Peripheral Vasc. Clinic Roy. Infirm. Edin.; SHO A & E Dept. Roy. Infirm. Edin.

NORTON, Anne Grove Medical Centre, 6 Uplands Terrace, Uplands, Swansea SA2 0GU Tel: 01792 643000 Fax: 01792 472800; 105 Bishopston Road, Bishopston, Swansea SA3 3EU Tel: 0144 128 2929 — MB ChB 1976 Dundee; DCH Eng. 1978. The Gr. Med. Centre.

NORTON, Aurelia Mary 2 Topiary Square, Stanmore Road, Richmond TW9 2DB — MB BS 1991 Lond.

NORTON, Bernard Derbyshire Royal Infirmary NHS Trust, London Road, Derby DE1 2QY Tel: 01332 347141 Fax: 01332 254764; 67 Green Lane, Liverpool L13 7BA — MB ChB 1986 Liverp.; MD Liverp. 1993; MRCP (UK) 1989; FRCP 2000. Cons. Phys. & Gastroenterol. Derbysh. Roy. Infirm. Socs: BMA; Brit. Soc. Gastroenterol.; Brit. Assn. Paren. & Ente. Nutrit. Prev: Sen. Regist. (Gen. Med. & Gastroenterol.) Derbysh. Roy. Infirm. & Nottm. City Hosp.; Regist. (Gen. Med., Gastroenterol. & Clin. Nutrit.) Roy. Lond. Hosp.; Regist. (Gen. Med. & Gastroenterol.) Countess of Chester Hosp.

NORTON

NORTON, Beverley Child and Family Mental Health Service, Royal Hospital for Sick Children, 3 Rillbank Terrace, Edinburgh EH9 1LL Tel: 0131 536 0534 Fax: 0131 536 0545 — MB ChB 1974 Ed.; MPhil Ed. 1982, BSc 1971; MRCPsych 1978. Cons. Child & Adolesc. Psychiat. Roy. Hosp. for Sick Childr., Lothian Primary Care Trust. Socs: Fell. Roy. Med. Soc. Edin. Prev: Cons. Child & Adolesc. Psychiat. Falkirk Roy. Infirm. Centr. Scotl. Healthcare; Sen. Regist. (Child & Adolesc. Psychiat.) Young People's Unit Roy. Edin. Hosp. & Roy. Hosp. Sick Childr. Edin.; Regist. (Psychiat.) Roy. Edin Hosp.

*NORTON, Brian 294 Rochdale Road, Bacup OL13 9TW — MB BS 1996 Newc.

NORTON, Catherine Anne University Hospital of Wales, Heath Park, Cardiff CF14 4XW; 32 Heol y Delyn, Lisvane, Cardiff CF14 0SQ Tel: 01222 520640 — MB BCh 1991 Wales; BSc; MRCP; DCH. (University of Wales College of Medicine) Specialist Regist.

NORTON, Mr Edward Raymond High Fell, Shann Lane, Keighley BD20 6NA — MB BCh 1960 Wales; FRCS Eng. 1967; FRCS Ed. 1967; MRCS Eng. LRCP Lond. 1960. (Cardiff) Cons. Orthop. Surg. Airedale Gen. Hosp. E.burn.

NORTON, Jane Department of Histopathology, University Hospital Lewisham, Lewisham High St., London SE13 6LH Tel: 020 8333 3046 Fax: 020 8333 3254 Email: jane.norton@uhl.nhs.uk — MB BS 1984 Lond.; MD Lond. 1994; MRCPath 1993. Cons. Histopath. Univ. Hosp. Lewisham Lond. Prev: Cons. Histopath. William Harvey Hosp. Ashford; Lect. (Histopath.) St. Marys' Hosp. Lond.; Regist. (Histopath.) Roy. Marsden Hosp. Sutton.

NORTON, John Christopher Gerard 27 Caledonia Road, Saltcoats KA21 5AJ Tel: 01294 63011; 17 South Crescent, Ardrossan Tel: 01294 63011 — MB BCh BAO 1981 NUI; MRCGP 1985. GP Ardrossan.

NORTON, Kathleen Grace (retired) Quince Cottage, Rye Road, Sandhurst, Hawkhurst, Cranbrook TN18 5JE — MRCS Eng. LRCP Lond. 1925; MA Oxf. 1926; BM Oxf. 1926.

NORTON, Keith John Kingsthorpe Medical Centre, Eastern Avenue South, Northampton NN2 7JN Tel: 01604 713823 Fax: 01604 721996 — MB ChB 1965 St. And.; DRCOG 1967; Cert JCC Lond. 1976. Hosp. Pract. (Psycho.-Geriat.) St. Crispin Hosp. N.ampton. Prev: Clin. Asst. (Psycho Geriat.) St. Crispin Hosp. N.ampton.

NORTON, Kenneth Ross (retired) 25 Granville Road, Barnet EN5 4DS Tel: 020 8440 2581 — MB BS 1951 Lond.; FRCP Lond. 1975, M 1958; DObst RCOG 1952; DCH Eng. 1956. Cons. Paediat. Barnet & Edgware Gen. Hosps. Prev: Regist. (Med.) Barnet Gen. Hosp.

NORTON, Kingsley Raymond William Henderson Hospital, 2 Homeland Drive, Brighton Road, Sutton SM2 5LT Tel: 020 8661 1611 — MB BChir 1977 Camb.; BA Camb. 1973; MD Camb. 1988; FRCPsych 1995, M 1980. Cons. Psychother. Henderson Hosp. Prev: Cons. Psychiat. Sutton Hosp.; Lect. (Psychiat.) St. Geo. Hosp. Med. Sch. Lond.

NORTON, Margaret Alice (retired) 163 Malvern Road, St. John's, Worcester WR2 4NN Tel: 01905 423183 — MB ChB 1939 Birm.; MRCGP 1953. Prev: Med. Off. Alice Ottley Sch. Worcester.

NORTON, Margot Lotte Sophie Park Gates, The Green, Richmond TW9 1QG Tel: 020 8940 4742 Fax: 020 8948 7211 — MB BS (Hons.) Lond. 1950; MRCS Eng. LRCP Lond. 1950. (Roy. Free)

NORTON, Mark Richard Cornerways Surgery, 50 Manor Road, Beckenham BR3 5LG Tel: 020 8650 2444; 61 Barnfield Wood Road, Beckenham BR3 6ST — MB BS 1984 Lond.

NORTON, Mark Ross Princess Elizabeth Orthopaedic Centre, Royal Devon & Exeter Hospital, Barrack Road, Exeter EX2 4UE Tel: 01392 411611; The Chapter House, 3 St Scholastica's Abbey, Teignmouth TQ14 8FF Tel: 01626 774734 Fax: 01626 774734 Email: nortm99@msn.com — MB ChB 1988 Cape Town; FRCS Eng. 1995. Specialist Regist. (Trauma & Orthop. Surg.) Roy. Devon & Exeter Hosp. Exeter. Socs: Assoc. Mem. BOA; Brit. Orthop. Train. Assn.

NORTON, Martyn Howard Shelfield Surgery, 144 Lichfield Road, Shelfield, Walsall WS4 1PW Fax: 01922 694069; 144 Lichfield Road, Shelfield, Walsall WS4 1PW Tel: 0121 353 6847 — MB ChB 1971 Liverp.

NORTON, Paul Gorvin Valley Medical Centre, Johnson Street, Stocksbridge, Sheffield S36 1BX Tel: 0114 288 3841 Fax: 0114 288 7897; 3 Royd Lane, Deepcar, Sheffield S36 2RZ — MB BS 1969 Lond.; DObst RCOG 1972.

NORTON, Peter Malcolm Banksfield, Lands Lane, Knaresborough HG5 9DE Tel: 01423 863156 — MB ChB 1967 Leeds; FFA RCS Eng. 1972; DA Eng. 1969; DObst RCOG 1969. Cons. (Anaesth.) Harrogate Health Care Trust. Prev: Ho. Phys. & Ho. Surg. (Obst.) York 'A' Gp. Hosps.; Regist. (Anaesth.) United Sheff. Hosps.; Sen. Regist. (Anaesth.) Leeds Gps. Hosps.

NORTON, Richard Christopher 19 Dobbins Lane, Wendover, Aylesbury HP22 6BZ — MB BChir 1952 Camb.; DObst RCOG 1953. (Middlx.) Prev: Sen. Princip. Med. Off. Med. Research Counc.; Ho. Phys. Middlx. Hosp.; Ho. Surg. O & G St. Mary Abbots Hosp. Kensington.

NORTON, Mr Robert Walsgrave Hospital, Clifford Bridge Road, Coventry CV2 2DX Tel: 024 76 538933; 6 Amherst Road, Kenilworth CV8 1AH Tel: 01926 857870 — MB BChir 1967 Camb.; MA, BChir 1966; FRCS Eng. 1972. (St. Thos.) Cons. Cardiothoracic Surg. Walsgrave Hosp. Coventry. Socs: Soc. Thoracic & Cardiovasc. Surgs. Prev: Cons. Thoracic Surg. Wentworth & King Geo. V Hosps. Durban, S. Afr.; Sen. Regist. (Cardiothoracic Surg.) Roy. Infirm. & City Hosps. Edin.

NORTON, Robert Nicholas 3 Cedar Walk, 45 Romsey Road, Winchester SO22 5EU — MB ChB 1991 Cape Town.

*NORTON, Rosalind Jane 7 Winsford Grove, Gilwern, Abergavenny NP7 0RL — BM BS 1997 Nottm.

NORTON, Ruth Helen Redham House, Redham Lane, Pilning, Bristol BS35 4HQ — MB BS 1996 Newc.

NORTON, Miss Sally Alexis The Old School House, Over Lane, Almondsbury, Bristol BS32 4DF — MB ChB 1989 Bristol; FRCS Ed. 1993; MD Bristol 1999. (Bristol)

*NORTON, Samuel Edward Strawberry Fields, Apsey Green, Framlingham, Woodbridge IP13 9RW — MB BS 1998 Lond.; MB. BS Lond 1998.

NORTON, Stephen Charles Doctors Surgery, Pembroke Road, Framlingham, Woodbridge IP13 9HA Tel: 01728 723627 Fax: 01728 621064 — MB BS 1971 Lond.; MRCS Eng. LRCP Lond. 1971; DObst RCOG 1973. (Char. Cross) Prev: SHO Profess. Obst. Unit Char. Cross Hosp. Lond.; Ho. Surg. Profess. Dept. Surg. Fulham Hosp.; Ho. Phys. Paediat. Dept. New Char. Cross Hosp. Fulham.

NORTON, William David Albany House Surgery, Albany Terrace, Barbourne, Worcester WR1 3DU Tel: 01905 26086 Fax: 01905 26888 — MB ChB Birm. 1980; MRCGP 1984; DRCOG 1983; DCH RCP Lond. 1983.

NORWELL, Nicholas Peter 4 Ladwell Close, Newbury RG14 6PJ — MB BS 1972 Lond.; MRCGP 1977; DA Eng. 1974; DCH Eng. 1977. (Guy's & King's Coll. Hosp.) Socs: MDU Secretariat.

NORWELL, Zoé McFadzean (retired) Holmlands, 1 Barbour's Park, Stewarton, Kilmarnock KA3 5HS Tel: 01560 82378 — MB ChB 1942 Glas.; MB ChB (Commend.) Glas. 1942. Prev: Urol. Samarit. Hosp. Wom. Glas.

NORWICH, Roger Peter, RD (cons. rooms), The Medico-Legal Consultancy, The Old Docks Office, Commercial Road, Gloucester GL1 2EB Tel: 01452 386242 Fax: 01452 386242; 21 Shrewsbury Road, Church Stretton SY6 6JB Tel: 01694 722951 — MB ChB 1982 Manch.; MRCGP 1986. Med. Dir. (Medico-Legal Consult.) Glos. Socs: Roy. Soc. Med.

NORWID-NIEKRASZEWICZ, Helena (retired) 18 Hamilton Road, London W5 2EH — Med. Dipl. Warsaw 1935.

NORWOOD, Christine Child Health Department, Willow House, St Mary's Hospital, Greenhill Road, Leeds LS12 3QE Tel: 0113 279 0121 Fax: 0113 231 9549; 31 Saxon Grove, Leeds LS17 5DY Tel: 0113 268 1365 — MB ChB 1982 Leeds; BSc (Biochem.) Leeds 1979. (Leeds) Staff Grade (Community Child Health) Leeds. Socs: Guild of Catholic Doctors (Sec. Leeds Br.).

NORWOOD, Fiona Lucinda Margaret 124 Grange Road, London SE1 3AL — MB BS 1991 Lond. (Guy's)

NORWOOD, Jeffrey Michael Walsall Health Authority, 27-31 Lichfield St., Walsall WS1 1TE Tel: 01922 720255 Fax: 01922 722051 — MB BChir 1974 Camb.; MFPHM RCP (UK) 1994; DCH RCP Lond. 1975. (Cambridge University/St. Thomas's Hospital) Cons. Pub. Health Med. Walsall HA; Lect. (Med. Managem.) Keele Univ. Socs: (Exec. Comm.) Pub. Health & Primary Care Gp. Prev: Sen. Regist. & Regist. (Pub. Health Med.) SW RHA; GP; Sen. Med. Off. Solomon Is.s.

*****NORWOOD, Michael Geoffrey Austin** The Rectory, Wiveton Road, Blakeney, Holt NR25 7NJ — MB ChB 1998 Leic.; MB ChB Leic 1998.

NOSENZO, Ivana c/o Drive H. Paul, 45 Barton Road, Canterbury CT1 1YQ — MB BCh 1985 Witwatersrand; MB BCh Wirwatersrand 1985.

NOSHIRVANI, Homa Fallah Maudsley Hospital, Denmark Hill, London SE5 8AZ Tel: 020 7919 3458 Fax: 020 7919 3455; Flat 25, Sandringham Court, Maida Vale, London W9 1UA Tel: 020 7289 7680 — DPM Eng. 1978; MRCPsych 1982; State Exam Med. Hamburg 1969. (Hamburg Uni.) Assoc. Specialist. Socs: MRCPsych.

NOSSEIR, Mohamed Nabil Abdel Hamid Queen Mary's Hospital, Sidcup DA14 6LT Tel: 020 8302 2678; 18 Langdon Shaw, Sidcup DA14 6AU — MB ChB 1965 Alexandria; FFA RCSI 1987.

***NOTARAS, Mr Mitchell James** Flat 11, Harmont House, 20 Harley St., London W1G 9PH — MB BS 1957 Sydney; FRCS Ed. 1961; FRCS Eng. 1961; FACS 1987.

NOTCUTT, William George James Paget Hospital, Gorleston, Great Yarmouth NR31 6LA Tel: 01493 452452 Fax: 01493 452753 Email: willy@tucton.demon.co.uk; 240 Brasenose Avenue, Gorleston, Great Yarmouth NR31 7EB Tel: 01493 665816 Fax: 0870 055 3847 — MB ChB 1970 Birm.; FRCA. 1976; DA Eng. 1973. Cons. Anaesth. Jas. Paget Hosp. Gt. Yarmouth; Hon. Sen. Lect. Univ. E. Anglia. Socs: BMA; Pain Soc.; Assn. Anaesth. Prev: Sen. Regist. (Anaesth.) Notts. AHA (T); Lect. (Anaesth. & Intens. Care) Univ. W. Indies Kingston, Jamaica; Med. Off. Lesotho Flying Doctor Serv.

NOTGHI, Alp Department of Nuclear Medicine, City Hospital NHS Trust, Dudley Road, Birmingham B18 7QH Tel: 0121 507 5228 Fax: 0121 507 5223; Brandhill Cottage, Lower Brand, Griffydam, Coalville LE67 8HE — MD 1976 Shiraz; FRCP Lond. 1999; FRCP Ed. 1998; MSc Nuclear Med. Lond. 1993; MRCP (UK) 1985; LRCP LRCS Ed. LRCPS Glas. 1984. Cons. Nuclear Med. City Hosp. NHS Trust Birm. Socs: Brit. Nuclear Med. Soc. (Counc. Mem.); Europ. Assn. of Nuclear Med. Prev: Sen. Regist. (Nuclear Med.) Dudley Rd. Hosp. Birm.

NOTLEY, John William (retired) Leat Farmhouse, Yeolmbridge, Launceston PL15 8NH Tel: 01566 2627 — MB BS 1928 Lond.; MRCS Eng. LRCP Lond. 1928.

NOTLEY, Mr Richard Guy Spindlewood, 59 Pewley Hill, Guildford GU1 3SW Tel: 01483 566295 Fax: 01483 579354 — MB BS Lond. 1959; MS Lond. 1968; FRCS Eng. 1963; MRCS Eng. LRCP Lond. 1959. (Guy's) Cons. Urol. Surg. Emerit. Roy. Surrey Co. & St. Luke's Hosp. Trust; Educat.al Adviser in Urol. to the Raven Dept. of Educat. Roy. Coll. of Surg.s of Eng. Socs: Fell. Roy. Soc. Med.; Hon. Mem. Brit. Assoc. Urol. Surgs.; BMA. Prev: Cons. Urol. Surg. & Med. Dir. Roy. Surrey Co. & St. Luke's Hosp. Trust; Sen. Lect. (Urol.) Lond. Hosp.; Leverhulme Research Fell. RCS Eng.

NOTMAN, Ian Andrew North Avenue Surgery, 18 North Avenue, Cambuslang, Glasgow G72 8AT Tel: 0141 641 3037 Fax: 0141 646 1905; 70 Stewarton Drive, Cambuslang, Glasgow G72 8DG — MB ChB 1977 Glas.; MRCGP 1982; Dip. Roy. Coll. Obst. & Gyn. Lond. 1980.

NOTMAN, James Andrew 54 Leap Park, Threemilestone, Truro TR3 6UB — MB ChB 1973 Glas. Prev: SHO (Gen. Surg.) Amersham Gen. Hosp.; SHO (Orthop.) Poole Gen. Hosp. Dorset; Ho. Off. (Gen. Med.) Glas. Roy. Infirm.

NOTT, Mr David Malcolm c/o Department of Surgery, Chelsea & Westminster Hospital, 369 Fulham Road, London SW10 9NH Tel: 020 8746 8464 Fax: 020 8746 8846; 39 Elmgrove Road, Barnes, London SW13 0BU — MD 1989 Manch.; BSc St. And. 1979; MB ChB Manch. 1981; FRCS Eng. 1985. (St Andrews and Manchester) Cons. Surg. Chelsea & W.minster Hosp.; Cons. Vasc. Surg. Roy. Brompton & Harefield NHS Trust & St Mary's Hosp. Lond.; Hon. Sen. Lect. (Surg.) Univ. of Lond.; Examr. (Surg.) Univ. of Lond.; Extern. Examr. (Surg.) Univ. of Glas. Socs: Vasc. Surg. Soc.; Surg. Research Soc.; BMA. Prev: Sen. Regist. (Gen. Surg.) Mersey RHA; Cancer Research Fell. Univ. Liverp.; Ho. Surg. Manch. Roy. Infirm. & Ho. Phys. Chapel Allerton Hosp. Leeds.

NOTT, James Gildon Harley Asplands Medical Centre, Wood Street, Woburn Sands, Milton Keynes MK17 8QP Tel: 01908 582069 Fax: 01908 281597; Rush Hill, Tyrells End, Eversholt, Milton Keynes MK17 9DS — MB BS 1976 Lond.; MA Camb. 1971; MRCP (UK) 1983; MRCGP 1988; DCH RCP Lond. 1982; DRCOG 1980. Mem. Heartlands PCT Exec. Comm.; Locality Clin. governance lead, Heartlands PCT. Prev: Trainee GP E. Lond. VTS; SHO (Neurol.) Harlow Dist.

NOTT, Mr Malcolm George (retired) AMI Highfield Hospital, Manchester Road, Rochdale OL11 4LX Tel: 01706 646209 — MB BS 1952 Madras; FRCS Ed. 1962; FRCS Eng. 1963. Prev: Cons. Traum. & Orthop. Surg. Rochdale & Dist. Hosp. Gp.

NOTT, Michael Richardson Royal West Sussex Hospital, St. Richard's, Chichester PO19 4SE Tel: 01243 788122 Fax: 01243 531269 Email: m.nott@rws_tr.sthames.nhs.uk; Chatsworth, 22 Church St, Littlehampton BN17 5PX Tel: 01903 713050 — MB BS Lond. 1966; FFA RCS Eng. 1972; DA Eng. 1970. (St. Geo.) Cons. Anaesth. Roy. W. Sussex Trust. Socs: Anaesth. Res. Soc.; Roy. Soc. Med. (Anaesth. Sect.). Prev: Lect. (Anaesth.) Univ. Soton. Fac. Med.; SHO (Clin. Meas.) W.minster Hosp. Lond.; Regist. (Anaesth) Chelmsford Essex.

NOTT, Peter Norman The Limberlost, St. Giles Hill, Winchester SO23 0HH Tel: 01962 869674 — MRCS Eng. LRCP Lond. 1962; MD Camb. 1984, MB 1963, BChir 1962; FRCP Ed. 1983, M 1969; FRCPsych 1984, M 1972; DPM Eng. 1967. Cons. Psychiat. Dept. Psychiat. Soton. Prev: Sen. Lect. (Psychiat.) Univ. Soton.; Research Regist. Guy's Hosp. Lond.; Lect. (Psychiat.) Univ. Oxf.

NOTT-BOWER, Thomas Mowbray (retired) Le Morne, 8 Maidstone Grove, Bleadon Hill, Weston Super Mare BS24 9NQ Tel: 01934 813844 — MRCS Eng. LRCP Lond. 1945; DObst RCOG 1957. Prev: Regist. (Gyn. & Obst.) Swindon & Dist. Hosp. Gp.

NOTT-BOWER, William George Penn Hill Surgery, St. Nicholas Close, Yeovil BA20 1SB Tel: 01935 74005 Fax: 01935 421841 — MB BS 1984 Lond.; BA Oxf. 1981; MRCGP 1989; DRCOG 1988; DCH RCP Lond. 1987. Prev: Trainee GP Taunton VTS; Cas. Off. Qu. Mary's Hosp. Roehampton.

NOTTINGHAM, John Frank Department of Cellular Pathology, Northampton General Hospitals, Cliftonville, Northampton NN1 5BD — MB ChB 1980 Sheff.; FRCPath 1997, M 1987. Cons. Histopath. N.ampton Gen. Hosp. Trust, N.ampton. Socs: Brit. Soc. Clin. Cytol.; Assn. Clin. Path. Prev: Sen. Regist. N.. Gen. & Roy. Hallamsh. Hosps. Sheff.; Regist. BRd. Green & Alder Hey Hosps. Liverp.; Cons. Geo. Eliot Hosp., Nuneaton, Warks.

NOUR, Hilal The Surgery, 77 Pickford Lane, Bexleyheath DA7 4RN Tel: 020 8304 3660 Fax: 020 8298 7736 — MB ChB 1961 Baghdad; MRCS Eng. LRCP Lond. 1971. Socs: Assur. Med. Soc.

NOUR, Mr Shawqui Abd El-Raheem Mohamed Leicester Royal Infirmary, Leicester LE1 5WW Tel: 0116 254 1414; 59 Guilford Road, Stoneygate, Leicester LE2 2RD Tel: 0116 221 7370 — MB BCh 1973 Cairo; MD 1992; FRCS (Paediat.) 1993; FRCS Ed. 1981; FRCS Glas. 1981. Cons. Paediat. Surg. Leicester Roy. Infirm. Prev: Sen. Regist. Childr. Hosp. Sheff.; Career Regist. (Paediat. Surg.) Sheff. Childr. Hosp.

NOUR-ELDIN, Fawzy 4 Rutland House, Marloes Road, Kensington, London W8 5LE Tel: 020 7937 0685 — MB BCh 1946 Cairo; PhD Manch. 1952; LMSSA Lond. 1958; FRCPath 1976, M 1963. Cons. Haemat. & Med. Writer STAT Laborat. Lond.; Vis. Cons. Blood Dis. Bakhsh Clinics & Hosps. Saudi Arabia; Edr. Excerpta Medica (Represen. UK Haemat. Sect.); Edr. Research Defence Soc. Lond.; Hon. Examr. (Path.) Brit. Sch. Osteop. Lond. Socs: Fell. Roy. Soc. Med.; BMA; Brit. Soc. Haematol. Prev: Cons. Clin. Path. NW Thames RHA; Clin. Research Fell. (Haemat.) Roy. Infirm. Manch. & Unit. Manch. Hosps.; Med. Off. Blood Transfus. Centre Brentwood.

NOURI-DARIANI, Esmael County Hospital, Greetwell Road, Lincoln LN2 5QY Tel: 01522 512512; 16 Geralds Close, Lincoln LN2 4AL Tel: 01522 512838 — MD 1971 Iran; DLO Eng. 1976. (Nat. Univ. Iran) Assoc. Specialist (ENT. Surg.) Co. Hosp. Lincoln; Cons. ENT Surg. John Coupland Hosp. GainsBoro. Socs: BMA. Prev: Cons. ENT Surg. Bougshan Hosp., Jeddah; Regist. (ENT) William Harvey & Roy. Vict. Hosps. Ashford; SHO (ENT) Poole Gen. Hosp. Dorset.

NOURIEL, Henry Tel: 01243 372161 Fax: 020 8906 8217 Email: henry@nouiel.freeserve.co.uk — MD 1983 Tel-Aviv; MRCP (UK) 1996. Socs: Brit. Cardiac Soc.; Roy. Coll. Phys.

NOURSE, Christopher Henry St. Helen's House, 571 Foxhall Road, Ipswich IP3 8LX Tel: 01473 275511 Fax: 01473 275512 Email: christopher.nouse@allingtn-tr.anglox.nhs.uk; 110 Christchurch Street, Ipswich IP4 2DE Tel: 01473 250969 Fax: 01473 445096 — MB BChir Camb. 1958; MA Camb. 1958; FRCP Lond. 1994; FRCP

NOURY

Ed. 1977, M 1965; DCH Eng. 1960; DObst RCOG 1959. (Camb. & Middlx.) Med. Dir. & Cons. Community Paediat. Allington NHS Trust. Socs: BMA (Ex-Pres. Suff. Div.); (Hon. Treas.) Brit. Paediat. Assn. Prev: Research Fell. (Med.) Harvard Coll. At Childr. Hosp. Med. Center Boston, USA; Lect. (Paediat.) St. Mary's Hosp. Med. Sch. Lond.

NOURY, Susana Ana Maria 28 Weller Grove, Chelmsford CM1 4YJ; 1 Digby Mansions, Hammersmith Bridge Road, London W6 9DE Tel: 020 8746 9883 — BM BCh 1996 Oxf.; MA (Camb.) 1993; MRC Ophth 1997. SHO (Neurosurg.) W. Lond. Neurosci.s Centre Char. Cross Hosp. Prev: Ho. Phys. Glos. Roy. Hosp.; Ho. Surg. John Radcliffe Hosp. Oxf.

NOVAK, Alan Zdenek Scott Coastal Villages Practice, Pippin Close, Ormesby St. Margaret, Great Yarmouth NR29 3RW Tel: 01493 730205 Fax: 01493 733120; Willow House, 54 North Road, Ormesby-St-Margaret, Great Yarmouth NR29 3LE Tel: 01493 731943 — MB BS 1971 Lond.; Cert Contracep. & Family Plann. RCOG, RCGP &; Cert FPA 1975. Prev: Trainee Gen. Pract. Mid-Sussex Vocational Train. Scheme.

NOVAK, Margaret Ruby (retired) The Oaks, Wick Road, Langham, Colchester CO4 5PG Tel: 01206 231318 — MRCS Eng. LRCP Lond. 1944; BSc Lond. 1937. Prev: Ho. Surg. Margate & Dist. Gen. Hosp.

NOVAK, Stephen Andrew 118B Wellsway, Bath BA2 4SD — MB BS 1985 Lond.; MRCP (UK) 1990.

NOVAK, Thomas Vladimir Leavesden Road Surgery, 141A Leavesden Road, Watford WD2 5EP Tel: 01923 225128; 27 Cassiobury Park Avenue, Watford WD18 7LA — MRCS Eng. LRCP Lond. 1976.

NOVELLI, Marco Riccardo Department of Histopathology, University College Hospitals, Rockefeller Building, University St., London WC1E 6JJ Tel: 020 7209 6033 Email: rmkdhmn.ucl.ac.uk; 29 Bardwell Road, St Albans AL1 1RQ — MB ChB 1987 Bristol; PhD Lond. 1997; MSc Experim. Path. (Toxicol.) 1989; MRC Path, Royal Coll. Pattrologists, 1999. Lect. (Histopath.) Univ. Coll. Lond. Prev: Clin. Fell. Imperial Cancer Research Fund Lincoln's Inn Fields Lond.

NOVELLI, Vas Great Ormond Street Hospital for Children, Great Ormond Street, London WC1N 3JH Tel: 020 7813 8504 Fax: 020 7813 8552 Email: novelv@gosh-nhs.uk; Tel: 020 8870 6519 Email: vasgos@cs.com — FRCPCH 1998; FRACP 1983; FRCP 1994; MRCP 1979 UK; MB BS 1974 Melbourne, Australia. (Melbourne University) Cons. in Paediatric Infec. Dis.s, Gt. Ormord St. Childr.s Hosp. Lond.; Hon. Sen. Lect., ImumunoBiol. Unit, Inst. of Child Health, Lond. Socs: Brit. Paediatric Allergy, Immunol., Infec. Dis.s Gp., (Retiring-Comm. Mem.); Immunocompromised Host Soc.; Paediatric Infec. Dis. Soc. (USA). Prev: Cons. in Paediatric Infec. Dis.s, Roy. Hosp., Muscat, Oman, (1989-1991); Cons. in Paediatric Infec. Dis.s, Hamad Hosp., Doha, Qatar (1986-1989); Fell. In Pediatric Infec. Dis.s, Univ. Of Texas Health Sci. Centre, San Antonio, Texas 1984-1986.

NOVICK, Stephen Maxwell 8 Ruith Field, Telford TF5 0PQ — MB ChB 1985 Manch. (Psychiat.) Shrops. Ment. Health NHS Trust.

NOVOSEL, Steven Hartwood Hill Hospital, Hartwood, Shotts ML7 4LA Tel: 01501 823366 — MB ChB 1978 Aberd.; MPhil Glasg. 1992; MRCPsych. 1983; T(Psychiat.) 1991. Cons. Community Psychiat. Socs: Roy. Coll. Psychiats.

NOWAK, Janik Josef Richard St Helen's Medical Centre, 151 St. Helens Road, Swansea SA1 4DF Tel: 01792 476576 Fax: 01792 301136 — MB BCh 1982 Wales.

NOWAK, Kazimierz The Surgery, Waterfall House, 223 Tooting High Street, London SW17 0TD Tel: 020 8672 1327 Fax: 020 8767 5615 — LMSSA 1971 Lond.; MPhil Lond. 1978; Med. Dip. Cracow 1963; FRCS Ed. 1975.

NOWAYHIO, Fadi Amin Department of Urology, University Hospital of Wales, Heath Park, Cardiff CF14 4XW — MD 1985 Lebabon.

NOWELL, Hilary Jane Dormer Cottage, York Road, West Habbourne, Didcot OX11 0NG Tel: 01235 851236 — MB BS 1984 Lond.; MRCGP 1989. GP Locum. Prev: GP Princip. Hanworth; Trainee GP W. Middlx. Hosp. Isleworth VTS.

NOWELL, Justin Lewis Cardiotheracic Surgery Department, Royal Bompton Hospital, Sydney Street, London SW3 6NP Tel: 020 7352 8121 — MB ChB 1995 Liverp.; MRCS 1999 England; BSc 1990 (Hons); 1990 (GRSC). Cardiothoracic Surg., Roy. Brompton Hosp.; SpR Cardiothoracic Surg. The London Chest Hosp, Bonner Rd, Lond.

NOWELL, Theresa Eve Bury Knowle Health Centre, Headington, Oxford OX3 9HY Tel: 01865 61651 — BM BCh 1988 Oxf.; MRCGP 1992; Cert. Family Plann. JCC 1991; DRCOG 1991; DGM RCP Lond. 1991. Prev: Trainee GP Oxf. VTS.

NOWERS, Christopher David Iver Medical Centre, High St., Iver SL0 9NU Tel: 01753 653008 Fax: 01753 650890; Elbury, Bassetbury Lane, High Wycombe Tel: 01494 523060, 01494 523113 Email: christopher@nowers.com — MB BS 1975 Lond.; BSc Lond. 1972; MRCS Eng. LRCP Lond. 1975. (Westm.) Prev: Regist. (Psychiat.) Atkinson Morley Hosp. Lond.

NOWERS, Michael Peter Avon & Wiltshire Mental Health Trust, Directorate of Mental Health Services, Cossham Hospital, Lodge Road, Kingswood, Bristol BS15 1LF Tel: 0117 975 8053 Fax: 0117 975 8034 — MB BS 1977 Lond.; MPhil. Lond. 1990; MRCS Eng. LRCP Lond. 1977; FRCPsych 1997, M 1985. Cons. Psychiat. (Old Age) Avon and Wilts. Ment. health trust; Hon. Sen. Lect. (Ment. Health) Univ. Bristol.

NOWIAK, Zofia (retired) 2 Dovedale Road, E. Dulwich, London SE22 0NF Tel: 020 8693 2476 — MRCS Eng. LRCP Lond. 1951. Prev: Princip. GP Lond.

NOWICKI, Margaret Tennant 37 Nimrod Road, London SW16 6SZ — MB BS 1976 Lond.; MRCS Eng. LRCP Lond. 1976; MFFP 1993.

NOWICKI, Robert Waclaw Antoni 22 Baker Avenue, Nottingham NG5 8FU — MB BS 1991 Lond.

NOWLAN, John Patrick (retired) 70 Parsonage Road, Heaton Moor, Stockport SK4 4JR Tel: 0161 432 1565 — LAH Dub. 1945. Prev: Flight Lt. RAuxAF.

NOWLAN, William Anthony 24 High Street, Marshfield, Chippenham SN14 8LP — MB BS 1983 Lond.; BA Oxf. 1978; MRCP (UK) 1986. Research & Developm. Cons. Hewlett Packard Mass, USA. Prev: Sen. Lect. (Epidemiol. & Pub. Health) & Clin. Research Fell. (Med. Informat.) Univ. Manch.

NOY SCOTT, Christopher Nuffield Hospital, Derriford, Plymouth PL6 8BG Tel: 01752 775861; Chaddlehanger, Tavistock PL19 0LG Tel: 01822 810734 — MB BS 1961 Lond.; MRCS Eng. LRCP Lond. 1961; DCH Eng. 1964; MMSA Lond. 1963; DObst RCOG 1963. (Char. Cross) Clin. Asst. (Psychiat.) Plymouth; Med. Off. Esso Petroleum & various Local Companies. Prev: GP Plymouth.

NOYELLE, Richard Mark Sandoz Pharmaceutics (UK) Ltd., Frimley Business Park, Frimley, Camberley GU16 5SG — MB BS 1977 Lond.; BSc (Pharmacol.) Lond. 1974, MB BS 1977; MFPM 1989; Dip. Pharm. Med. RCP (UK) 1985; DCH Eng. 1981; DRCOG 1980. (Univ. Coll. Hosp.) Med. Dir. Sandoz Pharmaceut. UK Ltd.

NOYES, Kathryn Joan 19 Edderston Road, Peebles EH45 9DT — MB ChB 1987 Ed. (Ed.) Staff Grade (Paediat. Diabetes) Roy. Hosp. Sick Childr. Edin. Prev: Research Fell. (Paediat.) Dept. Child Life & Health Edin.

NQUMAYO, Christopher Carl Flat E2, 101 Manthorpe Road, Grantham NG31 8DG Tel: 01476 65232 Fax: 01476 590441 — MB ChB 1984 Zambia; MRCOG 1993.

NRIALIKE, Patrick Olisa 21 Cumberland Road, Kirkholt, Rochdale OL11 2RP — MB BS 1979 Ibadan; MRCOG 1993.

NSAMBA, Mr Christian Royal Albert Edward Infirmary, Wigan Lane, Wigan WN1 2NN Tel: 01942 244000 — MB ChB 1964 Ed.; FRCS Ed. 1969; DLO Eng. 1966. (Ed.) Cons. Surg. (ENT) Wigan HA. Socs: Brit. Assn. Otol.; Otolaryngol. Research Soc. Prev: Research Fell. Inst. Laryng. & Otol. Lond.; Research Fell. Audio-Vestibular Unit Univ. Brit. Columbia Vancouver; Vis. Scientist Karoliska Inst. Sweden.

NSOFOR, Benjamin Ifeanyichukwu 20 Millfield Walk, Erskine PA8 6JB — MB ChB 1968 Glas.; FRCOG 1995, M 1980.

NTOUNTAS, Ioannis (John) c/o Paul Welsford Esq., 42 42 Willmore End, London SW19 3DF — State Exam Milan 1985.

NUBI, William Ajibola Olusegun New Stroud Surgery, 16 Upper, London N4 3EL; 224 Archway Road, London N6 5AX Tel: 020 8348 7155 — MB BS 1969 Newc.; Cert. Family Plann. JCC 1990; DPH Glas. 1978; DCH RCPSI 1972. Socs: BMA & Med. Defence Union.

NUGENT, Ailish Gabrielle Craiganon Area Hospital, 68 Lurgan Rd, Portadown, Craigavon BT635QQ; 6 Cleaner Gardens, Belfast BT9 5HZ Email: agnugent@aol.com — MB BCh BAO 1989 Belf.; MRCP (UK) 1992; MD 1996. (Queen's Univ. Belf.)

NUGENT, Anne Marie Royal Victoria Hosp, Grosvenor Road, Belfast BT12 6BA — MB BCh BAO 1987 Belf.; MD Belf. 1994; MRCP (UK) 1990.

NUGENT, Anthony Lowfield, Upton, Pontefract WF8 2RP — MB ChB 1950 Leeds. (Leeds) Socs: BMA. Doncaster Med. Soc. Prev: Ho. Phys. Pontefract Gen. Infirm.; Res. Obst. Off. Gen. Hosp. Wakefield; Capt. RAMC.

NUGENT, Colette Marie Station Road Practice, 66-68 Station Road, Ainsdale, Southport PR8 3HW Tel: 01704 574137 Fax: 01704 573875; 66 Burnley Road, Ainsdale, Southport PR8 3LR Tel: 01704 75466 — MB ChB 1985 Liverp. Prev: Trainee GP S.port VTS.

NUGENT, David 8 Cambridge Avenue, Middlesbrough TS5 5HQ — MB ChB 1990 Ed.

NUGENT, Desmond Andrew William (retired) Craigievar, 27 Golf Side, Cheam, Sutton SM2 7HA Tel: 020 8643 2052 — MB BS 1944 Madras; DTM & H Liverp. 1952; DPH Liverp. 1949. Prev: WHO Country Represen..

NUGENT, Elizabeth Mary Dr Nugent and Partners, 243 Abbey Road, Barrow-in-Furness LA14 5JY Tel: 01229 821599; 25 Croslands Park, Barrow-in-Furness LA13 9NH — MB ChB 1975 Manch.; DRCOG 1978. GP Barrow-in-Furness; Work for DHSS Bootle Merseyside. Socs: Disabil. Appeal Tribunals. Prev: SHO (Paediat.) Booth Hall Childr. Hosp. Manch.; SHO (O & G) N. Manch. Gen. Hosp.; SHO (Dermat.) Manch. Skin Hosp.

NUGENT, Mr Ian Michael The Royal Berkshire Hospital, London Road, Reading RG1 5AN Tel: 0118 987 5111; Newlands, Gypsy Lane, Kingwood Common, Henley-on-Thames RG9 5NB Email: iannugent@doctors.org.uk — MB BS 1983 Lond.; BSc (Hons.) Lond. 1980, MB BS 1983; FRCS (Orth.) 1994; FRCS Eng. 1987. (St. Thomass Hosp.) Cons. Orthop. Surg. Roy. Berks. Hosp. Reading. Socs: Brit. Orthopaedic Foot Surg. Soc.; Brit. Orthopaedic Assn. Prev: Sen. Regist. Bath & Swindon; Regist. Oxf. & Swindon.

NUGENT, John Joseph Dr Nugent and Partners, 243 Abbey Road, Barrow-in-Furness LA14 5JY Tel: 01229 821599; 243 Abbey Road, Barrow-in-Furness LA14 5JY Tel: 01229 21599 — MB ChB 1975 Manch.; MRCGP 1980; DRCOG 1979. Prev: SHO (Med./Neurol.) N. Manch. Gen. Hosp.; SHO (Paediat.) Booth Hall Childr. Hosp. Manch.; SHO (O & G) N. Manch. Gen. Hosp.

NUGENT, John Patrick Glenroyd Medical Centre, 164 whitegate Drive, Blackpool FY3 9HF — MB ChB 1982 Manch.; MRCGP 1986; DRCOG 1985.

NUGENT, Justine Lucy 10 Ingram Drive, Stockport SK4 3RH — MB ChB 1996 Manch.

NUGENT, Karen Patricia Professional Surgical Unit, Southampton General Hospital, Tremona Road, Southampton SO16 6YD Tel: 02380 796145 Fax: 02380 794020 Email: kpnugent@soton.ac.uk; 40 Porchester Road, Fareham PO16 8PT Tel: 01329 233849 — MB BS 1987 Lond.; MA Camb. 1988; MS Lond. 1994; FRCS Eng. 1991. Lect. & Hon. Sen. Regist. (Gen. Surg.) Univ. Soton.; Sen. Lect. & Hon. Cons. Uni. Soton. Prev: Research Regist. St. Mark's Hosp. Lond.

NUGENT, Serge 26 Highacres, Loders, Bridport DT6 3SE — MB ChB 1985 Manch.

NUGENT, Theodore Patrick Joseph Errigal Medical Centre, Old Dungannon Road, Ballygawley, Dungannon BT70 2EY; 21 Killymorgan Road, Tirnaskea, Ballygawley, Dungannon BT70 2JJ — MB BCh BAO 1983 Belf.; MB BCh Belf. 1983; MRCGP 1988; DRCOG 1986; DCH RCP Lond. 1985.

NUKI, George Western General Hospital, Edinburgh EH4 2XU Tel: 0131 537 1000 — MB BS 1960 Lond.; FRCP Ed. 1980; FRCP Lond. 1978, M 1964; MRCS Eng. LRCP Lond. 1960. (King's Coll. Lond. & King's Coll. Hosp.) Prof. (Rheum.) Univ. Edin. & Hon. Cons. Phys. Rheum. Dis. Unit.; N.. Gen. Hosp. & Roy. Infirm. Edin. Socs: Brit. Soc. Rheumat. & Med. Research Soc. Prev: Reader Welsh Nat. Sch. Med. Cardiff & Hon. Cons. Phys. Univ. Hosp.; Wales Cardiff.

NULLIAH, Krishnamurthi The Brock Street Clinic, 29 Brock St., Bath BA1 2LN; 8 Upper Church Street, Bath BA1 2PT — MB BS 1977 Lond.

NUNAN, Mary Ruth (retired) Meadow End, Woodmansterne Lane, Banstead SM7 3ES Tel: 0173 73 50341 — MB BCh BAO 1922 NUI. Prev: Ho. Surg. Childr. Hosp. Dub., Gen. Hosp. Altrincham & Roy. Infirm.

NUNAN, Thomas Oliver Department of Nuclear Medicine, St. Thomas' Hospital, London SE1 7EH Tel: +00 44 S(0)20 79289292 Fax: +00 44 (0) 20 79285634 — MD 1984 NUI; MB BCh BAO 1973; BSc NUI 1970, MD 1984; MSc Lond. 1979; FRCP Lond. 1991; MRCP (UK) 1975; FRCR 2000. Cons. Phys. St. Thos. Hosp. Lond.; Edr. Nuclear Med. Communications. Socs: Brit. Nuclear Med. Soc.; Pres. Brit. Nuclear Med. Soc. Prev: Sen. Regist. (Renal Med.) St. Thos. Hosp. Lond.; Research Fell. St. Thos. Hosp. Lond.; SHO (Med.) Hillingdon Hosp. Uxbridge.

NUNES, Michelle Doreen Anne 4 Catherine's Drive, Richmond TW9 2BX Tel: 020 8332 9868 — BSc (Clin. Scis.) Lond. 1990, MS BS 1991. (St. Mary's)

NUNEZ, Mr Desmond Antonio Department of Otolaryngology, Royal Infirmary, Aberdeen AB25 2ZN Tel: 01224 553903 Fax: 01224 554569 Email: d.a.nunez@abdn.ac.uk — MB BS 1982 West Indies; FRCS (Orl.) 1994; FRCS Ed. 1986; DLO RCS Eng. 1986; MD 1998. Cons. Otolaryngol. Aberd. Roy. Infirm. & Roy. Aberd. Childr. Hosp.; Sen. Lect. (Otolaryngol.) Univ. Aberd. Socs: Brit. Skull Base Soc.; Coun. Otolaryngol. Research Soc.; Brit. Assn. Paediat. Otol. Prev: Sen. Regist. Univ. Hosp. Nottm.; Sen. Regist. Leicester Roy. Infirm.; Tutor (Otolaryngol.) Univ. Leeds.

NUNEZ, Miss Valerie Ann 16 Beatrice Road, Richmond TW10 6DT Tel: 020 8332 9655 — MB BS 1992 Lond.; FRCS Eng. 1996; FRCS Ed. 1996. (Char. Cross & Westm. Med. Sch.) Specialist Regist. (Orthop. & Trauma) Roy. Surrey Co. Hosp. Guildford; Specialist Regist. (Orthop. & Trauma) St. Richard's Hosp. Chichester. Socs: Med. Defence Union; Roy. Soc. Med.; BMA. Prev: SHO (Orthop.) Roy. Surrey Co. Hosp. Guildford; SHO (Orthop. & Plastic Surg.) Qu. Mary's Univ. Hosp. Lond.; SHO (A & E) Char. Cross Hosp. Lond.

NUNEZ-AVELLANEDA, Julio Roberto University Hospital of Wales, Cardiff CF4 4XW Tel: 029 2074 3107 Fax: 01554 772271; 110 Oaklands Road, Bridgend CF31 4SX Tel: 01656 654404 — Medico y Cirujano 1982 Nat. Univ.; Medico y Cirujanoo Nat. Univ. 1982; LRCP LRCS Ed. LRCPS Glas. 1993; FRCA 1995; DA (UK) 1991. Specialist Regist. Univ. Hosp. Wales Cardiff. Prev: PostFell.sh. Regist. (Anaesth.) Morriston Singleton Hosp. Swansea; Regist. Rotat. Cardiff Teach. Hosp.

NUNEZ MIRET, Olga 11 Torbay Road, London NW6 7DX — LMS 1992 Barcelona. Regist. (Psychiat.) Halifax Gen. Hosp. Socs: Colegio De Medicos, Barcelona; BMA. Prev: SHO (Acute Adult Psychiat.) Qu. Charlotte's Hastings & E.bourne Dist. Gen. Hosp.

NUNLEY, Catriona Isabella 6 Llandennis Avenue, Cyncoed, Cardiff CF23 6JG — MB BCh 1985 Wales.

***NUNN, Andrew Nigel** 33 Heol Briwnant, Rhiwbina, Cardiff CF14 6QF — MB BCh 1997 Wales.

NUNN, Bryan Roger Filey Surgery, Station Avenue, Filey YO14 9AE Tel: 01723 515881 Fax: 01723 515197; 9-11 Church Hill, Hunmanby, Filey YO14 0JU Tel: 01723 891242 Fax: 01723 891242 Email: nunn@compuserve.com — MB ChB 1977 Sheff.; MRCGP 1982; DCH RCP Lond. 1982; Cert. Family Plann. JCC 1982; DRCOG 1981. (Sheff.) Lifeboat Med. Off. Filey RNLI; GP Trainer. Socs: MRC GP Research Framework. Prev: GP Regist. ChristCh., New Zealand; Med. Off. Scotts Base Antarctica; Emerg. Room Resid. Amer. Hosp. of Paris.

NUNN, Christopher Miles Hasler (retired) Barfad Beag, Ardfern, Lochgilphead PA31 8QN Tel: 01852 500321 Email: chrisnutn@compuserve.com — MB BS 1963 Lond.; MD Lond. 1974; FRCPsych 1985, M 1972; DPM Eng. 1966. Prev: Cons. Psychiat. Roy. S. Hants. Hosp. Soton.

NUNN, David Spring Hall Group Practice, Spring Hall Medical Centre, Spring Hall Lane, Halifax HX1 4JG Tel: 01422 349501 Fax: 01422 323091 — MB ChB 1968 St. And.; DA Eng. 1970.

NUNN, Mr David Department of Orthopaedics, Guy's Hospital, St Thomas St., London SE1 9RT Tel: 020 7955 5000 Fax: 020 7955 2759 — MB BS 1978 Lond.; FRCS Ed. Orthop. 1990; FRCS Ed. 1983; MRCS Eng. LRCP Lond. 1978; FRCS Eng. 1997. (St. Mary's) Cons. Orthop. Surg. Guy's & St. Thos. Hosps. Lond.; Mem. of the Ct. of Examrs. RCS Eng. Prev: Sen. Regist. (Orthop.) Guy's & St. Thos. Hosp. Lond.; Lect. (Orthop.) Lond. Hosp. Med. Coll.; Regist. (Orthop.) St. Geo. Hosp. Lond.

NUNN, Geoffrey Francis Old Vicarage, The Ginnel, Bardsey, Leeds LS17 9DU — MB BS 1975 Lond.; FFA RCS 1980. Cons. Anaesth. Wakefield Hosps.

NUNN

NUNN, Mr John Francis The Stocks, 3 Russell Road, Moor Park, Northwood HA6 2LJ — MB ChB 1948 Birm.; PhD Birm. 1958, DSc 1992, MD 1970; MD (Hon.) Uppsala 1996; FRCS Eng. 1983; FRCA 1955; FCA RCSI (Hon.) 1985; FANZCA (Hon.) 1984; Laurea (Honoris Causa) Turin 1993. (Birm.) Emerit. Cons. N.wick Pk. Hosp. Harrow. Socs: Hon. Fell. Roy. Soc. Med.; Hon. Mem. Europ. Acad. Anaesthesiol.; Hon. Mem. Assn. Anaesth. Prev: Head of Div. Anaesth. Clin. Research Centre (MRC) 1968-91; Dean Fac. Anaesth 1979-81; Prof. Anaesth. Univ. Leeds 1964-68.

NUNN, Nicola Kay Hawthorne House, Kilburn Road, Oakham LE15 6QL — MB ChB 1993 Liverp.

NUNN, Mr Paul Andrew 49 Highfield Hill, Upper Norwood, London SE19 3PT — MB BS 1983 Lond.; BSc (Hons.) Lond. 1980, MB BS 1983; FRCS Ed. 1988.

NUNN, Richard Andrew The Surgery, Angel Lane, Dunmow CM6 1AQ Tel: 01371 872105 Fax: 01371 873679; Haydens, Onslow Green, Barnston, Dunmow CM6 3PP Tel: 01371 820429 — MB BS 1969 Lond.; MRCS Eng. LRCP Lond. 1969; MRCGP 1978. (Roy. Free) Socs: Assoc. Mem. Roy. Coll. Homeop.

NUNN, Terence John 20 Cleghorn Road, Lanark ML11 7QR Tel: 01555 663139 — MB ChB 1971 Glas.; FFA RCS Eng. 1975; DObst RCOG 1973. Cons. (Anaesth.) Law Hosp. Carluke. Prev: Sen. Regist. (Anaesth.) Regionsykehuset I Trondheim, Norway; Sen. Regist. (Anaesth.) Bristol Roy. Infirm.; Regist. (Anaesth.) Glas. Roy. Infirm.

***NUNN, Thomas** 90 Norsey Road, Billericay CM11 1BG — MB ChB 1998 Glas.; MB ChB Glas 1998.

***NUNN, Timothy Richard** Haydens, Hounslow Green, Barnston, Dunmow CM6 3PP — MB BS 1996 Lond.

NUNNELEY, Joyce Beryl 1 Palace Gardens, Buckhurst Hill IG9 5PQ — MB BS 1952 Lond.; MRCS Eng. LRCP Lond. 1952. (Roy. Free) Vis. Venereal. H.M. Prison Holloway. Socs: Fell. Roy. Soc. Med.; Med. Soc. Study VD. Prev: Cons. Venereol. S. Lond. Hosp.; Clin Asst. (Venereol.) Roy. N.. Hosp. Lond.; Asst. Med. Off. Lond. Boros. Haringey & Barnet.

NUNNERLEY, Heather Bell (retired) 6 The Tudors, 10 Court Downs Road, Beckenham BR3 6LR Tel: 020 8658 8134 — MB ChB Liverp. 1956; FRCR 1975; DMRD Eng. 1967; DObst RCOG 1959; DCH Eng. 1958; FRCP 1997. Chairm. Ravensbourne NHS Trust. Prev: Cons. Radiol. King's Coll. Hosp. Lond.

NUNNS, David 163 Henrietta Street, Ashton-under-Lyne OL6 8PH Tel: 0161 339 5700 Email: d.nunns@virgin.net — MB ChB 1991 Manc.; MD 1995 Manc; MRCOG 1997. (Univ. Manch.) Subspenality Trainee Gyn. Lenetes Roy. Inirmary. Prev: Clin. Lect. (Pathol. Scis.) Manch. Med. Sch. Univ. Manch.; Regist. (O & G) St. Mary's Hosp. Manch.; Regist. (O & G) Derby City Hosp. Derby.

NUNNS, Mary Eleanor Beatrice The Mission Practice, 208 Cambridge Heath Road, London E2 9LS Tel: 020 8983 7300 Fax: 020 8983 6800; 22 Hadley Court, Cazenove Road, Stoke Newington, London N16 6JU — MB BS 1978 Lond. Prev: Trainee GP Hackney Hosp. VTS Lond.

NUNOO-MENSAH, Mr Joseph William 19A Coldershaw Road, London W13 9EA Tel: 020 8567 4697 — BM BS 1993 Nottm.; BMedSci Nottm. 1991; FRCS Eng. 1997. (Nottm. Med. Sch.) Specialist Regist. (Gen. Surg.) Manch.; USLME 1995. Socs: Med. Protec. Soc. Prev: SHO (Gen. Surg.) Frimley Pk. Hosp. Frimley Surrey; SHO Rotat. (Surg.) John Radcliffe Hosp. Oxf.; Anat. Prosector Camb. Univ.

NUR, Mr Oomar Ali Withybush Hospital, Fishguard Road, Haverfordwest SA61 2PZ Tel: 01437 764545; Eastleigh, Treffgarne, Haverfordwest SA62 5PH Tel: 01437741429 — MB BS 1982 Karachi; FRCSI 1991; FRCS Glas. 1991. (Dow Med. Coll. Karachi) Assoc. Specialist Surg., Withaybush Hosp., Haverford W. Prev: Regist.- Withaybush Hosp.; Regist., Urol., P. Phillip Hosp., Unaeup; SHO (Surg.) P.ss of Wales Hosp. Bridgend.

NURBHAI, Suhail Pfizer Central Research, Sandwich CT13 9NJ — MB ChB 1988 Dundee; MRCP (UK) 1992. Clin. Project Manager Pfizer Centr. Research Kent. Prev: Regist. (Med.) BRd. Green Hosp. Liverp.

NURENNABI, Abul Khair Mohamed 72 Half Edge Lane, Eccles, Manchester M30 9BA — MRCS Eng. LRCP Lond. 1968; MRCP (U.K.) 1971.

NURICK, Simon 40 Wilbury Road, Hove BN3 3JP Tel: 01273 206206 Fax: 01273 721411; 47 Park Crescent, Brighton BN2 3HB Tel: 01273 605795 — BM BCh Oxf. 1958; MA Oxf. 1959, DM 1971; FRCP Lond. 1978, M 1964. (Oxf. & Guy's) Hons. Cons. Neurol. Brighton Health Care NHS Trust & Hurstwood Pk. Neurol. Centre. Prev: Cons. Neurol. SE Thames RHA & Hurstwood Pk. Hosp. Haywards Heath; Sen. Regist. Nat. Hosp. Nerv. Dis. Maida Vale; Resid. Med. Off. Nat. Hosp. Qu. Sq. Lond.

NURMIKKO, Turo Juhani The Walton Centre for Neurology & Neurosurgery, Rice Lane, Liverpool L9 1AE — Lic Med Turku 1974.

NURMOHAMED, Akil GP Direct, 5/7 Welback Road, West Harrow, Harrow HA2 0RH Tel: 020 8515 9300 Fax: 020 8515 9300 — MB BS 1994 Lond.; BSc; DRCOG.

NUROCK, Leonard Max (retired) 28A Shawfield Street, London SW3 4BD Tel: 020 7352 5753 — LRCPI & LM, LRCSI & LM 1954; BA Dub. 1948. Prev: Local Treasury Med. Off.

NURSE, Ann Margaret 79 Sydenham Hill, London SE26 6TQ — MB BS 1975 Lond. Prev: Ho. Phys. (Gen. Med.) N. Middlx. Hosp.; Ho. Surg. (Gen. Surg.) Middlx. Hosp.; Cas. Med. Off. Middlx. Hosp.

NURSE, Diane Elizabeth Bromley Hospital, Cromwell Avenue, Bromley BR2 9AJ Tel: 020 8289 7010 — MB ChB 1979 Bristol; ChM Bristol 1995; FRCS (Urol.) 1990; FRCS Eng. 1985. (Univ. Bristol. Med. Sch.) Cons. Urol. Bromley Hosps. NHS Trust. Socs: Brit. Assn. Urol. Surgs.; Roy. Soc. Med. Prev: Sen. Regist. Rotat. (Urol.) Guy's Hosp. & Brighton HA; Regist. (Urol.) Adelaide Childr. Hosp., S. Austral.

NURSE, Joanna Mary 108 Alma Road, Southampton SO14 6UW — BM 1991 Soton.

NURUZZAMAN, Muhammad 61 Norman Road, Walsall WS5 3QS Tel: 01922 31782; 61 Norman Road, Walsall WS5 3QS Tel: 01922 31782 — MB BS 1959 Dacca; FRCP Glas. 1984, M 1967; FRCP Ed. 1985, M 1967; FCPS Bangladesh 1974; DTM & H Liverp. 1966. (Dacca Med. Coll.) Cons. Phys. (Geriat. Med.) Walsall AHA. Prev: Research Fell. (Gastroenterol.) Nuffield Dept. Clin. Med. Radcliffe; Infirm. Oxf.; Sen. Regist. (Geriat. Med.) Soton. & Poole Gen. Hosps.

NUSAIR, Aber-Rahman Qassem Tel: 01282 474747 Fax: 01282 474747; Tel: 00 962 2 210044 — Medic 1981 Romania; MD Romania 1981; MPsych. Liverpool 1995; DPM 1989; Board Psych. 1992. Cons. Psychiat. Burnley Gen. Hosp. Socs: Brit. Assn. Psychopharmacol.; CINP. Prev: SCMO (Psychiat.) Barnsley; Assoc. Specialist (Child Psychiat.) Nuneaton.

NUSEIBEH, Mr Isaac Mohamed National Spinal Injuries Centre, Stoke Mandeville Hospital, Mandeville Road, Aylesbury HP21 8AL Tel: 01296 315000 Fax: 01296 315868 — MB ChB Lond. 1960; LMSSA Lond. 1968; FRCS Ed. 1972. p/t Cons. Surg. Spinal Injuries & Hon. Lect. BPMF Univ. Lond. Socs: Hon. Sec. Internat. Med. Soc. Paraplegia.

NUSSBAUM, Fritz Helmut (retired) 14 Chiltern House, Hillcrest Road, London W5 1HL Tel: 020 8997 6771 Fax: 020 8997 6771 — LRCP LRCS Ed. LRFPS Glas. 1934; MD Berlin 1934. Prev: Sen. Ho. Surg. Centr. Lond. Throat, Nose & Ear Hosp.

NUSSBAUM, Toni 31 Barlow Moor Court, West Didsbury, Manchester M20 2UU Tel: 0161 448 1327 Email: toni@nussbaum.freeserve.co.uk — MB ChB 1992 Manch.; MRCGP 1998. (Manchester)

NUSSBAUMER, Andrea 25 Oakwood Hall Drive, Rotherham S60 3AQ — State Exam Med. Cologne 1991.

NUSSBAUMER, Michael c/o Doctors Mess, Rotherham General Hospital, Moorgate Road, Rotherham S60 2UD — State Exam Med 1991 Cologne.

NUSSEY, Andrew Paul Department of Anaesthetics, Addenbrooke's Hospital, Hills Road, Cambridge CB2 2QQ — MB BS 1986 Queensland.

NUSSEY, Fiona Elizabeth Department of Clinical Oncology, Western General Hospital, Crewe Road, Edinburgh EH4 2XU Tel: 0131 537 1000; 7 Murrayfield Drive, Edinburgh EH12 6EB — MB ChB 1995 Aberd.; MRCP UK (Edin) 1998. (Aberd.) Clin. Research Fell. Dept. of Clin. Oncol. W.ern. Gen. Hosp. Edin. Prev: SHO (Med.Oncol.); SHO (Clin. Oncol.); SHO (Gen. Med.).

NUSSEY, Stephen Spencer St. George's Hospital Medical School, London SW17 0RE Tel: 020 8725 5803 Fax: 020 8725 0240 Email: s.nussey@sghms.ac.uk; 51 Galveston Road, London SW15 2RZ — BM BCh 1977 Oxf.; MA, DPhil Oxf. 1974; FRCP Lond. 1992; MRCP (UK) 1979. Reader (Endocrinol.) St. Geo.'s Hosp. Med. Sch. Lond.; Cons. Phys. St. Geo. Hosp. Lond. Prev: Sen. Lect. & Lect. St. Geo.'s Hosp. Med. Sch. Lond.; Sen. Regist. St. Jas. Hosp. Lond.

NUTBEAM, Helen Mary The Surgery, Pound Close, Oldbury, Warley B68 8LZ Tel: 0121 552 1632 Fax: 0121 552 0848; 287 Lordswood Road, Harborne, Birmingham B17 8PR Tel: 0121 429 9096 — MB ChB 1974 Ed.; MRCP (UK) 1976; MRCGP 1980; DCH RCPS Glas. 1976. Prev: Lect. (Paediat.) Char. Cross Hosp. Lond.; Regist. (Paediat.) St. Stephen's Hosp. Lond.

NUTBOURNE, Patricia Anne Oulton House, Church St., Great Wilbraham, Cambridge CB1 5JQ — MB BS 1960 Lond.; FFA RCS Eng. 1981; DA Eng. 1976. (St. Mary's)

NUTHALL, Timothy Richard Alexander 117 Shepards Bush Road, London W6 7LP — MB BS 1992 Lond.

NUTLEY, Peter Graham Bishops Park Health Centre, Lancaster Way, Bishop's Stortford CM23 4DA Tel: 01279 755057 — MB BS 1978 Lond.; BA Open 1984; MRCS Eng. LRCP Lond. 1978; MFPHM 1990; DCH RCP Lond. 1982; DRCOG 1982. (Middlx.) GP Bishop's Stortford. Socs: Brit. Acupunc. Soc. Prev: Med. Dir. Til (Med.) Ltd.; Head of Quality Audit Med. & Clin. Managem. Ltd.

NUTT, Adrian Ernest Craig Thornhedge, 2 Kilcorig Road, Magheragall, Lisburn BT28 2QY Tel: 01846 621807 — MB BCh BAO 1977 Dub.; DO RCPSI 1986; DCH RCPSI 1979.

***NUTT, Christopher John** 7 Fieldfare Road, Hartlepool TS26 0SA — MB ChB 1997 Dundee.

NUTT, Professor David John University of Bristol, Psychopharmacology Unit, The Medical School, University Walk, Bristol BS8 1TD Tel: 0117 925 3066 Fax: 0117 927 7057 Email: david.j.nutt@bristol.ac.uk — MB BChir 1975 Camb.; MA Camb. 1982, BA 1972; DM Oxf. 1983; MRCP (UK) 1977; FRCPsych 1993, M 1983. (Guy's) Head (Clin. Med.) Univ. Bristol; Head Div. Psychiat. Univ. Bristol; Hon. Cons. Psychiat. United Bristol Health Trust; Prof. Psychopharmacol. Univ. Bristol; Edr. Jl. Psychopharmacol. Socs: (Pres.) Brit. Assn. Psychopharmacol.; Fell. CINP; Fell. ECNP. Prev: Dir. (PsychoPharmacol.) Univ. Bristol; Dir. (Clin. Research) NIAAA, USA; Wellcome Sen. Fell. (Clin. Sc.) Warneford Hosp. Oxf.

NUTT, Desmond John Pattison Liffock Surgery, 69 Sea Road, Castlerock, Coleraine BT51 4TW Tel: 028 7084 8206 Fax: 028 7084 9146; 71 Killane Road, Limavady BT49 0DL — MB BCh BAO 1976 Belf.; DRCOG 1979.

NUTT, Michael Neil The Dovercourt Surgery, 309 City Road, Sheffield S2 5HJ Tel: 0114 270 0997 Fax: 0114 276 6786 — MB ChB 1984 Sheff. Trainee GP Sheff. Prev: SHO (Paediat.) Sheff.; SHO (Psychiat.) Exeter.

NUTT, Michael Richard 61 Greenhill Road, Griffithstown, Pontypool NP4 5BG — BM BS 1990 Nottm.

NUTT, Nicholas Richard The West View Surgery, 9 Park Road, Keynsham, Bristol BS31 1BX Tel: 0117 986 3063 Fax: 0117 986 5061; 47 Charlton Road, Keynsham, Bristol BS31 2JG Tel: 0117 986 4439 Email: nnutt@fsmail.net — MB BS 1972 Lond.; MRCS Eng. LRCP Lond. 1972; MRCGP 1977; DObst RCOG 1974. (King's Coll. Hosp.) p/t Med. Off. (Geriat.) Keynsham Hosp. Prev: SHO P.ss Margt. Hosp. Swindon; Ho. Off. St. Giles Hosp. Lond.

NUTTALL, Andrew Makepeace High Street Surgery, 2 High Street, Macclesfield SK11 8BX Tel: 01625 423692 — MB ChB 1980 Manch.

NUTTALL, Ian Douglas Lynwood, 63 Bramhall Park Road, Bramhall, Stockport SK3 3NA Tel: 0161 486 9600 — MD 1985 Manch.; MB ChB 1972; FRCOG 1990, M 1977. Cons. O & G Stockport HA. Prev: Sen. Regist. (O & G) N. W.ern RHA; Clin. Research Fell. (O & G) Withington Hosp. Manch.; Regist. (O & G) Univ. Cape Town, S. Africa.

NUTTALL, Jayne Sonia The Surgery, Ruckinge Road, HamSt., Ashford TN26 2NJ Tel: 0123 373 2262 — MB BS 1987 Lond.; DRCOG 1991. Prev: Trainee GP Nottm. VTS.

NUTTALL, Joan Harston (retired) 4 Smithie Close, New Earswick, York YO32 4DG — MB BS 1954 Lond.

NUTTALL, John Barry Clarence Avenue Surgery, 14 Clarence Avenue, Northampton NN2 6NZ Tel: 01604 718464 Fax: 01604 721589; Church Cottage, 15 Church Street, Boughton, Northampton NN2 8SF — MRCS Eng. LRCP Lond. 1958; MA Camb. 1959; DObst RCOG 1960; MRCGP 1968. (Camb. & Leeds) Prev: Ho. Surg. St. Jas. Hosp. Leeds.

***NUTTALL, Martin Chandler** Corner House, Auclum Lane, Burghfield Common, Reading RG7 3DA Tel: 01189 832808 — MB BS 1998 Lond.; MB BS Lond 1998; MA Cantab 199.

NUTTALL, Norman David 34 Hawthorn Grove, Bramhall, Stockport SK7 1EF Tel: 0161 439 2479; Sunnyside, Preston Road, Ribchester, Preston PR3 3YA Tel: 01772 782272 — MB ChB 1992 Ed.; MRCPsych 1996. (Edinburgh) Specialist Registr. (Psychiat.) S. Manch. Train. Scheme Manch. Prev: Regist. (Psychiat.) SE Scotl. Psych. Train. Scheme Edin.; SHO (Psychiat.) SE Scotl. Psych. Train. Scheme Edin.; SHO (Pschiatry) Roy. Vict. Hosp. Edin. & Bellsdyke Hosp. Larbert Stirlingsh.

NUTTALL, Peter Julian Devaney Medical Centre, 40 Balls Road, Oxton, Prenton CH43 5RE Tel: 0151 652 4281 Fax: 0151 670 0445; 71 Forest Road, Medls, Wirral CH47 6AT — MB ChB 1987 Liverp.; DRCOG 1990. (Liverp.) Socs: Birkenhead Med. Soc. Prev: Trainee GP Wirral VTS; Regist. (Psychiat.) Melbourne Australia.

NUTTEN, Horace Edward (retired) Pantiles, Felsham Road, Cockfield, Bury St Edmunds IP30 0HW Tel: 01284 828414 — MB ChB Aberd. 1951; AFOM RCP Lond. 1978; MFCM RCP Lond. 1974; DPH Aberd. 1955. Prev: Regional Med. Off. Gen. Counc. Brit. Shipping Lond.

NUTTING, Christopher Martin Department of Radiotherapy, St Bartholomew's Hospital, West Smithfield, London EC1A 7BE Tel: 0207 377700 Fax: 0207 601 8364 — MB BS 1992 Lond.; BSc (Cell Path.) Lond. 1989; MRCP (UK) 1995; FRCR 1998. (Middlesex) Sen. Regist. (Clin. Oncol.) St. Bart. Hosp., Lond.,. Prev: Regist. (Clin. Oncol.) Roy. Marsden Hosp. Lond.; SHO (Med.) Univ. Hosp. Nottm.; Ho. Phys. Middlx. Hosp. Lond.

NUTTING, Linda Mary 27 Park Terrace, Dunston, Gateshead NE11 9PA Tel: 0191 460 1284; The Health Centre, Prince Consort Road, Gateshead NE8 1NR Tel: 0191 477 2243 Fax: 0191 478 6728 — MB BS 1988 Newc.; DRCOG 1991. GP Princip. Health Centre N. Tyneside. Prev: SHO (Community Paediat.) N. Tyneside.; SHO (Med.) N. Tyneside HA; Trainee GP N.d. VTS.

NUTTON, Miranda 49 Andes Close, Alexandra Quay, Ocean Village, Southampton SO14 3HS — BM BS 1975 Nottm.

NUTTON, Mr Richard William Princess Margaret Rose Orthopaedic Hospital, 41/43 Frogston Road W., Fairmilehead, Edinburgh EH10 7ED Tel: 0131 536 4602 Fax: 0131 536 4849; 5 Corrennie Gardens, Morningside, Edinburgh EH10 6DG Tel: 0131 447 3475 — MD 1984 Newc.; FRCS Ed. 1994; FRCS Eng. 1979. (Newcastle upon Tyne) Hon. Sen. Lect. Orthop. and Trauma Univ. of Edin.; Cons. Orthop. Surg. Roy. Infirm. Edin. NHS Trust. Socs: Brit. Elbow & Shoulder Soc.; Brit. Assn. Surg. Knee; Brit. Orthop. Research Soc.

NUVOLONI, Maureen Colette Christine 45 Northumberland Close, Warfield, Bracknell RG42 3XD — MB ChB 1965 Manch.; DObst RCOG 1967. Clin. Med. Off. E. Berks HA.

NWABINELI, Mr Nwachukwu James South Shields District Hospital, Harton Lane, South Shields NE34 0PL Tel: 0191 454 8888 Fax: 0191 202 4067; Bethel, 4 Elsdon Road, Whickham, Newcastle upon Tyne NE16 5HZ Tel: 0191 488 7178 Email: nwachukwul@yahoo.com — MB BS 1974 Ibadan; MB BS Ibadan, Nigeria 1974; MRCOG 1980; FRCOG 1995. (Ibadan, Nigeria) Cons. in O & G S. Tyneside Dist. Hosp. Socs: BMA; Brit. Menopause Soc.; Internat. Continence Soc. Prev: Train. Fell. (Gyn. & Oncol.) Stobhill Hosp. Glas.; Cons. Gyn. Univ. Benin Teach. Hosp. Nigeria; Research Fell. Freeman Hosp. Newc. u. Tyne.

NWABOKU, Mr Harold Chukwuemeka Ifeanyi 10 Tregothnan Road, London SW9 9JX — MB BS 1988 Lond.; FRCS Ed. 1992; FRCS Eng. 1992; FRCS (Orth.) 1997. (Middlesex) Orthop. Socs: BOTA; BMA.

NWABUEZE, Emmanuel Dibua Victoria Road Medical Centre, 166 Victoria Road, Prestatyn LL19 7UF Tel: 01745 852775 Fax: 01745 888998; 1A Ffordd Ffrith, Prestatyn LL19 7UD — BM BCh 1976 Nigeria. GP.

NWACHUKU, Oludotun Mofolusho 143 Rectory Path Avenue, Northolt UB5 6SB — MB ChB 1966 Aberd.

NWACHUKWU, Mr Ikechukwu Augustine 13 Deal Court, White Acre, Colindale, London NW9 5FT Tel: 020 8205 1982 — MB BS 1985 Nigeria; MB BS U. of Nigeria 1985; FRCS Eng 1991.

NWAGBARA, Patrick Nduruo Department of Obstetrics & Gynaecology, Warwick Hospital, Warwick CV34 5BW Tel: 01926 495321; 26 Parkinson House, Frampton Pk Road, London E9 7PH — MB BS 1979 Ibadan, Nigeria; MRCOG 1992. Regist. (O & G) S. Warks. Hosps. NHS Trust Warwick; Train. Fell. (Obst. Ultrasound) Birm. Wom. Hosp. Univ. Birm. Socs: Fell. W. Afr. Coll. Surgs. Prev:

NWAKAKWA

Regist. & SHO (O & G) New Cross Hosp. Wolverhampton; Sen. Regist. (O & G) Univ. Nigeria Teachg. Hosp.

NWAKAKWA, Victor Chinedu 26A Rowley Way, St Johns Wood, London NW8 0SQ — MB BS 1993 Ibadan, Nigeria; MRCP (UK) 1993.

NWAMARAH, Mr David Ezeakolam 91 Central Avenue, Welling DA16 3BG Tel: 020 8855 7238 — MB BS 1978 Lagos; FRCS Glas. 1989; FRCS Ed. 1988.

NWEKE, Anny Joseph 28 Patch Close, Horninglow, Burton-on-Trent DE13 0GE — MB BS 1974 Lagos.

NWOKOLO, Chukwuemeka Felix 25 Ashfield Crescent, Springhead, Oldham OL4 4NX Tel: 0161 652 8755 — MB BS 1980 Nigeria; MB BS Nigeria Univ. 1980; MRCOG 1992.

NWOKOLO, Chukwuka Uchemefuna University Hospitals Coventry & Warwickshire, Clifford Bridge Road, Coventry CV2 2DX Tel: 024 76 538759; 57 St Bernards, Solihull B91 3PH Tel: 0121 706 9567 Fax: 0121 711 4967 Email: chukanwokolog@compuserve.com — BM BCh 1978 Nigeria; MD Birm. 1993; FRCP 1998; FRCP Ed 1998. Hon Sen Lec Dep of Biological Sci.s Univ. of Warwick; Vis. Clin. Sen. Lect. Sch. Postgrad. Med. Educat. Univ. Warwick. Socs: Brit. Soc. Gastroenterol. & Midl. Gastrointestinal Soc.; Amer. Gastroenterol. Assn. Prev: Sen. Regist. (Med. & Gastroenterol.) Dudley Rd. Hosp. Birm.; Sen. Regist. (Med. & Gastroenterol.) Walsgrave Hosp. Coventry.; Clin. Research Fell. (Gastroenterol.) Roy. Free Hosp. Lond.

NWOKORA, Mr Gregory Ezennia Eye Department, Royal Hospital, Haslar, Gosport PO12 2AA Tel: 01705 584255 Ext: 2411; 10 Ashgrove Park, Altnagelvin, Londonderry BT47 5GN Tel: 01504 313090 — MB BS 1977 Lagos; FRCSI 1986; FRCOphth 1993; FCOphth 1988; DO RCPSI 1984. (College of Medicine University of Lagos, Nigeria) Assoc. Specialist (Ophth.) (Min. of Defence) Roy. Hosp. Haslar Gosport. Socs: BMA. Prev: Cons. (Ophth. Surg.) N W Armed Forces Hosp. Tabuk, KSA.

NWOSE, Macdonald Oliseyenum A5 William Gunn House, 50 Lawn Road, Hampstead, London NW3 2XA — MB BS 1987 Lagos.

NWOSU, Ezechi Callistus Whiston Hospital, Warrington Road, Prescot L35 5DN Tel: 0151 430 1495 Fax: 0151 430 1335; 15 South Mossley Hill Road, Mossley Hill, Liverpool L19 3PY — BM BCh 1978 Nigeria; MRCOG 1989; MObstG Liverp. 1992. (Univ. Nigeria Med. Sch. Enugu Campus) Cons. O & G Whiston Hosp. Prescot; Hon. Lect. (Obst. & Gyn.) Univ. Liverp. Socs: BMA; Blair Bell Res. Soc.; Med. Assn. Nigerian Specialists & GPs. Prev: Sen. Regist. (O & G) Liverp. Matern. Hosp.; Regist. Masters in Feto-Matern. Med. Mill Rd. Liverp. Matern. Hosp.; Regist. N. Tyneside Gen. Hosp. N. Shields & P.ss Mary Matern. Hosp. Newc.

NWOSU, Mr Lawrence Chidi 21 Remburn Gardens, Warwick CV34 5BH Tel: 01926 403652 — MB BS 1985 Ibadan; FRCS Ed. 1994. Staff Surg. Acc. & Emerg. Dept. Warwick Hosp. Warwick.

NWOZO, Mr James Chinyelu 180 Glastone Park Gardens, London NW2 6RL — MB BS 1962 Lond.; MRCS Eng. LRCP Lond. 1962; FRCS Eng. 1966.

NWULU, Bernard Nchewa Rampton Hospital, Retford DN22 0PD Tel: 01777 247706 Email: nchewanwulu@public online.co.uk; 146 Grange Road, Broom, Rotherham S60 3LL Tel: 0797 407 1721 Fax: 01709 519514 — MD 1972 National U, Zaire; MPhil Ed. 1984; FRCPsych 1996; MRCPsych 1982. (University of Zaire/Edinburgh) Cons. Psychiat. Rampton Hosp. Retford; Hon. Lect. Univ. Sheff.; Med Mem. Ment. Health Review Tribunal Eng. Socs: BMA & Soc. Clin. Psychiat.; Roy. Coll Psychiat. Prev: Sen. Regist. Balderton & E. Dale Unit Newark; Regist. (Psychiat.) Stratheden Hosp. Fife; Clin. Asst. Roy. Edin. Hosp.

NYAMUGUNDURU, Godfrey 6 Copeland Drive, Stone ST15 8YP. — MB BS 1986 Lond.; MRCP (UK) 1991. (St. Geo. Hosp.) Clin. Research Fell. Birm. Childr. Hosp. Prev: Regist. (Paediat.) Birm. Heartlands Hosp.; Regist. (Med.) Jas. Paget Hosp. Gt. Yarmouth.

NYAWO, Brian Westwood Hospital, Beverley HU17 8BU; 5 Oulton Drive, Woodlesford, Leeds LS26 8EN — MB ChB 1987 Leeds.

NYDAHL, Stefan 34 Knighton Grange Road, Leicester LE2 2LE — Lakarexamen Stockholm 1979; T(S) 1994.

NYE, Alan David Hopwood House, The Vineyard, Lees Road, Oldham OL4 1JN Tel: 0161 628 3628 Fax: 0161 628 4970 — MB ChB 1983 Sheff.; BMedSci (Hons.) Sheff. 1982. Trainee GP Oldham HA VTS.

NYE, Brenda Margaret Bradford Road Medical Centre, 60 Bradford Road, Trowbridge BA14 9AR Tel: 01225 754255 Fax: 01225 777342 — MB ChB 1980 Birm.; MRCGP 1985; DFFP 1996; DRCOG 1985; DCH 1984. (Birmingham Medical School) p/t Partnership in Gen. Pract. Bradford Rd. Med. Centre Trowbridge. Prev: Retainer GP Bath; GP Fernville Surg. Hemel Hempstead.

NYE, Christopher James Stewart Flat 1, 21 Mill St., St Peter Port, Guernsey GY1 1HG Tel: 01481 700152 — MB ChB 1963 St. And.; MLCOM 1980, L 1968; DFFP 1993; DPhysMed Eng. 1971; DObst RCOG 1966. Indep. Orthop. & Osteop. Phys. Socs: Fell. Roy. Soc. Med.; Brit. Osteop. Assn.; BIMM. Prev: Sen. GP Summerhill Surg. Ramsgate; Sen. Regist. (Rheum. & Rehabil.) Wilts. AHA & Hants. AHA (T) & Nuffield Med. Rehabil. Centre Odstock Hosp. Salisbury.

NYE, Frederick John ID Unit, University Hospital Aintree, Lower Lane, Liverpool L9 7AL; 23 Bonnington Ave, Great Crosby, Liverpool L23 7YJ — MRCS Eng. LRCP Lond. 1966; MD Lond. 1976, MB BS 1966; FRCP Lond. 1981, M 1969. (St. Geo.) Cons. Phys. Infec. Dis. Unit, Univ. Hosp.. Liverp.; Clin. Lect. Dept. Trop. Med. & Infec. Dis. Univ. Liverp. Socs: Brit. Soc. Antimicrobial Chemother. & Brit. Infec. Soc. Prev: Sen. Med. Regist. St. Geo. Hosp. Lond. & Dept. Communicable Dis. E.; Birm. Hosp.

NYE, Julie Frances 55 Barnsbury Street, London N1 1EJ — MB ChB 1991 Leic.

NYE, Matthew Yau Leung The Surgery, Aston University, 15 Coleshill Street, The Aston Triangle, Birmingham B4 7ET Tel: 0121 359 3611 Fax: 0121 333 6023; Priory Hospital, Priory Road, Edgbaston, Birmingham B5 7UG Tel: 0121 440 6611 — MB ChB 1981 Sheff.; AFOM 1994; MRCGP 1985; Dip. Pract. Dermat. Wales 1990; DCH RCP Lond. 1988; DRCOG 1986; Dip. Acupunc. 1984. (Sheff. Med. Sch.) Chief Univ. Phys. Univ. Aston.; VTS Course Organiser W. Birm.; Cons. Acupunc. Socs: Brit. Med. Acupunc. Soc. Prev: GP Birm.; GP Tutor.

***NYEKO, Christopher** UMDS, Boland House, Guy's Hospital, London SE1 9RT — LMSSA 1995 Lond.

NYHOLM, Elizabeth Shannon Yardley Green Medical Centre, 73 Yardley Green Road, Bordesley Green, Birmingham B9 5PU Tel: 0121 773 3838 Fax: 0121 506 2005; 35 Broad Oaks Road, Solihull B91 1JA Tel: 0121 705 5407 Fax: 0121 705 5407 — MB BS 1978 Lond.; MRCGP 1983; DCH RCPS Glas. 1984; DRCOG 1983. Princip. (Gen. Pract.) Hosp. Pract. (Gastroenterol.) Heartlands Hosp.

NYHOLM, Rosemary Erica Denton Turret Medical Centre, 10 Kenley Road, Slatyford, Newcastle upon Tyne NE5 2UY Tel: 0191 274 1840; 24 Queensway, Ponteland, Newcastle upon Tyne NE20 9RZ Tel: 01661 871663 — MB BS 1985 Lond.; MPhil Lond. 1980; BSc Reading 1975; MRCGP 1990; DRCOG 1987. (Univ. Coll. Sch. of Med.)

NYIRI, Polly Jennifer Flat 3, 26 Morwell St., London WC1B 3AZ — MB BChir 1990 Camb.

NYLANDER, Mr Arthur Gustavus Ekundayo Department of Ophthalmology, Blackburn Royal Infirmary, Bolton Road, Blackburn BB2 3LR Tel: 01254 687252 Fax: 01254 294050 Email: anylander@doctors.org.uk; Email: anylander@doctors.org.uk — MB BS 1980 Nigeria; FRCS Glas. 1987; FCOphth 1988; DO RCPSI 1984. (Ibadan, Nigeria) Cons. Ophth. Burnley Gen. Hosp. & Cons. Ophth. Blackburn Roy. Infirm. Socs: Amer. Acad. of Ophth.; UK & Irel. Soc. Cataract & Refractive Surg.; Brit. Soc. of Refractive Surg.

NYLANDER, David Leslie 176 Brantingham Road, Manchester M21 0TS — MB BS 1988 Newc.; MRCP (UK) 1992.

NYLANDER, Harold Hercules 92 Kirkland Avenue, Ilford IG5 0TN — MB BS 1974 Newc.; MRCPI 1982.

NYMAN, Cyril Richard Pilgrim Hospital NHS Trust, Sibsey Road, Boston PE21 9QS Tel: 01205 364801 Fax: 01205 359257 Email: cyril.nyman@uhl.nhs.uk; Stoke Lodge, 116 Tower Road, Boston PE21 9AU Tel: 01205 351748 Email: cnyman2@compuserve.com — MB BS 1968 Lond.; 1990 T (M) Roy. Coll. Physicians; 2000 FESC European Soc. Of Cardiology; FACC 2001 American Coll. Of Cardiology; FRCP Lond. 1987; MRCP (UK) 1971; MRCS Eng. LRCP Lond. 1968; DObst RCOG 1970. (St. Mary's) Cons. Phys. (Cardiorespirat. Med.) Pilgrim Hosp. Boston; Local Collaborator for "Search" and "Procardis" Studies Boston (Main Centre Oxf.). Socs: Brit. Cardiac Soc.; Brit. Thorac. Soc.; Brit. Soc. Echocardiogr. Prev: Sen. Regist. CardioRespirat. Med. Waller CardioPulm. Unit St Mary's Hosp. Lond.; Regist. (Gen. & Thoracic Med.) St. Thos. Hosp. Lond.

NYMAN, Joel Adam 1 Apthorpe Street, Fulbourn, Cambridge CB1 5EY — MB BS 1990 Lond.

NYMAN, Lorraine Esther 22 Bridgewater Way, Bushey, Watford WD23 4UA — MB BS 1991 Lond.

NYMAN, Valerie Anne Harbourside, 29 Esplanade, Fowey PL23 1HY Tel: 01726 832556 Fax: 01726 832556 Email: howardval@harbourside.swinternet.co.uk — MB ChB Liverp. 1966. p/t Clin. Asst. O & G Treliske Hosp. Truro; Clin. MO & Instruc. Dr. Fam. Plann. Cornw. Healthcare Trust. Socs: Fac. Comm. Health; Fac. Fam. Plann. & Reproduc. Health Care. Prev: Lead Clin. Community Serv. for Wom. & Young People N. Devon.

NYSENBAUM, Anthony Michael 87 Palatine Road, West Didsbury, Manchester M20 3JQ Tel: 0161 434 9126; Fir Trees, 88 Moss Lane, Sale M33 5BT Tel: 0161 973 5995 — MD 1980 Manch.; MB ChB 1977; MRCOG 1982. Cons. O & G Trafford HA. Socs: Fell. N. Eng. Obst. & Gyn. Soc.; Blair Bell Soc. Prev: Lect. (O & G) The Lond. Hosp.; Regist. (O & G) St. Bart. Hosp. Lond.; Research Fell. Dept. Child Health Univ. Manch.

NYUNT TIN, Mr 8 Nursery Grove, Kilmacolm PA13 4HW — MB BS 1971 Rangoon; FRCPS Glas. 1986; FRCS Ed. 1986. Prev: Cons. ENT Surg. King Abdul Aziz Naval Base Hosp. Jubail, Saudi Arabia.

NZEGWU, Grace Olufunmilayo 27 Woodnook Road, Streatham, London SW16 6TZ — MB BS 1956 Lond.

NZELU, Ernest Nnoruka 25 Delacourt Road, Manchester M14 6BU — MB BS 1980 Ibadan; MB BS Ibadan Nigeria 1980; MRCOG 1989.

NZEWI, Mr Onyekwelu Chibuike 4 Forest Drive, Bearsden, Glasgow G61 4SJ — BM BCh 1980 Nigeria; FRCSI 1991.

O'BEIRN, Diarmuid Peadar Department of Medicine for Elderly, General Hospital, Llandudno LL30 1LB Tel: 01492 860066 Fax: 01492 871668 — MB BCh BAO 1973 NUI; FRCPI 1989; MRCPI 1980; DCH Dub. 1976. Cons. Phys. (Med. for Elderly) Gen. Hosp. Llandudno. Socs: Brit. Geriat. Soc. Prev: Clin. Lect. & Sen. Regist. (c/o Elderly) Univ. Birm.; Regist. (Gen. Med.) Castlebar Gen. Hosp.; Regist. (Respirat. Med.) Merlin Pk. Hosp.

O'BEIRNE, Kathleen 17 Church Lane, Evenley, Brackley NN13 5SG — MB BCh BAO 1952 NUI.

O'BOYLE, Ciaran Patrick 26 Townview Avenue S., Omagh BT78 1HX — MB BCh BAO 1996 Belf.

O'BOYLE, Mr Patrick John Department of Urology, Taunton & Somerset Hosptial, MusGrove Park, Taunton TA1 5DA Tel: 01823 342103 Fax: 01823 343571 Email: pjoboyle@yahoo.co.uk; Wild Oak Cottage, Wild Oak Lane, Trull, Taunton TA3 7JS Tel: 01823 278057 Fax: 01823 343571 — MB ChB 1965 Glas.; ChM Liverp. 1978; FRCS Ed. 1970. (Glas.) Cons. Urol. Taunton & Som. NHS Trust. Socs: Fell. (Counc. Mem.) Roy. Soc. Med.; Internat. Continence Soc.; (Counc.) Brit. Assn. Urol. Surgs. Prev: Clin. Lect. Dept. Cancer Research Univ. Leeds; Sen. Regist. (Urol.) Liverp. Regional Urol. Centre Sefton Gen. Hosp. Liverp.; Regist. (Surg.) Glas. Roy. Infirm.

O'BRADY, Deirdre Siobhain 11 Rugby Mansions, Bishop Kings Road, London W14 8XD — MB BCh BAO 1979 NUI; LRCPI & LM, LRCSI & LM 1979.

O'BRART, Mr David Phillip Saul Department of Ophthalmology, St Thomas' Hospital, Lambeth Palace Road, London SE1 7EH Tel: 020 7928 9292 Fax: 020 7922 0586 — MB BS 1985 Lond.; MD Lond. 1995; FRCS Eng. 1990; FCOphth. 1990; DO RCS Eng. 1990. (Guy's) Cons. Ophth. Guy's & St. Thos. NHS Trust; Hon. Sen. Lect. Univ. of Lond. Socs: ARVO; UKIRCSS. Prev: Sen. Regist. (Ophth.) Addenbrooke's Hosp. Camb.; Regist. Rotat. & SHO (Ophth.) St. Thos. Hosp. Lond.

O'BRIEN, Mr Aidan Craigavon Area Hospital, Craigavon BT63 5QQ Tel: 028 3861 2634 Fax: 028 3833 3839 Email: aobrien@cah9t.n-i.nhs.uk; 12 Clover Hill, Moy, Dungannon BT71 7TP Tel: 028 8778 9494 Email: aidanpobrien@aol.com — MB BCh BAO 1978 Belf.; FRCSI 1983. (Queen's University, Belfast) Cons. Urol. Craigavon Area Hosp. Gp. Trust Craigavon. Socs: Irish Soc. Urol.; Fell. Roy. Acad. Med. Irel.; Fell. Ulster Med. Soc. Prev: Sen. Regist. (Paediat. Urol.) Bristol; Sen. Regist. (Urol.) Matern. Hosp. Dub.; Sen. Regist. (Urol.) Beaumont Hosp. Dub.

O'BRIEN, Aileen Ann Corwen Lodge, Castle Rising Road, South Wootton, King's Lynn PE30 — MB BS 1994 Lond.

***O'BRIEN, Alastair John** 6 The Hamlet, Champion Hill, London SE5 8AW.

O'BRIEN, Alice Nevis (retired) Riveredge, Normanby, Sinnington, York YO62 6RH — MB ChB 1951 Liverp.; MFCM 1975; DPH Liverp. 1964. Prev: Sen. Med. Off. Cumbria HA.

O'BRIEN, Ambrose Patrick Harley Street Medical Centre, Hanley, Stoke-on-Trent ST1 3RX Tel: 01782 281806 — MB BCh BAO 1952 NUI. (Univ. Coll. Dub.) Prev: Med. Off. Defence Forces of Irel. Att. Gen. Milit. Hosp. Curragh Camp; Sen. Res. Ho. Phys. St. Vincent's Hosp. Dub.; Res. Anaesth. City Gen. Hosp. Stoke-on-Trent.

O'BRIEN, Ann Elizabeth Oak Tree Medical Centre, 273-275 Green Lane, Seven Kings, Ilford IG3 9TJ Tel: 020 8599 3474 Fax: 020 8590 8277; 8 Audleigh Place, Chigwell IG7 5QT Tel: 020 8505 0536 Email: a.o'brien@virgin.net — MB BS 1975 Lond.; MRCGP 1980; DRCOG 1979. (Kings Coll.) Director, Redbridge GP OnCall. Prev: Non-Exec. Dir. Redbridge & Waltham Forest HA; Chairm. Local Med. Comm.; Clin. Asst. (Paediat.) King Geo. Hosp. Ilford.

O'BRIEN, Anthony Aloysius John Department of Medicine for Elderly, Southend General Hospital, Prittlewell Chase, Westcliff on Sea SS0 ORY Tel: 01702 435555 Fax: 01702 221377 Email: tonyobrien@aol.com — MB BCh BAO 1980 Dub.; MB BCh Dub. 1980; MD 1992; MRCPI 1983; FRCPI 1998. Cons. Phys. (Med.) S.end Gen. Hosp. Socs: Brit. Geriat.s Soc.; Amer. Geriat. Soc. Prev: Hon. Sen. Regist. (Geriat. Med.) Hammersmith Hosp. Lond.

O'BRIEN, Anthony Timothy James Brae Cottage, Rosemary Lane, Freshford, Bath BA2 7UF — MB BChir 1993 Camb.

O'BRIEN, Mr Barry Shaun Flat 1, 2 Burdon Terrace, Newcastle upon Tyne NE2 3AE — MB BS 1990 Newc.; MB BS (Hons.) Newc. 1990; FRCS Eng. 1994. Regist. (Orthop.) N. Regional Train. Scheme.

O'BRIEN, Bernard William Beechcroft, Ruff Lane, Ormskirk L39 4 — MB ChB 1972 Liverp.; DIH Lond. 1982.

O'BRIEN, Brendan Cornwall & Isles of Scilly Health Authority, John Kay House, St Austell PL25 4NQ Tel: 01726 627918 Fax: 01726 71777; 36 Lanyon Road, Playing Place, Truro TR3 6HF Tel: 01872 865801 Email: 101376.373@compurve.com — MB BCh BAO 1994 Belf.; Dip. Ment. Health Belf. 1997. Specialist Regist. (Pub. Health Med.) Cornw. & Isles of Scilly Health Auth. St Austell.

O'BRIEN, Brendan Patrick The Surgery, 29 Folkestone Road, Edmonton, London N18 2ER Tel: 020 8807 2176; 33 Arundel Gardens, London N21 3AG — MB BCh BAO 1980 NUI; DCH RCPSI 1986.

O'BRIEN, Catherine Geraldine North Mersey Community Trust, Arundel House, Sefton General Hospital, Smithdown Road, Liverpool L9 7JP Tel: 0151 330 8015 Fax: 0151 280 0929 — MB BCh BAO 1980 NUI; MRCPsych 1986. Cons. Psychiat. Sefton Gen. Hosp. Liverp. Prev: Sen. Regist. (Psychiat.) Mersey RHA; Sen. Regist. Bloomsbury HA & UCH.

O'BRIEN, Catherine Mary Bristol Childrens Hospital, Uppu Mandlin Street, Bristol — MB ChB 1991 Birm. (Birm.) Specialist Regist. (Paediat.) Bristol.

O'BRIEN, Miss Catherine Mary Brock Hall, Shawbury Lane, Shustoke, Birmingham B46 2SA Tel: 01676 540363 Fax: 01676 541175 — MB BS 1994 Lond.; FRCS (Eng) 1998. (Guy's & St. Thos. Hosp. Lond.) SHO Plastic Surg. Prev: SHO Rotat. (Surg.) Frenchay Hosp. Bristol; SHO (Orthop.) Bristol Roy. Infirm. & S.mead Hosp. Bristol; Cas. Off. Kent & Canterbury Hosp.

O'BRIEN, Charles Joseph Daisy Hill Hospital, Newry BT35 8DR Tel: 028 3083 5167 Fax: 028 3025 7965 Email: c.j.o'brien@dhn.n-i.nhs.uk; 40 Drumreagh Road, Rostrevor, Newry BT34 3DS — MB BCh BAO 1979 Belf.; MD Belf.1988; MRCP (UK) 1982; FRCP Lond. 1997; FRCPI 1997. Cons. Phys. & Postgrad. Clin. Tutor Daisy Hill Hosp. Newry. Socs: Brit. & Irish Soc. Gastroenterol.; Brit. Assn. Study Liver; BMA. Prev: Sen. Regist. (Med. & Gastroenterol.) Roy. Hallamsh. Hosp. Sheff.; Research Fell. Liver Unit King's Coll. Hosp. Lond.; Ho. Off. Mater Infirmorum Hosp. Belf.

O'BRIEN, Christine Department Respiratory Medicine, George Eliot Hospital, College Street, Nuneaton CV10 7DJ Email: christine.o'brian@geh.nhs.uk; Email: cob27@doctors.org.uk — MD 1989 Hamburg; State Exam Med 1988; MRCP (UK) 1992. (Hamburg) Cons. Phys. Respirat. and Gen. Med. Prev: Specialist Regist. (Respirat. Med.) W. Midl.

O'BRIEN, Christopher John Royal Victoria Infirmary, Queen Victoria Road, Newcastle upon Tyne NE1 4LP Tel: 0191 232 5131 Email: c.j.o'brien@ncl.ac.uk — MB BS 1986 Lond.; MRCP (UK) 1991; Dip. Obst. Auckland 1989. Cons. Paediat. Roy. Vict. Infirm., Uespuratory Paediat. Prev: Research Fell. Roy. Vict. Infirm. Newc.

O'BRIEN

O'BRIEN, Ciaran Joseph Department of Pathology, Swansea NHS Trust Morriston Hospital, Swansea SA6 6NL Tel: 01792 702222 Fax: 01792 703051 Email: ciaran.obrien@swansea-tr.wales.nhs.uk — MB BCh BAO 1977 Dub.; FRCPI 2001; MRCPI 1980; FRCPath 1995, M 1985. (Trinity Coll. Dub.) Cons. Histopath. Swansea NHS Trust, Morriston Hosp. Swansea. Prev: Lect. & Hon. Cons. Univ. Leeds.

O'BRIEN, David Charles 51 Chantry Road, Moseley, Birmingham B13 8DN — MB BS 1977 Lond.

O'BRIEN, David John 53 Hickmans Avenue, Cradley Heath, Sandwell, Cradley Heath B64 5NH — MB ChB 1981 Liverp.

O'BRIEN, David Pascal Department of Neurosurgery, Hope Hospital, Stott Lane, Salford M6 8HD — MB BCh BAO 1986 NUI.

O'BRIEN, David Vincent Haematology Department, Ormskirk and District General Hospital, Wigan Road, Ormskirk L39 2AZ Tel: 01695 656637 Fax: 01695656651 Email: davidobrien@soh-tr.nwest.nhs.uk — MB ChB 1983 Liverp.; MRCP (UK) 1986; MRCPath 1994. Cons. Haemat. S.port & Ormskirk Hosp. NHS Trust. Prev: Sen. Regist. (Haemat.) Birm. Childr. Hosp.; LRF Fell. Qu. Eliz. Med. Centre Birm.; Regist. (Haemat.) Roy. Liverp. Hosp.

O'BRIEN, Declan Francis 55 Moor Court, Westfield, Gosforth, Newcastle upon Tyne NE3 4YD — MB BCh BAO 1987 NUI; LRCPSI 1987.

O'BRIEN, Declan John King Street Surgery, 22A King Street, Hereford HR4 9DA Tel: 01432 272181 Fax: 01432 344725; 19 Aylestone Hill, Hereford HR1 1HR Tel: 01432 269336 — MB ChB 1978 Liverp.; MRCGP 1982; DRCOG 1981; DCH RCP Lond. 1982. Course Organiser Hereford & Worcs. VTS.

O'BRIEN, Deirdre Anne 55 High Street, Minster in Thanet, Ramsgate CT12 4BT Email: andrew@domneva.freeserve.co.uk — MB BCh BAO 1977 NUI; DRCOG 1981. (Univ. Coll. Dub.) Clin. Asst. (Dermat.) QEQMH Hosp. Margate Kent; Med. Off. (Psychosexual Med.) Margate & BRd.stairs; Mem. Inst. Psychosexual Med.; Clin. Asst. (GUM)Ramsgate; MO (FPC) Ramsgate. Prev: Trainee GP Thanet VTS; H.O. Surg. Laois Co. Hosp. Portlaoise; H.O. Med. St. Vincents Dub.

O'BRIEN, Denis Joseph Park Road Group Practice, The Elms Medical Centre, 3 The Elms, Dingle, Liverpool L8 3SS Tel: 0151 727 5555 Fax: 0151 288 5016; Talka House, 42 Ullet Road, Liverpool L17 3BP Tel: 0151 733 4785 Fax: 0151 733 0765 Email: djob@btinternet.com — MB BCh BAO 1982 NUI; MRCGP 1986; DCH NUI 1985; DObst. RCPI 1985.

O'BRIEN, Donogh Declan, OStJ, Brigadier late RAMC Retd. Park View, 38 Park Avenue, Bromley BR1 4EE Tel: 020 8464 0578 — MB BCh BAO NUI 1946; LM Coombe Hosp. Dub. 1948. (Univ. Coll. Dub.) Socs: Fell. Roy. Soc. Med.; BMA (Exec. Comm. Bromley Br.); Milit. Surg. Soc. Prev: Chief Med. Off. Brit. Red Cross Soc.; Hon. Phys. to HM the Qu.; CO Qu. Eliz. Milit. Hosp. Woolwich.

O'BRIEN, Edmund Noel (retired) 19 Beverley Gardens, Wargrave, Reading RG10 8ED Tel: 0118 940 2562 — MB BS 1952 Melbourne; FRACP 1970, M 1959; FRCPath 1978, M 1966. Prev: Hon. Med. Adviser Brit. Olympic Assn.

O'BRIEN, Eileen Assumpta 60 The Crescent, Belmont, Sutton SM2 6BN — MB BCh BAO 1980 NUI.

O'BRIEN, Elizabeth McQuilkan Davidson (retired) 53 Abingdon Villas, London W8 6XA — MB BChir 1950 Camb.; MRCS Eng. LRCP Lond. 1950; FRCPsych 1987, M 1971; DPM Eng. 1967. Prev: Cons. Child Psychiat. Newham HA Lond.

O'BRIEN, Fiona Geraldine Mary Light House, Newtonairds, Dumfries DG2 0JL — MB BCh BAO 1987 NUI; MRCGP 1991; DObst. RCPI 1990; DCH NUI 1989. SHO (Geriat.) Edin. Prev: A & E Roy. Infirm. Edin.; Trainee GP Edin.; SHO (Geriat.) Roy. Vict. Hosp. Edin.

O'BRIEN, Frances Clare Town End Surgery, 41 Town End, Caterham CR3 5UJ Tel: 01883 345613 Fax: 01883 330142; 47 Hartscroft, Croydon CR0 9LB — MB ChB 1978 Birm.; BA Camb.

O'BRIEN, Frances Elizabeth 59A Tollington Park, London N4 3QW — MB BS 1993 Lond.

O'BRIEN, Gregory 17 The Poplars, QGosforth, Newcastle upon Tyne NE3 4AE — MB ChB 1980 Aberd.

O'BRIEN, Hugh Anthony William 3 The Courtyard, Castle Carrock, Carlisle CA8 9LS — MB BS 1974 Lond.; MRCP (UK) 1977; MRCPath 1982; FRCP 1996. Cons. (Haemat.) Cumbld. Infirm. Carlisle. Prev: Sen. Regist. St. Bart. Hosp. Lond.

O'BRIEN, Iain Anthony Daniel Law Hospital, Carluke ML8 5ER Tel: 01698 361100; Murrayfield, Broughton Road, Biggar ML12 6HA Tel: 01899 220036 — MB BS 1973 Lond.; MD Bristol 1988; FRCP Ed. 1993; FRCP Glas. 1992; MRCP (UK) 1977. Cons. Gen. Med. Wishaw Gen. Hosp., Wishaw ML2 0DP. Prev: Sen. Regist. (Diabetes & Endocrinol.) Roy. Devon & Exeter Hosp. & Bristol Roy. Infirm.

O'BRIEN, Ian Michael 6 The Hamlet, Champion Hill, London SE5 8AW Tel: 020 7733 1792 — MB BS 1970 Lond.; FRCP Lond. 1987; MRCP (UK) 1972; MRCS Eng. LRCP Lond. 1970. (Char. Cross) Cons. Phys. Medway Health Dist.; Sen. Lect. (Med.) St. Thos. Hosp. Med. Sch. Lond. Prev: Regist. (Med.) & Lect. (Med.) St. Thos. Hosp. Lond.; Lect. (Clin. Immunol.) Brompton Hosp. Lond.

O'BRIEN, James Anthony South and West Devon Health Authority, The Lescaze Offices, Shinners Bridge, Dartington, Totnes TQ9 6JE Tel: 01803 866665 Fax: 01803 861853; 3 Elm Grove, Taunton TA1 1EG Tel: 01823 259819 — MB BCh BAO 1982 NUI; MFPHM RCP (UK) 1990; DObst. RCPI 1984. Cons. Pub. Health Med. Som. HA. Prev: Dir. Med. Servs. Guadalcanal, Solomon Is.s.

O'BRIEN, James Robert c/o The Fermoy Unit, Queen Elizabeth District General Hospital, King's Lynn Tel: 01533 766266 — MB BCh BAO 1960 NUI; MRCPsych 1971; DPM Eng. 1964. (Cork) Cons. Psychiat. W. Norf. & Wisbech HA. Prev: Sen. Regist. Long Gr. Hosp. Epsom; Regist. Whipps Cross Hosp. Leytonstone & Warley Hosp. Brentwood.

***O'BRIEN, Jennifer Mary** Royal Bolton Hospital, Minerva Road, Farnworth, Bolton BL4 0JR Tel: 01204 390390; Catshaw Green Cottage, Catshaw Lane, Millhouse Green, Sheffield S36 9ND — MB BS 1998 Lond.; MB BS Lond 1998; BSc.

O'BRIEN, Mrs Joan Elizabeth Mary Amerique, Castle St., Winchelsea TN36 4HU — MRCS Eng. LRCP Lond. 1950.

O'BRIEN, John Anthony Broad Lane Surgery, 684 Broad Lane, Coventry CV5 7BB Tel: 024 7646 6583 Fax: 024 7669 5972; Rose Cottage, Berryfields, Fillongley, Coventry CV7 8EX Tel: 01676 540312 — MB ChB 1968 Manch.; MRCGP 1977. Clin. Asst. (Obst. & Gyn.) Coventry Hosps.; Clin. Asst. (Genitourin. Med.) Coventry, Nuneaton & Rugby Hosps.

O'BRIEN, John Ignatius Westgate Surgery, 15 Westgate, Chichester PO19 3ET Tel: 01243 782866 — MB ChB 1990 Aberd.; BSc (Hons.) Lond. 1984; MSc Aberd. 1985, MB ChB 1990; DRCOG; MRCGP. (Kings Coll.) Clin. Asst. Ophthamology, Qu. Alexandra Hosp., Portsmouth.

O'BRIEN, John Joseph 1 Richmond Road, St. John's, Wakefield WF1 3LA — MB BCh BAO 1950 NUI; LM Coombe Hosp. 1951. (Univ. Coll. Dub.)

O'BRIEN, Mr John Michael Brock Hall, Shawbury Lane, Shustoke, Coleshill, Birmingham B46 2SA Tel: 01676 540363 Fax: 01676 541175 — MB BCh BAO 1958 Dub.; MA, MB BCh BAO Dub. 1958; FRCS Eng. 1970; FRCS Ed. 1969. (TC Dub.) Sen. Clin. Lect. (Surg.) Univ. Birm.; Cons. Surg. (Urol.) E. Birm. Gen. Hosp. & Solihull Hosp.; Mem. Panel Examr. RCS Ed. Socs: Brit. Assn. Urol. Surgs. Prev: Clin. Research Fell. Hosp. Sick Childr. Toronto, Canada; Sen. Regist. (Urol. Surg.) W.. Gen. Hosp. Edin.; Regist. (Surg.) Liverp. Roy. Infirm.

O'BRIEN, John Michael Low House, Ridsdale, Hexham NE48 2TF Tel: 01434 270368 Fax: 01434 270368 Email: tja146@aol.com — MB ChB Manch. 1961; FRCP Ed. 1996; Lond. 1990; FFCM 1980, M 1973; FRCPath 1992; FFPHM 1989; DPH (Distinc. & Trevor Lloyd Hughes Gold Medal); FFOM (Hon.) 1993; FFPHMI (Hon.) 1998. Chairm. N.d. HA. Socs: Fell. Roy. Soc. Med.; BMA; Internat. Epidemiol Assn. Prev: Regional Med. Dir. E. Anglian RHA; Area Med. Off. Durh. AHA; Tutor (Clin. Surg.) Univ. Manch.

O'BRIEN, Mr John Patrick 149 Harley Street, London W1N 2DE Tel: 020 7935 4444 Fax: 020 7486 5222 Email: obrien_spine@msn.com; 12 Wyndham Place, London W1H 2PY — MB BS 1960 Sydney; PhD Gothenburg 1975; FRCS Ed. 1966; FRACS 1988; FACS 1977. (Sydney) Socs: Internat. Soc. Study Lumbar Spine; Scoliosis Research Soc.; Cervical Spine Research Soc. Prev: Vis. Prof. Bioeng. Unit Strathclyde Univ. Glas. 1977-85; Dir. (Spinal Disorders) Robt. Jones & Agnes Hunt Orthop. Hosp. OsW.ry; Lect. (Orthop. Surg.) Univ. Hong Kong.

O'BRIEN, John Richard (retired) Glebe Cottage, South Hill, Droxford, Southampton SO32 3PB Tel: 01489 877876 — BM BCh Oxf. 1940; MA Oxf. 1947, BA 1937, DM 1950; FRCP Lond. 1975,

M 1970; MRCS Eng. LRCP Lond. 1940; FRCPath 1964. Hon. Cons. Haemat. Portsmouth & SE Hants. Health Dist. Path. Serv.; Hon. Clin. Reader Experim. Haemat. Soton. Univ. Prev: Cons. Path. S. Devon & E. Cornw. Hosp. Plymouth.

O'BRIEN, John Temple 42 Angel Hill Drive, Sutton SM1 3BX Tel: 020 8641 2917 — MB BChir 1988 Camb.; FRCS Eng. 1994. Specialist Regist. (Radiol.) Mersey. Prev: SHO (Surg.) William Harvey Hosp. Ashford; SHO (Surg.) Manch. Roy. Infirm.

O'BRIEN, John Tiernan Castleside Unit, Newcastle General Hospital, Newcastle upon Tyne NE4 6BE Tel: 0191256 3323 Fax: 0191 219 5051 Email: j.t.o'brien@ncl.ac.uk — BM BCh 1986 Oxf.; MA Camb. 1987; MRCPSych 1990; DM Oxf. 1996. (Oxford) Sen. Lect. & Cons. Old Age Psychiat. Newc. Gen. Hosp. & Univ. Newc. u. Tyne.

O'BRIEN, Joseph Dominic Department of Gastroenterology, Southend Hospital, Prittlewell Chase, Westcliff on Sea SS0 0RY Tel: 01702 221156 Fax: 01702 221379 — MB BS 1979 Lond.; BSc (1st cl. Hons. Physiol.) Lond. 1974, MD 1987; FRCP Lond. 1996. (Lond. Hosp.) Cons. Phys. (Gastroenterol.) S.end Hosp. Trust. Socs: Brit. Soc. Gastroenterol.; BMA. Prev: Sen. Regist. Rotat. W. Midl.; Clin. Research Fell. (Gastroenterol.) Lond. Hosp.; Regist. (Med.) St. Mark's Hosp. Lond.

O'BRIEN, Joyce Margaret (retired) 34 Torcross Road, South Ruislip, Ruislip HA4 0TB — MB BS 1949 Melbourne. Prev: Resid. Med. Off. Qu. Vict. Memor. Hosp. Melb., Austral.

O'BRIEN, Karen Anne 3 Fenwick Terrace, Newcastle upon Tyne NE2 2JQ — MB BS 1988 New South Wales.

O'BRIEN, Katherine 6 Churchwood Road, Didsbury, Manchester M20 6TY — MB ChB 1986 Manch.; MRCP (UK) 1989. Prev: SHO (Gen. Med.) Staffs. Gen. Infirm.

O'BRIEN, Kathrine Mary Courtfield Medical Centre, 73 Courtfield Gardens, London SW5 0NL Tel: 020 7370 2453 Fax: 020 7244 0018 — MB BS 1985 Lond.; BA Oxf. 1982; MB BS (Hons.) Lond. 1985; MRCP (UK) 1988; DRCOG 1989.

O'BRIEN, Kevin (retired) 23 The Spinney, Handsworth Wood, Birmingham B20 1NR — MB ChB 1941 Aberd.; DLO Eng. 1947. Prev: Regist. ENT Dept. United Birm. Hosps.

O'BRIEN, Laurence Stephen Ferndale Unit, University Hospital Aintree, Longmoor Lane, Liverpool L9 7AL — MB ChB 1979 Liverp.; MRCS Eng. LRCP Lond. 1979; MRCPsych 1985. (Liverp.) Clin. Dir. Ment. Health Servs., Aintree Hosp. NHS Trust, Liverp.

O'BRIEN, Margaret Deirdre The Queen Elizabeth Hospital, The Fermoy Unit, Gayton Road, King's Lynn PE30 4ET Tel: 01553 766266 — MB BCh BAO 1959 NUI; FRCPsych 1996, M 1972; DPM Eng. 1964; DCH NUI 1961; DObst RCOG 1960; Dip. Obst. Cork 1960. (Cork) Cons. Psychiat. King's Lynn & Norwich Health Dists. Prev: Sen. Regist. Banstead Hosp. Sutton; Regist. (Psychiat.) Warley Hosp. Brentwood; Ho. Phys. & Ho. Surg. St. Finbarr's Hosp. Cork.

O'BRIEN, Margaret Mary 36 Lanyon Road, Playing Place, Truro TR3 6HF — MB BCh BAO 1994 Belf.

O'BRIEN, Marion Kathryn New Court Surgery, Borough Fields, Wootton Bassett, Swindon SN4 7AX Tel: 01793 852302 — MB BCh BAO 1991 NUI; MRCGP Lond. 1998; DGM RCP Lond. 1997; DCH RCP Lond. 1996. (Univ. Coll. Cork) GP NewCt. Surg. Wootton Bassett; Clin. Asst. Dept. Gastroenterol. P.ss Margt. Hosp. Swindon.

O'BRIEN, Martin Joseph Brock End Surgery, Potton, Sandy SG19 2QS Tel: 01767 261777; 21 The Square, Potton, Sandy SG19 2NP Tel: 01767 261656 — MB BCh BAO 1992 NUI; MRCAP 1996; DObst RCPI 1995. (Univ. Coll. Dub.)

O'BRIEN, Mary 5 Kingsley Road, Dentons Green, St Helens WA10 6JN — MB BCh BAO 1938 NUI.

O'BRIEN, Mary Bridget 55 Marian Terrace, Killarney, Newtown — MB BCh BAO 1985 NUI.

O'BRIEN, Mary Elizabeth Rose Royal Marsden Hospital, Downs Rd, Sutton SM2 5PT Tel: 020 7352 8171; 115 Faraday Road, London SW19 8PA — MB BCh BAO 1980 Dub.; MD Dub. 1990; MRCP (UK) 1983. Sen. Regist. (Med. Oncol.) Roy. Marsden Hosp.; Cons. (Med. Oncol.) Roy. Marsden Hosp.; Cons. (Med. Oncol.) Kent Cancer Centre. Socs: ACP; ASCO; IASLC. Prev: Research Regist. Birm.; Regist. (Med. Oncol.) Edin.; Foreign Med. Resid. Creteil, France.

O'BRIEN, Mary Sharon Geraldine Department of Gastroenterology, The Central Middlesex Hospital, Acton Lane, London NW10 7NS — MB ChB BAO 1984; MD 1992 NUI; MRCPI 1986. Cons. Physican (Gastroenterol. & Gen. Med.) Centr. Middlx. Hosp. Lond. Prev: Sen. Regist., (Gastroenterol. & Gen. Med.) Centr. Middlx. Hosp. Lond.; Lect. (Gastroenterol.) Middlx. Hosp. Lond.

O'BRIEN, Mary Teresa 5 Heron Place, Johnstone PA5 0RW — MB ChB 1992 Aberd.

O'BRIEN, Michael (retired) Eastville Health Centre, East Park, Eastville, Bristol BS5 6YA Tel: 0117 951 0046 — LRCPI & LM, LRSCI & LM 1957; LRCPI & LM, LRCSI & LM 1957.

O'BRIEN, Michael Dermod Department of Neurology, Guy's Hospital, London SE1 9RT Tel: 020 7955 4499 Fax: 020 7955 4864 Email: michael.obrien@gstt.sthames.nhs.uk — MB BS Lond. 1962; MD Lond. 1973; FRCP Lond. 1981, M 1967; MRCS Eng. LRCP Lond. 1962. (Guy's) Cons. Neurol. Guy's & St. Thos. Hosp. NHS Trust; Hon. Cons. Neurol. Nat. Hosp. for Neurol. & Neurosurg.; Hon. Cons. Neurol. Neurosci.s Centre Kings Healthcare Trust. Socs: Fell. Med. Soc. Lond.; Fell. Roy. Soc. Med.; Assn. Brit. Neurols. Prev: Acad. Regist. Nat. Hosp. Nerv. Dis. Qu. Sq. Lond.; Sen. Regist. Regional Neurol. Centre Newc.; MRC Trav. Fell. (Neurol.) Univ. Minnesota, USA.

O'BRIEN, Michael James 27 South Station Road, Gateacre, Liverpool L25 3QE — MB ChB 1997 Manch.

O'BRIEN, Neil John Daisy Cottage, Front St, Seghill, Cramlington NE23 7TG — MB ChB 1998 Dund.

O'BRIEN, Padraig, OBE (retired) 42 Woodside Court, Dudlow Green Road, Appleton, Warrington WA4 5EH Tel: 01925 262015 — MB BCh BAO 1946 NUI; MD NUI 1963; FRCGP 1969, M 1953; LM Coombe 1948.

O'BRIEN, Patricia Mary (Sheldon) Brock Hall, Shawbury Lane, Shustoke, Birmingham B46 2SA Tel: 01676 540363 Fax: 01676 541175; Brock Hall, Shawbury Lane, Shustoke, Birmingham B46 2SA Tel: 01676 540363 Fax: 01676 541175 — MB ChB 1966 Liverp.; DA Eng. 1972; DObst RCOG 1968. (Liverp.) p/t Clin. Asst. Anaesth. Dept. Birm. Heartlands Hosp. Socs: Assn. Anaesth. Prev: Clin. Asst. (Anaesth.) Heartlands Hosp. Birm.; Regist. (Med.) St. Catherine's Hosp. Birkenhead; SHO (Anaesth.) W.. Gen. Hosp. Edin.

O'BRIEN, Patrick David 30 Jermyn Road, King's Lynn PE30 4AE — MB BCh BAO 1978 NUI; MRCPI 1992; MRCGP 1989; MRCPsych 1988; T(Psychiat.) 1994. (Univ. Coll. Dub.) Cons. Psychiat. Qu. Eliz. Psychiat. Hosp. Birm. Prev: Sen. Regist. (Psychiat.) E. Anglia Higher Psychiat. Train. Scheme; Regist. (Psychiat.) Qu. Eliz. Hosp. Kings Lynn; Ho. Surg. & Ho. Phys. St. Michael's Hosp. Dun Laoghaire.

O'BRIEN, Patrick James M.T.L. Medical Services, 24 Hatton Garden, Liverpool L3 2AN Tel: 0151 227 1874 Fax: 0151 236 5857 — MB ChB 1979 Glas.; AFOM RCP Lond. 1994; MRCGP 1985; T(GP) 1991. Occupat. Phys. M.T.L. Med. Servs. Prev: Occupat. Phys. Company Health Ltd. Blackpool; Med. Adviser Shell UK Ltd.; GP Bootle.

O'BRIEN, Patrick Michael John (retired) Carlrayne, Burley Road, Menston, Ilkley LS29 6NX Tel: 01943 874093 — MB BS 1951 Lond.; MRCP Lond. 1960; MRCS Eng. LRCP Lond. 1951; MRCPsych 1971; DPM Eng. 1957. Indep. GP Ilkley. Prev: Cons. Psychiat. Scalebor Pk. Burley-in-Wharfdale.

O'BRIEN, Professor Patrick Michael Shaughn School of Postgraduate Medicine, Thornburrow Drive, Stoke-on-Trent ST4 7QB — MD 1979 Wales; MB BCh 1972; FRCOG 1991, M 1979. Prof. Univ. Keele; Cons. N. Staffs. Hosp. Prev: Cons./Sen. Lect. Roy. Free Med. Sch.; SHO (Obst.) John Radcliffe Hosp. Oxf.; Regist. (O & G) Middlx. Hosp. Lond. & Brighton Health Dist.

O'BRIEN, Patrick William, VRD (retired) Heath Cottage, Herringswell, Bury St Edmunds IP28 6SS Tel: 01638 750252 — MB ChB 1950 St. And. Med. Adviser Albright & Wilson Ltd.; Surg. Lt.-Cdr. RNR. Prev: Regist. City Gen. Hosp. Sheff.

O'BRIEN, Paul Aloysius 19 Calthorpe Street, London WC1X 0JP — MB BCh BAO 1978 NUI; MSc (Econ.) Lond. 1983; LRCPI & LM, LRCSI & LM 1978; DRCOG 1994.

O'BRIEN, Paul William Martin 151 Cedars Avenue, Coventry CV6 1DP — MB BS 1994 Lond.

O'BRIEN, Richard Andrew Dermod Babbs Farm, Westhill Lane, Watchfield, Highbridge TA9 4RF — MB BS 1987 Lond.; PhD Lond. 1977; BSc (Hons.) Soton. 1973; MRCGP 1991; DRCOG 1991. Socs: BMA.

O'BRIEN, Russell James 98 Adderley Road, Leicester LE2 1WB Tel: 0116 2213 152 Email: rfob@dial.pipex.com; 36 Bowness

O'BRIEN

Avenue, Bromborough, Wirral CH63 0EZ — MB ChB 1994 Leic.; MRCP, UK 1998. Med. Specialist Regist. Leicester. Prev: SHO (A & E) P'boro.

O'BRIEN, Sarah Jane PHLS Communicable Disease Surveillance Centre, 61 Colindale Ave, London NW9 5EQ Tel: 0208 200 6868 Ext: 4422 Fax: 0208 200 7868 — MB BS 1986 Newc.; FFPHM RCP (UK) 1999; MFPHM RCP (UK) 1992; DTM & H RCP Lond. 1989. Cons. Epidemiologist. Socs: Roy. Soc. of Med.; Internat. Epidemiol. Assn.; Brit. Infec. Soc. Prev: Cons. in Pub. Health Med., Scott. Centre for Infec. and Environm. Health and Hon. Sec. Clin, Lect. Univ. of Glas.; Sen. Lect. (Epidemiol. of Infec.) Univ. Birm.; Lect. (Pub. Health Med.) Univ. Newc. u. Tyne.

O'BRIEN, Stephen Gerard Department of Haematology, * *, Newcastle upon Tyne NE1 4LP Tel: 0191 2824743/4262 Fax: 0191 201 0154 Email: s.g.o'brien@ncl.ac.uk — MB ChB 1987 Manch.; BSc (Hons.) Manch. 1985; MRCP (UK) 1990; MRCPath 1997; PhD 1998. Sen.Lect./Hon.Cons.Haem.Univ.Newc. Prev: Lect. (Haemat.) Univ. Wales Coll. Med. Cardiff; Research Fell. LRF Leukaemia Unit Roy. Postgrad. Med. Sch. Hammersmith Hosp. Lond.; Regist. (Haemat.) Hammersmith Hosp. Lond.

O'BRIEN, Mr Terence Edward Brendan (retired) Oakbank, 90 Manchester Road, Accrington BB5 2BN Tel: 01254 233944 — MB ChB 1965 Liverp.; ChM Liverp. 1982; FRCS Ed. 1974; DA Eng. 1972; DObst RCOG 1972. Cons. Surg. Blackburn, Hyndburn & Ribble Valley HA; Arris & Gale Lect. RCS Eng. Prev: Sen. Regist. (Surg.) Manch. AHA (T).

O'BRIEN, Terence Michael (retired) 84 Riseholme Road, Lincoln LN1 3SP Tel: 01522 524953 — MB BS 1951 Lond.; DA Eng. 1958; DObst RCOG 1953.

O'BRIEN, Thomas Gerard 52 Croxteth Hall Lane, Croxteth, Liverpool L11 4UG — MB BCh BAO 1982 NUI; MRCGP 1989; DObst. RCPI 1988; DCH NUI 1986. Trainee GP Crewe.

O'BRIEN, Thomas Patrick 38 Carisbrook Terrace, Chiseldon, Swindon SN4 — MB BCh BAO 1935 Dub.; BSc NUI 1939; DPH 1939; LM 1937. (Univ. Coll. Dub.) Socs: B.M.A. Prev: Ho. Surg. Gt. Yarmouth Gen. Hosp.; Extern Matern. Asst. Coombe Hosp.; Med. Off. Oakwood Hall Sanat. Rotherham.

O'BRIEN, Timothy Desmond 6 The Nook, off Manchester Road, Greenfield, Oldham OL3 Tel: 0145 773859 — MD 1971 NUI; MB BCh BAO 1955. (Cork) Cons. Phys. (Geriat.) Oldham & Dist. Gen. Hosp.

O'BRIEN, Timothy Philip 27 The Fairway, Leeds LS17 7QP — MB ChB 1993 Leeds; BEng. (Hons) Liverp. 1985. SHO (Psychiat.) St. Jas. Univ. Hosp. Leeds.; Airedale VTS (GP). Prev: SHO (Anaesth.); SHO (Paediat.); GP Regist.

O'BRIEN, Mr Timothy Stephen Department of Urology, Churchill Hospital, Oxford OX3 7DL Tel: 01865 225941; 16 Windsor Street, Oxford OX3 7AP Tel: 01865 741086 — BM BCh 1986 Oxf.; MA Camb. 1988; FRCS Lond. 1990. Research Fell. (Urol.) Ch.ill Hosp. Oxf. Socs: Brit. Assn. Urol. Surgs.

O'BRIEN, William, OBE, Maj.-Gen. late RAMC Retd. Kitfield Cottage, Ardingly, Haywards Heath RH17 6UP — MRCS Eng. LRCP Lond. 1941; MD (Distinc.) Lond. 1950, MB BS 1941; FRCP Lond. 1967, M 1948. (Char. Cross) Prev: Cons. Phys. to Army; Sen. Lect. Med. Univ. Coll. Khartoum; Med. Regist. Char. Cross Hosp.

O'BRYAN-TEAR, Charles Gillies 141-9 Staines Road, Hounslow TW3 3JA Tel: 020 8572 7422 Fax: 020 8754 3789; 2 Hereford Mansions, Hereford Road, London W2 5BA Tel: 020 7229 0789 — MB BS 1980 Lond.; BA Camb. 1977; MRCP (UK) 1983; MFPM RCP (UK) 1990. Med. Dir. Bristol-Myers Squibb, Hounslow. Socs: RCP; Brit. Assn. Pharmaceut. Phys.; Fac. Pharmaecut. Med. Prev: Dir. Med. Affairs Sanofi Winthrop Guildford; Dir. Clin. Research Searle Skokie Illinois, USA; Regist. (Med.) St. Mary's Hosp. Lond.

O'BYRNE, Ella Karen 8 Goosebrook Close, Comberbach, Northwich CW9 6BX — MB ChB 1997 Leeds.

O'BYRNE, Evan Paul Michael Ashlea, Market St., Whitworth, Rochdale OL12 8DY — MB BCh BAO 1991 NUI.

O'BYRNE, Mr Graham Arthur 6 Lansdown Drive, Abergavenny NP7 6AW; 8 Wimberley Way, Pinchbeck, Spalding PE11 3RY — MB BS 1977 Lond.; FRCSI 1984.

O'BYRNE, John Joseph Westlands Medical Centre, 20B Westlands Grove, Portchester, Fareham PO16 9AD; 4 Woodstock Close, Fareham PO14 1NW — MB BS 1978 Lond.; MLCOM 1991; MRCGP 1984; DCH RCP Lond. 1982; DRCOG 1983. (Char. Cross)

O'BYRNE, Kenneth John ICRF Clinical Oncology Unit, Churchill Hospital, Headington, Oxford OX3 7LJ — MB BCh BAO 1984 NUI.

O'BYRNE, Kevin Patrick The Health Centre, Lawson Street, Stockton-on-Tees TS18 1HX Tel: 01642 676520 Fax: 01642 614720; 9 Orchard Road, Linthorpe, Middlesbrough TS5 5PN Tel: 01642 819837 — MB BS 1975 Newc.; MRCGP 1979. Prev: Trainee GP Cleveland VTS.

O'BYRNE, Sharon Rose Therese Department of Clinical Pharmacology, St Bartholemew's & The Royal London School of Medicine & Dentistry, Chapterhouse Square, London EC1M 6BQ Tel: 020 7415 3416 Fax: 020 7415 3408 Email: s.r.o'byrne@mds.qmw.ac.uk — MB BCh BAO 1983 NUI; MSc (Clin. Pharm.) Aberd. 1992; MD Dub. 1997; MRCPI 1986. (Univ. Coll. Gallway Irel.) Lect./Gen. Regist. Clin. Pharmacol. St. Barts. Roy. Lond. Sch. Med. & Dent. Prev: Sen. Diabetes/Endocrinol. King's Coll. Hosp.; Postdoctoral Research Fell. Vanderbilt Univ. USA; Med. Regist. Aberd. Roy. Infirm.

O'CALLAGHAN, Abina Catherina P.O. Box 24488, London W5 2XT Tel: 020 8991 8198, 07831 537835 Fax: 020 8991 8198; Fax: 208 991 8198 — MB BS 1977 Lond.; MRCS Eng. LRCP Lond. 1977; FFA RCS Eng. 1981; FRCA Eng. 1981. (Roy. Free) Indep. Cons. Anaesth. & Pain Specialist Lond. Prev: Cons. Anaesth. Centr. Middlx. Hosp.; Clin. & Research Fell. (Paediat. Anaesth.) Toronto Sick Childr. Hosp., Canada; Sen. Regist. (Anaesth.) Middlx., Centr. Middlx. & N.wick Pk. Hosps.

O'CALLAGHAN, Ann Mary Portsmouth Oncology Centre, St Mary's Hospital, Milton Road, Portsmouth PO3 6AD Tel: 023 92 286000 Ext: 3880 Fax: 023 92 866313 Email: ann.ocallaghan@smail01.porthosp.swest.nhs.uk — MB BCh BAO 1988 NUI; MRCPI 1990. (UCD) Cons. in Med. Oncol. Prev: CRC Clin. Research Fell. & Hon. Sen. Regist. (Med. Oncol.) Wessex Med. Oncol. Unit Soton.

O'CALLAGHAN, Catherine Mary c/o Eimear O'Callaghan, 42 Grenfell Road, Maidenhead SL6 1HH — MB BCh BAO 1992 NUI.

O'CALLAGHAN, Christopher Anthony 3 Moorland Avenue, Great Crosby, Liverpool L23 2SN — BM BCh 1989 Oxf.; MA Oxf. 1992, BA (Hons.) 1986; MRCP (UK) 1992; DPhil. Oxford, 1998. (Oxf.) Clin. Lect. Nuffield Dept. Med. Univ. Oxf. Socs: Fell. Roy. Soc. Med.; Renal Assn. Prev: Regist. (Renal Med.) Renal Unit Guy's Hosp. Lond.; SHO (Intens. Care) St. Thos. Hosp. Lond.; SHO (Med.) Hammersmith Hosp. Lond.

O'CALLAGHAN, Christopher Liam School of Medicine, Clinical Sciences Building, Leicester Royal Infirmary PO Box 65, Leicester LE2 7LX — BM BS 1982 Nottm.; DM Nottm. 1992, BMedSci 1980, BM BS 1982; MRCP (UK) 1985; FRCP 1996; FRCPCH 1997. (Nottm.) Sen. Lect. (Child Health) & Hon. Cons. Paediat. Univ. Leicester. Prev: Cons. Thoracic Royd Childr. Hosp. Melbourne, Austral.; Lect. (Child Health) Univ. Nottm.

O'CALLAGHAN, Denis Joseph 65 Jermyn Street, Leicester LE4 6NS Tel: 0116 261340 — MB BCh BAO 1940 NUI. (Cork) Prev: Lt.-Col. RAMC.

O'CALLAGHAN, Desmin Pierce Park Avenue Medical Centre, 166-168 Park Avenue North, Northampton NN3 2HZ Tel: 01604 716500 Fax: 01604 721685 Email: des.ocallaghan@gp-k83042.northants.angeox.nhs.uk — MB BCh BAO 1982 NUI; MRCGP (Distinc.) 1987; DRCOG 1986. Clin. Asst. (Dermat.) Isebrook Hosp. WellingBoro.

O'CALLAGHAN, Eamonn Gabriel Winstree Road Surgery, 84 Winstree Road, Colchester CO3 5QF Tel: 01206 572372 Fax: 01206 764412; Greensleeves, Layer Breton Heath, Colchester CO2 0PP Tel: 01206 330668 — MB BCh BAO 1965 NUI; DObst RCOG 1974. (Univ. Coll. Dub.) Princip.Gen.pract., Visit.clin.asst. Socs: Colchester Med. Soc. Prev: Regist. (O & G) Milit. Hosp. Colchester; Paediat. Ho. Phys. St. Kevin's Hosp. Dub.

O'CALLAGHAN, Ellen Maria Whipps Cross Hospital, Leytonstone, London E11 1NR Tel: 020 8535 6744 Email: maria.o'callaghan@whippsx.nhs.uk; 48 Links Avenue, Gidea Park, Romford RM2 6ND Tel: 01708 782401 — MB BS 1983 Newc.; FRCPCH 1997; MRCP (UK) 1986; FRCP 1997. Cons. Paediat. Whipps Cross Hosp. Lond. Prev: Lect. (Child Health) St. Geo. Hosp. Med. Sch. Lond.; Regist. (Paediat.) Leic. Roy. Infirm. & P'boro. Dist. Hosp.

O'CALLAGHAN, Finbar Joseph Kevin Southampton General Hospital, Southampton SO9 4X7 Tel: 0117 942 7373; 5 Alexandra

Park, Redland, Bristol BS6 6QB — MB ChB 1990 Bristol; MA Oxf. 1988; MRCP (UK) 1993. Research Fell. & Hon. Sen. Regist. (Paediat.) Univ. Bath. Socs: Brit. Paediat. Assn.; BMA. Prev: Clin. Fell. (Neonat.) Hosp. Sick Childr. Toronto, Canada; Regist. (Paediat.) Birm. Childr. Hosp.; SHO (Paediat.) Roy. Hosp. Sick Childr. Bristol.

O'CALLAGHAN, Kathleen Mary Unsworth Medical Centre, Parr Lane, Unsworth, Bury BL9 8JR Tel: 0161 766 4448 Fax: 0161 767 9811; 126 Manchester Road, Accrington BB5 2PD Tel: 01254 235348 — MB ChB 1980 Leeds; MRCGP 1984.

O'CALLAGHAN, Mary Claremont, 2 Church Road, Evington, Leicester LE5 6FA — MB BCh BAO 1973 NUI; DObst RCPI 1979; DCH RCPSI 1975. Med. Off. Leics. AHA (T). Prev: SHO (Paediat.) St. Finbarr's Hosp. Cork & Mercy Hosp. Cork; SHO (Obst.) Erinville Hosp. Cork.

O'CALLAGHAN, Nigel Graham Sowerby and Partners, The Health Centre, Park Road, Tarporley CW6 0BE Tel: 01829 733456 Fax: 01829 730124; Ivy Farm, Tattenhall, Chester CH3 9NH Tel: 01829 770491 Email: nocallagha@aol.com — MB BS 1973 Lond.; Dip. Med. Acupunc. 1995 BMAS. (Roy. Free) Socs: Brit. Acupunc. Soc. Prev: SHO (A & E) Roy. Free Hosp. Lond.; SHO (Paediat.) St. Albans City Hosp.; SHO (O & G) Barnet Gen. Hosp.

O'CALLAGHAN, Patrick 10 Moss Close, Pinner HA5 3AY — MB BCh BAO 1960 NUI.

O'CALLAGHAN, Patrick Anthony Melbourne Street Medical Centre, 56 Melbourne Street, Leicester LE2 0AS Tel: 0116 262 2721; Claremont, 2 Church Road, Evington, Leicester LE5 6FA Tel: 0116 737857 — MB BCh BAO 1974 NUI; DObst RCPI 1979. (Cork) Prev: Trainee Gen. Pract. Leicester Vocational Train. Scheme; Intern S. Infirm. Cork.

O'CALLAGHAN, Patrick Joseph (retired) High Lea, Underwood Road, Alderley Edge SK9 7BR Tel: 01625 584863 — MB BCh BAO 1944 NUI; MB BCh BAO NUI (1st cl. Hons.) 1944; BSc NUI 1935. Prev: Asst. Phys. Castle Hill Hosp. Cottingham.

O'CALLAGHAN, Peter Augustine Department of Cardiological Science, St. Georges Hospital Medical School, Cranmer Terrace, London SW17 0RE — MB BCh 1988 N U Ireland.

O'CALLAGHAN, Sarah Elizabeth Southlea Surgery, 276 Lower Farnham, Aldershot GU11 3RB — MB ChB 1975 Bristol; MRCP (UK) 1978; MRCGP 1980.

O'CALLAGHAN, Timothy James Patrick (retired) The Arches, 515 Yarm Road, Eaglescliffe, Stockton-on-Tees TS16 9BG Tel: 01642 648348 Fax: 01642 866419 Email: typ.ocallaghan@ntlworld.com — MB BS Durh. 1961; DObst RCOG 1964. Prev: Sen. Med. Practitioner Eaglescliffe.

O'CALLAGHAN, Una Catherine Parsons Heath Medical Practice, 35A Parsons Heath, Colchester CO4 3HS Tel: 01206 864395 Fax: 01206 869047; 90 Egret Crescent, Colchester CO4 3FP — MB BCh BAO 1983 NUI; MRCGP 1988; DObst RCPI 1987; DCH NUI 1985.

O'CARROLL, Aisling Anne Woodlands Health Centre, Paddock Wood, Tonbridge TN12 6AR — MB BCh BAO 1991 NUI.

O'CARROLL, Anne-Marie 9 St Mary's Avenue, London E11 2NR — MB BChir 1993 Camb.

O'CARROLL, Aodhan (retired) The Surgery, 91 Dodworth Road, Barnsley S70 6ED Tel: 01226 282535 — MB BCh BAO 1972 NUI.

O'CARROLL, Aongus Finian Ely 97 Browning Road, Manor Park, London E12 — MB BCh BAO 1947 NUI; LM Coombe 1958. (Univ. Coll. Dub.) Med. Off. Refuge Insur. Co. & Britannia Insur. Co. Prev: Sen. Ho. Surg. Peace Memor. Hosp.; Sen. Ho. Phys. Salisbury Gen. Hosp.; Surg. Shaw Savill Shipp. Line.

O'CARROLL, Mr Charles Brian (retired) Fieldway, Woodbine Lane, Illogan, Redruth TR16 4ED — MB BS 1941 Lond.; MB BS Lond. (Hnrs. in Surg.) 1941; FRCS Ed. 1943; MRCS Eng. LRCP Lond. 1941. Prev: Maj. RAMC, Surg. Specialist.

O'CARROLL, Daniel Joseph 14 Patterdale Road, Davyhulme, Manchester M41 7DW — MB ChB 1996 Sheff.

O'CARROLL, Geraldine Teresa 97 Browning Road, Manor Park, London E12 — MB BCh BAO 1948 NUI; DPH Manch. 1956; DPH Eng. 1956. (Galw.) Prev: Ho. Surg. Peace Memor. Hosp. Watford; Med. Off. Pub. Health, Matern. & Child Welf. Servs. Birm.

O'CARROLL, Mary Geraldine Ridingleaze Medical Centre, Ridingleaze, Bristol BS11 0QE Tel: 0117 982 2693 Fax: 0117 938 1707 — MB BCh BAO 1977 NUI.

O'CARROLL, Patrick Joseph Anthony Church Lane Surgery, 24 Church Lane, Brighouse HD6 1AS Tel: 01484 714349 Fax: 01484 720479 — MB BCh BAO 1965 NUI. (Cork) Clin. Asst. (Diabetes) Roy. Infirm. Huddersfield. Prev: Regist. (Gen. Med.) & SHO (O & G) Huddersfield Roy. Infirm.; Regist. (Med.) Huddersfield Roy. Infirm.; SHO (Med. & Geriat.) St. Luke's Hosp. Huddersfield.

O'CARROLL, Timothy Michael 21 Southernhay Road, Leicester LE2 3TN Tel: 0116 270 6221 — MB BS Lond. 1970; MRCS Eng. LRCP Lond. 1970; FRCA 1975; DObst RCOG 1974. (St. Bart.) Cons. Anaesth. Leicester Roy. Infirm.

O'COLMAIN, Brendan Paul O'Colmain and Partners, Fearnhead Cross Medical Centre, 25 Fearnhead Cross, Fearnhead, Warrington WA2 0HD Tel: 01925 847000 Fax: 01925 818650 — MB BCh BAO 1974 NUI.

O'CONNELL, Beara Mary Susan Department of Microbiology, Southampton General Hospital, Southampton SO16 6UD Tel: 02380 796412 — LRCPI & LM, LRSCI & LM 1974; LRCPI & LM, LRCSI & LM 1974; Dip. Clin. Microbiol. Lond 1987. Assoc. Specialist (Microbiol.) Soton. Gen. Hosp. Socs: Brit. Soc. Study of Infec.; Assn. Clin. Pathol.; Assn. Med. Microbiol.

O'CONNELL, Brian Augustine 146 Kensington Park Road, London W11 2EP Tel: 020 7221 2725 — MB BCh BAO 1950 NUI; FRCPsych 1971; DPM RCPSI 1953. (Univ. Coll. Dub.) Socs: Founder Mem. Brit. Acad. Foren. Scs.; Trav. Fell. WHO. Prev: Med. Dir. & Cons. Psychiat. N.gate Clinic Lond.; Cons. Psychiat. Hammersmith & Fulham Health Auth. (T); Hon. Cons. Psychiat. St. Geo. Hosp. Lond.

O'CONNELL, Bridget 4 The Priory, Priory Park, London SE3 9XA Tel: 020 8852 3157 — MD NUI 1964, MB BCh BAO 1956; MRCP Lond. 1964; MRCP Ed. 1964; DCH Eng. 1960; FRCP (Ed.) 1997; FRCPCH 1997. (Cork) Hon. Cons. Paediat. Redbridge & N. Thames Health Auth. Socs: BMA; Fell. Roy. Soc. Med.; Fac. Paediat. Prev: Sen. Regist. (Paediat.) Hosp. Sick Childr. Gt. Ormond St. Lond.; Sen. Regist. (Paediat.) Lond. Hosp.; Lect. in Paediat. Dept. Physiol. Lond. Hosp. Med. Coll.

O'CONNELL, Cormac Roderic William 42 High Street, Sutton, Ely CB6 2RB — MB BCh BAO 1978 NUI; LRCPI & LM, LRCSI & LM 1977. (RCSI)

O'CONNELL, Daniel, KM, KCSG (retired) 17 Rosscourt Mansions, 13 Buckingham Palace Road, London SW1W 0PR Tel: 020 7834 5121 — MB BCh BAO 1945 Dub.; MD Dub. 1957; FRCR 1975; FFR RCSI 1962; FFR 1958; DMR Lond 1948. Prev: i/c Radiother. Dept. Char. Cross Hosp. Lond.

O'CONNELL, David Michael 321 Tettenhall Road, Wolverhampton WV6 0JZ; 1 Chilgrove Gardens, Tettenahll, Wolverhampton WV6 8XP — MB ChB 1966 Bristol.

O'CONNELL, Edmund Joseph (retired) Inniscarra, Old Bath Road, Sonning-on-Thames, Reading RG4 6TE — MB BCh BAO 1943 NUI. Prev: Med. Adviser AdW. Engin., W.ern Thompson Controls & Harris Lebus.

O'CONNELL, Elizabeth Philomena Genitourin Clinic, District General Hospital, Stafford; The Hall, Bednall, Stafford ST17 0SA Tel: 01785 712621 Fax: 01785 661064 Email: docshall@compuserve.com — MB BCh BAO 1977 NUI; DPH NUI 1981; DCH NUI 1980. (Univ. Coll .Cork) Staff Grade, GuGenitourin. Med., Dist. Gen. hosp. Stafford; Clin. Asst. N. Stafford Hosp. Stoke-on-Trent.

O'CONNELL, Francis Joseph (retired) 8 Down End Road, Drayton, Portsmouth PO6 1HT — MB BS Lond. 1955; DObst RCOG 1957.

O'CONNELL, Geoffrey Camowen Cottage, Omagh BT79 0DL — LM 1958 Rotunda; LAH Dub. 1956.

O'CONNELL, Gillian Sawrey Ground, Hawshead Hill, Ambleside LA22 0PP — MB ChB 1977 Dundee; FFA RCS Eng. 1983; DA Eng. 1979. Clin. Asst. (Anaesth.) N.wick Pk. Hosp. Middlx. Prev: Clin. Asst. & Regist. (Anaesth.) Lancaster Roy. Infirm.

O'CONNELL, Ian Patrick Michael Dept of Medicine, Royal Albert Edward Infirmary, Wigan Lane, Wigan WN1 2NN Tel: 01942 822292 — MB ChB 1987 Manch.; BSc (Hons.) St. And. 1984; MRCP (UK) 1991. Cons. Phys. (Diabetes & Endocrinol., Gen. Med.) Roy. Albert Edwd. Infirm. Wigan. Socs: RCP Edin.; Soc. Endocrinol.; Brit. Diabetic Assn. (Med. & Scientif. Sect.). Prev: Specialist Regist. (Endocrinol. & Gen. Med.) Hope Hosp. Salford; Research Fell. NW Injury Research Centre Salford; Regist. (Endocrinol. & Gen. Med.) Hope Hosp. Salford.

O'CONNELL, Janet Elisabeth City Hospital NHS Trust, Dudley Road, Birmingham B18 7QH Tel: 0121 554 3801 Ext: 5111 Fax: 0121 507 4557 — MB ChB 1976 Dundee; FRCS (Gen.) Ed. 1984;

O'CONNELL

FRCS (Oto.) Ed. 1986; O.R.L. 1996 Intercollegiate Examination: Cons. Otolaryngologist City Hosp. NHS Trust Birm. Socs: BMA; Brit. Assn. Paediat. Otol.; Brit. Assn. of Head and Neck Surg.s.

O'CONNELL, Janice Elizabeth Sunderland Royal Hospital, Sunderland SR4 7TP Tel: 0191 565 6256 Fax: 0191 569 9238 — MB ChB 1985 Glas.; MRCP (UK) 1988; FRCP 1998; FRCP 1999. Sen. Lect. (Geriat. Med.) Univ. Newc. Prev: Cons. Phys. (c/o Elderly) S. Tyneside Dist. Hosp.

O'CONNELL, John Francis 2 Old Court House, 24 Old Court Place, London W8 4PD Tel: 020 7937 6480 Fax: 020 7937 6480 — LRCPI & LM, LRCSI & LM 1954; MICGP; FRSM. (Royal College of Surgeons, Dublin) Med. Edr. (Irish Med. Times). Socs: Fell. Roy. Acad. Med. Irel.; Irish Coll. Gen. Pract.; Fell. Roy. Soc. Med. Prev: Resid. (Internal Med.) St. Rita's Hosp. Lima Ohio, USA; Regist. (Cardiol.) Mater Miser. Hosp. Dub.

O'CONNELL, Mr John Michael 46 Vanderbilt Road, London SW18 3BQ — MB BS 1984 Lond.; MPhil Sussex 1993; BSc Lond. 1981; FRCS (Orl.) 1996; FRCS (Otol.) 1990. (Westm.) Cons. ENT & Facial Plastic Surg., Brighton Healthcare NHS Trust, Brighton.; Edit. Bd. ENT News. Socs: Fell. Roy. Soc. Med.; Brit. Assn. Otol. Head & Neck Surg.; Coun. Mem. Europ. Acad. of Facial Plast. Surgs. Prev: Sen. Regist. Roy. Nat. Throat, Nose & Ear Hosp. Lond.; Sen. Regist. (Paediat. Otolaryngol.) Gt. Ormond St. Hosp.; SHO (Surg.) Profess. Unit Roy. Marsden Hosp. Lond.

O'CONNELL, John Paul Tramways Medical Centre, 54 Holme Lane, Sheffield S6 4JQ Tel: 0114 234 3418 Fax: 0114 285 5958 — MB ChB 1985 Sheff.

O'CONNELL, John Philip James 73 Harley Street, London W1N 1DE Tel: 07850 312252 Fax: 0208 788 8026 Email: johnpcon@aol.com; 69 Medfield St, Roehampton, London SW15 4JY — MB BS 1970 Lond.; FRCP Lond. 1991; MRCP (UK) 1976; MRCS Eng. LRCP Lond. 1970; FRCPCH 1999; DA 1974 Glasgow. (Middx. Hosp.) Cons. Paediat.Childr.'s Trust; Cons. Paediat. Epsom & St. Helier NHS Trust. Prev: Cons. Paediat. Epsom Health Care NHS Trust Lond.; Nat.Peadiat.Governm.Vanatu; Cons.peadiat/Sen. Lect. Child Health Fiji Sch. of Med.

O'CONNELL, Mary Agnes 190 Uppingham Road, Leicester LE5 0QG Tel: 0116 276 6605; 13 Beechwood Close, Evington, Leicester LE5 6SY Tel: 0116 241 9740 — MB BCh BAO 1976 NUI; DCH NUI 1979; DObst RCPI 1978. (Univ. Coll. Dub.) Prev: SHO (Med.) Midl. Health Bd. Irel.; SHO (Paediat.) Coombe Hosp. Dub. & Mercy Hosp. Cork.

O'CONNELL, Mary Elizabeth Ann Department of Radiotherapy, New Guy's House, Guy's Hospital, St Thomas' St., London SE1 9RT Tel: 020 7955 4400 Fax: 020 7955 4828; Flat 1 Ashleigh Court, 81 Lawrie Pk Road, Sydenham, London SE26 6EX Tel: 020 8659 9598 Fax: 020 8659 9598 — MB BS 1981 Lond.; MD Lond. 1993; MRCP (UK) 1984; FRCR 1989. (Roy. Free) Cons. Radiother. & Oncol. Guy's and St Thomas's Cancer Centre Lond. Socs: Fell. Roy. Coll. Radiol.; Brit. Inst. Radiol.; Eur. Soc. Therap. Radiol. & Oncol. Prev: Sen. Regist. (Clin. Oncol.) Addenbrooke's Hosp. Camb.; Hon. Sen. Regist. & Research Fell. (Radiother.) Roy. Marsden Hosp. Sutton; Regist. (Radiother.) Roy. Marsden Hosp.

O'CONNELL, Mary Susanna Paynes Farm House, Salcott-cum-Virley, Maldon CM9 8HG — MB BS 1981 Lond.; MRCS Eng. LRCP Lond. 1980; DRCOG 1983. (Char. Cross Hosp.)

O'CONNELL, Maureen Patricia c/o 1 Avington Close, London Road, Guildford GU1 1SL — MB BS 1964 Lond.; MRCS Eng. LRCP Lond. 1964; DObst RCOG 1966. (Roy. Free)

O'CONNELL, Maurice Charles Beacon Surgery, Beacon Road, Crowborough TN6 1AF Tel: 01892 652233 Fax: 01892 668840; 6 Beacon Gardens, Crowborough TN6 1BD Tel: 01892 663418 — MB BS 1978 Lond.; DRCOG 1982; DA Eng. 1980.

O'CONNELL, Michael Patrick 80 Ashdene Close, Gorton Road, Willerby, Hull HU10 6LW — MB BCh BAO 1989 NUI.

O'CONNELL, Morgan Ross, Surg. Capt. RN Combat Stress/Ex-Servicement's Mental Welfare Society, Tyrwhitt House, Oaklawn Road, Leatherhead KT22 0BX; Wickham House, Wickham, Fareham PO17 5JG Tel: 01329 834512 Fax: 01329 835150 Email: sprint@athene.co.uk — MB BCh BAO 1968 NUI; FRCPsych 1990, M 1976; DPM Eng. 1974. (Galw.) Chief Cons. Psychiat. Combat Stress/Ex- Serv.men's Ment. Welf. Soc.; Hon. Cons. Psychiat. RNLI. Socs: BMA; Fell., Roy. Soc., of Med.; Intern. Soc. Traum. Stress Studies. Prev: Cons. Adviser, Psychiat. to the Med. Dir. Gen. (Roy.

Navy); Cons. Psych. Roy. Naval Hosp. Haslar, Gosport, Hants.; PMO HMS Fearless.

O'CONNELL, Niall John Woodley Centre Surgery, 106 Crockhamwell Road, Woodley, Reading RG5 3JY Tel: 0118 969 5011 Fax: 0118 944 0382 — MB BS 1980 Lond.; LLM 1991; FRCGP 1995, M 1989; DRCOG 1984. (St. Mary's) Socs: Fell: Roy. Soc. Med.; BMA. Prev: SHO (Accid. & Traum. Surg.) Roy. Berks. Hosp. Reading; SHO (Obst.) Heatherwood Hosp.

O'CONNELL, Nicola Margaret 82 Moor Drive, Liverpool L23 2US — MB ChB 1998 Liverp.

O'CONNELL, Nuala Maria Department Laboratory Medicine, Salisbury District Hospital, Salisbury SP2 8BJ Tel: 01722 336262 — MB ChB 1980 Manch. Assoc. Specialist (Laborat. Med.).

O'CONNELL, Olivia 3 Woodvale, Ponteland, Newcastle upon Tyne NE20 9JR — MB ChB 1998 Sheff. SHO, A & E, Roy. Vic. Infirm., Newc. Gen. Hosp.,Newc. Prev: Ho. Off.; Roy. Hallanshire Hosp. W.on Pk. Hosp. Sheff.

O'CONNELL, Paul Timothy Joseph St Martins, Griffinstown, Kinnegad, Mullingar, County Westmeath, Republic of Ireland; 22 Egmont Road, Sutton SM2 5JN Tel: 020 8642 4007 — MB BCh BAO 1989 NUI; MRCPsych 1994. Sen. Regist. (Psychiat.) Maudsley Hosp. Lond.

O'CONNELL, Peter James 27 Cricklade Road, Highworth, Swindon SN6 7BW — MB BS 1990 Lond.

O'CONNELL, Rebeccaa 11A Queen Street, Henley-on-Thames RG9 1AR — MB BS 1993 Lond.

O'CONNELL, Shaun Michael 15 Queen's Down, Creech St Michael, Taunton TA3 5QY — BM 1990 Soton.; MRCGP 1995; DCH RCP Lond. 1994.

O'CONNELL, Thomas Joseph (retired) Kilcrea, 34 Laurel Road, St Helens WA10 4AZ Tel: 01744 609211 — MB BCh BAO 1949 NUI; LM Dub. 1953. Prev: Ho. Phys. S. Devon & E. Cornw. Hosp. Plymouth.

O'CONNELL, Una (retired) 17 Rosscourt Mansions, Buckingham Palace Road, London SW1W 0PR Tel: 020 7834 5121 — MB BS Lond. 1948; DMRD Lond 1951. Prev: Cons. Radiol. Sutton & W. Merton (St. Helier) Health Dist.

O'CONNELL, Una Cecilia c/o Cranswich, 5 Dudley Avenue S., Leith, Edinburgh EH6 4PH — MB BCh BAO 1989 NUI.

O'CONNELL, William Joseph (retired) 17 Portchester Road, Fareham PO16 8AN Tel: 01329 822443 — MB ChB Birm. 1953; DLO Eng. 1959. Prev: Ho. Surg. Qu. Eliz. Hosp. Birm.

O'CONNOR, Aidan Patrick The Family Medical Practice, 98 High St., Golborne, Warrington WA3 3DA — MB BCh BAO 1983 NUI. Prev: SHO (Paediat.) Hartlepool Gen. Hosp.; SHO (O & G) Doncaster Roy. Infirm.; Ho. Off. Belf. City Hosp.

O'CONNOR, Alison Mary 64 Park Road, Prestwich, Manchester M25 0FA — MB ChB 1990 Liverp.

O'CONNOR, Andrew 9 Calderstones Road, Liverpool L18 6HR — MB ChB 1992 Liverp.

O'CONNOR, Anthony, LVO (retired) c/o Lloyds Bank plc, 16 Broad St, Ludlow SY8 1NQ — MB BS 1941 Lond.; MRCS Eng. LRCP Lond. 1941; FFA RCS Eng. 1955; DA (UK) 1947. Prev: Dep. Med. Dir. Gen. RN.

O'CONNOR, Anthony Paul (retired) Deddington Health Centre, Earls Lane, Deddington, Banbury OX15 0TQ Tel: 01869 338611 Fax: 01869 37009 — LMSSA 1965 Lond.; MRCGP 1974; DObst RCOG 1970; DFFP 1995. Prev: Lt.-Col. RAMC.

O'CONNOR, Bernadette Sheila 14 Glencree Park, Newtownabbey BT37 0QS — MB BCh BAO 1997 Belf.

O'CONNOR, Brendan Bernard 21 Woodfield Road, Solihull B91 2DN Tel: 0121 704 1308 Email: ocobre@madasafish.com — MB ChB 1987 Birm.; ChB Birm. 1987; BSc Physiol. (Hons.) Birm. 1984; FRCA 1993. Cons. Anaesth. Birm. Heartlands & Solihull NHS Trust. Prev: Sen. Regist. (Anaesth.) Coventry Sch. Anaesth.; Lect. (Anaesth.) Univ. Sheff.; Regist. (Anaesth.) N. Staffs. Hosp. Stoke-on-Trent & Wolverhamton Hosps.

O'CONNOR, Brendan Gerard 6 Butler Place, Belfast BT14 7NY — MB BCh BAO 1990 Belf.; BDS Belf. 1983; MB BCh Belf. 1990.

O'CONNOR, Brendan Hayes East Sussex, Brighton & Hove Health Authority, 36/38 Friars Walk, Lewes BN7 2PB — MB BS 1973 Lond.; FFPHM RCP (UK) 1987, M 1980; T(PHM) 1991. (St. Bart.) Dep. Director of Pub. Health, E. Sussex, Brighton & Hove HA;

Princip. Lect. in Pub. Health, PostGrad. Med. Sch. Univ. of Brighton. Socs: Fell. (Ex-Hon. Sec.) Roy. Soc. Med. (Sect. Epidemiol.). Prev: Dir. Pub. Health E. Sussex HA & E. Sussex FHSA; Dir. Pub. Health Tunbridge Wells HA; Cons. Pub. Health Med. Bloomsbury HA.

O'CONNOR, Brian Dominic Greenbank Drive Surgery, 8 Greenbank Drive, Sefton Park, Liverpool L17 1AW Tel: 0151 733 5703; 69 Dovedale Road, Mossley Hill, Liverpool L18 5EP — MB ChB 1985 Liverp.

O'CONNOR, Brian Joseph Department of Respiratory Medicine, King's College School of Medicine & Dentistry, Bessemer Road, Denmark Hill, London SE5 9RS Tel: 020 7346 3583 Fax: 020 7346 3589 Email: b.o'connor@kcl.ac.uk; 14 Binns Road, Chiswick, London W4 2BS Tel: 020 7640 0945 Fax: 020 7498 4714 — MB BCh 1980 NUI; MRCPI 1984; DCH NUI 1987. (Univ. Coll. Dub.) Cons. Phys. (Respirat. Med.) King's Healthcare Lond.; Sen. Lect. King's Coll. Sch. Med. & Dent. Lond. Socs: Fell. Roy. Soc. Med. (Pres. Counc. Respirat. Sect.); Brit. Thorac. Soc.; Amer. Thoracic Soc. Prev: Cons. Phys. & Sen. Lect. (Thoracic Med.) Roy. Brompton Hosp., Imperial Sch. Med. & Nat. Heart & Lung Inst. Lond.; Lect. (Med.) Univ. Coll. Dub.

O'CONNOR, Mr Brian Thomas Robert Jones & Agnes Hunt Orthopaedic Hospital, Oswestry SY10 7AG Tel: 01691 655311 Fax: 01691 657968; Pen-isa'r Glyn Hall, Bronygarth, Oswestry SY10 7NE Tel: 01691 773523 — MB BS 1952 Queensland; MS Queensland 1964; MChOrth Liverp. 1959; FRCS Eng. 1958; FRACS 1964. (Queensld.) Prof. Orthop. Univ. Birm. at Inst. Orthop. Robt. Jones & Agnes Hunt; Orthop. Hosp. OsW.ry. Socs: Fell. Brit. Orthop. Assn. Prev: Cons. Orthop. Surg. & Dir. Clin. Studies Robt. Jones & Agnes Hunt; Orthop. Hosp. OsW.ry; 1st Asst. Nuffield Dept. Orthop. Surg. Univ. Oxf.

O'CONNOR, Catherine Mary Ita The Surgery, 241 Westbourne Grove, London W11 2SE Tel: 020 7229 5800 Fax: 020 7243 2058 — MB BCh BAO 1970 NUI.

O'CONNOR, David 62B Whartons Lane, Totton, Southampton SO40 7EF — MB BCh 1987 Wales.

O'CONNOR, David Oliver (retired) Cumberland House, Macclesfield SK10 1EG Tel: 01625 28081 — MB BCh BAO 1950 NUI. Prev: Sen. Ho. Surg. St. Martin's Hosp. Bath & Bon Secours Hosp. Cork.

O'CONNOR, Deirdre Mary Elizabeth Limes Medical Centre, The Plain, Epping CM16 6TL Tel: 01992 572727 Fax: 01992 574889 — MB BCh BAO 1975 NUI; MRCGP 1981; DObst RCPI 1979; DCH RCPSI 1979; Cert. Family Plann. JCC 1979.

O'CONNOR, Dermot Charles The Surgery, 30 Old Road West, Gravesend DA11 0LL Tel: 01474 351557 Fax: 01474 333952 — MB BCh BAO 1973 Dub.; BA; MRCGP 1979. (TC Dub.) GP Gravesend.; Covenor Dartford & Gravesham Trainers Gp. Prev: Ho. Off. (Surg.) & Ho. Off. (Med.) & Research Fell. in Vasc. Dis. Sir; P. Dun's Hosp. Dub.

***O'CONNOR, Dominic James** 1 Preston Close, Stanton under Bardon, Markfield LE67 9TX — MB ChB 1995 Manch.

O'CONNOR, Eric Joseph Michael (retired) 25 Minterne Avenue, Norwood Green, Southall UB2 4HW Tel: 020 8574 1727 — LRCPI & LM, LRSCI & LM 1949; LRCPI & LM, LRCSI & LM 1949; DCH RCPSI 1951.

O'CONNOR, Mr Fergus ENT Out Patient Department, Fairfield General Hospital, Rochdale Old Road, Bury BL9 7TD Tel: 0161 705 3671 Fax: 0161 705 3671 Email: ferguentryoc@hotmail.com; 12 Nabbs Fold, Greenmount, Bury BL8 4EH Tel: 0120 488 6418 Fax: 0161 705 3671 — MRCS Eng. LRCP Lond. 1964; FRCS Ed. 1970; FRCS Eng. ad eundem 1998. (Manch.) Cons. Surg. (ENT) Bury Gen. Hosp. & Birch Hill Hosp. Rochdale. Socs: Fell. Manch. Med. Soc.; Fell. Roy. Soc. Med. Prev: Sen. Regist. (ENT) Univ. Hosp. Wales Cardiff; Regist. (ENT) Liverp. ENT Infirm.; SHO (Surg.) Manch. Roy. Infirm.

O'CONNOR, Frances Patricia Carteknowle and Dore Medical Practice, 1 Carterknowle Road, Sheffield S7 2DW Tel: 0114 255 1218 Fax: 0114 258 4418 — MB BS 1986 Lond.

O'CONNOR, Francis Alexander Altnagelvin Area Hospital, Londonderry BT47 1JD Tel: 02871 345171; Tel: 01504 352188 — FACG (US); MB BCh BAO Belf. 1969; MD Belf. 1976; FRCP Lond. 1987; MRCP (UK) 1972; FRCP(I) 1997. (Belf.) Cons. Phys. & Gastroenterol. Altnagelvin Hosp. Lond.derry; Hon. Sen. Lect. Qu.'s Univ. Belf. Socs: Brit. & Irish Soc. Gastroenterol.; Amer. Coll.

Gastroenterol.; Amer. Soc. Dig. Endoscop. Prev: Sen. Tutor (Med.) Qu. Univ. Belf.; Sen. Fell. (Gastroenterol.) Univ. Washington Seattle, USA; Research Fell. Roy. Vict. Hosp. Belf.

O'CONNOR, Francis Anthony The Surgery, 9 Albion Street, Brighton BN2 2PS Tel: 01273 601122/601344 Fax: 01273 623450; 87 Stanford Avenue, Brighton BN1 6FA Tel: 01273 509535 — MB ChB 1980 Sheff.; RGN 1970; RMN 1968.

O'CONNOR, Graham John 6 Stretton Close, Birkenhead CH43 0XG — MB ChB 1994 Liverp.

O'CONNOR, Ian Oldcastle Surgery, South Street, Bridgend CF31 3ED Tel: 01656 657131 Fax: 01656 657134; Tyle Cottage, Penllyn, Cowbridge CF71 7RQ — MB BS 1990 Lond.; BSc (Hons.) Lond. 1986; MRCGP 1996; DCH RCP Lond. 1994. (St. Mary's) Socs: BMA; Brain Res. Assn.

O'CONNOR, Mr Ivan Mathew Thomas James, Group Capt. RAF Med. Br. Retd. (retired) 2 Vicarage Close, Wendover, Aylesbury HP22 6DS — MB BCh BAO 1942 NUI; BSc NUI 1944; MCh 1949, DPH 1944; FCOphth 1990; DOMS Eng. 1948; FRCOphth. Prev: Cons. Adviser Ophth. RAF.

O'CONNOR, James Azurdia and Partners, Bebington Health Centre, Civic Way, Bebington, Wirral CH63 7RX Tel: 0151 645 6936 Fax: 0151 643 1698; Merlewood, 73 Church Road, Bebington, Wirral CH63 3EA Tel: 0151 334 2585 — MB ChB 1974 Liverp.; DRCOG 1977. GP Princip.; Sec. Wirral Local Med. Comm. Socs: BMA; Birkenhead Med. Soc. Prev: Trainee GP Wirral VTS; Ho. Phys. & Ho. Surg. Wirral AHA.

O'CONNOR, James Patrick Bernard 10 Moss Lane, Timperley, Altrincham WA15 6SZ — MB BS 1998 Lond.

O'CONNOR, Janet Elizabeth Rosemary Medical Centre, 2 Rosemary Gardens, Parkstone, Poole BH12 3HF Tel: 01202 741300 Fax: 012020 721868 — MB BS 1970 Lond.; MRCS Eng. LRCP Lond. 1970; DObst RCOG 1974; DA Eng. 1972. (Univ. Coll. Hosp.) Prev: Clin. Med. Off. (Paediat.) E. Dorset HA; SHO (Anaesth. & Paediat.) P'boro. Dist. Hosp.; SHO (O & G) Poole Gen. Hosp.

O'CONNOR, Jayne Lesley Burley Park Medical Centre, 273 Burley Road, Leeds LS4 2EL Tel: 0113 275 9458; 9 Larchwood, Woodlands Drive, Rawdon, Leeds LS19 6JZ Tel: 0113 239 1716 — MB ChB 1984 Leeds. Socs: Assoc. Mem. Inst. Psychosexual Med. Prev: Regtl. Med. Off. 1 Glosters BFPO 45.

O'CONNOR, Joan Mary Ladybarn Group Practice, 177 Mauldeth Road, Fallowfield, Manchester M14 6SG Tel: 0161 224 2873 Fax: 0161 225 3276; 12 Ferndene Road, Manchester M20 4TT Tel: 0161 434 5148 — MB ChB 1990 Manch.; MRCGP 1995; DCH RCP Lond. 1993; DRCO Lond. 1993; Dip Family Plann Lond. 1993; Dip Pract Dermatol 1997. (Manc.) Princip. in Gen. Pract. Socs: MRCGP. Prev: Regist. GP Withershawe; SHO Withershawe UTS.

O'CONNOR, John Brendan Grove Village Medical Centre, 4 Cleeve Court, Grove Village, Bedfont, Feltham TW14 8SN Tel: 020 8751 6282; 3 Churchill Avenue, Harrow HA3 0AX — LRCPI & LM, LRSCI & LM 1961; LRCPI & LM, LRCSI & LM 1961.

O'CONNOR, John Charles Rosemary Medical Centre, 2 Rosemary Gardens, Parkstone, Poole BH12 3HF Tel: 01202 741300 — MB BS 1971 Lond.; MRCGP 1976; DObst RCOG 1975. (Univ. Coll. Hosp.) Clin. Asst. (Dermat.) Poole Gen. Hosp. Prev: GP Tutor & Trainee Course Organiser Poole.

O'CONNOR, Karen Ruth Heeley Green Surgery, 302 Gleadless Road, Sheffield S2 3AJ Tel: 0114 250 0309 Fax: 0114 250 7185 — MB ChB 1984 Sheff.; MRCGP 1994; DFFP 1993.

O'CONNOR, Katharine Mary 54 Canbury Avenue, Kingston upon Thames KT2 6JR — MB BS 1984 Lond.; MRCGP 1989; DRCOG 1988.

O'CONNOR, Kathleen Ann 41 Slaidburn Street, Chelsea, London SW10 0JW — MB BCh BAO 1979 NUI.

O'CONNOR, Kerry Michael Endless Street Surgery, 72 Endless Street, Salisbury SP1 3UH Tel: 01722 336441 Fax: 01722 410319 — MB ChB 1979 Bristol; BSc Bristol 1976, MB ChB 1979; MRCGP 1985; MRCOG 1984. Prev: Trainee GP Portishead Health Centre; SHO (Geriat.) Ham Green Hosp.; SHO (O & G) Bristol Matern. Hosp.

O'CONNOR, Kerstin Birgit 154 Silverhere Road, Catford, London SE6 4QT — MB ChB 1996 Leic.

O'CONNOR, Leo Declan Williams, O'Connor and Morgan, New Quay Surgery, Church Road, New Quay SA45 9PB Tel: 01545 560203 Fax: 01545 560916; Vaynor, High St, New Quay SA45 9NY Tel: 01545 560203 — MB BCh BAO 1984 NUI; DCH NUI 1986.

O'CONNOR

O'CONNOR, Louise Margaret 65 Gleneagles Road, Urmston, Manchester M41 8SB — MB ChB 1994 Leeds.

O'CONNOR, Margaret Thanet, 257 Abington Avenue, Northampton NN3 2BU Tel: 01604 713542 — LRCPI & LM, LRSCI & LM 1934; LRCPI & LM, LRCSI & LM 1934. Sch. Med. Off. N.ants.

O'CONNOR, Margaret Mary 8 Homelands Road, Sale M33 4BE — MB ChB 1998 Liverp.

O'CONNOR, Mark Dennis 85 Aylward Road, Merton Park, London SW20 9AJ — MB BS 1989 Lond.

O'CONNOR, Mary Brigid 46 Poppythorn Lane, Prestwich, Manchester M25 3BY — BM BS 1992 Nottm.

O'CONNOR, Mary Gerardine Royal Belfast Hospital for Sick Children, 180 Falls Road, Belfast BT12 6BE Tel: 028 9029 0503 Ext: 3976; 2 Sharman Road, Stranmills, Belfast BT9 5FW — MB BCh BAO 1984 Belf.; MRCP (UK) 1988. Cons. Paediat. (Nephrol.) Roy. Belf. Hosp. Sick Childr. Prev: Sen. Regist. (Paediat. Nephrol.) S.mead Hosp. Bristol.

O'CONNOR, Mary Regina Anaesthetic Department, Southern General Hospital, Glasgow G51 4TF Tel: 0141 201 1100; Tel: 0141 636 0493 Email: regina@quinn71.freeserve.co.uk — MB BCh BAO 1986 NUI; FFA RCSI 1990. Cons. Anaesth. Gtr. Glas. HB. Prev: Sen. Regist. & Career Regist. (Anaesth.) Gtr. Glas. HB.

O'CONNOR, Michael Department of Anaesthetics, Princess Margaret Hospital, Okus Road, Swindon SN1 4JU Tel: 01793 536231 Fax: 01793 431023 — MB ChB 1978 Bristol; FRCA 1982; T(Anaes.) 1991. Cons. Anaesth. Swindon & MarlBoro. NHS Trust. Socs: Pain Soc.; BMA & Assn. Anaesth. Prev: Sen. Regist. (Anaesth. Nuffield Dept. Anaesth. Oxf.; Sen. Regist. (Anaesth. & Intens. Care) Adelaide, S. Austral.; Regist. (Anaesth.) Sir Humphry Davy Dept. Anaesth. Bristol.

O'CONNOR, Mr Michael Andrew 12 Ferndene Road, Withington, Manchester M20 4TT Tel: 0161 434 5148 Email: mike@oconn49.freeserve.co.uk — MB ChB 1989 Manch.; FRCS Ed. 1994. Orthop. Specialist Regist., Mersey Region, Liverp.

O'CONNOR, Michael John Christopher 5 Viewpoint, Sandbourne Road, Alum Chine, Bournemouth BH4 8JP — MB BS 1981 Lond.; MRCS Eng. LRCP Lond. 1981. (Guy's)

O'CONNOR, Michael Pearse 47 Albany Road, New Malden KT3 3NY — MB BCh BAO 1991 NUI.

O'CONNOR, Niall Cormack 304 Pendelbury Drive, Leicester LE2 6HY — MB BCh BAO 1982 NUI; MRCGP 1989.

O'CONNOR, Niall Finbarr Dublin Road Surgery, 4 Dublin Road, Castlewellan, Newcastle BT31 9AG Tel: 028 4372 3221 Fax: 028 4372 3162 — MB BCh BAO 1979 NUI; MRCGP 1983; DRCOG 1983.

O'CONNOR, Nigel Timothy James 82 The Mount, Shrewsbury SY3 8PN Tel: 01743 343068 Fax: 01743 343068 — MB BS 1977 Lond.; MD Lond. 1986; FRCP Lond. 1996; MRCP (UK) 1981; MRCPath 1988. (St. Thos.) Cons. Haemat. Roy. Shrewsbury Hosp. Prev: Sen. Regist. Roy. Free Hosp. Lond.; MRC Train. Fell. Nuffield Dept. Med. John Radcliffe Hosp. Oxf.; Regist. (Gen. Med.) Norf. & Norwich Hosp.

O'CONNOR, Patricia Accident & Emergency Unit, Hairmyres Hospital, East Kilbride, Glasgow G75 8RG Tel: 014120292; Nethershields Farm, Quarter, Hamilton ML3 7XP — MB ChB 1987 Dundee; MRCP (UK) 1990; FRCS A&E 1995. (Dundee) Cons. (A & E) Hairmyres Hosp. Hairmyres E. Kilbride. Socs: BAEM; BMA.

O'CONNOR, Patricia Moira Flat 5, Greencroft Gardens, London NW6 3LP — MB ChB 1988 Cape Town.

O'CONNOR, Patrick Denis Hugh 41 Wallace Road, London N1 2PQ; Friary View, Kildare, Republic of Ireland Tel: 0145 21218 — MB BCh BAO 1986 Dub.; MRCOG 1992; MRCPI 1989; DCH NUI 1987. Research Regist. (Gyn. Endoscopic Surg.) Roy. Free Hosp. Lond. Prev: Regist. Rotat. Univ. Coll. Hosp. Lond.; SHO (Obst.) Qu. Charlottes Hosp.; SHO Rotat. (O & G) Rotunda & Hammersmith Hosp.

O'CONNOR, Patrick Joseph Gilbert Bain Hospital, Lerwick Tel: 01595 743000 — MB ChB 1989 Leeds; FRCA 1995. Cons. Anaesth.

O'CONNOR, Peter Francis Michael (retired) 75 The Ridgeway, Watford WD17 4TJ — MB BS 1964 Lond.; MRCS Eng. LRCP Lond. 1963; FRCOG 1989, M 1970. Prev: GP Watford.

O'CONNOR, Philip James Missy Cottage, Crag Lane, Huby, Leeds LS17 0BW — MB ChB 1987 Manch.

O'CONNOR, Phillip Joseph 33 Killeaton Park, Dunmurry, Belfast BT17 9HE — MB BCh 1998 Belf.

O'CONNOR, Rory Daniel 46 Poppythorn Lane, Prestwich, Manchester M25 3BY Tel: 0161 773 1603 — MB ChB 1990 Manch.; MSc Robert Gordon Aberd. 1998; DTM & H Liverp. Med. Off. Brit. Antarctic Survey. Prev: SHO (A & E) Stoke Mandeville Hosp.

O'CONNOR, Ruth Christine 1 Hermitage Close, Appley Bridge, Wigan WN6 9JQ — MB ChB 1988 Ed.; MRCP (UK) 1991.

O'CONNOR, Simon Philip John The Hollies Medical Centre, 20 St. Andrews Road, Sheffield S11 9AL Tel: 0114 255 0094 Fax: 0114 258 2863 — BM 1986 Soton.

O'CONNOR, Simon Roderick Department of Histopathology, Leicester Royal Infirmary, Leicester LE1 5WW Tel: 0116 254 1414; Chehalis, Ballyglan, Woodstown, Waterford, Republic of Ireland — MB BCh BAO 1993 NUI; Dip RCPath 1998. (University College Dublin)

O'CONNOR, Siobhan Anne Downshire Hospital, Ardglass Road, Downpatrick BT30 6RA Tel: 01396 613311 Email: siobhanoconnor@msn.com — MB BCh BAO 1977 Belf.; MMedSci (Psychother.) 1989; MRCPsych 1984; DRCOG 1980. Cons. Psychiat. Psychotherap. Downshire Hosp. Downpatrick. Prev: Sen. Regist. (Psychother.) Day Hosp. Belf.

O'CONNOR, Susan Barrow Hospital, Long Ashton, Bristol BS48 3SG Tel: 0117 939 2811; Yew Tree House, Brinsea Road, Congresbury, Bristol BS49 5JQ — MB BChir 1975 Camb.; BA Camb. 1972, MB BChir 1975; MRCPsych 1981. Clin. Dir. Ment. Health Servs. United Bristol Healthcare Trust.

O'CONNOR, Timothy John 4 Beauford House, The Hollow, Bamford, Hope Valley S33 0AU — MB BCh BAO 1955 NUI. (Cork) Socs: BMA. Prev: Ho. Off. St. Luke's Matern. Hosp. Bradford.

O'CONNOR, Helen Mary Nell Saltway Farm, Northleach, Cheltenham GL54 3QB Tel: 01285 720110 — MB BS 1975 Lond.; MRCS Eng. LRCP Lond. 1975. (St. Mary's) Prev: Med. Dir. Hospice of St. Francis Berkhamsted.

O'CUILL, Micheil Bhaillintin Bensham General Hospital, Saltwell Road, Gateshead NE8 8YL — MB BCh BAO 1986 NUI.

O'DAIR, Graham Nelson 4 Avondale Gardens, West Bolden, East Boldon NE36 0PR — MB ChB 1994 Manch.

O'DAIR, Jonathan David 4 Avondale Gardens, West Boldon, East Boldon NE36 0PR — MB ChB 1997 Liverp.

O'DALY, Eamon Francis Savile Road Surgery, 90 Savile Road, Savile Town, Dewsbury WF12 9LP Tel: 01924 465725 — LRCPI & LM, LRSCI & LM 1958; LRCPI & LM, LRCSI & LM 1958. (RCSI) GP Dewsbury. Prev: Maj. RAMC, Regtl. Med. Off. Yorks. Brig. Depot Strensall; Ho. Surg. & Ho. Phys. Chesterfield Roy. Hosp.

O'DEA, John Francis c/o Department of Anaesthetics, Dudley Road Hospital, Birmingham B18 7QH Fax: 0121 554 3801 Email: jfod@compuserve.com — MB BCh BAO 1982 NUI; FFA RCSI 1986. (Galway) Cons. Anaesth. & Intens. Care Dudley Rd. Hosp. Birm.; Hon. Clin. Lect., Univ. of Birm. Socs: Intens. Care Soc.; BMA. Prev: Sen. Regist. (Intens. Care Unit) Qu. Eliz. Hosp. Adelaide.

***O'DELL, Susan Mary** 38 Cradock Road, Leicester LE2 1TD Tel: 0116 270 1947 — MB ChB 1994 Leic.

O'DOHERTY, Andrew Hassengate Medical Centre, Southend Road, Stanford-le-Hope SS17 0PH Tel: 01375 673064 Fax: 01375 675196 — MB BS 1989 Lond.; BSc Lond. 1986, MB BS 1989.

O'DOHERTY, Ann Jacinta 17 Oakwood Park, Malone Court, Belfast BT9 6SE — MB BCh BAO 1981 NUI; LRCPI & LM, LRCSI & LM 1981; MRCPI 1983; FFR RCSI 1993; FRCR 1987. Cons. Radiol. Roy. Vict. Hosp. Belf. Prev: Regist. (Radiol.) Roy. Vict. Hosp. Hosp. Belf.

O'DOHERTY, Catherine Anne St. Francis' Hospice, The Hall, Havering-atte-Bower, Romford RM4 1QH — MB BS 1992 Lond.; PhD Camb. 1990; BSc (Hons.) Lond. 1986; MRCP (UK) 1995.

O'DOHERTY, Catherine Mary 8 Kendal Road, Hove BN3 5HZ — MB BCh BAO 1982 Dub.; MB BCh Dubl. 1982; MRCPI 1985.

O'DOHERTY, Conor St John 100 Harley Street, London W1N 1AF Tel: 0208 318 1818 Fax: 0208 265 1690 — MB BCh BAO 1970 NUI; MSc (Lond.) 1980; MRCP (UK) 1979; FRCP 1998. (Nat. Univ. Ire in Dublin) Cons. Dermat. Qu. Eliz. II Hosp. Welwyn Gdn. City & City & Co. Hosp. Hertford. Socs: Fell. Roy. Soc. Med.; Amer. Acad. Dermat.; Brit. Assn. Dermat. Prev: Cons. Dermatol.s N. Middsx

Hosp. Lond.; Lect. (Dermat.) Edin. Univ. Med. Sch.; Sen. Regist. Roy. Infirm. Edin.

O'DOHERTY, Mr Declan Patrick William Department of Orthopaedic Surgery, A4, University of Wales Hospital, Heath Park, Cardiff CF14 4XW Tel: 029 2074 3866 Fax: 029 2074 5399 — MD 1994 Sheff.; MD Univ. Sheff. 1994; MB BS Lond. 1981; FRCS Ed. 1985; MRCS Eng. LRCP Lond. 1981. Cons. Orthop. Surg. Univ. of Wales Hosp. Socs: Fell.Brit. Orthopaedic Assoc.; Brit. Orth. Foot Surg.s Soc.; Brit. Soc. Child Orthopaedic Surg.s. Prev: Lect. (Orthop.) Surg. Sheff.; Clin. Research Fell. (Human Metab. & Clin. Biochem.ry) Sheff.

O'DOHERTY, Kim Saundersfoot Medical Centre, Westfield Road, Saundersfoot SA69 9JW Tel: 01834 812407 Fax: 01834 811131; Tanglewood, Narberth Road, Tenby SA70 8HX — MB BCh 1979 Wales; MA Camb. 1979; MRCGP 1990; Dip. Palliat. Med. Wales 1994; DRCOG 1981.

O'DOHERTY, Moya-Anne Mount Cottage, Shawclough Rd, Rochdale OL12 7HR — MB ChB 1997 Bristol.

O'DOLAN, Carroll Anthony Temple Rusheen, Belcoo, Enniskillen BT93 5DU — MB BCh BAO 1990 Belf.; BAO Belf. 1990; LMCC (Ottawa, 1994); MRCGP (UK) 1997; DCH (UK) 1998; DFFP (UK) 1996. (Queen's Belfast)

O'DONNCHADHA, Benin Padhraic Cliff House, Ferryside SA17 5SP — MB BCh BAO 1979 Dub.; MB BCh Dub. 1979; FFA RCSI 1986; FFA RCS Eng. 1985. Cons. Anaesth. P. Philip Hosp. LLa.lli.

O'DONNCHADHA, Domhnall Seosamh Pear Tree Farm, Stubbins Lane, Chinley, High Peak SK23 6AE — MB BCh BAO 1983 NUI.

O'DONNCHADHA, Mr Eamon Proinseas Royal Eye Hospital, Oxford Road, Manchester M13 9WL Tel: 0161 276 5226 Fax: 0161 272 6618 — MB BCh BAO 1980 NUI; FRCS Ed. 1987; FRCOphth 1989. Cons. Ophth. Surg. Roy. Eye Hosp. Manch.; Lect. (Ophth.) Univ. Manch. Socs: Assn. for Research in Vision & Ophth., USA. Prev: Fell. Paediat. Ophth. Hosp. Sick Childr. Toronto, Canada; Fell. Glaucoma Moorfield Eye Hosp. Lond.; Resid. Moorfields Eye Hosp. Lond.

O'DONNELL, Aidan Mark St. John's Hospital at Howden, Howden Road W., Livingston EH54 6PP Tel: 01506 419666 — MB ChB 1996 Ed.; BSc (Hons.) Ed. 1994. SHO (Anaesth.) St. John's Hosp. Livingston. Socs: Ord. Mem. Assn. du Corps de Santé Internat. de Notre Dame de Lourdes.

O'DONNELL, Anne 63 Sandacre Road, Baguley, Wythenshawe, Manchester M23 1AP — MB ChB 1996 Dundee.

O'DONNELL, Anthony John St. Martin's Health Centre, Les Camps du Moulin, St Martin's, Guernsey GY4 6DA Tel: 01481 237757 Fax: 01481 239591; Le Vieux Rouvet, St. Saviours, Guernsey GY7 9NB Tel: 01481 64414 — MB BS 1966 Lond.; MRCS Eng. LRCP Lond. 1966; MRCGP 1976; DCH Eng. 1969; DObst RCOG 1968. (Guy's) Mem. Med. Staff P.ss Eliz. Hosp. Guernsey. Socs: BMA (Ex-Chairm. Guernsey & Alderney Div.). Prev: Dep. Res. Med. Off. Middlx. Hosp. Lond.; SHO (Paediat.) King's Coll. Hosp.; Ho. Phys. Guy's-Evelina Hosp. Childr. Lond.

O'DONNELL, Catherine Anne-Marie The Chase, Heathlands Road, Wokingham RG40 3AS — MB BS 1991 Lond.

O'DONNELL, Charles James 75 Osprey Close, Snaresbrook, London E11 1SZ Tel: 020 8491 6510 — MB BS 1989 Lond.; MRCP (UK) 1993. Cons. (A & E) Whipps Cross Hosp. Lond.

O'DONNELL, David Austen (retired) 21 Little Poulton Lane, Poulton-le-Fylde FY6 7ET — MB ChB 1968 Ed. Prev: GP Blackpool.

O'DONNELL, Declan Wake Green Surgery, 7 Wake Green Road, Moseley, Birmingham B13 9HD Tel: 0121 449 0300; 22 Woodlands Road, Birmingham B11 4HE Tel: 0121 449 8778 — MB BCh BAO 1987 NUI. Prev: SHO (O & G) Good Hope Hosp. Birm.; SHO (Paediat.) P.ss Roy. Hosp. Telford; SHO (A & E) Selly Oak Hosp. Birm.

O'DONNELL, Denis Rodney The Chase, Heathlands Road, Wokingham RG40 3AS — MB BCh BAO 1965 NUI.

O'DONNELL, Elizabeth Ann 1 Maners Way, Cambridge CB1 8SL — MB BCh 1980 Wales; MRCGP 1985; DCH RCP Lond. 1986; DRCOG 1983. Specialist Regist. Pub. Health Med. Anglia Regional Train. Scheme Ipswich. Socs: Med. Wom. Federat. Prev: GP Ruislip; Clin. Asst. (Community Adult Psychiat.) Mid-Anglia Community Health Trust Newmarket, Suff.

O'DONNELL, Emma Louise 16 Ashfield Road, Anderton, Chorley PR6 9PN — MB ChB 1994 Liverp.

O'DONNELL, Ennis Ignatius Ashton Health Centre, 67-69 Pedders Lane, Ashton-on-Ribble, Preston PR2 1HR Tel: 01772 726500 — MB ChB 1971 Glas.; DObst RCOG 1973.

O'DONNELL, Godfrey 3 The Saplings, Clayton, Newcastle ST5 4HW Tel: 01782 626291 — MB BCh BAO 1936 NUI. (Univ. Coll. Dub.) Prev: Ho. Surg. Mater Miser. Hosp. Dub.; Extern. Asst. Coombe Mat. Hosp. Dub.; Asst. Med. Off. Anlaby Rd. Hosp. Hull.

O'DONNELL, Helen Elizabeth 60 Upper Captain Street, Coleraine BT51 3LZ — MB BS 1998 Lond.; MB BS Lond 1998.

O'DONNELL, Hugh, Surg. Lt.-Cdr. RN Retd. Farnham Health Centre, Brightwells, Farnham GU9 7SA Tel: 01252 723122; Silver Hill, 53 Dene Lane, Farnham GU10 3RJ Tel: 01252 737480 — MB ChB 1973 Ed.; BSc (Med. Sci.) Ed. 1970, MB ChB 1973; MRCGP 1978; DRCOG 1981. Princip. Gen. Pract. Farnham. Prev: Gen. Pract. Vocational Trainee Helensburgh; Ho. Surg. Dunfermline & W. Fife Hosp.; Ho. Phys. (Cardiol.) W.. Gen. Hosp. Edin.

O'DONNELL, Hugh Anthony 8 The Gables, Sedgefield, Stockton-on-Tees TS21 3EU — MB BCh BAO 1979 NUI. Socs: Inceptor Roy. Coll. Psychiat.; BMA.

O'DONNELL, Hugh Francis Deddington Health Centre, Earls Lane, Deddington, Banbury OX15 0TQ Tel: 01869 338611 Fax: 01869 37009; Grove Cottages, High St, Deddington, Banbury OX15 0SL Tel: 01869 — MB BS 1968 Lond.

O'DONNELL, James Gerard Mary Unilabs Clinical Trials Ltd., Bewlay House, 32 Jamestown Road, London NW1 7BY Tel: 020 7333 8436 Fax: 020 7424 0607; Ambleside, 90 London Road, Datchet, Slough SL3 9LQ Tel: 01753 548065 Fax: 01753 541325 — MB BCh BAO 1978 NUI; MRCGP 1985; MFPM RCP (UK) 1993; Dip. Pharm. Med. RCP (UK) 1992; DObst RCPI 1982; DCH RCPSI 1981. Med. Dir. Chiltern Internat. Ltd.; Vis. Lect. Univ. Wales. Socs: Fell. Roy. Soc. Med.; Eur. Med. Research Gp. (Lond.). Prev: Sen. Clin. Research Regist. (Cardiol.) Wexham Pk. Hosp. Slough; Regist. (Med.) Ibn Al Bitar Parc, Baghdad; Regist. (Paediat.) Lourdes Hosp. Drogheda.

O'DONNELL, James Joseph, Col. late RAMC Retd. (retired) Primrose Cottage, Sandy Lane, Rushmoor, Farnham GU10 2ET Tel: 01252 790330 — LMSSA 1959 Lond.; FFA RCS Eng. 1971; DA Eng. 1962. Prev: Cons. Anaesth. K. Fahad Hosp. SANG Riyadh, Saudi Arabia.

O'DONNELL, James Joseph Park House Surgery, 55 Higher Parr Street, St Helens WA9 1BP Tel: 01744 23705 Fax: 01744 454601; 9 Hard Lane, St Helens WA10 6JP Tel: 01744 611075 Fax: 01744 454601 Email: odonnell@gpiag-asthma.org — MB ChB 1976 Liverp.; T(GP) 1990; DRCOG 1978. (Liverp.) Chairm. St. Helens S. PCG; Med. Sec. St. Helens & Knowsley LMC. Prev: SHO (Paediat.) Roy. Liverp. Child. Hosp. City Br.; Ho. Phys. & Ho. Surg. Birkenhead Gen. Hosp.; Ho. Off. Obst. Profess. Unit Mill Rd. Matern. Hosp. Liverp.

O'DONNELL, James Stewart 29 Five Acres, Dublin Road, Strabane BT82 9JD — MB BCh BAO 1990 Dub.; MB BCh Dub. 1990.

O'DONNELL, Jill Frances The Valley Medical Centre, 14 Waller Close, Liverpool L4 4QJ Tel: 0151 207 3447; 280 Greenhill Road, Allerton, Liverpool L18 9SY — MB ChB 1985 Liverp.; DRCOG 1992. GP Liverp. Prev: Clin. Med. Off./SHO (Community Paediat.) Sefton Gen. Hosp. Liverp.; SHO (Chest Med.) Regional Chest Unit Fazakerley Hosp. Liverp.; SHO (Med.) Arrowe Pk. Hosp. Wirral.

O'DONNELL, John White Lodge, Well Lane, Mollington, Chester CH1 6LD — MB ChB 1967 Manch.; MRCGP 1978.

O'DONNELL, John Desmond Wingate Medical Centre, 79 Bigdale Drive, Northwood, Kirby L33 6YJ Tel: 0151 546 2958 Fax: 0151 546 2914 Email: johnodonnell@doctors.org.uk; 62 Forest Grove, Eccleston Park, Prescot L34 2RZ Email: johnodonnell@doctors.org.uk — MB ChB 1981 Liverp. (Liverpool) Socs: Assoc. Mem. RCGP. Prev: SHO (A & E & O & G) Whiston Hosp. Prescot; SHO (Gen. Med.) Morriston Hosp. Swansea.

O'DONNELL, John Gerald 11 Watersmeet, Northampton NN1 5SQ — MB ChB 1983 Glas.; BSc (Hons.) Glas. 1980, MB ChB 1983.

O'DONNELL, John James Joseph Health Centre, Great James Street, Londonderry BT48 7DH Tel: 028 7137 8500; 5 Locarden,

O'DONNELL

Culmore, Londonderry BT48 8RP Tel: 01504 351408 — MB BCh BAO 1989 NUI; MRCGP 1994; DRCOG 1993.

O'DONNELL, Katrina Maria 7 Albany Avenue, Eccleston Park, Prescot L34 2QN — MB BCh BAO 1987 NUI; LRCPI 1987.

O'DONNELL, Louise Virginia 52 Waterloo Road, Southport PR8 2NB — MB ChB 1997 Liverp.

O'DONNELL, Maire Teresa Kennedy Centre Surgery, 568 Falls Road, Belfast BT11 9AE Tel: 028 9061 1411 — MB BCh BAO 1986 NUI.

O'DONNELL, Marie 28 Marine Drive, Hest Bank, Lancaster LA2 6EB — MB ChB 1980 Wales.

O'DONNELL, Marie Department of Pathology, University of Edinburgh Medical School, Teviot Place, Edinburgh EH8 9AG Tel: 0131 650 2945 — MB BCh BAO 1991 NUI. Regist. (Histopath.) Univ. Edin. Med. Sch.

O'DONNELL, Mark John Victoria Hospital, Whinney Heys Road, Blackpool FY3 1NR Tel: 01253 303861 Fax: 01253 306810 — MB ChB 1980 Liverp.; MD Birm. 1993; Dip. Rehabilt. Med. 1993; FRCP 1998. Cons. Phys. Vict., Clifton & Wesham Pk. Hosps. Socs: Hon. Life Mem. Liverp. Med. Stud.s Soc.; Liverp. Med. Inst. Prev: Hon. Life Mem. Liverp. Med. Studs. Soc.

O'DONNELL, Mr Mark Mary Overglinns, Fintry, Balfron, Glasgow G63 0LP — MB BCh BAO 1988 NUI; FRCS Ed. 1995; FRCSI 1993.

O'DONNELL, Martin Antony Clarence House, 14 Russell Road, Rhyl LL18 3BY Tel: 01745 350680 Fax: 01745 353293; 1 Cwrt-y-Dderwen, Colwyn Bay LL29 7BF Tel: 01492 535431 — MB BCh BAO 1985 NUI; MRCGP 1993. Mem. Denbighsh. A.C.P.C.; Vice-Chairm. N. Clwyd GP Co-op. Socs: Roy. Coll. Gen. Pract.; Brit. Diabetic Assn.

O'DONNELL, Michael Handon Cottage, Markwick Lane, Loxhill, Godalming GU8 4BD Tel: 01483 208295 Fax: 01483 208270 — MB BChir 1952 Camb.; FRCGP 1990. (Camb. & St. Thos.) Author & BRd.caster. Socs: GMC (Chairm. Professional Standards Comm.); BMA & Slagthorpe Med. Soc.; Hon. Mem. Alpha Omega Alpha Honor Med. Soc. Prev: GP; Edr. World Med.; Ho. Surg. St. Thos. Hosp. Lond.

O'DONNELL, Michael Joseph St. James Health Centre, 29 Great George Square, Liverpool L1 5DZ Tel: 0151 709 1120 — MB BCh BAO 1943 NUI.

O'DONNELL, Michael Joseph Medical & Industrial Servicies, MIS House, Eastbourne BN21 3UT Tel: 01323 724889 Fax: 01323 721161; 7 The Lords, Seaford BN25 2XP Tel: 01323 891232 Fax: 01323 891232 Email: michael.odonnel@lineone.net — MB ChB 1975 Manch.; AFOM RCP Lond. 1987. (Manch.) Sen. Med. Advisor, Med. & Insustrial Servicies, E. Bourne. Socs: Occupat. Med. Soc.; Inst. Occupat. Health & Safety. Prev: Force Med. Adviser (Occupat. Med.) Sussex Police; Med. Off. Brit. Nuclear Fuels Sellafield; Manager Med. Servs. Saudi Petrochem. Company, Saudi Arabia.

O'DONNELL, Neil Gerard Department of Anaesthesia, Western Infirmary, Dumbarton Drive, Glasgow G11 6NT Tel: 0141 211 2069 — MB ChB 1983 Glas.; FFARCS 1988. Cons. Anaesth. W.: Infirm. Glas.

O'DONNELL, Patrick James Dept. of Histopathology, 2nd Floor, North Wing, St. Thomas's Hospital, Lambeth Palace Road, London SE1 7EH Fax: 020 7401 3661 — MB BCh BAO 1975 NUI; FRCPath 1994; MRCPath 1982. (Univ. Coll. Galway Eire) Cons. Histopath. (Renal Path.) Guy's & St. Thos. Hosp. Trust Lond. Socs: Assn. of Clin. Pathologists; Renal Assn.; Europ. Renal Assn. Prev: Cons. (Histopath.) King's Coll. Hosp. Lond.; Lect. (Morbid. Anat.) St. Thos. Hosp. Lond.; Regist. (Path.) Sch. Med. Univ. Leeds.

O'DONNELL, Patrick Michael Joseph Sundon Medical Centre, 142-144 Sundon Park Road, Sundon Park, Luton LU3 3AH Tel: 01582 571130 Fax: 01582 564452; 6 Churchill Close, Streatley, Luton LU3 3PJ Tel: 01582 882502 Email: odon@ukonline.co.uk — MB BS 1961 Lond.; FRCGP 1981, M 1971; DObst RCOG 1963. (St. Mary's) Sen. Part. O'Donnell, Swan, Yip and Williams, Luton.

O'DONNELL, Paul Noel Simon 67 Ashdon Road, Saffron Walden CB10 2AQ — BM BS 1993 Nottm.

O'DONNELL, Paula Anne 9 Queen Street, Whittlesey, Peterborough PE7 1AY Tel: 01733 204611 Fax: 020 733 208926 Email: helena@queensheersurgery.com — MB ChB 1989 Glas.; MRCGP 1993. GP Whitlesey PeterBoro. Prev: SHO Psychiat. Boston; SHO Gynercology, PeterBoro.

O'DONNELL, Paula Sheila Fax: 020 8314 5557 — MB BS 1984 Lond.; BSc Lond. 1981; DCH RCP Lond. 1989. GP Princip., Brockley, Lond. Prev: Clin. Asst. (Blood Transfus. & Apheresis) S. Thames Blood Transfus. Serv. Lond.

O'DONNELL, Peter John The Old Court House Surgery, Throwley Way, Sutton SM1 4AF Tel: 020 8643 8866 Fax: 020 8770 2629; Tel: 0208 786 0606 — MB BS 1978 Lond.; MRCS Eng. LRCP Lond. 1978; DRCOG 1984. (St. Mary's) Prev: GP Principle, GP Med. Unit, The Manor Dr.Worchester Par, Surrey.

O'DONNELL, Peter Sean Richard Binscombe Medical Centre, 106 Binscombe Lane, Godalming GU7 3PR Tel: 01483 415115 Fax: 01483 414925 — MB BS 1989 Lond.

O'DONNELL, Roddy Department of Paediatrics, Addenbrooke's Hospital, Hills Road, Cambridge CB2 2QQ Tel: 01223 245151 Email: drod@addenbrookes.nhs.uk — MB BS 1989 Lond.; MRCP; MRCP (UK) 1992; PhD Lond. 1997. (UMDS (Guy's and St. Thomas' Hospital) London) Cons. in Paediatric Care, Addenbrooke's Hosp., Cambs. Socs: MRCPCH. Prev: Lect. (Paediat. Infec. Dis.s) Imperial Coll. of Sci. Technol. & Med. St. Mary's Hosp. Lond.; Clin. Fell. (Pulm. Med.) Childr.'s Hosp. Med. Centre Cincinnati USA; Wellcome Train. Fell. (Respirat. Med.) St. Mary's Hosp. Med. Sch. Lond.

O'DONNELL, Ruaidhri (retired) Sunningdale, 7 Albany Avenue, Eccleston Park, Prescot L34 2QN Tel: 0151 426 5083 — MB BCh BAO 1951 NUI.

O'DONNELL, Stanley John (retired) 39 Dean Road, South Shields NE33 4AS Tel: 0191 456 0232 — MB BS 1952 Durh. Prev: Ho. Surg. P.ss Mary Matern. Hosp. Newc.

O'DONNELL, Stephen Anthony Ivy Cottage, Waldrige, Chester-le-Street DH2 3SL Tel: 0191 387 1389 — MB BS 1989 Newc.; MRCGP 1994; DFFP 1994; DRCOG 1993.

O'DONNELL, Valerie Anne 1 South Drive, Sutton Coldfield B75 7TE — MB ChB 1987 Leic.

O'DONOGHUE, Alison 9 Castlemead Walk, Kingsmead, Northwich CW9 8GP — MB ChB 1991 Ed.; BSc Ed. 1991; DRCOG 1994; DFFP 1994; MRCGP 1995. (Edinburgh) Clin. Research Phys. Medeval Ltd. Manch.

O'DONOGHUE, Angela Elizabeth Marie Anna Derby City Hospital, Derby Tel: 01132 340141; The Coach House, Milicent Road, Nottingham NG2 7LD — BM BS 1994 Nottm.; BMedSci (Hons) 1992; MRCP UK 1997. Specialist Regist. (Renal) Derby City Hosp.

O'DONOGHUE, Beata Maria The Royal National Throat, Nose & Ear Hospital, Gray's Inn Road, London WC1X 8DA Tel: 020 7915 1300 Fax: 020 7833 5518; 150 Harley Street, London W1G 7LQ Tel: 020 7935 6000 Fax: 020 7584 4046 — MD Lodz, Poland 1969; FFA RCS Eng. 1980. Cons. Anaesth. Roy. Nat. Throat Nose & Ear Hosp. Lond. Socs: Brit. Sleep Soc.; Roy. Soc. Med.

O'DONOGHUE, Charles Reid 34 Camperdown Street, Broughty Ferry, Dundee DD5 3AB — MB ChB 1991 Dundee.

O'DONOGHUE, Dara Bartholomew 42 Hilltown Road, Mayobridge, Newry BT34 2HJ — MB BCh BAO 1993 Belf.

O'DONOGHUE, Dennis Michael 113 Cranley Gardens, London N10 3AE Tel: 020 8883 7090 Fax: 020 8883 7090 — MB ChB 1946 Otago; FRCA 1992; FFA RCS Eng. 1953; DA Eng. 1950. (Otago) Emerit. Cons. Anaesth. Univ. Coll. & Middlx. Hosp. Lond.; Hon. Cons. Anaesth. Roy. Nat. Orthop. Hosp. Lond. Socs: Fell. Roy. Soc. Med.; BMA. Prev: Cons. Anaesth. Univ. Coll. Hosp., Roy. Nat. Orthop. Hosp. Lond. & Hosp. Trop. Dis.; Cons. Anaesth. Nat. Dent. Hosp.; Sen. Regist. (Anaesth.) Univ. Coll. Hosp.

O'DONOGHUE, Donal Joseph Department of Renal Medicine, Hope Hospital, Salford Royal Hospitals NHS Trust, Eccles New Road, Salford M6 8HD Tel: 0161 787 4389 Fax: 0161 787 5775 Email: didonoghue@hope.spht.nwest.nhs.uk; 6 Millstone Close, Poynton, Stockport SK12 1XS Tel: 01625 871381 — MB ChB 1980 Manch.; BSc (1st cl. Hons. Physiol.) Manch. 1977; FRCP Lond. 1996; MRCP (UK) 1983. (Manch.) Cons. Renal & Gen. Phys. Hope Hosp. Salford; Hon. Lect. (Med.) Univ. Manch. Socs: Amer. Soc. Nephrol.; RCP Edin.; Renal Assn. Exec. 2000-2004. Prev: Sen. Regist. (Nephrol. & Gen. Med.) Roy. Infirm. Edin.; MRC Trav. Fell. Hopital Necker Paris; Regist. (Nephrol.) Manch. Roy. Infirm.

O'DONOGHUE, Eamon 16 Daryngton Avenue, Birchington CT7 9PS Tel: 01843 42449 — MB BCh BAO 1949 NUI; LM Nat. Matern. Hosp. 1949; AFOM RCPI 1978. (Cork) Dep. Chief Staff

O'DONOVAN

Med. Serv. ILEA. Prev: Cas. Off. Radcliffe Infirm. Oxf.; Res. Med. Off. Osler Sanat. Oxf.; Ho. Surg. (Gyn.) Ch.ill Hosp. Oxf.

O'DONOGHUE, Fiona Justine Margot Govanhill Health Centre, 233 Calder St., Glasgow G42 7DR — MB BCh BAO 1991 Belf.; MRCGP 1996; DRCOG 1996; DFFP 1996. Research Regist. (Menopause/Gyn.) Glas. Socs: Brit. Menopause Soc.

O'DONOGHUE, James 1 Reddish Avenue, Whaley Bridge, High Peak SK23 7DP — MB ChB 1948 Liverp.

O'DONOGHUE, John Patrick Marsh House Medical Centre, 254 Marsh House Avenue, Billingham TS23 3EN Tel: 01642 561282/565068 Fax: 01642 565982; Redwalls, 15 Thornton Road, Thornton, Middlesbrough TS8 9BS Tel: 01642 597443 — MB BCh BAO 1978 NUI; MRCGP 1982; DCH Dub. 1982; DRCOG 1980.

O'DONOGHUE, Maire Anne Therese Leighton Hospital, Middlewich Road, Crewe CW1 4QJ Tel: 01270 255141 — MB BCh BAO 1982 Dub.; MA Dub. 1992, MB BCh 1982; FRCPath 1998; MRCPath 1990. Cons. Microbiol. Leighton Hosp. Crewe.

O'DONOGHUE, Margaret Mary (retired) Greetwell Cottage, 1 Greetwell Gate, Lincoln LN2 4AW Tel: 01522 532728 — MB BCh BAO 1948 NUI; DA Eng. 1955; Cons. Anaesth. Co. Hosp. Lincoln. Prev: Cons. Anaesth. Lincoln Co. Hosp.

O'DONOGHUE, Michael Francis 1 Eaton Court, Water Eaton Road, Oxford OX2 7QT; Brentwood, Willoughby-on-the-Wold, Leicester LE12 6SZ Tel: 01509 880494 Fax: 01509 156467 — MB BS 1985 Lond.; BSc.Lond. 1982; MRCP (UK) 1988. (Univ. Coll. Hosp.) Cons. NeUrol., Nottm. Prev: SHO (Gen. Med.) Hammersmith Postgrad. Hosp. Lond. & Lond Chest Hosp.; Ho. Off. (Gen. Med.) Univ. Coll. Hosp. Lond.; SHO (Gen. Med.) John Radcliffe Hosp. Oxf.

O'DONOGHUE, Michael Geoffrey The Surgery, H. M. Tower of London, 2 Tower Green, London EC3N 4AB — LRCPI & LM, LRSCI & LM 1957; LRCPI & LM, LRCSI & LM 1957. Phys. BUPA Med. Centre Lond. Prev: Ho. Phys. & Ho. Surg. W. Cornw. Hosp. Penzance; Clin. Asst. Roy. Nat. Throat, Nose & Ear Hosp. Lond.

O'DONOGHUE, Mr Neil 99 Harley Street, London W1N 1DF Tel: 020 7935 6200 Fax: 020 7224 6177 — MB BCh BAO 1963 NUI; FRCS Eng. 1967. Cons. Urol. St. Peter's Hosp. Lond.; Sen. Lect. Inst. Urol. Lond. Socs: Internat. Soc. Urol. & Brit. Assn. Urol. Surgs. Prev: Vis. Assoc. Univ. Iowa Hosps., USA; Sen. Regist. St. Bart. Hosp. Lond.; Resid. Hammersmith Hosp.

O'DONOGHUE, Nora Brigid 12 Sandileigh Avenue, Manchester M20 3LW — MB ChB 1994 Glas.

O'DONOGHUE, Patrick 5 Stanmore Road, Stevenage SG2 2QA Tel: 01438 749734 Fax: 01438 749734 Email: podonog123@aol.com — MB BCh BAO 1982 NUI; MRCGP 1987; DObst RCPI 1985; DCH RCPSI 1984. (Cork)

O'DONOGHUE, Paula 42 Hilltown Road, Mayobridge, Newry BT34 2HJ — MB BCh BAO 1994 Belf. SHO (Med.) Antrim Area Hosp. Prev: Ho. Off. Belf. City Hosp.

O'DONOHOE, Jarlath Michael 21 Scaffog Avenue, Enniskillen BT74 7JJ — MB BCh BAO 1978 NUI; MSc Lond. 1986; MRCP (UK) 1986. Cons. Paediat. & Community Paediat. Qu. Mary's Univ. Hosp. Roehampton & Roehampton, Twickenham & Richmond HA. Prev: Lect. (Paediat.) Char. Cross & W.m. Med. Sch.; Cons. Paediat. Taif Saudi Arabia; Regist. Roy. Hosp. for Sick Childr. Glas.

O'DONOHUE, John William University Hospital Lewisham, London SE13 6LH Tel: 020 8333 3000 Ext: 6182 Fax: 020 83333 3093 Email: johnod13@yahoo.com; 50 Royal Hill, London SE10 8RT Tel: 020 8333 2828 Fax: 020 8333 1777 — MB BCh BAO 1987 Dub.; FRCPI 2001; MA 2000; MRCPI 1989; MD 1998. (Univ Dub.) Cons. Gastroenterol. Univ. Hosp. Lewisham & King's Coll. Hosp. Socs: Brit. Med. Assn. (BMA); (BSG) Brit. Soc. of Gastronetrology; (BASL) Brit. Assn. for the study of Liver Dis. W. Kent Chirurgic – Med. Soc. Prev: Sen. Regist. (Med & Gastroenterol.) W. Glas. Hosps. Trust; Research Fell. Inst. Liver Studies King's Coll. Hosp. Lond.; Regist. (Gastroenterol.) St. Bart. Hosp. Lond.

O'DONOHUE, Mary Bridget 2 Denbigh Road, Ealing, London W13 8PX — MB BCh BAO 1957 NUI.

O'DONOVAN, Anne Louise (retired) Mill Farmhouse, Martlesham, Woodbridge IP12 4PB — MRCS Eng. LRCP Lond. 1962. Prev: GP Leighton Buzzard.

O'DONOVAN, Carmel Philomena 43 Taylor Avenue, Richmond TW9 4EB Tel: 020 8876 6661 Fax: 020 8876 6661 — MB BS 1981 Lond.; MRCP (UK) 1984. (St. Mary's) Indep. Medico-Legal Cons. Richmond. Prev: Med. Secretariat Med. Defence Union.

O'DONOVAN, Dominic Gerard Histopathology Dept, Box 235 Addenbrookes Hospital, Hills Road, Cambridge CB2 2QQ Tel: 01223 217172 Fax: 01223 216980 — MB ChB 1983 Liverp.; MRCPath 1992. Cons. Neuropath Addenbrooke's Hosp., Camb.; Cons. Neuropathologist, Old Ch. Hosp., Romford. Socs: Brit. NeuroPath. Soc.; World Muscle Soc. Prev: Sen. Regist. (Neuropath.) N. W. Regional Health Auth..; Regist. (Path.) S.. Gen. Hosp. Glas.; SHO (Path.) Roy. Gwent Hosp. Newport.

O'DONOVAN, Donal John Cathal (retired) 1026 Alcester Road S., Kings Heath, Birmingham B14 5NG — MB BCh BAO 1941 NUI. Med. Off. W. H. Smith & Son (Birm.). Prev: Lect. & Demonst. Anat. Birm. Univ. Med. Sch.

O'DONOVAN, Ellen Christina c/o Westminster Bank, Market Place, Cirencester Tel: 01285 770456; The Corner House, Coates, Cirencester GL7 6NH Tel: 01285 770456 — MB BCh BAO 1941 NUI.

O'DONOVAN, Gerard Barry Ormskirk Street Surgery, 51A Ormskirk Stret, St Helens WA10 2TB Tel: 01744 29209; The Cottage, Rainford, St Helens WA11 8NG Tel: 01744 882534 — LRCPI & LM, LRCSI & LM 1962. (RCSI) Prev: Clin. Med. Off. St. Helens & Knowsley HA.; Ho. Surg. (Gyn. & Obst.) Billinge Hosp. Orrell.; Ho. Surg. Roy. Albert Edwd. Infirm. Wigan.

O'DONOVAN, Isabel Andrea Mary Risedale Surgery, 2-4 Gloucester Street, Barrow-in-Furness LA13 9RX Tel: 01229 822332 Fax: 01229 433636; Well House, Bardsea, Ulverston LA12 9QY — MB BS 1989 Lond.; DFFP 1995; DRCOG 1995; MRCGP 1995. (St George's Hosp.Med.Sch.) GP Princ.

O'DONOVAN, Jeremiah Timothy 34 Walsingham Road, Hove BN3 4FF — MB BCh BAO 1983 NUI.

O'DONOVAN, Maire Hammersmith Hospital, Du Cane Road, London W12 0HS — MB BCh BAO 1992 NUI; LRCPSI 1992.

O'DONOVAN, Marie Rosarie 22 Olive Road, London NW2 6TX — MB BS 1997 Lond.

O'DONOVAN, Mary Josephine (retired) 22 Hogarth Way, Hampton TW12 2EL — MB BCh BAO 1949 NUI; DPH NUI 1956; DCH NUI 1954; MFCM 1982.

O'DONOVAN, Michael Conlon Department of Psychological Medicine, University of Wales College of Medicine, Heath Park, Cardiff CF14 4XN Tel: 029 2074 3242 Fax: 029 2074 7839 Email: odonovanmc@cardiff.ac.uk — MB ChB 1983 Glas.; PhD Wales 1994; BSc (Hons.) Glas. 1980, MB ChB 1983; MRCPsych 1987; FRCPsych 1999. Prof. (Psychiat. Genetics) Univ. Wales Coll. Med.

O'DONOVAN, Nicholas Patrick Southlands, Park Lane, Barnstaple EX32 9AL — MB BCh BAO 1973 NUI; FFA RCS Eng. 1981. Cons. Anaesth. N. Devon Dist. Hosp. Barnstaple.

O'DONOVAN, Nicolas David 21 Orchard Road, Havant PO9 1AT Email: nick@thedonovans.freeserve.co.uk — MB ChB 1980 Birm.; DRCOG 1983. (Birm.) GP; Med. Mem. Disabil. Appeal Tribunals for Indep. Tribunal Serv.; EMP for Benefits Agency. Socs: Assur. Med. Soc.

O'DONOVAN, Norah Mary (retired) Loreto, 57 York Avenue, Finchfield, Wolverhampton WV3 9BX Tel: 01902 656269 — MB BCh BAO NUI 1946.

O'DONOVAN, Patricia Anne Department of Obstetrics & Gynaecology, Queen's Park Hospital, Haslingden Road, Blackburn — MB BCh BAO 1980 NUI; BSc NUI 1975; FRCS Ed. 1988; MRCOG 1987; FRCOG 1999. Cons. O & G Qu. Pk. Hosp. Blackburn. Prev: Lect. & Sen. Regist. (O & G) St. Jas. Univ. Hosp. Leeds; Asst. Master Combe Lying-in Hosp. Dub.; Regist. (O & G) Mater Infirmorum Hosp. Belf.

O'DONOVAN, Patrick (retired) Loreto, 57 York Avenue, Finchfield, Wolverhampton WV3 9BX Tel: 01902 656269 — MB BCh BAO NUI 1945.

O'DONOVAN, Mr Peter Joseph Cotswold, 3 Creskeld Crescent, Bramhope, Leeds LS16 9EH Tel: 01274 364888 Fax: 01274 366945 Email: podonovan@hotmail.com — MB BCh BAO 1978 NUI; FRCS Eng. 1982; MRCOG 1986. (National University of Ireland) Cons. O & G Bradford Roy. Infirm. Socs: Mem. Brit. Soc. Gyna. Endoscopy; Mem. Brit. Soc. Colposcopy and Cervical Pathol. Prev: Sen. Regist. (O & G) Leeds Gen. Infirm.; SHO (Perinatal Med.) Nat. Matern. Hosp. Dub.

O'DONOVAN, Timothy Joseph 160 Ribblesdale Road, Nottingham NG5 3HW Tel: 0115 263644 — MB BCh BAO 1951

O'DOWD

NUI. (Cork) Prev: Ho. Surg. Pk. Hosp. Davyhulme; SHO Paediat. Gen. Hosp. Burnley; Ho. Surg. Newc. Sanat. Co. Wicklow.

O'DOWD, Bernard Henry Nupend Court, Stonehouse GL10 3SP — MRCS Eng. LRCP Lond. 1940. (Birm.)

O'DOWD, Mr Brian Joseph 68 Plasturton Avenue, Pontacanna, Cardiff CF11 9HJ — MB ChB 1954 Liverp.; FRCSI 1963. (Liverp.)

O'DOWD, Clare Elizabeth The Limes, Pankridge St., Crondall, Farnham GU10 5QT Tel: 01252 850018 Email: odowds@compuserve.com — MB BS 1991 Lond.; MRCGP 1996; DFFP 1995; DRCOG 1995. (St Thomas' Hospital London)

O'DOWD, Gerard Michael 444 Aigburth Road, Liverpool L19 3QE — MB BCh BAO 1987 Dub.; MRCPath 1995, D 1994. Lect. (Path.) Univ. Liverp.

O'DOWD, John Gerard Mary Avenue Medical Centre, Wentworth Avenue, Slough SL2 2DG Tel: 01753 524549 Fax: 01753 552537 — MB BCh BAO 1981 Dub.; MRCPI 1983; MRCGP 1985; DCH RCP Lond. 1984.

O'DOWD, John James Mallon 29 Ballater Crescent, Woodlands Gate, Wishaw ML2 7YJ — MB ChB 1996 Glas.

O'DOWD, John Joseph Department of Histopathology, Airedale General Hospital, Skipton Road, Steeton, Keighley BD20 6TD Tel: 01535 652511 — MB ChB 1982 Leeds; FRCPath 1999; MRCPath 1990. Cons. Histopath. Airedale Gen. Hosp. Keighley.

O'DOWD, Mr John Kevin Centre for Spinal Studies & Surgery, Queens Medical Centre, Nottingham NG7 2UH Tel: 0115 924 9924 Fax: 0115 970 9991; 5 Tennis Drive, The Park, Nottingham NG7 1AE Tel: 0115 948 0760 — MB BS 1982 Lond.; FRCS Orth. 1994; FRCS Ed. 1988; FRCS Eng. 1988. BOA Spinal Fell. Qu. Med. Centre Nottm. Socs: Fell. Roy. Soc. Med.; Brit. Trauma Soc. Prev: Sen. Regist. (Orthop.) St. Geo. Hosp. Lond.; Sen. Regist. Qu. Mary's Hosp. for Childr. Carshalton; Research Fell. Acad. Dept. (Orthop.) St. Thos. Hosp. Lond.

O'DOWD, Lorien Rachel Maudsley Hospital, Denmark Hill, London SE5 8AZ Tel: 020 7703 6333 Fax: 020 7919 2171 — BM BS 1990 Nottm.; BMedSci Nottm. 1988. Regist. (Child Psychiat.) Maudsley Hosp. Lond.

O'DOWD, Sylvia 4 The Orchard, Malt House Lane, Wolverhampton WV6 9PF Tel: 01902 752311 — MRCS Eng. LRCP Lond. 1939. (Birm.) Prev: Sen. Med. Off. Wolverhampton Health Auth. Clin. Med. Off.; Wolverhampton Health Auth.; GP Wolverhampton.

O'DRISCOLL, Aisling Mary Department of Haematology, Worthing Hospital, Lyndhurst Road, Worthing BN11 2DH Tel: 01903 205111 Fax: 01903 285072 Email: aisling.o'driscoll@wash-tr.sthames.nhs.uk — MB BS 1986 Lond.; MRCP (UK) 1989; DRCPath 1992; MRCPath 1997, D 1992. Cons. Haematologist. Worthing & S.lands Hosp. Trust, Worthing. Prev: Sen. Regist. St. Geo.'s Hosp., Lond.; Regist. & Jun. Lect. (Haemat.) Univ. Coll. Hosp. Lond..

O'DRISCOLL, Anthony Micael Birmingham & Midland Eye Centre, Western Road, Birmingham B18 7QU Tel: 0121 236 4911; 12 Fetherston Grange, Glasshouse Lane, Packwood, Lapworth, Solihull B94 6PX Tel: 0121 704 9187 — MB ChB 1986 Cape Town; FRCOphth 1994. Regist. (Ophth.) Birm. & Midl. Eye Hosp. Socs: Midl. Ophth. Soc.; UK & Irel. Soc. of Cataract & Refractive Surgs.; Eur. Soc. Cataract & Refractive Surgs. Prev: SHO (Ophth.) Birm. & Midl. Eye Hosp. & Kent & Canterbury Hosp.; GP Canada; Regist. (Surg.) Vict. Hosp. Cape Town, S. Afr.

O'DRISCOLL, Barry Joseph 57 Priestnall Road, Heaton Mersey, Stockport SK4 3DL — MB ChB 1965 Manch. Clin. Asst. (Orthop.) Tameside Gen. Hosp. Prev: Ho. Off. (Med.) & Cas. Off. Salford Roy. Hosp.; Ho. Off. (Obst.) St. Mary's Hosp. Manch.

O'DRISCOLL, Bartholomew Ronan Campion Cardiorespiratory Medicine, Salford Royal Hospitals NHS Trust, Hope Hospital, Salford M6 8HD Tel: 0161 787 5154 Fax: 0161 787 4328; 1 South Road, Bowdon, Altrincham WA14 2JZ — MB BCh BAO 1977 NUI; MB BCh BAO (Hons.) NUI 1977; MD NUI 1983, BSc (1st cl. Hons.) 1974; MRCP (UK) 1980; MRCPI 1979; FRCP (UK) 1997. Cons. Phys. (Gen. & Respirat. Med.) Salford Roy. Hosps. NHS Trust. Socs: Brit. Soc. Allergy & Clin. Immunol.; Brit. Thorac. Soc.; Eur. Respirat. Soc. Prev: Sen. Regist. (Thoracic Med.) Hope & Wythenshawe Hosps.; Clin. Lect. & Hon. Regist. Cardiothoracic Inst. & Brompton Hosp. Lond.; Regist. (Med.) Guy's Hosp. Lond. & Merlin Pk. Hosp. Galway.

O'DRISCOLL, Catherine Mary 114 Upper Street, Islington, London N1 1QN — MB BS 1978 Lond.

O'DRISCOLL, David Lawrence 52 Moorfield Road, Salford M6 7QD — MRCS Eng. LRCP Lond. 1986. (Univ. Columbia) Regist. (Psychiat.) Salford; NY State Licensing Auth. (Flex) 1992. Prev: Intern & Resid. (Med.) Roosevelt Hosp., NY & Norwalk Hosp. Yale Univ.

O'DRISCOLL, Deirdre Patricia Springburn Health Centre, 200 Springburn Way, Glasgow G21 1TR Tel: 0141 531 9661 Fax: 0141 531 9666; 42 Upper Glenburn Road, Bearsden, Glasgow G61 4BN Tel: 0141 942 6976 — MB BCh BAO 1986 NUI; MRCGP 1992; DRCOG 1992. Prev: SHO (O & G) City Hosp. Nottm.; SHO (Psychiat.) Pastures Hosp. Derby; Trainee GP Devon.

O'DRISCOLL, Denis Peter 13 Crescent Road, Hale, Altrincham WA15 9NB — MB BCh BAO 1980 NUI.

O'DRISCOLL, Dilys Jane Fox Hollies Surgery, 511 Fox Hollies Road, Hall Green, Birmingham B28 8RJ Tel: 0121 777 1180; 6 Barbourne Close, Solihull B91 3TL — MB ChB 1988 Cape Town; DCH RCP Lond. 1993; DRCOG 1992. Trainee GP Hall Green, Birm. Prev: SHO (Paediat.) Kent & Canterbury Hosp.; SHO (Geriat., A & E & O & G) Kent & Canterbury Hosp.

O'DRISCOLL, Fergal Alexander Westwood Surgery, 47 Westwood Avenue, Lowestoft NR33 9RW Tel: 01502 588854; 403 London Road S., Lowestoft NR33 0BJ Tel: 01502 584485 — MB BCh BAO 1982 NUI. Clin. Asst. Lothingland Hosp.; Clin. Asst. LoW.oft & N. Suff. Hosp. Socs: BMA (Sec. Gt. Yarmouth & Waveney Div.). Prev: Trainee GP Merthyr & Cynon Valley HA VTS; SHO (Psychiat.) Bangour Village Hosp. W. Lothian Scotl.

O'DRISCOLL, Finnbarr Hugh Grange Road Welfare Centre, Grange Road, Widdrington, Morpeth NE61 5LX Tel: 01670 790229 Fax: 01670 791312 — MB BS 1968 Lond.; MRCS Eng. LRCP Lond. 1968; DObst RCOG 1970. Hosp. Pract. (Psychiat.) St. Geo. Hosp. Morpeth.

O'DRISCOLL, Hugh Michael Charles (retired) Verwood, Wimborne — MRCS Eng. LRCP Lond. 1948.

O'DRISCOLL, Jean Catherine Microbiology Department, Stoke Mandeville Hospital NHS Trust, Mandeville Road, Aylesbury HP21 8AL Tel: 01296 315330; 66 Woodstock Road S., St Albans AL1 4QH Fax: 01296 315389 Email: jeanodriscoll@hotmail.com — MB BCh BAO 1984 NUI; MSc Lond. 1989; MRCPath 1991; FRCPath 2000. Cons. Microbiol. Stoke Mandeville Hosp. NHS Trust Aylesbury. Socs: Hosp. Infec. Soc.; Assn. Med. Microbiol.; Brit. Soc. Antimicrob. Chemother. Prev: Sen. Regist. (Microbiol.) St. Geo. Hosp. Lond.; Regist. (Med. Microbiol.) Qu. Mary's Hosp. Lond.

O'DRISCOLL, John Brian The Beeches Consulting Centre, Alexandra Hospital Grounds, Mill Lane, Cheadle SK8 2PY Tel: 0161 428 4185 Fax: 0161 428 1692 — MB BS 1976 Lond.; MRCS Eng. LRCP Lond. 1976; MRCP (UK) 1984; FRCP 1998. (Westm.) Cons. Dermatol. Stepping Hill & Hope Hosps. Salford. Prev: Regist. (Dermat.) Manch. Skin Hosp.; SHO (Gen. Med.) Hope Hosp. Salford.; Regist. (Path.) Char. Cross Hosp. Lond.

O'DRISCOLL, John Patrick Spring Gardens Health Centre, Providence Street, Worcester WR1 2BS Tel: 01905 681681 Fax: 01905 681699 — MB BS 1982 Lond.; MRCGP 1987; DRCOG 1988. GP Worcester.

O'DRISCOLL, Kieran Jude Department Psychiatry, Withington Hospital, Nell Lane, West Didsbury, Manchester M20 2LR — MB BCh BAO 1976 NUI; MRCPsych 1987. (Univ. Coll. Dub.) Sen. Regist. (Psychiat.) S. Manch. Rotat. Univ. Dept. Psychiat. Withington Hosp. Manch. Prev: Regist. (Neurol.) Regional Unit Walton Hosp. Liverp.; Regist. (Neurol.) Leics. Roy. Infirm.; SHO/Regist. (Psychiat.) S. Manch. Rotat. Univ. Dept. Psychiat. Withington Hosp. Manch.

O'DRISCOLL, Maeve 15 Station Road, Verwood BH31 7PY Tel: 01202 825353 Fax: 01202 829697; Ormiston, Moorside Road, West Moors, Ferndown BH22 0EJ — MB BS 1981 Lond.

O'DRISCOLL, Margaret Christina 24 Gunterstone Road, London W14 9BU — MB BCh BAO 1979 Dub.

O'DRISCOLL, Melinda Jane The Brunswick Surgery, Oakhill Health Centre, Oakhill Road, Surbiton KT6 6EN Tel: 020 8390 5321 Fax: 020 8390 3223 — MB BS 1987 Lond.; BSc (Hons.) Lond. 1984, MB BS 1987; MRCGP 1992; DRCOG 1991. (St Georges Hospital Medical School)

O'DRISCOLL, Mr Michael The South Cheshire Private Hospital, Leighton, Crewe CW1 4QP; The Old Croft, Legh Road, Knutsford

WA16 8NR — MB ChB 1962 Leeds; ChM 1973 Bristol; FRCS 1967 Eng.; ChM Bristol 1973; FRCS Eng. 1967. (Leeds) Cons. Orthop Surg. S. Chesh. - Indep. Pract. Socs: S.I.C.O.T. Prev: Indep. Pract. S. Chesh. Private Hosp. Crewe; Cons. Orthop. Leighton Hosp. Crewe & The Robt. Jones & Agnes Hunt Orthop. Hosp. OsW.ry.

O'DRISCOLL, Patrick Michael 1 Harley Street, London W1N 1DA Tel: 020 7580 6191; Department of Oral & Maxillofacial Surgery, Guy's Hospital, London SE1 9RT Tel: 020 7955 4419 — MB BS 1961 Lond.; BDS (Hons.) Lond. 1958; MRCS Eng. LRCP Lond. 1961; FDS RCS Eng. 1963, L 1957. (Guy's) Cons. Oral & Maxillofacial Surg. Guy's Hosp.; Head Dept. Oral & Maxillofacial Surg. Guy's Dent. Hosp. Socs: Fell. Brit. Assn. Oral & Maxillofacial Surg.; Chairm. Dent. Provident Soc.; BMA. Prev: Sen. Regist. (Dent. Surg.) & Ho. Surg. Dent. Dept. Qu. Vict. Hosp. E. Grinstead; Sen. Regist. (Oral Surg.) Inst. Dent. Surg. & E.man Dent. Hosp.

O'DRISCOLL, Susan Catherine 2-6 Capitol Road, Higher Openshaw, Manchester M11 3SL — MB BS 1976 Lond.; BSc (Pharmacol.) Lond. 1973, MB BS 1976; DRCOG 1979. (Westm.) SHO (O & G) Heatherwood Hosp. Ascot. Prev: Ho. Surg. W.m. Hosp. Lond.; Ho. Phys. & Cas. Off. St. Stephen's Hosp. Lond.

O'DRISCOLL, Susan Leah The Old Croft, Legh Road, Knutsford WA16 8NR — MB ChB 1964 Leeds; MB ChB (Hons.) Leeds 1964; MRCP (U.K.) 1972. (Leeds)

O'DRISCOLL, Mr Thomas Gerard (retired) Calvert House, Greenway, Hutton Mount, Brentwood CM13 2NR Tel: 01277 223617 — MB BCh BAO NUI 1948; FRCS Eng. (Ophth.) 1956; FCOphth. 1989; DO RCS Eng. 1951. Prev: Cons. Ophth. Surg. Regional Eye Unit OldCh. Hosp. Romford.

O'DUCHON, Oscar 5 Linden Close, Saintfield, Ballynahinch BT24 7BH — MB BCh BAO 1991 NUI.

O'DUFFY, Desmond 142 Ravencroft, Bicester OX26 6YF — MB BCh BAO 1985 NUI; FCOphth 1991.

O'DWYER, Anne-Marie 63 Grandison Road, London SW11 6LT — MB BCh BAO 1986 Dub.; MRCPL (Irl) 1998; MRCPsych 1991; MD (Trinity Coll. Dublin) 1999. (Trinity Coll. Dublin.) Cons. Psychiat. Maudsley Hosp. Lond.

O'DWYER, Catherine Angela 10 Church Lane, Navenby, Lincoln LN5 0EG — MB BCh BAO 1987 NUI; FFA RCSI 1993.

O'DWYER, Mr Francis Gabriel Joseph Accident & Emergency Department, Burton District Hospital Centre, Belverdere Road, Burton-on-Trent DE13 0RB Tel: 01283 66333 — MB BCh BAO 1981 NUI; BSc (Hons.) Dub. 1983; FRCSI 1987. Cons. A & E Burton Dist. Hosp. Prev: Regist. (A & E) Leicester Roy. Infirm.

O'DWYER, Gearoid A Pontcae Surgery, Dynevor Street, Georgetown, Merthyr Tydfil CF48 1YE Tel: 01685 723931 Fax: 01685 377048.

O'DWYER, Gillian Margaret Llanfair Caereinion Health Centre, Llanfair Caereinion, Welshpool SY21 0RT Tel: 01938 810279 Fax: 01938 810955 — MB ChB 1966 Birm.; BSc, MB ChB Birm. 1966. (Birm.)

O'DWYER, Hugh Studdert 1 Craig-yr-Haul Drive, Castleton, Cardiff CF3 2SA — MB BCh 1970 Wales; FFA RCS Eng. 1975. Cons. (Anaesth.) Roy. Gwent Hosp. Newport. Prev: Sen. Regist. (Anaesth.) Univ. Hosp. Wales Cardiff; SHO (Cas.) Cardiff Roy. Infirm.; SHO (O & G) Neath Gen. Hosp.

O'DWYER, Jane Mary Eileen Department of Psychiatry, University of Sheffield, Northern General Hospital, Sheffield S5 7AU Tel: 01142 715216; 46 Carter Knowle Road, Sheffield S7 2DX — MB BCh BAO 1983 NUI; MD 1997; MRCPsych 1991. (Univ. Coll. Galway) Sen. Lect. (Psychiat. of Learining Disabil.) Univ. Sheff.; Hon. Cons. Psychiat. of Learning Disabil. Community Health Sheff. NHS Trust. Prev: Sen. Regist. (Psychiat.) Leeds; Regist. (Psychiat.) Leicester.

O'DWYER, John Studdert (retired) Troed-y-Bryn, Abertridwr, Caerphilly CF83 4BH — MB BCh BAO 1940 NUI. Prev: Capt. RAMC.

O'DWYER, Joseph Patrick Department of Anaesthesia, Southlands Hospital, Upper Shoreham Road, Shoreham-by-Sea BN43 6TQ Tel: 01273 455622; Hillbrook, London Road, Albourne, Hassocks BN6 9BJ — MB BCh BAO 1982 NUI; MRCP (UK) 1986; FCAnaesth 1989. Cons. Anaesth. Worthing & S.lands Hosps. NHS Trust. Prev: Sen. Regist. (Anaesth.) Soton. Gen. Hosp.; Vis. Asst. Prof. Anesthesiol. Univ. Maryland, Baltimore, USA.

O'DWYER, Mr Kevin John Department of Orthopaedic Surgery, Worcester Royal Infirmary, Castle St., Worcester WR1 3AS Tel: 01905 760163 Fax: 01905 760163; Thurlesbeg, 224 Malvern Road, Worcester WR2 4PA Tel: 01905 425230 Fax: 01905 425230 — MB BCh BAO 1978 Dub.; FRCS (Orth.) 1994; FRCS Eng. 1983. (Trinity Coll. Dublin) Cons. Orthop. Surg. Worcester Roy. Infirm. NHS Trust. Socs: Fell. BOA; Brit. Trauma Soc. Prev: Sen. Regist. Rotat. (Orthop.) Exeter & Truro; Regist. (Orthop.) P.ss Eliz. Orthop. Hosp. Exeter & Roy. Cornw. Hosp. Truro.

O'DWYER, Patrick Dermot Eithinog Hall, Cyfronydd, Welshpool SY21 9ED — MB BS 1964 Lond.; MRCS Eng. LRCP Lond. 1964; MRCOG 1971. (Univ. Coll. Hosp.)

O'DWYER, Professor Patrick Joseph University Department of Surgery, Western Infirmary, Glasgow G11 6NT Tel: 0141 339 8822 Fax: 0141 211 1972 Email: pjod25@clinmed.gla.ac.uk; 5 Fulton Gardens, Houston, Johnstone PA6 7NU Tel: 01505 324617 — MB BCh BAO 1979 NUI; MCh NUI 1986, MB BCh BAO 1979; FRCSI 1983. Prof. (Gastrointestinal Surg.) Univ. of Glas.; Hon. Cons. Surg. W.ern Infirm. Glas. Socs: Surg. Research Soc.; Assn. Surg. GR&G; Eur. Assn. Endoscopic Surg. Prev: Lect. (Surg.) Univ. Coll. Dub.

O'DWYER, Peter Francis The Surgery, 91 Dodworth Road, Barnsley S70 6ED Tel: 01226 282535 — MB BCh BAO 1973 NUI; BA Open 1992; MRCGP 1977; DGM RCP Lond. 1987; DRCOG 1978; DObst RCPI 1976; DCH NUI 1975; DCH RCPSI 1975. (Cork) Socs: BMA. Prev: Intern St. Finbarr's Hosp. Cork; SHO (Gen. Pract.) Barnsley AHA.

O'DWYER, Philip 5 Perry Green, Luton LU2 9QW — MB BS 1991 Lond.

O'DWYER, Sarah Theresa Patrice 31 Westbury Road, Crumpsall, Manchester M8 5RX — MB ChB 1979 Manch.; BSc St. And. 1976.

O'DWYER, Teresa Mary St. George's Hospital, Morpeth NE61 2NU Tel: 01670 512121 — MB ChB 1986 Leeds; MMedSci (Clin. Psychiat.) Leeds 1993; MRCPsych 1991. (Leeds) Cons. Psychiat. St. Geo. Hosp. N.d. Ment. Health Trust. Socs: BMA; Roy. Coll. Psychiats. Prev: Sen. Regist. Flexible Train. Scheme N. Deanary; Regist. Rotat. (Psychiat.) Leeds Train. Scheme; SHO (Psychiat.) St. Jas. Hosp. Leeds.

O'FARRELL, Anne Marie 41 Church View, Banbury OX16 9NB — MB ChB 1997 Bristol.

O'FARRELL, Brendan David West Bar Surgery, 1 West Bar Street, Banbury OX16 9SF Tel: 01295 256261 Fax: 01295 756848; 41 Church View, Banbury OX16 9NB Tel: 01295 264017 — MB BS 1971 Lond.; MRCS Eng. LRCP Lond. 1971; MRCGP 1976; DObst RCOG 1973. (St. Bart.) Prev: Trainee GP Kettering & Dist. VTS; Ho. Phys. & Ho. Surg. Redhill Gen. Hosp.

O'FARRELL, Jeanne Mary Department Medicine for Elderly People, Whipps Cross Hospital, Whipps Cross Rd, Leytonstone, London E11 1NR Tel: 020 8539 5522 Fax: 020 8535 6970; Flat 2, 546 Caledonian Road, London N7 9SJ Tel: 020 7609 6712 — MB BCh BAO 1977 NUI; MRCP (UK) 1985; MRCGP 1982. (Univ. Coll. Dub.) Cons. Med. for Elderly Whipps Cross Hosp. Lond. Socs: Brit. Geriat. Soc. Prev: Clin. Lect. (Geriat. Med.) Univ. Coll. & Middlx. Sch. Med. Univ. Coll. Hosp. Lond.; Regist. (Med.) Qu. Eliz. II Hosp. Welwyn Gdn. City Herts.; Ho. Surg. & Ho. Phys. Mater Miser. Hosp. Dub.

O'FARRELL, Nigel 44 Crookham Road, London SW6 4EQ — MB ChB 1976 Birm.; MRCPI 1984; MRCGP 1986.

O'FARRELL, Thomas Denis Paul Flat 4 Chartwell, 4B Church Hill, Edinburgh EH10 6BQ Tel: 0131 452 8335 — MB BCh BAO NUI 1967; FRCPsych 1988, M 1972; DPM Ed. & Glas. 1971. (Univ. Coll. Dub.) Cons. Psychiat. (Psychother.) Roy. Edin. Hosp.; Traing. Psychoanal. Scott. Inst. of Human Relations Edin.; Hon. Sen. Lect. Univ. Edin. Socs: Brit. Psychoanal. Soc. Prev: Sen. Lect. & Cons. (Psychother.) St. Geo. Hosp. Med. Sch. Lond.; Sen. Regist. (Adult) Tavistock Clinic Lond.; Sen. Regist. & Clin. Tutor (Psychiat.) Univ. Edin.

O'FLAHERTY, Kenneth Anthony Waterside Health Centre, Glendermott Road, Londonderry BT47 6AU Tel: 028 7132 0100 Fax: 028 7132 0117 — MB BCh BAO 1983; MRCGP 1989; DCH Glas. 1990; DRCOG 1987. (NUI Univ. Coll. Galway) SHO (Med.) Altnagelvin Hosp. Lond.derry. Prev: SHO (O & G & Paediat.) Altnagelvin Hosp. Lond.derry; Cas. Off. Roy. Preston Hosp.

O'FLANAGAN

O'FLANAGAN, Joyce Olwen 8 Marlfield Road, Grappenhall, Warrington WA4 2JT — MB ChB 1954 Birm.; DPM Eng. 1962, DCH 1957; DObst RCOG 1958.

O'FLANAGAN, Paul Henry Appletree Medical Practice, 47a Town Street, Duffield, Belper DE56 4GG Tel: 01332 841219 — MB BCh BAO 1972 Dub.; BA Dub. 1971; FRCGP 1988, M 1976; DObst RCOG 1976. Provost, Vale of Trent Fac. Bd.. Chairm., SDHA Dist. Clin. governance Comm. Socs: BMA & Chairm. Primary Care Quality Gp. Derbysh. Prev: Chairm. Vale of Trent Fac. Bd.; Course Organiser Derby VTS; Trainee GP Derby VTS.

O'FLANAGAN, Peter Malpas 8 Marlfield Road, Grappenhall, Warrington WA4 2JT Tel: 01925 63247 — LRCP & LM, LRSCI & LM 1945; LRCPI & LM, LRCSI & LM 1945; FRCPsych 1972; DPM RCPSI 1947. (RCSI) Prev: Cons. Psychiat. Winwick Hosp.; Psychiat. Regist. Pastures Hosp. Derby; Ho. Phys. Richmond Hosp. Dub.

O'FLANAGAN, William Joseph Dominic The Health Centre, Coatham Road, Redcar TS10 1SX Tel: 01642 484495 Fax: 01642 488701; 20 Hawthorn Road, Redcar TS10 3PA Tel: 01642 471436 — MB BS 1975 Newc.; MRCGP 1979. Prev: Clin. Asst. (Oncol.) Cleveland Hosp. Middlesbrough.

O'FLYNN, David William South London and Maudsley NHS Trust, Rehabilitation Services, Rehab Building, Lambeth Hospital, 108 Landor Rd, London SW9 9NT Tel: 020 7411 6306 Fax: 020 7411 6527 Email: david.o'flynn@slam-tr.nhs.uk — MB BS 1983 Lond.; MRCPsych 1989. p/t Cons. Psychiat., S. Lond. & Maudsley NHS Trust, Rehabil. Servs., Rehab Building. Lambeth Hosp., 108 Landor Rd, Lond. Prev: Research Fell. UMDS; SHO & Regist. (Psych. Med.) Guy's Hosp. Lond.; Specialist Regist.

O'FLYNN, Dermot Cornelius 57 Milton Road, London SE24 0NW Tel: 020 7733 8070 Email: dermot@docder.demon.co.uk — MB BCh BAO 1981 NUI. Socs: Brit. Med. Acupunct. Soc.

O'FLYNN, Desmond Robert The Maze, Leigh-on-Sea SS9 5RW — MB BS 1986 Lond.

O'FLYNN, Kieran Gerard 47 Third Cross Road, Twickenham TW2 5DY — MB BS 1990 Lond.

O'FLYNN, Mr Kieran Jeremiah 14 Broomfield Road, Stockport SK4 4ND — MB BCh BAO 1982 NUI; FRCSI 1986.

O'FLYNN, Mark William 6 Arum Close, Malvern WR14 2UT — MB BS 1992 Lond.

O'FLYNN, Nora Mary Flat 2, 27 Manville Road, London SW17 8JW — MB BCh BAO 1985 NUI; MRCGP 1993; DRCOG 1992; DGM RCP Lond. 1991.

O'FLYNN, Mr Paul Edward The Royal National Throat, Nose & Ear Hospital, Grays Inn Road, London WC1X 8DA Tel: 020 7915 1300; 55 Harley Street, London W1N 1DD Tel: 020 7580 4111 Fax: 020 7436 4901 — MB BS 1982 Lond.; FRCS Eng. 1988. (Univ. Coll. Lond.) Cons. Surg. Roy. Nat. Throat, Nose & Ear Hosp. Lond. Prev: Sen. Regist. (ENT Surg.) Nottm. & Derby Hosps.; Regist. (ENT Surg.) Char. Cross Hosp. Lond.; SHO (ENT Surg.) Roy. Nat. Throat, Nose & Ear Hosp. Lond.

O'FLYNN, Richard Redmond Department of Psychiatry, West Suffolk Hospital, Hardwick Lane, Bury St Edmunds IP33 2QZ Tel: 01284 713390 Fax: 01284 713694 — MB BS 1981 Lond.; MRCPsych 1985. (Char. Cross) Cons. Psychiat. W. Suff. Hosp. & Staff Cons. Psychiat. Priory Hosp. Chelmsford; Psychiat. Mem., the Parole Bd. for Eng. and Wales. Prev: Sen. Regist. (Psychiat.) SE Thames HA; Sen. Regist. (Psychiat.) SE Thames HA.

O'FRIEL, Arthur James, MBE (retired) Gartan Lodge, Ledsham Road, Little Sutton, South Wirral CH66 4QJ Tel: 0151 339 3500 — MB BCh BAO Belf. 1938. Prev: RNVR.

O'GALLAGHER, Deirdre Mary Bernadette Rylett Road Surgery, 45A Rylett Road, Shepherds Bush, London W12 9ST Tel: 020 8749 7863 Fax: 020 8743 5161; 16 Aycliffe Road, London W12 0LL — MB BS 1985 Lond.; MRCGP 1993.

O'GARA, Mary Geraldine Small Heath Medical Practice, 2 Gt. Wood Road, Small Heath, Birmingham B10 9QE Tel: 0121 766 8828 Fax: 0121 772 0097 — MB BCh BAO 1977 NUI; MRCGP 1982; DRCOG 1981. GP Partner, Small Heath Med. Pract., Small Heath, Birm.; Hosp. Practitioner, Diabetes, Heartlands Hosp., Birm.

O'GORMAN, Angela Jayne 21 Birchwood Avenue, Sidcup DA14 4JY — BM BS 1998 Nottm.

O'GORMAN, Ciaran 33 Hampton Parade, Sunnyside, Belfast BT7 3EQ — MB ChB 1995 Dundee.

O'GORMAN, Clare Josephine Antrim Health Centre, Station Road, Antrim BT41 4BS Tel: 028 9446 4939 — MB BCh BAO 1986 Belf.; MRCGP 1990; DRCOG 1991. Princip. in Gen. Pract., Antrim. Socs: BMA.

O'GORMAN, Ethna Catherine 134 Monlough Road, Saintfield, Ballynahinch BT24 7EU; Department of Mental Health, Whitla Medical Building, Queens University, Belfast BT9 7BL Tel: 01232 272169 Fax: 01232 324543 Email: eogorman@qub.ac.uk — MB BCh BAO NUI 1966; MD NUI 1974; FRCPsych 1985, M 1978; DPM RCPSI 1975. (Univ. Coll. Galway, Irel.) Cons. Psychiat. Belf. City Hosp. Trust; Dir. Clinic Skills Educat. Centre Qu.'s Univ. Belf. Socs: Fell. Rot. Soc. Med.; BMA; Ulster Med. Soc. Prev: Sen. Lect. Ment. Health Qu. Univ. Belf.; HA RVA RD Macy Schol. 1995; Clin. Research Fell. & Tutor/Regist. (Ment. Health) Belf.

O'GORMAN, Margaret 37 Hale Road, Hale, Liverpool L24 5RB Tel: 0151 425 2087 — MB BCh BAO 1948 NUI.

O'GORMAN, Margaret Elizabeth Nelson (retired) Westholm, Low Town, Thornhill, Stirling FK8 3PX Tel: 01786 85295 — MB ChB Glas. 1963; MRCPsych 1971; DPM Ed. & Glas. 1967. Prev: Cons. Child & Adolesc. Psychiat. Forth Valley HB.

O'GORMAN, Mary Elizabeth Victoria Road Surgery, 21 Victoria Road, Acocks Green, Birmingham B27 7XZ Tel: 0121 706 1129 Fax: 0121 765 4927 — MB ChB 1978 Liverp.; DRCOG 1980; DTM & H Liverp. 1982. Prev: Med. Off. Likuni Hosp. Malawi; Med. Off. Shisong Hosp. Cameroon.

O'GORMAN, Patrick (retired) Beechy Lees, Row Dow, Otford, Sevenoaks TN14 5RY Tel: 01959 522248 — MB BS 1954 Lond.; MD Lond. 1960; MRCS Eng. LRCP Lond. 1951; FRCPath 1964. Prev: Cons. Path. Brook Gen., Greenwich Dist. & Qu. Mary's Hosps. Lond.

O'GORMAN, Peter John 30 Blenheim Road, Cheadle Hulme, Cheadle SK8 7AN — MB BCh BAO 1990 NUI.

O'GORMAN, William Joseph The Square House, Peppard, Henley-on-Thames RG9 5EJ — MB ChB 1996 Manch.

O'GORMAN-LALOR, Olivia Anna Stephanie Nora Chelsea and Westminster Hospital, 369 Fulham Road, London W6 — MB BS 1994 Lond.; BSc 1991; MRCP (UK) 1997. (Char. Cross & Westm. Med. Sch.)

O'GRADY, Catherine Josephine (retired) Flat 6, Princess Court, 10-12 Canning Road, Croydon CR0 6QB Tel: 020 8654 1547 — MB BCh BAO NUI 1950. Prev: Ho. Phys. St. Luke's Hosp. Guildford.

O'GRADY, Elizabeth Anne 38 Harington Road, Formby, Liverpool L37 1NU — MB ChB 1985 Liverp.

O'GRADY, Professor Francis William, CBE, TD (retired) 32 Wollaton Hall Drive, Nottingham NG8 1AF Tel: 0115 978 3944 — MB BS (Hons.) Lond. 1950; MSc Lond. 1956, BSc (1st cl. Hons.) 1947, MD 1957; FRCP Lond. 1976, M 1971; FRCPath 1972, M 1963; Hon. FFPM RCP Lond. 1988. Prev: Prof. Microbiol. Univ. Nottm.

O'GRADY, Jane Tracy Oxfordshire Department of Public Health, Manor House, Headley Way, Headington, Oxford OX3 9DZ Tel: 01865 222599 — MB ChB 1984 Bristol; MRCPath 1991.

O'GRADY, Professor John Daiichi Pharmaceutical Co. Ltd., 76 Shoe Lane, London EC4A 3JB Tel: 020 7936 2850 Fax: 020 7583 6035; 47 Granville Road, Sevenoaks TN13 1HB Tel: 01732 453229 Fax: 01732 743122 — MB ChB Manch. 1967; MD Manch. 1983; FRCP Lond. 1988; MRCP (UK) 1976; FFPM 1989; T(M) 1991. Europ. Med. Dir. Daiichi Pharmaceut. Co. Ltd.; Dir. Imperial Cancer Research Technol. Ltd.; Cons. Health Protec. Br. Canada; Vis. Prof. Univ. Lond.; Vis. Prof. Clin. Pharmacol. Univ. Vienna, Austria; Examr. Dip. Pharmaceut. Med. RCP; Extern. Examr. Univ. Guildford. Socs: Fell. Roy. Soc. Med.; Fell. Roy. Statistical Soc.; Brit. Pharm. Soc. Prev: Med. Dir. May & Baker Ltd.; Head (Clin. Human Pharmacol.) Wellcome Foundat. Ltd.; Sen. Regist. St. Bart. Hosp. Lond.

O'GRADY, John Charles Ravenswood Home, Medium Secure Unit, Knowle, Fareham PO17 5NA Tel: 01329 836009 Fax: 01329 834780 Email: john.ogrady@wht.nhs.uk — MB BCh BAO 1975 NUI; MBA Durham 1995; FRCPsych 1995, M 1979. Cons. Psychiat. (Forens. Psychiat.) Ravenswood Ho. Fareham.

O'GRADY, John Gerard Mary King's College Hospital, Denmark Hill, London SE5 9PJ Tel: 020 7346 3367 Fax: 020 7346 3167 Email: john.g.o'grady@kcl.ac.uk — MB BCh BAO 1978 NUI; MD NUI 1983; FRCPI 1996. Cons. (Hepat.) King's Coll. Hosp. Lond.;

Hon. Sen. Lect. KCH Med. & Dent. Lond. Socs: Brit. Soc. Gastroenterol.; Eur. Assn. Study Liver; Amer. Assn. Study Liver Dis. Prev: Cons. (Hepat.) & Sen. Clin. Lect. St. James' Hosp. Leeds; Sen. Lect. Inst. Liver Studies King's Coll. Hosp. Lond.

O'GRADY, Margaret Mary Martina 9 The Mews, Sundrum Castle, By Coylton, Ayr KA6 5JY — MB BCh BAO 1990 NUI; MRCPsych 1997. (Galway) Cons. Psychiat. with s/i in Liason Psychiat. Socs: Roy. Coll. Psychiat. Prev: Specialist Regist. (Psychiat.) W. of Scot. Higher Train. Scheme.

O'GRADY, Michael Standish (retired) Spreets Rew, Arreton, Newport PO30 3AL Tel: 01983 865370 — MB BCh BAO 1948 Dub.; DObst RCOG 1953. JP.

O'GRADY, Timothy John Peter Hodgkinson Centre, Lincoln County Hospital, Lincoln LN2 5UA — MB ChB 1980 Leic.; MRCPsych 1984. Cons. Psychiat. Lincoln Co. Hosp.

O'HAGAN, Art Henry Knockaconey Road, Armagh BT61 8DU — MB BCh BAO 1994 Belf.

O'HAGAN, David Patrick 28 Cumbrian Way, Burnley BB12 8UF — MB BS 1993 Lond.

O'HAGAN, Dorothy Winifred (retired) Sounion, Mill Lane, Thimbleby, Horncastle LN9 5JS Tel: 01507 522382 — MB BS 1941 Durh. Prev: Asst. Co. Med. Off., Sch. Med. Off. & Family Plann. Med. Off. Lindsey CC.

O'HAGAN, Frances Theresa Friary Surgery, Dobbin Lane, Armagh BT61 7OG Tel: 375 21500 — MB BCh BAO 1989 Belf.; DCH; MRCGP; DGM; DRCOG; MRCGP; DCH; DGM; DRCOG. (Queens Belfast) p/t GP.

O'HAGAN, Jill 7 Norfolk Avenue, Heaton Chapel, Stockport SK4 5AG Tel: 0161 442 8828 — MB ChB 1983 Bristol. SHO (O & G) Hosp. St. Cross Rugby. Prev: SHO (Psychiat.) Tameside Gen. Hosp. Ashton-under-Lyne; Trainee GP Longsigh Manch.; SHO (Paediat.) Warwick Hosp.

O'HAGAN, Julie Elizabeth Clatterbridge Centre of oncology, Clatterbridge Road, Bebington, Wirral CH63 4JY; 13 Norfolk Avenue, Burton-upon-Stather, Scunthorpe DN15 9EW — MB BS 1993 Lond.; MRCP (UK) 1997.

O'HAGAN, Seamus 57 Glencregagh Drive, Belfast BT6 0NJ — MB BCh BAO 1993 Belf.

O'HAGAN, Simon James 21 William Alexander Park, Belfast BT10 0LX — MB BCh 1998 Belf.

O'HALLORAN, Paul David The Health Centre, Charlton Road, Andover SP10 3LD Tel: 01264 365031 Fax: 01264 336701; South View House, Ragged Appleshaw, Andover SP11 9HX Fax: 01264 772071 — MRCS Eng. LRCP Lond. 1985; MRCGP 1991; DFFP 1996; DObst Auckland 1989. (Char. Cross. Hosp. Lond.) GP Partner & Princip. Socs: (Sec.) Winchester & Andover Med. Golf Soc. Prev: Regist. (Psychiat.) Pk. Prewitt Hosp.; SHO (Psychiat.) Old Manor Hosp. Salisbury; SHO (O & G) & Regist. (Paediat.) Nat. Wom. Hosp. Auckland, NZ.

O'HANLON, Ann-Mary (retired) 5 Rubha Duig Heag, Fochdar, Lochboisdale HS8 — MB ChB 1944 Ed. Prev: JHMO (Surg.) Roy. Alexandra Infirm. Paisley.

O'HANLON, Christopher Houghton Tower Farm, Ramsbrook Lane, Hale, Liverpool L24 5RP — MB ChB 1970 Liverp.

O'HANLON, Denise Patricia Arrowe Sports Injuries Clinic, Archers Health Club, 132 Ford Road,Upton, Wirral CH49 0TQ Tel: 0151 604 0604; 22 Heron Road, Meols, Wirral CH47 9RU Tel: 0151 632 3946 — BM BS 1991 Nottm.; BMedSci 1989; Dip. Sports Med. (Scott. Roy. Colls.) 1997. Socs: BMA; Brit. Assn. Sport & Med.

O'HANLON, Donal Thomas John 56 Dundalk Street, Newtownhamilton, Newry BT35 0PB — MB BCh BAO 1990 NUI; LRCPSI 1990.

O'HANLON, John James 19 Richmond Court, Lisburn BT27 4QU — MB BCh BAO 1988 Belf.; BSc Belf. 1985, MB BCh BAO 1988.

O'HANLON, John Nangle, OStJ, TD (retired) 4 Leather Tor Close, Yelverton PL20 6EQ Tel: 01822 854034 Fax: 01822 854034 — LRCPI & LM, LRCSI & LM 1957. Prev: Sen. Med. Off. Home Office.

***O'HANLON, Karen Christina** Burnside, Closeburn Avenue, Heswall, Wirral CH60 4SP. — BM BS 1986 Nottm.

O'HANLON, Norah Mary Patricia (retired) Bermuda House, 1 Bakers Arms Hill, Arundel BN18 9DA — MB BS 1959 Lond.; BSc, MB BS Lond. 1959. Prev: Med. Asst. (Path.) Worthing & Chichester Health Dists.

O'HANLON, Peter Eric 52 Kingsknowe Road S., Edinburgh EH14 2JW — MB ChB 1978 Ed.

O'HANLON, Sean 22 Sourhille, Ballymena BT42 2LG — MB BCh BAO 1989 Belf.

O'HANLON, Stephen Gray The White Cottage, Western Avenue, Reading RG5 3BN — BChir 1997 Camb.; BChir Camb 1997.

O'HANLON, Sylvia North Tyneside General Hospital, Roke Lane, North Shields NE29 8NH Tel: 0191 253 6660 Fax: 0191 293 2563; 8 Alma Place, North Shields NE25 0LZ — Approbation Halle 1980; MSc (Pub. Health) Newc. 1993. (Univ. Halle Germany) Clin. Asst. (c/o Elderly) Newc. u. Tyne. Prev: Regist. (Pub. Health) Newc.

O'HANLON, Teresa Mary Old Hall Grounds Health Centre, Old Hall Grounds, Cowbridge CF71 7AH Tel: 01446 772237 Fax: 01446 775883; Stallcourt House, Stallcourt Close, Llanblethian, Cowbridge CF71 7JU — MB BS 1977 Lond.; MRCGP 1982.

O'HANRAHAN, Mr Timothy John Ward 33/34, Aberdeen Royal Infirmary, Foresterhill, Aberdeen AB25 2ZN Tel: 01224 681818; 1 Kingswood Gardens, Kingswells, Aberdeen AB15 8PE Tel: 01224 743080 — MB BCh BAO 1980 NUI; BSc Anat. (Hon.) NUI 1982, MCh 1991; FRCS (Gen.) 1995; FRCS Eng. 1986; FRCSI 1985. Cons. Gen. Surg. Aberd. Roy. Infirm. Socs: Assn. Surg.; BMA. Prev: Cons. Surg. Raigmore Hosp. Inverness; Lect. (Surg.) Aberd. Roy. Infirm.

O'HARA, Ann Wilson 5 Marine Terrace, Muchalls, Stonehaven AB39 3RD — MB ChB 1975 Glas.; DCH RCPS Glas. 1978; DRCOG 1977. SCMO (Community Child Health) Stonehaven.

O'HARA, Arthur Gerard Gransha Hospital, Clooney Road, Londonderry BT47 6WJ Tel: 01504 860261 — MB BCh BAO 1974 Belf. Cons. Psychiat. Gransha Hosp. Lond.derry.

O'HARA, Dermot Patrick Drs O'Hara, Finn + Bliss, 46-48 Grey Road, Walton, Liverpool L9 1AX Tel: 0151 525 1644; 5 Granville Park, Aughton, Ormskirk L39 5DS Tel: 01695 422247 — MB BCh BAO 1981 NUI; LRCPI & LM, LRCSI & LM 1981; DRCOG 1988; DCH RCSI 1983. GP Princip., Sen. Partner. Prev: Princip. GP Manch. & Warrington, Med. Off. DSS.

O'HARA, Fenella Rachel Judges Close Surgery, Judges Close, East Grinstead RH19 3AE Tel: 01342 324628; 19 Springfield, East Grinstead RH19 2RT Tel: 01342 328276 — MB BS 1990 Newc.; MRCGP 1995; DRCOG 1994. (Newcastle) GP Retainee Judges Cl. Surg. E. Grinstead. Prev: GP Princip.; Clin. Asst. (ENT) Wrexham Maelor Hosp.

O'HARA, Gerard Vincent 71 Naishcombe Hill, Wick, Bristol BS30 5QS — MB ChB 1991 Sheff.

O'HARA, Helena 128 Wolseley Road, Rugeley WS15 2ET — MB BCh BAO 1940 NUI. (Univ. Coll. Dub.)

O'HARA, Jean The Royal London Hospital, 130A Sewardstone Road, East London & the City Mental Health Trust, London E2 9HN Tel: 020 8981 7425 Fax: 020 8983 1026 — MB BS 1983 Lond.; MRCPsych 1988. Cons. Psychiat. Roy. Lond. Hosp.; Hon. Cons. - Barts & the Lond. NHS Trust; Hon. Sen. Clin. Lect. - Qu. Mary & W.field Coll. Univ. Of Lond. Socs: Fell. Roy. Soc. Med.; BMA; Roy. Coll. Psychiat. Prev: Sen. Regist. (Psychiat. of Ment. Handicap) Dept. Psychol. Med. St. Bart. Hosp. Lond. & Leytonstone Hse. S. Ockenden; SHO & Regist. Rotat. (Psychiat.) Waltham Forest & Enfield HA.

O'HARA, John 4 Cranleigh Avenue, Rottingdean, Brighton BN2 7GT Tel: 01273 302954 — MB ChB 1929 Glas. (Glas.) Mem. Med. Comm. Football Assn. (Chairm.). Socs: Fell. Roy. Soc. Med.; BMA. Prev: Med. Off. St. Dunstans Homes Brighton; Examr. Chest Med. Min. of Pens.; Chest Phys. E. Sussex CC.

O'HARA, Mr John Neary 7 Chad Road, Birmingham B15 3EN Tel: 0121 454 2991; Wind Flowers, The Drive, Burcot, Bromsgrove B60 1PP Tel: 0121 445 1386 — LRCPI & LM, LRSCI & LM 1976; LRCPI & LM, LRCSI & LM 1976; MCh NUI 1991; FRCS Eng. 1981; FRCSI Dub. 1981. (RCSI) Regist. (Orthop.) City Hosp. & Roy. Orthop. Hosp. Birm. Prev: Staff Sick Childr. Hosp. Toronto; Regist. Rotat. (Orthop.) Birm.; Regist. (Surg.) Bradford AHA.

O'HARA, Lawrence Joseph 18 Stonor Road, London W14 8RZ — MB BS 1991 Lond.

O'HARA, Liam Andrew 18 Melmerby Cl, Newcastle upon Tyne NE3 5JA — MB ChB 1997 Manch.

O'HARA, Mary Geraldine Ballymena Health Centre, Cushendall Road, Ballymena BT43 6HQ Tel: 028 2564 2181 Fax: 028 2565 8919; Leighinmohr Avenue, Ballymena BT42 2AT Tel: 01266 45974

O'HARA

— MB BCh BAO 1982 Belf.; MRCGP 1987; DCH Dub. 1987; DRCOG 1987.

O'HARA, Michael Denis Department of Pathology, Queen's University Belfast, Grosvenor Road, Belfast BT12 6BN Tel: 01232 894744 Fax: 01232 233643 Email: d.ohara@qub.ac.uk — MB BCh BAO 1966 Belf.; BSc (Hons. Anat.) Belf. 1963; FRCPath 1985, M 1973. (Qu. Univ. Belf.) Sen. Lect. Qu. Univ. Belf.; Cons. Roy. Vict. Hosp. Belf. Socs: Path. Soc.; Assn. Clin. Path.; (Treas.) Brit. Paediat. Path. Assn. Prev: Dunville Fell.sh. (Path.) Qu. Univ. Belf.; Sen. Regist. & Tutor Inst. Path. Qu. Univ. Belf.

O'HARA, Nora Patrica (retired) 118 St Marys Street, Latchford, Warrington WA4 1BH — MB, BCh BAO NUI 1946.

O'HARA, Patrick Joseph (retired) Foxwood, 10 Norton Lane, Halton, Runcorn WA7 2PR Tel: 0192 85 73509 — MB BCh BAO 1951 NUI. Prev: Ho. Phys. Co. Hosp. Castlebar.

O'HARA, Richard James 31 Branksome Road, Coundon, Coventry CV6 1FW — BM BS 1991 Nottm.; FRCS 1996. Specialist Regist. (Gen. Surg.) Oxf. Deanery.

O'HARA, Sheila Valerie Portland Medical Centre, 184 Portland Road, London SE25 4JQ Tel: 020 662 1233 Fax: 020 8656 7984, 020 8662 1223; Oakcroft, 12 Grimwade Avenue, Croydon CR0 5DG Tel: 020 8656 0213 — MB ChB 1969 Manch.; Cert. Family Plann. JCC 1975. (Manch.) GP Trainer Lond.; GP Tutor KCH Med. Sch. Lond. Prev: Ho. Surg. Univ. Hosp. S. Manch. Withington Hosp.; Ho. Phys. St. Mary Abbots Hosp. Lond.

O'HARA, Simon David North Long Barn, Lane End Farm, Hunger Hill Road, Ilkley LS29 0DP — MB ChB 1988 Liverp. SHO Rotat. (Med.) Leeds Gen. Infirm.

O'HARA, Adrian Gerard Mary 2 Rostrevor Road, Warrenpoint, Newry BT34 3RT — MB BCh BAO 1981 NUI.

O'HARA, Anne Elizabeth 39 Grange Road, Edinburgh EH9 1UG — MB BS 1978 Newc.; MD 1987; MRCP (UK) 1980.

O'HARE, Bernadette Ann Marie 13 Mountain Road, Cloughoge, Newry BT35 8NJ — MB BCh BAO 1988 Belf.

O'HARE, Brendan Joseph Castlederg Surgery, 13A Lower Strabane Road, Castlederg BT81 7AZ Tel: 028 8167 1211 Fax: 028 8167 9700 — MB BCh BAO 1985 Belf.; MRCGP 1989; DCH RCPS Glas. 1988; DRCOG 1988; DGM RCP Lond. 1987.

O'HARE, Conor Vincent 21 Barranderry Heights, Enniskillen BT74 6JW — MB BCh BAO 1990 Belf.; MB BCh Belf. 1990.

O'HARE, Deborah Jayne 2 Stamford Road, Exton, Oakham LE15 8AZ — MB ChB 1990 Manch. Demonst. (Anat.) St. And. Univ.

O'HARE, Deirdre Mary McDonnell and Partners, 139-141 Ormeau Road, Belfast BT7 1DA Tel: 028 9032 6030; 125 Shandon Park, Belfast BT5 6NZ Tel: 01232 795295 — MB BCh BAO 1984 Belf.; MRCGP 1989; DRCOG 1988.

O'HARE, Irene Paula 18 Drumnabey Road, Castlederg BT81 7NF — MB BCh BAO 1983 Belf.; MB BCh Belf. 1983; MRCGP 1989; DRCOG 1987.

O'HARE, John 21 Floral Park, Newtownabbey BT36 7RU — MB BCh BAO 1996 Belf.

O'HARE, Joseph Paul Hospital of St Cross, Barby Road, Rugby CV22 5PX Tel: 01788 545180 Fax: 01788 545251; 32 Waverley Road, Kenilworth CV8 1JN Tel: 01926 853783 — MB BS 1979 Lond.; MD Lond. 1986; FRCP Lond. 1994; MRCP (UK) 1982. Cons. Phys. (Diabetes & Endocrinol.) Hosp. St. Cross Rugby; Reader (Med. & Biol. Sci.) Univ. Warwick.

O'HARE, Kevin John 3F1, 121 Novar Drive, Hyndland, Glasgow G12 9TA Tel: 0141 339 1055 Email: kevin.o'hare@virgin.net — MB ChB 1991 Ed.; FRCA 1997; FFARCSI 1997. Specialist Regist. (Anaesth.) Glas. Roy. Infirm. NHS Trust. Prev: Specialist Regist. (Anaesth.) Glas. Roy. Infirm. NhS Trust.

O'HARE, Martin 23 Spelga Park, Hilltown, Newry BT34 5UU — MB ChB 1993 Birm.

O'HARE, Mary Patricia Dufferin Wards (ENT), Belfast City Hospital, Lisburn Road, Belfast BT9 7A; 6 Deramore Park S., Belfast BT9 5JY — MB BCh BAO 1983 Belf.; MRCGP 1988; DGM RCP Lond. 1986; DRCOG 1986; Cert. Family Plann. JCC 1986. GP Belf.

O'HARE, Michael Francis Daisy Hill Hospital, Newry BT35 8DR Tel: 028 3083 5000 Fax: 028 3026 8285 Email: m.f.ohare@btinternet.com; 39 Camlough Road, Newry BT35 7LS Tel: 028 3026 2445 Fax: 028 3026 8285 — MD Belf. 1983, MB BCh BAO 1970; FRCOG 1989, M 1975; DRCOG 1972. Cons. O & G Daisy Hill Hosp. Newry. Socs: Fell. Ulster Med. Soc. Prev: Sen. Tutor & Sen. Regist. Roy. Matern. Hosp. & Dept. Midw. & Gyn.; Qu.'s Univ. Belf.; Clin. Research Fell. Dept. Midw. & Gyn. Qu. Univ.; Belf.; Regist. (O & G) Harari Centr. Hosp. Salisbury, Rhodesia.

O'HARE, Patrick Austen Tel: 01582 712126 Fax: 01582 462414 — MB ChB 1977 Leeds; DRCOG 1979. Socs: Leeds Med. Soc. Prev: Ho. Phys. St. Jas. Univ. Hosp. Leeds; Ho. Surg. Chapel Allerton Hosp. Leeds.

O'HARE, Mr Peter Melville Department of Plastic Surgery, Castle Hill Hospital, Castle Road, Cottingham HU16 Tel: 01482 875875 Fax: 01482 622353 — MB ChB 1973 Bristol; BSc (Biochem., Hons.) Bristol 1970; FRCS Eng. 1977. (Bristol) Cons. (Plastic Surg.) Hull E. Yorks. NHS Trust. Socs: Brit. Assn. Plastic Surg.; Mem. Brit. Assn. Aesthetic Plastic Surgs.; Mem. Spec. Advisery Comm. For Plastic Surg. To Jt. Comm. For Higher Surg. Train. (Roy. Coll. Surg.s). Prev: Sen. Regist. (Plastic Surg.) Roy. Vict. Hosp. Belf. & The Ulster; Hosp. Dundonald.; Regist. E. Anglian Regional Plastic Surg. Serv. W. Norwich Hosp.

O'HARE, Ronan Andrew 21 Barranderry Heights, Enniskillen BT74 6JW — MB BCh BAO 1992 Belf.; MB BCh Belf. 1992.

O'HARE, Rosemary 6 Park Court, Giffnock, Glasgow G46 7PB Tel: 0141 638 5177 — MB ChB Glas. 1943; BSc Glas. 1940; MRCGP 1965. Socs: BMA. Prev: GP Glas.

O'HARE, Ruth The Surgery, 41 Connaught Square, London W2 2HL Tel: 020 7723 3338 Fax: 020 7402 3342 — MB BChir 1978 Camb.; MA Camb. 1979; MRCP (UK) 1981. Lect. (Gen. Pract.) St. Mary's Med. Sch. Lond.

O'HARE, Tom Joseph 9 Lincoln Drive, Smithybridge, Littleborough OL15 0NE — MB ChB 1984 Sheff.; BA (Hons) Med. Sci. Camb. 1981; MRCGP 1988; DRCOG 1988. Regist. Rotat. (Psychiat.) Gtr. Manch. Prev: SHO (Psychiat.) N. Manch. Gen. Hosp.; Trainee GP Rotat. Chesterfield; Psychiat. Rotat. N. Manch.

O'HEA, Anna-Marie Dormer Cortrage, Green End St., Aston Clinton, Aylesbury HP22 5EX — MB BCh BAO 1977 Dub.; MRCP (UK) 1980; MRCPath 1984. Cons. Haemat. Stoke Mandeville Hosp. Aylesbury.

O'HICKEY, Stephen Patrick Department of Respiratory Medicine, Worcester Royal Infirmary, Worcester WR1 3AS Tel: 01905 760240 Fax: 01905 760237 Email: steveohickey@writ.wmids.nhs.uk — MB ChB 1981 Manch.; MD Manch. 1990; MRCP (UK) 1984; FRCP 1999. Cons. Phys. (Respirat. Med.) Worcester Roy. Infirm. Prev: Cons. Phys. (Respirat. Med.) Solihull Hosp. W. Midl.; Sen. Regist. (Thoracic Med.) E. Birm. Hosp.; Research Asst. (Respirat. Med.) Guy's Hosp. Lond.

O'HIGGINS, Frances Margaret 27C Beaufort Road, Clifton, Bristol BS8 2JX — MB BS 1991 Lond.; BSc Lond. 1989; MRCP (UK) 1994; FRCA 1997.

O'HIGGINS, John William Department of Anaesthetics, Bristol Royal Infirmary, Bristol BS2 8HW Tel: 0117 923 0000; 4 Stoke Park Road S., Sneyd Park, Bristol BS9 1LS Tel: 0117 968 2365 — MB BS 1959 Lond.; FFA RCS Eng. 1968; DObst RCOG 1962; DA Eng. 1962. (Lond. Hosp.) Cons. Anaesth. United Bristol Healthcare Trust. Socs: Assn. Paediat. Anaesth. Prev: Treas. Soc. Anaesth. S. W.. Region; Educat. Adviser Anaesth. SW Region; Mem. Hosp. Accredit. Bd.

O'HIGGINS, Paul Department of Anatomy & Developmental Biology, University College London, Gower St., London WC1E 6BT — MB ChB 1982 Leeds; PhD Leeds 1989. Reader (Anat.) Univ. Coll. Lond. Prev: Sen. Lect. (Anat.) Univ. W.. Austral.; Lect. (Anat.) Univ. Leeds.

O'HORAN, Patrick The Burns Practice, 4 Albion Place, Bennetthorpe, Doncaster DN1 2EQ Tel: 01302 810888 Fax: 01302 812150 — MB BS 1982 Lond.; Cert. Family Plann. JCC 1986. (St. Mary's) Princip. GP Doncaster.; Med. Adviser Doncaster MBC. Socs: BMA; Soc. of Occup. Med. Prev: Trainee GP Doncaster VTS.

O'KANE, Agnes Elizabeth The Bungalow, 118 Malone Road, Belfast BT9 5HR — MB BCh BAO 1985 Belf.

O'KANE, Anne Genevieve Diamond Medical Centre, Meeting Street, Magherafelt BT45 6ED — MB BCh BAO 1983 Belf.; MRCGP 1988; DCCH RCP Ed. 1987; DCH Dub. 1987; DRCOG 1986.

O'KANE, Bronagh Mary Wynne Hill Surgery, 51 Hill St., Lurgan, Craigavon BT66 6BW Tel: 01762 326333; 75 Steps Road, Donaghcloney, Craigavon BT66 7NZ — MB BCh BAO 1985 Belf.; MRCGP 1991; DCH RCPSI 1989; DRCOG 1988.

O'KANE, Cecilia Majella 18 Foyle Av, Greysteel, Londonderry BT47 3EB — MB BCh BAO 1997 Belf.

O'KANE, Christopher Anthony John The Life Guards, Combermere Barracks, Windsor SL4 3DN — MB BChir 1984 Camb.; MA, MB BChir Camb. 1984. Regtl. Med. Off. to The Life Guards.

O'KANE, Damian Joseph Crumlin Road Health Centre, 130-132 Crumlin Road, Belfast BT14 6AR — MB BCh BAO 1987 Belf.; MRCGP 1992.

O'KANE, Declan 13 The Cedars, Jordanstown, Belfast BT5 6LU — MB BCh BAO 1991 Belf.

O'KANE, Dermot Patrick 148 Priory Road, Dungiven, Londonderry BT47 4LR — MB BCh BAO 1995 Belf.

O'KANE, Ellen Maria 185 Ballymena Road, Doagh, Ballyclare BT39 0TW — MB BCh BAO 1990 Belf.; MB BCh Belf. 1990.

O'KANE, Gerald St. Machar's House, Kilbarchan Road, Bridge of Weir PA11 3ET — MB ChB 1973 Glas.

O'KANE, Hugh Felix Gerald 9 Malone Pa, Belfast BT9 6NH — MB BCh 1998 Belf.

O'KANE, Mr Hugh Oliver 9 Malone Park, Belfast BT9 6NH Tel: 01232 665778 — MB BCh BAO 1960 Belf.; BSc Belf. 1957, MCh 1970, MB BCh BAO 1960; FRCS Ed. 1963. (Belf.) Cons. Cardiac Surg. Roy. Vict. Hosp. Belf. Socs: Brit. Soc. Thoracic & Cardiovasc. Surg. & Brit. Cardiac Soc.; Pres. Irish Cardiac Soc. Prev: Asst. Prof. Surg. Washington Univ. St. Louis, USA; on Attend. Staff Jewish Hosp. St. Louis, USA; Resid. (Cardiothoracic Surg.) Mayo Clinic Rochester, USA.

O'KANE, Jacinta Gerardene Paula 12 Ann Street, Ballycastle BT54 6AD — MB BCh BAO 1976 Belf.; DCH NUI 1978.

O'KANE, Jacintha Grace 51 Mullagh Meash Park, Feeny, Londonderry BT47 4TY — MB BCh 1998 Belf.

O'KANE, Janine Marie 613 antrim Road, Belfast BT15 4DY — MB BCh BAO 1981 Belf.

O'KANE, John Bernard The Oaks Family Medical Centre, 48 Orritor Road, Cookstown BT80 8BH Tel: 028 7976 2249 Fax: 028 7976 6793; 1 Tullagh Drive, Cookstown BT80 8ED — MB BCh BAO 1974 Belf.; DObst RCOG 1976. Mem. United Hosps. Trust (GP Forum). Socs: GMSC (N. I.); N. Irel. LMC.

O'KANE, Judith Jane Bridge Street Medical Centre, 30 Bridge Street, Londonderry BT48 6LA Tel: 028 7126 1137 Fax: 028 7137 0723 — MB BCh BAO 1977 Dub.; DCH Dub. 1981; DRCOG 1980. Socs: BMA.

O'KANE, Kevin Malachy 2 Cairnshill, Newry BT34 2ST — MB BCh BAO 1987 Belf.

O'KANE, Kevin Patrick James 41 Beechwood Drive, Broomhill, Glasgow G11 7ET — MB ChB 1987 Glas.

O'KANE, Martin Patrick 180 Vow Road, Ballymoney BT53 7NS — MB BCh BAO 1997 Belf.

O'KANE, Maurice John Clinical Chemistry Laboratory, Altnagelvin Hospital, Glenshane Road, Londonderry BT47 6SB Tel: 01504 45171 — MB ChB 1985 Ed.; BSc (Hons.) Ed. 1983; MD Belf. 1995; MRCP (UK) 1988; MRCPath 1993. Cons. Chem. Path. Altnagelvin Hosp. Lond.derry. Socs: Assn. Clin. Biochem.

O'KANE, Michael John Cwmfelin Medical Centre, 298 Carmarthen Road, Swansea SA1 1HW Tel: 01792 653941 — MB BS 1966 Lond.; MRCS Eng. LRCP Lond. 1966; DCH Eng. 1968. (Middlx.) Prev: Ho. Surg. O & G Middlx. Hosp.; Ho. Phys. Paediat. St. Albans City Hosp.

O'KANE, Patrick Joseph 16 Duncreggan Road, Londonderry BT48 0AD Tel: 01504 262034 — MB BCh BAO 1950 NUI.

***O'KANE, Roisin Maira Teresa** 19 Innisfayle Road, Belfast BT15 4ES; 19 Innisfayle Road, Belfast BT15 4ES — MB BCh BAO 1997 Belf.; DME 1999.

O'KANE, Rosa Dialhouse Medical Centre, 131 Mile End Lane, Stockport SK2 6BZ Tel: 0161 483 2535; 50 Siskin Road, Offerton, Stockport SK2 5JX Tel: 0161 419 9473 — MB ChB 1986 Leic.; DRCOG 1991; DMH Belf. 1991.

O'KANE, William Patrick 6 Leighimohr Avenue, Ballymena — MB BCh BAO 1957 Belf. (Belf.) Clin. Med. Off. N. Health & Social Servs. Bd. (N. Irel.).

O'KEEFFE, Anthony Guy 26 Eaton Terrace, London SW1W 8TS Tel: 020 7730 5070; 10 West Hill Road, London SW18 1LN — MB BS 1986 Lond.; MA Camb. 1982; MRCP (UK) 1986; Cert. Family Plann. JCC 1988. (Guy's Hosp.) Indep. GP Lond. Socs: BMA; Lister Hosp. Private Pract. Gp. Prev: Trainee GP St. Thos. Hosp. VTS; Regist. (Med.) Roy. Masonic Hosp.; SHO (A & E) Guy's Hosp. Lond.

O'KEEFFE, Caroline Jane 12 Haig Avenue, Poole BH13 7AJ — MB ChB 1998 Bristol.

O'KEEFFE, Charles James Maunsell (retired) 1 Brookedor, Kingskerswel, Newton Abbot TQ12 5BJ Tel: 01803 873861 — MB BS 1958 Lond.; DObst RCOG 1961. Prev: Ho. Surg., Ho. Phys. & SHO O & G Norf. & Norwich Hosp.

O'KEEFFE, Daniel Finnbarr Churchward and Partners, Croft Medical Centre, 2 Glen Road, Oadby, Leicester LE2 4PE Tel: 0116 271 2564 Fax: 0116 272 9000; 63 Linden Drive, Evington, Leicester LE5 6AJ — MB BCh BAO 1976 NUI; DCH RCPSI 1978; DObst RCPI 1979.

O'KEEFFE, Mr Declan (retired) 2 Roseville Apartments, Wandsworth Road, Bangor BT19 1DZ Tel: 01247 272143 — MB BS 1945 Lond.; FRCS Eng. 1950; MRCS Eng. LRCP Lond. 1945; DTM & H Eng. 1952. Prev: Vis. Lect. Prof. Calif. Med. Centre, Los Angeles.

O'KEEFFE, Declan Barry Cardiac Unit, Belfast City Hospital, Lisburn Road, Belfast BT9 7AB Tel: 028 329241 — MD 1970 Lond.; BSc (1st cl. Hons. Anat.) Lond. 1970, MD, MB BS 1973; FRCP Lond. 1989; MRCP (UK) 1975. (Guys) Cons. Cardiol. Belf. City Hosp.

O'KEEFFE, Kevin Anthony Glanworth, Brandy Hole Lane, Chichester PO19 4RJ Tel: 01243 527555 — MB BCh BAO 1956 NUI; FRCPsych 1984, M 1972; DPM Eng. 1962. (Univ. Coll. Dub.) Emerit. Cons. Child Psychiat. Chichester Health Dist. Prev: Sen. Regist. (Child Psychiat.) Guy's Hosp. Lond.; Regist. (Psychiat.) W.m. Hosp. Lond.; Ho. Surg. & Ho. Phys. St. Vincent's Hosp. Dub.

O'KEEFFE, Mr Leonard Joseph ENT Department, Royal Bolton Hospital, Minerva Road, Farnworth, Bolton BL4 0JR Tel: 01204 390018; 17 Greenmount Lane, Bolton BL1 5JE — MB BCh BAO 1984 NUI; FRCS (Orl.) 1996; FRCS Ed. 1994; FRCSI 1988. Cons. Otorhinolaryngologists, Bolton. Socs: Brit. Assoc. of OtorhinoLaryngol. and Head & Neck Surg.s; Roy. Soc. Med.; OtoLaryngol. Research Soc. Prev: Regist. (Gen. Surg.) Mercy Hosp. Cork; SHO (ENT) Bristol Roy. Infirm.; Sen. Regist. Rotat. NW Region.

O'KEEFFE, Nial John Department of Anaesthesia, Manchester Royal Infirmary, Oxford Road, Manchester M13 9WL Tel: 0161 276 4552 Fax: 0161 276 8027 Email: niall.okeeffe@man.ac.uk; 27 Elm Road, Didsbury, Manchester M20 6XD — MB BCh BAO 1984 NUI; FCAnaesth 1989; FFA RCSI 1988. Cons. Anaesth. Manch. Roy. Infirm. Prev: Sen. Regist. NW RHA; Regist. (Anaesth.) Withington Hosp. S. Manch. HA.

O'KEEFFE, Paul Timothy Andrew Princess Margaret Hospital, Okus Road, Swindon SN1 4JU Tel: 01793 480817; Frog Cottage, Green Lane, Milton-under-Wychwood, Oxford OX7 6JY — MB BS 1983 Lond.; BSc Lond. 1980; MRCP (UK) 1987. Cons. Paediat. Prev: Paediat. Sen. Regist. John Radcliffe, Oxf.; Research Fell. (Paediat.) P.ss Margt. Hosp. Perth, Austral.

O'KEEFFE, Mr Terence Sidney Fonbadet, Odstock, Salisbury SP5 4JB Tel: 01722 332083 Fax: 01722 332083 Email: okeeffet@msn.com — MB ChB 1994 Ed.; BSc (1st cl. Hons.) Ed. 1992; FRCS (Ed.) 1999. (University of Edinburgh) SHO (Orthop.) Salisbury Dist. Hosp. Prev: SHO (Gen. Surg.) Salisbury Dist. Hosp.; SHO (Gen. Surg.) Oregon Health Sci.s Univ. Portland, USA; SHO (A & E Med.) Roy. Infirm. Edin.

O'KEEFFE, Una Bridget 73 Belmont Church Road, Belfast BT4 3FG — MB BCh BAO 1960 NUI.

O'KEEFFE, Vincent Martin St. Winifrides School House, Llanasa Road, Glwespyr, Holywell CH8 9LU — MB BCh BAO 1986 NUI.

O'KELLY, Francis Joseph, OBE (retired) Large Barn, North Bersted St, Bognor Regis PO22 9AH Tel: 01243 826189 — MB BCh BAO 1946 NUI; DPH 1961; FACOM 1985; MFOM RCP Lond. 1980; FFCM 1977. Prev: Cons. (Occupat. Health) Governm. of Hong Kong.

O'KELLY, Francis Patrick, MBE Clare House, Newport St., Tiverton EX16 6NJ Tel: 01884 252337; Villa Franca, 9 Park Road, Tiverton EX16 6AU Tel: 01884 256570 — MB BS 1987 Lond.; MRCGP 1995; DRCOG 1995; DCH RCP Lond. 1994; DA (UK) 1993. (St. Bart. Hosp. Lond.) GP Princip.; Hosp. Pract. Anaesth. Prev: SHO (Anaesth.) Roy. United Hosp. Bath; Trainee GP Midsomer Norton; SHO (Med. & Geriat.) Jersey Gen. Hosp.

O'KELLY

O'KELLY, John Kevin Aberfoyle Terrace Surgery, 3-5 Aberfoyle Terrace, Strand Road, Londonderry BT48 7NP Tel: 028 7126 4868; 3 Waterstone Park, Trench Road, Londonderry BT47 2AG — MB BCh BAO 1984 Belf.; MRCGP 1989; DCH RCP Lond. 1987.

O'KELLY, Kate Francesca Bacon One Tree House, South Harting, Petersfield GU31 5NW — MB BS 1989 Lond.; BA Oxf. 1986; Dip. Paediat. Auckland 1992. Clin. Asst. (Gastroenterol.) St. Richard's Chichester; Clin. Asst. (Endocrinol.) St. Richard's Chichester.

O'KELLY, Lindsay Margaret 2 Moorgate, Lechlade GL7 3EH — BM 1982 Soton.; MRCGP 1994; DRCOG 1987; DCH RCP Lond. 1986. Prev: GP Soton.; Fell. (Family Pract.) Univ. Michigan, USA.

***O'KELLY, Noel Ignatius** The Surgery, Bull Yard, Simson Street, Spilsby PE23 5JE Tel: 01790 752555 Fax: 01790 754457 — MB BCh BAO 1986 Belf.; MRCGP 1990; DRCOG 1990.

O'KELLY, Rosaleen Mary 2 Burghley Road, Stone Manor Park, Lincoln LN6 7YE — MB BCh BAO 1976 NUI; MRCGP 1981. (Univ. Coll. Dub.)

O'KELLY, Sean William Princess Margaret Hospital, Okus Road, Swindon SN1 4JU Tel: 01793 426389 — BSc (Hons.) Bristol 1981, MB ChB 1984; FCAnaesth. 1991; DCH RCP Lond. 1989; DA (UK) 1988. Cons. Anaesth. P.ss Margt. Hosp. Swindon. Socs: Anaesth. Res. Soc.; Soc. Cardiovasc. Anaesth. Prev: Clin. Asst. Prof. Dept. Anaesth. Univ. Michigan, USA; Sen. Regist. (Anaesth.) Soton. & Portsmouth.

O'KELLY, Mr Terence James Whin Cottage, Ardoe, Aberdeen AB12 5XT — MB BS 1983 Lond.; BSc Lond. 1980, MB BS 1983; FRCS Eng. 1987. Research Fell. (Pharmacol.) & Nuffield Dept. Surg. Univ. Oxf.; Hon. Clin. Lect. Nuffield Dept. Surg. Univ. Oxf.; Hon. Regist. John Radcliffe Hosp. Oxf. Prev: Regist. (Surg.) John Radcliffe Hosp. Oxf.; SHO (Surg.) Glos. Roy. Hosp.

O'LEARY, Aeneas Francis 12 Wyndham Court, Commercial Road, Southampton SO15 1GS Tel: 02380 234644; Gort Mhuire, Cork Road, Killarney, County Kerry, Republic of Ireland Tel: 0164 31252 — MB BCh BAO 1984 NUI; DObst RCPI 1988.

O'LEARY, Amanda Jane Obsacitynae Department, South Mead Hospital, Westbury-onTrym, Bristol BS10 5NB Mobile: 01179 505050 Email: amandajoleary@hotmail.com — MB ChB 1992 Aberd.; MRCOG 1998. (Aberdeen) Research Fell. S. Mead Hosp. Bristol. Prev: Specialist Regist. (O & G) - Welsh Sotation.

***O'LEARY, Catherine Anne** 9 Buckingham Road, Bicester OX26 2NU — MB ChB 1996 Birm.; ChB Birm. 1996.

O'LEARY, Clare Louise 25 Quarry Hills Lane, Lichfield WS14 9HL — BM BS 1997 Nottm.

O'LEARY, Clare Marie 24 Springbank Road, Cheltenham GL51 0LU — MB ChB 1998 Liverp.

O'LEARY, Colin Peter Department of Neurology, Inst. of Neurological Sciences, Southern General Hospital, 1345 Govan Road, Glasgow G51 4TF Tel: 0141 201 1100 Fax: 0141 201 2993 Email: cpol1j@clinmed.gla.ac.uk — MB BCh BAO 1986 NUI; MRCP (UK) 1990. (Univ. Coll., Cork) Cons. (Neurol.) INS, SGH; Hon. Sen. Lect. (Neurol.), Univ. of Glas. Socs: Assn. Brit. Neurol.; Scott. Assn. Neurol. Scis.; RCP (Lond.). Prev: Clin. Lect. & Hon. Sen. Regist. (Neurol.) Inst. Neurol. Sci. S.. Gen. Hosp. Glas.; Career Regist. (Neurol.) Inst. Neurol. Sci. S.. Gen. Hosp. Glas.; Regist. (Gen. Med.) Nottm. City Hosp.

O'LEARY, Cornelia Frances Birchlands, 146 Forest Road, Liss GU33 7BU Tel: 01730 893741 — MB BCh BAO 1974 NUI; FFA RCS Eng. 1981; DCH Eng. 1977. (Univ. Coll. Cork, Irel.) Sen. Med. Off. Med. Control Agency Lond. Socs: FFPM.

O'LEARY, Mr Daniel Peter 16 Filton Avenue, Horfield, Bristol BS7 0AG — MB BCh BAO 1982 NUI; FRCSI 1986.

O'LEARY, David Reginald Dean Street Surgery, 8 Dean Street, Liskeard PL14 4AQ Tel: 01579 343133 Fax: 01579 344933 — MB 1976 Camb.; BA Camb. 1972, MB 1976, BChir 1975; MRCGP 1984; DRCOG 1979.

O'LEARY, Denis Andrew 3 Maybury Close, Frimley, Camberley GU16 7HH — MB ChB 1994 Liverp.

O'LEARY, Denis Anthony No. 34A Coton House, Addenbrooke's Hospital, Hills Road, Cambridge CB2 2QQ — MB BCh BAO 1987 NUI.

O'LEARY, Finbarr Child Guidance Clinic, 6 Southey Road, Worthing BN11 3HT — MB BCh BAO 1982 NUI; MRCPsych 1988.

O'LEARY, Gerard (retired) 22 Welford Road, Filey YO14 0AE Tel: 01723 514374 — MB BCh BAO 1940 NUI.

O'LEARY, Margaret Mary (retired) Queen Elizabeth Psychiatric Hospital, Birmingham B15 2QZ — MB BCh BAO 1977 NUI; MRCPsych 1984. Prev: Sen. Regist. (Psychiat.) W. Midl. RHA.

O'LEARY, Martin Anthony 133 Richmond Park, Tuebrook, Liverpool L6 5AB Tel: 0151 263 9316 — MB ChB 1986 Leeds.

O'LEARY, Maureen Loversall Hospital, Weston Road, Balby, Doncaster DN4 8NX Tel: 01302 796296 Fax: 01302 796134; 185 Chippinghouse Road, Nether Edge, Sheffield S7 1DQ Tel: 0114 258 2611 — MB ChB 1976 Bristol; MRCPsych 1981. Cons. Psychiat. Rehabil. Doncaster. Socs: BMA; Roy. Coll. Psychiat. Prev: Sen. Regist. Rotat. (Adult Psychiat.) Sheff. VTS.

O'LEARY, Paula Frances Gerardine 24B New High Street, Headington, Oxford OX3 7AQ — MB BCh BAO 1987 NUI.

O'LEARY, Mr Sean Thomas Tel: 0118 987 5111; Tel: 0118 940 1895 Fax: 0118 940 1895 — MB BChir 1989 Camb.; FRCS Eng. 1994; FRCS Ed. 1994; FRCS (Tr & Orth) 1998. (St. Mary's Hosp.) Cons. (Orthop.), Roy. Berks. Hosp. Reading. Socs: BMA; Assoc. Mem. BOA; Brit. Orthop. Train. Assn. Prev: Specialist Regist. St Mary's Hosp., Lond. W2; Specialist Reg. Centr. Middlx. Hosp., Lond.

O'LEARY, Thomas Dundalk Street Surgery, 53 Dundalk Street, Newtownhamilton, Newry BT35 0PB Tel: 028 3087 8204 Fax: 028 3087 8196; Bog Road, Mullaghbawn, Newry BT35 9TT — MB BCh BAO 1981 NUI; MRCGP 1985; DRCOG 1983. GP Newtownhamilton. Socs: BMA & Brit. Med. Acupunc. Soc. Prev: Trainee GP Warrenpoint Health Centre Newry; Trainee GP Daisy Hill Hosp. VTS Newry.

O'LEARY, Thomas Philip The Park Canol Group Practice, Park Carnol Surgery, Central Park, Church Village, Pontypridd CF38 1RJ Tel: 01443 203414 Fax: 01443 218218 — MB BCh 1985 Wales.

O'LEARY, Tony Derrick 100 Main Street, Invergowrie, Dundee DD2 5BE — MB ChB 1997 Dundee.

O'LEARY, Tracey Diane Greenland Surgery, Greenland, Millbrook, Torpoint PL10 1BA Tel: 01752 822576 Fax: 01752 823155; 1 Whiteford Road, Mannamead, Plymouth PL3 5LU — MB ChB 1992 Aberd.; MRCGP 1996; DRCOG 1995. (Aberd.) GP Millbrook Surg. Millbrook Torpoint Cornw. Prev: GP/Regist. (Gen. Pract.) Stonehaven Med. Centre.

O'LEARY, Victor Gabriel (retired) 100 St Mary's Avenue, Whitley Bay NE26 3TS Tel: 0191 252 0821 — MB BCh BAO 1946 NUI. Prev: Ophth. (Sch. Health Servs.) N.ld., Newc., N. Tyneside, Gateshead & Durh. HAs.

O'LOAN, Aidan Aloysius 19 Salisbury Gardens, Antrim Road, Belfast BT15 5EL — MB BCh BAO 1983 NUI.

O'LOAN, John Jackson Avenue Health Centre, Jackson Avenue, Culcheth, Warrington WA3 4DZ Tel: 01925 763077 — MB ChB 1987 Aberd.

O'LOAN, Maria Dolores Antrim Hospital, 45 Bush Road, Antrim BT41 2RL Tel: 01849 424000 Fax: 01849 424294; 48 Glen's Brae Road, Martinstown, Ballymena BT43 7LX Tel: 012667 58361 Fax: 012667 58361 — MB BCh BAO 1983 Belf.; MRCP & Glas. 1997; MRCGP 1988; DTM & H Liverp. 1990; DCH RCPS Glas. 1986; DRCOG 1986. (Belfast) Staff Grade (Paediat.) Antrim Hosp. Socs: Ulster Paediat. Soc. Prev: Med. Off. Ortum Mission Hosp. Kitale, Kenya; Trainee GP/SHO Waveney Hosp. Ballymena Vocations Train. Scheme; Trainee GP New Galloway.

O'LOAN, Philip Raymond Portstewart Medical Centre, Mill Road, Portstewart BT55 7PQ Tel: 028 7083 2600 Fax: 028 7083 6871 — MB BCh BAO 1982 Belf.; MRCGP 1987.

O'LOGHLEN, Niall Anthony Abbotswood Medical Centre, Defford Road, Pershore WR10 1HZ Tel: 01386 552424; The Pound House, Great Comberton, Pershore WR10 3DU — MB BS 1979 Lond.; MA Camb. 1975; MRCGP 1983; DCH RCP Lond. 1983; DRCOG 1982.

O'LOUGHLIN, Anne Marie Mourne Family Surgery, Newry Street, Kilkeel, Newry BT34 4DN Tel: 028417 65422; 3 Ardaveen Drive, Newry BT35 8UH — MB BCh BAO 1995 Belf.; DRCOG 1977 London; MRCGP 1999. (Qu. Univ. Belf.) GP Locum.

O'LOUGHLIN, Bernadette Ann Silver Lane Surgery, 1 Suffolk Court, Yeadon, Leeds LS19 7JN Tel: 0113 250 4953 Fax: 0113 250 9804; Beck House, Hebers Ghyll Drive, Ilkley LS29 9QH — MB ChB 1981 Leeds; MRCP (UK) 1984; MRCGP 1986; DRCOG 1986.

O'LOUGHLIN, Colm Joseph c/o Wythenshawe Hospital, Southmoor Road, Manchester M23 9LT — MB BCh N U Irel. 1991.

O'LOUGHLIN, James Peter (retired) 2 Fern Clough, Hillside, Chorley New Road, Bolton BL1 5DX Tel: 01204 847087 Email:

peter@poloughlin.freeserve.co.uk — MB ChB 1956 Manch.; FRCP Lond. 1977, M 1963. Prev: Phys. Bolton Dist. Gen. Hosp. & Bolton Roy. Infirm.

O'LOUGHLIN, Michael Alfred Ballygawley Road Surgery, 14 Ballygawley Road, Dungannon BT70 1EL — MB BCh BAO 1980 NUI; MRCGP 1984; DCH 1983. GP Dungannon.

O'MAHONY, Barbara Ann (retired) 2 Tranmere Drive, Guiseley, Leeds LS20 8NQ Tel: 01943 874888 — MB BS Durh. 1961; MRCP Lond. 1967.

O'MAHONY, Brian Joseph 4 Meadow Way, Wilmslow SK9 6JL — LRCPI & LM, LRSCI & LM 1966; LRCPI & LM, LRCSI & LM 1966.

O'MAHONY, Colm Pierce Countess of Chester Hospital, Countess of Chester, Health Park, Liverpool Road, Chester CH2 1UL Tel: 01244 363097 Fax: 01244 363095 Email: dr.o'mahony@coch-tr.nwest.nhs.uk — MB BCh BAO 1981 NUI; FRCP (Lond.) 2001; BSc (Microbiol.) Dub. 1975; MD NUI 1986; FRCPI 1995, M 1988; Dip. Ven. Liverp. 1986. (Univ. Coll. Dub.) Hon. Sen. Lect., Univ. of Liverp. Socs: Chairm., Assn. of Genitourin. Med. Prev: Lect. (Genitourin. Med.) Univ. Liverp.; Regist. (Immunol.) St. Jas. Hosp. Dub.

O'MAHONY, Denis 65 Jack Straw's Lane, Headington, Oxford OX3 0DW — MD 1993 NUI; MB BCh BAO 1985; MRCPI 1987. Sen. Regist. (Gen. & Geriat. Med.) Radcliffe Infirm. Oxf. Prev: Health Research Bd. of Irel. Research Fell. Merger's Inst. for Research on Ageing St. Jas. Hosp. Dub.; Research Regist. (Med. for the Elderly) St. Jas. Hosp. Dub.; Regist. (Gen. Med. & Gastroenterol.) Cork Univ. Hosp.

O'MAHONY, Grania Anne Mary St. Lulfstan Surgery, Southam Clinic, Pendicke St., Southam CV47 1PF Tel: 01926 810939; Fieldgate View, Pillory Green, Napton, Southam CV47 8LN Tel: 01926 815739 — MB BS 1983 Lond.; DRCOG 1987; MRCGP 1989; DCH RCP Lond. 1988. (St. Bart.) GP.

O'MAHONY, James Finbar 77 Old Park Road, London N13 4RG — MB BS 1973 Lond.

O'MAHONY, James Gerard Gastroenterology Unit, Leeds General Infirmary, Great George St., Leeds LS1 3EX Tel: 0113 392 6733 Fax: 0113 392 6968 Email: seamuso@ulth.northy.nhs.uk — MD 1991 NUI; MB BCh BAO 1983; MRCP (UK) 1988; MRCPI 1986; FRCP Ed 1998. Cons. Phys. Leeds Gen. Infirm. Prev: Sen. Regist. (Gen. Med. & Gastroenterol.) Yorks. RHA.; Regist. (Gen. Med. & Gastroenterol.) Cork Regional Hosp.; Research Fell. & Hon. Regist. Gastrointestinal Unit W.. Gen. Hosp. Edin.

O'MAHONY, Jeremiah B St. Annes Health Centre, Nottingham NG3 3PX; 49 Bridge Road, Welwyn Garden City AL8 6UH — MB BCh BAO 1947 NUI. (Cork) Prev: Ho. Surg. N. Infirm. Cork.

O'MAHONY, Marcella Sinead Third Floor, Academic Centre, Llandough Hospital, Penlan Road, Penarth CF64 2XX Tel: 01222 716984 Fax: 01222 711267 — MB BCh BAO 1986 NUI; MRCPI 1989. Sen. Lect. (Geriat. Med.) Univ. Wales Coll. Med. Cardiff.

O'MAHONY, Margaret Fidelma Mary 2 Mill Court, Mill Road, Shrewsbury SY3 9JT — MB BCh BAO 1987 NUI.

O'MAHONY, Mark Yves Cadbury Heath Health Centre, Parkwall Road, Cadbury Heath, Bristol BS30 8HS Tel: 0117 980 5700 Fax: 0117 980 5701; 8 Carnarvon Road, Redland, Bristol BS6 7DP Tel: 0117 924 3361 — BM 1979 Soton.; MRCP (UK) 1982; MRCGP 1986; DRCOG 1984; Cert. Evidence Based Healthcare 1997 (Oxon.). (Southampton) Prev: Trainee GP Avon VTS; SHO Rotat. (Med.) P.ss Margt. Hosp. Swindon; SHO Rotat. (Path.) John Radcliffe Hosp. Oxf.

O'MAHONY, Mary Catherine Public Health Laboratory Service Communicable Disease, Surveillance Centre, 61 Colindale Avenue, London NW9 5EQ Tel: 020 8200 4400 Fax: 020 8200 8130 — MB BCh BAO Dub. 1975; MSc Lond. 1980; MRCPI 1981; FFPHM 1992, M 1984.

O'MAHONY, Patrick Henry Michael Abernethy House, 70 Silver Street, Enfield EN1 3EP Tel: 020 8366 1314 Fax: 020 8364 4176 — MB BS 1976 Lond.; DPMSA 1998. (St. Geo.) Prev: GP Tutor Enfield Dist. Hosp. Postgrad. Centre.; Ho. Off. (Vasc. Surg.) St. Geo. Hosp. Lond.; SHO (O & G/Paediat.) Chase Farm Hosp. Enfield.

O'MALLEY, Antony Bernard Harley House, The Outwoods, Hinckley LE10 2UD Tel: 01455 2271 — MB BS 1948 Madras. (Madras) Prev: Med. Off. Kettering Gen. Hosp. & N.ampton Gen. Hosp.

O'MALLEY, Mr Austin Gerard (retired) Shalom, South Drive, Sandfield Park, Liverpool L12 1LH Tel: 0151 228 9738 — MB ChB 1939 Liverp.; MCh Orth. Liverp. 1947, MB ChB 1939; FRCS Ed. 1950. Prev: Orthop. Surg. Warrington Infirm. & Gen. Hosp. & Roy. S. Hosp.

O'MALLEY, Brendan Peter Kettering General Hospital, Rothwell Road, Kettering NN16 8UZ Tel: 01858 462840; Pine Lodge, 91 Fairfield Road, Market Harborough LE16 9QH Tel: 01858 462840 — MB BChir 1973 Camb.; FRCP (Lond.) 1995; MD Leic. 1987; MRCP (UK) 1976; BA (Hons.) Camb. 1969. Cons. Phys. Kettering Gen. Hosp. N.ants. Socs: Thyroid Club; Soc. Endocrinol.; Brit. Diabetic Assn. Prev: Lect. & Hon. Sen. Regist. (Therap.) Univ. Leicester; SHO Rotat. (Med.) Bath Health Dist.; Regist. (Med.) Leicester Roy. Infirm.

O'MALLEY, Daniel Noel 'Glengarriff', 19 Belgravia Road, Onchan, Douglas IM8 3TA — MB BCh BAO 1975 Belf. Socs: Roy. Coll. Psychiat.

O'MALLEY, Geraldine Washway Road Medical Centre, 67 Washway Road, Sale M33 7SS Tel: 0161 962 4354 Fax: 0161 905 4706 — MB ChB 1986 Sheff.; MRCGP 1990; DCH RCP Lond. 1989. GP Princip. Prev: Trainee GP Doncaster VTS.

O'MALLEY, Helen Anne 66 Tandle Hill Road, Royton, Oldham OL2 5UX — MB ChB 1995 Leic.

O'MALLEY, Helen Frances Medical Services, Grove House, 3 Grove Place, Swansea SA1 Tel: 01792 659840 — MB BCh 1974 Wales. Med. Adviser Med. Serv.s, Swansea. Socs: Brit. Med. Acupunct. Soc. Prev: Princip. GP Swansea; Dep. Designated Doctor Cervical Cytol. W.. Glam. HA; Regist. (Respirat. Med.) Morriston Hosp.

O'MALLEY, John Eustace Halton Heath Authority, 34 Halton Road, Runcorn WA7 5 Tel: 01928 74321 — MRCS Eng. LRCP Lond. 1951; MFCM 1972; DPH Liverp. 1957. (Liverp.) Dist. Med. Off. Halton Health Auth.; Med. Off. (Environm. Health) Halton & Vale Roy. Dist. Councs. Prev: Dist. Community Phys. Halton Health Dist.; MOH Runcorn, N.wich, Winsford & Middlewich UDs & Runcorn & N.wich RDs.

O'MALLEY, John Francis 17 Easingwold Gardens, Luton LU1 1UD — MB ChB 1991 Manch.

O'MALLEY, Michael Crofton Street Surgery, 1 Crofton Street, Oldham OL8 3DA Tel: 0161 624 4716 Fax: 0161 628 9513; Crofton House, 1 Crofton St, Oldham OL8 3BZ — MB ChB 1968 Birm.; BSc (Hons.) Birm. 1964, MB ChB 1968. Sec. Oldham Med. Soc.

O'MALLEY, Michael 132 London Road, Stockton Heath, Warrington WA4 6LE — MB ChB 1992 Liverp.; BSc (Hons.) Human Anat. & Cell Biol. Liverp. 1989. SHO (A & E) Wythenshawe & Withington Hosps. Manch.

O'MALLEY, Patricia Anne Moorside, Trafford General Hospital, Moorside Road, Davyhulme, Urmaston, Manchester M41 5SL — MB ChB 1984 Manch.; MSc Manch. 1992; MRCPsych 1989. Cons. Psychiat. i/c Elderly Trafford HA.

O'MALLEY, Mr Steven Patrick Milton Keynes NHS Trust, Standing Way, Milton Keynes MK6 5LD Tel: 01908 243141 Fax: 01908 243141 Email: sturm.omalley@mkg-tr.anglia.nhs.uk; Deiter House, Chase Park Road, Yardley Hastings, Northampton NN7 1HF Tel: 01604 696045 Fax: 01908 243141 Email: sturm.omalley@care.4free.net — MB BS 1977 Lond.; FRCS Eng. 1983. (St. Thos.) Cons. Otol. Milton Keynes Gen. Hosp.; Cons. Otol. N.ampton Gen. Hosp. Prev: Lect. & Sen. Regist. Manch.

***O'MARA, Lee** 72 Suffield Way, King's Lynn PE30 3DL — MB BS 1986 Lond.

O'MARA, Lucy Eve Hill Medical Practice, 29 Himley Road, Dudley DY1 2QD Tel: 01384 254423; Fax: 01384 373678 Email: lucy.o.@virgin.net — MB ChB 1996 Manch.; MRCGP 2001; DRCOG, RCOG 1998. p/t GP. Dudley; Clin. Asst. Palliat. Care, Mary Stevens Hospice Stourbridge.

O'MARA, Vanessa 13 Wildwood Avenue, Bricket Wood, St Albans AL2 3XG — MB ChB 1991 Leeds.

O'MEARA, Kevin Osin Manus Brendan (retired) 10 Silver Birch Drive, Kinver, Stourbridge DY7 6AW — MB ChB 1944 Birm.; MRCS Eng. LRCP Lond. 1944. Prev: Ho. Phys. Roy. S. Hants. & Soton. Hosp. & Roy. Hosp. Wolverhampton.

O'MEARA, Margaret Mary (retired) P.O. Box No 17317, London SW3 4WJ Tel: 020 7730 2800 Fax: 020 7730 0710 — MB BCh BAO NUI 1943; CPH Liverp. 1948. Prev: Ho. Surg. Jervis St. Hosp. Dub. & Temple St. Childr. Hosp. Dub.

O'MEARA

O'MEARA, Moira Elizabeth Primrose Cottage, Primrose Lane, Boston Spa, Wetherby LS23 6DL — MB ChB 1984 Leeds.

O'MOORE, Gerald Roderick (Surgery), 279 Katherine Road, Forest Gate, London E7 8PP Tel: 020 8472 0803 Fax: 020 8503 4490; 21 Stradbroke Drive, Chigwell IG7 5QU Tel: 020 8500 6502 — MB BCh BAO 1952 NUI; MICGP 1987. (Univ. Coll. Dub.) Socs: BMA; BMA. Prev: Ho. Phys. PeaMt. Sanat. Newc., Dub., Bon Secours Hosp. Glasnevin & Mater Hosp. Dub.

O'MOORE, John Charles Francis Devereux The Surgery, 96 Upminster Road, Hornchurch RM12 6PR Tel: 01708 440642 Fax: 01708 477329 Email: johnomoore@doctors.org.uk; 2 Oaklands Avenue, Romford RM1 4DB Tel: 01708 765996 Fax: 01708 765996 Email: johnomoore@doctors.org.uk — MB BCh BAO 1989 NUI; T.(GP) 1993; DFFP 1993. (Univ. Coll. Dub.) Princip. in Gen. Pract.; Med. Ref. - City of Lond. Crematorium. Socs: Fell. Roy. Soc. Med.; BMA. Prev: Trainee GP Glos.; SHO Barking Hosp. & King Geo. Hosp. Essex; Ho. Off. (Med. & Surg.) Walton Hosp. Liverp.

O'MUIRITHE, Barra Proinsias 134 Coombe Valley Road, Dover CT17 0HA — MB BCh BAO 1984 NUI; LRCPSI 1984.

O'MULLANE, Nicholas Matthew Tameside General Hospital, Darnton Road, Ashton-under-Lyne OL6 — MB ChB 1969 Birm.; FRCP Lond. 1990; MRCP (UK) 1974; DObst RCOG 1972; DCH Eng. 1972; Cert. Higher Med. Train. in Diabetes, Endocrinol. & Gen. (Int.) Med. 1981. Cons. Phys. Tameside Gen. Hosp. Ashton-under-Lyne. Prev: Clin. Tutor Tameside Gen. Hosp. Ashton-under-Lyne.

O'NEAL, Hugh Brighton General Hospital, Brighton BN2 3EW Tel: 01273 696955; 41 Wilbury Crescent, Hove BN3 6FJ Tel: 01273 724198 Email: hugh.oneal@cwcom.net — BM 1976 Soton.; BSc (Hons.) (Physiol. & Biochem.) Soton. 1971; FRCP Lond. 1994; MRCP (UK) 1980. Cons. Geriat. Brighton Health Care NHS Trust. Prev: Cons. Geriat. SE Thames RHA.

O'NEIL, Helen Alison Earwicker and Partners, The Health Centre, 97 Derby Road, Stapleford, Nottingham NG9 7AT Tel: 0115 939 2444 Fax: 0115 939 5625 — MB BS 1979 Lond.; MRCGP 1983; DCH RCP Lond. 1982; DRCOG 1981. (Univ. Coll.)

O'NEIL, James Edward Gerard Tel: 0141 778 0440 Fax: 0141 778 0143; 14 Alexandra Park, Lenzie, Glasgow G66 5BH — MB ChB 1983 Glas.; MPH Glas. 1995; MRCGP 1987. (Glas.) Prev: Med. Dir. Glas. Emerg. Med. Serv.; Trainee (Pub. Health Med.) Gtr. Glas. HB.

O'NEIL, Michael Jeffrey Holly Bank, Haughs Bay, Huddersfield HD3 4YS — MB ChB 1975 Leeds; FFA RCS Eng. 1983. Sen. Regist. (Anaesth.) Nottm. & E. Midl. Train. Scheme.

O'NEIL, Michael John Earwicker and Partners, The Health Centre, 97 Derby Road, Stapleford, Nottingham NG9 7AT Tel: 0115 939 2444 Fax: 0115 939 5625 — MB BS 1980 Lond.; BSc (Anat II 1) Lond. 1977, MB BS 1980; MRCP (UK) 1983. (Univ. Coll. Hosp.)

O'NEIL, Professor Raymund 49 Combermartin Road, Southfields, London SW18 5PP Tel: 020 8788 6609 — MRCS Eng. LRCP Lond. 1957; BDS Manch. 1948; FDS RCS Eng. 1952. (Westm.) Socs: Fell. Roy. Soc. Med.; BDA; BMA. Prev: Emerit. Prof. Oral Surg. Univ. Coll. Lond.

O'NEILL, Alice Elizabeth Norfolk & Norwich University Hospital, Brunswick Road, Norwich NR1 3SR Tel: 01603 286343; 20 Quebec Road, Dereham NR19 2DR — MB BS 1985 Lond.; MRCP (UK) 1996; Cert. Family Plann. JCC 1989; DRCOG 1989; DCH RCP Lond. 1988. (Roy. Free Hosp. Lond.) Cons. Community Paediat., Norwich. Socs: MRCPCH. Prev: Regist. (Paediat.) Addenbrooke's Hosp. Camb.; Specialist Regist. (Community Paediat.) Norwich; Regist. (Paediat.) Qu. Eliz. Hosp. King's Lynn.

O'NEILL, Ann-Marie St Catherine's, West Hill Road, Woking GU22 7UL — MB BCh BAO 1987 Dub.; DRCPath 1995. Sen. Regist. (Med. Microbiol.) Roy. Hants. Co. Hosp Winchester.

O'NEILL, Anne 50 Stuart Road, Corby NN17 1RL — MB BS 1993 Lond.

O'NEILL, Anthony Peter Forest Surgery, 11 Station Road, Loughton IG10 4NZ Tel: 020 8508 3818 Fax: 020 8508 2539; 6 Theydon Park Road, Theydon Bois, Epping CM16 7LW Tel: 01992 813643 — MB BS 1980 Lond.; MRCGP 1991. (Roy. Free Hosp. Sch. Med.) Clin. Asst. (Dermat.) St. Margt. Hosp. Epping.

O'NEILL, Anthony St John 12 Turnberry Road, Glasgow G11 5AE — MB BCh BAO 1988 NUI.

O'NEILL, Bridget Farmhill Lane, Holywood BT18 0HY — MB BCh BAO 1958 NUI; LAH Dub. 1957.

O'NEILL, Bronagh Mary 33 Mann's Road, Belfast BT5 7SS — MB BCh BAO 1992 Belf.

O'NEILL, Celine 66 Kelvin Drive, Glasgow G20 8QN — MB ChB 1987 Dundee.

O'NEILL, Ciara Anne Omagh Health Centre, Mountjoy Road, Omagh BT79 7BA Tel: 028 8224 3521; 12 Gleannan Park, Killyclogher, Omagh BT79 7XZ Tel: 01662 249026 — MB BCh BAO 1989 Belf.; MRCGP 1993; DRCOG 1992; DGM RCPS Glas. 1991.

O'NEILL, Claire 31 The Street, Kennington, Ashford TN24 9HB — MB BCh BAO 1990 Dub.

O'NEILL, Conor Patrick 26 Laurelvale, Crumlin BT29 4WW — MB BCh BAO 1994 Belf.

O'NEILL, Corina Mary Brigid Royal Free Hospital, Pond St., London NW3 2QG — MB BCh BAO 1985 NUI.

O'NEILL, Cornelius Omalley 27 Meeting Street, Magherafelt BT45 6BW — MB BCh BAO 1988 Belf.; MB BCh Belf. 1988.

O'NEILL, Cyril Patrick Norton Medical Centre, Harland House, Norton, Stockton-on-Tees TS20 1AN Tel: 01642 360111 Fax: 01642 558672 — MB BS 1982 Newc.; MRCGP 1987; DRCOG 1986; DCCH RCP Ed. 1986. GP Norton Med. Centre. Prev: Trainee GP Cleveland VTS.; Med. Off. Makiungu Hosp. Singida, Tanzania.

O'NEILL, Mr Damian Patrick c/o Eye Department, Leeds General Infirmary, Leeds LS1 3EX — MB BCh BAO 1986 NUI; FRCS Eng. 1990; MRCPI 1988; LRCPI & LM LRCSI & LM 1986; FRCOphth 1993; FCOphth 1990; DO RCS Eng. 1989. Sen. Regist. (Ophth.) Roy. Hallamsh. Hosp.; Cons. (Ophth.) Leeds Gen. Infirm.; Hon. Sen. Clin. Lect. Leeds Univ. Prev: Regist. Moorfields Eye Hosp. Lond.

O'NEILL, Daphne 17 Alfreton Close, Wimbledon, London SW19 5NS Tel: 020 8946 1498 — MB BS Durh. 1953.

O'NEILL, David 10 Providence Road, Bromsgrove B61 8EL — MB BChir 1980 Camb.; BA Camb. 1977, MA, MB BChir 1980; MRCP (UK) 1987.

O'NEILL, David Marnoch 10 Harling Drive, Troon KA10 6NF — MB ChB 1970 Glas.; MRCP (U.K.) 1974.

O'NEILL, Declan Finbarr Dower House, Fontridge Lane, Etchingham TN19 7DE — MB BCh BAO 1976 NUI; MPH Sydney 1988; MFPHM RCP (UK) 1993. Cons. Pub. Health Med. S. Thames RHA. Socs: Fell. Roy. Austral. Coll. Med. Admin.; Fell. Austral. Fac. Pub. Health Med. Prev: Dep. Dir. Fremantle Hosp.; Med. Off. Health Dept. W.. Austral.; Regist. Roy. Perth Hosp.

O'NEILL, Denis William James, TD, SBStJ (retired) 8 Oaklands Park, Warmwell, Dorchester DT2 8JQ Tel: 01305 852722 — MRCS Eng. LRCP Lond. 1946; MRCGP 1953. Prev: Ho. Surg. & Ho. Phys. Roy. Infirm. Sheff.

O'NEILL, Donagh Columba 30 Upper Healthmount, Dortstewosr, Belfast BT55 7AR Tel: 01232 329241 Email: donaghoneill@hotmail.com — MB BCh BAO 1989 NUI; MRCPsych 1994; DRCOG (RCOG) 1997; DCH 1997; MRCGP 1998. (University Coll. Dublin) Specialist Regis. Gen. Adult Psych., N. Irel. Prev: SHO Rotat. (Psychiat.) Gen. Pract. Regist., Lond., Merseyside RHA.

O'NEILL, Mr Eamon Canice 41 St. Brendan's Park, Tralee, Newtown — MB BCh BAO 1970 NUI; FRCS Ed. 1976.

O'NEILL, Edward George John 14 Chippendale Court, Belfast BT10 0DU — MB BCh BAO 1992 Belf.

O'NEILL, Eileen Moira 5 Amberley Gardens, Bedford MK40 3BT Tel: 01234 325800 — MD 1961 Sheff.; MB ChB 1953; FRCP Lond. 1976, M 1964; DCH Eng. 1957. Cons. Paediat. Emerit. Socs: Fell. Roy. Coll. Phys. Lond.; Brit. Paediat. Assn. Prev: Sen. Regist. (Paediat.) Whittington Hosp. Lond.; Regist. (Med.) Fulham Hosp. Lond.; Regist. (Paediat. Clin. & Research) N.. Gen. Hosp. Sheff.

O'NEILL, Elizabeth Mary 1 Marquis Close, Wembley HA0 4HF — MB ChB 1985 Liverp.

O'NEILL, Elizabeth Valerie Donmall and Partners, 87 Albion Street, London SE16 7JX Tel: 020 7237 2092 Fax: 020 7231 1435 — MB BCh BAO 1994 NUI.

O'NEILL, Emma Jane — MB ChB 1989 Glas.; MRCP (UK) 1994; FFARCSI 1998. GP LOCUM. Socs: BMA; Med. & Dent. Defence Union Scotl.

O'NEILL, Francis Anthony 14 Vauxhall Park, Belfast BT9 5GZ — MB BCh BAO 1984 Belf.; MD Belf. 1991; MRCPsych 1988. Lect. & Sen. Regist. (Ment. Health) Qu. Univ. Belf.

O'NEILL, Francis Charles Friends House, Abbeystead, Lancaster LA2 9DT Tel: 01524 791770 — MB ChB 1963 Manch.; MRCP

O'NEILL

Lond. 1968. (Manch.) Hosp. Pract. (Gen. Med.) Lancaster Dist. HA.; Mem. Med. Bd.ing Panel. Prev: Regist. (Med.) Addenbrooke's Hosp. Camb.; SHO (Med.) Manch. Roy. Infirm; Ho. Phys. & Ho. Surg. Manch. Roy. Infirm.

O'NEILL, George Dermot Springfield Road Surgery, 66-70 Springfield Road, Belfast BT12 7AH Tel: 028 9032 3571 Fax: 028 9020 7707 — MB BCh BAO 1971 Belf.

O'NEILL, Gordon Francis Allen Flat 1 Emerson Bainbridge House, 47 Cleveland St., London W1T 4JQ — MB BS 1987 New South Wales.

O'NEILL, Gregory Thomas John Dept of Radiology, Glasgow Royal Infirmary, Glasgow G4 0SF; 10 Main Street, Overtown, Wishaw ML2 0QA — MB ChB 1992 Ed. Specialist Regist. Radiol.

O'NEILL, Hilary Mary-Josephine Department of Radiology, North Hampshire Hospital, Aldermaston Road, Basingstoke RG24 9NA — MB BCh BAO 1979 NUI; MRCPI 1983; FFR RCSI 1986; DCH NUI 1982. Cons. Radiol. N. Hants. Hosp. Prev: Sen. Regist. (Radiol.) Soton. Gen. Hosp.; Regist. (Radiol.) Mater Hosp. Dub.

O'NEILL, Hugh Blaise Horsford Medical Centre, 205 Holt Road, Horsford, Norwich NR10 3DX Tel: 01603 898300 Fax: 01603 891818; 130 Lower Street, Salhouse, Norwich NR13 6RX Tel: 01603 722035 — MB BCh BAO 1980 NUI; MRCS Eng. LRCP Lond. 1980; Cert. Av. Med. 1987. Force Surg. Norf. Constab.; Sen. Cons. Clin. Forens. Med. B & C Div. Norf. Constab.; C. Med. Off. Norf. Army Cadet Force; Med. Examr. of Divers HSE. Socs: Assn. Police Surg.; Soc. Occupat. Med.; Soc. Orthop. Med. Prev: SHO (O & G, Orthop. & A & E) Norf. & Norwich Hosp.

O'NEILL, Hugh Finbarr 11 Rosetta Drive, Belfast BT7 3HL — MB BCh BAO 1992 Belf.; FFARCSI 1988.

O'NEILL, James Dermot Willowbrook Health Centre, Cottingham Road, Corby NN17 2UR Fax: 01536 402153 Email: dermott.oneill@gp-k83001.nhs.uk; 28 Skeffington Close, Geddington, Kettering NN14 1BA Tel: 01536 742305 — MB BCh BAO 1974 NUI; DRCOG 1977. (Galway)

O'NEILL, Jane Maria Bernadette Priory Court, Priory Hospital, Priory Lane, London SW15 5JJ — MB BCh BAO 1983 Dub.; MB BCh Dub. 1983.

O'NEILL, Janet (retired) Rose Cottage, Gosforth, Seascale CA20 1JB Tel: 0194 67 25216 — BM BCh 1963 Oxf.; MA Oxf. 1963; MRCP Lond. 1967; MRCPsych 1973; DPM Eng. 1972; DObst RCOG 1966; FRCP 1999. Prev: Princip. GP.

O'NEILL, Mr John Joseph Arus Na Greine, Killuney, Portadown Road, Armagh BT61 9HE — MB BCh BAO 1958 Belf.; FRCSI 1987; FRCS Ed. 1965. Cons. Surg. Craigavon Area Hosp. & Armagh City Hosp.

O'NEILL, John Marmion Radiology Department, Royal Infirmary, Lauriston Place, Edinburgh EH3 9HB Tel: 0131 536 2900; 17 Marchmount Road, Edinburgh EH9 1HY Tel: 0131 466 0639 Email: johnandal@aol.com — MB BCh BAO 1992 NUI; FRCR 2001; MSc 1999; MRCPI 1996. Specialist Regist. (Radiol.) Roy. Infirm. Edin. Prev: Regist. (Gen. Med. & Nephrol.) & SHO (Med.) Univ. Coll. Cork.

***O'NEILL, John Paul** Morpeth Health Centre, Gas House Lane, Morpeth NE61 1SR Tel: 01670 513657 Fax: 01670 511966 — MB BS 1986 Newc.; MRCGP 1991.

O'NEILL, Mr John Stephen Borders General Hospital, Melrose TD6 9BS Tel: 01896 826000 Fax: 01896 826924 Email: john.oneill@borders.scot.nhs.uk; Grianan, Gattonside, Melrose TD6 9NB — MB ChB 1978 Glas.; BSc (1st cl. Hons. Path.) Glas. 1976, MD 1989; FRCS Ed. 1983; FRCS Glas. 1983. Cons. Gen. Surg. Borders Gen. Hosp. Melrose. Prev: Lect. (Surg). Univ. Edin. & Roy. Infirm. Edin.

O'NEILL, Joseph Humphry (retired) 12 Fairfield Road, Widnes WA8 6SE — MB BCh BAO 1927 NUI; DPH NUI 1930.

O'NEILL, Joseph Marcus Margaret Thompson Medical Centre, 105 East millwood Road, Speke, Liverpool L24 6TH Tel: 0151 425 2885 Fax: 0151 425 2272 Email: kevin.gateley@gp-n82001.nhs.uk; 4 Hamilton Street, Chester CH2 3JG Tel: 01244 322440 — MB BCh BAO 1984 NUI; LRCPI & LM, LRCSI & LM 1984; MRCGP 1991; Dip. Palliat. Med. Wales 1995; DCH NUI 1986; CTCM & H RCSI 1983. (RCSI) Gen. Practitioner; Clin. Cancer Lead. Liverp. S PCG. 1 Childwall Pk Ave. Liverp. L16 0JE. Socs: Pain Soc.; Assn. Palliat. Med. Prev: Sen. Regist. (Palliat. Med.) Trent RHA; Assoc. Specialist

(Palliat. Med.) S. Downs Health NHS Trust; SHO (Palliat. Med.) St. Joseph's Hospice Lond.

O'NEILL, Kareen Ann 7 Douglas Park Crescent, Bearsden, Glasgow G61 3DS; Beechwood, 19 The Balk, York YO42 2QQ — MB ChB 1987 Manch. Princip. GP Goole.

O'NEILL, Kenneth Francis Midlock Medical Centre, 7 Midlock Street, Glasgow G51 1SL Tel: 0141 427 4271 Fax: 0141 427 1405; 20 Lawes Road, Glasgow G43 1BX — MB ChB 1983 Glas.; BSc (Holu Intercalate) 1980; MRCGP 1988.

O'NEILL, Kenneth Maurice Durham Road Surgery, 25 Durham Road, Edinburgh EH16 4DT Tel: 0131 669 1153 Fax: 0131 669 3633; 8 Hamilton Terrace, Edinburgh EH15 1NB Tel: 0131 669 1150 — MB ChB 1967 St. And. (St. And.) Socs: Clin. Club Edin. & Brit. Soc. Sport & Med. Prev: SHO (Gen. Med.) Edin. Roy. Infirm.; Ho. Phys. Maryfield Hosp. Dundee; Ho. Surg. Dundee Roy. Infirm.

O'NEILL, Kevin Peter Ipswich Hospital, Heath Road, Ipswich IP4 5PD Tel: 01473 712233; 12 Ipswich Road, Woodbridge IP12 4BU Tel: 01394 388308 — MB BS 1979 Lond.; MRCP (UK) 1984. Cons. Paediat. Ipswich Hosp. Socs: Brit. Paediat. Assn. Prev: Sen. Regist. (Paediat.) Dept. Child Health Ninewells Hosp. Dundee; Regist. (Paediat.) Dept. Child Health Newc. u Tyne; Research Clin. MRC, The Gambia.

O'NEILL, Kevin Richard 1 Crossley Terrace, Arthurs Hill, Newcastle upon Tyne NE4 5NY — MB BS 1992 Lond.

O'NEILL, Kevin Sean 63 Woodfarm Close, Leigh-on-Sea SS9 4PF — MB BS 1989 Lond.; BSc (Hons.) Lond. 1986, MB BS 1989. SHO (Orthop.) St. Geo. Hosp. Lond. Prev: SHO (Neurosurg.) Atkinson Morley's Hosp.; SHO (A & E) Ealing Gen. Hosp.; Ho. Surg. St. Mary's Hosp. Lond.

O'NEILL, Margaret Betty Edith 44 Salisbury Road, Cressington Park, Liverpool L19 0PJ Tel: 0151 427 2329 — MB BCh BAO 1949 Dub.; BA, MB BCh BAO Dub. 1949. (T.C. Dub.) Clin. Med. Off. (Community Health) Liverp. HA. Prev: Ho. Surg. Pk. Hosp. Davyhulme; Ho. Phys. Vict. Hosp. Blackpool & Dorking Gen. Hosp.

O'NEILL, Mark Francis Joseph (retired) 17 Alfreton Close, London SW19 5NS — MB BS 1954 Durh.

O'NEILL, Martin Patrick O'Malley Mourneside Medical Centre, 1A Ballycolman Avenue, Strabane BT82 9AF Tel: 028 7138 3737 Fax: 028 7138 3979; 6 Cedar Park, Urney Road, Strabane BT82 9ER — MB BCh BAO 1975 Belf.

O'NEILL, Mary Judith 16 Holborn Hall, Lisburn BT27 5AU — MB BCh BAO 1992 Belf.; MRCPsych 1997.

O'NEILL, Mary Margaret Meadowlands Surgery, Newry Health Village, Monaghan Street, Newry BT35 6BW Tel: 028 3026 7534; The Pines, 35 Windsor Hill, Newry BT34 1HS — MB BCh BAO 1983 Belf.; MRCGP 1987; DCH NUI 1986; DRCOG 1985. (Belf.)

O'NEILL, Mary Siobhan Gerandine 41 Duchy Road, Harrogate HG1 2HA; 41 Duchy Road, Harrogate HG1 2HA — MB BChir 1980 Camb.; MRCGP 1983; DRCOG 1983. Prev: GP Leeds.

O'NEILL, Maureen Patricia Mid-Ulster Hospital, 59 Hospital Road, Magherafelt BT45 5EX Tel: 01648 31031 Fax: 01648 32088; The St, 65 Tobermore Road, Magherafelt BT45 5EJ Tel: 01648 32124 — MB BCh BAO 1975 Belf.; FFA RCS Irel. 1980; DCH RCPSI 1977. Cons. Anaesth. Mid Ulster Hosp. Magherafelt. Socs: Assn. Anaesth.; Brit. Assn. Day Surg.; Med. Wom. Federat. Prev: Cons. Anaesth. Belf. City Hosp.; Sen. Regist. (Anaesth.) Roy. Vict. Hosp.; Hon. Lect. & Sen. Regist. Univ. Zambia.

O'NEILL, Michael Robert (retired) 11 Blakeley Brow, Raby Mere, Wirral CH63 0PS Tel: 0151 334 1905 Email: golfnuts@cwctv.net — MB BCh BAO 1960 Belf. Prev: Sen. Resid. Med. Off. Belf. City Hosp.

O'NEILL, Niall Patrick 63 Ballymena Road, Portglenone, Ballymena BT44 8BN — MB BCh BAO 1985 Belf.

***O'NEILL, Niamh Mary Deidre Rose** Flat 1, 89 Elgin Avenue, London W9 2DA — MB BS 1998 Lond.; MB BS Lond 1998.

O'NEILL, Owen Brian 21 Claremont Crescent, Edinburgh EH7 4HX Tel: 0131 557 3444 — MB BCh BAO 1971 NUI; BSc NUI 1968; MRCPsych 1976; T(Psych) 1991. (Univ. Coll. Cork) Hon. Cons. Psychother. Roy. Edin. Hosp. Socs: Brit. PsychoAnalyt. Soc.; Tavistock Soc. of Psychotherapists; N. Eng. Assn. for Train. in Psychother. Prev: Cons. Psychother. Portman Clinic Lond.; Dep. Dir. Lond. Clinic Psycho-Anal.; Cons. Psychother. Watford Gen. Hosp.

O'NEILL

O'NEILL, Patricia Alice (retired) 145 Perry Hill, London SE6 4LR Tel: 020 8699 1062 — BM BCh 1976 Oxf.; MRCS Eng. LRCP Lond. 1976.

O'NEILL, Patricia Josephine Grange Road Surgery, Grange Road, Bishopsworth, Bristol BS13 8LD Tel: 0117 964 4343 Fax: 0117 935 8422 — MB BChir 1989 Camb.

O'NEILL, Patricia Mary Public Health Laboratory, Royal Shrewsbury Hospital, Mytton Oak Road, Shrewsbury SY3 8XQ Tel: 01743 261161 Fax: 01743 261165 Email: poneill@mids.phls.nhs.uk — MB BS 1983 Lond.; BA Oxf. 1980; MRCPath 1992. (Westm. Med. Sch. Lond.) Cons. Microbiol. Pub. Health Laborat., Roy. Shrewsbury Hosp.; Cons. Communicable Dis. Control Shrops. HA. Socs: Assn. Med. Microbiol.; Hosp. Infec. Soc.; Assn. Clin. Pathologists. Prev: Sen. Regist. Rotat. (Microbiol.) W. Midl.; Regist. (Microbiol.) Char. Cross Hosp. Lond.

O'NEILL, Patrick 22 Somersall Park Road, Chesterfield S40 3LD Tel: 01246 566395 & profess. 01246 272139 — MB BCh BAO 1965 NUI.

O'NEILL, Pauline (retired) Stone House, Blocklands, Langton Matravers, Swanage BH19 3LD — BM BCh Oxf. 1952; DM Oxf. 1977. Prev: Cons. Microbiol. Lewisham Hosp. Lond.

O'NEILL, Pauline Mary 47 Manse Road, Kilkeel, Newry BT34 4BN — MB BCh BAO 1986 NUI; MRCGP 1994; DMH Belf. 1992; DRCOG 1991; DCH RCPSI 1990. (Univ. Coll. Dub.) Clin. Med. Off. (Child Health) Kilkeel. Socs: BMA.

O'NEILL, Mr Peter Balfe (retired) 44 Salisbury Road, Cressington Park, Liverpool L19 0PJ — MB BS 1948 Lond.; FRCS Eng. 1954; DLO Eng. 1950. Prev: Cons. ENT Surg. Warrington Dist. Gen. Hosp. & Whiston Hosp.

O'NEILL, Richard James 102 Yeldham Road, London W6 8JG — BChir 1995 Camb.

O'NEILL, Rory Conor O'Hagan Chard Road Surgery, Chard Road, St. Budeaux, Plymouth PL5 2UE Tel: 01752 363111 Fax: 01752 363611; Meadowlea, Bethany, Saltash PL12 5DA Tel: 01752 363111 — MB BS 1972 Lond.; MRCGP 1978. (St. Bart.) Prev: Surg. Lt.-Cdr. RN; Ho. Surg. Crawley Hosp.

O'NEILL, Ryan Joseph 4 Rannyglass, Dungiven, Londonderry BT47 4NE — MB BCh BAO 1997 Belf.

O'NEILL, Sarah Siobhan 14 Stanley Road, Stockport SK4 4HL — BM BCh 1998 Oxf.; BM BCh Oxf 1998.

O'NEILL, Sheena Berenice 13 Ashbourne Park, Lanberg, Lisburn BT27 4NS — MB BCh BAO 1996 Belf.

O'NEILL, Sheila Maria Keswick, 13 Woodburn Road, Newlands, Glasgow G43 2TN — MB ChB 1962 Glas. (Glas.) Assoc. Specialist Dermat. Glas. Roy. Infirm. Univ. NHS Trust.

O'NEILL, Suzanne Louise Top Floor Flat, 1 Walker St., Edinburgh EH3 7JY — MB ChB 1998 Ed.

O'NEILL, Terence William 42 Downview Park W., Antrim Road, Belfast BT15 5HP — MB BCh BAO 1984 Dub.; MRCPI 1986.

O'NEILL, Tracey Ann 9 Meadowside, Glenavy, Crumlin BT29 4FE Tel: 01849 459331 — MB BCh BAO 1996 Belf.

O'NEILL, Mr Trevor John Plastic Surgery Associates, Hill House, BUPA Hospital, Colney, Norwich NR4 7TD Tel: 01603 250368 Fax: 01603 250404 Email: plasticsurgery@enterprise.net — MB BS 1972 Lond.; FRCS Eng. 1976; MRCS Eng. LRCP Lond. 1972. Cons. Plastic Surg. Norwich. Socs: BAPS; BAAPS; Craniofacial Soc. Prev: Sen. Regist. (Plastic Surg.) Qu. Vict. Hosp. E. Grinstead; Regist. (Plastic Surg.) Mt. Vernon Hosp. N.wood & Univ. Coll. Hosp. Lond.

O'NEILL, Vincent John 6 Victory Way, Baillieston, Glasgow G69 7HH Tel: 0141 771 8258 Email: vjonlq@uclcf.gla.ac.uk — MB ChB 1993 Glas.; BSc Glas. 1991; MRCP (UK) 1996. (Univ. Glas.) Clin. Research Fell. (Med. Oncol.) Univ. Glas. Socs: BMA; Brit. Assn. Cancer Research; Eur. Soc. Med. Oncol. Prev: SHO Rotat. (Med.) Roy. Infirm. Glas.

O'NEILL, Vincent Mel 17 Norfolk Farm Road, Pyrford, Woking GU22 8LH — MB BCh BAO 1980 NUI.

O'NEILL, William Mary British Medical Association, 14 Queen St., Edinburgh EH2 1LL Tel: 0131 247 3000 Fax: 0131 247 3011; 11/7 Rennie's Isle, Edinburgh EH6 6QA — MB BCh BAO 1979 NUI; MRCGP 1985, FRCGP 2001; BSc NUI 1974; DCH NUI 1980. (Univ. Coll. Dub.) Scott. Sec., BMA. Socs: BMA; Assn. Palliat. Med. Prev: Developm. Cons. Primary Care Support Force; Cons. & Sen. Lect. (Palliat. Med.) St. Thos. Hosp. Lond. & Bristol Oncol. Centre; GP W. Lond.

O'NEILL-BYRNE, Katrina Erth Centre, Park Crescent, Erith DA8 3EE Tel: 01322 356110 — MB BCh BAO 1984 Dub.; MRCPsych. 1988. Cons. Psychiat. Oxleas NHS Trust Bexley; Hon. Sen. Lect. Psychiat. KGT Med. Sch., Lond.. Prev: Sen. Regist., Psychiat., Lewisham and Guy's NHS Trust.

O'NUNAIN, Sean Seosamh Cranfield Cottage, 27 Church St., Southwell NG25 0HQ — MB BCh BAO 1979 NUI.

O'RAHILLY, Professor Stephen Patrick Department of Clinical Biochemistry & Medicine, Addenbrooke's Hospital, Cambridge CB2 2QR Tel: 01223 336855 Fax: 01223 330160 Email: sorahill@hgmp.mrc.ac.uk; Email: sorahill@hgmp.ac.uk — MB BCh BAO 1981 NUI; MD NUI 1988; FRCP Lond. 1996; FRCPI 1996; MRCP (UK) 1984; MRCPI 1983. (NUI) Prof. Clin. Bioch. & Med. Univ. Camb.; Hon. Cons. Phys. Addenbrooke's Hosp. Camb.; Hon. Sen. Scient. MRC Human Nutrit. Research Cam.; Dir. Wellcome Trust Clin. Addenbrooke's Hosp. Camb. Socs: Fell.of Assocaiton of Phys.s; Diabetes UK; Soc. Endocrinol. Prev: Wellcome Sen. Clin. Research Fell. Addenbrooke's Hosp. Camb.; Research Fell. Nuffield Dept. Med. Diabetes Research Laborats. Oxf.; MRC Trav. Fell. Harvard Med. Sch. Boston, MA, USA.

O'RAWE, Angela Marie 53 Castle Gardens, Belfast BT15 4GB Tel: 028 779893 — MB BCh BAO 1983 Belf.; MRCP (UK) 1987; DCH RCPS Glas. 1987. Research Regist. (Paediat.) Dept. Child Health Qu. Univ. Belf. Socs: BMA & Nutrit. Soc.

O'RAWE, Bridget Mary Antoinette 53 Castle Gardens, Belfast BT15 4GB — MB BCh BAO 1987 Belf.

O'RAWE, Martin Gerard Daniel The Surgery, 80 Cambridge Gardens, London W10 6HS Tel: 020 8969 5517 Fax: 020 8964 4766; 53 Castle Gardens, Belfast BT15 4GB — MB BCh BAO 1984 Belf.; MB BCh Belf. 1984; DCH Dub. 1988. Dep. for Heathcall Med. Servs. Prev: GP Bletchley.

O'REGAN, Mr David John 59A Eaton Rise, London W5 2HE — BM 1985 Soton.; FRCS Ed. 1990.

O'REGAN, Josephine Mary Martha (retired) 30 Moor Way, Hawkshaw, Bury BL8 4LF Tel: 01204 885536 — LRCPI & LM, LRSCI & LM 1946; LRCPI & LM, LRCSI & LM 1946. Prev: Clin. Med. Off. Blackburn Hyndburn & Ribble Valley HA.

O'REGAN, Mary Elizabeth 3B Chalmers Crescent, Edinburgh EH9 1TW — MB BCh BAO 1983 Dub.

O'REGAN, Mary Helen 22 Cliftonville Road, Lowestoft NR33 7AY — MB BS 1993 Lond.

O'REGAN, Mr Michael Barry Queen Margaret Hospital, Whitefield Road, Dunfermline KY12 0SU; Glenlomond House, Glenlomond, Kinross KY13 9HF — MB BCh BAO 1977 NUI; BDS NUI 1983; FFD RCSI 1986; FDS (Hon.) Ed. 1997. Cons. Oral & Maxillofacial Surg. Qu. Margt. Hosp. NHS Trust Dunfermline; Postgrad. Tutor Qu. Margt. Hosp. Dunfermline; Hon Sen. Lect. Univ. of Edin.; Fell.sh. Examr. (FDS) Univ. of Edin. Socs: Scott. Oral and Maxillofacial Soc.; Fell. and Inaugrual Sec.; Brit. Assn. Oral & Maxfacial Surgs. Prev: Regist. Univ. Coll. Hosp. Lond.; Sen. Regist. The Roy. Lond. Hosp. Lond.

O'REGAN, Rita 9 Oxford Mews, Cromwell Raod, Hove BN3 3NF — MB BS 1991 Lond. (UCMSM)

O'REILLY, Adrian James Newnham Walk Surgery, Wordsworth Grove, Cambridge CB3 9HS Tel: 01223 366811 Fax: 01223 302706 — MB BCh 1984 Wales; MBA Cambs. 1992; MFPHM Part I (I) 1996; MRCGP 1988; DPH Camb. 1995; DCH RCP Lond. 1989; DObst RCOG 1988. (Wales) Princip. GP Camb.; PCG Bd. Mem., Camb. City PCG; 1-deg. Care Cancer Lead, Camb. City PCG (Prelim. care). Socs: Local Med. Comm. (Camb.shire). Prev: Regist. (Pub. Health) Camb. & Huntingdon Health Commiss.; Trainee GP S. Gwent VTS.

O'REILLY, Alexander Michael Lincoln Road Surgery, 62 Lincoln Road, Peterborough PE1 2SN Tel: 01733 551008 Fax: 01733 345399 — MB ChB 1977 Manch.; MRCGP 1981; DRCOG 1980; Dip. Occ. Med. 1997.

O'REILLY, Mr Brian Francis 21 Newlands Road, Glasgow G43 2JD Tel: 0141 649 1961 Fax: 0141 201 3162 Email: brian.o'reilly@northglasgow.scot.nhs.uk — MB ChB 1972 Glas.; FRCS Glas. 1977. Cons. ENT Surg. Stobhill Hosp. Glas.; Cons. Neuro-Otol. Inst. Neurol. Sci. S. Gen. Hosp. Glas. Socs: Scott. Otorhinolaryngological Soc.: Pat Sec.; Brit. Assn. of otorhinolaryngologists: Counc. Mem.; Roy. Soc. of Med.: Past Counc. Mem.

O'REILLY

O'REILLY, Mr Brian Joseph, Wing Cdr. RAF Med. Br. Retd. Essex Nuffield Hospital, Shenfield Road, Brentwood CM15 8EH Tel: 01277 263263 Fax: 01277 201158; Glasshouse Cottages, Mapletree Lane, Ingatestone CM4 0PP Tel: 01277 355794 Fax: 01277 355794 — MB ChB 1978 Bristol; FRCS Ed. 1984; DLO RCS Eng. 1982. (Bristol) Cons. Otorhinolaryngol. Orsett & Basildon Hosps. Essex. Socs: BMA; Brit. Assn. Otol. Head & Neck Surg.; Hosp. Cons. & Spec. Assn. Prev: Cons. Adviser (Otorhinolaryngol.) P.ss Mary's Hosp. RAF Halton.

O'REILLY, Brian Nestor Wombwell Medical Centre, George St., Wombwell, Barnsley S73 0DD — MRCS Eng. LRCP Lond. 1976; MB BCh BAO Dub. 1976; BDS Dub. 1963; DCH NUI 1981; DRCOG 1979; DObst RCPI 1979. (Univ. Coll. Dub.)

O'REILLY, Colum Vincent c/o McGee, 5 Beverley Road, Newlands, Glasgow G43 2RT — MB ChB 1976 Glas.

O'REILLY, David Terence West Suffolk Hospital, Hardwick Lane, Bury St Edmunds IP33 2QZ — MB BChir 1981 Camb.; MA Camb. 1982, MB BChir 1981; MRCP (UK) 1984. (Cambridge) Cons. Phys. & Rheum. W. Suff. Hosp. Prev: Sen. Regist. (Rheum.) Manch. Roy. Infirm.

O'REILLY, Denis St John Institute of Biochemistry, Royal Infirmary, Alexandra Parade, Glasgow G4 0SF Tel: 0141 211 4631 — MB BCh BAO 1975 NUI; FRCP 1999 Glasgow; FRCPath 1995; MD 1991; MRCP 1997; MRCPath 1983; MD 1991; MRCP 1997; FRCP (Glas) 1999. (Cork) Cons. Clin. Biochem. Glas. Roy. Infirm. Socs: Assn. Clin. Biochem. & Soc. Endrocrinol.; Brit. Thyroid Assn.. Prev: Sen. Regist. (Chem. Path.) Bristol Roy. Infirm.; Regist. (Clin. Chem.) Qu. Eliz. Med. Centre Birm.

O'REILLY, Derval Maeve Martine Cornmarket Surgery, Newry Health Village, Monaghan Street, Newry BT35 6BW — MB BCh BAO 1985 Belf.

O'REILLY, Eugene (retired) 37 Crossfield Drive, Worsley, Manchester M28 2QQ — MB BCh BAO 1949 NUI. Prev: Ho. Phys. & Ho. Surg. Hope Hosp. Salford.

O'REILLY, Fingal Erik 71 New Road, Bengeo, Hertford SG14 3JH — MB BS 1996 Lond.

O'REILLY, Francis William c/o Surgery, Charles St., Annan DG12 5AG Tel: 0146 122745 — MB BCh BAO 1981 Belf.; DRCOG 1985. Prev: SHO (A & E) Belf. City Hosp.; SHO (Infec. Dis.) Belvoir Pk. Hosp. Belf.; Ho. Off. Tyrone Co. Hosp. Omagh.

O'REILLY, Garrett Vincent Friary Surgery, Dobbin Lane, Armagh BT61 7QG Tel: 028 3752 3165 Fax: 028 3752 1514; 8 Mullinure Park, Armagh BT61 9EJ — MB BCh BAO 1971 Belf.; MRCGP 1975.

O'REILLY, Gerard Michael 21 Knockchree Road, Downpatrick BT30 6RP — MB BCh BAO 1984 NUI.

O'REILLY, Mr James Alphonsus (retired) 27 Westland Road, Cookstown BT80 8BZ Tel: 0164 87 62351 — MB BCh BAO 1948 NUI; FRCS Eng. 1960; FRCS Ed. 1960. Prev: Cons. ENT Surg. S. Tyrone Hosp. Dungannon.

O'REILLY, John Aura, Ballycolman Avenue, Strabane BT82 9A — MB BCh BAO 1961 NUI.

O'REILLY, John Francis Blackpool Victoria Hospital, Whinney Heys Road, Blackpool FY3 8NR Tel: 01253 303477 Fax: 01253 303475 Email: dr.oreilly@exch.buh-tr.nwest.nhs.uk; Email: johnoreilly@breathe.com — MB 1977 Camb.; MA Camb. 1977; MB Camb. 1976, BChir 1976; MRCP (UK) 1978. Cons. Gen. & Respirat. Med. Blackpool, Wyre & Fylde HA. Socs: BMA; Brit. Thorac. Soc.

O'REILLY, Josephine Kate Maudsley Hospital, London SE15; 3 Fontarabia Road, London SW11 5PE — BSc (Hons.) Lond. 1985, MB BS 1988; DCH RCP Lond. 1991. Regist. (Psychiat.) Maudsley Hosp. Lond. Prev: SHO (Paediat.) St. Mary's Hosp. Lond.; SHO (Psych.) Univ. Coll. Hosp.

O'REILLY, Karen Anastasia Ship House Surgery, The Square, Liphook GU30 7AQ Tel: 01428 723296 Fax: 01420 724022; 21 Winston Rise, Four Marks, Alton GU34 5HP — MB BS 1984 Lond.; MRCGP 1991.

O'REILLY, Kieran Miceal Leicester General Hospital, Gwendolen Road, Leicester LE5 4PW; Glennamaddy, 8 Link Road, Leicester LE2 3RA Tel: 0116 270 6334 — MB ChB 1972 Glas.; MB ChB (Commend.) Glas. 1972; FRCPath 1992, M 1980. Cons. Histopath. Leicester Gen. Hosp.

O'REILLY, Maria Antoinette Wellfield Surgery, 291 Oldham Road, Rochdale OL16 5HX Tel: 01706 355111 — MB ChB 1990 Manch.

O'REILLY, Marian Dorothy House, Winsley House, Winsley, Bradford-on-Avon BA15 2LE Tel: 01225 722988 Fax: 01225 722907; 4 St Catherine's Close, Bath BA2 6BS Tel: 01225 428657 Email: gelart428@aol.com — MB BS 1976 Lond.; MRCS Eng. LRCP Lond. 1976; MRCGP 1984; DRCOG 1981; DCH Eng. 1979; Dip. Palliat. Med. 1996. p/t Cons. (Palliat. Med.) Bath.

O'REILLY, Mary Anastasia Regan Dept. of Radiology, Queen Mary's University Hospital, Roehampton, London SW15 5PN — MB BCh BAO 1985 NUI; MSc NUI 1987, B Ed. 1978; MRCPI 1988; FFR RCSI 1993; FRCR 1993; DCH NUI 1988; FRCPI 1999. Cons. Radiol., Qu. Mary's Univ. Hosp., Lond.; Cons. Radiologist, Kingston Hosp., Surrey.

O'REILLY, Maurice Patrick Staplehurst, Portfield Bar., Whalley, Blackburn BB7 9DL Tel: 01282 71298 — LRCPI & LM, LRCSI & LM 1950. (RCSI) Prev: Ho. Surg. & Ho. Phys. Wigan Infirm.; Cas. Off. Leigh Infirm.; Regist. O & G Birch Hill Matern. Hosp. Rochdale.

O'REILLY, Michael Fraser Lifeline Medical Examiners, Ouseburn Building, East Quayside, Newcastle upon Tyne NE6 1LL Tel: 0191 224 4440 Fax: 0191 224 4440; 65 Cleveland Road, North Shields NE29 0NW — MB ChB 1989 Ed.; MRCGP 1995. Chief Med. Off. Lifeline Med. Examr. Newc.-upon.Tyne.

O'REILLY, Michael Henry (retired) 6 Beeston Road, Sale M33 5AG Tel: 0161 973 6707 — LRCPI & LM, LRCSI & LM 1929; DPH Belf. 1932. Prev: Ho. Surg. Jervis St. Hosp. Dub.

O'REILLY, Mr Michael Joseph 22 Norfolk Drive, Belfast BT11 8AE — MB BCh BAO 1970 Belf.; FRCS Ed. 1974; FRCSI 1974.

O'REILLY, Michael Kenneth 55 Burley Lane, Quarndon, Derby DE22 5JR — MB BCh BAO 1980 NUI.

O'REILLY, Nial The Health Centre, Newry BT35 8DE Tel: 01693 61236; 28 Hawthorn Hill, Dublin Road, Newry BT35 8DE Tel: 01693 63320 — MB BCh BAO 1949 NUI; DCH 1965; LM Coombe 1951.

O'REILLY, Mr Patrick Henry Stepping Hill Hospital, Hazel Grove, Stockport SK2 7JE Tel: 0161 419 5484 Fax: 0161 419 5699 — MRCS Eng. LRCP Lond. 1970; MD Manch. 1977, MB ChB 1970; FRCS Eng. 1974. (Manch.) Cons. Urol. Surg. Stepping Hill Hosp. Stockport; Vis. Prof. Austral. Kidney Foundat. 1993; Edit. Bd. Brit. Jl. Urol. Socs: Fell. Europ. Bd. Urol.; Amer. Urol. Assn. Prev: Sen. Regist. (Urol.) United Manch. Hosps.; Regist. (Surg.) Wythenshawe Hosp. Manch.; Lect. (Anat.) Univ. Manch.

O'REILLY, Patrick Joseph Dermot 26 Brook Street, Enniskillen BT74 7EU — MB BCh BAO 1980 Belf.

O'REILLY, Patrick Vincent 3 Railway Cottages, Burford Road, Lechlade — LRCPI & LM, LRSCI & LM 1933; LRCPI & LM, LRCSI & LM 1933. (RCSI)

O'REILLY, Paul Joseph 10 Albert Road, Harbourne, Birmingham B17 0AN — BM BCh 1986 Oxf.

O'REILLY, Pauline Veronica 21 Newlands Road, Glasgow G43 2JD Tel: 0141 649 1961 — MB ChB 1973 Glas.

O'REILLY, Ragnar Sean 2 Coeur de Lion, Colchester CO4 5WN — MB BS 1994 Lond.

O'REILLY, Rebecca Jane Glass House Cottages, Maple Tree Lane, Mill Green, Ingatestone CM4 0PP — MB ChB 1978 Bristol.

O'REILLY, Roisin 8 Mullinure Park, Armagh BT61 9EJ — MB BCh BAO 1996 Belf.

O'REILLY, Sean Talgarth Medical Centre, Talgarth, Brecon LD3 0AE Tel: 01874 711309 Fax: 01874 712033 Email: tybreffni@aol.com — MB BCh BAO 1983 NUI; MRCGP 1990; DCH RCP Lond. 1990; Dip. Geriat. Med. 1988. (Dubl.) Prev: Trainee GP Camberley & Talgarth.

O'REILLY, Sheila Catherine Department of Rheumatology, Derbyshire Royal Infirmary, London Road, Derby DE1 2QY Tel: 01332 347141 Fax: 01332 254989 Email: sheila.oreilly@sclah-tr.trent.nhs.uk; Tel: 0015 923 3269 — BM BS 1988 Nottm.; DM Nottm. 1997; MRCP (UK) 1991. Sen. Regist. (Rheum.) Derbysh. Roy. Infirm..

O'REILLY, Susan Margaret Mary Clatterbridge Centre for Oncology, Bebington, Wirral CH63 4JY Tel: 0151 334 1155 Fax: 0151 482 7675; 4 Hawthorn Cottages, Dee View Road, Heswall, Wirral CH60 0DN Email: smoreilly@hawthorn.freeserve.co.uk — MB BCh BAO 1981 NUI; MD NUI 1992; MRCPI 1984. (Dublin) Cons. Med. Oncol. Clatterbridge Centre for Oncol. Wirral. Prev: Sen.

O'REILLY

Regist. (Med. Oncol.) Char. Cross Hosp. Lond.; ICRF Research Fell. Clin. Oncol. Unit Guy's Hosp. Lond.

O'REILLY, Una Catherina 55 Lebanon Park, Twickenham TW1 3DH — MB BCh BAO 1984 NUI; MRCPI 1980; MRCGP 1993.

O'REILLY, Vivienne Halina 35 Svenskaby, Orton, Wistow, Peterborough PE2 6YZ — MB ChB 1977 Manch.; DRCOG 1980.

O'RIORDAN, Mr Brendan Gerard Mary West Wales General Hospital, Dolgwili Road, Carmarthen SA31 2AF Tel: 01267 235151 Fax: 01267 237662 — MB BCh BAO 1981 NUI; FRACS 1992; FRCSI 1985. Cons. Gen. & Specialist UGI Surg. W. Wales Gen. Hosp. Camarthen; Cons Gen Surg., Werndale Private Hosp., Camarthen. Socs: BMA & Med. Defence Union; Welsh Surgs.; Assn. Surg. Prev: Clin. Research Fell. (Surg. Oncol.) Jefferson Hosp. Philadelphia, USA.

O'RIORDAN, Mr Dermot Charles Princess Alexandra Hospital NHS Trust, Heastel Road, Harlow CM20 1QX Tel: 01279 444455 Fax: 01279 827071 Email: doriordan@rcseng.ac.uk; 72 Roding Road, London E5 0DW Tel: 020 8985 9538 Email: dermot@roding.demon.co.uk — MB BS 1988 Lond.; FRCS Eng. 1993; FRCS Ed. 1993. (St. Bart.) Specialist Regist. Rotat. Gen. Surg. NE Thames. Prev: Research Fell. Nat. Groin Hernia Outcomes Project RCS Eng. Lond.; Regist. Rotat. (Gen. Surg.) NE Thames.

O'RIORDAN, Donagh Kevin Flat 5, 22 Crawford Avenue, Wembley HA0 2JS — MB BCh BAO 1984 NUI; MRCPI 1988.

O'RIORDAN, Eithne Joan 15 Southwood Park, Southwood Lawn Road, London N6 5SG — MB BCh BAO 1944 Dub.; BA Dub. 1942; DOMS Eng. 1948. Prev: Outpat. Off. & SHO (Med.) Moorfields Eye Hosp. Lond.; SHO (Med.) City & E. Lond. & Camden & Islington AHAs (T).

O'RIORDAN, Jane Ann 28 Brodrick Road, London SW17 7DY — MB BS 1986 Lond.; FRCA 1992. Sen. Regist. (Anaesth.) St. Geo. Hosp. Lond.

O'RIORDAN, Professor Jeffrey Lima Hayes 14 Northampton Park, London N1 2PJ Tel: 020 7226 9676 Email: jeffrey@oriordan.demon.co.uk — DM Oxf. 1970, MA, BSc, BM BCh 1957; FRCP Lond. 1971, M 1959. (Middlx.) Emerit. Prof. Metab. Med. Univ. Coll. Lond.; Emerit. Hon. Cons. Phys. Middlx. Hosp. Lond. Socs: Assn. Phys.; Amer. Endocrine Soc. Prev: Regist. Middlx. Hosp. Lond.; Vis. Assoc. Nat. Inst. Arthritis & Metab. Dis. Bethesda, MD.

O'RIORDAN, Mr John Bosco Andrews 42 Brooklands Park, London SE3 9BL Tel: 020 8852 7237 — MB BCh BAO 1965 NUI; FRCSI 1970. Cons. Cardiac Surg. St. Thos. Hosp. Lond. Socs: BMA; Soc. Thoracic & Cardiovasc. Surg.; Brit. Cardiac Soc. Prev: Cons. Cardiac Surg. Brook Gen. Hosp.

O'RIORDAN, Jonathan Ignatius Department of Neurology, The National Hospital for Neurology, Queen Square, London WC1N 3BG — MB BCh BAO 1989 NUI.

O'RIORDAN, Joseph Edward Gerard Picton Road Surgery, 194 Picton Road, Liverpool L15 4LL Tel: 0151 733 1347 — MB BCh BAO 1978 NUI.

O'RIORDAN, Mary 2 First Avenue, Netherlee, Glasgow G44 3UB Tel: 0141 637 1819 — MB BCh BAO 1987 NUI; Diploma in Palliative Medicine; BSc (Biochem.) NUI 1984; MRCGP 1993; DRCOG 1993; DCH RCPSI 1991. (Univ. Coll. Galway, Irel.) p/t Specialist Regist. in Palliat. Med., W. of Scotl. Train. Scheme.

O'RIORDAN, Mr Michael David 15 Cedar Court, Somerset Road, London SW19 5HU Tel: 020 8946 6837 — MB BS 1952 Lond.; BA Open University 1989; FRCSC 1972; FRCS Eng. 1964; FRCP Ed. 1982, M 1963; LMCC 1967; FRCOphth. 1989; DO Eng. 1959. (Westm.) Emerit. Cons. Ophth. Croydon Eye Unit Mayday Univ. Hosp. Thornton Heath. Prev: Sen. Regist. Roy. Free Hosp. Lond.; Emerg. Off. Radcliffe Infirm. Oxf.; Ho. Phys. W.m. Hosp. Lond.

O'RIORDAN, Michael Denis John Terence 10 Lord Roberts Avenue, Leigh-on-Sea SS9 1NE — MB BCh BAO 1941 NUI. (Cork) Prev: on Staff Qu. Mary Hosp. Roehampton; Surg. Lt. RNVR; Surg. Regist. Whipps Cross Hosp. Lond.

O'RIORDAN, Mr Sean Michael The Old Stone School, Carlton Scroop, Grantham NG32 3AU Tel: 01400 250730; Rooms 6 Avenue Road, Grantham NG31 6TA Tel: 01476 593919 Fax: 01476 593919 — MRCS Eng. LRCP Lond. 1968; BSc Lond. 1965, MB BS 1968; FRCS Eng. 1975; DObst RCOG 1970. (Lond. Hosp.) Cons. Orthop. Surg. Co. Hosp. Lincoln & Grantham Kesteven Gen. Hosp. Prev: Sen. Regist. (Orthop.) Lond. Hosp.; Regist. (Orthop.)

Broomfield Hosp. Chelmsford; Resid. Med. Off. Gambo Leprosy Control & Rural Health Centre.

O'RIORDAN, Sean Peter 8 Cassiobury Park Avenue, Watford WD18 7LB — MB BChir 1993 Camb.; MRCP (Lond.) 1995. (Camb. Univ./CXWMS) Locum. Prev: Paediat. Regist. King Edwd. VIII Hosp., Durban, S. Africa.

O'RIORDAN, Shelagh Elizabeth 19 Azof Street, London SE10 0EG — MB BS 1990 Lond.

O'ROURKE, Alan John 72 Sandford Grove Road, Nether Edge, Sheffield S7 1RR Email: a.j.orourke@sheffield.ac.uk — MB ChB 1986 Sheff.; MSc Sheff. 1996. (Sheffield) Non-Clin. Lect. Sheff. Univ. Socs: BMA.

O'ROURKE, Brian 49 Lilybank Road, Port Glasgow PA14 5AW — MB ChB 1992 Aberd.; MRCP (UK) Glas. 1995. (Aberdeen)

O'ROURKE, Declan Martin Department of Patnology, Belfast City Hospital Trust, Lisbun Road, Belfast Tel: 01232 329241 Ext: 2332 — MB BCh BAO 1988 Belf.; MRCP (UK) 1991; MRCPath 1998; Dip RCPath. (Cytopathology) 1998. (Queen's University of Belfast) Cons. Histo/Cytopatnologist, Belf. City Hosp. Trust. Socs: Mem. Of the Roy. Coll. Of Physcians & Surg.s Glas.; Mem. Of the Roy. Coll. Of Patrologists. Prev: Regist. (Histopath.) Roy. Vict. Hosp. Belf.; SHO (Histopath.) Roy. Vict. Hosp. Belf.

O'ROURKE, Edward Joseph 41 Grange Avenue, Derby DE23 8DH — MB ChB 1994 Leeds.

O'ROURKE, Fintan Martin 2 Smalls Road, Warrenpoint, Newry BT34 3PL — MB BCh BAO 1995 Belf.

O'ROURKE, Florence Loraine (retired) 5 The Paddock, Foundry Road, Stamford PE9 2NE Tel: 01780 762294 — MB BCh BAO 1945 NUI; MFCM 1974; DPH Lond. 1957; DIH Eng. 1957. Prev: Med. Ref. Dept. Social Welf. Dub.

O'ROURKE, Mr John Seanan Department of Urology, Treliske Hospital, Truro TR1 3LJ — MB BCh BAO 1979 NUI; BSc NUI 1981, MCh 1990; FRCSI 1983.

O'ROURKE, Killian Patrick 22 Fortfield, Dromore BT25 1DD — MB BCh BAO 1996 Belf.

O'ROURKE, Lucy Elizabeth Shoreditch Park Surgery, 10 Ruston Street, London N1 5DR Tel: 020 7739 8525 Fax: 020 7739 5352 — MB BS 1993 Lond.; BSc (Hons.) Lond. 1990; MRCGP 1997. (UCMSM) GP Princip., ShoreditchPk. Surg., Hackney.; Mem. LMC, E. Lond.

O'ROURKE, Michael Hugh Beds & Luton Comm. NHS Trust Learning Disability Sevice, Specialist Medical Department, Twinwoods Health Resource, Milton Rd, Clapham, Bedford MK41 6AT Tel: 01234 310582; 14 Princes Road, Bromham, Bedford MK43 8QD — LRCPI & LM, LRCSI & LM 1976; MRCPsych 1982 Dublin; DCH 1979; DO Dublin 1978. Clin. Dir. (Learning Disabil. Serv.) Beds & Luton Community NHS Trust.

O'ROURKE, Nicholas Peter The Surgery, 280 Havant Road, Drayton, Portsmouth PO6 1PA Tel: 02392 370422 Fax: 02392 618383 Email: nporourke@hotmail.com — BM 1989 Soton.; MRCGP 1994; DRCOG 1993.

O'ROURKE, Noelle Patricia Beatson Oncology Centre, Western Infirmary, Glasgow G11 6NT — BM BCh 1986 Oxf.; MA Camb. 1987; MD Sheff. 1994; MRCP (UK) 1989; FRCR (Oncol.) 1995. Sen. Lect. & Hon. Cons. Clin. Oncol. Glas. Prev: Sen. Regist. (Radiother. & Clin. Oncol.) Oxf.; Regist. (Clin. Oncol.) Hammersmith Hosp. Lond.; Clin. Research Fell. (Human Metab.) Univ. Sheff.

O'RYAN, Michael Francis Nicholas 27 Central Avenue, Eccleston Park, Prescot L34 2QL Tel: 0151 426 5418 Fax: 0151 426 5418 — MB BCh BAO Dub. 1959; MA Dub. 1982; FRCGP 1990, M 1974; MICGP 1985. (Dub.) Indep. GP Merseyside; Course Organiser Mersey Region Train. Scheme. Socs: St. Helens Med. Soc.; Nat. Assn. Non-Princip. Prev: Hon. Clin. Tutor Univ. Liverp.; Med. Mem. & Assessor Indep. Trib. Serv.

O'SHAUGHNESSY, Denise Frances St Peter's Hosptial, Chertsey KT16 0PZ; Vynes Cottage, The Green, Pirbright, Woking GU24 0JE — BChir 1980 Camb.; DPhil Oxf. 1989; BSc (Hons.) St. And. 1978; MRCP (UK) 1983; MRCPath 1990. Cons. Haemat. St. Peter's Hosp. Chertsey. Prev: Sen. Regist. (Haemat.) Hammersmith Hosp. Lond.

O'SHAUGHNESSY, Donal Michael Kevin O'Shaughnessy, Rathfriland Health Centre, John Street, Rathfriland, Newry BT34 5QH Tel: 02840 630666 Fax: 02840 631198; 2 Bamneen Road, Rathfriland, Newry BT34 5AW Tel: 02840 630666 Fax: 02840 631198 — MB BCh BAO 1976 NUI; MICGP 1987.

O'SULLIVAN

(University College Galway) GP; Hon. Med. Off. Rugby Union.; Hon. Med. Off. Barbarians RFC. Socs: Irish Coll. Gen. Pract.; Brit. Assn. of Sport Med.

O'SHAUGHNESSY, Kevin Michael Clinical Pharma, Cology Unit, Level 6, ACCI, Box 110, Adden-Brooks Hospital, Cambridge CB2 2QQ Tel: 01223 762578 Fax: 01223 762376 Email: kmo22@medschl.cam.ac.uk; Tanglewood House, Cherry House, Duton Hill, Dunmow CM6 2EE Tel: 01371 870239 — BM BCh 1986 Oxf.; MA Camb. 1984, BA 1980; DPhil Oxf. 1983, BM BCh 1986; MRCP (UK) 1989. (Oxf.) Univ. Lect. Clin. Pharmacol. Univ. Camb. & Hon. Cons. Phys. Addenbrookes Hosp., Camb. Socs: Brit. Hypertens. Soc. Prev: Sen. Regist. (Clin. Pharmacol.) Hammersmith Hosp. Lond.; Research Fell. & Hon. Sen. Regist. Hammersmith Hosp. Lond.; SHO (Med.) Centr. Middlx. Hosp. Lond.

O'SHAUGHNESSY, Terence Conleth Newham General Hospital, Glen Road, Plaistow, London E13 8SL Tel: 020 7476 4000 Fax: 020 7363 8081 — MB BChir 1983 Camb.; BSc (Hons.) St. And. 1981; MRCPI. Cons. Respirat. & Gen. Med. Newham Gen. Hosp. Plaistow.

O'SHEA, Diarmuid Donal Paschal 10 Hardwick Place, Gosforth, Newcastle upon Tyne NE3 4SH — MB BCh BAO 1986 NUI; MRCPI 1988.

O'SHEA, Donal Brendan 145A Harbord Street, Fulham, London SW6 6PN — MB BCh BAO 1989 NUI.

O'SHEA, Elaine Maria Anne 79 Broomgrove Gardens, Edgware HA8 5RJ — MB ChB 1996 Bristol. (University of Bristol) SHO (Gen. Med.) The Ipswich Hosp. NHS Trust.

O'SHEA, Mr John Gerard Birmingham and Midand Eye Centre, Dudley Road, Birmingham B18 4EJ — MB BS 1983 Monash; FRCS Ed. 1991; MRCOphth 1991; DHMSA 1989; MD Monash 1991. Sen. Regist. Birm. & Midl. Eye Centre Dudley. Prev: Sen. Regist. (Ophth.) St. John Ophth. Hosp., Jerusalem.

O'SHEA, John Kevin Chichester Priority Care Services, 72 Stockbridge Road, Chichester PO19 2QJ Tel: 01243 782919 Fax: 01243 783919; Flat 18 Lombard Court, Lombard St, Old Portsmouth, Portsmouth PO1 2HU — MB BCh BAO 1986 NUI; MRCPsych 1994; DCH NUI 1988. Cons. Psychiat. Learning Disabil. Serv. Chichester Priority Care Servs. NHS Trust. Socs: Fell. Soc. Med.

O'SHEA, Judith Rowan 74 Mill Hill Road, Norwich NR2 3DS — MB BS 1990 Lond.

O'SHEA, Matthew James Staplands, Hinderton Road, Neston, South Wirral CH64 9PW — MB ChB 1993 Liverp.; BSc (Hons). 1990.

O'SHEA, Maureen Staplands, Hinderton Road, Neston, South Wirral CH64 9PW Tel: 0151 336 1422 — MB ChB 1960 Liverp.; DObst RCOG 1964. (Liverp.)

O'SHEA, Michael James 17 Kennedy Road, Shrewsbury SY3 7AB Tel: 01743 61148 — MD 1974 Camb.; MB 1959, BChir 1958; FRCPath. 1980, M 1968. Cons. Haemat. Salop AHA. Socs: Brit. Soc. Haemat. & Assn. Clin. Path. Prev: Lect. Haemat. King's Coll. Hosp. Inst. Child Health; Sen. Lect. & Cons. Haemat. Roy. Free Hosp. Lond.

O'SHEA, Patrick John 48 Southmeade, Maghull, Liverpool L31 8EF — MB ChB 1996 Glas.

O'SHEA, Peter John Anaesthetic Department, The London Hospital, Whitechapel, London E1 1BB — MB BS 1968 Lond.; FFA RCS Eng. 1973. (Lond. Hosp.) Cons. Anaesth. Lond. Hosp.

O'SHEA, Roger Aloysius 194 Burton Street, Melton Mowbray LE13 1DN — MB BCh BAO 1942 NUI; CPH 1948; LM Nat. Matern. Hosp. Dub. 1948; DObst RCOG 1949. (Univ. Coll. Dub.) Div. Surg. St. John Ambul. Brig. Socs: Foundat. Mem. Coll. of Gen. Pract.; Nottm. M-C Soc. & Derby Med. Soc. Prev: Res. Surg. Off. Leigh Infirm. Lancs.; Ho. Phys. Huddersfield Roy. Infirm.; O & G Regist. Stepping Hill Hosp. Stockport.

O'SHEA, Roger Michael John Ryle Health Centre, Southchurch Drive, Clifton, Nottingham NG11 8EW Tel: 0115 921 2970; 5 Manor Park, Ruddington, Nottingham NG11 6DS Tel: 0115 921 2177 — LRCPI & LM, LRCSI & LM 1972; DObst. RCPI 1977; DCH NUI 1976. Occupat. Health Phys. Jessop & Son. Ltd. Nottm. John Lewis Partnership.

O'SHEA, Sarah Jane Staplands, Hinderton Road, Neston, South Wirral CH64 9PW — MB BS 1991 Lond.; BSc Lond. 1989; MRCP (UK) 1994.

***O'SHEA, Sean Brian** 13 Pauls Row, Truro TR1 1HH — MB BS 1987 Lond.; MRCGP 1994.

O'SHEA, Thomas Stephen Hyde Park Surgery, 3 Woodsley Road, Leeds LS6 1SG Tel: 0113 295 1235 Fax: 0113 295 1220 — MB BCh BAO 1977 NUI; MRCGP 1981; DRCOG 1980.

O'SULLIVAN, Aideen Kathryn 25 Waterloo Park, Belfast BT15 5HU — MB BCh BAO 1996 Belf. (Belf.)

O'SULLIVAN, Anthony Gerard Priory Manor Child Development Centre, 1 Blagdon Road, Lewisham, London SE13 7HL Tel: 020 7771 4510 Fax: 020 7771 4540 Email: tony.o'sullivan@chsltr.sthames.nhs.uk; 88 Erlanger Road, New Cross, London SE14 5TH Tel: 020 7732 0304 Email: tony@osullivan17.freeserve.co.uk — MB ChB 1974 Liverp.; MRCP (UK) 1989; DCH RCP Lond. 1987. (Liverp.) Cons. Community Paediat. Community Health S. Lond. NHS Trust, Priory Manor Child Developm. Centre Lewisham. Socs: Fell.Roy. Coll. of Paediat. and Child Health; Brit. Paediat. Neurol. Assn.; BACCH.

O'SULLIVAN, Barbara Mary Philomena 57 Drones Road, Armoy, Ballymoney BT53 8YP — MB BCh BAO 1981 NUI; LRCPSI 1981; MRCGP 1990.

O'SULLIVAN, Bernadette Mary The Surgery, 2 Oxford Street, Southampton SO14 3DJ Tel: 023 8033 5157 — MB BS 1977 Lond.; MRCGP 2001; DA Eng. 1981. (Roy. Free)

O'SULLIVAN, Brian Columbanus Dalvennan Avenue Practice, 27 Dalvennan Avenue, Patna, Ayr KA6 7NA Tel: 01292 531367 Fax: 01292 531033; 14 Chalmer's Road, Ayr KA7 2RQ — MB BCh BAO 1987 NUI; MRCGP 1992; DRCOG 1990. (Dublin) GP Princip.; Forens. Med. Examr. Strathclyde Police. Socs: BMA. Prev: Trainee GP Peebles; Regist. (Psychiat.) Roy. Edin. Hosps.; SHO Ards Hosp. Newtownards.

O'SULLIVAN, Catherine Cecelia Pilgrim's Hospice, 56 London Road, Canterbury CT2 8JA Tel: 01227 459700; 3 Town Road, Petham, Canterbury CT4 5QT Tel: 01227 700898 — MB BCh BAO 1973 NUI; MA (Psychother. & Counselling) Regent's Coll. 1994; DTM & H Liverp. 1977. Hospice Phys. (Palliat. Med.) Pilgrim's Hosp. Canterbury. Socs: BMA. Prev: Clin. Med. Adviser Ellenor Foundat. Livingstone Community Hosp. Dartford.

O'SULLIVAN, Catherine Vivien 46 Woodbine Road, Gosforth, Newcastle upon Tyne NE3 1DD — MB BCh BAO 1983 NUI; MRCGP 1987.

O'SULLIVAN, Catherine Vivienne 46 Woodbine Road, Gosforth, Newcastle upon Tyne NE3 1DD — MB BCh BAO 1983 NUI; MRCGP 1987; MICGP 1987; Dobst RCPI 1986; DCH NUI 1985.

O'SULLIVAN, Clare Jennifer The Surgery, 48 Mulgrave Road, Belmont, Sutton SM2 6LX Tel: 020 8642 2050 — MB BS 1987 Lond.; MRCGP 1991; DRCOG 1989; Cert. Family Plann. JCC 1989. Prev: Trainee GP Wessex VTS.

O'SULLIVAN, Daniel Gerard 28 Whinmoor Road, West Derby, Liverpool L12 2AX — MB BCh BAO 1982 NUI.

O'SULLIVAN, Daniel John George Street, Wombwell, Barnsley S73 0DD Tel: 01226 752363; 29 South View Crescent, Nether Edge, Sheffield S7 1DG Tel: 0114 250 8035 Fax: 0114 250 8035 — MB BCh BAO 1987 Dub.; DFFP 1994; MRACGP 1994; MRCGP 1994; DFFP 1994; DCH NUI 1992; DGM RCP Lond. 1990. (Trinity College Dublin) GP.

O'SULLIVAN, Dawn Alice Maple House, Rue de la Vista, St Lawrence, Jersey JE3 1ED — MB BS 1996 Lond.

O'SULLIVAN, Mr Denis Christopher Department of Urology, Freeman Hospital, Newcastle upon Tyne NE7 7DN Tel: 0191 284 3111 — MB BCh BAO 1984 NUI; MCh NUI 1992; FRCSI (Urol.) 1995; FRCSI 1988. Cons. Urol. Freeman Hosp. Newc. u. Tyne.

O'SULLIVAN, Denis Michael 92 Cavendish Road, Cambridge CB1 3AF — MB BChir 1992 Camb.; MA Camb. 1992; MRCP (UK) 1995. (Cambridge) Specialist Regist. (Cardiol.) Papworth Hosp. Camb.

O'SULLIVAN, Desmond Patrick Llety Dawell, Greenhill Road, Griffithstown, Pontypool NP4 5BE — LRCPI & LM, LRSCI & LM 1937; LRCPI & LM, LRCSI & LM 1937.

O'SULLIVAN, Desmond Patrick Dominic Novartis Pharmaceuticals UK Ltd., Frimley Business Park, Frimley, Camberley GU16 5SG Tel: 01276 698276 Fax: 01276 698454 — MB BChir 1982 Camb.; Dip. Pharm. Med. RCP (UK) 1985. Head Clin. Safety & Epidemiol. Novartis Pharmaceuts. Surrey.

O'SULLIVAN, Donal Gerard Mary Lambeth, Southwark and Lewisham Health Authority, 1 Lower Marsh, London SE1 7NT Tel: 020 7716 7030 Fax: 020 7716 7018 Email:

O'SULLIVAN

donal.osullivan@ob.lslha.sthames.nhs.uk; Fairoaks, 221 Crofton Lane, Orpington BR6 0BL Tel: 01689 838125 — MB BCh BAO 1982 NUI; MB BCh BAO (NUI) 1982; FFPHM RCP (UK) 1997; MFPHM RCP (UK) 1990; MSc Lond. 1987. (University College, Cork) Cons. Communicable Dis. Control Lambeth, S.wark & Lewisham HA. Socs: BMA; Internat. Epidemiol. Assn.; Pub. Health Med. Environm. Gp. Prev: Sen. Regist. (Pub. Health Med.) S. E. Thames RHA.

O'SULLIVAN, Eileen Elizabeth Clountarrive, Gortalea, Tralee, County Kerry, Republic of Ireland; 2 Withey Close W., Westbury-on-Trym, Bristol BS9 3SX — MB BCh BAO 1981 NUI; MRCPsych 1986. Sen. Regist. (Psychiat.) S.mead Hosp. Bristol. Prev: Clin. Asst. Barrow Hosp. Bristol; Regist. (Psychiat.) Gransha Hosp. Lond.derry & Mater Hosp. Dub.; Regist. (Psychiat.) Holywell Hosp. Antrim.

O'SULLIVAN, Eleanor Meriel 151 Finborough Road, London SW10 9AP Tel: 01926 492522, 020 7373 6654 — MB BS 1966 Lond.; MRCS Eng. LRCP Lond. 1966; FRCR 1975; FFR 1974. Cons. (Radiol.) Qu. Mary's Hosp. Roehampton; Cons. (Radiol.) St. Helier's Hosp. Carshalton Surrey.

O'SULLIVAN, Eoin Patrick 77 Yale Court, Honeybourne Road, London NW6 1JH — MB BChir 1990 Camb.

O'SULLIVAN, Fergus Timothy HMP Littlehey, Perry, Huntingdon PE18 0SR Tel: 01480 812202; 63 Elton Road, Wansford, Peterborough PE8 6JS — MB BCh BAO 1977 NUI; DPM RCPSI 1989; DObst RCPI 1980. Sen. Med. Off. (Psychiat.) HMP Littlehey Cambs. Prev: Managing Med. Off. HMP Albany; Med. Off. HMP Pk.hurst I. of Wight.

O'SULLIVAN, Finbar Eugene Flat 8, 183 Sussex Gardens, London W2 2RH — MB BS 1998 Lond.

O'SULLIVAN, Geraldine Frances Mary Northamptonshire Hospital Trust, Aldermaston Road, Basingstoke RG24 9NA Tel: 01256 313492; Mallard's Close, Bourne Lane, Twyford, Winchester SO21 1NX Tel: 01962 713967 — MB BCh BAO 1973 Dub.; FRCR 1982; DMRD Eng. 1977. Cons. Radiol. Basingstoke N. Hants. Hosps. Trust; Q.A. Radiologist, S. E. (W.) Region, Dir. Of BrE. Screening. Socs: BMUS; Roy. Coll. of Raiologists BrE. Grp. Prev: Sen. Regist. (Diag. Radiol.) Soton. Gen. Hosp.; Sen. Regist. (Diag. Radiol.) Lond. Hosp. Whitechapel; Regist. (Diag. Radiol.) Roy. Free Hosp. Lond.

O'SULLIVAN, Geraldine Helen Albany Lodge Treatment Unit, Church Crescent, St Albans AL3 5JF Tel: 01727 834330 Fax: 01727 834182 — MB BCh BAO 1981 NUI; MD 1993; MRCPsych. 1986. (Univ. Coll. Cork Irel.) Cons. Community Psychiat. Herts. NHS Trust. Prev: Sen. Regist. Bethlem Roy. Maudsley Hosps.; Lect. & Research Work Inst. Psychiat. Lond.

O'SULLIVAN, Geraldine Mary Department of Anaesthetics, St Thomas Hospital, London SE1 7EH Tel: 020 7928 9292 Fax: 0207 960 5615 Email: geraldine.o'sullivan@gstt.sthames.nhs.uk — MB BCh BAO 1975 NUI; MD NUI 1985; FRCA. (Cork) Cons. St. Thos. Hosp. Lond. Obstetric Anasthesia; Pres. Elect. Obstetric Anaesth.s Assn. Socs: Comm. Mem. Anaesth. Assn.; Obst. Anaesth.s Assn.; Soc. for Obst. Anaesth. Prev: Sen. Regist. St. Thos.' Hosp. Lond.; Research Fell. Assn. Anaesth. Nuffield Dept. Anaesth. Oxf.; Regist. (Anaesth.) Nuffield Dept. Anaesth. Oxf.

O'SULLIVAN, Gerard Patrick Delamere Street Health Centre, 45 Delamere Street, Crewe CW1 2ER Tel: 01270 214046 — MB ChB 1984 Birm.; MRCGP 1988.

O'SULLIVAN, Helen Louise Shelton Hospital, Bilton Heath, Shrewsbury Tel: 01743 261000 — MB ChB 1995 Birm.; ChB Birm. 1995; MRCPsych Part 1 1998. SHO (Psychiat. & Learning Disabil.) Shelton Hosp. Bilton Heath Shrewsbury. Socs: Roy. Coll. Psychiatr. Inceptor. Prev: SHO (Psychiat. & Rehabil.); SHO (Gen. Adult Psychiat.).

O'SULLIVAN, Jerry Patrick, TD 3 Wiston Avenue, Donnington, Chichester PO19 2RJ Tel: 01243 527797 — MB ChB 1966 Glas.; BSc (Hons) Glas. 1961; FRCPath 1986, M 1973; BA (Hons) Open 1987. (Glas.) Cons. Histopath. St. Richard's Hosp. Chichester. Socs: Roy. Soc. Med.; Assn. of Clin. Pathologists. Prev: Cons. Histopath. St. Jas. Hosp. Lond.; Sen. Lect. (Histopath.) St. Geo. Hosp. Med. Sch. Lond.; Lect. (Path.) Glas. Roy. Infirm.

O'SULLIVAN, Mr John Conor 8 Pennant Mews, London W8 5JN Tel: 020 7580 6966 Fax: 020 7580 6966; 96 Arthur Road, Wimbledon, London SW19 7DT Tel: 020 8946 6242 — BM BCh 1959 Oxf.; BA (Hons.) Oxf. 1955, MA 1959; FRCS Eng. 1967; FRCOG 1983, M 1970; T(GP) 1996. (Westm.) Cons. Gyn. Oncol. Hammersmith Hosp. Lond.; Sen. Lect. Roy. Postgrad. Med. Sch. Hammersmith Hosp. Lond. & Inst. Obst. & Gyn.; Examr. Bd. Eng. & Univs. Lond. & Camb.; Examr. RCOG & Prof. & Linguistics Assessm. Bd. Socs: Founder Mem. Brit. Assn. Surg. Oncols.; Brit. Gyn. Cancer Soc. Prev: Sen. Regist. (O & G) Hammersmith Hosp. Lond.; Ho. Off. (Surg.) Qu. Charlotte's & Chelsea Hosps. Lond.; Cas. Off. & Ho. Off. (Surg.) W.m. Hosp. Lond.

O'SULLIVAN, Mr John Francis, OBE Belfast City Hospital, Lisburn Road, Belfast BT9 7AB — MB BCh BAO 1950 Belf.; FRCS Ed. 1956; FRCOG 1971, M 1959.

O'SULLIVAN, John Francis Xavier The Surgery, 1 Balliol Road, Coventry CV2 3DR Tel: 024 7644 9111 — LRCPI & LM, LRSCI & LM 1951; LRCPI & LM, LRCSI & LM 1951. Clin. Asst. (Rheum.) Coventry & Warks. Hosp.; Co. Med. Off. Various Midl. Firms. Prev: SHO Friern Hosp. Lond.; Ho. Surg. & Cas. Off. Metrop Hosp. Lond.

O'SULLIVAN, John James M, RD Ashling Occupational Health Ltd., Ashling House, Works Lane, Lostock Gralam, Northwich CW9 7FA Tel: 01606 330660 Fax: 01606 330644 Email: drjosullivan@ashling.co.uk; Ashling, 59 Mill Lane, Upton-by-Chester, Chester CH2 1BS Tel: 01244 372646 — MB BCh BAO NUI 1974; MSc (Occupat. Med.) Lond. 1977; LLM Cardiff 1996; FFOM RCP Lond. 1993, MFOM 1983; DIH Eng. 1977. Cons. Occupat. Health Ashling Occupat. Health Ltd N.wich; Tutor Distance Learning Course Manch. Univ.; Vis. Lect. Univ. Coll. Dub. Prev: Cons. Occupat. Health Brunner Mond & Co. N.wich; Sen. Med. Off. Imperial Chem. Indust. Chem. Gp. N.wich; Works Med. Off. Castner-Kellner Works, Imp. Chem. Indust. PLC, Mond Div. Runcorn.

O'SULLIVAN, John Jude 46 Woodbine Road, Gosforth, Newcastle upon Tyne NE3 1DD — MB BCh BAO 1983 NUI; MRCPI 1985.

O'SULLIVAN, John Laurence Twyford Surgery, Hazeley Road, Twyford, Winchester SO21 1QY Tel: 01962 712202 Fax: 01962 715158; Mallard's Close, Bourne Lane, Twyford, Winchester SO21 1NX Tel: 01962 713967 — MB BCh BAO 1973 Dub.; MRCGP 1981; DRCOG 1978; DCH Eng. 1977; DFP & RHC 1996. GP Winchester, Hants. Socs: BMA. Prev: Regist. St. Joseph's Hospice Lond.; MOH Ubon Refugee Camp Thailand (Save the Childr. Fund); SHO (Paediat.) Qu. Eliz. Hosp. Lond.

O'SULLIVAN, Joseph Philip (retired) 12 Upper Northgate Street, Chester CH1 4E — LRCPI & LM, LRSCI & LM 1948; LRCPI & LM, LRCSI & LM 1948. Prev: Ho. Surg. & Ho. Phys. Jervis St. Hosp. Dub.

O'SULLIVAN, Karen Mary Claire 28 Widmore Lodge Road, Bromley BR1 2QF — MB BCh 1984 Wales. SHO (Psychiat.) Ravensbourne NHS Trust FarnBoro. Hosp. Kent. Prev: SHO A & E Unit Cardiff Roy. Infirm.; Ho. Surg. Vasc. Unit Univ. Hosp. Wales Cardiff; Ho. Phys. Llandough Hosp.

O'SULLIVAN, Katherine Elizabeth — MB BS 1988 Lond.; DRCOG 1992. p/t GP, Non-Princip., Basingstoke; Health Screening BUPA.

O'SULLIVAN, Kevin Aelred 32 Hawthorn Lane, Wilmslow SK9 5DG — MB BCh BAO 1983 NUI; FFARCS 1988. Sen. Regist. (Anaesth.) NW RHA. Prev: Regist. (Anaesth.) Roy. Lancaster Infirm.; Regist. (Anaesth.) Univ. Hosp. S. Manch.

O'SULLIVAN, Kevin Miceal c/o AIKMO Medical Ltd., 62-63 Westborough, Scarborough YO11 1TS — MB ChB 1982 Manch.; DRCOG 1985. Managing Dir. AIKMO Med. Ltd. Prev: Med. Dir. BUPA Insur.; Regional Med. Dir. SmithKline Beecham Internat.; Med. Dir. The Harley Gp.

O'SULLIVAN, Kevin Thomas Cavendish Cottage, 25C Cavendish Road E., The Park, Nottingham NG7 1BB — MB ChB 1992 Liverp.

O'SULLIVAN, Kiaran Francis Oakwood Medical Centre, Oakwood Lane, Barnton, Northwich CW8 4HE Tel: 01606 74718 Fax: 01606 784529; Minaun, 4 Pear Tree Lane, Acton Bridge, Northwich CW8 3QR — MB ChB 1957 Liverp.; MRCS Eng. LRCP Lond. 1957. (Liverp.)

O'SULLIVAN, Maeve Coralie Banna House, 27 Heath End Road, Flackwell Heath, High Wycombe HP10 9DT — MB BS 1998 Newc.; PhD, Neurophysiology, Newc.1991; BSc (Hons), Physiology, Sheff 1987. SHO (Paediat.) Guy's & St Thomas' Hosp. Lond. Prev: JHO, Roy. Vichne Hosp. Belf.

O'SULLIVAN, Margaret Marian Wrexham Maelor Hospital, Croesnewydd Road, Wrexham LL13 7TD Tel: 01978 725091 — MB BCh BAO 1977 NUI; MD NUI 1989; MRCPI 1979; DCH NUI 1980. Cons. Rheum. Wrexham Maelor Hosp. Clwyd. Prev: Sen. Regist.

(Rheum.) Univ. Hosp. Wales Cardiff; SHO Hosp. Sick Childr. Crumlin; SHO (Med.) Regional Hosp. Cork.

O'SULLIVAN, Mr Mark Jonathan Benjamin North Hampshire Hospital, Basingstoke RG24 9NA; Email: benosullivan@doctors.org.uk — MB BS 1988 Lond.; MRCOG 1994; DM Soton. 1998. (Royal London Hospital Medical College) Cons. in Obst. & Gyn., N.Hants. Hosp. Socs: Brit. Fertil. Soc.; BSCCP. Prev: Specialist Regist. (O & G) Salisbury Dist. Hosp. Salisbury; IVF Research Fell. (O & G) Univ. Soton.; Regist. (O & G) P.ss Anne Hosp. Soton. & Roy. Hants. Co. Hosp. Winchester.

O'SULLIVAN, Mary Countisbury Avenue Surgery, 152 Countisbury Avenue, Llanrumney, Cardiff CF3 5YS Tel: 029 2079 2661 Fax: 029 2079 4537 — MB BCh BAO 1980 NUI. GP Cardiff Wales.

O'SULLIVAN, Mary Fiona East Surrey Hospital, Three Arch Road, Redhill RH1 5RH — MB BCh BAO 1982 NUI; MD NUI 1994; FRCS (Ophth.) Glas. 1987. (Univ. Coll. Cork, NUI) Cons. Ophth. E. Surrey Hosp. Redhill. Prev: Research Fell. (Glaucoma) Moorfields Eye Hosp. Lond.; Sen. Regist. St. Geo. Hosp. Lond.; Regist. W.. Ophth. Hosp. Lond.

O'SULLIVAN, Mary Josephine (retired) 11 Rowland Close, Wolvercote, Oxford OX2 8PW Tel: 01865 559269 — BA Open Univ. 1974; MRCS Eng. LRCP Lond. 1955; DPH Lond. 1962. Prev: Assoc. Specialist Blood Transfus. Serv. Oxf.

O'SULLIVAN, Michael Edward Howard Barton, Hittisleigh, Exeter EX6 6LP — MB ChB BAO 1949 NUI.

O'SULLIVAN, Michael Gerard 140 Churchfields, Shoeburyness, Southend-on-Sea SS3 8TW — MB BCh BAO 1983 NUI.

O'SULLIVAN, Mr Michael Gerard Joseph 175 Gilberstoun, Edinburgh EH15 2RG Tel: 0131 669 8766 — MB BCh BAO 1983 NUI; FRCSI 1987; BSc 1979. (University Coll. Cork Ireland) Cons. Neurosurg. Dept of Clin. Neurosc. W.. Gen. Hosp. Edin.

O'SULLIVAN, Michael John Bernard Shantallow Health Centre, Racecourse Road, Londonderry BT48 8NL Tel: 028 7135 3054; Aarhus, 27 Rock Road, Londonderry BT48 7NE Tel: 01504 265963 — MB BCh BAO 1959 NUI. Prev: Ho. Surg. & Ho. Phys. Waterside Gen. Hosp. Lond.derry; SHO Altnagelvin Hosp. Lond.derry; Cas. & Admission Off. Limerick Regional Hosp.

O'SULLIVAN, Nicole Therese 21 Brockley View, Forest Hill, London SE23 1SN — MB BS 1991 Queensland.

O'SULLIVAN, Nigel Noel Vincent Elm Park Clinic, 69 Elm Park, Stanmore HA7 4AU Tel: 020 8954 1333 Fax: 020 8420 7027 Email: drnigel@hotmail.com; 61 Parson Street, Hendon, London NW4 1QT Tel: 020 8203 1258 Email: drnigel@hotmail.com — MRCS Eng. LRCP Lond. 1960. (Guy's)

O'SULLIVAN, Patrick Finbarr (retired) High End, 33 Old Camp Road, Eastbourne BN20 8DL Tel: Ex Dir — MB BCh BAO NUI 1960; FRCR 1968; DMRD Eng. 1966; DObst RCOG 1962; DCH NUI 1962. Prev: Cons. Radiol. E.bourne HOsp. NHS Trust.

O'SULLIVAN, Patrick Joseph Gerard 44 Eight Avenue, Lancing BN15 9XD Tel: 01903 764769 — MB BCh BAO 1950 NUI.

O'SULLIVAN, Sheila Mary 81 Marlowe Drive, West Derby, Liverpool L12 7LR — MB BCh BAO 1985 NUI.

O'SULLIVAN, Mr William Joseph Orchard House, Three Gates Lane, Haslemere GU27 2LD Tel: 01428 654620 — MB BCh BAO NUI 1950; MD NUI 1961, MAO 1955; FRCS Ed. 1963; FRCOG 1971, M 1956, DObst 1953. (Galw.) Cons. (O & G) Sutton & W. Merton Health Dist.; Sen. Lect. St. Geo. Hosp. Med. Sch. Lond. Prev: Sen. Regist. Postgrad. Med. Sch. Lond.

O'TIERNEY, Donal Padraig O'Tierney, Murphy and Ryan, Health Centre, Summerhill, Warrenpoint, Newry BT34 3JD Tel: 028 4175 4100 Fax: 028 4175 4050; Belmont, 41 Seaview, Warrenpoint, Newry BT34 3NJ Tel: 028 4177 3630 — MB BCh BAO 1958 NUI; LAH Dub. 1957; FRCGP 1987, M 1968. (Univ. Coll. Dub.) Sen. Princip. GP DR O'Tierney Murphy & Ryan Partnership, Warren Point, Co. Down, Irel.; Med. Adviser SCA Packaging Ltd. Warrenpoint.

O'TOOLE, Conor Emmett Kevin 22 Blackstaff Road, Clough, Downpatrick BT30 8SW — MB BCh BAO 1994 Belf.

O'TOOLE, Mr Gregory Anthony 1 Eastcote View, Pinner HA5 1AT Email: gregoryotoole@hotmail.com — MB ChB 1992 Sheff.; FRCS Lond. 1996. Regist / Research Fell. (Plas Surg.) St Geo.s Hosp. Austral. Prev: SHO (Plastic Surg.) Qu. Mary's Hosp. Roehampton Lond.; SHO (Plastic Surg.) Leicester Roy. Infirm.

O'TOOLE, Helen Louise 34 Menlove Gardens S., Liverpool L18 2EL — MB BS 1933 Lond.

O'TOOLE, James Gerard Cambria Surgery, Ucheldre Avenue, Holyhead LL65 1RA Tel: 01407 762735 Fax: 01407 766900 Email: cambriasurgery@compuserve.com — MB ChB 1982 Ed.; BSc Ed. 1989, MB ChB 1982; MRCGP 1989.

O'TOOLE, Mr John J. Department of Cardiothoracic Surgery, St George's Hospital, Tooting, London SW17 0QT Tel: 020 8725 3288; 10 The Fieldings, Forest Hill, London SE23 3QA Tel: 07802 421872 — MB BCh BAO 1977 Dub.; FRCSI 1983. Locum Cons. Cardiothoracic Surg.St. Geo.'s Hosp. ,Tooting. Socs: Soc. of Cardiothoracic Surg. of GB & Irel.; Eur. Assn. Cardiothoracic Surg.; Irish Cardiac Soc. Prev: Cons. Cardiothoracic Surg. Al Hada Milit. Hosp. Taif, Saudi Arabia.; Regist. (Cardiothoric Surg.) Mater Hosp. Dub. & Glas. Roy. Infirm.

O'TOOLE, Laurence 32 Warrender Park Terrace, Marchmont, Edinburgh EH9 1ED — MB ChB 1989 Sheff.; MRCP Lond. 1992; BMedSci Sheff. 1989. Specialist Regist. (Cardio & Gen Med.) Edin.

O'TOOLE, Mark Anthony 2 Tawell Mews, Tiptree, Colchester CO5 0QU — MB BS 1994 Lond.

O'TOOLE, Oliver Bartholomew Kirby Road Surgery, 58 Kirby Road, Dunstable LU6 3JH Tel: 01582 609121 Fax: 01582 472002; 11 Friars Walk, Dunstable LU6 3JA Tel: 01582 606956 — MB ChB 1974 Birm.; MRCGP 1979; DRCOG 1978. GP Trainer NW Thames & Lond. Hosp. Train. Scheme. Prev: Clin. Asst. (Obst.) Luton & Dunstable Hosp. S. Beds. DHA; Trainee GP Luton & Dunstable VTS; SHO Luton & Dunstable Hosp. Beds.

O'TOOLE, Paul Anthony University Hospital Aintree, Longmoor Lane, Fazakerley, Liverpool L9 7AL Email: paul.otoole@aht.nwest.nhs.uk — FRCP Lond. 2001; BM BCh Oxf. 1985; MRCP (UK) 1989; BA (Hons) Oxf 1982. (Oxford) Cons. (Gastroenterol.) Univ. Hosp. Aintree Liverp.

O'TOOLE, Mr Stuart John 12 Cromwell Drive, East Leake, Loughborough LE12 6LZ — MB BS 1988 Newc.; FRCS Glas. 1993.

OADE, Yvette Alison Halifax General Hospital, Salterhebble, Halifax HX3 0PW; 25 Fall Lane, Hartshead, Liversedge WF15 8AP — MB ChB 1984 Leeds; BSc (Hons.) Leeds 1980; MRCP (UK) 1989. Cons. Paediat. Calderdale Healthcare NHS Trust. Prev: Sen. Regist. (Paediat.) Roy. Manch. Childr. Hosp.

OADES, Patrick John Royal Devon & Exeter Healthcare Trust (Wonford), Barrack Road, Exeter EX2 5DW Tel: 01392 411611 Fax: 01392 402715 — MB BCh 1985 Wales; MA Camb. 1996, BA (Hons.) 1982; MRCP (UK) 1988; FRCPCH 1997. Cons. Paediat. Roy. Devon & Exeter Healthcare Trust.

OAK, Mr Makarand Kumar, Lt.-Col. RAMC Retd. Mid Essex Hospitals, Services NHS Trust, Broomfield Court, Pudding Wood Lane, Broomfield, Chelmsford CM1 7WE; Ivydene, 52 Old Charlton Road, Shepperton TW17 8BH — MB BS 1972 Jiwaji; ChM Manch. 1989; MPH Glas. 1991; FRCOG 1995, M 1980. (Gajra Raja Med. Coll. Gwalior) Assoc. Med. Dir. Mid. Essex Hosps. NHS Trust & Hon. Cons. O & G Essex Rivers Healthcare NHS Trust Colchester. Socs: BMA; Brit. Assn. Med. Managers. Prev: Cons. O & G Camb. Milit. Hosp.; Sen. Lect. (Preven. Med.) RAMC Millbank Lond.; Research Fell. Univ. Hosp. S. Manch.

OAKDEN, Edward William Ralph The Health Centre, Goodly Date, Windermere LA23 2EG Tel: 015394 45159 Fax: 015394 46029 — MB BChir 1958 Camb.; MRCS Eng. LRCP Lond. 1957; MRCGP 1972. (St. Thos.) Prev: Cas. Off. Roy. W. Sussex Hosp. Chichester; Ho. Phys. & Ho. Surg. St. Richard's Hosp. Chichester.

OAKELEY, Penelope Susan Family Planning Services, Tooting Health Clinic, 63 Bevill Allen Close, Amen Corner, Tooting, London SW17 8PX Tel: 020 8700 0424 Fax: 020 8700 0426; Water Margin, 24 Hythe End Road, Wraysbury, Staines TW19 5AR Tel: 01784 481997 — MRCS Eng. LRCP Lond. 1966; MFFP 1993. (RCSI & St. Thos.) p/t Cons. Family Plann. & Reprod. Health S. W. Lond. Community NHS Trust; Hon. Sen. Lect. (Family Plann.) Dept. Obst. & Gyn. St. Geo. Hosp. Lond.; Sessional Med. Off. Amarant Menopause Clinic GainsBoro. Clinic Lond.; Clin. Asst. Genitourin. Med. St. Geogrs. Hosp. Lond. Socs: Bd. Mem. Fac. Community Health RIPHH; Med. Soc. Study VD; Assoc. Mem. Inst. Psycho-Sexual Med. Prev: Clin. Asst. (Genitourin. Med. & Sexual Problems) St. Thos. Hosp. Lond.; Med. Off. (Family Plann.) W. Lambeth, Camberwell, Lewisham, N. S.wark & Wandsworth HA's; Ho. Phys. (Psychiat.) St. Thos. Hosp. Lond.

OAKENFULL, Andrew Gordon Perrin Ferryhill Medical Practice, Durham Road, Ferryhill DL17 8JJ Tel: 01740 651238 Fax: 01740

OAKENFULL

656291; 2 Acle Meadows, Newton Aycliffe DL5 4XD Tel: 01325 301820 — MB BS 1982 Newc.; MRCGP 1987; DRCOG 1986. GP Ferryhill. Prev: Trainee GP W. Cumbld. VTS; SHO (Gen. Surg.) Qu. Eliz. Hosp. Gateshead; SHO (Neonat. Paediat.) Simpson Memor. Matern. Pavilion Edin.

OAKENFULL, Isabella Bethune (retired) Central House, 25 King St., Winterton, Scunthorpe DN15 9TP Tel: 01724 732278 — MB ChB 1951 Ed. Prev: Clin. Asst. (Dermat.) Gen. Hosp. Scunthorpe.

OAKERVEE, Heather Evelyn 66 Henshaw Street, London SE17 1PD Tel: 020 7252 6509 Email: hzjjones7@aol.com — MB BS 1993 Lond.; MRCP (UK) 1996. (United Medical and Dental Schools) Specialist Regist. (Haemat.) Homerton Hosp. Lond.

OAKES, John Laurence 28 Castle Road, Hythe CT21 5HW — MB BS 1996 Lond.

OAKES, Mary (retired) Meadowsweet, Whitchurch Road, Horrabridge, Yelverton PL20 7TZ Tel: 01822 852585 — MB ChB 1954 Sheff. Private Med. Homeopath. Prev: Gen. Pract., Plymouth.

OAKES, Sarah Marie 23 Wollaton Avenue, Sheffield S17 4LA — MB ChB 1998 Liverp.

OAKES, Stuart Victor (retired) 16 Far View Bank, Almondbury, Huddersfield HD5 8EP Tel: 01484 424183 — MB ChB 1970 Leeds; MRCPsych 1977. Prev: Cons. Psychiat. St. Lukes Hosp. Huddersfield.

OAKESHOTT, Philippa Department of General Practice & Primary Care, St. George's Hospital Medical School, London SW17 0RE Tel: 020 8672 9944 Fax: 020 8767 7697 Email: oakeshot@sghms.ac.uk; Manor Health Centre, 86 Clapham Manor St, London SW4 6FB Tel: 020 7622 3225 — MB BChir 1975 Camb.; MA Camb. 1975; MRCP (UK) 1979; MRCGP 1981; MD Camb. 1999. (Camb. & Barts.) p/t Sen. Lect. (Gen. Pract. & Primary Care) St. Geo. Hosp. Med. Sch. Lond. Socs: RCP; RCGP; AUDGP. Prev: Trainee GP Lond. (St. Thos.) VTS; Ho. Surg. St. Bart. Hosp. Lond.; Ho. Phys. N.wick Pk. Hosp. & Clin. Research Centre Harrow.

OAKESHOTT, Simon 17 Hinton Way, Great Shelford, Cambridge CB2 5AX Tel: 01223 844961 — MB BS Lond. 1966; MA Oxf. 1959; MRCPsych 1978. (St. Mary's) Indep. Psychother. Camb. Prev: Sen. Regist. (Child & Family Psychiat.) Camb. AHA; Regist. Fulbourn Hosp. Camb.; Demonst. (Anat.) Univ. Camb.

OAKEY, Helen Mary 64 Circular Road, Jordanstown, Whiteabbey, Newtownabbey BT37 0RQ; 64 Circular Road, Jordanstown, Whiteabbey, Newtownabbey BT37 0RQ — MB BS 1988 Lond.; MRCGP 1994; DRCOG 1992. (St. George's Hospital Medical School London) Med. Off. Roy. Flying Doctor Serv. Derby WA Australia. Socs: MRCGP; DRCOG; FRACGP. Prev: Med. Off. Roy. Flying Doctor Serv. Broken Hill NSW, Australia; Emerg. Regist. Roy. N. Shore Hosp. Sydney; GP Regist. Camb.

OAKEY, John Stuckey (retired) 37 Burses Way, Hutton, Brentwood CM13 2PL — MB BS 1946 Sydney; FRCPath. 1982, M 1970; FRCPA 1978. Prev: Cons. Haematol. Basildon & Thurrock Dist. Hosps.

OAKFORD, Andrew Charles 160 Newark Road, North Hykeham, Lincoln LN6 8LZ — MB ChB 1990 Sheff.

OAKHILL, Anthony Langford Cottage, Woollard, Pensford, Bristol BS39 4HT — MB ChB 1973 Birm.; MRCP (UK) 1976; DCH Eng. 1975. Cons. Paediat. Oncol. Bristol Roy. Sick Childr. Hosp.

OAKINS, Michael John Poundwell Meadow Health Centre, Poundwell Meadow, Modbury, Ivybridge PL21 0QL Tel: 01548 830666 Fax: 01548 831085; 1 Benedict Way, Modbury, Ivybridge PL21 0TJ — MB BS 1966 Lond.; MRCS Eng. LRCP Lond. 1966; DObst RCOG 1973. Prev: Maj. RAMC.

OAKLAND, Mr Christian David Hirst Accident & Emergency Department, Frenchay Hospital, Frenchay, Bristol BS16 1LE Tel: 0117 975 3840 Fax: 0117 918 6595 Email: frenchayed@cabteinet.co.uk; The Old Stables, The Street, Alveston, Bristol BS35 3SX Tel: 01454 416885 Fax: 01454 416881 Email: chris.oakland@btinternet.com — MB ChB 1978 Birm.; FRCS Eng. 1983; FRCS Ed. 1982. (Birm.) Cons. A & E N. Bristol NHS Trust; Cahir 'Avonsafe' Accid. Precaution. Socs: Fell. Fac. A & E Med. Prev: Sen. Regist. Basingstoke Dist. Hosp.

OAKLAND, Mr Desmond John (retired) 5 Breinton Lee, Hereford HR4 0SZ Tel: 01432 272262 Fax: 01432 272262 — MB ChB 1947 Birm.; ChM Birm. 1959; FRCS Eng. 1952; MRCS Eng. LRCP Lond. 1947. Prev: Cons. Surg. Gen. & Co. Hosps. Hereford & Ledbury Cott. Hosp.

OAKLAND, Michael Hurst (retired) Coromandel, Auberrow, Wellington, Hereford HR4 8AL Tel: 01432 830799 Email: michael.oakland@btinternet.com — MB ChB 1954 Birm.; BSc (Hons.) Birm. 1951; MRCGP 1963. Prev: Clin. Asst. United Birm. Hosps.

OAKLEY, Carol Jane Heath Hill Practice, Heath Hill Road South, Crowthorne RG45 7BN Tel: 01344 777915; Pinegrove, 100 Ellis Road, Crowthorne RG45 6PH Tel: 01344 762714 — BM 1984 Soton.; BM Soton 1984; MRCGP (Distinc.) 1988; DCH RCP Lond. 1987; DRCOG 1987. GP Crowthorne, Berks. Prev: Clin. Med. Off. N. Herts. HA; SHO (O & G & Paediat.) Heatherwood Hosp. Ascot; Trainee GP Sunningdale Berks.

OAKLEY, Professor Celia Mary Hammersmith Hospital, Du Cane Road, London W12 0NN Tel: 020 8383 3141 Fax: 020 8740 8373; Long Crendon Manor, Long Crendon, Aylesbury HP18 9DZ Tel: 01844 208246 Fax: 01844 208246 — MB BS 1954 Lond.; MB BS (Hons.) Lond. 1954; MD Lond. 1965; FRCP Lond. 1970, M 1956; MRCS Eng. LRCP Lond. 1954; FESC 1988; FACC 1972. (Roy. Free) Prof. Emerit. Clin. Cardiol. Roy. Postgrad. Med. Sch. Lond. & Hon. Cons. Cardiol. Hammersmith Hosp. & St. Mary's Hosp. Socs: Brit. Cardiac Soc.; Assn. Phys.; Med. Res. Soc. Prev: MRC Fell. Mem. Hosp. Rochester USA; Ho. Phys. Nat. Hosp. Qu. Sq. & Brompton Hosp.; Ho. Phys. & Ho. Surg. Roy. Free Hosp.

OAKLEY, Clifton Douglas (retired) Apt. 7 St Anne's court, llanrhos, Llandudno LL30 1SD — MB ChB 1952 Birm.; Local Treasury Med. Off.

OAKLEY, Dennis Elliott (retired) The Yetchleys, Lyneal, Ellesmere SY12 0QF Tel: 0194 875324 — MB ChB 1945 Birm.; MRCS Eng. LRCP Lond. 1945; DIH Soc. Apoth. Lond. 1968.

OAKLEY, Donald Percy (retired) 5 Woodlands Way, Barton, Preston PR3 5DU — MD 1962 Manch.; MB ChB 1952; FRCPsych 1975, M 1971; DPM Eng. 1958. Prev: Cons. Psychiat. Preston Health Dist.

OAKLEY, Edward Howard Nigel, Surg. Cdr. RN Brooklands Lodge, Park View Close, Wroxall, Ventnor PO38 3EQ Tel: 01983 853605 — MB BCh 1979 Wales; MSc Lond. 1987; BA Oxf. 1976. Head of Survival & Thermal Med. Inst. Naval Med. Socs: Eur. Undersea Biomed. Soc.; Brit. Med. Informat. Soc. Prev: Med. Off. Jt. Serv. Expedition to Brabant Is., Antarctica.

OAKLEY, Gary Mark Flat C, 8 Hartham Road, London N7 9JG — MB BS 1992 Lond.

OAKLEY, George David Gastineau Cardiothoracic Unit, Northern General Hospital, Herries Road, Sheffield S5 7AU Email: oakley@shef1.demon.co.uk — MD 1984 Camb.; MA 1972, MB BChir 1973; FRCP 1988, M 1975. (Westm.) Cons. (Cardiol.) N. Gen. Hosp. Sheff.; Hon. Clin. Lect. Univ. Sheff. Socs: Brit. Cedrac Soc.; Brit. Cardiac Soc. Prev: Sen. Regist. (Cardiol.) N.. Gen. Hosp. Sheff.; Regist. (Cardiol.); Roy. Postgrad. Med. Sch. Hammersmith Hosp. Lond.; Regist. (Gen. Med.); City Gen. Hosp. & N. Staffs Roy. Infirm. Stoke-on-Trent.

OAKLEY, Giles Anthony Montpelier Health Centre, Bath Buildings, Bristol BS6 5PT Tel: 0117 942 6811 Fax: 0117 944 4182; 47 Hillside Avenue, Worthing BN14 9QS Tel: 01903 237229 — MB ChB 1991 Leic.; MRCP (UK) 1994.

OAKLEY, Hazel Monkwearmouth Health Centre, Dundas St., Sunderland SR6 0AB Tel: 0191 567 4459 Fax: 0191 565 3336; 17 Rectory Green, West Boldon, East Boldon NE36 0QD Tel: 0191 536 3276 — MB BS 1964 Durh.; MFFP 1994.

OAKLEY, John Cyril (retired) Winchet Lodge, Winchet Hill, Goudhurst, Cranbrook TN17 1JX Tel: 01580 211773 — MB BS Lond. 1959; MRCS Eng. LRCP Lond. 1959; MRCGP 1971; DObst RCOG 1961. Med. Adviser Heritage Railway Assoc.

OAKLEY, John Richard 52 Bishops Way, Four Oaks, Sutton Coldfield B74 4XS Tel: 0121 308 8876; 161 Tamworth Road, Sutton Coldfield B75 6DY Tel: 0121 378 1251 Email: matt_oakley@msn.com — MB ChB 1972 Sheff.; DCH RCPS Glas. 1974; MRCP (UK) 1974. (Sheff.) Socs: Fell.Roy. Soc. of Med. Prev: Clin. Co-ordinator Multicentre PostNeonat. Study Project; Regist. (Med.) Childr. Hosp. Sheff.

OAKLEY, Judith Ellen (retired) Gibbs and Oakley, Doctors Surgery, Millend, Blakeney GL15 4ED Tel: 01594 510225 Fax: 01594 516074 — MB BChir 1975 Camb.; MRCP (UK) 1978. Prev: Sen. Regist. (Haemat.) W. Midl. Region.

OAKLEY, Louise Henderson (Weir) 7 Lismore Close, Maidstone ME15 9SN; 7 Lismore Close, Maidstone ME15 9SN Tel: 01622 746217 — MB ChB 1970 Ed.; MRCGP 1983; DTM & H Liverp. 1974; DCH RCP Lond. 1973; DObst RCOG 1972. p/t GP working in Health Assessm. Prev: Princip. GP Brook La. Med. Mission Pract.; Med. Off. HEED Bangladesh.; GP Kent FHSA Retainer Scheme.

OAKLEY, Mr Matthew John 2 Pickwick Close, Merryoaks, Eluet Moor, Durham DH1 3QU Tel: 0191 384 7204 — MB ChB 1991 Glas.; FRCS Glas 1996; FRCS Ed 1996. Specialist Regist. Trauma & Orthop. Surg. N.ern Rotat. Socs: BOA.

OAKLEY, Michael Charles The Oaks Lands Lane, Knaresborough — MB ChB 1971 Liverp.; MRCOG 1976. Cons. O & G Harrogate Health Auth.

OAKLEY, Mr Neil Royal Hallamshire Hospital, Glossop Road, Sheffield S10 2JF Tel: 0114 271 1900; 56 High Storrs Crescent, Sheffield S11 7JZ Tel: 01742 687224 Email: neil.oakley@bigfoot.com — MB ChB 1990 Sheff.; FRCS Eng. 1994; FRCS (Urol) 1998. (Sheffield) Specialist Regist. Urol., Roy. Hallamshire Hosp. Sheff. Prev: SHO Roy. Hallamsh. Hosp. Sheff.

OAKLEY, Nigel Wingate 44 Wimpole Street, London W1G 8SA Tel: 020 7935 0552 Fax: 020 7224 0629 Email: drnigeloakley@aol.com; The Homestead House, 113 Church Road, London SW13 9HL Tel: 020 8741 3311 Fax: 020 8563 0580 — MB BChir 1958 Camb.; MA Camb. 1959, MD 1974; FRCP Lond. 1978, M 1960; MRCS Eng. LRCP Lond. 1958. (Univ. Coll. Hosp.) Hon. Cons. Phys. & Hon. Sen. Lect. St. Geo. Hosp. Lond.; Hon. Cons. Phys. St. Luke's Hosp. for the Clergy. Socs: Diabetes UK; Med. Soc. Lond.; Assn. of Brit. Clin. Diabetologists. Prev: Sen. Lect. & Hon. Cons. Phys. St. Mary's Hosp. & Med. Sch. Lond.; Sen. Regist. Middlx. Hosp. Lond.

OAKLEY, Peter Anthony North Staffordshire Hospital, Princes Road, Hartshill, Stoke-on-Trent ST4 7LN Tel: 01782 715444 Fax: 01782 554627 — BChir 1979 Camb.; MA (Physics) Oxf. 1979, BA 1975; MB 1980; FFA RCS Eng. 1987; MRCGP 1983. (Cambridge) Cons. Anaesth. with s/i in Trauma & Intens. Care Stoke-on-Trent. Socs: Internat. Trauma Anaesth. & Critical Care Soc.; Brit. Trauma Soc. (Pres. 1998-1999). Prev: Wellcome Inst. Sen. Research Fell. & Hon. Sen. Regist. (Anaesth.) Nuffield Dept. Anaesth. Oxf.; Regist. (Anaesth.) Sir Humphry Davy Dept. Anaesth. Bristol; Clin. Fell. (Emerg. Med. & Trauma) Sunnybrook Med. Centre Toronto, Canada.

OAKLEY, Richard John 197 Worcester Road, Droitwich WR9 8AS — MB BS 1997 Lond.

OAKLEY, Robert Harvey 1 Oaklands Road, Bedford MK40 3AG — MB ChB 1976 Liverp.; FRCR Lond. 1982; DMRD Liverp. 1980. Cons. Radiol. Bedford Gen. Hosp.

***OAKLEY, Suzan Elizabeth** 26 The Spinnery, The Bryb, Pontllanfraith, Blackwood NP2 2BJ — MB BCh 1997 Wales.

OAKLEY, Timothy Neil Wallsend CMHC, The Green, Wallsend NE28 7PD Tel: 0191 262 4314 Fax: 0191 262 5228 — MB ChB 1987 Sheff.; MMedSci (Clin. Psychiat.) Leeds 1994; BMedSci 1986. Cons. (Psychiat.) Wallsend Community Ment. Health Centre. Prev: Sen. Regist. (Psychiat.) Newc. Gen. Hosp.

OAKLEY, Wendy Elizabeth Queens Hospital, Burton Hospitals NHS Trust, Belvedere Road, Burton-on-Trent DE13 0RB Tel: 01283 566333 — MB ChB 1987 Leic.; MRCOG 1992; MD Warwick 1998. Cons. (Obst. & Gyn), Qu.s Hosp. Burton. Socs: BMUS. Prev: Sen. Regist., W. Midl. Region; Research Fell. Assisted Conception Unit, Walsgrave Hosp. Coventry; Regist. Rotat. (O & G) Oxf. Region.

OAKMAN, Nicholas Mark Alma The Old School House, Narborough Road, Pentney, King's Lynn PE32 1JH Tel: 01760 338000 Email: nickoakman.free-online.co.uk — MB BS 1985 Lond.; DA (UK) 1992. (Westm. Med. Sch. Lond.) Staff Grade (Anaesth.) King's Lynn.

OAKSHOTT, Gordon Henry Leonard The Medical Physics & Bio Engineering Research Unit, Doncaster Royal Infirmary, Armthorpe Road, Doncaster DN2 5LT Tel: 01302 366666; 12 Bellwood Crescent, Thorne, Doncaster DN8 4BA Tel: 01405 812433 — MB ChB 1952 Leeds; MSc (Human Genetics) Ed. 1977; BA Open 1974; MRCGP 1960; AFOM RCP Lond. 1981. Hon. Med. Adviser (Med. Phys.) & Bioeng. Research Unit Doncaster Roy. Infirm. Socs: Leeds & W. Riding Medico-Legal Soc. Prev: GP Thorne; Teach. (Gen. Pract.) Univ. Leeds; Indust. Med. Off. GEC Thorne.

OATES, Alison Elizabeth 30 Overslade Manor Drive, Rugby CV22 6EB — MB BCh 1983 Wales.

OATES, Anita Paulette Hanscombe House Surgery, 52A St. Andrew Street, Hertford SG14 1JA Tel: 01992 582025 Fax: 01992 305511; 117 Ware Road, Hertford SG13 7EE — MB BS 1983 Lond.; MRCP (UK) 1987; DCH RCP Lond. 1986. (St. Geo.) Prev: Trainee GP Epsom VTS; Family Med. Duke Univ., USA.

OATES, Ann Muriel Burvill House Surgery, 52 Dellfield Road, Hatfield AL10 8HP Tel: 01707 269091 — MB ChB 1973 Sheff.; MRCP (UK) 1979; MRCGP 1984; DRCOG 1983. Hosp. Pract. (Diabetic Med.) St. Albans City Hosp.

OATES, Beverley Claire Dearden Brook, Edenwood Lane, Ramsbottom, Bury BL0 0EX — MB ChB 1993 Birm.; ChB Birm. 1993.

OATES, Bridget Daphne Royal Hospital For Sick Children, Yourk Hill, Glasgow G15 6PX — MB ChB 1992 Ed.; BSc (Hons.) Med. Sci. Ed. 1990; MRCP (UK) 1996. (Ed.) Regist., (Paediat.), RHSC, Yorkhill, Glas. Prev: SHO (Paediat.) Simpson Memor. Matern. Pavil. Edin.; SHO (Paediat.) Childr. Hosp. Birm.

OATES, Caroline Sinclair 71 Hunter House Road, Sheffield S11 8TU — MB ChB 1997 Sheff.

OATES, Christopher Glyn Mayford House Surgery, East Road, Northallerton DL6 1NP Tel: 01609 772105 Fax: 01609 778553; Malt House, Newby Wise, Northallerton DL7 9EX Tel: 01609 770850 — MB BS 1980 Newc.; MRCGP 1984; DCCH RCGP & FCM 1984; DRCOG 1983. Prev: Trainee GP N.umbria VTS; Ho. Off. Newc. Teach. Hosps.

OATES, David Eden Rayner Oughtibridge Surgery, Church Street, Oughtibridge, Sheffield S35 0FW Tel: 0114 286 2145 Fax: 0114 286 4031 — MB ChB 1971 Sheff.

OATES, Mr Geoffrey Donald (cons. rooms), 81 Harborne Road, Edgbaston, Birmingham B15 3HG Tel: 0121 455 9496 Fax: 0121 455 0288; 14 Hintlesham Avenue, Edgbaston, Birmingham B15 2PH Tel: 0121 454 3257 Fax: 0121 455 8315 Email: gdoates@doctors.org.uk — MB ChB 1953 Birm.; MS (Surg.) Univ. Illinois 1964; BSc (Anat. & Physiol. 1st cl. Hons.) Birm. 1950; FRCS Eng. 1959. (Birm.) Emerit. Cons. Surgic. Oncol. & Gen. Surg. Univ. Birm. NHS Trust; UKCCCR - Colorectal Cancer Gp.; MRC - Data Monitoring & Ethics Comm. (DMEC) Clasicc Trial. Socs: Brit. & Internat. Assns. Endocrine Surgs.; (Ex-Pres.) Assn. Coloproctol. Mem., Europ. Assn. of ColoProctol.; Fell. Roy. Soc. Med. (Mem. (Ex-Pres.) Sects. Oncol. & Colo-proctol., Mem. SectSurg.). Prev: Sen. Clin. Lect. (Surg.) Univ. Birm.; Capt. RAMC; Sen. Research Fell. & Instruc. (Surg.) Univ. Illinois, Chicago.

OATES, Mr John The ENT Department, Queen's Medical Burton, Belvedere Rd, Burton-on-Trent DE13 0RB Tel: 01889 504393 Fax: 01283 541683 — MB ChB 1979 Birm.; FRCS Ed. 1984. (Birmingham) Cons. Otolaryngol. Burton, Lichfield & Tamworth Hosps.; Educat.al Monitoring Team, W. Midl.s PostGrad. Deanery; Hon. Clin. Tutor, Univ. of Leics. Med Sch.; Cons. Otolaryngol Heartlands Hosp. Socs: Brit. Assn. of Otolaryngologists, head & neck Surg.s; Roy. Soc. Med. (RSM); Young Cons. Otolaryngol. Head & Neck Surg. (Pres.). Prev: Cons. Otolaryngol. Burton Hosps. Burton-on-Trent; Sen. Regist. (Otolaryngol.) Univ. Hosp. Nottm. & Derby Roy. Infirm.; Regist. (Otolaryngol.) Qu. Eliz. Hosp. Birm. & E. Birm. Hosp.

OATES, John Gordon Parkfield Health Centre, Sefton Road, New Ferry, Wirral CH62 5HS Tel: 0151 644 6665; 9 Buerton Close, Noctorum, Birkenhead CH43 9EA Tel: 0151 653 5014 — MB ChB 1980 Dundee; MRCGP 1986. Prev: GP Bootle, Merseyside.

OATES, John Kenyon (retired) 76 Glengall Road, Woodford Green IG8 0DL Tel: 020 8504 7379 Email: oatships@msn.com — MB BS Lond. 1946; MA Camb. 1973; FRCP Ed. 1970, M 1956. Prev: Hon. Cons. Phys. (Genitourin. Med.) Addenbrooke's Hosp. Camb. & W.m. Hosp. Lond.

OATES, Jonathan David Lawson South Glasgow University Hospitals NHS Trust, Victoria Infirmary, Langside Road, Glasgow G42 9TY Tel: 0141 201 5320 — BM 1983 Soton.; FFA RCSI 1988; DA (UK) 1985. Cons. Anaesth. S. Glas. Univ. Hosps. NHS Trust.

OATES, Kenneth Raymond Highland Health Board, Public Health Medicine Department, Beeckwood Park, Inverness IV2 3HG Tel: 01463 704886 Fax: 01463 717666 Email: kenoates@hhb.scot.nhs.uk; 8 Mayfield Road, Inverness IV2 4AE Tel: 01463 226236 — MB ChB 1985 Aberd.; MFPHM RCP (UK) 1995; MRCGP 1989; Cert. Family Plann. JCC 1989; DRCOG 1987. Cons. (Pub. Health Med.) Highland Health Bd. Inverness; Hon. Sen. Lect.

OATES

(Pub. Health) Aberd. Univ. Prev: Sen. Regist. (Pub. Health Med.) Highland HB Inverness; Med. Audit Facilitator Highland HB Inverness; Trainee GP Inverness VTS.

OATES, Margaret Rose Department of Psychiatry, University Hospital, Queens Medical Centre, Nottingham NG7 2UH Tel: 0115 970 9339 — MB ChB 1966 Liverp.; FRCPsych 1990, M 1972; DPM Eng. 1970. Hon. Cons. Psychiat. Univ. Hosp. Nottm.; Sen. Lect. (Psychiat.) Univ. Nottm. Med. Sch. Prev: Lect. (Psychiat.) Univ. Nottm. Med. Sch.; Sen. Regist. (Psychiat.) Manch. Roy. Infirm.; Regist. Roy. Edin. Hosp.

OATES, Nathalie Roberta The Old Kiln House, 79 Haymeads Lane, Bishop's Stortford CM23 5JJ Tel: 01279 659287 — MB BS 1985 Lond.

OATES, Peter Edward Lister House Surgery, The Common, Hatfield AL10 0NL Tel: 01707 268822 Fax: 01707 263990 — MB ChB 1973 Sheff.; DObst RCOG 1976.

OATES, Philip Damian 11 Skaterigg Drive, Jordanhill, Glasgow G13 1SR — MB ChB 1983 Dundee; FFA RCSI 1988; DA (UK) 1985. Cons. Anaesth. S.. Gen. Hosp. NHS Trust. Glas.; Hon. Sen. Lect., Univ. of Glas. Med. Soc..

OATES, Sharon Elizabeth Royal Shrewsbury Hospital, Mytton Oak Road, Shrewsbury SY3 8XQ Tel: 01743 261000; 181 Holyhead Road, Wellington, Telford TF1 2DP Tel: 01952 252498 — MB ChB 1982 Liverp.; MRCOG 1987; Dip. Human Sex Manch. 1992. Cons. O & G Shrops. & Powys HA. Socs: Shrewsbury Med. Institue; Brit. Assn. Sexual & Marital Ther. Prev: Lect. (O & G) St. Mary's Hosp. Manch.

OATES, Valerie Elizabeth Marshall 14 Craighlaw Avenue, Eaglesham, Glasgow G76 0EU — MB BS 1983 Lond.; BSc (Hons.) Aberd. 1977; MRCGP 1987; Dip. Palliat. Med. Wales 1995; DRCOG 1986. Hospice Phys. P. & P.ss of Wales Hospice, Glas.

OATES, William Keith Health Centre, Whyteman's Brae, Kirkcaldy KY1 2NA Tel: 01592 642902 Fax: 01592 644814 — MB ChB 1972 Ed.; MRCGP 1977.

OATHAM, Catherine Elizabeth Brentford Health Centre, Boston Manor Road, Brentford TW8 8DS Tel: 020 8321 3838 Fax: 020 8321 3814 — MB BS 1992 Lond.

OATWAY, Helen Beverley 58 Cambridge Road, Middlesbrough TS5 5HG — MB BS 1989 Newc. SHO (Anaesth.) S. Cleveland Hosp. Middlesbrough.

OBADIAH, Mercia (retired) 17 Alleyn Place, Westcliff on Sea SS0 8AT Tel: 01702 430685 — MB BS Calcutta 1951; MFCM 1974; DObst RCOG 1959.

OBADIAH, Rachel 52 Eastbury Road, Northwood HA6 3AW — MB 1937 Calcutta; DRCOG 1947.

OBAID, Matthew Paul 25 Celtic View, Bridgend CF31 1YG — MB BCh 1994 Wales.

OBAID, Sarah Louise 25 Celtic View, Litchard, Bridgend CF31 1YG — MB BS 1996 Lond.

OBAID, Shaza 132 Woodway Lane, Coventry CV2 2EJ — MD 1986 Damascus; MRCP (UK) 1994.

OBAIDULLAH, Mohammad The Surgery, Woodlands Terrace, Caerau, Bridgend CF32 7LB; 25 Celtic View, Litchard, Bridgend CF31 1YG — MB BS 1968 Peshawar; LLM (Legal Aspects of Med. Practice) Wales 1997; FRCOG 1991; MRCGP 1978; MRCOG 1976, DObst 1973; Dip. Pract. Dermat. Wales 1990; Dip. Palliat. Med. Wales 1991. (Khyber Med. Coll.) Mem. of the Local Research Ethics Comm. of Iechyd Morgannwy Health; Mem. of the Appeals Tribunal Mem. of the Multi Research Ethics Comm. of Wales; Mem. of the Buidford Local Health Gp. Prev: Hosp. Pract. (O & G) Bridgend Gen. Hosp. GP Trainer & Family.

OBAJI, Abdel Kader Kassem Horeb Street Surgery, Horeb Street, Treorchy, Cardiff CF42 6RU Tel: 01443 772185 Fax: 01443 773083 — MB BCh 1971 Al-Azhar Cairo; MB BCh Al-Azhar Egypt 1971.

OBARA, Lawrence Gordon 17 Maple Way, Cranfield, Bedford MK43 0DW — MB ChB 1970 East Africa; DLO Eng. 1978. (Makerere Univ. Coll.) Regist. (ENT Surg.) Gen. Hosp. & Univ. Hosp. Nottm. Prev: SHO (ENT Surg.) Gen. Hosp. Nottm.

OBARO, Steven Kolawole 10 Bramley Court, Ross Road, Wallington SM6 8QP Tel: 020 8773 0722 — MB BS 1982 Ahamadu Bello Univ. Nigeria; MB BS Ahmadu Bello Univ., Nigeria 1982; MRCP (UK) 1990. Lect. (Paediat. Immunol.) W.m., Char. Cross & W.m. Childr. Hosp. Lond.

OBASI, Angela Ijeoma Nwabuche Chukwu The London School of Hygiene & Tropical Medicine, Keppel St., London WC1E 7HT Email: aobasi@ishtm.ac.uk; 26 Mandela Court, Wimberley St, Blackburn BB1 7LT — MB BS 1988 Lond.; MSc Lond. 1996; MSc (Distinc.) Lond. 1992; MRCP (UK) 1994. Research Fell. Clin. Epidemiol. Lond. Sch. Hyg. & Trop. Med.

OBEID, Daisy Alexandra Hospital, Woodrow Drive, Redditch B98 7UB Tel: 01527 503030 Fax: 01527 512007; 111 Fitzroy Avenue, Harborne, Birmingham B17 8RG Tel: 0121 427 1955 Email: obeid@btnet.com — MB BCh Ain Shams 1965; FRCPath 1990, M 1978; DCH Eng. 1970. (Ain Shams) Cons. Haemat. W. Midl. RHA. Alexandra Healthcare NHS Trust Redditch. Prev: Sen. Regist. & Regist. (Haemat.) W. Midl. RHA; Gen. Duty Med. Off., Sudan.

OBEID, Mr El Moez Hayder 28 Ladywood Road, Oldhall, Warrington WA5 9QR — MB BCh 1978 Alexandria; MChOrth Liverp. 1993; FRCSI 1990; FRCS (Tr & Orth). 1998.

OBEID, Mr Magdi Latif 111 Fitzroy Avenue, Harborne, Birmingham B17 8RG Tel: 0121 427 1955 — MRCS Eng. LRCP Lond. 1973; MB BCh E' In Shams Univ. 1965; FRCS Eng. 1971; FRCS Ed. 1969. (E' In Shams Univ. Cairo) Cons. Surg. Dudley Rd. Hosp. & St. Chads Hosp. Birm. Socs: BMA & Brit. Transpl. Soc. Prev: Sen. Regist. (Surg.) Qu. Eliz. Hosp. Birm.; Regist. (Paediat. Surg.) Childr. Hosp. Birm.; Regist. (Surg.) Artific. Kidney & Renal Transpl. Unit Qu. Eliz. Hosp.

OBEL, Owen Abraham Flat 4, 68 Elmbourne Road, London SW17 8JJ — MB BCh 1986 Witwatersrand; MRCP (UK) 1993.

OBEN, Jude Augustine 3 Hart-Synott House, Leckford Road, Oxford OX2 6JL — BM BCh 1994 Oxf.

OBENG, Francis 230 Chalklands, Wembley HA9 9DY — State Exam Med 1977 Erlangen.

OBENG, Mark Atta 35 Bantock Way, Harborne, Birmingham B17 0LY — MB BS 1989 Lond.

***OBERAI, Bhavneet** 55 Chesterfield Road, Ashford TW15 2NE — BM BCh 1986 Oxf.; BSc Lond. 1983; DRCOG 1989.

OBERAI, Surendra K Pant Surgery, 57 Aberdare Road, Cwmbach, Aberdare CF44 0HL Tel: 01685 872434 Fax: 01685 878158. GP Aberdare, M. Glam.

OBERMAN, Anthony Stephen 39 The Ridgeway, Golders Green, London NW11 8QP — MB BS 1981 Lond.

OBEROI, Arjun 11 Hogan Mews, London W2 1UP — MB ChB 1997 Ed.

OBERTELLI, Andrea (retired) 11 View Road, London N6 4DJ — MD 1953 Parma; LAH Dub. 1956. Prev: Ho. Phys. Roy. E. Sussex Hosp. Hastings.

OBERTHUR, Eric Pierre Andre Westlake Surgery, West Coker, Yeovil BA22 9AH Tel: 01935 862212 Fax: 01935 864196 — MB 1964 Camb.; BChir 1963. (Westm.) Socs: BMA. Prev: Ho. Off. (Med.) St. Stephen's Hosp. Chelsea; SHO (Paediat.) Qu. Eliz. II Hosp. Welwyn Gdn. City; SHO (O & G) Centr. Middlx. Hosp. Lond.

OBEY, Pamela Ann Addenbrooke's Hospital, Cambridge CB2 2QQ Tel: 01223 217434 Fax: 01223 217223; The Cottage, Church Lane, Comberton, Cambridge CB3 7ED Tel: 01223 262337 Fax: 01223 262337 — MB BS Lond. 1967; FFA RCS Eng. 1984; DA Eng. 1975. (St. Geo.) Assoc. Specialist (Anaesth.) Addenbrooke's Hosp. Camb. Socs: Assn. Anaesth.; Brit. Assn. Day Surg. Prev: Clin. Asst. Addenbrooke's Hosp. Camb.; SHO (Anaesth.) St. Geo. Hosp. Lond.

OBEYESEKERA, Sharmin Lesrene 25 Barn Way, Wembley HA9 9NT — MB BS 1994 Lond.

OBHOLZER, Anton Meinhard Tavistock Clinic, 120 Belsize Lane, London NW3 5BA Tel: 020 7435 7111 Fax: 020 7447 3709 — MB ChB Cape Town 1963; FRCPsych 1987, M 1973; T(Psych) 1991; DPM Cape Town 1969. Chief Exec. Tavistock & Portman NHS Trust; Cons. Psychiat. Tavistock Clinic; Prof. Assoc. Brunel Univ.; Hon. Sen. Lect. Roy. Free Hosp. Med. Sch. Socs: Assoc. Mem. Brit. Psychoanalyt. Soc. Prev: Cons. Psychiat. Child Guid. Train. Centre Lond.; Sen. Regist. Adolesc. Dept. Tavistock Clinic Lond.; Regist. Groote Schuur Hosp. Cape Town, S. Afr.

OBHRAI, Mr Manjit Singh North Staffordshire Maternity Hospital, Hilton Road, Harpfields, Newcastle ST5 Tel: 01782 552402 Fax: 01782 552695; Little Croft, Tower Road, Ashley Health, Market Drayton TF9 4PU Tel: 01630 673723 Email: manjit@lineone.net — BM BS 1975 Nottm.; MRCOG 1982. (Nottingham University) Cons. Obst. & Obst. & Med. Dir. Fertil. Centre N. Staffs. Hosps. NHS Trust;

Sen. Clin. Lect. Univ. Keele. Socs: Brit. Fertil. Soc.; Eur. Soc. Human Reproduc. & Embryol. Prev: Cons. & Sen. Lect. & Sen. Regist. & Lect. (O & G) Univ. Birm.

OBI, Benedict Chibuzor 99 Trendlewood Park, Trendlewood Estate, Bristol BS16 1TD — MB BS 1991 Lond.

OBI, Bernard Chukwura Dr J E Barker and Partners, 85 Ross Road, Maidenhead SL6 2SR Tel: 01628 623767 Fax: 01628 789623; 5 Cheveley Gardens, Burnham, Slough SL1 8AX — MRCS Eng. LRCP Lond. 1970; MFFP 1993; MRCOG 1982; DObst RCOG 1975; DTM & H Eng. 1975. (St. Mary's) Hosp. Pract. (O & G) Wexham Pk. Hosp. Slough. Socs: Christ. Med. Fell.sh.; BMA; Assn. Police Surg. Prev: Regist. (O & G) Wexham Pk. Hosp. Slough; Sen. Med. Off. Iyi-Enu Miss. Hosp. Onitsha, Nigeria; Regist. (Gen. Med.) Croydon Gen. Hosp.

OBICHERE, Austin 28B Fairhazel Gardens, London NW6 3SJ — MB BS 1987 Lagos.

OBIECHINA, Nonyelum Evangeline 56 Kingfisher Grove, Bradford BD8 0NP Tel: 01274 880181 — LRCP LRCS 1993 Ed.; MB BS U. of Nigeria 1987; LRCP LRCS Ed. LRCPS Glas. 1993.

OBIEKWE, Margaret Ngozi Park Lodge Medical Centre, 3 Old Park Road, Palmers Green, London N13 4RG Tel: 020 8886 6866 Fax: 020 8882 8884 — MRCS Eng. LRCP 1989 Lond.; BM BCh Nigeria 1984; MRCS Eng LRCP Lond. 1989. Regist. (O & G) Roy. Lond. Hosp. Prev: SHO (O & G) Univ. Coll. Hosp. & Whipps Cross Hosp. Lond.

OBIN, Olive Mary (Surgery), 66A Portsmouth Road, Woolston, Southampton SO19 9AL Tel: 02380 436277 Fax: 02380 399751; Newstead, 32 Havelock Road, Warsash, Southampton SO31 9FX Tel: 01489 575970 — MB BS 1957 Lond.; MRCS Eng. LRCP Lond. 1957. (Roy. Free) Prev: Sen. Med. Off. (Family Plann.) Cosham & Fareham Health Centres; Ho. Surg. Mayday Hosp. Croydon; Ho. Phys. Croydon Gen Hosp.

OBINECHE, Professor Enyioma Nwaogu Acting \Chairman, Department of Internal Medicine, Faculty of Medicine & Health Sciences, United Arab Emirates University, PO Box 17666 Al-Ain, United Arab Emirates Tel: 971 3703 9420 Fax: 971 372995 Email: obineche@emirates.net.ae; 10 St Margarets Avenue, London N15 3DH Tel: 0208 881 0795 Fax: 0208 245 3498 — MB ChB 1963 Glas.; FRCPS Glas. 1978, M 1968; DCH RCP Lond. 1965. (Glasgow University School of Medicine) Director Kidney Dialysis Centre King Fahad Hosp. Al Baha, Saudi Arabia; Prof. Fac. Med. & Health Sci. UAE Univ., Al-Ain.; Acting Chairm. Dept of Internal Med. Socs: Int. Soc. Nephrol.; Eur. Dialysis & Transpl. Assn.; BMA. Prev: Director Renal Unit K. Fahd Hosp., Al-Baha, Saudi Arabia; Cons. Nephrol. Milit. Hosp. Tabuk, Saudi Arabia; Asst. Dean & Prof. Med. Ahmadu Bello Univ. Med. Sch., Kaduna & Zaria, Nigeria.

OBIYAN, Mary Ethel Inekhomo 87 Greyswood Street, London SW16 6QW Tel: 020 8677 4270 Fax: 020 8677 4270 — MB BS 1971 Ibadan; FRCS Glas. 1982; FWACS Lagos 1989. Prev: Cons. Surg. Milit. Hosp. Lagos & Enuqu Nigeria; Sen. Regist. Benin Teach. Hosp.

OBOMANU, William Agberenyana Itchie Henry Roun Unit, Horton Hospital, Long Grove Lane, Epsom Tel: 020 8237 2111 Fax: 020 8237 2256 — MB BS 1988 Lond.; MRCPsych 1994. Prev: Regist. (Psychiat.) Springfield Hosp. St. Geo. Train Scheme.

OBONNA, Rex 53 Langdale Way, East Boldon NE36 0UF — MB ChB 1983 Dundee. SHO (O & G) Edith Watson Matern. Unit Burnley Gen. Hosp. Prev: Ho. Off. (Surg.) Qu. Eliz. Hosp. Edgbaston; Ho. Off. S. Shields Gen. Hosp. Tyne & Wear.

OBONYO, Mr Henry Benjamin Princess Royal Hospital, Telford TF1 6TF Tel: 01952 641222; 36 Barringer Square, London SW17 8EE — MB ChB 1965 East Africa; MD Nairobi 1985; FRCS Ed. 1969. Cons. Urol. P.ss Roy. Hosp. Telford. Socs: Fell. Assn. Surgs. of E. Afr.; BMA; Brit. Assn. Urol. Surgs. Prev: Cons. Urol. Mulago Hosp., Uganda; Lect. (Urol.) Nairobi Univ., Kenya.

OBOTH OWINO, Nimrod 5A Woodland Road, New Southgate, London N11 1PN — MB ChB 1972 Glas.; MSc (Clin. Microbiol.) Lond. 1987; MSc (Clin Trop. Med.) Lond. 1980; DObst RCOG 1974. (Glas. Univ.) GP Regist. Enfield & Haringey GPVTS. Prev: Sen. Regist. (Microbiol.) Guy's & St. Thos. NHS Trust Lond.; Sen. Regist. (Microbiol.) Ashford PHL William Harvey Hosp. Kent; Regist. (Microbiol.) Lewisham Hosp. Lond., St. And. Hosp. & Lond. Hosp. Med. Coll.

OBRECHT, Karin Barbara Royal National Orthopaedic Hospital, Brockley Hill, Stanmore HA7 4LP — State Exam Med 1990 Freiburg.

OCHEFU, Oche Aaron University Hospital Aintree, Fazailerley, Liverpool L9 4AE Email: cooloche@yahoo.com; 32 Preston Road, Southport PR9 9EE — MB BS 1982 Benin. (Univ. of Benin Nigeria) Staff Grade (Otorhinolaryng. & Head & Neck Surg.) Aintree Hosps. Liverp. Socs: S.port Med. Soc. Prev: Regist. (ENT) Roy. Preston Hosp.

OCHOA GRANDE, Juan 9B Barnsbury Avenue, Aylesbury HP20 1NL — LMS 1982 Extramadura.

OCKELFORD, Olwyn Kathleen (retired) Flat 3, Burnage Court, 6 Martello Park, Canford Cliffs, Poole BH13 7BA Tel: 01202 701189 — MB BChir Camb. 1950; MA Camb. 1950; MRCS Eng. LRCP Lond. 1949; MRCPsych 1977; DCH Eng. 1952. Prev: Chairm. Dorset Healthcare NHS Trust.

OCKELFORD, Stuart John 22 Robin Down Lane, Mansfield NG18 4SW — MB ChB 1995 Bristol.

OCKENDEN, Barbara Georgina (retired) 4 Weavers Walk, Swynnerton, Stone ST15 0QZ — MB BS 1945 Lond.; FRCPath 1976, M 1964. Prev: Cons. Morbid Anat., Histopath. Centr. Path. Laborat. Stoke-on-Trent.

OCKRIM, Jeremy Louis 22 Braidholm Road, Giffnock, Glasgow G46 6HJ — MB ChB 1994 Glas.

OCKRIM, Jonathan Barry 22 Braidholm Road, Giffnock, Glasgow G46 6HJ — MB ChB 1989 Glas.

OCKRIM, Zoe Kate 22 Braidholm Road, Giffnock, Glasgow G46 6HJ Tel: 0141 620 3253 — MB ChB 1996 Glas.; MRCOphth. Part 1; MRCOpth Part 2. (University of Glasgow) SHO (Ophth) Qu. Marys Hosp, Sidcup, Kent. Socs: RCOphth; BMA; MDDUS. Prev: SHO (Ophth.) Vict. Eye Hosp. Hereford; Jun. Ho. Off. (Med. PRHO) Glas. Roy. Infirm.; Jun. Ho. Off. (Surgic. PRHO) Glas. Vict. Infirm.

ODAM, Richard (retired) Southfield Gate, 78 Sandy Lane, Charlton Kings, Cheltenham GL53 9DH Tel: 01242 580875 — MB BS Lond. 1966; MRCS Eng. LRCP Lond. 1965.

ODBER, Elizabeth Anne The Aldergate Medical Practice, The Mount, Salters Lane, Tamworth B79 8BH Tel: 01827 54775 Fax: 01827 62835 — BM 1983 Soton.; MRCGP 1990; DA (UK) 1987.

ODBERT, Reginald Massey Blue Sky House, 36 Grange Close, Everton, Lymington SO41 0TY Tel: 01425 271086 Email: blueskyodbert@virgin.net — MB ChB 1976 Sheff.; BSc Wales 1971; MRCGP 1981; Dip. IMC RCS Ed. 1995; DAvMed FOM RCP Lond. 1985; DRCOG 1982. Clin. Asst. (Ophth.) Roy. Bournemouth Hosp. Trust. Socs: Roy. Aeronaut. Soc.; RCS Edin.; Fac. Pre-Hosp. Care. Prev: Sen. Med. Off. RAF Akrotiri BFPO 57 & Aeromed Co-ordinating Off.; Sen. Med. Off. RAF Chivenor; Squadron Ldr. RAF.

ODD, David Edward 160 Conway Avenue, Great Wakering, Southend-on-Sea SS3 0BJ — MB ChB 1996 Leic.

ODDIE, Samuel Joseph Ripley 89 The Vineyard, Richmond TW10 6AT — MB BS 1991 Newc.

ODDY, Alice Virtue Llanberis Surgery, High Street, Llanberis, Caernarfon LL55 4SU — MB ChB 1992 Dundee; MRCGP 1996; DCH RCP Lond. 1996; DRCOG 1995.

ODDY, Clifford Gaunt (retired) 107 Pogmoor Road, Pogmoor, Barnsley S75 2LN Tel: 01226 206186 — MB ChB 1956 Sheff.; MFCM 1972; DPH Leeds 1961. Prev: Cons. Pub. Health Med. & Communicable Dis. Control Barnsley HA.

ODDY, Michael Jonathan 51 Christchurch Avenue, Finchley, London N12 0DG — BChir 1996 Camb.; MB Camb. 1997; MA Camb. 1998. (Univ. of Camb.)

ODEDRA, Nathalal Wolverton Health Centre, Gloucester Road, Wolverton, Milton Keynes MK12 5DF Tel: 01908 316633 Fax: 01908 225397 — MB BS 1972 Baroda; MB BS 1972 Baroda.

ODEDUN, Mr Titus Oyewole Brittania Medical Bureau, 12 Harley St., London W1 Tel: 020 7580 4903 Fax: 020 7580 4906; 6 Heather Drive, Rise Park, Romford RM1 4SP — MRCS Eng. LRCP Lond. 1978; MD Malta 1989; FRCS Eng 1982; FRCS Ed. 1981. Cons. Surg. Old Ct. Hosp. Lond.; Cons. Ormskirk & Dist. Hosp. Prev: Regist. (Surg.) Pinderfield Hosp. Wakefield; Lect. (Surg.) Univ. Calabar, Nigeria.

ODEGAARD, Esten Reidar ASnaesthetic Department, West Suffolk Hospital, Hardwick Lane, Bury St Edmunds IP33 2QZ — Cand Med 1961 Bergen.

ODEJINNI

ODEJINNI, Funmilayo Olukayode 36 New Way Road, London NW9 6PN — MB ChB 1986 Ife, Nigeria.

ODEKA, Benjamin Olugbola Child Health Department, Royal Oldham Hospital, Oldham OL1 2JH Tel: 0161 959 3759 Fax: 0161 627 8309 Email: egware@aol.com; 32 The Fairways, Ross Avenue, Whitefield, Manchester M45 7BN Tel: 0161 798 5862 Fax: 0161 959 3759 Email: egware@ad.com — MB BS 1980 Ibadan; MRCP (UK) 1987; DCH RCPS Glas. 1985; FRCP 2000. Cons. Paediat. Roy. Oldham Hosp.; Hon. Lect. Univ. of Manch.; Clin. Dir. (Child Health); UnderGrad. Tutor. Socs: Paediat. Research Soc.; Brit. Paediat. Assn. Brit. Soc. Paediat. Gastroenterol. & Nutrit. Prev: Sen. Regist. Rotat. Special Care Baby Unit Roy. Gwent Hosp.; Research Fell. Child Health (Paediat. Gastroenterol.) Univ. Manch. Booth Hall Childr. Hosp. Manch.; Regist. Rotat. (Paediat.) Roy. Manch Childr. Hosp. (Metab. Unit.), Pendlebury & Burnley Gen. Hosp.

ODEKU, Katherine Jill 81 Linford Avenue, Newport Pagnell MK16 8BX Tel: 01908 616850 — MB BS Lond. 1961; MRCS Eng. LRCP Lond. 1961; DObst RCOG 1963. (Roy. Free) SCMO Milton Keynes Community NHS Trust. Socs: Fac. Comm. Health; BMA; MRCPCH. Prev: Clin. Med. Off. Bucks. AHA; SHMO Gen. Outpat. Dept. Univ. Coll. Hosp. Ibadan; Regist. Paediat. Dept. Univ. Coll. Hosp. Ibadan, Nigeria.

ODELL, Mr Martin John Patrick 102 Stroud Road, Gloucester GL1 5JN; 291A Stroud Road, Gloucester GL1 5LB — MB ChB 1974 Leeds; BSc (Hons. Physiol.) St. And. 1970; FRCS Eng. 1979.

ODELL, Ruth Mary (retired) Elmbank, Church Lane, Ropley, Alresford SO24 0EA Tel: 01962 772499 — MB BChir Camb. 1947; MA Camb. 1955, BA (Nat. Sc. Trip.) 1944; MRCS Eng. LRCP Lond. 1947. Prev: Clin. Asst. (ENT) Roy. Free Hosp. & Connaught Hosp.

ODEMUYIWA, Olusola Department of Cardiology, Epsom General Hospital, Dorking Road, Epsom KT18 7EG Tel: 01372 735735 Fax: 01372 743421 — MB BS 1979 Lagos; FRCP 1999; MD Newc. 1991; MRCP (UK) 1983. Cons. Cardiol. Epsom Gen. Hosp. Socs: Brit. Cardiac Soc.; Brit. Cardiovasc. Interven. Soc. Prev: Sen. Regist. Wessex Cardiothoracic Centre Soton. Gen. Hosp.; Research Fell. (Cardiol. Sci.) St. Geo. Hosp. Med. Sch. Lond.

ODETOYINBO, Olusegun Abayomi Spitalfields Practice, 20 Old Montague St, London E1 5PB Tel: 020 7247 7070 — MB BS 1975 Ibadan; MRCP (UK) 1985; LMSSA Lond. 1986. GP City & E. Lond. FHSA. Prev: Med. Transpl. Off. Harefield Hosp.; Regist. (Med. of Elderly) Ealing Hosp.; SHO (Med.) Stepping Hill Hosp. Stockport.

ODGERS, Peter Brian The Cromwell Hospital, Cromwell Road, London SW5 0TU; 6 Devonshire Place, London W1G 6HN — MB ChB 1956 Leeds. (Leeds) Med. Adviser King Edwd. VII Hosp. Fund, Globtik Tankers Ltd. & other Cos. Socs: Fell. Roy. Soc. Med.; (Ex-Sec.) Chelsea Clin. Soc. Prev: Surg. Lt.-Cdr. RN, Staff Med. Off. W. Indies Squadron; SHO (Med.) Roy. Postgrad. Med. Sch. Lond.; SHO (Surg.) Leeds Gen. Infirm.

ODGERS, Mr Robin Charles Blake Corton Denham House, Corton Denham, Sherborne DT9 4LR Tel: 01963 220205 — BM BCh 1974 Oxf.; MA; FRCS Eng. 1979; DRCOG 1983. (Guy's) Prev: Regist. Surg. Qu. Mary's Hosp. Roehampton; Regist. (Surg.) St. Helier Hosp. Carshalton; SHO (Cas.) Guy's Hosp. Lond.

ODLING-SMEE, Mr George William Department of Surgery, Queen's University, Belfast City Hospital Trust, Lisburn Road, Belfast BT9 7AB Tel: 028 263909 Fax: 028 263875 — MB BS Durh. 1959; FRCSI 1987; FRCS Eng. 1968. (Newc.) Sen. Lect. (Surg.) Qu. Univ. Belf.; Cons. Surg. Belf. City Hosp. Prev: Sen. Tutor (Surg.) Qu. Univ. Belf.; Surg. & Act. Dir. Brit. Child Med. Care Unit Enugu; Surg. Unit Newc. Gen. Hosp.

ODLUM, Hugh Rupert Burgh Cottage, Burgh, Woodbridge IP13 6PT Tel: 01473 735226 — MB BChir. Camb. 1949; BA Camb. 1945, MA; MRCS Eng. LRCP Lond. 1947. (Camb. & St. Bart.) Socs: Fell. Roy. Soc. Med.; BMA. Prev: Ho. Surg. (Orthop.) Dept. St. Bart. Hosp.; Jun. Regist. (Anaesth.) Edgware Gen. Hosp.; Ho. Surg. Obst. St. Paul's Hosp. Hemel Hempstead.

ODOGU, Mr Kroneakegha Kitchener 2 Furness Avenue, West Derby, Liverpool L12 0HN — MB BS 1985 Lagos, Nigeria; FRCS Ed. 1994.

ODOI, Robert Emmanuel 30 Sackville Street, Kettering NN16 9DN Tel: 01536 521553 — MB ChB 1979 Ghana; MRCOG 1991.

ODONGA, Florence 5 Smithills Drive, Bolton BL1 5RB — LRCP LRCS 1978 Ed.; LRCP LRCS Ed. LRCPS Glas. 1978.

ODUFUWA-BOLGER, Titilayo Olubola 16 Moorside, Welwyn Garden City AL7 4QH — MB BS 1986 Lagos; MB BS Lagos, Nigeria 1986; FRCS Ed. 1993; FRCOphth 1993.

ODUKOYA, Mr Abiodun Olusegun Department Obstetrics and Gynaecology, Scunthorpe District Hospital NHS Trust, Scunthorpe DN15 7BH Tel: 01724 282282 Fax: 01724 290435 — MB BS 1980 Ibadan; MRCOG 1990; MD Sheff. 1995; FWACS 1991; FMCOG (Nigeria) 1987. (Ibadan, Nigeria) Cons. (O & G) Minimal Access Surg.; PostGrad. Clin. Tutor. Socs: BMA; Eur. Soc. Human Reproduc. & Embryol.; Brit. Fertil. Soc. Prev: Lect./Hon. Sen. Regist. (O & G) Jessop Hosp.; Centr. Univ. Teachg. Hosp. Sheff.

ODUM, Jonathan Renal Unit, New Cross Hospital, Wolverhampton WV10 0QP Tel: 01902 643086 Fax: 01902 643192 — MD 1993 Birm.; MB ChB 1984; MRCP (UK) 1987; FRCP 1999. Cons. Phys. & Nephrol. Roy. Wolverhampton Hosp. Trust. Socs: Brit. Renal Assn. & Internat. Soc. Nephrol. Prev: Sen. Regist. Roy. Adelaide Hosp.; Regist. N. Staffs. Roy. Infirm.

ODUM, Simon Brooklea Clinic, Wick Road, Bristol BS4 4HU Tel: 0117 971 1211 Fax: 0117 972 3370; 14 Claverton Road, Saltford, Bristol BS31 3DP — MB ChB 1989 Birm.

ODUMOSU, Timothy Adesegun 32 Scott Court, 50 Silverthorne Court, London SW8 3HD — MB BS 1986 Lagos; MRCOG 1994.

ODUNSI, Adekunle Omotayo Imperial Cancer Research Fund, Institute of Molcular Medicine, John Radcliffe Hospital, Headley Way, Headington, Oxford OX3 9DU — MB ChB 1984 Nigeria; MRCOG 1991.

ODUNSI, L O Cater Street Surgery, 1 Cater Street, Kempston, Bedford MK42 8DR Tel: 01234 853461 Fax: 01234 840536 — MB BS 1978 Lagos; MB BS 1978 Lagos.

ODUNUGA, Bankole Abidemi 133 Inverness Terrace, London W2 6JF — MB BS 1997 Lond.

ODURNY, Allan Department of Radiology, Southampton General Hospital, Tremona Road, Southampton SO16 6YD Tel: 02380 796862 Fax: 02380 794038 — MB ChB 1974 Birm.; FRCS Eng. 1978; FRCR 1986. Cons. Radiol. Soton. Gen. Hosp. Socs: Brit. Soc. Interven. Radiol.; Cardiovasc. & Interven. Soc. Europe. Prev: Cons. Radiol. E. Birm. Hosp.; Sen. Regist. (Radiol.) Soton. Gen. Hosp.; Fell. Angiogr. Toronto Gen. Hosp. & Univ. Toronto, Canada.

ODURO-DOMINAH, Asamoah Papworth Hospital NHS Trust, Papworth Hospital, Papworth Everard, Cambridge CB3 8RE Tel: 01480 830541 Fax: 01480 831143 — MB BS 1973 Newc.; FRCP 1999; FFA RCS Eng. 1982; MRCP (UK) 1978; FRCA Eng. 1982. (Newcastle Upon Tyne) Cons. Anaesth. Papworth Hosp. Socs: Assn. Cardiothoracic Anaesth.; Eur. Assn. Cardiothoracic Anaesth.; Eur. Soc. Intens. Care Med.

ODURO-YEBOAH, Adwoa Millway Medical Practice, Hartley Avenue, Mill Hill, London NW7 2HX Tel: 020 8959 0888 Fax: 020 8959 7050 — MB BS 1992 Lond.; MRCGP 1996; DRCOG 1995; DGM RCP Lond. 1994; DCH RCP Lond. 1994. (Univ. Coll. & Middlx. Sch. of Med.) GP Lond. Socs: (Chairm. & Asst. Sec.) Afr. Caribbean Soc. Prev: GP/Regist. Lond.

ODUTOLA, Taofeequat Abibayo Adedoyin c/o Mrs R F Bamgbala, 14 Sunnydene Lodge, Sunnydene Gardens, Wembley HA0 1AT — MB ChB 1965 Glas.

ODY, Andrew Wilmot 31 Frogston Raod W., Edinburgh EH10 7AB — MB BS 1994 Lond.

ODY, Catriona Luise McCormick 58 Shortheath Road, Farnham GU9 8SQ — MB BS 1994 Lond.

OELBAUM, Moses Hirsh (cons. rooms), 11 St John St., Manchester M3 4DW Tel: 0161 832 9999; 17 Sheepfoot Lane, Prestwich, Manchester M25 0BN Tel: 0161 740 4136 — BSc Manch. 1942, MD 1951, MB ChB (Hons., Distinc; Anat., Pharmacol. & Surg.) 1945; FRCP Lond. 1971, M 1947. (Manch.) Cons. Phys. Crumpsall Hosp., N. Hosp. & Vict. Memor. Jewish Hosp.; Hon. Clin. Lect. Med. Univ. Manch. Socs: Fell. Manch. Med. Soc. Prev: 1st Asst. Med. Unit, Manch. Roy. Infirm.; Med. Tutor Univ. Manch.; Sen. Ho. Phys. Manch. Roy. Infirm.

OELBAUM, Raymond Stuart Ormskirk District General Hospital, Wigan Road, Ormskirk L39 2AZ Tel: 01695 656066 Fax: 01695 656484 — MB ChB 1982 Manc; MD 1994; BSc (1st cl. Hons.) Med. Biochem. Manch. 1979; MRCP (UK) 1986. (Mancester) Cons. Phys. Diabetes & Endocrinol. Ormskirk Dist. Gen. Hosp. Prev: Sen. Regist. (Med.) St. Mary's Hosp. & N.wick Pk. Hosp.; Research Regist. (Diabetes & Lipid Research) St. Bart. Hosp. Lond.

OELBAUM, Sandra 14 Snaefell Avenue, Tuebrook, Liverpool L13 2EY Tel: 0151 228 2377 Email: sandra.oelbaum@free-internet.co.uk; 65 Dudlow Lane, Calderstones, Liverpool L18 2EY — MB ChB 1982 (Hons.) Manch.; BSc (1st cl. Hons.) Physiol. Manch. 1979; MRCP (UK) 1988. Tutor, Univ. of Liverp. Socs: Brit. Med. Soc. Prev: Princip. GP N.olt Middlx.; Lect. (Med.) Univ. Coll. Hosp. Lond.; GP Princip., Harrow, Middx.

OELMANN, Gareth John 66 Llanfair Road, Cardiff CF11 9QB — MB BCh 1994 Wales.

OEPPEN, Marion Heulwen Shelton House, Newton, Martley, Worcester WR6 6PR Tel: 01886 821497 — MB BCh 1959 Wales; DCH RCPS Glas. 1981. (Welsh Nat. Sch. Med.) Sen. Clin. Med. Off (Community Child Health & Paediat. Audiol.) Hearing & Speech Centre Hereford. Socs: Roy. Coll. Paediat. & Child Health.

OEPPEN, Rachel Suzanne Department of Radiology, Southampton General Hospital, Tremona Rd, Southampton SO16 6YD — MB ChB 1992 Bristol; FRCR 2000; MRCP (UK) 1996. (Bristol) Specialist Regist. Wessex Radiol. Train. Scheme.

OETIKER, Ursula Kingsfield Medical Centre, 146 Alcester Road South, Kings Heath, Birmingham B14 6AA Tel: 0121 444 2054 Fax: 0121 443 5856; 22 Amesbury Road, Moseley, Birmingham B13 8LD — MB BS 1985 Lond.; MRCGP 1994; DCH RCP Lond. 1990; DRCOG Lond. 1989. (St. Thos. Hosp. Lond.) GP Princip. Prev: GP Newc.; Trainee GP Lond.; SHO (Obst & Gyn., Paediat. & Geriat.) St. Geo. Hosp. Lond.

OFFEN, Mr David Nigel NHS Exec. Easter Region Office, Capital Park, Fulbourn, Cambridge CB1 5XB Tel: 01223 597500 Fax: 01223 597555 Email: nigekoffen@doh.ssi.gov.uk; 83 Drury Road, Colchester CO2 7UU Tel: 01206 570058 Fax: 01206 523636 Email: david.offen@dtn.nh.com — MB BS 1966 Lond.; FRCS Eng. 1971; LIHSM. (St. Bart.) Head of Clin. Qualiy E.R.O. NHS Exec. Socs: Chairm. Brit. Assn. Med. Managers; Fell. Roy. Soc. Med. & Hunt. Soc. Prev: Chier Exec., Essex Rivers NHS Trust; Cons. Clin. Audit & Quality Improvem. NE Thames RHA; Cons. Surg. Whipps Cross & Wanstead Hosps.

OFFER, Catherine Mary 26 The Close, Norwich NR1 4DZ — MB BS 1963 Lond.; MRCP Lond. 1969; MRCS Eng. LRCP Lond. 1963; DCH Eng. 1966. (St. Bart) Socs: Brit. Geriat. Soc. & BMA. Prev: Cons. Phys. (Geriat. Med.) Soton. & SW Hants. Health Dist. (T); Sen. Regist. Soton. Gen. Hosp.; Research Asst. RCP Lond.

OFFER, Mr Graham John 16 Lytham Road, Clarendon Park, Leicester LE2 1YD — MB ChB 1993 Leic.; BSc (1st cl. Hons.) Leic. (Pharmacol.) 1990; FRCS (Eng.) 1997. (Leic.) Specialist Regist., (Lat), Plastic Surg. Socs: Trent S. Jun. Doctor's Comm. BMA; Nat. Jun. Doctor's Comm. 1997; Full Mem., Brit. Burns Assoc. Prev: SHO (Neurosurg.) Qu.'s Med. Centre Nottm.; Demonst. (Anat.) Univ. Leic.; SHO (Plastic Surg.) Leic. Roy. Infirm.

OFFER, Mark 22 Malvern Road, London NW6 5PP — MB BS 1996 Lond.

OFFERMAN, Edward Leslie (retired) 11 Camden Row, Blackheath, London SE3 0QA Tel: 020 8852 7063 — MB BS 1959 Lond.; FRCPath 1986, M 1973; DObst RCOG 1961. Cons. Haemat. Qu. Mary's Hosp. Sidcup. Prev: Sen. Regist. (Haemat.) Univ. Coll. Hosp. & Whittington Hosp. Lond.

OFFIAH, Edward Curtis 77 Hamsterly Park, Northampton NN3 5DX — MB ChB 1994 Birm.; BSc Birm. 1991. SHO (Surg.) Oxf. Radcliffe NHS Trust.

OFFORD, Catherine Mary Belmont Surgery, St. James Square, Wadhurst TN5 6BJ Tel: 01892 782121 Fax: 01892 783989 — MB BS 1985 Lond.; BSc Lond. 1982, MB BS 1985; MRCGP 1989; DRCOG 1987.

OFFORD, George Brian (retired) 41 Woodland Grove, Weybridge KT13 9EQ Tel: 01932 843180 — MB BS 1963 Lond.; MRCS Eng. LRCP Lond. 1963; DObst RCOG 1966; DA Eng. 1971. Prev: Clin. Asst. (A & E) Roy. Hosp. Portsmouth.

OFILI, Esther Adesomo Eagle's Nest, Horsleyhead, Overtown, Wishaw ML2 0RS — MB BS 1979 Ibadan; MRCGP 1990; T(GP) 1992; DCCH RCP Lond. 1988.

OFILI, Gregory Ubaka Law Hospital NHS Trust, Carluke ML8 5ER Tel: 01698 361100 — MB BS 1978 Benin; BSc (Hons.) (Biochem.) Ahmadu Bello 1975; MRCOG 1988; T(OG) 1995. Research Fell. (Colposcopy Clinic) Dept. O & G Roy. Infirm. Edin.; Temp. Lect. & Sen. Regist. (Obst. & Gyn.) Univ. Edin. Socs: BMA & Glas. Obst. Soc. Prev: Regist. (O & G) E. Gen. Hosp. Edin.

OFOE, Victor Dotse 1 Valkyrie, Longfield, Grahame Park, Colindale, London NW9 5SN Tel: 020 8205 5908 — MB ChB 1983 Ghana; MRCP (UK) 1991.

OFORI, Joakin Apeadu Bosompra Friern Barnet Road Surgery, 79 Friern Barnet Riad, London N11 3EH Tel: 020 8368 9874 — MB BS 1971 Lond. (Univ. Coll. Hosp.) Prev: Ho. Surg. Edgware Gen. Hosp.; Ho. Phys. Dreadnought Seamen's Hosp. Lond.; SHO (Med.) King Geo. Hosp. Ilford.

OFORI-ATTA, Mr Paul 6 Talbot Road, Ashford TW15 3PN — MB ChB 1982 Univ. Ghana; FRCSI 1990.

OGAKWU, Michael Obioha c/o Mr. Emeka Agu, 152 Purves Road, Kensal Rise, London NW10 5TG — MB BS 1980 Nigeria; MB BS U of Nigeria 1980; MRCOG 1992.

OGANWU, Sylvanus Oyeshine 4 Rivereside Close, London E5 9SP Tel: 020 8806 7707 — MB BS 1978 Ibadan; MB BS Ibadan, Nigeria 1978; MRCOG 1991. Career Regist. (O & G) Edgware Gen. Hosp.

OGBO, Victor Ikechukwu Bolton General Hospital, Minerva Road, Farnworth, Bolton BL4 0JR Tel: 01204 390390; 126 Sandalwood, Rivermead Park, The Hoskers, Westhoughton, Bolton BL5 2RQ Tel: 01942 842056 — MB BS 1981 Benin; MB BS Benin, Nigeria 1981; MRCOG 1994; FWACS 1991; DFFP 1996. Clin. Asst. (O & G) Bolton Gen. Hosp. Socs: BMA; Brit. Soc. Psychosomatic Obst., Gyn. & Androl. Prev: Sen. Regist. (O & G) Univ. Benin Teachg. Hosp., Nigeria; Regist. (O & G) Ayrsh. Centr. Hosp.; Regist. Rutherglen Matern. & Vict. Infirm. Glas.

OGBOBI, Sale Emeje Flat 33, 38 Windsor Park, Belfast BT9 6FS — MB BS 1983 Lagos, Nigeria.

OGBONMWAN, Stephen Tel: 07813 656936 Fax: 0161 620 6974; Email: srosteve99@hotmail.com — MB BS 1980 Nigeria; Colposcopy Accredited; MMedSci (Assisted Reproduction Technol.) Nottm. 1996; FMCOG Nigeria 1992; MFFP 1995; MRCOG 1994. (University of Benin, Benin City, Nigeria) IVF Regist. Reproductive Med. Unit Withington Hosp. Univ. S. Manch. NHS Trust Hosp. Manch. Socs: Eur. Assn. Gyn. & Obst.; Brit. Soc. Colposc. & Cervical Path.; Brit. Fertil. Soc.

OGBORN, Anthony Douglas Ronald Riseley House, 10A Rotten Row, Bedford MK44 1EJ Tel: 01234 708010 — BM BCh 1963 Oxf.; MA Oxf. 1963; FRCOG 1982, M 1969, DObst 1966. (Univ. Coll. Hosp.) Cons. O & G Bedford Gen. Hosp. Prev: Sen. Regist. (O & G) N.ampton Gen. & Hammersmith Hosps.; Regist. Radcliffe Infirm. Oxf.; Ho. Phys. Univ. Coll. Hosp. Lond.

OGBUEHI, Nwabueze John 2D Grove Park Road, Rainham RM13 7BX — MB BS 1962 Lond.

OGDEN, Adrian David Clifton Lane Health Centre, Clifton Lane, Doncaster Road, Rotherham S65 1DU Tel: 01709 382315 Fax: 01709 512646 — MRCS Eng. LRCP Lond. 1975.

OGDEN, Alan Stanley 10 Farrington, 54 Westcliff Road, Bournemouth BH4 8BE Tel: 01202 767115 — MB ChB 1939 Manch. (Manch.) Socs: Fell. BMA.

OGDEN, Mr Andrew Chester Broadlands, Lochmaben, Lockerbie DG11 1RL — MB ChB 1969 Glas.; FRCS Glas. 1976.

OGDEN, Anne Barbara 21 Amberley Close, Send, Woking GU23 7BX Tel: 01483 223697 — MB ChB 1949 Bristol. (Bristol)

OGDEN, Barbara Eileen Patricia 14 Burlington Road, Ipswich IP1 2EU Tel: 01473 211661; Windmill Lodge, Mill Lane, Witnesham, Ipswich IP6 9HR Tel: 01473 785309 — MB BS 1959 Lond.; DObst RCOG 1960; DCH Eng. 1962. (Lond. Hosp.)

OGDEN, Mr Christopher William Department of Urology, Northwick Park & St Mark's Hospital, Watford Road, Harrow HA1 3UJ Tel: 020 8869 2478 Fax: 020 8869 2446; 19 Queensdale Road, Holland Park, London W11 4SB Tel: 020 7603 7584 Fax: 020 8869 2446 Email: chrisogden@compuserve.com — MB BS 1984 Lond.; MS Lond. 1993; FRCS (Urol.) 1995; FRCS Eng. 1990; FRCS Ed. 1989; FEBU 1996. (Char. Cross Hosp.) Cons. Urol. N.wick Pk. & St. Mark's Hosp. Harrow. Socs: Brit. Assn. Urol. Prev: Sen. Regist. Roy. Marsden, St. Mary's, Char. Cross & W.m. Hosps.

OGDEN, David James Stoneycroft House, Broadgreen Hospital NHS Trust, Thomas Drive, Liverpool L14 3LB — MB ChB 1994 Liverp.

OGDEN, David John Rothschild House Surgery, Chapel Street, Tring HP23 6PU Tel: 01442 822468 Fax: 01442 825889 — MB BS 1969 Lond.

OGDEN

OGDEN, Elizabeth Claire Broadlands, Lochmaben, Lockerbie DG11 1RL — MB ChB 1976 Glas.; DMRD Ed. 1980.

OGDEN, Elizabeth Mary Gateways Surgery, Andrew Close, Stenley, Radlett WD Tel: 01923 857190; Tel: 020 8894 4949 Email: assadbutt@hotmail.com — MB ChB 1975 Manch.; 2000 Dip. Of Inst. of Psychosexual Med.; DCH 1995; MFFP 1994; MRCGP 1979; Dip. Pract. Dermat. Wales 1993; DRCOG 1977; BSc St. And. 1972. (St Andrews & Manchester) Co Princip. (Gen. Pract.) Gateways Surg., Stenley Radlett & GP Non-Princip. Potters Bar & St Albans (p/t); Hosp. Practitioner Dermat. Lister Hosp. Stevenage; Sen. Clin. Med. Off. Dept. of Reproductive Sexual Healthcare Enfield Community Care NHS Trust; GP Specialist Outreach Clinic in Dermat. in Barehanwood; Examr. for the MFFP exam (Fac. of Family Plann. & Reproductive Health). Socs: BMA; Primary Care Dermat. Soc. (Comm. Mem.). Prev: Resid. Psychiat. St. Brendans Hosp., Bermuda; GP Broxbourne; Trainee GP Enfield VTS.

OGDEN, George Herbert, Surg. Lt.-Cdr. RN Retd. Kearsley Medical Centre, Jackson St., Kearsley, Bolton BL4 8EP Tel: 01204 573164; 2A Boothstown Drive, Worsley, Manchester M28 1UF — MB ChB 1989 Birm.; DRCOG 1994; MRCGP 1998. (Birmingham) GP Princip. Kearsley Med. Centre. Prev: Trainee GP Vanburgh Hill Health Centre Lond.

OGDEN, Jacqueline Noelle North Cardiff Medical Centre, Excalibur Drive, Thornhill, Cardiff CF14 9BB Tel: 029 2075 0322 Fax: 029 2075 7705; Pant y Gollen, Caerphilly Mountain, Caerphilly CF83 1LY — MB BCh 1988 Wales; BSc (Hons.) Wales 1985, MB BCh 1988; MRCGP 1994; T(GP) 1994; DRCOG 1993. Socs: Roy. Coll. Obst. & Gyn. Prev: SHO (Gen. Med.) Univ. Hosp. Wales Cardiff.

OGDEN, James Rennie 14 Reedley Grove, Burnley BB10 2LA — MB ChB 1963 Manch.; FRCOG 1982, M 1969, DObst 1965. Cons. (O & G) Burnley Gen. Hosp.

OGDEN, Jane 50 Leamington Street, Sheffield S10 1LW — MB ChB 1998 Sheff.

OGDEN, Jean Sheila Margaret 45 Grove Road, Norwich NR1 3RQ — MB BS 1955 Lond.; DObst RCOG 1957; FFA RCS Eng. 1966; DA Eng. 1962. (St. Mary's) Cons. Anaesth. United Norwich Hosps.

OGDEN, Mrs Lynne Mary Commercial Road Surgery, 75 Commercial Road, Leeds LS5 3AT Tel: 0113 275 2780; 19 Batcliffe Drive, Leeds LS6 3QB Tel: 0113 278 4576 — MB ChB 1980 Leeds.

OGDEN, Terence Lister c/o The Surgery, Caerffynnon, Dolgellau LL40 1LY — MB ChB 1972 Birm.; Cert. Family Plann. JCC 1975. Mem. Wales LMC; Hon. Teach. Welsh Nat. Sch. Med. Prev: Trainer (Gen. Pract.) Gwynedd; Sec. Meirionydd Med. Soc.; SHO (Obst., Anaesth. & Paediat.) Good Hope Hosp. Sutton Coldfield.

OGDEN, Thomas Tel: 0161 330 9880 Fax: 0161 330 9393; Bull Hill, Cobden Edge, Mellor, Stockport SK6 5NL — MRCS Eng. LRCP Lond. 1962. (Manch.) Socs: BMA.

OGDEN, William Stewart Winoma, Orchehill Avenue, Gerrards Cross SL9 8QJ Tel: 01753 884273 — MB BChir Camb. 1955; MA Camb. 1955; MRCS Eng. LRCP Lond. 1954. (Camb. & St. Bart.) Socs: BMA; (Ex-Pres.) Chiltern Med. Soc.; Brit. Assn. Pharmaceut. Phys. Prev: Flight Lt. RAF Med. Br.; Ho. Surg. (ENT) St. Bart. Hosp.; Ho. Phys. OldCh. Hosp. Romford.

OGDEN-FORDE, Fiona Elizabeth 12 Ewden Close, Liverpool L16 5HF — MB ChB 1989 Liverp.

OGDON, Colin Prestwich Health Centre, Fairfax Road, Prestwich, Manchester M25 1BT Tel: 0161 773 2483; Higher Red Lees Farm, Helmshore Road, Holcombe, Bury BL8 4PE Tel: 01706 825072 — MB ChB 1971 Manch.; MB ChB Manch. 1974; BSc (Hons. Med. Biochem.) Manch. 1971. Clin. Asst. (Med.) Bury Gen. Hosp.; Lect. (Gen. Pract.) Univ. Manch.; Med. Off. Gt.er Manch. Probation Serv.; Med. Off. Bury Community Drug Team. Socs: Fell. Manch. Med. Soc. Prev: Cons. Exec. & Indust. Health Screening BUPA Med. Centre; SHO (Psychiat.) Prestwich Hosp. Manch.; SHO Roy. Manch. Childr. Hosp.

OGEAH, John Chukwukadibia Fordwater, Cuddington Way, Sutton SM2 7JA — MB BS 1984 Ibadan; MB BS 1984 Ibadan.

OGEDEGBE, Mr Arikoge Joseph 17 Wynton Gardens, South Norwood, London SE25 5RS Tel: 020 8771 6955 Email: a.j.ogedegbe@alpha.gmw.ac.uk; 14 Crossways Road, Mitcham CR4 1DQ Tel: 0781 687 2859 Email: arikcoged@aol.com — MB BS 1987 Benin; MB BS Benin, Nigeria 1987; FRCS Ed. 1993. (Univ. Benin, Nigeria) Surg. Research Regist. & Lect. (Surg.) Surg. Roy. Lond. & St. Barth. NHS Trust; Specialist Regist., UCL Hosp. NHS Trust, Lond. Socs: Assoc. Mem. Assn. Surg. GB & Irel.; Assn. Surg. Train.; Brit. Assn. Surg. Oncol. Prev: Specialist Regist. (Surg.) Newham Gen. Hosp. Lond.; Career Regist. (Surg.) Havering Hosps. Trust.

OGG, Mr Archibald John (retired) Clearbury Cottage, Woodgreen, Fordingbridge SP6 2QU — BM BCh 1946 Oxf.; BM BCh Oxon. 1946; FRCS Eng. 1954; DO Eng. 1951. Surg. Lt. RNR. Prev: Opthalmic Cons., Salisbury Infirm.

OGG, Chisholm Stuart Evelegh's, High St., Long Wittenham, Abingdon OX14 4QH Tel: 01865 407724 — BSc (Physiol.) Lond. 1958, MD 1967, MB BS; (Distinc. Med.) 1961; FRCP Lond. 1975, M 1964; MRCS Eng. LRCP Lond. 1960; DObst RCOG 1963. (Guy's) Emerit. Cons. Nephrol. Guys & St. Thomas Hosp. Trust. Socs: Renal Assn. & Europ. Dialysis & Transp. Assn. Prev: Cons. Renal Phys. Guy's Hosp. Lond.; Dir. of Clin. Renal Servs. 1972-98; Civil Cons. Renal Dis. RN.

OGG, Elaine Catherine Serena, High Barnwood Road, Kilsyth, Glasgow G65 0EE — MB ChB 1983 Glas.; MRCGP 1987; MRCPsych 1990; DRCOG 1985. (Glas.) Cons. Psychiat. (Psychother.) Larkfield Centre, Glas. Socs: Roy. Coll. Psychiat.; Scott. Assn. of Analyt. Psychother.

OGG, Fiona Lindsay Mary Portlethen Medical Centre, Portlethen, Aberdeen AB12 4QP — MB ChB 1991 Aberd.; 1996 Diploma Family Plann.; MRCGP 1995. (Aberd.) p/t GP Princip. Portlethen Aberd. Prev: Aberd. P VTS; Ho. Off. Rotat. Aberd. Roy. Hosp.

OGG, Graham Stuart Molecular Immunology Group, Institute of Molecular Medicine, John Radcliffe Hospital, Oxford OX3 9DS Tel: 01865 222334 Email: gogg@worf.molbiol.ot.ac.uk; 19 St. Christophers Place, Oxford OX4 2HS — BM BCh 1992 Oxf.; BA (Hons.) Oxf. 1989; MRCP (UK) 1995; Dphil 1998. MRC Clin. Scientist Fell.ship, Nuffield Dept Clin med. Oxf. Prev: MRC Clin Train. Fell.sh.ip, Nuffield clinic med. Oxf.

OGG, Thomas Winchester (retired) 11 Worts Causeway, Cambridge CB1 8RJ Tel: 01223 248703 Fax: 01223 413005 — MB ChB 1964 Aberd.; MA Camb. 1977; FFA RCS Eng. 1971; DA Eng. 1968. Assoc. Lect. Camb. Univ; Dir. Day Surg. Addenbrooke's Hosp. Camb. Prev: Cons. Anaesth. Addenbrooke's Hosp. Camb.

OGHOETUOMA, Jerry Oghenekevbe 36 Winslow Road, Hunger Hill, Bolton BL3 4SP Email: j.ojhoetom@aog.com — MB BS 1985 Lagos; MRCOG 1993. Specialist Regist.

OGILVIE, Alan David 18 Applecourt, Newton Road, Cambridge CB2 2AN — MB ChB 1987 Ed.

OGILVIE, Alan James East Hill Surgery, 78 East Hill, Colchester CO1 2RW Tel: 01206 768393 Fax: 01206 869054 Email: aogilvie@f-81091.nhs.uk; 10 Fitzwalter Road, Colchester CO3 3SS Tel: 01206 768393 — MB ChB 1967 St. And.; DObst RCOG 1969. (St. And.) Socs: (Hon. Treas.) Colchester Med. Soc. Prev: SHO (Paediat.) St. John's Hosp. Chelmsford; Ho. Off. (O & G) Essex Co. Hosp. Colchester.

OGILVIE, Alan Leonard Northampton General Hospital, Cliftonville, Northampton NN1 5BD Tel: 01604 545567 Email: alan.ogilview@ngh-kr.anglox.nhs.uk; 26 Kingsley Road, Northampton NN2 7BL — MB BChir 1974 Camb.; MA Camb. 1974, MD 1986; FRCP Lond. 1991; FRCP Ed. 1989; MRCP (UK) 1976. (Univ. Camb.) Cons. Phys. N.ampton Gen. Hosp. Socs: Fell, Roy. Coll. Of Phys.s, Lond; Fell. Roy. Coll. Of Phys.s, Edin.; Mem, Brit. Soc. Of Gastroenterol. Prev: Sen. Regist. Edin. Teach. Hosps.; Research Fell. Univ. Hosp. Nottm.; Regist. (Med.) Luton & Dunstable Hosp.

OGILVIE, Alexander Collingwood Fitzwilliams (retired) 37 Nackington Road, Canterbury CT1 3NP Tel: 01227 452232 — MB BS 1944 Lond.; MD Lond. 1952; MRCS Eng. LRCP Lond. 1944; FRCPath 1966: Hon. Cons. Path. Kent & Canterbury Hosp. Prev: Cons. Path. W. Cumbld. Hosps.

OGILVIE, Bruce Campbell Wessex Cardiothoracic Centre, Southampton General Hospital, Southampton SO16 6YD Tel: 02380 794833 Fax: 02380 796341; 14 Russell Place, Southampton SO17 1NU Tel: 02380 556762 — MB ChB 1965 Ed.; FRCP Ed. 1987; MRCP (UK) 1970; FRCR 1975; DMRD Ed. 1972; DObst RCOG 1968. (Ed.) Cons. Radiol. Soton. Univ. Hosps. NHS Trust. Socs: Fell. Roy. Soc. Med.; Brit. Inst. Radiol.; Brit. Cardiac Soc. Prev:

Sen. Regist. & Research Fell. (Radiodiag.) Roy. Infirm. Edin.; Regist. (Med.) Vict. Hosp. Kirkcaldy.

OGILVIE, Charles Keith Meadowbank Health Centre, 3 Salmon Inn Road, Falkirk FK2 OXF Tel: 01324 715753 Fax: 01324 717565 — MB ChB 1968 Glas.

OGILVIE, Mr Colin Orthopaedic Department, Taunton & Somerset Hospital, Musgrove Park, Taunton TA1 5DA Tel: 01823 333444 — MB ChB 1979 Leeds; MD Leeds 1992; FRCS Eng. 1984. Cons. Orthop. Surg. Taunton & Som. NHS Trust Taunton. Socs: Fell. BOA. Prev: Sen. Regist. Bristol Hosps.; Action Research Fell. (BioMech.) Salford.

OGILVIE, Colin Macleod The Riffel, Woolton Park, Woolton, Liverpool L25 6DR Tel: 0151 428 3472 — MB ChB 1944 Liverp.; MD Liverp. 1954; FRCP Lond. 1968, M 1950. Emerit. Cons. Phys. Roy. Liverp. Hosp. & King Edwd. VII Hosp. Midhurst. Socs: (Ex-Pres.) Brit. Thoracic Soc.; Assn. Phys.; (Ex-Pres.) Liverp. Med. Inst. Prev: Cons. Phys. Roy. Liverp. Hosp. & Regional Cardiothoracic Centre; Postgrad. Trav. Fell. Univ. Lond.; Sen. Regist. & Lect. (Med.) Lond. Hosp.

OGILVIE, Danuta Maria Helena The Hyde Surgery, 37/39 The Hyde, Stevenage SG2 9SB Tel: 01438 365588 Fax: 01438 356013; All Saints Lodge, 6 Myddelton Park, Whetstone, London N20 0HX Tel: 020 8446 4671 — MB BS 1963 Lond.; MRCS Eng. LRCP Lond. 1963. (Guy's) GP Princip. 37/39 The Hyde Stevenage SG2 9SB. Socs: Med. Disab. Appeal Tribunals. Prev: Clin. Asst. (Rheum.) Lister Hosp. Stevenage.; Med. Disabil. Appeals Tribunal.

OGILVIE, David Queen Marys Hospital for Children, Wrythe Lane, Carshalton SM5 1AA Tel: 020 8296 3060 Fax: 020 8644 6878 Email: dogilvie@stheller.sghms.ac.uk — MB BS 1969 Lond.; FRCP Lond. 1990; MRCP (UK) 1972; MRCS Eng. LRCP Lond. 1969; DCH Eng. 1977. (Guy's) Cons. Paediat. Qu. Mary's Hosp. for Childr. & St. Helier Hosp. Carshalton. Prev: Sen. Regist. Hosp. Sick Childr. Lond. & Qu. Eliz. Hosp. for Childr. Lond.; Regist. Hammersmith Hosp. Lond.

OGILVIE, David Bruce Lanarkshire NHS Board, 14 Beckford St., Hamilton ML3 0TA Tel: 01698 281313 Fax: 01698 424316 Email: ogilvie@ecossetel.com; 2 Stuart Ave, Rutherglen, Glasgow G73 4JL — MB BChir 1994 Camb.; MRCGP 1998; 2001 DFPHM; MPH 2000 Glas.; MA Camb. 1995; DRCOG 1996; DFFP 1998. (Camb.) Specialist Regist. in Pub. Health Med., Lanarksh. NHS Bd., Hamilton. Socs: Soc. for Social Med. Prev: GP/Regist. W. Suff., VTS; SHO (A & E) Bedford Hosp.; Ho. Phys. Addenbrooke's Hosp. Camb.

OGILVIE, George Fleming Rhind (retired) Brooklands, Burnley Road, Crawshawbooth, Rossendale BB4 8BW Tel: 01706 215965 — MB ChB 1959 Manch.; DObst RCOG 1961.

OGILVIE, Ian Maurice (retired) 11 Cherry Tree Gardens, Balerno EH14 5SP Tel: 0131 449 3960 — MB ChB 1948 Ed.; AFOM RCP Lond. 1980; MFCM 1974; DPH Lond. 1961. Prev: Air Commodore RAF Med. Br.

OGILVIE, James Robertson The Medical Centre, 7 Hill Place, Arbroath DD11 1AE Tel: 01241 431144 Fax: 01241 430764 — MB ChB 1968 Ed.

OGILVIE, Mr John William The Clinic, Highfield, 22 Wymondley Road, Hitchin SG4 9PN Tel: 01462 431765 — LMSSA 1963 Lond.; MA, BM BCh Oxf. 1963; FRCS Eng. 1970. (Oxf. & Guy's) Indep. GP Nutrit. Med. Hitchin. Prev: GP Hitchin; Regist. (Gen. Surg.) Roy. Shrops. Infirm; Regist. (Cardiothoracic Surg.) BRd.green Hosp. Liverp.

OGILVIE, Katherine Elizabeth Ryehill Health Centre, St. Peter Street, Dundee DD1 4JH Tel: 01382 644466 Fax: 01832 646302; Kirkton House, Balmerino, Newport-on-Tay DD6 8SA Tel: 01382 330205 Email: keolgilvie@keogilvie.freeserve.co.uk — MB ChB 1983 Dundee; MRCGP 1987; DRCOG 1986; DFFP 1997.

OGILVIE, Marie Matheson Department of Medical Microbiology, Medical School, Teviot Place, Edinburgh EH8 9AG Tel: 0131 650 3153 Fax: 0131 650 6531 Email: marie.ogilvie@ed.ac.uk; 62/3 Blacket Place, Edinburgh EH9 1RJ Tel: 0131 668 1759 — MB ChB Ed. 1965; BSc (Hons.) Ed. 1963, MD 1970; MRCPath 1991. (Ed.) Sen. Lect. (Virol.) Univ. Edin. & Hon. Cons. Virol. Roy. Infirm. Edin. NHS Trust. Prev: Sen. Lect. & Hon. Cons. (Virol.) Univ. Soton.

OGILVIE, Patricia Joy Felin Bencoed, Llangybi, Pwllheli LL53 6SR — MB ChB 1997 Liverp.

OGILVIE, Paul Nicholas Felin Bencoed, Llangybi, Pwllheli LL53 6SR — MB ChB 1994 Liverp.

OGILVIE, William Alasdair (retired) 107 Balshagray Avenue, Glasgow G11 7EG Tel: 0141 959 1536 — LRCP LRCS 1942 Ed.; LRCP LRCS Ed. LRFPS Glas. 1942. Prev: Resid. Surg. (ENT) & Resid. Asst. (Out.-Pats.) W.. Infirm. Glas.

***OGILVY, Andrew James** 5 Huntsmans Close, Quorn, Loughborough LE12 8AR — MB ChB 1986 Leeds; FRCA. 1992.

OGILVY, Jennifer Elizabeth 14 Marlborough Square, Clifton Road, Ilkley LS29 8PU Tel: 01943 609424 — MB ChB 1985 Leeds.

OGILVY, Kathleen Mary (retired) 46 Dorward Road, Montrose DD10 8SB Tel: 01674 677633 — MB ChB 1948 Ed. Prev: Assoc. Specialist (Psychiat.) Sunnyside Roy. Hosp. Montrose.

OGILVY-STUART, Amanda Lesley Neonatal Unit, Rosie Hospital, Addenbrooke's NHS Trust, Cambridge CB2 2SW Tel: 01223 245151 Fax: 01223 217064 Email: staurt@addenbrookes.nhs.uk — BM 1983 Soton.; FRCP 2001; DM Soton. 1994; MRCP (UK) 1987; MRCPCH 1996. (Soton.) Cons. Neonatologist Addenbrooke's NHS Trust Camb. Socs: MRCPCH; Eur. Soc. Paediat. Endocrinol.; Brit. Soc. Paediat. Endocrinol. & Diabetes. Prev: Clin. Lect. (Paediat.) Univ. of Oxf.; Clin. Research Fell. (Paediat. Endocrinol.) Christie Hosp. & Holt Radium Inst. Manch.; Regist. (Paediat.) Taranaki Base Hosp. New Plymouth, NZ.

OGLE, John Lambert The Health Centre, Mill Lane, Cannington, Bridgwater TA5 2HB Tel: 01278 652335; Old Vicarage, Bromfield, Bridgwater TA5 2EQ Tel: 01823 451296 — MB BS 1973 Lond.; MRCS 1973 Eng.; DRCOG 1979; DA 1981 Eng.; LRCP 1973 Lond.; DA Eng. 1981; DRCOG 1979; MRCS Eng. LRCP Lond. 1973. (Guy's) Mem. S. W. MREC; Mem. Plymouth LREC. Socs: BMA; Plymouth Med. Soc. (Ex. Hon. Sec.). Prev: Med. Off. Roy. Geogr. Expedition to Borneo 1978.

OGLESBY, Alfred Ian 20 School Lane, Copmanthorpe, York YO23 3SG — MB ChB 1959 Leeds.

OGLESBY, Angela Jane 3 Farquhar Street, Newcastle upon Tyne NE2 2JJ Tel: 0191 281 2438 — MB BS 1993 Newc.; FRCS (Ed) 1998. Specialist Regist. A & E Med., Edin.

OGLESBY, Stuart David 39 Kildonan Road, Warrington WA4 2LJ — MB ChB 1995 Dundee.

OGLETHORPE, Rachel Jane Lindsay Department of Child and Family Psychiatry, 187 Old Rutherglen Road, Gorbals, Glasgow G5 0RE Tel: 0141 300 6360 Fax: 0141 300 6399 — MB ChB 1977 Birm.; MSc 2001 University of Prtsmouth; MRCPsych 1986. (University of Birmingham) p/t Cons. (Child Psychiat.) Dept. Child & Family Psychiat. Yorkhill NHS Trust Glas. Prev: Sen. Regist. (Child. & Adolesc. Psychiat.) WhitCh. Hosp. Cardiff & Roy. Hosp. Sick Childr. Edin.; Regist. (Psychiat.) Roy. Edin. Hosp. & WhitCh. Hosp. Cardiff; SHO (Paediat.) E. Birm. Hosp. & Bristol Roy. Hosp. Sick Childr.

OGLEY, Reginald 3 North Avenue, Ashbourne DE6 1EZ — MRCS Eng. LRCP Lond. 1942. (Univ. Coll. Hosp.) Prev: Ho. Surg. Leic. Roy. Infirm.; Obst. Ho. Surg. Matern. Hosp. Darlington; Capt. R.A.M.C. 1942-6.

OGSTON, Professor Derek, CBE (retired) 64 Rubislaw Den S., Aberdeen AB15 4AY Tel: 01224 316587 — MB ChB Aberd. 1957; DSc Aberd. 1975, PhD 1962, MD 1969; FRCP Lond. 1977, M 1967; FRCP Ed. 1973, M 1963; DTM & H Ed. 1959. Prev: Prof. Med. Univ. Aberd.

OGSTON, Keith Nicholas 64 Rubislaw Den S., Aberdeen AB15 4AY — MB ChB 1992 Aberd.

OGUEH, Onome All Saints Hospital, Magpie Hall Road, Chatham ME4 5NG Tel: 01634 407311 — MB BS 1986 Ibadan; MRCOG 1992.

OGUFERE, Mr Wallace Edafe Department of Ortropoedic Surgery, University Hospital, Lewishom High St., London SE13 6LH Email: wojufere@aol.com; 51 Uphill Grove, Mill Hill, London NW7 4NH — MB BS 1985 Benin; MB BS Benin, Nigeria 1985; FRCS Ed. 1992; FRCS (Trauma & Orth.) 1998. (University of Berlin Teaching Hospital, Bernin, Higeria) Cons. Orthop. Surg., Univ. Hosp. Lewisham. Prev: Specialist Regist. N. W. Thames Rotat.

OGUGUA, Viviene Obeagali 90 Wakeman Road, London NW10 5DH — MB ChB 1994 Bristol; MRCP Paeds. 1998.

OGUNBIYI, Mr Olagunju Adeolo Royal Free & University College Medical School, University Department of Surgery, Royal Free Hospital, Pond St., London NW3 2QG Tel: 020 7794 0500 Ext: 8666 Fax: 0870 162 3930 Email: ogunbiyi@dircon.co.uk, oogunbiyi@rfc.ucl.ac.uk; Email: ogunbiyi@dircon.co.uk — MB BS 1986 Lond.; CCST 1998; FRCS Eng. 1990; MD (Sheffield) 1994.

OGUNBIYI

(Charing Cross Hosp. Univ. of Lond) Sen. Lect./Cons. Surg. - colorectal Surg. Roy. Free & Univ. Coll. Sch. of Med. Socs: FRCS; Brit. Assn. of Surg. Oncol.; Assn. of coloProctol. of GB & Ire. Prev: Cold Rectal Fell. - The Roy. Lond. Hosp. 1997 - 1999; Lect./Sen. Regist. - The Univ. of Birm. In Surg. at Qu. Eliz. Hosp. Birm.; Colorectal Fell. - Washington Univ. Sch. of Med. St. Louis, Missouri, USA, 1995-97.

OGUNBIYI, Mr Theophilus Ayo James 28 Regent House, 43 Windsor Way, London W14 0UB — BM BCh 1961 Oxf.; FRCS Eng. 1966.

OGUNDIPE, Enitan Modupe Flat G01, Beaux Arts Building, Manor Gardens, London N7 6JY — MB BS 1985 Lagos; MRCP (UK) 1993. Clin. Research Fell. & Lect. (Child Health) King's Coll. Sch. Med. & Dent. UMDS Lond. Prev: Regist. (Paediat. & Neonat.) Lewisham Hosp.; SHO (Paediat.) N.wick Pk. Hosp. & King's Coll. Hosp. Lond.

OGUNLESI, Tolulola Olusesan Olusola Newland Avenue Surgery, 239-243 Newland Avenue, Hull HU5 2EJ Tel: 01482 448456 Fax: 01482 449536; 239-243 Newland Avenue, Hull HU5 2EJ Tel: 01482 448456 — MB BS 1967 Lond.

OGUNMUYIWA, Taiwo Adeyemi (retired) 125 Godric Crescent, New Addington, Croydon CR0 0HS Tel: (0802) 482816 — MB ChB Glas. 1967; DPH Glas. 1976. Prev: Dir. Health Servs. Univ. Lagos. Nigeria.

OGUNNAIKE, Olufemi Babatunde 390 Wells Road, Knowle, Bristol BS4 2QP — MB ChB 1970 Bristol; MRCS Eng. LRCP Lond. 1969; FFA RCSI 1975.

OGUNREMI, Adeyemi Oluwakemi Department of Obstetrics & Gynaecology, Farnborough Hospital, Orpington BR6 8ND — MB BS 1986 Ibadan; MRCOG 1994.

OGUNSANWO, Olugbenga Adeleke Olarewaju HM Prison Service HQ, Cleland House, Page St., London SW1P 4LN Tel: 020 7217 3000 — MB BS 1979 Ibadan; MRCOG 1985. Health Care Adviser (Princip. Med. Off.) Directorate of Health Care (S.) HM Prison HQ. Socs: Med. Protec. Soc.; BMA; Eur. Assn. Obst. and Gyn. Prev: Sen. Med. Off. HM Prison Swaleside, E.Ch., Kent; Locum Cons. O & G P.ss Roy. Hosp. Haywards Heath; Regist. (O & G) Cuckfield Hosp. Haywards Heath & MusGr. Pk. Hosp. Taunton.

OGUNYANKIN, Olufunso Kofoworola UCLA School of Medicine, Cardiology Section (111E), VAMC, 11301 Wilshire Boulevard, Los Angeles CA 90073, USA Tel: 00 1 310 2683643 Fax: 00 1 310 2684288; 11 Blurton Road, London E5 0NL — MB BS 1985 Lagos; MRCP (UK) 1991. Fell. (Cardiol.) UCLA Sch. Med. Los Angeles, USA. Prev: Fell. (Cardiol.) Nassau Co. Med. Center Long Is., NY, USA; Resid. (Internal Med.) State Univ. New York, Stony Brook, USA; Regist. (Med.) Brook Hosp. Lond.

OGUNYEMI, Olufemi Ayotunde Odunayo 9 St David's Place, Hendon, London NW4 3PJ — MB BS 1983 Ibadan; DA (UK) 1990.

OGUZ, Cenk Flat 1, 58 Fitzjohns Ave, Hampstead, London NW3 5LT — MB BS 1997 Lond.

OH, Colin Joo Eong The Oaks Surgery, Applegarth Avenue, Park Barn, Guildford GU2 8LZ Tel: 01483 563424 Fax: 01483 563789; Langley House, Gasden Copse, Witley, Godalming GU8 5QE — MB BS 1988 Lond.; DRCOG 1991.

OH, Sarah Yung An 9 Albany Court, 48 Oatlands Dr, Weybridge KT13 9JF — BM 1997 Soton.

OH, Vernon Min-Sen F & G Block, Level 2, Addenbrookes Hospital, Hills Road, Cambridge CB2 2QQ — MD 1979 Camb.; MB BChir 1972; FRCP Lond. 1987; MRCP (UK) 1974.

OHAISEADHA, Coilin Oscar Department of Paediatrics, Taunton & Somerset Hospital, Musgrove Park, Taunton TA1 5DA — MB BCh BAO 1989 NUI. SHO (Anaesth.) Nottm. City Hosp.

OHIORENOYA, Mr Bamidele Accident & Emergency Department, Arrowe Park Hospital, Arrowe Park Road, Upton, Wirral CH49 5PE Tel: 0151 678 5111 Fax: 0151 604 7114; Email: defeohio@doctors.org.uk — MB BCh 1980 Wales; BSc (Hons.) Salford 1975; FRCS Ed. 1988; FFAEM 1995. (Cardiff) Cons. A & E Arrowe Pk. Hosp. Wirral Merseyside. Socs: Brit. Assn. Accid. & Emerg. Med.; Hosp. Cons. & Spec. Assn.; Fell. Fac. Acc. & Emmerg. Med. Prev: Sen. Regist. (A & E) Bristol Roy. Infirm. & Frenchay Hosp. Bristol; Regist. (A & E) Wythenshawe Hosp. Manch.; Regist. (Gen. Surg.) Bolton Gen. Hosp. & Bolton Roy. Infirm.

OHLSEN, John Christopher 26 The Heights, London SE7 8JH — MB ChB 1983 Birm.

OHLSSON, Victoria 14 The Cottages, Station Road, Wrington, Bristol BS40 5LH Tel: 01934 863729 — BM BS 1995 Nottm.; MRCPCH Lond. 1999. (Nottingham)

OHRI, Anil Kumar Elephanta, 18 Courtney Road, London SW19 2ED Tel: 020 8543 4804 — BM 1989 Soton. SHO Rotat. (Surg.) St. Geo. Hosp. Lond. Prev: SHO (Surg.) Roy. Marsden Hosp.; Anat. Prosector Oxf. Univ.; SHO (Orthop.) Qu. Eliz. Milit. Hosp. Lond.

OHRI, Chandrika K Ardoch Medical Centre, 6 Ardoch Grove, Cambuslang, Glasgow G72 8HA Tel: 0141 641 3729 Fax: 0141 641 4339 — MB BS 1969 Bombay; MB BS 1969 Bombay.

OHRI, Kamal Mohan Ardoch Medical Centre, 6 Ardoch Grove, Cambuslang, Glasgow G72 8HA Tel: 0141 641 3729 Fax: 0141 641 4339; 52 Hamilton Avenue, Pollokshields, Glasgow G41 4HD Tel: 0141 427 6503 — MB BS 1972 All India Med. Scis.; MF HOM Faculty of Homoeopathy 1986. Socs: BMA; Fac. of Homoeopathy (Mem.).

OHRI, Prem Nath Department of Medicine and Care of the Elderly, Ysbyty Gwynedd, Bangor LL57 2PW Tel: 01248 384384 Fax: 01286 674680; Bryn Awel, 3 Rhoslan, Penrhosgarnedd, Bangor LL57 2NH Tel: 01248 353984 — MB BS 1975 Rajasthan. Assoc. Specialist (Med. & c/o Elderly) Gwynedd Hosp. Trust. Prev: Regist. (Geriat.) St. David's Hosp. Bangor; Clin. Asst. (Geriat.) Dist. Gen. Hosp. Bangor.

OHRI, Rita 107 Harley Street, London W1N 1DG Tel: 020 7580 3614 Fax: 020 7935 5187 — MB BCh 1972 Wales; FRCS Ed. 1981; FRCOphth.; DO Lond. 1979. Cons. Ophth. Surg. Whipps Cross Hosp. Lond. Socs: Roy. Soc. Med. Prev: Sen. Regist. W.. Ophth. Hosp. & Moorfields Eye Hosp.

OHRI, Mr Sunil Kumar Wessex Cardiothoracic Unit, Southampton General Hospital, Tremona Road, Southampton SO16 6YD Tel: 02380 796233 Fax: 02380 796614; Hamtun House, 9A Westrow Rd, Banister Park, Southampton SO15 2NA Tel: 02380 630885 Email: sohri.rph@excite.co.uk — MB BS 1985 Lond.; MD Lond. 1994; FRCS (Cth.) 1996; FRCS Eng. 1989; FRCS Ed. 1989. Cons. Cardiac Surg. Dept. fo Cardiothoracic Surg., Soton. Gen. Hosp., Soton., Hants.; Hon. Clin. Sen. Lect., Univ. of S.ampton. Socs: Soc. Cardiothoracic Surgs. GB & Irel.; Brit. Cardiac Soc.; Internat. Mem. Soc. Thoracic Surgs. (USA). Prev: Sen. Regist. (Cardiothoracic) Harefield Hosp. Middlx.; Sen. Regist. (Cardiac Surg.) Middlx. Hosp. Lond.; Sen. Regist. (Cardiac Surg.) Hammersmith Hosp. Lond.

OHUIGINN, Peadar South Croydon Medical Practice, 96 Brighton Road, South Croydon CR2 6AD Tel: 020 8688 0875; 50 Coombe Road, Croydon CR0 5SG — MB BCh BAO 1978 NUI. Socs: BMA. Prev: Trainee GP Redhill VTS; SHO (O & G) Wexford Gen. Hosp.; Ho. Surg. St. Vincents Hosp. Dub.

OIEN, Karin Anne University Department of Pathology, Western Infirmary, Dumbarton Road, Glasgow G11 6NT Tel: 0141 211 2473 Email: k.oien@clinmed.gla.ac.uk — MB ChB 1992 Glas.; BSc (Hons.) Glas. 1989; DRCPath 1997. (Univ. Glas.) CRC Clin. Research Fell. Univ. of Glas.; Hon. Specialist Regist. (Histopathol.) W.ern Infirm. Glas.

OJAGBEMI, Festus Oluwole 101 Hathaway Crescent, Manor Park, London E12 6LS — MB BS 1987 Benin.

OJAR, Davendra Hari 45/10 Caledonian Crescent, Edinburgh EH11 2AQ — MB BS 1988 W. Indies.

OJEDA DE LA PENA, Alicia 31 Castlegrange Close, Moreton, Wirral CH46 3SX — LMS 1993 Salamanca.

OJHA, Abha The Surgery, 119 Sheldon Health Road, Sheldon, Birmingham B26 2DB Tel: 0121 784 5465; The Surgery, 196 Green Lane, Castle Bromwich, Birmingham B36 0BU Tel: 0121 749 5115 Fax: 0121 749 5198 — MB BS 1982 Rajasthan; MRCOG 1992. Socs: Fac. Family Plann. Prev: Trainee GP Altrincham VTS; SHO (O & G) Roy. Oldham Hosp. & Hull Matern. Hosp.; SHO (Radiother. & Oncol.) P.ss Roy. Hosp. Hull.

OJHA, Rekha Rani 274 Union Road, Oswaldtwistle, Accrington BB5 3JB Tel: 01254 232351; 3 The Pastures, Beardwood, Blackburn BB2 7QR Tel: 01254 682575 — MBBS 1970; MBBS DRCOG FPCert. DFFP Roy. Coll. Obst. & Gyn. London. (Darbharga Medical College, Caheriasarai) GP Princip.; Clin. Med. Off., Family Plann. and Sexual Health of Hythe & Bury Community Clinic. Prev: CMO in Basic Advanced Centre, Blackburn; CMO at Accrington Surg. Dept., Vict. Hosp., Accrington.

OJI, Mr Erasmus Oluchukwu Eye Department, Rotherham District General Hospital, Moorgate Road, Rotherham S60 2UD Tel: 01709 820000; 369 Fulwood Road, Sheffield S10 3BS Tel: 0114 266 1360 — MRCS Eng. LRCP Lond. 1970; PhD Lond. 1980; BSc Ibadan 1966; FRCS Eng. 1976; DO Eng. 1974. (St. Mary's Hosp. Med. Sch. Lond.) Cons. Ophth. Surg. Rotherham Dist. Gen. Hosp.; Sen. Regist. Moorfields Eye Hosp. Lond. Socs: FRCOphth. Prev: Prof. Ophth. Univ. of Jos, Nigeria; Chief Med. Dir. Jos Teach. Hosp.; Dean Fac. Med. Scs. Univ. of Jos, Nigeria.

OJI, Mr Kalu Nwokeka 42 Fairview Road, London N15 6LJ Tel: 020 8802 6015 — LRCPI & LM, LRSCI & LM 1953; LRCPI & LM, LRCSI & LM 1953; FRCS Ed. 1967. (RCSI)

OJO, Mr Akinyede Abraham 51A Nicoll Road, London NW10 9AT — MB BS 1975 Lagos; FRCS Eng. 1983.

OJO, Mr Babatunde Abiodun RM175 Block 18, The University, Sunderland SR2 7PS — MB ChB 1986 Obafemi Awolowu Univ. Nigeria; MB ChB Obafemi Awolowu U Nigeria 1986; FRCSI 1993.

OJO, Oluropo Ebenezer 23 Bunkers Hill, Lincoln LN2 4QS — MB BS 1978 Nigeria.

OJO-AROMOKUDU, Mr Olumuyiwa Olugbenga 7 Hillside Grove, Mill Hill, London NW7 2LS — MB BS 1987 Ibadan; MB BS Ibadan, Nigeria 1987; MSc (Surgic. Sci.) Lond. 1997; FRCS Ed. 1995. Specialist Regist. Rotat. (Surg.) N. Thames. Prev: Specialist Regist. (Gen. Surg.) Edgware Gen. Hosp.; Research Regist. Middlx. Hosp. Univ. Coll. Lond.; Specialist Regist. Hemel Hempstead Gen. Hosp.

OJUKWU, Clifford Ikechukwu Gynaecology Department, Alexandra Hospital, Woodrow Drive, Redditch B98 7UB Tel: 01527 503030 Fax: 01527 512004 Email: cojukwu@aol.com; 114 Mercot Close, Redditch B98 7YY — MB BS 1984 Ibadan; MB BS Ibadan, Nigeria 1984; MFFP 1995; MRCOG 1992. Staff Grade, Obst. of Gyn., Alexandra Hosp., Redditch. Worcs.. Socs: Brit. Med. Assoc; Brit. Menopause Soc.; Bist. Soc. of Colposcopy & Cervical Path.

OJUKWU, Nnaemeka Jonathan St. Bartholmew's Surgery, 292A Barking Road, London E6 3BA Tel: 020 8472 0669 — FMCOG 1989; MB BS Nigeria 1975; DFFP 1996; DRCOG 1987. Socs: Fell. Med. Coll. Obst. & Gyn. Nigeria. Prev: SHO (O & G) Char. Cross Hosp. Lond., Barking Hosp. & N. Middlx. Hosp. Lond.

OJURO, Mr Ifeanyi Valentine c/o Mr J. Ukemenam, 7 Oxford Road, London E15 1DD — MB BS 1987 Nigeria; FRCS Glas. 1995.

OKAFOR, Mr Benignus Emeka 3 Sellincourt Road, Tooting, London SW17 9RX — MB BS 1987 Lond.; FRCS Eng. 1991. (St. Bart.) Regist. Rotat. (Orthop.) Roy. Nat. Orthop. Hosp. & Basildon & OldCh. Hosps. Socs: BMA.

OKAGBUE, Mr Chuma Ernest 10 Lake Way, Huntingdon PE29 6SU — MB BS 1977 Ibadan; FRCS Ed. 1992.

OKARO, Chukwuemeka Obianagha 2 Crescent Lodge, 15 Sunningfields Crescent, Hendon, London NW4 4RD — MB BS 1991 Nigeria.

OKE, Anthony Olawale 56 Kingfisher Grove, Lower Grange, Bradford BD8 0NP — MB ChB 1985 Ife, Nigeria; MRCPI 1994.

OKE, Olatokunbo Olutayo 23 Elmar Road, London N15 5DH Email: tayo@globalnet.co.uk — MB BS 1987 Ibadan; FRCS (Gen.Surg.); MMed Sc 2000 Keele; FRCS Ed. 1993. (Univ. Coll. Hosp. Ibadan) Gen. Surg. and ColoprOtol., Qu. Eliz. Hosp. Woolwich Lond. Socs: BMA; Assoc. of Surg.s in Train.; W Midl.s Surg. Soc. Prev: Specialist Regist. Stafford Cen. Hosp Stafford (Gen. Surg.); Specialist Regist. N. Staffs. Hospl Stoke-On-Trent (Gen. Surg.); Specialist Regist. Walsall Manor Hosp., Walsall (Gen. Surg.).

OKE, Peter Thompson (retired) 15 Gospelgate, Louth LN11 9JX Tel: 01507 602303 — MB BS 1957 Lond.; MRCS Eng. LRCP Lond. 1957. Prev: Ho. Surg. (Gyn.) & Resid. Obst. Off. Char. Cross Hosp. Lond.

OKE, Sarah Cecile Barrow Hospital, Barrow Gurney, Bristol BS48 3SG Tel: 01275 392811 — MB BS 1984 Lond.; BSc Lond. 1981; MRCPsych 1988. Cons. Psychiat. Barrow Hosp. Bristol (Mother & Baby Unit). Prev: Sen. Regist. Rotat. (Psychiat.) Exeter; SHO Rotat. (Psychiat.) St. Mary's Hosp. Lond. W2.

OKEAHIALAM, Majella Gerard Department of Obstetrics & Gynaecology, Bradford Royal Infirmary, Duckworth Lane, Bradford BD9 6RJ Tel: 01274 542200; 33 Aireville Avenue, Bradford BD9 4ER — MB BS 1982 Nigeria; MRCOG 1992. (Univ. Nigeria) Staff Grade Pract. (O & G) Bradford Roy. Infirm. Socs: Fell. W. Afr.

Coll. Surgs. (Obst. & Gyn. Sect.); BMA; Eur. Assn. Gyn. & Obst. Prev: Regist. (O & G) E. Glam. Gen. Hosp. Pontypridd.

OKECH, Mark Nuffield College of Surgical Sciences, Royal College of Surgeons of England, Lincoln's Inn Field, London WC2A 3PE — MB ChB 1968 East Africa.

OKELL, Roger William Grove Cottage, Chester Road, Acton, Nantwich CW5 8LD — MB ChB 1980 Manch.; MRCP (UK) 1988; FFA RCS Eng. 1985. Cons. Anaesth. Leighton Hosp. Crewe. Prev: Sen. Regist. (Anaesth.) Univ. Hosp. Wales; Sen. Regist. (Anaesth.) Gwynedd Hosp. Bangor; Regist. (Anaesth.) Arrowe Pk. Hosp. Wirral, BRd.green Hosp. Liverp. & Walton Hosp. Liverp.

OKEREKE, Robert Amobi 8 Holt Way, Holt Park, Leeds LS16 7QP Tel: 0113 267 6400 — MB BS 1978 Ibadan; MRCOG 1989.

OKHAH, Mr Michael Flat 1, Bridge Hey, Walton Hospital, Rice Lane, Liverpool L9 1AE — MB BS 1985 Ibadan; FRCS Ed. 1993.

OKHAI, Abdul Aziz Hassam 43 Dundee Road, Broughty Ferry, Dundee DD5 1NA Tel: 01382 739673 — MB ChB 1966 St. And. (St. And.)

OKHAI, Muhammed Farouk Department of Psychological Treatment Services, Addenbrookes Hospital, PO Box 190, Hills Road, Cambridge CB2 2QQ — MB ChB 1977 Dundee.

OKHANDIAR, Ashok Department of Haematology, Royal Hospital Haslar, Gosport PO12 2AA Tel: 01705 584255 Fax: 01705 762549 Email: okhandiar@haslar.demon.co.uk; Aashray, 1 Shorwell Place, Lakeside, Brierley Hill DY5 3TZ Tel: 01384 486099 — MB BS 1979 Poona; LMSSA Lond. 1985; MRCPath 1993. (Poona, India) Cons. Haemat. Roy. Hosp. Haslar, Gosport. Socs: Brit. Soc. Haematol.; Eur. Haemat. Assn. Prev: Staff Haemat. Russells Hall Hosp. Dudley.

OKHRAVI, Narciss Department of Clinical Ophthalmology, The Institute of Ophthalmology, 11-43 Bath St., London EC1V 9EL Tel: 020 7608 6872 Fax: 020 7608 6931 Email: nokhravi@menu.hgmp.mrc.ac.uk; Flat 72, Elm Quay Court, Nine Elms Lane, London SW8 5DF — MB BS 1989 Lond.; BSc Lond. 1986, MB BS (Hons.) 1989; FRCOphth 1994. Wellcome Vision Research Fell. Inst. Ophth. Lond. Socs: Roy. Soc. Med.; Med. Res. Soc. Prev: SHO (Ophth.) W.. Eye Hosp. Lond. & Roy. Lond. Hosp.; SHO (Neurosurg.) Brook Gen. Hosp. Woolwich.

OKINE, Emmanuel Ashaley Health Centre, Little Lane, South Elmsall, Pontefract WF9 2NJ Tel: 01977 465331 — Artsexamen 1992 Amsterdam. (Amsterdam) GP Pontefract, W. Yorks.

OKOCHA, Chike Oxleas House, Queen Elixabeth Hospital, London SE18 4QH Tel: 020 88366657 Fax: 020 88366659 — MB BS 1985 Ibadan; MB BS Ibadan, Nigeria 1985; PhD Lond. 1996; MRCPsych 1992. (Univ. Coll Hosp. University of Ibadan, Nigeria) Cons. Qu. Eliz. Hosp. Lond. Prev: Hon. Sen. Regist. MRC Unit Psychopharmacol. Inst. Psychiat. Lond.; Research Fell. King's Coll. Hosp. & Inst. of Psychiat.; Child & Adolesc. Psychiat. Elmsleigh Medway Hosp. Kent.

OKOKO, Acha Edegbanya Jeremiah Community Health Sheffield (NHS) Trust, Northern General Hospital, Psychiatric Unit, Sheffield S5 7AU Tel: 01742 716310; 228 Middlewood Road, Sheffield S6 1TE Tel: 01742 853635 — MB BS 1972 Ahmadu Bello Univ. Nigeria; MB BS Ahmadu Nigeria 1972; MRCPsych 1976; DPM Eng. 1977. Cons. Psychiat. N. Gen. Hosp. Sheff. Socs: Fell. Postgrad. Med. Coll. (Psychiat.) Nigeria; BMA; Nigerian Psychiat. Assn. Prev: Sen. Lect. (Psychiat.) Univ. Jos, Nigeria; Chief. Cons. Psychiat. MoH Jos, Nigeria.

OKOLO, Mr Stanley Obiora Department of Obstetrics and Gynaecology, Royal Free Hospital School of Medicine, Pond St., London NW3 2QG Tel: 020 7794 0500 Ext: 6274 Fax: 020 7830 2261 Email: okolo@rfhsm.ac.uk; 68 Northumberland Road, New Barnet, London EN5 1EE Tel: 0378 000097 — BM BCh 1979 Nigeria; MRCOG 1987; FWACS 1985; PhD Lond 1995. Cons Gyn. N. Middlx. Hosp. Lond.; Sen. Lect, Gyn. Roy. Free Hosp. Lond. Socs: ESHRE; RSM; BMS. Prev: Lect./Sen. Regist. Univ. of Bristol; Clin. Research Fell. (Reproduc. Endocrinol.) Roy. Free Hosp. Sch. Med. Lond.; Regist. (O & G) Roy. Sussex Co. Hosp. Brighton.

OKON, Moses Aniedi Abasi Biomedical Research Unit, Jessop Hospital for Women, Leavy Greave Road, Sheffield S3 7RE Tel: 0114 276 6333; 55 Eccleston Road, Kirk Sandall, Doncaster DN3 1NX Tel: 01302 885194 — MB BS 1984 Ibadan; MRCPI 1995; MRCOG 1994. Research Regist. (Biomed. Research) Jessop Hosp. for Wom. Sheff. Socs: BMA; Nigerian Med. Assn.

OKONKWO

OKONKWO, Mr Alfred Chigbo Ogochukwu 14 Southbourne Avenue, Drayton, Portsmouth PO6 2HN — MB BS 1974 Ibadan; FRCS Glas. 1980.

OKONKWO, Ndubisi Azubike 2 Victoria Avenue, London N3 1BD — MB BS 1982 Newc.

OKONKWO, Okechukwu Jonathan 19 Audley Gate, Netherton, Peterborough PE3 9PG Tel: 01733262125 Email: j.okonkwo@aol.com — BM BCh 1978 Nigeria; MFFP 1993; MRCOG 1987. GP; GP Regist., Dr Moyce & Partners, Iakham Med. Pract., Oakham. Prev: Staff Grade (O & G) P'boro. Dist. Hosp.; Regist. (O & G) Rochford & S.end Gen. Hosps.; Tutor (O & G) Aberd. Univ.

OKONKWO, Ozioma Obiageli Flat 23, 48-52 Coram St., Russel Square, London WC1N 1HE — MB BS 1996 Lond.

OKONKWO, Stella Ifeoma Health Centre, Brunswick Park Road, London N11 1EY Tel: 020 8368 1568; 2 Victoria Avenue, Fincheley Central, London N3 1BD — MB BS 1973 Newc.; MRCP (UK) 1977; DCH Eng. 1977. Socs: Fell. Roy. Soc. Med.; BMA. Prev: Lect. & Hon. Cons. Paediat. Univ. Nigeria Teach. Hosp.

OKOREAFFIA, Affia Chidi Athena Medical Centre, 21 Atherden Road, London E5 0QP Tel: 020 8985 6675 Fax: 020 8533 7775 — MRCS Eng. LRCP Lond. 1980. (Sheff.) Prev: SHO (Gen. Surg.) Scunthorpe Gen. Hosp.; SHO (A & E) Chesterfield Roy. Hosp.

OKORIE, N M Okorie, The Health Centre, 1a Ingfield Avenue, Sheffield S9 1WZ Tel: 0114 261 0623 Fax: 0114 261 0949.

OKORO, Disraeli Bemigho 144 Harley Street, London W1N 1AH Fax: 020 7935 5972 — MB BS 1978 Ibadan; MRCOG 1985.

OKORO, Mr Joseph Onyekachi Yare Valley Medical Practice, 202 Thorpe Road, Norwich NR1 1TJ Tel: 01603 437559 Fax: 01603 701773 — MB BCh 1977 Nigeria; FRCS Glas. 1990. Regist. (Gen. Surg.) Watford Gen. Hosp.

OKOSUN, Onoage Henry 81B Lechmere Avenue, Woodford Green IG8 8QG — MB BS 1992 Benin; MRCOG 1992.

OKOYE, David Obiefuna Chukwuemeka Bridge Surgery, St Peters Street, Stapenhill, Burton-on-Trent DE15 9AW Tel: 01283 563631 Fax: 01283 500896 — MB BS 1985 Ibadan; MRCP (UK) 1993; DRCOG 1996. (Ibadan, Nigeria) GP Princip., Bridge Surg., St. Peters St., Stapenhill, Burton-on-Trent. Prev: GP Regist. Measham Med. Unit Swadlincote; SHO Burton Hosp. NHS Trust VTS; Regist. (Cardiol. & Gen. Med.) Roy. Liverp. Univ. NHS Trust.

OKPARA, Mr Cyril Chinaka 109 Spring Street, Rishton, Blackburn BB1 4LP — Vrach 1971 Moscow; Vrach Peoples Friendship Univ. Moscow 1971; FRCSI 1980.

OKUBADEJO, Adedeji Abiodun 183 Woodruff Way, Tame Bridge, Walsall WS5 4SB — MB BS 1987 Lagos, Nigeria.

OKUBADEJO, Adeyoola Adrian Tejumade Peterborough District Hospital, Thorpe Road, Peterborough PE3 6DA Tel: 01733 874000; 50 West End, Langtoft, Peterborough PE6 9LU — MB BS 1986 Lond.; MRCP (UK) 1991. Sen. Regist. (Med. for Elderly) Homerton Hosp. Lond.; Cons. (Med. for Elderly) PeterBoro. Dist. Hosp. Socs: Brit. Geriat. Soc. Prev: Research Regist. (Respirat. Med.) Lond. Chest Hosp.; Regist. (Med.) Basildon Hosp.

OKUBADEJO, Olumade Adetola (retired) 39 Solent Road, Portsmouth PO6 1HH — MD 1966 Lond.; MB BS 1958; FRCPath. 1982, M 1972; DCP Lond 1963. Prev: Dir. Pub. Health Laborat. Portsmouth.

OKUGBENI, Gabriel Itobore 24 Fordyce Road, London SE13 6RH — MB BS 1982 Univ. Nigeria; MRCP (UK) 1994. Staff Grade (Paediat.) Qu. Mary's Univ. Hosp. Lond. Socs: MRCPCH; Coll. Mem. RCP Lond.; Coll. Mem. RCPS & Surg. Glas. Prev: Regist. (Paediat. & Gastroenterol.) Chelsea & W.m. Hosp.; Regist. (Paediat.) Ealing Hosp. Middlx.; SHO (Paediat.) Guy's Hosp. Lond.

OKUN, Taiwo Odion Stepney Green Medical Practice, 45-47 Ben Jonson Road, London E1 4SA Tel: 020 7790 9193 Email: taiokun@hotmail.com — MBBS 1977 Univ. Lagos Nigeria; DFFP. Lond. GP Princip. Lond. Socs: BMA.

OKUNDI, Anne Josephine Adhiambo Flat C, 16 Stoneygate Road, Leicester LE2 2AB — MB ChB 1992 Leic.

OKUNOLA, Olufunmilayo Olayemi 218 Broxburn Drive, South Ockendon RM15 5QY — BM 1995 Soton.

OKUONGHAE, Humphrey Osarenren Obasuyi Department of Paediatrics, Prince Charles Hospital, Merthyr Tydfil CF47 9DT Tel: 01685 721721; 25 Sweetwater Park, Trefechan, Merthyr Tydfil CF48 2LF Tel: 01685 350220 Email: hokuonghae@aol.com — MB BS 1980 Benin; MRCPCH 1996; MSC 1999; FMCPaed 1988; FWACP 1989; MB BS Benin, Nigeria 1980; DCH RCP Lond. 1996. (University Benin College Medicine, Nigeria) Staff Grade Paediat. P. Chas. Hosp. Merthyr Tydfil. Socs: BMA; FWACP W. African Coll. Phys. 1989; Welsh Paediat. Soc. Prev: Hon. Sen. Regist. Liverp. Matern. Hosp.; Cons. & Lect. Jos Univ. Teachg. Hosp., Nigeria.

OKUSI, Dolomena 75 Sarsfield Road, London SW12 8HS — MB BS 1993 Lond.

OKYERE, Kwame Marfo 2 Grace Avenue, OldBrook, Milton Keynes MK6 2XN — MB ChB 1975 Ghana; MB ChB U Ghana 1975. Staff Psychiat. Hellesdon Hosp. Norwich. Socs: Fell. Roy. Soc. Med. Prev: Staff Psychiat. ScarBoro. & NE Yorks. Healthcare NHS Trust.

OLA, Ayodele Olusegun New Medical Centre, 264 Brentwood Road, Romford RM2 5SU Tel: 01708 478800 Fax: 01708 471422 — MB BS 1985 Ibadan; LRCS 1994 England; LMSSA London; MB BS 1985 Ibadan; LRCP London.

OLADIPO, Mr Abiodun 25 Maple Leaf Close, Abbots Langley WD5 0SP — MB BS 1981 Lagos; FRCS Ed. 1995; MFFP 1994; MRCOG 1993. Specialist Regist. (O & G) Roy. United Hosp. Bath; Cons. Gyn. (with s/i in Oncol.) Lead Colposcopist, Roy. coirnwall hosp. Truro, TRI 3LJ. Socs: Brit. Med. Ultrasound Soc.; BMA; Brit. Menopause Soc. Prev: Regist. (O & G) Salisbury Dist. Hosp. & Roy. Gwent Hosp.; SHO Scunthorpe Gen. Hosp.; SpR (Gyn. Unit) Univ. of S.ampton Teachg. Hosp. (P.ss Anne Hosp.) S.ampton.

OLADIPO, Mr James Olarewaju Olagboyega 78 York Road, Linthorpe, Middlesbrough TS5 6LL Tel: 01642 812945 Fax: 01642 812945 — MB BS 1987 Ibadan; FRCS Ed. 1992; FRCS Glas. 1992.

OLÁH, Karl Steven Joseph 56 Dale Street, Rugby CV21 2LP — MB ChB 1984 Birm. Regist. (O & G) Selly Oak Hosp. Birm. Socs: BMA & Med. Protec. Soc. Prev: SHO (O & G) Sorrento Matern. Hosp. Moseley & Selly Oak Hosp.; Birm.; Ho. Off. (Gen. Med.) Walsall Manor Hosp.

OLAITAN, Adeola Flat 13 Northgates, 445 High Road, London N12 0AR — MB BS 1987 Lond.

OLAJIDE, Oladele Olugbenga Maudsley Hospital, Denmark Hill, London SE5 8AZ Tel: 020 7919 2951 Fax: 020 7919 2643 Email: dele.olajide@slam-tr.nhs.uk — MB BS 1977 Ibadan; PhD Lond. 1985; MRCPsych 1987, FRCPsych 1997; T(Psych) 1991. (Ibadan, Nigeria) Cons. Psychiat. Maudsley Hosp. Lond.; Clin. Sen. Lect. Dept. of Psychol. Med. Inst. of Psychiat. Lond.; Hon. Sen. Lect., Inst. of Psychiat., Lond. Socs: Fell. Collegium Internat.e Neuro-Psychopharmacol.; Eur. Coll. Neuropsychopharm.; Brit. Assn. Psychopharmacol. Prev: Cons. Psychiat. & Sen. Lect. Maidstone Priority Care NHS Trust & King's Coll. Hosptial Inst. Psychiat. Lond.

OLAJIDE, Victoria Feyishola South Tyneside District Hospital, Harton Road, South Shields NE34 0PL Tel: 0191 454 8888 Fax: 0191 202 4180; 16 Rothwell Road, Gosforth, Newcastle upon Tyne NE3 1TY Tel: 0191 284 4666 Fax: 0191 285 4820 — MB BS 1978 Ibadan; MB BS (Distinc. Obst. & Gyn.) Ibadan 1978; MRCOG 1986. Cons. O & G S. Tyneside Dist. Hosp. S. Shields. Socs: BMA; Brit. Fertil. Soc. Prev: Cons. O & G Ealing Hosp. Lond.; Lect. P.ss Mary & Roy. Vict. Infirm. Newc.; IVF Research Regist. St. Bart. Hosp. Lond.

OLAKANPU, Obasanmi Andrew 17 Ruskin Court, Winchmore Hill Road, London N21 1QJ — MB BS 1996 Lond.

OLATEJU, Mahmoud Abimbola Olatunji 3 Beachcroft Way, London N19 3HR — MB BS 1963 Lond.

OLAWO, Ayoola Oladoye 78 Bron-y-Nant, Croesnewydd Road, Wrexham LL13 7TZ Tel: 01978 291100 — MB BS 1987 Lagos, Nigeria; MRCOG 1995. (Coll. Med. Univ. Lagos) Specialist Regist. (O & G) Wrexham Maelor Hosp. Prev: Specialist Regist. (O & G) Ysbyty Gwynedd Bangor.

OLAYEMI, Agnes Oaikhohen 80 Hornby House, Clayton St., London SE11 5DB — MB BS 1986 Lond.

OLCZAK, Stephen Andrzej 45 Pilley's Lane, Boston PE21 9RA — MB BS 1975 Lond.; MD Lond. 1984, BSc (1st cl. Hons. Physiol.) 1972; FRCP Lond. 1994; MRCP (UK) 1978. Cons. Phys. Endocrinol. & Diabetes Pilgrim Hosp. Boston.

OLD, Eric Gordon (retired) 1 Glendower Street, Monmouth NP25 3DG Tel: 01600 712582 Email: eric.old@lineone.net — MB BS 1947 Lond.; MRCS Eng. LRCP Lond. 1947; DA Eng. 1966; DObst RCOG 1954. Prev: GP Monmouth.

OLD, Francis Tristram Elm Cottage, Townshend, Hayle TR27 6AG — MB ChB 1998 Leeds.

OLD, Peter John Isle of Wight, Portsmouth & S.E. Hampshire Health Authority, Finchdean House, Milton Road, Portsmouth PO3 3DP Tel: 023 9283 5104 — MB BS 1978 Lond.; LLM Wales 1992; MFPHM RCP (UK) 1993; MRCGP 1984; DCH RCP Lond. 1985; DRCOG 1984. Dir. Pub. Health Isle of Wight Portsmouth & S.E. Hants. Health Auth. Socs: Inst. Health Servs. Managem.; Medico-Legal Soc. Prev: Cons. Pub. Health Med. Soton. & SW Hants. Health Commiss.; GP Gosport; Med. Off. Save Childr. Fund Torit, S. Sudan.

OLD, Sally Emma 1 Merchants Walk, Baldock SG7 6TJ — MB BS 1991 Lond.; MRCP (UK) 1994. SHO (Clin. Oncol.) Mt. Vernon Hosp. Rickmansworth. Socs: Roy. Coll. Phys. Lond.; BMA. Prev: SHO (Med.) Lister Hosp.; SHO (A & E) Luton & Dunstable Hosp.

OLD, Simon Dept. of Anaesthesia, York District Hosp, Wigginton Road, York YO31 8HE Tel: 01904 631313; 16 Penley Grove Street, York YO31 7PN Tel: 01904 639094 Email: alexis_simon.old@virgin.net — MB ChB 1988 Bristol; MA Oxf. 1981; FRCA 1993; DA (UK) 1991. (Brist.) Cons., Anaesth., York Dist. Hosp. Socs: World Anaesth.; Obst. Anaesth. Assn.

OLDALE, Karine Natalie Margaret Yr Hen Efail, Llanllechid, Bangor LL57 3LE — MB BS 1994 Lond.; BSc Lond. 1990. SHO (Paediat.) Ysbyty Glan Clwyd Bodelwyddan.

OLDALE, Mark Jonathan 69 Adswood Road, Cheadle Hulme, Cheadle SK8 5QY — MB ChB 1998 Manch.

OLDAY, Susan Jane Flat 1, 17 Granville Terrace, Edinburgh EH10 4PQ — MB ChB 1990 Leeds; FRCA 1996.

OLDERSHAW, Catherine Mary 5 Park Close, Sonning Common, Reading RG4 9RY — MB ChB 1984 Bristol.

OLDERSHAW, Kenneth Leslie 6 Honor Oak, London SE23 3SF — MB BS 1949 Lond.; MRCGP 1968; DObst RCOG 1954. (Lond. Hosp.) Socs: BMA. Prev: Receiv. Room Off. Lond. Hosp.; Obst. Ho. Off. Roy. Berks. Hosp.

OLDERSHAW, Paul John 76 Carlton Hill, London NW8 0ET — MD 1991 Camb.; MB 1974, BChir 1973; FRCP Lond. 1990; MRCP (UK) 1975. (St. Thos. & Camb.) Cons. (Cardiol.) Brompton Hosp. Lond.; SHO & Regist. (Cardiol.) Brompton Hosp. Lond. Socs: Fell.Amer. Coll. of Cardiol. (FACC); Fell.Europ. Soc. of Cardiol. (FESC). Prev: Sen. Regist. (Cardiol.) St. Geo. Hosp. Lond.

OLDERSHAW, William Henry (retired) 23 Conalan Avenue, Sheffield S17 4PG Tel: 0114 235 2272 — MB ChB 1940 Sheff.; MFOM RCP Lond. 1978; Specialist Accredit (Occupat. Med.) RCP Lond.

OLDFIELD, Jessica Ann 72 Doeford Close, Culcheth, Warrington WA3 4DL — MB ChB 1998 Liverp.

OLDFIELD, Matthew David 42 Wellington Crescent, Shipley BD18 3PH — MB ChB 1992 Leic.; MRCP. SHO (Med. & Endocrinol.) Leicester.; Research Regist., Austin, Melbourne, Australia. Prev: Specialist Regist., Diabetes & Endociolgy.

OLDFIELD, Paul Douglas Weaverham Surgery, Northwich Road, Weaverham, Northwich CW8 3EU Tel: 01606 852168 Fax: 01606 854980 Email: oldfieldmanor@aol.com; Email: oldfieldmanor@aol.com — MB ChB Liverp. 1969; MRCGP 1977; DObst RCOG 1972. (Liverp.) GP; Clin. Asst. in Med., Vict. Infirm., N.wich. Socs: N.wich Med. Soc.; Sec. N.wich Med. Soc.

OLDFIELD, Raymond Henry 18 Roles Grove, Chadwell Heath, Romford RM6 5LT — MB BS 1950 Lond.; MRCS Eng. LRCP Lond. 1946. (St. Thos.)

OLDFIELD, William Laurence George 21 Queens Anne's Gardens, Ealing, London W5 5QD — MB BS Lond. 1992; MSc Human & Applied Physiol. Lond. 1987, BSc (Hons.) 1985; MRCP (UK) 1995. Clin. Research Fell. Dept. Allergy Clin. Immunol. Nat. Heart & Lung Inst. Lond. Prev: Regist. (Respirat. Med.) Char. Cross. Hosp. Lond.; SHO (Med.) Hammersmith Hosp. Lond.

OLDHAM, Barbara Firwood, Leycester Road, Knutsford WA16 8QR — MB ChB Manch. 1949; MRCS Eng. LRCP Lond. 1947.

OLDHAM, Eileen Patricia (retired) Gorsebank, 152 Upton Road, Bidston, Prenton CH43 7QG Tel: 0151 652 4579 — MB ChB 1950 Liverp.

OLDHAM, John, OBE Oldham and Partners, Manor House Surgery, Manor Street, Glossop SK13 8PS — MB ChB 1977 Manch.; MBA (Distinc.) Manch. 1992; MRCGP 1981; DCH Eng. 1980. GP Glossop; Nat. Primary Care Developm. Team, NHS. Prev: Med. Adviser Mersey RHA; Med. Adviser Primary Care Div. NHS Exec. HQ; Fac. Mem. Inst. of Health Care.

OLDHAM, Jonathan Richard Dial House Medical Centre, 131 Mile End Lane, Offerton, Stockport SK2 6BZ Tel: 0161 456 9905 Fax: 0161 456 7127 — MB ChB 1975 Manch.; MRCGP 1986.

OLDHAM, Judith Caroline Mount Pleasant Practice, Tempest Way, Chepstow NP16 5XR Tel: 01291 636500 Fax: 01291 636518 — MB ChB 1977 Manch. Prev: Clin. Asst., Dermat., Bristol.

OLDHAM, Kenneth William (retired) Three Gables, 53 Wrenbeck Drive, Otley LS21 2BP Tel: 01943 464914 — MRCS Eng. LRCP Lond. 1944; DA Eng. 1954. Asst. Anaesth. N.ampton & Dist. Gp. Hosps. Prev: Regist. (Anaesth.) St. Peter's Hosp. Chertsey.

OLDHAM, Mary Marian New Cross Surgery, 48 Sway Road, Morriston, Swansea SA6 6HR Tel: 01792 771419 — MB BCh 1972 Wales; MRCGP 1976; DObst RCOG 1974. (Welsh National School of Medicine) Socs: BMA. Prev: Clin. Med. Off. W. Glam. AHA; SHO (Cas.) Singleton Hosp. Swansea; SHO (Paediat.) Morriston Hosp. Swansea.

OLDHAM, Roger Department of Rheumatology, University Hospitals of Leicester NHS Trust, Leicester Royal Infirmary, Infirmary Square, Leicester LE1 5WW Tel: 0116 254 1414 Fax: 0116 258 6992 Email: roldham@talk21.com; Tel: 0116 259 2377 Email: roldham@talk21.com — MB BS 1969 Lond.; BSc (Hons.) Lond. 1966; FRCP Ed. 1995; FRCP Lond. 1992; MRCP (UK) 1974; MRCS Eng. LRCP Lond. 1969. (Char. Cross) Cons. Rheum. Univ. Hosp.s of Leicester NHS Trust. Socs: Brit. Soc. Rheum.; Leic. Med. Soc. Prev: Sen. Regist. (Med.) Leicester Roy. Infirm.; Regist. (Med.) Groby Rd. Hosp. Leicester; Ho. Surg. & Ho. Phys. Char. Cross Hosp. Gp.

OLDHAM, Rosemary Ann Stepping Hill Hospital, Poplar Grove, Stockport SK2 7SE Tel: 0161 483 1010; 16 Gladstone Road, Sheffield S10 3GT Tel: 0114 230 2884 — MB ChB 1997 Manch. SNO Adult Med., Stepping Hill Hosp. Stockport.

OLDHAM, Thomas Anthony 12 The Avenue, Whitchurch, Cardiff CF14 2EG — MB BS 1989 Lond.

OLDHAM, Trevor Peter Bridgegate Medical Centre, Winchester Street, Barrow-in-Furness LA13 9SH Tel: 01229 820304 Fax: 01229 836984; Dove Cottage, Aldingham, Ulverston LA12 9RT — MB ChB 1976 Birm.; MRCP (UK) 1982; DCH Eng. 1981.

OLDING, Ronald Brendan Haldens Surgery, 106 Haldens, Welwyn Garden City AL7 1DG Tel: 01707 323045 Fax: 01707 717569; 16B Woodside Road, Digswell, Welwyn AL6 0DR — MB BChir 1984 Camb.; MB BChir Camb. 1985; BA (Hons.) Camb. 1982; MRCGP 1988; DRCOG 1988. (Camb.) Tutor (Gen. Pract.) Welwyn Garden City. Socs: RCP. Prev: Lect. (Gen. Pract.) UMDS Lond.; Med. Off. Homeless & Rootless Leeds.

OLDMAN, Lynne Elizabeth Lyndhurst, 34 Newfield Road, West Hagley, Stourbridge DY9 0JR — MB ChB 1985 Birm.; MRCGP 1990; DRCOG 1988.

OLDMAN, Matthew John Derriford Hospital, Plymouth PL6 8DH; Delamere, The Common, Shotesham All Saints, Norwich NR15 1YD Email: oldman@globalnet.co.uk — MB BS 1994 Lond. (St Georges Hosp.) Specialist Regist. Anaesth. Derriford Hosp., Plymouth. Prev.: SHO Neonat. Med., Roy. Devon & Exeter Hosp.; SHO Anaesth. Roy. Devon & Exeter Hosp.; Sen. Ho. Off., Elderly Med. Roy. Devon & Exeter Hosp.

OLDREIVE, Peter David (retired) Wildwood, 85 Island Road, Sturry, Canterbury CT2 0EF Tel: 01227 710232 — BM BCh 1958 Oxf.

OLDREY, Timothy Branston Nugent, Brigadier late RAMC (retired) The Cottage, Figheldean, Salisbury SP4 8JJ — MB BS Lond. 1966; FRCP Lond. 1985; MRCP (UK) 1973; MRCS Eng. LRCP Lond. 1966. Prev: Dir. of Army Med. & Cons. Phys. to Army.

OLDRING, John Kennett Orchard Medical Practice, Orchard Road, Broughton Astley, Leicester LE9 6RG Tel: 01445 282599 Fax: 01445 286772; The White House, Main St, Ullesthorpe, Lutterworth LE17 5BT Tel: 01455 209337 — MRCS Eng. LRCP Lond. 1976; MA, BM BCh Oxf. 1976; MRCGP 1982; DRCOG 1982. GP Ullesthorpe.

OLDROYD, David The General Medical Centre, Surgery Lane, Hartlepool TS24 9DN Tel: 01429 266148 Fax: 01429 222416; Avis House, High Throston, Hartlepool TS26 0UG — MB ChB 1960 Birm.

OLDROYD, David Anthony Falsgrave Surgery, 33 Falsgrave Road, Scarborough YO12 5EA Tel: 01723 360835 Fax: 01723 503220; Overgreen Farm, Overgreen Lane, Burniston, Scarborough YO13 0HY Tel: 01723 870039 — MB BS Lond. 1971. (St. Thos.)

OLDROYD

OLDROYD, Glenda Jacqueline 2 Highfold, Yeadon, Leeds LS19 7DN — MB ChB 1983 Leeds; FRCA 1991. (Leeds) Cons. Anaesth. Bradford Hosps NHS Trust.

OLDROYD, Keith George Department of Medical Cardiology, Hairmyres Hospital, East Kilbride, Glasgow G75 8RG Tel: 01355 72636 Email: k.g.oldroyd@virgin.net; 5 Hamilton Drive, Cambuslang, Glasgow G72 8JG Tel: 0141 641 3759 — MB BS 1982 Aberd.; MB ChB Aberd. 1982; FRCP (Glas.) 1998; MD (Hons.) Aberd. 1993; MRCP (UK) 1985. Cons. Phys. & Cardiol. Hairmyres Hosp. E. Kilbride. Socs: Brittsh Cardiac Soc.; Scott. Cardiac Soc. Prev: Clin. Lect. (Med. Cardiol.) Glas. Roy. Infirm. & Univ. Glas.; Fell. Dept. of Cardiol., Toronto Gen. Hosp..

OLDROYD, Michael John, OBE 8 School Lane, Old Bricket Wood, St Albans AL2 3XU Tel: 01923 672082 — MB ChB 1955 Leeds; FRCGP 1978, M 1965; DA Eng. 1958. (Leeds) Sec. Emerit. Lond. LMCs. Socs: Fell. Roy. Soc. Med. Prev: Sec. Inner Lond. Local Med. Comms.; Clin. Asst. (Anaesth. & A & E) Dewsbury HA.

OLDROYD, Ruth Elizabeth The Granary, Stanton upon Hine Heath, Shrewsbury SY4 4LR — MB BS 1994 Newc.; DCH RCPS Glas. 1996; DRCOG 1997. GP Regist. Shrodihire. Prev: SHO Med. Shrewsbury; SHO (O & G) Shrewsbury.

OLDS, Elizabeth Mary Ninnis Farm, Lelant Downs, Hayle TR27 6NL — MB ChB 1993 Wales; BSc (1st cl. Hons.) Pharmacol. Wales, 1992, MB BCh 1993. SHO (Paediat.) Univ. Hosp. Wales.

OLEESKY, David Alan 8 Carew Court, Curlew Close, Cardiff CF14 1BQ Tel: 02920 617760 Email: david.oleesky@gwent.wales.nhs.uk — MB BS 1979 Lond.; BA (Hons.) Camb. 1976, MA 1980; MRCPath 1986. (Westm.)

OLEESKY, Samuel (retired) 1 Dunham Lawn, Bradgate Road, Altrincham WA14 4QJ Tel: 0161 928 8066 — MB ChB 1944 Manch.; MB ChB (Hons.) 1944; MSc Manch. 1951, BSc 1941; MD (Hons.) Washington Univ. St. Louis 1949; FRCP Lond. 1963, M 1946. Prev: Cons. Phys. Manch. Roy. Infirm.

OLESHKO, Christopher George Moss Lane Surgery, Moss Lane, Madeley, Crewe CW3 9NQ Tel: 01782 750274 Fax: 01782 751835 — MB BS 1985 Lond.

OLFORD, Colin Arthur Chichester Road Surgery, 34 Chichester Road, Portsmouth PO2 0AD — MB BS 1964 Lond.; DObst RCOG 1971. (Middlx.) Prev: Surg. Lt. RN; Ho. Phys. RN Hosp. Haslar; Ho. Surg. Roy. Portsmouth Hosp.

OLI, Professor Johnie Mbanefo c/o Dr B C Onyeabo, 25 Kelland Close, Park Road, London N8 8JS Tel: 0208 341 4874; Department of Medicine, University of Nigera Teaching Hospital, Enugy, Nigeria Tel: (00 23) (442) 451281 Fax: (00 23) (442) 451281 — MB ChB Manch. 1966; MRCP (U.K.) 1971; FRCP Ed 1984; FRCP (Lond.) 1986. (University of Manchester Medical School) Prof. Med. Univ. Nigeria Enugy, Nigeria; Hon. Cons. Phys. Univ. Nigeria Enugu, Nigeria. Socs: Diabetic Assn. Nigeria Trustee; Nigerian Soc. Endocrinol. & Metab.; Nutrit. Soc. Nigeria.

OLIN, Robert Henry 25 The Beeches, Park St., St Albans AL2 2PL Tel: 01727 74034; 1353 Hedman Way, White Bear Lake, Minnesota 55110, USA Tel: 612 653 1970 — MD 1958 Minnesota. Socs: Amer. Acad. Family Piys.; Minnesota Med. Soc.

OLIPHANT, Christopher John 83 Queens Road, Whitley Bay NE26 3AS — MB BS 1975 Newc.; MRCGP 1979; DRCOG 1977.

OLIVE, John Edward Victoria House, 28 Alexandra Road, Lowestoft, Norwich NR32 1PL Tel: 01603 288104 Fax: 01502 532147 — MB ChB 1969 Birm.; MRCPsych 1976. Cons. Psychiat. Norf. Trust, Med. Health Care; Assoc. Clin. Prof. of Psychiat. St. Geo.s Med. Sch., Grenada. Prev: Sen. Regist. (Psychiat.) All St.s' Hosp. Birm.; Hon. Clin. Lect. Univ. Birm.; Resid. (Paediat.) Ottawa Gen. Hosp.

OLIVEIRA, Professor David Benjamin Graeme Division of Renal Medicine, St. George's Hospital Medical School, Cranmer Terrace, Tooting, London SW17 0RE Tel: 020 8725 5038 Fax: 020 8725 5036 Email: doliveir@sghms.ac.uk; 62 Coombe Lane W., Kingston upon Thames KT2 7BY Tel: 020 8336 2446 — MB BChir 1979 Camb.; PhD 1987; MA Camb. 1981; FRCP Lond. 1996; MRCP (UK) 1981. Prof. Renal Med. & Hon. Cons. Nephrol. St. Geo. Hosp. Med. Sch. Lond.

OLIVER, Alexander Neville 16 Court Drive, Uxbridge UB10 0BJ — MB BS 1992 Lond.

OLIVER, Ann Patricia (retired) 8 Lyme Park, Chinley, High Peak SK23 6AG — MB ChB 1965 Manch. Prev: GP Chapel-en-le-Frith.

OLIVER, Anne Stragrane House, Dyan, Caledon BT68 4YA — MB ChB 1996 Aberd.

OLIVER, Barbara Kathleen (retired) 96 Dorset House, Gloucester Place, London NW1 5AF Tel: 020 7935 4519 — MRCS Eng. LRCP Lond. 1954; FFA RCS Eng. 1969; DA Eng. 1962. Prev: Cons. Anaesth. The Roy. Lond. Hosp.

OLIVER, Barry John Barnard Medical Practice, 43 Granville Road, Sidcup DA14 4TA Tel: 020 8302 7721 Fax: 020 8309 6579 — MB BS 1974 Lond.; Cert JCC Lond. 1976. (Middlx.) Sen. Partner NHS Gen. Pract.

OLIVER, Carol Anne Victoria Strathmore Medical Practice, 26-28 Chester Road, Wrexham LL11 7SA Tel: 01978 352055 Fax: 01978 310689; 4 Derwen Court, Wrexham LL13 7JA — MB ChB 1981 Manch.; BSc (Med. Sci.) St. And. 1978; DRCOG 1984; Cert. Family Plann. JCC 1984. Prev: Trainee GP S. Clwyd VTS; Ho. Surg. Maelor Gen. Hosp. Clwyd; Ho. Phys. Univ. Hosp. S. Manch.

OLIVER, Caroline Diane The Surgery, 1 Glebe Road, Barnes, London SW13 0DR Tel: 020 8748 1065 — MB BS 1993 Lond.

OLIVER, Charles Henry Teviot Medical Practice, Teviot Road, Hawick TD9 9DT Tel: 01450 370999 Fax: 01450 371025; Broomieknowe, Stirches Road, Hawick TD9 7HF Tel: 01450 73240 — MB ChB 1972 Ed.; MRCP (UK) 1978; DCH Eng. 1976. Clin. Tutor Gen. Pract. Univ. of Edin.; Police Surg. Lothian & Borders Police. Prev: Maj. RAMC.

OLIVER, Christopher John Russell Oliver and Partners, Millhill Surgery, 87 Woodmill Street, Dunfermline KY11 4JW Tel: 01383 621222 Fax: 01383 622862 — BM BCh 1972 Oxf.; DObst RCOG 1974. Prev: SHO Raigmore Hosp. Inverness.; Ho. Off. P.ss Margt. Hosp. Swindon.

OLIVER, Mr Christopher William Orthopaedic Trauma Unit, Royal Infirmary of Edinburgh, Lauriston Place, Edinburgh EH3 9YW Tel: 0131 536 3722 Fax: 0131 536 3413 Email: c.w.oliver@rcsed.ac.uk; Email: cwoliver@rcsed.ac.uk — MB BS 1985 Lond.; BSc (Physiol.) Lond. 1981, MD 1995; FRCS (Orth.) 1995; FRCS Eng. 1989; FRCS Ed. 1998. (Univ. Coll. Hosp.) Cons. (Trauma & Orthop.Surg.) Roy. Infirm. Edin.; p/t Sen. Lect. (Orthop.) Univ. Edin. Socs: Fell. Brit. Orthop. Assn.; AO Alumni; Orthopaedic Trauma Assoc. Prev: Fell. Musculoskeletal Trauma John Radcliffe Hosp. Oxf.; AO Fell. Harborview Med. Centre, Seattle, USA; Spinal Research Fell. (Orthop.) Middlesbrough Gen. Hosp.

OLIVER, Colin Barry Duncan Department of Clinical Radiology, Walsgrave Hospital, Coventry CV2 2DX Tel: 024 76 602020 Fax: 024 7684 4150 — MB BS Lond. 1986; BSc (Pharmacol.) Lond. 1983; MRCP (UK) 1990; FRCR 1994. Cons. (Diagn. Radiol.) Walsgrave Hosp. Coventry. Prev: Sen. Regist. (Diagn. Radiol.) Bristol Roy. Infirm.

OLIVER, David John Department of Surgery, University of Wales School of Medicine, Heath Park, Cardiff CF14 4XN — MB BS 1984 Western Australia.

OLIVER, David John Wisdom Hospice, St. William's Way, Rochester ME1 2NU Tel: 01634 830456 Fax: 01634 845890 Email: david.oliver@tgt.sthames.nhs.uk — MB BS 1978 Lond.; BSc Lond. 1975; FRCGP 1993, M 1982; DRCOG 1981. (Univ. Coll. Hosp.) Cons. Phys. (Palliat. Med.) Wisdom Hospice (Thames Gateway NHS Trust) Rochester; Hon. Sen. Lect. in Palliat. Care at Kent Inst. of Med. and Health Sci.s at Univ. of Kent at Canterbury. Socs: Fell. Roy. Soc. Med.; BMA; Assn. Palliat. Med. Prev: Trainee GP Swindon VTS; Sen. Regist. St. Christopher's Hospice Sydenham.

***OLIVER, David Jonathan** 14 Carlisle Close, Dunstable LU6 3PH Tel: 01582 727294 — MB ChB 1998 Birm.; ChB Birm. 1998, MBCLB.

OLIVER, David William 12 Oaklands Court, Aldcliffe, Lancaster LA1 5AT; Flat 4, The Hermitage, Parkstone, Poole BH14 0QG — MB ChB 1991 Birm.; ChB Birm. 1991.

OLIVER, Edward James Hoblyn 36 Woodstock Road, Redland, Bristol BS6 7EP Tel: 0117 924 6296 Fax: 0117 940 6555 Email: edit@msn.com — MB ChB 1984 Bristol; MSc (IT) Bristol 1990; BSc Bristol 1981; DCH RCP Lond. 1987. (Bristol Univ.) Managing Dir. Edit Ltd. Bristol. Socs: BMA. Prev: Informat. Manager S & W RHA; Managem. Cons. Price WaterHo.

OLIVER, Elizabeth Hawthorn Medical Centre, May Close, Swindon SN2 1UU Tel: 01793 536541 Fax: 01793 421049 — MB ChB 1977 Aberd.; MRCGP 1981. GP Swindon.

OLIVER

OLIVER, Elizabeth Mary Coleby Hall, Coleby, Scunthorpe DN15 9AL Tel: 01724 734531 — MB ChB 1972 Bristol; MRCS Eng. LRCP Lond. 1971; DA Eng. 1974.

OLIVER, Fred Tameside & Glossop Community & Priority Services NHS Trust, Tameside General Hospital, Fountain St., Ashton-under-Lyne OL6 9RW Tel: 0161 331 5063; Northenden, 25 Netherwood Road, Manchester M22 4BW — MB ChB Manch. 1966; FRCPsych 1997, M 1974; DPM Eng. 1973; DObst RCOG 1968. Cons. Psychiat. Tameside Gen. Hosp. Socs: Manch. Med. Soc. (Mem. Counc. Psychiat. Sect.). Prev: Sen. Regist. (Psychiat.) United Manch. Hosps.; Regist. (Psychiat.) Univ. Hosp. Withington; Dist. Med. Off. St. Lucia, W. Indies.

OLIVER, Gillian The Health Centre, Lawson Street, Stockton-on-Tees TS18 1HX Tel: 01642 672351 Fax: 01642 618112 — MB ChB 1992 Leeds.

OLIVER, Graeme 17 Woodlands Park Drive, The Parklands, Blaydon-on-Tyne NE21 5PQ Tel: 0191 414 3384 — MB BS 1968 Newc.; MRCGP 1972; DObst RCOG 1971.

OLIVER, Hugh Walter Latham, MBE (retired) 45 Tunwells Lane, Great Shelford, Cambridge CB2 5LJ Tel: 01223 842919 — MB BS 1954 Lond.; DObst RCOG 1959. Prev: GP Camb.

OLIVER, James 3 Kirkhill Drive, Oldmeldrum, Inverurie AB51 0FP — MB ChB 1979 Aberd.

***OLIVER, James** The Meads Surgery, Grange Road, Uckfield TN22 1QU Tel: 01825 765777 Fax: 01825 766220 — MB ChB 1986 Leic.

***OLIVER, James John** 14 Carlisle Court, Dunstable LU6 3PH — MB ChB 1996 Birm.; ChB Birm. 1996.

OLIVER, James Philip Nansmellion Road Health Centre, Nansmellion Road, Mullion, Helston TR12 7DQ Tel: 01326 240212 Fax: 01326 240420 — MB BChir 1987 Camb.; MA Camb. 1989, BA 1984. Prev: Trainee GP Truro VTS; Ho. Surg. MusGr. Pk. Hosp. Taunton; Ho. Phys. Tehidy & Treliske Hosp.

OLIVER, Miss Jane Margaret Accident & Emergency Department, Watford General Hospital, Vicarage Road, Watford WD18 0HB Tel: 01923 217506 Email: emerg@wathosp.force9.co.uk — MB ChB 1985 Bristol; BSc (Hons.) Bristol 1974; FRCS Ed. 1990; FFAEM 1997. Cons. (A & E) Mt. Vernon & Watford NHS Trust. Socs: BAEM.

OLIVER, Janice Elizabeth Balgonie Lodge, 5 Corsebar Lane, Paisley PA2 9LL — MB ChB 1986 Glas.; BSc St. And. 1984; MRCGP 1990; Dip. Pract. Dermat. Wales 1994; Dip. Forens. Med. Glas 1996; DRCOG 1990; DCH RCPS Glas. 1989.

OLIVER, Jayne Lynda 9 Beckett's Wood, Upstreet, Canterbury CT3 4DQ Tel: 01227 860366 — MB BCh 1983 Wales. (Cardiff) Community Med. Off. Hants.

OLIVER, Jean Mary (retired) 15 Falcon Drive, Mudeford, Christchurch BH23 4BA — MB ChB Ed. 1938; DPM RCPSI 1949. Prev: Cons. Psychiat. Epsom Dist. Hosp. & W. Pk. Hosp. Epsom.

OLIVER, Jeffrey Enrique The Surgery, 218 Ifield Drive, Ifield, Crawley RH11 0EP Tel: 01293 547846 — BM BCh 1978 Oxf.; 1978 MA Oxf.; MRCP (UK) 1980; DRCOG 1982. Tutor (Gen. Pract. & Primary Care) St. Geo.'s Hosp. Med. Sch. Lond.; Trainer (Gen. Pract.) Crawley; Tutor GP Crawley & Horsham Dist. Prev: SHO (Med.) Roy. Vict. Infirm. Newc.; Ho. Phys. John Radcliffe Infirm. Oxf..

OLIVER, Jill Rosemary 31 College Road, Isleworth TW7 5DJ — MB ChB 1965 Ed.; DA Eng. 1968. Clin. Asst. (Anaesth.) W. Middlx. Hosp. Isleworth.

OLIVER, Jill Susan Sheerwater Surgery, 290 Albert Drive, Sheerwater, Woking GU21 5TX Tel: 01932 343524 Fax: 01932 355908 — MB ChB 1971 Manch.

OLIVER, John Henry Huby, OBE, TD (retired) The Homestead, St. Michaels, Tenbury Wells WR15 8PH Tel: 01584 810246 — MRCS Eng. LRCP Lond. 1947. DL; Hon. Surg. to H.M. The Qu.; Cas. Off. & Anaesth. Tenbury & Dist. Hosp.; Brigadier RAMC TA & AVR; Co. Cdr. St. John Ambul. Assn. & Brig. (Heref. & Worcs.). Prev: Ho. Surg. & Res. Obst. Asst. St. Geo. Hosp.

OLIVER, Juliet Flat 7, Parade Mansions, E. Preston, Littlehampton BN16 1NT — MB BS 1991 Lond.; MRCP, Univ. Lond. Socs: RSM.

OLIVER, Karen Janet 12 Oaklands Court, Lancaster LA1 5AT — MB BS 1989 Lond.

OLIVER, Kathryn Jane Quorn Medical Centre, 1 Station Road, Quorn, Loughborough LE12 8PB Tel: 01509 412232 Fax: 01509 620652 — MB ChB 1990 Manch.; MRCGP 1995; DFFP 1993.

(Manch.) GP Princip.; Macmillan GP Facilitater, Leisc. Socs: (Treas.) Leic. Fac. RCGP. Prev: Course Organiser Leicesrer VTS; SHO (Palliat. Care) Loros Hospice Leics.; Trainee GP Leics. VTS.

OLIVER, Keith Robert (retired) Ailsa Hame, Cwrt Bryn-Y-Bia, Craigside, Llandudno LL30 3AU Tel: 01492 540263 — MA, MB BChir Camb. 1954. Prev: Ho. Surg. & Ho. Phys. Ashford Hosp. Middlx.

OLIVER, Krista 39 Oaklands Drive, Bebington, Wirral CH63 7NB — MB ChB 1993 Leic.

OLIVER, Lorna Sherbourne Medical Centre, 40 Oxford Street, Leamington Spa CV32 4RA Tel: 01926 424736 Fax: 01926 470884; 1, The Cedars, Warwick Place, Leamington Spa CV32 5YE Email: lornaoliver@homail.com — MB ChB 1992 Birm.; MRCGP 1996; DRCOG 1995. (Birm.) Princip. GP Leamington Spa.

OLIVER, Louise Elizabeth Low Farm, Saxlingham Nethergate, Norwich NR15 1TE — MB BS 1985 Lond.

OLIVER, Lucinda Jane Swyllmers Barn, The Lee, Great Missenden HP16 9NA Tel: 01494 837317 — MB ChB 1991 Leic.; MRCP (UK) 1996. Specialist Regist. (Palliat. Med.) Michael Sobell Ho. Oxf. Prev: SHO (Palliat. Care) Priscilla Bacon Lodge Norwich; Regist. Waikato Hosp. New Zealand.

OLIVER, Margaret Yool (retired) East Morningside, 5 Clinton Road, Edinburgh EH9 2AW Tel: 0131 447 1417 — MB ChB 1947 Ed. Prev: SCMO (Family Plann.) Lothian HB & Edin.

OLIVER, Maria Isabel 25 Grosvenor Place, Bath BA1 6BA — LMS 1992 Complutense Madrid.

OLIVER, Mark David 10 Browning Street, Stafford ST16 3AT Tel: 01785 258240 Fax: 01785 253119 — MB ChB 1984 Sheff.; MB ChB (Hons.) Sheff. 1984; MRCP (UK) 1987. Prev: Regist. (Renal Med.) Leeds Gen. Infirm.; Regist. (Med.) Edin. Roy. Infirm.

OLIVER, Matthew Charles 21 Marlborough Close, St Leonards-on-Sea TN38 0RY — MB BS 1998 Lond.

OLIVER, Maurice Herbert 4 Rawcliffe Grove, York YO30 6NR Tel: 01904 654122 — MB ChB (Hons.) Sheff. 1944; MRCGP 1956. (Sheff.) SBStJ. Socs: BMA; York Med. Soc. Prev: Supernum Med. Regist. Leeds Gen. Infirm.; Ho. Surg. Sheff. Roy. Hosp. & Winterton EMS Hosp.; Capt. RAMC.

OLIVER, Max Trahearn Windmill Medical Practice, 65 Shoot Up Hill, London NW2 3PS Tel: 020 8452 7646 Fax: 020 8450 2319; 14 Parkhill Road, London NW3 2YN — MB BS 1969 Lond.

OLIVER, Professor Michael Francis, CBE Cardiac Medicines, National Heart & Lung Institute, Dovehouse St., London SW3 6LY Tel: 020 7351 8855 Fax: 020 7351 8856; 12 Keepier Wharf, Narrow St, London E14 8DH Tel: 020 7790 4203 Fax: 020 7790 4203 — MB ChB Ed. 1947; FRACP 1987; FFPHM 1974; Hon. FACC 1973; FRSE 1987; MD (Gold Medal) Ed. 1957; MD (Hon. Causa) Karolinska 1980; MD (Hon. Causa) Bologna 1985; FRCP Lond. 1969, M 1963; FRCP Ed. 1957, M 1951; FRCPI 1987; FESC 1988. (Ed.) Emerit. Prof. Univ. Edin.; Hon. Prof. Nat. Heart & Lung Inst. Lond.; Cons. Cardiovasc. Div. WHO. Socs: Assn. Phys.; Brit. Cardiac Soc.; Med. Res. Soc. Prev: Dir. Wynn Inst. for Metabol. Research Inst. Lond.; Duke of Edin. Prof. Cardiol. Univ. Edin.; Pres. Brit. Cardiac Soc. & Roy. Coll. Phys. Edin.

OLIVER, Michael Henry North Devon District Hospital, Barnstaple EX31 4JB Tel: 01271 322577 Fax: 01271 322709; 7 Trafalgar Lawn, Barnstaple EX32 9BD Tel: 01271 374294 — MB BS 1976 (Hons.) Lond.; MD Lond. 1993; BA (Chem.) Oxf. 1971; FRCP Lond. 1996; MRCP (UK) 1978. (Univ. Coll. Hosp.) p/t Cons. Gen. & Chest Med. N Devon Dist. Hosp. Barnstaple. Socs: (Ex-Treas.) Brit. Thoracic Soc.; (Ex-Sec.) W. Country Chest Soc.; (Ex-Chairm. N. Devon Div.) Brit. Med. Assoc. Prev: Sen. Regist. (Gen. & Chest Med.) Bristol Roy. Infirm.; Clin. Lect. Cardiothoracic Inst. Brompton Hosp. Lond.; Regist. & SHO (Gen. Med.) Stoke City Gen. Hosp.

OLIVER, Neil McCrae Dr Wilkinson, Cardon and Oliver, Castle Douglas Health Centre, Academy St, Castle Douglas DG7 1EE Tel: 0155650250; 1 Whitecraigs, Whitepard Rd, Castle Douglas DG7 1EX — MB ChB 1992 Ed. GP Princip.

OLIVER, Paul Anthony David The Surgery, 577 Carlton Road, Nottingham NG3 7AF Tel: 0115 958 0415 Fax: 0115 950 9245 — BM BS 1980 Nottm.; BMedSci Nottm. 1978; MRCGP 1984; DRCOG 1983. Lect. (Gen. Pract.) Univ. Nottm. Prev: GP Nottm.

OLIVER, Peter James Robert 22 Woodlands Close, Hawsley, Camberley GU17 9HZ — MB BS 1998 Lond.

OLIVER

OLIVER, Peter John 20 St Johns Road, Chester CH4 7AL — MB BS 1984 Lond.; BSc Basic Med. Scs. & Pharmacol. 1981; AFOM RCP (UK) 1993; DA (UK) 1989. Sen. Regist. (Occupat. Med.) Chesh.; Asst. Med. Adviser Chesh. CC. Prev: SHO (Anaesth.) Manch. Roy. Infirm.; Trainee GP/SHO Macclesfield Dist. Gen. Hosp. VTS.

OLIVER, Peter Owen, RD Mill House, Milton Mills, Milton Abbas, Blandford Forum DT11 0BQ Tel: 01258 880675 Fax: 01258 880178 — MB BS Lond. 1949; MD Lond. 1964; MRCS Eng. LRCP Lond. 1948; FFOM RCP Lond. 1982, M 1978; DPH Eng. 1960; DIH Soc. Apoth. Lond. 1958. (King's Coll. & St. Geo.) Cons. Occupat. Health & Nautical Med. Soton.; Surg. Lt.-Cdr. RNR. Socs: Fell. Roy. Soc. Med.; Soc. Occupat. Med. Prev: Med. Dir. Cunard Line Ltd.; Chief Med. Off. Gillette Industs. Ltd.; Sen. Indust. Med. Off. Air Corps. Jt. Med. Serv. (BOAC).

OLIVER, Peter Stephen Russell's Hall Hospital, Dudley DY1 2HQ Tel: 01384 456111 Fax: 01384 244051; 9 The Heathlands, Old Swinford, Stourbridge DY8 1NR Tel: 01384 396062 — MB 1984 Camb.; MB BChir Camb. 1984; MA Camb. 1986; MRCP (UK) 1987; FRCR 1992. Cons. Radiol. Dudley Gp. Hosps. NHS Trust. Prev: Sen. Regist. (Diagn. Radiol.) W. Midl. RHA.; Regist. (Gen. Med.) Glos. Roy. Hosp. Gloucester; SHO (Gen. Med.) Norf. & Norwich Hosp.

OLIVER, Philip David Chard Road Surgery, Chard Road, St. Budeaux, Plymouth PL5 2UE — MRCS Eng. LRCP Lond. 1984; MRCGP 1990. (Guy's Hospital)

OLIVER, Philip Peter Market Surgery, Warehouse Lane, Wath-On-Dearne, Rotherham S63 7RA Tel: 01709 877524 — MB ChB 1984 Bristol; MRCGP 1988.

OLIVER, Raife Morgan Cromer Group Brachee, Ovestrand Road, Cromer Tel: 01263 513148 — MB ChB 1991 Leic.; MRCGP 1996; DRCOG 1995; DCH RCP Lond. 1993. (Leicester) Gen. Practitioner.

OLIVER, Raymond Ernest Willis (retired) 4 Crosslands Avenue, Ealing Common, London W5 3QH Tel: 020 8993 3345 — MRCS Eng. LRCP Lond. 1940; MFOM RCP Lond. 1978; FRCGP 1994, M 1953; DIH Eng. 1963; DIH Soc. Apoth. Lond. 1962. Prev: Squadron Ldr. RAFVR.

OLIVER, Richard Ecclesfield Group Practice, 96A Mill Road, Ecclesfield, Sheffield S35 9XQ Tel: 0114 246 9151, 0114 257 0935 Email: richard.oliver@gp-c88039.nhs.uk — MB ChB 1983 Sheff.; MRCGP 1988; Dip. Occ. Med. RCP Lond. 1996. (Sheff.) GP Adviser to N. Gen. Hosp. Trust; GP Mem. N. Sheff. PCT Exec. Comm. Lead Responsibil. for Prescribing/Commiss.ing. Prev: Trainee GP Sheff.; SHO (Psychiat.) Middlewood Hosp. Sheff.; SHO (Geriat.) N.. Gen. Hosp. Sheff.

OLIVER, Mr Richard Hywel Picton (retired) Cefn Coed, 22 Bronfelin, Llandegfan Anglesey, Menai Bridge LL59 5UY — MS Lond. 1966, MB BS 1948; FRCS Eng. 1954 MRCS Eng. LRCP Lond. 1948. Prev: Cons. Surg. Caernarvon & Anglesey Gen. Hosp. Bangor.

OLIVER, Richard Joseph 14 Partridge Road, South Yardley, Birmingham B26 2DA — MB BCh 1975 Wales. Clin. Asst. (Endoscopy) E. Birm. Hosp.

OLIVER, Richard Martin Cardiology Department, Ipswich Hospital NHS Trust, Heath Road, Ipswich IP4 5PD Tel: 01473 703516 Fax: 01473 703516 — MB BS 1980 Lond.; DM Soton 1992; MRCP (UK) 1985; FRCP Lond. 1998. (St. George's Hospital Medical School London) Cons. Cardiol. Ipswich Hosp. NHS Trust. Socs: Brit. Cardiac Soc.; BMA; FESC. Prev: Sen. Regist. & Regist. (Cardiol.) Middlx. & Univ. Coll. Hosp. Lond.; Clin. Research Fell. (Cardiovasc. Med.) Soton. Gen. Hosp.; Regist. (Med.) Portsmouth Hosps.

OLIVER, Robert Anthony Mawdsley (retired) The Firs, 3 Aldercombe Lane, Caterham CR3 6ED Tel: 01883 343884 — BM BCh 1947 Oxf.; MA, DM Oxf. 1957; FRCPath 1971, M 1964. Prev: Cons. Clin. Path. Croydon Hosp. Gp.

OLIVER, Professor Roderick Timothy Desmond Department Medical Oncology, St. Bartholomew's Hospital & Royal Lond. School Med. & Dent., 1st Floor KGV, West Smithfield, London EC1A 7BE Tel: 020 7601 8522 Fax: 020 7601 7577 — MB BChir 1966 Camb.; MD Camb. 1975; FRCP Lond. 1986, M 1968; MRCS Eng. LRCP Lond. 1966. (Lond. Hosp.) Prof. Med. Oncol. Med. Coll. Roy. Lond. Hosp.; Hon. Cons. & Hon. Sen. Lect. St. Bart. Hosp. Prev: Sen. Lect. (Med. Oncol.) Inst. Urol. Lond.; Sen. Scientif. Off. Dept. Med. Oncol. St. Bart. Hosp. Lond.; Lect. (Immunol.) Dept. Tissue Immunol. Lond. Hosp. Med. Coll.

OLIVER, Ronald Martin, CB, RD (retired) Greenhill House, Beech Avenue, Effingham, Leatherhead KT24 5PH Tel: 01372 452887 — MD Lond. 1965, MB BS 1952; MRCP (UK) 1987; FRCP (UK) 1998; MRCS Eng. LRCP Lond. 1952; MFCM 1987; MFOM RCP Lond. 1978; DCH Eng. 1954, DPH 1960, DIH 1961. Prev: Dep. Chief Med. Off. Dept. of Health.

OLIVER, Rosalind Mary A Block, Medway Maritime Hospital, Windmill Rd, Gillingham ME7 5NY Tel: 01634 833828 Fax: 01634 830082; 18 King's Avenue, Rochester ME1 3DS — MB BS 1972 Lond.; MRCS Eng. LRCP Lond. 1972; MRCPsych 1977; DPM Leeds 1975. Cons. Psychiat. Thames Gateway NHS Trust. Socs: BMA; NHS Cons. Assn. Prev: Cons. Psychiat. Thameslink Healthcare NHS Trust; Cons. Psychiat. Centr. Notts. NHS Trust; Cons. Psychiat. Invicta Community NHS Trust.

OLIVER, Rosemary 28 Dawlish Road, Dudley DY1 4LU Tel: 01902 885926 — MB ChB 1989 Liverp.; BSc (Hons.) Liverp. 1986, MB ChB 1989.

OLIVER, Sarah Elizabeth 25 Abbey Gate, Morpeth NE61 2XN — MB BS 1993 Newc.

OLIVER, Shirley Mary Morven, Blackhall Colliery, Hartlepool TS27 4EE Tel: 01429 586 4331 — MB BS 1959 Durh.

OLIVER, Stephen Francis Oliver and Partners, The Guildhall Surgery, Lower Baxter Street, Bury St Edmunds IP33 1ET Tel: 01284 701601 Fax: 01284 702943 — MB BS 1964 Lond.; FRCGP 1979, M 1972; DObst RCOG 1968. (Middlx.) Prev: Ho. Phys. Middlx. Hosp. Lond.; Ho. Surg. Centr. Middlx. Hosp.; Course Organiser W. Suff. VTS.

OLIVER, Steven Edward Bracken Hill Lodge, North Road, Leigh Woods, Bristol BS8 3PL — BM BS 1989 Nottm.; MRCP (UK) 1992.

OLIVER, Stuart Dean Covance Clinical Research Unit, Springfield House, Hyde St., Leeds LS2 9NG Tel: 0113 244 8071 Fax: 0113 237 3546; 5 Forest Hill Gardens, Outlane, Huddersfield HD3 3GA — MB BChir 1982 Camb.; MB Camb. 1982, BChir 1981; MA Camb. 1986; MFPM RCP (UK) 1996; MRCGP 1986; Dip. Pharm. Med. RCP (UK) 1991. Med. Dir. (Pharmaceut. Med.) Covance Clin. Research Unit.

OLIVER, Sybil Enid Kathleen (retired) 2 Courtenay House, Kingsway, Hove BN3 2WF Tel: 01273 732051 — BA, MB BCh BAO Dub. 1949. Prev: Sessional Med. Off. Brighton & Hove Family Plann. Assn.

OLIVER, Thomas Barry Clinincal Radiology Department, Ninewells Hospital and Medical School, Dundee Tel: 01382 660111 — MB ChB 1988 Ed.; MRCP (UK) 1991; FRCR 1996. Cons. Radiologist, Clin. Radiol. Dept., Ninewellas Hosp. and Med. Sch., Dundee.

OLIWIECKI, Simone Department of Dermatology, Bristol Royal Infirmary, Bristol BS2 8HW; Desmonde, Edgerton Road, Egerton, Huddersfield HD3 3AA — MB ChB 1982 Manch.; MRCP (UK) 1985. Research Regist. Bristol Roy. Infirm.

OLLERENSHAW, Katherine Judith 25 Meadowlands, Portstewart BT55 7FG — BM BS 1988 Nottm.; BMedSci Nottm. 1986; MRCGP 1992; DRCOG 1991. Socs: BMA.

OLLERHEAD, Elizabeth The Barn House, Orchard Farm, Cowfold Lane, Rotherwick, Hook RG27 9BP — MB BS 1986 Lond.; MSc (Pub. Health Med.) Lond. 1994; MRCGP 1995; DRCOG 1991; DCH RCP Lond. 1989; MFPHM 1998. Sen. Regist. (Pub. Health Med.) S & W RHA.

OLLERHEAD, Mr Keith John New Chineham Surgery, Reading Road, Chineham, Basingstoke RG24 8ND Tel: 01256 479244 Fax: 01256 814190; The Barn House, Orchard Farm, Cowfold Lane, Rotherwick, Hook RG27 9BP Tel: 01831 818063 — MB ChB 1982 Manch.; MB ChB (Hons.) Manch. 1982; BSc Manch. 1977; FRCS Ed. 1987; MRCGP 1989. Chair N. Hants. PCG. Socs: Manch. Med. Soc. Prev: Trainee GP Manch. VTS; Research Fell. (Surgic. Gastroenterol.) Manch. Roy. Infirm.; Regist. Rotat. (Surg.) Roy. Hallamsh. Hosp. Sheff.

OLLERTON, Andrew Hawkley Brook Surgery, Highfield Grange Avenue, Wigan WN3 6SU Tel: 01942 234740 Fax: 01942 820037 — MB ChB 1982 Birm.

OLLERTON, Stephen James Abraham 25 Chantrell Court, The Calls, Leeds LS2 7HA — MB ChB 1998 Leeds. SHO in A & E, at St James, Leeds. Socs: Affil. of Roy. Coll. of Surg.s. Prev: PRHO Surg., Roy. Halifax; PRHO Med. Halifax Gen.

OLLEY, Lorraine Michelle 166 Leesons Hill, Chislehurst BR7 6QL — MB BS 1998 Lond.

OLLEY, Peter Charles Department of Mental Health, Foresterhill, Aberdeen Tel: 01224 23423; 1 Corry Begg, 19 Cairn Road,

Bieldside, Aberdeen AB15 9AL — MB ChB 1958 Sheff.; BSc Birm. 1951; Dip. Psych. Ed. 1964. Prev: Regist. Roy. Edin. Hosp. Ment. & Nerv. Dis.

OLLEY, Peter William 29 Bridge Park, Gosforth, Newcastle upon Tyne NE3 2DX Tel: 0191 284 5560; The Village Green Surgery, The Green, Wallsend NE28 6BB Tel: 0191 295 8500 Fax: 0191 295 8519 — MB BS 1982 Newc.; DRCOG 1992; MRCGP 1995. (Newc. u. Tyne) Socs: Roy. Coll. Gen. Pract.; BMA. Prev: Trainee GP N.umbria VTS; Regist. (O & G) Bellshill Matern. Hosp. Lanarksh.; Regist. (O & G) S.. Gen. & Qu. Mothers Hosps. Glas.

OLLEY, Mr Stephen Francis c/o The Oral Surgery Department, Shrewsbury Hospital (Copthorne North), Mytton Oak Road, Shrewsbury SY3 8BR Tel: 01743 231122; (resid.) Carmel House, 47 The Mount, Shrewsbury SY3 8PP Tel: 01743 361714 — MB BS 1972 Lond.; BDS (Hons.) 1968; FRCS Ed. 1985; FDS RCS Eng. 1974. Cons. Oral & Maxillofacial Surg. W. Midl. RHA. Socs: Fell. BAOMS; EAOMFS.

OLLIFF, Jennifer Mary (retired) Grevels House, Chipping Campden GL55 6AG Tel: 01386 840395 — MB ChB Bristol 1949. Prev: Sen. Resid. Off. Bristol Eye Hosp.

OLLIFF, Julie Frances Caroline Clinical Radiology Department, Queen Elizabeth Hospital, Queen Elizabeth Medical Centre, Birmingham B15 2TH Tel: 0121 627 2458 Fax: 0121 697 8290 — BM BS 1979 Nottm.; BMedSci Nottm. 1977; MRCP (UK) 1983; FRCR 1987. Cons. Radiol. Qu. Eliz. Hosp. & Univ. Hosp. Birm. NHS Trust. Prev: Sen. Lect. (Diagn. Radiol.) Roy. Marsden Hosp. Sutton; Sen. Regist. (Diagn. Radiol.) St. Geo. Hosp. Lond.

OLLIFF, Simon Piers Clinical Radiology Department, Queen Elizabeth Hospital, Queen Elizabeth Medical Centre, Birmingham B15 2TH Tel: 0121 697 8488 Fax: 0121 697 8290 Email: simon.olliff@university-b.wmids.nhs.uk; 57 Moor Green Lane, Moseley, Birmingham B13 8NE — MB BS 1979 Lond.; MA Camb. 1980, BA 1976; MRCP (UK) 1983; FRCR 1988. (Camb. & Univ. Coll. Hosp.) Cons. Radiol. Qu. Eliz. Hosp. Birm. & Univ. Hosp. Birm. NHS Trust; Hon. Cons. Radiol., Birm. Childr.s Hosp. Socs: Liveryman Soc. Apoth. City Lond.; Brit. Soc. Interven. Radiol.; Gen. Interest Gp. For Gastrointestinal and Abdom. Radiol. Prev: Sen. Regist. (Radiol.) King's Coll. Hosp. Lond.

OLLIFF-COOPER, Anna Katharine Chalford Manor, Stoney Cross, Lyndhurst SO43 7GP Tel: 02380 812202 — MB BS 1973 Lond.; MRCP (UK) 1979; MRCS Eng. LRCP Lond. 1973; MRCGP 1985. (St. Bart.) Clin. Asst. (A & E) Soton. Gen. Hosp.

OLLIFFE, David James 5 Bryn y Gors, Morriston, Swansea SA6 6DQ — MB BCh 1988 Wales; MRCGP 1992.

OLLIFFE, Petra Elizabeth 45 Alderton Hill, Loughton IG10 3JD — MB BCh 1997 Wales.

OLLIVER, Mary Elizabeth 11 Pitter Close, Littleton, Winchester SO22 6PD — MB BS 1987 Lond.; MFFP 1994; T(GP) 1992. SCMO Margt. Pyke Centre Lond.; Clin. Asst Med./GUM Elderly Hosp.; Clin. Asst. BrE. Unit Roy. Harb Co. Hosp. Winchester. Socs: Chairm. Lond. Soc. of Family Plann. Doctors.

OLLIVER, Richard John The Health Centre, Kings Road, Horley RH6 7DG Tel: 01293 772686 Fax: 01293 823950; 2 Limes Avenue, Horley RH6 9DH Tel: 01293 786710 Email: richard.oliver@talk21.com — MB BS 1969 Lond.; MRCGP 1974; Cert. Family Plann. JCC 1974; DObst RCOG 1972; DCH Eng. 1971; PHEC certificate RCS (Ed) 1998. (St. Geo.) Socs: Co. Med.off.St John's Ambul. surrey. Prev: Trainee GP Wessex VTS; SHO (Paediat.) Qu. Mary's Hosp. Childr. Carshalton; SHO (O & G) Roy. Hants. Co. Hosp. Winchester.

OLNEY, Jonathan Simon Hurstwood Park Neuro Centre, Princess Royal Hospital, Lewes Road, Haywards Heath RH16 4EX Tel: 01444 441881 — MB BS 1974 Lond.; FRCR 1985. Cons. Radiol. Hurstwood Pk. Neurol. Centre. Prev: Sen. Regist. Nat. Hosp. Nerv. Dis. Lond.

OLNEY, Peter John (retired) 216 St Faith's Road, Old Catton, Norwich NR6 7AG Tel: 01603 426652 — MB BS 1953 Lond.; DObst RCOG 1956. Prev: SHO (Obst.) St. Mary's Hosp. Wom. & Childr. Manch.

OLNEY, Shelagh Mary The Surgery, 1 Glebe Road, Barnes, London SW13 0DR Tel: 020 8748 1065 Fax: 020 8741 8665 — MB BS 1986 Lond.; BSc Warwick 1981; MRCGP 1996; DCH RCP Lond. 1990; DRCOG 1989. (King's Coll. Sch. Med. & Dent.) Gen. Practitioner, Barnes; Clin. Asst. (Dermat.) Qu. Mary's Hosp. Lond.;

Occupat. Health Phys. BBC; Sen. Lect. Primary Care Imperial Coll. of Sci., Technol. & Med. Prev: Tutor (Gen. Pract.) Char. Cross & W.m. Med. Sch. Lond.

OLOBIA, Edirhiohwo Victoria Atamu 30 Mandarin Court, Edward St., London SE8 5HL — MB BS 1994 Lond.

OLOBO-LALOBO, James Henry 93 Harley Street, London W1N 1DF Tel: 020 7935 2627 Fax: 020 7935 4435; Obul, 49 Finchley Lane, London NW4 1BY — MB ChB 1973 Makerere; MSc Lond. 1978; MRCOG 1980. (Makerere Univ. Med. Sch. Kampala) Cons. O & G Harley St. Lond.; Cons. Gyn. Populat. Servs. Europe. Socs: BMA & Roy. Soc. Med. Prev: Regist. (O & G) Ealing Hosp.

OLOJOHUNGBE, Adebayo Babayide Kolade 59 Empire Court, North End Road, Wembley HA9 0AQ Tel: 020 8903 6854 — MB BS 1985 Ibadan; Dip. Haemat. Lond. 1989; MRCP (UK) 1992. Regist. (Haemat.) Roy. Free Hosp. Lond. Prev: Regist. (Haemat.) Edgware Gen. Hosp.

OLOJUGBA, Mr Oladeji Henry 16 Shenton Park Avenue, Sale M33 4NZ — MB BS 1988 Benin; MB BS Benin, Nigeria 1988; FRCS Ed. 1993.

OLORUNDA, Harry Ladipo Olufemi 56 Lewis Road, Mitcham CR4 3DE — MB BS 1971 Lagos; FRCOG 1995, M 1981.

OLOTO, Mr Emeka Josiah 74 Sunnigdale Ave, Alwoodley, Leeds W17 7SN Tel: 0113 2691 130 Fax: 0113 2691 130 Email: ejoloto@bigfoot.com — MB BS 1982 Nigeria; MB BS Univ. Nigeria 1982; MFFP 1994; MRCOG 1993. (Univ. of Nigeria) Specialist Regist. in D&G, P.ss Roy. Hosp., Hull. Socs: Fell. W. Afr. Postgrad. Med. Coll.; Eur. Soc. Contracep. Prev: Research Fell. & Hon. Sen. Regist. St. James Univ. Hosp. Leeds; Regist. (O & G) S. Tyneside Dist. Hosp., Furness Gen. Hosp., Roy. Vict. Infirm. & P.ss Mary Matern. Hosp. Newc.

OLSBURGH, Bernard Whitley Road Health Centre, Whitley Road, Whitley Bay NE26 2ND; 12 Westfield Grove, Newcastle upon Tyne NE3 4YA Tel: 0191 213 0668 — MB BS 1966 Newc.; FRCGP 1993, M 1971; DObst RCOG 1968. Local Med. Off. Whitley Bay; Train. N.umbria VTS.

OLSBURGH, Mr Jonathon David 28 Oakdene Drive, Leeds LS17 8XW — MB ChB 1993 Leeds; FRCS Eng. 1997.

OLSEN, Eckhardt Gerd Johannes (retired) Department of Histopathology (Cardiovascular Div.), Royal Brompton Hospital, Sydney St., London SW3 6NP Tel: 020 7351 8423 Fax: 020 7351 8293 — MB BS 1960 Lond.; MD Lond. 1971; MRCS Eng. LRCP Lond. 1960; FRCPath 1979, M 1976; FACC 1981. Cons. Path. Roy. Brompton Lond.; Hon. Sen. Lect. Cardiothoracic Inst.; Hon. Sen. Lect. (Morbid Anat.) Roy. Postgrad. Med. Sch. Lond. Prev: Sen. Lect. (Morbid Anat.) Roy. Postgrad. Med. Sch. Lond.

OLSEN, Noel David Lyche Oakdale, Court Wood, Newton Ferrers, Plymouth PL8 1BW Tel: 01752 873054 Fax: 01752 872653 — MB BS Lond. 1969; MSc (Social Med.) Lond. 1978; FRCP Lond. 1993; MRCP (UK) 1973; FFCM 1986, M 1979; FFPHM. (St. Geo.) p/t Indep. Pub. Health Phys.; Hon. Sec. Internat. Agency on Tobacco & Health; Chairm. SWCSC OFWAT; Cons. Adviser, Fuel Poverty & Clinic, DEFRA. Socs: (Ex.) BMA (Counc. 1993-98); (Ex. Hon. Sec.) Nat. Heart Forum; (Ex. Hon. Sec.) ASH (1975 - 1994). Prev: DPH Plymouth & Hampstead; DCP & Assoc. Lect. Camb.; Hon. Sen. Lect. Roy. Free Hosp. Sch. Med. Lond.

OLSON, Ewan Sinclair Department of Microbiology & Immunology, University of Leicester, PO Box 138, Medical Sciences Building, University Road, Leicester LE1 9HN Tel: 0116 252 2942 Fax: 0116 252 5030; 20 Burns Road, Aberdeen AB15 4NS — MB ChB 1990 Aberd.; MB ChB (Hons.) Aberd. 1990; DRCPath 1996. Lect. (Clin. Microbiol.) Univ. Leicester. Prev: Regist. (Med. Microbiol.) St. Bart. Hosp. Lond.

OLSON, Ian Alistair 20 Burns Road, Aberdeen AB15 4NS Tel: 01224 316497 — MD 1969 Aberd.; MB ChB 1962. (Aberd.) Socs: BMA & Assn. Study Med. Educat. Prev: Vice-Dean & Prof. (Human Morphol. & Experim. Path.) Kuwait Med. Sch.; Sen. Lect. (Anat.) Univ. Nottm. Med. Sch.; Lect. (Physiol.) Univ. Bristol Med. Sch.

OLSON, James John 28 Leven Close, Chandlers Ford, Eastleigh SO53 4SH — MB BS 1997 Lond. (St Georges) SHO in Anaesth., Carshalton.

OLSON, John Alexander The Eye Clinic, Aberdeen Royal Infirmary, Foresterhill, Aberdeen AB25 2ZN Tel: 0122468 1818 — MB ChB 1987 Aberd.; FRCP 2001 Edin.; MD 2000 Aberd.; MRCP UK 1990. Cons. Med. Opthalmology Aberd. Roy. Hosp. Trust. Prev:

OLSON

Sen. Regist. Med. Opthalmology Aberd. Roy. Hosp. Trust; Research Fell. Diabetic Retinopathy Aberd. Roy. Hosp. Trust; Regist. Gen. Med. Aberd. Roy. Hosp. Trust.

OLSON, Shona Department of Radiology, Aberdeen Royal Infirmary, Foresterhill, Aberdeen AB25 2ZN Tel: 01224 681818 — MB ChB Aberd. 1991. Specialist Regist. inDiagnostic Radiol.

OLUFUNWA, Philip Bandele Harrow Road Health Centre, 263-265 Harrow Road, London W2 5EZ Tel: 020 7286 1231 Fax: 020 7266 1253 — MB BS 1975 Ibadan; MB BS 1975 Ibadan.

OLUGBILE, Adedapo Olumuyiwa Babatunde 27 Lucien Road, London SW17 8HS — MB ChB 1966 Leeds; MRCPI 1972.

OLUONYE, Ngozi Margaret Dept. of Clinical Health, Royal Free Hospital, NHS Trust, Pond St., London NW3 Tel: 020 7830 2440 Fax: 020 7830 200 3 Email: noluonye@rfhsm.ac.uk; 1 Holly Farm Close, Caddington, Luton LU1 4ET Tel: 01582 452998 — MB BS 1986 Ibadan; MRCP (UK) 1993. (College of Medicine, Univ of Ibadau, Nigeria) Specialist Regist. Community Paediat., (p/t) · Roy. Free Hosp., NHS Trust, Pond St., Lond. Prev: Specialist Regist. Community Paediat. (p/t), Roy. Free Hosp. Lond.; Specialist Regist. Community Paediat. (p/t), S. Beds. Community Health Care Trust., Lutton; Paediat. Regis., Lutton & Dunstable Hosp., Dutton.

OLUSANYA, Adolphus Akinola Adesanya 18 Waterloo Close, Jack Dunning Estate, London E9 6EF — LRCPI & LM, LRSCI & LM 1965; LRCPI & LM, LRCSI & LM 1965.

OLUWAJANA, Mr Folajogun Michael Department of Surgery, Chesterfield & North Derbyshire Royal Hospital, Chesterfield S44 5BL; 6 Fairfield Drive, Ashgate, Chesterfield S42 7PU — MB BS 1979 Ibadan; MB BS Ibadan, Nigeria 1979; FRCS Ed. 1988. Staff Surg. (Gen. Surg.) Chesterfield & N. Derbysh. Roy. Hosp. NHS Trust. Prev: Regist. (Surg.) Scunthorpe HA.

OLUWOLE, Mr Matthew Olufunso Kolawole Dept of Otorlaryngology, Memorial Hospital, Darlington DL3 6HX; 19 Ettergill Drive, Darlington DL3 8UD — MB BS 1983 Ibadan; FRCS (Otol.) Ed. 1991; FRCS Part III 1997. Cons. Otolryngologist, Memor. Hosp., Darlington. Socs: RSM; BAOL; HNS.

OLVER, Miss Jane Madeleine Charing Cross Hospital, Fulham Palace Road, London W6 8RF Tel: 020 8846 1234 Fax: 020 8846 1111; Western Eye Hospital, Marylebone Road, London NW1 — MB BS 1979 Lond.; BSc (Hons.) Lond. 1976; FRCS Eng. 1984; DO RCS Eng. 1983. (St. Thos.) Cons. Ophth. & Oculoplastic Surg. Char. Cross Hosp. & W.. Eye Hosp. Lond. Socs: Roy. Soc. Med. Prev: Sen. Regist. Moorfields Eye Hosp. Lond.; Francis & Rene Hock Jun. Research Fell. Moorfields Eye Hosp.; Regist. (Ophth.) Univ. Hosp. Wales Cardiff & SHO (Neurosurg.) Brook Hosp. Lond.

OLVER, Julian John, TD 47 Myddelton Park, Whetstone, London N20 0JJ Tel: 020 8446 4315 Email: jjolver@cwcom.net — MB BS 1974 Lond.; FFA RCS Eng. 1981. (St. Thos.) Cons. Anaesth. Chase Farm Hosp. Enfield. Socs: Assn. Anaesth.; Intens. Care Soc. Prev: Sen. Regist. (Anaesth.) Roy. Free Hosp. Lond.; Regist. (Anaesth.) Univ. Coll. Hosp. Lond.; SHO St. Thos. Hosp. Lond.

OLVER, Julie Diane 36 The Grove, Hales Road, Cheltenham GL52 6SX — MB ChB 1984 Birm.; DRCOG 1989. GP Cheltenham & Staunton Retainer Scheme. Prev: Trainee GP Worcester.

OLVER, Michael John Middlewich Road Surgery, 6 Middlewich Road, Sandbach CW11 1DL Tel: 01270 767411 Fax: 01270 759305 — MB BS 1960 Lond.; MRCS Eng. LRCP Lond. 1960; DObst RCOG 1961. (Univ. Coll. Hosp.) Socs: BMA. Prev: Ho. Off. Obst. St. Mary's Hosps. Manch.; Ho. Phys. Paediat. Duchess of York Hosp. Babies Manch.

OLVER, Richard Edmund 45 West Side, Wandsworth Common, London SW18 2EE — MB BS 1966 Lond.; BSc (Physiol.) Lond. 1963, MB BS 1966; FRCP Lond. 1982, M 1970. Reader (Paediat.) Univ. Coll. Lond.; Cons. Paediat. Univ. Coll. Hosp. Lond. Prev: Ho. Phys. Med. Unit & Dept. Paediat. St. Thos. Hosp. Lond.; MRC Trav. Fell. Cardiovasc. Research Inst. Univ. Calif. San; Francisco USA; Vis. Prof. Physiol. Univ. New York USA.

OLVER, Robert Hartley (retired) Bay View Cottage, West Pentire, Crantock, Newquay TR8 5SE — MB ChB 1927 Leeds.

OLVER, William John 13 Queens Gardens, St Andrews KY16 9TA Tel: 01334 474531 — MB ChB 1993 Aberd.; BMedBiol. Aberd. 1992. (Aberd.) Specialist Regist. (Microbiol.) Qu. Med. Centre, Nottm. Socs: BMA; MDDUS. Prev: SHO (Microbiol.) Roy. Free Hosp.; SHO (Infect. Dis.) Roy. Free Hosp.; SHO (Cas.) W.. Infirm. Glas.

OLVERMAN, George Nicholson Department of Accident and Emergency, Macclesfield District General Hospital, 3 Victoria Road, Macclesfield SK10 3BL — MB ChB 1984 Glas.; BSc Hons. Glas. 1978; FFARCS Dub 1992. (Glas.) Cons. A & E Maeclesfield Dutet Gen. Hosp. Socs: BMA.

OM PRAKASH, Manni 19 The Loning, Colindale, London NW9 6DR — MB BS 1977 Madras.

OMAR, Mr Mohie El-Din Surgical Unit, Epsom General Hospital, Dorking Road, Epsom KT18 7EG — MB ChB 1978 Alexandria; FRCS Ed. 1990.

OMARA-BOTO, Tom Cabin Adie University College Hospital, Huntley St., London WC1E 6DH; 221 Rosendale Road, West Dulwich, London SE21 8LW — MRCS Eng. LRCP Lond. 1980; MRCOG 1986; Cert. Family Plann. RCOG 1982. Sen. Regist. (O & G) Univ. Coll. Hosp. Lond.; Mem. Europ. Soc. Hysteroscopy (Lond. Represen.). Socs: BMA. Prev: Research Fell. Lond. Hosp. Med. Coll. Newham Gen. Hosp.; Regist. (O & G) Whittington Hosp. Lond.; SHO (O & G) King's Coll. Hosp. Lond.

OMARI, Amy Anita Aika c/o Drive R. Morgan, 54 Rosemead Avenue, Pensby, Wirral CH61 9NW — MB BCh 1989 Wales; MRCP (Paediat.) 1997; DTM & H Liverp. 1990. SHO (Paediat.) Wirral. Prev: Trainee GP Wirral.

OMAYER, Mr Abdalla Salim 12 The Greenway, Hounslow TW4 7AJ — MB BCh 1973 Cairo; FRCS Glas. 1983.

OMER, Fazal The Headland Surgery, 113 Durham Street, Hartlepool TS24 0HU Tel: 01429 288100 Fax: 01429 282500; 21 Bankston Close, Hartlepool TS26 0PP — MB ChB 1984 Dundee. Prev: Trainee GP Scunthorpe VTS; SHO (Anaesth.) Gen. Hosp. Hartlepool.

OMER, Murwan Ibrahim 38 Jenner House, Restell Close, London SE3 7UW — MB BCh 1981 Zagazig, Egypt; MRCOG 1993.

OMOKANYE, Adenike Musili Bassetlaw NHS Trust, Worksop S81 0BD Tel: 01909 481156 Email: omokanye@aol.com; Wentworth House, 57 Water Meadows, Worksop S80 3DB Tel: 01909 481156 Email: omokanye@aol.com — 1993 DCH; 1985 MBBS; 1997 MRCPI; 1997 MRCPCH. (Ahmadu Bello Univ. Zaria Nigeria) GP Regist., Bawtry health centre. Prev: SHO (Paediat.) Pinderfields Hosp. Wakefield; SHO Obst. & Gynae. Wom.s hosp, Dorchester Roy.; SHO Psychiat., Doncaster Roy. Infirmary.

OMOKANYE, Salmon Ajikanle Rotherham Health Authority, Bevan House, Oakwood Hall Drive S60 3AQ Tel: 01709 302151 Fax: 01709 302154 Email: omokanye@aol.com; Wentworth House, 57 Water Meadows, Worksop S80 3DB Tel: 01919 481156, 07932 671921 Email: omokanye@aol.com — 1992 MRCOG; 2001 FFPCGC; 2001 cert.NEBS; 1998 Loc.PG.ED; 1989 FMCOG (Nigeria); 1980 MBBS, Ibadan; 1993 MFFP. (University of Ibadan Nigeria (1975-1980)) Vocational Train. scheme, Rotheram; VTS trainee, Ment. health Serv.s; Rotherham Gen. hHosp., Rotherham. Socs: Brit. Menopause Soc.; Europ. Soc. for Contracep. Prev: Sen. Clin. Med. Off., family Plann. and reproductive health care, Nottg; Staff Grade in OBS and Gynal.Bassetlaw Hosp.; Sen. Ho. Off. in obs &Gynae, Glousestershire Roy.

OMOLOLU, Mr Ajibade Gabriel 46 Pasquier Road, Walthamstow, London E17 6HB — MB BS 1983 Lagos; FRCS Ed. 1992.

OMOREGBEE, Mr Anthony Igbinoghodua Kayode 71 Albany Road, Hornchurch RM12 4AE — MB BS 1975 Lagos; FRCS Glas. 1990.

OMOREGIE, Teghese George 66 Rhodfa Fadog, Morriston, Swansea SA6 6NQ Tel: 01922 781602 — MB BS 1977 Benin; MRCP (UK) 1984; DCH RCPSI 1982.

OMRAN, Hany Talaat Ibrahim Yeovil District Hospital, Higher Kingston, Yeovil BA21 4AT Tel: 01935 475122; 11 Oakleigh, Sampson Wood, Yeovil BA20 2SR Tel: 01935 422880 Email: hanyomran@tinyonline.co.uk — MB BCh 1982 Cairo; MRCOG 1994. Staff Grade Practitioner, O & G, Yeovil Dist. Hosp. Yeovil. Socs: BMA.

ON, Fei Wen Flat 1/L, 314 St George's Road, Glasgow G3 6JR — MB ChB 1995 Glas.

ONAFOWOKAN, Jamilat Aduke 43 Denton Avenue, Leeds LS8 1LE — MB ChB 1980 Leeds; MD Leeds 1988; MRCP (UK) 1983.

ONEILL, Mary Frances 19 South Parade, Belfast BT7 2GL — MB BCh BAO 1983 Belf.; DO RCPSI 1988.

ONEN, Tom Sunny 186 Orchards Way, Beckenham BR3 3EU Tel: 020 8650 7809 — MB ChB 1976 Makerere; MRCPsych 1986. Cons. Psychiat. St. Thos. Hosp. Lond.; Hon. Sen. Lect. UMDS Guy's & St. Thos. Hosps. Lond. Prev: Regist. (Psychiat.) Crawley Hosp; Sen. Regist. Rotat. (Psychiat.) St. Thos. & Guy's Hosps. Lond.

ONG, Albert Chee Meng Clinical Sciences Centre, University Section of Medicine, Northern General Hospital, Herries Road, Sheffield S5 7AU — BM BCh 1984 Oxf.; MA Oxf. 1986, BA (Hons.) 1981; MRCP (UK) 1987; DM Oxf. 1997. (Oxford) Sen. Lect. & Cons. Nephrol., Univ. of Sheff. Prev: Sen. Regist., (Nephrol.), Oxf. Renal Unit; NKRF Sen. Research Fell., Oxf. Univ.; Clin. Lect. (Med.) Univ. Coll. Lond. Med. Sch.

ONG, Christina 9 West Heath Avenue, London NW11 7QS — MB BS 1997 Lond.

ONG, Mr Eng Kwee Highlans Acute Hospitals NHS Trust, Raigmore Hospital, Old Perth Rd, Inverness IV2 3UJ; 11 Waverlyey Drive, Prescot L34 1PU Email: engong@aol.com — MB BCh BAO 1995 N U Ireland; MB ChB BAO N U Ireland; MRCS 1999 Glasgow; FRCS 1999 Royal College of Surgeons, Ireland. (University College Cork) Specialist Regist. Urol. Raigmore Hosp., Inverness. Prev: Surgic. Train., Mersey Deanery.

ONG, Miss Evelyn Geok Peng 9 Ridgeway Gardens, * *, Highgate, London N6 5XR Tel: 020 7272 2841 Email: eong.@aol.com — MB BS 1994 Lond.; BSc Lond. 1991; FRCS Eng. 1998. (Royal Free Hospital) SHO Neonat. Unit, Chelsea & W.minster. Prev: SHO Surg., Derriford Hosp. Plymouth; SHO Paediat. Surg., Brist. Childr.s Hosp.

ONG, Florina Geok-Cheong 10 Holme Lacey Road, London SE12 0HR — MB BS 1992 Lond.

ONG, Grace May Leng 23 Martinville Park, Belfast BT8 7JH — MB BCh BAO 1993 Belf. (Qu. Univ. Belf.) SHO Microbiol. Roy. Vict. Dept. Belf. Socs: BMA; Med. Sicknes Soc.

ONG, Hean Yee 18 Rossdale Road, Belfast BT8 6TG Tel: 01232 793198 Email: heanong@doctors.org.uk; Lot 71A Jalan Tasek, Kuala Lumpur 58100, Malaysia Tel: 00 603 7811740 — MB BCh BAO 1994 Belf.; MRCP Edin. 1998.

ONG, Jeannie Peng Lan 5 Barnfield Close, Cardiff CF23 8LN — MB BCh 1995 Wales.

ONG, Juling 7 Chasely Crescent, Cheltenham GL51 3RY — MB BS 1996 Lond.

ONG, Kar-Binh FLat 12 Cathedral Lodge, 110-115 Aldersgate St., London EC1A 4JE — MB BS 1995 Lond.

ONG, Mr Kee Thiam Blackpool Victoria Hospital, Whinney Heys Road, Blackpool FY3 8NR; 37 Reeves Road, Chorlton-cum-Hardy, Manchester M21 8BU Tel: 0161 881 3372 — MB ChB 1985 Liverp.; FRCS Ed. 1989. Regist. (Gen. Surg.) Blackpool Vict. Hosp. Socs: MDU. Prev: Regist. (Gen. Surg.) Burnley Gen. Hosp., Hope Hosp. Salford & OrmskirkDist. Gen. Hosp.

ONG, Keh Oon Trust Office, Law Hospital NHS Trust, Carluke ML8 5ER — MB BS 1996 Melbourne.

ONG, Kenneth Kian Leong 76 Station Road, London N22 7SY Email: ken.ong@paediatrics.oxford.ac.uk — MB BChir 1991 Camb.; MA Camb. 1992; MRCP (UK) 1994. (Camb. & Guy's Hosp. Lond.) Research Fell. (Paediat. Endocrinol.) John Radcliffe Hosp. Oxf. Prev: Regist. (Paediat.) Wexham Pk. Hosp. Slough.

ONG, Liang Chai Edmund Department of Infection & Tropical Medicine, Newcastle General Hospital, Newcastle upon Tyne NE4 6BE Tel: 0191 273 8811 Fax: 0191 273 0900 Email: e.l.c.ong@ncl.ac.uk — MB BS 1983 Newc.; MSc Lond. 1987; FRCPI 1993, M 1986; DTM & H RCP Lond. 1987; FRCP 1997. (Univ. Newc. Med. Sch.) Cons. Phys. & Sen. Lect. (Med.) with interest Infec. Dis. Newc. Gen. Hosp. Socs: Fell. Roy. Soc. Trop. Med. & Hyg.; Internat. AIDS Soc.; Brit. Infec. Soc. Prev: Sen. Regist. & Regist. (Infec. Dis. & Gen. Med.) Monsall Hosp. Manch.; SHO Rotat. (Med.) S. Cleveland Hosp. Middlesbrough.

ONG, Paul Jau Lueng 122 Ruskin Park House, London SE5 8TL; 33B Estoril Court, 55 Garden Road, Mid-Level, Hong Kong Tel: 524 3831 — MB BChir 1992 Camb. Ho. Off. (Med.) Norf. & Norwich Hosp. Prev: Ho. Off. (Surg.) Addenbrooke's Hosp. Camb.

ONG, Poh Suan 134 Gainsborough Road, Hayes UB4 8PT — MB BS 1983 Lond.; MRCPath 1990.

ONG, Shong Meng 68 Queensborough Gardens, Hyndland, Glasgow G12 9TU — MB ChB 1993 Glas.; FRCS Glas. 1998. SHO (Gen. Surg.) S.ern Gen. Hosp. Prev: SHO (Gen. Surg.) Monklands Hosp.

ONG, Soo Heng Russell Court, Lisburn Road, Belfast BT9 7AB — MB BCh BAO 1995 Belf.

ONG, Thian Keh 17 Hazelmere Avenue, Melton Park, Gosforth, Newcastle upon Tyne NE3 5QL — MB ChB 1993 Sheff.; BDS Sheff. 1984; FDS RCS Eng. 1988.

ONG, Tuyen Binh 4 Norris House, Grove St., London SE8 5RF — MB BS 1998 Lond.

***ONG, Voon Hong** Room 700, Staff Residence, Hull Royal Infirmary, Anlaby Road, Hull HU3 2JZ Tel: 01482 328541 Ext: 4676; 17 Rmk Dusun Nylor, Seremban, Negeri Sembilan 70100, Malaysia — MS BS 1996 Melbourne; MB BS Melbourne 1996.

***ONG, Wei Wei** Walsgrave Hospital, Clifford Bridge Road, Coventry CV2 2DX Tel: 024 76 602020; 5 Melina Court, Grove End Road, London NW8 9SB Tel: 0973 369250 — MB BS 1996 Lond.

ONG, Yee Ean 19 Walsham Drive, Huddersfield HD3 3GS — MB BS 1993 Lond.

ONG, Yee Gan 19 Walsham Drive, Salendine Nook, Huddersfield HD3 3GS — MB BS 1991 Lond.

ONG, Yeu Theng 81 Leigh Hunt Drive, Southgate, London N14 6DF Tel: 020 8447 9225 — MB BCh BAO 1995 Belf. (Qu. Univ. Belf.) SHO (O & G) N. Middlx. Hosp. Lond. Socs: Med. Defence Union; BMA; MPA. Prev: SHO Roy. Vict. Hosp. Belf.

ONG, Yong Lee 101 Greer Park Avenue, Belfast BT8 7YF Email: docs@ljf13.demon.co.uk — MB BCh BAO Belf. 1991; MRCP (UK) 1995. (Queen's University of Belfast) Specialist Regist. Haemat.

ONG, Yuen Li 6 Hugh Street, Belfast BT9 7HH — MB BCh BAO 1990 Belf.; MB BCh Belf. 1990.

ONI, Mr John Queen's Medical Centre, Nottingham NG7 2UH — MB BCh BAO 1982 Dub.; MA Dub. 1987; FRCS Glas. 1987; FRCS (Orthop.) 1996. Cons. (QMC Nottm.). Socs: Roy. Soc. Med.; Assoc. Mem. BOA. Prev: Sen. Regist. (Orthop.) St. Jas. Hosp. Leeds; Regist. (Orthop.) Qu. Mary's Hosp. Sidcup, Huddersfield Roy. Infirm. & Roy. Halifax Infirm.

ONI, Mr Olusola Olumide Akindele Koro Lodge, 16 Sutherington Way, Meadowfields, Anstey, Leicester LE7 7TH Tel: 0116 236 7858 — MB BS 1973 Ibadan; MSc Leic. 1994, MD 1987; FRCS Ed. 1977. Cons. Orthop. Surg. Glenfield Gen. Hosp. Leicester; Lect. (Orthop. Surg.) Univ. Leicester. Socs: Brit. Assn. Surg. Knee; Fell. Nigerian Postgrad. Med. Coll. 1984; Fell. W. African Coll. Surgs. 1983. Prev: Sen. Lect. Univ. Leicester; Sen. Regist. (Orthop.) Watford Gen. Hosp.; Lect. (Orthop. Surg.) Univ. Benin, Nigeria.

ONI-ORISAN, John Edward Adetokubo Airdrie Health Centre, Monkscourt Avenue, Airdrie ML6 0JU Tel: 01236 769333; 14 Woodview Drive, Cairnhill, Airdrie ML6 9HJ Tel: 01236 769333 — MB BS 1964 Lond.; MRCS Eng. LRCP Lond. 1964; FRCOG 1989, M 1968. (Guy's) Med. Off. St. And.Hospice Airdrie; Mem. Airdrie LMC. Socs: Glas. Obst. Soc. Prev: Regist. (O & G) Ayrsh. Centr. Hosp. Irvine; Sen. Regist. (O & G) Univ. Coll. Hosp. Ibadan, Nigeria.

ONION, Carl William Reginald Wirral Health Authority, St. Catherines Hospital, 1st Floor Admin. Block, Church Road, Tranmere, Birkenhead CH42 0LQ Tel: 0151 651 0011 Fax: 0151 652 2668; 10 Ploughmans Way, Great Sutton, South Wirral CH66 2YJ Tel: 0151 339 2154 — MB ChB 1980 Liverp.; MSc Liverp. 1991; MRCGP 1989; MD Liverp. 1997. Med. Dir. & Med. Adviser Wirral HA; Hon. Lect. (Med. Educat.) Univ. Liverp.; Examr. Fac. Pub. Health RCP Lond., Ed., Glas. Socs: Assn. Primary Care Med. Advisers; Hon. Sec. Mersey Fac. RCGP. Prev: GP Birkenhead.

ONNIE, Clive Morris 31 Hill Rise, Hampstead Garden Suburb, London NW11 6LY Tel: 020 8455 5964; 31 Hill Rise, Hampstead Garden Suburb, London NW11 6LY Tel: 020 8455 5964 — MB BS 1996 Lond.; BSc (Hons) 1993 Lond. SHO Gen. Med. Rotat. N.wick Pk. Hosp. Harrow. Prev: Surgic. Ho. Off. Middlx. Hosp.; Med. Ho. Off. Roy. Hosp.

ONOCHE, Anne Ogugua 10 Arnal Crescent, Linstead Way, London SW18 5PX — MB BS 1988 Nigeria; MRCP (UK) 1993.

ONOJEJE-ORAKA, Augustine 28 Tylney Avenue, Dulwich Wood Park, London SE19 1LN — MB BS 1985 Benin.

ONON, Temujin Argyle Street Surgery, 141 Argyle Street, Heywood OL10 3SD Tel: 01706 366135 Fax: 01706 627706 — MB ChB 1983 Aberd. Prev: Trainee GP Coleshill Birm.; SHO (A & E) Hull Roy. Infirm.; Ho. Off. (Surg.) & Ho. Off. (Med.) Hull Roy. Infirm.

ONONYE

ONONYE, Lawrence Azubike 823 Finchley Road, London NW11 8AJ — MB ChB 1964 Glas. Med. Dir. Bendel Clinic Warri. Prev: Med. Off. Unilever Plantations, Nigeria.

ONORI, Kathleen Margaret The Richmond Practice, Health Centre, Dean Road, Bo'ness EH51 0DH Tel: 01506 822665 Fax: 01506 825939; 2 Kinglass Drive, Bo'ness EH51 9RB — MB ChB 1974 Ed.; MRCGP 1978; DRCOG 1976. (Ed.)

ONSLOW, Julie Marie Anaesthetic Department, Southampton General Hospital, Trenona Road, Southampton Tel: 02380 777222; 7 Hawthorn Close, Colden Common, Winchester SO21 1UX Tel: 01962 715383 — BM 1992 Soton.; DCH 1995; FRCA 1999. (Soton.) Specialist Regist. (Anaesth.) Soton Gen. Hosp. Prev: Specialist Regist., Partsmoth Qu.s Alexandra Hosp.; SHO (ITU) Portsmouth Qu. Alexandra Hosp.; SHO (Anaesth.) Salisbury Hosp.

ONUGHA, Chinye Okwudili Grantham & District Hospital, United Lincolnshire Trust, 101 Manthorpe Road, Grantham NG31 8DG Email: chibin@supanet.com; Email: chibin@supanet.com — MB BS Patna 1965; DA Ibadan 1971; FFA RCSI 1975. (Prince of Wales Med. Coll. Patna) Cons. Anaesth. Trent RHA. Socs: BMA & Soc. Anaesth. of Gt. Brit. & Irel.; Assn. Anaesth.; Soc. Low Flow Anaesth. Prev: Sen. Regist. (Anaesth.) N. Staffs. Hosps. Centre Stoke-on-Trent; Lect. (Anaesth.) Univ. Benin Teach. Hosp., Nigeria.

ONUGHA, Edwin Nwokedi 3 Wood Close, Salfords, Redhill RH1 5EE; East Surrey Hospital, Three Arch Road, Redhill RH1 5RH Tel: 01737 768511 — BM BCh 1976 Univ. Nigeria; DRCOG 1984. (University of Nigeria Medical School) Assoc. Specialist (O & G).

ONUOHA, Oyoyo Ogoegbunam 12 St Georges Avenue, London NW9 0JU — MB ChB 1996 Bristol.

ONWUBALILI, James Kenechukwu North Middlesex Hospital, Sterling Way, London N18 1QX Tel: 020 8887 4648 Fax: 020 8887 4491; 44 Little Bornes, London SE21 8SE Tel: 020 8670 9206 Fax: 020 8670 9206 Email: jko@doctors.org.uk — MB BS 1975 Ibadan; MD Ibadan 1985; FRCP Lond. 1992; MRCP (UK) 1979; T(M) 1995. (Ibadan Nigeria) Cons. Phys. & Nephrol. N. Middlx. & The Roy. Free Hosps. Lond. Socs: Brit. Renal Assn.; Europ. Dialysis & Transpl. Assoc.; Fell.sh. Roy. Soc. Of Med. Prev: Sen. Cons. Neprol. King Abdulaziz Hosp. Jeddah, Saudi Arabia; Cons. Nephrol. & Sen. Lect. (Med.) Univ. Nigeria Teach. Hosp. Enugu; MRC Research Fell Clin. Research Centre Harrow.

ONWUCHEKWA, Wilvar Ohiaeri 38 Bonsor House, Patmore Est., London SW8 4UR — MB BS 1963 Lond.; FMCGP (Nigeria) 1982; T(GP) 1993; DObst RCOG 1967; DCH RCP Lond. 1966. Socs: Assoc. Mem. Roy. Coll. Gen. Pract. Prev: Chief Med. Off. i/c Staff Health at Nat. Orthop. Hosp. Enugu, Nigeria.

ONWUDE, Joseph Loze St John's Hospital, Wood St., Chelmsford CM2 9BG Tel: 01245 513456; Springfield Medical Centre, Lawn Lane, Springfield, Chelmsford CM1 7GU Tel: 01245 461777 — MB BS 1981 Ibadan; MRCOG 1988; T(OG) 1993. Cons. St. Jas. Univ. Hosp. Leeds. Socs: Blair Bell Res. Soc. Prev: Sen. Regist. & Lect. Univ. Leeds.

ONWUDIKE, Mr Madu Dept of General Surgery, Bolton Hospitals NHS Trust, Royal Bolton Hospital, Bolton BL4 0JR Tel: 01204 390390 Fax: 01204 390109 Email: madu.onwudike@bolton-tr.nwest.nhs.uk; Tel: 020 484 1590 Fax: 020 8989 8884 Email: madu@frankford.clara.net — MB BS 1984 Ibadan; FRCS Ed. 1992; MSc (Surg. Sci.) Lond. 1996; FRCS 1999. Cons. Gen. and Vasc. Surg., Bolton Hosp. NHS Trust. Socs: Assn. Surg. Of GB & Irel.; Fell. W. African Coll. & Surg. 1996; Vasc. Surg. Soc. GB & Irel. Prev: Sp. Reg. Whipps Cross Hosp.; Sp. Reg. Vasc. Surg., Barts and the Lond. NHS Trust.; Sp. Reg. Vasc. Surg., Univ. Coll. Lond. Hosp. NHS Trust.

ONYALI, Mr Kenneth Obidigbo 30 Burwash Road, London SE18 7QZ Tel: 020 8855 9397 — MB BS 1985 Nigeria; FRCS Ed. 1990.

ONYEABO, Benjamin Chukwunwuba 25 Kelland Close, Park Road, Hornsey, London N8 8JS Tel: 020 8341 4874 — MB ChB BAO 1953 Belf.; DTM & H Liverp. 1955. Med. Specialist (Genitourin. Med.) Char. Cross Hosp. Gp. Lond. Socs: Fell. Roy. Soc. Trop. Med. & Hyg.

ONEADOR, Miriam Ijeoma Walm Lane Surgery, 114 Walm Lane, London NW2 4RT Tel: 0208 451 4100 — MB BS 1979 Nigeria; MFFP 1995; MRCOG 1988. GP Princip.; Forens. Med. Examr. for Victims of Sexual Assault for the Metrop. Police. Socs: Fac. of Family Plann.; BMA.

ONYEAMA, Warwick Paul Joseph Chukwuma Cygnet Wing Blackheath, 80-82 Blackheath Hill, London Tel: 0208 694 2111 Fax: 0208 692 0570; Email: warany@doctors.org.uk — MB BS 1967 Lond.; MRCS Eng. LRCP Lond. 1967; FRCPsych 1991, M 1991; T(Psych) 1991; MAE (Eng) 1997; DPM Eng. 1972. Independant Cons. Psychiat.,Hon.Cons., Slam (NHS) Trust. Socs: Brit. Med. Assn. (Mem.); Acad. of Experts (Mem.); Roy. Coll. of Psychiat.s (Fell.). Prev: Sen. Lect. (Psychiat.) Univ. Nigeria Teachg. Hosp. Enugu, Nigeria; Med. Dir. Staff Psychiat. Hosp. Enugu, Nigeria; Cons. Psychiat..Lect.S. Lond. Maldsley NHS Trust & Glct Med. Sch.

ONYEKWERE, Chukwuma Ugwoeze Chugozare 47 Wood End Way, Chandlers Ford, Eastleigh SO53 4LN — BM 1989 Soton.

ONYEKWULUJE, Chike Egbounu 36 Dovehouse Close, Bromham, Bedford MK43 8PS — MB BS 1976 Ibadan; MB BS Ibadan Nigeria 1976; FRCR 1985.

ONYETT, Roger Martin Mount Pleasant Health Centre, Mount Pleasant Road, Exeter EX4 7BW Tel: 01392 55262 Fax: 01392 270497; 36 Monmouth Street, Topsham, Exeter EX3 0AJ Tel: 01392 873853 — MB BS 1973 Lond.; MRCS 1973 Eng.; MRCGP 1979; BSc 1961 Nott.; LRCP 1973 Lond.; DCH 1975 Eng.; BSc Nottm. 1961; MRCS Eng. LRCP Lond. 1973; MRCGP 1979; DCH Eng. 1975. (Roy. Free) Trainer (Gen. Pract.) Exeter.

ONYIRIMBA, Faustinus Chidi Flat 16, Block 3, Flat 3 Residence, Walsgrave Hospital, Clifford Bridge Road, Coventry CV2 2DX — MB BS 1985 Nigeria; MRCP (UK) 1993.

OO, Mg Mg Bedwell Medical Centre, Sinfield Close, Bedwell Crescent, Stevenage SG1 1LQ Tel: 01438 355551 Fax: 01438 749704.

OO, Myint S. Cleveland Hospital, Marton Road, Middlesbrough TS4 3BW Tel: 01642 854869 Fax: 01642 854870; 46 The Green, Norton, Stockton-on-Tees TS20 1DU Tel: 01642 556291 Fax: 01642 556291 — MB BS 1960 Rangoon; FRCP Lond. 1982, M 1966; DCH Eng. 1962. (Rangoon Med. Coll.) Cons. Paediat. N. Tees Gen. Hosp. Stockton-on-Tees; Locum Cons. Comm. Paediat., Tees & N.E. Yorks. NHS Trust. Middlesbrough. Socs: BMA; Paediat. Assn.; N. Eng. Paediat. Soc.

OO, Myint Kyam Warrengate and Batley Road Surgery, Upper Warrengate, Wakefield WF1 4PR Tel: 01924 371011; 3 The Holloway, Amblecote, Stourbridge DY8 4DL — MB BS 1987 Med. Inst. (I) Rangoon.

OODIT, Ramesh Jugmohan 14 Hazelwood Close, Clondalkin, Dublin 22, Republic of Ireland Tel: 00 353 1 4592813; 33 Trajan Walk, Roman Way, Andover SP10 5JW Tel: 01264 365980 — MB BCh BAO 1989 Dub. Regist. (Obst. & Gyn.) Bishop Auckland Hosp. Co. Durh. Socs: BMA. Prev: Regist. (Obst.) Birm. Matern. Hosp.; SHO (Obst. & Gyn.) Whipps Cross Hosp.

OOI, Mrs Jane Louise — MB ChB 1990 Liverp.; FRCS Ed. 1995. Specialist Regist. (Gen. Surg.) Mersey Deanery. Prev: Specialist Regist. (Gen. Surg.) NW Deanery; SHO Rotat. (Surg.) Merseyside.

OOI, Kao Hua Centenary Surgery, 9 Centenary Gardens, Coatbridge ML5 4BY Tel: 01236 423355 Fax: 01236 606345 — MB ChB 1981 Glas.; DCH RCPS Glas. 1984; DRCOG 1983. GP Lanarksh.

OOI, Kheng Hong 40 North Linkside Road, Liverpool L25 9NT — MB ChB 1977 Liverp.; MRCS Eng. LRCP Lond. 1979; MRCGP 1986; DRCOG 1984; Dip. Ven. Liverp. 1981; DTM & H Liverp. 1979.

OOI, Laureen Gek Sim Department of Anaesthetics, Broomfield Hospital, Chelmsford CM1 7ET — MB ChB 1982 Ed.; FFA RCS Eng. 1988. Cons. Anaesth. Mid Essex Hosps. Trust. Prev: Cons. Anaesth. Kingston Hosp.; Sen. Regist. (Anaesth.) Roy. Lond. Hosp.; Lect. (Anaesth.) Lond. Hosp. Med. Coll.

OOI, May May Flat 50, Richmond Hill Court, Richmond Hill, Richmond TW10 6BE — MB BS 1991 Lond.

OOI, Richard Gek Beng Stonecroft, Northgate Drive, Camberley GU15 2AP — MB ChB 1984 Bristol; FRCA 1989. Cons. Anaesth. Chelsea & W.m. Healthcare Trust. Prev: Asst. Prof. Anaesth. Duke Univ. & Med. Center, USA; Lect. (Anaesth.) Char. Cross & W.m. Med. Sch. Lond.

OOI, Yang Wern The Charlton Stores, Charlton, Pershore WR10 3LG — BM BCh 1991 Oxf.

OOLBEKKINK, Marjon St Catharine's Hospital, Church Road, Birkenhead CH42 0LQ; 25 Heronpark Way, Spital, Wirral CH63 9FN Tel: 0151 340680 — Artsexamen 1985 Utrecht; PhD Amsterdam 1989. Clin. Asst. (Geriat. Med.) St Catharine's Hosp. Prev: SHO

(Gen. Med.) Bussum, Netherlands; Research Fell. Diabetic Research Amsterdam, Netherlands.

OOMMEN, Elizabeth Flat 1/2, 145 Yorkhill St., Glasgow G3 8NS — MB ChB 1998 Glas.; MB ChB Glas 1998. PRHO in Gen. Surg., Dumfries.

OOMMEN, Mr Puthenparambil Korah 14 Merwood Avenue, Heald Green, Cheadle SK8 3DN; Department of Cardiothoracic Surgery, Wythenshawe Hospital, Southmoor Road, Manchester M22 9RL — MB BS 1979 Mysore; MB BS Mysore 1979; FRCS Eng. 1989; FRCS Ed. 1988. Staff Grade, Cardiothoracic Surg. & ICU Wythenshawe Hosp. Manch.

OON, Lynette Lin Ean 25 Lisburne Road, London NW3 2NS; 3 Peach Garden, Singapore 437604, Singapore — MB BS 1992 Lond.; BSc Lond. 1989; MRCP (UK) 1995. SHO (Neurol.) Lond. Socs: BMA; MDU.

OON, Vincent Jin Huat 6 Woodsford Square, London W14 8DP; Academic Department of Obstetrics and Gynaecology, Imperial College School of Medicine, Chelsea and Westminster Hospital, London SW10 9NH — MB BChir 1991 Camb.; MA Camb. 1992, BA 1988. Research Lect. Acad. Dept. O & G Imperial Coll. Sch. Med. Chelsea & W.m. Hosp. Lond. Prev: SHO (Obst.) UCL Hosps. Lond.

OOSTHUYSEN, Stefanus Adrian Van Rooyen Downtown, Priory Road, St Olaves, Great Yarmouth NR31 9HQ — MB ChB 1980 Cape Town.

OPANEYE, Abayomi Adegboyega Department of Genitourinary Medicine, Middlesbrough General Hospital, Middlesbrough TS5 5AZ Tel: 01642 854548 Fax: 01642 854328; 6 Mallowdale, Nunthorpe, Middlesbrough TS7 0QA Tel: 01642 318236 Fax: 01642 854328 Email: yopaneye@btinternet.com — MB BS 1974 Ibadan; MFFP 1993; MRCOG 1982; FRCOG 1997; MPH 1989 Univ. Cali. Berkeley. Cons. Phys. (Genitourin. Med.) Middlesbrough Gen. Hosp. Cleveland; Cons. Phys. (Genitourin. Med.) Friarage Hosp. N.allerton. Socs: Fell. Roy. Soc. Health; Fell. W. African Coll. Surg.; Med. Soc. Study VD. Prev: Sen. Lect. & Cons. O & G Coll. Health Scs. Ogun State Univ, Nigeria; Cons. O & G King Khalid Hosp. Al-Kharj, Saudi Arabia; Regist. (Obst. Gyn.) Gen. Hosp. S. Shields.

OPDAM, Helen Ingrid Kent & Canterbury Hospital, Department of Anaesthetics, Ethelbert Road, Canterbury CT1 3NG — MB BS 1990 Monash.

OPDEBEECK, Goedele Patricia Edwarda Maria T 15 Eden Park, Scotforth, Lancaster LA1 4SJ Tel: 01524 63459 — MB BCh BAO 1975 NUI; MRCPsych 1989. Sen. Regist. (Psychogeriat.) NW RHA. Prev: Regist. (Psychiat.) Sheff.; Regist. (Psychiat.) Lancaster HA.

OPEMUYI, Isaac Olusoji Olumbamishe — MB BS 1977 Ibadan; FRCOG 2001; MRCOG 1988. Cons. (O & G) Barking, Havering & Redbridge HA.

OPENSHAW, David Rigby 6 Whitestone Close, Lostock, Bolton BL6 4RN — MB ChB 1993 Birm.; ChB Birm. 1993.

OPENSHAW, Professor Peter John Morland Department of Respiratory Medicine, Imperial College at St Mary's, Paddington, London W2 1PG Tel: 020 7594 3854 Fax: 020 7724 7349 Email: p.openshaw@ic.ac.uk — MB BS 1979 Lond.; PhD Brunel Univ. 1989; BSc (Physiol.) Lond. 1976; MRCP (UK) 1982. (Guy's) Prof. (Exp. Med.) Imperial Coll. of Sci. Technol. & Med. Nat. Heart & Lung Inst.; Sen. Lect. (Med.) & Hon. Cons. Phys. St. Mary's Hosp. Med. Sch. Lond. Socs: Fell. Roy. Coll. Phys.; Assn. Phys.; FASEB/Amer. Soc. of Immunol. Prev: MRC Train. Fell.; Regist. Roy. Postgrad. Med. Sch. Lond.

OPENSHAW, Mrs Susan Elizabeth (retired) 104 Bove Town, Glastonbury BA6 8JG Tel: 01458 32181 — BM BCh 1949 Oxf.; BM BCh Oxon. 1949.

OPENSHAW, William Arthur (retired) 104 Bove Town, Glastonbury BA6 8JG Tel: 01458 32181 — BM BCh 1950 Oxf.; MA, BM BCh Oxon. 1950; MRCGP 1974.

OPHER, Simon Joseph The Westgate Surgery, 40 Parsonage Street, Dursley GL11 4AA Tel: 01453 545981 — MB BS 1988 Lond.; MRCGP 1993.

OPIE, Neil John 45 Larch Way, Farnborough GU14 0QW — MB ChB 1998 Leeds.

OPIE, Peter Michael The Roxton Practice, The Surgery, Worsley Road, Immingham, Immingham DN40 1BE Tel: 01469 572058 Fax: 01469 573043 Email: peter.opie@virgin.net; Health Centre, Pelham Crescent, Keelby, Grimsby Tel: 01469 560202 Fax: 01469 573043 — MB BS 1981 Lond.; BSc Lond. 1978; MRCGP 1985; DRCOG 1985. (Westminster)

OPIRA-ODIDA, Mr Francis Xavier 44 Currer Walk, Thornhill Road, Steeton, Keighley BD20 6TL Tel: 01535 652208 Fax: 01535 652208 Email: francis@xavierodida.freeserve.co.uk — MD 1980 Dar-es-Salaam, Tanzania; MMed Uganda 1989; MRCOG 1996. Staff Grade (O & G) Airedale NHS Trust Keighley W. Yorks. Socs: BMA; BSGE; RCOG.

OPITZ, Eugen (retired) 36 Middleton Drive, off Manchester Road, Bury BL9 8DS Tel: 0161 766 3745 — Med. Dipl. Poznan 1938; DPM Eng. 1966. Prev: Asst. (Med.) Prestwich Hosp.

OPPE, Thomas Ernest, CBE 2 parkholme Cottages, Fife Road, Sheen common, London SW14 7ER Tel: 0208 392 1626 — MB BS (Hons., Distinc. Med.) Lond. 1947; FRCP Lond. 1966, M 1948; DCH Eng. 1950. (Guy's) Emerit. Prof. Paediat. Univ. Lond. Prev: Cons. Paediat. St. Mary's Hosp. Lond.; Sen. Censor (1st Vice-Pres.) RCP Lond.; Lect. (Child Health) Univ. Bristol.

OPPEL, Ariane Birgit Lotte Gerda 24 Pwllay Domen Road, Brondeg, Manselton, Swansea SA5 8PX Email: aboppel1@aol.com — State Exam Med 1992 Ulm; DCH 1999; DFFP 1999; ALS 1997; PALS 1998. Non-Princip., Locum Work. Socs: BMA; MDU. Prev: GP Regist., DOU Surg., Redditch.

OPPENHEIM, Audrey Isabelle North East Child and Family Services, Royal Liverpool Children's Hospital, Eaton Road, Alder Hey, Liverpool Tel: 0151 228 4811 — MB ChB 1983 Manch.; BSc Manch. 1983; MRCPsych 1988. Cons. Child Psychiat. & Paediat. Liasion Roy. Liverp. Childr. Hosp.; Mem. of the Nat. Disabil. Living Allowance Bd.; Professional Advisor to NYAS. Prev: Sen. Regist. (Child Psychiat.) Roy. Liverp. Childr. Hosp.; Regist. Withington Hosp. Manch.; Ho. Off. (Med. & Surg.) N. Manch. Gen. Hosp.

OPPENHEIM, Esther Margaret Jiggins Lane Medical Centre, 17 Jiggins Lane, Bartley Green, Birmingham B32 3LE Tel: 0121 477 7272 Fax: 0121 478 4319; 59 Weoley Park Road, Birmingham B29 6QZ Tel: 0121 472 1356 Fax: 0121 472 1356 — MB BCh 1975 Witwatersrand; BSc Witwatersrand 1972; MPH Hebrew Univ. Jerusalem 1980; Cert. Prescribed Equiv. Exp. JCPTGP 1982. (Witwatersrand) Socs: Assoc. Mem. RCGP. Prev: GP Ladywood Birm.; Trainee GP Glyncorrwg VTS; Med. Off. Moroka Hosp. Thaba Nchu, S. Afr.

OPPENHEIMER, Catherine Violet Rosalie P The Warneford Hospital, Oxford OX3 7JX Tel: 01865 226263 — BM BCh Oxf. 1968; FRCP Lond. 1992; MRCP (UK) 1972; FRCPsych 1989, M 1978. (Oxf.) Cons. Psychiat., Dept. of Psychiat. of Old Age, Warneford Hosp., Oxf.; Med. Dir. Oxon. Ment. Healthcare NHS Trust Oxf.

OPPENHEIMER, Christina Adrienne Leicester Royal Infirmary, Maternity Hospital, Infirmary Square, Leicester LE1 5WW Tel: 0116 254 1414 — MB BS 1980 Lond.; MA Camb. 1981; FRCS Eng. 1984; MRCOG 1989. (Cambridge, Westminster Medical School) Cons. O & G Leicester Roy. Infirm.

OPPENHEIMER, Matilda Magdalen Grenville Pangbourne Medical Practice, The Boat House Surgery, Whitchurch Road, Pangbourne, Reading RG8 7DP Tel: 0118 984 2234 Fax: 0118 984 3022 Email: mmgoppenheimer@aol.com; The White House, High St, Whitchurch-on-Thames, Reading RG8 7HA Tel: 01734 842915 Fax: 01734 841264 — MB BS 1981 Lond.; MA Oxf. 1978; MRCGP 1985; DRCOG 1984. p/t Gen. Practitioner. Socs: Wom. Med. Federat.; Reading Path. Soc.; RCGP.

OPPENHEIMER, Stephen James 81 Bainton Road, Oxford OX2 7AG — BM BCh 1971 Oxf.; BA (Hons. Physiol.) Oxf. 1968, DM 1988, BM BCh 1971; FRCP Ed. 1991; MRCP (UK) 1975; DTM & H Liverp. 1978. Assoc. Prof. (Paediat.) Univ. Sains Malaysia; Hon. Sen. Lect. Dept. Trop. Paediat. Liverp. Sch. Trop. Med. Socs: Brit. Paediat. Assn. Malaysian Med. Assn. Prev: Sen. Research Fell./Clin. Lect. Dept. Trop. Paediat. Liverp. Sch. Trop. Med.; Sen. Lect./Hon. Cons. Dept. Paediat. Univ. Oxf.; Dir. Wellcome Trust Research Laborat. Kilifi, Kenya.

OPPONG, Amma Caroline Kyerewaa 1 Hoveton Close, Shelton Lock, Derby DE24 9QH Tel: 01332 732371 Fax: 01332 732371 — BM BS 1988 Nottm.; MRCP (UK) 1992; DCH RCP Lond. 1990; MD Keele 1997. (Nottingham University) Sen. Regist. (Community Paediat.) S.. Derbysh. NHS Trust. Socs: BACCH; RCPCH; BMA. Prev: Regist. (Paediat.) City Gen. Hosp. Stoke-on-Trent; SHO (Neonat. &

OPPONG

Gen. Paediat.) Leicester Roy. Infirm.; SHO (Paediat.) Alder Hey & Roy. Liverp. Childr. Hosp.

OPPONG, Mr Fielding Christian Derriford Hospital, Derriford Road, Plymouth PL6 8DH Tel: 01752 777111 Fax: 01752 768976; 58 Hermitage Road, Mannamead, Plymouth PL3 4RY Tel: 01752 224184 Email: chris.oppong@phnt.swest.nhs.uk — MB ChB 1979 Ghana; FRCS Eng. 1989. (Univ. Ghana) Assoc. Specialist (Gen. Surg.). Socs: Fell. Roy. Coll. Surg. Eng.; Assoc. Mem. Assn. Surg. GB & Irel.; Assoc. Mem. Assn ColoProctol. of Gr. Britain & N. Irel. Prev: Staff Grade Surg. (Gen. Surg.); Regist. (Gen. Surg. & Urol.) Derriford Hosp. Plymouth; Regist. (Gen. Surg.) Derriford Hosp. Plymouth & Airedale Hosp. Keighley.

OPPONG, Kofi Ernest Nana Wadie 8 Berwick Hill Road, Ponteland, Newcastle upon Tyne NE20 9UU — BM 1987 Soton.; MRCP (UK) 1990. Research Fell. (Med.) Med. Sch. Univ. Newc. u. Tyne. Prev: Regist. (Med.) Sunderland Roy. Infirm.; Regist. (Med.) Roy. Vict. Infirm. Newc. u. Tyne.

OR, Christine — MB BS 1994 Lond.; DFFP 1997; DRCOG 1996; Dip Ther 1999. (UMDS) GP Locum. Socs: Med. Defence Union.; BMA. Prev: Vocationally Trained Acad. Assoc. VTAA Market Pl. Surg. Kent.

ORAEDU, Mr Ogugua Christian Department of General Surgery, Wycombe General Hospital, Queen Alexander Road, High Wycombe HP11 2TT — MB BS 1985 Lagos; FRCS Ed. 1993; FRCSI 1993.

ORAELOSI, Florence Nwakaego Obiamaka Ecclesbourne, Warwick Terrace, Lea Bridge Road, London E17 9DP Tel: 020 8539 2077; 504 Chigwell Road, Woodford Green IG8 8PA Tel: 020 8504 2126 — MB BCh BAO 1982 NUI. Prev: SHO (O & G) Birm. & Midl. Hosp. for Wom. & Birm. Matern. Hosp.; SHO (Paediat.) Roy. Gwent Hosp. Newport Wales; Regist. (O & G) Burton Dist. Hosp. Centre.

ORAKWE, Mr Samuel Ikemefuna 95 Berkeley Road, Shirley, Solihull B90 2HT — MB BS 1986 Univ. Nigeria; FRCS Ed. 1992.

ORAKZAI, Mr Nasir c/o Masood Khan, 14 Hillrise, Cardiff CF23 6UH — MB BS 1983 Peshawar; FRCSI 1991.

ORAM, David Andrew Tandon Medical Centre, Kent St., Upper Gornal, Dudley DY3 1UX Tel: 01902 882243; 5 Turf Cottages, Penn Common, Wolverhampton WV4 5LA — MB ChB 1980 Manch.; DRCOG 1986.

ORAM, David Charles Sunnyside Doctors Surgery, 150 Fratton Road, Portsmouth PO1 5DH Tel: 023 9282 4725 Fax: 023 9286 1014 — MB BS 1979 Lond.; BSc (Hons.) (Pharmacol.) Lond. 1976; MRCS Eng. LRCP Lond. 1979; MRCGP 1985; DCH RCP Lond. 1985; DRCOG 1984. (St. Bart.) Socs: BMA.

ORAM, Mr David Howard 121 Harley Street, London W1G 6AX Tel: 020 7935 7111 Fax: 020 7935 9001 Email: oram@gynaecology.freeserve.co.uk; Papplewick, 33 College Road, London SE21 7BG — MB BS 1971 Lond.; MRCS Eng. LRCP Lond. 1971.; FRCOG 1990, M 1977; DObst RCOG 1974. (King's Coll. Hosp.) Cons. Gyn. Oncol. Dept. Gyn. Oncol. St. Bart. Hosp. Lond. Socs: Blair Bell Res. Soc.; Brit. Gyn. Cancer Soc.; Internat. Gyn. Cancer Soc. Prev: Sen. Regist. King's Coll. Hosp. Lond.; Sen. Regist. King Edwd. VIII Hosp. Durban, S. Afr.; Research Fell. Geo.town Univ. Washington DC, USA.

ORAM, Edmund George 47 Rodney Road, West Bridgford, Nottingham NG2 6JH Tel: 0115 923 2746 — MB ChB 1953 Glas.; FRCPsych 1980, M 1971; DPM Eng. 1959. Emerit. Cons. Psychiat. Univ. Hosp. Qu. Med. Centre Nottm. Prev: Sen. Regist. Nuffield Research Unit Fulbourn Hosp. Camb.; SHO Gen. Hosp. W. Hartlepool; Ho. Phys. & Ho. Surg. Vict. Infirm. Glas.

***ORAM, Emma Louise** River Mead, Moor Road, Staverton, Totnes TQ9 6PB — MB ChB 1994 Birm.; ChB Birm. 1994.

ORAM, John Christopher 2 Devon Road, Failsworth, Manchester M35 0NR — MB ChB 1996 Leeds.

ORAM, Julian John 40 Vincent Square, London SW1P 2NP Tel: 020 7630 5154 Fax: 020 7630 5164 — MB BS 1974 Lond.; FRCP Lond. 1991; MRCP (UK) 1977; MRCS Eng. LRCP Lond. 1974; DObst RCOG 1976. (Guy's) Cons. Phys. (Geriat.) St. Geo. Hosp. Lond. Socs: Brit. Geriat. Soc.; Trustee Brit. Vasc. Foundat. Prev: Sen. Med. Regist. (Geriat.) St. Geo. Hosp. Lond.

ORAM, Matthew Department of Anaesthesia, Bristol Royal Infirmary, Marlborough Street, Bristol BS2 8HW — MB BCh 1993 Wales.

ORAM, Muriel Churchill Holmes Caer Eden, 47 Slamannan Road, Falkirk FK1 5NF Tel: 01324 21170 — MB ChB 1939 Glas.

(Glas.) Socs: BMA. Prev: Clin. Med. Off. Dept. Community Med. W. Lothian Health Dist. Res.; Med. Off. Stobhill Hosp. Glas. & Barnhill Inst. Glas.; Res. Obst. Surg. E.. Dist. Hosp. Glas.

ORAM, Suzanne Burton (retired) 43 London Road, Harston, Cambridge CB2 5QQ Tel: 01209 870320 — MB BS 1948 Adelaide; DObst RCOG 1956. Prev: Clin. Med. Off. Cambs. HA (T).

ORANGE, Gillian Valerie Department of Medical Microbiology, Ninewells Hospital, Dundee DD1 9SY — MB ChB 1979 Glas.

ORANGE, M Park Attwood Clinic, Trimpley, Bewdley DY12 1RE Tel: 01299 861444 Fax: 01299 861375 — Artsexamen 1983 Utrecht; Artsexamen 1983 Utrecht.

ORANGE, Robert William 3 Stonycroft Lane, Barkisland, Halifax HX4 0JD Tel: 01422 825162 — MB ChB 1990 Sheff.; MMedSc (Clin. Psychiat.) Leeds; MRCPsych 1995. Prev: Sen. Reg, Gen. Adult Psychiat. St. Jas. Univ. Hosp. Leeds.

ORANGE-LOHN, Bettina 41 Heath Street, Stourbridge DY8 1SE — State Exam Med 1987 Dusseldorf.

ORBACH, Nathan Suite 1, 3rd Floor, 1 Duchess St., London W1N 3DE — MB BS 1971 Melbourne; MRCP (UK) 1977.

ORBINSON, Helen Maureen 21 Calvertstown Road, Portadown, Craigavon BT63 5NY — MB BCh 1998 Belf.

ORCHARD, Ann Seymour (retired) 67 Croham Road, South Croydon CR2 7HF Tel: 020 8651 1222 — MB BS 1965 Lond.; MRCS Eng. LRCP Lond. 1965; DObst RCOG 1970. Prev: SHO (Obst.) Char. Cross Hosp. Lond.

ORCHARD, Jennifer Ann Milford Hill Cottage, Milford Hill, Salisbury SP1 2QZ — MB BS 1975 Lond.; MRCPath 1983.

ORCHARD, John Michael Limes Medical Centre, Limes Avenue, Alfreton, Derby DE55 7DW Tel: 01773 833133; Bramble Cottage, Main Road, Higham, Alfreton DE55 6EF Tel: 01773 831064 — MB ChB 1980 Liverp.; FRCGP 1995, M 1984; DRCOG 1983. Adviser Dept. of Postgrad. Gen. Pract. Univ. of Sheff. Socs: Chairm. Chesterfield Med. Soc. Prev: Course Organiser (Gen. Pract.) Chesterfield VTS.

ORCHARD, Kim Harold 130 Great Preston Road, Ryde PO33 1AZ; Royal Free Hospital, Hampstead, London NW3 2QG Tel: 020 7794 0500 Email: rfht0020@rfhsm.ac.uk — MB BS 1985 Lond.; BSc (Hons.) Warwick 1977; MRCP (UK); MRCPath 1997. (Royal Free) Research Fell. (Haemat.) Hammersmith & Roy. Free Hosp. Socs: Brit. Soc. Haematol. Prev: Sen.SR Regist. (Haemat.) Hammersmith Hosp. Trust; SHO (Med.) Rotat. N.wick Pk. Hosp. Middlx.; MRC Train. Fell.sh. HIV Research Chester Beatty Inst. Lond.

ORCHARD, Robin Theodore St. Helier Hospital, Wrythe Lane, Carshalton SM5 1AA Tel: 020 8296 2578 Fax: 020 8644 9419; 67 Croham Road, South Croydon CR2 7HF — MB BS Lond. 1965; FRCP Lond. 1982, M 1969; MRCS Eng. LRCP Lond. 1965. (Char. Cross) Cons. Phys. St. Helier, Sutton & Nelson Hosp.; Cons. Phys. St. Anthony's Hosp. Sutton; Hon. Sen. Lect. St. Geo. Hosp. Med. Sch. Socs: BMA; Roy. Soc. Med.; Brit. Soc. Gastroenterol. Prev: Sen. Regist. (Med.) Char. Cross Hosp. Lond.; Regist. (Med.) St. Stephen's Hosp. Chelsea; Ho. Phys. Lond. Chest Hosp.

ORCHARD, Timothy Robin 3 Wolsey Court, Woodstock Road, Woodstock OX20 1QP Email: timoth.orchard@ndm.ox.ac.uk — MB BChir 1991 Camb.; MA Camb. 1992; MRCP (UK) 1994; MD Camb 1999; MA DM Oxford 1999. (Char. Cross & Westm.) Clin. Research Fell. Gastroenterol. Unit Nuffield Dept. Med. Univ. Oxf.; Emmanoel Lee Research Fell. St. Cross Coll. Oxf. Socs: Brit. Soc. of Gastroenterol. Prev: Regist. Rotat. (Med.) St. Geo. Hosp. Lond.; SHO Frimley Pk. Hosp.; Ho. Off. W.m. Hosp. Lond.

ORCHARDSON, Robert Livingstone, MBE, TD (retired) 12A Anthony Court, Largs KA30 8TA Tel: 01475 675409 — MD 1958 Glas.; BSc Glas. 1935, MD 1958, MB ChB 1938; MRCGP 1958. Prev: RAMC 1939-45.

ORCHARTON, Alan MacKintosh (retired) 2 Glebe Avenue, Kilmarnock KA1 3DX Tel: 01563 524329 — MB ChB Glas. 1952; DObst RCOG 1956. Prev: Ho. Surg. W. Infirm. Glas.

ORCUTT, Roger Lee (retired) Tremorham House, Downderry, Torpoint PL11 3JX — BM BCh 1952 Oxf.; MA, BM BCh Oxon. 1952. Prev: ENT Ho. Surg. St. Thos. Hosp. Lond.

ORD, Jonathan Justin Department of General Surgery, The Royal Berkshire Hospital, London Road, Reading RG1 5AN Tel: 01189 875111; Hayes Barton, Jacobson, Okehampton EX20 3RJ Tel: 01837 851222 — MB BS 1995 Lond.; BSc UCL 1992. (St. Bartholomews) SHO Rotat. (Surg.) Reading.

ORD-HUME, Gail Celia Alma Road Surgery, 68 Alma Road, Portswood, Southampton SO14 6UX Tel: 023 8067 2666 Fax: 023 8055 0972; Cherry Tree Cottage, Coputhorne Crescent, Coputhorne, Southampton SO40 2PE — BM 1980 Soton.; MRCGP 1986; DRCOG 1984; DA Eng. 1983.

ORDE, Matthew Milburn 1 Oakfield Road, Clifton, Bristol BS8 2AH — MB ChB 1993 Dundee; Dip. Forens. Med. 1998; DMJ (Path.) Lond. 1998. Regist. (Forens. Med.) Univ. of Natal, S. Africa. Prev: Demonst. & Hon. Clin. Research Fell. (Histopath.) Univ. Bristol.

ORDMAN, Anthony James Department of Anaesthetics, The Royal Free Hospital, Hampstead, London NW3 2QG Tel: 0207 830 2623 Fax: 0207 830 2245 Email: anthony.ordman@rfh.nthames.nhs.uk; Tel: 020 8349 1990 Fax: 020 8371 0252 Email: ajordman@netcomuk.co.uk — MB BS 1978 Lond.; MRCS Eng. LRCP Lond. 1978; FFA RCS Eng. 1984. (Roy. Free) Cons. Anaesth. & Head Pain Managem. Serv. Roy. Free Hosp. Prev: Cons. Anaesth. Roy. Lond. Hosp.; Sen. Regist. (Anaesth.) Univ. Coll. Hosp. Lond.; Clin. Fell. (Anaesth.) Univ. Toronto Mt. Sinai Hosp., Canada.

ORDUNA MONCUSI, Modesto Royal Preston Hospital, Doctors Mess, Sharoe Green Lane, Fulwood, Preston PR2 9HT; 13 Whitehouse Close, Heywood OL10 2QU — LMS 1994 Barcelona.

OREN, Caroline Lucy Four Pads, California Lane, Bushey Heath, Watford WD2 1EP Tel: 020 8950 0643 Fax: 020 8950 1300 — MB BS 1989 Lond.; MRCP (UK) Paediat. 1993.

ORETTI, Rossana Graziana Whitchurch Hospital, Park Road, Whitchurch, Cardiff CF14 7XB Tel: 029 2069 3191; 12 Midlands Close, Newton, Swansea SA3 4SE — MB BS 1988 Lond.; MSc (Psychiat.) Cardiff 1993; BSc Lond. 1985; MRCPsych 1993. (Charing Cross & Westminster Med School) Sen. Regist. (Psychiat.) WhitCh. Hosp. Cardiff. Prev: Hon. Sen. Regist. (Psychiat.) Univ. Hosp. of Wales. Cardiff.

ORFORD, Christine Elizabeth 18 Myrtle Grove, Southport PR8 6BQ Tel: 01704 539930 — MB ChB 1971 Liverp.; DObst RCOG 1973. (Liverpool) Clin. Med. Off. (Contracep. & Sexual Health) N. Mersey NHS Trust; Clin. Med. Off. (Contracep. & Sexual Health) S.port Community Health Serv. NHS Trust. Socs: Foundat. Mem. Fac. Family Plann. & Reproduc. Health c/o RCOG. Prev: SCMO (Family Plann.) Wolverhampton HA.

ORFORD, Elaine Dawn 12 Mill Lane, Stock, Ingatestone CM4 9RY — MB ChB 1997 Leeds.

ORGAN, Joan Mary (retired) 6 Bawnmore Court, Bilton, Rugby CV22 7QQ Tel: 01788 812811 — MB ChB Glas. 1965; DCH RCPS Glas. 1970. Prev: SCMO Warks. AHA.

ORGEE, Jane Margaret Ashleigh, Walwyn Road, Colwall, Malvern WR13 6QT — MB ChB 1987 Sheff.

ORGLES, Clive Somerset Airedale General Hospital, Steeton, Keighley BD20 6TD Tel: 01535 652511; 26 Beverley Rise, Ilkley LS29 9DB — MB ChB 1983 Leeds; MRCGP 1991; FRCR 1996; DRCOG 1987. (Univ. Leeds Med. Sch.) Cons. Diagnostic Radiol. Airedale Gen. Hosp. Prev: Leeds/Bradford Radiol. Train. Scheme; GP Shipley Health Centre Bradford; Trainee GP Bradford VTS.

ORIFE, Stephen Oghale-Ufuoma 4 St Gabriels Avenue, High Barnes, Sunderland SR4 7TF — MB BS 1980 Nigeria; MB BS (Dinstinc. Phys.) Nigeria 1980; MRCOG 1989.

ORIMOLOYE, Adekola Oluwole Market Street Health Group, 52 Market Street, East Ham, London E6 2RA Tel: 020 8548 2200 Fax: 020 8548 2288 — MB BS 1985 Lagos; MRCOG 1993.

ORIOLOWO, Mr Adewunmi Munir Department of Pathology, Royal Victoria Infirmary, Queen Victoria Road, Newcastle upon Tyne NE1 4LP Tel: 0191 232 5131; 44 Sherfield Drive, Cochrane Park, Newcastle upon Tyne NE7 7LN Tel: 0191 266 4279 — MB BS 1986 Lagos; FRCS Ed. 1993; FRCS Eng. 1992. Regist. (Histopath.) Roy. Vict. Infirm. Newc. u. Tyne. Socs: BMA; Assn. Clin. Paths.; Roy. Coll. Surgs. Eng.

ORLANDI, Janet Robertson Occupational Health, ICI, PO Box 54, Wilton, Middlesbrough TS9 8JA Tel: 01642 433397 — MB ChB 1985 Dundee; MRCGP 1989; AFOM RCP Lond. 1992; MFOM Lond. 1998. Occupat. Phys. ICI Wilton Middlesbrough.

ORLANDI, Martin Ferryhill Medical Practice, Durham Road, Ferryhill DL17 8JJ Tel: 01740 651238 Fax: 01740 656291; 10 Southside, Hutton Rudby, Yarm TS15 0DD — MB ChB 1984 Dundee.

ORLANDO, Antonio Plastic Surgery Department, Frenchay Hospital, Frenchay Park Road, Bristol BS16 1LE Tel: 0117 970 1212; Bungalow 2, Frenchay Hospital, Frenchay Park Road, Bristol BS16 1LE Tel: 0117 970 1212 Ext: 2762 Fax: 0117 975 3846 — State Exam 1988 Florence; Spec. in Plastic Surgery, Univ of Parma, Italy 1996; Spec. Otolaryngology - Univ.of Florence, Italy, 1991; T(S) 1994. (Univ. Florence) Specialist Regist. Plastic Surg. Frenchay Hosp. Bristol; Hon. Sen. Lect. Sch. of Specialisation of Plastic Surg., Univ. Parma, Italy. Socs: Brit. Assn. of Head & Neck Oncol.; Italian Soc. Plastic Reconstruct. & Aesthetic Surg.; Italian Soc. Otolarkingol. & Head & Neck Surg. Prev: Resid. Plastic Surg. Parma Gen. Hosp. Parma Italy.

ORLANS, David Anthony Childwall Valley Road Surgery, 70 Childwall Valley Road, Liverpool L16 4PE Tel: 0151 722 7321 — MB ChB 1974 Liverp.

ORLANS, Marian Childwall Valley Road Surgery, 70 Childwall Valley Road, Liverpool L16 4PE Tel: 0151 722 7321 — MB ChB 1978 Liverp.; MRCGP 1982; DRCOG 1980.

ORME, Christopher Giles (retired) 16 Imperial Road, Matlock DE4 3NL Tel: 01629 582981 — MB ChB 1955 Sheff.

ORME, Gail Elizabeth 77 Gateland Lane, Shadwell, Leeds LS17 8LN — MB ChB 1984 Manch.

ORME, Leslie John The Health Centre, Fieldhead, Shepley, Huddersfield HD8 8DR Tel: 01484 602001 Fax: 01484 608125 — MB ChB 1974 Ed.; BA Camb. 1971.

ORME, Professor Michael Christopher L'Estrange NW Regional Office of NHS Executive, 930-932 Birchwood Boulevard, Millenium Park, Birchwood, Warrington WA3 7QN Tel: 01925 704149 Fax: 01925 704249 Email: morme@etnwest.demon.co.uk; Wychwood, Brimstage Road, Heswall, Wirral CH60 1XQ Tel: 0151 342 3269 Fax: 0151 342 8154 Email: morme@eandrhome.demon.co.uk — MB BChir Camb. 1965; MA Camb. 1965, MD 1974; FRCP Lond. 1980, M 1967. (Camb. & King's Coll. Hosp.) Dir. of Educat. & Train. NW Regional Off. NHS Exec. Warrington; Prof. Pharmacol. & Therap. Univ. Liverp.; Hon. Cons. Phys. Roy. Liverp. Univ. Hosps. Socs: Brit. Pharm. Soc.; Brit. Soc. Rheum.; Assn. Phys. Prev: Dean Fac. Med. Univ. Liverp.; Asst. Lect. Roy. Postgrad. Med. Sch. Lond.; Wellcome Research Fell. Karolinska Inst. Stockholm, Sweden.

ORME, Nicholas John 42 Mariners Road, Blundellsands, Liverpool L23 6SX — MB ChB 1988 Liverp.

ORME, Richard Colin L'Estrange (retired) Department of Child Heath, Postgraduate Medical School, University of Exeter, Church La, Heavitree, Exeter EX2 5SQ Tel: 01392 403145 Fax: 01392 403158 — MB BChir 1961 Camb.; MA, MB Camb. 1961; FRCP Lond. 1981, M 1967; MRCP Ed. 1967; FRCPCH 1997; DCH Eng. 1966. Hon. Sen. Lect. Dept. Child Health Postgrad. Med. Sch. Univ. Exeter. Prev: Sen. Regist. United Bristol Hosps. & S.W. RHB.

ORME, Richard Ian Royal Shrewsbury Hospital, Mytton Oak Road, Shrewsbury SY3 8XQ Tel: 01743 261000 — MB ChB 1986 Bristol; MRCP (UK) 1989; FRCR 1993. (Bristol) Cons. Diagn. Radiol. Roy. Shrewsbury Hosps. NHS Trust. Socs: Brit. Soc. Interven. Radiol. Prev: Sen. Regist. (Diagn. Radiol.) W. Birm. HA.

ORME, Robert Martin L'Estrange 6 Wrightons Hill, Helmdon, Brackley NN13 5UF Tel: 01295768944 Fax: 01295768624 Email: caroline.rob@virgin.net — MB ChB 1993 Dundee; BMSc (Hons.) Dund 1989. Specialist Regist., Anaesth. Oxf. Radcliffe, Hosp. Socs: Assoc. of Anaesth. Of Britian & Ire.; Obst. Anaesth. Assn. Prev: Regist. in Med., Whangarei Area Hosp. NZ; Resistrar in Anaesth., Denedin Pub. Hosp. Denedin, NZ.

ORME, Stephen Michael 3 Birchfields Garth, Skeltonwoods, Whinmoor, Leeds LS14 2JA — MB ChB 1984 Manch.

ORME, Susan Northern General Trust, Sheffield Tel: 0114 271 1900; 68 Charnock Hall Road, Sheffield S12 3HG — BM BS 1991 Nottm.; BM BS Hons. Nottm. 1991; MRCP (UK) 1994. Sen. Regist. (Cent. & Geriat. Med.) Centre Sheff. Univ. Trust. Prev: Regist. (Gen. Med.) N.. Gen. Trust.; SHO (Accid. & Med. & Dermat.) Roy. Hallamsh. Hosp. Sheff.; SHO (Med.) N.. Gen. Hosp.

ORME-SMITH, Elizabeth Ann Heathcote Medical Centre, Heathcote, Tadworth KT20 5TH Tel: 01737 360202; Lion Hill, 3 Tadworth St, Tadworth KT20 5RP Tel: 01737 358983 Email: 100604.724@compuserve.com — MB BS 1957 Lond.; FRCGP 1989, M 1981. (Guy's) Prev: Course Organiser Epsom GP VTS.

ORMEROD

ORMEROD, Alex Edward 17 Harley Street, London W10 9QH Tel: 020 7580 9854 Fax: 020 7636 2836; 8 Claygate Avenue, Harpenden AL5 2HF Tel: 01582 764045 — BM BCh 1967 Oxford; 1967 MA Oxf.; AFOM RCP Lond. 1981; DObst RCOG 1970. (Oxf.) Occupat. Phys. Herts. Socs: Fell. Roy. Soc. Med.; Soc. Occupat. Med. Prev: Sen. Med. Off. BRB Lond.; SHO & Ho. Off. Radcliffe Infirm. Oxf.

ORMEROD, Anthony David Ward 29, Aberdeen Royal Infirmary, Foresterhill, Aberdeen AB25 2ZN Tel: 01224 681818 Fax: 01224 840555 Email: a.d.ormerod@arh.granpian.scot.nhs.uk — MB ChB 1978 Manch.; FRCP Ed. 1996; MRCP (UK) 1981; MD 2000. (Manch.) Cons. Dermat. Aberd. Roy. Infirm.; Reader Med. & Therap. (Dermat.) Univ. Aberd. Socs: Brit. Assn. Dermat.; Brit. Soc. Investig. Dermat.; Eur. Soc. Dermat. Res. Prev: Sen. Regist. (Dermat.) Aberd. Roy. Infirm.

ORMEROD, Fiona The Surgery, Northwick Road, Pilning, Bristol BS35 4JF Tel: 01454 632393 — MB BS 1979 Lond.; MRCGP 1988; DA (UK) 1982; DRCOG 1980. (Middlx. Hosp.)

ORMEROD, Harry John Vernon Melancthon (retired) 221 Dryden Road, Gateshead NE9 5DA — MRCS Eng. LRCP Lond. 1947.

ORMEROD, I R The Plane Trees Group Practice, 51 Sandbeds Road, Pellon, Halifax HX2 0QL Tel: 01422 330860 Fax: 01422 364830 — MB ChB 1981 Sheffield; MB ChB 1981 Sheffield.

ORMEROD, Ian Edward Charlton Frenchay Hospital, Frenchay, Bristol BS16 1LE Tel: 0117 970 1212 — MB BS 1978 Lond.; MD Lond. 1987; FRCP Lond. 1995; FRCP. (Middlx. Hosp.) Cons. Neurol. Bristol Roy. Infirm (UBHT) N. Bristol NHS Trust. Socs: Assn. Brit. Neurol. Prev: Cons. Neurol. Nat. Hosp. Neurol. & Neurosurg. Qu. Sq. Lond. & St. Thos. Hosp. Lond.; Clin. Asst. Moorfields Eye Hosp. Lond.

ORMEROD, Jean Elizabeth Helen (retired) Silwood, Prescot Road, Hale, Altrincham WA15 9PZ Tel: 0161 928 0733 — MB ChB 1949 St. And.; DCH Eng. 1952. Prev: Trainer in Gen. Pract. & Family Plann. Manch.

ORMEROD, Professor Lawrence Peter Blackburn Royal Infirmary, Blackburn BB2 3LR Tel: 01254 263555 Fax: 01254 294549 — MB ChB 1974 Manch.; DSc 2000; BSc (Hons.) (Pharmacol.) Manch. 1971, MD 1986; FRCP Lond. 1990; MRCP (UK) 1977. Cons. Phys. (Chest Dis.) Blackburn Roy. Infirm.; Hon. Prof. Lancs. PostGrad. Sch. of Med. & Health Univ. of Centr. Lancs. Socs: Fell. Manch. Med. Soc.; Brit. Thorac. Soc. (Chairm. Jt. Tuberc. Comm.). Prev: Sen. Regist. N. Manch. Gen. Hosp.; Regist. (Gen. & Chest Med.) E. Birm. Hosp.; SHO (Gen. Med.) Univ. Hosp. S. Manch.

ORMEROD, Oliver John More Cardiac Department, John Radcliffe Hospital, Headington, Oxford OX3 9DU Tel: 01865 741166 Fax: 01865 221194; 4 Walton Crescent, Oxford OX1 2JG Tel: 01865 511957 — BM BCh 1978 Oxf.; BA Oxf. 1975, MA 1986, DM 1986; FRCP 1996; MRCP (UK) 1980. Cons. Cardiol. John Radcliffe Hosp. Oxf. Socs: BMA & Brit. Cardiac Soc. Prev: Clin. Lect. (Cardiovasc. Med.) Univ. Oxf.; Grimshaw Pk.inson Stud. (Cardiovasc. Dis.) Univ. Camb.; Regist. (Cardiol.) Papworth Hosp. Camb.

ORMEROD, Peter Stuart Medical Informatics Ltd., Ribble Bank Manor, Preston New Road Samlesbury, Preston PR5 0UL Tel: 01772 877111 Fax: 01772 877112 — MB ChB 1968 Glas.; MSc Occupat. Med. Lond. 1981; FFOM RCP Lond. 1982; DAvMed. FOM RCP Lond. 1973; T(OM) 1991. Med. Dir. Med. Informatics Ltd. Prev: Gp. Med. Off. WH Smith plc; Area Med. Off. CEGB; Sen. Med. Off. HM Naval Base Portsmouth.

ORMEROD, Raymond (retired) Silwood, Prescot Road, Hale, Altrincham WA15 9PZ Tel: 0161 928 0733 — MB ChB 1947 Manch.; MRCGP 1968.

ORMEROD, Simon James Health Centre, Handsworth Avenue, Highams Park, London E4 9PD Tel: 020 8527 0913 Fax: 020 8527 6597 — MB BS 1985 Lond.

ORMEROD, Thomas Edward (retired) 40 Rectory Lane, Orlingbury, Kettering NN14 1JH Tel: 01933 678373 — MB ChB 1952 Manch.

ORMEROD, Thomas Peter The Garden House, West Drive, Cheltenham GL50 4LB Tel: 01242 513896 Fax: 01242 512896 — MB BS Lond. 1956; MD Lond. 1966; FRCP Lond. 1977, M 1962; DCH Eng. 1959. (St. Bart.) Socs: Fell. Roy. Soc. Med.; BMA; Brit. Soc. of Gastroenerology. Prev: Cons. Phys. Cheltenham Gen. Hosp.; Chief Med. Off. Eagle Star Insur. Gp.; Chairm. Med. Panel Cheltenham Coll.

ORMEROD, Walter Edward London School of Hyg. & Trop. Medicine, Keppel St., London NW1 7HT Tel: 020 7636 8636; The Old Rectory, Padworth, Reading RG7 4JD — MB BCh 1944 Oxf.; MA, DSc, DM Oxf. 1963, BM BCh 1944. (Oxf.) Sen. Research Fell. Lond. Sch. Hyg. & Trop. Med.; Emerit. Reader (Med. Protozool.) Univ. Lond.; Hon. Sen. Lect. (Med. Microbiol.) King's Coll. Sch. Med. & Dent. Lond.

ORMEROD, William Paterson (retired) The Grey House, 102 West St., Corfe Castle, Wareham BH20 5HE — MB BChir 1961 Camb.; MA, MB Camb. 1961, BChir 1961. p/t Med.ly Qualified Panel Mem. (MQPM) for the Appeals Serv., Wales and S. W.ern Region. Prev: GP Poole,Dorset 1965-1995.

ORMISTON, Ian Nigel Robert Milton House Surgery, Doctors Commons Road, Berkhamsted HP4 3BY Tel: 01442 874784 Fax: 01442 877694 — MB BS 1974 Lond.; MRCP (UK) 1977; DRCOG 1982.

ORMISTON, Mr Ian William Department of Oral & Maxillofacial Surgery, Leicester Royal Infirmary, Infirmary Square, Leicester LE1 5WW Tel: 0116 258 5254 Fax: 0116 258 5205 — MRCS Eng. LRCP Lond. 1987; BDS Ed. 1981; FRCS Ed. 1994; FDS RCS Eng. 1992. Cons. Oral & Maxillofacial Surg., Maxillofacial unit, Leicester Roy. Infirmary. Socs: Fell. Coll. Surgs. Hong Kong; Fell.Brit. Assoc. Oral & Maxillofacial Surgs.; Fell.Hong Kong Acad. of Med. Prev: SHO (Head & Neck, ENT & Oral & Maxillofacial Surg.) Leics. HA; Lect. (Oral & Maxillofacial Surg.) Univ. Hong Kong.

ORMISTON, Mr Michael Charles Elliott Hemel Hempstead General Hospital, Hillfield Road, Hemel Hempstead HP2 4AD Tel: 01442 213141 — MB BChir 1974 Camb.; MChir Camb. 1984; FRCS Eng. 1978. Cons. Surg. St Albans & Hemel Hempstead NHS Trust. Socs: Vasc. Surgic. Soc. GB & Irel.; Assn. of Surg.s of Gt. Britain & Irel.; BMA. Prev: Sen. Regist. King's Coll. Hosp. Lond.

ORMISTON, Philip John Burnside Surgery, 365 Blackburn Road, Bolton BL1 8DZ Tel: 01204 528205 Fax: 01204 386409 — MB ChB 1978 Sheff.; DRCOG 1981; MSc Manch. 1997.

ORMONDE, Susan Elizabeth Ophthalmology Department, Royal Berkshire Hospital, Reading RG1 5AN Tel: 01734 875111 — MB ChB 1992 Bristol. SHO (Ophth.) Roy. Berks. Hosp. Prev: SHO (Ophth.) Roy. Berks. Hosp.; Ho. Phys. & Ho. Surg. Bristol Roy. Infirm.; Resid. Med. Off. BUPA Hosp. Sutton Coldfield.

ORMROD, Jean (retired) UCL Hospitals, Postgraduate Centre, 48 Riding House St., London W1P 7PN Tel: 020 7380 9371 Fax: 020 7380 9248 — MB ChB 1966 Ed.; FFA RCS Eng. 1972; DA Eng. 1970; DObst RCOG 1969. Asst. Dir. (Educat.) UCL Hosps. Postgrad. Centre Lond. Prev: Cons. Anaesth. & Clin. Dir. UCL Hosps.

ORMROD, Jessica 4 West View, Helmshore, Rossendale BB4 4LE — MB BS 1991 Newc.

ORMROD, Mr John Neville (retired) Malt House, Chart Road, Chart Sutton, Maidstone ME17 3RA — MB ChB 1944 Birm.; MB ChB (Hon.) Birm. 1944; FRCS Eng. 1956; FRCOphth. 1988; DO Eng. 1952. Prev: Cons. Ophth. Surg. Kent Co. Ophth. Hosp. Maidstone & Gravesend & N. Kent Hosp.

ORMSBY, James Matthew Ravenswood House, Knowle, Fareham PO17 5NA — BM 1991 Soton.; MRCPsyc 1996. Specialist Regist., Wessex.

ORMSTON, Brian John 6 Peckitt Street, York YO1 1SF Tel: 01904 639171; 322 Tadcaster Road, York YO24 1HF — MB BS 1968 Newc.; MRCP (UK) 1974; FRCGP 1997. GP York; Dep. Dir. Postgrad. Med. Educat. Yorks.

ORMSTON, Ronald Mark Ayton 6 Dorset House, Gloucester Place, London NW1 5AB Tel: 020 7935 7299 — LRCP LRCS Ed. LRFPS Glas. 1933; DPM RCPSI 1936. (Univ. & Roy. Colls. Ed. & Dub.)

ORNADEL, Dan Department of Chest Medicine, Northwick Park Hospital, Watford Road, London Tel: 020 8869 2613 Email: dan.ornadel@lineone.net — MB BS 1987 Lond.; BA Oxf. 1985; MRCP (UK) 1990; MD (London) 1999. (St Thomas' Hosp.) Cons. Respirat. Med. N.wick Pk. Hosp. Lond. Socs: Brit. Thoracic Sosciety; Roy. Soc. Med.; Amer. Thoracic Soc.

ORNSTEIN, Mr Marcus Henry (cons. rooms), 118 Harley St., London W1G 7JN Tel: 020 8423 8236 Fax: 020 8423 3339 Email: mark.ornstein@virgin.net; The Hill Studio, 23 Crown St., Harrow HA2 0HX Tel: 020 8423 8236 Fax: 020 8423 3339 Email:

mark.ornstein@virgin.net — MB ChB 1968 Bristol; 1973 FRCS Eng.; 1983 Accredit. Surg. (Univ. Bristol) Indep. Cons. Lond. Socs: Assn. of Surg.s of Gt. Briatin & Irel.; Brit. Soc. Gastroenterol.; Roy. Soc. of Med. Prev: Hon. Clin. Teach. St. Mary's Hosp. Med. Sch. Lond.; Sen. Regist. (Surg.) St. Mary's Hosp. Lond.; Regist. (Surg.) N.wick Pk. Hosp. Middlx.

ORPEN, Ian Michael St James Surgery, 8-9 Northampton Buildings, Bath BA1 2SR Tel: 01225 422911 Fax: 01225 428398; 22 Hantone Hill, Bathampton, Bath BA2 6XD — MB ChB 1982 Cape Town; MRCGP 1990; DGM RCP Lond. 1989; DCH RCP Lond. 1989. Prev: Asst. GP Bath; Trainee GP Bath VTS.

ORPHANIDES, D The Surgery, 74 Perry Hall Road, Orpington BR6 0HS Tel: 01689 837366 Fax: 01689 872990.

ORPIN, Madeleine Mary Tower House Practice, St. Pauls Health Centre, High Street, Runcorn WA7 1AB Tel: 01928 567404; 8 Borrowdale Close, Frodsham, Warrington WA6 7LN Tel: 01928 733611 — MB BS 1978 Lond.; MRCGP Lond. 1982; DRCOG 1983; DCH RCP Lond. 1981.

ORPIN, Richard Peter Ian Shelley Surgery, 23 Shelley Road, Worthing BN11 4BS; Green Banks, Mill Lane, Worthing BN13 3DE Tel: 01903 263813 — MB BS 1976 Lond.; MRCS Eng. LRCP Lond. 1976; MRCGP 1981; DRCOG 1981; DCH Eng. 1978. (Char. Cross) Prev: Trainee GP Portsmouth; SHO (O & G) St. Mary's Hosp. Portsmouth; SHO (Med.) Brook Hosp. Lond.

ORR, Alison Jane 4 Tempest Street, Stella, Blaydon-on-Tyne NE21 4ND Tel: 0191 414 4690 — MB BS 1989 Newc.; MRCGP 1993. Asst. GP Winlaton Tyne & Wear. Prev: Trainee GP N.umbria VTS; SHO (Paediat.) Bishop Auckland Gen. Hosp.; SHO (O & G) Shotley Bridge Gen. Hosp.

ORR, Andrew William Townhead Surgery, Townhead, Murray Lane, Montrose DD10 8LE Tel: 01674 676161 Fax: 01674 673151 — MB BS 1971 Lond.; FRCGP 1999; MRCS Eng. LRCP Lond. 1971; MRCGP 1977; DCH Eng. 1977; DObst RCOG 1974. (St. Bart.) Prev: SHO (Obst.) Rochford Gen. Hosp.; SHO (Paediat.) B.M.H. Munster; Maj. RAMC.

ORR, Anthony McNeill Moorfield House Surgery, 35 Edgar Street, Hereford HR4 9JP Tel: 01432 272175 Fax: 01432 341942; Highcroft, Longmeadow, Breinton, Hereford HR4 7PA Tel: 01432 354948 Email: amorr@doctors.org.uk — MB BS 1984 Lond.; DRCOG; LHMC. (The London Hospital Medical College) Gen. Pract.-Princip.

ORR, Barbara Marianne 'Bannits', Church St., Broadway WR12 7AE — BM BCh 1973 Oxf.

ORR, Brian Trevor Weston Park Hospital, Whitham Road, Sheffield S10 2SJ Tel: 0114 226 5000 Fax: 0114 226 5512 — MB BCh BAO 1984 Belf.; MSc Glas. 1992; MA Camb. 1981; MRCP (UK) 1989; FRCR 1993. Cons. (Clin. Oncol.) W.on Pk. Hosp, Sheff.. Prev: Sen. Regist. (Clin. Oncol.) Bristol Oncol. Centre.

ORR, Brian William Gordon (retired) 64 St Marys Road, Cowes PO31 7ST Tel: 01983 295527 Fax: 01983 295527 Email: b.w.orr@talk21.com — MB BChir 1956 Camb.; DRCOG 1961. Prev: Gen. Practioner, Portsmouth.

ORR, Carolyn Frances 38 Thorncliffe Gardens, Glasgow G41 2DE — MB ChB 1997 Glas.

ORR, Charles James Kirkpatrick (retired) 13 Hillside Park, Ballymena BT43 5ND Tel: 0285 656068 Email: candtott@amserve.net — MB BCh BAO 1939 Belf.; FRCA 1993; FFA RCS Eng. 1953; DA Eng. 1948. Hon. Cons. Anaesth. Mid Antrim Area Gp. Hosps. Prev: Sen. Cons. Anaesth. Mid-Antrim Area Gp. Hosps.

ORR, Charles Warden (retired) Alvenga, Godmans Lane, Kirk Ella, Hull HU10 7NY Tel: 01482 653217 — LRCP LRCS 1939 Ed.; LRCP LRCS Ed. LRFPS Glas. 1939; MRCGP 1953; DPH Belf. 1946. Prev: Med. Off. Brit. Transp. Docks Bd. & Nat. Dock Labour Bd. Hull & Goole.

ORR, David Hugh Musgrave & Clark House, Royal Victoria Hospital, Grosvenor Road, Belfast BT12 6BA — MB BCh 1997 Belf.

ORR, David Samuel Alexander Garvagh Health Centre, 110 Main Street, Garvagh, Coleraine BT51 5AE Tel: 028 2955 8210 Fax: 028 2955 7089; 78 Drumsaragh Road, Kilrea, Coleraine BT51 5XR — MB BCh BAO 1985 Belf.; MRCGP 1990; DRCOG 1988.

ORR, Desmond Alan Dept. Anaesthesia, Craigavon Area Hospital Group Trust, Craigavon BT63 5QQ Tel: 028 38 334444; 19

Corcreeny Road, Hillsborough BT26 6EH — MB BS 1979 Newc.; FFA RCS Eng. 1984; FFA RCSI 1983. Cons. Anaesth. Craigavon Area Hosp.

ORR, Donald Stuart (retired) Thatchers, Combe Raleigh, Honiton EX14 4TQ Tel: 01404 43198 — MRCS Eng. LRCP Lond. 1942. Prev: Ho. Phys. & Ho. Surg. EMS.

ORR, Mr Douglas James Monklands District General Hospital, Monkscourt Avenue, Airdrie ML6 0JS; 3 Dalnair Gardens, Yorkhill, Glasgow G3 8SD — MB ChB 1990 Glas.; BSc (Hons.) Glas. 1987, MB ChB 1990; FRCS Glas. 1994; FRCS Ed. 1994. SHO (Surg.) Monklands Dist. Gen. Hosp.

ORR, Elspeth Margaret (retired) 7 Kinkell Terrace, St Andrews KY16 8DS — MB ChB Ed. 1946; DObst RCOG 1954.

ORR, Mr Frederick George Geoffrey 48 Esplanade, Greenock PA16 7SD Tel: 01475 787038 — MB ChB 1971 Birm.; BSc (Hons.) Anat. Birm. 1968; FRCS Ed. 1976. Cons. Urol. Inverclyde Roy. Hosp. Greenock. Socs: Brit. Assn. Urol. Surg.; Assn. Surg. Prev: Sen. Regist. (Gen. Surg.) Aberd. Hosp.

ORR, Gary Mark Flat 34A, Marryat Square, London SW6 6UA — MB BS 1992 Lond.

ORR, George Alfred Birleywood Health Centre, Birleywood, Skelmersdale WN8 9BW Tel: 01695 723333 Fax: 01695 556193; 236 Elmers Green Lane, Skelmersdale WN8 6SN — MB ChB 1980 Liverp. Socs: W Lancs. Med. Soc.

ORR, Gordon David Front Street Surgery, 14 Front Street, Acomb, York YO24 3BZ Tel: 01904 794141 Fax: 01904 788304 — MB ChB 1990 Ed.; DRCOG 1994. Trainee GP/SHO Carlisle VTS.

ORR, Ian Alexander 3 Larchwood, Portadown, Craigavon BT63 5UL Tel: 01762 338037 Email: ianorr@aol.com — MB BCh BAO 1975 Belf.; MD (Hons.) Belf. 1981; FFA RCSI 1978; DRCOG 1979. (Belf.) Cons. Anaesth. Craigavon Area Hosp. Prev: Cons. Roy. Vict. Hosp. Belf.; Clin. Research Fell. (Anaesth.) Hosp. Sick Childr. Toronto, Canada; Sen. Regist. (Anaesth.) & Research Fell. Roy. Vict. Hosp. Belf.

ORR, Jacqueline Elizabeth Royal Alexandra Hospital Trust, Corsebar Road, Paisley PA2 9PN Tel: 0141 887 9111; 48 Esplanade, Greenock PA16 7SD Tel: 01475 787038 — MB ChB 1976 Aberd.; FFA RCS Eng. 1980. Cons. Anaesth. Roy. Alexandra Hosp. Paisley. Socs: Assn. Anaesth.; Obst. Anaesth. Assn.; Difficult Airway Soc.

ORR, James Henry (retired) c/o National Westminster Bank plc., 7 Manor Square, Otley LS21 3AP Email: jorr204459@aol.com — MB ChB 1955 Bristol; FRCPsych 1978, M 1972; DPM Eng. 1966. Prev: Cons. Forens. Psychiat. W. Yorks.

ORR, James Thomas 9 Hollinwell Court, Edwalton, Nottingham NG12 4DW — MB BS 1998 Lond.

ORR, Jane Elizabeth Keppel, Maj. RAMC Retd. Upper Gordon Road Surgery, 37 Upper Gordon Road, Camberley GU15 2HJ Tel: 01276 26424 Fax: 01276 63486; Selhurst, 119 Gordon Road, Camberley GU15 2JQ Tel: 01276 22584 Fax: 01276 502873 Email: jeko@selhurst.prestel.co.uk — MB BS 1974 Lond.; MRCS Eng. LRCP Lond. 1974; DRCOG 1980. (St. Mary's) Staff Grade Psychiat. BRd.moor Hosp. Prev: Clin. Asst. (Colposcopy) Frimley Pk. Hosp. Camberley; Cadets' Med. Off. Roy. Milit. Acad. Sandhurst; Clincal Med. Off. (Family Plann.) Surrey HA.

ORR, Jean Forbes Moonrakers, Forest Road, Binfield, Bracknell RG42 4HB — MB ChB 1957 Ed.; DA Eng. 1963. (Ed.)

ORR, John Anthony 428 Lanark Road, Colinton, Edinburgh EH13 0LT — MB ChB 1998 Aberd.

ORR, John Douglas Gilbert Road Medical Group, 39 Gilbert Road, Bucksburn, Aberdeen AB21 9AN Tel: 01224 712138 Fax: 01224 712239; 15 Glenhome Walk, Dyce, Aberdeen AB21 7FJ Tel: 01224 722801 Email: d.orr@easynet.co.uk — MB ChB 1969 Ed.; BSc (Med. Sci.) Ed. 1966; MRCP (UK) 1973; MRCGP 1975; Dip. Sports Med. Scot. 1992; DObst RCOG 1971; Primary Care Certificate in Homeopathy 1996; FPA 1975. (Ed.) GP; Sen. Lect. (Gen. Pract.) & Med. Asst. (Rheum.) Aberd. Prev: Regist. (Gen. Med.) Foresterhill & Assoc. Hosps. Aberd.; Ho. Phys. Milesmark Hosp. Dunfermline; Ho. Surg. Bangour Gen. Hosp. W. Lothian.

ORR, Mr John Douglas Royal Hospital for Sick Children, Sciennes Road, Edinburgh EH9 1LF Tel: 0131 536 0667 Fax: 0131 536 0666; 428 Lanark Road, Edinburgh EH13 0LT — MB ChB 1969 St. And.; FRCS Ed. 1975; MBA 1998 Stirling. Cons. Paediat. Surg. Roy. Hosp. Sick Childr. Edin.; Assoc. Med. Director, Wom., Childr. &

ORR

Assoc.d Serv.s, L.U.H.N.T. Socs: Scott. Comm. for Hosp. Med. Serv.s (Treas.); Brit. Asscoiation of Med. Managers (BAMM).; Brit. Asscoiation of Paediatric Surg. Prev: Sen. Regist. (Surg.) Roy. Hosp. for Sick Childr. Edin.; Sen. Regist. (Paediat. Surg.) Hosp. for Sick Childr Gt. Ormond St.; Lond.; Sen. Regist. (Surg.) Aberd. Roy. Infirm.

ORR, Jonathan Peter The Orchard Street Health Centre, Ipswich IP4 2PU Tel: 01473 213261 Fax: 01473 287741; 9 Orchard Close, Canons Drive, Edgware HA8 7RE — MB BS 1984 Lond.; Dip. Occ. Med. 1998; MRCGP 1997; BSc (Civil Engin) Loughborough 1973. (The London Hospital) Socs: RCGP. Prev: Trainee GP Lond. VTS; Capt. Roy. Engineers; Clin. Med. Off. (Child Health) Lond. Hosp.

ORR, Katherine Elizabeth Freeman Hospital, Freeman Road, High Heaton, Newcastle upon Tyne NE7 7DN Tel: 0191 284 3111 — MB ChB 1985 Bristol; FRCPath; MRCPath 1991. Cons. Med. Microbiol. Freeman Hosp. Newc. u. Tyne.

ORR, Keith Matthew Meadowbank Health Centre, 3 Salmon Inn Road, Falkirk FK2 0XF Tel: 01324 715753 Fax: 01324 717565 — MB ChB 1985 Glas.

ORR, Mr Kenneth Gibson (retired) 1 Avonbrook Gardens, Mountsandel Road, Coleraine BT52 1SS Tel: 028 7034 2355 — MB BCh BAO 1949 Belf.; FRCS Ed. 1956. Prev: Cons. Surg. Mid-Ulster Hosp. Magherafelt.

ORR, Lesley Ann Accident & Emergency Dept, Hairmyres Hosp, Eaglesham Road, East Kilbride, Glasgow G75 8RG Tel: 01355 220292; 6 Lochend Road, Bearsden, Glasgow G61 1DU — MB ChB 1983 Dundee; DA (UK) 1987. Staff Grade (A & E), Hairmyres Hosp., E. Kilbride. Prev: Regist. (Anaesth.) Law Hosp. Carluke; SHO (Surg.) Vict. Infirm. Glas.; SHO (A & E) Glas. Roy. Infirm.

ORR, Miss Linda Elizabeth 62 Seahill Road, Holywood BT18 0DW Tel: 01232 422648 — MB ChB 1991 Bristol; BSc (Hons.) Bristol 1986; Dip. App. Basic Sci. RCS Eng. 1997; FRSM; FRCS (Eng) 1999. (Bristol) SHO Ent, Roy. Hosp. HASLAR; Med. Off. Roy. Army Med. Corps. Socs: Wom. in Surg. Train.; Roy. Soc. Med. Prev: SHO (Burno & Plastics) Frenchay Hosp. Bristol; SHO ITU Middlx. Hosp. Lond.; Med. Off./Post Mistress S. Georgia.

ORR, Malcolm John 150 Chesterholm, Sandsfield Park, Carlisle CA2 7XY — MB ChB 1998 Dund.

ORR, Margaret Jane Parklands Surgery, 4 Parklands Road, Chichester PO19 3DT Tel: 01243 782819/786827 — BM (Hons.) Soton. 1979; DCH RCP Lond. 1983; MRCGP 1986; DRCOG 1982.

ORR, Marion Adele Graham (retired) Stangmore Lodge, Dungannon Tel: 02887 22782 — MB 1933 Dub.; M.B., B.Ch., B.A.O. Dub. 1933.

ORR, Mr Mark Monro (retired) Department of Surgery, Horton General Hospital Oxford Radcliffe Trust, Oxford Road, Banbury OX16 9AL Tel: 01295 229206 Fax: 01295 229271 — MB BS 1962 Lond.; BSc (Physiol.) Lond. 1959; FRCS Eng. 1969. Prev: Lect. (Surg.) St. Bart. Hosp. Lond.

ORR, Martin James 9 Lamond Place, Aberdeen AB25 3UT — MB ChB 1997 Glas.

ORR, Mr Michael McNeill CAMHS, Horsham Hospital, Hurst Road, Horsham RH12 2DR Tel: 01403 227014 — MB BS 1982 Lond.; FRCS (Orth) 1996; FRCS Eng. 1990. (Lond. Hosp. Med. Coll.) Cons. Orthop. & Traumatol. Cumbld. Infirm. Carlisle. Prev: Sen. Regist. (Orthop.) Dundee Roy. Infirm.; Regist. (Orthop.) & Research Regist. Dundee Roy. Infirm.; Regist. (Surg.) Orsett & Basildon Hosps.

ORR, Michael William Isham House, St. Andrew's Group of Hospitals, Billing Road, Northampton Email: xas93@dial.pipex.com; Flat 1, 12 Mecklenburgh Square, London WC1N 2AD Tel: 020 7833 3934 — MD 1967 Malta; DM Oxf. 1981; BSc Oxf. 1971, BA 1969; FRCPsych 1987, M 1974; DPM Eng. 1973. (Malta) Med. Director Isham Ho. St. Andrews Gp. of Hosps.; Cons. Psychiat. Warneford Hosp. Oxf. Prev: Dist. Clin. Tutor Oxon. HA; Lect. Univ. Dept. Psychiat. Warneford; Hosp. Oxf.; Research Fell. Clin. Psychopharmacol. Univ. Dept. & MRC; Unit of Clin. Pharmacol. Radcliffe Infirm. Oxf.

ORR, Mr Neil Wallace Morison (retired) 45 Lexden Road, Colchester CO3 3PY Tel: 01206 573854 — MB BChir 1966 Camb.; MA Camb. 1957, MD 1963, MChir 1966, MB 1957, BChir 1956; FRCS Eng. 1966. Prev: Cons. Surg. Colchester Gen. Hosp.

ORR, Paul Anthony 17 Glenview, Magheraconluce Road, Anahilt, Hillsborough BT26 6RD — MB BCh BAO 1991 Belf.; MRCGP 1995; DRCOG 1994. (Qu. Univ. Belf.)

ORR, Pauline Ann The Health Centre, Loftus Hill, Sedbergh LA10 5RX Tel: 015396 20218 Fax: 015396 20265; Farley Croft, Joss Lane, Sedbergh LA10 5AS Tel: 015396 21496 — MB ChB 1972 Aberd.; Fam. Planning Certif. 1975; MRCGP 1976; Dip. Ther. Newc. 1995; Dip. Pract. Dermat. Wales 1990; DCH Eng. 1975. GP Sedbergh, Cumbria; Med. Mem. Indep. Tribunal Serv. Prev: GP Morecambe; SHO (Gen. Med.) Roy. Lancaster Infirm.; SHO (O & G) Dudley Rd. Hosp. Birm.

ORR, Peter Kenneth 21 Durham Road, Bishop Auckland DL14 7HU — MB BS 1980 Newc.; FRCR 1987. Cons. Radiol. Bishop Auckland Gen. Hosp.

ORR, Mr Peter Stewart Dept. of Urology, Monklands Hospital, Airdrie ML6 0JS Tel: 01236 748748, 0161 795 8953 — MB ChB 1967 Glas.; MPhil (Law & Ethics in Med.) Glas. 1994; FRCS Glas. 1973; DObst RCOG 1969. (Glas.) Cons. (Urol.) Monklands, Hosp. Socs: BMA; Brit. Assn. of Urological Surg.s; Scottich Medico-Legal Soc. Prev: Sen. Regist. (Urol.) Glas. Roy. Infirm.; Ho. Off. (Surg.) Vict. Infirm. Glas.; Ho. Off. (Med.) S.. Gen. Hosp. Glas.

ORR, Raymond Michael 83 Mount Annan Dr, Kingspark, Glasgow G44 4RX — MB ChB 1997 Glas.

ORR, Richard Burnet Faris Mount Stuart Hospital, St Vincents Road, Torquay TQ1 4UP Tel: 01803 313881 Fax: 01803 313498 — MB BS 1959 Lond.; MRCS Eng. LRCP Lond. 1959; MRCPsych 1972; DPM Eng. 1968. (St. Thos.) Cons. S. Devon Healthcare Trust; Civil. Cons. Psychiat., Roy. Navy. Prev: Ho. Phys. St. Thos. Hosp. Lond.; Resid. in Med. New York Univ., U.S.A.; Sen. Regist. Profess. Unit, Warneford Hosp. Oxf.

ORR, Richard James 269 Manchester New Road, Middleton, Manchester M24 1LB — MB ChB 1978 Manch.; DRCOG 1980. GP Oldham; Sec. & Treas. Oldham LMC.

ORR, Robert Lindsay 76 Jackson Avenue, Mickleover, Derby DE3 5AT — MB ChB 1995 Leic.

ORR, Robin Gooch 9 Pointers Hill, Westcott, Dorking RH4 3PF Tel: 01306 888596 — MB BS 1953 Lond.; LMSSA Lond. 1953; MFOM RCP Lond. 1978; DIH Eng. 1957; DPH Lond. 1956; DObst RCOG 1955. (Guy's) Socs: BMA. Prev: Resid. Obst., Ho. Phys., Asst. Ho. Surg. & Outpats. Off. Guy's Hosp. Lond.

ORR, Roslyn Denise 133 Mountsandel Road, Coleraine BT52 1TA — MB BS 1995 Newc.

ORR, Sheila Christine (retired) 5 Gloucester Place, Edinburgh EH3 6EE Tel: 0131 225 5926 — MB ChB 1949 Glas.; DPH Lond. 1952. Prev: SCMO Lothian Health Bd.

ORR, Thomas Andrew Linlithgow Health Centre, 288 High Street, Linlithgow EH49 7ER Tel: 01506 670027; Bonnytounside, Linlithgow EH49 7RQ Tel: 01506 845237 — MB ChB 1973 Ed.; DObst RCOG 1975.

ORR, Valerie Anne Randerston, Kings Barns, St Andrews KY16 8QE Tel: 01333 450462 — MB ChB 1996 Aberd.

ORR, Mr Wilbert McNeill (retired) (cons. rooms), 11 St John St., Manchester M3 4DW Tel: 0161 832 9398 — MB BCh BAO 1954 Dub.; ChM Manch. 1967; FRCS Ed. 1960; FRCS Eng. 1961. Prev: Cons. Gen. Surg. Roy. Infirm. Manch.

ORR, William Graham The Health Centre, Loftus Hill, Sedbergh LA10 5RX — MB BS 1967 Lond.; MRCGP 1976. (St. Mary's) p/t Locum GP; Med. Mem. Appeals Tribunal Serv. Socs: Roy. Soc. Med. Prev: GP Morecambe.

ORR, William Peter Department of Cardiology, Royal Berkshire & Battle Hospitals, Oxford Road, Reading RG30 1AG Tel: 0118 963 6695 Fax: 0118 963 6622 Email: william.orr@rbbh-tr.nhs.uk; Outfield Cottage, 46 The Green, Marsh Baldon, Oxford OX44 9LP — MB BS 1989 Lond.; MRCP (UK) 1993. (Lond. Hosp. Med. Coll.) Cons. Cardiol. Roy. Berks. & Battle Hosp. Reading, Berk. Prev: BHF Jun. Research Fell. (Cardiovasc. Med.) Univ. Oxf. John Radcliffe Hosp.; Regist. Rotat. (Cardiol.) John Radcliffe Hosp. Oxf.; Specialist Regist. Cardiol. John Radcliffe Hosp. Oxf.

ORR, Mr William Stephen Michael Yarm Medical Centre, 1 Worsall Road, Yarm TS15 9DD Tel: 01642 786422 Fax: 01642 785617; The Old School, Crathorne, Yarm TS15 0BA — MB BCh BAO 1974 Dub.; BA (Hons.) Dub. 1971, MB BCh BAO 1974; FRCSI 1978; MRCGP 1984; DRCOG 1985. Prev: Clin. Research Fell. Roy. Vict. Hosp. Belf.

ORR-HUGHES, Kenneth (retired) 61 Madeira Park, Tunbridge Wells TN2 5SX Tel: 01892 521397 — MRCS Eng. LRCP Lond. 1949; MRCGP 1967.

ORRELL, Catherine Jane 24 Verdayne Avenue, Shirley, Croydon CR0 8TS Tel: 01946 693181 Fax: 01946 513513 — MB ChB 1992 Cape Town.

ORRELL, David Howard (retired) Royal Lancaster Infirmary, Lancaster LA1 4RP Tel: 01524 65944 — MB BChir 1962 Camb.; BA Camb. 1958, MA, MB 1962, BChir 1961; FRCP Lond. 1992, M 1964; FRCPath 1987, M 1970. Cons. Chem. Path. Roy. Lancaster Infirm. Prev: Cons. Chem. Path. Roy. Lancaster Infirm.

ORRELL, Jonathan Martin 12 Coldharbour, Chickerell, Weymouth DT3 4BG; Abbey Manor Surgery, Abbey Village Centre, Abbey Manor Park, Yeovil BA21 3TL Tel: 01305 33434 — MB BS 1985 Lond.; MRCGP 1990; DRCOG 1989. Socs: Christ. Med. Fell.sh.; Caring Professions Concern. Prev: Trainee GP Som. VTS.

ORRELL, Judith Clare 11 Beechwood Drive, Ormskirk L39 3NU Tel: 01695 574477; 63 Ash Close, Appley Bridge, Wigan WN6 9HU Tel: 0125 725 4695 — MB ChB 1988 Manch. Trainee GP Wrexham Maelor Hosp.

ORRELL, Julian Maxwell Department of Pathology, Ipswich Hospital NHS Trust, Ipswich IP4 5PD Tel: 01473 703359 — MB ChB 1985 Manch.; BSc Manch. 1982, MD Manch. 1994; MRCPath 1992. Cons. Histopath. Ipswich Hosp. NHS Trust. Prev: Lect. & Hon. Sen. Regist. (Path.) Ninewells Hosp. & Med. Sch. Dundee; Regist. (Histopath.) Ninewells Hosp. Med. Sch. Dundee; Regist. (Path. Biochem.) W.. Infirm. Glas.

ORRELL, Martin John (retired) 7 Brunel Drive, Weymouth DT3 6NU Tel: 01305 834049 Fax: 01305 834049 Email: orrellhg@globalnet.co.uk — MB BChir Camb. 1960; MA Camb. 1960; MRCGP 1967; DObst RCOG 1961. Prev: GP Weymouth.

ORRELL, Martin William Princess Alexandra Hospital, Harlow CM20 1QX Tel: 01279 827260 Fax: 01279 454018 Email: m.orrell@ucl.ac.uk; 27 Wickfield Avenue, Christchurch BH23 1JB — BM BS 1982 Nottm.; PhD Lond. 1994; BMedSci (Hons.) Nottm. 1980; MRCPsych. 1989. Reader (Psychiat. of Ageing) Univ. Coll. Lond.; Hon. Cons. Psychiat. of Elderly P.ss Alexandra Hosp. Harlow; Edr. Internat. Jl. Aging & Ment. Health. Socs: Eur. Assn. Sci. Eds. Prev: Sen. Regist. Maudsley Hosp. Lond.; Research Regist. Inst. Psychiat. Maudsley Hosp.

ORRELL, Mary Gillian Wick House, 17 Well Cross, Edith Weston, Oakham LE15 8HG Tel: 01780 720196 — MB BChir 1955 Camb.; MA Camb. 1956; DObst RCOG 1957. (Camb. & St. Thos.) Prev: Med. Adviser DSS; Clin. Asst. (Anaesth.) Dist. Hosp. P'boro.; Ho. Surg. (Obst.) St. Giles Hosp. Camberwell.

ORRELL, Richard William Department of Neurology, Royal Free Hospital, Bond Street, London NW3 2QG Tel: 020 7830 2387 Fax: 020 7431 1577 Email: r.orrell@rfc.ucl.ac.uk — MB ChB 1982 Manch.; BSc (Hons. Physiol.) Manch. 1979, MD 1996; MRCP (UK) 1987; DCH RCP Lond. 1984. Sen. Lect. (Clin. Neurosci.s) Roy. Free &Univ. Coll. Med. Sch., Lond.; Cons. NeUrol. Roy. Free Hosp. Lond. & Qu. Eliz. II Hosp.Welwyn Garden City; Nat. Hosp. For Neurol. & Neurosurg. Prev: Sen. Regist. (Neurol.) Hammersmith Hosp. & Char. Cross Hosp. Lond.; Hon. Lect. Acad. Unit. Neurosci. Char. Cross & W.m. Med. Sch. Univ. Lond.; Vis. Prof. MRC Trav. Fell. (Neurol.) Univ. Rochester Med. Center NY, USA.

ORRELL, Robert Frederick Edward Heavitree Health Centre, South Lawn Terrace, Heavitree, Exeter EX1 2RX Tel: 01392 211511 Fax: 01392 499451 — MB BS 1972 Lond.; DCH Eng. 1974; DObst RCOG 1975; MRCGP 1977. (Westm.)

ORRIDGE, Howard William St John's Group Practice, 1 Greenfield Lane, Balby, Doncaster DN4 0TH Tel: 01302 854521 Fax: 01302 310823; Stonecross Cottage, Wadworth Hall Lane, Wadworth, Doncaster DN11 9BH — MB BS 1981 Lond.

ORRITT, Sterry Gordon Charles Medical Centre, 1 Rawling Road, Gateshead NE8 4QS Tel: 0191 477 2180 — MB BS Newc. 1986; DRCOG 1991; DA (UK) 1989; MRCGP 1993. (Newcastle Upon Tyne)

ORSBORN, Raymond Christie 50 Vernon Avenue, Handsworth Wood, Birmingham B20 1DF — MB 1971 Camb.; BChir 1970; MRCGP 1979; DCH Eng. 1976; DTM & H Liverp. 1974; DObst RCOG 1974. GP Birm.

ORSI, Claudia Rosa 37 Balcombe Street, London NW1 6HH — BSc Lond. 1987, MB BS 1990; DCH RCP Lond. 1992. Trainee GP/SHO St. Mary's Hosp. Lond. VTS.

ORTEGA, Luis Salvador 274 West Way, Broadstone BH18 9LL — LMS 1988 U Autonoma Bilbao.

ORTEGA SIPAN, Anna Maria Royal Hospital for Sick Children, 129 Drumchapel Road, Glasgow G15 6PX — LMS 1992 U Autonoma Barcelona.

ORTEU, Catherine Helene Royal London Hospital, White Chapel, London E1 1BB Tel: 020 7377 7000 Fax: 020 7377 7383; 94 Eton Rise, Eton College Road, London NW3 2DB — MB BS 1987 Lond.; BSc Lond. 1984; MRCP (UK) 1992. Specialist Regist. (Dermat.) Roy. Lond. Hosp. Lond. Socs: Brit. Assn. Dermat.; Soc. Clinique Française. Prev: Hon. Sen. Regist. (Dermat) & Clin. Research Fell. Acad. Dept. Med. Roy. Free Hosp. Sch. of Med. Lond.; Regist. (Dermat.) Roy. Free Hosp. Lond.; Regist. Rotat. (Hosp. Med.) & SHO Lond. Hosp. Whitechapel.

ORTH, Astrid 75 Highcliffe Road, Sheffield S11 7LP — State Exam Med 1988 Munich; State Exam Med Technical Univ. Munich 1988. Regist. (Paediat.) Sheff. Prev: SHO King's Mill Hosp. Mansfield.

ORTOLANI, Maria Luisa 9 King Street, Loughborough LE11 1SB — State Exam Perugia 1992.

ORTON, Betty Frances Beach Hill, Bitton, Bristol BS30 6NU Tel: 0127 588 2306 — MB ChB 1939 Bristol. (Bristol)

ORTON, Caroline Jane Cookridge Hospital, Hospital Lane, Cookridge, Leeds LS16 6QB Tel: 0113 392 4035 Fax: 0113 392 4072 Email: j.orton@leedsth.nhs.uk — MB ChB 1982 Sheff.; MRCPsych 1988; FRCR 1994. Cons. (Clin. Oncol.) Cookridge Hosp. Leeds; Counc. Mem. of Brit. Gyn. Cancer Soc. 2000. Socs: Brit. Gyn. Cancer Soc. - Counc. Mem. Prev: Specialist Regist. (Clin. Oncol.) Christie Hosp. Manch.; Clin. Research Fell. Paterson Inst. Cancer Research Manch.; Regist. (Clin. Oncol.) Newc.

ORTON, Christine Margaret Park View Surgery, Haverflatts Lane, Milnthorpe LA7 7PS Tel: 015395 63327 Fax: 015395 64059; Brookside Cottage, Over Kellet, Carnforth LA6 1BS — MB ChB 1987 Dundee; BSc Sheff. 1983. Prev: Trainee GP Stoneleigh Surg. Milnthorpe; SHO (A & E & Psychiat.) Lancaster.

ORTON, Mr Clive Ian BUPA Hospital, Russell Road, Whalley Range, Manchester M16 8AJ Tel: 0161 861 0553 Fax: 0161 226 9014 Email: clive@cliveorton.com — MB BS 1967 Lond.; FRCS Eng. 1972; MRCS Eng. LRCP Lond. 1967; BDS Lond. 1962; FDS RCS Eng. 1969,. (Univ. Coll. Hosp.) Pres. of the Brit. Assn. of Aesthetic Plastic Surg.s. Socs: Brit. Assn. Plastic Surg.; Brit Assn. Of Aesthetic Plastic Surg.; Internat. Soc. Of Aesthetic Plastic Surg. Prev: Cons. Plastic Surg. at the Christie Hosp. and the Univ. Hosp. of S. Manch.

ORTON, David Arnold The Laurels CMHC, C/o Newton Abbot Hospital, 62 East Street, Newton Abbot TQ12 4PT Tel: 01626 357335 Fax: 01626 357338 — MB ChB Birm. 1970; MRCP (UK) 1974; MRCPsych 1982. Cons. Psychiat. S. Devon Healthcare Trust; Vis. Cons. The Priory N. Lond.. Prev: Cons. Psychiat. W. Herts. Community (NHS) Trust; Sen. Regist. P.ss Margt. Migraine Clinic & Hon. Lect. (Clin. Pharmacol.) St. Bart. Hosp. Lond.; Regist. (Psychiat.) N.wich Pk. & Shenley Hosps.

ORTON, David Ian Department of Dermatology, Amersham Hospital, Whielden Street, Amersham HP7 0JD Tel: 01492 734600; 110 Lord's View II, St John's Wood, London NW8 7HG — MB BS 1988 Lond.; BSc (Hons.) Lond. 1985; MRCP (UK) 1992. (Char. Cross & Westminster) Cons. Dermatol., Dermat. Dept. Amersham Hosp. Socs: Brit. Assn. of Dermatol.s; Europ. Soc. of Contact Dermatitis; Brit. Soc. of Allergy & Clin. Immunol. Prev: SpR Dermat. Rotat., Roy. Free Hosp. Lond. & Lond. Hosp.

ORTON, Dean Wells (retired) Mayfield, Ullesthorpe Road, Bitteswell, Lutterworth LE17 4SD — MRCS Eng. LRCP Lond. 1950; DObst RCOG 1952. Prev: SHO (Surg.) Bolton Roy. Infirm.

ORTON, Edward Maurice 109 Lords' View, St John's Wood Road, London NW8 7HG Tel: 020 7289 1786 — BA Camb. 1947, MA 1950, MB BChir 1952; MRCS Eng. LRCP Lond. 1950. (Camb. & Char. Cross) Prev: Med. Off. Tesco Stores Ltd. & Dentsply Ltd.; Ho. Phys. Char. Cross Hosp. Unit, Mt. Vernon Hosp. N.wood.

ORTON, John Kurt 8 Grosvenor House Mews, Holland Road, Crumpsall, Manchester M8 4NP — MB ChB 1979 Manch.

ORTON, Julian Jasper Bourne Hall Health Centre, Chessington Road, Ewell, Epsom KT17 1TG Tel: 020 8394 1500 Fax: 020 8786 8268 Email: julian.orton@gp-l81091.nhs.uk — MB ChB 1986 Manch.; MRCP (UK) 1990; DRCOG 1992. (Manch.) Prev: SHO (Paediat.) Epsom Gen. Hosp.; Regist. (Psychiat.) Priory Hosp. Roehampton; Trainee GP Fetcham, Surrey VTS.

ORTON, Katharine Anne The Surgery, Broomfields, Hatfield Heath, Bishop's Stortford CM22 7EH Tel: 01279 730616 Fax:

ORTON

01279 730408; Matching Parsonage Farm, Newmans End, Matching, Harlow CM17 0QX Tel: 01279 731536 — MB BS 1978 Lond.; MRCGP 1982; Dip. Addic. Behaviour Lond. 1994; DCH RCP Lond. 1981; DRCOG 1980. (Charing Cross Hospital Medical School) F/T Princip. in G.P at Broomfield N.Health; GP W.. Essex Community Drug & Alcohol Team. Socs: Fell.Roy. Soc. Med.; Pres. Sect. of Gen. Pract.1999-2000.

ORTON, Michael George 15 Porter Close, Rainhill, Prescot L35 6PY Fax: 0151 289 7974 Email: michaelorton@hotmail.com — MB BS 1981 Lond.; MRCS Eng. LRCP Lond. 1981; AFOM RCP Lond. 1994; MRCGP (Distinc.) 1986; DRCOG 1985; MFOM. RCP.Lond.1999. (Charing Cross Hospital London) Med. Director. OH Solutions, Liverp. Socs: Soc. Occupat.al Med. Prev: GP, Aylesbury, Bucks., 1986-1994; Head of Occupat.al Health, Marks & Spencer plc 1994-2000.

ORTON, Peggy Kathleen Lillian (retired) Oakwood, North Road, Chideock, Bridport DT6 6LE Tel: 01297 489742 — MRCS Eng. LRCP Lond. 1943; FRCS Eng. 1955; DLO Eng. 1947. Prev: Cons. Otolaryngol. Qu. Mary's Hosp. Childr., St. Helier Hosp. Carshalton, S. Lond. Hosp. Wom. & Eliz. Garrett Anderson Hosp. Lond.

ORTON, Peter Kenneth The Surgery, Broomfields, Hatfield Heath, Bishop's Stortford CM22 7EH Tel: 01279 730616 Fax: 01279 730408; Matching Parsonage Farm, Newmans End, Matching, Harlow CM17 0QX Tel: 01279 731536 Email: peterorton@email.msn.com — MB BS 1980 Lond.; MMedSc Leeds 1986; MRCS Eng. LRCP Lond. 1980; FRCGP 1995, M 1985; DRCOG 1984; Cert. Family Plann. JCC 1984; Cert. Av. Med. 1996; DFFP 1996. (Char. Cross) GP Princip.; Sen. Lect. (Postgrad. Med.) Centre for Continuing Educat. Bath Univ.; Sen. Lect. Inst. of Gen. Pract. Exeter. Socs: Fell. Roy. Soc. Med. (Ex-Pres. Gen. Pract. Sect.).

ORTON, Richard William (retired) Beach Hill, Bitton, Bristol BS30 6NU Tel: 0127 588 2306 — MB ChB 1940 Bristol.

ORTON, William Taylor (retired) 145 Thornton Road, Cambridge CB3 0NE Tel: 01223 277511 — MB BCh BAO 1948 Belf.; MFPHM 1974; DPH Belf. 1951. Hon. Sec. Inst. Sports Med. Lond. Prev: Dist. Community Phys. Haringey Health Dist.

ORUGUN, Enoch Oluwambe West Cumberland Hospital, Homewood, Whitehaven CA28 8JG; 58 Front Street, Sherburn, Durham DH6 1HB — MB BS 1979 Lagos; MSc Aberd. 1989; MRCPI 1987. Prev: Regist. (Gen. Med.) Whitehaven; Regist. (Gen. Med.) Stracatard Hosp Brechin.

ORWIN, Ashley Scarlett 9 Ashleigh Grove, West Jesmond, Newcastle upon Tyne NE2 3DJ — MB BS 1993 Newc.

ORWIN, John Michael (retired) 1 Mayen Place, Nightingale Road, Godalming GU7 3AH Tel: 01483 424663 — MB ChB 1963 Ed.; FFPM RCP (UK) 1990; FRCA 1968; DA Eng. 1965. Centre Dir. Marion Merrell Dow Research & Developm. Centre. Prev: Managing Dir. & Vice Pres. Global Clin. Research Marion Merrell Dow Inc. Kansas City, USA.

ORYEMA, Manackwe Benjamin Royal Victoria Hospital, Belfast BT12 6BA Tel: 028 40503 — MB ChB 1974 Makerere. (Mulago Med. Sch. Kampala) SHO (Gen. Surg.) Roy. Vict. Hosp. Belf.

OSAKWE, Edwin Aniamaka 10 Jeymer Avenue, London NW2 4PL — MB BS 1998 Lond.

OSBORN, Chester Alkermes Europe Ltd., The Quorum, Barnwell Road, Cambridge CB5 8RE Tel: 01223 401321 Email: chester.osborn@alkermes.co.uk; Wolfe Hall, Barrow, Bury St Edmunds IP29 5EZ Tel: 01284 811694 Fax: 01284 811694 Email: cosborn@doctors.org.uk — MB BS 1977 Lond.; MA Oxf. 1976; MRCP (UK) 1980. Dir. Med. Affairs Europe Alkermes Europe Ltd. Camb. Prev: Regional Dir. (Clin. Research) Rhone-Poulenc Rorer; Dir. (Clin. Research) SmithKline Beecham.

OSBORN, Mr David Eric The Dower House, Vicarage Lane, Barkby, Leicester LE7 — MRCS Eng. LRCP Lond. 1968; MS Lond. 1979, MB BS 1968; FRCS Eng. 1974. (Char. Cross) Cons. Urol. Leic. Gen. Hosp. Prev: Sen. Regist. (Urol.) Withington & Christie Hosps. Manch.; Regist. (Urol. & Transpl.) Hammersmith Hosp. Lond.; Lect. in Physiol. Char. Cross Hosp. Med. Sch. Lond.

OSBORN, David Philip John University Department of Psychiatry & Behavioural Sciences, Royal Free & Univ. Coll. Medical School, Rowland Hill St., London NW3 2PF Tel: 020 7794 0500 Email: dosborn@erfc.ucl.ac.uk — MB BS 1993 Lond.; 2000 MSC Lond.; BA. Cantab. 1990; MA Cantab. 1998; MRC Psych 1997. Lect. (Psychiat.) Roy. Free Hosp. Lond.; Hon. Specialist Regist. (Roy. Free Hosp. Lond). Socs: BMA; RCPsych. Prev: Regist. (Psychiat.) Roy. Free Hosp. Lond.

OSBORN, Donna Michelle 77 Goodrich Road, London SE22 0EQ — MB BS 1998 Lond.

OSBORN, Frances Ann 56 Thornyville Villas, Oreston, Plymouth PL9 7LD Tel: 01752 406595 — BM 1987 Soton. SHO (Anaesth.) Torbay Hosp. Prev: SHO (Obsts. & Gyn.) S. Glam. HA; Ho. Phys. St. Marys Hosp. Newport I. of Wight; Ho. Surg. Cumbld. Infirm. Carlisle.

OSBORN, Gillian Rosemary Health First Medical Group, King George Surgery, 135 High Street, Stevenage SG1 3HT Tel: 01438 361111 Fax: 01438 361227; Hicks Grove House, Halls Green, Weston, Hitchin SG4 7DX Tel: 01462 790454 — MB ChB 1967 Birm.; BSc Birm. 1965. (Birmingham) Prev: GP Taunton; Ho. Surg. Childr. Hosp. Birm.; Ho. Phys. Dudley Rd. Hosp. Birm.

OSBORN, Helen Mary St James Surgery, Gains Lane, Devizes SN10 1QU Tel: 01380 722206 Fax: 01380 721552 — MB BS 1988 Lond.; MRCGP 1993; DRCOG 1992.

OSBORN, Janet Anne Thorneloe Lodge Surgery, 29 Barbourne Road, Worcester WR1 1RU Tel: 01905 22445 Fax: 01905 610963; Pursers Orchard, Callow End, Worcester WR2 4TY Tel: 22445 — MB ChB 1963 Birm. Prev: Regist. Psychiat. Mabledon Hosp. Dartford.

OSBORN, Madeline Frances Graiglwyd, Graiglwyd Uchaf, Rhoscefnhir, Pentraeth LL75 8YS — MB ChB 1970 Ed.; MRCPsych 1975. Sen. Regist. (Psychiat.) Univ. Hosp. S. Manch.

OSBORN, Marian Lucy (retired) Weavers Hill House, Stoney Lane, Ashmore Green, Thatcham RG18 9HQ — MB BS 1955 Lond. Prev: Ho. Surg. & Sen. Cas. Off. Roy. Free Hosp. Lond.

OSBORN, Nicola Anne Pursers Orchard, Callow End, Worcester WR2 4UF — MB ChB 1988 Birm.; ChB Birm. 1988.

OSBORN, Stephanie Victoria 25A Scotts Av, Bromley BR2 0LG — MB ChB 1997 Sheff.

OSBORN, Thomas Welwyn 49 Hill Top, Hampstead Garden Suburb, London NW11 6EA Tel: 020 8455 4375 — MB BS 1947 Lond. (St. Bart) Hon. Research Fell. Nat. Heart & Lung Inst. Univ. Lond. Prev: Mem. Scientif. Staff, Nat. Inst. Med. Research & Nat. Inst. Biol. Standards & Control; Demonst. Path. St. Bart. Hosp.; Capt. RAMC.

OSBORN-SMITH, Erle Hamilton (retired) 5 Royal Walk, Ryde PO33 1NL Tel: 01983 563359 — MB BS Lond. 1959; MRCS Eng. LRCP Lond. 1958; LMSSA Lond. 1946 DPH Eng. 1957; MFCM 1974; Dip. Audiol. Univ. Manch. 1962. Prev: Sen. Med. Off. (Audiol.) E. Sussex AHA.

OSBORNE, Abraham Bertram (retired) 56/2 Spylaw Road, Edinburgh EH10 5BR Tel: 0131 337 2018 — MB ChB Ed. 1945. Prev: Med. Asst. in Psychiat. (Drug Addict) Guy's Hosp.

OSBORNE, Alice Jane Tel: 01926 770418 Fax: 01926 770418 Email: maxillofacialfagan@hotmail.com — BM BS 1993 Nottm.; DRCOG 1996; MRCGP 1997; DFFP 1997. (Nottm.) p/t GP Retainer. Prev: GP Regist. Clevedon Health.

OSBORNE, Andrew William 25 Wellfield Road, Culchetch, Warrington WA3 4JR — MB ChB 1987 Sheff.

OSBORNE, Andrew William Howard 76 Vineyard Hill Road, London SW19 7JJ — MB BS 1991 Lond.; FRCS Eng 1997. (The London Hospital Medical College)

OSBORNE, Mr Anthony Howard, Surg. Capt. RN Retd. Obsborne House, Brook Avenue, Warsash, Southampton SO31 9HP Tel: 01489 577652; 152 Harley Street, London W1N 1AH — MRCS Eng. LRCP Lond. 1967; MCh (Orthop.) Liverp. 1980; FRCS (Orthop.) Ed. 1980; FRCS Eng. 1976; FRCS Ed. 1976. (Guy's) Wessex Nuffield Hosp. E.leigh. Socs: Fell. Roy. Soc. Med.; Brit. Assn. Surg. Knee. Prev: Head (Orthop.) RNH Haslar Gosport.

OSBORNE, Bridget Virginia Llys Meddyg Surgery, Llys Meddyg, 23 Castle Street, Conwy LL32 8AY Tel: 01492 592424 Fax: 01492 593068; Tyddyn Ucha, Glan Conwy, Colwyn Bay LL28 5PN — MB BS 1980 Lond.; MRCP (UK) 1983; MRCGP 1987. (Roy. Free) Assoc. GP Conwy Retainer Scheme.

OSBORNE, Caroline Julie 6 Conner Avenue, New Carron Village, Falkirk FK2 7FS — MB ChB 1994 Aberd.; DRCOG 1996; DFFP 1996; MRCGP. 1998. (Aberdeen)

OSBORNE, Caroline Louise Elizabeth Homeleigh Cottage, Guineaford, Barnstaple EX31 4EA — MB BS 1996 Lond.

OSBORNE

OSBORNE, Christopher Derek Ian (retired) Nuttall Farmhouse, The Vale, Frostenden, Beccles NR34 7HZ Email: c.osborne@bt.internet.com — MB BS Lond. 1966; MRCS Eng. LRCP Lond. 1966; DObst RCOG 1968. Prev: Ho. Surg. W. Norwich Hosp.

OSBORNE, Christopher John 10 Danesboro Road, Bridgwater TA6 7LR — MB ChB 1980 Manch.

OSBORNE, Clifford Ernest The Health Centre, 55 High Street, Great Wakering, Southend-on-Sea SS3 0EF Tel: 01702 218678 Fax: 01702 577853; 17 Plymtree, Thorpe Bay, Southend-on-Sea SS1 3RA Tel: 01702 586934 — LRCPI & LM, LRSCI & LM 1970; LRCPI & LM, LRCSI & LM 1970. Prev: Ho. Phys. & Ho. Surg. Qu. Mary's Hosp. Sidcup.

OSBORNE, David Bruce Rowan (retired) Westacott House, Goodleigh, Barnstaple EX32 7NF Tel: 01271 323200 — MB Camb. 1955, BChir 1954; DObst RCOG 1956.

OSBORNE, David Carl Ashworth Street Surgery, 85 Spotland Road, Rochdale OL12 6RT Tel: 01706 44582 Fax: 01706 346767; 47 Bleakholt Road, Turn Village, Ramsbottom, Bury BL0 0RU — MB ChB 1992 Manch.; MB ChB St. Manch. 1992; BSc (Med Sci.) St. And. 1989. GP Rochdale. Lancs.

OSBORNE, David John Tel: 01792 843831 Fax: 01792 844902; 3 Graigola Road, Glais, Swansea SA7 9HS Tel: 01792 845312 — MB BS 1967 Lond.; MRCS Eng. LRCP Lond. 1967; DMJ Soc. Apoth. Lond. 1980. (Guy's) Med. Off. Clydach War Memor. Hosp; HM Coroner for Co. W. Glam.

OSBORNE, David Michael 90 Livingstone Road, Hove BN3 3WL — MB ChB 1993 Liverp.

OSBORNE, Mr David Robert Ladywell House, Ladywell Lane, Great Baddow, Chelmsford CM2 7AE — MRCS Eng. LRCP Lond. 1968; MS Lond. 1983, MB BS 1968; FRCS Eng. 1974. (Roy. Free) Cons. Surg. Basildon & Orsett Hosps. Prev: Lect. Surg. Roy. Free Hosp. Med. Sch. Lond.; Surg. Regist. Roy. Free Hosp. Lond. Surg. Regist. Cheltenham & Gloucester Health Dists.

OSBORNE, Elaine Marion (retired) 19 Alnwick Road, Newton Hall, Durham DH1 5NL Tel: 0191 386 1337 — MB ChB 1947 Leeds; MFCM 1974; DCH Eng. 1963; DPH Leeds 1961; DObst RCOG 1948. Prev: Cons. Phys. Sedgefield Dist. Counc.

OSBORNE, Elizabeth Sara Hopwood Medical Centre, 1-3 Walton Street, Hopwood, Heywood OL10 2BS Tel: 01706 369886 Fax: 01706 627619 — MB ChB 1992 Manch.; BSc (Med. Sci.) St. And. 1989; MRCGP. (Manchester) GP Princip. & GP Trainer. Socs: BMA; SPA; RCGP.

OSBORNE, Mr Eric Alexander (retired) Thorterburn Farm, nr. Neilston, Glasgow G78 3AX Tel: 0141 585222 — MB ChB 1960 Glas.; FRCS Ed. 1968; FRCS Glas. 1968; DObst RCOG 1962. Prev: Ho. Phys. Stobhill Gen. Hosp. Glas.

OSBORNE, Fiona Lesley 47 Fredrick Road, Selly Oak, Birmingham B16 1NZ — MB ChB 1998 Birm.; ChB Birm. 1998.

OSBORNE, Genevieve Emily Norah 82 Cadogan Lane, London SW1X 9DY — BM 1992 Soton.

OSBORNE, Mr Geoffrey Vaughan 26 Waterloo Road, Southport PR8 2NF Tel: 01704 65215 — MB ChB 1940 Liverp.; MCh Orth. Liverp. 1947, MB ChB 1940; FRCS Eng. 1973; FRCS Ed. 1946. Cons. Emerit. & Orthop. Surg., Roy. Liverp. Hosp. & S.port Gen. Hosp.; Hon. Research Fell. Sch. Engin. Liverp. John Mores Univ. Socs: Sen. Fell. BOA; Sen. Fell. Brit. Soc. Surg. Hand. Prev: Lect. (Orthop. Surg.) Univ. Liverp.

OSBORNE, Joanne 187 Battenhall Road, Worcester WR5 2BU — MB BS 1990 Lond. Regist. (O & G) NE Thames RHA.

OSBORNE, John Antony Bro-Morganning NHS Trust, Princess of Wales Hospital, Bridgend; Diamond House, Westgate, Cowbridge CF72 8SH Tel: 07968 141164 — MB BS 1988 Lond.; BSc 1985 (Psych.) Lond.; FRCA 1996. Cons. Anaesth. Socs: BMA; Fell. Roy. Coll. Anaesths.; Assn. Anaesths. Prev: Regist. (Cardiol. & Renal Med.) Wellington, NZ; SHO (Anaesth.) Gloucester Roy. Hosp.

OSBORNE, Mr John Leslie 212-214 Great Portland Street, London W1W 5QN Tel: 020 7387 7055 Fax: 020 7387 7066 Email: johnosborneobgyn@doctors.org.uk; 17 Grove Park Gardens, Chiswick, London W4 3RY Tel: 020 8995 0019 — MB BS 1966 Lond.; FRCOG 1985, M 1973. (Lond. Hosp.) Cons. Obst., Gynaecologist and Uro-gynaecologist, Univ. Coll. Hosp, Lond. Socs: Internat. Continence Soc.; Roy. Soc. Med.; Assoc. Mem. Brit. Assn. Urological Surg. Prev: Cons. Obst. & Gynaecologist to Qu. Charlotte's Hosp. & the Hosp. Forwonien; Sen. Regist. & Lect. Inst.

O & G Qu. Charlotte's & Chelsea Hosps. Wom.; Research Asst. & Hon. Sen. Regist. Urodynamic Unit Middlx. Hosp.

OSBORNE, Professor John Paul Royal United Hospital, Combe Park, Bath BA1 3NG Tel: 01225 824218 Fax: 01225 824212; 5 The Tyning, Widcombe Hill, Bath BA2 6AL Tel: 01225 420028 — MB BS 1971 Lond.; MD Lond. 1980; FRCP Lond. 1989; MRCP (UK) 1974; DCH Eng. 1974; DObst RCOG 1973. (St. Thos.) Cons. Paediat. Roy. United Hosp. Bath; Hon. Prof. Univ. Bath. Socs: Brit. Paediat. Neurol. Assn.; Fell. & Hon. Treas. Roy. Coll. Paediat. and Child. Health. Prev: Sen. Regist. (Paediat.) Roy. Hosp. Sick Childr. Bristol; Fell. (Neurol.) Hosp. Sick Childr. Toronto, Canada; Regist. (Paediat.) St. Thos. Hosp. Lond.

OSBORNE, Mr Jonathan Edward C/O ENT Department, Glan Clwyd Hospital, Bodelwyddan, Rhyl Tel: 01745 534233 Fax: 01745 534160 Email: jon.osborne@cd-tr.wales.nhs.uk; Tyddyn Ucha, Glan Conwy, Colwyn Bay LL28 5PN — MB BS 1978 Lond.; FRCS Eng. 1985; FRCS Ed. 1985. (Middlx. Hosp. Med. Sch.) Cons. ENT Surg., Glan Clwyd Hosp. Bodelwyddan. Socs: Sect. Otol. & Laryngol.; Roy. Soc. Med.; Treas. Welsh Assn. Otoloryngol. Prev: Sen. Regist. (ENT) Ninewells Hosp. Dundee & N. Riding Infirm. Middlesbrough; Med. Off. Save The Childr. Fund, Karamoja, Uganda.

OSBORNE, Joy Elizabeth Department of Dermatology, Leicester Royal Infirmary, Infirmary Square, Leicester LE1 5WW Tel: 0116 258 5762; 32 Church Lane, Ratcliffe-on-the-Wreake, Leicester LE7 4SF — BM BS 1978 Nottm.; MRCGP 1982. Assoc. Specialist Dermat. Leicester Roy. Infirm. NHS Trust.

OSBORNE, Julie Elaine Tel: 01332 880249 — MB BS 1986 Lond.; MA Camb. 1987; MRCGP (Distinc.) 1990; DRCOG 1989. Prev: Trainee GP Derby VTS; Dist. Med. Off. Mansa, Zambia (VSO).

OSBORNE, Kathleen Anne 158 Lindisfarne Road, Durham DH1 5YX — MB BS 1994 Lond.

OSBORNE, Keith Norman Alexander The Ayr Hospital, Dalmellington Road, Ayr KA6 6DX Tel: 01292 610555 Fax: 01292 288952; 5 Carrick Avenue, Ayr KA7 2SN Tel: 01292 289602 — MB ChB 1985 Glas.; BSc (Hons.) Glas. 1983; MRCP (UK) 1988; FRCR 1991. Cons. Radiol. Ayr Hosp. Socs: Roy. Coll. Phys. Surg. Glas.; Fell.Roy. Coll. of Radiologists. Prev: Sen. Regist. & Regist. (Radiol.) Roy. Infirm. Glas.; SHO (Gen. Med.) W.. Infirm. Glas.; Ho. Off. (Gen. Med. & Gen. Surg.) W.. Infirm. Glas.

OSBORNE, Margaret Anne (retired) Wildacrres, Consall, Wetley Rocks, Stoke-on-Trent ST9 0AH — MB ChB 1963 Birm. Prev: Sen. Med. Off. Staffs. AHA.

OSBORNE, Mr Martin John 28 Fotheringham Road, Enfield EN1 1QF Tel: 020 8292 2081 — MB BS 1982 Lond.; BA Oxf. 1979; FRCS Eng. 1988; FRCS Ed. 1986; FRCS (Gen.) 1998. (Middlx.) Sen. Regist. Rotat. (Gen. Surg.) Roy. Free & Whittington Hosps. Lond., Chase Farm Hosp. Middlx. & Sir Chas. Gairdner Hosp. Perth, W. Austral.

OSBORNE, Melanie Ann Withington Hospital, Nell lane, Manchester M20 2LR — MB ChB 1982 Leic.; MRCP (UK) 1986; FCAnaesth 1991; DA (UK) 1988. Cons. Anaesth. & ICU Lancs. Socs: RCP Edin.; Intens. Care Soc.; Assn. Anaesth. Prev: Sen. Regist. (Anaesth.) N. W.. Region; Regist. (Anaesth.) Manch. Roy. Infirm. & Wigan Roy. Albert Edwd. Infirm.; Regist. (Gen. Med.) N. Manch. Gen. Hosp.

***OSBORNE, Melanie Elizabeth** 2A Coalway Road, Renn, Wolverhampton WV3 7LR Tel: 0121 426 3221; Cornerways, South View Road, Pinner, Pinner HA5 3YB Tel: 0121 426 3221 — MB BS 1988 Lond.; FRCR 1997; BSc (Hons.) Lond. 1985; MRCP (UK) 1992.

OSBORNE, Melvyn Ambrose University Health Service, 2 Claremont Place, Sheffield S10 2TB Tel: 0114 222 2100 Fax: 0114 276 7223; Buck Trap, Andwell Lane, Sheffield S10 4QF Tel: 0114 230 1164 — MB ChB Sheff. 1969; MRCGP 1981; DObst RCOG 1973; DCH RCPS Glas. 1971; Cert Family Plann. RCOG RCGP & Family Plann Assn. 1976. (Sheff.) Med. Off. Univ. Sheff. Prev: SHO (Obst.) N.. Gen. Hosp. Sheff.; SHO (Paediat.) Hull Roy. Infirm.; Ho. Surg. Sheff. Roy. Hosp.

OSBORNE, Nigel Jonathan Russell First Floor Flat, 11 Lansdown Place, Clifton, Bristol BS8 3AF — BM BS 1993 Nottm.; MRCP (UK) 1996. (Univ. Nottm.) S. W. Deanery Calman Paediatri Specialist Regist. Prev: SHO Rotat. (Paediat.) Bristol; SHO (A & E) Bristol; Ho. Off. (Med.) Qu. Med. Centre Nottm.

OSBORNE, Nigel William Anstey Surgery, 21A The Nook, Anstey, Leicester LE7 7AZ Tel: 0116 236 2531 Fax: 0116 235 7867 — MB

OSBORNE

ChB 1982 Leic.; MRCGP 1986; DRCOG 1985; DCH RCP Lond. 1984. Clin. Asst. Minor Accid. Dept. Gen. Hosp. LoughBoro.

OSBORNE, Pamela Agnew (retired) Rosewood, Marley Common, Haslemere GU27 3PU — MB ChB 1947 Birm. Prev: Med. Off. S.W. Surrey HA.

OSBORNE, Patricia Mary (retired) Greenend Lodge, Ochtertyre, Crieff PH7 4LD Tel: 01764 652935 — MB ChB 1959 Liverp.; MSc (Comm. Med.) Manch. 1980. Prev: Cons. Pub. Health Med. Tayside HB.

OSBORNE, Paul Benjamin Church Street Surgery, Church Street, Starcross, Exeter EX6 8PZ Tel: 01626 890368 Fax: 01626 891330; 4 Westwood, Starcross, Exeter EX6 8RW Tel: 01626 890515 — MB 1974 Camb.; BChir 1973; MRCGP 1980; DCH Eng. 1976.

OSBORNE, Penelope Pauline Greyswood Practice, 238 Mitcham Lane, London SW16 6NT Tel: 020 8769 0845/8363 Fax: 020 8677 2960; 101 Nimrod Road, London SW16 6TH — MB BS 1989 Lond.; BSc (1st cl. Hons.) Lond. 1986; MRCGP 1995; DFFP 1993; DRCOG 1992. (St. George's) Prev: Trainee GP St. Helier Hosp. Carshalton VTS; GP Asst. Wrythe Green Surg. Carshalton.

OSBORNE, Richard John Dorset Cancer Centre, Poole Hospital, Longfleet Road, Poole BH15 2JB; The Engine House, Quarleston Farm, Winterbourne Stickland DT11 0NP — MD 1988 Manch.; MB ChB 1979; MRCP (UK) 1982; FRCP 1995. Cons Med Oncol. Dorset Cancer Centre. Prev: NCI-EORTC Vis. Research Fell. NCI-Navy Med. Oncol. Br. Nat. Cancer Inst. Maryland, USA.; Univ Lect Addenbrookes Hosp Camb.

OSBORNE, Sally Frances 18 Sunningdale, Bristol BS8 2NF — MB ChB 1998 Bristol.

OSBORNE, Sarah Ann Institute of Psychiatry, De Crespigny Park, London SE5 8AF — MB BS 1990 Lond. (Royal Free Hospital School of Medicine) Clin. Researcher and Hon. Staff Grade Psychiat., Inst. of Psychiat., Lond. Socs: Brit. Med. Assn.; Med. Protec. Soc. Prev: Regist. (Psychiat.) St Bart. Hosp. Lond.

OSBORNE, Simon Christopher Pollokshaws Doctors Centre, 26 Wellgreen, Glasgow G43 1RR Tel: 0141 649 2836 Fax: 0141 649 5238; 24 Marlborough Avenue, Broomhill, Glasgow G11 7BW Tel: 0141 334 4096 — MB ChB 1982 Glas.; BSc (Med. Sci.) St. And. 1979; MRCGP 1986.

OSBORNE, Stuart Anthony 8 Wyvis Avenue, Bearsden, Glasgow G61 4RD — MB ChB 1995 Glas.

OSBOROUGH, Fiona Kings Avenue Surgery, 23 Kings Avenue, Buckhurst Hill IG9 5LP Tel: 020 8504 0122 Fax: 020 8559 2984 — MB BCh 1974 Belfast. (Queens University) GP Partners in Gp. Pract.

OSBOURNE, Garrick Knox Hairmyres Hospital, Eaglesham Road, East Kilbride, Glasgow G75 8RG Tel: 01355 585098 Fax: 01355 234064; 1 Avenel Crescent, Strathaven ML10 6JF Tel: 01357 520862 Email: garryosbourne@hotmail.com — MB ChB 1972 Glas.; FRCOG 1990, M 1977. Cons. (O & G) Hairmyres Hosp., E. Kilbride and Wishaw Gen. Hosp. Prev: Sen. Regist. (O & G) Ninewells Hosp. Dundee; Regist. (O & G) Glas. Roy. Infirm., Glas. Roy. & Rutherglen; Matern. Hosps. & Roy. Samarit. Hosp. Glas.

OSBURN BOHEIMER, Nicholas Mount Stuart Hospital, St. Vincents Road, Torquay TQ1 4UP Tel: 01803 313881; Whilborough House, North Whilborough, Newton Abbot TQ12 5LP — MB BS 1979 Lond.; FRCA 1983. Cons. Anaesth. Torbay Hosp. Torquay.

OSCIER, David Graham 11 Littledown Avenue, Queens Park, Bournemouth BH7 7AT — MB BChir 1974 Camb.; MA Camb. 1974; FRCP Lond. 1990; MRCP (UK) 1976; FRCPath 1991. Cons. Haemat. Roy. Bournemouth Hosp.; Hon. Clin. Sen. Lect. Univ. Soton. Prev: Research Fell. MRC Leukaemia Unit Roy. Postgrad. Med. Sch. Lond.; Regist. (Haemat.) Hammersmith Hosp. Lond.; SHO (Path.) W.m. Hosp. Lond.

OSEI, Edward King George Hospital, Barley Lane, Goodmayes, Ilford IG3 8YB Tel: 020 8983 8000; 47 Sylvan Avenue, Emerson Park, Hornchurch RM11 2PW Tel: 01708 449759 — MB ChB 1976 Ghana; MFFP 1995; MRCOG 1981. Cons. O & G Redbridge Health Care Essex. Socs: Brit. Med. Ultrasound Soc. & BMA. Prev: Sen. Specialist K. Khalid Hosp. Hail, Saudi Arabia; Regist. (O & G) Barking Hosp.; Lect. (O & G) Univ. Bristol.

OSEI-BONSU, Michael Ampadu 72 Broadash, Greystoke Gardens, Jesmond, Newcastle upon Tyne NE2 1PZ — BChir 1991 Camb.

OSEI-FRIMPONG, Samuel 21 Clwydian Park Crescent, St Asaph LL17 0BJ — MB ChB 1976 Ghana; FFA RCSI 1985.

OSEN, Hyman Emmanuel 41 Cedra Court, Cazenove Road, London N16 6AT — MRCS Eng. LRCP Lond. 1934. (St. Bart.)

OSEN, Julian Sinclair 10 Courtland Drive, Chigwell IG7 6PN — MB BS 1998 Lond.

OSEN, Melvyn Alan 10 Courtland Drive, Chigwell IG7 6PN — MRCS Eng. LRCP Lond. 1962; MA Camb. 1962, MB BChir 1968; DMedRehab RCP Lond. 1984. (Lond. Hosp. & Camb.) Socs: BMA. Prev: SHO Wanstead Hosp.; Ho. Surg. Lond. Hosp.; Ho. Phys. Mile End. Hosp.

OSGOOD, Vicky Mary Holmleigh, Solomon's Lane, Shirrell Heath, Southampton SO32 2HU — MB BS 1977 Lond.; MRCOG 1983. Cons. Obst. Portsmouth Hosps. NHS Trust; Dir. Med. Educat. Portsmouth Hosp. NHS Trust.

OSHEA, Carmel Patricia Oakhill Health Centre, Oakhill Road, Surbiton KT6 6EN Tel: 020 8390 7839; 14 Westbank, Dorking RH4 3BZ Tel: 01306 883880 — MB BCh 1990 Wales; MRCGP 1994. Prev: SHO (Med.) E. Surrey Hosp. Redhill.

OSHINOWO, Omololu Sunday 48 South Manor Way, Woolton, Liverpool L25 9NR — MB BS 1978 Ibadan.

OSHO, Olushola Festus c/o Drive J. Ugbomba, 27 Wimpole St., London W1M 7AD — MB BS 1978 Benin; MB BS Benin, Nigeria 1978; MRCPI 1985.

OSHODI, Mustafa Akanni Milson Road Health Centre, 1-13 Milson Road, London W14 0LJ Tel: 020 8846 6262 Fax: 020 8846 6263; 91 West Drayton Road, Uxbridge UB8 3LE — MB ChB 1967 Wales; 1981 Fellow Medical Council (GP) Nigeria; 1986 Fellow West Africa of Physician (GP); DTM & H Liverp. 1970; Dip. Primary Care Therapeutics Lond. 1999. Sen. Partner. Socs: BMA; Nigeria Med. Assn.; RSM.

OSHODI, Mr Taohid Oladele The Royal Oldham Hospital, Rochdale Rd, Oldham OL1 2JH Email: taohid.oshodi@oldham-tr.nwest.nhs.uk; 6 Emsworth Drive, Sale M33 3PR — MB BS 1983 Lagos; FRCS 2000; FRCS Ed. 1990. Cons. Surg. (With s/i in Vasc. Surg.)The Roy. Oldham Hosp., Oldham. Socs: BMA; Vasc. Surg. Soc.; Assn. Surg. Prev: Roy. Lancaster Infirm. Lancaster.

OSHOWO, Mr Ayodele Oluwapelumi 26 Caversham Avenue, Sutton SM3 9AH — MB BS 1986 Ibadan; FRCS Ed. 1995.

OSIFODUNRIN, Olanrewaju Olukayode Olatokunbo 5 Craigmount Hill, Edinburgh EH4 8DP — MB BCh BAO 1984 NUI; LRCPI & LM, LRCSI & LM 1984.

OSINDERO, Adesola Olugbemiga Chells Way Surgery, 265 Chells Way, Stevenage SG2 0HN Tel: 01438 313001 Fax: 01438 362322 — MB BS 1983 Lond.; MRCGP; T(GP) 1993.

OSLER, David Farnworth Health Centre, Rosebery Avenue, South Queensferry EH30 9JA Tel: 0131 331 1396 Fax: 0131 331 5783; 7 Station Road, South Queensferry EH30 9HY Tel: 0131 331 1565 Fax: 0131 331 5783 — MB ChB 1961 Ed.; DObst RCOG 1965. Prev: Ho. Phys. E. Gen. Hosp. Edin.; Ho. Surg. Roy. Hosp. Sick Childr. Edin.; Ho. Surg. (O & G) W.. Gen. Hosp. Edin.

OSLER, Kay The Surgery, Main Street, Leiston IP16 4ES Tel: 01728 830526 Fax: 01728 832029 — MRCS Eng. LRCP Lond. 1973; MSc Univ. Lond. 1990, MB BS 1973; MRCGP 1980; DRCOG 1978. (Roy. Free)

OSMAN, Abd El Azim Abd El Monem City Way Surgery, 67 City Way, Rochester ME1 2AY Tel: 01634 843351 Fax: 01634 830421; Uplands, Gravelly Bottom Road, Kingswood, Maidstone ME17 3NS Tel: 01622 842066 Fax: 01662 842066 Email: azimosman@bigfoot.com — MB BCh 1974 Egypt. (Mansourah Univ. Egypt) GP Kent.

OSMAN, Abdel Karim Ahmed Orchard House, Joyce Green Hospital, Dartford DA1 5PL Tel: 01322 622487 — MB BS 1975 Khartoum, Sudan; MRCPsych 1984. Cons. (Gen. Adult Psychiat.) Thames Gateway NHS Trust Dartford Kent; Sen. Lect. Inst. of Psychiat. Univ. of Lond. Socs: Amer. Psychiatric Assoc.; Arab Federat. M.H. Prev: Cons. Psychiat. Wirral NHS Trust; Cons. Psychiat. Saudi Arabia.

OSMAN, Aheed El-Toam Fawzi 26 Twmpath Lane, Gobowen, Oswestry SY10 7AQ — MB ChB 1982 Alexandria, Egypt.

OSMAN, Ahmed El Murtada Department of Clinical Oncology, The Leicester Roayl Infirmary, NHS Trust, Infirmary Square, Leicester LE1 5WW — MB BS 1979 Khartoum.

OSMAN, Bader El Din Ismail Abd El Meguid 68 Fishbourne Lane, Ryde PO33 4EX — MB BCh 1969 Cairo.

OSMAN, Catriona Helen 7 Orchard Close, Monk Fryston, Leeds LS25 5EY — MB ChB 1987 Leeds.

OSMAN, Elsir Mohamed 10 Osborn Gardens, Mill Hill, London NW7 1DY Tel: 020 8346 5858 — MB BS 1978 Khartoum; MRCPI 1988. Cons. Phys. St. Albans & Hemel Hempstead NHS Trust. Socs: Roy. Soc. Med. Prev: Sen. Regist. Roy. Free Hosp. Lond.

OSMAN, Faizel 23 Deanston Croft, Coventry CV2 2NX — MB BCh 1995 Wales.

OSMAN, Gamal Osman Dewsbury District Hospital, Healds Road, Dewsbury WF13 4HS — MB BS 1983 Khartoum; MRCP (UK) 1993.

OSMAN, Hamdy Mohamed 7 Cuckoo Close, Woolton, Liverpool L25 4UA — MB BCh 1962 Ain Shams.

OSMAN, Inass Flat 2R, 8 Dunearn St., Glasgow G4 9EF — MB ChB 1998 Glas.; MB ChB Glas 1998.

OSMAN, Jeremy 7 Haven Gardens, Leeds LS16 6SN — MB ChB 1987 Leeds.

OSMAN, John Health & Safety Executive, Magdalen House, Stanley Precinct, Bootle L20 3QZ Tel: 0151 951 4000; 10 Suncroft Road, Heswall, Wirral CH60 1XZ — MB ChB 1973 Bristol; MRCP (UK) 1976; Specialist Accreditation, Roy. Coll. Of Phys., 1984. Sen. Employm. Med. Adviser Health & Safety Exec. Epidemiol. & Med. Statistics Unit Bootle.

OSMAN, Khalid Hussein Elsayed All Saints Hospital, Flat 32 Mackenzie Court, Lodge Road, Hockley, Birmingham B18 5SD — MB BS 1987 Khartoum; MRCP (UK) 1992.

OSMAN, Mohamed 195 Bath Road, Hounslow TW3 3BU Tel: 020 8570 6524 — MB BS 1946 Osmania; LMSSA Lond. 1965; DCH Eng. 1960. Socs: BMA. Prev: Sen. Regist. Paediat. St. Helier Hosp.; Paediat. Regist. Hope Hosp. Manch. & N.ampton Gen. Hosp.

OSMAN, Mohamed Ahmed 48 Ashcombe Gardens, Weston Super Mare BS23 2XD Tel: 01934 29233 — Ptychio latrikes 1975 Athens.

OSMAN, Mr Mohamed Fikry Aly Antrim Hospital, 45 Bush Road, Antrim BT41 2RL Tel: 01849 424000; 24 Castle Road, Mumbles, Swansea SA3 5TF — MB BCh 1969 Cairo; PhD Columbia 1992; ECFMG 1974; FRCS Ed. 1978. (Mansoura) Cons. ENT Antrim Hosps. Socs: BMA. Prev: Regist. (ENT) W. Wales Gen. Hosp. Glangwili & Univ. Hosp. Wales Cardiff.

OSMAN, Mr Monzir Khogali Department of General Surgery, Monklands Hospital, Monkscourt Avenue, Airdrie ML6 0JS Tel: 012361 748748; 20 Kiltongue Cottages, Monkscourt Avenue, Airdrie ML6 0JS Tel: 01236 748748 — MB BS 1980 Khartoum; FRCS Glas. 1989. Staff Surg. Monklands Hosp. Airdrie.

OSMAN, Mustafa 14 Azalea Road, Blackburn BB2 6JU — MB ChB 1993 Manch.

OSMAN, Noor Mahomed Omar (retired) Highfield, 139 The Avenue, Leigh WN7 1HR Tel: 01942 674158 — MB BS 1956 Karachi.

OSMAN, Rabia 37 Arnold Gardens, London N13 5JE — MB BS 1996 Lond.

OSMAN, Tasneem 29 Gally Lane, Arkley, Barnet EN5 4AR — MB BS 1989 Lond.; MRCGP 1994. Retainer GP Barnet.

OSMAN, Yahya Mohumed House 7, Bridlington & District Hospital, Bessingby Road, Bridlington YO16 4QP — MB BS 1982 Khartoum, Sudan; MRCPI 1993.

OSMAN, Zubeda Mattock Lane Health Centre, 78 Mattock Lane, London W13 9NZ Tel: 020 8567 8329; 280B Staines Road, Hounslow TW3 3LX Tel: 020 8570 1950/572 8610 — MB BS 1953 Hyberabad; MRCOG 1972; DGO Hyberabad 1958; DObst 1960. Osmania Med. Coll. Hyderabad) Prev: Hosp. Pract. (Gyn) Mt. Vernon Hosp. N.wood.

OSMASTON, Julie Ann Peter-Rosegger-Strasse 161, 72762 Reutlingen, Germany; 1 Burrows Close, Penn, High Wycombe HP10 8AR — MB ChB 1989 Manch.; BSc (Hons.) Med. Biochem. Manch. 1986. Trainee GP 72810 Gomaringen, Germany. Prev: SHO Renal Med.) Camberwell HA.

OSMOND, Alexander (retired) Pinetrees, 38 Willow Lane, Stanion, Kettering NN14 1DT Tel: 01536 443182 — MB BS 1956 Durh.; MRCGP 1965; DObst RCOG 1960.

OSMOND, David Frederick Risca Surgery, St. Mary Street, Risca, Newport NP11 6YS Tel: 01633 612666; 3 Woodville Road, Newport NP20 4JB Tel: 01633 669000 — MB BCh 1979 Wales; BA Camb. 1976. Socs: Roy. Coll. Gen. Practs.

OSMOND, Elizabeth Claire The Surgery, 4 Hardell Rise, Tulse Hill, London SW2 3DX Tel: 020 8674 6586 — MB BS 1980 Lond.; MRCP (UK) 1983; MRCGP 1986; DRCOG 1985. (Guy's)

OSMOND, Thomas George, MBE (retired) North Lodge, Lambourn, Newbury RG17 8XR Tel: 01488 71695 — MB BChir 1947 Camb.; BA Camb. 1944; DObst RCOG 1952. JP.; Local Treasury Med. Off.; Div. Surg. St. John Ambul. Brig. Prev: Ho. Phys. St. Thos. Hosp. Lond. & Roy. Portsmouth Hosp.

OSMOND-CLARKE, Lady Freda (retired) 46 Harley House, Marylebone Road, London NW1 5HJ Tel: 020 7486 9975 — MB ChB 1934 Manch.; MRCS Eng. LRCP Lond. 1934. Prev: Med. Asst. Endocrine Cytol. & Infertil. Dept. Chelsea Hosp. Wom.

OSMONT, Jonathan Mark, SBStJ Halkett Place Surgery, 84 Halkett Place, St Helier, Jersey JE1 4XL Tel: 01534 36301 Fax: 01534 887793; La Rochelle, Route D'Ebenezer, Trinity, Jersey JE3 5DT Tel: 01534 862255 — MB BS 1973 Lond.; DObst RCOG 1976. (St. Bart.) Co. Surg. St. John Ambul. Jersey. Socs: Jersey Med. Soc. Prev: SHO (Obst.) Redhill Gen. Hosp.; SHO (Gen. Med.) Gen. Hosp. Jersey.; Ho. Surg. & Ho. Phys. Ards Hosp. Newtownards.

OSRIN, David 19 Bancroft Avenue, London N2 0AR — MB BChir 1990 Camb.

OSRIN, Ivan Mill Lane Medical Centre, 112 Mill Lane, London NW6 1XQ Tel: 020 7431 1588 Fax: 020 7431 8919 Email: ivan.osrin@gp-f83055.nhs.uk; 7 Albermarle Mansions, Heath Drive, London NW3 7TA Tel: 020 7435 2069 — MB ChB 1964 Stellenbosch; BSc Stellenbosch 1960; DCH Eng. 1968. (Stellenbosch)

OSSEI-GERNING, Nicholas 6 Harper Avenue, Idle, Bradford BD10 8NU — MB BS 1990 Lond.

OSSELTON, Michael Friarwood Surgery, Carleton Glen, Pontefract WF8 1SU Tel: 01977 703235 — MB ChB 1985 Leeds; DRCOG 1989.

OSTBERG, Julia Elisabeth Brinkwood, Latimer Road, Barnet EN5 5NX — MB BS 1996 Lond.; BSc Hons. Lond. 1993; MRCP (UK) Part I 1998; MRCP (UK) Part 2. 1999. (University College, London)

OSTENFELD, Thor 15 Chamberlin Court, Westfield Lane, Cambridge CB4 3QX Email: to212@hermes.cam.ac.uk — MB ChB 1991 Dundee; BSc (1st cl. Hons.) Pharmacol. Dund 1986; FRCA 1996; DA (UK) 1993. Wellcome Trust Clin. Research Fell. MRC Centre for Brain Repair Univ. of Camb.; Hon. Specialist Regist. (Anaesth.) Addenbrooke's Hosp. Camb. Prev: Specialist Regist. (Anaesth.) PeterBoro. Dist. Hosps. Camb.; Regist. (Anaesth.) Addenbrooke's Hosp. & Papworth Hosp. Camb.; SHO (Anaesth.) W. Suff. Hosp. Bury St. Edmunds & Ashford Hosp. Middlx.

OSTERBERG, Mr Paul Harald (retired) 13 Ulsterville Avenue, Belfast BT9 Tel: 01232 667741 — MB BCh BAO 1953 Dub.; BA Dub. 1953; FRCS Eng. 1961; FRCSI 1959. Hon. Cons. Orthop. Surg. Roy. Vict. Hosp. Belf. & Musgrave Pk. Hosp. Belf. Prev: Vis. Prof. Surg. Pahlavi Univ. Iran.

OSTERLOH, Ian Howard Pfizer Central Research, Ramsgate Road, Sandwich CT13 9NJ Tel: 01304 648652 Fax: 01304 658143 Email: ian-osterloh@pfizer.com — MB BS 1982 Lond.; MSc Bristol 1976, BSc 1975; MRCP (UK) 1985. (Guy's Hospital) Global Candidate Team Ldr. Pfizer Centr. Research Sandwich Kent. Socs: Roy. Coll. Phys.; BMA; Internat. Soc. Impotence Research. Prev: Europ. Clin. Team Ldr. Pfizer Centr. Research Sandwich; Head of Phase 1 Operat. & Head Clin. Regulatory Affairs Pfizer Centr. Research Sandwich.

OSTERLUND, Pia Johanna 21 Telford Court, Guildford GU1 2EA — Lic Med Helsinki 1993.

OSTERMANN, Maria Elisabeth Intensive Care Unit, Royal Brompton Hospital, Sydney St., London SW3 6NP — State Exam. Med. Gottingen 1990.

OSTERRATH, Kai-Wilhelm c/o Sue Parvin Personnel Department, Friarage Hospital, Northallerton DL6 1JG — State Exam Med 1989 Marburg; MD Marburg 1992.

OSTICK, Mr David Graham Bridge House, Bolton Road, Bradshaw, Bolton BL2 3EU Tel: 01204 300214 — MB ChB 1966 Manch.; FRCS Eng. 1973. Cons. (Gen. Surg.) Bolton AHA.

OSTICK, Susan The James Cochrane Practice, Maude Street, Kendal LA9 4QE Tel: 01539 722124 Fax: 01539 734995 — MB BS 1982 Lond.; DRCOG 1984; Cert. Family Plann. RCOG & RCGP 1984. (St. Bart. Hosp. Med. Sch.) GP Kendal; Clin. Asst. (Obst. & Gyn. & Psychiat.) Cumbria; Clin. Asst. (Psychiat.) Cumbria.

OSTINS

OSTINS, Andrew William 4 Greenlands Way, Henbury, Bristol BS10 7PR; 62 Margards Lane, Verwood BH31 6JP — MB ChB 1974 Birm.; DRCOG 1978; DTM & H 1991. Med. Miss. Hosp. de Kipushya. Socs: Roy. Soc. Trop. Med. & Hyg. & Christian Med. Fell.sh. Prev: GP Verwood.

OSTLE, Kirstin Elizabeth Randolph Medical Centre, 4 Green Lane, Datchet, Slough SL3 9EX Tel: 01753 541268 Fax: 01753 582324; Estcourt, 1 Clayhall Lane, Windsor SL4 2SW Tel: 01753 868283 — MB ChB 1986 Ed.; MRCGP 1992; DRCOG 1991; DCH RCP Lond. 1989. (Ed.) GP Princip. Slough; Police Surg. Berks. Socs: Windsor Med. Soc.; Forens. Div. Roy. Med. Soc. Prev: SHO (Med., Paediat. & O & G) Heatherwood Hosp. Ascot.

OSTLER, Alec Michael 4 Aspen Close, Bishopsmead, Tavistock PL19 9LN — MB BS 1998 Lond.; MB BS Lond 1998.

OSTLER, Edward George 1 Queens Drive, Taunton TA1 4XW Tel: 01823 286244 — MB BS 1963 Lond.; MRCS Eng. LRCP Lond. 1963; FRCPsych 1992, M 1972; DPM Eng. 1967. (King's Coll. Hosp.) Med. Dir. Som. Patner NHS & Social Care Trust. Socs: BMA. Prev: Cons. Child Psychiat. & Ment. Handicap Som. NHS Trust; Sen. Regist. Tone Vale Hosp. Taunton; Regist. Glenside Hosp. Bristol.

OSTLER, Kevin John Cavendish House, 18 Victoria Road S., Southsea PO5 2BZ Tel: 023 9229 1867 Fax: 023 9287 2932 Email: kevin_ostler@doctors.org.uk — MB BS 1989 Lond.; BSc (2nd cl. Hons.) Lond. 1986. Cons. (Adult Ment. Health), Portsmouth Health NHS Trust. Socs: Roy. Coll. Psychiat. Prev: Clin. Research Fell. (Psychiat.) Roy S. Hants. Hosp. Soton.

OSTLER, Peter James 46 Cowper Road, Harpenden AL5 5NG — MB BS 1989 Lond.; MRCP (UK) 1992; FRCR 1996. Cons., Clin. Onicologist, Mt. Vernon Hosp., N.wood Lond.

OSTLERE, Lucy Sinclair 11A Routh Road, Wandsworth, London SW18 3SW Tel: 020 8875 9169 — MB BS 1986 Lond.; MB BS (Hons.) Lond. 1986; BSc (Hons) Lond. 1983; MRCP (UK) 1989; MD 1997. Cons. Dermat. St. Geo. Hosp. Lond & Kingston Hosp. Prev: Sen. Regist. (Dermat.) St. Geo. Hosp. Lond.; Regist. & SHO (Dermat.) Roy. Free Hosp. & W.m. Hosp. Lond.; Regist. (Med.) N.wick Pk. Hosp. Lond.

OSTLERE, Mary 22 St George's Road, Bromley BR1 2AU Tel: 020 8467 3128 — MB ChB 1947 Ed.; MRCP Ed. 1950; FFA RCS Eng. 1954; DA Eng. 1951. Socs: Assn. Anaesth. Prev: Research Asst. Nuffield Dept. Anaesth. Oxf.

OSTLERE, Simon John Gordon Dept. of Radiology, Nuffield Orthopaedic Centre, Oxford OX3 7LD Tel: 01865 74155 Fax: 01865 227347 — MB BS 1979 Lond.; FRCR 1988; MRCP (UK) 1983.

OSTROWSKI, Julian Leon Dept. of Pathology, Barnsley District General Hospital, Gawber Road, Barnsley S75 2EP Tel: 01226 730000 Fax: 012267300 00 Email: julian.ostrowskibdgh-tr.trent.nhs.uk — MB ChB 1988 Sheff.; BMedSci Sheff. 1987; MRCPath 1998. (Univ. Sheff.) Cons. Histopath./Cytopath., Barnsley Dist. Gen. Hosp. Prev: Kaberry Research Fell. Leeds NHS Trust; Regist. (Histopath.) Leeds Gen. Infirm.; Lect. (Histopath.) Univ. of Leeds.

OSTROWSKI, Marek Josef Department of Oncology, Norfolk & Norwich Hospital, Brunswick Road, Norwich NR1 3SR Tel: 01603 287225 Fax: 01603 287463 — MB ChB 1967 Birm.; FRCR 1974; DMRT Eng. 1970. Cons. Radiother. & Oncol. Norf. & Norwich Health Care Trust; Hon. Cons. Radiother. & Oncol. Addenbrooke's Hosp. Camb. Socs: Brit. Inst. Radiol.

OSTROWSKI, Nigel Michael Jan Bangholm Medical Centre, 21-25 Bangholm Loan, Edinburgh EH5 3AH Tel: 0131 552 7676 — MB ChB 1977 Dundee; MRCGP 1981; DCH Eng. 1981; DRCOG 1980. Princip. GP Edin.

OSU, Benjamin Asikadi 19 Fellpark Road, Manchester M23 0EX — State Exam 1984 Bologna.

OSUAGWU, Fiona Ifeyinwa 96 Brent Park Road, London NW4 3HP Tel: 020 8202 9751 Fax: 020 8202 9751 Email: fefe@infodial.demon.co.uk — MB BS 1990 Univ. Nigeria; DFFP 1995. Specialist Regist. in Obs. & Gyn., Lutton & Dunstable Hosp., Lewsey Rd., Luton. Socs: Brit. Matern. & Fetal Med. Soc. Prev: Research Regist. (Obst.) Qu. Charlotte's & Chelsea Hosp. Lond.; SHO (Obst.) Qu. Charlotte's & Chelsea Hosp. Lond.; Sen. SHO (Obst.) Birm. Wom.'s Hosp.

OSUHOR, Professor Paul Chukwunyeike (retired) 11 Oulton Way, Oxton, Birkenhead CH43 0XH Tel: 0151 608 0358 — MB BS 1963 Durh.; FFPHM RCP (UK) 1989; FFCM 1989, M 1982; MPH

1971; DIH Dund 1975; DPH Glas. 1970. Cons. Pub. Health Med. E. Lancs. HA. Prev: Prof. Community Health Univ. Benin & Cons. Community Phys. Univ. Benin Teach. Hosp. Benin City, Nigeria.

OSUNA CARRASQUILLA, Francisco Manuel Room 2, 3 Hollins Drive, Winwick Hospital, Winwich, Warrington WA2 8RR — LMS 1992 Cadiz.

OSUNKOYA, Abimbola Osunyele 21 West View, Ashington NE63 0RZ — MB BS 1986 Lagos; MRCOG 1993.

OSWAL, Mr Vasant Hansraj (retired) Far Shirby, Upleatham, Redcar TS11 8AG Tel: 01287 622000 Fax: 01287 625751 Email: voswal@aol.com — MB BS 1960 Poona; 1961 DORL BOM; MS Bombay 1963; FRCS Ed. 1968; DLO Eng. 1964. Hon. Cons. Ent. Surg. Cpt. James Cook Univ. Hosp. Middlesbrough, Cleveland.; Hon. Vis. Prof. & Head, ENT Dept. Deenath Mangeshkar Hosp. Pune, India. Prev: Cons. ENT Surg. S. Tees Acute Trust NHS Hosp.

OSWALD, Alexander George 10 Argyll Street, Brechin DD9 6JL — MB ChB 1979 Ed.

OSWALD, George Anthony The Medical Specialist Group, Alexandra House,Ruette Braye,, St Peter Port, Guernsey GY1 3EX Tel: 01481 238565 Fax: 01481 237782; Les Messieres, Route De Pleinmont, Torteval, Guernsey GY8 0LP — MB BS 1977 Lond.; BSc (Hons.) Physiol. Lond. 1973, MD 1986; FRCP Lond. 1995; MRCP (UK) 1980; T(M) 1991. (King's Coll. Hosp.) Phys. P.ss Eliz. Hosp. Guernsey, CI.

OSWALD, Iain Henry St George 55 Dartmouth Park Road, London NW5 1SL; 24 Dartmouth Park Avenue, London NW5 1JN — MB ChB 1976 Bristol; 1993 (Psychoanalyst) Mem. Brit. Psychanalytic Soc.; MRCPsych 1984. p/t Cons. Psychother. Watford Gen. Hosp.; Psychoanalyst Inst. Psychoanal. Lond. Socs: Brit. Psychoanal. Soc.; Assn. PsychoAnalyt. Psychtherap.; Tavistock Soc. Psychotherap. Prev: Sen. Regist. (Psychother.) Tavistock Clin. Lond.; Regist. Rotat. (Psychiat.) Maudsley Hosp. Train. Scheme; Field Dr. Brit. Nepal Med. Trust E.. Nepal.

OSWALD, Professor Ian The Birches, 41 St Ronan's Terrace, Innerleithen EH44 6RB Tel: 01896 830817 — BChir 1953 Camb.; 1954 MB BChir Camb.; 1963 DSc Ed.; 1950 BA (1st cl. Hons.) 1950. MA Camb. 1954,; 1971 FRCPsych; 1961 DPM Eng.; 1958 MD. (Camb. & Bristol) Emerit. Prof. Psychiat. Univ. Edin. Prev: Vis. Prof. (Psychiat.) Univ. W. Austral.; Lect. (Psychiat.) Univ. Edin.; Beit Memor. Fell. For Med. Research Univ. Oxf.

OSWALD, Janet Colinton Surgery, 296B Colinton Road, Edinburgh EH13 0LB Tel: 0131 441 4555 Fax: 0131 441 3963 — BSc (Med. Sci.) Ed. 1979, MB ChB 1982; MRCGP 1986; Dip. Rehab. Med. RCP Lond. 1988; DCH RCPS Glas. 1985; DRCOG 1985. GP Retainer Scheme for Wom. Doctors in Gen. Pract. Prev: Regist. (Rehabil. Med.) Astley Ainslie Hosp. Edin.

OSWALD, Neville Christopher, TD (retired) 4 St Martins Square, Chichester PO19 1NT Tel: 01243 784457 — MB BChir Camb. 1935; MD Camb. 1946; FRCP Lond. 1947, M 1935; MRCS Eng. LRCP Lond. 1934. Prev: Hon. Cons. St. Bart. Hosp. Lond., Brompton Hosp. Lond. & King Edwd. VII Hosp. Offs. Lond.

OSWALD, Professor Nigel Tatham Allan University of Teeside, Primary Care Resource & Development Centre, Grey Towers Ct., Stokesley Road, Middlesbrough TS7 0PN Tel: 01642 304146 Fax: 01642 304127 Email: nigel.oswald@tees.ac.uk; Hempsyke, Littlebeck Lane, Sneaton, Whitby YO22 5HY Tel: 01947 810302 Fax: 01947 810302 — MB BChir 1971 Camb.; MPhil Camb. 1985; FRCGP 1995, M 1977; DObst RCOG 1973. Prof. Primary Care Univ. Teeside & Newc. Prev: Lect. (Gen. Pract.) Univ. Camb.

OSWALD, Tamsin Fiona Bennett 40 Eastfield Road, Duston, Northampton NN5 6TQ — MB ChB 1998 Bristol.

OSWELL, Andrew David Kettering General Hospital, Rothwell Road, Kettering NN16 8UZ; 53 Wilford Avenue, Northampton NN3 9UQ — MB ChB 1992 Leic.

OTAKI, Alan Tadashi (retired) 63 Imperial Way, Chislehurst BR7 6JR Email: alan@otaki.freeserve.co.uk — MB BS 1954 Lond.; MD Lond. 1968; FRCP Lond. 1972, M 1960. Prev: Cons. Phys., Clin. Tutor & Phys. Medway Gp. Hosps.

OTENG-NTIM, Eugene 4 Zair Court, Voltaire Road, London SW4 6DE; 22 Briar Walk, Edgware HA8 0TX Tel: 020 8959 4077 — MB BS 1991 Lond.; MRCOG 1997. Spicialist Regist. O & G. Socs: Roy. Coll. Obs. & Gyn.

OTHMAN, Norlijah Room 310, Accommodation Building, Victoria Hospital, Kirkcaldy KY2 5AH — MB BS 1986 Malaya.

OTHMAN, Mr Walid Mohammed 11 Runnymede Green, Bury St Edmunds IP33 2LH Tel: 01284 68636 — MB ChB 1971 Alexandria; FRCS Ed. 1984.

OTIM-OYET, David Department of Oncology, Derbyshire Royal Infirmary, London Road, Derby DE1 2QY Tel: 01332 254843 Fax: 01332 254980; 12a Rachel Court, 30 Albion Road, Sutton SM2 5TF Tel: 01332 254843 Fax: 01332 254980 — MB ChB 1975 Makerere; FRCR 1986; T(R) (CO) 1991. (Makerere University) Cons. Clin. Oncol., Derbysh. Roy. Infirm. Socs: Fell.Roy. Coll. Radiol.; BMA. Prev: Sen. Regist. (Radiother. & Oncol.) Roy. Marsden Hosp. Lond.; WHO Cons. Radiotherapist & Oncol. Zimbabwe Oncological Train. Project Harare; Hon. Lect. Univ. Zimbabwe Med. Sch.

OTIV, S Castlefields Health Centre, Castlefields, Runcorn WA7 2HY Tel: 01928 566671 Fax: 01928 581631 — BM BS 1978 Nottingham; BM BS 1978 Nottingham.

OTLET, Alan Benjamin, MBE (retired) 6 Hutton Close, Westbury on Trym, Bristol BS9 3PS Tel: 0117 968 7116 Email: otletab@aol.com — MB ChB 1952 Bristol; FRCGP 1978, M 1966. Prev: GP S.mead Med. Centre Bristol.

OTLEY, Andrew John The Surgery, 1 Church Road, Mitcham CR4 3YU — MB BS 1993 Lond.; BSc 1990 (Hons) Lond. GP Prinicipal. Prev: GP Asst. Mitcham Surrey.

OTO LLORENS, Meritxell 9 Park Avenue, Stirling FK8 2QR — LMS 1992 Barcelona.

OTTEN, Katherine Anne 23 Ramsey Road, Sheffield S10 1LR — MB ChB 1995 Sheff.

OTTENSMEIER, Christian Hermann Heinrich Southampton General Hospital, CRC Wessex Oncology Unit, Tremona Road, Southampton SO16 6YD Tel: 02380 796184 Fax: 02380 783839 Email: cho@soton.ac.uk — State Exam Med 1986 Munster; MD Munster 1988. Sen. Lect. Med. Oncol. S.ampton Univ. Hosp. S.ampton.

OTTER, Alan Edwin Mytton Oak Medical Practice, Racecourse Lane, Shrewsbury SY3 5LZ Tel: 01743 362223 Fax: 01743 244 5811 — MB BS 1985 Lond.; MRCGP 1988; DRCOG 1988; DCH RCP Lond. 1987.

OTTER, Mark Ian Dept. of Histopathology, North East Wales Trust, Wrexham Maelor Hospital, Croesnewydd Road, Wrexham NP1 4PN Tel: 01978 291100 — MB BCh 1989 Wales; BSc (Hons.) Wales 1986; MRCPath 1997, D 1995. (Wales) Cons. Histopath., N. E. Wales Trust, Wrexham Maelor Hosp., Wrexham. Prev: Sen. Regist. (Histopath.) SW Thames; Regist. (Histopath.) SW Thames; SHO (Histopath.) Centr. Path. Laborat. N. Staffs. HA.

OTTERBURN, David Michael The Malthouse Surgery, The Charter, Abingdon OX14 3JY Tel: 01235 524001 Fax: 01235 532197; Thatched Cottage, 12 Kennel Lane, Steventon, Abingdon OX13 6SB Tel: 01235 834725 Email: dotterburn@aol.com — MB BS 1973 Lond.; MRCP (UK) 1977; Cert JCC Lond. 1976.

OTTEY, Dominic Sean 17 School Lane, Newbold, Coleorton, Leicester LE67 8PF — MB ChB 1991 Sheff.

OTTLEY, Geoffrey Bickersteth Ferndown Health Centre, Ferndown, Wimborne Tel: 01202 897200 Fax: 01202 875553; Willowcombe, Keepers Lane, Stapehill, Wimborne BH21 7NE — MB BS 1978 Lond.; MRCS Eng. LRCP Lond. 1978. (Char. Cross) Prev: SHO (Anaesth.) St. Richards Hosp. Chichester; SHO (Psychiat. & Dermat.) Char. Cross Hosp. Lond.; SHO (O & G) Roy. Sussex Co. Hosp. Brighton.

OTTLEY, Victoria Rachel 1 Augustus Gardens, Camberley GU15 1HL — MB ChB 1998 Bristol.

OTTMAN, Simon Charles Carlton Gardens Surgery, 27 Carlton Gardens, Leeds LS7 1JL Tel: 0113 295 2678 Fax: 0113 295 2679; 4 Shadwell Park Avenue, Roundhay, Leeds LS17 8TL Email: simon.ottman@dial.pipex.com — MB ChB 1987 Leeds; MRCGP 1994. (Leeds)

OTTO, Alison Dawn Roade Medical Centre, 16 London Road, Roade, Northampton NN7 2NN Tel: 01604 862218 Fax: 01604 862129; Otters Rest, Pk Road, Hartwell, Northampton NN7 2HP Tel: 01604 863031 Fax: 01604 863032 Email: alison@otto.softnet.co.uk — BM 1983 Soton.; MRCGP 1989; DRCOG 1987. (Soton.) GP Princip. N.ants.; Clin. Asst. (Gen. Med. & Gastroenterol.) N.ampton Gen. Hosp. Socs: Brit. Assn. Sport & Med.; Primary Care Soc. Gastroenterol. Prev: SHO (Geriat. & Gen. Med., Paediat. & O & G) Leic. Gen. & Leic. Roy. Infirm.; Ho. Off.

(Surg.) Roy. Hants. Co. Hosp. Winchester; Ho. Off. (Med.) Soton Gen. Hosp.

OTTO, Martina Hedwig Aberdeen Royal Infirmary, Ashgrove House, Room 172, Forester Hill, Aberdeen AB12 3XB — State Exam Med 1993 Heidelberg.

OTTO, Morkel Jacques 41 Worcester Crescent, Woodford Green IG8 0LX — MB ChB 1981 Pretoria.

OTTON, Sophie Helen 4 East Shrubbery, Redland, Bristol BS6 6SX — MB BChir 1993 Camb.

OTTY, Catherine Joy Donmall and Partners, 87 Albion Street, London SE16 7JX Tel: 020 7237 2092 Fax: 020 7231 1435; 57 Stradella Road, London SE24 9HL — MB BChir 1982 Camb.; MA Camb. 1984; MRCGP 1987; T(GP) 1991; DCH RCP Lond. 1986; Cert. Family Plann. JCC 1986; DRCOG 1985. (Camb.) p/t G.P. Princip.; GP Bd. Mem. N. S.wark PCG; LMC Mem. Lambeth S.wark Lewisham LMC. Prev: Trainee GP/SHO Addenbrooke's Hosp. Camb. VTS; Resid. Med. Off. P. Wales Childr. Hosp. Sydney, Austral.

OTUTEYE, Ernest Teye 28 Hollman Gardens, London SW16 3SJ Tel: 020 8679 0303 — MB ChB 1969 Ghana; LRCP LRCS Ed. LRCPS Glas. 1980; MRCOG 1979. (Ghana Med. Sch.) Cons. O & G King Saudi Univ. Riyadh; Gyn. Fertil. & Endocrinol. Unit Lister Hosp. Lond. Socs: Riyadh Perinatol. & Neonatol. Club. Prev: Sen. Med. Off. MoH Ghana; Vis. Cons. Gyn. & Regist. (O & G) Stobhill Hosp. Glas.

OUBRIDGE, John Victor The Spinney, Ramsey Road, St Ives, Huntingdon PE27 3TP Tel: 01480 492501 Fax: 01480 492504; Cross Keys, High St, Hemingford Abbots, Huntingdon PE28 9AE Tel: 01480 468600 — MB BChir 1965 Camb.; FRCGP 1996, M 1977. (St. Thos.) Course Organiser Huntingdon VTS. Prev: SHO Yeovil Gen. Hosp.; SHO Warneford Hosp. Oxf.; Ho. Off. Warwick Hosp.

OUDEH, Bashier Ahmed Rashied Mousa c/o 40 High Street, Dysart, Kirkcaldy KY1 2UG Tel: 01592 53590 — MB BCh 1974 Ain Shams; DObst RCPI 1983.

OUGH, Richard W Hardwicke Building, New Square, Lincolns Inn, London WC2A 3SB Tel: 0207 242 2523 — MB BS 1973 Lond.; MSc (Managem.) Lond. 1995; MA (Law) City Univ. 1986; MRCS Eng. LRCP Lond. 1972; LMCC 1975; Dip. Law City Univ. 1984. (St. Mary's Hosp. Lond.) Barrister; Dep. Chairm. NHS Tribunal. Socs: Fell. Roy. Soc. Med. Prev: Sloan Fell. Lond. Business Sch.

OUGHTIBRIDGE, David Brenan New Southgate Surgery, Borough Road, Wakefield WF1 3SW Tel: 01924 371946 Fax: 01924 200449; 40 Woodland Drive, Sandal, Wakefield WF2 6DD Tel: 01924 256599 — MB ChB 1961 Leeds; MB ChB (Distinc. Surg.) Leeds 1961. (Leeds) Socs: Wakefield Local Med. Comm. & BMA. Prev: Ho. Surg. Gen. Infirm. Leeds & St. Mary's Hosp. Leeds; Ho. Phys. St. Jas. Hosp. Leeds.

OUGHTON, Nora Marion (retired) Southlands, Walgrave, Northampton NN6 9QN Tel: 01604 978 1255 — MB ChB 1941 Birm.; DO Oxf. 1943.

OULD, Georgina Ann 10 Elgin Road, Lilliput, Poole BH14 8ER — MB BS 1990 Lond.

OULTON, Robert Anthony 15 Princes Drive, Rosehill, Marple, Stockport SK6 6NJ — MB BS 1977 Lond.

OUN, Hadi Abdalla Mohamed 197 Weedon House, Du Cane Road, London W12 0TZ — MB BS 1982 Garyounis, Libya; MRCP (UK) 1992.

OUNSTED, Christopher Martin Abbey Medical Practice, Health Centre, Merstow Green, Evesham WR11 4BS Tel: 01386 76111 Fax: 01386 769515; Greylyn, Broadway Lane, Fladbury, Pershore WR10 2QF Tel: 01386 860363 Fax: 01386 861412 Email: martinounsted@cs.com — MB BS 1974 Lond.; MRCS Eng. LRCP Lond. 1974; MRCGP 1981; DRCOG 1980. (Roy. Free) Mem. LMC. Socs: BMA; Roy. Coll. Gen. Pract. Prev: SHO Rotat. (Med.) Stoke Mandeville Hosp. Aylesbury; Ho. Phys. Worthing Hosp.; Ho. Surg. Roy. Free Hosp. Lond.

OUNSTED, Jean Mary Winyates Health Centre, Winyates, Redditch B98 0NR Tel: 01527 525533 Fax: 01527 517969; Greylyn, Broadway Lane, Fladbury, Pershore WR10 2QF — MB BS 1974 Lond.; MRCS Eng. LRCP Lond. 1974; MRCGP 1980; DRCOG 1978; DA Eng. 1976. (Roy. Free) Prev: Clin. Med. Off. Hereford & Worcester HA; Trainee GP Aylesbury VTS; Ho. Phys. Roy. Free Hosp. Lond.

OUSEY, Tamsin Jane 1 Strode Cottages, Strode, Ivybridge PL21 0LY — MB BCh 1997 Wales.

OUSTA

OUSTA, Basil Nihad 42 Oak Green, Abbots Langley WD5 0PH — MB BS 1985 Lond.

OUTAR, Kampta Persaud Orton Medical Practice, Orton Centre, Orton Goldhay, Peterborough PE2 5RQ Tel: 01733 238111 Fax: 01733 238236 — MB BCh BAO 1976 Dub.

OUTEN, Peter Ronald Avenue Road Surgery, 2 Avenue Road, Warley, Brentwood CM14 5EL Tel: 01277 212820 — MB BChir 1976 Camb.; 2000 (PGCAE) Ang; MA Camb. 1976; DCH Eng. 1978; DRCOG 1978. Primary Care Tutor Brentwood PCG. Socs: Primary Care Rheum. Soc. Prev: Clin. Asst. (Rheum.) Broomfield Hosp. Chelmsford.

OUTHOFF, Kim The Plough, 7 The Street, Wallington, Baldock SG7 6SW — MB ChB 1991 Cape Town. Phys. Guy's Drug Research Unit Guy's Hosp. Lond.

OUTON PERLA, Paula Elms, Block 96 New Health Close, New Cross Hospital, Wolverhampton Road, Heath Town, Wolverhampton WV10 0QP — LMS 1996 Granada.

OUTRAM, Donald Howarth (retired) 2 Lawhead Road W., St Andrews KY16 9NE — MB ChB 1956 St. And.; MSc Lond. 1964. Prev: Regist. Portsmouth Roy. Hosp. & Edenvale Hosp. Johannesburg.

OUTRAM, Duncan Peter The Surgery, School Lae, Alembury PE28 4EQ — BChir 1994 Camb.; MRCGP 1999 MA Camb. 1966, BChir 1964; MA Camb. 1996; DRCOG 1997; DFFP 1997. (Camb.) GP Princip.; Prescribing Lead Clinician Exec. Comm. Mem., Hunts. Primary Care Trust The Priory St. Ives Cambs. Socs: BMA. Prev: GP Regist., Dr Rawinsm & Partners, Hunters Way, Huttingdon; VTS Hinchingbrooke Hosp., Huntingdon; SHO (Gen. Med.) Hinchingbrooke Hosp. Huntingdon.

OUTRAM, Matthew The Mount, Dowlish Wake, Ilminster TA19 0NX — MB BS 1998 Lond.

OUTRED, Robert The Wootons Surgery, Priory Lane, North Wooton, King's Lynn PE30 3PT Tel: 01553 631550 Fax: 01553 631011; 54 Pilot Street, King's Lynn PE30 1QL Tel: 01553 691425 — MB ChB 1980 Manch. Clin. Asst. (Psychiat.) King's Lynn Norf.

OUTTRIM, Jane Elizabeth Nancy 80 Kirkstone Road, Walkley, Sheffield S6 2PP Email: janieout@aol.co.uk — MB ChB 1996 Sheff. (Sheffield) GP Regist. Rotherham.

OUTWIN, George Raymond 356 Thorne Road, Doncaster DN2 5AN Tel: 01302 367759 Fax: 01302 541913 — MRCS Eng. LRCP Lond. 1948; Cert. Av Med. MoD (Air) & Civil; Aviat. Auth. 1977. (Leeds) Med. Assessor Civil Aviat. Auth. Socs: Hon. Mem. Doncaster Local Med. Comm.; Fell. BMA; Brit. Med. Pilots Assn. Prev: Resid. Med. Off. Pontefract Gen. Infirm.; Gen. Med. Servs. Comm. & Counc. BMA; Ho. Surg. (Obst.) Leeds Matern. Hosp.

OUTWIN, Wendy Ruth The Park Surgery, 4 Alexandra Road, Great Yarmouth NR30 2HW Tel: 01493 855672; Tel: 01493 600359 — MB ChB 1987 Birm.; MRCGP 1991; DRCOG 1990. p/t Gen. Pract. Principle.

OVENDEN, Lynn Anne The Surgery, 178 Musters Road, West Bridgford, Nottingham NG2 7AA Tel: 0115 981 4472 Fax: 0115 981 2812 — MB ChB 1990 Sheff.

OVENDEN, Penelope Anne Hawthorn Cotttage, Kingsland, Leominster HR6 9QN Tel: 01568 708568 — MB BS Lond. 1963. (St. Thos.) Clin. Asst. (Dermat.) Co. Hosp. Hereford. Prev: Ho. Surg. Peace Memor. Hosp. Watford; Ho. Phys. Shrodells Hosp. Watford.

OVENDEN, Richard Nicholas (retired) North Acre, Kingsland, Leominster HR6 9RZ Tel: 01568 708762 Fax: 01568 708449 — MB BS Lond. 1962; DObst RCOG 1964; Cert Av. Med. MoD (Air) & CAA 1978. GP; Hon. Phys. Heref. Flying Club. Prev: Med. Adviser H & W FHSA.

OVENS, Joyce Elizabeth Anne Weavers House, 20 Dam Hill, Shelley, Huddersfield HD8 8JH Tel: 01484 605496 — LRCP LRCS 1952 Ed.; LRCP LRCS Ed. LRFPS Glas. 1952; DObst RCOG 1954. Clin. Asst. (Dermat.) Huddersfield Roy. Infirm.

OVENSTONE, Irene Margaret Kinnear (retired) 10 Moor Road, Calverton, Nottingham NG14 6FW Tel: 01158 477970 Fax: 01159 477975 — MB ChB St. And. 1954; MD (with commend.) Dundee 1972; FRCPsych 1979, M 1973; DPM Leeds 1963; DPH St. And. 1957. Locum Cons. Psychiat., Nottm. Health Care Trust, Mansfield. Prev: Emiritus Cons. Psychiat. (Geriat.) St Francis Unit City Hosp. Nottm.

OVER, Dawn Carol 16 Dyrham, Harford Drive, Frenchay, Bristol BS16 1NW — MB BS 1982 Lond.; FCAnaesth 1989. Prev: Cons. Anaesth. S.mead Hosp. Bristol; Medico-legal Adviser, Med. Protec. Soc.

OVER, Jacqueline Mary Alton Health Centre, Anstey Road, Alton GU34 2QX Tel: 01420 542542 Fax: 01420 549466 — MB BCh 1989 Wales; MRCGP 1994; DCH 1992; DFFP 1994. (UWCM)

OVER, Kathryn Elizabeth Flat 4, 1 Mossley Hill Drive, Liverpool L17 1AJ — MB ChB 1989 Liverp.; MRCP (UK) 1993. Sen. Regist. (Rheum. & Gen. Med.) Roy. Liverp. Univ. Hosp. Trust.

OVERAL, Susan Gillian Collings Park Medical Centre, 57 Eggbuckland Road, Hartley, Plymouth PL3 5JR Tel: 01752 771500 Fax: 01752 769946; Appletree House, Back Road, Calstock PL18 9QL Tel: 01822 832961 Mobile: 01822 832961 — MB BS 1979 Lond.; BSc (Pharmacol., Hons.) Lond. 1974; MRCS Eng. LRCP Lond. 1977; MRCGP 1984. (Guy's, London) p/t Princip. in Gen. Pract. Plymouth; Mem. S. W. Devon Local Med. Comm. Socs: BMA; Roy. Coll. Gen. Pract. (Tamar Fac.); Fac. Fam. Plann. & Reproduc. Health Care.

OVERELL, James Richard The Flat, 15 Cleveden Gardens, Glasgow G12 0PU — MB ChB 1994 Ed.

OVEREND, Alison Jane Maryport Group Practice, Alneburgh House, Ewanrigg Road, Maryport CA15 8EL Tel: 01900 815544 Fax: 01900 816626; Swan Cottage, Hayton, Aspatria, Carlisle CA7 2PD Tel: 016973 20610 Fax: 016973 23456 Email: the_overend_practice@compuserve.com — MB ChB 1988 Bristol; DFFP 1998; Dip. Primary Care Therap. Newc. 1995MRCGP 1992; Dip. Primary Care Therap. Newc. 1995; DRCOG Lond. 1991; MA Oxf. 1979. Socs: BMA; Med. Wom. Federat.; Roy. Coll. Gen. Pract. Prev: Trainee GP Airedale VTS; Ho. Off. S.mead Hosp.; Ho. Off. W.. Isles Hosp. Stornoway.

OVEREND, Gillian Sydney Ashcroft Surgery, 22 Sherwood Place, Bradford BD2 3AG Tel: 01274 637076 Fax: 01274 626979; 22 Harbour Crescent, Wibsey, Bradford BD6 3QG — MB ChB 1976 Leeds.

OVEREND, Jill 2 Hedingham Moira, Craigavon BT67 0MW Tel: 01846 613539 — MB BCh BAO 1997 Belf.

OVEREND, John Simpson Maghera Health Centre, 3 Church Street, Maghera BT46 5EA Tel: 028 7964 2579 Fax: 028 7964 3002 — MB BCh BAO 1976 Belf.; FFA RCSI 1981; MRCGP 1982.

OVERS, Karen GP Suite, Palmer Community Hospital, Jarrow NE32 3UX — MB BS 1980 Newc.; MRCGP 1985; Cert. Family Plann. JCC 1984; DRCOG 1984. GP Jarrow.

***OVERSHOTT, Ross Alexander** Felthorpe University, University of Wales, Caerleon, Newport — MB ChB 1996 Birm.; ChB Birm. 1996.

OVERSTALL, Peter Webb Age Care, General Hospital, Hereford HR1 2PA Tel: 01432 355444 Fax: 01432 274039; Little Cwm, Dulas, Hereford HR2 0HL — MB BS 1968 Lond.; FRCP Lond. 1984; MRCP (UK) 1971. (St. Geo.) Cons. Geriat. Med. Hereford Gen. Hosp. Socs: Brit. Geriat. Soc.; Internat. Continence Soc. Prev: Cons. Geriat. Med. Univ. Coll. Hosp. Lond.; Sen. Regist. (Geriat.) Univ. Coll. Hosp. Lond. & Whittington Hosp.; Lond.

OVERTON, Caroline Elizabeth Department Obstetrics and Gynaecology, Norfolk and Norwich University Hospital, Colney Lane, Norwich NR4 7UY Tel: 01603 287100 Fax: 01603 287532 Email: caroline.overton@norfolk-norwich; Tel: 01603 713656 Email: caroline@tenison.demon.co.uk — MB BS 1987 Lond.; MD Lond. 1996; MRCOG 1995. (Royal Free Hospital) Cons. Obstetrician and Gynaecologist. Prev: Subspecialist trainee in Reproductive Med. & Surg. at Univ. Coll. Hosp. Lond.; Regist. & Sen. Regist. Rotat (O&G) Addenbrookes', PeterBoro. and Norf. and Norwich Hosp.s.; Research Fell. Nuffield Dept (O&G) John Radcliffe Hosp. Oxf.

OVERTON, Christopher 7 Butterbache Road, Huntington, Chester CH3 6BY Tel: 01244 310199 — MB ChB 1982 Liverp.; MRCOG 1991; Dip. Ven. Liverp. 1986; Cert. Family Plann. JCC 1986. Regist. (O & G) Chester Roy. Infirm. Prev: Regist. (O & G) P.ss Margt. Hosp. Swindon.

OVERTON, Dennis James Holyoakes Farm, Holyoakes Lane, Hewell, Redditch B97 5SR — MB ChB 1985 Birm.; ChB Birm. 1985; FRCA 1993. (Birm.) Cons. Anaesth., Wycombe Gen. Hosp. High Wycombe, Buckshire.

OVERTON, John Geraint 6A Broomhill Gardens, Glasgow G11 7QD — BM 1987 Soton.; MRCGP 1993; Dip. Palliat. Med. Wales 1997. p/t Cons. in Palliat. Med., Salisbury Dist. Hosp. NHS Trust; Cons. in Palliat. Med., Soton. Univ. Hosps. NHS Trust,

Countess Mt.batten Ho. Prev: Specialist Regist., Palliat. Med., Soton. Univ. Hosp. NHS Trust; Regist. (Palliat. Med.) St. Josephs Lond.; SHO (Palliat. Med.) City Hosp. Nottm.

OVERTON, Marion Ruth Langley Health Centre, Common Road, Langley, Slough SL3 8LE Tel: 01753 544288; 8 Palmerston Avenue, Slough SL3 7PU Tel: 01753 572300 Fax: 01753 572300 — MB BS 1974 Lond.; MRCGP 1978; DRCOG 1978; DCH Eng. 1977. Prev: Trainee GP Ascot VTS.

OVERTON, Mark John Porthcawl Group Practice, The Portway, Porthcawl CF36 3XB — MB ChB 1991 Ed.

OVERTON, Michael Andrew (retired) Young, Ellis and Overton, 41 David Place, St Helier, Jersey JE2 4TE Tel: 01534 723318 Fax: 01534 611062 — MB ChB 1980 Manch.; DRCOG 1983. Prev: GP Manch.

OVERTON, Rachel Catherine 192 Scartho Road, Grimsby DN33 2BP — MB ChB 1985 Manch.

OVERTON, Robert David Charles The Keston House Medical Practice, 70 Brighton Road, Purley CR8 2LJ Tel: 020 8660 8292 Fax: 020 8763 2142 — MB BS 1988 Lond.; DRCOG 1993.

OVERTON, Mr Timothy Graeme Tel: 01603 286790 Fax: 01603 287532; Tel: 01603 713656 Email: toverton@tenison.demon.co.uk — MB BS 1986 Lond.; BSc (Immunol. & Physiol.) Lond. 1983; MRCOG 1994; MRCGP 1990; DRCOG 1990; MD 1999 (Univ. of Lond.). (Westm. Med. Sch.) Cons. (Obst. & Gyn), Subspecialist in Materno - Fetal Med., Norf. & Norwich Hosp. Socs: Blair Bell Res. Soc.; Brit. Matern. & Fetal Med. Soc.; Victor Bonney Soc. Prev: Sen. Regist. (Materno-Fetal Med.) Qu. Charlottes & Chelsea Hosp. Lond.; Sen. Regist. (O & G) Rosie Matern. Unit Camb.; Research Fell. Qu. Charlottes & Chelsea Hosp. Lond.

OVERY, Meriel Kate Dujardin Hook Green Farm, Lamberhurst, Tunbridge Wells TN3 8LL Email: m.sykes@tinyonline.co.uk — BM BS 1991 Nottm.; MRCGP 2000. GP Princip. Sch. La. Surg., Thetford, Norf. Prev: Ho. Phys. Pembury Hosp. Tunbridge Wells; Ho. Surg. Qu. Mary's Hosp. Sidcup.; VTS Trainee, N.er Staffs. 1992-1995.

OVERY, Richard Douglas Mulbarton Surgery, The Common, Mulbarton, Norwich NR14 8JG Tel: 01508 570212 Fax: 01508 570042; Corporation Farm House, Wymondham Road, Hethel, Norwich NR14 8EU Tel: 01953 607779 — MB ChB Leeds 1979; MRCGP 1986; DCH RCP Lond. 1984.

OVIEDO EXPOSITO, Maria Luz Flat 2, 14 Colville Terrace, London W11 2BE — LMS 1990 Basque Provinces.

OVINGTON, Nigel Robert 37 Albert Street, Cambridge CB4 3BE Tel: 01223 324234 — MA Dub. 1988, MB BCh BAO Dub. 1982; Cert. Family Plann. JCC 1990; Cert. Prescribed Equiv. Exp. JCPTGP 1988; DRCOG 1985; DCH NUI 1984.

OVIS, Simeon (retired) Spa Road Surgery, Spa Road East, Llandrindod Wells LD1 5ES Tel: 01597 824291 / 842292 Fax: 01597 824503 — MB BS 1957 Lond.; MRCS Eng. LRCP Lond. 1957. Prev: Gen. Practitioner, Llandrindod Wells.

OW, Kevin Khai Huat 14B Highnam Crescent Road, Sheffield S10 1BZ — MB ChB 1998 Sheff.

OWA, Mr Anthony Oloruntoba Flat 30, 133 East India Dock Road, London E14 6DE — MB BS 1987 Benin; FRCS Ed. 1993.

OWEN, Ailwen Meinir Llanishen Court Surgery, Llanishen Court, Llanishen, Cardiff CF14 5YU Tel: 02920 757025 Fax: 02920 747931; 12 Cae Garw, Thornhill, Cardiff CF14 9DX Tel: 02920 522924 — MB BCh 1977 Wales. (Univ. Hosp. of Wales) G.P. Princip.

OWEN, Mr Alan Ernest (retired) 4 Russell Field, Shrewsbury SY3 9AY Tel: 01743 231980 — MB BCh 1963 Wales; FRCS Ed. 1974; FRCOG 1983, M 1970. Prev: Cons. O & G Roy. Shrewsbury Hosp. Trust.

***OWEN, Alexander Guy Roger** Wonston Grange, Sutton Scotney, Winchester SO21 3LW Tel: 01962 760510 — MB BCh 1997 Wales; BSc Lond. 1991.

OWEN, Amanda Mehefin Mayday University Hospital, London Road, Thornton Heath, Croydon CR7 7YE Tel: 020 7401 3400; 3 Tradewinds Court, Asher Way, Wapping, London E1W 2JB Tel: 020 7480 6306 — MRCS Eng. LRCP Lond. 1978. (Guy's) Staff Grade (Liaison Psychiat.) Mayday Hosp. Thornton Heath. Socs: BMA; Med. Wom. Federat. Prev: Clin. Asst. (Psychiat.) E. Ham Day Hosp.; Regist. & SHO Guy's & Bexley Hosps. Lond.

OWEN, Andrew Nunnery Fields Hospital, Nunnery Fields, Canterbury CT1 3LP — MB BChir 1985 Camb.

OWEN, Andrew John 4 Wentworth Park Avenue, Birmingham B17 9QU — MB ChB 1992 Birm.

OWEN, Angela Christine Bryntirion Hospital, Swansea Road, Llanelli SA15 3DX — MB BCh 1979 Wales; MRCPsych 1984. Cons. Psychiat. Old Age Bryntirion Hosp. LLa.lli. Prev: Sen. Regist. (Psychiat.) Cefn Coed Hosp. Swansea; Hon. Sen. Research Regist., Regist. (Psychiat.) & SHO WhitCh. Hosp. Cardiff.

OWEN, Annaliese Catherine 61 Warwick Street, Oxford OX4 1SZ — MB BS 1993 Lond.

OWEN, Mr Anthony Wynn Michael Carton 21 Hale Road, Hale, Liverpool L24 5RB Tel: 0151 425 2288 — MB ChB 1968 Liverp.; BSc (Hons.) Liverp. 1965, MB ChB 1968; FRCS Eng. 1973; FRCS Ed. 1973. Lect. Surg. Univ. Hosp. S. Manch. Socs: BMA. Prev: Surg. Regist. Liverp. RHB & Chester Roy. Infirm.; Lect. Surg. Roy. Infirm. Edin.

OWEN, Brian Clifford Mountain View, Penrhos Road, Bangor LL57 2NA Tel: 01248 351127 Fax: 01248 371101 — MB BCh 1980 Wales; BSc Cardiff 1977; MFOM 1994; AFOM RCP Lond. 1988; MRCGP 1984; DRCOG 1983. Cons. (Occupat. Health) Bangor.

OWEN, Buddug, OBE (retired) Bwthyn, Cwm Road, Rhuallt, St Asaph LL17 0TP Tel: 01745 584446 — MB BCh Wales 1949; BSc Wales 1946; FFA RCS Eng. 1970; DA Eng. 1954. Trustee Museum of Med. & Health, Wales. Prev: Med. Off. (Complaints) Wales.

OWEN, Caroline Anne Flat 12, Stapylton Court St Peters Road, Harborne, Birmingham B17 0BE Tel: 0121 427 6417 — MB ChB 1984 Ed.; MB ChB (Hons.) Ed. 1984; MRCP (UK) 1987. Clin. Research Fell. Univ. Birm.; Hon. Regist. Gen. Hosp. Birm. Socs: RCP Ed.; RCP Land. Prev: SHO Rotat. (Gen. Med.) Qu. Eliza Hosp. Birm.

OWEN, Caroline Megan 12 Whitecroft Lane, Mellor, Blackburn BB2 7HA — MB ChB 1993 Bristol; MRCP (UK) 1996. Specialist Regist. (Dermat.) Lancaster Roy. Infirm. & Hope Hosp. Salford Manch.

OWEN, Colin Anthony PO Box 38, Spalding PE12 6XY — MB BS 1979 Newc.; BSc Leic. 1971, MPhil 1974; LLM Wales 1993; MRCGP 1984. Prev: Asst. Sec. Med. Protec. Soc. Lond.; GP Suff.

OWEN, Colin Griffith The Surgery, Swan Barton, Sherston, Malmesbury Tel: 01666 840270 — MRCS Eng. LRCP Lond. 1953. (St. Mary's) Prev: Clin. Asst. (Orthop.) Ormskirk & Dist. Gen. Hosp.; Ho. Surg. Orthop. Dept. St. Mary's Hosp. Lond.; Ho. Phys. Roy. Edwd. Infirm. Wigan.

OWEN, Mr David Ainslie 229 Coppermill Road, Wraysbury, Staines TW19 5NW Tel: 0128 125405 — MRCS Eng. LRCP Lond. 1962; MB Camb. 1963, BChir 1962; FRCS Ed. 1970; FRCS Eng. 1971; DO Eng. 1967. (St. Thos.) Socs: BMA.

OWEN, Lord David Anthony Llewellyn, PC, CH 78 Narrow Street, Limehouse, London E14 8BP Tel: 020 7987 5441 Fax: 01442 876108 Email: lordowen@nildram.co.uk — MA, MB Camb. 1963, BChir 1962. (St. Thos.) Fell. Sidney Sussex Coll. Camb.; Chairm. Middx. Holding plc; Dir. Abbott Laborat. Socs: Chairm. Humanitas. Prev: EU Chairm. Internat. Conf. on Former Yugoslavia; Ldr. of the SDP; Min. for the Navy, MoH & Sec. State Foreign & Commonw. Office.

OWEN, David Christopher 30 The Parade, Roath, Cardiff CF24 3AD — MB BCh 1984 Wales.

OWEN, David Granville Winch Lane Medical Centre, Winch Lane, Haverfordwest SA61 1RN Tel: 01437 763693 Fax: 01437 774389; The Hayes, 137 Haven Road, Haverfordwest SA61 1DL — MB BS 1965 Lond.; DObst RCOG 1967. (St. Bart.) Socs: BMA. Prev: Clin. Asst. (Anaesth.) Withybush Gen. Hosp. HaverfordW.; Hon. Med. Off. HaverfordW. Rugby Club; Ho. Surg. Orthop. Dept. & Dept. O & G, & Gen. Pract. Regist.

OWEN, David James Church View Cottage, Bridge St., Bampton OX18 2HA — MB ChB 1994 Leeds.

OWEN, David John Currie Road Health Centre, Currie Road, Galashiels TD1 2UA Tel: 01896 752476 Fax: 01896 751389; Fernlea, Ormiston Terrace, Melrose TD6 9SP Tel: 01896 822537 — MB ChB 1976 Ed.; DRCOG 1983; MRCGP 1982.

OWEN, David Kenny Bradford House, 106 Stockbridge Road, Winchester SO22 6RL Tel: 01962 856310 — MB BS 1982 Lond.; MRCS Eng LRCP Lond. 1982; FFHom 1983.

OWEN, David Norman Howell (retired) Bryn-y-mor, Fishguard SA65 Tel: 01348 872214 — MB BChir 1952 Camb.; MA; MRCS Eng. LRCP Lond. 1949; MRCGP 1962; DA Eng. 1968; DObst RCOG

OWEN

1954. Prev: Ho. Surg., Ho. Phys. & Paediat. Resid. Pembury Hosp. (Guy's Sector).

OWEN, David Roy (retired) The Old Vicarage, Soulbury, Leighton Buzzard LU7 0BX Tel: 01525 270305 Email: drowen@doctors.org.uk — MRCS Eng. LRCP Lond. 1957; DLO Eng. 1961; DObst RCOG 1962. Prev: GP Leighton Buzzard.

OWEN, Mr Dewi Wyn 9 Dolgwili Road, Carmarthen SA31 2AE Tel: 01267 235965 Email: dno.cartref@virgin.net — MB ChB 1957 Liverp.; FRCS Eng. 1965; MRCS Eng. LRCP Lond. 1957. Manager, Ment. Health Act Appeals Panel (Ment. Illness) Pembrokesh. NHS Trust Gen. Hosp. Fishguard Rd: Haverford W. Pembrokesh. Socs: Fell. BMA & Welsh Surgic. Soc.; Welsh Surgic. Travellers. Prev: Sen. Med. Off. Welsh Office Cardiff; Cons. Surg. W. Wales Gen. Hosp. Carmarthen; Sen. Regist. (Surg.) Liverp. Roy. Infirm.

***OWEN, Diane** 54 Glantawe Park, Ystradgynlais, Swansea SA9 1AE — MB BCh 1994 Wales.

OWEN, Dulcie Ann Lenthall (retired) 4 Cloutman's Lane, Braunton EX33 1NG Tel: 01271 890228 — MB BS 1955 Lond.

OWEN, Mr Edwin Nicholas (retired) 18 Kenton Drive, Shrewsbury SY2 6TH Tel: 01743 235858 — MB ChB Liverp. 1938; FRCS Eng. 1949; MRCS Eng. LRCP Lond. 1938; DLO Eng. 1946. Prev: Cons. ENT Shrewsbury Gp. Hosps.

***OWEN, Elin** Gwarcwm Bach, 18 Heol Ffynnon Asa, Eglwysbach, Colwyn Bay LL28 5BL — MB BCh 1997 Wales.

OWEN, Elizabeth Jane West Middlesex University Hospital Trust, Twickenham Road, Isleworth TW7 6AF Tel: 020 8565 5117 Fax: 020 8565 5973 — MB BS 1980 Lond.; MD Lond. 1993; MRCOG 1986; FRCOG 1998. (Royal Free Hospital) Cons. O & G W. Middlx. Univ. Hosp. Trust Isleworth. Socs: (Counc.) Roy. Soc. Med.; Brit. Fertil. Soc.; Brit. Menopause Soc. Prev: Sen. Regist. (O & G) St. Mary's Hosp. Lond.; Research Regist. (Gyn. Endocrinol.) Middlx. Hosp. Lond.; Regist. (Obst & Gyn.) Univ. Coll. Hosp. Lond.

OWEN, Mr Eoghan Ronan Thomas Carton Pipers Hollow, Forest Road, Horsham RH12 4HL Tel: 01403 242904 Fax: 01403 248773 Email: owen@uk-consultants.co.uk; Brookfield House, 21 Hale Road, Hale, Liverpool L24 5RB Tel: 0151 425 2288 — MB ChB 1978 Liverp.; FRCS Ed. 1984; FRCSI 1984. Cons. Surg. Gen. & Gastrointestinal Surg. Surrey & Sussex NHS Trust. Socs: Fell. New York Acad. Sci.; Surg. Research Soc. Prev: Resid. Surg. Off. St. Mark's Hosp. Lond.; Sen. Regist. St. Mary's & Hammersmith Hosps. Lond.; Regist. (Surg.) N.wick Pk. Hosp. & Clin. Research Centre Harrow.

OWEN, Garth Buchanan (retired) 26 Links Road, Romiley, Stockport SK6 4HU Tel: 0161 494 1416 Fax: 0161 494 1416 Email: owen@romiley26.fsnet.co.uk — MB ChB 1952 Manch. Prev: Gen. Practioner.

OWEN, Gerallt 10 Firgrove Corner, Wrexham LL12 7UF Tel: 01978 359219; Block D, 26 Wetherby Road, Harrogate HG2 7SA — MB ChB 1990 Liverp.; MRCP (UK) 1995. Regist. (c/o Elderly) Harrogate & St. Jas. Hosps. Leeds. Socs: BMA; Brit. Geriat. Soc. Prev: Regist. (Med.) Glan Clwyd Hosp. Rhyl; SHO (Nephrol.) Roy. Liverp. Univ. Hosp.

OWEN, Gerwyn Health Centre, Victoria Sq, Portishead, Bristol BS20 6AQ Tel: 01275 847474 Fax: 01275 817516; The Orchard, Sheepway, Portbury, Bristol BS20 7TE Tel: 01275 848346 — MB ChB 1984 Bristol; BSc (Hons.) Bristol 1981, MB ChB 1984; MRCGP 1994; DRCOG 1986. Prev: SHO (Paediat.) Bristol Childr. Hosp.; SHO (Gen. Med.) Frenchay Hosp. Bristol; SHO (Obst.) Bristol Matern. Hosp.

OWEN, Glyn Ward Bryn-yr-Ashwrn, Llanrhaeadr, Denbigh LL16 4PH — BM 1993 Soton.

OWEN, Griffith Tudor Penychen, Chwilog, Pwllheli LL53 6HJ — MRCS Eng. LRCP Lond. 1979. (Guy's) Prev: SHO (A & E) Guy's Hosp. Lond.; Ho. Surg. Guy's Hosp. Lond.; Ho. Phys. Harefield Hosp. Middlx.

OWEN, Gwen Ellis (retired) Gwenarth, 184 Hale Road, Hale, Altrincham WA15 8SQ Tel: 0161 928 1321 — MB ChB 1948 Liverp. SCMO S. Manch. HA.

OWEN, Gwyneth c/o Department of Paediatrics, West Wales General Hospital, Dolgwili Road, Carmarthen SA31 2AF — MB BCh 1979 Wales; MRCP (UK) 1984; DCH RCP Lond. 1981. Cons. Paediat. W. Wales Gen. Hosp. Carmarthen.

OWEN, Miss Gwyneth Olwen Lincoln Country Hospital, Greetwell Road, Lincoln LN2 5QY Tel: 01522 512512 — MB BS 1982 Lond.; FRCS Eng. (Orl.) 1990; FRCS Ed. 1987; Master of Surger, Univ. of Bath. 1994. (The Lond. Hosp. Med. Coll.)

OWEN, Gwynfryn Anwyl (retired) 11 Peters Way, Knebworth SG3 6HP Tel: 01438 812864 — MRCS Eng. LRCP Lond. 1939; DTM & H Eng. 1949.

OWEN, Harriet Alice 50 Hillside Crescent, Harrow HA2 0QX — MB BS 1998 Lond.; MB BS Lond 1998.

OWEN, Huw Gruffudd 1 Maes Afallen, Bow Street SY24 5BL — MB BCh 1977 Wales.

OWEN, Ian Glyn Kinnaird House, Curtis Street, Pemberton, Wigan WN5 9LB Tel: 01942 222304 Fax: 01942 214490; Kinnaird House, Curtis St, Pemberton, Wigan WN5 9LB Tel: 01942 222304 — LMSSA 1990 Lond.; MRCGP 1994; DRCOG 1994.

OWEN, Ivor Tudor, Squadron Ldr. RAF Med. Br. Retd. OHD, BAE Systems, W298, Warton Aerodrome, Preston PR4 1AX Tel: 01772 852798 Fax: 01772 855282 Email: ivor.owen@baesystems.com; 19 Cotswold Road, Lytham St Annes FY8 4NN Fax: 01253 732530 Email: ivorowen@doctors.org.uk — MB ChB 1986 Birm.; 1992 T (GP); 2001 AFOM; RCP Lond.; MRCGP 1994; D Occ Med. RCP Lond. 1996; DAvMed FOM RCP Lond. 1995; DFFP 1994; DCH RCP Lond. 1991; DRCOG 1991. (Univ.of Birm) Chief Med. Off., BAE Systems Warton Unit. Socs: Soc. Occupat. Med.; Aerospace Med. Assn.; Roy. Aeronaut. Soc. Prev: RAF Sen. Med. Off. RAF Decimomannu; Trainee GP Glos. FHSA Cheltenham VTS; Emiratas Airlines Clinic Doctor, Dubai.

OWEN, Mr James Edward 61 Warwick Street, Oxford OX4 1SZ — BChir 1992 Camb.; BA Camb. 1990; MA 1994 Camb.; FRCS Eng. 1997. (Camb.) Specialist Regist. Orthop. Oxf. Regional Train. Program. Socs: Assoc. Mem. BOA; Fell.of Roy. Coll. Of Surg.s of Eng.

OWEN, Lt. Col. Jeremy Peter, Lt.-Col. — MB ChB 1985 Birm.; MMedSc (Occupat. Health) Birm. 1994; MFOM RCP Lond. 1996, AFOM 1992. (Birm.) Cons. (Occupat. Med.) & Med. Off. RAMC. Socs: Soc. Occupat. Med. Prev: Med. Off. Brit. Antarctic Survey.

OWEN, Joan Catherine Dolycoed, Gowerton, Swansea SA4 3DJ Tel: 01792 873297 — MRCS Eng. LRCP Lond. 1932; MA, MB BChir Camb. 1937; FCPath 1963. (Camb. & Lond. Sch. Med. Wom.) JP; Hon. Cons. Path. W. Glam. AHA. Socs: Assn. Clin. Pathols. Prev: Pathol. Bermuda; Cons. Pathol. Welsh Hosp. Bd.

OWEN, Joanne Alison 5 Fairview Place, Danestone, Aberdeen AB22 8ZJ — MB ChB 1997 Aberd.

***OWEN, Joanne Claire** 2 Furzehatt Villas, Plymstock, Plymouth PL9 9HB — BM BS 1998 Nottm.; BM BS Nottm 1998.

OWEN, John Douglas, MBE (retired) 8 Achnacone Drive, Colchester CO4 5AZ — MB BChir 1959 Camb.; MA, MB Camb. 1959, BChir 1958; MRCS Eng. LRCP Lond. 1958; DObst RCOG 1960. Prev: Ho. Surg. Gordon Hosp. Lond.

OWEN, John Hughes c/o Cossham Hospital, Lodge Road, Kingswood, Bristol BS15 1LQ Tel: 0117 967 1661 — MB ChB 1982 Bristol; MRCPsych 1987. Cons. Psychiat. Cossham Hosp. Kingswood Bristol. Prev: Regist. (Psychiat.) Glenside Hosp. Stapleton, Bristol; Psychiat. Crisis Interven. Team Melbourne, Austral.; Lect. (Ment. Health) Univ. Bristol.

OWEN, Professor John Joseph Thomas Department of Anatomy, The Medical School, Edgbaston, Birmingham B15 2TT Tel: 0121 414 6812 Fax: 0121 414 6815 — FRS 1988; MA Oxf. 1964; BSc Liverp. 1955, MD 1963, MB ChB 1959. (Liverp.) Sands Cox Prof. Anat. Med. Sch. Univ. Birm. Prev: Prof. Anat. Med. Sch. Univ. Newc.; Fell. St. Cross Coll. Oxf.; Lect. Univ. Oxf.

OWEN, John Philip Glannrafon Surgery, Glannrafon, Amlwch LL68 9AG Tel: 01407 830878 Fax: 01407 832512 — MB ChB 1974 Liverp.; MRCP (UK) 1977.

OWEN, John Robson (retired) Mayfield, The Shore, Prinsted, Emsworth PO10 8HS Tel: 01243 373021 — MB ChB Birm. 1952. Prev: Med. Off. Dept. Health & Social Security BAMS.

OWEN, John Roger (retired) Brook Farm, Broadith Lane, Goosnargh, Preston PR3 2EJ Tel: 01772 865853 — MB 1964 Camb.; BChir 1963; FRCP Lond. 1982, M 1968; DCH Eng. 1965. Cons. Paediat. Preston Acute Hosps NHS Trust. Prev: Cons. Paediat. Preston Dist. HA & Chorley & S. Ribble HA.

OWEN, John Roger 81 Painswick Road, Cheltenham GL50 2EX — MB BS 1971 Lond.; FRCR 1977; FRCP (UK) 1998. Cons. Clin. Oncol. Cheltenham Gen. Hosp. Prev: Sen. Regist. (Radiother.) Roy.

OWEN

Marsden Hosp. Lond.; Regist. (Radiother.) Hammersmith Hosp. Lond.; Ho. Surg. Lond. Hosp.

OWEN, John Tudor (retired) 6 Eresby House, Rutland Gate, London SW7 1BG — MB BS 1948 Lond.

OWEN, Jonathan Richard Bower Offerton Health Centre, Offerton Lane, Stockport SK2 5AR Tel: 0161 480 0324; 105 Overdale Road, Romiley, Stockport SK6 3JB — MB ChB 1982 Manch.; MRCGP 1990; T(G) 1992; DCH RCP Lond. 1987. (Manchester) GP Princip. Prev: SHO (A & E Psychiat. & ENT) Tameside Gen. Hosp. Ashton u Lyne.

OWEN, Joyce Mary 11 Rotherwood Close, Mill Road, Bebington, Wirral CH63 5RG — MB ChB 1938 Liverp.; DObst RCOG 1942. (Liverp.) Mem. Liverp. Med. Inst. Prev: Res. Med. Off. Alder Hey Childr. Hosp. Liverp.; Ho. Surg. Liverp. Matern. Hosp.; Asst. M.O.H. & Res. Med. Off. Bank Hall Matern. Hosp. Burnley.

OWEN, Julie Clare 28 Sandbanks Road, Lower Parkstone, Poole BH14 8BU — MB ChB 1996 Liverp.

OWEN, Katharine Ruth 19 Tetbury Grove, Birmingham B31 5RB — MB ChB 1992 Birm.

OWEN, Katherine Clare 4 Wentworth Park Avenue, Birmingham B17 9QU — MB ChB 1993 Birm.

OWEN, Kathryn Ruth 13 Hart Road, Manchester M14 7LD — MB ChB 1991 Manch.

OWEN, Keith Rysseldene Surgery, 98 Conway Road, Colwyn Bay LL29 7LE Tel: 01492 532807 Fax: 01492 534846 — MB BCh 1977 Wales; DRCOG 1980.

OWEN, Kelyth Lloyd South Lawn, Moorend Park Road, Cheltenham Tel: 01242 522764 — MRCS Eng. LRCP Lond. 1948; FFA RCS Eng. 1954. (Univ. Coll. Hosp.) Cons. Anaesth. Cheltenham & Gloucester Health Dists. Socs: Assn. Anaesth.; S.W. Soc. Anaesths. Prev: Regist. & Sen. Regist. (Anaesth.) Cardiff Roy. Infirm.; RAMC, Clin. Off. Anaesth. Hong Kong.

OWEN, Mr Kenneth (retired) Hillside Farm, Adlestrop, Moreton-in-Marsh GL56 0YR Tel: 01608 658277 Fax: 01608 659170 Email: keno@adleside.u-net.com — MB BS Lond. 1944; MS Lond. 1957; FRCS Eng. 1950; MRCS Eng. LRCP Lond. 1944. p/t Cons. Surg. St. Mary's Hosp. Lond.; Cons. Urol. St. Peter's & St. Paul's Hosps. Lond. & King Edwd. VII Hosp Offs Lond. Prev: Research Asst. Harvard Univ.

OWEN, Louise Sarah Isobel 29 Avenue Rise, Bushey, Watford WD2 3AS — MB ChB 1996 Bristol. SHO (Paediat.) MusGr. Pk. Hosp. Taunton. Socs: BMA. Prev: Ho. Off. (Med.) Exeter; Ho. Off. (Surg.) Bristol.

OWEN, Lysa Edith Accident & Emergency Department, Dundee Royal Infirmary, Dundee DD1 9SY Tel: 01382 660111; 43 Hyndford Street, Dundee DD2 1HX Email: andyo.balnacraigschool@btinternet.com — MB ChB 1992 Dundee. Specialist Regist. (A & E) Dundee.

OWEN, Maldwyn Henry Dean Cross Surgery, 21 Radford Park Road, Plymstock, Plymouth PL9 9DL Tel: 01752 404743; Old Staddon Farm, Staddon Heights, Plymstock, Plymouth PS9 9SP Tel: 01752 404775 — MB 1975 Camb.; MA; BChir 1974; MRCGP 1980; DObst RCOG 1976.

OWEN, Marie Elizabeth Paediatric Department, Gloucestershire Royal Hospital, Great Western Road, Gloucester GL1 3NN Tel: 01452 528555; 81 Painswick Road, Cheltenham GL50 2EX Tel: 01242 522501 — MB BS 1972 Lond.; DCH Eng. 1978. Clin. Asst. (Paediat.) Gloucester Roy. Hosp. Prev: Regist. (Paediat.) Whittington Hosp. Lond.; SHO (Paediat.) Univ. Coll. Hosp. Lond.

OWEN, Mark Julian 1 The Park, London W5 5NE — MB BS 1982 Lond.; MSc Lond. 1975, BSc (Engineering) 1974, MB BS 1982.

OWEN, Mary 32 St Albans Road, Edinburgh EH9 2LU Tel: 0131 667 2222 — MB BCh 1962 Wales; DA Eng. 1965. (Cardiff) Clin. Asst. Colposcopy Clinic Edin. Roy. Infirm. Prev: Regist. (Anaesth.) SE RHB Scotl.

OWEN, Mary Dilys Maesgwyn, Grosvenor Road, Llandrindod Wells LD1 5NA Tel: 01597 2294 — MB ChB 1938 Wales; BSc Wales 1935, MB ChB 1938, DPH 1942; DObst RCOG 1948. (Cardiff) JP; Vis. Med. Off. Llandrindod Wells & Co. War Memor. Hosp. Prev: Res. Med. Off., Ho. Surg. & Ho. Phys. Llandough Hosp.

OWEN, Mererid Market Street Surgery, 3-5 Market Street, Caernarfon LL55 1RT Tel: 01286 673224 Fax: 01286 676405 — MB BCh 1985 Wales.

OWEN, Mervyn Edwards 3 Market Street, Caernarfon LL55 Tel: 01286 673224; Bryn Rhug, England Road N., Caernarfon LL55 1HS Tel: 01286 671122 — LRCPI & LM, LRSCI & LM 1957; LRCPI & LM, LRCSI & LM 1957; DObst RCOG 1965; Mem. BMA. Prev: Ho. Phys. Lincoln Co. Hosp.; Ho. Surg. City Hosp. Nottm.; Obst. Ho. Off. St. David's Hosp. Bangor.

OWEN, Professor Michael John Neuropsychatric Genetics Unit, Tenovus Building , Division Psychological Medicine, University of Wales College of Medicine, Heath Park, Cardiff CF14 4XN Tel: 029 2074 3248 Fax: 029 2074 6554 Email: owenmj@cf.ac.uk — MB ChB 1983 Birm.; PhD Birm. 1982, BSc 1977; FRCPsych 1997, M 1987; F.Med.Sci. 1999. Prof. Psychol. Med., Head Dept. Psychol. Med., Univ. of Wales, Coll. of Med., Cardiff; Hon. Cons. Psychiat. Univ. Hosp. Wales, Cardiff & Dist. Community, Health Care Trusts; Vis. Prof. Inst. of Psychiat. Lond. Socs: Director, Internat. Soc. of Psychiat. Genetics; Amer. Soc. of Human Genetics. Prev: MRC Research Fell. (Biochem. & Molecular Genetics) St. Mary's Hosp. Med. Sch. Lond.; Hon. Lect. Inst. Psychiat. Lond.

OWEN, Michael Robert Director of Public Health, North & East Devon Health Authority, Dean Clarke House, Southern Hay East, Exeter EX1 1PQ Tel: 01392 207380 Fax: 01392 207377; Tel: 01823 442681 Fax: 01392 207377 — MB BCh BAO 1972 Dub.; MSc Lond. 1981, MD 1983; FFPHM RCP (UK) 1995; MRCGP 1976; DObst RCOG 1976; DCH Eng. 1974. (Univ. Dub. Trinity Coll.) Dir. Pub. Health N. & E. Devon HA; Hon. Sen. Lect. Postgrad. Med. Sch. Univ. Exeter. Prev: Cons. Pub. Health Med. Exeter HA & SW RHA; Sen. Med. Adviser Overseas Developm. Admin.; Princip. in Gen. Pract. W.on Super Mare.

OWEN, Neil Macarthur Deerness Park Medical Centre, Suffolk Street, Sunderland SR2 8AD Tel: 0191 567 0961; Seaforth, 35B Sea View Road, Grangetown, Sunderland SR2 7UP Tel: 0191 514 0527 — MB ChB 1980 Glas.

OWEN, Neil Trevor Poyntz St Lawrence's Hospital, Boundary Road, Bodmin PL31 2QT Tel: 01208 251318 — MB ChB 1985 Ed.; MRCPsych 1991. Cons. Psychiat. (Gen. Adult) Cornw. Healthcare Trust. Prev: Sen. Regist. Rotat. Wessex Region; Research Fell. (Psychiat.) Roy. Edin. Hosp.; Regist. (Psychiat.) Ailsa Hosp. Ayr.

OWEN, Mr Nicholas John 58 Parliament Hill, London NW3 2TL — BM BCh 1988 Oxf.; BA (Hons.) Camb. 1985; FRCS Eng. 1992; FRCR 1998. (Oxford) Regist. (Radiol.) Roy. Lond. Hosp., GP Regist. Prev: Regist. (Surg., Urol. & Emerg. Med.) Monash Med. Centre Melbourne, Austral.; SHO (Surg. & Urol.) Reading Hosps.

OWEN, Norman Charles Watkin (retired) 11 Prestwick Drive, Blundellsands, Liverpool L23 7XB Tel: 0151 924 1574 — MB ChB 1948 Liverp.; MRCS Eng. LRCP Lond. 1949. Prev: Resid. Asst. Med. Off. Walton Hosp. Liverp.

OWEN, Mr Owen Elias (retired) Bryn Meurig, Bethesda, Bangor LL57 4YW Tel: 01248 600322 — MB ChB 1946 Ed.; FRCS Eng. 1953. Prev: Consult. in Gen. Surg. Gwynedd HA.

OWEN, Penelope Ann Heald Green Health Centre, Heald Green, Stockport; 12 Clarence Road, Hale, Altrincham WA15 8SG — BM 1986 Soton.; DRCOG 1989. Prev: SHO (Geriat. Med.) Portsmouth; Trainee GP Havant & Baddesley; SHO (O & G) P.ss Anne Hosp. Soton.

OWEN, Penelope Anne 3 Chester Court, Hendredenny, Caerphilly CF83 2UP — MB BCh 1978 Wales; MRCGP 1983.

OWEN, Penelope Judith Dawn 13 Highland Close, Cymdda, Sarn, Bridgend CF32 9SB — MB BCh 1997 Wales.

OWEN, Mr Peter Julian 32 Vale Road, Claygate, Esher KT10 0NJ Tel: 01372 802726 Email: jules@csi.com — MB BChir 1990 Camb.; MA Camb. 1990; FRCS Ed. 1994; FRCS (TRODRTH) 1999. (Cambridge) Specialist Regist. (Orthop. Surg.) SW Thames. Socs: BOA , Assoc. Mem.; BOTA Mem.; Fell. RCS (Ed.). Prev: Fell. in Orthop., Sunnybrook Heatlh Sci. Centre, Toronto, Ontario, Canada; Fell. (Callotasis) Robt. Jones & Agnes Hunt Orthop. Hosp. OsW.ry.

OWEN, Philip Glasgow Royal Maternity Hospital and Stobhill, General Hospital, Glasgow G21 3UW Tel: 0141 201 3432 Email: philipowen1@hotmail.com; 12 Craigievar Place, Newton Mearns, Glasgow G77 6YE — MB BCh 1985 Wales; DFM 2000; MD Wales 1998; MRCOG 1990. p/t The P.ss Roy. Matern. Unit and Stophill Hosp. Glas. Prev: Clin. Lect. & Hon. Sen. Regist. Ninewells Hosp. Dundee; Research Fell. (O & G) Ninewells Hosp. Dundee; Cons. Glas. Roy. Matern. Hosp. & Stobhill Gen. Hosp.

OWEN

OWEN, Philip Francis Bickford (retired) 19 Norfolk Road, Littlehampton BN17 5PW — BM BCh 1958 Oxf.; MA BM BCh Oxf. 1958; MRCS Eng. LRCP Lond. 1956.

***OWEN, Rachel Anne** 148 Lords Street, Cadishead, Manchester M44 5YB — MB ChB 1998 Manch.; MB ChB Manch 1998.

OWEN, Rhian Elin Y Bwthyn Newydd, Princess of Wales Hospital, Bridgend CF31 1RQ Tel: 01656 752014 Fax: 01656 752010 Email: rhian-owen@bromor-tr.wales.nhs.uk; Tel: 01222 842972 — MB BCh 1974 Wales; FRCP Lond. 1996; MRCP (UK) 1980; Dip. Palliat. Med: Wales 1992. (Welsh National School of Medicine) Macmillan Cons. Palliat. Med. Bridgend & Dist. NHS Trust. Socs: Brit. Geriat. Soc. (Sec. Welsh Br.); Rhondda Med. Soc. (Ex-Pres.); Fell. RSM. Prev: Sen. Med. Off. Welsh Off. Cardiff; Cons. Phys. (Geriat. Med.) Dewi Sant Hosp. Pontypridd; Cons. Phys. (Geriat. Med.) Tan Tock Seng Hosp., Singapore.

OWEN, Rhodri Wyn Bodnant Surgery, Menai Avenue, Bangor LL57 2HH Tel: 01248 364567 Fax: 01248 370654 — MB BCh 1978 Wales; MRCS Eng. LRCP Lond. 1978; DRCOG 1982.

OWEN, Rhys Prys The Health Centre, Bridge Street, Thorne, Doncaster DN8 5QH Tel: 01405 812121 Fax: 01405 741059 — MB ChB 1969 Leeds.

OWEN, Professor Robert, OBE Bryn Celyn, 41 Pwllycrochan Avenue, Colwyn Bay LL29 7BW Tel: 01492 533432 — MB BS 1946 Lond.; MCh Orth. Liverp. 1953; FRCS Eng. 1951. (Guy's) Emerit. Prof. Surg. Univ. Liverp. (Orthopaedic). Socs: Fell. Brit. Orthop. Assn.; (Ex-Pres.) Brit. Scoliosis Soc.; Counc. RCS Eng. Prev: Cons. Orthop. Surg. Robt. Jones & Agnes Hunt Orthop. Hosp. OsW.ry; Sen. Orthop. Regist. Liverp. United Hosps.; Squadron Ldr. RAFVR Med. Serv.

OWEN, Robert Andrew Department of Histopathology & Cytopathology, Whipps Cross Hospital, Whipps Cross Road, Leytonstone, London E11 1NR Tel: 020 8539 5522 — MB BChir 1980 Camb.; MRCPath 1989. (St. Geo.) Cons. Histopath. & Cytopath. Whipps Cross Hosp. Lond.

OWEN, Robert Arwyn (retired) Meadowbank, Greenfield Lane, Rowton, Chester CH3 6AU — MB BCh 1953 Wales; BSc Wales 1950, MB BCh 1953; FRCP Ed. 1977, M 1962; FRCR 1962; FFR 1962; DMRD Liverp. 1959; DMRD Eng. 1959. Prev: Cons. Radiol. Chester HA.

OWEN, Robert Elwy (retired) Cornel Penypentre, Llanfihangel Talyllyn, Brecon LD3 7TG Tel: 01874 658432 — MB BS Lond. 1957; MRCS Eng. LRCP Lond. 1957; LMSSA Lond. 1957; DPM Eng. 1964. Prev: Asst. Psychiat. Mid Wales Hosp. Talgarth.

OWEN, Robert Elwyn (retired) The Lugger, 21 Beach Road, Cemaes Bay LL67 0ES — MB BS 1976 Lond.; BA Oxf. 1973; MRCGP 1981. Prev: GP Amlwch.

OWEN, Robert Thomas Southern Derbyshire Mental Health (NHS) Trust, Derby City General Hospital, Psychiatric Unit, Uttoxeter Road, Derby DE22 3NE Tel: 01332 625587 — MB ChB 1973 Liverp.; MRCPsych 1979. Cons. Psychiat. Derby City Gen. Hosp. Prev: Cons. Psychiat. Pastures Hosp. Derby.

OWEN, Mr Robin Arthur (retired) Twitten End, Bickley Park Road, Bromley BR1 2AY Tel: 020 8467 4660 — MB BChir 1954 Camb.; MD Camb. 1965; FRCS Eng. 1960; FCOphth 1991; DO Eng. 1957. Prev: Cons. Ophth. Dartford, Sidcup, Lewisham Childr. & FarnBoro. Hosps.

***OWEN, Robin Dylan** 52 North Eastern Road, Thorne, Doncaster DN8 4AW — MB ChB 1998 Manch.; MB ChB March 1998.

OWEN, Roger Graham HMDS Laboratory, Leeds General Infirmary, Great George St., Leeds LS1 3EX Tel: 0113 392 6285 Fax: 0113 392 6286 Email: rgowen@hmds.org.uk — MB BCh 1988 Wales; BSc Wales 1985; MRCP (UK) 1991; MRCPath 1999; MD 1999. (Wales) Cons. Haematologist, Leeds Teachg. Hosps. NHS Trust. Prev: Research Fell. (Haemat.) Leeds Gen. Infirm.; Regist. (Haemat.) Leeds Hosps.; SHO Cardiff. Roy. Infirm. & Leeds Gen. Infirm.

OWEN, Rona Isabelle Pease Way Medical Centre, 2 Pease Way, Newton Aycliffe DL5 5NH Tel: 01325 312045; Seaforth, 35B Sea View Road, Grangetown, Sunderland SR2 7UP — MB ChB 1983 Ed.

OWEN, Ronald, OBE (retired) Oakengates, 24 Greenway, Harpenden AL5 1NQ Tel: 015827 715501 — MB ChB 1953 Liverp.; FFOM RCP Lond. 1982, MFOM 1978; DIH Soc. Apoth. Lond. 1961, DMJ (Clin.) 1964; FRSC 1987; CChem. Prev: Cons. to Trades Union Congr.

OWEN, Rosalind Janet 51 Stonehill, Street BA16 0PG Tel: 01458 443098; 51 Stonehill, Street BA16 0PG Tel: 01458 443098 — MB ChB 1967 Manch.; MFFP 1993. (Manch.) SCMO (Family Plann.) Som. HA; Asst. (Family Plann. & Well Wom.) Vine Surg. St.; Mem. UK Family Plann. Research Network Exeter Univ.

OWEN, Ruth (retired) 17 Devonhurst Place, Heathfield Terrace, London W4 4JB Tel: 020 8995 3228 Email: sg.owen@clara.co.uk — MD Univ. Pennsylvania 1955; LMSSA Lond. 1957; FRCA Eng. 1972. Prev: Cons. Anaesth. Ealing Hosp. Lond.

OWEN, Ruth Diana Child Health Department, Isaac Maddox House, Shrub Hill Road, Worcester WR4 9RW Tel: 01905 763333; Dovecote House, Charlton, Pershore WR10 3LL Tel: 01386 860712 — MB ChB Liverp. 1967; DCP Warwick 1985; DCCH RCP Ed. 1985; DCH Eng. 1971. SCMO Worcs. Community Healthcare Trust. Socs: Fac. Comm. Health; Brit. Assn. Community Drs in Audiol.

***OWEN, Samantha Jane** 28 Stafford Road, Bloxwich, Walsall WS3 3NL — MB ChB 1997 Birm.

OWEN, Samuel Griffith, CBE (retired) Flat 17, 9 Devonhurst Place, Heathfield Terrace, London W4 4JB Tel: 020 8995 3228 Email: sg.owen@clara.co.uk — MB BS Durh. 1948; MD Durh. 1955; FRCP Lond. 1965, M 1951. Prev: Second Sec. Med. Research Counc.

OWEN, Sandra 40 Parkhill Road, Bexley DA5 1HU Tel: 01322 522056 — MB BS 1966 Lond.; MRCS Eng. LRCP Lond. 1966. (St. Mary's)

OWEN, Sandra Jayne 18 Dulsie Road, Bournemouth BH3 7EA — MB BCh 1993 Wales.

OWEN, Sian Haf North West Wales NHS Trust, Women & Family Services Directorate, Beechwood House, Dolgellau LL40 1AU Tel: 01341 423121 Fax: 01341 422059; Crud - Yr - Awel, Ffrydan Road, Bala LL23 7RY Tel: 01678 521315 Fax: 01678 521375 Email: dlazarus@btinternet.com — MB BS 1985 Lond.; MRCGP 1991; Cert. Family Plann. JCC 1991; DFFP 1993; DCCH 1998. (Royal Free Hospital School of Medicine Univ.) Part - Time Sen. Community Paediat., N. W. Wales, NHST. Based in Dolgellau.; Staff Grade Doctor in Family Plann. N. W. Wales, NHST. (sessional). Socs: Med. Wom. Federat. (Counc. Mem. & Sec. local Assn.); BMA; Brit. Assoc. for Community Child Health.

OWEN, Stephen William 19 Greengates Crescent, Neston, South Wirral CH64 0XH — MB BS 1993 Liverp.

OWEN, Susan Judith 83 Main Road, Broughton, Chester CH4 0NR Tel: 01978 520099; 9 Lumley Road, Chester CH2 2AQ Tel: 01244 390230 Fax: 01244 390230 — MB BS 1975 Newc.; MRCGP 1979; DRCOG 1978.

OWEN, Terry Wawn Street Surgery, Wawn Street, South Shields NE33 4DX Tel: 0191 454 0421 Fax: 0191 454 9428; 7 Blagdon Avenue, South Shields NE34 0SG — MB BS 1980 Newc.; MRCGP 1984; DRCOG 1983.

OWEN, Thomas Emlyn (retired) 34 West End Avenue, Pinner HA5 1BJ Tel: 01248 353108 — MB BS 1945 Lond.; FRCP Lond. 1978, M 1951; MRCS Eng. LRCP Lond. 1945. Prev: Cons. Phys. (Geriat. Med.) Gwynedd HA.

OWEN, Thomas Meurig (retired) Bwthyn Bach, Knapwell, Cambridge CB3 8NW — MB BS 1950 Lond.; BSc (1st cl. Hons. Elec. Engin.) Wales 1940.

OWEN, Thomas Peter (retired) Trevaunance, Whitchurch, Tavistock PL19 9DD — MRCS Eng. LRCP Lond. 1963; MA Camb. 1959, MB BChir 1964; DA Eng. 1966; DObst RCOG 1967; DCH Eng. 1968. Prev: SHO Childr. Hosp. Sydenham.

OWEN, Timothy Clive Ethel Street Surgery, 88/90 Ethel Street, Benwell, Newcastle upon Tyne NE4 8QA Tel: 0191 219 5456 Fax: 0191 226 0300; 1 Lesbury Road, Heaton, Newcastle upon Tyne NE6 5LB Tel: 0191 265 8898 — MB BS 1979 Lond.; MRCGP 1983; DRCOG 1981.

OWEN, Mr Timothy David 49 Chillingham Drive, Chester-le-Street DH2 3TJ Tel: 029 2061 1565 — MB BCh 1986 Wales; FRCS Orth. 1995; FRCS Eng. 1990. Sen. Regist. (Orthop. Surg.) N. RHA. Prev: Regist. (Orthop Surg.) N.. RHA; Regist. Rotat. (Surg.) Cardiff.

OWEN, Tracy Amanda 85 Hermitage, Culcavy, Hillsborough BT26 6RJ — MB BCh BAO 1993 Belf.

OWEN, Trefor John 3 Market Street, Caernarfon LL55 1RT Tel: 01286 673224; Tyn y Coed, Caeathro, Caernarfon LL55 2TA Tel:

01286 671166 — MB BS 1959 Lond.; MRCS Eng. LRCP Lond. 1959; FFA RCS Eng. 1972; DA Eng. 1965. (St. Geo.) Hosp. Pract. (Anaesth.) Gwynedd HA; Med. Off. Ferodo Ltd. Caernarvon. Prev: Regist. (Anaesth.) Caernarvon & Anglesey Gen. Hosp. Bangor; Sen. Resid. (Anaesth.) Peter Bent Brigham Hosp. Boston, Mass.; Ho. Surg. St. Geo. Hosp. Lond.

OWEN, Trevor Richard 32 Morris Drive, Stafford ST16 3YE — MB ChB 1983 Manch.

OWEN, Tudor 10 Marine Road, Llandudno LL30 3NA Tel: 01492 541018 — MB ChB 1955 Liverp. Prev: GP Conwy N. Wales; Regist. (Paediat.) St. David's Hosp. Bangor; Ho. Phys. & Ho. Surg. Whiston Hosp.

OWEN, Victoria Jane 6 Ninelands Spur, Garfath, Leeds LS25 1NH Tel: 01132 866799 — MB ChB 1994 Dundee; Bmsc Dund 1994; DRCOG 1998; MRCGP 1998.

OWEN, Wanda Irena St George Health Centre, Bellevue Road, St. George, Bristol BS5 7PH Tel: 0117 961 2161 Fax: 0117 961 8761; 17 Normanton Road, Clifton, Bristol BS8 2TY Tel: 0117 973 2433 — MB ChB 1981 Bristol; MRCGP 1986. (Univ. Bristol) Prev: Clin. Asst. (Ment. Handicap) Phoenix Trust Bristol.

OWEN, Wendy Ann 32 North Park, Eltham, London SE9 5AP — MB BS 1968 Lond.; MRCS Eng. LRCP Lond. 1968. (Middlx.) Hon. Clin. Asst. Oesoph. Laborat. Guy's Hosp. Lond. Prev: Ho. Phys. St. Mary Abbot's Hosp. Kensington; Ho. Surg. Middlx. Hosp. Lond.; Asst. Lect. Bland-Sutton Inst. Path. Middlx. Hosp. Med. Sch. Lond.

OWEN, Wendy Anne Lanceburn Health Centre, Clarendon Surgery, Churchill Way, Salford M6 5AU Tel: 0161 736 4529 Fax: 0161 736 2724; 42 Lombard Grove, Fallowfield, Manchester M14 6AN — MB ChB 1985 Manch.; MRCGP 1990; DRCOG 1989.

OWEN, William Glyn (retired) 4 Cooper Hill Close, Walton-le-Dale, Preston PR5 4BE — MB BS Lond. 1952; FRCPath 1982, M 1966.

OWEN, Mr William Jones Department of Surgery, St. Thomas's Hospital, London SE1 7EH Tel: 020 928 9292 Ext: 3834 — MB BS 1969 Lond.; BSc (Hons.) Lond. 1966, MS 1980; FRCS Eng. 1974. (Guy's) Cons. & Dir. Surg. Guy's Hosp. Lond. & St. Thomas' Hosp.; Sen. Lect. Guy's Hosp. Med. Sch. Lond. Socs: Fell. Roy. Soc. Med. Prev: Sen. Regist. Guy's Hosp. Lond.; Surg. Regist. Bromley Hosp. Gp.; Jun. Lect. Anat. Guy's Hosp. Med. Sch.

OWEN, William Lewis (retired) Glennydd, Llanbedrog, Pwllheli LL53 7PG Tel: 01758 740009 — MB ChB 1947 Liverp.; MRCGP 1965. Prev: GP Llyn.

OWEN, Mr William Mervyn (retired) 17 Loyola Hey, Rainhill, Prescot L35 6PZ — MB BS 1938 Lond.; FRCS Eng. 1950; MRCS Eng. LRCP Lond. 1937; DLO Eng. 1948. Mem. BMA & Liverp. Med. Inst. Prev: Sen. Specialist, Otolaryng. RAMC.

OWEN, Yvonne Eleanor Mary Old Mill House, Tetford, Horncastle LN9 6QA Tel: 01507 533133 Fax: 01507 533489; Langton Hill Farm, Langton Hill, Horncastle LN9 5JP — BM BS 1985 Nottm.; Dip. IMC RCS Ed. 1991. Prev: Trainee GP Lincoln VTS.

OWEN-JONES, Jane Louise Horfield Health Centre, Lockleaze Road, Horfield, Bristol BS7 9RR Tel: 0117 969 5391; 91 Coombe Lane, Westbury on Trym, Bristol BS9 2AR — MB ChB 1979 Bristol; BA (Hons.) Bristol 1971, MB ChB 1979; MRCGP 1987; DRCOG 1985.

OWEN-JONES, Josephine Margaret Sarah Abbey Meads Medical Practice, Elstree Way, Swindon SN25 4YZ Tel: 01793 709100; Hollyhock Cottage, Union St, Ramsbury, Marlborough SN8 2PR Tel: 01672 520649 — MB BS 1976 Lond.; MSc (Univ. Westminster) 1999; MRCS Eng. LRCP Lond. 1976; MRCGP 1982; DRCOG 1979. (Roy. Free)

OWEN-JONES, Rodney James Ferguson Ramsbury Surgery, High Street, Ramsbury, Marlborough SN8 2QT Tel: 01672 520366 Fax: 01672 520180; Hollyhock Cottage, Union St, Ramsbury, Marlborough SN8 2PR Tel: 01672 520649 — MB BS 1977 Lond.; MRCS Eng. LRCP Lond. 1977; MRCGP 1982; DRCOG 1982. (Roy. Free) Prev: Clin. Asst. (Rheum.) P.ss Margt. Hosp. Swindon; Ho. Surg. Kent & Canterbury Hosp.; Ho. Phys. I. of Thanet Dist. Hosp. Ramsgate.

OWEN-REECE, Mr Aneurin Roy (retired) Hunters Cottage, Houghton, Stockbridge SO20 6LW Tel: 01794 388 8375 — MB BS 1960 Lond.; FRCS Eng. 1964; MRCS Eng. LRCP Lond. 1960. Prev: Regional Med. Off. DSS Birm.

OWEN-REECE, Huw 7A Clarendon Gardens, London W9 1AY Tel: 020 7286 2971 Email: 100676.3673@compuserve.com — MB BS 1988 Lond.; BSc Lond. 1985, MBBS (Hons. Clin. Pharm.) 1988; FRCA 1994. (St. Mary's Hosp.) Specialist Regist. (Anaesth.) Univ. Coll. Lond. Hosps.; Hon. Clin. Asst. (Nat. Hosp. Neurol. & Neurosurg.). Socs: Intens. Care Soc.; Anaesthetic Research Soc.; Anaesthetic Sect., Roy. Soc. Med. Prev: Lect. (Paediat.) UCL, Lond.; SHO (Intens. Care) Nat. Hosp. for Neurol. & Neurosurg. Lond.; SHO (Anaesth.) Centr. Middlx. Hosp. Lond.

OWEN-SMITH, Angela Mary (retired) Richmond House, 3 Old Houghton Road, Hartford, Huntingdon PE29 1YB Tel: 01480 458678 Fax: 01480 458678 — MB BS 1962 Lond.; MRCS Eng. LRCP Lond. 1962; FRCPCH 1997; DCH Eng. 1970. Prev: Cons. Community Paediat. Hinchingbrooke Healthcare NHS Trust.

OWEN-SMITH, Mr Bertram Awelon, Pentregat, Plwmp, Llandysul SA44 6HN Tel: 01239 654202 — MB BS 1950 Lond.; FRCS Eng. 1955; MRCS Eng. LRCP Lond. 1950. (Westm. Hosp. Lond.) Socs: Brit. Assn. Plastic Surg. Prev: Hon. Cons. Plastic & Reconstruc. Surg. Harare, Zimbabwe.

OWEN-SMITH, Brian David 48 Westgate, Chichester PO19 3EU Tel: 01243 786688 Fax: 01243 786688 — MB BChir 1963 Camb.; FRCP Lond. 1984; MRCP (U.K.) 1970; MRCS Eng. LRCP Lond. 1963; DPhysMed Eng. 1970. (Guy's) Cons. (Rheum. & Rehabil.) & Med. Dir. Donald Wilson Ho. Roy. W. Sussex Hosp. (St. Richard's) Chichester; Mem. Vis. Staff King Edwd. VII Hosp. Midhurst. Socs: Hunt. Soc.; Fell Roy. Soc. Med; Heberd. Soc. Prev: Sen. Regist. Roy. Nat. Hosp. Rheum. Dis. Bath & Hon. Lect. Clin.; Pharmacol. Univ. Bath; Lilly Fell. in Clin. Pharmacol. Indiana Univ. Sch. Med., U.S.A.

OWEN-SMITH, Mr Michael Stephen Richmond House, 3 Old Houghton Road, Hartford, Huntingdon PE29 1YB Tel: 01480 458678 Fax: 01480 458678 — MS BS 1962 Lond.; MB BS Lond. 1962; MA Camb. 1987; MD (hons. causa) Linkoping 1993; MS Lond. 1971; FRCS Eng. 1966; FRCS Ed. 1965; MRCS Eng. LRCP Lond. 1962. (Univ. Coll. Hosp.) Cons. Surg., Cromwell Clinic, Huntingdon. Socs: BMA. Prev: Sen. Cons. Surg. Hinchingbrooke Healthcare NHS Trust; Prof. Milit. Surg. RCS Eng. & RAM Coll. Lond.; Cons. Surg. Qu. Alexandra Milit. Hosp. Lond. & ANZUK Milit. Hosp.

OWEN-SMITH, Oliver Gregory Stephen The Spinney, 19 St Johns Avenue, Kidderminster DY11 6AU Tel: 015262 865363 Email: oliver.owen--smith@virgin.net — MB BS 1988 Lond. Cons. Anaesth. Roy. Orthopadic Hosp. Birm. Prev: Specialist Regist. in Anaesth. Leicester.

OWEN-SMITH, Richard John 20 The Russetts, Wakefield WF2 6JF — MB ChB 1993 Leeds.

OWEN-SMITH, Victoria Helen 5 Canterbury Park, Didsbury, Manchester M20 2UQ Tel: 0161 434 5712 Email: ryashleigh@cs.com — MB BS 1986 Lond.; MRCGP 1990; DRCOG 1990; DCH RCP Lond. 1988. (Royal Free Hospital School of Medicine) Specialist Regist. (Pub. Health) Gr. Manch. Train. Consortium.

OWENS, Alan Stephen 29 Hollocombe Road, West Derby, Liverpool L12 0RW — MB ChB 1994 Liverp.

OWENS, Catherine Mary 13 Eyot Gardens, London W6 9TN Tel: 020 8748 6729 — MB BS 1984 Lond.; BSc (Hons.) Lond. 1981, MB BS 1984; MRCP (UK) 1987; FRCR 1991. Cons. Radiol. St. Mary's Hosp. Lond. Socs: BMA. Prev: Fell. (Diag. Radiol.) HSC Toronto, Canada; Sen. Regist. (Diag. Radiol.) Middlx. & Univ. Coll. Hosps. Lond.; Regist. (Diag. Radiol.) Roy. Free Hosp. Lond.

OWENS, Christopher Thomas 7 Berkeley Road, Talbot Woods, Bournemouth BH3 7JL Tel: 01202 529606 Fax: 01202 242986 Email: 106515.3374@compuserve.com — MB BCh BAO 1982 NUI; DCM Beijing 1998. (University of Cork National University of Ireland) GP Traditional Chinese Med.; Gerson Ther. Practitioner. Socs: Primary Care Rheum. Soc.; Brit. Hyperlipid. Assn.; Chinese Med. Assn. Prev: Chef de Clinique Med. Hopital Ambroise Pare Paris.

OWENS, Christopher William Instone Dept. of Clinical Phaumacology, UCL School of Medicine, 5 University Street, London WC1E Tel: 020 7387 9300 Ext: 8339 Email: c.owens@ucl.ac.uk; 24 Pembridge Mews, London W11 3EQ — MB BS 1969 Lond.; BSc Wales 1961; PhD Lond. 1965, MB BS (Hons. Med.) 1969; FRCP Lond. 1989; MRCP (UK) 1971; FFPM RCP (UK) 1993. (Univ. Coll. Hosp.) Sen. Clin. Lect. (Clin. Pharmacol.) & Hon. Cons. Univ. Coll.

OWENS

Hosp. Lond. Prev: Lect. (Clin. Med.) & Ho. Phys. Med. Unit Univ. Coll. Hosp. Lond.; SHO Hammersmith Hosp.

OWENS, Colum Gerard 11 Strandview Street, Belfast BT9 5FF — MB BCh 1998 Belf.; MB BCh Belf 1998.

OWENS, Daniel Francis 16 Buckmaster Road, London SW11 1EN — MB BS 1987 Tasmania.

OWENS, David Morlais, Dwyran, Llanfairpwllgwyngyll LL61 6BJ Tel: 01248 430588 — MB ChB 1967 Liverp.; MB ChB (1st cl. Hons.) Liverp. 1967; MD Liverp. 1975; FRCP Lond. 1984; MRCP (UK) 1970. Cons. Phys. Gwynedd Hosp. Bangor. Socs: Brit. Soc. Gastroenterol. Prev: Cons. Phys. Walton Hosp. Liverp.; Regist. (Med.) Roy. Free Hosp. Lond.; Wellcome Research Fell. Liverp. Univ.

OWENS, Professor David Griffith Cunningham The University Department of Psychiatry, Kennedy Tower, Royal Edinburgh Hospital, Morningside Park, Edinburgh EH10 Tel: 0131 537 6262 Fax: 0131 537 6291 Email: david .owens@ed.ac.uk; Tel: 0131 662 1967 Email: dundyvan@aol.com — MD 1986 Glas.; MB ChB 1972 Glas; FRCP 1988; MRCP (U.K.) 1975; FRCPsych. 1989, M 1976. (Univ. Glas.) Prof. of Clin. Psychiat., Univ. Edin. & Hon. Cons. Psychiat. Roy. Edin. Hosp. Prev: Sen. Lect. (Psychiat.) Univ. Edin. & Hon. Cons. Psychiat. Roy. Edin. Hosp.; Cons. Psychiat. N.wick Pk. Hosp. Harrow; Mem. Scientif. Staff MRC.

OWENS, Professor David Raymond Diabetes Research Unit Academic Centre, Cardiff & Vale NHS Trust, Penlan Road, Penarth CF64 2XX Tel: 02920 716928 Fax: 02920 350147 Email: owensdr@cf.ac.uk — MB BCh 1966; MD Wales 1985; MRCP (UK) 1994; CBiol 1993, MIBiol 1986; FRCP. (Cardiff) Cons. Diabetologist; Prof. Socs: Fell. Roy. Soc. Med.; Brit. Pharm. Soc.; Fell.Inst. of Biol. Prev: Sen. Lect. (Med.) Univ. Wales Coll. Med. Cardiff; Lect. (Med.) Univ. Wales Coll. Med. Cardiff; Head Cardiovasc. & Metab. Research Ciba-Geigy Basle, Switz.

OWENS, David Wallace Division of Psychiatry, University of Leeds School of Medicine, 15 Hyde Terrace, Leeds LS2 9LT — MB ChB 1979 Leeds; BSc (Psychol.) Leeds 1976, MD 1990; MRCPsych 1983. Sen. Lect. (Psychiat.) Univ. Leeds; Hon. Cons. Psychiat. Leeds Community & Ment. Health Servs. NHS Trust. Prev: Lect. (Psychiat.) Univ. Leeds; Sen. Regist. (Psychiat.) Nottm. HA; Regist. (Psychiat.) Nottm. HA.

OWENS, Eifion Pryce 11 Windsor Road, Radyr, Cardiff CF15 8BQ Tel: 0161 773 9121 Fax: 0161 707 7430 — MB ChB 1967 Birm.; FRCPsych 1993, M 1973; DPM Eng. 1971. Clin. Lect. (Psychiat.) Univ. Manch. Socs: Foundat. Mem. Turning Point; Roy. Coll. Psychiat. (Subst. Misuse Sect.); Soc. for Addic. Prev: Cons. Psychiat. Alcoholism Treatm. Wentworth Hse. Eccles; Research Assoc. & Lect. (Psychiat.) Univ. Manch.; Sen. Regist. (Psychiat.) Univ. Hosp. S. Manch.

***OWENS, Miss Elisabeth Joy Clare** 36 Spring View Road, Sheffield S10 1LS Tel: 0114 268 0018 — MB ChB 1997 Sheff.

OWENS, Ellis Wynn Doctors Surgery, Glanfa, Orme Road, Bangor LL57 1AY Tel: 01248 370540 Fax: 01248 370637 — MB BCh 1976 Wales; BSc (Hons.) Wales 1973, MB BCh 1976.

OWENS, Gareth Wyn Bron Seiont Surgery, Bron Seiont, Segontium Terrace, Caernarfon LL55 2PH Tel: 01286 672236 Fax: 01286 676404; Y Gilfach, 4 Pen y Bryn, Caernarfon LL55 2YT Tel: 01286 673095 — MB BCh 1977 Wales; MRCGP 1988. (University Hospital Wales Cardiff)

OWENS, Geraint Griffith 66 Ffordd Glyn, Coed y Glyn, Wrexham LL13 7QW — BM BCh Wales 1970; FRCP Lond. 1992; MRCP (UK) 1975; FRCPCH 1997; DCH Eng. 1972. Paediat. Maelor Hosp. Wrexham.

***OWENS, Hazel Suzanne** 19 Shaw Road, Royton, Oldham OL2 6DA — MB ChB 1998 Manch.; MB ChB Manch 1998.

OWENS, Jane Mary The Surgery, Dedham Road, Ardleigh, Colchester CO7 7LD Tel: 01206 230224 Fax: 01206 231602 — MB BS 1980 Lond.; BSc Lond. 1977; MRCGP 1984; DRCOG 1983.

OWENS, Jennifer Lindsay 40 Poll Hill Road, Wirral CH60 7SW — MB ChB 1996 Liverp.

OWENS, John 56 Trumpington Street, Cambridge CB2 1RG Tel: 01223 61611 Fax: 01223 356837; 11 Clarendon Road, Cambridge CB2 2BH Tel: 01223 62760 — MB BS 1959 London; MRCGP 1975; DCH Eng. 1962. (St. Bart.) Med. Adviser Camb. Univ. Press; Med. Off. Electronic Indust. Camb.; Hon. Med. Off. Camb. Univ. Rugby Club & Tennis Club; Clin. Teach. Fac. Clin. Med. Univ. Camb. Socs: Pres. Camb. Med. Soc.

OWENS, John 2 Hollyfield Drive, Sutton Coldfield B75 7SF — MB ChB 1951 Glas.; DPM Eng. 1957. (Univ. Glas.) Socs: Fell. Roy. Soc. Med.; Roy. Med. Psych. Assn.

OWENS, John Raymond Macclesfield DGH, Victoria Rd, Macclesfield SK10 3BL Tel: 01625 661301 Fax: 01625 663055 Email: jowens@echeshire-tr.nwest.nhs.uk; 44 Ryles Park Road, Macclesfield SK11 8AH Tel: 01625 262335 — MB ChB 1969 Manch.; FRCP Lond. 1994; Dip. Hlth Mgt. Keele 1995; DCH Eng. 1972; FRCPCH 1997. (Manch.) Cons. Paediat. Macclesfield Dist. Socs: Brit. Assn. Community Child Health; Manch. Med. Soc. Prev: SCMO Liverp. AHA; Lect. (Child Health) Univ. Liverp.; Med. Superintendent Hôpital Yoseki, Zaire.

OWENS, Julie Fleming Noffield Unit, Burdon Terrace, Jesmond NE2 3AE; Email: richardsmith@ukgateway.net — MB BS 1992 Newc.; MRCPsych 1997. Specialist Child & Adolesc. Psychiat.; Specialist Regist. (Child & Adolesc. Psychiat.) Newc. Socs: Roy. Coll. Psychiat.

***OWENS, Kelly Elizabeth** 23 Clayford Cr, Liverpool L14 1PE — MB ChB 1997 Leeds.

OWENS, Lucy Alexandra Apsley House, Thicket Grove, Maidenhead SL6 4LW — MB ChB 1997 Bristol.

OWENS, Owen Joseph David BUPA Hospital Harpenden, Ambrose Lane, Harpenden AL5 4BP Tel: 01582 763191 Fax: 01582 712312; 12 Birch Way, Harpenden AL5 5TP Tel: 01582 760045 — MB BCh BAO 1980 NUI; MD Dub. 1991; MRCPI 1988; LRCPI & LM, LRCSI & LM 1980; MRCOG 1986; DCH NUI 1983. (Ireland) Cons. O & G Luton & Dunstable NHS Trust. Socs: Brit. Soc. Colpos. & Cerv. Path.; Brit. Gyn. Cancer Soc. Prev: Sen. Regist. (O & G) Gtr. Glas. HB; Hon. Regist. Gtr. Glas. HB; Clin. Research Fell. (Biochem.) Glas. Univ.

OWENS, Patricia Margaret Clinical Skills Resource, 2nd Floor E Block Centre, Old Infirmary, 70 Pembroke Place, Liverpool L69 3EF Tel: 0151 794 8235 Email: p.owens@liv.ac.uk — MB ChB 1979 Ed.; FRCGP 1998. Director. Clin. Skills Resource Centre. Univ. of Liverp. Prev: Princip. In Gen. Pract. Lache Health Centre Chester.

***OWENS, Paul James** 12 Broughton Gardens, Ravenhill Road, Belfast BT6 0BB — MB BCh BAO 1996 Belf.

***OWENS, Rachel Elizabeth** 220 Cyncoed Road, Cardiff CF23 6RS — MB BCh 1997 Wales.

***OWENS, Rebecca Wynne** 220 Cyncoed Road, Cyncoed, Cardiff CF23 6RS — BM 1996 Soton.

OWENS, Robert Paul Fairwater Health Centre, Plasmawr Road, Fairwater, Cardiff CF5 3JT Tel: 029 2056 6291 Fax: 029 2057 8870; 65 River Glade, Gwaelod-y-Garth, Cardiff CF15 9SP — MB BS 1983 Lond.; MA Camb. 1984; MRCGP 1988; DRCOG 1987. (Princip. - Gen. Pract) Socs: Roy. Coll. Gen. Practs. (Treas. SE Wales Fac.); BMA; S. Glam. Youth Princips. Gp. Prev: Trainee GP Nevill Hall Hosp. Abergavenny VTS; SHO (Gen. Med. & Geriat.) Merthyr Gen. & P. Chas. Hosps. Merthyr Tydfil; Ho. Phys. Co. Hosp. Hereford.

***OWENS, Stephen** 64 Archway Road, Huyton, Liverpool L36 9XE — MB ChB 1998 Ed.; MB ChB Ed 1998.

OWENS, Valerie Barbara 12 Birch Close, Oxton, Birkenhead CH43 5XE — MB ChB 1986 Manch. Clin. Asst. (Med. for Elderly) St. Catherine Hosp. Birkenhead.

OWENS, Mr William Andrew Department of Cardiothoracic Surgery, Freeman Hospital, High Heaton, Newcastle upon Tyne NE7 7DN Tel: 0191 284 3111 Fax: 0191 223 1175 Email: andrew.owens@ncl.ac.uk — MB BCh BAO 1990 Belf.; MB BCh BAO (Hons.) Belf. 1990; FRCS Eng. 1994; FRCSI 1994.

OWER, David Cheyne, TD (retired) 94 Coombe Lane W., Kingston upon Thames KT2 7DB Tel: 020 8942 8552 — MB BS Lond. 1954; FFPHM 1983, M 1976; DObst RCOG 1959. Lt.-Col. RAMC (TA). Prev: Sen. PMO Dept. Health & Social Security.

OWERS, Deborah Louise 5 Menlo Close, Oxton, Birkenhead CH43 9YD — MB BS 1985 Lond. (St. Mary's) SHO (Paediat.) Centr. Middlx. Hosp. Lond. Prev: Trainee GP Lond.; SHO (O & G) Hillingdon Hosp. Lond.; SHO (Geriat. Med.) Moriston Hosp, Swansea.

OWERS, Fred Max 5 Menlo Close, Birkenhead CH43 9YD Tel: 0151 652 2939 — MB BS 1952 Lond. (St. Mary's) Socs: (Pres.) Birkenhead Med. Soc. Prev: Clin. Asst. Ment. Handicap Wirral HA; Med. Off. Mobil Oil Co.; SHO (Med.) Walton Hosp. Liverp.

OWERS, Malca H (retired) 9 Brancote Court, Brancote Road, Birkenhead L43 Tel: 0151 652 2920 — MD 1924 Hamburg. Prev: Res. Ho. Phys. Birkenhead & Wirral Childr. Hosp.

OWERS, Russell Cameron, Lt.-Col. RAMC Garrison Medical Centre, Willoughby Road, Larkhill SP4 8QY Tel: 01980 845423 Fax: 01980 845056; 49 Clayfields Lane, Wentworth, Rotherham S62 7TD Tel: 01226 745486, 01980 597702 Email: cathy@collinson.freeserve.co.uk, russellowers@doctors.org.uk — MB BS 1987 Lond.; MA Camb. 1987, BA 1983; MRCGP 1993; DRCOG 1992. Princip. GPGMC Larkhill, Wilts S.M.D.; GP Trainer. Prev: Regt. Med. Off. 1 R.Irish BFPO 53; Trainee GP/SHO BMH BFPO 24; RMO 4/7 DG BFPO 41 & 3RGJ Colchester & IR Ang. Colchester.

OWINO, Edwin Walter James 235 Hampden Way, Southgate, London N14 7LD Tel: 020 8368 4157 Fax: 020 8368 7192 — MB ChB 1976 Nairobi; MRCPsych 1981; DPM Eng. 1980.

OWLETT, Ralph c/o Barclays Bank, 54 Lombard St., London EC3 — MRCS Eng. LRCP Lond. 1942. (St. Bart.) Socs: BMA. Prev: Capt. RAMC; Ho. Surg. Mt. Vernon Hosp. & Radium Inst. N.wood.

OWSTON, Ethel Winifred Wells (retired) Afton Cottage, Berks Hill, Chorleywood, Rickmansworth WD3 5AJ Tel: 01923 283708 — MB ChB Sheff. 1943; DObst RCOG 1949. Prev: Med. Off. Family Plann. Assn. Caryl Thomas Clinic Harrow.

OWUSUANSA, Ntow 3 Royal Lodge Gardens, Purdysburn Road, Belfast BT8 7YS — Lekarz 1970 Warsaw.

OXBORROW, Neil Jeffrey 14 Lidgett Park Grove, Leeds LS8 1HW — MB ChB 1991 Leeds.

OXBORROW, Susan Mary Prentice Building, Langdon Hospital, Dawlish EX7 0NR — MB BS 1985 Lond.; DTM & H RCP Lond. 1992. Prev: Asst. Dir. Lepra Eval. Project Chilumba, Malawi; Regist. (Genitourin. Med.) Bristol Roy. Infirm.; SHO (Med.) Roy. Devon & Exeter Hosp.

OXBURY, John Michael (retired) Felstead House, 23 Banbury Road, Oxford OX2 6NX Tel: 01865 558532 Fax: 01865 558532 Email: johnoxbury@aol.com — MB BChir 1964 Camb.; MA Oxf. 1972; MA, PhD Camb. 1962, MB 1964, BChir 1963; FRCP Lond. 1979; MRCP (U.K.) 1970. Cons. Neurol. (Private Practioner Only) at The Cromwell Hosp., Lond. SW5 0TU and The Acland Hosp., Oxf. OX2 6NX; Hon. Consg. NeUrol. to the Oxf. Radcliffe Hosp.s. Prev: Ment. Health Research Fund Sen. Research Fell. & Hon. Sen. Regist. (Neurol.) United Oxf. Hosps.

OXBY, Alison Diane Dept. O and G, Ashington Hospital, West View, Ashington NE63 0SA Tel: 01670 521212 Ext: 2240; 15 Barnard Road, Leigh on Sea SS9 3PH — MB BS 1989 Lond.; MRCGP 1994. p/t Lead Clinician, Reproductive and Sexual Health, N.umbria NHS Trust; Locum Gen. Practitioner, Seaton Hirst Primary Care Centre, Ashington; Mem. of Indep. Advis. Gp. Teenage Pregn. Unit, Dept. Of Health. Prev: Civil. Med. Practitioner.

***OXBY, Claire Louise** Squirrel Walk, Winder, Frizington CA26 3UH — MB ChB 1995 Manch.

OXENBURY, Julia Lynne Woodbridge Hill Surgery, 1 Deerbarn Road, Guildford GU2 8YB Tel: 01483 562230 Fax: 01483 452442; Hillerton House, Chandlers Lane, Yateley GU46 7SR Tel: 01252 860637 — MB BS 1978 Lond.; MRCGP 1983; DRCOG 1983; DCH RCP Lond. 1982; FRCGP 1997; M.Med. Dund. 1998. GP Tutor Frimley Pk. Hosp.

OXENHAM, Helen Caroline Western General Hospital, Crewe Road, Edinburgh EH4 2XU Tel: 0131 537 1000; 91 Mayfield Road, Edinburgh EH9 3AQ Tel: 0131 667 3530 — MB ChB 1989 Ed.; MRCP (Ed.) 1992. SHO (Gen. Med.) Lothian HB; Specialist Regist. (Cardiol.) W.ern Gen. Hosp. Edin. Prev: Staff Grade (Cardiol.) Roy. Infirm. Edin.; Ho. Off. & SHO (Renal) Roy. Infirm. Edin.

OXFORD, Peter Christopher Jude Doctors Surgery, 2 Danson Crescent, Welling DA16 2AT Tel: 020 8303 4204 Fax: 020 8298 1192; 12 Avery Hill Road, New Eltham, London SE9 2BD Tel: 020 8850 1804 Fax: 020 8850 4993 — MB BS 1981 Newc.; DRCOG 1984. (Newcastle uponTyne)

OXLEY, Charles Falcon Sterry Attleborough Surgeries (Station Road), Station Road, Attleborough NR17 2AS Tel: 01953 452394 Fax: 01953 453569 — MB BS 1968 Lond.; MRCS Eng. LRCP Lond. 1968; DObst RCOG 1971. (St. Thos.) Prev: Sen. Ho. Surg. Norf. & Norwich Hosp.; Ho. Surg. St. Thos. Hosp. Lond.

OXLEY, Jolyon Rawson 17 Shirley Road, London W4 1DD Tel: 0870 321 1753 Email: contact@ncssd.org.uk — MB BChir 1972 Camb.; MA Camb. 1973; FRCP Lond. 1991; MRCP (UK) 1973; MRCS Eng. LRCP Lond. 1971. (Univ. Camb. & St. Bart. Hosp. Lond.) Hon. Phys. Nat. Soc. for Epilepsy; Hon. Sec., Nat. Counselling Serv. for Sich Doctors (NCSSD). Prev: Hon. Sen. Lect. Inst. Neurol. Lond..; Sec. Standing Comm. Postgrad. Med. & Dent. Educat. (SCOPME) (1990-1999); Exec. Director, Acad. of Med. Sci. 1999-2000.

OXLEY, Jonathan David Dept of Cellular Pathology, Southmead Hospital, Westbury-on-Trym, Bristol BS10 5NB Tel: 0117 959 5623 Fax: 0117 959 0191; 5D Chertsey Road, Redland, Bristol BS6 6NB Email: jon@jon-oxley.freeserve.co.uk — MB BS 1993 Lond.; BSc Lond. 1990; Dip. Royal Coll. Of Pathologists 1999. (St. Bartholomews, Lond.) Specialist Regist. (Histopath.) S.mead Hosp. Bristol. Prev: Specialist Regist. (Histopath) Brist. Roy. Infirm.; Regist. (Histopath.) S.mead Hosp. Bristol; SHO (Histopath.) UMDS Lond.

OXLEY, Vernon Ernest Pathology Laboratory, Princess Alexandra Hospital, Hamstel Road, Harlow CM20 1QX Tel: 01279 827035 Fax: 01279 416846; Tel: 01279 659711 — MB BS 1970 Newc.; MRCP (U.K.) 1974; MRCPath 1979. (Newcastle-upon-Tyne) Cons. Haemat. P.ss Alexandra Hosp. Harlow. Prev: Sen. Regist. (Haemat.) Roy. Infirm. Bristol; Regist. (Haemat.) Lond. Hosp.; Regist. (Paediat. & Gen. Med.) St. Margts. Hosp. Epping.

OXTOBY, Alison Ella 24 Park Road, Bebington, Wirral CH62 4UT — MB ChB 1983 Leic. SHO (Psychiat.) Sefton Gen. Hosp. Liverp. Socs: Sec. Assn. Liverp. Psychiat. in Train.; Assoc. Mem. Liverp. Med. Inst. Prev: Ho. Surg. Roy. Halifax Infirm.; Ho. Phys. Newsham Gen. Hosp. Liverp.

OXTOBY, John William Chy An Drea, Moss Hill, Stockton Brook, Stoke-on-Trent ST9 9NW — MB ChB 1984 Ed.; MRCP (UK) 1990.

OXTOBY, Julie Dawn Chy-an-Drea, Moss Hill, Stockton Brook, Stoke-on-Trent ST9 9NW — BM 1988 Soton.

OXTOBY, Sarah Jane 10 Wallaford Road, Buckfastleigh TQ11 0AR — BM 1993 Soton.

OXYNOS, Costas 12 Ridgway Gardens, Lymm WA13 0HQ; 1 Arch Makarios Are C, Flat 104, Aglanjia 2107, Nicosia, Cyprus — MB BS 1994 Lond. SHO (Med.) Whittington Hosp. Manch. Prev: SHO (Med. & Cardiol.) Chase Farm Hosp. Lond.; SHO (c/o Elderly) Enfield Community Care Trust & Chase Farm Hosp.; Ho. Off. (Surg. & Med.) King's Coll. Hosp. Lond.

OYAIDE, Onajite Mavis 41 Old Farm Road, Birmingham B33 9HH Tel: 0121 784 5403 Fax: 0121 784 5403 — MB ChB 1997 Liverp. SHO Merseyside Paediat. Roatation Scheme. Aug 1998 - Aug 2000. Prev: Pre-Regist. Ho. Off., Fazakerley Hosp., Aintree.

OYARZABAL AMIGO, Mr Manuel Fernando Flat 2, 163 Marine Parade, Brighton BN2 1EJ Tel: 01273 687392 Email: m.oyarzab@tald21.com — LMS 1983 Santander; FRCS (Otol.) Ed. 1995; CST (Otolaryngol) Gen. Med. Counc 1994; FRCS (ORL); Intercollegiate Examination in Otolaryngology; Nov 1997. Specialist Regist. (otolaryngol) Guys Hosp. St Thomas Hosp & Kings Coll. Hosp. Lond.; Regist. Rotat. (Otolaryngol.) KCH Lond. & Roy. Sussex Co. Hosp. Brighton; Specialist Regist. (Otolaryn) Univ. Hosp. Lewisham Lond.; TWJ Fell. (Otolaryngol) Groote Schuur Hosp, Cape Town, S. Africa. Prev: SHO (Otolaryngol.) King's Coll. Hosp. Lond. & Roy. Sussex Co. Hosp.

OYEBODE, Babatunde Oyedeji Shaftesbury Clinic, Springfield Hospital, 61 Glenburnie Road, London SW17 7DJ Tel: 020 8682 6067 Fax: 020 8772 4345 Email: doyebode@sw1stg-tr.nhs.uk — MB BS 1980 Benin, Nigeria; MPhil Ed. 1993; MRCPsych 1987; Dip. Criminol. Lond. 1991. Cons. Forens. Psychiat. S. W. Lond. and St. Geo.'s Ment. Health NHS Trust; Hon. Sen. Lect. St. Geo. Hosp. Med. Sch. Univ. Lond. Prev: Sen. Regist. Rotat. (Forens. Psychiat.) Maudsley Hosp.; Sen. Regist. Rotat. (Psychiat.) N.. Region; Regist. & SHO (Psychiat.) Roy. Edin. Hosp.

OYEBODE, Professor Oluwafemi Akinwunmi Queen Elizabeth Psychiatric Hospital, Mindelsohn Way, Edgbaston, Birmingham B15 2QZ Tel: 0121 627 2999 Fax: 0121 627 2855 Email: femi.oyebode@sbaht.wmids.nhs.uk — MB BS 1977 Ibadan; MD Newc. 1989; FRCPsych 1996, M 1983; T(Psych) 1991; PhD Wales 1998. (Ibadan, Nigeria) Cons. Psychiat. Qu. Eliz. Psychiat. Hosp. Birm.; Med. Dir.; Prof. Univ. Birm. Socs: Fell. Roy. Soc. Med.; Birm. Med. Inst. Prev: Sen. Clin. Lect. Univ. of Birm.; Cons. Psychiat. John Conolly Hosp. Birm.; Sen. Regist. Roy. Vict. Infirm. Newc. u. Tyne.

OYEDE, Christopher Abolarinwa Psychiatric Rehab Unit, 1 Woodside, Downing Close, Knowle, Solihull B93 0QA — MB BS 1980 Ibadan; DPM RCPSI 1995. (Coll. of Med. UCH Ibadan Nigeria) Staff Psychiat. Dept. Psychiat. Vict. Hosp. Blackpool; Sen. Clin. Med.

OYEDIRAN

Off. (Psychiat.). Prev: Regist. Drug & Alocohol Unit Colchester, The Lakes Ment. Health Centre & Colchester Gen. Hosp.; Regist. Linden Centre Broomfield Gen. Hosp. Chelmsford.

OYEDIRAN, Muriel Ayodeji Flat 9, The Grange, The Knoll, Ealing, London W13 8JJ — MB BS 1965 Lond.; MRCS Eng. LRCP Lond. 1965.

OYELEYE, Mr Abiola Olatunbosun c/o Eye Department, James Paget Hospital, Lowestoft Road, Gorleston, Great Yarmouth NR31 6LA Tel: 01493 452648; 55 Gainsborough Drive, Gunton, Lowestoft NR32 4NJ Tel: 01502 518752 — MB BS 1987 Lagos, Nigeria; FRCOphth 1994. Staff Grade (Ophth.) James Paget Hosp. Gt. Yarmouth. Prev: Regist. (Ophth.) Roy. Infirm. Edin.; SHO Worthing Hosp.; SHO (Ophth.) E. Surrey Hosp.

OYESANYA, Olufunso Abiodun 16 Dunster Way, Harrow HA2 9PN — MB BS 1979 Ibadan; MRCOG 1988; FICS 1990.

OYSTON, Mr John Kenneth (retired) 7 Heath Gardens, Halifax HX3 0BD Tel: 01422 363272 — MB BS 1948 Durh.; FRCS Eng. 1955. Prev: Cons. Orthop. Surg. RAF & Halifax Roy. Infirm.

OYSTON, Margaret Greville (retired) 11 Alexandra Road, Epsom KT17 4BH Tel: 01327 23005 — MB BS 1948 Lond.; MRCS Eng. LRCP Lond. 1948; DObst RCOG 1949.

OZA, Amit Manulal Department of Medical Oncology, St. Bartholomew's Hospital, London EC1A 7BE Tel: 020 7601 7462; 14 Broadmead Road, Woodford Green IG8 0AY — MB BS 1983 Lond.; BSc (Hons.) Lond. 1980, MB BS 1983; MRCP (UK) 1986. (St. Bart.) ICRF Research Fell./Hon. Sen. Regist. (Med. Oncol.) St. Bart. Hosp. Lond. Prev: Regist. (Med.) Whipps Cross Hosp. Lond.; Resid. Med. Off. Nat. Heart Hosp. Lond.; SHO (Med. Rotat.) Ch.ill Hosp. & Radcliffe Infirm. Oxf.

OZA, Nandu Health Care Complex, 52 Low Moor Road, Kirkby in Ashfield, Nottingham NG17 3EE Tel: 01623 752312 Fax: 01623 723700; 5 Sheepwalk Lane, Ravenhead, Nottingham NG15 9FD Tel: 01623 793223 — MB BS 1966 Bombay; BSc Bombay 1960; DA Eng. 1970. (Grant Med. Coll.) Clin. Asst. (Anaesth.) Mansfield Gp. of Hosps. Prev: Regist. (Anaesth.) Mansfield & Dist. Hosp.; SHO (Anaesth.) Sheff. RHB; SHO (Cas.) Chesterfield Roy. Hosp.

OZA, Piush Health Care Complex, 52 Low Moor Road, Kirkby in Ashfield, Nottingham NG17 3EE Tel: 01623 752312 Fax: 01623 723700; 4 Darleydale Close, Berry Hill, Mansfield NG18 4TW Tel: 01623 633272 — MB ChB 1984 Leic.; DRCOG 1988.

***OZCAN, Kamile** 32 Howard Road, London N16 8PU — BM BS 1994 Nottm.

OZCARIZ EIZAGUIRRE, Jose Manuel 85 Mackenzie Road, London N7 8QY — LMS 1990 Basque Provinces.

OZDEMIR, Joanne (Vernon) Brywffynon Child & Family Centre, Pontypridd; 17 Heol Fair, Llandaf, Cardiff CF5 2EE — MB BCh 1989 Wales; MRCPsych 1998. Specialist Regist.in Child & Adolesc. Psychiat. Univ. of Wales Coll. of Med. Socs: Mem. Roy. Coll. of Psychiat.s.

OZUA, Christopher Irabor 12 Miller Road, Chalk, Gravesend DA12 4TP — MB BS 1988 Benin. (Benin, Nigeria) SHO (Psychiat.) Greenwich Dist. Hosp. Lond. Prev: Med. Off. The Chaucer Hosp. Canterbury; SHO (O & G) Harold Wood Hosp. Romford; SHO (O & G) Doncaster Roy. Infirm. Doncaster.

OZUA, Peter Osezua Dept of Histopathology, Luton Dunstable Hospital, Lewey Road, Luton Tel: 01582 497532; 152 Edgware Way, Edgware HA8 8JY Tel: 020 8621 3290 Fax: 020 8905 3728 Email: osezua@aol.com — MB BS 1982 Benin, Nigeria; DRC Path 1997; MRCPath 1998. Cons.(Histopat). Luton & Dunstable Hosp. Luton. Socs: Path. Soc. Prev: Specialist Regist. (Histopath.) Univ. Coll. Hosp. UCH Lond.; Specialist Regist. Whittington Hosp. Lond.; Specialist Regist. Roy. Devon & Exeter Hosp. Exeter.

OZUZU, Mr Gilbert Eberegbulam 8 Wellfield Terrace, Cherry Knowle Hospital, Ryhope, Sunderland SR2 0NB — MB BS 1986 Univ. Nigeria; MSc (Adv. Ophth.) Bristol 1992; FRCSI 1994; MRCOphth 1993; DCEH Lond. 1993. Specialist Regist. Rotat. (Ophth.) Roy. Vict. Infirm. Newc. Socs: Med. Protec. Soc. Prev: Regist. (Ophth.) Roy. Vict. Infirm. Newc.; SHO (Ophth.) Coventry & Warwick Hosp. & Bristol Eye Hosp.

***PABARI, Deepak** 490 Summerwood Road, Isleworth TW7 7QZ — BM 1996 Soton.

PABBINEEDI, Raghunath 33 Twmpath, Oswestry SY10 7AQ — MB BS 1980 Andhra.

PABLA, Herbel Singh Bulwell Health Centre, Main Street, Bulwell, Nottingham NG6 8QJ Tel: 0115 977 1181 Fax: 0115 977 1377; 18 Cheviot Road, Long Eaton, Nottingham NG10 4FU Tel: 0115 946 1154 — MB ChB 1983 Manch.; MRCGP 1989; DRCOG 1988; DA (UK) 1986. (Manchester) GP Partner; Clin. Asst. (Anaesth.) 1990. Prev: SHO (Anaesth.) Nottm. HA; SHO (Cas.) N. W.. RHA; Ho. (Surg.) Bolton HA.

PABLOT, Suzanne Mary 136 Glen Gall Road, Woodford Green IG8 0DS — MB BS 1971 Lond.; MRCS Eng. LRCP Lond. 1971; FRCR 1978.

PAC SOO, Chen Knien 11 Claremont Road, Norwich NR4 6SH — MB ChB 1984 Aberd.

PACE, Denise Department of Histopathology, Princess of Wales Hospital, Coity Road, Bridgend CF31 1RQ Tel: 01656 752752 — MB BS 1983 Lond.; MRCPath 1993, D 1994. Cons. Histopath. P. of Wales Hosp. Bridgend. Socs: BMA & Internat. Acad. Path. Prev: Sen. Regist. (Histopath.) Cardiff & Yorks.; Regist. (Histopath.) Grimsby HA; SHO (A & E) Scunthorpe HA.

PACE, Helen Elizabeth Lepton Surgery, Highgate Lane, Lepton, Huddersfield HD8 0HH Tel: 01484 606161; 15 Bilwell, Long Crendon, Aylesbury HP18 9AD — MB ChB 1980 Leeds. Clin. Asst., Accid. and Emerg., Bradford Roy. Infirm.

PACE, Ian Gerard Bourne Galletly Practice Team, 40 North Road, Bourne PE10 9BT Tel: 01778 562200 Fax: 01778 562207 — MB ChB 1985 Birm.; BSc (Physiol. Sci.) Birm. 1982; DRCOG 1992; DCH RCP Lond. 1991. (Birm.) Prev: Dep. Station Med. Off. RAF Cranwell; SHO (Psychiat.) RAF Hosp. Ely VTS; SHO (O & G) Hinchingbrooke Hosp.

PACE, Jacqueline Elizabeth Mount Vernon Hospital, Rickmansworth Road, Northwood HA6 2RN Tel: 01923 826111; 49 The Park, St Albans AL1 4RX — MB BS 1981 Lond.; MRCP (UK) 1984. Cons. Phys. (Elderly) Mt. Vernon Hosp. N.wood.

PACE, Joseph Alfred 367 Eastfield Road, Peterborough PE1 4RD Tel: 01733 52554 — MD 1962 Malta. (Roy. Univ. Malta)

PACE, Nicholas Adrian Department of Anaesthesia, Western Infirmary, Glasgow G12 Tel: 0141 339 2000 — MB ChB 1982 Glas.; MPhil Glas. 1992; MRCP Ed. 1989; FRCA. 1989. Cons. Anaesth. W.ern Infirm. Glas.; Hon. Sen. Lect. Prev: Vis. Asst. Prof. Univ. Texas 1991-92.

PACE, Richard Francis Everett 17 Walpole Road, Teddington TW11 8PJ — MB BS 1991 Lond.

PACE, Thomas, MBE, OStJ Central Surgery, Sussex Road, Gorleston-on-Sea, Great Yarmouth NR31 6QB Tel: 01493 414141 Fax: 01493 656253; Acornfield, Back Lane, Lound, Lowestoft NR32 5NE — MB ChB 1970 Sheff.; MSc (Occupat. Med.) 1981; FFOM RCP Lond. 1994, MFOM 1984, AFOM 1981; MRCGP 1976; DIH Eng. 1981. Dir. N. Sea Med. Centre. Prev: Surg. Cdr. RN.

PACE, Thomas Anastasi, OBE, Col. late RAMC Retd. 28 Cochrane Close, Cochrane St, London NW8 7NS Tel: 020 7722 2387 — MD 1937 Malta; BSc Malta 1934, MD 1937; DPH Eng. 1952. (Royal University of Malta) Socs: BMA; Harv. Soc. Prev: Med. Off. i/c Med. Centre MOD(A) Whitehall; Chief Med. Off. SHAPE; Chief Med. Off. United Nations Force in Cyprus.

PACE-BALZAN, Mr Albert St. John's Hospital, Wood St., Chelmsford CM2 9BG Tel: 012405 440761; Canonfylde, Porters Hall Road, Stebbing, Dunmow CM6 3TB — MRCS Eng. LRCP Lond. 1977; FRCS Eng. 1981; T(S) 1991. Cons. Surg. (ENT) Mid-Essex Hosps. NHS Trust.

***PACEY, Simon Christopher** 143 Elmsleigh Drive, Leigh-on-Sea SS9 3DS — MB BS 1998 Lond.; MB BS Lond 1998.

PACHMAYR, Henry K (retired) 17 Provost Road, London NW3 4ST Tel: 020 7722 5093 — MB BCh 1954 Wales. Prev: Ho. Off. (O & G) Roy. United Hosp. & St. Martin's Hosp. Bath.

PACHMAYR, John (retired) 17 Provost Road, London NW3 4ST Tel: 020 7722 0561 — MB BS Lond. 1951; MRCS Eng. LRCP Lond. 1951.

***PACIFICO, Marc Dominic** Flat 12, Stone House, 9 Weymouth St., London W1W 6DB — MB BS 1997 Lond.

PACIOREK, Paulina Mary X-Ray Department, William Harvey Hospital, Ashford — MB BS 1976 Lond.; MRCS Eng. LRCP Lond. 1976; FRCR 1983; DMRD Eng. 1983. (St. Geo.) Cons. Radiol. Nuclear Med. S.E. Kent HA. Prev: Sen. Regist. (Radiol.) Leic. Roy. Infirm.

PACK, Gordon James (retired) River Mead, Wherwell, Andover SP11 7JS Tel: 01264 860500 — MB BS Lond. 1947; DObst RCOG 1952. Prev: Ho. Phys. Roy. N.. Hosp.

PACK, Helen Margaret High Street Surgery, 15 High Street, Overton, Wrexham LL13 0ED Tel: 01978 710666 Fax: 01978 710494 (Call before faxing); Fairfield, 32 Salop Road, Overton-on-Dee, Wrexham LL13 0EH Tel: 01978 710595 — MB ChB 1982 Liverp.; DA (UK) 1987.

PACK, Mr Mowafaq Yousif Abdul-Maseeh 19 Northfield Avenue, Sudbrook, Lincoln LN2 2FB Tel: 01522 595752 Email: pack@otago.co.uk; 19 Northfield Avenue, Sudbrook, Lincoln LN2 2FB — MB ChB 1976 Mosul; MB ChB Mosul, Iraq 1976; FRCS Glas. 1989. Assoc. Specialist (Orthop.) Co. Hosp. Lincoln. Socs: BOA; Soc. of Hand Surg.; BMA. Prev: Regist. (Plastic Surg.) Univ. Coll. Hosp. Lond.

PACK, Susan Frances Hadwen Medical Practice, Glevum Way Surgery, Abbeydale, Gloucester GL4 4BL Tel: 01452 529933; Holcombe Farm Stable, Painswick, Stroud GL6 6RG — MB BS 1975 Lond.; MRCP (UK) 1978; MRCGP 1984; DRCOG 1977.

PACKARD, Mr Richard Bruce Selig Princess Christian's Hospital, 12 Clarence Road, Windsor SL4 5AG Tel: 01753 853121 Fax: 01753 831185 Email: eyequack@msn.com; 96 Harley Street, London W1N 1AF Tel: 020 7935 9555 — MD 1979 Lond.; MB BS 1970; FRCS Eng. 1977; FRCOphth. 1990; DO RCS Lond. 1975. (Middlx. Hosp.) Cons. Ophth. Surg. P. Chas. Eye Unit King Edwd. VII Hosp. Windsor. Socs: Internat. Mem. Amer. Acad. Ophth.; Amer. Soc. Cataract & Refractive Surg. Prev: Sen. Regist. Char. Cross Hosp. Lond.; Resid. Surg. Off. Moorfields Eye Hosp. Lond.

PACKARD, Robert Spencer 20 Quick Road, London W4 2BU Tel: 020 8994 6003 Fax: 0870 054 8199 Email: bob@packard.to; 12 Brunswick House, 96 Balcombe St, London NW1 6NG — MB BS Sydney 1951; FFPM RCP (UK) 1989; FRACP 1965, M 1955. Cons. Pharmaceut. Phys. Socs: Fell. Roy. Soc. Med.; Brit. Assn. Pharmaceut. Phys. Prev: Med. Dir. Pfizer Ltd. Sandwich; Phys. Roy. P. Alfred Hosp. Sydney, Austral.; Med. Dir. Pfizer Asia.

PACKE, Geoffrey Edward Department of Medicine, Newham General Hospital, Glen Road, Plaistow, London E13 8SL Tel: 020 7476 4000 Fax: 020 7363 8081 — MD 1989 Liverp.; MB ChB 1978; MRCP (UK) 1981; FRCP 1998. Cons. Phys. Thoracic & Gen. Med. Newham Gen. Hosp. Lond. Socs: Brit. Thorac. Soc. Prev: Sen. Regist. (Thorac. Med.) Aberd. Hosps.; Tutor (Thorac. Med.) Cardiothorac. Inst. & Brompton Hosp.

PACKE, Rosemary Irene (retired) 45 Mount Hermon Road, Woking GU22 7UN Tel: 01483 772662 — MB BS Lond. 1943; MRCS Eng. LRCP Lond. 1942; DCH Eng. 1949. Prev: Asst. Med. Off. Surrey CC.

PACKER, Claire Nancy 60 Dilmore Avenue, Fernhill Heath, Worcester WR3 7XA — BM BS 1983 Nottm.; BMedSci Nottm. 1981; MFPHM RCP (UK) 1994; DCH RCP Lond. 1986. Sen. Lect. (Pub. Health) Univ. Birm. Prev: Sen. Regist. (Pub. Health) N. Worcs. HA; Trainee GP Coventry VTS.

PACKER, Mr Gregory John Department of Orthopaedic Surgery, Southend District General Hospital, Prittlewell Chase, Westcliff on Sea SS0 0RY — MB BS 1983 Lond.; FRCS (Orth.) 1994; FRCS Ed. 1988. Cons. Orthop. Surg. S.end Health Care NHS Trust.

PACKER, John Michael Valentine (retired) 15 Tothill, Shipton under Wychwood, Chipping Norton OX7 6BX Tel: 01993 831113 — MB ChB 1954 Bristol; DPH Liverp. 1958; FFPHM 1981, M 1974. Prev: Cons. Pub. Health Med. (Epidemiol. & Environm. Health) Salford HA.

PACKER, Mary Elizabeth South Cleveland Hospital, Marton Road, Middlesbrough TS4 3BW Tel: 01642 850850; 81 South Parade, Northallerton DL7 8SJ Tel: 01609 777613 — MB ChB 1982 Aberd.; MRCOG 1996; DRCOG 1985; DFFP 1996. Specialist Regist. (O & G) S. Cleveland Hosp. Middlesbrough. Prev: CMO Fam.Plg. Bromley HA, Lond.; Trainee GP Grampian HB; SHO (O & G) Grampian HB.

PACKER, Paul Frederick Church Farm, Church Lane, Brigsley, Grimsby DN37 0RH — MB BS (Hons.) Newc. 1965; FRCR 1975; FFR 1972; DMRD Eng. 1970. (Newc.) Cons. Radiol. St Hugys Hosp. Grimsby. Prev: Cons. (Radiol.) Riyadh Milit. Hosp.; Cons. Radiol. Newc. Gen. Hosp. & Clin. Lect. (Radiol.) Univ. Newc.; Cons. Radiol. Grimsby HA.

PACKER, Timothy Francis 7 Newton House, Newton St Cyres, Exeter EX5 5BL Tel: 01392 851377 — MB BChir 1975 Camb.; BA Camb. 1972, MB BChir 1975; MRCPsych 1982. Cons. Psychiat. Exeter HA.

PACKHAM, Bruce Anthony Woodgate and Packham, Fairfield Surgery, High Street, Burwash, Etchingham TN19 7EU Tel: 01435 882306 Fax: 01435 882064; 18 Wedderburn Road, Willingdon, Eastbourne BN20 9EB Tel: 01323 502035 Fax: 01323 502035 — MB BS 1980 Lond.; DRCOG 1983. (King's Coll.) GP Burwash, E. Sussex. Socs: E.bourne Med. Soc. Prev: Dir. Med. Affairs Rorer Health Care E.bourne; GP E.bourne; Trainee GP E.bourne AHA.

PACKHAM, Christopher John Nottingham City PCT, Linoen House, Beechdale Lane, Nottingham NG8 3EY Tel: 0115 942 8702 Fax: 0115 942 8710 Email: chris.packham@nottingham.ac.uk, chris.packham@nottinghamcity-pct.nhs.uk — FRCP 2001; BM BS 1981 (Hons) Nottm.; FFPHM 2002; MMedSci Nottm. 1991, BMedSci 1979; MRCP (UK) 1984; MFPHM RCP (UK) 1994; MRCGP 1986; DFFP 1993; DRCOG 1986; DCH RCP Lond. 1986. (Nottm.) Director of Pub. Health Nottm. City PCT; Assoc. GP Nottm; Cons. Sen. Lect. (Pub. Health Med.) Nottm. HA & Nottm. Univ. Med. Sch. Socs: Nottm. M-C Soc. Prev: Special Clin. Lect. Nottm. Univ. Med. Sch.; GP Nottm; SHO (Med.) Freeman Hosp. Newc.

PACKHAM, Mr Derek Albert (retired) Foxes Wood, Shrub Lane, Burwash, Etchingham TN19 7ED Tel: 01435 882909 Email: derek.packham@virgin.net — MB BS Lond. 1956; FRCS Eng. 1959; MRCS Eng. LRCP Lond. 1956. Cons. Urol. Cromwell Hosp. Lond. Prev: Cons. Urol. Surg. King's Coll. & Brook Hosp. Lond.

PACKHAM, Gavin Bruce Central Buchan Medical Group, The Surgery, School Street, New Pitsligo, Fraserburgh AB43 6NE Tel: 01771 653205 Fax: 01771 653294 — MB ChB 1988 Aberd.; MRCGP 1992.

***PACKHAM, Iain Nicholas** 7 Priorswood, Compton, Guildford GU3 1DS — BM BS 1996 Nottm.

PACKHAM, Jonathan Charles 28 Silvermead, Worming Hall, Thame, Aylesbury HP18 9JS — BM 1991 Soton.; MRCP (UK) 1994. Specialist Regist. (Rheumatol.) Wexham Pk. Hosp. Slough. Socs: Brit. Soc. Rheum.; BMA; Brit. Soc. Med. (Coun. Young Mem.s Rep. Rheumatol. & Rehabil.).

PACKHAM, Roger Nigel 42 Nairn Road, Canford Cliffs, Poole BH13 7NH — MB BS 1972 Lond.; MRCS Eng. LRCP Lond. 1971; FFA RCS Eng. 1978. (St. Bart.) Cons. Anaesth. Poole Hosp. NHS Trust.; Med. Dir. Poole Hosps. NHS Trust.

PACKMAN, Charles Clifford 5 Seafield Park Road, Hill Head, Fareham PO14 3LT Tel: 01329 663708 — MB BS 1943 Lond.; MRCS Eng. LRCP Lond. 1942. (Middlx.) Socs: BMA & Soton. Med. Soc. Prev: Surg. Lt. RNVR; Resid. Med. Off. & Ho. Surg. Middlx. Hosp.

PACSOO, Tokefat Christian 77 Moor Park Drive, Addingham, Ilkley LS29 0PU Tel: 01943 830670 — MB ChB 1962 Aberd.; DMRD Eng. 1969.

PACTOR, Ronald (retired) 19 Coudray Road, Hesketh Park, Southport PR9 9NL Tel: 01704 537579 — MB ChB 1959 Liverp.

PACYNKO, Michael Kazimierz Meltham Village Surgery, Parkin Lane, Meltham, Huddersfield HD7 3BJ Tel: 01484 850638 Fax: 01484 854891; 3 Lower Hall Road, Lascelles Hall, Huddersfield HD5 0AZ Tel: 01484 420635 Email: 101741.1067@compuserve.com — MB ChB 1985 Leeds.

PADAYACHEE, Munoreedevi 8 Howard Road, Coulsdon CR5 2EA Tel: 020 8668 0336 — MB ChB 1984 Natal; PhD Lond. 1995; Dip. Human & Clin. Genetics Lond. 1990. Clin. Scientist (Molecular Genetics) Inst. Child Health Lond. Socs: Clin. Genetics Soc. Prev: Stud. MRC PhD 1990-95.

PADAYACHEE, Nithiananthan Sathasivan The Village Medical Centre, 20 Braemar Avenue, Neasden, London NW10 0DJ Tel: 020 8450 5405 Fax: 020 8450 1169; 70 Chambers Lane, London NW10 2RN Tel: 020 8451 7623 — LRCPI & LM, LRCSI & LM 1965. (RCSI) Socs: Hon. Fell. RMS. Prev: Div. Surg. St. John Ambul.; Sen. Cas. Off. Hampstead Gen. Hosp.; Hon. Clin. Asst. (O & G) Roy. Free Hosp. Lond.

PADDAY, Ruth The Medical Centre, 24-28 Lower Northam Road, Hedge End, Southampton SO30 4FQ Fax: 01489 799414; Yarrawonga, Brook Lane, Botley, Southampton SO30 2ER Tel: 01489 782783 Fax: 01489 796791 Email: ruthpadday@btinternet.com — BM 1979 Soton.; DRACOG 1985; DCH RCPS Glas. 1984. Teenage Drop-in Centre, Hedge End;

PADDISON

Teenage Drop-in Centre, Hedge End. Prev: GP Perth, W. Austral.; Regist. (Paediat.) Sydney & Perth, Austral.

PADDISON, David John (retired) Field Close, Joiners Road, Linton, Cambridge CB1 6NP Tel: 01223 893222 — MB BS 1946 Lond.; MRCS Eng. LRCP Lond. 1939. Prev: Ho. Surg. (ENT) Char. Cross Hosp.

PADDLE, John Stewart 2 Hast Hill House, Baston Manor Road, Keston BR2 7AH Tel: 020 8462 7575 — BA, MB Camb. 1959, BChir 1958; FFA RCS Eng. 1965. Private Pract. Specialist (Anaesth.). Prev: Cons. Anaesth. Guy's Hosp. Lond.; Sen. Regist. Anaesth. St. Thos. Hosp. Lond.; Regist. Anaesth. Soton. Hosp. Gp. & Hosp. Sick Childr. Gt.

PADDLE, Jonathan James 2 Hast Hill, Baston Manor Road, Keston BR2 7AH — MB BS 1989 Lond.; MRCP (UK) 1994; FRCA 1997. (Guy's Hospital) Specialist Regist. (Anaesth.) S. W.ern Deanery Derriford Hosp. Plymouth.

PADDOCK, Pamela Mary (retired) 113 Park Hall Road, Walsall WS5 3HS Tel: 01922 625726 — MB ChB 1950 Birm.; FRCA Eng. 1958. Prev: Cons. Anaesth. Sandwell AHA & Midl. Centre for Neurosurg. Smethwick.

PADDON, Alexander James The Rectory, Weybourne, Holt NR25 7SY Tel: 01263 70268 — MB BS 1991 Lond.; BSc (Hons.) Lond. 1988.

PADDON, Angela Margaret 22 Bramble Drive, Bristol BS9 1RE — MB BS 1994 Lond.

PADEL, Adam Frederick Department of Cellular Pathology, Stoke Mandeville Hospital, Aylesbury HP21 8AL Tel: 01296 315000; 50 Ellesborough Road, Wendover, Aylesbury HP22 6EL Fax: 01296 315595 Email: adam.padel@smh.nhs.uk — MB BS 1983 Lond.; BSc Lond. 1980; MRCPath 1991; FRCPath, 1999. (King's College, London) Cons. Histopath. Stoke Mandeville Hosp. Aylesbury. Prev: Sen. Regist. (Histopath. & Cytol.) & Regist. (Histopath.) John Radcliffe Hosp. Oxf. & N.ampton Gen. Hosp.; Regist. & SHO (Path.) Wycombe Gen. Hosp. High Wycombe.

PADFIELD, Adrian 351 Fulwood Road, Sheffield S10 3BQ Email: a.padfield@sheffield.ac.uk — MB BS Lond. 1961; FRCA Eng. 1968; DA Eng. 1963. (St. Bart.) Emerit. Cons. Anaesth. Centr. Sheff. Univ. Hosps. NHS Trust; Hon. Clin. Lect. Univ. Sheff. Socs: Fell. Roy. Soc. Med. (Ex-Pres. Sect. Anaesth.); Assn. Anaesth. Of Gt. Brit. & Ire.; (Ex-Pres.) Assn. Dent. Anaesth. Prev: Sen. Regist. (Anaesth.) United Bristol Hosps. & SW RHB; Regist. (Anaesth.) Roy. Free Hosp. Lond.; SHO (Anaesth.) St. Bart. Hosp. Lond.

PADFIELD, Charles James Henry Department of Histopathology, University Hospital, Queens Medical Centre, Nottingham NG7 2UH Tel: 01159709270 Fax: 0115 970 9759 Email: james.padfield@mail.qmcuh.tr.trent.nhs.uk — MB ChB 1977 Manch.; FRCS Eng. 1982; MRCPath 1989. Cons. Fetal & Neonat. Path. Univ. Hosp. Qu. Med. Centre Nottm. Prev: Sen. Regist. Rotat. (Histopath.) Bristol.

PADFIELD, Hazel Jean Lawn Farm, Straight Lane, Staunton, Gloucester GL19 3NX Tel: 01452 840371 Fax: 01452 840371 — MB BS 1971 Newc. Clin. Med. Off. (Community Child Health) Glos.

PADFIELD, Nicholas Leonard Room 8 Lister house, Lister hospital, Chelsea Bridge Road, London SW1W 8RH Tel: 020 7730 4706 Email: padfin@atlas.co.uk; 49 Smith Street, London SW3 4EP — MB BS 1976 Lond.; FFA RCS Eng. 1981. Cons. Anaesth. St. Thos. Hosp. Lond. Socs: Pain Soc.; Internat. Assn. Study of Pain; Ass of Anaethetists GBN1. Prev: Cons. Anaesth. Brook Gen. Hosp. & Greenwich Dist. Hosp. Lond.

PADFIELD, Nigel Norton Whitley The Medical Centre, East Street, Okehampton EX20 1AY Tel: 01837 52233; Upperton, Drewsteignton, Exeter EX6 6PY Tel: 01647 281660 Email: BNMTNP@aol.com — BChir Camb. 1970, MB 1971; MRCP (UK) 1974; DCH RCP Lond. 1972. (St. Mary's) p/t GP Okehampton Devon. Prev: Primary Health Care Adviser Actionaid Lond.; GP Thame.

PADFIELD, Paul Lynch 2/3 Albyn place, Edinburgh EH2 4NG Tel: 0131 226 1770, 0131 537 1716 Fax: 0131 537 1037 Email: paul.padfield@luht.nhs.uk — MB BCh 1970 Wales; FRCP Ed. 1983; MRCP (UK) 1973; MBA 2001. (Cardiff) Cons. Phys. in Endocrinol. & Gen. Med. W.. Gen. Hosp. Edin.; Reader. (Med.) Univ. Edin.; Assoc. Med. Director, Lothian Univ. Hosp.s NHS Trust. Socs: Endocrine Soc. USA & Internat. Soc. Hypertens.

PADGET, Kenneth Isaac (retired) The Jacobean Hsae., Church St., Burton Latimer, Kettering NN15 5LU — MB BS 1949 Lond.; FRCGP 1982, M 1953. Prev: Ho. Surg. St. Peter's Hosp. Chertsey.

***PADGHAM, Katharine Lindsay** Flat 2/R, 21 Hayburn Crescent, Glasgow G11 5AY Tel: 0141 339 6604; The Old Farm House, Norton, Sutton Scotney, Winchester SO21 3NE Tel: 01962 760383 — MB ChB 1997 Glas.

PADGHAM, Michael Richard John Charles The Old Farmhouse, Norton, Sutton Scotney, Winchester SO21 3NE Tel: 01962 760236 — MB BS 1965 Lond.; MRCS Eng. LRCP Lond. 1965; DO Eng. 1968. (Lond. Hosp.)

PADGHAM, Mr Nigel David ENT Department, Kent & Canterbury Hospitals NHS Trust, Ethelbert Road, Canterbury CT1 3NG Tel: 01227 766877; Rayham Farm, Rayham Road, Whitstable CT5 3DZ — MB ChB 1981 Leic.; FRCS Eng. 1988; FRCS Ed. 1987. (Leicester Univ. Med. Sch.) Cons. ENT Surg. E. Kent Hosp.s NHS Trust. Socs: Brit. Soc. Ocologol.; Roy. Soc. Surg.; Scott. Ocologol. Soc.

PADHANI, Anwar Roshanali Mount Vernon Hospital, Rickmansworth Road, Northwood HA6 2RN Tel: 01923 844353 Fax: 01923 844600 Email: anwar@padhani.fsnet.co.uk — MB BS 1985 Mysore; MRCP (UK) 1987; LRCP LRCS Ed. LRCPS Glas. 1984; FRCR 1991. Cons. (Radiol.) and Clin. Lead in MRI, Mt. Vernon Hosp. Lond.; Sen. Lect. Inst. Of Cancer Research; Cons. (Radiol.), The Lond. Clinic, Devonshire Pl. Lond. Prev: Sen. Regist. (Radiol.) Guy's Hosp. Lond.; Regist. (Radiol.) Addenbrooke's Hosp. Camb.; Fell.sh. (Chest Radiol.) John Hopkins Hosp. Baltimore, USA.

PADI, Ruby Koryo Glan Clwyd NHS Trust, Bodelwyddan, Rhyl LL18 5UJ; 2 Archway Cottages, Llanerch Park, St Asaph LL17 0BD — LRCPI & LM, LRSCI & LM 1963; LRCPI & LM, LRCSI & LM 1963; DCH Eng. 1968. (RCSI) Regist. & Clin. Asst. (Anaesth.) Glan Clwyd Hosp. Bodelwyddan; Assoc. Specialist (Anaesth.) Glan. Clwyd Hosp. Bodelwyddam. Socs: BMA; (Pres.) Med. Wom. Federat. (N. Wales Div.); Assn. Anaesth. Prev: Regist. (Paediat.) Warrington Gen. Hosp.; SHO (Cas.) Fulham Hosp. Lond.; SHO (Anaesth.) St. Mary's Hosp. Portsmouth.

PADKIN, Andrew John Royal United Hospital, Combe Park, Bath — MB ChB 1990 Bristol; BSc 1984 (Mech. Engin.) Bristol; MRCP (UK) 1993. Cons. Anaesth., Roy. United Hosp., Bath. Prev: Specialist Regist. Rotat. (Anaesth.) Treliske Hosp. Truro; SHO Rotat. (Anaesth.) Nottm.; SHO Rotat. (Med.) Qu. Med. Centre Nottm.

PADLEY, Noel Richard Oak Walk House, Oak Walk, Hythe CT21 5DN — MB ChB 1968 Birm.; FRCPath 1986, M 1974. Cons. Histopath. SE Kent Health Dist.

PADLEY, Robert George The Surgery, Traingate, Kirton Lindsey, Gainsborough DN21 4DQ Tel: 01652 648214 Fax: 01652 648398; Beckside House, Station Road, Hibaldstow, Brigg DN20 9EA Tel: 01652 659566 Email: rob.padley@ukgateway.net — MB ChB 1989 Sheff.; MRCGP 1993; Cert. Family Plann. JCC 1993; DRCOG 1993. (Sheffield) Socs: BMA. Prev: Trainee GP/SHO Scunthorpe VTS.

PADLEY, Timothy James Dean Cross Surgery, 21 Radford Park Road, Plymstock, Plymouth PL9 9DL Tel: 01752 404743; The Wicket, Elliotts Hill, Brixton, Plymouth PL8 2AG Tel: 01752 880931 Fax: 01752 880987 Email: tim.padley@plymouth.swis.net — BM BCh 1985 Oxf.; MA Oxf. 1987; DA (UK) 1991; DRCOG 1989. Prev: Trainee GP/SHO (Anaesth.) Plymouth VTS.

PADMAKUMAR, Beena 21 Deva Lane, Upton, Chester CH2 1BW Tel: 01244 364712 — MB BS 1992 Bharathiar, India; MRCP (UK) 1994. Regist. (Paediat.) Countess of Chester Hosp. Prev: Regist. (Paediat.) Alder Hey Childr. Hosp. Liverp.

PADMANABHAN, Hariharan (retired) Apple Tree Barn, Woodhouse Road, Todmorden OL14 5RJ — MB BS Nagpur 1956; FFA RCS Eng. 1967; DA Eng. 1963; Dip. Amer. Bd. Anaesth. 1963. Cons. Anaesth. Rochdale NHS Trust. Prev: Cons. Anaesth. Rochdale NHS Trust.

PADMANABHAN, Margaret Helen (retired) Apple Tree Barn, Woodhouse Road, Todmorden OL14 5RJ — MB ChB 1960 Manch.; MRCOG 1967, DObst 1964. Prev: Lect. (O & G) Radcliffe Infirm. Oxf. & Milnrow Health Centre.

PADMANABHAN, Neal Department of Medicine & Therapeutics, Gardiner Institute, Western Infirmary, Dumbarton Road, Glasgow G11 6NT — BM BCh 1993 Oxf.

PADMANATHAN, Chinnathambi King George Hospital, Barley Lane, Goodmayes, Ilford IG3 8YB Tel: 020 8983 8000; Aruna, 15A Manor Road, Chigwell IG7 5PF Tel: 020 8505 9306 — MB BS

1963 Ceylon; FRCR 1975; DMRD Eng. 1974. (Colombo) Cons. Radiol. King Geo. Hosp. Ilford & Barking Hosp.

PADMASRI, Poonati 18 Sydney Road, Woolaton, Nottingham NG8 1LH — MB BS 1988 Osmania U; MRCOG 1994. Post-grad. Stud. Univ. Nottm. Socs: Med. Soc.; BMA. Prev: Regist. Rotat. (O & G) N.W. RHA.

PADMORE, Susan Jane 4 Strathmore Drive, Kirklevington, Yarm TS15 9NS Tel: 01642 785311 — MB ChB 1971 Birm.; DA Eng. 1973. Clin. Asst. (Anaesth.) N. Tees Gen. Hosp. Stockton. Prev: Regist. Rotat. (Anaesth.) Birm. Accid. Hosp. & Selly Oak Hosp. Birm.; SHO (Anaesth.) & Ho. Surg. Selly Oak Hosp. Birm.

PADWELL, Mr Alan Birch Hill Hospital, Rochdale OL12 9QB — MB ChB 1969 Leeds; FRCS Eng. 1975; MRCPath.

PADWELL, Malcolm Anthony (retired) 15 Airedale Quay, Rodley, Leeds LS13 1NZ Tel: 0113 255 0379 Email: malc@mpadwell.freeserve.co.uk — MB ChB 1963 Leeds; Dip. Psychoth. 1983; DObst RCOG 1965. Course Organiser Leeds VTS.

PADWICK, Malcolm Lynn Watford General Hospital, Vicarage Road, Watford WD1 8HP Tel: 01923 244366; BUPA Bushey Hospital, Heathbourne Road, Bushey, Watford WD1 1RD Tel: 020 8950 9090 — MB BS 1980 Lond.; LMSSA Lond. 1980; T(OG) 1991; MD Lond. 1995. (Kings College London) Cons. O & G Watford Gen. Hosp. & Mt. Vernon Hosp. Socs: Brit. Gyn. Oncol. Soc.; Internat. Soc. Gyn. Endoscopy; Brit. Soc. Colpos. & Cerv. Path.

PAES, Alexandre 19 Greaves Sykes Lane, Micklebring, Rotherham S66 7RR Tel: 01709 817150 — LMSSA 1948 Lond. (Grant Med. Coll. Bombay) Socs: BMA. Prev: Ho. Surg. ENT & Eye Dept. Vict. Hosp. Blackpool; Ho. Phys. Leigh Infirm.; Sen. Ho. Off. Orthop. Doncaster Infirm.

PAES, Anthony Rabindranath Radiology Department, Huddersfield Royal Infirmary, Huddersfield HD3 3EA Tel: 01484 342186 Fax: 01484342161; 2 Spring Gardens, Holmfirth, Huddersfield HD9 3RT — MB BS 1978 Lond.; MRCP (UK) 1982; FRCR 1987, M 1984. (Lond. Hosp.) Cons. Radiol. Huddersfield Roy. Infirm.; Roy. Coll. of Radiologists Serv. Review Comm. Socs: Brit. Soc. of Skeletal Radiol.; Magnetic Resonance Radiologists Assn. Prev: Regist. & Sen. Regist. (Radiol.) Soton. Gen. Hosp.; Ho. Off. & SHO Roy. Lond. Hosp.

***PAES, Paul Vincent** 18 Roseworth Crescent, Newcastle upon Tyne NE3 1NR — MB BS 1997 Newc.

PAES, Mr Trevor Rudrah Franco The Hillingdon Hospital, Pield Heath Road, Uxbridge UB8 3NN Tel: 01895 238282 Email: paeshillingdon@cwlite.com — MRCS Eng. LRCP Lond. 1978; MS Lond. 1989; BSc Lond. 1973, MB BS 1978; FRCS Eng. 1982. (Bart's) Cons. (Surg.) Hillingdon & Mt. Vernon NHS Trust; Hon. Cons. (Surg.) Harefield Hosp. NHS Trust; Hon. Sen. Lec. Surg. Imperial coll. Socs: Vasc. Surg. Soc. UK; Assn. Roy. Coll. Sci. Prev: Lect. in Surg. Kings Coll. Hosp.; Hon. Surg. of St Barts Hosp.

PAFFENHOLZ, Michael c/o 117 Waverley Road, Harrow HA2 9RQ — State Exam Med 1993 Bonn.

***PAFFEY, Mark David** 201 Chelmsford Road, Shenfield, Brentwood CM15 8SA — MB ChB 1998 Sheff.; MB ChB Sheff 1998.

PAGADALA, Rama Krishna Rao Health Centre, Station Hill Road, Abertillery NP3 4JG — MB BS 1964 Andhra. (Guntur Med. Coll.) Socs: BMA. Prev: SHO (Gen. Surg.) Stracathro Hosp. Brechin; Regist. (Psychol. Med.) St. And. Hosp. Thorpe; Regist. (Orthop.) Greenock Roy. Infirm.

PAGADALA, Vasundhara The Surgery, 24 High Street, Colliers Wood, London E17 7LD Tel: 020 8542 1483 — MB BS Andhra 1962; DObst RCPI 1970. GP; Sessional Med. Assessor to the Benebits Agency.

PAGAN, Francis Stephen (retired) — MB BChir Camb. 1968; MA Camb. 1972; FRCPath 1987, M 1975. Cons. Microbiol. Darlington Memor. Hosp. Prev: Lect. (Bact.) Middlx. Hosp. Med. Sch. Lond.

PAGAN, William Hugh (retired) The Homestead, Holton, Halesworth IP19 8PN Tel: 01986 872342 — MB BS 1961 Lond.; DA Eng. 1964; DObst RCOG 1963. Prev: GP Clin. Asst. St. Bart. Hosp. Lond.

PAGANO, Kristin Christiania, Arkesden, Saffron Walden CB11 4EY — MB BS 1982 Lond.; MFPM RCP (UK) 1993; DRCOG 1993. (Guy's) Sen. Med. Adviser Cilaq Ltd. High Wycombe Bucks. Prev: Clin. Pharmacol. Beechams Research Div. Betchworth.

PAGDIN, George Hockley (retired) 29 Cranford Drive, Owlthorpe, Sheffield S20 6RP — MB ChB Sheff. 1949; MD Sheff. 1992; FRCGP 1994, M 1968.

PAGDIN, Judith Claire Church Grange Health Centre, Bramblys Drive, Basingstoke RG21 8QN Tel: 01256 329021 Fax: 01256 817466; 9 Beddington Court, Lychpit, Basingstoke RG24 8YZ Tel: 01256 460609 — BM 1981 Soton.; MRCGP 1985; DRCOG 1985. Socs: BMA. Prev: Trainee GP/SHO Basingstoke Dist. Hosp.VTS; Ho. Off. (Med.) W.. Hosp. Soton.; Ho. Off. (Surg.) Basingstoke Dist. Hosp.

PAGE, Mr Albert Brian 4 Old Fort, Helens Bay, Bangor BT19 1LL Email: page@trees.dnet.co.uk — MD 1988 Belf.; MB BCh BAO 1974; FRCS Ed. 1984; MRCGP 1981; DRCOG 1978. Cons. Ophth. Roy. Vict. Hosp. Belf.

PAGE, Alison Jane West Midlands Radiology Rotation City Hospital NHS Trust, Dudley Road, Winson Green, Birmingham B18 7QH Tel: 0121 554 3801 — MB ChB 1992 Birm.; FRCR 1999; BSc (Hons.) (Med. Biochem.) Birm. 1989; MRCP (UK) 1995. (Univ. of Birm. Med. Sch.)

PAGE, Andrew Clive Department of Radiology, Royal Hampshire County Hospital, Romsey Road, Winchester SO22 5DG — MB BS 1981 Lond.; FRCR 1988. (King's Coll.) Cons. Roy. Hants. Co. Hosp. Winchester. Socs: Roy. Coll. of Radiologists; BSIR; CIRSE. Prev: Sen. Regist. Kings Coll. Hosp. Lond.; Regist. Dept. Radiol. Freedom Fields Hosp. Plymouth.; SHO (Med.) N.. Gen. Hosp. Sheff.

PAGE, Anthony Dane Garth, Furness General Hospital, Dalton Lane, Barrow-in-Furness LA14 4LF — MB ChB 1980 Leeds; MRCPsych 1984. Cons. Psychiat. Furness Gen. Hosp. Barrow-in-Furness.

PAGE, Antony John Frederick Dept of Cardiology Norfolk & Norwich Hosp, Brunswick Road, Norwich NR1 3SR Tel: 01603 287516 Fax: 01603 287494 Email: tony.page@norfolk-norwich.thenhs.com; The Chestnuts, 215 Unthank Road, Norwich NR2 2PH Tel: 01603 25001 Fax: 01603 453091 Email: a.j.f.page@stinternet.com — MB BS 1971 Lond.; FRCP Lond. 1992; MRCP (UK) 1974. (Lond. Hosp.) Cons. Phys. & Cardiol. Norf. & Norwich Hosp. Socs: Brit. Cardiac Soc. Prev: Lect. (Cardiol.) Brit. Heart Foundat. Univ. Birm.

PAGE, Arthur Reginald Webster Testvale Surgery, 12 Salisbury Road, Totton, Southampton SO40 3PY; Forelands, Woodlands Drive, Woodlands, Southampton SO40 7HW — MB BS 1952 Lond.; MRCGP 1967. (St. Bart.) Admiralty Surg & Agent. Socs: Soton. Med. Soc. Prev: Ho. Surg. & Ho. Phys. Norf. & Norwich Hosp.; Ho. Surg. (O & G) Gen. Hosp. Soton.

PAGE, Barbara Elizabeth Abbots Cross Medical Practice, 92 Doagh Road, Newtownabbey BT37 9QW; 15 Lenamore Avenue, Jordanstown, Newtownabbey BT37 0PF — MB BCh BAO 1981 Belf.; MRCGP 1985; DRCOG 1984.

***PAGE, Barnaby Mills** Winterwood, Nyetimber Copse, West Chiltington, Pulborough RH20 2NE — MB ChB 1998 Manch.; MB ChB Manch 1998.

PAGE, Carol Susan 4 Bonhard Road, Scone, Perth PH2 6QL — MB ChB 1979 Dundee.

PAGE, Carolyn Jane Hathaway Surgery, 32 New Road, Chippenham SN15 1HR Tel: 01249 447766 Fax: 01249 443948; Godley's Farm House, Avon, Chippenham SN15 4LS — MB BS 1961 Lond.

PAGE, Catherine Ann 60 Hermiston, Currie EH14 4AQ — MB ChB 1992 Ed.; BSc (Hons.) Psychol. Ed. 1990, MB ChB 1992.

PAGE, Catherine Anne (retired) 9 Holt Hill Terrace, Birkenhead CH42 5LB Tel: 0151 201 2273 — MB ChB 1964 Leeds; BA (Hons.) Open 1985; DTM & H Liverp. 1973; DCH Eng. 1968; DObst RCOG 1967. Prev: Staff Grade Community Med. Off. Roy. Liverp. Childr. Hosp. & Community Serv. Trust.

PAGE, Cathleen Elizabeth Lingmell, 5 Old Lane, Bramhope, Leeds LS16 9AY Tel: 0113 843286 — MB BCh BAO 1972 Dub. (TC Dub.) Prev: Ho. Phys. Profess. Med. Unit Nottm. Gen. Hosp.; Ho. Surg. N.. Gen. Hosp. Sheff.; SHO (Med.) City Hosp. Nottm.

PAGE, Christopher Murray Temple Fortune Health Centre, 23 Temple Fortune Lane, London NW11 7TE Tel: 020 8458 4431 Fax: 020 8731 8257; 32 Wordsworth Walk, London NW11 6AU Tel: 020 8455 2785 — MB BS 1971 Lond.; MRCP (UK) 1975. Prev: Sen. Lect. (Primary Care & Pub. Health) Roy. Free Hosp. Lond.;

PAGE

Research Fell. & Hon. Sen. Regist. St. Mary's Hosp. Lond. & Cas. Med. Off. Middlx. Hosp. Lond.

PAGE, Elizabeth Anne 38 Fielding Street, Kennington, London SE17 3HD — LMSSA 1978 Lond.

PAGE, Ernest Donald 40 Harley Street, London W1N 1AB Tel: 020 7580 3478; 14 Devonshire Street, London W1N 1FS Tel: 020 7580 0655 — MB BS 1935 Lond.; MRCS Eng. LRCP Lond. 1933. (St. Mary's) Socs: BMA (Ex-Sec. St. Marylebone Div., Ex-Chairm. & Ex-Sec. Hampstead; Soc. Occupat. Med. Prev: Clin. Asst. Varicose Vein Clinic King Edwd. Memor. Hosp. Ealing; Sen. Clin. Asst. Varicose Vein Dept., &c. St. Mary's Hosp. Lond.; Clin. Asst. (Outpats.) Hosp. Wom. Soho Sq. Lond.

PAGE, Fiona Cameron The Royal Oldham Hospital, Rochdale Road, Oldham OL1 2JH — MB ChB 1981 Manch.; BSc St. And. 1979; MFOM RCP Lond. 1991, AFOM 1989; MRCGP 1985; DFFP 1993; DRCOG 1984; FFOM 1998. Cons. Occupat. Health Roy. Oldham Hosp.

PAGE, Frances Mary Larman 15 Sherwood Street, Whetstone, London N20 0NB — MB BS 1992 Lond.; BSc Lond. 1989; DA 1996. (Univ. College and Middlesex Hospital Medical School London) Specialist Regist. Rotat. N. Lond.

PAGE, Frank Bernard Tower House Medical Centre, Stockway South, Nailsea, Bristol BS48 2XX Tel: 01275 866700 Fax: 01275 866711; Rosedale, 108 Station Road, Nailsea, Bristol BS48 1TB Tel: 01275 852723 — MB BS 1968 Lond.; MRCGP 1981; DA Eng. 1970; DTM & H Liverp. 1970; TM 1998. (Lond. Hosp.) G.P. Socs: Christ. Med. Fell.sh. Prev: Med. Dir. Med. Asst. Program Inc. Afghanistan Project.

PAGE, Graham Wallace (retired) 9 Nightingale Lane, Beechwood Gardens, Coventry CV5 6AY Tel: 01203 673125 Fax: 01203 673125 — MB BChir 1948 Camb.; MRCGP 1966. Prev: Unit. Gen. Manager/Specialist in Comm. Med. N. Warks. HA.

PAGE, Gregory Christopher Thomas Skewen Medical Centre, Queens Road, Skewen, Neath SA10 6UL Tel: 01792 812316 Fax: 01792 323208 — MB BCh 1979 Wales.

PAGE, Hilary 43 Slayleigh Lane, Sheffield S10 3RG Tel: 0114 230 7826 — MD (Distinc.) Leeds 1992, MB ChB 1970; MRCGP 1978; MFPHM RCP (UK) 1987; DObst RCOG 1973; FFPHM RCP (UK) 1997. Ass. Dir. (Pub. Health) Trent Regional Office NHS Exec.; Hon. Sen. Lect. Sheff. Univ. Med. Sch. Socs: Nat. Assn. Family Plann. Doctors & BMA. Prev: Lect. (Epidemiol.) Sheff. Univ. Med. Sch.; Dir. (Pub. Health) Doncaster.

PAGE, Ian John (retired) Royal Lancaster Infirmary, Ashton Road, Lancaster LA1 4RP Tel: 01524 65944 Fax: 01524 583585 — MB BS 1979 Lond.; MRCS Eng. LRCP Lond. 1978; MRCOG 1985; T(OG) 1991; FRCDG 1998. Cons. O & G Roy. Lancaster Infirm. & W.morland Gen. Hosp. Kendal. Prev: Cons. O & G Army Med. Servs.

PAGE, James Martin The Village Green Surgery, The Green, Wallsend NE28 6BB Tel: 0191 295 8500 Fax: 0191 295 8519 — MB BCh BAO 1978 Belf.; MRCGP 1982; DRCOG 1981. GP Trainer.

PAGE, Janet Elizabeth 7 Hurstfield, Hayes Park, Bromley BR2 9BB — MB BS 1959 Lond.; MRCS Eng. LRCP Lond. 1959; DA Eng. 1961. (Roy. Free) Clin. Asst. (Rhesus Immunisation) Lewisham Hosp. Socs: Fac. Anaesth. RCS Eng. Prev: Clin. Asst. (Anaesth.) Dreadnought & Greenwich Dist. Hosps.; Regist. (Anaesth.) Qu. Mary's Hosp. Sidcup; SHO (Anaesth.) Bromley Hosp.

PAGE, Janet Elizabeth Medical Protection Society, 33 Cavendish Square, London W1G 0PS Tel: 020 7399 1327 Fax: 020 7399 1301 Email: janet.page@mps.org.uk; Coniston, 29 Westward House, Abbotswood, Guildford GU1 1UU Tel: 01483 453138 Email: drjanet.page@ntlworld.com — MB BS 1982 Lond.; BSc (Hons.) Lond. 1979; MRCP (UK) 1985; FRCR 1988. (St. Mary's) Medico Legal Adviser. Socs: BMA. Prev: Cons. Diagn. Radiol. E. Surrey Hosp. Redhill/18116; Cons. Radiologist, Surrey & Sussex Healthcare NHS Trust, Redhill.

PAGE, Jason David 130 Westcotes Drive, Leicester LE3 0QS — MB BS 1992 Lond.

PAGE, Jason McKinley 18 Wingrove Avenue, Newcastle upon Tyne NE4 9AL Tel: 0191 245 1489 Email: jason@page999.freeserve.co.uk — MB BS 1995 Newc. SHO Paediat, N. Shields. Prev: SHO Psychiat. Tranwell Unit AE Gateshead; SHO O & G Ashington; SHO A&E RVI & NGH, Newc.

PAGE, Jennifer Margaret 8 The Squirrels, Belmont Hill, London SE13 5DR — MB BS 1985 Lond.

PAGE, Joanne Maria Hook and Hartley Wintney Medical Partnership, 1 Chapter Terrace, Hartley Wintney, Hook RG27 8QJ Tel: 01252 842087 Fax: 01252 843145; 51 Longbridge Road, Bramley, Tadley RG26 5AN Tel: 01256 881231 — MB ChB 1988 Manch.; MRCGP 1996; Cert. Family Plann. JCC 1994; DRCOG 1994. (Manch.) GP Princip. Prev: Trainee GP Bramblys Grange Surg. Basingstoke; Ho. Surg. ChristCh. HA, NZ; Ho. Phys. & Ho. Surg. Vict. Hosp. Blackpool.

PAGE, Professor John Graham Accident & Emergency Department, Aberdeen Royal Infirmary, Aberdeen AB25 2ZN Tel: 01224 681818 Fax: 01224 840718 Email: g.page@abdn.ac.uk; 16 Kingswood Avenue, Kingswells, Aberdeen AB15 8AE Tel: 01224 742945 Fax: 01224 742945 — MB ChB Aberd. 1968; ChM Aberd. 1977; FRCS Ed. 1972; FFAEM 1993; FFOM 1998 RCP Lond. (Aberd.) Cons. A & E Aberd. Roy. Hosps. NHS Trust; Hon. Prof. Emerg. Med. Robt. Gordon Univ. Aberd.; Hon. Sen. Lect. (Surg.) Univ. Aberd. Socs: Eur. Undersea Biomed. Soc.; BMA. Prev: Regist. (Surg.) Grampian HB; Research Fell. Harvard Univ. Boston, USA; Terminable Lect. (Path.) Aberd. Univ.

PAGE, John Patrick Anthony, Col. late RAMC Medical Reception Station BFPO 36 Tel: 00 49 541 186532 Fax: 00 49 541 186529 Email: apage24334@aol.com — MB 1962 Camb.; BChir 1961; T(GP) 1991; DTM & H RCP Lond. 1964. (Camb. & St. Bart.) Civil Med. Pract. Osnabruck Germany. Socs: BMA; Caius Coll. Med. Soc. Prev: Staff Phys. NW AFH Tabuk, Saudi Arabia; Regtl. Med. Off. Blues & Roy.s; Specialist Dermat. Qu. Alexandra Milit. Hosp.

PAGE, Julian (Surgery) 30 Bradshaw Brow, Bradshaw, Bolton BL2 3DH Tel: 01204 302212; 89 Templecombe Drive, Bolton BL1 7TA Tel: 01204 592653 — MB ChB 1984 Manch.; FRCGP 1997; MRCGP 1989; DRCOG 1987. GP Tutor Bolton; Med. Off. Hick Hargreaves & Beliot Walmsley Ltd.; Ref. Brit. Sub.-Aqua Club.; Fell. Summative Assessm.

PAGE, Katharine Isabel 17 Gloucester Road, Almondsbury, Bristol BS32 4HD — MB BS 1986 Lond.

PAGE, Kathleen Margaret The White Cottage, 39 Blackbrook Park Avenue, Fareham PO15 5JN Tel: 01329 280455 — MB BS Lond. 1964; MRCS Eng. LRCP Lond. 1964; DCH Eng. 1969; DA Eng. 1967; DObst RCOG 1966. (Roy. Free) Hosp. Pract. (Anaesth.) Hants. Socs: BMA. Prev: GP Lee-on-the-Solent; Ho. Phys. Roy. Free Hosp. Lawn Rd.; Ho. Surg. St. Mary Abbott's Hosp. Kensington.

PAGE, Kevin Barry Department of Clinical Chemistry, Royal Hallamshire Hospital, Glossop Road, Sheffield S10 2JF Tel: 0114 271 3299 Email: kevin.page@csuh.tient.nhs.uk; 5 Rowell Cottages, Rowell Lane, Loxley, Sheffield S6 6SH — MB BS 1983 Lond.; MRCPath 1996. (Kings Coll. Hosp. Med. Sch.) Assoc. Specialist (Chem. Pathol.) Centr. Sheff. Univ. Hosps. Socs: Nutrit. Soc.

PAGE, Kim Elizabeth Rampton Hospital, Retford, Nottingham DN22 0PD Tel: 01777 248321 — MB ChB 1984 Birm.; MRCPsych 1993. Cons Forens. Psychiat. Rampton Hosp. Retford Notts. Socs: BMA. Prev: Regist. (Psychiat.) Mapperley Hosp. Nottm.; SHO (Med.) Kings Mill Hosp. Sutton-in-Ashfield; Sen Regis Forens. Psychiat. Trent scheme.

PAGE, Louise Jessamy Godley's Farmhouse, Avon, Chippenham SN15 4LS — MB ChB 1996 Leic. GP Registr., Nottm. VTS.

PAGE, Margaret Jane Claremont Bank Surgery, Claremont Bank, Shrewsbury SY1 1RL Tel: 01743 357355 — MB BS 1980 Lond.; MRCGP 1984; DA (UK) 1987; DRCOG 1985. (Middlx. Hosp.) Prev: Trainee GP/SHO (O & G, Med. & Anaesth.) Salop. HA VTS.

PAGE, Mary Elizabeth The Health Centre, Church Road, Thornton-Cleveleys; Five Gables, 67 Moorland Road, Poulton-le-Fylde FY6 7ER Tel: 01253 899449 — MB ChB 1979 Manch.

PAGE, Mercia Louise 4 Timber Lane, Woburn, Milton Keynes MK17 9PL — MB BS 1980 Lond.

PAGE, Mervyn James (retired) Whitegates, 29 Audley Park Road, Bath BA1 2XJ Tel: 01225 421171 — MB ChB 1954 Bristol; DObst RCOG 1960; DCH Eng. 1958. Prev: Ho. Surg. Frenchay Hosp. Bristol.

PAGE, Michael Clayton Medicines Control Agency, Room 1322, Market Towers, 1 Nine Elms Lane, London SW8 5NQ Tel: 020 7273 0529 Fax: 020 7273 0195; Little Orchard, Chiltern Road, Peppard, Henley-on-Thames RG9 5LP Tel: 01189 722576 — MB BS 1974 Lond.; MRCP (UK) 1980. (St. Bart.) Sen. Med. Off. Meds. Control Agency. Prev: Med. Dir. Fournier Pharmaceut. Ltd.

PAGE, Michael Denyer Solstice, Millcroft Court, St Mary Church, Cowbridge CF7 7LH — MD 1991 Wales; MB BCh 1980; FRCP 1998; MRCP (UK) 1984. Cons. Phys. Roy. Glam. Hosp. Prev: Sen. Regist. (Med.) Leeds.

PAGE, Michael James Scott Mount View Practice, London Street Medical Centre, London Street, Fleetwood FY7 6HD Tel: 01253 873312 Fax: 01253 873130; Five Gables, 67 Moorland Road, Poulton-le-Fylde FY6 7ER Tel: 01253 893194 — MB ChB 1975 Dundee; MRCGP 1980. (Dundee) Clin. Asst. EMI Unit Fleetwood Hosp.; Police Surg. to N. Fylde.

PAGE, Michael McBean Selly Oak Hospital, Raddlebarn Road, Birmingham B29 6JD Tel: 0121 627 1627; 532 City Road, Edobaston, Birmingham B17 8LN Tel: 0121 434 5516 Fax: 0121 434 5516 Email: michaelpg@aol.com — MB BChir 1969 Camb.; MD Camb. 1981; FRCP Lond. 1988, M 1972. (Cambridge) Cons. Phys. Selly Oak Hosp. Birm. Socs: Brit. Diabetic Assn. Prev: Sen. Regist. (Med.) Nottm. Gen. Hosp.; Regist. (Diabetes) King's Coll. Hosp. Lond.; Ho. Phys. St. Thos. Hosp. Lond.

PAGE, Nicholas Goodwin Richardson 15 Basil Mansions, Basil St., London SW3 1AP Tel: 020 7589 4780 Fax: 020 7581 0244 Email: nicdoc@aol.com; 72 Rodenhurst Road, London SW4 8AR — MB BS 1972 Lond.; MRCP (UK) 1976; FRCP Lond. 1998. (Westm.) Private Med. Pract. Socs: Med Soc. Lond.; Chelsea Clin. Soc. Prev: Resid. Fell. (Neurol.) Nat. Hosp. Lond.; Regist. (Med.) St. Thos. Hosp. & W.m. Hosp. Lond.

PAGE, Nicholas Philip Freeman The Surgery, 152 Melton Road, West Bridgford, Nottingham NG2 6ER Tel: 0115 945 2656 Fax: 0115 923 5166 — BSc (Hons.) Lond. 1980, MB BS 1983; MRCGP 1989; DRCOG 1988; DCH RCP Lond. 1988. (Guys)

PAGE, Mr Nigel Eric 5 The Rise, Southill, Weymouth DT4 0TD — MB ChB 1977 Birm.; FRCS Ed. 1983.

PAGE, Nigel Geoffrey Sandwell Health NHS Trust, Lyndon, West Bromwich B71 4HJ — MB ChB 1992 Birm; BSc (1st cl. Hons.) Pharmacol. Birm. 1989; MRCP (UK) 1995. Cons. Geriat., Sandwell Healthcare NHS Trust W. Bromwich.

PAGE, Renee Claire Lesley Department of Diabetes, Nottingham City Hospital, Hucknall Road, Nottingham NG5 1PB — MB ChB 1983 Manch.; MB ChB (Hons.) Manch. 1983; BSc Med. Sci. (St. And.) 1980; MRCP (UK) 1986. Cons. Phys. Prev: Regist. Radcliffe Infirm. Oxf. RHA.

PAGE, Mr Richard Denyer The Cardiothoracic Centre, Thomas Drive, Liverpool L14 3PE; 25 Barton Heys Road, Formby, Liverpool L37 2EY — MB ChB 1982 Liverp.; ChM Liverp. 1994; FRCS (Cth.) 1993; FRCS Ed. 1987. (Liverpool) Cons. Cardiothoracic Surg. Cardiothoracic Centre Liverp. Socs: Soc. Cardiothoracic Surg. GB & Irel. Prev: Sen. Regist. (Cardiothoracic Surg.) Cardiothoracic Centre Liverp.; Regist. (Cardiothoracic Surg.) BRd.green Hosp. Liverp.; Fell. (Cardiac Surg.) Harvard Med. Sch., Boston, USA.

PAGE, Richard James Holsworthy Health Centre, Western Road, Holsworthy EX22 6DH Tel: 01409 253692 Fax: 01409 254184; Sunnymeade, 6 Holnicote Road, Bude EX23 8EJ Tel: 01288 354464 — MB ChB 1975 Bristol; MRCGP 1980; DRCOG 1976. (Bristol) GP Trainer Holsworthy. Prev: Med. Off. I/C Amalo Refugee Camp Somalia.; Trainee GP Barnstaple VTS; SHO (Anaesth.) Roy. Devon & Exeter Hosp.

PAGE, Mr Richard John Page and Partners, Health Centre, Church Street, Audley, Stoke-on-Trent ST7 8EW Tel: 01782 721345 Fax: 01782 723808; Park Lane Farm, Park Lane, Audley, Stoke-on-Trent ST7 8HP — MB ChB 1981 Birm.; FRCS Ed. 1986; MRCGP 1990. (University of Birmingham) GP Princip.; Police Surg. Staffs. Police Force; Clin. Asst. in Gastroenterol.; Clin. Asst. in Orthop.

PAGE, Richard Louis St James's University Hospital, Beckett St., Leeds LS9 7TF Tel: 0113 243 3144 — MB BS 1967 Lond.; DM Nottm. 1978; FRCP Lond. 1986; MFOM RCP Lond. 1988; MRCP (U.K.) 1970; MRCS Eng. LRCP Lond. 1967. (Middlx.) Cons. Phys. St. Jas. Univ. Hosp. Leeds; Sen. Clin. Lect. Univ. Leeds. Socs: Brit. Thorac. Soc.; Soc. Occupat. Med. Prev: Sen. Regist. (Med.) Addenbrooke's Hosp. Camb.; MRC Fell. Med. Unit Nottm. Univ.; Regist. (Med.) Middlx. Hosp. Lond.

PAGE, Richard Mackay Yealm Medical Centre, Market St., Yealmpton, Plymouth PL8 2EA Tel: 01752 880392; Little Copse, New Road, Yealmpton, Plymouth PL8 2HH — MRCS Eng. LRCP Lond. 1969; DRCOG 1977; DA Eng. 1975. (St. Bart.) Socs: Chairm.

Plymouth LMC. Prev: Clin. Asst. Anaesth. Dept. Reinford Hosp. Plymouth.

PAGE, Mr Richard Samuel Wrightington Hospital, Hall Lane, Appley Bridge, Wigan WN6 9EP Tel: 0257 252211 Email: rbpage@ozemail.com.au — MB BS 1989 Tasmania; FRACS (orth) 2000; BMedSci. Tasmania 1985; FRACS (Pt 1) 1995. (Univ. Tasmania) Upper Limb Fell., Wrightington Hosp.; Orthopaedic Surg., Surg LCDR, RANR; Roy. Austral. Naval Reserves. Socs: Austral. Milit. Med. Assn.; Austral. Sports Med. Assn.; Assoc. Mem. Austral. Orthop. Assn. Prev: Orthop. Regist. Launceston Gen. Hosp. Tasmania; Cons. Orthopaedic Surg. Roy. Hosp. Haslar & Porrttsmouth Hosp.; Sen. Regist. & Fell. Orthopeaduc Trauma Unit, Roy. Inif. Edin.

PAGE, Ronald Mallis The Health Centre, Victoria Road, Leven KY8 4ET Tel: 01333 425656 Fax: 01333 422249 — MB ChB 1978 Ed.; BSc 1975; MRCGP (Distinc.) 1982; DRCOG 1981. Syntex Award Research in Gen. Pract.-Highlands & Is.s.

PAGE, Rosemary Beatrice (retired) Ardnamurchan, Thirlby, Thirsk YO7 2DJ Tel: 01845 597602 — MB 1972 Camb.; BChir 1971.

PAGE, Mrs Rosemary Fiona McLeish Witley Surgery, Wheeler Lane, Witley, Godalming GU8 5QR Tel: 01428 682218 Fax: 01428 685790; Fernside Cottage, Brook Road, Wormley, Godalming GU8 5UA Tel: 0142 684291 — MB BS 1959 Lond.; DObst RCOG 1961. (St. Mary's) Prev: Clin. Asst. (Cas.) Roy. Surrey Co. Hosp. Guildford.; Ho. Phys. & Ho. Surg. Roy. Hants. Co. Hosp. Winchester; Ho. Off. (Obst & Gyn.) St. Luke's Hosp. Guildford.

PAGE, Simon John The Lennard Surgery, 1-3 Lewis Road, Bishopsworth, Bristol BS13 7JD Tel: 0117 964 0900 Fax: 0117 987 3227 — MB ChB 1975 Bristol; MRCGP 1981. GP Princip. Bristol. Prev: Lead Gp Bristol S. Locality Commiss.ing; Clin. Asst. (ENT) W.on Gen. Hosp.; Clin. Teach. (Gen. Pract. & Child Health) Bristol Univ.

PAGE, Simon Richard Department of Diabetes, Endocrinology and Metabolism, University Hospital, Nottingham NG7 2UH Tel: 0115 924 9924 Fax: 0115 970 1080 Email: simon.page@mail.qmcuh-tr.trent.nhs.uk; 70 Watcombe Circus, Nottingham NG5 2DT Tel: 0115 960 9556 — MB ChB 1982 Bristol; MB ChB (Hons.) Bristol 1982; MD Bristol 1991; MRCP (UK) 1985; FRCP UK 1999. Cons. Phys. Univ. Hosp. Nottm. Prev: Sen. Regist. (Med., Diabetes & Endocrinol.) Nottm. & Derby Hosps.; Clin. Research Fell. Univ. Lond. St. Geo. Hosp. Med. Sch.; Regist. (Med.) St. Geo. Hosp. Lond.

PAGE, Valerie Joan 24 Grosvenor Avenue, Newcastle upon Tyne NE2 2NP — MB ChB 1982 Manch.

PAGE, William 4 Glebe Manor, Anahilt, Hillsborough BT26 6NS — MB BCh BAO 1976 Belf.; DMRD Eng. 1982; FRCR 1983. Cons. (Radiol.) Belvoir Pk. & Foster Green. Hosps. Belf. & Lagan Valley Lisburn.

PAGET, Cecil John Hayward (retired) Coombe Rise, 34 The Drive, Wallington SM6 9LX Tel: 020 8647 8084 — MB BChir 1945 Camb. Prev: Hon. Med. Off. Carshalton, Beddington & Wallington Memor. Hosp.

PAGET, Jacques Pierre Malezieux (retired) 15 Bladon Close, London Road, Guildford GU1 1TY Tel: 01483 571421 — MD Lille, France 1949; Lic. New Brunswick Med. Bd. 1961; Lic. Newfld. Med. Bd. 1968; Cert. Pathol, Canada 1961; DPH Bristol 1969.

PAGET, Richard Ian James North Ladbrook Hall, Penn Lane, Tanworth-in-Arden, Solihull B94 5HJ — MB ChB 1993 Birm.

PAGET, Richard James (retired) Glebe Farm House, Harthill, Sheffield S31 — MB ChB 1963 Bristol; MB ChB (Hons.) 1963; BSc (Hons.) Bristol 1960; MRCGP 1977; MIBiol 1976. Prev: SHO Cardiff Roy. Infirm.

PAGET, Sally Elizabeth Roebuck House, High Street, Hastings TN34 3ES Tel: 01424 420378 Fax: 01424 452824; 12 High Wickham, Hastings TN35 5PB Tel: 01424 714369 — MB BS 1981 Lond.; MRCP (UK) 1984; MRCGP 1987. (Guy's)

PAGET, Seaton Chamberlain Roebuck House Surgery, High St., Hastings TN34 3EY Tel: 01424 420378 — MB BS 1951 Lond.; MRCS Eng. LRCP Lond. 1951; DObst RCOG 1957. (Guy's)

PAGET, Timothy David 55 St Cross Road, Winchester SO23 9RE — MB BS 1990 Lond.; T(GP) 1994; Dip. Pharma. Med. 1997. Head of Med. Affairs (Pharma. Med.) Pk.e - Davis & Co. Ltd E.leigh Hants.

PAGLIERO, Mr Keith Michael High Water, 36c Countess Wear Road, Exeter EX2 6LR Tel: 01392 877520 Fax: 01392 877520 —

PAGLIUCA

MB BS 1962 Lond.; FRCS Eng. 1967; MRCS Eng. LRCP Lond. 1962. (Guy's) Indep. Cons. Thoracic Surg. Devon; Hon. Research Fell. Surgic. Oncol. Exeter Univ. Postgrad. Med. Sch. Socs: (Ex. Chairm.) Nat. Assn. Clin. Tutors; Soc. Thoracic & Cardiovasc. Surgs. Prev: Cons. Thoracic Surg. Roy. Devon & Exeter Hosp., N. Devon Infirm. & Torbay Hosps.; Dir. Educat. & Thoracic Surg. King Fahad Armed Forces Hosp. Jeddah; Sen. Regist. (Thoracic Surg.) Hammersmith & Guy's Hosps. Lond.

PAGLIUCA, Antonio Department of Haematological Medicine, King's College Hospital, Denmark Hill, London SE5 8RX Tel: 020 7346 3709 Fax: 020 7346 3514 Email: antonio.pagliuca@kcl.ac.uk; 15 Barnmead Road, Beckenham BR3 1JF — MB BS 1983 Lond.; MA Camb. 1984; MRCP (UK) 1986; MRCPath 1992; FRCPath 2000. (King's Coll. Lond.) Cons. Haemat. King's Coll. Hosp. Lond. Socs: Brit. Soc. of Haematol.; Amer. Soc. Haemat. Prev: Lect. (Haemat.) King's Coll. Sch. Med. & Dent.; SHO (Neurol.) Nat. Hosp. Nerv. Dis. Lond.; SHO (Med.) St. Geo. & Roy. Marsden Hosps. Lond.

PAGNI, Paul Anthony McKenzie House Surgery, Kendal Road, Hartlepool TS25 1QU Tel: 01429 233611 Fax: 01429 297713 — MB BCh BAO 1983 NUI.

***PAHAL, Gurmit Singh** 27 Campbell Road, Gravesend DA11 0JZ — MB BS 1994 Lond.

PAHOR, Mr Ahmes Labib ENT Department, City Hospital NHS Trust, Dudley Road, PO Box 293, Birmingham B18 7QH Tel: 0121 507 4559 Fax: 0121 507 4557 — MB BCh 1964 Cairo; FICS 1977 Fellow International College of Surgeons, USA; MA Cairo 1986; FRCS Ed. 1974; MRCS Eng. LRCP Lond. 1978; DHMSA Soc. Apoth. Lond. 1994; Specialist Accredit. (ENT) RCS Ed. 1977; DMSc (Path.) Ain Shams 1968; DLO Cairo 1966. (Kasr Al-Aini Med. Sch. Cairo) Cons. Surg. ENT City Hosp. Trust Birm., Sandwell NHS Trust, W. Bromwich; Hon. Sen. Clin. Lect. Univ. Birm.; Cert. Special Traing. Otolaryngol. (Europ. Union) 1995. Socs: Midl. Inst. Otol. (Hon. Libr.); Irish OtoLaryngol. Soc.; Brit. Soc. For the Hist. Of ENT (Hon. Sec.). Prev: Regist. Roy. Vict. Hosp. Belf.; Sen. Regist. Qu. Eliz. Hosp. Birm. & Walsgrave Hosp. Coventry, Roy. Infirm. Stoke-on-Trent.

PAHUJA, Saubhagya Omnamah, Roseberry Gardens, Dartford DA1 2NX Tel: 01322 271157 — MB BS 1975 Delhi; FFA RCSI 1990; DA Eng. 1982. (Maulana Azad Med. Coll.) Clin. Asst. (Anaesth.) Joyce Green & GNK Hosp. Dartford.

PAHWA, Balram Krishan 10 Leicester Road, Wanstead, London E11 2DP Tel: 020 8989 3224; 320 Commercial Road, London E1 2PY — MB BS 1957 Rajasthan. (Sawai Man Singh Med. Coll. Jaipur) Prev: Regist. W. Ham Chest Clinic Plaistow; Regist. Med. Post-Grad. Med. Inst. Chandigarh.

PAHWA, Mr Mahendra Kumar Goldthorn Medical Centre, 130a Park Street South, Off Goldthorn Hill, Wolverhampton WV2 3JF Tel: 01902 339283 Fax: 01902 339283 — MB BS 1963 Vikram; MS Delhi 1970.

PAI, Mr Ballambettu Yogish The Avenue, Linthorpe, Middlesbrough TS5 6 — MB BS 1954 Madras; MS Madras 1958, MB BS 1954; FRCS Eng. 1960; FRCS Ed. 1960. (Christian Med. Coll. Vellore) Cons. Orthop. Surg. S. & N. Tees Health Auths. Socs: Fell. Roy. Soc. Med.; Brit. Orthop. Assn. Prev: Sen. Orthop. Regist. N.. RHA. Newc.; MRC Research Regist. St. Helier Hosp. Carshalton & Guy's Hosp. Med.; Sch. Lond.

PAI, Elfreeda D'Souza 7 Daubeney Gate, Shenley Church End, Milton Keynes MK5 6EH — MB BS 1978 Mysore; LRCP LRCS Ed. LRCPS Glas. 1984; DCH Dub. 1981.

PAI, Haridas Upendra Shafton Lane Surgery, 20A Shafton Lane, Holbeck, Leeds LS11 9RE Tel: 0113 295 4393 Fax: 0113 295 4390 — MB BS 1974 Mysore. (Mysore) GP Leeds.

PAI, Mr Karkala Purushotham Department of General Surgery, The General Hospital, St Helier, Jersey JE2 3QS Tel: 01534 622000 Fax: 01534 622880 Email: purshot@hotmail.com; 126/A, Road 4, West Nehrunagar, Secunderabad, Andhra Pradesh 500026, India Tel: 780 1523 — MB BS 1983 Osmania; FRCS Ed. 1988. Ass. Staff Grade (Gen. Surg.), Gen. Hosp., St.Helier, Jersey. Prev: Regist. (Gen. Surg.) St. Helier Jersey.; Vis. Regist. (Gen. & Vasc. Surg.) N. Staffs. HA; Regist. (Gen. Surg.) P.ss Roy. Hosp. Telford & Burton Gp Hosps.

PAI, Kasturi Ganesh Atkinson Health Centre, Market Street, Barrow-in-Furness LA14 2LR Tel: 01229 821669 — MB BS 1970 Mysore. (Mysore) GP Barrow-in-Furness.

PAI, Mr Keshav Shrinivas Gudgeheath Lane Surgery, 187 Gudgeheath Lane, Fareham PO15 6QA Tel: 01329 280887 Fax: 01329 231321; High Pines, 30 Milvil Road, Lee-on-the-Solent PO13 9LX Tel: 01705 551700 — MB BS 1965 Karnatak; FRCS Ed. 1970. (Karnatak Med. Coll. Hubli) Hosp. Pract. (Gen. Surg.) Hants. AHA (T).

PAI, Manoj Sanathan Limbrick Wood Surgery, Jardine Crescent, Coventry CV4 9PN Tel: 024 7646 0800 Fax: 024 7646 7512 — MB BS 1980 Bombay.

PAI, Ming-Chu Pearl Thanet District General Hospital, St. Peter's Road, Margate CT9 4AN — MB ChB 1989 Aberd.; MD Liverpool 1999; MRCP (UK) 1992. Cons. Nephrologist, Sunderland Roy. Hosp.

PAI, Ramanath Umanath Sutherland Road Surgery, 44 Sutherland Road, Plymouth PL4 6BN Tel: 01752 662992 Fax: 01752 265538; 78 Windermere Crescent, Derriford, Plymouth PL6 5HX Tel: 01752 705702 Fax: 01752 265538 — MB BS 1966 Mysore; DA Eng. 1972. (Kasturba Med. Coll.) Socs: MDU. Prev: Regist. (Anaesth.) Canad. Red Cross Hosp. Taplow, Bucks.; Clin. Asst. (Anaesth.) Bronglais Gen. Hosp. Aberystwyth, Dyfed.

PAI, Shailaja Manoj 42 Glasshouse Lane, Kenilworth CV8 2AJ — MB BS 1979 Bombay; FRCS Ed. 1986.

PAI, Srinivas Hemachandra 24 Brookhus Farm Road, Walmley, Sutton Coldfield B76 1QP Tel: 0121 240 4818; 140 Coleshill Road, Hodge Hill, Birmingham B36 8AD Tel: 0121 776 6444 Fax: 0121 688 4544 — MB BS 1966 Mysore; DTM & H Liverp. 1972. (Kasthurba Med. Coll. Manipal.) Princip. GP. Prev: Med. Regist. St. Mary's Hosp. Isle of Wight; Med. Regist. S.port Infirm.

***PAI, Sripat Kasturi** 8 Windmill Court, Newcastle upon Tyne NE2 4BA — MB BS 1998 Newc.; MB BS Newc 1998.

PAI, Mr Vittaldas Panemangalore c/o 65 Herdman Close, Liverpool L25 2XS Tel: 0151 488 0181 — MB BS 1984 Mysore; FRCS (Ophth.) Ed. 1991; FCOphth. 1991; DO RCS Eng. 1990. Socs: UK Intraocular Implant Soc.; N. Eng. Ophth. Soc. Prev: Regist. Rotat. (Ophth.) Yorks. Train. Scheme.

PAICE, Brian Joseph 46 Fernlea, Bearsden, Glasgow G61 1NB Tel: 0141 772 6309; 46 Fernlea, Bearsden, Glasgow G61 1NB Tel: 0141 772 6309 — MB ChB 1976 Glas.; FRCP Ed. 1992; MRCP (UK) 1980; MRCGP 1984; FRCP Glas 1998.

PAICE, Elisabeth Willemien London Postgraduate, Medical and Dental Education, 20 Guilford St, London WC1N 1DZ Tel: 020 7692 3355 Fax: 020 7692 3396 Email: epaice@londoneanery.ac.uk — MB BCh BAO Dub. 1970; FRCP Lond. 1989; MRCP (UK) 1972; MRCS Eng. LRCP Lond. 1970; MA Dublin Univ. 1995; Dip. Med. Ed. Dund 1994. (Westm.) Dean Dir. Postgrad. Med. & Dent. Educat., Lond. Socs: Brit. Soc. Rheum.; Counc. Nat. Assn. Clin. Tutors (NACT); Counc. Assn. Study of Med. Educat. (ASME). Prev: Cons. Rheum. Whittington Hosp.; Sen. Regist. (Rheum.) Univ. Coll. Hosp.; Sen. Regist. (Rheum.) Stoke Mandeville Hosp.

PAIGE, David Geoffrey Dermatology Department, Royal London Hospital, Whitechapel, London E1 1BB Tel: 020 7377 7383 Fax: 020 7377 7383 — MB BS 1986 Lond.; MA Camb. 1987; FRCP (UK) 2000. Cons. Dermat. Roy. Lond. Hosp. & St. Bart. Hosp. Lond. Prev: Sen. Regist. (Dermat.) Bristol Roy. Infirm.; Clin. Research Fell. (Dermat.) Hosp. for Sick Childr. Gt. Ormond St. Lond.; Regist. (Dermat.) St. Mary's Hosp. Lond.

PAIGE, Graham John Balmore Park Surgery, 59A Hemdean Road, Caversham, Reading RG4 7SS Tel: 0118 947 1455 Fax: 0118 946 1766 — MB BS 1984 Lond.; MRCGP 1989; DRCOG 1987.

PAIGE, Helen Curtis House, Tokers Green Lane, Kidmore End, Reading RG4 9ED — MB BS 1986 Lond.; DRCOG 1989.

PAIGE, Peter George Mount Street Surgery, 69 Mount Street, Coventry CV5 8DE Tel: 024 7667 2277 Fax: 024 7671 7352; 3 Bransford Avenue, Cannon Park, Coventry CV4 7EP Tel: 024 76 412594 Email: george@ypaige.globalnet.co.uk — MB ChB 1979 Birm.; MA Oxf. 1981; FRCGP 1995, M 1983; DRCOG 1981. (Oxford/Birmingham) Prev: Clin. Asst. (Psychiat.) Walsgrave Ment. Health Unit Coventry; Trainee GP Swindon VTS.

PAILTHORPE, Mr Charles Andrew Royal Berkshire Hospital, London Road, Reading RG1 5AN — MB ChB 1977 Birm.; FRCS Ed. 1985. Cons. Orthop. Surg. Roy. Berks. Hosp. Reading.

PAILTHORPE, David Bruce Leonard (retired) North Cottage, Raughmere Drive, Lavant, Chichester PO18 0AB — MB BS 1944 Lond.; MRCS Eng. LRCP Lond. 1944. Prev: Regist. (Med.) & Ho. Phys. Mt. Vernon Hosp. N.wood.

PAIN, Amiya Kumar 2 Burleigh Avenue, Blackfen, Sidcup DA15 8QA Tel: 020 8859 1315 — MB BS 1958 Calcutta; MRCP (U.K.) 1974. (Calcutta Med. Coll.) Lect. Infec. Dis. Guy's Hosp. & King's Coll. Hosp. Lond.; Cons. Phys. Hither Green & Guy's Hosps. Lond. Socs: Brit. Soc. Study Infec. Prev: Sen. Regist. (Infec. Dis.) St. Ann's Gen. Hosp. Lond.; Regist. (Med. Unit) Hosp. Trop. Dis. & Univ. Coll. Hosp. Lond.; Med. Regist. Dreadnought Seamen's Hosp. Greenwich.

PAIN, Ashley Nigel The Hoppit Surgery, Butts Lane, Danbury, Chelmsford CM3 4NP Tel: 01245 222518 Fax: 01245 222116; 85 Main Street, Danbury, Chelmsford CM3 4DJ Tel: 01245 225882 — MB ChB 1980 Leeds; DRCOG 1986. GP Danbury; Mem. BASICS. Socs: Chelmsford Med. Soc.

PAIN, Mr James Andrew Poole Hospital, Longfleet Road, Poole BH15 2JB Tel: 01202 442951 Fax: 01202 448165; Stourbank House, Old Ham Lane, Little Canford, Wimborne BH21 7LB Tel: 01202 872782 Fax: 01202 890158 Email: japain@aol.com — MB BS 1978 Lond.; BSc Lond. 1975, MS 1986; FRCS Eng. 1981; FRCS Ed. 1981; MRCS Eng. LRCP Lond. 1978. (Guy's) Cons. Surg. Poole Gen. Hosp.; Vis. Surg. Vict. Hosp. Wimborne. Socs: Fell.Roy. Soc. Med.; Brit. Assn. Surg. Oncol.; Brit. Soc. Gastroenterol. Prev: Sen. Registar (Surg.) King's Coll. Hosp. Lond.; Registar (Surg.) St. Geo.'s. Hosp. Lond.; Hon. Physics & Hon. Surg. Guy's Hosp. Lond.

PAIN, Jonathan Hugh 12 Clos Waun Wen, Llangyfelach, Swansea SA6 6EF — MB ChB 1989 Leeds.

PAIN, Simon John Seafield House, Brantham, Manningtree CO11 1PT — MB BChir 1992 Camb.

PAIN, Vivian Maureen Huntsmans House, Kennel Lane, Billericay CM12 9RT Tel: 01277 658411 — MB BS 1963 Lond.; MRCS Eng. LRCP Lond. 1963; DCH Eng. 1965. (St. Bart.) Sen. Regist. Nuffield Hearing & Speech Centre Roy. Nat. ENT Hosp.; Sen. Med. Off. (Audiol.) Redbridge & Waltham Forest AHA. Socs: BMA. Prev: Regist. (Paediat.) Hillingdon Hosp. Uxbridge; Ho. Off. Qu. Eliz. Hosp. Childr. Lond.

PAINE, Sir Christopher Hammon (retired) Kings Farm, Withypool, Minehead TA24 7RE — BSc, MA Oxf. 1961; BM BCh 1961 Oxf.; FRCP 1976 Lond.; FRCR 1975; DM 1981; MRCP 1964 Lond.; DMRT 1967 Eng.; FFR 1969. p/t Trustee The Lond. Clinic; Immediate Past Pres. BMA (2001-02); Mem. Med. Advisory Bd. Internat. Hosp.s Gp.; Mem. Med. Advisery Bd. Medexonline. Prev: Pres. Roy. Soc. of Med. (1996-98).

PAINE, David Leon Stanley Centre for Complementary Medicine, Orchard Paddock, Bugbrooke, Northampton NN7 3QR Tel: 01604 832256 Fax: 01604 832256 — Dip. Med. Acup. Member British Medical Acupuncture Society; Dip. He. Beijing 1980; MF Hon. London 1990; MB ChB Manch. 1961; MRCGP 1972. (Manch.) Cons. in Acupunc. and Homeopathy and other Complementary Therapies. Socs: Fac. Homoep.; Brit. Med. Acupunct. Soc.; Brit. Soc. Med. & Dent. Hypn. Prev: GP; Hon. Cons. Acupunc. Abingdon Pain Relief Clinic Oxf.; SHO (Thoracic Surg. & Chest Dis.) Baguley Hosp. Manch.

PAINE, David Stevens 42 Newton Road, Cambridge CB2 2AL Tel: 01223 353300 — MB BChir 1948 Camb.; MA (Hons.) Camb. 1952, BA (Hons.) 1946, MB Bchir 1948; MRC Psych 1972; DPM Lond. 1966. (Middlx.) Psychiat. Adviser Camb. Marriage Guid. Counc.; Hon. Asst. Psychiat. Addenbrooke's Hosp. Camb. Prev: Regist. Netherne Hosp. Coulsdon; Res. Med. Off. St. And. Hosp. Dollis Hill; Sen. Regist. Fulbourn & Addenbrooke's Hosps. Camb.

PAINE, Douglas Harold Davey Aragon, 34 Dudsbury Road, Ferndown BH22 8RE Tel: 01202 861137 — MB BS 1943 Lond.; MRCS Eng. LRCP Lond. 1944; MRCPsych 1971; DPM Eng. 1948. (Middlx.) Cons. Psychiat. & Phys. Supt. Tatchbury Mt. Hosp. Calmore. Socs: Fell. Roy. Soc. Med. Prev: Cons. Psychiat. & Med. Supt. St. Margt. Hosp. Birm.; Sen. Phys. Botleys Pk. Hosp. Chertsey; Regist. (Med.) Middlx. Hosp.

PAINE, Malcolm Archibald First Floor, 74 Ridge Road, London N8 9LH — MB ChB 1996 Glas.

PAINE, Mark Andrew William Goodenough House, Flat 801, Mecklenburgh Square, London WC1 2AN — MB BS 1986 Melbourne.

PAINE, Peter Andrew 974A Garratt Lane, Tooting, London SW17 0ND Tel: 020 8767 7261 — MB BS 1996 Lond.; BSc 1993. (St. Geo.)

PAINE, Timothy Frank The Family Practice, Western College, Cotham Road, Bristol BS6 6DF Tel: 0117 946 6455 Fax: 0117 946 6410; 13 Limerick Road, Bristol BS6 7DY Tel: 0117 924 5332 — MB BChir 1966 Camb.; BA Camb. 1962; MRCP Lond. 1968; FRCGP 1986, M 1976. (Camb. & Lond. Hosp.) Socs: (Vice-Pres.) Nat. Assn. Pat. Participation. Prev: Hosp. Pract. (Rheum.) Univ. Bristol; GP Clin. Tutor Bristol Roy. Infirm.; Assoc. Adviser (Gen. Pract.) Univ. Bristol.

PAINTER, Andrew Neil Station Road Surgery, 46 Station Road, New Barnet, Barnet EN5 1QH Tel: 020 8441 4425 Fax: 020 8441 4957 — MB BS 1984 Lond. Trainee GP Barnet Gen. Hosp. VTS. Prev: Ho. Surg. Friarage Hosp. N.allerton; Ho. Phys. Chase Farm Hosp. Enfield.

PAINTER, Daniel John 10 Woodcroft Drive, Wirral CH61 6XJ — MB BS 1993 Lond.

PAINTER, Deborah Jane 13 Park Street, Charlton, Malmesbury SN16 9DF — MB ChB 1992 Bristol.

PAINTER, Gillian Elizabeth Audiology Department, Moss Side Health Centre, Monton St., Manchester M14 4GP Tel: 0161 232 4214 Fax: 0161 232 4210; 108 Wythenshawe Road, Northenden, Manchester M23 OPA Tel: 0161 998 9688 — MB BS 1973 Lond.; MSc (Audiol. Med.) Manch. 1990; FRCPCH 1996; DObst RCOG 1975. (St. Mary's) Cons. Community Paediat. (Audiol.) Centr. Manc. Primary Care NHS Trust. Socs: Brit Assn Of Community Doctors in Audiol.; Brit. Assn. Of Audiological Phys.s; Brit,. Assn. Of Community Child Health. Prev: SCMO (Audiol.) Mancunian Community Health NHS Trust; SCMO N. Manch. HA; Clin. Med. Off. (Child Health) Manch. HA.

PAINTER, Michael John Infection Control And Surveilance Unit, Gateway House, Picadilly Approach, Manchester M60 7LP Tel: 0161 236 2400 Fax: 01227 864055; Felder Lodge, Deal Road, Deal CT14 0BD Tel: 0161 236 2400 Fax: 01227 864055 — MB BS 1973 Lond.; MSc Manch. 1983; FFPHM RCP (UK) 1993; MFCM 1985. (St. Mary's) Cons. Communicable Dis. Control Manch. Socs: Fell. Manch. Med. Soc. Prev: Sen. Regist. (Community Med.) N. W.. RHA; SCMO & Assoc. Dir. Treloar Haemophilia Centre Alton.

PAINTER, Patricia (retired) 13 Springcroft Avenue, London N2 9JH — MB BS 1954 Lond.; MRCS Eng. LRCP Lond. 1954; FFA RCS Eng. 1958; DA Eng. 1956. Prev: Cons. Anaesth. Nat. Hosps. Nerv. Dis. Lond.

PAINTER, Susan Carole c/o Postgraduate Secretary, Tindal Centre, Bierton Road, Aylesbury HP20 1HU — BM 1994 Soton.

PAINTIN, Mr David Bernard Whitecroft, Broombarn Lane, Prestwood, Great Missenden HP16 9JD — MB ChB 1954 Bristol; FRCOG 1972, M 1960; FFP (Hon.) 1993. (Bristol) Emerit. Reader Obst. & Gyn. Imperial Coll. Sch. Med. St. Mary's Lond. Prev: Edr. Brit. Jl. O & G; Chairm. Birth Control Trust.

PAIRAUDEAU, Peter William Hull Royal Infirmary, Anlaby Road, Hull HU3 2JZ Tel: 01482 328541 6 — MB ChB 1980 Bristol; MRCP (UK) 1984. (Bristol) Cons. Paediat. Roy. Hull Hosp. NHS Trust.

PAIRO GARCIA, Alejandro Flat 5, 2 Riverview Place, Glasgow G5 8EB — LMS 1992 Barcelona.

PAIS, Victor 26 Avenue Clamart, Scunthorpe DN15 8EQ — MB BS 1973 Mysore.

PAIS, Winston Alexis Treetops, 17 Wilmerhatch Lane, Epsom KT18 7EQ — MB ChB 1967 East Africa; FFA RCS Eng. 1974. (Makerere Univ. Coll. Kampala) Cons. Anaesth. Epsom Dist. Hosp. Prev: Rotating Sen. Regist. (Anaesth.) Brighton & Guy's Hosps.

***PAISEY, John Robert** 14 Templar Court, Padwell Rd, Southampton SO14 6QZ — BM 1997 Soton.

PAISEY, Richard Bayley Torbay Hospital, Lawes Bridge, Torquay TQ2 7AA Tel: 01803 64567; Whitehill House, 18 Whitehill Road, Highweek, Newton Abbot TQ12 6PR — MD 1981 Bristol; MB Camb. 1974, BChir 1973; FRCP (UK) 1992; MRCP (UK) 1975. (Guy's Hospital) Cons. Phys. & Endocrinol. Torbay Dist. Hosp. Socs: Brit. Diabetic Assn.; Eur. Assn. Study Diabetes. Prev: Lect. (Med.) Univ. of Bristol; Regist. (Med.) N.wick Pk. Hosp.; SHO (Med.) Soton. Gen. Hosp.

PAISH, Nicholas Robert, Squadron Ldr. RAF Med. Br. 107 Eider Avenue, Lyneham, Chippenham SN15 4QQ — MB BS 1988 Lond.; MRCGP 1994; DCCH RCP Ed. 1992.

PAISLEY, Andrew Charles East Quay Medical Centre, East Quay, Bridgwater TA6 5YB Tel: 01278 444666 — MB ChB 1988 Bristol;

PAISLEY

PhD Bristol 1982; MB ChB 1988; T(GP) 1994. Trainee GP Bridgwater.

PAISLEY, Miss Anna Mary 15 Alnwickhill Park, Liberton, Edinburgh EH16 6UH — BM BCh 1993 Oxf.; MA Oxford; FRCS (Ed.) 1998. (Oxford) Res. Fell. (Gen. Surg.) Roy. Infirm. Edin. Prev: SHO (Basic Surg. Train. Scheme) SE Scotl.

PAISLEY, Jane Menzies 62 Stanford Avenue, Brighton BN1 6FD Tel: 01273 553837 — MB ChB 1984 Sheff.; MRCP (UK) 1991. Cons. in Med. for the elderly.

PAISLEY, Jennifer Ann Gallows Street Surgery, 50 Gallows Street, Dromore BT25 1BD Tel: 028 9269 2758; 9 Barronstown Court, Barronstown Road, Dromore BT25 1FB Tel: 01846 699454 — MB BCh BAO 1987 Belf.; MRCGP 1991; DMH Belf. 1992; DRCOG 1991. Socs: BMA; RCGP. Prev: Trainee GP HillsBoro., Co. Down; SHO Lagan Valley Hosp. Lisburn & Belvoir Pk. Hosp. Belf.

PAISLEY, John Carson (retired) 8 Victoria Park, Armagh BT61 9DX — MB BCh BAO 1923 Belf.; DTM & H RCPS Eng. 1926; DPH NUI 1935. Prev: Sen. Sleeping Sickness Off. Nigeria.

PAISLEY, Jonathan MacGregor Glenwood Health Centre, Napier Road, Glenrothes KY6 1HL Tel: 01592 611171 Fax: 01592 611931 — MB ChB 1984 Ed.; MRCGP 1989; DObst Auckland 1988. Clin. Asst. - Culposcopy; Clin., Forth Pk. Hosp., Kirkaloy.

PAISLEY, Thomas Allan 16 Branning Court, Kirkcaldy KY1 2PD — MB ChB 1974 Glas.

PAJOVIC, Slav Barton Surgery, Barton Terrace, Dawlish EX7 9QH Tel: 01626 888877 Fax: 01626 888360; Larkbeare Farm, Mamhead, Kenton, Exeter EX6 8HQ Tel: 01626 866297 — MB BS 1979 Lond.; MRCGP 1983. (Middx.)

PAJWANI, Kishor Shamlal Sydenham House, Monkswick Road, Harlow CM20 3NT Tel: 01279 424075 Fax: 01279 423936; 17 Walbrook, Woodford Road, South Woodford, London E18 2EG Tel: 020 8989 4456 — MB BS 1959 Karnatak; BSc (Hons.) Bombay 1952; LMSSA Lond. 1965. Hon. Adviser (Gen. Pract. Study) Kasturba Med. Coll. Manipal, India. Prev: Regist. (Chest Dis.) Kelling Hosp. Holt; Regist. (Geriat.) N.gate Hosp. Gt. Yarmouth; Ho. Surg. Dreadnought Seamens Hosp. Greenwich.

PAJWANI, Nileshrai Puskarrai The Surgery, 300 Ripple Road, Barking IG11 7RP Tel: 020 8594 2366 Fax: 020 8594 2775 — MB BS 1968 Gujarat.

PAKARIAN, Bouzourgmehr Farzin 27 Greenlaw Court, 1A Mount Park Road, London W5 2RX — MB ChB 1988 Leic.

PAKENHAM, Ralph William Medical Centre, 12 High Street, Fochabers IV32 7EP Tel: 01343 820247 Fax: 01343 820132 — MRCS Eng. LRCP Lond. 1975.

PAKENHAM-WALSH, Jean Thelma Keepers Cottage, Lythe Hill Park, Haslemere GU27 3BD — MB ChB 1942 Glas. Prev: Sen. Med. Off. i/c Uganda Blood Transfus. Serv.; Asst. Med. Off. Regional Blood Transfus. Serv. Camb.

PAKENHAM-WALSH, Neil Martin 16 Woodfield Drive, Charlbury, Oxford OX7 3SE Email: 101374.3615@compuserve.com; International Network for the Availability of Scientific Publications, 27 Park End St., Oxford OX1 1HU Tel: 01865 249909 Fax: 01865 251060 Email: inasp-health@gn.apc.org — MB BS 1983 Lond.; DRCOG 1986; DCH 1988.

PAKOULAS, Ms Christina Anthoula Emily (retired) 17 Homefield Road, Radlett WD7 8PX — MB BS 1984 Lond.; BSc (Hons.) Basic Med. Scs. & Physiol. Lond. 1981; FRCS Ed. (Ophth.) 1991. Prev: Specialist Regist. (Ophth.) Moorfields Eye Hosp. Lond.

PAKROOH, Mina Priscilla 21 Primley Park Crescent, Leeds LS17 7HY — MB BS 1993 Newc.

PAKTSUN, Lam Wai-Ping 8 Rose Court, Sherwood Road, Harrow HA2 8UU — MB BS 1964 Ceylon; DA Eng. 1976. Assoc. Specialist (Anaesth.) Mid Essex HA. Prev: Regist. (Anaesth.) Joyce Green Hosp. Dartford; Regist. (Anaesth.) Chelmsford Health Dist.

PAL, Abani Kumar (retired) Shanti, 27 Plastirion Avenue, Prestatyn LL19 9DU; MB BS Calcutta 1958; FICS 1988; MB BS 1958 Calcutta; FFAEM 1993. Cons. A & E Dept. Glan Clwyd Hosp. Rhyl. Prev: Resid. St. Vincent's Hosp. New York City, USA.

PAL, Ajita c/o Dr G. S. Pal, Horsham Hospital, Hurst Road, Horsham RH12 2DR — MRCS Eng. LRCP Lond. 1980.

PAL, Babi Rani 19 Warrington Close, Foxhollies Meadow, Walmley, Sutton Coldfield B76 2BL — MB ChB 1984 Glas.; MRCP (UK) 1988. SHO (Neonat.) St. Mary's Hosp. Manch.

PAL, Badal Department of Rheumatology, R10H4, Withington Hospital, Manchester M20 2LR Tel: 0161 291 4283 Fax: 0161 445 5631 Email: badal.pal@smuht.nwest.nhs.uk; 7 Poolcroft, The Nurseries, Sale Moor, Manchester M33 2LF Tel: 0161 973 6304 Fax: 0161 445 5631 Email: bpal@fs1.with.man.ac.uk — MB BS 1975 Calcutta; MD Newc. 1988; MRCP (UK) 1979; FRCP Lond. 1996; FRCP Ed. 1998. Cons. Rheum. & Withington Hosp. Manch.; Hon. Lect. (Rheum.) Univ. Manch. Socs: BMA; Brit. Soc. Rheum.; ODA Manch. Med. Soc. Prev: Sen. Regist. Roy. Vict. Infirm. Newc. & Durh.; Regist. (Med.) Wythenshawe Hosp. Manch.

PAL, Miss Cauvery 70 Mary Green, Abbey Road, London NW8 0BS — MB BS 1996 Lond.; BSc Lond. 1993. (UMDS, Guy's & St. Thos.)

PAL, Chhabi Rani 16 Chaldon Green, Lychpit, Basingstoke RG24 8YS Tel: 01256 471979 — MB BS 1985 Lond.; BSc Lond. 1982, MB BS 1985; MRCP (UK) 1988. Sen. Regist. (Radiol.) John Radcliffe Hosp. Oxf.

PAL, Deb Kumar Neuroscience Unit, Institute of Child Health, Wolfson Centre, Mecklenburgh Square, London WC1N 2AP Tel: 020 7837 7618 Fax: 020 7833 9469 Email: d.pal@ucl.ac.uk; Flat 3, 67/71 Yeldham Road, London W6 8JQ — MB BChir 1988 Camb.; MB BChir Camb. 1989; MA Camb. 1988; MRCP (UK) 1991; LMSSA 1988; MSc Lond. 1995; PhD Lond. 1998. (Camb. Univ.) Specialist Regist. (Paediat. Neurol.) Gt. Ormond St. Childr.'s Hosp. Nhs Trust, Lond. Socs: BMA; Brit Paed. Neuro. Assoc.; Internat. League Against Epilepsy. Prev: Wellcome Trust Res. Train. Fell., Inst. Of Child Health, Lond.; Sen. Regist. (Paediat. Neurol. & Complex Disabil.) Gt. Ormond St. Childr.'s Hosp. Nhs Trust, Lond.

PAL, Mr Dharam 1 Killowen Avenue, Northolt UB5 4QT — MB BS 1968 Delhi; FRCS Glas. 1983. (Maulana Azad Med. Coll.) SHO (Gen. Surg.) Warrington Infirm.

PAL, Dipti 27 Salisbury Mansions, St. Anns Road, London N15 3JP Tel: 020 8800 0611 — MB BS 1954 Calcutta.

PAL, Guru Saday c/o Dr P. Dasgupta, 54 Abbotts Park Road, London E10 6HX — MB BS 1974 Calcutta; MRCP (UK) 1983. (Calcutta Med. Coll.) Regist. (Haemat.) Clatterbridge Hosp. Wirral. Prev: Regist. (Gen. Med.) War Memor. Hosp. Wrexham; Regist. (Geriat. Med.) Leicester Gen. Hosp.; SHO (Gen. Med.) Dewsbury Gen. Hosp.

PAL, Madhu 1 Killowen Avenue, Northolt UB5 4QT Tel: 020 8864 7141 — MB BS 1974 Rajasthan; DRCOG 1984; DObst RCPI 1984. (Ravinder Nath Tagore Med. Coll. Udaipur) SHO (O & G) Chorley Dist. Hosp.

PAL, Mila 18 Duchy Road, Barnet EN4 0HU — MB BS 1972 Calcutta.

PAL, Naba Kumar Kernou, Moorgate Grove, Rotherham S60 2TR — MB BS 1955 Calcutta. (Nilratan Sarkar Med. Sch.) Med. Asst. A & E Dept. Rotherham Hosp. Prev: Sen. Ho. Surg. (Gen. Surg.) Bury Gen. Hosp.; Regist. (Orthop.) Dudley Rd. Hosp. Birm.; Resid. Surg. Off. (Gen. Surg.) Derwent Hosp. Derby.

PAL, Nibiti Ranjan Ash Grove, Cow Lane, Knottingley — MB BS Calcutta 1956, DTM & H 1961; DCH RCPS Glas. 1966. GP Knottingley. Prev: Regist. Killingbeck Hosp. Leeds.

PAL, Paragprasun Group Practice Surgery, 33 Newton Road, Great Barr, Birmingham B43 6AA Tel: 0121 357 1690 Fax: 0121 357 4253 — MB BS 1976 Calcutta; MB BS 1976 Calcutta.

PAL, Mr Praphulla Chandra (retired) 55 Cotysmore Road, Sutton Coldfield B75 6BL Tel: 0121 378 4446 — MB BS 1957 Calcutta; FRCS Ed: 1973; DTM & H Eng. 1963. Prev: Cons. Surg. Min. of Health Lusaka, Zambia.

PAL, Prasanta Kumar 91 Mossfield Road, Kings Heath, Birmingham B14 7JE Tel: 0121 444 2242; 48 Sellywick Drive, Selly Park, Birmingham B29 7JH Tel: 0121 414 1987 — MB BS Calcutta 1959; FFA RCSI 1974; DA Delhi 1964. (Calcutta) Indep. Pract. Cons. Anaesth. W. Midl. Socs: Assn. Anaesths. Prev: Cons. Anaesth. N.. RHA; Regist. (Anaesth.) Roy. Vict. Hosp. Belf.; Sen. Regist. (Anaesth.) Belf. City Hosp.

PAL, Rama Six Dials Surgery, 130-131 St. Marys Road, Southampton SO14 0BB Tel: 023 8033 5151 Fax: 023 8033 9677 — MB BS Calcutta 1974. (Culcutta) GP Soton.

***PAL, Rita** 55 Cotysmore Road, Sutton Coldfield B75 6BL — MB BS 1998 Lond.; MB BS Lond 1998.

PAL, Sandip Kumar 1 Vale Court, The Vale, Stock, Ingatestone CM4 9PX — MB BS 1977 Delhi.

PAL, Sankar Prosad Six Dials Surgery, 130-131 St. Marys Road, Southampton SO14 0BB Tel: 023 8033 5151 Fax: 023 8033 9677 — MB BS 1967 Calcutta. (Calcutta) GP Soton.

PAL, Santosh Kumar 65 Disraeli Road, London E7 9JU Tel: 020 8534 4388 Fax: 0208 472 3813 — MB BS 1963 Calcutta; BSc Calcutta 1954. (Med. Coll. Calcutta) p/t MQPM Appeals Serv. Lord Chancellors Dept Lond; Assist. GP Upton La. Med. Centre, Forest Gate Lond. E7 9PB. Socs: Companion Fell. BOA; Soc. Occupat. Med. Lond.; Fell. Hunt. Soc. Prev: Exam. Med. Off. Disablem. Servs. Auth.; Med. Off. i/c Balham & Kingston Appliances Centres DHSS; Med. Off. Limb-Fitting Centre Qu. Mary's Hosp. Roehampton.

PAL, Saphal Kanti Royton Medical Centre, Rochdale Road, Royton, Oldham OL2 5QB Tel: 0161 624 4857 Fax: 0161 628 5010 — MB BS 1965 Calcutta.

PAL, Sheena The Health Centre, Whyteman's Brae, Kirkcaldy KY1 2NA Tel: 01592 640600 Fax: 01592 641462.

PAL, Sipra Brinnington Road Surgery, 30-32 Brinnington Road, Stockport SK1 2EX Tel: 0161 480 4164 Fax: 0161 476 1996.

PAL, Uday 3 Index Drive, Dunstable LU6 3TU — MB BS 1969 Calcutta.

PALACCI, Alain Edward The Surgery, 22 Castelnau, London SW13 9RU Tel: 020 8748 7574 Fax: 020 8563 8821 — MB BS 1986 Lond. Assoc. Specialist Diabetic Unit Qu. Mary Hosp. Roehampton; Chairm. Therap. Comm. Richmond PCG.

PALACE, Jacqueline Ann Clinical Neurology, Radcliffe Infirmary, Woodstock Road, Oxford OX2 6HE Tel: 01865 224310 Fax: 01865 790493 — BM 1983 Soton.; MRCP (UK) 1986; DM 1992. Cons. (Neurol.) Oxf. RHA.

PALANIAPPAN, Rudrapathy Department of Audiological Medicine, Royal National Throat & Nose & Ear Hospital, Gray's Inn Road, London WC1X 8DA Tel: 020 7915 1559 Fax: 020 7915 1559 Email: rudipal@hotmail.com; 35 Axholme Avenue, Edgware HA8 5BE Tel: 020 8381 1323 Fax: 020 8381 1323 Email: rudipal@hotmail.com — MB BS 1986 Madras; MSc (Audiol. Med.) 1997; MS Madras 1986; FRCS Ed. 1995; DLO Madras 1985; DLO RCS Eng. 1991. (Jipmer, Pondicherry, India) Cons Audiologist Phys. Roy. Nat. Throat,Nose & Ear Hosp., Gray's Inn Rd. Lond. Socs: Brit. Soc. Audiol.; RCS Edin.; Brit. Assn. Audiol. Phys. Prev: Asst. Surg. Govt Gen. Hosp. Pondicherry, India.

PALANIAPPAN, Selambaram Moorfield Road Health Centre, 2 Moorfield Road, Enfield EN3 5PS Tel: 020 8804 1522 Fax: 020 8443 1465 — MB BS 1968 Ceylon; MRCOG 1980; DCH Ceylon 1974. GP Enfield. Socs: BMA. Prev: Regional Co-ordinator Rural Health Support Project Sudan (USAID Project).

PALAV, S S Comyns Close Clinic, 1 Comyns Close, Hermit Road, Canning Town, London E16 4JJ Tel: 020 7476 4862 Fax: 020 7473 6400 — MB BS 1959 Bombay; MB BS 1959 Bombay.

PALAZZO, Francesco Fausto 17 Wesley House, Little Britain, St Pauls, London EC1 7BX — State Exam Med 1992 Bari; FRCS Eng. 1997; FRSCI 1997. Prev: SHO Gen. Surg. Char. Cross Hosp. Lond.; Clin. Research Fell. Roy. Lond. & St Bart. Hosps.; Specialist Regist. Anglia & Oxf.

PALAZZO, Mark George Anthony 32 Holst Mansions, 96 Wyatt Drive, Barnes, London SW13 8AJ; Department of Anaesthetics, Charing Cross Hospital, Fulham Palace Road, London W6 8RF — MB ChB 1975 Bristol; MD Bristol 1989; FRCP Lond. 1995; MRCP (UK) 1978; FFA RCS Eng. 1982. Dir. (Intens. Care) Char. Cross Hosp. Lond. Prev: Sen. Lect. & Hon. Cons. Anaesth. Roy. Lond. Hosp.

PALCZYNSKI, Stephen Hunter Newlands Medical Centre, Borough Road, Middlesbrough TS1 3RX Tel: 01642 247401 Fax: 01642 223803; 106 Low Lane, Middlesbrough TS5 8EB Tel: 01642 593657 — MB BS 1969 Newc.; MRCGP 1974; DCH RCPS Glas. 1973; DObst RCOG 1972; FRCGP 1997. (Newc.) Princip. in Pract.; Year Tutor & Course Organiser Cleveland VTS; Trainer (Gen. Pract.) Cleveland; Mem. Micro PCG & Prescribing Lead. Socs: BMA & Med. Defence Union. Prev: Hosp. Pract. (Child & Family Psychiat.) N. Tees Gen. Hosp. Stockton-on-Tees; Police Surg. Cleveland Constab.; Trainee GP Newc. VTS.

PALEJWALA, Altaf Ali 27 Cherry Vale, Liverpool L25 5PX — MB ChB 1991 Liverp. Specialist Regist., Gastroenterol.

PALEJWALA, Razia 27 Cherry Vale, Liverpool L25 5PX — MB ChB 1993 Liverp.

PALEY, Helen Walnut Lodge Surgery, Walnut Road, Chelston, Torquay TQ2 6HP Tel: 01803 605359 Fax: 01803 605772; Venton Lodge, Dartington, Totnes TQ9 6DP Tel: 01364 73382 — MB BS 1988 Newc.; MRCGP 1993; DRCOG 1992. (New. u. Tyne) Prev: GP Newc.

PALEY, Judith Dorothy 11 Rodgersfield, Langho, Blackburn BB6 8HB — MB ChB 1995 Aberd.

PALEY, Mark Robert Department of Radiology, Frimley Park Hospital, Portsmouth Road, Frimley, Camberley GU16 7UJ Tel: 01276 604370 Fax: 01276 604546; 9 Portside, Brighton Marina Village, Brighton BN2 5UW Tel: 01273 605806 Email: paleym@globalnet.co.uk — BM BCh 1988 Oxf.; BA Oxf. 1985, BM BCh 1988; FRCR 1995. (Oxford) Cons. Radiol. Frimley Pk. Hosp. Surrey; Hon. Cons. Radiol. KCH Lond. Socs: Fell. Roy. Coll. Radiol.; Radiol. Soc. N. Amer. Prev: Fell. (Body Imaging & MRI) Univ. of Florida Gainesville USA; Sen. Regist. (Radiol.) King's Coll. Hosp. Lond.

***PALEY, Martin Douglas** 11 Rogersfield, Langho, Blackburn BB6 8HB — MB ChB 1997 Aberd.

PALEY, Olive Jane The Wing, Plas Hendy, Bryngeyn, Raglan NP15 2DA — MB ChB 1970 Liverp.

PALEY, Mr William George (retired) 11 Rogers Field, Langho, Blackburn BB6 8HB Tel: 01254 240124 — MB ChB 1958 Ed.; FRCS Eng. 1969; FRCS Ed. 1967. Prev: Cons. Surg. (Gen. & Vasc. Surg.) Blackburn & Dist. Gp. Hosps.

PALFERMAN, Thomas George Yeovil District Hospital, Higher Kingston, Yeovil BA21 4AT Tel: 01935 384302 Fax: 01935 426850 Email: palft@swest.nhs.uk — MB BS 1971 Lond.; FRCP Lond. 1992; MRCP (UK) 1977; MRCS Eng. LRCP Lond. 1971; DObst RCOG 1974; DCH Eng. 1974. (Char. Cross) Cons. Phys. & Rheum. Yeovil Dist. Hosp. Som.; Regional Adviser Rheumatol. S. W.. Deanery; Chair Clin. Affairs Comm. of Brit. Soc for Rheum.; Scientif. Adviser Nat. Osteoporosis Soc. Socs: MRCP Exam. RCP Lond.; Fell. Roy. Soc. Med. (Counc. Sect. Rheum.); (Counc.) Brit. Soc. Rheum. Prev: Sen. Regist. Rotat. (Gen. Med. & Rheum.) St. Bart. Hosp. Lond.; Regist. (Rheum.) St. Thos. Hosp. Lond.; Regist. (Med. & Neurol.) W.m. Hosp. Lond.

PALFRAMAN, Anthony Heathgate Surgery, The Street, Poringland, Norwich NR14 7JT Tel: 01508 494343; 120 The St, Rockland St. Mary, Norwich NR14 7HQ Tel: 01508 538382 — MB BS 1979 Lond.; MRCGP 1988; DRCOG 1987. Prev: Med. Regist. Roy. Cornw. Hosps.

PALFREEMAN, Adrian John The Cottage, Caldecott, Cheveston, Wellingborough NN9 6AR Tel: 01933 460807 Fax: 01933 460807 — MB ChB 1985 Sheff.; MRCPI 1994. Cons. (Genitourin. Med.) PeterBoro. Dist. Hosp.; Clin. Tutor PeterBoro. Dist. Hosp. Socs: Med. Soc. Study VD; Assn. Genitourin. Med.; Exec. Brit. HIV Assn. Prev: Sen. Regist. (Genitourin. Med.) Leicester Roy. Infirm.; Regist. (Genitourin. Med. & HIV) W.m. Hosp. Lond.; SHO Rotat. (Med.) Leicester Gp. Hosps.

PALFREEMAN, Roger Adam Olive House, Black Lane, Loxley, Sheffield S6 6SE Tel: 0114 234 3082 Email: rogandric@vwatt.freeserve.co.uk — MB ChB 1997 Sheff.

***PALFREMAN, Timothy Mark** 4 Loudhams Road, Little Chalfront, Amersham HP7 9NY — MB BS 1996 Lond.

PALFREY, Alec John 146 Hurlingham Road, London SW6 3NG Tel: 020 7736 2013 — MB BChir Camb. 1951; MA Camb. 1950, MD 1975. (Univ. Coll. Hosp.) Emerit. Reader (Func.al Morphol.) Char. Cross & W.m. Med. Sch. Lond. Socs: FRMS; Anat. Soc.; Brit. Assn. Clin. Anat. Prev: Sen. Lect. (Anat.) & Dir. Electron Microscope Unit Arthritis Rheum Counc. St. Thos. Hosp. Lond.; Lect. (Anat.) Univ. Coll., Ibadan.

PALFREY, Mr Edward Leslie Hinton Shepp House, Hamlash Lane, Frensham, Farnham GU10 3AU Tel: 01252 793481 Fax: 01252 793481 — MB BChir 1977 Camb.; MA, MB Camb. 1977, BChir 1976; FRCS Eng. 1980; FRCS Ed. 1980. (St. Mary's) Cons. Urol. Frimley Pk. Hosp. Surrey; Hon. Cons. Urol. Guy's & St. Thos. Hosp. Lond.; Med. Dir., Frimley Pk. Hosp. NHS Trust. Socs: Brit. Assn. Urol. Surg.; BSFE; BAUS - Sect. of Oncol. Prev: Sen. Regist. (Urol.) St. Thos. Hosp. Lond.; Asst. Dir. Lithotripter Centr. St. Thos. Hosp. Lond.; Research Fell. St. Thos. Hosp. Lond.

PALFREY, Penelope Ann (retired) 4 Sheaf Cottages, Weston Green, Thames Ditton KT7 0JR Tel: 020 8398 9209 — MB BChir

PALIA

1951 Camb.; BA Camb. 1951. Prev: Research Asst. (Anat.) Univ. Coll. Ibadan.

PALIA, Satnam Singh (retired) East Glam Mental health Unit, Church Village, Pontypridd CF38 1AB Email: sspalia@hotmail.com — MB BS 1976 Guru Nanak Dev; FRCPsych 1996, M 1981; DPM Eng. 1980. Cons. Psychiat. Old Age (Wales) E. Glam 1999-; Med. Mem. Ment. Health Review Tribunal. Prev: Sen. Regist. Rotat. (Adult Gen. Psychiat.) Glanrhyd & Penfai Hosp. Bridgend.

PALIN, Alastair Noel c/o The Ross Clinic, Royal Cornhill Hospital, Aberdeen AB25 2ZF — MB ChB 1982 Aberd.; MRCPsych 1987. Cons. Gen. Adult Psychiat. Grampian HB. Prev: Sen. Regist. (Psychiat.) Grampian HB; Regist. (Psychiat.) Lothian HB.

PALIN, Christopher Garden Flat, 15 Kitto Road, London SE14 5TW — MB ChB 1987 Birm.

***PALIN, Christopher Anthony** 19 Rylett Crescent, London W12 9RP — MB BS 1996 Lond.

PALIN, Donald John St Budeaux Health Centre, Stirling Road, St. Budeaux, Plymouth PL5 1PL Tel: 01752 361010 Fax: 01752 350675; 387 Fort Austin Avenue, Eggbuckland, Plymouth PL6 5TG Tel: 01752 788640 — MB BS 1972 Lond.; MRCS Eng. LRCP Lond. 1973. (Guy's Hospital) Prev: SHO (Paediat.) St. Richards Hosp. Chichester; SHO (O & G) Lewisham Hosp. Lond.

PALIN, Iain Stuart Clarendon Medical, 35 Northland Avenue, Londonderry BT48 7JW Tel: 028 7126 5391 Fax: 028 7126 5932 — MB ChB 1973 Ed.; BSc (Hons.) Ed. 1970, MB ChB 1973. Prev: Regist. (Med.) Raigmore Hosp. Inverness; SHO (Med.) Roy Infirm. Edin.

PALIN, Jonathan Ashley Broomwood Road Surgery, 41 Broomwood Road, St Paul's Cray, Orpington BR5 2JP Tel: 01689 832454 Fax: 01689 826165 Email: .palin@virgin.net; 13 Henham Gardens, East Peckham, Tonbridge TN12 5PD Tel: 01622 871176 — MB ChB 1989 Sheff.; MRCGP 1996; DRCOG 1994.

PALIN, Peter Haydn 17 Rowland Lane, Thornton-Cleveleys FY5 2QX — MB ChB 1965 St. And.; FFA RCS Eng. 1969; DA Eng. 1968. (St. And.) Cons. (Anaesth.) Vict. Hosp. Blackpool.

PALIN, Rachel Clare Wades Green Cottage, Church Minshull, Nantwich CW5 6DX Tel: 01270 522245 — MB ChB 1993 Leeds; DRCOG 1997. SHO (Psychiat.) N. Staffs. Hosp. Prev: Trainee GP (A & E) N. Staffs. VTS; Ho. Off. (Gen. Surg. & Gen. Med.) Huddersfield Roy. Infirm.

PALIN, Richard David 6 Morland Avenue, Leicester LE2 2PE — MB ChB 1991 Leic.

PALIN, Stephen John 19 Pencae, Llandegfan, Menai Bridge LL59 5TT — MB ChB 1996 Liverp.

PALIN, Suzanne Lydia Llys Teg, Pen Cae, Llandegfan, Menai Bridge LL59 5TT — MB ChB 1994 Birm.

PALING, John Bagshaw Fern Gardens, 29 Oxford Road, Garsington, Oxford OX44 9JT — MB BChir 1973 Camb.; BA Camb. 1969, MB 1973, MA, BChir 1972. Prev: GP Headington; PMO RMS Qu. Eliz. II.

PALIT, Arabinda 'Hillside', Cox Hill, Narberth SA67 8EH Tel: 01834860268 — MB BS 1960 Calcutta; FRCP Ed. 1983, M 1967; DCH Eng. 1964. (N.R.S. Med. Coll.) Cons. Paediat. Withybush Gen. Hosp. HaverfordW..

PALIT, Jayanta Department of Rheumatology, Basildon Hospital, Basildon SS16 5NL Tel: 01268 593397 Fax: 01268 593799; Department of Rheumatology, Orsett Hospital, Orsett, Grays RM16 3EU Tel: 01268 552267 Fax: 01268 592318 — MB BS 1971 Calcutta; MD All India Inst. Med. Scs. New Delhi 1976; MRCP (UK) 1982; FRCP Lond. 1997. (Calcutta) Cons. Rheum. Basildon Hosp. & Orsett Hosp. Socs: Brit. Soc. for Rheum. (B.S.R). Prev: Sen. Regist. (Rheum.) Withington Gen. Hosp. & Manch. Roy. Infirm.; Clin. Research Fell. (Rheum.) N. Gen. Univ. Edin.; Sen. Resid. (Rheum.) Dalhousie Univ. Halifax, Nova Scotia.

PALIT, Sanjit Lynwood Medical Centre, 4 Lynwood Drive, Romford RM5 2RA Tel: 01708 743244 Fax: 01708 736783 — MB BS 1976 Calcutta; LRCP LRCS Ed. LRCPS Glas. 1986.

PALIT, Tarun Department of Anaesthetics, Pilgrim Hospital, Sibsey Road, Boston PE21 9QS Tel: 01205 364801 Fax: 01205 442076 Email: palit@drtboston.freeserve.co.uk — MB BS 1981 Mithila U, India; MD (Anaesth.) Patna Univ. 1990; FFARCS (Irel.) 1998. Staff Grade (Anaesth.) Pilgrim Hosp. Boston. Socs: BMA. Prev: Vis. Regist. (Anaesth.) Pilgrim Hosp. Boston; SHO (Anaesth. & IC) Pilgrim Hosp. Boston; SHO (Anaesth. & Intens.. Care) Geo. Eliot Hosp. Nuneaton & Kettering Gen. Hosp.

PALIWALA, Abdulali Hasanali Potter Street, Harlow CM17 9BG; Osler House, Potter St, Harlow CM17 9BQ Tel: 01279 422664 Fax: 01279 422576 — MB BS 1968 Lond.; MRCP (UK) 1974; MRCS Eng. LRCP Lond. 1968; FRCGP 1996, M 1979; DCH Eng. 1971. (Univ. Coll. Hosp.) Prev: Course Organiser W. Essex GP VTS; Examr. MRCGP; Regist. (Paediat.) Qu. Mary's Hosp. Childr. Carshalton.

PALL, Abeed Ahmed 132 Hook rise N., Surbiton KT6 7JU — MB ChB 1984 Dundee.

PALL, Hardev Singh 22 Dunstall Way, East Molesey KT8 1PD — MB ChB 1979 Bristol; MRCP (UK) 1982.

PALL, Joginder The Surgery, Tinchbourne Street, Dudley DY1 1RH Tel: 01384 235540 Fax: 01384 458135; The Old Vicarage House, Vicarage Lane, Pensnett, Brierley Hill DY5 4JH Tel: 01384 262929 Email: j.pall@bt.internet.com — MB BS 1968 Punjab; MB BS Punjabi 1968. (Govt. Med. Coll. Patiala)

PALL, Navnit Kaur The Smethwick Medical Centre, Regent Street, Smethwick, Warley B66 3BQ — MB BS 1982 Maharshi Dayanand; MRCS Eng. LRCP 1991 London; MB BS 1982 Maharshi Dayanand. (Medical College, Lohrak, India)

***PALLAN, Arvind** 2 Derby Road, Bramcote, Nottingham NG9 3BA — MB ChB 1997 Birm.

PALLAN, Joginder Pal 2 Derby Road, Bramcote, Nottingham NG9 3BA Tel: 0115 925 4674 — MB ChB 1966 Manch.; FRCR 1976; DMRD Eng. 1972. Cons. Radiol. Derby City Gen. Hosp. Prev: Sen. Regist. & Regist. Gen. & City Hosps. Nottm.; SHO Roy. Manch. Childr. Hosp.

PALLANT, Eirwen Anne The Salvation Army Hospital, Chikankata, Mazabuka, Zambia; 4 Edward VII Avenue, Newport NP20 4NF Tel: 01633 267010 — MB ChB 1986 Leeds; BSc (Hons.) Physiol. Leeds 1983; DTM & H RCP Lond. 1992. Med. Off. Salvation Army Hosp. Chikankata, Mazabuka, Zambia.

PALLANT, Julia Madeleine Alexandra Surgery, 2 Wellington Avenue, Aldershot GU11 1SD Tel: 01252 332210 Fax: 01252 312490; 45 Bridgefield, Farnham GU9 8AW — MB ChB 1981 Birm.; MRCGP 1986; DRCOG 1985; DCH RCP Lond. 1984.

PALLAWELA, Mr Gunasiri D S Pallawela and Partners, Belmont Health Centre, 516 Kenton Lane, Kenton, Harrow HA3 7LT Tel: 020 8863 6863 Fax: 020 8863 9815; Red House, 188 Headstone Lane, North Harrow, Harrow HA2 6LY Tel: 020 8907 6046 — MB BS 1957 Ceylon; FRCS Ed. 1968. (Colombo) Police Surg. Metrop. Police.

PALLECAROS, Anna Sotira 30 Rollscourt Avenue, Herne Hill, London SE24 0EA — MB BS 1988 Lond.; BSc (Hist. of Med.) Lond. 1985; MRCP (UK) 1991; Cert. Family Plann. JCC 1993; DTM & H RCP Lond. 1992. Sen. Regist. (GUM & HIV) St. Mary's Hosp. Lond. Socs: Hellenic Med. Soc.; Med. Soc. Study VD. Prev: Clin. Research Fell. (Genitourin. Med.) St. Mary's Hosp. Lond.; Regist. Univ. Coll. Hosp. Sexual Health Clinic. Lond.

PALLETT, Ann Patricia Public Health Laboratory Service, Level B, South Laboratory Block, Southampton General Hospital, Southampton SO16 6YD Tel: 02380 796408 — MB BS 1978 Lond.; BSc (1st cl. Hons.) Lond. 1975; MRCPath 1986; FRCPath. (University College Hospital London) Cons. Med. Microbiol. Soton. & SW Hants. AHA. Prev: Sen. Regist. (Med. Microbiol.) Rotat. St. Richards Hosp. Chichester & St. Geo. Hosp. Lond; Regist. (Med. Microbiol.) W.m. Hosp. Lond.

PALLETT, Joan Lesley 9 The Glebe, Church Road, Copthorne, Crawley RH10 3RP Tel: 01342 713756 — MB BS 1967 Lond.; MFPM RCP (UK) 1995; Dip. Pharma. Med. RCP Lond. 1993; FFA RCS Eng. 1972; DA Eng. 1969. (Univ. Coll. Hosp.) Sen. Clin. Phys. Bibra Internat. Carshalton. Prev: Med. Adviser, Novartis Consumer Health; Assoc. Specialist (Anaesth.) Qu. Vict. Hosp. E. Grinstead.; Clin. Asst. (Anaesth.) Qu. Vict. Hosp. E. Grinstead.

PALLETT, Joyce Mary (retired) 36 Majorfield Road, Topsham, Exeter EX3 0ES — MB BS 1955 Lond.; MRCPsych 1972; DPM Eng. 1971; DObst RCOG 1958. Prev: Cons. Psychiat. Centr. Hosp. Warwick.

PALLEWELA, Constance Cordelia c/o Drive C. S. Pallewela, 3 Summerhill Court, Avenue Road, St Albans AL1 3PX Tel: 01727 68539 — MB BS 1956 Ceylon; DLO Eng. 1965. (Colombo) Clin. Asst. Outpat. Dept. Roy. Nat. Throat, Nose & Ear Hosp. Lond.

PALLEWELA, Cyril Samarawickrama (retired) 36 Kettering Road, Geddington, Kettering NN14 1AW — MB BS 1948 Madras; FRCOG 1980, M 1965, DObst 1957. Cons. (O & G) N.W. Thames RHA.

PALLIS, Doros John (retired) Old Lyminster House, Church Lane, Lyminster, Littlehampton BN17 7QJ Tel: 01903 882792 — Ptychio latrikes 1964 Athens; Ptychio latrikes (Distinc.) Athens 1964; MD (Commendat.) Aberd. 1977; FRCPsych 1994, M 1973; Cert. Neuropsychiat. 1979; Dip. Psychother. Aberd. 1970; DPM Eng. 1968. Cons. Psychiat. Med. Mem., Ment. Health Review Tribunal. Prev: Scientif. Off. MRC Clin. Psychiat. Unit.

PALLISTER, Deirdre Heather 4 King Edward Close, Christ's Hospital, Horsham RH13 7LX Tel: 01403 267159 — MB BS 1983 Lond. SCMO & BrE. Phys. Jarvis BrE. Screening Centre Guildford. Prev: Med. Off. (Orthop.) King Edwd. VII Hosp. Midhurst; Sen. Regist. (Pub. Health Med.) W. Midl. RHA.

PALLISTER, Ian 8 Cardinal Gardens, Darlington DL3 8SD; 4 St. Margaret's Road, Whitchurch, Cardiff CF14 7AA Email: ianpallister@hotmail.com — MB BS 1989 Newc.; FRCS (Eng) 1993; MMedSci Birm. 1995.

PALLISTER, Michael Alan, Air Commodore RAF Med. Br. (retired) Abbascombe Barn, Lily Lane, Templecombe BA8 0HN Tel: 01963 71163 — MRCS Eng. LRCP Lond. 1955; BA Camb. 1952, BChir 1955, MB 1956; MFOM RCP Lond. 1981; MFCM RCP (UK) 1976; MRCGP 1975; DIH Eng. 1963; DPH Lond. 1963; DTM & H Liverp. 1958. Station Commdr. P.ss Alexandra Hosp. RAF Wroughton; Cons. Community Med. RAF.

PALLISTER, William Knott 21 Denewood Road, Highgate, London N6 4AQ Tel: 020 8340 8438; (resid.), 21 Denewood Road, Highgate, London N6 4AQ Tel: 020 8340 8438 — MB BS Lond. 1949; FFA RCS Eng. 1955; DHMSA Lond. 1978; DA Eng. 1951. (King's Coll. Lond. & Westm.) Emerit. Cons. Anaesth. Middlx. Hosp. & Hosp. Wom. Soho; Hon. Sen. Lect. Univ. Coll. & Middlx. Sch. Med.; Emerit. Hon. Cons. Anaesth. Hosp. St. John & Eliz. Socs: Fell. Roy. Soc. Med.; Assn. Cardiothoracic Anaesths. Prev: Jt. Sen. Regist. (Anaesth.) Brompton Hosp. Dis. Chest & W.m. Hosp. Lond.; Squadron Ldr. RAF Med. Br., Graded Anaesth. Aden Command.

PALLOT, Doreen Betty (retired) 36 Parkway, Welwyn Garden City AL8 6HQ Tel: 01707 323115 — MB BS 1949 Lond.; MRCS Eng. LRCP Lond. 1949; FFA RCS Eng. 1955; DA Eng. 1952. Hon. Cons. Anaesth. Roy. Nat. Throat, Nose & Ear Hosp, & Moorfields Eye Hosp. Prev: Regist. (Anaesth.) Hosp. Sick Childr. Gt. Ormond St.

PALMER, Mr Alan (retired) 7 Wise Close, Beverley HU17 9GR Tel: 01482 873867 Fax: 01482 873867 Email: palmer@arpleby2000.fsnet.co.uk — MB BS Lond. 1964; MRCS Eng. LRCP Lond. 1964; FRCOG 1985, M 1972; DObst RCOG 1967. Prev: Cons. O & G Hull Health Dist.

PALMER, Alan Charles HMS Herald BFPO 296 — MB ChB 1990 Leic.

PALMER, Alastair Anderson Teviot Medical Practice, Teviot Road, Hawick TD9 9DT Tel: 01450 370999 Fax: 01450 371025; Newmill House, Hawick TD9 9UQ — MB ChB 1982 Glas.

***PALMER, Alison Rachel** 12 Brookside Road, Ruddington, Nottingham NG11 6AW Tel: 0115 921 1772 — MB ChB 1995 Birm.; DCH Lond. 1998; DRCOG Lond. 1998; DFFO Lond. 1999.

PALMER, Andrew Barlborough Medical Practice, The Old Malthouse, 7 Worksop Road, Barlborough, Chesterfield S43 4TY Tel: 01246 819994 — MB ChB 1984 Leic.; MRCGP 1988; DRCOG 1988. GP Chesterfield.

PALMER, Andrew Bernard David St. Mary's Hospital, Renal Unit, Praed St., Paddington, London W2 1NY Tel: 020 7886 1615 Fax: 020 7402 7784; Studd Cottage, Bedmond Road, Abbots Langley WD5 0QE Email: andypal@msn.com — MB BS 1980 Lond.; FRCP (UK) 1997; MRCP (UK) 1984. Cons. Nephrol. St. Mary's Hosp. Lond.; Hon. Cons. Nephrol. Centr. Middlx. Hosp. & N.wick Pk. Hosp. Socs: Renal Assn.; Brit. Transpl. Soc. Prev: Sen. Regist. (Nephrol.) St. Mary's Hosp. Lond.; Regist. (Nephrol.) Kings Coll. Hosp. Lond.

PALMER, Ann Patricia West Kent Health Authority, Preston Hall, Aylesford ME20 7NJ Tel: 01622 710161 Fax: 01622 719802; 49 St Margarets Street, Rochester ME1 1UG Tel: 01634 407198 — MD 1989 Ed.; MB ChB 1969; MSc (Community Med.) Lond. Sch. Hyg. & Trop. Med. 1983; FFPHM RCP (UK) 1992. (Ed.) Dir. of Pub. Health Medway HA; Sen. Research Fell. Health Servs. Research Unit Univ. Kent & Canterbury. Socs: Soc. Social Med.; Inst. Health Servs. Man.

Prev: SCM Medway HA; Sen. Regist. (Community Med.) Trent RHA; Regist. (Community Med.) N.W. Thames RHA.

PALMER, Audrey 722 Gower Road, Upper Killay, Swansea SA2 7HQ — BM 1976 Soton.; FRCS Eng. 1984. Cons. A & E Morriston Hosp. Swansea.

PALMER, Ayo Elizabeth Salome 272 Galton Road, Smethwick B67 5JL — MB ChB 1981 Bristol; BSc (Hons.) (Cell. Path.) Bristol 1981, MB ChB (Hons.) 1984; MRCP (UK) 1989.

PALMER, Bernard Kevin (retired) Brent Knoll, Glasllwch Lane, Newport NP20 3PR — MB ChB Bristol 1955; MRCGP 1963; DObst RCOG 1957. Prev: Clin. Asst. (Obst.) Gen. Pract. Matern. Unit Roy. Gwent Hosp. Newport.

PALMER, Mr Bernard Victor Lister Hospital, Stevenage Tel: 01438 781106; Southacre, 39 Pasture Road, Letchworth SG6 3LR Tel: 01462 683064 Email: bernardpalmer@ntlworld.com — MA, MB Camb. 1970, MChir 1981, BChir 1969; FRCS Eng. 1974; MRCP (UK) 1972. (Camb. & Lond. Hosp.) Cons. Gen. Surg. Lister Hosp. Stevenage. Socs: Christ. Med. Fell.sh.; Brit. Assn. Surg. Oncol.; B.M.A. Prev: Sen. Regist. (Surg.) Roy. Marsden Hosp. & King's Coll. Hosp. Lond.; Regist. (Surg.) Whipps Cross Hosp. & St. Bart. Hosp. Lond.

***PALMER, Beverley** Ann Cripps PGMC, Northampton General Hospital, Cliftonville, Northampton NN1 5BD — MB BS 1997 Lond.

PALMER, Bryan Mark 58 Burch's Close, Galmington, Taunton TA1 4TR Tel: 01823 252880 Email: bryanpalmer@hotmail.com — MB ChB Bristol 1993; DGM RCP Lond. 1996; DRCOG 1998; MRCGP 1998. (Bristol) Trainee GP Taunton Som. VTS. Prev: SHO (Geriat.) Whipps Cross Hosp. Lond.; Ho. Off. (Surg.) MusGr. Pk. Hosp. Taunton; Ho. Off. (Med.) Derriford Hosp. Plymouth.

PALMER, Celia Department of Occupational Health & Safety, King's College Healthcare NHS Trust, King's College Hospital, Denmark Hill, London SE5 9RS Tel: 020 7346 3387 / 3511 Fax: 020 7346 3261; 2 Horseshoe Wharf Apartments, Clink Street, London SE1 9FE Tel: 020 7378 0637 Fax: 020 7401 9158 — MB BS 1966 Lond.; MRCS Eng. LRCP Lond. 1966; AFOM RCP Lond. 1987; DA Eng. 1968. (Roy. Lond. Hosp.) Staff Grade Occupat.al Phys. Socs: Soc. Occupat. Med.; Roy. Soc. Med.; Dir. Soc. Relief of Widows & Orphans of Med. Men. Prev: Sen. Occupat. Phys. BMI Health Servs.; Occupat. Phys. Marks & Spencer plc Lond.; Med. Dir. Harlow Indust. Health Serv.

PALMER, Charles Rupert, TD Huntsland Barn, Crawley Down, Crawley RH10 4HB Tel: 01342 712313 Fax: 01342 712313 — MRCS Eng. LRCP Lond. 1944. (St. Thos.) Hon. Med. Off. Qu. Vict. Hosp. E. Grinstead. Socs: Fell. Hunt. Soc. & Roy. Soc. Med. (Mem. Sect. Gen. Pract.); Fell. Sy. Benevolent Med. Soc. Prev: Ho. Surg. Orthop. Dept. Roy. Vict. & W. Hants. Hosp. Bournemouth; Ho. Surg. Plastic Surg. & Maxillo-Facial Centre, Qu. Vict. Hosp. E.; Grinstead; Maj. RAMC TA (Sussex Yeomanry).

PALMER, Cheryl Anne 51 Priorswood, Thorpe Mamott, Norwich NR8 6FW Tel: 01603 864202 — BM BCh 1997 Oxf.; MA Camb. 1994. SHO (Gen. Med.) Norf. & Norwich Hosp. Prev: PRHO (Gen. Surg.) Roy. Surrey Co. Hosp. Guildford Surrey; PRHO (Gen. Med.) N.ampton Gen. Hosp.; Sen. Ho. Off. Qu. Eliz. Hosp. Kings Lynn.

PALMER, Christopher Douglas 151 Ecclesall Road S., Sheffield S11 9PJ Tel: 0114 235 2115 — MB BS 1990 Newc.; FRCA 1996. Specialist Regist. Rotat. (Anaesth.) Sheff. Socs: BMA; MRCAnaesth.; Train. Mem. Assn. Anaesth. Prev: SHO (Anaesth.) Chesterfield & N. Derbysh. Roy. Infirm.; SHO (Anaesth.) N.. Gen. Hosp. Sheff. & Rotherham Dist. Gen. Hosp.

PALMER, Mr Colin Attwell Lynch (retired) Rose Cottage, Whirlow Lane, Sheffield S11 9QF Tel: 0114 236 3773 — MB BS 1952 Lond.; FRCS Ed. 1962; FRCS Eng. 1962; DO Eng. 1957. Prev: Hon. Clin. Lect. (Ophth.) Univ. Sheff.

***PALMER, Daniel Harrison** 29 Chevril Court, Wickersley, Rotherham S66 2BN — MB ChB 1995 Birm.; ChB Birm. 1995.

PALMER, David Allan The Medical Centre, Forstgate Rd, Corby NN17 1TR Tel: 01536 202507 Fax: 01536 206099 — BM BS 1980 Nottm.; BMedSci Nottm. 1978; MRCGP 1984; Cert. Family Plann. JCC 1983; DRCOG 1982. (Nottingham) Police Surg. 1998. Socs: Roy. Coll. Gen. Pract.; Assn. Police Surg. Prev: Trainee GP Lincoln VTS; Ho. Off. Derby City Hosp.

PALMER, David John 5 King George Gardens, Chichester PO19 4LB Tel: 01243 788685 — MB BChir Camb. 1955; MRCS Eng. LRCP Lond. 1955; MRCGP 1965; DObst RCOG 1960. (Camb.

PALMER

& Guy's) Prev: GP Worthing; Asst. Ho. Surg. & Out-pat. Off. Guy's Hosp.; Med. Off. RAF.

PALMER, David Jonathan Lloyd 8 Chestnut Grove, Penkridge, Stafford ST19 5LX — MB ChB 1989 Birm.

PALMER, David Leslie (retired) Tremayne, Church Lane, Bearsted, Maidstone ME14 4EF — MB, BS Lond. 1948.

PALMER, Derek Edward 23 Sycamore Drive, Hamilton ML3 7HF — MB ChB 1984 Glas.

PALMER, Didier Jon Wilfred 24 Maitland Street, Cardiff CF14 3JU — MB BCh 1987 Wales.

PALMER, Edward Gray The Surgery, 71 The Avenue, Wivenhoe, Colchester CO7 9PP Tel: 01206 824447 Fax: 01206 827973 — MB BS 1954 Lond.; MRCS Eng. LRCP Lond. 1954; DObst RCOG 1957. (Guy's) Socs: BMA.

PALMER, Eileen Mary Workington Infirmary, Infirmary Road, Workington CA14 2UN — MB ChB 1979 Leeds; Cert. In Med. Edu. 1998 Newcastle; BSc (1st cl. Hons.) Leeds 1976; MRCGP 1985; Dip. Palliat. Med. Wales 1992; DRCOG 1984. Med.Dir. W. Cumbria Hospice at home; Cons Palliat. Med W Cumbria. Prev: Med. Dir. P. of Wales Hospice Pontefract; GP Leeds; SHO (Med.) Wharfedale Gen. Hosp. Otley.

PALMER, Elizabeth Ann 12 Brookvale Road, Highfield, Southampton SO17 1QP — MB BS 1977 Lond.; MRCGP 1981; DRCOG 1983. GP Soton.

PALMER, Elizabeth Nina Edith Garden Flat, 11 Manby Road, Malvern WR14 3BD — MB ChB 1992 Birm.

PALMER, Graham Robert Stockton Heath Medical Centre, The Forge, London Road, Stockton Heath, Warrington WA4 6HJ Tel: 01925 604427 Fax: 01925 210501; 5 Teddington Close, Appleton, Warrington WA4 5QG — MB ChB 1983 Manch. (Manch.)

PALMER, Harry James Graham Northfields, Jericho St., Thorverton, Exeter EX5 5PA — MB BS 1950 Lond.; MRCS Eng. LRCP Lond. 1950. (St. Mary's)

PALMER, Helen Elizabeth Department of Ophthalmology, St. Thomas' Hospital, London SE1 7EH Tel: 020 7928 9292 — MB BS 1988 Lond.; FRCS Ed. 1993. Regist. (Ophth.) St. Thos. Hosp. Lond.

PALMER, Helen Margaret South Tyneside Health Care Trust, Palmer Community Hospital, Wear St., Jarrow NE32 3UX Tel: 0191 451 6031 Fax: 0191 451 6000; 2 Coalburns Cottages, Coalburns, Greenside, Ryton NE40 4JN Tel: 0191 413 1211 — MB BS 1980 Newc.; MRCP (UK) (Paediat.) 1985; DTM & H Liverp. 1989. Cons. Community Paediat. S. Tyneside Health Care Trust. Prev: Sen. Regist. (Community Paediat.) Community Unit Newc. Gen. Hosp.

PALMER, Professor Ian Peter, Lt.-Col. RAMC Department of Military Psychiatry, RDMC, Fort Blockhouse, Gosport PO12 2AB Tel: 02392 765664 Fax: 02392 765653 Email: psych@milmed.demon.co.uk — MB ChB 1977 Bristol; MRCPsych 1992. TriServ. Prof. of Defence Pshyiatry Roy. Defence Med. Coll.; Hon. Cons. Psychiat. UMDS. Prev: Cons. Sen. Lect. (Milit. Psychiat.) Roy. Defence Med. Coll.; Sen. Regist. (Liaison Psychiat.) King's Coll. Hosp. Lond.; Psychiat. UNAMIR, Rwanda.

PALMER, Mr James David Derriford Hospital, Plymouth PL6 8DH Tel: 01752 792542 Fax: 01752 763395 Email: james.palmer@phnt.guest.nhs.uk — MB BS 1985 Lond.; FRCS (SN) 1996; FRCS Ed. 1989; MS Soton. 1998. (Lond. Hosp.) Cons. Neurosurg. Deffiford Hosp. Plymouth. Socs: Soc. Brit. Neurol. Surg.; Examr. Europe Bd. Europe Assoc. NeuroSurgic. Soc. Prev: Cons. Neurosurg. & Clin. Sen. Lect. Inst. Neurol. Nat. Hosp. Neurol. & Neurosurg. Lond.; Sen. Regist. (Neurosurg.) S.. Gen. Hosp. Glas.; Regist. (Neurosurg.) Wessex. Neuro Centre Soton.

PALMER, Mr James Gordon Cumberland Infirmary, Carlisle CA2 7HY Tel: 01228 23444 — MB BS 1973 Lond.; MS Lond. 1989; FRCS Eng. 1978. (Lond. Hosp. Med. Coll.) Cons. Surg. Cumbld. Infirm. Carlisle; Hon. Lect. (Surg.) Univ. Newc. Socs: (Counc.) Assn. Coloproctol. Prev: Research Fell. (Surg.) Univ. Michigan, USA; Clin. Fell. ICRF Colorectal Cancer Unit St. Mark's Hosp. Lond.; Resid. Surg. Off. St. Mark's Hosp. Lond.

PALMER, James Hector MacGowan Hope Hospital, Stott Lane, Salford M6 8HD Tel: 0161 787 5107 Email: jpalmer@hope.srht.nwest.nhs.uk; 22 Rutland Ave, West Didsbury, Manchester M20 1JD — MB ChB 1986 Manch.; BSc (Med. Sci.) St. And. 1983; FRCA 1992. Cons. Anaesth.Hope Hosp. Socs: Assn. Anaesth.& Manch. Med. Soc.; Difficult Airway Soc.; William Scott Memor. Soc. Prev: Cons (Anaesth.) Dumfries & Galloway RI.; Locum

Cons. (Anaesth.) Hope Hosp. Salford; Cons. (Anaesth.) SE Qu.sland Australia.

PALMER, Joanne Victoria 84 Towers Road, Poynton, Stockport SK12 1DF — MB BS 1992 Lond.

PALMER, Mr John Hendley Plastic & Reconstructive Surgery Unit, Royal Devon & Exeter Healthcare NHS Trust, Barrack Road, Exeter EX2 5DW Tel: 01392 411611; 8 Lyndhurst Road, Exeter EX2 4PA Tel: 01392 437138 — MB BS Lond. 1976; FRCS Eng. 1981; T(S) 1991. Cons. Plastic Surg. Devon, Exeter & Som. HAs. Socs: BMA; Brit. Assn. Plastic Surg.; (Counc.) Brit. Assn. Aesthetic Plastic Surgs. Prev: Cons. Plastic Surg. Bradford NHS Trust; Sen. Regist. Rotat. Leeds & Bradford; Regist. (Plastic Surg.) Edin.

PALMER, Mr John Herbert Medway Hospital, Windmill Road, Gillingham ME7 5NY; 1 King Edward Road, Rochester ME1 1UA Tel: 01634 407198 Fax: 01634 815811 — MB ChB 1970 Ed.; FRCS Ed. 1976. (Ed.) Cons. Urol. Medway Maritini Hosp. Gillingham. Prev: Sen. Regist. (Urol.) Roy. Hallamsh. Hosp. Sheff.; Regist. St. Paul's Hosp. Lond.; Research Fell. Inst. Urol. Lond.

PALMER, John Peter 11 Vicarage Avenue, Egham TW20 8NW — MB BCh BAO 1975 Dub.; DObst. RCPI 1980 DCH NUI 1979.

PALMER, Jonathan Charles Netherwood, Southwater, Horsham RH13 7DB Tel: 01403 733233 — MB BS 1980 Lond.; MRCS Eng. LRCP Lond. 1979. (Guy's)

PALMER, Joseph Maximiar c/o Mrs Teresa McCann, Lower Corr, Dungannon BT71 6HQ — MB BCh BAO 1992 Belf.

PALMER, Judith Angela Cornlands Road Clinic, Cornlands Road, Acomb, York YO24 3WY Tel: 01904 798278; 20 Bedern, York YO1 7LP Tel: 01904 637629 — MB ChB 1971 Bristol; DCH Eng. 1974. (Bristol) Clin. Med. Off. (Child Health) York Health NHS Trust. Socs: Christian Med. Fell.sh.; BMA. Prev: Princip. GP York; SHO (Paediat.) Roy. Alexandra Childr. Hosp. Brighton; Ho. Surg. (Obst.) Roy. Sussex Co. Hosp. Brighton.

PALMER, Julia Claire Woodland Centre, Hillingdon Hospital, Uxbridge UB8 3NN Tel: 01895 279969 Fax: 01895 279918 Email: julia.palmer@152.hillingh-tr.nthames.nhs.uk — MB BChir 1981 Camb.; MA, BA Camb. 1978; MRCPsych 1987. Cons. Old Age Psychiat. Hillingdon Hosp. Uxbridge. Prev: Sen. Regist. (Psychiat.) St. Geo. Hosp. Lond.

***PALMER, Julia Elizabeth** 39 Broadway, Pontypool NP4 6HW — MB BCh 1996 Wales.

PALMER, Justine Huette 14 The Mews, Leazes Park Road, Newcastle upon Tyne NE1 4DA — MB BS 1991 Newc.

PALMER, Karen Susan Community Mental Health Team, Inchkeith House, 137 Leith Walk, Edinburgh EH6 8NP Tel: 0131 467 8530; 50 Kingsknowe Road S., Edinburgh EH14 2JW Tel: 0131 443 2960 — MB ChB 1987 Glas.; BSc Aberd. 1982; MRCPsych 1992. (Glasgow) Staff Grade (Psychiat.) Roy. Edin. Hosp. Prev: Experienced SHO in Psychiat. (Retainer Scheme) Roy. Edin. Hosp.; Clin. Asst. (Learning Disabilities) Gogarburn, Edin.; Regist. Rotat. (Psychiat.) Gt.er Glas. Health Bd. Pk.head Hosp. Glas.

PALMER, Katherine Sarah Old Vicarage W., Castle Bank, Stafford ST16 1DJ; North Staffordford Hospital City General, London Road, Stoke-on-Trent ST4 6SD Tel: 01782 552445 — BM BS Nottm. 1985; MRCP (UK) 1989; DM Nottm. 1994; FRCPCH. Cons. Paediat. (Neonat.) N. Staffs. Hosp. NHS Trust.

PALMER, Keith Trevor MRC Environmental Epidemiology Unit, University of Southampton, Southampton General Hospital, Southampton SO16 6YD Tel: 02380 777624 Fax: 02380 704021; 12 Brookvale Road, Highfield, Southampton SO17 1QP — BM BCh 1981 Oxf.; MA Oxf. 1981; MRCGP (Distinc.) 1986; MFOM RCP Lond. 1994; Cert. Family Plann. JCC 1986; DRCOG 1984; FFOM RCP Lond. 1998. (Oxford Univ.) Clin. Scientist (Occupat. & Environm. Epidemiol.) MRC & Hon. Cons. Occupat. Health Phys. Soton. Univ. Hosps. NHS Trust. Prev: Employm. Med. Adviser Health & Safety Exec.; Asst. Regist. Fac. Occupat. Med.

PALMER, Kelvin Raymond 7 Abbotsfield Park, Edinburgh EH10 5DX; GI Unit, Western General Hospital, Edinburgh EH4 2XU Tel: 0131 537 1007 — MD 1981 Sheff.; FRCP 2000; MB ChB 1974; MRCP (UK) 1977; FRCP (Ed.) 1987. (Sheffield) Cons. Gastroenterol. W.ern Gen. Hosp. Edin.; Assoc. Postgrad. Dean, S.E. Scotl. Socs: Brit. Soc. Gastroenterol.

PALMER, Lindsay Anne Lambgates Doctors Surgery, 1-5 Lambgates, Hadfield, Glossop SK13 1AW Tel: 01457 869090 Fax: 01457 857367; 18 Hollybank, Manor Croft, Glossop SK13 8TS Tel:

PALMER

01457 852397 — MB ChB 1989 Manch.; BSc (Hons.) Anat. Manch. 1986; MRCGP 1993; DRCOG 1993; DCH RCP Lond. 1992; Cert. Family Plann. JCC 1991. (Manchester) Prev: SHO (A & E) Withington & Wythenshawe Hosp.; Trainee GP Bramhall Health Centre Chesh.; SHO (O & G, Geriat., Paediat. & Psychiat.) Stepping Hill Hosp. Stockport.

PALMER, Lyndon John Littlefield, Webbs Green, Soberton, Southampton SO32 3PY Tel: 01489 877174 — MB BS 1966 Lond.; MRCS Eng. LRCP Lond. 1966; DObst RCOG 1968. (St. Geo.) Socs: (Treas.) Fareham Med. Soc. (Ex-Chairm.). Prev: SHO (Midw. & Gyn.) Soton. Gen. Hosp.; Ho. Phys. & Ho. Surg. Cirencester Memor. Hosp.

PALMER, Margaret Anne The Oaklands Practice, Yateley Medical Centre, Oaklands, Yateley GU46 7LS Tel: 01252 872333 Fax: 01252 890084; 32 Masefield Gardens, Crowthorne RG45 7QS — MB ChB 1974 Manch. (Manch.)

PALMER, Mark Antony Lofthouse Surgery, 2 Church Farm Close, Lofthouse, Wakefield WF3 3SA Tel: 01924 822273 Fax: 01924 825168 — MB ChB 1990 Leeds; T(GP) 1994; DFFP 1994. (University of Leeds) GP.

PALMER, Mr Michael Alexander 8 Barcombe Road, Heswall Hills, Wirral CH60 1UZ Tel: 0151 342 8801 — MB ChB 1984 Glas.; FRCS Ed. 1989.

PALMER, Michael Ian 6 Brettenham Road, Hitcham, Ipswich IP7 7NT — MB BS 1993 Lond.

PALMER, Michael John The Surgery, Station Road, East Looe, Looe PL13 1HA Tel: 01503 263195; Teghyjy, Brentfields, Polperro, Looe PL13 2JJ Tel: 01503 272426 Fax: 01503 272426 — MRCS Eng. LRCP Lond. 1972; MFFP 1995; MRCGP 1983; DObst RCOG 1975. (Sheff.) Local Med. Off. Civil Serv. Dept. (Looe Dist.); CMO (Family Plann.) Liskeard.

PALMER, Michael Kenneth Flat 2, Flaxman House, 1-3 Coleherne Road, London SW10 9BS Tel: 020 7373 9208 — MB ChB 1974 Ed.; FRCR 1982. Cons. Radiol. St. Helier Hosp. Carshalton. Prev: Sen. Regist. (Radiol.) St. Geo. Hosp. Lond.; Ho. Surg. (Thoracic Surg.) Roy. Infirm. Edin.; Sen. Ho. Phys. (Gen. Med.) N. Middlx. Hosp. Lond.

PALMER, Michael Sydney Morton (retired) 24 Matham Road, East Molesey KT8 0SU Tel: 020 8979 1872 — MB BChir Camb. 1941; MD Camb. 1949. Prev: Cons. Phys. Roy. Free Hosp. Lond.

***PALMER, Natalie Jane** The Corner House, Round Oak Road, Weybridge KT13 8HT — MB ChB 1998 Liverp.; MB ChB Liverp 1998.

PALMER, Neil Ingamells The Old School House, Bramcote Lane, Wollaton, Nottingham NG8 2ND — MB BS 1969 Lond.; FFA RCS Eng. 1974. (St. Thos.) Cons. Anaesth. Univ. Hosp. Nottm. Prev: Sen. Regist. (Anaesth.) St. Thos. Hosp. Lond.; Regist. Dept. Anaesth. Hosp. Sick Childr. Gt. Ormond St. Lond.; Regist. Dept. Anaesth. Lond. Hosp.

PALMER, Nicholas David Department of Cardiology, Western General Hospital, Crewe Road S., Edinburgh EH4 2XU Tel: 0131 537 1851 Fax: 0131 537 1005; 3 Mearenside, East Craigs, Edinburgh EH12 8UQ Tel: 0131 476 0288 — MB BS 1991 Newc.; MRCP (UK) 1994. (Newc. u. Tyne) Hon. Regist. & Clin. Research Fell. (Cardiol.) W.. Gen. Hosp. Edin. Socs: Scott. Cardiac Soc. Prev: Regist. (Med. & Cardiol.) & SHO (Med.) N. Tees Gen. Hosp. Stockton; Ho. Off. (Med.) Freeman Hosp. Newc.

PALMER, Nigel William Park Grove Surgery, 94 Park Grove, Barnsley S70 1QE Tel: 01226 282345 — MB ChB 1986 Sheff.

PALMER, Pauline Anne 127 McDonald Road, Edinburgh EH7 4NW Tel: 0131 556 6996 — BChir 1993 Camb.; MB BChir Camb. 1993; BSc (Hons.) St. And 1991; DCH Lond. 1998. (St. Andrews/Camb.) N.umbria Vocational Train. Scheme Newc. u. Tyne.

PALMER, Rachel Mary Radbrook Green Surgery, Bank Farm Road, Shrewsbury SY3 6DU Tel: 01743 231816 Fax: 01743 344099 — MB ChB 1981 Birm.; MA Camb. 1982, BA (Hons.) 1978; MRCGP 1986; DRCOG 1985; DCH RCP Lond. 1984. GP.

PALMER, Rebecca Louise Broughton Holly Cottage, Low Road, Little Cheverell, Devizes SN10 4JY — BM 1995 Soton. SHO (Paediat.) Poole Gen. Hosp. Socs: BMA; MPS.

PALMER, Richard Holden, OStJ (retired) Sideways, 48 Station Road, Herne Bay CT6 5QH Tel: 01227 363595 — LRCPI & LM, LRCSI & LM 1959. Prev: Ho. Surg. (Obst.) I. of Thanet Gen. Hosps.

PALMER, Richard Mark Lisburn Health Centre, Linenhall St., Lisburn BT28 1LU Tel: 01846 603088; 6 Sequoia Park, Lambeg,

Lisburn BT27 4SJ Tel: 01846 604390 — MB ChB 1988 Manch.; MRCGP 1992; DRCOG 1993; Cert. Family Plann. JCC 1992; DCH Dub. 1991; DMH (Distinc.) Belf. 1990. Prev: Trainee GP Lisburn; SHO (O & G & Med.) Lagan Valley Hosp.; SHO (ENT) Roy. Vict. Hosp.

PALMER, Richard Michael (retired) Plovers, Church Road, Yapton, Arundel BN18 0EW Tel: 012343 555613 Fax: 012343 555995 Email: rmike.palmer@tesco.net — MB BS Lond. 1961; MRCS Eng. LRCP Lond. 1963; MRCGP 1969; DObst RCOG 1964. Prev: Med. Adviser Kingston & Richmond FHSA & Croydon FHSA.

PALMER, Robert George Birmingham, Heartlands & Solihull NHS Trust (Teaching), Solihull Hospital, Lode Lane, Solihull B91 2JL — MB BS 1976 Lond.; MA Oxf. 1977, DM 1985; MRCP (UK) 1978; MRCS Eng. LRCP Lond. 1976; MBA 1995; FRCP 1995; DM DM Oxon 1985. (Guy's) Cons. Phys. and Rheum.; Assoc. Postgrad. Dean W. Midl.s; Sen. Clin. Lect. (Univ. of Birm.). Prev: Clin. Sci. Clin. Med. Research Centre & N.wick Pk. Hosp. Harrow; Cons. Rheumatologist Dudley Rd. Hosp. Birm.

PALMER, Robert Julian Department of Anaesthetics, Queen Alexandra Hospital, Cosham, Portsmouth PO6 3LY; Tower Cottage, 67 Links Lane, Rowlands Castle PO9 6AF — MB BS 1968 Lond.; MRCS Eng. LRCP Lond. 1968; FFA RCS Eng. 1974. Cons. Anaesth. Portsmouth & SE Hants. Prev: Staff. Anaesth. Worcester Memor. Hosp., USA.

PALMER, Robert Leslie 61 Central Road, Leicester LE3 5EJ; University Department of Psychiatry, Leicester General Hospital NHS Trust, Gwendolen Road, Leicester LE5 4PW — MB BS 1966 Lond.; MRCS Eng. LRCP Lond. 1966; FRCPsych 1984, M 1972.

PALMER, Roger David 482 Bideford Green, Leighton Buzzard LU7 2TZ Tel: 01525 378526 Fax: 01525 378526 — BChir 1993 Camb.; MB BChir Camb. 1993; BSc (1st cl. Hons.) 1991; MRCO (UK) 1999. (St. And. Camb.) Sen. SHO (Paediat.) Dryburn Hosp. Durh. Prev: SHO Rotat. (Paediat.) Newc. Centr.

PALMER, Ronald (retired) 34 Whitney Drive, Stevenage SG1 4BH Tel: 01438 354919 — MB BS 1955 Lond. Prev: Ho. Phys. Guy's Hosp. Lond.

PALMER, Roy Alan The Clinic, Main Road, Ecclefechan, Lockerbie DG11 3BT Tel: 01576 300208 Fax: 01576 300694; Woodburn, Ecclefechan, Lockerbie DG11 3BT — MB ChB St. And. 1972. (St. And.) Sen. Med. Off. Carlisle Racecourse. Prev: SHO (Geriat.) Roy. Vict. Hosp. Dundee; SHO (O & G) Dundee Roy. Infirm.; SHO (Dermat.) Dundee Roy. Infirm.

PALMER, Roy Newberry HM Coroner's Court, Barclay Road, Croydon CR9 3NE Tel: 020 8681 5019 Fax: 020 8686 3491 Email: londoncoroner@aol.com; 2 Horseshoe Wharf Apartments, 6 Clink Street, London SE1 9FE Tel: 020 7378 0637 — MB BS 1968 Lond.; LLB Lond. 1974; MRCS Eng. LRCP Lond. 1968; DObst RCOG 1970; Barrister at Law Middle Temple 1977. (Roy. Lond. Hosp.) HM Coroner for the S.ern Dist. of Gt.er Lond..; Pres. Medico-legal soc; Governer, Expert Witness Inst. Socs: Medico-Legal Soc.(Pres.); Fell. Roy. Soc. Med.; Hon. Soc. Middle Temple. Prev: GP Herts.; Sec. & Med. Dir. Med. Protec. Soc.; Dep. Coroner Gt.er Lond.

PALMER, Ruth Bridget Manor Farm House, Manor Farm Drive, Sutton Benger, Chippenham SN15 4RW — MB BS 1986 Lond.; MRCGP 1991; DRCOG 1991.

PALMER, Sarah Catherine Dr Dow and Partners, 87-89 Prince of Wales Road, London NW5 3NT; 21a Burma Road, Stoke Newington, London N16 9BH — MB BS 1991 London; Member Royal College of General Practioners London 1998. (St. Bartholomews) GP Princip. Socs: Roy. Coll. Gen. Pract.

PALMER, Sarah Louise Liverpool Consulting and Psychotherapy Service, Mossley Hill Hospital, Park Avenue, Liverpool L18 8BU Tel: 0151 250 6128 Fax: 0151 729 0457 — MB ChB 1992 (Hons.) Liverp.; MRCPsych 1998. (Liverp.) Specialist Regist. (Adult Psychiat.) Mossley Hill Hosp. L'pool. Prev: Regist. (Psychiat.) Scott Clinic St Helen's Merseyside; SHO (Psychiat.) Chester; SHO (Gen. Psychiat.) Clatterbridge Hosp. Wirral.

PALMER, Sharon Manor Oak Surgery, Horebeech Lane, Horam, Heathfield TN21 0DS Tel: 01435 812116 Fax: 01435 813737; Woolbridge Cottage, Fir Toll Road, Mayfield TN20 6NE Tel: 01435 873509 — MB BS 1986 Lond.; MRCGP 1990. (St. Thos.) Prev: SHO (A & E Geriat.Paediat. & O & G) Qu. Marys Hosp. Sidcup; Ho. Phys. Poole Gen. Hosp.; Ho. Surg. St. Thos. Hosp. Lond.

PALMER

PALMER, Mr Simon Hastings 3 Mark Road, Headington, Oxford OX3 8PB — MB BS 1990 Lond.; FRCS Eng. 1994. Specialist Regist. Oxf. Rotat. Socs: BOA; Brit. Orthop. Trainee Assn.; Brit. Trauma Soc. Prev: Research Regist. (Orthop. & Trauma) Bath; Hon. Res. Fell. Bath Univ.

PALMER, Stephen John 5 Ancaster Crescent, New Malden KT3 6BD — MB BS 1990 Lond.

PALMER, Stephen John The Fairfield Centre, Fairfield Grove, Charlton, London SE7 8TX Tel: 020 8858 5738 Fax: 020 8305 3005 — MB BS 1976 Lond.; DRCOG 1980; MRCGP 1981; DCH Eng. 1980. (St. Thos.) GP Charlton Lond. Prev: GP VTS Greenwich Lond.; Ho. Surg. Qu. Alexandra Hosp. Cosham; Ho. Phys. Worthing Gen. Hosp.

PALMER, Professor Stephen Royston Department of Epidermiolgy and Public Health, University of Wales, College of Medicine, Heath Park, Cardiff CF14 4XN Tel: 029 2074 2321 Email: palmersr@cardif.ac.uk — MB BChir 1976 Camb.; MA Camb. 1976; FFCM 1987, M 1980; FRCP 1999. Dir. Welsh Combined Centres for Pub. Health Univ. Wales Coll. Med.; Head of Dept. of Epidemiol. & Pub. Health; Mansel Talbot Prof. of Epidemiol. & Pub. Health. Prev: Sen. Regist. Communicable Dis. Surveillance Centre; Lect. (Community Med.) St. Thos. Hosp. Med. Sch. Lond.; Ho. Phys. King's Coll. Hosp. Lond.

PALMER, Timothy Allan Dunorlan Medical Group, 64 Pembury Road, Tonbridge TN9 2JG Tel: 01732 352907 Fax: 01732 367408; Fax: 01732 838749 — MB BS 1982 Lond.; 2000 DMJ; BSc Lond. 1979; DRCOG 1986. (Guy's Hosp. Lond.) GP; Med. Off. Kent Sch. RFU; Princip. Forens. Med. Examr., Kent Police Auth., Tonbridge. Socs: Assn. Police Surg. Prev: Police Surg. Kent Police Auth. (Sevenoaks); Trainee GP Tunbridge Wells VTS.

PALMER, Timothy James Dun Macbeth, 14 Auldcastle Road, Inverness IV2 3PZ — MB BS 1978 Lond.; BSc Lond. 1975, MB BS 1978; MRCP (UK) 1982; MRCPath 1985. (Guy's) Cons. Histopath/Cytopath Raigmore Hosp. Inverness. Prev: Sen. Lect./Hon. Cons. Histopath./Cytopath. Guy's Hosp. Med. Sch., Guy's & Lewisham Hosps.; Lect. (Histopath.) United Med. & Dent. Sch. Guy's Hosp. Lond.; Sen. Regist. (Histopath.) Guy's & Lewisham Hosps.

PALMER, Valerie Frances Dalston Medical Group, Townhead Road, Dalston, Carlisle CA5 7PZ Tel: 01228 710451 Fax: 01228 711898 — BM BCh 1976 Oxf.; MA (Physiol.) Oxf. 1977; MRCGP 1984. (Oxf.) Prev: GP Lond.

PALMER, William Coningsby 2 Quarry Hill Lane, Wetherby LS22 6RY Tel: 01937 584755 — LRCP LRCS Ed. LRFPS Glas. 1947.

PALMER, Zoe Elizabeth St. Joseph's Hospice, Mare St., Hackney, London E8 4SA — BM BS 1987 Nottm.

PALMERI, Petra 2 Larch Close, Bourne PE10 9SS — LMS 1993 Cordoba.

PALMIER, Beryl Mary 115 Epsom Road, Sutton SM3 9EY Tel: 020 8644 7718 — MB ChB 1948 Birm.; MRCS Eng. LRCP Lond. 1948; MRCOG 1955; DCH Eng. 1956. Prev: Regist. O & G Whittington Hosp.; Ho. Phys. S.mead Hosp. Bristol; Cas. Off. Birm. Gen. Hosp.

PALMIERI, Carlo 23 Silverton Road, London W6 9NY — MB BS 1994 Lond.; BSc (1st cl. Hons.) Lond. 1991; MRCP (UK) 1997. (Char. Cross & Westm.) Clin. Research Fell. & Hon. Regist. (Med. Oncol.) Imperial Coll. Sch. Of Med., Lond. & Hammersmith Hosps. NHS Trust. Prev: SHO Med. Roy. Lond. Hosp.; SHO Med. Oncol. St. Bart. Hosp.

PALMOWSKI, Bogdan Maciej 6 Lane Ends, Hibson Road, Nelson BB9 0PX — LMSSA 1992 Lond.

***PALOMBO, Andrew Stewart** Larachan, 7 Dochfour Drive, Inverness IV3 5EB — MB ChB 1996 Aberd.

PALSINGH, Jasbinder Flat 1, 76 Portland Road, Edgbaston, Birmingham B16 9QU — MB ChB 1988 Dundee.

PALTA, Narinder Singh (retired) York District Hospital, Wigginton Road, York YO31 8HE Tel: 01904 631313 — MB BS 1959 Punjab; MB BS Punjab (India) 1959; FRCP Lond. 1991; MRCP (UK) 1971. Prev: Cons. Phys. York Dist. Hosp.

PALUCH, Nicholas Anthony Fleetwood La Gallie, Rue de la Gallie, St Peter Port, Guernsey GY7 9ED Tel: 01481 64242 — MB BS 1979; BSc (Hons.) 1976; MRCGP 1985; DPD Wales 1991; DRCOG 1982; DCH RCP Lond. 1982. (Univ. Coll. Hosp.) GP St. Peters, Guernsey.

PALUMBO, Luigina 6 Dundas St. West, Saltburn-by-the-Sea TS12 1BL Tel: 01287 622207 Fax: 01287 623803; Beechwood, Victoria Terrace, Saltburn-by-the-Sea TS12 1HN Tel: 01287 622822 — MB BS 1982 Nottm.; BMedSci Nottm. 1980, MB BS 1982; MRCP (UK) 1985; MRCGP 1992; DRCOG 1990. Princip. Gen. Pract. Prev: Regist. (Med.) Sheff.; SHO (Obst. & Gyn.) S. Cleveland Hosp.

PALWALA, Adamjee Joosab Clarehaven, 5 Mill Lane, Kirby, Liverpool L32 2AU — MB BS 1941 Bombay; MRCP Ed. 1954; DTM & H Liverp. 1953. (Grant Med. Coll. Bombay) Mem. Liverp. Med. Inst. Prev: Ho. Phys. Warrington Infirm.

PAMBAKIAN, Alidz Lucy Marina 41 Southdown Avenue, London W7 2AG — MB BS 1991 Lond.

PAMBAKIAN, Hosep 41 Southdown Avenue, Boston Manor, London W7 2AG — MB BS 1956 Lond.; MRCS Eng. LRCP Lond. 1956; LMSSA Lond. 1956.

PAMBAKIAN, Nazaret Haig Crown Street Surgery, 2 Lombard Court, Crown Street, Acton, London W3 8SA Tel: 020 8992 1963 — MB BS 1984 Lond.; MRCGP 1995; DRCOG 1987.

PAMBAKIAN, Samuel 41 Southdown Avenue, London W7 2AG — MB BS 1989 Lond.

PAMBAKIAN, Yvonne Emma Louise Arpi 5 Holders Hill Avenue, London NW4 1EN — MB BS 1993 Lond. SHO (Paediat.) Barnet Gen. Hosp. Prev: SHO (O & G) Edgware Gen. Hosp.; SHO (Orthop. & A & E) Barnet Gen. Hosp.

PAMPEL, Maralyn Marcia Bacon Lane Surgery, 11 Bacon Lane, Edgware HA8 5AT Tel: 020 8952 5073/7876 — MB BS 1974 Lond.; MRCGP 1995. (King's Coll. Hosp.) GP Trainer Edgware & Barnet VTS. Prev: SHO (Paediat.) Sydenham Childr. Hosp. Lond.; SHO (O & G) Barnet Gen. Hosp.; SHO (Orthop. & Cas.) Barnet Gen. Hosp.

PAMPHILON, Derwood Harold National Blood Service, Bristol Centre, Bristol BS10 5ND Tel: 0117 991 2096 Fax: 0117 991 2002 Email: derwood.pamphilon@nbs.nhs.uk — MB BS 1974 Bristol; MB BS Lond. 1974; MD Bristol 1991; MRCPath 1984; FRCPath 1996; MRCPCH 1998. (London) Cons. Haemat. Nat. Blood Serv.; Cons. & Sen. Clin. Lect. (Haemat.) Bristol Roy. Hosp. Sick Childr. Prev: Sen. Regist. Immunohaemat. S.mead Hosp. Bristol.; Regist. (Haemat.) Gen. Infirm. & St. Jas. Univ. Hosp. Leeds.

PAMPIGLIONE, Julian Sheridan The Bournemouth Nuffield Hospital, 67 Lansdowne Road, Bournemouth BH1 1RW Tel: 01202 292234 Fax: 01202 317848; 93 Canford Cliffs, Poole BH13 7EP — MB BS 1980 Lond.; MD Lond. 1992; MRCOG 1986; T(OG) 1992; FRCOG 1998. (Lond. Hosp.) Cons. O & G Roy. Bournemouth Gen. Hosp.; Cons. Obst. & Gyn. Poole Gen. Hosp.; Jt. Director, Dorset InFertil. Serv.s. Prev: Sen. Regist. (Human Reproduc. & Obst.) P.ss Anne Hosp. Soton.; Clin. Research Fell. Assisted Conception Unit King's Coll. Hosp. Lond.; SHO (Neonatol.) John Radcliffe Hosp. Oxf.

PANACER, Davinder Singh St Matthews Medical Centre, Prince Phillip House, Malabar Road, Leicester LE1 2NZ; 10 Waveney Rise, Oadby, Leicester LE2 4GG — BM BS 1988 Nottm.; BMedSci. Nottm. 1986; MRCGP 1994; DCCH 1993; DRCOG 1993; DFFP 1994. (Nott.) GP. Prev: Trainee GP Centr. Birm. VTS.

***PANAGAMUWA, Channa Sanjeewa Bandara** 57A Frederick Road, Selly Oak, Birmingham B29 6NX — MB ChB 1998 Sheff.; MB ChB Sheff 1998.

PANAGEA, Stavroula Elias c/o Microbiology Department, North Manchester General Hospital, Central Drive, Crumpsall, Manchester M8 5RL — Ptychio Iatrikes 1990 Athens.

PANAGIOTOPOULOS, Ioannis Department of Surgery, Broomfield Hospital, Chelmsford CM1 7ET — Ptychio Iatrikes 1981 Thessalonika.

PANAHLOO, Arshia Ali Dept. of Endocrinology & Diabetes, St. George's Hospital, Blackshaw Road, London SW17 0QT Tel: 020 8725 3902 Email: arshia.panahloo@stgeorges.nhs.uk — MB BS 1986 Lond.; MRCP (UK) 1989; MD Lond. 1998. (St. Thos.) Cons. Phys. (Diabetes & Endoc.) St. Geo.'s Hosp. Lond. Socs: Brit. Diabetic Assoc.; Brit. Endoc. Soc.; Eur. Assoc. for the Study of Diabetes. Prev: Sen. Regist. (Endocrinol. & Diabetes) Hammersmith Hosp. Lond.; Clin. Lect. (Med.) Whittington Hosp. Lond.; Regist. (Gen. Med.) St. Albans City Hosp. & St. Mary's Hosp. Lond.

PANAHLOO, Hassan Ali St. Augustines Hospital, Chartham, Canterbury CT4 7LL Tel: 01227 765976; 56 Beechworth House, Willesden Lane, London NW6 7YZ Tel: 020 8451 7387 — MD 1955 Tehran; FRCPsych 1985, M 1972; DPM Eng. 1968. Prev:

Supdt. Med. Dir. Razi Psychiat. Centre, Tehran; Sen. Lect. Vanak Psychiat. Centre, Tehran.

PANAHY, Mr Cambyse 6 Kingsmead Court, Avenue Road, Highgate, London N6 5DU Tel: 020 8341 4938 — MB ChB Bristol 1959; FRCS Eng. 1967; FRCS Ed. 1966. (Bristol) Socs: Fell. Roy. Soc. Med. Prev: Assoc. Prof. Surg. Nat. Univ. Iran; Lect. Surg. Unit Lond. Hosp.; Surg. Regist. City Hosp. Stoke on Trent.

***PANAKIS, Niki** 33 Ethelburt Avenue, Southampton SO16 3DG — BM BS 1994 Nottm.

PANAMA, Kathleen Wellcome Institute of the History of Medicine, 183 Euston Road, London NW1 2BE — MB BS 1977 Lond.; MSc Lond. 1992, MB BS 1977. Research Stud. Wellcome Inst. Hist. Med. Lond. Socs: Roy. Soc. Med. Prev: Princip. GP Lambeth, Lewisham & S.wark FPC.

PANANGHAT, Tony Paul 2 Knights Close, Thornton-Cleveleys FY5 3BF — MB BS 1971 Bangalor; MB BS Bangalore 1971.

PANARESE, Alessandro Dept of Ent., Royal Hallamshire Hospital, Sheffield S10 2JF; 75 Highcliffe Road, Sheffield S11 7LP — State Exam 1986 Milan. Specialist Regist., Dept of Ent. Roy. Hallamshire Hosp. Sheff.

PANAY, Nicholas Academic Department of Obstetrics & Gynaecology, 369 Fulham Road, London SW10 9NH Tel: 020 8746 8697 Fax: 020 8846 7796; 1 Shaftesbury Road, Richmond TW9 2TD Tel: 0973 543657 Email: nickpanay@msn.com — MB BS 1988 Lond.; BSc (Hons.) Lond. 1985; MRCOG 1994; MFFP 1996. (UCL/Middlesex) Research Fell. Chelsea & W.m. Hosp. Lond. Socs: Roy. Soc. Med.; Med. Defence Union; Med. Sickness Soc. Prev: Regist. Rotat. (O & G) Guy's Hosp. Lond. & Lewisham; SHO (Perinatol.) St. Mary's Hosp.; SHO (Gyn.) Univ. Coll. Hosp.

PANAYI, Professor Gabriel Stavros Guy's, King's, St Thomas' School of Medicine, Guys Hospital, London SE1 9RT Tel: 020 7955 4394 Fax: 020 7955 2472 Email: gabriel.panayi@kcl.ac.uk; 13 Bittacy Park Avenue, Mill Hill, London NW7 2HA — MB BChir Camb. 1966; ScD Camb. 1991; MD Camb. 1971; FRCP Lond. 1982; MRCP (UK) 1972. (Univ. Camb. & St. Mary's Hosp. Lond.) ARC Prof. Rheum. United Med.& Dent. Schs. Lond.; Hon. Cons. Rheum. Guy's & St. Thos. Hosp. Trust Lond. Socs: (Counc.) Brit. Soc. for Rheum.; Brit. Soc. Immunol.; Roy. Soc. Med. Prev: MRC Jun. Research Fell. Wright-Fleming Inst. & Kennedy Inst. Rheum. Lond.; Arthritis & Rheum. Counc. Research Fell. Dis. Unit N.. Gen.

PANAYIDES, Socrates Mathew Chartham Surgery, Parish Road, Chartham, Canterbury CT4 7JU Tel: 01227 738224; The White Lodge, 2 Abbots Barton Walk, Canterbury CT1 3AX Tel: 01227 768246 — LMSSA 1972 Lond.; Med. Dipl. Athens 1965. (Athens) Prev: Regist. (Thoracic Surg.) Roy. Infirm. Edin.; SHO (Orthop.) Kent & Canterbury Hosp.; Ho. Surg. Roy. Sussex Co. Hosp. Brighton.

PANAYIOTOU, Barnabas Nicos Department of Geriatrics, City General Hospital, Newcastle-under-Lyme ST4 6QG Tel: 01782 715444 Fax: 01782 747319 — BM BS 1983 Nottm.; BMedSci (Hons.) Nottm. 1981; MRCP (UK) 1988; MD (Keale) 1999; FRCP (London) 2000. Cons. Phys. & Geriat. City Gen. Hosp. Stoke-on-Trent; Hon. Sen. Clin. Lect. Keele Univ. Socs: BMA & Brit. Geriat. Soc.; Med. Res. Soc. Prev: Sen. Regist. (Gen. Med.) City Gen. Hosp. Stoke-on-Trent; Sen. Regist. (Geriat.) Manor Hosp. Walsall; Clin. Research Fell & Hon. Regist. (Med. Elderly) Leicester Gen. Hosp.

PANCH, Gnanie Whittington Hospital, Highgate Hill, London N19 5NF Tel: 020 7272 3070 Fax: 020 7288 5417; Tel: 020 8904 0987 — MB BS 1974 Sri Lanka; MRCS Eng. LRCP Lond. 1981; FRCA 1986. (Colombo (SRI Lanka)) Cons. (Anaesth.) Whittington Hosp. Lond. Socs: MRCAnaesth. & Pain Soc.; Assn. of Anaesth. Prev: Sen. Regist. in anE.hesia UCH; Clin. Asst. (Anaesth.) Univ. Coll. Hosp. Lond.; Regist. (Anaesth.) Centr. Middlx. & N.wick Pk. Hosp.

PANCHAM, Prem Kumar Aldersyde, 26 Rotchell Park, Dumfries DG2 7RH Tel: 01387 54541 — MB BS Nagpur 1959; MS (Ophth.) Lucknow 1963; DOMS Punjab 1960; FICS 1967. (Nagpur) Ophth. Med. Pract. Med. Free Lance. Prev: Assoc. Specialist (Ophth.) Dumfries & Galloway Roy. Infirm.; Asst. Prof. Ophth. Christian Med. Coll. & Hosp. Ludhiana, Punjab.

PANCHARATNAM, Mr Manoah Dhyanchand Consultant Urologist, West Hertfordshire NHS Trust, Hillfield Road, Hemel Hempstead HP2 4AD Tel: 01442 213141 Fax: 01442 287134 Email: manopanch@doctors.org.uk; 71 West Common, Harpenden AL5 2LD Tel: 01582 460281 Fax: 01582 761512 Email: manopanch@doctors.org.uk — MB BS 1974 Madras; FRCS Ed. 1977; T(S) 1991. (Jawaharlal Inst. Med. Educat. Pondicherry) Cons. Urol. W. Herts NHS trust Hosp.s. Socs: Brit. Assn. Urol. Surgs.; BAUS Oncol.; BMA. Prev: Cons. & Head Unit Urol. King Faisal Hosp. Taif, Saudi Arabia; Regist. & Cons. Gen. Surg. & Urol. King Geo. Hosp. Greenwich; Sen. Regist. (Urol.) St. Peters Gp. Inst. Urol.

PANCHAUD, Marcus Laurence Thomas Haslemere Health Centre, Church Lane, Haslemere GU27 2BQ Tel: 01483 783023 Fax: 01428 645065 — MB BS 1987 Lond.; MRCGP 1992; DRCOG 1991.

PANCHOLI, Mr Alok 59 Trenchard Avenue, Stafford ST16 3RD — MB BS 1986 Indore; FRCS Ed. 1990.

PANCHOLI, Prakash Spinney Hill Medical Centre, 143 St. Saviours Road, Leicester LE5 3HX Tel: 0116 251 7870; Tel: 0116 269 6221 — MB ChB 1983 Leic.; DRCOG 1986. Professional Exec. Comm. Mem. Of E.ern Leicester PCT.

PANDA, Jitendra Kumar 26 Cotton Close, Broadstone BH18 9AJ — MB BS Utkal 1973; BSc (Hons.) Utkal 1966; MD (Obst. & Gyn.) Chandigarh 1976; MRCOG 1984; FRCOG 1998. (S.C.B. Med. Coll. Cuttack) Specialist O & G Poole Hosp. NHS Trust Dorset; Regist. (Obst. & Gyn.) S.port Gen. Infirm. Socs: Roy. Coll. Obst. & Gyn. Lond.; Med. Protec. Soc.; BMA. Prev: Regist. (O & G) St. David's Hosp. Bangor & Fazakerley Hosp. Liverp.; Regist. (O & G) St. James Univ. Hosp. Leeds; Regist. (O & G) Soton. Gen. Infirm.

PANDA, Veena Pani 26 Cotton Close, Broadstone BH18 9AJ — MB BS 1986 Ravishankar U, India.

PANDALAI, Suresh Department of Surgery, Withybush Hospital, Ashguard Road, Haverfordwest SA61 2PZ — MB BS 1987 Madras.

PANDAY, Khaimchand 72 Kestrel Road, Basingstoke RG22 5PN — MB BS 1982 W. Indies.

PANDAY, Sheila 18 Stour Court, Stour St., Canterbury CT1 2PG — MB BCh BAO 1993 NUI; LRCPS 1993.

PANDAY, Sohrab Lincoln Road Practice, 63 Lincoln Road, Peterborough PE1 2SF Tel: 01733 565511 Fax: 01733 569230; 12 Livermore Green, Peterborough PE4 5DG — MB ChB 1984 Manch.; BSc Manch. 1982; MRCP (UK) 1987; MRCGP 1992; DCH RCP Lond. 1989. (Manchester) Socs: BMA; RCGP; RCP. Prev: Tutor Paediat. St. Jas. Univ. Hosp.; Trainee GP Leeds.

PANDE, Kanan Pear Garth, 9 Ferriby High Road, North Ferriby HU14 3LD; Spring Bank Group Practice, Walseley House, 168 Spring Bank, Hull HU3 1QW — MB BS 1984 Delhi; MRCOG 1992; MRCGP 1997. GP Princip.

PANDE, Mr Milind 33 Woodfield Crescent, London W5 1PD — MB BS 1981 Delhi; FRCS Glas. 1989; FCOphth 1989. Regist. Hull Roy. Infirm.

PANDE, Salil Kumar 18 Barnhurst Close, Childwall, Liverpool L16 7QT Tel: 0151 722 0872 Fax: 0151 280 7794 — MB BS 1996 Lond. (Univ. Coll. Hosp.) GP Regist. Liverp.

PANDE, Sandeep Kumar Longcroft Clinic, 5 Woodmansterne Lane, Banstead SM7 3HH — MB BS 1991 Lond.; MRCGP 1995; DCH RCP Lond. 1995. (University College and Middlesex Hospital Medical School) GP Princip.; Forens. Med. Examr. Socs: Roy. Soc. Med.; Assn. of Police Surg.

PANDE, Shiv Kumar, MBE Dr S K Pande, 14 North View, Edge Hill, Liverpool L7 8TS Tel: 0151 709 3779 Fax: 0151 709 6349; 18 Barnhurst Close, Childwall, Liverpool L16 7QT Tel: 0151 722 0872 Fax: 0151 280 7794 — MB BS Vikram 1962; MS Indore 1965; MRCGP 1996. (M.G.M. Med. Coll. Indore) GP/Presenter of TV Progr. Aap Kaa Hak; JP. Socs: Fell. Fac. Community Med.; Fell. Roy. Inst. Pub. Health & Hyg.; Fell. Overseas Doctors Assn. Prev: Regist. (Surg.) Lond. Chest Hosp., Roy. Liverp. Childr. Hosp. & Fazakerley Hosp. Liverp.

PANDE, Shyam Kumar (retired) 3 Sayers Close, Harlington, Doncaster DN5 7JA Tel: 01709 893066 — MB BS Nagpur 1956; MFCM 1974; DPH Eng. 1968. Prev: SCMO (Child Health) Doncaster HA.

***PANDEY, Manish** Flat 4, 34-35 Newman St., London W1T 1PZ — BChir 1992 Camb.

PANDEY, Radhakant Nuffield Orthopaedic Centre, Headington, Oxford OX3 7LD — MB BS 1989 Madras.

PANDEY, Surendra Kumar Department of Child Health, Stanley Health Centre, Stanley DH9 0XE Tel: 01207 214857 Fax: 01207 214800 Email: paed@skpandey.demon.co.uk — MB BS 1974 Patna; FRCP 1997 Lond.; MRCPI 1982; FRCPCH 1997. (P. Wales

PANDEY

Med. Coll. Patna) Cons. Paediat. Community Child Health Derwentside, Co. Durh. Hosp. Dryburn Hosp. Durh.

*PANDEY, Vikas Anand 10 Garth Edge, Whitworth, Rochdale OL12 8EH — MB ChB 1998 Liverp.; MB ChB Liverp 1998.

*PANDHER, Baltej Singh 7 Kelso Mews, Caversham Park, Reading RG4 6RJ — MB BS 1997 Lond.

PANDHER, Gurpreet Kaur 6 St Mary's Road, Heckford Park, Poole BH15 2LH Tel: 01202 673588 — MB BS 1990 Lond.; MRCOG 1996. (King's Coll. Sch. Med. & Dent.) Specialist Regist. (O & G) P.ss Anne Hosp. Soton.

PANDHER, Kulwant Singh Kidlington Health Centre, Exeter Close, Oxford Road, Kidlington OX5 1AP Tel: 01865 841941 — MRCS Eng. LRCP Lond. 1981; MB ChB Liverp. 1981. Research Regist. Nuffield Laborat. Ophth. Oxf. Univ. Socs: Fell. Roy. Soc. Med.

PANDIS, Vasilios Department of Orthopaedics, York Hill NHS Trust, Yorkhill, Glasgow G3 8SJ — Ptychio latrikes 1986 Athens.

*PANDIT, Adam Nisar 51 Langley Road, Watford WD17 4PB — MB BS 1998 Lond.; MB BS Lond 1998.

PANDIT, Anita 60 Ripplevale Grove, London N1 1HT Tel: 020 7700 6735 — MD 1986 Bombay; MBBS 1984; MRCP I 1991. (Grant Medical, Bombay)

PANDIT, Dayanand Ramrao (Surgery), 2 Avenue Road, Brentwood CM14 5EL; 68 Hamilton Crescent, Brentwood CM14 5ES Email: anne.pelham@uheane.net — MB BS 1965 Karnatak; T(GP) 1992. (Karnatak Medical College Hubli India) GP Brentwood, Essex.

PANDIT, Jaideep Jagdeesh Nuffield dept of Anaesthetics, John Radcliffe Hosp, Oxford OX3 9AJ — BM BCh 1988 Oxf.; DPhil Oxf. 1993, BA 1985; FRCA 1995. Lect. (Med.) St. John's Coll. Oxf. & cons. (Anaesth.) Nuffield Dept. Anaesth. Oxf.; Assessor Final Honour Sch. Physiol. Univ. Oxf. Socs: Sen. Common Room Corpus Christie Coll. Oxf.; BMA; Internat. Anaesthetic research centre. Prev: Wellcome Trust Research Fell. Univ. Oxf.; ass pro anE.hetics.uni Michigan.

PANDIT, Mr Jyotin Chittaranjan Bristol Eye Hospital, Lower Maudlin St., Bristol BS1 2LX Tel: 0117 923 0060 Fax: 0117 928 4686 Email: jyotin.pandit@virgin.net; 29 Vernon Avenue, Handsworth Wood, Birmingham B20 1DD Tel: 0121 554 1629 — MB BCh 1988 Wales; FRCS Ed. 1993. Specialist Regist. (Ophth.) Bristol Eye Hosp.; Clin. Lect. Univ. Bristol. Socs: BMA; Roy. Soc. Med.; Internat. Mem.-in-Train. Amer. Acad. Ophth. Prev: Specialist Regist. (Ophth.) REI Plymouth; Research Regist. Nuffield Laborat. of Ophth. Oxf.; Regist. (Ophth.) Torbay Hosp.

PANDIT, Mr Lakshmi Chand 48 Inner Park Road, London SW19 6DD — MB BS 1955 Punjab; MB BS Punjab, India 1955; FRCS Ed. 1963.

PANDIT, Nisar Ahmad Springfield, 51 Langley Road, Watford WD17 4PB Tel: 01923 32056 — MB BS 1959 Punjab; MB BS Punjab (Pakistan) 1959; FRCP Lond. 1985, M 1968. (King Edwd. VII Med. Coll. Lahore) Cons. Phys. Dept. Rheum. & Neurol. Rehabil. Watford Gen. Hosp. & Garston Manor Med. Rehabil. Centre. Prev: Sen. Regist. (Rheum. & Rehabil.) & Regist. Dept. Neurol. Middlx.; Hosp. Lond.; Sen. Regist. (Gen. Med. & Neurol.) W. Lond. Hosp.

PANDIT, Mr Ranjeet Jagdeesh Royal Victoria Infirmatory, Newcastle upon Tyne NE1 4LP — BM BCh 1990 Oxf.; BA (Hons.) Physiol. Oxf. 1987; MRCP (UK) 1993; FRCOphth 1998. Specialist Regist. (Med. Ophth.) Roy. Vict. Infirm. Newc. Upon Tyne. Prev: SHO (Ophth.) Gt. Ormond St. Hosp. Lond.; SHO (Ophth.) Radcliffe Infirm. Oxf.; SHO (Ophth.) Roy. Berks. Hosp. Reading.

PANDIT, Mr Ravi 33 Blenheim Road, Raynes Park, London SW20 9BA — MB BS 1983 Bombay; FRCS Eng. 1993.

PANDIT, Mr Sharad Shripadrao Highgate Medical Centre, 1 Brinklow Tower, Upper Highgate Street, Highgate, Birmingham B12 0XT Tel: 0121 440 3605 Fax: 0121 440 5063; 6 Sheringham, Edgbaston, Birmingham B15 3ND Tel: 0121 454 5612 Fax: 0121 440 5063 — MB BS 1971 Poona; FRCS Glas. 1981. (Poona) GP. Socs: BMA; LMC Birm.; ODA.

PANDIT, Sheela Dayanand 68 Hamilton Crescent, Brentwood CM14 5ES — MB BS Poona 1969. (B.J. Medical College, Poona)

PANDIT, Suchitra Narayan c/o Mr Laxman Pankhaniya, 704 Leyton High Road, London E10 6JP — MB BS 1984 Nagpur, India.

PANDIT, Versha 48 Charter Avenue, Ilford IG2 7AB — MB ChB 1994 Dundee.

PANDITA-GUNAWARDENA, Nandin Daya 132 Foxley Lane, Purley CR8 3NE Tel: 020 8660 7404 Fax: 020 8660 6491 — MB BS 1965 Ceylon; FRCP Lond. 1995; MRCP (UK) 1973. (Colombo) Cons. Phys. (Geriat. Med.) Hither Green Hosp. & Lewisham Hosp. Lond.; Hon. Sen. Lect. UMDS Guy's & St. Thos. Hosp. Lond. Prev: Sen. Regist. (Geriat. Med.) W. Middlx. Hosp. Isleworth & St. Mary's Hosp. Lond.; Regist. (Geriat.) St. Helier Hosp. Carshalton & W. Middlx. Hosp.

PANDITA-GUNAWARDENA, Vijitha Ranjanikanthi Beechcroft Living Skills Resource Centre, 120 Victoria Road, Horley RH6 7AB Tel: 01293 821183 Fax: 01293 822536; 132 Foxley Lane, Purley CR8 3NE Tel: 020 8660 7404 Fax: 020 8660 6491 — MB BS Ceylon 1965; FRCPsych 1996, M 1972; DPM Eng. 1971. (Colombo) Cons. Psychiat. Surrey Oaklands NHS Trust; Dep. Med. Director, Surrey Oaklands NHS Trust. Prev: Cons. Psychiat. Netherne Hosp. Coulsdon; Sen. Regist. (Psychiat.) W. Middlx. Hosp. Isleworth & Char. Cross Hosp. Lond.; Clin. Asst. (Psychiat.) W. Middlx. Hosp. Isleworth.

PANDOLFI, Andrew Lawrence The Surgery, Baird Road, Ratho, Newbridge EH28 8RA Tel: 0131 333 1062 — MB ChB 1973 Glas.; Cert. Family Plann. JCC 1980; DObst RCOG 1975. (Glas.) Socs: BMA. Prev: Ho. Phys. & Ho. Surg. Roy. Infirm. Stirling; Govt. Med. Off. Malawi; GP Arbroath.

PANDOR, Shamin Banu South Street Surgeries, 83 South St., Bishop's Stortford CM23 3AP — MB ChB 1990 Leic.

PANDURANGI, Vasudev Ramacharya Middlewood Hospital, Sheffield S6 1TP Tel: 0114 399491 — MD 1969 Bombay; MB BS 1955. (Grant Med. Coll.) SHO S. (Sheff.) Health Dist. (T).

PANDYA, Darshna 6 Styles Way, Beckenham BR3 3AJ — MB BS 1989 Lond.; T(GP) 1993.

PANDYA, Dinker Jagannath 10 Weald Way, Reigate RH2 7RG Tel: 01737 241933 — MB BS 1957 Bombay; FRCOG 1990, M 1967; DObst 1963. (Grant Med. Coll.) Regist. (O & G) Copthorne Hosp. Shrewsbury. Prev: Cas. Off. Roy. Gwent Hosp. Newport; Regist. (O & G) Gen. Hosp. Halifax.

PANDYA, Hament 14 Mylo Griffiths Close, Llandaf, Cardiff CF5 2RQ — MB ChB 1996 Sheff.

PANDYA, Hemendra Kashinath Wyken Medical Centre, Brixham Drive, Coventry CV2 3LB Tel: 024 7668 9149 Fax: 024 7666 5151 — MB BS 1972 Saurashtra.

PANDYA, Hitesh Champaklal 45 Disraeli Road, Forest Gate, London E7 9JR Tel: 020 8555 7449 — MB ChB 1987 Glas.; MRCP (UK) Paediat. 1993. Clin. Regist. Univ. of Leicester. Socs: Brit. Paediat. Soc. Prev: Research Regist. St. Thomas's Hosp. Lond.

PANDYA, Jayshree 324 Thorold Road, Ilford IG1 4HD Tel: 020 8262 6312 Email: jkp@amber9.force9.co.uk — MB BS 1988 Lond.; BSc BPharm. (Hons.) CNAA 1982. (Royal Free Medical School) Specialist Regist. Paediat. Oncol., St Bart./Roy. Lond. Hosp.

PANDYA, Jyotindra Keshavlal Laurence House, 107 Philip Lane, Tottenham, London N15 4JR; 101 Osidge Lane, Southgate, London N14 5JL Tel: 020 8361 6898 — MB BS 1973 Gujarat; MRCGP 1994; DFFP 1994; FRCGP. Mem. LMC.

PANDYA, Kirit Kashinath c/o Drive Koya, 77 Briarfield Avenue, London N3 2LG Tel: 020 8346 8309 — MB BS 1972 Saurashtra. (M.P. Shah Med. Coll. Jamnagar) SHO Accid. Unit E. Birm. Hosp. Prev: Ho. Off. (Gen. Surg.) Vict. Infirm. Glas.

PANDYA, Lalit 9 Partridge Close, Leegomery, Telford TF1 6WF Tel: 01952 223600 Email: lalit1000@hotmail.com — MB BS 1978 Indore; MSc (Biochem.) Indore 1971, MD (Gen. Med.) 1981, MB BS 1978; MRCP (UK) 1985; MRCPI 1985. (MGM Med. Coll. INDIA) Staff Grade (Phys. in Med.) Telford. Prev: Sen. Regist. (Med.) King Khalid Univ. Hosp. Saudi Arabia.

PANDYA, Mr Mukesh Dalpatbhai The Surgery, 48 Harrow View, Harrow HA1 1RQ Tel: 020 8427 7172 Fax: 020 8424 9375 — MB BS 1973 Gujarat; FRCS Ed. 1983.

PANDYA, Mr Pranav Department of Fetal Medicine, Obstetric Hospital, Huntley St., London WC1E 6AU Tel: 020 7387 9300 Email: pranav.pandya@uclh.org — MB BS 1988 Lond.; MD 1999 Univ. Of Lond.; BSc (Hons.) Lond. 1985; MRCOG 1997. (University College Hospital) Specialist Regist. (O & G) Univ. Coll. Hosp. Lond. & Cons. In Fetal Med. & Obst. Socs: Roy. Soc. Med.; BMA; RCOG Roy. Coll. Obs. & Gynae. Prev: Research Fell. (Fetal Med.) King's Coll. Hosp. Lond.; SHO (O & G) St. Mary's Hosp. Lond.; SHO (A & E) Univ. Coll. Hosp. Lond.

PANDYA, Rajesh Parmanand East Park Road Medical Centre, 264 East Park Road, Leicester LE5 5FD Tel: 0116 273 7700 Fax:

PANKHANIA

0116 273 5872 — MB BS 1986 Saurashtra; MRCS Eng. LRCP Lond. 1992; MRCGP 1996; DFFP 1994; DRCOG 1994. Gen. Practioner; Hosp. Pract. Glenfield Gen. Hosp. Leicester. Socs: Fell.of Roy. Soc. of Med. Prev: Trainee GP Leics.; SMC, Paeds, Rugby; SMC, MBSQ gynae, Leicester Hosp.

PANEGYRES, Peter Konstantinos c/o Park-Davis Research Unit, Addenbrooke's Hospital, Hills Road, Cambridge CB2 2QB — MB BS 1981 Western Australia; FRACP 1990.

PANESAR, Bhupinder Singh 10 Skaterigg Drive, Jordanhill, Glasgow G13 1SR — MB ChB 1986 Glasg.

***PANESAR, Harminder Singh** 82 Dale Street, Chatham ME4 6QG — MB BS 1996 Lond.

PANESAR, Mr Kanwar Jit Singh Altnagelvin Hospitals Trust, Londonderry BT47 6SB Tel: 01504 345171; Hinton House, 1 Clooney Park W., Londonderry BT47 6LA Tel: 01504 343935 Fax: 01504 343935 — MRCS Eng. LRCP Lond. 1974; MB BS Panjab (India) 1965; FRCS Eng. 1972; FRCS Ed. 1972; FRCBI 1994. (Med. Coll. Amritsar) Cons. Surg. Altnagelvin Hosp. Lond.derry. Socs: BMA; Assn. Surg.; Assn. Upper G.I. Surg. & Endoscop. Surgs. Prev: Sen. Regist. Lond.derry Matern. Hosp. & Prof.ial Unit. Roy. Vict.; Hosp. Belf.; Regist. (Gen. Surg.) St. Nicholas Hosp. Lond.; Sen. Tutor Dept. Surg. Qu. Univ. Belf.

PANESAR, Ravinder Singh 8 Wolds Drive, Orpington BR6 8NS — LMSSA 1979 Lond.; MB BS Guru Nanak 1973. (Glancy) CMP RAF MoD Lond. Prev: CMP RAF Biggin Hill; Vocational Train. in Gen. Pract. Lond.; SHO (Surg.) Whittington Hosp. Lond.

PANESAR, Satwant Kaur 10 Skaterigg Drive, Jordanhill, Glasgow G13 1SR — MB ChB 1992 Glas.

PANEZAI, Mr Amir Mohammad 51 Newton Garth, Leeds LS7 4HG Tel: 0113 262 1779 — MB BS 1973 Karachi; FRCS Glas. 1990; FRCSI 1990.

PANEZAI, Mr Jamil Ur Rehman 25 Helensburgh Close, Pogmoor Road, Barnsley S75 2EU — MB BS 1974 Karachi; FRCS Ed. 1992.

***PANG, Alison** 42 Buttermere Court, Boundary Road, London NW8 6NR — MB ChB 1995 Bristol.

***PANG, David** 21 Picardy Court, Rose St., Aberdeen AB10 1UG — MB ChB 1997 Aberd.

PANG, Esther Nui-Oi (retired) 33 London Street, Faringdon SN7 7AG — MB 1945 Calcutta. Prev: Med. Asst. Anaesth. Gen. Infirm. S.port.

PANG, Hin Tat 8 Colson Road, Loughton IG10 3RN — MB BS 1986 Lond.; MRCPsych 1993. Assoc. Prof. Dept. Psychiat. Chinese Univ. Hong Kong. Prev: Regist. (Psychiat.) NW Thames Regional Train. Scheme.

PANG, Kwok-Ki 3 Clarke Avenue, Nottingham NG5 8DL — BM BS 1990 Nottm.; BMedSci Nottm. 1988; MRCPI 1995. Regist. (Paediat. Intens. Care) Birm. Childr. Hosp.

PANG, Lillian Shu Chao 175 Salmon Street, Kingsbury, London NW9 8NE Tel: 020 8205 5442 — MD 1941 Shanghai; BSc, MD Women's Christian Med. Coll. Shanghai 1941; PhD Leeds 1957; FRCPath 1976, M 1964; LAH Dub. 1968. (Wom. Christian Med. Coll. Shanghai) Histopath. Imperial Cancer Research Fund. Socs: Path. Soc. Prev: Chief Resid. Margt. Williamson Hosp. Shanghai; Lect. (Path.) Hong Kong Univ.; Research Fell. St. Mark's Hosp. Lond.

PANG, Lyndon 16 The Beeches, Liverpool L18 3LT — MB ChB 1991 Liverp.

***PANG, Pauline** 16 The Beeches, Calderstones, Liverpool L18 3LT — MB BCh 1998 Wales.

PANGAYATSELVAN, Mr Thiyagarajah Orthopaedic Department, East Surrey Hospital, Canada Avenue, Redhill RH1 5RH Tel: 01737 768511; 58 Smitham Downs Road, Purley CR8 4NF Tel: 020 8660 1714 — MB BS 1979 Peradeniya; MSc (Orthop.) Lond. 1987; FRCS (Orthop.) Ed. 1990; FRCS Ed. 1985; LRCP LRCS Ed. LRCPS Glas. 1985. Cons. Trauma & Orthop. Surg. E. Surrey Hosp. Redhill. Socs: Fell. BOA. Prev: Assoc. Specialist (Orthop.) New E. Surrey Hosp. Redhill; Regist. (Orthop.) N. Middlx. Hosp. Lond. & Memor. Hosp. Darlington.

PANHWAR, Ghylam-Mustafa College Road Surgery, 4-6 College Road, Woking GU22 8BT Tel: 01483 771309; Goldsworth Park Health Centre, Denton Way, Woking Tel: 01483 770355 — MRCS Eng. LRCP Lond. 1980; MB BS Sind, Pakistan 1959; DCMT . Lond. 1968. (Liaquat Med. Coll.) Prev: SHO (Cas. & Orthop.) Bridgend Gen. Hosp. Mem Roy. Soc. Trop. Med.; SHO (Gen. Surg. & Cas.)

Waveney Hosp. Ballymena; SHO (Thoracic Surg. & Cardiac Surg.) Frenchay Hosp. Bristol.

PANIGRAHI, Krishna Donald Wilde Medical Centre, 283 Rochdale Road, Oldham OL1 2HG Tel: 0161 652 3184 Fax: 0161 620 2101 — MB BS 1972 Calcutta; MB BS 1972 Calcutta.

PANIGRAHI, Padmalochan The Surgery, 70 Winslow Drive, Immingham, Grimsby DN40 2DL Tel: 01469 574197 Fax: 01469 574198 — MRCS Eng. LRCP Lond. 1979; MB BS Utkal India 1965; DCH RCPSI 1972; Dip Ven. Liverp. 1969; DTM & H Lond. 1968. (Burla Med. Coll. Orissa) GP Grimsby. Prev: Regist. (Paediat.) York Dist. Hosp.; Regist. (Psychiat.) Hartwood Hosp. Shotts; SHO (Paediat.) Seacroft Hosp. Leeds.

PANIKKAR, Apsara 8A Collingwood Terrace, Newcastle upon Tyne NE2 2JP — MB BS 1991 Newc.

PANIKKAR, Jane Bromiley, Clayton-Le-Dale, Blackburn BB1 9EG — MB ChB 1989 Sheff.; MRCOG 1985. (Sheff.) Specialist Regist. (O & G) N. Trent.

PANIKKAR, Krishna Kumar Department of Anaesthetics, Stoke Man Deville Hospital, Mandeville Road, Aylesbury HP21 8AL Tel: 01296 315000; Moorfield, 87 Chaulkshire Road, Butlers Cross, Aylesbury HP17 0TJ — MB BS 1987 Lond.; FRCA 1994. Cons. (Anaesth. & Intens. Care) Stoke Mandeville Hosp. Aylesbury. Prev: Sen. Regist. Hammersmith Hosp. Lond.; Lect. (Anaesth.) Chelsea & W.m. Hosp. Lond.; Regist. Roy. Free Hosp. & Whittington Hosp. Lond.

PANIKKER, Narayana Ravindra Heath Lane Hopsital, Heath Lane, Sandwell, West Bromwich B71 2BQ Tel: 0121 5537676 Fax: 0121 8073229; 6 Canberra Crescent, Meir Park, Longton, Stoke-on-Trent ST3 7RA — MB ChB 1976 Ed.; BSc (Med. Sci.) Ed. 1973; MRCP (UK) 1983; MRCPsych 1990; DPM RCPSI 1990. (Univ. Ed.) Specialist Regist., Psychiat. of Learning Disabil., W. Midl.s Rotary. Socs: Brit. Soc. Rehabil. Med.; Brit. Inst. Learning Disabil.; Soc. Clin. Psychiats. Prev: Sen. Regist. (Rehabil. Med.) Soton. & Salisbury; Sen. Med. Off. (Brain Injury) Roy. Hosp. & Home Putney, Lond.; Regist. (Psychiat.) Pk.head, Duke St. & Gartloch Hosps. Glas.

PANIKKER, Sujatha Division of Bacteriology, University of Manchester, Clinical Sciences Building, Royal Infirmary, Oxford Road, Manchester M13 9WL Tel: 0161 276 8828 Fax: 0161 276 8826; 1 Grangelands, Macclesfield SK10 4AB Tel: 01625 611735 — MB BS 1963 Kerala; MSc Ed. 1967; DTM & H Ed. 1964. (Trivandrum Med. Coll.) Lect. (Bact.) Univ. Manch. Med. Sch. Prev: Regist. (Pub. Health) Laborat. Serv. Manch.

PANIS, Egidius Anna Hubertus 49 Trenchard Avenue, Stafford ST16 3RD — Artsexamen 1989 Utrecht.

PANJA, Kishan Kumar The Surgery, 4 Cross Street, Leicester LE4 5BA Tel: 0116 268 1242; 11 Grenfell Road, Stoneygate, Leicester LE2 2PA Tel: 0116 270 5099 — MB BS 1970 Calcutta. (R.G. Kar Med. Coll.)

PANJA, Mr Sanat Kumar Claude Nicol Centre, Royal Sussex County Hospital, Brighton BN2 5BE Tel: 01273 664717 Fax: 01273 664720; 135 Shirley Drive, Hove BN3 6UJ Tel: 01273 551530 Fax: 01273 551530 — MB BS 1967 Calcutta; FRCS Ed. 1976; FRCOG 1989, M 1973; DGO Calcutta 1969. (Med. Coll. Calcutta) Cons. Roy. Sussex Co. Hosp. Brighton. Prev: Sen. Regist. Cardiff Roy. Infirm.

PANJA, Shuba Rani Victoria Road Surgery, 27 Victoria Road, Horwich, Bolton BL6 7RF Tel: 01204 467197 — MB ChB 1979 Manch. GP Horwich.

PANJWANI, Suresh 18 Chailey Av, Enfield EN1 3LY — MB BS 1978 Delhi; LRCP LRCS Ed. LRCPS Glas. 1986; MRCS Eng. LRCP Lond. 1986; T(GP) 1991; DGM RCP Lond. 1988. Regist. (Geriat. Med.) St. Michael's Hosp. Enfield. Prev: SHO (Gen. Med.) Chingford Hosp.; SHO (A & E) Mt. Vernon Hosp. N.wood; SHO (Geriat.) N. Devon Dist. Hosp. Barnstaple.

***PANKHANIA, Ajay Chhaganlal** 40 Cambridge Close, Hounslow TW4 7BG — MB ChB 1996 Manch.

PANKHANIA, Bharat 38 Pantiles Close, St. John's, Woking GU21 1PT Tel: 01483 724028 Fax: 01483 837080 Email: bharat999@netscape.net; 83 Evington Drive, Leicester LE5 5PG Tel: 01483 724028 — MB BCh 1985 Wales; MRCGP 1989; DCH RCP Lond. 1992; DGM RCP Lond. 1990; MFPHM Lond. 1999. (Univ. Wales Coll. Med.) Communicable Dis. Control, Wilts. Health Auth. Prev: Sen. Regist. (Pub. Health Med.) S. Thames RHA.

PANKHANIA

PANKHANIA, Rajesh The Harlequin Surgery, 160 Shard End Crescent, Shard End, Birmingham B34 7BP Tel: 0121 747 8291 Fax: 0121 749 5497 — MB ChB 1991 Birm.; ChB Birm. 1991.

***PANKHURST, Maria-Teresa Anne** 3 Copley Park, London SW16 3DE — MB BS 1996 Lond.

PANNELL, Bryony Mary Burnet Brook Furlong, Priors Marston, Rugby CV47 7RH — MB ChB 1981 Aberd.; Dip. Community Paediat. Warwick 1987. Asst. GP Byfield, N.ants.; Gen. Pract. Clin. Asst. (Gen. Med.) Coventry HA.

PANNETT, Richard Neil Yare Medical Practice, 202 Thorpe Road, Norwich NR1 1TJ Tel: 01603 437559 Email: richard.pannett@gp-d82073.nhs.uk — MB ChB 1973 Manch.; DCH RCP Lond. 1979; DRCOG 1978.

PANNIKER, Clare Bernadette Chase View, Hilltop Drive, Oughtibridge, Sheffield S35 0AX Tel: 0116 286 3065 — LRCPI & LM, LRSCI & LM 1960. Sessional Benefits Agency Doctor DoH. Prev: GP Sheff.

PANNIKER, Richard Michael Wadsley Bridge Medical Centre, 103 Halifax Road, Sheffield S6 1LA Tel: 0114 234 5025; Bentwood Lodge, Bent Hills, High Bradfield, Sheffield S6 6LJ — MB BS 1983 Lond.; MRCGP 1989; DRCOG 1986. (St. Mary's) Prev: Trainee GP Bradford VTS; Ho. Phys. Bradford Roy. Infirm.; Ho. Surg. Derbysh. Roy. Infirm.

PANNU, Gurprit Singh 1 Forge Lane, Crawley RH10 1QS — BChir 1992 Camb.

***PANNU, Harpreet Singh** 236 Queens Road, Leicester LE2 3FT — MB ChB 1994 Leic.

PANNU, Upkar Singh Bensham Family Practice, 1 Sidney Grove, Bensham, Gateshead NE8 2XB Tel: 0191 477 1554 — MB BS 1963 Durh.

PANOS, George Zenon 75 Eyre Court, Finchley Road, St John's Wood, London NW8 9TX Tel: 020 7722 3700 — Ptychio Iatrikes 1983 Athens; BSc Salford 1978.

PANOS, Marios Zenon 75 Eyre Court, Finchley Road, London NW8 9TX Email: marzepanos@aol.com — MB BS 1981 Lond.; BSc Lond. 1976, MD 1990; MRCP (UK) 1984; FRCP 1998. (Middlx.) Private Pract. Socs: Brit. Soc. Gastroenterol.; Amer. Gastroenterol. Assn.; Europ. Assn. Of study of the Liver. Prev: Cons. Phys. (Med & Gastroenterol.) Roy. Berks Hosp. Reading; Lect. & Hon. Sen. Regist. (Med. & Gastroenterol.) Qu. Eliz. Hosp. & E. Birm. Hosp.; Clin. Research Fell. Liver Unit King's Coll. Hosp. Lond.

PANOSKALTSIS, Theodoros Department of Obstetrics & Gynaecology, Hammersmith Hospital-Queen Charlotte's Hosp., Du Cane Road, London W12 0HS; 5 Portobello Mews, London W11 3DQ — Ptychio Iatrikes 1987 Athens. Sen. Regist. (O & G). Socs: MRCOG.

PANSARI, Natwar Gopal Doctors Surgery, Short Street, Brownhills, Walsall WS8 6AD Tel: 01543 373222 Fax: 01543 454640 — MB BS 1971 Indore.

PANTA, Roshni 8 Edward Court, Edwards Lane, Nottingham NG5 3JB — MB BS 1969 Delhi; MRCP (UK) 1978.

PANTAGANI, Mr Babu Satya Vara Prasad Department of Ophthalmology, King's Mill Centre NHS Trust, Mansfield Road, Sutton-in-Ashfield NG17 4JL Tel: 01623 22515 — MD 1985 All India Inst. Med. Sci.; FRCS Ed. 1995; MRCOphth 1992.

PANTAZIS, Andreas 82 Clarence Road, London N22 8PW — BM 1992 Soton.; DFFP 2001; BSc Soton. 1991; MRCP (UK) 1996; DRCOG 1999. (Southampton University) Prev: SHO Renal Med., St. Mary's, Paddington; SHO, Gen. Med., Soton. Gen. Hosp.; GP (VTS) Hinchingbrooke NHS Trust.

PANTELEAKI, Alexandra 140 Lauderdale Mansions, Lauderdale Road, London W9 1NG — Ptychio Iatrikes 1985 Athens.

PANTELIDES, Michalakis Leonida 2 Farrer Road, Longsight, Manchester M13 0QX — MB ChB 1979 Manch. SHO (Surg. Rotat.) Manch. Roy. Infirm.

PANTER, Simon James 35 Crowles Road, Mirfield WF14 9PJ — MB ChB 1994 Ed.; BSc (Hons.) Ed. 1992; MRCP 1997. (Edinburgh) Specialist Regist. (Gastroenterol.) N.ern Deanery Based S. Cleveland. Prev: SHO Respirat. Unit Freeman Newc.; SHO GI RVI Newc.; SHO Neuro RVI Newc.

PANTIN, Charles Frank Alcock Directorate of Respiratory Medicine, North Staffordshire Hospital, Newcastle Road, Stoke-on-Trent ST4 6QG Tel: 01782 552331 Fax: 01782 552323 — MB BS 1977 Lond.; PhD, MA Camb. 1972; FRCP Lond. 1993; MRCP (UK) 1980. (St Bartholomews Hospital, University of London) Cons. Phys. N. Staffs. Hosp.; Sen. Lect. (Postgrad. Med.) Keele Univ. Prev: Sen. Regist. Brompton & W.m. Hosps. Lond.

PANTIN, Priscilla Leslie 9 Coalecroft Road, London SW15 6LW — BM BCh 1970 Oxf.; FFA RCS Eng. 1976; DA Eng. 1972. p/t Cons. Anaesth. Centr. Middlx. Hosp. Lond.

PANTING, Gerard Patrick The Medical Protection Society, 33 Cavendish Square, London W1M 0PS Tel: 020 7399 1300 Fax: 020 7399 1301; Waters Green, Marshalls Heath Lane, Wheathampstead, Hatfield AL48HJ Tel: 01582 831664 — MB BS 1976 Lond.; MA (Med. Ethics & Law) Lond. 1992; MRCS Eng. LRCP Lond. 1976; MRCGP 1985; DMJ Soc. Apoth. Lond. 1987; DCH RCP Lond. 1982; DRCOG 1981. (Char. Cross) Head of Policy. Prev: Dep. Police Surg. St. Albans & Hemel Hempstead; Course Organiser & Trainer St Albans GP VTS.

PANTING, Jonathan Rory MR Unit, Royal Brompton Hospital, Sydney St., London SW3 6NP Tel: 020 8898 7239 Fax: 020 8351 8816 Email: j.panting@rbh.nthames.nhs.uk; 57 Powder Mill Lane, Twickenham TW2 6EF — MB BChir Camb. 1989; BSc (1st cl. Hons.) St. And. 1985; MRCP (UK) 1992; DTM & H RCP Lond. 1990. Clin. Research Fell. MR Unit Roy. Brompton Hosp. Lond. Socs: Stud. Mem. Internat. Soc. Magnetic Resonance in Med.; Soc. Cardiovasc. Magnetic Resonance. Prev: SHO Rotat. (Med.) E. Birm. Hosp.; Regist. Rotat. (Cardiol.) Hull.

PANTING, Kim 2 Blacon Farm Cottages, Snitterfield Lane, Warwick CV35 8JJ Tel: 017889 730336; 2 Blacon Farm Cottages, Snitterfield Lane, Warwick CV35 8HH Tel: 01789 730336 — MB ChB 1987 Birm.; MRCGP 1995; DRCOG 1992. (Birm.) p/t Locum Gen. Practitioner.

PANTLIN, Adrian William Llanarth Court, Llanarth, Raglan NP15 2YD Tel: 01873 840555 Fax: 01873 840591 — MB ChB 1971 Bristol; MRCPsych 1975. Cons. Psychiat. Llanarth Ct. Raglan Gwent. Socs: Assoc. Mem. Gp. Anal. Soc. Lond. Prev: Cons. Psychiat. Basildon & Thurrock HA; Sen. Regist. N.W. Thames RHA; Sen. Regist. Uffculme Clinic Birm.

PANTO, Philip Nigel Department of Radiology, Kings Mill Centre for Health Care Services, Mansfield Road, Sutton-in-Ashfield NG17 4JL Tel: 01623 622515; 30 Summercourt Drive, Ravenshead, Nottingham NG15 9FT Tel: 01623 484186 — BM Oxf. 1975; MB BS Lond. 1979; MA Oxf. 1979; FRCR 1986. (King's Coll. Hosp.) Cons. Diag. Radiol. N. Notts. HA. Socs: Brit. Nuclear Med. Soc.; Brit. Soc. Interven. Radiol.; Cardiovasc. & Interven. Radiol. Soc. of Europe. Prev: Sen. Regist. (Diag. Radiol.) Nottm. Hosps.; SHO (Cardiol. & Gen. Med.) Kent & Canterbury Hosp.; SHO (Neurol. Surg.) Radcliffe Infirm. Oxf.

PANTON, David John Kelseys Doctors Surgery, Mill Road, Liss GU33 7AZ Tel: 01730 892184 Fax: 01730 893634; The Old Rectory, West Liss, Liss GU33 6JU Tel: 01730 892366 — MB BS 1974 Lond.; DRCOG 1979. (Lond. Hosp.) GP Staff Petersfield Hosp. Prev: Ho. Phys. & Ho. Surg. St. Stephen's Hosp. Lond.; Maj. RAMC.

PANTON, Heather Maureen (retired) 36 Lulworth Lodge, Palatine Rd, Southport PR8 2BS — MB ChB 1951 Manch.; FRCS Ed. 1965; FRCOG 1974, M 1960; DObst RCOG 1953. Prev: Cons. Gyn. St. Helens & Knowsley DHA.

PANTON, Ian Robert Oakmeadow Surgery, 87 Tatlow Road, Glenfield, Leicester LE3 8NF Tel: 0116 287 7911 — MB 1978 Camb.; BA Camb. 1974, MB 1978, BChir 1977; DRCOG 1980; MRCGP 1982. (St. Geo.)

PANTON, Nicholas Timothy MacIver Gervis Road Surgery, 14 Gervis Road, Bournemouth BH1 3EG Tel: 01202 293418 Fax: 01202 317866; 20 St. Leonard's Road, Charminster, Bournemouth BH8 8QN Tel: 01202 527761 Fax: 01202 549370 — MB BS 1972 Lond.; LRCP 1972 Lond.; MRCS Eng.; MRCGP 1981; DA 1976 Eng.; Dobst RCOG 1975. (Westm.) Course Organiser Dorset VTS. Socs: BMA.

PANTON, Robert Watt (retired) 2A Piercefield Road, Formby, Liverpool L37 7DQ Tel: 0170 48 70504 — MB ChB 1939 Aberd.; DCH Eng. 1950. Prev: Regist. (Paediat.) Mill Rd. Infirm. Liverp. & Roy. Liverp. Childr. Hosp.

PANTON, Sally Meadowbrook, 4 Flagshaw Lane, Kirk Langley, Derby DE6 4NW — MB ChB 1977 Ed.; MRCGP 1981; DCCH RCGP 1992; DRCOG 1981. (Edinburgh) Clin. Med. Off. (Child Health) Derby.

PANTON, Susanna The Surgery, 107 Wooley Castle Road, Wooley Castle, Birmingham B29 5QD Tel: 0121 427 1530 — MB BS 1988 Lond.; MRCGP 1993.

PANTRIDGE, Professor James Francis, CBE, MC (retired) Woodlands Corcreeny, Hillsborough BT26 6EH Tel: 01846 689976 Fax: 01846 689807 — MD 1946 Belf.; Hon. DSc Ulster 1981, Hon. DSc Open 1981; MB BCh BAO (Hons.) 1939; FRCP Lond. 1962, M 1947; Hon. FRCPI 1970. Prev: Phys. Roy. Vict. Hosp. Belf.

PAO, Caroline Shien-Lan Flat 4, 81 Alderney St., London SW1V 4HF — MB BS 1991 Lond.

***PAO, David Shien Phen** Mei-Lan, 5 Rosebriars, Esher KT10 9NN — MB BS 1994 Lond.

PAOLONI, Claudia Christina Erika 31 Green Lane, Oxhey, Watford WD19 4NL — MB BS 1991 Lond.; BSc (Hons.) Lond. 1988; FRCA 1997. Specialist Regist. (Anaesth.) Soton. Socs: Brit. Med. Assn.; Fell. Roy. Coll. Anaesth.; Eur. Acad. Anaesth. Prev: Med. Off. Roy. Flying Doctor Serv., Australia; SHO (Med.) Soton.; SHO (Anaesth.) Plymouth.

PAPACHRYSOSTOMOU EVGENIKOS, Maria Gastrointestinal Unit, Western General Hospital, Crewe Road S., Edinburgh EH4 2XU Tel: 0131 537 1756 Fax: 0131 336 4492 Email: mpapachrysostomou@ed.ac.uk; 17 Barnton Park Avenue, Edinburgh EH4 6ES Tel: 0131 336 4492 — Vrach 1984 Rostov Med. Inst.; MD Rostov Med. Inst. 1984; PhD (Med.) Ed. 1992. (Rostov Med. Institute and Edinburgh University) Staff Gastroenterol. W.ern Gen. Hosp. Edin. Socs: Caledonian Soc. Gastroenterol.; Eur. Soc. Gastroenterol. & Hepatol.; Assoc. of Coloproct. Gt. Brit. & Ire. Prev: Lect. (Med.) Univ. of Edin. W.ern Gen. Hosp.

PAPACONSTANTINOU, Helen 2 Shields, Lochwinnoch PA12 4HL — Ptychio Iatrikes 19984 Athens.

PAPACOSTOPOULOS, Demetrios 41 Northumberland Road, Bristol BS6 7BA — Ptychio Iatrikes 1962 Athens; PhD Bristol 1982.

PAPADAKIS, Mr Antonios c/o Urology Department, Ealing Hospital, Uxbridge Road, Southall UB1 3HW; 5 Broadway Close, Urmston, Manchester M41 7NR — Ptychio Iatrikes 1986 Athens; FRCS Ed. 1994. SHO Rotat. (Surg.) Whiston Hosp. Prescot; Mem. Bristol Urol. Inst. Socs: Hellenic Med. Soc. Prev: SHO (Urol. & Surg.) Dist. Gen. Hosp. Glan Clwyd; SHO (Surg.) Vict. Hopsp. Blackburn.

PAPADOPOULOS, Andreas John 5 The Murreys, Barnettwood Lane, Ashtead KT21 2LU — MB BS 1990 Lond.

***PAPADOPOULOU, Anthie Maria** First Floor Flat, 16 Crossfield Road, London NW3 4NT — MB BS 1998 Lond.; MB BS Lond 1998.

***PAPAGEORGHIOU, Aris Theodosis** 4 Portland Buildings, Sheffield S6 3DZ — MB ChB 1996 Sheff.

PAPAGEORGIOU, George Labros 17 Tedworth Green, Leicester LE4 2NG — Ptychio Iatrikes 1978 Athens.

PAPAGEORGIOU, Pantelis 6 Leinster Square, London W2 4PL — Ptychio Iatrikes 1989 Ioannina.

PAPAKOSTAS, Pavlos 169A Grey Turner House, Du Cane Road, London W12 0UA — Ptychio Iatrikes 1979 Athens.

PAPAMICHAEL, Demetrios Flat 16, Cedarland Court, 1A Roland Gardens, London SW7 3RW Tel: 020 7460 6491 — MB BS 1988 Lond.; MRCP (UK) 1992. (Char Cross & Westm.) Specialist Regist. (Med. Oncol.) & Clin. Research Fell. ICRF Dept. Med. Oncol. St. Bart. Hosp. Lond.

PAPANASTASSIOU, Maria Napsbury Hospital, Shenley Lane, Napsbury, St Albans AL2 1AA; Basement Flat, 144 Shirland Road, London W9 2BT — Ptychio Iatrikes 1991 Thessalonika.

PAPANASTASSIOU, Mr Varnavas Department of Neurosurgery, Institute of Neurological Sciences, The Southern General Hospital, Glasgow G51 4TF Tel: 0141 201 2107 Fax: 0141 201 2995 Email: vp7s@clinmed.gla.ac.uk — MB ChB 1985 Manch.; MD Manch. 1994; FRCS (SN) 1995; FRCS Eng. 1989; FRCS Ed. 1989. (University of Manchester) Sen. Lect. & Cons. Neurosurg. Inst. Neurol. Sc. Glasg. Socs: SBNS; Hellenic Med. Soc.; Brit. Neuro-oncol. Gp. Prev: Sen. Regist. (Neurosurg.) Radcliffe Infirm. Oxf.; Regist. (Neurosurg.) Radcliffe Infirm. Oxf.; Clin. Research Fell. Imperial Cancer Research Fund Frenchay Hosp. Bristol.

PAPAPANAGIOTOU, George 35 Elmwood Road, London SE24 9NS — Ptychio Iatrikes 1981 Athens.

PAPAS, Kyvelie 91 Westbourne Terrace, London W2 6QT Tel: 020 7262 5600 — MD 1969 Athens; MB 1954; LAH Dub. 1964; FRCPCH. (Athens) SCMO W. Lambeth HA. Socs: ACPP. Prev: Deptm. Med. Off. Lond. Boro. Haringey.

PAPASAVVAS, Georghios Kyriacos Department Rheumatology, Royal Sussex County Hospital, Eastern Road, Brighton BN2 5BE Tel: 01273 696955 Fax: 01273 673466 — MB BS 1980 Lond.; FRCP 1997; MRCP (UK) 1983. (Lond. Hosp.) Cons. Rheum. Roy. Sussex Co. Hosp. Socs: Brit. Soc. Rheum. Prev: Sen. Regist. (Rheum. & Rehabil.) King's Coll. Hosp. Lond.; Regist. (Rheum.) Middlx. Hosp.

PAPASIOPOULOS, Sophie West Middlesex University Hospital, Isleworth TW7 6AF Tel: 020 8560 2121 — Ptychio Iatrikes 1963 Thessalinika; Ptychio Iatrikes Thessalonika 1963; MD Athens 1975; FFA RCS Eng. 1972; FFA RCSI 1971; DA Eng. 1970. (Univ. Thessalonika) Cons. Anaesth. W. Middlx. Univ. Hosp. Isleworth.

PAPASTATHIS, Dimitrios ENT Department, Royal Hallamshire County Hospital, Winchester SO22 5DG — Ptychio Iatrikes 1972 Athens.

PAPAYANNAKOS, Efthimios 2 Gilston Road, London SW10 9SL — Ptychio Iatrikes 1957 Athens.

PAPE, Mrs Sarah Amanda Royal Victoria Infirmary, Newcastle upon Tyne NE1 4LP Tel: 0191 282 5336 Fax: 0191 227 5229 — MB ChB 1982 Leeds; FRCS (Plast) Ed. 1994; FRCS Ed. 1987. Cons. Plastic Surg. Roy. Vict. Infirm. Newc. u. Tyne. Prev: Sen. Regist. (Plastic Surg.) Newc. Teach. Hosp. Newc.; Regist. (Plastic Surg.) Whiston Hosp. Merseyside; Regist. & SHO Postgrad. Train Scheme (Surg.) St. Jas. Hosp. Leeds.

PAPEE, Eva (retired) 28 Grasmere Avenue, London W3 6JU Tel: 020 8992 3875 Fax: 020 8248 8284 — Lekarz 1960 Katowice; Dip. Anaesth. Katowice 1963. Prev: Clin. Asst. (Anaesth.) Edgware Gen. Hosp.

PAPENFUS, Carolyn Barbara 3 Aubrey Close, Marlborough SN8 1TS — LRCP LRCS Ed. LRCPS Glas. 1988; MB ChB Zimbabwe 1985; MRCP (UK) 1991; MRCGP 1993.

PAPINI, Mr Remo Pio Giuseppe Plastic Surgery Department, University Hospital Birmingham NHS Trust, Selly Oak Hospital, Raddlebarn Road, Birmingham B24 6JD Tel: 0121 627 8784 Fax: 0121 627 8782 Email: remo.papini@university-6.wmids.nhs.uk; 29 Hallcroft Way, Knowle, Solihull B93 9ET — MB BS 1984 Lond.; FRCS Ed. 1990; FRCS (Plast) Ed. 1998. (Royal Free Hosp. Sch. Of Med.) Cons. (Plastic & Burns Surg.). Socs: Brit. Burn Assoc.; Internat. Soc. For Burn Injury; Brit. Assoc. of Plastic Surgs. Prev: Burns Fell. Roy. Perth Hosp. Perth, W.ern Australia; Sen. Regist. (Plastic Surg.) Whiston Hosp. Merseyside; Regist. (Plastic Surg.) Newc. u. Tyne.

PAPOUCHADO, Mark 14 York Place, Clifton, Bristol BS8 1AH — MB BChir 1976 Camb.; BA Camb. 1972, MA, MB 1976, BChir 1975; MRCP (UK) 1982; DA Eng. 1978. (Camb. & Char. Cross) Cons. Cardiol. Frenchay Hosp. Bristol. Prev: Sen. Research Regist. (Cardiol.) Bristol Roy. Infirm.; Regist. (Cardiol.) Bristol Roy. Infirm.; Regist. (Med.) King Edwd. VII Hosp. Windsor.

PAPP, Marta 176 Gilbert Road, Frimley, Camberley GU16 7RE — MD 1985 Debrecen, Hungary; MRCP (UK) 1995.

PAPPACHAN, Joseph Vithayathil — MB BS 1964 Karnatak. (Kasturba Med. Coll. Mangalore)

PAPPACHAN, Vimala Meadowcroft, Primrose Hill, Bournmoor, Houghton-le-Spring DH4 6DY Tel: 01385 2508 — MB BS 1964 Karnatak; MRCOG 1973, DObst 1969. (Kasturba Med. Coll. Mangalore)

PAPPACHAN, Vithayathil John Fence Houses Surgery, Gill CrescentN., Fence House, Houghton-le-Spring DH4 6DW Tel: 0191 385 2508 — MB BChir 1991 Camb.

PAPPIN, Catherine Jane Eileen Netherlee, Roundham Avenue, Paignton TQ4 6DE Tel: 01803 551430 — MB BS 1996 Lond.; DFFP 1998; MRCOG Part I 1998. (Guys & St. Thos.) SHO (O & G) P.ss Anne Hosp. Soton. Socs: BMA; MDU. Prev: SHO (O & G) St. Mary's Hosp. Portsmouth; Ho. Phys. Worthing Hosp.; Ho. Surg. Roy. Sussex Co. Hosp. Brighton.

PAPPIN, John Christopher Anaesthetic Department, Torbay Hospital, Lawes Bridge, Torquay TQ2 7AA Tel: 01803 654310 Fax: 01803 654312; Netherlee, Roundham Avenue, Paignton TQ4 6DE Tel: 01803 551430 Email: jcpappin@hotmail.com — MB BS 1967 Lond.; MRCS Eng. LRCP Lond. 1967; FFA RCS Eng. 1972. (Middlx.) Cons. Anaesth. Torbay Hosp. Socs: BMA; Assn. Of Anaesth.s; S. W. Soc. Of Anaesth. Prev: Sen. Regist. Rotat. Avon AHA (T) & S. W.. RHA; Regist. (Anaesth.) Frenchay Hosp. Bristol; Regist. Chelmsford Gp. Hosps.

PAPWORTH

PAPWORTH, George William John (retired) 22 Graham Road, Weston Super Mare BS23 1YA Tel: 01934 628111 — MB ChB 1968 Leeds. Chairm. W.on Primary Care Co-Operat.; Med. Adv. W.on Area Health Trust Bd.; Audit Assessor Area Health Auth. Prev: Sen. Partner, Graham Rd Surg., W.on Super Mare.

PAPWORTH, James Edward John 12 Queens Road, Weston Super Mare BS23 2LQ — MB ChB 1994 Leeds.

PAPWORTH, Peter 11 Maidens Croft, Allendale Road, Hexham NE46 2QA Tel: 01434 607193 — MB BS 1951 Lond.; DA Eng. 1959. (King's Coll. Hosp. & Lond.) Pask Award Assn. Anaesth Gt. Brit. & Irel. 1981. Socs: Assn. Anaesth. Gt. Brit. & Irel. Prev: Cons. Anaesth. E. African Flying Doctor (AMREF).

PAPWORTH, Robert David John 1 Oakwood Mount, Roundhay, Leeds LS8 2JD — MB ChB 1964 Leeds; DA Eng. 1969. Anaesth. York A Hosp. Gp. Prev: Ho. Phys. St. Jas. Hosp. Leeds; Thoracic Ho. Surg. & Cas. Off. Leeds Gen. Infirm.

PAPWORTH, Susan Elizabeth Department of Paediatrics, Royal Gwent Hospital, Newport; 7 Trafalgar Road, Penylan, Cardiff CF23 5BQ — BM 1988 Soton.; MRCP (UK) 1994; MRCPCH 1996; DRCOG 1992; DCH RCP Lond. 1991. Specialist Regist. Paediat. Socs: MRCPCH.

PAPWORTH-SMITH, John William c/o Occupational Health Service, University Road, University of Leeds, Leeds LS2 9JT Tel: 0113 233 2997 Fax: 0113 233 2997 — MB ChB 1976 Leeds; BSc (Physiol.) Leeds 1973; MRCGP 1983; Dip. Pract. Dermat. Wales 1991; DCH RCP Lond. 1983; DRCOG 1982; Dip. Occupat. Med. 1996. (Leeds) Med. Off. Univ. Leeds.

PARAB, Suresh Bhikaji Ashirwad, Pen-y-Waun, Pentyrch, Cardiff CF15 9SJ — MB BS 1961 Vikram.

PARACHURI, Mr Venkateswara Rao c/o Mr B. Ramakrishna, 7 Fulton Close, Eaton, Norwich NR4 6HX Tel: 01603 57251 — MB BS 1980 Madras; FRCS Glas. 1986.

PARADINAS, Professor Fernando Juan Histopathology Department, Charing Cross Hospital, Fulham Palace Road, London W6 8RF Tel: 020 8846 7142 Fax: 020 8846 7139; 54 Eton Court, Eton Avenue, London NW3 3HJ Tel: 020 7722 8585 — LRCP LRCS Ed. LRCPS Glas. 1965; LMS Madrid 1962; MRCR 1994; FRCPath 1983, M 1971. (Madrid Univ.) Emerit. Prof. Imperial Coll. Sch. Med.; Hon. Cons. Path. Char. Cross Hosp. Lond. Hosps. Socs: Path. Soc. & Internat. Acad. Path.; Internat. Soc. Gyn. Path. Prev: Sen. Lect. (Path.) Char. Cross Hosp. Med. Sch.; Lect. (Path.) Char. Cross Hosp. Med. Sch.; Regist. (Path.) Roy. Marsden Hosp. Lond.

*PARAGREEN, Jane Louise 21 New Road, Geddington, Kettering NN14 1AT — MB ChB 1998 Birm.; ChB Birm. 1998.

PARAMAGNANAM, Nalliah Chestnut Green Surgery, 27 Chestnut Green, Upper Cwmbran, Cwmbran NP44 5TH Tel: 01633 482248 Fax: 01633 484228; 2 Meyricks, Coed Eva, Cwmbran NP44 6TU — MB BS 1962 Ceylon. (Colombo)

PARAMANATHAN, Kanjana 31 Manor Road N., Birmingham B16 9JS — MB BS 1976 Ceylon; LRCP LRCS Ed. LRCPS Glas. 1981. (Colombo) Regist. (Anaesth.) Geo. Eliot Hosp. Nuneaton. Prev: SHO (Anaesth.) St. Margts. Hosp. Epping; SHO (Anaesth.) Good Hope Gen. Hosp. Sutton Coldfield; SHO (Anaesth.) Roy. Hosp. Wolverhampton.

PARAMANATHAN, Nirmala Dept of Surgery, Royal Hampshire County Hospital, Romsey Road, Winchester SO22 5DG Tel: 01962 863535; 4 Elsham Rise, Ferriby Road, Hessle HU13 0HP Tel: 01482 641790 — MRCS Eng. LRCP Lond. 1987; FRCS Glas. 1996. Staff Grade (Gen. Surg.) Roy. Hamp. Co. Hosp. Winchester. Prev: Regist. (Gen. Surg.) Roy. Hamp. Co. Hosp. Winchester; SHO (Gen. Surg.) S.end Gen. Hosp.; SHO (Gen. Surg.) Co. Hosp. Lincoln.

PARAMANATHAN, Sivapragasam 31 Manor Road N., Birmingham B16 9JS — MB BS 1973 Ceylon; LRCP LRCS Ed. LRCPS Glas. 1981. (Univ. Ceylon) SHO (O & G) Hosp. of St. Cross Rugby. Prev: SHO (O & G) Wordsley Hosp. Stourbridge.

PARAMANATHAN, Veluppillai Otterfield Road Medical Centre, 25 Otterfield Road, Yiewsley, West Drayton UB7 8PE Tel: 01895 422611 Fax: 01895 431309; 11 Pastures Mead, Hillingdon, Uxbridge UB10 9PU — MB BS Ceylon 1970; T(GP) 1991; DFFP (1992). (University of Sri Lanka) GP.

PARAMESHWAR, Karat Jayan Transplant Unit, Papworth Hospital, Papworth Everard, Cambridge CB3 8RE Tel: 01480 830541 — MD 1981 All India Med. Scs.; MPhil Lond. 1992; MD (Med.) All India Med. Scs. 1981; MB BS Madras 1977; MRCP (UK) 1984. Cons. Transpl. Cardiol. Papworth Hosp. Socs: Brit. Cardiac Soc.; Internat. Soc. of Heart and Lung Transpl.ation. Prev: Regist. (Cardiol.) Roy. Brompton & Nat. Heart & Lung Hosps. Lond.; Regist. (Med. & Cardiol.) Hillingdon Hosp. Uxbridge; Regist. (Gen. Med.) Bedford Gen. Hosp.

PARAMESWARAM, Mr Sandrasekeram 14 The Crescent, Hartlepool TS26 8LY — MRCS Eng. LRCP Lond. 1981; MB BS Sr Lanka 1973; FRCS Eng. 1989; FRCS Ed. 1984.

PARAMESWARAN, Raghavannair 25 Whitemeadows, Darlington DL3 8SR Tel: 01642 813166 — MD 1970 Panjab; MD (Rad.) Panjab India 1970; MB BS Kerala 1968; FRCR 1979. (Trivandrum Med. Coll.) Cons. (Neuroradiol.) S. Tees HA, Middlesbrough Gen. & S. Cleveland. Socs: Brit. Soc. Neuroradiol. Prev: Sen. Regist. (Neuroradiol.) Regional Neurol. Centre Newc.; Regist. (Radiol.) & Sen. Regist. (Radiol.) Roy. Vict. Infirm. & Hosp.

PARAMESWARAN, Shanthy Santhanayagi 51 Blakes Avenue, New Malden KT3 6RF — MB BS 1966 Ceylon; MRCPsych 1978; T(Psychiat) 1991.

PARAMESWARAN, Umadevi Arulraja and Partners, 161 Wandle Road, Morden SM4 Tel: 020 8648 1877 Fax: 020 8648 4737 — MB BS 1982 Peradeniya, Sri Lanka.

PARAMOTHAYAN, Brinda Navaluxmi Glenlyn Medical Centre, 115 Molesey Park Road, East Molesey KT8 0JX Tel: 020 8979 3253 Fax: 020 8941 7914 — MB ChB 1992 Liverp.; BSc (Hons.) Physiol. Liverp. 1989. SHO Rotat. (O & G, Palliat. Med., Radiat. Oncol., Paediat. & Psychogeriat.) Wessex RHA VTS.

PARAMOTHAYAN, Niranjala Shanthimanoharie The Lighthouse, 47 Banstead Road S., Sutton SM2 5LG — MB BS 1993 Lond.; PhD Camb. 1987; BSc Birm. 1984; MRCP (UK) 1996. (St. Bartholomew's) Specialist Regist. (Respirat. & Gen. Med.) St. Geo.'s. Socs: Roy. Coll. Phys.; Brit. Thorac. Soc.; BMA.

PARAMSOTHY, Vijayaledchumy Plymouth General Hospital, Freedom Fields, Plymouth PL4 7JJ Tel: 01752 668080 — MB BS 1979 Colombo; MRCS Eng. LRCP Lond. 1984; MRCP (UK) 1986.

*PARANJAPE, Ruchira Nitin 30 Silverwood Close, Brackley Road, Beckenham BR3 1RN — MB BS 1996 Lond.

PARANJOTHY, Chellatturai Eric Moore Health Centre, Tanners Lane, Warrington WA2 7LY Tel: 01925 411210 Fax: 01925 632868; 18 Norlands Lane, Rainhill, Prescot L35 6NR Tel: 0151 289 8905 — MB BS 1962 Ceylon. Socs: BMA; ODA.

PARANJOTHY, Renuka 3 Cedar Walk, Osborn Park, Welwyn Garden City AL7 1HQ — MB ChB 1995 Manch.

*PARANJOTHY, Shantini Horton General Hospital NHS Trust, Banbury OX16 9BR — MB BCh 1995 Wales.

PARAPIA, Liakatali Gulamhussein Habib Bradford Royal Infirmary, Duckworth Lane, Bradford BD9 6RJ Tel: 01274 364203 Fax: 01274 364681 Email: parapia@doctors.org.uk; Farnhill, Kelcliffe Lane, Guiseley, Leeds LS20 9DE Tel: 01943 877282 Fax: 01274 364681 — MB BCh 1974 Wales; FRCP Lond. 1992; FRCP Ed. 1992; MRCP (UK) 1978; MRCPath. 1981; FRCPath 1991. (Univ. Coll. Cardiff, Welsh Nat. Sch. Med.) Cons. Haematolgy Bradford Roy. Infirm. & Dir. Haemophilia Centre; Hon. Cons. Leeds Teachg. Hosp.; Head of Haemat. Bradford; Hon. Lect. (BioMed. Sci.) Univ. Bradford; Ct. Dir. Haematolgy Research Unit Univ. Bradford; Dir. Pathol. Yorks. Clinic Bradford; Hon. Cons. Univ. of Leeds Hosp. Socs: Fell.Roy. Microscopical Soc.; Brit. Soc. Haemat.; Comm. mem. Hist. Med. Soc. Yorks. Prev: Sen. Regist. (Haemat.) Leeds AHA.

PARARAJASINGAM, Ravi 22 Lutterworth Road, Leicester LE2 8PE — MB ChB 1991 Leic. SHO (A & E Med.) N.ampton Gen. Hosp. Socs: BMA & Med. Protec. Soc. Prev: Demonst. (Anat.) St. Bart. Hosp. Lond.; Ho. Off. (Gen. Surg.) Leics. Gen. Hosp.

PARASHAR, Mr Karan Children's Hospital, Steelhouse Lane, Birmingham B4 6NH Tel: 0121 333 8082 Email: karan.parashar@bhamchildrens.wmids.nhs.uk; 145 Moor Green Lane, Moseley, Birmingham B13 8NT — MB BS 1978 Poona; MB BS Poona, India 1978; FRCS (Paediat.) 1994; FRCS Ed. 1987; FRCS Glas. 1983. Cons. Paediat. Surg. The Childr. Hosp. Birm.

PARASHCHAK, Myroslav Roman Longford Street Surgery, Longford Street, Heywood OL10 4NH Tel: 01706 621417 Fax: 01706 622915; Hawthorn House, White Horse Meadows, Broad Lane, Rochdale OL16 4PU Tel: 01706 712746 Email: mpdoc@zen.co.uk — MB ChB 1979 Manch.; BSc (Med. Sci.) St. And. 1976; MRCP (UK) 1983; MRCGP 1985; DRCOG 1984. (St Andrews Manchester)

PARASKEVA, Paraskevas Antonios 27 Crown Street, Harrow HA2 0HX — MB BS 1994 Lond.

PARASKEVAIDES, Mr Eftis Costas Hinchingbrooke Hospital, Hinchingbrooke Park, Huntingdon PE29 6NT Tel: 01480 416416; Clyde Farm, Silver St, Godmanchester, Huntingdon PE29 2LF — MB ChB 1980 Manch.; BSc Manch. 1977, MB ChB 1980; FRCS Ed. 1987; FRCS Glas. 1986; MRCPI 1993; MRCOG 1990. Cons. O & G Hinchingbrooke Hosp. Huntingdon. Socs: Manch. Med. Soc. (Surgic. Div.); E. Anglia Obst. & Gyn. Soc. Prev: Lect. (O & G) Roy. Coll. Surg. Irel. Rotunda Hosp. Dub.

PARASURAM, Pothina c/o Mr M. N. Patrudu, 52 Mellanear Road, Hayle TR27 4QT — MB BS 1974 Andhra.

PARBHOO, Ishverlal 57-59 East Dulwich Road, London SE22 9AP Tel: 020 8693 3047 — LRCPI & LM, LRSCI & LM 1953; LRCPI & LM, LRCSI & LM 1953. (RCSI) Prev: SHMO (Cas. & Orthop.) Roy. Infirm. Blackburn; Regist. Vict. Hosp. Burnley & Reedyford Memor. Hosp. Nelson.

PARBHOO, Krishnapathee 57-59 East Dulwich Road, London SE22 9AP Tel: 020 8693 3047 — LRCPI & LM, LRSCI & LM 1953; LRCPI & LM, LRCSI & LM 1953; DA Eng. 1957. (RCSI) Prev: Regist. (Anaesth.) Blackburn Hosp. Gp.; SHO (Cas.) Pub. Disp. & Hosp. Leeds; SHO (Anaesth.) Colchester Hosp. Gp.

PARBHOO, Pravinkumar Hurrilal The Paagon Suite, Wexham Park Hospital, Wexham St., Slough SL2 4HL — MB ChB 1975 Natal.

PARBHOO, Rakesh — MB BS 1991 Lond.; DCH 2000; MRCGP 2000; MRCP 1997.

PARBHOO, Mr Santilal Parag Cancerkin Centre, Royal Free Hospital, Pond St., London NW3 2QG Tel: 020 7830 2323 Fax: 020 7830 2324 Email: spparbhoo@doctors.net.uk; 6 Woodberry Way, London N12 0HG Tel: 020 8445 0348 Fax: 020 8445 0348 Email: spparbhoo@doctors.net.uk — MB ChB 1960 Cape Town; PhD Belf. 1967; FRCS Eng. 1967. (Cape Town) Hon. Cons. Surg. Roy. Free Hosp.; Med. Director, Cancerkin; Hon. Cons. Surg. Hosp. St. John & St. Eliz. Lond.; Vis. Prof. Univ. Amman (1983), Capetown (1987) & Cairo (1989); Vis. Prof. & Carlo Erba Lect. Univ. Milan 1973. Socs: Fell. Assn. Surgs.; Brit. Assn. Surg. Oncol.; Internat. Soc. Of Lymphology. Prev: Regist. & Tutor Profess. Surg. Unit Roy. Vict. Hosp. Belf.; Research Fell. (Med.) & Sen. Regist. Roy. Free Hosp. Lond.; Regist. (Gen. Surg. & Gastroenterol.) Frenchay Hosp. Bristol.

PARBROOK, Evelyn Ogilvie (retired) Kinord, 7 Buchanan St., Milngavie, Glasgow G62 8DB — MB ChB 1964 Aberd.; BSc Aberd. 1962. Prev: GP Glas.

PARBROOK, Margaret Jean (retired) 4 Delahays Drive, Hale, Altrincham WA15 8DP — MB BS 1947 Durh.; DA Eng. 1953. Prev: Cons. Anaesth. N. Manch.

PARCHURE, Nikhil c/o Dr Ashok Bhide, 143 Albury Drive, Pinner HA5 3RJ — MB BS 1987 Jiwaji; MRCP (UK) 1994.

PARDHANANI, Gianni Boehringer Ingelheim, Ellesfield Ave, Bracknell RG12 8YS Email: gpardhanani@doctors.org.uk — MB BS 1997 Lond.; MB BS (Hons.) Lond. 1997; BA Camb. 1994; MA Camb. 1998. (Camb. & St. Geo's.)

PARDOE, Celia Anne Bridge Cottage Surgery, 41 High Street, Welwyn AL6 9EF Tel: 01438 715044 Fax: 01438 714013; 15 Sherrardspark Road, Welwyn Garden City AL8 7JW Tel: 01707 331746 Email: nelsonpardoe@compuserve.com — MB ChB 1978 Liverp.; MRCGP 1983; DCH RCP Lond. 1982; Cert. Family Plann. JCC 1981; DRCOG 1981. (Liverpool) GP Trainer; Acupunc. Qu. Eliz. II Hosp. Pain Clinic. Socs: BMA; Brit. Med. Acupunct. Assn. Prev: Regist. (Pub. Health) N. Herts. HA; GP Alderley Edge Chesh.; GP Huyton Liverp.

PARDOE, Helen Dorothy — MB ChB 1989 Ed.; FRCS Ed. 1993; MSc 1996. (Edinburgh)

PARDOE, Ian Stuart The Old Priory Surgery, 319 Vicarage Road, Kings Heath, Birmingham B14 7NN Tel: 0121 444 1120 — MB ChB 1985 Birm.; MRCGP 1990; Dip. Med. Acupunc 1996. Socs: Accred. Mem. Brit. Med. Acupunc. Soc.

PARDOE, James Leslie (retired) Church Cottage, Church Road N., Portishead, Bristol BS20 6PS Tel: 01275 848249 — MB ChB 1942 Bristol. Post Office & Treasury Med. Off.

PARDOE, Robin Francis Carcroft Health Centre, Chestnut Avenue, Carcroft, Doncaster DN6 8AG Tel: 01302 723510; 91 Tenterbank Lane, Adwick-Le-Street, Doncaster DN6 — MB ChB 1969 Sheff.

PARDOE, Roger Braddy (retired) Innisfree, 79 Nore Road, Portishead, Bristol BS20 6JZ Tel: 01275 849497 — MB BS 1953 Lond.; MRCS Eng. LRCP Lond. 1953; DObst RCOG 1956.

PARDOE, Timothy Hugh Old Hall Grounds Health Centre, Old Hall Grounds, Cowbridge CF7 7AH Tel: 01446 772383 Fax: 01446 774022 — MB BCh 1978 Wales; MRCP (UK) 1981.

PARDOE, Timothy Savile The Stennack Surgery, The Old Stennack School, St Ives TR26 1RU Tel: 01736 796413 Fax: 01736 796245 — MB ChB 1972 Bristol. GP Princip.

PARDY, Mr Bruce James 144 Harley Street, London W1G 7LD Tel: 020 7935 0023 Fax: 020 7376 9708 Email: bruce@brucepardy.com; 49 Abingdon Villas, Kensington, London W8 6XA Tel: 020 7937 3417 Fax: 020 7376 9708 — MB ChB 1963 Otago; ChM Otago 1980, MB ChB 1963; BMedSc NZ 1961; FRCS Eng. 1973; FRACS 1969. (Otago) p/t Cons. Surg. Newnham Healthcare NHS Trust; Cons. Surg. Newham Gen. & St. And. Hosps. Lond. Socs: Med. Soc. Lond.; Eur. Vasc. Soc.; Fell. Roy. Soc. Med. Prev: Sen. Regist. (Gen. Surg.) St. Mary's Hosp. Lond.; Med. Adviser Raynaud's Assn.

PARDY, Karen 11 Maes Y Briallu, Morganstown, Cardiff CF15 8FA — MB BCh Wales 1997.

PARE, Charles Michael Bromiley Little Brook, Milton St., Westcott, Dorking RH4 3PX Tel: 01306 889633 — MB BChir 1948 Camb.; MD Camb. 1956; FRCP Lond. 1968, M 1950; FRCPsych 1971; Hon. FRCPsych 1987; DPM Lond. 1957. (Middlx.) Socs: Fell. Roy. Soc. Med. Prev: Treas. Roy. Coll. Psychiats.; Phys. Dept. Psychiat. St. Bart. Hosp. Lond.; US Pub. Health Serv. Trav. Fell. 1959-60.

PAREKH, Sailesh Jaswantrai Anukhil, Pen y Waun, Pentyrch, Cardiff CF15 9SJ — MB BS 1982 Mysore; MChOrth. 1991.

PAREKH, Shanti 14 Delamere Road, Hall Green, Birmingham B28 0ER Tel: 0121 243 5742 — MB BS 1973 Bombay; FRCS Eng. 1981.

PAREKH, Vistasp Jal The Surgery, 212 Richmond Road, Kingston upon Thames KT2 5HF Tel: 020 8546 0400 Fax: 020 8974 5771; 9 Brunswick Court, The Albany, Albany Park Road, Kingston upon Thames KT2 5SR — MB BS 1973 Bombay; MS Bombay 1978. (Grant Med. Coll.) Prev: Trainee GP Chessington Surrey; SHO (O & G) St. Helier Hosp. Carshalton; SHO (Paediat.) Qu. Mary's Hosp. Carshalton.

PAREMAIN, Mr Guy Perry 14 Glendale Drive, Wimbledon, London SW19 7BG — MB BS 1985 Lond.; FRCS Lond. 1991. SHO (Plastic Surg.) St. Geo. Hosp. Lond.

PAREMAIN, Tessa Jane 10 High Path Road, Merrow, Guildford GU1 2QG — MB BS 1991 Lond.

PARFITT, Mr Andrew 22 Dulais Road, Seven Sisters, Neath SA10 9EL; 36 Castellain Mansions, Castellain Road, London W9 1HA Email: andy.parfitt@virgin.net — MB BS 1990 Lond.; DRCOG 1993; FRCS Eng. 1995. Specialist Regist. (A & E) NW Thames. Socs: Brit. Assn. Sport & Med. Prev: Regist. (Cardiothoracics) St Mary's Hosp.; SHO (Surg.) St. Mary's Hosp. Paddington.; SHO (Gyn.) Samarit. Hosp. Lond.

PARFITT, Caroline Jane Health Centre, Old Street, Clevedon BS21 6DG Tel: 01275 871454 — MB BS 1987 Lond.; MRCGP 1992; Dip. Community Paediat. Warwick 1994; T(GP) 1991; DRCOG 1991. Prev: Clin. Med. Off. Community Child Health Kidderminster; Trainee GP Brighton VTS.

PARFITT, Catharine Jane Littlewick Medical Centre, 42 Nottingham Road, Ilkeston DE7 5PR Tel: 0115 932 5229 Fax: 0115 932 5413; 133 Parkside, Wollaton, Nottingham NG8 2NL Tel: 0115 916 3627 — MB BS Lond. 1970; MRCS Eng. LRCP Lond. 1970; MRCGP 1978; DCH Eng. 1975; DTM & H Liverp. 1974. (St. Bart.) Socs: BMA; Nottm. M-C Soc. Prev: Trainee GP Bristol VTS; Med. Off Wusasa Hosp. Zaria, Nigeria; Ho. Phys. & Ho. Surg. Hillingdon Hosp. Uxbridge.

PARFITT, Graham George 44 Mantilla Drive, Styvechale Grange, Coventry CV3 6LQ — MRCS Eng. LRCP Lond. 1966; BSc Physiol. Lond. 1963. (Guy's) Clin. Asst. in Ophth. Warneford Hosp. Leamington Spa. Socs: Leamington Med. Soc. Prev: Ho. Surg., Ho. Phys. & Ho. Surg. (O & G) Warneford Hosp.

PARFITT, Jeremy 22 Dulais Road, Seven Sisters, Neath SA10 9EL — MB BS 1994 Lond.; BSc Lond. 1991. (St Marys) SHO (Gen. Surg.) Hammersmith Hosp. Lond.; Vasc. SHO St Marys Hosp. Lond.

PARFITT

PARFITT, Julia Carolyn Royal Hampshire County Hosp., Romsey Road, Winchester, Hants SO22 5DG Tel: 01962 863535; 39 Hocombe Road, Chandlers Ford, Hants, Eastleigh SO53 5SP Email: parfittjulia@hotmail.com — BM 1986 Soton.; FRCA 1995; DA (UK) 1989. Staff Grade(Anaesth.) RHCH Winchester. Prev: Specialist Regist. Yr3 Winchester(Wessex RHA); Regist. (Anaesth.) Wessex RHA.; SHO (Anaesth. & Med.) Portsmouth & SE Hants. HA.

PARFITT, Matthew David 1 Brishing Close, Maidstone ME15 9LA Email: matthew.parfitt@kcl.ac.uk — MB BS 1996 Lond.; BSc Lond. 1992. SHO (Med.).

PARFITT, Ronald (retired) 165 Shirley Church Road, Croydon CR0 5AJ Tel: 020 8777 4746 — MRCS Eng. LRCP Lond. 1939; LDS RCS Eng. 1936; FRCR 1975; FFR 1958; DMRT Eng. 1949. Prev: Cons. (Radiother.) St. Thos. Hosp. Lond.

PARFITT, Vernon John Consultant Physician, Diabetes and Endocrinology, Diabetes and Endocrinology Service, Gloucestershire Royal Hospital, Great Western Road, Gloucester GL1 3NN Tel: 01452 394758 Fax: 01452 394755 — MB ChB 1983 Bristol; MD Bristol 1994; MRCP (UK) 1987. (Bristol) Cons. Phys. (Diabetes & Endocrinol.). Socs: Clin. Mem. BDA; Brit. Hyperlipid. Assn.; Med. Res. Soc. Prev: Sen. Regist. Rotat. (Gen. Med., Diabetes & Endocrinol.) Soton. & Bath; Lect. (Med.) Bristol Univ. & S.mead Hosp.; Research Regist. (Med.) Univ. Bristol.

PARFREY, Helen 1 Archerfield Road, Liverpool L18 7HS Tel: 0151 724 3867 — BM BCh 1993 Oxf.; MA Oxf. 1996; MRCP (UK) 1996. (Oxf.) Specialist Regist. (Gen. Med. & Respirat.) Camb.

PARGE, Frauke Maria Elizabeth 101A High Street, Waddesdon, Aylesbury HP18 0JE Tel: 01296 651282 — State Exam Med. Essen 1989. SHO (Neonat.) John Radcliffe Hosp. Headington Oxon. Prev: SHO High Wycombe Gen. Hosp.; Ho. Off. Mandeville Hosp. Aylesbury.

PARGETER, Jane Margaret Walton and Partners, West Street Surgery, 12 West Street, Chipping Norton OX7 5AA Tel: 01608 642529 Fax: 01608 645066; Easter Cottage, Southrop Road, Hook Norton, Banbury OX15 5PP — MB BS 1986 Lond.; MRCGP 1992; DGM RCP Lond. 1991; DCH RCP Lond. 1990.

PARGHI, Pratibha Dinesh St. Mary's Hospital, Dean Road, Scarborough YO12 7SW Tel: 01723 376111; 18 Mount View Avenue, Scarborough YO12 4EW Tel: 01723 500456 — MB BS 1969 Bombay; DPM Eng. 1981. Clin. Asst. (Psychiat.) Cross La. Hosp. ScarBoro..; Assoc. Specialist (Psychiat. of Old Age). Socs: MDU. Prev: Clin. Asst. (Psychiat.) St. Mary's Hosp. ScarBoro..

PARHAM, Andrew Leonard West End Medical Centre, 102 Stockport Road, Ashton-under-Lyne OL7 0LH Tel: 0161 339 5488 Fax: 0161 330 0945; Charity Farm, Millcroft Lane, Delph, Oldham OL3 5UX — MB ChB 1988 Manch.; MRCGP 1992.

PARHAM, Andrew Leslie Scott War Pensions Agency, Norcross, Blackpool FY2 0WP Tel: 01253 332440 — BM BCh 1975 Oxf.; MA Oxf. 1975; BA (Animal Physiol.) Oxf. 1971. (Oxf.) Sen. Med. Adviser War Pens. Agency Blackpool. Prev: Med. Adviser War Pens. Agency.

PARHAM, David McCausland Department of Pathology, Royal Bournemouth Hospital, Castle Lane E., Bournemouth BH7 7DW Tel: 01202 704832 Fax: 01202 704 8333 — MB ChB 1983 Dundee; BMSc (Hons.) Dund 1980, MD 1990; MRCPath 1990. Cons. Path. Roy. Bournemouth Hosp. Prev: Lect. & Hon. Sen. Regist. (Path.) Ninewells Hosp. Dundee; Regist. (Path.) Ninewells Hosp. Dundee; Ho. Off. Edin. Roy. Infirm.

PARIENTE, David 152 Harley Street, London W1G 7LH Tel: 020 7935 2477 Fax: 020 8455 2883 Email: parientedoc@lineone.net — MB ChB Aberd. 1967; MRCPsych 1974; DPM Eng. 1974; FRCPsych 1998. (University of Aberdeen) Cons. Adult Gen. Psychiat. Barnet Community Healthcare NHS Trust. Socs: Soc. Clin. Psychiats.; Acad. Experts; Soc. Expert Witnesses. Prev: Cons. Psychiat. Edgware Comm. Hosp. Lond.; Sen. Regist. Napsbury Hosp.; Hon. Clin. Asst. Univ. Coll. Hosp. Lond.

PARIHAR, P David Medical Centre, 274 Barlow Moor Road, Chorlton, Manchester M21 8HA Tel: 0161 881 1681 Fax: 0161 860 7071 — MB BS 1973 Delhi; MB BS 1973 delhi.

PARIHAR, S S David Medical Centre, 274 Barlow Moor Road, Chorlton, Manchester M21 8HA Tel: 0161 881 1681 Fax: 0161 860 7071 — MB BS 1973 kanpur; MB BS 1973 Kanpur.

PARIKH, Mr Aashish Madhusudan 73 The Vale, London NW11 8TJ — MB BS 1986 Gujarat; FRCS Eng. 1989; FRCS Ed. 1989.

PARIKH, Ami 3 Cringleford Chase, Norwich NR4 7RS — BM 1992 Soton.

PARIKH, Mr Balkrishna Kantilal High Bank, Addersgate Lane, Shibden, Halifax HX3 7TD Tel: 01422 205687 — MB BS 1959 Karnatak; FRCS Eng. 1964. (Kasturba Med. Coll. Mangalore) Cons. Surg. A & E Dept. Roy. Halifax Infirm.

PARIKH, Camilla Room 917, Market Towers, 1 Nine Elms Lane, London SW8 5NQ Tel: 020 7273 0374 Fax: 020 7273 0554 — MB BS 1982 Lond.; MSc Lond. 1991, MB BS 1982; MRCPsych 1989. (Westminster Medical School) Sen. Med. Off. Dept. of Health. Prev: Regist. (Pub. Health Med.) SE Thames RHA; Regist. (Psychiat.) W.m. & Char. Cross Hosp. Lond.

PARIKH, Chirag Orsett Road Surgery, 86 Orsett Road, Grays RM17 5EL Tel: 01375 372505 Fax: 01375 394596 — MB ChB 1988 Glas.; MRCGP 1994; DCH RCP Lond. 1994; DFFP 1994. Socs: BMA & RCGP.

PARIKH, Mr Daxesh Harivadan The Birmingham Childrens Hospital, Dept. of Paediatric Surgery, Steelhouse Lane, Birmingham B4 6MH Tel: 0121 333 9999 Fax: 0121 333 8081; 57 Moorcroft Road, Birmingham B13 8LT — MB BS 1980 Bombay; FRCS Glas. 1988; FRCS (Paed.) 1994; MD Bris 1994. Cons. (Paediat. Surg.) Birm. Childr.'s Hosp. Socs: Brit. Assn. Paediat. Surg. Prev: Sen. Regist. (Paediat. Surg.) Roy. Liverp. Childr. Hosp. Alder Hey.; Research Fell. (Paediat. Surg.) Univ. Liverp. Roy. Liverp. Childr. Hosp.; Regist. (Paediat. Surg. & Urol.) Alder Hey Childr. Hosp. Liverp.

PARIKH, Harshad Shantilal Potteries Medical Centre, Beverley Drive, Bentilee, Stoke-on-Trent ST2 0JG Tel: 01782 208755 — MB BS 1971 Gujarat; MB BS 1971 Gujarat.

PARIKH, Jitinkumar Kanchanlal The Surgery, 9 Beaconsfield Road, Brighton BN1 4QH Tel: 01273 698666 Fax: 01273 672742 — MB BS 1952 Bombay. (Bombay) GP Brighton.

PARIKH, Jyoti 15 Rayleas Close, London SE18 3JN; 15 Rayleas Close, London SE18 3JN — BM BCh Oxf. 1997; MA (Hons.) Cantab. 1998. (Cambridge and Oxford) SHO Med. Rotat. St Thomas' Hosp. Lond. Socs: BMA.

PARIKH, Ketankumar Satishchandra 12 Stangate, Royal St., London SE1 7EQ — MB BS 1988 Bombay.

PARIKH, Nalin Sakerlal (Surgery), 12 Movers Lane, Barking IG11 7UN Tel: 020 8594 4700 — MB BS 1955 Bombay.

***PARIKH, Paresh** 223 Styal Road, Heald Green, Stockport SK8 3UA Tel: 09058 582748 — MB ChB 1996 Leeds.

PARIKH, Rajesh Kantilal Ashfield Road Surgery, 70 Ashfield Road, Blackpool FY2 0DJ Tel: 01253 357739 Fax: 01253 596161 — MB BS 1975 Saurashtra. (M.P. Shah Med. Coll. Jamnagar) Clin. Asst. (Anaesth.) Vict. Hosp. Blackpool; Med. Off. Trinity Hospice in the Fylde. Prev: Regist. (Anaesth.) & SHO (A & E & O & G) Sunderland Dist. Gen. Hosp.

PARIKH, Ranjit Kantilal (retired) 62 Stokiemuir Avenue, Bearsden, Glasgow G61 3LX Tel: 0141 942 3925 — MB BS 1960 Bombay; FFA RCS Eng. 1971; FFA RCSI 1970; DObst RCOG 1964. Prev: Cons. Anaesth. Stobhill Gen. Hosp. Glas.

PARIKH, Rashmikant Vadilal Norfolk Street Surgery, 40 Norfolk Street, Glossop SK13 7QU Tel: 01457 864984 Fax: 01457 860966; Lee Mount, Marple Road, Charlesworth, Broadbottom, Hyde SK13 5DA — MB BS 1960 Bombay; DLO Eng. 1965; DA Eng. 1968. (Bombay) Prev: Regist. (ENT) Salford Hosp. Gp. & Angus Gp. Hosp.; SHO (Anaesth.) Salford Gp. Hosp.

PARIKH, Renuka Amulakhray Flat 17, Harwood Court, Harwood Road, Heaton Mersey, Stockport SK4 3BE — MB BS 1971 Saurashtra. (M.P. Shah Med. Coll. Jamnagar)

***PARIKH, Stanley** 62 Stanley Avenue, Harborne, Birmingham B32 2HA — MB ChB 1998 Birm.; ChB Birm. 1998.

PARIKH, Susan 62 Stanley Avenue, Harborne Road, Birmingham B32 2HA — MRCS Eng. LRCP Lond. 1992.

PARIS, Mr Andrew Martin Ingledew, OStJ 121 Harley Street, London W1N 1DH Tel: 020 7486 6324 Fax: 020 7935 5333; The Royal London Hospital, London E1 1DM Tel: 020 7377 7262 Fax: 020 7377 7292 — MB BS 1964 Lond.; FRCS Eng. 1971; MRCS Eng. LRCP Lond. 1964; DObst RCOG 1966. (Lond. Hosp.) Cons. Urol. Surg. Roy. Lond. Hosp. & St. Barts. Hosp.; Clin. Dir. Specialist Surg. Roy. Hosp. Trust. Socs: Fell. Roy. Soc. Med. (Vice Pres. Counc. Sect. Urol.); Brit. Assn. Urol. Surgs.; Brit. Assn. Transpl. Surgs. Prev:

Hon. Cons. Surg. Urol. Ital. Hosp. Lond.; Res. Surgic. Off. St. Peter's Hosps. Lond.; Sen. Regist. (Urol.) Lond. Hosp.

PARIS, James Alexander Gordon Bury and Rochdale Health Authority, 21 Silver St., Bury BL9 0EN — MB BS Lond. 1969; MRCP (UK) 1973; MFPHM RCP (UK) 1993. (Univ. Coll. Hosp.) Cons. Pub. Health Med., Head of Clin. Governance, Bury & Rochdale HA; Hon. Sen. Lect. Univ. of Centr. Lancs. Postgrad. Med. & Health Sch. Prev: GP Birm.

PARIS, Simon Tancred Flat 115, Bishops Mansions, Bishops Park Road, London SW6 6DY Tel: 020 7736 9912 — MB BS 1990 Lond.; BSc (Hons.) Lond. 1987, MB BS 1990. SHO (Anaesth.) Guy's Hosp. Lond. Socs: BMA; Assn. Anaesth. Gt. Brit. & Irel.

PARISH, Mr Christopher (retired) Church Farm, Boxworth, Cambridge CB3 8LZ Tel: 01954 267267 — MB ChB 1940 Manch.; MB ChB (Distinc. Surg.) 1940; MA Camb. 1956; BSc Manch. 1937; FRCS Eng. 1948; FFPHM 1983; FSA 1965. Fell. Sidney Sussex Coll. Camb. Prev: Postgrad. Dean Fac. Clin. Med. Univ. Camb.

PARISH, James Gordon (retired) Red Rocks, Perth Road, Stanley, Perth PH1 4NF Tel: 01738 828313 Fax: 01738 828313 — MB ChB 1947 Ed.; MD Ed. 1957; FRCP Canada 1972; DPhysMed. Eng. 1952; Cert Physical Med. RCPS Canada 1961. Prev: Cons. Phys. (Rheum. & Rehabil.) Colchester Health Dist.

PARISH, Penelope C/o Training Team Brunei BFPO 11 — MB ChB 1975 Sheff.; MRCGP 1981; DRCOG 1978.

PARISH, Stephen Peter Edward School House Surgery, Hertford Road, Brighton BN1 7GF Tel: 01273 551031 Fax: 01273 382036 — MB BS 1980 Lond. Socs: Brighton & Hove Med. Soc.; BMA. Prev: GP Swindon.

PARK, Adrian John Dept of Chemical Pathology, Charing Cross Hospital, Hammersmith, London W6 8RF; 10 Clare Avenue, Wokingham RG40 1EB — MB BS 1993 Lond.

PARK, Mr Alan John 45 Sharman Close, Stoke-on-Trent ST4 7LS — MB ChB 1988 Glas.; FRCS Glas. 1994. Regist. Rotat. (Plastic Surg.) W. Midl. Prev: SHO (Plastic Surg.) Addenbrooke's Hosp. Camb. & St. John's Hosp. Livingston; SHO Rotat. (Surg.) St. John's Hosp. Livingstone, Bangor & W.. Gen. Hosp. Edin.

PARK, Alison Victoria Health Centre, Meddygfa, Betws-y-Coed LL24 0BB Tel: 01690 710205 Fax: 01690 710051; The Cottage, Bunbury Common, Tarporley CW6 9QE Tel: 01829 261141 — MB ChB 1971 Liverp.; MRCGP 1994. Prev: VTS Gl Cruise Organiser Clan Clwyd N. Wales.

PARK, Alistair James Oakhill Medical Practice, Dronfield S18 2FA Tel: 01246 412073 Fax: 01246 291904; 11 Meadowbank Avenue, Sheffield S7 1PB — MB ChB 1988 Sheff.; MRCGP 1994. GP Bd. Mem. N. E. Derbysh. PCG.

PARK, Anne Elizabeth 6 Lower Brook Street, Oswestry SY11 2HJ Tel: 01691 655844; Plas Wilmot, Weston Lane, Oswestry SY11 2BB Tel: 01691 653615 — MB ChB 1959 Aberd.; DObst RCOG 1961. (Aberd.)

PARK, Miss Caroline Ann Accident & Emergency Department, Birmingham Heartlands Hospital, Bordesley Green E., Birmingham B9 5SS Tel: 0121 424 1257 Fax: 0121 424 0260 Email: parkc@heartsol.wmids.nhs.uk — MB ChB 1987 Birm.; FRCS Eng. 1992; FFAEM 1996. (Birmingham) Cons. A & E Med. Birm. Heartlands Hosp. Socs: Brit.ass of a+e Med.

***PARK, Christine Mary** 7 Burnside Road, Largs KA30 9BX — MB ChB 1994 Glas.

***PARK, Daniel Paul** Buttery Lodge, Kynnersley, Telford TF6 6DX — BChir 1996 Camb.

PARK, David John 2 Dunbar Avenue, Coatbridge ML5 5QJ — MB ChB 1975 Glas.

PARK, David Maxwell 19 Kings Road, Westcliff on Sea SS0 8LL Tel: 01702 343858 Fax: 01702 351059 — BM BCh 1965 Oxf.; MA Oxf. 1965; FRCP Lond. 1986, M 1969. (Oxf. Univ.) Cons. Neurol. Barts & Lond NHS Trust S.end Health Care. Socs: Fell. Roy. Soc. Med.; Med. Soc. Lond.; Assn. Brit. Neurol. Prev: Sen. Regist. (Neurol.) Char. Cross Hosp. Lond.; Research Fell. & Regist. (Neurol.) Univ. Glas.

PARK, David Samuel (retired) Yew Cottage, 34A Carrowdore Road, Greyabbey, Newtownards BT22 2LX Tel: 01247 788625 — MB BCh BAO 1959 Belf.; DCH Eng. 1962; DObst RCOG 1961. Prev: Ho. Off. Roy. Vict. & Roy. Matern. Hosps. Belf. & Roy. Belf. Hosp. Sick Childr.

PARK, Deryn Joyce The Richmond Practice, Health Centre, Dean Road, Bo'ness EH51 0DH Tel: 01506 822665 Fax: 01506 825939; 14 Grahams Dyke Road, Bo'ness EH51 9EG Tel: 01506 824383 — MB ChB Ed. 1970. GP. Socs: BMA.

PARK, Emily Stevenson Flat 1, 15 Grand Avenue, Hove BN3 2NG Tel: 01273 734460 Fax: 01273 734460 — MB ChB 1942 Aberd. (Aberd.) JP. Socs: Brighton & Sussex M-C Soc. Prev: Ho. Surg. Aberd. Roy. Infirm., Aberd. Matern. Hosp. & Roy. Sussex Co. Hosp. Brighton.

***PARK, Emma Jane** 21 Cloverhill Park, Belfast BT4 2JW — MB ChB 1997 Sheff.

PARK, George Edwin The Health Centre, North Road, Stokesley, Middlesbrough TS9 5DY Tel: 01642 710748 Fax: 01642 713037 — MB BS 1977 Newc.; MRCGP 1981; DRCOG 1980. GP Stokesley.

PARK, Gilbert Lindsay (retired) Barnetts Ridge, Barnetts Hill, Peasmarsh, Rye TN31 6YJ Tel: 01797 230852 Email: gil.park@virgin.net — LRCP LRCS Ed. LRFPS Glas. 1946. Hon. Phys. Roy. Scott. Corp. Lond.; Scientif. Adviser The Humane Research Trust Bramhall, Stockport. Prev: Regist. Roy. Infirm. Edin.

PARK, Gilbert Richard, TD Addenbrookes Hospital, Box 17, Hills Road, Cambridge CB2 2QQ Tel: 01223 217433 Fax: 01223 217898 Email: gilbertpark@compuserve.com; Malyons, 15 High Green, Great Shelford, Cambridge CB2 5EG — MB ChB 1974 Ed.; MA Camb. 1987; BSc (Med. Sci.) Ed. 1971, MD 1991; FFA RCS Eng. 1978; MD Edinburgh 1991; Honary Degree DMedSci Pleven. Cons. Anaesth. & Intens. Care Addenbrooke's Hosp. Camb. Socs: Intens. Care Soc. Prev: Vis. Prof. Duke Univ. 1995.

PARK, Helen Loreen 40 Chesterfield Road S., Mansfield NG19 7AQ — MB BS 1996 Newc.

PARK, Helen Murray 68 Union Street, Hamilton ML3 6NE; 11 Main Street, Uddingston, Glasgow G71 7HD Tel: 01698 817219 — MB ChB 1977 Glas. GP Uddingston.

PARK, Hilda Gillian Janet 10 Vestry Mews, Vestry Road, Camberwell, London SE5 8NS — MB BCh 1977 Wales.

PARK, James David Department of Anaesthetics, South Cleveland Hospital, Marton Road, Middlesbrough TS4 3BW Tel: 01642 850850 Fax: 01642 854613 — MB ChB 1985 Aberd. Cons. Cardiothoracic Anaesth. S. Cleveland Hosp. Middlesbrough.

PARK, John The Richmond Practice, Health Centre, Dean Road, Bo'ness EH51 0DH Tel: 01506 822665 Fax: 01506 825939 — MB ChB 1970 Ed.; MRCP (U.K.) 1973; MRCGP 1982.

PARK, John Beulah Lodge, Brookhouse Road, Lancaster LA2 9 Tel: 01524 770632 — MB ChB 1971 Liverp.

PARK, John Michael William Cloneen, 11 Belfast Road, Newtownards BT23 4BJ Tel: 01247 816449 — MB BCh BAO 1965 Belf.; FRCOG 1986, M 1971, DObst 1967. (Qu. Univ. Belf.) Cons. O & G Ards & Bangor Hosps. Socs: Ulster Obst. & Gyn. Soc.

PARK, Keith Charles Health Centre, Green Lane, Corwen LL21 0DN Tel: 01490 412362 Fax: 01490 412970; Trawscoed Bach, Maerdy, Corwen LL21 0PD Tel: 01490 81472 — MB ChB 1971 Liverp. (Liverp.) Prev: MoH Tristan Da Cunha.

PARK, Kenneth George Marquis Albyn Hospital, 21-24 Albyne Place, Aberdeen AB10 1RW — FRCS; MB ChB 1982 Ed.

PARK, Kirsten Anne 21 Main Street, Dalrymple, Ayr KA6 6DF — MB ChB 1976 Glas.

PARK, Lindsay Marian Eglinton Street Surgery, 16 Eglinton Street, Irvine KA12 8AS Tel: 01294 279178 Fax: 01294 313095; 13 Craven Grove, Stanecastle Village, South Stanecastle, Irvine KA11 1RY — MB ChB 1984 Aberd.; DRCOG 1989. Prev: Trainee GP Aviemore; SHO (Paediat.) Dist. Gen. Hosp. Grimsby; SHO (A & E & Psychiat.) N. Tees Hosp. Stockton.

PARK, Margaret Joan Queen Margaret Hospital NHS Trust, Whitefield Road, Dunfermline KY12 0SU Tel: 01383 623623; Gowanbrae House, 120 Garvock Hill, Dunfermline KY11 4JY Tel: 01383 729957 — MB ChB 1971 Ed.; DO Eng. 1978; DObst RCOG 1973. (Ed.) Staff Grade (Ophth.) Qu. Margt. Hosp. NHS Trust Dunfermline.

PARK, Pauline Mary Bell 42 Granville Park, Aughton, Ormskirk L39 5DU — MB ChB 1956 Liverp.

PARK, Philip Wesley 20 The Crest, Hillcrest, Whitehaven CA28 6TJ — MB ChB 1993 Leeds.

PARK, Rebecca Jane Developmental Psychiatry Section (University of Cambridge), Douglas House, 186 Trumpington Road, Cambridge CB2 2AH Tel: 01223 746122 Email: rjp42@cam.ac.uk; 22

PARK

Marlborough Road, Oxford OX1 4LP — MB ChB 1990 Bristol; BSc Bristol 1987; MRCPsych 1995. Cons. (Child & Adolesc. Psychiat.) Bedfordshire & Luton Community NHS Trust; Res. Assoc. (Devel. Psychiat.) Univ. of Camb.; Hon. Cons. (Child & Adolesc. Psychiat.) BrooksiDE CFC & Lifespan NHS Trust. Socs: ACPP; Assoc. of Cognitive Analytic Therapists; Assoc. of Infant Ment. Health. Prev: Regist. (Psychiat.) Roy. Edin. Hosp.; SHO (Psychiat.) Roy. Edin. Hosp.; SHO (Paediat.) Alder Hey Hosp. Liverp.

PARK, Richard Hammond Reid Southend General Hospital NHS Trust, 1345 Govan Road, Glasgow G51 4TF Tel: 0141 201 1100; 1 Melford Avenue, Glasgow G46 6NA Tel: 0141 638 0273 — MD 1992 Glas.; MB ChB 1979; MRCP (UK) 1983. Cons. Phys. & Gastroenterol. S.. Gen. Hosp. NHS Trust; Hon. Clin. Sen. Lect. Glas. Univ. Socs: Brit. Soc. Gastroenterol.

PARK, Richard Montgomery Clinical Oncology, Belvoir Park Hospital, Hospital Road, Belfast BT8 4HD; 14Kilmakee Park, Gilnahirk, Belfast BT5 7QY Tel: 01232 794809 Email: richardpark@kilmakee.fsnet.co.uk — MB BCh BAO 1996 Belf.; MRCP 2000 Edinburgh. Specialist Regist., Clin. Oncol., Belvoir Pk. Hosp.

PARK, Robert Robert Park, Warrington Hospital NHS Trust, Lovely Lane, Warrington; 112 Moor Drive, Crosby, Liverpool L23 2UT — MRCS Eng. LRCP Lond. 1973; FFA RCSI 1980; DObst. RCOG 1975. Cons. Anaesth., Warrington Hosp. NHS Trust. Socs: BMA; Assn. Anaesth.; The Pain Soc.

PARK, Robert Riverside Medical Practice, Roushill, Shrewsbury SY1 1PQ Tel: 01743 352371 Fax: 01743 340269 — MB ChB 1972 Liverp.; MRCS Eng. LRCP Lond. 1972; DObst. Univ. Auckland 1976.

PARK, Robert Hood Wright (retired) 4 The Paddock, Dirleton, Berwick, Edinburgh EH39 5AD Tel: 01620 850686 — MB ChB 1957 Ed.; FRCA 1968; DA Eng. 1962. Prev: Cons. Anaesth. Roy. Infirm. Edin. NHS Trust.

PARK, Robert Wilson George Street Surgery, 99 George Street, Dumfries DG1 1DS Tel: 01387 253333 Fax: 01387 253301; 99 George Street, Dumfries DG1 1DS Tel: profess. 53333 — MB ChB 1982 Glas.; MRCGP 1986; DRCOG 1884. Prev: Trainee GP Dumfries VTS; Ho. Phys. Stirling Roy. Infirm.; Ho. Surg. Vict. Infirm. Glas.

***PARK, Soo-Mi** Cambridge Institute for Medical Research, Box 139, Lab 4.36, Addenbrooke's Hospital, Cambridge CB2 2XY Tel: 01223 762618/9 Email: spark@hgmp.mrc.ac.uk — MB BS 1994 Lond.; BSc Lond. 1991; MRCP (UK) 1997.

PARK, Stewart Bertrand Geoffrey University Department of Psychiatry, Duncan MacMillan House, Porchester Road, Nottingham NG3 6AA Tel: 0115 969 1300 — BM BCh 1986 Oxf.; MRCP (UK) 1989; MRCPsych 1992. Sen. Lect. (Psychiat.) Univ. Nottm. Prev: Wellcome Train. Fell. MRC Clin. Psychopharmacol. Unit Littlemore Hosp. Oxf.; SHO & Regist. Rotat. (Psychiat.) Oxf.; Regist. (Med.) P.ss Margt. Hosp. Swindon.

PARK, Thomas (retired) Drumshiel, Thornhill DG3 5DW Tel: 01848 330513 — MB ChB 1952 Glas. Prev: GP Thornhill.

PARK, Thomas Harling (retired) Redlands, The Green, Acomb, York YO19 5XP Tel: 01904 798686 & 798329 — MB ChB 1945 Ed.

PARK, Wallace Galloway Meadowside, Cove Road, Silverdale, Carnforth LA5 0SQ Tel: 01524 701770 — MB ChB Ed. 1969; FFA RCS Eng. 1975. (Ed.) Cons. (Anaesth.) Morcambe Bay NHS Trust. Prev: Sen. Regist. (Anaesth.) S. W.. RHA.

PARK, Mr William Douglas, SJM (retired) The Beeches, 1 High Bungay Road, Loddon, Norwich NR14 6JT Tel: 01508 520991 — MS Lond. 1942, MB BS 1935; FRCS Eng. 1940; MRCS Eng., LRCP Lond. 1935. Hon. Cons. Surg. King Geo. Hosp. Ilford, Brentwood Dist. Hosp. OldCh. Hosp. Romford. Prev: Hon. Orthop. Surg. Connaught Hosp. Walthamstow.

PARK, William Douglas Station Road Surgery, 2 Station Road, Prestwick KA9 1AQ Tel: 01292 671444 Fax: 01292 678023 — MB ChB 1983 Glas.; FRCP 2000 Glas.; MRCP (UK) 1986; MRCGP 1988.

PARKAR, Hasratali Bhaudin 144-50 High Road, Willesden, London NW10 2PT Tel: 020 8459 5550; 28 Bromefield, Stanmore HA7 1AE — MB BS 1984 Newc.; MRCGP 1990. Mem. Brent & Harrow LMC. Socs: Brent & Harrow Med. Audit Advis. Gp. Prev: SHO (A & E) Roy. Vict. Infirm. Newc.; SHO (O & G) Newc. Gen. Hosp.; Ho. Phys. & Ho. Surg. Freeman Hosp. Newc u. Tyne.

PARKAR, Washik 89 Moorfield, Salford M6 7GD — MB ChB 1992 Liverp.

PARKASH, Vijay Kumari 20 Leila Parnell Close, Victoria Way, London SE7 7TD — MB BS 1988 Lond.; MRCPsych 1995.

PARKE, Margaret Eleanor Copley (retired) 33 Chock Lane, Westbury on Trym, Bristol BS9 3EX — MB ChB 1956 Bristol. Prev: Clin. Med. Off. (Community Med.) Avon Community Health Serv. S.mead Dist.

PARKE, Mr Roger Christopher Musgrave Park Hospital, Stockman's Lane, Belfast BT9 7JB Tel: 028 90669501 Fax: 028 90683662 Email: roger.parke@greenpark.n-i.nhs.uk; 3 Tudor Park, Holywood BT18 0NX Tel: 028 90423140 Fax: 028 90423140 — MB BCh BAO 1970 Belf.; FRCS Ed. 1976; FRCSI 1975. (Qu. Univ. Belf.) Cons. Rehabil. Med. Green Pk. Healthcare Trust Musgrave Pk. Hosp. Belf. Socs: Internat. Soc. Prosth.s & Orthotics; Brit. Soc. Rehabil. Med.; Brit. Orthopaedic Assn. Prev: Cons. Prosth. Surg. Musgrave Pk. Hosp. Belf.

PARKE, Roger Jeremy Greville 27 Oak Tree Drive, Aller Park, Newton Abbot TQ12 4NN — MB BS 1979 Lond.

PARKE, Simon Charles 8 Kensington Gate, Belfast BT5 6PF Tel: 01232 705805 — MB ChB 1993 Ed.; MRCP (UK) 1997. (Ed.) SHO (Paediat. Oncol. & Haemat.) Gt. Ormond St. Hosp. Lond.; Specialist Regist. Paediat. Birm. Heartlands Hosp. Prev: SHO (Paediat.) Roy. Berks. Hosp. Reading & John Radcliffe Hosp. Oxf.; Ho. Off. (Med.) Falkirk & Dist. Roy. Infirm.; Ho. Off. (Surg.) St. John's Hosp. Livingstone.

PARKE, Timothy John Department of Anaesthetics, Royal Berkshire Hospital, London Road, Reading RG1 5AN Tel: 01734 875111 — MB ChB 1980 Bristol; MRCP (UK) 1985; MRCGP 1989; FFA RCS Eng. 1986; DRCOG 1989. Cons. Anaesth. Roy. Berks. Hosp. Reading. Socs: Intens. Care Soc. Prev: Sen. Regist. (Anaesth.) Bristol Roy. Infirm.

PARKE, Timothy Robert James Accident & Emergency Department, Southern General Hospital, 1345 Govan Road, Glasgow G51 4TF Tel: 0141 201 1100 Fax: 0141 201 2997 — MB ChB 1986 Ed.; MRCP (UK) 1989; FFAEM 1996; DA (UK) 1995. (Ed.) Cons. A & E & Intens. Care S.. Gen. Hosp. Glas. Socs: Intens. Care Soc.; Brit. Assn. Emerg. Med. Prev: Sen. Regist. (A & E & ITU) W.. Infirm. Glas.; Regist. (A & E) Roy. Infirm. Edin.

PARKEN, Douglas Stuart (retired) Cascais Haven, 32B Lulworth Road, Birkdale, Southport PR8 2BQ — MB BS Lond. 1948; MRCS Eng. LRCP Lond. 1948; FFCM 1976, M 1974; DCH Eng. 1950; DPH Liverp. 1954. Prev: Area Med. Off. Lancs. AHA.

PARKEN, Helen Frances Mary Potter Health Centre, Gregory Boulevard, Hyson Green, Nottingham NG7 5HY Tel: 0115 942 0330; 115 Melton Road, West Bridgford, Nottingham NG2 6ET — MB BS 1975 Lond.; MRCP (UK) 1979; MRCS Eng. LRCP Lond. 1975. (St. Mary's)

PARKEN, Paul Nicholas Stuart Clifton Medical Centre, 571 Farnborough Road, Clifton, Nottingham NG11 9DN Tel: 0115 921 1288; 115 Melton Road, West Bridgford, Nottingham NG2 6ET — MRCS Eng. LRCP Lond. 1978. (St. Mary's)

PARKER, Alasdair Patrick John Child Development Centre, Box 107, Addenbrooke's Hospital, Cambridge CB1 1EZ Tel: 01223 311947 Email: alasdair.parker@addenbrookes.nhs.uk — MB BS 1987 Lond.; MD 2000 Lond.; MRCP (UK) 1990. Cons. Paediatric NeUrol., Addenbrookes Hosp., Camb. Prev: Co-ordinator Médecins Sans Frontières, Vietnam; SHO (Paediat.) Bristol & Brighton Childr. Hosp.; Regist., Cray's Hosp.

PARKER, Alfred Patrick The Surgery, 5 Enys Road, Eastbourne BN21 2DQ Tel: 01323 410088 Fax: 01323 644638 — MB BS 1977 Lond.; Cert. Family Plann. JCC 1979. Socs: BMA (Sec. E.bourne Div.). Prev: SHO (O & G) Roy. Sussex Co. Hosp. Brighton; Ho. Off. (Gen. Med.) St. Mary's Hosp. E.bourne; Ho. Off. Gen. Surg. (ENT & Orthop.) N. Middlx. Hosp. Lond.

PARKER, Alistair Cameron (retired) 2 Regent Terrace, Edinburgh EH7 5BN Tel: 0131 556 7164 — MB ChB 1967 Ed.; PhD Ed. 1976, BSc 1964; FRCP Ed. 1979; FRCPath. 1988, M 1977. Prev: Cons. Haemat. Roy. Infirm. Edin.

PARKER, Andrew Frank (retired) 14 Hobgate, Acomb, York YO24 4HF Tel: 01904 798850 — MRCS Eng. LRCP Lond. 1957; FFOM RCP Lond. 1988; MFOM 1978; DIH Soc. Apoth. Lond. 1972; DPH Leeds 1967. Prev: Sen. Regional Med. Off. BT plc NE Eng.

PARKER, Andrew John 2 West Lawn, Sunderland SR2 7HW — MB BS 1992 Lond.

PARKER, Mr Andrew John Department of Otolaryngology, Roual Hallamshire Hospital, Sheffield S10 2JF — MB ChB 1981 Leeds; ChM Bristol 1991; DLO RCS Eng. 1985; FRCS Ed 1986; FRCS Eng 1987. Cons. Otolaryngol. Head & Neck Surg. United Sheff. Hosp.; Sen. Lect. Univ. Sheff. Socs: Sheff. Med. Legal Soc.; Otorhinolaryngological Research Soc.; Europ. Gp. for Func.al Laryngeal Surg. Prev: Sen. Regist. (ENT) Sheff. United Hosps; Research Fell. (ENT) Bristol Roy. Infirm.; Regist. (ENT) Bristol & Bath Hosps.

PARKER, Angela Mary Torrington Park Health Centre, Torrington Park, North Finchley, London N12 9SS; 203 Holders Hill Road, London NW7 1ND — MB BS 1974 Lond.; BSc Lond. 1971; MRCGP 1979; DRCOG 1979; DCH Eng. 1978; DFP RHC RCOG 1993. (Univ. Coll. Hosp.) Socs: Primary Care Dermatol. Soc.; NAFPD. Prev: SHO (Med.) Whittington Hosp. Lond.; Trainee GP Barnet VTS.

PARKER, Ann (retired) South View, School Lane, Offley, Hitchin SG5 3AZ — MB BS 1960 Lond.; MRCS Eng. LRCP Lond. 1960; FRCOG 1980, M 1967, DObst 1962. Prev: Cons. (O & G) Lister & N. Herts. Gp. Hosps.

PARKER, Ann, OBE 17 Derwen Deg close, Govilon, Abergavenny NP7 9RJ Tel: 01873 830336; 17 Derwen Deg close, Govilon, Abergavenny NP7 9RJ Tel: 01873 830336 — MB BS 1963 Lond.; MRCS Eng. LRCP Lond. 1963. (Guy's) p/t Cons. psychosexual Med. Gwent healthcare NHS trust. Socs: Inst. Psychosexual Med.; Fac. Fam. Plann. & Reproduc. Health Care. Prev: Cons. Reproductive & Sexual Health Gwent Community NHS Trust; Clin. Dir. (Family Plann. & Sexual Health) Community Unit Gwent AHA; SCMO Gwent AHA.

PARKER, Mrs Ann Gwillim (retired) The Firs, Firs Road, Duxmere, Ross-on-Wye HR9 5BH Tel: 01989 563995 Fax: 01989 563995 — BM BCh Oxf. 1953; BA Oxf. 1953. Prev: Med. Off. Family Plann. Gloucester Health Dist.

PARKER, Anna Jane Department of Radiology, Southampton General Hospital, Tremona Road, Southampton SO16 6YD Tel: 02380 777222 — MB BS 1992 Lond.; BSc Lond. 1989; FRCS Lond. 1996. (St. Mary's Hospital Paddington) Specialist Regist. (Radiol.) Soton. Gen. Hosp.

PARKER, Anne Naomi Department Haematology, Glasgow Royal Infirmary, Castle St., Glasgow G4 0SF Tel: 0141 211 4672 Fax: 0141 552 8196 Email: anne.parker@northhglasgow.scot.nhs.uk — MB ChB 1987 Bristol; FRCP 2001 UK; BSc (Hons.) Biochem. Bristol 1984; MRCP (UK) 1991; MD MD Bristol 1998; MRCP MRCPATH 1997. (Univ. Bristol) Cons. haematologist; honary Sen. Lect. Univ. of Glas.; Cons. Haematologist, Health Care Internat., Glas. Prev: Clin. Research Fell. Beatson Inst. Cancer Research; Regist. (Haemat.) Leicester Roy. Infirm.; Sen. Lect., Haemat., W. of Scotl.

PARKER, Anne Shirley (retired) Northumberland House Surgery, 437 Stourport Road, Kidderminster DY11 7BL Tel: 01562 745715 Fax: 01562 863010 — MB ChB 1960 Birm.

PARKER, Anthony Leonard (retired) South Lodge, Pease Pottage, Crawley RH11 9AR Tel: 01293 542008 — MB ChB 1955 Birm.; FRCPsych. 1983, M 1971; DPM Eng. 1962. Prev: Cons. Psychiat. Crawley Hosp.

PARKER, Anthony Philip 16 Swathwick Close, Wingerworth, Chesterfield S42 6UA — MB ChB 1991 Birm.; MRCGP 1995; DCH RCP Lond. 1994.

PARKER, Arthur Stuart Renal Unit, Southmead Hospital, Westbury-on-Trym, Bristol BS10 5NB Tel: 0117 950 5050 — MB ChB 1961 Bristol. (Bristol) Socs: Renal Assn.; Eur. Dialysis & Transpl. Assn. Prev: Dep. Dir. Renal Unit & Nephrol. S.mead Hosp. Bristol.; Regist. (Med.) Renal & Respirat. Units & Asst. Phys. Ham Green Hosp.; Ho. Surg. Frenchay Hosp. Bristol.

PARKER, Barbara Doherty (retired) 52B Linden Road, Bournville, Birmingham B30 1JU Tel: 0121 472 2344 — MB BS 1942 Lond.; MRCS Eng. LRCP Lond. 1942; FFA RCS Eng. 1954; DA Eng. 1947. Prev: Cons. Anaesth. Birm. Regional Plastic Surg. Unit Wordsley.

PARKER, Barbara Louise Guidepost Health Centre, North Parade, Guidepost, Choppington NE62 5RA Tel: 01670 822071 Fax: 01670 531068; Greenside, Linden Avenue, Gosforth, Newcastle upon Tyne NE3 4HD Tel: 0191 285 5638 — MB BS 1978 Newc.; MRCGP 1982; Cert. Family Plann. JCC 1980. (Newcastle)

PARKER, Mr Barrie Charles Delaval, Furzefield, Oxshott, Leatherhead KT22 0UR Tel: 01372 842290 Fax: 01372 844091 Email: bparker@uk-consultants.co.uk — MB BS 1965 Lond.; FRCS Eng. 1970. (Char. Cross) Cons. Orthop. Surg. Kingston Hosp. Trust; Counc. Mem. Hon. Treas. Brit. Orthopaedic Assoc. Socs: Fell. (Mem. Counc & Hon. Treas.) BOA; Roy. Soc. Med. Prev: Sen. Regist. (Orthop.) Char. Cross Hosp. & Roy. Nat. Orthop. Hosp.; Clin. Tutor Kingston Hosp.; Regional Adviser (Orthop.) RCS.

PARKER, Brenda 378 Kilmarnock Road, Glasgow G43 2DH — MB ChB 1952 Liverp.; DPH 1957.

PARKER, Carl David McKenzie House Surgery, Kendal Road, Hartlepool TS25 1QU Tel: 01429 233611 Fax: 01429 297713; Cross Keys Farm, Borrowby, Thirsk YO7 4QY — MB BS 1987 Lond.; Section 12 Approved 1996; DRCOG 1991. Police Surg. N. Yorks. Police; Commiss.ing Lead, Hartlepool PCT.

PARKER, Catherine Sian Cross Keys Farm, Borrowby, Thirsk YO7 4QY — MB BS Lond. 1990.

PARKER, Charles Marcus The Surgery, Long Street, Topcliffe, Thirsk YO7 3RP Tel: 01845 577297 Fax: 01845 577128; Jubilee House, Long St., Topcliffe, Thirsk YO7 3RL Tel: 01845 577980 Fax: 01845 577140 Email: charles.parker@lineone.net — MB BS 1987 Lond. GP Princip. DRS Shaw & Pk.er Topcliffe Thirsk; Dir. N. Yorks. Emerg. Doctors York.

PARKER, Christopher Charles 9 Park Lane, Hartford, Northwich CW8 1PZ — BM BCh 1989 Oxf.; BA Camb. 1986; MRCP (UK) 1992. Regist. (Clin. Oncol.) Roy. Marsden Hosp. Lond.

PARKER, Mr Christopher John Yeovil District Hospital, Higher Kingston, Yeovil BA21 4AT Tel: 01935 384345 Fax: 01935 384643 Email: parkc@gwise.esomerset-tr.swest.nhs.uk — MB BS 1979 Lond.; FRCS (Urol.) 1993; FRCS Eng. 1985; FRCS Ed. 1984. (Guy's Hospital Medical School) Cons. Urol. Yeovil Dist. Hosp. Yeovil & Yeatman Hosp. Sherborne; Med. Directort, E. Somerst. NHS Trust, Yeovil. Prev: Sen. Regist. St. Peter's Hosp. & Inst. Urol. Lond.

PARKER, Christopher John Raymond, Lt.-Col. RAMC 3 Armd. Field Ambulance RAMC BFPO 16 — MB BS 1982 Lond.; MRCS Eng. LRCP Lond. 1981; DTM & H RCP Lond. 1989. (Westm.)

***PARKER, Christopher Paul** 18 Eight Street, Birkenshaw, Tannochside, Larkhall — MB ChB 1994 Aberd.

PARKER, Christopher Richard The Lindley Group Practice, 62 Acre Street, Lindley, Huddersfield HD3 3DY Tel: 01484 342190 — MB ChB Leeds 1984.

PARKER, Claire Elizabeth 6 Apsley Road, Oxford OX2 7QY — MB BChir 1980 Camb.; DPhil 1994; MRCGP 1983; DRCOG 1982.

PARKER, Claire Ruth 76 Pant-y-Celyn Road, Llandough, Penarth CF64 2PH — MB BCh 1994 Wales.

PARKER, Clare Luise Low Barn, Haydon Bridge, Hexham NE47 6AS — MB BS 1993 Lond.

***PARKER, Clare Rhian** 14 Western Terrace, Blaengwynfi, Port Talbot SA13 3YE — MB BCh 1998 Wales.

PARKER, Mr Clive (retired) 2 West Lawn, Ashbrooke, Sunderland SR2 7HW — MB ChB 1957 Ed.; FRCS Eng. 1966. Cons. Urol. Surg. Sunderland Gp. Hosps.

PARKER, Colin Ernest Albany Road Surgery, 5 Albany Road, Earlsdon, Coventry CV5 6JQ Tel: 024 7622 8606 Fax: 024 7622 9985; 59 Clinton Lane, Kenilworth CV8 1AS Tel: 01926 54852 — MB BS 1969 Lond.; MRCS Eng. LRCP Lond. 1969; DObst RCOG 1972. (Univ. Coll. Hosp.) Clin. Asst. (Dermat.). Socs: Midl. Dermatol. Soc. Prev: Ho. Surg. & Ho. Phys. Basingstoke & Dist. Hosp.; Ho. Off. Paediat. Gulson Hosp. Coventry; SHO Obst. N. Tees. Gen. Hosp. Stockton on Tees.

PARKER, Cornelle Ruth Division of Mineral Metabolism, Old Renal Unit, City Hospital, Hucknall Road, Nottingham NG5 1PB Tel: 0115 969 1169 Fax: 0115 962 7900 — MB ChB 1988 Liverp.; MRCP (UK) 1993. (Univ. Liverp.) Regist. Rotat. (Diabetes, Endoc., Gen. Med.) Trent region. Prev: Research Regist. Div. Mineral Metab. City Hosp. Nottm.; Regist. Rotat. (Clin. Diabetes & Endocrinol.) Trent Regional VTS; SHO Rotat. (Gen. Med.) Soton. Gen. Hosp.

PARKER, Cyril Stansfeld (retired) Stansfeld View, 871 Whittingham Lane, Goosnargh, Preston PR3 2AU Tel: 0177 476 865254 — LRCP LRCS 1935 Ed.; MD Manch. 1939, MB ChB 1935; LRCP LRCS Ed. LRFPS Glas. 1935; MRCPsych 1971; DPM RCPSI 1945. Prev: Dir., Child Guid. Clinic Blackpool.

PARKER, Mr David Alan Calder Farm, Taghole Lane, Mugginton, Ashbourne DE6 4PN — MB BChir 1980 Camb.; BA Camb. 1978, MA 1982, MB BChir 1980; FRCS Ed. 1985. Cons. ENT Derby Roy. Infirm. Prev: Sen. Regist. (ENT) W. Midl. Train. Scheme.

PARKER

PARKER, David Allan Wrexham Maelor Hospital, Croesnewydd Road, Wrexham LL13 7TD Tel: 01978 291100; Ty'r Graig, Ruthin Road, Bwlchgwyn, Wrexham LL11 5UT Tel: 01978 750620 — MB ChB 1979 Birm.; MRCP (UK) 1982; FRCR 1986. Cons. (Radiol.) Wrexham Maelor NHS Trust.

PARKER, David James Barton Surgery, 1 Edmunds Close, Barton Court Avenue, Barton-on-Sea, New Milton BH25 7EH Tel: 01425 620830 Fax: 01425 629812; Moonrakers, Woodcock Lane, Hordle, Lymington SO41 0FG Tel: 01425 638101 — MB BCh BAO 1971 Dub.; MB BCh BAO Dub 1971; MRCGP 1976.

PARKER, David Leonard Berinsfield Health Centre, Fane Drive, Berinsfield, Wallingford OX10 7NE Tel: 01865 340558 Fax: 01865 341973; 26 Manor Farm Road, Dorchester-on-Thames, Wallingford OX10 7HZ Tel: 01865 340402 — MB BChir 1965 Camb.; MA, MB Camb. 1965, BChir 1964; FRCGP 1997, M 1976; DObst RCOG 1967; DA Eng. 1968. (Cambridge & St. Thomas' Hospital) Clin. Asst. (Anaesth.) Oxon. DHA (T). Prev: Med. Off. Uganda Govt., Fort Portal; Cas. Off. St. Thos. Hosp. Lond.; Ho. Surg. & Ho. Phys. St. Mary's Hosp. Portsmouth.

PARKER, David Robert Department of Gastroenterology, Weston General Hospital, Grange Road, Uphill, Weston Super Mare BS23 4TQ — MB BCh 1986 Wales; BSc (Hons.) Wales 1983; MD Bristol 1996; MRCP (UK) 1989; FRCP Lond 1999. Cons. Phys. & Gastroenterol. W.on Gen. Hosp. W.on-Super-Mare; Sen. Clin. Lect. Univ. of Bristol. Socs: Brit. Soc. Gastroenterol.; The Physiological Soc. Prev: Sen. Regist. (Gen. Med. & Gastroenterol.) Singleton & Morriston Hosps. Swansea; Research Fell. Bristol Roy. Infirm.; Regist. (Gen. Med. & Gastroenterol.) Bristol Roy. Infirm.

PARKER, Deborah Ann Norwood Medical Centre, 360 Herries Road, Sheffield S5 7HD Tel: 0114 242 6208 Fax: 0114 261 9243 — MB ChB 1992 Manch.; BSc (Physiol.) Manch. 1989; DRCOG 1995. (Manch.) Partern Sheff. Norwood Med. Centre. Socs: BMA; Roy. Coll. Gen. Pract. Prev: Trainee GP Sheff. VTS.

PARKER, Deborah Francine South Farm Cottage, Sandhutton, Thirsk YO7 4RW — MB BS 1988 Lond.; BSc Lond. 1985, MB BS 1988.

PARKER, Dennis 29 St Paul's Square, York YO24 4BD Tel: 01904 620871 — MB BS 1969 Newc.; DPhil Oxf. 1973; BSc (Anat., Hons.) Newc. 1966; FRCP Lond. 1991; MRCP (UK) 1976. (Newc.) Cons. Phys. (Oncol.) Bradford Roy. Infirm. & St. Luke's Hosp. Bradford; Hon. Sen. Lect. Univ. Bradford. Prev: Sen. Regist. (Med.) Chapel Allerton Hosp. Leeds; Gordon Hamilton Fairley Fell. (Med. Oncol.) St. Bart. Hosp. Lond.; Regist. (Med.) Ninewells Hosp. Dundee.

PARKER, Dennis Mackinder, MBE (retired) — MB ChB Leeds 1953; MRCGP 1963. GP Sheff. Prev: GP Sheff.

***PARKER, Dianne** 18 Grenadier Close, Rainham, Gillingham ME8 8NQ — MB BS 1998 Lond.; MB BS Lond 1998.

PARKER, Mr Edward John Colton Northumberland House Surgery, 437 Stourport Road, Kidderminster DY11 7BL Tel: 01562 745715 Fax: 01562 863010; Tudor Lodge, Churchill, Kidderminster DY10 3LX Tel: 01562 700710 — MB BChir 1967 Camb.; MA Camb. 1969, BA 1963; FRCS Eng. 1971; MRCGP 1977. (Camb. & Lond. Hosp.) Socs: BMA. Prev: SHO Roy. Nat. Orthop. Hosp. Stanmore; Regist. (Surg.) Lond. Hosp.; Resid. Surg. Shanta Bhawan Hosp. Kathmandu.

PARKER, Edwin James Essex (retired) 11 Old Kilmore Road, Moira, Craigavon BT67 0LZ Tel: 01846 611595 — MB BCh BAO 1947 Belf.; FRCGP 1982, M 1968. Staff Med. Off. Craigavon Area Hosp. Prev: Res. Med. Off. Lurgan & Portadown Hosp.

PARKER, Elizabeth Mary Tel: 020 8318 1330/9 Fax: 020 8297 1448 — MB 1980 Camb.; BA Camb. 1976, BChir 1979; MRCPsych 1983. Cons. Psychiat. S. Lond. & Maudsley NHS Trust; Sen. Lect. GKT Lond. Prev: Cons. Psychiat. Springfield Hosp. Lond.; Sen. Regist. (Psychiat.) Guy's Hosp. Lond.; Regist. (Psychiat.) Guy's Hosp. Lond.

PARKER, Enid Agnes 25 Ashvale Drive, Hillsborough BT26 6DN — MB BCh BAO 1981 Belf. (Queens Belfast) Socs: BMA. Prev: Trainee GP Dundee; SHO (Gen. Psychiat.) St Luke's Hosp. Armagh N. Irel.

PARKER, Felicity Anne Riverside Surgery, Le Molay Littry Way, Bovey Tacey, Newton Abbot TQ13 9QP Tel: 01626 832666 — MB ChB 1982 Manch.; MRCGP 1986.

PARKER, Fiona Geraldine Maypole Health Centre, 10 Sladepool Farm Road, Maypole, Birmingham B14 5DJ Tel: 01121 430 2829 Fax: 0121 430 6080 — MB ChB 1982 Sheff. GP.

PARKER, Francis Bruce Wyndham, MBE (retired) 2 Tilsley Road, Chipping Norton OX7 5JA Tel: 01608 642822 Fax: 01608 642822 Email: g.parker1@mllworld.com — MB ChB Birm. 1954; DCH Eng. 1958; DObst RCOG 1956. Prev: Med. Off. Chipping Norton War Memor. Hosp. & Kingham Hill Sch.

PARKER, George Talbot 168 Spring Bank, Hull HU3 1QW; 247 Northgate, Cottingham HU16 5RL — MRCS Eng. LRCP Lond. 1956. (Leeds)

PARKER, Glynis 3 Devonshire Place, London W1G 6HE Tel: 020 7486 6181 Email: parkerg@the-medic.com — MB ChB 1978 Bristol; FFA RCS Eng. 1985; DRCOG 1986. Sen. Med. Claims Handler Med. Defence Union. Socs: Medico-Legal Soc. Prev: Regist. (Anaesth.) Bristol Train. Scheme Bristol Roy. Infirm.; Research Regist. & Tutor (Med. & Pharmacol.) Univ. Bristol; Trainee GP Bristol.

PARKER, Glynn North Trent Medical Audiology, Royal Hallamshire Hospital, Glossop Road, Sheffield S10 2JF; The Old Rectory, Churchtown, Darley Dale, Matlock DE4 2GL — MB ChB 1981 Leeds; MSc 1999 Manchester; MRCP (UK) 1985; DCH RCP Lond. 1983. Cons. Audiological Phys.; Cons. Audiological Phys. Childr.s Audiol.,Chesterfield. Prev: Clin. Med. Off. (Child Health) N. Derbysh.; Asst. GP Rotherham; Sen. Regist. (Audiol. Med.) Roy. Hallamsh. Hosp. Sheff.

PARKER, Gordon 1 Willaston Close, Chorlton, Manchester M21 8BJ Email: gordon.parker2@virgin.net — MB ChB 1979 Sheff.; MA Camb. 1980; MRCGP 1984; FFOM RCP Lond. 1998; MFOM 1993. Sen. Med. Adviser Ranks Hovis McDougall Ltd; Hon. Lect. (Occupat. Med.) Univ. Manch. Prev: Head of Health & Safety Servs. & Univ. Occupat. Phys. Univ. Manch.

PARKER, Graham The Archways Surgery, 86 Stockport Road, Romiley, Stockport SK6 3AA Tel: 0161 494 5337 Fax: 0161 406 7884 — BM BS 1989 Nottingham; BM BS Nottm 1989; BMedSci Nottm 1987; Post Graduate Certificate in GP University of Central Lanarkshire 1998. (Nottingham) Prev: Trainee GP Stockport VTS.

PARKER, Graham David Colne Medical Centre, 40 Station Road, Brightlingsea, Colchester CO7 0DT Tel: 01206 302522 Fax: 01206 305131 — MB BS 1976 Lond.

PARKER, Graham Stuart Keeling Street Doctors Surgery, Keeling Street, North Somercotes, Louth LN11 7QU — MB BS 1980 Lond.; DRCOG 1983.

PARKER, Harold Gordon (retired) Pont-Ar-Dulas, Llanafan Fawr, Builth Wells LD2 3LW Tel: 01591 620300 — MB ChB Birm. 1946. Prev: Ho. Surg. Qu. Eliz. Hosp. Birm. & Birm. Matern. Hosp.

***PARKER, Helen** 16 Swinburne House, Roman Road, London E2 0HJ — MB BS 1998 Lond.; MB BS Lond 1998.

PARKER, Hilary The Surgery, Marsh Gardens, Honley, Huddersfield HD9 6AG Tel: 01484 303366 Fax: 01484 303365 — MB ChB 1971 Birm.

PARKER, Ian 10 Allanton Road, Bonkle, Wishaw ML2 9QF Tel: 01698 384183 — MB ChB 1972 Ed.; FRCR 1980; DMRD Eng. 1978. (Ed.) Cons. Radiol St. John's Hosp. Howden Livingstone. Prev: Cons. Radiol. Bangour Gen. Hosp. Broxburn.

PARKER, Ian Richard Green End Surgery, 58 Green End, Comberton, Cambridge CB3 7DY Tel: 01223 262500 Fax: 01223 264401 — MB BChir 1978 Camb.; MSc E. Anglia 1976; MRCGP 1982; DRCOG 1981.

PARKER, Ian Wyndham 4 Collice Street, Islip, Kidlington OX5 2TB — MB BS 1986 Lond.; MRCGP 1993.

PARKER, James Barry 45 Hillpark Avenue, Edinburgh EH4 7AH Tel: 0131 336 3181 — MB ChB Ed. 1985; MRCGP 1989; DCCH RCP Ed. 1989. GP Edin.

PARKER, James Desmond Amylin Pharmaceuticals Inc., Magdalen Centre, Oxford Science Park, Oxford OX4 4GA Tel: 01865 784094 Fax: 01865 787901 Email: jparker@amylin.com — MB ChB 1979 Glas.; MRCP (UK) 1982; MFPM RCP(UK) 1990. Sen. Med. Dir. Europe; Hon. Cons. Guys Hosp. Lond. Prev: Sen. Regist. Rheum. Nuffield Orthop. Hosp. Oxf.

***PARKER, Jan Ceridwen** 59 Oakwood Road, Henleaze, Bristol BS9 4NT — BM 1996 Soton.

***PARKER, Jane** 8 Tottleworth, Rishton, Blackburn BB1 4AN — MB BS 1998 Newc.; MB BS Newc 1998.

PARKER, Jane Elizabeth 11 Austin Edwards Drive, Warwick CV34 5GW Tel: 01926 400325; 158 Barton Road, Luton LU3 2BE Tel: 01582 591360 — MB BS 1989 Lond.; MRCP (UK) 1992. Regist. (Haemat.) Pembury Hosp. Tunbridge Wells & Kings Coll. Hosp. Lond. Prev: SHO (Med.) S. Warks. Hosp.; SHO (Cas.) Cheltenham Gen. Hosp.; Ho. Phys. Ipswich Hosp.

PARKER, Jean Helen St Johns Medical Centre, 287A Lewisham Way, London SE4 1XF — MRCS Eng. LRCP Lond. 1974; BPharm (Hons.) Lond. 1969, MB BS 1974; MRCGP 1987; DCH RCP Lond. 1986; DRCOG 1977. (St. Bart.) Prev: Trainee GP Lewisham VTS; Med. Off. Lond. Brook Advis. Centres for Young People.; SHO (Paediat.) Sydenham Childr. Hosp.

PARKER, Jeremy Russell 28 Sunningvale Avenue, Biggin Hill, Westerham TN16 3BU Tel: 01959 571525 Email: jeremy@parkerpres.demon.co.uk — MB BS 1991 Lond.; FRCS Eng. 1996. (King's Coll. Hosp.) Specialist Regist. Roy. Lond. Hosp. Rotat.

***PARKER, Joanne Louise** 20 Wentworth Crescent, Mayals, Swansea SA3 5HT — MB BCh 1998 Wales.

PARKER, John Worden Medical Centre, West Paddock, Leyland, Preston PR5 5HA Tel: 01772 423555 Fax: 01772 623878; 12 Glenmore, Clayton Le Woods, Chorley PR6 7TA Tel: 01772 315117 — MB ChB 1977 Manch.; BSc Med. Sci St. And. 1974.

PARKER, John Anthony Richard (retired) Blue Gates, 2 Nayland Road, Mile End, Colchester CO4 5EG Tel: 01206 577510 — MB BS 1947 Lond.; DA Eng. 1953. Prev: GP & Asst. Anaesth. Colchester.

PARKER, John Charles 61 Bold Lane, Aughton, Ormskirk L39 6SG — MB ChB 1993 Sheff.

PARKER, John Howard Knight (retired) Pound Cottage, Pound Lane, Martock TA12 6LU Tel: 01935 823650 — MB ChB Bristol 1945; DObst RCOG 1948. Prev: Ho. Surg. & Res. Obst. Off. S.mead Hosp. Bristol.

PARKER, John Lauchlan Wilson County Hospital, Greetwell Road, Lincoln LN2 5QY Tel: 01522 573359; Torridon, 1 Cliff Avenue, Nettleham, Lincoln LN2 2PU Tel: 01522 750746 — MB ChB Glas. 1967; FRCP Glas. 1985; FRCP Ed. 1981; MRCP (UK) 1972. (Glas.) p/t United Lincs. Hosps. NHS Trust, Co. Hosp., Lincoln LN2 5QY, Cons. Phys. with interest in Diabetes & Endocrinology. Socs: BMA; Lincoln Med. Soc.; Assn. Of Brit. Clin. Diabetologists. Prev: Cons. Phys. St. Geo. Hosp. Lincoln; Sen. Regist. (Gen. Med.) Gartnavel Gen. Hosp. Glas. & Roy. Infirm. Glas.; Regist. (Gen. Med. & Endocrinol.) W.. Infirm. Glas.

PARKER, John Lee 11 Thurcaston Lane, Rothley, Leicester LE7 7LF — MB BS 1993 Lond.

PARKER, John Randolph Walsgrave NHS Trust, Rugby CV22 5PX Tel: 01788 572831 Fax: 01788 545267; Friz Hill House, Walton, Warwick CV35 9HH Tel: 01789 840321 — MB BChir 1961 Camb.; MA Camb. 1961, BA 1957; FRCA 1978; DObst RCOG 1962. (Camb. & Westm.) Cons. Anaesth. Rugby & Coventry NHS Trusts. Socs: Fell. Roy. Soc. Med.; Assn. Anaesth.; BMA. Prev: Sen. Regist. (Anaesth.) Qu. Eliz. Med. Centre. Birm.; Regist. (Med.) St. Stephen's Hosp. Lond.; Ho. Phys. W.m. Hosp. Lond.

PARKER, John Stephen Morrill Street Health Centre, Holderness Road, Hull HU9 2LJ Tel: 01482 320046; 1 Herne View, Beverley HU17 — MB ChB 1979 Leeds; MRCGP 1983; DRCOG 1983; DCH RCP Lond. 1982. Socs: Brit. Soc. Med. Dent. Hypn.

PARKER, Jonathan Chester 17 Paddockfields, Old Basing, Basingstoke RG24 7DB Tel: 01256 26460 — MB BS Lond. 1963; MRCS Eng. LRCP Lond. 1963; FRCR 1975; FFR 1970; DMRD Eng. 1968. (St. Mary's) Cons. Radiol. Basingstoke & Dist. Gen. Hosp. Prev: Sen. Regist. Univ. Coll. Hosp. Lond. & Hosp. Sick Childr. Gt. Ormond; St.; SHO W.. Hosp. Fulham.

PARKER, Joyce Mary (retired) The Hollies, Florida St., Castle Cary BA7 7AE Tel: 01963 50709 — MRCS Eng. LRCP Lond. 1949.

PARKER, Judith Alison The Lindley Group Practice, 62 Acre Street, Lindley, Huddersfield HD3 3DY Tel: 01484 342191 — MB ChB 1984 Leeds; MB ChB Leeds 1984.

PARKER, Julie Fairway, 6 Windle Hill, Church Stretton SY6 7AP — MB ChB 1981 Liverp.

PARKER, Julie Barrow Hospital, Barrow Gurney, Bristol BS48 3SG Tel: 0117 928 6655 — BM BCh 1978 Oxf.; BA Camb. 1975; MSc Bristol 1988; MRCPsych. 1982. Avon & W.ern Wilts. NHS Ment. Health Trust.

PARKER, Julius Clifford 3 Norden Meadows, Altwood Road, Maidenhead SL6 4SB — MB ChB 1988 Leic.; BA Oxf. 1983;

MRCGP 1992; T(GP) 1992; DRCOG 1991. Lect. (Child Health) Brit. Coll. of Naturopathy & Osteop. Socs: BMA. Prev: SHO (Community Paediat.) Banbury; Trainee GP N.ants. VTS.

PARKER, Kenneth James (retired) Selly Oak Health Centre, Katie Road, Selly Oak, Birmingham B29 6JG Tel: 0121 472 0016 — MB ChB 1967 Birm.

PARKER, Lewis (retired) 3 Dovercourt Avenue, Heaton Mersey, Stockport SK4 3QB — BM BCh 1944 Oxf.; MA Oxf. 1945, BM BCh 1944; FRCPath 1966. Hon. Cons. Microbiol. N. Manch. Gen. Hosp. Prev: Cons. Microbiol. N. Manch. Gen. Hosp.

PARKER, Linda Stella The Old Penny School House, St Johns Road, St Leonards-on-Sea TN37 6ET — MB BChir 1989 Camb.; MA Camb. 1990, BA (Hons.) 1986; ECFMG Cert. 1989; DRCOG 1995; DFFP 1995. (Univ. Camb. Clin. Sch.) GP Regist. Jenner Hse. Old Harlow. Prev: SHO (A & E Psychiat. & O & G) P.ss Alexandra Hosp. Harlow.

PARKER, Lisa Belinda 38 Crescent Avenue, Hornchurch RM12 4ED — MB BS 1992 Lond.

PARKER, Luke Robert Cowdy Close Farm Surgery, 47 Victoria Road, Warmley, Bristol BS30 5JZ Tel: 0117 932 2108 Fax: 0117 987 3977 Email: luke.parker@gp-l81050.nhs.uk — MB BS 1985 Lond.; BSc Lond. 1982; MRCGP 1993; DCH RCP Lond. 1991; DGM RCP Lond. 1989. Prev: Trainee GP Avon VTS.

PARKER, Margaret Beryl (retired) 68 Ladies Mile Road, Patcham, Brighton BN1 8TD Tel: 01273 555791 — MB ChB 1939 Birm.; MFCM 1974; DPH Eng. 1948. Prev: Sen. Med. Off. (Child Health) Brighton Health Dist.

PARKER, Marler Thomas (retired) 1 Douglas House, The Avenue, Beckenham BR3 5DJ Tel: 020 8658 7750 — MD 1956 Camb.; MB BChir 1937; FRCPath 1964; Dip. Bact. Lond 1939. Prev: Dir. Cross Infec. Ref. Laborat. Colindale, Manch. Regional Pub.

PARKER, Martyn John 113 Cumberland House, St Mary's Court, Peterborough PE1 1UN Tel: 01733 569945 — MB ChB 1979 Birm.; FRCS Ed. (Gen.) 1988; FRCS Ed. (A&E) 1987; DCH RCP Lond. 1984; DRCOG 1983; MD Birm. 1995. Research Fell. (Orthop.) PeterBoro. Dist. Hosp. Prev: Research Regist. (Orthop.) P.boro. Dist. Hosp.

***PARKER, Matthew Richard** 18 Laburnum Road, Chorley PR6 7BG — MB ChB 1998 Leeds.

PARKER, Melanie Community Child Health, 4th Floor, King Square House, Bristol BS2 8EF Tel: 0117 900 2350; 1 Cranbrook Road, Redland, Bristol BS6 7BJ — MB BCh 1980 Wales; MRCP Ed. 1994; DCCH 1988. (Welsh Nat. Sch. Med.) Staff Grade (Comm. Paediat.) United Bristol Healthcare Trust, Bris. Socs: BASPCAN; Brit. Paediat. Assn. Prev: Flexible Regist. (Paediat.) S.mead Hosp. Bristol; Clin. Med. Off. Fife HB.

PARKER, Michael Arthur Benefits Agency, Warbreck Hill Road, Blackpool FY2 0XW Tel: 01253 856123 — MB ChB 1984 Manch. Med. Off. Benefits Agency Blackpool.

PARKER, Mr Michael Christopher Owen Joyce Green Hospital, University Way, Dartford DA1 5PL Tel: 01322 227242 Fax: 01322 283564 Email: mike@surg24.freeserve.co.uk; 15 Church Road, Sundridge, Sevenoaks TN14 6DT Tel: 01959 564743 Fax: 01959 561209 Email: mikesurg@aol.com — MRCS Eng. LRCP Lond. 1973; MS Lond. 1987, BSc (Hons.) 1970, MB BS 1973; FRCS Eng. 1980; FRCS Ed. 1980. (Westm.) Cons. Surg. Joyce Green Hosp. Dartford. Socs: Fell. Roy. Soc. Med. (Vice Pres. Mem. Surg. Sect.); Brit. Assn. Surg. Oncol. (Mem. Nat. Comm.); Founder Mem. Assn. Colproctol. GB & Irel. Prev: Lect. & Sen. Regist. (Surg.) St. Geo. Hosp. Lond.; Regist. (Surg.) St. Geo. & St. Jas. Hosp. Lond.

PARKER, Michael Donovan (retired) Thornbers, Slaidburn Road, Waddington, Clitheroe BB7 3JJ Tel: 01200 425318 Email: parkerm@beeb.net — MB ChB 1953 Birm.; FRCGP 1985, M 1966; DCH Eng. 1958; DObst RCOG 1954. Prev: Ho. Phys. Childr. Hosp. Birm.

PARKER, Michael James Department of Clinical Genetics, The Leicester Royal Infirmary NHS Trust, Leicester LE1 5WW Tel: 0116 258 5736; The Gables, 4 Behay Gardens, Staythorpe, Newark NG23 5RL — MB ChB 1992 Leeds; BSc Leeds 1990, MB ChB 1992; MRCP (Paediat.) 1995. Specialist Regist.

PARKER, Michael Julian Reid Altnagelvin Area Hospital, Londonderry BT47 6SB; Ashton Lodge, 1 Rosswater, Limavady Road, Londonderry BT47 6YR — MD 1988 Belf.; FRCOG 1999; MB BCh BAO 1980; MRCOG 1985, D 1982. Cons. Obst. & Gyn.

PARKER

*PARKER, Michael Rowland 2 Ashdown Road, Heaton Moor, Stockport SK4 4JN — MB ChB 1994 Liverp.

PARKER, Myrtle Lee (retired) Ger-y-Plas, Talybont SY24 5HJ Tel: 01970 832449 Email: myrtle@talybont i.freeserve.co.uk — MB BS 1953 Lond. Prev: GP.

PARKER, Nicola Jane Main Road Surgery, 173 Main Road, Sundridge, Sevenoaks TN14 6EH Tel: 01959 562531; Winterton Surgery, Russell House, Westerham TN16 1RB — MB ChB 1986 Birm.; DCH RCP Lond. 1990; DRCOG 1989.

PARKER, Norman Eric Whittington Hospital, Highgate Hill, London N19 5NF Tel: 020 7288 5437 Fax: 020 7288 3485 — MB BS 1974 Lond.; FRCP Lond. 1993; MRCP (UK) 1976; FRCPath 1993, M 1981. (Univ. Coll. Hosp.) Cons. Haemat. Whittington Hosp. Lond.; Med. Director Whittington NHS Trust. Socs: Brit. Soc. Haematol. Prev: Lect. (Clin. Haemat.) Univ. Coll. Hosp. Med. Sch. Lond.

PARKER, Patricia Mary The Dial House, Frensham, Farnham GU10 3AZ Tel: 0125 125 4249 — MB BS 1969 Lond.

PARKER, Patrick William McLean Crossways, Chagford, Newton Abbot TQ13 8DA Tel: 01647 432430 — MB BS 1961 Lond.; DObst RCOG 1963. Prev: SHO (Obst.) St. Mary's Hosp. Kettering; Ho. Surg. Kettering Gen. Hosp.; Ho. Phys. Middlx. Hosp.

PARKER, Mr Paul Jeremy 18 Lancedean Road, Belfast, Milnthorpe BT6 9QP Email: ppark@nahs_tr.northy.nhs.uk — MB BCh BAO 1985 Belf.; FRCS Ed. 1992; Dip. IMC RCS Ed. 1990; FRCS (Orth) 1997. (Queen's Univ. Belfast) Cons. Orthop. Surg. Friarage Hosp. N. Allerton; ATLS Co-Dir. AO Instruc. Socs: Orthop. Dangerous Sports Soc. Prev: Osteoarticular Research Fell. Univ. Edin. Med. Sch.; Sen. Regist. (Orthop. & Traumatol.) Roy. Infirm. Edin.; Fell. (Orthop. Trauma) R. Adams Cowley Shock-Trauma Center Baltimore MD, USA.

PARKER, Richard Henry Oxlade (retired) The Firs, Firs Road, Ross-on-Wye HR9 5BH Tel: 01989 563995 — BM BCh 1953 Oxf.; BSc Oxf. 195; MRCGP 1972; DA Eng. 1970; DObst RCOG 1956. Med. Adviserr Ldr.ship trust, Ross On Wye. Prev: GP Ross-on-Wye.

PARKER, Richard Hugh c/ The Managaer, National Westminster Bank, 22 George St., Richmond TW9 1JW — MB BChir 1981 Camb.; MA, MB Camb. 1981, BChir 1980; MRCGP 1988; DRCOG 1986; DCH RCP Lond. 1986. Prev: Trainee GP Greenwich VTS; Med. Off. Brit. Antarctic Survey.

PARKER, Richard Lewis Edward South Ham House, 96 Paddock Road, Basingstoke RG22 6RL Tel: 01256 324666 Fax: 01256 810849; 7 Litton Gardens, Oakley, Basingstoke RG23 7JS — MB BS 1990 Lond.

PARKER, Robert Bunten (retired) 9 Tudor Way, Murton, Swansea SA3 3AZ Tel: 01792 234664 — MB BS 1953 Lond.; MRCS Eng. LRCP Lond. 1952.

PARKER, Robert Stansfeld 9 Rowton Grange Road, Chapel-en-le Frith, High Peak SK23 0LA Tel: 01298 812686 Fax: 01298 815287 — MB ChB 1960 Manch.; DObst RCOG 1964. (Manch.) Forens. Med. Examr. Derbysh. Constab.; Co. Path. High Peak Derbysh. Socs: BMA; Assn. Police Surg. Prev: Resid. (Clin. Path.) Bolton Roy. Infirm.; Ho. Off. (O & G) Bolton Dist. Gen. Hosp.; Ho. Off. (Surg.) Salford Roy. Hosp.

PARKER, Rodney Kevan Hassard Bushey Health Centre, London Road, Bushey, Watford WD23 2NN Tel: 01923 225224 Fax: 01923 213270; Oundle, 46 Little Bushey Lane, Bushey Heath, Watford WD23 4RN Tel: 020 8950 1013 Fax: 020 8950 1013 — MB ChB 1959 Bristol; MRCGP 1977; DObst RCOG 1961. Prev: Ho. Surg. (Obst.) Bristol Matern. Hosp.

PARKER, Roger The Health Centre, Doctor Lane, Mirfield WF14 8DU Tel: 01924 495721 Fax: 01924 480605; Pinfold Lodge, Pinfold Lane, Mirfield WF14 9HZ Tel: 01924 495549 — MB ChB 1969 Leeds. (Leeds) Socs: Hudds. Med. Soc. Prev: SHO (O & G), Ho. Phys. (Med. & Dermat.) & Ho. Surg. (Surg. & ENT) Staincliffe Gen. Hosp. Dewsbury.

PARKER, Roger Durnal Lloyd (retired) 24 Argarmeols Road, Formby, Liverpool L37 7DA — MB ChB Liverp. 1960; DObst RCOG 1962. Prev: Ho. Surg. & Ho. Phys. David Lewis N.. Hosp. Liverp.

PARKER, Roger John (retired) 17 Derwen Deg Close, Govilon, Abergavenny NP7 9RJ Tel: 01873 830336 — MRCS Eng. LRCP Lond. 1964; DMRD Eng. 1967. Cons. Radiol. P. Chas. Hosp. Merthyr Tydfil. Prev: Sen Regist. (Radiol) Bristol Roy. Infirm.

PARKER, Mr Ronald William Davenport Consulting Rooms, 5 Davenport Road, Coventry CV5 6QA — MB ChB 1963 Birm.; FRCS Eng. 1969; FRCS Ed. 1968. (Birm.) Governor Works. Private Hosp.; Cons. Gen. Surg. Walsgrave Hosp. Coventry. Socs: Chairm. Brit. Assn. Med. Managers; BMA & Brit. Assn. Surg. Oncol. Prev: Sen. Regist. Qu. Eliz. Hosp. Birm. & Selly Oak Hosp. Birm.

PARKER, Sally Elizabeth 6 Kempe's Close, Long Ashton, Bristol BS41 9ER Tel: 01275 392016 — BM 1986 Soton.; BM Soton 1986; FRCA 1994; DCH RCP Lond. 1992. (Soton.) Specialist Regist. (Anaesth.) St. Geo.s Hosp. Lond. Prev: Attend. (Pediatric Anesthesia) Childr.s Hosp. & Regional Med. Center Seattle, USA; Fell. (Paediat. Anaesth.) Hosp. Sick Childr. Toronto, Canada; Regist. (Anaesth.) Torbay Hosp. Torquay & Derriford Hosp. Plymouth.

PARKER, Sara Louise Ashford Public Health Laboratory, William Harvey Hospital, Willesborough, Ashford TN24 0LZ Tel: 01233 635731 Fax: 01233 643432; Stede Court, Stede Hill, Harrietsham, Maidstone ME17 1NR Tel: 01622 850944 — MB BS 1986 Lond.; MSc (Med. Microbiol.) Lond. 1993; MRCPath 1998. Cons. (Med. Microbiol.) Ashford Pub. Health Laborat. William Harvey Hosp. Prev: Sen. Regist. (Med. Microbiol.) Ashford Pub. Health Laborat. William Harvey Hosp.; Sen. Regist. (Med. Microbiol.) St. Geo. Hosp. Lond.

PARKER, Sarah Caroline Barrow Health Centre, 27 High Street, Barrow on Soar, Loughborough LE12 8PY Tel: 01509 413525 Fax: 01509 620664; Glebe Farm, 1 Main St, Hoby, Melton Mowbray LE14 3DT Tel: 01664 434263 Fax: 01664 434147 — MB BS 1982 Lond. (St. Mary's)

PARKER, Sheena Stevenson 2 Regent Terrace, Edinburgh EH7 5BN Tel: 0131 556 7164 — MB ChB 1967 Ed.; MFPHM RCP (UK) 1995; Dip Soc Med Ed. 1974; MFPHM 1995; FFPHM 1998; FRCP Ed 1998. (Ed.) Dir. Pub. Health, W. Sussex Health Auth. Prev: Cons. Pub. Health Med. Lothian HB.; Unit Gen. Manager Lothian HB.; Specialist (Community Med.) Lothian HB.

PARKER, Sheila Margaret Pasture Wood, Crawley Down, Crawley RH10 4LL Tel: 01342 2870 — MRCS Eng. LRCP Lond. 1946; FFA RCS Eng. 1956. (Roy. Free) Cons. Anaesth. Dudley & Stourbridge Hosp. Gp. Prev: Sen. Anaesth. Regist. United Birm. Hosps. & Regional Thoracic Centres.

PARKER, Sheila Morgan (retired) 2 Tilsley Road, Chipping Norton OX7 5JA Tel: 01608 642822 — MB ChB 1953 Birm.; FFA RCS Eng. 1956; DA Eng. 1956. Med. Off. Chipping Norton War Memor. Hosp. Prev: Regist. (Anaesth.), Ho. Phys. & Ho. Surg. Qu. Eliz. Hosp. Birm.

PARKER, Sidney James 85 Old Kilmore Road, Moira, Craigavon BT67 0NA Tel: 01846 611278; 52 Main Street, Moira, Craigavon BT67 0LQ Tel: 01846 611278 — MB BCh BAO 1978 Belf.; MRCGP 1982; DGM RCP Lond. 1985; DRCOG 1980.

PARKER, Mr Stephen John, Surg. Lt.-Cdr. RN 17 Coleby Close, Burton Green, Coventry CV4 8HN Tel: 024 76 474228 Email: parkeroz@globalnet.co.uk — MB BS 1988 Lond.; BSc Lond. 1985, MB BS 1988; FRCS Eng. 1994; FRCS Ed. 1994. (St. George's Hosp. Med. Sch.) Specialist Regist. (Gen. Surg.) W. Midl. Gen. Surgic. Train. Rotat. Prev: Regist. (Surg.) & Med. Off. RN.

PARKER, Steven John The Surgery, Revelstoke Way, Rise Park, Nottingham NG14 7DW — MB ChB 1983 Manch.; MRCGP 1989; DGM RCP Lond. 1993; DRCOG 1989. Socs: Nottm. Medico-Chirurgical Soc.

PARKER, Stuart Graeme Department of Medicine for the Elderly, University of Leicester, Leicester General Hospital, Gwendolen Road, Leicester LE5 4PW Tel: 0116 258 4081 — MB BS 1980 Newc.; MD Newc. 1991; MRCP (UK) 1983; FRCP 1998. Sen. Lect. (Med. for Elderly) Univ. Leicester. Prev: 1st Asst. in Med. (Geriat.) Univ. Newc.; BGS/Nuffield Trav. Fell. TNO-IVEG, Netherlands; Research Assoc. Univ. Newc.

PARKER, Stuart James 26 Romilly Park Road, Barry CF62 6RQ Tel: 01446 735282 — MB BCh 1966 Wales; BA (Hons.) Open 1989; MRCGP 1974; DMJ (Clin.) Soc. Apoth. Lond. 1981; DCH Eng. 1968; DObst RCOG 1968. (Cardiff) Med. Adviser SEMA Med. Servs. Cardff. Prev: Princip. GP Barry; Gen. Med. Off. Uganda.

PARKER, Stuart Samuel Ireland 75 Union Street, Larkhall ML9 1DZ Tel: 01698 882105 Fax: 01698 886332; 25 Burnside Place, Larkhall ML9 2EQ Tel: 01698 882724 Email: stuartparker@larkhall.demon.co.uk — MB ChB Glas. 1958; MB ChB Glas. 1958; DObst RCOG 1960; DObst RCOG 1960.

PARKER, Susan Clare Department of Dermatology, West Middlesex University Hospital, Twickenham Rd, Isleworth TW7 6AF Tel: 0208 785 9001; Tel: 0208 785 9001 — MB BChir 1980 Camb.; FRCP (Uk) 1999; MA Camb. 1981; MRCP (UK) 1983. (St. Thos.) p/t Cons. Dermat. W. Middlx. Univ. Hosps. & Chelsea and W.m. Hosp. Prev: Sen. Regist. St. Johns Dermat. Centre St. Thos. Hosp. Lond.; Regist. (Dermat.) St. Thos. Hosp. Lond.; Regist. Dermat. Roy. Vict. Infirm. Newc.

PARKER, Susan Lynne Deptartment of Medicine for the Elderly, Leicester General Hospital, Gwendolen Road, Leicester LE5 4PW — MB BS 1980 Newc.; MRCGP 1985; DRCOG 1984. Clin. Asst. (Med. for Elderly) Leicester Gen. Hosp.

PARKER, Susan Patricia 89 Preston New Road, Marton, Blackpool FY3 9ND — BM BCh 1991 Oxf.; BA Oxf. 1988; DRCOG 1996; DCH RCP Lond. 1995; DA (UK) 1993. (Oxf.) GP/Regist. Cawley Rd. Med. Centre, Chichester.

PARKER, Susan Woodward Oak House, 42 Glenferness Avenue, Bournemouth BH3 7ET — MB BS 1983 West. Austral.; MPsych (Clin.) 1973. Assoc. Specialist (Endocrinol.) Roy. Bournemouth Hosp.; Psychosexual Med. Specialist Dorset Healthcare Trust. Socs: Fell. Roy. Soc. Med.; BPS; BMA. Prev: Sen. Clin. Psychol. W.. Austral. Pub. Serv. Bd.; Trainee GP Dorset.

PARKER, Susanna Jane 14 Birley Park, Manchester M20 2TL — MB ChB 1991 Manch.

PARKER, Thomas Frederick James 17 Dingle Road, Abergavenny NP7 7AR Tel: 01873 3395 — MB ChB 1954 Bristol; FFA RCS Eng. 1966; DA Eng. 1957. (Bristol)

PARKER, Timothy Guy Church Stretton Medical Centre, Church Stretton SY6 6BL Tel: 01694 722127; Fairway, 6 Windle Hill, Church Stretton SY6 7AP — MB ChB 1984 Birm.; ChB Birm. 1984; DRCOG 1989. GP Ch. Stretton Shrops. Prev: Trainee GP Sandwell Dist. Gen. Hosp. VTS.

PARKER, Tom James 2 Ashdown Road, Stockport SK4 4JN — MB ChB 1993 Leeds.

PARKER, Valerie Anne Newpark Surgery, Talbot Green, Pontyclun CF72 8AJ Tel: 01443 224213 — MB BS 1981 Newc.; MRCGP 1987. (Univ. Newc. u. Tyne) Clin. Asst. in Diabetes Roy. Glamorgn Hosp. Prev: SHO (O & G) E. Glam. Gen. Hosp. Pontypridd; SHO (Haemat.) Roy. Infirm. Sunderland; Ho. Off. (Gen. Surg. & Gen. Med.) Newc. Gen. Hosp.

PARKER, Vernon Lester The Family Surgery, 7 High St, Green St Green, Orpington BR6 6BG Tel: 01689 850231 Fax: 01689 857122 Email: vernon.parker@gp-g84009.nhs.uk — MB BS 1983 Lond.

PARKER, Vivienne (retired) 3 Meadowgate, Tallington Road, Bainton, Stamford PE9 3AS Tel: 01780 740700 Fax: 01780 740700 Email: wardviv@warden30.bsnet.co.uk — MB ChB 1966 Leeds; FFPHM RCP (UK) 1989; FFCM RCP (UK) 1989, M 1982; DObst RCPI 1969. Prev: Dir. Pub. Health NW Anglia Health Commisss.

PARKER, William Arthur (retired) 44 Kenilworth Road, Bridge of Allan, Stirling FK9 4RP Tel: 01786 833342 — MB BCh 1941 MB BCh; FRCP 1967 FRCP Glas 1967; MRCP 1962 MRCP (uk) 1962. Prev: Cons. Phys. Stirling Roy. Infirm.

PARKER, William Neil Baron (retired) 67 Victoria Drive, Bognor Regis PO21 2TD Tel: 01243 823538 — MA Camb. 1969, MB BChir 1952; MRCS Eng. LRCP Lond. 1952; DObst RCOG 1954. Prev: GP Bognor Regis.

PARKER, Yvette-Marie Anne Department Child Psychiatry, Larkby Young Persons Unit, Victoria Park Road, Exeter EX2 4NU — MB ChB Leeds 1977; MRCPsych 1986; MRCGP (Distinc.) 1984. Cons. Child & Adolesc. Psychiat. Exeter Community Health Trust. Prev: Sen. Regist. (Child Psychiat.) St. Geo. Hosp. Lond.; Cons. St Peter's Hosp. Chertsey Surrey.

PARKER-WILLIAMS, Edward John St. George's Hospital, Blackshaw Road, London SW17 0QT Tel: 020 8725 5446 Fax: 020 8725 0245 — MB BS 1957 Lond.; FRCPath 1988. (Middlx.) Sen. Lect. & Cons. Haemat. St. Geo. Hosp. Med. Sch. Lond. (Emerit.); Director UKNEQAS, Gen' HaemOtol. Prev: Cons. Haemat. & Sen. Lect. Centr. Middlx. Hosp. Lond.; Lect. (Haemat.) Middlx. Hosp. Med. Sch. Lond.; Sen. Regist. Hammersmith Hosp. Lond.

PARKES, Adrian John 21 Merridale Avenue, Wolverhampton WV3 9RE Tel: 01902 772070 — MB ChB 1986 Birm.

PARKES, Alan Walton Adlerwood Precinct Surgery, 8 Alderwood Precinct, Northway, Sedgley, Dudley DY3 3QY Tel: 01902 85180/880825; (Surgery) 8 Alderwood Precinct, Dudley DY3 3QY Tel: 0190 735180 — MB ChB 1955 Birm.; BDS 1964. (Birm.)

PARKES, Andrew Michael Hackenthorpe Medical Centre, Main Street, Hackenthorpe, Sheffield S12 4LA Fax: 0114 251 0539 — MB ChB 1984 Sheff.

***PARKES, Andrew William** 15 Wellington Road, Lancaster LA1 4DN — MB BS 1998 Newc.; MB BS Newc 1998.

PARKES, Carol Ann West Kent Health Authority, Preston Hall, Aylesford ME20 7NJ Tel: 01978 760736 — MB BS 1985 Lond.; MSc Lond. 1990, MB BS 1985; MFPHM RCP (UK) 1994. p/t Cons. in Pub. Health Med.

PARKES, Colin Murray, OBE Tel: 01923 282746 Email: cmparkes@aol.com; Tel: 01923 282746 — MB BS Lond. 1951; MD Lond. 1962; FRCPsych 1975, M 1971; DPM Eng. 1959. (Westm.) Hon. Cons. Psychiat. St. Christopher's Hospice Sydenham & St. Josephs Hospice. Socs: Fell. Roy. Coll. Psychiat.; Roy. Soc. Med. Prev: Sen. Lect. Lond. Hosp. Med. Coll.; Mem. Research Staff Tavistock Inst. Human Relats. Lond.; Mem. Scientif. Staff, MRC Social Psychiat. Unit & Regist. Maudsley Hosp. Lond.

PARKES, Eric Charles Williams 18 Park Drive, Grimsby DN32 0EF Tel: 01472 78478 — MB ChB 1940 Birm. (Birm.) Prev: Ho. Surg. Selly Oak Hosp. Birm.; Asst. Res. Surg. Off. Bolton Roy. Infirm.; Orthop. Regist. Derbysh. Roy. Infirm.

PARKES, Gary The Limes Surgery, 8-14 Limes Court, Hoddesdon EN11 8EP Tel: 01992 464533 Fax: 01992 470729 — MB ChB 1980 Manch.; MRCGP 1985; DRCOG 1985; DCH RCP Lond. 1985. GP & Surg. Amp-Pipal Hosp. Kathmandu, Nepal; Princip. Gen. Pract. Hoddesdon. Prev: Trainee GP E.bourne.

PARKES, Georgina 17 Ewden Road, Wombwell, Barnsley S73 0RF; 7 Falcon Way, Colindale, London NW9 5DT Tel: 020 8203 4387 — MB BS 1994 Lond. (Royal Free Hospital School of Medicine) Socs: MPS.

PARKES, Helen Rosamond Flat 5, 70 Greencroft Gardens, London NW6 3JQ Tel: 020 7625 8934 — MB BS 1987 Lond.

PARKES, Howard Guy, MBE (retired) Nettlefields, Coat, Martock TA12 6AR Tel: 01935 823692 Email: guyparkes@hotmail.com — MB ChB Birm. 1953; FFOM RCP Lond. 1981 MFOM 1978. Prev: Med. Dir. Brit. Rubber Manufacturers' Assn. Ltd.

PARKES, Isobel Rose Park Lane Surgery, 2 Park Lane, Allestree, Derby DE22 2DS Tel: 01332 552461 Fax: 01332 541500; The Stackyard, Dale Abbey, Ilkeston DE7 4PN Tel: 0115 930 3000 Email: isobel@iwagstaff.freeserve.co.uk — BM BS 1991 Nottm.; BMedSci. (Hons.) Nottm. 1989; MRCP (UK) 1996. (Nottm.) GP, Pk. La. Surg. Derby. Prev: GP Regist. Derby VTS.

PARKES, Janet 17 Poplar Drive, Barnt Green, Birmingham B45 8NQ — MB ChB 1964 Manch.

PARKES, John Clifford (retired) Robin Cottage, Robins Folly, Thorleigh, Bedford MK44 2EQ Tel: 01234 772126 — MB BS 1952 Lond.; DObst RCOG 1958.

PARKES, John David 2 Boakes Meadow, Shoreham, Sevenoaks TN14 7SH Tel: 01959 523732 Fax: 020 7703 9989 — MD 1964 Camb.; MB 1960, BChir 1959; FRCP Lond. 1976, M 1961. (Camb.) Prof. Clin. Neurol. Univ. Dept. Neurol. Inst. Psychiat. & Kings Coll.; Hosp. Lond. Hon. Cons. Neurol. Maudsley Hosp. & KCH Lond. Prev: Reader Neurol. Univ. Dept. Neurol. Inst. Psychiat. & King's Coll. Hosp. Lond.; Acad. Regist. Nat. Hosp. Nerv. Dis. Qu. Sq. Lond.

PARKES, John Graham (retired) Ferndale, Low Lorton, Cockermouth CA13 9UW Tel: 01900 85337 — MB BS Lond. 1955; MRCS Eng. LRCP Lond. 1955; MRCGP 1970; DCH Eng. 1970. Prev: Ho. Surg. ENT Dept. & Ho. Phys. Childr. Dept. Guy's Hosp.

PARKES, Julian David The Health Centre, Alfred Squire Road, Wednesfield, Wolverhampton WV11 1XU Tel: 01902 575033 Fax: 01902 575013 — MB ChB 1984 Birm.; MRCGP 1989; DRCOG 1987.

PARKES, Julie 9 Lakewood Road, Chandlers Ford, Eastleigh SO53 1ER — BM BCh 1982 Oxf.

PARKES, Karen Nina Edwana, Woodland Way, Maidstone ME14 2EY — MB ChB 1989 Otago.

PARKES, Miles Gastroenterology Unit, Radcliffe Infirmary, Oxford Tel: 01865 224829; 9 Chiltern View, Little Milton, Oxford OX44 7QP Tel: 01844 278986 Email: miles.parkes@well.ox.ac.uk — MB BS 1990 Lond.; BA Oxf. 1987; MRCP (UK) 1993. MRC Clin. Train. Fell. Nuffield Dept. Med. Gastroenterol. Unit. Radcliffe Infirm. Oxf. Prev: Regist. (Med. & Gastroenterol.) John Radcliffe Hosp. Oxf.

PARKES

PARKES, Neal Richard Quine Bridge Street Surgery, Bridge Street, Louth LN11 0DR Tel: 01507 603121 Fax: 01507 605916; The Old Vicarage, School Lane, Hainton, Market Rasen LN8 6LW — MB BS 1993 Lond.; DFFP 1996; MRCGP 1997. (Royal Free Lond.) GP Princip.; CMO (Fam. Plg.) Race Course Doctor.

PARKES, Norman McNeill 1A Lynors Avenue, Strood, Rochester ME2 3NQ Tel: 01634 711463 — MB BCh BAO 1948 Dub.; BA Dub. 1945, MB BCh BAO 1948; LAH Dub. 1948. (TC Dub.) Prev: Cas. Off. & Ho. Phys. St. Bart. Hosp. Rochester.

PARKES, Peter William Joseph (retired) Turvy House, Holner, Hereford HR1 1LH Tel: 01432 358811 — MRCS Eng. LRCP Lond. 1938. Phys. Bristol Homoeop. Hosp.; Med. Off. Bristol Prison. Prev: Ho. Phys.Homeopath Hosp. Bristol.

PARKES, Robin Trevor The Surgery, St. Peters Close, Cowfold, Horsham RH13 8DN Tel: 01403 864204 Fax: 01403 864408 — MB BS 1969 Lond. (Middlx.)

PARKES, Stephen John 21 Hightrees Road, Copt Heath, Knowle, Solihull B93 9PR — MB ChB 1979 Sheff.; MRCGP 1984; DCH RCP Lond. 1984. GP Solihull.

PARKES, Thomas Alan Whitehouse (retired) Willow Cottage, Willow Green, Martley, Worcester WR6 6PT Tel: 01886 821332 — MB ChB Birm. 1945; DA Eng. 1963. Prev: GP Sutton Coldfield.

PARKES, William Raymond, OBE (retired) Pixham Firs Cottage, Pixham Lane, Dorking RH4 1PH — MB ChB Liverp. 1948 Kanthack Medal (Path.); MD Liverp. 1956; FRCP Ed. 1976, M 1959; FFOM RCP Lond. 1983, MFOM 1979; DIH Soc. Apoth. Lond. 1962. Hon. Clin. Lect. Prof. Unit Dept. Med. Nat. Heart & Lung Inst. Univ. Lond. Prev: Phys. (Respirat. Dis.) DSS Med. Bd.ing Centre Lond.

PARKES BOWEN, Malcolm David Marston (retired) The Manor House, 63 Anstey Lane, Thurcaston, Leicester LE7 7JB Tel: 0116 236 2434 Email: davidpb@netlineuk.net — MB BChir 1948 Camb.; MRCS Eng. LRCP Lond. 1948; FRCGP 1979, M 1960. Prev: Clin. Asst. (Phys. Med.) Leicester Roy. Infirm.

PARKHOUSE, Helen 149 Harley Street, London W1G 6DE Tel: 020 7935 8391 Fax: 020 7935 8391 Email: h.parkhouse@thelondonclinic.co.uk — MB ChB 1978 Birm.; FRCS (Urol.) 1989; FRCS Eng. 1982; FEBU 1992. (Birm.) Cons. (Urol.) The Lond. Clinic; Hon. Cons. Urol. St. Luke's Hosp. for Clergy Lond. Socs: Brit. Assn. Urol. Surgs.; Societe Internat.e d'Urologie; Amer. Acad. of Pediatrics. Prev: Cons. Urol. Hillingdon & Mt. Vernon Hosps.; Sen. Lect. (Urol.) St. Thos. Hosp. Lond.; Sen. Regist. (Urol.) St. Bart. Hosp. Lond.

PARKHOUSE, James 145 Cumnor Hill, Oxford OX2 9JA Tel: 01865 862822 — MB ChB 1950 Liverp.; MSc Manch. 1974; MA Oxf. 1960; MD Liverp. 1955; FFA RCS Eng. 1954; DA Eng. 1952. (Liverp.) Cons. Med. Careers Research Gp. Oxf. Prev: Dir. Med. Careers Research Gp. Ch.ill Hosp. Headington; Prof. Postgrad. Med. Educat. Univ. Newc.; Postgrad. Dean & Dir. Regional Postgrad. Inst. Med. & Dent. N.. RHA; Prof. (Anaesth.) Manch. Univ.

PARKHOUSE, Mr Nicholas Queen Victoria Hospital, East Grinstead RH19 3DZ Tel: 01342 410210; 149 Harley Street, London W1N 2DE Tel: 020 7224 0864 — MB BS 1981 Lond.; MA Oxf. 1985, BA 1978; MCh Oxf. 1991; FRCS Eng. 1985; DM Oxf. 1990. Cons. Plastic Surg. Qu. Vict. Hosp. E. Grinstead; Dir. McIndoe Burn Centre; Hon. Cons. St. Luke's Hosp. for Clergy Lond. Socs: Fell. Med. Soc. Lond.; Fell. Chelsea Clin. Soc. Prev: Cons. Plastic Surg. Mt. Vernon Hosp. N.wood Middlx.; Sen. Regist. (Plastic Surg.) Qu. Vict. Hosp. E. Grinstead; Clin. Lect. (Surg.) Studies Middlx. Hosp. Lond.

PARKIANATHAN, Mr Visuvanather George Eliot Hospital, College St., Nuneaton CV10 7DJ Tel: 01203 351351; 19 Norwich Close, Nuneaton CV11 6GF Tel: 01203 326625 — MB BS 1973 Sri Lanka; FRCS Ed. 1985; FRCS Glas. 1985. Staff Surg. Geo. Eliot Hosp. Nuneaton. Prev: Regist. (Gen. Surg.) Geo. Eliot Hosp. Nuneaton.

PARKIN, Andrew Westcotes House, Westcotes Drive, Leicester LE3 0QU Tel: 0116 225 2900 Fax: 0116 225 2899 Email: ap23@leicester.ac.uk — BM BS 1985 Nottm.; BMedSci Nottm. 1983; MRCPsych 1990. Sen. Lect. & Hon. Cons. Child & Adolesc. Psychiat. Leicester. Prev: Clin. Research Fell. & Hon. Sen. Regist. (Child & Adolesc. Psychiat.) Univ. Leicester; Sen. Regist. (Child & Adolesc. Psychiat.) Leicester & Trent RHA; Regist. & SHO (Psychiat.) Nottm. HA.

PARKIN, Andrew John The Surgeries, Lombard Street, Newark NG24 1XG Tel: 01636 702363 Fax: 01636 613037; The Old Rectory, Gainsborough Road, Winthorpe, Newark NG24 2NN Tel: 01636 703197 — BChir 1976 Camb.; BChir 1976, MB Camb. 1977; MRCP (UK) 1979; MRCGP 1990. GP Trainer Centr. Notts. VTS.

PARKIN, Anne Elizabeth Newland Avenue Surgery, 239-243 Newland Avenue, Hull HU5 2EJ Tel: 01482 448456 Fax: 01482 449536; 63 Canada Drive, Cottingham HU16 5EH — MB ChB 1975 Dundee; DRCOG 1989. Continuing Med. Educat. Tutor Postgrad. Centre Hull.

PARKIN, Mr Benjamin Thomas 107 Sandbanks Road, Poole BH14 8BT — BM 1989 Soton.; MD 2001 Bristol; FRCOphth 1995. (Southampton) Specialist Regist. (Ophth.) Eye Unit Soton. Gen. Hosp. Prev: Specialist Regist. (Ophth.) Qu. Alexandra Hosp. Portsmouth; Specialist Regist. (Ophth.) W.bourne Eye Hosp. Bournemouth.

PARKIN, Brian Derek Health Care Group, Rohais Health Centre, Rohais, St Peter Port, Guernsey GY1 1FF Tel: 01481 723322 Fax: 01481 725200; Le Vau Des Velines, Les Effards, St Sampsons, Guernsey GY2 4US Tel: 01481 52275 Fax: 01481 302275 — MB BS 1981 Lond.; BSc Lond. 1978; MRCP (UK) 1984; MRCGP 1987; DRCOG 1987; Cert. Family Plann. JCC 1987. (Lond. Hosp.) Mem. Med. Staff P.ss Eliz. Hosp. Guernsey; Dep. Med. Off. of Health Guernsey. Prev: Regist. Whipps Cross Hosp. Lond.; SHO N.wick Pk. Hosp. Harrow.; SHO Manch. Roy. Infirm.

PARKIN, David (retired) 55 Oakwood Grove, Rotherham S60 3ES Tel: 01709 366616 — MB ChB 1954 Sheff.; MRCPsych 1971; DPM Eng. 1960. Hon. Lect. Clin. Psychiat. Univ. Sheff. Prev: Cons. Psychiat. Rotherham Dist. Gen. Hosp.

PARKIN, David Emrys Department of Gynaecology, Aberdeen Royal Infirmary, Aberdeen Tel: 01224 681818; Corbie Pines, Kirkton of Maryculter, Aberdeen AB12 5FS Tel: 01224 733312 — MD 1988 Manch.; MB ChB 1978; MRCOG 1985. Cons. O & G Aberd. Matern. Hosp. & Aberd. Roy. Infirm.; Clin. Sen. Lect. (Obst. & Gyn.) Univ. Aberd. Prev: Regist. (O & G) Stobhill Hosp. Glas.; Sen. Regist. N. Staffs. Matern. Hosp.

PARKIN, Geoffrey James Scott 8 Wedgewood Grove, Roundhay, Leeds LS8 1EG — MB ChB 1964 Leeds; MB ChB (Hons.) Leeds 1967; BSc (1st. cl. Hons. Anat.) Leeds 1964; FRCR 1975; FFR 1972; DMRD Eng. 1970. Cons. Radiol. United Leeds Teachg. Hosps. NHS Trust; Sen. Clin. Lect. (Diag. Radiol.) Univ. Leeds. Prev: Cons. Radiol. St. James Univ. Hosp. Leeds.

PARKIN, Gillian Harrogate District Hospital, Lancaster Park Road, Harrogate HG1 7SX Tel: 01423 885959; 1 Green Way, Rossett Green, Harrogate HG2 9LR — MB BS 1980 Newc.; FFA RCSI 1989. Cons. (Anaesth.) Specialty: ICU Harrogate Dist. Hosp. Harrogate. Prev: Flexible Trainee Yorks. Region.

PARKIN, Gordon Tallyn The Surgery, 12 Victoria Road South, Southsea PO5 2BZ Tel: 023 9282 3857; 86 Bowes Hill, Rowlands Castle PO9 6BS — MB BS 1977 Lond.; MRCGP 1981; DRCOG 1981.

PARKIN, Ian Geoffrey Department of Anatomy, Downing St., Cambridge CB2 3DY Tel: 01223 339333 Email: igp20@mole.bio.cam.ac.uk — MB ChB 1975 Aberd. Clin. Anat. Univ. Camb. Socs: Fell. Brit. Assn. Clin. Anat. Prev: Sen. Lect. (Anat.) Birm. Univ.

PARKIN, Jacqueline Mary Department of Immunology, St. Bartholomew's Hospital Medical College, London EC1A 7BE Tel: 020 7601 8428 Fax: 020 7600 3839 — MB BS 1981 Lond.; PhD Lond. 1990; MRCP (UK) 1988; FRCP (UK) 1996. Sen. Lect. & Hon. Cons. Clin. Immunol. St. Bartholomews & the Roy. Lond Hosp Sch of Med & Dent.; Assoc. Director, St. Bart's. & The Lond. Med. & Dent. Edu. Dept.; Chair, Nth. Thames Specialist Train. Comm. in Immunol. Prev: Sen. Regist. (Clin. Immunol.) St. Mary's Hosp. Med. Sch. Lond.; Wellcome Research Fell. (Immunol.) St. Mary's Hosp. Med. Sch. Lond.

PARKIN, Jeffrey (retired) Rose Bank, 132 Chester Road, Northwich CW8 4AN — MB ChB 1953 Manch.

***PARKIN, Joanna Elizabeth** Flat 1 Top Left, 50 Cranworth St., Glasgow G12 8AG — MB ChB 1998 Glas.; MB ChB Glas 1998.

***PARKIN, John** 31 Brandling Place S., Newcastle upon Tyne NE2 4RU — MB BS 1994 Lond.

PARKIN, John Lewis Branston Surgery, Station Road, Branston, Lincoln LN4 1LH Tel: 01522 793081 Fax: 01522 793562 — MB BCh 1982 Witwatersrand.

PARKIN, John Whitehouse 12 Hawkesford Close, Sutton Coldfield B74 2TR — MB ChB 1950 Birm.; MRCS Eng. LRCP Lond. 1950; DObst RCOG 1955. (Birm.) Prev: Ho. Phys. Birm. Gen. Hosp. & Birm. Childrs. Hosp.; Capt. RAMC.; Capt. RAMC; Clin. Asst. (A & E) Gen. Hosp. Birm. Clin. Asst. A & E Dept. Gen. Hosp. Birm.

PARKIN, Jon Richard Institute of Psychiatry, De Crespigny Park, Denmark Hill, London SE5 8AF Tel: 020 7919 3365 Fax: 020 7703 5796 — MB ChB 1985 Aberd.; MRCPsych 1991. Clin. Research Worker & Hon. Sen. Regist. (Psychiat.) Inst. Psychiat. Lond. Prev: Trainee GP Aberd.; Aberd. Psychait. Train. Scheme.

PARKIN, Louise Healthcare Group, Rohais, St Peter Port, Guernsey Tel: 01481 723322 Fax: 01481 725200 — MB ChB 1983 Manch.

PARKIN, Louise Pamela Mary The Alma Partnership, Winton Health Centre, Alma Road, Winton, Bournemouth BH9 1BP Tel: 01202 519311; 107 Sandbanks Road, Poole BH14 8BT — BM 1990 Soton.; MRCGP 1996. (Soton.) p/t GP Retainer.

PARKIN, Michael Gerard St Peters Hill Surgery, 15 St. Peters Hill, Grantham NG31 6QA Tel: 01476 590009 Fax: 01476 570898; Ironstone Cottage, Stroxton, Grantham NG33 5DA Fax: 01476 570898 — BM BS 1987 Nottm.; BMedSci Nottm. 1985; MRCGP 1992.

PARKIN, Norman Derek Sycamores, Church Road, Freiston, Boston PE22 0NX Tel: 01205 760590 — MB BS 1958 Lond.; MRCS Eng. LRCP Lond. 1958; FRCPath 1986, M 1973; DCP Lond 1968. (King's Coll. Hosp.) Cons. Microbiol. Pilgrim Hosp. Boston S. Lincs. HA. Socs: Brit. Soc. Antimicrobial. Chemotherap. Hosp. Infec. Soc. Prev: Cons. Microbiol. Inst. Pathol. & Trop. Med. RAF Halton; Wing Cdr. RAF Med. Br.

PARKIN, Richard Anthony The Health Centre, Byland Road, Skelton-in-Cleveland, Saltburn-by-the-Sea TS12 2NN Tel: 01287 650430 Fax: 01287 651268; 17 Upleatham Village, Redcar TS11 8AG Tel: 01287 624225 — MB BS 1965 Durh.; MRCGP 1974; DObst RCOG 1973. Prev: Nuffield Research Fell. (Adverse Drug Reactions) Shotley Bridge Hosp. Consett; Regist. (Gen. Med.) Shotley Bridge Hosp.

PARKIN, Robert Tallyn (retired) Driftway House, Mill Lane, Langstone, Havant PO9 1RX Tel: 02392 450741 — MB BS 1943 Lond.; MRCP Lond. 1949; MRCS Eng. LRCP Lond. 1943. Prev: Maj. RAMC.

PARKIN, Roger Downend The Medical Centre, Beech Grove, Sherburn-in-Elmet, Leeds LS25 6ED Tel: 01977 682208/682974 — MB ChB 1970 Leeds; FRCGP 1986, M 1976; DObst RCOG 1972. Socs: York Med. Soc. Prev: Chairm. Educat. Subcomm: Yorks. Fac. Bd. RCGP.

PARKIN, Simon Graham 4 Storey Street, Cramlington NE23 6RL — MB ChB 1993 Ed.

PARKIN, Timothy Limes Medical Centre, Limes Avenue, Alfreton DE55 7DW Tel: 01773 833133 Fax: 01773 836099; Rough Close Farm, High Oredish, Ashover, Chesterfield S45 0JX Tel: 01629 580980 Fax: 01629 580980 Email: tparkin489@aol.com — MB ChB 1989 Sheff.; MRCGP 1994; DFFP 1994; DRCOG 1993. (Sheff.) GP Princip.; Med. Adviser Carlton TV (Peak Pract.); Clin. Asst. in Learning Disabilities S. Derbysh. Socs: BMA (Pl. of Work Accred. Represen.). Prev: Trainee GP Chesterfield VTS; Clin. Med. Off. (Family Plann.) N. Derbysh.

PARKINNEN, Sarah Anne 15 Granta Terrace, Great Shelford, Cambridge CB2 5DJ — BChir 1995 Camb.

PARKINS, Anthony Christopher Westbrook Medical Centre, 301 Westbrook Centre, Apleton, Warrington WA5 5UF Tel: 01925 232706; 81 Shepperton Close, Appleton, Warrington WA4 5JZ Tel: 01925 213359 Email: antonpark@aol.com — MB BS 1988 Lond.; BSc Lond. 1986; MRCP (UK) 1993; DRCOG 1994. (Charing Cross and Westminster London) Gen. Practitioner, W.brook Med. Centre, Warrington; Clin. Asst., Cardiol., Halton Hosp., Runcorn.

PARKINS, David Redvers James Cons. in Accident & Emergency Medicine, Wanbeck Gen. Hospital, Woodhorn Road, Ashington NE63 9JJ Fax: 0191 569 9215; Tel: 01670 827154 — MB BS 1985 Newc.; 2001 FIMC RCS Ed.; BDS Newc. 1980; MRCGP 1994; FDS RCS Eng. 1989; Dip. IMC RCS Ed. 1996; FRCS Ed. 1998. Cons in Accid. & Emerg. Wasnbeck Gen Hosp N.umberland; Pre-Hosp. Immediate Care (BMJ); Mem. BASICS Exec. Counc.; N.umbria E.

Ambul. Serv.; Clin. Advis. Gp.; Dir. Educat. BASICS. Socs: Brit. Assn. Immed. Care; Brit. Assn. Accid. & Emerg. Med.; RCS Ed, Fac. of Pre-Hosp. Care. Prev: Cons. A & E Med. City Hosp. Sunderland NHS Trust; Hon. Surg. Newc. Gen. Hosp.; Hon. Phys. Roy. Vict. Infirm. Newc.

PARKINS, Joanne 5 Saxilby Drive, Whitebridge Park, Gosforth, Newcastle upon Tyne NE3 5LS — MB BS 1986 Newc.; BMedSc Newc. 1983. Regist. N. RHA. Socs: Brit. Med. Assoc. & Assn. Anaesth. Gt. Brit. & Irel. Prev: Ho. Surg. Newc. Gen. Hosp.; Ho. Phys. Roy. Vict. Infirm Newc.

PARKINS, Kathryn Jane 15 Hunts Field Close, Lymm WA13 0SS Email: kateparkins@aol.com; 81 Shepperton Close, Appleton, Warrington WA4 5JZ Tel: 01925 213359 — MB BS 1988 Lond.; MRCPI 1995. (Charing Cross and Westminster London) p/t Specialist Regist. (Paediat. IC) Roy. Manch. Childr.s Hosp. Manch.; Specialist Regist. (Paediatric Intens. Care), Roy. Liverp. Childr.'s Hosp., Eaton Rd., Liverp. L12 2AP. Prev: Specialist Regist. (Paediat.) S. Manch. Univ. Hosps. (Wythenshawe); Specialist Regist. (Paediat.) Tameside Dist. Gen. Hosp. Ashton-under-Lyne; Research Fell. (Regist.) (Paediat.) N. Staffs. Hosp. Stoke-on-Trent.

PARKINS, Robert Anthony 5 York Avenue, E. Sheen, London SW14 7LQ Tel: 020 8878 4114 Fax: 020 8255 0766 — MB BS 1950 Lond.; MB BS (Hons.) Lond. 1950; MD Lond. 1962; FRCP Lond. 1971, M 1955. (Char. Cross) Hon. Cons. Phys. Gen. Med. & Gastroenterol. Char. Cross Hosp. Lond. Socs: Fell. Roy. Soc. Med.; Med. Soc. Lond. Prev: Lect. (Med.) Univ. Washington, Seattle; Regist. (Med.) Hammersmith Hosp.; Ho. Phys. Brompton Hosp. Lond.

PARKINSON, Adrian Michael Practice A, Hinckley Health Centre, 27 Hill Street, Hinckley LE10 1DS Tel: 01455 635362 Fax: 01455 619797; 5 Castlemaine Drive, Hinckley LE10 1RY — MB BS 1976 Lond.; MRCGP. 1981; DRCOG 1981; DCH Eng. 1980. (Lond. Hosp.)

PARKINSON, Bryan Francis The Medical Centre, 4 Craven Avenue, Thornton, Bradford BD13 3LG Tel: 01274 832110/834387 Fax: 01274 831694 — MB ChB 1975 Manch.; BSc Manch. 1972, MB ChB 1975; DRCOG 1978.

PARKINSON, Craig Stepping Hill Hospital, Stockport SK2 7JE; 42 Dovecote Green, Westbrook, Warrington WA5 7XH Tel: 01925 710026 — MB ChB 1992 Liverp.; MRCP (UK) 1996. (Liverpool) Specialist Regist. in Diabetes & Endocrinol. & Gen. Med., Manch.; Specialist Regist., Stepping Hill Hosp. Socs: BMA; Brit. Diabetic Assn.; N. W. Endocrine Soc. Prev: Specialist Regist., Trafford DGM; SHO, Trafford DGM; Sen. Ho. Off. Countess of Chester Hosp.

PARKINSON, David Richard Nelson Health Centre, Cecil Street, North Shields NE29 0DZ Tel: 0191 257 1204/4001 Fax: 0191 258 7191; 53 Earnshaw Way, Whitley Bay NE25 9UL — MB BS 1976 Newc.; MRCGP 1980.

PARKINSON, David William Wendover, Cavendish Road, Bowdon, Altrincham WA14 2NU Tel: 0161 941 6950 — MB ChB 1968 Liverp.; DRCOG 1973; DCH RCP Lond. 1972. Clin. Med. Off. Lymm.

PARKINSON, Derek John Department of Obstetrics & Gynaecology, Welsh Nat. School of Medicine, Heath Park, Cardiff CF14 4XN — MB ChB 1975 Liverp.; MRCOG 1980. Lect. (O & G) Welsh Nat. Sch. Med. Cardiff. Socs: N. Eng. Obst. & Gyn. Soc. Prev: Regist. (O & G) Mill Rd. Natern. Hosp. Liverp. & Liverp.; Matern. Hosp.

PARKINSON, Eileen Lilian (retired) 32 Waldens Park Road, Horsell, Woking GU21 4RW — MRCS Eng. LRCP Lond. 1942. Prev: Sen. Med. Off. N.ampton Co. Boro.

PARKINSON, Emma Jane 6 St John's Road, Coton, Cambridge CB3 7PU Tel: 01954 210650 — MB BS 1996 Lond.; BSc 1993. (UMDS Guy's & St. Thomas)

PARKINSON, Geoffrey Hope, Maj. RAMC (retired) Spout Hill, Kilmington, Axminster EX13 7RW Tel: 01297 32263 — MB BChir 1941 Camb.; MA Camb. 1941. Prev: Ho. Phys. & Ho. Surg. Lond. Hosp.

PARKINSON, Gillian Nelson Health Centre, Cecil Street, North Shields NE29 0DZ Tel: 0191 257 1204/4001 Fax: 0191 258 7191 — MB BS 1978 Newcastle; MB BS Newc. 1978. (Newcastle) GP N. Shields, Tyne & Wear.

PARKINSON, Graeme Francis Lytham Road Surgery, 352 Lytham Road, Blackpool FY4 1DW Tel: 01253 402546 Fax: 01253 349637;

PARKINSON

23 Windmill Close, Staining, Blackpool FY3 0EB Tel: 01253 895104 — MB ChB 1980 Manch.; DRCOG 1983.

PARKINSON, Heidi Samantha Blackwoods Medical Centre, 8 Station Road, Muirhead, Glasgow G69 9EE — MB ChB 1993 Glas.; DRCOG; MRCGP. p/t GP Glas.; Clin. Asst.; BrE. Phys. Socs: MRCGP.

PARKINSON, Helen The Surgery, Astonia House, High Street, Baldock SG7 6BP Tel: 01462 892458 Fax: 01462 490821; 63 Norton Road, Letchworth SG6 1AD Tel: 01462 482840 — MB BChir 1983 Camb.; MA Camb. 1984; MRCGP 1992; DRCOG 1990; DA (UK) 1985. (Camb.) GP Princip. Prev: Doctor Brit. Embassy Sofia, Bulgaria; GP Asst. Birchwood Surg. Letchworth; SHO (A & E & c/o the Elderly & O & G) Lister Hosp. Stevenage.

PARKINSON, Helen Mary 30 Mill Brow, Marple Bridge, Stockport SK6 5LW — MB ChB 1982 Leic.

***PARKINSON, Ian Mark** 113 Byrons Lane, Macclesfield SK11 7JS — MB ChB 1996 Ed.

PARKINSON, Jeremy Charles Ellis (retired) Blencathra, 3 Belfield Park Drive, Weymouth DT4 9RB Tel: 01305 784118 — MB ChB 1959 Birm.; MRCS Eng. LRCP Lond. 1959; DObst RCOG 1962. Prev: GP Weymouth.

PARKINSON, Joanne Maria Teresa Bristol Oncology Centre, Horfield Road, Bristol BS2 8ED Tel: 0117 923 0000; Flat 2, 68 Pembroke Road, Clifton, Bristol BS8 3ED Tel: 0117 973 5115 — MB BS 1989 Lond.; MRCP (UK) 1995. (Univ. Coll. & The Middx Sch. Of Med. Lond.) Specialist Regist. (Clin. Oncol.) Bristol Oncol. Centre.

PARKINSON, John David Hayes Barton, Totteridge Lane, Totteridge, London N20 Tel: 020 8445 0475 — MB ChB 1962 Aberd. (Aberd.) Prev: Clin. Asst. Finchley Memor. Hosp.; Paediat. Inverness Hosps.; Ho. Surg. & Ho. Phys. Woodend Hosp. Aberd.

PARKINSON, Karin Ann 11 Dinorben Avenue, Fleet GU52 7SQ Tel: 01252 622982 — MB BCh BAO Belf. 1960. (Queens, Belfast) Staff Grade (Paediat.) Loddon NHS Trust Basingstoke. Socs: BACCH; Assoc. Mem. BPA. Prev: Clin. Med. Off. Basingstoke Dist. Hosp.

PARKINSON, Kenneth Brook Medical Centre, 98 Chell Heath Road, Bradeley, Stoke-on-Trent ST6 6PD Tel: 01782 838355 Fax: 01782 836245; Squirrels Hollow, Church Lane, Endon, Stoke-on-Trent ST9 9HF — MB ChB 1982 Manch.; BSc Med. Sci. St. And. 1979.

PARKINSON, Margaret Constance Rockefeller Building, University College Hospital Medical School, University St., London WC1E 6JJ — MRCS Eng. LRCP Lond. 1966; BSc (Hons.) Lond. 1963; MD 1978, MB BS 1966; FRCPath 1986, M 1973. (Roy. Free) Cons. & Hon. Sen. Lect. (Histopath.) St. Peter's Hosp. & Inst. Urol. At UCL Hosp.s Trust; Hon. Lect. Roy. Free Hosp. Lond. Prev: Sen. Lect. (Foren. Path.) Guy's Hosp. Lond.; Sen. Regist. (Histopath.) Centr. Middlx. Hosp. Lond. & Middlx. Hosp. Lond.

PARKINSON, Mary Vere, OBE (retired) 205 Braemor Road, Calne SN11 9EA Tel: 01249 816127 — MB BCh BAO 1952 Dub.; MRCGP 1978. Prev: Civil. Med. Pract. RAF Hullavington.

PARKINSON, Mr Michael John Rose Cottage, Waldringfield, Woodbridge IP12 4QX Tel: 0147336 697 — BM BCh 1960 Oxf.; MA, BM BCh Oxf. 1960; FRCS Ed. 1968; DO Eng. 1963. (Oxf.) Cons. Ophth. Surg. Ipswich & E. Suff. Hosp. Prev: Sen. Regist. Birm. & Midl. Eye Hosp. Regist. Ophth. Norf. & Norwich; Hosp.

PARKINSON, Michael John Offerton Health Centre, 10 Offerton Lane, Offerton, Stockport SK2 5AR Tel: 0161 480 0324 — MB ChB 1982 Leic.

PARKINSON, Michael Stuart Northampshire Healthcare NHS Trust, Department of Community Paediatrics, St Mary's Hospital, Kettering NN15 7PW Tel: 01536 410141; Quarrybank House, 95 Parkview, Kettering Road, Moulton, Northampton NN3 7UZ Tel: 01604 645029 Email: parkinsn@qbh.u-net.com — MB ChB 1964 Manch.; DObst RCOG 1967; DCH Eng. 1968. (Manchester University) Assoc. Specialist Dept Community Paediat., Kettering; Med. Adviser Adoption/Fostering N.auts SCOH, Kettering. Socs: BMA, Mem. Prev: GP N.ampton; Regist. (Paediat. & Infec. Dis.) N.ampton Gen. Hosp.; Ho. Phys. & Ho. Surg. St. Geo. Hosp. Lincoln.

PARKINSON, Rachel Janet The Barn, Higher Mithian Farm, Mithian Downs, St Agnes TR5 0PY — BM BS 1995 Nottm.

***PARKINSON, Richard John** 68 Station Road, Alsager, Stoke-on-Trent ST7 2PD — BM BS 1995 Nottm.

PARKINSON, Mr Richard Wellesley Orthopaedic Department, Arrowe Park Hospital, Arrowe Park Road, Upton, Wirral CH49 5PE Tel: 0151 604 7023 Fax: 0151 604 7078 — MB ChB 1981 Manch.; FRCS (Orth.) 1992; FRCS Glas. 1985; FRCS Ed. 1985. Cons. Orthop. Surg. Arrowe Pk. & Clatterbridge Hosps. Socs: BOA; Brit. Assoc. for Surg. of the Knee (BASK); BMA. Prev: Sen. Regist. (Orthop. Surg.) Wrightington Hosp.; Vis. Fell. Austin Hosp. Melbourne, Austral.; Sen. Regist. Roy. Preston Hosp.

PARKINSON, Simon John St Stephens Surgery, Adelaide Street, Redditch B97 4AL Tel: 01527 65444 Fax: 01527 69218 — MB ChB 1982 Birm.; MRCGP 1986; DRCOG 1985; DFFD 1986. (Birmingham) Sec. Worcs. Local Med. Comm.

PARKINSON, Stephen Hugh 303 Mount Pleasant Road, London N17 6HD Tel: 020 8885 3830 — MB BS 1984 Lond.

PARKS, Lady Caroline Jean Whitefriars, Dunwich, Saxmundham IP17 3DW — MB BS 1954 Lond. (St. Bart.)

PARKS, Lorraine 25 Hampton Manor, Belfast BT7 3EL — MB BCh BAO 1991 Belf.; FFARCSI, Dub 1997. (Queens University Belfast) Specialist Regist. (Anaesth.) Roy. Gp. of Hosps.

PARKS, Robert John 142 Park Road, Timperley, Altrincham WA15 6TQ — MB BS 1987 Lond.; BSc (Hons.) Glas. 1980; DRCOG 1993.

PARKS, Roger Guy Merchiston Surgery, Highworth Road, Swindon SN3 4BF Tel: 01793 823307 Fax: 01793 820923 — MB ChB 1969 Bristol.

PARKS, Sharmila 5 Cheswick Drive, Gosforth, Newcastle upon Tyne NE3 5DF — MB ChB 1995 Sheff. SHO Rotat. (Anaesth.) Traom/ Wansbeck DGN; SHO (Gen. Med.) Wansbeck DGN; SHO (Anaesth.) Freeman Hosp. Prev: SHO (A & E) Hallamsh. Hosp.

PARKS, Mr Thomas George Department of Surgery, Belfast City Hospital, Lisburn Road, Belfast BT9 7AX Tel: 01232 329241 Fax: 01232 326614; 6 Malone View Road, Belfast BT9 5PH Tel: 01232 615013 — MB BCh BAO 1959 Belf.; Mch 1966; FRCSI 1983; FRCS Glas. 1981; FRCS Ed. 1963. (Qu. Univ. Belf.) Prof. Surg. Sc. Qu. Univ. Belf.; Cons. Surg. E. Health & Social Servs. Bd. Socs: Surg. Research Soc.; ((Ex-Pres.) Assn. Surgs. Prev: Sen. Regist. Roy. Vict. Hosp. Belf., St. Marks Hosp. Lond. & Lond.; Hosp.

PARKS, Yvonne Alyson Child Health, Temple Ward, St. Martins Hospital, Littlebourne Road, Canterbury CT1 1TD Tel: 01227 812009 Fax: 01227 812002; 105A London Road, River, Dover CT16 3AA — MB ChB 1980 Birm.; FRCPCH 1997; MD Leic. 1991; MRCP (UK) 1983. Cons. Paediat. (Community) E. Kent Community Trust. Prev: Sen. Regist. (Community Paediat.) Canterbury; Clin. Med. Off. Canterbury & Thanet HA; Clin. Research Fell. (Child Health) Leicester Univ.

PARKYN, James (retired) 4 St Lukes Mews, Searle St., Cambridge CB4 3DF Tel: 01223 316729 — MRCS Eng. LRCP Lond. 1946; MB BS Lond. 1946; MRCP (Lond.) 1952; MD Lond. 1952; DTM & H Eng. 1955. Prev: Civil. Med. Pract. MoD.

PARKYN, Theresa Mary Department of Paediatrics, Royal Devon & Exeter Hospital, Exeter; East Exstowe, Starcross, Exeter EX6 8PD — MB BS 1968 Lond.; MRCS Eng. LRCP Lond. 1968. (Roy. Free) Clin. Asst. (Paediat.) Roy. Devon & Exeter Hosp.; Asst. Specialist Paediat. Oncol. Roy. Devon & Exeter Hosp. Prev: SHO (Med. & Paediat.) & Ho. Phys. Lister Hosp. Hitchin; Ho. Surg. Hampstead Gen. Hosp.

PARLE, Hilary Jane Elizabeth Jiggins Lane Medical Centre, 17 Jiggins Lane, Bartley Green, Birmingham B32 3LE Tel: 0121 477 7272 Fax: 0121 478 4319 — MB ChB 1978 Birmingham; MB ChB 1978 Birmingham.

PARLE, James Vivian Jiggins Lane Medical Centre, 17 Jiggins Lane, Bartley Green, Birmingham B32 3LE Tel: 0121 477 7272 Fax: 0121 478 4319; 7 Harrisons Road, Edgbaston, Birmingham B15 3QR — MB ChB 1978 Birm.; MRCGP 1982; DRCOG 1981. Sen. Lect. (Gen. Pract.) Univ. Birm.

***PARMAR, Bina** 74 Parkfield Avenue, Harrow HA2 6NP — MB BS 1998 Lond.; MB BS Lond 1998.

PARMAR, Chhaganlal Savjibhai Wednesbury Road Surgery, 68 Wednesbury Road, Walsall WS1 3RT Tel: 01922 24480 Fax: 01922 614861 — MB BS 1967 Bombay; MCPS Bombay 1967. (Seth G.S. Med. Coll. Parel)

PARMAR, Dipak Navnitlal Specialist Registrar, Department of Opthalmology, Moorfields Eye Hospital, 162 City Road, London EC1V 2PD — MB BS 1993 Lond.; BSc (Hons.) Lond. 1991.

PARMAR, Hansraj Ravji Newbury Group Practice, Newbury Park Health Centre, 40 Perrymans Farm Road, Barkingside, Ilford IG2 7LE Tel: 020 8554 3944 Fax: 020 8518 5911 — MB BS 1969 Andhra; MRCP (UK) 1978. (Andhra Med. Coll. Visakhapatnam) SHO (Med.) Newsham Gen. Hosp. Liverp. Prev: Ho. Off Irwin Hosp. Jamnagar, India & Newsham Gen. Hosp. Liverp.

PARMAR, Mr Harishbhai Queen Elizabeth II Hospital, Howlands, Welwyn Garden City AL7 4HQ Tel: 01707 328111; 5 Connaught Road, St Albans AL3 5RX — MB BS 1982 Lond.; BSc (Hons.) Lond. 1979; FRCS (Orth.) 1995; FRCS Ed. 1986. Cons. Orthop. Surg. Qu. Eliz. II Hosp. Welwyn Garden City. Socs: Fell. BOA; Brit. Orthop. Research Soc.; BMA. Prev: Sen. Regist. (Orthop. Surg.) Roy. Nat. Orthop. Hosp. Stanmore; Lect. & Wishbone Research Fell. Univ. Leicester; Regist. (Orthop.) Leics. HA.

PARMAR, Harsukh 4 Kitson Road, Camberwell, London SE5 7LF Tel: 020 7701 5106 — MB ChB 1980 Aberd. Research Regist. (Oncol.) Char. Cross & W.m. Hosp. Med. Sch. Lond. Socs: Brit. Oncol. Assn.; Amer. Assn. of Cancer Research. Prev: Asst. Lect. (Med. Oncol.) St. Bart. Hosp. Med. Coll. Lond.; SHO (Gen. Med.) St. Bart. Hosp. Rochester; SHO (Med.) Medway Hosp. Gillingham.

PARMAR, Hitendra Parshottambhai 14 Kedleston Road, Evington, Leicester LE5 5HU — MB BS 1994 Lond.

PARMAR, Jasbir Singh 163 Fillongley Road, Meriden, Coventry CV7 7LT — MB ChB 1989 Leic.

PARMAR, Jasvir Singh 4 Rack & Manger Cottages, Crawley, Winchester SO21 2PH — BM 1990 Soton.

PARMAR, Mr Jitendra Maganlal Department of Cardiothoracic Surgery, North Staffordshire Hospitals, Royal Infirmary, Princes Road, Stoke-on-Trent ST4 7LN Tel: 01782 554865 Fax: 01782 554830; 208 Mansel Road, Birmingham B10 9NL — MB ChB 1977 Birm.; BSc Birm. 1974; FRCS Eng. 1982. Cons. Cardiothoracic Surg. N. Staffs. Roy. Infirm. Stoke-on-Trent. Prev: Sen. Regist. (Cardiothoracic Surg.) W. Midl. RHA; Lect. (Anat.) Univ. Birm.; Regist. (Cardiothoracic & Gen. Surg.) W. Midl. RHA.

PARMAR, Mr Jitendra Ratilal MO13 NSPD, City General Hospital, Stoke-on-Trent ST4 6QG Tel: 01782 715444 Fax: 01782 552012 Email: jitparmar@mailexcite.com; 7 Davis Close, Alsager, Stoke-on-Trent ST7 2YP Tel: 01270 883832 Fax: 01270 883832 — MB BS 1975 Bombay; FRCS Ed. 1981; FRCS Glas. 1981. Staff Grade Surg. Socs: Fell. ASGI.

***PARMAR, Kalpesh Amrit** Room 46, New Heath Close, New Cross Hospital, Wolverhampton WV10 0QP Tel: 01902 307999 Fax: 01902 644888; 34 Lamborne Road, West Knighton, Leicester LE2 6HL Tel: 0116 288 4969 — MB ChB 1995 Birm.; ChB Birm. 1995.

PARMAR, Kantilal Bhagoobhai Whitehall Road Surgery, 1 Whitehall Road, Rugby CV21 3AE Tel: 01788 561319 Fax: 01788 553762; 1 Whitehall Road, Rugby CV21 3AE Tel: 01788 561319 — MB BS 1964 Gujarat. (B.J. Med. Coll. Ahmedabad) GP Rugby; Clin. Asst. (Rheum.) St. Cross Hosp. Rugby; Med. Off. Fam. Plann. Clinic Rugby Area Health Office. Prev: SHO & Ho. Surg. (Obst.& Gyn.) St. Mary's Hosp. HarBoro. Magna; Ho. Surg. & Ho. Phys. Hosp. St. Cross Rugby.

PARMAR, Mahesh Chhabildas 21 Ashley Close, Winchester SO22 6LR Tel: 01772 792303 — MB BS 1988 Lond.; BSc (Hons.) Lond. 1985; MRCP (UK) 1992; FRCA 1994. Regist. (Specialist) Soton. Gen. & Salisbury Dist. Gen. Hosp. Prev: SHO (Anaesth.) Soton.; SHO (Anaesth., ITU & Gen. Med.) Chichester.

PARMAR, Pravinbhai Prahladbhai 17 Maplin Avenue, Salendine Nook, Huddersfield HD3 3GP — MB ChB 1978 Manch. GP Elland.

PARMAR, Mrs Samyukta 5 Naill Close, Agustus Road, Edgbaston, Birmingham B15 3LU Tel: 0121 454 7818 — MB BS 1958 Mysore. (Mysore) Mem. Birm. Med. Inst. Prev: Ho. Off. (Surg.) Selly Oak Hosp. Birm.; SHO Highcroft Hall Hosp. Birm.; Regist. (Psychiat.) Hollymoor Hosp. Birm.

PARMAR, Sanjay Jayanti Brownlow Medical Centre, 140-142 Brownlow Road, New Southgate, London N11 2BD; Tel: 020 8590 9621 — MB BS 1991 Lond.; DPD 1998; MRCGP 1996; BSc (Hons.) Radiol. Sci. Lond. 1988; DFFP 1994; DRCOG 1994. Princip. Clin. Asst. Dermat.; Woodgrange Med. Pract., 40 Woodgrange Rd., Forest Gate, Lond. E7 0QH Tel: 020 8250 7585 Fax: 020 8250 7587. Prev: SHO (Med.) Basildon Dist. Gen. Hosp.; SHO (Paediat.) P.ss Alexandra Hosp. Harlow.; Trainee GP Lond.

PARMAR, Satyesh Chimanlal 27 Belfry Way, Edwalton, Nottingham NG12 4FA — BM BS 1995 Nottm.; BChD Leeds 1986; FDS RCS Eng. 1990; BMedSci Nottm. 1993; FRCS 1997. Specialist Regist. (Oral & Maxillofacial Surg.) Trent Region. Prev: SHO (Gen. Surg.) Trent Region; SHO (Orthop.) Trent Region; SHO (A & E) Trent Region.

***PARMAR, Tajinder Singh** 11 Talbot Road, Smethwick, Smethwick B66 4DX — MB BS 1994 Lond.

PARMENTER, John Grantley 15 Eirene Terrace, Pill, Bristol BS20 0ET Tel: 01275 372137 — MB ChB Bristol 1962.

PARNABY, Philip Bertram Icknield, Aylesbury Road, Princes Risborough HP27 0JW — MB ChB Manch. 1956; MRCS Eng. LRCP Lond. 1956. Prev: Capt. RAMC.

PARNABY, Roberta Mary Department of Microbiology, George Eliot Hospital, College St., Nuneaton CV10 7DJ Tel: 01203 351351 — BM BS 1981 Nottm.; MSc Lond. 1992; MRCPath 1993; DRCOG 1986; Dip. Health Mgt. Keele 1997; FRCPath 2001. p/t Cons. Clin. Microbiol. Geo. Eliot Hosp. Nuneaton.

PARNABY-PRICE, Adrian Ocular Immunology Group, Rayne Institute, St Thomas' Hospital, Lambeth Palace Road, London SE1 7EH Tel: 020 7928 9292 ext 6414 Email: aparnaby@geocities.com; 39 The Hawthorns, Charvil, Reading RG10 9TS — MB BChir 1987 Camb.; MA, MB BChir Camb. 1987; FRCS Ed. 1992. Fell. cular immunol. St. Thos. Hosp. Lond.

PARNACOTT, Sarah Margaret Ashgate Hospice, Ashgate Road, Old Brampton, Chesterfield S42 73E — MB ChB 1989 Sheff.; BMedSci (Hons.) Sheff. 1988; MRCP (UK) 1994. p/t Cons. (Palliat. Med.) Ashgate Hospice, Chesterfield. Prev: Specialist Regist. (Palliat. Med.) W.on Pk. Hosp. & St. Lukes Hospice Sheff.; Regist. (Clin. Oncol.) W.on Pk. Hosp. Sheff.; SHO Med. Rotat., Dundee.

PARNAIK, Vijaykumar G Castle Practice, 2 Hawthorne Road, Castle Bromwich, Birmingham B36 0HH Tel: 0121 747 2422 Fax: 0121 749 1196 — MB BS 1966 Poona; MB BS 1966 Poona.

PARNELL, Adrian Paul 17 Rosedale Court, West Denton, Newcastle upon Tyne NE5 2JH — MB ChB 1978 Manch.; BSc Manch. 1975, MB ChB 1978; MRCP (UK) 1982; FRCR 1985. Sen. Regist. (Radiol.) N. RHA.

***PARNELL, Caroline Emma** The Old Vicarage, Pennington, Ulverston LA12 7NY — MB BS 1996 Lond.

PARNELL, Cathryn Rooley Lane Medical Centre, Rooley Lane, Bradford BD4 7SS Tel: 01274 770777 — MB ChB 1975 Leeds; DRCOG 1978. GP Bradford.

PARNELL, Christopher John 83 St Margaret's Street, Rochester ME1 3BJ — MB BS 1975 Lond.; MRCS Eng. LRCP Lond. 1975; FFA RCS Eng. 1981; T(Anaesth.) 1991. (Univ. Coll. Hosp.) Clin. Dir. (Anaesth. & Intens. Care) Medway NHS Trust Gillingham. Prev: Cons. & Sen. Lect. Anaesth. & Resusc. RAMC.

PARNELL, Mr Edward John Princess Royal Hospital, Lewes Road, Haywards Heath RH16 4EX Tel: 01444 441881; Kemps House, East Chiltington, Lewes BN7 3QT Tel: 01273 891143 Fax: 01273 891143 — MB BS 1978 Lond.; FRCS Ed. 1984. Cons. Orthop. Surg. P.ss Roy. Hosp. Haywards Heath; cons. Orthopaedic surge, Qu. Vic Hosp, E.Grinstead. Socs: Fell. BOA; Mem. RSM; Mem. BORS.

PARNELL, Katherine Elizabeth The Surgery, 1 Streatfield Road, Harrow HA3 9BP Tel: 020 8907 0381 Fax: 020 8909 2134; Highcroft, Brookshill, Harrow HA3 6RW Tel: 020 8385 7397 — MB BS 1992 Lond.; MRCGP (Distinc.) 1996; DRCOG 1995; DCH RCP Lond. 1994. (Roy. Lond. Hosp.)

PARNELL, Nicholas David Jeffrey Willingdon, Worster Road, Cookham, Maidenhead SL6 9JG — MB BS 1989 Lond.

PARNELL, Stephen John Moss Grove Surgery, 15 Moss Grove, Kingswinford DY6 9HS Tel: 01384 277377 Fax: 01384 402329; Pound Cottage, 8 School Road, Himley, Dudley DY3 4LG Tel: 01902 326112 Email: drsparnell@aol.com — MB ChB 1978 Birm.; MRCGP 1982; DRCOG 1982; DCH RCP Lond. 1981. Hosp. Pract. (Diabetes) Corbett Hosp. Stourbridge.

PARNHAM, Alan 91 Kendon Drive, Manor Farm, Southmead, Bristol BS10 5BU — MB BS 1985 Lond.

PARNHAM-COPE, Delia Anne 47 Westfield Crescent, Patcham, Brighton BN1 8JA — MB BS 1990 Lond.; MB BS (Lond.) 1990; BSc Lond. 1987; FRCS Ed. 1997; DGM RCP Lond. 1993; DRCOG 1992. Socs: Med. Protec. Soc.

PAROS

PAROS, Norman Leonard, KStJ (retired) 55 Malting Green Road, Layer-de-la-Haye, Colchester CO2 0JJ Tel: 01206 734595 — MB BS Lond. 1946; FRCGP 1979, M 1960; Cert. Av. Med. 1982; DObst RCOG 1953. Clin. Asst. (Infec. Dis.) NE Essex HA. Prev: Provost. Essex Fac. RCGP.

PARR, Alison Marie St Ann's Hospice, Peel Lane, Little Hulton, Manchester M28 0FE Tel: 0161 702 8181 Fax: 0161 790 0186 — MB BS 1992 Newc.; 1999 MSc Oncology, University of Manchester; MRCP (UK) 1995. (Newc. Upon Tyne) Specialist Regist. (Palliat. Med.) St. Ann's Hospice Manch. & Christie Hosp. Manch. Socs: Jun. Mem. NW Pall. Care Phys. Grp.; Assoc. of Pall. Med.; Fell. Roy. Soc. of Med. Prev: Specialist Regist. (Med. Oncol.) Christie Hosp. Manch.; SHO (Palliat. Care) St. Ann's Hospice Manch.; SHO Rotat. (Med.) N. Manch. Gen. Hosp.

PARR, Mr David Caffrey Home Layne, Annington Road, Steyning BN44 3WA Tel: 01903 812505 — MB 1966 Camb.; MA Camb. 1968, MB 1966, BChir 1965; FRCS Eng. 1972; FRCS Ed. 1971. (Camb. & St. Bart.) Cons. Surg. Worthing HA. Prev: Sen. Regist. (Gen. Surg. & Urol.) Nottm. Hosp. & Derby Roy. Infirm.; Demonst. (Anat.) Univ. Camb.; Ho. Surg. & Jun. Surg. Regist. St. Bart. Hosp. Lond.

PARR, Denis John 3 Kingfisher Way, Horsham RH12 2LT Tel: 01403 261547 — MB BS 1948 Lond.; MD Lond. (Univ. Gold Medal) 1952; MRCS Eng. LRCP Lond. 1948; FRCPsych 1972; DPM Lond. 1951. (Univ. Coll. & Univ. Coll. Hosp.) Socs: Fell. Roy. Soc. Med. (Ex-Vice Pres. Psychiat. Sect.). Prev: Lord Chancellor's Med. Visitor; Cons. Psychiat. Lady Chichester, St. Francis & Roy. Sussex Co. Hosps.; Psychiat. 1st Asst. & Research Fell. St. Geo. Hosp. Lond.

PARR, Evan John (retired) 5 Park Road, Barry CF62 6NU Tel: 01446 736293 — MB BCh 1944 Wales; BSc Wales 194; CPH Wales 1947; DCH Eng. 1948. Prev: Clin. Asst. Asthma Clinic Llandough Hosp. Cardiff.

PARR, Gwendolen Doris (retired) Lordings, Station Road, Pulborough RH20 1AH Tel: 01798 872872 — MB BChir 1961 Camb.; FFPHM RCP (UK) 1993, M 1991; Dip. Pharm. Med. RCP (UK) 1983. Prev: Head Pharma Policy & Head Drug Monitoring Dept. Ciba Pharmaceut. Horsham.

PARR, Jeremy Ross 29 Hambalt Road, London SW4 9EA — MB ChB 1996 Leic.

PARR, John Henry South Tyneside District Hospital, Harton Lane, South Shields NE34 0PL Tel: 0191 454 8888 — MBChb 1974; MD Liverp. 1989, MB ChB 1974; MRCP 2001 Edin.; FRCP Lond. 1994; MRCP (UK) 1979. (Liverp.) Cons. Phys. S. Tyneside Healthcare Trust. Socs: Soc. Endocrinol.; Brit. Diabetic Assn.; Caledonian Endocrine Soc. Prev: Lect. (Diabetes & Endocrinol.) Centr. Middlx. Hosp. & St. Mary's Hosp. Med. Sch. Lond.; Regist. (Med.) N. Middlx. Hosp. Lond., Chester City Hosp. & St. Catherine's Hosp. Birkenhead.

PARR, Linda Susan Adcroft Surgery, Prospect Place, Trowbridge BA14 8QA Tel: 01225 755878 Fax: 01225 775445; Mistletoe Cottage, 24 High St, Steeple Ashton, Trowbridge BA14 6EL — MB BS 1975 Lond.; FRCOG 1995, M 1980, D 1977. (St. Mary's) Trustee Bath GP Educat. & Research Fund; Dep. Cons. (Obst.) Ante Natal Clinic Trowbridge Hosp. Wilts. Prev: SHO (Obst.) Qu. Charlottes Hosp. Lond.; Resid. Med. Off. Samarit. Hosp. Wom. Lond.; Ho. Surg. St. Mary's Hosp. Lond.

PARR, Margaret Ann Wigan & Bolton Health Authority, Bryan House, 61 Standishgate, Wigan WN1 1AH Tel: 01942 822843; 22 Parkway, Shevington Moor, Wigan WN6 0SJ Tel: 01257 424168 — MB ChB 1966 Sheff.; MSc (Community Med.) Manch. 1979; MFCM 1980; DObst RCOG 1970; DCH Eng. 1970. (Sheff.) Dir. Pub. Health Wigan & Bolton HA. Socs: BMA. Prev: Ho. Off. Chesterfield Roy. Hosp.; Med. Off. Clinic Welf. Centre Zerka Jordan; SHO (Paediat.) Pk. Hosp. Davyhulme.

PARR, Michael Joseph Anthony Stockland, Beechen Cliff Road, Bath BA2 4QR — MB BS 1983 Lond.; MRCP (UK) 1987; FRCA 1989; DA (UK) 1986.

PARR, Michelle Dawn 8 Inhsmere Court, Fairburn, Knottingley WF11 9JN — BChir 1994 Camb.

PARR, Mr Nigel John Wirral Trust Hospital, Upton, Wirral Tel: 0151 678 5111; Centaur House, 33 Tower Road N., Heswall, Wirral CH60 6RS Tel: 0151 342 6100 Fax: 01513426100 Email: nigelparr@lineone.net — MD 1989 Liverp.; MB ChB 1980; FRCS (Urol.) Ed. 1984. Cons. Urol. Wirral Trust Hosp. Socs: Brit. Assn.

Urol. Soc.; Am. Urol. Assn.; Brit. Soc. Endocrinol. Prev: Sen. Regist. W.. Gen. Hosp. Edin.; Lect. (Urol.) Scott. Lithotriptor Centre Edin.

PARR, Penelope Jane Ladybridge Surgery, 10-12 Broadgate, Ladybridge, Bolton BL3 4PZ Tel: 01204 653267 Fax: 01204 665350 — MB ChB 1988 Leeds; MRCGP 1992; DRCOG 1991. (Leeds) Socs: BMA; Bolton Med. Soc. Prev: Trainee GP Bolton; SHO Wigan HA VTS.; Clin. Asst. Bolton Hospice.

PARR, Robert Thornton (retired) The Barn House, Broughton, Stockbridge SO20 8AA Tel: 01794 301401 — MB BS 1947 Durh.; MRCS Eng. LRCP Lond. 1947; DObst RCOG 1952.

PARR, Stephen Matthew 35 Alder Lane, Balsall Common, Coventry CV7 7DZ — BM 1982 Soton.; FRCA 1989. Cons. Anaesthetist, Heartlands & Solihull Hosp.

PARR-BURMAN, Stephen John North Shore Surgery, 95 Holmfield Road, Blackpool FY2 9RS Tel: 01253 593971 Fax: 01253 596039; Norwood, 15 Lockwood Avenue, Poulton-le-Fylde FY6 7AB Tel: 01253 899328 — MB ChB 1982 Dundee; MRCGP 1989; DRCOG 1988; DCH RCP Lond. 1984. (Dundee) GP; Dir. of Ltd. Company specialising in Medico-legal Pract.; Medico-legal expert witness. Socs: Soc. Occup. Med.; Inst. Expert Witnesses; Brit. Acupunc. Soc.

PARRACK, Stella Margaret (retired) Willow Bank, Blendellsands Road W., Blundellsands, Liverpool L23 6TE Tel: 0151 924 8499 Email: stella_parrack@doctors.org.uk — MB ChB 1957 Manch.; DObst RCOG 1959. Locum GP. Prev: GP Liverp.

PARRATT, David 91 Strathern Road, Broughty Ferry, Dundee DD5 1JT Tel: 01382 477305 — MD 1977 Dundee; MB ChB St. And. 1969; FRCPath 1988, M 1975. Sen. Lect. & Hon. Cons. (Med. Microbiol.) Ninewells Hosp. Dundee.

PARRATT, Jennifer Ruth 47 Brookside Glen, Chesterfield S40 3PG — MB ChB 1990 Liverp.; MRCOG 2001; BSc Liverp. 1987; MD Liverp. 1997. Socs: BMA. Prev: SHO (O & G) Arrowe Pk. Hosp.; SHO (O & G) Liverp. O & G Trust.

PARRATT, Jon Taunton Road Medical Centre, 12-16 Taunton Road, Bridgwater TA6 3LS Tel: 01278 444400 Fax: 01278 423691 — MB ChB 1985 Birm.; MRCGP 1990. Prev: Trainee GP Taunton VTS.

PARRES, Hillar 11 Scotts Green Close, Dudley DY1 2DX — Med. Dipl. Tartu 1940. (Tartu)

PARRIS, John Bower 28 Craigleith View, Ravelston, Edinburgh EH4 3JZ — MB ChB 1984 Ed.

PARRIS, May Ruhiyyih 28 Craigleith View, Edinburgh EH4 3JZ — MB ChB 1981 Manch. SHO (Anaesth.) P.ss Margt. Rose Orthop. Hosp. Edin. Prev: SHO (Anaesth.) Roy. Infirm. Edin.; Ho. Off. (Surg.) Roy. Infirm. Edin.; Ho. Off. (Med.) Manch. Roy. Infirm.

***PARRIS, Michael Paul** 223 Croxted Road, London SE21 8NL — MB BS 1996 Lond.

PARRIS, Richard John 4 Mapeshill Place, London NW2 5LA — MB ChB 1991 Ed.; BSc (Hons) Ed. 1990; MRCP (UK) 1995. Lect. & Regist. (Med.) Univ. Edin. W.. Gen. Hosp.

PARRIS, Robert Crahamel Medical Practice, Crahamel House, Duhamel Place, Jersey JE2 4TP Tel: 01534 735419/735742 — MB BS 1995 Lond.; BSc 1994 (Hons.) Clin. Sciences, Lond.; DFFP 1998; MRCGP 2000; DCH 1999; Loclnt 1998; DRCOG 1998. GP, Crahamel Med. Pract., St Helier, Jersey.

PARRIS-PIPER, Timothy William 24 Church Street, Boughton Monchelsea, Maidstone ME17 4HW — MB BS 1992 Lond.; MRCA 1997. (St George's London) Specialist Regist. (Anaesth.) N. Thames E. Socs: Assn. Anaesthes.; BMA. Prev: SHO (Anaesth.) Addenbrooke's Hosp. Camb.; SHO (Anaesth.) PeterBoro. Dist. Gen.

PARRISH, David John Dawley Medical Practice, Dawley, Telford TF4 3AL Tel: 01952 505213 Fax: 01952 503089; 31 Church Road, Lilleshall, Newport TF10 9HE Tel: 01952 505213 — MB ChB 1982 Birm.

PARRISH, Frances Mary Ashdown Cottage, Tanyard Lane, Danehill, Haywards Heath RH17 7JW Email: fmp1768@aol.uk; Chailey Heritage Clinical Services, North Chailey, Lewes BN8 4JN Tel: 01825 722112 — MB ChB Ed. 1968; MRCP (UK) 1974; DObst RCOG 1970. (Ed.) Staff Grade Paediat. Chailey Heritage Clin. Servs.

PARRISH, Frank John Old Fleet, Grimsby DN37 9RT — MB ChB 1987 Leeds; FRCR 1996. Fell. (Radiol.) & Clin. Assoc. Lect. Univ. Qu.sland, Austral. Prev: Sen. Regist. (Radiol.) N.. Train. Scheme.

PARRISH, Jane Endellion, 36 Callington Road, Saltash PL12 6DY — MB BCh 1974 Wales.

PARRISH, John Anthony Kingsmead, 47 The Ridge, Purley CR8 3PF Tel: 020 8660 8317 — MB BS 1951 Lond.; MD Lond. 1964; FRCP Lond. 1973, M 1957; MRCS Eng. LRCP Lond. 1951. (St. Bart.) Emerit. Cons. Phys. Mayday Hosp. Croydon; Chief Med. Off. Woolwich Life Assur. Soc. Prev: Cons. Phys. Shirley Oaks Hosp. Croydon; Regional Adviser RCP Lond. (SW Thames Region); Sen. Regist. (Med.) St. Bart. Hosp.

PARRISH, John Richard The Surgery, 212 Richmond Road, Kingston upon Thames KT2 5HF Tel: 020 8546 0400 Fax: 020 8974 5771; 27 Turner Road, New Malden KT3 5NL — MCRS Eng. LRCP 1983 Lond.; MRCGP 1988; DCH RCP Lond. 1988; DRCOG 1986. Clin. Asst. (Ophth.) Kingston Hosp. Prev: Trainee GP Croydon; SHO (Geriat.) Qu. Hosp. Croydon; SHO (O & G) & (Paediat.) Mayday Hosp. Croydon.

PARRISH, Mark McKenzie, Surg. Lt.-Cdr. RN Flat 7, Bramley House, Crescent Road, Gosport PO12 2DJ — MB ChB 1983 Birm.; MRCGP 1991. DPMO HMS Neptune. Prev: SMO HMS Kutnabul Sydney, Austral.; Trainee GP/SHO (Med.) RN Hosp. Haslar.

PARRISH, Richard William Endellion, 36 Callington Road, Saltash PL12 6DY — MB BCh 1974 Wales; MRCP (UK) 1978; FRCR 1988.

***PARROTT, Charles Edward** Merrymead, Stanford-on-Soar, Loughborough LE12 5QL — MB ChB 1994 Birm.; ChB Birm. 1994.

PARROTT, David (retired) 29 West Tytherley, Salisbury SP5 1NF Tel: 01794 40621 — MB BS Lond. 1956; MRCS Eng. LRCP Lond. 1956; FFPM RCP (UK) 1989; DObst RCOG 1963; DPhil Med. (SA) 1982. Med. Dir. (Europe) Syntex Research Palo Alto, USA. Prev: Gen. Duties Med. Off. HM Overseas Civil Serv., Nigeria.

PARROTT, David Robert John (retired) North Edge, 18 Whidborne Avenue, Torquay TQ1 2PQ Tel: 01803 212309 — MB BS 1956 Lond.; DObst RCOG 1959. Prev: Ho. Phys. & Ho. Surg. Mt. Vernon Hosp. N.wood.

PARROTT, Janet Mary Bracton Centre, Bracton Lane, Dartford DA2 7AF — MB ChB 1976 Manch.; BSc (Hons.) St. And. 1973; FRCPsych. 1993, M 1981; Dip. Criminol Lond. 1983. Cons. Psychiat. Bracton Centre, Oxleas NHS Trust; Hon. Lect. Guy's Hosp. Lond. Prev: Sen. Regist. & Regist. Bethlem Roy. & Maudsley Hosps. Lond.

PARROTT, Jeffrey Peter Stanley Eastville Health Centre, East Park, Bristol BS5 6YA Tel: 0117 951 1261 Fax: 0117 935 5056 — MB ChB 1981 Bristol.

PARROTT, Mr Neil Raymond Department of Surgery, Manchester Royal Infirmary, Oxford Road, Manchester M13 9WL Tel: 0161 276 4535 Fax: 0161 273 3428 Email: nparrott@renal.cmht.nwest.nhs.uk; 43 Hazlewood Road, Wilmslow SK9 2QA Tel: 01625 539582 Email: n.parrott@virgin.net — MB BS 1978 Newc.; MD Newc. 1989; FRCS Eng. 1984; FRCS Ed. 1983. Sen. Lect. (Surg.) Univ. Manch.; Cons. Gen. & Transpl. Surg. Manch. Roy. Infirm. Socs: Tranpl. Soc.; Brit. Assn. Of Endocrine Surg.; Am. Assn. Of Tranpl. Surg.s. Prev: Asst. (Surg.) Univ. Newc.; Hon. Research Assoc. (Surg.) Univ. Newc.

PARROTT, Rachel Janet Eaglescliffe Health Centre, Sunningdale Drive, Eaglescliffe, Stockton-on-Tees TS16 9EA Tel: 01642 780113 Fax: 01642 791020; Swiss Cottage, 21 The Green, Romanby, Northallerton DL7 8NL Tel: 01609 776467 — MB ChB 1986 Bristol; MRCGP 1991; T(GP) 1991; DRCOG 1988. GP Asst. N. Region Retainer Scheme. Socs: Christian Med. Fell.sh.; Christians in Caring Professions. Prev: Trainee GP N.allerton VTS.

PARROTT, Richard Humphrey (retired) Blackdown Cottage, Lerryn, Lostwithiel PL22 0NW Tel: 01208 873828 — MB BS 1960 Lond.; FRCGP 1981; DObst RCOG 1963. Prev: GP St. Germans.

PARROTT, William Francis (retired) 27 Glendale Close, Woking GU21 3HN Tel: 01483 723746 — MB ChB 1954 Ed.; MFOM RCP Lond. 1978; Specialist Accredit (Occupat. Med.) RCP Lond 1980; DIH Dund 1978; DPH Ed. 1964; DObst RCOG 1959. Prev: Med. Off. Specialist Occupat. Health Woking.

PARRY, Alan Charles 206 Queen's Court, Ramsey IM8 1LG — MB BS 1945 Durh.; LRCP LRCS Ed. LRFPS Glas. 1945.

PARRY, Alison James House Doctors Surgery, Maryport Street, Usk NP15 1AB Tel: 01291 672633 Fax: 01291 672631 — BM 1993 Soton.; DRCOG 1996; MRCGP 1997; DFFP 1995. (Southampton) GP Partner The Surg. James Ho. Usk. Prev: SHO (Psychiat.) St. Jas. Hosp. Portsmouth; SHO (Paediat.) Jersey Gen. Hosp., CI; SHO (O & G) St. Mary's Hosp. Portsmouth.

PARRY, Alister Richard John 421 Mile End Road, London E3 4PB — MB BS 1989 Lond.

PARRY, Allyson Margaret Morgan 22 Skene Close, Headington, Oxford OX3 7XQ — MB ChB 1995 Birm.; ChB Birm. 1995.

PARRY, Alun Wyn Lindum House Surgery, 32 Turney St., Meadows, Nottingham NG2 2LG Tel: 0115 952 8200 Fax: 0115 952 8282 — MB BCh 1976 Wales. Force Med. Off. Notts. Constab.; Prison Med. Off. HMP Whatton; Clin. Tutor (Gen. Pract.) Qu. Med. Centre Nottm. Prev: Clin. Asst. (Anaesth.) Nottm.; Prison Med. Off. Lowdham Grange Notts.

PARRY, Alwyn Llewelyn Llanberis Surgery, High Street, Llanberis, Caernarfon LL55 4SU Tel: 01286 870634 Fax: 01286 871722 — MB BCh 1988 Wales. Socs: Welsh Med. Soc.; Arfon Med. Soc. Prev: Trainee GP Bodannt Bangor.

PARRY, Mr Andrew David The Cottage, Entwistle Hall Lane, Entwistle, Bolton BL7 0LR — MB ChB 1987 Bristol; FRCS Eng. 1992. Tutor (Surg.) Withington Hosp. Manch.

PARRY, Mr Andrew John Department of Paediatric Cardiac Surgery, Bristol Royal Hospital for Sick Children, Upper Mandlin Street, Bristol BS2 8BJ Tel: 0117 928 5083 — MB BCh 1985 Oxf.; MA Oxf. 1986, MB BCh 1985; FRCS Eng. 1990; FRCS (CTH) Eng 1995. (Oxford) Cons Paedia Cardiac Surg Bristol Roy. Hosp. for sick Childr.; Hon. sen lec Instit of child health Univ of Bristol. Socs: Soc. of Cardiothoracic Surg. of GB & Irel.; Europ. Assoc of cardiothoracic Surg; Soc. of Thoracic Surg. Prev: Asst. Prof (Paediactric Cardiac Surg) Univ of Calif, San Francisco USA; Fell (Paediatric cardiac surg Univ of Calif., San Francisco USA; Sen. Regist. (Cardiothoracic Surg.) Oxf. Heart Centre.

PARRY, Angela Karen Woodlands Surgery, Woodlands, Shadsworth Road, Blackburn BB1 2HR Tel: 01254 665664 Fax: 01254 695883; 69 Highercroft Road, Lower Darwen, Darwen BB3 0QT Tel: 01254 694633 — MB ChB 1987 Manch.; BSc (Med. Sci.) St. And. 1985; MRCGP 1992.

PARRY, Anthea Catherine Hillingdon Hospital, Pield Heath Road, Hillingdon, Uxbridge UB8 3NN Tel: 01895 238282; 23 Homefield Road, Chiswick, London W4 2LW Fax: 01895 279454 Email: anthea.parry@406.hillingh-tr.nthames.nhs.uk — MBBS 1981 Lond.; FRCP 2000; MRCP 1984 UK. Cons. Phys. (c/o Elderly) Hillingdon Hosp. Uxbridge. Prev: Sen. Regist. St. Geo. Hosp. Lond.

PARRY, Anthony James Bridge Street Surgery, 67 Bridge Street, Cambridge CB2 1UR Tel: 01223 355060 Fax: 01223 460812 — MB BS 1986 Lond.; MRCGP 1991; Dobst 1990.

***PARRY, Bethan Sian** 15 Fore Street, Ivybridge PL21 9AB — MB ChB 1995 Birm.; ChB Birm. 1995.

PARRY, Carmel Frances Maria Tang Hall Surgery, 190 Tang Hall Lane, York YO10 3RL Tel: 01904 411139 Fax: 01904 431224 — MB ChB 1983 Dundee.

PARRY, Celia Rosamund 8 Dovepoint Road, Meols, Wirral CH47 6AR — MB ChB 1971 Liverp.

PARRY, Christine Susan Spring Hall Group Practice, Spring Hall Medical Centre, Spring Hall Lane, Halifax HX1 4JG Tel: 01422 349501 Fax: 01422 323091; 112 Huddersfield Road, Brighouse HD6 3RH — MB ChB 1978 Aberd.; MRCGP 1982. Socs: BMA.

PARRY, Christopher Adrian, Surg. Lt. RN 7 Vernon Close, Gosport PO12 3NU Tel: 01705 581100 — MB BS 1993 Lond.; BSc (Hons.) Cell Path. Lond. 1987. Med. Off. RN.

PARRY, Christopher Martin Nuffield Department of Clinical Medicine, Level 5, John Radcliffe Hospital, Headington, Oxford OX3 9DU — MB BChir 1984 Camb.; MA Camb. 1984; MRCP (UK) 1987; MRCPath 1993. Clin. Microbiol. John Radcliffe Hosp. Oxf. Prev: Lect. (Microbiol.) Roy. Liverp. Hosp.

PARRY, Christopher William Kickham Mill Road Surgery, 61 Mill Road, Mile End, Colchester CO4 5LE Tel: 01206 845900 Fax: 01206 844090 — MB BS 1984 Lond.; LF Hon. 1999 University fo Glasgow; DRCOG 1990. (St. Bartholomew's Hospital)

PARRY, Dafydd Emyr Grovehurst, Middle Lane, Denbigh LL16 3UW — MRCS Eng. LRCP Lond. 1990.

PARRY, David (retired) Greyholme, West Road, Nottage Village, Porthcawl CF36 3SS Tel: 01656 784211 Fax: 01656 786828 Email: davidparry@greyholme.freeserve.co.uk — MB BCh Wales 1962; FRCGP 1980, M 1971; Dip. Pract. Dermat. Wales 1989; DPH Manch. 1968; DObst RCOG 1965; DCH Eng. 1964. Clin. Complaints Adviser MDU. Prev: Princip. GP.

PARRY, David Gareth West Kirby Health Centre, Grange Road, Wirral CH48 4HZ Tel: 0151 625 9171 Fax: 0151 625 9171; 8 Dovepoint Road, Meols, Wirral CH47 6AR — MB ChB 1971 Liverp.

PARRY

Hon. Med. Adviser (RNLI Hoylake Offshore Station & RNLI W. Kirby Inshore Station).

PARRY, David Gratton Cross Street Health Centre, Cross Street, Dudley DY1 1RN Tel: 01384 459044 Fax: 01384 232467; 4 Station Drive, Hagley, Stourbridge DY9 0NX Tel: 01562 886129 — MB BS 1982 Lond.; MRCGP 1986; DCH RCP Lond. 1986; DRCOG 1985. (Guy's) Prev: Trainee GP Doncaster VTS; Ho. Phys. Roy. Cornw. Hosp.; Ho. Surg. Worcester Roy. Infirm.

PARRY, David Hugh Bryniau, Llangoed, Beaumaris LL58 8ND Tel: 0124 878269 — MB BS 1969 Lond.; MRCPath 1977. (St. Geo.) Cons. Haemat. Gwynedd Hosp. Bangor. Prev: Lect. (Haemat.) Welsh Nat. Sch. Med. Cardiff.

PARRY, David Lewis Clarence House, Rhyl LL18 6BY Tel: 01745 350980 Fax: 01745 353293; Tan yr Onnen, Waen, St Asaph LL17 0DU Tel: 01745 583821 — MB ChB 1958 Liverp. (Liverp.) Clin. Asst. (Geriat.) Roy. Alexandra Hosp. Rhyl. Socs: Assoc. Mem. RCGP & Mem. BMA. Prev: Ho. Phys. & Ho. Surg. Alexandra Hosp. Rhyl; Ho. Surg. H.M. Stanley Hosp. St. Asaph.

PARRY, David Lloyd 26 High Street, Erdington, Birmingham B23 6RN Tel: 0121 373 0086; 10 Ashfern Drive, Sutton Coldfield B76 1JD Tel: 0121 313 1315 — MB ChB 1984 Birm. Prev: Ho. Off. (Med.) Sandwell Dist. Gen. Hosp.; Ho. Off. (Surg.) Good Hope Hosp.; Trainee GP Sandwell VTS.

PARRY, Deborah Elizabeth Albert Road Surgery, Albert Road, Penarth CF64 1BX Tel: 029 2070 5884 Fax: 029 2071 1735 — MB BS 1985 Lond.; MFFP 1993; DRCOG 1989; Cert. Family Plann. JCC 1987. Clin. Asst. (Cytol.).

PARRY, Deborah Margaret Elizabeth House Surgery, 515 Limpsfield Road, Warlingham CR6 9LF Tel: 01883 625262; 110 Norfolk Avenue, South Croydon CR2 8BS — MB BS 1990 Lond.; BSc Lond. 1987; MRCGP 1994; DFFP 1994; DGM RCP Lond. 1993; DRCOG 1993. (Middlesex Hospital) Asst. GP Warlingham, Surrey; Community Med. Off. Family Plann.

PARRY, Delyth Meredydd Oak Vale Medical Centre, 158-160 Edge Lane Drive, Liverpool L13 4AQ Tel: 0151 259 1551 Fax: 0151 252 1121; 18 Brentwood Ave, Aigburth, Liverpool L17 4LD Tel: 0151 727 2635 — MB BCh 1989 Wales; BSc 1986; MRCGP 1996. GP Princip. Oakdale Med. Centre, L'pool; Clin. Asst. in Drug Dependency.

PARRY, Miss Diane Susan 158 Ffordd-y-Parc, Bridgend CF31 1RA — MB BCh 1988 Wales.

***PARRY, Dominic James** Marshall Cottage, Great Peatling Lodge, Foston La, Peatling Magna, Leicester LE8 5UH — MB ChB 1997 Leic.

PARRY, Douglas Neville (retired) Cedar Cottage, Newlands Manor, Everton, Lymington SO41 Tel: 0159 069 3157 — MRCS Eng. LRCP Lond. 1935.

PARRY, Duncan John 5 Ashfield Park, Leeds LS6 2QT — MB ChB 1993 Sheff.

PARRY, Dylan Clwyd Meddygfa Cadwgan, 11 Bodelwyddan Avenue, Old Colwyn, Conwy LL29 9NP Tel: 01492 515410 — MB BCh 1994 Wales; DRCOG; MRCGP; DFFP; BSc (Hons.) Wales 1991. GP Princip.

PARRY, Mr Edgar Williams (retired) Brynteg Cottage, Brynteg Lane, Llandegfan, Menai Bridge LL59 5NU Tel: 01248 714612 — MB ChB 1943 Liverp.; ChM Liverp. 1953; FRCS Ed. 1949; FRCS Eng. 1955. Prev: Cons. Surg. BRd.green Hosp. Liverp.

PARRY, Ednyfed Wyn (retired) Department of Human Anatomy & Cell Biology, The University, PO Box 147, Liverpool L69 3BX — MB ChB 1962 Liverp.; MB ChB (Hons.) Liverp. 1962; MD Liverp. 1967; FRCPath 1991. Prev: Sen. Lect. (Histol.) Univ. Liverp.

PARRY, Edward Elwyn Corwen House Surgery, Corwen House, Market Place, Penygroes, Caernarfon LL54 6NN Tel: 01286 880336 Fax: 01286 881500 — MB ChB 1973 Liverp.; MRCGP 1978; DCH Eng. 1977; DObst RCOG 1975. (Liverp.)

PARRY, Eileen Jennifer Tameside General Hospital, Fountain Street, Doddington Park OL6 9RW Tel: 0161 331 6618 — MB ChB 1988 Liverp.; BSc (Hons.) Liverp. 1985, MB ChB 1988; MRCP (UK) 1991. Cons. (Dermatol.s) Tameside Gen.Hosp..Lancs.; Custultant Dermatol.s, 1.Hope Hosp. (Dermat. Centre) Salford; 2. Christie Hosp.,Manch.

PARRY, Eldryd Hugh Owen, OBE THET, 1 Park Square W., London NW1 4LJ Tel: 020 7486 1725 Fax: 020 7486 1724 — MB BChir 1956 Camb.; MD Camb. 1965; FRCP Lond. 1970, M 1958. Vis. Prof. Lond. Sch. Hyg. & Trop. Med. Socs: Hon. Fell. Roy. Soc. Trop. Med. Hyg.; Assn. Phys. Prev: Dean & Prof. of Med. Sch. Med. Sc. Univ. Sc. Technol. Kumasi, Ghana; Foundat. Dean & Prof. of Med. Fac. Health Sc. Univ. Ilorin, Nigeria; Assoc. Prof. of Med. Univ. of Addis Ababa Ethiopia.

PARRY, Elizabeth Ann 5 Abingdon Road, Bramhall, Stockport SK7 3EU — MB ChB Liverp. 1987. CMO Family Plann. Specialty Family Plann. Bose Palatine Centre Manch. Socs: BMA; Fac. Family Plann. and Reproductive Health Care (Diplomat). Prev: GP Retainee Devonshire Lodge Health Centre Abbotsbury Gdns. Middlx.

PARRY, Elizabeth Frances Hilton Payton Cottage, 11 Payton St., Stratford-upon-Avon CV37 6UA — MB BS 1961 Lond.; LMSSA Lond. 1961.

PARRY, Emma Clare Email: daveandemma@clear.net.nz; Treetops, 9 Greenhaugh Way, Dunblane FK15 9PT Tel: 01786 880389 — MB BS 1991 Lond.; FRANZ COG 2001; MRANZ COG 1998; 1997 MRCOG. (Guys) Sen. Lect. O & G Dept., Nat. Wom.'s Hosp., Auckland, NZ.

PARRY, Emyr Hafod, Ruthin Roadd, Denbigh LL16 3EU — MB ChB 1962 Manch.; MRCS Eng. LRCP Lond. 1962; MRCOG 1967.

PARRY, Enid Brynteg Cottage, Brynteg Lane, Llandegfan, Menai Bridge LL59 5NU Tel: 01248 714612 — MB ChB 1948 Liverp.; CPH 1949. (Liverp.) Clin. Med. Off. Gwynedd HA. Socs: BMA. Prev: Clin. Med. Off. Sefton HA; Sch. Med. Off. Pub. Health Dept. Bristol; Med. Off. Rochester State Hosp. Minn., USA.

PARRY, Gareth Department of Cardiac Transplantation, Freeman Hospital, Newcastle upon Tyne NE7 7DN Tel: 0191 284 3111 Fax: 0191 223 1152; 20 Foxhills Covert, Fellside Park, Whickham, Newcastle upon Tyne NE16 5TN Tel: 0191 488 0487 — MB BCh 1981 Wales; MRCP (UK) 1985; FRCP Ed 1998. (Wales) Assoc. Specialist Cardiac Transpl. Freeman Hosp. Newc. u. Tyne. Socs: Brit. Cardiac Soc. Prev: Regist. (Cardiol.) Freeman Hosp. Newc.; Regional Research Regist. Profess. Cardiol. Unit Freeman Hosp. Newc.

PARRY, Gareth Michael Horsman's Place Surgery, Instone Road, Dartford DA1 2JP Tel: 01322 01322 228363; Copthorne, Ash Road Hartley, Longfield DA3 8EY Tel: 01474 708906 Email: gareth@parryfy.demon.co.uk — MB BS 1981 Lond.; MSc 2000; BSc Lond. 1978; MRCGP 1985; DRCOG 1985. (Guy's) Prev: GP Tutor Dartford & Gravesham Dist.

PARRY, Mr Gareth Wyn Thoracic Surgical Unit, Norfolk & Norwich Univesity Hospital, Colney Lane, Norwich NR4 7UZ Tel: 01603 286396 Fax: 01603 287882 Email: wyn.perry@norfolk-norwich.itenhs.com — MB BCh 1984 Wales; FRCS (Clth) 1996; BSc Wales 1981, MB BCh 1984; FRCS Eng. 1989. Cons. (Thoracic Sug.) Norf. & Norwich Univ. Hosp. Norwich; Mem. of the Ct. of Examin.s Roy. Coll. Of Surg. Eng. Socs: Pres. Norwich Div. BMA. Prev: Sen. Regist. (Cardiothoracic Surg.) Glenfield Hosp. Leicester; Sen. Regist. (Cardiothoracic Surg.) N. Gen. Hosp. Sheff.; Cons. (Cardiothoracic Surg.)Freeman Hosp. Newc. upon Tyne.

PARRY, George Robert Oak Vale Medical Centre, 158-160 Edge Lane Drive, Liverpool L13 4AQ Tel: 0151 259 1551 Fax: 0151 252 1121; 6 Sandhurst, Blundellsands Road E., Liverpool L23 8UJ — MB ChB 1978 Liverp.; MRCGP 1982; DRCOG 1981; DCH RCPSI 1981. Phys. (Occupat. Health) NW Water & Evans Meds.

PARRY, Harry Vaughan (retired) 9 Avondale Road, St Leonards-on-Sea TN38 0SA — BM BCh 1957 Oxf.; BA 1953, BSc 1956, BM BCh 1957; DObst RCOG 1960. Prev: Ho. Phys. Univ. Coll. Hosp.

PARRY, Heather Mary Anaesthetic Department, Watford General Hospital, Vicarage Road, Watford WD18 0HB Tel: 01923 217604; 33 Orchard Close, Cassiobury, Watford WD17 3DU Tel: 01923 228942 — MB ChB 1974 Bristol; FFA RCS Eng. 1979. Cons. Anaesth. Watford Gen. Hosp. Prev: Sen. Regist. (Anaesth.) St. Geo. Hosp. Lond. & Hosp. Sick Childr. Gt.; Ormond St.; SHO (Anaesth.) Chester Roy. Infirm.

***PARRY, Helen Kathryn** 2 Yew Tree Walk, Harrogate HG2 9JT Tel: 01423 569913 — MB BS 1998 Newc.; MB BS Newc 1998.

PARRY, Helen Stephanie Garstang Road Surgery, 229 Garstang Road, Ribbleton, Preston PR2 8XE Tel: 01772 792512 — MB ChB 1977 Birm.; MRCGP 1982.

PARRY, Hilary Rosamund 6 Upper Belmont Road, Bishopston, Bristol BS7 9DQ Tel: 0117 942 2873 — MB BS 1990 Lond.; BA (Hons.) Oxf. 1984; MRCGP 1994; DRCOG 1993. (Med. Coll. St. Bart. Hosp. Lond.)

PARRY, Hugh Evan (retired) 21 Rose Place, Aughton, Ormskirk L39 4UJ Tel: 01695 421154 — MB BS Lond. 1945; FRCP Lond. 1974, M 1951; MRCS Eng. LRCP Lond. 1944; DCH Eng. 1945. Prev: Cons. Phys. (Infec. Dis.) Fazakerley Hosp. Liverp.

PARRY, Hugh Francis Danewell House, The Borough, Downton, Salisbury SP5 3LT — MB BS 1972 Lond.; MRCS Eng. LRCP Lond. 1972; MRCPath 1981. (Guy's) Cons. Haemat. Gen. Infirm. Salisbury; Clin. Tutor, Salisbury HA. Socs: Brit. Soc. Haemat.; Assn. Clin. Path. Prev: Sen. Regist. (Haemat.) St. Thos. Hosp. Lond.; Jules Thorn Research Fell. & Hon. Sen. Regist. Univ. Coll. Hosp.; Lond.; Regist. (Clin. Path.) Univ. Coll. Hosp. Lond.

PARRY, Huw Cambria Surgery, Ucheldre Avenue, Anglesey, Holyhead LL65 1RA Tel: 01407 762735 Email: cambriasurgery@compuserve.com; Tyn Pwll, Bodedern, Holyhead LL65 3PB — MB ChB 1982 Leeds; BSc (Hons.) Pharmacol. Leeds 1979.

***PARRY, Huw David** Greyholme, West Rd, Nottage Village, Porthcawl CF36 3SS — MB BCh 1996 Wales.

PARRY, James Charles 1 Rectory Close, Sutton-cum-Duckmanton, Chesterfield S44 5JT — MB ChB 1978 Sheff.

PARRY, James Dennis (retired) (Surgery), Margaret St., Ammanford SA18 2TJ — MB ChB 1952 Sheff.; DObst RCOG 1956. Prev: Treas. Med. Off. & Med. Examr. Dept. Educat. & Civil Serv. Comms. BritTelecom.

PARRY, Jayne Morgan 17 Sandiway, Shrewsbury SY3 9BN — MB ChB 1993 Birm.; ChB Birm. 1993.

PARRY, Jean Corfield (retired) Bridge House, Rowton Bridge Road, Christleton, Chester CH3 7BD Tel: 01244 332066 — MB ChB 1943 Liverp. Prev: Med. Off. Chesh. HA.

PARRY, Jennifer Imogen Bennets End Surgery, Gatecroft, Hemel Hempstead HP3 9LY — MB BS 1985 Lond.; MRCP (UK) 1988; DRCOG 1991; DCH RCP Lond. 1990. Prev: Trainee GP/SHO St. Albans City Hosp.

PARRY, Joanna Margaret Flat 8, Hillymead, 1A Thornton Hill, Wimbledon, London SW19 4JJ — MB BS 1990 Lond.

PARRY, Rev. John Edward (retired) 5 Hawthorn Close, Haughton, Stafford ST18 9HG Tel: 01785 780577 Email: john@parry-haughton.freeserve.co.uk — MB ChB 1947 Manch.; DTM & H Liverp. 1953. Prev: Med. Supt. Livingstone Hosp., Zambia.

PARRY, John Gareth Greyholme, West Road, Nottage, Porthcawl CF36 3SS — BM 1992 Soton.

PARRY, John Henry (retired) Slouths farm house, Slapton, Kingsbridge TQ7 2PR Tel: 01548 581110 Fax: 01548 581110 — MB BS Lond. 1949.

PARRY, John Hilary Holycroft Surgery, The Health Centre, Oakworth Road, Keighley BD21 1SA Tel: 01535 602010 Fax: 01535 691313; Spring House, 157 Keighley Road, Cowling, Keighley BD22 0AH Tel: 01535 635510 — MB BChir 1981 Camb.; MA Camb. 1982; MRCGP 1985; DRCOG 1983. Prev: Med. Off. Sue Ryder Home Oxenhope; Trainee GP Camb. VTS; SHO (Radiother.) Addenbrooke's Hosp. Camb.

PARRY, John Morton (retired) Waterside Cottage, Tyrley Wharf, Market Drayton TF9 2AH Tel: 01630 654228 — MB BS Lond. 1962; MRCS Eng. LRCP Lond. 1962; DObst RCOG 1965. Prev: Ho. Surg. Mile End Hosp.

PARRY, Mr John Niall Meredydd, OBE, KStJ (retired) 139 Tyglas Road, Llanishen, Cardiff CF14 5EF Tel: 01222 752637 — MB BS 1942 Lond.; FRCS Eng. 1947; MRCS Eng. LRCP Lond. 1938; FRCGP 1967. Prev: Mem. Roy. Commiss. on Med. Educat.

PARRY, Mr John Rhys Williams Church Farm, Tuddenham St Martin, St Martin, Ipswich IP6 9BT Tel: 01473 785614 — MB BS 1976 Lond.; FRCS Ed. 1982; MRCS Eng. LRCP Lond. 1976. (St. Bart.) Cons. (Urol.) Ipswich Hosp. NHS Trust. Prev: Mem. Brit. Ann. Urol. Surgs.; Mem. BMA; Mem. RSM.

PARRY, John Stephen Westcotes Health Centre, Fosse Road South, Leicester LE3 0LP Tel: 0116 254 8568 — MB BCh 1968 Wales.

PARRY, Jonathan Edward Parry, The Surgery, Spring Wells, Billingborough, Sleaford NG34 0QQ Tel: 01529 240234 Fax: 01529 240520; Westhill House, Hangman's Lane, Stainfield, Bourne PE10 0RS Tel: 01778 570888 Fax: 01778 570478 — MB BS 1982 Lond.; MRCGP 1986; DGM RCP Lond. 1986. (Lond. Hosp.) Dep. Police Surg. Sleaford; St John Ambul., Bourne, Med. Off.; Lincs. Integrated Volun. Emerg. Serv.; Gen. Practitioner Trainer.

PARRY, Joseph Jones Evergreen, Gannock Park W., Deganwy, Conwy LL31 9HQ Tel: 01492 583338 — MB BS 1953 Lond.; MRCS Eng. LRCP Lond. 1953. (St. Geo.) Prev: Squadron Ldr. RAF Med. Br.; Ho. Surg. & Ho. Phys. Mayday Hosp. Croydon.

PARRY, Keith Teasdale Forest Gate Surgery, Hazel Farm Road, Totton, Southampton SO40 8WU Tel: 023 8066 3839 Fax: 023 8066 7090 — MB ChB 1971 Manchester; MB ChB Manch. 1971. (Manchester) GP Soton.

PARRY, Kenneth Michael, OBE (retired) 9 Moray Place, Edinburgh EH3 6DS Tel: 0131 226 3054 — MB ChB 1956 Bristol; FRCP Ed. 1973, M 1970; FRCGP 1982, M 1976; FFPHM 1974; DCH Eng. 1961. Prev: Sec. Scott. Counc. Postgrad. Med. Educat. & UK Conf. Postgrad. Med. Deans.

PARRY, Llewellen Graham Mill Road Surgery, Mill Road, Market Rasen LN8 3BP Tel: 01673 843556 Fax: 01673 844388; The Water Mill, Middle Rasen, Market Rasen LN8 3TY — MRCS Eng. LRCP Lond. 1965. (Guy's) Prev: SHO (Surg.) St. Mary's Hosp. E.bourne; Regist. (O & G) Pembury Hosp. Tunbridge Wells.

PARRY, Mair Afallom, FFordd Caergybi, Porthaethwy, Ynys Mon, Menai Bridge LL59 5RH — MB BCh 1991 Wales.

PARRY, Margaret Olwen Lloyd Student Health Service, 25 Belgrave Road, Bristol BS8 2AA Tel: 0117 973 7716 Fax: 0117 970 6804; 5 Pembroke Vale, Clifton, Bristol BS8 3DN — MB BS 1962 Lond.; MRCS Eng. LRCP Lond. 1962. (St. Mary's) JP; Med. Off. Bristol Univ. Stud. Health Serv. Prev: Ho. Surg. Surgic. Unit & Med. Outpat. Asst. St. Mary's Hosp. Lond.; Ho. Phys. King Edwd. Memor. Hosp. Ealing.

PARRY, Marianne Isabelle 14 Cae Gwyn, Caernarfon LL55 1LL; 35 Primrose Hill, Chalcot Square, London NW1 8YP Email: mip70@hotmail.com — MB ChB 1994 Manch.; DTM & H 1997. Prev: Ho. Off. (Surg.) Macclesfield Dist. Gen. Hosp.; Ho. Off. (Med.) N. Manch. Dist. Gen. Hosp.

PARRY, Mark Stephen Community Health Sheffield NHS Trust, Fulwood House, Old Fulwood Road, Sheffield S10 3TH; Email: mparry@doctors.org.uk — MB ChB 1986 Sheff.; MRCPsych 2000. Specialist Regist. in Psychiat. Community Health Sheff. NHS Trust, Sheff. Socs: Brit. Med. Assn. Prev: Trainee GP Bassetlaw VTS; SHO Psychiat., Sheff. & N.Trent; GPTS Worksop.

PARRY, Martin Edwin, OBE (retired) Tyn-Y-Caeau, Nannerch, Mold CH7 5RQ Tel: 01352 741252 — MB ChB Bristol 1951; DObst RCOG 1958; DCH Eng. 1956. Prev: GP Clwyd.

PARRY, Martin Gratton The Royal Sussx County Hospital, Eastern Road, Brighton BN2 5BE Tel: 01273 696955 — MB BS 1989 Lond.; BSc (Hons.) Lond. 1987, MB BS 1989; FRCA 1995. (Guy's Hospital Medical School) Cons. (Anaesth.). Socs: Roy. Soc. Med.; Difficult Airway Soc.; Assn. Paed. Anaesth. Prev: Clin. Fell. The Hosp. For Sick Childr., Toronto, Canada; Specialist Regist. (Anaesth.) Middlx. Hosp. & The Hosp. for Sick Childr. Gt. Ormond St. Lond.

PARRY, Mary Wyn (retired) 97 Long Road, Cambridge CB2 2HE Tel: 01223 501487 — MRCS Eng. LRCP Lond. 1958; DObst RCOG 1960. Med. Off. Hinchinbrooke Trust Huntingdon Cambs. Prev: Med. Off. Hinchinbrooke Trust Huntingdon Cambs.

PARRY, Michael Anthony McHarg The Glenlyn Medical Centre, 115 Molesey Park Road, East Molesey KT8 0JX — MRCS Eng. LRCP Lond. 1966.

PARRY, Michael Richard Hexham General Hospital, Hexham NE46 1QJ; Bank House, Shield Court, Hexham NE46 1RA — MB ChB 1978 Ed.; BSc (Med. Sci.) Ed. 1975, MB ChB 1978; MRCPsych 1984. Cons. Psychiat. Hexham Gen. Hosp. Hexham N.d.; Hon. Clin. Lect. (Psychiat.) Univ. Newc. Prev: Sen. Regist. (Psychiat.) Roy. Vic. Infirm. Newc.; Sen. Regist. (Psychiat.) Newc. Gen. Hosp.; Regist. (Psychiat.) Roy. Edin. Hosp.

PARRY, Nicholas Sebastian 40 Elm Grove, Didsbury, Manchester M20 6PN — MB ChB 1990 Manch.; FRCA 1997.

PARRY, Patricia Anne Portway Surgery, 1 The Portway, Porthcawl CF36 3XB Tel: 01656 304204 Fax: 01656 772605; Greyholme, West Road, Nottage, Porthcawl CF36 3SS Tel: 01656 784211 Fax: 01656 786828 Email: patparry@greyholme.co.uk — MB BCh 1965 Wales. (Cardiff)

PARRY, Peter Gratton (retired) Llannerch, Morfa Bychan Road, Porthmadog LL49 9UR Tel: 01766 512921 — MB BS 1959 Lond.; MRCS Eng. LRCP Lond. 1958. Prev: GP Porthmadog & Dist.

***PARRY, Richard John** 31 Mornington Terrace, London NW1 7RS — MB BS 1998 Lond.; MB BS Lond 1998.

PARRY

PARRY, Richard Tonson Ribbleton Medical Centre, 243, Ribbleton Avenue,, Preston PR2 6RD Tel: 01772 792512; 229 Garstang Road,, Fulwood, Preston PR2 8XE — MB ChB 1977 Manch.; MRCGP 1981; DRCOG 1979. GP Preston; Med. Director, Heartbeat (Cardiac Rehab. Charity).

PARRY, Robert Langhorne 74 Trafalgar Road, Birkdale, Southport PR8 2NJ Tel: 01704 562712 — MB ChB 1979 Liverp.; MRCP (UK) 1986; FRCR 1990. Cons. Vasc. Radiol. S.port Dist. Gen. Hosp. Prev: Merck Lect. (Cardiovasc. Radiol.) Univ. Bristol; Sen. Regist. (Radiol.) Univ. Hosp. Wales Cardiff.

PARRY, Robin Llanberis Surgery, High Street, Llanberis, Caernarfon LL55 4SU Tel: 01286 870634 Fax: 01286 871722; Rhiwerfa, Frongoch, Llanberis, Caernarfon LL55 4LE Tel: 012486 872211 — MB ChB 1984 Manch.; MRCGP 1988; DRCOG 1987. Socs: BMA; Cadeirydd Cymdeithas Feddygol Arfon. Prev: Trainee GP Gwynedd VTS.

PARRY, Robin Geoffrey 13 Lingwood Road, Great Sankey, Warrington WA5 3EN — MB ChB 1989 Leeds.

PARRY, Rosemary Margaret Whiteparish Surgery, Common Road, Whiteparish, Salisbury SP5 2SU Tel: 01794 884269 Fax: 01794 884109; Danewell House, 130 The Borough, Downton, Salisbury SP5 3LT Tel: 01725 20425 — MB BS 1972 Lond.; MRCS Eng. LRCP Lond. 1972; DCH Eng. 1974; DObst RCOG 1974. (Guy's) Hon. Clin. Teach. Univ. Soton.; GP Trainer. Prev: SHO (Paediat.) Qu. Eliz. Hosp. Childr. Lond.; SHO (O & G) FarnBoro. Hosp. Kent; Ho. Phys. Hither Green Hosp.

PARRY, Ruth North Wales Health Authority, University of Wales, IMSCAR, Wheldon Building, Deiniol Rd, Bangor LL57 2UW Tel: 01248 388069 Email: ruth.parry@nwales-ha.wales.nhs.uk; Tel: 01248 490269 — MB BCh 1971 Wales; MFPHM 1997. Cons. (Pub. Health Med.) N. Wales Health Auth. Prev: SCMO Pub. Health Med. N. Wales HA; Clin. Med. Off. Anglesey; Health Promotion Facilitator Gwynedd HA.

PARRY, Sally Davina 55 Buckthorn Avenue, Stevenage SG1 1TW; 53 Tudor Close, Brixton Hill, London SW2 2AB Tel: 0589 598512 Email: sallyparry@compuserve.com — MB BS 1993 Lond.; BPharm (Hons.) Lond. 1987; MRCP (UK) 1996. (Univ. Coll. & Middlx. Sch. Med.) Specialist Regist. (Gen. Med. & Gastro.) King's Coll. Hosp. & S. Thames Rotat. Prev: SHO (Gen. Med.) Qu. Med. Centre Nottm.; Regist. Rotat. (Gen. Med. & Gastroenterol.) King's Coll., Roy. Sussex Co., Brighton, Kent & Sussex, Tunbridge Wells.

PARRY, Steve Wayne c/o Ward 13 Office, Freeman Hospital, Newcastle upon Tyne; 45 Lonsdale Road, Stamford PE9 2RW — MB BS 1991 Newc.

PARRY, Thomas Mervyn 18B Cabul Road, London SW11 2PN Tel: 020 7223 7057 — MB BS 1984 Lond.; FCAnaesth. 1990.

PARRY, Tom Evelyn (retired) Awelon, Pen-y-Turnpike, Dinas Powys CF64 4HG Tel: 02920 512338 Fax: 029 2076 2208 — MB ChB 1941 Manch.; FRCP Lond. 1974, M 1950; MRCS Eng. LRCP Lond. 1941; FRCPath 1963. Hon. Cons. Haemat. S. Glam. HA (T); Recognised Clin. Teach. (Haemat.) Univ. Wales Coll. Med. Cardiff; Hon. Vice-Pres. Leukaemia Research Appeal for Wales. Prev: Cons. Haemat. S. Glam. HA (T).

PARRY, Tomos Health Services Centre, Wynne Road, Blaenau Ffestiniog LL41 3DW Tel: 01766 830205 Fax: 01766 831121; Afallon, Holyhead Road, Menai Bridge LL59 5RH Tel: 712633 — MB BCh 1983 Wales. Trainee GP/SHO Gwynedd HA VTS. Socs: BMA; Med. Defence Union. Prev: Ho. Phys. & Ho. Surg. Llandudno Gen. Hosp.

PARRY, Wilfrid Hocking (retired) 135 Dore Road, Dore, Sheffield S17 3NF Tel: 0114 236 6925 — MB ChB 1948 Liverp.; MD Liverp. 1960, MB ChB (Distinc. in Pub. Health) 1948, DPH 1952, DTM & H 1964; FFPHM 1972. Cons. Smallpox Trent RHA & DHSS; Med. Ref. City of Sheff. Crematoria; Examr. Environm. Health Offs. Educat. Bd. Prev: Area Med. Off. Sheff. AHA (T) & Hon. Clin. Lect. (Community Med.) Univ. Sheff.

PARRY, William Gwyn Wakefield Llys Meddyg, Pen-y-Groes, Caernarfon LL54 6HD Tel: 01286 207 — MB ChB 1952 Liverp. (Liverp.)

PARRY, William Ronald 15 The Drive, Park Lane, Retford DN22 6SD Tel: 01777 702340 — MB ChB 1949 Liverp.; MD Liverp. 1957; Dip. Bact. Lond 1952. (Liverp. & Lond.) Emerit. Cons. Histopath. Vict. Hosp. Worksop. Prev: Cons. Gen. Path. Worksop & Retford Hosp. Gp.; Asst. Pathol. St. Helier Hosp.; Princip. Scientif. Off. Min. of Supply M.R.D. Porton.

PARRY DAVIES, Miss Michaela Frances Department of Plastic Surgery, Aberdeen Royal Infirmary, Foresterhill, Aberdeen AB25 2ZN — MB BS 1982 Lond.; FRCS Lond. 1986; FRCS (Plast.) 1996. (Univ. Coll. Lond.) Cons. (Plastic Surg.).

***PARRY-JONES, Adrian** Tegfan, Llandegfan, Menai Bridge LL59 5PY — MB ChB 1998 Manch.; MB ChB Manch 1998.

PARRY-JONES, Alexander Jack Duncan 57 Scholars Road, London SW12 0PF — MB BS 1992 Lond.; MRCP (Lond.) 1995; FRCA (Lond.) 1998. (UCMSM) Specialist Regist., Anaesth., N. Thames.

PARRY-JONES, Charles Edward Ty Bodafon, Mynydd Bodafon, Llanerchymedd LL71 8BN — MB ChB 1993 Ed.

PARRY-JONES, Gareth Bron Seiont Surgery, Bron Seiont, Segontium Terrace, Caernarfon LL55 2PH Tel: 01286 672236 Fax: 01286 676404; Bryn Eglwys, Caeatho, Caernarfon LL55 2TA Tel: 01286 671195 — MB ChB 1975 Liverp.; MSc (Med. Educat.) Wales 1996; FRCGP 1991, M 1979; DFFP 1993; DRCOG 1978. Sen. Lect. & Assoc. Adviser (Gen. Pract.) Gwynedd; Clin. Asst. MacMillan Terminal Care Unit; Examr. RCGP. Socs: (Chairm.) Welsh Med. Soc.; FRCGP. Prev: Trainee GP Gwynedd VTS; Ho. Surg. Univ. Hosp. Wales; Ho. Phys. (Paediat.) Llandough Hosp. Cardiff.

PARRY-JONES, John (retired) Bodynys Penrodyn, Valley, Holyhead LL65 3BE Tel: 01407 741118 — MRCS Eng. LRCP Lond. 1954; BSc Wales 1949.

PARRY-JONES, Mary (retired) Bodynys, Penrodyn, Valley, Holyhead LL65 3BE Tel: 01407 741118 — MRCS Eng. LRCP Lond. 1945; DPH Eng. 1949.

PARRY-JONES, Nicholas Owen Douglas Grove Surgery, Douglas Grove, Witham CM8 1TE Tel: 01376 512827 Fax: 01376 502463 — MB BChir 1970 Camb.; MRCP (UK) 1975; DRCOG 1979. (Camb. & St. Thos.) Prev: Sen. Lect. (Gen. Pract.) UMDS & Hon. Cons. Guy's & St. Thos. Hosps. Lond.

PARRY-JONES, Nilima Dept. Of Academic Haematology, Royal Marsden Hospital, 203 Fulham Road, London SW3 6JJ — MB BS 1992 Lond.; DRCPath 2001; MRCP (UK) 1995. (Univ. Coll. & Middlx.) Clin. Research Fell., Dept. Of Acad. Haemat. Roy. Marsden Hosp. Inst. of Cancer Research, Lond. Sw3.

PARRY-JONES, Owen Charles Craigle, Beach Road, Benllech, Tyn-y-Gongl LL74 8SW Tel: 01248 853853 Email: ocpj@hotmail.com — LRCPI & LM, LRSCI & LM 1958; LRCPI & LM, LRCSI & LM 1958; MICGP 1986; LM Coombe 1960. (RCSI) Med. Off. advising allocation of Pub. housing to Conwy, Gwynedd & Ynys Mon Co. Counc.s; Anglesey Co. Surg. St. John's Ambul.; Hon. Med. Off. Moelfre Lifeboat; Chief MO Anglesey Motor Racing Circuit. Socs: BASICS. Prev: Clin. Asst. (Geriat.) Gwynedd AHA; Sen. Res. Paediatr. Rotunda Hosp. Dub.; Clin. Clerk Coombe Lying-in Hosp. Dub.

PARRY-JONES, Owen John Carey Whitenap Cottage, Romsey SO51 5RR Tel: 01794 512497 — MB BS 1965 Lond.; DObst RCOG 1966. (St. Thos.) Socs: (Treas.) Brit. Med. Acupunc. Soc. Prev: Ho. Surg. St. Thos. Hosp. Lond.; Ho. Surg. (O & G) Lambeth Hosp.; Dist. Surg. & Med. Off. Montebello Miss. Hosp. Dalton, S. Africa.

PARRY-MORTON, Monica 11 Maynard Court, Llandaff, Cardiff CF5 2LS Tel: 029 2056 9106 — MB BCh 1941 Wales; BSc, MB BCh Wales 1941. (Cardiff) Clin. Med. Off. Mid Glam. AHA.

PARRY OKEDEN, Peter Christopher Uvedale Pemberley Avenue Surgery, 32 Pemberley Avenue, Bedford MK40 2LA Tel: 01234 351051 Fax: 01234 349246; 38 Kimbolton Avenue, Bedford MK40 3AA Tel: 01234 344148 Email: peterparryokeden@compuserve.com — MB ChB 1979 Sheff.; MRCGP 1984; DRCOG 1982. (Sheff.) Chairm. Bedford PCG. Prev: Trainee GP Bedford VTS; Ho. Surg. & Ho. Phys. Rotherham Dist. Gen. Hosp.

PARRY-SMITH, Hywel John Meddygfa Surgery, Meddygfa Rhydbach, Botwnnog, Pwllheli LL53 8RE Tel: 01758 730266 Fax: 01758 730307; 8 Glyn y Mor, Llanbedrog, Pwllheli LL53 7NW — MB BS 1979 Lond.; MRCGP 1985; DRCOG 1982. (Middlesex Hospital Medical School) Prev: Ho. Surg. Harefield Hosp. Ho. Phys. Cent. Middlx. Hosp. Lond.

PARRY-WILLIAMS, Ann Wyn Cadwgan Surgery, 11 Bodelwyddan Avenue, Old Colwyn, Colwyn Bay LL29 9NP Tel: 01492 515410

Fax: 01492 513270 — MB ChB 1982 Liverp.; BSc Liverp. 1977; DRCOG 1985.

PARRY-WILLIAMS, Henry Wyn (retired) The Randolph Medical Centre, Green Lane, Datchet, Slough SL3 9EX Tel: 01753 41268 Fax: 01753 582324 — MB Camb. 1956, BChir 1955; MA Camb. 1956; DObst RCOG 1957. Prev: Ho. Off. (Med. & Surg.) Univ. Coll. Hosp.

PARSHALL, Alice Margaret Gordon Hospital, Bloomberg St., London SW1 Tel: 020 8746 8000; 55 Bridge View, London W6 9DD — PhD Lond. 1983; MRCPsych 1990. Cons. Psychiat. S. Marylebone & Gordon Hosp. Lond. Prev: Sen. Regist. & Regist. (Psychiat.) Maudsley Hosp. Lond.; SHO (Rheum.) Hammersmith Hosp. Lond.

PARSLEW, Richard Anthony Gerard 10C Link, Royal Liverpool University Hospital, Prescot Street, Liverpool L7 8XP Tel: 0151 706 3477; Norwood, 26 Merrilocks Road, Blundellsands, Liverpool L23 6UN Tel: 0151 932 9023 — MB ChB 1990 Liverp.; MRCP (UK) 1993. (Liverpool) Cons. Dermatol. Roy. Liverp. Hosp. & Alder Hey Roy. Liverp.. Socs: MDU; Brit. Assn. Dermat..; Brit. Soc. for Investigative Dermat. Prev: Sen. Regist. (Dermat.) Roy. Liverp. Univ. Hosp.; Regist. (Dermat.) Roy. Liverp. Hosp.; SHO (Med.) Roy. Liverp. Hosp.

PARSLEY, John Flat 5, 31 Sussex Square, Brighton BN2 5AB — BM 1984 Soton.

PARSLOE, Justin Bruce Kingsley St Annes Group Practice, 161 Station Road, Herne Bay CT6 5NF Tel: 01227 742226 Fax: 01227 741439; 11 Seymour Close, Herne Bay CT6 7AS — MB BS 1984 Lond.; MRCGP 1989; DRCOG 1988. Prev: Trainee GP S. Warks. VTS.

PARSLOE, Malcolm Richard Justin Department of Anaesthesia, Leeds General Infirmary, Great George St., Leeds LS1 3EX Tel: 0113 392 6672 Fax: 0113 392 2645; 22 Elmete Avenue, Oakwood, Leeds LS8 2QN Tel: 0113 293 1625 Email: mparsloe@btinternet.com — MB ChB 1981 Manch.; FFA RCS Eng. 1986. (Manchester) Cons. Anaesth. Leeds Gen. Infirm. Prev: Sen. Regist. (Anaesth.) N.. RHA; Regist. (Anaesth.) St. Jas. Univ. Hosp. Leeds; SHO (Paediat. & Anaesth.) Warwick Hosp.

PARSLOW, Sara Frances 9 Southfield Road, Oxford OX4 1NX — MB BS 1981 Lond.; DCH RCP Lond. 1989; MRCPsych 1991. (Char. Cross) Regist. (Child Psychiat.) Oxf. Prev: Clin. Med. Off. (Paediat.) Soton HA.

PARSON, Alison Mary Yule Lytham Road Surgery, 2A Lytham Road, Fulwood, Preston PR2 8JB Tel: 01772 716033 Fax: 01772 715445 — MB ChB 1976 Manch.; MRCGP 1981; DRCOG 1980. Gen. Practitioner; Clin. Asst. Paediat.; Roy. Preston Hosp., Preston, Lancs. Prev: Ho. Off. Blackpool Vict. Hosp.; SHO (Paediat.) Hull Roy. Infirm. & (Neonat. Paediat.) St. Mary's; Hosp. Manch.

PARSON, Andrew Francis The Surgery, 42 High Street, Chislehurst BR7 5AX Tel: 020 8467 5551 Fax: 020 8468 7658 — MB ChB 1988 Liverp.; MRCGP 1993; DRCOG 1992.

PARSON, David Anthony Bedford General Hospital, South Wing, Bedford MK42 9DJ — MB BS 1982 Lond. Trainee GP Bedford VTS.

PARSON, Ian Stuart Ross The Surgery, Rockfield Road, Tobermory, Isle of Mull PA75 6PN Tel: 01688 302013 Fax: 01688 302092 — MB ChB 1972 Manch.; FRCOG 1994, M 1978; DObst 1975.

PARSONAGE, Maurice John (retired) BUPA Hospital Leeds, Jackson Avenue, Roundhay, Leeds LS8 1NT Tel: 0113 269 3939 Fax: 0113 268 1340 — MB ChB 1939 Manch.; BSc Manch. 1936; FRCP Lond. 1959, M 1945; MRCS Eng. LRCP Lond. 1940; DCH Eng. 1940. Indep. Cons. BUPA Hosp. Leeds; Mem. Hon. Med. Advis. Panel Driving & Disorders of The New System (Dept. of Transport); Med. Adviser Brit. Epilepsy Assn. Prev: Cons. Phys. (Neurol.) & Phys. (Electroenceph.) Gen. Infirm. Leeds.

PARSONAGE, Mirella Jane The Karis Medical Centre, Waterworks Road, Edgbaston, Birmingham B16 9AL Tel: 0121 454 0661 Fax: 0121 454 9104; 48 Woolacombe Lodge Road, Selly Oak, Birmingham B29 6PX — MB ChB 1987 Birm.; MRCGP 1992; DCH RCP Lond. 1991; DRCOG 1989. Socs: BMA. Prev: Trainee GP Birm.; SHO (O & G, Geriat., Psychiat. & Paediat.) S. Birm. HA.

PARSONAGE, Sarah Madeleine 86 Broadwood Avenue, Ruislip HA4 7XR — BM BS 1989 Nottm.; FRCR 2000; BMedSci 1987; FRCS Glas. 1997. Specialist Regist. (Radiol.) City Hosp. Birm.

PARSONAGE, William Anthony The Cottage, 2 Cross Lane Head, Bridgnorth WV16 4SJ — BM BS 1991 Nottm.

PARSONS, Adrian Priory Medical Centre Partnership, Cape Road, Warwick CV34 4JP Tel: 01926 494411 Fax: 01926 402394; 2 Verden Avenue, Warwick CV34 6RX — BM BCh 1989 Oxf.; BA Oxf. 1986; MRCGP 1994.

PARSONS, Anthony David Hospital of St Cross, Barby Road, Rugby CV22 5PX Tel: 01788 545208 Fax: 01788 822802 Email: tonyparsons@doctors.org.uk; Department of Postgraduate Medical Education, University of Warwick, Coventry CV4 7AL Tel: 02476 522913 Fax: 02476 524311 Email: a.d.parsons@warwick.ac.uk — MB BS 1971 Lond.; MA Wales 1989; FRCOG 1990, M 1978; MFFP 1993; MFCH 1991. (King's Coll. Hosp.) Cons. O & G Walsgrave NHS Trust; Sen. Lect. (Obst. & Gyn.) Univ. Warwick. Socs: Fell. Roy. Soc. Med.; (Ex-Chairm.) Brit. Menopause Soc. Prev: Lect. (O & G) Birm. Univ.; Sen. Regist. (O & G) Stoke-on-Trent; Regist. (Psychiat.) King's Coll. Hosp. Lond.

PARSONS, Anthony Stephen Brynderwen Surgery, Crickhowell Road, St. Mellons, Cardiff CF3 0EF Tel: 029 2079 9921 Fax: 029 2077 7740 — MB BCh 1968 Wales.

PARSONS, Beate Elisabeth Annick West Riding, Billingham, Newport PO30 3HE Tel: 01983 721804 — State Exam Med 1989 Aachen; State Exam Med. Aachen 1989.

PARSONS, Benedicte Lawrence The Surgery, 319 Westdale Lane, Carlton, Nottingham NG3 6EW Tel: 0115 952 5320 Fax: 0115 952 5321; The Grange, Main St, Farnsfield, Newark NG22 8EA Tel: 01623 882903 — MB BS 1976 Lond.; MRCGP 1980; DRCOG 1979. (UCL)

PARSONS, Carol Ruth The Health Centre, Rikenel, The Park, Gloucester GL1 1XR Tel: 01452 891110 Fax: 01452 891111; Health Centre, Rikenel, The Park, Gloucester GL1 1XR Tel: 01452 891110 — MB ChB 1978 Liverp.; MRCGP 1982.

PARSONS, Charles Anthony (retired) Woodford House, Knightwick, Worcester WR6 5PH Tel: 01886 821630 — MB ChB 1948 Birm.; MRCS Eng. LRCP Lond. 1948; MRCGP 1960. Prev: GP Kt.wick, Worcs.

PARSONS, Christopher John The Meeting House, New Road, Flaxley, Newnham GL14 1JS Tel: 01594 544566 — MB ChB 1971 Birm.; FLCOM 1980; DMS Med. Soc. Apoth. Lond. 1993. Indep. Specialist (Musculoskeletal Med.) Mitcheldean, Glos.; Specialist (Muskuloskeletal Med.) NHS Dilke Hosp. Cinderford, Glos. Socs: (Pres.) Brit. Osteop. Assn.; Brit. Inst. Musculoskel. Med.; Med. Acupunct. Soc.

PARSONS, Claire Elizabeth Mary 1 Holmesdale Road, Dronfield S18 2FA Tel: 0114 241 2073; 39 Smithywood Crescent, Woodseats, Sheffield S8 0NT Tel: 0114 258 8454 — MB ChB 1982 Sheff. Clin. Asst. BrE. Clinic Chesterfield & N. Derbysh. Roy. Hosp. Prev: Trainee GP Chesterfield VTS.

PARSONS, Corinne Anita 10 Pitchens End, Broad Hinton, Swindon SN4 9PR — MB ChB 1987 Birm.

PARSONS, David Leslie Thomas St. John's Medical Centre, 287A Lewisham Way, London SE4 1XF; Two Ridges, Summerhill, Chislehurst BR7 5NY Tel: 020 8467 4099 Fax: 020 8467 1944 Email: dltparsons@aol.com — MB ChB 1957 St. And.; MRCGP 1966. Socs: Worshipful Soc. of Apoth.; (Chairm.) Benefits Agency Sessional Docs. Assn. Prev: Resid. Obst. Off. Matern. Hosp. Cheltenham; Resid. Therap. Unit. Maryfield Hosp. Dundee; Resid. (Surg. & Gyn. Units) Gen. Infirm. S.port.

PARSONS, Dennis Shirley Merton College, Oxford OX4 Tel: 01865 276310 Fax: 01865 276361; 56 Holywell Street, Oxford OX1 3SD Tel: 01865 243880 — BM BCh 1942 Oxf.; BA Oxf. 1939, MA 1946, DM 1950. (Oxf.) Emerit. Reader (Physiol. Biochem.) Oxf; Fell. Merton Coll. Oxf.; Mem. Edit. Bd. Biomembranes Reviews. Socs: Physiol. Soc. Prev: Chairm. Europ. Ed. Bd. Physiol. Rev.; Mem. Edit. Bd. Biochim. Biophys. Acta.; Hon. Maj. RAMC.

PARSONS, Mr Derek Walter 10 Harley Street, London W1N 1AA Tel: 020 7436 5252; Meon House, Meon Close, Tadworth KT20 5DJ Tel: 01737 813762 — MB BS 1957 Lond.; FRCS Eng. 1963. (Univ. Coll. Hosp.) Hon. Cons. Orthop. St. Anthony's Hosp. Cheam; Cons. Orthopaedic Surg. St Helier and Epsom Hosp.s Trust. Socs: Fell. Roy. Soc. Med. & BOA; SICOT; Brit. Hip Soc.,Europ. Hip Soc. Prev: Sen. Regist. (Orthop.) Roy. Nat. Orthop. Hosp. Lond.; John Marshall Fell. Univ. Coll. Hosp. Med. Sch.

PARSONS

PARSONS, Mr Donald Colin Stuart Top Farmhouse, Shrubbery Lane, Wilden, Bedford MK44 2PH; Top Farm House, Shrubbery Lane, Wilden, Bedford MK44 2PH Tel: 01234 792064 Fax: 01234 792322 — MB BS 1966 MB BS Lond. 1966; MS Lond. 1978; FRCS Eng. 1971; MRCS Eng. LRCP Lond. 1966. (St. Mary's) Cons. Surg. Vasc. unit Bedford Hosp. NHS Trust; Recognised Clin. Teach. Sch. Clin. Med. Addenbrooke's Hosp. Camb.; Chairm. N. Beds. Hospice Care; Examr. Ct. of RCS Eng. Socs: Assn. Surg.; Vasc. Surgic. Soc. GB & Irel. Prev: Sen. Regist. (Surg.) & Research Regist. St. Mary's Hosp. Lond.; Regist. (Vasc. Surg.) Chelmsford Gp. Hosps.; Regist. (Surg.) Lewisham Hosp.

*PARSONS, Emma Jane 68 Wallingford Avenue, London W10 6PY — MB ChB 1995 Dundee.

PARSONS, Gary John The Health Centre, Worcester Street, Stourport-on-Severn DY13 8EH Tel: 01299 827141 Fax: 01299 879074 — MB ChB 1980 Birm.; MRCP (UK) 1983; MRCGP 1986.

PARSONS, Gary Jonathan Glebelands, Broughton-in-Furness LA20 6HS — MB ChB 1983 Liverp.; DRCOG 1986.

PARSONS, Gillian Mary Bacon Lane Surgery, 11 Bacon Lane, Edgware HA8 5AT Tel: 020 8952 5073/7876 — MB BS 1989 Lond.; MA Camb. 1994; MRCGP (Distinc.) 1994; DCH RCP Lond. 1992; DRCOG 1991. Socs: BMA. Prev: Trainee GP Barnet.

*PARSONS, Heather Elizabeth 25 Ince Crescent, Liverpool L37 1XR — MB BS 1998 Newc.; MB BS Newc. 1998.

*PARSONS, Helen Grace 15 Waverley Close, Hayes UB3 4AJ — MB ChB 1994 Dundee.

PARSONS, Helen Mary Willow Cottage, Brook Road, Chilworth, Guildford GU4 8ND — BM BCh 1992 Oxf.

PARSONS, Helena Kate 233 Carter Knowle Road, Sheffield S11 9FW — MB ChB 1995 Sheff. SHO (Gen. Med.) Chesterfield Roy. Hosp.

PARSONS, Henry 66 Worsley Road, Worsley, Manchester M28 2SN Tel: 0189 086 3149 — MB BCh BAO 1950 Dub.; LAH Dub. 1949. (T.C. Dub.)

PARSONS, Mr Howard Michael (retired) 22 Manor Way, South Croydon CR2 7BR Tel: 020 8686 2121 — FRCS Eng. 1956; MRCS Eng. LRCP Lond. 1942; DLO Eng. 1949. Prev: Cons. ENT Surg. Croydon HA.

PARSONS, Jean Mary (retired) 68A St Wilfred's Road, West Hallam, Derby DE7 6HH Tel: 0115 932 0340 — MB ChB 1957 Ed.; FRCGP 1992, M 1972. Prev: GP Ilkeston.

PARSONS, John Arthur West Billingham Farm, Chillerton, Newport PO30 3HE — MB BS 1964 Lond.; FRCP Lond. 1986; MRCP (U.K.) 1971; MRCS Eng. LRCP Lond. 1964; DObst RCOG 1966. (Westm.) Cons. Rheum. I. of Wight AHA. Prev: Sen: Regist. (Rheum. & Physical Med.) Roy. Free Hosp. Lond.

PARSONS, John Bruce (retired) 59 Bleadon Hill, Weston Super Mare BS24 9JW — MB BS 1950 Lond.; MB BS (Hns.) Lond. 1950; MRCS Eng. LRCP Lond. 1950; FFA RCS Eng. 1962. Prev: Cons. Anaesth. W.on-super-Mare Gen. Hosp.

PARSONS, John Howard Assisted Conception Unit, King's College Hospital, Denmark Hill, London SE5 8RX Tel: 020 7274 3242 — MB ChB 1970 Dundee; MRCOG 1979; DA Eng. 1979. (Dundee) Sen. Lect. (O & G) King's Coll Sch. Med. & Dent. Lond. Prev: Regist. (O & G) Hammersmith Hosp. Lond.; Regist. (O & G) Roy. Hants Co. Hosp. Winchester; Gen. Med. Off. Malawi Govt.

PARSONS, John Warwick Bassett Western House, Pershore WR10 1AJ — M.B., B.S. Lond. 1951. (St. Thos.) Prev: Cas. Off., Ho. Surg. & Obst. Ho. Phys. St. Thos. Hosp.

PARSONS, John Whitehill 9 The Paddocks, Ramsbury, Marlborough SN8 2QF — LRCP LRCS 1952 Ed.; LRCP LRCS Ed. LRFPS Glas. 1952; FFCM 1983, M 1974; DPH Lond. 1963; DTM & H Eng. 1962; DIH Soc. Apoth. Lond. 1963. (Roy. Colls. Ed.) Dist. Med. Off. Swindon HA. Socs: Soc. Community Med. & BMA. Prev: SCM (Child Health) Dudley AHA; Col. late RAMC, DDMS H.Q. Scotl. (Army); ADAH W. Midl. Dist.

PARSONS, Jonathan Michael Ashbery House, Main St., Wighill, Tadcaster LS24 8BQ — MB BS 1981 Lond.; FRCP Lond. 1995; MRCP (UK) 1985. Cons. Paediat. Cardiol. Killingbeck Hosp. Lond. Prev: Sen. Regist. (Paediat. Cardiol.) Killingbeck Hosp. Leeds; Research Fell. Dept. Paediat. Cardiol. Guy's Hosp. Lond.; Regist. (Cardiol., Thoracic Med.) Harefield Hosp.

PARSONS, Judith Mollie 8 Lon-Ysgubor, Cardiff CF14 6SG — MB ChB 1992 Leic.

PARSONS, Mr Keith Francis (Surgery) Roscoe House, 27 Rodney St., Liverpool L1 9EH Tel: 0151 709 2003; 31 Derby Road, Freshfield, Liverpool L37 7BN — MB ChB Liverp. 1970; FRCS Ed. 1975; FRCS Eng. 1975. Cons. Urol. (Surg.) Roy. Liverp. & BRd.green Univ. Hosp. NHS Trust; Dir. Urol. Studies Univ. Liverp.; Hon. Cons. Urol. to the Regional Spinal Injuries Centre, S.port and Formby Dist. Hosps. NHS Trust. Socs: Fell. Europ. Bd. Urol.; Fell. Roy. Soc. Med; (Former Hon. Sec.) Brit. Assn. Urol. Surgs. Prev: Sen. Regist. (Urol.) Hants. AHA (T); Research Fell. Merseyside Assn. Kidney Research; Chief Exec., the Roy. Liverp. and BRd. Green NHS Trust.

PARSONS, Kenneth Charles (retired) Trevonny, Eastfield Road, Ross-on-Wye HR9 5JZ Tel: 01989 562091 — MB BCh 1952 Wales; BSc Wales 1952; DObst RCOG 1954.

PARSONS, Linda Marguerite Neurology Department, St. Albans City Hospital, Waverley Road, St Albans AL3 5PN — MB ChB 1973 Sheff.; MD Sheff. 1983; MRCP (UK) 1977; FRCP 2000 UK. (Sheffield) p/t Cons. Neurol. St. Albans Hemel Hempstead & Roy. Free Hosps.; Assoc. Specialist (Neurol.) Luton & Dunstable Hosp. Socs: Fell. Roy. Soc. Med.; Assn. Brit. Neurol.; BMA. Prev: Sen. Regist. (Neurol.) St. Mary's Hosp. Lond.; Sen. Research Fell. Neurovirol. Unit & Hon. Clin. Asst. (Neurol.) St. Thos. Hosp. Lond.; Regist. (Neurol.) Dudley Rd. Hosp. Birm.

PARSONS, Malcolm (retired) 1 Ancaster View, Leeds LS16 5HR — MB BChir 1958 Camb.; MA Camb. 1957; FRCP Lond. 1978, M 1963. Prev: Cons. Neurol. Gen. Infirm. Leeds.

PARSONS, Maria Andrea 92 Salop Road, London E17 7HT — MB BS 1990 Lond.

PARSONS, Marjorie (retired) 11 Breary Court, Breary Lane, Bramhope, Leeds LS16 9LB Tel: 0113 284 2211 — MB ChB 1943 Leeds. Prev: Med. Off. Leeds AHA.

PARSONS, Matthew St John 144 Wyndcliffe Road, Charlton, London SE7 7LF Tel: 020 8480 9441 Fax: 07771 879066 Email: stjohn@dircon.co.uk — MB ChB 1993 Bristol; DFFP 1997. Specialist Regist. (O & G) NE Thames Deanery Lond. Prev: SHO (A & E) Qu. Mary's Sidcup Lond.; SHO (GUM) King's Healthcare NHS Trust Lond.

PARSONS, Michael Andrew Ophthalmic Sciences Unit, Royal Hallamshire Hospital, Glossop Road, Sheffield S10 2JF Tel: 0114 271 2745 Fax: 0114 276 6381 Email: a.parsons@sheffield.ac.uk — MB ChB 1974 Sheff.; FRCPath. 1982. Sen. Lect. & Hon. Cons. Ophth. Path. Univ. Sheff. & Roy. Hallamsh. Hosp. Sheff.; Dir. Ophth. Sci. Unit Univ. Sheff. Socs: Eur. Ophth. Path. Soc.; Internat. Soc. Ophth. Pathol.; Soc. Endocrinol. Prev: Sen. Lect. & Hon. Cons. Path. Univ. Sheff. & Roy. Hallamsh. Hosp. Sheff.

PARSONS, Michael Hume 7 Swanage Road, Lee-on-the-Solent PO13 9JW Tel: 01705 553525 — BM BCh Oxf. 1957; MA Oxf. 1958; DObst RCOG 1959. Prev: GP Gosport; Hosp. Pract. (Psychiat.) St. Jas. Hosp. Portsmouth.; Surg. Lt.-Cdr. RN.

PARSONS, Patricia Ann Cellular Pathology Department, Uited Lincolnshire Hospitals NHS Trusts, Lincoln County Hospital, Lincoln LN2 5QY Tel: 01522 512512 Ext: 2707 Fax: 01909 502462; Park Farm, 45 Main St, Hayton, Retford DN22 9LF — MB BS 1982 Lond.; PhD Lond. 1974, BSc 1970, MB BS 1982; MRCPath 1993. Cons. Histopath. & Cytopathologist United Lincs. Hospitals NHS Trust Lincoln. Prev: Sen. Regist. (Cytol. & Histopath.) St. Stephens & Char. Cross Hosp. Lond.; Regist. (Histopath.) W.m. Hosp. Lond.; Cons. Histopath & CytoPath. Bassetlaw Dist. Gen. Hosp. Worksop. Notts.

PARSONS, Paul William 30 Warkworth Close, Banbury OX16 1BD — MB ChB 1991 Birm.; DRCOG 1998; DFFP 1998. (Birm.) GP Non-Princip., Banbury, Oxon. Prev: GP Trainee Banbury VTS.

PARSONS, Peter Henry Irving (retired) 103 Park Road, Brentwood CM14 4TT Tel: 01277 210569 — MB BS 1956 Lond.; MRCS Eng. LRCP Lond. 1955; LMSSA Lond. 1950. Assoc. Specialist Nat. Blood Transfus. Centre Brentwood. Prev: Regist. (Surg.) Lambeth Hosp.

PARSONS, Raymond Leslie 3 St Mary's Gardens, London SE11 4UD — MB BS 1964 Lond.; MRCP Lond. 1968; MRCS Eng. LRCP Lond. 1964; DCH Eng. 1966. (Westm.) Hon. Lect. Sect. Clin. Pharmacol. Acad. Dept. Med. Roy. Free Hosp.; Lond. Socs: Brit. Pharmacol. Soc. & Brit. Soc. Gastroenterol. Prev: Cons. (Clin. Pharmacol.) May & Baker Ltd. Dagenham; Sen. Med. Off. Glaxo

Research Co. Ltd. Ware; Lect. Dept. Clin. Pharmacol. Guy's Hosp. Med. Sch. Lond.

PARSONS, Richard Simon Department of anaesthetics, Guys hospital, St Thomas Street, London SE1 9RT Tel: 020 7955 4051 Fax: 020 7955 8844 — BM BCh Oxf. 1968; MA Camb. 1969; MA Oxf. 1969; FFA RCS Eng. 1973. (Oxf.) Cons. Anaesth. Guy's Hosp. Lond. Prev: Sen. Regist. (Anaesth.) W.m. Hosp. Lond.; Regist. (Anaesth.) Guy's Hosp. Lond.; SHO Nuffield Ho. & Resid. Anaesth. Guy's Hosp. Lond.

***PARSONS, Samantha Louise** 41 De Burgh Street, Cardiff CF11 6LB — MB BS 1998 Lond.; MB BS Lond 1998.

***PARSONS, Samuel Joseph** 4 St Johns Row, Long Wittenham, Abingdon OX14 4QG — MB BS 1997 Lond.

PARSONS, Sarah Aerona (retired) Trevonny, Eastfield Road, Ross-on-Wye HR9 5JZ Tel: 01989 562091 — MB BCh 1948 Wales; BSc Wales 1948. JP.

PARSONS, Sarah Luise Foley 214 East Ferry Road, London E14 3AY — MB BS 1977 Lond.

PARSONS, Mr Simon Leslie 35 Bunny Lane, Keyworth, Nottingham NG12 5JU Tel: 0115 937 7292 — BM BS 1989 Nottm.; MD Nottm. 1996; FRCS Eng. 1993. (Nottm.) Specialist Regist. (Surg.) Nottm. Socs: Brit. Assn. Surgic. Oncol.

PARSONS, Simon Tobias 21 Velvet Court, Granby Row, Manchester M1 7AB — BM 1989 Soton.

PARSONS, Mr Stephen Wyndham c/o Department of Orthopaedics, Royal Cornwall Hospital, Infirmary Hill, Truro TR1 2HZ; The Beeches, Greensplatt, Perranwell Station, Truro TR3 7LZ Tel: 01872 74242 — MB BS 1979 Lond.; FRCS Eng. 1984; FRCS Ed. 1984. (Middlx. Hosp. Med. Sch.) Cons. Orthop. Surg. Roy. Cornw. Hosps. Trust. Socs: Fell. BOA; Brit. Childr. Orthop. Surg. Soc.; (Ex-Pres.) Brit. Orthop. Foot Surg. Soc. Prev: Lect. (Orthop. Surg.) Univ. Soton.

PARSONS, Terence Danvers (retired) 9 Walton Terrace, Aylesbury HP21 7QY Tel: 01296 82894 — MB BS 1946 Lond. Prev: Ho. Phys. Tindal Gen. Hosp. Aylesbury.

PARSONS, Terence Michael Caradoc 54 Primrose Gardens, London NW3 4TP — MA Oxf. 1968; MB BS Lond. 1970; MRCP (UK) 1973; MRCPsych 1976. (Middlx.) Indep. Psychoanalyst Lond. Socs: Brit. Psychoanal Soc.; Train. Analyst. Brit. Psycho-Analyt. Soc. Prev: Sen. Regist. (Psychiat.) UCH Lond.; Asst. Lect. Bland-Sutton Inst. Path. Middlx. Hosp. Med. Sch. Lond.; Ho. Phys. Middlx. Hosp.

PARSONS, Vincent John Hope Hospital, Eccles Old Road, Salford M6 8HD — MB BCh BAO 1986 NUI; MRCPI 1989; FRCR 1993; FFR RCSI 1993. Sen. Regist. Manch. Socs: BMA. Prev: Regist. (Radiol.) Manch.

PART, Maiu 55 Warman Close, Stockwood, Bristol BS14 8LY Tel: 01275 835592 — MB ChB Bristol 1964; Cert. Family Plann. JCC 1974. (Bristol)

PARTHA, Jagadish Staploe Medical Centre, Brewhouse Lane, Soham, Ely CB7 5JD Tel: 01353 624123 Fax: 01353 624203; 5 The Birches, Townsend, Soham, Ely CB7 5FH — MB BS 1973 Mysore.

PARTHASARADHI, Karri 10 Jonquil Way, Colchester CO4 5UW — MB BS 1972 Andhra.

PARTHASARATHY, Doralsamy Front Street Surgery, 16 Front Street, Annfield Plain, Stanley DH9 8HY Tel: 01207 281888 — MB BS 1975 Madras; MB BS 1975 Madras; LMSSA Lond 1989. (Madras) GP Stanley, Co. Durh.

PARTHASARATHY, Mallika 9 West Road, Annfield Plain, Stanley DH9 7XT Tel: 01207 231112 — MB BS 1975 Madras; MB BS 1975 Madras; LMSSA Lond 1989. (Madras) GP Stanley, Co. Durh.

PARTHASARATHY, Pobbathi Balaramaiah Chesterfield & North Derbyshire Royal Hospital, Orthopaedics Department, Calow, Chesterfield S44 5BL — MB BS 1974 Bangalor; MB BS Bangalore 1974.

PARTHIPAN, Kanthapillai 61 Reynolds Drive, Edgware HA8 5PU — LMSSA 1993 Lond.

PARTINGTON, Andrew Lamond Cottage, Over Kellet, Carnforth LA6 1DN Tel: 01524 734565 — MB ChB 1989 Leeds; MRCGP 1993; DFFP 1993; DRCOG 1992. Prev: Trainee GP/SHO Bolton AHA VTS; Ho. Off. (Med.) Bolton Gen. Hosp.; Ho. Off. (Surg.) Bolton Roy. Infirm.

PARTINGTON, Andrew Gareth Chy-an-Bron, St Tudy, Bodmin PL30 3NH — BM BCh 1981 Oxf.; MA Camb. 1978; MRCGP 1986; DRCOG 1986. GP St. Columb Maj..

PARTINGTON, Christopher Terence The Medical Centre, Forest Oate Road, Corby NN17 1TR — MB ChB 1990 Leic.; DMJ 2000 (Clin); DRCOG 1995. GP; Police Surg. Leics.; Police Surg. N.ants. Socs: BMA & Assn. Police Surgs. Prev: Trainee GP Leicester VTS.

PARTINGTON, Colin Kjeld, Squadron Ldr. RAF Med. Br. Retd. St. John's Hospital, Wood St., Chelmsford CM2 9BG Tel: 01245 513047 — MB BS 1975 Lond.; MD Lond. 1992; MRCOG 1983. (Westm.) Cons. O & G Mid Essex Hosps. Socs: Brit. Gyn. Cancer Soc.; Brit. Soc. Gyn. Endoscopy; Brit Soc. Colp & Cervical Path. (BSCCP). Prev: Sen. Regist. (O & G) Inst. O & G Hammersmith Hosp. Lond.; Regist. (O & G) Centr. Middlx. Hosp. Lond.; Sen. Specialist (O & G) RAF Med. Br.

PARTINGTON, Eileen Patricia The Surgery, Port Isaac; Chy-an-Bron, St Tudy, Bodmin PL30 3NH — MB ChB 1982 Bristol; MRCGP 1986; DRCOG 1985. GP Asst. Prev: GP Trainee Plymouth HA VTS.; Ho. Phys. Plymouth HA; Ho. Surg. Plymouth HA.

PARTINGTON, Francis Ian (retired) High Bank, 183 Havant Road, Drayton, Portsmouth PO6 1EE Tel: 01705 375450 — MB BS Lond. 1952; MRCS Eng. LRCP Lond. 1952; DObst RCOG 1954. Prev: Med. Examr. Roy. Lond. Mutual Insur. Soc. & Other Insur. Cos.

***PARTINGTON, Jane Rebecca** 2 The Old Bobbin Mill, Wray, Lancaster LA2 8QR — BM BS 1997 Nottm.

PARTINGTON, John Stanley The New City Medical Centre, Tatham Street, Hendon, Sunderland SR1 2QB Tel: 0191 567 5571 — MB BS 1987 Newc.

PARTINGTON, Michael James Hope House, Anstey, Buntingford SG9 0BP — MB ChB 1984 Otago.

PARTINGTON, Mr Paul Francis Wansbeck General Hospital, Woodhorn Lane, Ashington NE63 9JJ Tel: 01670 529672 Fax: 01670529656 Email: paul.partigan@cwcom.net; 8 McCracken Close, Gosforth, Newcastle upon Tyne NE3 2DW Tel: 0191 217 1768 Fax: 0191 217 1768 — MB BS 1987 Newc.; FRCS Eng. 1992; FRCS (Orth) 1997. (Univ. of Newc upon Tyne) Cons. (Orthop. Surg.) Ashington, N.umberland. Prev: Sen. Regist. (Orthop. Surg.) Newc.; Clin. Fell. Lower UMB Reconstruction Univ. Hosp. Lond. Ont. Canada.

PARTINGTON, Phyllis Elizabeth The Barn, Edale Road, Hope, Hope Valley S33 6ZF — MB ChB 1967 Sheff.; DA Eng. 1970; MFFP 1994. (Sheff.) Med. Asst. (Genitourin Med.) Chesterfield Dist. Gen. Hosp.; Clin. Med. Off. Sheff. Community Med. Prev: Regist. (Anaesth.) & Ho. Off. (Gen. Med.) N.. Gen. Hosp. Sheff.; SHO (Anaesth.) United Sheff. Hosps.; SHO (Genitourin Med.) Roy. Hallamsh. Hosp. Sheff.

***PARTINGTON, Robert John** 33 Camm Street, Walkley, Sheffield S6 3TR — MB ChB 1994 Sheff.

PARTINGTON, Susan Isabel Perrancoomb House, Perrancoomb, Perranporth TR6 0HZ — MB BS 1974 Lond. Clin. Med. Off. Child Health Cornw. & I. of Scilly AHA. Prev: Ho. Phys. & Ho. Surg. Cornw. & I. of Scilly AHA.

***PARTLETT, Polly** 4 Westbridge Road, Launceston PL15 8HS — MB BS 1998 Lond.; MB BS Lond 1998.

PARTON, Andrew Brian 7 Calderwood Close, Tottington, Bury BL8 3LE Tel: 01204 884873 Email: a.b.parton@talkzi.com — MB ChB 1992 Liverp.; BSc (Molecular Biol.) Liverp. 1987, MB ChB 1992; DCH 1997; DRCOG 1998; DFFP 1998; MRCGP (merit) 1999. (Liverp.) SHO (A & E) Roy. Liverp. Hosp. & Demonst. (Anat.) Liverp. Univ. Prev: GP VTS Bury. Lancs.

PARTON, Elizabeth Querida 31 Ambleside Avenue, London SW16 1QE — MB BS 1980 Lond.

PARTON, Jeremy (retired) Sue Ryder Palliative Care Home, Nettlebed, Henley-on-Thames RG9 5DF Tel: 01491 641384 Fax: 01491 641169 — MB BS Lond. 1958; MRCGP 1981; Dip. Palliat. Med. Wales 1996. Assoc. Specialist (Palliat. Med.) Sue Ryder Home Nettlebed Oxon. Prev: Ho. Phys. Kettering Gen. Hosp.

PARTON, John Bayard (retired) The Hollies, Higher St., Norton Sub Hamdon, Stoke-sub-Hamdon TA14 6SN Tel: 01935 881445 — MB BS Lond. 1950; MRCS Eng. LRCP Lond. 1950; DO Eng. 1958. Prev: Clin. Asst. Ashford Hosp. Middlx. & Char. Cross Hosp. Lond.

PARTON, Matthew James Department of Neurology, King's College Hospital, London SE5 8AF — BChir 1992 Camb.

PARTON, Michael James 45 Brooklet Road, Wirral CH60 1UJ — MB ChB 1993 Liverp.; BSc Liverpl 1990; DLO RCS (Eng) 1999. (L'pool)

PARTON

*PARTON, Simon Dominic 99 Hassett Road, London E9 5SL — MB BS 1995 Lond.

PARTRIDGE, Alan Bernard (retired) 55 Hipwell Court, Olney MK46 5QB — MB ChB 1952 Ed.; BA Nat. Sc. Trip. Camb. 1946, MA 1952; DMRD Eng. 1967. Prev: Radiol. Christian Med. Coll. Hosp. Vellore, S. India.

PARTRIDGE, Barbara Winifred Mary (retired) Cheriton, Redcliffe Road, Torquay TQ1 4QG Tel: 01803 329998 — MB BCh BAO 1952 Dub.; MA Dub. 1954, MD 1961. Assoc. Specialist (A & E) Torbay Hosp. Prev: SHO (Phys.) Torbay Hosp. Torquay.

PARTRIDGE, Brian Edward Cobbs Garden Surgery, West Street, Olney MK46 5QG Tel: 01234 711344; 12 St. Josephs Close, Olney MK46 5HD Tel: 01234 712583 — MB ChB 1983 Leic.; DRCOG 1986. Prev: Trainee GP Kettering VTS.

PARTRIDGE, Carolyn Gallinae, Old Coach Road, Cross, Axbridge BS26 2EQ — MB BCh 1995 Wales; BMedSc (Path. Sci.) Wales 1994; Dip. Biomed. Methods Wales 1997. (Univ. Wales Coll. Med. Cardiff) CMO(Psychiat.)Priory Pk., Wells. Socs: Med. Protec. Soc. Prev: SHO(Psychiat.) Beech Ct., Bridgwater; SHO (Psychiat.) Phoenix Ho., Wells.; Ho. Off. (Surg.) Univ. Hosp. Wales Cardiff.

PARTRIDGE, Carolyn Rosemary-Anne Wellington House Practice, Wades Field, Stratton Rd, Princes Risborough HP27 9AX Tel: 01844 344281 Fax: 01844 274719; 1 Upper Ashlyns Road, Berkhamsted HP4 3BW Tel: 01442 864582 — MB BChir 1973 Camb.; 1972 MB (conferred); BA Camb. 1969; MRCP (UK) 1975. (Camb. & Newc.) Clin. Asst. (Rheum.) Watford Gen. Hosp.

*PARTRIDGE, Christiaan James 29 Windgap Lane, Haughley, Stowmarket IP14 3PB — MB ChB 1998 Dund.; MB ChB Dund 1998.

*PARTRIDGE, Craig Andrew 23 Barnes Avenue, Stockport SK4 4DR — MB ChB 1994 Leeds.

PARTRIDGE, David Ralph 45 Pembroke Road, Clifton, Bristol BS8 3BE — MB ChB 1982 Bristol; BSc Psychol. Bristol 1979, MB ChB 1982; MRCGP 1986; DRCOG 1985. Prev: Trainee GP Avon VTS.

PARTRIDGE, Edward Deverall Pentlands Cottage, High Road, Chipstead, Coulsdon CR5 3SB — MB ChB 1996 Birm.; ChB Birm. 1996.

PARTRIDGE, Elspeth Murray Macclesfield District General Hospital, Victoria Road, Macclesfield SK10 3BL — MB ChB 1985 Glas.; MRCP (UK) 1988; FRCR 1992. Cons. Radiol. E. Chesh. NHS Trust. Prev: Sen. Regist. (Radiol.) Mersey RHA.

PARTRIDGE, Fiona Jane The Hedges Medical Centre, Pasley Road, Eyres Monsell, Leicester LE2 9BU Tel: 0116 225 1277; 18 Blacket Place, Edinburgh EH9 1RL Tel: 0116 270 3260, 0131 667 2885 — MB ChB 1994 Leic.; MA Cantab. p/t GP Princip., The Hedges Med. Centre, Leicester; Staff Grade in Genitourin. Med. & Infec. Dis.s, Leicester Roy. Infirm. Prev: SHO (Ophth.) Leicester Roy. Infirm.

PARTRIDGE, Gerald William Holycroft Surgery, The Health Centre, Oakworth Road, Keighley BD21 1SA Tel: 01535 602010 Fax: 01535 691313 — BM BCh 1976 Oxf.; MA Oxf. 1976; MRCGP 1982. (Oxford) Cardiac NSF Lead, Airedale Primary Care Trust. Socs: BMA; Primary Care Cardiovasc. Soc.; Christian Med. Fell. Prev: Trainee GP Kettering VTS; Regist. (Path.) Radcliffe Infirm. Oxf.; Ho. Phys. & Ho. Surg. Gen. Infirm. Leeds.

PARTRIDGE, James William (retired) 85 Willes Road, Leamington Spa CV31 1BS Tel: 01926 427452 — MB BChir 1962 Camb.; MA Camb. 1967; FRCP Lond. 1982, M 1965; DObst RCOG 1963; DCH Eng. 1963. Prev: Cons. Paediat. S. Warks. Hosp. Gp.

PARTRIDGE, John The Medical Centre, Upper Green Road PO33 1UG Tel: 0198 872772; 49 Foreland Road, Bembridge PO35 5XN — MB ChB 1977 Bristol; FRCGP 2000; DRCOG 1979. Princip. in Gen. Pract.

PARTRIDGE, John Barry Department of Radiology, Harefield Hospital, Harefield, Uxbridge UB9 6JH Tel: 01895 828628 Fax: 01895 828590 — MB BS Lond. 1969; FRCP 1998; FRCR 1975; FFR 1974; FRACR 1984. (UCHMS London) Cons. Cardiothoracic Radiol. Harefield Hosp. Middlx. Socs: Cardiac Radiol. Gp. RCR; Cardiac Soc.; Brit. Soc. Echocardiogr. Prev: Assoc. Prof. Radiol. Univ. Qu.sland, Austral.; Specialist Cardiac Radiol. P. Chas. Hosp. Brisbane, Austral.; Cardiac Radiol. Killingbeck Hosp. Leeds.

PARTRIDGE, Mr John Philip (retired) Tawton House, Bishop's Tawton, Barnstaple EX32 0DB — MB BS 1944 Lond.; FRCS Eng. 1951; MRCS Eng. LRCP Lond. 1943. Prev: Cons. Surg. N. Devon Dist. Hosp. Barnstaple.

*PARTRIDGE, Jonathan Miles Flat 1F1, 27 Montague St., Edinburgh EH8 9QT — MB ChB 1996 Ed.

PARTRIDGE, Martyn Richard Chest Clinic, Whipps Cross Hospital, London E11 1NR Tel: 020 8535 6675 Fax: 020 8535 6709 Email: mrp@wxhchest.demon.co.uk; Westfields, 4 Westfield, Loughton IG10 4EB Tel: 020 8502 1156 Email: martyn.partridge@btinternet.com — MB ChB 1972 Manch.; MD Manch. 1980; FRCP Lond. 1989; MRCP (UK) 1975. Cons. Phys. Whipps Cross Hosp. Lond.; Chief Med. Adviser Nat. Asthma Campaign; Mem. (Exec. Comm.) Global Initiative on Asthma; Chairm. (Exec. Comm.) Brit. Thoratic Soc.; Regional Adviser, RCP Lond. Prev: Sen. Regist. (Med.) Lond. Chest. & Univ. Coll. Hosps. Lond.; Sir Jules Thorn Research Fell. Middlx. Hosp. Med. Sch. Lond.; Regist. Hammersmith Hosp. Lond.

PARTRIDGE, Rena Elizabeth (retired) 55 Hipwell Court, Olney MK46 5QB Tel: 01234 240018 — MB ChB 1952 Ed.; DObst RCOG 1955. Prev: Family Plann. Off. Christian Med. Coll. Hosp. Vellore, S. India.

*PARTRIDGE, Richard Francis c/o 10 Dickens Drive, Stamford PE9 2GS — BM BS 1998 Nottm.; BM BS Nottm 1998.

PARTRIDGE, Mr Richard James 23 Middle Bourne Lane, Farnham GU10 3NH Tel: 01252 719244 Fax: 01252 719244 Email: rich@partridger.freeserve.co.uk — MB BS 1978 Lond.; FRCS Ed. 1983; FFAEM 1993. (St.Geo.) Cons. A & E Med., Clin. Dir. A & E, Out Pats. & Pat. Servs. Staff Health Frimley Pk. Hosp. Surrey; Lect. (Orthop. & Rheum.) Brit. Sch. Osteop. Lond.

PARTRIDGE, Sally Joy The Limes Surgery, 172 High Street, Lye, Stourbridge DY9 8LL Tel: 01384 422234 — MB ChB 1983 Birm.; MB ChB (Hons.) Birm. 1983; MRCGP 1987; DRCOG 1986; DCH 1988. GP Stourbridge. Prev: Trainee GP E. Birm. Hosp. VTS.

PARTRIDGE, Samuel James Musgrove Park Hospital, Taunton TA1 5; 134 Broadoak Road, Langford, Bristol BS40 5HB Tel: 01934 853381 — MB ChB 1996 Bristol. SHO (Gen. Med.) MusGr. Pk. Hosp. Taunton.

PARTRIDGE, Sarah Elizabeth Department of Clinical Oncology, Hammersmith Hospital, Ducane Road, London W12 2NN Tel: 020 8743 2030; 207 Sandycombe Road, Richmond TW9 2EW Tel: 020 8948 5614 — MB BS 1990 Lond.; MRCP (UK) 1994. Regist. (Clin. Oncol.) Hammersmith Hosp. Lond. Socs: Assoc. Mem. Roy. Soc. Med. Prev: SHO (Gen. Med.) Chelsea & W.m. Hosp. Lond.; SHO (Med.) Watford Gen. Hosp.; Ho. Surg. Qu. Alexandra Hosp. Portsmouth.

PARTRIDGE, Susan Marie Dept. of Pathology, Furness General Hospital, Dalton Lane, Barrow-in-Furness LA14 4LF Tel: 01229 491022 Fax: 01229 491044 — MB ChB 1987 Leic.; BSc (Hons) Med. Sci. Leic 1984; MRCPath 2000. Cons. Microbiol., Furness Gen. Hosp. Prev: SHO (Microbiol.) Qu. Med. Centre Nottm.; Regist./Specialist Regist. (Microbiol.) Sheff. Teachg. Hosps.

PARTRIDGE, Suzanne Brough and South Cave Medical Practice, 4 Centurion Way, Brough HU15 1AY Tel: 01482 658446 Fax: 01482 665090 — BM BS 1993 Nottm.; BMedSci Nottm. 1991; MRCGP Lond. 1997; DRCOG Lond. 1979. (Nottm.) GP Princip. Hull.

PARTRIDGE, Thomas Murray Upton Group Practice, 32 Ford Road, Wirral CH49 0TF Tel: 0151 677 0486 Fax: 0151 604 0635; 26 Croome Drive, West Kirby, Wirral CH48 8AH — MB ChB 1985 Ed.; MRCGP 1992.

PARUMS, Dinah Velta Department of Pathology, Papworth Hospital, Cambridge CB3 8RE Tel: 01480 364306 Fax: 01480 831192 Email: dup@dinahmac.demon.co.uk; The Keysmith,, High Street, Boxworth, Cambridge CB3 8LY Tel: 01954267738 Fax: 01954 267738 Email: dvp@dinahmac.demon.co.uk — BM BCh 1983 Oxf.; PhD Camb 1987, MA 1984, BA 1980; MRCPath 1992; FCCP 1998; FRCPath 1999. (Camb. & Oxf.) Cons. Cardiothoracic Path. Papworth Hosp. Camb.; Edit. Bd. Cardiovasc. Path. Socs: Fell.Roy. Soc. Med.; (Counc.) Soc. Cardiovasc. Path.; Fell.Coll. of Chest Pysicians. Prev: Cons. Cardiothoracic Path. Freeman Hosp. Newc.; Sen. Lect. & Cons. (Histopath.) Roy. Postgrad. Med. Sch. Hammersmith Hosp. Lond.; Clin. Tutor, Clin. Lect. & Hon. Sen. Regist. Nuffield Dept. Path. John Radcliffe Hosp. Oxf.

PARVEEN, Shada Shane Maybury Surgery, Alpha road, Maybury, Woking GU22 8HF Tel: 01483 728757 Fax: 01483 729169 — MB BS 1982 Lond. (Charing Cross Hosp. Med. Sch.) Socs: BMA.

PARVIN, Mr Simon Dudley Royal Bournemouth Hospital, Castle Lane E., Bournemouth BH7 7DW Tel: 01202 704621 Fax: 01202 704623 Email: sdp@rbh.org.uk; 12 Spencer Road, Canford Cliffs, Poole BH13 7EU Tel: 01202 709626 Fax: 01202 709626 — MD 1988 Leic.; MB BS Lond. 1975; FRCS Eng. 1981; FRCS Ed. 1980. Cons. Gen. & Vasc. Surg. Bournemouth & Poole Hosps. Prev: Lect./Hon. Sen. Regist. Leic. Univ.

PARVIS, Alexander Home (retired) 954 Chelsea Cloisters, Sloane Avenue, London SW3 3EU — MRCS Eng. LRCP Lond. 1947; BA, MD Amer. Univ. Beirut 1941; DOMS Eng. 1949. Prev: Cons. Lect. (Ophth.) City Univ. Lond.

PARWAIZ, Mr Khalid Staff Urologist, Hinchingbrooke Hospital, Hinchinbrooke Park Road, Huntingdon PE29 6NT Tel: 01480 416416; 39 Crane Street, Brampton, Huntingdon PE28 4UX Tel: 01480 417784 Email: knhif@aol.com — MB BS 1986 Patna; FRCS Ed. 1991; Dip. Urol.1994. (Patna.med.Coll) Staff Grade Surg. (Urol.) Huntingdon. Socs: BMA.

PARWAIZ, Paul Ratby Surgery, 122-124 Station Road, Ratby, Leicester LE6 0JP — MRCS Eng. LRCP Lond. 1979. (Manch.)

PARWANI, Mr Ghanshyam Shivaldas 64 Kingsway, Gillingham ME7 3BD — MB BS 1956 Nagpur; FRCS Eng. 1966. (Nagpur Med. Coll.) Cons. Rehabil. Med. Disabil. Servs. Centre Harold Wood Hosp. Romford. Socs: Fell. Brit. Soc. Orthop. Assn.; Internat. Soc. Prosth.s & Orthotics. Prev: Ho. Surg. Safdarjung Hosp. New Delhi, India; Regist. (Orthop.) Notley Orthop. Centre Braintree; Regist. (Surg.) NE Essex HA.

PARYS, Mr Bohdan Tadeusz Department of Urology, Rotherham District General Hospital, Moorgate Road, Rotherham S60 2UD Tel: 01709 304061 Fax: 01709 307193 Email: parys.sec@rgh-tr.trent.nhs.uk; 3 Castle Dyke Mews, Ringinglow Road, Sheffield S11 7TA — MB BS 1979 Lond.; ChM Liverp. 1990; FRCS (Urol.) 1993; FRCS Ed. 1985. (Roy. Free) Cons. Urol. Rotherham Dist. Gen. Hosp. Socs: Brit. Assn. Urol. Surgs.; BMA; Internat. Continence Soc. Prev: Sen. Regist. (Urol.) Roy. Hallamsh. Hosp. Sheff.; Regist. (Urol.) Roy. Preston Hosp.; Research Fell. (Urol.) Roy. Liverp. Hosp.

***PASAPULA, Chadra Seker** 5 Dickens Close, Cheshunt, Waltham Cross EN7 6BG — MB BS 1996 Lond.

PASCALL, Anna Child & Family Services, Delancey Hospital, Charlton Lane, Cheltenham GL53 9DU Tel: 01242 275015 Fax: 01242 272105 — MB BS 1983 Lond.; MRCPsych 1988. Cons. Child & Adolesc. Psychiat. Delancey Hosp. Cheltenham. Prev: Cons. Child & Adolesc. Psychiat. W. Wales Gen. Hosp. Carmarthen; Sen. Regist. (Child Psychiat.) St. Geo. Hosp. Lond.

PASCALL, Caroline Margaret Emma 46 Brandon Village, Brandon, Durham DH7 8SU — MB BS 1983 Lond.; MRCGP 1988.

PASCALL, Mr Charles Richard Williton and Watchet Surgeries, Robert Street, Williton, Taunton TA4 4QE Tel: 01984 632701 Fax: 01984 633933; Heddon House, Crowcombe, Taunton TA4 4BJ — MB BS 1974 Lond.; FRCS Eng. 1979. Clin. Asst. Gen. Surg. Som. HA. Prev: Surgic. Regist. Norwich HA.

PASCALL, Emma Jane Heddon House, Crowcombe, Taunton TA4 4BJ Tel: 01984 618642 — MB ChB 1978 Liverp.; FFA RCS Eng. 1987. Assoc. Specialist (Anaesth.) Taunton & Som. NHS Trust.

PASCALL, Mr Keith Gardner (retired) Wiverton House, Plympton, Plymouth PL7 5AA Tel: 01752 337276 — MB BS Lond. 1938; FRCS Ed. 1946; LMSSA Lond. 1937. Prev: Sen. Cas. Off. Plymouth Gen. Hosp.

***PASCALL, Nicola Jayne** 10 Abinger Dr, Redhill RH1 6SY — BM 1997 Soton.

PASCALL, Olive Joyce The Glade, Grindley Bank, Mickle Trafford, Chester CH2 4EQ — MB BCh BAO 1947 NUI; DA Eng. 1956. Med. Off. Blood Transfu. Serv. Mersey RHA; Sessional Med. Off. Chesh. HA. Prev: Sessional Med. Off. Sheff. Blood Transfu. Serv.; Regist. (Anaesth.) N. Sheff. Gen. Hosp.

PASCOE, Karen Frances 28 Heol Y Foel, Llawtwit Fardre, Pontypridd CF38 2EQ — MB ChB 1988 Liverp.; MRCGP 1992. GP Retainer Scheme M. Glam.

PASCOE, Keith Laurence Crown Medical Practice, Tamworth Health Centre, Upper Gungate, Tamworth B79 7EA Tel: 01827 58728 Fax: 01827 63873 — MB BCh 1973 Wales.

PASCOE, R J M Belgrave Medical Centre, 22 Asline Road, Sheffield S2 4UJ Tel: 0114 255 1184.

PASCOE, Sarah Jane 5 Russell Court Gardens, Tavistock PL19 0DR Tel: 01822 610515 — MB BS 1991 Lond.; MRCGP 1995; DCCH RCP Ed. 1995. (St. Geo. Hosp. Lond.) Specialist Regist. (Oncol.) Derriford Hosp. Plymouth. Socs: BMA; Roy. Coll. Gen. Pract. (Tamar Fac.). Prev: SHO (Oncol.); Trainee GP Plymouth VTS.

PASCOE-WATSON, David 7 Avon Road, Barnton, Edinburgh EH4 6LA — MB ChB 1987 Bristol.

PASCUAL, Juanita Aurelia 1 Graig Cottage, Miskin, Pontyclun CF72 8JR — MB BS 1986 Newc.; BMedSc Newc. 1985; MRCP (UK) 1990. Sen. Regist. (Geriat. Med.) Univ. Hosp. Wales Cardiff.

PASH, Jonathan David 5 Oxford Mews, Hove BN3 3NF — MB ChB 1993 Dundee.

PASH, Raphael (retired) 31 Tormead Road, Guildford GU1 2JA Tel: 01483 838290 — MB BCh 1957 Wales; DA Eng. 1966.

PASHA, Mahmood Seymour Grove Health Centre, 70 Seymour Grove, Old Trafford, Manchester M16 0LW; 381 Wilbraham Road, Whalley Range, Manchester M16 8NG Tel: 0161 881 0171 — MB BS 1960 Karachi; BSc. Punjab 1955; DIH Eng. 1974. (Dow Med. Coll.) Socs: Fell. Manch. Med. Soc. Prev: SHO Memor. Hosp. Darlington; Asst. Resid. Med. Off. Salford Roy. Hosp.

PASHA, Mohamed Abdulla (retired) 31 Willingale Way, Thorpe Bay, Southend-on-Sea SS1 3SN Tel: 01702 586610 — MB BS 1953 Andhra; FRCP Glas. 1979, M 1965. Cons. Phys. (Geriat.) S.end-on-Sea Hosp. Gp. Prev: Med. Asst. Chest Unit, S.end-on-Sea Hosp. Gp.

PASHA, Nadeem 536 Chelsea Cloisters, Sloane Avenue, London SW3 3EH — MB BS 1993 Lond.

PASHANKAR, Dinesh Shrikrishna 6 Amity Road, London E15 4AT — MB BS 1987 Poona; MRCP (UK) 1993.

PASHANKAR, Farzana Dinesh 6 Amity Road, London E15 4AT — MB BS 1989 Poona.

PASHBY, Mr Nigel Lowthrop Northgate, Church St., Uttoxeter ST14 8AG Tel: 01889 562010 — MB BS 1969 Lond.; FRCS Eng. 1977; MRCS Eng. LRCP Lond. 1969. (Roy. Free) GP Uttoxeter. Prev: Research Fell. Dept. Surg. Univ. Hosp. Wales Card.; Regist. (Surg.) Bristol Roy. Infirm.

PASHLEY, Camilla Elizabeth The Surgery, 1 Troy Close, Tadworth Farm, Tadworth KT20 5JE Tel: 01737 362327 Fax: 01737 373469; 25 Belmont Road, Reigate RH2 7ED Tel: 01737 242502 — BM BS 1986 Nottm.; MRCGP 1991; DRCOG 1991. GP Princip. Prev: Regist. (Palliat. Med.) P.ss Alice Hospice Esher.

PASHLEY, Julia Kathryn 2 Chestnut Spinney, Droitwich WR9 7QD — MB BS 1993 Lond.

PASI, Kanwal Chandra 2 Castel Close, Seabridge, Newcastle ST5 3EG — MB BS 1954 Punjab; MB BS Punjab (India) 1954; DPH Leeds 1965. Prev: GP Stoke-on-Trent; PMO Lond. Boro Havering; Admin. Med. Off. City of Birm.

PASI, Kanwal John Division of Haematology, University of Leicester, Leicester Royal Infirmary, Leicester LE2 7LX Tel: 0116 252 3256 Email: jp69@le.ac.uk, kjp@rfhsm.ac.uk — MB ChB 1983 Birm.; FRCPath 2001; PhD 1994 Birm.; MRCP (UK) 1986; MRCPath 1993; FRCPCH 1997; FRCP Lond. 1998. Prof. of Haemat., Univ. of Leicester, Hon. Cons., Univ. Hosp. of Leicester NHS Trust. Prev: Lect. (Haemat.) Roy. Free Hosp. Lond.; Research Fell. (Haemat.) Childr. Hosp. Birm.; Con. Haemat. & Hon Gen. Lect. Roy. Free Hosp. Lond.

PASKA, Lubomyr Mychajlo 11 Lucknow Street, Rochdale OL11 1RH — MB BS 1990 Lond.; BSc (Hons.) Lond. 1984, MB BS 1990. SHO (Gen. Med.) Maidsstone Hosp. Barming. Prev: SHO (Geriat. Med.) Qu. Mary Univ. Hosp. Lond.; SHO (A & E) Ashford Hosp. Middlx.

PASKIN, Donald George (retired) Chestnut Tree Cottage, Whitegate, Northwich CW8 2BY — MRCS Eng. LRCP Lond. 1956; DObst RCOG 1958. Prev: GP N.wich.

PASKINS, Mr John Roderick 17 Birchwood Dell, Doncaster DN4 6SY — MB BS 1972 Lond.; FRCS Eng. 1977. (Char. Cross) Cons. A & E Med., Doncaster Roy. Infirm. Socs: Cas. Surgs. Assn. Prev: Sen. Regist. (A & E Med.) Roy. Hallamshire Hosp. Sheff.; Research Fell. Paediat. Surg. St. Thos. Hosp. Lond.; Regist. (Surg.) St. Thos. Hosp. Lond.

PASMORE, Henry Stephen (retired) South Cottage, Ham Gate Avenue, Richmond TW10 5HB Tel: 020 8940 8803 — MB BS 1935 Lond.; MRCS Eng. LRCP Lond. 1933; FRCGP 1969. Prev: Ho. Phys. Univ. Coll. Hosp.

PASOLA, Mark 33 Gladstone Road, Orpington BR6 7EA — MB BS 1984 Lond.; DA (UK) 1990. Prev: Regist. (Anaesth.) St. Geo. Hosp. Lond.

PASPATIS

PASPATIS, Gregory Brierley House, Room 111, Walden St., Whitechapel, London E1 2RD — Ptychio Iatrikes 1985 Athens.

PASQUAL, Robert Steuart Hylton (retired) The Old Smithy, Skirling, Biggar ML12 6HD — MB ChB 1949 Ed.; DPH 1956. Med. Off. Pneumoconiosis Med. Panel Min. of Social Security. Prev: Med. Off. Kenya Govt.

PASSANI, Stefano Little Blakes, South View Road, Danbury, Chelmsford CM3 4DX — State Exam 1978 Rome; Stat Exam Rome 1978.

PASSANT, Carl Damien Apartment 4, Byron Court, Pittville Circus Road, Cheltenham GL52 2GA — MB ChB 1994 Bristol; BSc Physiol. (Hons.) Bristol 1991.

PASSANT, Colin Charles Windhill Green Medical Centre, 2 Thackley Old Road, Shipley BD18 1QB Tel: 01274 584223 Fax: 01274 530182 — MB ChB 1985 Leeds; MRCGP 1990; DRCOG 1988. Socs: Brit. Med. Acupunct. Soc. Prev: Ho. Phys. & Ho. Surg. Airedale Gen. Hosp. Keighley.

PASSANT, Wendy Sharon Grey Haigh Hall Medical Centre, Haigh Hall Road, Greengates, Bradford BD10 9AZ Tel: 01274 613326 — MB ChB Leeds 1985; BSc (Hons.) Leeds 1982; DRCOG 1990; DCH RCP Lond. 1989. (Leeds) p/t GP Principle.

PASSEY, Joanne Lorraine 48 Kielder Square, Eccles New Road, Salford M5 4UL — MB ChB 1990 Manch.

PASSI, Man Mohan Lal Leicester Street Medical Centre, Leicester Street, Wolverhampton WV6 0PS Tel: 01902 24118; 16 Showell Lane, Wolverhampton WV4 4UA Tel: 01902 58846 — MB BS 1957 Rajasthan; DIH Eng. 1964; DTM & H Lond1964; DPH Calcutta 1960. (Rajasthan)

PASSI, Uma 16 Showell Lane, Wolverhampton WV4 4UA Tel: 01902 58846 — MB BS 1961 Punjab; MB BS Punjab (India) 1961; DObst RCOG 1964; DA Eng. 1964. (Punjab)

***PASSI, Vimmi** 16 Showell Lane, Wolverhampton WV4 4UA — MB BCh 1995 Wales.

PASSMORE, Anna Margaret 2 School Lane, Weldon, Corby NN17 3JN — MB ChB 1995 Birm.; ChB Birm. 1995.

PASSMORE, Anthony Peter 108 Malone Road, Belfast BT9 5HP Tel: 02890 272158 Fax: 02890 325839 Email: p.passmore@qub.ac.uk; 108 Malone Road, Belfast BT9 5HP Tel: 02890 272158 Fax: 02890 325839 Email: p.passmore@qub.ac.uk — MB BCh 1981 Belf.; FRCP (Lond. 1995, Glas. 1996); BSc Physiol. (1st cl. Hons.) Belf. 1978, MD 1987, MB BCh BAO 1981; MRCP (UK) 1984. Sen. Lect. Dept. Geriat. Med., Qu.s Univ. Belf.; Cons. Phys. Socs: Mem. Brit. Geriatics Soc.; Mem. Brit. Hypertens. Soc.; Fell. Ulster Med. Soc. Prev: Sen. Regist. Dept. Therap. & Clin. Pharmacol. Qu. Univ. Belf.

***PASSMORE, Kirsty Emma** 36 Avon Way, Portishead, Bristol BS20 6JQ — MB ChB 1996 Leeds.

PASSMORE, Reginald 54 Newbattle Terrace, Edinburgh EH10 4RX — BM BCh 1935 Oxf.; MA, DM Oxf. 1942; BM BCh (1st cl. Hons. Sch. Physiol. 1931) 1935; FRCP Ed. 1976. (Oxf. & St. Mary's) Prev: Reader in Physiol. Univ. Edin.; Lt.-Col. IMS.

PASSMORE, Sarah Jane Hospital for sick children, Gt Ormond Street, London WC1N Tel: 020 7405 9200 x0112 Fax: 020 7813 8588 Email: jane@ccrg.ox.ac.uk — MB BS 1984 Newc.; MRCP (UK) 1987; DCH RCP Lond. 1989. p/t Cons. paediatric oncologist; Snr Regist..Childh. cancer research grp. Prev: Clin. Research Fell. (Haemat. & Oncol.) Hosp. for Sick Childr. Gt. Ormond St. Lond.; Regist. (Paediat.) Roy. Devon & Exeter Hosp. & S.mead Hosp.

PASTERSKI, Jerzy Kazimierz Altrincham Priory Hospital, Rappax Road, Hale, Altrincham WA15 0NX Tel: 0161 904 0050 Fax: 0161 980 4322 — Lekarz 1969 Warsaw; Lekarz Warsaw Poland 1969; MRCPsych. 1979; T(Psych.) 1991. Med. Dir. Altrincham Priory Hosp.

PASTOR, Thomas Greenacres & Homefield, Homefield Road, Worthing BN11 2HS Tel: 01903 212206 Fax: 01903 218799; Goring Hall Hospital, Bodiam Avenue, Goring-by-Sea, Worthing BN12 5AT Tel: 01903 506699 Fax: 01903 700782 — MB BS 1968 Lond.; MRCS Eng. LRCP Lond. 1968; MRCPsych 1975; DPM Eng. 1974. (Univ. Coll. Hosp.) Cons. Psychiat. (Psychother.) Worthing Priority Care NHS Trust. Socs: Fell. Roy. Soc. Med.; BMA. Prev: Lect. (Psychiat.) Univ. Lond. & Hon. Sen. Regist. St. Mary's Hosp. Lond.; Regist. (Psychiat.) Roy. Free Hosp. Friern Hosp.; SHO Univ. Coll. Hosp. Lond.

PASUPATHY, Amirtha 26 Lapstone Gardens, Harrow HA3 0ED — MB BS 1983 Peradeniya, Sri Lanka.

***PASUPATHY, Dharmintra** Flat 1, Block 10, Wilsford Green, Oakhill Drive, Edgbaston, Birmingham B15 3UG; Flat 1, Block 10,, Wilsford Green, Oakhill Drive, Edgbaston, Birmingham B15 3UG — MB ChB 1997 Liverp.; MBGB Liverpool 1997.

PASVOL, Professor Geoffrey Imperial College School of Medicine, Infection & Tropical Medicine Unit, Northwick Park Hospital, Harrow HA1 3UJ Tel: 020 8869 2831/2 Fax: 020 8869 2836 Email: g.pasvol@ic.ac.uk; 85 Fordington Road, Highgate, London N6 4TH Tel: 020 8444 7784 — MB ChB 1972 Cape Town; MA Oxf. 1987, DPhil 1978; FRCP Ed. 1996; FRCP Lond. 1990; MRCP (UK) 1975. (Univ. Cape Town) Prof. Infec. Dis. & Trop. Med. Imperial Coll. Sch. Med. Harrow; Hon Cons in Infec dis & Trop Med N.W. Lond. Hosp.s Trust & St Mary's Hosp.; Hon Prof. Kings Coll. Lond. Socs: Fell. RCP; Fell. Roy. Soc. Trop. Med. & Hyg.; Assn. Phys. Prev: Wellcome Sen. Lect. & Dep. Univ. Med. Off. Univ. Oxf.; Clin. Lect. (Trop. Med.) Nuffield Dept. Med. John Radcliffe Hosp. Oxf.; Research Stud. Nuffield Dept. Med. Radcliffe Infirm. Oxf.

PASZKIEWICZ, Jolanta Maria The Medical Centre, H.M. Naval Base, Rosyth, Dunfermline KY11 2YA — MB BS 1974 Tasmania.

PASZKOWSKA, Kazimiera Netheravon Road Surgery, 29 Netheravon Road, Chiswick, London W4 2NA Tel: 020 8994 2506 — LRCPI & LM, LRSCI & LM 1957; LRCPI & LM, LRCSI & LM 1957. Socs: BMA. Prev: Ho. Phys. St. Leonard's Hosp.; SHO Cas. & Orthop. Roy. Hosp. Richmond; SHO Anaesth. W. Middlx. Hosp. Isleworth.

PATALAY, Mr Tuljaram Jasmine House, Great North Road, Barnet EN5 4PZ — MB BS 1967 Osmania; FRCS Ed. 1974. (Osmania Med. Coll.) Socs: Med. Defence Union.

PATANKAR, Mr Roy Suneel Vasudev University Surgical Unit, F Level, Southampton General Hospital, Southampton SO16 6YD — MB BS 1988 Bombay; FRCS Glas. 1993; FRCS Ed. 1993.

PATANWALA, Saifuddin Kamruddin John Coupland Hospital, Ropery Road, Gainsborough DN21 2TJ Tel: 01427 816500 Fax: 01427 810785 / 816517; 11 Southlands Gardens, Morton, Gainsborough DN21 3EX Tel: 01427 610071 — MB BS 1971 Rajasthan; MRCPI 1981; FRCP (I) 1998. (R.N.T. Med. Coll. Udaipur) Assoc. Specialist (Geriat. & Gen. Med.) John Coupland Hosp. GainsBoro. & Co. Hosp. Lincoln. Socs: Lincoln Med. Soc.; BMA; Brit. Geriat. Soc. Prev: SCMO (Geriat. & Gen. Med.) John Coupland Hosp. GainsBoro.; Regist. (Geriat. & Gen. Med.) Pilgrim Hosp. Boston; SHO (Geriat. Med.) Vict. Hosp. Mansfield.

PATCH, David William Michael Dept of surgery,9th floor, Royal Free Hospital, Pond St., London NW3 2QG Tel: 020 7794 4688 — MB BS 1987 Lond.; MRCP (UK) 1990. Cons. & Hon. Sen. Lect.dept of liver translantation & hepatolary Med.

PATCHETT, Douglas Robert, MC (retired) 58 Regency House, Newbold Terrace, Leamington Spa CV32 4HD Tel: 01926 423679 — MRCS Eng. LRCP Lond. 1944. Prev: Capt. RAMC.

PATCHETT, Ian Douglas Groby Road Medical Centre, 9 Groby Road, Leicester LE3 9ED Tel: 0116 253 8185 — MB ChB 1984 Leic.; MRCGP 1989; DRCOG 1988. GP Leics.

PATCHETT, Paul Anthony Waterloo House Surgery, Waterloo House, 42-44 Wellington Street, Millom LA18 4DE Tel: 01229 772123 — MB ChB 1975 Bristol; MRCGP 1984; MRCP (UK) 1979.

PATCHETT, Stephen Edmund 216 Windsor Road, Maidenhead SL6 2DW — MB BCh BAO 1984 NUI; MRCPI 1987.

PATCHETT, Una Margaret Mary Binfield Surgery, Terrace Road N., Binfield, Bracknell RG42 5JG Tel: 01344 425434 Fax: 01344 301843; 216 Windsor Road, Broy Borders, Maidenhead SL6 2DW — MB BCh BAO 1984 NUI; MRCGP 1991; DObst RCPI 1988; DCH RCP Lond. 1988. (Univ. Coll. Dub.)

PATE, Elizabeth Gilmore 13 Laurel Avenue, Lenzie, Glasgow G66 4RX — MB ChB 1960 Glas.; DPH Glas. 1969; DCH RCPS Glas. 1964.

PATEL, Aarron Neil Annie Prendergast Health Centre, Ashton Gardens, Chadwell Heath, Romford RM6 6RT — MB BS 1995 Lond.

PATEL, Abdul Rahim Ahmed Queen Elizabeth Psychiatric Hospital, Mindlesohn Way, Edgbaston, Birmingham B15 2QZ Tel: 0121 678 2027 Fax: 0121 678 2075; 5 Fitzroy Avenue, Harborne, Birmingham B17 8RL — MB ChB 1982 Zambia; MSc Clin. Trop. Med. Lond. 1985; MRCPsych 1992. (University of Zambia) Cons. (Old Age Psychiat.), Qu. Eliz. Psychiatric Hosp. Prev: Sen. Regist. (Old Age Psychiat.) W. Midl. RHA.; Regist. Birm. Train. Scheme.

PATEL, Abhilash 3 Fugelmere Close, Harborne, Birmingham B17 8SE Tel: 0121 429 2488 — MB BS 1974 Newc.; FFA RCS Eng. 1978. (Univ. Newc. u. Tyne) Cons. Anaesth. Univ. Hosp. Birm. NHS Trust & Sandwell NHS Trust. Prev: Sen. Regist. (Anaesth.) W. Midl. RHA; Regist. & SHO (Anaesth.) Notts. AHA (T).

PATEL, Alberta Elizabeth 119 Chester Road, St.ly, Sutton Coldfield B74 2HE Tel: 0121 353 1888; 96 Chester Road N., Sutton Coldfield B73 6SL — MB BCh BAO 1957 Belf.; DObst RCOG 1960. Socs: Med. Wom. Federat. (Hon. Br. Sec. Birm. & W. Midl.).

PATEL, Alka Manish 114 Francklyn Gardens, Edgware HA8 8SA Tel: 020 8958 3657 Fax: 020 8357 3471 Email: dralka@hotmail.com — MB BS 1995 Lond.; DFFP 1997; DRCOG 1997; DCH 1998. (UMDS)

PATEL, Allison 5 Betony Walk, Haverhill CB9 7YA — MB BCh BAO 1991 NUI; MRCOG 1997; LRCPSI 1991. Regist. (O & G) P'boro. Dist. Hosp., Cambs; Regist. (O & G). Prev: Regist. (O & G) Whipps Cross Hosp. Lond.; Regist. (Obst. & Gyn.) Homerton Hosp. Lond.; Regist. (O & G) P.ss Alex Andra Hosp., Harlaw.

***PATEL, Alpa Mohanbhai** 70 Lawn Street, Bolton BL1 3AY — MB ChB 1998 Manch.; MB ChB Manch 1998.

PATEL, Alpesh 7 Lens Road, London E7 8PU — MB ChB 1992 Manch.; BSc (Hons.) Manch. 1989; DCH RCP Lond. 1994; MRCGP 1997. (Manch.) Princip. GP Loughton Health Centre.

PATEL, Ambalal Shankerlal The Surgery, Station Road, Shotton Colliery, Durham DH6 2JL Tel: 0191 526 5913 Fax: 0191 526 2651; Peterlee Health Centre, Peterlee SR8 1AD Tel: 0191 586 7414 — MB BS 1973 Gujarat; DObst RCPI 1979; Cert. Family Plann. JCC 1977. (B.J. Med. Coll. Ahmedabad) Prev: Regist. (O & G) Gen. Hosp. Bishop Auckland, Middlesbrough Matern. Hosp. & Middlesbrough Gen. Hosp.; SHO (Obst.) Craigtoun Matern. Hosp. St. And.; SHO (O & G) N.. Gen. Hosp. Sheff.

PATEL, Mr Ameet Ghanshyam Dept. of Surgery, King's College Hospital, Denmark Hill, London SE5 9RS Tel: 020 7346 3065 Fax: 020 7346 3438 Email: agp@ameet.dircon.co.uk — MB BS 1985 Lond.; FRCS Ed. 1991; FRCS (Eng) 1992; MS 1999. (St. George's Hosp. Med. Sch. Lond.) Cons. (Surg.) King's Coll. Hosp. Lond.

PATEL, Amish 19a Birch Park, Harrow HA3 6SP — MB ChB 1996 Manch. (Manch.) SHO (Gen. Med.) Rotat. Roy. Berksh. & Battle NHS Trust. Socs: MDU; BMA. Prev: Ho. Off. Roy. Preston Hosp. Lancs.

***PATEL, Amish** 12 Belvoir Close, Oadby, Leicester LE2 4SG Tel: 0116 2719 295; 12 Belvoir Close, Oadby, Leicester LE2 4SG Tel: 0116 2719 295 — MB BS 1998 Lond.; MB BS Lond 1998.

PATEL, Mr Amratlal Norfolk & Norwich Hospital, Brunswick Road, Norwich NR1 3SR Tel: 01603 286711 Fax: 01603 287160; 77 Newmarket Road, Norwich NR2 2HW Tel: 01603 763645 Fax: 01603 763645 Email: adpatel@paston.co.uk — MB ChB 1976 Sheff.; FRCS Eng. 1981. Cons. Orthop. Surg. & Specialist Trauma & Shoulder Disorders Norf. & Norwich Hosp. Socs: Brit. Trauma Soc.; Brit. Shoulder & Elbow Soc. Prev: Sen. Regist. SW Thames Region Train. Scheme; Clin. Fell. (Trauma) Sunnybrook Med. Centre Toronto, Canada; Regist. St. Geo. Hosp. Lond.

PATEL, Amrish Chimanlal St John's Hill Surgery, 39 St. John's Hill, Sevenoaks TN13 3NT Tel: 01732 747202 Fax: 01732 747218; 25 Hollman Gardens, Norbury Hill, London SW16 3SJ Tel: 020 8764 4837 Fax: 020 8764 4837 Email: jpatel3501@aol.com — MB BS 1984 Lond.; MRCGP 1988; DFFP 1995; DRCOG 1987. (Lond. Hosp. Med. Coll. Univ. Lond.) Hosp. Pract. (Geriat., A & E) Sevenoaks Hosp.; Clin. Asst. (A & E & Rehabil. Med.) Kent. Prev: Asst. Prof. Dept. Family Med. Univ. Mass. USA; Clin. Med. Off. (Community Paediat.) Chelmsford; Trainee GP/SHO (Gen. Med.) Broomfield Hosp. Chelmsford VTS.

PATEL, Angela 1 Ennerdale Close, Huntingdon PE29 6UU — MB ChB 1993 Liverp.

PATEL, Anil Royal National Throat Nose and Ear Hospital, Grays Inn Road, London WC1X 8DA Tel: 020 7915 1669 Fax: 020 7278 3018 — MB BS 1991 Lond.; FRCA 1995. (University College and Middlesex School of Medicine(London University)) Cons. Anaesth., The Roy. Nat. Throat, Nose & Ear Hosp., Lond.; Hon. Sen. Roy. Fre & Univ. Coll. Med. Sch., UCL. Socs: Difficult Airway Soc. Prev: research fell., Paediat. IC Unit, Guy's Hosp.; Sen. Regist., Anaesth. Dept., Guy's Hosp.; Regist. Rotat. (Anaesth.) Qu. Vict. Hosp. E. Grinstead.

PATEL, Anilkumar Maganbhai 224 Balgores Lane, Romford RM2 6BS — MRCS Eng. LRCP Lond. 1991.

PATEL, Anita 12 Pinewood Drive, Potters Bar EN6 2BD — MB BCh 1993 Wales.

PATEL, Anita Givindji 21 Farrans Court, Northwick Avenue, Harrow HA3 0AT — MB ChB 1986 Glas.

PATEL, Anjana 20 Brecknock Road, London N7 0DD — MB BS 1993 Lond.

PATEL, Anooj Kanubhai 39 Bluebell Close, Rush Green, Romford RM7 0XN — MB ChB 1998 Sheff.; MB ChB Sheff 1998.

PATEL, Anuj 4 Limes Avenue, London N12 8QN — MB BS 1993 Lond.

PATEL, Mr Anup Tel: 020 886 1033/1006 Fax: 0207 7986 1546 — MB BS 1983 Lond.; BSc (1st cl. Hons.) Lond. 1980; FRCS Eng. 1987; ECFMG 1993; MS 1994; (Urol.) FRCS 1994. (St. Bart.) Cons Urological Surg St Mary's Hosp Lond. Socs: Full mem BAUS; Full Mem EALL; Corr. mem AUA. Prev: Sen. Regist. (Urol.) Roy. Marsden Hosp. Lond.; Clin Instruc. in EndoUrol. & Urological Oncol. UCLA Calif.

PATEL, Anup Madhusudan 5 Broadcroft Avenue, Stanmore HA7 1NT Tel: 020 8357 5858 — MB BS 1993 Lond.; MRCGP 1998. (UMDS of Guy's and St. Thomas's Hosps.) Princip. in Gen. Pract. Socs: BMA & Med. Defence Union. Prev: SHO (Palliat. Care & A & E) N. Lond. Hospice; Trainee GP/SHO (O & G) Edgware.

PATEL, Arati Bhavesh Lawnside, St. Georges Road, Bickley, Bromley BR1 2LB Tel: 020 8467 6094 — MB ChB 1990 Sheff.; T(GP) 1995; DFFP 1994. Trainee GP Lewisham & N. S.wark HA VTS. Prev: Ho. Off. Qu. Mary's Hosp. Sidcup; Ho. Off. Joyce Green Hosp. Dartford.

PATEL, Arti Manaharlal 10 Park Court, Sandy SG19 1NP — MB ChB 1986 Glasg. SHO (Paediat.) Luton & Dunstable Hosp.

PATEL, Aruna Ramanbhai St James House Surgery, County Court Road, King's Lynn PE30 5SY Tel: 01553 774221 Fax: 01553 692181 — MB BCh BAO 1981 NUI; LRCPI & LM, LRCSI & LM 1981.

PATEL, Arunbhai Bhagwanbhai Health Centre, Wardles Lane, Great Wyrley, Walsall WS6 6EW Tel: 01922 411948 Fax: 01922 412994 — MB BS 1971 Gujarat.

PATEL, Arunkumar Naginbhai 38 Calder Gardens, Edgware HA8 5PT — MB BS 1974 Saurashtra.

PATEL, Arvind Chhotu c/o Boydens Estate Agents, Aston House, 57-59 Crouch St., Colchester CO3 3EL — MB ChB 1975 Bristol; MRCGP 1979; DRCOG 1978. Princip. Med. Off. (Communicable Dis.) Dept. Health, Wellington, NZ. Socs: Roy. NZ Coll. GP's & NZ Coll. Community Med.

PATEL, Arvind Manibhai (retired) Haematology Department, New Cross Hospital, Wolverhampton WV10 0QP Tel: 01902 307999 Fax: 01902 643104 — MB BS Gauhati 1965; FRCPath 1984, M, 1972. Cons. Haemat. New Cross Hosp. Wolverhampton. Prev: Demonst. (Path.) King's Coll. Hosp. Med. Sch. Lond.

PATEL, Ashok Nanubhai Deepdale Road Healthcare Centre, Deepdale Road, Preston PR1 5AF Tel: 01772 655533 Fax: 01772 653414; 7 Langport Close, Fulwood, Preston PR2 9FE — MB ChB 1983 Manch.; MRCGP 1990.

PATEL, Ashokkumar Gordhanbhai Bedford Hospital, Weller Wing, Bedford MK42 PDJ Tel: 01234 355122 Fax: 01234 792279; 26 Aubreys, Letchworth SG6 3TZ Tel: 01462 676714 Fax: 01462 638513 — MB BS 1976 Baroda; FRCPsych 1997, M 1983; DPM Eng. 1981. (Baroda, India) Cons. Psychiat. Bedford Hosp.; Clin. Dir. (Ment. Health) Bedford Hosp. Prev: Sen. Regist. St. Bernards Hosp. S.all; Regist. & SHO Rotat. (Psychiat.) Char. Cross Hosp. Lond.; Clin. Tutor (Psychiat.) Fairfield Hosp.

***PATEL, Ashokkumar Ramanbhai** 50 Sheffield Drive, Lea, Preston PR2 1TS — MB ChB 1994 Manch.

PATEL, Ashvinkumar Raojibhai Leicester Road Surgery, 57 Leicester Road, Bedworth, Nuneaton CV12 8AB Tel: 024 7631 2288 Fax: 024 7631 3502; 5 Mill Close, Nuneaton CV11 6QD Tel: 01203 642009 — MB BS Baroda 1968; Cert. Family Plann. JCC 1974; DCH RCPSI 1972; DTM & H Liverp. 1971. (Med. Coll. Baroda) Sch. Med. Off. Exhall Grange Sch. for Handicap. Childr. Coventry. Socs: Dent. & Hypnotic Assn.

***PATEL, Ashwin Mukesh** 230 Turncroft Lane, Stockport SK1 4AX — MB ChB 1994 Manch.

PATEL

PATEL, Mr Ashwinkumar Rambhai Preston Medical Centre, 23 Preston Road, Wembley HA9 8JZ Tel: 020 8904 3263; 11 Ford End, Denham Village, Uxbridge UB9 5AL — MB BS 1972 Bombay; MB BS Bombay 1970; FRCS Eng. 1979; FRCS Ed. 1979.

PATEL, Atulkumar The Health Centre, Gibson Lane, Kippax, Leeds LS25 7JN Tel: 0113 287 0870 Fax: 0113 232 0746; 3 The Coppice, Sherburn-in-Elmet, Leeds LS25 6LU — MB ChB 1985 Manch.; Cert. Family Plann. JCC 1989; DRCOG 1989. GP N. Yorks.; Hosp. Pract. Endoscopy Unit St. Jas. Univ. Hosp. Leeds.

PATEL, Avni 22B Crookham Road, London SW6 4EQ; Flat 3, 14 Brunswick Terrace, Hove BN3 1HL Tel: 01273 823304 — MB BS 1994 Lond.; DRCOG 1998; MRCGP 1998. (King's Sch. Of Med. & Dent.)

PATEL, Azad Jashbhai St Giles Surgery, 40 St. Giles Road, London SE5 7RF Tel: 020 7252 5936; 38a Stanley Avenue, Beckenham BR3 6PX Tel: 020 8658 3944 — MB BS 1973 Gujarat. (B.J. Med. Coll. Ahmedabad)

PATEL, Babubhai Khodabhai (retired) 70 St Michael's Avenue, Wembley HA9 6SA Tel: 020 8900 0993 — MB BS 1946 Lond.; MRCS Eng. LRCP Lond. 1944.

PATEL, Bachubhai Bhogilal 39 The Paddocks, Wembley HA9 9HG — MB BS 1971 Saurashtra.

***PATEL, Bakula** 15 Albert Promenade, Loughborough LE11 1RB — MB ChB 1995 Leic.

PATEL, Bela 23 The Dene, Wembley HA9 7QS — MB BCh 1989 Wales; MRCGP 1994; DRCOG 1993.

PATEL, Bhanukumar Ambalal 3 Downs Walk, Peacehaven BN10 7SN — MB BS 1973 Indore.

PATEL, Bharat Radiology Department, Singleton Hospital, Sketty, Swansea SA2 8QA Tel: 01792 285431 Fax: 01792 286090 Email: bharat.patel@swansea-tr.wales.nhs.uk; Inshallah, Bishopston Road, Bishopston, Swansea SA3 3EW — MB BCh 1981 Wales; FRCR 1987; Dip Health Managem 1998. (Welsh National School of Medicine) Cons. & Clin. Dir. (Diagnostic Radiol.) Singleton Hosp. Swansea.

PATEL, Bharat Chunibhai 21 Compton Close, London NW11 8SX Tel: 020 7267 2868 — MB BS 1992 Lond. SHO (Geriat.) St Helier Hosp. Carshalton. Prev: SHO (A & E) E. Surrey Hosp. Redhill.

PATEL, Bharatkumar Chimanbhai PHLS Collaborating Centre, Department of Microbiology, North Middlesex University Hospital, Sterling Way, London N18 1QX Tel: 020 8887 2472 Fax: 020 8887 4227 — MB BS 1980 Lond.; MSc Lond. 1992; MRCPath 1993. Cons. Med. microbiologist Med. microBiol. Pub. health Laborat. Serv..Lond. Socs: Hosp. Infec. Soc.; Brit. Soc. Antimicrob. Chemother.; Assn. Med. Microbiol. Prev: Cons. Med. Microbiol. Pub. Health Laborat. Serv. Ashford; Sen. Regist. Pub. Health Laborat. Serv. Centr. Middlx. Hosp.; Regist. & Hon. Asst. Lect. (Med. Microbiol.) King's Coll. Hosp. Lond.

PATEL, Bharatkumar Popatlal 1 Comyns Close, Canning Town, London E16 4JJ; 131 Prince Regent Lane, Plaistow, London E13 8RY Tel: 020 7476 1964 — MB BS 1973 Baroda. (Med. Coll. Baroda)

PATEL, Bhasker Chunibhai 134 Bath Road, Hounslow TW3 3ET Tel: 0208 570 9609 Fax: 0208 572 0935 — MB BS 1977 Gujarat; MRCS Eng. LRCP Lond. 1980; MRCOG 1983. Socs: Roy. Coll. of Obst. & Gynae.

PATEL, Bhavesh Kantibhai The Surgery, 188 Ann Street, London SE18 7LU Tel: 020 8854 6444 Fax: 020 8855 7656; Lawnside, St. Georges Road, Bickley, Bromley BR1 2LB Tel: 020 8467 6094 — MB ChB 1989 Sheff.; T(GP) 1993; DFFP 1993. Trainee GP Qu. Mary's Hosp. Sidcup VTS. Prev: Ho. Off. (Med.) Bassettlaw Dist. Gen. Hosp.; Ho. Off: Joyce Green Hosp. Dartford.

***PATEL, Bhavesh Sarajchandra** 13 Triumph Road, Glenfield, Leicester LE3 8FR — MB BS 1997 Lond.

PATEL, Bhikhubhai Devrajbhai Hospital of St Cross, Barby Road, Rugby CV22 5PX Tel: 01788 572831; 29 Lime Tree Avenue, Rugby CV22 7QT — MB BS 1975 Saurashtra; FRCPCH 1997, MR 1996; DCCH RCP Ed. 1985; DCH RCPS Glas. 1980. Cons. Paediat. Hosp. St. Cross. Socs: Med. Protec. Soc.; BACCH; BMA. Prev: Locum Cons. Paediat. P.ss Alexandra Hosp. Harlow.

PATEL, Bhupen Motibhai The Surgery, 54 Thorne Road, Doncaster DN1 2JP Tel: 01302 361222; 34 Cantley Lane, Bessacarr, Doncaster DN4 6ND Tel: 01302 538478 — MB ChB 1983 Manch.; MRCGP 1989; DRCOG 1987.

PATEL, Bhupendra Dahyabhai Longton Health Centre, Drayton Road, Longton, Stoke-on-Trent ST3 1EQ Tel: 01782 332176 Fax: 01782 598602 — MB BS 1965 Gujarat; MB BS 1965 Gujarat.

PATEL, Bhupendra Purshottam Charnwood Health Centre, 1 Spinney Hill Road, Leicester LE5 3GH Tel: 0116 262 5102; 12 Belvoir Close, Oadby, Leicester LE2 4SG — MB BS 1966 Calcutta. (Calcutta Nat. Med. Coll.)

PATEL, Bhupendra Ramanlal 24 Stockport Road, Streatham Vale, London SW16 5XF Tel: 020 8764 5709 — MB BS 1969 Bombay. (T.N. Med. Coll. Bombay)

PATEL, Bhupendra T The Dowlais Medical Practice, Ivor Street, Dowlais, Merthyr Tydfil CF48 3LU Tel: 01685 721400 Fax: 01685 375287.

PATEL, Bijesh Family Doctor Unit Surgery, 92 Bath Road, Hounslow TW3 3LN Tel: 020 8577 9555 Fax: 020 8570 2266; Orchard Lodge, 88 Sandy Lane, Teddington TW11 0DF Email: bijesh1@aol.com — MB ChB 1985 Dundee; BMSc (Hons.) 1982; MRCGP 1989; DRCOG 1987. (Univ. of Dundee) GP Tutor Char. Cross Hosp. Prev: Trainee GP Croydon; SHO (A & E, O & G, Geriat. & Rheum.) Mayday Hosp. Croydon.

PATEL, Bina 36 Longaford Way, Hutton Mount, Brentwood CM13 2LT — BM 1990 Soton. Cons. Phys. Socs: Amer. Coll. Phys. Prev: Resid. (Internal Med.) Temple Univ. & Hahnemann Univ. Philadelphia, USA; Ho. Surg. Univ. Soton.

***PATEL, Binit Ramnik** 40 Avondale Road, Benfleet SS7 1EJ — MB ChB 1996 Manch.

PATEL, Bipen Dahyabhai 8 Bilberry Close, Leicester LE3 2JA — MB BS 1992 Lond.; BSc (Hons.) Human Physiol. Lond. 1989; MRCP (UK) 1996. Health Serv. Research fell. Inst. Of Pub. Health, Forvic Uni. Site Hills Rd Camb.; Hon. SpR (Resp. Med.) Addenbrookes Hosp. Camb. Socs: Brit. Thorac. Soc. Prev: Specialist Regist. (Respirat. Med.) S.mead Hosp. Bristol; SpR (Resp. Med.) Roy. Devon & Exeter Hosp. Exeter.

PATEL, Bipin Bhikhabhai Watling Vale Medical Centre, Burchard Crescent, Shenley Church End, Milton Keynes MK5 6EY Tel: 01908 501177 Fax: 01908 504916; 6 Stonegate, Bancroft, Milton Keynes MK13 0PX — MB BCh 1982 Wales; MRCP (UK) 1993; MRCGP 1987; DCH RCP Lond. 1986; DRCOG 1985. Prev: Trainee GP/SHO Milton Keynes Hosp.; SHO (Anaesth.) E. Birm. Hosp.; Ho. Off. Univ. Hosp. Wales Cardiff.

PATEL, Bipinchandra Oakham Surgery, 213 Regent Road, Tividale, Oldbury B69 1RZ Tel: 01384 252274 Fax: 01348 240088; 55 The Broadway, Dudley DY1 4AP — MB BCh 1978 Wales.

PATEL, Bipinchandra Naginbhai The Sorrels Surgery, 7 The Sorrels, Stanford-le-Hope SS17 7DZ Tel: 01375 671344 Fax: 01375 676913 — MB BS 1969 Bombay; DObst. RCOG 1974; Cert. FPA 1974. (Seth G.S. Med. Coll. Bombay) Med. Off. Basildon Family Plann. Clin.

***PATEL, Biral Pratap** 66 Somerset Street, Kingsdown, Bristol BS2 8NB — MB ChB 1995 Bristol.

PATEL, Chaitanya, CBE Westminster Healthcare Ltd, Westminster House, Randalls Way, Leatherhead KT22 7TZ Tel: 01372 860302 Fax: 01372 860336 Email: cpatel@whc.co.uk — BM 1979 Soton.; FRCP (UK) 1999. Chief Exec. W.m. Healthcare Grp.; Chief Exec. W.m Healthcare Grp. Socs: Brit. Geriat.Soc. Prev: Chairm. And Chief Exec. Ct. Cavendish Gp. plc Lond. And Chief Exec.; Chief Exec., Care 1st Gp.

PATEL, Mrs Chandra Vinodchandra The Surgery, 117 Knypersley Road, Norton-in-the-Moors, Stoke-on-Trent ST6 8JA Tel: 01782 545728 Fax: 01782 570069; Sanmay, Basnetts Wood, Endon, Stoke-on-Trent ST9 9DQ Tel: 01782 504403 — MB BS 1964 Gujarat; DA Eng. 1966; DGO Gujarat 1965. (B.J. Med. Coll. Ahmedabad)

PATEL, Chandrakant Great Barr Group Practice, 912 Walsall Road, Great Barr, Birmingham B42 1TG Tel: 0121 357 1250 Fax: 0121 358 4857 — MB BCh 1986 Wales. Socs: Birm. Med. Inst.

PATEL, Chandrakant Bhailal Bhai Medical Centre, Chatsworth Road, Chesterfield S40 Tel: 01246 568065; 173 Old Road, Brampton, Chesterfield S40 3QL Tel: 01246 206341 — MB ChB 1963 Manch. Prev: Ho. Off. (Surg.) Pk. Hosp. Davyhulme; SHO (Anaesth.) City Gen. Hosp. Stoke-on-Trent.

PATEL, Chandrakant Jashbhai The Cottage Surgery, 179 South Coast Road, Peacehaven BN10 8NR Tel: 01273 581629 Fax: 01273 584648 — MB BS 1967 Gujarat.

PATEL, Chandrakant Prabhudas Patel's Surgery, 90-92 Malvern Road, Gillingham ME7 4BB Tel: 01634 578333 Fax: 01634 852581 — MB BS 1963 Bombay.

PATEL, Chandrakant Rambhai London Road Surgery, 519 London Road, Thornton Heath CR7 6AR Tel: 020 8684 2161; Westdean, 5 Downsway, Sanderstead, South Croydon CR2 0JB — MB BCh 1972 Wales; Dip Therp 1998. (University of Wales) GP Tutor St. Geo. Hosp. Med. Sch. Lond. Socs: BMA. Prev: Trainee GP Hackney VTS; Ho. Phys. (Med.) Singleton Hosp. Swansea; Ho. Surg. E. Glam. Gen. Hosp. Pontypridd.

PATEL, Chandrakant Ranchhodbhai Pickhurst Surgery, 56 Pickhurst Lane, Bromley BR2 7JF Tel: 020 8462 2880 Fax: 020 8462 9581; Manraj, 19 Pk Avenue, Farnborough Park, Orpington BR6 8LJ Tel: 01689 855312 — MB ChB 1964 East Africa; MRCP (UK) 1972. (Makerere Med. Sch.)

PATEL, Chandrakant Shankerbhai Roundwood Day Hospital, Willesden Hospital, Harlesdon Road, London NW10 3RY Tel: 020 8451 8284; 112 Princess Avenue, Palmers Green, London N13 6HD — MB BS 1975 Baroda. Staff Grade Psychiat. NW Lond. Ment. Health NHS Trust Lond. Prev: Regist. (Psychiat.) Wexham Pk. Hosp. Slough.

PATEL, Chandresh Ratilal Woodlands Surgery, 301 Newtown Road, Bedworth, Nuneaton CV12 0AJ Tel: 01203 490909 — MB BS 1971 Baroda.

PATEL, Chandresh Thakorbhai 165 Woodmansterne Road, London SW16 5UB — MB BCh 1990 Wales.

PATEL, Chandubhai Bhailalbhai 51 Newdene Avenue, Northolt UB5 5JE — MB BS 1961 Gujarat.

PATEL, Chetan Kantibhai Oxford Eye Hospital, Radcliffe Infirmary, Oxford OX2 9AN; 20 Elms Drive, Marston, Oxford OX3 0NJ — MB BS 1988 Lond.; BSc (Hons.) Lond. 1987; FRCOphth 1993. (Lond. Hosp. Med. Coll.) Regist. Rotat. Oxf. Prev: Research Regist. Cataract Research Unit Oxf. Eye Hosp.; SHO Rotat. (Ophth.) St. Geo. Hosp., E. Surrey Hosp. & Worthing Dist. Gen. Hosp.; SHO (Neurosurg.) Brook Gen. Hosp.

PATEL, Chetankumar 57 Burnley Road, London NW10 1EE Tel: 0976 620973 Email: chetan@globalnet.co.uk — MB BS 1992 Lond.

PATEL, Daksha 60 Holmfield Avenue, Stoneygate, Leicester LE2 2BF; 57 Redcar Road, Broomhill, Sheffield S10 1EX Tel: 0114 266 8589 — MB ChB 1985 Sheff.; MRCOG 1990; MD Sheff. Univ. 1999. Sen. Lect. / Hon. Cons.

PATEL, Davandra North West Regional Health Authority, Manchester M20 2PL; 25 Truro Drive, Sale M33 5DF — MB ChB 1986 Manch.; FRCA 1991; DA (UK) 1988. Sen. Regist. (Anaesth.) NW RHA Manch. Socs: Train. Mem. Assn. AnE.h.; Manch. Med. Soc. Prev: Instruc. (Anesthesiol.) Univ. Michigan Ann Arbor, USA.

PATEL, Dayavanti Shashikant The Surgery, 1A Oak Road, Canvey Island SS8 7AX Tel: 01268 692211 — MB BS 1968 Gujarat. (B.J. Med. Coll. Ahmedabad) Med. Off. Family Plann. Clinics Essex AHA.

***PATEL, Deepal Arunbhai** 115 Hatherton Road, Cannock WS11 1HH — MB BS 1997 Lond.

***PATEL, Deevia Chandrakant** 79 Regal Way, Harrow HA3 0SD Tel: 020 8907 2055; 79 Regal Way, Harrow HA3 0SD Tel: 020 8907 2055 — MB BS 1998 Lond.; MB BS Lond 1998.

PATEL, Deven Jashbhai 87 Pine Walk, Carshalton Beeches, Carshalton SM5 4HL Tel: 020 8642 6395 — MB BS 1985 Lond.; MRCP (UK) 1988. Sen. Regist. (Cardiol.) Harefield Hosp. Middlx. Prev: Regist. (Cardiol.) Roy. Brompton Nat. Heart & Lung Hosp. Lond.; Regist. (Gen. Med. & Cardiol.) Hillingdon Hosp. Uxbridge; Regist. (Cardiol.) Roy. Free Hosp. Lond.

PATEL, Devendra Pravin 18 Manor Road, Chigwell IG7 5PD — MB BS 1994 Lond.

PATEL, Devyani Ramubhai Dartmouth Medical Centre, 1 Richard St., West Bromwich B70 9JL Tel: 0121 553 1144 Fax: 0121 580 1914; Central Clinic, Horseley Road, Tipton DY4 7NB Tel: 0121 557 4377 — MB BS 1966 Gujarat; DGO Dub. 1969; LM Rotunda 1969. (B.J. Med. Coll. Ahmedabad) Med. Off. Family Plann. Assn. Birm. Prev: SHO (Gyn. & Obst.) Leicester Gen. Hosp.

***PATEL, Dharmesh** Paradise Medical Centre, Broad Street, Coventry CV6 5BG Tel: 024 7668 9343 Fax: 024 7663 8733 — MB ChB 1994 Leic.

***PATEL, Dharmesh** 20 Windermere Street, Castle Gardens, Leicester LE2 7GT — MB ChB 1995 Manch.

PATEL, Dheeren 1 Crossway, Raynes Park, London SW20 9JA Tel: 020 8543 1059 — BM 1987 Soton.; Cert. Family Plann. JCC 1991; DRCOG 1991. Prev: SHO (Paediat.) Soton. Gen. Hosp.; SHO (Geriat. Med.) Univ. Coll. Hosp. Lond.; SHO (A & E) Epsom Dist. Hosp.

PATEL, Dhruva Doncaster Drive Surgery, 45 Doncaster Drive, Northolt UB5 4AT Tel: 020 8864 8133; 6 Thomas A Beckett Close, Sudbury Hill HA0 2SH — MB ChB 1990 Aberd.; MRCGP 1994. (Univ. Aberd.)

PATEL, Dilip Kumar Chhotabhai Civic Medical Centre, 18 Bethecar Road, Harrow HA1 1SE Tel: 020 8427 9445 Fax: 020 8424 0652; 3 Arnside Gardens, Wembley HA9 8TJ Tel: 020 8908 21444 — MB BCh BAO 1984 NUI; LRCPSI 1984.

PATEL, Dilip Kumar Kunverji Email: dilip_k_patel@yahoo.co.uk — MB ChB 1978 Bristol; FRCA. 1982. Cons. Anaesth. Mt. Vernon Hosp. Trust Middlx. Socs: Assn. Anaesth. & Intens. Care Soc. Prev: Sen. Regist. Middlx. Hosp. Lond.

PATEL, Dilip Maganlal 24 Ernest Street, Bolton BL1 4RZ — MB ChB 1994 Manch.; DRCOG 1996; DCH RCP Lond. 1996; DFFP 1998; MRCGP 1998. (The Victoria University of Manchester) GP Locum Preston. Prev: SHO (Paediat.) & Ho. Off. (Gen. Surg. & Urol.) Roy. Preston Hosp.; SHO (A & E) Roy. Preston Hosp.; SHO (Psychiat.) Chorley Hosp.

PATEL, Dilipkumar Chaturbhai 21 Knights Manor Way, Dartford DA1 5SB — MB BS 1980 Ranchi; LMSSA Lond. 1989.

PATEL, Dinesh Kumar Kantibhai The Consulting Rooms, Oxhey Drive, South Oxhey, Watford WD1 6RU Tel: 020 8428 2292; 3 Holbein Gate, Eastglade, Northwood HA6 3SH — MB BS 1973 Banaras Hindu. (Inst. Med. Sc. Varanasi) Prev: SHO (Med., A & E & Orthop.) Hertford Co. Hosp.

PATEL, Dineshchandra Broadway Surgery, 2 Broadway, Fulwood, Preston PR2 9TH Tel: 01772 717261 Fax: 01772 787652 — MB ChB 1984 Manch.; MRCGP 1990; DRCOG 1990; DCH RCP Lond. 1988. Occupat. Health Off. Preston; Represen. Lancs. LMC; NW Lorg Represen.; EMCS Nat. User Gp. Comm. Mem.; Edr. EMCS NUG. Socs: Subfac. Represen. Roy. Coll. Gen. Pract. Prev: Trainee GP Preston VTS.

PATEL, Dinkerrai Purshottamdass Health Centre, Lake Lock Road, Stanley, Wakefield WF3 4HS Tel: 01924 822328 Fax: 01924 870052 — MB BS 1967 Bombay. (Bombay) GP Wakefield, W. Yorks.

PATEL, Dipak 5 Charles Road, London E7 8PT — MB ChB 1992 Liverp.

***PATEL, Dipesh Chandrakant** 139 Overbrook, Eldene, Swindon SN3 6AU — MB BS 1998 Lond.; MB BS Lond 1998.

***PATEL, Dipika Vandravanbhai** 9 Hurst Road, Eastbourne BN21 2PJ — BM BCh 1998 Oxf.; BM BCh Oxf 1998.

PATEL, Dipti UMDS/Guys & St Thomas' NHS Trust, Lambeth Palace Road, London SE1 7EH — MB BS 1989 Lond.; DRCOG 1992; MRCGP 1993; Dip. Occ. Med. RCP Lond. 1997. Lect. (Occupat. Health) UMDS Guys & St. Thomas' NHS Trust Lond. Prev: Med. Adviser to the Foreign & Commonw. Office Lond.

PATEL, Ela Dayalji Park Surgery, 278 Stratford Road, Shirley, Solihull B90 3AF Tel: 0121 241 1700 Fax: 0121 241 1821; 12 Stoneleigh Road, Solihull B91 1DG — MB ChB 1983 Leic.

PATEL, Falgun 219 Charlton Road, Harrow HA3 9HT — MB ChB 1992 Manch.

PATEL, Geeta Devi Salisbury Road Surgery, 1 Salisbury Road, Seven Kings, Ilford IG3 8BG Tel: 020 8590 1143 Fax: 020 8599 7162 — MB BCh 1989 Wales; BSc (Hons.) Wales 1989. Socs: Roy. Coll. Gen. Pract. Prev: Trainee GP Harlow; SHO (O & G, Med. & c/o Elderly)) Harlow; SHO (A & E) St. Margt. Hosp. Epping.

PATEL, Geeta Harendra Patel, Latimer Health Centre, 4 Homerton Terrace, off Morning Lane, Hackney, London E9 6RT Tel: 020 8985 2249 Fax: 020 8985 7333; Rosedene, 4 Mellish Gardens, Woodford Green IG8 0BH — MB BS 1979 Rajasthan. GP; Clin. Asst. Psychiat. Homerton Hosp. Prev: Regist. (Psychiat.) Claybury Hosp. Woodbridge Essex & Warley Hosp. Brentwood.

PATEL, Ghanashyambhai Umedbhai Meersbrook Medical Centre, 243-245 Chesterfield Road, Sheffield S8 0RT Tel: 0114 258 3997 — MB BS 1972 Jiwaji. (Gajra Raja Med. Coll. Gwalior)

PATEL, Ghanshyam Maganbhai 57 Woodfield Road, Oadby, Leicester LE2 4HQ — MB BS 1969 Gujarat.

PATEL, Girish Khandubhai 23 St. George's Lodge, Queen's Road, Weybridge KT13 0AB — MB BS 1993 Lond.

PATEL

PATEL, Girishchandra Keshavlal 22 Church View, Roger Lane, Rd. 1, Laleston, Bridgend CF32 0HF Tel: 01656 659745; 83 Tremains Court, Brackla, Bridgend CF31 2SS Tel: 01656 669519 — MB BS 1969 Baroda; DTCD Wales 1972. (Med. Coll. Baroda) Regist. (Geriat. Med.) Bridgend Gen. Hosp. Socs: Brit. Tuberc. & Thoracic Assn. & BMA.

PATEL, Gokul Maganlal Tawe Medical Centre, 6 Thomas Street, St. Thomas, Swansea SA1 8AT Tel: 01792 650400 Fax: 01792 464914; St Davids Medical Centre, Caldicot Close, Winchwen, Swansea SA1 7HT Tel: 01792 702700 — MB ChB 1979 Wales; MRCGP 1983. (Cardiff)

PATEL, Govindbhai Ranchhodbhai 99 Whiteacre Road, Ashton-under-Lyne OL6 9PJ Tel: 0161 339 2034 — MB BS 1963 Bombay. (Grant Med. Coll.) Trainee Gen. Pract. Manch. Vocational Train. Scheme.

PATEL, Gulam Ahmed Abdulla Musa Flat 7, 55 Woodville Gardens, London W5 2LN — MB BS 1987 Lond.

PATEL, Gunjan Bhachubhai 4 Outwood Close, Burton-on-Trent DE13 0QY — MB ChB 1980 Glas.; DRCOG 1983; DCH RCP Lond. 1982. SCMO (Child Health) S. E. Staffs. HA.

PATEL, Gunvantbhai Jashubhai Department of Orthopaedics, Queen Margaret Hospital, Dunfermline KY12 0SU Tel: 01383 623623; 44 Townhill Road, Dunfermline KY12 0JD — MB BS 1973 South Gurarat; FRCS Glas. 1987. Staff Grade (Orthop. Surg.) Qu. Margt. Hosp. Dunfermline.

PATEL, Gunvantrai Dalabhai Petworth Drive Medical Centre, 5 Petworth Drive, Leicester LE3 9RF Tel: 0116 255 0030 — MB BS 1974 Bombay.

PATEL, H R Seabank Road Surgery, 213/215 Seabank Road, Wallasey CH45 1HE Tel: 0151 630 6577 Fax: 0151 639 7477.

PATEL, Hamina Jayantibhai — MB BCh 1990 Wales; MSc Glasgow 1998; MRCPI 1995. (University of Wales, College of Medicine) Clin. Research Phys., Lond. Prev: Regist. (Pharmacol. & Gen. Med.) Univ. Coll. Hosp. Lond.

PATEL, Hansa Thakor 1 Banckside, Hartley, Longfield DA3 7RD Tel: 0147 475644 — MB BS 1970 Bombay; FFA RCSI 1976; DA Eng. 1972. (Grant Med. Coll.) Cons. Anaesth. Dartford & Gravesham Health Dist. Prev: Sen. Regist. (Anaesth.) Guy's Hosp. Lond.

PATEL, Harendra Gordhanbhai Patel, Latimer Health Centre, 4 Homerton Terrace, off Morning Lane, Hackney, London E9 6RT Tel: 020 8985 2249 Fax: 020 8985 7333; Rosedene, 4 Mellish Gardens, Woodford Green IG8 0BH — MB BS 1978 Baroda; MRCS Eng. LRCP Lond. 1984. GP. Prev: Princip. GP Redbridge.

PATEL, Harikrishna Purushottamdas 3 Ashleigh Court, Preston PR2 9WU — MB BS 1958 Gujarat; FFCM 1981; MFCM 1974; DPH Eng. 1962. (B.J. Med. Coll. Ahmedabad) Specialist Community Med. Preston HA. Prev: Area SCM Acute & Scientif. Servs. Blackburn; Princip. Ahmadu Bello Univ. Med. Auxil. Train. Sch. Kaduna, Nigeria; PMO Min. of Health & Social Welf. Kano State, Nigeria.

PATEL, Harischandra Chimanbhai Ore Clinic, Old London Road, Hastings TN35 5BH Tel: 01424 448410; 40 Bowmans Drive, Battle TN33 0LU Tel: 01424 775245 — MB BS 1981 Mysore; MFFP 1995; MRCOG 1988; Dip GU Med 1990 Lond. Cons. Genitourin. Med. Hastings & E.bourne. Socs: BMA; Soc. Study of VD. Prev: Sen. Regist. (Genitourin. Med.) Roy. Lond. Hosp.; Regist. (Genitourin. Med.) St. Geo. & St. Helier Hosp. Lond.; Regist. (O & G) Hope Hosp. Salford & Rochford Gen. Hosp.

PATEL, Harshadaben Maheshkumar Westbury Medical Centre, 205 Westbury Avenue, Wood Green, London N22 6RX Tel: 020 8888 3021 Fax: 020 8888 6898; 44 Vicass Moor Lane, Winchmore Hill, London N21 2QJ Tel: 020 8364 0605 Fax: 020 8364 1399 — MB BS 1974 Saurashtra. (M. P. Shah Medical College Jamnagar, India) Socs: FRSH.

PATEL, Harshadrai Prabhubhai (retired) Queen Victoria Hospital, East Grinstead RH19 3DZ Tel: 01342 24111 — MB BS 1962 Gujarat; MD Gujarat 1965; FFA RCS Eng. 1969. Cons. Anaesth. Qu. Vict. Hosp. E. Grinstead. Prev: Sen. Regist. (Anaesth.) King's Coll. Hosp. Lond.

PATEL, Harshadrao Dahyabhai Lynwood Medical Centre, 4 Lynwood Drive, Romford RM5 2RA Tel: 01708 743244 Fax: 01708 736783 — MB BS 1968 Gujarat. (B.J. Med. Coll. Ahmedabad)

PATEL, Mr Hashumati Dajibhai Laxman 14 Evans Close, Tipton DY4 8BG — MB ChB 1989 Aberd.; FRCS Ed. 1995.

PATEL, Hasmukh Rambhai Darent Valley Hospital, Dartford DA2 8ND Tel: 01322 428100 Ext: 8221 Fax: 01322 428231; Freeby, The Green, Sidcup DA14 6BS Tel: 020 8302 7400 Fax: 020 8302 7400 Email: hrzp@hotmail.com — MB BS Lond. 1967; FRCP Lond. 1986; FRCP Ed. 1985; MRCP (UK) 1972; MRCS Eng. LRCP Lond. 1967; DCH Eng.1970; FRCPCH 1997. (King's Coll. Hosp.) Cons. Paediat. Darent Valley hosp., Dartford, Kent. Socs: Pres., N. W. Kent Med. Assoc. Prev: Chairm. Specialist Train. Comm. Paediat. S. Thames RHA; Postgrad. Assoc. Dean. S. Thames RHA; Sen. Regist., Regist. & SHO (Paediat.) King's Coll. Hosp. Lond.

PATEL, Hasmukh Shivabhai St Bartholomews Surgery, 292A Barking Road, London E6 3BA Tel: 020 8472 0669/1077 Fax: 020 8471 9122 — MB BS 1973 Gujarat. (B.J. Med. Coll. Ahmedabad) Ho. Surg. OldCh. Hosp. Romford.

PATEL, Heather Frances Capelfield Surgery, Elm Road, Claygate, Esher KT10 0EH Tel: 01372 462501 Fax: 01372 470258; The Thatched House, Manor Way, Oxshott, Leatherhead KT22 0HU Tel: 01372 843995 — BM 1982 Soton.; MRCGP 1986; DRCOG 1984. Socs: Bd. Mem. E. Elmbridge PCG (Vice Chairm.).

PATEL, Heena The Surgery, 577 Carlton Road, Nottingham NG3 7AF Tel: 0115 958 0415 Fax: 0115 950 9245 — BM BS 1980 Nottm.; BMedSci Nottm. 1978; MRCGP 1987; DRCOG 1985; DCH RCP Lond. 1984. (Univ. Nottm. Med. Sch.) Tutorsh. Nottm. Med. Sch.; Clin. Asst. Asian Diabetes Nottm. City Hosp.

***PATEL, Heman Kumar Bhanubhai** 113 Godfrey House, Bath St., London EC1V 9ET — MB BS 1996 Lond.

PATEL, Hemanshu 53 Chapel Fields, Charterhouse Road, Godalming GU7 2BX — MB BS 1996 Lond.

PATEL, Hemantkumar 20 Eastmead Avenue, Greenford LB6 9RB Tel: 020 8578 1244; 7 Rundell Crescent, Hendon, London NW4 3BS Email: hkpatel1@aol.com — MB BS 1988 Lond.; MRCGP 1994; DRCOG 1992. (St. Georges) GP Princip.

PATEL, Hemlata 36 Lamorrey Close, Sidcup DA15 8BA — MB BS 1973 Rajasthan.

PATEL, Hemlata Ashokkumar The Warren Medical Centre, The Warren, Uxbridge Road, Hayes UB4 0SF Tel: 020 8573 2476/1781 Fax: 020 8561 3461; 5 Sandy Lodge Lane, Moor Park, Northwood HA6 2JA Tel: 01923 829276 Fax: 01923 823063 — MB BS 1972 Baroda; DA Eng. 1975. (Baroda Med. Coll.) GP.

PATEL, Hemlata Bharatkumar 228 Watford Road, Harrow HA1 3TY — MB BS 1979 Baroda. Gen. Practitioner, Primary Care Lond.

PATEL, Himanshu 3 Windermere Close, Dartford DA1 2TX — MB BCh 1991 Wales.

***PATEL, Himanshu Jairamdas** 21 Blakes Avenue, New Malden KT3 6RJ — MB BS 1994 Lond.

PATEL, Himanshu Jayantilal Myatts Field Health Centre, Patmos Road, London SW9 7RX Tel: 020 7587 5300 Fax: 020 7793 8792; 35 Hitherwood Drive, College Road, London SE19 1XA Tel: 020 8670 8222 — MB BS 1983 Lond.; DRCOG 1987. Clin. Asst. (Dermat.) KCH Lond. Prev: SHO (A & E) N. Middlx. Hosp. Lond.; SHO (Psychiat.) E. Glam. Gen. Hosp.; SHO (Paediat.) P. Chas. Hosp. Merthyr Tydfil.

PATEL, Hiren Chandrakant 22 Alliance Court, Hills Road, Cambridge CB1 7XE — MB ChB 1995 Sheff.

PATEL, Hitan 14 Penney Close, Wigston LE18 1AN — MB ChB 1995 Leic.

***PATEL, Hiten** 94 Arundel Drive, Harrow HA2 8PP — MB ChB 1998 Manch.; MB ChB Manch 1998.

PATEL, Hitendra Ramesh Himanshu School of Surgical Sciences, The Medical School, Framlington Place, Newcastle upon Tyne NE2 4HH Tel: 0191 232 5131 Fax: 0191 222 8514 Email: h.r.h.patel@ncl.ac.uk — MB ChB 1992 Dundee; BMSc (Hons.) Dund 1990. (Dundee) Med. Research Counc. Clin. Train. Fell. (Surg.) Univ. Newc. Socs: Fell. Roy. Microscopical Soc.

PATEL, Hitesh 50 Blenheim Gardens, Wembley HA9 7NP; 56 Intwood Road, Cringlefield, Norwich NR4 6TH — MB ChB 1982 Aberd.; MRCP (UK) 1988; MRCGP 1993; DRCOG 1993.

PATEL, Hitesh 40 Rissington Avenue, Selly Oak, Birmingham B29 7SX — MB BCh BAO 1992 Dub.

PATEL, Mr Hitesh 1 Steele Road, London W4 5AE Tel: 020 8746 8231 Email: hitesh.patel@ic.ac.uk — MB ChB 1994 Liverp.; FRCS (Eng) 1998. (University Liverpool Medical School) Res. Fell. (Surg.) Acad. Surg. Chelsea & W.minster Hosp. Lond. Prev: SHO (Surg.)

Chelsea & W.m. Hosp. Lond.; SHO (Surg.) Watford Gen. Hosp.; Demonst. (Anat.) Char. Cross & W.m. Med. Sch.

PATEL, Indira Ghanshyam Melbourne Road Medical Centre, 47 Melbourne Road, Leicester LE2 0GT Tel: 0116 255 9869 — MB BS 1969 Gujarat.

PATEL, Indravadan Purshottamdas (Surgery), 85/87 Acton Lane, Harlesden, London NW10 8UT Tel: 020 8961 1183 Fax: 020 8961 4785; 113 Green Lane, Stanmore HA7 3AD — MB BS 1965 Gujarat; DLO Eng. 1976. (B.J. Med. Coll. Ahmedabad) ENT Surg. Lond. Hosp.; ENT Surg. N.wick Pk. Hosp. Wembley Hosp. Socs: Brit. Otol. Soc. & BMA. Prev: Regist. (ENT) Lewisham Hosp. Lond.; Regist. (ENT), Ho. Surg. & Ho. Phys. Mulago Hosp. Kampala, Uganda.

PATEL, Irem Suzan Queen Mary's Hospital, Sidcup DA14 6LT Tel: 020 8302 2678 Email: rkpandisp@aol.com; 190 Farnaby Road, Bromley BR2 0BB Tel: 020 8290 6932 — MB BS 1994 Lond.; MRCP (UK) 1997. (University College and Middlesex) Specialist Regist. (Respir. Med.) SE Thames. Socs: Brit Thoracic Soc.; SE Thames Thoracic Soc.; Lond. Int. Care Grp.

PATEL, J D Highbury Park, 94 Highbury Park, London N5 2XE Tel: 020 7226 5360 — MB BS 1969 Bombay; MB BS 1969 Bombay.

PATEL, Jagdish Babubhai Priory Lodge, 72 Grosvenor Way, Barton Seagrave, Kettering NN15 6TZ — MB BS 1965 Gujarat; DLO 1968. (B.J. Med. Coll. Ahmedabad) Socs: BMA. Prev: Regist. (ENT) Kettering Gen. Hosp.; SHO Oldham Roy. Infirm. & W. Kent Gen. Hosp. Maidstone.

PATEL, Jagdishchandra Maganbhai Park House Surgery, 2 St. Georges Road, Stoke, Coventry CV1 2DL Tel: 024 7622 4438 Fax: 024 7622 9782 — MB BS 1968 Baroda; FRCOG 1974. (Baroda)

PATEL, Jagdishchandra Nagjibhai 1 Whitehall Road, Rugby CV21 3AE Tel: 01788 561319 — MB BS 1968 Gujarat; MD (Anaesth.) Gujarat 1972; DA Gujarat 1970. (B.J. Med. Coll. Ahmedabad) Prev: Regist. (Anaesth.) Gen. Hosp. N.ampton; SHO (Anaesth.) P.ss Margt. Hosp. Swindon & Ashton-under-Lyne Gen. Hosp.

PATEL, Jai Vinodray 10 Manton Croft, Dorridge, Solihull B93 8TD Email: jai@jvpatel.freeserve.co.uk — MB ChB 1990 Manch.; MRCP (UK) 1994; FRCR 1998. (Univ. Manch.) Specialist Regist. Qu. Elis. Hosp. Birm. Prev: Regist. (Radiol.) Birm. Heartlands Hosp.

PATEL, Jaikrishna Rambhai Dhulabhai 14 Northwick Park Road, Harrow HA1 2NU — MB BS 1986 Lond.; MB BS (Hons.) Lond. 1986; BSc (Hons.) Lond. 1983; MRCP (UK) 1989. Dir. Diabetes & Metabol. SmithKline Beecham Philadelphia. Prev: Regist. (Med.) King's Coll. Hosp. Lond.; SHO (Gen. Med.) St. Bart. Hosp. Lond.; Ho. Phys. Med. Profess. Unit St. Bart. Hosp. Lond.

PATEL, Janmejay Jayantilal 2300 Corporate Circle, Suite 100, Henderson NV 89074, USA Tel: 720 731 8224 Email: jjpatelmd@aol.com — BM 1987 Soton. Cons. Cardiol. Cardiovasc. Cons. Of Nevada, Las Vegas, Nevada, USA. Socs: Amer. Coll. Phys.; Fell. Amer. Coll Cardiol.; Fell. Amer. Coll. Chest Phys. Prev: Instruc. (Cardiol.) Hahnemann Univ. Philadelphia, USA; Clin. Instruc. (Gen. Med.) & Resid. Internal Med. Hahnemann Univ., Philadelphia, USA; Ho. Surg. Prof. Surg. Unit. Univ. Soton.

PATEL, Jatin Kumar Vishnooprasad Melbourne Road Surgery, 71 Melbourne Road, Leicester LE2 0GU Tel: 0116 253 9479 Fax: 0116 242 5602; 25 Carisbrooke Avenue, South Knighton, Leicester LE2 3PA Tel: 0116 270 3792 — MB ChB 1983 Leeds; MRCGP 1987; DRCOG 1988; Cert. Family Plann. JCC 1986. (Leeds) Prev: Intern. Psychiat. Med. Coll. Georgia Augusta, USA; Trainee GP Leicester VTS; SHO (Psychiat. & O & G) ScarBoro. HA.

PATEL, Jatin Suresh Box 134, Department of Clinical Genetics, Addenbrooke's NHS Trust, Addenbrooke's Hospital, Cambridge CB2 2QQ Tel: 01223 274568 Email: j.patel@hgmp.mrc.ac.uk; 3 Sheridan Place, Hampton TW12 2SB — MB ChB 1989 Ed.; BSc Ed. 1985; MRCP (UK) 1992; DCH RCP Lond. 1991. (Univ. Ed.) Specialist Regist. (Clin. Genetics) Addenbrooke's Hosp. Camb. Prev: Regist. Roy. Childr. Hosp. Melbourne, Austral.; Research Fell. & SHO Gt. Ormond St. Hosp. Lond.

***PATEL, Jay Kantilal** 7 Oakleigh Road N., Whetsone, London N20 9HE — MB BCh 1986 Wales.

PATEL, Jayantibhai Ashabhai Thorns Road Surgery, 43 Thorns Road, Quarry Bank, Brierley Hill DY5 2JS Tel: 01384 77524 Fax: 01384 486540; 10 Ironbridge Walk, Pedmore, Stourbridge DY9 0SF Tel: 01562 886465 — MB BS Indore 1966. (M.G.M. Med. Coll. Indore) GP.

PATEL, Jayesh Purushottamdas A & E Department, Southampton General Hospital, Tremona Road, Southampton SO16 6YD — LRCP LRCS 1983 Ed.; LRCP LRCS Ed. LRCPS Glas. 1983.

PATEL, Jayesh Rajnikant Ambalal 34 Fairview Road, Istead Rise, Gravesend DA13 9DR Tel: 01474 355331 — MB ChB 1982 Sheff.

PATEL, Jayeshkumar Slab Cottage, 11 Old Cottage Close, West Wellow, Romsey SO51 6RL Tel: 01794 324154 — MB BS 1987 Lond.; BSc Lond. 1984; MRCP Lond. 1991; DCH 1990. (St. Geo. Hosp. Lond.) Paediat. Neurol. Sen. Regist. Soton. Gen. Hosp. Soton. Socs: Neonat. Soc.; MRCPCH.

PATEL, Jayshree Narrendra Dudley Park Medical Centre, 28 Dudley Park Road, Acocks Green, Birmingham B27 6QR Tel: 0121 706 0072 Fax: 0121 707 0418 — MB BS 1974 Bombay; DRCOG 1976.

PATEL, Jigisha 38 St Mary's Road, London E13 9AD — MB BS 1991 Lond.

PATEL, Jignesh Indravadan 113 Green Lane, Stanmore HA7 3AD Tel: 020 8854 9922 Fax: 020 8961 4785 — MB BS 1993 Lond.; BSc Lond. 1990. Demonst. (Anat.) Char. Cross & W.m. Med. Sch. Lond. Prev: SHO (Cas.) & Ho. Off. (Med.) Char. Cross Hosp. Lond.; Ho. Off. (Surg.) W. Middlx. Univ. Hosp.

PATEL, Mr Jignesh Vinodrai 55 Westmoreland Road, Bromley BR2 0TQ; 10 Sutherland Avenue, Ealing, London W13 8LE Tel: 020 8991 9825 — BM 1991 Soton.; FRCS Eng. 1996; FRCSI 1994. (Southampton) Specialist Regist. (Orthop.) Chelsea & W.m. Hosp. Lond. Prev: SHO (Plastics) Char. Cross Hosp. Lond.; SHO (Orthop.) Chelsea & W.m. Hosp. Lond. & Addenbrooke's NHS Trust Camb.

PATEL, Jitendra 38 Deptford Broadway, Deptford, London SE8 4PQ — MB ChB 1980 Sheff.

PATEL, Jitendra 23 Colin Drive, Colindale, London NW9 6ES — BM 1980 Soton.

PATEL, Jitendra Ishwarbhai c/o D. M. Patel, 17 Watford Road, Wembley HA0 3ET — MB BS 1969 Gujarat.

PATEL, Jyotsana Suresh The Surgery, 1 Uxendon Crescent, Wembley HA9 9TW Tel: 020 8904 3883 Fax: 020 8904 3899; 119 Pinner Hill Road, Pinner HA5 3SQ — MB BS 1978 Baroda; MRCS Eng. LRCP Lond. 1980; MRCGP 1983; DRCOG 1982; Dip Chinese Med Bejing 1999.

***PATEL, Kalpana Lallubhai** 2 Berners Road, London N22 5NE — MB BS 1997 Lond.

PATEL, Kalpana Prakash Wallasey Crescent Practice, 1 Wallasey Crescent, Ickenham, Uxbridge UB10 8SA Tel: 01895 674156 Fax: 01895 623334 — MB BS 1974 Bombay; MB BS 1974 Bombay.

PATEL, Mr Kalpesh Santuram Department of Otolaryngology - Head & Neck Surgery, St. Mary's Hospital, Praed St., London W2 1NY Tel: 020 7725 2151 Fax: 020 7725 1847 Email: mrkspatel@aol.com; Tel: 020 7262 0297 Fax: 020 7886 1390 — MB BS Lond. 1984; BSc (Hons.) Lond. 1981; FRCS (Orl.) 1994; FRCS Eng. (Orl.) 1989. (St. Bart.) Cons. ENT Surg. St. Mary's Hosp. Lond. Socs: Fell. Roy. Soc. Med.; Am. Acad. Otolaryngol - Head & Neck Surg.; Europ. Acad. Facial Surg. Prev: Sen. Regist. Rotat. (ENT Surg.) St. Mary's Hosp. & Roy. Marsden Hosp. Lond.; Regist. (ENT & Plastics) King's Coll. Hosp. Lond.; Demonst. Univ. St. And. Fife.

PATEL, Kamal Chelsea & Westminster Hospital, Fulham Road, London SW10 9NH; 23 Bernard Street, St Albans AL3 5QW Tel: 01727 811287 — MB BS 1990 Lond.; MRCP (UK) 1993. Regist. (Paediat.) Chelsea & W.m. Hosp. Lond. Prev: Regist. Watford Gen. Hosp.; SHO (Paediat.) St. Jas. Univ. Hosp. Leeds; SHO (O & G) St. Peter's NHS Trust Chertsey.

PATEL, Kamini 28A Milton Avenue, London N6 5QE — MB BS 1983 Lond.

PATEL, Kanak Kumar 26 Archer Close, Leicester LE4 7RA — MB ChB 1997 Manch.; BDS 1987; FDS RCPS 1991. SHO Basic Surg. Trainee. Socs: BMA; RCS (Eng.); RCS (Glas.). Prev: SHO (Gen. Surg.); Ho. Off. (Surg.); Ho. Off. (Med.).

PATEL, Kantibhai Maganbhai The Surgery, 47 Boundaries Road, Balham, London SW12 8EU Tel: 020 8673 1476; 7 Willows Avenue, Morden SM4 5SG Tel: 020 8648 6354 — MB BS Bombay 1956; FRCP Ed. 1994; MRCP Ed. 1961; MRCP Glas. 1960; MRCS Eng. LRCP Lond. 1958; DCH Eng. 1958; DTM & H Eng. 1958; FRCP

PATEL

Ed 1995. (Grant Med. Coll.) Prev: Sen. Lect. & Cons. Phys. Makerere Med. Sch. Mulago Hosp. Kampala, Uganda.

PATEL, Kantilal Chhaganbhai Littleover Medical Centre, 640 Burton Road, Littleover, Derby DE23 6EL Tel: 01332 207100 Fax: 01332 342680; 640 Burton Road, Littleover, Derby DE23 6EL Tel: 01332 44441 — MB BS 1971 Banaras; DObst. RCPI 1977. Socs: Derby Med. Soc.

PATEL, Kantilal Motibhai (retired) 42 Buckhurst Way, Buckhurst Hill IG9 6HJ — MB BS Bombay 1951; MRCGP 1962.

PATEL, Kantilal Rambhai Department of Respiratory Medicine, Gartnavel General Hospital, Glasgow G12 OYN Tel: 0141 211 3000; 9 Lomond Place, Linburn, Erskine PA8 6AP Tel: 0141 812 4569 — MB BS 1967 Bombay; PhD Glas. 1976; FRCP Lond. 1985; FRCP Glas. 1980; MCPS Bombay 1967. (Grant Med. Coll.) Cons. Phys. Respirat. Med. & Gartnavel Gen. Hosp. Glas.; Hon. Clin. Sen. Lect. (Med.) Univ. Glas. Socs: Brit. Thorac. Soc. & Scott. Thoracic Soc.; Amer. Thoracic Soc.; Europ. Thoracic Soc. Prev: Sen. Regist. (Gen. Med. & Respirat. Dis.) Gt.er Glas. Health Bd.; Research Fell. & Regist. (Respirat. Dis.) W.. Infirm. Glas.

PATEL, Kantilal Raojibhai Royton Medical Centre, Market Street, Royton, Oldham OL2S 5QA Tel: 0161 652 6336 Fax: 0161 620 3986; 182 Castleton Road, Royton, Oldham OL2 6UP Tel: 0161 652 5486 — MB BS 1963 Bombay; MRCP Glas. 1969; MRCGP 1978; DTM & H Liverp. 1967. (Grant Med. Coll.) Socs: BMA & Cardiol. Soc. India. Prev: Clin. Asst. (Geriat.) Tameside Gen. Hosp.; Regist. (Med.) Cheltenham Gen. Hosp.; Med. Adviser Sandoz (India) Ltd. Bombay.

PATEL, Kanubhai Mangalbhai Patel and Partners, Thornley Road Surgery, Thornley Road, Wheatley Hill, Durham DH6 3NR Tel: 01429 820233 Fax: 01429 823667 — MB BS 1969 Baroda.

PATEL, Karen Elizabeth Lime Tree Surgery, Lime Tree Avenue, Findon Valley, Worthing BN14 0DL Tel: 01903 264101 Fax: 01903 695494; 7 Longlands Glade, Charmandean, Worthing BN14 9NR Tel: 01903 232246 — MB ChB 1987 Leic.; DRCOG 1991. GP.

PATEL, Kashyap Bhogilal 3 Ashleigh Court, Fulwood, Preston PR2 9WU — MB BS 1984 Gujarat; MB BS Gujarat India 1984.

PATEL, Kaushik Ramanbhai Kingston Hospital, Galsworth Road, Kingston upon Thames KT2 7QB Tel: 020 8934 2515 Fax: 020 8934 3288 Email: kaushik@doctors.org.uk — MB ChB 1987 Sheff.; BMedSci Sheff. 1986; MRCPath 1994. Cons. (Histopath. & Cytol.). Prev: Sen. Regist. (Histopath.) Leeds Gen. Infirm.; Regist. (Histopath.) Watford Gen. Hosp.; SHO (Clin. Path.) Roy. Hallamsh. Hosp. Sheff.

PATEL, Kersasp Rustomji 57 Butt Lane, Farnley, Leeds LS12 5AY Tel: 0113 263 1815 — MB BS 1952 Bombay; DTM & H Eng. 1955. (Seth. G.S. Med. Coll.) Prev: GP Leeds; Med. Off. HM Prison Leeds; Regist. (Med.) Kilton Hosp. Worksop & Beckett Hosp. Barnsley.

PATEL, Ketan Central Park Surgery, Balfour Street, Leyland, Preston PR25 2TD Tel: 01772 451940 Fax: 01772 623885 — MB ChB 1989 Bristol.

***PATEL, Ketan Chandubhai** 279 Main Road, Sidcup DA14 6QL — MB BS 1994 Lond.

PATEL, Ketan Jayakrishna 11 North Terrace, Cambridge CB5 8DJ — MB BS 1986 Lond.

PATEL, Ketankumar Jerambhai Avondale Health Centre, Avondale Street, Bolton BL1 4JP; "Kirkstone", 374A Bocton Road, Hawkshan, Bury BL8 4JP — MB ChB 1991 Manch.; MRCGP 1995; DRCOG 1994. (Manchester) eneral Practitioner Bogon. Prev: Trainee GP/SHO Rochdale VTS.

***PATEL, Khalid Ismail** 59 Chaucer Road, London E7 9LZ — LMSSA 1996 Lond.

PATEL, Kinnari 43 Mapplewell Crescent, Grat Sankey, Warrington WA5 1UT — MB ChB 1990 Bristol.

PATEL, Kiran P Tel: 01204 883375 Fax: 01204 887431; 28 Humber Drive, Bury BL9 6SJ Tel: 0161 764 3953 — MB ChB 1988 Manch.; MRCGP 1993; Cert. Prescribed Equiv. Exp. JCPTGP 1993; DRCOG 1992.

PATEL, Kiranbhai Chhaganbhai Department of Cardiology, Bristol Royal Infirmary, Upper Maudlin Street, Bristol BS2 8MW Tel: 0117 923 0000 Fax: 0117 928 2666; 19 Rowley View, West Bromwich B70 8QR — MB BChir 1994 Camb.; PhD 2002 Bristol; MA 1995 Camb.; BA 1991 (Hons.) Cantab; MRCP 1997 Lond. (Cambridge) SpR In Cardiol., Bristol Roy. Infirm. Socs: BMA; Chairm. Of The Indian Foundat. (UK); Chairm. S. Asian Health Foundat. UK. Prev: SHO (Cardiol.) Bristol Infirm.; SHO (Gen. Med., Rheum., Therap. & c/o Elderly) Bristol Infirm.; SHO (A & E) Leicester Roy. Infirm.

PATEL, Kiritkumar Punjabhai 23 Geneva Drive, Westlands, Newcastle ST5 2QQ Tel: 01782 622650 — MB BS 1967 Baroda; FRCP Lond. 1988; MRCP (UK) 1973. (Baroda Med. Coll.) Cons. Phys. Gen./Geriat. Med. City Gen. Hosp. Stoke-on-Trent.

PATEL, Kiritkumar Raojibhai 34 Matlock Avenue, Mansfield NG18 5DW Tel: 01623 32659 — MB BS 1974 Bombay. (Grant Med. Coll.)

***PATEL, Kirti** 14 Whitton Avenue E., Greenford UB6 0PU — MB BS 1994 Lond.

PATEL, Kirtikbhai Amratlal 79 Belmont Road, Penn, Wolverhampton WV4 5UE — MB ChB 1993 Manch.; FRCS 1997; FRCS Ed 1997. (Manchester)

***PATEL, Kishor Kantilal** 25 Churchfields Road, Wednesbury WS10 9DX — MB BCh 1994 Wales.

PATEL, Krutika 3 Freeman Street, Coventry CV6 5FF — MB ChB 1993 Leic.

PATEL, Lalitkumar Chaturbhai Patel, Brocklebank Health Centre, 249 Garrett Lane, London SW18 4UE Tel: 020 8870 1341; Triangle Surgery, Unit 3, Triangle House, 2 Broomhill Road, London SW18 4HX Tel: 020 8874 1700 Fax: 020 8870 7695 — MB BS 1957 Baroda; DObst & DGO Dub. 1960; LM Rotunda 1960; DTM & H Eng. 1959.

PATEL, Lata Manojkumar Lynwood Medical Centre, 4 Lynwood Drive, Romford RM5 2RA Tel: 01708 743244 Fax: 01708 736783 — MB BS 1977 Saurashtra.

PATEL, Lata Vinubhai 158 Tokyngton Avenue, Wembley HA9 6HL Tel: 020 8900 1584 — MB BS 1968 Gujarat.

PATEL, Leena Department of Child Health, Booth Hall Children's Hospital, Manchester M9 7AA Tel: 0161 795 7000 Fax: 0161 795 7542 — MB BS 1982 Gujarat; MRCP (UK) 1989; MD Gujarat 1985; MHPE (Maastricht) 1996; MD (Manchester) 1998. Sen. Lect. (Child Health) & Hon. Cons. Paediat. Manch. Childr.s Hosp. Prev: Sen. Lect. Booth Hall Childr. Hosp. Manch.; Lect. (Child Health) Booth Hall Childr. Hosp. Manch.; Regist. (Paediat.) Hammersmith Hosp. & Hillingdon Hosp. Lond.

PATEL, Lily Sashikant Chichester Road, Romiley, Stockport SK6 4QR.

PATEL, Madhu Ganeshbhai The Surgery, 44 Broadway, Twydall, Gillingham ME8 6BD Tel: 01634 231364 — LRCP LRCS 1981 Ed.; MB BS Saurashrta 1976; LRCP LRCS Ed. LRCPS Glas. 1981; MRCGP 1984. (M.P. Shah Med. Coll. Jamnagar) GP Gillingham.

PATEL, Maganlal Popatlal Department of Radiology, Walsgrave Hosp NHS Trust, Coventry CV2 2DX; Ledbury, 10 Cannon Close, Coventry CV4 7AS — MB ChB 1959 Sheff.; DMRD Ed. 1966. Cons. Radiol. Walsgrave Hosp. NHS Trust; Mem. Coventry LMC. Socs: BMA (Chairm. Coventry Div.); RCR; ODA (Exec. Comm. Coventry Div.). Prev: Sen. Regist. (Radiol.) Roy. Infirm. Aberd.; SHO (Radiodiag.) Roy. Hosp. Edin.; Med. Off. Mulago Hosp. Kampala, Uganda.

PATEL, Mahendra Shay Lane Medical Centre, Shay Lane, Hale, Altrincham WA15 8NZ Tel: 0161 980 3835 Fax: 0161 903 9848; 6 Oldbrook Fold, Wood Lane, Timperley, Altrincham WA15 7PA — MB ChB 1984 Manch.; MRCGP (Distinc.) 1988; DCH RCP Lond. 1988; DRCOG 1987.

PATEL, Mahendra Maganbhai 55A Thomas Drive, 132 Parrock St., Gravesend DA12 5PY Tel: 01474 363217 Fax: 01474 353746; Southlands, 363 Singlewell Road, Gravesend DA11 7RL Tel: 01474 363217 Fax: 01474 353746 — MB BS Baroda 1969. (Med. Coll. Baroda) Hosp. Pract. (Geriat. Med.) Gravesend Hosp., Gravesend. Socs: BMA. Prev: Ho. Off. (Med. & Surg.) Mulago Hosp. Kampala, Uganda.

PATEL, Mahendrakumar Chimanbhai Hartington Street Surgery, 28-30 Hartington Street, Barrow-in-Furness LA14 5SL Tel: 01229 870170 Fax: 01229 834677 — MB BS 1971 Bombay. (Bombay) GP Barrow-in-Furness, Cumbria.

PATEL, Mamta 1/R 50 Kelbourne Street, Glasgow G20 8PR — MB ChB 1993 Glas.

PATEL, Manashkumar 23 Freeman Road N., Leicester LE5 4NB — MB BCh 1984 Wales; FRCA. 1990. Sen. Regist. (Anaesth.) Char. Cross Hosp. Lond. Prev: Research Regist. Middlx. Hosp. Lond.

PATEL

PATEL, Maneesh Chandrakant 19 Park Avenue, Farnborough Park, Orpington BR6 8LJ — MB BS 1990 Lond.

PATEL, Mr Maneklal Bhaktibhai 30 Tranmere Road, London SW18 3QQ — MB BS 1968 Bombay; MS Bombay 1971, MB BS 1968; DO RCPSI 1974; DO Eng. 1974. (Grant Med. Coll.) Regist. (Ophth.) Roy. Surrey Co. Hosp. Guildford.

PATEL, Manibhai Hirabhai 7 Shapland Way, London N13 4EZ — LAH Dub. 1963.

***PATEL, Manish** Flat 2/L, 32 Highburgh Road, Downhill, Glasgow G12 9EF — MB ChB 1997 Glas.

PATEL, Mr Manu Dept of Maxillofacial Surgery, Withington Hospital, Manchester M20 2LR; 6 Old Hall Crescent, Handforth, Wilmslow SK9 3AX — LRCP LRCS Ed. LRCPS Glas. 1987; FRCS Eng. 1992. Cons. Withinghton Hosp. Manch.

PATEL, Manu Khandubhai Longshoot Health Centre, Scholes, Wigan WN1 3NH Tel: 01942 242610 Fax: 01942 826612 — MB ChB 1976 Manch.

PATEL, Manubhai Kevaldas Neasden Medical Centre, 21 Tanfield Avenue, Neasden, London NW2 7SA Tel: 020 8450 2834 Fax: 020 8452 4324; 63 Alicia Gardens, Harrow HA3 8JB Tel: 020 8907 9698 — MB BS 1968 Bombay. (Grant Med. Coll.)

***PATEL, Mayank Bhaskar Rao** 126 Kingston Road, New Malden KT3 3ND — BM 1995 Soton.

PATEL, Mayur Vinod 53 Basnetts Wood, Endon, Stoke-on-Trent ST9 9DQ — MB BS 1993 Lond.

***PATEL, Meeta** 1 Marshfield Drive, Off Stoneleigh Road, Coventry CV4 7ER — BM BS 1998 Nottm.; BM BS Nottm 1998; HB BS (Hons) 1998; BMedSci 1996.

PATEL, Mehool Devendrakumar 92 Carlton Avenue W., North Wembley, Wembley HA0 3QU — MB BS 1990 Baroda; MRCP (UK) 1996. (Baroda Med. Coll.) Specialist Regist., SE Thames.

PATEL, Minal Myra 13 Powis Gardens, London NW11 8HH — MB BCh BAO 1984 NUI; LRCPSI 1984; MRCGP 1991.

***PATEL, Minesh** 19 Rowsley Street, Leicester LE5 5JN — MB ChB 1994 Birm.; ChB Birm. 1994.

PATEL, Minesh Kumar 33 Sutlej Road, London SE7 7DD Tel: 020 8856 6575 — MB BS 1991 Lond.

PATEL, Minoti Kalpesh Station Road Surgery, 46 Station Road, New Barnet, Barnet EN5 1QH Tel: 020 8441 4425 Fax: 020 8441 4957; 3 Gatcombe Way, Barnet EN4 9TT Tel: 020 8441 9630 — MB BS 1982 Baroda.

PATEL, Mohamed Salim Ahmed Carmondean Medical Group, Carmondean Health Centre, Livingston EH54 8PY Tel: 01506 430031 Fax: 01506 432775; Roshni, 11 Northwood Park, Livingston EH54 8BD Tel: 01506 415591 — MB ChB 1973 Glas.

PATEL, Motilal Rambhai Abercynon Health Centre, Abercynon, Mountain Ash CF45 4SU Tel: 01443 740447 Fax: 01443 740228; The Grove, 1 Aberfrwdd Road, Caegarw, Mountain Ash CF45 4DD Tel: 01443 478087 — MB BS 1972 Bombay; Dip. Pract. Dermat. Wales 1991. (Seth G.S. Med. Coll.) Prev: Clin. Asst. (Dermat.) Aberdare Gen. Hosp.; SHO (Paediat. & Obst.) E. Glam. Hosp.; SHO (Dermat. & O & G) E. Glam. Hosp.

PATEL, Mukesh 16 Westwood Lane, Welling DA16 2HE — MB BCh 1983 Wales; MRCGP 1988; DRCOG 1987.

***PATEL, Mukesh Kantilal** 35 Shale Street, Bilston WV14 0HF — MB BS 1996 Lond.

PATEL, Mukesh Narendra Vine House Surgery, Vine Street, Grantham NG31 6RQ Tel: 01476 576851 Fax: 01476 591732; Waltham House, 34 Swinegate, Grantham NG31 6RL Email: mukeshnpatel@hotmail.com — MB ChB 1979 Glas. Prev: Regist. Rotat. (Anaesth.) Liverp. HA; SHO (Anaesth.) Walton Hosp. Liverp.; SHO (Anaesth.) Roy. Liverp. Hosp.

PATEL, Mukundchandra Kanubhai Westbury Medical Centre Tel: 020 8445 8733 Fax: 020 8888 6898; 205 Westbury Avenue, London N22 6RX Tel: 020 8888 3021 Fax: 020 8888 6898 — MB BS 1971 Rajasthan. (S.P. Med. Coll. Bikaner)

***PATEL, Mumtaz** 141 Sharoe Green Lane, Fulwood, Preston PR2 8HE Tel: 01772 787786; 141 Sharoe Green Lane, Fulwood, Preston PR2 8HE Tel: 01772 787786 — MB ChB 1996 Manch.; MB ChB (Hons) Manch. 1996.

PATEL, Mumuksh Bhupendra The Surgery, 1 Glebe St., Chiswick, London W4 2BD Tel: 020 8747 4800 Fax: 020 8995 4388; 322 Goldhawk Road, Stamford Brook, London W6 0XF Tel: 020 8563 1863 — MB ChB 1992 Manch. (Manchester) GP; GP Private GP Clinic Stamford Hosp. Lond. W6. Prev: GP Assit. Chiswick.

PATEL, Murji Premji 118 Johnston Street, Blackburn BB2 1HY — MB ChB 1975 Manch.

PATEL, N M Broad Lane, Norris Green, Liverpool L11 1AD Tel: 0151 226 1976 Fax: 0151 270 2873 Email: narendra.patel@gp-82019.nhs.uk; 18a Druids Cross Road, Calderstones, Liverpool L18 3HW Tel: 0151 428 9119 — M.B.B.S.; 1982 RCOG; 1978 MBBS; 1982 (Scottish Cojoint Board) LRCP, LRCS, LRCPSS. (MRM Medical College, Gulbarga) GP Principle, Liverp. FMSA; Wavertree Lodge, Clin. Asst. in Learning Disabil. & Challenging Behaviour organisation, Liverp. Health Auth. Socs: BMA; Overseas Doctors Assoc.; Med. Protec. Soc. Prev: Colposcopy (Clin. Asst.) '87-'01, Whiston Hosp. Prescott.

PATEL, Mrs Nalini 40 Whitgift Avenue, South Croydon CR2 6AY Tel: 020 8688 6975 — MB BS 1973 Gujarat.

PATEL, Narendra Whinshiels, Main Road, Wrinehill, Crewe CW3 9BJ — MB ChB 1981 Manch. GP Crewe.

PATEL, Narendrakumar Babubhai 19 Cansip Crescent, Gowrie Park, Dundee DD2 4TP — MB ChB 1964 St. And.; MRCOG 1969; FRCOG 1988.

PATEL, Naresh Ambalal Patel and Partners, Broom Lane Medical Centre, 70 Broom Lane, Rotherham S60 3EW Tel: 01709 364470 Fax: 01709 820009; 4 Newman Court, Moorgate, Rotherham S60 3JA Tel: 01709 366294 — MB BS 1977 Bombay; MRCS Eng. LRCP Lond. 1978. (Topiwala Nat. Med. Coll. Bombay) GP Tutor Med. Stud. Sheff. Med. Sch. Prev: Trainee GP Rotherham VTS; SHO (Thoracic Med.) Milford Chest Hosp. Godalming; Ho. Off. (Gen. Med.) Staincliffe Gen. Hosp. Dewsbury.

PATEL, Mr Natwarlal Gangjibhai Oxford Road Surgery, 292 Oxford Road, Reading RG30 1AD Tel: 0118 957 4614 Fax: 0118 959 5486 — MB BS 1956 Bombay; FRCS Ed. 1960; DLO RCS Eng. 1958.

PATEL, Natwarlal Shivabhai 19 Dewhurst Road, London W14 0ET Tel: 020 7603 2103 Fax: 020 7603 2103 — MB BS Gujarat 1960; PhD Lond. 1972; DMJ Soc. Apoth. Lond. 1965. (Roy. Lond. Hosp.) State Forens. Path. & Hon. Lect. Lusaka, Zambia. Socs: Brit. Acad. Forens. Med.; Assn. Police Surg. Prev: Sen. Lect. & Forens. Path. The Lond. Hosp. Med. Coll.; Lect. & Asst. Forens. Path. The Lond. Hosp. Med. Coll.; Regist. (Path.) Moorgate Gen. Hosp. Rotherham.

PATEL, Navnitbhai Hargovindbhai Southey Green Medical Centre, 281 Southey Green Road, Sheffield S5 7QB Tel: 0114 232 6401 Fax: 0114 285 4402 — MB BS 1973 Baroda.

PATEL, Nayan 48 Ragburn Road, Sidcup DA15 8RB — MB BS 1993 Lond.

PATEL, Nayana Pravin 507 Kenton Road, Harrow HA3 0UL — MB BS 1973 Gujarat; DGO 1976.

PATEL, Neera Kanubhai Department of Histopathology, Royal Sussex County Hospital, Eastern Road, Brighton BN2 5BE Tel: 01273 664502 Fax: 01273 664412 Email: neera.patel@brighton-healthcare.nhs.uk — MB BS 1990 Lond.; BSc (Hons.) Lond. 1987; DRCPath 1995; MRCPath 1997. (Univ. Coll. Hosp.) Cons. (Histopath. & Cytopath.) Roy. Sussx Co. Hosp. Brighton. Prev: Lect. & Hon. Sen. Regist. (Histopath. & Cytopath.) St. Thos. Hosp. Lond.

PATEL, Neeta 37c Elm Park Road, London N3 1EG — MB ChB 1992 Manch.

***PATEL, Neil Dinesh** 20 Sycamore Tree Close, Radyr, Cardiff CF15 8RT — MB BS 1994 Lond.

PATEL, Nikhil Raman 24 Codrington Hill, London SE23 1LW — MB BS 1989 Lond.; MRCP Lond. 1992. Regist. (Cardiol.) Guy's Hosp. Lond.

***PATEL, Nikunj Kantilal** 4 Streatham Vale, London SW16 5TE; 205 Westway, Raynes Park, London SW20 9LW Tel: 020 8542 1580 — MB BS 1994 Lond.; BSc Lond. 1991; FRCS 1998.

PATEL, Nila Dilip Worle Village Surgery, Hill Road East, Worle, Weston Super Mare BS22 9HF Tel: 01934 516671 Fax: 01934 520664 — MB BS 1977 Mysore; LRCP LRCS Ed. LRCPS Glas. 1982.

PATEL, Nilam DVLA, Longview Road, Swansea SA99 1TU Tel: 01792 783780 Fax: 01792 783784 — MB BCh 1981 Wales; MRCGP 1986. Med. Adviser Dept. Transport Swansea.

PATEL, Nilesh Rajnikant North Brink Practice, 7 North Brink, Wisbech PE13 1JR Tel: 01945 585121 Fax: 01945 476423; 55 Clarkson Avenue, Wisbech PE13 2EH — MB BCh BAO 1980 NUI;

PATEL

MRCGP 1986; DRCOG 1986. (Royal College of Surgeons in Ireland) GP N. Brink Pract., Wisbech.

*PATEL, Nilesh Ravji 38 Dale Avenue, Edgware HA8 6AE; 29 Fairway Avenue, Kingsbury, London NW9 0ET Tel: 020 8206 0066 — MB BS 1997 Lond.

PATEL, Mr Nimesh Narendra — MB ChB 1992 Manch.; FRCS 1997. (Manchester)

*PATEL, Nina Rasikbhai 93 Michleham Down, London N12 7JL — MB BS 1991 Lond.

PATEL, Niranjana Ramanlal 14 Sinclair Grove, Golders Green, London NW11 9JG Tel: 020 8455 0430 — MB BS 1973 Rajasthan. (S.M.S. Med. Coll. Jaipur) Ho. Off. Dept. Gen. Med. & Chest Unit Bangour Gen. Hosp. Broxburn.

PATEL, Niranjanbhai Ratilal The Surgery, 27 Burges Road, East Ham, London E6 2BJ Tel: 020 8472 0421 Fax: 020 8552 9912; 34 Hillington Gardens, Woodford Green IG8 8QT Tel: 020 8550 3413 Fax: 020 8550 3413 — MB BS 1977 Lond. (London Hospital Medical College)

*PATEL, Nishal Basildon Hospital, Nether Mayne, Basildon SS16 5NL — MB BS 1998 Lond.; MB BS Lond 1998.

*PATEL, Nitesh 5 Nutfield Road, Thornton Heath, Croydon CR7 7DP — MB ChB 1994 Manch.

PATEL, Mr Nitin Kumar Ratilal 50 Hillside Court, Gledhow Lane, Leeds LS7 4NJ — MB BCh 1987 Wales; FRCS Eng. 1992. Sen. Regist. (Neurosurg.) Frenchay Hosp. Bristol. Socs: MDU. Prev: SHO Rotat. (Surg.) St. Jas. Hosp. Leeds; SHO (Neurosurg.) Hope Hosp. Salford; Ho. Off. (Gen. Med. & Neurol.) Singleton Hosp. Swansea.

*PATEL, Or Timeer Shantilal 102 Sidcup High Street, Sidcup DA14 6DS — MB BS 1996 Lond.

PATEL, Pankaj Stoney Stanton Medical Centre, 475 Stoney Stanton Road, Coventry CV6 5EA Tel: 024 7688 8484 Fax: 024 7658 1247; 23 Cotswold Drive, Finham, Coventry CV3 6EZ Tel: 024 76 690588 — BM 1983 Soton.

PATEL, Panna Kantibhai 33 Moorville Drive, Lowry Hill, Carlisle CA3 0AN — MB BS 1981 Gujarat; FRCS Ed. 1985.

PATEL, Parag Wolverhampton Road Surgery, 13 Wolverhampton Road, Stafford ST17 4BP Tel: 01785 258161 Fax: 01785 224140 — MB BS 1989 Lond.

PATEL, Parimal Rushey Mead Health Centre, 8 Lockerbie Walk, Leicester LE4 7ZX Tel: 0116 266 9616; 5 Southland Road, South Knighton, Leicester LE2 3RJ — MB ChB 1986 Manch.

PATEL, Parindkumar Bipinchandra 17 Orchard Rise, Ruislip HA4 7LR Tel: 0410 597320 — MB BS 1995 Lond. (St George's) SHO (Surg.) Mayday Univ. Hosp. Socs: MDU. Prev: SHO (Med.) St Geo.'s Hosp.; SHO (Med.) Frimley Pk. Hosp.; SHO (Anaesth.) Mt. Vernon Hosp.

PATEL, Paritosh Chandubhai 43 Fircroft Road, London SW17 7PR — MB BS 1994 Lond.

PATEL, Pinakin Bhanubhai 21 Tylers Court, Vicars Bridge Close, Alperton, Wembley HA0 1XT — MB BS 1989 Lond.

PATEL, Mr Piyush Jashbhai 11 Dalton Road, Earlsdon, Coventry CV5 6PB Tel: 024 76 677444 Fax: 024 76 691436 — MB BChir 1980 (Distinc. Surg.) Camb.; MA (Hons.) Camb. 1981, BA (Hons.) 1977; FRCS Ed. 1987; FRCS Eng. 1987. (Univ. of Camb.) Cons. EN Surg. Walsgrave Hosp. NHS Trust Coventry. Prev: Sen. Regist. (ENT Surg.) W. Midl. Otolaryngol. Train. Scheme.

PATEL, Piyush Ranchhodbhai 38 Lavington Road, Croydon CR0 4PP — MB BS 1982 Lond.

PATEL, Poulam Manubhai ICRF Cancer Medicine Research Unit, St. James University Hospital, Leeds LS9 7TF — MB BS 1983 Lond.; PhD Lond. 1994; MRCP (UK) 1989. ICRF Sen. Clin. Scientist & Hon. Cons. Med. Oncol. St. Jas. Univ. Hosp. Leeds. Prev: ICRF Clin. Research Scientist & Hon. Sen. Regist. St. Jas. Univ. Hosp. Leeds; CRC Clin. Research Fell. Inst. Cancer Research Chester Beaty Laborat. Lond.; Regist. (Med.) Mayday Hosp. Croydon.

PATEL, Prabhudas Govindbhai 193 Chase Side, London N14 5JB — MB ChB 1966 Makerere.

PATEL, Pradeepkumar Chimanbhai (Patrick) The Surgery, 1 Tollington Court, Tollington Park, London N4 3QT Tel: 020 7272 2121 Fax: 020 7561 1901; 3 Neeld Crescent, Wembley HA9 6LW Tel: 020 8903 4501 Fax: 020 8903 5397 — MB BS 1975 Bombay; MRCS Eng. LRCP Lond. 1980; ECFMG 1980. (Topiwala National Medical College Bombay University India) GP Princip. Socs: Camden & Islington Local Med. Comm., Med. Audit Advisory Gp. & Primary Care Educat. Bd. Commiss.ing Sub-Gp.; BMA. Prev: Clin. Asst. in the c/o the Elderly Geo. Eliot Hosp. Nuneaton Warks; Trainee GP Manch.; Hosp. posts.

PATEL, Pradipkumar Rambhai Radiology Dept., Ealing Hospital, Uxbridge Road, Ealing UB1 3HW Tel: 020 8967 5373; 34 High Drive, New Malden KT3 3UG Tel: 020 8949 9202 — MB BCh 1977 Wales; FRCR 1982; DMRD 1982. (University of Wales Cardiff) Cons. Radiol. Ealing Hosp. Middlx. & Hon. Clin. Sen. Lect. Imperial Coll. Lond. Prev: Cons. Radiol. Ealing Hosp. Lond.; Sen. Regist. & Regist. (Radiol.) St. Mary's Hosp. Lond. W2; SHO (Paediat.) King's Coll. Hosp. Lond.

PATEL, Prafulchandra 31 Leven Close, Chandlers Ford, Eastleigh SO53 4SH — MB ChB 1986 Manch.; MD Manch. 1995; MRCP (UK) 1990. (Manch.) Cons. Gastroenterol. & Hon. Sen. Lect. Soton. Univ. Hosp. Trust. Socs: Brit. Soc. Gastroenterol.; RCP.

PATEL, Prafulchandra Chimanbhai Charnwood Health Centre, 1 Spinney Hill Road, Leicester LE5 3GH; 37 Carisbrooke Gardens, Leicester LE2 3PR — MB ChB 1970 Glas.; MRCP (UK) 1974.

PATEL, Prafulchandra Chunibhai Rectory Park Drive Surgery, 6 Rectory Park Drive, Pitsea, Basildon SS13 3DW Tel: 01268 552999 Fax: 01268 559986 — MB BS 1972 Bombay.

PATEL, Prafulchandra Jashbhai 167 Ellesmere Road, London NW10 1LG Tel: 020 8208 0188 — MB BS 1965 Gujarat. Clin. Med. Off. Enfield HA.

PATEL, Prafull Ambalal 154 Rothley Road, Mountsorrel, Loughborough LE12 7JX Tel: 0116 230 3642; 63 Belvoir Drive, Loughborough LE11 2SN Tel: 01509 236906 — MB BS 1952 Bombay. (Seth G.S. Med. Coll.)

*PATEL, Pratiksha Satish 29 Sonning Meadows, Sonning, Reading RG4 6XB Tel: 01189 699710 Fax: 01189 263231 Email: pratiksha74@yahoo.com — MB BS 1998 Lond.; MB BS Lond 1998.

PATEL, Mr Pravin Chaturbhai 507 Kenton Road, Harrow HA3 0UL — MB BS 1973 Gujarat; FRCS Ed. 1980.

PATEL, Pravina Kantilal Littleover Medical Centre, 640 Burton Road, Littleover, Derby DE23 6EL Tel: 01332 207100 Fax: 01332 342680 — MB BS 1973 Poona; DO RCPSI 1977. (B.J. Med. Coll.)

PATEL, Pravinbhai Kantilal 9 Athlone Road, Walsall WS5 3QU Tel: 01922 29395; 291 Walsall Road, West Bromwich B71 3LN Tel: 0121 588 2286 — MB BS 1968 Baroda. (Med. Coll. Baroda) GP W. Midl.

PATEL, Pravinkumar Maganbhai The Surgery, 24 Suttons Avenue, Hornchurch RM12 4LF Tel: 01708 442711 Fax: 01708 471756 — MB BS 1980 Bombay; MB BS 1980 Bombay; MRCS Eng. LRCP Lond. 1989 London.

PATEL, Mr Prem Swaroop 9 Hanging Water Close, Sheffield S11 7FH — MB BS 1979 Jabalpur; MS Jabalpur 1982, MB BS 1979; FRCS Ed. 1985.

PATEL, Priti City of London Migraine Clinic, 22 Charterhouse Square, London EC1M 6DX — MB ChB 1988 Dundee; DA (UK) 1993. Socs: BMA; IMS; BASH. Prev: Regist.(Anaesth.) NE Thames Regional Plastics Burns Unit St. And. Hosp. Billericay,Essex; SHO (Anaesth.) Leicester Teachg. Hosps.

PATEL, Priti 40B Allcroft Road, London NW5 4NE — MB BS 1992 Lond.; BSc Lond. 1988; MRCPsych 1996. (King's Coll.) Specialist Regist. (Child & Adolesc. Psychiat.) Tavistock Centre Lond.

PATEL, Punambhai Somabhai 7 Coape Road, Stockwood, Bristol BS14 8TN — MB BS 1955 Bombay. (Grant Med. Coll.)

PATEL, R S Holmlands Medical Centre, 16-20 Holmlands Drive, Oxton, Prenton CH43 0TX Tel: 0151 608 7750 Fax: 0151 608 0989.

PATEL, Mr Rahmikant Haridas CARE, Victoria Park, 108 -112 Daisybank Road, Manchester M14 5QH Tel: 0161 257 3799 Fax: 0161 224 4283; Ashtree Cottage, South Hill Avenue, Harrow HA1 3PA Tel: 020 8864 2400 — MB BS 1975 Baroda; MRCOG 1983; FRCOG 1999. CARE, The Alexandra Hosp. Cons. Gynaecologist/Reproductive Med. Vict. Pk. 108-112 Daisybank Toad, Manch. M14 5QH. Socs: BMA; Brit. Menopause Soc.; BSPOGA. Prev: Clin. research Fell. & Hon. Regist. St Geo.'s Hosp. Lond.; Med: Off. & Research Lect. (O & G) St Geo.'s Hosp. Lond.; Assoc. Specialist (Obst.& Gyn.) St Geo.'s Hosp. Lond.

*PATEL, Rahul Vinayak 16 Endcliffe Hall Avenue, Sheffield S10 3EL — MB BS 1998 Lond.; MB BS Lond 1998.

PATEL, Raina 94 Flodden Street, Sheffield S10 1HA — MB ChB 1985 Sheff.

PATEL, Mr Rajan Shashi 22 Stormont Road, London N6 4NL — MB ChB 1995 Glas.; MRCS Glas. 1998. SHO (Gen. Surg.) Vict. Roy. Infirm. NHS Trust Glas. Socs: BMA.

PATEL, Mr Rajankumar Russells Hall Hospital, Dudley DY1 2HQ Tel: 01384 244021 Email: rajtpatel@aol.com; 90 Fitzroy Avenue, Harborne, Birmingham B17 8RQ Email: rajtpatel@ed.com — MB BCh 1984 Wales; MD Birm. 1995; FRCS Eng. 1989; FRCS (Gen) 1997. (Cardiff) Cons. Gen. Surg. Socs: Fell. Roy. Coll. of Surg.s of Eng.; Assn. Surg.; Mem. Vasc. Surg. Soc. Prev: Sen. Regist. (Gen. Surg.), Qu. Eliz. Hosp. Birm.; Sen. Regist. (Gen. Surg.) Good Hope Hosp. Birm.; Sen. Regist. (Gen. Surg.) City Hosp. Birm.

PATEL, Rajen Flat F, Clarence Avenue, London SW4 8JR — MB BS 1993 Lond.; BSc (Hons.) Lond. 1990. SHO (Med.) Hastings & Rotherham NHS Trust.

PATEL, Rajendra Melbourne Road Surgery, 71 Melbourne Road, Leicester LE2 0GU Tel: 0116 253 9479 Fax: 0116 242 5602 — MB ChB 1977 Manch. Prev: Princip. GP Leic.; SHO (O & G) Tameside Matern. Hosp.; SHO (Orthop./A & E) Leicester Roy. Infirm.

PATEL, Rajendra Bhailalbhai The Health Centre, Trenchard Avenue, Thornaby, Stockton-on-Tees TS17 0DD Tel: 01642 762636 Fax: 01642 766464; 26 Church Lane, Middleton Saint George, Darlington DL2 1DF Tel: 01325 333179 — MB BS 1980 Saurashtra.

PATEL, Rajendra Nagindas 6 Wedgwood Way, London SE19 3ES — MB BS 1987 Lond.; DCH RCP Lond. 1991.

***PATEL, Rajendra Upendrabhai** 12A Sidney House, Royal Herbert Pavillions, Shooters Hill Road, London SE18 4PP — MB ChB 1986 Glas.

PATEL, Rajesh The Brooke Surgery, 20 Market St., Hyde SK14 1AT Tel: 0161 368 3312 Fax: 0161 368 5670 Email: patel@which.net; 51 Brownsville Road, Heaton Moor, Stockport SK4 4PF Tel: 0161 442 8720 — MB ChB 1985 Manch.; MRCGP 1992; Dip. Pract. Dermat. Wales 1996. Gen. Med. Practitioner; Hosp. Pract. (Dermat.); Vice-Chairm. Tameside & Glossop PCG.

PATEL, Rajesh Bhailalbhai Fullwell Avenue Surgery, 272 Fullwell Avenue, Clayhall, Ilford IG5 0SB Tel: 020 8550 9988 Fax: 020 8550 1241; 96 Cheriton Avenue, Clayhall, Ilford IG5 0QL Tel: 020 8551 1586 — MB BS 1979 Mysore; MRCS Eng. LRCP Lond. 1981. GP Ilford. Prev: SHO (O & G, A & E Radiother. & Oncol.) Redbridge & Waltham Forest HA.

PATEL, Rajesh Chandrakant 3 Alton Road, Bournbrook, Birmingham B29 7DU — MB ChB 1991 Birm.; ChB Birm. 1991.

PATEL, Rajesh Kantilal 190 Farnaby Road, Bromley BR2 0BB Email: bkpandisp@aol.com — MB BS 1994 Lond.; MRCP 1997. (University College London) Specialist Regist. (Haemat.) King's Coll. Hosp. Lond.

PATEL, Rajesh Manubhai Bethnal Green Health Centre, 60 Florida Street, London E2 6LL Tel: 020 7739 4837 Fax: 020 7729 2190 — MB BS 1979 Lond.; BSc (Physiol.) Lond. 1976, MB BS 1979. (King's Coll.)

PATEL, Rajesh Rasikbhai Manchester Road Surgery, 57 Manchester Road, Southport PR9 9BN Tel: 01704 532314 Fax: 01704 539740; 46 Cambridge Road, Southport PR9 9PP — MB BS 1985 Newc.; FRCGP 1999; MRCGP 1989; DRCOG 1988. Civic Serv. Clin. Local Med. Off. S.port. Prev: SHO Geriat. S.port & Formby Dist. Gen. Hosp.; Trainee GP S.port; SHO (Geriat. & A & E) Middlesbrough.

PATEL, Rajnika Niranjan 94 Mackenzie Road, London N7 8RE — MB BS 1972 Baroda.

PATEL, Rajnikant Bhanabhai Bourne Galletly Practice Team, 40 North Road, Bourne PE10 9BT Tel: 01778 562200 Fax: 01778 562207; 79 West Road, Bourne PE10 9PX — MB BCh 1977 Wales; Dip. Pract. Dermat. Wales 1992; DRCOG 1982. GP Bourne. Prev: Trainee GP P'boro. VTS; Ho. Surg., Surg. Unit Univ. Hosp. Cardiff; Ho. Off. (Med.) War Memor. & Maelor Hosps. Wrexham.

PATEL, Rajnikant Jorabhai Department of Radiology, George Eliot Hospital, Nuneaton CV10 7DJ Tel: 01203 865391 Fax: 01203 865095; 29 Norwich Close, Nuneaton CV11 6GF Tel: 01203 865164 — MB BS Baroda 1970; MS Univ. Barado 1974; FFR RCSI 1981; DMRD Liverp. 1978. (Med. Coll. Baroda) Cons. Radiol Geo. Eliot. Hosp. Nuneaton NHS Trust. Socs: Roy. Coll. Radiol.; BMA.

Prev: Sen. Cons. Roy. Hosp.; Cons. Radiol. MOH Muscat Sultanate of Oman; Sen. Regist. Walton Hosp. Liverp.

PATEL, Rajnikant Kantilal The Group Practice, Victoria House, 405 Shooters Hill Road, Woolwich, London SE18 4LH Tel: 020 8781 4350 Fax: 020 8781 4358; 145 Hurst Road, Sidcup DA15 9AH Tel: 020 8300 4092 — MB BS 1973 Bombay; MSc Lond. 1995; MRCS Eng. LRCP Lond. 1978; LMSSA Lond. 1978; FRCGP 1996, M 1989; MFFP Lond. 1992; Dip. Med. Educat. Dund 1993; DRCOG 1978; DOBst. Dub. 1978. (Grant Med. Coll. Bombay) Civil. Med. Pract. MoD; Trainer (Gen. Pract.) & Course Organiser Lond. Dist. Socs: Fell. Roy. Soc. Med. (Hon. Sec. GP Sect.); Fell. Roy. Soc. Health; RCGP (Counc. SW Thames Fac.).

PATEL, Rajnikant Manibhai Glascote Health Centre, 60 Caledonian, Tamworth B77 2ED Tel: 01827 281000 Fax: 01827 262048; 5 Blackdown, Wilnecote, Tamworth B77 4JQ Tel: 01827 895462 — MB BS Vikram 1969. (Gandhi Med. Coll. Bhopal)

PATEL, Rajnikant Shambhubhai Shakespeare Street Surgery, 1 Shakespeare Street, Loughborough LE11 1QQ Tel: 01509 268060 Fax: 01509 216146; 283 Forest Road, Loughborough LE11 3HT — MB BS 1973 Bombay.

PATEL, Rajul 608 Manchester Road, Sheffield S10 5PT — MB ChB 1984 Sheff.

PATEL, Rakesh 19 Hodgson Street, Darwen BB3 2DS — MB ChB 1991 Manch.

***PATEL, Rakesh** 135 Somerton Road, Breightmet, Bolton BL2 6LW — MB ChB 1996 Sheff.

PATEL, Rakesh Maganbhai 25 Spring Grove Road, Hounslow TW3 4BE — MB ChB 1983 Leeds; MRCGP 1987; DGM RCP Lond. 1986; DRCOG 1985.

PATEL, Ramanbhai Vaghajibhai The Health Centre, Wallsgreen Road, Cardenden, Lochgelly KY5 0JE Tel: 01592 722443 Fax: 01592 721679 — MB BS 1941 Bombay. (Bombay) GP Lochgelly, Fife.

PATEL, Ramanlal Gopalji Royal Manchester Chilren's Hospital, Hospital Road, Swinton, Manchester M27 4HA — MB BS 1966 Bombay; FRCP Lond. 1984; MRCP (UK) 1971; DCH Eng. 1968. (Grant Med. Coll.) Cons. Paediat. Cardiol. Roy. Manch. Childr. Hosp. Pendlebury & Wythenshawe Hosp. Manch. Socs: Brit. Paediat. Assn. & Brit. Cardiac Soc. Prev: Staff Cardiol. Hosp. Sick Childr. Toronto Canada & Asst. Prof.; Paediat. Univ. Toronto; Sen. Regist. Hosp. Sick Childr. Lond.

PATEL, Ramesh Walsgrave Hospital, Coventry CV2 2DX; The North Lodge, Coventry Road, Berkswell, Coventry CV7 7AZ — MB ChB 1980 Sheff.; MD 1994; FRCS (CTh) 1994; FRCS (Ed.) 1985. (Sheff.) Regist. (Cardiothorocic Surg.) Harefield Hosp.; Research Fell. Rayne Inst. St. Ths. Hosp.; Sen. Regist. Qu. Eliz. Hosp. Birm.; Sen. Regist. Birm. Childr. Hosp.; Sen. Regist. Birm. Heartlands Hosp. Socs: Fell. Roy. Coll. Surgs. Edin.; Soc. Cardiothorocic Surgs. GB.

PATEL, Ramesh Chandra Paston Health Centre, Chadburn, Peterborough PE4 7DG Tel: 01733 572584 Fax: 01733 328131; 18 Lakeside, Werrington, Peterborough PE4 6QZ Tel: 01733 578288 Fax: 01733 578288 — MB BS 1976 Lond.; MRCS Eng. LRCP Lond. 1976; MRCGP 1980. (St. Mary's) Prev: Trainee GP Dudley VTS; Ho. Surg. & Ho. Phys. Roy. Hosp. Wolverhampton.

PATEL, Ramesh Dhanjibhai 22 Rowbank Way, Loughborough LE11 4AJ — BM BS 1994 Nottm.; BMedSci Nottm. 1992.

PATEL, Ramesh Girdharlal 3 Eaton Road, Norwich NR4 6PY Tel: 01603 503700 Fax: 01603 503700; E.W. 3 Kamaldeep Flats, Opp. Navarangpura, Ellisbridge, Ahmedabad 380006, India Tel: 00 91 79 460013 Fax: 00 91 79 460013 — MB BS 1971 Gujarat; FFA RCSI 1979; DA Eng. 1973. (B.J. Med. Coll. Ahmedabad) Prev: Sen. Cons. Anaesth. King Fahad Hosp. Al-Baha, Kingdom Saudi Arabia; Regist. (Anaesth.) King Geo. Hosp. Ilford, ScarBoro. Gen. Hosp. & Moorfields Eye Hosp. Lond.

PATEL, Ramesh Govindji St George's Medical Centre, Field Road, New Brighton, Wallasey CH45 5LN Tel: 0151 630 2080 Fax: 0151 637 0370 — MB BS 1971 Gujarat.

PATEL, Rameshbhai Ramubhai The Health Centre, Main Road, Radcliffe-on-Trent, Nottingham NG12 2GD Tel: 0115 933 3737; Email: rambhai@ntlworld.com — MB BS 1984 Lond.; MRCP (UK) 1987; MRCGP 1989; DCH RCP Lond. 1989. (Royal Free Hospital) GP Trainer Nottm. VTS. Prev: Trainee GP Nottm. VTS.

PATEL, Rameshchandra Ashabhai 32 Baldwyns Park, Bexley, Dartford DA5 2BA Tel: 01322 529026; 32 Baldwyns Park, Bexley

PATEL

DA5 2BA Tel: 01322 529026 Fax: 01322 529026 — MB BS Punjab (India) 1962; DObst RCOG 1967; DA Eng. 1967; MFFP 1994 Lond. (Amritsar) Clin. Asst. Chistlehurst; Family Plann. Instruc. Doctor. Socs: BMA; Med. & Dent. Assn. Prev: Clin. Asst. W. Hill Hosp. Dartford & Clin. Med. Off. FPC Memor. Hosp.; Med. Off. Kenya Govt.; SHO (Anaesth.) Essex Co. Hosp. Colchester.

PATEL, Rameshchandra Chhotabhai Ascot Medical Centre, 690 Osmaston Road, Derby DE24 8GT Tel: 01332 348845; 163 Pastures Hill, Littleover, Derby DE23 7AZ — MB BS 1971 Bombay.

PATEL, Rameshchandra Harmanbhai Patel and Partners, 4 Bedford Street, Bletchley, Milton Keynes MK2 2TX Tel: 01908 377101 Fax: 01908 645903; 7 Carnoustie Grove, Bletchley, Milton Keynes MK3 7RP — MB ChB 1974 Manch.

PATEL, Rameshchandra Maganbhai Stroud Avenue, 250 Stroud Avenue, Willenhall WV12 3DA Tel: 01902 609500 Fax: 01902 603625; 233 Stroud Avenue, Willenhall WV12 4DA — MB BS 1965 Bombay. Socs: BMA; ODA; MDU. Prev: Clin Dermat New Cross Hosp Wolverhampton.

PATEL, Rameshchandra Nathabhai East Park Road Medical Centre, 264 East Park Road, Leicester LE5 5FD Tel: 0116 273 7700; 10 Campbell Avenue, Thurmaston, Leicester LE4 8HB Tel: 0116 25100 — MB BS 1964 Baroda. (Baroda)

PATEL, Ramilaben Ramanlal Chorlton Health Centre, 1 Nicolas Road, Chorlton, Manchester M21 9NJ Tel: 0161 881 7941 Fax: 0161 861 7567; 2 Rowantree Drive, Brooklands, Sale M33 3PA — MB BS 1966 Baroda; MRCOG 1974; DRCOG 1968. Prev: GP Greenford; Train. GP Birm.; Regist. (O & G) Dudley Rd. Hosp. Birm.

PATEL, Ramnik Mathurbhai Rushbottom Lane Surgery, 91 Rushbottom Lane, Benfleet SS7 4EA Tel: 01268 754311 Fax: 01268 795150; 40 Avondale Road, Benfleet SS7 1EJ Tel: 01268 755150 Fax: 01268 795150 — MB BS Baroda 1969. (Med. Coll. Baroda) Med. Adviser SW Essex Adopt. Panel. Prev: SHO (Gen. Med. & O & G) Hallam Hosp. W. Bromwich; Ho. Off. (Gen. Surg. & Med.) Kenyatta Nat. Teachg. Hosp. Nairobi, Kenya.

PATEL, Ramubhai Mitthalbhai Dartmouth Medical Centre, 1 Richard Street, West Bromwich B70 9JL Tel: 0121 553 1144 Fax: 0121 580 1914; Central Clinic, Horseley Road, Tipton DY4 7NB Tel: 0121 557 4377 — MB BS 1964 Gujarat; DTM & H Liverp. 1972. (B.J. Med. Coll. Ahmedabad) Prev: Regist. Summerfield Hosp. Birm.; SHO Maelor Gen. Hosp. Wrexham & Dudley Rd. Hosp. Birm.

PATEL, Ranchhodji Hansjibhai (retired) 22 Severn Road, Oadby, Leicester LE2 4FY — MRCS Eng. LRCP Lond. 1932; MRCS Eng., LRCP Lond. 1932.

PATEL, Rasiklal Somabhai 93 Michelham Down, London N12 7JL — MB BS 1954 Bombay. (Grant Med. Coll.)

PATEL, Ravindrabhai 7 Chelsea Close, Worcester Park KT4 7SF — MB BS 1988 Lond.

***PATEL, Rayhana** 439 Bridgeman Street, Bolton BL3 6TH — MB ChB 1998 Manch.; MB ChB Manch 1998.

PATEL, Rekha Dhirubhai 23 Geneva Drive, Newcastle ST5 2QQ Tel: 01782 622650 — MB BS 1972 Mysore; FFA RCSI 1977; DA Eng. 1975. (Kasturba Med. Coll. Mangalore) Cons. Anaesth. Wolverhampton DHA. Prev: Sen. Regist. (Anaesth.) Birm. AHA (T).

PATEL, Rekha Kantilal Compton Health Centre, High St., Shaw, Oldham; Shawdale, Castleton Road, Royton, Oldham OL2 6UP — MB BS 1964 Bombay; DObst RCOG 1967. (Grant Med. Coll.) Prev: SCMO Rochdale AHA; SHO (O & G) Ashton-under-Lyne Gen. Hosp.; Deptm. Med. Off. Essex CC.

***PATEL, Rita Mohanbhai** 70 Lawn Street, Bolton BL1 3AY — MB ChB 1996 Manch.

PATEL, Roger Nagindas 7 Chaston Road, Great Shelford, Cambridge CB2 5AS — MB BChir 1995 Camb.; 1999 MRCP (UK). Specialist Regist. (Radiol.) Camb. Rotat.

***PATEL, Roshni Raman** 36 Meadow Brook Road, Birmingham B31 1NE — MB ChB 1995 Bristol.

PATEL, Rupal 178 Halley Road, London E7 8DU — MB ChB 1996 Dundee.

PATEL, Ruth Shahani 51 Heybridge Drive, Ilford IG6 1PE — MB BS 1993 Lond.; DRCOG Lond. 1996. GP Regist. Prev: GP Trainee.

***PATEL, Sameer** 9 Lomond Place, Erskine PA8 6AP — MB ChB 1995 Glas.

PATEL, Samir 147 Turner Road, Edgware HA8 6AS — BM 1993 Soton.; (American Board of Internal Medicine 2000); MRCP 1997. Regist. Elderly Care Barnet Hosp.; Fell. in Pulm. and Critical Care Med., Yale Univ. Connecticut, USA. Socs: Assoc. Mem. Amer. Coll. of Chest Phys.s.

PATEL, Samir Niranjan Pavilion Practice, 9 Brighton Terrace, London SW9 8DJ Tel: 020 7274 9252 Fax: 020 7274 0740 — MB BS 1988 Lond.

***PATEL, Sandip** 204 Whitehall Road, Leeds LS12 4AR — MB BS 1994 Lond.

PATEL, Sangeeta Balham Park Surgery, 92 Balham Park Road, London SW12 8EA Tel: 020 8767 8828 Fax: 020 8682 1736 — MB BS 1986 Lond.; MRCGP (Distinc.) 1990; DRCOG 1990; MA (Med. Anthropology) 1997. (Kings College Hosp. School of Med.) GP Princip.; Clin. Lect. (Gen. Pract.) St. Geo. Hosp. Med. Sch. Lond.

PATEL, Sangita 4 Hatherleigh Road, Leicester LE5 5NR — MB ChB 1990 Sheff.

PATEL, Sanjay 19 Courtleigh Avenue, Barnet EN4 0HT — MB ChB 1988 Manch.; MRCGP 1992; DRCOG 1991.

***PATEL, Sanjay** 208 Church Hill Road, Barnet EN4 8PP — MB BS 1998 Lond.; MB BS Lond 1998.

PATEL, Sanjay Kumar Sanderson and Partners, Adan House Surgery, St. Andrews Lane, Spennymoor DL16 6QA Tel: 01388 817777 Fax: 01388 811700 — MB ChB 1986 Leeds; MRCGP 1992; DRCOG 1991; DCCH RCGP 1991. (Leeds) GP. Socs: BMA.

PATEL, Sanjay Vinod Sanmay, Basnetts Wood, Endon, Stoke-on-Trent ST9 9DQ Fax: 01782 570069 — BM BS 1995 Nottm.; BMedSci Nottm. 1993. (Nottm.) Demonst. (Biomed. Sci.) & SHO (Ophth.) Sheff. Univ. & Roy. Hallamsh. Hosp.

PATEL, Sanjaykumar 42 Sheridan Street, Walsall WS2 9QX — MB ChB 1993 Leeds.

PATEL, Sanjeev Rasikbhai Department of Rheumatology, St. Helier Hospital, Carshalton SM5 1AA Tel: 020 8296 2473; 24 Haverhill Road, London SW12 0HA — BM 1984 Soton.; DM Nottm. 1995; MRCP (UK) 1989. (Univ. Soton.) Cons. Phys. & Rheum. St. Helier Hosp. Carshalton; Sen. Lect. (Rheum.) St. Helier Hosp. Carshalton. Socs: Brit. Soc. Rheum. Prev: Sen. Regist. (Med. & Rheum.) St. Geo. Hosp. Lond.

PATEL, Sanjiv Shashikant 60 Park Avenue, Mitcham CR4 2EN — MB BS 1990 Lond.; MRCP (UK) 1993; MRCGP 1998. (Guy's Hosp. Med. Sch. Lond.) GP Princip., Lond. Prev: Resid. Internal Med. Cleveland Clinic Foundat. Ohio, USA; SHO (Med.) Crawley Hosp.; GP Regist. Lond.

PATEL, Sarit Amritlal 7 Cambridge Court, Sussex Gardens, London W2 1EU — MB BS 1991 Lond.

PATEL, Satish Manibhai London Road Practice, 172 London Road, Reading RG1 3PA Tel: 0118 926 4992 Fax: 0118 926 3231; 5 Whitley Wood Road, Reading RG2 8HX Tel: 01734 311377 — MB BS 1969 All India Inst.; MB BS All India Inst. Med. Scs. 1969. (All India Inst. Med. Scs. New Delhi)

PATEL, Satiskumar Purshotamdas 4 Willcox Drive, Melton Mowbray LE13 1HH — MB ChB 1994 Leeds.

PATEL, Shailendra Bhanubhai 247 Burnt Oak Broadway, Burnt Oak, Edgware HA8 5ED — BM BCh 1985 Oxf.

PATEL, Shailesh Jayantilal 1 Troutbeck Road, Gatley, Cheadle SK8 4RP — MB ChB 1982 Manch.

PATEL, Shailesh Somabhai Saffron Lane Health Centre, 612 Saffron Lane, Leicester LE2 6TD Tel: 0116 291 1212 Fax: 0116 291 0300; 49 Spon Lane, Grendon, Atherstone CV9 2PD Tel: 01827 714035 — MB ChB 1981 Glas.; DRCOG 1986; DA (UK) 1984. (Univ. Glas.) Prev: SHO (Anaesth.) Geo. Eliot Hosp. Nuneaton; SHO (O & G & A & E) Bedford Gen. Hosp.

PATEL, Mr Shaileshkumar Bhailalbhai 36 Doyle Gardens, Kensal Rise, London NW10 3DA — MB BS 1985 Lond.; BSc (Hons.) Lond. 1982, MB BS 1985; FRCS Eng. 1990; FRCS Ed. 1990. Research Fell. (Paediat. Surg.) St. Thos. Hosp. Lond. Prev: Regist. (Paediat. Surg.) St. Thos. Hosp. Lond.; Regist. (Gen. Surg.) St. Mary's Hosp. Lond.; Regist. (Gen. Surg.) Hillingdon Hosp. Middlx.

PATEL, Shalini Narendra c/o The Osteopathic Surgery, Worton Hall, Worton Road, Isleworth TW7 6ER; 73 Constance Road, Whitton, Twickenham TW2 7HX — MB BS 1996 Lond.; BSc Lond. 1995; DRCOG 1999. (St. George's Hosp. Med. Sch.) GP VTS, St. Peter's Hosp. Chertsey. Prev: Ho. Off. (Med.) Luton & Dunstable Hosp.; Ho. Off. (Surg.) St. Peter's Hosp. Chertsey.

PATEL, Shamima (retired) 107 Drewstead Road, London SW16 1AD Tel: 020 8769 7359 — MB ChB 1949 Sheff.

PATEL, Shantilal Devshibhai 172 Wandsworth Bridge Road, London SW6 2UQ — MB BS 1977 Gujarat; LRCP LRCS Ed. LRCPS Glas. 1983. GP Lond.

PATEL, Shashikant Haribhai (retired) Oak Road Surgery, 1 Oak Road, Canvey Island SS8 7AX Tel: 01268 692211 — MB BS 1966 Poona.

PATEL, Shashikant Jethabhai 60 Park Avenue, Mitcham CR4 2EN Tel: 020 8640 4984 — MB BS 1964 Bombay.

PATEL, Shashikant Ratilal Penvale Park Medical Centre, Hardwick Road, East Hunsbury, Northampton NN4 0GP Tel: 01604 700660 Fax: 01604 700772; 15 Rixon Close, Western Favell, Northampton NN3 3PF Tel: 01604 404843 — MB BS 1976 Calicut; DRCOG 1987; DA Eng. 1981.

PATEL, Sheetal Thakor 1 Banckside, Hartley, Longfield DA3 7RD Tel: 01474 705644 Email: sheetal50@hotmail.com — MB BS 1997 Lond.

PATEL, Sheila 173 Old Road, Brampton, Chesterfield S40 3QL Tel: 01246 206341 — MB ChB 1963 Manch. (Manch.) SCMO (Audiol.) N. Derbysh. Health Auth.

PATEL, Shetal 44 Dudley Avenue, Kenton, Harrow HA3 8SS — MB ChB 1990 Manch.

PATEL, Shirish Chunibhai Mill Road Surgery, Mill Road, Pontnewynydd, Pontypool NP4 6NG Tel: 01495 757575 Fax: 01495 758402 — MB BS Bombay 1973.

PATEL, Shobana 51 Dalkeith Grove, Stanmore HA7 4SQ Tel: 020 8958 5982 — MB BS 1974 Gujarat; MB BS Gujarat India 1974; FRCA 1994.

PATEL, Shobhana Oxford Road Surgery, 292 Oxford Road, Reading RG30 1AD Tel: 0118 957 4614 Fax: 0118 959 5486 — MB BS 1972 Delhi.

PATEL, Shruti Devyani 27 St Michael's Hill, Kingstown, Bristol BS2 8DZ — MB ChB 1993 Bristol.

PATEL, Shveta Thakorlal Princess Margaret Hospital, Perth, Australia Tel: 020 8882 0974; Tel: 0061 893415654 — MB BS 1990 Lond.; DRCOG 1995; DCH RCP Lond. 1994. Socs: Med. Protec. Soc. Prev: GP/Regist. Forest Rd. Health Centre Edmonton; Trainee GP/SHO (Psychiat.) Enfield HA.

PATEL, Siddharth Ramkrishna Oxnead, Marsham Way, Gerrards Cross SL9 8AW Tel: 01753 882492 — MB BS 1964 Gujarat; DMRD Eng. 1972. (B.J. Med. Coll. Ahmedabad) Cons. Radiol. Ashford Hosp. Middlx. Prev: Sen. Regist. (Diag. Radiol.) Windsor Gp. Hosps. & N.wick Pk. Hosp.; Harrow; Trainee Regist. (Radiol.) Roy. Free Hosp. Lond.

PATEL, Smita Chimanbhai 37A St. Johns Road, Watford WD17 1LS — MB BS 1985 Lond.; MRCGP 1992; DRCOG 1990. (St. Georges Hosp. Med. Sch. Lond.) Prev: Trainee GP Belmont Health Centre Harrow; SHO (Obst.) Basildon Hosp.; SHO (A & E & Paediat. S.end Hosp.

PATEL, Smita Hasmukh Mawney Road Practice, 34 Mawney Road, Romford RM7 7HD Tel: 01708 743627 Fax: 01708 738244; 14 Tyle Green, Nelmes Park, Hornchurch RM11 2TB Tel: 01707 459156 — MB BS 1974 Gujarat. (B.J. Med. Coll.) Princip. GP Romford.

PATEL, Smita Virendrabhai 15 Marlpit Lane, Coulsdon CR5 2HF — MB BS 1984 Gujarat; MRCP (UK) 1991. Regist. Rotat. (Gen. Med.) Univ. Hosp. Wales Cardiff. Prev: SHO Rotat. (Gen. Med.) Coventry HA.

***PATEL, Smitaben Yashwantbhai** 62 Foxbourne Road, London SW17 8EW — MB BS 1994 Lond.

PATEL, Smruti High Peak, Rownhams Lane, Rownhams, Southampton SO16 8AR — BM 1991 Soton.

PATEL, Sneha Narsing 42 High Drive, New Malden KT3 3UB — MB BS 1993 Lond.; MRCP (UK) 1997. (Roy. Free Hosp. Lond.)

PATEL, Snehlata Mukundchandra St Johns Villas Surgery, 16 St Johns Villas, Friern Barnet Road, London N11 3BU Tel: 020 8368 1707; 16 St. John's Villas, Friern Barnet Road, London N11 3BU Tel: 020 8368 1707 — MB BS 1972 Gujarat. (B.J. Med. Coll. Ahmedabad)

***PATEL, Soonie Rameshchandra** 73 Warlingham Road, Thornton Heath, Croydon CR7 7DF — MB ChB 1994 Leeds.

PATEL, Subhash Chandrakant The Surgery, Welbeck Street, Creswell, Worksop S80 4HA Tel: 01909 721206; The Stables, Old Hall Lane, Whitwell, Worksop S80 4QX — MB ChB 1980 Glas.; DRCOG 1987; DCH RCP Lond. 1986.

PATEL, Suhasini Sureshchandra The Surgery, 114 Woodside, Wigmore, Gillingham ME8 0PW Tel: 01634 234131 — MB BS 1967 Bombay; MSc Bombay 1956, MB BS 1967. (Grant Med. Coll.) Clin. Asst. (O & G) Medway Health Dist.

***PATEL, Sujal Suryakant** 13 Badgers Holt, Oadby, Leicester LE2 5PU — MB ChB 1995 Leeds.

PATEL, Suliman Mohamed (retired) 107 Drewstead Road, London SW16 1AD Tel: 020 8769 7359 — MB ChB 1946 Sheff.

PATEL, Sumitraben Mukundbhai 16 Timber Pond Road, London SE16 6AG — MB BS 1970 Gujarat.

PATEL, Sundeept 78 Butler Road, Harrow HA1 4DR — MB BS 1991 Lond.

PATEL, Sundip Jagdishchandra 1 Marshfield Drive, Coventry CV4 7ER — MB BCh 1992 Wales; MRCP (UK) 1996. (Univ. Wales Coll. Med.) Specialist Regist. Cardio. S. Thames. Prev: Clin. Research Fell. Blood Pressure Unit St Geo.s Hosp.; SHO Med. Rotat. Leicester.

PATEL, Surendra Ambalal The Surgery, 86 Audley Road, Hendon, London NW4 3HB Tel: 020 8203 5150 Fax: 020 8202 5682 — MB BS 1969 Gujarat.

PATEL, Surendra Purshottam 39 Winchester Way, Ashby-de-la-Zouch LE65 2NR Tel: 01530 411064 — MB BS 1970 Gujarat. (B.J. Med. Coll. Ahmedabad) GP Midway & Ch. Greasley. Prev: Med. Off. Homa Bay Dist. Hosp. Kenya; Med. Off. Kapsabet Dist. Hosp. Kenya; Clin. Asst. Groby Rd. Hosp. Leicester.

PATEL, Suresh Kanubhai The Surgery, 11-13 Charlton Road, Blackheath, London SE3 7HB Tel: 020 8858 2632 Fax: 020 8293 9286 — MB BS 1975 Bombay; MB BS 1975 Bombay.

PATEL, Suresh Kumar 38 Mollison Way, Edgware HA8 5QW — MB BCh 1992 Wales; FRCS (Oto) 1998; BSc (Hons) (Anat.) 1989; FRCS Ed. 1996. (Univ. Wales) Specialist Regist.Oxf. Region; SHO ENT Roy. Nat. Throat, Nose & Ear Hosp. W. Midl. Gen. Surg. Rotat.; SHO St Mary's Hosp.; SHO St Bart's Hosp.; LAT Spr Bristol & S.W. Eng.

PATEL, Suresh Madhavlal Wenlock Street Surgery, 40 Wenlock Street, Luton LU2 0NN Tel: 01582 27094 — MB BS 1962 Gujarat. (B.J. Med. Coll. Ahmedabad)

PATEL, Sureshchandra Chhaganbhai The Surgery, 114 Woodside, Wigmore, Gillingham ME8 0PW Tel: 01634 234131; Abbotts Court Farm, The St, Bredhurst, Gillingham ME7 3LQ — MB BS 1963 Bombay; MRCGP 1976; DCH RCP Lond. 1969. Prev: Hosp. Pract. (Rheum.) St. Bart. Hosp. Rochester.

PATEL, Sureshchandra Rambhai The Health Centre, High Street, Arnold, Nottingham NG5 7BG Tel: 0115 926 7257 — MB BS 1969 Newc.; DObst RCOG 1973; DCH Eng. 1972.

PATEL, Sushila Deveshi 2 Cedar Tree Drive, off Copse Hill, Wimbledon, London SW20 — MB BS 1966 Calcutta; DObst RCOG 1970. (R.G. Kar Med. Coll.) Med. Off. (Community Med.) Wandsworth & Merton HAs.

PATEL, Swati South Ham House, 96 Paddock Road, Basingstoke RG22 6RL Tel: 01256 324666 Fax: 01256 810849; Malabar House, 2 The Baredown, Nately Scures, Hook RG27 9JT Tel: 01256 763702 Fax: 01256 760274 Email: clegg@malabar.demon.co.uk — BM 1980 Soton.; DRCOG 1984. GP Basingstoke. Prev: Trainee GP Overton VTS; SHO (Psychiat.) Basingstoke Dist. Hosp.; SHO (Med. & O & G) Basingstoke Dist. Hosp.

PATEL, Swati Rajendra c/o Mrs S. Patel, 4 Crofton Way, Enfield EN2 8HX — MB BS 1987 Lond.; DRCOG 1991.

***PATEL, Tapin Barindra** Devoran Lime Grove, London N20 8PU — MB BS 1996 Lond.

PATEL, Tarangini Purushottam Whitehill House Surgery, 1 Crayford Road, Dartford DA1 4AN Tel: 01322 225603 Fax: 01322 293244 — MB BS 1971 Baroda.

PATEL, Tarulata Khandubhai 2E Verwood Road, Harrow HA2 6LD Tel: 020 8428 7692 — MB BS 1984 Lond.; MRCP (UK) 1986; DRCOG Lond. 1988; DCH RCP Lond. 1987. Prev: SHO (Gen. Med.) NW Herts. HA.

PATEL, Thakor Dahyabhai Kent House Surgery, 36 Station Road, Longfield DA3 7QD Tel: 01474 703550; 1 Banckside, Hartley, Longfield DA3 7RD Tel: 01474 705644 — MB BS 1963 Baroda; MRCOG 1971. (Med. Coll. Baroda) Socs: MDU.

PATEL

PATEL, Thakorlal Bhailalbhai Connaught Surgery, 144 Hedge Lane, Palmers Green, London N13 5ST Tel: 020 8886 2284 Fax: 020 8372 7246 — MB BS 1963 Bombay. (Grant Med. Coll.) Mem. of Lions Club of Enfield. Socs: BMA.

PATEL, Trilok Bercharbhai Craven Road Medical Centre, 60 Craven Road, Leeds LS6 2RX Tel: 0113 295 3530 Fax: 0113 295 3542 — MB ChB 1973 Leeds; DRCOG RCOG 1975; MRCGP Royal College of General Practioners 1981. (Leeds) GP Leeds; GP Trauma.

PATEL, Uday Department of Radiology, St. George's Hospital, Blackshaw Road, London SW17 0QT Tel: 020 8725 1481 Fax: 020 8725 2936; 6 Fontarabia Road, London SW11 5PF — MB ChB 1982 Dundee; MRCP (UK) 1985; FRCR 1992. Cons. & Hon. Sen. Lect. St. Geo. Hosp. Lond. Prev: Fell. (Interven. Radiol.) Univ. Texas Med. Br., USA; Sen. Regist. (Radiol.) Middlx. Hosp. Lond.; Hon. Regist. Univ. Dept. Med. Glas. Roy. Infirm.

PATEL, Uresh Sureshbhai Kanders, Norwich Avenue, Camberley GU15 2JX — MB BS 1987 Lond.

***PATEL, Urmil** Kanders, Norwich Avenue, Camberley GU15 2JX — MB BS 1988 Lond.

PATEL, V R Southey Green Medical Centre, 281 Southey Green Road, Sheffield S5 7QB Tel: 0114 232 6401 Fax: 0114 285 4402.

PATEL, Valabh Shambhubhai Patel, Erith Health Centre, Queen Street, Erith DA8 1TT Tel: 01322 330283 Fax: 01322 351504; 11 Lansdown Road, Sidcup DA14 4EF Tel: 020 8300 6217 — MB BS 1973 Bombay; DRCOG 1976. (Topiwala Nat. Med. Coll. Bombay India)

PATEL, Venita 58 Foscote Road, Hendon Central, London NW4 3SD — MB BS 1993 Lond.; DRCOG 1995. SHO (Paediat.) St. Geo. Hosp. Lond. Prev: SHO (A & E) Kingston Gen. Hosp.; SHO (O & G) Newham Gen. Hosp.

PATEL, Vijaychandra Jashbhai Annie Prendergash Health Centre, Ashton Gardens, Romford RM6 6RT Tel: 020 8590 1461 Fax: 020 8597 7819 — MB BS 1989 Lond.; MRCGP 1993.

PATEL, Vijaykumar Maganbhai 224 Balgores Lane, Gidea Park, Romford RM2 6BS — MB BS 1981 Baroda; MRCS Eng. LRCP Lond. 1988.

***PATEL, Vikesh** 7 Gatley Drive, Guildford GU4 7JJ — MB ChB 1998 Dund.; MB ChB Dund 1998.

PATEL, Vimla Harikrishna 3 Ashleigh Court, Fulwood, Preston PR2 9WU — MB BS 1960 Gujarat.

PATEL, Vinaben 19 Factory Street, Loughborough LE11 1AL — MB ChB 1992 Birm.; MRCGP 1996; DRCOG 1995.

PATEL, Vinaykumar 1 Poynton Close, Grappenhall, Warrington WA4 2NG — MB ChB 1993 Liverp.

PATEL, Vinod Kumar 30 Newstead Drive, Bolton BL3 3RE — MB BS 1995 Lond.

PATEL, Mr Vinod Shamalji (retired) White Gables, Kitnocks Hill, Curdridge, Southampton SO32 2HJ Tel: 01489 781789 — MB BS Bombay 1952; FRCS Eng. 1965; FRCS Ed. 1965. Cons. Rehabil. Med. St. Mary's Hosp. Portsmouth. Prev: Sen. Med. Off. DHSS.

PATEL, Vinodchandra Ambalal The Surgery, 117 Knypersley Road, Norton-in-the-Moors, Stoke-on-Trent ST6 8JA Tel: 01782 545728 Fax: 01782 570069; Sanmay, Basnetts Wood, Endon, Stoke-on-Trent ST9 9DQ Tel: 01782 504403 — MB BS 1963 Bombay; MRCOG 1971; DObst RCOG 1966; DObst RCPI 1965; DGO Dub. 1965. (Seth Gordhandas Sunderdas Med. Coll.)

PATEL, Vinodkumar Natubhai Manor House Health Centre, Manor Lane, Feltham TW13 4JQ Tel: 020 8321 3737 Fax: 020 8321 3739 — MB BS 1973 Saurashtra.

PATEL, Vinodray Chaturbhai 1 Oaks Avenue, London SE19 1QY — MB BS 1969 Poona. (B.J. Med. Coll.) Assoc. RCGP. Socs: BMA. Prev: Intern (Paediat.) New Mulago Hosp. Kampala, Uganda; Intern (Surg.) Jinja Hosp., Uganda; SHO Pumwani Matern. Hosp. Nairobi, Kenya.

PATEL, Vinubhai Natubhai 11 Moorlands View, Bolton BL3 3TN Tel: 01204 64957 — MB BS 1974 Indore; BSc Vikram 1961. (M.G.M. Med. Coll.) Socs: Med. Protec. Soc. Prev: GP Asst. Essex; SHO (A & E) Birkenhead Gen. Hosp. & Vict. Centr. Hosp. Wallasey; SHO (Gyn. & Obst.) St. Catherine Hosp. Birkenhead.

PATEL, Vipin Family Doctor Unit Surgery, 92 Bath Road, Hounslow TW3 3LN Tel: 020 8577 9666 Fax: 020 8577 0692; 8 Kingsbridge Road, Norwood Green, Southall UB2 5RT Tel: 020 8574 5683 — BM BS 1975 Nottm.; DRCOG 1977.

PATEL, Vipinchandra Chhotabhai Water Lane Surgery, 48 Brixton Water Lane, London SW2 1QE Tel: 020 7274 1521 Fax: 020 7738 3258 — LRCPI & LM, LRSCI & LM 1969; LRCPI & LM, LRCSI & LM 1969.

PATEL, Vipul 145 Kingston Road, Teddington TW11 9JP; Flat 6, 75 Ravenhurst Road, Harborne, Birmingham B17 9SR Tel: 0121 427 4887 — BM 1992 Soton.; MRCP (UK) 1997. (Soton.) Specialist Regist. Diagnostic Radio. W. Midl. Rotat. Birm.

PATEL, Mr Vipul Ramubhai Department of Trauma & Orthopaedics, Mayday University Hospital, London Road, Croydon CR7 7YE; 63 Greenway, Raynes Park, London SW20 9BQ — MB BS 1986 Gujarat; MS (Orth.) Gujarat 1988; FRCS Eng. 1991. Sen. Regist. (Orthop.) S. Thames (W.) Orthop. Train. Scheme. Prev: Regist. (Orthop.) St. Helier NHS Trust Carshalton & St. Geo. Healthcare Lond.

PATEL, Vishnubhai Rambhai Melbourne Road Surgery, 71 Melbourne Road, Leicester LE2 0GU Tel: 0116 253 9479 Fax: 0116 242 5602; (branch Surgery), 24 Moira St., Leicester LE4 6FL Tel: 0116 266 5384 — MB BS 1958 Bombay. (Grant Med. Coll.) Socs: BMA & LM Soc.; Med. Protec. Soc.

PATEL, Yajurbala Sharadchandra 47 Shirley Hills Road, Croydon CR0 5HQ Tel: 020 8654 5075 — MB BS 1967 Bombay; DA Eng. 1972. (Grant Med. Coll.) Prev: SHO (Anaesth.) Cumbld. Infirm. Carlisle; SHO (Anaesth.) Roy. Surrey Co. Hosp. Guildford; Regist. (Anaesth.) Bolingbroke Hosp. Lond.

PATEL, Yakub Valibhai Suleman Slaithwaite Road Surgery, 140 Slaithwaite Road, Thornhill Lees, Dewsbury WF12 9DW Tel: 01924 461369; Tel: 01924 464736 — MB ChB 1978 Leeds; BSc 1975 (Hon.) Leeds. (Leeds Un) GP Dewsbury.

PATEL, Yashvant Ashabhai New Medical Centre, Main Road, Highley, Bridgnorth WV16 6HG Tel: 01746 861572 Fax: 01746 862295 — MB BS 1969 Baroda.

***PATEL, Yasmin** 197 Milton Avenue, London E6 1BN — MB BS 1996 Lond.

PATEL, Yusuf Ahmed Llysmeddyg Surgery, Dew Road, Sandfields Estate, Port Talbot SA12 7HE Tel: 01639 871039 Fax: 01639 898616 — MB ChB 1974 Zambia; BSc Zambia 1971; MRCOG 1981. (Univ. Zambia) Princip. Gen. Pract.; Clin. Asst. (Colposcopy & Ophth.) Neath Gen. Hosp.; Med. Adviser (Palliat. Care) Iechyd Morgannwg Health Swansea; Police Surg. S. Wales Constab.; Clin. Asst. (Chest Clinic) Neath Gen. Hosp.; Clin. Asst. (Ophth.) Neath Gen. Hosp. Socs: BMA; Med. Protec. Soc.; (Sec.) Overseas Doctors Assn. Prev: Lect. (O & G) Sch. of Med. Univ. Teachg. Hosp. Lusara, Zambia; Sen. Regist. & Regist. (O & G) W. Middlx. Hosp. Isleworth.

PATEL, Yusuf Ismail Woodgrange Medical Practice, 40 Woodgrange Road, Forest Gate, London E7 0QH Tel: 020 8250 7585 — MB ChB 1984 Sheff.; MRCGP 1988.

***PATEL, Zaki** 5 The Dene, Beardwood, Blackburn BB2 7QS — MB ChB 1998 Aberd.; MB ChB Aberd 1998.

PATEMAN, Jane Ann Brighton General Hospital, Elm Grove, Brighton BN2 3EW Tel: 01273 696955; Silverthorn, Minsted, Midhurst GU29 0JH — MB BS 1982 Lond.; FFA RCS Eng. 1987; DA Eng. 1985. Cons. Anaesth. Brighton Health Care Trust. Prev: Vis. Asst. Prof. Anesthesiol. Univ Maryland, Baltimore, USA; Sen. Regist. (Anaesth.) St. Thos. Hosp. Lond.

PATEMAN, John Atkinson Morley's Hospital, 31 Copse Hill, Wimbledon, London SW20 0NE Tel: 020 8946 7711 Fax: 020 8947 8389; 17 Eversfield, Southwater, Horsham RH13 7GF Tel: 01403 734219 Email: j.pateman@clara.net — MB BChir 1988 Camb.; MA (Hons.) Camb. 1989; FRCA 1995; DA (UK) 1993. Specialist Regist. (Anaesth.) St. Geo. Hosp. Lond. Socs: SCATA; Obst. Anaesth. Assn. Prev: Regist. (Anaesth.) St. Richard's Hosp. Chichester & Worthing & S.lands Hosp.; SHO (Anaesth.) Soton. Gen. Hosp. & P.ss Roy. Hosp. Haywards Heath.

PATEMAN, Myrtle Thelma Chattis Hill, Moulsham Thrift, Chelmsford CM2 8BP — MB BS 1951 Calcutta; DObst RCOG 1954. Prev: Regist. (O & G) OldCh. Hosp. Romford; Ho. Surg. Eliz. G. Anderson Hosp.; Ho. Phys. Rush Green Hosp. Romford.

PATEMAN, Sally Elizabeth (retired) Craig y Trwyn, Wattsville, Cross Keys, Newport NP11 7QW Tel: 01495 273045 Fax: 01495 270370 — MRCS Eng. LRCP Lond. 1966; Cert. Family Plann. JCC 1976. GP Gwent; Police Surg. Gwent. Prev: SCMO (Geriat., Young Chronic Sick & Renal Dialysis) Gwent HA.

PATERNOSTRO, Giovanni MRC Clinical Sciences Centre, Hammersmith Hospital, Du Cane Road, London W12 0NN — State Exam 1987 Rome.

PATERSON, Abigail Ann 53 Midrow, Charleston, Forfar DD8 1UG Tel: 01307 840307 — MB ChB 1996 Dundee; DFFP 1998; DRCOG 1999. (Univ. of Dundee) SHO (Med.) GP Train. Scheme. Prev: SHO (Infec. Dis.s) GP Train. Scheme; SHO (O & G) GP Train. Scheme.

PATERSON, Aileen Margaret Elizabeth Milngavie Road Surgery, 85 Milngavie Road, Bearsden, Glasgow G61 2DN Tel: 0141 211 5621 Fax: 0141 211 5625 — MB ChB 1983 Glas.; MRCGP 1987; DRCOG 1986. Socs: Roy. Coll. Gen. Pract.

PATERSON, Mr Alastair Glen Department of Surgery, West Cornwall Hospital, St Clare St., Penzance TR18 2PF Tel: 01736 62382 Fax: 01736 50134; St. Loy Farm, St. Buryan, Penzance TR19 6DH Tel: 01736 810430 — MB ChB 1972 Ed.; BSc (Med. Sci.) Ed. 1969, MD 1988; FRCS Ed. 1977. Cons. Surg. W. Cornw. Hosp. Penzance & Dir. Mermaid Centre Roy. Cornw. Hosps. Trust Treliske. Socs: Brit. Assn. Surgic. Oncol.; Surgic. Research Soc.; Assn. Surg. GB & Irel. Prev: Cons. Surg. CrossHo. Hosp. Kilmarnock; Sen. Regist. (Surg.) Univ. Hosp. Wales Cardiff & Roy. Marsden Hosp. Lond.; Research Fell. Univ. Dept. Surg. Welsh Nat. Sch. Med. Cardiff.

PATERSON, Alexander Bernard Terrace Surgery, 17 Bernard Terrace, Edinburgh EH8 9NU Tel: 0131 667 2240 — MB ChB 1978 Dundee; MRCGP 1983.

PATERSON, Alexander 18 Denbigh Drive, Shaw, Oldham OL2 7EQ — MB ChB 1957 Ed. (Ed.)

PATERSON, Mr Alexander Dumgoyach House, Blanefield, Glasgow G63 9AJ — MB ChB 1940 Glas.; FRFPS Glas. 1947; FRCS Glas. 1962. (Univ. Glas.) Cons. Neurosurg. Glas. & W. Scotl. Neurosurg. Unit, Killearn Hosp.; W.. Infirm. Glas. & S.. Gen. Hosp. Glas. Socs: Soc. Brit. Neurol. Surgs. Prev: 1st Asst. Neurosurg. Dept. St. Geo. Hosp. Lond.; Neurosurg. Fell. Montreal Neurol. Inst. & Montreal Gen. Hosp.; Regist. Hosp. Nerv. Dis. Qu. Sq. Lond.

PATERSON, Alexander MacGregor St Thomas Surgery, Rifleman Lane, St. Thomas Green, Haverfordwest SA61 1QX Tel: 01437 762162 Fax: 01437 776811 — MB ChB 1987 Aberd.

PATERSON, Alistair Graham Friary Surgery, Queens Road, Richmond DL10 4UJ Tel: 01748 822306 Fax: 01748 850356; Tel: 01748 824358 — MB ChB 1978 Aberd.; MRCGP 1984. Prev: Maj. RAMC.

PATERSON, Allan Wilson (retired) Stafla Lodge, 19 Midton Road, Ayr KA7 2SE Tel: 01292 264402 — LRCP LRCS Ed. LRFPS Glas. 1941. Prev: Ho. Phys. Ross & Cromarty Co. Fev. Hosp.

PATERSON, Andrew David North End House, Hutton Rudby, Yarm TS15 0DG Tel: 01642 700056 — BM BCh 1975 Oxf.; MA Oxf. 1976, BM BCh 1975; MRCP (UK) 1978; FRCP Lond. 1994; FRCP Ed. 1997. (King's Coll. Hosp.) Cons. Phys. & Nephrol. S. Cleveland Hosp. Middlesbrough. Socs: Renal Assn. Prev: Sen. Regist. (Nephrol.) City Hosp. Nottm.; Regist. (Med.) Hallamsh. Hosp. Sheff.; Epidemiol. WHO Smallpox Eradicat. Progr. Bangladesh.

PATERSON, Andrew James The Surgery, Park Lane, Stubbington, Fareham PO14 2JP Tel: 01329 664231 Fax: 01329 664958 — MB BChir 1983 Camb.; MA Camb. 1983; MRCGP 1986; DRCOG 1985. (Middlx.) Gen. Practitioner, Pk. La. Surg., Stubbington, Fareham; GP Bd. Mem., Fareham PCG. Prev: Trainee GP Portsmouth VTS; SHO (Paediat.) Soton Gen. Hosp.; SHO (Geriat.) Upton Hosp. Slough.

PATERSON, Andrew Munro 2 Park Terrace, Stirling FK8 2NA — MB ChB 1988 Ed.

PATERSON, Anne Radiology Department, Royal Belfast Hospital for Sick Children, 180 Falls Road, Belfast BT12 6BE Tel: 01232 894963 Fax: 01232 313798; 9 Farm Lodge Way, Greenisland, Carrickfergus BT38 8YA Tel: 01232 864380 Fax: 01232 864380 Email: anniep@csi.com — MB BS 1990 Lond.; MRCP (UK) 1993; FRCR 1997. (St. Bartholomew's Hospital) Cons. (Paediat. Radiol.) Roy. Belf. Hosp. For Sick Childr. Socs: Brit. Paediat. Soc. Imaging Gp.; Eur. Soc. Of Paed. Radiol.; Radiol. Soc. of N. Amer. Prev: Specialist Regist. (Radiol.) Roy. Vict. Hosp. Belf.; Fell. Sect. of Pediatric Radiol. Duke Univ. Med. Center Durh. NC 27710, USA.

PATERSON, Mr Anthony William Southwaite House, Southwaite, Carlisle CA4 0ER — MRCS Eng. LRCP Lond. 1987; BDS Ed. 1977; FRCS Ed. 1991; FDS RCS Ed. 1981; DOrth. 1982. Sen. Regist. (Maxillofacial Surg.) Roy. Lond. Hosp. Trust.

PATERSON, Antony Zdzislaw Church House, Shaw St., Ruddington, Nottingham NG11 6HF Tel: 0115 984 7101 Fax: 0115 945 6503 — MB ChB 1972 Manch. Prev: SHO (Paediat. & O & G) City Hosp. Nottm.; SHO (A & E) Univ. Hosp. Nottm.

PATERSON, Barbara Ann 119 Newark Avenue, Peterborough PE1 4NL Tel: 01733 343658; 4/260 Casuarina Drive, Nightcliff, Darwin NT 0810, Australia Tel: 00 61 0889 480221 Email: barbara.paterson@nt.gov.au — MB ChB 1984 Manch.; MPH NSW Austral. 1995; MRCGP 1990; FAFPHM 1995; T(GP) 1991; DRCOG 1989; DGM RCP Lond. 1987; DCH RCP Lond. 1986. Specialist (Pub. Health Med.) Matern. & Child Health Policy. Socs: BMA; Austral. Med. Assn.; Fell. Austral. Fac. Pub. Health Med. Prev: Dist. Med. Off. Territory Health Servs. Austral.

PATERSON, Brodie Charles 22 North Meggetland, Edinburgh EH14 1XG — MB ChB 1990 Aberd.

PATERSON, Charlotte Frances 13 York Place, Bristol BS8 1AH Tel: 0117 973 4672 Email: c.paterson@dial.pipex.com; Top Flat, 13 York Place, Bristol BS8 1AH Tel: 0117 973 4672 Email: c.paterson@dial.pipex.com — MB ChB 1972 Bristol; MSc Lond. 1995; MRCGP 1978; DObst RCOG 1975. Research Fell. Self Employed.

PATERSON, Mrs Christina Craig Christie (retired) Watsonhead Cottage, Newmains, Wishaw ML2 9PL Tel: 01698 382487 — MB ChB Glas. 1941. Prev: Late. Med. Asst. Motherwell & Hamilton Geriat. Serv.

PATERSON, Colin Ralston Department of Medicine, Ninewells Hospital & Medical School, Dundee DD1 9SY Tel: 01382 632517 Fax: 01382 660675 Email: c.r.paterson@dundee.ac.uk; Temple Oxgates, Longforgan, Dundee DD2 5HS Tel: 01382 360240 Email: c.s.paterson@btinternet.com — BM BCh Oxf. 1962; MSc Oxf. 1986, BSc 1961, BA 1958, MA 1962, DM 1970; FRCP Ed. 1988, M 1985; FRCPath 1981, M 1971. (Oxf. & Univ. Coll. Hosp.) Reader Med. Dundee Univ.; Hon. Sen. Lect. St. And. Univ.; Hon. Cons. Tayside Univ. Hosp.s NHS Trust. Socs: Scot. Soc. Phys.s; Internat. Bone & Mineral Soc.; BMA- Bone and Tooth Soc. Prev: Sen. Lect. (Med.) Dundee Univ.; Sen. Lect. (Biochem. Med.) Univ. Dundee; Regist. (Med.) York Hosp. Gp.

PATERSON, Cordelia Lynn Reevy Hill Health Centre, 50 Reevy Road West, Buttershaw, Bradford BD6 3LT Tel: 01274 691098 Fax: 01274 694008 — MB BS 1981 Lond.

PATERSON, David Alexander Department of Pathology, Weston General Hospital, Grange Road, Uphill, Weston Super Mare BS23 4TQ — MB ChB 1983 Manch.; BSc (Hons.) St And. 1980; MRCPath 1990. Cons. Histopath. W.on Area Health Trust W.on Gen. Hosp. W.on-super-Mare. Prev: Lect. (Histopath.) Univ. Edin.; Demonst. (Histopath.) Brist. Roy. Infirm.; SHO (Path.) S.mead Hosp. Bristol.

PATERSON, David Hood (retired) 14 Landsborough Drive, Kilmarnock KA3 1RY Tel: 01563 522282 — MB ChB 1948 Glas.; DPH 1956; MFCM 1972; DObst RCOG 1955. Prev: SCM Ayrsh. & Arran Health Bd.

PATERSON, Dorothy Maeve 2 Greenbank Gardens, Little Urswick, Ulverston LA12 0RN Tel: 0122 988677 — MB BCh BAO 1948 NUI. (Cork) Med. Off. for DHSS Bootle Merseyside. Socs: BMA. Prev: Clin. Med. Off. S. Cumbria HA; Asst. MOH & Sch. Med. Off. Bolton Co. Boro.; JHMO (Psychiat.) St. Thos. Hosp. Stockport.

PATERSON, Douglas Robert 6B Castle Terrace, Edinburgh EH1 2DP; Medical Flats, St. George's Hospital, Morpeth NE61 2NU Tel: 01670 512121 — MB ChB 1996 Ed.; BSc 1994. (Edin. Univ.) SHO (Psychiat. Rotat.) St. Geo.'s Hosp. S. Tyneside Area. Prev: SHO (Infec. Dis.s) Kirkaldy; SHO (Oncol.) Edin.; SHO (Med.) Dumfermline.

PATERSON, Miss Elfriede Katherine Jessie (retired) Wood End, Labour-in-Vain Road, Wrotham, Sevenoaks TN15 7NY Tel: 01732 822465 — MRCS Eng. LRCP Lond. 1938. Prev: Deptm. Med. Off. Kent CC.

***PATERSON, Elizabeth Ann** 600 Old Chester Road, Birkenhead CH42 4NW — MB ChB 1997 Manch.

PATERSON, Emma Helen 7A Baswich Lane, Stafford ST17 0BH — MB BS 1994 Lond.; BSc Lond. 1991; DRCOG 1998; DFFP 1998. (King's College Hospital London) GP Regist. Mid Staffs. Prev: SHO (O & G) Stafford Gen. Hosp.; VTS Train. Scheme N. Staffs. Hosp.

PATERSON, Eric Horsburgh (retired) Glenview, 38 Station Road, Carluke ML8 5LN Tel: 01555 751311 — MB ChB 1956 Glas. Prev: GP Carluke.

PATERSON

PATERSON, Evelyn Jean (retired) The Ochils, Brimstage Road, Heswall, Wirral CH60 1XA Tel: 0151 342 3184 — MB ChB St. And. 1949; FRCPath 1971. Prev: Cons. Path. Clatterbridge Hosp. Bebington.

PATERSON, Mr Fergus William Nigel Cromwell Hospital, Cromwell Road, London SW5 0TU Tel: 020 7460 5914 Fax: 020 7460 5709 Email: fergus.paterson@knee-surgery.co.uk — MB BS 1971 Lond.; FRCS Eng. 1977; FRCS Ed. 1976. (St. Mary's) Cons. Orthop. Surg. W. Middlx. Univ. Hosp. Trust Isleworth; Hon. Lect., Imperial Coll., Lond. Socs: Fell. BOA. Prev: Clin. Lect. Inst. Orthop. Lond.; Sen. Regist. Roy. Nat. Orthop. Hosp. Lond.

PATERSON, Fiona Campbell Ailsa Hospital, Dalmellington Road, Ayr KA6 6AB Tel: 01292 610556; 10 Beechwood Paddock, Loans, Troon KA10 7LX Tel: 01292 311209 — MB ChB 1985 Glas. Staff Grade (Psychiat. Old Age) Ailsa Hosp. Ayr. Prev: GP Dukes Rd. Troon; Trainee GP Alloway Pl. Ayr; SHO (Psychiat. & O & G) CrossHo. Hosp.

PATERSON, Fiona Moira 22 North Meggatland, Edinburgh EH14 1XG — MB ChB 1991 Aberd.; BMedBiol. Aberd. 1991; MRCGP (Distinc.) 1996; DFFP 1995; DRCOG 1995.

PATERSON, Francis Lyle (retired) Willowbrae, Alexandra Terrace, Forres IV36 1DL Tel: 01309672355 — LRCP LRCS 1945 Ed.; LRCP LRCS Ed. LRFPS Glas. 1945.

PATERSON, Fraser Neil Grove House Surgery, 80 Pryors Lane, Rose Green, Bognor Regis PO21 4JB Tel: 01243 265222/266413 Fax: 01243 268693 — MB BS 1987 Lond.; DRCOG 1991.

PATERSON, Gavin William Hausen 4 Westfield Road, Ayr KA7 2XN Tel: 0292 268096 — MB ChB Glas. 1943.

PATERSON, Gordon Murray Charles McDonald, RD Nuffield Department of Anaesthetics, The John Radcliffe Hospital, Oxford OX3 9DU Tel: 01865 221590 Fax: 01865 464038 Email: gordon.paterson@nda.ox.ac.uk — MB ChB Ed. 1959; FRCA 1964. Cons. Anaesth. Oxf. Radcliffe NHS Trust.

PATERSON, Hamish Robert 34 Sandringham Road, South Gosforth, Newcastle upon Tyne NE3 1PY — MB BS 1985 Newc.

***PATERSON, Hugh Mackenzie** Dept of General Surgery, Stirling Royal Infirmary, Stirling FR8 2AU; 27 Bredero Drive, Ellon AB41 9QF — MB ChB 1994 Aberd.

PATERSON, Mr Iain MacKenzie Frimley Park Hospital NHS Trust, Portsmouth Road, Frimley, Camberley GU16 7UJ Tel: 01276 604588; Sherwood, 14 Middle Avenue, Farnham GU9 8JL Tel: 01252 711201 Fax: 01252 712580 — MB ChB 1976 Aberd.; PhD Aberd. 1984; FRCS 1980. (Aberd.) Cons. Surg. Frimley Pk. Hosp. Surrey. Socs: Fell. Assoc. Surg.s GB & Irel.; Brit. Soc. Gastroenterol.; Assn. Upper G.I. Surg. Prev: Vis. Prof. Univ. Hong Kong 1997; Sen. Registar (Surgury) St. Geo.'s Hosp. Lond.; Clin. Fell. Univ. Hong Kong.

PATERSON, Iain Wallace 1 Arlington Road, Eastbourne BN21 7DH Tel: 01323 727531 Fax: 01323 417085 — MB BS 1965 Lond.; MRCS Eng. LRCP Lond. 1965; MRCGP 1982; DObst RCOG 1967. (St. Mary's) Med. Off. Chaseley Home for Disabled Serv.men & E.bourne Coll. Art & Technol.; Chairm. Trustees Seadoc. Doctors Co-op.. Prev: Ho. Surg. St. Mary's Hosp. Lond.; Ho. Phys. & Ho. Surg. (O & G) Paddington Gen. Hosp.

PATERSON, Ian Charles 21 The Green, Ingham, Lincoln LN1 2XT Tel: 01522 730545 — MB ChB 1968 Manch.; BSc (Hons.), MB ChB Manch. 1968; FRCP Eng. 1988; FRCP Ed. 1988; MRCP (UK) 1972. Cons. Phys. (s/i Respirat. Dis.) N. Lincs. (Lincoln) Dist. Socs: Brit. Thorac. Assn. Prev: Regist. (Respirat. Dis.) N.. Gen. Hosp. Edin.; Sen. Regist. (Gen. Med.) N. Lothian Health Dist.; Ho. Surg. & Ho. Phys. Manch. Roy. Infirm.

PATERSON, Ian Douglas, Maj. RAMC Retd. (retired) 52 Free Trade Wharf, 340 The Highway, London E1W 3ES Tel: 020 7791 0367 Fax: 020 7790 9073 — MB ChB 1939 Ed. Prev: Maj. RAMC.

PATERSON, Ian Gavin 16 Devonshire Road, Sheffield S17 3NT Email: ian@cosmos.uk.org — MB BS 1986 Lond.; MA Camb. 1983; FRCA 1992. Cons. Anaesth. N. Gen. Hosp. Sheff. Prev: Sen. Regist. Rotat. (Anaesth.) UCL; Regist. Rotat. (Anaesth.) Char. Cross Hosp. Lond.; SHO (Anaesth.) St Geo. Hosp. Lond.

PATERSON, Irene Dalkeith Road Medical Practice, 145 Dalkeith Road, Edinburgh EH16 5HQ Tel: 0131 667 1289; 26 Danube Street, Edinburgh EH4 1NT Tel: 0131 332 0370 — MB BS 1977 Lond.; MRCP (UK) 1981; MRCGP 1982; DRCOG 1981; Dip. Thev. 1998. Teachg. Med. Stud.s (Univ. of Edin.).

PATERSON, Isabel Eleanor (retired) 129 Georgetown Road, Dumfries DG1 4BE Tel: 01387 253639 Fax: 01387 253639 — MB ChB Ed. 1955; DCH RCPS Glas. 1958; DPH Ed. 1962.

PATERSON, James Alexander (retired) 1 Austen Avenue, Oliver's Battery, Winchester SO22 4HP Tel: 01962 854762 — MB ChB 1944 Ed. Prev: GP Winchester.

PATERSON, Jean (retired) Comraich, The Green, Sinnington, York YO62 6RZ Tel: 01751 31907 — MB BS 1945 Durh.; DObst RCOG 1948. Prev: Med. Off. City Fev. Hosp. Little Bromwich.

PATERSON, Jeremy Robert Mount Chambers Surgery, 92 Coggeshall Road, Braintree CM7 9BY Tel: 01376 553415 Fax: 01376 552451; Winnipeg, Church Road, Gosfield, Halstead CO9 1TL Tel: 01787 472514 — MB BS 1976 Lond.; MRCS Eng. LRCP Lond. 1976; MRCGP 1980; DCH Eng. 1979; DRCOG 1979. (Guy's) Prev: Trainee GP Worthing VTS; Ho. Phys. & Ho. Surg. Greenwich Dist. Hosp. Lond.

PATERSON, Joan Catherine 13 Craigstewart Crescent, Alloway, Ayr KA7 4DB Tel: 01292 43484 — MB ChB 1964 Glas. (Glas.)

PATERSON, Joan Patricia The Surgery, Northwick Road, Pilning, Bristol BS35 4JF Tel: 01454 632393 — MB ChB 1973 Aberd.

PATERSON, Joan Sheila Kennedy Galton Centre, NW London NHS Trust, Watford Road, Harrow HA1 3UJ Tel: 020 8869 2795 Fax: 020 8869 3106 Email: j.paterson@ic.ac.uk — MB ChB 1983 Glas.; BSc (Hons.) (Genetics) Glas. 1980; MRCP (UK) (Paediat.) 1988. (Glas.) Cons. (Clin. Genetics) NW Lond. NHS Trust. Prev: Regist. (Med. Genetics) Roy. Hosp. Sick Childr., Glas.

PATERSON, John Gordon (retired) Hamilton Medical Group, 4 Queens Road, Aberdeen AB15 4ZT Tel: 01224 622345 Fax: 01224 627426 — MB ChB Ed. 1965; FRCP Ed. 1994; FFCM 1986, M 1977; DObst RCOG 1968; Dip. Community Med. Ed. 1975. Chief Med. Adviser Brit. Red Cross. Prev: GP Selkirk.

PATERSON, John Gray Thorncliffe, Tighnabruaich PA21 2DU Tel: 0170 0811 387 — MB ChB Glas. 1961; FRCR 1975; FFR 1972; DMRD Eng. 1967. (Glas.) Cons. Radiol. Roy. Alexandra Infirm. Paisley.; Cons. Radiol. Ross Hall Hosp. Prev: Wing. Cdr. RAF Med. Br., Cons. Radiol. P.ss Alexandra Hosp.; Wroughton & RAF Hosp. Wegberg Germany; Sen. Regist. Middlx. Hosp. Lond.

PATERSON, John Kirkpatrick (retired) The Old Dairy, Dullingham, Newmarket CB8 9UP — MB BS 1950 Lond.; MRCGP 1956. Prev: Chairm. Scientif. Advis. Comm. Federat. Internat. Médecine Manuelle.

PATERSON, John Maclaine 20 Greenwood Drive, Bearsden, Glasgow G61 2HA Tel: 0141 942 2983 — MB ChB 1952 Glas.; FFPHM 1989; FFCM 1987, M 1974; DPH Glas. 1959. (Glas.) Socs: Fell. Inst. Health Serv. Admin.s 1971. Prev: Cons. Pub. Health Med. Lanarksh.; Community Med. Specialist (Acute Servs.) Lanarksh. HB; Asst. Sen. Admin. Med. Off. W.. RHB (Scotl.).

PATERSON, Mr John Mark Hamilton Email: jmhpaterson@doctors.org.uk; 8 Creighton Avenue, London N10 1NU Tel: 020 8444 2404 Fax: 020 8473 9519 Email: jmhpaterson@csi.com — MB BS 1977 Lond.; FRCS Eng. 1982. (Middlesex Hosp) Cons. Orthop. Surg. Roy. Lond. Hosp. Socs: Hon. Sec Orthopaedic sec Roy. Soc. Med.; Hon Sec. Brit. Soc. for Surg. in Cerebral Palsy. Prev: Sen. Regist. (Orthop.) Lond. Hosp. & Roy. Nat. Orthop. Hosp. Lond.; Regist. (Orthop.) Portsmouth & Alton.

PATERSON, John McDonald (retired) The Elmes, 148 Whitehouse Loan, Edinburgh EH9 2EZ Tel: 0131 447 8034 — MB ChB Ed. 1941; MA (Hons.) Ed. 1932. Prev: Resid. Med. Off. Craiglockhart Hosp. Edin. & Roy. Infirm. Falkirk.

PATERSON, John Robert Area Biochemistry Department, Dumfries & Galloway Royal Infirmary, Dumfries Tel: 01387 46246; Glencaple House, Church St, Glencaple, Dumfries DG1 4QY — MB ChB 1985 Dundee; PhD Strathclyde 1983; MRCP (UK) 1988; FRCP (Ed)1999. Cons. Clin. Chem. Dumfries & Galloway Roy. Infirm. Prev: Sen. Regist. (Clin. Chem.) Roy. Infirm. Glas.; Regist. (Clin. Chem.) W.. Infirm. Glas.; SHO (Med.) Freeman Hosp. Newc.

PATERSON, John Thomson 33 Newton Road, Great Barr, Birmingham B43 6AA Tel: 0121 357 1690 Fax: 0121 357 4253; 62 Charlemont Road, Walsall WS5 3NQ Tel: 01922 26780 — MB ChB Aberd. 1963; DObst RCOG 1966. (Aberd.)

PATERSON, John William Links Medical Centre, 4 Hermitage Place, Edinburgh EH6 8BW Tel: 0131 554 1036 Fax: 0131 555 3995; 18 Clarendon Crescent, Edinburgh EH4 1PU Tel: 0131 343

1645 — MB ChB 1980 Aberd.; MRCGP 1985; DCH RCP Glas. 1984; DRCOG 1982. (Aberdeen) Lect. (Gen. Pract.) Univ. Edin.

PATERSON, Joseph Craig 8 Stanton Drive, Chichester PO19 4QN — MB BS 1971 Lond.; BSc (Hons.) Lond. 1968, MB BS 1971; Assoc. Fac. Occupat. Med. RCP Lond. 1980. Div. Med. Off. I.C.I. (Plant Protect. Div.); Assoc. Mem. Bioengin. Soc. Prev: Works Med. Off. I.C.I. Pharmaceut. Div.; Regist. (Gen. Med.) Foresterhill Gp. Hosps.; Ho. Phys. & Cas. Off. W.m. Hosp. Lond.

PATERSON, Joseph Dunbar (retired) 77 Greenbank Crescent, Morningside, Edinburgh EH10 5TB Tel: 0131 447 1515 — MB ChB 1946 Glas. Prev: Med. Dir, M.M.R.U. Manch. Regional Health Bd.

PATERSON, Joy 12 Sutherland Avenue, Bearsden, Glasgow G61 3JW — MB BChir 1953 Camb.; MRCP Ed. 1963. (Camb. & Bristol) Prev: Ho. Phys. Roy. Vict. Hosp. Edin.; Sen. Ho. Phys. Chest Unit, City Hosp. Edin.; Regist. Geriat. Assessm. Unit S.field Hosp. Edin.

***PATERSON, Katherine Elizabeth** Katherine Paterson Mhordon, St James Place, Inverurie AB51 3UB Tel: 01467 622566 Email: katherine@doctors.org.uk — MB ChB 1998 Glas.; MB ChB Glas 1998.

PATERSON, Kenneth Ross Diabetes Centre, Royal Infirmary, Castle St., Glasgow G4 0SF Tel: 0141 211 4745 Fax: 0141 800 1971 Email: ken.paterson@northglasgow.scot.nhs.uk; Strathcashel, Lochlibo Road, Uplawmoor, Glasgow G78 4AA Tel: 01505 850344 Email: ken.mairi@dial.pipex.com — MB ChB 1977 Glas.; FRCP Ed. 1990; FRCP Glas. 1989; MRCP (UK) 1980. Cons. Phys. Roy. Infirm. Glas. Socs: Hon. Sec. - Roy. Coll. of Phys.s & Surg.s of Glas. Prev: Sen. Regist. (Gen. Med.) Roy. Infirm. & S.. Gen. Hosp. Glas.; Regist. (Gen. Med.) Roy. Infirm. Glas. & Roy. Alexandra Infirm. Paisley.

PATERSON, Laura Margaret — MB ChB 1994 Bristol; MRCGP 1999. p/t Gen. Pract. Principle Nailsea. Socs: BMA.

PATERSON, Lorraine Mary (retired) Ansonhill House, Crossgates, Cowdenbeath KY4 8HA Tel: 01863 610146 — MB ChB 1948 Ed.

PATERSON, Margaret Tran 10 Machrie Place, Kilwinning KA13 6RW Tel: 01294 554393 Fax: 01294 554393 Email: ipaterson@aol.com; Department of Community Child Health, Ayrshire Central Hospital, Irvine KA12 8SS Tel: 01294 323441 — MB ChB 1971 Glas.; BSc Glas. 1967, MB ChB 1971, DFFP 1995. (Glasgow) Staff Grade (Community Child Health) Ayrsh. Centr. Hosp. Irvine; Clin. Med. Off. (Family Plann.) Ayrsh. & Arran Community Health Care Trust. Prev: Regist. (Clin. Biochem.) Roy. Hosp. Sick Childr. Glas.

PATERSON, Margarita Mary Frances 16 Devonshire Road, Sheffield S17 3NT — MB BS 1989 Lond.; MRCP (UK) 1994; DRCOG 1995.

***PATERSON, Mark Anthony** 72 Middlebeck Drive, Arnold, Nottingham NG5 8AF — MB BS 1996 Lond.

PATERSON, Mark Eian Oak Lodge Surgery, 32 Miller Street, Almada Lane, Hamilton ML3 7EN Tel: 01698 282350 Fax: 01698 282502 — MB ChB 1983 Glas.; MRCGP 1988; DRCOG 1987. GP Lanarksh.

PATERSON, Mary Caffyn Wright (retired) 13 Catherine Street, Gatehouse-of-Fleet, Castle Douglas DG7 2JD Tel: 01557 814000 — MB ChB 1951 Ed.; FRCOG 1976, M 1960.

PATERSON, Mary Tregelles 50 South Grove House, Highgate, London N6 6LR Tel: 020 8340 3818 — MB BS 1932 Lond.; DPH Eng. 1940. (Char. Cross) Socs: Fell. Roy. Soc. Med. Prev: Dep. MoH City W.m.; Asst. MoH Boro St. Pancras; Asst. Phys. Roy. Edin. Hosp.

PATERSON, Mr Maurice Peacock Longwood House, The Bath Clinic, Claverton Down Road, Bath BA2 7BR Tel: 01225 835555 — MB BCh 1978 Witwatersrand; FRCS Ed. (Orthop.) 1989; FCS (Orthop.) S. Afr. 1987. (Univ. Witwatersrand) Cons. Orthop. Surg. Bath Clinic. Socs: Brit. Soc. Surg. Hand; Brit. Scoliosis Soc.; Brit. Orthop. Assn.

PATERSON, Mr Maurice Wingate 30 Abbotsford Court, 18 Colinton Road, Edinburgh EH10 5EJ Tel: 0131 447 5315 — MB ChB 1937 Ed.; MA Ed. 1932; FRCS Ed. 1947; FRCOphth 1988. Prev: Ophth. Surg. Glas. Eye Infirm.; Ophth. Surg. Stobhill Gen. Hosp. Glas.; Hon. Clin. Lect. (Ophth.) Univ. Glas.

PATERSON, Mr Michael Edward Lockhart 54 Clarendon Road, Fulwood, Sheffield S10 3TR Tel: 0114 230 8054 Fax: 0114 230 7871 Email: michael.paterson@btconnect.com — MD 1980 Birm.; MB ChB 1971; FRCS Ed. 1981; FRCOG 1989, M 1977. Cons. O & G Jessop Wing Roy. Hallamshire Hosp. Sheff. Socs: Brit. Gyn.

Cancer Soc.; Gyn. Travellers; Brit. Med. Assn. Prev: Sen. Regist. Rotat. (O & G) Bradford & Leeds; Regist. Birm. & Midl. Hosp. Wom.; Regist. (Surg.) United Birm. Hosps.

PATERSON, Patricia Mary Margaret Orr (retired) 14 Dick Place, Edinburgh EH9 2JL Tel: 0131 667 1245 — M.B., Ch.B. Ed. 1945.

PATERSON, Peter Dept of Anaesthesia, Monklands Hospital, Monkscourt Avenue, Airdrie ML6 0JS Tel: 01236 748748 Fax: 01236 760015; Firhill, Woodburn Avenue, Airdrie ML6 9DT — MB ChB 1971 Glas.; FFA RCS Eng. 1977; DObst RCOG 1974; FRCA 1992. (Univ of Glasgow) Cons. Anaesth. Monklands . Hosp. Airdrie. Prev: GP Airdrie.

PATERSON, Peter 7A Baswich Lane, Stafford ST17 0BH — MB BS 1992 Lond.

PATERSON, Mr Peter John Nuffield McAlpin Clinic, 25 Beaconsfield Road, Glasgow G12 0PJ Tel: 0141 334 9441; Ross Hall Hospital, 221 Crookston Road, Glasgow G52 3NQ — MB ChB 1969 Liverp.; FRCS Eng. 1974. (Liverp.) Cons. Urol. Glas. Roy. Infirm.; Hon. Sen. Lect. (Urol.) Univ. Glas. Prev: Sen. Regist. (Urol.) Glas. Roy. Infirm.

PATERSON, Rhona Anton Aldershot Health Centre, Wellington Avenue, Aldershot GU11 1PA Tel: 01252 24577; 19 Church Road W., Farnborough GU14 6QG Tel: 01252 517001 — MB BS 1985 Lond.; MRCGP 1994; DCH RCP Lond. 1990; DGM RCP Lond. 1987.

PATERSON, Richard Graham The Croft Surgery, Barnham Road, Eastergate, Chichester PO20 6RP — MB BS 1990 Lond.; MRCGP 1994.

PATERSON, Robert Alexander Harcourt Queensway Clinic, 226 Queensway, Bletchley, Milton Keynes MK2 2TE Tel: 01908 643200 Fax: 01908 368943 — BM BCh 1968 Oxf.; MA Oxf. 1968; MRCPsych 1980. Cons. Community Ment. Health Team Bletchley. Prev: Sen. Regist. (Psychiat.) Oxf. Rotat Train. Scheme; Regist. (Psychiat.) St. John's Hosp. Stone; Med. Off. Brit. Antarctic Survey.

PATERSON, Robert Craig (retired) 38 Belleve Crescent, Ayr KA7 2DR Tel: 01292 288128 — MB ChB 1955 Glas.

PATERSON, Robert Euan Govan Health Centre, 5 Drumoyne Road, Glasgow G51 4BJ Tel: 0141 531 8490 Fax: 0141 531 8487; 467 Kilmarnock Road, Glasgow G43 2TJ — MB ChB 1981 Glas.; MRCGP 1985; DRCOG 1984.

PATERSON, Robert James Rosebank Surgery, 153B Stroud Road, Gloucester GL1 5JQ Tel: 01452 522767; Lealands, 2 Kenilworth Avenue, Gloucester GL2 0QJ Tel: 01452 306651 — MB ChB 1970 Birm.; DCH Eng. 1972. Prev: SHO (Paediat.) E. Birm. Hosp.; SHO (Psychiat.) Coney Hill Hosp. Gloucester; Ho. Phys. (Paediat.) Birm. Childr. Hosp.

PATERSON, Robert McGart West Styx Cottage, Bolfracks, Aberfeldy PH15 2EY — MB ChB 1984 Dundee.

PATERSON, Mr Robert William Walker 13 Craigstewart Crescent, Alloway, Ayr KA7 4DB Tel: 01292 43484 — MB ChB 1962 Glas.; FRCS Ed. 1968; DO Eng. 1965; DObst RCOG 1964. Cons. Ophth. Heathfield Hosp. Ayr.

PATERSON, Roger Wellwood St Margarets Health Centre, St. Margaret's Drive, Auchterarder PH3 1JH — MB ChB 1984 Glas.; MRCGP 1992. (Glasgow) GP Princip.; GP Trainer.

***PATERSON, Ross Lindsey** 2 Corstorphine Hill Crescent, Edinburgh EH12 6LH — MB ChB 1994 Aberd.

PATERSON, Samuel Muir 22 Silverknowes Drive, Edinburgh EH4 5LQ — MB ChB 1969 Ed.; MRCGP 1975.

PATERSON, Sarah Llywela Susan (retired) 10 Lyndhurst Drive, Hale, Altrincham WA15 8EA — MB ChB 1948 Leeds. Prev: Jun. Anaesth. Off. Leeds Gen. Infirm.

***PATERSON, Stuart** Firhill, Woodburn Avenue, Airdrie ML6 9DT — MB ChB 1998 Glas.; MB ChB Glas 1998.

PATERSON, Stuart Neil 7 Racecourse Road, Swinton, Mexborough S64 8DW — MB ChB 1997 Sheff.

PATERSON, Terence Andrew The Surgery, Northwick Road, Pilning, Bristol BS35 4JF Tel: 01454 632393 — MB ChB 1972 Aberd.; MRCGP 1994; DObst. RCOG 1975; DA Eng. 1974; FRACGP 1978.

PATERSON, Thomas Macilvean (retired) Ty-Bach, Moreton Avenue, Newcastle ST5 4DE Tel: 01782 641444 — MB ChB Glas. 1942; BSc Glas. 1939, MD 1949; FRCGP 1978, M 1953. Prev: Hsopital Practitioner, Diabetic Clinic, Nth. Staffs. Hosp.

PATERSON

PATERSON, Mr Walter Gouinlock Balchrystie House, Colinsburgh, Leven KY9 1HE Tel: 01333 340517 — MB ChB 1955 Ed.; FRCS Ed. 1962; FRCOG 1962, M 1975; MRCOE 1962; FRCOE 1974.

PATERSON, William (retired) Old Orchard, Lifton PL16 0AE — MB ChB 1937 Glas.; MFCM 1974; DPH Glas. 1947. Prev: Lect. Pub. Health Univ. Glas.

PATERSON, Mr William (retired) 10 Lyndhurst Drive, Hale, Altrincham WA15 8EA Tel: 0161 980 4727 — MB ChB Leeds 1941; FRCS Eng. 1950. Prev: Cons. ENT Surg. Wythenshawe Hosp. Manch. & St. Anne's Hosp. Bowdon.

PATERSON, Mr William David (retired) Black Hough Farm, Allimore Green, Haughton, Stafford ST18 9JG Tel: 01785 780599 — MB ChB 1945 St. And.; FRCS Ed. 1948. Prev: Cons. ENT Surg. Mid. Staffs. HA.

PATERSON, William David Carolina, 56 Longlands Road, Carlisle CA3 9AE Tel: 01228 521166 — MB ChB 1967 Ed.; FRCP Lond. 1985; FRCP Ed. 1983; MRCP (UK) 1972; DObst RCOG 1970. (Ed.) Cons. Dermat. N. Cumbria Health Distr. Carlisle. Socs: Brit. Assn. Dermat. & BMA. Prev: Sen. Regist. (Dermat.) Roy. Infirm. Edin.; Regist. (Med.) Chalmers Hosp. Edin.; Ho. Surg. Bellshill Matern. Hosp.

PATERSON, Mr William Ian Craig Dhu, North Queensferry, Inverkeithing KY11 Tel: 01383 2647 — MB ChB 1938 Ed.; FRCS Ed. 1946. (Ed.) Adviser (Orthop.) El Fateh Hosp. Tripoli. Socs: Fell. Brit. Orthop. Assn. & Roy. Med. Soc. Edin. Prev: Cons. Orthop. Surg. P.ss Margt. Rose Orthop. Hosp. Edin., Vict. Hosp. Kirkcaldy & Dunfermline & W. Fife Hosp.; Sen. Hosp. Med. Off. Orthop. Dept. Roy. Infirm. Edin.

PATERSON-BROWN, June, CBE (retired) Norwood, Hawick TD9 7HP Tel: 01450 372352 Fax: 01450 379697 Email: pbnorwood@btinternet.com — MB ChB Ed. 1955. Dir. Border Television plc; Trustee MacRobt.s Trusts; Lord Lt Roxburgh Ettrick & Lauderdale. Prev: Med. Off. Family Plann. & Well Woman Clinics Borders HB.

PATERSON-BROWN, Peter Neville (retired) Norwood, Hawick TD9 7HP Tel: 01450 372352 Fax: 01450 379697 Email: pbnorwood@btinternet.com — MB ChB 1955 Ed.; DObst RCOG 1958. Dir. Childr. Hospice Assn. Scotl. Prev: Hon. Med. Adviser Red Cross Scotl.

PATERSON-BROWN, Sara Queen Charlottes & Chelsea Hospital, Ducane Rd, London W12 0NN Tel: 020 8748 4666 Fax: 020 8383 3419 Email: s.paterson-brown@htnt.org; 24 Mount Park Crescent, London W5 2RN — MB BChir 1984 Camb.; FRCS Eng. 1988; MRCOG 1990. Cons. O & G Qu. Charlottes & Chelsea Hosp. Lond. Socs: RSM. Prev: Sen. Regist. (O & G) Qu. Charlottes & Chelsea Hosp. Lond.; Regist. (O & G) Ashford Middlx. & St. Thos. Hosp. Lond.; SHO (Gyn.) Qu. Charlotte's & Chelsea Hosps.

PATERSON-BROWN, Sheila Philomena Princess Alexandra Eye Pavillion, Edinburgh EH3 9YW Tel: 0131 536 1000 Fax: 0131 536 1001 — MB BS 1982 Lond.; MRCP (UK) 1985; MRCGP 1987; DRCOG 1986. (St. Mary's Hosp. Med. Sch.) Clin. Asst. (Ophth.) P.ss Alexandra Eye Pavil. Edin. Prev: GP Lond.; GP Hong Kong; Trainee GP Yateley VTS.

PATERSON-BROWN, Mr Simon Department of Surgery, Royal Infirmary, Lauriston Place, Edinburgh EH3 9YW Tel: 0131 536 1000 Fax: 0131 228 2661 Email: s.keggie@ed.ac.uk — MB BS 1982 Lond.; MPhil Lond. 1989, MS 1993; FRCS Ed. 1986; FRCS Eng. 1986. (St Mary's Hospital London) Cons. Surg. Roy. Infirm. Edin.; Lead Clinician, Gen. surg.; Hon. Sen. Lect. Univ. Edin.; Hon. Sen. Lect. univ. Edin.; Chairm., Basic Surgic. Train. scheme, S.E, Scotl. Socs: Surgic. Research Soc.; Assn. Surg.; Brit. Soc. Gastroenterol. Prev: Sen. Lect. (Surg.) St Mary's Hosp. Lond.; Sen. Regist. (Surg.) Hammersmith & St Mary's Hosp. Lond.; Lect. (Surg.) Roy. Infirm. Edin.

PATEY, David Geoffrey Hamilton, TD 1 Bures House, Nayland Road, Bures CO8 5BX Tel: 01787 227096 — BM BCh Oxf. 1952; MA Oxf. 1952; FFCM 1980, M 1974; DPH Eng. 1960. (Oxf. & Middlx.) Prev: Co. MOH W. Suff.; PMO W. Sussex CC.

PATEY, George Laurence Thomas Macnamara 29 Conisboro Avenue, Caversham, Reading RG4 7JE Tel: 01734 472466 — LMSSA 1943 Lond.; MA Oxon. 1943, BM BCh 1948. (Oxf.)

PATEY, Mrs Jean (retired) 36 Keyberry Park, Newton Abbot TQ12 1DF Tel: 01626 54958 — MB ChB 1938 Manch.; FRCS Ed. 1942. Prev: Asst. Radiotherap. Middlx. Hosp. Lond.

PATEY, Richard Antony 128C Barry Road, London SE22 0HW — MB BS 1993 Lond.

PATEY, Rona Elizabeth Department of Anaesthetics, Aberdeen Royal Infirmary, Foresterhill, Aberdeen AB25 2ZN Tel: 01224 681818 Fax: 01224 685307; 61 Gray St, Aberdeen AB10 6JD — MB ChB 1982 Aberd. Cons. Anaesth. Aberd. Roy. Infirm.

PATHAK, Binay Kumar Wollaton Vale Health Centre, Wollaton Vale, Nottingham NG8 2GR Tel: 0115 928 1151 Fax: 0115 928 8703 — MRCGP; MB BS Gauhati 1966. (Assam Med. Coll. Dibrugarh) GP Wollaton Vale Health Centre, Wollaton. Prev: Regist. (Gen. Med.) & Resid. SHO (Paediat.) City Hosp. Chester; Regist. (Geriat. Med.) W. Chesh. Hosp. Chester.

PATHAK, Catherine Anne 11 Northfield Crescent, Beeston, Nottingham NG9 5GR — MB ChB 1995 Sheff.

PATHAK, Mrs Madhu Lata Rush Green Medical Centre, 261 Dagenham Road, Romford RM7 0XR Tel: 01708 728261 Fax: 01708 722645; 84 Parkway, Gidea Park, Romford RM2 5PL Tel: 01708 726835 Fax: 01708 722645 — MB BS 1967 Aligarh; Dip. Law 1996; MRCGP 1986; LMSSA Lond. 1979; DCH Eng. 1974; DA Eng. 1973; DTM & H Liverp. 1969. (J.L.N. Med. Coll. Aligarh) GP; Trainer (Gen. Pract.) Romford; Sec. LMC. Socs: BMA. Prev: Regist. (Paediat.) OldCh. Hosp. Romford & Rush Green Hosp. Romford.

PATHAK, Nisha Dattatray 52 Lake Avenue, Walsall WS5 3PA — MB BS 1973 Baroda.

PATHAK, Pankaj 17 Hill Field, Oadby, Leicester LE2 4RW — MB BS 1976 Punjab, Pakistan; MChOrth Liverp. 1993.

PATHAK, Pransanta Kumar Caerphilly District Miners Hospital, Martin's Road, Caerphilly CF8 2WN — MB BS 1971 Calcutta.

PATHAK, Mr Pratap Narayan (rooms), 41 The Downs, Altrincham WA14 2QG Tel: 0161 928 0611; 19 The Avenue, Sale M33 4PB Tel: 0161 969 6311 — MB BS 1961 Vikram; FRCS Ed. 1968; MRCS Eng. LRCP Lond. 1966; DLO Eng. 1968. (Gandhi Med. Coll. Bhopal) Cons. Surg. (Otolaryngol.) Trafford Gen. Hosp. Davyhulme. Socs: N. Eng. Otolaryngol. Soc. & Roy. Soc. Med. Prev: Sen. Regist. (ENT Surg.) Newc. Gen. Hosp.

PATHAK, Prem Lata Wilmslow Road Medical Centre, 156 Wilmslow Road, Rusholme, Manchester M14 5LQ Tel: 0161 224 2452 Fax: 0161 248 9261 — MB BS 1961 Delhi; DObst RCOG 1967. (Lady Hardinge Med. Coll.) Prev: SHO (O & G) Newc. Gen. Hosp.

PATHAK, Priscilla Lotha 17 Hill Field, Oadby, Leicester LE2 4RW — MB BS 1983 Delhi.

PATHAK, Sanjeev Kumar 85 Oak Lane, West Bromwich B70 8PR — MB ChB 1994 Leic. SHO (Orthop.) Roy. Urthopaedic Hosp. Prev: SHO (Urol.) Roy. Preson Hosp.; Prosector Anat. Oxf. Univ.; SHO (A & E) Solihull Hosp.

***PATHAK, Miss Smriti** 101 Fishponds Road, London SW17 7LL Tel: 020 8672 5626; 101 Fishponds Road, London SW17 7LL Tel: 020 8672 5626 — MB BS 1996 Lond.; BSc (Hons.) Lond. 1993.

PATHAK, Suresh Kumar Rush Green Medical Centre, 261 Dagenham Road, Romford RM7 0XR Tel: 01708 728261 Fax: 01708 722645; 84 Parkway, Gidea Park, Romford RM2 5PL Tel: 01708 726835 Fax: 01708 722645 — MB BS 1963 Vikram; DFFM 1998; DObst RCPI 1969. (G.R. Med. Coll. Gwalior) Trainer, Tutor (Gen. Pract.) Med. Sch. Lond. Socs: Balint's Soc.; GP Writers Assn.; Fell. Roy. Soc. Med. Prev: SHO Waterford Matern. Hosp. Waterford & Pinderfields Gen. Hosp. Wakefield; Med. Off. Tuberc. Hosp. Hathras, India.

PATHAN, Abdul Hafiz 83 Lynmouth Avenue, Enfield EN1 2LS — MB ChB 1985 Aberd.

PATHAN, Mohammed Aslam Longford Medical Centre, 18a Sydnall Road, Coventry CV6 6BW Tel: 024 7664 4123 Fax: 024 7636 3157 — MB BS 1966 Peshawar.

PATHAN, Nazima Academic Department of Paediatrics, St. Mary's Hospital, 7th Floor, QEQM Building, London W2 Tel: 020 7886 6377; Apartment 3.G., The Ziggurat, 60-66 Saffron Hill, London EC1 Email: n. pathan@sm.ic.ac.uk — MB BS 1993 Lond.; BSc Lond. 1990; MRCP (UK) 1996. Clin. Research Fell. (Paediat.) St. Mary's Hosp. Lond. Prev: Specialist Regist. (Paediat.) N.wick Pk. Hosp.; SHO (Neonates) John Radcliffe Hosp. Oxf.; SHO (Paediat.) John Radcliffe Hosp. Oxf.

PATHANSALI, Rohan 83 Seaford Road, London W13 9HS — MB BS 1988 Lond.; MRCP (UK) 1992.

PATHARE, Soumitra Ramesh Academic Unit of Psychiatry, North Wing 4th Floor, St Thomas Hospital, London SE1 Tel: 020 7928 9292 Fax: 020 7633 0061; 403 City View, 463 Bethnal Green Road, London E2 9QH Tel: 020 7739 5028 Email: 100701.3527@compuserve.com — MB BS 1988 Bombay; MD Bombay 1991; MRCPsych 1994; DPM Bomaby 1990. (Seth G.S. Med. Coll. Bombay India) Wellcome Research Fell. (Psychiat.) UMDS (Guy's & St. Thos.). Prev: Research Assoc. & Regist. (Psychiat.) UMDS.

PATHINAYAKE, Bethmage Dona Achirawathie Chulakantha 19 Milton Road, Sutton Courtenay, Abingdon OX14 4BP Tel: 01235 848375 — MB BS 1986 Colombo; MRCP (UK) 1994; MRCGP 1997. (University of Columbo Sri Lanka) Prev: GP Regist. Ch. St. Pract. Wantage; SHO (Gen. Paediat.) P.ss Margt. Hosp. Swindon; SHO (O & G) Hoxton Gen. Hosp. Banbury.

PATHIRANA, Chandrawansa Kankanamge 225 Hoo Road, Kidderminster DY10 1LT Tel: 01562 639189 Email: pathick@hotmail.com — MB BS 1968 Ceylon; MRCPI 1981. Staff Phys. (Gen. Med. & Geriat.) Gen. Hosp. Kidderminster.

PATHIRANA, Ranjith Senarath 92 Reighton Avenue, Clifton, York YO30 5QW Tel: 01904 690879 — MB BS 1979 Colombo; FFA RCSI 1985. Staff Anaesth. York Dist. Hosp. Prev: Regist. (Anaesth.) York. Dist. Hosp.; Regist. (Anaesth.) Luton & Dunstable Hosp.

PATHMABASKARAN, Selvaranee 63 Fishponds Road, Tooting Broadway, London SW17 7LH — MRCS Eng. LRCP Lond. 1987; MB BS Colombo, Sri Lanka 1983.

PATHMADEVA, Chryshanthi 6 Buriton Road, Harestock, Winchester SO22 6HX Tel: 01962 880770; Connaught House, 63B Romsey Road, Winchester SO22 5DE Tel: 01962 825128 Fax: 01962 840912 — MB BS 1972 Sri Lanka; MRCPsych 1988. SCMO (Psychiat.) Connaught Ho. Day Hosp. Winchester. Prev: Regist. (Psychiat.) Pk. Prewett Hosp. Basingstoke.

PATHMADEVA, Thiraviyam Wesley 6 Buriton Road, Harestock, Winchester SO22 6HX Tel: 01962 880770 — MB BS 1973 Sri Lanka. Assoc. Specialist St. Jas. Hosp. Portsmouth.

PATHMANABAN, Praveen 36 Upton Gardens, Worthing BN13 1DA — MB BCh 1993 Wales.

***PATHMANANDAM, Hemachandran** 50 Old Park Ridings, London N21 2ES — MB BS 1997 Lond.

PATHMANATHAN, Hariharan 75 The Crosspath, Radlett WD7 8HP — MB ChB 1994 Manch. (Manch.)

PATHMANATHAN, Ishwara Kumar 14 Grafton Close, Worcester Park KT4 7JY — MB BS 1989 Lond.

PATHMANATHAN, Ravi Kumar Department of Cardiology, Leicester General Hospital, Gwendolen Road, Leicester LE5 4PW Tel: 0116 258 4436 Email: ravi.pathmanathan@uhl.tr.nhs.uk; Four Gables, 33 Elms Road, Stoneygate, Leicester LE2 3JD — MB BS 1989 Newc.; MRCP (UK) 1992. (Newcastle-Upon-Tyne) Cons. Cardiol., Leicester.

PATHMANATHAN, Sironmany 70 Kirkcroft, Wiggington, York YO32 2GH Tel: 01904 762329 — MB BS 1966 Sri Lanka. SHO (Psychiat.) Hartlepool Gen. Hosp. Cleveland; Staff Grade (Psychiat.), Whitby & ScarBoro. Prev: SHO (O & G) York. Dist. Gen. Hosp. & Barnsley Dist. Hosp.; Unified SHO S. Tyneside NHS Rotat.al Scheme.

PATHMANATHAN, Thillainathan Ruxley Ward, Queen Mary's Hospital, Frognal Av., Sidcup DA14 6LT — MB BChir 1985 Camb.; FRCPS Glas. 1991.

PATHMANATHAN, Yoshana Flat 12, Mellior Court, 79 Shepherds Hill, London N6 5RQ — MB BS 1983 Lond.

PATHY, Damian John Gallwey Cathays Surgery, 137 Cathays Terrace, Cardiff CF24 4HU Tel: 029 2022 0878 Fax: 029 2038 8771 — MB BS 1987 Lond.; MRCP (UK) 1991; MRCGP 1994. (St. Bartholomew's) Prev: Regist. (Dermat.) Skin Hosp. Birm.; SHO Rotat. (Med.) MusGr. Pk. Hosp. Taunton; Ho. Off. (Cardiol. & Gen. Med.) St Bart. Hosp. Lond.

PATHY, Harish 41 Mere Road, Leicester LE5 3HS — MB ChB 1992 Leic.

PATHY, Professor Mohan Sankar John, OBE Tel: 029 2075 5476 Fax: 029 2076 5040 Email: johnpathy@aol.com; Mathern Lodge, 3 Cefn Coed Crescent, Cyncoed, Cardiff CF23 6AT Tel: 029 2075 5476 Fax: 029 2076 5040 Email: johnpathy@aol.com — MRCS Eng. LRCP Lond. 1948; FRCP Lond. 1973, M 1960; FRCP Ed. 1968, M 1957; FRCP Glas. 1997. (King's Coll. Hosp.) Prof. Emerit. Univ. Wales; Health Research & Developm. Assoc., Cardiff. Socs: BMA & Brit. Geriat. Soc.; Amer. Geriat. Soc. Prev: Prof. Geriat. Med. Univ. Wales Coll. Med. Cardiff; Cons. Phys. (Geriat. Med.) Univ. Hosp. Wales Cardiff; Ho. Phys. King's Coll. Hosp. Lond.

PATI, Jhumur 1 Aldridge Walk, Southgate, London N14 6AF Tel: 020 7601 8387 — MB BS 1985 Dacca; FRCS Ed. 1992; FRCS Eng. 1992.

PATI, Upendra Mohan 147 Liverpool Road, Birkdale, Southport PR8 4NT — MB BS 1963 Utkal; FRCP Glas. 1986, M 1966; MRCGP 1975. (S.C.B. Med. Coll. Cuttack) Mem. S.port & Formby HA. Socs: BMA (Pres. Sefton Div.). Prev: Med. Regist. S.port Gen. Infirm.; Neurol. Regist. Walton Hosp. Liverp.

PATIENCE, Lesley Anne Dryden Cottage, Robert St., Stonehaven AB3 — MB ChB 1980 Aberd.

PATIENCE, Wendy Ann 113A Loftus House, Marton Road, Middlesbrough TS4 3TQ — MB BS 1992 Lond.

PATIENT, Miss Charlotte Jane Addenbrookes Hospital, Hills Road, Cambridge CB2 2QQ; 3 Coniston Road, Cambridge CB1 7BZ — MB BS 1991 Lond.; MRCOG 1996. (Lond.) Specialist Regist. (O & G) Camb.

PATIENT, David Neil 114 Lower Ham Road, Kingston upon Thames KT2 5BD — MB BS 1981 Lond.; MRCP (UK) 1986; MRCGP 1996; DRCOG 1988; Dip. Occ. Med. RCP Lond. 1997.

PATIENT, Dennis Willoughby (retired) 8 Chattis Hill, Spitfire Lane, Stockbridge SO20 6JS Tel: 01264 810779 — MB BS Lond. 1957; MRCS Eng. LRCP Lond. 1957; DA Eng. 1964; DObst RCOG 1959. Prev: GP Heathcote Med. Centre Tadworth Surrey 1978-95.

PATIENT, Peter Stuart 22 Sinnington End, Highwoods, Colchester CO4 4RE — MB BS 1986 Lond.; BSc Lond. 1983; FRCA 1996; DRCOG 1991. Cons. (Anaesth.) Colchester Gen. Hosp. Prev: Specialist Regist. Rotat. (anaseth.) UCLH & Roy. Free; Regist. Rotat. (Anaesth.) UCLH.

PATIENT, Mr Stafford Mortimer (retired) 24 Park Road, Ipswich IP1 3SU Tel: 01473 250728 — MB BS 1960 Lond.; FRCS Ed. 1968; MRCS Eng. LRCP Lond. 1960; DCH Eng. 1963; FRCOG 1979, M 1966, DObst 1962. Prev: Cons. O & G Ipswich Hosp.

PATIL, Dilip Bhimagouda Department of Obstetrics & Gynaecology, James Paget Hospital, Great Yarmouth NR31 6LA; 10 Diana Way, Caister on Sea, Great Yarmouth NR30 5TP Tel: 01493 377060 Fax: 01493 377060 Email: dilippatil@compuserve.com — MB BS 1982 Karnatak; MRCOG 1992. Assoc. Specialist (O & G) Jas. Paget Hosp. Gt. Yarmouth. Prev: Regist. (Obst.) Roy. Lond. Hosp.; Regist. (O & G) Shotley Bridge Gen. Hosp. Consett; SHO (Fertil. Regulat.) Newc. Gen. Hosp. Newc. u. Tyne.

PATIL, Mr Krishnaji Pandurang c/o Department of Urology, St Peters Hospital, Guildford Road, Chertsey KT16 0PZ — MB BS 1978 Bombay; FRCS Ed. 1992.

PATIL, Muralidhar Bhivrao 99 Downs Park Road, London E8 8JE — MB BS 1966 Nagpur.

***PATINIOTT, Anthony Kieron** 15 Castleway, Halebarns, Altrincham WA15 0AD — MB ChB 1995 Birm.; ChB Birm. 1995.

PATINIOTT, Francis Joseph Birchwood Medical Centre, 15 Benson Road, Birchwood, Warrington WA3 7PJ Tel: 01925 823502 Fax: 01925 852422; Mosswood, 15 Castleway, Hale Barns, Altrincham WA15 0AD Tel: 0161 980 5507 — MRCS Eng. LRCP Lond. 1962; DObst RCOG 1965. (Manch.) Prev: Regist. (O & G) Stepping Hill Hosp. Stockport; SHO (Paediat.) Birch Hill Hosp. Rochdale; Ho. Surg. Pk. Hosp. Davyhulme.

PATKAR, Ashwin Anand 17 Perryford Drive, Solihull B91 3XE — MB BS 1988 Bombay; MRCPsych 1993.

PATMORE, Jane Elizabeth 3 Thornleys, Cherry Burton, Beverley HU17 7SJ — BM BS 1989 Nottm.; MRCP (UK) 1992. Specialist Regist. Yorks. Rotat. Flexible Train. Socs: BDA; Soc. Edocrinol. Prev: Regist. (Chem. Path.) St. Jas. Univ. Hosp. Leeds; SHO (Gen. Med.) Harrogate Dist. Hosp.

PATMORE, Russell David department of Haematology, Hull Royal infirmary, Anlaby rd, Hull HU3 2JZ Tel: 01482 607742 Fax: 01482 607739; 3 Thornleys, Cherry Burton, Beverley HU17 7SJ Tel: 01964 550007 — BM BS 1989 Nottm.; MRCP (UK) 1992; MRCPath 1997. Cons. hamatology Hull & E Yorks. Hosp. NHS trust Hull. Socs: Brit. Soc. Haematol. Prev: Cons. (Haematol.) Roy. Hull Hosp. Hull; Regist. (Haemat.) Yorks. RHA.

PATMORE

PATMORE, Susan Jane Harriet 5 Cavendish Place, Cavendish Crescent S., The Park, Nottingham NG7 1ED — BM 1996 Soton. SHO (Surg.) Rotat. QMC Nottm.

PATNAIK, Bhakta Kishore Pilgrim Hospital, Sibsey Road, Boston PE21 9QS Tel: 01205 64801 — MB BS 1953 Utkal; PhD Ed. 1965; BSc (Hons.) Utkal 1948; TDD Wales 1958. (S.C.B. Med. Coll. Cuttack) Cons. Phys. (Geriat. Med.) Trent RHA. Socs: Amer. Assn. Advancem. of Sc. & Brit. Geriat. Soc. Prev: Asst. Chest Phys. Welsh RHB; Research Fell. Univ. (Pfizer Med. Monograph 1) 1965; Papers On Electron Microscopic Edin.

PATNAIK, Sharmistha Brookeside House, Brookside Cottages, Ashbrooke Road, Sunderland SR2 7HQ — MB BS 1969 Utka.

PATNAIK, Surya Narayan The New City Medical Centre, Tatham Street, Hendon, Sunderland SR1 2QB Tel: 0191 567 5571 — LRCP LRCS 1980 Ed.; MB BS Sambalpur 1969; LRCP LRCS Ed. LRCPS Glas. 1980.

PATODI, Mamta c/o Drive K.C. Jain, 24 Redlake Drive, Stourbridge DY9 0RX — LMSSA 1986 Lond.

PATODI, Sanat Kumar The Surgery, 33 Keynell Covert, Kings Norton, Birmingham B30 3QT Tel: 0121 458 2619 Fax: 0121 459 9640 — MB BS 1971 Indore; MB BS 1971 Indore.

PATON, Alastair George Peter (retired) Ben Ard, The Mount, Peebles EH45 9EX Tel: 01721 20098 — MB ChB 1954 Ed.; DObst RCOG 1960.

PATON, Alexander (retired) Knollbury, Chadlington, Oxford OX7 3NJ Tel: 01608 676305 — MRCS Eng. LRCP Lond. 1947; MD Lond. 1958, MB BS 1947; FRCP Lond. 1967, M 1951. Prev: Postgrad. Med. Dean NE Thames RHA.

PATON, Alexander Campbell Kingfisher Surgery, 26 Elthorne Way, Newport Pagnell MK16 0JR Tel: 01908 618265 Fax: 01908 01908 217804 — MB ChB 1973 Glas.; MRCP (UK) 1975. Dep. Coroner Beds.

PATON, Andrew Lindsay Dalton Square Surgery, 8 Dalton Square, Lancaster LA1 1PP Tel: 01524 842200; 11 Eden Park, Lancaster LA1 4SJ Tel: 01524 39633 — MB ChB 1979 Ed.; MA Oxf. 1982; DRCOG 1982; MRCGP 1983.

PATON, Andrew Nicholas Compass House Medical Centres, 25 Bolton Street, Brixham TQ5 9BZ Tel: 01803 855897 Fax: 01803 855613; 1 The Drive, Upton Manor, Brixham TQ5 9RA Tel: 01803 851494 Email: drpaton@aol.com — MB ChB 1981 Bristol; MRCGP (Distinc.) 1987; DCH RCPS Glas. 1985.

PATON, Calum Cameron 157 Clepington Road, Dundee DD3 7SN — MB ChB 1994 Dundee. Demonst. (Anat.) Univ. Dundee.

PATON, Catherine Anne The Pump House, Olwey Road, Weston Underwood, Olney Tel: 01234 711951 — MB ChB 1972 Glas. GP Newport Pagnell.

PATON, David (retired) Purbeck Lodge, 48 Britwell Road, Burnham, Slough SL1 8DE Tel: 01628 604993 — MB ChB Glas. 1938. Prev: Clin. Asst. Co. Lanark Matern. Hosp. Bellshill.

PATON, Mr David Frederic (retired) Grove Cottage, Sidestrand Road, Southrepps, Norwich NR11 8XB Tel: 01263 833540 Fax: 01263 833540 — MB ChB 1958 Cape Town; FRCS Eng. 1965; FRCS Ed. 1964. Prev: Prof. (Orthop. Surg.) Head Dept. Orthop. Surg. Univ. Cape Town.

PATON, David Hill Tryst Medical Centre, 431 King Street, Stenhousemuir, Larbert FK5 4HT Tel: 01324 551555 Fax: 01324 551925; Muirlands, 69 Bellsdyke Road, Larbert FK5 4EQ Tel: 01324 557584 — MB ChB 1974 Ed.; BSc Ed. 1971, MB ChB 1974; MRCGP 1978; DObst RCOG 1976.

PATON, Douglas Henry Hay War Memorial Health Centre, Crickhowell NP8 1AG Tel: 01873 810255 — MB ChB 1983 Ed.; MRCGP 1990; DCH RCPS Glas. 1989. Prev: Trainee GP Gwent VTS.

PATON, Maj-Gen Douglas Stuart, CBE, CStJ, Maj.-Gen. late RAMC (retired) Brampton, Springfield Road, Camberley GU15 1AB Tel: 01276 63669 — MB ChB Bristol 1951; FFPHM 1989; FFCM 1982, M 1974. Prev: Hon. Phys. to HM the Qu.

PATON, Edward Robert Ley, Col. late RAMC Retd. (retired) 10 Ettrick Road, Edinburgh EH10 5BJ — MB ChB 1956 St. And.; MRCGP 1974; DCH Eng. 1970; DTM & H Eng. 1963. Clin. Med. Off. Lothian HB. Prev: Sen. Med. Off. & Med. Off. Berlin Garrison Germany.

PATON, Gerald Maybole Health Centre and Day Hospital, 6 High Street, Maybole KA19 7BY Tel: 01655 882278 Fax: 01655 889616 — MB ChB 1982 Glas.

PATON, Mr Iain Campbell Eildon, 27 Middlepenny Road, Langbank, Port Glasgow PA14 6XB — MB ChB 1972 Glas.; FRCS Ed. 1978. Cons. ENT Surg. Inverclyde Hosp. Greenock. Prev: Sen. Regist. Leeds.

PATON, Irene Kennedy 66 Crawford Road, Milngavie, Glasgow G62 7LF Tel: 0141 956 3802 — MB ChB 1965 Glas.; DCH RCPS Glas. 1967.

PATON, James Stewart Henry Yewlands, Crundalls Lane, Bewdley DY12 1ND — BM BCh 1973 Oxf.; MA. Prev: Med. Off. Tugela Ferry Hosp., S. Africa; Ho. Phys. Amersham Hosp.; Ho. Surg. Ch.ill Hosp. Oxf.

PATON, James Young Department of Child Health, Royal Hospital for Sick Children, Yorkhill, Glasgow G3 8SJ Tel: 0141 201 0238 Fax: 0141 209 0387 Email: j.y.paton@clinmed.gla.ac.uk — MB ChB 1977 Leic.; MB ChB (Hons.) Glas. 1977; BSc (Hons.) Glas. 1973; MD Leic. 1987; FRCP Glas. 1995; MRCP (UK) 1979; DCH Eng. 1979. Socs: Americain Thoracic Soc.; Eur. Respirat. Soc.; Brit. Thorac. Soc. Prev: Sen. Regist. Roy. Hosp. Sick Childr. Glas.; MRC Trav. Fell. Childr. Hosp. Los Angeles, USA.

PATON, Janet Forth View Practice, Dean Road, Bo'ness EH51 0DQ Tel: 01506 822466 Fax: 01506 826216; 28 Linlithgow Road, Bo'ness EH51 0DN Tel: 01506 822418 — MB ChB 1977 Ed.; MRCGP 1981. (University of Edinburgh)

PATON, Joseph Train (retired) Crouch End, Wargrave, Reading RG10 8LT Tel: 01734 403338 — MB ChB 1944 St. And.; DObst RCOG 1950. Prev: Ho. Surg. (O & G) Radcliffe Infirm. Oxf.

PATON, Nicholas Iain James 34 Dundonald Road, London SW19 3QN — MB BChir 1989 Camb.; MA Camb. 1990, MB BChir 1989; MRCP (UK) 1993.

PATON, Richard Stewart The Hawthorns, Stonepit Lane, Inkberrow, Worcester WR7 4ED Tel: 01386 792784 Fax: 01386 792637 — MB ChB 1967 Glas. (Glas.) GP Princip. The Hawthorns PMS Pilot, Inkberrow, Worcs WR7 4ED.

PATON, Robert Colin Milton Keynes General Hospital NHS Trust, Eaglestone, Milton Keynes MK6 5LD Tel: 01908 243006; 7 Dene Close, Aspley Hill, Woburn Sands, Milton Keynes MK17 8NL — MD 1983 Ed.; MB ChB 1972; FRCP Ed. 1986; FRCP Lond. 1989; MRCP (UK) 1974. Cons. Phys. Milton Keynes Gen. Hosp. Prev: Lect. Med. Univ. Leeds.

PATON, Robert Hamish 8 Lime Street, Ossett, Wakefield — MB ChB 1985 Sheff.; FRCA 1994; DCH RCP Lond. 1987.

PATON, Robert McCracken (retired) 5 Monks Road, Airdrie ML6 9QW Tel: 01236 762322 — MB ChB Glas. 1929. Prev: Ho. Surg. Clayton Hosp. Wakefield.

PATON, Mr Robin William Blackburn Royal Infirmary, Bolton Road, Blackburn BB2 — MB ChB 1980 Glas.; FRCS Glas. 1985; FRCS Ed. 1984; FRCS (Orth.) Ed. 1989. Cons. Orthop. Surg. Blackburn Roy. Infirm.; Hon. Clin. Lect. Univ. of Manch. 1997. Socs: Sec. Childr.'s Orthop. Gp. NW Eng. Prev: Sen. Regist. (Orthop. Surg.) N.. W.. Region.

PATON, Mr Sidney Leopold (retired) 384 Higham Lane, Nuneaton CV11 6AP — MB ChB 1947 Ed.; FRCS Ed. 1958. Prev: Cons. Traum. & Orthop. Surg. Manor Hosp. Nuneaton & Coventry & Warwick Hosp.

PATON-PHILIP, Mr Philip, VRD 77 Harley Street, London W1N 1HH; The Ship, Hurst Drive, Walton-on-the-Hill, Tadworth KT20 7QT Tel: 0207 2251 — MB BChir Camb. 1946; MA, MChir Camb. 1959; FRCS Eng. 1955; MRCS Eng. LRCP Lond. 1946. (Camb., St. Bart. & St. Thos.) Cons. Urol. Surg. St. Geo. Hosp. Lond., St. Helier Hosp. Carshalton & Epsom Dist. Hosp.; Sen. Cons. Urol. Surg. St. Anthony's Hosp. Cheam & Ashstead Private Hosp. Surrey; Hon. Sen. Lect. St. Geo. Hosp. Med. Sch. Univ. Lond.; Surg. Lt. Cdr. RNR. Socs: Fell. Roy. Soc. Med.; Brit. Assn. Urol. Surgs. Prev: Surg. Chief Asst. & Sen. Regist. (Surg.) St. Bart. Hosp. Lond.; Demonst. (Anat.) St. Thos. Hosp. Lond.

***PATRE, Pamela** 11 Manor Place, London SE17 3BD — MB BS 1998 Lond.; MB BS Lond 1998.

PATRICK, Alan William Royal Infirmary, Lauriston Place, Edinburgh EH3 9YW Tel: 0131 536 1000 Fax: 0131 536 2091; 50 Braid Road, Edinburgh EH10 6AL Tel: 0131 447 9402 — MB ChB 1981 Ed.; MRCP (UK) 1984; MD Ed. 1994; FRCP Ed. 1996. (Edinburgh) Cons. Phys. (Diabetes & Endocrinol.) Roy. Infirm. Edin.

PATRICK, Andrew Godson 35 Norwood Avenue, Alloa FK10 2BY Tel: 01259 724198 — MB ChB 1960 Glas. (Glas.)

PATRICK, Anthea Alison Rock Cottage, Hartington, Buxton SK17 0AX Tel: 01298 84275 — MB BS 1930 Melbourne; DObst RCOG 1936.

PATRICK, Clifford Thomas Station Medical Centre, Royal Air Force, Boscombe Down, Salisbury SP4 0JF; Fluters Field, White Lane, Guildford GU4 8PS Tel: 01483 504050 — MSc Wales 1965; MA; MB Camb. 1971, BChir 1970; DCMT . Lond. 1974; BVetMed Lond. 1964; MRCVS 1964; AFOM RCP Lond. 1981. (Cambridge University and King's College Hospital London) Sen. Med. Off. RAF Boscombe Down Aviat. Med. Socs: Occupat. Health (Soc. Occup. Med.) AFOM; Roy. Aeronautical Soc. Assoc. Prev: Univ. Med. Off. RAF Brize Norton; Univ. Med. Off. RAF Finningley; Univ. Med. Off. RAF Odiham.

PATRICK, David Hexham General Hospital,, Hexham NE46 1QJ; 9 Green Close, Stannington, Morpeth NE61 6PE — MB BS 1974 Newc.; BSc Newc. 1971, MB BS 1974; FRCR 1981; DMRD Eng. 1980. Cons. Radiologist Hexham Gen. Hosp., Hexham, N.umberland; Cons. Radiol., Wansbew Gen. Hosp., Ashington, N.umberland.

PATRICK, David Anthony 10 Langdale Road, Bebington, Wirral CH63 3AW — BM BS 1996 Nottm. SHO (Anaesth.) Derby City Hosp. Prev: SHO (A & E) Chorley & S. Ribble Hosp.; SHO (Paediat.) Roy. Preston Hosp.

PATRICK, Elizabeth Anne Shenton Sunnyside Surgery, 4 Sunnyside Road, Clevedon BS21 7TA Tel: 01275 873588 Fax: 01275 341381 Email: elizabethpatrick@gp-l81102.nhs.uk — MB ChB 1982 Leic.; 2000 D.Occ.Med London; MRCGP 1986; DCH RCP Lond. 1986; DRCOG 1985. (Leicester) Occupat.al Med., Bupa Occupat.al Med. Div. Prev: Trainee GP Leics. VTS; SHO (Geriat. Ophth. Cas.) Leic. HA.

***PATRICK, Emma May** Lavrock, 7 Forgan Drive, Drumoig, North Leuchars, St Andrews KY16 0BF — MB BS 1998 Lond.; MB BS Lond 1998.

PATRICK, Guy Michael IBAH (UK), Wessex Business Centre, Bumpers Farm, Chippenham SN14 6NQ Tel: 01249 440727 Fax: 01249 463004 Email: patrickg@ibah.com — MB ChB 1984 Bristol; MRCP 1990 UK; BSc 1981 Bristol. (Bristol University) Pharmacutical Phys.; Sen. Lect. Keele Univ., Staffs. Research Fell. in Gen. Pract., Regional GP Unit, Birm.; Med. Adviser to C.E. andersons & Sons Ltd., Barclays Bank Ltd. & other Cos.; Primary Care Phys. (UK & abRd.); Vis. Cons. Learning Assessm. Centre, Horsham, W. Sussex; HP. Rshit S.port; HS RSCH Guildford; RAF Med. Pract. Prev: Cons. Nephrologist.

PATRICK, Ian Thomas, OStJ (retired) Ochiltree, Merse Way, Kippford, Dalbeattie DG5 4LH — MB ChB 1948 Glas. Prev: Co. Surg. St. John Ambul. Brig.

PATRICK, James Alexander Directorate of Anaesthesia, Glasgow Royal Infirmary, Glasgow G4 0SF Tel: 0141 211 4620/1 Fax: 0141 211 4622 — MB ChB 1981 Glas.; BSc Glas. 1976; FRCA 1986. Cons. Anaesth. Glas. Roy. Infirm. Prev: Sen. Regist. (Anaesth.) St. Thos. Hosp. Lond.; Regist. (Anaesth.) Glas. Roy. Infirm.; SHO (Anaesth.) Roy. Infirm. Edin.

PATRICK, Janet Frances Royal Oldham Hospital, Rochdale Road, Oldham OL1 2JH — MB ChB 1975 Sheff.; BSc Ed. 1969; MRCOG 1983. Cons. O & G Roy. Oldham Hosp. Lancs.

PATRICK, Janice Station Approach Health Centre, Station Approach, Bradford-on-Avon BA15 1DQ Tel: 01225 866611; 70 The Retreat, Whitehill, Bradford-on-Avon BA15 1SG — MB BS 1988 Newc.; DRCOG 1991; MRCGP 1992; Dip. Ther. Wales 1998.

PATRICK, Jenneth Mary Witton Street Surgery, 162 Witton Street, Northwich CW9 5QU Tel: 01606 42007 Fax: 01606 350659; Barberry Cottage, Mill Lane, Cuddington, Northwich CW8 2TA — MB ChB 1982 Manch. Prev: SHO (A & E) Stockport Infirm.; SHO (Psychiat.) Univ. Hosp. S. Manch.; SHO/Trainee GP Bolton Gen. Hosp. VTS.

PATRICK, Mr John Francis (retired) 2 Pledwick Grove, Sandal, Wakefield WF2 6DW — MB ChB 1952 Manch.; FRCS Ed. 1966; DObst RCOG 1961. Fell. Brit. Orthop. Assn. Prev: Cons. Orthop. Surg. Pinderfields Hosp. Wakefield.

PATRICK, Mr John Howard 27 Kennedy Road, Shrewsbury SY3 7AB; 27 Kennedy Road, Shrewsbury SY3 7AB Tel: 01743 249303 Fax: 01691 404236 — MB BS 1966 Lond.; FRCS Eng. 1972. (St. Thos.) p/t Dir. ORLAU & Cons. Orthop. Surg. Robt. Jones & Agnes Hunt Hosp. OsW.ry. Socs: Fell. BOA; Fell. Roy. coll. Surgs.

Prev: Sen. Lect. (Orthop. Surg.) Univ. Liverp.; Specialist (Surg.) RAF Med. Br.; Chief Asst. (Orthop. Surg.) St. Thos. Hosp. Lond.

***PATRICK, Kathryn Antoinette** 10 Langdale Road, Bebington, Wirral CH63 3AW — MB ChB 1998 Birm.; ChB Birm. 1998.

PATRICK, Kevin, Capt. Anaesth. Department, Royal Hospital Hasler, Gosport PO12 2AA; The Cottage, Cairnbulg Castle, Fraserburgh AB43 8TN — MB ChB 1996 Aberd. SHO (Anaesth.) Roy. Hosp. Hasler, Gosport. Prev: Regt.. Med. Off. Med. Centre QRH Catterick Garrison.

PATRICK, Mark Ronald Department of Anaesthesia, Wythenshawe Hospital, Southmoor Road, Manchester M23 9LT Tel: 0161 946 2502 Fax: 0161 291 2979; Lindow Cottage, 65 Racecourse Road, Wilmslow SK9 5LJ Tel: 01625 522499 — MB BS 1976 Lond.; BSc Lond. 1973; FRCA 1981. (St. Bart.) Cons. Anaesth. Wythenshawe Hosp. Manch.; Hon. Clin. Lect. Univ. Manch. Socs: BMA & Assn. Anaesth.; Assn. Cardiothoracic Anaesth. Prev: Sen. Regist. (Anaesth.) Lond. Hosp.; Regist. (Anaesth.) Hosp. Sick Childr. Lond. & St. Bart. Hosp. Lond.

PATRICK, Matthew Paul Hugh Adult Department, Tavistock and Portman NHS Trust, 120 Belsize Lane, London NW3 5BA Tel: 020 7435 7111 Fax: 020 7447 3745 — MB BS 1985 Lond.; BSc (1st cl. Hons.) Lond. 1982; MRCPsych 1990. (Roy. Lond. Hosp.) Cons. Psychother. Tavistock & Portman NHS Trust Lond. Socs: Full. Mem. Brit. Psychoanalyt. Soc. Prev: MRC Train. Fell. Univ. Coll. Lond.; Hon. Sen. Regist. (Psychother.) Tavistock Clinic Lond.; Regist. (Psychiat.) Maudsley & Bethlem Roy. Hosp. Lond.

PATRICK, Paul Richard Patrick and Partners, Rise Park Surgery, Revelstoke Way, Nottingham NG5 5EB Tel: 0115 927 2525 Fax: 0115 979 7056; George's Hill House, George's Hill, Arnold, Nottingham NG5 8PU Tel: 0115 920 7795 — BM BS 1976 Nottm.; BMedSci Nottm. 1974; DRCOG 1979. (Nottm.) Hosp. Pract. (Disabil. Med.) City Hosp. Nottm.; Clin. Tutor (Gen. Pract.) Univ. Nottm.

PATRICK, Mr Robert Kenneth 9 Heatherstones, Queens Gate, Halifax HX3 0DH — MB BS 1968 Sydney; FRCS Ed. 1973.

PATRICK, Sharon Public Health Laboratory, Salisbury District Hospital, Salisbury SP2 8BJ Tel: 01722 336020 Fax: 01722 412636 — MB ChB 1970 Sheff.; FRCPath 1989, M 1977; Dip. Bact. Manch. 1976. Dir. & Cons. Med. Microbiol. Pub. Health Laborat. Salisbury. Socs: Brit. Infec. Soc.; Assn. Med. Microbiologists. Prev: Sen. Regist. & Regist. Roy. Hosp. Sheff.

PATRICK, Mr William John Ainslie Dept of Paediatric Pathology, Yorkhill NHS Trust, Yorkhill, Glasgow G3 8SJ Tel: 0141 201 0401 Fax: 0141 201 0397 — MB ChB 1962 Glas.; FRCS Eng. 1970; FRCS Ed. 1970; FRCPath 1990, M 1978. (Glas.) Cons. Path. Roy. Hosp. Sick Childr. Glas.; Hon. Clin. Sen. Lect. Univ. Glas.; cons and Gardiner lec. Roy.hosp.sick.childr.glas. Socs: Paediat. Path. Soc.; Brit. & Irish Paediat. Path. Assn. Prev: Sen. Regist. Path. Roy. Hosp. Sick Childr. Edin.

PATROCLOU, Aristotelis c/o Mr. A. Pickles, 69 Lewsey Road, Luton LU4 0EN — MD 1985 Liege.

PATRONI, Bruno Flat 4, 51 St James Road, Sutton SM1 2TG — MB BS 1984 West. Austral.

PATRUDU, Mr Makena Narasimha St Michael's Hospital, 4 Trelissick Road, Hayle TR27 4HY Tel: 01736 753234; 52 Mellanear Road, Hayle TR27 4QT — MB BS Andhra 1970; FRCS Ed. 1985. (Andhra Med. Coll.) Assoc. Specialist (Surg.) St. Michael's Hosp. Hayle.

PATSALIDES, Mr Christodoulos Theodosiou Knee Research Room, 4th Floor, Musculoskeletal Science, UCD Building, Royal Liverpool University Hospital, Liverpool L69 3GA Tel: 0151 706 4126 Fax: 0151 706 5815 Email: c.t.patsalides@liverpool.ac.uk; Flat 10, 2 Strathmore Road, Newsham Park, Liverpool L6 7UD Tel: 0151 281 4645 — MB ChB 1994 Leic.; FRCS (I) Dubl. 1998. Clin. Res. Asst., Roy. L'pool & Braodgreen Hosps Knee Serv., L'pool.

***PATSIOS, Demetris Andrea** 68 Green Bridges, Headington, Oxford OX3 8PL — BM BCh 1994 Oxf.

PATTABHI, Jayanidhi The Surgery, 20 Lavender Road, Battersea, London SW11 2UG Tel: 020 7223 1056 Fax: 020 7978 4112 — MB BS 1972 Osmania.

PATTANAYAK, Mr Kalidas 25 Valley View Road, Rochester ME1 3PB Tel: 01634 826289 — MB BS 1967 Calcutta; FRCS Eng. 1978. (Sir Nilratan Sircar Med. Coll.) Socs: Fell. Roy. Soc. Med.; Fell. Assn. Surgs. India; Assoc.Mem.Brit.Assoc.s.Urol.Surg. Prev: Cons. Surg. & Chief Surg. P. Salman Hosp. Riyadh, Saudi Arabia; Regist.

PATTANI

(Surg.) Friarage Hosp. N.allerton; Surg. Specialist Calcutta Nat. Med. Coll. Hosp., India.

PATTANI, Shriti Mansukh Occupational Health & Safety Unit, Royal Free Hampstead NHS Trust, London NW3 2QG — MB ChB 1991 Leic.

PATTANI, Sumitra Kanjibhai Fryent Medical Centre, 331 Church Lane, London NW9 8JD Tel: 020 8205 6262; 72A Pinner View, Harrow HA1 4QD Tel: 020 8863 4837 — MB BS 1964 Bombay; DCH Lond. 1982.

PATTAR, Subhas Mahadev 23 Pickering Close, Leicester LE4 6ER — MB BS 1974 Karnatak.

PATTARA, Alexander Joseph The Surgery, High Road, Horndon-on-the-Hill, Stanford-le-Hope SS17 8LB Tel: 01375 642362 Fax: 01375 641747 — MB BS 1972 Mysore.

PATTEKAR, Bhanuvilas Digamber Orthopaedic Department, Queen Elizabeth Hospital, Sheriff Hill, Gateshead NE9 6SX Tel: 0191 403 2833; 1 Brenkley Court, Seaton Burn, Newcastle upon Tyne NE13 6DR Tel: 0191 236 7375 Fax: 0191 403 2833 — MB BS 1971 Jabalpur. Assoc. Specialist (Orthop.) Qu. Eliz. Hosp. Tyne & Wear. Prev: Regist. (Orthop.) CrossHo. Hosp. Kilmarnock, StoneHo. Hosp. & Kilmarnock Infirm.; Regist. Ayr Hosp.

PATTEKAR, Jyotsna Bhanuvilas 1 Brenkley Court, Seaton Burn, Newcastle upon Tyne NE13 6DR Tel: 0191 236 7375 — MB BS 1971 Univ. Marathwada; MB BS Univ. Marathwada India 1971; DObst RCPI 1980. GP (Long Term Locum) Gateshead, Tyne & Wear. Prev: Regist. (O & G) Ayrsh. Centr. Hosp. Irvine; SHO (Gyn.) Cross Hse. Hosp. Kilmarnock; SHO (Paediat.) Seafield Childr. Hosp. Ayr.

PATTEN, George Deryck Rudall (retired) The Cottage, 1 Church Lane, Wareham BH20 4NQ Tel: 01929 552212 — MRCS Eng. LRCP Lond. 1941. Prev: Ho. Surg. Roy. Vict. & W. Hants. Hosp. Bournemouth.

PATTEN, John Philip Pelham, Mead Road, Hindhead GU26 6SG Tel: 01428 604975 Fax: 01428 607085 — MB BS 1960 Lond.; BSc Lond. 1957; FRCP Lond. 1979, M 1964. (Westm.) Private Pract. Socs: Assn. Brit. Neurols. Prev: Hon. Cons. Neurol. King Edwd. VII Hosp. Midhurst; Cons. Neurol. SW Thames RHA; Sen. Regist. Maida Vale Hosp. Nerv. Dis. & Univ. Coll. Hosp.

PATTEN, Maria Juliette 21 Gosling Grove, Downley, High Wycombe HP13 5YS — MB BS 1991 Lond.

PATTEN, Mark Thomas Luton & Dunstable, Hosp., Lewsey Road, Luton LU4 0DZ Tel: 01582 497230; 8 High Ash Road, Wheathampstead, St Albans AL4 8DY Tel: 01582 833038 — MB ChB 1988 Glas.; FRCA 1994. Cons. (Intensive Care & Anaesth.) Luton & Dunstable Hosp. Prev: Sen. Regist. (Anaesth.) NW RHA; Clin. Fell. (Intens. Care) Academisch Ziekenhuis Groningen, Netherlands; Regist. Rotat. (Anaesth.) NW RHA.

PATTEN, Michael Gordon 23 Hawker Close, Merley, Wimborne BH21 1XW; 272 Wimborne Road, Winton, Bournemouth BH3 7AT Tel: 01202 512549 — BM 1980 Soton.; MRCGP 1985; DRCOG 1984. Princip. GP Bournemouth. Prev: SHO (Med. & Oncol.) Roy. Marsden Hosp. Sutton; SHO (Med. & O & G) Bedford Gen. Hosp.

***PATTEN, Piers Edward Major** 121 Blenheim Crescent, London W11 2EQ — MB ChB 1997 Bristol; BSc (Hons.) Bristol 1994.

PATTEN, Timothy James Cheviot Road Surgery, 1 Cheviot Road, Millbrook, Southampton SO16 4AH Tel: 02380 773174 Fax: 02380 702748 — MB BS 1983 Lond.; MA Oxf. 1979; MRCGP 1987; DRCOG 1987. (Oxford St. Mary's Paddington) Sen. Lect., Primary Care, Univ. of S.ampton. Prev: Trainee GP Som. HA VTS.

PATTERSON, Agnes Campbell Woodlands, Inverdale, Aviemore PH22 1QH — MB ChB 1961 Ed.

PATTERSON, Aileen Dept of Pathology, Hinchingbrooke NHS Trust, Hinchingbrooke Park, Huntingdon PE29 6NT Tel: 01480 416150 Fax: 01480 416527 Email: aileen.patterson@hbuc-tr.anglox.nhs.uk — MB BS 1981 Lond.; MRCPath 1993; FRCPath 2001. (Roy. Free) p/t Cons. (Path.) Hinchingbrooke Hosp. Huntingdon.

***PATTERSON, Ainslie Anne** Law Hospital, Airedrie Road, Carluke ML8 5ER Tel: 01698 361100; The Birches, 2 Old Creamery, Stewarton Road, Kilmarnock KA3 6AS Tel: 01560 600193 — MB ChB 1997 Aberd.; BSc (Med. Sci.) Aberd. 1995.

PATTERSON, Mr Alan (retired) Blythe Wood Lodge, Lady Alice Drive, Blythe Lane, Ormskirk L40 5UD — MB ChB Liverp. 1956; MD Liverp. 1960; FRCS Eng. 1965; FRCOphth 1989; DO Eng. 1962 Cons. Ophth. Liverp. HA (T). Prev: Sen. Regist. Lond. Hosp.

PATTERSON, Alan Herbert 3 Ruskin Park, Hillsborough Old Road, Lisburn BT27 5QN — MB BCh BAO 1978 Belf. Indust. Med. Off. Harland & Wolff Ltd., Belf. Mem. Soc. Occupat.

PATTERSON, Alison Sandra 328 Stranmillis Road, Belfast BT9 5EB — MB BCh BAO 1994 Belf.

PATTERSON, Andrew Barry Burnside, 12 Ballynahinch Road, Dromore BT25 1DJ; 106 Hillsborough Road, Dromore, Down, Dromore BT25 1QW Tel: 01846 693876 Fax: 01846 693876 Email: barry@patterson106.freeserve.co.uk — MB BCh BAO 1995 Belf. (Queen's Univ. Belf.)

PATTERSON, Angus James 11 Lenamore Avenue, Newtownabbey BT37 0PF — MB BCh BAO 1988 Belf.; MRCP Glas. 1991. Regist. (Clin. Oncol.) Belvoir Pk. Hosp. Belf.

PATTERSON, Anne Elizabeth Jane Sth. Ken. & Chelsea Mental Hlth. Centre, 1 Nightingale Place, London SW10 9NG Tel: 020 8846 6051 Fax: 020 8237 5282 — MB ChB 1985 Manch.; MRCPSych 1991. p/t Cons. Psychiat. in Psychother., Chelsea & W.. Hosp., Lond. Prev: Sen. Regist. (Psychother.) Glas.

PATTERSON, Brian George Portglenone Health Centre, 17 Townhill Road, Portglenone, Ballymena BT44 8AD Tel: 028 2582 1551 Fax: 028 2582 2539; Stoneleigh House, 20 Largy Road, Portglenone, Ballymena BT44 8BX Tel: 01266 821263 Fax: 01266 822539 — MB BCh BAO 1977 Belf.; MRCGP 1985; DRCOG 1979. Socs: BMA.

PATTERSON, Carole Anne Whitley Vicarage, Hexham NE46 2LA — MB BS 1990 Newc.

***PATTERSON, Catherine Anne** 13 Prestonhall Avenue, Glenrothes KY7 5RH — MB ChB 1998 Dund.; MB ChB Dund 1998.

PATTERSON, Cathryn Emma 21 Monlough Road W., Ballygowan, Newtownards BT23 6ND — MB BCh BAO 1995 Belf. SHO Rotat. (Med.) Belf. City Hosp.

PATTERSON, Christopher John Care of the Elderly Department, St. Luke's Hospital, Little Horton Lane, Bradford BD5 0NA Tel: 01274 365148 — MB ChB 1990 Leeds; MRCP (UK) 1993; BSc 1987.

PATTERSON, Colin Brunswick House Medical Group, 1 Brunswick Street, Carlisle CA1 1ED Tel: 01228 515808 Fax: 01228 593048 — MB BCh BAO 1986 Belf.

PATTERSON, Damian David Lister The Doctor's Mess, Derriford Hospital, Plymouth Tel: 01752 777111; 26 Kingswood Park Avenue, Peverell, Plymouth PL3 4NQ Tel: 01752 227625 — MB BS 1992 Lond.; BSc (Hons.) Lond. 1989; MRCP (UK) 1996. SHO (Med.) Derriford Hosp. Plymouth. Prev: SHO (Oncol.) ChristCh. Hosp., NZ; SHO (Med.) Torbay Hosp.; SHO (A & E) St. Richards Hosps. Chichester.

***PATTERSON, Daniel Mark** 8 David Close, Aylesbury HP21 9XF — MB BS 1996 Lond.

PATTERSON, David Llewhelin Hood Department of Cardiovascular Medicine, Whittington Hospital, Highgate Hill, London N19 5NF Tel: 020 7288 5292 Fax: 020 7288 5010 Email: d.patterson@ucl.ac.uk; 25 South Villas, Camden Town, London NW1 9BT Tel: 020 7267 2394 Fax: 0870 054 3737 — MB BS Lond. 1965; MD Lond. 1973; FRCP Lond. 1980, M 1969; MRCS Eng. LRCP Lond. 1965. (Univ. Coll. Hosp.) Cons. Phys. & Cardiol. Whittington Hosp. & Univ. Coll. Lond. Hosps.; Vice-Dean Whittington Campus, Roy. Free & Univ. Coll. Sch. of Med., UCL. Socs: Brit. Cardiac Soc.; Brit. Med. Informat. Soc.; Europ. Soc. Cardiol. Prev: Sen. Regist. Roy. Free Hosp. Lond.; Regist. Nat. Heart Hosp. Lond.; Regist. Univ. Coll. Hosp. Lond.

PATTERSON, David Robert Main Street Surgery, 29 Main Street, Eglinton, Londonderry BT47 3AB Tel: 028 7181 0252 Fax: 028 7181 1347 — MB BCh BAO 1985 Belf.; MRCGP 1990.

PATTERSON, Diana Georgina, OBE Shaftesbury Square Hospital, 116-120 Great Victoria St., Belfast BT2 7BG Tel: 01232 329808 Fax: 01232 312208 — MB BCh BAO 1977 Belf.; MD Belf. 1983; MRC Psych 1981; FRCPsych 1996. (Queen's University Belfast) Cons. Psychiat. Shaftesbury Sq. Hosp. Belf.; Hon. Lect. Qu. Univ. Belf.

PATTERSON, Donald Howard (Surgery) 6 East Mount Road, York YO2 2DB; 100 Tadcaster Road, Dringhouses, York YO24 1LT — MB ChB 1968 Leeds; DObst. RCOG 1975; DCH Eng. 1970. Prev: Med. Dir. Brit. Nepal Med. Trust; Princip. Gen. Pract. Watton; Regist. (Paediat.) St. John's Hosp. Chelmsford.

PATTERSON, Edna Rosemary Ellen 16 Lindrick Close, Tickhill, Doncaster DN11 9RB Tel: 01302 742584 Email: rosemary.patterson@virgin.net — MB BCh BAO 1979 Belf.; Dip. Occ Med 1996; DA (UK) 1986. (Qu. Univ. Belf.) Med. Adviser (Med. Servs.) Sheff.

PATTERSON, Edward Loudon (retired) Greenlands, Sand Lane, Nether Alderley, Macclesfield SK10 4TS — MB ChB 1934 Manch.; BSc Manch. 1931, MD (Gold Medal) 1944, MB ChB. Prev: Reader in Anat. Manch. Univ.

PATTERSON, Eleanor Jill Handforth Health Centre, Handforth, Wilmslow SK9 3HL Tel: 01625 529421 Fax: 01625 536560; Parkend, Bradford Lane, Nether Alderly, Macclesfield SK10 4TR — MB ChB 1974 Manch.; DRCOG 1977; DCH Eng. 1976. (Manch.) Princip. GP.

PATTERSON, George Charles Cardiac Catheterisation Unit, Royal Victoria Hospital, Belfast BT12 6BA — MD 1955 Belf.; PhD Belf. 1968, MD 1955, MB BCh BAO 1950. Cons. Cardiol. Roy. Vict. Hosp. Belf.

PATTERSON, Gillian Mary 3 Cumberland Avenue, Basingstoke RG22 4BG — MB ChB 1980 Bristol; T(GP) 1991; Cert. Family Plann. JCC 1985. Asst. GP Basingstoke; Community Med. Off. (Family Plann.) Loddon Trust Basingstoke.

PATTERSON, Gordon Joseph 2A Grey Point, Helen's Bay, Bangor BT19 1LE — MB BCh BAO 1979 Belf.; MRCGP 1983; AFOM RCP Lond. 1992. Med. Off. Civil Serv. Occupat. Health Serv. Socs: Soc. Occupat. Med. Prev: GP Co. Fermanagh; GP Bournemouth.

PATTERSON, Helen 4 Hartington Road, North Shields NE30 3SA — BM BCh 1986 Oxf.; MRCP (UK) 1989. CRC Clin. Research Fell. Inst. Cancer Research Sutton.

PATTERSON, Jacoby Vivien Mary 42 Springfield Road, Windsor SL4 3PQ — MB BChir 1988 Camb.; MA Camb. 1989. Clin. Lect. (Pub. Health Med.) Oxf. Univ. Prev: Sen. Regist. (Pub. Health Med.) Oxf. HA.; Regist. (Pub. Health Med.) Berks. HA; SHO (Radiother.) Roy. Berks. Hosp. Reading.

PATTERSON, James Alexander 95 Cinderhill Lane, Scholar Green, Stoke-on-Trent ST7 3HR — MB ChB 1984 Dundee. Prev: Trainee GP Pathhead Midlothian; SHO (O & G) E.. Gen. Hosp. Edin.; SHO (Paediat.) Falkirk & Dist. Roy. Infirm.

PATTERSON, James Andrew 2 Hedingham, Moira, Craigavon BT67 0NW — MB BCh BAO 1997 Belf. Gen. Surg. Craigavon Area Hosp.

PATTERSON, James Fleming (retired) Heron's Hill, Cherry Lane, Great Bridgeford, Stafford ST18 9SL Tel: 01785 282749 — MB ChB 1946 Glas.; DCH Eng. 1956. Assoc. Specialist Paediat. Stafford Dist. Gen. Hosp. Prev: ass specialist paediat Stafford Gen. Hosp.

PATTERSON, Jane Elizabeth Queens Medical Centre, University Hospital, Clifton Boulevard, Nottingham NG7 2UH; 15 Storth Park, Fulwood, Sheffield S10 3QH — MB ChB 1985 Liverp.; MB ChB (Hons.) Liverp. 1985; BSc (Hons.) Liverp. 1982; FRCS Eng. 1991. (Liverp.) Specialtiy Career Regist. (Surg.) Mid Trent Scheme. Prev: PeriFell.sh. Rotat. & Research Fell. (Surg.) Roy. Hallamsh. Hosp. Sheff.; SHO Walton & Fazakerley Hosps. Liverp.

PATTERSON, Janet Allison Tel: 01865 778911 — MB ChB 1984 Manch.; MRCPsych. 1991. Cons. In Rehabil. Psychiat., Oxf. Ment. Hlth. Care NHS Trust. Socs: Roy. Coll. Psychiat. Prev: Sen. Regist. (Gen. Psychiat.) Oxf. & Anglia RHA; Sen. Regist. & Regist. (Psychiat.) N. W.. RHA; Staff Psychiat. N. Mersey Community Trust.

PATTERSON, Joan Elizabeth 18 Braehead Terrace, Milltimber AB13 0ED — MB ChB 1990 Aberd.

***PATTERSON, John Kenneth** 19 Glennor Crescent, Carryduff, Belfast BT8 8HW — BChir 1996 Camb.

PATTERSON, John Lonsdale (retired) 5 Beechways, Appleton Park, Warrington WA4 5EL Tel: 01925 264599 — MB ChB 1948 Glas.; DPH Liverp. 1954. Prev: Div. MOH Runcorn.

PATTERSON, John Simon Zeneca Pharmaceuticals, Alderley House, Alderley Park, Macclesfield SK10 4TF Tel: 01625 582828; Park End, Bradford Lane, Nether Alderley, Macclesfield SK10 4TR — MB ChB 1971 Manch.; FRCP 1997; FFPM RCP (UK) 1990. Territorial Business Dir. Zeneca Pharmaceut. Macclesfield. Prev: Internat. Med. Dir. Zeneca Phamaceut. Macclesfield; Vice Pres. Clin. & Med. Affairs ICI Americas Wilmington Del., USA; Head of Med. Research Dept. ICI Pharmaceut. Div. Macclesfield.

PATTERSON, John Stitt (retired) 67 Great King Street, Edinburgh EH3 6RP Tel: 0131 556 7647 Fax: 0131 557 6587 — MB ChB Ed. 1951; FRCGP 1976, M 1968. Prev: Med. Adviser Austrian Relief Comm. for Afghans, Pakistan.

PATTERSON, Judith Ingrid 2/L 27 Huntly Gardens, Glasgow G12 9AU — MB ChB 1987 Glas.

PATTERSON, Mr Julian Alexander 25 Manor Drive, Aylesbury HP20 1EW — MB BS 1984 Lond.; FRCS Ed. 1991.

PATTERSON, Julie Anne Wilsden Medical Practice, Health Centre, Townfield, Wilsden, Bradford BD15 0HT Tel: 01535 273227 Fax: 01535 274860 — MB ChB 1990 Leeds; DRCOG 1992.

PATTERSON, Keith Graham Department of Haematology, University College Hospital, Gower St., London WC1E 6AU — MB BS 1972 Lond.; FRCP Lond. 1995; MRCP (UK) 1976; MRCS Eng. LRCP Lond. 1972; FRCPath 1995, M 1979. Cons. Haemat. Univ. Coll. Hosp. Lond. Prev: Sen. Lect. & Hon. Cons. Haemat. Middlx. Hosp. Lond. & Univ. Coll Hosp. Lond.

PATTERSON, Laura Claire 93 Drift Way, Cranham Park, Cirencester GL7 1WN — MB ChB 1994 Bristol; DFFP 1997; DCH 1996; MRCGP 1998. (Bristol) Locum GP.

PATTERSON, Linda Joyce, OBE Commission for Health Improvement, Finsbury Tower, 103-5 Bunhill Row, London EC1Y 8TG Tel: 020 7448 9263 Email: linda.patterson@chi.nhs.uk; Knott Hall, Charlestown, Hebden Bridge HX7 6PE Tel: 01422 845390 Email: l.patterson@ztn.co.uk — MB BS 1975 Lond.; FRCP Lond. 1993; FRCP Ed. 1991; MRCP (UK) 1979. (London) Med. Director Commiss. for Health Improvement; Clin. Lect. Univ. Manch.; Cons. Phys. (Gen. and Geriat. Med.), Burnley Health Care NHS Trust. Socs: GMC. Prev: Asst. Prof. Univ. Sashatchewan, Canada; Sen. Regist. (Gen. & Geriat. Med.) Univ. Hosp. S. Manch.; Tutor (Med.) Univ. Manch.

PATTERSON, Lindsey Jane 7 Holbeck Avenue, Healey, Rochdale OL12 6DN — MB ChB 1990 Leeds; FRCA 1996. Regist. Rotat. (Anaesth.) Cardiff. Prev: SHO (Paediat.) St Mary's Hosp. Lond.; SHO (Anaesth.) Bradford Hosps. NHS Trust.

PATTERSON, Lorna Margaret Jenny 7 Dolphin Road, Glasgow G41 4LE — MB ChB 1987 Glas.

PATTERSON, Malcolm David Torrington Health Centre, New Road, Torrington EX38 8EL Tel: 01805 622247 Fax: 01805 625083 — MB BS 1980 Lond.; MRCGP 1987; DA Eng. 1983.

PATTERSON, Mr Marc Henry Princess Royal Hospital, Lewes Road, Haywards Heath RH16 4EX Tel: 01444 441881; Ladywell, Black Hill, Haywards Heath RH16 2HE Tel: 01444 483097 — MB BS 1977 Lond.; Associate King's College 1977; FRCS Eng. 1981. (King's Coll.) Cons. Trauma & Orthop. Surg. P.ss Roy. Hosp. Haywards Heath; Examr., Roy. Coll. of Surg.s of Eng. Socs: Fell. BOA; S.I.C.O.T.; Expert Witness Inst. Prev: Sen. Regist. (Orthop.) St. Mary's Hosp. Lond.; Microsurg. Research Fell. Univ. Singapore; Regist. (Orthop.) St. Geo. Hosp. Lond.

PATTERSON, Marion Ruth 6 Parkwood, Lisburn BT27 4EF — MB BCh BAO 1939 Belf. (Belf.) Prev: Cas. Off. Altnagelvin Hosp.; Res. Med. Off. Musgrave Clinic Belf; GP Asst. Cas. Off. Ulster Hosp. Dundonald.

PATTERSON, Mark Jonathan Lister Department of Haematology, Leighton Hospital, Crewe CW1 4QJ Tel: 01270 612345 Fax: 01270 250639 Email: mark.patterson@mcht.nhs.uk; Wolverton Manor, Shorwell, Newport PO30 3JS Tel: 01983 740609 Fax: 01983 740977 Email: markl.patterson@btinternet.com — MB BS 1959 Lond; MB BS Lond. 1959; MRCP (UK) 1963; MRCS Eng. LRCP Lond. 1959. (St Barts) Cons. Haemat. Leighton Hosp. Crewe & Hon. Cons. (Haematol.) Manch. Roy. Infirm.

PATTERSON, Mark Simon 43 Ware Road, Hoddesdon EN11 9AB — MB BS 1991 Lond.

PATTERSON, Mervyn Lee House Surgery, Eves Corner, Danbury, Chelmsford CM3 4QA Tel: 01245 225522 Fax: 01245 222196; Woodford, Elm Green Lane, Danbury, Chelmsford CM3 4DW Tel: 01245 222515 — MB BS 1984 Lond.; DCH RCP Lond. 1988.

PATTERSON, Michael Campbell (retired) 44 Gipsy Lane, Earley, Reading RG6 7HD Tel: 01189 264141 Email: patterson@fullnet.com.ar — MB BS Lond. 1958; DTM & H Eng. 1968; DRCOG 1962. Director of Health Progr. of the African Ch., Argentine Chaco, Argentina. Prev: Dir. Anglican Med. Miss. Argentine Chaco.

***PATTERSON, Paul Robindra Nath** 92 Leechmere Road, Sunderland SR2 9NF — MB BS 1994 Lond.

PATTERSON

PATTERSON, Paula Maria Luisa 3 Preston Close, Strawberry Hill, Twickenham TW2 5RU Tel: 020 8894 1744 — MB BS 1982 Lond. SHO (Geriat.) Qu. Mary's Hosp. Roehampton. Prev: SHO (A & E) & (Geriat.) Qu. Mary's Hosp. Roehampton.; SHO (Obst.) Basildon Hosp.; SHO (Orthop.) Kingston Hosp. Kingston upon Thames.

PATTERSON, Rebekah Dean Pool House Cottage, Ellerton, Newport TF10 8AW — MB ChB 1986 Manch. Trainee GP Stafford VTS; Clin. Asst. (Psychogeriat.) St. Geo. Hosp. Stafford.

PATTERSON, Robert Charles 44 Granville Park, Aughton, Ormskirk L39 5DU; Claremont Medical Centre, 171 Liverpool Road S., Liverpool L31 8AA — MB ChB 1986 Liverp.

PATTERSON, Robert Neil 91 Tadworth, Bangor BT19 7WG Tel: 01247 464601 — MB BCh BAO 1996 Belf.

PATTERSON, Ronald Springburn Health Centre, 200 Springburn Way, Glasgow G21 1TR Tel: 0141 531 9660 Fax: 0141 531 9666 — MB ChB 1965 Glas. (Glas.) Prev: SHO (Gen. Surg. & Urol.) & Ho. Off. (Gen. Surg.) Vict. Infirm. Glas.; Ho. Phys. Stobhill Hosp. Glas.

PATTERSON, Samuel Clive Alexander 14 Richmond Av., Lisburn BT28 2DL — MB BCh BAO 1991 Belf.

PATTERSON, Stephen 18 Westwood Rise, Ilkley LS29 9SW — MB ChB 1989 Leeds.

PATTERSON, Sybil Margaret (retired) 36 Meadow Lane, Beadnell, Chathill NE67 5AJ Tel: 01665 720769 — MB BS 1943 Durh. Prev: Med. Off. Dept. Health & Social Security.

PATTERSON, Mr Thomas John Starling (retired) 80 St Bernard's Road, Oxford OX2 6EJ Tel: 01865 553892 — DM Oxf. 1965; MD Camb. 1960, MChir 1967, MA, MB BChir 1945; FRCS Eng. 1951; MRCS Eng. LRCP Lond. 1944. Prev: Clin. Lect. in Plastic Surg. Univ. Oxf.

PATTERSON, Victor Howard 58 Lisnabreeny Road E., Belfast BT6 9SS — MB BChir 1973 Camb.; FRCP Lond. 1990; MRCP (UK) 1974. Cons. Neurol. Roy. Vict. Hosp. Belf. Prev: MDA Clin. Fell. Washington Univ. Sch. Med., USA; Sheldon Clin. Research Fell. & Regist. (Neurol.) N. Staffs. Hosp. Centre Stoke-on-Trent.

PATTERSON, William James North Yorkshire Health Authority, Clifton Moor, York YO3 4XF Tel: 01904 825110 Fax: 01904 825245 — MB BCh BAO 1983 Belf.; MPH 1989; MFPHM RCP (UK) 1992; MRCGP 1987; DCH Dub. 1986; DRCOG 1986; DGM RCP Lond. 1986; FFPHM RCP (UK) 1998. Cons. Pub. Health Med. N. Yorks. HA.

PATTERSON, William Michael Potter Sherwood, Hengist Road, Westgate, Margate Tel: 01843 32175 — MRCS Eng. LRCP Lond. 1961; MB Camb. 1962, BChir 1961; FRCOG 1979, M 1966, DObst 1963. (Guy's) Cons. Gyn. & Obst. Canterbury & I. of Thanet Gps. Hosps. Socs: Fell. Roy. Soc. Med. Prev: Sen. Regist. (O & G) Guy's Hosp. Lond.; Resid. Med. Off. Qu. Charlotte's Matern. Hosp. Lond.; Regist. (O & G) Addenbrookes Hosp. Camb.

PATTERSON, William Morgan (retired) Braid Farm House, 40 Braid Hills Road, Edinburgh EH10 6LA Tel: 0131 447 4426 Fax: 0131 452 9628 Email: bill.patterson@ukonline.co.uk — MB ChB 1958 Ed.; FRCGP 1980, M 1971. Prev: Hon. Sen. Lect. Univ. Edin.

PATTERSON, William Rodney Maurice 44 Knockdarragh Park, Lisburn BT28 2XZ — MB BCh BAO 1996 Belf.

PATTINSON, Brian Pattinson Clinic, The Forge, 37 Red Lion St., Richmond TW9 1RJ Tel: 020 8332 6184 Fax: 020 8332 0424; East Sheen, London SW14 8BE Tel: 020 8878 5611 Fax: 020 8876 1965 — MB BS Durh. 1962; LRCP LRCS Ed. LRCPS Glas. 1964; DMS Med. Soc. Apoth. Lond. 1994; MLCOM 1973; MRO 1973; DObst RCOG 1973; Dip Med Ac. Specialist in Musculo-Skeletal Med. Pattinson Clinic, Richmond-upon-Thames.

PATTINSON, Catherine Pamela Central Clinic, Victoria Place, Carlisle CA1 1HP; Linden House, Plumpton, Penrith CA11 9PA — MB BS 1978 Newc. Clin. Med. Off. E. Cumbria HA.

PATTINSON, Christopher John 16 Woodcote Park Road, Epsom KT18 7EX Tel: 01372 812985 — MB BChir 1954 Camb.; MA, MB Camb. 1954, BChir 1953; MRCPsych 1971; DPM Eng. 1963. (Guy's) Cons. Psychiat. Private Pract. Socs: Brit. Soc. Med. & Dent. Hypn. Metrop. & S. (Gen. Comm. Mem.). Prev: Cons. Psychiat. W. Lambeth HA; Ho. Off. Guy's Hosp.; SHO Guy's-Maudsley Neurosurg. Unit Lond.

PATTINSON, Jonathan Kyle Larch Corner, Ballinger Road, South Heath, Great Missenden HP16 9QJ — MB BS 1981 Lond.

PATTINSON, Kyle Thomas Shane Ridgens Farm, Mynthurst, Leigh, Reigate RH2 8RJ — BM 1993 Soton.

PATTINSON, Maureen Frances Azes Cottage, Atherington, Umberleigh EX37 9HY Tel: 01769 60730 — LRCP LRCS 1951 Ed.; LRCP LRCS Ed. LRFPS Glas. 1951. (Roy. Colls. Ed.) JP. Prev: Squadron Ldr. RAF Med. Br.; Ho. Phys. Gen. Hosp. Leicester.

PATTISON, Mr Andrew 77 London Road, Shrewsbury SY2 6PQ Tel: 01743 366230 — MB ChB 1972 Birm.; BSc Birm. 1969, MB ChB 1972; FRCS Eng. 1977; MRCGP 1982.

PATTISON, Andrew Christopher 16 Newton Drive, Wakefield WF1 3HZ — MB ChB 1993 Leeds.

PATTISON, Mr Charles William 42 Wimpole Street, London W1M 7AF Tel: 020 7486 7416 Fax: 020 7487 2569 — MB ChB 1980 Birm.; FRCS Eng. 1984; FRCS Ed. 1984. (Birm.) p/t Cons. Cardiothoracic Surg. Univ. Coll. Hosps. Lond.; Clin. Lect. (Cardiac Surg.) Nat. Heart & Lung Inst. Lond.; Fell. & Mem. Scientif. Counc. Internat. Coll. Angiol. NY. Socs: Brit. Cardiac Soc.; Soc. Cardiothoracic Surgs.; Amer. Assn. Thoracic Surg. Prev: Sen. Regist. (Cariothoracic Surg.) Nat. Heart & Chest Hosp.; Regist. (Cardiothoracic Surg.) Harefield Hosp. & St. Thos. Hosp. Lond.; Regist. (Surg.) Centr. Birm. Health Dist.

PATTISON, Christina Jane — MB BCh 1981 Wales; BSc (Hons) Birm 1975; MRCP (UK) 1985. GP N.wich.

PATTISON, Denise Carol Belvedere Medical Centre, 15 Albert Road, Belvedere DA17 5LP Tel: 01322 446700 Email: rpatpcc@aol.com; 65 Whitworth Road, Woolwich, London SE18 3QG Tel: 020 8854 8520 — MB BS 1987 Lond. (King's College Medical School London) GP. Prev: Trainee GP Lond. VTS.

PATTISON, Mr Giles Thomas Ridley Department of Orthopaedics & Trauma, Yeovil District Hospital, Higher Kingston, Yeovil BA21 4AT Tel: 01935 75122; Farndon Thatch, Puckington, Ilminster TA19 9JA Tel: 01460 57392 Email: gillspattison@hotmail.com — MB BS Lond. 1991; FRCS Ed 1996. Specialist Regist., Trauma & Orthop. Bristol & S.W. Rotat. Socs: BOTA. Prev: SHO (Orthop.) S.mead Hosp.; SHO (Orthop.) Taunton & Som. Hosp.; SHO (Orthop.) Frenchay Hosp. Bristol.

PATTISON, Helen Fiona Rose Holding, Latteridge Road, Iron Acton, Bristol BS37 9TW — MB ChB 1985 Birm.

PATTISON, Ian 86 Horsley Hill Road, South Shields NE33 3EP — MB BS 1996 Newc.

PATTISON, James Michael Renal Unit, Guy's Hospital, St Thomas St., London SE1 9RT Tel: 020 7955 4151 Fax: 020 7955 4909; 93 Vanbrugh Park, Blackheath, London SE3 7AL Tel: 020 8293 0254 — BM BCh 1987 Oxf.; BA Oxf. 1984; MRCP (UK) 1990; DM Oxf. 1996. (Oxf.) Cons. Nephrol. Renal Unit Guys' Hosp. Lond. Socs: Renal Assn.; Amer. Soc. Nephrol. Prev: Sen. Regist. & Regist. (Renal) Guy's Hosp. Lond.; Research Fell. Stanford Univ. Calif., USA; SHO Brompton & Hammersmith Hosps. Lond.

PATTISON, Jill 57 Esmond Road, London W4 1JG — MB BS 1983 Lond.; FFA RCS Eng. 1988; DA (UK) 1985. Cons. Anaesth. & ITU Heatherwood Hosp. Ascot & Wexham Pk. Hosp. Socs: Roy. Soc. Med. & Intens. Care Soc. Prev: Sen. Regist. (Anaesth.) W.m. & Char. Cross Hosp. Lond.; Regist. (Anaesth.) St. Mary's Hosp. Lond.; SHO (Anaesth. & ITU) Middlx. Hosp. Lond.

PATTISON, Professor Sir John Ridley Director of Research, Analysis and Information, Department of Health, Richmond House, 79 whitehall, London SW1A 2NS Tel: 020 7210 5556 Fax: 020 77210 5868 Email: john.pattison@doh.gsi.gov.uk — BM BCh Oxf. 1968; BA Oxf. 1964, BSc 1967, DM 1975; FRCPath 1989, M 1975. Dir.Research, Anal. & Informat., Dept. of Health; Hon. Cons. UCL Hosps. NHS Trust & Pub. Health Laborat. Serv.; Prof. Med. Microbiol. UCL (on secondment to Dept. of Health). Prev: Prof. Med. Microbiol. King's Coll. Hosp. Med. Sch. Lond.; Hon. Cons. Camberwell HA.

PATTISON, Philip Brian HM Prison Service HQ, Cleland House, Page St., London SW1P 4LN — MB BS 1961 Lond.; MRCS Eng. LRCP Lond. 1960; DRCOG 1962. Health Care Adviser Directorate of Operats. (N.) Prison Serv. HQ.

PATTISON, Roderick Brown Muiredge Surgery, Merlin Crescent, Buckhaven, Leven KY8 1HJ Tel: 01592 713299 Fax: 01592 715728; 71 Alexandra Street, Kirkcaldy KY1 1HH Tel: 01592 200474 — MB ChB 1989 Aberd.; MRCGP 1995; DFFP 1995; DRCOG 1995. Trainee GP/SHO (Geriat.) Vict. Hosp. Kirkcaldy. Socs: BMA. Prev: SHO

(Psychiat.) Vict. Hosp. Kirkcaldy; Trainee GP Glenrothes; SHO (Clin. Path.) Nat. Hosp. Neurol. & Neurosurg.

PATTISON, Roger Michael 17 Thames Haven, Portsmouth Road, Surbiton KT6 4JA — MB BS 1989 Lond.

***PATTISON, Sophie Harriet** Ground Floor Flat, 21 Trelawney Rd, Bristol BS6 6DX — MB ChB 1997 Bristol.

PATTISSON, Peter Richard Merriman, OBE (retired) Waterfield House Surgery, 186 Henwood Green Road, Pembury, Tunbridge Wells TN2 4LR Tel: 01892 825488 — MB Camb. 1964, BChir 1963. Prev: Med. Off. Save The Childr. Fund Masan, Korea.

PATTMAN, Mary Geraldine Denton Park Health Centre, Denton Park Centre, West Denton Way, Newcastle upon Tyne NE5 2QZ Tel: 0191 267 2751 Fax: 0191 264 1588; Balnakeil, 9 Westfield, Gosforth, Newcastle upon Tyne NE3 4YE Tel: 0191 285 3049 Email: camisp@aol.com — MB ChB 1973 Glas.; Dip. Ther. Newc. 1995; DFFP 1994; DObst RCOG 1975.

PATTNAIK, Dhirendra Kumar Law Hospital, Carluke ML8 5ER Tel: 01698 351100 — MB BS 1965 Utkal; BSc Utkal 1958; DMRD Eng. 1972. (S.C.B. Med. Coll. Cuttack) Cons. Radiol. Law Hosp. Carluke & Strathclyde Hosp. Motherwell. Prev: Sen. Regist. (Radiol.) Manch. Roy. Infirm.; Regist. (Radiol.) Glas. Roy. Infirm.; Edr Jl. S.C.B. Med. Coll.

PATTNI, Bhikhu Ladhabhai The Surgery, 1222 Coventry Road, Hay Mills, Birmingham B25 8BY Tel: 0121 772 1898 Fax: 0121 608 1222 — MB ChB 1979 Nairobi; LMSSA 1984; DRCOG 1989.

***PATTNI, Tejal Ashvin** 15 Glebe Road, London N3 2BA — MB BS 1998 Lond.; MB BS Lond 1998.

PATTON, Alexandra Park Road Surgery, 37 Park Road, Teddington TW11 2AU Tel: 020 8977 5481 — MB BChir 1993 Camb.; MRCGP 1997; DRCOG 1996; DCH 1995. (Cambridge University) GP Partner.

PATTON, David Thomas Carrick Brae, 146 Gilford Road, Portadown, Craigavon BT63 5LD — MB BCh BAO 1946 Belf.

PATTON, Mr David William, TD Penmaen Cottage, Penmaen, Swansea SA3 2HH Tel: 01792 371607 Fax: 01792 371605 Email: jaw@dpatton.demon.co.uk — BDS Dundee 1969; FDS RCS Eng. 1975; FDS RCPS Glas. 1975; MB BS Lond. 1980; FRCS Ed. 1985. (Guy's) Cons. Maxillofacial Surg. Morriston Hosp. Swansea; Hon. Sen. Lect. (Maxillofacial Surg.) Sch. Postgrad. Studies in Med. & Healthcare Swansea; Hon. Civil. Cons. Oral & Maxillofacial Surg. to the Army. Socs: Fell. Brit. Assn. Oral & Maxillofacial Surg.; Fell. Brit. Assn. Head & Neck Oncol.; Craniofacial Soc. Prev: Sen. Regist. (Maxillofacial Surg.) Canniesburn Hosp. Glas.

PATTON, George, MC 34 Highfield Road, Littleover, Derby DE23 7DG Tel: 01332 762739 — MB BCh BAO 1937 Belf.; MRCGP 1953. (Qu. Univ. Belf.) Prev: Ho. Surg. Stanley Hosp. Liverp.; Res. Med. Off. Fev. Hosp. Fazakerley, Liverp.; RAMC.

PATTON, Hugh Fergus 4 The Dell, Fulbeck, Morpeth NE61 3JY Tel: 01670 515782 Fax: 01670 515782; 4 The Dell, Fulbeck, Morpeth NE61 3JY Tel: 01670 515782 Fax: 01670 515782 Email: hf.mpatton@talk21.com — MB BCh BAO 1974 Dub.; MA Dub. 1977, BA, MB BCh BAO 1974; MICGP 1984. (TC Dub.) Forens. Med. Examr. (FT). N.umbria Police. Prev: Capt. RAMC; Ho. Off. Roy. City of Dub. Hosp.; GP.

PATTON, Hugh Henry Terence 39 Dromore Road, Hillsborough BT26 6HU — MB BCh BAO 1981 Belf.; MB BCh Belf. 1981.

PATTON, Mr James Terence Fallows Hall, Chelford Road, Macclesfield SK10 4SZ; TFR, 10 Hope Park Crescent, Edinburgh EH8 9NA — MB ChB 1991 Ed.; FRCS Ed. 1995. Specialist Regist. (Orthop.) S. E. Scotl. Prev: SHO Rotat. (Orthop.) Glas. Roy. Infirm.

PATTON, John Terence, RD 23 Anson Road, Victoria Park, Manchester M14 5BZ Tel: 0161 224 0006; Fallows Hall, Chelford, Macclesfield SK10 4SZ Tel: 01625 861252 — MRCS Eng. LRCP Lond. 1951; Hon. FRCP Ed. 1984; FRCR 1975; FFR 1963; DMRD Eng. 1959. (Liverp.) Hon. Cons. Manch. Roy. Infirm.; Hon. Lect. (Radiol.) Univ. Manch.; Chairm. Armed Servs. Cons. Approval Bd. (Radiol.). Socs: Fell. Manch. Med. Soc. Prev: Cons. Radiol. to RN; Cons. i/c (Radiol.) Manch. Roy. Infirm.; Ed. Brit. Jl. Radiol.

PATTON, Lara 23 Rosepark, Belfast BT5 7RG — MB BCh BAO 1993 Belf.

PATTON, Margaret 146 Gilford Road, Portadown, Craigavon BT63 5LD — MB BS 1949 Lond.

PATTON, Melanie Kay West Bar Surgery, 1 West Bar Street, Banbury OX16 9SF Tel: 01295 256261 Fax: 01295 756848;

Oakleigh, Weeping Cross, Bodicote, Banbury OX15 4ED — MB ChB 1984 Sheff.; MRCGP 1989; DTM & H Liverp. 1988.

PATTON, Professor Michael Alexander St. Georges Hospital Medical School, Cranmer Terrace, London SW17 0RE Tel: 020 8725 5335 Fax: 020 8725 3444 Email: mpatton@sghms.ac.uk; 126 Woodlands Road, Little Bookham, Leatherhead KT23 4HJ — MB ChB 1974 Ed.; MA Camb. 1975; MSc (Human Genetics) Ed. 1976; FRCP Lond. 1993; MRCP (UK) 1979; FRCPCH 1997; DCH Eng. 1977. Cons. & Prof. (Med. Genetics) St. Geo. Hosp. Med. Sch. Lond.; Med. Dir. Birth Defects Foundat.; Chrm ethics Comm. RCPCH. Socs: Fell. Roy. Soc. Med.; Brit Soc human genetics. Prev: Insp. Human Fertilization & Embryol. Auth.; Pres. Jenner Soc. 1997-1998; Sen. Regist. (Clin. Genetics) Hosp. Sick Childr. Gt. Ormond St. Lond.

***PATTON, Michael Sean** 7 Dukes Lane, Ballykelly, Limavady BT49 9JT — MB ChB 1997 Aberdeen.

PATTON, Michelle The Village Surgery, Dudley Lane, Cramlington NE23 6US Tel: 01670 712821; 4 The Dell, Fulbeck, Morpeth NE61 3JY Tel: 01670 515782 Fax: 01670 515782 Email: patton@btinternet.com — MB BS 1989 Lond. Priciple Gen. Practioner; Clin. Asst. (Psychogerat.), St Geo. Hosp.,Morpeth.; Dep. Forens. Med. Examr.), N.umbria Police. Socs: MRCQP; Assoc.s of Police Surg.s.

PATTON, Niall 6 Rossbay, Waterside, Londonderry BT47 6JF — MB ChB 1996 Manch. SHO (Opthal.) Roy. Eye Hosp. Manch.

PATTON, Nicholas David The Surgery, 9 Albion Street, Brighton BN2 2PS Tel: 01273 601122/601344 Fax: 01273 623450 — MB BS 1979 Lond.; MRCGP 1989; DRCOG 1984.

PATTON, Stephen Nadim 90 Lisnafin Park, Strabane BT82 9DH — MB BCh 1996 Belf.; DRCOG. (Queen's University Belfast) SHO (Psychiat.) Mater Hosp. Belf. Prev: A & E; O & G.

PATTON, Walter John (retired) 199 Romsey Road, Winchester SO22 5PG Tel: 01962 854183 — MB ChB 1937 Liverp.

PATTON, William Collim 23 Rosepark, Dundonald, Belfast BT5 7RG — MB BCh BAO 1966 Belf.; BSc (Hons.) Belf. 1963, MB BCh BAO 1966; FRCPsych 1974. (Qu. Univ. Belf.) Cons. Psychiat. Downsh. Hosp. Downpatrick.

PATTON, Mr William Henry Gordon (retired) The Croft, Weston Road, Weston-on-Road, Derby DE72 2BH Tel: 01332 701024 — MB ChB 1937 Liverp.; BSA Toronto 1932; MCh Orth. Liverp. 1948, MB ChB 1937. Prev: Asst. Surg. Bretby Hall Orthop. Hosp. Burton-on-Trent.

PATTOO, Bashir Ahmad Bollington Road Surgery, 126 Bollington Road, Ancoats, Manchester M40 7HD Tel: 0161 205 2979 Fax: 0161 205 6368 — MB BS 1974 Kashmir.

PATTRICK, Francis Gilson Marham House, Marham, King's Lynn PE33 9HS Tel: 01760 223 — LMSSA 1941 Lond.; BA Camb. 1937, MA 1943, MB BChir 1948; MRCP Ed. 1949; DTM & H Eng. 1942. (Camb. & St. Mary's) Cons. Phys. N. Cambs. & Doddington Hosp. Gp. Socs: B.M.A. Prev: Med. Regist. St. Mary's Hosp.; Ho. Surg. Redhill Co. Hosp. Edgware.

PATTRICK, Martin Graham 44 Tunis Street, Sculcoates Lane, Hull HU5 1EZ — MB ChB 1981 Bristol; BSc (Cellular Path.) Bristol 1978, MB ChB 1981; MCRP (UK) 1983. Clin. Research Fell. & Hon. Regist. (Rheumat.) Nottm. HA. Socs: Brit. Soc. Rheumat. Prev: SHO (Med.) & Regist. N. Staffs. HA; Ho. Off. Bristol & W.on HA.

***PATTULLO, Simon James** The Park, Bank St., Elie, Leven KY9 1BW — MB ChB 1997 Aberd.

PATUCK, David Fram Wharf Lane, Ilminster TA19 0DT Tel: 01460 52354; Chatsworth, Broadway Road, Broadway, Ilminster TA19 9RX Tel: 01460 52088 Email: david@patucks.co.uk — MB BS 1975 Lond.; MRCS Eng. LRCP Lond. 1974; DRCOG 1980. Prev: Med. Off. Brit. Antarctic Survey.

PATUCK, Dina Rowantree House, Robinson Lane, Woodmancote, Cirencester GL7 7EN Tel: 01285 831700 — MB BS 1950 Lond.; MRCS Eng. LRCP Lond. 1949; DObst RCOG 1954; DCH Eng. 1952. (Roy. Free) Regist. (Paediat.) King Edwd. VII Hosp. Windsor. Prev: Ho. Phys. Roy. Free Hosp.; Ho. Surg. (O & G) Canad. Red Cross Memor. Hosp. Taplow.

PATUCK, Fram (retired) Rowantree House, Robinson Lane, Woodmancote, Cirencester GL7 7EN Tel: 01285 831700 Email: fram@patuck.freeserve.co.uk — MRCS Eng. LRCP Lond. 1946; FRCGP 1989, M 1977; Assoc. Fac. Occupat. Med. RCP Lond. 1980. Prev: Surg. S. Div. Metrop. Police.

PATUCK

PATUCK, Julie Frances 22 North Street, Ilminster TA19 0DG Tel: 01460 52284; Chatsworth, Broadway Road, Broadway, Ilminster TA19 9RX Tel: 01460 52088 — MB ChB 1977 Liverp.; MRCGP 1981; DRCOG 1980. (Liverp.)

PATWALA, D Y Church Road Surgery, 64 Church Road, Bebington, Wirral CH63 3EB — MBBS 1972; DGO, DFP. (Topiwala National Medical School)

PATWARDHAN, Kiran 1 West Kensington Court, Edith Villas, London W14 9AA — MB BS 1986 Nagpur; MRCP (UK) 1994.

PAU, Henry Poon Hang Bedfont House, Prospect Place, Hythe, Southampton SO45 6AT Tel: 01703 848011; 25 Fernleigh Avenue, Royal Oak, Auckland, New Zealand Tel: 00 64 96256102 — MB ChB 1994 Leic. SHO (A & E) Leicester Roy. Infirm.; Demonst. (Anat.) Leicester Univ. Prev: Ho. Off. (Orthop. & Surg.) Leicester Roy. Infirm.; Ho. Off. (Med.) Geo. Eliot Hosp. Nuneaton.

PAUFFLEY, John Hamilton (retired) Pengymill, Chignal St James, Chelmsford CM1 4TZ Tel: 01245 440515 — MRCS Eng. LRCP Lond. 1949; DObst RCOG 1954. Prev: Ho. Phys. Poplar Hosp.

PAUL, Mr Alan Burnett Pyrah Department of Urology, St James' Univ.Hosp., Beckett St., Leeds LS6 7TF Tel: 0113 206 4949 Email: alan.paul@leedsth.nhs.uk — MB ChB 1985 Ed.; FRCS Ed. 1990; FRCS Ed (Urol.) 1998; MD (Edin.) 1999. (Edinburgh) Cons. Urological Surg., St James, Leeds. Socs: BMA; Assoc. Mem. BAUS. Prev: Clin. Research Fell. Nuffield Transpl. Unit W.. Gen. Hosp. Edin.; Sen. Regist. Withington Hosp. Manch.

***PAUL, Alison** Marsh Farm, North Molton, South Molton EX36 3HQ — MB ChB 1998 Birm.; ChB Birm. 1998.

***PAUL, Amal Chandra** 4 Bayswater Row, Leeds LS8 5LH — MB ChB 1994 Leeds.

PAUL, Anindita 40 Alton Road, Birmingham B29 7DU — MB ChB 1992 Birm.

PAUL, Mr Ashok Samuel 9 Tilby Close, Urmston, Manchester M41 6JN — MB BS 1983 Madras; FRCS Ed. 1987.

PAUL, Beverley Bassetlaw Hospital, Kilton, Worksop S81 0BD Tel: 01909 500990 Fax: 01909 502462 Email: beverley.paul@dbh.nhs.uk; Stonebeck, Low St, Carlton in Lindrick, Worksop S81 9EJ Tel: 01909 730284 Email: bevpaul@lineone.net — MB BS 1973 Lond.; MRCS Eng. LRCP Lond. 1973; FRCPath 1995, M 1983; T(Path.) 1991. (Univ. Lond.) Cons. Haemat.Doncaster & Bassetlaw Hosps. NHS Trust. Socs: Brit. Soc. Haematol.; Brit. Blood Transfus. Soc.; Eur. Haematol. Assn. Prev: Lect. (Haemat.) Univ. Zimbabwe; Sen. Regist. (Haemat.) N.. RHA.

***PAUL, Carolyn Ann** 167 Moss Lane, Bramhall, Stockport SK7 1BG — MB ChB 1994 Manch.

PAUL, Carolyn Patricia 5A Gerrard Road, London N1 8AY — MB BS 1988 Lond.; MRCOG 1994.

PAUL, Clive Conrad The Old Rectory Surgery, 18 Castle Street, Saffron Walden CB10 1BP Tel: 01799 522327 Fax: 01799 525436 — MB BS 1980 Lond.; BSc Lond. 1976; MRCS Eng. LRCP Lond. 1979; MRCGP 1988; DRCOG 1988. (Guys)

PAUL, David Hendrie Greencroft Medical Centre (South), Greencroft Wynd, Annan DG12 6GS Tel: 01461 202244 Fax: 01461 205401; 63 Hecklegirth, Annan DG12 6HL — MB ChB 1971 St. And.; MRCGP 1983; DObst RCOG 1973. (St. And.) Socs: BMA. Prev: Gen. Med. Off. Nchanga Consolidated Copper Mines Hosp. Kitwe, Zambia; SHO (Paediat.) Perth Roy. Infirm.; SHO (O & G) W.. Gen. Hosp. Edin.

PAUL, Derek Lindsay 28 Birkdale Crescent, Dullatur, Glasgow G68 0JZ Tel: 0141 722078 — MB ChB 1980 Ed.; FRCA 1986. (Ed.) Cons. Cardiothoracic Anaesth. Roy. Infirm. Glas. Socs: Assn. Anaesth. Prev: Sen. Regist. (Anaesth.) W.. Infirm. Glas.; Astra Research Fell. (Anaesth.) Roy. Infirm. Edin.

PAUL, Eric Andre Albert Salisbury Road Surgery, 1 Salisbury Road, Seven Kings, Ilford IG3 8BG Tel: 020 8597 0924 Fax: 020 8598 8254 — Artsexamen 1986 Amsterdam; T(GP) 1992.

PAUL, Euan Hector Menzies 12 Market Street, Chipping Norton OX7 5NQ Tel: 01608 645566 Fax: 01608 645300 Email: cosic@btinternet.com — MB BS 1960 Lond.; FFOM RCPI 1984; FFOM RCP Lond. 1996; DObst RCOG 1962. (St. Thos.) Scientif. Adviser COSIC; Cons. Occupat. Health & Safety Oxon. Socs: Fell. Roy. Soc. Med.; SOM; BMA. Prev: Dir. Health, Safety & Risk Managem. Europe; Ho. Phys. & Ho. Surg. Kent & Canterbury Hosp.; Ho. Surg. (Obst.) St. Mary's Matern. Hosp. W. Croydon.

PAUL, George 6 Wolverley Grange, Alvaston, Derby DE24 0SS — MB BS 1977 Kerala; MRCP (UK) 1985.

***PAUL, Gideon Andrew** 50 Green Lane, Edgware HA8 7PX — MB BS 1998 Lond.; MB BS Lond 1998.

PAUL, Hans-Joerg Health Centre, East St., Thame OX9 3JZ; 14 Onslow Drive, Thame OX9 3YX — State Exam Med 1990 Freiburg; State Exam Med. Freiburg 1990; MD Freiburg 1990; MRCP (UK) 1993; DRCOG 1997. GP Regist. Thame VTS. Prev: Sen. Regist. (Radiol.) W.. Infirm. Glas.; SHO (Gen. Med.) Roy. Alexandra Hosp. Paisley.

PAUL, Heather Elizabeth 63 Hecklegirth, Annan DG12 6HL — MB ChB 1970 Ed.; DObst RCOG 1972; DCH RCPS Glas. 1972. Staff Grade (Geriat.) Dumfries & Galloway Roy. Infirm.

PAUL, Helga Judith Channel Watch, 123 Coast Drive, Greatstone, New Romney TN28 8NR — MB BS 1987 Lond.; DRCOG 1995; Cert. Prescribed Experience. 1995. Ship's Doctor. Prev: Regist. (c/o the Elderly) Kent & Canterbury Hosp. Canterbury.; SHO (Med.) Kent & Canterbury Hosp.; SHO (A & E) Wexham Pk. Hosp. Slough.

PAUL, Henryck Marian Pawel (retired) 23 Windermere Road, Bolton Le Sands, Carnforth LA5 8LL Tel: 01524 824071 — MB BS 1964 Lond.; MRCS Eng. LRCP Lond. 1964. Prev: Ho. Surg. (Orthop.) Qu. Mary's Hosp. Roehampton.

PAUL, Ian Robert Coniston Medical Practice, The Parade, Coniston Road, Patchway, Bristol BS34 5TF Tel: 0117 969 2508 Fax: 0117 969 0456 — MB BCh BAO 1985 Belf.; MRCGP 1992; DRCOG 1989. GP, Coniston Med. Pract., Bristol.

PAUL, Israel Pep (retired) 26 Seagry Road, London E11 2NH Tel: 020 8989 0741 — MB ChB Ed. 1938. Prev: Ho. Surg. Roy. Infirm. Oldham.

PAUL, James Rupert 23 Vineyard Hill Road, London SW19 7JL Email: jamespaul@compuserve.com — MB BS 1994 Lond.; BSc Lond. 1992; MRCP 1998. (RFHSM London) SHO (Med.). Socs: Mem. Christian Med. Fell.ship.

PAUL, Mrs Jill Barns Street Surgery, 3 Barns Street, Ayr KA7 1XB Tel: 01292 281439 Fax: 01292 288268; 2 Inverkar Road, Ayr KA7 2JT Tel: 01292 263669 — MB ChB 1988 Glas.; MRCGP 1992; DRCOG 1991. (Glasgow) GP Princip. Prev: Trainee GP Ayr; SHO (Geriat.) Vict. Hosp. Glas.; SHO (Psychiat.) Levendale Hosp. Glas.

PAUL, John Brighton PHL, Royal Sussex County, Eastern Road, Brighton BN2 5BE Tel: 01273 696955; Downsflint, High St, Upper Beeding, Steyning BN44 3WN — MB ChB 1985 Birm.; MSc Lond. 1990; BSc Birm. 1982; MD Birm 1999. Cons. Microbiol. Brighton PHL. Socs: Fell. Roy. Soc. Trop. Med. & Hyg. Prev: Hon. Sen. Regist. & Regist. Oxf. PHL; Microbiol. Wellcome Trust Research Laborats., Nairobi.

PAUL, Kusem 8 Sequoia Park, Pinner HA5 4BS — MB BS 1983 Lond.

PAUL, Leela Department of Psychiatry, Ashford Hospital, Ashford TW15 3AA Tel: 01784 884488; 11 Percy Avenue, Ashford TW15 2PB Tel: 01784 255540 — MB BS Kerala 1968; DPM Eng. 1980; DRCOG 1975. (Trivandrum) Assoc. Specialist (Psychiat.) Ashford Hosp. Prev: SHO (O & G) Grantham & Kesteven Hosp.; SHO (Psychiat.) St. Mary's Hosp. ScarBoro.; CL. Asst. Psychiat. Ashford Hosp.

***PAUL, Mark Nicholas** Watersmeet House, Yarde, Williton, Taunton TA4 4HW — MB BS 1997 Lond.

PAUL, Martin Bedgrove Surgery, Brentwood Way, Aylesbury HP21 7TL Tel: 01296 330330 Fax: 01296 399179; 5 Orchard Way, Botolph Claydon, Buckingham MK18 2NG — MB BS 1971 Lond.; MRCGP 1983; DRCOG 1977; DCH Eng. 1976. GP Aylesbury; Course Organiser Aylesbury VTS. Socs: Roy. Coll. GPs. Prev: Chairm. of Aylesbury GP fundholding forum.

PAUL, Matthew Leon Henry The New Surgery, Lindo Close, Chesham HP5 2JN Tel: 01494 782262; 13 Chartridge Lane, Chesham HP5 2JJ Tel: 01494 793284 Email: thepauls@nildron.co.uk — MB BS 1990 Lond.; BSc Lond. 1985, MB BS 1990. (King's College Hospital) Prev: Ho. Surg. (Cardiothoracic & Gen. Surg.) & Ho. Phys. (Oncol. & Gen. Med.) KCH Lond.

***PAUL, Meenu** 56 Goodman Park, Slough SL2 5NN — MB BS 1996 Lond.

PAUL, Michael General Medical Clinics PLC, 2-3 Salisbury Court, Brushfield St., London Tel: 020 7427 0605 Fax: 020 7427 0608 Email: michael.paul@genmed.org.uk — MB ChB 1972 Manch.;

MRCGP 1977; DObst RCOG 1975. Med. Dir. Gen. Med. Clinics. Socs: Fell. Roy. Soc. Med. Prev: GP Sunninghill Ascot; Clin. Asst. Infertil. Clinic Heatherwood Hosp. Ascot; Med. Off. Priory Convent Ascot.

PAUL, Michael Braithwaite (retired) Orchard House, Newchurch, Burton-on-Trent DE13 8RH — MB BChir 1944 Camb.; MA Camb. 1942, MD 1948; MRCS Eng. LRCP Lond. 1942. Prev: Cons. Chest Phys. & Cons. Geriat. SE Staffs. Health Dist.

PAUL, Mr Milan Rudolph (retired) 8 Summerfield Road, Wolverhampton WV1 4PR Tel: 01902 429044 Fax: 01902 710290 — MRCS Eng. LRCP Lond. 1970; FRCS Eng. 1973; DO Eng. 1970.

PAUL, Milena Mary (retired) 1 Greenacres, Tettenhall, Wolverhampton WV6 8SR Tel: 01902 753284 — MRCS Eng. LRCP Lond. 1976; DA Eng. 1972. Prev: Clin. Asst. (Anaesth.) Walsall Gen. Hosp.

PAUL, Narinder Radiology Department, Bradford Royal Infirmary, Duckworth Lane, Bradford BD9 6RJ — BM 1987 Soton.; MRCP (UK) 1991; FRCR 1994. (Soton.) Cons. Radiol. St. Jas. Univ. Hosp. Leeds. Prev: Regist. (Radiol.) Freeman Hosp. Newc.; SHO (Renal & Respirat. Med., Neurol. & A & E) Soton.

PAUL, Natasha Kamaljeet 245 Popes Lane, London W5 4NH — MB BS 1993 Lond.

***PAUL, Neil Robin** 21 Portland Close, Hazel Grove, Stockport SK7 5HF — MB ChB 1994 Manch.

PAUL, Nigel Croyard Road Surgery, Croyard Road, Beauly IV4 7DT Tel: 01463 782794 Fax: 01463 782111 — MB ChB 1984 Aberd. Prev: SHO (O & G) Falkirk Roy. Infirm.

PAUL, Pallipurathukaren Joseph 110 Ecclesfield Road, Eccleston, St Helens WA10 5ND — MB BS 1968 Andhra; MRCP (UK) 1977. (Kakinada Med. Coll.) Cons. (Geriat. Med.) St. Helens Hosp. Prev: Regist. (Gen. Med.) King's Mill Hosp. Sutton-in-Ashfield.

PAUL, Mr Prasanta Kumar 72 Windmill Avenue, St Albans AL4 9SN Tel: 01727 762291 — MRCS Eng. LRCP Lond. 1987; FRCS Glas. 1995. Regist. (Trauma & Orthop. Surg.) Hemel Hempstead Gen. Hosp. Herts. Socs: BMA; Assn. Surg. Train. Prev: Regist. (Gen. Surg.) Milton Keynes Gen. Hosp.; Ho. Off. (Gen. Surg.) Ormskirk & Dist. Gen. Hosp.

***PAUL, Raymond Thomas** 68 Ballycrochan Road, Bangor BT19 6NF — MB BCh 1998 Belf.; MB BCh Belf 1998.

***PAUL, Rini** 252 Boundary Road, Wood Green, London N22 6AJ — MB BS 1997 Lond.

PAUL, Roger Graham The Park Surgery, 375 Chepstow Road, Newport NP19 8XR Tel: 01633 277333 Fax: 01633 279078 — MB BS 1971 Lond.; MRCS Eng. LRCP Lond. 1970.

PAUL, Sheila Sarah The Misbourne Surgery, Church Lane, Chalfont St Peter, Gerrards Cross SL9 9RR Tel: 01753 891010; 40 Batchelors Way, Amersham HP7 9AJ Tel: 01494 434718 — MB ChB 1975 Manch.; DMJ 1999; DRCOG 1977; ATLS 1983 & 1995; Section 12 approved 1998. (Manch.) Police Surg. Thames Valley Police; Med. Off. Community Drug & Alcohol Team Aylesbury. Socs: Assn. Police Surg.; Fell. Roy. Soc. Med.; Brit. Acad. Forens. Sci. Prev: Gen. Phys. US Army Hosp. Frankfurt, W. Germany.

PAUL, Simon Neil Mayday Hospital, Croydon CR7 7YE — MB BS 1994 Lond.; BSc Kingston 1996; MRCP (UK) 1998. (Univ. Coll. Lond. Med. Sch.)

PAUL, Mr Sudhansu Bhusan (retired) 70 Abinger Avenue, Cheam, Sutton SM2 7LW — MB BS 1955 Calcutta; FRCS Eng. 1969. Prev: Assoc. Specialist (Orthop.) SW Thames Regional Auth.

PAUL, Mr Surendramohan Chandpal Hinchingbrooke Hospital, Hinchingbrooke Park, Huntingdon PE29 6NT — MRCS Eng. LRCP Lond. 1974; MB Camb. 1976, BChir 1975; FRCS Ed. 1979.

PAUL, Thankam 111B Camberwell Grove, London SE5 8JH — MB BS 1988 Lond.

PAUL, Vincent Edward Department of Cardiology, Harefield Hospital, Harefield, Uxbridge UB9 6JH Tel: 01895 823737 — MB ChB 1981 Manch.

PAUL CHOUDHURY, Saumitra Kumar Dunstable Road Surgery, 163 Dunstable Road, Luton LU1 1BW Tel: 01582 23553; 2 Milburn Close, Luton LU3 4EH — MB BS 1975 Dacca; DLO RCS Eng. 1984. Clin. Asst. (Gen. Psychiat.) Luton & Dunstable Hosp. Trust; Clin. Dir. GP Liaison Luton & Dunstable Hosp. NHS Trust (Exec. Bd.).

PAULDING, Elizabeth Anne The Alton Practice, 208 Roehampton Lane, London SW15 4LE Tel: 020 8788 4844 Fax: 020 8788 4844;

8 Stuart Road, London SW19 8DH Tel: 020 8946 8495 — MB BCh BAO 1964 Dub. Socs: BMA.

PAULEAU, Anne Essex Lodge, 94 Greengate Street, Plaistow, London E13 0AS Tel: 020 8472 4888 Fax: 020 8472 5777 — MB BS 1986 Lond.; MRCGP 1992; DRCOG 1993. Clin. Lect Qu. Mary W.field Coll. Prev: Vis. Hon. Lect. King's Coll.

PAULEAU, Nitza Francoise 56A Cleveden Drive, Glasgow G12 0NX — MB BS 1958 Lond.; MRCS Eng. LRCP Lond. 1958.

PAULI, Helen Mary Triangle Cottage, Englishcombe, Bath BA2 9DU Tel: 01225 311134 — MB BChir 1990 Camb.; MA Camb. 1989; MRCGP 1995; DRCOG 1993. GP Princip. Bath. Prev: Asst. GP Bath; Trainee GP/SHO Bath HA; Ho. Off. (Surg.) Swindon HA.

PAULI, Monica Aileen (retired) 6 Eastmead Court, Stoke Hill, Bristol BS9 1HP — MB BCh BAO 1927 NUI.

PAULIN, Mary Neilson Macqueen 41D Sans Souce Park, Belfast BT9 5BZ Tel: 028 665864 — MB BCh BAO 1941 Belf.; DPH Eng. 1946. (Qu. Univ. Belf.) Prev: Asst. MOH Co. Antrim.; Hon. Clin Asst. Fertil. Clinic Samarit. Hosp. Belf.; Asst. MoH Lees.

PAULLEY, Jean Susan 25 Clarksfield Street, Clarksfield, Oldham OL4 3AW — MB ChB 1968 Manch. (Manch.) Clin. Med. Off. Oldham HA.

PAULLEY, John Wylmer (retired) Sufolk Nuffield Hospital at Christchurch Park, 57 Fonnereau Rd, Ipswich IP1 3JN Tel: 01473 623771 — MB BS 1940 Lond.; MD Lond. 1944; FRCP Lond. 1959, M 1941; MRCS Eng. LRCP Lond. 1939. Will. Edmunds' Clin. Research Fell. RCP. Prev: Cons. Phys. Ipswich Health Dist.

PAULUS, Eira-Wyn 50 Parc Wern Road, Sketty, Swansea SA2 0SF — MB BS 1986 Lond.

PAULUS, Jonathan Neal 50 Parc Wen Road, Shetty, Swansea SA2 0SF — MB BS 1986 Lond.; MRCGP 1990. Prev: SHO (Paediat.) Singleton Hosp. Swansea; SHO (Psychiat.) Cefn Coed Hosp. Swansea; SHO (ENT) Singleton Hosp. Swansea.

PAULUS, Ulrike Staff Residence, Monkland District General Hospital, Monkscourt Avenue, Airdrie ML6 0JS — State Exam Med 1992 Kiel.

PAUN, Sadguna Manharlal Archadian Gdns Surgery, 1 Arcadian Gardens, Bowes Park, London N22 5AB; 15A Eversleigh Road, New Barnet, Barnet EN5 1NE — MB BS 1965 Gujarat; DGO 1967. (B.J. Med. Coll. Ahmedabad) GP Lond. Prev: Res. SHO Obst. Bearstead Hosp. Stoke Newington.

PAUN, Santdeep Harilal 4 Sudbury Court Drive, Harrow HA1 3TA — MB BS 1991 Lond.

PAVAGADHI, Bijal 7 Lime Tree Walk, Rickmansworth WD3 4BX — MB BS 1993 Lond.

PAVAR, Jayashri Sreenivasarao Boundfield Road Medical Centre, 103 Boundfield Road, London SE6 1PG Tel: 020 8697 2920; 2 Silverdale Drive, Mottingham, London SE9 4DH Tel: 020 8851 2259 — MB BS 1974 Marathwada; DO RCPSI 1980; DA (UK) 1978. (Avramgabad India) GP; Ophth. Med. Pract. Lond. Socs: Med. Protec. Soc. Prev: Regist./SHO (Ophth.) Arrowe Pk. Hosp. Wirral; SHO (Ophth.) Lister Hosp. Stevenage & Whipps Cross Hosp. Lond.; SHO (Anaesth.) St. Mary's Hosp. Lond.

PAVELEY, William Frederick (retired) Edina Cottage, Main St., Wilson, Melbourne, Derby DE73 1AD Tel: 01332 864717 — MB ChB Ed. 1952; DObst RCOG 1955.

PAVESI, Lucy Anne Proctor & Gamble (Technical Centres) Limited, Rusham Park Technical Centre, Whitehall Lane, Egham TW20 9NW Tel: 01784 474346 Fax: 01784 498787 Email: pavesi.l@pg.com; 72 Lavington Road, Ealing, London W13 9LR Tel: 020 85673728 — MB BChir 1991 Camb.; MA Camb. 1992; Dip. Pharm. Med. 1997; AFPM. (Camb. Univ. Roy. Free Hosp. Lond.) p/t Med. Adviser Procter & Gamble (Technical Centres) Ltd. Socs: Assoc. Mem., faculty of pharmaceltical Med. Prev: Clin. Research Phys. Roche Products Ltd. Welwyn Garden City; SHO (Cas.) Lister Hosp. Stevenage; SHO (Med. for Elderly) Hemel Hempstead Hosp.

PAVEY, Ina Shelagh Joan Moor Park Surgery, 49 Garstang Road, Preston PR1 1LB Tel: 01772 252077 Fax: 01772 885451; Bridge House, Knowle Green, Longridge, Preston PR3 2YN Tel: 01254 878235 — MB BS 1968 Lond. (Lond. Hosp.) Prev: Ho. Surg. & Ho. Phys. Roy. Vict. Hosp. Folkestone.

PAVEY, Kevin Michael Francis Gordon Stonebridge Surgery, Preston Road, Longridge, Preston PR3 3AP Tel: 01772 783271 Fax: 01772 782836 — MB BS 1968 Lond.; MRCGP 1977. (Lond. Hosp.)

PAVEY

Hosp. Practitioner, Rheum., Roy. Preston Hosp. Prev: SHO (O & G), SHO (Paediat.) & SHO Emerg. & Accid. Dept.; Preston Roy. Infirm.

PAVEY, Susan Kate 64 Manor Road, Barnet EN5 2LG Tel: 020 8449 1805 — MB ChB 1994 Glas.; BA (Hons.) Medieval & Modern Hist. Birm. 1986. SHO (Emerg.) Roy. Perth Hosp. Perth, W. Austral. Prev: Ho. Off. Dumfries & Galloway Roy. Infirm.

PAVEY-SMITH, John Holmacre, Park End Road, Workington CA14 4DE Tel: 01900 603020 — MRCS Eng. LRCP Lond. 1946. (Camb. & St. Bart.) Admiralty Surg., Agent & Police Surg. Prev: Ho. Surg. Harlow Wood Orthop. Hosp. Mansfield; Orthop. Ho. Surg. St. Bart. Hosp.; O & G Ho. Surg. Gen. Hosp. Harrogate.

PAVIER, Peter Colin (retired) The Health Centre, High Street, Arnold, Nottingham NG5 7BG Tel: 0115 926 7257 — MB BS 1960 Lond.

***PAVIOUR, Dominic Curtis** 62 Burges Road, Thorpe Bay, Southend-on-Sea SS1 3HT — MB BS 1998 Lond.; MB BS Lond 1998.

PAVIS, Hilary Margaret Hayward House, Macmillan Specialist Palliative Care Unit, Nottingham City Hospital NHS Trust, Nottingham NG5 1PB; 12 Old Hall Close, Calveton, Nottingham NG14 6PU — BM BCh 1982 Oxf.; MA Oxf. 1983; DRCOG 1991; MRCGP 1995. (Oxford University) Prev: SHO (Psychiat.) Fulbourn Hosp. Camb.; SHO (Gen. Med.) Roy. Sussex Co. Hosp.; Ho. Off. Nuffield (Surg.) John Radcliffe Hosp. Oxf.

PAVITT, Jane Anne Orchard Medical Practice, Orchard Street, Ipswich IP4 2PU Tel: 01473 213261 — MB BS 1976 Lond.; DCH Eng. 1978.

PAVLIDIS, Sotira 12 Saundersfoot Way, Oakwood, Derby DE21 2RH — MD Brussels 1980; Dip Trop. Med. Univ. Antwerpen (Belgium) 1980. (Faculty of Medicine - University of Brussels)

PAVLOU, Mr Criton 48 Wimpole Street, London W1M 7DG Tel: 020 7935 7886 Fax: 020 7935 7886; Manor Lodge, 37 College Road, London SE21 7BA — MB BS 1963 Lond.; FRCS Ed. 1973; FRCOG 1991, M 1970. (Middlx.) Indep. O & G Lond. Socs: Fell. Roy. Soc. Med.; BMA. Prev: Hon. Sen. Regist. (O & G) Qu. Charlotte Hosp. Wom. Lond.; SHO & Regist. (O & G) Hammersmith Hosp. Lond.

***PAVLOU, Philip Theoklis** 23 Woodcote Close, Enfield EN3 4NZ — MB BS 1998 Lond.; MB BS Lond 1998.

PAVLOU, Stelios Chase Farm Hospital NHS Trust, The Ridgeway, Enfield EN2 8JL Tel: 020 8366 6600; 13 Bancroft Avenue, East Finchley, London N2 0AR Tel: 020 8340 0777 — Ptychio latrikes 1976 Athens; T(Anaes.) 1994. Cons. Anaesth. Chase Farm Hosp. NHS Trust. Socs: Assn. Anaesth.; Obst. Anaesth. Assn.; BMA.

PAVORD, Ian Douglas Glenfield Hospital NHS Trust, Groby Road, Leicester LE3 9QP Tel: 0116 287 1471 Fax: 0116 236 7768; 17 Maplewell Road, Woodhouse Eaves, Loughborough LE12 8RG Tel: 01509 890927 Email: pavord@aol.com — MB BS 1984 Lond.; DM Nottm. 1992; MRCP (UK) 1987; FRCP FRCP Lond 2000. (Westm.) Cons. Phys. Glenfield Hosp. Leicester; Hon. Sen. Lect. Univ. Leics. Prev: Lect. & Hon. Sen. Regist. (Respirat. Med.) City Hosp. Nottm.; Clin. Fell. St. Josephs Hosp. McMaster Univ. Hamilton, Canada; Research Fell. (Respirat. Med.) City Hosp. Nottm.

PAVORD, Susannah Ruth Department of Haematology, Leicester Royal Infirmary, Leicester LE1 5WW; 17 Maplewell Road, Woodhouse Eaves, Leicester LE12 8RG — MB ChB 1988 Leic.; MRCP (UK) 1991; MRCPath 1997. p/t Cons. (Haemat.) & Sen. Lect. In Med. Educ. Socs: Brit. Soc. Haematol.; Brit. Soc. Homeo. & Throm. Prev: Clin. Fell. McMasters Univ. Hamilton, Ontario, Canada; Regist. (Haemat.) Leicester Roy. Infirm.; SHO Rotat. (Med.) Leicester Hosps.

***PAVY, Corinne Rose** 17 Circus, Bath BA1 2ET — BM 1994 Soton.

PAW, Henry Gee Wai 17 Mander Way, Cambridge CB1 7SF Tel: 01223 411806 — MB BS Newc. 1990; BPharm (1st cl.) Cardiff 1984; FRCA 1994; MRPharmS 1985; DA (UK) 1992. (Newc.-u-Tyne) Specialist Regist. (Anaesth.) Norf. & Norwich Hosp. Prev: Regist. (Anaesth.) Addenbrooke's, Papworth & P'boro. Dist. Hosp.; Specialist Regist. (Anaesth.) Jas. Paget Hosp. Gt. Yarmouth.

PAW, Jayantilal Devji Pleck Health Centre, 16 Oxford Street, Pleck, Walsall WS2 9HY Tel: 01922 647660 Fax: 01922 629251; Jay Nivas, 123 Longwood Road, Aldridge, Walsall WS9 0TB Tel: 01922 629251 Fax: 01922 633397 — MB BS 1960 Poona. (B.J. Med. Coll.) Prev: Police Surg. Walsall; Med. Off. Govt. Hosps. Uganda.; Police Surg. Uganda Govt.

PAW, Rajan Chimanlal 54 Eastlands Road, Birmingham B13 9RG Email: rajan@rpaw.freeserve.co.uk — MB ChB 1997 Birm.

PAWA, Chandra Mohan Fieldway Surgery, 15A Danebury, New Addington, Croydon CR0 9EU Tel: 01689 84166 Fax: 01689 800643; 7 Pampisford Road, Purley CR8 2NG Tel: 020 8660 0641 Fax: 01689 800643 — MB BS 1965 Lucknow; MSc (Gen. Pract.) Lond. 1991. (G.S.V.M. Med. Coll. Kanpur) Clin. Asst. (Diabetes & Endocrinol.) St. Hellier Hosp. Carshalton. Prev: Regist. (Med.) Markfield Hosp.; SHO & Regist. (Gen. Med.) Kilton Hosp. Worksop.

PAWADE, Mr Ashwinikumar Madhukar The Red Lodge, Abbots Leigh Road, Leigh Woods, Bristol BS8 3PX Tel: 0117 973 3473 — MB BS 1978 Nagpur; FRCS Ed. 1987. Cons. Paediat. (Cardiac Surg.) Roy. Bristol Hosp. for Sick Childr.; Cons. Cardiac Surg. Bristol Roy. Infirm.; Cons. & Sen. Lect. (Surg.) Univ. Bristol. Prev: Dep. Dir. Vict.n Paediat. Cardiac Surgic. Unit Roy. Childr. Hosp. Melbourne, Austral.

***PAWAR, Jo Eluned** 5 Stanley Pl, Cadoxton, Neath SA10 8BE — MB ChB 1997 Birm.

PAWAR, Mr Narendrasing Mohansing Central Park Surgery, Balfour St., Leyland, Preston PR25 2TD Tel: 01772 421205 Fax: 01772 623885 — MB BS 1976 Bombay; MS Bombay 1980, MB BS 1976; FRCS Glas. 1985; T(GP) 1991. Prev: Regist. (Gen. Surg.) GT Hosp., Bombay; Regist. (Paediat. Surg.) Childr. Hosp. Dub.; Chief Resid. (Surg.) Salmaniya Med. Centre, Bahrain.

PAWAR, Pratap Baburao (retired) 5 Stanley Place, Cadoxton, Neath SA10 8BE Tel: 01639 56659 — MB BS Bombay 1961; MRCPI 1972; FRCPI 1991. Cons. Phys. (Geriat. Med.) Cymla Hosp. Neath.

PAWAROO, Lalldhar Pawaroo and Partners, The Old Forge Surgery, Pallion Pk, Pallion, Sunderland SR4 6QE Tel: 0191 510 9393 Fax: 0191 510 9595; 1 Nookside, Grindon, Sunderland SR4 8PH Tel: 0191 528 55320 — MB ChB 1969 Glas. (Glas.)

PAWLEY, Ann Frances Shepherd Spring Medical Centre, Cricketers Way, Andover SP10 5DE Tel: 01264 361126 Fax: 01264 350138 — MB ChB 1985 Bristol; MRCGP 1990; DRCOG 1992. Prev: Trainee GP Nailsworth Glos.

PAWLEY, Gillian Ruth 29 Stafford Road, Warrington WA4 6RP — MB BS 1991 Lond.

PAWLEY, Jeremy John 12 Spinney Drive, Great Shelford, Cambridge CB2 5LY; Flat 5, 9 Kingston Hill, Kingston upon Thames KT2 7PN Tel: 020 8541 1474 — MB BS 1991 Lond.; DRCOG 1996; MRCGP 1997. (King's College School of Medicine and Dentistry)

PAWLEY, Martin Kenneth 30 Blaen-y-Coed, Radyr, Cardiff CF15 8RL Tel: 029 2084 3140; 30 Blaen-y-Coed, Radyr, Cardiff CF15 8RL Tel: 029 2084 3140 — MB BCh 1980 Wales. (Welsh Nat. Sch. of Med. Cardiff)

***PAWLEY, Susannah Elisabeth** 21 Cobbold Av, Eastbourne BN21 1UY — BM 1997 Soton.

PAWLIKOWSKI, Teresa Rosalia Barbara 2 Scarsdale Place, London W8 5SX Tel: 020 7938 1885; 6 Poplar Grove, London W6 7RE — MB BS 1978 Lond.; BSc, MB BS Lond. 1978. (Univ. Coll. Hosp.) Sen. Lect. (Dept. Primary Care & Pop. Scis.) Roy. Free & Univ. Coll. Med. Sch. Lond.

PAWLOWICZ, Anna Queen Elizabeth Hospital, Gayton Road, King's Lynn PE30 4ET Tel: 01553 613712 Fax: 01553 613984 Email: anna.pawlowicz@klshosp.anglox.nhs.uk — Lekarz 1985 Warsaw; MRCP (UK) 1995; FRCP 2000. Cons. Gen. Med. with an interest in Respirat. Med. Socs: BMA; E. Angl. Thoracic Soc.

PAWLOWICZ, Wladyslaw, OBE (retired) 50 The Vineyard, Richmond TW10 6AT — MD 1925 Warsaw.

PAWLOWSKA, Elzbieta St Johns Medical Centre, 287A Lewisham Way, London SE4 1XF — MRCS Eng. LRCP Lond. 1985; DRCOG 1989.

PAWSEY, Stephen David 21 The Orchard, Virginia Water GU25 4DT — MB BS 1988 Lond.; FRCA 1993. Clin. Research Phys. Upjohn Laborat. Europe. Prev: Regist. Rotat. (Anaesth.) NE Thames Region; SHO (Anaesth.) St. Mary's Hosp. Lond.

PAWSON, Margaret Elizabeth (retired) 3 St John's Ave, Filey YO14 9AZ Tel: 01723 513042 Email: postmaster@mepawson.demon.co.uk — MB ChB 1959 Ed.; LRCP

LRCS Ed. LRFPS Glas. 1959; DObst RCOG 1961. Prev: Med. Off. Kalyani Hosp. (Ch. of S. India) Mylapore, India.

PAWSON, Michael Edward 55 Wimpole Street, London W1G 8YL Tel: 020 7935 1964 Email: mike.pawson@virgin.net; Braywood House, Drift Road, Windsor SL4 4RR Tel: 01344 882670 Email: mike.pawson.@virgin.net — MB BS Lond. 1962; MRCS Eng. LRCP Lond. 1962; FRCOG 1983, M 1970; DObst RCOG 1964. (St. Thos.) p/t Cons. Chelsea & W.m. Hosp. Lond.; Examr. Univ. Lond. & Roy. Coll. Obst. & Gyn.; UK Represen. Comm. ISPOG. Socs: Brit. Fertil. Soc.; Brit. Holistic Med. Assn.; Past Chairm. Brit. Soc. of Psychosomatic Obst., Gyn. & Androl. Prev: Regist. (O & G) King Edwd. VII Hosp. Windsor & Upton Hosp. Slough; SHO Qu. Charlotte's Hosp. Lond.

PAWSON, Rachel NBS Oxford Centre, John Radcliffe Hospital, Headington, Oxford OX3 9DU Tel: 01865 447910 Email: rachael.pawson@nbs.nhs.uk — MB BS 1988 Lond.; MD 1998; BSc (Hons.) Lond. 1985; MRCP (UK) 1991; MRCPath 1998. (King's College Hospital London) Cons. (Haemat.), Nat. Blood Serv. & John Radcliffe Hosp., Oxf.

PAWSON, Robert Hugh Belford Medical Practice, The Belford Health Centre, Croftfield, Belford NE70 7ER Tel: 01668 213738 Fax: 01668 213072; Redeford, South Road, Belford NE70 7DP Tel: 01668 213384 — MB ChB 1970 St. And.; MRCGP 1974; DObst RCOG 1972.

PAWSON, Roger Michael Mitchell and Partners, The Park Surgery, Old Tetbury Road, Cirencester GL7 1US Tel: 01285 654733 Fax: 01285 641408 — BM BCh 1977 Oxf. GP Cirencester; Clin. Asst. in Psychiat. & Old Age Psychiat. Prev: Trainee GP Swindon VTS; Ho. Phys. Radcliffe Infirm. & Ch.ill Hosp. Oxf.

PAWULSKI, Yvonne Maria 10 Hudsons, Tadworth KT20 5TZ — MB BS 1986 Lond. SHO (ENT) Wexham Pk. Hosp. Slough.

PAXTON, Adam Guy North Hykeham Health Centre, Moor Lane, North Hykeham, Lincoln LN6 9BA Tel: 01522 682848 Fax: 01522 697930; 9 Thurlby Road, Bassingham, Lincoln LN5 9LG — MB ChB 1983 Leic.

PAXTON, Albert Etherington 27 Deneside Avenue, Gateshead NE9 6AD Tel: 0191 876545 — MB BS 1935 Durh.; BHyg., DPH 1937. (Durh.) Med. Supt. Qu. Eliz. & Bensham Gen. Hosps. Gateshead; Cons. Phys. (Infec. Dis.) Regional Infec. Dis. Unit Qu. Eliz. Hosp. Gateshead. Prev: Lt.-Col. RAMC.

PAXTON, Ann Margaret (retired) Birchwood Cottage, Birchwood, Chard TA20 3QH — MB BS 1962 Lond.; MRCS Eng. LRCP Lond. 1962; MRCPath 1970. Prev: Cons. Haemat. E. Surrey & Mid Downs HA's., St. Bart. Hosp. Lond. & Oncol. Unit. Hackney Hosp.

PAXTON, Christopher Patrick Charles Courtside Surgery, Kennedy Way, Yate, Bristol BS37 4DQ Tel: 01454 313874 Fax: 01454 327110; Coppinhall, 23 Church Lane, Old Sodbury, Bristol BS37 6NB — MB BS 1979 Lond.; DRCOG 1983; LFHom. 1998. (St. Mary's Hosp. Lond.)

PAXTON, George Clifford Wards Medical Practice, 25 Dundonald Road, Kilmarnock KA1 1RU Tel: 01563 526514 Fax: 01563 573558 — MB ChB 1990 Glas.; MRCGP 1994; DRCOG 1994; DFFP 1993. Socs: BMA. Prev: Trainee GP Lanarksh.

PAXTON, Jane Ralston 4 Seaford Street, Kilmarnock KA1 2DA Tel: 01563 33911 — MB ChB 1992 Glas.; BSc (1st cl. Hons.) Pharmacol. Glas. 1989, MB ChB 1992. SHO (Histopath.) Stobhill Hosp. Glas. Prev: Ho. Off. (Surg. & Med.) Paisley Roy. Alexandra Hosp. & Glas. Roy. Infirm.

PAXTON, Lionel Douglas Dept. of Clinical Anaesthesia, Royal Victoria Hospital, Grosvenor Road, Belfast BT12 6BA Tel: 01232 240503 Fax: 01232 325725; 12 Waterloo Road, Lisburn BT27 5NW — MB ChB 1984 Zimbabwe; LRCP LRCS Ed. LRCPS Glas. 1986; FFA RCSI 1992. Cons. (Cardio thoracic anaesth.).

PAXTON, Michael John The Penryn Surgery, Saracen Way, Penryn TR10 8HX Tel: 01326 372502 Fax: 01326 378126; Chy Worval, Old Tram Road, Devoran, Truro TR3 6NF Tel: 01872 863950 — MB 1974 Camb.; BChir 1973. (Camb. & Middlx.) Prev: SHO (O & G) & SHO (A & E) Ipswich Hosp.

PAXTON, Paul James Lensfield Medical Practice, 48 Lensfield Road, Cambridge CB2 1EH Tel: 01223 352779 Fax: 01223 566930 — MB ChB 1975 Birm; MRCGP 1979; DRCOG 1977. Course Organiser Addenbrooke's Hosp. VTS Scheme.

PAXTON, Ross Meuros (retired) Caradon Villa, Downgate, Upton Cross, Liskeard PL14 5AJ — MB BS 1967 Lond.; FRCR 1975; FFR

1974; DMRD Eng. 1971. Cons. Neuroradiol. Plymouth Hosps. NHS Trust.

***PAY, Charlotte Louise** Hode Oast, Hode Lane, Patrixbourne, Canterbury CT4 5DH — MB BS 1996 Lond.

PAY, Graham Victor Watling Street Surgery, 25 Watling St., Canterbury CT1 2UD Tel: 01227 463570 — MRCS Eng. LRCP Lond. 1968. (Guy's) Prev: SHO (Gen. Med.), SHO (Obst.) & SHO (Gen. Surg.) Kent & Canterbury; Hosp.

PAY, Jennifer Anne Hode Oast House, Hode Lane, Patrixbourne, Canterbury CT4 5DH — MB BS 1967 Lond.; MRCS Eng. LRCP Lond. 1967. (Char. Cross) Clin. Asst. (Ophth.) Kent & Canterbury Hosp. Prev: Clin. Asst. (Ophth.) Greenwich Dist. Hosp.; Jun. Regist. (Ophth.) Guy's Hosp. Lond.; Ho. Phys. & Ho. Surg. Char. Cross Hosp. Lond.

***PAY, Rachel Karen** 4 Patcham Grange, Grangeways, Brighton BN1 8UR — MB BS 1998 Lond.; MB BS Lond 1998.

PAYAN, José d'Aumale Cottages, 19 The Embankment, Twickenham TW1 3DU Tel: 020 8892 9231 — MB BS 1956 Lond.; FRCP Lond. 1980; MRCP (UK) 1961. (Guy's) Emerit. Cons. Clin. Neurophysiol. Guy's Hosp. Lond. Socs: Fell. Roy. Soc. Med.; Assn. Brit. Neurol. Prev: Sen. Regist. (Clin. Neurophysiol.) Nat. Hosp. Nerv. Dis. Qu. Sq.; Regist. (EMG) RigsHosp.et, Copenhagen; Fell. (Neurol.) Stanford Univ., USA.

PAYKEL, Professor Eugene Stern Department of Psychiatry, University of Cambridge, Addenbrooke's Hospital, Cambridge CB2 2QQ Tel: 01223 336960 Fax: 01223 336968 — MB ChB 1956 Otago; MA Camb. 1986, MD 1988; MD Otago 1971; FRCP Ed. 1978, M 1960; FRCP Lond. 1977, M 1961; FRCPsych 1977, M 1971; DPM Lond. 1965; F Med Sci 1998. (Otago) Prof. Psychiat. Univ. Camb.; Fell. Gonville & Caius Coll.; Edr. Psychol. Med. Prev: Prof. Psychiat. St. Geo. Hosp. Med. Sch. (Univ. Lond.); Vice-Pres. RCPsych.; Pres. Brit. Assn. Psychopharmacol.

PAYLER, David Kingsley (retired) The Court Road Surgery, Court Road, Malvern WR14 3BL Tel: 01684 573161 Fax: 01684 561593 — MB BS 1959 Lond.; MRCS Eng. LRCP Lond. 1959; DObst RCOG 1964. Hosp. Pract. (Surg.) Worcester Roy. Infirm.; Med. Off. Malvern Coll.

PAYLING, Sandra Mary The Surgery, Bach Victoria Terrace, Thiochly, Newcastle upon Tyne NE18 0PF Tel: 0191 267 4005; 17 Algernon Terrace, Wylam NE41 8AX Tel: 01661 85281 — MB BS 1964 Durh. (Newc.) Socs: BMA. Prev: Ho. Off. (Paediat.) & Ho. Off. (Gen. Med.) Newc. Gen. Hosp.; Med. Off. Stud. Health Serv. Newc. Univ.

PAYMASTER, Nalin Jagmohandas The Department of Community Dental Health, Ground Floor, G Block, St Catherine's Hospital, Church Road, Birkenhead CH42 0LQ Tel: 0151 604 7295 Fax: 0151 604 0085; The Close, Chantry Walk, Lower Village, Heswall, Wirral CH60 8PX Tel: 0151 342 4143 — MB BS 1955 Bombay; DA Eng. 1960; DA Bombay 1958; FRCA Eng. 1961. (G.S. Med. Coll. Bombay) Cons. (Anaesth.) Wirral & W. Chesh. Community NHS Trust. Socs: Liverp. Soc. Anaesth.; Birkenhead Med. Soc. Prev: Cons. Anaesth. Wirral Hosp. NHS Trust Mersey RHA; Fell. Anaesthesiol. Hosp. of Univ. Penna Philadelphia, Pa., USA; Sen. Regist. (Anaesth.) Newc. RHB.

***PAYNE, Alison Judith** Department of Orthopaedics, Royal Hallamshire Hospital, Sheffield S10 Tel: 0114 271 1900; 71 Southgrove Road, Sheffield S10 2NP — MB ChB 1995 Sheff.; MB ChB (Hons.) Med. Sheff. 1995; BSc (Hons.) Pharmacol. & Chem. Sheff. 1989.

PAYNE, Amanda Community Health Branch, Broyle Road, Chichester PO19 4YD Tel: 01243 781111; Ranfold Farm House, Toat Hill, Slinfold, Horsham RH13 7RL — MB BS Lond. 1977; MRCS Eng. LRCP Lond. 1976; DRCOG 1979. (Guy's) Clin. Med. Off. (Priority Care) Worthing.

PAYNE, Andrew John Broadmoor Hospital, Crowthorne RG45 7EG Tel: 01344 773111 — MB BS 1984 Lond.; BSc Lond. 1981; MRCP (UK) 1988; MRCPsych 1991. Clin. Director & Cons. Forens. Psychiat. BRd.moor Hosp. Prev: Sen. Regist. & Regist. (Forens. Psychiat.) Roy. Bethlem & Maudsley Hosp. Lond.; SHO Rotat. (Med.) Walsgrave Hosp. Coventry.

PAYNE, Arthur Dudley, SBStJ (retired) Randwick, Amroth, Narberth SA67 8NQ — MA Camb. 1942, MB BChir. 1940; MRCS Eng. LRCP Lond. 1943. Prev: Capt. RAMC (Mentioned in Despatches).

PAYNE

PAYNE, Brian Victor Norfolk and Norwich, University Hospital, Colney Lane NR4 7UY Tel: 01603 288000 Email: brian.payne@norfolk-norwich.thenhs.com; 15 Wentworth Green, Norwich NR4 6AE Tel: 01603 452393 — MB BChir 1970 Camb.; FRCP Lond. 1989; MRCP (UK) 1974. (Camb. & Middlx.) Cons. Phys. the Elderly Norf. & Norwich Univ. hosp NHS trust. Socs: Brit. Geriat.s Soc. Prev: Sen. Regist. (Geriat. Med.) Chesterton Hosp. Camb.

PAYNE, Miss Caroline Elizabeth 22 Barnhill, Pinner HA5 2SX — MB BS 1994 Lond.; BSc (Hons.) Lond. 1989; FRCS (Eng) 1998. (Guy's & St. Thos.)

PAYNE, Christopher James Irving Avon Health Authority, King Square House, King Square, Bristol BS2 8EE Tel: 01630 654064 — MB ChB 1978 Bristol; MFPHM 2000; MRCGP 1982; MPH Wales 1998. Cons. in Pub. Health Med., Avon Health Auth.

PAYNE, Christopher Oliver Bermondsey and Lansdowne Medical Centre, The Surgery, Decima Street, London SE1 4QX Tel: 020 7407 0752 Fax: 020 7378 8209; 90 Kidbrooke Park Road, Blackheath, London SE3 0DX — MB BS 1963 Lond.; MRCP (UK) 1971; MRCS Eng. LRCP Lond. 1963. (King's Coll. Hosp.) Socs: W. Kent M-C Soc.; BMA. Prev: Dir. Community Health Servs. Lewisham & N. S.wark HA; Cons. Phys. The Christian Hosp. Shiraz, Iran; Med. Specialist RAF Hosp. Nocton Hall.

PAYNE, Christopher Robert Consulting Suite, Alexandra Hospital, Mill Lane, Cheadle SK8 2PX Tel: 0161 428 3656 Fax: 0161 282 5005; Ramillies, 2 Marlborough Road, Bowdon, Altrincham WA14 2RT Tel: 0161 928 0177 Fax: 0161 331 6401 — MB ChB 1971 Manch.; FRCP Lond. 1992; MRCP (UK) 1976; DObst RCOG 1975. Cons. Phys. Tameside Gen. Hosp., Ashton-under-Lyne. Socs: Brit. Thorac. Soc.; BMA. Prev: Sen. Regist. (Med.) Manch. Roy. Infirm.; Sen. Regist. (Med.) Withington Hosp. Manch.; Regist. (Med.) Brompton Hosp. Lond.

PAYNE, Clare Elisabeth Butlers Farm, Chittlehamholt, Umberleigh EX37 9NT — MB BChir 1985 Camb. (Univ. & Westm. Hosp. Camb.) Clin. Asst. (Genitourin. Med.) N. Devon Health Care Trust Barnstaple, Roy. Devon & Exeter Health Care Trust, Exeter & Family Plann. N. Devon Health Ca. Prev: Family Plann. N. Devon HA.

***PAYNE, David Anthony** 4 Murrayfield, Bamford, Rochdale OL11 5UQ — MB ChB 1994 Leic.

PAYNE, David John The Surgery, The Street, Shorne, Gravesend DA12 3EA Tel: 01474 355331; 11 Millfield Drive, Northfleet, Gravesend DA11 8BH — MB BS 1988 Lond.; MRCGP 1992; DRCOG 1990.

PAYNE, Donald Neil Russell Glendevon, Nately Scures, Basingstoke RG27 9JS Tel: 01256 762661 — MB BChir 1990 Camb.; BA (Hons.) Camb. 1987; MRCP (UK) 1993. (Univ. Camb. & Lond. Hosp. Med. Coll.) Specialist Regist. (Paediat.) Roy. Brompton Hosp. Lond.

PAYNE, Elizabeth Heather 4 Glyncoed Road, Glyncoed, Cardiff CF23 7DX — MB BS 1980 Lond. Socs: Card. Med. Soc.; Hist. of Med. Soc. Wales.

PAYNE, Elizabeth Mary Margaret (retired) 23 Blenheim Road, Penylan, Cardiff CF23 5DS Tel: 01222 214067 — MB BCh 1950 Wales; BSc Wales 1947.

PAYNE, Elizabeth Susan Princess of Wales Womens Unit, Birmingham Heartlands Hospital, Bordesley Green E., Birmingham B9 5SS Tel: 0121 685 5951 — MD 1991 Birm.; MB ChB 1977; MRCOG 1983; FRCOG 1997. (Birmingham) Cons. O & G Birm. Heartlands Hosp. Socs: Brit. Menopause Soc.; Brit. Fertillity Soc.; Brit. Soc. paediatric and Adolesc. Gyn. Prev: Cons. O & G; City Hosp. NHS Trust 1990-1995.

***PAYNE, Elspeth Margaret Conroy** 17 Deanburn Road, Linlithgow EH49 6EY — MB ChB 1997 Glas.

PAYNE, Emma Clare Highcliffe, Eden Park, Lancaster LA1 4SJ — MB BS 1991 Newc.

PAYNE, Eric Eustace 23 Blenheim Road, Penylan, Cardiff CF23 5DS Tel: 029 2021 4067 — MB BCh 1953 Wales; BSc Wales 1950, MD 1958. (Welsh Nat. Sch. Med. Cardiff) Indep. Med. Pract. Cardiff; Research Investig. Cardiff; Hon. Med. Off. Cardiff Inst. Blind; Hon. Curator Museum Hist. Med. UWCM. Socs: Cardiff Med. Soc. Prev: Sen. Lect. (Path.) Welsh Nat. Sch. Med. Cardiff.

PAYNE, Eric Guy Mark 20 Coppice Walk, Cheswick Green, Shirley, Solihull B90 4HY Tel: 015646 2186 Fax: 015646 3337 — MB BS 1977 Lond.; MA Oxf. 1978. (Westm.) Dir. Vict. Homoeop. & Allergy Clinic Solihull; Tutor (Environm. Med.) Breakspear Hosp. Watford; Clin. Asst. (A & E Dept.) Birm. Gen. Hosp. Prev: Solihull FDC Serv. Comm. Represent. Solihull LMC Mem.; GP Represent. Solihull Community Unit Managem. Gp.

PAYNE, Fiona Beverley The Cottage, Duck Lane, Kenn, Clevedon BS21 6TP — MB ChB 1988 Bristol; DRCPath 1993. Clin. Research Fell. (Path.) St Michael's Hosp. Bristol. Prev: Regist. (Histopath.) Leics. Roy. Infirm.

PAYNE, Fiona Margaret The Surgery, 327D Upper Richmond Road, London SW15 6SU Tel: 020 8788 6002 Fax: 020 8789 8568 — MB BS 1989 Lond. (St. Thomas's Hosp.)

PAYNE, Geoffrey Paul Ingleby The New Surgery, Lindo Close, Chesham HP5 2JN Tel: 01494 782262; Winstons, Weedon Hill, Hyde Heath, Amersham HP6 5RN — BM BCh 1975 Oxf.; MA Oxf. 1975; MRCP (UK) 1977; MRCGP 1979; DRCOG 1979; DCH Eng. 1978. GP; Med. Adviser, Bucks HA; Bd. Mem. Chiltern PCG. Socs: Fell.Roy. Soc. of Med.

PAYNE, George Stuart Alford Medical Practice, 2 Gordon Road, Alford AB33 8AL Tel: 019755 62253 Fax: 019755 62613; Suilven, The Lang Stracht, Alford AB33 8AW Tel: 019755 62976 — MB ChB 1976 Aberd.; MRCGP 1982; DRCOG 1980.

PAYNE, Gillian Elizabeth Doncaster Royal Infirmary, Armthorpe Lane, Doncaster DN2 5LZ Tel: 01302 366666; 6 Oaklands, Warning Tongue Lane, Bessacarr, Doncaster DN4 6XW — MB ChB 1987 Leeds; MD Leic. 1996; MRCP (UK) 1990. (Univ. Leeds) Cons. Gen. Phys. (Cardiol.) Doncaster Roy. Infirm. Prev: Research Regist. (Cardiol.) Glenfield Hosp. Leicester.

PAYNE, Graham Spencer Yeovil District Hospital, Higher Kingston, Yeovil BA21 4AT — MB ChB 1974 Bristol.

PAYNE, Heather Ann 117 Aveling Park Road, Walthamstow, London E17 4NS Tel: 020 8527 4071 — MB BS 1983 Lond.; MRCP (UK) 1988; FRCR. (St. Mary's Hospital Medical School) Cons. (Clin. Oncoloy) The Middlx. Hosp. Lond. Prev: Sen. Regist. (Clin. Oncol.) The Middlx. Hosp. Lond.; Sen. Regist. Mt. Vernon Hosp.

PAYNE, Mr Ian William (retired) Swallow Cottage, Teigngrace, Newton Abbot TQ12 6QW — MB ChB 1946 Manch.; FRCS Eng. 1953; DOMS Eng. 1949. Prev: Surg. Roy. Eye Infirm. Plymouth.

PAYNE, Jacqueline Dorfold Cottage, Wrexham Road, Acton, Nantwich CW5 8LP — MB BCh BAO 1980 NUI; FFA RCS Eng. 1987.

PAYNE, Jacqueline Station House Surgery, Station Road, Kendal LA9 6SA Tel: 01539 722660 Fax: 01539 734845 — MB BS 1986 Newc.; MRCGP 1990; DRCOG 1990; Cert. Family Plann. JCC 1990.

PAYNE, Jacqueline Mary Pound House Surgery, 8 The Green, Wooburn Green, High Wycombe HP10 0EE; 70 Westwood Drive, Little Chalfont, Amersham HP6 6RW — MB BS 1989 Lond.; BSc (Hons.) Lond. 1986; MRCGP 1993; DRCOG 1993; DCH RCP Lond. 1992.

PAYNE, Professor James Patrick, OStJ 36 Raymond Road, Wimbledon, London SW19 4AP Tel: 020 8946 8456 — MB ChB Ed. 1946; DSc (Med.) Lond. 1988; MD (Hon. Causa) Uppsala 1984; FRCA 1992; FFA RCS Eng. 1954; DA Eng. 1951. (Ed.) Emerit. Prof. Anaesth. RCS Eng.; Emerit. Prof. Anaesth. Univ. Lond. (Lond. Hosp. Med. Coll.); Hon. Cons. Anaesth. Lond. Hosp. & St. Peter's Hosps. Lond. Socs: Fell BMA (Ex-Chairm. Merton & Sutton Div.); Hon. Mem. (Ex-Vice Pres.) Assn. Anaesth.; Liveryman Soc. Apoth. Lond. Prev: Lect. (Anaesth.) Postgrad. Med. Sch.; Research Asst. (Anaesth.) Univ. Manch.; Sen. Regist. (Anaesth.) Roy. Infirm. Edin.

PAYNE, John Allan Greenscombe House, Luckett, Callington PL17 8LF Tel: 01579 370149 Fax: 01579 370149 — MB BS Lond. 1950; LMSSA Lond. 1949; DObst RCOG 1955. (Guy's) Socs: Guild Psychother.; Affil. RCPsych. Prev: Dir. Stud. Health Serv. Lond. Sch. Economics; Asst. Ho. Surg. & Out Pat. Off. Guy's Hosp. Lond.; Stud. Health Phys. Univ. Sussex.

PAYNE, Mr John Gordon Fordie House, 82 Sloane St., London SW1X 9PA Tel: 020 7259 6308 Fax: 020 7225 0914; 10 Moore Street, London SW3 2QN Tel: 020 7584 2035 Fax: 020 7225 0914 — MB BS 1968 Lond.; MD Lond. 1976; FRCS Eng. 1974; MRCS Eng. LRCP Lond. 1968. (Guy's) Cons. Surg. Qu. Mary's Sidcup NHS Trust; Mem. Ct. Examrs. RCS Extern. Examr. Qu. Univ. Belf.; Hon. Surg. Tutor Char. Cross & W.m. Med. Sch. Lond. Socs: Coloproctol. Soc.; Internat. Soc. Univ. Colon & Rectal Surg. Prev: Assoc. Staff Surg. (Colon & Rectal Dis.) Ochsner Med. Inst. New Orleans; Sen. Regist. (Surg.) St. Mark's Hosp. & Guy's Hosp. Lond.

PAYNE, John Halliday Rowland Monnow St, Monmouth NP25 3EQ Tel: 01600 713811; Ingleside, Lone Lane, Penallt, Monmouth NP25 4AJ Tel: 01600 712170 — MB BS 1972 Lond.; MRACGP 1978; DCH 1977 Eng.; MRCS 1972 Eng.; LRCP 1972 Lond.; MRCS Eng. LRCP Lond. 1972; MRCGP 1978; DCH Eng. 1977. (St. Bart.) Clin. Asst. (Geriat.) Bridges Day Hosp. Monmouth.

PAYNE, John Martin Victor Barton House Surgery, Barton House, Beaminster DT8 3EQ Tel: 01308 862233 Fax: 01308 863785 — MB BS 1978 Lond.; MRCP (UK) 1981; MRCGP 1986.

PAYNE, John Nicholas School of Health and Related Research, Sheffield University, 30 Regent St., Sheffield S1 4DG Tel: 0114 222 0819 Fax: 0114 272 4095 Email: n.payne@sheffield.ac.uk — BM BCh 1977 Oxf.; PhD Sheff. 1987; MA Camb. 1978; FFPHM RCP (UK) 1998; FFA RCS Eng. 1981. (Oxford University) Sen. Lect. (Pub. Health Med.) Sheff. Univ.; Hon. Cons. Pub. Health Med. Sheff. HA. Prev: Cons. Pub. Health Med. Sheff. HA; Regist. (Pub. Health Med.) Trent RHA; Lect. Dept. Biomed. Sc. Univ. Sheff.

PAYNE, John Stiling The Avenue Surgery, 14 The Avenue, Warminster BA12 9AA Tel: 01985 846224; 87 Boreham Road, Warminster BA12 9JX Tel: 01985 214030 — MB ChB 1971 Bristol; DObst RCOG 1973. Prev: SHO (Psychiat.) Barrow Hosp. Bristol; Obst. Ho. Off. S.mead Gen. Hosp. Bristol.

PAYNE, Jonathan Frank Anaesthetic Department, Norfolk & Norwich Hospital, Brunswick Road, Norwich NR1 3RS Tel: 01603 287086; 15 Nursery Lane, Costessey, Norwich NR8 5BU — MB BS 1987 Lond.; FRCA 1991. (Lond.) Cons. Anaesth. Norf. & Norwich Hosp. Prev: SR (Anaesth.) Birm. Sch. Anaesth.; Clin. Fell. (Anaesth.) Childr. Hosp. Birm.; Regist. (Anaesth.) Kingston Hosp. Surrey & St. Geo. Hosp. Lond.

PAYNE, Julia Helen EMI Academic Unit, St. Catherine's Hospital, Church Raod, Birkenhead CH42 — BM BS 1992 Nottm. Clin. Lect. (Old Age Psychiat.) Univ. of L'pool; Specialist Regist. Hon. Mersey Deanery.

PAYNE, Leonard Robert (retired) 125D Beechwood Avenue, Coventry CV5 6FQ Tel: 024 7667 2406 Fax: 024 7667 2406 — MB ChB 1957 St. And.

PAYNE, Margaret Anne Breast Screening Office, Wycombe Hospital, Queen Alexandra Road, High Wycombe HP11 2TT Tel: 01494 425689; Winstons, Weedon Hill, Hyde Heath, Amersham HP6 5RN Tel: 01494 783167 — BM BCh 1975 Oxf.; MA Oxf. 1975; DCH Eng. 1978; DRCOG 1977. Assoc. Specialist (BrE. Screening & Fam. Plg.) S. Bucks. HNS Trust, High Wycombe. Prev: Clin. Med. Off. (Child Health) High Wycombe; SCMO & Clin. Co-ordinator BrE. Screening Serv. S. Bucks. NHS Trust High Wycombe.

PAYNE, Mrs Margaret Catherine (retired) Barnstones, Old Seaview Lane, Seaview PO34 5BJ — MB BS Lond. 1940; MRCS Eng. LRCP Lond. 1940.

PAYNE, Mark Nicholas Birmingham Heartlands Hospital, Bordesley Green E., Birmingham B9 5TA Tel: 0121 766 6611 Fax: 0121 753 0613; 104A Bellingdon Road, Chesham HP5 2HF Tel: 01494 785525 — MB BS 1984 Lond.; MRCP (UK) 1988. Regist. (Cardiol.) Birm. Heartlands Hosp. Prev: Regist. (Med. & Cardiol.) Selly Oak Hosp. Birm.

PAYNE, Martin Richard Department of Anaesthetics, Cumberland Infirmary, Carlisle CA2 7HY Tel: 01228 814196 — MB ChB 1977 Bristol; FFA RCS Eng. 1982; DTM & H Eng. 1987. Cons. Cumbld. Infirm. Carlisle. Socs: Eur. Soc. Regional Anaesth. Prev: Sen. Regist. Roy. Infirm. Edin.; Specialist Med. Off. (Anaesth.) Angau Memor. Hosp. Lae Papua New Guinea; Regist. (Anaesth.) Univ. Hosp. Wales, Cardiff & W.mead Centre, NSW Australia.

PAYNE, Mary Rosalind 66 Netherby Road, Edinburgh EH5 3LX Tel: 0131 552 4584 Email: dsphk@compuserve.com — MB ChB 1980 Dundee; MRCGP 1987; Cert. Family Plann. JCC 1983. Prev: Princip. GP Howden HC 1988-99; Locality Coordinator W. Lothian 1992-1997; Regist.ar (O & G) Tayside HB.

PAYNE, Michael James Butlers Farm, Chittlehamholt, Umberleigh EX37 9NT — MB BS 1985 Lond.

PAYNE, Mr Michael John, Col. late RAMC Retd. Tiree Cottage, West Ridge, Hogs Back, Seale, Farnham GU10 1JU Tel: 01252 782014 — MB BS 1966 Lond.; FRCS Ed. 1973; MRCS Eng. LRCP Lond. 1966; Dip. IMC RCS Ed. 1995. (Westm.) Cons. Gen. Surg. King. Edwd. VII Hosp. Midhurst. Socs: Fell. Assn. Surgs.; Milit. Surg. Soc.; BASO.

PAYNE, Michael Lawrence Harborne Medical Practice, 4 York Street, Harborne, Birmingham B17 0HG Tel: 0121 427 5246 — MB ChB 1979 Manch.; MRCGP 1983.

PAYNE, Michael Robert 409 City View House, 463 Bethnal Green Road, London E2 9QY Tel: 020 7729 4979 Email: doctormike.payne@virgin.net — MB BS 1990 Lond.; MRCPsych 1995. Specialist Regist. St Clements Hosp. Lond.

PAYNE, N M The Surgery, Southview Lodge, South View, Bromley BR1 3DR Tel: 020 8460 1932 Fax: 020 8323 1423.

PAYNE, Nicholas David Gerhard 57A Constantine Road, London NW3 2LP Tel: 020 7482 7122 Fax: 020 7482 7122 — MB BS 1993 Lond. (Roy. Free Hosp. Sch. Med.) Staff Grade (A & E) Lister Hosp. Stevenage.

PAYNE, Nicola Louise 6 Courtney Road, London SW19 2ED — MB BS 1992 Lond.

PAYNE, Nigel Edric Sven 10 Justice Avenue, Saltford, Bristol BS31 3DR — MB BS 1985 Lond.; FCAnaesth 1990. Cons. (Anaesth.) Guildford Roy Surrey Co. Hosp. Socs: Fell. Roy. Coll. Anaesths.

PAYNE, Paul Anthony Gullock Gloucester Road Medical Centre, Tramway House, 1A Church Road, Horfield, Bristol BS7 8SA Tel: 0117 949 7774 Fax: 0117 949 7730; The South Barn, Lower Almondsbury, Bristol BS32 4EF Tel: 01454 615553 — MB BS 1969 Lond.; MRCS Eng. LRCP Lond. 1969; DO Eng. 1972. (St. Bart.) Police Surg.; Hosp. Pract. Bristol Eye Hosp. Prev: SHO Croydon Eye Unit; Ho. Surg., Ho. Phys. & Cas. Off. Bethnal Green Hosp. Lond.

PAYNE, Mr Peter Russell (retired) The Hampshire Clinic, Basing Road, Basing, Basingstoke RG24 7AL Tel: 01256 57111 Fax: 01256 397517 — MB BCh BAO Dub. 1954; FRCS Ed. 1959; FRCOG 1979, M 1966. Prev: Cons. Gyn. Hants. Clinic Basingstoke.

PAYNE, Reginald Brian (retired) 50 North Park Avenue, Leeds LS8 1EY Tel: 0113 266 1577 Email: rbrianpayne@netscapeonline.co.uk — MB BCh 1954 Wales; PhD Leeds 1970; MD Wales 1963; FRCPath 1977, M 1965. Prev: Cons. Chem. Path. St. Jas. Univ. Hosp. Leeds.

PAYNE, Reuben Frederick (retired) Huxtable Farm, West Buckland, Barnstaple EX32 0SR Tel: 0159 86 254 — MRCS Eng. LRCP Lond. 1945; BA Camb. 1942; DTM & H Eng. 1952. Prev: Assoc. Specialist Accid. Dept. N. Devon Dist. Hosp. Barnstaple.

PAYNE, Mr Richard Frederick 18 Stansted Road, Bishop's Stortford CM23 2DX Tel: 01279 503578 — MB BS 1993 Lond.; BSc Lond. 1990, MB BS 1993; FRCS Lond. 1997.

PAYNE, Richard Wyman (retired) 22 Silverwell Park, Modbury, Ivybridge PL21 0RJ Tel: 01548 831053 — MB BChir 1954 Camb.; MA Camb. 1955, BA (Hons.) 1951, MD 1960; FRCP Glas. 1977, M 1974; FRCPath 1973, M 1963. Prev: Cons. Haemat. Worcester Roy. Infirm. & Vict. Infirm. Glas.

PAYNE, Robert Orlando (retired) Room 2, Upton Grange, 214 Prestbury Road, Macclesfield SK10 4AA Tel: 01625 827919 — MRCS Eng. LRCP Lond. 1930. Prev: Ho. Surg. ENT Dept. & Ho. Phys. Childr. Dept. Guy's Hosp.

PAYNE, Roger John Ward End Medical Centre, 794A Washwood Heath Road, Ward End, Birmingham B8 2JN Tel: 0121 327 1049 Fax: 0121 327 0964; 5 Anton Drive, Walmley, Sutton Coldfield B76 1XQ — MB ChB 1981 Birm.; MRCGP 1985; DRCOG 1983; Cert. FPA 1983. Socs: BMA & Med. Defence Union. Prev: Trainee GP Birm.

PAYNE, Ronald John Top Flat Left, 318 Queen St., Broughty Ferry, Dundee DD5 2HQ — MB ChB 1990 Dundee.

PAYNE, Sandra Anne North Wales Health Authority, Preswylfa, Hendy Road, Mold CH7 1PZ Tel: 01352 700227; Whiteacres, Llanelian Heights, Colwyn Bay LL29 8YB Email: sandrapayne@fsmail.net — MB BS 1977 Lond.; FFPHM 2000; MRCS Eng. LRCP Lond. 1977; MFPHM 1990. Dir. of Pub. Health; Hon. Sen. Lect. Univ. Bangor. Prev: Sen. Registar (Community Med.) Clwyd HA; Sen. Clin. Med. Off. (Child Health) Clwyd HA.

PAYNE, Scott Morgan Longley Flat 5, 5 Moorland Road, Leeds LS6 1AL — MB ChB 1990 Leeds.

PAYNE, Simon David Nottingham RCCS, Westminster House, Mapperley Hospital, Nottingham NG3 6AA; 10 Grosvenor Avenue, Nottingham NG3 5DX — MB ChB 1981 Leic.; MRCPsych 1988. Cons. Psychiat. Rehabil. & Community Care Nottm. Healthcare Unit Mapperley Hosp. Prev: Sen. Regist. (Adult Psychiat.) Nottm. VTS.

PAYNE

PAYNE, Mr Simon David William A/E Department, Ealing Hospital, Uxbridge RD, Southall UB1 3HW Tel: 020 8967 5421 Fax: 020 8967 5311 Email: simon.payne@eht.nhs.uk; 28 Emanuel Avenue, Acton, London W3 6JJ Tel: 020 8992 1880 Email: simonpayne10@hotmail.com — MB BS 1978 Lond.; LLM Wales 1992; FRCS Eng. 1984; FRCS Ed. 1983; FFAEM 1995. (Middlx. Hosp. Med. Sch.) Cons. & Clin. Dir. A & E Ealing Hosp. Lond.; Hon. Sen. Lect. in A/E Med. Imperial Coll. Med. Sch. Lond. Socs: Cardiff Med. Soc. - Mem.; Roy. Soc. Med. - Mem.; Medico-Legal Soc. - Mem. Prev: Cons. A & E Roy. Hants. Co. Hosp. Winchester; Sen. Regist. Rotat. (A & E) Basingstoke, Portsmouth & Soton.; Regist. Rotat. (A & E) Lincoln & Nottm.

PAYNE, Simon Nicholas Lester Department of Pathology, University Medical Buildings, Foresterhill, Aberdeen AB25 2ZD Tel: 01224 681818 Fax: 01224 633002; 6H Belgrave Terrace, Aberdeen AB25 2NS Tel: 01224 658534 — MB ChB 1991 Aberd.; BMedBiol. (Hons.) Aberd. 1988; MRCPath (UK) 1999. Cons. (Histopath./Cytopath.) Aberd. Prev: Specialist Regist. (Path.) Aberd.; SHO & Hon. Lect. (Path.) Univ. Aberd.; Research Fell. (Path.) Univ. Aberd.

PAYNE, Simon Philip Kent 52 Flatford Place, Kidlington OX5 1TH Tel: 0186 754886 — MB ChB 1986 Leic. SHO (Surg.) Hammersmith Hosp. Lond. Prev: Prosector Univ. Oxf.

PAYNE, Mr Stephen Richard 23 Anson Road, Victoria Park, Manchester M14 5BZ Tel: 0161 2482010 Fax: 0161 276 4221 Email: stevepayne.urol@btinternet.com; 21 Ollerbarrow Road, Hale, Altrincham WA15 9PP Tel: 0161 941 1267 Fax: 0161 941 1267 — MB BS 1977 Lond.; MS Lond. 1987; FRCS Eng. 1981; FEBU 1992. (Roy. Free) p/t Cons. Urol. Centr. Manch.and Manch.s Childr. Hosp. Univ. Trust, Manch. Infirm, & St. Marys Hosp. Manch; Hon. Clin. Lect. (Urol.) Univ. Manch. Socs: Brit. Assn. Urol. Surgs.- Counc. Mem. 2001-2004; Manch. Med. Soc. Prev: Sen. Registar (Urol.) St. Mary's Hosp. Portsmouth; Lect. (Percutaneous Renal Surg.) Inst. Urol. Univ. Lond.; RSO St. Peter's Hosp. Lond.

PAYNE, Susan Ann 43 Brompton Place, Tredegar NP22 4NF — MB BCh 1976 Wales.

PAYNE, Susan Karen 109 Portnall Road, London W9 3BB — MB BS 1986 Lond.

PAYNE, Thomas Christopher 103 Sidney Grove, Newcastle upon Tyne NE4 5PE — MB BS 1993 Newc.

PAYNE, Wendy Sharon 22 Shearwater Drive, Bradwell, Great Yarmouth NR31 9UL — BM BS 1990 Nottm. SHO Jas. Paget Hosp. Gt. Yarmouth VTS.

PAYNE, William Nigel (retired) Wareham Health Centre, Streche Road, Wareham BH20 4PG Tel: 01929 553444 Fax: 01929 550703 — MB BS 1962 Lond.; MRCS Eng. LRCP Lond. 1962. Prev: Ho. Surg. (O & G), Ho. Surg. & Ho. Phys. Dorset Co. Hosp.

PAYNE-JAMES, Mr John Jason 19 Speldhurst Ropad, London E97EH Tel: 0208 5250269 Fax: 0208 5250269 Email: jasonpaynejames@cs.com; Farensic Healthcare, Services Ltd, Po Box 5507, Southend-on-sea SS0 7GW Tel: 01702 333399 Fax: 01702 344450 Email: jpj@forensic-healthcare.com — MB BS 1980 Lond.; 1989 Rnutr; LLM 1995; FRCS Eng. 1986; FRCS Ed. 1985; DFM 2000. (Royal London Hospital) p/t Forens. Phys. Lond. & Endoscopist Gastroenterol. Qu.sway Surg. S.end-on-Sea; Freelance Med. Writer Lond.; Edr. Jl. Clin. Forens. Med.; Hon. Sen. Research Fell. (Gastroenterol. & Nutrit.) Centr. Middlx. Hosp.; Registered Nutrit.ist; Co. Edr. Curr. Med. Literature - Clin. Nutrit.; Med. Edr.; Dir. Forens. Healthcare Serv.s Ltd. Socs: Fell. Roy. Soc. Med.; Fell. & Licentiate Assoc. of Lawyers; (Counc.) Assn. Police Surgs. Prev: Regist. (A & E) Whipps Cross Hosp. Lond.; Regist. & Research Fell., (Gastroenterol. & Nutrit.), Lond.; Director, Greenwich Med. Media LTD.

PAYNTER, Arthur Stephen Central Clinic, 50 Victoria Place, Carlisle CA1 1HP Tel: 01228 603274 Fax: 01228 603201; 26 Tullie Street, Carlisle CA1 2BA Tel: 01228 819318 — MB BS 1971 Madras; DCH RCPS Glas. 1974; FRCP 1997. (Christian Med. Coll. Vellore) Cons. Paediat. (Community Child Health) N. Lakeland Health Care. Socs: FRCP; FRCPCh. Prev: Cons. Paediat. (Community Child Health) W. Cumbria Health Care; Cons. Paediat. (Community Child Health) NW Durh. HA; Cons. Paediat. to Govt. Solomon Is.s.

PAYNTER, Helen Elizabeth Gloucestershire Royal Hospital, Great Western Road, Gloucester GL1 3NN Tel: 01452 528555; 47 Fabian Drive, Stoke Gifford, Bristol BS34 8XL Tel: 0117 969 9263 Email: hep@paynter1.demon.co.uk — MB ChB 1992 Bristol; MRCP (UK) 1996; DRCOG 1994. Specialist Regist. (Renal/Gen. Med.) Gloucestershire Roy. Hosp.

PAYNTON, David John Bath Lodge Practice, Bitterne Health Centre, Commercial Street, Bitterne, Southampton SO18 6BT; 210 Bridge Road, Sarisbury Green, Southampton SO31 7ED Tel: 0148 95 573049 — MB ChB 1975 Manch.; FRCGP 1994, M 1980; DCH Eng. 1979; DRCOG 1978. Chair of Exec. Comm., Soton. City Primary Care Trust.

PAYTON, Colin David Royal United Occupational Health & Safety, Royal United Hospital, Combe Park, Bath BA1 3NG Tel: 01225 824064 Fax: 01225 825427 Email: colin.payton@ruh-bath.swest.nhs.uk — MB ChB 1977 Manch.; FRCP Glas. 1994; MRCP (UK) 1982; MFOM RCP Lond. 1994. (Manch.) Cons. Occupat. Phys. Roy. United Occupat. Health & Safety Bath; Clin. Dir. Occupat. Health & Safety Roy. United Hosp. Bath. Socs: Soc. Occupat. Med.; Assn. NHS Occupat. Phys. Prev: Sen. Regist. Leicester Roy. Infirm.

***PEACE, Aaron James George** 335A Clooney Road, Ballykelly, Limavady BT49 9PL — MB BCh 1998 Belf.; MB BCh Belf 1998.

PEACE, Julian Miles Valley Medical Centre, Johnson Street, Stocksbridge, Sheffield S36 1BX — MB ChB 1990 Sheff.; 2000 (Dip. Practical Dermat.) Cardiff; BMedSci Sheff. 1987.

PEACE, Mary Mima Norton, Stenness, Orkney KW17 — MB BS 1944 Durham.

PEACE, Mr Peter Kirkby Frere House, Kenwyn, Truro TR1 3DR — MB BS 1966 Lond.; BSc (Hons. Anat.) Lond. 1963; FRCS Eng. 1972; MRCS Eng. LRCP Lond. 1966. (Guy's) Cons. Surg. (Orthop. & Trauma) Roy. Cornw. Hosps. Trust. Socs: Fell. BOA; BMA. Prev: Ho. Phys. Guy's Hosp. Lond.; Jun. Lect. (Anat.) Guy's Hosp. Med. Sch.; Sen. Regist. P.ss Eliz. Orthop. Hosp. Exeter.

PEACE, Mr Richard Henry Nightingale Surgery, Greatwell Drive, Cupernham Lane, Romsey SO51 7QN Tel: 01794 517878 Fax: 01794 514236; The Well House, Canada Road, West Wellow, Romsey SO51 6DE Tel: 01794 322970 Email: t-peace@virgin.net — MB BS 1976 Lond.; FRCS Eng. 1981; MRCS Eng. LRCP Lond. 1975.

PEACE, Savita 51 Peckover Drive, Pudsey LS28 8EH — MB ChB 1996 Liverp.

PEACEY, Mrs Jean Menzies 46 Riverside Court, Nine Elms Lane, London SW8 5BY Tel: 020 7627 2818 Fax: 020 7627 2818; The Old Grain House, 27 High St, Bourn, Cambridge CB3 7SQ Tel: CB3 7SQ Fax: 01954 718310 — MB BS Lond. 1957; MRCGP 1968. (St. Bart.) Prev: Sen. Med. Off. MoD; Ho. Surg. King Geo. Hosp. Ilford; Ho. Phys. St. And. Hosp. Bow.

PEACEY, Steven Raymond Department of Endocrinology and Diabetes, Bradford Royal Infirmary, Duckworth Lane, Bradford BD9 6RJ Tel: 01274 364370 — MB ChB 1985 Leeds; MRCP (UK) 1988; MD Sheff. 1998. Cons. (Endocrinol. & Diabetes) Bradford Hosps. NHS Trust Bradford. Socs: Soc. Endocrinol.; Diabetes UK; Roy. Coll. Phys. Lond. Prev: Sen. Regist. (Endocrinol. & Diabetes) Christie Hosp. Manch.; Lect. & Research Fell. (Endocrinol. & Diabetes) Univ. Sheff.; Regist. (Endocrinol.) Leeds Gen. Infirm.

PEACH, Alan Howard Skyrme 35 Cowper Road, Redland, Bristol BS6 6NZ — MB ChB 1989 Bristol.

PEACH, Mr Alfred Nowell Hamilton (retired) 124 Brighton Road, Horsham RH13 6EY Tel: 01403 262573 — MB ChB 1937 Bristol; FRCS Eng. 1948. Prev: Surg. Horsham Hosp.

PEACH, Mr Barry Griffith Skyrme (retired) Cranford House, 244 Clifton Drive Sth., Lytham St Annes FY8 1NH Tel: 01253 726203 Email: peachbgs@gobalnet.co.uk — MB ChB 1959 Birm.; MChOrth Liverp. 1970; FRCS Ed. 1968. Prev: Cons. Surg. (Orthop.) Blackpool Health Dist.

PEACH, Christopher John David The Surgery, 77 Thurleigh Road, Balham, London SW12 8TZ Tel: 020 8675 3521 Fax: 020 8675 3800 — MB BS 1974 Lond.; MSc (Community Med.) 1983; MRCGP 1984. (Char. Cross) GP Battersea Lond.; Chief Med. Off. Gesa Asst.ance (UK) Lond. Socs: Chairm. Brit. Aeromed. Pract. Assn. Prev: Regist. (Community Med.) S.W. Thames RHA; Regist. (Gen. Med.) P.ss Margt. Hosp. Nassau, Bahamas.

PEACH, Fiona Jane Cross Plain Surgery, 84 Bulford Road, Durrington, Salisbury SP4 8DH Tel: 01980 652221; 4 Heath Road, Salisbury SP2 9JS — BM 1986 Soton.; MRCGP 1991. Prev: Trainee GP Salisbury VTS.

PEACH, Ian David (Surgery), Recreation Drive, Billinge, Wigan WN5 7LY Tel: 01744 892205 — MB ChB 1990 Manch.; MRCGP 1994.

PEACH, Rosalind Margaret (retired) Cranford House, 244 Clifton Drive S., Lytham St Annes FY8 1NH Tel: 01253 726203 — MB ChB Ed. 1960; MFFP 1994; DA Eng. 1963. Locum Med. Off. Family Plann. Prev: SCMO (Family Plann.) Blackpool, Wyre & Community Health Servs. NHS Trust.

PEACHEY, Geoffrey Robert Weybridge Health Centre, Minorca Road, Weybridge KT13 8DU Tel: 01932 853366 Fax: 01932 844902; Waverley Lodge, Elgin Road, Weybridge KT13 8SN — MB BS 1958 Lond.; MRCS Eng. LRCP Lond. 1958. (Guy's) Prev: Res. Med. Off. Nuffield Ho., Guy's Hosp.; Res. (Obst.) & Asst. Ho. Phys. & Ho. Surg. Guy's Hosp. Lond.

PEACHEY, Jean Aylott 58 Parkway, Welwyn Garden City AL8 6HH Tel: 01707 323284 — MB BS 1957 Lond.; MRCS Eng. LRCP Lond. 1957; DO Eng. 1959. (King's Coll. Hosp.) Prev: Assoc. Specialist (Ophth.) Qu. Eliz. II Hosp. Welwyn Gdn. City; Ho. Phys. Dulwich Hosp.; Cas. Off. & Ho. Off. (Anaesth.) King's Coll. Hosp. Lond.

PEACHEY, Robin David Gordon (retired) Litfield House, 1 Litfield Place, Clifton Down, Bristol BS8 3LS Tel: 0117 973 1323 — MB BS 1956 Lond.; BSc (Anat.) Lond. 1953, MD 1972, MB BS 1956; FRCP Lond. 1975, M 1958. Prev: Cons. Dermat. Bristol Roy. Infirm. & Frenchay Hosp. Bristol.

PEACHEY, Ronald Sidney 58 Parkway, Welwyn Garden City AL8 6HH Tel: 01707 323284 — MRCS Eng. LRCP Lond. 1956; BSc (1st cl. Hons.) Lond. 1950, MB BS 1956; FFA RCS Eng. 1967; DObst RCOG 1958. (King's Coll. Hosp.) Prev: Cons. Anaesth. Qu. Eliz. II Hosp. Welwyn Garden City; Sen. Regist. Dept. Anaesth. Hammersmith Hosp. Lond. Regist. Dept.; Anaesth. St. Thos. Hosp. Lond.

PEACHEY, Timothy David Dept of Anaesthesia, The Royal Free Hospital, Pond Street, London NW3 2QP Tel: 0207 794 0500 Ext: 6503 Fax: 0207 830 2245 Email: tim.peachey@rfh.nthames.nhs.uk — MB BS 1983 Lond.; FFA RCS Eng. 1988. (King's college Hospital) Cons. Anaesth. Roy. Free Hosp. Lond.

PEACOCK, Andrew John Scottish Pulmonary Vascular Unit, Department Respiratory Medicine, Western Infirmary, Glasgow G11 6NT Tel: 0141 211 6327 Fax: 0141 211 6334 Email: apeacock@udcf.gla.ac.uk; 6 Roman Road, Bearsden, Glasgow G61 2SW — MB BS 1973 Lond.; MPhil Camb. 1978, MD 1984; BSc (Hons.) Lond. 1971; FRCP Lond. 1995; FRCP Glas. 1994; MRCP (UK) 1976. (St. Bart.) Cons. Phys. (Respirat. Med.) W.. Infirm. Glas.; Vis. Sci. Nat. Heart & Lung Inst.; Respirat. Research Fell.sh. Socs: Assn. Phys. Of Gt. Britain & Irel.; Amer. thoracic Soc.; Europ. thoracic Soc. Prev: Sen. Regist. (Thoracic Med.) Soton. Hosps.; Vis. Scientist Cardiovasc. Pulm. Research Laborat. Denver, Colorado; Research Regist. Brompton Hosp. Lond.

PEACOCK, Brian Silver Street Surgery, 26 Silver Street, Great Barford, Bedford MK44 3HX Tel: 01234 870325 Fax: 01234 871323; Last Straw Cottage, Brook End, Keysoe, Bedford MK44 2HR — MB BS 1983 Lond.; DRCOG 1988. (St. Mary's) Prev: SHO (Paediat., O & G & Orthop.) Bedford Gen. Hosp.

PEACOCK, Christine Elizabeth (retired) Bliss Cottage, Hentland, Ross-on-Wye HR9 6LP Tel: 01989 730427 Fax: 01298 815506 Email: chrispeacock@doctors.org.uk — MB ChB 1962 Manch.; MB ChB Manch. 1980; BSc (1st cl. Hons.) Physiol. Manch. 1962; MFCH 1990; DRCOG 1982. Prev: Sen. Med. Off. i/c Stud. Health Centre Manch.

PEACOCK, Clare Top Flat, 50 Gloucester St., Pimlico, London SW1V 4EH — MB BS 1989 Lond.; MRCP (UK) 1993. Regist. (Radiol.) Soton. Gen. Hosp. Prev: Regist. (ITU) Roy. N.shore Hosp. Sydney, Austral.; Acting Regist. (Cardiol. & Chest) Roy. Sussex Co. Hosp.; SHO Rotat. (A & E & Med.) Roy. Sussex Co. Hosp.

PEACOCK, David MDP Practice, 44 High Street, Portaferry, Newtownards BT22 1QT Tel: 028 9128 420 Fax: 028 4272 9834 — MB BCh BAO 1972 Belf.; MRCGP 1976; DObst RCOG 1974.

PEACOCK, Duncan Antony 27 Scott Street, Dundee DD2 2AH — MB ChB 1991 Dundee.

PEACOCK, Gillian Frances The Old Manor, Ubley, Bristol BS40 6PJ — MB ChB 1952 Bristol.

PEACOCK, Ian David Allan Derbyshire Royal Infirmary, London Road, Derby DE1 2QY; Castle House, 2 Castle Hill, Duffiled, Belper DE56 4EA Tel: 01332 842663 Fax: 01332 843075 Email: ip@btinternet.com — MB BChir 1974 Camb.; MD Camb. 1985; FRCP Lond. 1994. Prev: Sen. Regist. (Med.) Nottm. City Hosp.; Research Fell. (Diabetes) & Regist. (Med.) Univ. Hosp. Nottm.; Cons. Phys. (Diabetes) Derbysh. Roy. Infirm.

PEACOCK, Joanna Elizabeth Margaret The Surgery, 75 Bank St., Alexandria G83 0NB Tel: 01389 752626 Fax: 01389 752169; 25 Mansewood Drive, Dumbarton G82 3EU Tel: 01389 767174 — MB ChB 1956 Glas. Prev: Med. Miss. Duncan Hosp. Raxaul India; SHO (Surg.) Vale of Leven Hosp. Alexandria.

PEACOCK, John Stable Fold Surgery, Church St., Westhoughton, Bolton BL5 3SF Tel: 01942 813678 Fax: 01942 812028; Blythewood, 13 Towncroft Lane, Heaton, Bolton BL1 5EW Tel: 01204 847626 — MB ChB 1966 Sheff.; DObst RCOG 1968. (Sheff.)

PEACOCK, John Edward Department of Anaesthetics, C Floor, Royal Hallamshire Hospital, Glossop Road, Sheffield S10 2JF Tel: 0114 271 2494 Fax: 0114 279 8314 Email: john.peacock@sth.nhs.uk; 10 Crimicar Lane, Fulwood, Sheffield S10 4FB — MB ChB 1979 Sheff.; FRCA 1985. (Sheff.) Cons. Anaesth. Roy. Hallamsh. Hosp. Sheff. Socs: Soc. Intravenous Anaesth. (UK). Prev: Sen. Lect. (Anaesth.) Univ. Sheff.

PEACOCK, Kate Elizabeth 124 Broadway N., Walsall WS1 2QE — MB ChB 1993 Bristol.

PEACOCK, Kim Field House Medical Centre, 13 Dudley Street, Grimsby DN31 2AE Tel: 01472 350327; 12 Dudley Street, Grimsby DN31 2AB Tel: 01472 50327 — MB ChB 1974 Sheff.; DRCOG 1976.

PEACOCK, Matthew Lockhart (retired) 25 Mansewood Drive, Dumbarton G82 3EU Tel: 01389 767174 — MB ChB 1956 Glas. Prev: GP Alexandria.

PEACOCK, Sharon Jayne Nyfield Department of Pathology & Baderology, Level 4 Academic Block, John Radcliffe Hospital, Oxford OX3 9DU Tel: 01865 741166 Email: sharon.peacock@ndp.ox.ac.uk — BM 1988 Soton.; BA (Open) 1995; MSc Lond. 1994; MRCP (UK) 1991; MRCPath 1997; DTM & H RCP Lond. 1994. Univ. Lect. & Hon. Cons. (MicroBiol.). Prev: Wellcome Research Fell. & Hon. Sen. Regist. (Microbiol.) John Radcliffe Hosp. Oxf.; Regist. (Microbiol.) John Radcliffe Hosp. Oxf.; SHO (Med.) John Radcliffe Hosp. Oxf., Whittington Hosp. Lond. & Roy. Sussex Co. Hosp. Brighton.

PEACOCK, Simon Gregory Leeds Student Medical Practice, 4 Blenheim Court Walk, Leeds LS2 9AE Tel: 0113 295 4488 — MB ChB 1989 Leeds; MRCGP 1993.

PEACOCK, Stephen Richard The Surgery, Woden Road, Wolverhampton WV10 0BD Tel: 01902 454242 Fax: 01902 352438 — BM 1982 Soton.

***PEACOCK, Timothy Edward** The Old Vicarage, Easthall Road, North Kelsey, Market Rasen LN7 6HA — MB ChB 1997 Manch.

PEACOCK, Timothy Guy Meadowcroft Surgery, Jackson Road, Aylesbury HP19 9EX Tel: 01296 425775 Fax: 01296 330324; 4 Spenser Road, Aylesbury HP21 7LR Tel: 01296 81364 — MB ChB Bristol 1979; MRCGP 1985; DRCOG 1987. Prev: Surg. Lt. RN.

PEACOCK, Vanessa Anne 70 Rannoch Drive, Mansfield NG19 6QX — MB BS 1992 Newc.

***PEAD, Michael Elliott** 70 Putnoe Street, Bedford MK41 8HL — MB BS 1986 Lond.

PEAKE, David Ronald Queen Elizabeth Hospital, Edgbaston, Birmingham B15 2TH Tel: 0121 697 8350 — MB ChB 1984 Liverp.; MRCP (UK) 1989; FRCR 1994. Cons. Clin. Oncologist, Qu. Eliz. Hosp., Birm. Prev: Regist. (Med.) Roy. Liverp. Hosp.; Regist. (Med.) Arrowe Pk. Hosp. Wirral Merseyside.; Regist. (Radiotherap. & Oncol.) Clatterbridge Hosp. Merseyside.

PEAKE, Michael David Respiratory Medicine Unit, Glenfield Hospital, Groby Rd, Leicester LE3 9QP Tel: 0116 250 2610 Fax: 0116 250 2777 Email: mick.peake@uhl-tr.nhs.uk; Riverlea, Hodge Lane, Little Smeaton, Pontefract WF8 3LG Tel: 01977 620235 — MB ChB 1973 Birm.; FRCP Lond. 1990; MRCP (UK) 1976. Cons. Phys. Glenfield Hosp, Leicester; Lead clinician for lung cancer; assoc director, CEEU, Roy. Coll. of Phys.s of Lond.; Nat. Lead Clinician for Lung Cancer, Cancer Servs. Collaborative. Socs: Brit. Thorac. Soc. (Chairm. of Research Comm.); Med. Research Soc.; Eur. Respirat. Soc. Prev: Cons. Phys. Pontefact Gen. Infirm.; Peel Trust Research Fell. Johns Hopkins Hosp. Baltimore, USA; Lect. & MRC Research Fell. Profess. Med. Unit Univ. Sheff.

PEAKMAN

PEAKMAN, David John 16 Rectory Terrace, Gosforth, Newcastle upon Tyne NE3 1YB Tel: 0191 213 2863 Email: dj@peakman.com — MB BS 1979 Lond.; MS Newc. 1994; BSc (Hons.) Lond. 1976; FRCR 1986. (Univ. Coll. Hosp.) Cons. Radiol. Qu. Eliz. Hosp. Gateshead; Hon. Lect. Med. Sch. Newc.

PEAKMAN, Mark 12 Ferndene Road, London SE24 0AQ — MB BS 1984 Lond.; MSc Lond. 1988, BSc 1981, MB BS 1984; PhD 1993; MRCPath 1992. (Univ. Lond.) Lect. (Immunol.) & Hon. Sen. Regist. (Immunol.) King's Coll. Sch. Med. Dent. Prev: Wellcome Research Train. Fell. & Hon. Sen. Regist. (Immunol.) King's Coll. Hosp. Lond.

PEALING, Vivien Margaret 4 Dunkery Road, Weston Super Mare BS23 2TD — MB ChB 1976 Leeds; DA Eng. 1979.

PEARCE, Adrian Colven Department of Anaesthetics, Guy's Hospital, London SE1 9RT — MB BChir 1976 Camb.; MA, MB Camb. 1976, BChir 1975; MRCP (UK) 1981; FFA RCS Eng. 1980. Cons. Anaesth. Guy's Hosp., Lond.

PEARCE, Alan John (retired) — MB ChB 1945 Birm.; MRCS Eng. LRCP Lond. 1945; FRCGP 1970, M 1953. Prev: Clin. Asst. Migraine Clinic Birm. & Midl. Eye Hosp.

PEARCE, Alan John Seaforth Farm Surgery, Vicarage Lane, Hailsham BN27 1BH Tel: 01323 848494 Fax: 01323 849316; 36 Pitreavie Drive, Hailsham BN27 3XG — MB BS 1984 Lond.; MRCGP 1988; Dip. IMC RCS Ed. 1995; DCH RCP Lond. 1988; DRCOG 1987.

PEARCE, Alison Virginia 44 Bettwys-y-Coed Road, Cardiff CF23 6PL — BM 1989 Soton.; MRCP (UK) 1994.

PEARCE, Andrew Francis Bissett Lydbrook Health Centre, Lydbrook GL17 9LG Tel: 01594 860219 Fax: 01594 860987 — MB BS 1974 London; MB BS 1974 Lond. (London) GP Lydbrook, Glos.

*PEARCE, Andrew James 52 Clementson Road, Sheffield S10 1GS — MB ChB 1997 Sheff.

PEARCE, Anthony John (retired) 22 Park Road, Wollaston, Stourbridge DY8 3QX Tel: 01384 392723 — MB ChB Birm. 1951; DObst RCOG 1958. Prev: Ho. Surg. (O & G) Ronkswood Hosp. Worcester.

PEARCE, Anthony John (retired) Berners House, 2 Mill Hill, Newmarket CB8 0JB Tel: 01638 665709 Fax: 01638 665709 — MB BS Lond. 1959; FFA RCS Eng. 1969; DA Eng. 1963; DObst RCOG 1962. Prev: Cons. Anaesth. Addenbrooke's Hosp. Camb. & Newmarket Gen. Hosp.

PEARCE, Callum Bruce 31 Orchards Way, Highfield, Southampton SO17 1RF — MB ChB 1992 Liverp.

*PEARCE, Caroline Elizabeth 30 Beehive Road, Crookesnoor, Sheffield S10 1EP — MB ChB 1998 Sheff.; MB ChB Sheff 1998.

*PEARCE, Catherine Rebecca 33 Forest Drive W., London E11 1JZ — MB BS 1998 Lond.; MB BS Lond 1998.

*PEARCE, Christopher Jon West Cottage, Grandon Lodge, South Holmwood, Dorking RH5 4LT — MB ChB 1998 Manch.; MB ChB Manch 1998.

PEARCE, Christopher Jonathan Department of Clinical Biochemistry, The Ipswich Hospital NHS Trust, Heath Road, Ipswich IP4 5PD Tel: 01473 703725 Fax: 01473 703259 Email: christopher.pearce@ipsh-tr.anglox.nhs.uk — BM BCh 1972 Oxon.; MRCP 1975; FRCP (UK) 1997; MRCPath 1989; FRCPath 1998. (Middlesex) Cons. Clin. Biochem. Ipswich Hosp. Socs: Soc. Endocrinol. Prev: Hon. Sen. Regist. Clin. Research Centre N.wick Pk. Hosp. Harrow; Regist. (Med.) W.m. Hosp. Lond.; Ho. Phys. Middlx. Hosp. Lond.

PEARCE, Christopher Patrick Smugglers Lane Surgery, Smugglers Lane, Reepham, Norwich NR10 4QT Tel: 01603 870271 Fax: 01603 872995 — MB BChir 1989 Camb.

*PEARCE, Daniel Jon 55 Hillside Av, Plymouth PL4 6PS — BM 1997 Soton.

PEARCE, Daryl Elizabeth 51 Middle Park Road, Birmingham B29 4BH Tel: 0121 475 3600 — MB BS 1991 Lond.; BSc (Hons.) Lond. 1988; BDS Birm. 1981; MRCGP 1995; DFFP 1995. Prev: Trainee GP Croydon VTS; GP Asst. Croydon.

PEARCE, David Nigel Edith Morgan Centre, Torbay Hospital, Lawes Bridge, Torquay TQ2 7AA — MB BCh 1986 Wales. Staff Grade (Psychiat.) Torquay Hosp. Prev: SHO Rainhill Hosp. Prescot; Ho. Off. Ysbyty Gwynedd; Ho. Off. Ysbyty Glan Clwyd.

PEARCE, Douglas John (retired) The Old Vicarage, Forest Park Road, Brockenhurst SO42 7SW Tel: 01590 622001 — MB BS 1950 Lond.; MRCS Eng. LRCP Lond. 1950; FFA RCS Eng. 1954; DA Eng. 1952. Prev: Cons. Anaesth. Soton. & SW Hants. Health Dist.(T).

PEARCE, Drusilla Ann Bromley NHS Trust, Orpington Hospital, Sevenoaks Road, Orpington BR6 9JU Tel: 01689 815100 Fax: 01689 815285; Coldharbour, Bletchingley, Redhill RH1 4NA Tel: 01883 742685 Fax: 01883 743661 — MB BS 1971 Lond.; BSc (Pharmacol.) Lond. 1968, MB BS 1971; FRCR 1977. (King's Coll. Hosp.) Clin. Dir. - diagnostic imaging; Cons. Radiol. Bromley HA. Prev: Sen. Cons. Dept. Diag. Radiol. Riyadh & Al Khari Hosp. Progr. Saudi Arabia; Sen. Regist. (Radiol.) King's Coll. Hosp. Lond.

PEARCE, Florence Muriel (retired) 30 Dulwich Common, London SE21 7EX Tel: 020 8693 4189 — MB BS 1946 Lond.

PEARCE, Gillian 10 Kings Hill Fields, Wednesbury WS10 9JF — BM BCh 1997 Oxf.; BSc (Hons.) Wolverhampton 1994; BSc (Hons.) CNAA 1980; PhD Keele Univ. 1983; Fell Roy Astronom Soc. 1981. (Oxf.) Ho. Off. (Med.) Wordsley Hosp. Stourbridge; SHO (Orthop.) P.ss Roy. Hosp. Telford, Shrops. Socs: Med. Protec. Soc. Prev: Res. Fell. (Astrophysics) Univ. Wolverhampton 1992-1999; Lect. & Atlas Research Fell. (Astrophysics) Oxf. Univ. 1987-1992, 1993; Vis. Res. Fells. GSFC/NASA 1991, Univ. Glas. 1992.

PEARCE, Hilary Lockhart 23 Carnethy Av, Edinburgh EH13 0DL — MB ChB 1997 Dundee. SHO (Paed) Yorkhill Hosp. Glas.

PEARCE, Mr Ian 1 Lowrie Place, Chapeltown, Strathaven ML10 6RJ Tel: 01357 300419; 7 Brockholes, Simmondley, Glossop SK13 6YT Tel: 0411 696217 — BM BS 1993 Nottm.; BMedSci (Hons.) 1991; FRCS Glas. 1997. (Univ. of Nottm.) Specialist Regist. Rotat. Urol. Manch. Socs: Roy. Soc. Med.; Assn. Surg. Train.

PEARCE, Ian Andrew 50 Bridge Street, Golborne, Warrington WA3 3QB — MB ChB 1990 Liverp.

PEARCE, Iris 304 Beverley Road, Anlaby, Hull HU10 7BG Tel: 01482 654165 — MB BS 1960 Durh.; MB BS (Hnrs.) Durh. 1960. (Newc.) Clin. Research Fell. Dept. Neurol. Hull Roy. Infirm. Prev: Ho. Surg. Roy. Vict. Infirm. Newc.; SHO Regional Neurol. Centre, Newc.; Med. Regist. Roy. Hosp. Sheff.

PEARCE, Jack Fred, Lt.-Col. RAMC c/o Glyn Mills & Co., Whitehall, London SW1 — MRCS Eng. LRCP Lond. 1942; DTM & H Eng. 1963. (St. Bart.) Jun. Med. Specialist RAMC. Socs: Fell. Roy. Soc. Med. Prev: Ho. Surg. Harlowwood Orthop. & Peripheral Nerve Injury EMS Centre; Mansfield; Med. Clin. Asst. St. Bart. Hosp. Lond.

PEARCE, James Frederick Bryony Cottage, New House Lane, Poslingford, Clare, Sudbury CO10 8QX Tel: 01787 278624 — MB BS 1954 Lond.; BSc (1st cl. Hons.) Lond. 1951, MD 1964; DPM 1963; MRCPsych 1972. (St. Bart.) Socs: BMA. Prev: Cons. Psychiat. Home Office Prison Dept.; Sen. Regist. (Med.) Roy. N.. Hosp. Lond.; Regist. Bethlem & Maudsley Hosps.

PEARCE, Jennifer Jane Sunbury Health Centre Group Practice, Green Street, Sunbury-on-Thames TW16 6RH Tel: 01932 713399 Fax: 01932 713354; 181 French Street, Sunbury-on-Thames TW16 5JY — MB BS 1974 Lond.; MRCP (UK) 1976. (Middlesex)

PEARCE, Professor John Barber 4 Knighton Drive, Leicester LE2 3HB Tel: 0116 270 4004 Fax: 0116 270 4004 Email: johnpearce@mcmail.com — MB BS Lond. 1965; MPhil Lond. 1974; FRCP Lond. 1991; MRCP (UK) 19/0; FRCPsych 1984, M 1973; DCH RCP Lond. 1968. (Univ. Coll. Hosp.) Prof. Child & Adolesc. Psychiat. Nottm. Univ. Prev: Cons. Child & Adolesc. Psychiat. Guy's Hosp. Lond.; Sen. Regist. Maudsley Hosp. Lond.; Regist. (Paediat.) St. Bart. Hosp. Lond.

PEARCE, John Leonard Tel: 01753 634603 — MB BS 1967 Lond.; FRCPCH 1999; FRCP Lond. 1993; FRACP 1976; DCH Eng. 1969. (St. Thos.) Cons. (Paediat.) E. Berks. Health Dist. Socs: Brit. Paediat. Assn. Prev: Cons. Paediat. Taranaki Hosp. Bd., NZ; Sen. Regist. (Paediat.) ChristCh. Pub. Hosp., NZ; Resid. Hosp. Sick Childr. Toronto, Canada.

PEARCE, John Macfarlane Church Street Surgery, 30 Church Street, Dunoon PA23 8BG Tel: 01369 703482/702778 Fax: 01369 704502; Lochview, Ardnadam, Dunoon PA23 8QG Tel: 01369 706241 — MB ChB 1979 Manch. Prev: Trainee GP Paisley VTS.

PEARCE, Mr John Malcolm Frederick Department of Obstetrics & Gynaecology, St. George's Hospital, London SW17 0RE Tel: 020 8672 9944; 37 Louisville Road, London SW17 8RL Tel: 020 8672 1682 — MD 1989 Sheff.; MB ChB 1973; FRCS Eng. 1978; MRCOG 1979. Sen. Lect. St. Geo. Hosp. Lond. Socs: Gyn. Research Soc.; Brit. Med. Ultrasound Soc. (Obst. Represen.). Prev: Research Fell.

King's Coll. Hosp. Lond.; Regist. Whipp's Cross Hosp. Lond.; Lect. King's Coll. Hosp. Lond.

PEARCE, John Michael Schofield 304 Beverley Road, Anlaby, Hull HU10 7BG Tel: 01482 654165 Fax: 01482 654165 Email: jmsp@dial.pipex.com — MB ChB 1959 Leeds; MB ChB (Hons.) Leeds 1959; MD Leeds 1965; FRCP Lond. 1975, M 1962. Emerit. Cons. Neurol. Hull. Socs: Assn. Brit. Neurol. (Ex. Counc.); (Exec Comm.) Assn. Phys.; (Pres. Counc.) N. Eng. Neurol. Assn. Prev: Sen. Regist. (Neurol.) Gen. Infirm. Leeds; Fulbright Trav. Fell. (Neurol.) Mass. Gen. Hosp. Boston, USA; Clin. Research Fell. & Regist. (Neurol.) Regional Neurol. Centre Newc.

PEARCE, Jonathan Christopher The Surgery, Stone Drive, Colwall, Malvern WR13 6QJ Tel: 01684 540323; Woostock, Walwyn Road, Upper Colwall, Malvern WR13 6PR Tel: 01684 541144 — MB ChB 1981 Birm.; DRCOG 1985; DA Eng. 1983. Prev: SHO (O & G) Worcs.; SHO (Anaesth.) Shrewsbury; SHO (Med.) Abergavenny.

PEARCE, Mr Jonathan Gale St. Sampsons Medical Centre, Grandes Maison Road, St Sampsons, Guernsey Tel: 01481 45915 — MB ChB 1983 Zimbabwe; FRCS Glas. 1990; LRCP LRCS Ed. LRCPS Glas. 1983.

PEARCE, Juliet Anne Meadowcroft, Andrews Lane, Waltham Cross EN7 6SP — MB BS 1993 Lond.

PEARCE, Katherine Anne 14 Furness Close, South Wootton, King's Lynn PE30 3TR Tel: 01553 674430 — BM BCh 1988 Oxf.; MRCGP 1994.

PEARCE, Katherine Jane Dr Conrad & Partners, Willow Surgery, Coronation Road, Downend, Bristol BS16 Tel: 0117 956 2979, 0117 970 9500; Tel: 01454 326638 — BM 1989 Soton. p/t GP Retainer, Willow Surg., Coronation Rd. Prev: SHO (Paediat.) S.mead Hosp. Bristol; SHO (Psychiat.) S.mead Hosp. Bristol; SHO (O & G) Fairfield Hosp. Bury.

PEARCE, Keith William Hamilton Road Surgery, 201 Hamilton Road, Felixstowe IP11 7DT Tel: 01394 283197 Fax: 01394 270304 — MB BS 1982 Lond.

PEARCE, Kenrick Maplesden (retired) Grasmere, The Lane, Little Barningham, Norwich NR11 7LR — MB ChB Manch. 1948; DCH Eng. 1952; DMSA Ed. 1961. Prev: SCM Salford HA.

PEARCE, Mark Quentin 42 Dorchester Road, Tolpuddle, Dorchester DT2 — MB BS 1991 Lond.

PEARCE, Mark Stephen Flat 58, G Block, Broomfield, Willesborough, Ashford TN24 0LY — MB BS 1981 Queensland.

PEARCE, Mary-Jane The Fulbrook Centre, Churchill Hospital, Old Road, Headington, Oxford OX3 7JU Tel: 01865 223840 Fax: 01865 223853; 72 Lonsdale Road, Oxford OX2 7EP — BM BS 1976 Nottm.; BMedSci Nottm. 1974; MRCPsych 1983; MRCGP 1980. Cons. Psychiat. Oxf. Ment. Healthcare Trust. Prev: Cons. Psychiat. Oxf. HA.

PEARCE, Meryn McLachlan 23 Carnethy Avenue, Edinburgh EH13 0DL Tel: 0131 441 2142 — MB ChB 1961 Ed.; DCH Eng. 1963. (Ed.) Clin. Med. Off. Edin. Sick Childr. Hosp. Trust. Socs: Assoc. Mem. BPA.

***PEARCE, Michael John** 503 Welford Road, Leicester LE2 6BN — MB ChB 1998 Leic.; MB ChB Leic 1998.

PEARCE, Neil William University Surgical Unit, F Level, Centre Block, Southampton General Hospital, Southampton SO16 6YD Tel: 02380 796815; 57 Cedar Road, Portswood, Southampton SO14 6TQ Tel: 02380 228720 — BM 1990 Soton. Specialist Regist. (Gen. Surg.) Wessex Rotat.

PEARCE, Nicholas Ricardo Sunbury Health Centre Group Practice, Green Street, Sunbury-on-Thames TW16 6RH Tel: 01932 713399 Fax: 01932 713354; 181 French Street, Sunbury-on-Thames TW16 5JY — MB BS 1976 Lond.; BSc Cardiff 1970.

PEARCE, Nigel Seward Kinson Road Surgery, 440 Kinson Road, Bournemouth BH10 5EY Tel: 01202 574604 Fax: 01202 590029; Seward, 91 Orchard Avenue, Parkstone, Poole BH14 8AH Tel: 01202 745573 — MB BS 1976 Lond.; BSc (Hons.) (Physical Oceanogr. & Electronic; Engin Wales 1970; MRCS Eng. LRCP Lond. 1976; DRCOG 1982. (St. Thos.) GP Bournemouth. Prev: Trainee GP Pk.stone Health Centre; SHO (O & G & Paediat.) Poole Gen. Hosp.; Med. Off. Atlantic & Panama Expedition Drake.

PEARCE, Paula Ann 5 Churchmere Drive, Crewe CW1 4SN — BM BS 1992 Nottm.

PEARCE, Peter Edwin Christchurch Health Centre, Saxon Square, Christchurch BH23 1DQ Tel: 01202 473531 — MB BS 1959 Lond.; MRCS Eng. LRCP Lond. 1959; DObst RCOG 1961. (Guy's) Prev: Ho. Surg. Orpington Hosp.; Ho. Phys. Roy. Vict. Hosp. Bournemouth; Ho. Surg. (O & G) Brighton Gen. Hosp.

PEARCE, Richard (retired) The Meadow, Coulsdon Lane, Chipstead, Coulsdon CR5 3QG Tel: 0173 75 52982 — MD 1933 Camb.; MRCS Eng. LRCP Lond. 1927; FRCPath. 1964. Prev: Dir. of Path. W. Lond. Hosp.

PEARCE, Richard David (retired) Staithe House, Belaugh, Wroxham, Norwich NR12 8XA Tel: 01603 783520 — MRCS Eng. LRCP Lond. 1947; FFCM 1981, M 1974; DPH Eng. 1953. Prev: Area Med. Off. Essex AHA.

PEARCE, Richard Jack Ivry Street Medical Practice, 5 Ivry Street, Ipswich IP1 3QW Tel: 01473 254718 Fax: 01473 287790 — MB BS 1972 Lond.; DObst RCOG 1974. (King's Coll. Hosp.) Prev: SHO (Paediat.), (Cas.) & (O & G) Ipswich Hosp.

PEARCE, Robert Handel (retired) 32 Gloster Gardens, Wellesbourne, Warwick CV35 9TQ — MB BS Lond. 1961; MRCS Eng. LRCP Lond. 1960; MRCGP 1976; DFFP 1994; Dip. Pract. Dermat. Wales 1991. Prev: Med. Off. Myton Hamlet Hospice Warwick.

PEARCE, Robert Leslie Vernon (retired) Dorincourt, 51 The Glade, Leatherhead KT22 9TB Tel: 01372 453559 — MB BS Lond. 1956; MRCS Eng. LRCP Lond. 1956; FRCPC 1971; DCH RCP Lond. 1960. Prev: Regist. (Med.) Stoke Mandeville Hosp.

PEARCE, Rodney Aubrey James 42 The Croft, Meadow Drive, Devizes SN10 3BJ Tel: 01380 724703 — MB ChB Bristol 1945; MRCS Eng. 1945, LRCP Lond 1946; MRCGP 1957; DRCOG Lond. 1946. (Bristol) Med. Off. (Brit. Racing & Sports Car Club) S.W. Bristol. Socs: Hon. Mem. Bath Clin. Soc. & Hon. Mem. Med. Defence Union. Prev: Apptd. Police Surg. Chippenham Div.; Cas. Off. & Dep. Sen. Resid. Off. Gen. Hosp. Bristol; Ho. Phys. Roy. Infirm. Bristol.

PEARCE, Mr Roger Malcolm Pembroke House, Chorleywood Road, Rickmansworth WD3 4EP — MB BS 1968 Lond.; FRCS Eng. 1979; MRCS Eng. LRCP Lond. 1971; FCOphth 1988; DO Eng. 1974. (St. Mary's) Cons. Ophth. Surg. Watford Gen. Hosp.; Sen. Regist. W. Ophth. Hosp. Lond.; Chief Clin. Asst. Moorfields Eye Hosp. Lond. Prev: Sen. Regist. Moorfields Eye Hosp. Lond.; Med. Off. Save the Childr. Fund; SHO (Paediat.) Barnet Gen. Hosp.

PEARCE, Ruth Elizabeth Dale End Surgery, Danby, Whitby YO21 2JE Tel: 01287 660739 Fax: 01287 660069; 4 Bridge End, Harrogate HG3 2NP — MB BS 1986 Lond.; DRCOG 1991. SHO (Med.) S. Cleveland Hosp. Middlesbrough. Prev: Ho. Off. (Surg.) Pinderfields Hosp. Wakefield; Ho. Off. (Med.) Bedford Gen. Hosp.

PEARCE, Sally Louise 25 Queens Road, Cheltenham GL50 2LX — MB BS 1988 Lond.; DRCOG 1991; DCH RCP Lond. 1991.

PEARCE, Sarah Jane 9 Almoner's Barn, Durham DH1 3TZ Tel: 0191 383 2469 Fax: 0191 383 9859 — MB ChB 1967 Cape Town; Cert. of Med. Educat. Newc. 2000; FRCP Lond. 1985; MRCP (UK) 1970. (Cape Town) Cons. Gen. Med. & Respirat., Dis. Univ. Hosp. of N. Durh.; Hon. Clin. Sen. Lect. Univ. Newc. Socs: Europ. Respiratoy Soc.; Roy. Soc. of Med.; Brit. Thorac. Soc. Prev: Sen. Regist. (Med.) Newc. AHA (T); Regist. (Med.) S.mead Hosp. Bristol; Regist. Chest Unit City Hosp. Edin.

PEARCE, Sarah Nicole Palace Flop House, Manor Farm, Chillington, Ilminster TA19 0PU Tel: 01460 52646 Fax: 01460 52646 — MB ChB 1994 Bristol. SHO Barley Wood Alcohol & Drug Rehabil. Centre, Bristol.

PEARCE, Simon Henry Schofield Dept. of Medicene, The Medicla School, Newcastle upon Tyne NE2 4HH Email: spearce@hgmp.mrc.ac.uk — MB BS 1989 Newc.; MB BS (1st cl. Hons.) Newc. 1989; MRCP (UK) 1992; MD 1998. Advanced Research Fell & Hon. Sen. Regist. (Med.) Univ. Newc. u. Tyne. Socs: Soc. Endocrinol.; Bone & Tooth Soc.; Amer. Soc. Bone & Mineral Research. Prev: MRC Train. Fell. Roy. Postgrad. Med. Sch. Lond.; Regional Regist. Rotat. (Diabetes & Endocrinol.) N.. Region.

PEARCE, Stephen Dept. of Psychiatry, Royal Southants Hospital, Brintons Terrace, Southampton SO14 0YG — MB ChB 1990 Manch.; BSc St. And. 1987; MRCP (UK) 1993; MRCPsych 1996.

PEARCE, Sushmita 8 Whinney Lane, Langho, Blackburn BB6 8DQ; 6 Rider Road, Hillsborough, Sheffield S6 2LH Tel: 0114 234 9618

PEARCE

— BM BS 1993 Nottm.; BMedSci (Hons.) Nottm. 1991; MRCP (UK) 1997.

PEARCE, Thomas Trien Surgery, Trien, Carbost, Isle of Skye IV47 8ST Tel: 01478 640202 Fax: 01478 640464 — MB ChB 1972 Manch. Prev: Med. Off. Brit. Antarctic Survey 1974-75; Chief Med. Off. Govt. Med. Dept. Falkland Is.

PEARCE, Valerie Margaret St Johns House Surgery, 28 Bromyard Road, St. Johns, Worcester WR2 5BU; St. Johns House, 28 Bromyard Road, Worcester WR2 5BU Tel: 01905 423612 Fax: 01905 740003 — MB ChB 1975 Manch.; MMedSci Birm. 1996.

PEARCE, Vanessa Lynne Health Centre, St. John Street, Mansfield NG18 1RH Tel: 01623 622541 Fax: 01623 423821; The Beeches, Main St, Eakring, Newark NG22 0DD — MB ChB 1989 Leeds; MRCGP 1994; DFFP 1994; DRCOG 1992. (Leeds)

PEARCE, Vaughan Roy Royal Devon & Exeter Hospital (Wonford), Barrack Road, Exeter EX2 5DW — MRCS Eng. LRCP Lond. 1972; BSc Lond. 1969, MB BS 1972; FRCP Lond. 1989; MRCP (UK) 1975. (St Mary's Hospital) Cons. Phys. Roy. Devon & Exeter Hosp. (Wonford); Med. Dir. Exeter & Dist. Community Trust; Sen. Lect. (Geriat. Med.) Univ. Exeter. Prev: Sen. Regist. Chesterton Hosp. Camb.

PEARCE, Walter Brian (retired) West Hill House, Blunsdon, Swindon SN26 7BN Tel: 01793 721218 — MB BS 1959 Lond.; MRCS Eng. LRCP Lond. 1959; DObst RCOG 1963. Prev: Clin. Asst. (Obst.) P.ss Marg. Hosp. Swindon.

PEARCY, Patricia Alison Mary 11 Woodlands, Darras Hall, Ponteland, Newcastle upon Tyne NE20 9EU Tel: 01661 24555 — MB BS 1960 Durh.; DPH Newc. 1968; DObst RCOG 1961. (Durh.) Prev: Sen. Research Asst. Dept. Midw. & Gyn. Univ. Newc.

PEARCY, Richard Malcolm 1 Winchcombe Road, Frampton Cotterell, Bristol BS36 2AG Tel: 01454 773102 — MB BS 1993 Lond.; MB BS (Hons.) Lond. 1993; BSc (Hons.) Lond. 1990; FRCS Eng. 1997; FRCS Ed. 1997; FRCSI 1997. (St. Geo. Hosp. Lond.) Research Regist. (Urol. Surg.) Taunton. Prev: SHO Rotat. (Surg.) Bristol.

PEARD, Mary Catherine (retired) 2 Squires Close, Crawley Down, Crawley RH10 4JQ Tel: 01342 712540 — MB BS 1952 Lond.; FRCP Lond. 1979, M 1965; MRCS Eng. LRCP Lond. 1952; DCH Eng. 1955. Prev: Cons. Paediat. Crawley & Redhill Hosps.

PEARL, Bradley Andrew The Foreland Medical Centre, 188 Walmer Road, London W11 4EP Tel: 020 7727 2604 Fax: 020 7792 1261; 47 Vespan Road, London W12 9QG — MB BS 1983 Lond.; BSc Lond. 1980, MB BS 1983; MRCGP 1987; DRCOG 1985.

***PEARL, Robert Ashley** 26 Gatehill Road, Northwood HA6 3QQ — BM 1998 Soton.; BM Soton 1998.

PEARL, Stephanie Ann 8 Culcabock Road, Inverness IV2 3XQ — MB ChB 1997 Glas.; DRCOG 1999; BA (Oxon) 1987. GP Train. Scheme, Highlands,.

PEARLGOOD, Morris, SBStJ 40 Westmount Road, Eltham Park, London SE9 1JE Tel: 020 8850 2870 Fax: 020 8850 4501 Email: mpearlgood@doctors.net.uk — MB ChB 1962 Sheff.; MRCGP 1972; DObst RCOG 1964. (Sheff.) Indep. Cons., Med. Adviser Non-Princip. GP; Cons. Med. Adviser to Bexley, Bromley & Greenwich HA and Bexley PCT; Med. Mem. of Appeals Tribunals; Med. Adviser - Publishing. Prev: Gp. Med. Edr. Modern Med. Gp. UK; Hosp. Pract. (Psychiat.) FarnBoro. Hosp. Kent; Ho. Surg. & Ho. Phys. City Gen. Hosp. Sheff.

PEARLMAN, Juliet Ann 29 Firbeck Road, Bramham, Wetherby LS23 6NE — MB ChB 1983 Leeds; MRCGP 1987; DRCOG 1987; AFOM RCP Lond. 1993. Dep. Force Med. Off. W. Yorks. Police.

***PEARMAIN, Brendan Michael Paul** 20 Scratton Road, Southend-on-Sea SS1 1EN — MB BS 1994 Lond.

PEARMAN, Mr Kenneth ENT Department, Birmingham Heartlands Hopsital, Bordeslet Green East, Birmingham B9 5SS Tel: 0121 4242351; 33 Rollswood Drive, Solihull B91 1NL Tel: 0121 7044429 Email: k@pearman.demon.co.uk — MB BS 1970 Lond.; FRCS Eng. 1975; MRCS Eng. LRCP Lond. 1970. (Roy. Free) Cons. ENT Surg. Birm. Heartlands & Solihull Hosp. Trust, Childr. Hosp. Birm. Socs: Roy. Soc. Med. & Brit. Assn. Paediat. Otorhinlaryng.

PEARS, Carl Richard Hereward Medical Centre, Exeter Street, Bourne PE10 9NJ Tel: 01778 394188 Fax: 01778 393966 — MB BS 1990 Lond.; MRCGP 1995; DFFP 1995. (St. George's Hospital Medical School) GP Partner. Prev: GP The Doctors Ltd. Napier, Hawkes Bay, New Zealand; Duke of Cornw. Spinal Injuries Unit Salisbury; GP VTS Gr. Ho. Surg. & Salisbury Dist. Hosp.

***PEARS, Jane** Reedsford, Mindrum TD12 4QQ — MB ChB 1996 Manch.

PEARS, John Stuart Medical Research Department, Zeneca Pharmaceuticals, Mereside, Macclesfield SK10 4TG Tel: 01625 515617 Fax: 01625 585626; 17 Hall Road, Wilmslow SK9 5BN Tel: 01625 524453 — MB ChB 1983 Ed.; MD Ed. 1993; MRCP (UK) 1987; Dip. Pharm. Med. RCP (UK) 1994. Med. Advisor Zeneca Pharmaceut. Macclesfield.; Clin. Asst. Manch. Diabetes Centre. Prev: Dep. Dir. Drug Developm. (Scotl.) Ltd.; Novo Research Fell. (Diabetic) Ninewells Hosp. Dundee; Regist. (Med. & Endocrinol.) Ninewells Hosp. Dundee.

PEARS, Peter Edwin 27 Parkfield Road, Coleshill, Birmingham B46 3LD Tel: 01675 463165 — MB ChB 1972 Dundee; MRCGP 1977; DObst RCOG 1974. (Dundee) Med. Adviser (Adoptions) Father Hudson's Soc. Socs: Birm. & Midl. Med. Inst. Prev: SHO (Paediat.) Maelor Gen. Hosp. Wrexham; SHO (O & G) Norf. & Norwich Hosp. Norwich; Ho. Surg. & Ho. Phys. Bridge of Earn Hosp.

PEARSALL, Fiona Jean Burns Directorate of Anaesthesia, Royal Infirmary, Castle St., Glasgow G4 0SF — MB ChB 1986 Glas.; MSc (Med. Sci.) Glas. 1993; FRCA 1991. Cons. (Anaesth.) Roy. Infirm. Glas.; Hon. Sen. Clin. Lect. Glas. Univ. Socs: GMC (Counc. Mem.); BMA; Assn. Anaesths. Prev: Sen. Regist. (Anaesth.) Glas. Roy. Infirm.; Research Regist. (Anaesth.) W.. Infirm. Glas.; Regist. (Anaesth.) Vict. Infirm. Glas.

PEARSALL, Robert William Harold 54 Newark Drive, Pollokshields, Glasgow G41 4PX — MB ChB 1988 Glas.

***PEARSE, Andrew John** Windlake House, Coaley, Dursley GL11 5DX — MB ChB 1998 Manch.; MB ChB Manch 1998.

PEARSE, Anthony Guy Everson Church Cottage, Cheriton Bishop, Exeter EX6 6HY Tel: 01647 231; Culverhill Farm, George Nympton, South Molton EX36 4JE Tel: 017695 8039 — MB BChir Camb. 1941; MA Camb. 1942, MD 1950; MD (hon causa) Basel 1960; FRCP Lond. 1964, M 1957; MRCS Eng. LRCP Lond. 1940; FRCPath 1963; DCP Lond 1947. (Camb. & St. Bart.) Emerit. Prof. HistoChem. Prev: Cons. Path. Hammersmith Hosp. Lond.

PEARSE, Dorothy Jill 98 Marsh Lane, Stanmore HA7 4HP Tel: 020 8954 4075 — MB BS 1949 Lond.; MRCS Eng. LRCP Lond. 1949. (King's Coll. Hosp.)

PEARSE, Elizabeth (retired) Church Cottage, Cheriton Bishop, Exeter EX6 6HY Tel: 01647 24231 — MB BS 1942 Sydney; DCP Lond 1947. Prev: Cons. Path. Hammersmith Hosp.

***PEARSE, Hazel Anne** 82 Bolingbroke Road, Cleethorpes DN35 0HQ — MB ChB 1994 Leeds.

PEARSE, Helen Roxane Amherst Medical Practice, 21 St. Botolphs Road, Sevenoaks TN13 3AQ Tel: 01732 459255 Fax: 01732 450751 — MB BCh 1991 Witwatersrand; DCH RCP Lond. 1996; MRCGP, UK 1998. (Univ. Witwatersrand) Socs: Med. Protec. Soc.; BMA.

PEARSE, Henry Arthur Chernocke Caen Medical Centre, Braunton EX33 1LR Tel: 01271 812005; Fullabrook Mill, Little Comfort, Braunton EX33 2NJ Tel: 0127 814735 — MRCGP 1998; MB ChB Birm. 1988; BSc Physiol. (1st cl. Hons.) Birm. 1985; DCH Otago 1992. (Birm.) GP Braunton N. Devon. Prev: Govt. Med. Off. (Police & Prisons) Bermuda; SHO (Paediat.) Poole Gen. Hosp.; Regist. (Paediat.) Wellington NZ.

PEARSE, Mr Michael Department Orthopaedic Surgery, Central Middlesex Hospital, Acton Lane, Park Royal, London NW10 7NS Tel: 020 8453 2423 Fax: 020 8453 2579 Email: m.pearse@ic.ac.uk; Department of Orthopaediac Surgery, Charing Cross Hospital, Fulham Palace Road, London W6 8RF Tel: 020 8846 1473 — MB ChB 1984 Leic.; FRCS (Orth.) 1993; FRCS Ed. 1988. Sen. Lect. (Orthop. Surg.) Hammersmith Hosps. Trust; Vis. Asst. Prof. Univ. Texas Med. Sch. Houston, USA 1995; Hon. Cons. Centr. Middlx. Hosp. Lond. Socs: Assoc. Mem. BOA; Brit. Orthop. Research Soc. Prev: Sen. Regist. Rotat. (Orthop.) Bristol, Frenchay & Plymouth Hosps.; Clin. Research Fell. (Arthritis & Rheum. Counc.) Univ. Dept. Orthop. Surg. Bristol Roy. Infirm.; Regist. (Orthop.) P.ss Eliz. Orthop. Hosp.

PEARSE, Patricia Alcyone Everson Highgate Group Practice, 44 North Hill, London N6 4QA Tel: 020 8348 6628 — MB BS 1973 Lond.; DCH Eng. 1978. GP Highgate.

PEARSE, Richard Granville The Jessop Wings, Sheff. Teachg. Hosps. NHS Trust, Sheffield S10 2SF Tel: 0114 226 8000; Bourne House, 49 Westbourne Road, Sheffield S10 2QT Tel: 0114 268 3027 Fax: 0114 267 1300 Email: rgpearse@hotmail.com — MB BChir 1970 Camb.; MA Camb. 1970; FRCP Lond. 1988, M 1974. (St. Thos.) Cons. Neonat. Paediat. Jessop Wing, Sheff. Teachg. Hosps. NHS Trust. Prev: Chef De Clin. Neonat. Unit Acad. Hosp. Rotterdam, Netherlands; Lect. (Paediat.) & Hon. Sen. Regist. St. Thos. Hosp. Lond.; Fell. (Paediat. Cardiol.) Hosp. Sick Childr. Toronto, Canada.

***PEARSE, Rupert Mark** Flamstead House, Flamstead, St Albans AL3 8BZ — MB BS 1996 Lond.

PEARSE, Sonja Blyton Ciba-Geigy Pharmaceuticals, Wimblehurst Road, Horsham RH12 4AB Tel: 01403 272827; 14 The Murreys, Barnett Wood Lane, Ashtead KT21 2LU Tel: 01372 278530 — MB BCh 1968 Wales; MFPM RCP (UK) 1989; FFA RCS Eng. 1975; FFPM 1992. (Cardiff) Head Clin. Drug Safety & Pharmacoepidemiol. Ciba-Geigy Pharmaceut. Horsham. Socs: Fell. Roy. Soc. Med.; Assn. Anaesth. Prev: Dir. Clin. Research (UK & Eire) Cyanamid Internat. Research Centre Richmond; Research Phys. Dept. Internat. Clin. Research Warner Lambert-Pk.e Davis Pontypool; Sen. Regist. (Anaesth.) Qu. Eliz. Hosp. Birm.

PEARSE-DANKER, Steven Christian The Surgery, 9 Ebdon Road, Worle, Weston Super Mare BS22 6UB Tel: 01934 514145 Fax: 01934 521345 — MB BS 1982 Lond.

PEARSON, Alan Ernest Gerald (retired) 29 Birchwood Road, Parkstone, Poole BH14 9NW — MB BChir 1977 Camb.; PhD Lond. 1959; MA Camb. 1954, BA (Nat. Sc. Trip.) 1952. Prev: Assoc. Specialist (Psychiat.) Alderney Hosp. Dorset.

PEARSON, Alexander Frederic (retired) 22 North Road, Holsworthy EX22 6HB Tel: 01409 253205 — MB ChB Manch. 1937; FRCOG 1989, M 1949. Prev: Asst. Pathol. & Res. Obst. Surg. St. Mary's Hosp. Manch.

PEARSON, Alison Jane Derwent House Surgery, Derwent House, Wakefield Road, Cockermouth CA13 0HZ Tel: 01900 822345 Fax: 01900 828469 — MB ChB 1988 Sheff.; DRCOG; DFFP. (Sheff.) GP. Prev: Trainee GP Cumbria FHSA.

PEARSON, Andrew David Chest Department, 1st Floor Lambeth Wing, Guy's & St Thomas Hospital Trust, Lambeth Palace Road, London SE1 7EH Tel: 020 7922 8046 Fax: 020 7620 2596 — BM BCh 1968 Oxf.; BA, BM BCh Oxf. 1968; Dip Bact Lond. 1972. (Oxf. & Lond. Hosp.) Cons. Communicable Dis. Control for Lambeth Lond.; Infect. Control Doctor St. Thos. Hosp. Lond.; Sec. PHLS AIDS Co-ordinating Comm. Socs: Amer. Soc. Microbiol. & Brit. Soc. Study Infec. Prev: Dir. Soton. Pub. Health Laborat.; Hon. Clin. Sen. Lect. Soton Univ.; Hon. Cons. Microbiol. Soton & S.W. Hants. HA.

PEARSON, Professor Andrew David John Sir James Spencer Institute of Child Health, Royal Victoria Infirmary, Queen Victoria Road, Newcastle upon Tyne NE1 4LP Tel: 0191 202 3036 Fax: 0191 202 3060 Email: a.d.j.pearson@ncl.ac.uk; 2 Queensway, Ponteland, Newcastle upon Tyne NE20 9RZ — MD 1989 Newc.; MB BS (1st Cl. Hons.) 1977; FRCP Lond. 1992; MRCP (UK) 1979; DCH Eng. 1980. Prof. Paediat. Oncol. Univ. Newc.; Hon. Cons. Child Health Roy. Vict. Infirm. Newc. Socs: Internat. Soc. Paediat. Oncol. & UK Childr. Cancer Study Gp.; Eur. Neuroblastoma Study Gp. Prev: Sen. Lect. & Lect. (Paediat. Oncol.) Univ. Newc.; Hon. Sen. Regist. (Paediat.) Dept. Child Health Roy. Vict. Infirm. Newc.; Lilly Internat. Med. Research Counc. Trav. fell. Univ. Minnesota, USA.

PEARSON, Andrew James Department of Radiology, Borders General Hospital, Melrose TD6 9BS Tel: 01896 826423 Fax: 01896 826438; Birchdale, Boleside, Galashiels TD1 3NV Tel: 01896 758317 — MB ChB 1979 Glas.; FRCR 1987. Cons. Radiol., Borders Gen. Hosp., Melrose. Socs: Brit. Nuclear Med. Soc.; Eur. Assn. Nuclear Med.; Soc. Nuclear Med. Prev: Sen. Regist. (Radiol.) Manch. Teach. Hosps.; Regist. W.. Infirm., Glas.

PEARSON, Andrew Robert Pyewipe House, Waddingham, Gainsborough DN21 4TG — MB BChir 1989 Camb.; MA Camb. 1989; MRCP (UK) 1993; FRCOphth 1996. (Camb. & St. Mary's) Specialist Regist. (Ophth.) Leicester Roy. Infirm.

PEARSON, Anne Mary Locksley House, Main St., Sutton on Derwent, York YO41 4BT Tel: 01904 607770 — MB ChB 1976 Glas.; MRCGP 1980; DRCOG 1978. (Glasgow)

PEARSON, Anne Rachel Newtyle Farmhouse, Drums of Foveran, Ellon AB41 6AS — MB ChB 1987 Aberd.; BA York 1978; MRCGP 1991. GP Retainer Scheme Ellon. Prev: Trainee GP Aberd. VTS.

PEARSON, Anthony John Fairway Surgery, 475 Bordesley Green East, Yardley, Birmingham B33 8PP Tel: 0121 783 2125 Fax: 0121 785 0416; Willowbrook Barn, Preston Fields Lane, Lowsonford, Solihull B95 5EZ — MB ChB 1971 Birm.; Dip. Occ. Med. 1995.

PEARSON, Anthony John Grayhurst Barnet General Hospital, Wellhouse Lane, Barnet EN5 3DJ — MRCS Eng. LRCP Lond. 1966; MB Camb. 1967, BChir 1966; MRCP Lond. 1969. Cons. Phys. Barnet Gen. Hosp.

PEARSON, Audrey Vilma Ann 49 High Bannerdown, Batheaston, Bath BA1 7JZ Tel: 01225 858293 Email: pearson@bannerdown.fsnet.co.uk; 49 High Bannerdown, Batheaston, Bath BA1 7JZ Tel: 01225 858293 — MRCS Eng. LRCP Lond. 1969; MFHom Lond. 1989. (Sheffield) p/t Indep. Pract. Homoeopathy & Acupunc. Socs: Fac. Homoeop.; Accred. Mem. Brit. Med. Acupunc. Soc. Prev: Homoeop. Phys. Roy. Lond. Homeop. Hosp.; GP Bath.

PEARSON, Benedict Joseph 29 Horton Street, Lincoln LN2 5NG Tel: 01522 511704 — MB BS 1993 Lond.

PEARSON, Beryl Coline Low Lickbarrow Farm, Lickbarrow Close, Heathwaite, Windermere LA23 2NF — MB ChB 1949 Liverp.; DCH Eng. 1951. (Liverp.) Prev: Ho. Surg. Profess. Unit BRd.green Hosp. Liverp.; Paediat. Ho. Phys. Taunton & Som. Hosp.; Ho. Surg. O & G Chester City Hosp.

PEARSON, C Michael G Ash Cottage, Farley Common, Westerham TN16 1UB Tel: 01959 65347 — MB BS 1946 Lond. (Guy's) Prev: Ho. Phys. Childr. Dept. Pembury Hosp.; Res. Med. Off. Qu. Eliz. Hosp. Childr. Shadwell.

PEARSON, Mr Charles Justly Probyn, Surg. Capt. RN Retd. Northernhay, Pathfields, Townstal, Dartmouth EX39 2HL — FRCS Ed. 1935; MRCS Eng. LRCP Lond. 1932. (St. Thos.) Prev: Ho. Surg. & Cas. Off. St. Thos. Hosp.

PEARSON, Christine Freya Rodwell, East Dean Road, Lockerley, Romsey SO51 0JQ — MB BS 1995 Lond.

PEARSON, Christopher Alan Robert Stirchley Medical Practice, Stirchley Health Centre, Stirchley, Telford TF3 1FB Tel: 01952 660444 Fax: 01952 415139; 48 Lincoln Hill, Ironbridge, Telford TF8 7QA — MB ChB 1982 Sheff.; MRCGP 1986; DRCOG 1985.

PEARSON, Christopher Almack Aldershot Health Centre, Wellington Avenue, Aldershot GU11 1PA Tel: 01252 324577 Fax: 01252 324861; Lorien, 1 Highlands Close, Shortheath, Farnham GU9 8SP Tel: 01252 24577 — MB BS 1971 Lond. (Middlx.)

PEARSON, Clive Henry Crown House Surgery, Chapelgate, Retford DN22 6NX Tel: 01777 703672 Fax: 01777 710534 — MB ChB 1979 Sheff.

PEARSON, Daphne Mary (retired) Camelot, 21 The Ridgway, Sutton SM2 5JX Tel: 020 8642 4770 — MB BS Lond. 1966; MRCS Eng. LRCP Lond. 1966. Community Paediat. (SCMO) Richmond, Twickenham & Roehampton.

PEARSON, David Anthony Woolpit Health Centre, Heath Road, Woolpit, Bury St Edmunds IP30 9QU Tel: 01359 240298 Fax: 01359 241975; Poplar Farm, Great Green, Thurston, Bury St Edmunds IP31 3SL Tel: 01359 232325 — MA, MB BChir Camb. 1980; MRCGP 1986; DCH RCP Lond. 1984; DRCOG 1982; Cert. Av. Med. 1990. (Middlx.) Socs: BMA.

PEARSON, David Charles (retired) Woodland Cottage, Eggerslack, Grange-over-Sands LA11 6EX — MB ChB 1955 Birm.; FFA RCS Eng. 1964; DObst RCOG 1957. Prev: Cons. Anaesth. W. Birm. Health Dist.

PEARSON, David Gerald Roger Doctors Surgery, Salisbury Road, Southsea PO4 9QX Tel: 023 9273 1458 — MB BS 1977 Lond.; BSc (Pharmacol.) Lond. 1974; MRCGP 1982; DRCOG 1979; Dip. Occ. Med. 1997. (Univ. Coll. Hosp.) Socs: Soc. Occupat. Med.

PEARSON, David John Royd House, 224 Hale Road, Hale, Altrincham WA15 8EB Tel: 0161 998 1999, 0161 946 1697 Email: david@allergy.uk.com — MB BS 1968 Lond.; PhD Manch. 1976; FRCP Lond. 1987; MRCP (UK) 1972; MRCS Eng. LRCP Lond. 1968. (St. Geo.) Cons. Phys. Univ. Hosp. S. Manch. Socs: Brit. Soc. Allergy & Clin. Immunol.; Eur. Acad. Allergy & Clin. Immunol.; Amer. Acad. Asthma, Allergy & Clin. Immunol. Prev: Sen. Lect. (Med.) Univ. Manch.; Vis. Scientist Nat. Occupat. Safety & Health Pub. Health Serv.; Asst. Prof. (Med.) W. Virginia Univ.

PEARSON

PEARSON, David John Fisher Medical Centre, Millfields, Coach Street, Skipton BD23 1EU — MB ChB 1988 Ed.; BA Camb. 1982; MRCGP 1993. Prev: GP/SHO (Gen. Med.) Airedale Gen. Hosp. VTS.

PEARSON, Deborah Christine 12 Sherbourne Drive, Maidenhead SL6 3EP Tel: 01628 672518 — BM BCh Oxf. 1986; MA Camb. 1987; Dip. Pharm. Med. RCP (UK) 1991. Socs: Fac. Pharmaceut. Med. Prev: Clin. Research Phys. Syntex Pharmaceuts. Med. Research Europe Maidenhead; Sen. Med. Adviser Clinpharm Ltd. Maidenhead & Boehringer Ingelheim Ltd. Bracknell.

PEARSON, Deborah Jane Compton Hospice, 4 Compton Road West, Wolverhampton WV3 9DH — MB ChB 1984 Birm.; MRCGP 1988. Med. Dir. Compton Hospice Wolverhampton. Prev: GP Bushbury Wolverhampton; SHO (A & E) Roy. Hosp. Wolverhampton; SHO (Paediat. & O & G) New Cross Hosp. Wolverhampton.

PEARSON, Derek Thomas (retired) 9 Lowther Glen, Eamont Bridge, Penrith CA10 2BP Email: dtpearson@medix-uk.com — MB BS 1959 Durh.; FRCP Lond. 1976, M 1962; FRCA Eng. 1964. Prev: Cons. Anaesth. Regional Cardiothoracic Centre Freeman Hosp. Newc.

PEARSON, Donald 62 Park Road, Hale, Altrincham WA15 9LR Tel: 0161 980 2237 — MD 1969 Liverp.; MB ChB 1960; FRCP Lond. 1978, M 1964. (Liverp.) Cons. Phys. Warrington Hosp. NHS Trust; Sen. Regist. (Med.) Liverp. Roy. Infirm. Socs: BMA & Liverp. Med. Inst. Prev: Regist. (Med.) Walton Hosp. Liverp. & Vict. Centr. Hosp. Wallasey; Ho. Surg. Mill Rd. Matern. Hosp. Liverp.

PEARSON, Donald William MacIntyre Diabetic Clinic, Woolmanhill, Aberdeen Royal Infirmary, Gampian University Hospitals NHS Trust, Aberdeen Tel: 01224 681818 Fax: 01224 681818; 19 Corunna Place, Aberdeen AB23 8DA Tel: 01224 702463 — MB ChB 1976 Glas.; BSc (Hons.) Glas. 1972; FRCP Ed. 1990; FRCP Glas. 1988. Cons. Phys. (With s/i in Diabetes Mellitus) Aberd. Teach. Hosps.; Clin. Sen. Lect. Univ. Aberd. Socs: Scott. Soc. Phys.; Brit. Diabetic Assn.; Diabetic Pregn. study Gp. of EASD. Prev: Sen. Regist. (Gen. Med.) (With s/i in Endocrinol. & Diabetes) Aberd. Teach. Hosps.; Lect. (Med.) Univ. Aberd.; Regist. (Gen. Med.) Glas. Roy. Infirm.

PEARSON, Dorothy (retired) 5 Meadowfields, Whaley Bridge, High Peak SK23 7AX Tel: 01663 732570 Fax: 01663 732570 — MB ChB 1948 Manch.; FRCR 1975; FFR 1958; DMRT Eng. 1951. Prev: Cons. Radiotherap. Christie Hosp. & Holt Radium Inst. Manch.

PEARSON, Elaine Janet Stoneleigh Surgery, Police Square, Milnthorpe LA7 7PW Tel: 015395 63307; 5 Heron's Quay, Sandside, Milnthorpe LA7 7HW — MB ChB 1983 Manch.; MRCP (UK) 1986; MRCGP 1990; DRCOG 1989.

PEARSON, Elizabeth Margaret 355 Harrogate Road, Leeds LS17 6PZ Tel: 0113 268 0066 Fax: 0113 288 8643 — MB BS 1973 Lond.; MRCGP 1980; DCH Eng. 1976; DRCOG 1976. (Lond. Hosp.) Prev: Trainee GP Nottm. VTS; SHO Wom. Hosp. Nottm.; SHO (Paediat.) Childr. Hosp. Nottm.

***PEARSON, Ewan Robert** 2 St Johns Close, East Grinstead RH19 3YR — BChir 1995 Camb.

PEARSON, Gale Adrian Birmingham Childrens Hospital, Steelhouse Lane, Birmingham B4 6NH; 205 Northfield Road, Kings Norton, Birmingham B30 1EA — MB BS 1985 Newc.; MRCP (UK) 1990; FRCPCH 1997. Cons. Paediat. Intensivist Birm. Childr. Hosp.; Hon. Sen. Lect. Dept. of Anaesth. & Int. Care, Birm. Univ. Socs: Chairm. PICS; PRS; ICS. Prev: Chief Regist. PICU Roy. Childr. Melbourne, Austral.; ECMO Fell. Leicester Univ.

PEARSON, George Halley (retired) Hadrian, 34 High West Road, Crook DL15 9NS Tel: 01388 762552 — MB ChB 1943 Ed. Prev: Ho. Surg. OldCh. Co. Hosp. Romford.

PEARSON, Gillian Charlotte Osteoporosis Research Unit, Southampton General Hospital, Southampton SO16 6YD Tel: 02380 794857 Fax: 02380 798505; 75 Christchurch Road, St. Cross, Winchester SO23 9TG — MB ChB 1977 Bristol; MF Hom Lond. 1997. Research Fell. (Osteoporosis Research Unit) Soton. Gen. Hosp.; Homeopathic Physican, Winch. Homeopathic. Pract. Prev: GP VTS; Med. Off. RAMC.

PEARSON, Gillian Lesley 2 Queensway, Ponteland, Newcastle upon Tyne NE20 9RZ — MB BS 1976 Newc.; MRCGP 1980. GP Wom. Retainer Scheme Morpeth. Prev: Regist. Dept. Radiother. Newc. Gen. Hosp.

PEARSON, Gordon Horden Group Practice, The Surgery, Sunderland Road, Horden, Peterlee SR8 4QP Tel: 0191 586 4210 Fax: 0191 587 0700; 37 Elsdon Close, Peterlee SR8 1NE — MB ChB 1977 Ed.; MRCGP 1981; DRCOG 1981. (Edinburgh)

PEARSON, Ian Barrie (retired) 94 Tamworth Drive, Fleet GU51 2UP — MB ChB 1965 Sheff.; MD Sheff. 1965; MRCPsych 1971; DPM Eng. 1967. Cons. Psychiat. Dumfries & Galloway HB., Crichton Roy. Hosp. Prev: Head of Clin. Research, Roche Products Ltd.

***PEARSON, Ian Christopher** 21 The Ridgeway, Sutton SM2 5JX — MB BS 1996 Lond.

PEARSON, James (retired) Glencart House, 5 Glencart Grove, Kilbarchan, Johnstone PA10 2DH Tel: 01505 705314 — MB ChB 1944 Glas.; MRCGP 1964; FRCGP 1999. Prev: Regional Med. Off. Scott. Home & Health Dept. Glas.

PEARSON, James Francis (retired) 14 Sherborne Avenue, Cyncoed, Cardiff CF23 6SJ Tel: 029 2075 2909 Fax: 029 2075 3050 — MB BS 1960 Lond.; MD Lond. 1973; FRCOG 1978, M 1965; DObst RCOG 1963. Prev: Sen. Regist. (O & G) United Birm. Hosps. & Birm. RHB.

PEARSON, James Gordon Royal Crescent Surgery, 11 Royal Crescent, Cheltenham GL50 3DA Tel: 01242 580248 Fax: 01242 253618; Quintain, Old Mansion Drive, Prestbury, Cheltenham GL52 3AS Tel: 01242 580198 — MB BS 1971 Lond.; MRCS Eng. LRCP Lond. 1971. (Roy. Free) Med. Off. Cheltenham Coll.; Med. Off. Cheltenham Tour AFC; Clin. Asst. in Psychiat. (Learning Disabilities).

PEARSON, Joanna Mary 31 Pennine Walk, Tunbridge Wells TN2 3NW — MB BS 1991 Lond.; DPD 1999; BSc Lond. 1982; Dip. Dietetics Lond. 1983; MRCGP 1996; DFFP 1996; DRCOG 1994. (University College and Middlesex School of Medicine London) Prev: Vocationally Trained Assoc. W. Kent; GP/Regist. Tunbridge Wells VTS.

PEARSON, Mr John Brian (retired) Copthall Green House, Upshire, Waltham Abbey EN9 3SZ Tel: 01992 711273 Email: upshirepearson@yahoo.co.uk — MB ChB 1953 Birm.; FRCS Eng. 1961; FACS 1977; DObst RCOG 1955. Cons. Surg. Redbridge Dist. HA. Prev: Sen. Surg. Regist. United Birm. Hosps.

PEARSON, John Dale West Cairn, The Shore, Hest Bank, Lancaster LA2 6HW — MB ChB 1964 Liverp.; DTM & H 1965; MRCP (U.K.) 1970. (Liverp.) Cons. Phys. Roy. Lancaster Infirm., Lancaster Moor & Kendal Hosps. Socs: Fell. RCP Lond.; Brit. Geriat. Soc. Prev: Sen. Regist. Liverp. Regional Hosp. Bd.; Regist. United Liverp. Hosp.

PEARSON, John Egan 292 Victoria Park Road, Leicester LE2 1XE Tel: 0116 270 8641 — MB ChB 1990 Leic.; BSc (Biol. Sc.) Leic. 1982; DA (UK) 1994. Specialist Regist. (Anaesth.) Leicester Roy. Infirm. Prev: SHO (Anaesth.) Leicester Roy. Infirm.

PEARSON, John Gilbert Havelock 10 Morley Road, Twickenham TW1 2HF — MRCS Eng. LRCP Lond. 1974; BSc Lond. 1972, MB BS 1975.

PEARSON, John Michael Henry (retired) 3 Swan Cottage, Asthall Leigh, Witney OX29 9PZ Tel: 01993 878384 — BM BCh Oxf. 1955; DM Oxf. 1975; FRCP Lond. 1981, M 1963. Prev: Mem. Scientif. Staff Med. Research Counc.

PEARSON, John Robert Centre Surgery, Health Centre, Hill St., Hinckley LE10 1DS Tel: 01455 632277 — MRCS Eng. LRCP Lond. 1963.

PEARSON, Mr John Roy (retired) 66 Arthur Road, Edgbaston, Birmingham B15 2UW — MB ChB 1950 Birm.; FRCS Eng. 1958; FRCS Ed. 1958. Prev: Cons. Surg. (Orthop.) Birm. Gen. Hosp. & Roy. Orthop. Hosp. Birm.

PEARSON, Jonathan Mark Department of Pathology, Royal Bolton Hospital, Minerva Road, Farnworth, Bolton BL4 0JR Tel: 01204 390534 — MB ChB 1985 Manch.; FRCPath 2000; MB ChB (Hons.) Manch. 1985; BSc (Hons.) Manch. 1982; MRCPath 1992. Cons. Histopath. Roy. Bolton Hosp.

PEARSON, Joseph Robert 14 Sherborne Avenue, Cyncoed, Cardiff CF23 6SJ Tel: 029 2075 2909 — MB BCh 1995 Wales. (UWCM) SHO (Anaesth.) Swansea. Socs: MPS; MSS. Prev: Cardiff-Llandough Hosp.

PEARSON, Julia Melissa Nelson Health Centre, Leeds Road, Nelson BB9 9TG Tel: 01282 698036; Acorn House, Lanehouse, Trawden, Colne BB88SN — MB BS 1983 Lond.; DRCOG 1987; DCH 1988.

PEARSON

*****PEARSON, Julie Claire** Belves, The Chantry, Rooksbridge, Axbridge BS26 2TR — MB ChB 1998 Liverp.; MB ChB Liverp 1998.

PEARSON, Kathleen Marianne (retired) Tollgate, 28 Church St., Milnthorpe LA7 7DX Tel: 015395 63121 — MB ChB 1936 Liverp.; FRCGP 1971, M 1953. Prev: Pres. Lancs. Med. Book Club.

PEARSON, Mr Kenneth William 29 Knowsley Street, Bury BL9 0ST Tel: 0161 797 9771 — MD 1974 Manch.; MB ChB 1964; FRCS Eng. 1972; FRCS Ed. 1970; DObst RCOG 1966. Cons. Gen. Surg. Bury AHA. Socs: Fell. Manch. Med. Soc. Prev: Sen. Surg. Regist. Manch. AHA (T).

PEARSON, Lezli Ann The Stewart Medical Centre, 15 Hartington Road, Buxton SK17 6JP Tel: 01298 22338 Fax: 01298 72678 — MB BS 1984 Lond. Trainee GP Hillingdon Hosp. VTS. Prev: SHO (Orthop.) Kingston & Esher HA; Ho. Off. (Med. & Surg.) W. Cumbria HA.

PEARSON, Linda Claire 4 The Fairways, Leamington Spa CV32 6PR — MB ChB 1987 Manch.; DA (UK) 1992. Staff Grade Anaesth. Warwick Hosp. Prev: SHO (Anaesth.) Oldham Hosp.

PEARSON, Linsey Jane The Stables, Westfield, Wood Lane, Chapel Allerton, Leeds LS7 3QF — MB ChB 1992 Leeds.

PEARSON, Lorraine Crescent Villa, Crescent St., Cottingham HU16 5QS — MB ChB 1982 Manch.

PEARSON, Lucy Samantha Farthings, Park Road, Slinfold, Horsham RH13 7SD — MB ChB 1993 Leic. SHO (Nephrol.) Leicester Gen. Hosp. Prev: SHO (A & E) Selly Oak Hosp.; Ho. Off. (Med.) Leicester Roy. Hosp.; Ho. Off. (Surg.) Geo. Eliot Hosp. Nuneaton.

PEARSON, Margaret (retired) 82 Harrison Gardens, Edinburgh EH11 1SB — MB ChB 1947 Ed.; MB ChB (Hnrs.) Ed. 1947. Prev: Med. Asst. (Path.) Bangour Gen. Hosp. Broxburn.

PEARSON, Margaret Joan Beechgrove, Strachan, Banchory AB31 6NL Tel: 01330 822072 — MB ChB 1991 Aberd.

PEARSON, Marjory Morison (retired) 3 Garscube Terrace, Edinburgh EH12 6BH — MB ChB 1933 Ed.

PEARSON, Mark Joseph 41 Alderbrook Road, Solihull B91 1NW — MB ChB 1979 Birm.; MA Camb. 1980; MSc (Psychother.) Warwick 1986; MRCPsych 1983.

PEARSON, Maurice Robert Wick Medical Centre, Martha Terrace, Wick KW1 5EL Tel: 01955 605885 Fax: 01955 602434; 22 Port Dunbar, Port Dunbar, Wick KW1 4JJ Tel: 01955 602450 Fax: 01955 606637 Email: mrpwick@aol.com — MB BS Durh. 1965; BSc Durham. 1962. (Durh.) Socs: BMA. Prev: Regist. Gen. Med. Qu. Eliz. Hosp. Gateshead; SHO Artific. Kidney Unit, & Ho. Surg. & Ho. Phys. Roy. Vict. Infirm. Newc.

PEARSON, Max (retired) Price of Peace, Hatherleigh, Okehampton EX20 3QA Tel: 01837 810509 — MB ChB 1953 Liverp.; DObst RCOG 1962. Prev: Ho. Phys. St. Catherine's Hosp. Birkenhead.

PEARSON, Michael Carden (retired) Bleak House, Horsted Keynes, Haywards Heath RH17 7ED — MB BChir 1963 Camb.; MA Camb. 1963; MSc (Med.) Lond. 1993; FRCP Lond. 1994; MRCP Lond. 1967; FRCR 1975; FFR 1971; DMRD Eng. 1969. Prev: Cons. Radiol. Lond. Chest Hosp. Roy. Hosps. NHS Trust & Roy. Brompton & Nat. Heart Hosps.

PEARSON, Michael David Stourview Medical Centre, Crown Passage, High Street, Haverhill CB9 8BB Tel: 01440 761177 Fax: 01440 714688; 23 Bladon Way, Haverhill CB9 0AB Tel: 01440 61177 — MB ChB 1966 Sheff. (Sheff.) Home Off. Prison Med. Off.; Occupat. Health Phys. Prev: Ho. Surg. St. Luke's Matern. Hosp. Bradford & Roy. Infirm. Sheff.; Ho. Phys. Nottm. Gen. Hosp.

PEARSON, Michael George Aintree Chest Centre, University Hospital, Aintree, Longmoor Lane, Liverpool L9 7AL Tel: 0151 529 3857 Fax: 0151 529 2873 — MB BChir 1976 Camb.; MA Camb. 1976; FRCP Lond. 1991; MRCP (UK) 1978. Cons. Phys. Aintree Chest Centre Univ. Hosp., Aintree, Liverp.; Dir. Clin. Effectiveness & Eval. Unit of RCP Lond.; Vis. Prof. Univ. Salford. Socs: Brit. Thorac. Soc.; Amer. Thoracic Soc.; Eur. Respirat. Soc. Prev: Hon. Lect. (Med.) Univ. Liverp.; Clin. Research Fell. Univ. of W. Ontario & Lond., Canada; Sen. Regist. Rotat. (Gen. & Respirat. Med.) Mersey RHA.

PEARSON, Michael John 11 Millholme Close, Southam, Leamington Spa CV47 1FQ — MB ChB 1982 Birm.; MD Birm. 1995; MRCOG 1988. Cons. O & G S. Warks. Hosps. NHS Trust.

PEARSON, Michael Lawrence 5 Woodland Place, Bathwick Hill, Bath BA2 6EH; 15 Choir Green, Knaphill, Woking GU21 2NQ — MB BS 1989 Lond. Trainee GP St. John's Health Centre Woking.

PEARSON, Mr Morton Gilmour (retired) 27 Bryanston Drive, Dollar FK14 7EF Tel: 01259 742444 — MB ChB 1941 Ed.; FRCS Ed. 1953; FRCOG 1963, M 1950. Prev: Cons. O & G Roy. Infirm. Edin., Simpson Memor. Matern. Pavil. Edin. & Scott. Borders Hosp. Gp.

PEARSON, Nanette Mirrington Pant Hywel, Llandegfan, Menai Bridge LL59 5SB — MB BS 1971 Lond.; DCH Eng. 1974; DObst RCOG 1973. (Middlx.) Med. Off. (Community Med.) Gwynedd Health Auth. Prev: Regist. (Paediat.) W. Middlx. Hosp. Isleworth; SHO (Paediat.) Centr. Middlx. Hosp. Lond. & W.m. Childr. Hosp.; Lond.

PEARSON, Nicholas David Oakley Bungalow, Oakley Lane, Canford Magna, Wimborne BH21 1SF Tel: 01202 849048 Fax: 01202 886207 — MB BS 1977 Lond.; MRCPsych 1987. Cons. Psychiat. (Old Age Psychiat.) Oakley Hse. Bungalow.

PEARSON, Nicola Jane Somerset Health Authority, Wellsprings Road, Taunton TA2 7PQ; The Anchorage, Othery, Bridgwater TA7 0PY Tel: 01823 698036 — MB BS 1986 Lond.; MFPHM RCP (UK) 1995. (Lond. Hosp. Med. Coll.) Cons. (Pub. Health Med.) Som. HA. Prev: Lect. (Epidemiol. & Pub. Health Med.) Dept. Social Med. Bristol Univ.

PEARSON, Nigel Ian Campbell 86 Cornwallis Road, Florence Park, Oxford OX4 3NL Tel: 01865 773253 — MB ChB 1987 Bristol; DTM & H Liverp. 1991; DCH RCPS Glas. 1990; Cert. Equiv Experience. (Bristol) Locum Gen. Practitioner, Oxf.; Freelance Cons. in Health Care in Poor, deprived and dEstab. areas. Prev: Trainee GP I. of Mull; SHO (Paediat. & O & G) Boston.; Dist. Med. Off. Health Dist. of Boga, Zaire.

PEARSON, Nigel Ralph Maudsley Hospital, Denmark Hill, London SE5 8AZ Tel: 020 7703 6333 — MB BS 1991 Lond.; BA Oxf. 1988; MRCP (UK) 1994; MCRPsych (UK) 1996.

PEARSON, Nina Rosemary Saltaire Medical Centre, Richmond Road, Saltaire, Shipley BD18 4RX Tel: 01274 593101; 7 Bramham Drive, Baildon, Shipley BD17 6SZ — MB BS 1983 Newc.; MRCGP 1987; Cert. Family Plann. JCC 1987; DRCOG 1986. GP Shipley Retainer Scheme. Prev: Trainee GP Harrogate VTS.

***PEARSON, Owen Rhys** 5 Bryneglwys Gardens, Porthcawl CF36 5PR — MB BCh 1997 Wales.

PEARSON, Patricia Frithwood Surgery, 45 Tanglewood Way, Bussage, Stroud GL6 8DE Tel: 01453 884646 Fax: 01453 731302; Rectory Barn, Bisley, Stroud GL6 7AD Tel: 01452 770707 — MB BS 1967 Durh.; MRCGP 1977. (King's Coll. Newc.) Prev: Clin. Asst. (Gyn.) Gloucester Roy. Hosp.

PEARSON, Patricia Joan Margaret Dovecote, Synton, Selkirk TD7 4BP — MB BS 1965 Durh. (Durh.) Prev: Anaesth. Co. Hosp. & Lewis Hosp. Stornoway; Regist. Anaesth. Gateshead Hosp. Gp.; Ho. Surg. & Ho. Phys. Qu. Eliz. Hosp. Gateshead.

PEARSON, Patrick Joseph Thomas Longcroft Clinic, 5 Woodmansterne Lane, Banstead SM7 3HH Tel: 01737 359332 Fax: 01737 370835; Myrtle Cottage, 20 Myrtle Road, Sutton SM1 4BX Tel: 020 8643 8680 — MB BChir 1979 Camb.; MA Camb. 1978; MRCGP (Distinc.) 1984; DRCOG 1982. (Kings Coll. Hosp.) Dep. Police Surg. Epsom; Med. Adviser Catholic Childr. Adoption Soc. Socs: BMA; Sutton Med. Soc. Prev: Trainee GP Croydon VTS; SHO (A & E) Kingston Hosp.; Ho. Surg. King's Coll. Hosp. Lond.

PEARSON, Paul (retired) Low Lickbarrow Farm, Lickbarrow Close, Heathwaite, Windermere LA23 2NF — MRCS Eng. LRCP Lond. 1949; MRCGP 1962; DObst RCOG 1964; DA Eng. 1963. Prev: Ho. Surg. Liverp. Stanley Hosp.

PEARSON, Randall Murray Gloynes, Capt. RAMC Retd. 14 Stapenhill Road, Burton-on-Trent DE15 9AF Tel: 01283 568427 Email: rmgpearson@aol.com — MB BS 1975 Lond.; FFA RCS Eng. 1984. (Lond. Hosp.) Cons. Anaesth. Burton-on-Trent. Socs: BMA & Assn. Anaesths. Gt. Brit. & Irel.; Fell. Roy. Soc. Med.; Obst. Anaesth. Assn. Prev: Sen. Regist. (Anaesth.) Nottm. & E. Midl. Higher Profess. Train. Scheme; Regist. (Anaesth.) Norf. & Norwich Hosp.; Specialist (Anaesth.) RAMC.

PEARSON, Richard Alan 17 Shillingford Drive, Stoke-on-Trent ST4 8YG — MB ChB 1990 Manch.

PEARSON, Richard Eaton The Maudsley Hospital, Denmark Hill, London SE5 8AZ Tel: 020 7919 2327 — MB BS 1983 Lond.;

PEARSON

MRCPsych 1992. Sen. Regist. Bethlem Roy. & Maudsley Hosp. Lond. & BRd.moor Hosp. Prev: Research Sen. Regist. (Psychiat.) Inst. Psychiat. Lond.; Regist. (Psychiat.) Char. Cross Hosp. Lond. & Roy. Lond. Hosp.

PEARSON, Richard Francis (retired) 78 Woodside Avenue, Muswell Hill, London N10 3HY Tel: 020 8883 1965 — MRCS Eng. LRCP Lond. 1947; MA Camb. 1947, MB BChir 1952. Prev: Ho. Phys. Hope Hosp. Salford.

PEARSON, Richard James Pyewip House, Waddingham, Gainsborough DN21 4TG — MB BS 1985 Lond.; MA Camb. 1986; MRCGP 1990; FRACGP 1993; DA (UK) 1995; DTM & H Liverp. 1995; DCH RCP Lond. 1989; DRACOG 1988. Prev: SHO (Anaesth.) Countess of Chester Hosp.

PEARSON, Richard Martin St Bartholomew's & the Royal London School of Medicine, & Dentistry, Charterhouse Square, London EC1M 6BQ Tel: 020 7415 3411 Fax: 020 7415 3404 Email: r.m.pearson@mds.qmw.ac.uk; 152 Harley Street, London W1N 1HH Tel: 020 7935 3834 Fax: 020 7354 1501 Email: richard.pearson@which.com — MB BChir 1968 Camb.; MA, MB Camb. 1968, BChir 1967; FRCP (UK) 1996, MRCP 1970. (Camb. & St. Mary's) Cons. Phys. Harold Wood & Oldchurdh Hosp. Romford & Sen. Lect. Clin. Pharmacol. St. Bart. Hosp. Lond. Socs: Fell. Roy. Soc. Med.; Brit. Pharm. Soc.; BMA. Prev: Cons. Phys. Nottm. AHA.; Sen. Regist. (Med.) Roy. Free Hosp. Lond.; Research Fell. Roy. Postgrad. Med. Sch. Hammersmith Hosp. Lond.

PEARSON, Robert Red House Farm, Thame Road, Longwick, Princes Risborough HP27 9SW Tel: 01844 342843 — MB ChB 1970 Bristol; MSc Bristol 1970, BSc (Physiol.) 1966; MRCP (UK) 1974; DObst RCOG 1976. (Univ. Bristol) Assoc. Med. Dir. (Respirat.) Glaxo Wellcome UK Uxbridge. Socs: BMA; Brit. Thorac. Soc. Prev: Regional Med. Adviser Glaxo Pharmaceut. UK Ltd. Uxbridge; GP Stratford-upon-Avon; SHO (Obst., Path. & Neonat. Paediat.) S.mead Hosp. Bristol.

PEARSON, Mr Robert Charles 23 Anson Road, Victoria Park, Manchester M14 5BZ Tel: 0161 428 9326; 55 Bramhall Park Road, Bramhall, Stockport SK7 3NA — MB ChB 1978 Manch.; MB ChB (Hons.) Manch. 1978; BSc St. And. 1975; MD Manch. 1989; FRCS Eng. 1983. (Manchester) Cons. Surg. Manch. Roy. Infirm.

PEARSON, Robert Edmund Moresdale Lane Surgery, 95 Moresdale Lane, Leeds LS14 6GG Tel: 0113 295 1200 Fax: 0113 295 1210 — MB ChB 1981 Manch.; BSc Manch. 1979; MRCGP 1989; DGM RCP Lond. 1986; DRCOG 1986; Adv Professional Dip (Mentoring) LMU 1997. Prev: SHO (Orthop.) Pontefract Gen. Infirm.; SHO (O & G) Huddersfield Roy. Infirm.; SHO (Gen. Med.) Bury Gen. Hosp.

PEARSON, Robert Henry Dept. of Radiology, Perth Royal Infirmary, Perth PH1 1NX — MB ChB 1988 Manch.; MD Aberdeen 2000; BSc MedSci St. Andrews. 1985; MRCP (UK) 1992; FRCR 1998. (Manch.) Cons. (Radiol.) Perth Roy. Infirm. Perth.

PEARSON, Robert Neville (retired) 47 Church Lane, South Crosland, Huddersfield HD4 7DD — LMSSA 1950 Lond.

PEARSON, Robin Lochrie Elgin Medical Centre, 10 Victoria Crescent, Elgin IV30 1RQ Tel: 01343 547512 Fax: 01343 546781; The Grange, 14 Seafield Crescent, Elgin IV30 1RE Tel: 01343 542146 — MB ChB 1976 Glas.; MRCGP 1985; DRCOG 1978.

PEARSON, Roger Hardacre Lowther Medical Centre, 1 Castle Meadows, Whitehaven CA28 7RG Tel: 01946 692241 Fax: 01946 590617; 17 Eden Drive, Moresby Parks, Whitehaven CA28 8XA Tel: 01946 694494 Fax: 01946 590617 — MB BS 1964 Durh. (Durh.) Prev: SHO Sunderland Matern. Hosp.; Ho. Surg. & Ho. Phys. Roy. Infirm. Sunderland.

***PEARSON, Ronald Carl Alan** 12 Kingswood Avenue, Newcastle upon Tyne NE2 3NS — BM BCh 1980 Oxf.; MA Oxf. 1984, DPhil 1980, BA 1974, BM BCh 1980.

PEARSON, Ronald Norman Bosmere Medical Practice, PO Box 41, Civic Centre Road, Havant PO9 2AJ Tel: 023 9245 1300 Fax: 023 9249 2524 Email: bosmeremedical@cs.com; Applegarth, Church Lane, Hayling Island PO11 0SB Tel: 023 9246 3565 — MB BS 1964 Lond.; MRCS Eng. LRCP Lond. 1964; DObst RCOG 1967. (Guy's) Hosp. Pract. (Geniourin. Med.) St. Mary's Hosp. Portsmouth. Socs: BMA. Prev: Ho. Phys. & Ho. Surg. Roy. Sussex Co. Hosp. Brighton; Ho. Surg. (Obst.) Brighton Gen. Hosp.; Med. Off. King Edwd. VII Memor. Hosp. Bermuda.

PEARSON, Rowan Elisabeth 32 Bankside Close, Upper Poppleton, York YO26 6LH — MB ChB 1986 Leeds; MRCPsych 1991. Staff Grade Malham Hse. Day Hosp. Leeds CMH Trust.

PEARSON, Mr Russell Vaughan Ophthalmology Department, Southend General Hospital, Prittlewell Chase, Southend-on-Sea SS0 0RY Tel: 01702 435555; 59 Priests Lane, Shenfield, Brentwood CM15 8BX Tel: 01277 214577 Fax: 01277 848580 Email: russell.pearson1@virgin.net — MB BS 1980 Lond.; BSc (Physiol.) Lond. 1977, MB BS 1980; FRCS Eng. 1986; MRCP (UK) 1985; FRCOphth. 1989. (Lond. Hosp.) Cons. Ophth. Surg. S.end Health Care Trust and Basildon & Orsett Hosp. Socs: Fell. Roy. Soc. Med.; Oxf. Ophth. Congr.; Euro. Soc. Of Cataract & Refractive Surg.s. Prev: Sen. Regist. (Ophth.) Lond. & Moorfield Eye Hosps. Lond.; Resid. Regist. (Surg.) Moorfields Eye Hosp. Lond.; SHO (Ophth.) W.. Ophth. & Char. Cross Hosps. Lond.

PEARSON, Ruth Hutchison Dept of Radiology, Queen Mary's University Hospital, Roehampton, London SW15 5PN Tel: 020 8789 6611; Jasmine House, 190 New King's Road, London SW6 4NF Tel: 020 7731 0818 — MB BCh BAO 1973 Dub.; BA Dub. 1971, MB BCh BAO 1973; FRCR 1978; DMRD Eng. 1977. (TC Dub.) Cons. Radiol. Qu. Mary's Hosp. Roehampton Lond. Prev: Sen. Regist. Radiol. Hammersmith Hosp. Lond.

PEARSON, Sally Anne Department of Ultrasound, Derriford Hospital, Derriford, Plymouth PL6 8DH; Langston, Kingston, Kingsbridge TQ7 4HB Tel: 01548 810234 Fax: 01548 810453 — MB BS 1972 Lond.; MRCS Eng. LRCP Lond. 1972; DObst RCOG 1974. (Roy. Free) Assoc. Specialist Radiol. (Ultrasound) Derriford Hosp. Plymouth. Socs: Plymouth Med. Soc.; Brit. Med. Ultrasound Soc.

PEARSON, Sally Elizabeth Gloucestershire Health Authority, Victoria Warehouse, The Docks, Gloucester GL1 2EL Tel: 01452 300222 — MB ChB 1984 Leeds; MPH Leeds 1989; MFPHM RCP (UK) 1991; FFPHM RCP (UK) 1997. Dir. Pub. Health Glos. HA. Prev: Cons. Pub. Health Med. Wakefield & Pontefract HA.

PEARSON, Sally Jane 11 Thirlestane Road, Edinburgh EH9 1AL — MB ChB 1993 Aberd.

PEARSON, Sandra Wessex Deanery, Highcroft, Romsey Road, Winchester SO22 5EY Tel: 01962 863511 — MB ChB 1981 Leeds; MRCPsych. 1998. Specialist Regist. (Psychiat.) Wessex Rotat. Prev: Staff Grade (Psychiat.) Alderney Hosp. Poole; Regist. (Psychiat.) St. Ann's Hosp. Poole.

***PEARSON, Sarah** Laneside, West Bradford Rd, Waddington, Clitheroe BB7 3JE — MB ChB 1997 Birm.

PEARSON, Sheila Elizabeth Cumberland Infirmary, Carlisle CA2 7HY — MB BS 1981 Newc.; MRCOG 1987; FRCOG 1999. (Newcastle upon Tyne) Cons. O & G Carlisle Hosps.

PEARSON, Sheila Hamilton Crawford (retired) Askernish, 45 Polmaise Road, Stirling FK7 9JH — MB ChB 1964 Glas.

PEARSON, Stanley Barwis Department of Respiratory Medicine, Leeds general infirmary, Great George Street, Leeds LS1 3EX Tel: 0113 392 2891 Fax: 0113 392 6316 Email: stan.pearson@leedsth.nhs.uk; 14 Charville Gardens, Leeds LS17 8JL — DPhil Oxf. 1971, MA 1972, BA (1st Cl. Hons.) 1968, DM 1990, BM BCh; Oxf. 1974; MRCP (UK) 1976; FRCP Lond. 1988. (Lond. Hosp.) Cons. Phys. Leeds Gen. Infirm.; Sen. Clin. Lect., Univ. of Leeds. Socs: Brit. Thorac. Soc. & Europ. Respirat. Soc. Prev: Sen. Regist. (Gen. & Thoracic Med.) Hants. AHA; Regist. (Gen. Med.) Nottm. City Hosp.; SHO (Gen. Med.) Univ. Med. Unit. Nottm. Gen. Hosp.

PEARSON, Stephen William Wonford House Hospital, Dryden Road, Exeter EX2 5AF Tel: 01392 403433; 43 Leys Road, Chelston, Torquay TQ2 6EB Tel: 01803 606897 — MB ChB 1983 Bristol; MRCGP 1990; DRCOG 1990. SHO (Psychiat.) Wonford Ho. Hosp. Exeter. Prev: GP Paignton.

PEARSON, Susan Grace Leeds BAMS, Government Buildings, Otley Road, Leeds LS16 5PU Tel: 0113 230 9247; 10 Summerhill Gardens, Roundhay, Leeds LS8 2EL — MB ChB 1970 Leeds. Socs: BMA. Prev: Clin. Med. Off. Leeds AHA (T); Ho. Phys. St. Jas. Hosp. Leeds; Ho. Surg. Seacroft Hosp. Leeds.

PEARSON, Susan Lynn West Wing, Esk Medical Centre, Ladywell Way, Musselburgh EH21 6AB Tel: 0131 665 2594 Fax: 0131 665 2428; Old Bank House, 18 Hillhead, Bonnyrigg EH19 2JG Tel: 0131 660 3407 — MB ChB 1986 Ed.; DRCOG 1989.

PEARSON, Professor Thomas Claud Department of Haematology, St Thomas Hospital, London SE1 7EH Tel: 020 7928 9292 Fax: 020 7928 5698 Email: tom.pearson@gstt.sthames.nhs.uk — MD Lond. 1977, MB BS 1966; MRCP Lond. 1997; MRCS Eng. LRCP Lond. 1966; FRCPath 1989, M 1977. (Char. Cross) Prof. Haemat. The Guy's, King's Coll. & St. Thomas' Hosps.' Med. & Dent. Sch.; Hon. Cons. Haemat. Guy's & St. Thos. Trust.

PEARSON, Thomas Eric Mellows, Brayton Lane, Selby YO8 9DZ — MB BS 1992 Lond.

PEARSON, Thomas Noel (retired) Wasbister, Newton Hill, Lentran, Inverness IV3 8RN Tel: 0146 383794 — MB BCh BAO 1956 Dub.; DObst RCOG 1958. Prev: Ho. Off. Derbysh. Roy. Infirm., Derby & New Cross Hosp.

PEARSON, Timothy Friary Surgery, Queens Road, Richmond DL10 4UJ Tel: 01748 822306 Fax: 01748 850356 — MB ChB 1990 Sheff.

PEARSON, Timothy John Holmside Medical Group, 142 Armstrong Road, Benwell, Newcastle upon Tyne NE4 8QB Tel: 0191 273 4009 Fax: 0191 273 2745 — MB BS 1981 Newc.

PEARSON, Veronica Ashville Medical Centre, 430 Doncaster Road, Barnsley S70 3RJ Tel: 01226 282280 Fax: 01226 216002 — MB ChB 1976 Leeds.

PEARSON, Veronica (retired) 21 Orrin Close, York YO24 2RA Tel: 01904 708521 — MB BChir Camb. 1955; BA (Nat. Sc. Trip. Pts. I & II Path.) Camb. 1952; MFFP 1993; DCH Eng. 1958; DObst RCOG 1957. Prev: GP Pontefract.

PEARSON, Virginia Alison Hardy Somerset Health Authority, Wellsprings Road, Taunton TA2 7PQ Tel: 01823 333491 Fax: 01823 272710 — MB BChir 1985 Camb.; MA Oxf. 1985, BA 1981; MFPHM RCP (UK) 1993; MRCGP 1988; DCH RCP Lond. 1988; DRCOG 1987.

PEARSON, William John Christopher 110 Station Road, Mickleover, Derby DE3 5FP Tel: 01332 512646 — MB BCh BAO 1952 Dub.; BA Dub. 1949, MB BCh BAO 1952. (T.C. Dub.)

PEARSONS, David Ernest (retired) 37 Chadwick Road, Westcliff on Sea SS0 8LD Tel: 01702 353551 — MB BS 1953 Lond. Mem. (Ex-Chairm.) Essex Local Med. Comm.; Mem. Family Plann. Pract. Prev: Ho. Surg. & Ho. Phys. Rochford Gen. Hosp.

PEARSTON, Gordon James Walker Medical Group, Church Walk, Walker, Newcastle upon Tyne NE6 3BS Tel: 0191 220 5905 Fax: 0191 220 5904; 14 Woodlands, Gosforth, Newcastle upon Tyne NE3 4YL Tel: 0191 284 7363 — MB ChB 1979 Ed.; BSc Ed. 1976, MB ChB 1979; MRCGP 1983; DRCOG 1982.

PEARSTON, Mary Kathleen Tel: 0191 265 5755 Fax: 0192 276 2921; 14 Woodlands, Gosforth, Newcastle upon Tyne NE3 4YL Tel: 0191 284 7363 Email: mkpearston@aol.com — MB BS 1981 Lond.; BSc Lond. 1978; MRCGP 1987. (University College London) Princip. (Gen. Med.).

PEART, Charlotte Louise Practice 3, Abbey Health Centre, East Abbey St, Arbroam DD2 5EU Tel: 01241 870311; 28 Cortachy Cres., Balgillo Park, Dundee DD5 3BF Email: charlotte1972@hotmail.com — MB ChB 1996 Dundee; MRCGP 2000 Edinburgh; DFFP. Prev: GP Regist. Maryfield Health Centre, Dundee; GP Princip., Abbey Health Centre, Pract. 3, Arbroam.

PEART, Emma Jane Felix House Surgery, Middleton Lane, Middleton St. George, Darlington DL2 1AE Tel: 01325 332235 Fax: 01325 333626 — BM BS 1991 Nottm.; BMedSci Nottm. 1989; DCH RCP Lond. 1994. GP Regist. Darlington.

PEART, Ian 1 Birkdale Close, Huyton with Roby, Liverpool L36 4QW Tel: 0151 449 1401 — MB ChB 1976 Manch.; MRCP (UK) 1979. Cons. Paediat. Cardiol. Roy. Liverp. Childr. Hosp. Prev: Sen. Regist. (Paediat. Cardiol.) Freeman Hosp. Newc.; Nat. Heart Research Fund Research Fell. (Cardiol.) Roy. Vict. Infirm. Newc.; Regist. (Cardiol.) Regional Cardiothoracic Centre Freeman.

PEART, Sir (William) Stanley (retired) 17 Highgate Close, Highgate, London N6 4SD Tel: 020 8341 3111 Fax: 020 8341 3111 — MB BS (Hons.) Lond. 1945; FRS; MD Lond. 1949; FRCP Lond. 1958, M 1946. Chairm. N.wick Pk. Inst. Med. Research; Trustee Beit Research Fell.sh. Prev: Prof. Med. St. Mary's Hosp. Lond.

PEASE, Colin Thomas Leeds General Infirmary, Great George St., Leeds LS1 3EX; 4 Lancaster Road, Harrogate HG2 0EZ — MB BS 1976 Lond.; MD Lond. 1988; FRCP Lond. 1995; MRCP (UK) 1979. Cons. Rheum. Leeds Gen. Infirm.; Sen. Clin. Lect. (Rheum.) Univ. Leeds. Socs: Brit. Soc. Rheum. Prev: Cons. Roy. Bath Hosp. Harrogate; Sen. Regist. Rotat. (Rheum. & Gen. Med.) Char. Cross Hosp.; Research Regist. Bone & Jt. Research Unit Lond. Hosp.

PEASE, Elizabeth Hamilton Errol Kingsley, 64 Woodford Road, Bramhall, Stockport SK7 1PA; Department Reproductive Medicine, St. Mary's Hospital, Hathersage Road, Manchester M13 0JH Tel: 0161 276 6494 Fax: 0161 224 0957 — MB ChB 1972 Manch.; FRCS Ed. 1978; FRCOG 1994, M 1978. Cons. (Reproductive Med.) St. Mary's Hosp. Manch.; Insp. Human Fertilisation & Embyology Auth. Lond. Prev: Mem. Brit. Fertil. Soc.; Mem. Brit. Andrology Soc.

PEASE, Mr Hon William Simon (retired) 29 Upper Addison Gardens, London W14 8AJ Tel: 020 7371 1776 — MB BS 1956 Lond.; MA Oxf. 1957; FRCS Eng. 1960. Prev: Cons. ENT Surg. Centr. Middlx., N.wick Pk. Wembley & Acton Hosps.

PEASE, James Jonathan 10 Headlands, Kettering NN15 7HP Tel: 01536 518022 Fax: 01536 517002 — MB BS Lond. 1970; FRCPsych 1993, M 1976. (Middlx.) Cons. Child Family Psychiat. N.hamptonshire Health Care NHS Trust. Prev: Sen. Regist. (Child Psychiat.) Cambs. AHA (T).

PEASE, John Clifford The Ark, Church St., Wells-next-the-Sea NR23 1JB Tel: 01328 710605 — BM BCh 1941 Oxf.; DM Oxf. 1950; FRCP Lond. 1970, M 1948. (Oxf. & Middlx.) Emerit. Cons. Phys. Centr. Notts. (Mansfield) Health Dist. Socs: Liveryman of Worshipful Soc. Apoth. Prev: Ho. Phys. & Sen. Med. Regist. Radcliffe Infirm. Oxf.; Phys. i/c Langwith Lodge Diabetic Unit; Clin. Teach. Univ. Nottm. Med. Sch.

PEASE, Nicola Jane Frances 23 Station Road, Llanfennech, Llanelli SA14 8UD — MB BCh 1992 Wales.

***PEASEGOOD, Joanna Aislinn** 27 Keele Road, Newcastle ST5 2JT — MB ChB 1998 Ed.; MB ChB Ed 1998.

PEASEGOOD, Mary 82 Stumperlowe Hall Road, Sheffield S10 3QT — MRCS Eng. LRCP Lond. 1945; MRCPsych 1976; DPM Eng. 1972. (Sheffield)

PEASTON, Michael John Thorpe (retired) Wheatmill House, 7 New Wood Lane, Blakedown, Kidderminster DY10 3LD — MB ChB 1959 Liverp.; PhD Liverp. 1967; FRCP Lond. 1981, M 1968; FRCP Glas. 1979, M 1964. Prev: Cons. Phys. Countess of Chester Hosp.

PEAT, Christopher John Addington Street Surgery, 69 Addington Street, Ramsgate CT11 9JQ Tel: 01843 593544 Fax: 01843 594310 — MB BS 1974 Lond.; MRCS Eng. LRCP Lond. 1974. (Roy. Free)

PEAT, Clive Cecil 36 Glebe Road, Sheffield S10 1FB — MB ChB 1960 Sheff.

PEAT, Danielle Susan Dept. of Histopathology, Southmead Hospital, Westbury-on-Trym, Bristol BS10 5NB Tel: 0117 959 5623 Fax: 0117 959 0191 Email: danipeat@msn.com; 4 Falcondale Road, Westbury on Trym, Bristol BS9 3JU Tel: 0117 959 5623 — MB BChir 1991 Camb.; PhD (Path.) Camb. 1986; BSc (1st cl. Hons. Biol.) Manch. 1982; DRCPath 1995; MRCPath 1996. Cons. (Histopath.) S.mead Hosp. Bris.; Sen. Lect. Bristol Univ. Prev: Sen. Regist. (Histopath.) Addenbrooke's Hosp. Camb.; Regist. (Histopath.) Ipswich Hosp.; SHO (Histopath.) Addenbrooke's Hosp. Camb.

PEAT, Ian David 47 Craigasy Quadrant, Milngavie, Glasgow G62 7BX Email: dave-peat@talk21.com — MB ChB 1995 Aberd.; BSc (Hons) 1994. (Aberd.) SHO (Diabetes & Gen. Med.) Edin. Roy. Infirm.

PEAT, Irene Mary The Leicester Royal Infirmary, Leicester LE1 5WW — MB BS 1975 Lond.; FRCP Lond. 1994; MRCP (UK) 1978; FRCR 1983. (Univ. Coll. Hosp.) Cons. Clin. Oncol. Leicester Roy. Infirm. Prev: Sen. Regist. (Radiother. & Oncol.) Qu. Eliz. Hosp. Edgbaston Birm.; Regist. (Radiother. & Oncol.) Ch.ill Hosp. Oxf.; Lect. (Med. Oncol.) W.m. Med. Sch. Lond.;330.

PEAT, Janet 36 Glebe Road, Broomhill, Sheffield S10 1FB — MB ChB 1962 Sheff.

PEAT, Judith Mary Glen Farm, Church Hill, Honiton EX14 9TE — MB BS 1975 Lond.; MRCP (UK) 1979.

PEAT, Meryl Lesley 25 Granby Road, Edinburgh EH16 5NP Tel: 0131 667 7983 — BM BS 1989 Nottm.; MRCGP 1995. (Nottm.)

PEAT, Michael John 10 Prospect Drive, Hest Bank, Lancaster LA2 6HX — MB ChB 1983 Leic.

PEAT, Susan Joan 29 Museum House, Roman Road, London E2 0JA — MB BS 1982 Lond.; BSc Lond. 1979; FFA RCS Eng. 1986.

PEATFIELD, Barry John Durrant Foxley Lane Clinic Limited, 86 Foxley Lane, Purley CR8 3EE Tel: 020 8660 0905 Fax: 020 8763

PEATFIELD

1828 — MB BS Lond. 1961; MRCS Eng. LRCP Lond. 1961. GP Foxley Clinic Purley Foxley Care Clinic Ltd; Authorized Med. Examr. Civil Aviat. Auth. Socs: Brit. Menopause Soc.; Roy. Soc. Med.

PEATFIELD, Richard Crompton 23 Mount Park Road, Ealing, London W5 2RS — MB BChir 1973 Camb.; MA Camb. 1974, MD Cam 1982; FRCP Lond. 1995; MRCP (UK) 1976. (Middlx.) Cons. Neurol. Char. Cross Hosp. Lond. & Mt. Vernon Hosp. N.wood. Socs: Fell. Roy. Soc. Med.; Internat. Headache Soc. Prev: Sen. Regist. (Neurol.) Leeds & Wakefield Hosps.; Research Fell. (Neurol.) Char. Cross Hosp. Lond.; Regist. (Med.) Centr. Middlx. Hosp. Lond.

PEATMAN, Suzanne Jane 9 Claremont Street, Newcastle upon Tyne NE2 4AH — MB BS 1992 Newc.; BA (Hons.) Newc 1985. (Newcastle upon Tyne) Specialist Regist. (O & G) N.ern Deanery.

PEATTIE, Alison Brunton Department of Obstetrics & Gynaecology, Countess of Chester Hospital, Liverpool Road, Chester CH2 1UL Email: 106376.2107@compuserve.com; Penketh House, Church Lane, Neston, South Wirral CH64 9UU Email: peattiebushby@compuserve.com — MB ChB 1978 Glas.; MRCOG 1983. (Univ. Glas.) Cons. O & G Countess of Chester Hosps. Socs: Internat. Continence Soc.; Blair Bell Res. Soc. Prev: Sen. Lect. (O & G & Gyn. Urol.) St. Geo. Hosp. Med. Sch. Lond.; Lect. (O & G) St. Geo. Hosp. Med. Sch. Lond. & St. Helier Hosp. Carshalton.

PEBERDY, Mary (retired) Norney Cottage, Whittingham, Alnwick NE66 4UP Tel: 01665 574268 — MRCS Eng. LRCP Lond. 1939. Prev: Lect. (Family Plann.) Univ. Newc.

PEBERDY, Robert John Walton Grove Surgery, Walton Grove, Aylesbury HP21 7SU Tel: 01296 82554; 3 First Court, Aylesbury Road, Bierton, Aylesbury HP22 5AY — MB BChir 1963 Camb.; BA, MB BChir Camb. 1963. (Middlx.) Socs: BMA. Prev: Ho. Surg. Middlx. Hosp. Lond.; Ho. Phys. Bolingbroke Hosp. Lond.

PEBERDY, Roger Michael (retired) Wistley, 79 Corbett Avenue, Droitwich WR9 7BH Tel: 01905 772847 Email: rmperdy@lineone.net — MB ChB 1962 Birm.; DA Eng. 1965. Prev: GP Droitwich Spa.

***PECCHIA, Kiersten Antoinette** 104 Lower Northend Farm, Northend, Batheaston, Bath BA1 7HA — MB BS 1998 Lond.; MB BS Lond 1998.

PECHAL, Arthur James, Surg. Cdr. RN 9A Catsfield Road, Fareham PO15 5QP Tel: 01329 43752 — MB BS 1958 Lond.; MRCS Eng. LRCP Lond. 1958; DO Eng. 1970; DTM & H Eng. 1965. (Roy. Free) Ophth. Specialist RN Hosp. Haslar. Socs: S. W.. Ophth. Soc. Prev: PMO HMS St. Angelo & Ophth. Specialist RN Hosp. Imtarfa, Malta; Ophth. Specialist RN Hosp. Plymouth; Dep. PMO HMS Nelson Portsmouth.

PECHAN, Jiri Tel: 020 8500 0066 — MUDr 1982 Prague; LRCP LRCS Ed. LRCPS Glas. 1985; DRCOG 1988. GP Chigwell. Socs: BMA; Ilford Med. Soc.

PECK, Anthony Wilson (retired) Pavilion End, Bickley Park road, Bromley BR1 2AT Tel: 020 8467 1406 — MB BS Lond. (Distinc. Med., Path. & Therap. Univ. Medal) Lond. 1958; PhD Lond. 1967, BSc (1st cl. Hons.) 1955; FRCP Lond. 1981; MRCP (UK) 1963; FFPM RCP (UK) 1992. Sen. Med. Off. Med. Control Agency. Prev: Clin. Neuropharmacol. Wellcome Foundat. Ltd.

PECK, Audrey Barbara The Surgery, 139 Valley Road, London SW16 2XT Tel: 020 8769 2566 Fax: 020 8769 5301 — MB BChir 1982 Camb.; MA 1983; MRCGP 1986; DRCOG 1985. Princip. GP Streatham.

PECK, Barbara Wendy Upton Medical Partnership, 18 Sussex Place, Slough SL1 1NS Tel: 01753 522713 Fax: 01753 552790; Greenacres, Bracken Close, Farnham Common, Slough SL2 3JP — MB BS 1982 Lond.; MRCGP 1988; DRCOG 1985.

PECK, Bernard Joseph (retired) Flat 3, Forest Lodge, Portland Road, East Grinstead RH19 4EZ — MRCS Eng. LRCP Lond. 1943. Prev: Hosp. Pract. Dermat. Plymouth Gen. Hosp.

PECK, David John St Andr. Centre for Burns & Plastics, Broomfield Hospital, Chelmsford; 53 Lukins Drive, Dunmow CM6 1XQ Fax: 01371 879823 Email: dai@tesco.net — MB BS 1985 Lond.; FRCA 1993. (St Bartholomews) Cons. (Anaesth.) St Andrews Centre Broomfield Hosp. Essex. Prev: Sen. Regist. Rotat. (Anaesth.) Roy. Free Hosp. NHS Trust; Regist. Rotat. (Anaesth.) Leicester Hosps.; Pre-Fell.sh. Regist. (Cardiothoracic Anaesth.) Gree La. Hosp. Auckland, NZ.

PECK, John Derek Weston (retired) Bilboa House, Dulverton TA22 9DW Tel: 01398 23475 — MB BS 1953 Lond.; MRCS Eng. LRCP Lond. 1953; DCH Eng. 1958; DObst RCOG 1955. Prev: Sen. Ho. Off. Paediat. Bury. Gen. Hosp.

PECK, John Eric (retired) Rivendell, Halifax Road, Todmorden OL14 6DW Tel: 01706 810619 — MB BS Lond. 1961; FRCOG 1982, M 1969, DObst 1964. Prev: Cons. (O & G) Halifax Gen. Hosp. & Halifax Roy. Infirm.

***PECK, Marcus John Edwards** 51 Dukes Avenue, Theydon Bois, Epping CM16 7HQ — MB BS 1998 Lond.; MB BS Lond 1998.

PECK, Mark Andrew 2 Antoinette Court, Abbots Langley WD5 0QL — MB BS 1982 Lond.

PECK, Richard Wilson Smithkline Beecham Pharmaceuticals, New Frontiers Science park, Third Avenue, Harlow CM19 5AW Tel: 01279 622000 Fax: 01279 644404 Email: richard_w_peck@sbphrd.com — MB BChir 1985 Camb.; MB BChir Camb. 1984; MA Camb. 1986; MRCP (UK) 1987; MFPM 1996. Gp. Dir. (Clin. Pharmacol.) SmithKline Beecham Pharmaceut. Socs: Brit. Pharm. Soc.; (Comm.) Assn. Human Pharmacol. in Pharmaceut. Industry. Prev: Sen. Clin. Pharmacologist Research & Developm. Glaxo Wellcome; Regist. (Med.) Leicester Roy. Infirm.

PECK, Robert James Royal Hallamshire Hospital, Glossop Road, Sheffield S10 2JF Tel: 0114 276 6222; 1 Stone Delf, Fulwood, Sheffield S10 3QX — MB BS 1980 Lond.; BSc Lond. 1977, MB BS 1980; FRCR 1986. (Guy's) Cons. (Radiol.) Sheff. HA. Prev: Lect. (Radiol.) Chinese Univ., Hong Kong; Sen. Regist. (Radiol.) Trent RHA; Regist. (Radiol.) Sheff. HA.

PECK, Rodney Miles D3 Monument Mansions, Wigan Lane, Wigan WN1 2LE — LAH Dub. 1949.

PECK, Sibel Private GP Services, Springfield Hospital, Lawn Lane, Chelmsford CM1 7GU Tel: 01245 234000 Fax: 01245 234107; Fax: 01371 879823 — MB BS 1988 Lond.; MRCGP 1993; DCH RCP Lond. 1992; DRCOG 1991. (Univ. Lond. Med. Sch. St Bart.) Private GP - set up own Pract. Prev: Trainee GP Leicester VTS; Trainee GP Surrey VTS.

PECK, Simon Richmond Firefly, Westmore Road, Tatsfield, Westerham TN16 2BJ — MB BS 1984 Lond. Hosp. Admin. Sen. Managem. Account Basildon NHS Trust. Prev: Regist. (Anaesth.) Kings Coll. Hosp. Lond.; SHO (Anaesth.) St. Bart. Hosp. & Roy. Free Hosp. Lond.; SHO (Med.) Newham Gen. Hosp.

PECK, Thomas Eyton 1 Valley Close, La Route de la Hougue Bie, St Saviour, Jersey JE2 7UX Email: tepeck@aol.com — MB BS 1992 Lond.; BSc Lond. 1989; FRCA 1997. (Lond. Hosp. Med. Coll.) Specialist Regist. (Anaesth.) Soton.

PECKAR, Mr Clive Orde Warrington Hospital NHS Trust, Lovely Lane, Warrington WA5 1QG Tel: 01925 662188 Fax: 01925 662395 Email: clive.peckar@warrh-tr.nwets.nhs.uk; BUPA North Cheshire Hospital, Fir Tree Close, Stretton, Warrington WA4 4LU Tel: 01925 265000 Fax: 01925 215038 — MRCS Eng. LRCP Lond. 1971; MSc Oxf. 1983; FRCS Eng. 1979; FRCOphth 1989; DO Eng. 1974; FRCS Ed. 2000. (St. Thos.) Cons. Ophth. Surg. Warrington Hosp. NHS Trust; Edr. Cataract & Refractive Surg. Eurotimes. Socs: Fell. Coll. Ophth. And Fell. Roy. Coll. of Surg.s, Edin.; Internat. Intraocular Implant Club.; Pub.ations Comm. And Director of Surgic. Skills Train. Europ. Soc. Cat. & Ref. Surg. Prev: Sen. Regist. St. Pauls Eye Hosp. Liverp.; Sen. Research Regist. Oxf. Univ. & Oxf. Eye Hosp.; Regist. Manch. Roy. Eye Hosp.

PECKETT, Mr William Robert Charles 29 Sherbrooke Road, London SW6 7QJ; Bosky Barn, Church Lane, Ripe, Lewes BN8 6AS Tel: 01323 811839 Email: willpecket@msn.com — MB BS Lond. 1991. (Uniersity College & Middlesex Hospital Medical School) Specialist Regist. Trauma & Orthop. S. E. Thames Rotat.

PECKHAM, Anna Victoria Gahard, 2 Ridge Close, Lane End, High Wycombe HP14 3BX Tel: 01494 883501 — MB ChB 1996 Liverp. (Liverp.) SHO (Psychiat.) in Liverp.

PECKHAM, Professor Catherine Stevenson, CBE Centre for Paediatric Epidemiology & Biostatics, The Institute of Child Health, 30 Guildford St., London WC1N 1EH Fax: 020 7242 2723 Email: c.peckham@ich.ucl.ac.uk — MB BS 1960 Lond.; 1997 FRCPCH; MD Lond. 1975; FRCP Lond. 1988; MRCS Eng. LRCP Lond. 1960; FFCM 1980, M 1974; MFPHM 1973; Hon. FRCOG 1994; Hon. FRCPath 1991. (University College Hospital, London) Prof. Paediat. Epidemiol. Inst. of Child Health Lond. & Hon. Cons. Hosp. for Sick Childr. Gt. Ormond St. Lond.; Hon. Cons. Community Med. (Epidemiol.) PHLS (Communicable Dis. Surveillance Centre. Socs: Founder Mem. of Acad. of Med. Sci.s. Prev: Reader (Community Med.) & Hon Cons.

Char. Cross Hosp. Lond.; Sen. Med. Research Off. Nat. Childr. Bureau.

PECKHAM, Clare Louise 3 Ashley Gardens, Eastleigh SO53 2JH Tel: 01703 265954; 50 Marcliffe Road, Wadsley, Sheffield S6 4AG Tel: 0114 233 7907 — MB BS 1989 Lond.; MRCPI 1996; MRCPCH 1996; DCH RCP Lond. 1993. (Char. Cross & Westm. Med. Sch.) Specialist Regist. Rotat. (Paediat.) Sheff. Childr. Hosp. Prev: SHO (Paediat. Cardiol.) Alder Hey Liverp.; SHO (Neonat.) St. Geo. Hosp. Lond.; SHO (Paediat.) Kingston Hosp. Surrey.

PECKHAM, Daniel Gavin Seacroft & St James's Hospitals, Leeds LS14 6UH Tel: 0113 206 3752 Fax: 0113 206 3540 — MB BS 1987 Lond.; DM Nottm. 1994; MRCP (UK) 1991. Regist. (Med.) Roy. Berks. Hosp.

PECKHAM, Professor Sir Michael John School of Public Policy, University College London, 29 Tavistock Square, London WC1H 9EZ Tel: 020 7679 4966 Fax: 020 7679 4969 Email: spp@ucl.ac.uk — MB BChir 1960 Camb.; MD Camb. 1969; FRCP Lond. 1986, M 1974; FRCS 1996; FRCPath 1991; FRCR 1975. (Univ. Coll. Lond. Med. Sch.) Dir. Sch. Pub. Policy Univ. Coll. Lond. Prev: Dir. Research Developm. NHS DoH; Dir. Brit. Postgrad. Med. Federat.

PECKHAM, Mr Timothy James Tel: 01268 592335 Fax: 01268 592254 — MB BS 1984 Newc.; BMedSc Newc. 1981; FRCS (Orth.) 1996; FRCS Eng. 1990. (Newc. u. Tyne) Cons. Orthop. Surg. Basildon & Thurrock Gen. Hosps. NHS Trust. Socs: Fell. BOA; Fell. Roy. Soc. Med.; Brit. Elbow & Shoulder Soc. Prev: Sen. Regist. Rotat. (Orthop.) Guy's & St. Thos. Hosp. Lond.; Regist. Rotat. (Orthop.) King's Coll. Hosp. Lond.; Shoulder Fell., Guy's Hosp. Lond.

PECKITT, Gavin Beattie Clifton Lane Health Centre, Clifton Lane, Doncaster Road, Rotherham S65 1DU Tel: 01709 382315 Fax: 01709 512646 — MB ChB 1973 Aberd.; DObst RCOG 1975. Clin. Asst. (ENT Surg.) Rotherham Dist. Gen. Hosp. Prev: SHO Aberd. Matern. Hosp.; Ho. Off. Aberd. Roy. Infirm.

***PECKITT, Kenneth** 7 Herringthorpe Avenue, Rotherham S65 3AA — MB ChB 1998 Manch.; MB ChB Manch 1998.

PECKITT, Mr Ninian Spenceley Email: peckitt@maxfac.com; St. Chad's House, Hooton Pagnell, Doncaster DN5 7BW Tel: 01977 644535 Fax: 01977 644535 Email: nspeckitt@maxfac.com — MB ChB 1979 Sheff.; BDS Ed. 1974; FRCS Ed. 1984; MRCS Eng. LRCP Lond. 1979; FDS RCS Eng. 1987; FFD RCSI 1986. Cons. Oral & Maxillofacial Surg. Doncaster Roy. Infirm.; Cons Pk. hill hosp Thorne Rd Doncaster; Dir computer gen Implants ltd. Socs: BMA; BAOMS. Prev: Sen. Regist. (Oral & Maxillofacial Surg.) S. Wales; Regist. (Oral & Maxillofacial Surg.) Ysbyty Glan Clwyd; Dir. Dent. Surg. King Khalid Hosp. Hail, Kingdom Saudi Arabia.

PEDDER, Claire Elizabeth Eyre Medical Practice, 31 Eyre Crescent, Edinburgh EH3 5EU Tel: 0131 556 8842; 23 Edinburgh Road, Musselburgh EH21 6EA Email: pedlam@epulse.net — MB ChB 1990 Ed.; BSc (Med. Sci.) Hons. Ed. 1989; MRCGP 1996; DRCOG 1994. (Edinburgh) GP Princip.; Clin. Asst. Cardiol., Roy. Infirm. Edin.

PEDDER, Gillian Helen 45 Stonnall Road, Aldridge, Walsall WS9 8JZ Tel: 01922 454355 — MB ChB 1993 Leeds. (Leeds).

PEDDER, Jonathan Richard (retired) 26 Alwyne Road, London N1 2HN Tel: 020 7226 3807 — BM BCh Oxf. 1961; MA Oxf. 1961; FRCP Lond. 1992, M 1965; FRCPsych 1979, M 1971; DPM Lond. 1967. Prev: Cons. Psychother. Bethlem Roy. & Maudsley Hosps.

PEDDER, Samantha Jane 6 Providence Court, Morley, Leeds LS27 9RP — BSc (Hons.) Anat. & Human Biol. Liverp. 1989, MB ChB 1992. SHO (Anat.) NHS Trust, Aintree Walton Hosp. & Fazakerley Hosp. Liverp.

***PEDDI, Nagabhushanam Choudary** 15 Stowe Close, Liverpool L25 7YE — MB ChB 1998 Ed.; MB ChB Ed 1998.

PEDDI, V Belle Vale Health Centre, Hedgefield Road, Liverpool L25 2XE Tel: 0151 487 0514 Fax: 0151 488 6601.

PEDDIE, Mary Margaret The Wallace Medical Centre, 254 Thornhill Road, Falkirk FK2 7AZ Tel: 01324 622826 Fax: 01324 633447; 8 Greenhorn's Well Drive, Falkirk FK1 5HJ — MB ChB 1979 Glas.; MRCGP 1984; DRCOG 1981. GP Falkirk.

PEDEN, Alan Trevor 3 Mount Pleasant Road, Rothesay PA20 9HQ — MB ChB 1990 Aberd.

PEDEN, Carol Jane Royal United Hospital, Bath BA1 3NG Tel: 01225 428331 — MB ChB 1983 Ed.; MD Ed. 1996; FRCA 1988. Cons. Anaesth. & Intens. Care Roy. United Hosp. Bath; Primary Fell.

Examr., Roy. Col. Of Anaesth.s; Course Organiser, Bristol/Bath Primary Fell.sh. Course. Prev: Lect. (Anaesth.) Bristol Roy. Infirm.; Hon. Sen. Regist. & MRC Research Fell. Hammersmith Hosp. Lond.

PEDEN, Karen Irene 41 Ballynagarrick Road, Belfast BT8 8LU — MB ChB 1989 Aberd.; MRCGP 1995; DRCOG 1995. (Aberdeen University)

PEDEN, Norman Robert Falkirk & District Royal Infirmary, Major's Loan, Falkirk FK1 5QE Tel: 01324 616128 Fax: 01324 616020 Email: nrpeden@sri.scot.nhs.uk — MB BChir 1976 Camb.; MA, MB Camb. 1976, BChir 1975; MRCP (UK) 1977; FRCP Ed. 1988. (Middlesex hospital) Cons. Phys. Falkirk & Dist. Roy. Infirm.; Hon. Sen. Lect. Dept. of Postgrad. Med. Unversity of Glas. Socs: Brit. Diabetic Assn.; Brit. Thyroid Assn.; Caledonian Soc. Endocrinol. Prev: Lect. (Pharmacol./Ther.) Univ. Dundee & Hon. Sen. Regist. (Gen. Med.) Ninewells Hosp. Dundee; Registar (Gen. Med.) Ninewells Hosp. & Med. Sch. Dundee; Chief Resid. (Endocrinol. Metab.) Univ., Ottawa.

PEDEN, Thomas Craig (retired) 202 Glasgow Road, Paisley PA1 3LS Tel: 0141 889 9040 — MB ChB 1951 Glas.

PEDERSEN, David Lawrence (retired) The Knoll House, Hinksey Hill, Oxford OX1 5BN Tel: 01865 735345 Fax: 01865 327660 — MB BS 1950 Lond.; MRCS Eng. LRCP Lond. 1950; MRCGP 1968. Prev: Hosp. Pract. (ENT) Orsett Hosp.

PEDERSEN, Karen Staff Bungalow 3, Newton Road, Worcester WR5 1HP — MB BCh 1991 Witwatersrand.

PEDERSEN, Sarah Wendy Family Consultation Centre, Newtown Centre, Nursery Road, Huntingdon PE29 3RJ Tel: 01480 415331 Fax: 01480 415393 Email: sarah.pederson@hbhc-tr.anglox.nhs.uk — MB BS 1979 Lond.; MRCPsych 1983. (St. Mary's) Cons. Child & Adolesc. Psychiat. Hinchingbrooke Hosp. Huntingdon. Prev: Sen. Regist. (Child & Adolesc. Psychiat.) Camb. HA.

PEDLER, Stephen John 12 Rudby Close, Whitebridge Park, Gosforth, Newcastle upon Tyne NE3 5JF — MB ChB 1978 Bristol; MRCPath 1984. Cons. (Microbiol.) Roy. Vict. Infirm. Newc. u. Tyne. Socs: BMA & Brit. Soc. Antimicrobial Chemother. Prev: Sen. Regist. (Microbiol.) Roy. Vict. Infirm. Newc.; Regist. (Microbiol.) Bristol Roy. Infirm.

***PEDLEY, David Keith** 3 Higher Tunsteads, Greenfield, Oldham OL3 7NX Tel: 01457 875259 Fax: 0161 343 2716; Blafrual House, Lod Backello, Ancterhouse, Dundee DD3OQy Tel: 0131 662 0021 Fax: 01382 320430 Email: finped@msn.uk — MB ChB 1994 Dundee; MRCP (UK) 1997.

PEDLEY, Ian David 334 Stainbeck Road, Chapel Allerton, Leeds LS7 3PP Tel: 0113 294 0771 — MB ChB 1990 Leeds; BSc Chem. Path. (Hons.) Leeds 1987; MRCP (UK) 1994. Regist. (Clin. Oncol.) Yorks. Regional Cancer Centre Cookridge Hosp. Leeds.

PEDLEY, Julian Eric Medical Protection Society, 33 Cavendish Square, London W1G 0PS Tel: 020 7399 1300 Fax: 020 7399 1301; 4 Andrewes Croft, Marsh Drive, Great Linford, Milton Keynes MK14 5HP Tel: 01908 660706 Email: julian_pedley@tinyworld.co.uk — MB BS 1967 Lond.; MB Land. 1967; MSc (Social Med.) Lond. 1976; FFPHM 1987, M 1979; DTPH 1970; DTM & H Liverp. 1968. (Middlx.) Medico-Legal Advis. (Internat. Div.) Med. Protec. Soc. Lond.; Chairm. Willen Hospice Counc. of Managem. Milton Keynes. Socs: Medico-Legal Soc.; IAPOS; Roy. Soc. Med. Prev: Chief Exec. Bucks. HA; Dist. Gen. Manager & Dir. Pub. Health Milton Keynes HA; Sen. Med. Off., Commonw. Developm. Corp. Swaziland.

PEDLOW, Paula Leslie Department of Child & Family Mental Health, Homoeopathic Hospital, 41 Church Road, Tunbridge Wells TN1 1JU Tel: 01892 522598 Fax: 01892 532629 — MB BS Newc. 1970; MRCPsych 1978. Cons. Child Psychiat. & Clin. Dir. Child & Family Servs. Invicta Community Care NHS Trust. Prev: Cons. Child Psychiat. & Med. Dir. Hastings & Rother NHS Trust; Sen. Regist. (Child Psychiat.) W. Midl. RHA.

PEDLOW, Pauline Joyce 175 Malone Road, Belfast BT9 6TB — MB BCh BAO 1971 Belf.

PEDLOW, Mr Peter Robert Bradley (retired) c/o Pinehill Hospital, Benslow Lane, Hitchin SG4 9QZ Tel: 01462 422822 — MB BCh BAO 1954 Belf.; FRCS Ed. 1963; FRCS Glas. 1963; FRCOG 1975, M 1960, DObst 1956. Prev: Cons. Gyn. Pinehill Hosp. Hitchin.

PEDRAZZINI, Anne Elizabeth Bedford House Clinic, Havelock Place, Shelton, Stoke-on-Trent ST1 4PR Tel: 01782 425012 Fax:

PEDRAZZINI

01782 425006; Fig Tree House, 15 Sandy Lane, Newcastle ST5 0LX Tel: 01782 613830 — MB ChB Birm. 1963; DObst RCOG 1965. SCMO Family Plann. (Community Med. & Sexual & Reproduc. Med.) N. Staffs. HA. Socs: Assoc. Mem. Inst. Psychosexual Med; Assn. Marital & Sexual Therapists; Assoc. Mem. Inst. Psycho-Sexual Med. Prev: Med. Off. (Community Med.) N. Staffs. Health Dist.; Clin. Asst. (Dermat.) Mid. Staffs. Health Dist.

PEDRAZZINI, Sarah-Louise 44 Eason Drive, Abingdon OX14 3YD — MB BCh 1997 Wales. SHO (A&E) Morriston Hosp. Swansea. Prev: Ho. Off. (Gen. Med.) P.ss of Wales Hosp. Bridgend; Ho. Off. (Gen. Surg.) Singleton Hosp. Swansea.

PEDUZZI, Mr Remo Derek (retired) Woodlands, Hopesyke Woods, Carlisle CA6 5SS — MB BS 1950 Lond.; FRCS Eng. 1961. Prev: Cons. Surg. Cumbld. Infirm. Carlisle.

PEEBLES, Charles Robert 16 Cherville Street, Romsey SO51 8FD — MB BS 1990 Lond.

PEEBLES, Donald Mark 25 Finsen Road, London SE5 9AX — MB BS 1986 Lond.

PEEBLES, Douglas James (retired) 101 Plaistow Lane, Bromley BR1 3AR Tel: 020 8460 0871 — MB BS 1959 Lond.; FFA RCS Eng. 1965; DObst RCOG 1962. Cons. Anaesth. Sydenham Childr. Hosp. & Bromley Hosp. Gp. Prev: Sen. Regist. Dept. Anaesth. Lond. Hosp.

PEEBLES, Jennifer Payne The Old Rectory, The Green, Wickhambreaux, Canterbury CT3 1RQ; 14 Riverbank, East Molesey KT8 9BH — MB BS 1960 Lond.; MB BS (Hons.) Distinc. Midw. & Gyn.) Lond. 1960; MRCS Eng. LRCP Lond. 1960; DObst RCOG 1962. (Guy's) Med. Off. Pilgrims Canterbury Hospice; Mem. Inst. Psychosexual Med.

PEEBLES, Margaret Kerr 36 Crieff Road, Perth PH1 2RS — MB ChB 1988 Ed.

PEEBLES, Mary Anne Clark Durrockstock, 8 Castle Terrace, Ullapool IV26 2XD — MB ChB 1947 Glas. (Univ. Glas.)

PEEBLES, Robert Anthony, RD The Old Rectory, Wickhambreaux, Canterbury CT3 1RQ; 14 Riverbank, East Molesey KT8 9BH — MRCS Eng. LRCP Lond. 1961; MB BS Lond. 1961, BDS 1957; FDS RCS Eng. 1964. (Guy's) Cons. Oral & Maxillofacial Surg. Kingston & NW Surrey Hosp. Gps.

PEEBLES-BROWN, Anne Elizabeth Mayday University Hospital, Mayday Road, Croydon CR7 7YE Tel: 020 8401 3268 Fax: 020 8401 3438; 238 Chaldon Way, Coulsdon CR5 1DH — MB ChB 1976 Glas.; FFA RCS Eng. 1980; DRCOG 1978. Cons. Anaesth. Mayday Univ. Hosp. Croydon.

PEEBLES BROWN, David (retired) 8 St. Marys Close, Hessle HU3 0HJ — MB ChB 1972 Glas.; MRCGP 1977; DObst RCOG 1975. Prev: Regist. (Geriat. Med.) & Ho. Off. (Paediat.) Stobhill Hosp. Glas.

PEEBLES BROWN, Doris Agnes Rothery (retired) 18 The Chestnuts, Winscombe BS25 1LD Tel: 01934 844377 — MB ChB Glas. 1943. Prev: Clin. Med. Off. Chesh. Co. Counc.

PEECOCK, Fiona Patricia Mary 563 Felixstowe Road, Ipswich IP3 8TE — MB BS 1982 Newc.; DRCOG 1986. Prev: Ho. Off. (Med.) Preston Hosp. N. Shields; Ho. Off. (Surg.) S. Shields Gen. Hosp.

***PEEDELL, Clive** 1 Sweetmans Road, Oxford OX2 9BA — BM 1995 Soton.

PEEK, Brenda Mains of Melginch Farmhouse, Balbeggie, Perth PH2 6HJ Tel: 01821 640528 — MB ChB 1978 Dundee; MRCGP 1986. Staff Grade Phys. Perth Roy. Infirm.

PEEK, Mr Giles John ECMO Office, Glenfield Hospital, Leicester LE3 9QP Tel: 0116 256 3256 Email: ycq57@dial.pipex.com — MB BS 1990 Lond.; FRCS Eng. 1994; MD Leic. 1998. (Kings College Hospital London) Lect. (Cardiac Surg.) Univ.of Leic.; Hon. Specialist Regist. (Cardio-Thoracic Surg.). Socs: BMA; Soc. Of Cardiothoracic Surg. of GB & Irel. Prev: Specialist Regist. (Cardio-Thoracic Surg.) Trent Rotat.; Research Fell. (Cardiothoracic Surg.) Glenfield Hosp. Leicester; Regist. & SHO (Cardiothoracic Surg.) Glenfield Hosp. Leicester.

PEEK, Ian Maurice (retired) Daleham Practice, 5 Daleham Gardens, London NW3 5BY Tel: 020 7530 2510 Fax: 020 7530 2511 — MB BS 1966 Lond.; MRCS Eng. LRCP Lond. 1966; MRCGP 1976; DCH Eng. 1971; DObst RCOG 1968. Prev: Regtl. Med. Off. 4th Bn. Roy. Green Jackets (T & AVR).

PEEK, William Henry Yew Tree, Lymington Road, Milford on Sea, Lymington, Southampton SO4 0QL — MRCS Eng. LRCP Lond.

1939; FRCOG 1963, M 1948. (Westm.) Prev: Res. Obst. Asst. W.m. Hosp.; Med. Off. RAFVR 1940-5; Obstetr. & Gynaecol. Walsall Gp. Hosps.

PEEL, Andrew James Headwell House, Headwell Lane, Saxton, Tadcaster LS24 9PX; Medical Centre, Beech Grove, Sherburn in Elmet, Leeds LS25 6ED — BM BS 1988 Nottm.

PEEL, Andrew Joseph Northern General Hospital, Herries Road, Sheffield S5 7AU Tel: 0114 243 4343 — MB ChB 1987 Sheff. SHO (Psychiat.) Sheff. Prev: SHO (O & G) Sheff.

PEEL, Mr Anthony Lawrence Geoffrey 77 Junction Road, Norton, Stockton-on-Tees TS20 1PU Tel: 01642 554354 — MB 1966 Camb.; MChir Camb. 1977, MB 1966, BChir 1965; FRCS Ed. 1969; FRCS Eng. 1970. (St. Thos.) Cons. Surg. N. Tees Dist: Gen. Hosp. Stockton-on-Tees. Prev: Sen. Regist. (Surg.) St. Thos. Hosp. Lond.

PEEL, Darryl Michael The Surgery, Market Place, Halesworth IP19 8HP Tel: 01986 874136 — MB ChB 1986 Sheff.

PEEL, David Jonathan Dean Lane Family Practice, 1 Dean Lane, Bedminster, Bristol BS3 1DE Tel: 0117 966 3149 Fax: 0117 953 0699 — MB BS 1992 Lond.

PEEL, Edwin Timothy North Tyneside General Hospital, North Shields NE29 8NH Tel: 0191 293 2722 Fax: 0191 293 2722 Email: tim.peel@northumbra-healthcare.nhs.uk — MB BS 1974 Lond.; BSc (Hons.) Lond. 1971; FRCP (Lond.) 1992, M 1977. (UCHMS) Cons. Phys. (Gen. & Respirat. Med. & Palliat. Med.) N. Tyneside Gen. Hosp. Socs: Brit. Thorac. Soc. Assoc. Palliat. Med. Prev: Sen. Regist. (Respirat. Med.) Gwent & S. Glam. HA; Regist. Dept. Respirat. Med. & Chest Unit City Hosp. Edin.; Regist. Newc. AHA (T).

PEEL, Elizabeth Mary The Surgery, 46 Stewkley Road, Wing, Leighton Buzzard LU7 0NE Tel: 01296 688949 Fax: 01296 688575. — MB BS 1989 Lond.; MRCGP 1993. Socs: BMA.

PEEL, Fiona Carolyn The Surgery, Lochgoilhead, Cairndow PA24 8AQ Tel: 01301 703258 Fax: 01301 703258; Gleniffer, Lochgoilhead, Cairndow PA24 8AA Tel: 01301 703258 — MB BS 1986 Lond.; BSc (Hons.) Lond. 1983. Prev: Trainee GP/SHO (Cas.) E. Cumbria HA VTS; SHO (Paediat.) Qu. Pk. Hosp. Blackburn.

PEEL, George William Bryan (retired) Haygrove House, Roman Lane, Bridgwater TA6 7JB Tel: 01278 423044 — MB ChB 1950 Bristol; DObst RCOG 1951. Prev: O & G RAMC.

PEEL, Jessica Scott 36 Merrywood Park, Ashurst Drive, Tadworth KT20 7LR — MRCS Eng. LRCP Lond. 1973; LDS Durh. 1961. (St. Geo.) Prev: Regist. & SHO (Anaesth.) St. Geo. Hosp. Lond.; Regist. (Maxillofacial) Roy. Surrey Co. Hosp.; SHO (Orthop.) Roy. Sussex Co. Hosp.

PEEL, Sir John, KCVO 11 Harnwood Road, Salisbury SP2 8DD Tel: 01722 334892 — BM BCh 1932 Oxf; FRCOG 1944; Hon. FRCOG 1989; Hon. FACOG 1971; Hon. MMSA Lond. 1970; Hon. FACS 1970; Hon. FCM (S. Afr.) 1968; BA (1st cl. Hons. Nat. Sc.) Oxf. 1928, MA 1932; Hon. DCh Newc. 1980; Hon. DM Soton. 1974; Hon. DSc Birm. 1972; FRCP Lond. 1971; FRCS Eng. 1933; Hon. FRCS Canada 1967; MRCS Eng. LRCP Lond. 1930. (Oxf. & King's Coll. Hosp.) Consg. O & G Surg. King's Coll. Hosp. Lond.; Emerit. Lect. KCH Med. Sch. Socs: Hon. Fell. Roy. Soc. Med. (Ex-Pres. Obst. Sect.); Hon. Fell. Amer. Assn. Obst. & Gyn. & Amer. Gyn. Soc. Prev: Surg. Gyn. to HM The Qu.; O & G Surg. King's Coll. Hosp. 1936-69; Pres. RCOG.

PEEL, Juliet Margaret (de Galleani) School House, Hassop, Bakewell DE45 1NT Tel: 01629 640324 Fax: 01629 640324 Email: pjpeel@netcomuk.co.uk — MB BS 1966 Lond.; MFFP 1992; DObst RCOG 1968. (Middlx.) p/t Coloscopy Pract. Jessop Wing Hallamshire Hosp. Sheff. Teachg. Hosp. Trust; Fam. Plann. SCMO N. Derbysh.; Cervical Screening Co-ordinator N. Derbysh. Prev: SCMO (Colposcopy) Rotherham Gen. Hosp. Trust; SHO (O & G) N.. Gen. Hosp. Sheff.

PEEL, Mr Kenneth Roger The Mid-Yorkshire Nuffield Hospital, Outwood Lane, Horsforth, Leeds LS18 4HP Tel: 0113 258 8756 Fax: 0113 258 3108; Borrings Cottage, Hawkswick, Skipton BD23 5QA Tel: 01756 770279 — MB ChB 1958 Leeds; FRCS Ed. 1965; FRCOG 1977, M 1965; DObst RCOG 1960. (Leeds) Cons. Gynaecologist, Mid Yorks. Nuffield Hosp.. Leeds. Socs: BMA; Soc. Apoth. Lond. Prev: Se.Aclin.Lect.(Obst. & Gyn.) Uni. Leeds; Hon. Cons. Gyn. Regional RadiopTher.. Centre Cookridge Hosp. Leeds.; Gyn.Surg. Leeds Gen. Infirm..

PEEL, Martyn David c/o Occupational Health Unit, St. Woolos Hospital, Stow Hill, Newport NP20 4SZ Tel: 01633 234234 — BM 1983 Soton.; AFOM RCP Lond. 1996; DRCOG 1986. (Soton.) SCMO (Occupat. Med.) St Woolos Hosp. Newport. Socs: Soc. Occupat. Med. Prev: Trainee GP Rotat. Bedford VTS; Ho. Off. P.ss Margt. Hosp. Swindon; Ho. Surg. Qu. Alexandra Hosp. Portsmouth.

PEEL, Michael John (retired) Millstone, Mill Lane, St Ippolyts, Hitchin SG4 7NN Tel: 01462 459748 — MB BChir 1950 Camb.; MA, MB BChir Camb. 1950.

PEEL, Michael Robert Occupational Health Department, St. Thomas Hospital, London SE1 7EH Tel: 020 7928 9292; Flat 3, 47 Pembridge Villas, London W11 3EP — MB BS 1978 Lond.; MRCGP 1984; MFOM RCP Lond. 1989. (St. Mary's) Sen. Lect. (Occupat. Med.) UMDS Guy's & St. Thos. Hosps.; Med. Adviser Hse. of Parliament; Sen. Med. Examr. Med. Fundat. Socs: Fell. Roy. Soc. Med.; Soc. Occupat. Med. Prev: Sen. Manager Health, Safety & Welf. Brit. Telecom Internat.; Med. Off. Brit. Airways Med. Serv.

PEEL, Nicola Frances Anne Northern General Hospital, Herries Road, Sheffield S5 7AU Tel: 0114 226 6044 Email: nicola.peel@sth.nhs.uk — BM BS 1984 Nottm.; DM 1984; BMedSci Nottm. 1982; MRCP (UK) 1988. Cons., Metab. Bone Med.; Hon. Sen. Clin. Lect. Socs: Bone and Tooth Soc.; Brit. Soc. for Rheum.; Amer. Soc. for Bone and Mineral Research. Prev: Regist. (Gen. Med.) Roy. Hallamsh. Hosp. Sheff.; SHO (Gen. Med.) Chesterfield Roy. Hosp.; SHO (Rheum. & Gen. Med.) Harold Wood Hosp.

PEEL, Philip Hedley 3 Brancepeth Close, Durham DH1 5XL — MB ChB 1988 Leeds.

PEEL, Robert Kemsley 116 Moor Lane, York YO24 2QY — MB BS 1994 Lond.

PEEL, Robert Nigel (retired) 116 Moor Lane, Dringhouses, York YO24 2QY Tel: 01904 704375 — MB BS Lond. 1964; FRCPath 1983, M 1971. Prev: Cons. Med. Microbiol. & Dir. Regional Pub. Health Laborat. Leeds.

PEEL, Sheelagh Patricia (retired) Hollybank, Ward Lane, Higher Disley, Stockport SK12 2BZ Tel: 01663 762253 Fax: 01663 762253 — MB ChB Liverp. 1955; MFPHM RCP (UK) 1974; DPH Liverp. 1962. Prev: SCMO Stockport DHA.

PEEL, Stephen 5 Cousins Grove, Southsea PO4 9RP Tel: 01705 732043 — MB BS 1942 Durh. (Durh.) Prev: Asst. Res. Med. Off. Roy. Vict. Infirm. Newc.; Surg. Lt. RNVR 1943-7; Med. Off. H.M. Prison Portsmouth.

PEEL, Willis John 1 Drimmie Place, Letham, Forfar DD8 2DW Tel: 01307 818905 — MB ChB 1987 Ed.; FRCA 1995.

PEEL-WHITE, Angela Lesley Flat 3, 28 Queensland Road, Bournemouth BH5 2AB — MB BS 1984 Lond. Socs: Brit. Holistic Med. Assn. Prev: SHO (Gen. Surg.) Heatherwood Hosp. Ascot; SHO (Neurosurg.) Walton Hosp. Liverp.; SHO (Orthop.) Qu. Med. Centre Nottm.

PEELING, Audrey Margaret (retired) 17 Stow Park Circle, Newport NP20 4HF Tel: 01633 255463 Fax: 01633 223357 Email: ampeeling@aol.com — MB BS 1955 Lond.; FFA RCS Eng. 1960; DA Eng. 1958. Prev: Cons. Anaesth. S. Gwent Health Dist.

PEER, Emily Jane 2 Scotsmansfield, Burway Road, Church Stretton SY6 6DP Tel: 01694 722437 — BM BS 1991 Nottm.; BMedSci Nottm. 1989; MRCGP 1997; DRCOG 1997; DFFP 1997. (Nottm.) GP Regist. Hunting Rd. Surg. Cambs. Socs: BMA & Med. Defence Union. Prev: SHO (Paediat.) Roy. Shrewsbury Hosp.; Sen. Med. Off. Proserpine Hosp. N. Qu.sland, Austral.

PEER, Rachel Margaret Wasen Hill, Evesham Road, Binton, Stratford-upon-Avon CV37 9UD — MB BS 1975 Lond.; FFA RCS Eng. 1979. Assoc. Specialist (Anaesth.) Warwick Hosp.

PEEREBOOM, Jeffery Mark Flat 2, Girdlestone Close, Headington, Oxford OX3 7NS — MB BS 1985 Queensland.

PEERMAHOMED, Rafic Conifers Resource Centre, Church Road, Caterham CR3 5RA Tel: 01883 347373 Fax: 01883 346492; 57 Mulgrave Road, Sutton SM2 6LR Tel: 020 8661 9285 — MB BS 1966 Osmania; MRCPsych 1974; DPM RCPSI 1973. (Gandhi Med. Coll. Hyderabad) Cons. Psychiat. E. Surrey Learning Disabil. Ment. Health Serv. NHS Trust Redhill, Surrey. Prev: Med. Asst. (Psychiat.) Tooting Bec. Hosp. Lond.; Regist. (Psychiat.) Clifton Hosp. York.

PEERS, Christina Maria — MB BS Lond. 1983; DRCOG 1986; Cert. Family Plann. JCC. 1986; MFFP. p/t Cons. (Family Plann. & Reprod. Healthcare). Prev: GP Cuckfield Sussex VTS; Med. Off. St. Catherines Hospice Crawley.

***PEERS, Lesley Anne** 121 Brookhouse Hill, Fulwood, Sheffield S10 3TE — MB ChB 1996 Sheff.

PEERS, Louisa Fir Lodge, 120 Park Road, Camberley GU15 2LW — MB BS 1977 Melbourne.

PEET, Andrew Charles Birmingham Childrens Hospital, Steelhouse Lane, Birmingham B4 6NH; 82 Underdale Road, Shrewsbury SY2 5EE Tel: 01743 340038 Fax: 01743 340038 — MB BS 1994 Lond.; MRCP UK 1998. (St Georges London) Specialist Regist., Birm. Childr.s Hosp., Birm.

PEET, Angela Suzanne 27 Park Avenue, Barbourne, Worcester WR3 7AJ Tel: 01905 612371 — MB BS 1993 Lond.; FRCS (A&E) 1998. (Royal London)

PEET, Eleanor Joan Robertson Penarth Health Centre, Stanwell Road, Penarth CF64 3XE Tel: 029 2070 0911; 47 Clive Place, Penarth CF64 1AX Tel: 01222 711216 — MB ChB 1977 Manch.; MRCGP 1981; DRCOG 1979.

PEET, John Spencer Lethbridge Farmhouse, Lovacott, Newton Tracey, Barnstaple EX31 3PY — MB BS 1954 Lond.

***PEET, Julia Anne** Le Chene, Forest GY8 0BB — MB BS 1969 Lond.; MRCS Eng. LRCP Lond. 1969.

PEET, Katharine Mary Skrine (retired) 4 Stephen Road, Headington, Oxford OX3 9AY Tel: 01865 761763 — BM BCh 1948 Oxf.; MA Oxf. 1949; MRCP Lond. 1953. Cons. Phys. Younger Disabled Ch.ill Hosp. & Migraine Clinic Dept. Neurol. Radcliffe Infirm. Oxf. Prev: Med. Asst. (Physical. Med.) Rivermead Hosp. Oxf.

PEET, Professor Malcolm Swallownest Court Hospital, Aughton Rd, Swallownest, Sheffield S31 0TH Tel: 0114 287 2570 Fax: 0114 287 9147 Email: malcolmpeet@yahoo.com — MB ChB 1968 Leeds; BSc (Physiol.) Leeds 1965, MB ChB 1968; FRCPsych 1990, M 1973; DPM Eng. 1972. (Leeds) Prof. Assoc., Sheff. Univ. Prev: Med. Adviser (Clin. Research) ICI Pharmaceuts. Div. Alderley Edge; Med. Adviser Med. Unit. Organon Oss, Holland.; Cons. Psychiat. Scarsdale Hosp. Chesterfield.

PEET, Mrs Suzanne Elizabeth Ethel (retired) Flat 4, Shaftesbury House,, Trinity St., London SE1 4JF Tel: 020 7407 5158 — MB BS 1965 Lond.; MRCS Eng. LRCP Lond. 1965. Prev: Clin. Asst. Dept. Occupat. Health Univ. Coll. Hosp. Lond.

PEET, Mr Timothy Nigel Dexter (retired) Le Chene, Forest, Guernsey GY8 0BB — MB BS Lond. 1965; FRCS Eng. 1973; MRCS Eng. LRCP Lond. 1965. Prev: Cons. Surg. P.ss Eliz. Hosp. Guernsey.

PEFFERS, Gillian Mary Bridge Surgery, 8 Evesham Road, Redditch B97 4LA Tel: 01527 550131 — MB BS 1986 Newc.; DFFP 1995; DRCOG 1993. (Newcastle upon Tyne)

PEGG, Mr Christopher Arthur Sunley The Convent Hospital, 748 Mansfield Road, Woodthorpe, Nottingham NG5 3FZ Tel: 0115 920 9209 Fax: 0115 967 3005 — MB BS 1962 Lond.; ChM Aberd. 1969; FRCS Eng. 1967. (St. Thos.) Cons. Gen. Surg. Nottm. Univ. Hosp. & Gen. Hosp. Nottm. Socs: Fell. Assn. Surgs.; Thyroid Club & Europ. Thyroid Assn. Prev: Sen. Regist. (Surg.) Roy. Infirm. Aberd.; Sen. Surg. Cas. Off. & Ho. Surg. Profess. Unit, St. Thos. Hosp. Lond.

PEGG, David Edward Medical Cryobiol. Unit, Department Biology, University of York, Heslington, York YO10 5DD Tel: 01904 434080 Fax: 01904 434090; 10 St. Paul's Square, Holgate, York YO24 4BD Tel: 01904 630751 — MD 1963 Lond.; MB BS 1956; MRCPath. 1968. (Westm.) Dir. Med. Crybiol. Unit. Socs: Fell. Roy. Soc. Med.; Brit. Transpl. Soc. Prev: Dir. E. Anglian Regional Tissue Bank; Head, MRC Med. Cryobiol. Gp. Douglas Ho. Camb.; Research Haemat. W.m. Med. Sch. Lond.

PEGG, Mr Derek Jonathan Leighton Hospital, Middlewich Road, Crewe CW1 4QJ Tel: 01270 612150 Fax: 01270 612150 Email: derek.pegg@mcht.nhs.uk — MB BS 1984 Lond.; FRCS (Orth.) 1996; FRCS Ed. 1989. (Westm.) Cons. Orthop. Surg. Leighton Hosp. Crewe, Chesh.

PEGG, Elizabeth Margaret (retired) Holden Cottage, 2 West St., Withycombe, Minehead TA24 6PX Tel: 01984 640781 — MRCS Eng. LRCP Lond. 1951; DObst RCOG 1954. Prev: Regist. (O & G) Eliz. G. Anderson Hosp. Lond.

PEGG, Graham Charles Whiteladies Health Centre, Whatley Road, Clifton, Bristol BS8 2PU Tel: 0117 973 1201 Fax: 0117 946 7031; 17 Downs Cote View, Westbury-on-Trym, Bristol BS9 3TU Tel: 0117 962 1513 — MB ChB 1970 Bristol. Prev: SHO (Gen. Surg.) Bristol Homoeop. Hosp.; SHO (Neurosurg.) Frenchay Hosp. Bristol; SHO (Orthop. Surg.) Winford Orthop. Hosp.

PEGG

PEGG, John Gordon (retired) Sunnyside, Venn Ottery, Ottery St Mary EX11 1RX Tel: 01404 812166 — MB BS 1959 Lond.; DObst RCOG 1969.

PEGG, John Graham (retired) The White House, 31 Woodmarket, Lutterworth LE17 4BX Tel: 01455 552428 — MRCS Eng. LRCP Lond. 1943; FRCA Eng. 1954; DA Eng. 1949. Hon. Cons. Anaesth. Hosp. of St. Cross, Rugby. Prev: Sen. Regist. (Anaesth.) FarnBoro. Hosp. Kent.

PEGG, Michael Stuart Newstead, 3 Canons Close, Radlett WD7 7ER — MB BS 1972 Lond.; LLM Wales. 1995; BSc Lond. 1969; MRCS Eng. LRCP Lond. 1972; FFA RCS Eng. 1977; DObst RCOG 1974. (Westm.) Cons. Anaesth. Roy. Free Hosp. Lond.; Hon. Sen. Lect. Roy. Free Hosp. Med. Sch. Lond.; Hon. Cons. Anaesth. St. Lukes Hosp. for Clergy. Socs: Assn. Anaesths.; BMA. Prev: Sen. Regist. (Anaesth.) St. Geo. Hosp. Lond.; Staff Anaesth. Univ. Amsterdam & Willhelmina Hosp. Amsterdam Holland; Regist. (Anaesth.) King's Coll. Hosp. Lond.

PEGG, Rachel Jane Wybourne, Wheatlands, Elmstead Market, Colchester CO7 7EW Tel: 01206 824322 — MB ChB 1996 Sheff.; ATLS RCS Eng. 1997; ALS 1998; APLS 1999. (Sheffield) SHO (Paed) Whipps Cross Hosp. Prev: SHO (A & E) Chase Farm Hosp. Enfield Middlx.; SHO (Med.) Chase Farm Hosp. Enfield Middlx.

PEGG, Rachel Lisa 8 Cherrytree Road, Rowledge, Farnham GU10 4AB Email: rachel_pegg@hotmail.com — MB BS 1992 Lond.; MRCP (Paed.) UK 1997. (King's College London)

PEGG, Stephen Mark 8 Davan Place, Broughty Ferry, Dundee DD5 3HG — MB ChB 1989 Dundee.

PEGGE, Nicholas Christopher University of Wales College of Medicine, Dept. of Cardiology, Heath Park, Cardiff CF14 4XN Tel: 029 2074 7747 Fax: 029 2074 3500 Email: peggenc@cardiff.ac.uk; Bryher, 39 Village Farm, Bonvilston, Vale of Glamorgan, Cardiff CF5 6TY Tel: 01446 781553 — MB BS 1993 Lond.; MA Camb. 1990; MRCP (UK) 1996. (Jesus Coll. Camb. & St. Thos. Hosp. Lond.) Regist. (Cardiol.) Univ. Hosp. of Wales Cardiff. Prev: Regist. (Cardiol.) Morriston Hosp. Swansea; Regist. (Cardiol.) Singleton Hosp. Swansea.

PEGGE, Stephanie Margaret 11 Ilkeston Road, Bramcote, Nottingham NG9 3JP — MB BS 1987 Lond.; MRCGP 1992.

PEGGIE, David Anderson Reform Street Health Centre, Reform Street, Beith KA15 2AE Tel: 01505 502888 Fax: 01505 504151; 1 Whitelea Crescent, Kilmacolm PA13 4JP Tel: 01505 873776 Email: david.peggie@virgin.net — MB ChB 1978 Ed.; DRCOG 1981. GP Princip. Beith; Occupat. Health Med. Off. N. Ayrsh. & Arran NHS Trust; Police Surg. Ayrsh.

PEGGS, Karl Stuart 20 Upper Hollis, Great Missenden HP16 9HP — BM BCh 1991 Oxf.

PEGLER, Gillian 3 Heathfield Road, Gabalfa, Cardiff CF14 3JX — MB BCh 1997 Wales. (UWCM) Jun. Ho. Off. T&O Cardiff Roy. Infirm. Cardiff; SHO (A& E) Univ. Hosp. Of Wales, Cardiff. Prev: Jun. Ho. Off. Gen. Surg. Llondough Hosp. Cardiff; Jun. Ho. Off. (Gen. Med.) Neath Gen. Hosp.; Jun. Ho. Off. (Gen. Med.) Morriston Hosp. Swansea.

PEGMAN, Amanda Jane 9 The Chase, Rickleton, Washington NE38 9DX — BM BCh 1988 Oxf.

PEGRUM, Anthony Charles 46 Alleyn Road, London SE21 8AL — MB BS 1993 Lond.; BSc Lond. 1990; DA (UK) 1996. (St. Geo. Hosp. Med. Sch.)

PEGRUM, Helen Louise 11 Barley Mead, Warfield, Bracknell RG42 3SA — MB BS 1989 Lond.; MRCGP 1995; DRCOG 1993; DCH RCP Lond. 1992.

PEGUM, Joseph Stephen The Primary, Langley Upper Green, Saffron Walden CB11 4RZ Tel: 01799 550226 — BChir 1944 Camb.; MA Camb. 1952, BA 1939, MD 1952; FRCP Lond. 1966, M 1948; LMSSA Lond. 1943. (Camb. & Guy's) Cons. Dermat. Lond. Hosp. Socs: Hon. Mem. (Ex.-Pres.) Brit. Assn. Dermat.; Fell. Roy. Soc. Med. (Ex-Pres Sect. Dermat.). Prev: Phys. Skin Dept. Lond. Hosp.; Civil Cons. Dermat. to RN; Cons. Dermat. Qu. Eliz. Hosp. Childr. Lond.

PEI, Kee Cheong Benjamin 15 Holmdene Avenue, London NW7 2LY — MB ChB 1990 Glas.

PEI, Yuk Man Debra 15 Holmdene Avenue, London NW7 2LY — MB ChB 1992 Bristol.

PEI YAW LIANG, Gordon 15 Holmdene Avenue, Mill Hill, London NW7 2LY Tel: 020 8959 4792 Fax: 020 8906 0598; Penthouse 121, Regent on the River, Watermans Quay, Sands Wharf, Townmead Road, London SW6 2RR — MB BS 1959 Hong Kong; DTM & H RCP Lond. 1996.

PEILE, Edward Basil Aston Clinton Surgery, 136 London Road, Aston Clinton, Aylesbury HP22 5LB Email: ed.peile@dphpc.ox.ac.uk; Chiltern Waters, 1 Stablebridge Road, Aston Clinton, Aylesbury HP22 5ND Tel: 01296 631337 Fax: 01296 631727 Email: ed.peile@btinternet.com — MB BS 1975 Lond.; MRCP (UK) 1981; MRCS Eng. LRCP Lond. 1975; FRCP 1999; MRCPCH 1997; FRCGP 1993; MRCGP 1980; DCH Eng. 1978; DRCOG 1978. (Middlx.) Research Fell. (Med. Educ.) Dept. of Primary Care Univ. of Oxf. Prev: Med. Off. Community Drugs & Alcohol Team Tindal Centre Aylesbury; Sen. Specialist Renal Unit PMRAF Hosp. Halton; SHO Profess. Unit Sheff. Childr. Hosp.

PEIRCE, Clive Ronald Glendevon Medical Centre, Carlton Place, Teignmouth TQ14 8AB Tel: 01626 770955; Little Court, Shaldon Road, Combeinteignhead, Newton Abbot TQ12 4RR — MB ChB 1989 Dundee; MRCGP 1994; DGM RCP Lond. 1995; DFFP 1995.

PEIRCE, Kate Sarah 79 Lauriston Road, London E9 7HJ — MB BS 1994 Lond.

PEIRCE, Nicholas Sheridan 51 Kelly Street, London NW1 8PG — BM BS 1988 Nottm.

PEIRIS, Mr Collin Sweithin Linton (retired) 6 Argyle Road, Southport PR9 9LH Tel: 01704 532123 — MB BS 1952 Ceylon; FRCS Ed. 1963; DO Eng. 1957. Prev: Cons. Ophth. Surg. S.port & Formby Dist. Gen. Hosp. & Ormskirk & Dist. Gen. Hosp.

PEIRIS, Jeffrey Gordon Christopher 31 Oakfield Avenue, Kenton, Harrow HA3 8TH Tel: 020 8907 0606 — MB BS 1959 Ceylon; DCH Ceylon 1967. (Ceylon) Clin. Med. Off. Brent & Harrow AHA.

***PEIRIS, Lokukankanamge Heshanth Sandun** 69 Shirley Park Road, Addiscombe, Croydon CR0 7EW — MB BS 1996 Lond.

PEIRIS, Mahapitiyage Viveka Sudharma Infectious Disease Unit, East Riding Health Authority, Victoria House, Park St., Hull HU2 8TD Tel: 01482 617800 Fax: 01482 617840 — MB BS Lond. 1983; MRCPath 1991. (St. Thos.) Cons. Communicable Dis. Control E. Riding HA.

PEIRIS, Mathew Laith Quintus 6 Langworth Close, Dartford DA2 7ET — MB BS 1968 Ceylon; MRCP (UK) 1977; T(GP) 1991.

PEISACH, Carole Melanie Torrington Park Health Centre, 16 Torrington Park, North Finchley, London N12 9SS Tel: 020 8445 7622/4127 — MB ChB 1989 Cape Town; MRCGP Lond. 1995; DCH Lond. 1994. GP Princip. Lond.; Clin. Asst. Gyn.

PEJOVIC, Ivan 128 Barrowgate Road, London W4 4QP — Lekar Sarajevo, Yugoslavia 1964. (Sarajevo)

PEKTAS, Tevfik 143 Conisborough Crescent, Catford, London SE6 2SQ — LMSSA 1972 Lond.; DCH RCPS Glas. 1970. Clin. Med. Off. (Child Health) Optimum Health Servs. Lond. Socs: Med. Protec. Soc.

PELEKOUDA, Eleni Queens Hospital, Block B Flat B, Belvedere Road, Burton-on-Trent DE13 0RB — Ptychio Iatrikes 1991 Thessalonika.

PELEKOUDAS, Nicolaos 11 Belsize Road, London NW6 4RX — Ptychio Iatrikes 1990 Athens.

PELENDRIDES, Eleni Lichfield Grove Surgery, 64 Lichfield Grove, Finchley, London N3 2JP Tel: 020 8346 3123 Fax: 020 8343 4919; 112 Creighton Avenue, London N2 9BJ — MB BS 1984 Lond.; DRCOG 1988. (Guy's Hospital London)

PELFRENE, Eric 255 Kennington Road, London SE11 6BY — MD 1983 Ghent; T(M) 1994.

PELGER, Hans Christian Queen's Medical Centre, Currie Court, Block C11/24, Nottingham NG7 2UH — State Exam Med 1988 Bochum.

PELHAM, Anne 230 Jesmond Dene Road, Jesmond, Newcastle upon Tyne NE2 2JU; 68 Hamilton Crescent, Brentwood CM14 5ES Email: anne.pelham@uheane.net — MB ChB 1986 Aberd.; Dipl Cognitive Therapy 2000; MRCGP 1990. p/t Specialist Regist., N.ern Region.

PELL, Gerard Melvyn (retired) Frenchay Hospital, Bristol BS16 1LE Tel: 0117 970 1212 — MB BS 1969 Lond.; BDS Lond. 1962; MRCS Eng. LRCP Lond. 1969; FDS RCS Eng. 1971, LDS 1962. Cons. Maxillofacial & Oral Surg. Frenchay Hosp. Bristol; Univ. Clin. Tutor Frenchay Hosp. Prev: Sen. Regist. (Oral & Maxillofacial Surg.) Qu. Vict. Hosp. E. Grinstead & Kings Coll. Hosp. Lond.

PELL, Heather (retired) 23 Parkgate, Blackheath, London SE3 9XF — MB BS Lond. 1960; MRCS Eng. LRCP Lond. 1960.

PELL, Jill Patricia Department Public Health, Greater Glasgow Health Board, Dalian House, 350 St Vincents St., Glasgow G3 8YU Tel: 0141 201 4544 Fax: 0141 201 4949 — MB ChB 1987 Ed.; MD 1999 ed; MSc Ed. 1994, MB ChB Ed. 1987; MFPHM RCP (UK) 1995; MRCGP 1991; DCH Glas. 1989. (Ed.) Cons. Pub. Health Med. Gt.er Glas. HB; Hon. Clin.sen Lect. (cardiol) Univ. Glas.full time. Prev: Sen. Regist. (Pub. Health) Glas.; Research Fell. (Health Servs.) Univ. Edninburgh; GP Trainee, Fife.

PELL, Judith Barbara West Hayes Lodge, Sarum Road, Winchester SO22 5EZ — BM 1981 Soton.; MFFP 1993; MFFP 1993; MRCGP 1985. Asst. GP, S.ampton. Socs: Fac. Fam. Plann. & Reproduc. Health Care. Prev: GP Winchester.

PELL, Mr Rodney Lang Tel: 01843 823604 Fax: 01843 823461 Email: rodneypell@aol.com — MB BS 1961 Lond.; BSc (Hons.) Lond. 1958; FRCSI 1969; MRCS Eng. LRCP Lond. 1961; Cert. T.A. (1993). (Lond. Hosp.) Cons. Orthop. Surg. Chaucer Hosp. Canterbury, Kent.; Cons. Othop. Surg. The Spencer Wing, Qu. Eliz. the Qu. Mother Hosp. Margate, Kent. Socs: Fell. BOA; Fell. Roy. Soc. Med.; Acad. Experts. Prev: Cons, Orthop. Surg. City & E. Lond. HA; Regist. St. Bart. Hosp. Lond.; Regist. (Orthop.) Guy's Hosp. Lond.

PELL-ILDERTON, Richard (retired) The New House, Ryme Intrinseca, Sherborne DT9 6JX — MB ChB 1953 Manch.; FRCPath 1973, M 1963; DPath Eng. 1961. Prev: Cons. Path. N. Manch. Gen. Hosp.

PELLEGRINI, Arthur Vincent 87 Larkfield Road, Liverpool L17 9PS — MB ChB 1980 Liverp.

PELLER, Sally Elizabeth Collurian, Gilly Lane, Whitecross, Penzance TR20 8BZ Tel: 01736 740441 Fax: 01736 740441 — MB ChB 1982 Bristol; MRCGP 1989. p/t GP Locum, Cornw. Socs: BMA; RCGP. Prev: GP Regist. Cornw. VTS; Staff Grade (A & E) GTruro Cornw.; GP Regist. Soton. VTS.

PELLERITO, Rosolino Leinster House, 46 Leinster Gardens, London W2 3AT — State Exam Palermo 1992.

PELLING, Marc Xavier 46 Aberdeen Gardens, London NW6 3QA — MB ChB 1984 Bristol.

PELLOW, Roy John Newman, MC (retired) 32 Lansdowne Road, Luton LU3 1EE Tel: 01582 731700 — MB BS 1943 Lond.; MRCS Eng. LRCP Lond. 1941.

PELLUET, Emma Jane 10 Roland Mews, London E1 3JT; 12 The Windmills, Broomfield Hospital, Chelmsford CM1 7ET — MB BS 1996 Lond.

PELLY, Hugh John Wordsworth Dean Lane Surgery, Dean Lane, Sixpenny Handley, Salisbury SP5 5PA Tel: 01725 552500 Fax: 01725 552029; Doves Meadow Surgery, Broadchalke, Salisbury SP5 5EL Tel: 01722 780282 Fax: 01722 780041 — FRCGP 2000; MB BS Lond. 1969; MRCGP 1980; DCH Eng. 1971. (Middlx.) Socs: Expert Witness Inst.; Brit. Inst. Manip. Med. Prev: Clin. Asst. (Rheumatol.) Salisbury Gen. Hosp.; Med. Off. Brit. Nepal Med. Trust; Resid. Med. Off. Middlx. Hosp. Lond.

PELLY, Michael Eliot Chelsea & Westminster Hospital, 369 Fulham Road, London SW10 9NH Tel: 020 8746 8071 Email: m.pelly@ic.ac.uk; 15 Crondace Road, Parsons's Green, London SW6 4BB Tel: 020 7731 0559 — MB BS 1978 Lond.; MSc (Clin. Trop. Med.) Lond. 1987; MRCP (UK) 1980; MRCGP 1986; DTM & H RCP Lond. 1987; FRCP UK 1997. (St. Mary's) Cons. Phys. Gen. Med. & Sen. Lect. (Med. for Elderly) Chelsea & W.m.Hosp. Lond.; Med. Adviser Med. Emerg. Relief Internat.; Sen. Health Adviser (Extern. Cons.) Internat. Federat. of Red Cross & Red Cresc. Societies. Socs: FRCP; Liveryman of Soc. of Apoth.; Fell. Roy. Soc. of Trop. Med. and Hyg.

PELOSI, Anthony Joseph Department of Psychiatry, Hairmyres Hospital, East Kilbridge, Glasgow G75 8RG Tel: 0135 572620 Fax: 0135 572615 Email: anthonypelosi@compuserve.com — MB ChB 1977 Glas.; MSc (Epidemiol.) Lond. 1987; FRCP Glas. 1992; MRCP (UK) 1980; MRCPsych 1985.

PELOSI, Luciana 18 Reservoir Road N., Prenton, Birkenhead CH42 8LU Tel: 0151 608 1482 — State Exam Naples 1979.

PELTA, David Elliott Queensway Surgery, 75 Queensway, Southend-on-Sea SS1 2AB Tel: 01702 463333 Fax: 01702 603026 — MB ChB 1973 Bristol; MRCP (UK) 1976; MRCGP 1977; DCH Eng. 1975.

PELTON, Christopher Ian Wellington Health Centre, Chapel Lane, Wellington, Telford TF1 1PZ Tel: 01952 242304; Hillside, 13 Princes End, Lawley bank, Telford TF4 2JN Tel: 01952 630108 Email: chris@peltons.freeserve.co.uk — MB BS 1978 Lond.; MRCGP 1985; FFA RCS Eng. 1982; DRCOG 1987. (Middlesex) Prev: Regist. (Anaesth.) Univ. Hosp. Wales Cardiff; Sen. Med. Off. Jane Furse Hosp. Lebowa S. Afr.

***PELTON, Ginette Michelle** Brambles, Birchland Way, Sparkwell, Plymouth PL7 5DW — BM BS 1998 Nottm.; BM BS Nottm 1998.

PELTON, Jane Tel: 01952 620077; Hillside, 13 Princes End, Lawley Bank, Telford TF4 2JN Tel: 01952 630108 Email: peltons@tinyworld.co.uk — MB ChB 1980 Birm.; DRCOG 1982. Princip. in Gen. Pract., Telford. Prev: GP Telford; Med. Off. Jane Furse Memor. Hosp. Lebowa, S. Afr.; Trainee GP Cardiff VTS.

PELTZ, Samuel Lionel 49 Broadwick Street, London W1 Tel: 020 7437 4040 — LRCPI & LM, LRSCI & LM 1957; LRCPI & LM, LRCSI & LM 1957. (RCSI) Clin. Asst. (Surg.) Roy. Lond. Homoeop. Hosp.; Teach. Gen. Pract. Middlx. Hosp. Lond. Univ. Socs: Inst. Indust. Med.

PEMBERTON, Anthony John (retired) Alveston, Oak End Way, Woodham, Weybridge KT13 3DY Tel: 01932 345031 — BM BCh 1956 Oxf.; MA Oxf. 1956; Cert Av Med MoD (Air) & CAA; Aviat. Auth. 1977.

PEMBERTON, Colin James (retired) 8 Gleneagles Road, Heald Green, Cheadle SK8 3EL Tel: 0161 491 6953 — MB ChB 1964 Manch.; MRCS Eng. LRCP Lond. 1966; FFA RCS Eng. 1971; DA Eng. 1968. Cons. Anaesth. Stockport NHS Trust. Prev: Sen. Regist. (Anaesth.) United Manch. Hosps. & Manch. RHB.

PEMBERTON, David Almond (retired) 16 High Street, Dunblane FK15 0AD Tel: 01786 822927 — MB ChB 1961 Ed.; MRCPsych 1972; DPM Eng. 1965. Prev: Cons. & Unit Med. Manager Bellsdyke Hosp. Larbert.

PEMBERTON, Mr David John Royal Glamorgan Hospital, Pontyclun CF72 8XR Tel: 01443 443576 — MB BCh 1984 Wales; FRCS (Orth.) 1992; FRCS Ed. 1988. (Welsh Nat. Sch. Med.) Cons. Orthop. Surg.Roy. Glam. NHS Trust. Socs: BASK; BOSTA. Prev: Sen. Regist. (Orthop. Surg.) Cardiff Roy. Infirm.; Lect. (Orthop. Surg.) Univ. Wales Coll. Med.

PEMBERTON, Derek John Circuit Lane Surgery, 53 Circuit Lane, Reading RG30 3AN Tel: 0118 958 2537 Fax: 0118 957 6115 — MB BCh 1983 Wales; MRCGP 1989; DA (UK) 1986.

PEMBERTON, Douglas Pye Apartment 4, The Empire, Grand Parade, Bath BA2 4DF — BA Camb. 1956; MRCS Eng. LRCP Lond. 1961. (Camb. & Royal Lond. Hosp.) Life Insur. Med. Examr. Socs: BMA. Prev: Sen. Med. Off. ADMA-OPCO Med. Dept. Das Is., Abu Dhabi, UAE; Dist. Med. Off. Long Is., Bahamas; MOH Elgin N. Dakota, USA.

PEMBERTON, Elaine 118 Main Road, Ravenshead, Nottingham NG15 9GW — MB ChB 1967 Ed. SCMO (Family Plann.) Nottm. HA (T); Sen. Clin. Med. Off. Centr. Notts. HA. Socs: Fac. Fam. Plann. & Reproduc. Health Care (Regional Assessor); Inst. Psychosexual Med.

PEMBERTON, James 18 Village Way, Dulwich, London SE21 7AN Tel: 020 7737 2220 — MRCS Eng. LRCP Lond. 1967; BSc Lond. 1963, MB BS 1967; MRCP (U.K.) 1971; FRCR 1975; FFR 1974; DMRD Eng. 1972. (St. Bart.) Cons. (Diag. Radiol.) St. Thos. Hosp. Lond. Prev: Jun. Regist. (Med.) & Regist. (Diag. Radiol.) St. Bart. Hosp. Lond.; Sen. Regist. (Diag. Radiol.) King's Coll. Hosp. Lond.

***PEMBERTON, James Anthony** 161 Osborne Road, West Jesmond, Newcastle upon Tyne NE2 3JT — MB BS 1996 Newc.

PEMBERTON, Janet Mary Scunthorpe Community Healthcare Trust, Brumby Hospital, Scunthorpe DN16 1QQ Tel: 01724 290068 — MB BS Lond. 1970. (King's Coll. Hosp.) SCMO Scunthorpe Community Healthcare Trust. Prev: Ho. Phys. Belgrave Hosp. Childr.; Ho. Surg. (Gen. Surg.) Wythenshawe Hosp. Manch.

PEMBERTON, John Central Surgery, King St., Barton-upon-Humber DN18 5ER Tel: 01652 635435 Fax: 01652 636122 — MB BS 1969 Lond.; BDS Lond. 1964; FDS RCS Eng. 1972. (King's Coll. Hosp.) Prev: Lect. (Oral Med.) Univ. Manch.; Ho. Surg. (ENT) Kings Coll. Hosp. Lond.; Ho. Phys. Belgrave Hosp. Childr. Lond.

PEMBERTON, John (retired) Iona, Cannonfields, Hathersage, Hope Valley S32 1AG — MB BS Lond. 1936; MD Lond. 1940; FRCP Lond. 1964, M 1941; MRCS Eng. LRCP Lond. 1936; FFCMI 1976; FFCM 1974; DPH Leeds 1956. Prev: Acad. Co-ordinator N.. Consortium Community Med. Univ. Sheff.

PEMBERTON

*PEMBERTON, Laura Shelley 79 1/L Lumsden Street, Yorkhill, Glasgow G3 8RH — MB ChB 1996 Glas.

PEMBERTON, Michael Neal University Dental Hospital of Manchester, Manchester M15 6FH — MB ChB 1995 Sheff. Cons. Oral Med. Univ. Dent. Hosp. Manch.

PEMBERTON, Nicholas Charles 528 Upper Brentwood Road, Romford RM2 6HX — MB BS 1995 Lond.

PEMBERTON, Philippa Louise 18 Village Way, London SE21 7AN — MB BS 1993 Lond.

PEMBERTON, Phillip Edward Health Centre, Victoria Sq, Portishead, Bristol BS20 6AQ Tel: 01275 847474 Fax: 01275 817516 Email: ppemberton@cix.co.uk — MB ChB 1978 Bristol; MRCGP 1994; MRCOG 1984. Course Organiser, Bristol Vocational Train. Scheme.

PEMBERTON, Mr Richard Mark Queen Alexandra Hospital, Cosham, Portsmouth PO6 3LY Tel: 023 92 286000 — MB BS 1986 Lond.; FRCS Eng. 1990; BA Camb. 1982; MA Camb. 1985; MS (Gen.) 1998. (Kings College Hospital) Cons. Vasc. Srugeon Portsmouth Hosps.

*PEMBLETON, Alec 14c St Bridge Street, Liverpool L8 7PL — MB ChB 1996 Liverp.

PEMBREY, John Seymour The Surgery, 48 Mulgrave Road, Belmont, Sutton SM2 6LX Tel: 020 8642 2050 Fax: 020 8643 6264; 50 Mulgrave Road, Sutton SM2 6LX Tel: 020 8643 3596 Email: pembrey@blueyonder.co.uk — MB BS 1966 Lond.; MRCS Eng. LRCP Lond. 1966; MRCGP 1974; DObst RCOG 1969; DCH Eng. 1968. (St. Bart.) Socs: BMA; Sutton Med. Soc. Prev: SHO (Paediat.) Sydenham Childr. Hosp.; Ho. Surg. Metrop. Hosp. Lond.; Ho. Off. (Obst.) St. Bart. Hosp. Lond.

PEMBREY, Professor Marcus Edred Institute of Child Health, 30 Guilford St., London WC1N 1EH Tel: 020 7242 9789 Fax: 020 7831 0488; Picketts S., Picketts Lane, Redhill RH1 5RG Tel: 01293 785776 — MRCS Eng. LRCP Lond. 1966; BSc (Hons.) Lond. 1963, MD 1978, MB BS 1966; FRCP 1981, M 1968. (Guy's) Mothercare Prof. Paediat. Genetics Inst. Child Health Univ. Lond.; Hon. Cons. Clin. Geneticist Hosp. for Childr. Gt. Ormond St. Lond. Socs: Fell. Roy. Soc. Med. Prev: Research Assoc. (Med. & Paediat. Research) Guy's Hosp. Med. Sch. Lond.

PEMBREY, Mr Michael Robert Abbotsfield, Saxonwood Road, Battle TN33 0EY Tel: 01424 775502 Fax: 01424 772754 Email: pembraymr@hotmail.com — MB BS 1972 Lond.; MRCS Eng. LRCP Lond. 1972; FRCS Ed. 1981; MRCOG 1984. (St. Bart.) Cons. O & G Hastings & Rother NHS Trust Conquest Hosp. St. Leonards on Sea. Socs: Brit. Soc. Colpos. & Cerv. Path.; Internat. Continence Soc. Prev: Sen. Regist. (O & G) John Radcliffe & Ch.ill Hosps. Oxf.; Resid. Med. Off. (Obst.) Qu. Charlotte's Matern. Hosp.; Resid. Med. Off. (Gyn.) Samarit. Hosp. for Wom.

PEMBREY, Rachel Lisa Birchwood, 2 College Road, Upper Beeding, Steyning BN44 3TB; Birchwood, 2 College Road, Upper Beeding, Steyning BN44 3TB — MB BS 1998 Lond.; MB BS Lond 1998. (St. George's Hosp. Med Sch.) SHO (A&E) St. Richard's Hosp. Chichester, W. Sussex. Prev: Ho. Off. (Med.) P.ss Roy. Hosp. Hayward's Heath; Ho. Off. (Surg.) St. Richard's Hosp. Chichester, W. Sussex.

PEMBRIDGE, Bette Theresa Marcham Health Centre, Marcham Road, Abingdon OX14 1BT Tel: 01235 522602; Sutton Wick Barn, Sutton Wick, Drayton, Abingdon OX14 4HJ Tel: 01235 559291 — MB BS 1974 Lond.; MRCS Eng. LRCP Lond. 1974; MRCGP 1992; T(GP) 1991; DCH Eng. 1978; DRCOG 1977. (Roy. Free) Gen. Practitioner Princip.

*PEMBRIDGE, Jonathan Mark Maesmarchog House, Cross Inn, Llantrisant, Pontyclun CF7 8PF — MB BCh 1994 Wales.

PEMBROKE, Andrew Charles 28 Dartford Road, Sevenoaks TN13 3TQ Tel: 01732 450197 — MB BChir 1971 Camb.; MA Camb. 1972; FRCP Lond. 1988; MRCP (UK) 1974. (St. Bart.) Cons. Dermat: Bromley Hosps. NHS Trust. Prev: Cons. Dermat. King's Coll. Hosp. Lond.; Sen. Regist. (Dermat.) King's Coll. Hosp. Lond.; Regist. (Dermat.) Lond. Hosp.

PENA, Mr Milton Arquimides Tameside General Hospital, Fountain St., Ashton-under-Lyne OL6 9RW Tel: 0161 331 6768 Fax: 0161 331 6300; Ribbleton House, 30 Crow Lane W., Newton-le-Willows WA12 9YG Tel: 01925 226122 — Medico Cirujano Chile 1973; FRCS Ed. 1984; T(S) 1991. Cons. Orthop. Surg. Tameside Gen. Hosp. Prev: Sen. Regist. (Orthop.) Wrightington Hosp., Manch Roy. Infirm. & Hope Hosp. Salford.

PENCHEON, David Charles 51 Mill Road, Lode, Cambridge CB5 9EN — BM BCh 1982 Oxf.

PENCHEON, Pamela Edna (retired) — MB ChB Leeds 1952; MRCPsych 1972; DPM Eng. 1966. Prev: Cons. Psychiat. (Adult Psychiat.) Roy. Cornw. Hosp. Truro.

PENDER, James Blackwoods Medical Centre, 8 Station Road, Muirhead, Glasgow G69 9EE Tel: 0141 779 2228 Fax: 0141 779 3225 — MB ChB 1972 Glas.

PENDERED, John Hamilton, MBE (retired) Little Way, West Furlong Lane, Hurstpierpoint, Hassocks BN6 9RH Tel: 01273 835209 — MB BS 1946 Lond.; FRCGP 1988, M 1976; DObst RCOG 1948. Prev: Ho. Surg., Ho. Phys. & Res. Accouch. Lond. Hosp.

PENDERED, Lucy Frances Clifton Lodge, 17 Cheddon Road, Taunton TA2 7BL Tel: 01823 282151 Fax: 01823 326755; Lower Comeytrowe Farm House, Comeytrowe Lane, Taunton TA1 5HY — MB ChB 1985 Bristol; MRCGP 1990; T(GP) 1991; DRCOG 1989. (Bristol) Partner.

PENDLEBURY, Donald Granville (retired) Southern Pines, Little London Road, Horam, Heathfield TN21 0BD Tel: 01435 812300 — MB BS Lond. 1959; MRCPsych 1971; DPM Eng. 1962. Prev: Cons. Psychiat. Hellingly Hosp. Hailsham.

PENDLEBURY, Sarah Tamsin 5 Ferry Road, Marston, Oxford OX3 0ET Tel: 01865 721344 Fax: 01865 221122 Email: stpendle@bioch.ox.ac.uk; Oxford Centre for Functional Magnetic, John Radcliffe Hospital, Oxford OX3 9DU Tel: 01865 222738 Fax: 01865 221122 — BM BCh Oxf. 1992; MA Camb. 1993; MRCP (UK) 1995. (Univ. Camb. & Univ. Oxf.) Clin. Research Fell. & Hon. Regist. (Neurol.) Oxf. Prev: SHO (Neurol.) Radcliffe Infirm.; Clin. Attaché (Respirat. Med.) Centre Hosp.ie Universitaire de Grenoble, France; SHO (Intens. Care) Roy. Sussex Co. Hosp. Brighton.

PENDLETON, Adrian 82 Willowvale Gardens, Belfast BT11 9JW — MB BCh BAO 1993 Belf.

PENDLETON, Ann Pia Mary Mount Pleasant Practice, The Health Centre, Tempest Way, Chepstow NP16 5XR Tel: 01291 636500 Fax: 01291 636518 — MB BCh BAO 1982 NUI; MRCGP 1991.

PENDLETON, Neil 43 Elmswood Road, Liverpool L17 0DH — MB ChB 1985 Liverp.

PENDLINGTON, Matthew, TD 49 Cannock Road, New Invention, Willenhall WV12 5SA Tel: 01922 76477 Fax: 01922 476477 — MB ChB Birm. 1957. (Birm.) Prev: Ho. Surg. Gen. Hosp. Birm.; Ho. Phys. & Sen. Ho. Surg. O & G Dryburn Hosp. Durh.

PENDOWER, Mr John Edward Hicks (retired) Rosemary, Promenade de Verdun, Purley CR8 3LN Tel: 020 8660 8949 — MB BS 1950 Lond.; FRCS Eng. 1955; MRCS Eng. LRCP Lond. 1950. Barrister-at-Law Inner Temple 1972. Prev: Dean Char. Cross & W.m. Med. Sch.

PENDREIGH, Gladys Margaret (retired) 22 Bonaly Avenue, Edinburgh EH13 0ET Tel: 0131 477 3750 — MB ChB 1954 Ed. Prev: SCMO Lothian HB.

PENDRIGH, David Croll (retired) 24 Scarbrough Avenue, Skegness PE25 2SY Tel: 01754 3050 — MB ChB 1949 Glas. Prev: Anaesth. Skegness & Dist. Hosp.

PENDRY, Katherine Royal Albert Edward Infirmary., Wigan Lane, Wigan WN1 2NN — MB ChB 1983 Bristol; MRCP (UK) 1986; MRCPath 1991; FRCP 1999; FRCPath 2000. Cons. Haemat. Wigan & Leigh health Serv.s NHS Trust; Cons. Haemat. Wrightington Wigan & Leigh Health Serv.s NHS Trust. Prev: Cons Haemat. Bury Health Ccare NHS Trust; Cons Haematol BUPA healthcare NHS Trust; Sen. Regist. (Haemat.) N. W.. RHA.

PENFIELD, Beverley South Woodford Health Centre, 114 High Road, London E18 2QS; 14 Chester Road, Chigwell IG7 6AJ Tel: 020 8500 7018 — MB BS 1982 Lond.; DA Eng. 1985. p/t GP Princip.; Family Plann. Doctor Chigwell. Prev: Trainee GP Epping VTS; SHO (O & G/Anaesth.) Whipps Cross Hosp. Lond.

PENFOLD, Bernard Mark 45 Fairways Drive, Blackwell, Bromsgrove B60 1BB — MB ChB 1972 Liverp.; MRCS Eng. LRCP Lond. 1972; DObst RCOG 1975. Med. Adviser, Med. Servs., SEMA Gp., Birm. Socs: Soc. Occupat. Med.

PENFOLD, Mr Christopher Neil Glan Clwyd Hospital, Rhyl LL18 5UJ Tel: 01745 583910; Tyddyn Llan, Corwen LL21 9SL Tel: 01824 750472 Email: cnp@globalnet.co.uk — MB BS 1988 Lond.;

BDS 1978; FDS RCS Ed. 1982; FRCS Ed. 1991. Cons. Oral & Maxillofacial Surg., Glan Clwyd Hosp. Socs: Fell. Brit. Assoc. Oral & Maxillofacial Surg.s; Craniofacial Soc.; Brit. Assn. Head & Neck Oncol. Prev: Regist. (Oral & Maxillofacial Surg.) S.ampton Gen. Hosp.; Sen. Regist. KCH Lond.; Sen. Regist., Qu. Vict. Hosp., E. Grinstead.

PENFOLD, Grace Kent The Nest, Higher Porthpean, St Austell PL26 6AY — MB BS 1963 Lond. (Univ. Coll. Hosp.)

PENFOLD, Helen Margaret Waterlooville Health Centre, Dryden Close, Waterlooville PO7 6AL Tel: 02392 257321 Fax: 02392 230739 — MB ChB 1976 Sheff.; MRCP (UK) 1980; MFFP 1993; DRCOG 1978. (Sheff.)

PENFOLD, Hilary Anne Wootton Medical Centre, 36-38 High Street, Wootton, Northampton NN4 6LW Tel: 01604 709933 Fax: 01604 709944; Harlestone House Lodge, Church Lane, Lower Harlestone, Northampton NN7 4EN — MB ChB 1987 Sheff.; DRCOG 1991.

PENFOLD, Jason John 350 Scalby Road, Scarborough YO12 6ED — MB BS 1996 Lond.

PENFOLD, Nigel William Department of Anaesthesia, West Suffolk Hospital, Hardwick Lane, Bury St Edmunds IP33 2QZ Tel: 01638 750269 Fax: 01284 713100; St. Helier, Bury Road, Kentford, Newmarket CB8 7PT Tel: 01638 750269 Fax: 01638 555124 Email: nigelwpenfold@aol.com — MB BS 1980 Lond.; FFA RCS Eng. 1985. (St. Bart.) Cons. Anaesth. W. Suff. Hosp. Bury St. Edmunds; Dep. Regional Adviser (Anglia) Roy. Collaege of Anaesth.s. Socs: Assn. Anaesth.; Obst. Anaesth. Assn.; Brit. Assn. Day Surg. Prev: Sen. Regist. Rotat. (Anaesth.) E. Anglian HA; Regist. (Anaesth.) Char. Cross & Brompton Hosps. Lond.; Ho. Surg. St. Bart. Hosp. Lond.

PENFOLD, Susan Elizabeth Handsworth Wood Medical Centre, 110 Church Lane, Handsworth Wood, Birmingham B20 2ES Tel: 0121 523 7117 Fax: 0121 554 2406; 35 Lee Crescent, Edgbaston, Birmingham B15 2BJ — BM 1987 Soton.; MRCGP 1991. Socs: Comm. Mem. Birm. Med. Inst.

PENGE, Daniela Joy 14 Strathblaine Road, London SW11 1RJ Tel: 020 7228 0726 — MB BS 1992 Lond. GP Regist. W. Middlx. Hosp. Lond. Prev: SHO (Generam Med.) King's Coll. Hosp. Lond.

PENGELLY, Mr Andrew William 72 Berkeley Avenue, Reading RG1 6HY Tel: 0118 955 3452 Fax: 0118 958 8110; Fieldgate House, Hollington, Woolton Hill, Newbury RG20 9XR Tel: 01635 254429 Fax: 01635 253741 Email: awp@ab12.demon.co.uk — BM BCh Oxf. 1968; MA Oxf. 1968; FRCS Eng. 1974; FEBU 1989. (Oxf. & Middlx.) Cons. Urol. & Med. Exec. Dir. Roy. Berks. & Battle Hosps. NHS Trust Reading. Socs: Brit. Assn. Urol. Surgs.; Roy. Soc. Med.; Internat. Continence Soc. Prev: Sen. Regist. Middlx. Hosp.; SHO Gloucester Roy. Hosp.; Ho. Phys. Addenbrooke's Hosp. Camb.

PENGELLY, Charles Desmond Ross (cons. rooms), 60 Manchester Road, Altrincham WA14 4PJ Tel: 0161 928 2833; The Oasis Hotel, 46 Barrington Road, Altrincham WA14 1HN Tel: 0161 928 4523 — MB ChB 1946 Bristol; MD Bristol 1959; FRCP Ed. 1969, M 1952; FRCP Glas. 1986, M 1984; FRCP Lond. 1968, M 1954. (Bristol) Hon. Cons. Phys. Altrincham Gen. Hosp., St. Anne's Hosp. Bowdon & Trafford Gen. Hosp. Davyhulme; Examr. PLAB. Socs: Fell. Roy. Soc. Med.; Fell. Manch. Med. Soc.; Hon. Mem. Nat. Assn. Clin. Tutors. Prev: Univ. Manch. Postgrad. Tutor Altrincham; Sen. Regist. (Med.) Manch. RHB, Manch. Roy. Infirm. & W. Cornw. Clin. Area.

***PENGIRAN SUHAILI, Dayangku Norsuhazenah** 45 Earle Road, Liverpool L7 6AD — MB ChB 1994 Liverp.

PENGIRAN TENGAH, Dayangku Siti Nur Ashikin Derbyshire Royal Infirmary, London Road, Derby DE1 2QY; 3 Newcastle Drive, The Park, Nottingham NG7 1AA — BM BS 1996 Nottm. SHO (Med.) Derbysh. Roy. Infirm. Derby. Socs: BMA. Prev: Jun. Ho. Off. (Surg.) Derby City Gen. Hosp.; Jun. Ho. Off. (Med.) Kings Mill Centre for Health Care Servs. Sutton-in-Ashfield.

PENIKET, Andrew James Water Works Cottage, Simons Lane, Shipton-under-Wychwood, Chipping Norton OX7 6DH — MB BChir 1992 Camb.

PENIKET, John Bernard 11 The Avenue, Churchdown, Gloucester GL3 2HB Tel: 01452 713727 Fax: 01452 713727 Email: jpeniket@compuserve.com — MB BChir Camb. 1966; MRCP Lond. 1969; MRCS Eng. LRCP Lond. 1965; MRCGP 1981; DObst RCOG 1967. (King's Coll. Hosp.) Med. Adviser Med. Servs. by Sema. Prev: Med. Servs. Manager Benefits Agency; GP Gloucester; Research Asst. (Cardiac) Radcliffe Infirm. Oxf.

PENISTAN, Thomas Richard Penistan and Partners, Cordell Road, Long Melford, Sudbury CO10 9EP Tel: 01787 378226 Fax: 01787 311287; The Old Rectory, Lavenham, Sudbury CO10 9SA Tel: 01787 247991 — MB ChB 1971 Bristol; MRCS Eng. LRCP Lond. 1971.

PENKETH, Andrea Regan Lea Roscalen, 19 Eldorado Road, Cheltenham GL50 2PU — MB BS 1977 Lond.; BSc Lond. 1974, MD 1984; MRCP (UK) 1980; T(M) 1991. (St. Mary's) p/t Cons. Phys. Cheltenham Gen. Hosp. Prev: Cons. Phys. Worcester Roy. Infirm.; Lect. (Thoracic Med.) Cardiothoracic Inst. Lond.; SHO (Med.) Hammersmith Hosp. Lond.

PENKETH, Antony Clive Alec — MB BS 1981 Lond.; DCH RCP Lond. 1984; DRCOG 1983. Gen. Practitioner.

PENKETH, Richard John Anderson Doctor's Mess, Block A, St. Peters Hospital, Chertsey KT16 0PZ — MB BS 1980 Lond.; BSc (Human Genetics) Lond. 1977, MB BS 1980. (Univ. Coll. Hosp.) MRC Jun. Clin. Scientif. Off. Sect. Perinatal & Child Health Clin. Research Centre N.wick Pk. Hosp. Harrow; RP Winfrey Research Fell. (Sir Halley Stewart Trust). Prev: Hon. Research Asst. (Prenatal Diag.) Dept. Genetics Univ. Coll. Lond.; SHO (O & G) Whittington Hosp. & Univ. Coll. Hosp. Lond.; Ho. Phys. & Ho. Surg. Chase Farm Hosp. Enfield.

PENKETHMAN, Andrew John Felixstowe Road Surgery, 235 Felixstowe Road, Ipswich IP3 9BN Tel: 01473 719112; 14 Borrowdale Avenue, Ipswich IP4 2TN Tel: 01473 251260 — MB BS 1980 Lond.; MRCGP 1984; DRCOG 1983.

PENLINGTON, Elizabeth Ruth (retired) 2 Leighton Close, Gibbet Hill, Coventry CV4 7AE Tel: 024 7641 9707 Email: napierpenlington@compuserve.com — MB BCh 1959 Wales; MFCH 1989. Bishop's Represen. for Child Protec. (Coventry Diocese). Prev: Princip. Clin. Med. Off. (Child Health I/c Child Protec.) Coventry Health Care NHS Trust.

PENLINGTON, (Gilbert) Napier (retired) 2 Leighton Close, Gibbet Hill, Coventry CV4 7AE Tel: 024 7641 9707 — MB 1954 Camb.; BChir 1953; FFA RCS Eng. 1965; DA Eng. 1961; DObst RCOG 1961. Prev: Regist. (Anaesth.) Addenbrooke's Hosp. Camb.

PENMAN, Mr David Gerard Fetal Medicine Unit, Medway Maritime Hospital, Windmill Road, Gillingham ME7 5NY Tel: 01634 825110 Email: penman@ndirect.co.uk — MB BS 1984 Lond.; MRCOG 1993. (St. Thos.) Cons. In O & G, Specialist in Fetal Med., Fetal Med. Unit, Medway Maritime Hosp.; Hon. Cons. Harris Birthright Centre KCH Lond. Socs: Milit. Surg. Soc.; Brit. Matern. & Fetal Med. Soc.; Brit. Med. Ultrasound Soc. Prev: Cons. (Matern. & Foetal Med.) All St.s Hosp. Chatham; Sen. Regist. (Matern. & Foetal Med.) St. Michael's Hosp. Bristol; Regist. Rotat. (O & G) St. Geo.'s Hosp. Lond.

PENMAN, Edward Hugh Giles The Old House, Baschurch Road, Bomere Heath, Shrewsbury SY4 3PN Email: ed@ehgp.com — MB BS Lond. 1990; MRCGP 1996; DFFP 1995; DRCOG 1994; DCH RCP Lond. 1993. (Roy. Free)

PENMAN, Hugh Gerard (retired) Kaduna, Lyons Road, Slinfold, Horsham RH13 7QS — MB BChir Camb. 1953; MA Camb. 1954, MD 1966; MRCP Lond. 1955; FRCPath 1975, M 1963; DTM & H Eng. 1960. Prev: Cons. Path. Histopath. & Clin. Dir. (Path.) Crawley Hosp.

PENMAN, Ian Douglas 4 Howe Park, Edinburgh EH10 7HF — MB ChB 1988 Glas.; BSc (Hons.) Glas. 1986, MD 1995; MRCP (UK) 1991. Cons. Gastroenterol. W.. Gen. Hosp. Edin.; Sen. Lect. Univ. Edin. 1997-. Socs: Brit. Soc. Gastroenterol. Prev: Advanced Fell. (Med.) Univ. S. Carolina USA; Sen. Regist. & Regist. (Med. & Gastroenterol.) W.. Gen. Hosp. Edin.; Research Fell. (Gastroenterol.) W.. Infirm. Glas.

PENMAN, Robert Anthony The Surgery, East Parade, Harrogate HG1 5LW Tel: 01423 566574 Fax: 01423 568015 — MB ChB 1983 Leeds; BSc (Hons.) Biochem. Leeds 1980; MRCGP 1988; DRCOG 1986; DCH RCP Lond. 1987. Prev: Trainee GP Harrogate VTS; Ho. Off. (Surg.) St. James Hosp. Leeds; Ho. Off. (Med.) Huddersfield Roy. Infirm.

PENMAN, Walter Andrew (retired) 3 St Cuthberts Avenue, Dumfries DG2 7NZ Tel: 0131 228 3398 — MB ChB 1950 Edinburgh; MB ChB Ed. 1950; FRCP Ed. 1971, M 1958. Prev: Cons. Phys. Dumfries & Galloway Health Bd.

PENMAN SPLITT

PENMAN SPLITT, Miranda Claire South Thames Regional Genetics Centre(East), 7th Floor New Guys House, Guys Hospital, London SE1 9RT Tel: 0207 955 4648 Fax: 0207 955 2550 Email: miranda.splitt@gstt.sthames.nhs.uk; 5 Union Square, London N1 7DH — MB BS 1985 Lond.; MRCP (UK) 1989; MD University of London, 1999. (St. Mary's Hospital) p/t Cons. Clin. Geneticist, Guys Hosp., Lond.

PENN, Adrian Falklands Surgery, Falkland Way, Bradwell, Great Yarmouth NR31 8RW Tel: 01493 442233 — MB BS 1982 Lond.

PENN, Christopher Robert Howard (retired) Sprey House, 1 Holcombe Road, Teignmouth TQ14 8UP Tel: 01626 778448 — MB BChir 1965 Camb.; MA Camb. 1965; FRCR 1975; FFR 1972; DMRT Eng. 1970. Prev: Sen. Regist. (Radiother.) & Ho. Surg. & Ho. Phys. Lond. Hosp.

PENN, George Kempton Hillside, North Road, Whitland SA34 0AY — MB BCh 1951 Wales. (Cardiff)

PENN, Michael Anthony Southbourne Surgery, 17 Beaufort Road, Southbourne, Bournemouth BH6 5BF Tel: 01202 427878 Fax: 01202 430730 — MB BS Lond. 1964; LMSSA Lond. 1961; MRCOG 1969. (St. Mary's) Prev: SHO (Gyn.) Jessop. Hosp. Wom. Sheff. Regist. (O & G) Roy. Vict. Hosp. Bournemouth; Ho. Surg. King Edwd. VII Hosp. Windsor.

PENN, Naomi Kathryn Shaftesbury Medical Centre, 480 Harehills Lane, Leeds LS9 6DE Tel: 0113 248 5631 Fax: 0113 235 0658; Dale Brow, Breary Lane E., Bramhope, Leeds LS16 9ET Tel: 0113 267 2959 — MB ChB 1983 Leeds; MRCGP 1987; DRCOG 1988.

PENN, Neil David St. James University Hospital, Beckett St., Leeds LS9 7TF; Dale Brow, Breary Lane E., Bramhope, Leeds LS16 9FT Tel: 0113 267 2959 — MB ChB 1982 Leeds; MRCP (UK) 1985. Cons. Phys. Med. for Elderly St. Jas. Univ. Hosp. Leeds.

PENN, Raymond George (retired) 5 Springfield Crescent, Sherborne DT9 6DN — MB BCh Wales 1956; MD Wales 1982; DHMSA Soc. Apoth. Lond. 1978. Prev: Dept of Health.

PENN, Sophie Astrid 3 Higher Shapter Street, Topsham, Exeter EX3 0AW — MB ChB 1991 Manch.

PENN, Stephen William (retired) 2F Queen Elizabeth Walk, London N16 0HX — MB BS 1977 Lond.

PENN, Zoe Jillian Chelsea & Westminster Hospital, 369 Fulham Road, London SW10 9NM Tel: 020 8846 7902 Fax: 020 8846 7998; 3 Walerand Road, London SE13 7PE Tel: 020 8318 4950 — MB BS 1982 Lond.; MRCOG 1986; MD Lond. 1997. (Westm.) Cons. Obst. Chelsea & W.m. Hosp. Lond. Prev: Research Regist. (Obst.) Char. Cross & W.m. Med. Sch. W. Lond. Hosp.; Regist. (O & G) W.m. Hosp. Lond. & Barnet Gen. Hosp.; SHO (Surg.) Roy. Marsden Hosp. Lond.

PENNA, Leonie Kay St. Helier Hospital, Carshalton SM5 1AA Tel: 020 8296 2985; 81 Upland Road, Sutton SM2 5JA — MB BS 1986 Lond.; MRCOG 1993. Cons. Obst., St. Helier Hosp., Carshalton, Surrey. Prev: Lect. (O & G) St. Geo. Hosp. Lond.

PENNANT-LEWIS, Rhian Anaesthetic Department, Ysbyty Gwynedd, Bangor; 7 Tyin y Cae, Llanfairpwllgwyngyll LL61 6UX Tel: 01248 715925 — MB ChB 1982 Manch.; FFA RCS Eng. 1987. Cons. Anaesth. Ysbyty Gwynedd Bangor. Prev: Sen. Regist. (Anaesth.) Addenbrooke's Hosp. Camb.; Regist. (Anaesth.) Leicester Roy. Infirm.; Lect. (Anaesth.) Roy. Hallamsh. Hosp. Sheff.

PENNEFATHER, Marguerite Eleanor (retired) Church Gate, Church Lane, Northiam, Rye TN31 6NN Tel: 01797 253341 — MB ChB Bristol 1953; DObst RCOG 1956. Prev: Med. Asst. (Geriat.) Dept. Med. for the Elderly Bexhill.

PENNEFATHER, Philippa Marion Royal Liverpool University Hospital, Prescott St., Liverpool L7 8XP; Cronton Hall, Cronton, Widnes WA8 5DH — MB BS 1985 Newc.; BMedSc Newc. 1983; FRCOphth 1990. Sen. Regist. (Ophth.) Roy. Liverp. Univ. Hosp.

PENNELL, Angela Mary Taverham Surgery, Sandy Lane, Taverham, Norwich NR8 6JR Tel: 01603 867481 Fax: 01603 740670 — MB ChB 1970 Birm.

PENNELL, Dudley John Magnetic Resonance Unit, Royal Brompton Hospital, Sydney St., London SW3 6NP Tel: 020 7351 8810 Fax: 020 7351 8816 Email: d.pennell@ic.ac.uk — MB BChir 1983 Camb.; MB BChir (Distinc. Med.) Camb. 1983; MA Camb. 1983, BA 1980, MD 1992; FRCP 1997, M 1986; FESC 1996; FACC 1996. (St. Thos.) Pres. & Hon. Cons. Roy. Brompton Hosp.; Dir. Clin. Cardiac MRI. Socs: Pres. Soc. Cardiovasc. MR; Chairm., Euro. Soc. Of Cardiol. Working Grp. On CMR; Chairm., Study Grp. On CMR of the Internat. Soc. Of MR in Med. Prev: Lect. Roy. Brompton Nat. Heart & Lung Hosp. Lond.; Regist. (Med. & Cardiol.) St. Thos. Hosp. Lond.; SHO (Med.) Hammersmith & St. Thos. Hosps. Lond.

PENNELL, Ian Philip Worcestershire Community Services NHS Trust, Newtown Hospital, Newtown Road, Worcester WR5 1JG Tel: 01905 763333 — MB ChB 1980 Manch.; BSc Manch. 1977, MB ChB 1980; MRCPsych 1985. Cons. Psychiat. Worcs. Community Servs. NHS Trust. Prev: Sen. Regist. (Psychiat.) Warneford Hosp. Oxf.

PENNELL, Simon Craigen Southbourne Surgery, 17 Beaufort Road, Southbourne, Bournemouth BH6 5BF Tel: 01202 427878 Fax: 01202 430730 — BM 1981 Soton.; DA (UK) 1986. Prev: SHO Rotat. (Surg.) Roy. Hants. Co. Hosp. Winchester; Ho. Surg. Roy. Vict. Hosp. Bournemouth; Ho. Phys. Poole Gen. Hosp. Dorset.

PENNELLS, Robert Arthur Pennells and Partners, Gosport Health Centre, Bury Road, Gosport PO12 3PN Tel: 023 9258 3344 Fax: 023 9260 2704; Bury Cottage, 79 Bury Road, Gosport PO12 3PR Tel: 02392 523510 — MB BS 1971 Lond.; DObst RCOG 1975. (St. Mary's) GP Gosport. Prev: Regist. (Anaesth.) Hillingdon Hosp. Uxbridge; Regist. (Paediat.) Palmerston N. Hosp., N.Z.

PENNEY, Adrian Peter St John School House Lane Surgery, School House Lane, Bishops Castle SY9 5BP Tel: 01588 632285 — MB BS 1980 Lond.; MRCS Eng. LRCP Lond. 1980.

PENNEY, Basil Francis Carmel Surgery, Nunnery Lane, Darlington DL3 8SQ Tel: 01325 463149; 3 Glenfield Road, Darlington DL3 8DZ — MB BCh BAO 1982 Dub.; MRCGP 1986; DObst RCPI 1986; DCH RCPSI 1985.

PENNEY, Christopher Charles 42 Langton Way, Blackheath, London SE3 7TJ — MA Camb. 1969, MB 1967, BChir 1966; FRCP Lond. 1986; MRCP (U.K.) 1970; FRCR 1975; FFR 1974; DMRD Eng. 1972. Cons. Neuroradiol. Kings Coll. Hosp. Lond.

PENNEY, David James 17 Broadway, Wheathampstead, St Albans AL4 8LW — MB BS 1993 Lond.

PENNEY, Gerald Norman St John (retired) Black Lion House, Bishops Castle SY9 5BS Tel: 01588 638128 — MB BChir 1950 Camb.; MA Camb. 1951; FRCGP 1987, M 1977; DRCOG 1976; DCH Eng. 1954. Prev: Admiralty Surg. & Agent.

PENNEY, Gillian Constance Knapperna House, Udny, Ellon AB41 6SA — MD 1981 Ed.; MB ChB 1975; MFFP 1993; MRCOG 1980. Sen. Regist. (Community Gyn.) Aberd. Roy. Infirm.

PENNEY, Michael David Lower House Cottage, Earlswood, Chepstow NP16 6RH — MB BS 1975 Lond.; BSc (Hons.) Birm. 1970; MD Lond. 1985; FRCPath 1993, M 1981. (Middlx.) Cons. Chem. Path. Roy. Gwent. Hosp. Newport; Clin. Teach. Univ. Hosp. Wales Cardiff; Hon. Cons. Chem. Path. Bristol Roy. Infirm.; Dir. (Path.) Gulent Healthcare Trust. Prev: Sen. Regist. (Chem. Path.) Leeds Gen. Infirm.; Regist. (Path.) Bristol Roy. Infirm.

PENNEY, Oliver James St John The Surgery, Staunton-on-Wye, Hereford HR4 7LT Tel: 01981 500227 Fax: 01981 500603 — MB BS 1983 Lond.; MRCGP 1988; DCH RCP Lond. 1988; DRCOG 1985. (Guy's) Prev: Med. Off. I/c Raihu Hosp., Aitape, Papua New Guinea.

PENNEY, Rachel Marion The Surgery, Gadbridge Road, Weobley, Hereford HR4 8SN; Comp Corner, Seven Mile Lane, St. Mary's Platt, Sevenoaks TN15 8QZ — BM 1983 Soton.; BM Soton 1983; MRCGP 1988; DRCOG 1987; DCH 1985. Med. Off. Raihu Hosp.,Aitape Papua New Guinea.

PENNEY, Richard John Cwmavon Health Centre, Cwmavon, Port Talbot SA12 9PY Tel: 01639 896244 Fax: 01639 895183 Email: penney-rj@doctors.org.uk — MB BChir 1991 Camb.; MRCGP 1995; T(GP) 1995. (Princip. (General Practice)) Prev: Trainee GP/SHO Rotat. Neath Gen. Hosp. W. Glam. HA VTS; Ho. Off. (Med.) Hull Roy. Infirm.; Ho. Off. (Surg.) Castle Hill Hosp. Cottingham.

PENNEY, Sarah Christine 45 Springkell Drive, Pollokshields, Glasgow G41 4EZ Tel: 0141 427 2023 — MB ChB 1976 Glas.; MRCGP 1983. Staff Grade (Gastroenterol.) Glas.

PENNEY, Tony Martin Linden Medical Group, Linden Medical Centre, Linden Avenue, Kettering NN15 7NX Fax: 01536 415930 — MB BS 1984 Lond.; DRCOG 1987. (Roy. Free Sch. of Med.) Prev: Ho. Off. Luton & Dunstable Hosp.; Ho. Off. Roy. Free Hosp. Lond.; Trainee GP Luton & Dunstable Hosp. VTS.

PENNI, Mr Ack Nichodemus Department of ENT, District General Hospital, Warrington WA5 1QG Tel: 01925 35911; 36 Reaper Close, Great Sankey, Warrington WA5 1DX Tel: 01925 416762 Fax: 01925 416762 — MB ChB 1978 Ghana; FRCS Ed. 1990; DLO RCS Eng. 1994.

PENNIE, Mr Bruce Hamilton University Hospital Aintree, Longmoor Lane, Liverpool L9 7AL Tel: 0151 529 2547 Fax: 0151 529 2549; 23 Hillside Drive, Woolton, Liverpool L25 5NR Tel: 0151 421 1526 — MB ChB 1980 Ed.; MCh (Orthop.) Liverp. 1987; FRCS Ed. 1984. Cons. Orthop. Surg. Aintree Hosp.s, NHS Trust. Socs: BOA; Liverp. Med. Inst.; Brit. Assn. of Spinal Surg.s. Prev: Sen. Regist. (Orthop. Surg.) Roy. Liverp. Hosp.; SHO (Accid & Emerg. & Orthop.) Walton Hosp. Liverp.; Ho. Off. (Med.) Bangour Hosp. W. Lothian.

PENNIE, Donald Durance (retired) 24 Turfbeg Avenue, Forfar DD8 3LL Tel: 01307 462592 — MB ChB 1942 Aberd.; MRCGP 1958. Prev: RAMC.

PENNIE, Ian Durance (retired) 5 Badcall, Scourie, Lairg IV27 4TH Tel: 01971 502206 — MSc Aberd. 1967, MB ChB 1939. Prev: Maj. RAMC.

PENNING-ROWSELL, Virginia Wintringham Dept. of Anaesthesia, Bristol Royal Infirmary, Bristol BS2 8HW Tel: 0117 928 2163; Corners, Stone Allerton, Axbridge BS26 2NW Tel: 01934 712567 — MB BS 1968 Lond.; FFA RCS Eng. 1972. (Univ. Coll. Hosp.) p/t Cons. Anaesth. United Bristol Hosps. Trust. Prev: Sen. Regist. (Anaesth.) Bristol W.on, S.mead & Frenchay HAs; Sen. Regist. (Anaesth.) Addenbrooke's Hosp. Camb.; Regist. (Anaesth.) Guy's Hosp. Lond.

PENNINGTON, Professor Christopher Royston Department of Gastroenterology, Ninewells Hospital & Medical School, Dundee DD1 9SY Tel: 01382 60111 Fax: 01382 632317 Email: chrisp@tuht.scot.nhs.uk; Balnagowan, Braehead, Invergowrie, Dundee DD2 5DD — MB ChB 1970 Manch.; MB ChB Mahc. 1970; MD Manch. 1977, BSc (Hons. Physiol.) 1967; FRCP Lond. 1993; FRCP Ed. 1983, M 1972. (Manch.) Cons. Phys. & Gastroenterol. Ninewells Hosp. Dundee; Clin. Gp. director in Med. Tayside uni trust. Socs: Brit. Soc. Gastroenterol.; Nutrit. Soc.; Chairm. Brit. Assn. for parenteral & enteral Nutrit. Prev: Cons. Phys. Kings Cross Hosp. Dundee; Regist. (Med.) Aberd. Teachg. Hosps.; Ho. Off. Manch. Roy. Infirm.

PENNINGTON, Elizabeth Rebecca Moorside Surgery, 1 Thornbridge Mews, Bradford BD2 3BL Tel: 01274 626691 — MB ChB 1989 Leeds; MRCGP 1994.

PENNINGTON, Eric The Surgery, 247 Cateswell Road, Tyseley, Birmingham B11 3DU Tel: 0121 706 1214; 6 Berkley Crescent, Birmingham B13 9YD — MB ChB 1985 Birm.; BSc (Hons.) Birm. 1982, MB ChB 1985; DRCOG 1988. Prev: Trainee GP Birm. VTS.

PENNINGTON, George William (retired) Sullane, Eaton Hill, Baslow, Bakewell DE45 1SB Tel: 01246 582212 — MB ChB Liverp. 1956; MA Dub. 1962; MSc Calif. 1961; MD Liverp. 1959; MRCS Eng. LRCP Lond. 1956; FRCOG 1987; FRCPath 1973, M 1963. Prev: Cons. Chem. Path. Jessop Hosp. Wom. & Sheff. HA.

PENNINGTON, Honor Ruth Dykebar Hospital, Dykebar, Paisley PA2 7DE; 170 Prospecthill Road, Mount Florida, Glasgow G42 9LH Tel: 0141 632 9161 — MB ChB 1988 Glas. SHO (Psychiat.) Dykebar Hosp. Paisley.

PENNINGTON, John Hilton (retired) 42 Elizabeth Crescent, Queen's Park, Chester CH4 7AZ — MD 1966 Camb.; MB 1961, BChir 1960; FRCPath 1979, M 1967. Prev: Cons. Microbiol. & Dir. Pub. Health Laborat. Fazakerley Hosp. Liverp.

PENNINGTON, Jonathan Mark 192 Maney Hill Road, Sutton Coldfield B72 1JX Email: john.pennington@xtra.co.nz — MB ChB 1993 Liverp.

***PENNINGTON, Sarah Helen** 311 Tag La, Ingol, Preston PR2 3XA — MB ChB 1997 Manch.

PENNINGTON, Sheila Jane 6 Berkley Crescent, Birmingham B13 9YD — MB ChB 1985 Birm.; BSc (Hons.) Birm. 1982, MB ChB 1985; DRCOG 1987. Trainee GP Wolverhampton VTS.

PENNINGTON, Sylvia Elizabeth Forest Hall Medical Centre, Station Road, Forest Hall, Newcastle upon Tyne NE12 9BQ Tel: 0191 266 5823 — MB ChB 1974 Sheffield; MB ChB Sheff 1974. (Sheffield) GP Newc.

PENNINGTON, Professor Thomas Hugh Department of Medical Microbiology, Medical School Buildings, Foresterhill, Aberdeen AB25 2ZD Tel: 01224 681818 Fax: 01224 685604 — MB BS 1962 Lond.; PhD Lond. 1967; FRCPath 1990, M 1978. (St. Thos.) Prof. Bact. Univ. Aberd.; Hon. Cons. (Bact.) Grampian HB. Prev: Sen. Lect. Dept. Virol. Univ. Glas.; Lect. (Bact.) St. Thos. Hosp. Med. Sch. Lond; Project Assoc. Univ. Wisconsin Med. Sch. Madison, USA.

PENNOCK, Charles Anthony Warners Cottage, Chewton Keynsham, Bristol BS31 2SU Tel: 01179 862320 Email: charles.pennock@btinternet.com — BSc Bristol 1968, MD 1973, MB ChB 1962; FRCPath 1982, M 1970; FRCPCH 1998. (Bristol) Cons. Paediat. Chem. Path. United Bristol Hosps. Trust & S.mead Hosp. Trust; Sen. Lect. (Child Health) Univ. Bristol; Vis. Fell. Univ. Bath 1979-. Socs: Hon D Se (U.W.E.) 2000. Prev: Vis. Prof. Sci. Sheff. Hallam Univ. 1994-1997.

PENNOCK, Helen Claire 32 Nash Lane, Belbroughton, Stourbridge DY9 9SW — MB ChB 1989 Manch.

PENNOCK, Philip Francis Louis The Bull Ring Surgery, 5 The Bull Ring, St. John's, Worcester WR2 5AA Tel: 01905 422883 Fax: 01905 423639; The Barley House, Clevelode Farm, Clevelode, Malvern WR13 6PD Tel: 01684 311201 Fax: 01684 311975 Email: ppennock@aol.com — MB BS 1980 Lond.; BA Oxf. 1975; Dip. Occupational Medicine 1999; DRCOG 1984. (Barts)

PENNY, Alison Elizabeth 145 Wigton Lane, Leeds LS17 8SH — MB ChB 1986 Glas.; MRCPsych 1992. Clin. Med. Off. (Rehabil. Psychiat.) Lynfield Mt. Hosp. Bradford. Prev: Regist. (Psychiat.) RHA.

PENNY, Elizabeth Philomena Cardiff & Vale NHS Trust, Child Health Directorate, Lansdowne Hospital, Cardiff, Cardiff CF11 8PL Tel: 029 2037 2451 Fax: 029 2023 7378 — MB BCh BAO 1976 NUI; MPH Wales 1995; DCH Eng. 1979; Dip. POS. Lond. 2000. (Cork) p/t Cons. Community Paediat. Cardiff Community Healthcare Trust. Socs: Fell. Roy. Coll. Paediat. & Child Health; Welsh Paediat. Soc.; Brit. Assn. Community Child Health. Prev: Project Ldr. Audit of Cerebral Palsy for Childr. in Wales; SCMO (Child Health) S. Glam. AHA; SHO (Paediat.) Morriston Hosp. Swansea.

PENNY, Emma Clare Berkeley Place Surgery, 11 High Street, Cheltenham GL52 6DA Tel: 01242 513975; 11 Pirton Meadow, Churchdown, Gloucester GL3 2RW — MB BS 1989 Lond.; BSc Lond. 1986; MRCGP 1994; DFFP 1994; DCH RCPS Glas. 1992.

PENNY, Gordon Pine Cottage, Benenden, Cranbrook TN17 4DR — MB ChB 1954 St. And.; DObst RCOG 1956. Socs: MRCGP. Prev: Ho. Surg. Midw. & Gyn. & Ho. Phys. WillesBoro. Hosp. Ashford.

PENNY, James Alexis 74 Elborough Street, London SW18 5DN — MB BS 1988 Lond. SHO (Obst.) N.wick Pk. Hosp. Middlx.

PENNY, James Leith (retired) Beechwood, Ewanfield, Crieff PH7 3DA Tel: 01764 652744 Fax: 01764 652744 — MB ChB 1958 St. And.; DObst RCOG 1960.

PENNY, Judith Margaret West Calder Medical Practice, Dickson Street, West Calder EH55 8HB Tel: 01506 871403; 124 Viewforth, Edinburgh EH10 4LN — MB ChB 1986 Ed.; MRCGP 1991; DCH RCP Ed. 1992; DObst RCOG 1988. Partner Gen. Pract. W. Calder. Prev: Trainee GP Edin.

***PENNY, Lisa Antonia** Robin House, Garden Close La., Newbury RG14 6PP — MB ChB 1995 Bristol.

PENNY, Philip Trevor Overton House, West Monkton, Taunton TA2 8RA Tel: 01823 413013 Fax: 01823 413707 Email: pennyswims@hotmail.com — MB BS 1956 Lond.; MRCS Eng. LRCP 1956 Lond; AFOM 1983 RCP Lond. (Univ. Coll. Hosp.) Dir. S. W.. Indust. Med. Servs. SWIMs; Occupat. Phys. W.on Area Health Trust; HM (Dep.) Coroner W. Som.; Med. Adviser Inst. Swimming Teachs. & Coaches & ASA (Amateur Swimming Assn.). Socs: Soc. Occupat. Med.; Assn. Local Auth. Med. Advisors.

PENNY, Ronald Maxwell (retired) Pennys, Cutlers Green, Thaxted, Dunmow CM6 2PZ Tel: 01371 831166 — MRCS Eng. LRCP Lond. 1946; MRCGP 1970. Prev: Res. Med. Off. St. Mary's Hosp. E.bourne.

PENNY, William John Department of Cardiology, University of Wales College of Medicine, Heath Park, Cardiff CF14 4XN Tel: 029 2074 7747 Fax: 029 2074 5360 Email: william.penny@uhw_tr.wales.nhs.uk — MB BCh BAO 1976 NUI; FRCP Lond. 1995; MRCP (UK) 1980; MD NUI 1984. (Cork) Cons. Cardiol. Cardiff & Wales NHS Trust. Prev: Lect. (Cardiol.) Univ. Wales Coll. Med.; Cardiol. Fell. Mayo Clinic Rochester MN, USA; Regist. (Cardiol.) Lond. Chest Hosp.

PENNYCOOK, Charlotte Frances Spring Cottage, Longford Road, Thornford, Sherborne DT9 6QQ Tel: 01935 872331 — MB BS 1993 Lond.

PENNYCOOK, Julie Alison 364 Glasgow Road, Ralston, Paisley PA1 3BQ — MB ChB 1990 Glas.

PENRICE, Gillian Mary 1 Hughenden Drive, Glasgow G12 9XS — MB ChB 1986 Glas.; MRCGP 1990; DRCOG 1990.

PENRICE

PENRICE, Juliet Mellanby The Neonatal Unit Chelsea & Westminster Hospital, 369 Fulham Road, London SW10 9NH — MB BChir 1989 Camb.; MA Camb. 1985; MRCP (UK) 1992. Cons. (Neonat. Paediat.) Chelsea & W.minster Hosp. Lond. Socs: RCPCH; Eur. Soc. Of Paed. Res.; Perinatal Soc. Of Aust. & NZ.

PENRICE, Miss Lisa Margaret 185 Coombe Lane, London SW20 0RG — MB ChB 1988 Manch.

PENROSE, Andrew John 5 Ballard Close, Littleborough OL15 9HN Tel: 01706 76302 — MB ChB 1986 Sheff.; DRCOG 1990.

PENROSE, Catherine Veronica Flat 4b, 28 Great Ormond St., London WC1N 3JH — MB BS 1990 Newc.

PENROSE, Gaynor Louise 4 Green Row, Machen, Caerphilly CF83 8NU — MB BCh 1994 Wales; DCH 1996; DRCOG 1997; MRCGP 1998. (Univ. Wales) GP.

PENROSE, Mr Joscelyn Hugh (retired) Glebe Field, 21 St Michael's Road, Claverdon, Warwick CV35 8NT Tel: 01926 842802 — MB BChir Camb. 1939; MA Camb. 1939; FRCS Eng. 1946; MRCS Eng. LRCP Lond. 1939. Prev: Cons. Orthop. Surg. Coventry Hosp. Gp. & Warks. Orthop. Hosp. Coleshill.

PENROSE, Richard James Jackson (retired) 16 The Orangery, Ham, Richmond TW10 7HJ Tel: 020 8392 4297 — MB BS 1966 Lond.; MRCS Eng. LRCP Lond. 1966; MRCPsych 1973; DPM Eng. 1970. Cons. Psychiat. The Priory Hosp. Roehampton Lond. Prev: Cons. Psychiat. Epsom Gen. Hosp. Surrey.

PENROSE-STEVENS, Ana 292 Maidstone Road, Gillingham ME8 0HH Tel: 01634 232452 — LMS 1983 Santiago; FRCS Glas. 1993. Regist. (Neurosurg.) Univ. Wales Cardiff. Socs: Brit. Neurosurg. Soc. Prev: Regist. (Neurosurg.) Morriston Hosp.; Regist. (Neurosurg. & Paediat. Neurosurg.) Manch.

PENRY, Elizabeth Margaret Forsythe (retired) Brincliffe, 20 Westbury Lane, Coombe Dingle, Bristol BS9 2PE Tel: 0117 968 1471 — MB ChB 1956 Bristol; DObst RCOG 1959; DCH Eng. 1958. Prev: SCMO (Paediat. & Audiol.) United Bristol Hosp. Trust.

PENRY, Ifan Emyr Wyn 37 Hendrefoilan Avenue, Sketty, Swansea SA2 7NA Tel: 01792 299064 — MB BS 1970 Lond.; MRCOG 1978. (St. Mary's)

PENRY, John Bernard (retired) Brincliffe, 20 Westbury Lane, Coombe Dingle, Bristol BS9 2PE Tel: 0117 968 1471 — MB BCh 1957 Wales; FRCR 1975; FFR 1964; DMRD Eng. 1961. Prev: Cons. Radiol. S.mead Hosp. & Ham Green Hosp. Bristol.

PENRY, Karen Sian Tel: 01970 624545 Fax: 01970 615612; Plas Bryn Y Mor, Bryn Y Mor Road, Aberystwyth SY23 2HY Tel: 01970 627871 — BM 1986 Soton.; PGCME 2001 Cardiff; MRCGP 1991; DRCOG 1991; DCH RCP Lond. 1990. (Southampton)

PENSTON, James Geoffrey Mary 8 West Field Garth, Ealand, Scunthorpe DN17 4JR; Scunthorpe General Hospital, Cliff Gardens, Scunthorpe DN15 7BH — MB BS 1975 Lond. Cons. (Phys./Gastroenterol.) Scunthorpe & Goole NHS Trust.

PENTECOST, Mr Alan Frederick (retired) 24 Bower Mount Road, Maidstone ME16 8AU — MB BS 1962 Lond.; FRCS Ed. 1970; MRCS Eng. LRCP Lond. 1962; FRCOG 1982 M 1969. Cons. (O & G) Maidstone Hosp.

PENTECOST, Professor Brian Leonard, OBE 37 Farquhar Road, Edgbaston, Birmingham B15 3RA Tel: 0121 454 1287 Email: bpentecost@supanet.com — MB BS (Hons. Med. & Path.) Lond. 1957; MD Lond. 1965; FRCP Lond. 1971, M 1959; Hon DSc (Aston) 1998. (St. Mary's) Emerit. Prof. Med. Univ. Birm. Socs: Fell. Europ. Soc. Cardiol.; Brit. Cardiac Soc. & Assn. of Phys. Prev: Med. Dir. Brit. Heart Foundat.; Linacre Fell. Roy. Coll. Phys. Lond.; Cons. Phys. United Birm. Hosps.

PENTER, Gail Radiology Department, Warwick Hospital, Lakin Road, Warwick CV34 5BW Tel: 01926 495321 — MB BCh 1980 Wales; FRCR 1986. Cons. Radiol. Warwick Hosp. & Stratford u. Avon Hosp. Prev: Sen. Regist. (Radiol.) W. Midl. RHA.

PENTLAND, Brian Lothian Primary Care Trust, Astley Ainslie Hospital, Grange Loan, Edinburgh EH9 2HL Tel: 0131 537 9039 Fax: 0131 537 9030 — MB ChB 1974 Ed.; BSc Ed. 1972; FRCP Ed. 1986; MRCP (UK) 1978. (Edinburgh) Cons. Neurol. (Rehabil. Med.) & Clin. Dir. Astley Ainslie Hosp. Edin.; Dip. Europ. Bd. Phys. Med. & Rehabil. Socs: Assn. Brit. Neurols.; Hon. Fell. Roy. Coll. Speech & Language Therapists; Brit. Soc. Rehabil. Med. Prev: Lect. (Med. Neurol.) Roy. Infirm. Edin.; Regist. King's Cross Hosp. Dundee; SHO N.. Gen. Hosp. Edin.

PENTLOW, Mr Barry Dennis Consulting Rooms, The Glen Hospital, Bristol BS6 7JJ Tel: 0117 973 2562; 36 Great Brockeridge, Bristol BS9 3TZ Tel: 0117 962 1166 — MB BS 1968 Lond.; FRCS Eng. 1974; MRCS Eng. LRCP Lond. 1968. Cons. Surg. S.mead Hosp. Bristol. Prev: Sen. Lect. (Surg.) Univ. Bristol & Hon. Cons. Surg. S.mead Hosp. Bristol; Lect. (Surg.) Univ. Camb. & Hon. Sen. Regist. Addenbrookes Hosp. Camb.

PENTNEY, Millicent Joy (retired) 4 Desenfans Road, London SE21 7DN Tel: 020 8693 3635 — MB BS 1952 Lond. Assoc. Specialist (Psychiat.) Bexley Hosp. Kent. Prev: Asst. Specialist (Psychiat.) Castlewood Day Hosp. Bexley Hosp. Kent.

PENTZ, Anthon Jasper Ley Goodmayes Hospital, 157 Barley Lane, Ilford IG3 8XJ — MB ChB 1965 Cape Town.

PENWARDEN, David Brian The Surgery, Marlpits Road, Honiton EX14 2DD Tel: 01404 41141 Fax: 01404 46621; The Surgery, Marlpits Road, Honiton EX14 2DD Tel: 01404 41141 Fax: 01406 46621 — MB BS 1970 Lond.; MRCS Eng. LRCP Lond. 1970; MRCGP 1976; DObst RCOG 1973. (Westm.)

PEOPLES, Joseph Anthony 28 Henstead Road, Southampton SO15 2DD — MB BS 1994 Lond.; BSc (Hons.) Lond. 1990, MB BS 1994.

***PEOPLES, Sharon** 13 Beach Road, Whitehead, Carrickfergus BT38 9QS — MB ChB 1996 Ed.

PEPE, Gloria Brookvale Adolesent Services, 30 Brookvale Road, Southampton SO17 1QR Tel: 02380 586154; 18 Stoke Road, Winchester SO23 7ET Tel: 01962 862122 Fax: 01962 622533 Email: gloria@pepe_woodcock.demon.co.uk — State Exam 1981 Rome; Dip. Specialist Psychiat. Rome 1985. (La Sapienza University of Rome) Sen. Regist. (Child & Adolesc. Psychiat.) Soton. Socs: Mem. Italian Med. Soc. UK; Mem. Brit Assn. Psychopharmacol.; Mem. Assn. Child Psychol. & Psychiatr. Prev: Clin. Asst. Clinica Belvedere Montello Rome; Regist. (Psychiat.) St. Jas. Hosp. Portsmouth; Regist. (Psychiat.) Pk. Prewitt Hosp. Basingstoke.

PEPELASSIS, Dionissios Doctors Mess, Joyce Green Hospital, Dartford DA1 5PL — Ptychio Iatrikes 1989 Thessalonika.

PEPERA, Theodora Audrey Ansoma c/o MSL (UK) Ltd., 16 Victoria Way, Burgess Hill RH15 1NF Email: tpepera_hibber@yahoo.com — MB BS 1987 Lond.; MRCOG 1996. (Roy. Free Hosp. Sch. Med. Univ. Lond.) Regist. (O & G) Roy. Free Hosp. Lond. Prev: SHO (Obst.) St. Mary's Hosp. Lond.; SHO (Gyn.) Leicester Gen. Hosp.; SHO (Genitourin. Med.) Guy's Hosp. Lond.

***PEPIN, Roger** 24 Bousley Rise, Ottershaw, Chertsey KT16 0JX — MB ChB 1996 Glas.

PEPKE-ZABA, Joanna Wanda Chest Medical Unit, Papworth Hospital, Papworth Everard, Cambridge CB3 8RE Tel: 01480 830541; 56 Melvin Way, Histon, Cambridge CB4 9HY Tel: 01223 503770 — MB BS 1977 Warsaw; PhD Warsaw 1995. Assoc. Specialist (Resp. Med.) Papworth Hosp. Camb. Socs: Brit. Thoracic Soc. Prev: Regist. (Chest Med.) Papworth & Addenbrooke's Hosps. Camb.

PEPPER, Anne Vivienne Norah Hedon Group Practice, 4 Market Hill, Hedon, Hull HU12 8JD Tel: 01482 899111 Fax: 01482 890967 — MRCS Eng. LRCP Lond. 1970. (Roy. Free)

PEPPER, Bryan James (retired) Heavitree Health Centre, South Lawn Terrace, Heavitree, Exeter EX1 2RX Tel: 01392 211511 Fax: 01392 499451 — MB ChB Birm. 1964. Med. Off. Dept. Educat. Univ. Exeter.

PEPPER, Christopher Bryan Dept of Cardiology, Yorkshire Heart Centre, Leeds General Infirmary, Leeds LS1 Tel: 0113 274 2499 — MB ChB 1989 Birm.; BSc (Hons.) Birm. 1986; MD 1997; MRCP (UK) 1992. Cons. Cardiol. Prev: Research Fell. & Hon. Regist. (Cardiol.) Univ. Wales Coll. Med.; SHO (Med. Cardiol.) Glas. Roy. Infirm.; SHO (Med.) Sandwell Hosp. W. Bromwich.

PEPPER, Gregory James Amberley, 89 High St., Sidford, Sidmouth EX10 9SA — MB BS 1984 Lond.; MRCGP 1989; DRCOG 1988; DCH RCP Lond. 1987.

PEPPER, Helen Mary Hetton Group Practice, Hetton Medical Centre, Francis Way, Hetton-le-Hole, Houghton-le-Spring DH5 9EZ Tel: 0191 526 1177 Fax: 0191 517 3859; 176 Burnpark Road, Houghton-le-Spring DH4 5DH — MB BS 1971 Newc.; MRCPsych 1978; DCH RCPS Glas. 1974.

PEPPER, John Mark 23 Belvidere Road, Shrewsbury SY2 5LS — MB ChB 1990 Sheff.; BMedSci Sheff. 1990; MRCGP 1994; DFFP 1994; DRCOG 1993.

PEPPER, Jonathan Mark Carriage House, Carriage Drive, Frodsham, Warrington WA6 6EB — BM BS 1989 Nottm.

PEPPER, Karel Mark Wingate, Chilton Avenue, Kearsney, Dover CT16 3EF — MB BS 1972 Lond.; MRCS Eng. LRCP Lond. 1972.

PEPPER, Michael Bernard (retired) The Birches, 115 Station Road, Hugglescote, Coalville, Leicester LE67 2GB Tel: 01530 35397 — MB BS 1954 Lond.; MFCM 1974; DPH Bristol 1966. Prev: Med. Off. DHSS.

PEPPER, Sarah Helen 52 Apsley Road, Bristol BS8 2ST — MB ChB 1993 Bristol.

PEPPER, Susan Jane 2F2, 6 Gardners Crescent, Edinburgh EH3 8BZ Tel: 0131 229 3488 — MB ChB 1987 Ed.; MRCGP 1992.

PEPPERCORN, Miss Penelope Delia 17 Chantry Street, London N1 8NR — MB ChB 1988 Birm.

PEPPERELL, Irene Avondale Medical Practice, Strathaven Health Centre, The Ward, Strathaven ML10 6AS Tel: 01357 529595 Fax: 01357 529494 — MB ChB 1975 Glas.

PEPPERELL, Justin Charles Thane The Old Bakery, 51 Castle St., Nether Stowey, Bridgwater TA5 1LW — MB BChir 1992 Camb.; MA Camb. 1992, MB BChir 1992. Specialist Regist. (Respir. Med.) SW Rotat. Socs: Brit. Thoracic Soc.

PEPPERMAN, Mark Andrew Pepperman and Partners, The Cottons, Meadow Lane, Raunds, Wellingborough NN9 6YA Tel: 01933 623327 Fax: 01933 623370 — MRCS Eng. LRCP Lond. 1975; BSc (Hons.) (Physiol.) Lond. 1972, MB BS 1975; DMedLaw 1995; DRCOG 1979. (King's Coll. Hosp.) GP Raunds. Socs: Fell. Roy. Soc. Med. Prev: SHO (Communicable & Trop. Dis.) E. Birm. Hosp.; SHO Metab. & Renal Unit E. Birm. Hosp.; Ho. Off. Liver Unit King's Coll. Hosp. Lond.

PEPPERMAN, Michael Leon Leicester Royal Infirmary NHS Trust, Infirmary Close, Leicester LE1 5WW Tel: 0116 254 1414 Fax: 0116 258 5389; Farcroft, Links Road, Kirby Muxloe, Leicester LE9 2BP Tel: 0116 239 3048 — MB ChB Birm. 1968; BSc (Anat., Hons.) Birm. 1965; MRCS Eng. LRCP Lond. 1968; FFA RCS Eng. 1972. p/t Cons. Anaesth. Leicester Roy. Infirm. NHS Trust; Nat. Clin. Lead - Med., NHS Modernisation Agency Critical Care Progr. Prev: Cons. Anaesth. P.ss Margt. Hosp. Nassau, Bahamas; Sen. Regist. (Anaesth.) Wolverhampton Gp. Hosps. & United Birm. Hosps.

PEPPIATT, Roger Dartford West Health Centre, Tower Road, Dartford DA1 2HA Tel: 01322 228032/223960 — MB BS 1974 Lond.; MB BS (Hons.) Lond. 1974; MRCP (UK) 1976; MRCGP 1978; Dip. Palliat. Med. Wales 1994; DCH RCP Lond. 1978. (St. Bart.) Trainer (Gen. Pract.) Joyce Green Hosp. Dartford; Clin. Asst. Lions Hospice N.fleet. Socs: Fell.Roy.Soc.Med. Prev: Tutor (Gen. Pract.) Dartford; Trainee GP Univ. Exeter VTS; Sen. Med. Off. Nixon Memor. Hosp., Segbwema, Sierra Leone.

PEPPIATT, Timothy Neil 2 Leys Avenue, Cambridge CB4 2AW — BM 1990 Soton.

PEPYS, Elizabeth Olga Department of Medicine, Royal Free & University College Medical School, Rowland Hill St., London NW3 2PF Tel: 020 7433 2801 Fax: 020 7433 2803 Email: m.pepys@rfc.ucl.ac.uk; 22 Wildwood Road, London NW11 6TE — BM BCh 1968 Oxf.; MA Oxf. 1968. (Univ. Coll. Hosp.) Clin.Asst. Allergy Roy. Free. Univ. Coll. Med. Sch.Lond. Socs: Brit. Soc. Allergy & Clin. Immunol. Prev: Res. Fell. Roy. Post-Grad. Med. Sch. Lond; Ho. Phys. Med. Unit Univ. Coll. Hosp. Lond.; Jun. Asst. Path, Camb. Univ.

PEPYS, Professor Mark Brian Department of Medicine, Royal Free & University College Medical School, Rowland Hill St, London NW3 2PF Tel: 020 7433 2801 Fax: 020 7433 2803 Email: m.pepys@rfc.ucl.ac.uk; 22 Wildwood Road, London NW11 6TE Tel: 020 8455 9387 — MB BChir Camb. 1968; MA Camb. 1968; PhD Camb. 1974, MD 1982; FRCP Lond. 1981; MRCP (UK) 1970; FRCPath 1991, M 1981; FRS 1998; F Med Sci 1998. (Univ. Coll. Hosp.) Prof. Med., Roy. Free & Univ. Coll. Med. Sch. Lond. Socs: Fell. of the Roy. Soc.; Former Fell. Acad. of Med. Sci.; Hon. Mem. Assoc. of Phys. Prev: Prof. (Immunol. Med.) & Cons. Phys. RPMS Hammersmith Hosp. Lond.; Sen. Lect. & Cons. (Immunol.) Roy. Free Hosp. Lond.; Fell. Trinity Coll. Camb.

***PEPYS, Miriam Elizabeth** 22 Wildwood Road, London NW11 6TE — MB BS 1998 Lond.; MB BS Lond 1998.

PERACHA, Mr Amjad Mumtaz King Faisal Specialist Hospital & Research Centre, Department of Surgery, MBC 40, PO Box 3354, Riyadh 11211, Saudi Arabia; 43 Broadmayne Avenue, High Barnes, Sunderland SR4 8LT Tel: 0191 528 5172 — MB BS 1982 Sind, Pakistan; FRCS Glas. 1990; MRCS Eng. LRCP Lond. 1987. Regist. (Gen. Surg.) Qu. Eliz. Hosp. Tyne & Wear. Socs: Med. Protec. Soc. Prev: Regist. (Gen. Surg.) S. Tyneside Dist. Hosp.

PERAHIA, David Gunther Sam 56 Harthall Lane, Kings Langley WD4 8JH Tel: 01923 268437 — MB BS 1992 Lond.; BSc (Hons.) Lond. 1989, MB BS 1992.

PERAVALI, Mr Buddhababu 26 Wharncliffe Close, Hadfield, Hyde SK13 1QE; 26 Wharncliffe CloseTameside General Hospital, Fountain St, Ashton-under-Lyne OL6 9RW — MB BS 1976 Sri Venkateswara; FRCS Glas. 1983.

***PERCHARD, Bryony Jane** Elisabeth, South Dock Marina, Rope St., London SE16 7SZ — MB BS 1998 Lond.; MB BS Lond 1998.

PERCHARD, Stanley Drelaud 2 Edwards Cottages, Compton avenue, London N1 2XL Tel: 020 7226 2478 — MB BS 1940 Lond.; MD Lond. 1951; MRCS Eng. LRCP Lond. 1939; FRCOG 1963, M 1948. (Univ. Coll. Hosp.) Emerit. Cons. O & G Lond. Hosp. Socs: BMA; Liveryman Soc. Apoth.; Fell.Munterian Soc. Prev: Examr. Univ. Lond. RCOG & RCS; Cons. O & G Lond. Hosp.; Cons. Gyn. Guy's Health Dist.

PERCIVAL, Professor Alan 3 Coudray Road, Southport PR9 9NL Tel: 01704 534530 — BM BCh 1958 Oxf.; MA, BM BCh Oxf. 1958; MRCPath 1970. (Oxf. & St. Mary's) Emerit. Prof. Clin. Bact. Univ. Liverp. Socs: Ex-Pres Assoc.med.Micro; Ex pres Brit.soc.Antimicros.chemother. Prev: Prof. Bact. Univ. Manch.; Lect. (Bact.) St. Mary's Hosp. Med. Sch. Lond.; Regist. (Path.) Edgware Gen. Hosp.

***PERCIVAL, Elisabeth Jane** 6 Regent Close, Wilmslow SK9 6LF — BM BS 1996 Nottm.

PERCIVAL, Geoffrey Nigel The Surgery, White Cliff Mill Street, Blandford Forum DT11 7BH Tel: 01258 452501 Fax: 01258 455675; Cob Cottage, Tarrant Gunville, Blandford Forum DT11 8JR — MB ChB 1981 Birm.; DA (UK) 1988; DCH RCP Lond. 1985; DRCOG 1984.

PERCIVAL, George Oliver 18 Orchard Close, Roughton, Norwich NR11 8SR — MRCS Eng. LRCP Lond. 1964.

PERCIVAL, Helen Jane Ryecroft Street, Surgery, Stapleford, Nottingham NG10 Tel: 01159 395555; 45 Poplar Road, Breaston, Derby DE72 3BH — BM BS 1982 Nottm.; BMedSci (Hons.) Nottm. 1980. BUPA Screening Doctor Clawson Lodge Nottm. Prev: GP Stapleford, Nottm.

PERCIVAL, Mr Hubert George 94 Islip Road, Oxford OX2 7SW — MB ChB 1962 Birm.; FRCS Eng. 1976; MRCS LRCP Lond. 1962.

PERCIVAL, Ian Duncan Cleveland House, 16 Spital Terrace, Gainsborough DN21 2HF Tel: 01427 613158 Fax: 01427 616644 — MB ChB 1990 Sheff.

PERCIVAL, Ingrid Monica 3 Hill Rise, Twyford, Winchester SO21 1QH — BM BS 1990 Nottm.; DRCOG 1995. Trainee GP Roy. Hants. Co. Hosp. Winchester. Prev: Trainee GP Winchester VTS.

PERCIVAL, Mr Nicholas John Department of Plastic Surgery, Charing Cross Hospital, Fulham Palace Road, London W6 8RF Tel: 020 8846 1723; 2 Ormond Avenue, Hampton TW12 2RU — MB BS 1977 Lond.; FRCS Eng. 1984. Cons. Plastic Surg. Char. Cross Hosp. Lond. & Chelsea & W.m. Hosp. Lond. Socs: Brit. Assn. Plastic Surg.; Brit. Assn. Aesthetic Plastic Surgs.; Brit. Soc. Surg. Hand. Prev: Sen. Regist. (Plastic Surg.) Edin.; Regist. (Plastic Surg.) Chepstow; Lect. (Anat.) Stanford Univ. Med. Sch. Calif., USA.

PERCIVAL, Richard Newland Avenue Surgery, 129 Newland Avenue, Hull HU5 2ES Tel: 01482 343671 Fax: 01482 448839; 249 Willerby Road, Hull HU5 5HH Tel: 01482 353671 — MB ChB 1978 Manch.

PERCIVAL, Richard Edward 3 Hill Rise, Twyford, Winchester SO21 1QH Tel: 01962 713668 — BM 1990 Soton.; DRCOG 1995; MRCGP 1996. GP Hants. Prev: Trainee GP Twyford, Hants.

PERCIVAL, Robert Kirkhall Surgery, 4 Alexandra Avenue, Prestwick KA9 1AW Tel: 01292 476626 Fax: 01292 678022; 17 Trinity, 35 Lynedoch St, Glasgow G3 — MB ChB 1977 Glas.; MRCGP 1981.

PERCIVAL, Mr Robert Hugh, KStJ (retired) 2 Cloth Hall Gardens, Biddenden, Ashford TN27 8AT Tel: 01580 291456 — MCh Oxf. 1951, MA, BM BCh 1941; FRCS Eng. 1943; MRCS Eng. LRCP Lond. 1941; DCH Eng. 1952. Hon. Cons. Surg. W. Kent Hosp. Maidstone & Qu. Mary's Hosp. Sidcup. Prev: Cdr. St. John Ambul. Brig. Kent.

PERCIVAL

PERCIVAL, Mr Stanley Piers Bassnett The Manor House, Hutton Buscel, Scarborough YO13 9LL Tel: 01723 862811 Fax: 01723 377223 — MA Camb. 1964, MB 1962, BChir 1961; FRCS Eng. 1970; FCOphth 1989; DO Eng. 1964; DObst RCOG 1964. (St. Thos.) p/t Cons. Ophth. Surg. BUPA Belvedere Hosp. ScarBoro. Socs: (Ex-Pres.) UK Intraocular Implant Soc.; Internat. Intraocular Implant Club; (Ex-Pres.) N. Eng. Ophth. Soc. Prev: Cons. Ophth. Surg. ScarBoro. Health Care Trust; Sen. Regist. Birm. & Midl. Eye Hosp.; Ho. Surg. (Ophth.) St. Thos. Hosp. Lond.

PERCY, Mr Anthony John Leahy Tadhurst, Hill Brow, Bickley, Bromley BR1 2PQ Tel: 020 8460 6513 Fax: 020 8460 6513 — MB BS 1965 Lond.; FRCS Eng. 1973; FRCS Ed. 1972; MRCS Eng. LRCP Lond. 1964; DObst RCOG 1966. (Westm.) p/t Cons. Orthop. Surg. Qu. Mary's Hosp. Sidcup. Socs: BMA; Fell. BOA; Acad. Experts. Prev: Sen. Regist. Orthop. W.m. Hosp. Lond. & Univ. Coll. Hosp. Lond.; Orthop. Regist. Roy. Nat. Orthop. Hosp. Lond.

PERCY, Catherine Mary The New Surgery, The Nap, Kings Langley WD4 8ET; Cottingham Farm, Flaunden Lane, Bovingdon, Hemel Hempstead HP3 0PD — MB BS 1975 Lond.; MRCS Eng. LRCP Lond. 1975; DCH Eng. 1977. (Royal Free Hospital School of Medicine) p/t Asst. GP Kings Langley Herts.; Clin. Asst. (Orthop.) Hemel Hempstead Hosp. Prev: Regist. (Paediat.) Stobhill Hosp. Glas.

PERCY, David Bryden NHS Executive South East, 40 Eastbourne Terrace, London W2 3QR Tel: 020 7725 2745 Fax: 020 7725 2741 Email: dpercy@doh.gov.uk; 10 Nightingale Close, Winchester SO22 5QA Tel: 01962 877962 Email: 113777.3604@compuserve.com — MB BS 1972 Lond.; FRCGP 1995, M 1976. (Roy. Free) Dir. Educat. & Train.; Indep. Psychother. Socs: Guild Psychother. Prev: Trainee GP Soton. VTS; GP Princip. Soton.; Assoc. Postgrad. Dean Winchester.

PERCY, Henry Gordon, MBE (retired) Hawthorns, Hyde, Fordingbridge SP6 2QL Tel: 01425 652191 — MB BChir 1946 Camb.; MRCS Eng. LRCP Lond. 1938. Prev: Ho. Phys. St. James' Hosp. Lond.

PERCY-HUGHES, Huw Cynvoel (retired) Brookside, St. George Road, Abergele LL22 7HB Tel: 01745 833232 — MB ChB Liverp. 1941.

PERCY-ROBB, Professor Iain Walter Medical Education Unit, 11 Southpark Terrace, Glasgow G12 8LG Tel: 0141 339 8855 Fax: 0141 330 2776 Email: iwpr1h@clinmed.gla.ac.uk — MB ChB 1959 Ed.; PhD Ed. 1968; FRCP Ed. 1980, M 1976; FRCPath 1980, M 1972; DObst RCOG 1962. (Edin.) Prof. Path. Biochem. Univ. Glas.; Assoc. Dean of Med. Educat. Glas. Med. Sch; Cons. Biochem. Gtr. Glas. HB. Socs: Brit. Soc. Gastroenterol. & Assn. Clin. Biochems. Prev: Reader Clin. Chem. Univ. Edin.

PEREGRINE, Anthony David Llynfi Surgery, Llynfi Road, Maesteg CF34 9DT Tel: 01656 732115 Fax: 01656 864451 — MB BCh 1970 Wales.

PEREIRA, Albert Anthony Lazarus Moreton Medical Centre, 27 Upton Road, Wirral CH46 0PE Tel: 0151 677 2327 Fax: 0151 604 0419 — MB ChB 1991 Liverp.; DRCOG 1995; MRCGP 1997. (Liverpool) Communication Skills Tutor Univ. of Liverp. Prev: Trainee GP Birkenhead; SHO (Paediat.) Wirral NHS Trust.

PEREIRA, Alison Marissa 5 Wellington Terrace, Cotham, Clifton, Bristol BS8 4LE Tel: 0117 9466 971 Fax: 0117 9466 471 — MB ChB 1990 Birm.; FRCOphth 1994. Regist., Bristol Roy. Infirm. Socs: RCOphth.

PEREIRA, Anthony Chrysoligo 122 South Parkside Drive, West Derby, Liverpool L12 8RP — MB BChir 1992 Camb.; MA Camb. 1993, BA (Hons.) 1989; MRCP (UK) 1994. Lect. (Clin. Neurosci.) St. Geo. Hosp. Med. Sch. Lond.; Hon. Regist. (Neurol.) Atkinson Morley's Hosp. Lond. Prev: SHO (Med.) Qu. Med. Centre Nottm.; Cas. Off. Char. Cross Hosp. Lond.; Ho. Phys. Qu. Eliz. II Hosp. Welwyn Gdn. City.

***PEREIRA, Bernadette Livramenta Sandra** 80 Norbury Crescent, Norbury, London SW16 4LA Tel: 020 8764 8348 Email: bernadettep@iname.com — LRCP LRCS LRCPS 1998 Ed., Glas.; LRCP Ed LRCS Ed LRCPS Glas 1998.

PEREIRA, Celina Maria The Health Centre, Laindon, Basildon SS15 5TR Tel: 01268 546411 Fax: 01268 491248 — MB BS Lond. 1987; MA Camb. 1988; DCH RCP Lond. 1991; MRCGP 1994. GP Laindon. Prev: Trainee GP Frimley Pk. Hosp. Camberley VTS.

PEREIRA, Daphne Teresa Maria (retired) Rm 109 Albert Bridge House, Bridge Street, Manchester M60 9DA Tel: 0161 831 2094 — MB ChB 1973 Manch.; AFOM RCP Lond. 1995; MRCGP 1985; DMRO 1985; MSc Occupat. Health Sciences Manchester 1997. Med. Adviser Schlumbergersema Med. Serv.s. Prev: Regist. (Radiother. & Oncol.) Christie Hosp. Manch.

PEREIRA, Diana Aldina St Philomena 17 Hayes Gardens, Hayes, Bromley BR2 7DQ — MB BCh BAO 1961 NUI; DPH Eng. 1965; DCH Eng. 1964. (Galway) Clin. Med. Off. Optimum Health Servs. Lond. Prev: Med. Off. Nairobi City Counc.

PEREIRA, Edgar Paul (retired) 142 Wricklemarsh Road, Kidbrooke, London SE3 8DR Tel: 020 8319 2029 — MRCS Eng. LRCP Lond. 1960; DObst RCOG 1963. Prev: Capt. IMS, Staff Capt. to Dir.-Gen.

PEREIRA, Eric Denzil 36 Linden Way, Boston PE21 9DS — MB BS 1969 Lond.; MRCS Eng. LRCP Lond. 1969; FRCOG 1993, M 1977; DObst 1971. (Char. Cross) Cons. O & G Pilgrim Hosp. Boston, Lincs. Prev: Cons. O & G Vict. Hosp. Mahe, Seychelles; Lect. (O & G) Char. Cross Hosp. Med. Sch. Lond.; Regist. (O & G) St. Jas. Univ. Hosp. Leeds.

PEREIRA, Eric Michael (retired) 6 Brantwood Road, Luton LU1 1JJ Tel: 01582 459125 — MB BS 1966 Nagpur; Cert JCC Lond. 1976. Prev: Regist. (Paediat.) St. Martha's Hosp. & St. Johns Med. Coll.

PEREIRA, Mr Jerome Harry James Paget Hospital, Lowestoft Road, Gorleston, Great Yarmouth NR31 6LA Tel: 01493 452452 Fax: 01493 452666 Email: pereirajh@yahoo.co.uk; Fir House, Priory Road, St. Olaves, Great Yarmouth NR31 9HQ — MB BS 1976 Madras; FRCS Ed. 1983; MD Univ. East Angl. 2000. (Stanley Med. Coll. Madras) Cons. (Surg.) James Paget Hosp.; Hon. Sen. Lect. Univ. of E. Anglia, Norwich. Socs: Fell. Assoc. of Surgs. Of GB & Ire.; Brit. Assn. Surg. Oncol. Prev: Sen. Regist. (Gen. Surg.) Luton & Dunstable Hosp.; Hon. Sen. Regist. (Plastic Surg.) Qu. Vict. Hosp.; Bern. Surg. Res. Fell. Roy. Coll. Of Surgs. of Eng.

PEREIRA, Joaquim Matthew Da Santana 4 All Hallows Road, London N17 7AD — MB ChB 1992 Aberd.

PEREIRA, Mr John Anthony Anmaryn, Luxford Road, Crowborough TN6 2PP Email: johnpereira@compuserve.com — MB BS 1991 Lond.; FRCS (Eng) 1994. (Guy's Hosp. Lond.) Specialist Regist. (Plastic & Reconstruc. Surg.) Pan-Thames Rotat. Socs: Roy. Soc. Med.; Brit. Assoc. of Plastic Surg.

PEREIRA, John Reginald 31 Parkfield Road S., Didsbury, Manchester M20 6DH — MB BS 1941 Bombay. (Grant Med. Coll.)

PEREIRA, Mr Jose Filomeno (retired) Lark Lodge, The Street, Fornham St Martin, Bury St Edmunds IP31 1SW — MB BS 1955 Bombay; FRCS Ed. 1966; DO Eng. 1960. Prev: Cons. Ophth. Surg. W. Suff. Hosp. Gp.

PEREIRA, Madhu Leon Blackfriars, 25 George Square, Edinburgh EH8 9LD — MB ChB 1997 Leeds.

PEREIRA, Marshall Chrysoligo (retired) 'Aldona', 3/B Haymans Green, Liverpool L12 7JG Tel: 0151 226 5613 — MB BS 1933 Bombay; BSc, MB BS Bombay 1933.

PEREIRA, Nigel Hugh Tapton Heights, 29 Taptonville Road, Broomhill, Sheffield S10 5BQ — MB ChB 1975 Sheff.; FFA RCS Eng. 1979. Cons. Anaesth. Sheff. Childr. Hosp.

PEREIRA, Noel Bertram Michael Mount Chambers Surgery, 92 Coggeshall Road, Braintree CM7 9BY Tel: 01376 553415 Fax: 01376 552451 — MB BS Lond. 1969; MRCS Eng. LRCP Lond. 1969; DObst RCOG 1973. (Guy's)

PEREIRA, Raul Scott Immunology Department, Northwick Park Hospital, Watford Road, Harrow HA1 3UJ Tel: 020 8869 2120; Yacht Lilian, 3 Ducks Walk, Twickenham TW1 2DD Tel: 020 8892 5086 Fax: 020 8255 9494 Email: scott.periera@which.net — MB BChir Camb. 1973; PhD Lond. 1985; MA Camb. 1973; FRCPath 1993, M 1981. (Oxf.) Cons Immunol, NW Lond. Hosp.s Trust; Cons Immunol, The Doctors Laborat., Lond.; Hon. Cons. Immunol, Roy. Brompton Hosp Lond. Socs: Fell. Roy. Soc. Med.; Assn. Clin. Path.; Brit Soc for allergy & Clin. Immunol. Prev: Sen Cons Immuno Imperial Coll; Cons. Immunol. St. Helier Hosp. Carshalton & Sen. Lect. (Immunol.) St. Geo. Hosp. Med. Sch. Lond.; Research Sen. Regist. W. Middlx. Univ. Hosp.

PEREIRA, Stephen Maxim Pathways PICU, Goodmayes Hospital, Barley Lane, Ilford IG3 8YB Tel: 020 8970 5833 Fax: 020 8970 5838 — MB BS 1986 Bombay; DPM 1987, MD 1989 Bombay; MRCPysch 1993; BCPsych Lond. 1992; MSc Lond. 1995. Cons. Psychiat. Pathways PICU Goodmayes Hosp. Essex; Hon. Sen. Lect. (Psychiat.) United Med. & Dent. Sch., Guys Hosp. Socs: Med. Defense Union.

PEREIRA, Stephen Paul Department of Gastroenerology, The Middlesex Hospital, Mortimer Street, London W1N 8AA Tel: 020 7380 9011 Fax: 020 7380 9162 Email: steve.pereira@uclh.org; Flat 1, 12 Mecklenburgh Square, London WC1N 2AD Tel: 020 7833 3934 — MB BS 1989 New South Wales; BMedSc NSW 1987; MRCP (UK) 1991; DGM RCP Lond. 1991. (Univ. of NSW) Cons. (Gastro. & Gen. Med.) Univ. Coll. Lond. Hosp. Socs: Brit. Soc. of Gastroenterol.; Amer. Gastro. Assoc.; Amer. Assoc. for the study of Liver Dis.s. Prev: Sen. Regist. Univ. Hosp. Lewisham, Lond.; Regist. (Liver Transpl.) King's Coll. Hosp.; Research Fell. (Gastroenterol.) Guy's Hosp. Lond.

PEREPECZKO, Biruta 2 Braemar Mansions, Cornwall Gardens, London SW7 4AF Tel: 020 7937 7969 — MD 1937 Warsaw.

PERERA, A D The Surgery, 123 Towncourt Lane, Petts Wood, Orpington BR5 1EL Tel: 01689 821551 Fax: 01689 818692.

PERERA, Antony Nihal Ranjit Chesterfield Royal Hospital, Calow, Chesterfield S44 5BL Tel: 01246 277271; 102 Morland View Road, Walton, Chesterfield S40 3DF Tel: 01246 276683 Email: nihalper@lineone.net — MB BS Sri Lanka 1972; DCH RCPSI 1987. (University of Sri Lanka Colombo Faculty) Trust Paediat. Socs: BMA. Prev: Regist. (Paediat.) Geo. Eliot Hosp. Nuneaton; Staff Grade (Paediat.) Grimsby NHS Trust.

PERERA, Balasooriyage Leelananda 11 Bidle Grove, Wigmore Gardens, Water Lane, West Bromwich B71 3SF — MB BS 1968 Ceylon; DPM 1981. Prev: Regist. (Psychiat.) Arrowe Pk. Hosp. Upton & Clatterbridge Hosp Bebington; Regist. Dist. Gen. Hosp. Bangor.

PERERA, Mr Bodiyabaduge Sumith Felix Highview, 22A Fenton Road, Redhill RH1 4BN — MB BS 1983 Colombo; FRCS Ed. 1993; MRCOphth 1991. Assoc. Specialist (Ophth.) RN Hosp. Haslar Gosport.

PERERA, Christopher Nihal 25 Bron y Nant, Croesnewydd Road, Wrexham LL13 7TX — Vrach 1988 People's Freindship, U Moscow; Vrach People's Freindship U, Moscow 1988; DA (UK) 1997; FFARCSI Dub. 1996. Specialist Regist. (Anaesth.) All Wales Higher Train. Prog. Cardiff. Socs: Fac. Anaesth. Coll. Surgs. Dub. Irel.; Vasc. Anaesth. Soc. UK. Prev: Staff Grade (Anaesth.) Scunthorpe Gen. Hosp.

PERERA, Cuthbert Aelian Maurice Top Flat, 9 Wolseley Road, London N8 8RR — MB BS 1959 Ceylon.

PERERA, Devamullage Devapriya Tikakarsiri 2 Woodend Close, St Johns Hill Road, Woking GU21 1RJ — MB BS 1958 Ceylon.

PERERA, Devi Chandra Thavapalan and Partners, 55 Little Heath Road, Bexleyheath DA7 5HL Tel: 01322 430129 Fax: 01322 440949 — MRCP UK 1982; MB BS 1974 Sri Lanka; MRCS Eng. LRCP Lond. 1980 London.

PERERA, Dona Marina Dilukshi Manchester Cytology Centre, Christie Hospital NHS Trust, Kinnaird Road, Withington, Manchester Tel: 0161 446 3656; 3 Clarence Park, Blackburn BB2 7FA Tel: 01254 681997 — MB BS 1979 Colombo; FRCPath 1997; MSc (Cytol.) Lond. 1994; DRCPath 1995, MRCPath 1989. p/t Cons. Cytopath. Christie Hosp. NHS Trust Manch. Socs: Brit. Soc. Clin. Cytol. Prev: Sen. Regist. NW RHA & W. Midl. HA; Regist. Wigan Infirm.

***PERERA, Gayathri Kanchania** 15 Virginia Road, Thornton Heath, Croydon CR7 8EL — BM BCh 1997 Oxf.

PERERA, Gerard Sheran George Stuart Montague Health Centre, Oakenhurst Road, Blackburn BB2 1PP Tel: 01254 263631; 3 Clarence Park, Berardwood, Blackburn BB2 7FA — MB BS 1980 Colombo; MRCP (UK) 1985; DCH RCP Lond. 1985. Cons. Paediat. Community Child Health Communicare NHS Trust Blackburn,Hyndburn & Ribble Valley. Prev: Sen. Train. Post (Community Paediat.) Smallwood Health Centre Redditch; Regist. (Paediat.) Roy. Manch. Childr. Hosp., Glas. Roy. Matern. Hosp.& Roy. Hosp. Sick Childr. Glas.

PERERA, Gunatungamudalige Leslie Senarath St. Mary's Hospital, London Road, Kettering NN15 7PW Tel: 01536 410141 Fax: 01536 493244; 41 Hall Close, Kettering NN15 7LQ Tel: 01536 392580 — MB BS Ceylon 1966; MRCP (UK) 1978. Assoc. Specialist St. Mary's Hosp. Kettering. Socs: Sri Lanka Med. Assn.; Sri Lanka Coll. Phys. Prev: Cons. Phys. DoH, Sri Lanka.

***PERERA, Hasitha Roshal** 208 Beverley Drive, Edgware HA8 5NB — MB ChB 1998 Leic.; MB ChB Leic 1998.

PERERA, Herath Muditanselage Gnana 16 Fairway, Whitestone, Nuneaton CV11 6NP — Vrach 1974 Moscow; Vrach 2nd Moscow Med. Inst. 1974.

PERERA, Hewage Don Padmasiri Wijeratne 8 Sudley Grange, North Sudley Road, Liverpool L17 6DY — MB BS 1978 Sri Lanka.

PERERA, Irma Marie Frances 44 Sigrist Square, Kingston upon Thames KT2 6JT — MB BS 1973 Sri Lanka.

PERERA, Jayantha Lalith Chrysantha Anaesthetic Department, Monklands Hospital, Airdrie ML6 Tel: 01236 748748 Email: thrys1205@yahoo.com — MB BS 1969 Ceylon; MRCPsych 1992. Cons. Psychiat., Cherry Knowle Hosp., Ryhope, Sunderland. Prev: SCMO (Psychiat. of Old Age).

PERERA, Mr John Kenneth Percival (retired) 10 Brickwall Green, Sefton Village, Liverpool L29 9AF Tel: 0151 531 9407 — MB BChir 1947 Camb.; MA Camb. 1959, BA (Hons.) 1944; FRCS Ed. 1959; FRCOG 1968, M 1956. Prev: Cons. O & G N. Liverp. Hosp. Gp.

PERERA, Mahesh Jude Department of Obstetrics & Gynaecology, University of Glasgow, Queen Mothers Hospital, Yorkhill, Glasgow G3 8SJ Tel: 0141 201 0550 Fax: 0141 357 3610 Email: mahesh.perera@clinmed.gla.ac.uk; Derwent Court, 108H North Woodside Road, Glasgow G20 7DN Tel: 0141 353 1790 — MB ChB 1992 Ed.; BSc Sri Lanka 1989; DFFP 1996. (Univ. Ed.) Clin. Research Fell. Univ. Glas.; Clin. Med. Off. (Family Plann.). Socs: BMA; W Scotl. Obst. Soc.; Scott. Family Plann. Doctors Assn. Prev: SHO (O & G) Qu. Mothers Hosp. Glas.; SHO (Gyn.) Stobhill Gen. Hosp. & W.. Infirm. Glas.; SHO (Oncol.) Beatson Oncol. Centre Glas.

PERERA, Panawalage George Alfred Alexander 59 Nicola Close, South Croydon CR2 6NA Tel: 020 8688 6510 — MB BS 1963 Ceylon; MRCPsych 1973; DPM Eng. 1972. (Ceylon)

***PERERA, Panawalage Suraj Alfred** 59 Nicola Close, South Croydon CR2 6NA — BM BCh 1996 Oxf.

PERERA, Mr Peter Hemelge Meary Arnott ENT Depart. Farnborough Hospital, Farnborough Common, Orpington BR6 8ND — MB BS 1973 Sri Lanka; FRCS Ed. 1986; MRCS Eng. LRCP Lond. 1979. Assoc. Specialist (ENT Surg.) Bromley HA.

PERERA, Preethi 22 Clareville Road, Orpington BR5 1RS — MB BCh 1989 Wales.

***PERERA, Rohan Chandra** 18 Eland Road, London SW11 5JY — MB BS 1994 Lond.

PERERA, Rohanta Kumar Netherton Health Centre, Halesowen Road, Dudley DY2 9PU Tel: 01384 254935 Fax: 01384 242468; 69 Greyhound Lane, Norton, Stourbridge DY8 3AD — MB ChB 1984 Bristol; BSc (Hons.) Bristol 1979, MB ChB 1984. Prev: SHO (Dermat.) Falmouth Hosp.; SHO (Geriat. & A & E) Bristol & W.on HA.

PERERA, Saman Devapriya Southend Hospital, Prittlewell Chase, Westcliff on Sea SS0 0RY Tel: 01702 348911; 35 Tyrone, Thorpe Bay, Southend-on-Sea SS1 3HE Tel: 01702 587716 — MB BS 1982 Newc.; FRCR 1988; DMRD Aberd. 1988. Cons. Radiol. S.end Hosp. W.cliff-on-Sea. Prev: Sen. Regist. (Diag. Radiol.) Roy. Hallamsh. Hosp. Sheff.; Regist. (Diag. Radiol.) Aberd. Roy. Infirm.; SHO (A & E & Neurosurg.) Middlesbrough Gen. Hosp.

PERERA, Samantha Rovina 104a Highbury Park, London N5 2XE — MB ChB 1993 Bristol.

***PERERA, Sattambiralalage Anthony Michael Nirdosh** 35 Farthing Court, Graham Street, Birmingham B1 3JR — MB ChB 1995 Birm.; ChB Birm. 1995.

PERERA, Senerath Jayanthi Department of Paediatrics, Southend Health Care NHS Trust, Southend Hospital, Prittlewell Chase, Westcliff on Sea SS0 0RY — MB BS 1982 Peradeniya, Sri Lanka.

***PERERA, Shamira Asith** 10 Winchester Close, Rochdale OL11 5NE — MB BS 1997 Lond.

PERERA, Shyam Divaka 10 Chalmers Road, Cambridge CB1 3SX — BChir 1995 Camb.

PERERA, Srilal Mahendra Queen Elizabeth II Hospital, Howlands, Welwyn Garden City AL7 4HQ Tel: 01707 328111 — MB BS 1970 Ceylon; DA (UK) 1979.

PERERA, Srimathie Therese Benodini 126 Wandle Road, Morden SM4 6AE — MB BS 1970 Ceylon. (Colombo) Regist. Manor Hosp. Epsom.

***PERERA, Sunimalee Himalika Bernadine** 13 Dalcross Road, Hounslow TW4 7RA — MB BS 1994 Lond.

PERERA

PERERA, Varahenage Tilakapala 28 Park Lane, Retford DN22 6TY Tel: 01777 709389 — MB BS 1947 Ceylon; FRCPsych 1987, M 1975; DMJ Soc. Apoth. Lond. 1979; DPM Eng. 1973. (Ceylon) Socs: BMA. Prev: Cons. Forens. Psychiat. Rampton Hosp. Retford; Med. Off. HM Prison Hosp. Wormwood Scrubs Lond.; Regist. & Med. Asst. Leavesden Hosp. Abbots Langley.

PERERA, Weditantirige Nihal Ranjit 16 Fairway, Whitestone, Nuneaton CV11 6NP Tel: 01203 325489 — MRCS Eng. LRCP Lond. 1978; MRCP (UK) 1984; FRCP Lond. 1998. Cons. Phys. c/o Elderly ScarBoro. Hosp. Prev: Lect. & Hon. Sen. Regist. (c/o the Elderly) King's Coll. Hosp. Lond.

PERERA, Wijesinghe Aratchige Titus Edward 48 Uplands Way, London N21 1DT — MB BS 1962 Ceylon.

PEREZ, Adrian Apple Tree House, Butcher's Lane, Boughton, Northampton NN2 8SL — LMS 1967 Madrid; MRCPsych 1977; DPM Eng. 1976. Cons. Psychiat. St. Crispin & N.ampton Gen. Hosps.; Vis. Cons. St. And. Hosp. N.ampton. Prev: Regist. (Psychiat.) Acad. Dept. Newc.; Sen. Regist. (Psychiat.) S.. Gen. Hosp. Glas.

PEREZ, Jose Manuel Second Floor, 9 Lower Granton Road, Edinburgh EH5 3RY — LMS 1990 U Complutense Madrid.

PEREZ, Mr Joseph Valentine Mark Email: perezjv@hotmail.com — MB BS 1987 Lond.; FRCS 1999 (Tr & Orth); FRCS Ed. 1993. (UMDS) Specialist Regist. (Orthop.) S. Thames Region.

***PEREZ, Lisa Anne** 11 Coda Avenue, Bishopthorpe, York YO23 2SE — BM 1995 Soton.

PEREZ-AVILA, Mr Carlos Arturo, OBE Accident & Emergency Department, Royal Sussex County Hospital, Brighton Tel: 01273 696955 — DMed 1970 El Salvador; FRCS Eng. 1994; FRCS Ed. 1981; FFAEM 1994. (Univ. El Salvador) Cons. A & E Roy. Sussex Co. Hosp. Brighton. Socs: Brit. Assn. for Accid. & Emerg. Med. Prev: Sen. Regist. (A & E) Plymouth HD.

PEREZ-CAJARAVILLE, Juan Jesus Department of Anaesthesia, Royal Preston Hospital, Sharoe Green Lane, Fulwood, Preston PR2 9HT Tel: 01772 716565 — Licenciated in Med. & Surg. Pamplona 1991.

PEREZ-CARRAL PANCHUELO, Francisco Jesus Leeds General Infirmary, Staff Residence, Room 313, Woodhouse Hall, 18 Clarendon Road, Leeds LS2 9NT; 92 Low Lane, Horsforth, Leeds LS18 5PX — LMS 1990 Cantabria.

PEREZ CELORRIO, Inigo Dept of Stroke Medicine, Guy;s King's & St Thomas's School of Medicine, London SE5 9PJ; Crysie Cottage, Stanton, Ashbourne DE6 2DA — LMS 1986 Basque Provinces. Research. Fell. Dept. Stroke. Med. Guy's. King's & St Thomas's. Sch. Med. Lond.

PEREZ DE ALBENIZ, Alberto Javier Caludon Centre, Clifford Bridge Road, Walsgrave, Coventry CV2 2TE Tel: 02476 602020 — LMS 1987 Basque Provinces; MRCPsych 1994. Cons. Psychi. In Psychother., Coventry, W Midl.s. Socs: Inst. Gp. Anal.; Soc Psychoth. Research; Internat. Attachment Network. Prev: Sen. Regist. (Psychother.) W. Midl. Scheme.

PEREZ JARA, Javier Research Office, Ward 10 Office, Department of Medicine for the Elderly, Newcastle General Hospital, Newcastle upon Tyne NE4 6BE — LMS 1994 U Complutense Madrid.

PEREZ-MORALES, Maria de las Mercedes Princess Alexandra Hospital, Hamstel Road, Harlow CM20 1QX — LMS 1986 Zaragoza; BSc Zaragoza 1987; DCH Lond. 1997.

PEREZ ROMAN, Maria Dolores 1 Valley Close, St Saviours Hospital, St Saviour, Jersey JE2 7UA — LMS 1987 Cadiz.

PEREZ SALES, Santiago BUPA Murrayfield Hospital, 122 Corstorphine Rd, Edinburgh EH12 6UD — LMS 1993 U Autonoma Barcelona.

PEREZ TERUEL, Maria Isabel 20 Florence Road, West Bridgford, Nottingham NG2 5HR — LMS 1987 Navarre.

PERFECT, Arthur John Strode (retired) Clipper Cottage, Point Green, Devoran, Truro TR3 6NH Tel: 01872 862256 — MRCS Eng. LRCP Lond. 1944; MA Oxon.; MFOM RCP Lond. 1979. Med. Cons. & Advis. to the Oil Industry Nat. & Internat. Prev: Sen. Med. Adviser Chevron Oil (UK) Ltd.

PERHAM, Elizabeth Greystone, Milnthorpe LA7 7QW — MB ChB 1952 Liverp.

PERHAM, Timothy Geoffrey Maslen Baccamore, Sparkwell, Plymouth PL7 5DF Tel: 01752 837404 — MB ChB 1966 Bristol; MB ChB (Hons.) Bristol 1966; FRCP Lond. 1986, M 1971; DCH Eng. 1973; DObst RCOG 1968. (Bristol) Cons. Paediat. Plymouth Gen.

Hosp.; OCC Lect. (Social Studies) Plymouth Univ.; Hon. Tutor (Child Health) Guy's Hosp. Lond. Socs: Brit. Paediat. Assn. & Plymouth Med. Soc. Prev: Regist. (Paediat.) Plymouth Gen. Hosp. & United Bristol Hosps.; Sen. Regist. (Med. Paediat.) Hosp. Sick Childr. Gt. Ormond St. Lond.; Regist. (Med.) Frenchay Hosp. Bristol.

PERIAPPURAM, Mathew John Radcliffe Hospital, Headley Way, Headington, Oxford OX3 9DU Tel: 01865 741166; 64 Ivy Lane, Headington, Oxford OX3 9DY Tel: 01865 220786 — MB BS 1980 Kerala; DCH RPCSI 1985. Regist. (Paediat.) John Radcliffe Hosp. Oxf. Prev: Regist. (Paediat.) Milton Keynes Gen. Hosp.

PERIASAMY, Mr Paramasivan 20 Salt Market Place, Glasgow G1 5NF Tel: 0141 552 6610 — MB BS 1986 Madras; FRCS Ed. 1990; FRCS Glas. 1991.

PERIES, Aubrey Cromwell Hospital, Cromwell Road, London SW5 0TU Tel: 020 7460 2000 Fax: 020 7460 5555; Chanterelle, Hook Heath Gardens, Woking GU22 0QG Tel: 01483 730022 Fax: 01483 730022 — MB BS 1976 Lond.; BSc Biochem. Lond. 1970; MRCS Eng. LRCP Lond. 1976; DCH RCP Lond. 1991. (St. Bart. Hosp. Med. Coll. Lond.) Gen. Phys. Cromwell Hosp. Lond.; Hon. Regist. (Paediat.) Nat. Heart & Lung Hosp. Brompton. Socs: Fell. Roy. Soc. Med.; Roy. Coll. Of Paediat. & Child Health; Internat. Coll. of Paediat., Child & Adolesc. Care. Prev: Med. Off. (Paediat.) Cromwell Hosp. Lond.; Regist. (Paediat.) Frimley Pk. Hosp. Surrey (SW AHA).

PERINGER, Jane Elizabeth 35 Josephine Avenue, London SW2 2JY — MB BS 1978 Lond.; BA Camb. 1975; MRCPsych 1982. Indep. Psychoanal. Lond. Socs: Assoc. Mem. Brit. Psychoanal. Soc.; Lincoln Centre & Inst. for Psychother. Prev: Sen. Regist. (Child Psychiat.) St. Mary's Hosp. Lond.; Regist. Child Guid. Train. Centre Lond.; Regist. (Psychiat.) Middlx. Hosp. Lond.

PERINI, Anthony Francis Northgate & Prudhoe NHS Trust, Northgate Hospital, Morpeth NE61 3BP Tel: 01670 394070 Fax: 01670 394004 — MB BS 1980 Newc.; MRCPsych 1985; MSc Lond. 1997. (Newc. u. Tyne) Med. Dir. & Cons. Psychiat. (Learning Disabil.) N.gate & Prudhoe NHS Trust. Socs: Brit. Neuropsychiat. Assn. Prev: Cons. Psychiat. & Clin. Dir. (Learn. Disabil.) Rampton Hosp.; Sen. Regist. (Ment. Handicap) N.gate Hosp.; Clin. Research Fell. Brain Metab Unit, Edin. Univ.

PERINPANAYAGAM, Kanthirani Nirmala St. Quintin's Health Centre, London W10 6NX Tel: 020 8960 5677; 50 Wyndham Road, London W13 9TE Tel: 020 8567 0447 — MB BS 1969 Ceylon. (Colombo) Prev: Regist. (Anaesth.) St. Chas. Hosp. Lond.

PERINPANAYAGAM, Kulenthiran Savunthararaj (retired) 72 Fordwych Road, London NW2 3TH Tel: 020 8452 3489 Fax: 020 7813 5723 Email: sounthyperin@compuserve.com — MB BS 1961 Ceylon; MRCPsych 1972; DPM Eng. 1967. Cons. Psychiat. & Chief Exec. Sheperd's Youth Trust; Vis. Cons. Gr.lands Priory Hosp. Lond. N14. Prev: Cons. (Psychiat.) & Med. Dir. Brookside Young People's.

PERINPANAYAGAM, Ruth Manorangitham 72 Fordwych Road, London NW2 3TH Tel: 020 8452 3489 — MB BS 1959 Ceylon; MRCPath 1970; DPath Eng. 1967. (Ceylon) Cons. (Microbiol.) Merton, Sutton & Wandsworth AHA (T). Socs: Assn. Clin. Pathols. Prev: Rotat. Sen. Regist. (Microbiol.) Univ. Coll. Hosp. Lond. & Whittington Hosp. Lond. & Edgware Gen. Hosp. & St. Mary's Hosp. Lond.; Regist. (Microbiol.) Hammersmith Hosp. Lond.

PERINPANAYAGAM, Sandy True Vijeyasingam Hanwell Health Centre, 20 Church Road, Hanwell, London W7 1DR Tel: 020 8567 5738 — MB BS 1970 Ceylon; MRCGP 1982. Socs: Brit. Performing Arts Med. Trust.

PERISELNERIS, Savirimuthu Rayappu Beach Road Surgery, 15 Beach Road, Lowestoft NR32 1EA Tel: 01502 572000 Fax: 01502 508892 — MB BS 1976 Sri Lanka; MRCS Eng. LRCP Lond. 1988. Trainee GP RavensCt. Surg. Barry S. Glam. VTS. Socs: Med. Defence Union. Prev: SHO (Paediat.) Manor Hosp. Walsall; SHO (O & G & Anaesth.) Ponterfract Gen. Infirm.; SHO (Gyn.) Walsgrave Hosp. Coventry.

PERIYASAMY, Thiyagarajah Om Sai Clinic, 248 Earls Court Road, London SW5 9AD Tel: 020 7935 1455 Fax: 020 7370 7497 — MB BS 1973 Sri Lanka; MB BS 1973 Sri Lanka.

PERKIN, George David Regional Neurosciences Unit, Charing Cross Hospital, Fulham Palace Road, London W6 8RF Tel: 020 8846 1153 Fax: 020 8846 7487 Email: d.perkin@ic.ac.uk; 29 Dalmore Road, West Dulwich, London SE21 8HD Tel: 020 8244 8668 — BA Camb. 1963, MB 1967, BChir 1966; FRCP Lond. 1985, M 1969;

MRCS Eng. LRCP Lond. 1966. (Camb. & King's Coll. Hosp.) p/t Cons. Neurol. Char. Cross Hosp. Lond. Prev: Sen, Regist. (Neurol.) Maida Vale & Univ. Coll. Hosps.; Regist. Nat. Hosp. Nerv. Dis. Qu. Sq.; Ho. Phys. & Ho. Surg. King's Coll. Hosp. Lond.

PERKIN, Malcolm Alexander Lambeth, Southwark & Lewisham HA, 1 Lower Marsh, Waterloo, London SE1 7NT Tel: 020 7716 7030 Fax: 020 7716 7070; 32 Albury Ride, Cheshunt, Waltham Cross EN8 8XF Tel: 01992 425542 Email: gg672@dial.pipex.com — MB BS 1973 Newc.; MSc (Pub. Health) Lond. 1997; MSc (Gen. Pract.) Lond. 1990; MRCGP 1983; T(GP) 1991; DTM & H. (Newcastle upon Tyne) Specialist Regist. (Pub. Health Med.); GP; Hon. GP Tutor. Socs: BMA; Soc. Pub. Health. Prev: Eval. of Educat. Materials Project, Inst. of Pub. Health Camb.; Sen. Lect. (Gen. Pract.) St. Bart. Hosp. Med. Coll. Lond.; Med. Dir. Herts. FHSA Hertford.

PERKIN, Michael Richard 26 Barrington Road, Carshalton, Sutton SM3 9PP — MB BS 1993 Lond.; MB BS (Hons.) Lond. 1993; BSc (Hons.) Lond. 1990; MRCP (UK) 1996; MRCPCH 1997. Specialist Regist. (Paediat.) St. Heliers Hosp. Carshalton, Lond. Prev: SHO (Paediat. Oncol.) Gt. Ormond St. Hosp.

PERKINS, Adrian Dryland Surgery, 1 Field Street, Kettering NN16 8JZ Tel: 01536 518951 Fax: 01536 486200 — MB ChB 1990 Leeds; MRCGP 1994. (Leeds) Prev: GP Asst. Bradford; Trainee GP Harrogate VTS.

PERKINS, Andrew Stuart Road Surgery, Stuart Road, Pontefract WF8 4PQ Tel: 01977 703437 Fax: 01977 602334; 5 Parkside Close, Leeds LS6 4LZ Tel: 0113 230 4348 — MB BS 1983 Lond.; MSc (Gen. Pract.) Lond. 1993; DRCOG 1986. (Lond. Hosp.) Prev: Trainee GP Medway VTS.

PERKINS, Andrew Leonard c/o 71 Basing Way, London N3 3BP — MB BS 1977 Lond.; MCOphth 1989; DO RCPSI 1985; DRCOG 1979.

PERKINS, Anne Marie Yorwerth The Clift Surgery, Minchens Lane, Bramley, Tadley RG26 5BH Tel: 01256 881228 — MB BS 1983 Lond.; MRCGP 1996; DFFP 1995; DCH RCP Lond. 1990. (St. Geo. Hosp.) Socs: RCGP (Fac. Family Plann.). Prev: Volunteer GP Romania; SHO (O & G) Roy. Shrewsbury Hosp.

PERKINS, Benedick Antony Webb (retired) 17B Warmdene Road, Brighton BN1 8NL Tel: 01273 508811 — MB 1960 Camb.; BChir 1959; DObst RCOG 1964. Prev: GP Brighton.

PERKINS, Brian 21 Cherry Tree Avenue, Farnworth, Bolton BL4 9SB — BM BCh 1993 Oxf.

PERKINS, Carol Ann 28-30 Kings Road, Harrogate HG1 5JP; Ceylon House, 11 Robert St, Harrogate HG1 1HP Tel: 01423 521733 — MB ChB 1985 Leeds; T(GP) 1991; DRCOG 1987.

PERKINS, Mr Charles Shepherd Department of Maxillofacial Surgery, Cheltenham General Hospital, Sandford Road, Cheltenham GL53 7AN Tel: 01242 222222 — BM 1989 Soton.; BDS Liverp. 1980; FRCS Ed. 1993; FFD RCSI 1985; FDS RCS 1984. Cons. Oral & Maxillofacial Surg. Cheltenham Gen. & Glos. Roy. Hosps. Socs: BMA; Fell. Brit. Assoc. Oral & Maxillofacial Surg.; Eur. Assoc. Craniomaxillofacial Surg. Prev: Sen. Regist. (Oral & Maxillofacial Surg.) Cheltenham Gen., Gloucester Roy & John Radcliffe Hosp. Oxf.; Regist. (Oral & Maxillofacial Surg.) Soton. Gen. Hosp. & Odstock Hosp. Salisbury; SHO (Gen. Surg.) Qu. Alexandra Hosp. Portsmouth.

PERKINS, Colin Michael Zeneca Pharmaceuticals, Alderley Park, Macclesfield SK10 4TG Tel: 01625 515997 Fax: 01625 512406 — MD 1983 Leeds; MB ChB 1974; FRCP Ed. 1988; MRCP (UK) 1977; FFPM 1990. Gp. Manager Regulatory Strategy Zeneca Pharmaceuts. Alderley Pk. Socs: Brit. Inst. Regulatory Affairs. Prev: MRC Clin. Scientist (Med.) Univ. Oxf.; Research Fell. (Med.) Univ. Leeds.

PERKINS, Douglas Henry The Chimneys, Hall Road, Hemsby, Great Yarmouth NR29 4LF — LMSSA 1958 Lond.

PERKINS, Elizabeth Lilian Madeleine (retired) Thorpe Lee, Denne Park, Horsham RH13 7AY Tel: 01403 252186 — MB BS Lond. 1953; DObst RCOG 1955; DA Eng. 1957.

PERKINS, Gavin David Research Fellow, Intensive Care Medicine, Birmingham Heartlands Hospital, Bordesley Green Easst, Birmingham B9 5SS Tel: 0121 424 3562 Email: perking@heartsol.wmids.nhs.uk — MB ChB 1995 Birm.; ChB Birm. 1995; Dip. IMC RCS Ed. 1998; MRCP (Lond) 1998. (Birmingham) SHO (Med.) Rotat. Heartlands Hosp. Birm.

PERKINS, Hugh David 199 East Dulwich Grove, London SE22 8SY — MB BS 1962 Lond.; FFA RCS Eng. 1967. (St. Mary's) Cons. Anaesth. Greenwich Health Dist. Prev: Sen . Anaesth. Regist. St. Mary's Hosp. Lond.; Anaesth. Regist. Roy. Marsden Hosp. Lond.

PERKINS, Hywel Hopcyn Bowen (retired) Netherdon, 3 Beech Walk, Ewell, Epsom KT17 1PU — LMSSA 1948 Lond. Prev: Resid. Med. Off. & Regist. (Cas.) Sutton & Cheam Gen. Hosp.

PERKINS, Jane Deborah Alison Toddington Medical Centre, Luton Road, Toddington, Dunstable LU5 6DE Tel: 01525 872222 Fax: 01525 876711; St. Andrews, Pk Road, Toddington, Dunstable LU5 6AB — MB BS 1980 Lond.; DRCOG 1982. (Lond.)

PERKINS, Jennifer Anne 8 Brunstath Close, Barnston, Wirral CH60 1UH — MB ChB 1994 Liverp.; DRCOG. (Liverpool)

***PERKINS, Jeremy Mark Michael** 3 Ribblesdale, Whitby, Ellesmere Port, South Wirral CH65 6RF — MB ChB 1994 Liverp.

PERKINS, John Saunton, Broseley Avenue, Culcheth, Warrington WA3 4HH Tel: 0192 576213 — MB ChB 1953 Manch.; FRCP Lond. 1977, M 1962.

PERKINS, John Hilmar Church Street Surgery, Church Street, Starcross, Exeter EX6 8PZ Tel: 01626 890368 Fax: 01626 891330 — MB BS 1982 Lond.; MRCGP 1987. GP. Exeter.

PERKINS, Kate Sophia Mary 17 Ashgrove Road, Aberdeen AB25 3AE — MB ChB 1997 Birm.

***PERKINS, Katrina Mary** Gibbs Marsh Farm, Stalbridge, Sturminster Newton DT10 2RU Tel: 01963 362655 Fax: 01963 362655 Email: perkins@gibbsmarsh.freeserve.co.uk — MB ChB 1998 Bristol.

PERKINS, Marian Joan Park Hospital, Headington, Oxford OX3 1LQ — MB BS 1981 Lond.; BSc (Hons.) Anat. Lond 1978, MB BS 1981; MRCP (UK) 1984; MRCPsych 1988. Drummond Prize Biochem. 1977.

PERKINS, Peter Doré Southbourne Surgery, 17 Beaufort Road, Southbourne, Bournemouth BH6 5BF Tel: 01202 427878 Fax: 01202 430730 Email: postmaster@gp-j81059.nhs.uk; 26 Carbery Avenue, Bournemouth BH6 3LF — MB BS 1977 Lond.; MRCS Eng. LRCP Lond. 1977; MRCGP 1981; Cert. Family Plann. JCC 1978; Dip Ad. Educat. Soton 1986; DRCOG 1979. (Westm.) Clin. Pract. (Accid.) Bournemouth Gen. Hosp.; Clin. Dir. Flat Earth Soc.; Clin. Tutor Univ. Soton.; Med. Dir. to Latter Day Luddities; Chairm. Dept. of Minimally Invasive Gen. Pract.; Fell. Roy. Soc. of Med.; Pres. Bournemouth and ChristCh. Br. of the Roy. Coll. of Midw. Socs: Fell. of the Roy. Soc. of Med. Prev: SHO & Ho. Phys. (O & G) Roy. Vict. Hosp. Boscombe, Bournemouth; Ho. Surg. Qu. Mary's Hosp. Roehampton.

PERKINS, Peter John Veor Surgery, South Terrace, Camborne TR14 8SN Tel: 01209 612626 Fax: 01209 886569; Walpole Cottage, South Tehidy, Camborne TR14 0HU — MB BS 1978 Lond.; DRCOG 1982. (Lond. Hosp.)

***PERKINS, Peter Paul** 58 Eaton Crescent, Swansea SA1 4QN — MB BCh 1996 Wales.

PERKINS, Philip James 8 Ivelbury Close, Buckden, St Neots, Huntingdon PE19 5XE — MB BS 1985 Lond.

PERKINS, Mr Ralph Douglas Garth, Holyhead Road, Wellington, Telford TF1 2DP Tel: 01952 641848 Fax: 01952 641848 Email: perkins@enta.net — MB BS 1976 Lond.; FRCS Eng. 1982. (Guy's) Cons. Orthop. Surg. P.ss Roy. Hosp. Telford. Socs: Fell. BOA. Prev: Sen. Regist. (Orthop.) P.ss Eliz. Orthop. Hosp. Exeter; Hon. Research Fell. Univ. Exeter; Cas. Off. & Ho. Surg. Guy's Hosp. Lond.

PERKINS, Roger Joseph Department of Obstetrics & Gynaecology, St. Mary's Hospital, Milton Road, Portsmouth PO3 6AD — MB BS 1982 West. Austral.; BSc West. Austral. 1977, MB BS 1982; DA (UK) 1988; DRACOG 1985.

PERKINS, Rosslyn Mary 301 Kingston Road, Wimbledon Chase, London SW20 8LB Tel: 020 8296 8154 — BM 1995 Soton.; DCH 1999. SHO (GP Train. Scheme) Roy. Surrey Co. Hosp. Guildford. Socs: MPS; BMA. Prev: SHO (A & E) Roy. Berks. Hosp. Reading.

PERKINS, Russell James Kevin Dept of Anaesthesia, Booth Hall Childrens Hospital, Blackley, Manchester — MB BS 1988 Lond.; FRCA 1994; DA (UK) 1990. Cons. Manch. Childr. Hosp. NHS Trust. Prev: Sen. Regist. NW Region; Research Fell. Hope Hosp. Salford; Anaesth. NW Regional Train. Scheme.

PERKINS, Sarah Louise Eaton Wood Medical Centre, 1128 Tyburn Road, Erdington, Birmingham B24 0SY Tel: 0121 373 0959 Fax: 0121 350 2719; 4 Shottery Close, Walmley, Sutton Coldfield

PERKINS

B76 2WS Tel: 0121 313 1466 — MB ChB 1981 Birm.; MRCGP 1985; DRCOG 1985. (Birmingham) GP; Hon. Clin. Lect. Dept Gen. Pract. Birm. Med. Sch.

***PERKINS, Scott Marcus** 1 Osprey Close, Worcester WR2 4BX — MB ChB 1997 Manch.

PERKINS, Susanne Alderton Health Centre, Alderton, Woodbridge IP12 3DA — BM 1988 Soton.

PERKINS, Vincent Dumfries & Galloway NHS Trust, Anaesthetic Department, Dumfries DG1 4AP; 39 Jeffreys Road, Wrexham LL12 7PD — MB ChB 1987 Aberd.; FRCA 1994. Cons. Anaesth. Dumfries & Galloway NHS Trust. Socs: BMA. Prev: Sen. Regist. Rotat. (Anaesth.) Cardiff; Regist. Rotat. (Anaesth.) Cardiff; SHO (Med. & Cas.) ChristCh., NZ.

PERKINS, William Department of Dematology & Dermatologic Surgery, The University Hospital, Nottingham NG7 2UH; The Manor House, Old Main Road, Bulcote, Nottingham NG14 5GU — MB BS 1984 Newc.; FRCP (UK) 2000. Cons. Dermat. Qu. Med. Centre Nottm. Socs: Brit. Assn. Dermat. Prev: Cutaneous Surg. Fell. Univ. Minnesota, USA; Sen. Regist. Soton. Univ. Hosps. Trust.

PERKO, Christopher Darko Draycott Hall, Draycott, Derby — MRCS Eng. LRCP Lond. 1976.

PERKS, Alan The Oaklands, Bromfield Road, Ludlow SY8 1DW — MB BS 1985 Lond.; DRCOG 1988.

PERKS, Mr Anthony Graeme Bowman Department of Plastic & Reconstructive Surgery, City Hospital, Hucknall Road, Nottingham NG5 1PB Tel: 0115 969 1169 Ext: 46428 Fax: 0115 962 7939 — MB BS 1979 Lond.; FRCS (Plast) 1994; FRACS 1991; FRCS Eng. 1984. (King's Coll. Hosp. Lond.) Cons. Plastic & Reconstruc. Surg. City Hosp. & Qu. Med. Centre Nottm.; Cons. Plastic & Reconstruc. Surg. King's Mill Hosp. Manfield; Cons. Plastic & Reconstruc. Surg. Newark Hosp. Newark; Cons. Plastic & Reconstruc. Surg. The Pk. Hosp. Nottm. Socs: Nat. Comm. Mem. Brit. Assn. Head & Neck Oncologists; Brit. Assn. Surg. Oncol.; Brit. Assn. Aesthetic Plastic Surgs.

PERKS, Barbara Mary Helena Hunnington Meadows, Long Itchington Road, Hunnington, Leamington Spa CV33 9EN Tel: 01926 633318 — MB ChB 1969 Birm. p/t Cons. Anaesth. S. Warks. Community Dent. Serv.; Clin. Asst. (Anaesth.) Birm. Heartland Hosp. Prev: Regist. (Anaesth.) United Birm. Hosps.

PERKS, Bryan Peter Walter Burham Court, Burham, Rochester ME1 3XX Tel: 01634 64951; 1 The Esplanade, Rochester ME1 1QW Tel: 01634 43142 — MB BS 1955 Lond. (Lond. Hosp.) Prev: Ho. Surg. Hillingdon Hosp.; Obst. Ho. Surg. & Sen. Ho. Phys. All St.'s Hosp. Chatham.

PERKS, Christian Edward Pershore Health Centre, Priest Lane, Pershore WR10 1RD Tel: 01386 502030 Fax: 01386 502058; South Mede House, Lower End, Birlingham, Pershore WR10 3AD — MB BChir 1989 Camb.; MA Camb. 1990.

PERKS, Geoffrey Thomas (retired) The Grange Coach House, Yarm Lane, Great Ayton, Middlesbrough TS9 6PJ Tel: 01642 722595 — MB BS 1955 Durh.

PERKS, Janet Mary North Road West Medical Centre, 167 North Road West, Plymouth PL1 5BZ Tel: 01752 662780 Fax: 01752 254541; 7 Thorn Park, Mannamead, Plymouth PL3 4TG Tel: 01752 266078 — MB ChB 1976 Birm.; MRCGP 1980; DRCOG 1978.

PERKS, John Stewart (retired) Hunnington Meadows, Long Itchington Road, Hunnington, Leamington Spa CV33 9EN Tel: 01926 633318 — MB ChB 1969 Birm.; FFA RCS Eng. 1974. Cons. Anaesth. Coventry AHA.

PERKS, Mr Nigel Francis 58 Royal Hill, Greenwich, London SE10 8RT Tel: 020 8691 3183 — MB BS 1982 Newc.; MRCOG 1988; FRCOG 2000. Cons. O & G Greenwich Dist. Hosp. Lond.; Cons. Reproductive Med. & Asst.ed Conception St. Bart Hosp. Lond. Socs: Brit. Fertil. Soc.; Treas. & Sec. Forum for Qual. in Healthcare; Acad. Bd., Roy.Soc. Of Med.

PERKS, Richard Henry George (retired) 18 St Peters Close, Church Lane, Goodworth Clatford, Andover SP11 7SF Tel: 01264 354680 — BM BCh Oxf. 1952; MA Oxf. 1952; MRCGP 1963. Prev: Cas. Off. & Ho. Surg. St. Thos. Hosp.

PERKS, Ruth Dyke (retired) 32 Melbury Close, Chislehurst BR7 5ET — MB ChB Bristol 1939.

PERKS, Warren Hamilton 25 Ridgebourne Road, Shrewsbury SY3 9AA Tel: 01743 232028 Fax: 01743 357652 Email: wazperks@hotmail.com — MB ChB 1971 Manch.; MD Manch.

1980; FRCP Lond. 1990; FRCP Ed. 1989; MRCP (UK) 1975. Cons. Phys. Roy. Shrewsbury Hosp. Socs: Brit. Thorac. Soc.; Eur. Sch. Respirat. Med. Prev: Cons. (Phys.) P.ss Roy. Hosp. Telford; Research Regist. Brompton Hosp.; Regist. (Neurol.) Manch. Roy. Infirm.

PERLIK-KOLACKI, Danuta Bozena Bredon Avenue Surgery, 232 Bredon Avenue, Binley, Coventry CV3 2FD Tel: 02476 447139 Fax: 02476 431839; 7A St. Martins Road, Finham, Coventry CV3 6ET Tel: 024 76 411148 Fax: 02476 412 — Med. Dipl. Poznan 1963; LAH Dub. 1970. (Poznan) Socs: BMA. Prev: SHO (Med. & Geriat.) Horton Gen. Hosp. Banbury; SHO (Med. & O & G) New Cross Hosp. Wolverhampton.; SHO (Med. & Chest), Creation Hosp., N.ampton.

PERLMAN, Francesca Jane Andrea 8 Sutton Lane, Banstead SM7 3QP — MB BS 1989 Lond.; MRCGP 1994. Prev: GP Lambeth, S.wark & Lewisham; Trainee GP Kent VTS.

PERLOW, Bernard Woolf 17 Hillcrest Gardens, Finchley, London N3 3EY Tel: 020 8349 9913 — MRCS Eng. LRCP Lond. 1946. (Lond. Hosp.) Socs: BMA & Brit. Med. Acupunc. Soc. Prev: Capt. RAMC; Ho. Surg. Lewisham Hosp.; Res. Med. Off. Haslemere & Dist. Hosp.

PERN, Peter Oliphant Woodside House, Cromarty IV11 8XU — MB ChB 1970 Ed.; BSc (Med. Sci.) Ed. 1967, MB ChB 1970; FRCP Ed. 1986; FFOM RCP Lond. 1994, MFOM 1984, AFOM 1981; DIH Soc. Apoth. Lond. 1977.

PERRAUDEAU, Mohini Kamala 102 Lavenham Road, London SW18 5HF — MB BS 1990 Lond.; BSc Lond. 1987, MB BS 1990; MRCP (UK) 1993. Regist. (Rheum.) Hammersmith Hosp. Lond. Prev: Regist. (Gen. Med.) Wrexham Pk. Trust; SHO (Renal Med.) St. Mary's Hosp. Lond.; SHO Hammersmith Hosp. Lond.

PERREN, John Frederick (retired) 1 Graysfield, Welwyn Garden City AL7 4BL — MB BS 1953 Lond.; D.Occ.Med. RCP Lond. 1996; DObst RCOG 1958. Prev: GP Force Med. Off. Herts. Constab. Welwyn Gdn. City.

PERREN, Timothy John ICRF Cancer Medicine Research Unit, St. James' University Hospital, Beckett St., Leeds LS9 7TF Tel: 0113 206 4670 Fax: 0113 242 9886 Email: t.j.perren@cancermed.leeds.ac.uk — MB BS 1978 Lond.; MD Lond. 1990; FRCP Lond. 1995; MRCP (UK) 1982; MRCS Eng. LRCP Lond. 1978. (Char. Cross) Hon. Sen. Lect. & Cons. Med. Oncol. ICRF Cancer Med. Research Unit Univ. Leeds & St. Jas. Univ. Hosp. NHS Trust Leeds; Lead Clinician (Chemother.) Leeds Teachg. Hosps. NHS Trust; Speciality Lead (Gyn. cancer) Leeds Cancer Centre. Prev: Sen. Lect. In Med. Oncol., Leeds Univ.; Research Fell. (Med. Oncol.) Qu. Eliz. Hosp. Birm.; Regist. & SHO (Gen. Med.) N. Staffs. Hosp. Centre Stoke-on-Trent.

PERRETT, Andrew Gordon 124 Victoria Road, Cambridge CB4 3DZ — BChir 1993 Camb.

PERRETT, Anthony David (retired) 22 St Johns Terrace, Devoran, Truro TR3 6NE Tel: 01872 863358 — MB ChB Otago 1958; MD Otago 1968; FRCP Lond. 1979, M 1965. Prev: Cons. Phys. Roy. Cornw. Hosp. Treliske.

***PERRETT, Conal Martin** 31 Shelwood Road, Brentwood CM14 6AD — MB ChB 1996 Bristol.

PERRETT, Jennifer Margaret 22 St Johns Terrace, Devoran, Truro TR3 6NE Tel: 01872 863358 — MRCS Eng. LRCP Lond. 1969; DA Eng. 1971. (Guy's.) Clin. Asst. (Ophth.) Roy. Cornw. Hosps. Trust.

PERRETT, Kevin 53 Endowood Road, Millhouses, Sheffield S7 2LY Tel: 0114 236 5973 Email: perretts@aol.com — MB ChB 1985 Sheff.; MRCGP 1990; T(GP) 1991; MFPHM 1997. (Sheff.) Sen. Regist. (Pub. Health Med.) Trent RHA; Cons. (Communicable Dis. Control/Pub. Health Med. Rotherham HA. Socs: BMA; Fac. Publ. Health Med.; Soc. Social Med.

PERRETT, Richard Guy 4 Hillhead, Chittlehampton, Umberleigh — MB BS 1993 Lond.; DCH; DRCOG; DFFP; MRCGP.

PERRICONE, Vittorio Blackpool Victoria Hospital, Whinney Heys Road, Blackpool FY3 8NR; 25 Infirmary Road, Blackburn BB2 3LP — State Exam 1992 Palermo.

PERRIN, Clifford Edwin 1 Washington Street, Chichester PO19 3BN — MB BS 1958 Lond. (St. Thos.)

***PERRIN, Felicity Margaret Roche** 19 Sidney Square, London E1 2EY — MB BS 1994 Lond.

PERRIN, Janet Anne St. James' Surgery, St. James', Quedgeley, Dundalk Co. Louth, Republic of Ireland Tel: 01452 722280; 21 Alexandra Road, Gloucester GL1 3DR Tel: 01452 539116 — MB ChB 1959 Birm.; MRCS Eng. LRCP Lond. 1959. (Birm.) Sen. Clin.

Med. Off. (Psychosexual Med.) S. Worcs. Community Trust & Frenchay Healthcare Trust & St. Michael's Hosp. United Bristol Hosps. Trust; Police Surg. Glos. Constab. Socs: BMA; Assn. Police Surg.; Inst. Psychosexual Med. Prev: Clin. Asst. (Orthop.) Gloucester Roy. Hosp.; GP Glos.; Ho. Surg. Gen. Hosp. Birm.

PERRIN, John (retired) Woodmans, Copthorne, Crawley RH10 3JU — MB BChir 1941 Camb.; MD Camb. 1952; MRCP Lond. 1948. Cons. Immunol. Lond. Hosp. Prev: Asst. Dir. Clin. Laborats. Lond. Hosp.

PERRIN, John Eric (retired) 21 Alexandra Road, Gloucester GL1 3DR Tel: 01452 539116 — MB ChB 1959 Birm.; MRCS Eng. LRCP Lond. 1959; FRCGP 1985, M 1968; DObst RCOG 1964. Prev: GP Gloucester.

PERRIN, Mandy Elizabeth 6 Norwood Gardens, Belfast BT4 2DX — MB ChB 1992 Birm. SHO (Anaesth.) Nottm.

PERRIN, Peter Francis 22 Eastway, Maghull, Liverpool L31 6BR — MB ChB 1985 Liverp.

***PERRIN, Sarah Margaret** 13 Larkfield Close, Caerleon, Newport NP18 3EX — MB ChB 1996 Bristol.

PERRIN, Val Lawrence 13 Pettitts Lane, Dry Drayton, Cambridge CB3 8BT Email: val.perrin@dial.pipex.com — MB BS 1972 Lond.; BSc Lond. 1969; MFPM 1992. (St. Geo.) Cons. Pharmaceut. Med. Camb. Prev: Sen. Research Phys. Glaxo Gp. Research Ltd. Greenford; GP Camb.; Med. Off. i/c Port Saunders Community Health Centre Newfld.

PERRING, Jeffrey 121 Burlington Court, Adderstone Crescent, Jesmond, Newcastle upon Tyne NE2 2HR — MB ChB 1988 Liverp.

PERRING, Michael Arthur Optimal Health of Harley Street, 114 Harley St., London W1N 1AG Tel: 020 7935 5651 Fax: 020 7935 3858 — MB BChir Camb. 1964; MA Camb. 1964; FCP(SA) 1969; DPM Eng. 1974. (St. Bart.) Socs: Fell. Roy. Soc. Med.; BMA; Brit. Erectile DysFunc. Soc. Prev: Dir. Lond. Inst. Study Human Sexuality; Regist. (Med.) Groote Schuur Hosp. Cape Town, S. Afr.; Ho. Phys. & Ho. Surg. St. Bart. Hosp. Lond.

PERRINS, Mr David John Dyson 7 Fairlawn Wharf, East Saint Helen St., Abingdon OX14 5ED Tel: 01235 521592 — MD 1973 Camb.; MB BChir 1950; FRCS Eng. 1960; FRCS Ed. 1958. Hon. Med. Adviser Federat. Multiple Sclerosis Treatm. Centres. Socs: Vice-Pres. Internat. Soc. Hyperbaric Med.

PERRINS, Edward John Department of Cardiology, The General Infirmary, Great George St., Leeds LS1 3EX Tel: 0113 392 2650 Fax: 0113 392 6343; 28 Foxhill Crescent, Leeds LS16 5PD Tel: 0113 230 4174 — MB ChB 1975 Leeds; MB ChB (Hons.) Leeds 1975; BSc (Anat.) (1st cl. Hons.) Leeds 1972, MD 1985; FRCP Lond. 1989; MRCP (UK) 1977; FACC 1983. Cons. Cardiol. Gen. Infirm. Leeds. Socs: Brit. Cardiac Soc. Prev: Pres. Soc. Cardiol. Technicians; Sec. Brit. Pacing Gp.

PERRINS, John Kenneth Perrins and Partners, Trinity Medical Centre, New George Street, South Shields NE33 5DU Tel: 0191 454 7775 Fax: 0191 454 6787; Shanklin, 20 Underhill Road, Cleadon Village, Sunderland SR6 7RS — MB BS 1981 Newc.; MRCP (UK) 1988; MRCGP 1985. (Newcastle upon Tyne)

***PERRIS, Allison Jane** 36 Aireburn Avenue, Keighley BD20 6NH — MB ChB 1998 Leeds.

PERRIS, Thomas Michael 97 Lichfield Road, Sutton Coldfield B74 2RR — MB ChB 1993 Bristol.

PERRISS, Brian William Department of Anaesthetics, Royal Devon & Exeter Hospital, Barrack Road, Exeter EX2 5DW Tel: 01392 402474; Lyneham Farm, Chudleigh, Newton Abbot TQ13 0EH Tel: 01626 854513 — MB BS 1963 Lond.; BSc (Hons.) Lond. 1959, MB BS 1963; FFA RCS Eng. 1968; DA Eng. 1965. (St. Bart.) Cons. Anaesth. Roy. Devon & Exeter Hosps. Socs: BMA & Soc. Anaesth. SW Region. Prev: Sen. Regist. (Anaesth.) S.W. RHA & United Bristol Hosps.; Sen. Clin. Fell. Univ. Colorado, Denver, USA; Regist. (Anaesth.) United Bristol Hosps.

PERRISS, Richard William 6 Windsor Court, South Gosforth, Newcastle upon Tyne NE3 1YN Email: rperriss@globalnet.co.uk — MB ChB 1993 Sheff. Demonst. (Anat.) Univ. of Newc. Upon Tyne. Prev: SHO (Surg.) Darlington Memor. Hosp.; SHO (ENT) Freeman Hosp. Newc.; SHO (Cardiothoracic) N.. Gen. Hosp. Sheff.

PERRITT, Simon Jeremy 2 French Street, Widnes WA8 0BT — MB ChB 1996 Liverp.

PERRONS, Anthony John Tigh Nan Sgeiran, Isle of Islay PA49 7UN — MB ChB 1959 Birm.

PERROS, Petros Ward 15, Level 6, Freeman Hospital, Freeman Road, Newcastle upon Tyne NE7 7DN Tel: 0191 284 3111 Fax: 0191 213 1968 — MB BS 1983 Newc.; BSc (Hons.) 1978, MD 1992; MRCP (UK) 1986; FRCP 2000. Cons. Phys. (Endocrinol.) Freeman Hosp. Newc. u. Tyne; Hon. Sen. Lect. Newc. Univ.

PERROTT, Barry David Flat 4, 18 Campden Hill Gardens, London W8 — MRCS Eng. LRCP Lond. 1961. (Westm.) Prev: Ho. Surg. W.m. Hosp.; Ho. Phys. St. Mary's Hosp. Newport, I. of Wight; Cas. Sen. Ho. Off. St. Jas. Hosp. Balham.

PERROTT, Charles Stephen Halse Road Health Centre, Halse Road, Brackley NN13 6EJ Tel: 01280 703460 Fax: 01280 703460; The Old Stone House, Greatworth, Banbury OX17 2DZ — MB BS 1987 Lond.; MRCGP 1992; DCH RCP Lond. 1989. Prev: Trainee GP Banbury VTS; SHO (A & E) Gen. Hosp. St. Helier, Jersey; Ho. Surg. Roy. Free Hosp. Lond.

PERRY, Aideen Dorothy Campbell Manor Cottage, Kingstone, Ilminster TA19 0NS — MB ChB 1961 Liverp.; MRCP (U.K.) 1972; DObst RCOG 1964; DCH Eng. 1966.

PERRY, Alastair James House Doctors Surgery, Maryport Street, Usk NP15 1AB Tel: 01291 672633 Fax: 01291 672631; Tyn-y-Caeau Farm, Llangibby, Usk NP15 1PS Tel: 01291 2888 — MB BCh BAO NUI 1958. (National University of Ireland University College Galloav) Med. Off. HM Prison & HM Young Offenders Inst. Usk. Socs: BMA. Prev: Med. Off. Balfour Beatty (Overseas) Ltd. W. Pakistan; Regist. (Path.) Roy. N.. Hosp. & Char. Cross Hosp. Lond.

PERRY, Amanda Ruth Department of Academic Haematology, Institute of Cancer Research, Cotswold Road, Sutton SM2 5NG Tel: 020 8643 8901 Email: aperry@icr.ac.uk; 195C Camberwell Grove, London SE5 8JU Tel: 020 7924 0497 — BM BCh 1990 Oxf.; MRCP (UK) 1993; Dip. RCPath 1996.

PERRY, Andrew John Warwick House Medical Centre, Holway Green, Upper Holway Road, Taunton TA1 2YJ Tel: 01823 282147 Fax: 01823 338181; Orchard Cottage, Nailsbourne, Taunton TA2 8AG Tel: 01823 451415 Email: harris.perry@which.net — MB BS 1985 Lond.; BSc Lond. 1982; MRCGP 1990; DRCOG 1990; DCH RCP Lond. 1989; DA (UK) 1987. (Char. Cross) Hosp. Practitioner (Anaesth.) MusGr. Pk. Hosp. Taunton.

PERRY, Mr Andrew Richard 108 Faraday Road, London SW19 8PB — MB BS 1992 Lond.; BSc Lond. 1989; FRCS Eng. 1997; FRCS Ed. 1997. Specialist Regist. Rotat. (Orthop.) S. W. Thames. Socs: BOA; Brit. Orthop. Train. Assn. Prev: SHO (Plastics & Reconstrüc. Surg.) Qu. Mary's Roehampton; SHO Rotat. (Surg.) Roy. Surrey Co. Hosp.; SHO (A & E) St. Thos. Hosp. Lond.

PERRY, Anne Catherine Psychotherapy Department, 50-52 Clifden Road, Hackney, London E5 OLJ Tel: 020 8510 7842, 020 8510 8242 — MB BS 1991 Lond.; MRCPsych 1995; Dip. Cog Therapy Oxf. 1998. (Univ. Lond. & St. Geo. Hosp. Med. Sch.) Cons. Psychiat. in Psychother. (CBT). Prev: Sen. Regist. (Behavioural & Cognitive Psychother.) Springfield Hosp. Lond.

PERRY, Anthony Treetops, Penycoedcae, Pontypridd CF37 1PY Tel: 01443 402448; 5 Tythebarn Lane, Dicken's Heath, Solihull B90 1RN Tel: 0121 745 2556 — BM BS 1993 Nottm.; BMedSci (Hons.) 1991; FRCS Ed. 1997; FRCS Glas. 1997. (Nottm.) Specialist Regist. (Gen. Surg.) W. Midl. Rotat. Prev: Sen. SHO Gen. Surg. Birm. Heartlands & Solihill Trust.

PERRY, Catherine Ann Grace The Brant Road Surgery, 291 Brant Road, Lincoln LN5 9AB Tel: 01522 722853 Fax: 01522 722195 — BM BS 1989 Nottm.; BMedSci 1987 Nottm.; MRCGP 1993; DRCOG 1993. (Nottm.) p/t GP Princip. Lincoln. Prev: Lincoln VTS.

PERRY, Lady (Catherine Hilda) Glenholm, 2 Cramond Road S., Davidsons Mains, Edinburgh EH4 6AD — MB ChB 1970 Ed. (Ed.) Socs: Med.. Wom. Federat. & Cas. Surgs. Assn. Prev: Regist. (A & E) N.ampton Gen. Hosp.; Med. Off. (Gen. Surg. & Traum. & Orthop. Surg.) Stoke; Mandeville Hosp.; Ho. Off. Stoke Mandeville Hosp.

PERRY, Charles Lyn, SJM (retired) Windrush, 39 Haven Road, Haverfordwest SA61 1DU Tel: 01437 762973 — MB BCh 1949 Wales; BSc Wales 1944; MRCGP 1960; DObst RCOG 1954. Prev: GP HaverfordW.

PERRY, Christopher Michael 2 Woodhall Avenue, London SE21 7HL Tel: 020 7351 4173 — MB BS Lond. 1969; FRCOG 1989, M 1976. (King's Coll. Lond. & St. Geo.) Cons. Gyn. St. Helier NHS Trust & Roy. Marsden Hosp. Lond.; Edit. Bd. Mem. of Cytopathol. Socs: Brit. Soc. Colpos. & Cerv. Path. Prev: Sen. Regist. St. Helier Hosp. Carshalton & Roy. Marsden Hosp.; Regist. (O & G)

PERRY

St. Helier Hosp. Carshalton; Ho. Surg. Surgic. Unit & Regist. (O & G) St. Geo. Hosp. Lond.

PERRY, Colin Graham 1/R 103 Woodford Street, Shawlands, Glasgow G41 3HW — MB ChB 1991 Glas.; MCP (UK) 1995. (Glas.) Specialist Regist. (Diabetics/Endocrinol.) Glas.

PERRY, David Andrew 1 Orchard Crescent, Nether Adderley, Macclesfield SK10 4TZ — MB ChB 1989 Liverp. SHO (Surg.) BRd.green Hosp. Liverp.

PERRY, David James Haemophilia Centre & Haemostasis Unit, Royal Free & University Colege Medical School, Rowland Hill St., London NW3 2PF Tel: 020 7830 2068 Fax: 020 7830 2178 Email: djp@rfhsm.ac.uk; 17 Long Road, Cambridge CB2 2PP Tel: 01223 244299 — MB ChB 1978 Ed.; PhD Camb. 1993; BSc Ed. 1975, MD 1992; MRCP (UK) 1980; FRCPath 1995, M 1985; FRCP 1998. Sen. Lect. (Haemat.) Roy. Free Hosp. Sch. Med. Lond. Prev: Lect. (Molecular Haemat.) Wellcome Trust.

PERRY, David William 20 Ufton Close, Shirley, Solihull B90 3SB — MB ChB 1987 Birm.

PERRY, Mr Dexter 39 West Street, Ryde PO33 2UH Tel: 01983 564983 Email: dexter.perry@qmail01.porthosp.swest.nhs.uk; 39 West Street, Ryde PO33 2UH Tel: 01983 564983 — BM 1991 Soton.; FRCS Eng. 1995. Specialist Regist. (Gen. Surg.) Qu. Alexandra Hosp. Ports. Prev: Specialist Regist. (Gen. Surg.) I. of Wight Health Care Trust St. Mary's Hosp. Newport.

PERRY, Diana Parsonage House, 17 Orlingbury Road, Pytchley, Kettering NN14 1ET — MB BS 1964 Lond.; MRCS Eng. LRCP Lond. 1964; DCH Eng. 1967; DObst RCOG 1966. (King's Coll. Hosp.)

***PERRY, Duncan Ross Alastair** Tyn-Y-Caeau Farm, Llanbadoc, Usk NP15 1PS — MB BS 1994 Lond.

PERRY, Eileen Elizabeth (retired) Movilla House Nursing Home, 51 Movilla Road, Newtownards BT23 8RG Tel: 028 9182 6390 — MB BCh BAO Belf. 1937; MFCM 1974; DObst RCOG 1942; DCH Eng. 1946; DPH 1939. Prev: Div. Med. Off. Antrim Co. Health Comm.

PERRY, Elizabeth Mary Cornerstone Surgery, 469 Chorley Old Road, Bolton BL1 6AH Tel: 01204 495426 Fax: 01204 497423 — MB ChB 1983 Liverp.

PERRY, Fiona Mary The Surgery, 138 Beaconsfield Villas, Brighton BN1 6HQ Tel: 01273 552212/555401 Fax: 01273 271148; Bankside, Ditchling Common, Burgess Hill RH15 0SJ Tel: 01444 233307 — MB BS 1981 Lond. (Roy. Free)

PERRY, Geoffrey Lawrence Bloomfield, Yarmouth Road, Hales, Norwich NR14 6AB — MB BS 1990 Lond.

PERRY, Huw Miles 4 St Anne's Court, Talgarn, Pontyclun CF72 9HH — MB BS 1985 Lond.

PERRY, Ian 103 Quinton Lane, Birmingham B32 2TT Tel: 0121 682 3285; Department of Medicine, University of Birmingham, Vincent Drive, Birmingham B15 2TH — MB ChB 1993 Birm.; BSc 1992; MRCP (UK) 1996. Research Fell. (Gastroenterol.) Univ. Birm. Prev: Regist. (Gastroenterol.) City Hosp. Birm.

PERRY, Ian Charles Old Farm House, Grateley, Andover SP11 8JR Tel: 0126 488 9659 Fax: 0126 488 9639 Email: ian@ianperry.com; 19 Cliveden Place, London SW1W 8HD Tel: 020 7730 8045 Fax: 020 7730 1985 — MB BS 1963 Lond.; MRCS Eng. LRCP Lond. 1963; MFOM RCP Lond. 1979; DAvMed RCP Lond. 1968. (Guy's) Cons. Occupat. Med. Various Cos.; Authorised Sen. Med. Examr. Civil Aviat. Auth. (UK), Federal Aviat. Agency (USA) & Other Foreign Aviat. Auths.; Med. Cons. to Various Airlines & Companies; Med. Cons. Brit. Helicopter Advis. Bd. & IAOPA; Sen. Cons. Avimed Ltd. & Twinnings & HAS; Cons. (Occup. Med.) Winchester & Eversleigh NHS. Socs: FRAeS; FIOSH; Internat. Acad. Aviat. Med. & Space. Prev: Master of Guild. Air Pilots & Air Navigators; Maj. RAMC, Sen. Med. Off. & Aviat. Med. Adviser RAMC & Army Air Corps; UK Delegate NATO Agard Aerospace Med. Panel.

PERRY, James Herbert (retired) 2 Combe Street Lane, Yeovil BA21 3PB Tel: 01935 475504 — MB ChB Bristol 1953; DObst RCOG 1960. Prev: Sen. Res. Off. Bristol Matern. Hosp.

PERRY, Jane Elizabeth 11 Cherry Gardens, Sawbridgeworth CM21 9DW — MB BS 1988 Lond.

PERRY, Jeremy David Dept. of Rheumatology, Barts. And The London Trust, Royal London Hospital, Mile End, Bancroft Road, London E14 DG Tel: 020 7377 7859 Fax: 020 7377 7801 — MB BS 1970 Lond.; FRCP Lond. 1986; MRCP (UK) 1973; Acad. Dip. Biochem. Univ. Lond. 1967. (Middlx.) Cons. Rheumatologist, Barts and the Lond. Trust, Roy. Lon. Hosp.; Cons. Adviser Crystal Palace Nat. Sports Centre; Hon. Sen. Lect. Lond. Hosp. Med. Coll., Q.M.W. Lond. Sch. Med. & Dent Teach. Univ. Lond. Socs: Brit. Soc. Rheum.; Roy. Soc. Med. (Comm. Mem. Sect. Sports Med.); Brit. Assn. Sport & Med. Prev: Cons. Rheum. Newham Health Care; Sen. Regist. (Rheum.) Colchester and P. Of Wales Hosp.; Regist.&SHO (Med.) Lond. Hosp.

PERRY, John Fraser Unit 8, Torbay Hospital, Newton Road, Torquay TQ2 7AA — MB ChB 1995 New Zealand.

PERRY, John Gilbert (retired) Appleyard, Santon Downham, Brandon IP27 0TQ Tel: 01842 813456 Fax: 01842 813456 Email: jperry9@compuserve.com — MB BS 1958 Lond.; LMSSA Lond. 1958; DTPH Lond 1975; DObst RCOG 1963. Prev: Med. Supt. Sinoia Gen. Hosp., Zimbabwe.

PERRY, John Reginald (retired) 49 New Wokingham Road, Crowthorne RG45 6JG Tel: 01344 774210 Fax: 01344 762753 — MB ChB 1959 Birm.; DCH Eng. 1963; DObst RCOG 1961. Prev: Med. Off. Wellington Coll.

PERRY, John Richard Health Clinic, 407 Main Road, Dovercourt, Harwich CO12 4ET Tel: 01255 201299 Fax: 01255 201270; 116 Fronks Road, Dovercourt Bay, Harwich CO12 4EQ Tel: 01255 502649 — MB BS 1969 Lond.; MRCGP 1976; DObst RCOG 1972; DA Eng. 1971. Socs: Brit. Med. Acupunct. Soc.; Roy. Soc. Med. Prev: Hosp. Pract. (Anaesth.) Essex Rivers Trust.

PERRY, John Rodham Nuffield Road Medical Centre, Nuffield Road, Chesterton, Cambridge CB4 1GL Tel: 01223 423424 Fax: 01223 566450 — MB BCh 1970 Wales; MSc 1998; FRCGP 1987, M 1974; DObst RCOG 1973. (Welsh National School of Medicine) Dir. (Studies in Gen. Pract.) Univ. Camb.

PERRY, Jonathan James Dilston Mill House, Corbridge NE45 5QZ — MB BS 1997 Lond.

PERRY, Jonathan Neil, Surg. Cdr. RN Department of Radiology, Derriford Hospital, Derriford Road, Plymouth PL6 8DH Tel: 01752 763297 Email: jon.perry@phnt.swest.nhs.wk; Westlake Brake, Renny Road, Down Thomas, Plymouth PL9 0BG — MB ChB 1984 Birm.; FRCR 1994. Cons. Radiol. Derriford Hosp. Plymouth. Prev: Med. Off. HMS Revenge.

PERRY, Joseph John 2 Adenburgh Drive, Attenborough, Nottingham NG9 6AZ — MB ChB 1948 Birm.; MRCGP 1961; DA Eng. 1969. (Birm.) Prev: Ho. Phys. Gen. Hosp. Birm.

***PERRY, Katherine Joy** 8 Belle Baulk, Towcester NN12 6YH — BM 1998 Soton.; BM Soton 1998.

PERRY, Keith Alan Worcester Street Surgery, 24 Worcester Street, Stourbridge DY8 1AW Tel: 01384 371616 — MB ChB 1961 Birm.; DObst RCOG 1963. (Birm.) Socs: BMA. Prev: Clin. Asst. (Ophth.) Corbett Hosp. Stourbridge; Clin. Asst. Birm. & Midl. Eye Hosp.; Ho. Phys. & Ho. Surg. Corbett Hosp. Stourbridge.

PERRY, Louise Jane 11 Shropshire Gardens, Warfield, Bracknell RG42 3XP — MB BS 1987 Lond.; JCPTGP 1991; MSc (Distinc. Experim. Path. & Toxicol.) Lond. 1993; MRCPath 2000.

PERRY, Mark Stephen The Robert Darbishire Practice, Walmer Street, Rusholme, Manchester M14 5NP Tel: 0161 225 6699 Fax: 0161 248 4580 — MB ChB 1979 Leeds.

***PERRY, Mark Stephen** 38 Mount Street, Aberdeen AB25 2QT — MB ChB 1997 Aberd.

PERRY, Mrs Mary Elisabeth Rhael Windrush, 39 Haven Road, Haverfordwest SA61 1DU Tel: 01437 762973 — MRCS Eng. LRCP Lond. 1952. (Cardiff) JP. Prev: Med. Advisor to Schs. & Clin. Med. Off. Pembrokesh. HA.

PERRY, Matthew Giles Bampton Surgery, Landells, Bampton OX18 2LJ Tel: 01993 850257; Blackthorn Cottage, Queen St, Bampton OX18 2LP — MB BS 1973 Lond.; BSc (Genetics) Lond. 1970, MB BS 1973; DObst RCOG 1975. (Univ. Coll. Hosp.) Prev: SHO (A & E) & SHO (O & G) P.ss Margt. Hosp.; Swindon; Ho. Surg. Bolingbroke Hosp. Lond.

PERRY, Mr Matthew James Alexander 16 Beatrice Road, Richmond TW10 6DT Tel: 020 8332 9655 — MB BS 1993 Lond.; BSc (Hons.) Lond. 1990; FRCS (Eng.) 1997. (Char. Cross & Westm. Med. Sch.) Research Fell. (Urol.) St. Geo.'s Hosp. Med. Sch. Socs: Med. Defence Union; BMA; BAUS. Prev: SHO (Surg.) Epsom Gen. Hosp.; SHO (Surg.) Roy. Surrey Co. Hosp.; SHO (Orthop. & Urol.) Roy. Surrey Co. Hosp.

PERRY, Matthew Robert The Surgery, Shaw Lane, Albrighton, Wolverhampton WV7 3JF Tel: 0190 722 2301 Fax: 01902 373807;

Cloverleigh, Shaw Lane, Albrighton, Wolverhampton WV7 3DT — MB ChB 1982 Birm.; MRCGP 1986; DRCOG 1985; MSc Warwick University Primary Care Management 1998. Chair S. E. Shrops. PCG.

PERRY, Mr Michael John Maxillofacial Unit, North Staffs NHS Trust, COPD, Hartshill Road, Stoke-on-Trent ST4 7PA Tel: 91782 554696 — MB ChB 1988 Leeds; BSc Leeds 1985; BChD Leeds 1993; FRCS Eng. 1995; FDS Lond. 1995. Cons. Maxillofacial Surg. N. Staff NHS Trust Stoke-on-Trent. Prev: SHO (Oral Surg.) Sunderland Dist. Gen. Hosp.; SHO (Gen. Surg. & Orthop.) York Dist. Gen. Hosp.; SpR Maxillofacial Surg. S. Thames.

PERRY, Nicholas David 13 Aylmer House, Eastney St., London SE10 9NU — MB BS 1992 Lond.

PERRY, Nicholas Keith 27 Lansdown Park, Lansdown, Bath BA1 5TG — BM BS 1982 Nottm.

PERRY, Nicholas Mark Breast Ass Centre, St Barts, London EC1A 7BE Tel: 020 7601 8074; Jasmine cottage, Arlington Green, Bilbury, Cirencester GL7 5NE — MB BS Lond. 1975; FRCS Eng. 1980; FRCR 1984. (St. Bart.) Cons. Radiol. St Bartholomews Hosp. Lond.; Quality Assur. Manager N. Thames BrE. Screening Progr.; Cons. Europ. Commiss. Europe. Against Cancer BrE. Screening Progr.; QA Dir.Lond. region BrE. screening prog; Clin. Dir.Centr. and E.Lond. BrE. screening prog. Prev: Sen. Regist. (Radiol.) St. Bart. Hosp. Lond.

PERRY, Nicola Ground Floor Flat, 22 Steerforth St., London SW18 9HE — MB ChB 1996 Bristol.

PERRY, Nigel Braeside Surgery, Gorse Hill, Farningham, Dartford DA4 0JU Tel: 01322 862110 Fax: 01322 862991; 19 Eardley Road, Sevenoaks TN13 1XX Tel: 01732 458443 Email: drnperry@aol.com — MB ChB 1976 Cape Town; BSc Cape Town 1971. (Cape Town) Asst. Med. Adviser Nuclear Electric plc & Magnox Electric; Apptd. Dr under ionizing Radiat. Regulat.s.

***PERRY, Philip Lewis** 1 Harrow Close, Stoke Heath, Bromsgrove B60 3QT — MB ChB 1998 Aberd.; MB ChB Aberd 1998.

PERRY, Professor Philip Michael (retired) Queen Alexandra Hospital, Cosham, Portsmouth PO6 3LY Tel: 023 92 286000 — MB BS Lond. 1962; MS Lond. 1974; FRCS Eng. 1968. Cons. Surg. Qu. Alexandra Hosp. Portsmouth; Vis. Prof. Postgrad. Med. Fac. Univ. Portsmouth; Cons. Surg. Portsmouth & SE Hants. Health Dist.; Arris & Gale Lect. & Erasmus Wilson Demonst. RCS Eng; Hon Cons. jure. Prev: Lect. (Surg.) Unit St. Bart. Hosp. Lond.

***PERRY, Rachel Elizabeth** 1 Bowling Leys, Middleton, Milton Keynes MK10 9BD Tel: 01908 395235 Fax: 01908 395235 — MB BS 1998 Lond.; MB BS Lond 1998.

PERRY, Rachel Kitrick Kaye 23 Barnfield Road, Petersfield GU31 4DQ; Adelaide Cottage, Church Path, London SW14 8HD Tel: 020 8876 8883 — BChir 1994 Camb.; MRCP 1998. Specialist Regist. (Clin. Oncol.) Roy. Marsden NHS Trust, Lond. Prev: SHO (Gen. Med.) Kent & Canterbury NHS Trust; Locum Regist. (c/o Elderly) St. Chas. Hosp. Lond.

PERRY, Raphael Adam Cardiothoracic Centre, Thomas Drive, Liverpool L14 3PE Tel: 0151 228 1616 Fax: 0151 220 8573 Email: rperry@ccl-tr.nwest.nhs.uk; 15 Acrefield Park, Woolton Village, Liverpool L25 6JX Tel: 0151 428 2031 Fax: 0151 428 2146 Email: raphbabs@aol.com — BM BS 1980 Nottm.; DM Nottm. 1990, BMedSci 1978; FRCP Lond. 1995; MRCP (UK) 1984; FACC 1993; FACA 1992. Cons. Cardiol. Cardiothoracic Centre Liverp.; Postgrad. Clin. Tutor & Clin. Lect. (Med.) Cardiothoracic Centre Liverp. Socs: Brit. Cardiac Soc.; Brit. Cardiovasc. Interven. Soc. Prev: Sen. Registar (Cardiol.) Regional Adult Cardiothoracic Unit BRd.green Hosp. Liverp.; Brit. Heart Foundat. Research Fell. Deptartment Cardiovasc. Med. Qu. Eliz. Hosp. Birm.

PERRY, Rebecca Jane 11 St Tristan Close, Locks Heath, Southampton SO31 6XR Tel: 01489 576828 — MB ChB 1994 Glas.; MRCP Glasgow 1998. SHO (Paediat. Med.) Roy. Hosp. For Sick Childr., Glas. Socs: Roy. Coll. Phys.s and Surg. Glas.; BMA. Prev: SHO (Paediat. Med.) Roy. Alexandra Hosp.; SHO (Paediat. Med.) S.ern Gen. Hosp.; SHO (Paediat. Med.) Roy. Hosp. Sick Childr. Glas.

PERRY, Richard James 20C Queensdown Road, London E5 8NN — MB BS 1990 Lond.; MRCP (UK) 1994.

PERRY, Richard John Parkside Family Practice, Green Road Surgery, 224 Wokingham Road, Reading RG6 1JT Tel: 0118 966

3366 Fax: 0118 926 3269; 3 Knossington Close, Lower Earley, Reading RG6 4EU — MB BS 1996 Lond.

PERRY, Richard Jolyon Doctor's Mess, Level 3, John Radcliffe Hospital, Headley Way, Oxford OX3 9DU Tel: 01865 741166; 8 Pembroke Court, Rectory Road, Oxford OX4 1BY Tel: 01865 721830 — BM BCh 1993 Oxf.; PhD Camb. 1991; MA Oxf. 1993. SHO Rotat. (Gen. Med.) Oxf. Radcliffe NHS Trust. Prev: Ho. Phys. John Radcliffe Hosp. Oxf.; Ho. Surg. Wycombe Gen. Hosp. High Wycombe.

PERRY, Professor Robert Henry Neuropathology Department, Newcastle General Hospital, Westgate Road, Newcastle upon Tyne NE4 6BE Tel: 0191 273 8811 Fax: 0191 256 3196 Email: robert.perry@ncl.ac.uk; Dilston Mill House, Corbridge NE45 5QZ Tel: 01434 632308 Email: r@perry.net — MB ChB 1969 St. And.; DSc Newc. 1993; FRCP Ed. 1992; MRCP (UK) 1972; FRCPath 1990, M 1978; FRCP (Lond) 1993. (St Andrews) Cons. Neuropath.Newc. Upon Tyne Hosp.s NHS Trust; Prof. Neuropothology Newc. Univ.; Clin. Scientist Developm. in brain ageing. Socs: Brit. Neuropath. Soc.

PERRY, Robin Charles Macdonald 10 (2F4) Lochrin Place, Edinburgh EH3 9QS Tel: 0131 622 1279 — MB ChB 1996 Aberd. SHO (Paediat. Surg.) Roy. Hosp. for Sick Childr. Edin.

PERRY, Roger Malcolm Gordon and Partners, The Redwell Medical Centre, 1 Turner Road, Wellingborough NN8 4UT Tel: 01933 400777 Fax: 01933 671959 — MB ChB 1977 Birm.; MRCGP 1981.

PERRY, Samantha Frances 7 Turnberry Road, Glasgow G11 5AF — BM BS 1988 Nottm.; MRCP (UK) 1991. Regist. (A & E) W.. Infirm. Glas. Socs: BMA; Brit. Accid. & Emerg. Med. Soc. Prev: SHO (A & E) CrossHo. Kilmarnock; SHO (A & E & Clin. Pharmacol.) Glas. Roy. Infirm.

PERRY, Stella Margaret Beryl (retired) 78 Holmead Road, Glasgow G44 3AG — MB ChB 1939 Glas.; DPH 1941. Prev: Sch. Med. Off. Glas.

PERRY, Mr Stephen Robert Kidderminster Hospital, Bewdley Road, Kidderminster DY11 6RJ Tel: 01562 823424; Hillhampton farmhouse, Hillhampton lane, Great Willy, Worcester WR6 6DV — MB BChir 1983 Camb.; MA Camb. 1980; FRCS Ed. 1989; FCOphth 1989; DO RCS Lond. 1986. Worcester Acute Hosp.s NHS Trust. Socs: Roy. Soc. Med.; Midl. Ophth. Soc. Prev: Fell. Oculoplastic & Orbital Surg. Univ. Brit. Columbia; Sen. Regist. (Ophth.) Bristol Eye Hosp.

PERRY, William Rodham (retired) 15 Cherry Tree Lane, Edwalton, Nottingham NG12 4AL Tel: 0115 923 1359 Fax: 0115 923 3639 — MB BS Durh. 1941; DPH Birm. 1947. Prev: Dist. Community Phys. S.. Nottm. Health Dist. (T).

PERRY-KEENE, Gillian Heather Prices Mill Surgery, New Market Road, Nailsworth, Stroud GL6 0DQ Tel: 01453 832424 Fax: 01453 833833; Street Farm Cottage, 22 The St, Uley, Dursley GL11 5TB — MB BS 1968 Lond.; MRCS Eng. LRCP Lond. 1968. (Univ. Coll. Hosp.) Dep. Police Surg. Glos. Constab. Socs: Assn. Police Surg.; Fell. Roy. Soc. Med. Prev: Dep. Police Surg. Glos. Constab.; Clin. Asst. (Geriat.) Qu.s Hosp. Cirencester; Ho. Off. (Surg. & Phys.) Cirencester Memor. Hosp.

PERRYER, Carolyn Jane Delapre Medical Centre, Gloucester Avenue, Northampton NN4 8QF Tel: 01604 761713 Fax: 01604 708589; 1 High Street, Greens Norton, Towcester NN12 8BA Tel: 01327 353681 — MRCS Eng. LRCP Lond. 1984; T(GP) 1991. (Char. Cross)

PERRYER, Susan Elizabeth Summertown Group Practice, 160 Banbury Road, Oxford OX2 7BS Tel: 01865 515552 Fax: 01865 311237; 7 Walton Crescent, Oxford OX1 2JG Tel: 01865 522416 — MB BS 1983 Lond.; MRCP (UK) 1987.

PERSAD, Mr Krishna 41 Mercer's Road, London N19 4PP — MB ChB 1967 St. And.; FRCS Ed. 1974; MRCOG 1976.

PERSAD, Mr Rajendra Asita Rajkrishna Department of Urology, Bristol Royal Infirmary, Bristol BS2 8HW Tel: 0117 928 3509 Fax: 0117 928 3505 Email: raj.persad@ubht.swest.nhs.uk; 10 Clifton Park Road, Bristol BS8 3HL Tel: 0117 377 7173 Fax: 01275 846 117 — MB BS 1983 Lond.; ChM Bristol 1993; FRCS (Urol.) 1994; FRCS Eng. 1987; FEBU 1994. (Univ. Coll. Hosp.) Cons. Urol. Surg. & Surg. Uro-Oncol. Bristol Roy. Infirm.; Sen. Clin. Lect. Univ. Bristol; Hon. Assoc. Prof. of Med. Univ. Pittsburgh. Socs: Roy. Soc. Med.; Brit. Assn. Urol. Surg.; Brit. Prostate Gp. Exec. Mem. Prev: Regist. Rotat. (Gen. Surg.) Guy's Hosp. Lond. & Kent & Sussex Hosp.; SHO

(Surg.) Frenchay & S.mead HA; Ho. Phys. (Gen. Med. & Gastroenterol.) N.wick Pk. Hosp.

PERSAUD, Janki London Road Surgery, 64 London Road, Wickford SS12 0AH Tel: 01268 765533 Fax: 01268 570762 — MB ChB 1982 Dundee.

PERSAUD, Mark Christopher Insurance Medical Services, Unit 8 Cambridge Court, 210 Shepherds Bush Road, London W6 7NL — MB BS 1990 Lond.

PERSAUD, Rajendra Dhwarka Westways, 49 St James Road, Croydon CR9 2UR Tel: 020 8700 8512 Fax: 020 8700 8504; The Maudsley Hospital, Denmark Hill, London SE5 Tel: 020 7703 6333 — MB BS 1986 Lond.; MPhil 1991 Lond; BSc 1983 Lond; MSc 1995 City; 1990 Dip. Phil; MRCPsych 1990; DHMSA 1988 Soc. Apoth.; 1994 Dip Hlth Econ. (Univ. Coll. Lond.) Cons. Psychiat. Bethlem Roy. & Maudsley Hosps. Lond.; Research Worker Inst. Neurol. Univ. Lond.; Resid. Doctor Granada TV Programs; columnist for Hosp. Doctor. Socs: Fell. Worshipful Soc. Apoth.; Fell. Roy. Soc. Med.; Aristotlean Soc. Prev: Regist. & SHO Bethlem Roy. & Maudsley Hosps.; Research Schol. John Hopkins Hosp., USA; Post Doctoral Fell. Johns Hopkins Hosp. USA (1990).

PERSAUD, Ricardo Abraham Petember 50 Waller Road, Telegraph Hill, London SE14 5LA — MB BS 1996 Lond.; MPHIL Lond. 1994. (Univ. Coll. Lond. Med. Sch.) S. Thames Basic Surg. Rotat.; Orthop. SHO, Joyce Green Hosp. Dartford Kent; Gen. Surg. SHO, Mayday Hosp. Mayday Rd. Surrey; Neurosurg. SHO, KCH Lond. Socs: Grad. Mem. Inst. Biol. Lond.; Middlx. Hosp. Med. Soc. Prev: Surg. Ho. Off. Whittington Hosp. Lond.; Med. Ho. Off. N. Middlx. Hosp. Lond.

PERSEY, Alexander (retired) 62 Stanton Road, Sandiacre, Nottingham NG10 5EL Tel: 0115 939 7356 — MB BS 1944 Lond.; MRCS Eng. LRCP Lond. 1944; MRCOG 1952; DObst 1949, (Middlx.); Mem. Coll. GP. Prev: Surg. Lt. RNVR.

PERSEY, Dorothy Joyce (retired) 62 Stanton Road, Sandiacre, Nottingham NG10 5EL Tel: 0115 939 7356 — MB ChB 1945 Bristol; DCH Eng. 1950; DObst RCOG 1952. Prev: Asst. Matern. & Child Welf. Off. & Sch. Med. Off. Derbysh. CC.

PERSEY, Malcolm Robert Northwick Park Hospital, Watford Road, Harrow HA1 3UJ Tel: 020 8864 3232; 14 Thanet Lodge, Mapesbury Road, London NW2 4JA Tel: 020 8451 6229 — MB BS 1988 Lond.; BA (Hons.) Oxf. 1985; MRCP (UK) 1992. Regist. Rotat. Centr. Middlx., N.wick Pk. & Hammersmith Hosps. Socs: Roy. Soc. Med. & Brit. Soc. Rheum. Prev: SHO Rotat. (Med.) St. Mary's Hosp. Lond.

***PERSHAD, Nirvisha** 9 Langton Gate, Newton Mearns, Glasgow G77 6TP — MB ChB 1998 Glas.; MB ChB Glas 1998.

PERSOFF, David Asher 152 Harley Street, London W1G 1HH Tel: 020 8202 8877 Email: dpersoff@aol.com ; dr.dap@doctors.net.uk; 5 Raleigh Close, London NW4 2SX Tel: 020 8202 6161 — MSc Lond. 1959; BSc 1955, MB BS 1961; FRCP Lond. 1982, M 1969. (Lond. Hosp.) Hon. Cons. Phys. Newham HA (Retd.). Socs: Fell. Roy. Soc. Med. Prev: Cons. Phys. St. And.& Newham Dist. Gen. Hosps. Lond.; Lect (Med.) Univ. Lond.; Cons. Phys. Poplar Hosp. Lond.

PERTHEN, Katharine Sarah 21 Corbison Close, Warwick CV34 5EZ — MB ChB 1997 Liverp. Whiston Hosp. Prescot, Merseyside.

***PERTWEE, Richard** Rayne Hall, Shalford Road, Rayne, Braintree CM7 5BT — MB BS 1998 Lond.; MB BS Lond 1998.

PERUMAINAR, Manohara 3 Paddock Rise, Beechwood, Runcorn WA7 3HL Tel: 01928 715531 — MB BS 1972 Ceylon; LMSSA Lond. 1990; DGM RCP Lond. 1990.

PERUMAL, Joseph Remy Ayam (retired) — MB BS 1963 Ceylon; FRCP Lond. 1991; MRCP (UK) 1974; FACP 1998. Locum Cons. Rheumatologist, Surrey & Sussex Healthcare NHS Trust. Prev: Cons. Rheum. & Gen. Med. Scunthorpe & Goole Hosps. Trust.

PERUMALPILLAI, Mr Ravi Gnanasundaram The John Radcliffe Hospital, Headley Way, Headington, Oxford OX3 9DU — MB BS 1974 Lond.; FRCS Ed. 1979; FRCS Eng. 1979. (Middlx.) Cons. Cardiothoracic Surg. John Radcliffe Hosp. Oxf. Prev: Sen. Regist. (Cardiothoracic Surg.) Brompton Nat. Heart & Chest Hosp. Lond.; Regist. Rotat. (Surg.) Middlx. Hosp. Lond.; Regist. (Cardiothoracic Surg.) Harefield & Brompton Hosps.

PERVAIZ, Mr Khalid Queen Marys hospital, Sidcup DA16 8LT Tel: 020 8302 2678 Fax: 020 8308 3041; Email: khalidpervaiz@compuserve.com — MB BS 1984 Karachi; FRCS Ed. 1994; FFAEM 1998. (Dow Med. Coll. Karachi) Cons.A & E Med. Qu. Marys Hosp., Sidcup. Socs: Mem. Specialist Train. Comm. A & E Med.. S Thames. Prev: Sen. Regist. A+E Med. Basildon; Sen. Regist. A+E Med. Roy. Free Hosp.; Sen. Regist. A+E Med. OldCh. Hosp.

PERVAIZ KHAN, Nasir 13 Seafield Terrace, South Shields NE33 2NP; 19-N Gulberg II, Lahore, Pakistan Tel: 878967 — MB BS 1964 Sind; MB BS Lond. 1974; FRCOphth 1990, M 1989; DO RCS Eng. 1974. Assoc. Eye Specialist Sunderland Eye Infirm. Prev: Sen. Regist. (Ophth.) Punjab Med. Coll. Pakistan; Asst. Prof. Ophth. King Edwd. Med. Coll. & Postgrad. Med. Inst. Lahore, Pakistan.

PESKETT, David John Peskett, 38 Old Shoreham Road, Lancing BN15 0QT Tel: 01903 754358 — MB BS 1976 Lond.; MRCGP 1980; DCH Eng. 1979; DRCOG 1978. GP Lancing. Prev: Trainee GP Chelmsford VTS; Ho. Phys. Qu. Mary's Hosp. Stratford; Ho. Surg. Lond. Hosp. (Mile End).

PESKETT, Sheila Anne 137 Priests Lane, Shenfield, Brentwood CM15 8HJ Tel: 01277 223010 Fax: 0374 595735 Email: majictorch@ad.com — MA Oxf. 1974, BA 1966, BM BCh 1969; FRCP (UK) 1990, M 1975. (St. Mary's) Cons. (Rheum. & Rehabil.) Mid Essex Health Dist. Socs: Brit. Assn. Rheum.; Roy. Soc. Med.; Brit. Assn. Rehabil. Med. Prev: Sen. Regist. (Rheum.) Middlx. Hosp. Lond.

PESKETT, Timothy Roper 36 Bron Deg, Dyserth, Rhyl LL18 6BG — MB BCh 1982 Wales; DCH RCP Lond. 1986.

PESTELL, Anne Main Street Surgery, 45 Main Street, Willerby, Hull HU10 6BP Tel: 01482 652652 — MB BS 1983 Newc.

PESTON, Samantha Aydit 48 The Reddings, London NW7 4JR.— MB ChB 1997 Manch.

PESTRIDGE, Andrew David 8 Charlton House Court, Charlton Marshall, Blandford Forum DT11 9NT — BM 1993 Soton.

PETANGODA, Gamini Dogsthorpe Medical Centre, Poplar Avenue, Peterborough PE1 4QF — MBBS 1972 (Ceylon). (Univ. of Ceylon) GP Princip., P'boro.

PETCH, Edward William Adrian West London Mental Health NHS Trust, The Three Bridges Unit, Uxbridge Road, Southall UB1 3EU Tel: 020 8354 8874 Fax: 020 8354 8877 Email: edward.petch@ehf-tr.nthames.nhs.uk — MB BS 1990 Lond.; MSc Lond. 1995; MRCPsych 1995; DFP 1997; Dip.Criminol. Lond.1999. (Royal Free Hospital School of Medicine) Cons. (Foren. Psychiat.) W. Lond. Ment. Health NHS Trust, Lond. Prev: Sen. Regist. (Forens. Psychiat.) Maudsley Hosp. Lond.

***PETCH, Matthew John** 32 Partridge Close, The Country Park, West Derby, Liverpool L12 0SQ — MB ChB 1998 Liverp.; BSc (Hons) 1993.

PETCH, Michael Charles, OBE Cardiac Unit, Papworth Hospital, Cambridge CB3 8RE Tel: 01480 364351 Fax: 01223 302858 Email: janet.barrett@papworth-tranglex.nhs.uk; 20 Brookside, Cambridge CB2 1JQ Tel: 01223 365226 Fax: 01223 302858 — MB BChir 1965 Camb.; MA Camb. 1966, MD 1977; FRCP Lond. 1980, M 1967. (St. Thos.) Cons. Cardiol. Papworth Hosp. NHS Trust; Assoc. Lect. Camb. Univ. Socs: Fell. Europ. Soc. Cardiol.; Fell. Amer. Coll. Cardiol.; Brit. Cardiac Soc. Prev: Sen. Regist. (Med.) Nat. Heart Hosp. Lond.; Regist. (Med.) & Ho. Phys. St. Thos. Hosp. Lond.

PETCHEY, David Rodney (retired) 151 Ellesmere Road, Shrewsbury SY1 2RA Tel: 01743 241754 Email: david@petcheyd.fsnet.co.uk — MB ChB Manch. 1959. Prev: GP Shrewsbury.

PETER, Antonypillai Manuelpillai The Medical Centre, 144-150 High Road, London NW10 2PT Tel: 020 8459 5550 Fax: 020 8451 7268; Chartwell, 2B Sudbury Hill Close, Sudbury, Wembley HA0 2QR — MB BS 1973 Sri Lanka; MRCOG 1985.

PETER, Beverly Maralyn Tel: 020 8863 3333; Tel: 020 8866 6739 Fax: 020 8866 6739 — MB BS 1974 Lond.; MRCS Eng. LRCP Lond. 1974; MRCGP 1980; DCH Eng. 1977; DRCOG 1976. (Westm.) Assoc. GP N.wick Pk. Hosp. Harrow; Tutor (Gen. Pract.) UCL Sch. Med.; Mem. Harrow Area Child Protec. Comm.; Facilitator (Gen. Pract.) Imperial Coll. Sch. of Med.; Sen. Lect. Imperial Coll. Fac. of Med. Prev: Trainee GP N.wick Pk. (Harrow) VTS; Ho. Phys. W.m. Hosp. Lond.; Ho. Surg. St. Luke's Hosp. Guildford.

PETER, Judith 21 Langley Avenue, Surbiton KT6 6QN — State Exam Med. Munich 1987.

PETER, Justin Luke Timothy Millway Medical Practice, Hartley Avenue, Mill Hill, London NW7 2HX Tel: 020 8959 0888 Fax: 020

8959 7050 — MB BS 1992 Lond.; BSc BioMedSci. (1st cl. Hons.) Lond. 1989.

PETER, Leonard Harold The Medical Centre, 45 Enderley Road, Harrow Weald, Harrow HA3 5HF Tel: 020 8863 3333 Fax: 020 8901 3307 Email: leonard.peter@gp-e84009.nhs.uk — MB BS 1974 Lond.; MRCGP 1978; DRCOG 1977; DCH Eng. 1976. (King's Coll. Hosp.) Prev: Trainee GP N.wick Pk. Hosp. VTS; Ho. Phys. King's Coll. Hosp. Lond.; Ho. Surg. Roy. Surrey Co. Hosp. Guildford.

PETER, Michael William Littlebury Medical Centre, Fishpond Lane, Holbeach, Spalding PE12 7DE Tel: 01775 22231/22054 — MB BS 1967 Lond. (King's Coll. Hosp.) Socs: BMA. Prev: Med. Off. RAF; Ho. Phys. Gen. Med. Freedom Fields Hosp. Plymouth; Ho. Surg. (Ophth.) King's Coll. Hosp. Lond.

PETER, Thankamma 16 Chestnut Avenue, Langley, Slough SL3 7DE — MB BS 1976 Kerala.

PETERKIN, Conon William Grant Group Practice Surgery, Green Street, Forfar DD8 3AR Tel: 01307 462316 Fax: 01307 463623; 44 Brechin Road, Kirriemuir DD8 4DD Tel: 01575 575232 Fax: 01575 57239 Email: wpeterkin@cmpuserve.com — MB ChB Ed. 1967; MRCGP 1978; DObst RCOG 1970. (Ed.) Socs: Forfarshire Med. Assn. Prev: Ho. Off. Roy. Infirm. Edin.; SHO (Obst.) & Ho. Off. W.. Gen. Hosp. Edin.

PETERKIN, Douglas Brock, MBE (retired) — MB ChB Ed. 1937; MD (Commend.) Ed. 1947; MRCGP 1962. Prev: Ho. Phys. Profess. Unit W.. Gen. Hosp. Edin.

PETERKIN, Gordon Stuart David Graupiam Primary Care Trust, Summerfield House AB17 Tel: 01224 557860 Email: gordon.peterkin@gpct.nhs.scot.uk; Thistlecroft, Carseburm, Forfar DD8 3NJ Tel: 01307 63556 — MB ChB 1971 Glas.; FRCP 2000; FRCGP 1997; MRCP (U.K.) 1974; MRCGP 1977. Med. Director Graupiam Primary Care Trust; Hon.Sen.Lect. dept of GP,Univ. of Aberd. Socs: Scott. Assoc of Community Hosps,Comm. Mem. (Past Secy).

PETERKIN, Myrtle Ann Glasgow & West Scotland Blood Transfusion Service, Law, Carluke ML8 5ES Tel: 01698 373315 Fax: 01698 356770; 83 Hyndland Road, Hyndland, Glasgow G12 9JE Tel: 0141 339 8359 — MB BS W. Indies 1974; FRCPath 1996; MRCPath (Haemat.) 1985. (Univ. W. Indies) Cons. Glas. & W. Scotl. Blood Transfus. Serv.; Hon. Clin. Sen. Lect. Univ. Glas. Socs: Brit. Blood Transfus. Soc.; Internat. Soc. Blood Transfus. Prev: Sen. Regist. & Regist. Glas. & W. Scot. Blood Transfus. Serv.

PETERMANN, Astrid Gabriele 56 Melbreck, Skelmersdale WN8 6SZ — State Exam Med 1986 Marburg; FRCS Glas. 1993. SHO (Gen. Surg.) Leicester Gen. Hosp.

PETERS, Professor Adrien Michael Nuclear Medicine, Addenbrookes hospital, Hills rd, Cambridge CB2 2QQ Tel: 01223 217147 Fax: 01223 586671 Email: nina.hedderick@msexc.addenbrookes.anglox.nhs.uk; 32 Station Road, Waterbeach, Cambridge CB5 9HT — MB ChB 1970 Liverp.; BSc (Physiol.) Lond. 1967, MSc (Nuclear Med.) 1987; MD Liverp. 1974; MRCP (UK) 1993; FRCPath 1996, M 1984; FRCR 1995; FRCP 1997. Nuclear Med., Camb. Univ. Socs: Hon. Mem. Brit. Inst. Radiol.; Brit. Nuclear Med. Soc.; Soc. Nuclear Med. Prev: Prof. Diagn. Radiol. Hammersmith Hosp. Lond.; Prof.(Diagn. Radiol.) Imperial Coll. Med. Sch.

PETERS, Alexander John (retired) 7 New Edinburgh Road, Uddingston, Glasgow G71 6BT Tel: 01698 813662 — MB ChB 1956 Glas.; DPH Glas. 1965. Sen. Med. Off. Sch. Health Serv. Gtr. Glas. HB.

PETERS, Anthony Russell (retired) William Budd Health Centre, Leinster Avenue, Bristol BS4 1NL Tel: 0117 963 6201 — MB ChB 1965 Bristol.

PETERS, Antoinette Jeyarahini 9 Burdett Avenue, London SW20 0ST Tel: 020 8241 8715 — MB BS 1966 Ceylon; DPM Eng. 1978. Staff (Psychiat.) W. Lambeth. Community Care Trust.

PETERS, Barry Stephen Harrison Wing, St. Thomas' Hospital, Lambeth Palace Road, London SE1 7EH Tel: 020 7928 9292 Fax: 020 7922 8291 Email: barry.peters@gstt.sthames.nhs.uk — MD 1994 Lond.; MB BS 1979; MRCP (UK) 1985; FRCP Lond. 1998. (St. Bartholomew's) Sen. Lect & Hon. Cons. (Genitourin. Med. & HIV) GKT Med. Sch. Socs: Med. Soc. Study VD; Assn. Genitourin. Med.; Exec. Mem. Brit. HIV Assn. Prev: Lect. (Genitourin. Med. & Communicable Dis.) St Mary's Hosp. Lond.

*PETERS, Catherine Jane 39 Willifield Way, London NW11 7XU — MB BS 1994 Lond.

*PETERS, Catherine Jane 37 Blake Hill Crescent, Lilliput, Poole BH14 8QP — MB ChB 1995 Birm.; ChB Birm. 1995.

PETERS, Charles Douglas, VRD 34 Combe Road, Combe Down, Bath BA2 5HY Tel: 01225 833605 Email: cdpeters@ukhome.net — MB BS Lond. 1949; MRCS Eng. LRCP Lond. 1949; DObst RCOG 1954. (Char. Cross) Prev: Hon. Phys. to HM the Qu.; Surg. Capt. RNR; Asst. Cas. Off. & Ho. Phys. Char Cross Hosp. Lond.

*PETERS, Christine Jennifer 5 Iona Street, Edinburgh EH6 8SG — MB ChB 1998 Ed.; MB ChB Ed 1998.

PETERS, Colin 18 Wemyss Drive, Blackwood, Cumbernauld, Glasgow G68 9NP — MB ChB 1998 Glas.; MB ChB Glas 1998.

PETERS, Colin George Anaesthetic Department, New Cross Hospital, Wolverhampton WV10 0QP Tel: 01902 307999 — MB ChB 1973 Manch.; FFA RCS Eng. 1977. Cons. Anaesth. Wolverhampton AHA; Dir. Wolverhampton Pain Relief Clinic. Socs: Assn. Anaesth.; The Pain Soc. Prev: Sen. Regist. (Anaesth.) Sheff. Higher Prof. Train. Scheme; Regist. (Anaesth.) Bristol Gen. Prof.ial Train. Scheme; SHO (Anaesth.) Salford AHA.

PETERS, David Marylebone Health Centre, 17 Marylebone Road, London NW1 5LT — MB ChB 1971 Manch. (Manchester) Sen. Lect. (Community Care Primary Health) Univ. of W.minster; Dir. Complementary Ther. Unit Marylebone Health Centre. Socs: Fac. Homoeop.; Brit. Holistic Med. Assn. Prev: Sen. Research Fell St Mary's Waites Project; Lect. (Gen. Pract.) St Mary's.

PETERS, David John, RD Avisford Medical Group, North End Road, Yapton, Arundel BN18 0DU Tel: 01243 551321 Fax: 01243 555101 — MB BChir 1968 Camb.; MA, BChir 1967; MRCS Eng. LRCP Lond. 1967; DObst RCOG 1971. (Camb. & Guy's) Med. Off. Ford Prison. Socs: Anglo-German Med. Soc. Prev: SHO (Cas.) St. Richard's Hosp. Chichester; Ho. Surg. (Thoracic Med.) Guy's Hosp.; Ho. Phys. Addenbrooke's Hosp. Camb.

PETERS, Professor Sir David Keith University of Cambridge School of Clinical Medicine, Addenbrooke's Hospital, Hills Road, Cambridge CB2 2SP Tel: 01223 336738 Fax: 01223 336721 — MB BCh 1961 Wales; FRS 1995; FRCP Ed. 1995; FRCP Lond. 1975; MRCP (UK) 1964; FRCPath 1991. Regius Prof. of Physic Univ. Camb.; Hon. Cons. Phys. Addenbrooke's Hosp. Camb. Prev: Prof. Med. Roy. Postgrad. Med. Sch. Hammersmith Hosp. Lond.; Reader (Med.) Roy. Postgrad. Med. Sch. Lond.; Lect. (Med.) & Hon. Cons. Phys. Roy. Postgrad. Med. Sch. Hammersmith Hosp. Lond.

PETERS, Diogu Arulanandam (retired) 9 Burdett Avenue, London SW20 0ST Tel: 020 8241 8715 — MB BS 1954 Ceylon; MRCPsych 1972; DPM Eng. 1966. Prev: Cons. Psychiat. Health Serv. Sri Lanka.

PETERS, Edward John The Surgery, 148 Forton Road, Gosport PO12 3HH Tel: 023 9258 3333 Fax: 023 9260 1107 — MB BS 1977 Lond.; MRCS Eng. LRCP Lond. 1977; MRCGP 1987; DRCOG 1981. GP Gosport.

PETERS, Elizabeth Eileen (retired) 67 Tor Bryan, Ingatestone CM4 9HN Tel: 01277 353998 Fax: 01277 355497 — MB ChB 1960 Glas.; FRCPath 1991, M 1979. Prev: Cons. Histopath. & Cytol. Basildon & S.end Hosps.

PETERS, Eric (retired) Leacroft, 19 St John's Road, Stafford ST17 9AS Tel: 01785 223516 — MB ChB Birm. 1955. Prev: GP Stafford.

PETERS, Esmeralda Margery 60 Audley Road, London NW4 3HB — MB BS 1993 Lond.

*PETERS, Francesca Hedda 27 Castle Road, Colchester CO1 1UW — MB ChB 1997 Liverp.

PETERS, Gerald 65 Thames Drive, Leigh-on-Sea SS9 2XQ — MB BS 1971 Lond.; MRCS Eng. LRCP Lond. 1971; DObst RCOG 1973. (Guy's) Prev: SHO (Path.) & Ho. Surg. Greenwich Dist. Hosp.; Ho. Surg. (O & G) Glos. Roy. Hosp.

*PETERS, Gordon 7 1F1 Rankeillor Street, Edinburgh EH8 9JA — MB ChB 1998 Ed.; MB ChB Ed 1998.

PETERS, Graeme Kearley Clare House Practice, Clare House Surgery, Newport Street, Tiverton EX16 6NJ Tel: 01884 252337 Fax: 01884 254401; The Old Vicarage, Cove, Tiverton EX16 7RX Tel: 01398 31859 — MB ChB 1977 Bristol; MRCP (UK) 1981; MRCGP 1988; DRCOG 1988. Princip. in Gen. Pract. Clare Ho. Tiverton; Hosp. Practitioner Gen. Med. Tiverton & Dist. Hosp.; Med. Off. Blundell's Sch. Tiverton; Endoscopist Tiverton & Distmct Hosp.

PETERS

Socs: Roy. Coll. Phys.; Med. Off.s Sch.s Assn.; Devon & Exeter Med. Soc.

PETERS, Helen 107 Egerton Street, Wallasey CH45 2LS — MB ChB 1992 Birm.

PETERS, Henry Gordon The Medical Centre, Bulford, Wellington TA21 8PW Tel: 01823 663551 Fax: 01823 660650; Burts House, Wellington TA21 9PG Tel: 01823 662820 — MB BS 1960 Lond.; BSc (Anat.) Lond. 1956; MRCS Eng. LRCP Lond. 1960; MRCGP 1978. (Univ. Coll. Hosp.)

PETERS, Henry John 72 Hartburn Lane, Stockton-on-Tees TS18 4EW Tel: 01642 678660 — MB BS 1930 Durh.; BHyg., DPH 1936; DPA Lond. 1946. (Durh.) Assoc. MOH Co. Boro. Tees. Socs: Fell. Soc. MOH; FRSH. Prev: MOH Stockton-on-Tees; MOH & Sch. Med. Off. Leigh; Asst. MOH, Asst. Tuberc. Off. & Sen. Sch. Med. Off. Co. Boro. Gateshead.

PETERS, Janet Anne 67 Falcon Court, Edinburgh EH10 4AG Tel: 0131 447 6531 — MB ChB 1959 Ed.; MFCM 1974; DCH Eng. 1962; DObst RCOG 1962. SCMO S. W. Edin. Lothian Health Bd. Prev: SCMO Forth Valley Health Bd.

PETERS, Jean Mair 22 Mustow Place, London SW6 4EL — MB BCh Wales 1961; MRCS Eng. LRCP Lond. 1962; MCOphth 1990; DO Eng. 1975. (Welsh Nat. Sch. Med.) Med. Pract. (Ophth.) Surrey; Med. Pract. (Ophth.) Surrey. Socs: Med. Contact Lens & Ocular Surface Assn. Prev: Assoc. Specialist (Ophth.) W.. Eye Hosp. & St. Mary's Hosp. Lond.; Assoc. Specialist Char. Cross Hosp. Lond.; Clin. Asst. Cardiff Roy. Infirm. & Birm. & Midl. Eye Hosp.

PETERS, Joanne West Street Surgery, 89 West Street, Dunstable LU6 1SF Tel: 01582 664401 Fax: 01582 475766 — MB BS 1981 Newc.; MRCGP 1985; DRCOG 1984.

PETERS, John Gerard 31 Acres Lane, Stalybridge SK15 2JR — MB BCh BAO 1987 NUI; LRCPSI 1987.

PETERS, Mr John Leslie 67 Tor Bryan, Ingatestone CM4 9HN; 27 Lewin Road, East Sheen, London SW14 8DR Tel: 020 8392 2314 Fax: 020 8392 2626 Email: jlp1966@aol.com — MB BS 1991 Lond.; BSc Lond. 1988; FRCS Eng. 1995. Specialist Regist. W. Lond. Urol. Scheme. Socs: RSM; EAU; BAUS. Prev: Regist. (Urol. & Gen. Surg.) W. Middlx. Univ. Hosp. Lond.

PETERS, John Redmond Department of Medicine, University Hospital of Wales, Heath Park, Cardiff CF14 4XW Tel: 029 2074 2344 Fax: 029 2074 4581; 24 Ty Draw Road, Roath Park, Cardiff CF23 5HB Tel: 029 2049 6410 — MB BCh 1972 Wales; BSc (1st cl. Hons.) Wales 1969, MD 1980, MB BCh 1972; FRCP Lond. 1989; MRCP (UK) 1974. Cons. Phys. Univ. Hosp. Wales Cardiff. Prev: Lect. (Med.) Welsh Nat. Sch. Med. Card.; Wellcome Research Fell. & Hon. Sen. Regist. MRC Unit Dept. Clin. Pharmacol. Radcliffe Infirm. Oxf.

PETERS, Jonathan Morland Surgery, 40 New Road, Tadley RG26 3AN Tel: 0118 981 6661; Hedgerows, 1B Church Road, Tadley, Basingstoke RG26 3AU — BM 1983 Soton.; AFOM 2001; MRCGP 1987; DRCOG 1987. Gen. Practitioner; Occupat.al Phys.

PETERS, Mr Joseph Lennox Highfield, Little Widbury Lane, Ware SG12 7AU Tel: 01920 466349 Fax: 01920 486783 Email: josephpeters@btinternet.com; Highfield, Little Widbury Lane, Ware SG12 7AU Tel: 01920 466349 Fax: 01920 486783 Email: josephpeters@btinternet.com — MB BS 1969 Lond.; BSc (Hons. Physiol.) Lond. 1967; FRCS Eng. 1975. (Univ. Coll. Hosp.) Cons. Surg., The P.ss Alexandra Hosp., Harlow, Essex. Socs: Fell. Roy. Soc. Med.; Fell. Assn. of Surg.s; Fell. Assn. of Colo-Proctol. of Gt. Britain and Irel. Prev: Resid. Asst. Surg. Univ. Coll. Hosp. Lond.; Sen. Surg. Regist. Middx. Hosp. Lond.; Resid. Surg. Off. Brompton Hosp. Lond.

PETERS, Julia Jane Riverside Surgery, 48 Worthing Road, Horsham RH12 1UD Tel: 01403 262700 Fax: 01403 275158 — MB BS 1974 Lond.; MB BS Lond 1974.

PETERS, Lesley Anne Drugs North W., Mental Health Services of Salford, Bury New Road, Prestwich, Manchester M25 3BL Tel: 0161 772 3694 Fax: 0161 772 3595 — MB ChB 1989 Ed. (Edinburgh) Clin. Res. Fell.

PETERS, Margaret Wallace Leacroft, 19 St Johns Road, Rowley Park, Stafford ST17 9AS Tel: 01785 223516 — MB ChB 1955 Birm.; DA Eng. 1966. (Birm.) Benefits Agency Med. Servs. Prev: Assoc. Specialist (Anaesth.) Stafford Dist. Hosp.; Ho. Surg. Qu. Eliz. Hosp. Birm.; Ho. Phys. Noble's I. of Man Hosp. Douglas.

PETERS, Mark John 55 Battlefield Road, St Albans AL1 4DB — MB ChB 1989 Bristol.

PETERS, Martin Godfrey (retired) Basildon & Thurrock Occupational Health Service, Basildon Hospital, Nethermayne, Basildon SS16 5NL Tel: 01268 280585 Fax: 01268 534127 — MB BS 1959 Lond.; MRCS Eng. LRCP Lond. 1959; FFOM RCP Lond. 1995; DObst RCOG 1960. Dir. Basildon & Thurrock Dept. Occupat. Health & Safety; JP.; Med. Off. Various Ltd. Companies; Occupat. Health Adviser MGP Consults. Ltd. Lond.; Hon. Lect. (Occupat. Health) Barking Coll. Technol. Prev: Employm. Med. Adviser EMAS.

PETERS, Martin John 204 Yoxall Road, Shirley, Solihull B90 3RN — MB BS 1987 West Indies; MRCP (UK) 1994.

PETERS, Michael Arthur 17 Milestone Road, Knebworth SG3 6DA — MB ChB 1988 Leeds; BSc Leeds 1985. Prev: Ho. Off. (Surg.) Dewsbury Dist. Hosp.; Ho. Off. (Med.) Leeds Gen. Infirm.

PETERS, Michael David 111 Adelaide Road, London NW3 — MB BS 1974 Lond.

PETERS, Nicholas John Monrad 69 Bury Road, Gosport PO12 3PR Tel: 02392 580363; 70 Newtown Road, Warsash SO31 9GB Tel: 01489 573360 — BM 1978 Soton.; DFFP 1995. Gen. Practitioner in Gosport at Bury Rd. Surg. Prev: Trainee GP Is. of Thanet VTS; SHO Rotat. (Surg.) Yeovil Dist. Hosp.; Ho. Surg. & Ho. Phys. Soton. Gen. Hosp.

PETERS, Nicholas Simon St Marys hospital, Praed St, London W2 1NY Tel: 020 7886 2468 Fax: 020 7886 1763 Email: n.peters@ic.ac.uk — MD 1994 Lond.; MB BS 1984; MRCP (UK) 1987; FRCP 1999 FRCP 1999. Prof. of Cardiol. St Marys Hosp. Lond.; Adj Prof. of Pharmacol., Columbia Univ., New York USA.

PETERS, Norman 119 Friern Barnet Lane, London N20 0XZ Tel: 020 8366 2122 — MB BS 1958 Lond.; FRCP Lond. 1977, M 1963; MRCS Eng. LRCP Lond. 1958. (St. Geo.) Cons. Phys. Chase Farm Hosp. Enfield. Socs: Brit. Diabetic Assn. Prev: Sen. Regist. (Med.) & Ho. Phys. St. Geo. Hosp. Lond.; Resid. Med. Off. Brompton Hosp.

PETERS, Roderick Michael 55 Clancarty Road, Fulham, London SW6 3AH Tel: 020 7736 7256 Fax: 020 7736 7256 Email: rodpeters@msn.com; Weavers, Ewhurst Green, Cranleigh GU6 7RR Tel: 01483 278481 Fax: 020 7736 7256 — MB BS Lond. 1966; MSc (Occupat. Med.) Lond. 1978; MRCP (UK) 1970; MRCS Eng. LRCP Lond. 1966. (St. Geo.) Prev: Specialist Phys. Brunei Shell Petroleum Ltd., Brunei.

PETERS, Samuel Boyd Ian Charles Cottage Hospital, The Health Centre, Castle Road East, Grantown-on-Spey PH26 3HR Tel: 01479 872484 Fax: 01479 873503; 6 Anagach Hill, Old Spey Bridge, Grantown-on-Spey PH26 3NF Tel: 01479 873700 — MB BCh BAO 1988 Belf.; MRCGP 1992.

PETERS, Seija Erica 87 Riccarton Road, Linlithgow EH49 6HX — MB ChB 1993 Glas.

PETERS, Sharon Elizabeth Hobs Moat Medical Centre, Ulleries Road, Solihull B92 8ED Tel: 0121 742 5517 Fax: 0121 743 4217; 5 Naseby Road, Solihull B91 2DR Tel: 0121 705 6843 — BM 1984 Soton; MRCGP 1988; DRCOG 1987; DCH RCP Lond. 1986. Prev: Asst. GP Birm. Doctors Retainer Scheme; Trainee GP Wythall; SHO (O & G) Selly Oak Hosp. Birm.

PETERS, Sheila Anne St Mary's Hospital, Milton Rd, Portsmouth PO3 6AD Tel: 02392 866102 Fax: 02392 866101 Email: sheila.peterson@smail01.porthosp.swest.nhs.uk — BM Soton. 1983; MRCP (UK) 1988; FRCPCH (UK) 1999. p/t Cons. Paediat. St. Mary's Hosp. Portsmouth. Prev: Sen. Regist. St. Mary's Hosp. Portsmouth.

PETERS, Stephen Academic Department of Psychiatry, Northern General Hospital, Herries Road, Sheffield S5 7AU Tel: 0114 226 1517; Oakwood, Lincoln Road, East Markham, Newark NG22 0SW — MB BS 1988 Lond.; MRCPsych 1993. Sen. Lect. (Psychiat.) Sheff. Univ.; Hon. Cons. Psychiat. Bassetlaw Hosp. Notts.

PETERS, Stephen Raymond 31 Fairfax Road, Leicester LE4 9EH — MRCS Eng. LRCP Lond. 1985.

PETERS, Professor Timothy John Department of Clinical Biochemistry, Kings College School of Medicine, Bessemer Road, London SE5 9PJ Tel: 020 7346 3008 Fax: 020 7737 7434 Email: timothy.peters@rcl.ac.uk — MB ChB 1964 (Hons) St. And.; MSc St. And. 1967; PhD. Lond. 1971; DSc St. And. 1986; FRCP Ed. 1981, M 1967; FRCP Lond. 1976, M 1968; FRCPath 1984, M 1980. (Univ. of St Andrews, Scotl.) Prof. & Head Clin. Biochem. King's Coll. Sch. Med. & Dent. Lond. - Assoc. Dean for Flexible Train. Lond. And Kent, Surrey and Sussex Deaneries; Cons. Chem. Path. & Phys. KCH Lond.; Edr. in Chief Addic. Biol.; Edit. Bd. Addic., Alcohol. Socs: Assn. Phys. Med. Research Soc. & Biochem. Soc.;

Counc. Mem. & Trustee Sir Richard Stapley Educat. Trust; Chairm. and Trustee, Area Concern. Prev: Head Div. Clin. Cell. Biol. MRC Clin. Research Centre Harrow; Sen. Lect. & Reader Roy. Postgrad. Med. Sch. Lond.; MRC Trav. Research Fell. The Rockefeller Univ. New York City, USA.

PETERS, Timothy Malcolm West Middlesex University Hospital NHS Trust, Twickenham Road, Isleworth TW7 6AF Tel: 020 8565 5826; 85 Hamlet Gardens, London W6 0SX Tel: 020 8741 2447 Email: tim.peters@btinternet.com — MB BS 1985 Lond.; MA Camb. 1982; FRCA 1994; MRCGP 1990; DCH RCP Lond. 1989; DA (UK) 1988. (Westminster) Cons. (Anaesth. & ITU) W. Middlx. Hosp. Lond. Socs: Assn. Anaesth.s; Eur. Soc. Regional Anaesth.; Intens. Care Soc. Prev: Sen. Regist. Rotat. (Anaesth.) Roy. Free Hosp. Lond.; Regist. (Anaesth.) Walsgrave Hosp. Coventry; Med. Off. Roy. Flying Doctor Serv. Broken Hill, Austral.

PETERS, Professor Wallace Northwick Park Institute for Medical Research, Tropical Parasitic Diseases Unit, Watford Road, Harrow HA1 3UJ Tel: 0208 869 3292 Fax: 0208 422 7136 Email: w.peters@ic.ac.uk — MB BS (Hons.) Lond. 1947; DSc Lond. 1976, MD 1966; FRCP Lond. 1978, M 1973; MRCS Eng. LRCP Lond. 1948; DTM & H Eng. 1950. (St. Bart.) Dir. Trop. Parasitic Dis.s Unit; Emerit. Prof. Med. Protozool. Univ. Lond. 1989 & Prof. 1979. Socs: Fell.. Roy. Soc. Med.; Fell. (Ex-Pres.) Roy. Soc. Trop. Med. Hyg.; BMA. Prev: Walter Myers Prof. Parasitol. Univ. Liverp.; Dean Liverp. Sch. Trop. Med.; Sen. Malariol. Territory of Papua & New Guinea.

PETERS, William Martin Department of Pathology, District General Hospital, Scartho Road, Grimsby DN33 2BA Tel: 01472 874111 Fax: 01472 875333 Email: martin.peters@nlg.nhs.uk — MB ChB 1977 Sheff.; MRC Pathology 1985; FRCPath 1995. (Sheffield) p/t Cons. Histopath. Grimsby Dist. Gen. Hosp. Prev: Sen. Regist. (Histopath.) Yorks. RHA.

PETERSEN, Jane Sara Flat 3/2, Glasgow Street, Hillhead, Glasgow G12 8JN — MB BS 1997 Newc.

PETERSEN, Katharine Sara 50 Brentwood Avenue, Newcastle upon Tyne NE2 3DH — MB BS 1993 Newc.

***PETERSEN, Lorraine Anne** 3 Alowick Drive, Maidenhead SL6 4JQ — BM BCh 1996 Oxf.

PETERSEN, Mark Erik Victor c/o Ward 13 Cardiology Office, Gloucester Royal Hospital, Great Western Road, Gloucester GL1 3NN Tel: 01452 528555; The Manor, Aston-on-Carrant, Tewkesbury GL20 8HL — MB BS 1984 Lond.; MB BS (Hons.) Lond. 1984; MRCP (UK) 1987. Cons. Phys. (Cardiol.) Glouc. Roy. NHS Trust.

PETERSON, Angus Cameron (retired) Dunham Cottage, 3 Blidworth Lodge, Rigg Lane, Mansfield NG21 0NX Tel: 01623 797145 — MB ChB Manch. 1958; FFA RCS Eng. 1965; DA Eng. 1962. Prev: Cons. Anaesth. N. (Manch.) Health Dist.

PETERSON, David Bernard Luton & Dunstable Hospital NHS Trust, Lewsey Road, Luton LU4 0DZ Tel: 01582 491122 — MB BChir 1975 Camb.; MA Camb. 1976, MD 1990; MRCP (UK) 1978; FRCP 1998. (Middlx.) Cons. Phys. (Gen. Med. & Diabetes) Luton & Dunstable Hosp.; Clin. Director of Med. Prev: Sen. Regist. Rotat. (Gen. Med.) St. Geo. Hosp. Lond.; MRC Train. Fell. & Hon. Sen. Regist. Oxf. HA; Regist. (Med.) Centr. Middlx. Hosp. Lond.

PETERSON, Mr David Charles Department of Neurosurgery, Charing Cross Hospital, Fulham Palace Road, London W8 8RF Tel: 020 8846 1186 Fax: 020 8846 7487 — MB BS 1985 Lond.; BSc Lond. 1982; FRCS (SN) 1994; FRCS Eng. 1989. Cons. Neurosurg. Char. Cross Hosp. & Chelsea & W.m. Hosp.

PETERSON, David John Maxwell Eynsham Medical Group, Conduit Lane, Eynsham, Witney OX29 4QB Tel: 01865 881206 Fax: 01865 881342; The Shrubbery, 26 High St, Eynsham, Witney OX29 4HB — MB BS Lond. 1969; MRCS Eng. LRCP Lond. 1969; MRCGP 1986. (Roy. Free) Med. Off. Boggles Racing Club. Prev: Sen. Resid. Med. Off. Roy. Free Hosp. Lond.; Resid. Amer. Hosp. Paris, France.

***PETERSON, Katharine Ann** Balhaldie House, High St., Dunblane FK15 0ER — MB ChB 1997 Aberd.

PETERSON, Mark Maple House, 7 College Avenue, Leicester LE2 0JF; 23 Whitewell Drive, Upton, Wirral CH49 4PE — MB ChB 1991 Leic.

PETERSON, Pamela Louise 52 Bolton Drive, Glasgow G42 9DR — MB ChB 1993 Glas. SHO (Med.) Vict. Infirm. Glas.

***PETERSON, Sarah Elizabeth** 23 Earnsdale Avenue, Darwen BB3 1JW — MB BS 1998 Newc.; MB BS Newc 1998.

PETERSON, Mr Stephen 25 Ridgway Road, Kettering NN15 5AQ — MB ChB 1981 Liverp.; FRCS Ed. 1985; FRCR 1992. Sen. Regist. (Radiol.) N. Staffs. Hosp. & Roy. Shrewsbury Hosp.

***PETHEN, Samantha** 11 Poolmans Road, Windsor SL4 4PB — BM 1996 Soton.

PETHER, John Victor Sebastian (retired) The Old School, Church Lane, Kingston St Mary, Taunton TA2 8HR Tel: 01823 451311 — BM BCh 1959 Oxf.; MA Oxf. 1959; FRCPath 1979, M 1967; Dip. Bact. Lond 1966; DTM & H Eng. 1963. Prev: Dir. Pub. Health Laborat. Taunton.

PETHERAM, Christine Dorothy Five Lanes Farmhouse, Rhiwderin, Newport NP1 9RQ — MB BCh 1970 Wales.

PETHERBRIDGE, Sean Paul 26 Cliff Road, Welton, Lincoln LN2 3JJ Tel: 0410 407902 — MB BS 1997 Lond. (St George's Hosp. Med. Sch.) Psychiat. SHO, Coventry. Socs: BMA; MDU. Prev: A & E SHO, Kings Lynn.

***PETHERICK, Colin Samuel** 13 Beverley Close, Newtownards BT23 7FN — MB BCh BAO 1994 Belf.; BDS Belf. 1983.

PETHICA, Brian Damian 37 Shooters Hill, Pangbourne, Reading RG8 7EA Tel: 073 572643 — MB BS 1981 Lond.; MA Maths. Oxf. 1979; MRCGP 1985. (Univ. Coll. Hosp.) SHO (Anaesth.) W. Berks. HA. Prev: Trainee GP Oxf. VTS.

***PETILLON, Claudia Maria** 4 Station Street, Kibworth Beauchamp, Leicester LE8 0LN — BM BS 1997 Nottm.

PETIT, Christopher Gerard Curzon The Mill House, Buxted, Uckfield TN22 4DP Tel: 01826 733620 — MB BCh BAO 1955 Dub.; LM Rotunda 1956. (T.C. Dub.)

PETO, Professor Timothy Edward Alexander Nuffield Department Medicine, John Radcliffe Hospital, Headington, Oxford OX3 9DU Tel: 01865 220154 Fax: 01865 222962 Email: tim.peto@ndm.ox.ac.uk — BM BCh 1977 Oxf.; FRCPath 2000; DPhil Oxf. 1974, MA, BM BCh 1977; FRCP Lond. 1992; MRCP (UK) 1978. (Oxford) Cons. Phys. Infec. Dis. Nuffield Dept. Med. John Radcliffe Hosp. Oxf.; Prof. (Med.); Sec. MRC AIDS Therap. Trials Comm.; Chairm., interDept.al Acad. unit of Infec. Dis.s and microBiol. Socs: Brit. Infec. Soc.; Fell. Roy. Soc. Trop. Med.; Ass. Of Phys.s. Prev: Clin. Lect. Nuffield Dept. Med. John Radcliffe Hosp. Oxf.; MRC Train. Fell. & Wellcome Fell. Nuffield Dept. Med. Oxf.; SHO (Med.) Hammersmith Hosp. Lond.

PETRE, Henrietta Claire Gladstone Medical Centre, Fallingbostel BFPO 38; Caryhill House, Castle Cary BA7 7HL — MB BS 1993 Lond. GPVT RAMC. Prev: Ho. Off. Camb. Milit. Hosp. Aldershot; Ho. Off. St. Thos. Hosp. Lond.

PETRI, Gianfranco John James Paget Hospital, Lowestoft Road, Gorleston, Great Yarmouth NR31 6LA Tel: 01493 452699 Fax: 01493 452066 Email: john.petri@jpaget.nhs.uk — State Exam 1981 Naples; Specialist (Orthop.) Univ. Naples 1987; D.U. Hand & Upper Limb Surg Paris 1994. Cons. Orthop. Surg. James Paget Healthcare NHS Trust; Clin. Dir. Socs: Fell. BOA; A. O. Alumni; BMA. Prev: Cons. Orthop. Surg. Centre Hosp.ier de Macon, France.

PETRI, Michael Philip 28 Burlington Road, Swanage BH19 1LT Tel: 01929 425464 — MB BS 1977 Lond.; FRCP Ed. 1993; MRCP (UK) 1980; MRCS Eng. LRCP Lond. 1977. (Char. Cross) Prev: Cons. Phys. Poole Gen. Hosp.; Sen. Regist. (Gen. Med. & Geriat. Med.) Bath; Regist. (Cardiol. & Med.) Birm. Gen. Hosp.

PETRICCIONE DI VADI, Pierluigi University Hospital Lewisham, Lewisham High St., London SE13 6LH Tel: 020 8690 9127 Fax: 020 8333 3248 — State Exam 1978 Naples; Post Graduate Degree Endocrinology Naples 1981; Post Graduate training in Anaesthetic and Intensive Care Naples 1991. Cons. in Pain Managem. Unit Lewisham Hosp., Lond.; Hon. Cons., Dept. of Anaesth., Guy's & St Thos. Hosp. Trust, Lond. Socs: Europ. Acad. Anaesth.; Internat. Soc. Study Pain; Assn. Palliat. Med. Prev: Med. Advisor Europ. Research & Developm. Procter & Gamble Pharmaceut.; Locum Cons. Pain Relief Unit Guy's Hosp. Lond.; Regist. (Anaesth. & Intens. Care) A. Cardarelli Hosp. Naples, Italy.

PETRIDES, Simon Peter Blackberry Orthopaedic Clinic, Blackberry Court, Walnut Tree, Milton Keynes MK7 7PB Tel: 01908 604666 Fax: 01908 692711 Email: info@boc.powernet.co.uk — MB BS 1985 Lond.; Dip. Sports Med. Soc. Apoth Lond. 1991; Dip. Osteop 1988. Dir. Milton Keynes Sports Injury Clinic & Blackberry Orthop. Clinic. Socs: Coun.lor Brit. Inst. Musculoskeletal Med.; Brit. Assn.

PETRIE

Sport & Med.; Gen. Counc. & Register Osteop. Prev: Treas. Soc. Orthop. Med.; Med. Off. Everest Marathon.

PETRIE, Alan James 11 South Street, Greenock PA16 8TZ — MB ChB 1994 Glas.

PETRIE, Alison Margaret 2 Bradley Mews, Bradley Hall, Wylam NE41 8JL — BM BS 1989 Nottm.; MRCGP 1994; DCH RCP Lond. 1991.

PETRIE, Allyson Marie 11 South Street, Greenock PA16 8TZ — MB ChB 1992 Glas.

***PETRIE, Colin James** Sauchur Garden Cottage, Wadeslea, Elie, Leven KY9 1EA — MB ChB 1997 Aberdeen.

PETRIE, Gavin Ross Chest Unit, Ward 16, Victoria Hospital, Mayfield Road, Kirkcaldy KY2 5AH Tel: 01592 643355 Fax: 01592 647078; Mol Hall, Dewars Mill, St Andrews KY16 9TY — MB ChB 1971 Aberd.; FRCP Ed. 1985; MRCP (UK) 1974. Cons. Chest. Phys. Vict. Hosp. Kirkcaldy Fife. Socs: BTS; ATS; BRS. Prev: Research Fell. in Med. Aberd. Univ.; Regist. (Respirat. Dis.) S. Lothian Health Dist.; Sen. Regist. Glas. Roy. Infirm.

PETRIE, Gillian Alison Flat 2nd Left, 13 Naseby Avenue, Broomhill, Glasgow G11 7JQ — MB ChB 1996 Glas.

PETRIE, Graham Maxwell (retired) College Farmhouse, 2 Balsham Road, Fulbourn, Cambridge CB1 5BZ Tel: 01223 881429 Fax: 01223 882733 — MB BChir 1956 Camb.; MRCS Eng. LRCP Lond. 1955; FRCPsych 1983, M 1972; DPM Eng. 1970; DObst RCOG 1959. Prev: Cons. Psychiat. Addenbrooke's Hosp. Camb.

PETRIE, Henry Peterson Surrey Lodge Group Practice, 11 Anson Road, Victoria Park, Manchester M14 5BY Tel: 0161 224 2471 Fax: 0161 257 2264 — MB ChB 1984 Leic.; DRCOG 1987.

PETRIE, John Ross University Department of Medicine & Therapeutics, Gardiner Institute, Western Infirmary, Glasgow G11 6NT Tel: 0141 211 2000 Fax: 0141 339 2800 Email: jrpls@clinmed.gla.ac.uk; 24 Station Road, Bearsden, Glasgow G61 4AL Tel: 0141 942 9523 — MB ChB 1989 Ed.; PhD (Glasgow) 1997; BSc (Ed) 1987; MRCP (UK) 1992. Lect. (Diabetes & Endocrinol.) & Hon. Specialist Regist. Univ. Glas. Socs: Chairm. Brit. Hypertens. Research Gp. Prev: Clin. Research Fell. (Med. & Therap.) Univ. Glas.; Brit. Heart Foundat. Jun. Research Fell.

PETRIE, Kathryn (retired) College Farmhouse, Balsham Road, Fulbourn, Cambridge CB1 5BZ Tel: 01223 881429 — MB BS Lond. 1955. Prev: Clin. Asst. (Ophth.) Addenbrooke's Hosp. Camb.

PETRIE, Margaret Xanthe Patricia 126 Desswood Place, Aberdeen AB15 4DQ Tel: 01224 640537 — MB ChB Aberd. 1964. Med. Off. Diabetes & Rheumat. Foresterhill & Assoc. Hosps. Gp. Prev: Regist. Gastroenterol. Research Project Foresterhill & Assoc. Hosps. Gp.

PETRIE, Mark Colquhoun 126 Desswood Place, Aberdeen AB15 4DQ — MB ChB 1993 Ed.

PETRIE, Mary Agnes 45 Rosslyn Road, Bearsden, Glasgow G61 4DL — MB ChB 1971 Glas.

***PETRIE, Nicola Clare** First Floor Flat, 3 Vyvyan Terrace, Clifton, Bristol BS8 3DF Tel: 0117 974 1403 — MB ChB 1997 Bristol.

PETRIE, Paula Jane Bolton Hospitals, Mineria Road, Farnworth, Bolton BL4 0JR Tel: 01204 390390; 14 Copperfields, Chew Moor, Lostock, Bolton BL6 4HZ — MB ChB 1993 Ed.; MRCP Ed 1996. (Edinburgh) Staff Grade Stroke, Bolton Hosps., Bolton. Prev: Lect. Geriat.s, Hope, Manch.; Specialist Regist. Geriat. Hope, Manch.

PETRIE, Rachel Xanthe Ann Department of Psychiatry, University of Dundee, Ninewells Hospital, Dundee DD1 9SY Tel: 01382 660111 Ext: 33111 Fax: 01382 633923 Email: r.petrie@dundee.ac.uk; Northwest Cottages, Middlebank Farm, Westown, Perth PH2 7SX Tel: 01828 686769 — MB ChB 1991 Ed.; BSc (Hons.) Psychol. Ed. 1989; MRCPsych 1996. (Edinburgh Univ.) Sim Research Fell. (Psychiat.) Univ. Dundee. Prev: Regist. Tayside Psychiat. Train. Scheme.

PETRIE, Robert Alexander Neill, TD (Surgery) Walpole Court, 1A Park Road, Wallington SM6 8AW Tel: 020 8647 4485 — MRCS Eng. LRCP Lond. 1952; MA, MB BChir Camb. 1957. (Camb. & King's Coll. Hosp.) Maj. RAMC (V). Prev: Ho. Surg. ENT Dept. King's Coll. Hosp.

***PETRIE, Sarah Elizabeth** Homerton Hospital, Homerton Row, London E9 6SR Tel: 020 8510 5555 — MB BS 1998 Lond.; MB BS Lond 1998.

PETRIE, Sheena Edwards (retired) 4 Transy Place, Dunfermline KY12 7QN Tel: 01383 723622 — MB ChB 1962 Ed.; MFFP 1993;

DObst RCOG 1965. SCMO (Family Plann.) Fife HB. Prev: SHO (O & G) Roy. Infirm. Edin.

PETROPOULOS, Maria-Christina The Cheyne Developmental Service, Chelsea & Westminster Hospital, 369 Fulham Road, London SW10 9NH Tel: 020 8746 8000; Email: petromcj@doctors.org.uk — MB BS 1990 Lond.; MRCP (UK) 1995; DCH RCP Lond. 1992. (St. Geo. Hosp. Med. Sch.) Specialist Regist. Community Paediat., Chelsea and W.minster Hosp., Lond.; Specialist Regist. (Paediat.) N.wick Pk. Hosp. (1998-1999). Socs: Roy. Coll. of Paedatrics and Child Health (RCPCH); Brit. Assn. of Community Child Health (BACCH). Prev: Specialist Regist. Neurol./NeuroDisabil., Gt. Ormond St. Hosp., Lond. (1999-2001; Regist (Paediat.) Roy. Free Hosp (1996-1998); SHO (Neonat.) St. Geo. Hosp. Lond. (1995).

PETROS, Andranick Joseph Paediatric Intensive Care Unit, Great Ormond Street Hospital, London WC1 3JH — MB BS 1979 Lond.; FRCP 1998 uk. (Middlx.) Cons. Paediatric Intens. Care, Gt. Ormond St.

PETROU, Marios Sotiris 58 Sandgate House, Pembury Est., London E5 8JH — MB BS 1990 Lond.; BSc Lond. 1987.

PETROU, Petros Panoyiotis Crowndale Road Surgery, 53 Crowndale Road, London NW1 1TU Tel: 020 7387 7762 — MB ChB 1972 Leeds. (Leeds) Prev: Ho. Phys. (Gen. Med.) & Ho. Surg. Pontefract Gen. Infirm.

PETROVIC, Marko North Wales Health Authority, Preswylfa, Hendy Road, Mold CH7 1PZ Tel: 01352 744046 Fax: 01352 700043 — MB BS 1986 Lond.; FRCS Eng. 1992. Specialist Regist. (Pub. Health Med.) N. Wales HA.

PETRUS, Leonard Victor c/o Department of Radiology, Leeds General Infirmary, St George St., Leeds LS1 3EX; 51 Hollin Park Mount, Leeds LS8 2NP — MB ChB 1982 Ed.; MRCP (UK) 1985. Regist. (Diag. Radiol.) Leeds Gen. Infirm. Prev: Regist. & SHO (Gen. Med.) N. Tees Gen. Hosp.

PETT, Adrian Nicholas 21 Devonshire Avenue, Ripley DE5 3SS — MB BS 1985 Lond.; MRCGP 1988.

PETT, Raymond John (retired) Wisteria Lodge, 15 Millbourn Close, Winsley, Bradford-on-Avon BA15 2NN Tel: 01225 723477 — MB BS 1951 Lond.; MRCS Eng. LRCP Lond. 1951; MRCGP 1963; DCH Eng. 1955; DObst RCOG 1952.

PETT, Simon The Surgery, Grove Street, Petworth GU28 0LP Tel: 01798 342248 Fax: 01798 343987 — MB BS 1977 Lond.; MRCP (UK) 1980; MRCGP 1989; DRCOG 1983; DCH RCP Lond. 1981; DTM & H Lond 1981. (Middlx. Hosp.) Socs: Fell. Roy. Soc. Trop. Med. & Hyg.; Fell. Roy. Soc. Med. Prev: Research Fell. (Liver Dis. Childr.) King's Coll. Hosp. Lond.; Perinatal Research Fell. Hammersmith Hosp. Lond.; SHO (Med. & Neurol.) Soton. Gen. Hosp.

PETT, Stephen Jonathan Dental Surgery, 31 Bridge Avenue, Hammersmith, London W6 9JA Tel: 020 8748 5246 Fax: 020 8748 5248 — MB BS 1984 Lond.

PETTER, John Roger Coles Lane Health Centre, Coles Lane, Linton, Cambridge CB1 6JS Tel: 01223 891456 Fax: 01223 890033 — MB BChir 1987 Camb.; MA Camb. 1989; MRCGP 1992; DRCOG 1992; DGM RCP Lond. 1991. (Univ. Camb.)

***PETTERS, Sophie Catherine** 5 Eaton Place, Luton LU2 9LB — BM BS 1997 Nottm.

PETTERSON, Diane Margaret Consett Medical Centre, Station Yard, Consett DH8 5YA Tel: 01207 216116 Fax: 01207 216119 — MB ChB 1987 Liverp.; Cert. Family Plann. JCC 1990; DRCOG 1990.

PETTERSON, Jane Anne 232 Albany Road, Roath, Cardiff CF24 3RZ — MB BCh 1991 Wales; MRCGP 1995. SHO Anaesth. Newport.

PETTERSON, Louise Elaine 2nd Floor, East Wing, Homerton Hospital, Homerton Row, London E9 6SR Tel: 020 8510 8297 Fax: 020 8510 8716 Email: louise.petterson@chpct.nhs.uk — MB BS 1978 Monash; MRCPsych 1984; DPM Eng. 1983. (Univ. Monash) Cons. Rehabil. Psychiat. E. Lond. & The city Ment. health Serv.s NHS trust. Prev: Cons. Psychiat. S.. Psychiat. Servs. Network & Heatherton Hosp. Vict., Austral.

PETTERSON, Timothy Acorn Cottage, Iveston, Consett DH8 7TL — MB ChB 1986 Liverp.; BSc (Hons.) Liverp. 1982; MD Manch. 1995; MRCP (UK) 1991. Clin. Research Fell. (Geriat. Med.) Univ. Manch. Hope Hosp. Socs: Brit. Geriat. Soc.

PETTIFER, Brenda Jane Pettifer and Mok, Colville Health Centre, 51 Kensington Park Road, London W11 1PA Tel: 020 7727 4592

PETTY

Fax: 020 7221 4613 Email: pettmok@globalnet.co.uk — MB BS Lond. 1969; MRCS Eng. LRCP Lond. 1969. (Roy. Free) p/t Lect. (Gen. Pract.) Imperial Coll. Socs: RSM. Prev: Ho. Phys. (Endocrinol.) Roy. Free Hosp. Lond. (New End Br.); Ho. Phys. Roy. Free Hosp. Lond. (Lawn Rd. Br.); Ho. Surg. Whipps Cross Hosp. Lond.

PETTIFER, Claudia Fenella 18 Bassett Close, Bassett, Southampton SO16 7PE Tel: 02380 768470 — BM 1985 Soton.; DFFP 1993.

PETTIFER, Matthew William Coquet Medical Group, Amble Health Centre, Percy Drive, Amble, Morpeth NE65 0HD Tel: 01665 710481 Fax: 01665 713031; 1 Old Barns, Warkworth, Morpeth NE65 0TH Tel: 01665 710145 — MB BS 1989 Newc.; MRCGP 1993.

PETTIFER, Rachel Janet Anne 27 Lambourne Drive, Wollaton, Nottingham NG8 1GR Tel: 0115 985 4547 Email: rachel@japettifer.freeserve.co.uk — BM 1989 Soton.; DCH RCP Lond. 1993; FRCA Lond. 1997. Specialist Regist. (Anaesth.) Nottm & E. Midl. Socs: RCA; Assoc. of Anaesth. Prev: GCNO Fell. Clonfield Hosp. Leic.

PETTIFORD, Geoffrey Hugh 80 Keith Road, Bournemouth BH3 7DX Tel: 01202 514163 — MB 1966 Camb.; BChir 1965. (Guy's)

PETTIGREW, Mr Alastair Morrison ENT Department, Royal Infirmary, Stirling FK8 2AU Tel: 01786 434000; Tel: 01786 474275 Email: xpettigrew@aol.com — MB ChB Glas. 1968; FRCS Ed. 1973. Cons. Otolaryngol. Stirling Roy. Infirm.

PETTIGREW, Anna Frances Springburn Health Centre, 200 Springburn Way, Glasgow G21 1TR Tel: 0141 531 9611 Fax: 0141 531 6706; 617 Kilmarnock Road, Glasgow G43 2TH — MB ChB 1975 Glas.; BSc (Hons. Biochem.) Glas. 1972, MB ChB 1975. Prev: Clin. Asst. (Haemat. & Oncol.) Roy. Hosp. Sick Childr. Glas.

PETTIGREW, Anne Margaret Ardgowan Medical Practice, 2 Finnart Street, Greenock PA16 8HW Tel: 01475 888155 Fax: 01475 785060 — MB ChB 1974 Glas.; MFHom 1997; MFFP 1994. (Glas.) GP NHS Private Homoep. Pract. Prev: Trainee GP Kilbride VTS; SHO Rotat. (Med.) Gartnavel Gen. Hosp. Glas. & W.. Infirm. Glas.; Ho. Off. Roy. Hosp. Sick Childr. Glas.

PETTIGREW, Mr Gavin 41 Southbrae Drive, Jordanhill, Glasgow G13 1PU — MB ChB 1990 Glas.; FRCS Glas. 1994.

PETTIGREW, Naomi Margaret Elizabeth Eckford Cottage, 38 Broomieknowe, Lasswade EH18 1LN — MB ChB 1986 Manch.

PETTIGREW, Rachel Alyson Assisted Conception Unit, Department of Obstetrics and Gynaecology, St Thomas Hospital, Lambeth Palace Road, London SE1 7EH Tel: 020 7928 9292 ext 2773 Fax: 020 7633 0152 Email: r.pettigrew@umds.ac.uk — MB ChB 1992 Birm. Research Assoc. Reproductive Med. O & G St. Thos. Hosp. Lond.

PETTIGREW, Richard Christopher Bruce (retired) 5 Edale Avenue, Haslingden, Rossendale BB4 6QL — MB ChB Sheff. 1966; DObst RCOG 1968. Clin. Asst. in Rheum. & Rehabil. Med., Burnley Gen. Hosp., Burnley; Clin. Asst. in Rheum., Dept. of Rheum., Rochdale Infirm., Rochdale. Prev: Regist. (Psychiat.) Burnley Gen. Hosp.

PETTINGALE, Keith William Department of Health Care for the Elderly, GKT School of medicine, Kings College Hospital (Dulwich), East Dulwich Grove, London SE22 8PT Tel: 020 7346 6077 Fax: 020 7346 6476 Email: keith.pettingale@kcl.ac.uk; 32 Buckingham Close, Orpington BR5 1SA — MB BS 1964 Lond.; MD Lond. 1971; FRCP Lond. 1980, M 1966; MRCS Eng. LRCP Lond. 1964. (King's Coll. Hosp.) Guy's, Kings and St Thomas's (GKT) Sch. of Med.; Hon. Cons. Phys. KCH Lond. Socs: Assn. Palliat. Med.; Brit. Geriat. Soc.; Me.Brit.Psycho.Ssocial.Oncolog.Soc. Prev: Director of underGrad. studios kings Coll. Med. 95/98; Med. Dir. MacMillan Continuing Care Team Camberwell HA; Vis. Prof. Lund Univ. (Sweden) 1994.

PETTINGER, Andrew John Catherine House Surgery, New Walk, The Plains, Totnes TQ9 5HA Tel: 01803 862073 Fax: 01803 862056; Watsons, Belsford, Haberton, Totnes TQ9 7SP Tel: 01803 863687 — BM 1987 Soton. GP.

PETTINGER, Graham Devonshire Green Medical Centre, 126 Devonshire Street, Sheffield S3 7SF Tel: 0114 272 1626; 73 Hallam Grange Crescent, Fulwood, Sheffield S10 4BB — MB ChB 1984 Sheff.

PETTINGER, Mrs Rachel Bluebell Medical Centre, 356 Bluebell Road, Sheffield S5 6BS Tel: 0114 242 1406 Fax: 0114 261 8074 — MB ChB 1986 Sheff.

PETTIT, Andrew Ian 103 Knighton Church Road, Leicester LE2 3JN Email: pettite@lineone.net — MB ChB 1994 Leic.; MRCP 1998. Clin. Res. Fell. (Med. & Therap.) Univ. of Leic.

PETTIT, Barry The Upper Surgery, 27 Lemon Street, Truro TR1 2LS Tel: 01872 74931 Fax: 01872 260339; Summerville, Crescent Road, Truro TR1 3EP Tel: 01872 73222 — MB ChB 1969 Bristol; DA Eng. 1972; DObst RCOG 1971. Hosp. Pract. (Gastrointestinal Endoscopy) Roy. Cornw. Hosp. Truro. Prev: SHO (Anaesth. & Obst.) Treliske Hosp. Truro; Ho. Phys. Torbay Hosp. Torquay.

PETTIT, Derek Richard South Birmingham mental heath trust, Queen Elizabeth Pyschiatric hospital, Mindgone john Drive, Birmingham; 32 Cockshute Hill, Droitwich WR9 7QP Tel: 01905 774265 — MB ChB 1973 Birm.; BSc (Anat. 1st cl. Hons.) Birm. 1969; MRCGP 1979; DFFP 1994; DRCOG 1977; Cert. JCC Lond. 1978; MRCP MRCP Uk 1990. (Birm.) Clin. Asst. Adult Psychiat., Qu. Eliz. Psychiatric Hosp. Socs: Brit. Soc. Colpos. & Cerv. Path.; Fac. Pre-Hosp. Care; Brit. Med. ass. Prev: Med. Adviser SEMA Gp. Fiveways Complex Edgbaston, Birm.; GP Princip., Droitwich, Worcs; Regist. (Gen. Med.) Hollymoor Hosp. Birm.

PETTIT, Elizabeth Kirsty Fishponds Health Centre, Beechwood road, Fishponds, Bristol BS16 3TD — MB ChB 1993 Leic.; DRCOG 1997; MRCGP 1998. p/t GP Princip.

***PETTIT, James David** Coldbrook House, Hardwick, Abergavenny NP7 9BT — MB ChB 1997 Leeds.

PETTIT, Jane Rosina (retired) 83 Eastwood Road, Boston PE21 0PN Tel: 01205 369930 — MB ChB 1972 Leeds; MRCGP 1978; DCH Eng. 1976; DObst RCOG 1974.

PETTIT, John Gregory Gable House, 46 High Street, Malmesbury SN16 9AT Tel: 01666 825825; Pinkney Cottage, Pinkney, Malmesbury SN16 0NZ — BM 1987 Soton.; MRCGP 1993. (Univ. Soton.)

PETTIT, Katrina Erica Olivia 1 Claremont Street, Spital Tongues, Newcastle upon Tyne NE2 4AH — MB BS 1996 Newc.

PETTIT, Mark Linthorpe Road Surgery, 378 Linthorpe Road, Middlesbrough TS5 6HA Tel: 01642 817166 Fax: 01642 824094; Millfield House, Little Ayton Lane, Middlesbrough TS9 6HU — MB ChB Ed. 1968; DObst RCOG 1970. (Edinburgh)

PETTIT, Philippa Clare The Tolsey Surgery, High Street, Sherston, Malmesbury SN16 0LQ Tel: 01666 840270 Fax: 01666 841074 — BM 1987 Soton.; MRCGP 1993; DRCOG 1990. (Southampton)

PETTIT, Mr Stephen Harold Dept. of Surgery, Victoria Hospital NHS Trust, Whinney Heys Road, Blackpool FY3 8NR Tel: 01253 303564; 1 The Oaks, St. Michaels, Preston PR3 0TF — MB ChB 1976 Manch.; MA Oxf. 1977; ChM 1986; FRCS Ed. 1981; FRCS Eng. 1981; DRCOG 1978. (Manchester and Oxford) Cons. Gen. Surg. Vict. Hosp. Blackpool & Lytham Hosp. Prev: Sen. Regist. (Gen. Surg.) Manch. Roy. Infirm., Withington Hosp. Manch.& Hope Hosp. Salford.

PETTIT, Tor Angus Cheruiyot Lenzing Southwood Hospital, 70 Southwood Lane, Highgate Village, London N6 Tel: 020 8340 8778 — BM BCh 1994 Oxf.

PETTIT, William John 19 Cobbs Lane, Hough, Crewe CW2 5JN — MB ChB 1973 Manch.; MRCGP 1977; DObst RCOG 1975.

PETTITT, Andrew Royston Department of Haematology, Royal Liverpool University Hospital, Prescot St., Liverpool L7 8XP Tel: 0151 706 4343 Fax: 0151 706 5810 Email: andrew.pettitt@rlbuh-tr.nwest.nhs.uk — MB BChir 1989 Camb.; BA Camb. 1986; MRCP (UK) 1991; PhD 2000; MRCPath 2000. Sen. Lect. & Hon. Cons. (Haemat.) Roy. Liverp. Univ. Hosp. Prev: Regist. (Haemat.) Roy. Liverp. Univ. Hosp.; Lect. & Hon. Sen. Regist. (Haemat.) Roy. Liverp. Univ. Hosp.

PETTMAN, Jean Calvert (retired) 107 Northampton Road, Kettering NN15 7JY Tel: 01536 485799 — MB BS Durh. 1955.

PETTMAN, Sarah Barbara Bedford Road Surgery, 273 Bedford Road, Kempston, Bedford MK42 8QD Tel: 01234 852222 Fax: 01234 843558 — BM BCh 1987 Oxf.; MRCGP 1992; DRCOG 1991.

PETTY, Mr Alfred Holdsworth (retired) 7 Elmfield Park, Newcastle upon Tyne NE3 4UX Tel: 0191 285 1706 Email: ahv@onyxnet.co.uk — MB BS Durh. 1948; FRCS Eng. 1958. Prev: Cons. Surg. Newc. Gen. Hosp.

PETTY

*PETTY, Daniel Robert 15 Beech Hill, Hexham NE46 3AD — MB ChB 1994 Birm.; ChB Birm. 1994.

PETTY, David John Health Centre, Eaton Place, Bingham, Nottingham NG13 8BE Tel: 01949 837338; Greenhedge Farm, Thoroton Rd, Thoroton NG13 9DT — BM BS 1984 Nottm.; BDS Lond. 1976; LDS RCS Eng. 1977. (Nottm.) Prev: SHO Odstock Hosp. Salisbury; Ho. Surg. Salisbury Gen. Infirm.; Ho. Phys. York Dist. Hosp.

PETTY, Hugh Richard 32 Weymouth Street, London W1M 3FA Tel: 020 7352 6351 Fax: 020 7637 2109 — MB BChir 1965 Camb.; MA, MB Camb. 1965, BChir 1964; MRCS Eng. LRCP Lond. 1964. (Camb. & St. Bart.) Med. Dir. The Wellman Clinic & The Med. Centre Lond. Prev: Med. Adviser Roy. Commonw. Soc., Blick Internat. & other Cos.; Regist. & Resid. Med. Off. (Gen. Med. & Neurol.) Gen. Hosp. Rochford; Ho. Phys. St. Bart. Hosp. Lond.

PETTY, Jane Windhill Green Medical Centre, 2 Thackley Old Road, Shipley BD18 1QB Tel: 01274 584223 Fax: 01274 530182 — MB ChB 1990 Leeds; BSc (Hons.) Physiol. Lond. 1985; MRCGP 1995; DRCOG 1994; DFFP 1994. (Leeds) Neurol. Clin. Asst. Socs: BMA; Roy. Coll. Obst. & Gyn.; Roy. Coll. GP's.

PETTY, Laurence Gilbert 5 Hardy Road, Blackheath, London SE3 7NS — MB BS 1964 Lond.

PETTY, Martyn Glyn David Victoria Surgery, 5 Victoria Road, Holyhead LL65 1UD; Clydfan, Gorad Road, Valley, Holyhead LL65 3AT Tel: 01407 740706 — MB ChB 1986 Manch.; MB ChB Hons. Manch. 1986; BSc (Physiol.) Manch. 1982; DRCOG 1989; Cert. Family Plann. JCC 1989.

*PETTY, Melanie Joanne 145 Birmingham Road, Wylde Green, Sutton Coldfield B72 1LX — MB BS 1996 Lond.

PETTY, Richard Kenneth Holdsworth Institute of Neurological Science, Southern General Hospital, Glasgow G51 4TF Tel: 0141 201 1100 — MB BS 1978 Newc.; MD Newc. 1989; MRCP (UK) 1980; FRCP 1999. Cons. Neurol. S.. Gen. Hosp. Glas. Socs: Assn. Brit. Neurol.; World Muscle Soc. Prev: Lect. (Neurol. & Neurovirol.) Univ. Glas.

PETTY, Russell David 35 Gordondale Road, Midstocket, Aberdeen AB15 5LZ — MB ChB 1996 Dundee.

PETTY, William Harry 123 Church Road, Worle, Weston Super Mare BS22 9EL — MRCS Eng. LRCP Lond. 1942; MA Camb. 1942. (Guy's & Camb.) Prev: Asst. Surg. Regist. St. Bart Hosp. Rochester; Dep. Res. Surg. Off. King Edwd. Memor. Hosp. Ealing; Ho. Surg. Co. Hosp. Dartford.

PEUTHERER, John Forrest Department of Mewdical Microbiology, Medical School, Teviot Place, Edinburgh EH8 9AG Tel: 0131 650 3159 Fax: 0131 650 6531; 44 Bridge Road, Edinburgh EH13 0LQ Tel: 0131 441 1201 — MD 1975 Ed.; BSc Ed. 1957, MD 1975, MB ChB 1962; FRCP Ed. 1988 M 1986; FRCPath 1986, M 1975. Hon. Cons., Head of Dept. & Sen. Lect. Med. Microbiol. Edin. Univ. Med. Sch.

PEUTRELL, Jane Margaret 48 Victoria Crescent Road, Glasgow G12 9DE; Department of Anaesthetics, Royal Hospital For Sick Children, Yorkshill NHS Trust, Dalnair St., Glasgow G3 8SJ Tel: 0141 201 0000 Fax: 0141 201 0821 — MB BS Newc. 1982; MRCP (UK) 1985; FCAnaesth. 1989; DA (UK) 1986; FRCP Ed 1998. Cons. Paediat. Anaesth. Roy. Hosp. for Sick Childr. Yorkshill NHS Trust, Glas.

PEVELER, Professor Robert Charles UniversityMental Health Group, Royal South Hampshire Hospital, Brinitons Terrace, Southampton SO14 0YG Tel: 02380 825533 Fax: 02380 234243 — BM BCh 1982 Oxf.; MA Oxf. 1980, DPhil 1980; FRCPsych 1998. (Univ. Oxf.) Prof. & Cons. (Psychiat.) Univ. Dept. Psychiat. Soton.; Hon. Cons. W. Hants. NHS Trust. Prev: Clin. Lect. (Psychiat.) Univ. Dept. Psychiat. Oxf.; Wellcome Trust Research Fell. Univ. Dept. Psychiat. Oxf.; Regist. & SHO (Psychiat.) Oxf. HA.

PEVERLEY, Martin Christopher 63 Castledene Court, South Gosforth, Newcastle upon Tyne NE3 1NZ — MB BS 1989 Newc.

PEVERLEY, Philip Mark Griffin House, View Lane, Stanley, Crook DL15 — MB BS 1987 Newc.

PEXTON, Nigel Frederick Williamwood Medical Centre, 85 Seres Road, Clarkston, Glasgow G76 7NW Tel: 0141 638 7984 Fax: 0141 638 8827 — MB ChB 1985 Glas.; MRCGP 1990; DRCOG 1988.

PEYMAN, Michael Anthony 37B New Cavendish Street, London W1G 8JR Tel: 020 7735 7128 — BM BCh 1948 Oxf.; MA Oxf. 1950, DM 1957; MRCP Lond. 1950. (Oxf. & St. Thos.) Prev: Med. Adviser Brit. Home Stores Ltd; Clin. Asst. Med. Profess. Unit & Sen. Regist. (Med.) Char. Cross Hosp.; Evans Med. Research Fell. New Eng. Center Hosp. Boston, USA.

PEYSER, Edith Erna Charlotte (retired) Woodrow, Asheldon Road, Wellswood, Torquay TQ1 2QN Tel: 01803 299551 — Staatsexamen Univ. Berlin 1934.

PEYSER, Mr Paul Michael 7 Cedar Walk, 45 Romsey Road, Winchester SO22 5EU Tel: 01962 824575 — MB BS 1990 Lond.; BSc (Hons.) Lond. 1984; FRCS Eng. 1995. Career Regist. Rotat. (Gen. Surg.) S. Thames (W.) Roy. Hants. Co. Hosp. Winchester. Prev: SHO Rotat. Derriford Hosp. Plymouth.

PEYTON, Henry Newnham 10 Manor Road, Ipswich IP4 2UX Tel: 01473 57842 — MRCS Eng. LRCP Lond. 1939. (St. Bart.) Prev: Resid. W. Herts. Hosp.; Ho. Surg. King Edwd. Memor. Hosp. Ealing; RAMC 1940-46.

PEYTON, Mr James William Rodney, TD Beechlyn Court, Ballynorthland Park, Dungannon BT71 6DY Tel: 02887 727134 Fax: 02887 724255 Email: rpeyton@rpeyton.demon.co.uk — MB BCh BAO 1993 Belf.; MSc Cardiff 1995; BSc (Hons.) Belf. 1970, MD 1982; FRCS Eng. 1996; FRCSI 1993; FRCS Ed. 1978; MRCP (UK) 1975; FRCP Lond. 1997. (Queen's University, Belfast) Cons. Surg. S. Tyrone Hosp. Dungannon; Tutor (Educat.) RCS Eng.

PEYTON, Patricia Anne Hospital Hill Surgery, 7 Izatt Avenue, Dunfermline KY11 3BA Tel: 01383 731721 Fax: 01383 623352 — MB ChB 1973 Ed.

PEYTON-JONES, Benjamin 37 Swallowfields, Totnes TQ9 5LB — MB ChB 1996 Leic. SHO (O & G) Bath.

PEZESHGI, Djallilah Sadri 6 Roman Road, Bearsden, Glasgow G61 2SW — MRCS Eng. LRCP Lond. 1973; BA (Hon) Lond. 1984, MB BS 1974; DRCOG 1978. (St. Bart.) Prev: GP Soton.

PEZESHKIAN, Hratch Villa Armenia, 23 Mount Avenue, Ealing, London W5 1PZ — MD 1971 Iran; ECFMG Cert. 1984; FLEX Lic. (USA) 1984; DObst RCPI 1982.

PFANG, Jennifer Anne PO Box 900, Norwich NR2 3ER — MB BS 1988 Lond.

PFEFFER, Jeremy Michael 97 Harley Street, London W1N 1DF Tel: 020 7935 3878 Fax: 020 7935 3865; 84 Southover, London N12 7HD Tel: 020 8446 4475 — MB BS 1971 Lond.; BSc (Hons. Biochem.) Lond. 1968; FRCP Lond. 1990; MRCP (UK) 1974; FRCPsych 1988, M 1977. (Univ. Coll. Hosp.) Cons. Psychiat. & Hon. Sen. Lect. The Roy. Brompton Hosp. Socs: Fell. Roy. Soc. Med. Prev: Sen. Regist. (Psychiat.) The Maudsley Hosp. Lond.; Regist. (Chest Med.) Papworth Hosp. Camb.; Ho. Surg. Univ. Coll. Hosp. Lond.

PFEIFER, Christine Zdenka Crosby, Skene and Partners, College Way Surgery, Comeytrowe Centre, Taunton TA1 4TY Tel: 01823 259333 Fax: 01823 259336; Park Gate House, Ash Priors, Taunton TA4 3NF Tel: 01823 432122 — MB BS Lond. 1970; MRCGP 1977; Cert. JCC Lond. 1976; DCH Eng. 1974; DObst RCOG 1972. (St. Geo.) Family Plann. Doctor Som. HA. Prev: GP Nottm.; SHO (Obst.) Roy. Berks. Hosp. Reading; SHO (Anaesth.) Frenchay Hosp. Bristol.

PFEIFER, Peter Michael Anaesthetic Department, Robert Jones Agnes Hunt Orthopaedic Hospital, Oswestry SY10 7AG Tel: 01691 404000 Fax: 01691 404068; Ochr, The Llawnt, Rhydycroesau, Oswestry SY10 7HY Email: pfeiferp@rjahoh_trwmids.nhs.uk — MB BS 1978 Lond.; PhD (Biochem.) Liverp. 1969, BSc (Hons.) 1966; FFA RCS Eng. 1984. (St. Bart.) Cons. Anaesth. Robt. Jones & Agnes Hunt. Orthop. Hosp. Socs: Soc. for Computing & Technol. in Anaesth.; Free Radical Soc.; Brit. Soc. of Orthopaedic Anaesth.s. Prev: research fell. Oklahoma Med. Research Foundat. Oklahoma City, USA.

PFEIFFER, U Meldrum, Vitty and Pfeiffer, 40-42 Kingsway, Waterloo, Liverpool L22 4RQ Tel: 0151 928 8800 Fax: 0151 928 3775 Email: upfeiffer@rcsed.ac.uk — State Exam Med., Bonn 1981; Regis. Spec. in Gen. Surg. 1995; MD 1984 (Bonn); FRCS 1988 (Ed.); MRCGP 1994; DFFP 1995. (Bonn University, Guy's Hospital) GP Princip.

PFLANZ, Sebastian The Clinic, Mill Isle, Craignair Street, Dalbeattie DG5 4HE Tel: 01556 610331 — MB ChB 1988 Aberd.; BMedBiol. 1986; MRCP (UK) 1992; DRCOG 1994. Prev: Regist. (Med.) Dundee; SHO (Med.) Aberd.

PFLUG, Josef Johann Robert Swollen Limb Clinic, Royal Masonic Hospital, Ravenscourt Park, London W6 Tel: 020 8748 4611 — MUDr 1953 Charles Univ. Prague; MUDr Charles U, Prague

Czechoslovakia 1953; PhD 1971; FACS 1969. Cons. Surg. Phiebol. & Lymphol. Hammersmith Hosp. Lond.

PHADKE, Anil Sriram Bryncelyn Clinic Premises, Bryncelyn, Nelson, Treharris CF46 6HL Tel: 01443 450340 Fax: 01443 453127 — MB BS 1966 Calcutta; BA Open Univ. 1991. (Nat. Med. Coll. Calcutta)

PHADNIS, Sunil Gangadhar 26 The Bourne, London N14 6QS — MB BS 1975 Poona.

PHAIR, Mr Ivan Charles 8 Hampton Drive, Belfast BT7 3DE — MB BCh BAO 1980 Belf.; FRCS Ed. 1985.

PHALKE, Indrajit Madhavarao (retired) North Hampshire Hospitals NHS Trust, Aldermaston Road, Basingstoke RG24 9NA — MB BS Agra 1956; DMRE Vikram 1959; DMRD Eng. 1965. Prev: Cons. Radiol. P.ss Margt. Hosp. Swindon.

PHALP, Charles George Anderson Rother House Medical Centre, Alcester Road, Stratford-upon-Avon CV37 6PP Tel: 01789 269386 Fax: 01789 298742; Cherry Tree Cottage, Loxley, Warwick CV35 9JS Tel: 01789 842902 — MB ChB 1972 Birm.; MMedSci Birm. 1994; DObst RCOG 1974. Chairm. Warks. Health Auth. Strategy Comm. Socs: Roy. Soc. Med.

***PHAN, Phuong-Anh Thi** 40 Kelly Street, London NW1 8PH — MB BS 1997 Lond.

PHANJOO, Andre Ludovic 29 Blacket Place, Edinburgh EH9 1RJ Tel: 0131 667 9809 Fax: 0131 537 6112 Email: andrepha@cs.com — MB ChB 1966 Ed.; FRCPsych 1984, M 1972; DPM Ed. 1969. Cons. Psychiat. Roy. Edin. Hosp.; Clin. Dir. (c/o the Elderly) Roy. Edin. Hosp.; Hon. Sen. Lect. Fac. Med. Univ. Edin.

PHARAOH, Alice Mary The Old Dispensary, 32 East Borough, Wimborne BH21 1PL Tel: 01202 880786 Fax: 01202 880736; Corfe Cottage, Broadmoor Road, Corfe Mullen, Wimborne BH21 3RB Tel: 01202 693215 — MB BS 1972 Lond.; Cert. Family Plann. (St. Geo.) Clin. Asst. ESMI & Wimborne Community Hosp.; Mem. PCG. Socs: BMA. Prev: Clin. Asst. Lipid Clinic & Diabetic Clinic.

***PHARAOH, Amy Jane** Corfe Cottage, Broadmoor Road, Corfe Mullen, Wimborne BH21 3RB — BM BS 1998 Nottm.; BM BS Nottm 1998.

PHARAOH, James Mark Hadleigh House Medical Centre, 20 Kirkway, Broadstone BH18 8EE Tel: 01202 692268 Fax: 01202 658954; Corfe Cottage, Broadmoor Road, Corfe Mullen, Wimborne BH21 3RB Tel: 01202 693215 — MB BS 1971 Lond.; DA Eng. 1974; DObst RCOG 1973. (St. Geo.)

***PHARE, Alexis Jonathon** Longacre, Compton, Paignton TQ3 1TD — MB BCh 1996 Wales.

PHAROAH, Fiona Margaret Lifespan Healthcare NHS Trust, Block 14, The Ida Darwin Hospital, Fulbourn, Cambridge CB1 5EE Tel: 01223 884243; c/o 11 Fawley Road, Allerton, Liverpool L18 9TE — MB ChB 1991 Manch.; MA Camb. 1986; MRCPsych. Specialist Regist. (Gen. Psychiat.). Prev: Regist. Rotat. BRd.moor Hosp. Crowthorne; Regits. (Psychiat) Warneford Hosp.; SHO (Psychiat.) Fairmile Hosp. Oxon.

PHAROAH, Paul David Peter Strangeways Research Laboratories, Worts Causeway, Cambridge CB1 8RN Tel: 01223 740166 Email: paul.pharoah@slr.cam.ac.uk; 71 Hinton Avenue, Cambridge CB1 7AR — BM BCh 1986 Oxf.; PhD (CAMB) 2000; DPH (CAMB) 1993; MA (CAMB) 1986; MRCP (UK) 1990; MFPHM RCP (UK) 1995. Cancer Research Campaign Sen. Clin. Research Fell. & Hon. Cons. Pub. Health.

PHAROAH, Professor Peter Oswald Derrick Department of Public Health, University of Liverpool, Liverpool L69 3GB Tel: 0151 794 5577 Fax: 0151 794 5272 Email: p.o.d.pharoah@liverpool.ac.uk; 11 Fawley Road, Liverpool L18 9TE Tel: 0151 724 4896 — MB BS Lond. 1958; MSc Lond. 1974, BSc 1955, MD 1972; FRCP 1997; MRCS Eng. LRCP Lond. 1958; FRCPCH 1997; FFPHM 1980. (St. Mary's) Emeri. Prof. Pub. Health Univ. Liverp. Prev: Prof. Pub. Health Univ. Liverp.; Sen. Lect. Lond. Sch. Hyg. & Trop. Med.; Med. Off. Inst. Human Biol. Goroka, New Guinea.

PHATAK, Mr Prabhakar Shankar (retired) 2 Longlands Park Crescent, Sidcup DA15 7NE Tel: 020 8302 1535 — MB BS Nagpur 1960; FRCS Eng. 1967.

PHAURE, Trevor Albert Joseph (retired) 76 Weeping Cross, Stafford ST17 0DL — MB BS Lond. 1963; FRCPath 1984, M 1972. Prev: Sen, Regist. (Path.) United Oxf. Hosps.

PHEAR, David Norman (retired) 1 Beech Hyde, Hogg End Lane, St Albans AL3 6RF Tel: 01727 850456 — MB BChir 1949 Camb.; MD Camb. 1956, MA 1949; FRCP Lond 1973, M 1954; FRACP 1972, M 1961; Nat. Sc. Trip. cl. 1 Pts. 1 & 2. Prev: Cons. Phys. St. Albans City Hosp. & Qu. Eliz. II Hosp. Welwyn Gdn. City.

PHEARA, Jezziniah c/o Anaesthetics Department, Darlington Memorial Hospital NHS Trust, Hollyhurst Road, Darlington DL3 6HX — MB ChB 1994 Stellenbosch.

PHEBY, Derek Francis Henry Unit of Applied Epidemiology, University of the West of England, Frenchay Campus, Coldharbour Lane, Bristol BS16 1QY Tel: 0117 3443912 Fax: 0117 34443940 Email: derek.pheby@uwe.ac.uk; Hadspen Cottage, Hadspen, Castle Cary BA7 7LR — MB BS Lond.1969; MPhil York 1983; BSc Lond. 1966; LLM 1992; MRCS Eng. LRCP Lond. 1969; MFPHM 1986; DObst RCOG 1973. (St. Thos.) Dir. Unit Applied Epidemiol. Univ. W. Eng. Socs: Medicolegal Soc; Assoc. Mem. Brit. Assn. Clin. Terminology Special.; Melvyn Ramsey Soc. Prev: Dir. Cancer Epidemiol. Unit Univ. Bristol; Cons. Pub. Health Med. Gloucester HA; Sen. Regist. (Community Med.) Wessex RHA.

PHEILS, Mr Peter John Oaktree House, 36 Callis Court Road, Broadstairs CT10 3AG Tel: 01843 863170 Fax: 01843 602343 — MB BS 1968 Lond.; MS Lond. 1981; FRCS Eng. 1973. (St. Thos.) Cons. Gen. Surg. E. Kent Hosp.Trust. Socs: Fell. Assn. Surgs.; Fell. Roy. Soc. Med.; Brit. Assn. Surg. Oncol. Prev: Sen. Regist. (Gen. Surg.) St. Bart. Hosp. Lond.; Lect. (Surg.) St. Thos. Hosp. Lond.; Regist. (Surg.) Brighton & High Wycombe Health Dists.

PHELAN, Aideen Elizabeth 47 Albany Road, New Malden KT3 3NY — MB BCh BAO 1991 NUI.

PHELAN, Declan Richard Statham Grove Surgery, Statham Grove, London N16 9DP Tel: 020 7254 4327 Fax: 020 7241 4098; 68 Malvern Road, Hackney, London E8 3LJ Email: dphelan@doctors.org.uk — MB BCh BAO 1983 NUI; MRCGP 1988; DObst. RCPI 1987; DCH NUI 1985. (UCD)

PHELAN, Francis Joseph Department of Elderly Medicine, Seacroft Hospital, Leeds LS14 Tel: 0113 264 8164; 17 Kingscroft Gardens, Moortown, Leeds LS17 6PB Tel: 0113 216 5791 — BM 1991 Soton.; MSc Cork 1984; MRCP (UK) 1996. (Soton.)

PHELAN, Lorna Karen 137 Sandy Lane S., Wallington SM6 9NW — BM BS 1992 Nottm.

PHELAN, Margaret Sarah 19 Asmara Road, London NW2 3SS — MB BCh BAO 1976 NUI; MRCPI 1980; FRCR 1981; DMRD Eng. 1980. Cons. Radiol. The Chelsea & W.m. Hosp. Lond.

PHELAN, Martin Richard 148 Harley Street, London W1G 6DH Tel: 020 7935 3356 Fax: 020 7224 0557 — MB BChir 1980 Camb.; BDS Lond. 1963; LMSSA Lond. 1977; MLCOM 1987; FDS RCS Eng. 1970; DOrth 1969. (Addenbrooke's & Univ. Coll. Hosp. Lond.) Specialist Orthop. & Sports Med. Lond. And Psychosocratic Med.; Medico-Legal Expert Witness; Sen. Mem. Clare Coll. Camb.

PHELAN, Mary Bernadette 35 Park Road, London W4 3EY — MB BS 1964 Lond.; MRCS Eng. LRCP Lond. 1964.

PHELAN, Michael Boland 53 Great Cumberland Place, London W1H 7LH Tel: 020 7723 6482 — MB BS 1962 Lond.; MRCS Eng. LRCP Lond. 1962; LAH Dub. 1963; AMQ 1964; DTM & H Liverp. 1965. (St. Mary's) Socs: BMA; Chelsea Clin. Soc.; Med. Soc. Lond. Prev: Resid. Fell. Geo.town Univ. Hosp. Washington, USA; Ho. Surg. (Orthop.) St. Mary's Hosp.; Ho. Phys. Rochford Gen. Hosp.

PHELAN, Michael Cornelius Dept. of Psychiatry, Charing Cross Hospital, Fulham Palace Road, London W6 8RF — MB BS 1984 Lond.; BSc (Psychol.) Lond. 1981, MB BS 1984. Cons. (Psychiat.) Char. Cross Hosp.

PHELAN, Mr Peter Stephen Sunderland Eye Infirmary, Queen Alexandra Road, Sunderland SR2 9HP Tel: 0191 569 9068 Fax: 0191 569 9264 Email: psphin@globalnet.co.uk; 13 Ashwood Terrace, Thornhill, Sunderland SR2 7NB Tel: 0191 567 6901 — MB BCh BAO 1979 NUI; FRCS Ed. (Ophth.) 1987; FCOphth 1988; DO RCPSI 1984. Cons. Ophth. Sunderland Eye Infirm.; Cons. Ophth. S. Shields Hosp.; Head Glaucoma Dept. Sunderland Eye Infirm. Socs: BMA; Hosp. Cons. & Spec. Assn. Prev: Regist. (Ophth.) Roy. Free Hosp. Lond.; Clin. Tutor (Ophth.) UCC; Sen. Regist. (Ophth.) Univ. Coll. Hosp. & Moorfield Eye Hosp. Lond.

PHELLAS, Andrew The Cambridge Medical Group, 10A Cambridge Road, Linthorpe, Middlesbrough TS5 5NN Tel: 01642 851177 Fax: 01642 851176 — MB ChB 1984 Ed.; MRCGP 1989; DRCOG 1989.

PHELLAS

PHELLAS, Anne Jacqueline Linthorpe Road Surgery, 378 Linthorpe Road, Middlesbrough TS5 6HA Tel: 01642 817166 Fax: 01642 824094 — MB BS 1986 Lond.; BSc Lond. 1983, MB BS 1986; MRCGP 1990; DRCOG 1990.

PHELLAS, Georgina Doris (retired) 10 Fern Drive, Magherafelt BT45 5HZ Tel: 028 796 32965 — MB BCh BAO 1954 Belf.; DA Eng. 1958.

PHELLAS, Paul Medical Group Practice, Fairhill, Magherafelt, Londonderry Tel: 01648 32621; 10 Fern Drive, Magherafelt BT45 5HZ Tel: 01648 32965 — MB ChB 1957 Ed.; DObst RCOG 1959.

PHELLAS, Renos (retired) 67 Paddock Road, London NW2 7DH Tel: 020 8452 7916 — MB ChB 1952 Ed. Prev: Dir. Surg. Unit. St. And. Clinic Famagusta.

PHELPS, Miss Fiona Avrille The Surgery, 20 New St., Lord Harr Square, Port of Spain, West Indies Tel: 627 2466 Fax: 627 8231 Email: sphelps@nail.cablenet.net; 12 Rossdale Road, Putney, London SW15 1AD Tel: 020 8789 7895 — MB BS 1988 West Indies; MRCOG 1995. Regional Regist. (Obst. & Gyn.) SW Thames RHA. Prev: Regist. Qu. Charlotte's Hosp., Univ. Coll. Hosp. & St. Geo. Hosp. Med. Sch. Lond.

PHELPS, Peter David (retired) Department of Radiology, Royal Throat Nose & Ear Hospital, Grays Inn Road, London WC1X 8DA Tel: 020 7915 1300 Fax: 020 7833 5518 — MB BS 1962 Lond.; MD Lond. 1984; FRCS Eng. 1968; FFR 1973; FRCR 1975; DMRD Eng. 1971. Cons. Radiol. Walsgrave Hosp. Coventry; Hon. Cons. Radiol. Hosp. for Childr. Gt. Ormond St. Lond. Prev: Cons. Radiol. & Dir. Radiol. Roy. Nat. ENT Hosp. Lond.

PHELPS, Richard Grenville 22 Argyle Court, Edinburgh EH15 2QD — MB BChir 1986 Camb.

PHELPS, Mr Simon Richard 42 Station Road, Alvechurch, Birmingham B48 7SD — MB BS 1986 Lond.; FRCS Ed. 1991. (Charing Cross Hospital) Fell. (Paediat. IC) Roy. Manch. Childr.s Hosp.

PHELPS, Susan Vicky Health Centre, High Street, Bedworth, Nuneaton CV12 8NQ Tel: 024 7631 5432 Fax: 024 7631 0038; Doric House, Main St, Easenhall, Rugby CV23 0JA Tel: 01788 832347 — MB BS 1969 Lond.; MRCS Eng. LRCP Lond. 1969. (Char. Cross)

PHELPS, Thelma Marjorie (retired) 3 Bromley Road, West Bridgford, Nottingham NG2 7AP Tel: 0115 981 0563 — MB BS 1946 Lond.; MRCS Eng. LRCP Lond. 1945; MFPHM 1990; MFCM 1974; DPH Bristol 1970. Prev: Cons. Pub. Health Nottm.

PHEMISTER, John Clark Belaire, Chagford, Newton Abbot TQ13 8AT Tel: 01647 432477 — MB ChB 1946 Ed.; FRCP Ed. 1972, M 1954. Socs: Assn. Brit. Neurol. Prev: Cons. Neurol. Centr. Middlx. Hosp., Hillingdon Hosp. & Wexham Pk. Hosp. Slough; Surg. Antarctic Whaling Expedit.; Clin. Tutor Roy. Infirm. Edin.

PHIBBS, Peter Alban Thorburn 27 The Square, Latimer, Chesham HP5 1TY — MB BChir 1938 Camb.; MRCS Eng. LRCP Lond. 1937. (St. Thos.) Surg. Lt.-Cdr. RNVR. Prev: Regist. (Med.) King Geo. Hosp. Ilford; Ho. Phys. Roy. N.. Hosp.; Ho. Surg. W. Lond. Hosp.

PHILBIN, John Christopher The Surgery, 221 Whaddon Way, Bletchley, Milton Keynes MK3 7EA Tel: 01908 373058 Fax: 01908 630076 — MB BCh 1980 Wales; DCH RCP Lond. 1986; DRCOG 1985.

PHILBIN, Karen Hilary 12 Great Brickhill Lane, Little Brickhill, Milton Keynes MK17 9NW — MB BCh 1980 Wales.

PHILIP, Colin John Stennack Surgery, The Old Stennack School, St Ives, Penzance TR20 1RU Tel: 01736 795237 Fax: 01736 795362; Booby's Castle, Nancledra, Penzance TR20 8NE — MB ChB 1978 Bristol; MRCGP 1983; DRCOG 1980.

PHILIP, Dawn Barn Brae, Dalcross, Inverness IV2 7JH — MB ChB 1987 Aberd.; MRCGP 1992. SHO (Obst.& Gyn.) St. Richard's Hosp. Chichester.

PHILIP, George Department of Histopathology, St Helier Hospital, Wrythe Lane, Carshalton SM5 1AA — BM BCh 1970 Oxf.; MA Oxf. 1970; MRCPath 1977. (Oxf. & Univ. Coll. Hosp.) Cons. Path.St Helier Hosp., Surrey.

PHILIP, George Eugene Newton Medical Centre, 14/18 Newton Road, London W2 5LT Tel: 020 7229 4578 — MB ChB 1960 Ed. Socs: Fell. BMA.

PHILIP, Ian Grant (retired) 1 Orchard Road, Maldon CM9 6EW Tel: 01621 841560 Fax: 01621 841560 Email: iph6789582@aol.com — MB ChB Glas. 1957; DObst RCOG 1959. Prev: Ho. Phys. Univ. Med. Unit, Stobhill Hosp. Glas.

PHILIP, Professor James Fiddes (retired) Broomhill, Lumphanan, Banchory AB31 4QH Tel: 013398 83672 — ChM (Hons.) Aberd. 1937, MB ChB 1933; FRCS Ed. 1938. Hon. Cons. Malig. Dis. Grampian HB. Prev: Clin. Dir. Roxburghe Hse. Milltimber.

PHILIP, Mr John Pennine Screening Programme, Trinity Road, Bradford BD5 0JX Tel: 01274 365521 Fax: 01274 727322 — MB BS 1972 Madras; PhD Leeds 1985; FRCS Ed. 1976. (Jawaharlal Inst. Postgrad. Med. Educat. Pondicherry) Clin. Dir. DHSS BrE. Screening Progr. Bradford; Surg. BrE. Screen. & Advis. Centre. Socs: BASO. Prev: Clin. Research Fell. BrE. Unit St. Lukes Hosp. Huddersfield; Med. Off. Nigeria; Regist. Gen. Hosp. Nottm.

PHILIP, John Murray Ure (retired) Penlan, Holm Farm Road, Catrine, Mauchline KA5 6TA — MB ChB Ed. 1945; DTM & H Ed. 1949. Prev: Princip., Gen. Pract., Catrine.

***PHILIP, Laura Margaret** 84 Ennerdale Road, Liverpool L37 2EA Tel: 017048 72700; 98 Causeway Head Road, Dore, Sheffield S17 3DW Tel: 0114 236 1796 Email: lmphilip@aol.com — MB ChB 1997 Sheff.

PHILIP, Lynne Liberton Medical Group, 55 Liberton Gardens, Edinburgh EH16 6JT Tel: 0131 664 3050 Fax: 0131 692 1952 — MB ChB 1982 Aberd.; MRCGP 1987.

PHILIP, Mary Frances (retired) 3 Ferguson Gardens, Musselburgh EH21 6XF Tel: 0131 653 2310 Email: jamesphilip@lineone.net — MB ChB Ed. 1958; MRCPsych 1980. Prev: Cons. Psychiat. Gogarburn Hosp. Edin.

PHILIP, Mr Peter Forbes (retired) Toldrum Cottage, Winksley, Ripon HG4 3PG Tel: 01765 658650 Email: jandpphilip@toldrumcottage.fsnet.co.uk — MB BS Lond. 1945; MS Lond. 1953; FRCS Eng. 1948. Prev: Cons. Urol. Char. Cross Hosp. Lond. & Roy. Masonic Hosp.

PHILIP, Rebecca Anne 12 Burnet Place, Aberdeen AB24 4QD — MB ChB 1991 Aberd.; MRCGP 1995; MRCPsych. 1997. Specialist Regist. (Child & Adolesc. Psychiat.) Aberd. Roy. Hosps. NHS Trust Aberd. Prev: Trainee GP Grampian HB VTS.; SHO (Psychiat.) Grampian Health Care Aberd.

PHILIP, Valerie Jane 23 New Road, Ham, Richmond TW10 7HZ — MB ChB 1976 Bristol; DCH Eng. 1980; DRCOG 1979.

PHILIP, William James Unwin 12 Burnett Place, Kittybrewster, Aberdeen AB24 4QD Tel: 01224 492038 — MB ChB 1990 Aberd.; MRCP (UK) 1993. Clin. Research Fell. & Hon. Regist. (Cardiol.) Aberd. Roy. Infirm.

PHILIP, William Marshall 4 Carpenter Road, Edgbaston, Birmingham B15 2JT Tel: 0121 454 3981 — MB BS 1938 Lond.; FRCP Lond. 1975, M 1939; MRCS Eng. LRCP Lond. 1936. (Guy's) Hon. Cons. Phys. Birm. HA. Prev: Cons. Phys. E. Birm. Gen. Hosp.; Squadron Ldr. RAFVR; Ho. Phys. Brompton Hosp. & Guy's Hosp.

PHILIP-SMITH, Peter Bellamy (retired) Old Lodge Farm, Church Lane, Cransley, Kettering NN14 1PX Tel: 01536 790320 — MB BChir Camb. 1944; BA Camb. 1944; MRCS Eng. LRCP Lond. 1944. Prev: Clin. Asst. Midw. & Gyn. Dept. & Ho. Phys. St. Thos. Hosp.

PHILIPP, Anthony Bertram 7 Bracknell Gardens, London NW3 7EE — MRCS Eng. LRCP Lond. 1942. (Univ. Coll. Hosp.) Socs: BMA. Prev: Ho. Phys. Roy. Bucks. Hosp. Aylesbury; Flight Lt. RAFVR Med. Br.

PHILIPP, Mr Elliot Elias (retired) 166 Rivermead Court, Ranelagh Gardens, London SW6 3SF Tel: 020 7736 2851 Fax: 020 7736 2851 — MB BChir 1947 Camb.; BA Camb. 1936, MA 1942; FRCS Eng. 1951; MRCS Eng. LRCP Lond. 1939; FRCOG 1962, M 1947. Hon. Cons. Obst. & Gyn. City Lond. Matern. Hosp., Whittington & Roy. N. Hosps Lond; Hon. Cons. Gyn. French Disp. Lond. Prev: Cons. O & G OldCh. Hosp. Romford.

PHILIPP, Robin Department of Occupational Medicine, Bristol Royal Infirmary, Bristol BS2 8HW Tel: 0117 928 2223 Fax: 0117 928 3840 — MB ChB Otago 1968; MSc Bristol 1979; FFOM RCP Lond. 1991, MFOM, 1984, AFOM 1979; FAFPHM 1994, FFPHM RCP (UK) 1990, M 1985; MCCM (NZ) 1980; MFCMI 1977; DIH Dund 1976; DCH Eng. 1974; DPH Bristol 1974; FRCP Lond. 1999. Cons. Occupat. Phys. United Bristol NHS Health Care Trust; Hon. Sen. Lect. Occupat. & Pub. Health Med. Univ. Bristol. Prev: Vis. Lect. (Environm. Epidemiol.) Wellington Clin. Sch. Univ. Otago;

Regist. (Med.) Wellington Pub. Hosp., NZ; Dir. WHO Collaborating Centre for Environm. Health Promotion & Ecology Univ Bristol.

PHILIPPAS, Antonios 5 Uxbridge Court, Uxbridge Road, Kingston upon Thames KT1 2LJ — Ptychio Iatrikes 1992 Athens.

***PHILIPPIDIS, Pandelis** 277 Otley Road, Leeds LS16 5LN — MB ChB 1994 Ed.

PHILIPPOU, George Nicolaou 1 Bury Hall Villas, Great Cambridge Road, London N9 9LE Tel: 020 8360 0319 — State Exam. Med. Sofia 1969.

PHILIPPSON, Margaret Elizabeth Anne Longrove Surgery, 70 Union Street, Barnet EN5 4HT Tel: 020 8441 9440/9563 Fax: 020 8441 4037 — MB BS Lond. 1976; DRCOG 1980. (Guy's) Clin. Asst. (Genitourin. Med.) Barnet. Prev: Prinicip. GP Broxbourne, Herts; Med. Off. Turks & Caicos Isles; Trainee GP Tunbridge Wells VTS.

PHILIPS, Barbara Janet Department of Anaesthetics, St Goeorge's Hospital Intesive Care Medical School, Cranmer Terrace, Tootins, London SW17 0RE Email: bphilips@sghms.ac.uk — MB BS 1988 Lond.; 1999 Lond; MD 1999 Lond.; FRCA 1993 Lond. Sen. Lect.. Intens. Care Med. St Geo.'s Hosp. Med. Sch.. Lond. Socs: Europ. Intens. care Soc. Ordinary Mem.; Europ. Shock Soc. Ordinary Mem.; Intesive Care Soc. Ordinary Mem. Prev: Specialist Regist. Intens. care. Roy. Infirm. Edin.; Sen. Regis. Anaesth. Roy. Infirm. Edin.; Clin. Research Fell.. Liver Transpl. Serv.. Roy. Infirm. Edin.

PHILIPS, Frances Katharine Shieldaig, La Rocque, Grouville JE3 9FD Tel: 01534 854149 — MB ChB Glas. 1954; DObst RCOG 1957.

PHILIPSON, Gavin Patrick 29 Westgate, Leslie, Glenrothes KY6 3LR — MB ChB 1992 Ed.

PHILIPSON, Mr John Anthony Moore (retired) Clifton Farm House, Pullover Road, West Lynn, King's Lynn PE34 3LS Tel: 01553 775619 Fax: 01553 775619 — MB BChir 1963 Camb.; MB Camb. 1963, BChir 1962; MA Camb. 1963; FRCS Ed. 1969; MRCS Eng. LRCP Lond. 1962. Prev: Sen. Cons. Orthop. The Qu. Eliz. Hosp., King's Lynn.

***PHILIPSON, Mark Robert** 19 Holly Avenue, Jesmond, Newcastle upon Tyne NE2 2PU — MB ChB 1998 Leeds.

PHILIPSON, Richard Simon GSK CRU, ACCI, Addenbrooke's Hospital, Hills Road, Cambridge CB2 2GG Tel: 01223 296040 Fax: 01223 296002 Email: Richard_S_Philipson@gsk.com; 24 Teversham Road, Fulbourn, Cambridge CB1 5EB — MB BS 1988 Lond.; BSc Lond. 1985; MRCP (UK) 1992; MRCGP 1994; T(GP) 1995; Dip. Pharma. Med. 1998. (Middlx. Hosp. Med. Sch.) Clin. Pharmacol.

***PHILIPSZ, Mary Louise** Wellwood House, Saline, Dunfermline KY12 9TD — MB ChB 1993 Glas.

PHILLIMORE, Catherine Elizabeth 26 Welland Way, Oakham LE15 6SL — MB BS 1994 Lond.; BSc Lond. 1991.

PHILLIP, Clifford Edgar (retired) 5 Helmsley Drive, Leeds LS16 5HY Tel: 0113 252772 — LRCP LRCS 1943 Ed.; LRCP LRCS Ed. LRFPS Glas. 1943; DPH Eng. 1949. Prev: Ho. Surg. Killearn E.M.S. Hosp.

PHILLIPPS, Mr James John Singleton Hospital, Sketty, Swansea SA2 8QA; Tawel Fryn, Cae Mansel Road, Gowerton, Swansea SA4 3HN — MB BS 1977 Lond.; FRCS Eng. 1983. Cons. Surg. ENT W. Glam HA. Prev: Sen. Regist. (ENT) Soton. Gen. Hosp.

***PHILLIPPS, Jennifer Susan** Wootton, Pyle Hill, Mayford, Woking GU22 0SR — MB ChB 1998 Bristol.

PHILLIPS, Adrian Wilkin Wolverhampton Health Authority, Loncston House, Chapel Ash, Wolverhampton WU3 OXE — MB ChB 1985 Birm.; MRCP (UK) 1990; MFPHM 1997. (Birm.) Prev: Sen. Regist. (Pub. Health Med.) NHS Exec. W. Midl.; Regist. (Med.) Goodhope Hosp. Sutton Coldfield.

PHILLIPS, Alan Hewett (retired) Myrtle Bank, Allt-yr-Yn Avenue, Newport NP20 5DE Tel: 01633 263546 — MB BS 1949 Lond.; MRCS Eng. LRCP Lond. 1949; FFA RCS Eng. 1956. Cons. Anaesth. Roy. Gwent Hosp. Newport. Prev: Sen. Regist. & Regist. Dept. Anaesth. Roy. Infirm. Cardiff.

***PHILLIPS, Aled Myrddin** Llysgwyn, Cellan, Lampeter SA48 8HY — MB BCh 1994 Wales.

PHILLIPS, Aled Owain Institute of Nephrology, Cardiff Royal Infirmary, Cardiff Tel: 029 2049 2233 Fax: 029 2045 3643 Email: phillipsao@cf.ac.uk; 3 Cyncoed Avenue, Cyncoed, Cardiff CF23 6ST — MB BCh 1986 Wales; BSc Wales 1983; MD Wales 1995; MRCP (UK) 1989. Sen. Lect. (Nephrol.) Cardiff Roy. Infirm.; Research Fell.

Inst. Nephrol. Cardiff Roy. Infirm.; Hon. Cons. Nephrologist/Gen. Phys. Socs: Renal Assn.; Amer. Soc. Nephrol. Prev: Sen. Regist. (Renal & Gen. Med.) Cardiff Roy. Infirm.; Regist. (Renal) Dulwich Hosp. Lond.; Regist. & SHO Rotat. (Med.) S. Glam. HA.

PHILLIPS, Alexander Blackwood Riverside Medical Centre, Victoria Road, Walton-le-Dale, Preston PR5 4AY Tel: 01772 556703 — MB ChB 1975 Dundee; DRCOG 1978.

PHILLIPS, Andrea Jayne 49 Demesne Furze, Headington, Oxford OX3 7XG Tel: 01865 741142 — MB BS 1989 Lond.; BSc Lond. 1986; MRCP (UK) 1992; FRCR 1996. Specialist Regist. (Radiol.) John Radcliffe Hosp. Oxf. Prev: SHO (Cardiol.) Roy. Brompton Nat. Heart & Lung Hosp. Lond.; SHO (Med. & Infec. Dis.) N.wick Pk. Hosp. Harrow.

PHILLIPS, Andrew Jonathan Department of Anaesthetics, New Cross Hospital, Wolverhampton WV10 0QP Tel: 01902 307999 — MB BS 1980 Lond.; BSc Lond. 1977; FRCA 1985. Cons. Anaesth. New Cross Hosp. Wolverhampton.

PHILLIPS, Mr Andrew Mark 76 Ormiston Road, London SE10 0LN Tel: 020 8853 4009 — MB BChir 1989 Camb.; FRCS Eng. 1993. Specialist Regist. (Orthop.) King's Coll. Hosp. Lond.

PHILLIPS, Ann Allister Southfields Group Practice, 7 Revelstoke Road, London SW18 5NJ Tel: 020 8947 0061 Fax: 020 8944 8694; 1 Grangemuir, 2 Southside Common, Wimbledon, London SW19 4TG Tel: 020 8946 1446 — MB BS 1965 Lond.; MRCS Eng. LRCP Lond. 1965. (St. George's Hospital) Prev: Sch. Med. Off. St. Paul's Girls' Sch. Lond.; Clin. Asst. (Chest Med.) St. Geo. Hosp. Lond.

PHILLIPS, Ann Elizabeth Margaret Tal-y-Coed Court, Monmouth NP25 5HR Tel: 01600 85272 — MB BCh 1955 Wales.

PHILLIPS, Anne Fiona The Glebeland Surgery, The Glebe, Belbroughton, Stourbridge DY9 9TH Tel: 01562 730303 Fax: 01562 731220; 67 Love Lane, Stourbridge DY8 2DZ — MB ChB 1987 Birm.

PHILLIPS, Anne Frances Crookes Valley Medical Centre, 1 Barber Rd, Sheffield S10 1EA Tel: 0114 266 0703, 02920 747747 Fax: 0114 267 8354; 33 Cliffe Road, Walkley, Sheffield S6 5DR Tel: 0114 233 8529 — MB ChB 1953 Birm. (Birm.) Asst. GP Crookes Valley Med. Centre Sheff.; Med. Adviser Benefits Agency Med. Servs. Socs: BMA & Christian Med. Fell.sh. Prev: Dir. of Diocesan Med. Servs. Diocese on the Niger; Med. Supt. Iyi Enu Hosp. Onitsha, Nigeria; Med. Off. Emevor Nigeria.

PHILLIPS, Anne Sarah Department of Aneasthetics, Royal Hospitals Trust, Grosvenor Road, Belfast BT12 6BA Tel: 01232 240503; 364 Beersbridge Road, Belfast BT5 5DZ — MD 1993 Belf.; MB BCh BAO 1984; FFA RCSI 1988; DA (UK) 1987.

PHILLIPS, Anthony Graham Sky Larks, Hutton Village, Guisborough TS14 8ER — MB BS 1984 Lond.; MA Camb. 1985; DCH RCP Lond. 1987. Trainee GP Kingston Hosp. Surrey.

PHILLIPS, Arnold Morley (retired) 74 Chaffers Mead, Ashtead KT21 1NH Tel: 01372 272567 — MB ChB 1937 Ed.; DA Eng. 1962.

PHILLIPS, Barbara Elizabeth Child Development Centre, Pat Lewis Child Development Centre, Heath Lane, Hemel Hempstead Tel: 01442 232022; 51 Watling Street, St Albans AL1 2QF Tel: 01727 831481 — MB ChB 1974 Bristol. Clin. Med. Off. (Community Health) W. Herts. Community Health NHS Trust. Socs: Inst. Psychosexual Med.

PHILLIPS, Barbara Helen (retired) 7 Bathwick Hill, Bath BA2 6EW — MB BS 1955 Lond.; MRCS Eng. LRCP Lond. 1954.

PHILLIPS, Barbara May Alder Hey Children's Hospital, Eaton Road, Liverpool L12 2AP Tel: 0151 228 4811 Fax: 0151 252 5033 — MB ChB Birm. 1969; FRCP Lond. 1990; MRCP (UK) 1973; FFAEM 1993; FRCPCH 1997. Cons. Paediat. (A & E Med.) Alder Hey Childr. Hosp. & Manch. Roy. Infirm.; Chairm. Paediat. Life Support Comm. of Rususcitation Counc. UK; Chairm. Europ. Resusc. Counc. PLS Comm.; Chairm. APLS Working Party. Socs: Chairm. Brit. Paediat. A & E Gp.; Fell. Fac. A & E Med. (Exam. Comm.). Prev: Cons. Paediat. A & E Med. Booth Hall Childr. Hosp. Manch.

PHILLIPS, Berkeley Simon 15 Rhodes Drive, Bury BL9 8NH — MB BS 1993 Lond.

PHILLIPS, Brenda Joyce 23 Moel Famau View, Liverpool L17 7ET — MB ChB 1979 Ghana; FFA RCS Eng. 1987. Cons. Liverp. O & G Servs. NHS Trust.

PHILLIPS

PHILLIPS, Brian Lester David 5 White Orchards, London N20 8AQ — BM BCh Oxf. 1954; MA Oxf. 1956, BA (Hons.) 1951; AFOM RCP Lond. 1979; T(GP) 1991; DObst RCOG 1959. (Oxf. & Roy. Free) Occupat. Health Phys. BMI Health Servs. Socs: Soc. Occupat. Med. Prev: Occupat. Health Phys. Glaxo Holdings plc; Resid. Med. Off. Matern. Hosp. Beckenham; SHO (Paediat.) Memor. Hosp. P'boro.

PHILLIPS, Brian Morgan (retired) Waitawhiti, Nicholston, Gower, Swansea Tel: 01792 371633 — MB BS Lond. 1958; FRCP Lond. 1974, M 1960; MRCS Eng. LRCP Lond. 1958. Prev: Cons. Neurol. Glantawe Hosp. Gp. & Morriston Hosp.

PHILLIPS, Professor Calbert Inglis 5 Braid Mount Crest, Edinburgh EH10 6JN — MB ChB 1946 Aberd.; Hon. FBOA 1975; MSc Manch. 1969; PhD Bristol 1961; MD Aberd. 1957; FRCS Ed. 1973; FRCS Eng. 1955; FRCOphth 1993; DPH Ed. 1950; DO Eng. 1953. (Aberd.) Emerit. Prof. Edin. Prev: Prof. Ophth. Univ. Edin. & Hon. Cons. Ophth. Surg. Roy. Infirm. Edin.; Prof. Ophth. Univ. Manch. & Hon. Cons. Ophth. Surg. Univ. Manch.; Cons. Surg. St. Geo. Hosp. Lond.

PHILLIPS, Catherine Jane Cheslyn, Barlaston, Stoke-on-Trent ST12 9DE — BM BS 1990 Nottm.

PHILLIPS, Charles Edward William 51A St Georges Square, Pimlico, London SW1V 3QN Tel: 020 7821 8934 Fax: 020 7821 8934; Whitethorn House, Tilford, Farnham GU10 2DF — MB BS 1992 Lond. SHO Epsom Gen. & Roy. Marsden Hosp. Prev: Ho. Off. St. Thos. Hosp. Lond.

PHILLIPS, Charles Russell (retired) Millennium Medical Centre, 121 Weoley Castle Road, Weoley Castle, Birmingham B29 5QD Tel: 0121 427 5201 Fax: 0121 427 5052 — MB ChB 1958 Birm.; DObst RCOG 1961. Prev: Ho. Surg. & Ho. Phys. Dudley Rd. Hosp. Birm.

PHILLIPS, Charles William Derek (retired) Ebbor House, Barrack Hill, Hythe CT21 4BY Tel: 01303 267884 Email: zoekenyor@msn.com — MB BCh BAO Belf. 1956; FRCGP 1981, M 1972.

***PHILLIPS, Christian Guy Hambro** 2 Cricket Close, Crawley, Winchester SO21 2PX — BM 1995 Soton.

PHILLIPS, Mr Christopher Edward 62 Cardigan Terrace, Heaton, Newcastle upon Tyne NE6 5NU Tel: 0191 224 1357 — MB BS 1986 Newc.; FRCS Ed. 1991.

PHILLIPS, Christopher John 34 Rotherwick Road, London NW11 7DA Tel: 020 8455 2421 Email: jw59@dial.pipex.com — MB BS 1974 Lond.; MRCPsych Lond. 1986. (Univ. Coll. Hosp. Lond.) Vis. Cons. Rhodes Farm Clinic Lond.; Vis. Cons. Harrow Sch. Middx.

PHILLIPS, Christopher John Department of Radiology, Alexandra Hospital, Redditch B98 7UB Tel: 01527 512059 Fax: 01527 512005 — MB ChB 1980 Leeds; FRCR 1989; MBA Keel University 1999. Cons. Radiol. Alexandra Hosp. Redditch. Prev: Cons. Radiol. Qu. Eliz. Hosp. Lond.; Sen. Regist. (Radiol.) King's Coll. Hosp. Lond.

PHILLIPS, Claire Patricia 5 Chestnut Rise, Droxford, Southampton SO32 3NY — MB BS 1988 Lond.

PHILLIPS, Clare Frances 132 Old Ford Road, London E2 9PW — MB BS 1984 Lond.; BSc (Hons.) Lond. 1981, MB BS 1984.

PHILLIPS, Clive William Eveswell Surgery, 254 Chepstow Road, Newport NP19 8NL Tel: 01633 277494 Fax: 01633 290709 — MB BCh 1983 Wales; MRCGP 1988; DRCOG 1987; DA (UK) 1985.

PHILLIPS, Mrs Cynthia Mary 10 Hawkswell Gardens, Oxford OX2 7EX — BM BCh 1943 Oxf.; MA, BM BCh Oxf. 1943. (Oxf. & Univ. Coll. Hosp.)

PHILLIPS, David 2 Gsrecian Road, Tunbridge Wells TN1 1TG — MB BS 1977 Lond.

PHILLIPS, David Edmund (retired) Bryn Hyfryd, Rhydwyn, Holyhead LL65 Tel: 01407 730744 — MRCS Eng. LRCP Lond. 1952; DPH Liverp. 1963. Prev: Assoc. Specialist (Gen. Med.) Crossley Hosp. Kingswood.

PHILLIPS, Mr David Esmond ENT Department, Warwick Hospital, Lakin Road, Warwick CV34 5BW Tel: 01926 495321 Fax: 01926 482607; Struan, 47 Kenilworth Road, Leamington Spa CV32 6JJ Email: david.phillips@sworkhosp-tr.wmids.nhs.uk — MB BS 1982 Lond.; FRCS Eng. 1989; FRCS Ed. 1988; T(S) 1992. (Lond. Hosp.) Cons. ENT Surg. Warwick Hosp. Prev: Hon. Cons. ENT Roy. Liverp. Univ. Hosp. & Aintree Hosp.; Sen. Lect. (ENT) Univ. Liverp.; Sen. Regist. (ENT) Roy. Liverp. Univ. Trust. Hosp.

PHILLIPS, Professor David Ivor Wyn Medical Research Council, Epidemiology Unit, Southampton General Hospital, Tremona Road, Southampton SO16 6YD Tel: 02380 777624 Fax: 02380 704021 Email: diwp@mrc.soton.ac.uk; 48 Welbeck Avenue, Highfield, Southampton SO17 1SS Tel: 02380 325081 — MB 1978 Camb.; FRCP (Lond) 1997; PhD Soton. 1985; MSc Lond. 1981; MA Camb. 1978, MB 1978, BChir 1977; MRCP (UK) 1979. Prof. of Endocrine and Metab. Proramming, MRC Environ Epidemiol Unit, Univ. of S.ampton; Hon. Cons. Phys.S.ampton Univ. Hosp. NHS Trust. Socs: Endocrine Soc.; Brit. Diabetes Assn.; Brit. Endocrine Soc. Prev: Lect. (Med.) Univ. Wales Coll. Med.; Wellcome Research Fell. (Clin. Epidemiol.) Univ. Soton.

PHILLIPS, David John The Anchorage, Gromford Lane, Snape, Saxmundham IP17 1RG — MB BChir 1966 Camb.; MA, MB Camb. 1966, BChir 1965; MRCS Eng. LRCP Lond. 1965; FRCR 1975; DMRD Eng. 1973. (Camb. & St. Thos.) Prev: Cons. Radiol. Norf. & Norwich Hosp. & Ipswich Health Dist.; Sen. Regist. (Radiol.) St. Thos. Hosp. Lond.; Vis. Specialist (Radiol.) Adelaide Childr. Hosp., Austral.

PHILLIPS, David Llewellyn Caldicot Medical Group, Gray Hill Surgery, Woodstock Way, Caldicot, Newport NP26 4DB Tel: 01291 420282 Fax: 01291 425853; Brookside, Well Lane, Llanvair Discoed, Chepstow NP16 6LP Tel: 01633 400669 — MB BS 1974 Lond.; PhD Lond. 1970, BSc (Hons.) 1964, MB BS 1974. (Kings Coll. Hosp.) Princip. Gen. Pract. Caldicot. Prev: Ho. Phys. & Regist. King's Coll. Hosp. Lond.; Lect. (Physiol.) Kings Coll. Lond.

PHILLIPS, David Lynn The Surgery, 75 Longridge Avenue, Saltdean, Brighton BN2 8LA Tel: 01273 305723 Fax: 01273 300962; The Farriers, Mill Lane, Rodmell, Lewes BN7 3HS Tel: 01273 475241 Fax: 01273 477823 Email: rnlidoc@aol.com — MRCS Eng. LRCP Lond. 1974. Hon. Med. Adviser Brighton Lifeboat.

PHILLIPS, David Wyndham Penton House, Queen Anne Street, Shelton, Stoke-on-Trent ST4 2EQ Tel: 01782 848642 Fax: 01782 747617; Alpine View, Stone Road, Hill Chorlton, Newcastle ST5 5DR Tel: 01782 680709 Email: 100025.660@compuserve.com — MB ChB 1978 Liverp.

PHILLIPS, Deborah Clare St. Peter's Lodge, 18 1/2 Eastgate, Lincoln LN2 4AA — MB ChB 1976 Leeds; FFA RCS Eng. 1980.

PHILLIPS, Deborah Joan 12 Crown Mews, Ock St., Abingdon OX14 5DS Tel: 01235 536822 — BM BS 1994 Nottm.; FRCS Ed. 1994. Regist. (Gen. Surg.) John Radcliffe Hosp. Oxf. Prev: SHO (Gen. Surg.) Derriford Hosp. Plymouth & Cheltenham Gen. Hosp.; SHO (Orthop. & ITU) Derriford Hosp. Plymouth; SHO (Orthop. & A & E) & Ho. Off. (Surg.) Qu. Med. Centre Nottm.

PHILLIPS, Diana Margaret 5 Elfort Road, London N5 1AX — MB ChB 1971 Liverp.; FFA RCS Eng. 1980. (Liverp.) Cons. Anaesth. Worcester HA. Prev: Sen. Regist. Nuffield Dept. Anaesth. Oxf.

PHILLIPS, Diane Heather c/o The Manager, Natwest Bank Plc, PO Box 306, 36 Earlsdon St, Coventry CV3 5ZZ — MB BS 1985 Lond.; DA RCA 1987.

PHILLIPS, Donald Leslie (retired) Stock Lodge, Stock, Ingatestone CM4 9BS Tel: 01277 840546 Fax: 01277 841050 — MRCS Eng. LRCP Lond. 1948; FRCOG 1978, M 1954; FRCR 1975; FFR 1960; DMRT Eng. 1956; DObst RCOG 1952. Cons. Radiotherap. S.end Hosp. Prev: Cons. Radiotherap. W.. Infirm. Glas.

PHILLIPS, Mr Douglas George 42 Over Lane, Almondsbury, Bristol BS32 4BW — MB ChB 1935 N.Z.; FRCS Eng. 1939. (Otago) Socs: Soc. Brit. Neurol. Surgs. Prev: Surg. i/c S.W. Regional Neurosurg. Unit Bristol; Clin. Lect. (Neurosurg.) Univ. Bristol; Chief Asst. Neurosurg. Dept. Lond. Hosp.

PHILLIPS, Dylan Gwynne Leyshon Elms Medical Practice, 5 Stewart Road, Harpenden AL5 4QA Tel: 01582 769393 Fax: 01582 461735; 24 Amenbury Lane, Harpenden AL5 2DF — MB BS 1981 Lond.; BSc (Hons.) Lond. 1978; DFFP 1993; DRCOG 1985. (St. Marys) Socs: BMA. Prev: Trainee GP Frimley Pk. Hosp. VTS.; Ho. Phys. Profess. Med. Unit St. Mary's Hosp. Lond. W2; Ho. Surg. St. Mary's Hosp. Lond. W2.

PHILLIPS, Edward Hamilton Dalrymple (retired) Herne Cottage, Smuggler's Way, The Sands, Farnham GU10 1NA Tel: 01252 782850 — MRCS Eng. LRCP Lond. 1935; BA Camb. 1932; DA Eng. 1945. Prev: Maj. RAMC, Specialist Anaesth.

PHILLIPS, Edward James Brynhedyn, Cwmcoy, Newcastle Emlyn SA38 9PF — MB BCh 1951 Wales; BSc Wales 1948, MB BCh 1951; FRCPath 1975, M 1964. (Cardiff)

PHILLIPS

PHILLIPS, Eileen Blossom Field House, 53 Knowsley Road, Wilpshire, Blackburn BB1 9PN — MB ChB 1959 Ed.

PHILLIPS, Eileen Margaret East Surrey Hospital, Canada Avenue, Redhill RH1 5RH Tel: 01737 231796 Fax: 01737 231736; Tel: 01342 842752 — MB BS 1966 Lond.; MD 1975; BSc 1970 (Hons. Pharmacol.); BSc (Hons. Pharmacol.) Lond. 1970, MD 1975, MB BS 1966; FRCP Lond. 1985, M 1969. (St. Bart.) Cons. Phys. Gastroenterol. E. Surrey Hosp. Surrey Sussex Healthcare Trust; Chairm., STC G(1)M, S. Thames; CME Adv., S. Thames W., Roy. Coll. of Phys.s. Socs: Fell. Roy. Soc. Med.; Brit. Soc. Gastroenterol. Prev: Sen. Regist. (Med.) St. Geo. Hosp. Lond.; MRC Clin. Research Fell. & Hon. Assoc. Chief Asst. St. Bart. Hosp. Lond.

PHILLIPS, Elfyn Arfon 32 Melyd Avenue, Johnstown, Wrexham LL14 2TB — MB ChB 1994 Liverp.

PHILLIPS, Elizabeth Mary Gibbon The Liver Unit, Freeman Hospital, Newcastle upon Tyne; 132 Kenton Lane, Gosforth, Newcastle upon Tyne NE3 3QE — MB BS 1986 Newc.; BMedSc Newc. 1983; MRCP (UK) 1989. Sen. Regist. (Med.) Freeman Hosp. Newc. u. Tyne. Prev: Research Regist. (Med.) Univ. Newc.; Regist. (Med.) Ashington Gen. Hosp. N.d.

PHILLIPS, Ernest Prabhu Kumar Trent View Medical Practice, 45 Trent View, Keadby, Scunthorpe DN17 3DR Tel: 01724 782209 Fax: 01724 784472; 9 Acer Grove, Silica Lodge, Scunthorpe DN17 2AJ — MB BS 1965 Osmania. (Osmania Med. Coll. Hyderabad)

PHILLIPS, Gareth Rhys The Rogerstone Practice, Chapel Wood, Western Valley Road, Rogerstone, Newport NP10 9DU Tel: 01633 890800 — MB BCh 1988 Wales; MRPharms 1980; DPD 1992; BPharm (Hons.) 1979. GP Princip. Socs: Roy. Pharmaceut. Soc. Gt. Brit.

PHILLIPS, Geoffrey 7 Garth Drive, Calderstones, Liverpool L18 6HN — MB BCh 1976 Wales; FRCP Lond. 1993; MRCP (UK) 1978. Cons. Geriat. BRd.green Hosp. Liverp. Prev: Sen. Regist. (Geriat. Med.) Newsham Gen. Hosp. Liverp.; Regist. (Med.) BRd.green Hosp. Liverp.; Ho. Phys. Llandough Hosp. Penarth.

PHILLIPS, Geoffrey David 18-20 Woodland Road, St Austell PL25 4QY Tel: 01726 63311; Roskear, 67 Penwinnick Road, St Austell PL25 5DS Tel: 01726 73806 — MB BS 1951 Lond.; MRCS Eng. LRCP Lond. 1951; DObst RCOG 1958. (St. Bart.) Police Surg. Devon & Cornw. Constab.; Clin. Asst. Penrice Psychogeriat. Hosp. St. Austell.

PHILLIPS, George Bevan 104 Belgrave Road, Loughor, Swansea SA4 6RE Tel: 01792 2218 — MB BS 1956 Lond.; MRCS Eng. LRCP Lond. 1955. (St. Geo.) Anaesth. Glantawe, Hosp. Gp.; Med. Off. Bowden Engin. Co. (LLa.lly); Apptd. Fact. Doctor. Socs: BMA. Prev: Ho. Surg., Ho. Phys. & Ho. Off. Anaesth. Roy. Hosp. Wolverhampton.

PHILLIPS, Gerrard David Dorset County Hospital, Williams Avenue, Dorchester DT1 2JY — MB BS 1978 Lond.; MA Oxf. 1975; DM Soton. 1991; MRCP (UK) 1982; LMSSA Lond. 1978; FRCP 1998. Cons. Thoracic & Gen. Med. W. Dorset Gen. Hosps. NHS Trust. Socs: Eur. Respirat. Soc.; BMA; Brit. Thorac. Soc., Chairm. Educat. and Train. Comm. Prev: Sen. Regist. (Thoracic & Gen. Med.) Brompton Hosp. St. Geo. Hosp. Lond.; Clin. Research Fell. Soton. Univ.; Regist. (Med.) Roy. Vict. Hosp. Boscombe & W.m. Hosp. Lond.

PHILLIPS, Gillian Moir H2, Bolton General Hospital, Minerva Road, Farnworth, Bolton — BM 1984 Soton.; FRCS Ed. 1991. Staff Grade (Ophth.) Bolton Gen. Hosp. Prev: Regist. (Ophth.) Manch. Roy. Eye Hosp.; SHO Wythenshawe Hosp. Manch. & N. Manch. Gen. Hosp.; Tutor (Anat.) & SHO (Ophth.) Manch. Eye Hosp.

PHILLIPS, Glenys 22 Downham Chase, Timperley, Altrincham WA15 7TJ — MB BCh 1968 Wales; FFA RCS Eng. 1972. Cons. Anaesth. Wythenshawe Hosp. Manch.

PHILLIPS, Glyn Michael Greenhills Health Centre, 20 Greenhills Square, East Kilbride, Glasgow G75 8TT Tel: 01355 236331 Fax: 01355 234977; 36 Queensberry Avenue, Clarkston, Glasgow G76 7DU — MB ChB 1980 Leeds; MRCGP 1986; DRCOG 1988. (Univ. Leeds) Prev: Med. Off. HMS Revenge (S); SHO (A & E) RN Hosp. Plymouth; SHO (Dermat.) S.. Gen. Hosp. Glas.

PHILLIPS, Gwen Elizabeth Hodgson Oxford Road Medical Centre, 25 Oxford Road, Burnley BB11 3BB Tel: 01282 423603 Fax: 01282 832827; Meadow Bank, 7 Watt St, Burnley BB12 8AA Tel: 01282 426716 — MB BS 1980 Newc.; BA (Hons.) Camb. 1977. Prev: Clin. Med. Off. (Family Plann.) Burnley, Pendle & Rossendale HA.

PHILLIPS, Gwyn William (retired) Maes-yr-Afon, Felindre Road, Pencoed, Bridgend CF35 5PB Tel: 01656 860998 — MB BCh 1962 Wales; DObst RCOG 1969. Prev: Research Schol. (Pharmacol.) Welsh. Nat. Sch. Med. Cardiff.

PHILLIPS, Hamish Andrew Dept. of Clinical Oncology, Western General Hospital, Edinburgh EH4 2XU Tel: 0131 537 1000; 11 Comely Bank Avenue, Edinburgh EH4 1EW Tel: 0131 332 0207 — MB BChir 1986 Camb.; MSc (Clin. Oncol.) Ed. 1993; BSc (Hons.) St. And. 1984; MRCP (UK) 1990; FRCR 1995; MD Edin. 1998. Cons. (Clin. Oncol.) W. Gen. Hosp. Edin. Prev: Sen. Regist. (Clin. Oncol.) W.. Gen. Hosp. Edin.; Clin. Research Fell. (Clin. Oncol.) W.. Gen. Hosp. Edin.; Regist. (Clin. Oncol.) W.. Gen. Hosp. Edin.

PHILLIPS, Helen Claire Langholm Health Centre, Langholm, Langholm DG13 0LR; Arresgill Farm, Langholm DG13 0LR — MB ChB 1989 Manch.; MRCGP 1996; DCH 1991. GP Princip. Langholm. Socs: RCGP.

PHILLIPS, Helen Margaret Burney Street Practice, 48 Burney Street, London SE10 8EX Tel: 020 8858 0631 Fax: 020 8293 9616; 25 Wemyss Road, Blackheath, London SE3 0TG Tel: 020 8297 1600 Fax: 020 8297 1600 Email: helen@phillipsfamily.demon.co.uk — MB BS 1988 Lond.; MRCGP 1994; DRCOG 1992; DCH RCP Lond. 1991.

PHILLIPS, Helen Victoria 53 Tottehale Close, North Baddesley, Southampton SO52 9NQ Tel: 01703 733490 — MB ChB 1995 Birm.; MRCGP 1999; DRCOG 1997; Dip. Fac. Family Planning 1998. (Birm.) GP. Prev: Trainee GP/SHO Soton.; GP Regist. Soton.; GP Locum.

PHILLIPS, Mr Hugh 77 Newmarket Road, Norwich NR2 2HW Tel: 01603 613640 Fax: 01603 761554 Email: hphillip77@aol.com; Ashwellthorpe Grange, Ashwellthorpe, Norwich NR16 1ET Tel: 0150 841713 Fax: 01508 489644 — MB BS 1964 Lond.; BSc (Hons.) Lond. 1961; FRCS Eng. 1970. (St. Bart.) Cons. Orthop. Surg., Norf. & Norwich NHS Health Care Trust; Examr. Intercollegiate Bd. Orthop. Surg.; Extern. Examr. Final MB Camb.; Edit. Bd. JBJS & Hip. Internat.; Elected Mem. Counc. Roy. Coll. of Surg.s of Eng. Socs: Fell. BOA; Roy. Soc. Med.; Brit. Hip Soc. Prev: Regional Advisor Orthop. Surg. Roy. Coll. Surg. Eng.; Pres. RSM (Orthop. Sect.); Past Chairm. Specialist Adv. Comm. Orthop. Surg 1995-1997.

PHILLIPS, Iain Geoffrey The Health Centre, Carrington Way, Wincanton BA9 9JY Tel: 01963 32000 Fax: 01963 32146 Email: dr.phillips@wincantonhc.nhs.uk — MB BS 1985 Lond.; MRCGP 1990. (Charing Cross and Westminster)

PHILLIPS, Professor Ian 30 Fentiman Road, London SW8 1LF Tel: 020 7735 2489 Fax: 020 7735 2489 Email: iphillips@attglobal.net — MB BChir Camb. 1961; MA Camb. 1962, MD 1966; FRCP Lond. 1983, M 1978; FRCPath 1981, M 1969; FFPHM RCP (UK) 1997. (Camb. & St. Thos.) Emerit. Prof. Med. Microbiol. United. Med. & Dent. Schs. Guy's & St. Thos. Hosp. Lond.; Emerit. Hon. Cons. Bacteriol. Guy's & St. Thos. Hosp. Lond. Socs: (Ex-Pres.) Assn. Med. Microbiol.; (Ex-Chairm.) Brit. Soc. Antimicrobial Chemother.; (Ex-Pres.) Eur. Soc. Clin. Microbiol. & Infect. Dis. Prev: Civil Cons. (Microbiol.) RAF; Edr. Clin. Microbiol. & Infec.; Lect. (Med. Microbiol.) Makerere Univ. Coll. Kampala, Uganda.

PHILLIPS, Jack Herzyl 62 Montagu Court, Newcastle upon Tyne NE3 4JL Tel: 0191 285 3492 — MB ChB 1927 Leeds. (Leeds) On Surg. Staff Ellison Hall Hosp. Hebburn; Clin. Asst. Palmer Memor. Hosp. Jarrow; Cas. Off. Ingham Infirm. S. Shields; Fact. Doctor Vickers Armstrong, Newc. & Chas. Lennig & Co.; Mem. Local Med. Comm.; Admiralty Surg. & Agent; Chairm. Med. Bd. Nat. Insur. (Indust. Injuries) Act, 1946; Lect. & Examr. St. John Ambul. Assn.; Med. Ref. Pearl & Other Assur. Cos. Socs: N.. Cos. Med. Soc. Prev: Ho. Surg. Roy. Eye Hosp. Manch.; Res. Med. Off. Walsall Gen. Hosp.; Asst. MOH Maltby UDC.

PHILLIPS, James (retired) 65 Woodcote Road, West Timperley, Altrincham WA14 5PN Tel: 0161 969 4839 — MB ChB Aberd. 1936. Prev: SHO (Surg.) Roy. Albert Edwd. Infirm. Wigan.

PHILLIPS, James Neil Janssen-Cilag Ltd, PO Box 79, Saunderton, High Wycombe HP14 4HJ — MB ChB 1988 Bristol; MBA Lond. 1991; MRCGP 1994; DFFP 1994. Prev: Non-Exec. Dir. W. Sussex DHA.

PHILLIPS, James Ronald Nigel Consultant Physician, Queen Elizabeth Hospital, Gayton Road, King's Lynn PE30 4ET Tel: 01553

PHILLIPS

613895 Fax: 01553 613900 Email: james.phillips@klshosp.anglox.nhs.uk — MB BS 1989 Lond.; MRCP (UK) 1993. (Char. Cross & Westm.) Cons. Phys. (Gen. Med.) c/o the Elderly. Prev: Sen. Regist. (Gen. Med. & Elderly Care) Chelsea & W. Hosp. Lond.; Sen. Regist. (Gen. Med. & Elderly Care) Lister Hosp. Stevenage.

*PHILLIPS, James William 32 Villiers Road, Woodthorpe, Nottingham NG5 4FB — MB BS 1996 Newc.

PHILLIPS, Jane Hilary 95 Park Avenue, Ruislip HA4 7UL — MB ChB 1996 Leic.

PHILLIPS, Jason 20 Wellfield Close, Gorseinon, Swansea SA4 6BD — MB BCh 1992 Wales.

PHILLIPS, Jean Dorothy (retired) Bryn Hyfryd, Rhydwyn, Holyhead LL65 4ED Tel: 01407 730744 — MB ChB Liverp. 1951. Prev: SCMO Community Child Health Serv. Liverp. HA.

PHILLIPS, Jeannette Veronica Constantia, 18 Mill Road, Rochester ME2 3BT — MB BS 1980 Lond.; MRCP (UK) 1987; MRCPsych 1994.

PHILLIPS, Jeffrey Alan James Princess Alexandre Hospital, Harlow CM20 1QX — MB BS 1990 Lond.; BSc Lond. 1987; FRCA 1996. (St. Mary's Hosp. Med. Sch.) Cons. In Intens. Care & Anaesthetics. Prev: SHO (Anaesth.) St. Bart. Hosp., Homerton Hosp. Lond. & Hillingdon Hosp. Middx.; Specialist Regist. Rotat. (Anaesth.) UCH & Middlx. Hosps. Lond.

PHILLIPS, Jeremy Keith The Surgery, Lorne Street, Lochgilphead PA31 8LU Tel: 01546 602921 Fax: 01546 606735 — MRCS Eng. LRCP Lond. 1984; MRCGP 1990; DRCOG 1988.

PHILLIPS, John 26 Buckingham Terrace, Edinburgh EH4 3AE — MB ChB 1975 Ed.; MRCGP 1979.

PHILLIPS, John Andrew (retired) 60 Old Rossorry Road, Enniskillen BT74 7LF Tel: 028 6632 9359 Email: john@thephillipses.freeserve.co.uk — MB ChB Ed. 1962; MSc Lond. 1992; FRCP Ed. 1995; FRCP Lond. 1992; MRCP (UK) 1971; FRCPCH 1996; DCH Glas. 1964; DRCOG Lond. 1965. Prev: Paediat. Erne Hosp. Enniskillen.

PHILLIPS, Mr John Barrie (cons. rooms), 7 Greenhill Court, 25B Green Lane, Northwood HA6 2UZ Tel: 01923 826948; 15 Hill Crescent, Totteridge, London N20 8HB Tel: 020 8445 0932 Fax: 020 8445 8499 Email: johnbarriephillips@compuserve.com — MB BS Lond. 1959; FRCS Eng. 1965; MRCS Eng. LRCP Lond. 1960. (Univ. Coll. Lond. & Univ. Coll. Hosp.) N.wood & Pinner Dist. Hosp. & St. Vincent's Orthop. Hosp. Pinner; Assoc. Cons. Roy. Masonic Hosp. Lond; Hon. Cons. Orthop. Surg. Roy. Masonic Sch. Girls & Merchant Taylors Sch. Boys N.wood. Socs: Fell. Roy. Soc. Med. & BOA. Prev: Cons. Orthop. Surg. Mt. Vernon Hosp. N.wood, Harefield Hosp.; Sen. Regist. (Orthop.) Roy. Free Hosp. Lond. & Windsor Gp. Hosps.; Regist. Roy. Nat. Orthop. Hosp.

PHILLIPS, John Dale The Burnham Surgery, Foundry Lane, Burnham-on-Crouch CM0 8SJ Tel: 01621 782054 Fax: 01621 785592; 33 Maple Way, Burnham-on-Crouch CM0 8DF — MB BS 1963 Lond.; MRCS Eng. LRCP Lond. 1963; MRCGP 1976; DObst RCOG 1966. (St. Bart.) Socs: BMA (Clin. Ecology Gp.) & Brit. Soc. Med. & Dent. Hypn. Prev: Obst. Ho. Off. Forest Gate Hosp.; SHO (Neurol. & Chest Dis.) Whipps Cross Hosp. Lond.; SHO (Psychiat.) Claybury Hosp. Woodford Bridge.

PHILLIPS, Mr John Edward 32 Dalhousie Terrace, Edinburgh EH10 5PD Tel: 0131 447 3334 — MB ChB 1973 Liverp.; FRCS Ed. 1979. Cons. Orthop. Surg. Borders Gen. Hosp. Melrose. Prev: Sen. Regist. Lothian Health Bd; Lect. Univ. Edin.; Cons. Orthop. Surg. Khoula Hosp. Muscat, Oman.

PHILLIPS, John Ernest (retired) Hawkes Barn, Hawkes Lane, Bracon Ash, Norwich NR14 8EW Tel: 01508 578576 Fax: 01508 578576 — MB BCh 1959 Wales; FRCPsych 1987, M 1971; CRCP Canada 1968; DPM Eng. 1965. Prev: Cons. Psychiat. S. Devon Health Care Trust & Exe Vale Hosp. Exminster.

PHILLIPS, John Gareth Maxillo-Facial Unit, Glan Clwyd Hospital, Bodelwyddan, Rhyl LL18 5UJ Tel: 01745 534309 Fax: 01745 534309; 81 Marine Drive, Colwyn Bay LL28 4HT — MB ChB 1980 Bristol; LDS Durham 1962; MRCS Eng. LRCP Lond. 1981; FDS RCS Eng. 1974; FFD RCSI 1974; FDS RCPS Glas. 1973. Cons. Maxillofacial Unit Glan Clwyd Hosp. Bodelwyddan.

PHILLIPS, John Jeffery (retired) 102 Harewood Avenue, Bournemouth BH7 6NS Tel: 01202 394919 — MB ChB 1941 Leeds; MFCM 1974. Prev: Sen. Med. Off. E. Dorset Health Dist.

PHILLIPS, John Kendrick Field House, 53 Knowsley Road, Wilpshire, Blackburn BB1 9PN — MB ChB 1957 Ed.

PHILLIPS, John Martin (retired) 100A Hamilton Terrace, London NW8 9UP — MRCS Eng. LRCP Lond. 1954.

PHILLIPS, John Michael (retired) 25 Leverton Gate, Broome Manor, Swindon SN3 1ND Tel: 01793 527844 — MB BS 1957 Lond.; BSc Lond. 1954, MB BS 1957. Prev: GP Swindon.

PHILLIPS, John Norman 2 Kitcat Terrace, London E3 2SA — LMSSA 1947 Lond. (Lond. Hosp.)

PHILLIPS, John Peter Keith Avondale Health Centre, Avondale St., Bolton BL1 4JP Fax: 01204 493751; 8 Grasmere Avenue, Whitefield, Manchester M45 7GN Email: john@collis.demon.co.uk — MB ChB 1982 Manch.

PHILLIPS, Julia Katharine Haematology Department, Royal Hallamshire Hospital, Glossop Road, Sheffield S10 2JF Tel: 0114 271 1900; 57 Evelyn Road, Crookes, Sheffield S10 5FE Tel: 0114 268 7397 — MD Liverp. 1996; MB ChB Liverp. 1981; MRCP (UK) 1985; MRCPath 1997. (Liverp.) Sen. Regist. (Haemat.) Sheff. Train. Scheme. Prev: Lect. & Hon. Sen. Regist. (Haemat.) St. Thos. Hosp. Lond.; Regist. (Haemat.) Roy. Liverp. Hosp. & BRd.green Hosp. Liverp.; Research Fell. & Hon. Sen. Regist. (Haemat.) Roy. Liverp. Hosp.

PHILLIPS, Julia Margaret 87 Mayals Avenue, Mayals, Swansea SA3 5DD — MB ChB 1964 Birm.

PHILLIPS, June (retired) 17 Wilberforce Road, Cambridge CB3 0EQ Tel: 01223 358212 — MB BChir 1952 Camb.; MA, MB BChir Camb. 1952; Dip. Ven. Soc. Apoth. Lond. 1977. Clin. Asst. Dept. Genitourin. Med. Univ. Coll. Hosp. Lond.; Sessional Med. Off. Family Plann. Clinics Lond. Boro. Hampstead. Prev: Ho. Phys. Bedford Gen. Hosp.

PHILLIPS, June (retired) 15 Greenhill Road, Liverpool L18 6JJ Tel: 0151 724 1940 — MB ChB 1956 Liverp.; FFPHM RCP (UK) 1982, M 1974; DPH Liverp. 1959. Prev: Dir. Pub. Health Liverp. HA.

*PHILLIPS, Karin Anne 46 Granby Road, Edinburgh EH16 5NW — MB ChB 1994 Aberd.

PHILLIPS, Karl 10 Islay Drive, Newton Mearns, Glasgow G77 6UD — MB ChB 1981 Dundee; BMSc (Hons.) Dund 1978; MB ChB 1981; MRCPsych 1985. Cons. Psychiat. Dykebar Hosp. Paisley. Prev: Sen. Regist. Gtr. Glas. HB; Research Regist. Crighton Roy. Hosp. Dumfries; Regist. (Psychiat.) Roy. Dundee Liff Hosp.

PHILLIPS, Katherine Gemma Peacock Farmhouse, 29 Main St., Kirby Bellars, Melton Mowbray LE14 2EA — BM BS 1993 Nottm.

PHILLIPS, Kay Anne Pensby Walk Practice, 8 Pensby Walk, Miles Platting, Manchester M40 8GN Tel: 0161 205 2867 Fax: 0161 205 2972 — MB ChB 1990 Manch.

PHILLIPS, Keith Anthony 107 The Farthings, Astley Village, Chorley PR7 1SH — MB ChB 1973 Manch.; FFA RCS Eng. 1980. Cons. (Anaesth.) Wigan HA.

PHILLIPS, Kenneth David 10 Harley Street, London W1N 1AA Tel: 020 8868 0338; 47 Azalea Walk, Pinner HA5 2EH Tel: 020 8868 7426 Fax: 020 8868 7426 Email: kenneth.p@which.net — MB BS 1954 Lond. Socs: Brit. Soc. Med. & Dent. Hypn.; Brit. Soc. Experim. & Clin. Hypn.

PHILLIPS, Kevin Willow Tree Lodge, 9 Grosvenor Place, Beverley HU17 8LY — MB ChB 1986 Leeds; MRCOG 1991. Cons. (O & G) Castlehill Hosp. Cotttingham. Socs: Glas. Obst. & Gyn. Soc. Prev: Sen. Regist. (O & G) Glas. Roy. Infirm Glas.; Regist. (O & G) Ayrsh. Centr. Hosp. & Qu. Mother's Hosp. Glas.; Regist. (O & G) ChristCh. Wom. Hosp., NZ.

PHILLIPS, Laurence (Surgery), 266 Lea Bridge Road, London E10 Tel: 020 8539 1221; 194 Clarence Gate Gardens, Glentworth St., London NW1 6AU Tel: 020 7723 5439 — MRCS Eng. LRCP Lond. 1947. (Middlx.) Socs: Local Med. Comm. Co. Lond. Prev: Clin. Asst. (Gyn.) Hackney Hosp.

*PHILLIPS, Leighton John Brockencote, Chaddesley Corbett, Kidderminster DY10 4PT — MB ChB 1996 Leic.

PHILLIPS, Lesley Jane City Way Surgery, 67 City Way, Rochester ME1 2AY Tel: 01634 843351 Fax: 01634 830421 — MB BS 1986 Lond.; DRCOG 1988. Prev: Trainee GP Dartford & Gravesham VTS.

PHILLIPS, Lionel (retired) High Prospect, Jarman Road, Sutton, Macclesfield SK11 0HJ — LRCP LRCS Ed. LRFPS Glas. 1940; FRCPath 1971, M 1963. Prev: Cons. Path. Macclesfield Dist. Gen. Hosp.

PHILLIPS, Lisa Cripps Postgraduate Centre, Northampton General Hospital, Cliftonville, Northampton NN1 5BD — MB BS 1992 Lond.

PHILLIPS, Louis Arthur 17 Albion Square, London E8 4ES Tel: 020 7249 2891 Fax: 020 7249 2891 Email: louis.phillips@bt.internet.com — MB BS Lond. 1953; DA Eng. 1956. (Middlx.) Freelance Med. Writer. Prev: Clin. Research Phys. May & Baker Ltd. Dagenham; Med. Adviser Allen & Hanburys Ltd. Bethnel Green; Cons. Anaesth. S. Pacific Health Serv. Fiji.

PHILLIPS, Louise Angela 325 Boldmere Road, Sutton Coldfield B73 5HQ — MB ChB 1997 Manch. (Manchester) Alder Hey Childr.s Hosp. Liverp.

PHILLIPS, Malcolm Edward Charing Cross Hospital, Fulham Palace Road, London W6 8RF Tel: 020 8846 7592 Fax: 020 8846 7589; The Ridings, 26 Pelhams Walk, Esher KT10 8QD Tel: 01372 461098 — MB BS 1964 Lond.; MD Lond. 1979; FRCP Lond. 1986; MRCP (UK) 1970; MRCS Eng. LRCP Lond. 1964. (Char. Cross) Cons. Phys. & Nephrol. Char. Cross Hosp. Lond.; Hon. Cons. Nephrol. Chelsea & W.m. Hosp. Lond.; Hon. Cons. Phys. & Nephrol. W. Middlx. Univ. Hosp. Isleworth. Socs: Europ. Dialysis & Transpl. Assn. Prev: Lect., Hon. Sen. Regist. & Regist. (Med.) Char. Cross Hosp. Lond.; Wellcome Research Fell. (Nephrol.) Univ. Naples, Italy.

PHILLIPS, Malcolm John (retired) Luffield Cottage, Rumwell, Taunton TA4 1EJ Tel: 01823 461509 — MB ChB 1954 Sheff.; FRCPath 1976, M 1964; DTM & H Eng. 1964; DCP Lond 1960. Hons. Cons. Clin. Haemat. Taunton & Som. Hosp. NHS Trust; Clin. Tutor Univ. Bristol; Research Fell. Univ. Exeter. Prev: Ho. Phys. Profess. Med. & Cardiol. Units City Gen. Hosp. Sheff.

PHILLIPS, Malcolm Kenneth Crawcrook Medical Centre, Back Chamberlain Street, Crawcrook, Ryton NE40 4TZ Tel: 0191 413 2243 Fax: 0191 413 8098; Tynedale, 53 Woodcroft Road, Wylam NE41 8DH Tel: 01661 852546 — MB BS 1970 Newc.; MRCGP 1974. Prev: Trainee GP VTS.

PHILLIPS, Margaret Frances Pulmonary & Rehabilitation Research Group, University Clinical Department at Aintree, University Hospital Aintree, Liverpool L9 7AL Tel: 0151 529 2946 Fax: 0151 529 2931 Email: mphillip@liv.ac.uk — MB BCh 1989 Wales; BSc (Hons.) Physiol. Wales 1986; MRCP 1992. (Univ. Wales Coll. Med.) Hon. Specialist Regist. (Rehabil. Med.) Fazakerley Hosp. Liverp.; Lect. (Med. Rehabil.) Univ. of Liverp. Socs: Brit. Soc. Rehabil. Med.; Soc. for Research in Rehabil.; World Muscle Soc. Prev: Research Fell. Inst. Med. Genetics Univ. Wales Coll. Med.; SHO (A & E) Sandwell Dist. Gen. Hosp. W. Bromwich; SHO (Med.) Dudley Rd. Hosp. Birm. & Roy. Gwent Hosp. Newport.

PHILLIPS, Marie Gabrielle Anne 3 Ardleigh Court, Ardleigh, Colchester CO7 7LA — MB BS 1981 Lond.; MRCPath 1988. Cons. Microbiol. Ninewells Hosp. & Med. Sch. Dundee. Prev: Sen. Regist. & Hon. Lect. Ninewells Hosp. & Med. Sch. Dundee.

***PHILLIPS, Mark Anthony Thomas** 69 Walter Street, Stockton-on-Tees TS18 3PP — MB ChB 1995 Sheff.

PHILLIPS, Mark Christopher Read Bird-in-Eye Surgery, Uckfield Community Hospital, Framfield Road, Uckfield TN22 5AW Tel: 01825 763196; Delgany, Belmont Road, Uckfield TN22 1BP Tel: 01825 763191 — MB BS 1973 Lond. (St. Bart.) Clin. Asst. Uckfield Hosp. Prev: SHO (Orthop.) Barnet Gen. Hosp.; Ho. Phys. & Ho. Surg. Orpington Hosp.

PHILLIPS, Mark Leslie Clifford The Health Centre, Charles Street, Langholm DG13 0JY; Arresgill Farm, Langholm DG13 0LR — MB ChB 1988 Liverp.; MRCGP 1992; DTM & H Liverp. 1993. (Univ. Liverp.) SHO (Orthop. & Trauma) Lancaster; Resid. Med. Off. Chatham Is. NZ. Prev: Trainee GP Lancaster VTS; Ho. Phys. & Ho. Surg. Ormskirk Dist. Gen. Hosp.

PHILLIPS, Martin The Newbridge Surgery, 255 Tettenhall ROad, Wolverhampton WV6 0ED Tel: 01902 751420 Fax: 01902 747936 — MB BS 1977 Lond.; DA (UK) 1985. (St. Mary's)

PHILLIPS, Martin Geoffrey Dept. of Gastroenterology, University Hospital Lewisham, Lewisham High St., London SE13 6LH; 14 Camborne Road, Southfields, London SW18 4BJ — MB BS 1991 Lond.; BSc Lond. 1988; MRCP (UK) 1994. (St Mary's Hospital) Specialist Regist.Univ. Hosp. Lewisham. Socs: Asst. Sec. BMA; BASL. Prev: Regist. (Hepatol.) Inst. Of Liver Studies, King's Coll. Hosp. Lond.; Regist. (Gastrol.) Roy. Surrey Co. Hosp. Guildford; SHO (Gen. Med.) Addenbrooke's Hosp. Camb.

PHILLIPS, Martin Ronald James Street Practice, 40 James Street, Crossgar, Downpatrick BT30 9JU — MB BCh BAO 1967 Belf. (Belf.)

PHILLIPS, Mary (retired) 8 The Lancers, Old Barrack Road, Woodbridge IP12 4TZ Tel: 01394 380143 — MB BS Lond. 1964; DObst RCOG 1966.

PHILLIPS, Mary Gordon (retired) Southwood, Gordon Road, Horsham RH12 2EF Tel: 01403 52894 — MB BS Lond. 1945.

PHILLIPS, Mary Louise Institute of Psychiatry, De Crespigny Park, London SE5 8AF Tel: 020 7848 0379 Fax: 020 7848 0379 — MB BChir 1990 Camb.; MD 2000 Camb.; MSc Keele 1989; MA Camb. 1990, BA 1986; MRCPsych 1994. (Cambridge) Sen. Lect. Inst. of Psychiat. Lond.; Co Dir. Depersonalisation Research Unit, Maudsley Hosp.; Hon. Cons. Psychiat., Maudsley Hosp. Prev: Hon. Lect. Inst. of Psychiat. Lond.; Clin. Lect. Inst. of Psychiat. Lond.; Hon Sen. Lect.. Inst. of Psychiatary Lond.

PHILLIPS, Mr Michael John Department Vascular Surgery, Southampton General Hospital, Southampton SO16 6YD — BM 1986 Soton.; 1998 FRCS (Gen. Sug.); 1998 MS Southampton; FRCS Eng. 1990. Cons. Vasc. & Gen. Surg., Soton. Univ. NHS Trust. Socs: VSS GB & Ire.; Assn. of Surg.s. Prev: Regist. (Gen. Surg.)Wessex Rotat.; Vasc. Research Fell. Thrombosis Research Inst. Lond.; Vasc. Fell., Roy. Adelaide Hosp.

PHILLIPS, Michelle Elaine 22 Bramley Road, Bramhall, Stockport SK7 2DP — MB BS 1993 Lond.

PHILLIPS, Morley Clayton Owen (retired) Pendragon, Station Hill, Lelant, St Ives TR26 3DJ Tel: 01736 752282 — MA Camb. 1955; MB BS Lond. 1961; MRCS Eng. LRCP Lond. 1960; DObst RCOG 1962. Prev: Ho. Surg. Surgic. Unit St. Mary's Hosp. Lond.

PHILLIPS, Nansi Eluned Local Health Partnerships NHS Trust, Elm Street Clinic, Elm St., Ipswich IP1 1HB Tel: 01473 275200 Email: nansi@copthall.freeserve.co.uk; Great Copt Hall, Bildeston, Ipswich IP7 7BH — MB BCh 1975 Wales; FRCPCH 1997; DCH Eng. 1978. p/t Cons. Community Child Health (Audiol.), L.H.P. NHS Trust, Ipswich. Prev: SCMO (Child Health) E. Suff. HA.

PHILLIPS, Naomi Noble Vinayakumar Radford Health Centre, Ilkeston Road, Nottingham NG7 3GW Tel: 0115 979 1313 Fax: 0115 979 1470 — MB BS 1971 Osmania; DObst RCOG 1974. (Gandhi Med. Coll. Hyderabad) Prev: SHO (O & G) Doncaster Roy. Infirm. & Nottm. Hosp. Wom.

PHILLIPS, Mr Nicholas Ian Department of Neurosurgery, Leeds General Infirmary, Great George St., Leeds LS1 3EX — MB ChB 1988 Ed.; PhD Lond. 1983; BSc Leeds 1980; FRCS Eng. 1992; FRCS (SN) 1996. SHO Rotat. (Surg.) Leeds Gen. Infirm.; Regist. (Neurosurg.) Qu. Med. Centre Nottm.; Cons. Neurosurg. Leeds Gen. Infirm. Prev: SHO (Cas.) Manch. Roy. Infirm.; Ho. Phys. Edin. Roy. Infirm.

PHILLIPS, Nicholas James 12 Peregrine Close, Hartford, Huntingdon PE29 1UZ — BChir 1990 Camb.

PHILLIPS, Noble Vinaya-Kumar 14 Pavillion Road, Bestwood Lodge, Nottingham NG5 8NL Tel: 0115 202077; (Surgery) 112 Graylands Road, Bilborough, Nottingham NG8 4FD Tel: 0115 929 2358 — MB BS 1969 Osmania; DA Eng. 1975. (Osmania Med. Coll. Hyderabad & India) Prev: Regist. (Anaesth.) Nottm. City Hosp.

PHILLIPS, Patricia Coulson The Keston House Medical Practice, 70 Brighton Road, Purley CR8 2LJ Tel: 020 8660 8292 Fax: 020 8763 2142 — MB BS 1974 Lond.

PHILLIPS, Paul David Scarborough Hospital, Scarborough YO12 6QL; 4 Welbourn Drive, Seamer, Scarborough YO12 4RP — MB ChB 1993 Leeds. (Leeds) GP/Regist. ScarBoro. VTS.

PHILLIPS, Penelope Kate 9 Witham Lodge, Witham CM8 1HG — BM 1991 Soton.

PHILLIPS, Peter Alan Department of Medicine for the elderly, Ipswich Hospital, Heath Road Wing, Ipswich IP4 5PD Tel: 01473 704134 Fax: 01473 704166 Email: peter.phillips@ntlworld.com; 118 Constable Road, Ipswich IP4 2XA Tel: 01473 401184 Fax: 01473 704166 — MB BS 1974 Queensland; MB BS (1st cl. Hons.) Queensland 1974; FRCP Lond. 1995. Cons. Phys. (Geriat. Med + Gen. Med..) Ipswich Hosp.; Lead Clinician, Dept. of Med. for the Elderly, Ipswich Hosp. Socs: Brit. Geriat. Soc. (Regional Sec.); Tissue Viability Soc.; Internat. Continence Soc. Prev: Dir. Geriat. Med. P. Chas. Hosp. Brisbane, Austral.

PHILLIPS, Peter David Department of Anaesthesia, Norfolk & Norwich, Health Care NHS Trust, Norwich NR1 3SR Tel: 01603 287086 — MB BS 1976 Lond.; BSc (Biochem.) Birm. 1967; FFA RCS Lond. 1981. Cons. Anaesth. Norf. & Norwich Healthcare NHS Trust.

PHILLIPS

PHILLIPS, Peter Gerard 67 Penwinnick Road, St Austell PL25 5DS — MB BS 1993 Lond.

PHILLIPS, Peter James Giffords Surgery, 28 Lowbourne, Melksham SN12 7EA Tel: 01225 703370; Giffords, Lowbourne, Melksham Tel: 01225 703320 — MB ChB 1974 Bristol; MRCGP 1981; DCH Eng. 1980; DRCOG 1979. Gen. Med. Pract. Melksham.

PHILLIPS, Peter Rolleston Pendyffryn Medical Group, Ffordd Pendyffryn, Prestatyn LL19 9DH Tel: 01745 886444 Fax: 01745 889831 — MB ChB 1981 Manch.; BSc (Med. Sci.) St. And. 1978.

PHILLIPS, Philippa Margaret 76 Ormiston Road, Greenwich, London SE10 0LN Tel: 020 8853 4009 — BM BCh 1987 Oxf.; MA Camb. 1988; FRCOphth 1994; MCOphth 1990. (Oxf.) Clin. Asst. Qu. Mary's Hosp. Lond. Prev: Regist. (Ophth.) Greenwich Dist. Hosp. Lond.; Research Fell. (Ophth.) Roy. Free Hosp. Lond.; SHO (Ophth.) Roy. Free Hosp. Lond.

PHILLIPS, Rachel Rhodes 144 Walton Street, Oxford OX1 2HG Email: rachelrp@aol.com — MB ChB 1982 Leeds; MRCP (UK) 1986; FRCR 1990; DCH RCP Lond. 1984. (Univ. Leeds) Cons. Radiol. Whittington Hosp. Lond.; Hon. Sen. Lect. Dept. Med. Imaging UCL. Socs: Radiol. Soc. N. Amer.; Brit. Soc. Skeletal Radiol.; NW Soc. Paediat. Radiol. (USA, Canad). Prev: Mem. Standing Comm. Mems. RCP; Mem. Manpower Advisory Panel RCP; Clin. Fell. (Magnetic Resonance) Leopold Muller Magnetic Resonance Unit St. Bart. Hosp. Lond.

PHILLIPS, Rex Philip, CB, OBE, Surg. Rear-Admiral Retd. Langstone House, Langstone Vill., Havant PO9 1RY Tel: 01705 484668 — MB BS 1937 Durh.; DO Eng. 1951. (Durh.) Socs: BMA. Prev: Med. Off. i/c RN Hosp. Plymouth & Command Med. Off. to Flag Off.; Plymouth; Hon. Surg. to HM the Qu..

PHILLIPS, Rhodri Linkwood, Hornbeam Lane, London E4 7QT — MB BCh 1992 Wales.

PHILLIPS, Richard Charles Saxonbrook Medical, Maidenbower Square, Crawley RH10 7QH Tel: 01293450400 Fax: 01293 450401 Email: richard@saxonbrook.co.uk; 156 Buckswood Drive, Crawley RH11 8JF Tel: 01293 513317 — MB BS 1972 Lond.; MRCGP 1976; DObst RCOG 1975; Cert FPA 1976. (St. Geo.) Sen. Partner Saxonbrook Med.; Med. Off. to Fire Brig. Prev: Trainee GP Mid-Sussex VTS; Ho. Phys. Good Hope Hosp. Sutton Coldfield; Ho. Surg. Cuckfield Hosp.

PHILLIPS, Richard John Maxwell The Goffin Consultancy Ltd., The Riding House, Bossingham Rd., Stelling Minnis, Keighley CT4 6AZ Tel: 01227 709220 Fax: 01227 709220 Email: goffin.network@virgin.net; Riding House, Bossingham Road, Stelling Minnis, Canterbury CT4 6AZ Tel: 01227 709618 Email: richard_jm.phillips@virgin.net — MB BS 1980 Lond.; MBA Kingston 1991; MFPM RCP (UK) 1990; DPM Eng. 1987. (St. Mary's Hospital Medical School) Princip. & Managing Dir.; Hon. Sen. Lect. Dept. Managem. Univ. St. And. Socs: Brit. Soc. Antimicrob. Chemother.; Health Economic Study Gp.; Brit. Assn. Pharm. Phys. Prev: Head of Outcomes Research Pfizer Ltd. Sandwich Kent; Gp. Med. Adviser Pfizer Ltd. Sandwich Kent; SHO (Anaesth.) Dewsbury Gen. Hosp. & Wakefield HA.

PHILLIPS, Richard John Wyndham The New Surgery, Linom Road, Clapham, London SW4 7PB Tel: 020 7274 4220 Fax: 020 7737 0205 — BM BCh 1978 Oxf.; MA Camb. 1980; MRCP (UK) 1985. Sen. Lect. (Gen. Pract.) UMDS. Prev: Brit. Heart Foundat. Research Fell. (Cardiovasc. Med.) St. Geo. Hosp. Med. Sch. Lond.

PHILLIPS, Richard Kenneth (retired) 4 Channel View, Penarth CF64 5DQ Tel: 01222 709437 — MRCS Eng. LRCP Lond. 1941; DIH Eng. 1950. Prev: Sen. Med. Off. David Brown Corp.

PHILLIPS, Richard Morgan (retired) Cheslyn, Station Road, Barlaston, Stoke-on-Trent ST12 9DE Tel: 0178 139 2638 — MB BS 1953 Lond.; MRCS Eng. LRCP Lond. 1943; FRCPsych 1972; DPM Lond. 1950. Prev: Chief Asst. (Psych. Med.) St. Thos. Hosp.

PHILLIPS, Robert Charles, Wing Cdr. RAF Med. Br. 9 Mansion Hill, Halton, Aylesbury HP22 5NL — MB ChB 1980 Ed.; MRCGP 1986; DRCOG 1985; Dip. Family Plann. 1982; DAvMed. 1995.

PHILLIPS, Robert Charles Stuart Colne Health Centre, Market St., Colne BB8 0LJ Tel: 01282 863230 Fax: 01282 870381; Lansdowne, Coates Lane, Barnoldswick, Colne BB18 6HJ Tel: 01282 815434 — BM BS 1984 Nottm.; BMedSci Nottm. 1981; DRCOG 1986; DCH RCP Lond. 1986.

PHILLIPS, Robert Hugh Stanford Cade Department of Clinical Oncology, Westminster Hospital, Dean Ryle St., London SW1P 2AP Tel: 020 8746 8000 Fax: 020 8746 8111; 7 Wonford Close, Kingston upon Thames KT2 7XA Tel: 020 8949 1705 — BM BCh 1971 Oxf.; MA, BM BCh Oxf. 1971; FRCP Lond. 1989; FRCR Eng. 1977; MRCP (UK) 1978; DMRT Eng. 1975. Cons. Radiother. & Phys. Med. Oncol. W.m. Hosp. Lond.; Hon. Cons. Radiother. Richmond, Twickenham, Roehampton & Kingston & Esher Has; Hon. Cons. Radiother. The Army. Socs: FRCR; Fell. Roy. Soc. Med. (Mem. Counc., Sect. Radiol); Fell. RCP.

PHILLIPS, Robert Michael 94 Malcolm Road, Peterculter AB14 0XB — MB ChB 1987 Aberd.

PHILLIPS, Mr Robert Sneddon (retired) 11 St John Street, Manchester M3 4DW Tel: 0161 832 9999 Fax: 0161 834 7855 — MB ChB 1956 Ed.; FRCS Eng. 1991; FRCS Ed. 1959. Prev: Cons. Orthop. Surg. N. Manch. Health Dist.

***PHILLIPS, Robert Stephen** 35 Church La, Marston, Oxford OX3 0PT — BM BCh 1997 Oxf.

PHILLIPS, Professor Robin Kenneth Stewart St Marks Hospital, Harrow HA1 3UJ Tel: 020 8235 4251 Fax: 020 8235 4277 Email: marie.gun@cancer.org.uk — MB BS 1975 Lond.; MS Lond. 1985; FRCS Eng. 1979. (Roy. Free) p/t Cons. Surg. St. Marks Hosp. Lond.; Hon.Prof. of colorectal Surg. Imperial Coll. Lond.; Dean St Mark's Acad. Inst.; Dir. Thames Region Polyposis Registry; Cancer Research UK; Pres, Brit Colostomy Assoc; Civil. cons in colorectal surg to the Roy. Navy. Socs: FRSM; Assn. Coloproct.Counc. mem for NW Thames; Roy. Soc. Med. (Vice-Pres. Counc. Coloproctol. Sector). Prev: Cons. Surg. Homerton Hosp. Lond.; Sen. Lect. & Hon. Cons. Surg. St. Bart. Hosp. Lond.; CRC Research Fell. & Hon. Sen. Regist. (Surg.) Large Bowel Cancer Project St. Mary's Hosp. Lond.

PHILLIPS, Mr Rodney (retired) 16 Old Hall Road, Whitefield, Manchester M45 7QW Tel: 0161 740 7824 — MB ChB 1961 Manch.; FRCS Eng. 1967; MRCS Eng. LRCP Lond. 1961. Prev: Sen. Regist. Welsh Hosp. Bd. & United Cardiff Hosps.

PHILLIPS, Professor Rodney Ernest Nuffield Department of Clinical Medicine, John Radcliffe Hospital, Headington, Oxford OX3 9DU Tel: 01865 221478 Fax: 01865 220993 Email: profmed@ndm.ox.ac.uk — MD 1987 Oxf.; MA Ox. 1995; MD Melbourne 1987; MB BS Melbourne 1976; FRACP 1983; FRCP 1995. Prof. of Med. Univ. Oxf.; Prof.ial Fell. Wolfson Coll. Oxf.; Hon. Cons. Phys. Oxon. Radcliffe Ch.ill Trust. Prev: Clin. Reader (Clin. Med.) Univ. Oxf.; Wellcome Trust Sen. Clin. Research Fell.; Wellcome Lect. (Trop. Med.) John Radcliffe Hosp. Oxf.

PHILLIPS, Rosalind Alethea (retired) Cheslyn, Barlaston, Stoke-on-Trent ST12 9DE Tel: 01782 372638 — MB BS 1952 Lond.; DCH Eng. 1955; DObst RCOG 1954. Prev: Clin. Asst. (Cardiac) City Gen. Hosp. Stoke-on-Trent.

PHILLIPS, Rosemary Helen (Maxwell) Princess Alexandra Hospital NHS Trust, Harlow CM20 1QX Tel: 01279 444455 — MB BS 1990 Lond.; BSc Lond. 1987; MRCP (UK) 1993. (St. Mary's Hosp. Med. Sch. Lond.) p/t Specialist Regist. (Gastrol.) S. E. Thames. Socs: Assoc. Mem. Roy. Soc. Med. Prev: SpR (Liver Unit) King's Coll. Hosp. Lond.; Research Regist. (Gastroenterol.) St. Thos. Hosp, Rayne Inst.; Regist. (Gen. Med. & Gastroenterol.) St. Thos. Hosp. Lond.

PHILLIPS, Roy Percy, VRD (retired) 51 Church Road, Whitchurch, Cardiff CF14 2DY Tel: 01222 625300 — BSc Wales 1948, MB BCh 1951; MRCGP 1962. Prev: Ho. Surg. & SHO (Paediat.) Llandough Hosp.

PHILLIPS, Russell Langley 15 Underne Avenue, London N14 7ND — MB BS 1997 Lond. (Royal Free)

PHILLIPS, Mr Russell Picton Department of Ophthalmology, Arrowe Park Hospital, Upton, Wirral CH49 5PE Tel: 0151 604 7193; Redstones, Redstones Farm, Arrowe Brook Lane, Wirral CH49 3NY Tel: 0151 677 9545 — MB ChB 1982 Birm.; MD Birm. 1982; FRCS (Ophth.) Ed. 1987; FCOphth 1988; DO RCS Eng. 1986. Cons. Wirral Hosps. Trust; Hon. Lect. Univ. Liverp.; Hon. Research Assoc. Univ. Aberd. Prev: Sen. Regist. (Ophth.) Aberd. Roy. Infirm.; Regist. (Ophth.) Aberd. Roy. Infirm.; SHO (Ophth.) Birm & Midl. Eye Hosp.

PHILLIPS, Ruth Swarna Latha (surgery) Bramley Crescent, Valley Park, Bottesford, Scunthorpe — MB BS 1971 Osmania. (Osmania Med. Coll. Hyderabad) Clin. Med. Off. Scunthorpe HA. Prev: SHO (O & G) Montagu Hosp. MexBoro..

PHILLIPS, Sally Joyce Family Planning Service, Cornwall Healthcare Trust, 2 St Clement Vean, Tregolls Road, Truro TR1 1RN Tel: 01872 74242 — MB BS 1960 Lond.; MRCS Eng. LRCP Lond. 1960. (St. Mary's) Clin. Dir. (Family Plann. Serv.) Cornw. Healthcare

Trust. Prev: Ho. Phys. Paddington Green Childr. Hosp.; Ho. Surg. Paddington Gen. Hosp.

PHILLIPS, Samantha Jane 54 Audmore Road, Gnosall, Stafford ST20 0HE — MB BS 1989 Lond.

PHILLIPS, Samuel Graham (retired) 98 Stafford Road, Bloxwich, Walsall WS3 3PA Tel: 01922 476670 — MB ChB 1948 Birm.; FFPHM 1983, M 1974; DPH Glas. 1961; DObst RCOG 1958; DTM & H Eng. 1955. Prev: Cons. Pub. Health Med. Wolverhampton HA.

***PHILLIPS, Sara Dawn** 15 Rhodes Drive, Sunnybank, Bury BL9 8NH — BChir 1996 Camb.

PHILLIPS, Sarah Louise Orthopaedic Department, King's College Hospital, Denmark Hill, London SE5 9RS Tel: 020 7346 3523 Email: sarah.phillips@kingshc.nhs.uk; 69B Shoorers Hill Road, Blackheath, London SE3 7HU Tel: 01423 781618, 020 8853 4847 Email: slphillips@btinternet.com — MB BS 1986 Lond.; BSc Lond. 1983; FRCS Eng. 1991; FRCS (Orth.) 1997. Cons. Orthop. Surg. King's Coll. Hosp. Prev: Sen. Regist. Rotat. (Orthop.) King's Coll. Hosp.

PHILLIPS, Sharon 12 The Crest, Surbiton KT5 8JZ Tel: 020 8399 7451; 14 Camborne Road, Southfields, London SW18 4BJ Tel: 020 8875 1512 — MB BS 1994 Lond.; BSc Lond. 1993; DRCOG Lond. 1996. (Charing Cross & Westm.) GP Regist.; SHO (Paediat.) Epsom Gen. Hosp.

PHILLIPS, Sharon Louise The Oakwood Surgery, Masham Road, Cantley, Doncaster DN4 6BU Tel: 01302 537611 Fax: 01302 371804 — MB ChB Sheff. 1988; MRCGP 1992; DRCOG 1992. Prev: Trainee GP/SHO Doncaster Roy. Infirm. VTS; Ho. Phys. Doncaster Roy. Infirm.; Ho. Surg. (Orthop.) N.. Gen. Hosp. Sheff.

PHILLIPS, Sheelagh Helen 13 Westbourne Crescent, Bearsden, Glasgow G61 — MB BCh BAO 1970 Dub.; DCH RCPS Glas. 1974; DPH Glas. 1974; DObst RCOG 1972. Clin. Med. Off. Gtr. Glas. Health Bd. Prev: Mem. Wom. Doctors Retainer Scheme Gtr. Glas. Health Bd.; Clin. Med. Off. Gtr. Glas. Health Bd.

PHILLIPS, Shon 7 Gladeside Close, Thornhill, Cardiff CF14 9HU — MB BCh 1992 Wales.

PHILLIPS, Sian 10 Hanbury Close, Whitchurch, Cardiff CF14 2TB Tel: 029 2052 1048 Email: drsian@msn.com; Department of Radiology, University Hospital of Wales, Heath Park, Cardiff CF4 4XN Tel: 029 2074 7747 Email: phillipss1@cardiff.ac.uk — MB BCh 1989 Wales; MRCP (UK) 1993; FRCR 1998. (University of Wales College of Medicine) Specialist Regist. (Radiol.).

PHILLIPS, Sian Eleri Briton Ferry Health Centre, Hunter Street, Briton Ferry, Neath SA11 5SF Tel: 01639 812270 Fax: 01639 813019; 3 Llys Hebog, Birchgrove, Swansea SA7 9PY Tel: 01792 814813 — MB BCh 1987 Wales; MRCGP 1991. Princip. in Gen. Pract.

PHILLIPS, Simon Jeremy Church Holding, Etchilhampton, Devizes SN10 3JL Tel: 01380 860291 — MB BS Lond. 1966; MPhil Bath 1990; MRCS Eng. LRCP Lond. 1966; DCH Eng. 1970; DObst RCOG 1968. (St. Bart.) Hon. Co-Dir. Inst. Refugee Healthcare Studies PG Med. Sch., Univ. of Bath. Socs: Clin. Soc. Bath. Prev: Phys. Devizes & Dist. Hosp.; Research Regist. (Neonat. Paediat.) & SHO (Paediat.) Roy. Berks. Hosp. Reading; SHO (Obst.) Battle Hosp. Reading.

PHILLIPS, Simon Marcus The Paddocks, 50 Bristol Road, Frenchay, Bristol BS16 1LQ — MB BChir 1994 Camb.; MA Oxon. 1998; FRCS (Eng) 1997. (Univ. of Cambridge) Specialist Regist. (Gen. Surg.) NW Thames.

***PHILLIPS, Simon Robert** Thatchers' Court, Traps Lane, New Malden KT3 4SQ Tel: 020 8949 1705 Fax: 020 8942 3545 — MB BS 1998 Lond.; MB BS Lond 1998.

PHILLIPS, Sophie Anne Queen Alexandra Hospital, Cosham, Portsmouth PO6 3LY; 5 Tilford Road, Farnham GU9 8DJ — BM 1990 Soton.; FRCS 1999 (Trauma & Orthopaedics); FRCS Eng. 1994. Regist. Rotat. (Orthop.) Wessex.

PHILLIPS, Spencer Lea Bridge Road Surgery, 266 Lea Bridge Road, Leyton, London E10 7LD Tel: 020 8539 1221 Fax: 020 8539 2303 — MB BS 1978 Lond.; MRCS Eng. LRCP Lond. 1977.

PHILLIPS, Stephen John 47 Oakwood Drive, Clydach, Swansea SA8 4DF — MB BCh 1996 Wales.

PHILLIPS, Stephen Walter High Street Surgery, High Street, Pewsey SN9 5AQ Tel: 01672 563511 Fax: 01672 563004; Bield House, Church Road, Woodborough, Pewsey SN9 5PH Tel: 01672 851564 — MB BS 1975 Lond.; MRCS Eng. LRCP Lond. 1975; MRCGP 1980; DRCOG 1979.

PHILLIPS, Stewart Mark Anthony 132 Highfield Road, Hall Green, Birmingham B28 0HU — MB ChB 1983 Birm. Regist. (Surg.) Gen. Hosp. Birm.

PHILLIPS, Susan 12 Lymister Avenue, Rotherham S60 3DD — MB ChB 1975 Sheff.; MRCPsych 1981. Sen. Regist. Brighton Clinic Newc. Gen. Hosp.; Cons. Psycho. Geriat. Kingsway Hosp. Derby. Prev: Sen. Regist. Doncaster Roy. Infirm.; Regist. Sheff. HA; Hon. Sec. Coll. Trainee Comm. Roy. Coll. Psychiat.

PHILLIPS, Susan Elizabeth Caldicot Medical Group, Gray Hill Surgery, Woodstock Way, Caldicot, Newport NP26 4DB Tel: 01291 420282 Fax: 01291 425853; Brookside, Well Lane, Llanfair Discoed, Chepstow NP16 6LP Tel: 01633 400669 — MB BS Lond. 1970; MRCS Eng. LRCP Lond. 1970; DObst RCOG 1973; DCH RCP Lond. 1972. (Roy. Free) GP.

PHILLIPS, Suzanne 19 Dragon Close, Burnham-on-Crouch CM0 8PW — MB BS 1992 Lond.; DRCOG 1996; MRCGP 1997. (Royal Free Hospital) Asst. GP.

PHILLIPS, Suzanne Mary 130a Upper Westwood, Bradford-on-Avon BA15 2DE — MB BS 1998 Lond.; MB BS Lond 1998; BSc Lond. 1995. (St. George's)

***PHILLIPS, Tania** 16 Thornhill Road, Uxbridge UB10 8SF — BM 1994 Soton.

PHILLIPS, Tania Jane 3 The Hill, Pury End, Towcester NN12 7NU Tel: 01327 811292 — MB ChB 1988 Liverp.; MRCPsych 1996. (Univ. Liverp.) Specialist Regist. (Psychiat.) Oxf. & Anglia Region. Prev: Regist. (Psychait.) Manch. Region; SHO (Psychiat.) Liverp. Region; Trainee GP Bedford Gen. Hosp.

PHILLIPS, Tessie (retired) 52 Lavinia Way, East Preston, Littlehampton BN16 1EF Tel: 01903 775755 — BSc Wales 1939, MB BCh 1942; FRCPath 1975, M 1963. Prev: Path. Roy. Infirm. Leicester.

PHILLIPS, Thomas (retired) 41 Bentinck Drive, Troon KA10 6HY Tel: 01292 314468 — MB BCh BAO 1948 Belf.; DTM & H Eng. 1963. Prev: Med. Off. Unit 2 Ayrsh. & Arran HB.

PHILLIPS, Thomas John The Croft, 8 Clifford Road, Ilkley LS29 0AL Tel: 01943 608536 — MB ChB 1959 Leeds; FRCOG 1981, M 1968; T(OG) 1991; DObst RCOG 1962. (Leeds) Cons. Gyn. Yorks. Clinic Bingley, W. Yorks. Prev: Cons. O & G Airedale Gen. Hosp. Steeton; Hon. Sen. Regist. United Leeds Hosps.; Resid. Surg. Off. Matern. Hosp. Leeds.

PHILLIPS, Toby Teresa Bloomer (retired) Tilt Cottage, 6 Tilt Road, Cobham KT11 3EZ Tel: 01932 863354 — MB ChB 1958 St. And. Immunol. Community Child Health. Prev: Clin. Med. Off. Croydon Community Health Trust & Ealing, Hammersmith & Hounslow HA.

PHILLIPS, Trevor John Graham (retired) 2 Blenheim Gardens, Sanderstead, South Croydon CR2 9AA Tel: 020 8657 2960 — MB BS 1952 Ceylon; FRFPS Glas. 1961; MRCP Glas. 1962; MFOM RCP Lond. 1980; DCH Eng. 1958. Prev: Princip. Med. Off. (Pneumoconiosis) DHSS Lond.

PHILLIPS, Ugo Neil (retired) 8 Strensham Court Mews, Strensham, Worcester WR8 9LR Tel: 01684 299560 Email: neil27@supanet.com — MB ChB 1955 Sheff.; DObst RCOG 1956; MRCGP 1965. Prev: Sen. Team Phys. Eng. Football Team.

PHILLIPS, Ugo Neil (retired) 8 Strensham Court Mews, Russell Drive, Strensham, Worcester WR8 9LR Tel: 01684 299560 Email: neil27@supanet.com — MB ChB 1955 Sheff; MB ChB Sheff. 1955; Obst. RCOG Lond. 1956. Chairm. The Fitness League Surrey. Prev: Chief. Exec. S. Worcs. Community NHS Trust.

PHILLIPS, Vivian John Sinnet Court, 84 The Avenue, Mortimer, Reading RG7 3QX Tel: 0118 983 2879 Fax: 0118 933 2894 Email: viv.phillips@medicalis.co.uk — MB ChB 1971 Bristol; AFOM 1989 RCP Lond.; MFPM 1989 RCP (UK); MBA 1999; FFPM 1993 RCP (UK); DIH 1978 Eng.; DObst 1973 RCOG; MRCS Eng. LRCP 1970 Lond.; MRCS Eng. LRCP Lond. 1970; FFPM RCP (UK) 1993; MFPM RCP (UK) 1989; AFOM RCP Lond. 1978; DIH Eng. 1975; DObst RCOG 1973; MBA 1999. MD, Med.is Ltd. Socs: BMA; Fell Fac. Pharm. Med. Roy. Coll. Phys. Prev: Managing Dir. Med. Monitoring & Research Ltd. Hertford; Med. Dir. Wyeth Laborat. Ltd. & Wyeth Research (UK) Ltd.; Dir. Med. Servs. Boehringer Ingelheim Ltd.

PHILLIPS, Wayne Stephen Double Helix Development, Rowan House, 9-31 Victoria Road, London NW10 6BP Tel: 020 8963 0337 Fax: 020 8963 0336 Email: wphillips_doublehelix@compuserve.com; 33A Redington Road,

PHILLIPS

London NW3 7QY Tel: 020 7431 5989 Fax: 020 7431 4225 — MB ChB 1976 Liverp.; FFPM 1992, M1990; Dip. Pharm. Med. RCP Lond. 1981; MIBiol 1992, C 1992. (L'pool) Man. Dir. Double Helix. Socs: Fell. Fac. Pharmaceutical Phys.s; Fell. Roy. Soc. Med.; (Ex-Chairm.) Brit. Assn. Pharmaceut. Phys. Prev: Europ. Med. Dir. Genentech; Med. Dir. Sandoz Pharmaceut. Frimley Surrey; Head Clin. Med. Beecham Pharmaceut. UK Ltd.

PHILLIPS, Wendy Susan 47 Annesley Road, Sheffield S8 7SD — MB ChB 1982 Sheff.

PHILLIPS, William Denstone Powell Department Obstetrics & Gynaecology, Perth Royal Infirmary, Perth PH1 1NX Tel: 01738 623311 Fax: 01738 473212; Greylag House, Forteviot, Perth PH2 9BT Tel: 01764 684245 Email: denny@bizonline.co.uk — MB BCh 1971 Wales; FRCOG 1989, M 1976; DObst RCOG 1974. Cons. O & G Perth Roy. Infirm. Socs: BSCCP; BSGE; TENS. Prev: Clin. Fell. Foetal Monitoring Unit Univ. Brit. Columbia, Vancouver; Regist. Univ. Hosp. Wales Cardiff; Lect. (O & G) Aberd. Univ.

PHILLIPS, William George Royal Free Hospital, London NW3 2TG Tel: 020 7794 0500 Fax: 020 7431 2743 — MB 1985 Camb.; MA Camb. 1987, MB 1985, BChir 1984; MRCP (UK) 1989; DRC Path 1995; MRCGP 1990; DCH RCP Lond. 1987. Cons. (Dermat.) Roy. Free Hosp. Lond.

PHILLIPS, William John Oakfields, 50 Winterbourne Road, Solihull B91 1LX — MB ChB 1971 Birm.

PHILLIPS, William Roger Spence Group Practice, Westcliffe House, 48-50 Logan Road, Bishopston, Bristol BS7 8DR Tel: 0117 944 0701 — MB ChB 1968 Bristol; DMJ(Clin) Soc. Apoth. Lond. 1986; DObst RCOG 1971.

PHILLIPS-HUGHES, Jane Radiology Department, John Radcliffe Hospital, Headington, Oxford OX3 9DU Tel: 01865 741166; 8 Oxford Road, Old Marston, Oxford OX3 0PQ — MB BCh 1986 Wales; MRCP (UK) 1989; FRCR 1992. Cons. Radiol. John Radcliffe Hosp. Oxf. Socs: Brit. Soc. Interven. Radiol.; Cardiovasc. & Interven. Radiol. Soc. of Europe; Radiol. Soc. N. Amer. Prev: Lect. (Diagn. Radiol.) & Sen. Regist. (Radiol.) Univ. Hosp. Wales Cardiff; SHO (Gen. Med.) Roy. Gwent Hosp. Newport Gwent.

PHILLIPSON, Mr Andrew Peter Forest Way, Waste Lane, Kelsall, Tarporley CW6 0PE Email: andyorth@aol.com — MB ChB 1985 Liverp.; FRCS (Orth.) 1995; FRCS Eng. 1989. (Liverp.) Cons. Orthop. & Trauma. Socs: Brit. Orthop. Assn.

PHILLIPSON, Elizabeth Mary The Old Rectory, Chapel Lane, Costock, Loughborough LE12 6UY — MB BS 1969 Lond.; MRCS Eng. LRCP Lond. 1969.

PHILLIPSON, Harold Oliver (retired) 263 Tring Road, Aylesbury HP20 1PH Tel: 01296 5139 — MB BS 1951 Lond.; MRCS Eng. LRCP Lond. 1951; FRCGP 1980, M 1959; DObst RCOG 1953.

PHILLPOTS, Stacey 1 Silverdale Croft, Ecclesall, Sheffield S11 9JP Tel: 0114 220 8266 Email: randsbin@senet.com.au — MB ChB 1988 Leic.; DFFP. GP Adelaide; Wom. Health & Family Plann. S. Australia. Socs: Roy. Coll. Gen. Pract.; Fell. Roy. Austral. Coll. Gen. Practitioners.

PHILLPOTTS, Ian Sherwood Tracy Health Centre, Richmond Road, Catterick Garrison DL9 3JL Tel: 01748 833431 — MB BS 1955 Lond.; DObst RCOG 1958. (St. Thos.) Prev: Ho. Off. Ashford Hosp. Middlx.; Ho. Phys. St. Stephen's Hosp. Lond.; Obst. Ho. Surg. City of Lond. Matern. Hosp.

PHILP, Mr Bruce Malcolm 12 Windermere Road, Northfields, Ealing, London W5 4TD — BM BCh 1987 Oxf.; FRCSI 1992.

PHILP, George 13 Ashton Road, Glasgow G12 8SP Tel: 0141 339 4044 — BSc (Hons.) Ed. 1959, MB ChB 1955; LLCO 1961. (Univ. Ed.) Prev: Sen. Ho. Off. (Orthop.) Vict. Infirm. Glas.; Ho. Surg. Roy. Samarit. Hosp. Glas.; Asst. Bacteriol. Fife Dist. Laborat. Windygates.

PHILP, Professor Ian Northern General Hospital, Sheffield S5 7AU Tel: 0114 243 4343; 24 Sterndale Road, Sheffield S7 2LB — MD 1991 Ed.; MB ChB 1981; FRCP Ed. 1993; T(M) 1993. Prof. Healthcare for the Elderly N. Gen. Hosp. Sheff.; Hon. Cons. Phys. N. Gen. Hosp. Sheff. Socs: Brit. Geriat. Soc.; Brit. Soc. Gerontol. Prev: Sen. Lect. (Geriat. Med.) Soton. Gen. Hosp.; Sen. Regist. (Geriat. Med.) Roy. Vict. Hosp. Dundee.

PHILP, Lawrence Douglas The Rookery, 15 Scotby Village, Scotby, Carlisle CA4 8BS Tel: 01228 513554; The Rookery, 15 Scotby Village, Scotby, Carlisle CA4 8BS Tel: 01228 513554 — MB ChB 1940 Ed.; DMRD 1948. (Ed.) Prev: Cons. Radiol. Diag. Special Area Cumbld. & N. W.mld.; Sen. Regist. (Radiol.) Salford Hosp. Gp.; Maj. RAMC.

PHILP, Margaret Ruth Jessamine Cottage, Bowling Bank, Wrexham LL13 9RL Tel: 01978 661619 Fax: 01978 661619 — MB BS 1966 Lond.; MRCS Eng. LRCP Lond. 1966; DFFP 1995; DObst RCOG 1968.

PHILP, Mr Nigel Hastings 8 Summerfield Road, Wolverhampton WV1 4PR Tel: 01902 429044; Quartford Wood House, Chapel Lane, Quatford, Bridgnorth WW15 6QH Tel: 01746 763132 — MB ChB 1970 Liverp.; FRCS Eng. 1976; FRCS Ed. 1976. (Liverpool) Cons. Urol. New Cross Hosp. Wolverhampton. Socs: Brit. Assn. Urol. Surg. Prev: Sen. Regist. (Urol.) St. Jas. Hosp. Leeds; Research Regist. (Urol./Spinal Injs.) Lodge Moor Hosp. Sheff.; Regist. (Urol.) Roy. Hallamsh. Hosp. Sheff.

PHILP, Mr Timothy 30 Cleveland Road, South Woodford, London E18 2AL Tel: 020 8530 4917 Fax: 020 8530 4917 Email: timphilp@uk-consultants.co.uk — MB BChir 1973 Camb.; MA Camb. 1974, MChir 1987; FRCS Eng. 1979. (Camb. & St. Thos. Hosp. Med. Sch.) Cons. Urol. Whipps Cross Hosp. Lond.; Cons. Urol. St. Peters. Hosp. & Middlx. Hosp. Lond. Socs: Fell. Roy. Soc. Med.; Brit. Assn. Urol. Surgs.; Corr. Mem. Amer. Urol. Assn. Prev: Sen. Regist. (Urol.) St. Peter's Gp. Hosps. Lond.; Research Regist. (Urol.) Radcliffe Infirm. Oxf.; Regist. (Urol.) Whittington Hosp. Lond.

PHILPOT, Joanne 20 Newton Court, Burfield Road, Windsor SL4 2SN — MB BS 1988 Lond.; DRCOG 1989.

***PHILPOT, Kate Anne** Hillcroft, Hillcourt Road, Cheltenham GL52 3JL — MB ChB 1994 Birm.; ChB Birm. 1994.

PHILPOT, Kimberley Simone 83 Hartopp Road, Leicester LE2 1WG — MB ChB 1991 Leic.

PHILPOT, Michael Peter Department of Old Age Psychiatry, Maudsley Hospital, Denmark Hill, London SE5 8AZ Tel: 020 7919 2193 — MB BS 1978 Lond.; BSc Lond. 1975; MRCPsych 1983; FRCPsych 1998. (Univ. Coll. Hosp.) Cons. & Hon. Sen. Lect. (Old Age Psychiat.) Maudsley Hosp. Lond. Socs: Europ. Assoc. for Geriat. Psychiat. (Sec.). Prev: Cons. & Sen. Lect. (PsychoGeriat.s) Lewisham & Guy's Ment. Health NHS Trust; Registar Bethlem Roy. & Maudsley Hosp. Lond.; Clin. Lect. Inst. Psychiat. Lond.

PHILPOTT, Bruce Honeywood, 12 Kingswood Firs, Grayshott, Hindhead GU26 6EU Tel: 01428 604712 — MB BS 1956 Lond.; MRCS Eng. LRCP Lond. 1956; FRCA 1992; FFA RCS Eng. 1964; DA Eng. 1958. (Char. Cross) Cons. Anaesth. King Edwd. VII Hosp. Midhurst & Mt. Alvernia Hosp. Guildford; Emerit. Cons. Anaesth. Roy. Surrey Co. Hosp. Guildford. Socs: Assn. Anaesths. & BMA. Prev: Cons. Anaesth. King Edwd. VII Hosp. Midhurst & Mt. Alvernia Hosp. Guildford; Cons. Anaesth. Roy. Surrey Co. Hosp. Guildford & Moorfields Eye Hosp. Lond.; Tutor (Clin.) SW Surrey.

***PHILPOTT, Carl Martin** 144 Howard Road, Leicester LE2 1XJ — MB ChB 1998 Leic.; MB ChB Leic 1998.

PHILPOTT, David Neil Homecroft Surgery, Voguebeloth, Illogan, Redruth TR16 4ET Fax: 01209 843707; Little Treweege Farm House, Stithians, Truro TR3 7DX Tel: 01209 860164 — MB ChB 1976 Birm.; BSc (Hons.) Birm. 1973, MB ChB 1976; MRCGP 1984.

PHILPOTT, Graham John 1 Parsonage Cottage, The Street, High Easter, Chelmsford CM1 4QS — MB BS 1983 Lond.; FRCA 1993; DRCOG 1987. Cons. Anaesth. Broomfield & St. Johns Hosps. Chelmsford.

PHILPOTT, Hedley Guy Leadburnlea, Leadburn, West Linton EH46 7BE — MB ChB 1984 Dundee; PhD Physiol. Dundee 1980, MB ChB 1984; BSc Physiol. Newc. 1977. Rotat. SHO (Med.) Leeds Gen. Infirm.

***PHILPOTT, Jonathan Mark** The Cottage, Wyatts Green Road, Doddinghurst, Brentwood CM15 0PT — MB BS 1994 Lond.

PHILPOTT, Maurice George (retired) 4 Crofter's Drive, Thwaite St., Cottingham HU16 4SD Tel: 01482 876606 — MB BS 1943 Lond.; MD Lond. 1952; FRCP Lond. 1971, M 1946; MRCS Eng. LRCP Lond. 1943; FRCPCH 1997; DCH Eng. 1944. Prev: Cons. Paediat. Hull & E. Yorks. Health Dists.

***PHILPOTT, Megan Elizabeth** 17 Shrubbery Av, Worcester WR1 1QN — BM 1997 Soton.

PHILPOTT, Megan Jane Grovehurst Surgery, Grovehurst Road, Kemsley, Sittingbourne ME10 2ST Tel: 01795 430444 Fax: 01795 410539 — MB ChB 1983 Birm.; BSc Birm. 1980; DRCOG 1987. (Birm.) MacMillan GP Facilitator, Swale PCG.

PHILPOTT, Nicola Jane Dept. of Haemotology, Ealing Hospital NHS Trust, Uxbridge Rd, Southall UB1 3HW Tel: 020 8967 5432 Email: nphilpott@ent.org.uk; Flint Cottage, Hampden, Chalfont St Peter, Gerrards Cross SL9 9DP Tel: 01753 892541 — BM BCh 1988 Oxf.; BA (Hons.) Oxf. 1985; DM Oxf. 1997; MRCP (UK) 1991; MRCPath 1999. (Oxf.) Cons. Haemotol. Ealing Hosp. NHS Trust Middx. Socs: BMA; BSH; UK Myeloma Forum. Prev: LRF Research Fell. St. Geo. Hosp. Med. Sch. Lond.; Regist. Rotat. (Haemat.) SW Thames RHA; SHO Rotat. (Med.) St. Geo. Hosp. Lond.

PHILPOTT, Robert Martin Sir Douglas Crawford Unit, Park Avenue, Liverpool L18 8BU Tel: 0151 724 2335 — MB BS 1968 Lond.; MRCS Eng. LRCP Lond. 1968; MRCPsych 1973; FRCPsych 1985. (King's Coll. Hosp.) Cons. Psychiat. Old Age N. Mersey Community NHS Trust; Dir. Age Concern Liverp.; Med. Dir. N. Mersey Community Trust; Chairm. Dist. Med. Advis. Comm. Liverp. Dist. HA; Trustee Health Advisery Serv. Socs: Liverp. Med. Inst.; BMA; Brit. Geriat. Soc. Prev: Cons. Psychiat. Airedale Gen. Hosp.; Sen. Regist. Maudsley Hosp. Lond.

PHILPOTT, Ruth Grace Edith The Community Unit, Isaac Maddox House, Shrub Hill Road, Worcester WR4 9RW Tel: 01905 763333; 17 Shrubbery Avenue, Worcester WR1 1QN Tel: 01905 613545 — MB ChB 1968 Bristol. (Bristol) SCMO (Community Health) S. Worcs. Community Trust. Prev: Med. Off. VOM Plateau State MoH, Nigeria.

PHILPOTT-HOWARD, John Nigel Department of Infection, GKST School Medicine, Bessemer Road, London SE5 9PJ Tel: 020 7346 3213 Fax: 020 7346 3404 Email: john.philpott-howard@kcl.ac.uk; 80 Charlton Road, London SE7 7EY Tel: 020 8858 4692 Email: jphilpotth@cs.com — MB BCh 1977 Wales; MRCPath 1983; Dip. Clin. Microbiol. Lond. 1983. (Welsh Nat. Sch. of Med.) Socs: Brit. Infec. Soc.; Brit. Soc. For Antimicrobial Chemother.; Am. Soc. For Microbio. Prev: Lect. (Med. Microbiol.) Lond. Hosp. Med. Coll.

PHIMESTER, Mary Eryl Tynemouth Medical Practice, 24 Tynemouth Road, Tottenham, London N15 4RH Tel: 020 8275 4062 Fax: 020 8275 4120; 30 Church Crescent, Finchley, London N3 1BJ Tel: 020 8346 1397 — MB BS 1977 Lond.; MRCGP 1982; DRCOG 1979. (St. Mary's) Prev: Trainee GP Watford VTS.

PHIN, Nicholas Fulton 3 Woodlands, Escrick, York YO19 6LU — MB ChB 1981 Glas.; LLM (Legal of Aspects Med.) Wales 1996; MFPHM RCP (UK) 1991; FFPHM RCP (UK) 1998. (Glasgow) Dir. Pub. Health Dwfed Powys HA. Socs: Vice-Chairm. Bolam Soc. Prev: Dir. Pub. Health & Plann. United Health Grimsby & Scunthorpe HA; Dir. Pub. Health Grimsby HA; Sen. Regist. (Pub. Health Med.) Yorks. RHA.

PHIPP, Ian David 38 Crosby Row, London SE1 3PT — MB BS 1985 Lond.

PHIPP, Laura Helen 456 Stonegate Road, Moortown, Leeds LS17 5BG — MB BS 1993 Lond.; FRCS Eng. 1997. (Roy. Free Hosp. Lond.) Specialist Regist. (Gen. Surg.) Leeds. Prev: SpR Gen. Surg., York Dist. Hosp.; SpR Gen. Surg., Harrogate Dist. Hosp.; SpR Gen. Surg., Dewsbury Dist. Hosp.

PHIPPEN, Alison Ruth 116 Rosemullion House, Treliske Hospital, Truro TR1 3LJ — MB ChB 1991 Bristol; MB ChB (Hons.) Bristol 1991.

PHIPPS, Mr Alan Roderick Pinderfields General Hospital, Aberford Road, Wakefield WF1 4DG Tel: 01924 201688 Fax: 01924 814938 Email: alan.phipps@paup-tr.northy.nhs.uk; 7 Lowther Avenue, Garforth, Leeds LS25 1EP Tel: 0113 287 5489 Fax: 0113 287 5489 Email: arphipps@aol.com — BM BCh 1978 Oxf.; MA Camb. 1976; FRCS (Plast) 1995; FRCS Ed. 1983. Cons. Plastic Surg. Pinderfields & Pontefract Hosp. NHS Trust. Socs: Brit. Assn. Plast. Surgs.; Brit. Assn. Aesthetic Plastic Surgs.; Brit. Burns Assn. Prev: Sen. Regist. (Plastic Surg.) St. Thos. Hosp. Lond.; Regist. (Plastic Surg.) Qu. Mary's Hosp. Roehampton & W. Midl. Regional Burns Unit.

PHIPPS, Alleyne Elizabeth 21 Highfields, Brackland, Bridgend CF31 2PA — MB ChB 1987 Liverp.; MRCGP 1994; DFFP 1993. p/t Long-term GP Locum. Treorchy, S. Wales. Socs: MPS; RCGP; BMA. Prev: GP Asst., Lond.; G Locum; Trainee GP Kilburn Pk. Med. Centre Lond.

PHIPPS, Andrew John 41 Orchard Drive, The Sands, Durham DH1 1LA Tel: 0191 383 1036 — MB BS 1980 Lond.; MRCGP 1984; DRCOG 1983; MRCPsych 1998. SHO Rotat. (Psychiat.) Newc.

PHIPPS, Barbara Mary 2 Killaire Road, Carnalea, Bangor BT19 1EY — BM BS 1997 Nottm.

PHIPPS, Claire Kathleen Louise Thrum Mill Farm, Rothbury, Morpeth NE65 7XH — MB BS 1992 Lond.

PHIPPS, Mr Jeffrey Howard Nuneaton Private Hospital, 132 Coventry Road, Nuneaton CV10 7AD Tel: 01203 353000; Wykin Fields Farm, Stoke Lane, Wykin, Hinckley LE10 3EB Tel: 01455 619502 Fax: 01455 619705 — MB ChB 1983 Leic.; BSc Lond. 1978; MD Leic. 1992; MRCOG 1988. Cons. Gyn. Geo. Eliot Hosp. Nuneaton; Sen. Lect. (Minimal Access Surg.) Univ. Warwick. Prev: Sen. Regist. (O & G) Watford & Char. Cross Hosp. Lond.; Hon. Sen. Regist. (O & G) Hammersmith Hosp. Lond.; Regist. (Gyn. & Oncol.) Hammersmith Hosp.

PHIPPS, Jeremy Simon Key The Deepings Practice, Market Deeping, Peterborough PE6 7DD Tel: 01778 579000 — MB 1987 Camb.; BA Oxf. 1984; BChir 1986; MRCGP 1992; Cert. Family Plann. JCC 1991.

PHIPPS, Jonathan Andrew 299 Green Lane, Norbury, London SW16 3LU — MB BS 1975 Lond.; FFA RCS Eng. 1979.

PHIPPS, Kathryn 16 St Andrews Avenue, Ashton, Preston PR2 1JN Tel: 01772 732494 — BM 1985 Soton.; MRCGP 1990; DRCOG 1988. Med. Off. Preston. Prev: Trainee GP/SHO (O & G) Sharoe Green Hosp. Fulwood VTS; Trainee GP Lancs. Family Plann. Comm.

PHIPPS, Kevin Nigel Marsh, Kennedy, Phipps, Chapman and Wilde, Netherfield Medical Practice, 2A Forester Street, Netherfield, Nottingham NG4 2NJ Tel: 0115 940 3775 Fax: 0115 961 4069; 3 Pool Meadow, Colwick, Nottingham NG4 2DF — BM BS 1985 Nottm.; BMedSci Nottm. 1983. (Nottingham)

PHIPPS, Madeleine Elizabeth 11 Wilson Closse, Willesborough, Ashford TN24 0HX — MB BS 1991 Lond.; BSc Lond. 1988, MB BS 1991.

PHIPPS, Martyn Richard Glen Moriston Farm, Eastham Rake, Eastham, Wirral CH62 9AL — MB BCh 1975 Wales; MRCGP 1979.

PHIPPS, Phyllis Hilda (retired) c/o Mr and Mrs G Suckling, Blue Firs, Camilla Drive, Westhumble, Dorking RH5 6BU — MRCS Eng. LRCP Lond. 1946; BSc Lond. 1931, MB BS 1946.

PHIRI, Duke Edward Dalliance 43 Boundary Lane, Howlands, Welwyn Garden City AL7 4EG — MB ChB 1982 Univ. Zambia; MRCPI 1994.

PHIZACKERLEY, Patrick John Ruthven 365A Woodstock Road, Oxford OX2 8AA — BM BCh 1952 Oxf.

PHIZACKLEA, Sheila Fairfield Surgery, Station Road, Flookburgh, Grange-over-Sands LA11 7SY Tel: 015395 58307 Fax: 015395 58442 Email: shielaphizacklea@angelfire.com; Allithwaite Lodge, Allithwaite, Grange-over-Sands LA11 7RJ Tel: 015395 33422 Fax: 015395 33882 — MB BS 1973 Lond.; DCH Eng. 1976; DObst RCOG 1975. (Middlx.) Chair Med. Audit Advis. Gp. Morecambe Bay HA. Prev: GP Barrow-in-Furness.

PHONGSATHORN, Virach East Surrey Hospital, Canada Avenue, Redhill RH1 5RH Tel: 01737 768511 — MB BS 1976 Mahidol, Thailand; MRCP (UK) 1980; FRCP 1998. Cons. Elderly Med. E. Surrey Hosp.; Lead clinician in Med. Surrey & Sussex healthcare NHS Trust. Prev: Sen. Regist. (Geriat. Med.) Whittington Hosp. Lond.

***PHORNNARIT, Jedth** 81 Crane Court, Gurnell Grove, London W13 0AQ — MB BCh 1994 Wales.

PHOTIOU, Mr Sophocles Photiou and Partners, 1 Warren Road, Blundellsands, Liverpool L23 6TZ Tel: 0151 924 6464 Fax: 0151 932 0663; 14 Heatherways, Formby, Liverpool L37 7HL — MB ChB 1971 Aberd.; MB ChB Aberd.1971; FRCS Ed. 1978; MRCGP 1982; DRCOG 1983.

PHOTOS, Elias Turnpike Lane Surgery, 114 Turnpike Lane, London N8 0PH — MRCS Eng. LRCP Lond. 1977, Prev: Regist. Whipps Cross Hosp. Lond.

PHUA, Miss Vanessa Mae Flat 2, 5 Middle St., Taunton TA1 1SH; Flat 65, Charlesworth House, Stanhope Gardens, London SW7 5RD Tel: 020 7370 1121 Email: vphua@hotmail.com — BM BS 1996 Nottm. (Nottm.) SHO (Ophth.) MusGr. Pk. Hosp. Taunton, Som. Socs: BMA; MDU. Prev: SHO (Ophth.); SHO (Neurosurg.); SHO (Neurol.).

PHULL, Elizabeth Anne Elmbark Group, Foresthill Health Centre, Westburn Rd, Aberdeen AB25 2AY Tel: 01224 696949; Tel: 01661 872018 — MB BS 1990 Lond.; MRCGP 1994; DCH RCP Lond. 1993; DRCOG 1992.

PHULL, Perminder Singh Gastroenterology Unit, Aberdeen Royal Infirmary, Foresterhill, Aberdeen AB25 2ZN Tel: 01224 681818 Fax: 01224 840711 — MB BS 1984 Lond.; MD Lond. 1997; MRCP (UK)

PHYPERS

1991. (Guy's Hosp. Med. Sch.) Cons. (Phys. & Gastrol.) Aberd. Roy. Infirm.; Hon. Sen. Clin. Lect. Aberd. Univ. Med. Sch. Socs: Brit. Soc. Gastroenterol. Prev: Sen. Regist. & Hon. Clin. Lect. Aberd. Roy. Infirm.; Clin. Research Fell. (Gastroenterol.) N.wick Pk. Hosp. Harrow.

PHYPERS, Michael Gordon 14 Lower Port View, Saltash PL12 4BY — MRCS Eng. LRCP Lond. 1974; BDS Lond. 1968, MB BS 1974; FDS RCS Eng. 1974, L 1968.

PHYTHIAN-ADAMS, Julia Mary 24 Oakbrook Road, Sheffield S11 7EA Email: sheffieldbk@aol.com; 88 Howard Road, Clarendon Park, Leicester LE2 1XH — MB ChB 1991 Sheff.; MRCGP 1997. (Sheff.) p/t Darnall Community Health Sheff. - GP Salaried to S.-E. PCT Sheff. Socs: BMA; Med. Protec. Soc. Prev: SHO (O & G) PCT Chesterfield & N. Derbysh. Roy. Hosp.; Trainee GP Chesterfield; SHO (Paediat.) N.. Gen. Hosp. Sheff.

PHYU PHYU, Dr Paediatric Department, North Tees General Hospital, Stockton-on-Tees TS19 8PE Tel: 01642 617617; 3 Bulmer Close, Yarm TS15 9UX Tel: 01642 898230 — MB BS 1982 Med. Inst. (I) Rangoon; MRCP (UK) 1994. Regist. (Paediat.) N. Tees Gen. Hosp. Stockton-on-Tees. Prev: SHO N. Tees Gen. Hosp. Stockton-on-Tees; SHO S. Cleveland Hosp. & Middlesbrough Gen. Hosp.

PIACHAUD, Michael James Henry Horizon Trust, Harperbury Hospital, Harper Lane, Radlett WD7 9HQ Tel: 01923 427214 Email: m.piachaud@ic.ac.uk — BM BCh 1973 Oxf.; MRCPsych 1978; FRCPsych 1996. Cons. Psychiat./Med. Dir. Harperbury Hosp. & Eric Shepherd Unit; Hon. Sen. Lect. St. Mary's Hosp. Lond.

PIACHAUD, Mr Raoul Alfred (retired) 18 Princes Avenue, London N10 3LR — MRCS Eng. LRCP Lond. 1934; FRCS Eng. 1942. Prev: Surg. Newc. Gen. Hosp.

PICARD, John James 48D St Lukes Road, London W11 1DH Email: john.picard@globalnet.co.uk — BM BCh 1995 Oxf.

PICARD, Laurence Appley Castle, Princess Royal Hospital, Telford TF1 6TF Tel: 01952 541222; 11 Swan Gate, Shawbirch, Telford TF1 3QF — MD 1992 Besancon. Staff Grade Practitioner Rehabil. Unit.

***PICARDO, Karen Joanna Maria** 15 Woodridge Way, Northwood HA6 2BE — MB ChB 1998 Bristol.

PICARDO, Luciano 38 Victoria Road, Whalley Range, Manchester M16 8DP — MB ChB 1987 Manch.

PICCAVER, James George The Barley Close, Butts Road, Ashover, Chesterfield S45 0AY Tel: 01246 590230 — MB ChB 1945 Birm.; MRCS Eng. LRCP Lond. 1945. (Birm.) Socs: Derby Med. Soc; BMA.

PICCHIONI, Mark Michael 28 St Stephens Road, London W13 8HH — MB BS 1992 Lond.

***PICCINELLI, Katherine Jane** 32 Russet Way, Melbourn, Royston SG8 6HE Tel: 01763 261386; 32 Russet Way, Melbourn, Royston SG8 6HE Tel: 01763 261386 — MB BS 1997 Lond.

PICCINI, Paola MRC Clinical Sciences Centre, Hammersmith Hospital, Du Cane Road, London W12 0NN Tel: 020 8383 3773 Fax: 020 8383 2029 Email: paola@cu.rpms.ac.uk; 11A Addison Grove, Chiswick, London W4 1EP Tel: 020 7792 7765 — State DMS 1985 Pisa. Regist. (Neurol.) Hammersmith Hosp. Lond.; Lect. (Neurol.) Hammersmith Hosp. Lond. Prev: Sen. Regist. & Regist. (Neurol.) Pisa Univ.

PICH MARTINEZ, Santiago Flat 5, 22 Mavisbank Gardens, Glasgow G51 1HG — LMS 1991 Barcelona; LMS Autonoma Barcelona 1991.

PICHEL, Adam Conrad 38 Lacey Green, Wilmslow SK9 4BA — MB ChB 1995 Sheff.

PICK, Frederick Walter (retired) 18 St Marys Avenue, Gosport PO12 2HX — MB BS 1959 Lond.; FRCR 1975; FFR 1973; DMRD Eng. 1971. Cons. Radiol. MoD. Prev: Cons. radiologist Min. of defence.

PICK, James Timothy Hessel (retired) 25 Victoria Road, Barnsley S70 2BE Tel: 01226 206532 — MB BChir 1952 Camb.; MA Camb., MB BChir. 1952. JP. Prev: SHO (O & G) St. Helen Hosp. Barnsley.

PICK, Michael John (retired) — MB BS 1969 Lond.; MRCS Eng. LRCP Lond. 1969; FCAnaesth. 1973. Cons. Anaesth. Medway NHS Trust. Prev: Cons. Anaesth. Benenden Hosp. Kent.

PICK, Michael John Tel: 01843 592576 Fax: 01843 852980 — MB BS 1986 Lond.; MA Oxf. 1988, BA 1983; MRCGP 1990; DRCOG 1990; DCH RCP Lond. 1988. (Oxford/UCH/Middlesex) GP Partner Ramsgate; Med. Adviser Air Atlanta/Avia Serv.s; Clin. Asst. in Occupat.al Health Kent and Canterbury Hosp. Socs: RCGP;

Primary Care Dermatol. Soc.; Soc. Occupat. Med. Prev: Trainee GP Ipswich VTS; Ho. Off. (Med.) Chase Farm Hosp. Enfield; Ho. Off. (Surgic. & Orthop.) NW Herts. HA.

PICK, Stephen Grovelands Medical Centre, 701 Oxford Road, Reading RG30 1HG Tel: 0118 958 2525 Fax: 0118 950 9284; 100 Oaktree Road, Tilehurst, Reading RG31 6JY — MB BS 1973 Lond.; MRCGP 1977; Cert JCC Lond. 1976; DObst RCOG 1975. Prev: Trainee Gen. Pract. Reading Vocational Train. Scheme.

PICKARD, Mr Brian Harold Cromwell Hospital, Cromwell Road, London SW5 0TU; 19 Waltham Way, Frinton-on-Sea CO13 9JE Tel: 01255 674808 Fax: 01255 674808 — MB BS Lond. 1946; LMSSA Lond. 1945; DLO Eng. 1947; FRCS Eng. 1954. (Guy's) Hon. Cons. ENT Surg. St. Geo., Moorfields Eye Hosp. & Dispensaire Français Lond.; Authorised Med. Examr. for Civil Aviat. Auth.; Vis. Cons. Is. of St. Helena. Socs: Fell. Roy. Soc. Med.; (Ex-Pres.) Brit. Med. Pilots Assn.; Fell. Roy. Aeronautical Soc. Prev: Sen. Regist. ENT Dept. King's Coll. Hosp., Nat. Hosp. Nerv. Dis. Qu. Sq. & Hosp. Sick Childr. Gt. Ormond St. Lond.

PICKARD, Cecil (retired) Anston House, 30 Strathern Road, Dundee DD5 1PN — MD 1952 Leeds; BSc Leeds 1936, MD 1952, MB ChB 1939; MRCP Ed. 1966; DMRD Eng. 1946.

PICKARD, Christine Alice Margaret Robert Street Surgery, 89D Robert Street, London NW1 3QT Tel: 020 7387 4576; Springfield, Barnoldswick, Colne BB8 7EA Tel: 01282 3348 — MB ChB 1962 Liverp. (Liverp.) Prev: Ho. Surg. Ho. Phys. Whiston Gen. Hosp. Prescot.

***PICKARD, Grant Alexander** 81 Hollow Road, Anstey, Leicester LE7 7FR — MB ChB 1996 Leeds.

PICKARD, Huia Masters 14 Kingsdown, 115A Ridgway, London SW19 4RL — MRCS Eng. LRCP Lond. 1936; FDS RCS Eng. 1949. (Char. Cross) Emerit. Prof. Conserv. Dent. Univ. Lond. Socs: Fell. Roy. Soc. Med. (Ex-Pres. & Hon. Mem. Odont. Sect.); BMA. Prev: Hon. Cons. & Dir. Dept. Restorat. Dent. Roy. Dent. Hosp.; Reader (Conserv. Dent.) Univ. Lond.; Capt. Graded Surg. Specialist RAMC.

PICKARD, Mr John Douglas Department of Neurosurgery, Addenbrooke's Hospital, Hill Road, Cambridge CB2 2QQ Tel: 01223 336946 — MB BChir 1971 Camb.; MA Camb. 1970, MChir (Distinc.) 1981; FRCS Lond. 1989; FRCS Ed. 1974; T(S) 1991. (Camb. & King's Coll. Hosp.) Prof. Neurosurg. & Cons. Neurosurg. Addenbrooke's Hosp. Camb.; Edr. World Federat. of Neurosurgic. Studies. Socs: (Advis. Counc.) Soc. Brit. Neurol. Surg. Prev: Prof. Clin. Neurol. Sci. & Cons. Neurosurg. Wessex Neurol. Centre Soton.; Lect. (Neurosurg.) Inst. Neurol. Scs. Glas.; Research Fell. (Neurosurg.) Hosp. Univ. Pennsylvania Philadelphia, USA.

PICKARD, John Gimson Beaumont Villa Surgery, 23 Beaumont Road, Plymouth PL4 9BL Tel: 01752 663776 Fax: 01752 261520; Prospect Farm, Latchley, Gunnislake PL18 9AX Tel: 01822 832008 — MB BChir 1978 Camb.; MA, MB Camb. 1979, BChir 1978; MRCGP 1987; DMRT 1985. Clin. Asst. (Radiother.) Plymouth Gen. Hosp. Prev: SHO (A & E) & Regist. (Radiother.) Plymouth Gen. Hosp.; SHO (Gen. Med.) Univ. Hosp. Nottm.

PICKARD, Mr Malcolm Alexander Dunn Carolside Medical Centre, 1 Carolside Gardens, Clarkston, Glasgow G76 7BS Tel: 0141 644 3511 Fax: 0141 644 5525 — MB ChB 1981 Glas.; FRCS Glas. 1985.

PICKARD, Marjorie Annette Dingly Dell, 2 Liquorstane, Falkland, Cupar KY15 7DQ Tel: 01337 857297 — MB ChB 1972 St. And.

PICKARD, Richard James Beechcroft Cottage, School Lane, Baslow, Bakewell DE45 1RZ — BM 1993 Soton.

PICKARD, Robert Stephen 66 Brockmer House, Crowder St., London E1 0BJ — MB BS 1984 Lond.

PICKARD, Sally Juliet Basement Flat, 81 Pepys Road, London SE14 5SE — MB BS 1992 Lond.

***PICKARD, Sarah Grace** 6 Danestream House, Sea Road, Milford on Sea, Lymington SO41 0DA — MB BS 1996 Lond.

PICKARD, Mr Simon John Benchmark Cottage, Marchanley, Shrewsbury SY4 5LQ — MB BS 1992 Lond.; FRCS 1997. (CXWMS) Regist. (Ortho) Stoke OsW.ry Rotat.

PICKARD, Timothy Martin Tennyson House Surgery, 20 Merlin Place, Chelmsford CM1 4HW Tel: 01245 260459 Fax: 01245 344287; 6 Fanners Green, Great Waltham, Chelmsford CM3 1EA — MB BChir 1970 Camb.; MA, MB BChir Camb. 1970; DObst RCOG 1973.

PICKARD, William Russell Allerton, 8 Orleans Avenue, Jordanhill, Glasgow G14 9LA Tel: 0141 959 3575; Department of Radiology, Victoria Infirmary NHS Trust, Langside Road, Glasgow G42 9TY Tel: 0141 201 5556 Fax: 0141 201 5497 — MB ChB 1976 Glas.; FRCS Glas. 1980; FRCR 1990. (Glasgow) Cons. Radiol. Vict. Infirm. Glas. Prev: Sen. Regist. (Radiol.) Glas. Roy. Infirm.

PICKARD-MICHELS, Patricia Michele Helene Bench Mark Cottage, Rookery Lane, Marchamley, Shrewsbury SY4 5LQ; Bench Mark Cottage, Rookery Lane, Marchamley, Shrewsbury SY4 5LQ — MB BS 1992 Lond. GP - work in local Pract. as locum Curr.ing. Socs: MDU. Prev: SHO O & G; GP Regist.

PICKAVANCE, Gillian The Newbridge Surgery, 255 Tettenhall ROad, Wolverhampton WV6 0ED Tel: 01902 751420 Fax: 01902 747936; Holly Tree Cottage, Tong, Shifnal TF11 8PW Tel: 01902 375179 — MB ChB Birm. 1990; MRCGP 1994; DCH RCP Lond. 1993; DFFP 1993; DRCOG 1992. (Birmingham)

PICKEN, David Kennedy Watt, TD, OStJ 68 St Michael's Road, Llandaff, Cardiff CF5 2AQ Tel: 029 2056 1146 — MB BCh 1941 Wales; BSc Wales 1938, MB BCh 1941; FFA RCS Eng. 1953; DA Eng. 1948. (Cardiff) JP; DL; Cons. Anaesth. Univ. Hosp. of Wales Cardiff; Clin. Teach. Anaesth. Welsh Nat. Sch. Med. Socs: (Ex-Pres.) Soc. Anaesths. Wales. Prev: Hon. Phys. To H.M. the Qu. 1964-66; Sen. Anaesth. Regist. United Cardiff Hosps.; RAF Med. Serv. 1942-6.

PICKEN, Gary The Ipswich Hospital, Heath Road, Ipswich IP4 5PD Tel: 01473 712233 Fax: 01473 703400 — MB ChB 1985 Bristol; MRCP (UK) 1989; FRCR 1991. Cons. Radiol. Ipswich Hosp., E. Suff. Prev: Sen. Regist. (Radiol.) Addenbrooke's Hosp. Cambs.; Cons. Radicol. Wellington Hosp. NZ.

PICKEN, Sheila Dialysis Unit, Addenbrookes Hospital, Hills Road, Cambridge CB2 2QQ Tel: 01223 217832; 3 Lansdowne Road, Cambridge CB3 0EU — MB ChB 1967 Ed.; MRCP (UK) 1972; DCH Eng. 1971. (Ed.) Clin. Asst. (Dialysis Unit) Addenbrooke's Hosp. Camb.; Med. Adviser Adoption Panel Adopt Anglia (CORAM). Socs: Med. Wom.'s Federat. Prev: Regist. (Med) Deaconess Hosp. Edin.; Resid. (Paediat.) Janeway Child Health Centre, St. John's, Newfld.

PICKENS, Peter Tudor (retired) 20 Eldon Grove, Hartlepool TS26 9LY — BM BCh 1954 Oxf.; FRCP Lond. 1977, M 1960. Prev: Cons. Phys. Hartlepool Health Dist.

PICKENS, Samuel 7 Crowtrees Grove, Roughlee, Nelson BB9 6NE — MB ChB 1966 Ed.; FRCP Lond. 1994; FRCP Ed. 1985; MRCP (UK) 1971. Cons. Phys. Burnley Gen. Hosp. Prev: Sen. Regist. (Diabetic Outpat. & Gen. Med.) Edin. Roy. Infirm.; Sen. Regist. (Communicable Dis.) City Hosp. Edin.

PICKER, Jonathan David Department of Biological & Nutritional Sciences, Agriculture Building, Newcastle University, Newcastle upon Tyne NE1 Tel: 0191 222 6000; Apartment 2, 11 Garrison Road, Brookline MA 02146, USA Tel: 00 1 617 738 1948 — MB ChB 1988 Aberd.; BMedBiol (Commend.) 1985; MSc 1993. (Aberdeen) Prev: SHO (Child Psychiat.) N.d. HA.

PICKERELL, Lindsay Mark Warren The Bull Ring Surgery, 5 The Bull Ring, St. John's, Worcester WR2 5AA Tel: 01905 422883 Fax: 01905 423639 — MB ChB 1986 Bristol.

***PICKERING, Alastair** 7 Arundel Road, Harwood Park, Bromsgrove B60 2HE — MB ChB 1998 Birm.; ChB Birm. 1998.

PICKERING, Annette Mary Avenue Road Surgery, 3 Avenue Road, Dorridge, Solihull B93 8LH Tel: 01564 776262 Fax: 01564 779599 — MB BS 1983 Lond.; DRCOG 1987. Retainer Scheme Croydon HA. Socs: BMA. Prev: Trainee GP/SHO St. Geo. Hosp. Lond. VTS.

PICKERING, Mr Anthony 18 The Bryn, Sketty, Swansea SA2 8DD Tel: 01792 299384 — MB ChB 1965 Ed.; BSc (Hons. Physiol.) Ed. 1962, MB ChB 1965; FRCS Ed. 1969; DO Eng. 1968. (Ed.) Cons. Ophth. Singleton Hosp. Swansea. Prev: Ho. Surg. & Ho. Phys. Roy. Infirm. Edin.

PICKERING, Anthony Edward 388 Rowallan Road, Fulham, London SW6 6AG — MB ChB 1994 Birm.; PHD Birm. 1993, BSc (Hons.) Physiol. 1988. SHO (Anaesth.) Roy. Free Hosp. Lond.

PICKERING, Anthony Jean-Marie Coutin Orchard Lane Surgery, Orchard Lane, Denton, Northampton NN7 1HT Tel: 01604 890313 Fax: 01604 890143 — BM BCh 1980 Oxf.; MA, DPhil. Oxf. 1978. Prev: Tutor (Gen. Pract.) N.ampton.

PICKERING, Arthur Holmes Hambro Lodge, 141 Slough Road, Datchet, Slough SL3 9AE Tel: 01753 547707 Fax: 01753 547707 Email: aholmespick@aol.com — MB BS Lond. 1960; FFOM RCP Lond. 1991, MFOM 1981; Specialist Accredit. (Occupat. Med.) ICHMT 1980; CIH Dund 1973; DObst RCOG 1965. (St. Mary's) Med. Adviser Transco; JP Slough; Mem. Med. Appeal Tribunal. Socs: Hon. Mem. Soc. Occupat. Health Phys. of Nigeria; Liveryman Worshipful Soc. Apoth. Lond.; Fell. Roy. Inst. Pub. Health & Hyg. Prev: Regional Med. Dir. Gulf Oil Co. & Chevron Corpn. E. Hemisphere Lond.; Ho. Off. (Surg. & Cas.) & Admitting Off. Paddington Gen. Hosp.; Med. Off. Unilever & United Afr. Co. Cameroons & Nigeria.

PICKERING, Brian James Seaford Health Centre, Dane Road, Seaford BN25 1DH Tel: 01323 490022 Fax: 01323 492156 — MB BS 1975 Lond.; DCH Eng. 1980; Cert. Family Plann. JCC 1980; DRCOG 1978. (King's Coll. Hosp.)

PICKERING, Mr Brian Neil (retired) 19 Manscombe Road, Livermead, Torquay TQ2 6SP Tel: 01803 607641 — MB BS 1956 Lond.; FRCS Eng. 1966; MRCS Eng. LRCP Lond. 1956. Cons. Thoracic Surg. Plymouth Health Dist.; Civil. Cons. in Thoracic Surg. RN. Prev: Cons. Thoracic Surg. Colindale & Harefield Hosps.

PICKERING, Catherine Patricia Northcote Surgery, 2 Victoria Circus, Glasgow G12 9LD Tel: 0141 339 3211 Fax: 0141 357 4480; 6 Marlborough Avenue, Glasgow G11 7BW Tel: 0141 357 0743 — MB ChB 1984 Glas.; MRCGP 1989. Prev: GP Aberd.

PICKERING, Professor Charles Anthony Cary Department of Thoracic Medicine, Northwest Lung Centre, Wythenshaw Hospital, Manchester M23 9LT Tel: 0161 946 2832; 10 The Mount, Church St, Altrincham WA14 4DX — MB BS Lond. 1966; FRCP Lond. 1987; MRCP (UK) 1970; MRCS Eng. LRCP Lond. 1966; FFOM RCP Lond. 1991, MFOM 1981; DIH Eng. 1976. Cons. Thoracic Phys. Wythenshawe Hosp. & Withington Hosp. Manch. Prev: Sen. Regist. Brompton & W.m. Hosps. Lond.

PICKERING, David George Lowthian Kent Oncology Centre, Maidstone Hospital, Herritage Lane, Maidstone ME16 9QQ Tel: 01622 225023; 2 Millstream Cottages, 217 Tunbridge Road, East Peckham, Tonbridge TN12 5JU Tel: 01622 872701 Email: dpickering@lineone.net — MB BS Lond. 1972; MRCP (UK) 1978; MRCS Eng. LRCP Lond. 1972; FRCR 1985. (Westm.) Cons. Clin. Oncol. Kent Oncol. Centre. Prev: Cons. Radiother. & Oncol. Pembury Hosp. Tunbridge Wells; Sen. Regist. (Radiother.) Hammersmith Hosp. Lond.; Regist. (Radiother.) W.m. Hosp. Lond.

PICKERING, Derek Frank Tel: 0114 222 2100 Fax: 0114 276 7223 — MB ChB 1979 Sheff.; AFOM RCP Lond. 1987; MRCGP 1983; DCH RCP Lond. 1983; DRCOG 1982. Med. Off. Sheff. Univ. Health Serv.; Occupat. Health Phys. Sheff. Univ.

***PICKERING, Elspeth Evelyn** Sketty, Swansea SA2 8DD — MB ChB 1998 Birmingham; ChB Birm 1998.

PICKERING, Frederick Charles Avondale Clinic, 4 Avondale Court, Onchan, Douglas Tel: 01624 621883; 53 Cronk Ny Greiney, Tromode Park, Douglas IM2 5LW Tel: 01624 663746 — MB BS 1951 Durham. Med. Dir. Rheum. Dis. Foundat. (UK); Med. Dir. Avondale Clinic I. of Man. Prev: Med. Off. Winthrop Laborat.; SHO Guy's & Maudsley Hosps. Neurosurg. Units Lond.; Ho. Surg. Roy. Vict. Infirm. Newc. upon Tyne.

PICKERING, Frederick Charles Sanofi Winthrop Ltd., Edgefield Avenue, Newcastle upon Tyne NE3 3TT Tel: 0191 250 0471 Fax: 0191 213 3129 Email: oh@sanpd.onyxnet.co.uk; 18 Glastonbury Grove, Newcastle upon Tyne NE2 2HA Tel: 0191 281 5177 — MB BS 1969 Newc.; DIH Eng. 1978. Gp. Occupat. Phys. Sanofi Winthrop Ltd. Socs: Fac. Occupat. Med. Prev: Sen Occupat. Phys. Sterling Winthrop Gp.

PICKERING, Geraldine Bowland Road, 52 Bowland Road, Baguley, Manchester M23 1JX Tel: 0161 998 2014 Fax: 0161 945 6354; 10 The Mount, Church St, Altrincham WA14 4DX — MB BS 1965 Lond.; MRCS Eng. LRCP Lond. 1965; DPH NUI 1968; DObst RCOG 1967. (St. Mary's)

***PICKERING, Ian Frederick** 64 Hartley Avenue, Woodhouse, Leeds LS6 2LP — MB ChB 1998 Leeds.

PICKERING, John Gilbert The Hawthorns, 1 Oxford Road, Redhill RH1 1DT Tel: 01737 762902 Fax: 01737 762902; 38 West Street, Reigate RH2 9BX — MB BChir 1968 Camb.; B.Chir 1967; MB Camb. 1968; MA Camb. 1968; MRCP (UK) 1971; MRCS Eng. LRCP Lond. 1967; DObst RCOG 1975. (Camb. & Guy's) Med. Off. E. Surrey Water Co.; Med. Adviser Roy. Philanthropic Soc.; Med. Adviser Boro. of Reigate & Banstead. Prev: Regist. (Med.) Guy's

PICKERING

Hosp. Lond.; Ho. Phys. (Neurol.) Guy's Hosp.; Ho. Surg. (Obst.) St. Bart. Hosp. Lond.

PICKERING, Margaret Ann 5 The Pastures, Narborough, Leicester LE9 5DY Tel: 0116 286 7557 — MB ChB 1973 Manch. Med. Adviser, SEMA Gp. Med. Servs.

PICKERING, Mary Evelyn Anne Clavell Shovers Green House, Wadhurst TN5 7JY — MB BS 1962 Durh. (Newc.) Socs: BMA. Prev: Community Med. Off. (Community Health Servs.) CrowBoro. & E.bourne HA; Sch. Med. Off. Heref. & Worcs. AHA & Hexham; Clin. Asst. (Med.) Roy. Vict. Infirm. Newc.

PICKERING, Matthew Caleb Dept. of Rheumatology, Hammersmith Hospital, London W12 0NN — MB BS 1992 Lond.

PICKERING, Nigel The Medical Centre, Cranwell Road, Driffield YO25 6UH Tel: 01377 253334 Fax: 01377 241728; 37 St. Johns Road, Driffield YO25 6RS Tel: 01377 256741 — MB BS 1982 Lond.

PICKERING, Nigel John Gable House, 46 High Street, Malmesbury SN16 9AT Tel: 01666 825825 — BM BCh 1982 Oxf.; BA Oxf. 1979; MRCGP 1987; DRCOG 1985.

***PICKERING, Rachel Anna** 224 Ashenden, Deacon Way, London SE17 1UB — MB BS 1998 Lond.; MB BS Lond 1998.

PICKERING, Robert Spencer The Avenue Surgery, 71 The Avenue, Wivenhoe, Colchester CO7 9PP Tel: 01206 824447 Fax: 01206 827973 — MB BS 1987 Lond. Prev: SHO (O & G) Essex. Co. Hosp. Colchester; SHO (Gen. Med.) Severalls Hosp. Colchester; SHO (Geriat. Med.) St. Mary's Hosp. Colchester.

PICKERING, Mr Simon Anthony William 35 Mapperley Orchard, Arnold, Nottingham NG5 8AH — MB ChB 1993 Birm.; FRCS Eng. 1998.

PICKERING, Veronica Ridingleaze Medical Centre, Ridingleaze, Bristol BS11 0QE Tel: 0117 982 2693 Fax: 0117 938 1707; 243 Canford Lane, Westbury-on-Trym, Bristol BS9 3PD — MB ChB 1992 Birm.

PICKERING, William Graham 7 Moor Place, Gosforth, Newcastle upon Tyne NE3 4AL Tel: 0191 284 2259 Email: wgpi@hotmail.com — MB BS 1973 Lond.; MRCP (UK) 1976; AFOM RCP Lond. 1985; MRCGP 1981; DRCOG 1980; DCH Eng. 1975. (King's Coll. Hosp.)

***PICKERING, Zoe Gail** 123 Moyallan Road, Portadown, Craigavon BT63 5JY — MB BCh 1998 Belf.; MB BCh Belf 1998.

PICKERING-PICK, Margaret Elizabeth (retired) 35 Battlefield Road, St Albans AL1 4DB Tel: 01727 860651 — MB BS 1954 Lond.; FFA RCS Eng. 1963; DA Eng. 1958. Prev: Cons. Anaesth. St. Albans City Hosp. & Hemel Hempstead Gen. Hosp.

PICKERSGILL, Andrew Billinge Hospital, Up Holland Road, Billinge, Wigan WN5 7ET Tel: 01942 244000; 20 Sandiway Place, Altrincham WA14 1HT Email: andypick@aol.com — MB ChB 1989 Liverp.; MRCOG 1994. Specialist Regist. (O & G). Prev: Lect. (O & G) Univ.of Manch.

PICKERSGILL, David Eric Birchwood Surgery, Park Lane, North Walsham NR28 0BQ Tel: 01692 402035 Fax: 01692 500367 — MB ChB 1969 Bristol; DObst RCOG 1971. (Bristol) Socs: Gen. Med. Servs. Comm.; (Mem. Counc.) BMA. Prev: Regist. (Gen. Med. & Dis. Chest.) & SHO (Orthop.) Worcester Roy. Infirm.; Ho. Off. S.mead Hosp. Bristol.

PICKERSGILL, David Eric Upper Snape Farm, Sowerby Bridge HX6 1PB — MB ChB 1981 Leeds.

PICKERSGILL, Hilary Beryl Birchwood Surgery, Park Lane, North Walsham NR28 0BQ Tel: 01692 402035 Fax: 01692 500367 — MB ChB 1964 Bristol. (Bristol) Prev: SHO (Cas. & Anaesth.) S.mead Hosp. Bristol; Demonst. (Anat.) Univ. Bristol.

PICKERSGILL, Trevor Paul University Hospital of Wales, Heath Park, Cardiff CF14 4XW Tel: 029 2074 7747; 10 Brambling Drive, Thornhill, Cardiff CF14 9FD Tel: 02920 754172 Fax: 07970 057519 Email: ndirect.co.uk — MB BCh 1991 Wales; MRCP (UK) 1994. (Univ. Wales Coll. Med.) Specialist Regist. (Neurol.) Morriston Hosp. Swansea. Socs: Brit. Soc. Rehabil. Med.; Assoc. Mem. Assn. Brit. Neurol.; Assn. Study Med. Educat. Prev: Research Fell. (Neurol.) Univ. of Wales Coll. of Med.; SHO (Neurol. & Rehabil.) Rookwood Hosp. Cardiff; SHO (Med.) Singleton Hosp. Swansea.

PICKETT, Denise Ada Disability Benefits Centre, Government Buildings, Flowers Hill, Bristol BS4 5LA Tel: 0117 971 8343 Fax: 0117 971 8482; Cotswold, 19A Pedlars Grove, Frome BA11 2SL Tel: 01373 451650 — MB BS 1971 Newc.; MBA Birm. 1995; DMRD Eng. 1975. Area Med. Adviser Benefits Agency Med. Servs.

Bristol; Tutor Open Univ. Prev: GP N.d.; Regist. (Radiol.), Ho. Phys. & Ho. Surg. Roy. Vict. Infirm. Newc.; SHO (Med.) Newc. Gen. Hosp.

PICKETT, Janet Anne 1 Divert Road, Gourock PA19 1DR — MB ChB 1984 Glas.

PICKETT, Liza Clare The Portmill Surgery, 114 Queen Street, Hitchin SG4 9TH Tel: 01462 434246; 3 Pullman Drive, Hitchin SG4 0ED — BM BCh 1986 Oxf.; MA Camb. 1987; MRCGP 1990; DCH RCP Lond. 1991; DRCOG 1990. GP. Prev: Clin. Med. Off. (Paediat.) Worthing HA; Lister Hosp. Stevenage VTS.

PICKETT, Margaret Elizabeth Jacqueline Knightswood Clinic, 129 Knightswood Road, Glasgow G13 2XF Tel: 0141 211 9069; The Hollow, 22 Kirkhouse Road, Blanefield, Glasgow G63 9BX — MB ChB 1982 Glas.; MRCPsych 1988. Cons. Adolesc. Psychiat. Gtr. Glas. Primary Care NHS Trust.

PICKETT, Thomas Mark Department of Renal Medicine, Lister Hospital, Stevenage SG1 4AB Tel: 01438 314333; 3 Pullman Drive, Hitchin SG4 0ED Email: tmpickett@aol.com — MB BS 1986 Lond.; MA Camb. 1987; MRCP (UK) 1990. Specialist Regist. (Nephrol.) Lister Hosp. Stevenage. Prev: Train. Fell. Nat. Kidney Research Fund St. Thomas's Hosp. Lond.; Regist. (Nephrol.) St. Thomas's Hosp. Lond.; Regist. (Gen. Med.) Worthing Hosp.

PICKFORD, Alison Mary Department of Anaesthetics, Queen Alexandra Hospital, Portsmouth Tel: 023 92 286000 — MB BS 1989 Lond.; BSc Lond. 1986; MRCP (UK) 1992; FRCA 1995.

PICKFORD, Professor Lillian Mary Winton Nursing Home, Wallop House, Nether Wallop, Stockbridge SO20 8HE Tel: 01264 781014 — MRCS Eng. LRCP Lond. 1934; FRS Lond. 1966; FRS Ed. 1954; DSc Lond.; Hon. DSc Heriot-Watt 1991; FRCP Ed. 1977; MRCS Eng. LRCP Lond. 1934. (Univ. Coll. Hosp.) Emerit. Prof. Dept. Physiol. Univ. Coll. Lond.; Special Prof. Endocrinol. Univ. Nottm. Socs: Hon. Mem. Physiol. Soc. & Brit. Pharmacol. Soc. Prev: Jun. Beit Memor. Research Fell.; Asst. Dept. Pharmacol. Univ. Coll. Lond.; Ho. Phys. Stafford Gen. Infirm.

PICKFORD, Louise Jayne Clwydian Community NHS Trust, Royal Alexandra Hospital, Rhyl — MB ChB 1989 Birm.; DRCOG 1992. Clin. Med. Off. (Family Plann.) Clwydian Community & Gwynedd Community NHS Trusts. Prev: Trainee GP Glan Clwyd Hosp. Bodelwyddan VTS.

PICKFORD, Mr Mark Ashton The Queen Victoria Hospital NHS Trust, Holtye Road, East Grinstead RH19 3DZ Email: pickford@picky.demon.co.uk — MB BS 1983 Lond.; MS 1991; FRCS (Plast.) 1995; FRCS Eng. 1987. (King Coll. Hosp. Med. Sch.) Cons. Plastic & Hand Surg. Qu. Vict. Hosp. E. Grinstead. Socs: Brit. Soc. Surg. Hand; Brit. Assn. Plastic Surg. Prev: Hand Surg. Fell. Christine M. Kleinet Inst. Hand & Microsurg. Louisville Kentucky, USA; Sen. Regist. Plastic Surg. Qu. Vict. Hosp.; Regist. Plastic Surg. Cannierbum Hosp. Glas.

PICKFORD, Steven (retired) Castle Acre, Grosmont, Abergavenny NP7 8LW Tel: 01981 240091 — MB BS 1943 Lond.; MRCP Lond. 1945; MRCGP 1965. Prev: Jun. Phys. Harold Wood EMS Hosp.

PICKHAVER, Kathleen Mary Ground Floor Flat, 49 Thornby Road, London E5 9QL — MB BS 1988 Lond.

PICKIN, Christine Anne 20 Windsor Road, Levenshulme, Manchester M19 2EB — MB ChB 1982 Liverp.

PICKIN, David Mark Medical Care Research Unit, Regent Court, 30 Regent St., Sheffield S1 4DA Fax: 0114 222 0749 — MB ChB 1986 Bristol; MRCGP 1991; DRCOG 1989; DCH RCP Lond. 1989; MFPHM 1996. (Bris.) Clin. Sen. Lect. in Health Serv. Research, Med. Care Research Unit, Sch. Of Health & related Research, Sheff. Univ.; Hon. Cons. In Pub. Health Med., Nth Derbysh. Health Auth. Chesterfield. Prev: MRC Special Train. Research Fell. (Pub. Health Med.) Univ. Sheff.; Sen. Regist. (Pub. Health Med.) NHS Exec. Trent.

PICKIN, Jacqueline Heidi Oxshott Medical Centre, Holtwood Road, Oxshott, Leatherhead KT22 0QJ Tel: 01372 844000; 126 Woodlands Road, Little Bookham, Leatherhead KT23 4HJ Fax: 01372 453151 — MB ChB 1974 Ed.; MRCP (UK) 1978.

PICKIN, John Michael 235 Brooklands Road, Manchester M23 9HF Tel: 0161 973 1036 — MB BS 1977 Lond. GP Manch.

PICKIN, Margaret Claire Keresley Road, 2 Keresley Road, Coventry CV6 2JD Tel: 024 7633 2628 Fax: 024 7633 1326 — MB ChB 1981 Liverp.; BSc (Hons.) Biochem. Liverp. 1973; MFHom 1998.

PICKIN, Richard Brian Upton Group Practice, 32 Ford Road, Wirral CH49 0TF Tel: 0151 677 0486 Fax: 0151 604 0635 — MB ChB 1972 Liverp.; MRCGP 1976.

PICKLES, Basil George (retired) — MB BS 1947 Lond.; MRCS Eng. LRCP Lond. 1947; FRCOG 1970, M 1953; MMSA Lond. 1956. Cons. O & G Tunbridge Wells Health Dist. Examr. Centr.; Surg. Lt.-Cdr. RNR.; Midw. Bd. & RCOG Capt. RAMC. Prev: Sen. Regist. (O & G) King's Coll. Hosp. Lond.

PICKLES, Bryan Christopher Beaumont (retired) 41 Walsall Road, Little Aston, Sutton Coldfield B74 3BA Tel: 0121 353 1547 — MB ChB 1957 Birm.; MRCS Eng. LRCP Lond. 1957; DObst RCOG 1959. Indep. GP Sutton Coldfield.

PICKLES, Clive John Kings Mill Centre, Mansfield Road, Sutton-in-Ashfield NG17 4NA; Stud Farm, Hardstoft, Pilsley, Chesterfield S45 8AE Tel: 01773 875994 — MB ChB 1976 Manch. Cons. O & G Kingsmill Hosp. Sutton-in-Ashfield. Socs: Roy. Coll. Obst. & Gyns. Prev: Sen. Regist. (O & G) Univ. Hosp. Nottm.; Research Fell. (O & G) Univ. Hosp. Nottm.; Regist. (O & G) Univ. Hosp. Nottm. & Burnley Gen. Hosp.

***PICKLES, Edward James William** Westbury Cottage, Panarama Drive, Ilkley LS29 9RA — MB ChB 1996 Dundee.

PICKLES, Hilary Glen 3 Ducks Walk, Twickenham TW1 2DD Tel: 020 8892 5086 — MB BChir 1973 Camb.; PhD Lond. 1978; MA Camb. 1972; MRCP (UK) 1974; MFPHM 1998; FRCP 1997. Dir. (Pub. Health & Health Strategy) Hillingdon HA. Prev: Princip. Med. Off. Dept. Health, Elephant & Castle Lond.; MRC Fell. Clin. Pharmacol. St. Bart. Hosp. Med. Coll. & Nat. Hosp. Lond.; Teachg. Fell. Dept. Pharmacol. Lond. Sch. Pharmacy.

PICKLES, Mr John Michael Luton and Dunstable Hospital, Dunstable Road, Luton LU4 0DZ; Topstreet Farm House, Crabtree Lane, Harpenden AL5 5NU — MB ChB 1976 Dundee; FRCS Eng. 1984; FRCS Ed. 1982. Cons. Otolaryngol. Luton & Dunstable Hosp. Socs: Brit. Assn. Otolaryngol.; Brit. Voice Assn. Prev: Sen. Regist. Yorks. RHA.

PICKLES, John Stephen Health Centre, Holme Lane, Cross Hills, Keighley BD20 7LG Tel: 01535 632147 Fax: 01535 637576; The Barn, Glusburn Moor, Keighley BD20 8DY Tel: 01535 635717 Fax: 01535 637576 — MB BS 1972 Newc.; MRCGP 1976. Med. Off. Malsis Preparatory Sch. Socs: Keighley & Dist. Med. Soc. Prev: Trainee GP Airedale VTS.

PICKLES, Lisa Jane Union Lodge, Scammonden Road, Barkisland, Halifax HX4 0AY — MB BS 1987 Newc.; MRCGP 1991; T(GP) 1991.

PICKLES, Margaret Muriel (retired) Chaucer's House, Woodstock OX20 1SP Tel: 01993 811244 — BM BCh 1939 Oxf.; DM Oxf. 1947, MA 1939; FRCPath 1970. Prev: Cons. Path. AHA (T).

PICKLES, Richard Mark Plas y Bryn Surgery, Chapel Street, Wrexham LL13 7DE Tel: 01978 351308 Fax: 01978 312324 — MRCS Eng. LRCP Lond. 1968. (Guy's)

PICKLES, Roger Llewellyn Silverdale Medical Centre, Mount Avenue, Heswall, Wirral CH60 4RH Tel: 0151 342 6128 Fax: 0151 342 2435 — MB ChB 1976 Liverp.

PICKLES, Stanley Thomas (retired) Pengwerne, St. Nicholas Close, Penn Hill, Yeovil BA20 1SB Tel: 01935 475866 — MB BChir Camb. 1950; MLCOM 1963. Prev: Med. Off. Summerlands Hosp. Yeovil.

PICKLES, Valerie Ann Park Lane House Medical Centre, 187 Park Lane, Macclesfield SK11 6UD Tel: 01625 422893 Fax: 01625 424870 — MB ChB 1989 Aberd.; BSc Aberd. 1984. (Aberd.) Princip. GP. Socs: RCGP.

PICKLES, Victoria Marylin Clarendon Wing, Leeds General Infirmary, Leeds LS2 9NS — MB ChB 1994 Leeds.

PICKRELL, Morgan David Birchend Farmhouse, Ockeridge, Wichenford, Worcester WR6 6YR Tel: 01886 888414 Email: d.pickrell@ukonline.co.uk — MB BS 1975 Lond.; MRCOG 1983; DRCOG 1980; FRCOG 2000. (Univ. Coll. Hosp.) Cons. O & G Worcester Roy. Infirm. Prev: Sen. Regist. (O & G) Birm. Matern. Hosp.

PICKSTOCK, Colette Cecilia, OStJ, Surg. Lt.-Cdr. RN Retd. (retired) 35 Portsdown Avenue, Drayton, Portsmouth PO6 1EL Tel: 01705 219084 Fax: 01705 649004 — MB ChB Liverp. 1957; FRCS Ed. 1964; DObst RCOG 1960. Cons. Forens. Gyn. MoD. Prev: Clin. Asst. (Orthop.) Qu. Alexandra Hosp. Cosham.

PICKSTOCK, Nicholas Jon 25 Jack Lane, Davenham, Northwich CW9 8LF — MB ChB 1994 Manch.; BSc (Hons.) Manch. 1989. SHO (Gen. Med.) Roy. Preston Hosp. Prev: Ho. Surg. (Gen. & Neurosurg.) Manch. Roy. Infirm.; Ho. Phys. (Gen. Med.) Roy. Preston Hosp.

PICKTHALL, Pamela Dorothy, Wing Cdr. RAF Med. Br. Retd. (Scholefield) Medical Centre, Hullavington Barracks, Stanton St Quintin, Chippenham SN14 6BT Tel: 01666 508906 Fax: 01666 508906; Glebelands, Easton Road, Sherston, Malmesbury SN16 0LS Tel: 01666 841072 — MB ChB 1974 Manch.; DA Eng. 1979. (Manchester) Civil. Med. Practitioner Med. Centre Hullavington Barracks, Chippenham. Prev: GP Rowden Surg. Chippenham; Med. Off. RAF.

PICKUP, Anthony John The Old Chapel, Drury Lane, Mortimer, Reading RG7 2JN Tel: 0118 933 2135 Fax: 0118 933 1273 Email: ajpickup@aol.com — MRCS Eng. LRCP Lond. 1973; BSc (1st cl. Hons. Physics appl. Med.) Lond. 1970; FFPM RCP (UK) 1995. (Guy's) Head Med. Aff. Merck Pharmaceut. Socs: Fell. Roy. Soc. Med. Prev: Med. Dir. Otsuka Pharmaceut. Co. Ltd.; Med. Dir. Abbott Laborat.

PICKUP, John Christopher 60 Dorrington Court, South Norwood Hill, London SE25 6BG Tel: 020 8771 1963 — BM BCh 1974 Oxf.; DPhil, MA Oxf. 1972, BM BCh 1974. Hon. Lect. Unit Metab. Med. Guy's Hosp. Lond.; Asst. Endocrine Physiol. & Pharmacol. Laborat. Nat. Inst. Med Research Lond. Prev: SHO (Endocrinol. & Gen. Med.) Hammersmith Hosp. Lond.; Ho. Surg. N.ampton Gen. Hosp.; Ho. Phys. Radcliffe Infirm. Oxf.

PICKVANCE, Nicholas John Warner Lambert, Lambert Court, Chestnut Avenue, Eastleigh SO53 3ZQ Tel: 02380 628625 Fax: 02380 629726 Email: pickvan@el1.uk.wl.com; Littlewood House, Cowesfield, Whiteparish, Salisbury SP5 2RB Tel: 01794 884783 — MB ChB 1972 Bristol; MRCP (UK) 1977; FRCP (UK) 1998. Vice Pres. R&D Warner Lambert Consumer Health.

PICKWORTH, Anthony James Department of Anaesthetics, Princess Margaret Hospital, Okus Road, Swindon SN1 4JU Tel: 01793 536231 Fax: 01793 480817 — BM BCh 1987 Oxf.; MA Camb. 1988; MRCP (UK) 1992; FRCA 1993. (Oxf.) Cons. Anaesth. P.ss Margt. Hosp. Swindon. Prev: Sen. Regist. Rotat. (Anaesth.) Addenbrooke's Hosp. & W. Suff. Hosp. Bury St. Edmunds; Regist. Rotat. (Anaesth.) Addenbrooke's Hosp. Camb. & Heath Rd. Hosp. Ipswich; SHO (Anaesth.) City Gen. Hosp. Stoke-on-Trent.

PICKWORTH, David Christopher The Darley Dale Medical Centre, Two Dales, Darley Dale, Matlock DE4 3FD Tel: 01629 733205; Clevedon House, Brookleton, Youlgrave, Bakewell — MB BS 1973 Newc.; MRCGP 1977; DObst RCOG 1976. Princip. in Gen. Pract.; Clin. Asst. Psychiat. of Learning Disabil.; Clin. Asst. in Elderly Med.; PCG Bd. Mem.

PICKWORTH, Frederick Edward Norfolk & Norwich Hospital, Brunswick Road, Norwich NR1 3SR Tel: 01603 286737 Fax: 01603 286088 Email: fpickworth@pactec.demon.co.uk; Mundham Grange, Mundham, Norwich NR14 6EP Tel: 01508 550718 Fax: 01508 550718 Email: 106062.537@compuserve.com — LMSSA 1983 Lond.; MA Camb. 1984, MB BChir 1983; MRCP (UK) 1987; FRCR 1992. (Cambridge) Cons. Radiol. Norf. & Norwich Health Care NHS Trust.; Hon. Cons. Jas. Paget Hosp. NHS Trust. Prev: Sen. Regist. (Radiol.) Mersey RHA.

PICKWORTH, Frederick John (retired) The Coach House, 10 Cherry Hill Road, Barnt Green, Birmingham B45 8LJ Tel: 0121 445 3066 Email: johnpickworth@b-g.demon.co.uk — MB ChB 1956 Birm.; DObst RCOG 1959. Prev: GP Worcs.

PICKWORTH, Julia Christine Pinfold Lane Surgery, 40 Pinfold Lane, Butterknowle, Bishop Auckland DL13 5NU Tel: 01388 718230 Fax: 01388 718808 — MB BS 1975 Newcastle; MB BS Ncle 1975. (Newcastle) GP Bishop Auckland, Co. Durh.

PICKWORTH, Kenneth Hart (retired) 41 Woodside, Barnard Castle DL12 8DZ Tel: 01833 638398 — MB BS Durh. 1944; MRCGP 1960.

PICKWORTH, Michael John Wylie 36 The Drive, Powick, Worcester WR2 4SA — MB ChB 1993 Birm.; ChB Birm. 1993; MB Ch.B Birm. 1993; DCH 1996. (Birm.) GP Locum. Prev: GP Regist. Lowesmoor Med. Centre, Worcester; Worcester Roy. Infirm. GP VTS.

PICKWORTH, Richard William Alderman Jack Cohen Health Centre, Springwell Road, Sunderland SR3 4HG Tel: 0191 528 2727 Fax: 0191 528 3262; 13 Thornhill Terrace, Sunderland SR2 7JL — MB ChB 1978 Leeds.

PICKWORTH

PICKWORTH, Sarah Anne Margaret 13 Pevensey Road, Worthing BN11 5NP Tel: 01903502220 Fax: 01903502220 Email: sarah.pickworth@onet.co.uk; 13 Pevensey Road, Worthing BN11 5NP Tel: 01903502220 Fax: 01903502220 — MB BS Lond. 1990; BSc. (1st cl. Hons.) Nutrit. & Basic. Med. Sc. Lond. 1987; DFFP 1997; PHEC 1997; DTM & H 1999; Cert Prescribed Exp. (Char. Cross & Westm.) MB BS Lond. 1990. Socs: BMA; Roy. Soc. Hyg. And Trop. Med.

PICKWORTH, Sheila Mary (retired) The Coach House, 10 Cherry Hill Road, Barnt Green, Birmingham B45 8LJ Tel: 0121 445 3066 — MB BS 1956 Lond.; MRCS Eng. LRCP Lond. 1956. Prev: Clin. Asst. (Gen. Med.) BromsGr. Gen. Hosp.

PICOZZI, Mr Gerard Louis 8 Muir Street, Coatbridge ML5 1NH — MB ChB 1974 Glas.; FRCS Glas. 1980.

PICOZZI, Joan 8 Muir Street, Coatbridge ML5 1NH — MB ChB 1974 Glas. Clin. Asst. Diabetes Opd Glas. Roy. Infirm.

PICTON, Catherine Ellison The Medical Centre, 6 The Green, West Drayton UB7 7PJ Tel: 01895 442026 Fax: 01895 430753; Fortune Gate, Manor Crescent, Seer Green, Beaconsfield HP9 2QX — MB ChB 1983 Dundee; BSc Leeds 1973; DCH RCP Lond. 1989; DRCOG 1986. (Dundee)

PICTON, Paul 6 Salisbury Avenue, Old Waltham, Grimsby DN37 0DA — MB ChB 1993 Sheff.; BMedSci Sheff. 1990; MRCP (UK) 1996. (Sheff. Univ. Med. Sch.) SHO (Anaesth.) Soton Univ. Hosps. NHS Trust, Soton.

PICTON, Susan Flat 6, Victoria Court, Victoria Avenue, Manchester M20 1FR — MB ChB 1996 Manch.

PICTON, Susan Vanessa Department of Paediatric Oncology, Childrens Day Hospital,, St. James's Hospital, Leeds LS9 7TF Tel: 0113 206 4986 Fax: 0113 247 0248; 37 Gledhow Wood Road, Leeds LS8 4BZ Email: pictostah@doctors.org.uk — BM BS 1986 Nottm.; BMedSci. Nottm. 1984; MRCP (UK) 1990. (Nottm.) Cons. Paediat. Oncol. St. Jas. Univ. Hosp. NHS Trust Leeds. Prev: Lect. (Paediat. Oncol.) Manch. Univ. & Roy. Manch. Childr. Hosp.; Regist. (Paediat.) Qu. Pk. Hosp. Blackburn.

PICTON, Thomas Andrew 80 Clyde Crescent, Chelmsford CM1 2LL — MB BS 1994 Lond.

***PICTON, Tracy Elizabeth** 2 Warwick Road, Milford Haven SA73 2LP — MB BCh 1994 Wales.

***PICTON-JONES, Evan Ceredig** Fountain Hill, Eglwyswrw, Crymych SA41 3RY — MB BCh 1995 Wales.

PICTON-JONES, Jennifer (retired) 12 Shirley Avenue, Cheam, Sutton SM2 7QR Tel: 020 8642 2760 — MB BS 1962 Lond.; MRCS Eng. LRCP Lond. 1962; FRCPsych 1985, M 1972; T(Psych.) 1991; DPM Eng. 1966. Prev: Med. Dir. Croydon Ment. Health Serv.

PICTON-ROBINSON, Ian 221 Sutton Park Road, Kidderminster DY11 6LD Tel: 01562 751518 — MB BS Lond. 1963; BSc (Anat.) Lond. 1960; FFOM RCP Lond. 1992, MFOM 1979; DIH Soc. Apoth. Lond. 1968; DObst RCOG 1965. (St. Thos.) Sen. Med. Off. Jaguar Cars Ltd. Prev: Regional Med. Off. Austin-Rover Ltd.; SHO St. Matthew's Hosp. Burntwood.

PICTS, Alexandra Claire 65 Shakespeare Road, St Ives, Huntingdon PE27 6TT Tel: 01480 468369 — MB ChB 1996 Bristol. (Univ. of Bris.) SHO (Surgic. Rotat.) Roy. Sussx Co. Hosp. Brighton. Prev: Demonst. (Anat.) Roy. Free Med. Sch.; SHO (Orthop.) Soton. Gen. Hosp.; SHO (A&E) W.ern Gen. Hosp.

***PIDCOCK, Jacqueline** 289 Thorpe Road, Longthorpe, Peterborough PE3 6LU — BM BS 1996 Nottm.

PIDD, Sally Anne Victoria House, Thornton Road, Morecambe LA4 5NN Tel: 01524 400445 Fax: 01524 400357 — MB ChB 1972 Birm.; FRCPsych 1991, M 1976. Cons. Psychiat. Bay Community. NHS Trust. Prev: Sen. Regist. (Psychother.) Whittingham Hosp. Preston; Sen. Regist. (Psychiat.) Lancaster Moor Hosp.; Research Fell. Dept. Psychiat. Univ. Birm.

PIDGEON, Colleen Alison Sandhurst Group Practice, 72 Yorktown Road, Sandhurst GU47 9BT Tel: 01252 872455 Fax: 01252 872456 — MB BCh 1976 Wales; BSc Bristol 1973; MRCGP 1982; DCH Eng. 1979; DRCOG 1979.

PIDGEON, Nigel David New Hall Lane Practice, The Health Centre, Geoffrey Street, Preston PR1 5NE Tel: 01772 401730 Fax: 01772 401731; Jonah House, 19 Sheraton Park, Ingol, Preston PR2 7AZ Tel: 01772 727094 — MB BS 1978 Lond.; MRCS Eng. LRCP Lond. 1978; MRCGP 1985; DRCOG 1984. (Char. Cross) Hosp. Pract. (Gastroenterol.) Roy. Preston Hosp. Socs: Christ. Med. Fell.sh.

PIDSLEY, Charles Godfrey Laurence Bridge Surgery, St. Peters Street, Stapenhill, Burton-on-Trent DE15 9AW Tel: 01283 563451 Fax: 01283 500896; 46 Meadow View, Rolleston on Trent, Burton-on-Trent DE13 9AN — MB BS 1982 Lond.; MRCGP 1987; DRCOG 1986.

PIDSLEY, Godfrey Kenneth (retired) Tanglewood, Elmbridge, Droitwich WR9 0DA Tel: 01299 851667 — MB BS 1954 Lond. Prev: Ho. Off. (Cas.) Mt. Vernon Hosp. N.wood Middlx.

PIECHOWSKI, Leszek Dryland Surgery, 1 Field Street, Kettering NN16 8JZ Tel: 01536 518951 Fax: 01536 486200 — MB BS 1980 Lond.; MRCGP 1989; Primary FRCS London 1982; Cert Family Plann 1985. Chairm. Kettering PCG; N.amptonshire Heartlands PCT Lead Clinician. Prev: Regist. (Geriat. & Gen. Med.) Upton Hosp. Slough; SHO (Paediat.) Wexham Pk. Hosp. Slough; SHO (A & E) St. Geo. Hosp. Tooting.

PIECZORA, Marek Stanislav Susan Britton Wills Centre, Bristol General Hospital, Guinea St., Bristol BS1 6SY Tel: 0117 928 6333 Fax: 0117 929 4250; Barrow Hospital, Barrow Gurney, Bristol BS48 3SG Tel: 0117 928 6602 Fax: 0117 928 6650 — MB BS 1981 Lond.; MSc Wales 1997. (Middlx.) Staff Psychiat. United Bristol Healthcare (NHS) Trust; Tutor (MSc Family Ther. & Systemic Pract.) Bristol Univ. Socs: Affil. Mem. Roy. Coll. Psychiat.; Assn. Family Ther.; Fam. Inst. Cardiff.

PIENAAR, Georg Frederick 22 Tylsworth Close, Amersham HP6 5DF — MB ChB 1995 Orange Free State.

PIENKOS, Anna Veronica 12 Warren Road, Banstead SM7 1LA — MB BS 1985 Melbourne.

PIENKOWSKI, Czeslaw Franciszek (Surgery), 12 Goldington Road, Bedford MK40 3NE Tel: 01234 52493; 502 Broadway, Letchworth SG6 3PT — MB BCh BAO 1964 Dub.; MA 1966, MB BCh BAO Dub. 1964. (T.C. Dub.) Socs: BMA. Prev: Ho. Surg. Dr. Steevens' Hosp. Dub.; Ho. Phys. Gulson Hosp. Coventry; Police Surg. Mid-Herts.

PIEPER, Frederick Antonius 20B Park Lane, Llangennech, Llanelli SA14 8YR — Artsexamen 1990 Nijmegen.

PIEPER, Hans The Ayr Hospital, Dalmellington Road, Ayr KA6 6DX Tel: 01292 610555; 53 Ottoline Drive, Troon KA10 7AN — State Exam Med 1984 Hanover; MD Hanover 1986; MRCGP 1994; DA (UK) 1990. Staff Grade (A & E) The Ayr Hosp. Prev: Staff Grade (A & E) Aberd. Roy. Infirm.; Trainee GP Salen Isle of Mull; Sen. Anaesth. Ahli Hosp. Gaza, Israeli Occupied Territories.

PIERCE, Agnes Main (retired) 11 Roseacre, West Kirby, Wirral CH48 5JW — MB ChB 1952 Ed. Cons. Child Abuse Merseyside Police Auth. Prev: Med. Off. (Paediat.) Alder Hey Hosp. Liverp.

PIERCE, Alison Agnes Bootham Park Hospital, Bootham, York YO30 7BY Tel: 01904 454072 — MB ChB 1984 Ed.; BSc (Hons.) Ed. 1982; MRCPsych 1991. (Ed.) Specialist Regist. Old Age Psychiat. Bootham Pk. Hosp., York. Prev: Staff Grade Psychiat. Springwood Community Unit for the Eldrly, Malton, NY; Staff Grade Psychiat. ScarsBoro. & NE Yorks. Health Care.; Regist. (Psychiat.) Roy. Edin. & Assoc. Hosp. Edin.

PIERCE, Christine Marie 39A Belsize Square, London NW3 4HL — MB BS 1988 Lond.; MRCP (UK) 1991. (Univ. Coll. Lond.) Cons. (Paediat. Intens. Care) Gt. Ormond St. Hosp. Lond. Prev: Regist. (Paediat.) St. Mary's Hosp. Lond.

PIERCE, David William St. Tydfil's Hospital, Merthyr Tydfil CF47 0SJ Tel: 01685 723244; 77 High Street, Cowbridge CF71 7AF Tel: 01446 773248 — MB BS 1961 Lond.; FRCP Ed. 1992; MRCP Ed. 1968; MRCS Eng. LRCP Lond. 1961; FRCPsych 1990, M 1972; DPM Eng. 1965. (Westm.) Cons. Psychiat. N. Glam. Health Trust. Prev: Cons. Psychiat. E. Glam. Hosp.; Sen. Regist. Pk. Prewett Hosp. Basingstoke; Mem. Scientif. Staff MRC Clin. Psychiat. Unit Graylingwell Hosp.

PIERCE, Elsbeth Wyn Bron-y-Fedw, 6 Llysgwyn, Caernarfon LL55 1EN — MB ChB 1985 Liverp.

PIERCE, Emma Louise 38 Cleveland Road, Brighton BN1 6FG — BM 1996 Soton.

PIERCE, Geoffrey Frederick Markham (retired) The Limes, Clewer Village, Windsor SL4 5JE Tel: 01753 866432 — MB BS 1950 Lond.; MRCS Eng. LRCP Lond. 1950; FFA RCS Eng. 1963; DA Eng. 1955. Cons. Anaesth. Windsor Hosp. Gp. Prev: Sen. Regist. St. Mary's Hosp. Lond.

PIERCE, Jonathan Mark Thomas Southampton General Hospital, Remona Road, Southampton SO16 6YD Tel: 02380 796135 Email:

tom.pierce@publiconline.co.uk; 44 Brookvale Road, Southampton SO17 1RA Tel: 02380 553500 — BM 1981 Soton.; MRCP (UK) 1985; FFA RCS Eng. 1988; DA (UK) 1986. (Soton.) Cons. Cardiac Anaesth. Wessex Cardiac Centre Soton. Gen. Hosp. Socs: Eur. Assn. Cardiothoracic Anaesth. Prev: Sen. Regist. (Anaesth.) Soton. & Portsmouth Hosps.; Fell. (Cardiothoracic Anaesth.) Groningen, Netherlands.

PIERCE, Julie Francis Flat B, 34 Hans Road, London SW3 1RW — MB BS 1991 Lond.

PIERCE, Mary Bridget 8 Eliot Place, London SE3 0QL Tel: 0208 852 4423 Mobile: 07774 759213 Email: yof30@uk.uumail.com — MB BChir 1978 Camb.; MD Lond. 1997; MRCGP 1982; LMSSA Lond. 1977. Sen. Lect. (Gen. Pract.) Univ. of Warwick. Prev: Lect. (Gen. Pract.) UMDS Lond.; Sen. Lect. (Gen. Pract.) Imperial Coll., Lond.

PIERCE-WILLIAMS, Gwyn Clarence House, 14 Russell Road, Rhyl LL18 3BY Tel: 01745 350680 Fax: 01745 353293; Brithdir, 24 Bryntirion Avenue, Rhyl LL18 3NP — MB ChB 1977 Liverp.; MRCGP 1981; DFFP 1994; DRCOG 1980.

PIERCY, Joanna Altacraig, Leighton Gardens, Ellon AB41 9BH Tel: 01358 720442, 01926 491019 Fax: 01358 725236 — MB ChB 1993 Birm.; MRCGP 2000; MRCP (UK) 1996. Socs: BMA. Prev: SHO (Med.) Warwick; SHO Rotat. (Med.) Warwick Hosp.; Specialist Regist. (Haem.) Soton.

***PIERCY, Melanie Louise** Royal Devon & Exeter Hospital, Barrack Road, Exeter EX2 5DW — MB ChB 1994 Bristol.

PIERCY, Norman MacLennan (retired) Shandon, 4 Rosehill, Montrose DD10 8RZ Tel: 01674 673665 Email: norman@percy44.freeserve.co.uk — MB ChB St. And. 1952; MRCGP 1968; DObst RCOG 1970. Prev: GP Montrose.

PIERECHOD, Bogdan Antony Newsom View, Alma St., Woodlesford, Leeds LS26 8PN — MB ChB 1975 Leeds.

PIERI, Marco North Tees General Hospital, Hardwick Road, Stockton-on-Tees TS19 8PE; 35 Northgate, Tickhill, Doncaster DN11 9HZ — State Exam Rome 1990.

PIERI, Sarah Elizabeth 10C Bird Cage Court, Bird Cage Walk, Otley LS21 3HH — MB BS 1986 Lond.

***PIERINI, Stephen Victor** 4 Halter Path, Hamworthy, Poole BH15 4HT — BM BCh 1997 Oxf.; MA.

***PIERIS, Malwattage Janaka Asitha** 11 Linley Court, Rouse Gardens, London SE21 8AQ — MB BS 1994 Lond.

PIERONI, Joyce Elaine Shaftesbury Medical Centre, 480 Harehills Lane, Leeds LS9 6DE Tel: 0113 248 5631 Fax: 0113 235 0658 — MB ChB 1984 Leeds; MRCGP 1988; DRCOG 1987.

PIERPOINT, Steven Hill and Partners, 36 Belmont Hill, London SE13 5AY Tel: 020 8852 8357 Fax: 020 8297 2011 — BM 1984 Soton.

PIERRE, Germaine Marsha Flat 3, George Eliot Hospital NHS Trust, Lewis House, College Street, Nuneaton CV10 7DJ — MB BS 1997 West Indies.

PIERRE, Sylvan Lyndon 14 Teynton Terrace, London N17 7PZ — MB BS 1988 West Indies.

PIERREPOINT, Marcus John Department of Child Health, University Hospital Wales, Heath Park, Cardiff CF14 4XW — MB BCh 1991 Wales; MRCP (UK) 1995; MRCPCH. (UWCM) Res. Fell. (Cystic Fibrosis) UWCM. Socs: MDU. Prev: SHO (Cardiopulm. Med.) S. Glam. HA; Specialist Regist. (Paediat.) Mid Glam.; SHO (Paediat.) UHW Cardiff.

PIERREPOINT, Susan Elizabeth The Park Canol Group Practice, Park Carnol Surgery, Central Park, Church Village, Pontypridd CF38 1RJ Tel: 01443 203414 Fax: 01443 218218; The Blackthorns, Chapel Lane, Upper Church Village, Pontypridd CF38 1EE Tel: 01443 202312 — MB ChB 1962 Liverp.; MB ChB (Hons.) Liverp. 1962; DObst RCOG 1964. (Liverp.)

PIERRO, Mr Agostino Department of Paediatric Surgery, Institute of Child Health & Great Ormond Street Hospital NHS Trust, 30 Guildford St., London WC1N 1EH Tel: 020 7905 2175 Fax: 020 7404 6181 Email: a.pierro@ich.ucl.ac.uk; 80 Etheldene Avenue, London N10 3QB Tel: 020 8444 8605 — State Exam 1978 Rome; FRCS Ed.; FRCS Engl. Prof. of Paediat. Surg.; Hon. Cons. in Paediat. Surg. UCL. Socs: Counc. Mem. Brit. Assn. of Paed. Surgs.; Canad. Assn. of Paed. Surg.; Clin. Nutrit. & Metabol. Gp. (Chairm.). Prev: Cons. Paediat. Surg. & Reader Lond.; Cons. & Sen. Lect. Paediat. Surg. Liverp. Alderlhey Hosp.

PIERRY, Adrian Arrau Cardiff Road Medical Centre, 31 Cardiff Road, Llandaff, Cardiff CF5 2DP Tel: 029 2057 6675 Fax: 029 2057 5367; Coast Guard Cottage, 2 Marine Parade, Penarth CF64 3BE Tel: 029 2070 4609 — MRCS Eng. LRCP Lond. 1975; Medico Cirujano Chile 1970; MRCPI 1978; MRCGP 1983; DRCOG 1983. (Univ. Chile) Clin. Tutor Univ. Wales Sch. Med. Prev: Trainee GP Cardiff VTS; Sen. Health Off. Regist. (Med.) Hope Hosp.; Regist. (Med.) Glas. Roy. Infirm.

PIERSON, Janet Gagnon P & O Cruises, Richmond House, Terminus Terrace, Southampton SO14 3PN Tel: 02380 534209 Fax: 02380 534210; Byways, South Harting, Petersfield GU31 5PH — BM 1979 Soton.; BM Soton 1979; MRCGP 1984; DCH RCP Lond. 1984; AFOM Lond. 1996. Med. Off. P & O Cruises Soton. Socs: BMA; SOM. Prev: GP Portsmouth.

PIERZCHNIAK, Piotr 8 Medgbury Road, Swindon SN1 2AS — MB BS 1987 Lond.; MRCPsych 1992.

PIESOWICZ, Alina Teresa (retired) 78 Grosvenor Avenue, Carshalton SM5 3EP Tel: 020 8647 2917 — MB BS Lond. 1958; FRCP Lond. 1979, M 1961; MRCS Eng. LRCP Lond. 1958; FRCPCH 1997; DCH Eng. 1960. Prev: Cons. Paediatr. Qu. Mary's Hosp. Childr. & St. Helier Hosp. Carshalton.

PIETERSE, Louisa Renee Pauline West Anchorage, 19 High Cross Avenue, Melrose TD6 9SQ Tel: 0189 682 3446 — MB ChB 1983 Glas.; MRCGP 1989.

PIETERSEN, Sheila Christine 251 Chesterfield Road, Sheffield S8 0RT — MB ChB 1980 Bristol. Prev: SHO (Paediat.) Bristol Childr. Hosp.; SHO (Gyn.) Frenchay Hosp. Bristol.

PIETRONI, Mark Arthur Charles Lamb Hospital, Po Parbntipur, Dist. Dinajpur 5250, Dinajpur, Bangladesh Tel: 00 880 552 69011 Email: lamb@citechco.net; 54 Medway Road, London E3 5BY Tel: 020 8980 3969 — MB BChir 1992 Camb.; MA Camb. 1992; MRCP (UK) 1994; DTM & H RCP Lond. 1996; MA (Open Univ.) 1997. (Lond.) Med. Cons. Lamb Hosp. TB Control Progr.; Chief Dept. of Med. Lamb Hosp. Socs: BMA; Christ. Med. Fell.sh. Prev: Regist. (Infec. Dis. & Trop. Med.) N.wick Pk. Hosp.; Regist. (Chest Med.) N.wick Pk. Hosp.; SHO (Med.) & Ho. Phys. OldCh. Hosp.

PIETRONI, Mr Michael Cyril (retired) Delta House, 66 High Road, Buckhurst Hill IG9 5RW Tel: 020 8505 6389 — MB BS Lond. 1961; FRCS Eng. 1968; MRCS Eng. LRCP Lond. 1961. Cons. Surg. Whipps Cross & Wanstead Hosps. Lond.; Assoc. Dean of Postgrad. Med. Univ. Lond; Hon. Lect. St. Barts. Hosp. Lond. Prev: Mem. Ct. Examrs. RCS.

PIETRONI, Professor Patrick Claude Marylebone Health Centre, 17 Marylebone Road, London NW1 5LT; 57 Fitzroy Road, London NW1 8TP — MB BS 1966 Lond.; MRCP (UK) 1972; MRCS Eng. LRCP Lond. 1966; FRCGP 1985, M 1974. Prof. Community Care & Primary Health Univ. W.m. Socs: Fell. Roy. Soc. Med. Prev: Sen. Lect. (Gen. Pract.) St. Mary's Hosp. Med. Sch. Lond.; Assoc. Prof. Family Med. Univ. Cincinnati, Ohio, USA.

PIETRONI, Raymond Allan Yves Princess Street Group Practice, 2 Princess Street, London SE1 6JP Tel: 020 7928 0253 Fax: 020 7261 9804 — MRCS Eng. LRCP Lond. 1964; BSc (Anat.) Lond. 1962, MB BS 1965; MRCGP 1970; DCH Eng. 1968. (Guy's) GP P.ss St. Gp. Pract.; Sen. Lect. (Gen. Pract.) United Med. & Dent. Sch. Lond. Univ.; Med. Adviser Ch. Eng. Childr. Soc. Socs: BMA. Prev: SHO (Chest) Whittington Hosp. Lond.; Ho. Surg. & Cas. Off. & Ho. Phys. Guy's Hosp. Lond.

PIETRONI, Roger Gabriel Ealing Park Health Centre, 195A South Ealing Road, Ealing, London W5 4RH Tel: 020 8758 0570 Fax: 020 8560 5182; 2 Layer Gardens, London W3 9PR Tel: 020 8992 4362 Email: ripietroni@ic.ac.uk — MB BS 1972 Lond.; MMed. Dundee 1992; MRCS Eng. LRCP Lond. 1972; FRCGP 1992, M 1976; Dip. Med. Educat. Dund 1989. (Guy's Hospital) GP; Sen. Teachg. Fell. Imperial Coll. Sch. of Med. Prev: Assn. Adviser Gen. Pract. NW Thames; RCGP Schering Schol.ship 1987; Course Organiser VTS Ealing Hosp.

PIETRONI, Teresa Lesley Chrisp Street Health Centre, 100 Chrisp St., London E14 6PG Tel: 020 7515 4860; 54 Medway Road, London E3 5BY Tel: 020 8980 3969 — MB BChir 1992 Camb.; MA Camb. 1992; MRCGP 1996; DRCOG 1994. Prev: Trainee GP/SHO Roy. Lond. Hosp. VTS.

PIGEM RICART, Isabel Leicester Royal Infirmary, Leicester LE9 5WW Tel: 0116 254 1414 Fax: 0116 258 5631; 6 Blawith Road, Harrow HA1 1TN — LMS 1991 Barcelona. SHO (Radiother. &

PIGGOT

Oncol.) Leicester Roy. Infirm. Socs: BMA; Med. Protec. Soc. Prev: SHO (Urol.) Leicester Gen. Hosp.; SHO (O & G) Co. Hosp. Lincoln; SHO (O & G & A & E) Airedale Gen. Hosp.

PIGGOT, Judith Innes Flat 3/3, 179 Kingarth St., Glasgow G42 7JT — MB ChB 1991 Glas.

PIGGOT, Mr Thomas Alan, TD (retired) Ardlui, 3 Osbaldeston Gardens, Gosforth, Newcastle upon Tyne NE3 4JE Tel: 0191 285 8934 — MB BCh BAO 1953 Belf.; FRCS Ed. 1961. Prev: Sen. Regist. (Plastic Surg.) Wythenshawe Hosp. Manch.

PIGGOTT, Andrea Grosvenor Medical Centre, Grosvenor Street, Crewe CW1 3HB Tel: 01270 256348 Fax: 01270 250786; 56 Millbeck Close, Weston, Crewe CW2 5LR — MB ChB 1986 Liverp.; MRCGP 1990.

PIGGOTT, Mr Harry (retired) Orchard House, 28 Bradshaw Drive, Holbrook, Belper DE56 0SZ — MB BChir Camb. 1948; FRCS Eng. 1955. Hon. Cons. Orthop. Surg. United Birm. Hosps., Roy. Orthop. Hosp. Birm. & Midl. Centre For Neurosurg. & Neurol. Smethwick. Prev: Sen. Regist. (Orthop.) Middlx. Hosp. Lond.

PIGGOTT, Rosemary Margaret Moorland Practice Centre, Regent St., Leek ST13 6LU — MB ChB 1983 Birm.; MRCPsych 1987. GP Retainer Scheme Leek, Staffs. Prev: Clin. Med. Off. (Community Paediat.) Stoke-on-Trent; Clin. Asst. (Psychiat.) Parent & Baby Unit Stoke-on-Trent; Regist. (Psychiat.) N. Staffs. VTS.

PIGGOTT, Susanna Elizabeth — MB ChB 1980 Birm.; FRCA 1987.

***PIGOTT, Ailie Elizabeth** Amilla House, Windmill Lane, Wheatley, Oxford OX33 1TA — MB BS 1998 Lond.; MB BS Lond 1998.

PIGOTT, Brian (retired) 20 Beaufort Close, Lynden Gate, Putney Heath, London SW15 3TL Tel: 020 8789 2513 Fax: 020 8789 2513 — BM BCh 1952 Oxf.; BA Oxf. 1949. Prev: Regist. (Med.) & Ho. Phys. Guy's Hosp. Lond.

PIGOTT, Mr Humphrey William Shilton (retired) The Stone House, Felsham Road, Cockfields, Bury St Edmunds IP30 0AB Tel: 01284 828727 — MRCS Eng. LRCP Lond. 1962; BA Camb. 1959, MB 1963, BChir 1962; FRCS Eng. 1967. Prev: Regist. (Surg.) Middlx. Hosp. Lond.

PIGOTT, Jacqueline Dawn 17 Burnaby Gardens, London W4 3DR — MB BChir 1988 Camb.; MA Camb. 1989.

PIGOTT, Janet Barbara Broadfield House, Dent, Sedbergh LA10 5TG — MB BS 1970 Lond. Appeal Co-ordinator Cancer Relief MacMillan Fund Cumbria. Socs: Fell. Soc. Pub. Health; Fac. Comm. Health. Prev: Sen. Med. Off. Jane Furse Hosp. S. Africa; Clin. Med. Off. S. Cumbria HA; Clin. Med. Off. Holland & Kesteven Dist. Lincs.

PIGOTT, Jean Lesley Child and Family Department, Tavistock Clinic, 120 Belsize Lane, London NW3 5BA Tel: 020 7435 7111; 4 Olive Road, London NW2 6DB — MB BS 1985 Lond.; PhD Lond. 1981, BA 1977; MRCPsych. 1991; DCH RCP Lond. 1989. (University College Hospital (London)) Cons. in Child & Adolesc. Psychiat. Tavistock & Portman NHS Trust & Clin. Dir. Tavistock Munrae Young Family Centre. Socs: RCPsych - ACPP. Prev: Sen. Regist. Rotat. (Child & Adolesc. Psychiat.) Tavistock & Portman NHS Trust.

PIGOTT, Julia Elizabeth Kerigan and Partners, The Surgery, Captain French Lane, Kendal LA9 4HR Tel: 01539 720241 Fax: 01539 725084; Tel: 015395 60869 — MB ChB 1982 Manch.; BSc (Hons.) Manch. 1979; MRCGP 1986. (Manch.) Med. Off. Family Plann. & Police Surg. Kendal.

PIGOTT, Katharine Hamilton Royal Free Hospital, Pond St., London NW3 2QG Tel: 020 7794 5000 — MB BS 1985 Lond.; MRCP (UK) 1988; FRCR 1992; MD MD 1995. (Middlesex hospital) Cons. (Clin. Oncol.) Roy. Free Hosp. Lond. Prev: Sen. Regist. (Radiother.) Mt. Vernon Hosp.

PIGOTT, Nicholas Brian Great Ormond Street Hospital for Children NHS Trust, Great Ormond Street, London WC1N 3JH Tel: 020 7405 9200 Fax: 020 7829 8673 Email: pigotn@gosh.nhs.uk; 88a Melbury Gardens, West Wimbledon, London SW20 0DN Email: nicholap@nch.edu.au — MB BS 1984 Lond.; 1994 MRCPI; 1996 MRCPCH. (St. Thos. Hosp. Med. Sch. Lond.) Cons. Paediatric Intens. Care, Gt. Ormond St. Hosp. for Childr., Lond.. Socs: Med. Protec. Soc.; MRCPCH; Paediat. Intens. Care Soc.

PIGOTT, Peter Vilven Fairhurst, Peppard Common, Henley-on-Thames RG9 — MB BChir 1959 Camb.; MA Camb. 1959; DO Eng. 1961. (St. Thos.) Med. Dir. YRCR Ltd. Henley-on-Thames. Socs: Fell. Roy. Soc. Med.; BMA. Prev: Specialist (Ophth.) Brit. Milit. Hosp. Dhekelia, Cyprus; Regist. (Ophth.) Aylesbury & High Wycombe Hosps.; Ho. Surg. (Ophth.) St. Thos. Hosp. Lond.

PIGOTT, Mr Ronald Wellesley (retired) Bitthams Cottage, Gunnislake PL18 9PD — MB BCh BAO 1956 Dub.; FRCSI 1960; FRCS Eng. 1962. Prev: Hon. Cons. Plastic Surg. Frenchay Hosp. Bristol.

PIGOTT, Stephen Christopher Merchiston Surgery, Highworth Road, Swindon SN3 4BF Tel: 01793 823307 Fax: 01793 820923 — MB BS 1974 Lond.; MRCS Eng. LRCP Lond. 1974; GP(T) 1978. Lect. & Course Organiser Sch. Postgrad. Med. Univ. Bath. Socs: Med. Equestrian Assn.

PIGOTT, Susan Jane Plymyard Avenue Surgery, 170 Plymyard Avenue, Eastham, Wirral CH62 8EH Tel: 0151 327 1391 — BM BS 1984 Nottm.; BMedSci Nottm. 1982, BM BS 1984; MRCGP 1990; DRCOG 1990. Prev: Trainee GP Nottm. VTS.

PIGOTT, Tara Grace 9 Woodland Avenue, Hemel Hempstead HP1 1RG — MB BS 1991 Lond. Trainee GP Carlisle VTS.

PIGOTT, Mr Timothy John Drummond The Walton Centre for Neurology and Neurosurgery, Rice Lane, Liverpool L9 1AE Tel: 0151 525 3611 — MB ChB 1982 Birm.; DM Nottm. 1990; FRCS (SN) 1992; FRCS Eng. 1986. Cons. Neurosurg. Walton Centre Neurol. & Neurosurg. Liverp. Prev: Sen. Regist. (Neurosurg.) Gen. Infirm. Leeds; Regist. (Neurosurg.) Qu. Med. Centre Nottm.; Stanhope Research Fell. (Neurosurg.) S. Derbysh. HA.

PIHLENS, Hugh Lynton Hungerford Surgery, The Croft, Hungerford RG17 0HY Tel: 01488 682507 Fax: 01488 681018; Canver House, 2 Canal Walk, Hungerford RG17 0EQ — MB BS 1971 Lond.; MRCS Eng. LRCP Lond. 1971. (Roy. Free)

PIHLENS, Lois Patricia East Wiltshire Health Care NHS Trust, Community Services, Empire House, Clarence St., Swindon SN1 2LL Tel: 01793 533181; Canver House, 2 Canal Walk, Hungerford RG17 0EQ — MB BS 1972 Lond.; MRCS Eng. LRCP Lond. 1972; MFPP 1993. (St. Bart.) Med. Off. & Instruc. (Family Plann.) E. Wilts. Health Care NHS Trust. Prev: Ho. Surg. & Ho. Phys. P.ss Margt. Hosp. Swindon.

PIILBERG, Olaf (retired) 4 Withers Road, Worcester WR2 4AG Tel: 01905 424246 — Med. Dip. Tartu 1941.

PIKE, Alison Anne 61 Forester Avenue, Bath BA2 6QB — MB BS 1984 Lond.; MRCP (UK) 1988; DCH RCP Lond. 1986; MD 1997.

PIKE, Alison Carol Newton Heath HC, 2 Old Church St, Newton Heath, Manchester M40 2JF Tel: 0161 684 9696 — MB BS 1988 Lond.; MRCP (UK) 1993. Sen. Regist. Rotat. (Paediat. & Community Paediat.) Roy. Manch. Childr. Hosp. Prev: Regist. Rotat. (Paediat.) Roy. Manch. Childr. Hosp.; Clin. Med. Off. (Paediat.) Leicester; SHO (Paediat.) Birm. Childr. Hosp.

PIKE, Brian Richard Bishopgate Medical Centre, 178 Newgate Street, Bishop Auckland DL14 7EJ Tel: 01388 603983 Fax: 01388 607782; The Old Vicarage, Kingsway, Bishop Auckland DL14 7JN Tel: 01388 608191 — MB BS 1968 Newc.; MRCGP 1972; DObst RCOG 1970. (Newc.) Trainer (Gen. Pract.) & Hosp. Pract. (Geriat.) Bishop Auckland. Socs: BMA. Prev: GP, New Zealand; Med. Off. W. Austral. Govt.; Ho. Off. Roy Vict. Infirm. Newc.

PIKE, Catherine Provan (retired) Blatchfield, Littleford Lane, Blackheath, Guildford GU4 8QY Tel: 01483 892358 — MB ChB 1943 Glas. Prev: Cons. Histopath. (Cytopath.) S.W. Surrey Health Dist.

PIKE, Eileen Elizabeth Department of Radiology, Queen Elizabeth Hospital, Gateshead NE9 6SX Tel: 0191 487 8989 Fax: 0191 491 1823; The Old Vicarage, Kingsway, Bishop Auckland DL14 7JN — MB BS 1970 Newc.; FRCR 1985; DObst RCOG 1972. (Newc.) Cons. Radiol. Gateshead Hosps. NHS Trust. Prev: Cons. Radiol. Darlington Memor. Hosp.

***PIKE, Helen Sarah** Sarella, 25 Grange Road, Bromley Cross, Bolton BL7 9AU — MB ChB 1998 Manch.; MB ChB Manch 1998.

PIKE, Mr Jeremy Martin Frimley Park Hospital, Portsmouth Road, Frimley, Camberley GU16 7UJ Tel: 01276 604456 Fax: 01276 604457; 4 Lakeside Grange, Weybridge KT13 9ZE Tel: 01932 821362 — BM 1984 Soton.; FRCS (Orth.) 1995; FRCS Eng. 1990. Cons. Orthop. Frimley Pk. Hosp. Camberley. Prev: Sen. Regist. (Orthop.) St. Geo. Hosp. Lond.

PIKE, John Kingswood Health Centre, Alma Road, Kingswood, Bristol BS15 4EJ Tel: 0117 961 1774 Fax: 0117 947 8969; 17 Kennington Avenue, Bishopston, Bristol BS7 9EU Tel: 0117 944 4084 — MB BS 1987 Lond.; MRCGP 1991; Cert. Family Plann. JCC

1990. Socs: BMA; Med. Protec. Soc. Prev: Trainee GP Dorset; SHO (O & G, Gen. Med. & A & E) W. Dorset Hosps.

*PIKE, John Lindsay The Warren, 17 Meadowfield Road, Stocksfield NE43 7PY — MB ChB 1995 Leeds; MRCP 1999.

PIKE, Jonathan Maxwell 23 High Street, Alconbury, Huntingdon PE28 4DS — BM BS 1991 Nottm. Prev: Ho. Off. (Med.) St. Geo. Hosp. Lincoln; Ho. Off. (Surg.) MusGr. Pk. Hosp. Taunton.

*PIKE, Katherine Claire West Suffolk Hospital, Hardwick Lane, Bury St Edmunds IP33 2QZ — BM BCh 1998 Oxf.; BM BCh Oxf 1998.

PIKE, Lawrence Charles James Street Family Practice, 49 James Street, Louth LN11 0JN Tel: 01507 611122 Fax: 01507 610435; High Bridge House, High Bridge Road, Alvingham, Louth LN11 0QE Tel: 01507 327875 — MB ChB 1980 Birm.; MRCGP 1985.

PIKE, Michael Graham John Radcliffe Hospital, Oxford OX3 9DU — MB BS 1977 Lond.; MA Oxf. 1971; MD Lond. 1989; FRCP Lond. 1997; MRCP (UK) 1981; MRCS Eng. LRCP Lond. 1977; FRCPCH 1997. (Guy's) Cons. Paediat. Neurol. Oxf. Radcliffe Hosp.; Hon. Sen. Clin. Lect. (Paediat.) Univ. of Oxf. Socs: Brit. Paediat. Neurol. Assn. Prev: Sen. Regist. (Paediat. Neurol. & Neurodevelopm. Paediat.) Hosp. Sick Childr. Gt. Ormond St. Lond.; Fell. (Paediat. Neurol.) BC Childr. Hosp. Vancouver, BC, Canada.

PIKE, Shaun Hugo Elgar House Surgery, Church Road, Redditch B97 4AB Tel: 01527 69261 Fax: 01527 596856; Tel: 01527 542472 — MB ChB 1984 Birm. GP Redditch.

PIKE, Stephen Charles Selden Medical Centre, 6 Selden Road, Worthing BN11 2LL Tel: 01903 234962 — MB BS 1986 Lond.; MRCGP 1991; DFFP 1994; DRCOG 1990; DCH RCP Lond. 1989; Dip. Ther. 1998. (St. Geo. Hosp. Med. Sch. Lond.) GP Worthing. Prev: Trainee GP/SHO (Psychiat.) Medway VTS.

*PIKE, Susan Jane 5 Mill Quay, London Road, St Ives PE27 5GT — BChir 1995 Camb.

PIKE, Warwick John, Air Commodore RAF Med. Br. Director Primary Health Services, HQ Personnel and Training Command, Royal Air Force Innsworth, Gloucester GL3 1EZ Tel: 01452 712612 Fax: 01452 510841; 25 Nicolson Close, Innsworth, Gloucester GL3 1DN Tel: 01452 859451 Email: warwick.pike@virgin.net — MB BS Lond. 1968; MSc Lond. 1988; MRCS Eng. LRCP Lond. 1968; MFOM RCP 1992, AFOM 1981; MRCGP 1975; DAvMed Eng. 1979; DObst RCOG 1975. (Guy's) Dir. Primary Health Servs. RAF. Socs: Soc. Occupat. Med. Prev: Dir. Med. Personnel RAF; Command. Off. P.ss Mary's RAF Hosp., Akrotiri; Sen. Med. Off. (Radiat. Med.) Centre Med. Estab.

PILAPITIYA, Rahula Bandara Ashburne Medical Centre, 74-75 Toward Road, Sunderland SR2 8JG Tel: 0191 567 4397 Fax: 0191 567 1035; 2 Seaton Park, Seaham SR7 0HH Tel: 0191 581 8705 — Vrach 1971 2nd Moscow Med. Inst. USSR; Cert. Family Plann. JCC 1984; Cert. Prescribed Equiv. Exp. JCPTGP 1983; DRCOG 1981; DA Eng. 1980. (2nd Moscow State Pyzogovs Med. Inst.) Staff Grade (Anaesth.) City Hosps. Sunderland. Socs: Obst. Anaesth. Assn. Prev: Trainee GP Som.; Trainee GP Newc. VTS; Regist. & Clin. Asst. (Anaesth.) Som. AHA.

PILBROW, Lisa Katharine 56 Copthall Lane, Chalfont St Peter, Gerrards Cross SL9 0DJ — MB BS 1991 Lond.

PILCH, David John Fuller The Blofield Surgery, Plantation Road, Blofield, Norwich NR13 4PL Tel: 01603 712337 Fax: 01603 712899 — BM BCh 1974 Oxf.

PILCHER, Christopher John Chatsworth Road Medical Centre, Chatsworth Road, Brampton, Chesterfield S40 3PY Tel: 01246 568065 Fax: 01246 567116 — MB ChB 1981 Sheff.; DRCOG 1985.

PILCHER, David Vytas 15 Roebuck Lane, Rochester ME1 1UE Tel: 01634 832509 Email: dvp@dvpilcher.freeserve.co.uk — MB BS 1993 Lond.; MRCP 1996. (Camb. Univ. & Royal Lond. Hosp. Med. Sch.)

PILCHER, James Martin 7 St Nicholas Mansions, Trinity Crescent, London SW17 7AF — MB BS 1990 Lond.

PILCHER, Mr Richard, Air Commodore RAF Dent. Br. c/o National Westminster Bank plc, PO Box 2DG, 208 Picadilly, London W1A 2DG; 14 Westwell Court, Castle Dene, South Gosforth, Newcastle upon Tyne NE3 1YY Tel: 0191 285 2667 — LMSSA 1993 Lond.; BSc (Hons.) Dund 1977, BDS 1981; FDS RCPS Glas. 1987; FRCS Glas. 1998. (University College and Middlesex Hospital London) Staff Grade (Oral & Maxillofacial Surg.) Newc. Gen. Hosp. Socs: Brit. Assn. Oral & Maxillofacial Surg.; BMA; Med. Protec. Soc. Prev: Specialist Regist. Rotat. (Oral & Maxillofacial Surg.); Sen. Specialist (Oral Surg.) Camb. Milit. Hosp. Aldershot.; Specialist (Oral Surg.) Brit. Milit. Hosp. Munster, Germany.

PILCHER, Richard Kendall, MC, Col. late RAMC Retd. (retired) The Old Bell, 20 Long St., Cerne Abbas, Dorchester DT2 7JF Tel: 01300 341225 — MRCS Eng. LRCP Lond. 1938; DOMS Eng. 1948. Prev: Cons. Adviser Ophth. MoD (Army).

PILE, Alun Edward 3 Tree Tops Close, Kewferry Road, Northwood HA6 2PL — MB BS 1966 Lond.; MRCS Eng. LRCP Lond. 1966; DA Eng. 1973. (King's Coll. Hosp.) Clin. Asst. (Anaesth.) Edgware Gen. Hosp.

PILE, Horace Francis (retired) 104 Summercourt Way, Brixham TQ5 0RB Tel: 01803 852857 — MB BS 1950 Lond.; MRCS Eng. LRCP Lond. 1950.

PILE, Nicholas Richard Phoenix Surgery, 33 Bell Lane, Burham, Rochester ME1 3SX Tel: 01634 367982 Fax: 01634 864513; Foley View, Farleigh Lane, Barming, Maidstone ME16 9LX — MB BS 1982 Lond.; MRCGP 1988; DRCOG 1988; DCH RCP Lond. 1985. (Roy. Free)

PILE, Richard James Horton General Hospital NHS Trust, 81A Oxford Road, Banbury OX16 9AL — BM BS 1996 Nottm.

PILGRIM, Jane Moreton Lodge, Farmhouse, Culworth, Banbury OX17 2HL — MB BS 1970 Lond.; MRCS Eng. LRCP Lond. 1970; MRCGP 1981; FFA RCS Eng. 1978; DRCOG 1982. (St. Bart.) Semi Retd. GP Locum.

PILGRIM, John Anthony Department of Psychiatry, Doncaster Royal Infirmary, Armthorpe Road, Doncaster DN2 5LT Tel: 01302 366666 Fax: 01302 761317 Email: john.pilgrim@dsh.nhs.org — MB BS 1986 Lond.; MA (Hons.) St And. 1980; MRCPsych 1990. (University college London) Cons. Psychiat. Doncaster Roy. Infirm. Socs: MRCPsych. Prev: Sen. Regist. Bethlem & Maudsley Hosp. Lond.

PILGRIM, Lisa Louisa Pilgrims Rest, Sudbury Road, Bures CO8 5JL — MB ChB 1988 Leeds.

PILKINGTON, Adele IOM, 8 Roxburgh Place, Edinburgh EH8 9SU Tel: 0131 667 5131; 120 Candlemakers Park, Edinburgh EH17 8TL — MB BS 1985 Lond.; MFOM RCP Lond. 1996; MRCGP 1990; DRCOG 1989; Cert. Family Plann. JCC 1989; DCH RCP Lond. 1988; DA (UK) 1987. Cons. Occupat. Phys. Inst. Occupat. Med. Edin. Prev: Occupat. Phys. Inst. Occupat. Med. Edin.; Sen. Regist. (Occupat. Med.) IBH Company Health Ltd. & Blackpool Vict. Hosp. & Community Trusts; Asst. Med. Edr. The Practitioner.

PILKINGTON, Anna Clare 206 Queensbridge Road, London E8 3NB; 35 Balfour Road, London N5 2HB — MB BS 1981 Lond.

PILKINGTON, Barbara Susan 1 Claddach Carinish, Lochmaddy HS6 5HP Tel: 01876 580218 — MB BS 1982 Lond.; BSc Lond. 1979, MB BS 1982; MRCGP 1986.

PILKINGTON, Carole Elaine 2 Beeches Close, Marton Road, Gargrave, Skipton BD23 3NL — MB ChB 1986 Manch.

PILKINGTON, Clare Joanne Westgate Practice, Greenhill Health Centre, Church Street, Lichfield WS13 6JL Tel: 01543 414311 Fax: 01543 256364; 14 Rock Farm Road, Whittington, Lichfield WS14 9LZ — MB BS 1987 Lond.

PILKINGTON, Clarissa Anne Department of Rheumatology, Middlesex Hospital, Tottenham St., London W1 Tel: 020 7636 8333; 23 Sulgrave Road, London W6 7RD — MB BS 1984 Lond.; BSc Lond. 1981; MRCP (UK) 1989. Sen. Regist. (Paediat. Rheum.) & Hon. Lect. Univ. Coll. Lond. Med. Sch. Prev: Research Fell. (Bacteriol.) Univ. Coll. Med. Sch. Lond.

PILKINGTON, Edward Michael (retired) 3 Bellsmeadow, necton, Swaffham PE37 8NE Tel: 01760 721355 Fax: 01760 720924 Email: empilkington@necton.fsbusiness.co.uk — MB BS 1953 Lond.; MRCS Eng. LRCP Lond. 1952; DObst RCOG 1955.

PILKINGTON, George Anthony 19 Pine Walk, Great Bookham, Leatherhead KT23 4AS Tel: 01372 459235 — MB ChB 1951 Bristol. (Bristol) Socs: (Ex-Pres.) Epsom Med. Soc.

PILKINGTON, Guy Stephen Cruddas Park Surgery, 178 Westmoreland Road, Newcastle upon Tyne NE4 7JT Tel: 0191 226 1414 — MB BS 1983 Newc.; BA Oxf. 1980; MRCP (UK) 1986; MRCGP 1989. Prev: Trainee GP N.d. VTS; SHO (Med. & Geriat.) Newc. Gen. Hosp.; SHO (Med.) Shotley Bridge Gen. Hosp. Consett.

PILKINGTON

PILKINGTON, Harriet The Victoria Clinic, 6 Osbert St., London SW1; 9 Avoca Road, Tooting Bec, London SW17 8SQ — MRCS Eng. LRCP Lond. 1978. Clin. Asst. GU Med.

PILKINGTON, Pamela (retired) 16 Lichfield Road, Kew, Richmond TW9 3JR Tel: 020 8940 0369 — MB BS 1951 Lond.; MRCPsych 1977. Prev: Cons. Psychiat. Long. Gr. Hosp. Epsom.

PILKINGTON, Miss Rachel Sarah 6 Brabham Mews, Swinton, Manchester M27 0HH Tel: 0161 728 3486 — MB ChB 1991 Manch.; FRCS Ed. 1996. (Manchester) Specialist Regist. A & E Med. Manch. Deanery; Forens. Police Surg. Gt.er Manch. Police. Prev: Research Fell. Min. of Defence.

***PILKINGTON, Sophie Anne** Oaklands, Backwoods Close, Lindfield, Haywards Heath RH16 2EG — BM BCh 1996 Oxf.

PILKINGTON, Thomas Roger Edward 16 Lichfield Road, Kew, Richmond TW9 3JR Tel: 020 8940 0369 — MD 1949 Lond.; MB BS 1945; FRCP Lond. 1965, M 1946. (Middlx.) Prof. Emerit. Med. St. Geo. Hosp. Med. Sch. Lond.

PILL, Stephen Howard Christopher Health Centre, Old Street, Clevedon BS21 6DG Tel: 01275 871454; 5 Canowie Road, Redland, Bristol BS6 7HP Tel: 0117 973 9501 Email: pill@btinternet.com — MB ChB 1980 Bristol; MSc Bristol 1990; MRCGP 1989; DRCOG 1985; DCH RCP Lond. 1985. (Bristol) Cons. Med. Electronic Data Interchange. Socs: RCGP Represent. RCGP/GMSC Jt. Computing Gp.; RCGP Represent. MIG(Med. Informat. Gp.). Prev: GP Melbourne; SHO Bristol VTS.

PILLAI, Aravind 246 Chiswick Village, London W4 3DF — MB BS 1997 Lond.

PILLAI, Chittaranjan Narayana The Surgery, 57 Plains Road, Mapperley, Nottingham NG3 5LB Tel: 0115 962 1717; 1 Furleys Cottages, Old Epperstone Road, Lowdham, Nottingham NG14 7DG — MB BS 1976 Lond.; FRCGP 1994, M 1982; DCH Eng. 1979. (King's Coll. Hosp. & Guy's) Trainer (GP) Nottm. VTS.; G. P. Adviser, PostGrad. Dept. Nottm. Univ. Med. Sch.; Exec. Comm. Mem., Gedling PCT. Prev: SHO Univ. Hosp. Nottm. & Hammersmith Hosp. Lond.; Ho. Off. King's Coll. Hosp. Lond.; Course Organiser Nottm. VTS.

PILLAI, Mr Kanapathipillai Oppilamani Hertford Road Surgery, 459 Hertford Road, London N9 7DU Tel: 020 8804 2190; 123 Fitzjohn Avenue, Barnet EN5 2HR Tel: 020 8441 8748 — MB BS 1973 Ceylon; FRCS Eng. 1982; MRCGP 1989; DRCOG 1987.

PILLAI, Krishna Charles 16 Stodmarsh House, Cowley Road, London SW9 6HH — MB ChB 1992 Otago.

PILLAI, Mary Bernadette St. Paul's Wing, Cheltenham General Hospital, Cheltenham GL53 7AN Tel: 01242 222222 Fax: 01242 272403; Glenfall Lodge, Mill Lane, Charlton Kings, Cheltenham GL54 4EP Tel: 01242 578453 Fax: 01242 269528 — MB ChB 1980 Bristol; MD Bristol 1992; MRCP (UK) 1985; MRCOG 1987; DCH RCP Lond. 1985. Cons. O & G Cheltenham Gen. Hosp. Prev: Cons. O & G (Fetal Med.) St. Michael's Hosp. Bristol; Perinatal Fell. Wom. Hosp. Winnipeg, Canada; Sen. Regist. (O & G) Glos. Roy. Hosp.

PILLAI, Padmanabha Madhav (retired) Croglin, 70 Whitburn Road, Cleadon Village, Sunderland SR6 7QY Tel: 0191 536 2894 — MB BS 1952 Lucknow; DCH Eng. 1962; DTM & H Calcutta 1954. Prev: Regist. (Paediat.) Roy. Manch. Childr. Hosp.

PILLAI, Mr Parasu Pillai Chidambarathanu c/o Professor Dua, B Floor, South Block, Department of Ophthalmology, Queens Medical Centre, University Hospital, Nottingham NG7 2UH — MB BS 1980 Madras; FRCS Ed. 1989; FCOphth 1990; DO RCS Eng. 1988.

PILLAI, Sarah Watson 459 Hertford Road, Edmonton, London N9 7DW Tel: 020 8804 2190; 123 Fitzjohn Avenue, Barnet EN5 2HR Tel: 020 8441 8748 — MB BS 1984 Lond.; BA Open 1992; DFFP. (Middlx. Hosp.) Lead. Sen. CMO (Fam. Plann.) Barnet Primary Care Trust; GP Asst.; Clin. Asst. GUM.

PILLAI, Mr Sivathanu Subramania 27 Longmeadows, East Herrington, Sunderland SR3 3SB — MB BS Madras 1950; FRCS Eng. 1962; FRCS Ed. 1959. (Madras Med. Coll.) Cons. Surg. (ENT) N. RHA.

***PILLAI, Sunil Kumar** 12 Carlton Avenue W., Wembley HA0 3QU — MB BS 1998 Lond.; MB BS Lond 1998.

PILLAY, Deenan Regional Virus Laboratory, Birmingham Heartlands Hospital, Bordesley Green East, Bordesley Green, Birmingham B9 5SS — MB BS 1987 Newc.; BSc (1st. cl. Hons.) Biochem. Lond. 1979; PhD Sheff. 1982; MRCPath 1993. Cons. Virol. Birm. Pub. Health Laborat. Birm. Heartlands Hosp. Prev: Lect. & Hon. Sen. Regist. (Virol.) Div. Communicable Dis. Roy. Free Hosp. Sch. Med. Lond.; Research Fell. (Med. & Path.) Univ. Calif., San Diego, USA; Asst. Lect. & Hon. Regist. (Virol.) UMDS Guys & St. Thos. Hosp. Lond.

PILLAY, Mr Jayapragassen Govindasamy Accident & Emergency Department, County Hospital, Greetwell Road, Lincoln LN2 5QY Tel: 01522 512512; Stonegarth, Northgate, Lincoln LN2 1QT — MB ChB 1977 Glas.; FRCS Glas. 1981; FFAEM 1995. Cons. A & E Dept. Co. Hosp. Lincoln.

PILLAY, Thaseegaran Marisusay 13 Louisville Road, London SW17 8RL — MB ChB 1989 Natal.

PILLAYE, Jayshree Health Education Authority, Hamilton House, Habledon Place, London WC1H 9TX Tel: 020 7413 1915 Fax: 020 7413 0342; 1 Tudor House, Pinner Hill Road, Pinner HA5 3RY Tel: 020 8429 2344 Email: jayshree.pillaye@hea.org.uk — MB ChB 1972 Natal; MSc Lond. Sch. Economics 1990; DFFP 1993; Cert. Internat. Studies Lond. 1986; Cert. Family Plann. JCC 1984; DA Hamburg 1979. Sen. Med. Off. (Pub. Health) Health Educat. Auth. Socs: Fell. Roy. Soc. Med.; Med. Soc. Study VD. Prev: GP Lond.; SHO (O & G) K. Edwd. VII Hosp. Durban, S. Afr.; Anaesth. Allgemeines Krankenhaus, Hamburg.

PILLER, Wolfgang Konrad 87 Clonmell Road, London N17 6JT — State Exam Med. Frankfurt 1990.

PILLEY, Christine Helen Frances 20 Colbourne Road, Hove BN3 1TB — MB ChB 1991 Birm.; ChB Birm. 1991.

PILLING, Adrian Charles Kensington Group Practice, Kensington Road, Road, Douglas IM1 3PF Tel: 01624 676774 Fax: 01624 614668 — MB BS 1972 Lond.; MRCS Eng. LRCP Lond. 1972; MRCGP 1979; DObst RCOG 1975. (St. Mary's) Prev: Sen. Med. Off. Station Med. Centre RAF Henlow. Sqdn. Ldr. RAF Med.; Br.

PILLING, Allen (retired) Primrose Bank, 4 Daggers Lane, Preesall, Poulton-le-Fylde FY6 0QN Tel: 01253 810699 — MB BS 1947 Lond.; MRCS Eng. LRCP Lond. 1947. Prev: Ho. Surg. & Cas. Off. Gen. Hosp. Bootle.

PILLING, David John Kelso Avenue Health Centre, Kelso Avenue, Thornton-Cleveleys FY5 3LF Tel: 01253 823215 Fax: 01253 860640 — MB ChB 1974 Liverp.; DObst RCOG 1976. Prev: Trainee GP Blackpool VTS; SHO (O & G) St. Catherine's Hosp. Birkenhead; Ho. Phys. & Ho. Surg. Whiston Hosp. Prescot.

PILLING, David William 7 Slessor Avenue, West Kirby, Wirral CH48 6ED Tel: 0151 625 1011 — MB ChB 1970 Liverp.; FRCR 1975; DMRD Eng. 1974; DCH Eng. 1972; FRCPCH 1997. (Liverpool) Cons. Radiol. Alder Hey Childr. Hosp. & Liverp. Wom.s Hosp. Prev: Cons. Radiol. BRd.green & Alder Hey Childr. Hosp.; Sen. Regist. (Radiol.) Sheff. AHA; Regist. (Radiol.) United Sheff. Hosps.

PILLING, Gillian Mary Elizabeth Dalton Square Surgery, 8 Dalton Square, Lancaster LA1 1PP Tel: 01524 842200; 6 Wyresdale Gardens, Wyresdale Road, Lancaster LA1 3FA Tel: 01524 382856 — MB BS 1974 Lond.

PILLING, John Barry Sutton Lodge, 15 Ipswich Road, Norwich NR2 2LN Tel: 01603 610249 Fax: 01603 610249 — MB BS 1966 Lond.; FRCP Lond. 1984; MRCP (U.K.) 1970; MRCS Eng. LRCP Lond. 1966. (St. Bart.) Cons. Neurol. Norf. & Norwich Hosp. & Addenbrooke's Hosp. Camb. Prev: Sen. Regist. (Neurol.) Nat. Hosp. Nerv. Dis. & St. Bart. Hosp. Lond.; Regist. (Neurol.) Addenbrooke's Hosp. Camb.

PILLING, John Richard Norfolk & Norwich Hospital, Brunswick Road, Norwich NR1 3SR Tel: 01603 286086 Email: john.pilling@norfolk.thenhs.com; 10 Old Grove Court, Catton Grove Road, Norwich NR3 3NL — BM BCh 1972 Oxf.; MA Oxf. 1973; FRCR 1978; DCH Eng. 1974. Cons. (Radiol.) Norf. & Norwich Hosp. Norwich. Prev: Sen. Regist. (Diag. Radiol.) Addenbrooke's Hosp. Camb.; Regist. (Diag. Radiol.) Addenbrooke's Hosp. Camb.; SHO (Paediat. Med.) Childr. Hosp. Sheff.

PILLING, Keith James Occhea Ltd, 32 Oldway Drive, Solihull B91 3HP Tel: 0121 246 5432 Fax: 0121 689 3748 Email: occhea@aol.com; 32 Oldway Drive, Solihull B91 3HP Tel: 0121 247 5569 Fax: 0121 246 5432 — MB BCh 1982 Wales; BSc Wales 1977; FFOM RCP Lond. 1995, MFOM 1992, AFOM 1988; Spec. Accredit. Occupat. Med. JCHMT 1992. (Wales) Man. Dir. Occhea Ltd.; Hon. Sen. Clin. Lect. Inst. Occupat. Health Birm. Prev: Dir. Health & Safety Rover Gp. Ltd; Chief Med. Off. UK Atomic Energy Auth.

PILLING, Patricia Jane Penny's Hill Practice, St Mary's Road, Ferndown BH22 9HB Tel: 01202 897200 Fax: 01202 877753 — MB ChB 1977 Liverp.; DRCOG 1979.

PILLINGER, John Edward Terence Highcliffe Medical Centre, 248 Lymington Road, Highcliffe, Christchurch BH23 5ET Tel: 01425 272203 Fax: 01425 271086; 1 Howe Close, Mudeford, Christchurch BH23 3JA — MB ChB 1982 Liverp.; DRCOG 1984. Prev: Trainee GP/SHO W. Lancs. HA VTS; Ho. Off. Roy. Liverp. Hosp.

PILLITTERI, Angelo John 157 Clare Road, Maidenhead SL6 4DL — MB ChB 1990 Liverp.

PILLMAN, Florence Ruth (retired) The Manor Linneys, Stogumber, Taunton TA4 3TP Tel: 0198 46 56696 — MB BS 1940 Lond.; MRCP Lond. 1947; MRCS Eng. LRCP Lond. 1940. Prev: Cons. Chest Phys. Chichester Health Dist.

PILLOW, Joan Rosalie (retired) 9 Orchard Walk, Stoney Lane, Winchester SO22 6DL Tel: 01962 880984 — MRCS Eng. LRCP Lond. 1936.

PILLOW, Stephen John Azurdia and Partners, Bebington Health Centre, Civic Way, Bebington, Wirral CH63 7RX Tel: 0151 645 6936 Fax: 0151 643 1698; Fieldside Cottage, 38 Spital Road, Spital, Wirral CH63 9JF Tel: 0151 334 6318 — MB ChB 1972 Leeds; MRCGP 1976; DObst RCOG 1976. Hospice Practitioner St. John's Hospice Wirral. Prev: Trainee GP Doncaster VTS.

PILPEL, James Malcolm The New Surgery, Old Road, Tean, Stoke-on-Trent ST10 4EG Tel: 01538 722323 Fax: 01538 722215 — BM BS 1976 Nottm.; BMedSci Nottm. 1974, BM BS 1976; DA Eng. 1983; DRCOG 1980; Cert FPA. 1980; DCH Eng. 1979.

PILPEL, Pamela Jean The Firs, Firbob Lane, Hollington, Stoke-on-Trent ST10 4HT — BMedSci Nottm. 1974, BM BS 1976; DCH RCP Lond. 1983; Cert. Family Plann. JCC 1979. Clin. Med. Off. N. Staffs. HA.

PILSTON, Matthew John 15 Prebend Street, Islington, London N1 8PF Tel: 020 7226 9090 — BM 1986 Soton.

PILSWORTH, Roy (retired) 8 Sidwell Park, South Benfleet, Benfleet SS7 1LQ Tel: 01268 754822 — MB BS 1943 Lond.; MD Lond. 1951, MB BS 1943, Dipl. Bact. (Distinc.) 1947; MRCS Eng., LRCP Lond. 1942.

PILTON, Donald William (retired) St. Michael's Surgery, Walwyn Close, Twerton, Bath BA2 1ER Tel: 01225 428277 — MB ChB 1959 Bristol. Prev: Clin. Asst. in Orthop. Roy. United Hosp. Bath.

PILZ, Daniela Theresa Institute of Medical Genetics, University Hospital of Wales, Cardiff CF14 4XW Email: daniela.pilz@uhw-tr.wales.nhs.uk — State Exam Med 1986 Hannover; State Exam Med. Hannover 1986; MRCP (UK) 1990; MD 1997. (Medizinische Mochschule, Hannover, Germ.) Cons. (Med. Genetics) Inst. Med. Genetics. Univ. Hosp. Wales Cardiff.

PIM, Arthur Joseph (retired) Vane House, Nuffield, Henley-on-Thames RG9 5RT Tel: 01491 641444 Fax: 01491 641444 — MB BS 1958 Lond.; DObst RCOG 1960. Coroner Reading.

PIMBLETT, Geoffrey Holland, MC (retired) Nancy's Cottage, Brookside, Balderstone, Blackburn BB2 7LD Tel: 01254 812947 — MB ChB 1941 Liverp.

PIMBLETT, John Hugh Sutcliffe Apple Tree Cottage, Sutton Marsh, Cross Keys, Hereford HR1 3NL Tel: 01432 72523 — MB BS 1960 Durh.; BA Open 1985; DA Eng. 1965; DObst RCOG 1963.

PIMENIDIS, Dimitrios 81 Glisson Road, Cambridge CB1 2HG — Ptychio Iatrikes 1988 Thessalonika.

***PIMENTA, Darren Joseph** 19 Blackberry Walk, Lychpit, Basingstoke RG24 8SN — MB ChB 1995 Aberd.

PIMENTA, Neale Gerard Horsman's Place Surgery, Instone Road, Dartford DA1 2JP Tel: 01322 228363/277444 — BM 1985 Soton.; MRCGP 1989; Cert. Family Plann. JCC 1987. Socs: BMA & Med. Protec. Soc. Prev: Trainee GP E. Dorset VTS; Ho. Phys. & Ho. Surg. Roy. Vict. Hosp. Bournemouth.

PIMENTA, Susan Mary Horsman's Place Surgery, Instone Road, Dartford DA1 2JP Tel: 01322 228363/277444 — BM 1986 Soton.; DRCOG 1991; Cert. Family Plann. JCC 1990; DCH RCP Lond. 1988. Socs: Med. Protec. Soc.

PIMLEY, Kenneth Gordon (retired) — MB ChB 1946 Aberd. Prev: Cons. Psychiat. Cranage Hall Hosp. Crewe.

PIMLEY, Mrs Sheila King (retired) Ben Shiel, 1 Gordon St., Fochabers IV32 7DL Tel: 01343 821396 — MB ChB St. And. 1955. Prev: Assoc. Specialist (Child & Family Psychiat.) Bilbohall Hosp. Elgin.

PIMM, James Tait Brookside Group Practice, Brookside Close, Gipsy Lane, Earley, Reading RG6 7HG Tel: 0118 966 9222 Fax: 0118 935 3174; 66 Beech Lane, Earley, Reading RG6 5QA Tel: 0118 986 3073 — MB ChB 1981 Univ. Zimbabwe; LRCP LRCS Ed. LRCPS Glas. 1981; MRCGP 1989. (Godfrey Huggins) Gen. Pract.; Lord Harris Ct. Med. Off. - c/o the Elderly.

PIMM, John Borstal Cottage, 138 Borstal Road, Rochester ME1 3BB Tel: 01634 42323 — MB BS 1957 Lond. (Lond. Hosp.) Prev: SHO Lond. Hosp.; Gen. Med. Off. S.. Rhodesia; Sen. Med. Off. N.. Rhodesia.

PIMM, Jonathan 138 Borstal Road, Rochester ME1 3BB — MB BS 1987 Lond.

PIMM, Mr Lionel Henry (retired) Barken Cottage, Courtlands Lane, Bower Ashton, Bristol BS3 2JS Tel: 0117 909 9397 Email: lionel@lpimm.fsnet.co.uk — MB BS 1945 Lond.; FRCS Eng. 1952. Prev: Cons. Orthop. Surg. Ipswich Hosp. & Suff. AHA.

PIMM, Michael Henry James The Surgery, 87 New Bristol road, Worle, Weston Super Mare, Bristol BS22 6AJ Tel: 01934 515878 Fax: 01934 520263; 42 Uphill Road S., Weston Super Mare BS23 4SQ Tel: 01934 413407 — MB ChB 1982 Bristol; MRCGP 1986; DRCOG 1985; Cert. Family Plann. JCC 1985; DCH RCP Lond. 1985. (Bristol) Prev: Trainee GP Rugby VTS.

***PINCH, Edward Thomas** 1 Tor Close, Hartley, Plymouth PL3 5TH Tel: 01752 705372 — MB BS 1994 Lond.

PINCHBECK, Frank Walter Sleaford Road Surgery, 1 Sleaford Road, Heckington, Sleaford NG34 9QP Tel: 01529 460213 Fax: 01529 460087; 12 Houldon Way, Hockington, Sleaford NG34 9TY Tel: 01529 460600 — MB ChB 1960 Sheff.

PINCHEN, Christopher John The Surgery, Margaret Street, Thaxted, Dunmow CM6 2QN Tel: 01371 830213 Fax: 01371 831278 — MB BS 1978 Lond.; BSc (Pharm.) CNAA 1969; MRCS Eng. LRCP Lond. 1978; MPS 1970; DRCOG 1981. (St. Bart.) GP Thaxted.; CMP 33 Eng Regt. (EOD) Wimbish; HSE Approved Diving Doctor. Prev: GP Trainee Addenbrooke's Hosp. Camb. VTS.; Ho. Phys. OldCh. Hosp. Romford; Ho. Surg. Hackney Hosp. Lond.

PINCHES, Claire Elaine Elm Lane Surgery, 104 Elm Lane, Sheffield S5 7TW Tel: 0114 245 6994 Fax: 0114 257 1260 — MB ChB 1986 Bristol; MRCGP 1990; DCH RCP Lond. 1991; DGM RCP Lond. 1989; DRCOG 1988. GP Princip. Prev: SHO (Paediat.) Rotherham Dist. Gen. Hosp.; Trainee GP Bristol VTS.

PINCHES, Patricia Joyce Elizabeth Faringdon Health Centre, Coxwell Road, Faringdon SN7 7ED Tel: 01367 242388 Fax: 01367 243394; April Cottage, 32C London St, Faringdon SN7 7AA Tel: 01367 243316 — MB ChB St. And. 1961. (St. And.) Clin. Asst. Paediat.Oncol.P.ss Margt. Hosp. Swindon Wilts.

PINCHES, Robert Smythe Marcham Road Family Health Centre, Abingdon OX14 1BT Tel: 01235 522602 — MB ChB 1961 St. And.; MRCGP 1975; DObst RCOG 1971. (St. And.) Socs: Medico-Legal Soc.

PINCHIN, Roberta Mary Erasmus Paynesfield House, Tatsfield, Westerham TN16 2BQ Tel: 01959 541212 — MB BS 1970 Lond.; FFA RCS Eng. 1974; T(Anaesth.) 1991. Cons. Anaesth. Bromley Hosps. NHS Trust. Prev: Cons. Anaesth. Barnet Gen. Hosp.; Sen. Regist. (Anaesth.) Barnet Gen. Hosp. & Roy. Free Hosp. Lond.; Regist. (Anaesth.) W.m. Hosp. Lond.

PINCHING, Professor Anthony John Department of Immunology, St. Bartholomew's Hospital, West Smithfield, London EC1A 7BE Tel: 020 7601 8428 Fax: 020 7600 3839 Email: a.j.pinching@mds.qmw.ac.uk; 22 Cuckoo Hill Road, Pinner HA5 1AY — BM BCh 1973 Oxf.; MA Oxf. 1973, DPhil 1972, BA 1968; FRCP Lond. 1986; MRCP (UK) 1976. Prof. Immunol. St. Bart. & Roy. Lond. Sch. Med. & Dent., Qu. Mary & W.field Coll. Lond. Prev: Reader & Hon. Cons. Clin. Immunol. St. Mary's Hosp. Med. Sch. Lond.; Sen. Regist. (Med.) Hammersmith Hosp. Lond.

PINCHING, John Hillbury House, Wells Tel: 01749 3356 — MRCS Eng. LRCP Lond. 1942; BM BCh Oxon. 1942; MRCPLond. 1948. (Oxf. & Guy's) Clin. Asst. (Med.) Bath Gp. Hosps. Prev: Res. Med. Off. St. Cross Hosp. Rugby; Asst. Med. Off. Co. Hosp. FarnBoro..

PINCHING, Nicola Jane Adelaide Street Health Centre, Norwich NR2 5DL Tel: 01603 625015; 7 High Street, Marsham, Norwich NR10 5AE — MB ChB 1990 Leic.; MRCGP 1996. GP Asst.

PINCOTT, John Raymond The R.W. Johnson Pharmaceutical Research Institute, Wycombe Road, Saunderton, High Wycombe HP14 4HX Tel: 01494 567496 Fax: 01494 567408 — MB BS 1968

PINCOTT

Lond.; MD Lond. 1985; FFPM RCP (UK) 1996, MFPM 1993, AFPM 1990; FRCPath 1986, M 1975; MRCPCH 1996; CBiol, FIBiol 1992. (Univ. Coll. Hosp.) Sen. Dir. Pharmacovigilance, RW Johnson Pharmaceut. Research Inst.; Hon. Cons. Path. Hosp. Sick Childr. Gt. Ormond St. Lond.; Hon. Research Fell. St. Bart. Hosp. Med. Coll. Lond. Socs: Fell. Roy. Soc. Med. (Hon. Sec. Comparative Med. Sect.); Hon. Fell. Scoliosis Research Soc.; (Hon. Treas.) Soc. Pharmaceut. Med. Prev: Med. Dir. Europ. Safety Pfizer Inc., NY, USA; Gp. Dir. Path. & Toxicol. SmithKline & French Research Ltd.; Sen. Lect. & Hon. Cons. Inst. Child Health Gt. Ormond St. Lond.

PINCOTT, Richard Glynne Sway Road Surgery, 65 Sway Road, Morriston, Swansea SA6 6JA Tel: 01792 773150 / 771392 Fax: 01792 790880 — MB BS 1971 Lond.; DCH Eng. 1974. (King's Coll. Hosp.)

PINCUS, Celia Tziona Flat 2, 10 Parkhill Road, London NW3 2YN Tel: 020 7482 4639 Fax: 020 7482 4639 Email: guler@global.net.co.uk — MB ChB 1991 Cape Town. (Cape Town S. Afr.)

PINDER, Alison Orchard Cottage, Cranford Way, Highfield, Southampton SO17 1RN — MB BS 1975 Lond.; DRCOG 1978. (St. Bart.)

PINDER, Amanda Jane 28 Elm Tree Close, Colton, Leeds LS15 9JE Email: drajppig@aol.com — MB ChB 1994 Leeds; BSc (Chem. Path.) Leeds 1991. (Leeds) Specialist Regist. (Anaesth.) N. & W. Yorks. Socs: Assn. Anaesth. Prev: Clin. Fell. (NeuroIC) Leeds Gen. Infirm.; SHO (Anaesth.) Dewsbury Dist. Hosp.; SHO (Anaesth.) Pontefract Gen. Infirm.

PINDER, Carole Ann Ferrybridge Medical Centre, 8-10 High Street, Ferrybridge, Knottingley WF11 9NQ Tel: 01977 672109 Fax: 01977 671107; Manor Grange, Church St, Brotherton, Knottingley WF11 9HE — MB ChB 1975 Leeds; DOCC Med 1997. Dr Capinder, GP Ferrybridge Med. Centre, 8-10 High St., Ferrybridge, Knottingley WF11 8NQ; Med. Adviser Pioneer Electronics Castleford; Med. Adviser Monkhill Confectionery Pontefract, Dunhill Haribo (Pontefract) Ltd; Med. Adviser, Monkhill Confectionery, York; Med. Adviser Constar, Sherburn in Elmet. Socs: Soc. Occupat. Med. Prev: SHO (Paediat., A & E & O & G) Pontefract Gen. Infirm.

PINDER, Christopher Gerard 31 Chichele Road, Oxted RH8 0AE — MB BS 1975 Lond.; FRCR Lond. 1983. (Guy's) Cons. Radiol. Qu. Mary's Hosp. Sidcup.

PINDER, Colin Anthony Frederick 47 Buttermere Road, Bolton, Bradford BD2 4JA Tel: 01274 641916 — MB ChB 1988 Leeds; MRCP (UK) 1994. (Leeds) Regist. (Rehabil. Med.) St. Mary's Hosp. Leeds.

PINDER, Darren Kenneth The Holmes, Ryarsh, West Malling ME19 5LQ — BChir 1992 Camb.

PINDER, David Charles West Surrey HA, Ridgewood Centre, Old Bisley Road, Frimley, Camberley GU16 9QE Tel: 01276 605549 Fax: 01276 605493; 31 Grasmere Road, Lightwater GU18 5TG Tel: 01276 476721 — MB BChir Camb. 1969; BA Open 1975; MA Camb. 1970; FFPHM RCP (UK) 1995, M 1977; DPH Manch. 1972. p/t Cons. Pub. Health Med. W Surrey DHA. Prev: SCM (Informat. & Primary Care) Leics. HA & (Informat. & Research) Mersey RHA; Med. Off. DHSS.

PINDER, Fiona Anne McNeil 7 Oliver Road, Heckmondwike WF16 9QA — MB ChB 1991 Leeds.

PINDER, Gillian Anne 6 St Helens Grove, Wakefield WF2 6RR — MB ChB 1979 Birm.; MFPHM RCP (UK) 1990; MFCM 1988. Cons. Pub. Health Med. Wakefield HA. Prev: Sen. Regist. (Community Med.) Yorks. RHA; Trainee GP E.. Dist. Wakefield AHA.

PINDER, Gordon Whittaker (retired) Moor Garth, Hutton-le-Hole, York YO62 6UA Tel: 01751 417581 — MRCS Eng. LRCP Lond. 1940; BA Camb. 1937; DObst RCOG 1948. Prev: Lt.-Col. RAMC 1942-46.

PINDER, Ian Fred Manor Grange, Church Lane, Brotherton, Knottingley WF11 9HE Tel: 01977 676777 Fax: 01977 673111 — MB ChB 1975 Leeds; MRCP (UK) 1979; AFOM 1999. (Leeds) Occupat. Phys. Covance, Harrogate; Internat. Speciality Chem. Ltd, Scott. & Newc. Breweries, Regromac Indep. Media, Nestle UK. Socs: Soc. Occupat. Med.; Chairm. Yorks. Grp. Prev: CMO Courage Ltd.

PINDER, Mr Ian Maurice Newcastle Nuffield Hospital, Clayton Road, Jesmond, Newcastle upon Tyne NE2 1JP; 126 Darras Road, Newcastle upon Tyne NE20 9PG — MB ChB 1961 Sheff.; FRCS Ed. 1966. Cons. (Orthop.) Surg. Newc. Nuffield Hosp. Prev: Cons. (Orthop.) Surg. Newc. AHA (T).

PINDER, Joe Rawdon Sycamore House, High St., Barmby-on-the-March, Goole DN14 7HU — MB ChB 1993 Leeds.

PINDER, Mary 97 Kingsmead Road, London SW2 3HZ — MB BS 1982 Lond.

PINDER, Norman Richard Pond Farm, Kirby Bedon, Norwich NR14 7DY — MB BS 1972 Lond.; MSc (Community Med.) Lond. 1988, MB BS 1972; MFPHM RCP (UK) 1991; DObst RCOG 1975; FFPHM 1998. (Guy's) Cons. Pub. Health Med. E. Norf. Health Auth. Prev: Dir. Community Med. Grenfell Regional Health Serv. Newfld., Canada.

PINDER, Sarah Elizabeth Dept. of Histopathology, Nottingham City Hospital NHS Trust, Hucknall Road, Nottingham NG5 1PB Tel: 0115 691169 Fax: 0115 962 7768 Email: sarah.pinder@nottingham.ac.uk; 14 Cotgrave Raod, Plumtree, Nottingham NG12 5NX — MB ChB 1986 Manch.; MRCPath 1993. Sen. Lect. & Hon. Cons. Univ. of Nottm. Prev: Clin. Research Fell. & Hon. Sen. Regist. City Hosp. Nottm.

PINDER, Sarah Jane 15 Mill Street, Warwick CV34 4HB — BChir 1992 Camb.

PINDER, Stephen Paul Hetherington The Deepings Practice, Market Deeping Health Centre, Market Deeping, Peterborough PE6 8DD Tel: 01778 579000 Fax: 01778 579009; 10 Whattoff Way, Baston Fields, Baston, Peterborough PE6 9QS — MB BS Lond. 1976; D.Occ.Med. RCP Lond. 1996; DAvMed FOM RCP Lond. 1990.

PINDOLIA, Narendra Kumar Braeside Medical Group, Escomb Road, Bishop Auckland DL14 6AB Tel: 01388 663539 Fax: 01388 601847 — MB BS 1983 Lond.; MRCGP 1988.

PINE, Isabel Mary (retired) 22 Norfolk Street, Southsea PO5 4DS — MB BS Lond. 1950; DPH Eng. 1965; MFCM 1974; MFPHM 1989; FRIPHH. Prev: Sen. Med. Off. Portsmouth & SE Hants. Health Dist.

PINE, Mr Richard Campbell 29 Sunnydale Gardens, Mill Hill, London NW7 3PD — MB BS 1966 Lond.; FRCS Ed. 1980; FRCS Glas. 1980; MRCS Eng. LRCP Lond. 1965; LMSSA Lond. 1971. (St. Bart.) Surg. Roy. Fleet Auxil. Prev: Ho. Surg. Roy. Vict. Hosp. Bournemouth; SHO (Gen. Surg.) Roy. Berks. Hosp. Reading; Demonst. (Anat.) Roy. Free Hosp. Sch. Med.

PINES, Dinora 16 Bracknell Gardens, Hampstead, London NW3 7EB Tel: 020 7794 3644 — MB BS 1945 Lond.; BA (Hons.) Lond. 1939, MB BS 1945. (Lond. Sch. Med. Wom.) Socs: Inst. Psychoanal. Prev: Hon. Sen. Tutor (Psychother.) Maudsley Hosp. Lond.; Therap. & Research Asst. Brent Consultation Centre; Clin. Asst. (Dermat.) Eliz. G. Anderson Hosp. & S. Lond. Hosp. Wom.

PINFOLD, Terence James 4 Southwood Close, Kingswinford DY6 8JL — MB ChB 1961 Birm. Cons. (Accid. Emerg.) Dudley & Stourbridge AHA. Socs: Fell. Brit. Orthop. Assn. Prev: Med. Asst. (Trauma & Orthop.) Dudley & Stourbridge AHA.

***PING, Emma Claire** 38 The Paddocks, Old Catton, Norwich NR6 7HD — MB ChB 1998 Sheff.; MB ChB Sheff 1998.

PINGREE, Brian James William, RD Institute of Naval Medicine, Alverstoke, Gosport PO12 2DL; Long Durford, Upper Durford Wood, Petersfield GU31 5AW — MB ChB 1968 Bristol; MSc (Bioeng.) Strathclyde 1974; BSc (Engin.) Bristol 1960, MB ChB 1968; MFOM RCP Lond. 1983; DAvMed. FOM RCP Lond. 1982. (Bristol) Sen. Med. Off. Submarine Med. Inst. Naval Med. Gosport. Socs: Soc. Occupat. Med. Prev: Sen. Med. Off. (Environm. Med.) Inst. Naval Med. Alverstoke; Princip. Med. Off. Clyde Submarine Base; Head of Human Factors Inst. Naval Med. Alverstoke.

PINHEIRO, Neville Leslie Acreswood Surgery, 5 Acreswood Close, Coppull, Chorley PR7 5EJ Tel: 01257 793578 Fax: 01257 794005 — MRCS Eng. LRCP Lond. 1976; LSM Spain 1973. (Navarra, Spain)

PINHORN, Anja 19 Marston Lane, Rolleston-on-Dove, Burton-on-Trent DE13 9BH — MB BS 1989 Lond.; BSc Lond. 1986, MB BS 1989. SHO Rotat. (Med.) St. Mary's Hosp. Lond.

PINION, Sheena Barbara Forth Park Maternity Hospital, Bennochy Road, Kirkcaldy KY2 5RA Tel: 01592 643355 — MB ChB 1981 Ed.; MD (Ed) 1997; FRCS Glas. 1990; MRCOG 1988. Cons. O & G Forth Pk. Matern. Hosp. Kirkcaldy. Prev: Sen. Regist. (O & G) Dundee; Research Fell. (Gyn.) Univ. Aberd.; Regist. (O & G) Glas.

PINK, Edith Jean (retired) 10 Balgove Avenue, Gauldry, Newport-on-Tay DD6 8SQ — MB ChB 1955 St. And.; FRCP Canada 1973;

DA Eng. 1960. Prev: Cons. Anaesth. Monklands Dist. Gen. Hosp. Coatbridge.

*PINK, Edward 24 Lawrence Road, Biggleswade SG18 0LS — MB ChB 1998 Birm.; ChB Birm. 1998.

PINK, Quintin James (retired) Hawthorn Cottage, East Farndon, Market Harborough LE16 9SH Tel: 01858 467717 — MRCS Eng. LRCP Lond. 1973; MB Camb. 1974, BChir 1973. Prev: GP Market HarBoro. Leics.

PINKER, Sir George Douglas, KCVO (retired) 96 Harley Street, London W1N 1AF Tel: 020 7935 2292 — MB BS 1947 Lond.; FRCS 1989; FRCS Ed. 1957; FRCOG 1964, M 1954; DObst 1949; Hon. FACOG 1990; Hon. FRACOG 1989; Hon. FRCSI 1988. Cons. Gyn. Surg. & Obst. St. Mary's Hosp., Samarit. Hosp. Lond. & King Edwd. VII Hosp. for Offs.; Hon. Cons. Roy. Wom. Hosp. Melbourne, Austral.; Examr. FRCS Ed.; Examr. (Obst. & Gyn.) Univs. Camb., Birm., Glas., Lond., Dub. & Dundee. Prev: Pres. Roy. Soc. Med. 1992-1994 & RCOG 1987-1990 (Vice-Pres. 1980).

*PINKERTON, Amanda Louise Lubards Lodge Farm, Ranreth Lane, Rayleigh SS6 — MB ChB 1996 Leeds.

PINKERTON, Professor Charles Ross Children's Department, Royal Marsden NHS Trust, Downs Road, Sutton SM2 5PT Tel: 020 8661 3498 Fax: 020 8770 7168 Email: rossp@icr.ac.uk — MB BCh BAO 1974 Belf.; MD (Hons.) Belf. 1981; FRCPI (Paediat.) 1979, M 1979; DCH RCPSI 1978; FRCPCH 1997. Prof. Paediat. Oncol. Roy. Marsden Hosp. & Inst. Cancer Research Lond.

PINKERTON, Florence (retired) 41C Sans Souci Park, Belfast BT9 5BZ Tel: 02890 682956 — MB BCh BAO 1945 Belf. Prev: Clin. Med. Off. (Community Health) Clinic EHSSB.

PINKERTON, George Eustace, MC (retired) 17 Church Lane, Upwood, Huntingdon PE26 2QF Tel: 01487 813946 Email: gpapajakl@aol.com — MB BChir 1941 Camb.; BA Camb. 1938, MB BChir 1941. Prev: Capt. RAMC.

PINKERTON, Ian Watt, OBE, OStJ, TD (retired) 10 Langside Drive, Comrie, Crieff PH6 2HR Tel: 01764 670578 — MB ChB 1951 Glas.; FRCP Ed. 1979, M 1960; FRCP Glas. 1970; FRFPS Glas. 1957. Hon. Lect. (Infec. Dis.) Univ. Glas. Prev: Cons. Phys. Dept. Infec. Dis. Ruchill Hosp. Glas.

PINKERTON, (Isabella) Madeleine (retired) 64 Portsmouth Road, Surbiton KT6 4HT Tel: 020 8399 0067 — MB BCh 1944 Wales; FFOM RCP Lond. 1978; DPH Lond. 1949. Prev: Gp. Med. Adviser Marks & Spencer Ltd.

PINKERTON, John Henry McKnight, CBE 41c Sans Souci Park, Belfast BT9 5BZ Tel: 02890 682956 — MB BCh BAO 1943 Belf.; DSc Hon. NUI 1986; MD Belf. 1948; FRCPI 1977, M 1974; FRCOG 1960, M 1950. (Belf.) Emerit. Prof. Midw. & Gyn. Qu. Univ. Belf. Socs: BMA; Hon. Mem. Gyn. Vis. Soc. Prev: Prof. O & G Univ. Lond. at Inst. O & G & Surg. Chelsea Hosp. Wom. Obst. Surg. Qu. Charlotte's Matern Hosp.; Sen. Lect. (O & G) Univ. Coll. W. Indies.; Rockefeller Research Fell. Harvard Univ. 1956-7.

*PINKERTON, Rachel Mariama 15 Colenso Pde, Belfast BT9 5AN — MB BCh BAO 1997 Belf.

PINKERTON, Stuart Melvyn Old Barn House, Nomansland Farm, Wheathampstead, St Albans AL4 8EY Tel: 01582 831029 Fax: 01582 834965 Email: stuart@pinkertonhealthcare.com — MB ChB 1979 Liverp.; MFPM RCP (UK) 1989; FFPM RCP (UK) 1997; Dip. Pharm. Med. RCP (UK) 1985; Cert. Family Plann. JCC 1982; Cert. Prescribed Equiv. Exp. JCPTGP 1982. Chairm. Europ. Healthcare. Burson- Marsteller; Hon. Clin. Asst. (Cardiol.) St. Albans City Hosp. Socs: BMA; FFPM. Prev: Med. Dir. Roche Products Ltd. Welwyn Gdn. City; Med. Dir. Syntex UK & Scand.; Head Europ. Clin. Research Syntex Internat.

PINKEY, Basil 2 Edith Marriage House, 5 Cambridge Road, Colchester CO3 3NS — MB BCh BAO 1959 Belf.; MRCP (UK) 1969.

PINKHAM, Kathryn Louise 1 Dehewydd Isaf, Llantwit Fardre, Pontypridd CF38 2EX — MB BCh 1992 Wales.

PINKNEY, Jonathan Henley University Department of Medicine, Bristol Royal Infirmary, Marlborough St., Bristol BS2 8HW Email: j.pinkney@bris.ac.uk; 2 Marlborough Hill Place, Kingsdown, Bristol BS2 8HA — MB BS 1985 Lond.; BSc Lond. 1982; MD Lond. 1997; MRCP (UK) 1988. (Char. Cross & Westm.) Sen. Lect. (Med., Cons Phys.). Socs: Brit. Diabetic Assn.; Brit. Endocrine Soc. Prev: Research Fell. Univ. Coll. Lond. Sch. Med.; Lect. (Med.) Univ. Bristol; Vis. Fell. Louisiana State Univ.

PINKNEY, Moira Ann 7 George Frost Close, Ipswich IP4 2UG Tel: 01473 252798 — MB ChB 1973 Bristol; MRCP (UK) 1978; MRCGP 1990; DGM RCP Lond. 1985; DCH Eng. 1975; DObst RCOG 1975. Cons. community Paediat..local health partnerships trust Ipswich; GP Ipswich. Prev: Sen. Regist. (Community Paediats.) Allington NHS Trust Ipswich; Regist. (Med.) Norf. & Norwich Hosp.; SHO Rotat. (Med.) Oxon. AHA (T).

PINNELL, Jeremy Robert 28 Bedford Close, Kettering NN15 6TQ Tel: 01536 723976 — MB ChB 1994 Leeds. SHO (Anaesth.).

PINNER, Gillian Tracy Dencourt, London rd, Newark, Nottingham NG7 2UH Tel: 01636 685948 Fax: 0115 942 3618 — MB BS 1989 Lond.; MSc Lond. 1994; MRCPsych 1995. (Kings College Hospital London) Cons. old age Psychiat., Centr. Nottm. Health Care Trust; acedemic Cons.. Old age psychiatry. Socs: Roy. Coll. Psychiat. Prev: Lect. & Hon. Sen. Regist. (Old Age Psychiat.) Univ. Hosp. Nottm.; Research Assoc. (Psychiat.) UMDS.; Regist. Bexley Hosp. Oxleas NHS Trust.

*PINNER, Jason Roderick Garden Flat, 369 Liverpool Road, London N1 1NL — MB BS 1997 Lond.

PINNER-HARTH, Johanna A (retired) 29 Thanet Lodge, Mapesbury Road, London NW2 4JA Tel: 020 8459 6776 — MD 1931 Vienna. Prev: Regist. Qu.'s Hosp. Croydon.

PINNEY, David Charles Dal Na Beigh, Corriechoillie, Spean Bridge PH34 4EY — MB BS 1987 Lond.

PINNEY, Deborah Elizabeth Foxie Cottage, Romsey Road, Copythorne, Southampton SO40 2PF — BM 1988 Soton.

PINNEY, Philip David 331 Kingston Road, Willerby, Hull HU10 6PY — MB ChB 1990 Leic.; MRCGP 1994; DRCOG 1993. Socs: Med. Protec. Soc. Prev: Trainee GP Lincoln VTS.

PINNEY, Sally Ann Elthorne Park Surgery, 106 Elthorne Park Road, Hanwell, London W7 2JJ — MB BS 1984 Lond.; BSc (Hons.) Anat. Lond. 1981; DRCOG 1987; Cert. Family Plann. JCC 1987. (Charing Cross Hospital) GP Princip.

PINNINGTON, Julie 10 Peacock Drive, Bottisham, Cambridge CB5 9EF Tel: 01223 812595 — BChir 1994 Camb.

PINNINGTON, Susan Osborne Road Surgery, 17 Osborne Road, Newcastle upon Tyne NE2 2AH Tel: 0191 281 4588 Fax: 0191 212 0379 — MB BS 1993 Lond.; BSc Lond. 1977; MRCGP 1997; DRCOG 1998. (Univ. Coll. & Middx Sch. Med.) GP.

PINNOCK, Colin Andrew 8 Pear tree way, Church Lane, Wychbold, Worcester WR9 7SW — MB BS 1977 Lond.; FFA RCS Eng. 1982. Cons. Anaesth. Alexandra Hosp. Redditch. Prev: Cons. Anaesth. BromsGr. & Redditch Dist. Gen. Hosp.

PINNOCK, Eileen Mary (retired) Meadow Rise, Atch Lench, Evesham WR11 5SP Tel: 01386 870718 — MB ChB Birm. 1947. Prev: Med. Asst. (Anaesth.) Worcester Roy. Infirm.

PINNOCK, Hilary Joan Whitstable Health Centre, Harbour Street, Whitstable CT5 1BZ Tel: 01277 594400 Fax: 01277 771474; Email: hpinnock@gpiag-asthma.org — MB ChB 1974 Leeds; MRCGP 1982. (Leeds) Princip. in Gen. Practise, Whitstable Med. Pracrise; Course Organiser Primary Focus; Clin. research Fell.ship, Dept of Gen. Practise& Primary core; Aberd. Uni. Socs: Brit. Thorac. Soc.; Comm. Mem. GP in Airways grp; Europ. Respiratary Soc. Prev: GP Prestwich Manch. & Burgess Hill W. Sussex; SHO (Gen. Med.) Salford AHA.

PINNOCK, Malcolm Raymond (retired) Meadow Rise, Atch Lench, Evesham WR11 5SP Tel: 01386 870718 — MB ChB 1950 Aberd. Prev: Princip. in Gen. Pract., Worcs.

PINNOCK, Roger Graham North Street Surgery, 28 North Street, Ashford TN24 8JR Tel: 01233 661133 Fax: 01233 662727; Yew Tree House, Westwell Leacon, Charing, Ashford TN27 0EE Tel: 01233 712840 — MB BS 1974 Lond.; Cert. Family Plann. JCC 1984. (St Mary's) Chairm. E. Kent MAAG. Prev: Clin. Asst. (Dermat.) William Harvey Hosp.

PINSENT, Susan Elizabeth Mallett Higher Ludbrook, Ermington, Ivybridge PL21 0LL — MB ChB 1978 Liverp.; DA Eng. 1982; DRCOG 1980.

PINSON, Kenneth Donovan 58 Orson Street, Leicester LE5 5EN — MB ChB 1949 Manch. (Manch.)

PINTO, Alan Lawrence Premkumar Wigan & Leigh Health Services NHS Trust, Royal Albert Edward Infirmary, Wigan Lane, Wigan WN1 2NN; 50 Bempton Road, St. Michaels Wood, Liverpool L17 5BB Tel: 0151 727 0820 Email: alanpinto@lineone.net — MB

PINTO

BS 1980 Bangalor; MB BS Bangalore 1980; FRCPS Glas. 1992; FFAEM 1997. (St. John's Med. Coll. Bangalore) Cons. (A&E).

PINTO, Mr Anthony Phillip Rozario 125 Carshalton Park Road, Carshalton SM5 3SJ — MB BS 1940 Bombay; MS Bombay 1943, MB BS 1940; FRCS Eng. 1946; FRCS Ed. 1946.

PINTO, Ashwin Arnold 4 Collice Street, Islip, Kidlington OX5 2TB — MB BCh 1992 Oxf.; MRCP (UK) 1995.

PINTO, Mr Domingos Joseph Diago Teodoro, OBE 89 Kevlin Road, Coolnagard, Omagh BT78 1PQ Tel: 028 8224 6854 — MB BS Lond. 1962; MS Lond. 1970; FRCSI 1996; FRCS Eng. 1967; FRCS Ed. 1966; MRCS Eng. LRCP Lond. 1962. (Lond. Hosp.) Cons. Surg. Tyrone Co. Hosp. Socs: Fell. Assn. Surgs.; Fell. Assn. Upper G.I. Surg. Prev: Scientif. Asst. & Hon. Cons. Med. Research Counc.; Regist. Rotat. (Surg.) Middlx. Hosp. Lond.; Sen. Lect. Makerere Univ. Kampala, Uganda.

PINTO, Robin Trevor 354 Old Bedford Road, Luton LU2 7BS Tel: 01582 31065 — LMSSA 1967 Lond.; MPhil (Psychiat.) Lond. 1970; MRCP Glas. 1966; FRCPsych. 1984, M 1972. Cons. Psychiat. Luton & Dunstable Hosp. Socs: Fell. Roy. Soc. Med. Prev: Sen. Regist. Bethlem Roy. & Maudsley Hosps.; Med. Regist. King's Lynn Gen. Hosp.

PINTO, Stella Matilda Cradley Road Surgery, 62 Cradley Road, Cradley Heath, Warley B64 6AG Tel: 01382 569586 — MB ChB 1987 Birm.; MRCGP 1992; DRCOG 1991; DCH RCP Lond. 1989.

PINTO, Sunil Christopher 354 Old Bedford Road, Luton LU2 7BS — MB BS 1989 Lond.; DCH RCP Lond. 1993; DRCOG 1992.

PINTO, Tara (retired) Homestead, 18 Cambridge Road, Linthorpe, Middlesbrough TS5 5NN — MB BS 1961 Vikram; MRCOG 1965.

PINTO, Thelma Queen Elizebeth Hospital, Stadium Road, Woolwich, London SE18 4QH Tel: 020 8836 5656 — MB BS 1977 Lond.; MRCP (UK) 1980; FRCPath 1995. Cons. (Histopath.) Qu. Eliz. Hosp., Woolwich, Lond.

PINTO, Zoe Anne Penshurst Gardens Surgery, 39 Penshurst Gardens, Edgware HA8 9TN Tel: 020 8958 3141 Fax: 020 8905 4638; 2 Stoneyfields Gardens, Edgware HA8 9SP — MB ChB 1983 Bristol; MRCGP 1988; DRCOG 1987.

PINTO WRIGHT, Ricardo Jose City Hospitals Sunderland, Kayall Road, Sunderland SR4 7TP; 6 Wellfield Terrace, Ryhope, Sunderland SR2 0NA Tel: 0191 565 6256 — LMS 1994 Navarre; BA Kingston, Ontario 1985. SHO (A & E) Sunderland City Hosp. Socs: BMA. Prev: SHO (Paediat.) Sunderland City Hosp.

PIOTROWICZ, Andrzej Jan Krzysztof 133 Whitaker Road, Derby DE23 6AQ — MB ChB 1989 Bristol; BSc Bristol 1986, MB ChB 1989; MRCP (UK) 1992. Regist. (Gen. Med.) Guy's Hosp. Lond.

PIOTROWICZ, Andrzej Leszek Maria (retired) 133 Whitaker Road, Derby DE23 6AQ — MB BCh BAO 1956 NUI; FFR 1968; DMRD Eng. 1965. Cons. Radiol. Derby Hosp. Gp. Prev: Regist. Dept. Radiol. United Sheff. Hosps.

PIOTROWSKI, Anthony George The Surgery, 232-234 Milton Road, Weston Super Mare BS22 8AG Tel: 01934 625022 Fax: 01934 612470; 7 Highpath, Wellington TA21 8NH — MB BS 1991 Lond. (St. George's HMS Lond.)

PIPE, Mr Norman Geoffrey James Huntersfield, Highlands Road, Reigate RH2 0LA Tel: 01737 244029 Fax: 01737 226267 — MRCS Eng. LRCP Lond. 1968; MB BS Lond. 1969; FRCOG 1987, M 1973, DObst 1971. (Char. Cross) p/t Cons. O & G Surrey & Sussex Healthcare NHS Trust. Socs: Brit. Soc. Colpos. & Cerv. Path.; BMA; Blair Bell Res. Soc. Prev: Sen. Regist. (O & G) Guy's Hosp. Lond. & Farnbororough Hosp. Kent; Regist. (O & G) Luton & Dunstable & Hammersmith Hosps.

PIPE, Roderic Alan The Priory Ticehurst House, Ticehurst, Wadhurst TN5 7HU Tel: 01580 200391; 2 Riverview Road, London W4 3QH Tel: 020 8995 9265 — MB ChB 1984 Ed.; MRCPsych 1989. Cons. Psychiat. (Child & Adolesc. Psychiat.), The Priory Ticehurst Ho.; Vis. Cons., Sturt Priory Hosp. and The Priory Hosp. Rochampton. Socs: Assn. Child Psychol. & Psychiat.; Assn. for Profess. in Servs. for Adolesc.; Roy. Coll. Psychiat. Prev: Sen. Regist. (Child & Adolesc. Psychiat.) Bethlem & Maudsley Hosps. Lond.; Regist. & SHO (Psychiat.) St. Geo. Hosp. Lond.; Cons. Psychiat. (Child & Adolesc. Psychiat.) Bethlem & Maudsley NHS Trust Lond.

PIPER, Alison Jane Holmbushes Nursery, Billingshurst Road, Loxwood, Billingshurst RH14 0AL — MB BS 1986 Lond.; MRCGP 1992; DCH RCP Lond. 1990; DRCOG 1989.

PIPER, Anthony Richard Rosedean Surgery, 8 Dean Street, Liskeard PL14 4AQ Tel: 01579 343133 — MB BS 1967 Lond.; MRCS Eng. LRCP Lond. 1967; MRCGP 1980; DA Eng. 1971; DObst RCOG 1969. (Char. Cross)

PIPER, Mr Ian Hedley Orthopaedic Department, Barnsley General Hospital, Gawber Road, Barnsley S75 2EP Tel: 01226 777741 Fax: 01226 380470; Week Cottage, Week Hill, Notton, Dartmouth TQ6 0JT Tel: 01226 380180 Fax: 01226 380470 — MB BS 1968 Lond.; LRCP 1978 Canada; AFPM CSPQ 1981, Canada; FRCS Eng. 1974; MRCS Eng. LRCP Lond. 1968. (St Thomas's, London) Cons. Orthop. Surg. Barnsley Dist. Gen. Hosp. Socs: Brit. Orthop. Assn.; BMA; BESS. Prev: Staff Surg. Santa Cabrini Hosp. Montreal, Quebec; Staff Surg. Omineca Clin, Vanderhoof, Brit. Columbia.

PIPER, Julia Alison 3 Knighton Grange Road, Stoneygate, Leicester LE2 2LF; 3 Knighton Grange Road, Stoneygate, Leicester LE2 2LF Tel: 0116 270 0373 Fax: 0116 270 1660 Email: drjpiperataol.com — BM BS 1980 Nottm.; BMedSci 1978 Nottm.; MRCGP 1984; Cert. FPA 1984. (Nottingham) p/t Regional Phys. i/c Bupa Health Screening Leicester, Birm. & Lincoln; Private GP Leicester. Socs: BMA (Brit. Med. Assn.); RCGP (Roy. Coll. of GPs); BMAS (Brit. Med. Acupunc. Soc.). Prev: GP Chorleywood; Screening Clinic Dr. Bupa Hosps., Bushey & Harpenden; Phys. i/c BUPA Med. Centre Leeds.

PIPER, Mark Patrick Peter 13 Westley Avenue, Whitley Bay NE26 4NW — MB ChB 1988 Ed.; BSc (Med. Sci.) Hons. Ed. 1986; FRCA 1996. (Univ. Ed.)

PIPER, Mary North Thames RHA, 40 Eastbourne Terrace, London W2 — MB BS 1971 Lond.; FRCP Lond. 1986; MRCP (UK) 1974; MRCS Eng. LRCP Lond. 1971; MFPHM RCP (UK) 1995. Cons. (Geriat. Med.) N.wick Pk. Hosp. Harrow. Prev: Lect. (Geriat. Med.) Univ. Coll. Hosp. Lond.; Sen. Regist. (Geriat. Med.) N.wick Pk. Hosp. Harrow.

PIPER, Mary Evelyn, Maj. RAMC Department of Psychiatry, Mrs Tidworth, Delhi Barracks, Tidworth SP9 — LMSSA 1978 Lond.; MRCPsych 1983. Cons. Psychiat. Dept. Psychiat. Delhi Barracks Tidworth.

PIPER, Philippa Claire 14 Hillside Close, Southgate, Crawley RH11 8PQ Tel: 01293 440222 Email: philpiper@aol.com — MB ChB 1978 Manch. Trainee GP Cleveland VTS; Clin. Asst. Family Plann. Prev: SHO (Paediat.) Booth Hall Childr. Hosp. N. Manch.; Ho. Off. (Med.) Hope Hosp. Salford; Ho. Off. (Surg.) Chester Roy. Infirm.

***PIPER, Rosalind Olivia Jane** Bramblecote, 42 Tupwood Lane, Caterham CR3 6DP — MB BS 1996 Lond.

PIPER, Sally Joanne Corial, Northlands Road, Warnham, Horsham RH12 3SQ — MB BS 1989 Lond.; MRCGP 1993; DRCOG 1991.

PIPER, Simon Austen Road Surgery, 1 Austen Road, Guildford GU1 3NW Tel: 01483 564578 Fax: 01483 505368 — MB BS 1977 Lond. (St Marys) Med. Off. Probation Hostels Guildford. Socs: Soc. Occup. Med.

PIPKIN, Christopher, Surg. Cdr. RN Royal Hospital, Haslar, Gosport PO12 2AA Tel: 01705 584255 Fax: 01705 762549 Email: chrispipk@dsca.gov.uk — MB BS 1982 Lond.; MRCPath 1992; Dip. Clin. Microbiol. Lond 1991. (Univ. Coll. Hosp.) Cons. Microbiol. Roy. Hosp. Haslar. Socs: Assn. Med. Microbiol.; Hosp. Infec. Soc.; Brit. Soc. Antimicrob. Chemother. Prev: Hon. Sen. Regist. (Microbiol.) Roy. Lond. Hosp.; Sen. Regist. (Microbiol.) Pub. Health Laborat. St. Mary's Hosp. Portsmouth; Trainee (Path.) RN Hosp. Haslar.

***PIPON, Madeleine Louise** 3 Shakespeare Road, London W7 1LT — MB BS 1994 Lond.

PIPPARD, John Sutton (retired) 9 Princes Avenue, Woodford Green IG8 0LL — MB BChir 1942 Camb.; MD Camb. 1955; FRCP Lond. 1965, M 1942; FRCPsych 1971; DPM Lond. 1951. Prev: Cons. Psychiat. Claybury Hosp. Woodford Bridge.

PIPPARD, Kathleen Marjorie (retired) 9 Princes Avenue, Woodford Green IG8 0LL — MB ChB 1943 Birm.; MFFP 1993. Prev: Med. Off. Family Plann. Clinics W. Essex & E. Herts HAs.

PIPPARD, Professor Martin John Department of Molecular & Cellular Pathology, Ninewells Hospital & Medical School, Dundee DD1 9SY Tel: 01382 660111 Fax: 01382 633952 Email: m.j.pippard@dundee.ac.uk — MB ChB 1972 Birm.; FRCP 1998 Ed; BSc 1969 Birmingham; FRCPath 1994; MRCPath 1982. (Birmingham) Profess. Haemat. Univ. Dundee & Cons. Haemat. Ninewells Hosp. & Med. Sch. Dundee. Socs: Brit. Soc. Haematol.; Assn. Clin. Path.; Amer. Soc. Hemat. Prev: Cons. Haemat. N.wick

Pk. Hosp. & Clin. Research Centre Harrow Middlx.; Research Fell. & Clin. Lect. Nuffield Dept. Clin. Med. John Radcliffe Hosp. Oxf.; Sen. Fell. Div. Hemat. Dept. Med. Univ. Washington, USA.

PIPPEN, Catherine Ann Rhoda The White House, 103 Cyncoed Road, Cardiff CF23 6AD Tel: 029 2075 1750 — MB BCh 1956 Wales; MRCP Ed. 1968. (Cardiff) Cons. Phys. (Geriat. Med.) S. Glam. AHA (T). Socs: Brit. Geriat. Soc. & Cardiff Med. Soc. Prev: Sen. Regist. (Geriat. Med.) St. David's Hosp. Cardiff; Regist. (Gen. Med.) Cardiff Roy. Infirm.

PIPPET, Diana June 18A Monalla Road, Ballinamallard, Enniskillen BT94 2GS Tel: 01365 324377 — MB BS Lond. 1954; DCH Eng. 1956. (St. Bart.)

PIQUERAS ARENAS, Ana Isabel Department of Nephrology, Birmingham Children's Hospital, Ladywood Middleway, Birmingham B16 8ET — LMS 1988 Valencia.

PIRA, Almas Mocha Parade Surgery, 4-5 Mocha Parade, Salford M7 1QE Tel: 0161 839 2721 Fax: 0161 819 1191.

PIRACHA, Arshid The Surgery, Exchange Road, Alrewas, Burton-on-Trent DE13 7AS; 66 Chads Road, Derby DE23 6RQ — MB ChB 1985 Manch.

PIRES, Philip (retired) 12 Woodside Close, Tolworth, Surbiton KT5 9JU Tel: 020 8241 4987 — LAH Dub. 1961. Prev: Med. Asst. Manor Hosp. Epsom.

PIRIE, Alexander McKenzie Department of Obstetrics & Gynaecology, City Hospital, Dudley Road, Birmingham B18 7QH Tel: 0121 507 4706 Email: alexander.pirie@cityhospbham.wmids.nhs.uk; Mobile: 07970 748748 — MB ChB 1989 Ed.; MRCOG 1998; BSc (Hons.) Ed. 1984; MRCP (UK) 1993; DFFP 1995; DRCOG 1993. (Univ. Ed.) Cons. in Obst. & Gyn., Hon. Sen. Lect., Univ. of Birm..; Private Pract.- The Priory Hosp., Birm. Socs: Brit. Matinal & Fetal Med. Soc. Prev: Regist. & SHO Rotat. (Gen. Med.) Ninewells hosp.; Teachg. Hosp. posts in Edin, Glas, Dun, Cardiff, S. hamp; Acting Cons. (O&G) S.ampton Univ. Hosp.

PIRIE, Antoinette 188A Sutherland Avenue, London W9 1HR — MB BS 1981 Lond.; MA Oxf. 1982, BA 1978; MBA Warwick 1990; MRCOG 1989. Med. Dir. W. Herts NHS Trust. Prev: Med. Dir. Mt. Vernan & Watford NHS Hosps Trust.

PIRIE, Bruce Geddes (retired) Orchard End, Amenbury Lane, Harpenden AL5 2DQ Tel: 01582 715656 — MB ChB 1951 Aberd.; FFA RCS Eng. 1961; DA Eng. 1956. Prev: Cons. Anaesth. Qu. Eliz. II Hosp., Welwyn Gdn. City & St. Albans City Hosp.

PIRIE, Catherine Mary Department of Community Child Health, Divisional Headquarters, Berryden Road, Aberdeen AB25 3HG; 59 Hazledene Road, Aberdeen AB15 8LA — MB ChB 1972 Aberd. Staff Grade Doctor Grampian Healthcare NHS Trust. Prev: Clin. Med. Off. Grampian Healthcare NHS Trust; Ho. Phys. Woodend Gen. Hosp. Aberd. & Roy. Aberd. Childr. Hosp.; Ho. Surg. Aberd. Roy. Infirm.

PIRIE, Clare Armour 35 Spottiswoode Gardens, St Andrews KY16 8SA Tel: 01334 1662 — MB ChB 1967 St. And.; DO Eng. 1970. SHO Eye Dept. Roy. Infirm. Dundee.

PIRIE, Keith The Surgery, Mackenzie Avenue, Auchenblae, Laurencekirk AB30 1XU Tel: 01561 320202 Fax: 01561 320774 — MB ChB 1981 Aberd.

PIRIE, Lesley Kathryn Ian Charles Cottage Hospital, The Health Centre, Castle Road East, Grantown-on-Spey PH26 3HR Tel: 01479 872484 Fax: 01479 873503 — MB BCh BAO 1982 Dub.; MB BCh Dub. 1982; MRCGP 1986. Prev: Trainee GP Renfrewsh. VTS.

PIRIE, Linda Ellen Farriers House, 35 Main St., Middleton, Market Harborough LE16 8YU Tel: 01536 771140 — MB BS 1983 Lond.; LLB (Hons.) Leics. 1994. Indep. Med. Practitioner. Socs: Brit. Soc. Med. & Dent. Hypn. Prev: Sen. Regist. (Histopath.) Lewisham Hosp. & Guy's Hosp. Lond.; Regist. & SHO (Histopath.) Roy. Free Hosp. Lond.

PIRIS, Juan Cellular Pathology, John Radcliffe Hospital, Headington, Oxford OX3 9DU Tel: 01865 222891 Fax: 01865 222891 Email: juan.piris@orh.nhs.uk — LMS 1972 Spain; MBA Ed. 1996; DPhil Oxf. 1975; FRCPath 1991, M 1979. (Univ. Navarra) Cons pathol interest in gastrointestinal path. Socs: Brit. Soc. Gastroenterol. Path. Soc.; Assn. ColoProctol. of GB & Ire; Brit Assoc for study of liver. Prev: Sen. Lect. (Path.) Univ. Edin; Clin. Lect. & Hon. Sen. Regist. Nuffield Dept. Univ. Oxf.; Ho. Off. Clinica Univ. Pamplona, Navarra, Spain.

***PIRIS, Monica** 2F2 13 Brunsfield Avenue, Edinburgh EH10 4EL — MB ChB 1998 Ed.; MB ChB Ed 1998.

PIRMOHAMED, Professor Munir Department of Pharmacology & Therapeutics, The University of Liverpool, PO Box 147, Liverpool L69 3BX Tel: 0151 794 5549 Fax: 0151 794 5540 Email: munirp@liv.ac.uk; Tel: 0151 62548408 — MB ChB 1985 Liverp.; FRCP 1999 Edin.; FRCP 2000 London; MB ChB (Hons.) Liverp. 1985; PhD Liverp. 1993; MRCP (UK) 1988. (Liverp. Univ. Med. Sch.) Prof. od Clin. Pharmacol. Liverp. Univ.; Hon. Cons. Phys. Roy. Liverp. & BRd.green Univ. Hosp. Trust. Socs: Brit. Pharmacological Soc.; Med. Research Soc.; Fac. of PostGrad. Med. Prev: Lect. (Clin. Pharmacol). Liverp. Univ.; MRC Train. Fell. (Pharmacol.) Liverp. Univ.; Regist. (Gen. Med.) Hope Hosp. Manch.

PIROTTA, David Anthony Department of Anaesthesia, Bristol Royal Infirmary, Marlborough Street, Bristol BS2 8HW — MB ChB 1995 Bristol.

PIRRET, Marie Frances Park Surgery, Baker Street, Glasgow G41 3YE Tel: 0141 632 0203 Fax: 0141 636 5349 — MB ChB 1975 Glas.; DCH RCPS Glas. 1977.

PIRRIE, Alexander Laurenson (retired) Flat 6, Chynance, Alexandra Road, Penzance TR18 4LY — MB ChB 1928 Glas.

PIRRIE, Augusta Jane 15 Onslow Road, Burwood Park, Walton-on-Thames KT12 5BB — MB BS 1966 Lond.; MRCS Eng. LRCP Lond. 1966; DCH RCP Lond. 1983.

PIRRIE, John Miller (retired) Conlig, Copt Hill, Danbury, Chelmsford CM3 4NN — MB BS 1954 Lond.; MRCS Eng. LRCP Lond. 1950.

PIRWANY, Imran Rahmetullah Queen Mothers Hospital, Yorkhill, Glasgow G3 8SJ Tel: 0141 201 0000 Fax: 0141 357 3610 Email: ipirwany@hotmail.com; Flat PF1, 3 Marchmont St, Edinburgh EH9 1EJ Tel: 0131 228 8635 Fax: 0131 228 8635 Email: ipirwany@compuserve.com — MB BS 1986 Karachi; MFFP 1994; MRCOG 1994. (University of Karachi) Sen. Regist. (Obsterics & Gyn.) Qu. Marys Hosp. Yorkhill. Socs: Glas. Obst. Soc.; Ed. Obst. Soc.; Munroe Kerr Soc. Prev: Clin. Research Fell. Univ. of Glas.; Career Regist. Edin. Roy. Infirm. & Simpson Memor. Hosp. Edin.; Regist. S.mead Hosp. Bristol.

***PIRZADA, Aslam Fiaz** 10 Lancia Crescent, Bracebridge Heath, Lincoln LN4 2QN — MB BS 1997 Lond.

PIRZADA, Mr Badr-ul-Islam St. Catherine Surgery, 19 St Catherines, Lincoln LN5 8LW Tel: 01522 20389; 10 Lancia Crescent, Bracebridge Heath, Lincoln LN4 2QN Tel: 01522 524326 — MB BS 1950 Punjab; MB BS Punjab (Pakistan) 1950; FRFPS Glas. 1960; FRCS Glas. 1962; FRCS Ed. 1966; MRCGP 1976; FRCGP 1989, M 1976. (King Edwd. Med. Coll. Lahore) Med. Off. Smith Clayton Forge GKN Lincoln; Clin. Tutor (Gen. Pract.) N. Lincs. HA; Sec. N. Lincs. Gen. Practs. Comm. Socs: Fell. Roy. Soc. Med.; Lincs. LMC; Trent Regional Med. Comm. Prev: Sen. Regist. (Surg.) Co. Hosp. Lincoln; Regist. (Orthop.) Brighton & Lewes Hosp. Gp. & Halifax Roy. Infirm.

PIRZADA, Omar Masood 10 Lancia Crescent, Bracebridge Heath, Lincoln LN4 2QN — MB BS 1993 Lond.

PISKO-DUBIENSKI, Janina 18 Hanger Lane, Ealing, London W5 3HH — LRCPI & LM, LRSCI & LM 1958; LRCPI & LM, LRCSI & LM 1958.

PISKOROWSKYJ, Nicola 19 Bryngwili Road, Pontardulais, Swansea SA4 1XB — MB BCh 1988 Wales.

PITALIA, Mr Anil Kumar 34 Haydock Park Gardens, Newton-le-Willows WA12 0JF — MB ChB 1992 Manch.; FRCS Ed 1997; BSc Hons 1990. (Manchester)

PITALIA, Pyare Lal 34 Haydock Park Gardens, Newton-le-Willows WA12 0JF — MB BS 1961 Vikram. (Gandhi Med. Coll. Bhopal)

PITALIA, Sanjay Kumar Wigan Road Surgery, 120 Wigan Road, Ashton-in-Makerfield, Wigan WN4 9ST Tel: 01942 727325 Fax: 01942 709081 — MB ChB 1983 Manch.; MRCGP 1987; DCH RCPS Glas. 1986; DRCOG 1985. (Manchester) Chairm. Ashton PLC.

PITALIA, Shikha The Bowery Medical Centre, Elephant Lane, St Helens WA9 5PR Tel: 01744 816837 Fax: 01744 850800; Lakeview, 28 Willow Bank, Newton-le-Willows WA12 0DQ Tel: 01925 224242 — MB ChB 1987 Manch.; MRCGP 1991. (Manchester)

PITCHER, Christopher Sotheby (retired) Rother View, 24 Military Road, Rye TN31 7NY Tel: 01797 226015 Fax: 01797 226015 —

PITCHER

DM Oxf. 1963, BM BCh 1950; FRCPath 1974; DPath Eng. 1960. Prev: Cons. Haematol. Stoke Mandeville Hosp. Aylesbury.

PITCHER, David Corbett Reid 144 Harley Street, London W1N 1AH Tel: 020 7935 0023; 37 The Croft, Barnet EN5 2TN Tel: 020 8440 0100 — MB BS Lond. 1965; MPhil (Psychiat.) Lond. 1971; MRCS Eng. LRCP Lond. 1965; FRCPsych 1979, M 1972; DPM Eng. 1969. (Westm.) Hon. Cons. Psychiat. Roy. Free Hosps. Lond. Socs: Fell. Roy. Soc. Med.; Brit. Acad. Forens. Sci.; Medico-Legal Soc. Prev: Regist. Bethlem & Maudsley Hosps.; Sen. Lect. (Psychiat.) Roy. Free Hosp. Sch. Med. Lond.

PITCHER, David William Hereford Heart Unit, County Hospital, Hereford HR1 2ER Tel: 01432 364071 Fax: 01432 364054; 6 Clarksons lane, Hereford HR1 1RN — MB BS 1973 Lond.; MD Lond. 1986; FRCP Lond. 1991; MRCP (UK) 1975. (St. Geo.) Cons. Cardiol. Co. Hosp. Hereford. Socs: Brit. Cardiac Soc. & Brit. Hypertens. Soc.; Exec. Resusc. Counc. (UK). Prev: Sen. Regist. (Med. & Cardiol.) Plymouth Gen. Hosp. & Bristol Roy. Infirm.; Lect. (Clin. Pharmacol. & Cardiol.) Guy's Hosp. Med. Sch. Lond.; Regist. (Med.) Guy's Hosp. Lond.

PITCHER, Maxton Charles Leighton Northwick Park Hospital, Dept. of Gastroenterology, Watford Road, Harrow HA1 3UJ Tel: 020 8869 2628 Fax: 020 8869 2626 — BM BCh 1988 Oxf.; MA Camb. 1989, BA (Hons.) 1985, MD 1996; MRCP (UK) 1991. Cons. (Phys. & Gastro.) N.wick Pk. & St. Mark's Hosp. Harrow. Socs: Brit. Soc. Gastroenterol.

PITCHER, Melanie Sara Hillcrest, Quinneys Lane, Redditch B98 7WG — MB ChB 1995 Birm.; MRCGP 2001; DRCOG 1998; DFFP 1998. (Birm.) p/t GP Asst., St Johns Surg., BromsGr.; Staff Grade Psychiat., Hillcrest, Redditch. Prev: GPUTS Alexandra Hosp. Redditch.

PITCHER, Robert William Department Path., Royal Cornwall Hospital (Treliske), Truro TR1 3LJ — MB ChB 1977 Bristol.

PITCHES, David William 26 Springbridge Road, Manchester M16 8PW Tel: 0956 123230 Email: dwp@ukgateway.net — MB BS 1997 Lond.; BSc 1994; ACK 1994; DCH 1999. (King's Coll. Lond.) Specialist Regist. (Pub. Health) Birm. Prev: SHO (Palliat. Med.) Mildmay Hosp. Lond.; SHO (c/o the Elderly) Qu. Hosp. Burton-on-Trent; SHO (Paediat.) Good Hope Hosp. Sutton Coldfield.

PITCHFORTH, Anthony Edmund Inzievar Surgery, 2 Kenmore Street, Aberfeldy PH15 2BL Tel: 01887 820366 Fax: 01887 829566 — MB BS 1964 Durh.; DTM & H 2001 Liverpool; DObst RCOG 1970; DCH RCPS Glas. 1970.

PITHER, Charles Edward St. Thomas' Hospital, London SE1 7EH Tel: 020 792208107 Fax: 020 7922 8229 Email: charles.pither@gstt.sthames.nhs.uk; 20 Corkran Road, Surbiton KT6 6PN Tel: 020 8225 0911 Fax: 020 8225 0939 Email: cpither@doctors.org.uk — MB BS 1977 Lond.; FFA RCS Lond. 1982. (St. Thos.) Cons. In Pain Med. St. Thos. Hosp. Lond.; Med. Dir.; Pain Managem. Progr. Bronnllys Hosp. Brecon Powys. Socs: Fell. Med. Soc. Lond.; Eur. Soc. Regional Anaesth.; Internat. Assn. Study of Pain. Prev: Sen. Regist. (Anaesth.) St. Thos. Hosp. Lond.; Fell. (Regional Anaesth. & Pain Control) Univ. Cincinnati Med. Centre Ohio, USA.

PITHIE, Alan David Brownler Centre Infection Service, Gartnavel General Hospital, Great Western Road, Glasgow G12 0YN — MB ChB 1993 Dundee; MB ChB Dundee 1982; MD Dundee 1993, BMSc (Hons.) 1979; MRCP (UK) 1985; DTM & H RCP Lond. 1988. Cons. Phys. (Gen. Med. & Infec.s Dis.s) Glasglow.

PITKEATHLY, Denis Aitken (retired) 4C Victoria Square, Meamskirk Road, Newton Mearns, Glasgow G77 5TD Tel: 0141 616 3421 — MB ChB 1957 St. And.; FRCP Ed. 1972, M 1962; FRCP Glas. 1972, M 1962. Med. Off.. Appeals Serv.. Glas. Prev: Cons. Phys. S.; Gen. Hosp. Glas.

PITKEATHLY, Isabella Gilmour (retired) Govan Health Centre, 295 Langlands Road, Glasgow G51 4BJ — MB ChB 1960 Glas.; DObst RCOG 1962. Prev: Asst. Div. Med. Off. Lancs. CC.

PITKEATHLY, William Thomas Nigel 10 Huntsmans Gate, Burntwood, Walsall WS7 9LL — MB ChB 1967 St. And.

PITKIN, Andrew David Institute of Naval Medicine, Alverstoke, Gosport PO12 2DL Tel: 01705 768026 Fax: 01705 504823 Email: ye30@mail.pipex.com; 61 Village Road, Alverstoke, Gosport PO12 2LE Tel: 01705 524879 Email: apitkin@cix.compulink.co.uk — MB BS 1990 Lond.; MRCP (UK) 1994. Civil. Med. Pract.

(Undersea Med.) Inst. Naval Med. Gosport, Hants. Socs: Undersea & Hyperbaric Med. Soc.

***PITKIN, Lisa Jane** Stoke Road Farm, Stoke Road, Newton Longville, Milton Keynes MK17 0BQ — MB BS 1994 Lond.

***PITMAN, Ian John** 4 Brook Place, Cwm, Ebbw Vale NP23 7QZ — MB BCh 1994 Wales.

PITMAN, Jane 2 Kingswood Way, Wallington SM6 8PB Tel: 020 8681 0880 — MB BS 1992 Lond.; DRCOG 1996. (King's Coll. Lond.)

PITMAN, Marianne Alice 60 Bishops Road, Cleeve, Bristol BS49 4NG — MB BCh 1968 Wales; FRCOG 1993, M 1974, DObst 1970; FFPHM RCP (UK) 1994, M 1980; MFFP 1996; T(PHM) 1991. p/t Locum Family Plann. CMO UBHT, N. Bristol Trust. Prev: Cons.Health.Pub.Med.NHSE S & W. Regional Off; Sen. Regist. (Community Med.) SE Thames RHA; Regist. (Community Med.) S. W.. RHA.

PITMAN, Mr Martyn Clive The Princess Anne Hospital, Southampton University Hospital, Coxford Road, Southampton SO16 5YA Tel: 023 8077 7222; 10 Long Barrow Close, South Wonston, Winchester SO21 3ED Tel: 01962 889421 Fax: 01962 889421 — MB BS 1991 Lond.; MRCOG 2001; BSc (Hons.) Physiol. Lond. 1988. (Char. Cross & Westm. Med. Sch.) Specialist Regist. (O & G) Soton. Univ. Hosp. NHS Trust. Socs: BMA; MDU. Prev: Specialist Regist. (O & G) Wessex Regional Rotat.; Research Fell. & Hon. Regist. (O & G) Chelsea & W.m. Hosp. Lond.; SHO (O & G) Chels. & W.m. Hosp. Lond.

PITMAN, Richard Hugh 27 Lemon Street, Truro TR1 2LS — MB ChB 1960 Bristol; DObst RCOG 1964. (Bristol)

PITSIAELI, Andreas Plisi Heathcote Medical Centre, Heathcote, Tadworth KT20 5TH Tel: 01737 360202; 43 Chequers Lane, Walton on the Hill, Tadworth KT20 7SF — MB BS 1988 Lond.; BSc Lond. 1985; MRCGP 1992; DRCOG 1992. (Char. Cross & Westm. Med. Sch. Lond.) Prev: SHO (Gen. Med.) Qu. Mary's Univ. Hosp. Lond.

PITT, Alison Flat C, 15 Elm Grove, Wimbledon, London SW19 4HE — MB BS 1997 Lond.

PITT, Angela Elizabeth Rylett Road Surgery, 45A Rylett Road, Shepherds Bush, London W12 9ST Tel: 020 8749 7863 Fax: 020 8743 5161 — MB BS 1984 Lond.; DGM RCP Lond. 1986; DRCOG 1987. Prev: Trainee GP Lond.; SHO (O & G) W. Middlx. Univ. Hosp. Isleworth; SHO (Geriat., Cas. & Paediat.) W. Middlx. Univ. Hosp. Isleworth.

PITT, Professor Brice Masterman Norman Memory Clinic, Department of Psychological Medicine, Royal Postgraduate Medical School, Hammersmith Hospital, Du Cane Road, London W12; Palmer's House, Maltings Drive, Epping CM16 6SH Tel: 01992 574748 Fax: 01992 575471 — MB BS 1955 Lond.; MD Lond. 1966; FRCPsych 1979, M 1971; DPM Eng. 1958. (Guy's) Prof. Psychiat. Elderly Roy. Postgrad. Med. Sch. Lond. Socs: (Ex-Pres.) Marcé Soc.; (Chairm.) Assn. Postnatal Illness; Roy. Soc. Med. (Vice-Chair Sect. Psychiat.). Prev: Prof. Psychiat. of Old Age. St. Mary's Hosp. Med. Sch. Lond.; Cons. Psychiat. & Sen. Lect. St. Bart. Hosp. Lond.; Cons. Psychiat. Lond. Hosp., Ch.ill Clinic, Harlow Hosp. & Claybury Hosp.

PITT, Bronwen Mary Melbourne House Surgery, 12 Napier Court, Queensland Crescent, Chelmsford CM1 2ED Tel: 01245 354370 Fax: 01245 344476; Pipers Farm, Good Easter, Chelmsford CM1 4RL — MB BCh 1987 Wales; DRCOG 1990.

PITT, Deborah June Gabalfa Community Clinic, 213 North Road, Cardiff CF14 3AG Tel: 029 2069 3941 Fax: 029 2062 7954; 10 Erw'r Delyn Close, Penarth CF64 2TU Tel: 029 2071 1762 — MB BS 1972 Lond.; Dip. (Psychol Med.) Wales. (St. George's Hospital London) Staff Grade Psychiat. Socs: BMA; Christ. Med. Fell.sh. Prev: SHO Rotat. (Psychiat.) Gwent; SHO Rotat. (Psychiat.) S. Glam.; SHO Rotat. (Psychiat.) Mid Glam.

PITT, Miss Elspeth Sheena A&E Department, Aberdeen Royal Infirmary, Foresthill, Aberdeen AB25 2ZN Tel: 01224 681818; 14 Leddach Gardens, Westhill AB32 6FX — MB ChB 1992 Aberd.; DRCOG 1995; MRCGP 1996; Dip. IMC RCS Ed 1998; FRCS (Ed) A&E 1998. (Aberd.) Specialist Regist. (A&E).

PITT, Frances Ann Sheffield Health, 5 Old Fulwood Road, Sheffield S10 3TG Tel: 0114 271 1250; 44 Bannercross Road, Sheffield S11 9HR — MB ChB 1978 Sheff.; MFPHM RCP (UK) 1991. Cons. Pub. Health Med. Sheff. Health. Socs: Fac. Pub. Health Med. Prev:

Cons. Pub. Health Med. Barnsley HA; Sen. Regist. (Pub. Health Med.) Trent RHA; Regist. (Anaesth.) Doncaster Roy. Infirm.

PITT, Giles Hugh Townsend House, 49 Harepath Road, Seaton EX12 2RY Tel: 01297 20616 Fax: 01297 20810 — BM BCh 1982 Oxf.; MA Camb. 1986; FRCGP 2000 (FBA); DObst. Otago 1987; Cert. Family Plann. JCC 1986. Princip. in GP.

PITT, Ian Victor Street Surgery, Victor Street, Shirley, Southampton SO15 5SY Tel: 023 8077 4781 Fax: 023 8039 0680; 360 Winchester Road, Shirley, Southampton SO16 6TW — MB 1975 Camb.; BChir 1974; MRCGP 1979. Prev: Med. Off. Kapsowar Hosp. Kenya.

PITT, Jacqueline Mary JA - Rose, Post Office Rd, Toft Monks, Beccles NR34 OEH Tel: 01502 677342 — MB BS 1965 Lond.; DObst RCOG 1967. (St Bart.)

PITT, Mr James The Ipswich Hospital, Heath Road, Ipswich IP4 5PD Tel: 01473 703755 Email: james.pitt@ipsh-tr.anglox.nhs.uk; Newson Farm, Clopton, Woodbridge IP13 6SS Tel: 01473 735467 Fax: 01473 738655 Email: james.pitt@talk21.com — MB BS 1989 Lond.; FRCS 2000 (Gen. Surg.); MSc (Hons.) Lond. 1996; FRCS Eng. 1994. (Lond. Hosp. Med. Coll.) Cons. (Gen. Surg.) The Ipswich Hosp. NHS Trust Ipswich. Socs: Roy. Soc. Med.; Hunt. Soc.; Livesyman Soc. of Apoth. Prev: Research Fell. Univ. Coll. Hosp. Lond.; Specialist Regist. (Gen. Surg.) Char. Cross Hosp.; Specialist Regist. St. Mary's Hosp.

PITT, John Brian Mount Oriel Surgery, 2 Mount Oriel, Belfast BT8 7HR Tel: 028 9070 1653; 23 Glencregagh Road, Belfast BT8 6FZ Tel: 01232 799241 — MB BCh BAO 1963 Belf.; MB BCh BAO (Hons.) Belf. 1963; MRCGP 1971; DObst RCOG 1967. (Qu. Univ. Belf.) Prev: Resid. Med. Off. Belf. City Hosp.; SHO Roy. Vict. Hosp. Belf.

PITT, Mark Adrian Department of Histopathology, Royal Preston Hospital, Sharoe Green Lane North, Fulwood, Preston PR2 9HT Tel: 01772 710148 — MB ChB 1986 Manch.; BSc Manch. 1983; MRCPath 1993. Cons. Histopath. Roy. Preston Hosp.

PITT, Matthew Carey Department of Clinical Neurophysiology, The Hospital for Children, Great Ormond St., London WC1N 3JH Tel: 020 7405 9200; St Maximin, Blakes Lane, East Clandon, Guildford GU4 7RR — MD 1989 Camb.; MB 1978, BChir 1977; FRCP (UK) 1997. Cons. Clin. Neurophysiol. Hosp. Sick Childr. Gt. Ormond St. Lond.

PITT, Michael Peter Ian Hob Cottage, Wheeley Road, Alvechurch, Birmingham B48 7DD — MB ChB 1990 Birm.; ChB Birm. 1990.

PITT, Nicola Sara 30 Damer Gardens, Henley-on-Thames RG9 1HX — MB ChB 1987 Sheff. Prev: Jun. Ho. Off. (Gen. Surg.) W. Cornw. Hosp. Penzance; Jun. Ho. Off. (Gen. Med.) N. Devon Dist. Hosp. Barnstaple.

PITT, Pauline Isobel Orpington Hospital, Severn Oaks Road, Orpington BR6 8JG Tel: 01689 815239 Fax: 01689 815073 — MB BS 1975 Lond.; MD Lond. 1989; FRCP. (Univ. Coll. Lond.) p/t Cons. Rheum. Bromley Hosp. NHS Trust. Socs: Brit. Soc. of Rheum. Prev: Sen. Regist. (Rheum. & Rehabil.) King's Coll. Hosp. Lond.

PITT, Mr Peter Clive Crawford, TD Garnish Hall, Margaret Roding, Dunmow CM6 1QL Tel: 01245 231209 Fax: 01245 231224 Email: peter@garnishhall.fsnet.co.uk — FRCP Ed 1998; MB BS Lond. 1957; FRCS Eng. 1964; FRCS Ed. 1963; MRCP Ed. 1961; MRCS Eng. LRCP Lond. 1957; DTM & H Eng. 1960. (Guy's) p/t Private Con. Surg. BUPA Roding Hosp. Redbridge. Socs: Fell. Roy. Soc. Med.; (Counc.) Hunt. Soc. Prev: Cons. Gen. Surg. Havering Hosps. Romford; Sen. Regist. (Surg.) Guy's Hosp. Lond. & Chase Farm Hosp. Enfield; Maj. RAMC Sen. Surg. Specialist.

***PITT, Shaun Michael** 515A Clifton Drive N., Lytham St Annes FY8 2QX — MB BS 1994 Lond.

PITT, William Edward Robert Houstoun House, 48 Crescent Road, Worthing BN11 1RQ Tel: 01903 38262; 11 Manchester Square, London W1U 3PW — MRCS Eng. LRCP Lond. 1943. (St. Geo.) Prev: Capt. RAMC; Ho. Surg. & Cas. Off. St. Geo. Hosp.

PITT, William Henry Paisley Road West Surgery, 1314 Paisley Road West, Glasgow G52 1DB Tel: 0141 882 4567 Fax: 0141 882 4548; 6 Lednock Road, Cardonald, Glasgow G52 2SJ Tel: 0141 882 2245 — MB ChB 1960 Glas. Socs: BMA; Scott. Assn. Auth. Med. Examr.s Aviat.

PITT-PAYNE, James Henry 12 Top Park, Beckenham BR3 6RU Tel: 020 8650 4377 — MB BS 1970 Lond; MB BS Lond. 1970; MRCS Eng. LRCP Lond. 1970; DObst RCOG 1972. (Guy's) Mem.

Indep. Doctors Forum. Socs: Fell. Med. Soc. Lond. Prev: SHO (O & G) FarnBoro. Hosp. Kent; Ho. Surg. & Ho. Phys. & Ho. Surg. BrE. & Plastic Surg. Units Guy's Hosp. Lond.

PITTAM, Joan Kathryn Templehill Surgery, 23 Templehill, Troon KA10 6BQ Tel: 01292 312012 Fax: 01292 317594; 52 Wilson Avenue, Troon KA10 7AJ — MB ChB 1972 Manch. GP Templehill Troon. Prev: Ho. Surg. & Ho. Phys. Manch. Roy. Infirm.; SHO (Psychiat.) Univ. Hosp. S. Manch.

PITTAM, Mr Michael Robert Luton & Dunstable Hospital, Lewsey Road, Luton LU4 0DZ Tel: 01582 497097 Fax: 01582 497176; Vicarage Cottage, Valley Road, Studham, Dunstable LU6 2NN Tel: 01582 872264 Fax: 01582 873843 — MB 1973 Camb.; MA Camb. 1973, MChir 1986; FRCS Eng. 1977. Cons. Gen. BrE. & Vasc. Surg. Luton & Dunstable Hosp. Prev: Sen. Regist. (Surg.) W.m. Hosp. Lond.; Vandervell Research Fell. & Lect. (Surg.) Inst. Cancer Research Lond.; Regist. (Surg.) St. Jas. Hosp. Leeds.

PITTARD, Alison Jane General Intensive Care Unit, The General Infirmary at Leeds, Great George St., Leeds LS1 3EX Tel: 0113 392 6672 Email: apittard@ulth.northy.nhs.uk; 6 Tudor Lawns, Wetherby Road, Oakwood, Leeds LS8 2JR Tel: 0113 265 7300 Fax: 0113 265 7300 — MB ChB 1988 Leeds; FRCA Lond. 1993; MD (Leeds) 1998. (Leeds) Cons. (Int. Care) The Gen. Infirm. at Leeds. Prev: Sen. Regist. (Anaesth.) St. Jas. Univ. Hosp. Trust Leeds.; Research Fell. (Intens. Care) Leeds; Regist. (Anaesth.) Yorks.

PITTARD, John Barry Chertsey Lane Surgery, 5 Chertsey Lane, Staines TW18 3JH Tel: 01784 454164 Fax: 01784 464360; 31 Oaktree Close, Virginia Water GU25 4JF — BM BCh 1972 Oxf.; MSc (Social Med.) Lond. 1978; BSc (1st cl. Hons.) Newc. 1969. Clin. Asst. (Cardiol.) St. Peter's Hosp. Chertsey. Socs: Sec. Primary Care Cardiovasc. Soc. Prev: Sen. Regist. (Community Med.) Oxf. AHA (T) & Lond. Sch. Hyg. & Trop. Med.; SHO (Med.) Hammersmith Hosp. Lond.

PITTAWAY, Andrew John 48 Sandrock Drive, Bessacarr, Doncaster DN4 6DT — BM BS 1991 Nottm.; FRCA 1998.

PITTMAN, James Alexander Leader The Old Rectory, Poyntington, Sherborne DT9 4LF — MB BS 1992 Lond.; BSc (Hons.) Lond. 1989, MB BS 1992.

***PITTS, Christopher Mark** 33 Wyston Brook, Hilton, Derby DE65 5JB — MB BS 1998 Lond.; MB BS Lond 1998.

PITTS, Isabella Deri Queens Corner Surgery, 1 New Queen Street, Scarborough YO12 7HL Tel: 01723 378078 Fax: 01723 378010; Fax: 01723 378010 — State DMS 1968 Siena; State Exam Siena 1968. (Pisa & Siena) Socs: BMA & Med. Defence Union. Prev: Clin. Asst. (Dermat. & A & E) ScarBoro. Hosp.

PITTS, John Elliot (retired) Stable Cottage, School Road, Bursledon, Southampton SO31 8BW Tel: 01703 402433 — MB BChir 1946 Camb.

PITTS, John Richard Waterside Health Centre, Hythe, Southampton SO45 5WX Tel: 02380 845955; 31 Sir Christopher Court, Hythe, Southampton SO45 6JR Tel: 02380 847155 — MB BS 1973 Lond.; BSc (Hons.) Lond. 1970; MSc (Med. Educat.) Cardiff 1991; MRCP (UK) 1975; MRCGP 1979. Assoc. Adviser Wessex; Edr., "Educat. for Primary Care". Prev: Ho. Surg. Univ. Coll. Hosp. Lond.; SHO (Med.) & Ho. Phys. Whittington Hosp. Lond.

PITTS, Jonathan Edward Emergency Medical Assessment Unit, Llandough Hospital, Penlan Road, Penarth CF64 2XX Tel: 01222 711711; 13 Llansamor Drive, Cardiff CF1 5BW Email: jpitts@ndirect.co.uk — MB BS 1993 Lond. (Char. Cross & Westm.) Staff Grade Phys. Emerg. Med. Assessm. Unit Llandough Hosp. Penarth. Socs: Fell. Roy. Soc. Med. Prev: Regist. (Emerg. Admissions) William Harvey Hosp. Ashford; SHO (Gen. Med.) S. Kent Hosps.; SHO (Gen. Med.) Mardstone Hosp.

PITTS, Sarah 18 Hart Street, Lenton, Nottingham NG7 1SF — BM BS 1996 Nottm.

PITTS, Thomas Bellamy (retired) Weaver's Mead, Curry Mallett, Taunton TA3 6SY — MRCS Eng. LRCP Lond. 1929; DA Eng. 1939. Prev: Cons. Anaesth. Taunton Hosp. Gp.

PITTS-TUCKER, Thomas John Pershore Health Centre, Priest Lane, Pershore WR10 1RD Tel: 01386 502030 Fax: 01386 502058 — BM BCh 1978 Oxf.; MMedSci Birm. 1996; MRCP (UK) 1980; MRCGP 1982; DCH RCP Lond. 1983; DRCOG 1980.

PIXLEY, Fiona Jane 31 Park Town, Oxford OX2 6SN Tel: 01865 511562 — MB BS 1981 Western Australia; MB BS (Hons.) Western Australia 1981. (Univ. West. Australia) Regist. Oxon. AHA.

PIYARISI

PIYARISI, Mr Dadallage Lalitha 33 Ripley Road, Ilford IG3 9HA — MB BS 1980 Peradeniya, Sri Lanka; FRCS Ed. 1991.

PIYASENA, Chandrani 191 Bishopsford Road, Morden SM4 6BH Tel: 020 8648 3187 Fax: 020 8440 3157; 33 Shirley Avenue, Cheam, Sutton SM2 7QS — MB BS 1972 Sri Lanka; MRCS Eng. LRCP Lond. 1976; DRCOG 1977. (Colombo) GP Morden. Prev: SHO (O & G) Merton, Sutton & Wandsworth AHA (T); Ho. Off. (Gyn.) Merton, Sutton & Wandsworth AHA (T); Ho. Off. (Gyn.) Barnet AHA.

PIZER, Barry Leonard 8 Mervyn Road, Bishopston, Bristol BS7 9EL — MB ChB 1981 Bristol; PhD 1992; MRCP (UK) 1984. Lect. (Child Health) & Hon. Sen. Regist. Univ. Bristol. Socs: Brit. Paediat. Assn. & Assn. Paediat. Research Soc. Prev: Clin. Research Fell. Imperial Research Fund Paediat. & Neuro-Oncol. Laborat. Bristol; Regist. (Paediat.) Kingsmill Hosp. Mansfield; Regist. (Paediat.) Univ. Hosp. Notts.

PIZEY, Mr Noel Cyril Douglas Horsecombe House, Shepherd's Walk, Bath BA2 5QU Tel: 01225 833510 — MB BS 1947 Lond.; FRCS Eng. 1950; MRCS Eng. LRCP Lond. 1946; FFR 1966; DMRT Eng. 1963. (St. Thos.) Cons. Radiotherap. Radiother. Centre Bristol & Roy. United Hosp. Bath. Socs: Assn. Head & Neck Oncol.; Brit. Inst. Radiol. Prev: Sen. Regist. Dept. Radiother. Addenbrooke's Hosp. Camb.; Research Asst. Dept. Radiother. & Sen. Surg. Regist. St. Thos. Hosp.; Lond.

PIZURA, Volodimir Alexander Chancellor House Surgery, 6 Shinfield Road, Reading RG2 7BW Tel: 0118 931 0006 Fax: 0118 975 7194 — MB BS 1983 Lond.; BSc Lond. 1980, MB BS 1983; MRCGP 1988; DRCOG 1990. (St. Geo.) Socs: Pharmaceut. Soc. Prev: GP Crowthorne; Regist. (Psychiat.) Fairmile Hosp.; Med. Off. Jane Furze Hosp., Africa.

PLAAT, Felicity Sarah Department of Anaesthesia, Queen Charlotte's and Chelsea Hospital, Du Cane Road, London W12 0HS Tel: 020 8383 3991 Fax: 020 8838 5373 Email: fplaat@hhnt.org; 34 Aubert Park, London N5 1TU Tel: 020 7354 5252 — MB BS 1985 Lond.; FRCA 1994; BA Camb. 1981. (Middlesex Hospital) Lead Cons. Anaesth. Qu. Charlotte's & Chelsea Hosp.; Coll. Tutor. Socs: Assn. Anaesth.; Obst. Anaesth. Assn.; BMA. Prev: Sen. Regist. Rotat. (Anaesth.) Hammersmith Hosp. Lond.

PLACE, Collin (retired) The Coppice, The Green, Thornborough, Buckingham MK18 2DL Tel: 01280 812514 Fax: 01280 813796 — MB ChB 1963 St. And.; DObst RCOG 1965. Prev: Princip. GP, Verney Cl. Family Pract., Buckingham.

PLACE, David Gregory University Hospital of Wales, Cardiff CF4 3EA; 66 Gelligaer Street, Cathays, Cardiff CF24 4LB — MB BS 1987 Newc.; FRCA 1993; Dip. IMC RCS Ed. 1990. Regist. (Anaesth.) Univ. Hosp. Wales Cardiff. Prev: SHO (Med.& Anaesth.) Nevill Hall Hosp. Abergavenny; SHO (A & E) Pontefract Gen. Infirm.

PLACE, Francis Callow (retired) Three Greens, Mutton Hall Hill, Heathfield TN21 8NL Tel: 01435 864936 — LRCP LRCS Ed. LRFPS Glas. 1945. Prev: Pub. Vaccinator City of Edin. 1942.

PLACE, Gregory Francis Ashfield House, Forest Road, Annesley Woodhouse, Kirkby in Ashfield, Nottingham NG17 9JB Tel: 01623 752295/153 — MB BChir 1984 Camb. LMC Chairm., N. Nottm. LMC Chairm. N. Nottm. LMC LMC Chairm.

PLACE, Professor Maurice Child, Adolescent & Family Psychiatry Department, Sunderland General Hospital, Sunderland SR4 7TP Tel: 0191 569 9026 Email: maurice.place@unn.ac.uk — MD 1988 Newc.; MB BS Newc. 1975; FRCPsych 1994, M 1979; LLB Univ Northumbria 1995. Cons. Child & Adolesc. Psychiat. Sunderland Gen. Hosp.; Prof. Child & Family Psychiat. Univ. of N.umbria at Newc. Socs: Assn. Child Psychol Psychiat.; Fell. Child Psychiat. Research Soc. Prev: Med. Dir. of City Hosps Sunderland; Sen. Regist. (Psychiat.) Newc. Teach. Hosp.; Research Assoc. Human Developm. Unit Newc. Univ.

PLACZEK, Monica Maria Crinkle Cottage, 9 The Green, Silverdale, Carnforth LA5 0TJ Tel: 0524 701318 — MB ChB 1973 Manch.; FRCP (UK) 1979; FRCPCH 1995; DRCOG 1976; DCH Eng. 1976. Cons. Paediat. Lancaster HA & N. RHA.

PLAGARO COWEE, Samantha 84 East Street, Littlehampton BN17 6AN — LMS 1993 La Laguna. SHO (A & E) Roy. Gwent Hosp., Gwent, Newport. Prev: SHO (Gen. Surg.); SHO (Urol.); SHO (A & E).

PLAHA, Mr Harbhajan Singh BUPA Hartswood Hospital, Eagle Way, Brentwood CM13 3LE Tel: 01277 232525 Fax: 01277 200128; 1 Warwick Dene, Ealing Common, London W5 3JG Tel: 020 8840 0946 Fax: 020 8840 0946 — MB BS 1973 Bombay; MS Bombay 1975, MB BS 1973; FRCS Ed. (Orth.) 1983; FRCS Eng. 1979; FRCS Ed. 1979 FCPS Bombay 1975. (Topiwala Nat. Med. Coll.) Cons. Orthop. Surg. Havering Hosps NHS Trust. Prev: Tutor (Gen. Surg.) Lokmanya Tilak Municip. Med. Coll. Univ. Bombay; Sen. Regist. (Gen. Surg.) Topiwala Nat. Med. Coll. Univ. Bombay; Regist. (Orthop. Surg.) Ealing Hosp. S.all.

PLAIL, Mr Roger Oliver Conquest Hospital, The Ridge, St Leonards-on-Sea TN37 4BD Tel: 01424 755255 — MB BS 1976 Lond.; BSc Lond. 1973, MS 1990, MB BS 1976; FRCS Eng. 1981. Cons. Urol. Conquest Hosp. St. Leonards-on-Sea. Prev: Sen. Regist. (Urol.) Roy. Marsden Hosp. Lond.

PLANA VIVES, Fausto 11 Lock Chase, London SE3 9HB — LMS 1982 Barcelona.

PLANCHE, Timothy David 4 Warren Road, Banstead SM7 1LA — MB BS 1991 Lond.

PLANE, Andrew Raymond The Surgery, 3 Heyward Road, Southsea PO4 0DY Tel: 023 9273 7373; 15 Magdala Road, Cosham, Portsmouth PO6 2QG Tel: 02392 380694 — MB BS 1987 Lond.; BSc (Physiol.) Lond. 1980; MRCGP 1991; DGM RCP Lond. 1994; DCH RCP Lond. 1994; DRCOG 1991; Cert. Family Plann. JCC 1991. (Univ. Coll. Lond.) GP Princip.; Clin. Asst. (Elderly Med.) Hants.; Hosp. Practitioner, Elderly Med., Qu. Alexandra and St Mary's Hosp., Portsmouth. Prev: Trainee GP Petersfield Hants.; SHO (Elderly Med.) Portsmouth; SHO (Paediat.) Jersey.

PLANGE, Theresa Nyanchi 1 Diamond EStreet, 61 Glenburnie Road, London SW17 7DJ — MB BS 1968 Lond.; MRCS Eng. LRCP Lond. 1968.

***PLANNER, Andrew Charles** Tallawalla, Long La, Shaw, Newbury RG14 2TH — MB ChB 1997 Bristol.

PLANT, Alan Russell House Surgery, Bakers Way, Codsall, Wolverhampton WV8 1HD Tel: 01902 842488; Moleshill, Mill Lane, Codsall, Wolverhampton WV8 1EG Tel: 01902 843819 — MB ChB 1964 Birm.; MRCS Eng. LRCP Lond. 1964; DA Eng. 1967. (Birm.) Prev: Clin. Asst. Anaesth. Wolverhampton HA; SHO (Anaesth. & O & G) Walsall Hosp. Gp.

PLANT, Arthur Maxwell (retired) Tanglewood, Summerhill, Kingswinford DY6 9JG Tel: 01384 274060 — MB ChB 1941 Edin.; MB ChB (Edin.) 1941. Prev: Ship's Surg. Merchant Navy 1942-46.

PLANT, Berwyn (retired) 22 Lancaster Way, Scalby, Scarborough YO13 0QH Tel: 01723 370928 Email: plantmed@aol.com — MRCS Eng. LRCP Lond. 1949; MRCGP 1966. Prev: Regist. Gen. Surg. Hull 'A' Hosp. Gp.

PLANT, Gillian Dorne Fox and Partners, South Park Surgery, 250 Park Lane, Macclesfield SK11 8AD Tel: 01625 422249 Fax: 01625 502169; Field Bank, 172 Chester Road, Macclesfield SK11 8PT — MB ChB 1979 Manch.; FRCGP 1994, M 1983; DCCH Ed. 1986; DRCOG 1982. (Manchester) Socs: Fell. Manch. Med. Soc. Prev: GP Postrad. Tutor Macclesfield 1991-1998; Trainee GP Bramhall Health Centre Stockport FPC; SHO GP VTS Stockport HA.

PLANT, Gordon Terence The National Hospital for Neurology and Neurosurgery, Queen Square, London WC1N 3BG Tel: 020 7837 3611 Fax: 020 7829 8720 Email: gordon@plant.globalnet.co.uk; Tel: 020 8876 7455 — MB BChir 1978 Camb.; MA Camb. 1978, MD 1986; FRCP Lond. 1993; MRCP (UK) 1979. (Camb. & St. Thos.) Cons. Phys. Nat. Hosps. for Neurol. & Neurosurg. Lond.; Cons.NeUrol.. St. Thos. Hosp. & Moorfields Eye Hosp. Lond.; Hon. Cons., Neurol.St Lukes Hosp.Lond.; Hon. Sen.lct Univ. Coll. Lond.; Hon. Sec. Lect. Guys, Kings, St Thomas, Med. Sch. Lond. Socs: Eur. Neurol. Soc.; Eur. Brain & Behaviour Soc.; Assn. Research in Vision & Ophth. Prev: Sen. Regist. Middlx. & Univ. Coll. Hosps. Lond.; Wellcome Research Assoc. Physiol. Laborat. Camb.; MRC Trav. Fell. Smith-Kettlewell Eye Research Inst., San Francisco.

PLANT, Graham Richard Tudor Department of Radiology, North Hampshire Hospital, Basingstoke RG24 9NA Tel: 01256 313477 Fax: 01256 314773; Email: graham.plant@bas.swest.nhs.uk — MB BS 1978 Lond.; MRCS Eng. LRCP Lond. 1977; FRCR 1986. (Westm.) Cons. Radiol. N. Hants. Hosp.; Edr.Cardiovasc. and Interven.al Radiol. Socs: Brit. Inst. Radiol.; Fell. Cardiovasc. Interven. Radiol. Soc. Europ.; Brit. Soc. Interven. Radiol. Prev: Sen. Registar (Radiol.) W.minster, Brompton & Roy. Marsden Hosps. Lond.

PLANT, Ian David Connaught House, 63B Romsey Road, Winchester SO22 5DE — MB ChB 1967 Liverp.; FRCPC 1987;

LMCC 1986; FRCPsych 1991, M 1973; DPM Eng. 1972. (Liverp.) Cons. Psychiat. Roy. Hants. Co. Hosp. Winchester; Cons. Psychiat. Marchwood Priory Hosp. Soton. Prev: Sen. Regist. (Psychiat.) Profess. Unit Knowle Hosp. Fareham; Specialist in Psychiat. RAMC; Ho. Off. Clatterbridge Hosp. Bebington & Ashford Hosp., Middlx.

PLANT, Irene Mary Premier Health Trust, Greenhill Health Centre, Church St, Lichfield WS13 6JL Tel: 01543 414311; Wellcroft, Stanley, Stoke-on-Trent ST9 9LX Tel: 01782 502693 — MB ChB Liverp. 1968; MSc (Primary Med. Care) Keele 1995; DCH RCP Lond. 1971; DRCOG 1970. Cons. Community Paediat. (Lichfield). Socs: Roy. Coll. Paediat. & Child Health; MRCPCH; Fac. Community Health. Prev: SCMO (Community Paediat.) Stoke on Trent.

***PLANT, Lee Anthony** 231A Manchester Road W., Little Hulton, Manchester M38 9XD — MB ChB 1997 Birm.

PLANT, Marilyn Jane The Surgery, 1 Glebe Road, Barnes, London SW13 0DR Tel: 020 8748 1065 Fax: 020 8741 8665 — MB BChir 1977 Camb.; MPhil Camb. 1983, MA 1978; MRCP (UK) 1980; MRCGP 1988; DRCOG 1985.

PLANT, Michael James Department of Rhematology, University Hospital Wales, Cardiff CF4 4XW Tel: 029 2074 2346; 4 Egerton Walk, Dodleston, Chester CH4 9NS Tel: 01244 660052 — MB BS 1984 Lond.; MD Lond. 1996; MA Camb. 1984; MRCP (UK) 1987. Sen. Regist. (Rheum.) Univ. Hosp. Wales Cardiff & Wrexham Maelor Hosp. Prev: Regist. (Rheum.) Staffs. Rheum. Centre Stoke-on-Trent; Regist. (Diag. Radiol.) Manch. Roy. Infirm.; Regist. (Med.) Char. Cross Hosp. Lond.

PLANT, Nicholas Anthony The Surgery, Summerhill, Kingswinford DY6 9JG; Carr House, 32 Moss Grove, Kingswinford DY6 9HU — MB ChB 1974 Birm. Chairm. Duvky S. Primary Care Gp., Paryton's Ho., Ridge Hill, Brievley Hill Rd., Stowbridge, W. Midl.s, DY8 5ST. Prev: Sen. Ho. Surg. (O & G) New Cross Hosp. Wolverhampton; Ho. Phys. Roy. Hosp. Wolverhampton; Ho. Surg. Dept. Urol. Qu. Eliz. Hosp. Birm.

PLANT, Nicholas David Children's Kidney Unit, Royal Victoria Infirmary, Queen Victoria Road, Newcastle upon Tyne NE1 4LP Tel: 0191 2325131 Fax: 0191 261 5881 Email: n.d.plant@ncl.ac.uk — MB BCh 1984 Wales; MRCP (UK) 1988; FRCPCH; FRCP FRCP 2000. (Welsh National School of Medicine) Cons. & Paediat. Nephrol.

PLANT, Patricia Anne 3 Wintney Close, Harborne, Birmingham B17 8SQ — MB ChB 1963 Bristol.

PLANT, Paul Keith 5 Sandhill Drive, Leeds LS17 8DU — BM BS 1990 Nottm.; MRCP 1993.

PLANT, Sara Jane Withymoor Surgery, Turners Lane, Brierley Hill DY9 2PG Tel: 01384 366740 Fax: 01384 350444; Prospect House, 17 Birmingham Road, Blakedown, Kidderminster DY10 3JD — MB ChB 1993 Birm.; DRCOG 1997; DFFP 1997. Salaried GP, PMS Pilot, Withymoor Surg., Brierley Hill; CMO Family Plann., Dudley Priority Community NHS Trust, W. Mids. Prev: SHO (A & E) Russells Hall Hosp. Dudley.; GP Partner, Aston Univ. Health Centre, Birm.; Asst. GP Worcs.

PLANT, Simon Haddon Lyle and Partners, The Surgery, 4 Silverdale Road, Burgess Hill RH15 0EF Tel: 01444 233450 Fax: 01444 230412 — MB BS 1991 Lond.; BSc (Hons.) Lond. 1987; DCH RCP Lond. 1995. (King's Coll. Hosp. Lond.)

PLANT, William David Department of Renal Medicine, Royal Infirmary of Edinburgh, Lauriston Place, Edinburgh EH3 9YW Tel: 0131 536 2281 Fax: 0131 536 1441 Email: wdp@globalnet.co.uk; 19A Blackford Road, Grange, Edinburgh EH9 2DT Tel: 0131 447 0791 Email: wdp@globalnet.co.uk — MB BCh BAO 1985 NUI; MB BCh BAO (Hons.) NUI 1985; BSc (Hons.) NUI 1982; MRCPI 1988; FRCP 1999 FRCP Edinburgh 1999. (Cork, Ireland) Cons. renal Phys. Roy. Infirm. of Edin.; Hon. Sen. Lect. (Med.) Univ. Edin. Socs: Scott. Renal Assn.; Eur. Soc. Philosophy in Med. & Health Care; Renal Assn. Prev: Sen. Regist. (Renal Med.) Roy. Infirm. Edinbugh; Regist. (Renal Med.) Roy. Infirm. Edin.; Regist. (Nephrol. & Gen. Med.) Cork Univ. Hosp.

PLANTEVIN, Odile Marie Emma Paule (retired) 23 Broom Park, Teddington TW11 9RS Tel: 020 8943 0412 — MB ChB Manch. 1951; FFA RCS Eng. 1958; DA Eng. 1955. Prev: Cons. Anaesth. St. Thos. Hosp. Lond.

PLASTOW, Susan Elizabeth 78 Dartnell Park Road, West Byfleet, Weybridge — MB BS 1984 Lond.

PLATER, Marianne Elaine 8 Hillside Road, Marlow SL7 3JY; 27 Charles Road, Cowes PO31 8HG — MB ChB 1988 Liverp.; MRCP (UK) 1991. Specialist Regist. (Gen. Med. & c/o the Elderly). Socs: Brit. Geriat. Soc.

PLATFORD, Joan Camphill, Japonica Lane, Willen Park S., Milton Keynes MK15 9JY Tel: 01908 235505 — MB ChB 1983 Bristol.

PLATMAN, Andrew Maurice Sydenham Green Group Practice, 26 Holmshaw Close, London SE26 4TH Tel: 020 8676 8836 Fax: 020 7771 4710; 203 Lennard Road, Beckenham BR3 1QN Tel: 020 8659 1990 — MB BChir 1977 Camb.; MA Camb. 1978; MRCP (UK) 1980; MRCGP 1983. (Camb. & King's Coll. Hosp.)

PLATT, Mr Alastair James 17 The Mount, Wrenthorpe, Wakefield WF2 0NZ Email: ajplatt@demon.co.uk — BM BCh 1989 Oxf.; FRCS Eng. 1993. Specialist Regist. (Plastic Surg.) Yorks.

PLATT, Audrey Mary (retired) 47 Windermere Drive, Rishton, Blackburn BB1 4EG — MB ChB 1959 Liverp.; MRCS Eng. LRCP Lond. 1959; FRCOG 1983, M 1970; DObst RCOG 1965. Prev: Cons. O & G Blackburn, Hyndburn & Ribble Valley HA.

PLATT, Celia Lesley New Road Surgery, 60 New Road, Willenhall WV13 2DA Tel: 01902 607590 Fax: 01902 609403 — MB ChB 1959 Sheff. (Sheff.) GP Willenhall. Socs: BMA. Prev: SHO (Cas.) Clatterbridge Hosp. Bebington.

PLATT, Craig Charles Department of Pathology, Birmingham Women's Health Care NHS Trust, Metcheley Park Road, Birmingham B15 2TG; 8 Romford Meadow, Eccleshall, Stafford ST21 6SP — MB ChB 1984 Leic.; MRCPath 1993. Socs: Paediat. Path. Soc.

PLATT, Graham Norris Road Surgery, 356 Norris Road, Sale M33 2RL Tel: 0161 962 5464 — MB BCh 1981 Wales; BSc Wales 1978, MB BCH 1981; MRCGP 1986.

PLATT, Hugh Shuter, TD, OStJ, OBE Royal College of Pathologists, 2 Carlton House Terrace, London SW1Y 5AF Tel: 020 7451 6758; 6 Rewland Drive, Winchester SO22 6PA Tel: 01962 881050 Email: platty@eclipse.co.uk — FRCP 2001; FRCOphth 1999; MB BS (Hons. Surg.) Lond. 1958; BSc Lond. 1955, MD 1970; FRCPath (Hon.) 1986. (Univ. Coll. Hosp.) p/t Dir. of Studies RCPath; Scientif. Fell. Zool. Soc. Lond. Socs: Fell. Roy. Soc. Med.; BMA; Scientif. Fell. Zool. Soc. Lond. Prev: PostGrad Dean (Wessex); Hon. Sen. Clin. Lect. Soton Med. Sch.; Hon. Phys. to HM the Qu.

PLATT, Ian Thomas Skellern and Partners, Bridport Medical Centre, North Allington, Bridport DT6 5DU Tel: 01308 421109 Fax: 01308 420869 — BM 1990 Soton.; BSc Durham 1986; MRCGP 1995. (Soton.) GP Trainee GP W. Dorset Gen. Hosps. NHS Trust.

PLATT, James Alexander (retired) 214 Preston Road, Chorley PR6 7BA Tel: 012572 62654 — MB ChB 1949 Manch.

PLATT, John Old School Medical Centre, School Lane, Greenhill, Sheffield S8 7RL Tel: 0114 237 8866 Fax: 0114 237 3400 — MB ChB 1974 Sheff.

PLATT, John Stephen West Middlesex University Hospital NHS Trust, Twickenham Road, Isleworth TW7 6AF Tel: 020 8565 5449 Fax: 020 8565 5318 Email: maria.classick@wmuh-tr.nthames.nhs.uk — MB BChir 1980 Camb.; MB Camb 1979, BChir 1980; MA Camb. 1979; FRCP Lond. 1996; MRCP (UK) 1982. (St Catharines College Cambridge and Middlesex Hosp. Med. Sch) Cons. Phys. (c/o the Elderly & Gen. Med.) W. Middlx. Univ. Hosp. NHS Trust; Brit. Geriat. Soc. Regional sec 94-97 & Brit. Geriat. Soc. Counc. Represen. for N. W. Thames 2000. Prev: Sen. Regist. (Geriat. Med.) N.. Gen. Hosp. Sheff. & Barnsley Dist. Gen. Hosp.; Regist. (Geriat. Med.) Char. Cross Hosp. Lond.; Regist. (Gen. Med.) Greenwich Dist. Hosp. Lond.

***PLATT, Julie Elizabeth** 29 Forsyth Road, Newcastle upon Tyne NE2 3DB — MB BS 1997 Newc.

PLATT, Kaye Alison 66 Fairlawn Road, Tadley, Basingstoke RG26 3SP — MB BCh 1990 Wales; MB BCh (Hons.) Wales 1990; MRCP (UK) 1993. Specialist Regist. (Radiol.) Univ. Coll. Lond. Hosp. Trust. Prev: Research Regist. (Med.) Univ. Wales Coll. Med. Cardiff.; SHO (Gen. Med.) P.ss of Wales Hosp. Bridgend; SHO Rotat. (CardioPulm.) Cardiff.

PLATT, Kenneth Frederic (retired) West Howtown Cottage, Winsford, Minehead — MB ChB 1925 Bristol. Prev: Ho. Surg. Bristol. Gen Hosp.

PLATT, Mark Richard 49 Cherville Street, Romsey SO51 8FB — MB BChir 1982 Camb.; MA Camb. 1982; FFA RCS 1987. Cons. Anaesth. Soton. Gen. Hosp. Prev: Sen. Regist. (Anaesth.) Soton. Univ. Hosp.

PLATT, Mark Robson South Sefton Child and Family Services, Emire House, 138-148 Linacre Road, Litherland, Liverpool L21 8JU

PLATT

Tel: 0151 285 6500 Fax: 0151 285 6503 — MB BS 1981 Lond.; MA Oxf. 1985; MRCPsych 1986. Cons. Child & Adolesc. Psychiat. Roy. Liverp. Childr.s NHS Trust, Liverp.

PLATT, Mary Jane Department of Public Health, University of Liverpool, Whelan Building Quadrangle, Liverpool L69 3GB Tel: 0151 794 5580 Fax: 0151 794 5588 Email: mjplatt@liv.ac.uk — MB BS 1982 Lond.; MPH John Hopkins Univ. Baltimore; FRCPCH 1997; MFPHM RCP (UK) 1995; MRCGP 1985; DRCOG 1987. (Char. Cross Hosp. Med. Sch.) Sen. Lect. (Pub. Health Med.) Univ. Liverp. Prev: Sen. Regist. (Pub. Health Med.) Mersey Region; Post Doctoral Fell. John Hopkins Univ. Sch. Hyg. & Pub. Health Baltimore, USA; Trainee GP Swindon & Cirencester VTS.

PLATT, Michael William Department of Anaesthetics, St. Mary's Hospital, Praed St., London W2 1NY Tel: 020 7725 6216 Fax: 020 7725 6425; 44 Lammas Park Road, Ealing, London W5 5JB Tel: 020 8567 2248 Email: m.platt@ic.ac.uk — MB BS 1977 West. Austral.; FRCA 1988. Cons. Anaesth. & Pain St. Mary's Hosp. Trust Lond.; Asst. Vice-Princip. Undergrad. Teachg. Imperial Coll. Sch. of Med., St Mary's Campus; Dir. Clin. Studies St Mary's Campus; Hon. Sen. Lect. (Anaesth.) Imperial Coll. of Sci., Technol. & Med. Lond. Socs: (Pres.) Age Anaesth. Assoc.; Roy. Soc. Med. (Anaesth. Sect.); Assn. Anaesth. Prev: Sen. Lect. (Anaesth.) St. Mary's Hosp. Med. Sch., Imperial Coll. Sci., Technol. & Med. Lond.

PLATT, Neville Douglas 1 Old Vicarage, Edensor, Bakewell DE45 1PH Tel: 01246 583176 — MB BS 1964 Lond.; FFA RCS Eng. 1969.

PLATT, Philip Neil 31 Mitchell Avenue, Jesmond, Newcastle upon Tyne NE2 3JY — MD 1988 Birm.; MB ChB Birm. 1976; FRCP Lond. 1992; MRCP (UK) 1980. Cons. Rheum. Freeman Hosp. Trust; Hon. Lect. (Med.) Univ. Newc. Prev: Cons. Rheum. Roy. Vict. Infirm. Newc.

PLATT, Rosemary 34 Blackroot Road, Four Oaks, Sutton Coldfield B74 2QP — MB ChB 1974 Manch.; MRCGP 1979; DRCOG 1977; DCH Eng 1976.

PLATT, Sarah Gillian Selly Park Surgery, 2 Reaview Drive, Pershore Road, Birmingham B29 7NT Tel: 0121 472 0187 Fax: 0121 472 0187; 49 Moor Green Lane, Moseley, Birmingham B13 8NE Tel: 0121 449 2764 — MB ChB 1975 Birm. Socs: Treas. Birm. Med. Inst.; Sec. Midl. Med. Soc.

PLATT, Simon Robert 67 Lake View, Edgware HA8 7SA — MB ChB 1993 Bristol.

***PLATT, Tracey Louise Clifton** Applewood, Alleyns Lane, Cookham-Dean, Maidenhead SL6 9AD — MB BS 1998 Lond.; MB BS Lond 1998.

PLATTEN, Harriet Maud Jenny Charles Hicks Centre, 75 Ermine Street, Huntingdon PE29 3EZ Tel: 01480 453038 Fax: 01480 434104; 13 Hawkes End, Brampton, Huntingdon PE28 4TW Tel: 01480 453978 Fax: 01480 453978 — MB ChB 1976 Bristol; MRCGP 1982. p/t Hosp. Practitioner (Rheum.) Hinchingbrooke Hosp. Huntingdon.

PLATTEN, Michael Cotterell Elm Rise, 46 High St., Finstock, Chipping Norton OX7 3DW — MB ChB 1942 Birm.; MA Camb.

PLATTS, Alan Samuel Gregory Helsby Street Medical Centre, 2 Helsby Street, Warrington WA1 3AW Tel: 01925 637304 Fax: 01925 570430; 2 Stoneacre Gardens, Appleton, Warrington WA4 5ET Email: ap@appleton.demon.co.uk — MB ChB 1980 Manch.; BSc St. And. 1977; DRCOG 1984. Trainer (Gen. Pract.) Warrington.

PLATTS, Amanda Jill Parkbury House Surgery, St. Peters Street, St Albans AL1 3HD Tel: 01727 851589; 60 Worley Road, St Albans AL3 5NN Tel: 01727 832046 — MB BS 1977 Lond.; MRCP (UK) 1982. (Roy. Free) Course Organiser NW Herts. Train. Scheme.

PLATTS, Mr Andrew Duncan Radiology Department, Royal Free Hampstead NHS Trust, Pond St., London NW3 2QG Tel: 020 7830 2013 Fax: 020 7830 2969 Email: andrew.platts@rfh.nthames.nhs.uk; 60 Worley Road, St Albans AL3 5NN Tel: 01727 832046 — MB BS 1977 Lond.; FRCS Ed. 1981; FRCS Eng. 1981; FRCR 1985. Cons. Neuroradiol. Roy. Free Hampstead NHS Trust; Hon. Sen. Lect. Roy. Free and Univ. Coll. Med. Sch.

PLATTS, Anthony John (retired) 9 Blackley Close, Watford WD17 4TE Tel: 01923 243394 — MB BS Lond. 1952; MRCS Eng. LRCP Lond. 1952; DObst RCOG 1958. Prev: Ho. Surg. St. Mary's Hosp. (Harrow Rd. Br.) & Camb. Matern. Hosp.

PLATTS, Brian William, TD Park Cottage, Nottingham Road, Southwell NG25 0LG Tel: 01636 812587 Fax: 01636 812587 Email: drbrianplatts@hotmail.com; Park Cottage, Nottingham Road, Southwell NG25 0LG Tel: 01636 812587 — MB ChB 1975 Manch.; MRCGP 1979; FFOM RCP Lond. 1995, MFOM 1984, AFOM 1982; DIH Eng. 1981. Indep. Cons. Occ. Phys. Socs: (Ex-Chairm. Sec. & Treas.) Soc. Occupat. Med. (E. Midl. Gp.); Ex-Treas. Assn. NHS Occupat. Phys. (Ex-Chairm. Educat. Comm.). Prev: Regional Med. Off. Brit. Gas E. Midl.; Employm. Med. Adviser Health & Safety Exec. Nottm.; Med. Off. Brit. Steel Sheff.

PLATTS, Christopher Hanson The Medical Centre, King George Dock, Hull HU9 5PQ Tel: 01482 712113 Fax: 01482 704373; 5 Driffield Road, Beverley HU17 7LP Tel: 01482 882304 Fax: 01482 882304 — MB ChB 1964 Leeds; MRCGP 1971; DObst RCOG 1967. (Leeds) Med. Off. Assoc. Brit. Ports, Hull. (PT). Prev: GP. Princip. Beverley; SHO (O & G) W.wood Hosp. Beverley; Ho. Phys., Ho. Surg. & Ho. Off. (Paediat. & Dermat.) St. Jas. Hosp. Leeds.

PLATTS, Dorothy Edwina (retired) Occupational Health Department, Billing House, Northampton General Hospital NHS Trust, Cliftonville, Northampton NN1 5DB Tel: 01604 634700 — MB BS 1961 Lond.; MRCS Eng. LRCP Lond. 1961; AFOM RCP Lond. 1982; DIH Soc. Apoth. 1982; DCH Eng. 1964; DObst RCOG 1963. Med. Off. Occupat. Health Serv. N.ampton Gen. Hosp. NHS Trusts. Prev: Ho. Phys. Roy. Free Hosp. Lond. & P.ss Louise Kensington Hosp. Childr.

PLATTS, Hazel Florence Mary Ashworth Street Surgery, 85 Spotland Road, Rochdale OL12 6RT Tel: 01706 44582 Fax: 01706 346767; Buckley Hill House, Buckley Hill Lane, Milnrow, Rochdale OL16 4BU — MB ChB 1978 Manch.; MRCGP 1982.

PLATTS, Hilary Adele The Health Centre, St. Peters Crescent, Selsey, Chichester PO20 0NN Tel: 01243 604321/602261 Fax: 01243 607996; 19 Bonnar Road, Selsey, Chichester PO20 9AT — MB ChB 1982 Leic.; BSc Leic. 1980; DRCOG 1989. GP Princip. Chichester; Med. Off. (Family Plann.) Chichester; Hosp. Practitioner, BrE. Clinic.

PLATTS, Julia Karen Wrexham Maelor Hospital, Croesnewydd Road, Wrexham LL13 7TD; 8 Farmhouse Mews, Wrexham LL13 9SX — MB BS 1989 Lond.; MRCP (UK) 1993. Specialist Regist. Rotat. (Diabetes & Endocrinol.) Wrexham Maelor Hosp.

PLATTS, Karena Anne The Surgery, High Street, Epworth, Doncaster DN9 1EP Tel: 01427 872232 Fax: 01427 874944 — MB ChB 1983 Sheff.; MRCGP 1987; DRCOG 1987; MFFP 1993; Dip. Genitourin. 1996. (Sheffield) Prev: Mem. Humberside MAAG; Clin. Asst. (Genitourin. Med.); Clin. Asst. (Genitourin. Med.).

PLATTS, Margaret Machon (retired) 47 Coldwell Lane, Sheffield S10 5TJ Tel: 0114 230 7300 Email: margaret.platts@care4free.net — MB ChB Sheff. 1948; BSc Sheff. 1947, MD (Commend.) 1957; FRCP Lond. 1971, M 1950; DObst RCOG 1950. Prev: Cons. Phys. Lodge Moor Hosp. & Roy. Hallamsh. Hosp. Sheff.

PLATTS, Marina Margaret 106 Hillview Drive, Clarkston, Glasgow G76 7JD — MB ChB 1993 Glas.; MRCPI 1998. Specialist Regist. Rehabil. Med. S.ern Gen. Hosp. Glas.

PLATTS, Paul Health Centre, Blaby Road, Wigston, Leicester — BM BS 1975 Nottm.; MRCGP 1980.

PLATTS, Sydney Herbert Bingley (retired) 16 Pannal Avenue, Harrogate HG3 1JR — MRCS Eng. LRCP Lond. 1932; MB Camb. 1937, BChir 1932.

PLATTS, Timothy Simon Castleton Health Centre, 2 Elizabeth Street, Castleton, Rochdale OL11 3HY Tel: 01706 658905 Fax: 01706 343990; Buckley Hill House, Buckley Hill Lane, Milnrow, Rochdale OL16 4BU — MB ChB 1978 Manch.; MRCGP 1982.

PLATZ, Christine Linda Mary 40 The Pines, St. James Road, Purley CR8 2DZ Tel: 020 8668 5465 — MB ChB 1980 Liverp.; MPhil (Psychiat.) Ed. 1986; MRCS Eng. LRCP Lond. 1980; MRCPsych 1985. Sen. Regist. (Psychiat.) Stone Ho. Hosp. Dartford. Prev: Regist. (Psychiat.) Roy. Edin. Hosp.; SHO Roy. Edin. Hosp.; Ho. Off. Roy. Liverp. Hosp.

PLAUT, Mr Gustav S, TD (retired) 18 North Mill Place, Mill Chase, Halstead CO9 2FA Tel: 01787 478114 — MB BChir 1947 Camb.; MA Camb. 1947; FRCS Eng. 1955; FRCS Ed. 1954; FRCGP 1980, M 1965. Prev: GP Lond.

PLAXTON, Michael Robert Kirby (retired) Dean's Orchard, Angel Lane, Mere, Warminster BA12 6DH Tel: 01747 860523 — MB BChir 1954 Camb.; BA, MB BChir Camb. 1954; DObst RCOG 1958.

PLAYER, David Arnott (retired) 7 Ann Street, Edinburgh EH4 1PL Tel: 0131 332 1088 — MB ChB 1950 Glas.; FRCP Ed 1979, M 1977; FRCPsych 1981, M 1972; FFCM 1978, M 1974; DPM RCPSI 1965; DPH Glas. 1959. Chairm. Pub. Health Alliance. Prev: Dir. Gen. Health Educat. Counc.

PLAYER, Mark Hort Patwell Lane Surgery, Patwell Lane, Bruton BA10 0EG Tel: 01749 812310 Fax: 01749 812938; Bird's Hill Farm, Upton Noble, Shepton Mallet BA4 6AP Tel: 0174 985244 — MB BS 1980 Lond.; BSc (Hons.) Leeds 1974; MRCGP 1986; DRCOG 1984. (St. Mary's) Socs: BMA. Prev: Regist. (Med.) Wexham Pk. Hosp. Slough; SHO (Paediat. & O & G) Hillingdon Hosp. Uxbridge; Ho. Surg. St. Mary's Hosp. Lond.

PLAYER, Peter Val North Ridge Medical Practice, North Ridge, Rye Road, Hawkhurst, Cranbrook TN18 4EX Tel: 01580 753935 Fax: 01580 754452; Keeper's Cottage, Hastings Road, Flimwell, Wadhurst TN5 7PR Tel: 01580 879503 Fax: 01580 879640 Email: ring4en@aol.com — MB BS 1975 Lond.; BSc (Hons. Ecological Sc.) Ed. 1970; DRCOG 1978. (Middlx.) Socs: Weald & Marsh Med. Soc. Prev: SHO (Otolaryng.) Cheltenham Gen. Hosp.; SHO (Paediat.) St. Mary's Hosp. Lond.; Ho. Phys. Centr Middlx. Hosp.

PLAYFAIR, Christopher James Adam Practice, Heath Cottage Surgery, 40 High Street, lytchett Matravers, Poole BH16 6BG Tel: 01202 632764; Siyabonga, 69 Kingland Road, Poole BH15 1TN — BM 1978 Soton.; MRCGP 1988; DO RCS Eng. 1986. GP Princip.; Clin. Asst. Opthalmology Roy. Bournmouth Hosp. Castle La. Bournemouth.

PLAYFAIR, James Ronald St James Surgery, 6 Northampton Buildings, Bath BA1 2SR Tel: 01225 422911 Fax: 01225 428398; 13 Bathwick Hill, Bath BA2 6EW Tel: 012255 462105 — MB BS 1977 Lond.; MRCGP 1982; DRCOG 1979. (Lond. Hosp. Lond. Univ.) GP Princip. Prev: SHO (Radiotherap. & Oncol.) Addenbrooke's Hosp. Camb.; Ho. Phys. Lond. Hosp.; Ho. Surg. Epsom Dist. Hosp.

PLAYFAIR, Mary Lois (retired) 62 Coniger Road, London SW6 3TA — MB BS Lond. 1940; MRCS Eng. LRCP Lond. 1940.

PLAYFER, Jeremy Robin Embleton, 59 Brimsgate Road, Hewswall, Wirral L60 1XE — MB ChB 1970 Liverp.; MD Liverp. 1977; FRCP Lond. 1988; MRCP (UK) 1974. Cons. Phys. Roy. Liverp. Hosp.; Clin. Lect. Univ. Liverp. Socs: (Treas.) Brit. Geriat. Soc. Prev: Sen. Regist. Cowley Rd. Hosp. Oxf.; Research Fell. (Med.) Univ. Liverp.; Regist. (Med.) Liverp. RHB.

PLAYFOR, Bridget Emma 21 Hawkshead Drive, Knowle, Solihull B93 9QE — MB BS 1992 Lond.

PLAYFOR, Stephen Derek 27 Mounthouse Road, Freshfield, Liverpool L37 3LA — MB BS 1991 Lond.

PLAYFORD, Edith Diane 28 Holmfield Road, Leicester LE2 1SA — MD 1994 Lond.; MB BS 1984; MRCP (UK) 1987. Sen. Lect. Univ. of Nottm.; Hon. Cons. (Neurol. & Rehabil.) S.ern Derbys. Acute Hosps. NHS Trust. Prev: Lect. (Neurol.) Nat. Hosp. for Neurol. & Neurosurg. Lond.; Regist. Nat. Hosp. for Neurol. & Neurosurg. Lond.; Regist. (Med.) Atkinson Morley Hosp. Lond.

PLAYFORD, Professor Raymond John Department of Gastroenterology, Leicester General Hospital, Gwendoline Road, Leicester LE5 4PW Tel: 0116 258 8180 Fax: 0116 258 8183 Email: rjp13@le.ac.uk — MB BS 1984 Lond.; PhD Lond. 1992; MRCP (UK) 1987; FRCP (UK) 1997. Prof. Gastroenterol. Leicester Univ.; Vis. Prof. Imperial Coll. Sch. of Med. Socs: Brit. Soc. Gastroenterol.; Amer. Gastroenterol. Assn. Prev: MRC Clin. Sci. (Gastroenterol.) & Train. Fell. Hammersmith Hosp. Lond.; Regist. (Med.) Hammersmith Hosp. Lond.

PLAYFORD, Vanda Jane Gill Street Health Centre, 11 Gill Street, London E14 8HQ Tel: 020 7515 2211; 145 Glenarm Road, London E5 0NB Tel: 020 8985 6506 Fax: 020 8985 6506 Email: vanda@chats.demon.co.uk — MB BS 1982 Lond.; MA Derby 1996. Lect. Gen. Pract. 1997-. Socs: Med. Practs. Union (MSF Br.).

PLAYFORTH, Mr Michael John Accident and Emergency Department, Pontefract General Infirmary, Friarwood Lane, Pontefract WF8 1PL Tel: 01977 600600 Fax: 01977 606909 Email: micheal.playforth@panp-tr.northy.nhs.uk — MB ChB 1976 Leeds; MD Leeds 1988; FRCS Ed. 1984; FFAEM 1993. Cons. A & E Pontefract Gen. Infirm.

PLEASANCE, Clive Martin Whiteway, 2 Ryecroft Road, Heswall, Wirral CH60 1XB — MB ChB 1979 Liverp.; DCH NUI 1981; DRCOG 1981.

PLEASANT, Elizabeth Ann St. Gerardines, Lossiemouth IV31 6RD Tel: 0134 381 2055 — MB BS 1955 Lond.; MRCS Eng. LRCP Lond. 1955.

PLEDGE, Simon David Department of Clinical Oncology, Weston Park Hospital, Whitham Road, Sheffield S10 2SJ — BM BCh 1988 Oxf.; MA Oxf. 1985, BM BCh 1988; MRCP (UK) 1992; FRCR 1998. Cons. Clin. Oncol., W.on Pk. Hosp. Socs: UKCCSA (full). Prev: Research Fell. Paterson Inst. for Cancer Research; Regist. (Clin. Oncol.) City Hosp. Nottm.; Lect. & Hon. Sen. Regist. Univ. Sheff..

PLEDGER, Herbert Gordon (retired) Oaktree Cottage, Mitford, Morpeth NE61 3PN Tel: 01670 513339 — MD 1964 Newc.; MB BS Durh. 1953; FFCM 1986, M 1982; FFA RCS Eng. 1960. Prev: Dist. Med. Off. Newc. HA.

PLEMING, Aled Wyn Bryn Hafod, Pen-y-Berth, Llanfairpwllgwyngyll LL61 5YT — MB BS 1989 Lond.

PLENDERLEITH, Anne Caroline Hay Kinning Park Medical Centre, 42 Admiral Street, Glasgow G41 1HU Tel: 0141 429 0913 Fax: 0141 429 8491; 17 Rowan Road, Glasgow G41 5BZ — MB ChB 1977 Glas.

PLENDERLEITH, John Louie Western Infirmary, Glasgow G11 6NT; 17 Rowan Road, Glasgow G41 5BZ — MB ChB 1979 Ed.; BSc Ed. 1976; FFA RCS Eng. 1984. Cons. Anaesth. (Intens. Care) W.. Infirm. Glas.

PLENDERLEITH, Mark Flat 12, 27 Demesne Road, Whalley Range, Manchester M16 8HJ — MB ChB 1988 Manch.

PLENDERLEITH, Stephen James St. Rocco's Hospice, Lockton Lane, Bewsey, Warrington WA5 0BW Email: dr.steve@st-roccos-hospice.co.uk; steve@gooseberry.netkonect.co.uk — MB ChB 1991 Liverp.; DRCOG 1993; MRCGP 1997. Sen. Med. Off. (Pall. Care) St. Rocco's Hospice, Warrington.

PLENTY, David Ronald Lake Road Health Centre, Nutfield Place, Portsmouth PO1 4JT Tel: 023 9282 1201 Fax: 023 9287 5658 — BM 1980 Soton.; BSc Manch. 1974; MRCGP 1984; DRCOG 1984.

PLESSAS, Spyridon 10 Centre Court, Barlow St., Derby DE1 2TQ — Ptychio latrikes 1987 Athens.

PLESTER, George Leonard Abbotsford, 9 Briars Close, Hinckley Road, Nuneaton CV11 Tel: 02476 384073 — LRCP LRCS 1944 Ed.; LRCP LRCS Ed. LRFPS Glas. 1944; AFOM RCP Lond. 1981. (Ed.) Med. Off. Occupat. Health Dept. Nuneaton (N. Warks.) Health Dist.; Med. Advis. to Various Local Firms. Socs: Med.-Leg. Soc. Prev: Sen. Med. Off. E. Gen. Hosp. Edin.; Res. Surg. Off. Gen. Infirm. Burton-on-Trent.

PLETTS, Robert Charles White Wings, 4 Broadsands Road, Paignton TQ4 6JY — MB BS 1975 Lond.; BSc Bristol 1969; MRCS Eng. LRCP Lond. 1975; FFAEM 1993; DIP IMC RCS Ed. 1991. Assoc. Specialist (A & E) Torbay Hosp.

PLEVRIS, Ioannis 50 Gogarloch Syke, Edinburgh EH12 9JB — Ptychio latrikes 1983 Athens; MRCP (UK) 1993.

PLEWES, Mr John Lawrence The Royal Orthopaedic Hospital, Northfield, Birmingham B31 2AP Tel: 0121 485 4291; Selvas Cottage, Withybed Green, Alvechurch, Birmingham B48 7PR Tel: 0121 445 1624 — BM BCh 1964 Oxf.; MA Oxf. 1964; FRCS Eng. 1970. (Middlx.) Cons. Orthop. Surg. Roy. Orthop. Hosp. Birm.; Clin. Sen. Lect. (Surg.) Univ. Birm. Prev: Orthop. Surg. Chaleur Gen. Hosp. Bathurst, Canada; Sen. Regist. (Orthop.) Robt. Jones & Agnes Hunt Orthop. Hosp. OsW.ry; Research Fell. (Orthop.) St. Joseph's Hosp. Toronto, Canada.

PLEWS, Christina Mackenzie Stonelaw, Poole End Close, Tytherington, Macclesfield SK10 2LD — MB ChB 1949 Glas. (Glas.)

PLEWS, David Julian Market Surgery, Warehouse Lane, Wath-On-Dearne, Rotherham S63 7RA Tel: 01709 877524 — MB ChB 1982 Leeds; MRCGP 1986; Cert. Family Plann. JCC 1986.

PLEWS, Dianne Elaine 9/5 Great King Street, Edinburgh EH3 6QW — MB ChB 1992 Ed.; MRCP 1996. Specialist Regist. (Blook Transfus.) Scott. Nat. Blood Transfus. Serv.

PLEWS, Normana Rose Imphal, 3 Banks Howe, Onchan, Douglas IM3 2EN Tel: 01624 629247 — MB ChB 1942 Glas. (Glas.) Prev: Med. Off. E.M.S. Hosp. StoneHo.; Ho. Phys. Roy. Infirm. Glas.; Ho. Surg. Vict. Infirm. Glas.

PLIETH, Charlotte E.A.C. Boga, Dem. Rep. of Congo, PO Box 21285, Nairobi, Kenya; Downs Cottage, Rivar Road, Shalbourne, Marlborough SN8 3QE Tel: 01672 870514 — State Exam Med 1989 Kiel; State Exam Med. Kiel 1989.

PLIMMER

PLIMMER, Anna Louise 97 Gladstone Road, London SW19 1QR — MB BS 1993 Lond. (Univ. Lond.) SHO (Gen. Med. & Geriat.) E. Surrey Hosp. Redhill. Prev: SHO (Cas.) Ashford Hosp. Middlx.; Ho. Off. (Med.) W. Middlx. Hosp.; Ho. Off. (Surg.) Frimley Pk. Hosp. Surrey.

PLIMMER, Michelle Maria 37 Burbage Road, London SE24 9HB — MB BS 1990 Lond.

PLIMMER, Wendy Nicola 2 Herbert Villa, Pelham Road, London SW19 1NW — MB BS 1992 Lond.

PLINT, Simon John Beaumont Street Surgery, 19 Beaumont Street, Oxford OX1 2NA Tel: 01865 240501 Fax: 01865 240503; 16 Farndon Road, Oxford OX2 6RT — MB BS 1984 Lond.; MA (Mod. & Medieval Langs.) Camb. 1981; MRCGP 1988; DRCOG 1989; DCH RCP Lond. 1986. Med. Off. Oxf. Univ. Rugby Football Club; Course Organiser Oxf. Sub-Regional GP VTS.

PLOTNEK, Jonothan Stuart Field House Medical Centre, 13 Dudley Street, Grimsby DN31 2AE Tel: 01472 350327; Greenways, 10 Park Drive, Grimsby DN32 0EF — MB ChB 1982 Leeds; Cert. Developm. Paediat. Leeds 1985.

PLOWMAN, Jacqueline Rae Heywood Villa, Heywood Road, Pill, Bristol BS20 0ED — MB BS 1985 Lond.

PLOWMAN, Margaret Anne (retired) Eastgate Surgery, 31B York Place, Knaresborough HG5 0AD Tel: 01423 557200 Fax: 01423 557201 — MB ChB 1967 Sheff.

PLOWMAN, Patricia Elizabeth (retired) Fiveacres, Browning Hill Green, Baughurst, Basingstoke RG26 5JZ Tel: 01734 816172 — MB BS 1966 Lond.; MRCS Eng. LRCP Lond. 1966; FFA RCS Eng. 1970. Prev: Cons. Anaesth. Basingstoke Dist. Hosp.

PLOWMAN, Piers Nicholas 14 Harmont House, 20 Harley St., London W1G 9PH Tel: 020 7631 1632 Fax: 020 7323 3487; 101 Barnsbury Street, Islington, London N1 1EP Tel: 020 7607 5307 Fax: 020 7323 3487 — MB BChir 1974 Camb.; MD Camb. 1980, MA, MB BChir (Hons.) 1974; FRCP Lond. 1989; MRCP (UK) 1976; FRCR 1980. Cons. Phys. Radiother. & Oncol. St. Bart. Hosp. (Head) & Hosp. for Sick Childr. Lond.; Hon. Sen. Lect. Inst. Child Health Lond.

PLOWMAN, Raymond Albert (retired) 4 Rectory Garth, Hemsworth, Pontefract WF9 4NB Tel: 01977 611298 — MB ChB Leeds 1959; MRCPsych 1993; DPM Eng. 1963. Prev: Sen. Regist. & Regist. (Psychiat.) St. Jas. Hosp. Leeds.

PLOWS, Charles David (retired) 31 Roman Lane, Little Aston, Sutton Coldfield B74 3AE Tel: 0121 353 2243 — MB BChir 1958 Camb.; MB BChir Camb. 1957; MA Camb. 1958; FRCPath 1980, M 1968; Dip. Bact. Lond 1965. Cons. Microbiol. Good Hope Dist. Gen. Hosp. Sutton Coldfield. Prev: Sen. Bacteriol. Pub. Health Laborat. Serv. Sheff.

PLOYE, Philippe Maurice (retired) 45A Beauchamp Road, East Molesey KT8 0PA Tel: 020 8979 9181 — MD 1941 Montpellier; FRCPsych 1978, M 1972. Prev: Hon. & Cons. Psychother. Cassel Hosp. Ham Common.

PLUCK, Judith Catherine Broomfields, Hatfield Heath, Chelmsford CM3 7EH Tel: 01279 730616; 4 Snows Court, Great Waltham, Chelmsford CM3 1DE Tel: 01245 360145 — MB BS 1987 Lond.; BPharm (Hons.) Bradford 1979. GP Hatfield Heath. Socs: MRCP; Roy. Plann. Soc.

PLUCK, Nigel David 29 Barn Close, Oxford OX2 9JP — BM BCh 1985 Oxf.; MA, DPhil, BM BCh Oxf. 1985.

PLUGGE, Emma Harriet 75 Boyne Road, Lewisham, London SE13 5AN Tel: 020 8318 6018 — MB BChir 1991 Camb.; MA Camb. 1991; DTM & H 1992. Regist. (Pub. Health Med.) W. Sussex.

PLUMB, Mr Andrew Philip 15A Bolton Road, Eastbourne BN21 3JT Tel: 01323 736626 Fax: 01323 736626 — MB BS 1977 Lond.; MRCS Eng. LRCP Lond. 1977; FRCS Eng. 1983; FCOphth 1988; DO Eng. 1980. (Guy's) Cons. Ophth. Surg. E.bourne HA. Prev: Sen. Regist. (Ophth.) Univ. Coll. Hosp., Roy. Free Hosp. Lond. & Moorfield Hosp. Lond.; Regist. (Ophth.) St. Thos. Hosp. Lond.

PLUMB, Elizabeth Anne Dennis and Partners, The Medical Centre, Folly Lane, Bewsey, Warrington WA5 0LU Tel: 01925 417247 Fax: 01925 444319; 7 Caversham Close, Appleton, Warrington WA4 5JX Tel: 01925 860167 — MB ChB 1982 Manch.

PLUMB, John Martin Tudor Gate Surgery, Tudor Street, Abergavenny NP7 5DL Tel: 01873 855991 Fax: 01873 850162 — MB BS 1969 Lond.; MRCP (U.K.) 1973; MRCS Eng. LRCP Lond. 1969; MRCGP 1982. (Westm.) Prev: Ho. Phys. St. Stephen's Hosp. Lond.; Sen. Ho. Phys. Nevill Hall Hosp. Abergavenny; Med. Off. Nchanga Consolidated Copper Mines Ltd. Konkola, Zambia.

PLUMB, Marjory Ernestine (retired) Claremont, 2 Woodland Avenue, Leighton Buzzard LU7 3JW Tel: 01525 373165 — MB BS 1956 Lond.; DCH Eng. 1960. Prev: GP Tring Herts.

PLUMB, Nicholas John Lancing Health Centre, Penstone Park, Lancing BN15 9AG Tel: 01903 763144 Fax: 01903 750288 — MB BS 1987 Lond. (Roy. Free Hosp. Sch. Med. Lond.)

PLUMB, Richard David 27a Fairhead View, Ballycastle BT54 6LU — MB BCh BAO 1995 Belf.

PLUMB, Stephen Argyle Street Surgery, 141 Argyle Street, Heywood OL10 3SD Tel: 01706 366135 Fax: 01706 627706 — BM BCh 1973 Oxf.; MA Oxf., BM BCh 1973; MRCGP 1980; DObst RCOG 1976. (Oxf.)

PLUMLEY, Michael Hugh Department of Anaesthetics, Queen Elizabeth Hospital, Gayton Road, King's Lynn PE30 4ET Tel: 01553 766266; Bridge House, Winch Road, Gayton, King's Lynn PE32 1QP — MB BS 1975 Lond.; BA Oxf. 1972; FFARCS Eng. 1982. (St Marys) Cons. Anaesth. W. Norf. & Wisbech HAs. Socs: Intens. Care Soc.; Fell. Roy. Soc. Med.; Assn. Anaesth. Prev: Sen. Regist. (Anaesth.) W.m. Hosp. & W.m. Childr. Hosp. Lond.; Clin. Fell. Roy. Vict. Hosp., Montreal; Clin. Fell. Montreal Childr. Hosp. Quebec, Canada.

PLUMLEY, Mr Peter Francis (retired) 8 Marina Court Avenue, Bexhill-on-Sea TN40 1BN Tel: 01424 213618 — MB BChir 1952 Camb.; MChir Camb. 1967, MA, MB BChir 1952; FRCS Eng. 1958. Prev: Cons. Gen. Surg. Roy. E. Sussex & St. Helen's Hosps. Hastings & Bexhill Hosp.

PLUMLEY, Susan Mary Putneymead Medical Centre, 350 Upper Richmond Road, London SW15 6TL Tel: 020 8788 0686; 1 St. Margaret's Crescent, London SW15 6HL — MB BS 1982 Lond.; MRCGP 1988; DRCOG 1987.

PLUMLEY, Thomas Alfred (retired) 16 Ashley Court, Ashley Road, Epsom KT18 5AJ Tel: 01392 722693 — MB BS Lond. 1951; MRCS Eng. LRCP Lond. 1955; AFOM 1978; MFCM 1972; DObst RCOG 1955; DPH Lond. 1954. Prev: Employm. Med. Adviser Health & Safety Exec.

PLUMMER, Christopher John Department of Cardiology, Freeman Hospital, High Heaton, Newcastle upon Tyne NE7 7DN Tel: 0191 284 3111 Fax: 0191 213 0498 Email: c.j.plummer@ncl.ac.uk; Tel: 01661 853177 — BM BCh 1992 Oxf.; BSc 1986 Bristol; PhD Bristol 1989, BSc 1986; MRCP (UK) 1995. (Oxf.) Specialist Regist. (Cardiol.) N. Deanery. Socs: Brit. Cardiac Soc. (Mem.). Prev: Regist. (Acad. Cardiol.) Freeman Hosp. Newc.; SHO Rotat. (Med.) Newc. u. Tyne; Ho. Phys. John Radcliffe Hosp. Oxf.

PLUMMER, Elizabeth Ruth Northern Centre for Cancer Treatment, Newcastle General Hospital, Westgate Road, Newcastle upon Tyne NE4 6BE Tel: 0191 219 4200; Rudchester Manor, Haddon-on-the-Wall, Newcastle upon Tyne NE15 0JA Email: e.r.plummer@ncl.ac.uk — BM BCh 1992 Oxf.; MA Camb. 1990; DPhil Oxf. 1989; MRCP (UK) 1995. (Oxf.) Clin. Lect. in Med. Oncol., Univ. of Newc. Prev: Specialist Regist. (Med. Oncol.) Newc. u. Tyne; Research Regist. (Med. Oncol.) Newc.; Ho. Phys. John Radcliffe Hosp. Oxf.

PLUMMER, Hugh Exwick Surgery, New Valley Road, Exwick, Exeter EX4 2AD Tel: 01392 70063; Orchard View, Kenn, Exeter EX6 7UH Tel: 01392 833033 — BM 1979 Soton.; BSc Soton. 1966; PhD Lond. 1969; MRCGP 1984; DRCOG 1983. Prev: Princip. GP Exeter.

PLUMMER, Jonathan Richard Flat 23, Didsbury Court, Wilmslow Road, Manchester M20 6AD — MB ChB 1996 Manch.

PLUMMER, Richard Bruce Leys House, Bridge St., Great Kimble, Aylesbury HP17 9TW Tel: 01844 346532 Fax: 01844 346532 Email: plummer@compuserve.com — MRCS Eng. LRCP Lond. 1969; FFCA Eng. 1975; DObst RCOG 1972; FRCA FRCA Eng 1975. (Guy's) Cons. Anaesth. Stoke Mandeville Hosp. Aylesbury. Prev: Sen. Regist. (Anaesth.) Guy's Health Dist. (T) & Brighton Health Dist.

PLUMMER, Sarah Jane Grove Cottage, Siginstone, Cowbridge CF71 7LP Tel: 01446 775492; Spindrift, 10 Smugglers Close, Old Hunstanton, Hunstanton PE36 6JU Tel: 01485 533953 — MB BS 1990 Lond.; FRCA 1995; DA (UK) 1992. Regist. (Anaesth.) Univ. Hosp. Wales Cardiff. Socs: Fell. Roy. Coll. Anaesth.; Assn. Anaesth.

Prev: SHO (Neonates) Exeter; SHO (Anaesth.) Bristol Roy. Infirm. & Worthing Gen. Hosp.

PLUMMER, Thomas Royston (retired) 3 Wharfeside Cottages, Leatherbank, Burley-in-Wharfedale, Ilkley LS29 7HP — BM BCh 1931 Oxf.; MRCS Eng. LRCP Lond. 1928.

PLUMMER, William Philip East Kent Community Alcolol Service, Mount Zeehan Unit, St. Martin's Hospital, Little Bourne Road, Canterbury CT1 1TD Tel: 01227 761310 Fax: 01227 463254 — MB BS 1980 Lond.; BSc 1977 Lond.; BSc Lond. 1977, MB BS 1980; MRCPsych 1990; MRCGP 1985; DRCOG 1986. (St. Thomas' Hospital Medical School) Cons. Psychiat. E. Kent Community NHS Trust; Hon. Sen. Lect. (Psychiat) KIMHS Univ. of Kent at Canterbury. Prev: Sen. Regist. (Psychiat.) UMDS SE Thames RHA; Regist. (Psychiat.) Guy's Hosp. Lond.; GP Herne Bay.

PLUMMER, Yvonne Myra 122 Maltby Drive, Enfield EN1 4EN Tel: 020 8804 2928 — MB BS 1979 Lond.; MRCS Eng. LRCP Lond. 1977; DFFP 1993; DRCOG 1993. (Roy. Free) Clin. Asst. (Gyn.) Homerton Hosp. NHS Trust. Socs: Fell. Roy. Soc. Med. Prev: Regist. (O & G) N. Middlx. Hosp. Lond.; Regist. (O & G) St. Jas. & St. Geo. Hosp. Lond.; Regist. (Surg.) S. Lond. Hosp.

PLUMMERIDGE, Martin James Lung Research Group, University of Bristol, Medical School Unit, Southmead Hospital, Westbury on Trym, Bristol BS10 5NB Tel: 0117 959 5156 Email: m.j.plummeridge@bristol.ac.uk; 13 Apsley Road, Clifton, Bristol BS8 2SH Tel: 0117 973 3440 — MB ChB 1990 Bristol; MRCP (UK) 1994. Clin. Research Fell. Lung Research Gp. Univ. Bristol. Prev: Regist. (Thoracic Med.) Roy. United Hosp. Bath; Regist. (Gen. & Thoracic Med.) P.ss Margt. Hosp. Swindon & Salisbury Dist. Hosp.; Regist. (Gen. & Thoracic Med.) Gold Coast Hosp. Qu.sland.

PLUMPTON, Frederic Salkeld (retired) 241 Wishing Tree Road, St Leonards-on-Sea TN38 9LA Tel: 01424 854077 Fax: 01424 854077 — BM BCh Oxf. 1958; MA Oxf. 1958; FFA RCS Eng. 1965; DA Eng. 1964; DObst RCOG 1960. Vice-Pres. St. Michael's Hospice Hastings; Hon. Cons. Anaesth. Hastings Hosp. Gp. Prev: Examr. FFA RCS Eng.

PLUMPTON, Helen Patricia The Surgery, 24 Albert Road, Bexhill-on-Sea TN40 1DG Tel: 01424 730456/734430 Fax: 01424 225615 — MB ChB 1991 Manch.; BSc St. And. 1988; MRCGP 1995; DRCOG 1994. (St. Andrews & Manchester) Prev: Trainee GP/SHO Roy. Lancs. Infirm.

PLUMPTON, Rosamund Joan 16 Sandwich Road, Worthing BN11 5NT — MB BS 1990 Lond.; DCH RCP Lond. 1994.

PLUMPTRE, Aubrey Martin Macdonald (retired) Ragdon Cottage, Ragdon, Church Stretton SY6 7EY — MB BS 1957 Lond.; Cert. Family Plann. JCC 1975; DObst RCOG 1959. Prev: GP Soton.

***PLUMTREE, Jane Rebecca** 19 Hazon Way, Epsom KT19 8HD Tel: 01372 812038; 19 Hazon Way, Epsom KT19 8HD Tel: 01372 812038 — MB ChB 1998 Leeds.

PLUNKETT, Ciaran Nial 30 The Ridgeway, London N11 3LJ Tel: 020 8368 4433 — MB BCh BAO 1959 NUI.

PLUNKETT, Gerald Barry (retired) 3 St Mark's Place, The Mall, Armagh BT61 9BH Tel: 01861 510716 — MB BCh BAO NUI 1951; FRCPsych 1991; FRCPI 1969, M 1958; DPM TCDI 1961. Prev: Cons. Psychiat. St. Luke's Hosp. Armagh.

PLUNKETT, Luke 30 Stanley Park, Bristol BS5 6DU — MB ChB 1985 Bristol.

PLUNKETT, Michael Charles Academic Department of Paediatrics, City General Hospital, Stoke-on-Trent ST4 6QG Tel: 01782 552663 Fax: 01782 713946 Email: mcplunkett@aol.com — BM 1987 Soton.; MRCPI 1993. Specialist Regist. (Paediat.) N. Staffs. Hosp. NHS Trust Stoke-on-Trent.

PLUNKETT, Nicholas Patrick Drumadd Cottage, Armagh BT61 9EA — MB ChB 1991 Aberd.

PLUNKETT, Simon Gerald 4 The Square, Lymm WA13 0HX — MB ChB 1989 Aberd.

PLUNKETT, Timothy Andrew ICRF Clinical Oncology Unit, Guy's Hospital, London SE1 9RT — MB BS 1992 Lond.; BSc (Hons.) Lond. 1989; MRCP (UK) 1995. (Guy's Hosp.) ICRF Clin. Research Fell. Guy's Hosp. Lond.

PLUNKETT, Trevor George Yare Valley Medical Practice, 202 Thorpe Road, Norwich NR1 1TJ Tel: 01603 437559 Fax: 01603 701773; 13 South Avenue, Thorpe St. Andrew, Norwich NR7 0EY Tel: 01603 435622 Email: tevorg@talk21.com — MB ChB Ed. 1961. (Ed.) Socs: Brit. Soc. Rheum.; Fell. Roy.Soc.Med.

PLUSA, Mr Stefan Murray Dept. of Surgery, Royal Victoria Infirmary, Newcastle upon Tyne NE1 4LP Tel: 0191 282 4744 — MB ChB 1984 Leeds; FRCS Eng. 1989; FRCS Ed. 1989; FRCS (Gen) 1997. Cons. (Colorectal Surg.) Roy. Vict. Infirm. Newc. Upon Tyne. Socs: Surg. Research Soc. & Nutrit. Soc.; Brit Soc. Of Castroent.; Assoc. of Coleproct. Prev: Lect. & Sen. Regist. (Surg.) Roy. Vict. Infirm. Newc.; Research Regist. (Surg.) St. Jas. Univ. Hosp. Leeds; Regist. (Transpl. & Urol.) St. Mary's Hosp. Portsmouth.

PLYMING, Annabelle Virginia Louise 10 Brass Thill, St Margaret's Garth, Durham DH1 4DS Tel: 0191 386 5272 Email: avplyming@lineone.net — MB ChB 1997 Ed.

POATE, Timothy William John Martlet Cottage, Runcton, Chichester PO20 6QA — MB BS 1996 Lond.; BDS Lond. 1990; LDS RCS Eng. 1990; FDS RCS Eng. 1996. (Bartholomews) SHO (Oral & Maxillofacial Surg.) Roy. United Hosp. Bath.

POBERESKIN, Mr Louis Howard Department of Neurosurgery, Derriford Hospital, Plymouth PL6 8DM Tel: 01752 792539 Fax: 01752 763395 Email: louis.pobereskin@phnt.swest.nhs.uk; Tel: 01822 859026 — MD Case Western Reserve 1970; FRCS Ed. (SN) 1987. Cons. Neurosurg. Socs: Soc. Brit. Neurol. Surg.s.

POBLETE GRIBBELL, Maria Ximena Northwick Park Hospital, Watford Road, Harrow HA1 3UJ — MRCS Eng. LRCP Lond. 1981; MSc (Community Paediat.) Lond. 1991; MRCP (UK) 1995; DCH RCP Lond. 1985. Cons. Paediat. N.wick Pk. Hosp. Harrow. Prev: Sen. Regist. (Community Paediat.) Optimum NHS Trust; Clin. Med. Off, City & Hackney Hlth. Auth.; Clin. Res. Fell., Behavioural Sci., Inst. Child Hlth.

POCHA, Meher J The Child Development Centre, Hill Rise, Kempston, Bedford MK42 7EB Tel: 01234 310278 Fax: 01234 310277; Homefield, 3 Baldock Road, Letchworth SG6 3LB Tel: 01462 686987 — MB BS 1971 Bombay; MD (Paediat.) Bombay 1974; MRCP (UK) 1977; DCH CPS Bombay 1972. (Grant Med. Coll.) Cons. Paediat. Child Developm. Centre Bedford & Bedford Hosp. Socs: MRCP; FRCPCH; Mem. BPNA. Prev: SCMO (Child Health) Pk.side HA; Regist. (Paediat.) Alder Hey Childr. Hosp. Liverp.; Research Fell. Inst. Child Health & Hon. Clin. Asst. Gt. Ormond St. Hosp. Lond.

POCHIN, Rosalynd Sidonee Barkby 81C Lewisham Way, London SE14 6QD — MB BS 1994 Lond.

POCKLINGTON, Anthony Geoffrey 25 Clifton Road, Heaton Moor, Stockport SK4 4DD — MB ChB 1968 Manch.; FFA RCS Eng. 1977; DObst RCOG 1971.

POCKLINGTON, Susan Lynne Boarden Barn, Bicton, East Budleigh, Budleigh Salterton EX9 7BR — MB ChB 1969 Leeds; MRCGP 1978. (Leeds) Socs: BMA. Prev: Regist. (Anaesth.) United Birm. Hosps.; Ho. Surg., Ho. Phys. & SHO (Anaesth.) Corbett Hosp. Stourbridge.

***POCKNEY, Peter Graham** 23 Greville Road, Southampton SO15 5AW — MB BS 1996 Lond.

POCOCK, Christopher Francis Elliott 34 Longridge House, Falmouth Road, London SE1 6QN Email: c.pocock@ic.ac.uk — MB BS 1987 Lond.; MRCP (UK) 1991; PhD Lond. 1995; Dip. RCPath 1998. Allogeneic BMT Coordinator, Hammersmith Hosp. Lond. Prev: Clin. Research Fell. & Hon. Lect. (Haemat.) Roy. Lond. Trust Whitechapel.

POCOCK, David Ian Gordon 66A Station Approach, South Ruislip, Ruislip HA4 6SA — MB BS 1996 Lond.

POCOCK, Jessica Dept. of Ophthalmology, King's College Hospital, London SE5 9RS Tel: 020 7346 3534; 111 Babington Road, Streatham, London SW16 6AN Tel: 020 8769 3194 — MB ChB 1971 Bristol; BSc (Anat.) Bristol 1967; MRCOphth 1994. (Bris.) Assoc. Specialist (Ophth.) King's Coll. Hosp. Lond. Prev: Clin. Asst. (Ophth.) King's Coll., St. Geo. Hosp. & Roy. Hosp. for Neurodisabil. Lond.; Clin. Asst. Bristol Eye Hosp.; Lect. (Anat.) St. Geo. Hosp. Med. Sch. Lond.

POCOCK, Kenneth Norman Johnston, OStJ Ridge Cottage, 305 Luton Road, Harpenden AL5 3LW Tel: 01582 461624 — MA Camb. 1953, BA, MB BChir 1949; MRCS Eng. LRCP Lond. 1949; MFOM RCP Lond. 1978; DIH Soc. Apoth. Lond. 1955; CPH Eng. 1955. (Camb. & Bristol) Socs: Fell. Roy. Soc. Med.; Soc. Occupat. Med. Prev: Chief Med. Off. Vauxhall Motors Ltd.; Squadron Ldr. RAF Med. Br.; Area Commr. St. John Ambul. Brig.

POCOCK, Marilyn Ann Josephine Royal Devon & Exeter Hospital, Exeter; Chilton, Bickleigh, Tiverton EX16 8RT — MB ChB 1970

POCOCK

Manch.; FRCP Lond. 1996; MRCP (UK) 1977; FRCPath 1992, M 1981. Cons. Haemat. Roy. Devon & Exeter Hosp. Socs: Brit. Soc. Haematol. Prev: Cons. Haemat. Cheltenham Gen. Hosp.; Leukaemia Research Fund Fell. 1982/84; Lect. & Sen. Regist. (Haemat.) King's Coll. Hosp. Lond.

POCOCK, Mr Richard Duncan Royal Devon & Exeter Hospital, Barrack Road, Exeter EX5 2DW Tel: 01392 402133 Email: rdp@quadrant1.u-net.com; Chilton, Cadeleigh, Tiverton EX16 8RT — MB ChB 1973 Bristol; FRCS Eng. 1978. Cons. Urol.Roy. Devon & Exeter NHS Trust. Prev: Sen. Regist. (Urol.) Bristol Roy. Infirm. & S.mead Hosp. Bristol.; Regist. St. Geo. Hosp. Lond.; Regist. St. Jas. Hosp. Lond.

POCOCK, Sarah Margaret Queens Park Medical Centre, Farrer Street, Stockton-on-Tees TS18 2AW Tel: 01642 679681 Fax: 01642 677124 — MB ChB 1986 Bristol; MRCGP 1991; DRCOG 1991.

POCOCK, Mr Timothy John Wellesley Hospital, Eastern Avenue, Southend-on-Sea SS2 4XH Tel: 01702 258262 Fax: 01702 258262 — MB ChB 1971 Bristol; FRCOG 1995; FRCS Ed. 1979; MRCOG 1978, DObst 1975. (Bristol) Cons. O & G S.end Gen. Hosps. Socs: Roy. Coll. Obitetrician Gynaecologist; Roy. Coll. Med.; Brit. Soc. Colposcopy Clin. Path. Prev: Sen. Regist. (O. & G) W.m. Hosp. Lond.; SHO (Obst.), SHO (Paediat.) & SHO (Surg.) Avon AHA (T).

PODAS, Thrasyvoulos 15 Stevenstone Close, Oadby, Leicester LE2 4TF — Ptychio Iatrikes 1980 Thessalonika; MRCPI 1992. Specialist Regist. (Gastroenterol.) Leicester Gen. Hosp. Socs: Med. Res. Soc.; Roy. Coll. Phys. Irel.; Hellenic Med. Soc. Prev: Regist. (Gastroenterol.) Glenfield Gen. Hosp. Leicester.

PODD, Mr Timothy James Radiotherapy Department, Newcastle General Hospital, Westgate Road, Newcastle upon Tyne NE4 6BE — MB BChir 1982 Camb.; MA Oxf. 1984; FRCS Ed. 1987; FRCS Eng. 1987; FRCR 1992. Cons. Clin. Oncol. Newc. Gen. Hosp. Prev: Sen. Regist. (Radiother.) Newc. Gen. Hosp.; Regist. Rotat. Poole Gen. Hosp.; Regist. (Radiol. & Oncol.) Roy. S. Hants. Hosp.

PODDAR, Mohan Lal 25 Sandringham Avenue, Newton Mearns, Glasgow G77 5DU — MB BS 1954 Bihar; MRCGP 1972; DCH RCPS Glas. 1965; DTM & H Calcutta 1956. (Darbhanga Med. Coll. Bihar) Socs: BMA.

PODDAR, Subhashish 35 Delafield Road, Abergavenny NP7 7AW — MB BCh 1988 Wales.

PODICHETTY, Madhavi 5 Skene Close, Headington, Oxford OX3 7XQ — MB ChB 1991 Manch.; BSc St And. 1988; MRCPsych 1997.

PODKOLINSKI, Marek Thomas Endless Street Surgery, 72 Endless Street, Salisbury SP1 3UH Tel: 01722 336441 Fax: 01722 410319 — MB BS 1974 Lond.

PODMORE, Mr Malcolm Dennis Elms Hall Cottage, Elms Hall Road, Colne Engaine, Colchester CO6 2JL Tel: 01787 222006 Email: sussie@malcolm106.freeserve.co.uk — MB BS 1987 Lond.; FRCS 2001 (Orth); BSc (Hons.) Lond. 1984; FRCS Eng. 1992. (Middlesex Hospital) Cons. Orthopaedic Surg. N. Devon & Destrict Hosp. Barnstaple Devon; Hon. Cons. Orthopaedic Surg. Roy. Devon & Exeter Hosp. Devon. Prev: Specialist Regist. Roy. Nat. Orthapaedic Hosp. Stanmore.

PODOGROCKI, Adam John 40 Elmfield Gardens, Newcastle upon Tyne NE3 4XB — MB BS 1987 Newc.

***POELS, Jonathan Anthony David** 52 Doncaster Avenue, Manchester M20 1DJ — MB ChB 1998 Manch.; MB ChB Manch 1998.

POELS, Peter John Sandpitts, Heathstock, Stockland, Honiton EX14 9EX — MRCS Eng. LRCP Lond. 1942. (St. Thos.) Prev: ENT & Gyn. Ho. Surg. St. Thos. Hosp.

POEPPINGHAUS, Vanessa Jane Ida Department of Accident & Emergency, Ysbyty Gwynedd, Bangor LL57 2PW Tel: 01248 384384 Fax: 01248 384936; Mefus, Glyn Garth, Menai Bridge LL59 5PF Tel: 01248 712365 — MB BCh 1984 Wales; BSc (Hons.) St. And. 1980. Assoc. Specialist (A & E) Ysbyty Gwynedd Bangor.; Community Med. Off. Wom. & Childs. Health; Police Surg. N. Wales Police. Prev: Trainee GP Cardiff VTS; SHO (Psychiat.) Ysbyty Gwynedd Bangor; SHO (O & G) Univ. Coll. Wales Cardiff.

POGGO, Colin The Stone House, Sandy Lane, Maidstone ME14 3DJ Tel: 01622 762575 Fax: 01622 762934 Email: c.poggo@poggo.co.uk; The Stone House, Boxley, Maidstone ME14 3DJ Tel: 01622 757524 — MB BCh 1978 Witwatersrand. Direct. Poggo Anaesth Ltd.

POGMORE, Mr John Richard, Wing Cdr. RAF Med. Br. Retd. The Birmingham Womens Hospital, Edgbaston, Birmingham B15 2TG Tel: 0121 6074711 Fax: 0121 627 2667 Email: john.pogmore@bham-womens.thenhs.com; 15 St. Mary's Road, Harborne, Birmingham B17 0EY Tel: 0121 427 2590 Fax: 0121 682 7555 Email: jpog@doctors.org.uk — MB BS Lond. 1965; MRCS Eng. LRCP Lond. 1965; FRCOG 1988, M 1975; DObst 1970. (St. Bart.) p/t Cons. O & G Birm. Wom. Healthcare NHS Trust; Ex-Chairm. Hosp. Recognition Comm. Roy. Coll. Obst. & Gyn. Socs: Birm. medico-legal soc (counc mem); Fell. Birm. & Midl. Obst. & Gyn. Soc.Vice Pres.; Hon Treas. Brit.Soc. Colposcopy & Cervical Path. Prev: Cons. O & G RAF Hosp. Wroughton; Hon. Lect. & Sen. Regist. (O & G) Nottm. City Hosp.; Resid. Surg. Off. Hosp. Wom. Soho Sq. Lond.

POGREL, Graham Philip Waterloo House Surgery, Waterloo House, 42-44 Wellington Street, Millom LA18 4DE Tel: 01229 772123 Fax: 01229 771300 Email: grahampogrel@hotmail.com; 1 Low Beck Stones, The Green, Millom LA18 5HZ Tel: 01229 773144 Email: grahampogrel@hotmail.com — MB ChB 1971 Liverp.; FRCGP 2000; Cert in Medical Education (Durham) 2000; MRCS Eng. LRCP Lond. 1971; MRCGP 1975; DObst RCOG 1973; DCH Eng. 1973. Police Surg. Cumbria. Socs: RCGP; BMA. Prev: SHO (Med.) Liverp. Roy. Infirm.; G.P Trainer 1977-1999; Course Organiser SW Cumbria VTS 1982-1988.

POGSON, Caroline Jane 30 Ross Road, Wallington SM6 8QR — MB BS 1991 Lond.

POGSON, David Graeme Anaesthetic Department, Singleton Hospital, Swansea SA2 8QA Tel: 01792 205666; Manor Cottage, Thorpe Bassett, Rillington, Malton YO17 8LU — MB BCh 1992 Wales. SHO (Anaesth.) Singleton Hosp. Swansea. Socs: BMA; Med. Protec. Soc.; Assn. Anaesth. Prev: SHO (Med.) Roy. Gwent Hosp.

POGUE, Laura Jane Justine Mar-Rowee, Bradda East, Port Erin IM9 6QB — MB ChB 1993 Liverp.

POH, Choo Hean 33 Meadowlands, Jordanstown, Newtownabbey BT37 0UR — MB BCh BAO 1996 Belf.

***POHL, Debbie Susan** 9 Woodland Avenue, Leicester LE2 3HG — MB ChB 1998 Leic.; MB ChB Leic 1998.

POHL, Jurgen Ernst Friedrich (retired) 9 Woodland Avenue, Stoneygate, Leicester LE2 3HG Tel: 0116 270 8129 Fax: 0116 249 0064 — BSc Melbourne 1955, MB BS 1959; FRCP Lond. 1979, M 1964. Prev: Lect. (Therap.) Univ. Manch.

POHL, Keith Richard Erik Newcomen Centre, Guy's Hospital, London Bridge, London SE1 9RT Tel: 020 7955 4270 Fax: 020 7955 4950 Email: keith.pohla@gstl.sthame.nhs.uk; 7 Oakley Avenue, Ealing, London W5 3SA Tel: 020 8992 7366 — BSc (Basic Med. Sci.) Lond., MB BS 1981; MRCP (UK) 1985; DCH RCP Lond. 1983; FRCPCH 1997. (Royal Free Hospital London) Cons. Paediat. Neurol. Guy's & St. Thos. Trust Lond. Prev: Sen. Regist. (Paediat.) Univ. Coll. Hosp. Lond.; Fell. & Regist. (Neurol.) Brit. Columbia's Childr. Hosp., Vancouver & Hosp. Sick Childr. Lond.

***POINTEN, Emma Juliet** 21 Nayland Croft, Birmingham B28 0QH — MB ChB 1995 Manch.

POINTING, Teresa Dawn Westfield Surgery, Waterford Park, Radstock, Bath BA3 3UJ Tel: 01761 463333; 7 Sarabeth Drive, Tunley, Bath BA2 0EA — MB BS 1987 Lond. GP Princip.; Clin. Asst. (Psychiat.) Barrow Hosp. Bristol. Prev: GP Bonnybrigg, Midlothian.

POINTON, Andrew David University Laboratory of Physiology, Parks Road, Oxford OX1 3PT Tel: 01865 272500 — MB BS 1992 Lond.; BA (Hons.) Oxf. 1989. MRC Clin. Train. Fell. Neurophysiol.

POINTON, Gweneth Irene (retired) 23 Marcuse Fields, Bosham, Chichester PO18 8NA — MRCS Eng. LRCP Lond. 1953; FRCGP 1981, M 1962. Prev: Ho. Phys. Fulham Hosp. Lond.

POINTON, Robert Charles Snow (retired) Bridge End House, Lower Frankton, Oswestry SY11 4PU — MB BChir 1947 Camb.; MA Camb. 1950, BA, MB BChir 1947; MRCS Eng. LRCP Lond. 1947; FRCP Glas. 1981 M 1978; DMRT Eng. 1952; DMRT Lond. 1952; FRCR 1975; FFR 1954. Dir. Radiother. Christie Manch. & Holt Radium Inst. Prev: Cons. Radiotherap. Christie Manch. & Holt Radium Inst.

POIRIER, Mr Henry, TD (retired) Hangerlea, Stansted Road, Bishop's Stortford CM23 2DA Tel: 01279835880 Fax: 01279 835880 — MB BS 1954 Lond.; FRCS Eng. 1960. Hon. Cons. Orthop. Surg. Herts. & Essex Hosp. Bishop's Stortford & P.ss

Alexandra Hosp. Harlow; Cons. Orthop. Surg. Rivers Hosp. Sawbridgeworth. Prev: Regist. Roy. Nat. Orthop. Hosp. & St. Bart. Hosp. Lond.

POKINSKYJ, Stefanie Katrina Longford Street Surgery, Longford Street, Heywood OL10 4NH Tel: 01706 621417 Fax: 01706 622915 — MB BCh 1979 Wales; MRCGP 1983; DRCOG 1982. Clin. Asst. (Psychiat.) Prestwich.

POKORNY, Michael Robert 167 Sumatra Road, London NW6 1PN Tel: 020 7431 4693 Fax: 020 7435 5712 Email: mrp@mpokorny.freeserve.co.uk — MB ChB Sheff. 1961; FRCPsych 1994, M 1972; DPM Eng. 1966. (Sheff.) Socs: Brit. Psychoanal Soc.; Hon. Mem. Assn. Grp. & Individual Psychother.; Forum for inDepend. psychotherapists. Prev: Cons. Psychiat. Prestwood Lodge Sch. Bucks. CC.; Hon Cons Psychiat. Lond centre for Psychother.

POLACARZ, Stephen Victor Department of Pathology, Withybush General Hospital, Fishguard, Haverfordwest SA61 2PZ Tel: 01437 773269 Fax: 01437 773549 Email: stephen.polacarz@pdt-tr.wales.nhs.uk — MB ChB 1981 Sheff.; PhD Lond. 1984; BSc (Hons.) Hull 1973; MRCPath 1991; FRCPath 1999. Cons. Histopath. Withybush Gen. Hosp. HaverfordW.. Socs: Brit. Soc. Clin. Cytol.; Assn. Clin. Path.; Internat. Acad. Path. Prev: Lect. (Path.) Univ. Sheff. Med. Sch.

POLACK, Clare 224 Hills Road, Cambridge CB2 2QE Tel: 01223 247661 — MB BS 1994 Newc.; BSc Ed. 1989; MRCP 1997. (Univ. Newc.) GP. Prev: SHO (Med.) N. Tyneside Gen. Hosp. Tyne & Wear.

POLAK, Adolf (retired) The Old Rectory, Bidbury Lane, Bedhampton, Havant PO9 3JG — MD Camb. 1955, MB BChir 1949; FRCP Lond. 1970, M 1953. Prev: Cons. Phys. Wessex Regional Renal Unit.

POLAK, Gerard Jan Anton HMYOI Glen Parva, Tigers Road, Wigston LE18 4TN Tel: 0116 264 3101 Fax: 0116 264 3000 — Artsexamen 1982 Amsterdam; Dip. Addic. Behaviour Lond. 1996. (University Vrye Amsterdam) Med. Off. HMYOI Glen Parva Wigston. Prev: Med. Off. HMP Hull; Staff Psychiat. (Psychiat. for Deaf People) Whittingham Hosp. Preston; Regist. (Psychiat.) De La Pole Hosp. Hull.

POLAK, Professor Julia Margaret Histochemistry Department, ICSM,Hammersmith Hospital, Du Cane Road, London W12 0NN Tel: 020 8740 3231 Fax: 020 8743 5362 Email: julia.polack@ic.ac.uk; 8 Denbigh Road, Ealing, London W13 8PX — MD 1964 Buenos Aires; DSc Lond. 1980; Medico 1961; FRCPath 1986, M 1973; MRCP Eng. 1992. (Buenos Aires) Prof. Endocrinol. Pathol. Roy. Postgrad. Med. Sch. Lond.; Hon. Cons. Path. Hammersmith Hosp. Lond.; Dep. Dir. Dept. Histopath. Hammersmith Hosp. Lond. Socs: Fell. Roy. Microscop. Soc.; Path. Soc. Prev: Vis. Prof. Neuroendocrine Path. Milan Univ.; Reader, Sen. Lect. & Lect. Roy. Postgrad. Med. Sch. Lond.; Sen. Regist. (Path.) Univ. Buenos Aires.

POLAK, Louisa North Hill Surgery, 18 North Hill, Colchester CO1 1DZ Tel: 01206 578070 Fax: 01206 769880; The Latch, Church St, Boxted, Colchester CO4 5SX — BM BCh 1979 Oxf.; MRCP (UK) (Paediat.) 1982; DRCOG 1982. GP Colchester.

POLAKOFF, Sheila (retired) 31 Templemead Close, Gordon Avenue, Stanmore HA7 3RG — MB BCh BAO 1948 Dub.; MD Dub. 1971.

***POLAND, Karen Monica** 1 Millbrook Drive, Ballynahinch BT24 8HQ — MB BCh BAO 1996 Belf.

POLANI, Professor Paul E Division of Medical & Molecular Genetics, Paediatric Research Unit, Prince Philip Research Laboratories, Guy's Hospital, London SE1 9RT Tel: 020 7955 4456 Fax: 020 7955 4644; Little Meadow, West Clandon, Guildford GU4 7TL Tel: 01483 222436 — MD 1938 Pisa; FRS 1973; FRCPI 1989; FRCP Lond. 1961, M 1948; FRCPath 1985; FRCOG 1979; FRCPCH 1997; DCH Eng. 1945. (Siena & Pisa, Italy) Geneticist Paediat. Research Unit Div. Med. Molec. Genetics UMDS, Guy's & St. Thos. Hosps. Lond.; Emerit. Prof. Paediat. Research Lond.; Hon. Fell. Guy's St. Thos. & King's Coll., Fell. King's Coll., Lond. Socs: Genet. Soc.; Clin. Genetics Soc.; Assn. Brit. Neurol. Prev: Vis. Prof. (Human Genetics & Developm.) Coll. of Phys. & Surg. Columbia Univ., New York; Dir. Paediat. Research Unit Guys Hosp. Med. Sch. & SE Thames Regional Genetics Centre; P. Phillip Prof. Paediat. Research & Hon. Childr. Phys. Guy's Hosp. Lond. & Geneticist Guy's Hosp. & Med. Sch., Lond.

POLANSKA, Antonina Isabella 6 Revell Road, Kingston upon Thames KT1 3SW — MB ChB 1965 Glas.; MSc (Biochem.) Lond. 1976; MRCPath 1977. (Glas.) Cons. Chem. Path. Qu. Mary's Hosp. Lond. Socs: BMA & Assn. Clin. Biochems. Prev: Rotat. Sen. Regist. (Chem. Path.) Roy. Free Hosp. Lond. & W. Middlx.; Hosp. Isleworth; Regist. (Path.) Dept. Chem. Path. & Metab. Unit Roy. Infirm. Liverp.

POLDING, Aileen 968 Dumbarton Road, Clydebank G81 4LG — MB ChB 1993 Glas.

POLE, Deborah Mary (Vincent) Tel: 0161 962 4625; Tel: 0161 860 0367 — MB ChB 1994 Manch.; MRCGP Lond. 1999; BSc St. And. 1991; MRCP Lond. 1996. (St. Andrews and Manchester) GP Bodmin Rd. Surg., Sale. Socs: RCGP. Prev: SHO (Chest Med.) Wythenshawe Hosp. Manch.; Ho. Off. (Surg.) Blackpool Vict. Hosp.; Ho. Off. (Med.) Withington Hosp. Manch.

POLE, Indira Yashvant Blackwoods Medical Centre, 8 Station Road, Muirhead, Glasgow G69 9EE Tel: 0141 779 2228 Fax: 0141 779 3225; 11A Fraser Gardens, Kirkintilloch, Glasgow G66 1DB — MB BS 1974 Bombay; FFA RCS Eng. 1980; FFA RCSI 1980. (Grant Med. Coll.)

POLE, Julia Margaret St Johns House Surgery, 28 Bromyard Road, St. Johns, Worcester WR2 5BU Tel: 01905 423612 Fax: 01905 740003; 9 Stoneleigh Close, Greenhills, Worcester WR5 3RQ — BM BS 1983 Nottm.; MRCGP 1987.

POLE, Pamela Margaret 7 Hadfield Cross, Hadfield, Glossop, Hyde SK13 1NT — MB ChB 1991 Manch.

POLEY, Bryan Anthony (retired) 6 Grosvenor Avenue, Torquay TQ2 7LA — MB ChB 1955 Bristol; FFA RCS Eng. 1963; DA Eng. 1958. Prev: Cons. Anaesth. Torbay Hosp. Gp.

POLGE, Christopher Mark Roysia Surgery, Burns Road, Royston SG8 5PT Tel: 01763 243166 Fax: 01763 245315 — MB ChB 1983 Bristol.

POLIAKOFF, Lucinda Jane 3 Waverley Road, Norwich NR4 6SG — MB BChir 1982 Camb.; DRCOG 1984.

POLIHILL, Sara Louise Flat L, 90 Warwick Square, London SW1V 2AJ — BM 1996 Soton.

POLITO, Thomas Charles The Garden Flat, 16 York Place, Harrogate HG1 1HL — MB ChB 1995 Sheff. (Sheff.) GP Regist. Harrogate. Prev: Ho. Off. (Med.) Bassetlaw Hosp. Worksop; Ho. Off. (Gen. Surg.) Norf. & Norwich Hosp.

POLKEY, Anne Elizabeth 121 Court Lane, London SE21 7EE — MB ChB 1990 Leeds.

POLKEY, Professor Charles Edward Dept. of Neurosurgery, King's College Hospital, Denmark Hill, London SE5 9RS; 121 Court Lane, Dulwich, London SE21 7EE — MD 1968 Bristol; BSc Bristol 1960, MD 1968, MB ChB 1963; FRCS Eng. 1971. (Bristol) Prof. Of Func.al Neurosurg. GKST Sch. of Med.; Hon. Cons. Neurosurg. King's Healthcare Trust. Socs: Soc. Brit. Neurol. Surgs.; Europ.Soc. Funct. Neurosurg. Prev: Sen. Regist. Neurosurg. Unit Maudsley Hosp. Lond.; MRC Jun. Research Fell. Dept. Physiol. Univ. Bristol.; Cons. Neurosurg. Guy's Hosp. & Bethlem Roy. Hosp. & Maudsley Hosp. Lond.

POLKEY, Michael Iain Respiratory Muscle Laboratory, Department of Thoracic Medicine, King's College School of Medicine, Bessemer Road, London SE5 9PJ Tel: 020 7346 4493 Fax: 020 7346 3589 Email: michael.polkey@kcl.ac.uk; 23 Ashmead Road, Deptford, London SE8 4DY — MB ChB 1988 Bristol; MRCP (UK) 1991; PhD Lond. 1998. Specialist Regist. (Thoracic & Gen. Med.) King's Coll. Hosp. Lond.; Hon. Regist. Roy. Brompton Hosp. Socs: Brit. Thorac. Soc.; Eur. Respirat. Soc.; Amer. Thoracic Soc. Prev: Lect. (Med.) King's Coll. Sch. Med. & Dent.; Regist. (Med.) Guy's Hosp. Lond.; SHO Rotat. (Med.) Middlx. Hosp. Lond.

POLKINGHORN, Andrew Verwood Surgery, 15 Station Road, Verwood BH31 7DY Tel: 01202 825353 Fax: 01202 829697 — BM 1992 Soton.; MRCGP Lond. 1997 - RCGP; DCH RCP Lond. 1996; DRCOG Lond. 1997; DFFP Lond. 1997. GP Princip., Sandy & Partners, Verwood.

***POLKINGHORN, Claire Louise Hunter** 2 Bassett Crescent W., Southampton SO16 7DZ — BM 1994 Soton.

POLKINGHORN, David Gareth Market Surgery, Warehouse Lane, Wath-On-Dearne, Rotherham S63 7RA Tel: 01709 877524; Woodfalls, 14 New Road, Wath-upon-Dearne, Rotherham S63 7LQ Tel: 01709 877900 — BM 1978 Soton.; MRCGP 1982. GP Princip.; GP Tutor Continuing Professional Developm. Socs: BMA & Soc. Med. & Dent. Hypn. Prev: GP Trainee Rotherham; Ho. Phys. Gen. Hosp. Poole Dorset; Ho. Surg. Roy. S. Hants. Hosp. Soton.

POLKINGHORNE

POLKINGHORNE, Kevan Roy 109A Chiswick High Road, Chiswick, London W4 2ED — MB ChB 1994 Auckland.

POLKINHORN, John Skewes Dr Polkinhorn and Partners, The Surgery, Boyden Close, Nunnery Green, Wickhambrook, Newmarket CB8 8XU Tel: 01440 820140 Fax: 01440 820534; Jack's Cottage, Ousden, Newmarket CB8 8TN Tel: 01638 500483 — MB BChir 1972 Camb.; FRCGP 1999; MB Camb. 1972, BChir 1971; MRCGP 1976; DCH Eng. 1975; DObst RCOG 1974. (Guy's)

POLKINHORN, Mary Ethna Newmarket Road Surgery, 125 Newmarket Road, Cambridge CB5 8HA Tel: 01223 364116 Fax: 01223 366088; Jack's Cottage, Ousden, Newmarket CB8 8TN Tel: 01638 500483 — MB Camb. 1974, BChir 1973; MRCGP 1986. (King's Coll. Hosp.)

POLL, David James Riversdale, 59 Bridge St., Belper, Derby DE56 1AY Tel: 0177 382 2386 — MB BS 1980 Lond.; BSc (Hons.) Immunol. Lond. 1977, MB BS 1980; MRCGP 1986; DRCOG 1983; Cert. Family Plann. JCC 1985. GP Belper, Derbysh.

POLLACK, Jonathan Stockbridge Village Health Centre, The Withens, Liverpool L28 1NL; 33 Rockbourne Avenue, Liverpool L25 4TQ Tel: 0151 428 1007 — MB BS 1969 Newc.; MRCGP 1975; DObst RCOG 1972.

POLLAK, Benno Beech Cottage, Gibson Hill, London SW16 3EP Tel: 020 8670 3241 — MRCS Eng. LRCP Lond. 1949; FRCGP 1977. (Leeds) Emerit. Clin. Assoc. Maudsley Hosp. Prev: Clin. Tutor (Gen. Pract.) St. Thos. Hosp. Med. Sch. Lond.; Hon. Clin. Assoc. Bethlem Roy. Maudsley Hosp.; Clin. Asst. Bethlem Roy. Maudsley Hosp.

POLLAK, Thomas Edward 30 Thames Rise, Kettering NN16 9JL — MB ChB 1976 Sheff.

POLLARD, Alfred James Department Radiology, Stepping Hill Hospital, Stockport SK2 7JE; 41 Sevenoaks Avenue, Heaton Moor, Stockport SK4 4AU — MB ChB 1974 Manch.; FRCR 1982. Cons. Radiol. Stockport HA.

POLLARD, Andrew John Department of Paediatrics, University of Oxford, John Radcliffe Hospital, Oxford OX3 9DU Tel: 01865 221068 Fax: 01865 221068 Email: andrew.pollard@paediatrics.ox.ac.uk; Tel: 01865 725935 Email: ajpollard@compuserve.com — MB BS 1989 Lond.; BSc Lond. 1986; MRCP (UK) 1993; MRCPCH 1996; PhD Lond. 1999; DIC Imperial Coll. 1999. (St. Bart's Med. Sch. Lond.) Sen. Lect. in Paediat. Infec.s Dis.s, Univ. of Oxf., Oxf.; Hon. Cons. Paediat., Univ. of Oxf., Oxf. Prev: SpR (Paed. Int. Care) St. Mary's Hosp. Lond.; Action Research Train. Fell. & Hon. NHS Regist. (Paediat. Infec. Dis.) St. Mary's Hosp. Lond.; Regist. (Paed. Infec. Dis.) St. Mary's Hosp. Lond.

***POLLARD, Andrew Michael** Old Farm House, High St., South Cerney, Cirencester GL7 5UG — MB ChB 1998 Leeds.

POLLARD, Professor Brian James Department of Anaesthesia, Manchester Royal Infirmary, Oxford Road, Manchester M13 9WL Tel: 0161 276 8650 Fax: 0161 273 5685 Email: brian.pollard@man.ac.uk; Dial House, 1 Pownall Avenue, Bramhall, Stockport SK7 2HE — MB ChB 1977 Sheff.; MD Sheff. 1992; BPharm Lond. 1971; FFA RCS Eng. 1981. (Sheffield) Prof. Anaesth. Univ. Manch.; Hon. Cons. Anaesth. Manch. Roy. Infirm. & UHSM; Dep. Edr. Europ. Jl. Anaesthsiol.; Edr. Curr. Anaesth. & Critical Care. Socs: Anaesth. Res. Soc.; Assn. Anaesth. GB & Irel.; Roy. Soc. Med. (Sect. Anaesth.). Prev: Sen. Lect. (Anaesth.) Univ. Manch.

POLLARD, Brian John Wycliffe Surgery, Elliott Road, Plymouth PL4 9NH Tel: 01752 660648 Fax: 01752 261468 — MB ChB 1977 Birm.

POLLARD, Brian John (retired) Mullion Court, Linton Hill, Linton, Maidstone ME17 4AP Tel: 01622 743330 Email: bpol187976@cs.com — MB BS Lond. 1954; MRCGP 1977.

POLLARD, Claire Elizabeth 29Greenbank Road, Sefton Park, Liverpool L18 1HG Tel: 0151 734 1168 Fax: 0151 734 5147 — MB ChB 1990 Liverp.; MRCGP (Distinc.) 1996; DRCOG 1993. (Liverp.) p/t GP Princip. Liverp.

POLLARD, Corinna Mary 49 Selcroft Road, Purley CR8 1AJ — MB BS 1974 Lond.; FRCP Lond. 1995; MRCP (UK) 1979; FRCPath 1996, M 1983. Cons. Haemat. Mayday Hosp. Croydon. Socs: Brit. Soc. Haematol. Prev: Sen. Regist. (Haemat.) St. Geo. Hosp. Lond.

POLLARD, Danuta Elzbieta Kolodziejska (retired) Department of Child & Family Psychiatry, Peterborough District Hospital, Thorpe Road, Peterborough PE3 6DA — MB BCh BAO 1954 Dub.; MRCPsych. 1971.

POLLARD, David Edward 6 Darley Avenue, Gatley, Cheadle SK8 4PQ — MB ChB 1994 Sheff.

POLLARD, David John Kingsclere Medical Practice, Kingsclere, Newbury RG20 5QX Tel: 01635 296000 Fax: 01635 299 282; Mote Cottage, The Dell, Kingsclere, Newbury RG20 5NL Tel: 01635 297124 Email: davidpollard@cs.com — MB ChB 1972 Aberd.; MRCGP 1980; Dip. IMC RCS Ed. 1992; DObst RCOG 1976. GP Princip.

POLLARD, Hugh Charles 64 The Brow, Widley, Waterlooville PO7 5DA Tel: 023 92 321184 Email: juliandhugh@thenebion.fsnet.co.uk — MB BS Lond. 1986; DRCOG 1991. (St. Mary's Hospital Medical School London)

POLLARD, Ian Geoffrey (retired) — MB ChB 1969 Manch.; MRCGP 1977.

POLLARD, Ilene Isabel (retired) Broadgate, Storrs Park, Bowness on Windermere, Windermere LA23 3LT Tel: 015394 43097 — MB ChB Leeds 1948.

POLLARD, John Geoffrey 2 Fore Street, Hessenford, Torpoint PL11 3HP — MB ChB 1987 Bristol.

POLLARD, Mr John Patrick Horton Hospital, Oxford Road, Banbury OX16 9AL Tel: 01295 275500 Fax: 01295 229055; Berry Hill House, Berry Hill Road, Adderbury, Banbury OX17 3HF Tel: 01295 810534 — MB BChir 1969 Camb.; MA 1967, MChir Camb. 1983; FRCS Eng. 1973. (Camb.) Cons. Orthop. Surg. Horton Hosp., Oxf. Radcliffe NHS Trust. Socs: Fell. BOA. Prev: Sen. Regist. (Orthop. Surg.) Middlx. Hosp., Centr. Middlx. Hosp. & Roy. Nat. Orthop. Hosp.; Regist. (Orthop. Surg.) Bath Health Dist.

POLLARD, Kenneth Philip South Tyneside District Hospital, Harton Lane, South Shields NE34 0PL Tel: 0191 454 8888 Fax: 0191 202 4145 — MB ChB 1977 Sheff.; FRCPath 1996. Cons. Histopath. S. Tyneside Dist. Hosp.

POLLARD, Kirsten Jane 35 Imperial Road, Beeston, Nottingham NG9 1FN — MB ChB 1993 Leic.

POLLARD, Maria Ann Western Road Surgery, 41 Western Road, Billericay CM12 9DX Tel: 01277 658117 Fax: 01277 658119 — MB BS 1986 Lond.

POLLARD, Martin, Squadron Ldr. RAF Med. Br. Retd. High Street Surgery, High Street, Willingham by Stow, Gainsborough DN21 5JZ Tel: 01427 788277 Fax: 01427 787630; Heywoods House, Willingham Road, Kexby, Gainsborough DN21 5ND — MB BS 1971 Lond.; MRCS Eng. LRCP Lond. 1971; MRCGP 1977 (Lond. Hosp.). GP Willingham. Prev: Sen. Med. Off. RAF Marham; Sen. Med. Off. Episkopi Garrison, Cyprus.

POLLARD, Michael Fallon and Partners, 1 Houghton Lane, Shevington, Wigan WN6 8ET Tel: 01257 253311 Fax: 01257 251081 — MB ChB 1986 Manch.; BSc (Hons.) Physiol. Manch. 1983; MRCGP 1990; T(GP) 1991; DRCOG 1989. Scheme Organiser Wigan VTS. Prev: Trainee GP Bolton VTS; SHO (Med. & Paediat.) Wigan Infirm.; SHO (O & G) Billinge Hosp.

POLLARD, Neil Adrian The Hops, 9 Leys Farm, Tarrington, Hereford HR1 4EX — MB BS 1984 Lond.; MRCP (UK) 1990.

POLLARD, Rachel Clare 12 Purcell Road, Marston, Oxford OX3 0HB Tel: 01865 725935 Fax: 01865 725935 — MB BChir 1988 Camb.; FRCA 1993; DA (UK) 1990. Regist. (Anaesth.) John Radcliffe Hosp. Oxf. Prev: Regist. Rotat. (Anaesth.) Centr. Birm. Hosp.; SHO (Anaesth.) Leicester Gen. Hosp.; SHO (A & E & Cardiothoracic Surg.) Leicester.

POLLARD, Richard Charles Hayward (retired) 102 Looseleigh Lane, Crownhill, Plymouth PL6 5HH Tel: 01752 774033 — MB BS Lond. 1959. Prev: GP Plymouth.

POLLARD, Mr Roy North Tyneside General Hospital, North Shields NE29 8NH Tel: 0191 596660 Fax: 0191 293 2578; 5 Camp Terrace, North Shields NE29 0NE Tel: 0191 259 5823 Fax: 0191 280 1113 Email: roypollard@freenet.co.uk — MB ChB 1961 Leeds; FRCS Ed. 1968; FRCS (Eng) 1996. (Leeds) Cons. Surg. N. Tyneside Dist. Gen. Hosp. N. Shields. Prev: Sen. Regist. (Surg.) Guy's Hosp. Lond.

POLLARD, Stella Marguerite 69 Forest Lane, Kirklevington, Yarm TS15 9NE Tel: 01642 780941 — BChir 1969 Camb.; MB; MRCPath 1987, M 1975. (Camb. & St. Geo.) Cons. Histopath. & Cytol. Hartlepool Gen. Hosp. Prev: Lect. in Path. Univ. Nottm.; Regist. (Path.) Radcliffe Infirm. Oxf.; Ho. Phys. St. Geo. Hosp. Lond.

POLLARD, Mr Stephen Geoffrey Department of Surgery, St James's University Hospital, Leeds LS9 7TF Tel: 0113 243 3144;

Lime Kiln House, Woodhall, Linton, Wetherby LS22 4HZ Tel: 01937 587706 — MB BS 1981 Lond.; MA Camb. 1993; BSc Lond. 1978, MS 1994, MB BS 1981; FRCS Lond. 1986. Cons. Surg. St. Jas. Hosp. Leeds; Regent & Ethicon Trav. Schol.. 1990; Vis. Asst. Prof. Surg. Indianapolis Univ. Hosp. USA. Prev: Clin. Lect. & Sen. Regist. (Surg.) Addenbrooke's Hosp. Camb.; E. Anglian Research Fell.; Regist. Rotat. Addenbrookes Hosp. Camb.

POLLARD, Valerie Audrey Clipstone Health Centre, First Avenue, Clipstone, Mansfield NG21 9DA Tel: 01623 626132 Fax: 01623 420578 — MB ChB 1980 Sheff.; DRCOG 1984. Exec. Comm. Mem. Newark & Sherwood PCT.

POLLEN, Mr Andrew Gerald (retired) 313 Lauderdale Tower, Barbican, London EC2Y 8NA Tel: 020 7588 5434 — MB BS 1946 Lond.; FRCS Eng. 1954. Prev: Cons. Orthop. & Traum. Surg. Bedford Gen. Hosp.

POLLEN, Roseanna Mary Bethnal Green Health Centre, 60 Florida Street, London E2 6LL Tel: 020 7739 4837 Fax: 020 7729 2190; 62 Malvern Road, London E2 3LJ — MB BS 1979 Lond.; MRCGP 1984; MSc BEcon Lond. 1995. (St. Bartholomew's Hospital) Socs: Inst. Psychosexual Med. Prev: Trainee GP Whipps Cross Hosp. Lond. VTS.

POLLER, David Nigel Department of Histopathology, Queen Alexandra Hospital, Cosham, Portsmouth PO6 3LY Tel: 023 92 286000 Fax: 023 92 286493 — MB ChB Liverp. 1984; MRCPath 1994; MD 2000. Cons. Histopath. Portsmouth Acute Hosps. NHS Trust.

POLLER, Professor Leon School of Biological Sciences, Stopford Building, The university of Manchester, Oxford Road, Manchester M13 9PT Tel: 0161 27533161 Fax: 0161 275 5316 Email: ecaa@man.ac.uk — MB ChB 1951 Manch.; DSc Manch. 1980, MD 1957; MRCS Eng. LRCP Lond. 1951; FRCPath 1973, M 1964. (Manch.) Co-ordinator EC Concerted Action on Anticoagulation of the E.C.; Hon. Prof. Univ. Manch.1989-; Co-Chairm. Standardisation Subcomm. ISHT Anticoagulant Contr.; Mem. Counc. ICSH/ICTH Expert Panel on APTT Standardisation. Socs: Assn. Clin. Pathols.; Brit. Soc. Haematol.; Internat. Soc. Haematol. Prev: Dir. Nat. (UK) Ref. Laborat. Anticoagulant Reagents & Contr. (WHO Centre) & Haemat. Withington Hosp. Manch.; Resid. (Clin. Path.) & Cons. Haemat. Withington Hosp. Manch.; Maj. RAMC.

POLLERT, Jan (retired) 4 Glenalmond House, Manor Fields, Putney, London SW15 3LP — MD 1939 Prague. Prev: Med. Asst. Lewisham Chest Clinic Lond.

POLLET, Mr John Eugene Halton General Hospital, Hospital Way, Runcorn WA7 2DA Tel: 01928 714567 Fax: 01928 753440 Email: jep@j_pollet.demon.co.uk — MB ChB 1972 Aberd.; PhD Aberd. 1984, MD 1985, BMedBiol 1968, MB ChB 1972; FRCS Ed. 1977. Cons. Surg. Halton Hosp. Mersey RHA. Prev: Regist. & Sen. Regist. (Gen. Surg.) Grampian HB; Lect. (Path.) Univ. Dundee.

POLLET, Sheena Margaret Thorn Road Clinic, Thorn Road, Runcorn WA7 5HQ Tel: 01928 575073 Fax: 01928 576969; Cherry Tree Farm, Kingswood, Frodsham, Warrington WA6 6HX Tel: 01928 740296 — MB ChB 1972 Aberd.; BMedBiol (Hons.) Aberd. 1969; FRCPsych 1997; MRCPsych 1979; Dip. Psychother. Aberd. 1983. (Aberdeen) Cons. Psychother. Halton Gen. Hosp. NHS Trust; Lect. & Acad. Tutor (Psychother.) Liverp. Socs: Merseyside Psychother. Inst.

POLLING, Michael Roy James Street Surgery, 2 James Street, Boston PE21 8RF Tel: 01205 362556 Fax: 01205 359050 — MB ChB 1970 Leeds; MRCS Eng. LRCP Lond. 1970; MRCGP 1977; MLCOM 1981. Socs: Brit. Osteop. Assn.; Soc. Orthop. Med.; Brit. Med. & Dent. Hypn. Soc.

POLLINGTON, Bruce Ian Marsham Street Surgery, 1 Marsham Street, Maidstone ME14 1EW Tel: 01622 752615/756129 — MB ChB 1992 Manch.

POLLINGTON, Graham David Auchtermuchty Health Centre, 12 Carswell Wynd, Auchtermuchty, Cupar KY14 7AW Tel: 01337 828262 Fax: 01337 828986; Taybank, Cupar Road, Cupar KY14 Tel: 01337 840541 — MB ChB 1990 Dundee. Clin. Asst. (A & E) Qu. Margt. NHS Trust Dunfermline. Prev: SHO (A & E Gen. Med. & Palliat. Care) Qu. Margt. NHS Trust Dunfermline.

***POLLINGTON, Tamara** Taybank, Cupar Road, Newburgh, Cupar KY14 6HA — MB ChB 1993 Dundee.

POLLITT, Christine Ormskirk & District General Hospital, Wigan Road, Ormskirk L39 2AZ — MB BS 1991 Newc.

POLLITT, Geoffrey (retired) c/o Lloyds Bank, 14 Church St., Sheffield S1 1HP — MRCS Eng. LRCP Lond. 1945; FRCPsych 1979, M 1971; DMJ (Clin.) Soc. Apoth. Lond. 1966; DPM Eng. 1958. Prev: Surg. Cdr. RN.

POLLITT, John Deryk (retired) Leahurst, 49 Park Avenue, Dover CT16 1HD — MB BS Lond. 1950; MD Lond. 1959; FRCP Lond. 1969, M 1954; FRCPsych 1971; DPM Eng. 1955. Prev: Phys. i/c Dept. Psychol. Med. St. Thos. Hosp. Lond.

***POLLITT, Michael John Kensey** 96 Caerleon Road, Newport NP19 7GZ — MB BCh 1997 Wales.

POLLITT, Norman Travers (retired) 18 Curzon Place, Eastcote, Pinner HA5 2TQ Tel: 020 8868 4082 Email: ntp@waitrose.com — MB BS Lond. 1952; MRCS Eng. LRCP Lond. 1952; MRCGP 1961. Prev: Phys. BUPA Med. Centre Lond. & Bushey.

POLLITT, Peter Geoffrey Harris Tomlin (retired) Sharrow, Bidford Road, Cleeve Prior, Evesham WR11 5LQ — MB ChB 1944 Birm. JP. Prev: Med. Asst. (A & E) Walsall Gen. Hosp.

POLLITT, William Alfred (retired) Touchstone, Greenfields Lane, Rowton, Chester CH3 6AU Tel: 01244 335689 — MRCS Eng. LRCP Lond. 1950; FFCM 1978, M 1974; DPH Liverp. 1953. Prev: Dist. Med. Off. Chester HA.

POLLITT, Yvonne S. A. F. E. Family Planning Office, Seventrees Clinic, Baring St., Greenbank, Plymouth PL4 8NF Tel: 01753 389531; Langmans Quarry, West Buckland, Thurlestone, Kingsbridge TQ7 3AG Tel: 01548 561713 — MB BS Lond. 1964; MRCS Eng. LRCP Lond. 1964; MFFP 1993. (Middlx.) Med. Head (Family Plann. & Wom. Health Servs.) Plymouth Community Servs. NHS Trust. Prev: Clin. Asst. (Genitourin. Med.) Freedom Fields Hosp. Plymouth; Clin. Asst (Ultrasound) Plymouth Hosps. Trust.

POLLITZER, Melanie Paediatric Department, Royal Berkshire Hospital, Reading RG1 5AN Tel: 0118 9877993 Fax: 0118 9878383 Email: mjpollitzer@doctors.org.uk; Bear Place Farm, Hare Hatch, Reading RG10 9TA Tel: 0118 940 3016 Fax: 0118 940 4487 Email: bearplacefarm@compuserve.com — MB BS 1973 Lond.; DCH Eng. 1976. (Roy. Free Hosp. Lond.) p/t Assoc. Specialist (Paediat.) Roy. Berks. Hosp. Reading. Socs: MRCPCH; Neonat. Soc.

POLLOCK, Mr Alan Victor (retired) Scarborough Hospital, Scarborough YO12 6QL Tel: 01723 368111 Fax: 01723 501692 Email: alan@meded.demon.co.uk — MB ChB 1943 Cape Town; FRCS Ed. 1984; FRCS Eng. 1948. Edr. Curr. Opinion in Surg. Infects.; Edr. Bd. Europ. Jl. Surg. Prev: Hon. Cons. Surg. ScarBoro. Hosp.

POLLOCK, Alexander Chapman West Linton Health Centre, Deanfoot Road, West Linton EH46 7EX Tel: 01968 660808 Fax: 01968 660856; Corra Linn, Medwyn Road, West Linton EH46 7HA Tel: 01968 60691 Fax: 01968 660856 — MB ChB 1970 Glas.; MRCGP 1986. (Glas.) JP.

***POLLOCK, Alison Ann** Stobhill Hospital, 133 Balornock Road, Glasgow G21 3UW Tel: 0141 201 3000; 1 Fern Avenue, Lenzie, Glasgow G66 4LE Tel: 0141 776 1072 — MB ChB 1998 Manch.; MB ChB Manch 1998; BSc Ed. 1996.

POLLOCK, Professor Allyson Mary Flat 1, 20 Streatham Common N. Side, London SW16 3HJ Tel: 0208 769257 — MB ChB 1983 Dundee; FFPath 1996 (UK); BSc (Hons.) Dund 1979; MSc Lond. 1988; MFPHM RCP (UK) 1990. Cons. & Sen. Lect. St. Geo. Med. Sch. Lond.

POLLOCK, Angus James Elliot (retired) Belwood, 3 Seacroft Square, Skegness PE25 3AQ Tel: 01754 767433 — MB ChB 1949 Glas. Prev: Ho. Surg. Roy. Infirm. Glas. & City Matern. Hosp. Carlisle.

POLLOCK, Anne Maclean Dunblane Medical Practice, Well Place, Dunblane FK15 9BQ Tel: 01786 822595 Fax: 01786 825298 — MB ChB 1969 Glas.; MFFP 1993; DObst RCOG 1971. Princip. GP DunbLa..

POLLOCK, Anthony Louis Park Grove Surgery, 94 Park Grove, Barnsley S70 1QE Tel: 01226 282345 — MB ChB 1977 Manchester; MB ChB Manch. 1977. (Manchester) GP Barnsley, S. Yorks.

POLLOCK, Bruce James 96 Moor Lane, Rickmansworth WD3 1LQ — MB BS 1991 Lond.

POLLOCK, Catherine Louise Mountsandel Surgery, 4 Mountsandel Road, Coleraine BT52 1JB Tel: 028 7034 2650 Fax: 028 7032 1000; Macleary Lodge, 9 Macleary Road, Coleraine BT51 3QX — MB BCh BAO 1983 Belf.; MRCGP 1988; DRCOG

POLLOCK

1986. Prev: Clin. Med. Off. Lisburn Health Centre; Trainee GP Ballymena Health Centre VTS.

POLLOCK, Christopher George Holme Farm, Rowley, Little Weighton, Cottingham HU20 3XR Tel: 01482 843578 — MB ChB 1976 Ed.; FFA RCS Eng. 1981. Cons. Anaesth. Hull & E. Yorks. Dist.

POLLOCK, Colin Thomas Stephen Wakefield Health Authority, White Rose House, West Parade, Wakefield WF1 1LT Tel: 01924 213041 Email: colin.pollock@gw.wakeha.northy.nhs.uk; 15 Holray Park, Carlton, Goole DN14 9QP Tel: 01405 860607 Email: pollock1@which.net — MB BChir 1982 Camb.; BA Camb. 1980, MB BChir 1982; MRCGP 1986; MFPHM 1993; MPH Leeds 1991; DRCOG 1985. Med. Dir. (Pub. Health) White Rose Hse. Wakefield.

POLLOCK, Mr David (retired) The Ridge, 26 Radbrook Road, Shrewsbury SY3 9BE Tel: 01743 344397 Email: davjan@zoom.co.uk — MB ChB Glas. 1957; FRCS Glas. 1964; FRCS Ed. 1965; FRCS Eng. 1992. Prev: Sen. Regist. (Surg.) Glas. Roy. Infirm.

POLLOCK, David Josephus Ratmoyle, 96 Moor Lane, Rickmansworth WD3 1LQ Tel: 01923 72361 — MB ChB 1956 Liverp.; BSc (Hons.) Liverp. 1953, MB ChB 1956; FRCPath 1977, M 1965. (Liverp.) Sen. Lect. Path. Inst. Lond. Hosp. Socs: Fell. Roy. Soc. Med. Prev: Sen. Regist. Dept. Histopath. & Regist. Path. Dept. W. Middlx. Hosp.; Isleworth; Regist. Dept. Morbid Anat. Postgrad. Med. Sch. Lond.

POLLOCK, Deborah Marion Pynes Farmhouse, Pitney, Langport TA10 9AG — MB BChir 1962 Camb.; FRCS Ed. 1979; DO RCPSI 1976. (St. Bart.) Prev: Assoc. Specialist (Ophth.) N. Irel. Hosp. Auth.; Regist. St. Geo. Hosp. Lond.; Ho. Phys. & Ho. Surg. Barnet Gen. Hosp.

POLLOCK, Elaine Elizabeth Clarkston Manse, Forrest St., Airdrie ML6 7BE — MB ChB 1983 Glas.; MRCGP 1987. GP Glas. Prev: Clin. Asst. (Colposcopy) Glas. Roy. Infirm.

POLLOCK, Ellen Mary Teresa (retired) 136 Highcross Road, Poulton-le-Fylde FY6 8BX — MB BCh BAO 1920 NUI.

POLLOCK, Estella Gertrude (retired) 7 Greenacre Walk, Southgate, London N14 7DB Tel: 020 8886 0157 — MB BS 1947 Lond.; DCH Eng. 1954. Prev: SCMO Enfield DHA.

POLLOCK, Evelyn Marian Margaret 5 Essex Court, Temple, London EC4Y 9AH Tel: 020 7410 2000 Fax: 020 7410 2011; 21 Thomas More House, Barbican, London EC2Y 8BT Tel: 020 7638 0023 — MB ChB 1978 Ed.; BSc Ed. 1975, MD 1991; FFA RCS Eng. 1983. Dep. Coroner Lond. S. Dist.; Barrister at Law Inner Temple Lond. Socs: BMA; Medico-Legal Soc. Prev: Sen. Regist. (Anaesth.) W.. Infirm. Glas.; Clin. Fell. (Critical Care Med.) Hosp. for Sick Childr. Toronto, Canada; Regist. (Anaesth.) Glas. Roy. Infirm.

POLLOCK, Geoffrey George (retired) 10 Dunstall Road, Wimbledon, London SW20 0HR Tel: 020 8946 9879 — MB BS 1955 Lond.; MRCP Lond. 1968; MRCS Eng. LRCP Lond. 1955; FRCGP 1983; FFA RCS Eng. 1971; DA Eng. 1966; DObst RCOG 1957. Prev: GP Wimbledon.

POLLOCK, George (retired) 238 Holyhead Road, Wellington, Telford TF1 2DZ — MD 1937 Glas.; MB ChB 1932; FRCP Glas. 1979, M 1962. Prev: Ho. Phys. W.. Infirm. Glas. & Roy. Hosp. Sick Childr. Glas.

POLLOCK, George Tullo Department Public Health & Epidemiology, University of Birmingham, Edgbaston, Birmingham B15 2TT Tel: 0121 414 3163 Fax: 0121 414 7878 Email: pollocgt@hsrc1.bham.ac.uk — MB ChB 1953 Aberd.; FFPHM RCP (UK) 1989; FFCM RCP (UK) 1981, M 1974; DPH Aberd. 1957; MD Birm. 1999. (Aberdeen) Hon. Sen. Clin. Lect. (Pub. Health Med.) Univ. Birm. Socs: Fell. Roy. Soc. Med.; BMA. Prev: Vis. Lect. (Pub. Health) Univ. Malta; Cons. Epidemiol. PHLS Communicable Dis. Surveillance Centre; Dir. Pub. Health Coventry HA.

POLLOCK, Henry Bernard (retired) 23 Coach Road, Warton, Carnforth LA5 9PR Tel: 01524 735181 — MB BS 1952 Lond.; DObst RCOG 1954. Prev: GP (Sen. Partner) Morecambe.

POLLOCK, Ian Chase Farm Hospital, The Ridgeway, Enfield EN2 8JL Tel: 020 8967 5902 Fax: 020 8367 3577 Email: childhealth@chasefarmhospital.org.uk — MB BS 1976 Lond.; MRCP 1982; DCH Eng. 1981; DRCOG 1979; FRCPCH 1997. (Lond. Hosp.) Cons. Paediat. Chase Farm Hosp. Enfield; Charm of Paediative & Clin. Managem. Gp. Socs: Brit. Soc. Allergy & Clin. Immunol.; BMA. Prev: Sen. Regist. (Paediat.) St. Geo. Hosp. Lond.; Research Fell. Cardiothoracic Inst. Lond.; Regist. (Paediat.) St. Mary's Hosp. Lond.

POLLOCK, Ilse c/o Stewart, 22 Watling House, 4 Woolwich Common, London SE18 4HP — LRCP 1954 Ed.; LRCP Ed. LRCS Ed. LRFPS Glas. 1954.

POLLOCK, Mr James Campbell Shaw 60 Balshagray Drive, Glasgow G11 7BZ Tel: 0141 339 3944 — MB ChB 1972 Glas.; FRCS Canada 1979; FRCS Glas. 1976. (Glas.) Cons. Cardiac Surg. Roy. Hosp. Sick Childr. Glas. & Glas. Roy. Prev: Sen. Resid. & Fell. Dept. Cardiac Surg. Univ. Toronto; Regist. Glas. Roy. Infirm.; Resid. (Gen. Surg.) St. Luke's Hosp. New York City, U.S.A.

POLLOCK, Janet Elizabeth Bloomfield Medical Centre, 118/120 Bloomfield Road, Blackpool FY1 6JW Tel: 01253 344123 Fax: 01253 349696; 242 Clifton Drive S., St Annes, Lytham St Annes FY8 1NH Tel: 01253 723759 — MB ChB 1985 Glas.; MRCGP 1989; DRCOG 1988; DCH RCPS Glas. 1988. (Glasgow)

POLLOCK, Janet Somerville Shaw Girthill Farm, Warlock Road, Bridge of Weir PA11 3SR — MB ChB 1976 Glas.; FFA RCS Eng. 1982.

POLLOCK, Joan Margaret Macpherson Airdrie Health Centre, Monkscourt Avenue, Airdrie ML6 0JU Tel: 01236 769388 — MB ChB 1961 Glas. Socs: BMA.

POLLOCK, John Alan Morden Lodge, Lion Road, Bexleyheath DA6 8PE Tel: 020 8303 2121 — MB BS 1954 Lond. (Guy's) Prev: Asst. Ho. Surg. Guy's Hosp.; Ho. Phys. Glos. Roy. Infirm. Gloucester; Ho. Phys. Roy. Infirm. Glouc.

POLLOCK, John Alexander Russell (retired) Leckonby Lodge, Blackpool Old Road, Little Eccleston, Preston PR3 0YQ — MB BCh BAO 1953 Dub.

POLLOCK, Mr John Graham (retired) Nuffield and Ross Hall Hospitals, Glasgow Tel: 0141 334 9441/810 3151 — MB ChB Glas. 1958; FRCS Ed. 1965; FRCS Glas. 1965. Prev: Research Regist. (Surg.) W.. Infirm. Glas.

POLLOCK, John Graham 5 Imperial Avenue, Beeston, Nottingham NG9 1EZ Tel: 0115 922 9011 Email: j.pollock@btinternet.com — BM BCh 1992 Oxf.; MA (Med. Sci.) Camb. 1989; MRCP (UK) 1995; FRCR 1998. Regist. (Radiol.) Qu. Med. Centre Nottm. Prev: SHO (Gen. Med.) Qu. Med. Centre Nottm.; Ho. Off. (Med.) John Radcliffe Hosp. Oxf.; Ho. Off. (Surg.) Roy. United Hosp. Bath.

POLLOCK, John Jackson The Grange, Victoria Road, Liversedge Tel: 01924 3929 — MB ChB 1948 Glas. (Univ. Glas.) Ho. Surg. Glas Roy. Infirm. Prev: Ho. Surg. O & G Falkirk & Dist. Roy. Infirm.; ENT Ho. Surg. Roy. Infirm. Glas.

POLLOCK, John Sprott (retired) 5 Park Close, Sprotbrough, Doncaster DN5 7LT Tel: 01302 854997 — MB ChB 1944 Glas.

POLLOCK, Mr Jonathan Robert Dept of Surgical Neurology, National Hospital for Neurology & Neurosurgery, Wueen Square, London WC1N 3BG — BM BCh 1990 Oxf.; FRCS 2000 Ed. (Surg. Neurol.); MA Camb. 1991; FRCS Ed. 1994. Pituitary Research Fell. Socs: Assoc. Mem. Soc. Brit. Neurol. Surgs. Prev: Specialist Regist. Neurosurg.; N. Thames Train. Rotat.

POLLOCK, Karin Janet 173 Newbridge Hill, Bath BA1 3PY Tel: 01225 330728; 27 Gay Street, Bath BA1 2PD Tel: 01225 22911 — MB BCh 1977 Wales.

POLLOCK, Keith Douglas Windsor House Surgery, 2 Corporation Street, Morley, Leeds LS27 9NB Tel: 0113 252 5223 Fax: 0113 238 1262 — MB ChB 1982 Leeds.

POLLOCK, Kenneth McKenzie 15 Mansion Street, Cambuslang, Glasgow G72 7JP — MB ChB 1993 Glas.

POLLOCK, Lucy Elizabeth Department of Histopathology, Kings College Hospital, Denmark Hill, London SE5 9RS — MB BS 1983 Lond.; BA Oxf. 1980; MRCPath 1992. Cons. Histopath. Kings Coll. Hosp. Lond.

POLLOCK, Lucy Mary Drayton Cottage, Drayton, Langport TA10 0LL — MB BChir 1991 Camb.; MRCP Lond. (Trinity Coll. Camb.)

POLLOCK, Marian Ruth The Old Schoolhouse, Station Road, Hatton, Peterhead AB42 7RX — MB ChB 1991 Aberd. SHO (Ophth.) Wolverhampton Eye Infirm.

POLLOCK, Marjory Adela (retired) 9 Downview Crescent, Seacon Road, Ballymoney BT53 — MB BCh BAO Dub. 1947; FFA RCSI 1971; FFA RCS Eng. 1954; DA Eng. 1950. Prev: Cons. Anaesth. S. Belf. Hosp. Gp.

POLLOCK, Myra Welsh Penicuik Health Centre, 37 Imrie Place, Penicuik EH26 8LF Tel: 01968 72612; Corra Linn, Medwyn Road, West Linton EH46 7HA — MB ChB 1970 Glas. (Glas.) Princip. GP

POLWIN

Penicuik. Prev: Jun. Ho. Off. (Med. & Surg.) Stirling Roy. Infirm.; Jun. Ho. Off. (O & G) Stobhill Hosp. Glas.

POLLOCK, Nigel Charles Omagh Health Centre, Mountjoy Road, Omagh BT79 7BA Tel: 028 8224 3521 — MB BCh BAO 1980 Belf.; DRCOG 1983.

POLLOCK, Richard Sayles St George's Surgery, 46A Preston New Road, Blackburn BB2 6AH Tel: 01254 53791 Fax: 01254 697221 Email: richard.pollock@gp_p81058.nhs.uk — MB ChB 1982 Manch.; BSc St. And. 1979; Cert. Family Plann. JCC 1988; MRCGP 1986; DRCOG 1985. Lead GP for Ment. Health & Commiss.ing Blackburn with Darwen Primary Care Trust. Prev: Ho. Phys. & Ho. Surg. Noble's Isle of Man Hosp.; SHO GP VTS Blackburn, Hyndburn & Ribble Valley HA; SHO (Psychiat.) Qu. Pk. Hosp. Blackburn.

POLLOCK, Mr Robin Charles Dept. Orthopaedics, Middlesex Hospital, Martiner St., London W1N 8AA Tel: 0207 636 8333 Email: rob@pollock39.freeserve.co.uk; Tel: 01473 737749, 0207 731 5790 Fax: 01473 737227 — MB BS 1993 Lond.; BSc Lond. 1990; FRCS Eng. 1997. (Univ. Coll. & Middlx. Sch. Med.) Specialist Regist. (Orthop.) The Middlx. & Univ. Coll. Hosps. Lond. Socs: Brit. Orthop. Assn.

POLLOCK, Ronald Matthew MPA Health Strategy & Planning, 105 - 111 Euston St., London NW1 2EW Tel: 020 7388 2454 Fax: 020 7387 2320 Email: 106537.3212@compuserve.com; 67 Scott's Sufferance Wharf, Mill St, London SE1 2EW Tel: 020 7237 3131 Fax: 020 7237 3131 Email: synergyuk@compuserve.com — MB BChir 1957 Camb.; MA; FFCM 1977, M 1972. (Middlx.) Partner, MPA Health Strategy & Plann. Socs: Fell.Roy. Soc. of Med.; (Counc.) Sect. of Epidemiol. & Pub. Health. Prev: Regional Med. Off. & Dir. Pub. Health Med. Oxf. RHA; Dep. Regional Med. Off. Regional Plann. Manager Oxf. RHA; Surg. Regist. Roy. N.. Infirm. Inverness.

POLLOCK, Ruth (retired) 23 Coach Road, Warton, Carnforth LA5 9PR Tel: 01524 735181 — MB ChB 1957 St. And. Prev: SCMO (Child Health) Lancs. AHA.

POLLOCK, Stephen Swinnerton Department of Neurology, Mapother House, Regional Neurosciences Unit ,, De Crespigny Park, Denmark Hill, London SE5 8AZ Tel: 020 7346 5355 — MB BS 1973 Lond.; MD Lond. 1985; FRCP Lond. 1993; MRCP (UK) 1976; MRCS Eng. LRCP Lond. 1973. (Royal Free) Cons. (Neurol.) Kent & Canterbury Acute Hosp. NHS Trust & Regional Neurosci.s Unit King's Coll. Hosp. Healthcare Trust Lond.; Clin. Dir. (Neurol.) King's Health Care Trust. Socs: Fell. Roy. Soc. Med.; Coun. Stroke Assoc.; BMA. Prev: Sen. Regist. (Neurol.) Manch. Roy. Infirm.; Research Asst. (Neurol.) Middlx. Hosp. Lond.; Regist. (Neurol. Sci.s) Roy. Free Hosp. Lond.

POLLOCK, William Cockenzie & Port Seton Health Centre, Avenue Road, Prestonpans EH32 0JL Tel: 01875 812998 Fax: 01875 814421 — MB ChB 1970 Ed.; DObst RCOG 1972.

POLLOCK, Mr William Somerville Thomson Blackpool Victoria Hospital, Whinney Heys Road, Blackpool FY3 8NR Tel: 01253 300000 — MB ChB 1985 Glas.; FRCS Glas. 1991; MRCP (UK) 1989. Cons. Ophth. Surg. Blackpool Vict. Hosp. Prev: Sen. Regist. Rotat. Sunderland, MiddlesBoro. & Newc.; Regist. Rotat. (Ophth.) St. Thos. Hosp. Lond. & Brighton & Canterbury Hosps.; SHO Rotat. (Ophth.) Bristol Eye Hosp.

POLLOK, Antony John 13/1 Rocheid Park, E. Fettes Avenue, Edinburgh EH4 1RU — MB ChB 1979 Ed.

POLLOK, Arthur (retired) Wellwood, Scott St., Galashiels TD1 1DU Tel: 01896 753487 — LRCP LRCS Ed. LRFPS Glas. 1950; MRCGP 1965. Prev: Hosp. Pract. (Geriat.) Borders Gen. Hosp. Melrose.

POLLOK, Richard Charles Goodall Digestive Diseases Research Centre, St. Bart's & Royal London School of Medicine & Dentistry, Turner St., London E1 2AT Tel: 020 7295 7191 Fax: 020 7295 7192 Email: r.c.pollok@mds.qmw.ac.uk — MB BS 1989 Lond.; BSc Lond. 1987; MRCP (UK) 1992; DTM & H Liverp. 1991. Res. Fell. (Gastro.) Wellcome Trust, St. Bart's Hosp. Lond. Socs: RCP. Prev: Regist. (Gastroenterol.) Qu. Mary's Hosp. Lond.; Regist. (Gastroenterol. & HIV Med.) Chelsea & W.m. Hosp. Lond.

POLLOK, William Mowat Aberfoyle Medical Centre, Main Street, Aberfoyle, Stirling FK8 3UX Tel: 01877 382421 Fax: 01877 382718 — MB ChB 1970 Glas.

POLMEAR, Andrew Fraser 20 Sackville Road, Hove BN3 3FF Tel: 01273 778585; 9 Powis Square, Brighton BN1 3HH Tel: 01273 328085 — MB BChir 1971 Camb.; MRCP (UK) 1973; MRCS Eng. LRCP Lond. 1971; FRCGP 1993, M 1978; DObst RCOG 1973. (St. Geo.) Prev: Sen. Med. Off. United Christian Hosp., Hong Kong.; SHO St. Geo. Hosp. Lond.; Ho. Off. Roy. Hants. Co. Hosp. Winchester.

POLNAY, Janet Carole Nottingham City Hospital NHS Trust, Hucknall Road, Nottingham NG5 1PB Tel: 0115 969 1169 Ext: 46809 Fax: 0115 962 7715; 41A Valley Road, West Bridgford, Nottingham NG2 6HG Tel: 0115 923 3718 Fax: 0115 974 3666 Email: janetpolnay@hotmail.com — MB BS 1975 Lond.; BSc 1972 (Hons) Lond.; MA 1999 Leics. (Lond. Hosp. & St. Mary's) p/t Assoc. Specialist in Paediat. (Cystic Fibrosis & Child Protec.) & named Doctor in Child Protec., Notts. City Hosp. NHS Trust, Notts. Socs: Nottm. M-C Soc. Prev: Sen. Doctor Child Protec. (Primary Care) Nottm. Community NHS Trust; Med. Adviser Notts. FHSA; Princip. (Gen. Pract.) Nottm.

POLNAY, Professor Leon Division of Child Health, School of Human Development, Floor E East Block, Hospital Queens Medical Centre, Nottingham NG7 2UH Tel: 0115 970 9255 Fax: 0115 970 9382 Email: leon.polnay@nottingham.ac.uk; Tel: 0115 923 3718 — MB BS 1971 Lond.; BSc Lond. 1968; FRCP Lond. 1988; MRCP (UK) 1974; DObst RCOG 1975; DCH Eng. 1974; FRCPCH 1997. (Lond. Hosp.) Prof. (Community Paediat.) Univ. Nottm. Socs: Fell. Brit. Assn. Comm. Child Health; RCP Lond.; Roy. Coll. Paediat. & Child Health. Prev: Clin. Med. Off. S. Hammersmith Health Dist.; Hon. Lect. (Paediat.) Char. Cross Hosp. Med. Sch.; SHO (Paediat.) W. Middlx. Hosp. Isleworth.

POLSON, David William Hope Hospital, Eccles Old Road, Salford M6 8HD Tel: 0161 789 7373 Fax: 0161 787 5475; 31 New Forest Road, Manchester M23 9JT Tel: 0161 969 2057 — MB BS 1980 Lond.; MRCOG 1987; MD Lond. 1990. (St. Mary's) Cons. (O & G) Salford Roy. Hosps NHS Trust, Salford. Socs: Brit. Fertil. Soc.; ESHRE. Prev: Sen. Regist. (O & G) Manch.; Clin. Research Fell. Monash Med. Centre, Australia; SHO (Obst.& Gyn.) St. Mary's & Qu. Charlotte's Hosps. Lond.

POLSON, Gertrude Mary (retired) 16 Tewit Well Road, Harrogate HG2 8JE Tel: 01423 503434 — MB ChB Leeds 1950; BSc (Hons.) Leeds 1947; MFCM RCP (UK) 1974; DObst RCOG 1953. Prev: SCMO Harrogate HA.

POLSON, Hamish William Morrison Leith Mount, 46 Ferry Road, Edinburgh EH6 4AE Tel: 0131 554 0558 Fax: 0131 555 6911; 16 Blinkbonny Terrace, Edinburgh EH4 3NA Tel: 0131 332 3227 — MB ChB 1962 Ed.; DObst RCOG 1965. (Ed.) Socs: BMA & Soc. Occupat. Med.

POLSON, Rex James Solihull Hospital, Lode Lane, Solihull B91 2JL Tel: 0121 424 4549 Fax: 0121 424 4549 — MB BS Lond. 1979; BSc Lond. 1976, MD 1990; FRCP Lond. 1996; MRCP (UK) 1983. (St. Mary's) Cons. Phys. (Gastroenterol.) Birm. Heartlands & Solihull NhS Trust; Hon. Sen. Lect., Univ. of Birm. Socs: Brit. Soc. Gastroenterol.; Brit. Ass. Study Liver.; Fell. of Roy. Coll. of Phys.s. Prev: Sen. Regist. Rotat. (Gen. Med. & Gastroenterol.) Centr. Middlx. Hosp. & St. Mary's Hosp. Lond.; Clin. Research Fell. (Liver Unit) King's Coll. Hosp. Lond.; SHO & Regist. Rotat. (Med.) Lond. Hosp.

POLSON, Richard Gordon Osborn Clinic, Osborn Road, Fareham PO16 7ES Tel: 01329 288331 — MB BS 1982 Lond.; MRCPsych 1989. Cons. Psychiat. Portsmouth Healthcare Trust. Prev: Sen. Regist. (Psychiat.) St. Jas. Hosp. Portsmouth; Regist. (Psychiat.) Friern Hosp. Lond.

POLTOCK, Tracy Louise 1 Manor House Lane, Yardley, Birmingham B26 1PE Tel: 0121 743 2273 Fax: 0121 722 2037; 14 Swinbrook Way, Shirley, Solihull B90 3LZ — MB ChB 1986 Sheff. (Sheff.) Socs: BMA. Prev: Trainee GP/SHO Mold VTS; SHO (Psychiat.) Arrowe Pk. Hosp.; SHO (O & G) Wrexham Maelor Hosp.

POLURI, Ram Mohan 3 Eson Wood Road, Whiston, Prescot L35 3QR Tel: 0151 426 8499 — MB BS 1983 Nagarjuna; MD (Obst. & Gyn.) Nagarjuna 1983, MB BS 1979, DGO 1982; LRCP LRCS Ed. LRCPS Glas. 1985.

POLWIN, Philip John Stephen The Surgery, Roman Way, Billingshurst RH14 9QZ Tel: 01403 782931 Fax: 01403 785505 — MB BS 1978 Lond.; Cert. Aviation Med. 1993; Cert. Family Plann. JCC 1982; DRCOG 1982. (Lond.) Prev: Trainee GP Portsmouth VTS; SHO (A & E) Qu. Alexandra Hosp. Portsmouth; Ho. Surg. Qu. Mary's Hosp. for the E. End Lond.

POLWIN, Stephen John Sidney, RD (retired) 18 Lower Bere Wood, Waterlooville PO7 7NQ — MB BCh 1950 Wales; BSc Wales

POLYCHRONIS, 1947; MRCGP 1974; Cert Contracep. & Family Plann. RCOG; RCGP & Family Plann. Assn. 1975; DObst RCOG 1952. Prev: Princip. GP Waterlooville.

POLYCHRONIS, Andreas Guy's Hospital, London SE1 9RT Tel: 020 7955 5000; 277 Camberwell New Road, London SE5 0TF — MB BCh 1995 Wales. SHO (Gen. Med.) Guy's Hosp. Lond.

POMERANCE, Ariela (retired) 42 Davenham Avenue, Northwood HA6 3HQ Tel: 01923 22773 — MRCS Eng. LRCP Lond. 1951; MD Lond. 1958, MB BS 1951; MRCPath 1970. Cons. Histopath. Harefield & Mt. Vernon Laborat. N.wood.

POMEROY, Ann 10 Tivoli Road, Cheltenham GL50 2TG Tel: 01242 233168 Fax: 01242 255658 — MB BS 1972 Lond.; MRCS Eng. LRCP Lond. 1972. (St. Mary's) Assoc. Specialist (Dermat.) Gloucester Roy. Hosp., Cheltenham Gen. Hosp. & Stroud Gen. Hosp.

POMEROY, Richard Thomas, MBE The Medical Centre, Craig Croft, Chelmsley Wood, Birmingham B37 7TR Tel: 0121 770 5656 Fax: 0121 779 5619; 22 The Cricketers, Meriden Road, Hampton in Arden, Solihull B92 6BT Tel: 01675 443663 Fax: 0121 779 5619 — MB BCh BAO 1965 NUI; FRCGP 1987, M 1973; DObst RCOG 1966. Socs: BMA. Prev: Ho. Off. Gen. Hosp. Stratford-on-Avon & Manor Matern. Hosp. Walsall.

POMEROY, William Shubrook The Oaks, Nightingale Way, Swanley BR8 7UP Tel: 01322 668775 Fax: 01322 668010 — MB ChB 1975; DCH London; MRCGP UK. (UCT Cape Town, South Africa) GP. Socs: BMA.

POMFRET, Steven Mark The Knoll Surgery Partnership, 46 High Street, Frodsham, Warrington WA6 7HF Tel: 01928 733249 Fax: 01928 739367; 29 Ashlands, Frodsham, Warrington WA6 6RG — BM 1987 Soton.; MRCGP 1991; DRCOG 1991.

POMIRSKA, Maria Bernadeta 61 Lower Redland Road, Redland, Bristol BS6 6SR — MB ChB 1982 Birm.

POMPA, Peter Anthony Philip (retired) 5 Haslar Crescent, Waterlooville PO7 6DB — MB BS Lond. 1954; MRCS Eng. LRCP Lond. 1954; DObst. RCOG 1956; DA Eng. 1957; MRCGP 1965. Prev: Dep. Med. Dir. Lederle Laborats.

POMPHREY, Elizabeth O'Hara Trust Research Office, 4th Floor, Queen Elizabeth Building, 10 Alexandra Parade, Royal Infirmary, Glasgow G31 2ER Tel: 0141 211 4587 Fax: 0141 553 2558; The Gardeners House, Formakin, Bishopton PA7 5NX — MB ChB 1963 Glas.; DObst RCOG 1965. (Glas.) Research & Developm. Manager Glas. Roy. Infirm. NHS & Univ. Trust. Prev: Clin. Research Fell. (Path., Biochem. & Med. Cardiol.) Univ. Glas.; Clin. Research Asst. (Cardiol.) Univ. Glas.; Med. Off. (Cytol.) Gtr. Glas. HB.

POMSON, Hyman Robert 38 South Grove House, South Grove, London N6 6LR — MB BS 1940 Lond. (Char. Cross) Prev: Ho. Surg. Char. Cross Hosp. & Bolingbroke Hosp. Lond.; Res. Surg. Off. P. of Wales Hosp. Plymouth.

***PONCIA, James Robert** 15 Durham Road, London N2 9DP — MB ChB 1994 Birm.

PONCIA, John 26 Eccleston Street, London SW1W 9PY Tel: 020 7730 2828; 8 Laxford House, Cundy St, London SW1W 9JU Tel: 020 7730 9365 Fax: 020 7823 6195 — MB ChB 1961 Ed.; MRCPsych 1972; DPM Eng. 1965. (Ed.) Indep. Cons. Psychotherapist Lond.; Cons. Psychiat. Florence Nightingale Hosp.s Lond. Socs: BMA; Roy. Coll Psychiat. Prev: Cons. Psychotherapist BRd.moor Hosp. Crowthorne; Psychotherapist & Chief Asst. W.m. Hosp. Lond.; Regist. (Psychiat.) St. Geo. Hosp. Lond.

***POND, Eleanor Zoe** 52 Brocco Bank, Sheffield S11 8RR — MB ChB 1997 Bristol.

POND, John Bellingham (retired) Dromore, 10 Granville Road, Walmer, Deal CT14 7LU Tel: 01304 372977 — MB BChir 1955 Camb.; MA Camb. 1955; MRCS Eng. LRCP Lond. 1954; DObst RCOG 1957. Prev: Clin. Asst. (Orthop.) Kent & Canterbury Hosp. & Vict. Hosp. Deal.

POND, Margaret Helen (retired) 38 Strand Court, The Strand, Topsham, Exeter EX3 0AZ Tel: 01392 873189 — MB BChir Camb. 1945; MA Camb. 1946, MD 1953; MRCS Eng. LRCP Lond. 1946. Prev: Clin. Asst. (Diabetic) King's Coll. Hosp. Lond.

POND, Michael Neil Lynfield, 9 Malvern Road, Chellow Dene, Bradford BD9 6AR — MB BS 1986 Lond.; MA Camb. 1987, BA 1983; MRCP (UK) 1990. Regist. (Chest Med.) Glenfield Hosp. Leicester. Socs: Brit. Thorac. Soc. Prev: Clin. Fell. Adult Cystic Fibrosis Unit Seacroft Hosp. Leeds.

PONDA, Bipin Gatubhai (retired) 32 Beeston Drive, Winsford CW7 1ER Tel: 01606 861201 Email: bsponda@hotmail.com — MB BS 1960 Bombay; DTM & H Liverp. 1963. Private Pratise; GP Locum work. Prev: Regist. (Med.) S. Chesh. Hosp. Gp.

PONDER, Professor Bruce Anthony John Department of Oncology, Addenbrooke's Hospital, Hills Road, Cambridge CB2 2QQ Tel: 01223 336900 Fax: 01223 336902 Email: bajp@mole.bio.cam.ac.uk; 43 High Street, Cottenham, Cambridge CB4 8SA Tel: 01954 252163 Fax: 01954 252103 — MB 1969 Camb.; MB BChir Camb. 1969; PhD Lond. 1977; MA Camb. 1972; FRCP 1988. (Camb. & St. Thos.) CRC Prof. Clin. Oncol. Univ. Camb.; Dir. Cancer Research Campaign Human Cancer Genetics Research Gp.; Gibb Fell. CRC; Fell. Jesus Coll. Camb.; Hon. Cons. Phys. Addenbrooke's Hosp. Camb.; Co-Dir. Strangeways Research Laborat. Socs: (Ex-Treas.) Brit. Assn. Cancer Research; Fell. Acad. Med. Sc.; Amer. Soc. Human Genetics. Prev: Prof. Human Cancer Genetics Univ. Camb.; Head Sect. Human Cancer Genetics Inst. Cancer Research; Reader (Human Cancer Genetics) Univ. Lond.

PONDES, Sandra 393 Archway Road, Highgate, London N6 4ER — MB BS 1969 Adelaide.

***PONNAMPALAM, Joanna Sharmila** 4 Whitehall Road, Sittingbourne ME10 4HB — MB BS 1994 Lond.

PONNAMPALAM, Mr Mark Saundarasingam Tower Hamlets Racial Equality Council, 45-55 Commercial Street, London E1 6BD Tel: 020 7537 3666; PO Box 35257, London E1 7WE — MB BS Lond. 1960; FRCSC 1974; FRCS Eng. 1972; FRCS Ed. 1971; LMCC 1974. (St. Bart. Hosp. Med. Coll.) GP Non-Princip.; Co-ordinator UK Counc. Human Rights; Assoc. Internat. Federat. Surg. Coll; Specialist Cert. (Gen. Surg.) RCSC. Socs: Fell. Roy. Soc. Med.; FICS. Prev: Regist. Rotat. (Surg.) N.. Irel. Hosps. Auth.; Sen. Resid. W.m. Hosp. Ontario, Canada; Ho. Surg. St. John's Hosp. Chelmsford.

PONNAMPALAVANAR, Anusha 26 Chepstow Rise, Croydon CR0 5JB — MB BS 1996 Lond.

PONNAPPA, Muruvanda Aiyappa Yiewsley Health Centre, 20 High St., Yiewsley, West Drayton UB7 8DP — MB BS 1964 Mysore.

PONSFORD, Joan Margaret (retired) 17 Buttsfield Lane, E. Hoathly, Lewes BN8 6EE Tel: 0182 584615 — LRCP LRCS 1949 Ed.; LRCP LRCS Ed. LRFPS Glas. 1949; DObst RCOG 1952; DPH Lond. 1961. Clin. Med. Off. E. Herts. AHA. Prev: SHO Pk. Hosp. Davyhulme.

PONSFORD, John Richard c/o C5 Ward, Walsgrave Hospital, Coventry — MB BS 1969 Lond.; BSc (Physiol.) Lond. 1965, MB BS 1969; FRCP Lond. 1987. (St. Geo.) Cons. Neurol. Coventry & Warks. HAs. Prev: Sen. Regist. (Neurol.) St. Mary's Hosp. Lond. & Nat. Hosp. Lond.

PONSFORD, John Steel The Medical Centre, 24-28 Lower Northam Road, Hedge End, Southampton SO30 4FQ Tel: 01489 785722 Fax: 01489 799414; 17 Crowsnest Lane, Boorley Green, Botley, Southampton SO32 2DD — MB BS 1974 Lond.; MRCGP 1978; DRCOG 1977. (Middlx.)

PONSONBY, Christine Elizabeth The Manor Street Surgery, Manor Street, Berkhamsted HP4 2DL Tel: 01442 875935; Street Farm, Bovingdon, Hemel Hempstead HP3 0JR Tel: 01442 834149 — MB BS 1968 Lond.; MRCP (UK) 1973; MRCGP 1986; DCH Eng. 1973. (St Thomas Hosp. Med. Sch.) Prev: Ho. Phys. St. Thos. Hosp. Lond.; SHO Wexham Pk. Hosp.

PONSONBY, William John Carleton The Cottage, Twentyman Court, Penrith Road, Keswick CA12 4HF Tel: 017687 75101 Email: willponsonby@yahoo.com — MB ChB 1986 Birm.; 2002 AFOM; 2002 FRIPH; MBA Durham Univ. 1997; MRCGP 1991. (Birm.) Med. Director Med. Serv.s CIS Region, Internat. SOS; Internat. Med. Support OMS Baku. Socs: BMA; RIPH Fell.; Fac. of Occupat.al Med. (Assoc.). Prev: Gen. Manager Med. Operat.s Azerbaijan.

PONT, Jean Mary Wright (retired) 8 Balmoral Drive, Cambuslang, Glasgow G72 8BG — MB ChB 1962 Glas.; DObst RCOG 1964. Prev: Assoc. Specialist (Ultrasonics) Rutherglen Matern. Hosp.

PONTE, Jose Castelhano Department of Anaesthesia, GKST School of Medicine & Dentistry, Denmark Hill, London SE5 9RS Tel: 020 7346 3358 Fax: 020 7346 3632 — Lic Med 1967 Lisbon; Lic. Med. Lisbon 1967; PhD Bristol 1973; FFA RCS Eng. 1979; DIC Lond. 1971. (Lisbon, Portugal) Sen. Lect., Cons. & Dep. Head Anaesth. GKST Sch. Med. & Dent. Lond. Socs: Roy. Coll. Anaesth.; Physiol. Soc.; Europ. Acad. Anaesthesiol.

PONTE TELLECHEA, Pedro Queen Elizabeth Hospital, Gayton Road, King's Lynn PE30 4ET; The Old Post Office, Lynn Road, Castle Rising, King's Lynn PE31 6AJ — LMS 1990 Navarre.

PONTEFRACT, Carolyn Ann Grove Hill Medical Centre, Kilbride Court, Hemel Hempstead HP2 6AD Tel: 01442 212038; 16 Alzey Gardens, Harpenden AL5 5SZ Tel: 01582 768912 — BM BS Nottm. 1988; MRCGP 1992; DGM RCP Lond. 1990.

***PONTEFRACT, David Robert** 4 The Woodlands, Eccleston Park, Prescot L34 2TN — MB ChB 1996 Ed.

PONTEFRACT, Lesley Gorton Road Family Surgery, 306 Gorton Road, Reddish, Stockport SK5 6RN Tel: 0161 432 1235 Fax: 0161 442 2495; 1 Oaklands Road, Oaklands Wood, Hyde SK14 3DD — MB ChB 1982 Manch.; MRCGP 1986; DRCOG 1986. Prev: SHO (O & G, Psychiat. & Paediat.) Tameside Gen. Hosp. Ashton-under-Lyne.

PONTIN, Mr Alan Roger c/o 18 Whychford Drive, Sawbridgeworth CM21 0HA — MB ChB 1968 Birm.; FRCS Ed. 1973.

PONTIN, Alyson Jane The Minster Practice, Cabourne Court, Cabourne Avenue, Lincoln LN2 2JP Tel: 01522 568838 Fax: 01522 546740; Gilcrest, 32 Washdyke Lane, Nettleham, Lincoln LN2 2PY Tel: 01522 595698 — MB BS 1981 Lond.; FRCGP 1999; DFFP 2000; MRCGP 1985; DRCOG 1985. (Roy. Free Hosp. Lond.)

***PONTIN, Mark John** 26 Hermitage Woods Crescent, Woking GU21 1UE — MB BS 1994 Lond.

PONTON, Alastair William Gordon Heatherview Medical Centre, Alder Road, Parkstone, Poole BH12 4AY Tel: 01202 743678 Fax: 01202 739960 — MB ChB Leic. 1985.

PONTY, Ralph Medical Centre, Church Road, Tiptree, Colchester CO5 0HB Tel: 01621 816475 Fax: 01621 819902 — MB BS 1965 Lond.; MRCS Eng. LRCP Lond. 1965.

POOBALASINGAM, Nagalingam 61 Oakleigh Park N., Whetstone, London N20 9AT Tel: 020 8445 7924 — MB BS 1964 Ceylon; FRCA 1971; DA Eng. 1971. (Univ. Sri Lanka) Cons. Anaesth. N. Middlx. Hosp. Prev: Cons. Anaesth. Haringey Dist. Hosp. (N. Middlx., St. Ann's & P. of Wales Hosps.); Sen. Regist. Research Dept. Anaesth. Roy. Coll. Surg. Eng. & Whittington Hosp.

POOK, Clifford Wilford Pantiles, Raglan NP15 2YE — MB BS 1954 Lond.; MRCS Eng. LRCP Lond. 1954; DObst RCOG 1957.

POOK, John Anthony Ronald 18 Cedars Road, Beckenham BR3 4JF — MB BS 1970 Lond.; MRCS Eng. LRCP Lond. 1970; FFA RCS Eng. 1974; DA Eng. 1972.

POOL, Andrew John 18 Armadale Road, Fulham, London SW6 1JP — MB BS 1986 Lond.

POOL, Mr Christopher John Fenton Cherrywynd House, High St., Ballinger, Great Missenden HP16 9LF Tel: 01494 837254 — MB BS 1960 Lond.; FRCS Eng. 1968; MRCS Eng. LRCP Lond. 1960; DObst RCOG 1963. (Lond. Hosp.)

POOL, Mr Kenneth Raymond Stanley (retired) 18 Radnor Cliff, Sandgate, Folkestone CT20 2JJ Tel: 01303 48387 — MB BS 1952 Lond.; FRCS Eng. 1958; MRCS Eng. LRCP Lond. 1952; FRCOG 1976, M 1963. Prev: Cons. O & G S.E. Kent.

POOL, Richard John Greenfield Surgery, 1 Claremont Avenue, Woking GU22 7SF Tel: 01483 771171; Lindsay Cottage, Guildford Road, Woking GU22 7UT Tel: 0148 62 768545 — MB BS 1984 Lond.; DRCOG 1987. GP Woking. Prev: Trainee GP W. Dorset HA.; Ho. Off. Med. Roy. Sussex Co. Hosp.; Ho. Off. Surg. N. Devon Dist. Hosp.

POOL, Richard William 14 Lambert Road, Grimsby DN32 0HT — MB BS 1991 Lond.

POOL, Roger Watson Brig Royd Surgery, Brig Royd, Ripponden, Sowerby Bridge HX6 4AN Tel: 01422 822209; Little Merrybent Farm, Ripponden, Sowerby Bridge HX6 4NH — MB ChB 1976 Leeds; MRCP (UK) 1979; MRCGP 1983.

POOL, Mr Rowan Donald The Willows, 32 Allen House Park, Hook Heath, Woking GU22 0DB Tel: 01483 730795 — MB ChB 1974 Leeds; FRCS Eng. 1980. Cons. Traum. & Orthop. Surg. Rowley Bristow Orthop. Unit. St. Peter's Hosp. Chertsey. Socs: Brit. Limb Reconstruc. Soc. Prev: Sen. Regist. (Orthop.) St. Geo. Hosp. Lond.

***POOLE, Abigail Elizabeth** 33 Parkwood Drive, Rawstenstall, Rossendale BB4 6RP; 3 Cottingham, Kettering General Hospital, Rothwell Raod, Kettering NN16 8UZ Tel: 01536 492000 — MB ChB 1998 Leic.; MB ChB Leic 1998; BSc Leic. 1995.

POOLE, Adam James Flat 1, 331 Shirland Road, London W9 3JJ Tel: 020 8968 1612 — MB BS 1996 Lond.; MB BS (Hons.) Lond. 1996; BSc (Hons.) Lond. 1993. (Imperial College School of Medicine) SHO (A & E Med.) St. Mary's Hosp. Lond. Prev: SHO (Orthop. & Trauma) Wexham Pk. Hosp. Slough; Ho. Off. Acad. Surgic. Unit St Mary's Hosp. Lond.

POOLE, Alan Julian Sanford House, Rock Hill, Wrantage, Taunton TA3 6DW — MB BS 1961 Lond.; BSc Lond. 1957, MB BS 1961; MRCP Lond. 1966; FRCPsych 1984, M 1972; DPM Eng. 1971. (Lond. Hosp.) Prev: Ho. Phys. Med. Unit Lond. Hosp.; Ho. Phys. Endocrine Unit Hammersmith Hosp. & Postgrad. Med. Sch.; Lond.

POOLE, Alexander Geoffrey Bruce (retired) Ednam East Mill, Kelso TD5 7QB Tel: 01573 224000 Fax: 01573 226288 Email: poole@scotborders.co.uk — MB ChB Ed. 1947; MRCGP 1956; DA Eng. 1969.

POOLE, Bernard Joseph Branton House, North Road, Hembsy, Great Yarmouth NR29 4LR — MB BS 1954 Lond.

POOLE, Charles Jonathan Mortiboy Haelth Centre, Cross St., Dudley DY1 1RN Tel: 01384 366422; Hunters Rise, Holy Cross Green, Clent, Stourbridge DY9 0HG Tel: 01562 730804 — MB BS 1978 Lond.; MD Lond. 1988; FRCP Lond. 1995; MRCP (UK) 1981; FFOM RCP Lond. 1996, MFOM 1992, AFOM 1989; AKC 1975. (Westm.) Cons. Occupat. Phys. Dudley Priority Health NHS Trust; Hon. Reader in Occupat. Med. Univ. of Wolverhampton; Trustee Leber's Optic Neuropathalogy Trust. Socs: Soc. Occup. Med.; Assn. NHS Occupat.al Phys.; Assn. Local Auth. Med. Advisors. Prev: Sen. Occupat. Phys. Rover Gp. Birm.; Occupat. Phys. Brit. Steel W. Midl.; Research Fell. (Med.) W.minster Hosp. Lond.

POOLE, Christopher John CRC Institute for Cancer Studies, The Medical School, University Hospital Birmingham, Birmingham B15 2TH Tel: 0121 472 4311 Fax: 0121 414 3700; 112 Oxford Road, Moseley, Birmingham B13 9SQ Tel: 0121 449 3784 Email: pookcj@aol.com — MB BChir 1979 Camb.; MA Camb. 1980, BA (Med. Sci.) 1976; MRCP (UK) 1983. (King's Coll. Hosp.) Macmillan Sen. Lect. (Med. Oncol. & Palliat. Care) Qu. Eliz. Hosp. & City Hosp. Birm. Socs: Brit. Assn. for Cancer Res.; Assn. Cancer Phys.; W Midl. Oncol. Assn. Prev: CRC Clin. Research Fell. Beatson Inst. Glas. & ICRF Research Fell. St. Bart. Hosp. Lond.; Regist. (Med.) St. Thos. Hosp. Lond.; SHO (Med.) Roy. Marsden Hosp. Sutton.

POOLE, David The Hurley Clinic, Ebenezer House, Kennington Lane, London SE11 4HJ Tel: 020 7735 7918 Fax: 020 7587 5296 — MB ChB 1967 Ed. GP Hurley Clin. Lond.

POOLE, David Robert Scarborough Hospital, Woodlands Drive, Scarborough YO12 6QL — MB BS 1971 Newc.; FRCOG 1991, M 1977. Cons. (O & G); Med. Dir.

POOLE, Elman William 18 Victoria Road, Oxford OX2 7QD Tel: 01865 59489 — MB ChB 1950 New Zealand; FRCP Ed. 1965, M 1956; MRCPsych 1972; DPM Eng. 1957. (Otago) Cons. Clin. Neurophysiol. Oxf. HA & RHA; Clin. Lect. (Neurol.) Univ. Oxf. Prev: Lect. Inst. Psychiat. Lond.; Rockefeller Trav. Fell. 1960-61; Regist. Nat. Hosp. Nerv. Dis. Qu. Sq. Lond.

POOLE, Garth Harcourt City Hospital, Hucknall Road, Nottingham NG5 1PJ — MB ChB 1985 Otago.

POOLE, Gillian Gwyneth Ty Croes, Llanymynech SY22 6ER Tel: 01691 830872 Fax: 01691 839202 — MB BCh 1962 Wales; DCH Eng. 1964; DObst RCOG 1964. Clin. Asst. (Rheum.) Robt. Jones & Agnes Hunt Orthop. & Dist. Hosp. OsW.ry. Prev: Regist. (Obst.) Sorrento Matern. Hosp. Birm.; Ho. Off. United Cardiff Hosps.

POOLE, Graham White (retired) Mayflower Waters, Beacon Lane, Kingswear, Dartmouth TQ6 0BU Tel: 01803 752738 — MB ChB 1944 Birm.; MB ChB (Distinc. Med. Paediat. & Midw.) Birm; FRCP Lond. 1976, M 1949; MRCS Eng. LRCP Lond. 1944. Prev: Cons. Phys. Respirat. Dis. & Sen. Lect. Hammersmith Hosp. & Roy. Postgrad. Med. Sch.

POOLE, Mrs Helen (retired) 14 Custom House Street, Ullapool IV26 2XF Tel: 01854 2810 — MB ChB 1947 Liverp.

POOLE, Jacqueline 11 St. Georges Road, Hexham NE46 2HG — MB BS 1986 Lond.

POOLE, Jill (retired) Mayflower Waters, Beacon Lane, Kingswear, Dartmouth TQ6 0BU Tel: 01803 752738 — MB ChB 1949 Birm.; MRCS Eng. LRCP Lond. 1949; DCH . Lond. 1952.

***POOLE, Kenneth Eric Sealy** The Wagon House, Manor Farm, Old Alresford, Alresford SO24 9DH Email: kenpode@hotmail.com — BM 1997 Soton.

***POOLE, Kingsley Kahlil** Arun, The Close, Ashington, Pulborough RH20 3LJ — BM BCh 1996 Oxf.

POOLE

*POOLE, Norman Alan 11 Barassie Drive, Bridge of Weir PA11 3HB — MB ChB 1997 Dund.

POOLE, Pauline Marcia (retired) Fairy's Oak, 19 Pentre Close, Ashton, Chester CH3 8BR — MB BCh BAO 1950 Dub.; MA, MD Dub. 1961; FRCPath 1972, M 1963; Dip. Bact. Lond 1954. Prev: Dir. Pub. Health Laborat. Chester.

POOLE, Rebecca Anne 5 The Budding, Stroud GL5 1XU Tel: 01453 759363 Email: rebecca.poole@bigfoot.com; 5 The Budding, Stroud GL5 1XU Tel: 01453 759363 — MB ChB 1994 Ed. (Edinburgh)

POOLE, Richard Roy Graydon Richardson Road Surgery, 56 Richardson Road, East Bergholt, Colchester CO7 6RR Tel: 01206 298272 Fax: 01206 299010; The Beeches, Gaston St, E. Bergholt, Colchester CO7 6SD — MB ChB 1973 Dundee; BSc St. And. 1969; DObst RCOG 1975.

POOLE, Robert Godfree North Mersey Community (NHS) Trust, Windsor House, 40 Upper Parliament St., Liverpool L8 7LF Tel: 0151 250 5322 — MB BS 1980 Lond.; FRCPsych 1997, M 1984. (St. Geo. Hosp. Lond.) Cons. Psychiat. N. Mersey Community (NHS) Trust; Hon. Clin. Lect. (Psychiat.) Univ. Liverp. Prev: Sen. Regist. (Psychiat.) Oxf. RHA; Regist. (Psychiat.) St. Geo. Hosp. Lond.

*POOLE, Robin Geoffrey 34 Selwyn Dr, Broadstairs CT10 2SW — MB ChB 1997 Birm.

POOLE, Ruth Burnet 2 The Vineyards, Southampton SO52 9PP; 2 The Vineyards, North Baddesley, Southampton SO52 9PP — BM 1995 Soton.

POOLE, Simon Benedict Firs House Surgery, Station Road, Impington, Cambridge CB4 9NP Tel: 01223 234286 Fax: 01223 235931 — MB BS 1987 Lond.

POOLE, Simon Maurice Department of Histopathology, Royal Free Hospital, Pond St., London NW3 2QG Tel: 020 7830 2227 Fax: 020 7435 3289 — MB BS 1991 Lond.; BSc (Hons.) Lond. 1986. Sen. Regist. (HP) Roy. Free & Univ. Coll. Med. Sch. Lond. Prev: Sen. Regist. (Histopath.) Roy. Marsden. Hosp.; Sen. Regist. (Histopath.) Roy. Postgrad. Med. Sch. Lond.; Regist. Roy. Marsden Hosp. & Hammersmith Hosp. Lond.

POOLE, Mr Thomas Robert Guimaraes 26B Edbrooke Road, London W9 2DG — MB BS Lond. 1992; BSc Lond. 1991; FRCOphth 1997. (St Marys Hospital London) Specialist Regist. Ophth. St Thomas Hosp. Lond. Prev: Ophth. Kilimanjaro Christian Med. Centre Tanzania.; SHO Ophth. W.ern Eye Hosp. Lond.

POOLE, Thomas Williams (retired) Conifers, 13 Wealden Way, Haywards Heath RH16 4AF Tel: 01444 450877 — LRCP LRCS 1945 Ed.; LRCP&S Glas. 1945; MFOM RCP Lond. 1983. Prev: Chief Med. Off. P & O Steam Navigation Co.

POOLE-WILSON, Professor Philip Alexander National Heart & Lung Institute, Imperial College School of Medicine, Dovehouse St., London SW3 6LY Tel: 020 7351 8179 Fax: 020 7351 8113 Email: p.poole-wilson@ic.ac.uk; 174 Burbage Road, Dulwich Village, London SE21 7AG Tel: 020 7274 6742 — MB BChir Camb. 1968; MA Camb. 1991, BA 1969, MD 1975; FRCP Lond. 1983; MRCP (UK) 1970; FACC 1992; FESC 1988. (Camb. & St. Thos.) Head of Nat. Heart & Lung Div., Imperial Coll. Sch. of Med.; Simon Marks Brit. Heart Foundat. Prof. Cardiol. Nat. Heart & Lung Inst. Imperial Coll Sch Med; Hon. Cons. Phys. Roy. Brompton Nat. Heart & Lung Hosp.; Brit.-Amer. Trav. Fell.sh. Socs: (Pres.) Europ. Soc. Cardiol.; (Treas.) Internat. Soc. Heart Research; Pres. Elect World Heart Federat. Prev: Lect. (Med.) St. Thos. Hosp. Lond.; Regist. St. Thos. Hosp. Lond.; SHO St. Thos., Brompton & Hammersmith Hosps. Lond.

POOLER, Alan David Hollies (retired) Roseneath, 195 Holyhead Road, Wellington, Telford TF1 2DP Tel: 01952 412433 — LMSSA 1957 Lond.; MA Camb. 1960, MB BChir 1957. Prev: GP Telford.

POOLER, Alan Francis William Marshall (retired) 7 Priory Gardens, Old Basing, Basingstoke RG24 7DS Tel: 01256 462332 — MB BS 1953 Lond.; FRCP Lond. 1982; MRCP (UK) 1972; MRCS Eng. LRCP Lond. 1953; FCP(SA) 1968. Prev: Cons. Phys. (Geriat. Med.) Basingstoke Dist. Hosp.

POOLEY, Andrew Stuart 5 Kingsdown Road, Epsom KT17 3PU — MB BS 1987 Lond.; MRCOG 1993. (St. George's Hosp. Lond.) Cons. (O & G) Kingston Healthcare Trust, Surrey. Socs: BMA; Brit. Soc. CCP.

POOLEY, Mr Joseph 12 Darras Road, Ponteland, Newcastle upon Tyne NE20 9PA — MD 1983 Newc.; MB BS 1971; FRCS Eng. 1977. Brit. Orthop. Research Soc. Pres. Medal 1982; Cons. & Sen. Lect. Orthop. Surg. Univ. Newc. upon Tyne. Prev: Sen. Regist. Orthop. Surg. N.. RHA; Lect. (Orthop. Surg.) Univ. Newc. upon Tyne; Ho. Surg. & Ho. Phys. Roy. Vict. Infirm. Newc.

POOLEY, Simon Francis Lambert Medical Centre, 2 Chapel Street, Thirsk YO7 1LU Tel: 01845 523157 Fax: 01845 524508; Village Farm, Little Thirkleby, Thirkleby, Thirsk YO7 2AZ Tel: 01845 501539 — BM BS 1981 Nottm.; BMedSci Nottm. 1979, BM BS 1981; MRCGP 1987; DRCOG 1987.

POOLEY, Stewart Sandeman Favell (retired) 31 Ockfields, Milford, Godalming GU8 5JT Tel: 0148 685741 — MB BS 1938 Lond.; MRCS Eng. LRCP Lond. 1938; FRCOG 1965, M 1947. Prev: Cons. O & G S. W. Surrey Health Dist. & Cobham Cott. Hosp.

POOLOGANATHAN, Saravanamuthu Rush Green Medical Centre, 261 Dagenham Road, Romford RM7 0XR Tel: 01708 740730 Fax: 01708 725388; 25 Butts Green Road, Hornchurch RM11 2JS Tel: 01708 438382 — MB BS 1978 Sri Lanka; MRCS Eng. LRCP Lond. 1988; Dip Immediate Care RCS Ed. 1988. Dep. Doctor Health Call Ltd. Leigh-on-Sea.

POON, Choong Leng Department of Radiology, Royal Albert Edward Infirmary, Wigan Lane, Wigan WN1 2NN Tel: 01942 822402 Fax: 01942 822402; 11 Thurlestone Road, Altrincham WA14 4NB Email: clpoon@compuserve.com — MB ChB 1984 Manch.; BSc St. And. 1981; MRCP (UK) 1990; FRCR 1994. Cons. Radiol. Roy. Albert Edw. Infirm. Wigan. Socs: Brit. Soc. Interven. Radiol.; Radiol. Soc. N. Amer.; Cardiovasc. & Interven. Radiol. Soc. Europe. Prev: Sen. Regist. & Regist (Diagn. Radiol.) N. W.. RHA; Regist. (Gen. Med. & Diabetol.) Wythenshawe Hosp. Manch.; Regist. & SHO (Gen. Med.) Stepping Hill Hosp. Stockport.

POON, Fat Wui Glasgow Royal Infirmary, Glasgow G4 0SF; 60 Colonsay Drive, Newton Mearns, Glasgow G77 6TY — MB ChB 1979 Aberd.; MB ChB (Commend.) Aberd. 1979; MBA 1996; FRCS Glas. 1984; FRCR 1988.

*POON, Jasmine Hei-Wan 38 Heron Drive, Lenton, Nottingham NG7 2DE — BM BS 1998 Nottm.; BM BS Nottm 1998.

*POON, Karen 15 Braddock Close, Lenton, Nottingham NG7 2FN — BM BS 1998 Nottm.; BM BS Nottm 1998.

POON, Pui Yee Alice Anaesthetic Department, Barnsley District General Hospital, Barnsley S75 2EP Tel: 01226 730000 — MB ChB 1986 Leeds; DA (UK) 1988; FRCA 1998. Cons. Anaesth., Barnsley DGH. Socs: Fell. Roy. Coll. Anaesths.; Assn. of Anaesth.s; Obst. Anaesth.s Assn. Prev: Specialist Regist. (Anaesth.) S. Thames W. Region.

POON, Wai Sang 20 Annan Drive, Bearsden, Glasgow G61 1EZ — MB ChB 1978 Glas.

POON, Wallace Ka Ming 17 Brocas Close, London NW3 3LD — MB BS 1991 Lond.

POONAWALA, Mr Shabbir Saleh Block 1516 (Staff Quarters), Barnsley District General Hospital, Pogmoor Road, Barnsley S75 2EP Tel: 01226 730000 Email: shabbirsp@hotmail.com — MB BS 1985 Bombay; FRCS Glas. 1992. (Grant Medical College, Bombay)

POONI, Jagtar Singh 3 Wicket Close, Checkley Grange, St Georges, Telford TF2 9PL — MB ChB 1986 Manch.; BSc (Hons) Manch. 1983; MRCP (UK) 1990; FRCA 1993. Sen. Regist. Rotat. (Anaesth.) W. Midls. Socs: Assn. Anaesth.; Gp. Anaesth. in Train. (GAT Comm.). Prev: Regist. (Anaesth.) N. Staffs. NHS Trust Stoke-on-Trent, P.ss Roy. Hosp. Telford & Roy. Shrewsbury Hosp.; SHO (Anaesth.) Countess of Chester Hosp.; SHO (A & E) Hope Hosp, Salford.

*POOR, Stephen Hedrick 1st Floor Flat, 36 Rainville Road, London W6 9HA — MB BS 1996 Lond.

POOR, Stephen Joseph 10 Russell Street, Bath BA1 2QF — LMSSA 1974 Lond.

POORE, Peter David Save The Children Fund, 17 Grove Lane, Camberwell, London SE5 8RD; Reading Green Farm House, Denham, Eye IP21 5DH — MB BS 1964 Lond.; DTM & H Liverp. 1978; DCH RCP Lond. 1970. Health Adviser Save the Childr. Fund UK.

POORNAN, Annamalai Mudaliar Cauveri, Springhill Lane, Lower Penn, Wolverhampton WV4 Tel: 01902 34821 — MB BS 1949 Madras. (Madras Med. Coll.) Prev: Ho. Off. Govt. Gen. Hosp. Madras; Med. Off. IAMC; SHO Childr. Hosp. Nottm.

POOTS, David Frederick John 8 St Michael's Road, Farnborough GU14 8NE — MB BS 1987 Lond.

POOTS, Eileen Dorothy Miriam Helena (retired) 4 Abercorn Park, Hillsborough BT26 6HA Tel: 01846 682024 — MB BCh BAO 1948 Belf. Prev: Regist. Perivale Matern. Hosp. Middlx.

POOTS, Gwendoline Gladys Lowry Kilsorrel, Rew Lane, Summersdale, Chichester PO19 4QH — MB BCh BAO 1949 Dub.

POOTS, Samuel James Staines Health Centre, Knowle Green, Kingston Road, Staines TW18 1AJ — MB BCh BAO 1946 Dub. (TC Dub.)

POOTS, Stephen Allan Mourne Family Surgery, Mourne Hospital, Newry Street, Kilkeel, Newry BT34 4DN — MB BCh BAO 1981 Belf.; MRCGP 1985; DRCOG 1983.

POPAT, Dhirendra 52 Marine View, Rhos-on-Sea, Colwyn Bay LL28 4PQ — MB BS 1980 Racnchi.

POPAT, Jayantilal Thakarshi Station Road Surgery, 42 Station Road, London NW4 3SU Tel: 020 8202 3733 Fax: 020 8203 8096 — MB BS 1969 Baroda. Socs: BMA.

POPAT, Ramniklal Thakarshi Tynemouth Medical Practice, 24 Tynemouth Road, Tottenham, London N15 4RH Tel: 020 8275 4062 Fax: 020 8275 4120 — MB BS 1972 Baroda.

POPAT, Sanjaykumar Batuklal Institute of Cancer Research, Haddow Laboratories, 15 Cotswold Road, Sutton SM2 5NG Tel: 020 8722 4113 Fax: 020 8643 0257 Email: s.popat@icr.acc.uk — MB BS 1994 Lond.; MB BS (Hons.) Lond. 1994; BSc (Hons.) Lond. 1991; MRCP (UK) 1997. (United Medical and Dental Schools) Clin. Res. Fell. (Cancer Genetics) Inst. Of Cancer Res./ Roy. Marsden NHS Trust, Sutton. Prev: SHO (Gen. Med.) Lewisham Hosp.; SHO (Med. Oncol.) Roy. Masden Hosp.; SHO (Chest/ICU) Roy. Brompton Hosp.

POPAT, Uday Rameshchandra 10 Glebe Road, Finchley, London N3 2AX — MB BS 1986 Bombay; MRCP (UK) 1991.

POPAT-HADDEN, Alpha Olympia — MB ChB 1988 Aberd.; FRCS 1995 Edin.

POPE, Mr Alvan John, TD Hillingdon Hospital, Pield Heath Road, Uxbridge UB8 3NN Tel: 01895 279698 Fax: 01895 279890; Sakura, 73 Camp Road, Gerrards Cross SL9 7PF Tel: 01753 893068 Email: ajpope@compuserve.com — MB BS 1980 Lond.; BSc Lond. 1977, MB BS 1980; MD Lond. 1992; FRCS (Urol.) 1994; FRCS Eng. 1985. (Middlx.) Cons. Urol. Char. Cross & Hillingdon Hosps. Socs: Brit. Assn. Urol. Surg.; Brit. Soc. Endocrinol. Prev: Sen. Regist. (Urol.) St. Peters Hosp. Lond.; Research Regist. Inst. Urol. Lond.; RSO St. Peter's Hosps. Lond.

POPE, Andrew James Dept. of Clinical Radiology, Southampton Hospital, Tremona Raod, Southampton SO16 6YD Tel: 02380 777222; 20 Shaftesbury Street, Fordingbridge SP6 1JF — MB BS 1994 Lond.; MRCP (UK) 1998; FRCR (1) 1999. (Charing Cross & Westminster)

POPE, Mr David Charles Quarter Jack Surgery, Rodways Corner, Wimborne BH21 1AP Tel: 01202 882112 Fax: 01202 882368; Huish House, Winterborne Zelston, Blandford Forum DT11 9ES Tel: 01929 459461 — MB BS 1967 Lond.; FRCS Eng. 1972; MRCS Eng. LRCP Lond. 1967. (St. Bart.) Clin. Dir. & Surg. Off. Vict. Hosp. Wimborne. Socs: (Comm.) Community Hosp. Assn. Prev: Regist. (Surg.) Poole Gen. Hosp. & St. Bart. Hosp. Lond.; Resid. Surg. Off. (Thoracic Surg.) Brompton Hosp. Lond.

POPE, David Graham La Solaize, Rue Du Craslin, St Peter, Jersey JE3 7YN Tel: 01534 36301 — MB ChB 1970 Bristol. Prev: SHO Obst. Bristol Matern. Hosp.

POPE, Dean Granville West End Medical Practice, 21 Chester Street, Edinburgh EH3 7RF Tel: 0131 225 5220 Fax: 0131 226 1910; 1 St Bernards Crescent, Edinburgh EH4 1NR Tel: 0131 332 8480 — MB ChB 1986 Ed.; MRCGP 1990; DRCOG 1990. Prev: Trainee GP Cumbria VTS.

POPE, Professor Francis Michael Division of Life Sciences, King's College London, Franklin Wilkins Building, 150 Stamford Street, London SE1 9NN; 91 Marsh Road, Pinner HA5 5PA — MB BCh Wales 1963; MD Wales 1974; FRCP Ed. 1994; FRCP Lond. 1981, M 1968; FRCP Glas. 1981, M 1967; MRCP Ed. 1968. (Welsh Nat. Sch. Med. (Univ. Wales)) Cons. Dermatol. W. Middlx. Univ. Hosp. and Chelsea & W.m. Hosp. (Nov 2001); Hon. Cons. Clin. Genetics Inst. Med. Genetics UHW Cardiff; Vis. Prof. Connective Tissue Matrix Genetics, Kings Coll. Lond.; Hon. Head Connective Tissue Genetics Gp. Div. Life Sci. Kings Coll. Lond. (Nov 2001). Socs: Assn. Phys.; Brit. Assn. Dermat.; Amer. Soc. of Human Genetics. Prev: Hon. Cons. Clin. Genetics Addenbrooke's Hosp. Camb.; Hon. Cons. Phys. Div. of Clin. Sci. & MRC Clin. Research Centre & N.wick Pk. Hosp.; Hon. Sen. Lect. & Cons. Dermat. Inst. Dermat. & St. John's Hosp. Dis. Skin. Lond.

POPE, Mr Ian Michael 16 Merlin Gardens, Brickhill, Bedford MK41 7HL — BM BCh 1991 Oxf.; BA (Hons.) Camb. 1988; FRCS Ed. 1995. (Oxford) Specialist Regist. (Gen. Surg.) S. E. Scot. Higher Surg. Train. Rotat. Edin. Socs: Brit. Assn. Surg. Oncol. Prev: Research Fell. (Surg.) Univ. Liverp.; SHO (Gen. Surg.) Roy. Liverp. Univ. Hosp.; SHO (Gen. Surg.) Roy. Liverp. Univ. Hosp.

POPE, Isabel Joy Kildonan House, Ramsbottom Road, Horwich, Bolton BL6 5NW Tel: 01204 468161 Fax: 01204 698186; 10 Ansdell Road, Horwich, Bolton BL6 7HL — MB ChB 1979 Manch.; MRCGP 1985; DTM & H Liverp. 1985; DCH RCPS Glas. 1985; DRCOG 1981. (Manch.)

POPE, Joanna Brownfield Wyndhams, Quarry Lane, Chicksgrove, Tisbury, Salisbury SP3 6LY — MB ChB 1996 Ed.

POPE, John Alfred ffitch Essex Way Surgery, 34 Essex Way, Benfleet SS7 1LT Tel: 01268 792203 Fax: 01268 759495 — MB BS 1960 Lond.; DObst RCOG 1962. (St. Bart.)

POPE, John David Kitson Roslin Surgery, 6 Main Street, Roslin EH25 9LE Tel: 0131 440 2043 Fax: 0131 448 2558 — MB ChB 1965 St. And.; FFA RCS Eng. 1972; DA Eng. 1972. (Dundee)

POPE, Laysan Edward Roy 18 Bury Street, Norwich NR2 2DN — MB BS 1996 Lond.

***POPE, Mark Edward** 59 Sunray Avenue, London SE24 9PX — MB BS 1994 Lond.

POPE, Mary Halcyon Meredith Marcham Health Centre, Marcham Road, Abingdon OX14 1BT Tel: 01235 522602; 16 Bostock Road, Abingdon OX14 1DW Tel: 01235 532120 — BM BCh 1990 Oxf.; MRCGP 1995. (Oxf.) Prev: Trainee GP Abingdon; SHO (O & G) P.ss Margt. Hosp. Swindon.

POPE, Rachel Trixie Yarra House, 73 Camp Road, Gerrards Cross SL9 7PF — MB BS 1984 Lond.; MRCGP 1988; DRCOG 1987; DCH RCP Lond. 1986. (Middlx. Hosp.) Prev: GP Lond.; Clin. Med. Off. W. Lambeth HA; Trainee GP/SHO Qu. Eliz. II Hosp. Welwyn Gdn. City VTS.

POPE, Richard Martin Airedale General Hospital, Skipton Road, Steeton, Keighley BD20 6TD Tel: 01535 652511 — MB BCh 1981 Wales; MD Wales 1990; FRCP 1997. Cons. Phys. (Diabetes & Endocrinol.) Airedale Gen. Hosp. Prev: Lect. (Med.) Univ. Leeds; MRC Train. Fell. King's Coll. Hosp. Lond. & Cardiff HA.

POPE, Romney Jane Elliott 2 Bradiston Road, London W9 3HN — MB BS 1994 Lond.

POPE, Mr Stephen John 53 Disraeli Road, Ealing, London W5 5HS — MB BS 1989 Lond.; BSc (Hons.) Lond. 1986; FRCS Eng. 1994; FRCSI 1993; FRCS (Tr & Orth) 1998. (London Hospital Medical College)

POPE, Stephen Paul The Bishop's Cottage, Church Hill, Crayke, York YO61 4TA — MB ChB 1973 Liverp.; MRCGP 1988; FFA RCS Eng. 1980; T(GP) 1991; DRCOG 1988. GP Asst. (p/t) Derwent Surg. Multon. Prev: Staff Phys. (Palliat. Med.) St. Gemma's Hospice Leeds; GP Benfleet; Regist. (Anaesth.) BRd.green Hosp. Liverp.

POPE, Ursula Clair Pen Y Gaer Isa, Llanfihangel G.M., Corwen LL21 9UH — MB ChB 1949 Liverp.

POPE, Miss Vanessa 15 Barwell Road, Sale M33 5FE — MB BS 1993 Lond.; BSc (Hons.) Lond. 1990; FRCS Eng. 1997. (Univ. Coll. & Middlx. Lond.) p/t Specialist Regist. Gen. Surg., Manch. Prev: Sen. SHO (Surg.) Bolton; Sen. SHO (Surg.) Shrewsbury; SHO Rotat. (Surg.) Leic.

***POPELY, Claire Sarah** 14 Harrod Dr, Southport PR8 2HA — MB BS 1997 Newc.

POPERT, John Bransford House, Bransford, Worcester WR6 5JL Tel: 01886 832373 — MB BS 1948 Lond.; MD Lond. 1962; FRCP Lond. 1973, M 1956. (St. Bart.) Hon. Cons. Phys. Worcester Roy. Infirm.; Hon. Cons. Rheum. Roy. Orthop. Hosp.Birm. Socs: Brit. Soc. Rheum.; Midl.s Rheum. Soc. Prev: Lect. & Asst. Dir. Clin. Sect. Rheum. Research Clinic Manch. Univ.; Hon. Cons. Phys. Manch. Roy. Infirm.

POPERT, Mr Richard John Mackay Peter Department of Urology, King's College Hospital, Denmark Hill, London SE5 Tel: 020 7274 6222; Flat 1, 22 Grove Park, Camberwell, London SE5 8LH Tel: 020 7733 4859 — MB BS 1985 Lond.; FRCS Ed. 1989; FRCS Eng. 1989. Research Regist. (Urol.) King's Coll. Hosp. Lond. Socs: Fell. Roy. Soc. Med.; Assoc. Mem. BAUS. Prev: Regist. (Urol.) King's

Coll. Hosp. Lond.; Regist. (Gen. Surg.) Qu. Alexandra Hosp. Portsmouth; Demonst. (Anat.) Camb. Univ.

POPERT, Sheila Jane 22 Ullathorne Road, Streatham, London SW16 1SA Tel: 020 8664 6725 — MRCS Eng. LRCP Lond. 1985; BDS (Hons.) Lond. 1980. p/t Cons. (Palliat. Med.) St. Christopher's Hospice, Sydenham; Cons. (Pall. Med.) Mayday Univ. Hosp. Croydon. Prev: Med. Dir. St. Raphael's Hospice Sutton.

POPHAM, Carolyn Mary Knowl Rose, Hockering Road, Woking GU22 7HP — BM 1978 Soton.; BM (Hons.) Soton. 1978.

POPHAM, Philip Andrew Bryan Dept of Anaesthesia, Addenbrookes' Hospital, Hills Road, Cambridge CB2 2QQ Email: popham@lineone.net — MB BS 1982 Lond.; BSc (Hons.) Lond. 1979, MD 1992; FFA RCS 1987. Cons. Anaesth. Addenbrooke's Hosp. Camb. Socs: BMA; (Treas.) E. Anglian Obst. Anaesth. Gp.; Assn. Anaesth. Prev: Staff Specialist (Anaesth.) Roy. Woms. Hosp. Melbourne, Austral.; Sen. Regist. (Anaesth.) Addenbrooke's Hosp. Camb.; Sir Jules Thorn Research Fell. (Physiol.) St. Thos. Hosp. Lond.

***POPLAR, Christopher Charles Edward** 22 Farlers End, Nailsea, Bristol BS48 4PG — BM 1997 Soton.

POPLE, Andrew Robert Wordsworth Health Centre, 19 Wordsworth Avenue, Manor Park, London E12 6SU Tel: 020 8548 5960 Fax: 020 8548 5983; 8 The Vale, Woodford Green IG8 9BT — MB BS 1986 Lond. Prev: SHO (Psychiat.) Goodmayes Hosp.; SHO (O & G & A & E) Newham Gen. Hosp.; SHO (Paediat.) Newham Gen. Hosp.

POPLE, Mr Ian Kenneth Frenchay Hospital, Frenchay Park Road, Frenchay, Bristol BS16 1LE Tel: 0117 975 3960 Email: ikpople@hotmail.com; 49A Shirehampton Road, Stoke Bishop, Bristol BS9 2DN Tel: 0117 968 7026 — MB ChB 1983 Sheff.; MD Sheff. 1992; FRCS (SN) 1993; FRCS Eng. 1987; ECFMG Cert. 1992; Fell Paedc Neurosurg Univ Tennessee USA 1995. (Sheff.) Cons. Neurosurg. Frenchay Hosp. Bristol. Socs: Soc. Brit. Neurolog. Surg.; Soc. for Research into Hydrocephalus & Spina Bifida; Brit. Paediat. Neurosurg. Gp. Prev: Sen. Registar & Registar (Neurosurg.) Frenchay Hosp. Bristol; Registar (Neurosurg.) Hosp. Sick Childr. Gt. Ormond St. Lond.; SHO (Neurosurg.) Leeds Gen. Infirm.

POPLETT, Neil David Charing Surgery, Charing, Ashford TN27 0HZ Tel: 01233 714141 Fax: 01233 713782 — MB BS 1990 Lond.; BSc Lond. 1987, MB BS 1990; DRCOG 1993 or 94; MRCGP 1995. (Univ. Lond.) SHO (O & G) Pembury Hosp. Tonbridge. Prev: SHO (A & E) Kent & Canterbury Hosps.; SHO (Geriat. & Paediat.) William Harvey Hosp. Ashford; Ho. Off. (Med. & Surg.) Maidstone Hosp. Kent.

POPLI, Sanjeev c/o Mapledown, Little Windmill Hill, Chipperfield, Kings Langley WD4 9DG — MB ChB 1991 Liverp.; DRCOG 1996.

***POPOV, Alain** 39 Berwick Chase, Peterlee SR8 1NQ — MB ChB 1997 Manch.

POPOVIC, Sara Brighton House, 14 Droitwich Road, Worcester WR3 7LJ — MB BS 1991 Lond.

POPPER, Stefan Leopold 8 Colwick Park Close, Colwick, Nottingham NG4 2DZ Tel: 0115 987 9002 — BM BS 1981 Nottm.; BMedSci Nottm. 1979, BM BS 1981.

POPPINGHAUS, Claus-Michele c/o Doctors Mess, Royal Cornwall Hospital, Treliske, Truro TR1 3LJ — State Exam Med 1991 Cologne.

POPPLE, Anthony Willis Green Head House, 37 The Green, Dalston, Carlisle CA5 7QD — MB BS 1969 Lond.; BSc, MB BS Lond. 1969; MRCPath 1978. Cons. (Histopath.) Cumbld. Infirm. Carlisle.

POPPLE, Mark David Hollies Medical Practice, Tamworth Health Centre, Upper Gungate, Tamworth B79 7EA Tel: 01827 68511 Fax: 01827 51163; Wigginton Lodge, Wigginton Road, Tamworth B79 8RH Tel: 01827 62808 — MB BS 1982 Lond. Prev: Regist. (A & E) Derbysh. Roy. Infirm.; Trainee GP Tamworth.

POPPLESTONE, Gaynor Anne 11 Tickenor Drive, Finchampstead, Wokingham RG40 4UD — MB ChB 1986 Liverp.; MRCGP 1995; DCH RCP Lond. 1994. (Liverpool) p/t Gen. Practitioner. Prev: Gen. Practitioner, Swallowfield Med. Pract.

POPPLESTONE, Mark Fax: 020 8738 9757 Email: mark1.popplestone@british-airways.com — MB ChB 1983 Liverp.; MB ChB Liverpool 1983; AFOM RCP Lond 1992; MFOM (RCP) London 1998. Cons. Occupat. Phys. Brit. Airways. Prev: Occupat. Phys., Nestlé Rowntree, York; Med. Off. Brit. Steel Scunthorpe.

POPPLETON, John Frank (retired) 6 Graham Close, Paradise, Scarborough YO11 1RU Tel: 01723 373143 — MB ChB 1955 Leeds; AFOM RCP Lond. 1983. Prev: Occupat. Phys. McCain Foods (GB) plc.

POPPLEWELL, Julie Ann Coppers, Temple Grafton, Alcester B49 6NR — MB ChB 1975 Birm.; DRCOG 1978.

POPPLEWELL, Martin Coppers, Temple Grafton, Alcester B49 6NR — MB ChB 1975 Birm.; DA Eng. 1980; DRCOG 1978.

PORCHERET, Mark Ernest Paul The John Kelso Practice, Park Medical Centre, Ball Haye Road, Leek ST13 6QR Tel: 01538 399007 Fax: 01538 370014 — MB BS 1978 Lond.; MRCGP 1983; DRCOG 1983; DCH RCP Lond. 1982.

PORCHEROT, Roger Charles Crahamel Medical Practice, Crahamel House, 2 Duhamel Place, St Helier, Jersey JE2 4TP; Le Flieurion, Rue de L'Eglise, St John, Jersey JE3 4BA Tel: 01534 864025 Fax: 01534 864834 — MB BS 1967 Lond.; MRCS Eng. LRCP Lond. 1967; BA O.U. 1997. (St. Bart.) Prev: Ho. Surg. St. Bart. Hosp. Lond.; Ho. Phys. Brook Hosp. Lond.; Ho. Surg. Woolwich Memor. Hosp.

PORCZYNSKA, Krystyna Regina 4 Thomas Telford Basin, Piccadilly Village, Manchester M1 2NH — MB ChB 1989 Manch. Clin. Asst. (Haemat.) Bolton Gen. Hosp.

PORCZYNSKA, Wladyslawa Irena 24 Argyle Road, Wolverhampton WV2 4NY — MB ChB 1987 Manch.

PORE, Padmaja Suhas 7 Kernel Close, Littleover, Derby DE23 7SA — MB BS 1977 Bombay; MRCPI 1995.

PORE, Suhas Vishnu 3 Litchurch Street, Derby Royal Infirmary, Derby DE1 2RG — MB BS 1973 Poona; MRCPsych 1982.

***POROOHAN, Rowshanak** 54A Barber Road, Sheffield S10 1ED — MB ChB 1998 Sheff.; MB ChB Sheff 1998.

PORRITT, Andrea Janice 110 Hazelhurst Road, Worsley, Manchester M28 2SP — MB ChB 1989 Ed.

PORRITT, Siobhan Frances Mary 48 Tamworth Road, Hove BN3 5FH Tel: 01273 770487 — MB BS 1988 Lond.; MRCGP Lond. 1996; DRCOG Lond. 1993; DFFP Lond. 1993. Clin. Asst. (Psychiat.).

PORRU, Daniele Department of Urology, Gartnavel General Hospital, 1053 Great Western Road, Glasgow G12 0YN — State DMS 1992 Cagliari; T(S) 1994.

PORT, Mr Andrew Michael 53 Brigadene Close, Warrior Park, Hartlepool — MB ChB 1988 Manch.; BSc (Hons.) Manch. 1985, MB ChB 1988; FRCS Ed. 1992. Regist. (Orthop.) N. RHA. Prev: SHO (A & E) Middlesbrough Gen. Hosp.

***PORT, Ann** 30 Sandmoor Green, Leeds LS17 7SB — MB BCh 1985 Wales.

PORTAL, Pamela The Briars, Beech Hill Road, Swanland, North Ferriby HU14 3QY Tel: 01482 631567 — MB BS 1963 Lond.; MB BS (Distinc. Surg., Midw. & Gyn.) Lond. 1963; DA Eng. 1966. (Middlx.) Clin. Asst. Dept. Anaesth. Hull Hosp. Gps. Prev: Regist. (Anaesth.) Gr. Hosp. Tooting & Qu. Mary's Hosp. Childr.; Carshalton.

PORTAL, Richard Wallace The Nuffield Hospital, 81 Westbourne Avenue, Hull HU5 3HP Tel: 01482 42327; The Briars, Beech Hill Road, Swanland, North Ferriby HU14 3QY Tel: 01482 631567 — MB BS 1956 Lond.; MA Camb. 1966, BA 1948, LLB 1949; MD Lond. 1966; FRCP Lond. 1975, M 1959. (Middlx.) Prev: Cons. Cardiol. Humberside AHA; Sen. Regist. (Cardiol.) Middlx. Hosp. Lond.

PORTANIER, John (retired) 10 Vivian House, Seven Sisters Road, London N4 1QZ Tel: 020 7503 9836 — LM 1938 Rotunda; PhC Malta 1933, MD 1937.

PORTAS, Charles David Wrington Vale Medical Group, Station Road, Wrington, Bristol BS40 5NG Tel: 01934 862532 Fax: 01934 863568 — MB BCh 1984; BSc 1977 Wales; MRCGP 1988; DRCOG 1987; DCH RCP Lond. 1987. GP Bristol. Prev: Trainee GP Dept. Gen. Pract. Univ. Wales Coll. of Med. Cardiff; SHO (Paediat.) Gwent HA; SHO (O & G & Geriat. Med.) S. Glam. HA.

PORTAS-DOMINGUEZ, Luis-Carlos 8 College Road, London SW19 2BS — State Exam Med. Tubingen 1990.

PORTCH, Hilary Ruth Royal Commercial Hospital NHS Trust TR1 3LJ Tel: 01872 250000 — BM 1988 Soton.; MRCGP 1996; DFFP 1995; DRCOG 1993. Staff Grade Cardiol., Roy. Cornw. Hosp. Socs: Brit. Soc. Of Endocardiography; Brit. Med. Assn.; Primary Care Cardiovasc. Soc. Prev: Clin. Asst. (Cardiol.); Clin. Asst. Cardiol., Brit. Roy. Infirm.

PORTE, Aileen McKenzie 3 Crosshill Road, Strathaven ML10 6DS Tel: 01357 522464 — MB ChB 1990 Glas.; MRCGP 1994. Prev: Trainee GP Lanarksh.

PORTE, Mr Hubert Eran (retired) Springwood Cottage, Shenmore, Madley, Hereford HR2 9NX Tel: 01981 250561 — MB ChB 1960 Manch.; FRCS Ed. 1964; DLO Eng. 1967. Prev: Cons. ENT Surg. Lincs AHA.

PORTE, Mr Michael Eran 179 Mountview Road, Stroud Green, London N4 4JT — MB BS 1982 Lond.; BSc Lond. 1979, MB BS 1982; FRCS Eng. 1986.

PORTELLY, John Edward (retired) 169 Coombe Lane, West Wimbledon, London SW20 0QX Tel: 020 8946 7006 — MB BChir 1957 Camb.; MA Camb. 1952; LMSSA Lond. 1952. Prev: SHO (Surg.) S. Devon & E. Cornw. Hosp.

PORTELLY, John Patrick The Ross Practice, Keats House, Bush Fair, Harlow CM18 6LY Tel: 01279 692747 Fax: 01279 692737 — MB BS 1982 Lond.; MRCGP 1986; DRCOG 1986. (Royal London Hospital) Gen. Practitioner. Socs: BMA. Prev: Trainee GP Harold Wood Hosp. VTS.

PORTEOUS, Alexander Calvert (retired) Quantocks, 81 Church Road, Ryde PO33 4PZ Tel: 01983 882840 — MB BS 1947 Lond.; MRCS Eng. LRCP Lond. 1942. Prev: Postgrad. Regist. (Med.) St. Mary's Hosp.

PORTEOUS, Alison Olwen Ross 2 Clos Nant Y Cor, Chatfield Park, North Pentwyn, Cardiff CF23 8LD — MB BCh 1990 Wales.

PORTEOUS, Colin 101 Brisbane Street, Greenock PA16 8PA — MB ChB 1980 Aberd.

PORTEOUS, Colin Ross (retired) The Glebe, 200 Prescot Road, Aughton, Ormskirk L39 5AG Tel: 0695 423771 — MB ChB 1953 Liverp.; FRCOG 1975, M 1961, DObst 1958. Cons. O & G Ormskirk & Dist. Gen. Hosp. Prev: Lect. Obst. Univ. Liverp.

PORTEOUS, David John Fishponds Health Centre, Beechwood Road, Fishponds, Bristol BS16 3TD Tel: 0117 908 2365 Fax: 0117 908 2377; 10 Marlfield, Pensby, Wirral CH61 1AJ — MB BS 1991 Lond.; BSc (Hons) Lond. 1988.

PORTEOUS, Elizabeth Mary Ellen 16 Overton Drive, West Kilbride KA23 9LH Tel: 01294 823134 — MB ChB 1977 Ed.

PORTEOUS, George Alexander The Surgery, Victoria Gardens, Lockerbie DG11 2BJ Tel: 01576 203665 Fax: 01576 202773; Janalla, Cargenbridge, Dumfries DG2 8LW Tel: 01387 264042 — MB ChB 1990 Glas. (University of Glasgow)

PORTEOUS, Gordon Sloane 16 Overton Drive, West Kilbride KA23 9LH Tel: 01294 823134 — MB ChB 1976 Ed. GP Ardrossan.

PORTEOUS, Ian Brenton (retired) 79 Woodlands Road, Shotley Bridge, Consett DH8 0DT Tel: 01207 503063 — MB BS 1952 Durh.; MRCPath 1964; DPath Eng. 1961. Prev: Cons. Path. NW Durh. Hosp. Gp.

PORTEOUS, Jean Margaret 140 Hamilton Place, Aberdeen AB15 5BB Tel: 01224 50110 — MB ChB 1949 Liverp. (Liverp.) Med. Off. N.E. Scotl. Transfus. Centre Aberd. Prev: Ho. Phys. & Ho. Surg. Vict. Hosp. Burnley.

PORTEOUS, Leonard Duncan (retired) 13 Dukes Drive, London Road, Leicester LE2 1TP — MRCS Eng. LRCP Lond. 1918. Prev: Temp. Surg. Lt. RN.

PORTEOUS, Lorna Anderson 6 Denecroft, Wylam NE41 8DE — MB ChB 1987 Ed.; MRCGP 1991; DRCOG 1991; DCH RCP Lond. 1990.

PORTEOUS, Margaret Ann 20 Heswall Avenue, Wirral CH63 5QD — MB ChB 1983 Ed.; MRCGP 1988.

PORTEOUS, Mary Elizabeth Muir Clinical Genetics Service, Western General Hospital, Crewe Road, Edinburgh EH4 2XU Tel: 0131 651 1012 Fax: 0131 651 1013 Email: mary.porteous@ed.ac.uk — MB ChB Manch. 1983; MSc Clin. Genetics Glas. 1988; MD Manch. 1992; MRCP (UK) 1989; FRCP Ed 1999. Cons. Clin. Geneticist W.ern Gen. Hosp. Edin.; Sen. Lect. (Clin. Genetics) Univ. Edin.

PORTEOUS, Mr Matthew John Le Fanu West Suffolk Hospital, Hardwick Lane, Bury St Edmunds IP33 2QZ Tel: 01284 713334 Email: matthew.porteous@wsufftrust.org.uk; Hamling House, Bull Road, Pakenham, Bury St Edmunds IP31 2LW — MB BS 1982 Lond.; FRCS (Orth.) 1992; FRCS Eng. 1986. (London Hospital) Cons. (Orthop. Surg.) W. Suff. Hosp. Bury St Edmunds. Socs: Fell. BOA; BMA. Prev: Cons. (Orthop. Surg.) King's Coll. Hosp. Lond.; Sen. Regist. (Orthop.) King's Coll. Hosp. Lond.

PORTEOUS, Michael Belgrave Medical Centre, 22 Asline Road, Sheffield S2 4UJ Tel: 0114 255 1184 — MB ChB 1964 Sheff.; DObst RCOG 1968.

PORTEOUS, Myfanwy Rhiwen Hughes The Glebe, 200 Prescot Road, Aughton, Ormskirk L39 5AG — MB ChB 1949 Liverp.; DPH 1956.

PORTEOUS, Patrick Joseph (retired) Castlebalfour, Lisnaskea, Enniskillen BT92 0LT Tel: 01365 21800 — MB BCh BAO 1947 NUI; FRCGP 1982, M 1961. Prev: Med. Off. Gen. Med. Servs. Bd. Dub.

PORTEOUS, Robert (retired) 4 Merchants Quay, Bristol BS1 4RL — MB BS 1955 Lond.; FFA RCS Eng. 1961. Prev: Cons. Anaesth. Swindon & MarlBoro. NHS Trust.

PORTER, Ada Margaret Grange Road Surgery, Dudley DY1 2AW Tel: 01384 255387/252095 Fax: 01384 242109; 17 Foley Road, Pedmore, Stourbridge DY9 0RT — MB ChB 1958 Birm.; DObst RCOG 1961. (Birm.)

PORTER, Alan Newton Surgery, Park Street, Newtown SY16 1EF Tel: 01686 626221/626224 Fax: 01686 622610 — MB ChB 1982 Glas.

PORTER, Alan Michel Woodward (retired) Redcrest, Heath Rise, Camberley GU15 2ER Email: aporter@talk21.com — MB BS 1954 Lond.; MD Lond. 1968; PhD Lond. 1996.

PORTER, Alexandra Fiona Ivy Cottage, Alpha Place, Trallwn, Pontypridd CF37 4RT Tel: 01443 404556 Email: fiporter@aol.com — MB BCh 1997 Wales. GP Regist. Bridgend S. Wales.

PORTER, Amber Durdana Woolsthorpe Surgery, Main Street, Woolsthorpe, By Belvoir, Grantham NG32 1LX Tel: 01476 870166 Fax: 01476 870560 — MB BS 1968 Punjab; MB BS Punjab (Pakistan) 1968; DCH Eng. 1972. (Fatima Jinnah Med. Coll. Lahore)

PORTER, Andrew Charles 6 Tenter Terrace, Durham DH1 4RD — MB BS 1989 Lond.

PORTER, Andrew John Carlton Street Surgery, Carlton Street, Horninglow, Burton-on-Trent DE13 0TE Tel: 01283 511387 Fax: 01283 517174; 181 Horninglow Street, Burton-on-Trent DE14 1NU Tel: 01283 63561 — MB BS 1974 Lond.

*PORTER, Andrew John 6 Abbey Crescent, Beauchief, Sheffield S7 2QX — MB BS 1996 Newc.

PORTER, Anita 65 Pinner Road, Northwood HA6 1QN — MB BS 1991 Lond.; MRCGP Lond. 1999; DRCORG 1995. (St. Geo. Hosp.) p/t GP Retainer.

PORTER, Barbara Helen Temple Cowley Health Centre, Templar House, Temple Road, Oxford OX4 2HL Tel: 01865 777024 Fax: 01865 777548; Green Glades, 3 bayswater farm Road, Headington OX3 8BX — MB ChB 1987 Ed.; MRCGP 1996. (Ed.) Gen. Practitioner Temple Cowley Med. Gp., Oxf. Socs: BMA; Christian Med. Fell.ship; Med. Wom.s Federat., Treas., Oxf. Br. Prev: Trainee GP Edin.; SHO (O & G) E.. Gen. Hosp. Edin.; SHO (Geriat.) Roy. Vict. Hosp. Edin.

PORTER, Belinda Jane 114 Laurel Avenue, Bridge of Don, Aberdeen AB22 8QJ — MB ChB 1993 Aberd.

*PORTER, Benjamin Gareth 19 Cheriton Place, Westbury-on-Trym, Bristol BS9 4AW — MB BS 1998 Lond.; MB BS Lond 1998.

PORTER, Mr Bertram Butterworth (retired) Glebe House, Tweeds Muir, Biggar ML12 6QP Tel: 01899 880204 — MB ChB 1958 Ed.; MB ChB (Hnrs.) Ed. 1958; FRCS Eng. 1963. Med. Mem. Approach Serv.s (Scotl. Region). Prev: Cons. Orthop. Surg. Dryburn Hosp. Durh.

PORTER, Bryan John Guardian Medical Centre, Guardian St., Warrington WA5 1UD Tel: 01925 650226 — MB ChB 1959 Sheff.; DObst RCOG 1966; DTM & H Eng. 1962. (Sheff.)

PORTER, Charles Andrew 18 Chequers Park, Wye, Ashford TN25 5BB — MB BS 1961 Lond.; MRCP Lond. 1969; MRCS Eng. LRCP Lond. 1961; DObst RCOG 1963. (Middlx.) Cons. Paediat. S.E. Kent, & Canterbury & Thanet Health Dist. Prev: Resid. (Paediat.) Bellevue Hosp. New York City; Regist. Renal Unit Roy. Sussex Hosp. Brighton; Ho. Surg. Whittington Hosp. Lond.

PORTER, Charlotte Lawson House, Sawley, Clitheroe BB7 4NJ — MB BS 1988 Lond.

PORTER, Clement Ian (retired) Elm Cottage, Little Burstead, Billericay CM12 9TJ Tel: 01277 623054 — MRCS Eng. LRCP Lond. 1960. Prev: GP Billericay.

PORTER

PORTER, Crispin Jon, Capt. MDHU Frimley Park, Frimley Park Hospital, Portsmouth Road, Frimley, Camberley Tel: 01276 604604; Garrison Officers Mess, Hospital Road, Aldershot GU11 2AR Tel: 04107 53010 Fax: 01252 669485 — MB ChB 1994 Dundee. (Dundee) SHO (Med.) Frimley Pk. Socs: BASICS. Prev: SHO (A & E) Frimley Pk.; RMO Belf.; RMO Cyprus.

PORTER, Mr Daniel Edward Nuffield Department of Orthopaedic Surgery, Nuffield Orthopaedic Centre, Headington, Oxford OX3 7LD Tel: 01865 741155 Fax: 01865 742348; Green Glade, 3 Bayswater Farm Road, Headington, Oxford OX3 8BX — MB ChB 1989 Ed.; BSc Ed. 1987; MD Ed. 1995; FRCS Glas. 1995; FRCS Ed. 1994. Clin. Lect. (Orthop. Surg.) Univ. Oxf. Prev: Regist. (Orthop.) Lothian HB.; Research Fell. (Surg.) MRC Unit of Human Genetics W.. Gen. Hosp. Edin.

***PORTER, David** Birmingham Childrens Hospital, Steelhouse Lane, Birmingham B4 6NH Tel: 0121 333 9999; Reynolds Barn, Burys Bank Road, Thatcham RG19 8DD Tel: 01635 31839 — MB BS 1998 Lond.; MB BS Lond 1998; BA (Hons) Oxf 1995.

PORTER, Mr David Geoffrey Department of Neurosurgery, Frenchay Hospital, Frenchay Park Road, Bristol BS16 1LE Tel: 0117 975 3959 Fax: 0117 970 1161 — MB BS 1987 Lond.; FRCS 1992; FRCS (SN) 1997. (Royal Free) Cons. (Neurosurg.) Frenchay Bristol. Socs: SBNS; MPS. Prev: Sen. Regist. (Neurosurg.) Leeds Gen. Infirm.; Research Regist. Inst. Neurol. Qu. Sq.; Regist. (Neurosurg.) Roy. Free & Char. Cross.

PORTER, David Ian (retired) Hospital of St Cross, Barby Road, Rugby CV22 5PX Tel: 01788 545196 Fax: 01788 561561 — MB BS 1958 Lond.; FRCP Lond. 1984, M 1962. Prev: Cons. Dermat. Hosp. St. Cross Rugby.

PORTER, David Michael 17 Longmoor Road, Long Eaton, Nottingham NG10 4FQ — MB BS 1982 Nottm.

PORTER, David Robert Flat 2, 5 The Riding, London NW11 8HL — MB ChB 1992 Otago.

PORTER, David Valley (retired) Skeo Green, Lunning, Vidlin, Lerwick ZE2 9QB Tel: 01806 577302 — MB ChB St. And. 1939. Prev: GP Shetland, Wombwell & Dodworth.

PORTER, David William 6 Abbey Crescent, Sheffield S7 2QX — MB ChB 1993 Sheff.

PORTER, Mr Derek Spencer London Independent Hospital, Beaumont Square, London E1 4NL Tel: 020 7790 0990 Fax: 020 7795 0112; 31 Redburn Street, London SW3 4DA Tel: 020 7351 3090 Fax: 020 7351 3090 — MB BS Lond. 1954; FRCS Eng. 1963. (St. Thos.) Socs: Fell. Roy. Soc. Med.; Fell. BOA. Prev: Cons. Orthop. & Trauma Surg. Greenwich Dist. HA; Sen. Regist. (Orthop.) King's Coll. Hosp. Lond.; Regist. (Orthop.) Rowley Bristow Orthop. Hosp.

PORTER, Duncan Roderick Gartnavel General Hospital, 1053 Great Western Road, Glasgow G12 0YN Tel: 0141 211 3262 — BM BCh 1985 Oxf.; MRCP (UK) 1988. Cons. Rheum. Gartnavel Gen. Hosp. Glas.

PORTER, Edward Joseph Brian 89 Elers Road, Ealing, London W13 9QE — MRCS Eng. LRCP Lond. 1976; BSc Lond. 1972, MB BS 1976; FFA RCS Eng. 1980.

PORTER, Edward Robert 10 Lethbridge Park, Bishops Lydeard, Taunton TA4 3QU — MB BS 1998 Lond.; MB BS Lond 1998.

***PORTER, Elizabeth** 146 Maidstone Road, Borough Green, Sevenoaks TN15 8HQ; 2/2 Iseggielea Road, Jordanhill, Glasgow G13 1XJ Tel: 0141 954 8317 — MB ChB 1996 Glas.

PORTER, Fiona Vivien (Smith) 94 Broom Park, Broom Road, Teddington TW11 9RR Tel: 020 8977 1617 Email: fionav.porter@virgin.net — MB BS 1993 Lond.; FRCA 1998; BSc (Hons.) Lond. 1990. (Univ. Coll. & Middlx. Sch. Med.) p/t Specialist Regist. (Anaesth.)Roy. Brompton and Harefield NHS Trust, Lond. Socs: Roy. Coll. Anaesth.; BMA; Assn. Anaesth. Prev: Specialist Regist. (Anaesth.) Roy. Marsden Hosp., Lond.; Specialist Regist. (Anaesth.) Roy. Nat. Throat, Nose and Ear Hosp. Lond..; Specialist Regist. (Anaesth.) Ealing Hosp.

PORTER, Frederick John The Health Centre, Linenhall St., Lisburn BT28 1LU Tel: 01846 666266; 611 Kensington Gardens, Hillsborough BT26 6HP Tel: 01846 682766 — MB BCh BAO 1965 Belf.; FRCGP 1990, M 1973. (Belf.) Hosp. Pract. E. Health & Social Serv. Bd.

PORTER, Frederick Nelson The Croft, 95 Manthorpe Road, Grantham NG31 8DE Tel: 01476 564204 — MB ChB 1970 Sheff.; FRCP Lond. 1994; MRCP (UK) 1975; MRCS Eng. LRCP Lond. 1970; DCH Eng. 1973; FRCPCH 1996; MSc 1999; Post Grad Cert.Managem. 1994. (Sheff.) Cons. Paediat. Child Developm. Centre Nottm. City Hosp. Socs: Collegiate Mem. RCP Edin.; Fell.Roy.Coll.Paediat.Child Health; BMA. Prev: Lect. (Child Health) Univ. Aberd.; Sen. Regist. (Paediat.) Waikato Hosp. Hamilton, NZ; Cons. Paediat. Grantham & Kesteven Gen.

***PORTER, Gareth James Richard** 77 Galwally Avenue, Belfast BT8 7AJ — MB ChB 1996 Bristol.

PORTER, Geoffrey Duncan Gaston Wood, Upper Wyke, St Mary Bourne, Andover SP11 6EA — MB ChB 1957 Ed. Prev: Ho. Surg. Addenbrooke's Hosp. Camb.; Ho. Phys. & Ho. Surg. (Obst.) St. Mary's Hosp. Portsmouth.

PORTER, George Robert York Road, Green Hammerton, York YO26 8BN Tel: 01423 330030 Fax: 01423 331433; Moss House, Crayke YO61 4TQ Tel: 01347 822228 — MRCS Eng. LRCP Lond. 1968. (Univ. Coll. Hosp.) Hon. Med. Off. York City AFC; Examr. in 1st Aid for St. John Ambul. Socs: Roy. Soc. Med.; York Med. Soc. Pres. 2001-2002. Prev: Med. Off. Whixley Hosp. York; Dep. Med. Off. HMP Full Sutton; SHO Lond. Hosp.

PORTER, Mr Graham Charles 1a Briarfield Road, Heswall, Wirral CH60 2TH — MB BS 1990 Lond.; BSc Lond. 1987; FRCS (CSiG) Eng. 1995; FRCS (Oto.) Eng. 1996. Specialist Regist. (OtoLaryngol.) Mersey Region.

PORTER, Mr Graham Peter Frome Farm, West Stafford, Dorchester DT2 8AA Tel: 01305 266872 — MB BS 1973 Newc.; BSc (Hons.) Newc. 1970; FRCS Ed. 1978; FRCOphth 1989; DO RCS Eng. 1978. Cons. Ophth. W. Dorset Gen. Hosp. Trust Dorchester. Socs: S.. Ophth. Soc. & Oxf. Congr. Ophth. Prev: Sen. Regist. Addenbrooke's Hosp. Camb. & Norf. & Norwich Hosp.; Specialist Ophth. Groote Schuur Hosp. Cape Town, S. Afr.

PORTER, Guy Greig Parrot Brow, Woodside Lane, Conoley, Keighley BD20 8PE Tel: 01535 634541 — MB BS 1978 Lond.; MRCP (UK) 1982; FRCR 1988. Cons. Radiol. Airedale Gen. Hosp. Keighley. Prev: Asst. Prof. Radiol. Univ. Miami Florida, USA; Sen. Regist. (Radiol.) St. Jas. Hosp. Leeds.

PORTER, Gwenda Elizabeth The Old Barn, The Street, Shotesham, Norwich NR15 1YL — MB BS 1977 Newc.; FFA RCS Eng. 1982. Cons. Anaesth. Norf. & Norwich Hosp.

PORTER, Helen 69 Fitzgerald House, 169 East India Dock Road, London E14 0HH — MB BS 1990 Lond.

PORTER, Helen Jane Department of Paediatric Pathology, St Michaels Hospital, Southwell St., Bristol BS2 8EG Tel: 0117 928 5310 Fax: 0117 928 5312 Email: helen.porter@bristol.ac.uk — MD 1990 Manch.; MB ChB 1981; FRCPath. Cons. Sen. Lect. Perinatal Path. Univ. Bristol. Prev: Sen. Regist. (Histopath.) Leicester Roy. Infirm.

***PORTER, Helen Patricia** 52 Warmington Road, Birmingham B26 3SY — MB ChB 1996 Leeds.

PORTER, Ian Alexander (retired) Byethorn, Abergeldie Road, Ballater AB35 5RR — MB ChB 1945 Glas.; MD Glas. 1960; FRCPath 1973, M 1963. Prev: Cons. Bact. & Cons. i/c Admin. Regional Laborat. City Hosp. Aberd.

PORTER, Ian John 36 Downend Park, Horfield, Bristol BS7 9PU — MB ChB 1984 Bristol; MRCPsych 1992. Regist. (Psychiat.) Blackberry Hosp. Bristol. Prev: SHO (Psychiat.) Glenside Hosp. Bristol; SHO (ENT & A & E) S.mead Hosp. Bristol; SHO Whakatane Hosp., New Zealand.

PORTER, Jacqueline Sarah Department Anaesthetics, St. Thomas' Hospital, London SE1 7EH Tel: 020 7928 9292; 41 St Martins Road, London SW9 0SP — MB BS 1987 Lond.; MD 2001 Lond.; FRCA 1993. (Univ. Coll. Hosp.) Cons. (Anaesth.) St Thos. Hosp. Lond. Prev: Sen. Regist. St. Thos. Hosp. Lond.

PORTER, James Harrison Lawson House, Bolton-by-Bowland Road, Clitheroe BB7 4NJ — MB BS 1992 Lond.

PORTER, Jane Kreewood, Vicarage Road, Whaddon, Milton Keynes MK17 0LU Tel: 01908 501709 — MB ChB 1967 Liverp.; FFA RCS Eng. 1973. Cons. Anaesth. Milton Keynes Hosp. Socs: Assn. Anaesths.; Obst. Anaesth. Assn. Prev: Sen. Regist. (Anaesth.) Nuffield Dept. Anaesth. John Radcliffe Hosp. Oxf.; Sen. Regist. (Anaesth.) St. Geo. Hosp. Lond.; Regist. (Anaesth.) Kingston-upon-Thames Hosp. & Centr. Middlx. Hosp. Lond.

PORTER, Miss Janet Elizabeth 114 Woodside, Leigh-on-Sea SS9 4RB Tel: 01702 421704 Fax: 01702 421661 Email: j.porter@doctors.org.uk — MA 1972 Camb. 1968; BChir 1971;

FRCS Eng. 1977; FFAEM 1991. Lect. in Med. Eduation, St. Geo.s Hosp. Med. Sch., Lond.; Medico-Legal Cons.; Accid. & Emerg. Cons., P.ss Alexandra Hosp., Harlow. Prev: Cons. (A & E) S.end Hosp.

PORTER, Jayne Margaret 52 Stoneypath, Londonderry BT47 2AF — MB BCh BAO 1986 Belf.

PORTER, Joanna Catherine Mary 114 Hemingford Road, London N1 1DE Email: joporker@114hr.freeserve.co.uk — BM BS 1988 Oxf.; BM BCh Oxf. 1988; MA Camb. 1989; MRCP (UK) 1991; PhD Lond. 1998. (Oxford University) Specialist Regist. (Respirat. / Gen. Med. NE Thames. Prev: ICRF Clin. Fell. ICRF Lond.; MRC Train. Fell. ICRF Lond.; Regist. (Intens. Care) St. Geo. Hosp. Lond.

PORTER, Joanne Norma Chorlton Fold Farm, Rocky Lane, Monton, Eccles, Manchester M30 9NA — MB BS 1987 Lond.; MRCP (UK) 1990. Regist. (Gen. Med. & Cardiol.) W.. Gen. Hosp. Edin.

PORTER, John David The Surgery, Station Lane, Farnsfield, Newark NG22 8LA Tel: 01623 882289 Fax: 01623 882286; 117 Station Lane, Farnsfield, Newark NG22 8LB Tel: 01636 883126 — BMedSci (Hons.) Nottm. 1979, BM BS 1981; MRCGP 1985; DCH RCP Lond. 1984.

PORTER, John David Henley 17 Rigault Road, London SW6 4JJ — MB BS 1977 Lond.; MPH Harvard 1984; MRCP (UK) 1982; MFPHM 1988; DA Eng. 1980; DCH RCP 1982. (King's Coll. Hosp.) Sen. Lect. (Clin. Sci.) Lond. Sch. Hyg. & Trop. Med.; Cons. Epidemiol. Communicable Dis. Surveillance Centre Lond. Prev: Sen. Regist. (Communicable Dis.) Surveillance Centre Lond.; SHO (Neonat. Paediat.) Qu. Charlottes Hosp. Lond.; Epidemic Intellig. Serv. Off. Centers for Dis. Control Atlanta, USA.

PORTER, John Francis Hugh The Cripps Health Centre, University Park, Nottingham NG7 2QW Tel: 0115 950 1654 — MB ChB 1987 Leic.; MSc 1999 (Travel Medicine) Glasgow University; MRCGP 1991; DRCOG 1991. Socs: MRCGP; Mem. of Internat. Travel Med.; Mem. of Brit. Travel Health Assn.

PORTER, Mr John Michael 2 Five Elms Drive, Whitenap, Romsey SO51 5RN Tel: 01794 512784 — MB BS 1969 Lond.; MS Soton. 1988; FRCS Eng. 1974; MRCS Eng. LRCP Lond. 1969; AKC 1969. (King's Coll. Lond. & King's Coll. Hosp.) Prev: SHO (Plastic Surg.) Odstock Hosp. Salisbury; Regist. (Plastic Surg.) Odstock Hosp. Salisbury; Hon. Regist. (Plastic Surg.) Odstock Hosp. Salisbury.

PORTER, John Rendall 327 Salters Road, Gosforth, Newcastle upon Tyne NE3 4HN Tel: 0191 284 0599 — MB BS 1995 Newc.; BA (Hons.) Oxf. 1992. (Oxf. & Newc. u. Tyne) SHO (A & E) Sunderland Dist. Gen. Hosp.

PORTER, Jonathan Mark Walsgrave Hospital, University Hospitals Coventry and Warwickshire NHS Trust, Coventry CV2 2DX Tel: 07770 837901 Fax: 08701 376261 Email: mark.porter@wh_wmids.nhs.uk; 6 Broadsword Way, Burbage, Hinckley LE10 2QL Tel: 07770 837901 Email: mark@porter-home.com — MB ChB 1989 Leic.; BSc Leic. 1983; FRCA 1994; Dip. ATLS RCS Eng. 1996. (Leic.) Cons. Anaesth. with s/i in Obstetric Anaesth. Univ. Hosp.s Coventry & Warks. NHS Trust. Coventry; Co-Clin. director of critical care, Anaesth. & theatres,UHCW NHS Trust. Socs: Obst. Anaesth. Assn.; Assn. Anaesth. GB & Irel.; BMA (former Chairm., Jun. Doctor Comm.; Mem., Centr. Cons.s & Specialists Comm.). Prev: Specialist Regist. (Anaesth.) Coventry Sch. of Anaesth.; SHO (A & E & Intens. Care) Derbysh. Roy. Infirm.; SHO (Anaesth.) P'boro. Dist. Hosp. & Leicester Gp. Hosps.

PORTER, Kamilla Kiron 2 Berners Mansions, 34-36 Berners St., London W1T 3LU Tel: 020 7323 2892 Email: kamillaporter@hotmail.com; 2 Berners Mansions, 34-36 Berners St, London W1T 3LU Tel: 020 7323 2892 — MB BS 1996 Lond.; BSc Lond. 1993; MRCP (UK) Part 1 1998; DCH 1999. (Univ. Coll. Lond. Med. Sch.) SHO (Infec. Dis.s) St. Geo.'s Hosp. Lond. Socs: BMA. Prev: SHO (Gen. Paed) Univ. Coll. Lond. Hosp.; SHO (A&E) Roy. Lond. & Homerton Hosps.

PORTER, Kathryn 108 Pembroke Road, Clifton, Bristol BS8 3EW — MB ChB 1991 Liverp.; MRCP (UK) 1995; DCH RCP Lond. 1996.

PORTER, Mr Keith Macdonald University Hospital Birmingham NHS Trust, Selly Oak Hospital, Raddlebarn Road, Selly Oak, Birmingham B4 6NH Tel: 0121 627 1627 Fax: 0121 627 8075; Woodlands Farm, Chapel Lane, Lower Rowney Green, Alvechurch, Birmingham B48 7QJ Tel: 01527 64466 Email: kmp999uk@compuserve.com — MB BS 1974 Lond.; FRCS Eng. 1978; Dip. IMC RCS Ed. 1992; FRCS Ed. 1998. Cons. Trauma Surg. Univ. Hosp. Birm. NHS Trust. Prev: Cons. Trauma & Orthop. Surg. Birm. Accid. Hosp.; Sen. Regist. & Regist. (Orthop.) Roy. Orthop. Hosp. Birm.; Surg. Regist. Roy. Hosp. Wolverhampton.

PORTER, Professor Kendrick Arthur Reynolds Barn, Burys Bank Road, Thatcham RG19 8DD Tel: 01635 31839 Fax: 01635 33793 — MB BS Lond. 1948; DSc Lond. 1961, MD 1953; MRCS Eng. LRCP Lond. 1948; FRCPath 1972. (St. Mary's) Emerit. Prof. Path. Imperial Coll. Sch of Med. At St Mary's, Univ. Lond.; Vis. Prof. Path. Univ. Pittsburgh Sch. Med.; Hon. Cons. Path. St. Mary's Hosp. Lond. Socs: Path. Soc.; Transpl. Soc. Prev: Research Fell. Harvard Med. Sch.; Brit. Postgrad. Med. Federat. Trav. Fell.; Fulbright Fell.sh.

PORTER, Kevin Greaves Garforth Medical Centre, Church Lane, Garforth, Leeds LS25 1ER Tel: 0113 286 5311 Fax: 0113 281 2679; Blythe House, St. John's Road, Boston Spa, Wetherby LS23 6DD — MB ChB 1974 Leeds; DObst RCOG 1976. (Leeds)

PORTER, Lissy c/o Clifton Ward, Southmead Hospital, Westbury-on-Trym, Bristol BS10 5NB Tel: 0117 959 5871; 52 Devonshire Road, Bristol BS6 7NL Tel: 0117 924 1717 — MD 1983 Aarhus. Clin. Asst. (Psychiat.) S.mead Hosp. Bristol.

PORTER, Lynn Joyce Weavers Lane Surgery, 1 Weavers Lane, Whitburn, Bathgate EH47 0QU Tel: 01501 740297 Fax: 01501 744302; 4 Kettilstoun Mains, Linlithgow EH49 6SN — MB ChB 1980 Aberd.; MRCGP 1984.

PORTER, Margaret Adelaide (retired) Larch Hill, 4 Church Close, Ballylesson, Belfast BT8 8JX Tel: 02890 826805 — MB BCh BAO 1949; MD 1955 Belfast.

PORTER, Mark Christopher Milsom Locking Hill Surgery, Stroud GL5 1UY Tel: 01453 764222 Fax: 01453 756278 Email: drmarkp@aol.com; Email: drmarkp@aol.com — MB BS 1986 Lond.; DCH RCP Lond. 1990; DA (UK) 1989. (Westminster Hospital) p/t GP Strond.; Med. BRd.caster & Med. Jl.ist.

PORTER, Martin Herdman (retired) Len Valley Practice, Tithe Yard, Church Square, Lenham, Maidstone ME17 2PJ Tel: 01622 858341 Fax: 01622 859659 — MB BS 1967 Lond.; MRCGP 1977; DObst RCOG 1969. Prev: SHO (Obst. & Med.) Orsett Hosp.

PORTER, Mr Martin John Worcester Royal Infirmary, Castle St., Worcester WR1 3AS Tel: 01905 760179; Dovecote Barn, Blackhouse Lane, Suckley, Worcester WR6 5DP Tel: 01886 884797 — BM BCh 1984 Oxf.; MD 1997; FRCS (Orl.) 1994; FRCS Eng. 1989. Cons. (ENT) Worcs. Roy. Infirm. & Hereford Co. Hosp. Prev: Head & Neck Fell. Green La. Hosp. Auckland, NZ; Hon. Lect. Chinese Univ. Hong Kong.

PORTER, Mr Martyn Lonsdale Wrightington Hospital for Joint Disease, Hall Lane, Appley Bridge, Wigan WN6 9EP Tel: 01257 256288 Fax: 01257 256291; Email: matyn.porter@ukgateway.net — MB ChB 1979 Manch.; FRCS Ed. (Orth.) 1989; FRCS Ed. 1983. Cons. Orthop. Surg. Hip Centre Wrightington Hosp.; Hon. Sen. Research Fell. (Med. Biophysics) Manch.; Hon. Sen. Lect. Univ. of Centr. Lancs. Socs: BOA Counc. Mem. 2001-2003; Brit. Hip Soc.; B.A.S.K. Prev: Cons. Orthop. Roy. Preston Hosp.; Sen. Regist. (Orthop.) NW RHA; Tutor (Orthop. Surg.) Univ. Manch.

PORTER, Matthew Charles Bromley Crossroads Medical Practice, Moore Lane, North Hykeham, Lincoln LN6 9BA Tel: 01522 682848 — MB ChB 1994 Sheff.; DRCOG 1999 London; DFFP 1998 London. GP Princip.

PORTER, Mr Michael Francis (retired) 30 Anstruther Road, Edgbaston, Birmingham B15 3NW Tel: 0121 684 6644 Fax: 0121 684 6644 Email: michaelporter@compuserve.com — MB BS 1953 Lond.; FRCS Ed. 1960; MRCS Eng. LRCP Lond. 1953. Prev: Cons. Orthop. Surg. E. Birm. Hosp. & Birm. Accid. Hosp.

PORTER, Moira Elaine 8 Moorfoot Way, Baljaffray, Bearsden, Glasgow G61 4RL — MB ChB 1984 Glas.; MB ChB Glas. l984; MRCGP 1988; DRCOG 1986. Trainee GP Glas. VTS. Prev: Regist. (Dermat.) Inverclyde Hosp. Greenock.

PORTER, Mr Nigel Harry (retired) (cons. rooms), 98 The Drive, Hove BN3 6GP Tel: 01273 731807 Fax: 01273 723105 — MB BS 1949 Lond.; FRCS Eng. 1954; LMSSA Lond. 1949. Prev: Sen. Regist. (Surg.), Out-pat. Off. & Ho. Surg. Guy's Hosp. Lond.

PORTER, Patricia Jacqueline Regents Park Surgery, Park Street, Shirley, Southampton SO16 4RJ Tel: 023 8078 3618 Fax: 023 8070 3103; Little Elcombes, Elcombes Close, Lyndhurst SO43 7BB — BM 1982 Soton.; BSc (Psych.) Durham. 1974.

PORTER

PORTER, Mr Paul 53 Kings Road, Weymouth DT3 5ES — BM 1991 Soton.; BSc Glas. 1979; FRCS Glas. 1996. Specialist Regist. Rotat. (Trauma & Orthop.) Castle Hill Hosp. Hull.

PORTER, Mr Richard Royal Victoria Infirmary, Newcastle upon Tyne NE1 4LP Tel: 0191 232 5131; 11 Graham Park Road, Gosforth, Newcastle upon Tyne NE3 4BH Tel: 0191 285 7500 — MB BS 1964 Durh.; FRCS Eng. 1970; FRCOphth 1989; DO Eng. 1968. (Newc.) Cons. Ophth. Roy. Vict. Infirm. Newc. u. Tyne; Hon. Clin. Lect. Univ. Newc. Prev: Clin. Asst. Moorfields Eye Hosp. Lond.; Sen. Regist. (Ophth.) Roy. Vict. Infirm. Newc.; 1st Asst. Dept. Ophth. Univ. Newc.

PORTER, Richard Howell John Elliott Unit, Department of Psychiatry, Birch Hill Hospital, Rochdale OL12 9QB — MB ChB 1982 Manch.; MSc (Psychiat.) Manch. 1991; MRCPsych 1986. Cons. Ment. Illness Rochdale Healthcare Trust. Prev: Sen. Regist. (Psychiat.) NW RHA.

PORTER, Richard James Royal United Hospital, Combe Park, Bath BA1 3NG Tel: 01225 824657 Fax: 01225 825077; Weston Lea, Weston Park, Bath BA1 4AL Tel: 01225 425618 Fax: 01225 429223 Email: rjporter@community.co.uk — BM BCh 1977 Oxf.; MA Oxf. MSc Oxf. 1977; MRCOG 1983; FRCOG 1998. (Oxford) Cons. O & G Roy. United Hosp. NHS Trust & Wilts. Health Care NHS Trust; Clin. director Matern. Serv.s Wilts. Healthcare trust; Hon. Sen. Lect. Soton. & Bristol Univs. Socs: Roy. Soc. Med.; Chairm., Assn. for community based Matern. care. Prev: Sen. Regist. (O & G) St. Mary's Hosp. Lond. & Rosie Matern. Hosp. Camb.; Med. Dir. Wilts. Health Care NHS Trust:.

PORTER, Richard John Flat 8, 6 Riverview Place, Glasgow G5 8EB — MB BS 1989 Newc.; DO Otago 1992. Regist. (Psychiat.) Newc. Gen. Hosp.

PORTER, Professor Richard William 34 Bawtry Road, Doncaster DN4 7AZ Tel: 01302 538888 Fax: 01302 538471 Email: ric.porter@virgin.net — DSc Ed. 2001; MB ChB Ed. 1958; MD Ed. 1981; FRCS Eng. 1966; FRCS Ed. 1961; DObst RCOG 1961. 1st Syme Prof. RCS Ed. Socs: (Pres.) Back Pain Research Soc.; (Counc.) Brit. Orthop. Assn.; Soc. Clin. Anatomists. Prev: Prof. Sir Harry Platt Chair of Orthop. Surg. of Aberd.; Dir. Educat./Train. RCS Ed.; Prof. Orthop. Aberd. Univ.

PORTER, Ruth (retired) Pittville Lodge Cottage, 39 Malden Road, Cheltenham GL52 2BU — MB ChB Ed. 1948; FRCP Lond. 1973, M 1958; FRCPsych 1980, M 1974; DCH Eng. 1951. Prev: Psychotherapist (Old Age Psychiat.) Roy. Free Hosp. & St. Chas. Hosp. Lond.

PORTER, Sally-Anne Mary Department of Addictive Behaviour, St. Georges Hospital Medical School, London SW17 0RE — MB BS 1987 Lond.; MRCPsych 1991. Sen. Lect. & Hon. Cons. Psychiat. St. Geo. Hosp. Med. Sch. Lond. Prev: Sen. Regist. (Addic. Behaviour) St. Geo. Hosp. Med. Sch. Lond.

PORTER, Stephen O'Neill 65 Pinner Road, Northwood HAG 1QN Email: steveporter@hotmail.com — MB BS 1992 Lond.; MRCOG 2001; BSc Lond. 1991. (St. Geo. Hosp.) Specialist Regist. (O & G) NW Thames Rotat. Socs: Blair-Bell research Soc.; Roy. Soc. of Med. Prev: SPR (O & G) Qu. Charlottes & Chelsea Hosps.; SPR (O & G) W.ford Gen. Hosp.; Clin. Research Fell. Roy. Free Hosp.

PORTER, Professor Stephen Ross Department of Oral Medicine, Eastman Dental, Institute for Oral Health Care Sciences, 256 Gray's Inn Road, London WC1X 8LD Tel: 020 7915 1197 Fax: 020 7915 2341 Email: s.porter@eastman.ncl.ac.uk — MB ChB 1991 Bristol; BSc Glas. 1979, BDS 1982; PhD Bristol 1987, MD 1993; FDS RCS Eng. 1987; FDS RCS Ed. 1987. (Bristol) Prof. (Oral Med.) E.man Dent. Inst. for Oral Health Care Scis. & Univ. Coll., Lond.

PORTER, Steven Michael Grove House Surgery, 102 Albert Street, Ventnor PO38 1EU Tel: 01983 852427 — MB ChB 1985 Bristol; MRCGP 1989; DRCOG 1988. Gen. Practitioner, Gr. Ho. Surg., Ventnor. Prev: Trainee GP Bristol.

***PORTER, Stuart William** 23 Blucher Street, Ashton-under-Lyne OL7 9NG — MB ChB 1996 Sheff.

PORTER, Ms Susan MD Alexandra Hospital, Woodrow Drive, Redditch B98 7UB Tel: 01527 503030; Ingeva, Tutnall Lane, Tutnall, Bromsgrove B60 1NA — MB BS 1976 Lond.; BSc (Hons.) Lond. 1973; FRCS Eng. 1982; DO Eng. 1981; FRCOphth. (Westm.) Cons. Ophth. Surg. Alexandra Hosp. Redditch. Prev: Sen. Regist. St. Paul's Eye Hosp. Liverp.

PORTER, Suzanne, Surg. Lt. RN 3A Rutland Lane, Sale M33 2GG Tel: 0161 969 1631 Fax: 0161 969 1631 — MB ChB 1995 Manch.; BSc (Med. Sci.) St. And. 1993. SHO Higher Med. Train. RN; SHO HMS Neptune FasLa. Scotl.; SHO Roy. Hosp. Hasler, Gosport, Hants. Socs: Life Mem. Bute Med. Soc. (St. And.). Prev: SHO (A & E) R Hosp. Haslar; Ho. Off. (Surg.) RN Hosp. Haslar; Ho. Off. (Med.) Blackpool Vict. Hosp.

PORTER, Suzanne Maria Bootham Park Hospital, York YO30 7BY; 134 Glen Road, Oadby, Leicester LE2 4RF — MB ChB 1991 Birm.; MRC Psych. Specialist Regist. (Old Age Psychiat.) Bootham Pk. Hosp. York. (p/t).

PORTER, Timothy Aberhoyw Farmhouse, Cyffredin Lane, Llangynldr, Crickhowell NP8 1LR — MB BS 1988 Lond.

***PORTER, Vanessa Jane** 76 London Road, Hailsham BN27 3DD — BM BS 1998 Nottm.; BM BS Nottm 1998.

PORTER, William Northern General Hospital, Herries Road, Sheffield S5 7AU — MB ChB Glas. 1965; FRCOG 1983, M 1970. Cons. O & G N. Gen. Hosp. Sheff.; Clin. Teach. (Obst. & Gyn.) Univ. Sheff.; Lect. & Examr. Centr. Midw. Bd.; Fell. N. Eng. Obst. & Gyn. Soc. Prev: Cons. O & G Nether Edge Hosp. Sheff.; Sen. Regist. Jessop Hosp. for Wom. Sheff.; Regist. (Obst.) Glas. Roy. Matern. Hosp.

PORTER, William Arthur 38 Woodruff Avenue, Hove BN3 6PH Tel: 01273 550443 — MB BS 1947 Lond.; MRCS Eng. LRCP Lond. 1941. (Guy's) Socs: BMA & Brighton & Sussex M-C Soc. Prev: RAFVR Med. Br.; Ho. Surg. Roy. I. of Wight Hosp. Ryde; Ho. Phys. St. Olave's Hosp. Lond.

***PORTER, William Aubrey Blackwood** 17 Foley Road, Stourbridge DY9 0RT — MB ChB 1986 Manch.

PORTER, William Davis (retired) 19 Annadale Avenue, Belfast BT7 3JJ Tel: 01232 643441 — LAH Dub. 1953. Prev: Sen. Med. Off. Somme Hosp. Belf.

PORTER, William Morier Department of Dermatology, Gloucestershire Royal Hospital, Great Western Road, Gloucester GL1 3NN Tel: 01452 395554 — MB BS 1992 Lond.; BSc 1989; MRCP 1996. (St Mary's) Cons. Dermatol. Gloucestershire Roy. Hosp.; Cons. Cheltenham & Cirencester Gen. Hosps. (NHS); Winfield Hosp. Gloucester (Private). Socs: Brit. Assn. Dermatol.; Dowling Soc.; St John's Dermatological Soc. Prev: SHO Rotat. St Mary's Hosp. Med.; SHO (ITU, A & E & Orthop.) Roy. Sussex Co. Hosp. Brighton; REG (OERM) St. Mary's, Chelsea & W.minster & Char. Cross Hosp.s.

PORTER-BOVERI, Katharina Angelika Morwyn Dundee Royal Infirmary, Barrack Road, Dundee DD1 9ND Tel: 01382 660111 — MB ChB 1976 Birm.; MRCP (UK) 1980; MFCM 1987.

PORTERFIELD, Alexander Gourley (retired) 18 Kings Park, Kingswood Road, Tunbridge Wells TN2 4XF — MB ChB Liverp. 1939.

PORTERFIELD, Alexandra June (retired) The Little Manor House, 9 Manor Close, Tunbridge Wells TN4 8YB Tel: 01892 528261 — MB ChB 1965 Liverp.; FFA RCS Eng. 1968. Prev: Cons. Anaesth. Kent & Sussex Weald Trust.

PORTERFIELD, James Stuart Green Valleys, Goodleigh, Barnstaple EX32 7NH Tel: 01271 345325 Fax: 01271 345325 Email: porterfield@sosi.net — MB ChB Liverp. 1947; MD Liverp. 1949; MRCS Eng. LRCP Lond. 1947. (Liverp.) Emerit. Fell. Wadham Coll. Oxf. Socs: Fell. (Ex-Vice Pres. & Ex-Counc.lor) Roy. Soc. Trop. Med. & Hyg.; Soc. Gen. Microbiol. (Meetings Sec.). Prev: Reader (Bacteriol.) Sir William Dunn Sch. Path. Univ. Oxf.; Mem. Scientif. Staff Nat. Inst. Med. Research Mill Hill.

PORTERFIELD, John Arnold (retired) 4 Princes Close, Berkhamsted HP4 1JS Tel: 01442 876697 — MB BChir 1963 Camb.; MA, MB Camb. 1963, BChir 1962.

PORTERFIELD, Norman Nathaniel The Haven, 1 Horse Lane, Shaldon, Teignmouth TQ14 0BW Tel: 0162 687 2252 — MB ChB 1930 N.Z. (Otago)

PORTERFIELD, Philip Norman Stannery Surgery, Abbey Rise, Whitchurch, Tavistock PL19 9BS Tel: 01822 613517 Fax: 01822 618294 — MB BS 1975 Lond.

PORTERGILL, Nicola Clare The Surgery, Great Lumley, Chester Le Street DH3 4LE Tel: 01474 770 6473, 0191 388 5600 Fax: 01474 705279 Email: narayanasamiramu@aol.com — MB BS 1990 Newc.

PORTLOCK, Kim Michelle 128 Crookes Road, Sheffield S10 5BE — MB ChB 1993 Sheff.

PORTMAN, Eric The Coach House, Newland, Coleford GL16 8NJ — BM 1980 Soton.; PhD, BSc, BM Soton. 1980; DRCOG 1983.

PORTMANN, Professor Bernard Claude Institute of Liver Studies, King's College Hospital, Denmark Hill, London SE5 9RS Tel: 020 7346 3734 Fax: 020 7346 3125 Email: bernard.portmann@kcl.ac.uk; 20 Ewelme Road, Forest Hill, London SE23 3BH Tel: 020 8699 6717 Fax: 020 8291 4006 — MD 1972 Geneva; Dip Federal Switzerland 1966; FRCPath 1989, M 1977. (Geneva) Cons. & Prof. (Histopath.) Inst. Liver Studies King's Coll. Hosp. Lond.; Prof. Hepatpathol. Lond. Univ. 1997. Socs: Brit. Soc. Gastroenterol. Path. Soc. & Internat. Acad. Pathol. Prev: 1st Asst. (Histopath.) Univ. Hosp., Geneva; Research (Histopath.) Clin. Asst. Liver Unit King's Coll. Hosp. Lond.

PORTNOY, Amanda Elizabeth Ilkeston Health Centre, South Street, Ilkeston DE7 5PZ Tel: 0115 932 2933; 6 Birdsall Avenue, Wollaton, Nottingham NG8 2EH — MB ChB 1982 Leic.; BSc Lond. 1976; DRCOG 1986; AKC. GP Princip.; Clin. Asst. (Dermat.) Nottm.; CME Course Organiser Nottm.

PORTNOY, Benjamin, TD (retired) Forest Lodge, Bollinway Hale, Altrincham WA15 0NZ Tel: 0161 980 2307 Email: benann@ndirect.co.uk — MB ChB (Distinc.) Pharmacol. Path. Med. Manch. 1936; PhD New York 1951; MD Manch. 1938; FRCP Lond. 1976, M 1945. JP.; Hon. Cons. Phys. Manch. & Salford Hosp. Skin Dis.; Clin. Lect. (Dermat.) Univ. Manch. 1960; Mem. Gray's Inn. Prev: Chief Med. Asst. (Clin. Investigs. & Research) Manch. Univ. & Infirm.

PORTNOY, David 42 Nottingham Road, Ilkeston DE7 5RE Tel: 0115 932 5229 Fax: 0115 932 5413 — MB ChB 1982 Leic.; BSc Lond. 1976; MRCGP 1988; DRCOG 1987; DA (UK) 1986; AKC 1976.

PORTO, Luiz Otavio da Rocha 102 Ramillies Road, Bedford Park, Chiswick, London W4 1JA — Medico Gama Filho 1976; DMR 1983. Dir. Clin. Research & Developm. Antisoma plc; Clin. Asst. St. Mary's NHS Trust Lond. Socs: Fell. Roy. Soc. Med.; Fac. Pharmaceut. Med. Prev: Med. Dir. Gensia Europe Ltd; Head Clin. Developm. Bayer plc; Regist. (Med.) King's Coll. Hosp. Lond.

PORTSMOUTH, Owen Henry Donald 12 Paddock Drive, Dorridge, Solihull B93 8BZ Tel: 01564 775032 — MB BS Lond. 1953; MA Keele 1993; FRCP Lond. 1977, M 1960; FRCP Ed. 1971, M 1960; DTM & H Eng. 1956. (St. Thos.) Hon. Sen. Clin. Lect. (Biomed. Ethics) Univ. Birm.; Hon. Cons. Phys. (Geriat. & Gen. Med.) Birm. Heartlands & Solihull NHS Trust (Teachg.); Pres. W. Midl. Inst. Geriat. Med. & Gerontol. Socs: Fell. Roy. Soc. Trop. Med. & Hyg.; Brit. Geriat. Soc.; Fell.Roy.Soc.Med. Prev: Cons. Phys. (Geriat.) E. Birm. Hosp. & Solihull HA; Specialist (Med.) Kenya.

PORTSMOUTH, Simon David 20 Falmer Road, London N15 5BA Tel: 020 8800 4164 — MB ChB 1992 Sheff.

PORTWOOD, John Keith (retired) 105 Lansdown Road, Gloucester GL1 3JF Tel: 01452 527116 Email: john.portwood@tesco.net — MB ChB 1961 Birm.; DObst RCOG 1964. Prev: GP Gloucester.

PORTWOOD, Mrs Rosemary (retired) 3 Belmont Villas, The Avenue, Truro TR1 1HS Tel: 01872 273856 — MB BS Lond. 1954; MFFP 1993. SCMO (Instruc.) St. Austell, Truro & Bodmin Family Plann. Clinics & Cervical Cytol. Clinics Cornw. HA.

POSFORD, Peter Cecil Alexandre 16 Harestone Hill, Caterham CR3 6SX Tel: 01883 344563 — MRCS Eng. LRCP Lond. 1936; DObst RCOG 1947. (St. Thos.) Socs: BMA. Prev: Clin. Asst. Mothercraft Dept. & Sen. Obst. Ho. Phys. St. Thos. Hosp.

POSKITT, Elizabeth Margaret Embree, OBE (retired) International Nutrition Group, London School of Hygiene & Tropical Medicine, 49-51 Bedford Square, London WC1B 3DP Tel: 020 7636 8636 — MB 1964 Camb.; BChir 1963; FRCP Lond. 1980, M 1966; FRCPCH 1997. Hon. Sen. Lect. Int. Nutrit. Gp. Lond. Prev: Head of Station, MRC Dunn Nutrit. Gp., Kemeba, Banjul, The Gambia.

POSKITT, Mr Keith Richard Department of Surgery, Cheltenham General Hospital, Sandford Road, Cheltenham GL54 7AN Tel: 01242 222222 — MB ChB 1977 Sheff.; MD Sheff. 1988; FRCS Eng. 1981. Cons. Gen. Vasc. Surg. Cheltenham Gen. Hosp. Socs: Surgic. Research Soc.; Vasc. Surgic. Soc. GB & Irel.; BMA. Prev: Sen. Regist (Gen. Surg.) Bristol Roy. Infirm. & S.mead Hosp. Bristol; Regist. (Gen. Surg.) Char. Cross Hosp. Lond.; Regist. Rotat. (Gen. Surg.) Roy. Hallamsh. Hosp. Sheff.

POSKITT, Michael Graeme 2 Franklins Way Surgery, Franklins Way, Wickford SS11 8AT Tel: 01268 733020 — MB BS 1980 Newc.; DRCOG 1991.

POSKITT, Vivienne Jayne 149 Knighton Field Road E., Leicester LE2 6DR — MB ChB 1993 Leic.

POSMYK, Boleslaw Marek 32 Goodman Park, Slough SL2 5NN — MB ChB 1981 Leeds.

POSNER, Brian Hyman (retired) 39 Moor Crescent, Gosforth, Newcastle upon Tyne NE3 4AQ Tel: 0191 213 1122 Fax: 0191 213 1122 — MB BS Durh. 1957; MRCGP 1965. Sec. Sunderland LMC; Med. Adviser Univ. Sunderland. Prev: GP Sunderland.

POSNER, John BIOS, Consultancy & Contract Research Ltd., Bagshot GU19 5ER Tel: 01276 473363 Fax: 01276 473928; 95 Copers Cope Road, Beckenham BR3 1NY Tel: 020 8650 7521 Fax: 020 8325 8856 — MB BS 1974 Lond.; PhD Lond. 1971, BSc (Hons.) 1968; FRCP Lond. 1991; MRCP (UK) 1976; FFPM RCP (UK) 1995. Med. Dir. BIOS Ltd. Surrey; Hon. Sen. Lect. (Med.) Kings Coll. Sch. Med. & Dent. Lond. Socs: Brit. Pharm. Soc. Prev: Dir. Clin Pharmacol. Studies Glaxo Wellcome Unit N.wick Pk. Hosp.

POSNER, Nicholas Charles Parkway Medical Centre, 2 Frenton Close, Chapel House Estate, Newcastle upon Tyne NE5 1EH Tel: 0191 267 1313 Fax: 0191 229 0630 — MB ChB 1990 Leeds; MRCGP 1994; DFFP 1994; DRCOG 1993. (Leeds) GP Newc.u.Tyne. Prev: Trainee GP N.umbria VTS; Ho. Off. Airedale Hosp. W. Yorks.

POSNER, Philip Joseph James Wigg Group Practice, Kentish Town Health Centre, 2 Bartholomew Road, London NW5 2AJ Tel: 020 7530 4747 Fax: 020 7530 4750; 7 Spencer Rise, London NW5 1AR Tel: 020 7267 5043 — MB ChB 1987 Leeds; MRCGP 1991; DFFP 1993; DRCOG 1990. (Leeds) Socs: BMA. Prev: Trainee GP ScarBoro. Hosp. VTS.; SHO (Palliat. Med.) Edenhall Hospice; SHO (Geriat.) St. Albans City Hosp.

POST, Felix 7 Leeward Gardens, Wimbledon, London SW19 7QR Tel: 020 8946 5600 — MD Lond. 1961, MB BS 1939; FRCP Lond. 1963, M 1944; MRCS Eng. LRCP Lond. 1939; FRCPsych 1971; DPM Eng. 1942. (St. Bart.) Emerit. Phys. Bethlem Roy. & Maudsley Hosps. Socs: Fell. Roy. Soc. Med.; Hon. Fell. Roy. Coll. Psychiats.; Fell. Roy. Coll. Phys. Prev: Maj. RAMC; Assn Phys Edin Hosp; Hon Phys Hammersmith.

POSTINGS, Samantha Jane 8 White's Meadow, Ranton, Stafford ST18 9JB Tel: 01785 282444; 8 White's Meadow, Ranton, Stafford ST18 9JB Tel: 01785 282444 — MB ChB 1990 Leeds. Staff Grade (Paediat.) Shrops. Community NHS Trust Shrewsbury.

POSTIUS CONDE, Camilo Westmorland General Hospital, Burton Road, Kendal LA9 7RG — LMS 1991 Barcelona.

POSTLETHWAITE, Dennis Leslie (retired) Lyndene, 15 Highbury Avenue, Springwell, Gateshead NE9 7PX Tel: 0191 416 3315 Fax: 0191 416 3315 — MB BS Durh. 1948; MRCS Eng. LRCP Lond. 1948. Prev: Flight Lt. RAF Med. Br.

POSTLETHWAITE, Mr John Crispian (retired) Hollybush, Hammonds Lane, Sandridge, St Albans AL4 9BG Tel: 01582 833401 Email: john.pos@tinyworld.co.uk — MB BS Lond. 1963; FRCS Eng. 1971; FRCS Ed. 1969; MRCS Eng. LRCP Lond. 1963. Cons. Surg. Barnet Gen. Hosp.; Hunt. Prof. RCS Eng. Prev: Sen. Regist. (Surg.) Roy. Free Hosp. Lond.

POSTLETHWAITE, Mr Keith Roy High Level Cottage, Prospect Hill, Corbridge NE45 5RU Tel: 01431 633998 Fax: 01434 633998 Email: keith.postlethwaite@virgin.net — MB ChB 1982 Birm.; FRCS Ed. 1987; FDS RCS Eng. 1977. p/t Cons. Oral & Maxillofacial Surg. Newc. Gen. Hosp. W.gate Rd. Newc. u. Tyne; Hon. Clin. Lect. Univ. Newc. Prev: Sen. Regist. (Oral & Maxillofacial Surg.) Clwyd HA; Regist. (Oral & Maxillofacial Surg.) Roy. Surrey Co. Hosp.

POSTLETHWAITE, Robert Joseph Royal Manchester Childrens Hospital, Hospital Road, Pendlebury, Manchester M27 4HA — MB ChB 1970 Manch.; FRCP Lond. 1988; MRCP (UK) 1973. Cons. Paediat. Nephrol. Roy. Manch. Childr. Hosp.; Hon. Lect. (Child Health) Univ. Manch. Prev: Lect. (Child Health) Univ. Manch.; Regist. Hammersmith Hosp. Lond. & Booth Hall Childr. Hosp. Manch.

POSTLETHWAITE, Professor Roy (retired) 6 Rendcomb Drive, Cirencester GL7 1YN Tel: 01285 885345 — MB ChB 1954 Manch.; BSc (Hons. Physiol.) Manch. 1951, MD (Gold Medal) 1959; FRCPath 1973, M 1963. Prev: Personal Chair Virol. Univ. Aberd.

POSTON, Bernard Leslie The Hazeldene Medical Centre, 97 Moston Lane East, New Moston, Manchester M40 3HD Tel: 0161

POSTON, 681 7287 Fax: 0161 681 7438; 73 Bishops Road, Prestwich, Manchester M25 0AS Tel: 0161 773 1008 Fax: 0161 773 1008 — MB ChB Manch. 1956; MRCGP 1976. Prev: Ho. Phys. & Cas. Off. Crumpsall Hosp. Manch.; Ho. Surg. Ancoats Hosp. Manch.

POSTON, Mr Graeme John Royal Liverpool University Hospital, Prescot St., Liverpool L7 8XP Tel: 0151 706 3484 Fax: 0151 706 5827; Linkstone, 201 The Serpentine, Blundellsands, Liverpool L23 6TJ Tel: 0151 924 1820 Email: gjpjap@aol.com — MB BS 1979 Lond.; MS Lond. 1988; FRCS Eng. 1984; FRCS Ed. 1984. (Univ. Lond. & St. Geo. Hosp. Med. Sch.) Cons. Surg. Roy. Liverp. Univ. Hosp.; Lect. (Surg.) Univ. Liverp.; Edit. Bd. Europ. Jl. Surg. Oncol. Socs: (Sec.) Brit. Assn. Surg. Oncol.; (Counc.) Europ. Soc. Surg. Oncol. Prev: Lect. (Surg.) St. Mary's Hosp. Med. Sch. Univ. Lond.; Instruc. (Surg.) Univ. Texas Med. Br. Galveston, Texas; Regist. (Surg.) Hammersmith Hosp. Lond.

POSTON, Margaretta McLean (retired) 4 Alexandra Mews, Queens Road, Oldham OL8 2BN Tel: 0161 665 2528 — MB BCh BAO 1922 Belf. Prev: Cons. Anaesth. Oldham Roy. Infirm. & Oldham & Dist. Gen. Hosp.

POSTON, Richard George Macmillan 105 Queens Road, Oldham OL8 2BA Tel: 0161 624 8364 — MB ChB 1953 St. And. (St. And.) Prev: Paediat. Ho. Phys. & Cas. Off. Dundee Roy. Infirm.

POSTON, Robert Nigel King's College London, Centre for Cardiovascular Biology Medicine, New Hunt's House, Guy's Hospital Campus, London SE1 1UL Tel: 020 7848 6232 Fax: 020 7848 6220 Email: robin@poston.eurobell.co.uk; 11 Marlborough Crescent, Riverhead, Sevenoaks TN13 2HH Tel: 01732 454575 Email: poston@eclipse.co.uk — MD Camb. 1981, MB 1970, BChir 1969; FRCPath 1994, M 1981. (Middlx.) Sen. Lect. (Immunopath.) Kings coll Lond Guy's Hosp. Lond.; Hon. Cons. (Immunol.) Guy's & St Thos. Hosp. Trust. Socs: Roy. Soc. Med.; Path. Soc.; Brit. Soc. Immunol. Prev: Lect. (Path.) Guy's Hosp. Med. Sch.; Brit. Heart Foundat. Jun. Research Fell.; Research Assoc. (Immunol.) Middlx. Hosp. Med. Sch.

POSTON, Rosemary Anne — MB BS 1972 Lond.; MRCGP 1984. (Middlx.) Prev: Princip. GP Melbourne, Derbysh. & Oadby, Leics.

POTAMITIS, Theodoros 26 Cedar Road, Dudley DY1 4HW — MB ChB 1987 Leic.; FCOphth. 1992.

POTDAR, Mr Nandkishore Purushottam Department of Surgery, Grantham & Kesteven General Hospital, 101 Manthorpe Road, Grantham NG31 8DG — MB BS 1978 Bombay; FRCSI 1982.

POTE, Allan Herbert 3 Ripplevale Grove, London N1 1HS Tel: 020 7607 2629 — MB BS 1944 Lond.; LMSSA Lond. 1944. (Lond. Hosp.) Hon. Lect. in Gen. Pract. Univ. Coll. Hosp. Med. Sch. Prev: Asst. Chest Phys. Walthamstow Chest Clinic; Asst. Med. Off. Whipps Cross Hosp.; Graded Chest Phys. RAMC.

POTE, Francis William (retired) Cornheys Farm, Wash, Chapel en le Frith, High Peak SK23 0QW — MRCS Eng. LRCP Lond. 1939. Prev: Med. Admin. War on Want.

POTE, Jonathan Lamington, 32 Willoway Lane, Braunton EX33 1BS Tel: 01271 814412 Email: potes@enterprise.net; Lamington, 32 Willoway Lane, Braunton EX33 1BS Tel: 01271 814412 — MB BS 1972 Lond.; BSc (Human Physiol.) Lond. 1969; MRCS Eng. LRCP Lond. 1972; MRCGP 1982; Dip. IMC RCS Ed. 1993. (Char. Cross Hosp.) Med. Off. AeroMed. Evac. 4626 (Aeromed Evac) Squadron, R Aux AF, Roy. Air Force Lyneham, Wilts. Prev: GP Braunton; Regist. (Gen. Orthop. & Cardiothoracic Surg.) Roy. Brisbane Hosp., Austral.

POTELIAKHOFF, Alexander (retired) Sudbury, 16B Prince Arthur Road, London NW3 6AY Tel: 0207 435 1872 — MB BS 1941 Lond.; MD Lond. 1949; MRCP Lond. 1947; MRCS Eng. LRCP Lond. 1941. Prev: Sen. Regist. (Med.) St. Mary Abbots Hosp. Lond.

POTHANIKAT, Mr George South Tyrone Hospital, Dungannon BT71 4AU Tel: 018657 22821; 8 Viewfort, Killymeal Road, Dungannon BT71 6LP Tel: 018687 26428 — State DMS 1965 Padua; BSc Madras 1958; FRCSI 1985. Assoc. Specialist (Gen. Surg.) S. Tyrone Hosp.

POTHANIKAT, Mary George Waveney Hospital, Cushendall Road, Ballymena BT43 6HH Tel: 01266 653377; 8 Viewfort, Killymeal Road, Dungannon BT71 6LP Tel: 018687 26428 — State DMS 1966 Padua; BSc Mysore 1959; DGO TC Dub. 1976; LM 1975.

***POTHECARY, Ian Colin** 31 Hurst Avenue, Horsham RH12 2EL — MB BS 1998 Lond.; MB BS Lond 1998.

POTIPHAR, Darren Wayne, Surg. Lt. RN 8 Southways, Stubbington, Fareham PO14 2AG Tel: 01329 668039 — MB ChB 1993 Liverp. Med. Off. HMS Collingwood. Prev: Med. Off. HMS Drake; Mixed Module SHO RNH Haslar; Med. Off. HMS Glas. & RNAS Culdrose.

POTKINS, Dawn Victoria 211 Windsor Walk, Kingston Park, Newcastle upon Tyne NE3 2TX — MB BS 1981 Lond.

POTLURI, Mr Bernard Shaw Department Urology, Princess Alexandra Hospital, Hamstel Road, Harlow CM20 1QX Tel: 01279 827092 Fax: 01279 827093 Email: potluri@bigfoot.com — MB BS 1977 Andhra; MS Andhra 1981; FRCS 1989; Dip. Urol. Lond 1991. Cons. Urological Surgeeon P.ss Alexandra Hosp., Harlow. Socs: Brit. Assn. Urol. Surgs. & BMA; Life Mem. Assn. Surg. India; Eur. Assn. of Urol. Prev: Cons. Urol. Hairmyres Hosp. E. Kilbride; Cons. Urol. P.ss Alexandra Hosp. Harlow.

POTOKAR, John Piers Psychopharmacology Unit, School of Med. Sci., Bristol Univ., Bristol BS8 1TD Email: john.potokar@bristol.ac.uk — MB ChB 1987 Birm.; MRCPsych 1991; MD Birm. 2000. Hon. Cons. In Liaison Psychi. Bristol Roy. Infirm. Socs: Coll. Internat. Neuropsychopharmacologicum; Brit. Assn. For Psychopharm. Prev: Lect., Div. of Psychiat. Bristol Univ.; Hon. Sen. Regist. (Psychopharmacol.) Bristol Roy. Infirm.

POTOKAR, Mr Thomas Stephen No 3, Vyvyan Terrace, Clifton, Bristol BS8 — MB ChB 1988 Birm.; FRCS Ed. 1995; DA (UK) 1992; DTM & H Liverp. 1989.

POTRYKUS, Michael The Tollerton Surgery, 5-7 Hambleton View, Tollerton, York YO612EW Tel: 01347 838231 Fax: 01347 838699; 26 Mallison Hill Drive, Easinghold, York YO61 3RY Tel: 01347 821505 — MB ChB 1981 Ed.; BSc Ed. 1979; MRCGP 1985; DRCOG 1985. Bd. Mem. York PCG. Prev: Trainee GP N.allerton VTS.

POTTAGE, Anthony Astra Zeneca Rand D Headquarters, Södertälje S-15185, Sweden Tel: 00 46 8553 26350 Fax: 00 46 8553 28822 Email: anthony.pottage@astrazeneca.com; 14 Caiystane Hill, Edinburgh EH10 6SL Tel: 0131 445 3456 Fax: 0131 445 3456 — MB ChB 1972 Ed.; FRCP Ed. 1985; MRCP (UK) 1975; FFPM RCP (UK) 1989. Vice Pres. R&D Admin. Astra Zeneca Sweden. Prev: Director Clin. Research Astra Clin. Research Unit; Med. Dir. Astra Pharmaceut. Ltd.; Vice-Pres. Clin. Affairs, AB Astra, Sodertalje, Sweden.

POTTAGE, Philip 41 Kendal Road, Stockton-on-Tees TS18 4PU — MB ChB 1976 Ed.

POTTER, Alan (retired) 219 Crofton Lane, Orpington BR6 0BL Tel: 01689 871571 — MB BS 1960 Durh. Prev: Surg. P & O S.N. Co.

POTTER, Alexander Wilson Clydebank Health Centre, Kilbowie Road, Clydebank G81 2TQ Tel: 0141 531 6475 Fax: 0141 531 6478; 19 Campbell Drive, Bearsden, Glasgow G61 4NF Tel: 0141 942 8366 Email: awplg@clinmed.gla.ac.uk — MB ChB 1982 Glas.; MRCGP 1986; DRCOG 1985. (Glasgow) GP Princip.; Vocat. Studies Tutor Glas. Univ.

POTTER, Alice Naghlia 64 Ryecroft Road, London SW16 3EH — LRCPI & LM, LRSCI & LM 1956; LRCPI & LM, LRCSI & LM 1956. (RCSI) Princip. Phys. (Child Health) Richmond Twickenham & Roehampton HA. Socs: Brit. Paediat. Assn. & Fac. Community Health of Soc. Community Med. Prev: SCMO (Community Health) Merton, Sutton & Wandsworth; AHA (T); Hon. Clin. Asst. (Child Health) King's Health Dist. (T).

POTTER, Andrew Boyce North Road West Medical Centre, 167 North Road W., Plymouth PL1 5BZ — MB ChB 1989 Bristol; MRCGP 1995; DRCOG 1992; Dip. IMC RCS Ed. 1993; DFFP 1995. (Bristol)

POTTER, Andrew Robert, MBE 7 St Peter's Close, Goodworth Clatford, Andover SP11 7SF; BP 924, Parakou, Benin Tel: 229 61 11 09 Fax: 229 61 08 91 Email: postmast@parakou.sim.org — MB BChir 1975 Camb.; MA Camb. 1976; MRCGP 1981; MRCOphth 1988; DTM & H Liverp. 1989; DO RCPSI 1985; DA Eng. 1980; Cert. JCC Lond. 1980; DRCOG 1979. (Cambridge University and Westminster Medical School) Ophth. Hopital St. Jean De Dieu Boko. Parakou, Benin; Vis. Ophth. Hosps. In Benin, Burkina Faso & Niger. Socs: BMA. Prev: Ophth. Centre Hosp.ier, Abomey, Benin.

***POTTER, Andrew William** 6 Patterdale Road, Bebington, Wirral CH63 3BN — MB ChB 1998 Manch.; MB ChB Manch 1998.

POTTER, Caroline Ruth Grace Hungerford Medical Centre, School Crescent, Crewe CW1 5HA Fax: 01270 216330; Hassall Gate

Cottage, Hassall, Sandbach CW11 4SB Tel: 01270 767527 — MB ChB 1986 Manch.; BSc (Hons.) Physiol. 1983; MRCGP 1990; DCH RCP Lond. 1989; Cert. Family Plann. JCC 1989; DRCOG 1989. (Manch.) Retainer Scheme; Clin. Asst. Palliat. Care, St. Luke's Hospice, Guildford. Prev: Trainee GP Wigan VTS; SHO (O & G) Billinge Hosp. Wigan; Clin. Med. Off. (Child Health) Tunbridge Wells.

POTTER, Christian Paul Sheridan 12 Nursery Close, Headington, Oxford OX3 7AG — BM BCh 1994 Oxf.; MA (Hons.) Oxf. 1994. (Oxf.) SHO (ENT) S.mead Hosp. Bristol.

POTTER, Christopher John Frederick (retired) 45 Seabrook Road, Hythe CT21 5LX Fax: 01303 267116 — MA, MB BChir Camb. 1955; FFA RCS Eng. 1963; DA Eng. 1958. Cons. Anaesth. SE Kent NHS Trust. Prev: Sen. Regist. St. Mary's Hosp. Lond.

POTTER, Christopher Michael 34 Beachcroft Road, Kingswinford DY6 0HX — MB ChB 1983 Birm. Ho. Off. (Surg.) E. Birm. Hosp. Prev: Ho. Off. (Med.) Good Hope Hosp. Sutton Coldfield.

POTTER, Mr David Northern General Hospital, Herries Road, Sheffield S5 7A Tel: 0114 243 4343; 89 High Storrs Drive, Greystones, Sheffield S11 7LN — MB ChB 1990 Sheff.; FRCS Eng. 1995. Socs: Assoc. Mem. BOA; BESS; BOTA. Prev: Regist. (Orthop. Surg.) Rotherham Dist. Gen. Hosp.; Specialist Regist. (Orthop. Surg.) Barnsley Dist. Gen. Hosp.; Specialist Regist. (Orthop. Surg.) N. Gen. Hosp.

POTTER, Dennis Ralph (retired) 64 Ryecroft Road, London SW16 3EH — MB BS 1957 Lond.; MRCS Eng. LRCP Lond. 1957; FFA RCS Eng. 1964. Prev: Cons. Anaesth. King's Coll. Hosp. Lond.

POTTER, Elizabeth Sara 4 Bramford Terrace, 23 Westfield Park, Redland, Bristol BS6 6LT — MB ChB 1981 Bristol; DRCOG 1985.

POTTER, Frances Aileen (retired) 63 Polwarth Road, Brunton Park, Newcastle upon Tyne NE3 5NE Tel: 0191 236 2059 — MB ChB 1941 Manch.; BSc Manch. 1938, MB ChB 1941; DCH Eng. 1947. Prev: Sen. Med. Off. Family Plann. N. Tyneside AHA.

POTTER, Francis Anthony 17 Shaws Drive, Wirral CH47 5AP — MB ChB 1983 Manch.

POTTER, Geoffrey James Arthur The Surgery, Denmark Street, Darlington DL3 0PD Tel: 01325 460731 Fax: 01325 362183; 17 Abercorn Court, High Grange, Darlington DL3 0GF Tel: 01325 361309 — MB ChB 1980 Leeds; MRCGP 1984; DRCOG 1983; Dip. Med. Educat. 1995. Course Trainer, Cleveland VTS.

***POTTER, Gillian Margaret** 2F3 139 Buccleuch Street, Edinburgh EH8 9NE; 22 Howieston Avenue, Boiness, Edinburgh EH51 9JG Tel: 01506 510505 Email: potter22@hotmail.com — MB ChB 1998 Ed.; MB ChB Ed 1998; BSc (Hons) Med Sci 1995.

POTTER, Heather Christine Skewen Medical Centre, Queens Road, Skewen, Neath SA10 6UL Tel: 01792 812316 Fax: 01792 323208; 68 Derwen Fawr Road, Derwen Fawr, Swansea SA2 8AQ Tel: 01792 203440 — MB ChB 1985 Manch.; MRCGP 1991.

***POTTER, Helen Louise Zoe** 14 Gallacher Way, Saltash PL12 4UT — MB BS 1997 Lond.

POTTER, Hilary Anne Furnace House Surgery, St. Andrews Road, Carmarthen SA31 1EX Tel: 01267 236616 Fax: 01267 222673; Y Wern, Capel Dewi, Carmarthen SA32 8AY Tel: 01267 290084 — MB BCh 1978 Wales; DCH RCP Lond. 1983. (Welsh Nat. Sch. Med.)

POTTER, Jacobus Louw (retired) 40A Morningside Park, Edinburgh EH10 5HA Tel: 0131 447 8467 Email: 113000.162@compuserve.com — MB ChB 1948 Ed.; FRCP Ed. 1971, M 1953. Prev: Exec. Dean Fac. Med. Univ. Edin.

POTTER, Jane Rhoda 7 Longlands, Worthing BN14 9NS — MRCS Eng. LRCP Lond. 1979; BSc (Hons.) Lond. 1976, MB BS 1979; MRCGP 1985; T(GP) 1992; DCH RCP Lond. 1989. (Guy's)

POTTER, Janette Marie 25 Penrith Avenue, Giffnock, Glasgow G46 6LU — MB ChB 1985 Glas.; FRCP Glas.; MRCP (UK) 1989. Cons. Phys. Med. for Elderly & Stroke Vict. Infirm. Glas.; Hon. Clin. Sen. Lect. Glas. Univ.; Hosp. sub dean Vict. Infirm. Glas.

POTTER, Jeanette Dawn Francesca 2 Sycamore Close, Chalfont St Giles HP8 4LF — MB BS 1993 Lond.

POTTER, Jennifer Gae Lower Gnd. Floor, Adamson Centre, Sth. Wing, Block 8, St. Thomas's Hospital, Lambeth Palace Road, London SE1 7EH Tel: 0207 928 9292 Ext: 2272 Fax: 0207 960 5663 Email: jenny.potter@slam-tr.nhs.uk — MB ChB 1977 Cape Town; MRCPsych 1982; BSc Natal 1972. p/t Cons. Psychotherapist St. Thomas's Hosp. Lond. Prev: Sen. Reg. Tavistock Clinic (Psychoth.) Tavistock & Portman NHS Trust; Sen. Reg. Cassel Hosp. (Psychoth.) Riverside NHS Trust Lond.; SHO. & Reg. (Psychiat.) Roy. Beth. & Maudsley Hosps. Lond.

POTTER, Mr John 1 Greystoke Park, Gosforth, Newcastle upon Tyne NE3 2DZ — MB BS 1938 Durh.; FRCS Ed. 1942. (Durh.) Socs: Brit. Assn. Plastic Surg. Prev: Plastic Surg. Teesside, Darlington & N.allerton Hosp. Gps.; Plastic Surg. Shotley Bridge Hosp. & Newc. Gen. Hosp.; Maj. RAMC. Surg. Specialist.

POTTER, Professor John Francis University Department of Medicine for the Elderly, The Glenfield Trust Hospital, Groby Road, Leicester LE3 9QP Tel: 0116 256 3365 Fax: 0116 232 2976 Email: jp34@le.ac.uk — BM BS 1976 Nottm.; DM Nottm. 1989, BM BS 1976; FRCP Lond. 1992; MRCP (UK) 1979. Prof. Med. for Elderly. Univ. Leicester; Frohlich Vis. Prof. Roy. Soc. Med. Socs: Internat. Soc. Hypertens.; Exec. Comm. Mem. Brit. Hypertens. Soc.; Assn. Phys.

POTTER, John Maclaren 15 Lynton Road, Queens Park, London NW6 6BD — BM BCh 1988 Oxf.; FRCS Eng.; BA Camb. 1985. Specialist Regist. Urol. The Roy. Free Hosp. Lond. Prev: SHO Urol. Battle Hosp. Reading.

POTTER, Mr John McEwen 47 Park Town, Oxford OX2 6SL Tel: 01865 557875 — MB BChir 1943 Camb.; MA Camb. 1945; DM Oxf. 1964; FRCS Eng. 1951; MRCS Eng. LRCP Lond. 1943. (Camb. & St. Bart.) Socs: Emerit. Mem. (Ex-Hon. Sec. & Arch.) Soc. Brit. Neurol. Surg.; Corr. Mem. Amer. Assoc. Neurol. Surgs.; Roy. Soc. Med. Ex-Pres. Sect. Neurol. Prev: Emerit. Fell. Wadham Coll. Oxf.; Dir. Postgrad. Med. Educat. Univ Oxf.; Cons. Neurosurg. Radcliffe Infirm. Oxf. & Manch. Roy. Infirm.

***POTTER, John Michael** 8A Neptune Close, Murdishaw, Runcorn WA7 6JX — MB ChB 1997 Dund.

POTTER, John Richard Crisop Woodford Surgery, 29-31 Chantry Lane, Grimsby DN31 2LS Tel: 01472 342325 Fax: 01472 251739; 2 Devonshire Avenue, Grimsby DN32 0BW Tel: 01472 276228 Email: 101623.2123@compuserve.com — MB ChB 1980 Sheff.; FRCGP 1996, M 1984. Course Organiser N. Lincs. VTS.

POTTER, Jonathan Martin Kent and Canterbury Hospital, Canterbury CT1 3NG Tel: 01227 766877; Tyler Hall, Summer Lane, Tyler Hill, Canterbury CT2 9NJ Tel: 01227 471682 — BM BCh 1973 Oxf.; DM 1983 Oxf.; FRCP (UK) 1992. (St Thomas's) Cons. Phys. (Geriat. Med.) Kent & Canterbury Hosp.; Hon. Sen. Research Fell. Centre for Health Serv. Studies Univ.of Kent; Hon. Sen. Lect. Kent Inst. of Health & Med. Scis.; Assoc. Director, Clin. Effectivness and Eval. Unit, Roy. Coll. of Phys.s, Lond. Socs: Brit. Geriat. Soc. Prev: Sen. Regist. (Gen. & Geriat. Med.) Roy. Hallamsh. Hosp. & Nether Edge Hosp. Sheff.; Radcliffe Trav. Fell. N.W.. Univ. Med. Center, USA.

***POTTER, Lucy Mary** 29 West End, Whittlesford, Cambridge CB2 4LX — BM 1997 Soton.

POTTER, Mr Mark Adrian 33 Muir Wood Drive, Currie EH14 5EZ — MB ChB 1990 Ed.; FRCS Eng. 1994.

POTTER, Michael Neil Department of Haematology, Royal Free Hospital School of Medicine, Rowland Hill St., London NW3 2PF Tel: 020 7794 0500 Fax: 020 7794 0645 Email: potter@rfc.ucl.ac.uk; 141 North Hill, Highgate, London N6 4DP Tel: 020 8348 4040 — MB BS 1984 Lond.; PhD Bristol 1993; MA Camb. 1984; MRCP (UK) 1987; MRCPath 1993. (Univ. Camb., Univ. Lond. & Middlx. Hosp.) Cons. & Sen. Lect. (Haemat.) Roy. Free Hosp NHS Trust & Roy. Free & Univ coll med sch Lond.; Hon Cons (Haemat) Gt Ormond St. Hosp for Childr. NHS Trust. Socs: ASH; BSH; (Sec.) Brit. Soc. Blood & Marrow Transpl. Prev: Cons. & Sen. Lect. (Haemat. & Bone Marrow Transpl.) United Bristol Healthcare Trust & Univ. Bristol; Sen. Regist. (Haemat.) Yorks. RHA; Research Regist. (Paediat. Haemat.) Bristol Childr. Hosp. & Bristol Univ. Med. Sch.

POTTER, Neil David Mowbray Marden Medical Centre, Church Green, Marden, Tonbridge TN12 9HP Tel: 01622 831257 Fax: 01622 832840; 1A Mill Bank, Headcorn, Ashford TN27 9QX Tel: 01622 891971 Fax: 01622 891971 — MB BChir 1991 Camb.; MA Camb. 1992; MRCGP 1995; DFFP 1996; DCH RCP Lond. 1993. (Cambridge) GT Princip. Socs: (Founder Mem.) Maidstone Area New Genuinely Young Principles and Recent Train.s Soc. Prev: Trainee GP Maidstone VTS; SHO Nat. Wom. Hosp. Auckland, NZ.

POTTER, Patricia Eustace Holywell Hospital, Steeple Road, Antrim BT41 2RJ; 39 Osborne Park, Belfast BT9 6JP — MB BCh BAO 1959 Belf.; BSc Belf. 1956, MB BCh BAO 1959; MRCPsych 1972; DPM

POTTER

RCPSI 1963. (Qu. Univ. Belf.) Cons. Psychiat. Holywell Hosp. Antrim. Socs: Roy. Med.-Psych. Assn. Prev: Asst. Psychiat. Purdysburn Hosp. Belf.

*POTTER, Rachel Louisa 4 Barrington Road, Rushden NN10 0NJ Tel: 01933 56982 — MB BS 1994 Lond.

POTTER, Robert Graham Department of Child & Family Psychiatry, Royal United Hospital, Bath BA1 3NG Tel: 01225 825075 Fax: 01225 825076; Abbey View House, Abbey View, Bath BA2 6DG Tel: 01225 333774 Email: bob.potter@argonet.co.uk — MB ChB 1971 Bristol; MRCPsych 1975. (Bristol) Cons. Child Psychiat. Roy. United Hosp. Bath. Socs: Assn. Psychiat. Study Adolesc.; Assn. Child Psychol. & Psychiat. Prev: Sen. Regist. (Child & Adolsc. Psychiat.) Warneford & Pk. Hosp. Oxf.; Sen. Regist. (Psychiat.) Profess. Dept. Psychiat. Warneford Hosp. Oxf.

POTTER, Robert John 68 Derwen Fawr Road, Sketty, Swansea SA2 8AQ — MB ChB 1985 Manch.

POTTER, Russell Shaw 47 Earls Way, Ayr KA7 4HQ — MB ChB 1994 Glas. Dir. Medic8.com.

POTTER, Samantha Margaret Balmore Park Surgery, 59A Hemdean Road, Caversham, Reading RG4 7SS — MB BS 1991 Lond.; BSc (Med. Microbiol.) Lond. 1988; MRCGP 1996; DFFP 1996; DRCOG 1995. p/t GP Princip., Balmore Pk. Surg. Prev: SHO (Cas.) Chase Farm Hosp. Enfield; GP Regist. Wycombe VTS.

POTTER, Samuel James Owen 30 Brisbane House, The Fairway, Midhurst GU29 9JE Tel: 01730 813727 — MB ChB 1996 Dundee; BSc (Hons.) Pharm. Dund 1989.

POTTER, Sara Maureen (retired) Honey House, Lodes Lane, Kingston St Mary, Taunton TA2 8HU — MB BCh 1944 Wales; LM Rotunda 1947. Prev: Ho. Surg. Roy. W. Sussex Hosp. Chichester & Roy. Surrey Co. Hosp.

POTTER, Sarah Frances Kelso Medical Group Practice, Health Centre, Inch Road, Kelso TD5 7JP Tel: 01573 224424 Fax: 01573 226388; Ferneyhill Cottage, Kelso TD5 7SU — MB ChB 1990 Ed.

*POTTER, Stephen Mark 3 Halterburn Close, Kingsmere, Gosforth, Newcastle upon Tyne NE3 4YT — MB ChB 1994 Ed.

POTTER, Susan Jane 12 Colshaw Road, Stourbridge DY8 3AS — BM BS 1989 Nottm.; DRCOG 1992. Socs: Roy. Coll. Gen. Pract.

*POTTER, Susan Michelle 106 St James Road, Upper Shirley, Southampton SO15 5HF — MB BS 1998 Lond.; MB BS Lond 1998.

*POTTER, Tanya Buchanan 1 Margaret Street, Derby DE1 3FE — MB ChB 1994 Sheff.

POTTER, Vanessa Alice Joyce 8 Mithras Close, Dorchester DT1 2RF — MB ChB 1992 Birm.

POTTER, Vanessa Jane Faversham Health Centre, Bank St., Faversham ME13 8QR Tel: 01795 562011; Tyler Hall, Tyler Hill, Canterbury CT2 9NJ Tel: 01227 471682 — MB BS 1974 Lond.; DRCOG 1988. (St. Thomas's Hosp. Med. Sch.) GP.

POTTERTON, Amanda Jane Department of Radiology, Royal Victoria Infirmary, Newcastle upon Tyne NE1 4LP Tel: 0191 282 4431 Email: ajpotterton@ukonline.co.uk; 15 Gosforth Terrace, South Gosforth, Newcastle upon Tyne NE3 1RT Tel: 0191 284 6193 — MB BS 1985 Newc.; MRCP (UK) 1989; FRCR 1992. (Newcastle) Cons. Diagnostic Radiol. Newc. Hosps. NHS Trust; Cons. radiologist.brE. screening & Assessm. centre,Qu. Eliz. Hosp. Prev: Sen. Regist. (Diag. Radiol.) N.. RHA Newc. u Tyne; Regist. (Gen. Med.) Gateshead HA; SHO (Gen. Med.) Sunderland HA.

POTTERTON, Karen Louise Woodlands Health Centre, Paddock Wood, Tonbridge TN12 6AX Tel: 01892 833331 Fax: 01892 838269 — MB BS 1992 Lond.

POTTERTON, Olivia Maud 88 Huntington Road, York YO31 8RN; 5 Mossley Hill Drive, Liverpool L17 1AJ Tel: 0151 724 6376 — MB BCh BAO 1987 Dub.

*POTTINGER, Gillian Ruth Field House, Brimfield, Ludlow SY8 4NX — BM BCh 1996 Oxf.; BA Oxf. 1993.

POTTINGER, Kenneth Hay Sinclair 239 Westminster Road, Liverpool L4 4LS Tel: 0151 922 3510 — MB ChB 1945 Ed. (Ed.)

POTTINGER, Kerry Anne 1 Finchall Croft, Solihull B92 9QP — MB ChB 1983 Birm.; FCAnaesth 1991.

POTTINGER, Ronald Forbes 8 West View, Alveston, Bristol BS35 3RN — MB ChB 1959 Ed.; DO Eng. 1963; Regist. Bristol Eye Hosp.

POTTS, Mr David John c/o Accident & Emergency Department, Wycombe General Hospital, High Wycombe HP11 2TT Tel: 01494 425318 — MB BCh 1981 Wales; BSc (Hons.) Anat. Wales 1978; FRCS Eng. 1987. Cons. A & E Wycombe Gen. Hosp.

POTTS, Donald Agar c/o The Old New House, Avon Dassett, Leamington Spa; 1228 Kensington Road, Calgary Alb. T2N 4PQ, Canada — MRCS Eng. LRCP Lond. 1953; MD Alberta 1958. Asst. Prof. Univ. of Calgary Med. Sch.; Chief of Staff Sarcee Auxil. Hosp. Calgary Alta; Med. Dir. Bowcrest Nursing Home Calgary Alta. Prev: Chief of Staff Col. Belcher Hosp. Calgary.

POTTS, Elizabeth Deirdre Ann Oakwood Lodge, 6 Park Avenue, Leeds LS8 2JH — MB BCh BAO 1972 Belf.; MB BCh BAO (Hons.) Belf. 1972; FRCP Lond. 1993; MRCP (UK) 1976; DObst RCOG 1974. Cons. Dermat. Halifax Gen. Hosp.

POTTS, Mr Hamish Elder 132 Bentinck Drive, Troon KA10 6JB Tel: 01292 318789; The Ayr Hospital, Dalmellington Road, Ayr KA6 6DX — MB ChB 1976 Glas.; BSc Glas. 1970; FRCS Ed. (Orth.) 1990; FRCS Glas. 1984. Cons. Orthop. Surg. The Ayr Hosp. Socs: Fell. BOA. Prev: Sen. Regist. Edin.; Surg. Lt. RN.

POTTS, Jane Jason 27 Murray Road, Northwood HA6 2YP Tel: 01923 825318 — MB ChB 1971 Leeds; DObst RCOG 1976. Psychiat. Hounslow & Spelthorne AHA.

*POTTS, Katherine Anne 51A Northcross Road, London SE22 9ET — MB BS 1998 Lond.; MB BS Lond 1998.

POTTS, Lindsay Fraser Raigmore Hospital, Inverness IV2 3UJ Tel: 01463 704000 Fax: 01463 705460 Email: lindsay.potts@raigmore.scot.nhs.uk; Hillside, Upper Myrtlefield, Nairnside, Inverness IV2 5BX — MB ChB 1985 Ed.; BSc Physiol. Ed. 1983; MRCP (UK) 1989. Cons. (Phys.) Raigmore Hosp. Inverness. Socs: BMA; Roy. Soc. Med.; Brit. Soc. Gastro. Prev: Regist. (Geriat.) Edin.

POTTS, Mrs Lorna Anne Village Green Surgery, The Green, Wallsend NE28 6BB Tel: 0191 262 3252 Fax: 0191 263 4260; 5 Beverley Park, Monkseaton, Whitley Bay NE25 8JL — MB BS 1959 Durh. Prev: Ho. Phys. Sunderland Roy. Infirm.; Ho. Off. (Paediat.) Sunderland Child. Hosp.

POTTS, Mary Anne 1 Chapel Row, Sandhutton, Thirsk YO7 4RW Tel: 01845 587333 — MB ChB 1978 Cape Town. GP Trainee.

POTTS, Michael 10 High Bury, Newcastle upon Tyne NE2 3DX — MB BS 1985 Newc.; FRCS Glas. 1995; FFAEM (UK) 1999.

POTTS, Mr Michael John (private rooms), 2 Clifton Park, Clifton, Bristol BS8 3BS Tel: 0117 973 5904 Fax: 0117 973 0887; 192 Stoke Lane, Westbury on Trym, Bristol BS9 3RU Tel: 0117 968 7550 — PhD Bristol 1979, BSc (Hons.) (Physics) 1973, MB ChB 1981; FRCS Eng. (Ophth.) 1986; FRCOphth 1989. Cons. Ophth. Bristol Eye Hosp. Socs: Europ. Soc. Plastic. & Reconstruc. Surg. Prev: Oculoplastic Fell. Moorfields Eye Hosp. Lond.; Sen. Regist. Moorfields Eye Hosp. Lond.; Regist. (Ophth.) Bristol & W.on HA.

POTTS, Nicolette Jane 12 Holt Park Gardens, Leeds LS16 7RB — MB ChB 1994 Leics.

POTTS, Roger Karl Shadwell Medical Centre, 137 Shadwell Lane, Leeds LS17 8AE Tel: 0113 293 9999 Fax: 0113 248 5888 — MB BS 1972 Lond.; MRCS Eng. LRCP Lond. 1972. (King's College Hospital Medical School London)

POTTS, Stephen Graham Royal Infirmary of Edinburgh, Edinburgh EH3 9YW Tel: 0131 536 2875 Fax: 0131 536 3408 — BM BCh 1982 Oxf.; MA Camb. 1985, BA 1979; MRCPsych 1990. (Oxf.) p/t Cons. Liaison Psychiat. (Psychol. Med.) Roy. Infirm. Edin. Socs: Roy. Coll. Psychiat. Prev: Regist. (Psychiat.) Maudsley Hosp. Lond.; Sen.Regist. (Psychiat.) Roy. Edin. Hosp.; Hon.Sen.Regist. (Psychiat.) & Research Fell.Unov.Edin.

POTTS, Timothy Marc Victoria Surgery, Victoria Road, Rhymney NP22 5NU Tel: 01685 840614 Fax: 01685 843770; Wenallt Fach, Gilwern, Abergavenny NP7 0HP Tel: 01873 832221 — MB BCh 1986 Wales; BDS Wales 1977; MRCGP 1993; FDS RCS Eng. 1982; Dip. IMC RCS Ed. 1989; DCH RCP Lond. 1988. (University of Wales) Med. Off. Longtown Mt.ain Rescue Team; Mem. Mid. Glam. Emerg. Doctor Serv. Socs: Brit. Assn. Immed. Care Schemes. Prev: Trainee GP N. Gwent VTS; Regist. (Oral & Dent. Surg.) Bristol Dent. Hosp.

POTTS, Wendy Ann 53 Parkway, New Mills, High Peak SK22 4DU — MB ChB 1992 Ed.

POTU, Mr Prabhakar Hadleigh, Rolvenden Road, Benenden, Cranbrook TN17 4EH — MB BS 1970 Osmania; FRCS Ed. 1988; FRCOphth 1989; DO RCPSI 1978.

POULDEN, Mr Mark Alan 9 Dysgwylfa, Sketty, Swansea SA2 9BG Tel: 01792 207458 — MB BCh 1992 Wales; FRCSI 1997. Specialist

Regist. All Wales A & E Team. Prev: SHO (A & E) Morriston Hosp. Swansea.

POULIER, Robin Arcot Ilkley Health Centre, Springs Lane, Ilkley LS29 8TQ; 53 Ben Rhydding Road, Ilkley LS29 8RN — MB BS 1980 Newc.; MRCGP 1984; Dip. Palliat. Med. Wales 1992; DCCH RCGP & FCM 1984; DRCOG 1983; Cert. Family Plann. RCOG & RCGP 1982. Med. Off. Marie Curie Cancer Care Ilkley. Prev: Trainee GP N.Id. VTS; Ho. Phys. Freeman Hosp. Newc.; Ho. Surg. Sunderland Roy. Infirm.

POULLIS, Andrew Patroclos 8 Butlers Close, Amersham HP6 5PY — MB BS 1994 Lond.; BSc 1991; MRCP 1997.

POULSEN, Helle 10 Parkside, High St., Worthing BN11 1NB — MD 1983 Copenhagen.

POULSEN-HANSEN, Alfred Gerhardt (retired) 24 Noel Road, London N1 8HA Tel: 020 7226 8037 — MD 1941 Copenhagen; MFCM 1974; DPH Lond. 1952; DTM & H Liverp. 1948. Prev: Dep. MOH Harlow & Epping UDCs & Epping & Ongar RDC & Asst. Co. Med. Off. Essex CC.

POULSOM, William John High Walls, Over Court, Over La., Almondsbury, Bristol BS32 4DG — MB BS 1966 Lond.; MRCS Eng. LRCP Lond. 1966; MFCM 1979; DPH Bristol 1972; DObst RCOG 1969.

POULSON, Arabella Valentine 46 Ross Street, Cambridge CB1 3BX — MB BS 1989 Lond.; FRCOphth 1995.

***POULTER, Andrea Elizabeth** 20 Manse Road, Newtownards BT23 4TP — MB BCh BAO 1996 Belf.

POULTER, Professor Neil Reginald Cardiovascular Studies Unit, Clinical Pharmacology & Therapeutics, Imperial College School of Medicine, St Mary's Campus, London W2 1PG Tel: 020 7594 3446 Fax: 020 7594 3411 Email: n.poulter@ic.ac.uk; 149 Park Road, Chiswick, London W4 3EX Tel: 020 8580 1611 — MB BS 1975 Lond.; MSc Lond. 1986; FRCP Lond. 1994; MRCP (UK) 1977; MRCS Eng. LRCP Lond. 1974. Dir. Cardiovasc. Studies Unit Dept. of Clin. Pharm. & Therap.; Hon. Cons. Phys. & Epidemiol. St. Mary's Hosp. Lond.; Prof. Preven. Cardiovasc. Med. St. Mary's Hosp. Lond. (1997-). Socs: Sec. Brit. Hypertens. Soc.; Internat. Soc. Hypertens.; BHF. Prev: Reader in Clin. Epidem. Univ. Coll. Lond. Med. Sch.; Sen. Lect. in Clin. Epidem. Univ. Coll. Lond. Med. Sch.

POULTER, Simon David Anaesthetic Department, Royal Gwent Hospital, Cardiff Road, Newport NP20 2UB Tel: 01633 234234; 20 Yr Efail, Treoes, Bridgend CF35 5EG Tel: 01656 766975 Email: simon.poulter@bigfoot.com — MB BCh 1990 Wales; FRCA 1996. (Univ. Wales Coll. Med. Cardiff) Specialist Regist. (Anaesth.) Roy. Gwent Hosp.

***POULTNEY, Joanne Michelle** 56 Cole Bank Road, Hall Green, Birmingham B28 8EY — MB ChB 1996 Leic.

POULTON, Brodyn Bryant Norfolk & Norwich Hospital, Brunswick Rd, Norwich NR1 3SR; Corner House, Plump Road, Tharston, Norwich NR15 2YR — MB ChB 1989 Cape Town; FRCA 1994. Cons. (Anaesth.) Norf. & Norwich Hosp.

POULTON, David John Adeline Road Surgery, 4 Adeline Road, Boscombe, Bournemouth BH5 1EF Tel: 01202 309421 Fax: 01202 304893; 12 Leicester Road, Poole BH13 6BZ Tel: 01202 760054 — MB ChB 1975 Liverp.; MRCGP 1979; DRCOG 1979. Police Surg. Bournemouth. Prev: Clin. Asst. Cardiol. Roy. Bournmuth Hosp.

POULTON, Joanna University of Oxford, Department of Paediatrics, John Radcliffe Hospital, Headington, Oxford OX3 9DU Tel: 01865 221227 Fax: 01865 220479 Email: joanna.poulton@paediatrics.ox.ac.uk; 5 West Street, Oxford OX2 0BQ — BM BCh 1979 Oxf.; DM Oxf. 1991; MRCP (UK) 1982. (Oxf.) Univ. Research Fell. (Roy. Soc.) (Paediat.) Univ. Oxf.; Hon. Cons. (Mitochondrial Genetics) Oxf.; Convenor Mitochondrial Workshop for the Europ. Neuromuscular Centre; Hon. Readership in Mitochondrial Genetics, Univ. of Oxf. Socs: BPA; Clin. Genetics Soc. Prev: Wellcome Sen. Research Fell. in Clin. Sc.; Action Research Train. Fell.sh. (Paediat.) Univ. Oxf.; Regist. (Paediat.) Birm. Childr. Hosp.

***POULTON, Julian Walker** 3 The Beeches, Guilddown Road, Guildford GU2 4EN — MB ChB 1998 Liverp.; MB ChB Liverp 1998.

POULTON, Mary Bernadette Antonfold, Moss Lane, Garstang, Preston PR3 1HB — MB BS 1992 Lond.; MRCP (UK) 1996; Dip GU Med. Soc Apoth 1997; DFFP 1998. (King's Coll. Lond.) Specialist Regist. (GUM/HIV) Kings Coll. Hosp. Lond. Socs: MSSVD; BHIVA.

Prev: SHO (Immunol. & HIV) St. Bart. Hosp. Lond.; SHO (Genitourin. Med.) Char. Cross Hosp. Lond.; SHO (Paediat.) Greenwich Hosp.

POULTON, Susan Elizabeth Dept of Elderly Medicine, Queen Alexandra Hospital, Cosham, Portsmouth PO6 3LY Tel: 023 9228 6423 Fax: 02392200381; Tel: 01705 286423 — BM Soton. 1983; MRCP (UK) 1986; DRCOG 1989. Cons. (Geriat. Med.) Qu. Alexandra Hosp. Portsmouth. Prev: Sen. Regist. (Geriat. Med.) Soton. Gen. Hosp.; Sen. Regist. (Geriat. Med.) Qu. Alexandra Hosp. Portsmouth; Regist. & SHO (Med.) Qu. Alexandra & St. Mary's Hosps. Portsmouth.

POUNCEY, Catherine Margaret Godwin The Surgery, Malthouse Meadows, Portesham, Weymouth DT3 4NS Tel: 01305 871468 Fax: 01305 871977; Bridehead, Littlebredy, Dorchester DT2 9JA Tel: 01308 482232 — MB BS 1972 Lond.; MRCP (UK) 1975; DObst RCOG 1974; DCH Eng. 1975. (King's Coll. Hosp.) Prev: Sen. Regist. & Regist. (Paediat.) Horton Gen. Hosp. Banbury; Regist. (Paediat.) Soton. Gen. Hosp.

POUNCEY, David Anthony Columba Godwin Marlow and Partners, The Surgery, Bell Lane, Minchinhampton, Stroud GL6 9JF Tel: 01453 883793 Fax: 01453 731670; 18 Rodborough Avenue, Stroud GL5 3RS — MB BS 1983 Lond.; MA Camb. 1984, BA 1980; MRCGP 1987; DTM & H Lond. 1988; DRCOG 1986.

POUND, David Philip Benjamin (retired) Danetre Medical Practice, London Road, Daventry NN11 4EJ Tel: 01327 703333 Fax: 01327 311221 Email: david.pound@btinternet.com — MRCS Eng. LRCP Lond. 1965; MRCGP 1974; DObst RCOG 1969. Prev: Ho. Phys. & Ho. Surg. Harrogate Gen. Hosp.

POUND, Neil 3 Regency Close, Littleover, Derby DE23 7TR Tel: 01332 776488 Email: npound@npound.demon.co.uk — BM BS 1990 Nottm.

POUND, Susan Elizabeth 17 Corrennie Gardens, Edinburgh EH10 6DG Tel: 0131 447 0044 — MB ChB 1986 Ed.; BSc (Med. Sci.) Ed. 1984; MD Ed. 1994; MRCP (UK) 1989. Cons. Phys. (Gen. Med. & c/o Elderly) Qu. Margt. Hosp. Dunfermline. Prev: Sen. Regist. (Geriat. & Gen. Med.) St. John's Hosp. Livingston; MRC Clin. Train. Fell. MRC Human Genetics Unit W.. Gen. Hosp. Edin.; Regist. (Gen. Med.) Roy. Infirm. Edin.

POUNDALL, Clare Elise 16 Ralliwood Road, Ashtead KT21 1DE Tel: 01372 275160 — MB BCh BAO 1952 NUI; DObst RCOG 1954. (Univ. Coll. Dub.) Socs: Brit. Assn. Dermat. Prev: Assoc. Specialist (Dermat.) Roy. Surrey Co. Hosp. Guildford & Nelson Hosp. Lond.

POUNDER, Derek 79 Bowes Hill, Rowlands Castle PO9 6BS Tel: 01705 412437 Fax: 01705 412437 — MB ChB 1973 Dundee; FFA RCS Eng. 1979; DA Eng. 1977. Cons. (Anaesth.) Portsmouth Hosps. Acute Unit Trust. Prev: Sen. Regist. (Anaesth.) Soton. & Portsmouth Hosps.; Regist. (Anaesth.) Addenbrooke's & Papworth Hosps. Camb.

***POUNDER, Fiona Alison** 23 Wellcroft Close, Wheatley Hills, Doncaster DN2 5RU; Morton Grange, The Avenue, Morton, Lincoln LN6 9HW — MB ChB 1986 Sheff.

POUNDER, Leanne Wye Valley Surgery, 2 Desborough Ave, High Wy Combt CV35 7QR — BM BS 1996 Nottm.; MRCGP 2000; DFFP 2000; DRCOG 1999. GP Princip., High Wy Combe; Clin. Asst. - Palliat. Care, Sueryder Home, Nettlebed, Henry-on-Thames.

POUNDER, Professor Robert Roy Edward Centre for Gastroenterology (10th floor), Royal Free and University College Medical School, Rowland Hill St., London NW3 2PF Tel: 020 7830 2243 Fax: 020 7431 5261 Email: r.pounder@rfc.ucl.ac.uk — MB BChir 1969 Camb.; BA Camb. 1966, MD 1977, MA 1970; DSc (Med.) Lond. 1992; FRCP Lond. 1984; MRCP (UK) 1971. (Camb. & Guy's) Prof. Med. Roy. Free & Univ. Coll. Med. Sch. of Univ. Med. Coll. Lond. - Vice-Pres., Roy. Coll. of Phys.sm, Lond.; Co-Edr. Alimentary Pharmacol. & Therap.; Hon. Cons. Phys. & Gastroenterol. Roy. Free Hosp. Lond.; Co-Edr., GastroHep.com. Socs: Brit. Soc. Gastroenterol.; Amer. Gastroenterol. Assn.; FACG. Prev: Sen. Regist. (Med.) St. Thos. Hosp. Lond.; Sen. Regist. (Gastroenterol.) Centr. Middlx. Hosp. Lond.; SHO (Gastroenterol.) Hammersmith Hosp.

POUNDER, Ronald The Pease Way Medical Centre, 2 Pease Way, Newton Aycliffe DL5 5NH Tel: 01325 301888 — MB BS 1983 Newc.; MRCGP 1987.

POUNDS, Frances Jessie (retired) Fairlic House, 2 -6 Uppington Road, West Norwood, London SE27 0RP Tel: 020 8693 8396 — MD 1943 Lond.; MB BS 1938; MRCP Lond. 1942. Prev: Med. Off. Resid. Staff Health Serv. King's Coll. Hosp. Lond.

POUNSFORD

POUNSFORD, John Christopher Frenchay Day Hospital, Frenchay, Bristol BS16 1LE Tel: 0117 970 1212 Fax: 0117 970 2290; 1 Knoll Hill, Stoke Bishop, Bristol BS9 1QY Tel: 0117 968 4934 — MB BS 1975 Lond.; MD Lond. 1986; FRCP Lond. 1994; MRCP (UK) 1978; MRCS Eng. LRCP Lond. 1975. (Westm.) Cons. Phys. Frenchay Hosp. Bristol; Sen. Clin. Lect. Univ. Bristol. Socs: Brit. Geriat. Soc. & Brit. Thoracic Soc. Prev: Cons. Sen. Lect. (Med.) Univ. Bristol; Regist. & Research Fell. St. Geo. Hosp. Lond.; Ho. Phys. & Ho. Surg. W.m. Hosp. Lond.

POUNTAIN, Gillian Diane Hinchingbrooke Hospital, Hinchingbrooke Park, Huntingdon PE29 6NT Tel: 01480 416416; 13 Church Street, Bourn, Cambridge CB3 7SJ — MB BS 1976 Lond.; BSc (Pharmacol.) Lond. 1973; MD Lond. 1995; MRCP (UK) 1980; FRCP 1999. (University College Hosp London) p/t Cons. Rheum. Hinchingbrooke Hosp. Huntingdon. Socs: E. Anglian Rheum. Soc; Paediatric E Anglian Rheum Soc. (Chair.); Brit. Soc. for Rheum. Prev: Sen. Regist. (Rheum.) Addenbrooke's Hosp. Camb.; Regist. (Rheum.) Manch. Roy. Infirm.; Regist. (Rheum.) Canad. Red Cross Memor. Hosp. Taplow.

POUNTNEY, Alison Mary Claremont Surgery, Wilderness Medical Centre, 2 Cookham Road, Maidenhead SL6 8AN Tel: 01628 673033; Wingates, 32 Boyn Hill Road, Maidenhead SL6 4HG Tel: 01628 37918 — MB BS 1981 Lond.; BSc Lond. 1978, MB BS 1981; DRCOG 1984. (Univ. Coll.) Prev: SHO (A & E) Wexham Pk. Hosp. Slough; SHO (O & G) Heatherwood Hosp. Ascot; SHO (Anaesth.) E. Berks. HA.

***POUNTNEY, Andrew James** 75 Bridle Lane, Streetly, Sutton Coldfield B74 3QE — MB ChB 1998 Leeds.

POURAMINI, Morteza The Body Sculpture Clinic, 54A Pennhill Avenue, Poole BH14 9NA Tel: 01202 737274 Fax: 01202 737444 — MD 1966 Tehran; OB Gyn UK 1976. (Tehran Med. Univ.) Cons. "Cosmetic Surg."; Med. Dir. Of Body Sculpture Clinic, Dorset UK. Socs: Fell. Europ. Acad. Cosmetic Surg.; Amer. Acad. of Cosmetic Surg.; Internat. Soc. Of Lipos. Surg.

POURGHAZI, Saied 34 Montague Street, Glasgow G4 9HX — MB ChB 1992 Glas.

POURGOURIDES, Christina Kyriacou Sutton South CMHT, Chilternn Wing, Sutton Hospital, Cotswold Road, Sutton SM2 5NF Tel: 0208 296 4239 Fax: 0208 296 4239 — MB ChB 1989 Birm.; MRC Psych 1994.

POURGOURIDES, Effie Kyriacou Garden Flat, 5 Gladwyn Road, Putney, London SW15 1JY — MB ChB 1992 Birm.; MBChB (Hons.) 1992; MRCP (UK) 1996. (Birm.) Specialist Regist. in Haemat.

POURGOURIDES, Mrs Emilia 40 Northfield Road, Kings Norton, Birmingham B30 1JH — Ptychio Iatrikes 1963 Athens.

POURGOURIDES, Kyriacos Christofi — MB ChB 1964; LRCP 1964; MRCS 1964. (Birmingham)

POURIA, Shideh 22 Grovelands Close, London SE5 8JN — MB BS 1991 Lond.

POUYA, Amitis 17 Argie Gardens, Leeds LS4 2JL — MB ChB 1992 Aberd.

POVEDANO CANIZARES, Cristobal Eduardo 6 Victoria Crescent, Ashton Road, Lancaster LA1 5FD — LMS 1991 Cordoba.

POVEDANO CANIZARES, Jose Eneique Flat 7, Eaton House, 41 St Peters Road, Margate CT9 1TJ — LMS 1987 Cordoba.

POVER, Andrew Benedict Town House, Station Road, Madeley, Crewe CW3 9PW — MB ChB 1992 Dundee.

POVER, Gillian Margaret Powder Ject Technologies Ltd., 4 Robert Robinson Avenue, The Oxfprd Science Park, Oxford OX4 4GP Tel: 01865 782800 Fax: 01865 782801 Email: gillian_pover@powderject.com; 23 Upper Hill Rise, Rickmansworth WD3 7NU — MB ChB 1976 Birm.; FFPM RCP (UK) 1994; DRCOG 1979. (Birm.) Vice Pres. Head of Res. & Dev. Powder Ject Technologies Ltd. Prev: Managing Dir. Leicester Clin.Research Centre PPD Pharmaco; Exec. Dir. Clin. Research & Developm. Bristol-Myers Squibb; Assoc. Med. Dir. Glaxo (Allen & Hanburys).

POVEY, Jane Margaret Mytton Oak Surgery, Racecourse Lane, Shrewsbury SY1 1RL Tel: 01743 362223; 1 The Huntons, Off Grove Lane, Bayston Hill SY5 7BD Tel: 01743 872345 — MB BS 1991 Lond.; T(GP 1996; DRCOG 1995; DFFP 1994. (St. Bart.) p/t GP Retainer; Clin. Asst. InFertil., Roy. Shrewsbury Hosp. Prev: SHO (O & G) N.ampton Hosp.; SHO (A & E) Bendigo Base Hosp. Vict., Australia; SHO (Paediat.) P.ss Roy. Hosp. Telford.

POVEY, Janet Rowan The Haybarn, Home Farm Court, Holdenby, Northampton NN6 8EE Tel: 01604 770124 Fax: 01604 770124 — MB ChB 1982 Liverp. Med. Advisor SR Pharma Ltd.; Cons. Mapleleaf Assocs. Ltd. Prev: Med. Dir. Pasteur Merieux MSD Ltd.; Vaccines Business Manager Lederle Laborat.; Med. Affairs Manager Lederle Laborat. Gosport.

POVEY, John Sullivan (retired) Martlets, Westerland, Marldon, Paignton TQ3 1RR Tel: 01803 557054 — MRCS Eng. LRCP Lond. 1957; MRCGP 1965; DObst RCOG 1959. Prev: GP Paignton.

POVEY, Julian David Pontesbury Medical Practice, Pontesbury, Shrewsbury SY5 0RF Email: julian.povey@gp-m82030.nhs.uk; Tel: 01743 790406 — MB BS Lond. 1991; MRCGP 1996; DFFP 1996; Cert. Prescribed Equiv. Exp. JCPTGP 1996. (St. Bart.) Prev: SHO (Paediat.) P.ss Roy. Hosp. Telford; SHO (A & E) Milton Keynes Hosp.; SHO (Med.) Echuca Hosp. Vict., Austral.

POVEY, Margaret Susan 20 Church Lane, Cheddington, Leighton Buzzard LU7 0RU — MD 1977 Camb.; MB BChir 1967; DTM & H Liverp. 1968. (Camb. & Univ. Coll. Hosp.) Scientif. Staff MRC Unit Galton Laborat. Univ. Coll. Lond.

POVEY, Mr Robert William, CStJ (retired) Heath Rise, 48 Horncastle Road, Woodhall Spa LN10 6UZ Tel: 01526 53379 — MB BS 1945 Lond.; FRCS Eng. 1953; MRCS Eng. LRCP Lond. 1945. Prev: Cons. Adviser Orthop. Surg. RAF.

POVEY, Wilhelmina Rutherford Balvicar Centre, 46 Balvicar St., Glasgow G42 8QU Tel: 0141 201 0912 — MB ChB 1968 Glas. (Glas.) Clin. Med. Off. (Community Child Health & Sch. Health Serv.) Yorkhill NHS Trust Glas. Socs: BMA; BACCH & SACCH.

POVEY, William Peter (retired) The Gables, 153 Chester Road, Grappenhall, Warrington WA4 2SB — MRCS Eng. LRCP Lond. 1961; MSc Manch. 1982; FFPHM RCP (UK) 1990; FFCM 1979, M 1972; DPH Liverp. 1968; DObst RCOG 1966. NSM Assoc. Priest, All St.s Ch., Daresbury, Chesh.; Hon. Cons. Pub. Health Med. Wigan & Bolton HA. Prev: Dir. Pub. Health Centr. M/C HA.

POVLSEN, Professor Bo Guy's Hospital, St. Thomas Street, London SE1 9RT Tel: 0207 955 5000 Ext: 5607. — MD 1984 Copenhagen; 1998 Assoc. Professor; PhD Sweden 1994. (Copenhagen 1984) Cons. Orthop. Guy's & St. Thos. Hosps. NHS Trust. Socs: Brit. Elbow & Shoulder Soc.; Brit. Soc. Surg. Hand; Brit. Orthop. Assn. Prev: Cons. & Trainee Hand Surg. Univ. Hosp. Linköping, Sweden; Fell. (Microsurg.) St. Jas. Univ. Hosp. Leeds.

POW, Arthur Alexander (retired) 45 Esplanade, Greenock PA16 7RY Tel: 01475 20977 — MB ChB 1940 Glas. Prev: Maj. RAMC, TA.

***POW, Colin Edward Lindsay** 134 Newton Street, Greenock PA16 8SJ — MB ChB 1997 Aberd.

POWAR, Michael Paramjit 10 Vanilla and Sesame Court, Curlew Street, London SE1 2NN — BM BS 1997 Nottm.

POWAR, Motilal R Porth Farm Surgery, Porth Street, Porth CF39 9RR Tel: 01443 682579 Fax: 01443 683667.

POWELL, Adele Patricia South Uist Medical Practice, The Surgery, Daliburgh, Lochboisdale HS8 5SS Tel: 01878 700302 Fax: 01878 700675; 26 Aldwickbury Crescent, Harpenden AL5 5RR Tel: 015827 64513 — MRCS Eng. LRCP Lond. 1966; FRCSI 1978. (Liverp.) Princip. GP Lochboisdale, I. of S. Uist. Socs: BMA. Prev: Sen. Surg. Resid. (A & E) Univ. Hosp. Jamaica; Regist. (Surg.) Belf. VTS; Ho. Surg. United Liverp. Hosp.

POWELL, Aileen Margaret (retired) 52 The Boulevard, Worthing BN13 1LB Tel: 01903 40424 — MB BS 1953 Lond.

***POWELL, Alexandra** 81 Ardwyn, Cardiff CF14 7HE — MB ChB 1995 Bristol.

***POWELL, Amanda Jane** 11 Kelburn Av, Chesterfield S40 3DG — MB ChB 1997 Manch.

POWELL, Andrew Philip Park Medical Centre, 2 Park Road, West Kirby, Wirral CH48 4DW Tel: 0151 625 6128; 32 Beacon Drive, West Kirby, Wirral CH48 7ED — MB BChir 1985 Camb.; MA Camb. 1987, MB BChir 1985; Cert. Family Plann. JCC 1989. Prev: Trainee GP N. Staffs. Hosp. Centre; Ho. Phys. & Ho. Surg. N. Staffs. Hosp. Centre.

POWELL, Andrew Stephen The Warneford Hospital, Warneford Lane, Headington, Oxford OX3 7JX Tel: 01865 226330 Fax: 01865 226507 — MB BChir 1970 Camb.; MA Camb. 1972; MRCP (UK) 1972; FRCPsych 1988, M 1975. (St. Thos.) Cons. Psychother. & Hon. Sen. Lect. Univ. Oxf. Socs: Assoc. Mem. Brit. Assn. Psychother.; Inst. Gp. Anal.; Brit. Psychodrama Assn. & Mem. Inst.

Gp. Anal. Prev: Cons. & Head Psychother. St. Geo. Hosp. Lond.; Sen. Lect. (Psychiat.) St. Geo. Med. Sch. Lond.; Sen. Regist. (Psychother.) Maudsley & Bethlem Roy. Hosps. Lond.

POWELL, Anna Louise Hendy, Church St., Addingham, Ilkley LS29 0QS — BM BS 1991 Nottm.

POWELL, Anthony Richard 210 Liverpool Road, Reading RG1 3PJ — MB BS 1991 Lond.

POWELL, Arnold 5 Canons Close, London N2 0BH Tel: 020 7624 4414 — MB ChB 1957 Sheff.; MRCS Eng. LRCP Lond. 1958.

POWELL, Barbara Joan 22 King Street, Shrewsbury SY2 5ER — MB ChB 1992 Leeds.

POWELL, Mr Barry Willoughby Eric Merrick 51 George's Hospital, Blackshaw Road, London SW17 0QT Tel: 020 8672 1255 Fax: 020 8725 2416 Email: bpowell@sghms.ac.uk; Baronsmead, Pachesham Park, Leatherhead KT22 0DJ Tel: 01372 844419 Fax: 01372 844742 Email: bpowell@sghms.ac.uk — MB BCh BAO 1978 Dub.; MA Dub. 1992, MCh 1992; FRCS Ed. 1984. (Dublin University) Cons. Burns, Plastic & Reconstruc. Surg. St. Geo. Hosp. Lond.; Represen. on Plastic Surg. STC Pan Thames; Regional Adviser Plastic Surg. S. Thames Deanery & KSS Deanery; Examr. Specialist Fell.sh. plastic Surg. Socs: Brit. Assn. Plastic Surg.; Brit. Assn. Aesthetic Plastic Surgs.; Brit. Assn. Tissue Banks.

POWELL, Benedict Walter (retired) The Willows, Theberton, Leiston IP16 4SF Tel: 01728 830588 — MB BChir 1939 Camb.; FRCP Lond. 1970, M 1946; MRCS Eng., LRCP Lond. 1939; DCH Eng. 1947. Prev: Cons. Paediat. P'boro. Area.

POWELL, Bruce Patrick 218 Chippinghouse Road, Nether Edge, Sheffield S7 1DR Tel: 0114 255 6371 — MB BS 1991 Lond.; MRCP Lond. 1997. (Royal Free) Specialist Regist. (Nephrol.) N.ern Gen. Hosp. Sheff. Socs: Roy. Coll Phys.

***POWELL, Catherine Elizabeth** 7 Dan-y-Felin, Llantrisant, Pontyclun CF72 8EH — MB BS 1992 Lond.

POWELL, Catherine Georgina Bransom 3 Parfrey Street, London W6 9EW Tel: 020 8741 9278; Efford Farm, Yealmpton, Plymouth PL8 2LB Tel: 01752 881387 — MB BS 1988 Lond.; FRCA 1991. (Char. Cross & Westm. Hosp. Lond.) Specialist Regist. Rotat. (Anaesth.) SW Region.

POWELL, Catherine Riva The Chimes, Felix Manor, Old Perry St., Chislehurst BR7 6PL — MB BS 1979 Lond.; MB BS (Hons.) Lond. 1979. Clin. Asst. (Dermat.) Greenwich Healthcare.

POWELL, Charles Edward Adam Practice, Upton Health Centre, Blandford Road North, Poole BH16 5PW Tel: 01202 622339 — BM 1987 Soton.; MRCGP 1992; DCH RCP Lond. 1992. Clin. Asst. (Paediat.) Poole.

POWELL, Christopher Duncan New Hayesbank Surgery, Cemetery Lane, Kennington, Ashford TN24 9JZ Tel: 01233 624642 Fax: 01233 637304; 127 Lakemead, Ashford TN23 4XZ — MB ChB 1981 Manch.

POWELL, Mr Christopher Stephen Department of Urology, Countess of Chester Hospital, Liverpool Road, Chester CH2 1UL Tel: 01244 366588 Fax: 01244 366587; Tel: 01829 782225 Fax: 01829 782225 — MB BS 1975 Lond.; FRCS Eng. 1979; MRCS Eng. LRCP Lond. 1975. Cons. Urol. Surg. Countess of Chester Hosp. Socs: Brit. Prostate Gp.; Brit. Assn. Urol. Surgs. Prev: Cons. Urol. Surg. Leighton Hosp. Crewe; Sen. Regist. (Urol.) Swansea & Cardiff Gp. Hosps.; Research Regist. (Urol. & Transpl.) Roy. Hallamsh. Hosp. Sheff.

POWELL, Claire Elaine Wallis and Partners, The Health Centre, 5 Stanmore Road, Stevenage SG1 3QA Tel: 01438 313223 Fax: 01438 749734 — MB BS 1981 Lond.; BSc Lond. 1978, MB BS 1981; DRCOG 1987. (Westm.) GP Lond. Prev: Trainee GP Sheff. VTS; Regist. (Anaesth.) Glos. Roy. Hosp.

POWELL, Colin Victor Eric Knowles House Farm, Hollin Lane, Sutton, Macclesfield SK11 0HR — MB ChB 1984 Manch.; MRCP (UK) 1989; DCH RCP Lond. 1987. Hon. Regist. Research Fell. (Respirat.) Univ. Sheff. Prev: Tutor (Child Health) Univ. Manch.; SHO (Paediat.) Wythenshawe Hosp. Manch.; SHO (Paediat.) Booth Hall Childr. Hosp. Manch.

POWELL, David (retired) Piranhuthlant, Hatches Green, Gunnislake PL18 9BX — MB BS 1956 Lond. EMP Benefits Agency. Prev: SHO (O & G) St. Mary's Hosp. Kettering.

POWELL, David Edward Baden Maesmor, 4 West Farm Close, Ogmore-by-Sea, Bridgend CF32 0PT — MB ChB 1952 Ed.; MA Wales 1992; MD (Commend.) Ed. 1959; FRCP Lond. 1981, M 1955; FRCPath 1974, M 1963. (Ed.) Chairm. Panel D Bro Taf LREC Cardiff. Socs: Path. Soc.; BMA. Prev: Cons. Path. Mid Glam. AHA; Sen. Regist. (Path.) United Bristol Hosps.; Asst. Lect. (Path. & Bact.) Welsh Nat. Sch. Med. Cardiff.

POWELL, David Fred Three Villages Medical Practice, Audnam Lodge, Wordsley, Stourbridge DY8 4AL Tel: 01384 395054 Fax: 01384 390969; 16 Dark Lane, Kinver, Stourbridge DY7 6JB Tel: 01384 873761 — MB BS 1968 Newc.

POWELL, David Grant Machattie 24 St Keyna Court, Temple St., Keynsham, Bristol BS31 1HB — MB BChir 1980 Camb.; MA, MB BChir Camb. 1980; MRCGP 1984; DRCOG 1984.

POWELL, David Howel Thomas Eastleigh Surgery, Station Road, Westbury BA13 3JD Tel: 01373 822807 Fax: 01373 828904 — MB BS 1981 Lond.; MRCGP 1986. (St. Bart.) Prev: Trainee GP Hythe Med. Centre Soton.; SHO (O & G) St. Geo. Hosp. Lond.; SHO (Med.) Soton. Gen. Hosp.

POWELL, David John Hope Hospital, Stott Lane, Salford M6 Tel: 0161 789 7373; 5 Elishaw Row, Eccles New Road, Salford M5 4UJ — MB ChB 1989 Manch.; BSc (Med. Sci.) St. And. 1986. SHO Rotat. (Neurosurg.) Hope Hosp. Salford.

POWELL, David Jolyan Stroud Whittington Road Surgery, 9 Whittington Road, Norton, Stourbridge DY8 3DB Tel: 01384 393120 Fax: 01384 353636; 2 Riverside Court, Caunsall, Kidderminster DY11 5YW — MB BS 1974 Lond. (St. Thos. Hosp. Lond.) Prev: Trainee GP Torquay VTS; SHO (O & G) Torbay Hosp. Torquay; Ho. Surg. (ENT) St. Thos. Hosp. Lond.

POWELL, David Lewis 21 Elizabeth Crescent, Queens Park, Chester CH4 7AY Tel: 01244 679236 — MB BS 1961 Lond.; FFA RCS Eng. 1970; DObst RCOG 1964. (Char. Cross) Cons. Anaesth. Chester Roy. Infirm.; Clin. Tutor Chester HA. Socs: Assn. Anaesths. Prev: Maj. RAMC T & AVR; Sen. Regist. United Liverp. & Liverp. Regional Hosps.; Lect. Dept. Anaesth. Univ. Liverp.

POWELL, Eileen Felvus Crichton Royal Hospital, Dumfries DG1 4TE Tel: 01387 244331 Fax: 01387 244337; Lherghydoo, 7 Robertson Avenue, Dumfries DG1 4EY — MB ChB Glas. 1974; MRCPsych 1980. Cons. Psychiat. Child Psychiat. & Ment. Handicap Dumfries & Galloway HB. Prev: Cons. (Child & Adolesc. Psychiat.) Forth Valley HB.

POWELL, Elizabeth Anne Crinnis, 3 Woodland Avenue, Teignmouth TQ14 8UU Tel: 01626 775328 — MB BS 1982 Lond.; MRCGP 1986; DRCOG 1985; Cert. Family Plann. JCC 1985. Clin. Med. Off. (Family Plann.) Devon. Prev: GP St. Austell; Trainee GP N. Devon Dist. Hosp. Barnstaple VTS; SHO Worcester Eye Hosp.

***POWELL, Elizabeth Jane** 3 Morlands, East Hanney, Wantage OX12 0JW — MB ChB 1998 Leeds.

POWELL, Florence Mary Noreen Burn Brae Surgery, Hencotes, Hexham NE46 2ED Tel: 01434 603627 Fax: 01434 606373 — MB ChB 1980 Leeds; MRCGP 1984; DRCOG 1983; DCH RCP Lond. 1983. Partner Burn Brae Med. Gp. Hencotes Hexham. Socs: RCGP; Fac. Fam. Plann. & Reproduc. Health Care. Prev: Trainee GP Wakefield VTS; Partner Almondbury Huddersfield W. Yorks.; Partner Middlestown W. Yorks.

POWELL, Francis Iorwerth 249 Cwmamman Road, Garnant, Ammanford SA18 1LS Tel: 01269 822115 — MB BCh Wales 1947; BSc Wales 1944; DMJ (Clin.) Soc. Apoth. Lond. 1970. (Cardiff) Socs: BMA; Assn. Police Surg. Prev: Clin. Asst. Amman Valley Hosp. Glanamman.; Regist. (Orthop. & Fract.) Roy. Infirm. Cardiff; Asst. Surg. Off. Accid. Unit St. David's Hosp. Cardiff.

POWELL, Frederic James (retired) Summerfield Lodge, Compton Chamberlayne, Salisbury SP3 5DB Tel: 01722 714705 — MRCS Eng. LRCP Lond. 1948; MB BS Lond. 1949; FRCGP 1988, M 1960; DObst RCOG 1952. Prev: Gp Shaftesbury.

POWELL, Gareth John 31 Upper Simpson Street, Crosshouse Hospital, Kilmarnock KA2 0BE Tel: 01563 521133; Ty'r Capel, Bishops Frome, Worcester WR6 5AS Tel: 01885 490316 — MB ChB 1994 Dundee. SHO (O & G) CrossHo. Hosp. Kilmarnock. Prev: SHO (Paediat.) Ayr Hosp.; SHO (A & E) Darlington Memor. Hosp.; Ho. Off. (Gen. Surg.) S. Cleveland Hosp. Middlesbrough.

POWELL, Glyn Douglas, TD (retired) 35 Cavendish Avenue, Dore, Sheffield S17 3NJ Tel: 0114 236 3578 — MB BCh 1944 Wales; BSc Wales 1941; FRCPath 1975, M 1963. Maj. RAMC, TARO. Prev: Cons. Path. Rotherham Dist. Gen. Hosp.

POWELL, Guy Alan Cowslip Farm, Devizes Road, Salisbury SP2 7NB — BM 1989 Soton.

POWELL

POWELL, Hazel Department Cardiothoracic Anaesthesia, Freeman Hospital, High Henton, Newcastle upon Tyne NE7 7DN Tel: 0191 284 3111 Ext: 26488 Fax: 0191 223 1175 Email: hazel.powell@tfh.nuth.northy.nhs.uk — MB BS 1980 Lond.; FFA RCS Eng. 1987. Cons. (Anaesth.) Freeman Hosp. Newc. upon Tyne. Socs: Assn. of Anaesth.s; Assn. of Cardiothoracic Anaesth.s; Intens. Care Soc. Prev: Sen. Regist. (Anaesth.) Hammersmith Hosp. Lond.; Regist. (Anaesth.) Harefield Hosp.; Regist. (Anaesth.) Univ. Hosp. Nottm. & N.ampton Gen. Hosp.

POWELL, Hazel Morag Pangbourne Medical Practice, The Boat House Surgery, Whitchurch Road, Pangbourne, Reading RG8 7DP Tel: 0118 984 2234 Fax: 0118 984 3022; Rickstools, Manor Farm Lane, Tidmarsh, Reading RG8 8EX Tel: 01189 843129 — MB BS 1972 Lond.; MRCS Eng. LRCP Lond. 1972; MRCGP 1983; DObst RCOG 1974. (Guy's)

POWELL, Helen Kathleen Roma Ballaloch, Nethermill Road, Lochmaben, Lockerbie DG11 1QA — MB BCh BAO 1965 NUI; Cert. Prescribed Equiv. Exp. JCPTGP 1981; DA Eng. 1969. Community Med. Off. E. Cumbria HA. Prev: Anaesth. Regist. Dumfries & Galloway Roy. Infirm.; Med. Off. Blood Transf. Serv.

POWELL, Mr Henry Denis Whitwell (retired) Old Fox Cottage, Heath End Road, Great Kingshill, High Wycombe HP15 6HS Tel: 01494 713176 — MB ChB 1944 Ed.; MA Camb. 1945; FRCS Eng. 1953. Prev: Cons. Surg. Orthop. High Wycombe & Amersham Dist.

***POWELL, Howell William Robert** Redwood, Lisvane Road, Cardiff CF14 0SD — MB BS 1998 Lond.; MB BS Lond 1998.

POWELL, Hugh Benedict Bockhampton Road Surgery, Bockhampton Road, Lambourn, Hungerford RG17 8PS Tel: 01488 71715 Fax: 01488 73569; The Old Vicarage, Eastbury, Hungerford RG17 7JN Tel: 01488 71407 — MB BChir 1979 Camb.; MRCGP 1984; DRCOG 1983; DCH Eng. 1981.

POWELL, James Francis Department of Anaesthesia, Royal Cornwall Hospital, Treliske, Truro TR1 3LJ Tel: 01872 253134 Fax: 01872 252480; Kerthen Wood Farm House, Townshend, Hayle TR27 6AH Tel: 01736 851001 — MB BS 1980 Lond.; FRCA 1991; DA (UK) 1987; DRCOG 1983. (Univ. Lond. & Guy's Hosp.) Cons. Anaesth. Roy. Cornw. Hosp. Teliske Truro. Prev: Sen. Regist. (Anaesth.) Qu. Eliz. Hosp. Kings Lynn; Sen. Regist. (Anaesth.) Addenbrooke's Hosp. Camb.

POWELL, James Hugo Peplow Royal Surrey County Hospital, Egerton Road, Guildford GU2 7XX Tel: 01483 571122 Fax: 01483 302683 Email: hugopowell@royalsurrey.nhs.uk — MRCS Eng. LRCP Lond. 1982; MA Camb. 1983, MB BChir 1982; MRCP (UK) 1987; FRCP 1999. Cons. Phys. Geriat. Med. Roy. Surrey Co. Hosp. Guildford. Socs: Brit. Geriat.s Soc. (Counc. Mem. & Hon. Sec. SW Thames Regional Br.); Fell.and Coll. tutor Roy. Coll. Phys. Prev: Sen. Regist. (Geriat. Med.) St. Geo. Hosp. Lond.

***POWELL, James John** 2/2, 10 Sandbank Street, Glasgow G20 0PJ — MB ChB 1994 Glas.

POWELL, James Shanklin Horning Road Surgery, Horning Road West, Hoveton, Norwich NR12 8QH Tel: 01603 782155 Fax: 01603 782189 — MB ChB Ed. 1970; MRCGP 1976. Prev: Surg. Lt. RN.

POWELL, Janice Anne 6 Chichester Close, East Wellow, Romsey SO51 6EY — MB ChB 1984 Auckland; FANZCA 1992.

POWELL, Jean Charlotte Milngavie Road Surgery, 85 Milngavie Road, Bearsden, Glasgow G61 2DN Tel: 0141 211 5621 Fax: 0141 211 5625 — MB ChB 1979 Glas.; MRCGP 1983; DRCOG 1981.

POWELL, Jennifer Jean The Old Vicarage, Eastbury, Newbury RG17 7JN Tel: 01488 71407; Department of Dermatology, The Churchill, Old Road, Headington, Oxford OX3 7LJ Tel: 01865 228257 Fax: 01865 228260 — MB BS 1979 Lond.; BA Oxf. (Hons.) 1976; MRCP (UK) 1982. (St. Thos.) Specialist Regist. (Dermat.) Oxf. Radcliffe Hosps. Socs: Train. Mem. Brit. Assn. Dermatol.

***POWELL, Jennifer Margaret** 4 Langbank Rise, Kilmacolm PA13 4LF — MB ChB 1994 Glas.

POWELL, Joan Veronica Tudor Cottage, The Street, South Stoke, Reading RG8 0JS Tel: 01491 874113 — MB BS 1942 Lond.; MRCS Eng. LRCP Lond. 1942. (Lond. Sch. Med. Wom.) Clin. Asst. (Accid. Dept.) Orpington Hosp.; Med. Off. Family Plann. Clinic Bromley AHA & Tunbridge Wells Health Dist. Prev: Ho. Surg. Roy. Free Hosp.; Ho. Phys. & Ho. Surg. Chester City Hosp.; Res. Obst. Off. St. Helier's Hosp. Carshalton.

POWELL, John Antony Buckinghamshire Health Authority, Aylesbury HP19 8ET Email: j.powell@lshtm.ac.uk; Haining Chace, Brockenhurst Road, Ascot SL5 9HB — MB BChir Camb. 1992; MA Camb. 1994; BA (Hons.) Camb. 1990; MRCPsych 1997. (Univ. Camb.) Regist. Rotat. (Psychiat.) Oxf. Regional Train. Scheme. Prev: SHO (Psychiat.) Oxf. Train. Scheme; SHO (Old Age Psychiat.) N.wick Pk. Hosp.

POWELL, John Christopher (retired) Crichton Royal Hospital, Dumfries DG1 4TE Tel: 01387 255327 Fax: 01387 244337 — MB BCh BAO 1965 NUI; BSc St. Peter's Coll. New Jersey 1960; FRCPsych 1989, M 1972; DPM Eng. 1970. Cons. Dept. Child & Adolesc. Psychiat. & Cons. i/c Adolesc. Unit Crichton Roy. Hosp. Dumfries; Hon. Clin. Sen. Lect. Univ. Glas. Prev: Sen. Regist. (Psychiat.) Hollymoor Adolesc. Unit Birm.

POWELL, John Frederick PPD Pharmaco, Lookton House, Clarendon Road, Cambridge CB2 2BH Tel: 01223 272243 Fax: 01223 314724; 28 Short Road, Stretham, Ely CB6 3LS — MB ChB 1978 Manch.; MFPM RCP (UK) 1994. Med. Advis. Pharmaceut. Med. Pharmaco LSR Camb. Prev: Clin. Pharmacol. Napp Research Centre Camb.

POWELL, John Gerald (retired) 23 Dodd Avenue, Myton Grange, Warwick CV34 6QR Tel: 01926 497585 — MB ChB 1953 Birm.; DObst RCOG 1955. Prev: Sen. Hosp. Pract. & Lect. (Dermat.) Warneford Hosp. & Warwick Hosp.

POWELL, Mr John Michael Orthopaedic Department, Ipswich Hospital, Heath Road, Ipswich IP4 5PD Tel: 01473 702032 Fax: 01473 702032 Email: jmspine@hotmail.com — MB BS 1977 Lond.; FRCS Eng. 1981. (St. Bart.) Cons. Orthop. Surg. Ipswich Hosp. Socs: Brit. Orthop. Spinal Soc.; Brit. Orthop. Assn.; Brit. Assn. of Spinal Surg.s. Prev: Clin. Research Fell. Univ., Toronto; Spinal Research Fell. WCB Rehabil. Centre, Toronto; Sen. Regist. Rotat. (Orthop. Surg.) St. Bart. Hosp. Lond.

POWELL, John Nevill 17 Gloucester Road, Almondsbury, Bristol BS32 4HD Tel: 01454 613027 Email: john.powell6@virgin.net — MB BChir Camb. 1960; MRCS Eng. LRCP Lond. 1958; FFA RCS Eng. 1963; DA Eng. 1961. (Guy's) Emerit. Cons. Anaesth. S.mead Health Servs. NHS Trust. Socs: Assn. Anaesth.s; (Ex-Pres.) Soc. Anaesth. SW Region. Prev: Instruc. (Anaesth.) Univ. Colorado Med. Center Denver, USA; Cons. Sen. Lect. (Anaesth.) Univ. Bristol.; Cons. Anaesth. S.mead Health Servs. NHS Trust.

POWELL, John Owen James 24 Gladstone Street, Skipton BD23 1PT — MB ChB 1990 Bristol; MRCP (UK) 1993. Trainee GP Skipton. Prev: SHO (Med.) Morriston Hosp. Swansea; Regist. (Radiol.) St. Jas. Hosp. Leeds; Ho. Phys. Ham Green Hosp.

POWELL, Karen Josephine 76 Buxton Street, London E1 5AT — MB BS 1987 Lond.

POWELL, Katayoun Yasamin 2 Curzon Mews, Wilmslow SK9 5JN; 30 Spruce Avenue, Loughborough LE11 2QW — BM BS 1990 Nottm.; BMedSci. (Hons.) Nottm. 1988, BM BS 1990; MRCGP 1994. Asst. Gen. Pract. LoughBoro. Leics.

POWELL, Katharine Ursula Ley The Cottage, Thorpe Lane, Trimley St Martin, Felixstowe IP11 0RZ Tel: 01394 273688 — MB BS 1977 Lond.; MRCS Eng. LRCP Lond. 1977; MRCGP 1981; DRCOG 1981; DCH Lond. 1980. (Roy. Free) Clin. Research Asst. (Gastroenterol. & Neurol.) Ipswich Hosp.; Assoc. specialist (Rheum. & Neurol.) Ipswich Hosp. Socs: Brit. Soc. Gastroenterol.

POWELL, Kathleen (retired) Coastal View, Residential Home, 54 Mark St., Portrush BT56 8BU — MB BCh BAO 1945 Belf.

POWELL, Katie Annabel Medical Adviser, Foreign and Commonwealth Office, London Tel: 01246 260772 Email: tribhubanv@yahoo.co.uk; Tel: 01246 260772 Email: tribhubanv@yahoo.co.uk — MB BS 1994 Lond.; BSc Lond. 1991; DRCOG 1997; DFFP 1997. (St. Thos. Hosp. Lond.) GP Locum Holland Pk., Holland Pk. Avenue, Lond.; Bank Family Plann., Riverside Community Healthcare Trust. Socs: MRCGP. Prev: GP Regist. Chelsea & W.m. VTS.

POWELL, Kelly Damask 20A St Anne's Road, Barnes, London SW13 9LJ Tel: 020 8878 1647 Email: kellypowell@o.net.co.uk — MB BS 1990 Lond.; DRCOG 1995; MRCGP 1995; MFPHM (P. I) 1998; MSc Public Health (Lond.), 1998. (Charing Cross & Westminster) Regist. (Pub. Health Med.) W. Surrey Health Auth. Prev: SHO (A & E) Char. Cross Hosp. Lond.; GP Train.

POWELL, Kendra Jane 51 Ashworth Park, Knutsford WA16 9DG — MB ChB 1990 Manch.

POWELL, Mrs Lilian Jean 4 Watts Close, High Cross, Newport NP10 0DW; J Bwythan Bach, 4 Watts Close, Rogerstone, Newport NP10 0DW — MB BCh 1950 Wales; BSc Wales 1950; MFCM RCP (UK) 1974; DPH Bristol 1968; DObst RCOG 1966. (Cardiff) Med. Off. Welsh Office Cardiff. Socs: Fell. Soc. Community Med.; BMA. Prev: Ho. Off. St. David's Hosp. Cardiff; Ho. Surg. O & G Cardiff Roy. Infirm.; Dist. MOH Magor & St. Mellons RD & Risca & Bedwas & Machen UDs.

POWELL, Linda Jane Kings Cottage, Sandy Lane, Tilford, Farnham GU10 2ES — MB BCh 1980 Wales.

POWELL, Louise Ann Kennedy Way Surgery, Kennedy Way, Yate, Bristol BS37 4AA Tel: 01454 313849 Fax: 01454 329039 — MB ChB 1989 Birm.; MRCGP 1993.

POWELL, Mair Medicines Control Agency, Market Towers, 1 Nine Elms Lane, London SW8 5NQ Tel: 020 7273 0486 Fax: 020 7273 0170 — MB BS 1980 Lond.; MB BS (Hons.) Lond. 1980; MSc (Med. Microbiol.) Lond. 1987, MD 1989; MRCP (UK) 1984; FRCPath 1997, M 1988. Sen. Med. Assessor Meds. Control Agency Lond. Prev: Sen. Assoc. Med. Dir. Pfizer Incorp. New York, USA; Assoc. Med. Dir. Lederle Internat. Wayne, New Jersey, USA; Sen. Lect. (Med. Microbiol.) Lond. Hosp. Med. Coll.

POWELL, Marie Jose Endless Street Surgery, 72 Endless Street, Salisbury SP1 3UH Tel: 01722 336441 Fax: 01722 410319 — BM 1991 Soton.; BM (Hons.) Soton. 1991. SHO (Geriat.) Odstock Hosp. Salisbury. Prev: Ho. Off. Roy. S. Hants. Hosp. Soton.; Ho. Off. Poole Gen. Hosp.

POWELL, Martin Barry Manor Brook Medical Centre, 117 Brook Lane, London SE3 0EN Tel: 020 8856 5678 Fax: 020 8856 8632; The Chimes, Felix Manor, Old Perry St, Chislehurst BR7 6PL Tel: 020 8295 0868 Fax: 020 8856 8632 Email: martin@the-chimes.freeserve.co.uk — MB BChir 1978 Camb.; MA, MB Camb. 1978, BChir 1977; DRCOG 1980. (Gonville and Caius College Cambridge) GP Bexley & Greenwich HA; Employm. Med. Off. DoH Attendance & Disabil. Living Allowance Units. Socs: W Kent Med. Soc. Counc. Mem. & Hon. Sec. 1999-2000. Prev: Trainee GP Greenwich & Brook Hosps. VTS; Ho. Surg. Brook Hosp. Lond.; Ho. Phys. King's Coll. Hosp. Lond.

POWELL, Mr Martin Charles Consultant Obstetrician and Gynaecologist, East Block, Queens Medical Centre, Nottingham NG8 2UH Tel: 0115 924 9924 Ext: 44872 — MB ChB 1978 Sheff.; DM Nottm. 1990; FRCS Ed. 1984; MRCOG 1989. Cons. O & G Qu. Med. Centre Nottm.

POWELL, Melanie Estelle Barrington Department of Radiotherapy, St Bartholomwes hospital, London EC1 7BE Tel: 020 7601 8353 — MB BS 1986 Lond.; MRCP (UK) 1989; FRCR 1994; MD Lond. 1998. Cons. Clin. Oncol. St. Bart's. Hosp. Lond. Prev: Clin. Research Fell. Marie Curie Research Wing Mt. Vernon Hosp.; Regist. (Radiother. & Oncol.) Roy. Marsden Hosp.

POWELL, Michael Allan Rysseldene Surgery, 98 Conway Road, Colwyn Bay LL29 7LE Tel: 01492 532807 Fax: 01492 534846 — MB BS 1971 Newc.; MRCGP 1975; DObst RCOG 1973.

POWELL, Michael Edward Arthur (retired) 37 Ridgeway Road, Redhill RH1 6PQ Tel: 01737 763991 — MD 1969 Lond.; MB BS 1952; FRCPath 1972, M 1964. Prev: Cons. (Histopath.) Kingston Hosp. Surrey.

POWELL, Michael Francis 4 Balfour Close, Little Thornton, Thornton-Cleveleys FY5 5AY — MB ChB 1984 Liverp.

POWELL, Michael Leonard (retired) c/o The Royal Bank of Scotland, 1 Market Place, Poulton-le-Fylde, Blackpool FY1 1LE — MRCS Eng. LRCP Lond. 1962; Cert. Av. Med. 1982.

POWELL, Michael Pearce Pangbourne Medical Practice, The Boat House Surgery, Whitchurch Road, Pangbourne, Reading RG8 7DP Tel: 0118 984 2234 Fax: 0118 984 3022; Rickstools, Manor Farm Lane, Tidmarsh, Reading RG8 8EX Tel: 01723 573129 — MB BS 1972 Lond.; MRCS Eng. LRCP Lond. 1972; DObst. RCOG 1974. GP Reading. Prev: SHO (Obst.) St. Helier Hosp. Carshalton; SHO (Paediat.) Auckland Hosp. Bd., N.Z.

POWELL, Mr Michael Peter National Hospital for Neurology & Neurosurgery, Queen Square, London WC1N 3BG Tel: 020 7837 3611 Fax: 020 7833 8658; 66 The Avenue, London NW6 7NP — MB BS 1975 Lond.; MA Oxf. 1988, BA 1972; FRCS Eng. 1980. Cons. Neurosurg. Nat. Hosp. Neurol. & Neurosurg. UCLH (Trust) & Roy. Nat. Orthop. Hosp. Trust; Hon. Cons. Neurosurg. & Roy. Free Hosp. Trust, St. Luke's Hosp. for Clergy, Whittingtoin Hosp & K

Edwd VII Hosp for Offs; Hon. Cons. Surg. St. Thos. Hosp. Lond.; Civil. Adviser (Neurosurg.) RAF.

POWELL, Muriel Rachel (retired) 27 Langdon Lane, Galmpton, Brixham TQ5 0PH Tel: 01803 2423 — MB ChB 1923 Sheff.

POWELL, Niels Department of Radiology, Morriston Hospital NHS Trust, Swansea Tel: 01792 703135 Fax: 01792 703674; 121 Summerland Lane, Caswell, Swansea SA3 4RS — MB BCh 1974 Wales; FRCR 1983; DMRD Eng. 1982; DCH Eng. 1976. (Welsh Nat. Sch. Med.) Cons. Neuroradiol. Morriston Hosp. Swansea. Socs: Fell.Roy. Coll. of Radiologists; Radiol. Soc. N. Amer.; Brit. Inst. Radiol. Prev: Cons. Radiol. W. Glam. HA; Sen. Regist. (Radiol.) S. Glam. HA.

POWELL, Olive Joyce Hawthorn Drive Surgery, 206 Hawthorn Drive, Ipswich IP2 0QQ Tel: 01473 685070 Fax: 01473 688707; Appletree Cottage, The St, Harkstead, Ipswich IP9 1BN Tel: 01473 328678 — MB BS 1970 Lond.; MRCP (UK) 1973; DObst RCOG 1972. (Univ. Coll. Hosp.) Prev: Regist. (Rheum.) Roy. Free Hosp. Lond.

POWELL, Patricia Copeland (retired) Knowles House, Hollin Lane, Sutton, Macclesfield SK11 0HR Tel: 01260 252334 — MB BS 1956 Durh. Prev: Research Asst. (Paediat. Nephrol.) Roy. Manch. Childr. Hosp.

POWELL, Paula Marie Bridge Road Surgery, 30 Bridge Road, Litherland, Liverpool L18 5EG Tel: 0151 949 0249 — MB BS 1989 Lond.; MRCGP 1993.

POWELL, Peter David (retired) Cwmbach Lodge, Glasbury-on-Wye, Hereford HR3 5LT Tel: 01497 847218 — MB ChB 1951 Ed. Prev: SHO & Ho. Phys. Gen. Hosp. Grimsby.

POWELL, Peter David Ahern (retired) The Old Barn, Whiteshill Common, Hambrook, Bristol BS16 1SN Tel: 0117 956 5760 — MB BS 1956 Lond. Prev: Sen. Cas. Off. & SHO (Surg.) Bristol Roy. Infirm.

POWELL, Mr Philip Hugh 38 Rectory Road, Gosforth, Newcastle upon Tyne NE3 1XP — MD 1981 Bristol; MB ChB 1973; FRCS Eng. 1977. Cons. (Urol.) Freeman Hosp. Newc.

POWELL, Reginald Maldwyn (retired) The Coach House, Legsheath Lane, East Grinstead RH19 4JW — MRCS Eng. LRCP Lond. 1946; MRCGP 1962. Prev: Ho. Surg. Univ. Coll. Hosp. Lond.

POWELL, Richard Adam Whitby Group Practice, 114 Chester Road, Whitby, Ellesmere Port CH65 6TG Tel: 0151 355 6151 Fax: 0151 355 6843; South Woodlands, Welsh Road, Childer Thornton, South Wirral CH66 5PG Tel: 0151 339 2210 — MB ChB 1978 Liverp.; MRCGP 1982; DRCOG 1981. Clin. Asst. (Dermat.) Countess of Chester Hosp.

POWELL, Richard John Clinical Immunology Unit, Queen's Medical Centre, Nottingham NG7 2UH Tel: 0115 970 9130 Fax: 0115 970 9919 Email: richard.powell@nottingham.ac.uk — MB BS 1971 Lond.; FRCP Lond. 1992; MRCP (UK) 1974; MRCS Eng. LRCP Lond. 1971; DM Nottm 1994. (Char. Cross) Cons. Clin. Immunol. Qu. Med. Centre Nottm.; Sen. Lect. Univ. Med. Sch. Socs: Brit. Soc. Rheum.; Brit. Soc. Allergy & Clin. Immunol.; Amer. Coll. Rheum.

POWELL, Robin Barrington Park Royal Centre for Mental Health, Central Middlesex Hospial, Acton Lane, London NW10 7NS Tel: 020 8453 2780 Fax: 020 8961 6339 Email: robin.powell@dial.pipex.com — MB BS 1984 Lond.; MSc Lond. 1992; MRCPsych 1989. (Westminster) Cons. Old Age Psychiat. Centre Middlsex Hosp. Lond.; Hon. Sen. Lect. Imperial Coll. Sch. of Med. Prev: Sen. Regist. (Psychiat.) Maudsley Hosp. Lond.; Regist. Rotat. (Psychiat.) Roy. Free Hosp. Lond.

POWELL, Royden James (retired) 52 The Boulevard, Worthing BN13 1LB Tel: 01903 40424 — MRCS Eng. LRCP Lond. 1950; MRCGP 1968. Prev: Chest Regist. Worthing Hosp. & Rochford Hosp.

POWELL, Sarah Lucy 82 Park Lea, East Herrington, Sunderland SR3 3SZ — MB BS 1991 Newc.

POWELL, Sharon Jeanne The Medical Centre, Kingston Avenue, East Horsley, Leatherhead KT24 6QT; Cranley Cottage, 12 Cranley Close, Guildford GU1 2JN — MB BCh 1989 Witwatersrand; MRCGP (UK) 1995. GP Retainer.

POWELL, Sheila Margaret Fax: 01865 228260; 3 Morlands, East Hanney, Wantage OX12 0JW Tel: 01235 868518 Fax: 01865 228260 — MB BS Lond. 1965; FRCP Lond. 1993, M 1969; MRCS Eng. LRCP Lond. 1965. (Roy. Free) Cons. Dermat. Oxon. HA. Socs: BMA & Brit. Contact Dermat. Gp.; Eur. Soc. Contact Dermat. Prev:

POWELL

Lect. (Community Med.) Univ. Sheff.; SHO (Med.) Lusaka Centr. Hosp., Zambia; Ho. Phys. Hampstead Gen. Hosp.

POWELL, Simon Nicholas 153 Melrose Avenue, Wimbledon Park, London SW19 8AU — MB BS 1981 Lond.; BA Oxf. 1976; MRCP (UK) 1985; FRCR 1988. Clin. Scientist Inst. Cancer Research Lond.; Hon. Sen. Regist. Roy. Marsden Hosp.

POWELL, Stephen Mark John 49 Woollin Crescent, Tingley, Wakefield WF3 1ET — MB ChB 1989 Leeds.

POWELL, Stephen William Wellington Road Surgery, Wellington Road, Newport TF10 7HG Tel: 01952 811677 Fax: 01952 825981; The Brook Cottage, Longford, Newport TF10 8LS Tel: 01952 825544 — MB BS 1982 Lond.; MRCGP 1986; DRCOG 1986; DCH RCP Lond. 1984. (St. Bart.) Prev: Trainee GP Stafford VTS; SHO (Psychiat.) Lister Hosp. Stevenage.

***POWELL, Steven Kevin** 5 Benvie Road, Dundee DD2 2LH — MB ChB 1997 Dundee.

POWELL, Teyrnon Glyn Paediatric Department, Ysbyty Gwynedd, Bangor LL57 2PW Tel: 01248 384125 Fax: 01248 370629; Tyddyn Eden, Tynygongl, Isle of Anglesey Tel: 01248 851006 Email: tgp@doctors.org.uk — MB BChir 1975 Camb.; MA Camb. 1975, MD 1987; FRCP 1997; FRCPCH 1997; DCH Eng. 1976. (Lond.) p/t Cons. Paediat. Ysbyty Gwynedd Bangor. Prev: Cons. Paediat. Neath Gen. Hosp. W. Glam.; Regist. (Paediat.) Melbourne, Austral.; Sen. Regist. (Paediat.) Manch.

POWELL, Thomas Paul Stansfield (retired) Bryn Eryl, Bryn Goodman, Ruthin LL15 1EL Tel: 01824 703199 — MB ChB Leeds 1950; MRCS Eng. LRCP Lond. 1952; FRCPsych 1980, M 1952; DPM Eng. 1959. Prev: Cons. Psychiat. N. Wales Hosp. Denbigh.

POWELL, Trevor Adrian St Bartholomews Surgery, 292A Barking Road, London E6 3BA Tel: 020 8472 0669/1077 Fax: 020 8471 9122 — MB 1976 Camb.; BChir 1975; MRCGP 1980; DRCOG 1980.

POWELL, William David Gareth 21 Ditchfield, Formby, Liverpool L37 4EQ — MB ChB 1970 Liverp.

POWELL, William Malcolm Court View Surgery, Rosemary Street, Mansfield NG19 6AB Tel: 01623 623600 Fax: 01623 635460 — MB ChB 1974 Sheff.; Dip. Pract. Dermat. Wales 1991. (Sheffield)

POWELL-BRETT, Christopher Francis 3 Basil Street, London SW3 1AU Tel: 020 7235 6642 Fax: 020 7235 6052; 13 Alderney Street, London SW1V 4ES Tel: 020 7834 1118 — MB BS 1966 Lond.; MFOM RCP Lond. 1980; MRCS Eng. LRCP Lond. 1966; DObst RCOG 1968. (St. Thos.) Med. Examr. United Nations in Gt. Brit.; Med. Adviser Jaine Spencer Ch. and transmitter Computer. Socs: Med. Soc. Lond.; Chelsea Clin. Soc.; Skane Med. Soc.

POWELL-JACKSON, John David Newick, Edward Road, St Cross, Winchester SO23 9RB — MB BChir 1967 Camb.; MD Camb. 1977, MA, MB 1967, BChir 1966; FRCP Lond. 1983, M 1969; MRCS Eng. 1966; LRCP Lond. 1967. (Camb. & Guy's) Cons. Phys. Roy. Hants. Co. Hosp. Winchester. Socs: Internat. Soc. Hypertens; Brit. Cardiac Soc. Prev: Ho. Phys. & Sen. Regist. (Med.) Guy's Hosp. Lond.; Clin. Research Fell. MRC Blood Pressure Unit W.m. Infirm. Glas.

POWELL-JACKSON, Mary Ann Newick, Edward Road, St Cross, Winchester SO23 9RB — MB BS 1966 Lond.; MRCS Eng. LRCP Lond. 1966; FFA RCS Eng. 1971. (St. Geo.) Clin. Asst. (Anaesth.) Basingstoke Dist. Hosp. Prev: Anaesth. Sen. Regist. St. Geo. Hosp. Lond.; Anaesth. Regist. St. Geo. Hosp. Lond.; Ho. Surg. St. Geo. Hosp. Lond.

POWELL-JACKSON, Paul Richard The Maidstone Hospital, Maidstone & Tunbridge Wells NHS Trust, Hermitage Lane, Maidstone ME16 9QQ Tel: 01622 723052 Fax: 01622 723053 — MB BChir 1973 Camb.; MA Camb. 1970, BA (Hons.) 1969, MD 1985; FRCP Lond. 1994; MRCP (UK) 1975. (Guy's) Cons. Phys Maidstone & Tunbridge Wells NHS Trust. Socs: Brit. Soc. Gastroenterol. Prev: Lect. King's Coll. Sch. Med. & Dent. Lond.; Regist. St. Geo. Hosp. Lond.; Resid. Med. Off. Nat. Heart Hosp. Lond.

POWELL-TUCK, Jeremy St Bart. & The Royal London. Hospital School of Med. & Dent., Turner St., London E1 2AD Tel: 020 7426 5603 Fax: 020 7247 9594 Email: j.powell-tuck@mds.qmw.ac.uk; 9 Horbury Crescent, London W11 3NF Tel: 020 7727 2528 — MD Birm. 1980, MB ChB 1970; FRCP Lond. 1992; MRCP (UK) 1973. (Birm.) Sen. Lect. (Human Nutrit.) Lond. Hosp. & St. Bart. Hosp. Med. Colls.; Hon. Cons. Phys. Roy. Hosps. Trust. Prev: Sen. Regist. (Med.) Char. Cross, W.m. & W. Middlx. Hosps. Lond.; Wellcome Research Fell. (Clin. Nutrit & Metab. Unit) Lond. Sch. Hyg. & Trop. Med.; Research Fell. & Hon. Sen. Regist. St. Mark's Hosp. Lond.

POWER, Aidan Colman Pfizer Central Research, Sandwich CT13 9NJ Tel: 01304 648140 Fax: 01304 655614 Email: aidan_power@sandwich.pfizer.com; 4 Oaks Park, Rough Common, Canterbury CT2 9DP — MB BCh BAO 1984 NUI; MSc History of Sci. & Med. Lond. 1991; MRCPsych 1989. Pharmaceut. Phys. Pfizer Centr. Research Sandwich Kent.

POWER, Andrew c/o Clinical Pharmacology, Glasgow Royal Infirmary, Glasgow G4 0SF Tel: 0141 211 4212 Fax: 0141 211 5515; 51 Rodger Avenue, Newton Mearns, Glasgow G77 6JS Tel: 0141 639 7048 Email: apower@net.ntl.com — MB ChB 1988 Glas.; BSc (Hons.) Glas. 1985; MRCGP 1992; Dip. Therap. Wales 1997; DRCOG 1991. (Glas.) Asst. Med. Prescribing Adviser Gtr. Glas. HB. Prev: GP Glas.; SHO (Psychiat.) Levendale Hosp. Glas.; SHO (O & G) Rutherglen Matern. Hosp. Glas.

POWER, Andrew Patrick 1A Grange Park Avenue, Leeds LS8 3BA; Whitkirk Medical Centre, 9A Austhorpe View, Leeds LS15 8NN — MB ChB 1985 Leeds.

POWER, Anthony Lyn 27 Rhyd-y-Defaid Drive, Derwen Fawr, Sketty, Swansea SA2 8AJ Tel: 01792 299760 — MB BCh 1969 Wales; FFR 1974; FRCR 1975. Clin. Dir. (Radiol.) Singleton Hosp. Swansea; Cons. Radiol. Swansea NHS Trust. Socs: BMA. Prev: Cons. Radiol. W. Glam. AHA; Sen. Regist. & Trainee Regist. (Radiodiag.) Univ. Hosp. of Wales; SHO (Cardiothoracic Med.) Sully Hosp.

POWER, Mr Brian John Department of Ophthalmology, Dumfries and Galloway Royal Infirmary, Dumfries DG1 4AP — MB BS 1970 Lond.; FRCS Eng. 1978; DO Eng. 1974.

POWER, Bryan Edward Victoria House Surgery, 228 Dewsbury Road, Leeds LS11 6HQ Tel: 0113 270 4754 Fax: 0113 272 0561 — MB BCh BAO 1982 NUI.

POWER, Catherine Clare 11 Banchory Road, Blackheath, London SE3 8SL Tel: 020 8853 0679 — MB BCh BAO NUI 1941, DPH 1943; LM Nat. Matern. Hosp. Dub. 1942. (NUI) Socs: BMA. Prev: Ho. Phys. St. Vincent's Hosp. Dub.; Ho. Surg. Eliz. G. Anderson Hosp.; Asst. Med. Off. Brook Gen. Hosp.

POWER, Christine Anne Cottage Farm, Main St., Keyham, Leicester LE7 9JQ — MB BS 1980 Lond.; DA (UK) 1988. Clin. Asst. (Anaesth.) Glenfield Hosp. Leicester. Prev: SHO (Anaesth.) Roy. Devon & Exeter Hosp.; Regist. (Microbiol.) Kingston Hosp. Kingston upon Thames; Trainee GP Exeter VTS.

POWER, Damian Edward 22 Deuchar Street, Newcastle upon Tyne NE2 1JX — MB BS 1996 Newc.

POWER, Dominic Michael 14 Thoday Street, Cambridge CB1 3AS — BChir 1994 Camb.

POWER, Eileen Laura (retired) 10 Johnson Mansions, Queen's Club Gardens, London W14 9SJ Tel: (20) 7385 0155 — MB BCh BAO 1942 NUI; LAH Dub. 1951; MFCM 1974; DPH Eng. 1961; MPSI 1952. PMO King's Health Dist. (T). Prev: Ho. Phys. St. Vincent's Hosp. Dub. & Alder Hey Childr. Hosp. Liverp.

POWER, Francis John Upper Portclew House, Freshwater East, Pembroke SA71 5LA Tel: 01646 672661 — MB BCh Wales 1971; MRCGP 1976.

POWER, Jacqueline Anne Susan Silverdale, Fieldhouse Lane, Hepscott, Morpeth NE61 6LT — MB BS 1990 Newc.; MRCGP 1994. Community Doctor Child & Adolesc. Ment. Health City Health Trust Newc.

POWER, Jennifer Susan Fiona 3 West View, Wylam NE41 8DT — MB ChB 1993 Manch.; MA (Medieval Archaeology) Univ. Lond. 1984, BA (Modern Hist.) 1983.

POWER, Joanna 25 Yeoman's Row, London SW3 2AL — BM BCh 1991 Oxf.

POWER, Mr John Washington 130 Harley Street, London W1N 1AH Tel: 020 7235 2190 Fax: 020 7460 0985 Email: 101705.2321@compuservce.com — MB BS 1959 Sydney; FRCS Eng. 1964; FRCS Ed. 1964. Cons. Orthop. Cromwell Hosp. Lond.; Cons. Repatriation Dept. Austral. Socs: Fell. Austral. Orthop. Assn.; Roy. Soc. Med.; Internat. Coll. Surgs. (Ex-Pres. Austral.). Prev: Governor & Mem. Nominating Comm. Represen. WHO; Princip. OMAES Pty Ltd. Sydney, Austral.; Cons. Harley St. Clinic Lond.

POWER, Kenneth John Ronald Fisher Department of Anaesthesia, Poole Hospital NHS Trust, Longfleet Road, Poole BH15 2JB Tel: 01202 442443; 23 Penn Hill Avenue, Parkstone, Poole BH14 9LU — BM 1980 Soton.; MRCP (UK) 1983; FFA RCS Eng. 1986. Cons.

Anaesth. & Intens. Care Poole Gen. Hosp. Prev: Sen. Regist. (Anaesth.) Roy. United Hosp. Bath.

POWER, Lucy Mary Department of Psychiatry, East Wing, Homerton Hospital, Homerton Road, Hackney, London E9 6SR — BChir 1990 Camb. SHO Barts and The Homerton Psychiat. Train. Rotat.

POWER, Michael James Patrick Department Elderly Medicine, Ulster Hospital, Dundonald, Belfast BT16 1RH Tel: 028 9048 4511 Ext: 2845 Fax: 028 9055 0415 Email: michael.power@ucht.n-i.nhs.uk; 5 Brooklands Road, Newtownards BT23 4TL Tel: 028 9181 7313 — MB BCh BAO 1979 NUI; MRCPI 1982; FRCP 1994 Ed.; FRCP 1997 (L); MRCP 1983 UK; FRCPI 1994. (Nat. Univ. Ire. Galway) Cons. Phys. Dept. Elderly Med. Ulster Hosp.

POWER, Michael Patrick Waterfoot Health Centre, Cowpe Road, Waterfoot, Rossendale BB4 7DN Tel: 01706 215178 — MB ChB 1988 Manch.

POWER, Neil Richard 52 Noblehill Avenue, Dumfries DG1 3HX — MB ChB 1993 Glas.

POWER, Norman Athol Mill Pond House, Iping, Midhurst GU29 0PE Tel: 01730 812970 — MRCS Eng. LRCP Lond. 1950; LDS RCS Eng. 1941.

POWER, Peter Colin (retired) 91 Cottage Grove, Southsea PO5 1EH Tel: 02392 872490 — MB ChB Bristol 1959; 1988 (MLCOM) (Mem. Of London college of osteopathic med.); DObst RCOG 1966.

POWER, Mr Richard Anthony Department of Orthopaedic Surgery, Glenfield Hospital, Groby Road, Leicester LE3 9QP Tel: 0116 256 3440; Cottage Farm, Main St, Keysham, Leicester LE3 9JQ Tel: 0116 259 5263 — MB BS 1980 Lond.; FRCS (Orth.) 1993; FRCS Ed. 1986. Cons. Orthop. Glenfield Hosp. & Leicester Roy. Infirm.

POWER, Richard John 79 Gallys Road, Windsor SL4 5QS — MB ChB 1992 Sheff.

POWER, Sharon Jane Department of Anaesthetics, Greenwich District Hospital, Vanbrugh Hill, Greenwich, London SE10 9HE Tel: 020 8858 8141; The Knoll, 17 Kidbrooke Grove, Blackheath, London SE3 0LE — MB BS 1976 Lond.; FFA RCS Eng. 1982. Cons. Anaesth. Greenwich Healthcare Trust Lond.

POWER, Simon Flat C1 Elm Court, Barlow Moor Road, Didsbury, Manchester M20 2QQ — MB ChB 1990 Manch.

POWER-BREEN, Patricia Anne 3 Hillview Avenue, George Town, Dumfries DG1 4DX — MB BCh BAO 1976 NUI; MRCGP 1984. Clin. Asst. (Psychogeriat.) Crichton Roy. Hosp. Dumfries. Prev: Clin. Asst. (ENT) Dumfries & Galloway Roy. Infirm. Dumfries; Clin. Asst. (Ophth.) Edin. Roy. Infirm.; Asst. GP Kerry, Eire.

POWERS, Anthony Michael (retired) — MB ChB 1971 Liverp.; DA Eng. 1977.

***POWERS, David Samuel** 14 Meadowbrook Court, Stone ST15 8LX Tel: 01785 286115 — MB ChB 1996 Dundee.

POWERS, Lynette Ann The Gainsborough Practice, Warfield Medical Centre, 1 County Lane, Whitegrove, Bracknell RG42 3JP Tel: 01344 428742 Fax: 01344 428743 — BM BCh 1982 Wales.

POWERS, Michael John 4 Paper Buildings., Temple, London EC4Y 7EX Tel: 020 7353 3366 Fax: 020 7353 5778 Email: powersqc@medneg.co.uk; 11 Old Square, Lincoln's Inn, London WC2A 3TS — MB BS 1972 Lond.; BSc Lond. 1969; DA Eng. 1975. (Middlx.) Socs: Medico-Legal Soc.; Roy. Soc. Med.; Soc. Of Doctors in Law. Prev: Barrister-at-Law Lincoln's Inn 1979, Inner Temple 1984 & Qu.'s Counsel 1995; Regist. (Anaesth.) N.wick Pk. Hosp. Harrow; Ho. Surg. (O & G) Middlx. Hosp. Lond.

POWERSMITH, Parsley Sheena Mary St. James University Hospital, Beckett St., Leeds LS9 7TF Tel: 0113 243 3144 — MRCS Eng. LRCP Lond. 1981; MRCPsych 1985; Dip. Clin. Hypn. Sheff. 1991. Cons. Psychiat. & Sen. Clin. Lect. St. Jas. Univ. Hosp. & Univ. Leeds. Socs: BMA.

POWICK, Dawn Rose 3 Elizabeth Mews, Lower St., Cleobury Mortimer, Kidderminster DY14 8AL; Inverbeg, Pinkham, Cleobury Mortimer, Kidderminster DY14 8QE Tel: 01299 271181 — MB ChB 1985 Birm.; ChB Birm. 1985.

POWIS, Judith Alison Abington Hill, 504 Wellingborough Road, Northampton NN3 3HX Tel: 01604 405555 — MB ChB 1963 Birm.; DObst RCOG 1965. (Birm.) SCMO (Family Plann.) N.ampton HA; Clin. Asst. (Family Plann.) N.ampton Gen. Hosp. Prev: Clin.

Asst. (Paediat.) Birm. Matern. Hosp.; Med. Off. Birm. Family Plann. Assn.

POWIS, Mr Mark Robert Flat 1, 47 Gondar Gardens, London NW6 1EP Tel: 020 7433 1456 Email: mark@lobsang.rfeeserve.co.uk — MB BS 1987 Lond.; BSc (Hons.) Lond. 1984; FRCS Eng. 1992; FRCS 1999 FRCS(PAED.SURG)1999. (St. Mary's Hosp. Med. Sch.) Specialist Regist. Paediat. Surg. Roy. Lond. Hosp. Socs: Fell. Roy. Soc. Med.; Assoc. Mem. Brit. Assn. Paediat. Surgs.; Brit. Assn. Paediatric Endoscopic Surg. Prev: SPR Paediatric Surg..Gt Ormond St Hosp; SPR Paediatric Surg.. Kings Coll. Hosp; SPR Paediatric Surg.. Qu. Eliz. Hosp.

POWIS, Martin David Meadowside Family Health Centre, 30 Winchcombe Road, Solihull B92 8PJ Tel: 0121 743 2560/742 5666 Fax: 0121 743 4216; 218 Stoney Lane, Yardley, Birmingham B25 8YJ Tel: 0121 783 4584 Fax: 0121 783 4584 — MB ChB 1976 Birm.; MRCGP 1980; DRCOG 1978; DFFR 1998. (Birmingham) Undergrad. Tutor Birm. Univ. Prev: SHO (O & G) Solihull Hosp.; SHO (Infect. Dis.) E. Birm. Hosp.; Ho. Off. (Radiother.) Qu. Eliz. Hosp. Birm.

POWIS, Rachel Anne 40 Greatwood Terrace, Topsham, Exeter EX3 0EB Tel: 01392 877685 — MB BS 1993 Lond. (St Georges Hospital)

POWIS, Professor Stephen Huw Centre for Nephrology, Royal Free & University College Medical School, Rowland Hill St., London NW3 2PF Tel: 020 7830 2695 Fax: 020 7830 2125 Email: powis@rfhsm.ac.uk — BM BCh 1985 Oxf.; PhD Univ. Lond. 1995; BSc (Hons.) Glas. 1981; MRCP (UK) 1988; FRCP 1998. Prof. (Renal Med.) Roy. Free Hosp. Sch. Med. Lond. Socs: Renal Assn. (Exec. Comm. 1998-2001); Brit. Transpl. Soc.; Brit. Soc. Immunol. Prev: Sen. Lect. (Renal Med.) Guy's Hosp. Lond.; Regist. (Renal Med.) Guy's Hosp. Lond.

POWLES, Allan Badgett Jubilee Farm, Fen Road, Washingborough, Lincoln LN4 1AE Tel: 01522 793620 — MB BS 1974 Lond.; FFA RCS Eng. 1978; FFA RCSI 1977. Cons. Anaesth. Lincoln Co. Hosp.

POWLES, Anne Veronica St. Mary's Hospital, Praed St., London W2 2NY Tel: 020 7725 1194; St. Ibbs Bush, St. Ippolytts, Hitchin SG4 7NL Tel: 01462 457956 — MB ChB 1972 Aberd.; MD Aberd. 1989; FRCP Lond. 1995. Cons. Dermat. St. Mary's Hosp. & Centr. Middlx. Hosp. Lond. Prev: Sen. Regist. (Dermat.) St. Mary's Hosp. Lond.

POWLES, Mr David Pritchard Lister Hospital, Coreys Mill Lane, Stevenage SG1 4AB Tel: 01438 314333 Fax: 01438 781274; St. Ibbs Bush, St. Ippolytts, Hitchin SG4 7NL Tel: 01462 457956 — MD 1973 Queen's Univ. Kingston, Canada; BSc McGill 1969; FRCS Eng. 1978. (Qu. Univ., Canada) Cons. Orthop. Surg. Lister Hosp. Stevenage. Socs: Fell. BOA; Brit. Assn. Surg. Knee; Eur. Soc. Knee Surg. Sports Med. Arthroscopy. Prev: Sen. Regist. (Orthop.) King's Coll. Hosp. Lond.

POWLES, Mr James Watson Green Hedges, Coulsdon Lane, Coulsdon CR5 3QL Tel: 01737 556352; Green Hedges, Coulsdon Lane, Coulsdon CR5 3QL Tel: 01737 556352 — MB BS 1994 Lond.; FRCS (Eng) 1998; BSc (Hons) 1991. (St.Bart's, Lond.) SHO (Otoaryn.) Radcliffe Infirm. Oxf.

POWLES, John William Department of Public Health and Primary Care, Institute of Public Health, Robinson Way, Cambridge CB2 2SR Tel: 01223 330310 Fax: 01223 330330 Email: jwp11@cam.ac.uk; 164 Gwydir Street, Cambridge CB1 2LW Tel: 01223 740245 — MA 1997 Camb.; MB BS Sydney 1968; FFPHM RCP (UK) 1987, M 1974. Univ. Lect. (Pub. Health Med.) Univ. Camb.; Hon. Cons. Pub. Health Med. Camb. Socs: Internat. Epidemiol. Assn.; Soc. for Epidemiological Research; Soc. for Social Med. Prev: Lect., Dept. of Social and Preven. Med., Monash Med. Sch., Melbourne, Australia, 1975-1991.

POWLES, Professor Raymond Leonard Little Garratts, 19 Garratts Lane, Banstead SM7 2EA Tel: 01737 353632; The Royal Marsden Hospital, Downs Road, Sutton SM2 5PT Tel: 020 8770 1027 — MB BS Lond. 1964; BSc (Special) Lond. 1961, MD 1976; FRCP Lond. 1980, M 1968; FRCPath Lond. 1993. (St. Bart.) Head & Prof. Haematological Oncol. i/c Leukaemia & Myeloma Units & Cons. Phys. Roy. Marsden Hosp. Sutton; Mem. Med. Research Counc. Working Party on Adult Leukaemia. Socs: (Advis. Comm.) Internat. Bone Marrow Transpl. Registry; Internat. Soc. Experim. Haematol.; Amer. Soc. Haemat. Prev: Imperial Cancer Research

POWLES

Fund. Sen. Scientif. Off. St. Bart. Hosp. Lond.; Ho. Phys. St. Bart. Hosp. Lond.; Ho. Phys. Brompton Hosp. Lond.

POWLES, Professor Trevor James Breast Unit, Royal Marsden Hospital, Downs Road, Sutton SM2 5PT Tel: 020 8642 6011 Fax: 020 8770 7313 Email: trevor.powles@rmh.nthames.nhs.uk; Green Hedges, Coulsdon Lane, Chipstead, Coulsdon CR5 3QL Tel: 01737 556352 — PhD Lond. 1975, BSc 1961, MB BS 1964; FRCP Lond. 1983; MRCP (UK) 1969; MRCS Eng. LRCP Lond. 1964; Specialist Accredit. (Gen. Med. & Med. Oncol.) RCP Lond. 1983. (St. Bart.) Cons. Med. Oncol. Roy. Marsden Hosp. Lond. & Sutton; Prof. (BrE. Oncol.) Inst. Cancer Research Lond. 1998-; Head BrE. Unit Roy. Marsden Hosp, 1994-; Med. Director.Common Cancers Div.,Roy. Marsden Hosp. Socs: Soc. Endocrinol.; Brit. BrE. Gp.; Assn. Cancer Phys. Prev: Sen. Lect. (Med.) & Hon. Cons. Phys. Roy. Marsden Hosp. & St. Geo. Hosp. Lond.; MRC Clin. Research Fell. Chester Beatty Research Inst. Lond.; Ho. Phys. Hammersmith Hosp. Lond.

POWLEY, Elaine The Kirkbymoorside Surgery, Tinley Garth, Kirkbymoorside, York YO62 6AR Tel: 01751 431254 Fax: 01751 432980; Lund Head, Skiplam, Nawton, York YO62 7RH Tel: 01751 431249 Fax: 01751 432980 — MB ChB 1968 Bristol; DPM Leeds 1971. Course Organiser Postgrad. Centre & Gen. Hosp. ScarBoro. VTS. Prev: Clin. Asst. (Child & Adolesc. Psychiat.) Clifton Hosp. York; Regist. (Psychiat.) York Hosps.; Ho. Off. (Obst.) Matern. Hosp. Fulford.

POWLEY, Mr John Michael (retired) 18 Compton Drive, Eastbourne BN20 8BX Tel: 01323 727520 — MB BS 1951 Lond.; FRCS Eng. 1958; MRCS Eng. LRCP Lond. 1951. Prev: Cons. Surg. E.bourne Health Dist.

POWLEY, Mr Philip Harold (retired) 47 Corby Avenue, Swindon SN3 1PS Tel: 01793 536570 — MB BS 1958 Lond.; FRCS Ed. 1962; FRCS Eng. 1962. Prev: Cons. Surg. Swindon Dist. Hosps.

POWLS, David Andrew Princess Royal Maternity, 16 Alexandra Parade, Glasgow Tel: 0141 211 5400 Email: powlsa@northglasgow.scot.nhs.uk — MB BCh 1986 Wales; MD (Univ. Liverp.) 1997; MRCP Ed. 1991. Cons. Neonatologist. Prev: Research Regist. (Child Health) Liverp. Univ.

POWLSON, Mark Medicines Control Agency, Room 1202 Market Towers, 1 Nine Elms Lane, London SW8 5NQ Tel: 020 7273 0908 Email: mark.powlson@mca.gov.uk; Vellum Lodge, 2A Read Road, Ashtead KT21 2HS — MB BS 1983 Lond.; BSc (Hons.) Lond. 1979; MRCS Eng. LRCP Lond. 1982. (Guy's) Edr.ial & Pub.ations Co-ordinator, MCA. Socs: Fell. Roy. Soc. Med.; Fell. Roy. Soc. Arts; Eur. Assn. Sci. Edr.s. Prev: Head, Med. Edit Unit DoH; Asst. Edr. The Lancet; Regist. (Med.) Roy. Shrewsbury Hosp.

POWNALL, Charles Hoole Bank Cottage, Hoole Bank, Chester CH2 4ES Tel: 01244 351077 — MRCS Eng. LRCP Lond. 1942. (Liverp.) Prev: Sen. Ho. Surg. Burton-on-Trent Gen. Infirm.

POWNALL, Christine Catherine Graham (retired) — MB ChB 1952 Ed. Prev: Ho. Surg. Simpson Matern. Hosp. Edin.

POWNALL, Denys 49 Belle Vale Road, Liverpool L25 2PB Tel: 0151 487 8660 — MRCS Eng. LRCP Lond. 1954. (Liverp.)

POWNALL, Mr Philip John 22 Bottom O'Th Moor, Horwich, Bolton BL6 6QF Tel: 01204 669096 — MB ChB 1961 Manch.; FRCS Eng. 1972; FRCS Ed. 1971. (Manch.) Cons. Orthop. Surg. Bolton Gp. Hosps. Socs: Fell. Manch. Med. Soc. Prev: Tutor/ Hon. Sen. Regist. (Orthop. Surg.) Univ. Leeds.

POWNER, Helen Ruth 3 Grange Crescent, Bridgend CF35 5HP — MB ChB 1989 Birm.

POWNEY, Alan (retired) 4 The Barn, Garden Farm, Chester-le-Street DH2 3RD Tel: 0191 387 3251 — MB BS 1958 Durh.; MB BS Durh., 1958.

POWNEY, Jolyon Geary 120 Bulwer Road, New Barnet, Barnet EN5 5EX — MB BS 1982 Lond.; BSc (Hons.) Lond. 1979, MB BS 1982; DA (UK) 1986; FFA RCS Eng. 1987. Cons. Anaesth. Newham Gen. Hosp. Prev: Sen. Regist. (Anaesth.) Roy. Lond. Hosp.; Regist. Rotat. (Anaesth.) Bloomsbury HA; SHO (Anaesth.) W.m. Hosp. Lond.

POWRIE, James Kenneth Diabetes & Endocrine Unit, Thoma Guy House, St Thomas St., London SE1 9RT Tel: 020 7955 5000 Fax: 020 7955 2121 Email: jake.powrie@kcl.ac.uk — MB ChB 1982 Aberd.; MB ChB Aberdeen 1982; MD Aberdeen 1992; BMedBiol Aberdeen 1979; MRCP (UK) 1986; FRCP Ed 1999; FRCP Lond. 2000. (Aberd.) Cons. Phys. & Hon. Sen. Lect. (Gen. Med., Diabetes & Endocrinol.) Guy's & St. Thos. NHS Trust Lond. Socs: Brit. Diabetic Assn.; Brit. Endocrine Soc.; Roy. Soc. Med. Prev: Lect.

(Med.) St. Thos. Hosp. Lond.; Research Fell. (Clin.) St. Thos. Hosp. Lond.; Regist. (Med.) Aberd. Roy. Infirm.

POWRIE, Suzanne Elizabeth 21 Chipstead Street, Fulham, London SW6 3SR Tel: 020 7731 5697 — MRCS Eng. LRCP Lond. 1967; FFA RCS Eng. 1974; FFA RACS 1972; DA Eng. 1969. (Sheff.) Cons. (Anaesth.) Moorfields Eye Hosp. Lond. Socs: Assn. Anaesths. Prev: Sen. Regist. (Anaesth.) Hammersmith Hosp. Lond.; Regist. (Anaesth.) Brompton Hosp. Lond. & Roy. Wom. Hosp. Melb.; Australia.

POWROZNYK, Arsenyj Vasyl Volodyslav Department of Anaesthesia, St Thomas' Hospital, Lambeth Palace Road, London SE1 7EH Tel: 020 7928 9292 Ext: 2353 Fax: 020 7960 5615 — MB BS 1986 Lond.; MA Camb. 1987, BA 1983; DA (UK) 1988; FRCA 1993. (Charing Cross Hospital Medical School) Cons. Anaesth. St. Thomas' Hosp. Lond. Socs: Assn. Anaesth.; Eur. Assn. Cardiothoracic Anaesth.; Assn. Cardiothoracic Anaesth. (UK). Prev: Sen. Regist. (Cardiothoracic Anaesth.) Roy. Brompton Hosp. Lond.; Sen. Regist. (Anaesth.) St. Thomas' Hosp. Lond.; Clin. Fell. (Caerdiothoracic Anaesth.) Papworth Hosp. Camb.

POXON, Ian Mark 28 The Drive, Walsall WS4 1PT Tel: 01922 684686 Email: ianpoxon@doctors.net.uk — MB ChB 1992 Sheff.; FRCA 2000 Lond. Specialist Regist. (Anaesth.) W. Midl. Higher Specialist Train. Scheme, Staffs. Prev: SHO (Anaesth.) Derbys Hosp.; SHO (Med.) Roy. Hull Hosps.

***POYNER, Amy Louise** Vine Cottage, Lower Road, Adgestone, Sandown PO36 0HN — MB BS 1998 Lond.; MB BS Lond 1998.

POYNER, Fiona Elizabeth Accident and Emergency Department, Northampton General Hospital Trust, Cliftonville, Northampton NN1 5BD Tel: 01604 634700 Fax: 01604 545615; 3 Woodland Walk, Northampton NN3 5NS — MB BCh 1986 Oxf.; MRCP (UK) 1992; FFAEM. Cons. A & E N.ampton Gen. Hosp. Trust.

POYNER, John Gerard St Annes Road East, 24 St. Annes Road East, Lytham St Annes FY8 1UR Tel: 01253 722121 Fax: 01253 781121; 42 St Annes Road E., St Annes, Lytham St Annes FY8 1UR Tel: 01253 722121 — MB ChB 1981 Manch.; MRCGP 1985; DRCOG 1986.

POYNER, Kenneth George (retired) Leach Heath Medical Centre, 14 Leach Heath Lane, Rubery, Birmingham B45 9BU Tel: 0121 453 3516 — MB BChir 1968 Camb.; MB Camb. 1968, BChir 1967; MA Camb. 1968; MRCGP 1975; DCH Eng. 1971; DObst RCOG 1969. Hosp. Pract. (Geriat.) W. Heath Hosp. Birm.; Mem. Birm. LMC. Prev: Ho. Surg. St. Thos. Hosp. Lond.

POYNER, Thomas Francis Queens Park Medical Centre, Farrer Street, Stockton-on-Tees TS18 2AW Tel: 01642 679681 Fax: 01642 677124 — MB BS 1974 Lond.; FRCP 2001 Lond.; MRCP (UK) 1981; MRCS Eng. LRCP Lond. 1974; MRCGP 1978; Dip. Pract. Dermat. (Merit) Wales 1993; DRCOG 1978. (Roy. Free) Hosp. Practitioner. Socs: Edit. Bd. Dermat. Pract.; (Vice Chairm.) Primary Care Dermat. Soc.; Mem. of the Assur. Med. Soc.

POYNOR, Margaret Ursula 586 Chorley New Road, Bolton BL6 4DW — MB BS 1975 Lond.; MRCP (UK) 1980; MRCS Eng. LRCP Lond. 1975; DCH Eng. 1978; DRCOG 1977. (Guy's) Cons. Community Paediat. Bolton HA.

***POYNTER SMITH, Paul Nicholas** Pinewood, Hannington Rd, Hannington, Tadley RG26 5TW — MB BS 1997 Lond.

POYNTON, Amanda Mary Rawnsley Building, Manchester Royal Infirmary, Oxford Road, Manchester M13 9BX Tel: 0161 276 5354 — MB BS 1981 Lond.; MA Oxf. 1984, BA (Physiol. Sci.) 1978; MRCPsych 1985. Cons. Psychiat. Manch. Roy. Infirm. Prev: Cons. Psychiat. & Sen. Lect. Guy's Hosp. Lond.; Lect. (Biol. Psychiat.) United Med. & Dent. Sch. Lond.; Regist. Rotat. (Psychiat.) Guy's Hosp. Lond.

POYNTON, Christopher Hilton Department of Haematology, University Hospital of Wales, Heath Park, Cardiff CF14 4XN Tel: 029 2074 7747 Fax: 029 2074 3895 Email: poynton@cardiff.ac.uk; 47 Stanhope Road, Croydon CR0 5NS — BM BCh 1974 Oxf.; DM Oxf. 1991; FRCP Lond. 1995; MRCP (UK) 1979; MRCPath 1986; FRCPath 1997; FRCP Ed 1999. (Oxford) Sen. Lect. & Hon. Cons. Haemat. Univ. Hosp. Wales Cardiff; State of Texas Med. License (Hemat. & Oncol.). Socs: Amer. Soc. Haemat.; Internat. Soc. Hemat. & Graft Engin.; Brit. Soc. Haematol.

POYSER, John Tramways Medical Centre, 54a Holme Lane, Sheffield S6 4JQ Tel: 0114 233 9462; Newstead, 76 Langsett

Avenue, Sheffield S6 4AA — MB ChB 1976 Sheff.; MPhil. Sheff. 1995. (Sheff.) Chair Sheff. W. PCG; Lect. (GP) Univ. Sheff.

POYSER, Louisa Margaret 7 Palace Road, Llandaff, Cardiff CF5 2AF Tel: 01222 577117 — BM BS 1986 Nottm.; BMedSci Nottm. 1984, BM BS 1986; MRCGP 1993; DRCOG 1989. Asst. GP Cardiff.

POZNIAK, Anton Louis HIV Unit Chelsea and Westminster Hospital NHS Trust, 369 Fulham Road, London SW10 9NH Tel: 020 8746 5620 Fax: 020 8746 5628 Email: antonp@crusaid-star.co.uk; 8 Eynella Road, Dulwich, London SE22 8XF Tel: 020 8693 4057 Fax: 020 8693 4057 Email: pozniak@dircon.co.uk — MB ChB 1979 Bristol; MD Bristol 1994; FRCP Lond. 1996; MRCP (UK) 1982. (University of Bristol) Cons. Phys. GUM/HIV Chelsea & W.minster Hosp. NHS Trust; Hon. Sen. Lect. Imperial Coll. Lond. Socs: Brit. Thorac. Soc.; MSSVD; Brit. HIV Assn. Prev: Sen. Lect. Kings Coll. Sch. Med.; Lect. Acad. Dept. Genitourin. Med. Middlx. Hosp.; Lect. (Med.) Univ. Zimbabwe.

POZO, Mr Joseph Louis The Royal United Hospital, Combe Park, Bath BA1 3NG; The Royal National Hospital for Rheumatic Diseases, Upper Borough Walls, Bath BA1 1RL — BM BCh 1974 Oxf.; MA, BM BCh Oxf. 1974; FRCS Eng. 1980. Cons. Orthop. Surg. Roy. United Hosp. Bath. Socs: Fell. BOA; Brit. Assn. Surg. Knee; Eur. Soc. Sports Traumatol. Knee Surg. & Arthroscopy. Prev: Sen. Regist. (Orthop. Rotat.) Univ. Coll. Hosp. & W.m. Hosp. Lond.

POZUELO LIMA, Eloy Carlos 13B Burton Street, Melton Mowbray LE13 1AE — LMS 1986 Malaga.

POZYCZKA, Teofil Andrzej Tel: 01493 452654 Fax: 01493 452270 Email: andy.pozyczka@jpaget.nhs.uk; The Poppins, Thrioby Rd, Filby, Great Yarmouth NR29 3HJ Tel: 01493 369204 — MB BS 1971 Lond.; FRCOG 1997; MRCOG 1980, DObst RCOG 1973. (Westm.) Cons. O & G James Paget Healthcare NHS Trust, Gt. Yarmouth; Clin. Director Wom. and Childhealth Directorate. Socs: Brit. Med. Assn.; Brit. Soc. for Colposcopy and Cervical Path. Prev: RAF Med. Br. Wg. Cdr. (Ret'd) - Cons. O & G; Hon. Lect. Nuffield Dept. O & G John Radcliffe Hosp. Oxf.

POZZI, Marco 16 College Road, Liverpool L23 0RW — State Exam 1981 Milan. (Univ. Milan) Cons. Cardiac Surg. Roy. Liverp. Childr. Hosp.; Clin. Lect. Univ. Liverp. Socs: Eur. Soc. Cardiothorac. Surg.; Brit. Paediat. Cardiac Assn.; Soc. Cardiothoracic Surgs. GB.

POZZILLI, Paolo Department of Diabetes & Metabolism, St. Bartholomew's Hospital, West Smithfield, London EC1A 7BE Tel: 020 7601 7454 Fax: 020 7601 7449 Email: p.p.pozzilli@qmul.ac.uk — State Exam 1976 Rome; Dip. Endocrinol. Univ. Lond. 1979. (Univ. Rome) Prof. of Clin. research St. Bartholomews Hosp. Lond.; Prof. Endocrinol. & Metab. Dis.s, Univ. Campus Biomedico, Rome 2001. Socs: Fell.Roy. Soc. Med.; Fell.Int. Diabetes Federatation.; Eur. Assn. Study Diabetes. Prev: Wellcome Foundat. Fell. 1980; Juvenile Diabetes Foundat. Fell. (USA) 1983; Sen. Investigator, Asst. Prof., Univ. of Rome "La Sapienza".

POZZONI, Lynda Suzanne 19 Bowness Avenue, Southfront, Southport PR8 3QP — MB BS 1995 Lond.

PRABHAKAR, Deepak Trilok Chand Prestwich Health Centre, Fairfax Road, Prestwich, Manchester M25 1BT Tel: 0161 773 2483 Fax: 0161 773 9218; Branch Surgery, The Uplands, Whitefield Health Centre, Bury New Road, Whitefield, Manchester M45 8GH Tel: 0161 796 2296 — MB BS 1972 Poona; DA Eng. 1976. (Armed Forces Med. Coll.) Prev: Regist. (Anaesth.) Bury Gen. Hosp.; SHO (Anaesth.) Bury Gen. Hosp.

PRABHAKAR, Narinder 36 Sergeants Lane, Whitefield, Manchester M45 7TS Tel: 0161 766 9911 — MB BS 1974 Poona; DCCH RCGP Warwick 1995; DObst RCOG 1976. (Armed Forces Med. Coll.) SCMO (Paediat. & Child Health) Bury Health Care NHS Trust. Prev: Clin. Med. Off. (Community Med.) Bury AHA; SHO (Gyn. & Obst.) Fairfield Gen. Hosp. Bury; Ho. Off. (Gen. Surg.) Bury Gen. Hosp.

PRABHAKARAN, Narayanan Cambridge House, 124 Werrington Road, Bucknall, Stoke-on-Trent ST2 9AJ Tel: 01782 219075 Fax: 01782 279047 — MB BS 1971 Kerala; MB BS 1971 Kerala.

PRABHAKARAN, Unniparambath Pattaveettil Pontynewynydd Clinic, Mill Road, Pontynewynydd, Pontypool NP4 6NG Tel: 01495 752115 — MB BS 1974 Kerala; MSc (Med. Sci.) Gen. Pract. 1985; MLCOM 1987; MFHom 1985; MRCGP 1983. (Med. Coll. Trivandrum) RCGP/Syntex Fell.sh. Rheum. 1981; Univ. Glas. Fell.sh.

1982; RCGP Fac. Tutor; Sen. Lect. in Gen. Pract. Socs: RCGP Research Sec.

PRABHAKER, Shakti Kumar Carters Lane House, 41 Brunswick Road, Shoreham-by-Sea BN43 5WA — MB BS 1977 Panjab.

PRABHU, Manur Radhakrishna Kildean Day Hospital, Drip Road, Stirling FK8 1RW Tel: 01786 458607 Fax: 01786 458605 — MB BS 1971 Madras; MRCPsych 1980; DPM Leeds 1976. (Jawaharlal Inst. Postgrad. Med. Educat Pondicherry) Cons. Psychiat.Forth Valley Primary CareHealthcare NHS Trust. Prev: Regist. (Psychiat.) Middlx. Hosp. Lond. & Gtr. Glas. HB.

PRABHU, Matti Achuth 6 St James Mount, Rainhill, Prescot L35 0QU Tel: 0151 426 4332 — MB BS 1971 Dibrugarh; MB BS Dibrugarh, India 1971. Assoc. Specialist. Socs: MDU. Prev: Clin. Asst. A & E Warrington NHS Trust Hosp.

PRABHU, Mudar Anantha 43 Hallington Drive, Heanor, Derby DE75 7QX Tel: 01773 765632; 43 Hallington Drive, Heanor, Derby DE75 7QX — MB BS 1970 Bangalor; MB BS Bangalore 1970. (Bangalore Med. Coll.) GP Derby.

PRABHU, Mrs Poornima Shrinivas Ashok East Glamorgan General Hospital, Church Village, Pontypridd CF38 1AB Tel: 01443 204242; 4 Clos Darran Las, Cardiff Road, Creigiau, Cardiff CF15 9SL Tel: 01222 892525 — MB BS 1979 Bombay; MRCOG 1986; DObst RCPI 1981. Clin. Med. Off. Community Family Plann. & RHC; Clin. Asst. (Obst. & Gyn.).

PRABHU, Suman 93 Waterslea Drive, Heaton, Bolton BL1 5FA — MB ChB 1996 Manch.; DRCOG 1998; DCH 1999. (Manchester) SHO Bury GP Train. Scheme.

PRABHU, Usha Achuth 6 St James Mount, Rainhill, Prescot L35 0QU Tel: 0151 426 4332 — Vrach 1972 Moscow; Vrach People's Friendship U. Moscow 1972; MRCOG 1981; DCH Eng. 1979; MFFP 1993; FRCOG 1996. (People's Friendship U.) SCMO (Wom. Health) N. Mersey Community NHS Trust. Socs: Med. Protec. Soc.; BMA; Brit. Menopause Soc. Prev: Clin. Med. Off. (Childhealth) St Helens & Knowsley HA; Regist. (O & G) Warrington Dist. Gen. Hosp.; SHO & Regist. (O & G) Halifax Gen. Hosp.

PRABHU, Mr Vithaldas Ramchandra Galleries Health Centre, Washington Centre, Washington NE38 7NQ Tel: 0191 416 6130 Fax: 0191 416 6344 — MB BS 1962 Karnatak; MS Bombay 1969; FRCS Ed. 1975. (Kasturba Med. Coll. Mangalore)

*PRABHU-KHANOLKAR, Deepa 12 Fairlie, Stewartfield, East Kilbridge, Glasgow G74 4SE — MB ChB 1996 Glas.

PRABHU-KHANOLKAR, Mr Sudhir Dinkar 12 Fairlie, E. Kilbridge, Glasgow G74 4SE; 109 Calderbraes Avenue, Uddingston, Glasgow G71 6ES Tel: 0141 818724 — MB BS 1971 Poona; FRCS Glas. 1978. (B.J. Med. Coll.) Regist. (Gen. Surg.) Roy. Alex. Hosp. Paisley; Regist. (Gen. Surg.) Vict. Infirm. Glas; Regist. (Paediat. Surg.) Roy. Hosp. Sick Childr. Glas.

PRACH, Andrzej Tomasz Monklands Hospital, Monkscourt Avenue, Airdrie ML6 0JS Tel: 01236 748748 Fax: 01236 760015 — MB ChB 1987 Glas.; BSc (Pharmacol.) Ed. 1982; MRCPI 1993. Cons. Phys. & Gastroenterol., Monklands Hosp., Airdrie. Prev: Specialist Regist. (Med. & Gastroenterol.), Ninewells Hosp. & Med. Sch., Dundee; Clin. Research Fell. (Gastroenterol.) Ninewells Hosp. & Med. Sch. Dundee.; SHO (Gen. Med. & Gastroenterol.) Stobhill Gen. Hosp. Glas.

PRACY, John Paul Myles 98 Liverpool Road, Islington, London N1 0RE; 98 Liverpool Road, London N1 0RE — MB BS 1987 Lond.; FRCPS Glas. 1992.

PRACY, Mr Robert (retired) Ginkgo House, New Road, Moreton-in-Marsh GL56 0AS Tel: 01608 650740 Fax: 01608 651893 — MPhil Lond. 1984, MB BS 1945; Hon. FRCSI 1983; FRCS Eng. 1953; MRCS Eng. LRCP Lond. 1944. Mem. & Chairm. (Med.) Pension Appeals Tribunals. Prev: Dean Inst. Laryngol. & Otol. Lond.

PRADEEP KUMAR, Narasimhan 236 Nottingham Road, Burton Joyce, Nottingham NG14 5BD — MB BS 1986 Madras.

PRADHAN, Abhay Madhav Pradhan and Partners, Traps Hill Surgery, 25 Traps Hill, Loughton IG10 1SZ Tel: 020 8508 4403 Fax: 020 8508 7269; 10 Eleven Acre Rise, Loughton IG10 1AN Tel: 020 8508 7333 — MB BS 1974 Poona; DRCOG 1985; DA (UK) 1980. (Armed Forces Medical College)

PRADHAN, Mr Chandra Bahadur 36 Wyatt Close, Edgbaston, Birmingham B5 7QR Tel: 0121 249 2838 Fax: 0121 249 2839 Email: chandna@cpradhan.freeserve.co.uk — MB BS 1975 India; FRCSI 1985; MCh (Ortho) L'pool 1990. (All India Institute of

PRADHAN

Medical Sciences, New Delhi) Staff Grade (Orthop.) Roy. Orthop. Hosp. NHS Trust, Birm.; Staff Orthop. Surg.; Cons. Orthop. Surg. Birm. Nuffield Hosp. Birm. Socs: BMA; BOA; Life Mem. Nepal Med. Coun. Prev: Assoc. Prof. & Head of Dept. of Orthop., Tribhuvan Univ. Teachg. Hosp. Kathmandu, Nepal.

PRADHAN, Mr Keshav Tularam 121 Old Road, Neath SA11 2DF Tel: 01639 631929; 6 The Avenue, Eagles Bush Valley, Neath SA11 2FD Tel: 01639 631929 — MB BS 1970 Marathwada; FRCS Ed. 1987; FRCS Glas. 1987. Staff Grade (Gen. Surg.) Singleton Hosp. NHS Trust Swansea.

PRADHAN, Manoj Jayant 138 Elmstead Avenue, Wembley HA9 8NZ — MB BS 1984 Bombay.

PRADHAN, Mr Nitin Shripad 22 Church Road, Wootton, Ryde PO33 4PX — MB BS 1976 Bombay; MS Bombay 1980, MB BS 1976; FRCS Ed. 1984.

PRADHAN, Rizwan Mohamedtaki High Street Surgery, 301 High Street, Epping CM16 4DA Tel: 01992 572012 Fax: 01992 572956; 1 Wedgwood Close, Theydon Grove, Epping CM16 4QD Tel: 01992 575064 Email: rizrosyshafiq@msm.com — MB BS 1983 Lond.; MRCGP 1988; DRCOG 1987.

***PRADHAN, Shubhra** 2 Dunlin Cl, Rochdale OL11 5PZ — MB ChB 1997 Manch.

PRADHAN, Tajdin Alibhai 61 Melbourne Road, Leicester LE2 0GU — MRCS Eng. LRCP Lond. 1975.

PRADHAN, Vijaykumar Shyamsunder Newham General Hospital, Glen Road, Plaistow, London E13 8SL Tel: 020 7476 4000; 39 The Drive, Loughton IG10 1HB — MB BS 1961 Jabalpur; DA Bombay 1964; FFA RCS Eng. 1970. Cons. Anaesth. Newham Gen. Hosp. Socs: Research Soc. Anaesth. Prev: Sen. Regist. Whittington Hosp. Lond.; Sen. Regist. (Research) Roy. Coll. Surgs. Lond.; Regist. (Anaesth.) Roy. Infirm. & Canniesburm Hosp. Glas.

PRAGNELL, Anthony Arthur (Surgery), Charing Surgery, Charing, Ashford TN27 0HZ Tel: 01233 713782; Stonebridge Green House, Egerton, Ashford TN27 9AP Tel: 01233 756216 — MB BS Lond. 1962; DObst RCOG 1964. (Char. Cross)

PRAGNELL, Cyril Albert, VRD 30A Wimpole Street, London W1G 8YA Tel: 020 7580 1185; 4 Crown Street, Harrow-on-the-Hill, Harrow HA2 0HR Tel: 020 8864 4878 — MB BS 1943 Lond.; MRCS Eng. LRCP Lond. 1943. (St. Bart.) Lic. Fac. Osteop. 1960; Mem. Regist. Osteop. 1960; Mem. DHSS Working Gp. on Back Pain. Socs: Fell. Roy. Soc. Med.; (Ex-Pres.) Brit. Osteop. Assn. Prev: Ho. Surg. Orthop. Dept. & Ho. Surg. Profess. Surg. Unit St. Bart.; Hosp. Lond.; Clin. Asst. (Manip.) P. of Wales Hosp. Tottenham.

PRAHALIAS, Andreas Aggelos 32 Rodenhurst Road, London SW4 8AR — Ptychio latrikes 1990 Crete.

***PRAHMS, Astrid Mary** Doctors' Residence, Arrowe Park Hospital, Arrowe Park Road, Wirral CH49 5PE — MB ChB 1998 Liverp.; MB ChB Liverp 1998.

PRAIN, John Henry, TD (retired) Ruadhchre, Longforgan, Dundee Tel: 01382 360308 — MD (Commend. & Silver Medal) St. And. 1950, MB ChB; FRCPath 1963. Cons. Pathol. Perth City & Co. Hosp. Gp.; Lect. in Path. Univ. Dundee. Prev: JP.

PRAIS, Lesley Birmingham Skin Centre, City Hospital, Dudley Road, Birmingham B15 5TS; 64 Arthur Road, Edgbaston, Birmingham B15 2UW Tel: 0121 454 1049 — MB ChB 1976 Birm.; D.Occ.Med. RCP Lond. 1996. Clin. Asst. (Occupat. Dermat.) Birm. Skin Hosp. Prev: SCMO (Community Health) Centr. Birm. HA.

PRAIS, Susan Sarah 4 Heath Drive, Hampstead, London NW3 7SY — MB ChB 1969 Glas.; Cert FPA 1971.

PRAJAPATI, Chandravadan Laxmanlal East Surrey Hospital, Canada Avenue, Redhill RH1 5RH Tel: 01737 768511; 2 Taunton Close, Poundhill, Crawley RH10 7XT Tel: 01293 889058 — MB BS 1978 Saurashtra; MRCPI 1991. Cons. Phys. (Gen./Elderly Med.) E. Surrey Hosp. Redhill. Socs: Brit. Diabetic Assn.; Geriat. Soc.; BMA. Prev: Sen. Regist. Rotat. (Gen. /Elderly Med.) Guy's Hosp. Lond.; Sen. Regist. Rotat. (Gen./Elderly Med.) Brighton Health Care; Regist. Rotat. (Gen. Med., Diabetes & Endocrinol.) BRd.green Hosp. Liverp.

PRAJAPATI, Devant Pradhan and Partners, Traps Hill Surgery, 25 Traps Hill, Loughton IG10 1SZ Tel: 020 8508 4403 Fax: 020 8508 7269; 51 Fontayne Avenue, Chigwell IG7 5HD — MB BS 1994 Lond.; DFFP 1998. (St. Bartholomew's) GP Loughton, Essex. Socs: Assoc. Mem. Roy. Coll. Gen. Pract.; MDU; BMA. Prev: GP Regist. Gen. Pract. Romford Essex; SHO (Psychiat.) Warley Hosp. Essex; SHO (Paediat.) Old Ch. Hosp. Romford.

PRAKASAM, Stanley Francis Reginald 15 Hallamshire Road, Sheffield S10 4FN — MB BS 1961 Madras.

PRAKASH, Mr Dhruva Hairmyres Hospital, East Kilbride, Glasgow G75 8RG Tel: 01355 58500 Fax: 01355 584473 Email: letitham.evans@laht.scot.nhs.uk — MB BS 1967 Madras; MS Madras 1970, MCh (Cardiothoracic) 1976; FRCS Ed. 1973. (Madras Med. Coll., India) Cons. Thoracic Surg. Hairmyres Hosp. Glas.; Coll. Tutor RCS Edin.; Hon. Sen. Lect. In Thoracic Surg., Univ. of Glas. Socs: Scott. Thoracic Soc.; Assn. Cardiothoracic Surg. GB & Irel.; Eur. Assn. Cardiothoracic Surg. Prev: Hon. Sen. Regist. Frenchay Hosp. Bristol; Sen. Regist. (Cardiothoracic Surg.) Roy. Vict. Hosp. Belf.; Clin. Research Fell. Oesoph. Func. Laborat. Toronto Gen. Hosp. Canada.

PRAKASH, Halahally Channaiah Harrogate General Hospital, Harrogate HG2 7ND Tel: 01423 885959; 14 Masham Road, Harrogate HG2 8QF — MB BS 1975 Karnatak. Sen. Staff Anaesth. Harrogate Gen. Hosp. N. Yorks.

PRAKASH, Hari Victoria Hospital, Blackpool FY3 8NR Tel: 01253 300000 — MB BS 1977 Delhi; DA Eng. 1982. (Maluna Azad) Staff Grade (Anaesth.) Vict. Hosp. Blackpool.

PRAKASH, Mr Kudigae Gurappagowda Meddygfa Penygroes, Bridge Street, Penygroes, Llanelli SA14 7RP Tel: 01269 831193 Fax: 01269 832116 — MB BS 1970 Mysore; MS Mysore 1974, MB BS 1970; FRCS Ed. 1978. (Kasturba Med. Coll.)

PRAKASH, Nandhini Govinda 2 Langdale Avenue, Rochdale OL16 4SA — MB BS 1981 Madras; MRCPI 1990.

PRAKASH, Mr Om Dilkush, 73 Ringwood Road, Luton LU2 7BG; 25 Gadebridge Road, Hemel Hempstead HP1 3DT Tel: 61820 — MB BS 1968 Agra; MS Agra 1971, MB BS 1968; DO Eng. 1972. (S.N. Med. Coll. Agra)

PRAKASH, Raj Shriniwas 10 Wykeham Road, Guildford GU1 2SE — MB BS 1966 Nagpur; DLO Eng. 1971. Clin. Asst. (ENT) Roy. Surrey Co. Hosp. Guildford. Socs: BMA. Prev: SHO (Otolaryng.) Addenbrooke's Hosp. Camb., Sussex Throat & Ear Hosp.; Brighton & Norf. & Norwich Hosp.

PRAKASH, Swatantra Devi (retired) 11 Bracewell Avenue, Greenford UB6 7QU Tel: 020 8903 4325 Fax: 020 8204 0721 — MB BS Lucknow 1951; DRCOG Lond. 1962; DCH Lond. 1962.

PRAKASH, Mr Udai 20 Colliston Drive, Balgillo Road, Broughty Ferry, Dundee DD5 3TL Tel: 01382 779253 Email: uprakash@aol.com — MB BS 1990 Gulbarga; FRCS Eng. 1994; FRCS Ed. 1994. Specialist Regist. (Orthop.) Dundee Roy. Infirm.; Hon. Clin. Tutor (Orthops. & Trauma) Univ. Dundee. Prev: SHO (Plastic Surg.) St. John's Hosp. Livingston.

PRAKASH, Vineet 36 Hallamshire Road, Sheffield S10 4FP — MB ChB 1995 Leeds.

PRAKASH-BABU, Pandichary Chandra Westfield Medical Centre, 2 St Martin's Terrace, Chapeltown Road, Leeds LS7 4JB Tel: 0113 295 4750 Fax: 0113 295 4755 — MB BS 1974 Calcutta. (Calcutta) GP Leeds.

PRAMANIK, Amit Flat No 5, Worthington House, 3rd Floor, Hope Hospital, Stott Lane, Salford M6 8HD — MB BS 1982 Calcutta; MRCP (UK) 1992.

PRAMANIK, K Hornspit Medical Centre, Hornspit Lane, Liverpool L12 5LT Tel: 0151 256 5755.

PRAMANIK, P The Surgery, 142 Marshland Road, Moorends, Doncaster DN8 4SU Tel: 01405 740094 Fax: 01405 741063 — MB BS 1972 Calcutta; MB BS 1972 Calcutta.

PRAMSTALLER, Peter Paul Institute of Neurology, 6th Floor, Queen Square, London WC1N 3BG; 27 Carmel Court, King's Drive, Wembley Park, Wembley HA9 9JE — MD 1990 Innsbruck.

PRANCE, Sarah Elizabeth Department of General Surgery, Derriford Hospital, Derriford Road, Plymouth PL6 8DH — MB BS 1993 Lond.; BA Univ. Rochester, USA 1988. (St George's Hospital Medical School)

PRANGNELL, Dennis Roy The Bungalow, Church Farm, Swinethorpe Road, Harby, Newark NG23 7ED Tel: 01522 703844 Fax: 01522 703844 Email: dennis@pragndr.demon.co.uk — MB ChB 1971 Birm.; FRCPath 1983, M 1977. Cons. Haemat. Lincoln Co. Hosp.

PRANK, Christopher John Brockwell Medical Group, Northumbrian Road, Cramlington NE61 6PE Tel: 01670 392700 — MB BChir 1989 Camb.; MA Camb. 1989; MRCGP 1994; DRCOG

1991. (Camb.) Princip. in Gen. Pract., Brockwell Med. Gp., Cramlington. Prev: SHO (A & E Med.) Kettering Gen. Hosp.

PRANKERD, Thomas Arthur John (retired) 6 Stinsford House, Stinsford, Dorchester DT2 8PT Email: prankerd@abbaslake.freeserve.co.uk — MB BS 1947 Lond.; MD (Gold Medal) Lond. 1949; FRCP Lond. 1962, M 1951; MRCS Eng. LRCP Lond. 1947. Prev: Dean & Prof. Clin. Haemat. Univ. Coll. Hosp. Med. Sch. & Hon. Cons.

PRASAD, Amoolya Kumar 63 Bloxwich Road, Willenhall WV13 1AZ Tel: 01902 608838 Fax: 01902 604866 Email: amooly@aol.com — MB ChB 1982 Manch. (Manchester University) GP Willenhall W. Midl. Socs: Brit. Med. Acupunct. Soc.; Birm. Med. Inst.; Primary Care Spec. Gp. of Brit. Computer Soc. Prev: MRC Research Stud.ship (Physiol.) Univ. Manch. 1983-4; SHO (Geriat. Med.) Burnley, Pendle & Rossendale HA; SHO (A & E) Bury HA.

PRASAD, Amrita 229 Portland Road, Edgbaston, Birmingham B17 8LS — MB ChB 1984 Birm.

PRASAD, Anant Deansgate Health Centre, Deansgate, Bolton BL1 1HQ Tel: 01204 383911 — MB BS 1974 Patna; MS Patna 1979. (Patna, India) GP Princip. Socs: Med. Protec. Soc.

PRASAD, Arjun The Health Centre, Welbeck Street, Castleford WF10 1DP Tel: 01977 465777 Fax: 01977 519342; 1 Dale View, Pontefract WF8 3SE Tel: 01977 600258 — MB BS 1966 Bihar. (Darbhanga Med. Coll.) Clin. Asst. Castleford & Normanton Dist. Hosp. Prev: Regist. (Psychiat. & Ment. Handicap) Stanley Royd & Field Head Hosps. Wakefield; SHO (Psychiat.) Fairfield Gen. Hosp. Bury.

PRASAD, Avinashi Clarendon Park Road Health Centre, 296 Clarendon Park Road, Leicester LE2 3AG Tel: 0116 270 5049 — MB ChB 1981 Leic.; ECFMG Cert. 1984; DRCOG 1985. (Leicester) GP Leics.

PRASAD, Birendra Belle Isle Medical Centre, Middleton Road, Leeds LS10 3DZ Tel: 0113 270 9139 Fax: 0113 270 9139 — MB BS 1963 Prasad; MB BS Patna 1963. (Prasad) GP Leeds.

PRASAD, Mr Bollina Ramachandra 1F3, 85 Comely Bank Road, Edinburgh EH4 1AW Tel: 0131 343 6472 — MB BS 1979 Andhra; FRCS (Urol) 1994; FRCS Ed. 1986.

PRASAD, Brij Kishore Ridge Lea Hospital, Quernmore Road, Lancaster LA1 3JT — MB BS 1962 Patna; T(Psych) 1991.

PRASAD, Jwala The Surgery, 137 Straight Road, Harold Hill, Romford RM3 7JJ Tel: 01708 343281 Fax: 01708 345386 — MB BS 1962 Patna. (P. of Wales Med. Coll. Hosp. Patna, India)

PRASAD, Kalyanaraman Hallam Street Hospital, Hallam St., West Bromwich B71 4NH Tel: 0121 607 3911 Fax: 0121 607 3901 — MB BS 1973 Osmania; MRCPsych 2001; Dip. Psychiat. W. Indies 1977; DM (Psychiat.) Univ. W. Indies 1980. Cons. Psychiat., Black Country Ment. Health NHS Trust. Socs: BMA; Med. Protec. Soc.; Brit. Indian Psychiat.s Assn. Prev: Cons. (Psychiat.) All St.s Hosp. Birm.; Assoc. Specialist Fairfield Hosp. Hitchin; Resid. Psychiat. Tobago, W. Indies.

PRASAD, Kavita 31 Tootswood Road, Bromley BR2 0PB Tel: 020 8289 8957; 60 Bridge Lane, Golders Green, London NW11 0EH Tel: 020 8455 5209 — MB BS 1994 Lond.; BSc (Hons.) Clin. Nutrit. Lond. 1992, MB BS 1994. Resid. (Internal Med.) Mayo Clinic, Rochester, MN 55905, USA. Prev: Ho. Off. Univ. Hosp. Wales Cardiff.; Research Fell. Nat. Inst. of Aging/NIH Bethesday, Maryland, USA.

PRASAD, Kumar Tripurari Prasad, Blackford and Commander, 6 Dyas Road, Great Barr, Birmingham B44 8SF Tel: 0121 373 1885 — MB BS 1974 Patna.

PRASAD, Leonie Rita 26 Greenstone Mews, Voluntary Place, London E11 2RS — MB BS 1989 Lond.; MRCGP 1994; DRCOG 1993.

PRASAD, Mr Mangalore Govinda 28 Queensway, Ponteland, Newcastle upon Tyne NE20 9RZ Tel: 01661 821329 — MB BS 1981 Mysore; FRCS Glas. 1989; FRCS (Orthop.) 1998. Specialist Regist. Newc. Prev: Trainee Regist. (Orthop.) N.. RHA Newc.

PRASAD, Manoj First Floor, The Moore Group Business Centre, 19 West Bromwich St., Walsall WS1 7BJ — MB ChB 1988 Dundee; MB ChB Dundee 1989.

PRASAD, N Stockbridge Lane Surgery, 45 Stockbridge Lane, Huyton, Liverpool L36 3SA Tel: 0151 489 2888.

PRASAD, Neelam DARTT, 20 Albion St., Hull HU1 3TG Tel: 01482 215214 Fax: 01482 336916; 1 Barleycorn Close, Pindersheath,

Wakefield WF1 4TD Tel: 01924 379334 Fax: 01924 211418 — MB BS 1978 Patna; LRCP LRCS Ed. LRCPS Glas. 1985; DFFP 1993; DPM 1997. (Patna Med. Coll., India) Socs: Affil. Mem. Roy. Coll. Psychiat. 1995; BMA; Med. Protec. Soc. Prev: Staff Grade Psychiat. Hull & Holderness Community Health NHS Trust; Regist. (Psychiat.) Wakefield HA.

PRASAD, Neeraj Jasmine Cottages, High St., Church Eaton, Stafford ST20 0AG — MB ChB 1988 Dundee.

PRASAD, Mr Palimar 17/2 East Parkside, Edinburgh EH16 5XL — MB BS 1981 Bangalor; MB BS Bangalore 1981; FRCS Ed. 1987; FCOphth 1989.

PRASAD, Patricia Margaret Brunswick Health Centre, 139/140 St Helen's Road, Swansea SA1 4DE; 22 Chestnut Avenue, West Cross, Swansea SA3 5NL — MB BCh 1985 Wales; MRCGP 1989; DRCOG 1990.

PRASAD, Pradip Nath 33 Croydon Road, London SE20 7TJ Tel: 020 8778 5135; 11 Bucknall Way, Beckenham BR3 3XL Tel: 0208 650 1726 — MB BS 1958 Bihar; BSc Bihar 1953; MD Delhi 1961; FRCP Ed. 1990; MRCP (UK) 1970. (Darbhanga Med. Coll.) Princip. GP Bromley Family Pract. Comm. Prev: Med. Specialist Safdarjang Hosp. New Delhi, India; Asst. Prof. Med. Univ. Mosul, Iraq; Assoc. Prof. Med. Univ. Benghazi, Libya.

PRASAD, Priyajit Pines, Westbourne Road, Edgbaston, Birmingham B15 3TR — MB BS 1994 Lond.

***PRASAD, Punam** 25 Poppleton Road, West Ardsley, Wakefield WF3 1UX — MB ChB 1995 Manch.

PRASAD, Raghavan Shankar NICU, Harold Wood Hospital, Gubbins Lane, Harold Wood, Romford RM3 0BE Tel: 01708 746090 Fax: 01708 708374 — MB BS 1978 Mysore; MRCP (UK) 1989; T(M) (Paed.) 1995. Cons. Paediat. (Neonat.) Harold Wood Hosp. Essex.

PRASAD, Raghureshwar The Surgery, 74 Brooksbys Walk, London E9 6DA Tel: 020 020 8985 2797 Fax: 020 8985 0999; 30A Grove Park, Wanstead, London E11 2DL Tel: 020 8989 5637 — MD 1965 Bihar; MB BS 1960 Bihar; MB BS 1960; MRCGP 1972. (P. of Wales Med. Coll. Patna) Socs: Med. Protec. Soc.

PRASAD, Mr Rajendra 3 Orchard Court, Royal National Orthopaedic Hospital, Brockley Hill, Stanmore HA7 4LP — MB BS 1980 Ranchi; FRCS Glas. 1983.

PRASAD, Rajendra 3 George Lane, Notton, Wakefield WF4 2ND — MB BS 1973 Bihar; T(GP) 1991.

PRASAD, Ramesh Chander Kings Road Medical Centre, 73 Kings Road, North Ormesby, Middlesbrough TS3 6HA Tel: 01642 244766 Fax: 01642 246243 — MB BS 1973 Osmania. (Osmania Med. Coll. Hyderabad) GP Middlesbrough.

PRASAD, Ranjit Pendeford Health Centre, Whitburn Close, Wolverhampton WV9 5NJ Tel: 01902 781728 Fax: 01902 781728; 10 Elviron Drive, Tettenhall, Wolverhampton WV6 8SZ — MB BS 1967 Patna; DTM & H Bihar 1975. (P.W. Med. Coll.) Prev: Trainee GP Neath; SHO (Chest Dis. & Geriat.) Mt. Pleasant Hosp. Chepstow; SHO (Geriat. Med.) Withybush Hosp. HaverfordW..

***PRASAD, Roopa** 40 Beaumaris Way, Grove Park, Blackwood NP12 1DE — MB BCh 1995 Wales.

PRASAD, Mr Roopendra Kumar Lostock Hall Medical Centre, 410 Leyland Road, Lostock Hall, Preston PR5 5SA Tel: 01772 518080 Fax: 01772 518086; Rulyn House, Parkside Drive, Whittle le Woods, Chorley PR6 7PL Tel: 01257 261771 — FRCGP 2001; MB BS Patna 1965; MS Patna 1968; FRCS Glas. 1971. (P. of Wales Med. Coll.) Chairm. NW Regional Med. Comm.; Chairm. S. Lancs. LMC. Socs: BMA (Gen. Med. Servs.) (Counc. Mem. BMA); Preston Medico Ethical Soc.; BMA Counc. Prev: Regist. (Cardiothoracic Surg.) Trafford AHA; SHO (Thoracic Surg.) Hull 'B' Gp. Hosps.; SHO (Orthop.) Clwyd & Deeside Gp. Hosps.

PRASAD, Sachida Nand The Surgery, 40 Brooke Road, London N16 7LR — MB BS 1966 Ranchi.

PRASAD, Sanjay 18 Acland Crescent, Camberwell, London SE5 8EQ — MB BCh 1990 Wales.

PRASAD, Sheo Narayan 25 Poppleton Road, Tingley, Wakefield WF3 1UX — MB BS 1963 Patna.

PRASAD, Shyam King's College Hospital, Denmark Hill, London SE5; 398 Tempest Road, Chew Moor, Bolton BL6 4HL — MB BS 1994 Lond.; MA Oxf. 1995. SHO (Med.) King's Coll. Hosp. Lond.

PRASAD, Subhash 22 Cochrane Street, Barrhead, Glasgow G78 1RF; 35 Poplar Avenue, Newton Mearns, Glasgow G77 5QZ — MB BS 1974 Patna.

PRASAD, Sudama Rosemary Surgery, 2 Rosemary Avenue, Finchley, London N3 2QN Tel: 020 8346 1997; 42 Bancroft Avenue, London N2 0AS — MB BS 1966 Patna.

PRASAD, T St James Health Centre, 29 Great George Square, Liverpool L1 5DZ Tel: 0151 709 1120.

***PRASAD, Usha Kumari** 25 Poppleton Road, Tingley, Wakefield WF3 1UX — MB ChB 1994 Leeds.

***PRASAD, Vineet** 1 Dale View, Pontefract WF8 3SE — MB ChB 1995 Leeds.

PRASAD, Mr Vireshwar 4 The Causeway, London N2 0PR — MB BS 1980 Patna; FRCS Glas. 1988.

***PRASAD, Vishal** 35 Poplar Avenue, Newton Mearns, Glasgow G77 5QZ — MB ChB 1996 Manch.

PRASAD, Yadu Nandan Kelvin Grove Surgery, Kelvin Grove, Wombwell, Barnsley S73 0DL Tel: 01226 752361 Fax: 01226 341577; 2 Upper Hoyland Road, Hoyland, Barnsley S74 9NJ Tel: 01226 742302 Fax: 01226 742302 — MB BS 1965 Bihar. (Darbhanga Med. Coll.) Clin. Asst. Family Plann. Clinic Barnsley. Socs: BMA & Overseas Doctors Assn. Prev: Med. Pract. & Hosp. Pract. (ENT) Barnsley Gen. Hosp.

PRASAD RAO, Mr Garikapati St. Paul's Eye Unit, Royal Liverpool Hospital, Prescot St., Liverpool L7 8XP Tel: 0151 706 2000 Fax: 0151 706 5861; 16 Newbury Close, Widnes WA8 9YX Tel: 0151 495 3078 — MB BS 1982 Osmania; MS (Ophth.) Osmania 1987; FRCS Ed. 1991; FCOphth 1991. (Gandhi Med. Coll., A.P. India) Sen. Regist. (Ophth.) St. Paul's Eye Unit Roy. Liverp. Hosp. Socs: Med. Protec. Soc.; Assn. Research in Vision & Ophth. Prev: Dir. (Primary Care in Ophth.) Liverp.

PRASAD REDDY, Kasu 85A Thealby Gardens, Doncaster DN4 7EQ — MB BS 1974 Andhra.

PRASAI, Mr Janak Keshar 7 Valley Prospect, Newark NG24 4QH — MB BS 1973 Calcutta; MS Chandigarh 1977; FRCS Ed. 1980.

PRASEEDOM, Mr Raaj Kumar Transplant Unit, Box 210, Addenbrooke's Hospital, Cambridge CB2 2QQ Tel: 01223 245151 Fax: 01223 216111; 120 Lucerne Close, Cambridge CB1 9SA Tel: 01223 412850 Email: rpraseedom@aol.com — MB BS 1988 Kerala; FRCS Ed. 1993; MS Kerala 1991; FRCS. (Trivandrum, India) Specialist Regist. (Transpl. Surg.) Addenbrooke's Hosp. Camb. Socs: Affil. Fell. ASGBI; BMA; IHPBA. Prev: Specialist Regist. (Gen. Surg.) Roy. Infirm. Edin.; Specialist Regist. (Gen. Surg.) W.ern Gen. Edin.; Specialist Regist. (Gen. Surg.) Qu. Margt. Dunfermline.

PRASHAD, Hari Har (Surgery) 10 Millfordhope Road, Knights Place, Strood, Rochester ME2 2TE Tel: 01634 76262 — MB BS 1955 Rajputana. (S.M.S. Med. Coll. Jaipur)

PRASHAR, Sanjeev 15 Gurney Road, Northolt UB5 6LJ — MB ChB 1986 Manch.

PRASHARA, Krishan Gopal (retired) 8 Acacia Close, Green Acres, Greasby, Wirral CH49 3QE Tel: 0151 678 1752 — MB BS 1962 Nagpur; DPH Eng. 1969.

PRASHER, Verinder Paul Department of Psychiatry, Queen Elizabeth Psychiatric Hospital, Birmingham B15 2QZ Tel: 0121 627 2840 Fax: 0121 627 2832 — MB ChB 1985 Birm.; MD Birm. 1994; MMedSc Birm. 1992; MRCPsych 1990. Sen. Clin. Lect. (Learning Disabil.) Qu. Eliz. Psychiat. Hosp. Birm.

PRASHNER, Philip Louis (retired) Loughton Health Centre, The Drive, Loughton IG10 1HW Tel: 020 8508 8117 Fax: 020 8508 7895 — MB BS Lond. 1963; DObst RCOG 1968. Therapist Sexual Dysfunc. Clinic Holly Hse. Hosp. Buckhurst Hill, Loughton HC & Loughton Clinic, Loughton. Prev: Regist. (Psychiat.) Claybury Hosp. Woodford.

PRASUNA, Kola c/o Mr. David Beach, 73 Aster St., Oldham OL1 2LA — MB BS 1973 Andhra.

PRATAP, Bhoom Raj 38 Crewe Road, Alsager, Stoke-on-Trent ST7 3DD — MB BS 1954 Osmania; DCH Eng. 1957.

PRATAP, Ravi (retired) 1 Pine View, Ashgate, Chesterfield S40 4DN Tel: 01246 234224 — MB BS 1960 Lucknow.

***PRATAP, Rohit** 249 Court Road, London SE9 4TQ — MB BS 1996 Lond.

PRATAP VARMA, Mr Medavaram Jagdish Clifton House Medical Centre, 263-265 Beverley Road, Hull HU5 2ST Tel: 01482 341423 Fax: 01482 449373; 5 Feren's Gardens, Park Lane, Cottingham HU16 5SP Tel: 01482 842675 Fax: 01482 842675 Email: varma-vijaya@hotmail.com — MB BS 1965 Osmania; MS 1973 Osmania. (Osmania Med. Coll. Hyderabad) Clin. Asst. Cardio Thorach Surg. Castle Hill Hosp. Cottingham Clin. Assis. Orthop. Surg. Both at Castle Hill Hosp. Cottingham. Socs: BMA.

PRATHIBHA, Bandipalyam Vamanarao 45 Bron-y-nant, Maelor Hospital Residences, Croesnewydd Road, Wrexham LL13 7TZ — MB BS 1985 Bangalor; MB BS Bangalore 1985.

PRATLEY, Jonathan Spring Gardens Health Centre, Providence Street, Worcester WR1 2BS Tel: 01905 681681 Fax: 01905 681699; 92 Hallow Road, Worcester WR2 6BY Tel: 01905 428929 — MB ChB 1975 Leeds. Princip. GP Worcester. Prev: SHO (Paediat. & Neonates) S.mead Hosp. Bristol; SHO (Paediat.) Battledown Hosp. Cheltenham.

PRATT, Albert Edward (retired) Hawthorns, 8 Mill Road, Swanland, North Ferriby HU14 3PL Tel: 01482 632264 — MB BS 1960 Lond.; FRCR 1975; FFR 1972; DMRD Eng. 1964. Prev: Cons. Radiol. Hull & E. Yorks. Health Trust.

PRATT, Barbara Anne (retired) Greenlands, Chorley Hall Lane, Alderley Edge SK9 7UL Tel: 01625 583397 — MB ChB 1953 Manch.; DObst RCOG 1954; DA Eng. 1956. Prev: Anaesth. Crew & Macclesfield DHA.

PRATT, Charles William McElroy Huntington House, Huntington Lane, Hereford HR4 7RA Tel: 01432 350927 — MB ChB Manch. 1949; MA Camb. 1953; MD Manch. 19641. (Manch.) Prev: Lect. (Anat.) Camb.; Fell. & Dir. of Studies in Med. Pembroke Coll. Camb.; Vis. Assoc. Prof. Univs. Illinois & Calif., USA.

PRATT, Charlotte Frances Wilson Care of Elderly Department, St. Andrews Hospital, Devons Road, London E3 3NT — MB BS 1985 Lond.; BSc Lond. Psychol. 1982; MRCP (UK) 1988. Cons. Geriat. Newham Healthcare NHS Trust Lond. Socs: Brit. Geriat. Soc.; Roy. Soc. Med. Prev: Sen. Regist. UCH & Whittington Hosps. Lond.; Lect. & Hon. Sen. Regist. St. Geo. Hosp. Med. Sch. Lond.; Regist. (Med.) Centr. Middlx. Hosp.

PRATT, Clarence Lucan Gray, OBE Far End, Chideock, Bridport DT6 6JW Tel: 01297 89300 — MD 1931 Liverp.; MA Camb. 1946; MA Liverp. 1936, MSc 1933, MD 1931, MB ChB 1929. (Liverp.) Fell. Christ's Coll. Socs: Physiol. Soc. Prev: Lect. Physiol. Univ. Camb.; Sen. Lect. Physiol. St. Thos. Hosp.; Med. Off. i/c RN Physiol. Laborat. Alverstoke.

PRATT, Mr Clive Alan Department of Maxillo-Facial Surgery, Kettering General Hospital, Rothwell Road, Kettering NN16 8UZ — MB BS 1990 Lond.; MB BS (Hons.) Lond. 1990, BDS (Hons.) 1983, BSc (Hons.) Med. Sci. &; Anat. 1980; FRCS Ed. 1993; FDS RCS Eng. 1990.

PRATT, Clive Ian Medical Specialists Group Guernsey, Alexandra House, Les Friteaux, St Martin's, Guernsey GY1 1XE Tel: 01481 38565; La Marcherie, La Villette, St. Martins, Guernsey GY4 6QG Tel: 01481 37344 — BM BCh 1974 Oxf.; MRCGP 1979; FFA RCS Eng. 1982; DRCOG 1978; DCH Eng. 1979.

PRATT, Mr David BUPA Hospital, Roundhay Hall, Jackson Avenue, Leeds LS8 Tel: 0113 269 3939; 101 Southway, Horsforth, Leeds LS18 5RW Tel: 0113 258 4561 — MB ChB 1951 Leeds; MB ChB (1st cl. Hons.) Leeds 1954; BSc (1st cl. Hons. Anat.) Leeds 1951; FRCS Eng. 1962. (Leeds) Cons. Surg. St. Jas. Hosp. & Chapel Allerton Hosp. Leeds; Tutor (Clin. Surg.) Univ. Leeds. Socs: Vasc. Surg. Soc.; Trav. Surg. Soc. GB & N. Irel.

PRATT, David Alastair Hayman (retired) St. Andrews Lodge, 51 The Avenue, Fareham PO14 1PF Tel: 01329 284443 — MB BS 1957 Lond.; BSc St. And. 1951; MRCS Eng. LRCP Lond. 1956; FRCPath 1978, M 1966. Prev: Head Path. Dept. Glaxo Gp. Research Ltd. Ware.

***PRATT, David Anthony** 110 Cofton Road, Birmingham B31 3QR — MB BS 1994 Lond.

PRATT, David George St. Stephen's Surgery, St. Stephen's Green, Canterbury CT2 7JT Tel: 01227 454085; Glebe House, St. Stephen's Green, Canterbury CT2 7JT Tel: 01227 760667 — MB BS 1964 Lond.; DObst RCOG 1973. (St. Thos.) Prev: Regist. (Cardiac) & Ho. Phys. & Ho. Surg. Profess. Surgic. Unit St. Thos. Hosp. Lond.; Regist. (Med.) Peace Memor. Hosp. Watford.

PRATT, Mrs Denise Elaine Fairholme, Golf Lane, Church Brampton, Northampton NN6 8AY — MB BS 1982 Lond.; MFFP 1993; MRCGP 1993; MRCOG 1990; Cert. Prescribed Equiv. Exp.

JCPTGP 1986. Prev: Trainee GP Wessex VTS; Regist. Rotat. (O & G) S.lands & Guy's Hosp. Lond.

PRATT, Donald Reginald Winton Health Centre, Alma Road, Bournemouth BH9 1BP Tel: 01202 519311; Church Cottage, Burton Green, Christchurch BH23 7JN Tel: 474144 — MB ChB 1954 Aberd.; MA Aberd. 1949, MB ChB 1954; DObst RCOG 1958. (Aberd.) Clin. Asst. (A & E) Bournemouth Gen. Hosp.

PRATT, Edward John 26 Salterns Road, Lower Parkstone, Poole BH14 8BJ — BM 1992 Soton.; BSc (Hons.) Soton. 1991; MRCP (UK) 1996. Regist. (Med.) Roy. Bournemouth Gen. Hosp. Socs: BMA. Prev: SHO (Med.) Roy. Bournemouth Gen. Hosp.

PRATT, Guy Edward Dickens 8 Mill Road, Swanland, North Ferriby HU14 3PL — MB BChir 1989 Camb.; MRCP (UK) 1993; DRCPath 1995. Regist. (Haemat.) Mersey RHA.; Regist. (Haemat.) Yorks. RHA.

***PRATT, Hazel Anne** 40 Plasturton Gardens, Cardiff CF11 9HF — MB BCh 1997 Wales.

PRATT, Helenor Ferguson (retired) Town Farm, West St, Marlow SL7 2BP Tel: 01628 483896 — MB ChB 1946 Ed.; DCH Eng. 1951. Prev: Regist. Hosp. Sick Childr. Gt. Ormond St. Lond.

PRATT, Joyce Diana 110 Cofton Road, West Heath, Birmingham B31 3QR — MB BS 1987 Lond.

PRATT, Julian Charles 15B Collegiate Crescent, Sheffield S10 2BA Tel: 0114 266 0777 Fax: 0114 268 7414 Email: ep66@dial.pipex.com — BM BCh 1973 Oxf.; MRCP (UK) 1980; MRCGP 1982; DRCOG 1978. (Univ. Coll. Hosp.) Vis. Fell. Primary Care Gp. King's Fund Developm. Centre. Prev: GP Heeley.

PRATT, Karen 9 Belsize Road, Lisburn BT27 4AL — BChir 1992 Camb.

PRATT, Michael Alexander North Wing, Denburn Health Centre, Rosemount Viaduct, Aberdeen AB25 1QB Tel: 01224 643333/642757 Fax: 01224 404989; 9 Abbotshall Crescent, Cults, Aberdeen AB15 9JQ — MB ChB 1967 Aberd.; FRCP Ed. 1989; MRCP (UK) 1972.

PRATT, Noel James 8 Bluebell Crescent, Norwich NR4 7LE Tel: 01603 452851 — MRCS Eng. LRCP Lond. 1940; FFHom 1983, M 1956. (Univ. Coll. Hosp.) Prev: Regist. Jenny Lind Hosp. Childr. Norwich; Flight Lt. RAFVR; Resid. Med. Off. Weir Hosp. Balham.

PRATT, Oliver William 12 The Shroggs, Steeton, Keighley BD20 6TG — MB BS 1994 Newc.

PRATT, Peter Leslie Greenwood Farm, Ham, West Wittering, Chichester PO20 7NX Tel: 01243 641046 — LMSSA Lond. 1956. (King's Coll. Hosp.)

PRATT, Mr Roland Kristian 51 Hartburn Avenue, Stockton-on-Tees TS18 4ES — MB BChir 1991 Camb.; MA Camb. 1991; FRCS Eng. 1995. Specialist Regist., Orthop., N.ern Deanery.

PRATT, Stanley Dennington (retired) Greenlands, Chorley Hall Lane, Alderley Edge SK9 7UL Tel: 01625 583397 — MB ChB 1948 Manch.; MRCGP 1962; DA Eng. 1953. Prev: Princip. GP Chelford.

PRATT, Stephen Francis The Portland Practice, St Paul's Medical Centre, 121 Swindon Road, Cheltenham GL50 4DP Tel: 01242 707792; Tall Trees, 8 Shrublands, Charlton Kings, Cheltenham GL53 0ND — MB ChB 1977 Bristol; MRCGP 1983; DRCOG 1982. Prev: GP Postgrad. Clin. Tutor Cheltenham HA.

PRATT, Steven 85 Ross Road, Maidenhead SL6 2SR Tel: 01628 23767; 63 Wavell Road, Maidenhead SL6 5AB Tel: 01628 781688 — MB BS 1974 Lond.; MB BS (Distinc. Path. & Therap.) Lond. 1983; MSc (Pub. Health) Lond. 1993; MRCP (UK) 1986; MRCGP 1988; DRCOG 1987; Cert. Family Plann. JCC 1987. (St. Geo.) Socs: Windsor Med. Soc. Prev: Sen. Regist. (Pub. Health Med.) Anglia & Oxf. RHA; Regist. (Med.) Ealing Hosp. Lond.; SHO (Med.) St. Geo. Hosp. Lond.

PRATT, Tunde Sekweyama and Pratt, 10 Trafalgar Avenue, London SE15 6NR Tel: 020 7703 9271 Fax: 020 7252 7209 — MB BS 1978 Lond.; MRCS Eng. LRCP Lond. 1977.

PRATT, William Robert (retired) Essex County Hospital, Lexden Road, Colchester CO3 3NB Tel: 01206744582 Fax: 01206 744739 — MB BS 1972 Lond.; MRCP (UK) 1975; FRCR 1979. Prev: Cons. Radiother. & Oncol. Essex Co. Hosp. Colchester.

PRATT-JOHNSON, John Herbert (retired) 2 Kingsmead Close, Holcombe, Bath BA3 5DR — MB Calcutta 1942; FRCP Lond. 1977, M 1948. Prev: Cons. Chest Phys. Tottenham Chest Clinic.

PREBBLE, Sylvia Ethel (retired) 18 Greysfield Flats, Ferma Lane, Great Barrow, Chester CH3 7HU Tel: 01829 741767 — MRCS Eng. LRCP Lond. 1952; DObst RCOG 1954. Prev: Asst. Specialist (O & G) Chester City Hosp., Chester Roy. Infirm. & New Matern. Unit Chester.

PRECIOUS, Sheila Helen West Cumberland Hospital, Whitehaven CA28 8JG Tel: 01946 693181; North Cross, Prospect House, Distington, Workington CA14 4PP Tel: 01946 832603 — MB ChB 1978 Manch.; FRCP (UK) 1997; MRCP (UK) 1982; FRCPCH 1997. Cons. Paediat. W. Cumbria Health Care.

PREDDY, John Spencer Whiteoak, Burrington, Umberleigh EX37 9LT — BM BS 1984 Nottm.; BMedSci 1982. SHO (Cas.) Taunton Hosp. Prev: SHO (Paediat.) MusGr. Pk. Hosp. Taunton; SHO (Med.) Qu. Med. Centre Nottm.; Ho. Off. (Surg.) Derbysh. Roy. Infirm. Derby.

PREDOLAC, Olivera Dominika 23 Baston Road, Hayes, Bromley BR2 7BD — MB BS 1988 Lond.

PREECE, Arthur Patrick James (retired) The Old Buck, Church Lane, Sedgeford, Hunstanton PE36 5NA Tel: 01485 570905 Fax: 01485 570891 — MA, MB Camb. 1965, BChir 1964; DObst RCOG 1966. Prev: GP Fakenham.

PREECE, Joanna Margaret The Grange, Harewood Road, Collingham, Wetherby LS22 5BL — MB ChB 1993 Leeds.

PREECE, John Fryer (retired) Cliff House, Yealm Road, Newton Ferrers, Plymouth PL8 1BN — MA Camb. 1949; MB BChir Camb. 1952; DObst RCOG 1954; MRCGP 1995. Cons. Ed. Health Serv. Computing Magazine. Prev: Edr. Pract. Computing Magazine.

PREECE, John Mark Yew Tree Cottage, Tredunnock, Usk NP15 1LY Tel: 01633 450464 Email: mark@preecem.demon.co.uk — MB BS 1983 Lond.; BSc (Hons.) Lond. 1979; FRCS (Otol.) Eng. 1990. (King's Coll.) Cons. ENT Roy. Gwent Hosp. Newport. Prev: Sen. Regist. & Regist (ENT) Univ. Hosp. Wales; SHO (ENT) Gt. Ormond St. Hosp. Lond.; SHO (ENT) Radcliffe Infirm. Oxf.

PREECE, Michael Andrew Institute of Child Health, 30 Guildford St., London WC1 Tel: 020 7242 9789 — MRCS Eng. LRCP Lond. 1967; MSc (Statistics) Lond. 1977, MD 1976, MB BS 1967; FRCP Lond. 1982; MRCP (U.K.) 1971; DCH Eng. 1969. (Guy's) Prof. (Child Health & Growth) Inst. Child Health Lond.; Hon. Cons. Phys. Hosp. Sick Childr. Gt. Ormond St. Socs: Fell. Roy. Soc. Med. FSS. Prev: Reader (Child Health & Growth) Inst. Child Health Lond.; Research Fell. Middlx. Hosp. Med. Sch. Lond.

PREECE, Mr Paul Edward clinical Skill Centre, Ninewells Hospital & Medical School, Dundee DD1 9SY Tel: 01382 660111 Fax: 01382 641795 Email: pe.preece@dundee.ac.uk; 11 Marchfield Road, Dundee DD2 1JG Tel: 01382 668126 — MB BCh Wales 1966; MD Wales 1983; FRCS Eng. 1974; FRCS Ed. 1972. Hon.Sen.Lect.Centre.Med.Ed.; Edit. Bd. Europ. Jl. Surgic. Oncol.; Mem. Brit. BrE. Gp. Socs: BMA; Surgic. Research Soc.; Brit. Assn. Surgic. Oncol. Prev: SHO Accid. Serv. Radcliffe Infirm. Oxf.; Research Regist. Univ. Hosp. Wales; Lect. Univ. Dept. Surg. Welsh Nat. Sch. Med. Cardiff.

PREECE, Philip Milburn Chesterfield & North Derbyshire Royal Hospital, Calow, Chesterfield S44 5BL Tel: 01246 277271 — MD Ed. 1988, MB ChB 1975; MRCP (UK) 1980; DCH RCPS Glas. 1978; DRCOG 1977. Cons. Paediat. Chesterfield & N. Derbysh. Roy. Hosp. Socs: FRCPCH.

PREECE, Richard Mark Astrazeneca, Alderley Park, Macclesfield SK10 4TF Tel: 01625 513276 Fax: 01625 513527 Email: richard.preece@astrazeneca.com; 14 The Crescent, Mottram St. Andrew, Macclesfield SK10 4QW — MB ChB 1987 Manch.; MFOM 1998 RCP, Lond. (Manch. Univ.) Occupat. Phys.Astrazeneca. Prev: Regist. (Occupat. Med.) HM Naval Base Clyde; Regist. (Diving Med.) Inst. Naval Med. Gosport; Regist. (Occupat. Med.) Naval Base Devonport.

PREECE, Vanessa Elizabeth Joy 26 Poulett Gardens, Twickenham TW1 4QR — BM 1986 Soton.; MRCGP 1990.

PREES, Karen Adele Cottles, 32 Tutton Hill, Colerne, Chippenham SN14 8DN Tel: 01225 744496 — MB ChB 1989 Bristol; DRCOG 1992. (Bristol) Prev: Trainee GP Box Surg. Wilts.; SHO (Paediat., Geriat., O & G & A & E) Roy. United Hosp. Bath.

PREEST, Annette Ruth Barrie 22 Heathmead, Heath, Cardiff CF14 3PJ — MB BCh 1989 Wales; MRCP (UK) 1994. Sen. Regist. (Rehabil. & Spinal Injuries) Rookwood Hosp. Cardiff.

PREEST, Geraint Arwyn — MB BCh 1992 Wales; BSc (Hons.) Pharmacol. Wales 1987.

PREJBISZ

PREJBISZ, Jan Wojciech Southend Hospital, Prittlewell Chase, Westcliff on Sea SS0 0RY Tel: 01702 345555 Fax: 01702 226145 Email: jprejbisz@southend.nhs.uk — Lekarz 1977 Warsaw; DMRT 1989. Ass. Spec., Clin. Oncol., Cancer Centre, S.end Hosp. NHS Trust. Socs: Roy. Coll. Radiol. Prev: SHO (Radiother. & Oncol.) Christie Hosp. Manch.; Clin. Research Regist. (Radiother. & Oncol.) Roy. Lond. Hosp.; Staff Grade (Radiother. & Oncol.) S.end Health Care NHS Trust.

PRELEVIC, Gordana Department of Endocrinology, The Royal Free Hospital, Pond Street, London NW3 2QG Tel: 020 7794 0500 Fax: 020 7380 2416 Email: g.prelevic@ucl.ac.uk; Flat 2, 20 Crossfield Road, London NW3 4NT Tel: 020 7433 1337 Fax: 020 7813 6233 — MD 1971 Belgrade; MSc Belgrade 1978; DSc Belgrade 1985; FRCP (Lond.) 1995. p/t Sen. Lect. & Hon. Cons. Reproductive Med. Roy. Free & Univ. Coll. Med. Sch. Lond.; Prof. (Med.) Belgrade Univ. Sch. of Med. Yugoslavia. Socs: RSM; Soc. Endocrinol.; Amer. Endocrine Soc. Prev: Cons. (Endocrinol.) Zvezdara Univ. Med. Centre Belgrade Yugoslavia; Head of Dept. (Endocrinol.) Zvezdara Univ. Med. Centre Belgrade Yugoslavia.

PREM, Alan Govindan 64 London Road, Wickford SS12 0AN Tel: 01268 765533; 35 Riverside Walk, Wickford SS12 0DU Tel: 01268 560521 — MB BS 1960 Madras. (Stanley Med. Coll.) Prev: Regist. (Paediat.) St. John's Hosp. Chelmsford; SHO (Paediat.) Roy. Vict. Infirm. Newc.; Regist. (Med.) Newc. Gen. Hosp.

***PREM, Daniel Matthew** 35 Riverside Walk, Wickford SS12 0DU — BM BS 1997 Nottm.

PREM SWARUP, Mr Immaraju Joel Department of Accident & Emergency, Basildon Hospital, Basildon SS16 5NL Tel: 01268 533911 — MB BS 1979 Sri Venkatatewara; FRCS Glas. 1988. Staff Grade Doctor Basildon Hosp. Prev: Regist. (Surg.) Bromley Hosp.

PREMACHANDRA, Mr Don Jayantha James Paget Hospital, Great Yarmouth NR31 6LA Tel: 01493 452452; Asconia, Gunton Cliff, Lowestoft NR32 4PF Tel: 01502 585779 Fax: 01502 585779 Email: dpremachan@aol.co.uk — MB BS 1975 Ceylon; FRCS Ed. 1984; DLO RCS Eng. 1984. Cons. ENT Surg. James Paget Hosp. Gt. Yarmouth & Norf. & Norwich Hosp.; Hon. Sen. Lect. Univ. E. Anglia. Socs: BMA; Med. Protec. Soc.; Roy. Soc. Med. Prev: Research Fell. Blood McIndoe Centre for Research; Sen. Regist. (ENT) Kent & Sussex Hosp. Tunbridge Wells; Regist. (ENT) Metrop. ENT Hosps. Lond.

PREMACHANDRAN, Sandrasekeram 1 Callow Field, Purley CR8 4DU — MB BS 1983 Sri Lanka; FRCP Ed. 1992; MRCS Eng. LRCP Lond. 1987. Career Regist. (A & E) Mayday Univ. Hosp. Surrey. Prev: Critial Care Fell. Trauma Centre N. Staffs. Hosp. Stoke-on-Trent; Regist. (Surg.) Altnagelvin Area Hosp. Lond.derry; Regist. (Surg.) Whiteabbey Hosp. Belf.

PREMARATNE, Robolge Vijayalakshmi The Medical Centre, Gun Lane, Strood, Rochester ME2 4UW Tel: 01634 720220 — MB BS 1979 Peradeniya; MRCS Eng. LRCP Lond. 1986; MRCP (UK) 1986.

PREMAWARDHANA, Lakdasa Devananda Kuvera Ellawela 19 Coedyafarn, Lisvane, Cardiff CF4 5RQ; 9 Timothy Rees Close, Cardiff CF5 2RH — MB BS 1975 Ceylon; MRCP (UK) 1982.

PREMCHAND, Vattakkatt Balakrishnan Ellergreen, 3 Willoughby Close, Kings Coughton, Alcester B49 5QJ — MB BS 1987 Kerala; MRCP (UK) 1994.

PREMKUMAR, Chittor Shadaksharam Solva Surgery, Cysgod-Yr-Eglwys, Solva, Haverfordwest SA62 6TW Tel: 01437 721306 Fax: 01437 720046 — MB BS 1974 Madras.

PREMKUMAR, Gopalakrishna 9 Coggles Causeway, Bourne PE10 9LN Tel: 01778 421623 — MD (Paediat.) Madras 1974, MB BS 1966; DCH Eng. 1979; DCH Madras 1969. (Madurai) SCMO N. Lincs. HA.

PREMNATH, Mr TFL, 12 Hill Square, Edinburgh EH8 9DR — MB BS 1981 Mysore; FRCS Ed. 1990.

PREMNATH, Pankaj 143 Folkestone Road, Dover CT17 9SG Tel: 01304 216224 — MBBS. (Armed Forces Medical College, Pouna, India) Gen. Pract. Princip. Socs: LMC; PCG.

PREMNATH, Ramal The White Cliff Medical Centre, 143 Folkestone Road, Dover CT17 9SG Tel: 01304 201705 — MBBS; DA Royal Coll. Anaest. Lond.; LMSSA Soc. Of Apoth. Lond. (Gandhi Medical College, Bhopal, India) Gen. Med. Practitioner.

PREMPEH, Thomas Bonsu 40 Greenfield Gardens, London NW2 1HX — MB ChB 1966 Aberd.; MRCP (U.K.) 1972.

PREMRAJ, Koppada 5 'Toulouse', Brooklands Road, Sale M33 3QH Tel: 0161 973 4647 — MB BS 1978 Osmania U, India; DLO, London 1994. Clin. Asst. (ENT), Warrington Dist. Gen. Hosp., Lovely La., Warrington, Chesh.

PREMRAJ, Kumudini c/o Dr T. George, 82 Mellor Brow, Mellor, Blackburn BB2 7EX — MB BS 1980 Madras; FRCA 1994.

PREMSEKAR, Rajasekaran 3 Partridge Road, Parkhurst Estate, Newport PO30 5NS — MB BS 1988 Madras; MRCPI 1995.

PRENDERGAST, Anne Elizabeth Muirhouse Medical Group, 1 Muirhouse Avenue, Edinburgh EH4 Tel: 0131 332 2201; 83 Dundas Street, Edinburgh EH3 6SD Tel: 0131 556 3983 — BM BS 1987 Nottm.; BMedSci Nottm. 1985; MRCGP 1992; DCH RCP Lond. 1991; DRCOG 1990. (Nottingham) p/t GP Retainee.

PRENDERGAST, Bernard David Department of Cardiology, North West Regional Cardiotherapic Centre, Wythemshawe Hospital, Manchester N23 9LT Fax: 00 33 1 48742315 Email: bernard.prendergast@smuht.nwest.nhs.uk — BM BS 1987 Nottm.; DM 1998; BMedSci Nottm. 1985; MRCP (UK) 1990. (Univ. Nottm.) Cons. Cardiol. Wythemshawe Hosp. Manch., UK. Socs: BMA; Brit. Cardiacsaler Intereation Soc.; Brit. Soc. of Echocardiography. Prev: BHF Jun. Research Fell. (Cardiol.) Univ. Wales Coll. of Med. Cardiff; Regist. (Cardiol.) Univ. Hosp. Wales Cardiff; Regist. (Gen. Med.) Soton. & Salisbury Gen. Hosps.

PRENDERGAST, Mr Brian Cathcart House, New Lane, Beal, Goole DN14 0RN Tel: 0197 676570 — MB ChB Liverp. 1987; BSc Liverp. 1982; FRCS Ed. 1993. Regist. (Cardiothoracic Surg.) Edin. Prev: Research Fell. (Transpl. & Cardiac) Sheff.; SHO Rotat. (Surg.) Pontefract.

PRENDERGAST, Mr Colin Henry Luton & Dunstable Hospital NHS Trust, Lewsey Road, Luton LU4 0DZ Tel: 01582 491122; The Garden Flat, 117 The Grove, Ealing, London W5 3SL Tel: 020 8840 1810 Fax: 020 8840 1810 — MB BCh BAO 1990 NUI; MRCOG 1997; MRCPI 1998. (University College Dublin) Specialist Regist. (O & G) N. Thames (W.). Socs: Blair Bell Res. Soc.; Roy. Acad. Med. Irel. Prev: Research Regist. Acad. Dept. of Metab. Med. St Mary's Hosp. Med. Sch.; SHO (O & G) St Mary's Hosp.; SHO (O & G) Nat. Matern. Hosp. Dub., Irel.

PRENDERGAST, Colm Michael Lister Hospital, Stevenage SG1 4AB Tel: 01438 314333 Fax: 01438 781176; 83 Station Road, Harpenden AL5 4RL Tel: 01582 761947 — MB BCh BAO 1980 Dub.; MA Dub. 1981; MRCP (UK) 1985; FRCR 1989. Cons. Radiol. Lister Hosp. Stevenage.; Med. Dir. E &N Herts NHS Trust. Prev: Sen. Regist. (Radiol.) W.m., Brompton & Roy. Marsden Hosps. Lond.; Regist. (Radiol.) W.m. Hosp. Lond.

PRENDERGAST, Jayne Mary 22 Frenchmans Close, Toddington, Dunstable LU5 6BD — MB BCh BAO 1992 NUI.

PRENDERGAST, Kenneth Francis 88 Landor Road, London SW9 9PE — MB BCh BAO 1979 Dub.; BDentSc Dub. 1983; FDS RCS Eng. 1990.

PRENDERGAST, Marie Theresa Anne 20 Devonshire Avenue, Dartford DA1 3DW — MB ChB 1990 Liverp. Trainee GP/SHO (A & E) Qu. Mary's. Hosp. Carshalton VTS.

PRENDERGAST, Mary Carmel High Street, Ruabon, Wrexham LL14 6NH — MB BCh BAO 1979 NUI; 1989 MRCGP; 1985 D Obst. Univ. Coll. Dub.; 1984 DCH Univ. Coll. Dub. (Galway)

***PRENDERGAST, Matthew Patrick,** Surg. Lt. 23 Pine Bank, Bishops Cleeve, Cheltenham GL52 8JW — BM BS 1998 Nottm.; BM BS Nottm 1998; BMedSci Nottm. 1995.

PRENDERGAST, Michael Prudhoe Hospital, Prudhoe NE42 5NT Tel: 01661 514305 — MB BS 1972 Lond.; FRCP 1997, MRCP 1975; FRCPCH 1997, MRCPsych 1980; FRCPsych 1997; T(Psych) 1991; DCH Eng. 1974. (St. Thomas') Cons. (Child & Adolesc. Psychiat.) Prudhoe Hosp. Socs: Brit. Paediat. Neurol. Assn.; Mac Keith Meetings; Brit. Neuropsychiat. Assn. Prev: Cons. (Child Psychiat.) Birm. Childr.s Hosp.; Cons. (Child Psychiat.) Hosp. Sick Childr. Gt. Ormond St. Lond.; Clin. Lect. (Child Adolesc. Psychiat.) Maudsley Hosp. & Inst. Psychiat. Lond.

PRENDERGAST, Michael Patrick Medway Maritime Hospital, Windmill Road, Gillingham ME7 5NY Tel: 01634 830000; 29 Longhill Road, Chatham ME5 7AR Tel: 01634 402532 Email: 106205.251@compuserve.com — MB ChB 1971 Sheff.; FRCP Lond. 1993; DCH Eng. 1974; FRCPCH. Cons. Paediat. (Community Child Health Medway NHS Trust.

PRENELLE, Ian 9 Haybridge House, Mount Pleasant Hill, London E5 9NB — MB BS 1993 Lond.

PRENTICE, Alfred Ian Douglas, MC (retired) 21 Sandy Lane, Woodbridge IP12 4DW Tel: 0139 438 3565 Email: i.prentice@virgin.net — MA, MB BChir Camb. 1948; MRCS Eng. LRCP Lond. 1942; FRCPath 1968, M 1964. Hon. Pathol. Colchester Dist. Hosps. Prev: Cons. Path. Colchester Dist. Hosps.

PRENTICE, Allan Cameron Liberty Occupational Health, 12 Sunnybank Road, Aberdeen AB24 3NG Tel: 01224 492884 Fax: 01224 487812 Email: allanprentice@libetyhealth.co.uk — MB ChB 1982 Dundee; AFOM RCP Lond. 1989; CIH Dund 1989. Sen. Med. Adviser Liberty Occupat. Health Aberd. Prev: SHO (O & G) Ayrsh. Centr. Hosp. Irvine; Ho. Off. (Gen. Med.) The Infirm. Arbroath.

PRENTICE, Andrew Department of Obst. & Gyn., Rosie Maternity Hospital, Robinson Way, Cambridge CB2 2SW Tel: 01223 336876 Fax: 01223 215327 Email: ap128@mole.bio.cam.ac.uk; 20 Rotherwick Way, Cambridge CB1 8RX — MB ChB 1983 Glas.; MA Camb. 1994; MD Newc. 1992; BSc 1980 Glas.; MRCOG 1988. Sen. Lect., Univ. of Camb. Socs: BMA; Europ. Soc. of Embryology and Human Reprodich; World Endonetriosis Soc. Prev: Univ. Lect., Hon. Cons., Univ Camb.; Clin. Lect. Univ. Camb.; Research Assoc. Univ. Newc.

PRENTICE, Colin Richard Murray Department of Medicine, The Martin Wing, The General Infirmary, Leeds LS1 3EX Tel: 0113 243 2799 Fax: 0113 242 3811 — MD 1970 Camb.; MB BChir 1959; FRCP Glas. 1977, M 1974; FRCP Lond. 1977, M 1964; DTM & H Eng. 1961. (Westm.) Prof. Med. Gen. Infirm. Leeds. Prev: Reader & Hon. Cons. Phys. (Med.) Roy. Infirm. Glas.; Research Fell. Amer. Heart Assn. W. Reserve Univ. Cleveland, USA; Ho. Surg. W.m. Hosp. Lond.

***PRENTICE, Elaine** 9 Thornwood Avenue, Ayr KA8 0NR — MB ChB 1998 Glas.; MB ChB Glas 1998.

PRENTICE, Professor Hugh Grant Academic Department of Haematology, Royal Free and University College Medical School, Pond Street, Hampstead, London NW3 2QG Tel: 020 7830 2300 Fax: 020 7794 0645 Email: g.prentice@rfc.ucl.ac.uk; 7 Kendalls Hall, New End, Hampstead, London NW3 1DD Tel: 020 7435 5210 — MB BS Lond. 1968; FRCP Lond. 1984; MRCP (UK) 1972; FRCPath 1988, M 1976. (St. Geo.) Head Dept. of Haemat.; Prof. Haemat. Oncol.Roy. free & Univ. Coll. Med. Sch.; Dir. Bone Marrow Transpl. Progr. Socs: Brit. Soc. Haematol. & Internat. Soc. Experim. Haemat.(Chair); Mem. Internat. Bone Marrow Transpl. Registry (Chair. Nominations Comm.) Prev: Sen. Regist. St. Geo. Hosp. Lond. & Roy. Marsden Hosp. Lond. & Sutton; Regist. W.. Gen. Hosp. Edin.

***PRENTICE, Ian James** 34 Ash Grove, Kirklevington, Yarm TS15 9NQ — MB ChB 1996 Sheff.

PRENTICE, Janet Mary (retired) 5 Borage close, Pontprennau, Cardiff CF23 8SJ — MB ChB Leic.1983; DTM & H Liverp. 1988; DRCOG 1987; MFPHM (Pt. I) 1995. Prev: Sen. Regist. (Pub. Health Med.) Wessex RHA.

PRENTICE, Lesley-Ann Valleyfield Health Centre, Chapel Street, High Valleyfield, Dunfermline KY12 8SJ Tel: 01383 880511 Fax: 01383 881848 — MB ChB 1986 Leeds.

PRENTICE, Malcolm George Tel: 020 8401 3034 Fax: 020 8401 3487 Email: malcolm.prentice@mhc-tr.sthames.nhs.uk — MB BS 1974 Lond.; BSc (Hons.) Pharmacol. Lond. 1971; FRCP Lond. 1994; MRCP (UK) 1978. (King's College Hospital) Cons. Phys. (Gen. Med., Endocrinol. & Diabetes) Mayday Univ. Hosp. Croydon; Hon. Cons. St. Geo. Hosp. Lond.; Clin. Teach. UCL. Socs: Sec. of Brit. Thyroid Assn.; Soc. Endocrinol.; Brit. Nuclear Med. Soc. Prev: Sen. Regist. (Med. Diabetes & Endocrinol.) Middlx. Hosp. Lond.; Regist. (Med.) Char. Cross Hosp. Lond.; Ho. Phys. King's Coll. Hosp. Gp. Lond.

PRENTICE, Margaret Helen (retired) Ridge End Farm, Marple, Stockport SK6 7ET Tel: 0161 427 2184 — MRCS Eng. LRCP Lond. 1934; MRCS Eng., LRCP Lond. 1934.

***PRENTICE, Matthew Grant** 2 Woodlands Road, Surbiton KT6 6PS — MB ChB 1998 Bristol.

PRENTICE, Michael Barron Department of Medical Microbiology, St Bartholomews Hospital, West Smithfield, London EC1A 7BE Tel: 020 7601 8411 Fax: 020 7601 8409 Email: m.b.prentice@qmul.ac.uk — MB ChB 1980 Birm.; MRCP (UK) 1985; MRCPath (Med. Micro) 1991; PhD London 1998; FRCPath 1999. Sen. Lect. & Hon. Cons. (Med. MicroBiol.) St Bart's & The Lond.Sch. of Med. & Dent.

PRENTICE, Michael Charles 5 Lingmell Dene, Coundon, Bishop Auckland DL14 8QX — MB ChB 1989 Leic.; MRCGP 1995; DRCOG 1994; DFFP 1994. SHO (A & E) Stockton-on-Tees. Socs: BMA; PHCSG. Prev: Trainee GP P'boro. VTS; Ho. Off. (Surg. & Orthop.) Leics. HA; Ho. Off. (Med.) P'boro.

PRENTICE, Neil Paterson Murray Royal Hospital, Perth PH2 7BH Tel: 01738 621151 Fax: 01738 440431; 26 Hillpark Terrace, Wormit, Newport-on-Tay DD6 8PN — MB ChB 1985 Dundee; MRCPsych 1991. Sen. Lect. old age Psychiat. Murray Roy. Hosp. Prev: SHO (Psychiat.) Roy. Edin. Hosp.; Ho. Off. (Surg.) Stracathro Hosp. Brechin; Ho. Off. (Med.) Falkirk & Dist. Roy. Infirm.

PRENTICE, Patricia Ann 2 Woodlands Road, Surbiton KT6 6PS Tel: 020 8390 7445 — MB BS 1968 Lond.; DO Eng. 1979. (St. Geo.) Assoc. Specialist (Ophth.) Roy. Eye Unit Kingston Hosp. Socs: Coll. Ophth.

PRENTICE, Robert Thomson West (retired) 7 Kings Park, Torrance, Glasgow G64 4DX Tel: 01360 620204 Email: roy@twprentice.freeserve.co.uk — MB ChB (Commend.) Glas. 1961; BSc (Hons.) Glas. 1958; FRCP Glas. 1982, M 1965. Prev: Princip. in Gen. Pract. 68/97, Glas.

PRENTICE, Wendy Mary Marie Wrie Centre, Marie Wrie Drive, Newcastle upon Tyne NE4 6SS — MB BS 1992 Newc.; MRCP (UK). (Newc. Upon Tyne) Specialist Regist. (Palliat. Med.) Newc. Socs: MRCP Lond.

PRENTON, Michael Antony Moor Edge Farm, Moorwood Lane, Owler Bar, Sheffield S17 3BP — MB BChir 1963 Camb.; MSc Lond. 1967; BA Camb. 1959, MB 1963; BChir 1962; FRCPath 1981, M 1969. (Westm.) Cons. Chem. Pathol. Roy. Hosp. Chesterfield. Prev: Sen. Regist. (Chem. Path.) W.m. & Kingston Hosps.; Lect. in Chem. Path. St. Thos. Hosp. Lond.; Cons. Chem. Pathol. Roy. Hallamshire Hosp. Sheff.

PRESCOTT, Professor Laurence Francis Clinical Pharmacology Unit & Research Centre, University Department of Medicine, Western General Hospital, Crewe Road, Edinburgh EH4 2XU Tel: 0131 537 2553 Fax: 0131 537 1009; Redfern, 24 Colinton Road, Edinburgh EH10 5EQ Tel: 0131 447 2571 Fax: 0131 447 4140 Email: laurie.prescott@ed.ac.uk — MB BChir 1960 Camb.; FRSE 1988; MA Camb. 1960, MD 1968; FRCP Lond. 1991; FRCP Ed. 1970, M 1968; FFPM RCP (UK) 1990. (Camb. & Middlx.) Emerit. Prof. Clin. Pharmacol. Edin. Univ. Socs: Hon. Mem. Assn. Phys. & Scot. Soc. Phys.; Brit. Pharm. Soc. Prev: on Staff Roy. Infirm. Edin.; on Staff (Med.) Div. of Clin. Pharmacol. Johns Hopkins Sch. of Med. Baltimore, USA; Cons. Phys. W.. Gen. Hosp. Edin.

PRESCOTT, Mr Mark Vincent Royal Shrewsbury Hospital, Mytton Oak Road, Shrewsbury SY3 8XQ Tel: 01743 261000; Willow Brook, Church Road, Meole Brace, Shrewsbury SY3 9HQ Tel: 01743 249637 — MB ChB 1973 Dundee; FRCS Ed. 1979. Cons. A & E Med. Roy. Shrewsbury Hosp. Socs: Fell. Fac. Accid. & Emerg. Med.; Brit. Assn. Accid. & Emerg. Med. Prev: Cons. N. Staffs. Hosp. NHS Trust; Cons. A & E Med. Roy. Shrewsbury & Telford Hosps.; Sen. Clin. Lect., Dept. Orthop. s, Keel Univ.

PRESCOTT, Mary Cordelia Nuclear Medicine Department, Manchester Royal Infirmary, Oxford Road, Manchester M13 9WL Tel: 0161 276 4780 — MB ChB 1975 Manch.; FRCR 2001; MD Manch. 1982; MRCP 1999. Cons. Nuclear Med. Manch. Roy. Infirm. Socs: Brit. Nuclear Med. Soc.; Eur. Assn. Nuclear Med.; Brit. Inst. Radiol. Prev: Research Asst. Nuclear Med. Manch. Roy. Infirm.

PRESCOTT, Richard John Department of Histopathology, Blackburn Royal Infirmary, Bolton Road, Blackburn BB2 3LR Tel: 01254 678300; 24 The Dene, Blackburn BB2 7QS Tel: 01254 690953 — MB ChB 1983 Manch.; MRCPath 1992. Cons. (Histopathoogy) Blackburn Roy. Infirm. Prev: Sen. Regist. (Histopath.) Hope Hosp. Manch.

PRESCOTT, Richard William George 18 Blaidwood Drive, Durham DH1 3TD — MB BS 1977 Newc.; MB BS (Hons.) Newc. 1977; MBA Dunelm 1995; MD Newc. 1983; FRCP Lond. 1992; FRCP Ed. 1990; MRCP (UK) 1979. Cons. Phys. (Special Responsibil. for Elderly) Bishop Auckland Gen. Hosp.

PRESCOTT, Mr Stephen c/o Department of Urology, St. James' Hospital, Beckett St., Leeds LS9 7TF Tel: 0113 206 4949 Fax: 0113 206 4920; Anscot House, Brackenthwaite Lane, Pannal, Harrogate HG3 1PJ Tel: 01423 871009 Fax: 01423 871009 — MB ChB 1981 Manch.; MD Manch. 1990; FRCS (Urol.) 1993; FRCS Ed. 1986. Cons. Urol. St. Jas. Univ. Hosp. & Gen. Infirm. Leeds. Socs: Brit.

PRESHAW

Assn. Urol. Surgs.; BMA. Prev: Sen. Lect. (Urol.) Univ. Edin. & W.. Gen. Hosp. Edin.

PRESHAW, Colin Taylor Roy. Scot. Nat. Hospital, Old Denny Road,, Larbert FK5 4SD Tel: 01325 570700 Fax: 01324 563788; 2 Allander Avenue, Bardowie, Milngavie, Glasgow G62 6EU — MB ChB 1967 Aberd.; DPM Ed. & Glas. 1970; MRCPsych 1973. (Aberd.)

PRESHAW, John Mulligan Kilmeny Surgery, 50 Ashbourne Road, Keighley BD21 1LA Tel: 01535 606415 Fax: 01535 669895 — MB ChB Leeds 1969; MRCGP 1978. (Leeds) Clin. Asst. (Dermat.) Airedale Gen. Hosp. Keighley. Socs: Keighley & Dist. Med. Soc.; BMA. Prev: Regist. (Med.) Airedale Gen. Hosp. Keighley; Ho. Surg. & Ho. Off. (Med.) Chapel Allerton Hosp. Leeds.

PRESKEY, Mark Stephen Waterloo Road Surgery, 178 Waterloo Road, Blackpool FY4 3AD Tel: 01253 348619 Fax: 01253 404330 — MB BS Lond. 1983; BSc (Hons.) Lond. 1980; MRCGP 1987; DCH RCP Lond. 1987; DRCOG 1986; DGM RCP Lond. 1985. Prev: Trainee GP Ulverston VTS.

PRESLAND, Andrew Hamon 47 Priory Avenue, Harlow CM17 0HJ — MB BS 1992 Lond. SHO (A & E) King Geo. Hosp. Goodmayes.

PRESLEY, Robert Anatomy Department, University of Wales, Cardiff CF1 3YF Tel: 029 2087 4000; La Frenaie, Bryn Rhedyn Close, Llanfrechfa, Cwmbran NP44 8UB Tel: 01633 482856 — MB BChir 1963 Camb.; MB Camb. 1964, MA, BChir 1963. (Univ. Coll. Hosp.) Sen. Lect. (Anat.) Univ. Coll. Cardiff. Socs: Fell. Zool. Soc. Lond.; FLS. Prev: Ho. Phys. Paediat. Unit Univ. Coll. Hosp. Lond.; Ho. Surg. (Orthop.) W. Middlx. Hosp. Isleworth; Univ. Demonst. (Anat.) & Fell. Emmanuel Coll. Univ. Camb.

PRESS, Anthony Martin Doctors Surgery, Great Melton Road, Hethersett, Norwich NR9 3AB Tel: 01603 810250 Fax: 01603 812402 — MB BS 1978 Lond.; MA Camb. 1979, BA 1975; MRCS Eng. LRCP Lond. 1978; MRCGP (Distinc.) 1986; Dip. IMC RCS Ed. 1991; DRCOG 1983; DA Eng. 1981. (Char. Cross) Princip. (GP); Med. Adviser to Fitness Express. Prev: Trainee GP Norwich VTS; SHO (Anaesth.) Norf. & Norwich Hosp.; Ho. Off. (Med.) Char. Cross Hosp. Lond.

PRESS, Christopher Martin 99 Highfield Lane, Southampton SO17 1NN — MB BChir 1968 Camb.; MSc Lond. 1972; MA Camb. 1969; FRCP Lond. 1996; MRCP (UK) 1971. (Univ. Coll. Hosp. Cambridge) Cons. Phys. & Hon. Sen. Lect. Roy. Free Hosp. & Med. Sch. Lond. Socs: RSM (Sec. Sect. for Transpl.ation); EASD (Sec., Study Gp. on Insulin Pumps and Pancreatic Transpl.s. '97-'01). Prev: Asst. Prof. Med. & Paediat. Yale Univ. Sch. of Med. New Haven CT, USA; Lect. (Metab. Med.) Soton. Univ.; Regist. (Med.) Hammersmith Hosp. Lond.

PRESS, James David 87 Gorsty Lane, Hereford HR1 1UN — MB BS 1994 Lond.

PRESS, John Randolph 9A Magheralave Road, Lisburn BT28 3BE — MB BCh BAO 1960 Dub. Cons. Path. Inst. Forens. Med. Belf.

PRESS, Vivienne Rose Fountayne Road Health Centre, 1A Fountayne Road, London N16 7EA Tel: 020 8806 3311 — BSc (Hons.) Lond. 1974, MB BS 1977; DCH RCP Lond. 1982; DRCOG 1980. (Lond. Hosp.)

PRESSLER, Janice Mary Greenmount Medical Centre, 9 Brandlesholme Road, Greenmount, Bury BL8 4DR Tel: 01204 883375 Fax: 01204 887431; 11 Henwick Hall Avenue, Ramsbottom, Bury BL0 9YH Tel: 01706 825448 — MB ChB 1979 Sheff.; MRCGP 1983.

PRESSLEY, Kieran Joseph Totley Rise Medical Centre, 96 Baslow Road, Totley, Sheffield S17 4DQ Tel: 0114 236 5450 Fax: 0114 262 0942 Email: senlac@doctors.org.uk — MB ChB 1978 Manch.; MRCGP 1986; DRCOG 1982; DA 1981; Dip. Ther. Wales Coll Med 1998. (Manchester)

PRESTON, Alan Eley Botolph House, Botolph Claydon, Winslow, Buckingham MK18 2LR Tel: 0129 671 4555 Fax: 0129 671 4806 — BM BCh 1944 Oxf.; BM BCh Oxon. 1944; FRCPath 1971, M 1963. Socs: Brit. Soc. Haematol. & Assn. Clin. Path.

PRESTON, Andrew Paul Doctors Surgery, Salisbury Road, Southsea PO4 9QX Tel: 023 9273 1458; 95 Festing Grove, Southsea PO4 9QE — MB BS 1977 Lond.; BA Oxf. 1974; MRCGP 1981; DRCOG 1980. (Univ. Coll. Hosp.) Prev: GP Bromley.

PRESTON, Bryan John 124 Parkside, Wollaton, Nottingham NG8 2NP Tel: 0115 928 3650 — MB BS Lond. 1961; FRCS Ed. 1967; MRCS Eng. LRCP Lond. 1961; FRCR 1975; FFR 1971; DMRD Eng. 1969. Cons. (Diag. Radiol.) Nottm. Univ. Gp. Hosps. Socs: Brit. Inst. Radiol. & Internat. Skeletal Soc.; Europ. Soc. of Skeletal Radiologist. Prev: Sen. Regist. (Diag. Radiol.) St. Mary's Hosp. Lond.; SHO N. Middlx. Hosp. Lond.; Ho. Surg. St. Mary's Hosp. Paddington.

PRESTON, Caroline Longwood, Parklands, Scruton, Northallerton DL7 0QT — MB ChB 1982 Ed.

PRESTON, Catherine Wray 39 Boulevard, Weston Super Mare BS23 1PF Tel: 01934 624242; Church Farm, The Bury, Locking, Weston Super Mare BS24 8BZ Tel: 01934 823468 Email: cathpreston@hotmail.com — MB ChB 1972 Bristol.

PRESTON, Clive Ian Tel: 01592 648004 Fax: 01592 642787; 64 Inverleith Row, Edinburgh EH3 5PX Tel: 0131 551 1919 — MB ChB 1977 Ed.; BSc (Hons.) Ed. 1974; FRCR 1988; DMRT Ed. 1985. (Univ. Edin.) Cons. Palliat. Med. Fife Primary Care NHS Trust. Prev: Cons. Radiother. & Oncol. P.ss Roy. Hosp. Hull; Sen. Regist. (Radiother. & Oncol.) Velindre Hosp. Cardiff; Regist. (Radiat. Oncol.) W.. Gen. Hosp. Edin.

PRESTON, David Michael Princess Alexandra Hospital, Hamstel Road, Harlow CM20 1QX Tel: 01279 444455; Amwellbury House, Walnut Tree Walk, Great Amwell, Ware SG12 9RD Tel: 01920 462108 Fax: 01920 485190 Email: dmpreston@compuserve.com — MB BS 1974 Lond.; MD Lond. 1985; FRCP Lond. 1993; MRCP (UK) 1977; MRCS Eng. LRCP Lond. 1974; T(M) 1991. (Guy's) Cons. Gastroenterol. P.ss Alexandra NHS Trust. Socs: Brit. Soc. Gastroenterol.; Brit. Soc. Med. & Dent. Hypn. Prev: Cons. Phys. Louth Co. & Lincoln Co. Hosps. & Postgrad. Tutor Louth Co. Hosp.; Sen. Regist. (Med.) John Radcliffe Hosp. Oxf.; Research Fell. St. Mark's Hosp. Lond.

PRESTON, Denys Wallwork (retired) 15 Parkstone Lane, Worsley, Manchester M28 2PW Tel: 0161 793 4914 — MB ChB Manch. 1951; MFCM 1974; DPH Manch. 1958.

PRESTON, Elizabeth Mary Aintree Hospitals NHS Trust, University Hospital Aintree, Longmoor Lane, Liverpool L9 7AL Tel: 0151 529 2231 Fax: 0151 529 3286 Email: elizabeth.preston@ahton.west.nhs.uk; Jack Leg Farm, Cranes Lane, Lathom, Ormskirk L40 5UJ Tel: 01695 575026 Fax: 01695 571032 Email: elizabethmpreston@hotmail.com — MB ChB 1968 Liverp.; FFA RCSI 1971. (Liverp.) Med. Dir. Aintree Hosps. NHS Trust, Liverp.; Cons. Anaesth. Aintree Hosp. NHS Trust Liverp. Socs: Brit. Assn. Anaesth.; Liverp. Inst.; Brit. Assn. of Med. Managers. Prev: Sen. Registar (Anaesth.) BRd.green, Alder Hey & Walton Hosps. Liverp.; Registar (Anaesth.) Walton Hosp. Liverp.; SHO (Anaesth.) David Lewis N.ern Hosp. Liverp.

PRESTON, Professor Francis Eric Department of Haematology, Royal Hallamshire Hospital, Sheffield S10 2JF Tel: 0114 273 9107 Fax: 0114 275 6126; 7 Broomhall Road, Sheffield S10 2DN — MD 1970 Liverp.; MB ChB 1963; FRCP Lond. 1992; FRCPath 1982, M 1970. Prof. Haemat. Univ. Sheff. & Hallamsh. Hosp. Sheff.; Dir. Sheff. Ref. Haemophilia Centre. Socs: (Pres.) Brit. Soc. Haemostasis & Thrombosis. Prev: Reader & Cons. Haemat. Univ. Sheff. & Hallamsh. Hosp. Sheff.

PRESTON, Frank Samuel, OBE, VRD, CStJ 2 Ravensmead, Chalfont St Peter, Gerrards Cross SL9 0NB Tel: 01494 876143 Fax: 01494 870403 Email: frankp@ravensmead.fsnet.co.uk — MB ChB Glas. 1947; FFOM RCP Lond. 1982; DA Eng. 1954. (Univ. Glas.) Cons. Aviat. & Occupat. Med.; Mem. Parliamentary Adv. Comm. On Transport Safety; Mem. Hse. of Commons Air Safety Gp.; Mem. (Ex-Vice-Pres.) Internat. Acad. Aviat. & Space Med.; Dir., P. Michael Internat. Rd. Safety Counc.. Socs: Fell. Roy. Soc. Med.; Fell. Aerospace Med. Assn. USA; (Ex-Pres.) Soc. Occupat. Med. Prev: Med. Dir. Brit. Airways; Hon. Phys. to HM the Qu.; Surg. Capt. RNR.

PRESTON, George Mason Hurley Clinic, Kennington Lane, London SE11; e55 Court Lane, Dulwich Village, London SE21 7DP — MRCS Eng. LRCP Lond. 1959; BSc Lond. 1957, MB BS 1960; MRCGP 1971. (Guy's) Sen. Police Surg. Metrop. Police. Prev: Lect. Physiol. Guy's Hosp. Med. Sch. Lond.

PRESTON, Helen Sarah 518 Chatsworth Road, Chesterfield S40 3BA — MB ChB 1996 Leic.

PRESTON, Hilary Gay Loddon NHS Trust, North Hampshire Hospital, Basingstoke RG24 9NA; Summerdown House, Malshanger, Basingstoke RG23 7ES — MB BS 1968 Lond.; MRCS Eng. LRCP

Lond. 1968; DObst RCOG 1970; FRIPHH. Staff Grade Paediat. (Community Child Health) Basingstoke & N. Hants. HA. Socs: Assoc. Mem. BPA; Fac. Comm. Health.

PRESTON, Hilary Veronica 1 Sherwood Close, Herne Bay CT6 7DX — MB ChB 1988 Liverp.

PRESTON, James William Peter Austin Friars House, 2-6 Austin Friars, London EC2N 2HD Tel: 020 76284001 Fax: 020 76286002 Email: prestonj@BUPA.com; Flat 3, 25 Hornsey Lane Gardens, London N6 5NX Email: jwpp@clara.co.uk — MB BCh 1991 Wales; MRCGP 1998. Dep. Head Phys., BUPA wellness, Lond. Prev: SHO (Gen. Med.) Morriston Hosp. Swansea.

PRESTON, Jane Thomas 458 Unthank Road, Norwich NR4 7QJ — MB ChB 1984 Aberd.; BMedBiol Aberd. 1981; MRCOG 1989. (Aberd.) Cons. James Paget Hosp. Gorleston-on-Sea Norf. Prev: Sen. Regist. Norf. & Norwich Hosp.; Research Regist. (O & G) Addenbrooke's Hosp. Camb.; Regist. (Obst.) Qu. Mother's Hosp. Glas.

PRESTON, Jean Elizabeth (retired) 14 Four Oaks Road, Sutton Coldfield B74 2TH Tel: 0121 308 0346 — MB ChB 1936 Glas.; MFCM 1974. Prev: SCM (Social Servs.) Walsall AHA.

***PRESTON, Jennifer Ann Helen** 127 Nottingham Road, Belper DE56 1JH — MB ChB 1998 Sheff.; MB ChB Sheff 1998.

***PRESTON, Joanne Elizabeth** 31 Crosswood Crescent, Balerno EH14 7LX — MB ChB 1994 Glas.

PRESTON, John Grainger Group Practice Surgery, Middle Chare, Chester-le-Street DH3 3QD Tel: 0191 388 4857 Fax: 0191 388 7448; 28 Denwick Close, Chester-le-Street DH2 3TL Tel: 0191 389 2479 — MB BS 1983 Newc.; MRCGP 1987. Chairm. of Durh. & Chester-le-St. Community Alliance.

***PRESTON, Katherine Elaine** Botolph House, Botolph Claydon, Buckingham MK18 2LR — MB BCh 1998 Wales.

PRESTON, Lucinda Jane Kents, High St., Great Chesterford, Saffron Walden CB10 1PL Tel: 01799 531437 — MB BS 1988 Lond.; BSc Lond. 1985; MRCP (UK) 1995; MRCGP 1994; DRCOG 1992; DCH RCP Lond. 1990. Regist. (Paediat.) Addenbrooke's Hosp. Camb. Socs: Brit. Paediat. Assn.; Camb. Med. Soc.

PRESTON, Mark Richard Preston and Austin, Killingworth Health Centre, Citadel East, Killingworth, Newcastle upon Tyne NE12 6UR — MB BS 1984 Newc.; DFFP 2000; MRCGP 1988; DRCOG 1987; Cert. Family Plann. 1988. GP Killingworth.; Police Surg./Forens. Med. Examr.

***PRESTON, Michelle Joanne** Barnfield, Main St., Bishampton, Pershore WR10 2NH — MB ChB 1997 Bristol.

PRESTON, Morag Samantha 21 Mount Pleasant, Houghton-le-Spring DH5 8AQ — MB ChB 1993 Manch.

PRESTON, Noel Wallace (retired) 36 Queen's Drive, Heaton Mersey, Stockport SK4 3JW Tel: 0161 432 2870 — LRCP LRCS 1946 Ed.; MD Manch. 1954, MB ChB 1946; LRCP LRCS Ed. LRFPS Glas. 1947; FRCPath 1971, M 1963; Dp. Bact. Manch. 1950. WHO Expert Advis. Panel on Bacterial Dis.; Hon. Fell. Microbial Immunol. Univ. Manch. Prev: Dir. WHO Pertussis Ref. Laborat. Univ. Manch.

PRESTON, Paul Robin Sherwood House, Sherwood Road, Bearwood, Smethwick, Smethwick B67 5DE Tel: 0121 429 1289; 26 Oak Hill Drive, Edgbaston, Birmingham B15 3UG Tel: 0121 454 3741 — MB ChB 1958 Birm.; MRCS Eng. LRCP Lond. 1958.

PRESTON, Penelope East Street Surgery, 6-7 East Street, Ware SG12 9HJ Tel: 01920 468777 Fax: 01920 484892.

PRESTON, Penelope Jane 239 Victoria Road, London N22 7XH — MB ChB 1989 Manch.

PRESTON, Peter George 74 Eaton Road, Norwich NR4 6PR — MB ChB 1976 Ed.; BSc Ed. 1973, MB ChB 1976; MRCP (UK) 1978; FRCR 1984. (Ed.) Cons. Radiol. Norf. & Norwich Hosp. Norwich. Prev: Sen. Regist. (Radiol.) Lothian Health Bd.

PRESTON, Roger Clifford The Surgery, 6 Longton Grove Road, Weston Super Mare BS23 1LT Tel: 01934 628 118/ Fax: 01934 645893; Church Farm, The Bury, Locking, Weston Super Mare BS24 8BZ — MB ChB Bristol 1969; DObst RCOG 1971. GP W.on-super-Mare. Prev: SHO Gen. Pract. Train. Scheme Roy. Hosp. Wolverhampton; Ho. Phys. Ham Green Hosp. Bristol; Ho. Surg. Cossham Hosp. Bristol.

PRESTON, Mr Shaun Ralph Division of Surgery, Level 8, Clinical Sciences Building, St Jame's Univesity Hospital, Leeds LS9 7TF Tel: 0113 206 5282 Fax: 0113 244 9618 Email: medsrp@leeds.ac.uk; 12 Brookfield Place, Headingley, Leeds LS6 4EH — MB ChB 1990 Leeds; BSc (Hons) Leeds 1987; Md Leeds 1997. (Leeds) Lect. (Surg.) Univ. Div. Of Surg., St James Univ. Hosp. Leeds; Hon. Specialist Regist.

PRESTON, Stanley David Grosvenor Street Surgery, 4 Grosvenor Street, St Helier, Jersey JE1 4HB Tel: 01534 30541 Fax: 01534 887948; Hautes Murailles, Rue de Samares, St Clement, Jersey JE2 6LS Tel: 01534 53229 — MB ChB 1960 Aberd.; MB ChB (Commend.) Aberd. 1960. (Aberd.)

PRESTON, Thomas Russell (retired) Priorsford, Vetch Park, Haddington EH41 3LH Tel: 0162 082 2634 — MB ChB 1948 Ed.

PRESTON, Mr Timothy Russell (retired) 72 Rodney Street, Liverpool L1 9AF Tel: 0151 709 5644 Fax: 01695 571032 — MB BChir 1957 Camb.; MA Camb. 1969, BA 1957; FRCS Ed. 1965; FRCS Eng. 1965. InDepend. Med. appeals tribunal Serv. Liverp. Prev: Cons. Gen. Surg. Whiston Hosp. & St. Helens Hosp.

PRESTON, Wilfrid Edwin Bentley Rose Cottage, Wroxham Road, Coltishall, Norwich NR12 7AE — MB BS 1950 Lond.; DObst RCOG 1954. (Middlx.) Socs: BMA & Norwich M-C Soc. Prev: Ho. Surg. Jenny Lind Childr. Hosp. & Norf. & Norwich Hosp.; Ho. Phys. Roy. S. Hants. Hosp. Soton.

PRESTON-WHYTE, Margaret Elan Department of General Practice and Primary Healthcare, University of Leicester, Leicester Gen Hospital, Gwendolen Road, Leicester LE5 4PW Tel: 0116 258 4078 Fax: 0116 258 4982 Email: mep5@le.uk; 3 The Poplars, Billesdon, Leicester LE7 9AT Tel: 0116 259 6636 — MB BCh Wales 1961; FRCGP 1983, M 1976; DA Eng. 1966. Lect. (Gen. Pract. & Primary Health Care) Univ. Leicester. Socs: Assn. Univ. Depts. Gen. Pract.; Leic. Med. Soc. Prev: GP Leicester; SHO MRC Pneumoconiosis Research Unit Llandough Hosp. Cardiff; Regist. (Anaesth.) Groote Schuur Hosp. Cape Town, S. Afr.

PRESTWICH, Albert (retired) 3-5 Chancery Lane, Thrapston, Kettering NN14 4JL Tel: 01832 732456 Fax: 01832 734854 — MB BS 1961 Lond.; MRCS Eng. LRCP Lond. 1961. Prev: Dist. Med. Off. Inagua, Bahamas.

PRESTWICH, Heather Rachel Bennett Street Surgery, Stretford, Manchester M32 8SG Tel: 0161 865 1100; 13 River Street, Wilmslow SK9 4AB Tel: 01625 520078 — MB ChB 1988 Manch.; MRCGP 1994; DRCOG 1993; DCH RCP Lond. 1992. GP Princip. Stretford Manch. Prev: Asst. GP Macclesfield.

***PRESTWICH, Robin James Daniel** 46 Albert Street, Durham DH1 4RJ — BM BCh 1998 Oxf.; MB BCh Oxf 1998.

PRESTWOOD, John Michael Brecon, 26 St Aubins Park, Hayling Island PO11 0HQ Tel: 023 9246 2070 — MB ChB 1965 Bristol. (Bristol) Prev: GP Hayling Is.

***PRETLOVE, Samantha Jane** 160 Tiverton Road, Selly Oak, Birmingham B29 6BU — MB ChB 1996 Birm.; ChB Birm. 1996.

PRETORIUS, Marina 73 Manor Road, Scarborough YO12 7RT — MB ChB 1990 Pretoria.

PRETSELL, Alexander Ogilvy 17 Law Road, North Berwick EH39 4PT; Seaview, 17 Law Road, North Berwick EH39 4PT Tel: 01620 2766 — MB ChB 1964 Ed.; DObst RCOG 1967. (Ed.)

PRETTEJOHN, Edward Joseph Tucker (retired) Kings Gatchell Cottage, Gatchell Green, Trull, Taunton TA3 7ER Tel: 01823 338041 — MB BChir Camb. 1943; FRCP Lond. 1974, M 1948; MRCS Eng., LRCP Lond. 1942. Prev: Cons. Dermatol. Taunton & Bridgwater Hosps.

PRETTY, Madeline Ann Dipple Medical Centre, South Wing, Wickford Avenue, Pitsea, Basildon SS13 3HQ Tel: 01268 553321 Fax: 01268 556231; 24 The Finches, Thundersley, Benfleet SS7 3LR Tel: 01268 775356 — MB BS 1967 Lond. (Roy. Free) Prev: Regist. (Surg.) S. Lond. Hosp. Wom.; Cas. Off. Roy. Free Hosp. Lond.

PRETTYMAN, Richard John Bennion Centre, Groby Road, Leicester LE3 9DZ Tel: 0116 250 2752 Fax: 0116 250 2770 Email: pd12@le.ac.uk — MB ChB 1985 Leic.; MRCGP 1990; MRCPsych 1992; DRCOG 1988; DGM RCP Lond. 1987. Sen. Lect. (Old Age Psychiat.) Univ. Leicester. Socs: Brit. Geriat. Soc.; Brit. Neuropsychiat. Assn.; Brit. Neurosci. Assn. Prev: Lect. (Health c/o Elderly) Univ. Nottm. Med. Sch.; Regist. (Psychiat.) Leicester; Trainee GP Leicester VTS.

PREVETT, Martin Charles Wessex Neurological Centre, Southampton General Hospital, Southampton Tel: 023 8079 4793 — BM 1987 Soton.; DM Soton. 1995; MRCP (UK) 1990. (Univ. Soton.) Cons. (Neurol.) Wessex Neurol. Centre Soton. Socs: Counc. Clin. Neurosci.s Sect.; Roy. Soc. of Med. Prev: Sen. Regist. (Neurol.)

PREZIOSI

Nat. Hosp. Neurol. & Neurosurg. Lond. & St. Mary's Hosp. Lond.; Regist. & SHO (Neurol.) Nat. Hosp. Neurol. & Neurosurg. Lond.; Research Regist. (Neurol.) Hammersmith Hosp. Lond.

PREZIOSI, Josef John 57/6 Holland Park, London W11 3RS — MRCS Eng. LRCP Lond. 1981.

PRIAULX, Mr Le-Roy Yeovil General Hospital, Yeovil BA22 4AT; Rowe Croft, Rimpton, Yeovil BA22 8AD Tel: 01935 850321 — MB ChB 1961 Liverp.; FRCS Eng. 1967; MRCS Eng. LRCP Lond. 1961; MChOrth Liverp. 1969. Prev: Cons. Orthop. Surg. Yeovil Dist. Hosp.

PRICE, Adam Stainton Portscatho Surgery, Gerrans Hill, Portscatho, Truro TR2 5EE Tel: 01872 580345 Fax: 01872 580788 — MB BChir 1975 Camb.; MA Camb. 1972; FRCGP 1993, M 1980. Course Organiser (Gen. Pract.) Cornw. VTS Scheme Postgrad. Centre Treliske Hosp. Truro.

PRICE, Mr Alan John The Alexandra Hospital, Woodrow Drive, Redditch B98 7UB Tel: 01527 503030; Vicarage House, Himbleton, Droitwich WR9 7LE Tel: 01905 391404 — MB BS 1969 Lond.; FRCS Ed. 1975; T(S) 1991. (Univ. Coll. Hosp.) Cons. Orthop. & Traum. Surg. Alexandra Healthcare Trust Redditch, Worcs. Socs: Fell. BOA; Brit. Assn. Surg. Knee. Prev: Sen. Regist. (Orthop.) King's Coll. Hosp. Lond.; Regist. (Gen. Surg.) Roy. E. Sussex & St. Helens Hosps. Hastings & Bexhill Hosp.

PRICE, Alan Richard West Kirby Health Centre, Grange Road, Wirral CH48 4HZ Tel: 0151 625 9171 Fax: 0151 625 9171 — MB ChB 1968 Liverp. (Liverp.) GP Hoylake.

PRICE, Alfred Cecil (retired) Greenways, 1 Fayre Oakes Drive, Hereford HR4 0QS Tel: 01432 2759 — MRCS Eng. LRCP Lond. 1930.

PRICE, Alison Nicola Clare Blackbrook Surgery, Lisieux Way, Taunton TA1 2LB Tel: 01823 259444 Fax: 01823 322715; West Lodge, Pitminster, Taunton TA3 7AZ Tel: 01823 421396 — MB BS 1977 Lond.; DRCOG 1980.

PRICE, Professor Allan Department of Oncology, University of Edinburgh, Western General Hospital, Edinburgh EH4 2XU Tel: 0131 537 2205 Fax: 0131 537 2240 Email: a.price@ed.ac.uk — MB BCh 1980 Wales; PhD Lond. 1992; FRCP Ed. 1997; MRCP (UK) 1984; FRCR 1988; DMRT Ed. 1986. (Wales) Prof. Radiat. Oncol. Univ. Edin. Prev: Cons. Clin. Oncol. Addenbrooke's NHS Trust & Papworth Hosp. NHS Trust Camb.

PRICE, Althea Grace Hill Brow Surgery, Long Croft, Staincross, Barnsley S75 6FH Tel: 01226 383131; 62 Huddersfield Road, Barnsley S75 1DR Tel: 01226 206205 Fax: 01226 380100 — MB BS 1951 Lond.; MRCP Lond. 1954; DCH Eng. 1953. (Roy. Free) Prev: SHO Roy. United Hosp. Bath.; Ho. Phys. Roy. Free Hosp. & Hosp. Sick Childr. Gt. Ormond St.

***PRICE, Andrea Louise** 11 Edinburgh Close, Maes-y-Rhiw, Cwmbran NP44 5HR — MB ChB 1998 Birm.; ChB Birm. 1998.

PRICE, Andrew Frederick Holmside Medical Group, 142 Armstrong Road, Benwell, Newcastle upon Tyne NE4 8QB Tel: 0191 273 4009 Fax: 0191 273 2745; 6 Saxilby Drive, Whitebridge Park, Gosforth, Newcastle upon Tyne NE3 5LS Tel: 0191 284 0060 — MB BS 1984 Newc.; MRCGP 1988; DRCOG 1988. Prev: SHO (Obst.) Qu. Eliz. Hosp. Gateshead; Trainee GP N.d. VTS; SHO (Med.) Preston Hosp. N. Shields.

PRICE, Mr Andrew James 81 Warwick Street, Oxford OX4 1SZ — MB BChir 1993 Camb.; BA Camb. 1989; FRCS Eng. 1996. (Camb. & St. Thos. Hosp.) SHO (Orthop.) N.wick Pk. Hosp. Harrow; Specialist Regist. (Orthop.) Oxf. Rotat. Socs: BMA; BOA.

***PRICE, Andrew Jonathan** 29 Inverallan Drive, Bridge of Allan, Stirling FK9 4JR — MB ChB 1998 Glas.; MB ChB Glas 1998.

PRICE, Andrew Richard Tel: 01323 440022 Fax: 01323 649674 Email: andy.price@each-tr.sthames.nhs.uk; Email: andy.price@each-tr.stames.nhs.uk — MB ChB 1981 Leeds; MRCPsych 1986. Cons. in Child and Adolesc. Psychiat., CAMHS, E.bourne & Co. NHS Trust. Prev: Sen. Regist. (Child & Adoles. Psychiat.) Soton. Child Guid. Clinic.; Clin. Director CAMHS, E.bourne and Co. Healthcare Trust.

PRICE, Ann 45 Heol Maendy, North Cornelly, Bridgend CF33 4DF — MB ChB 1993 Bristol.

PRICE, Anne Bapty (retired) Rome Radcliffe, 96-98 Brighton Road, Coulsdon CR3 2YY — MB ChB 1927 Glas.; BSc, MB ChB Glas. 1927; DTM & H Eng. 1928. Prev: Med. Off. The Lawn, Lincoln & Stoke Pk. Colony Bristol.

PRICE, Annis Rebecca 11 The Drive, Hopwood, Alvechurch, Birmingham B48 7AH — MB ChB 1968 Birm.

PRICE, Professor Ashley Beresford 40 Cleveland Road, Ealing, London W13 8AL Tel: 020 8998 6208 Fax: 020 8864 1933 — BM BCh 1964 Oxf.; FRCPath 1984. Cons. Histopath. N.wick Pk. & St. Mark's NHS Trust. Prev: Research Fell. & Hon. Sen. Regist. St. Mark's Hosp. Lond.; Sen. Regist. (Path.) St. Mary's Hosp. Portsmouth & St. Thos. Hosp. Lond.

PRICE, Audrey Joyce Nadine (retired) Little Manor, Church Lane, Burghfield, Reading RG30 3TG Tel: 0118 983 2569 Email: aud@ajprice.fsnet.co.uk — MB BS Lond. 1957; MRCS Eng. LRCP Lond. 1957; DObst RCOG Lond. 1960. Prev: Ho. Phys. S.lands Hosp. Shoreham-by-Sea.

PRICE, Mr Barrie Anthony, Lt.-Col. RAMC Frimley Park Hospital NHS Trust, Portsmouth Road, Frimley, Camberley GU16 7UJ Tel: 01276 604772 Fax: 01276 604019; 7 Minorca Avenue, Deepcut, Camberley GU16 6TT Tel: 01252 837432 Fax: 01252 837432 Email: barriep@aol.com — MB BS 1977 Lond.; MS Lond. 1987, MD 1995; FRCS Ed. 1981; FRCS Eng. 1981; MRCS Eng. LRCP Lond. 1977. (Guy's) Cons. Vasc. Surg. Frimley Pk. Hosp. NHS Trust. Socs: Surgic. Research Soc.; Vase. Surg. Soc. Gt. Brit. & Irel. Prev: Cons. Surg. Musgrave Pk. Hosp. BFPO 801; Cons. Surg. P.ss Mary's RAF Hosp. RAF Akrotiri, BFPO 57; Hon. Sen. Regist. (Surg.) St. Bart. Hosp. Lond.

PRICE, Carol Ann Singleton Medical Centre, 10 Singleton Court, Ashford TN23 5GR Tel: 01233 646036/646037 Fax: 01233 663150; Old Forge Cottage, 81 The St, Willes Borough, Ashford TN24 0NA — MB BCh BAO 1977 Dub. (Trinity College, Dublin) GP.

PRICE, Catherine Mary Child Development Centre, Leicester Royal Infirmary, Leicester LE1 5WW; 59 Gartree Road, Oadby, Leicester LE2 2FD — MB BS 1971 Lond.; MRCP (UK) 1978. Clin. Asst. (Paediat.) Leicester Roy. Infirm.

PRICE, Charles Hedley Godfrey (retired) The Wood, Wrington Road, Congresbury, Bristol BS19 5AS Tel: 01934 838910 — MRCS Eng. LRCP Lond. 1934; MD Bristol 1938, MB ChB 1934; FRCPath 1963. Prev: Research Fell. Univ. Bristol Dept. Osteoarticular Path. Bristol Roy.

PRICE, Christopher Gerard Adrian Bristol Oncology Centre, Horfield Road, Bristol BS2 8ED Tel: 0117 928 2238 Fax: 0117 928 2027 Email: chris.price@ubht.swest.nhs.uk; 13 Woodhill Road, Portishead, Bristol BS20 8ED Email: portprice@supanet.com — MB BS 1981 Lond.; BSc (Pharmacol.) Lond. 1978; MD Lond. 1993; MRCP (UK) 1984. (King's Coll. Hosp.) Cons. Med. Oncol. Bristol Oncol. Centre Bristol Roy. Infirm. Prev: Sen. Regist. (Med. Oncol.) Soton. Univ. Hosps.; ICRF Research Fell. (Med. Oncol.) St. Bart. Hosp. Lond.; Ho. Phys. Liver Unit King's Coll. Hosp. Lond.

PRICE, Christopher Ian Morgan 29 Four Ashes Road, Brewood, Stafford ST19 9HX — MB ChB 1992 Birm.

PRICE, Christopher John Little Maristone, 53 Western Avenue, Glasllwch, Newport NP20 3SN — MB BCh 1985 Wales.

PRICE, Christopher John Simon 6B Westfield Park, Bristol BS6 6LT — MB BS 1994 Lond. SHO (A & E Med.) St. Geo. Hosp. Lond.

PRICE, Christopher Patrick Joseph Old Hall, Little Plumstead Hospital, Norwich NR13 5EW Tel: 01603 711401 — MB ChB 1979 Bristol; MRCGP 1984. CEO, NORWICH PCT. Prev: CEO Norwich City pcg; Regist. (Pub. Health Med.) Trent RHA.; GP LoughBoro. Univ.

PRICE, Mr Colin NHS Centre for Coding & Classification, Woodgate, Loughborough LE11 3SD Tel: 01509 211411; 317 Beacon Road, Loughborough LE11 2RA Email: cprice@l-boro.demon.co.uk — MB ChB 1978 Manch.; BSc Manch. 1976; MPhil Sheff. 1996; FRCS Eng. 1982. Sen. Med. Coding Cons. NHS CCC LoughBoro. Socs: BMA; Manch. Med. Soc.; Amer. Med. Informatics Assn. Prev: Regist. (Surg.) N. Manch. Roy. HA; Lect. (Anat.) Univ. Manch.; Ho. Phys. Preston Roy. Infirm.

PRICE, Dallas John Alistair South Cleveland Hospital, Marton Road, Middlesbrough TS4 3BW Tel: 01642 850850 Fax: 01642 854190; 5 South Cresent, Sowerby, Thirsk YO7 1QZ Tel: 01845 522209 Email: djap@free4all.co.uk — MB BS 1987 Lond.; MRCP (UK) 1996; MRCPI 1994. (St. Thomas Hospital London) Specialist Regist. (Cardiol.) S. Cleveland Hosp. Middlesbrough. Prev: Regist. (Gen. Med. & Cardiol.) Derriford Hosp. Plymouth; Med. Off. RN; Ho. Phys. (Med. Unit) St. Thos. Hosp. Lond.

PRICE, David Alun Chatsworth Road Medical Centre, Chatsworth Road, Brampton, Chesterfield S40 3PY Tel: 01246 568065 Fax: 01246 567116; The Old Rectory, 408 Chatsworth Road,

Chesterfield S40 3BQ Tel: 01246 205900 Email: alun@doctor.gp — MB ChB 1980 Dundee. Clin. Asst. (Pychogeriats.) Walton Hosp. Chesterfield.

PRICE, David Anthony 2 Rickett's Farm House, Bullocks Farm Lane, Wheeler End, High Wycombe HP14 3NH — MB BChir 1991 Camb.; MA Camb. 1992, BA 1988.

PRICE, David Anthony Royal Manchester Children's Hospital, Pendlebury, Manchester M27 4HA Tel: 0161 794 4696; Woodside, 2 Ringley Road, Whitefield, Manchester M45 7LB — BM BCh 1967 Oxf.; FRCPCH 1997; MA Oxf. 1967; FRCP (UK) 1983, M 1970. (Oxf.) Sen. Lect. (Child Health) Manch. Univ.; Hon. Cons. Roy. Manch. Childr. Pendlebury. Prev: Ho. Off. (Med. & Surg.) Radcliffe Infirm. Oxf.; Research Fell. Sophia Kinderziekenhuis, Rotterdam.

***PRICE, David Ashley** Pine View, Cwm Crawnon Road, Llangynidr, Crickhowell NP8 1LS — MB ChB 1995 Sheff.; MRCP II 1998.

PRICE, David Barry The Surgery, London Lighthouse, 111-117 Lancaster Road, London W11 1QT Tel: 020 7792 1200 — MB ChB 1988 Dundee; MRCGP 1992. Princip. Med. Off. Lond. LightHo. (Centre for HIV & AIDS).

PRICE, David Brendan Thorpe Wood Surgery, 140 Woodside Road, Norwich NR7 9QL Tel: 01603 701477 Fax: 01603 701512 — MB 1985 Camb.; BChir 1984. Hon. Sen. Lect. Univ. of E. Anglia; Nat. Comm. of GPIAG. Prev: Course Organiser Norwich VTS.

PRICE, David Brian, OBE (retired) 22 Bryntyrion Hill, Bridgend CF31 4DA — MB BCh 1945 Wales; MRCGP 1962; DObst RCOG 1949. Regist. Obst. St. Davids Hosp. Cardiff. Prev: Maj. RAMC.

PRICE, David Elwyn Morriston Hospital, Swansea SA6 6NL Tel: 01792 703182; 40 West Cross Lane, West Cross, Swansea SA3 5LS Email: price.westcross@ntlworld.com — MD 1990 Camb.; MB BChir 1979; MRCP (UK) 1982; FRCP Lond. 1997. Cons. Gen. Med., Endocrinol. & Diabetes Morriston Hosp. Swansea; Sen. Lect. Univ. Wales. Swansea. Socs: Diabetes UK; Brit. Endocrine Soc. Prev: Sen. Regist. (Gen. Med., Endocrinol. & Diabetes) Leicester Roy. Infirm.; Research Fell. (Med.) Univ. Leeds; Regist. (Med.) Gen. Infirm. Leeds.

PRICE, David Gareth Royal Well Surgery, St Pauls Medical Centre, 121 Swindon Road, Cheltenham GL50 4DP; 75 Shaw Green Lane, Prestbury, Cheltenham GL52 3BS — MB BS 1974 Lond.; BSc (Physiol.) Lond. 1971; DCH Eng. 1980. (Lond. Hosp.)

PRICE, David Gerard 201 Edgeside Lane, Rossendale BB4 9TY — MB ChB 1989 Manch.

PRICE, David Glynne (retired) The Little Manor, Church Lane, Burghfield, Reading RG30 3TG Tel: 0118 983 2569 — MB BS Lond. 1948; MRCS Eng. LRCP Lond. 1948; FFA RCS Eng. 1965; DA Eng. 1959; DObst RCOG 1953. Prev: Cons. Anaesth. Roy. Berks. Hosp. Reading.

PRICE, David John Wishing Gate, Mount Road, Bebington, Wirral CH63 6HB — BM BS 1988 Nottm.; MRCGP 1993; DCH RCP Lond. 1993.

PRICE, David John 82 Gravelly Bank, Lightwood, Stoke-on-Trent ST3 7EF Tel: 01782 318862 Fax: 01782 316102 Email: davej.price@btopenworld.com; 82 Gravelly Bank, Lightwood, Stoke-on-Trent ST3 7EF Tel: 01782 318862 Fax: 01782 316102 — MB ChB 1965 Sheff.; D.Occ. Med. RCP Lond. 1995. (Sheff.) Med. Off. various companies. Socs: Soc. Occupat. Med. Prev: SHO (O & G) City Gen. Hosp. Stoke-on-Trent; Ho. Off. (Gen. Med., Dermat. & Gen. Surg.) N. Staffs. Roy. Infirm.; Chairm. Centr. Stoke PCG.

PRICE, David K Dept of Community Psychiatry, HMS Drake, HMNB Devonport, Plymouth PL2 2BG; Tel: 01579 370399 — MBBS 1974 London; MRCPsych 1986. (St Bartholomews Hospital Medical School) Cons.Psychiat., MOD UK (RN) Plymouth; Cons. Psychiat., Community Alcohol Serv., plymouth Community Trust. Prev: Cons. Psychiat., Cornw. Health Care Trust; Surg. Cdr., Head of Community Psychiat., Plymouth.

PRICE, David Malcolm Charlotte Keel Health Centre, Seymour Road, Easton, Bristol BS5 0UA Tel: 0117 951 2244 Fax: 0117 935 4447; 18 Maurice Road, St Andrews, Bristol BS6 5BZ Tel: 0117 942 1616 — MB BS 1979 Newc.; MRCGP 1986; DRCOG 1984; DCH RCP Lond. 1981.

PRICE, Dean Robert Gregory 149 Hawthorn Rise, Haverfordwest SA61 2AZ — BM BCh 1975 Oxf.

PRICE, Dennis Thornton (retired) 83 Manchester Road, Wilmslow SK9 2JQ Tel: 01625 528024 — MB ChB 1961 Manch.; MRCGP 1974; DObst RCOG 1963. Prev: GP Wilmslow.

PRICE, Dora Elizabeth 35 Alleyn Road, West Dulwich, London SE21 8AD — M.B., B.S. Lond. 1930. (Lond. Sch. Med. Wom.) Prev: Asst. Med. Off. Grosvenor Sanat. Ashford; Ho. Surg. Roy. Vict. Hosp. Folkestone; Res. Med. Off. Childr. Hosp. Hampstead.

PRICE, Doris May Clewett (retired) 19 Oaklands Park, Bishop's Stortford CM23 2BY Tel: 01279 652629 — MB ChB 1953 Birm.; DO Eng. 1956; FRCS Ed. (Ophth.) 1963; FRCS Eng. (Ophth.) 1963; FCOphth 1988. Prev: Cons. Ophth. Surg. W. Essex & E. Herts. HAs.

PRICE, Douglas James (retired) Box Cottage, Balls Cross, Petworth GU28 9JS Tel: 01403 820302 — MB BS Lond. 1949; FRCGP 1974, M 1957. Prev: Postgrad. Adviser Gen. Pract (SW Thames Region) Brit. Postgrad. Med. Federat. Univ. Lond.

PRICE, Mr Edgar Charles Vincent, TD (retired) Purey Cust Nuffield Hospital, Precentor's Court, York YO1 7EL Tel: 01759 371465 Fax: 01904 673253 — MB BS 1952 Lond.; FRCS Eng. 1990; FRCS Ed. 1962; MRCS Eng. LRCP Lond. 1952. Prev: Cons. Orthop. Surg. York Hosp. Gp.

PRICE, Edith Patricia (retired) Tircwm, Leigh Road, Pontypool NP4 8HY — MB BCh 1959 Wales; DObst RCOG 1961. Prev: SCMO (Child Health) Gwent DHA.

PRICE, Edward David Peregrine Corinthian Surgery, St Paul's Medical Centre, 121 Swindon Road, Cheltenham GL50 4DP Tel: 01242 707777 Fax: 01242 707776; Dowdeswell House, Dowdeswell, Cheltenham GL54 4LX Tel: 01242 820993 — MB BS 1967 Lond.; LRCP 1967 Lond.; MRCS 1967 Eng.; DObst RCOG 1969. (St. Geo.) Med. Off. Cheltenham Coll. Prev: Ho. Off. (Med.) Cheltenham Gen. Hosp.; Ho. Surg. St. Geo. Hosp. Lond.; Ho. Off. (Obst.) Cheltenham Matern. Hosp.

PRICE, Eifion Wyn Anaesthetic department, Royal Brompton Hospital, Minerva Road, Farnworth, Bolton BL4 0JR Tel: 01204 390762 Email: wyn.price@bolton-tr.nwest.nhs.uk — MB BS 1990 Lond.; FRCA 1996. Cons. Anaesth. Roy. Bolton Hosp. Prev: Specialist Regist. (Anaesth.) N. W. Region.

PRICE, Elinor Myles Morland House Surgery, 2 London Road, Wheatley, Oxford OX33 1YJ Tel: 01865 872448 Fax: 01865 874158; Alan Court, Mill Lane, Old Marston, Oxford OX3 0PY — MB BS 1972 Lond.; MRCGP 1979. (Univ. Coll. Hosp.) Prev: Ho. Phys. Med. Unit Univ. Coll. Hosp. Lond.; Ho. Phys. Endocrine Unit Roy. Free Hosp. Lond.

PRICE, Elizabeth Helen 48 Middleway, London NW11 6SG — MB BS Lond. 1967; MRCS Eng. LRCP Lond. 1967; MRCPath 1975; DCH Eng. 1969; FRCPath 1988. (Westm.) Cons. Med. Microbiol. Roy. Lond. Hosp. Whitechapel Lond. Prev: Cons. Med. Microbiol. Qu. Eliz. Hosp. for Childr. & Hosp. for Childr. Gt. Ormond St. Lond.; Sen. Lect. (Microbiol.) Qu. Eliz. Hosp. Childr. Lond. & Inst. Child Health Lond.

PRICE, Elizabeth Jayne Princess Margaret Hospital, Okus Road, Swindon SN1 4JU Tel: 01793 426205 Fax: 01793 426205; 2 Manor Courtyard, Ogbourne Maizey, Marlborough SN8 1RN Tel: 01672 841174 — MB BCh 1987 Wales; MD Wales 1997; MRCP (UK) 1990. (Univ. Wales Coll. Med.) Cons. Rheum. P.ss Margt. Hosp. Swindon. Prev: Sen. Regist. (Rheum. & Gen. Med.) Char. Cross. Hosp. Lond.; Research Regist. Kennedy Inst. Rheum. Lond.; Regist. (Med.) Univ. Hosp. Wales Cardiff.

PRICE, Elizabeth Margaret Schopwick Surgery, Everett Court, Romeland, Elstree, Borehamwood WD6 3BJ Tel: 020 8953 1008 — MB BS 1977 Lond.; MA Camb. 1972 PhD Lond. 1972, MB BS 1977; MRCGP 1982; DRCOG 1980. (Univ. Coll. Hosp.) Course Organiser N.wick Pk. Hosp. GP VTS; Examr. MRCGP Exam.

PRICE, Elizabeth Mary (retired) Pear Tree Cottage, Hewelsfield, Lydney GL15 6UU — MB ChB 1953 Manch.; DObst RCOG 1955; DCH Eng. 1956.

PRICE, Emily Eileen (retired) Merry Piece, Oxford Road, Woodstock, Oxford OX20 1QW — MB BCh 1956 Wales.

PRICE, Mrs Erika Burscough Health Centre, Stanley Court, Lord Street, Burscough, Ormskirk L40 4LA Tel: 01704 892229; 63 Harridge Lane, Scarisbrick, Ormskirk L40 8HD — MB ChB 1971 Manch.

PRICE, Mr Evan Reginald (retired) 62 Huddersfield Road, Barnsley S75 1DR Tel: 01226 206205 Fax: 01226 231418 — MB BCh Wales 1944; MB BS Lond. 1948; FRCS Eng. 1955; MRCP Lond. 1949. Prev: Cons. Orthop. Surg. Barnsley Hosp. Gp.

PRICE

PRICE, Felicity Margaret Spring Hall Group Practice, Spring Hall Medical Centre, Spring Hall Lane, Halifax HX1 4JG Tel: 01422 349501 Fax: 01422 323091 — BM BS 1989 Nottm.

PRICE, Fiona Jane The Coach House, Crawford Park, Perth Road, Dunblane FK15 0HA Tel: 01786 825045 — MB ChB 1989 Glas.

PRICE, Frances Mary The Surgery, 60 Hungate Street, Aylsham, Norwich NR11 6AA Tel: 01263 733693 — MB ChB 1977 Manch.; MRCGP 1988. Prev: Med. Miss. Segbwema Sierra Leone.

PRICE, Gail Victoria Pencoed and Llanharan Medical Centres, Heol-yr-Onnen, Pencoed, Bridgend CF35 5PF Tel: 01656 860270 Fax: 01656 861228; Haulfa, 7 Rogers Lane, Laleston, Bridgend CF32 0LB Tel: 01656 638753 — MB BCh 1988 Wales; BA (Hons.) Wales 1983. (Univ. Wales Coll. Med.)

***PRICE, Gary** 16 Carr Close, Liverpool L11 4UA — MB ChB 1996 Liverp.

PRICE, Mr Gavin Fontaine Watson Riverbank, Victoria Park, Londonderry BT47 2AD — MB BCh BAO 1967 Belf.; FRCS Ed. 1973. Orthop. Surg. Altnagelvin Hosp. Lond.derry. Prev: Princip. Orthop. Surg. & Sen. Lect. Univ. Natal, S. Africa.

PRICE, Geoffrey John Royal Sussex County Hospital, Main X-Ray Department, Eastern Road, Brighton BN2 5BE Tel: 01273 696955 — MB ChB 1978 Sheff.; FRCR 1988. Cons. Radiol. Main X-Ray Dept. Roy. Sussex Co. Hosp. Brighton.

***PRICE, Gillian** 68 Barfield Park, Lancing BN15 9DG — MB BS 1996 Lond.

PRICE, Gillian Mary Cramond Surgery, 2 Cramond Glebe Road, Edinburgh EH4 6NS Tel: 0131 336 5432 Fax: 0131 336 2203 Email: s.price@scotland.com; Basement Flat, 104 St. Stephens St., Edinburgh EH3 5AQ Tel: 0131 225 3595 — MB ChB 1987 Ed.; BSc Med. Sci. (Hons.) 1985 Ed. (Edinburgh)

PRICE, Godfrey Charles (retired) 34 Bury Road, Branksome Park, Poole BH13 7DG — MRCS Eng. LRCP Lond. 1941.

PRICE, Graham Anthony Roscoe Paston Surgery, 9-11 Park Lane, North Walsham NR28 0BQ Tel: 01692 403015 Fax: 01692 500619 — MB BCh 1972 Wales; MRCP (UK) 1975; MRCGP 1978; DFFP 1993; DRCOG 1978. Hosp. Pract. (Dermat.) Cromer Hosp. & W. Norwich Hosp.; Mem. Med. Staff N. Walsham War Memor. Cottage Hosp. Prev: Regist. (Dermat.) Liverp. Roy. Infirm.; Ho. Off. Univ. Hosp. of Wales Cardiff.

PRICE, Graham David Lewis Takeda Europe R&D ltd., Savannah House, 11 Charles II St., London SW1Y 4QU; 131 Saltram Crescent, Maida Vale, London W9 3JT Tel: 020 8960 8420 Fax: 020 8964 2845 Email: graham.price.1@btinternet.com — MB BS 1991 Lond.; BSc (Hons.) Lond. 1989; DFFP 1995; DRCOG 1994. Med. Man. Takeda Res. & Dev. Europe. Lond.; Mem. Osler Club Lond. Socs: Roy. Soc. Med. Prev: Pharmaceut. Phys. Servier Laborats. Ltd., Paris; SHO (O & G) Roy. Free Hosp. Lond. & St. Mary's Hosp. Lond.; SHO (Med.) Centr. Middlx. Hosp. Lond.

PRICE, Grant Crichton 3FL, 37 Arden St., Edinburgh EH9 1BS — MB ChB 1995 Manch.

PRICE, Harold 47 Oakleigh Park N., London N20 9YT Tel: 020 8445 9985 — MB ChB 1953 Bristol; DCH Eng. 1955. (Bristol) Coroner E. Lond. Dist. Socs: Med.-Leg. Soc.; Coroners Soc. Prev: Barrister-at-Law Lincoln's Inn 1967; Ho. Off. Alder Hey Child Hosp. Liverp.; Ho. Surg. S.mead Hosp. Bristol.

PRICE, Hazel Margaret Vue De La Saline, Petit Val, Alderney GY9 3UX — MB BS 1955 Lond.; MB BS (Hnrs. Therap.) Lond. 1955; FRCR 1978; DMRD Eng. 1973; DA Eng. 1959. (Roy. Free) Prev: Cons. Radiol. Univ. Hosp. Nottm.

PRICE, Heather Mary Rea Kidlington Health Centre, Exeter Close, Kidlington OX5 1AP — BM 1991 Soton.; MRCGP 1995. GP. Prev: Trainee GP Reading; SHO (Paediat., Rheum., Gen. Med. & O & G) Basingstoke Dist. Hosp.

PRICE, Helen Jean (retired) Tigh Bahn, 2a Merrion Ave, Exmouth EX8 2HX — MB ChB 1943 Birm. Prev: Ho. Surg. Matern. Hosp. Birm.

PRICE, Helen Louise Princes Margaret Hospital, Okus Road, Swindon SN1 4JU Tel: 01793 426183 Fax: 01793 426774 Email: helen.price@smnhst.swest.nhs.uk — MD 1982 New York; BSc Yale 1978. p/t Cons. Paediat. P.ss Margt. Hosp. Swindon. Socs: Roy. Coll. Paediat. & Child Health; BMA; Fell. Roy. Coll. Paediat. and Child Health. Prev: Sen. Regist. (Paediat.) Kings Coll. Hosp. Lond.

***PRICE, Helen Louise** Sadlers End, 52 Sadlers Way, Ringmer, Lewes BN8 5HG — MB BS 1996 Lond.

PRICE, Helen Samantha 10 Manchester Road, Knutsford WA16 0NT — MB ChB 1989 Bristol; MRCOG 1995; Cert. Family Plann. JCC 1993; DRCOG 1993. (Bristol) Med. Adviser Zeneca Pharmaceuts. Chesh. Prev: Trainee GP Wycombe Gen. Hosp. VTS; SHO (O & G) Macclesfield Dist. Gen. Hosp.

PRICE, Hugh Francis (retired) 15 Castle Hill, Duffield, Derby DE56 4EA Tel: 01332 840115 — MB BS Lond. 1955. Prev: Asst. Med. Off. Babington Hosp. Belper.

PRICE, Isabel Mary Shirvell Bright's Orchard, Hole-in-the-Wall, Ross-on-Wye HR9 7JW Tel: 01989 565804 Fax: 01989 565804 Email: isabel@pebody.freeseve — MB ChB 1960; MFCM RCP (UK) 1974; FRCPCH 1997; DCH Eng. 1967; DObst RCOG 1962. (Bristol) p/t SCMO Hereford Community Health Trust. Socs: MEDACT. Prev: Cons. Pub. Health Med. Mid Downs HA; SCMO (Audiol.) W. Sussex; Specialist Community Med. (Child Health) Chichester HA.

PRICE, Jacqueline Frances 4 Strathalmond Road, Edinburgh EH4 8AD; 107 Candlemaker's Park, Edinburgh EH17 8TL — MB ChB 1992 Ed.; BSc Ed. 1990. Clin. Lect. Dept. of Pub. Health Sci.s Univ. Edin.; Hon. Specialist Regist. (Pub. Health Med.) Lothian Health Edin. Socs: Soc. Social Med. Prev: Clin. Research Fell. Epidemiol. Wolfson Unit for Preven. of Peripheral Vasc. Dis. Univ. Edin.; SHO (Gen. Med.) St. John's Hosp. at Howden Livingston.

PRICE, James David Sabrina House, 98 Abingdon Road, Grandpoint, Oxford OX1 4PX Tel: 01865 727770 Email: a2037510@infotrade.co.uk; Radcliffe Infirmary, Woodstock Road, Oxford OX2 6HE — BM BCh 1991 Oxf.; BSc (Hons.) Bristol 1988; MRCP (UK) 1994. Res. Fell. (Clin. Gerat.) Radcliffe Infirm. Oxf. Prev: Specialist Regist. (Gen. Med. & Geratology) Radcliffe Infirm. Oxf.; SHO Rotat. (Gen. Med.) Gen. Infirm. Leeds; Ho. Surg. Nuffield Dept. Surg. John Radcliffe Hosp. Oxf.

PRICE, James Michael Parklands Surgery, 4 Parklands Road, Chichester PO19 3DT Tel: 01243 782819/786827; Downview, Summersdale Road, Chichester PO19 4PW Tel: 01243 787062 Fax: 08700 568514 Email: jmp@jimprice.demon.co.uk — MB BChir 1984 Camb.; MA Camb. 1985; MRCP (UK) 1989; MRCGP 1992; DFFP 1993; T(GP) 1992; DRCOG 1991. (Camb. & St. Thos.) Princip. in GP; Vice Chairm. & Clin. Governance Lead Chichester & Rural PCG. Socs: Primary Care Soc. Gastroenterol. (Comm.); BAMM; NHS Primary Care Gp Alliance. Prev: Hosp. Practitioner (Gastroenterol.) St Richards Hosp., Chichester.

PRICE, Jane Rosalyn Westbury House, Belmont St., Bognor Regis PO21 1LE — MB BChir 1969 Camb.; MA Camb. 1969; DObst RCOG 1973. (Camb. & Middlx.) Clin. Asst. Regis Day Hosp. Bognor Regis. Prev: Princip. Rochdale Gp. Pract. Lond.

PRICE, Jean North Bristol Trust c/o Community Child Health, Southmead Hospital, Southmead Road, Westbury on Trym, Bristol BS10 5NB Tel: 0117 950 8906 Fax: 0117 959 5363; 18 Great Brockeridge, Westbury on Trym, Bristol BS9 3TY Tel: 0117 962 8296 — MB BS Durh. 1966; DPM Eng. 1974; DPH Bristol 1971; DObst RCOG 1969; FRCPCH 1996. (Durh.) Cons. Community Paediat.; Forens. Examr. Socs: BACCH; PCAIG (Exec. Comm. Mem.); CCP, Chairm. CPIG. Prev: SCMO S.mead HA; Sen. Regist. (Child Psychiat.) Bristol Childr. Hosp.; Regist. (Gen. Med.) Jersey Gp. Hosps.

PRICE, John David Springhead Medical Centre, 376 Willerby Road, Hull HU5 5JT Tel: 01482 352263 Fax: 01482 352480 — LRCPI & LM, LRSCI & LM 1968. Chairm. Exec. Comm. W. Hull Primary Care Trust. Socs: Brit. Soc. Gastroenterol. Prev: Ho. Phys. & Ho. Surg. Mercer's Hosp. Dub.; SHO Hull Matern. Hosp.

PRICE, John David 144 Harley Street, London W1G 7LD Tel: 020 7935 0023 Fax: 020 7935 5972; 12 Fitzjames Avenue, Croydon CR0 5DH Tel: 020 8654 3862 Mobile: 07956 597177 — MB BS 1958 Lond.; MRCS Eng. LRCP Lond. 1958; Dip Pharm Med RCP (UK) 1977; DObst RCOG 1960. (Westm.) Socs: Fell. Roy. Soc. Med.; Brit. Assn. Manip. Med.; Primary Care Soc. Prev: Med. Dir. Beecham Pharmaceut. Lond.; Med. Dir. Clin. Research Glaxo Laborats. Greenford; Assoc. Cons. Char. Cross Hosp. Lond.

PRICE, John David 144 Harley Street, London W1G 7LD Tel: 020 7935 0023 Fax: 020 7935 5972 — L.R.C.P. MR.CS Lond. 1958; D.Ph. Med. Edinburgh 1977; D.R.C.O.G. 1960 Lond.; M.B. B.S. (Lond.) 1958. (Westminster) Cons. Orthopaedic Physcian Lond. Socs: F.R.S.M.; Apothecarion Hall; Brit. Soc. Manip. Med. Prev: Med. Director Research Pharmaceutical Lond.; Med. Director Clin.

Research & Developm. New Products Glaxo Lab Lond.; Assn. Char. Cross & Roy. Free Hosp. Lond.

PRICE, Professor John Frederick Department of Child Health, King's College Hospital, London SE5 9RS Tel: 020 7326 3562; 119 Dacre Park, London SE13 5BZ Tel: 020 8318 5450 — MB BChir 1970 Camb.; MA, MB Camb. 1970, MD 1986, BChir 1969; FRCP Lond. 1985, M 1972; DCH Eng. 1973. (Camb. & Guy's) Prof. Paediat. Respirology & Cons. Paediat. King's Coll. Hosp. Lond.; Prof. Paediat. Respirology King's Coll. Sch. Med. Lond. Socs: (Counc.) Brit. Thoracic Soc. & Europ. Respirat. Soc. Prev: Ho. Phys. Brompton Hosp. Lond.; Regist. Hosp. Sick Childr. Gt. Ormond St.; MRC Research Fell. Inst. Child Health Lond.

PRICE, John Hardy (retired) Pear Tree Cottage, Hewelsfield, Lydney GL15 6UU — MB ChB 1953 Manch.; FRCGP 1977, M 1962. Prev: Hon. Sen. Clin. Lect. Univ. Birm.

PRICE, John Hazlett Department of Gynaecology, Belfast City Hospital, Lisburn Road, Belfast BT9 7AB Tel: 01232 263810 Fax: 01232 263953 — MD 1989 Belf.; MB BCh BAO Belf. 1977; MRCOG 1982, D 1979; FRCOG 1995. Cons. O & G Belf. City Hosp.; Hon sen Lec Qu.s Univ Belf. Socs: Brit. Gyn. Cancer Soc. (Counc. Mem.); BSCCP; Irish Gyn. Oncol. Soc. (Ulster Represent.).

PRICE, Mr John Jeffrey The Yorkshire Clinic, Bradford Road, Bingley BD16 1TW — MB ChB 1965 Leeds; MB ChB (Hons.) Leeds 1965; MRCP Lond. 1968; FRCS Eng. 1971; FRCP 1999. Cons. (Gen. Surg.) Bradford Hosps.

PRICE, Mr John Lawrence, TD (retired) 70 Brackenrig Crescent, Eaglesham, Glasgow G76 0HF Tel: 0141 644 3395 — MB ChB 1956 Glas.; FRCS Ed. 1972; FRCOG 1980, M 1966, DObst 1960. Prev: Cons. Lanarksh. Area Health Bd.

PRICE, John Lewis, OBE, RD (retired) 1 Little Warren Close, Guildford GU4 8PW Tel: 01483 563868 — MB BS 1950 Lond.; FRCR 1963; DMRD Eng. 1961. Prev: Profess. Fell. Radiol. Dept. Phys. Univ. Surrey.

PRICE, John Scott Odintune Place, Plumpton, Lewes BN7 3AN Tel: 01273 890362 Fax: 01273 890614 Email: john.price@lycosmail.com — DM Oxf. 1969, BM BCh 1958; MRCP Lond. 1973; FRCPsych 1979, M 1971; T(Psych) 1991; DPM Lond. 1965. (St. Bart.) Cons. Psychiat. Milton Keynes Health Dist. Socs: Chairm. Sect. on Psychother., World Psychiatric Assn. Prev: Cons. Psychiat. N.wick Pk. Hosp. & Clin. Research Centre Harrow; Mem. Scientif. Staff MRC Psychiat. Genetics Unit Inst. Psychiat.; Sen. Lect. (Psychol. Med.) Univ. Newc.

PRICE, John Stephen Wingham Lodge, High St, Wingham, Canterbury CT3 1AZ — MB ChB 1983 Ed.; PhD Camb. 1990; BSc (Hons.) Ed. 1980. (Ed.) Sen. Director and Global Head Clin. Regulatory Submissions Grp. Centr. Res. Socs: Fell. Roy. Soc. Med. Prev: Sen. Clin. Submissions Manager Pfizer Centr. Research; Head Clin. Eval. Unit, Med. Centre Agency, DOH; Sen. Med. Off. Med. Control Agency DoH.

PRICE, Jonathan Neil Moat House, Crescent Road, Ivybridge PL21 0BP — BM 1992 Soton.

PRICE, Jonathan Paul David Osborne Practice Surgery, 25 Osborne Road, Southsea PO5 3ND Tel: 023 9282 1371 — BMSc Nottm. 1983, BM BS 1985; MRCGP 1989; DCH RCP Lond. 1990; DRCOG 1988. Prev: Trainee GP Portsmouth; SHO Portsmouth VTS; Ho. Off. Univ. Hosp. Nottm.

PRICE, Jonathan Raymond University of Oxford, Department of Psychiatry, The Warneford Hospital, Oxford OX3 7JX Tel: 01865 226 467 Fax: 01865 793101 Email: jonathan.price@psych.ox.ac.uk — BM BCh 1991 Oxf.; 2001 Dip in Learning & Teaching of Higher Education, Oxford; MA Camb. 1992; BA Oxf. 1988; MRCPsych 1995; Dip. Evid. Based Healthcare, Oxf. 1998; Dip. Cognitive Ther, Oxf. 1999. (Oxf.) Clin. Tutor in Psychiat.; Hon. Specialist Regist. The Warneford Hosp. Oxf. Prev: Regist. Rotat. (Psychiat.) Oxf. Train. Scheme; SHO (Rheum., Rehabil. & Metab. Med.) Nuffield Orthop. Centre Oxf.; SHO (Oncol.) Qu. Eliz. Hosp. Birm.

PRICE, Judith-Ann Willow Wood Surgery, Crook Lane, Winsford CW7 3GY Tel: 01606 861220 Fax: 01606 863354; 87 Chester Road, Winsford CW7 2NG — MB ChB 1987 Manch.; BSc 1984; DRCOG 1989. Socs: Roy. Coll. Gen. Pract.

PRICE, Julie Hillingdon Hospital, Pield Heath Rd, Hillingdon UB8 3NN Tel: 01895 279889 Fax: 01895 279444 — MB BS 1978 Lond.; BSc Lond. 1975; MRCOG 1984. (King's Coll. Hosp.) Cons. O & G Hillingdon Hosp. Uxbridge. Prev: Sen. Regist. & Lect. (O & G) Char. Cross Hosp. Lond.; Regist. & Lect. (O & G) St. Thos. Hosp. Lond.

PRICE, Katherine Jean Fax: 0114 273 0522 Email: kjprice@sheffon-tr.trent.nhs.uk; 8 Woodvale Road, Sheffield S10 3EX — MB ChB 1979 Sheff.; MRCP (Paediat.) (UK) 1985; DCH RCP Lond. 1983. Cons. Paediat. N. Gen. Hosp. Sheff. & Sheff. Childr. Hosp. Prev: Sen. Regist. (Paediat.) Roy. Devon & Exeter Hosp.; SHO (Paediat.) & (Med.) Exeter HA; Med. Off. Kwa Zulu Rep. S. Afr.

PRICE, Kathryn Anne 3 Thornholme Road, Sunderland SR2 7QF — MB ChB 1978 Liverp.; FFA RCS Eng. 1983. Cons. (Anaesth.) Newc. Gen. Hosp. Socs: Dep. Regional Adviser (Anaesth.) N.. Region; Counc., SEA UK. Prev: Cons. (Anaesth.) Sunderland DGH; Sen. Regist. & Regist. (Anaesth.) Newc. HA; Clin. Research Fell. (Neurosurg.) Newc. HA.

PRICE, Keith Gerrard University Health Centre, University of York, Heslington, York YO10 5DD Tel: 01904 430000 — MB ChB 1974 Liverp.

PRICE, Kenneth John Probert Battle End House, Battle, Brecon LD3 9RW Tel: 01874 2121 — MB BS 1948 Lond. (Lond. Hosp.) Emerg. Off. Lond. Hosp. Prev: Surg. Brecon War Memor. Hosp.; Ho. Surg. Roy. Gwent Hosp. Newport; Med. Off. Crosfield Ho. Brit. Legion Home.

***PRICE, Laura Claire** 9 Wellgarth Road, London NW11 7HP — MB ChB 1998 Bristol.

PRICE, Leonard Anthony (cons. rooms), 147 Harley St., London W1G 1BL Tel: 020 7486 2545 Fax: 020 7935 6324 — MB BS 1962 Lond.; MD Lond. 1980; MRCP (UK) 1972. (Westm.) Stem Cell Transpl. Phys./Med. Oncol.; UK Represen. New York Chemother. Foundat. Socs: New York Acad. Sci. (Sect. Med.); Amer. Soc. Clin. Oncol.; Fell. Roy. Soc. Med. Prev: Sen. Lect. (Med.) Inst. Cancer Research Lond.; Hon. Cons. Phys. Roy. Marsden Hosp. Lond; MRC Clin. Scientist Inst. Cancer Research Lond.

PRICE, Leonie Jones The Surgery, Bennett St., Stretford, Manchester M32 8SG Tel: 0161 865 1100 Fax: 0161 865 7710 — MB BCh 1992 Wales; MRCGP 1996. (Univ. of Wales Coll. Of Med.)

PRICE, Lindsay James Roscoe Bangor Medical Centre, Bryn Hydd, Holyhead Road, Bangor LL57 2EE Tel: 01248 372373 Fax: 01248 372244 — MB BS 1974 Newc.

PRICE, Lois Emilie Noble Brewery Cottage, South Stoke, Bath BA2 7DL Tel: 01225 832122 — MB ChB 1943 Manch.; MRCPsych 1973; DCH Eng. 1948; DPM Eng. 1968. (Manch.) Assoc. Specialist Dept. Ment. Health Bristol. Socs: Roy. Med.-Psych. Assn. Prev: SHO Dept. Ment. Health Bristol Roy. Infirm.; Regist. (Psychiat.) Bath Clin. Area; Ho. Phys. Booth Hall Childr. Hosp. Manch.

PRICE, Lorna Duncan 23 Pennine Close, Oadby, Leicester LE2 4TB — MB ChB 1980 Glas.

PRICE, Lynfa The Surgery, 30 Old Road West, Gravesend DA11 0LL Tel: 01474 352075/567799 Fax: 01474 333952 — MB BCh 1968 Wales.

PRICE, Malcolm Alexander Bezeck 6 Post Office Lane, Slitting Mill, Rugeley WS15 2UP — MB BS 1983 Lond.; BSc (Hons.) Lond. 1979, MB BS 1983; MCOphth 1990; DRCOG 1989.

PRICE, Margaret Louise Brighton General Hospital, Elm Grove, Brighton BN2 3EW Tel: 01273 696955 Fax: 01273 665025 — BM BCh 1973 Oxf.; FRCP Lond. 1992; MRCP (UK) 1977. Cons. Dermatol. Brighton HA; Hon. Lect. Brighton Univ. Socs: Roy. Soc. Med. (Dermatol. Sect.); Brit. Assn. Dermatol.; Chairm. CPD Comm. Prev: Sen. Registar Guy's Hosp. & Brighton HA.

PRICE, Margaret Mary Park Road Health Centre, Park Road, Radyr, Cardiff CF15 8DF Tel: 029 2084 2767 Fax: 029 2084 2507; 23 Lon Y Fro, Pentyrch, Cardiff CF15 9TE — MB BCh 1978 Wales; MRCGP 1982.

***PRICE, Mark** 2 Greenlawns, Cardiff CF23 6AW — BM 1997 Soton.

PRICE, Mark Alexander 86 Angus Street, Cardiff CF24 3LX — MB BCh 1988 Wales.

PRICE, Martin Laurence 54 Eland Road, London SW11 5JY — MB BS 1980 Lond.; BSc (cl. 2 Hons.) Lond. 1978; FFA RCS Eng. 1984. Cons. Anaesth. St. Mary's Hosp. Lond. Prev: Sen. Regist. St. Geo. Hosp. Lond.; Regist. Qu. Charlottes Matern. Hosp. Lond.; Regist. (Anaesth.) King's Coll. Hosp. Lond.

PRICE, Mary (retired) Leith Mount, 46 Ferry Road, Edinburgh EH6 4AE Tel: 0131 554 0558 Fax: 0131 555 6911 — MB BCh

PRICE

1955 Wales; BSc Wales 1952; DCH Eng. 1957. Prev: Asst. Med. Off. Pub. Health Dept. City Edin. SHO (Paediat.) Llandough.

PRICE, Melinda Ann Meddygfa'r Llan, Church Surgery, Portland Street, Aberystwyth SY23 2DX — MB BCh 1984 Wales; AFOM 2001; DRCOG 1987. Clin. Assit. Occupat.al Health, Bronglais Hosp. Aberystwyth. Prev: Trainee GP Aberystwyth VTS.

PRICE, Michael Price and Partners, The Surgery, Park Road, Holbeach, Spalding PE12 7EE Tel: 01406 423288 Fax: 01406 426284 — MB ChB 1965 St. And.

PRICE, Michael Ernest Smugglers Lane Surgery, Smugglers Lane, Reepham, Norwich NR10 4QT Tel: 01603 870271 Fax: 01603 872995 — MB BS 1977 Lond.; MA Camb. 1979; MRCP (UK) 1980; MRCGP 1988. Prev: Regist. (Med.) W. Norwich Hosp.; Med. Miss. Segbwena, Sierra Leone.

PRICE, Michael Gregory (retired) Windrush, Cocklawelva, Rock, Wadebridge PL27 6LW Tel: 01208 863622 — BSc (Hons. Physiol.) Lond. 1949, MB BS 1952; MRCGP 1965; DObst RCOG 1956. Prev: Sen. Ho. Phys. St. Bart. Hosp. Lond.

PRICE, Michael John Moat House, Crescent Road, Ivybridge PL21 0BP — MB BS 1965 Lond.; MRCPsych 1972; DPM Eng. 1971. (Univ. Coll. Hosp.) Cons. Psychiat. of Old Age Cotehele Unit Mt. Gould Hosp. Plymouth. Prev: Sen. Regist. (Psychiat.) Barrow & United Bristol Hosps.; Regist. (Geriat.) Qu. Alexandra & St. Mary's Hosps. Portsmouth; Regist. (Psychiat.) St. Francis Hosp. Haywards Heath.

PRICE, Michael Leslie Hulbert, Price, Hulbert and Davies, Laurel Bank Surgery, Old Hall Street, Malpas SY14 8PS Tel: 01948 860205 Fax: 01948 860142; Rock Cottage, Sarn, Threapwood, Malpas SY14 7LN Tel: 01948 770329 — MB ChB 1972 Bristol; DRCOG 1977.

PRICE, Michael Richard Jan First Floor Flat, 125 Newbridge Road, Bath BA1 3HG Email: mrjp@globalnet.co.uk — BM BS 1994 Nottm.

***PRICE, Mitchel** The Limes Surgery, 172 High Street, Lye, Stourbridge DY9 8LL Tel: 01384 422234; Roundhill Farmhouse, Whittington, Hall Lane, Stourbridge DY7 6PH — MB ChB 1986 Birm.

PRICE, Mr Neil 35 Chiltern View, Little Milton, Oxford OX44 7QP — BM BCh 1987 Oxf.; MA Camb. 1988; FRCS Eng. 1992.

PRICE, Mr Nicholas Charles (cons. rooms), Lansdown Lodge, Lansdown Road, Cheltenham GL51 6QL Tel: 01242 522475 Fax: 01242 253816 Email: ncp@l-lodge.fsbusiness.co.uk; Church Farm House, Mill St., Prestbury, Cheltenham GL52 3BG Tel: 01242 244810 Email: nicholas.price@egnhst.swest.nhs.uk — MB BS 1978 Lond.; BSc Lond. 1975; FRCS Eng. 1985; FCOphth 1989; T(Ophth.) 1991. (Westm.) p/t Cons. Ophth. E. Gloucester NHS Trust. Socs: BMA; Roy. Soc. of Med.; SWOS (Hon. Rec). Prev: Sen. Regist. Oxf. Eye Hosp.; Resid. Surg. Off. Moorfields Eye Hosp. Lond.; SHO (Ophth.) W.. Ophth. Hosp. Lond.

***PRICE, Nicholas Henley** Upper Royd House Farm, Black Moor Road, Oxenhope, Keighley BD22 9ST — MB ChB 1986 Leeds.

PRICE, Mr Nicholas James Wolverhampton & Midland Counties Eye Infirmary, Compton Road, Wolverhampton WV3 9QR Tel: 01902 307999 Fax: 01902 645019 — MB BS 1979 Lond.; MA Camb. 1978; FRCS Eng. 1986; FRCOphth 1988. (St. Thos. Hosp. Lond.) Cons. Ophth. Wolverhampton & Midl. Co. Eye Infirm. & Stafford Gen. Hosp.; Wolverhampton Nuffield Hosp. Rowley Hall Hosp. Stafford. Prev: Sen. Regist. Wolverhampton, Stoke, Birm. & Moorfields, Lond.

PRICE, Nicholas Martin Department of Infections Diseases, Imperial College School of Medicine, Hammersmith Hospital, Du Cane Road, London W12 0NN Tel: 020 8383 2069 Fax: 020 8383 3394 Email: n.price@rpms.ac.uk — MB ChB 1988 Birm.; MB ChB Birm. 1991; BSc Birm. 1988; DTM & H Lond. 1995; MRCP (UK) 1994. (Birm.) Med. Research Coun. Fell., Dept. of Infect. Dis., Imperial Coll. Sch. of Med. Hammersmith Hosp. Lond. Socs: Roy. Soc. of Trop. Med. and Hyg. Prev: Regist. Hammersmith Hosp.

PRICE, Nicola Sir William Dunn School of Pathology, University of Oxford, South Parks Road, Oxford OX1 3RE Tel: 01865 275540 Email: nicky.price@path.ox.ac.uk; Flat 5, 42 Nelson St, Oxford OX2 6BD Tel: 01865 514952 — MB BChir 1991 Camb.; MA Camb. 1992, BA 1991. (Camb.) Research Scientist (Path.) Sir William Dun Sch. Path. Oxf. Socs: BMA. Prev: SHO (Ophth.) Arrowe Pk. Hosp. Wirral.

PRICE, Nicolette Sian 239 Botley Road, Burridge, Southampton SO31 1BJ — MB BS 1993 Lond. Trainee GP/SHO (Adult Med.) Roy. Oldham Hosp. Lancs. Prev: SHO (A & E) Roy. Oldham Hosp.

PRICE, Nigel Carsley Poole Road Medical Centre, 7 Poole Road, Bournemouth BH2 5QR; 33 Compton Avenue, Lilliput, Poole BH14 8PU Tel: 01202 701127 — MB BS Lond. 1984; MRCGP 1988; DRCOG 1989. (Roy. Free Hosp. Sch. Med.) Princip. GP Bournmouth. Socs: Bournemouth & Poole Med. Soc. Prev: SHO (O & G) St. Mary's Hosp. I. of Wight; SHO (Paediat.) Chase Farm Hosp. Enfield; SHO (Geriat.) Whipps Cross Hosp. Lond.

PRICE, Mrs Patricia Emily (retired) 17 Bay Court, Cliff Road, Falmouth TR11 4NP Tel: 01326 319260 — MB ChB Ed. 1951; DObst RCOG 1953. Prev: Occupat. Health Solihull MB Counc.

PRICE, Professor Patricia Mary Academic dept of Radiation, Christie Hospital, Uni of Manchester, Manchester M20 4BY Tel: 0161 446 8003 Fax: 0161 446 8111 Email: anne.mason@christie-tr.nwest.nhs.uk — BChir 1981 Camb.; MA Camb. 1982, MD 1991; FRCP Lond. 1995; MRCP (UK) 1984; FRCR 1987. Ralston Paterson Prof & head of Acad. deptof Rudration Oncol. & hon Cons. Clin. oncologist, Christie Hosp.; Head MRC PET Oncol. Gp. & CRC PET Research Gp.; MRC Cyclotron Unit Hammersmith Hosp. Lond. Socs: Pres. elect of Brit. Oncol. Assn. 2000/2002. Prev: Reader (Clin. Oncol.)& Head of Sect. of Cancer Therap., Imp. Coll. Sch Med. & Cons. Hammersmith Hosp ., St. Mary's Hosp. & Ealing Hosp. Lond.; Clin. Scientist & Hon. Sen. Regist. Inst. Cancer Research & Roy. Marsden Hosp. Sutton; Regist. (Radiother.) Roy. Marsden Hosp. Lond.

PRICE, Paul Anthony 33 Gloucester Street, Cirencester GL7 2DJ Tel: 01285 654524 Fax: 01285 654524 — MB BS 1973 Lond.; BSc (Hons. Pharmacol.) Lond. 1970; FRCP Lond. 1993. (University College Hospital Medical School) Cons. Phys. & Endocrinol. Swindon & MarlBoro. Hosps. NHS Trust. Socs: Soc. Endocrinol. (Clin, Comm. Mem.); Diabetes UK. Prev: Sen. Regist. (Med.) St. Geo. Hosp. Lond.; Hon. Lect. (Endocrinol.) St. Bart. Hosp. Lond.; Regist. (Gen. Med.) Univ. Coll. Hosp. Lond.

PRICE, Paul Terence Manor Street Surgery, Manor Street, Ruskington, Sleaford NG34 9EN Tel: 01526 832204 — MB BS 1980 Lond. (Univ. Coll. Hosp.) Prev: Trainee GP Kings Lynn VTS; Ho. Off. (Cardiorespirat. Med.) Pilgrim Hosp. Boston; Ho. Surg. Lincoln Co. Hosp.

PRICE, Pauline Muriel The Dekeyser Group Practice, The Fountain Medical Centre, Little Fountain, Leeds LS27 9EN Tel: 0113 295 1600 Fax: 0113 238 1901; Westwood, Pk Avenue, Morley, Leeds LS27 0JW Tel: 0113 252 8849 — MB ChB 1969 Leeds; MMedSci (Gen. Pract.) Leeds 1985. (Leeds)

PRICE, Peter Harry Woodlands, Preston Road, Lonsonford, Solihull B95 5EY — MB ChB 1962 Birm.

PRICE, Rhys Michael John The Surgery, Parkwood Drive, Warners End, Hemel Hempstead HP1 2LD Tel: 01442 250117 Fax: 01442 256185; 38 Oakwood, Berkhamsted HP4 3NQ Tel: 01442 866871 — MB BChir 1969 Camb.; MB Camb. 1969, BChir 1968; MA Camb. 1969; FRCGP 1984, M 1976. (Camb. & Middlx.) Mem. Edit. Bd. RCGP. Socs: BMA.

PRICE, Richard Alan 587 Lichfield Road, Sutton Coldfield B74 4EG — MB BS 1990 Lond.

PRICE, Richard Dafydd Over Compton House, Waverley Lane, Farnham GU9 8BW — MB BS 1993 Lond.; BSc Lond. 1990; FRCS Eng. 1997. (Char. Cross & Westm.)

PRICE, Richard Edward The Health Centre, Magna Lane, Dalton, Rotherham S65 4HH Tel: 01709 850229; Silverdale, 234 Doncaster Road, Thrybergh, Rotherham S65 4NU — MB BS 1954 Lond. (Univ. Coll. Hosp.)

***PRICE, Richard John** 33 Ripley Road, Willesborough, Ashford TN24 0JP — MB ChB 1998 Aberd.; MB ChB Aberd 1998.

PRICE, Richard Norman Orchard Lodge, Cranleigh Road, Ewhurst, Cranleigh GU6 7RJ — MB BChir 1989 Camb.; MA Camb. 1990, MB BChir 1989; MRCP (UK) 1993.

PRICE, Richard Vaughan Rydal, 375 High Road, Woodford Green IG8 9QJ Tel: 020 8504 0532 Fax: 020 8559 1503; 5 High Road, Buckhurst Hill IG9 5HT Fax: 020 8559 1503 — MB BS 1983 Lond.

PRICE, Robert 43 Crossfield Drive, Worsley, Manchester M28 2QQ — MB ChB 1950 Manch. (Manch.) Clin. Asst. Bridgwater Hosp. Patricroft. Socs: Fell. Manch. Med. Soc.; Manch. Med. Engineer. Soc.

PRICE, Robert Kimberley 12 Fitzjames Avenue, Croydon CR0 5DH — MB BS 1993 Lond.

PRICE, Rodney Bernard Four Gables, 5 Ferry Lane, Hook, Goole DN14 5NZ — Artsexamen 1983 Maastricht.

PRICE, Roger John Anthony Pinfold Medical Practice, The Health Centre, Pinfold Gate, Loughborough LE11 1DQ Tel: 01509 263753 Fax: 01509 264124; 42 Holywell Drive, Loughborough LE11 3JY — MB BS 1975 Lond.; MRCS Eng. LRCP Lond. 1975; MRCGP 1979; DRCOG 1979. Course Organiser Leics. VTS.

PRICE, Rosemary May Blackburn Street Health Centre, Blackburn Street, Radcliffe, Manchester M26 1WS; 2 Ringley Road, Whitefield, Manchester M45 7LB — BM BCh 1967 Oxf.; DFFP 1993.

PRICE, Mr Rupert Francis Western General Hospital, Crewe Road, Edinburgh EH4 2XU Tel: 0131 332 2525; Old Bank House, 18 Hillhead, Bonnyrigg EH19 2JG — MB ChB 1990 Ed.; PhD Ed. 1991, BSc (Hons.) 1985, MB ChB 1990; FRCS Ed. 1995. SHO (Surg.) SE Scotl. Train. Scheme.

PRICE, Russell John 9 Beaufort Close, Oadby, Leicester LE2 4TP — MB BS 1983 Queensland.

PRICE, Sandra Elizabeth — BM 1985 Soton. Princip. in Gen. Pract. - Weymouth; Family Plann. Doctor Dorchester.

PRICE, Sarah Ann (retired) New House Surgery, 142A South Street, Dorking RH4 2QR Tel: 01306 881313 Fax: 01306 877305 — MB BS Lond. 1964; MRCS Eng. LRCP Lond. 1964. Prev: Clin. Med. Off. E. Surrey AHA.

PRICE, Sarah Margaret Holmside Medical Group, 142 Armstrong Road, Benwell, Newcastle upon Tyne NE4 8QB Tel: 0191 273 4009 Fax: 0191 273 2745; 6 Saxilby Drive, Gosforth, Newcastle upon Tyne NE3 5LS Tel: 0191 284 0606 — MB BS 1984 Newc.; MRCGP 1988; DRCOG 1986. GP Newc. Prev: SHO (Med.) Hexham Gen. Hosp.; SHO (Obst.) Newc. Gen. Hosp.; Trainee GP N.d. VTS.

PRICE, Sarah Penelope Top Floor Flat, 106 Hampton Road, Bristol BS6 6JD — MB ChB 1992 Birm.

PRICE, Scott Richmond Flat 8, Woodlands Court, Woodlands Road, Rouken Glen, Glasgow G46 7SA Tel: 0141 638 6466 — MB ChB 1990 Manch.; BSc St. And. 1987; FRCA 1995. Regist. Rotat. (Anaesth.) Glas. Roy. Infirm. Univ. NHS Trust. Socs: Assn. Anaesth.; BMA; Glas. & W. Scot. Soc. Anaesth. Prev: SHO Rotat. (Anaesth.) W. Glas. Hosps. Univ. NHS Trust; SHO Rotat. (Anaesth.) Ayrsh.; SHO (Gen. Surg.) Kirkcaldy.

PRICE, Septimus Harold Mervyn White Gates, 66 The Drive, Harefield Place, Uxbridge UB10 8AQ Tel: 01895 33782 — MB BS 1947 Lond.; MRCS Eng. LRCP Lond. 1939; DObst RCOG 1948. (Westm.) Prev: Ho. Surg. & Cas. Off. Connaught Hosp. Walthamstow; Ho. Phys. Staines EMS Hosp.

PRICE, Sian Elen 69 Ridding Close, Southampton SO15 5PN; 69 Ridding Close, Shirley, Southampton SO15 5PN — MB BS 1988 Lond.; BSc (Hons.) Lond. 1985, MB BS 1988; MRCP (UK) 1991; AKC 1985.

PRICE, Simon David St Julians Medical Centre, 13A Stafford Road, Newport NP19 7DQ Tel: 01633 251304 Fax: 01633 221977; 11 Alwyn Close, Rogerstone, Newport NP10 9HW Tel: 01633 893649 — MB BCh 1980 Wales; MB BCh Wales. 1980; MRCGP 1986; Cert. Family Plann. JCC 1983; DRCOG 1982. Socs: BMA.

PRICE, Stanley Adrian Clevedon, 9 Park Drive, Heaton, Bradford BD9 4DP Tel: 01274 47527 — MB ChB 1951 Leeds; MRCGP 1963. (Leeds) Clin. Asst. (Psychiat.) Storthes Hall Hosp. Kirkburton; Med. Dir. Sherrington Ho. Nurs. Home Bradford. Socs: Fell. Roy. Soc. Med.; FRSH. Prev: Ho. Surg. Gen. Infirm. Leeds; Ho. Phys. Roy. Infirm. Bradford; Flight Lt. (Surg. Div.) RAF Hosp. Ely.

PRICE, Mr Stephen John 41 Rayfield, Epping CM16 5AD Tel: 01992 576864 Email: stephenjprice@hotmail.com — MB BS 1994 Lond.; BSc (Hons.) Lond. 1991; FRCS Eng. 1998. (St. Barts. Hosp. Med. Coll.) RCS Res. Fell. Univ. Dept. of Neurosurg. Addenbrooke's Hosp. Prev: Specialist Regist. (Neurosurg.) OldCh. Hosp. Romford; SHO Neurosurg. Addenbrookes; SHO Neurosurg. Qu. Med. Centre Nottm.

PRICE, Stephen Rhys Exmouth Health Centre, Claremont Grove, Exmouth EX8 2JF Tel: 01395 273001 Fax: 01395 273771 — MB ChB 1972 Bristol; BSc (Hons., Biochem.) Bristol 1969, MB ChB 1972; MRCGP 1982; DRCOG 1977; DA Eng. 1978.

PRICE, Stephen Rowland Department of Clinical Biochemistry, Wycombe General Hospital, High Wycombe HP11 2TT Tel: 01494 425244 Fax: 01494 425220 Email:

100265.3011@compuserve.com; Chiltern Retreat, Queens Road, Princes Risborough HP27 0JR Tel: 01844 342018 — MB ChB 1979 Birm.; MRCPath 1988; FRCPath 1998. (Birmingham) Cons. Chem. Path. Wycombe Gen. Hosp. Prev: Sen. Regist. (Chem. PAth.) Oxf. HA.; Regist. (Chem. Path.) W. Midl. RHA.

PRICE, Stephen Vincent, Flight Lt. RAF Med. Br. (retired) West Street Surgery, 89 West St., Dunstable LU6 1SF Tel: 01582 602082 Fax: 01582 475766 — MB BS 1990 Lond.; MRCGP 1996; DRCOG 1995; DFFP 1995; T(GP) 1995; DCCH RCP Ed. 1993; Cert. Av. Med. 1991. GP W. St. Surg. Dunstable. Prev: Family Care Med. Serv. Brisband Australia.

PRICE, Susan Margaret Child Health Directorate, Northampton General Hospital NHS Trust, Cliftonville, Northampton NN1 5BD Tel: 01604 544638 Fax: 01604 545988 Email: suep@chngh.denom.co.uk; The Old Bake House, 6 Corby Road, Cottingham, Market Harborough LE16 8XH — MB ChB 1982 Manch.; MRCP (UK) 1985; Dip Clin Genetics 1992. Cons. (Clin. Genetics) N.ampton Gen. Hosp. NHS Trust. Socs: Brit Soc of Human Genetics. Prev: Regist. & Sen. Regist. (Clin. Genetics) Leicester Roy. Infirm.; Regist. (Paediat.) Roy. Infirm. Leicester.

PRICE, Susan Mary Carlisle House Surgery, 53 Lagland Street, Poole Tel: 01202 672534; 169 Albian Way, Verwood BH31 7LT — MB ChB 1992 Birm; DCH RCP Lond. 1996; DRCOG 1994. GP Retainer, Dorset.

PRICE, Susanna 7 Canada Rise, Market Lavington, Devizes SN10 4AD — MB BS 1990 Lond.

PRICE, Sydney Lionel The Surgery, 75 Gloucester Place, London W1H 3PF Tel: 020 7935 4153; F1, 133-135 Park Road, The Beverley, London NW8 7JB Tel: 020 7586 2759 — MB BS 1956 Lond.; MRCS Eng. LRCP Lond. 1956. (King's Coll. Hosp.) Socs: Brit. Assn. Manip. Med.; Assoc. Mem. Brit. Assn. Rheum. & Rehabil. Prev: Clin. Asst. (Physical Med.) Guy's Hosp. Lond.; Ho. Phys. & Ho. Surg. Mayday Hosp. Croydon.

PRICE, Thomas Cannock Chase Hospital, Brunswick Road, Cannock WS11 2XY Tel: 01543 576451 Fax: 01543 576455 Email: tom.price@msgh-tr.wimds.nhs.uk; Fielden House, Stowe Lane, Stowe-by-Chartley, Stafford ST18 0NA Tel: 01889 270962 Fax: 01889 271588 Email: thomas.price@btinternet.com — BM BCh 1973 Oxf.; MA, BM BCh Oxf. 1973; FRCP Lond. 1992; MRCP (UK) 1977. (Univ. Coll. Hosp.) Cons. Rheum. Mid. Staffs. Hosps. Prev: Sen. Regist. Middlx. Hosp., N.wick Pk. Hosp. & Roy. Nat. Orthop. Hosp. Lond.

***PRICE, Thomas Matthew Dodds** 57 Cambridge Road, London SW20 0PX — MB BS 1996 Lond.

PRICE, Thomas Michael Lloyd (retired) Hobbs Cottage, Piltdown, Uckfield TN22 3XB Tel: 01825 722028 — MRCS Eng. LRCP Lond. 1939; MD Lond. 1948, MB BS 1939; FRCP Lond. 1963, M 1947. Prev: Cons. Phys. Lewisham Hosp. & St. Nicholas' Hosp. Plumstead.

PRICE, Thomas Richard 5 North Several, Orchard Drive, London SE3 0QR — MB BS 1976 Lond.; PhD Lond. 1974, BSc 1968, MB BS 1976; MRCP (UK) 1979.

PRICE, Thomas Richard Hughes Jesmond Clinic, 48 Osborne Road, Jesmond, Newcastle upon Tyne NE2 2AL Tel: 0191 281 4060 Fax: 0191 281 0231; 32 Waterbury Road, Brunton Park, Newcastle upon Tyne NE3 5AJ Tel: 0191 217 0365 — MB BS Nottm. 1986; BMedSci Nottm. 1984; MRCGP 1992; DCH RCP Lond. 1990. Lect. (Gen. Pract.) Univ. Newc. u. Tyne. Prev: Trainee GP VTS.

PRICE, Thomas Waldron Beacon Surgery, Beacon Road, Crowborough TN6 1AF Tel: 01892 652233 Fax: 01892 668840; Redfold, Rannoch Road, Crowborough TN6 1RB Tel: 01892 652233 — MB BS 1965 Lond.; MRCS Eng. 1965, LRCP Lond. 1966; DObst RCOG 1973; DA Eng. 1971. (Middlx.) Prev: Ho. Phys. Middlx. Hosp.; Ho. Surg. Centr. Middlx. Hosp.

PRICE, Thomas Wentworth (retired) Long Acre, Yawl Uplyme, Lyme Regis DT7 3XA Tel: 01297 443214 — BM BCh 1945 Oxf.; BA, BM BCh Oxf. 1945. Prev: GP S.sea.

PRICE, Vanessa Hinchingbrooke Hospital, Hinchingbrooke Park, Huntingdon PE29 6NT Tel: 01480 416416; 42 Hinton Way, Great Shelford, Cambridge CB2 5BB — MB BS 1967 Lond.; FFA RCS Eng. 1973; DA Eng. 1969. (Middlx.) p/t Lead Cons. Acute Pain Hinchingbrooke Hosp. Huntingdon. Socs: Assn. Anaesths. Gt. Brit. & Irel.; Pain Soc. (uk chapter). Prev: Sen. Regist. (Anaesth.) Addenbrookes Hosp. Camb.; Sen. Regist. (Anaesth.) Roy. Free Hosp. Lond.; Regist. (Anaesth.) Middlx. Hosp. Lond.

PRICE

PRICE, Victoria Jane — MB ChB 1998 Manch.; DRCOG 2001; MB ChB Manch 1998. (Manchester) GP Regist., Alderley Edge. Prev: SHO Obs & Gynae. Arrowe Pk. Hosp. Wirral; SHO Paediat. Arrowe Pk. Hosp. Wirral; SHO Medine, Arrowe Pk. Hosp. Wirral.

***PRICE, Victoria Juliette** 62 Llanrhos Road, Penrhyn Bay, Llandudno LL30 3HY — MB ChB 1998 Ed.; MB ChB Ed 1998.

PRICE, Walter John (retired) Tor Cragg, Slade Lane, Kiln Bank, Riddlesden, Keighley BD20 5DT — MB ChB 1954 Leeds; FFA RCS Eng. 1965. Prev: Cons. Anaesth. Bradford Trust Hosps.

PRICE, Walter Rostron Regis Medical Centre, Darby Street, Rowley Regis, Warley B65 0BA Tel: 0121 559 3957 Fax: 0121 502 9117; 31 Whitehall Road, Pedmore, Stourbridge DY8 2JT Tel: 01384 394544 — MB ChB 1974 Birm.; MB ChB (Hons.) Birm. 1974; PhD Liverp. 1965, BSc (Hons.) 1962; MRCGP 1980; DRCOG 1977; Cert. Family Plann. JCC 1978. Hosp. Pract. (Gastroenterol.) Russells Hall Hosp. Dudley. Prev: Clin. Asst. (Gastroenterol.) Wordsley Hosp. Stourbridge & Russells Hall Hosp. Dudley.

PRICE, William Henry (retired) 4 Strathalmond Road, Barnton, Edinburgh EH4 8AD Tel: 0131 339 2129 Fax: 0131 476 3432 Email: drwhprice@aol.com — MB BCh 1955 Wales; BSc Wales 1952; FRCP Ed. 1972, M 1962. Hon. Fell. Molecular & Clin. Med. Univ. Edin. Prev: Hon. Cons Phys. & Clin. Dir. Med. Serv. W.. Gen. Hosp. Edin.

PRICE, William James Pembroke Mere Surgery, Dark Lane, Mere, Warminster BA12 6DT Tel: 01747 860001 Fax: 01747 860119; Apple Tree Cottage, Huntingford, Gillingham SP8 5QQ Tel: 01747 861233 — MB BS 1979 Lond.; MRCP (UK) 1982; MRCGP 1987. Clin. Asst. Diabetic Clinic Salisbury Dist. Hosp. Prev: Regist. Rotat. (Med.) Salisbury & Soton.; SHO (Paediat.) St. Richard's Hosp. Chichester; SHO Rotat. (Med.) Bath.

PRICE-DAVIES, Rona (retired) Sunnyside Cottage, Westra, Dinas Powys — BSc., M.B., B.Ch. Wales 1936. Prev: Mem. Chairm. Med. Bd. DHSS.

PRICE-FORBES, Alec Nicholas 109 West Pottergate, Norwich NR2 4BW; Cripps Medical Centre, Northampton General Hospital, Northampton NN1 5BD Tel: 01604 634700 — MB ChB 1996 Leic. (Leicester) SHO Rotat. (Med.) N.ampton.

PRICE-JONES, Jonathan Christian Oxford Street Surgery, Oxford Street, Aberaeron SA46 0JB Tel: 01545 570273 Fax: 01545 571625 — MB BCh 1985 Wales.

PRICE-THOMAS, Simon Phillip, Maj. RAMC Broadgate Frm., Cookbury, Holsworthy EX22 7YG; 39 Blenheim Park, Aldershot GU11 2HS Tel: 01252 324270 — MB ChB 1988 Aberd.; MRCGP 1995; DRCOG 1994. GP Aldershot.

PRICE WILLIAMS, Deborah Anne 33 St Margaret's Road, Ruislip HA4 7NX; The Child Development Centre, The Hillingdon Hospital, Pield Heath Road, Uxbridge UB8 3NN Tel: 01895 279395 Fax: 01895 279299 — MB BCh 1981 Wales; MSc Warwick 1997; Cert. Family Plann. JCC 1988. Clin. Med. Off. (Child Health) Hillingdon HA.; Med. Adviser to Lond. Boro. of Hillingdon. Socs: Assoc. Mem. RCPCH. Prev: Clin. Med. Off. (Child Health) Richmond & Roehampton HA; Ho. Phys. (Med./Geriat./Cardiol.) Cardiff Roy. Infirm. & Univ. Hosp. Wales Cardiff; Ho. Surg. (Surg.) Mt. Vernon Hosp. N.wood Middlx.

PRICE-WILLIAMS, Ruth Dorothy 3 Hawtrey Drive, Ruislip HA4 8QW Tel: 01895 673722 — MB ChB 1954 Bristol. (Bristol) Med. Off. C.D.T. Fountains Mill, Uxbridge. Prev: Div. Surg. St. John's Ambul.; GP Fell. HIV Med. Hillingdon HA; Vis. Med. Off. Hillingdon.

PRICHARD, Mr Andrew John Norman Head & Neck Centre, Royal Shrewsbury Hospital, Mytton Oak Road, Shrewsbury SY3 8AX — MB BS 1983 Lond.; FRCS Ed. 1989; Intercollegiate FRCS (ORL) 1992. (UCH) Cons. (Otolaryngol.) Shrewsbury. Prev: Sen. Regist. (Otolaryngol.) Freeman Hosp. Newc.; Regist. (Otolaryng.) Leic. Roy. Infirm.; SHO (Otolaryng.) Roy. Surrey Co. Hosp. Guildford.

PRICHARD, Professor Brian Norman Christopher, CBE Clinical Pharmacology Centre, University College, 5 University St., London WC1E 6JJ Tel: 020 7209 6205 Fax: 020 7209 6212; 24 Lyford Road, Wandsworth Common, London SW18 3LG Tel: 020 8870 3066 — MB BS 1958 Lond.; FACC 1977; MSc Lond. 1954, BSc 1953; FRCP Lond. 1977, M 1966; MRCS Eng. LRCP Lond. 1957; FESC 1996; FFPM RCP (UK) 1989. (St. Geo.) Prof. Clin. Pharmacol. Univ. Coll. & Middlx. Sch. Med.; Cons. Phys. Univ. Coll. Hosp. Lond. Socs: Assn. Phys.; Internat. Soc. Hypertens.; Brit. Pharm. Soc. Prev: Reader (Clin. Pharmacol.) & Sen. Lect. (Med.) Univ. Coll. Hosp. Med. Sch. Lond.; Regist. (Med.) St. Geo. Hosp. Lond.

PRICHARD, David Robert Gwynedd Hospital NHS Trust, Ysbyty Gwynedd, Bangor LL57 2PW; Hillside, Chwarel Goch, Tregarth, Bangor LL57 4NU — MB ChB 1973 Ed.; FRCP Lond. 1994; MRCP (UK) 1976; Dip. Health Care Law 1997. Cons. Phys. Med. for Elderly Ysbyty Gwynedd Bangor. Prev: Sen. Regist. (Geriat.) Clatterbridge Hosp. Bebington; Research Regist. Sheff. AHA (T); Regist. (Med.) N.. Gen. Hosp. Sheff.

PRICHARD, Jonathan Edgar Birchgrove Surgery, 104 Caerphilly Road, Cardiff CF14 4AG Tel: 029 2052 2344 Fax: 029 2052 2487; 22 Llwyd Coed, Rhiwbina, Cardiff CF14 7TT — MB BCh 1981 Wales; MRCGP 1993; DRCOG 1983.

PRICHARD, Owain Merfyn Tristan, Penrhyndeudraeth LL48 6AY Tel: 01766 77304 — MB ChB 1936 Ed. (Univ. Ed.) Med. Off. Bron-y-Garth Chronic Sick Hosp. Penrhyndeudraeth. Prev: Ho. Phys. Roy. United Hosp. Bath; Ho. Surg. P.ss Beatrice Hosp. Lond.; Sen. Ho. Surg. Caern. & Anglesey Infirm. Bangor.

PRICKETT, Frances Mary Emma Room 2 Staff Corridor, Llandough Hospital, Penlan Road, Llandough, Penarth CF64 1XX — MB ChB 1988 Leic.; DCH RCP Lond. 1991. Prev: Trainee GP Oxf. VTS; Ho. Off. (Med.) P'boro; Ho. Off. (Gyn. & Surg.) Leicester.

PRIDDLE, Deborah Jane Drumchapel Health Centre, 80/90 Kinfauns Drive, Glasgow G15 7TS Tel: 0141 211 6110; 3 Sanda Street, North Kelvinside, Glasgow G20 8PU Tel: 0141 946 2933 — MB ChB 1981 Glas. Socs: Assoc. Mem. Roy. Coll. Gen. Pract.

PRIDDLE, Evelyn Susan 99 Westmoreland Road, Bromley BR2 0TQ Tel: 020 8464 8040 — BM BCh 1961 Oxf.; MFFP 1993; DCH Eng. 1965. (St. Bart.) Asst. Dir. (Community Med. Servs.) Ravensbourne NHS Trust. Socs: Fac. Comm. Health.

PRIDDY, Alvan Robert Adrian Northwick Park Hospital, Department of Obstetrics & Gynaecology, Watford Road, Harrow HA1 3UJ Tel: 020 8864 3419 Fax: 020 8869 2864 — MB ChB 1983 Manch.; MD Manch. 1992; MRCOG 1989. Cons. O & G N.wick Pk. Hosp. Socs: Brit. Fertil. Soc.; Brit. Soc. Gyn. Endoscopy; BMA. Prev: Sen. Regist. (O & G) Hammersmith Hosp. & N.wick Pk. Hosp. Lond.; Regist. (O & G) Roy. Oldham Hosp., St. Mary's Hosp. Manch & Fairfield Gen. Hosp. Bury; Research Fell. (O & G) Withington Hosp. Manch.

PRIDDY, Ronald Joseph 17 Butterworth Drive, Westwood Heath, Coventry CV4 8JL — MB BS 1962 Lond.; DTM & H RCP Lond. 1969; LMSSA Lond. 1958. (Lond. Hosp.) Prev: Maj. RAMC; Ho. Surg. Mile End Hosp. Lond.; Ho. Phys. St. Albans City Hosp.

PRIDE, Andrew John Tel: 01442 863119/864448 Fax: 01442 879909 — MB BS 1976 Lond.; MRCS Eng. LRCP Lond. 1976; DRCOG 1980. (Roy. Free) GP Berkhamstead. Prev: Trainee GP/SHO (Paediat.) Qu. Mary's Hosp. Lond. VTS; SHO (Obst.) Profess. Unit O & G W.m. Hosp. Lond.; SHO (Psychiat.) W.m. Hosp. Lond.

PRIDE, Neil Blair 49 Ranelagh Road, London W5 5RP Tel: 020 8567 2705 Fax: 020 8566 4075 Email: m.pride@ic.ac.uk; 49 Ranelagh Road, London W5 5RP Tel: 020 8567 2705 Fax: 020 8566 4075 — MB BChir Camb. 1956; MD Camb. 1968; FRCP Lond. 1974, M 1959. (Camb. & St. Mary's) Prof. Emerit. Respirat. Med. Imperial Coll. Sch. Med.

PRIDEAUX, Christopher Patrick 19 Powys Avenue, Oadby, Leicester LE2 2DQ — MB BS 1977 Lond. (Westm.)

PRIDEAUX, Cyril Frank Gifford 9 Parklands Road, Chichester PO19 3DP Tel: 01243 531528 — MB BS 1950 Lond.; MRCS Eng. LRCP Lond. 1944; FFA RCS Eng. 1954; DA Eng. 1949. (St. Thos.) Emerit. Cons. Anaesth. Chichester Health Dist. Prev: Sen. Cons. Anaesth. Chichester & Graylingwell Hosp. Gp. & King Edwd. VII Hosp. Midhurst; Sen. Regist. (Anaesth.) Univ. Coll. Hosp.

***PRIDGEON, Jennie Madeline** 68 Spur Hill Avenue, Poole BH14 9PL — MB ChB 1994 Dundee.

PRIDIE, Angus Kenneth Anaesthetic Department, Freeman Hospital, High Heaton, Newcastle upon Tyne NE7 7DN Tel: 0191 284 3111; 12 Queen's Gardens, Benton, Newcastle upon Tyne NE12 9PL Tel: 0191 266 2440 Email: morgapridi@aol.com — MB ChB Bristol 1968; FFA RCS Eng. 1973; DObst RCOG 1970; DA Eng. 1971. Cons. (Anaesth.) Freeman Hosp. Newc. Prev: Sen. Regist. Anaesth. Newc. Univ. Hosp. Gp.

PRIDIE, Joanna Mary (retired) 58 St John's Road, Clifton, Bristol BS8 2HG — MRCS Eng. LRCP Lond. 1931. Prev: Ho. Surg. King's Coll. Hosp.

*PRIDMORE, Peter John Wayside, Ratcliffe-Upon-Soar, Nottingham NG11 5 — MB BCh 1994 Wales.

PRIEST, Alison Vanessa 12 Linksway, Gatley, Cheadle SK8 4LB Tel: 0161 428 6160 — MB ChB 1992 Bristol; DRCOG 1996. (Bristol) SHO (Surg.) ChristCh. Hosp., NZ. Prev: SHO Bristol Matern. Hosp.; SHO (Psychiat.) S.mead Hosp. Bristol; SHO (Paediat.) Tameside Hosp. Manch.

PRIEST, Martin Stuart The Surgery, Trekenning Road, St Columb Major, St Columb TR9 6AA Tel: 01637 880359; Little Tregustick, Withiel, Bodmin PL30 5NG Tel: 01208 815948 — BM BS 1987 Nottm.; MRCP (UK) 1991; MRCGP 1995; DRCOG 1993. (Nottm.) Princip.

PRIEST, Matthew 89 Stagborough Way, Stourport-on-Severn DY13 8TX — MB ChB 1993 Birm.

*PRIEST, Oliver Hartwell Melrose, 3 Argyle Rd, Whitby YO21 3HS — MB ChB 1996 Manch.

PRIEST, Mrs Pamela (retired) Old Manor Farmhouse, Hewish, Crewkerne TA18 8QT — MRCS Eng. LRCP Lond. 1951; DPM Durham. 1960.

PRIEST, Peter James 7 Kinlock Drive, Heaton, Bolton BL1 4LZ — MB ChB 1986 Sheff.; MRCGP 1990; DRCOG 1990.

PRIEST, Professor Robert George 29 Old Slade Lane, Richings Park, Iver SL0 9DY Tel: 01753 653178 — MB BS Lond. 1956; MD Lond. 1970; FRCP Ed. 1974, M 1964; FRCPsych 1974, M 1971; T(Psych) 1991; DPM Eng. 1963. (Univ. Coll. Hosp.) Prof. Emerit. Univ. Lond.; Prof. Psychiat. Imperial Coll. Sch. Med. St. Mary's Hosp. Socs: Fell. Roy. Coll. Psychiat.; Hon. Corr. Fell. Amer. Psychiat. Assn.; Hon. Corr. Fell. Assn. Francaise de Psychiatrie. Prev: Regist. Roy. Coll. Psychiat.; Sen. Lect. St. Geo. Hosp. Med. Sch. Lond.; Vis. Lect. Univ. Chicago.

PRIEST, Timothy David INPUT Pain Management Unit, St. Thomas's Hospital, London SE1 7EH Tel: 020 7922 8107 Fax: 020 7922 8229; 34 Thames Drive, Ruislip HA4 7AY Tel: 01895 633848 Email: tpriest@globalnet.co.uk — MB BS 1990 Lond.; PhD Glas. 1983; MA Oxf. 1984; FRCA 1995. (Univ. Coll. & Middlx. Hosp.) Clin. Fell. (Pain Managem.) St. Thomas's Hosp. Lond. Socs: Fell. Roy. Coll. Of Anaesth.; The Pain Soc.; Int. Assn. Study of Pain. Prev: Specialist Regist. Rotat. (Anaesth.) St. Mary's Hosp. Lond.

PRIESTLEY, Anne Catherine Crawcrook Surgery, Crawcrook, Ryton NE40 4TZ; Craigmont, Barlow, Blaydon-on-Tyne NE21 6JT — MB BS 1972 Newc.; MRCP (UK) 1975. Prev: Regist. (Gen. Med.) Newc. Gen. Hosp.; SHO (Gen. Med.) Newc. Gen. Hosp.; Ho. Surg. Hexham Gen. Hosp.

PRIESTLEY, Betty Leila (retired) 3A Eastbury Avenue, Northwood HA6 3LB Tel: 01923 840889 — MB BS 1958 Lond.; FRCP Lond. 1977, M 1961; MRCS Eng. LRCP Lond. 1958; FRCPCH 1997; DCH Eng. 1963. Hon. Cons. Paediat. Sheff. Childrs. Hosp. Prev: Cons. Paediat. Sheff. Childr. Hosp., Chesterfield Roy. & Scarsdale Hosps. & N.wick Pk. Hosp. Harrow.

PRIESTLEY, Cecilia Juliette Fiona Department of Genitourinary Medicine, Weymouth Community Hospital, Melcombe Avenue, Weymouth DT4 7TB Tel: 01305 762682 Fax: 01305 762695 Email: cecilia.priestley@dorch.wdgh-tr.swest.nhs.uk — MB ChB 1985 Sheff.; MRCP (UK) 1990. Cons. (Genitour. Med.) W. Dorset Gen. Hosps. NHS Trust Weymouth. Socs: MSSVD; AGUM. Prev: Sen. Regist. (Genitourin. Med.) Roy. Hallamsh. Hosp. Sheff.; Regist. (Genitourin. Med.) Stoke-on-Trent; Regist. (Gen. Med.) Macclesfield Dist. Gen. Hosp. & Walton Hosp. Liverp.

PRIESTLEY, Colin Thomas Penketh Health Centre, Honiton Way, Penketh, Warrington WA5 2EY Tel: 01925 725644 Fax: 01925 791017 — MB ChB 1974 Ed.

PRIESTLEY, Edward (retired) 195 Highfield Road, South Shore, Blackpool FY4 3NS — MB ChB Manch. 1946.

PRIESTLEY, George Shearer 10 Dryden Avenue, Cheadle SK8 2AW Tel: 0161 491 3720 Fax: 0870 055 9647 Email: george@maddys.demon.co.uk — MB ChB 1985 Manch.; MRCP (UK) 1992; FRCA 1993; DA (UK) 1992. (Manch.) Cons. (Int. Care & Anaesth.) York Dist. Hosp. Socs: Intens. Care Soc. & Assn. Anaesth.; Europ. Soc. of Intens. Care Med. Prev: Specialist Regist. (Anaesth.) Soton. Gen. Hosp.

PRIESTLEY, Hugh Stephen Abbotsbury Road Surgery, 24 Abbotsbury Road, Weymouth DT4 0AE Tel: 01305 786257 — MB BS 1983 Lond. (Westminster)

PRIESTLEY, Kim Anita Solihull Hospital, Lode Lane, Solihull B91 2JL Tel: 0121 711 4455 — MB ChB 1982 Leic.; MRCP (UK) 1985. Cons. Phys. (Cardiol.) Solihull Hosp. W. Midl.

PRIESTLEY, Nicholas (retired) 111 Burges Road, Thorpe Bay, Southend-on-Sea SS1 3JL Tel: 01702 588585 — MB ChB Leeds 1963.

PRIESTLEY, Stuart Edward 4D Lake Road N., Fairhaven, Lytham St Annes FY8 1AG — MB ChB 1976 Manch.; MRCP (UK) 1979.

PRIESTLEY, Veronica Ruth The Grove Medical Centre, Church Road, Egham TW20 9QJ Tel: 01784 433159 Fax: 01784 477208; 46 Northcroft Road, Englefield Green, Egham TW20 0EA — MB ChB 1984 Sheff.; MRCGP 1994.

PRIESTMAN, Geoffrey Michael (retired) Roseland, Walberton Green, Arundel BN18 0AT Tel: 01243 543266 — MB ChB 1951 Ed.; MFCM 1974; DPH Leeds 1967; MRCGP 1961. Prev: Med. Adviser UK Sangmed Team Jeddah, Saudi Arabia.

PRIESTMAN, John Frederick Walter Health Services Centre, Shelley Lane, Kirkburton, Huddersfield HD8 0SJ Tel: 01484 602040 Fax: 01484 602012; 18 Cleveland Way, Shelley, Huddersfield HD8 8NQ Email: 100717.3066@compuserve.com — MB ChB 1978 Leeds; MRCGP 1982. (Leeds) Trainer Huddersfield VTS; Examg. Med. Pract. for Benefits Agency. Socs: BMA; Hudds. Med. Soc.; Brit. Med. & Dent. Hypn. Soc. Prev: Trainee GP Huddersfield VTS; Ho. Phys. Leeds Gen. Infirm.; Ho. Surg. Clayton Hosp. Wakefield.

PRIESTMAN, Kathleen Gordon (retired) 49 Pleasant View Road, Crowborough TN6 2UU Tel: 01892 653579 — MRCS Eng. LRCP Lond. 1934; Hon. FFHom 1974. Prev: Hon. Asst. Phys. Dis. Childr. Lond. Homoeop. Hosp.

PRIESTMAN, L Frances Gordon, OBE (retired) Sandalls, Southview Road, Crowborough TN6 1HG Tel: 01892 662802 Fax: 01892 662802 — MB BS Lond. 1936; MRCS Eng. LRCP Lond. 1936.

PRIESTMAN, Samuel (retired) 5 Church Street, Woolley, Bath BA1 8AS Tel: 01225 858075 Email: sampriestman@onetel.net.uk — MB BChir Camb. 1955; MA MB Camb. 1956; DObst RCOG 1957; MRCGP 1966. Prev: Princip. GP Bath.

*PRIESTMAN, William Steven 29 Thurlow Road, Leicester LE2 1YE — MB ChB 1998 Leic.; MB ChB Leic 1998.

PRIGG, Nicholas James West Suffolk Hosp, Bury St Edmunds IP33 2QT; 12 Wheelers, Great Shelford, Cambridge CB2 5UD Tel: 01223 473491 Fax: 01223 473492 Email: nicholas.prigg@lineone.net — MB ChB 1996 Birm.; ChB Birm. 1996. (Birm.) SHO (Paediat.).

PRIGMORE, Gerrard Timothy Camarthen Road Health Centre, Carmarthen Road, Cross Hands, Llanelli SA14 6SU Tel: 01269 831091 — MB BCh 1991 Wales.

PRIMAVESI, John Francis Parkstone Health Centre, Mansfield Road, Poole BH14 0DJ Tel: 01202 741370 Fax: 01202 730952; 40 Kings Avenue, Parkstone, Poole BH4 9QQ Tel: 01202 734206 — MB BS 1978 Lond.; DLO RCS Eng. 1984.

PRIMAVESI, Richard John Paediatric Consulting Suite, 234 Great Portland St., London W1W 5QT Tel: 020 7390 8355 Fax: 020 7390 8356 Email: primadoc@easynet.co.uk; Marlefield, Shalden Green Road, Shalden, Alton GU34 4DT — MB BS 1974 Lond.; MRCP (UK) 1980; FRCP (1997); FRCP (CH) 1998. (Roy. Lond.) Cons. Paediat. The Portland Hosp. Gt. Portland St. Lond. Socs: Worshipful Soc. of Apoth.; Treas. Livery Comm.; Roy. Soc. Med. Prev: Cons. Paediat. N. Hants. Hosp. Basingstoke.

PRIMAVESI, Sarah Margaret Mitchell Road Surgery, 9 Mitchell Road, Canferd Heath, Poole BH17 8UE Tel: 01202 672474 Fax: 01202 660926 — MB BS 1978 Lond.; MRCS Eng. LRCP Lond. 1978; DRCOG 1981. p/t Gen. Practitioner.

PRIME, Alison Judith 1E Urquhart Street, Aberdeen AB24 5PL Tel: 01224 635826 — MB ChB 1993 Aberd.

PRIME, Carl Francis 35 Steel Road, Birmingham B31 2RQ — MB 1976 Camb.; BChir 1975.

PRIME, Katarina Petia B-01 Du Cane Court, Balham High Rd, London SW17 7JD — MB ChB 1996 Manch.; BSc (Hons. Med. Microbiol.) Manch. 1993. (Manch.) SHO GU Med., Mortimer Market Centre, ULL. Prev: SHO (Med.) N.middlx. Hosp. Sterling Way Edmunton Lond.; PRHO Surg. Mayday Hosp. Thornton Heath; PRHO Med./Infec. Dis. N. Manch. Gen. Hosp.

PRIMHAK, Robert Anthony Sheffield Children's Hospital, Western Bank, Sheffield S10 2TH Tel: 0114 276 1111 Fax: 0114 275 5364

PRIMROSE

Email: r.a.primhak@sheffield.ac.uk; 45 Whiteley Wood Road, Sheffield S11 7FF — MD 1986 Sheff.; MB BS Lond. 1975; FRCP Lond. 1993; MRCP (UK) 1980; FRCPCH (UK) 1997. (King's Coll. Hosp.) Sen. Lect. (Paediat.) Univ. Sheff. Socs: Eur. Respirat. Soc.; Brit. Thorac. Soc. Prev: Sen. Lect. (Child Health) Univ., Papua New Guinea.

PRIMROSE, David Alexander Anderson (retired) 26 Garngaber Avenue, Lenzie, Glasgow G66 4LL Tel: 0141 776 1600 — MB ChB 1951 Glas.; MD Glas. 1966; FRCP Glas. 1978, M 1975; FRCPsych 1974, M 1971; MRCGP 1958. Hon. Sec. Internat. Assn. Scientif. Study Ment. Defic. Prev: Phys. Supt. Roy. Scott. Nat. Hosp. Larbert.

PRIMROSE, Evangelene Daphne S&E Belfast H+SS Trust, Holywood Arches Health Centre, Westminster Avenue North, Belfast BT4 1QQ Tel: 01232 563318 Fax: 01232 563327 Email: daphne.primrose@sebt.n-i.nhs.uk; 23 Station Road, Craigavad, Holywood BT18 0BP — MB BCh BAO Belf. 1982; MD Belf. 1992; MRCP (UK) 1985. Cons. (Paediat.) S&E Belf. H+SS Trust, Belf.; Cons. (Paediat.) Ulster Comm. & Hosps. Trust, Belf. Socs: Brit. Paediat. Assn.; BACCH; UPS.

PRIMROSE, Mr John Neil University Surgical Unit, Level F, Centre Block, Southampton General Hospital, Southampton SO16 6YD Tel: 02380 796144 — MB ChB 1977 Glas.; MB ChB (Hons.) Glas. 1977; MD Glas. 1984; FRCS Glas. 1981. Prof. & Cons. Surg. Soton. Gen. Hosp. Prev: Cons. Surg. & Sen. Lect. St. Jas. Hosp. Leeds; Lect. & Sen. Regist. (Surg.) Leeds Gen. Infirm.; Regist. (Surg.) Glas. Roy. Infirm.

PRIMROSE, Kathleen Mary Tel: 023 9273 6000 Fax: 023 9278 2999; 14 Cousins Grove, Southsea PO4 9RP — MB BS 1976 Lond.; MRCS Eng. LRCP Lond. 1976; MRCGP 1981; DRCOG 1978. (Roy. Free) Prev: Ho. Surg. Roy. Portsmouth Hosp.; Ho. Phys. Qu. Alex. Hosp. Portsmouth.

PRIMROSE, Pauline Ann Brooklea Clinic, Wick Road, Bristol BS4 4HU Tel: 0117 971 1211 Fax: 0117 972 3370 — MB ChB Bristol 1962; DObst RCOG 1964. (Bristol)

PRIMROSE, Mr William John 59 Richmond Court, Lisburn BT27 4QX — MB BCh BAO 1977 Belf.; FRCSI 1981. Cons. Roy. Vict. Hosp. Belf.

PRIMROSE, William Robertson Woodend Hospital, Aberdeen AB15 6XS Tel: 01224 681818 Fax: 01224 556339 Email: willie.primrose@arh.grampion.scot.nhs.uk; 41 Richmondhill Road, Aberdeen AB15 5EQ Tel: 01224 311276 — MB ChB 1976 Aberd.; BMedBiol. Aberd. 1973; FRCP Glas. 1990; MRCP (UK) 1978; MRCGP 1981; DObst Otago 1980; FRCP 1999 Edin. Cons. Phys. (Geriat. Med.) Woodend Hosp. Aberd. Socs: Brit. Geriat. Soc. Prev: Sen. Regist. (Geriat. & Gen. Med.) City Hosp. Edin.; Regist. (Respirat. Med. & Infec. Dis.) King's Cross Hosp. Dundee; SHO Regist. (Gen. Med.) S.. Gen. Hosp. Glas.

PRINCE, Arthur Wilfred The Park Surgery, 116 Kings Road, Herne Bay CT6 5RE Tel: 01227 742200 Fax: 01227 742277; Cheveney House, 12 Chantry Park, Sarre, Birchington CT7 0LG Fax: 01843 848112 — MB BS 1969 Newc.; MRCGP (Distinc. & Fraser Rose Gold Medal) 1973; Cert. Family Plann. JCC 1976; DObst RCOG 1971. Postgrad. Teach. (Gen. Pract.) SE Thames RHA; Port Med. Insp. H. M. Immigr. Serv. Socs: Beckett Med. Soc. Prev: Trainee GP Newc. Univ. VTS; Postgrad. Teach. (Gen. Pract.) N.. RHA.

PRINCE, Carolyn Ann Heston Health Centre, Cranford Lane, Heston, Hounslow TW5 9ER Tel: 020 8321 3400 Fax: 020 8321 3413; 45 Dene Avenue, Hounslow TW3 3AQ — MB ChB 1988 Leic.; BSc (1st cl. Hons.) Leic. 1985; DFFP 1993. (Leic.) Clin. Med. Off. (Houns. HA) Wom.s Servs. Prev: SHO (Gen. Med.) Ealing Hosp.; SHO (Chem. Path. & Research) Char. Cross Hosp. Lond.; Ho. Phys. (Coronary Care) Leicester Roy. Infirm.

PRINCE, Clive Benjamin Bewdley Medical Centre, Dog Lane, Bewdley DY12 2EG Tel: 01299 402157 Fax: 01299 404364; The Stables, Park Farm, Ribbesford, Bewdley DY12 2TW Tel: 01295 403115 Email: clive@bewdleymedicalcentre.force9.net — MB ChB 1979 Birm.; MRCGP 1984; DCH RCP Lond. 1983; DRCOG 1982; Cert. Family Plann. JCC 1982. Lead Partner Advanced Train. Pract.; Examr. (Gen. Pract.) Birm. Med. Sch.; Author Computerised Med. Textbk. of Gen. Pract.; Summative Assessm. Examr.; Computer Manager Wyre Forest Primary Care Centre. Socs: Primary Care Spec. Gp. of Brit. Computer Soc.

PRINCE, George Harrald Abingdon Family Health Centre, 361/365 Queens Drive, Liverpool L4 8SJ Tel: 0151 525 1298 — MB ChB 1958 Liverp. (Liverp.)

PRINCE, Graham David Jersey General Hospital, St Helier, Jersey JE1 3QS Tel: 01534 622492 Fax: 01534 617245; Hamilton House, Le Chemin Des Hautes Croix, Trinity, Jersey JE3 5DT Email: gdprince@iti.net — MB BS 1977 Lond.; FFA RCS Eng. 1983; DRCOG 1979. Cons. Anaesth. Jersey Gen. Hosp. Prev: Sen. Regist. (Anaesth.) Newc. HA.

PRINCE, Heather Gail 6 Chartwell Grove, Nottingham NG3 5RD; Oakbank, 6 Chartwell Grove, Mapporley Plains, Nottingham NG3 5RD — MB ChB 1972 Liverp.; FRCS Eng. 1978. Cons. spinal Surg..Univ. Hosp. Nottm. Socs: BMA, BOA. Prev: Cons. Orthop. Kingsmill Hosp. Mansfield & Univ. Hosp. Nottm.; Sen. Lect. (Orthop. & Accid. Surg.) Univ. Nottm. Harlow Wood Orthop. Hosp. & Mansfield Gen. Hosp.; Hon. Cons. Mansfield & Dist. Gen. Hosp., Harlow Wood Orthop. Hosp. & Univ. Hosp. Nottm.

PRINCE, John Anthony Tower Medical Centre, 129 Cannon Street Road, London E1 2LX Tel: 020 7488 4240 Fax: 020 7702 2443 — BM BCh 1966 Oxf.; MA, BM BCh Oxf. 1966; MFOM RCP Lond. 1985, A 1981; MRCGP 1981; DFFP 1984; DIH 1981. Exam. Med. Off. DSS; Local Med. Off. Civil Serv. OHS. Socs: BMA & Soc. Occupat. Med. Prev: Occupat. Phys. Tower Hamlets DHA & Cons. to Lond. Boro. Tower Hamlets & Dockland Developm.; Ho. Surg. St. Thos. Hosp. Lond.; Mem. GP Tower Hamlets HA.

PRINCE, Karen Laura 8 South Morton Street, Joppa, Edinburgh EH15 2NB — MB ChB 1979 Ed.; BA Oxf. 1976; MRCP (UK) 1983; MRCGP 1983.

PRINCE, Martin Ivor 48 Alwinton Terrace, Gosforth, Newcastle upon Tyne NE3 1UD Tel: 0191 284 5022 — BM BS 1992 Nottm.; BMedSci Nottm. 1990; MRCP (UK) 1995. Regist. (Gastroenteral.) Freeman Hosp. Newc. Prev: Regist. (Gen. Med.) N. Tyneside Dist. Gen. Hosp.

PRINCE, Martin James Flat 3, 43 Granville Park, London SE13 7DY — MB BChir 1984 Camb.

PRINCE, Michael Fred Charles (retired) Tan Yr Allt, Cefn Canol, Rhydycroesau, Oswestry SY10 7PS — MB ChB Birm. 1959; DObst RCOG 1965. Med. Off. Benefits Agency Birm. Disablem. Centre. Prev: GP Handsworth Birm.

***PRINCE, Sarah** 2 West End Av, Guisborough TS14 6NP — MB ChB 1997 Birm.

PRINCE, Sharon Elizabeth Yeoman House, 23 High St., Broughton, Kettering NN14 1NF — MB ChB 1992 Sheff.

PRINCE, Simon Richard The Surgery, High Street, Lowestoft NR32 1JE Tel: 01502 589151 Fax: 01502 566719 — MB BS 1982 Lond.; BSc Pharmacol. Lond. 1978, MB BS 1982; MRC Psych 1988; MRCGP 1990; DRCOG 1989. (Univ. Coll. Hosp.) Socs: Princip. Fell. Roy. Soc. Med. Prev: SHO Rotat. (Med.) Univ. Coll. Hosp.; Ho. Surg. St. Pancras Hosp. Lond.; Ho Phys. Harefield Hosp.

PRINCE, William Tom 18 St Albans Avenue, Weybridge KT13 8EN — MB BChir 1980 Camb.; PhD Camb. 1971 MA 1970, BA 1967; Dip. Pharm. Med. RCP (UK) 1987. Dir. Clin. Graduation Acad. Therap. Chelsea & W.m. Hosp. Lond.; Mem. Fac. Pharmaceut. Med. Socs: Fell. Roy. Soc. Med.; Brit. Pharm. Soc.; Soc. Pharmaceut. Med. Prev: Phys. i/c Clin. Pharmacol. SmithKline Beecham Pharmaceut.

PRINCEWILL, Opribo Mpakaboari Orthopaedic Department, Newham General Hospital, Glen Road, Plaistow, London E13 8SL; 6 Stanmore House, Smedley Street, Union Grove, London SW8 2QT — MB BS 1979 Ibadan; MBBS IBADAN 1979; FRCS 1992 Edinburgh; FRCS 1992 England. (IBADAN) Orthopaedic Regist., Newham Gen. Hosp., Plaistow. Socs: BOA; BMA. Prev: Dept. of Orthop., Stepping Hill Hosital, Stockport.

PRING, Christopher Michael 22 Tinwell Road, Stamford PE9 2SD — MB BChir 1994 Camb.; FRCS (Gen.) 1998.

PRING, Mr David James The Princess Elizabeth Hospital, Le Vauquiedor, St Martin's, Guernsey GY4 6UU Tel: 01481 725241; The Medical Specialist Group, PO Box 113, Alexandra House, Les Frieteaux, St Martins, Guernsey GY1 3EX Tel: 01481 38565 Fax: 01481 37782 Email: davidp@medspec.demon.co.uk — MB BS 1974 Newc.; FRCS Eng. 1979; FRCS Ed. 1979. Cons. Orthop. Guernsey Med. Specialist Gp. Prev: Sen. Regist. (Orthop.) Roy. Nat. Orthop. Hosp. Lond.; Regist. (Orthop.) Hammersmith Postgrad. Hosp.; Surg. Leprosy Mission Asia.

PRING, David William Department of Obstetrics and Gynaecology, York District Hospital, York YO31 8HE Tel: 01904 631313 Fax: 01904 454848; The Old Vicarage, Main St, Wilberfoss, York YO41 5NN Tel: 01759 380256 Fax: 01759 380526 Email: dr@pring.net — MB BS 1975 Lond.; BSc (Hons.) Lond. 1971; FRCOG 1994, M 1981; DRCOG 1978. (Lond. Hosp.) Cons. Gyn. & Obst. York Dist. Hosp. Socs: Fell. Med. Soc. Lond.; York Med. Soc.; Ospreys Gyn. Soc. Prev: Sen. Regist. (O & G) St. Bart. Hosp. Lond.; Regist. (O & G) St. Mary's Hosp. Lond.; SHO (Obst.) Qu. Charlotte's Hosp. Wom.

PRING, John Ernest 5 Lidden Road, Penzance TR18 4PG; West Cornwall Hospital, St. Clare St, Penzance TR18 2PF — MB BS 1971 Lond.; MRCS Eng. LRCP Lond. 1971; FFA RCS Eng. 1978; DA Eng. 1975; DObst RCOG 1974. (Lond. Hosp.) Cons. Anaesth. Cornw. & Isles of Scilly HA. Socs: Assn. Anaesths. Prev: Sen. Regist. Withington Hosp. Manch.; Res. Accouch. & SHO (Anaesth.) Lond. Hosp.

***PRING, Rachel Caroline** 22 Tinwell Road, Stamford PE9 2SD — MB BS 1998 Lond.; MB BS Lond 1998.

PRINGLE, Adam James Lawley Medical Practice, Lawley, Telford SY4 2DD Tel: 01952 501601 Fax: 01952 501502 — MB ChB 1990 Birm.; Dip Occ Med 2000; DCH RCPS Glas. 1995; DRCOG 1993; MRCGP 1996. (Birm.) GP Princip.; Occupat. Health Med. Adviser.

PRINGLE, Alexander (retired) 17 Crescent Road, Chingford, London E4 6AT Tel: 020 8529 4402 — BSc (Hons.) Glas. 1952, MB ChB (Commend.) 1955; FRCP Lond. 1975, M 1961; FRCP Glas. 1968; FRFPS Glas. 1959; MRCP Ed. 1960; FRCP Ed. 1994. Prev: Cons. Phys. N. Middlx. Hosp.

PRINGLE, Alexander Ferguson The Cannons, Fisher St., Methil, Leven KY8 3HE Tel: 01333 426083; The Paddock, Main St, Upper Largo, Leven KY8 6EW Tel: 0133 336707 — MB ChB 1960 Aberd.

PRINGLE, Dorothy Lindsay Deas (retired) North Lodge, Torwoodlee, Galashiels TD1 2NE Tel: 01896 57458 — LRCP LRCS 1941 Ed.; LRCP LRCS Ed. LRFPS Glas. 1941; FDS RCS Ed. 1968. Prev: Lect. (Orthodont.) Univ. Edin.

PRINGLE, Edward, TD (retired) Kingswood, McBean Road, Wolverhampton WV6 0JQ Tel: 01902 751661 Email: prignlehoned@fsnet.co.uk — MB BChir 1946 Camb.; BA Camb. 1939, MA, MB BChir 1946; MRCS Eng., LRCP Lond. 1942; DCH Eng. 1948; MRCGP. Prev: Ho. Phys. Lond. Hosp.

***PRINGLE, Edward Marc** 54 Cayser Drive, Kingswood, Maidstone ME17 3QD — BM BCh 1998 Oxf.; BM BCh Oxf 1998.

PRINGLE, Gordon Mitchell Benreary Surgery, Seaview Place, Buckie AB56 1JT Tel: 01542 831555 Fax: 01542 835799 — MB ChB 1976 Glas.; MRCGP 1980; DRCOG 1978.

PRINGLE, Jane Karen Waterlooville Health Centre, Dryden Close, Waterlooville PO7 6AL Tel: 023 9225 7321; 3 Abbotts Way, Highfield, Southampton SO17 1QU — MB BCh BAO 1982 Belf.; MRCGP 1986; DRCOG 1986; DCH RCP Lond. 1985.

PRINGLE, Jean Anne Smellie Morbid Anatomy Department, Institute of Orthopaedics, Royal National Orthopaedic Hospital, Brockley Hill, Stanmore HA7 4LP Tel: 020 8954 5908 Fax: 020 8954 5908; 17 Crescent Road, Chingford, London E4 6AT Tel: 020 8529 4402 — MB ChB 1959 Glas.; FRCS 1995. (Glas.) Sen. Lect., Hon. Cons. & Head Dept. (Morbid Anat.) Inst. Orthop. Lond.; Pathol. Lond. Bone & Soft Tissue Tumour Serv. Socs: Internat. Skeletal Soc.; Eur. Musculoskeletal Oncol. Soc.; Nat. Bone Tumour Panel (Sec.).

PRINGLE, Jean Rosemary 4 Hermand Gardens, West Calder EH55 8BT — MB ChB 1981 Glas.; MFHom 1988; DRCOG 1984.

PRINGLE, Jonathan James Austen Shirley Avenue Surgery, 1 Shirley Avenue, Shirley, Southampton SO15 5RP Tel: 023 8077 3258/1356 Fax: 023 8070 3078; 3 Abbotts Way, Highfield, Southampton SO17 1QU Tel: 02380 558688 Fax: 01703 558688 — MB BS 1980 Lond.; MRCP (UK) 1985; MRCGP 1987; DRCOG 1986; DCH Otago 1983. (Guy's Hospital Medical School)

PRINGLE, Keith Holmcroft Surgery, Holmcroft Road, Stafford ST16 1JG Tel: 01785 242172 — BM BCh 1978 Oxf.; BA 1975 Oxf.

PRINGLE, Mary Willows Brook, Llangoed, Beaumaris LL58 8NY — MB BS 1943 Lond.; BSc (Physiol.) 1939; MRCS Eng. LRCP Lond. 1942; DCH Eng. 1948. (King's Coll. Lond.) Prev: Regist. (Med.) Whiston Hosp.; Capt. RAMC.

PRINGLE, Professor Michael Alexander Leary The Medical Centre, High Street, Collingham, Newark NG23 7LB Tel: 01636 892156 Fax: 01636 893391; Department of General Practice, Queens Medical Centre, Nottingham NG7 2UH Tel: 0115 970 9391 Fax: 0115 970 9389 Email: mike.pringle@nottingham.ac.uk — MB BS 1973 Lond.; MD 1987 Lond.; MRCS Eng. LRCP 1973 Lond; DRCOG 1977; FRCGP 1989; MRCGP 1978. (Guy's) Prof. Gen. Pract. Univ. Nottm.

PRINGLE, Mr Michael Blair Queen Alexandra Hospital, Cosham, Portsmouth PO6 3LY Tel: 023 92 379451 — MB BS 1983 Lond.; FRCS (Orl.) 1994; FRCS (Orl.) Eng. 1990; FRCS Eng. 1988. (St. Geo. Hosp. Med. Sch.) Cons. ENT Qu. Alexandra Hosp. Portsmouth; Hon. Cons. ENT Soton. Gen. Hosp.; Cons. ENT S. Eng. Cochear Implant Centre Soton.

PRINGLE, Mr Robert (retired) Taynuilt, Kilspindie, Errol, Perth PH2 7RX Tel: 01821 670289 Email: robert@pringle000.freeserve.co.uk — MB ChB Glas. 1950; ChM Glas. 1964; FRCS Glas. 1987; FRCS Eng. 1961; FRCS Ed. 1958. Prev: Prof. & Head Clin. Sci.s Internat. Med. Coll. Kuala Lumpur, Malaysia.

PRINGLE, Mr Robert Greig Burnell House, 82 Berwick Road, Shrewsbury SY1 2NF Tel: 01743 353012 — MB ChB 1960 New Zealand; FRCS Eng. 1966. Indep. Cons. Orthop. Surg. Shrops. Prev: Cons. Orthop. Surg. Robt. Jones & Agnes Hunt Orthop. Hosp. OsW.ry & Roy. Shrewsbury Hosp.; Cons. Orthop. Midl. Spinal Injuries Centre Robt. Jones & Agnes Hunt Orthop. Hosp.; Sen. Regist. (Orthop.) United Birm. Hosps.

PRINGLE, Mr Robert Macaulay 15 Lenzie Road, Stepps, Glasgow G33 6DU Tel: 0141 779 2179 & profess. 0236 748748 — MB ChB 1964 Aberd.; FRCS Ed. 1971. Cons. Orthop. Surg. Monklands Dist. Gen. Hosp. Airdrie. Socs: Fell. BOA. Prev: Sen. Regist. (Orthop.) Vict. Infirm. Glas.; Regist. (Orthop. & Accid.) Div. Glas. Roy. Infirm.

PRINGLE, Stewart 8 Woodend Drive, Glasgow G13 1QS Email: 100724.2333@compuserve.com — MB ChB 1983 Glas.; BSc Glas. 1981; MRCOG 1994; MRCGP 1988. Specialist Regist. (O & G) S.ern Gen. Hosp. Glas. Prev: Career Regist. (O & G) Stirling Roy. Infirm.; Regist. (O & G) Stobhill Hosp. & Roy. Matern. Hosp. Glas.; SHO (Obst.) Qu. Mother's Hosp. Glas.

PRINGLE, Stuart David Ninewells Hospital & Medical School, Dundee DD1 9SY Tel: 01382 660111; Bankview, Main St, Longforgan, Dundee DD2 5EW — MB ChB 1979 Dundee; MD Dundee 1990; FRCP Glas. 1994; MRCP (UK) 1983; FRCP Ed. 1996. Cons. Cardiol. & Hon. Sen. Lect Ninewells Hosp. & Med. Sch. Dundee. Socs: Brit. Cardiac Soc.; Scot. Cardiac Soc.; Brit. Soc. Of Echocardiography. Prev: Sen. Lect. Ninewells Hosp. Dundee; Sen. Regist. (Cardiol.) Roy. Infirm. Edin.; Regist. (Cardiol.) Glas. Roy. Infirm.

PRINGLE, Terence Harold Cardiac Department, Ninewells Hospital, Dundee DD1 9SY Tel: 01382 60111; Balnagar, Tealing, Dundee DD4 0QZ Tel: 01382 380463 — MB BCh BAO 1972 Dub.; MD Dub. 1987; FRCP Ed. 1992; FRCPI 1989, M 1975. (TC Dub.) Cons. Cardiol. Ninewells Hosp. Dundee; Hon. Sen. Lect. (Med.) Univ. Dundee. Prev: Sen. Regist. (Gen. Med.) Belf. City Hosp. & Roy. Vict. Hosp. Belf.; Regist. (Cardiol.) Roy. Infirm. Glas.

PRINGLE, Timothy Greenlaw 20 Boadicea Way, Colchester CO2 9BQ — MRCS Eng. LRCP Lond. 1974.

PRINGLE, Victoria Alexandra — MB ChB 1993 Aberd.; MRCGP 1998; Dip FP 1996; DRCOG 1996.

PRINJA, Aparna Flat 1, 14 Carols Place, London W1Y 5AG — MB BS 1992 Lond. (St. Thos. UMDS) SHO (Paediat.) Chelsea & W.minster Hosp. Lond.

PRINN, Mr Michael George (retired) Four Seasons, Brockley Grove, Hutton Mount, Brentwood CM13 2JJ Tel: 01277 219698 Fax: 01277 219698 — MB BS 1961 Lond.; FRCS Eng. 1966; MRCS Eng. LRCP Lond. 1961; DObst RCOG 1964. Prev: Cons. Gen. Surg. Harold Wood Hosp. & Brentwood Hosp. Gp.

PRINSEN, Agatha Krista Elisabet 84 Malmesbury Road, Southampton SO15 5FQ — Artsexamen 1993 Nijmegen.

PRINSLEY, Mr Peter Richard 26 Eaton Road, Norwich NR4 6PZ Tel: 01603 506482 — MB ChB 1982 Sheff.; BMedSci Sheff. 1981; FRCS Eng. 1989; FRCS Ed. 1987. Cons. ENT Surg. Norf. & Norwich Hosp. & Jas. Paget Hosp. Gt. Yarmouth Norf. Prev: Sen. Regist. (ENT Surg.) Yorks. Region; Regist. (ENT Surg.) Barnet Gen. Hosp. & Roy. Free Hosp.

PRINTER, Keki Dinshaw, Col. late RAMC Retd. (retired) 13 Deben Crescent, Greenmeadow, Swindon SN25 3QB — MB BS 1952

PRIOR

Bombay; FRCOG 1974, M 1959; DObst 1955. Prev: Cons. Gyn. & Obst. & Command Cons. BAOR BMH Rinteln, BFPO 29.

PRIOR, Alison Department of Gastroenterology, Woodlands House, West Norwich Hospital, Bowthorpe Road, Norwich NR2 3TU; Hackford Hall, Reepham, Norwich NR10 4RL — MB ChB 1981 Manch.; BSc Manch. 1978, MD 1990; MRCP (UK) 1984; FRCP 1999. Cons. Phys. (Gastroenterol.) Norwich. Prev: Sen. Regist. Rotat. E. Anglia; Lect. (Med.) Univ. Hosp. S. Manch.

PRIOR, Mr Andrew John Bromley Hospitals NHS Trust, Farnborough Hospital, Farnborough BR6 8ND Email: aj.prior@virgin.net; Tel: 020 8467 7087 Fax: 020 8468 7488 Email: aj.prior@virgin.net — MB ChB 1987 Birm.; BSc (Hons.) Birm. 1984; FRCS Eng. 1992; FRCS Ed. 1992; FRCS FRCS(ORL-HNS) 1998. (Birmingahm) Cons. E.N.T Surg..Bromley Hosp.s NHS Trust; Hon. Sen. Lect. Univ. Coll. Lond. Prev: Sen. Regist.Throat Nose and Ear Hosp.

PRIOR, Andrew Ronald John, MBE, Wing Cdr. RAF Med. Br. Prior Data Sciences Ltd, 12 Pondtaic Road, Fleet GU51 3JW Tel: 01252 819959 Email: andyprior@pdsl.dircon.co.uk — MB BS 1978 Lond.; PhD Lond. 1992, BSc 1974, MB BS 1978.

PRIOR, Andrew William Old Court House Surgery, 27 Wood Street, Barnet EN5 4BB Tel: 020 8449 2388 — MB BS 1980 Lond.; BSc Lond. 1977, MB BS 1980; MRCGP 1984. GP Barnet.

PRIOR, Eileen Mary (retired) 23 Eaton Court, Augusta St., Grimsby DN34 4UD Tel: 01472 343748 — MRCS Eng. LRCP Lond. 1942. Prev: Asst. Med. Off. Grimsby.

PRIOR, Gethin Thomas James Bryntirion Surgery, Cardiff Road, Bargoed CF81 8NN Tel: 01443 830796 Fax: 01443 835962 — MB BS 1990 Lond.; BSc Lond. 1987. (UCH Lond.) Prev: SHO Salisbury VTS.

PRIOR, John Gareth Winfield Hospital, Tewkesbury Road, Gloucester GL2 9WH Tel: 01452 331111 Fax: 01452 331200 Email: drjohnprior@compuserve.com; Stonecourt, Stone, Berkeley GL13 9JY Tel: 01454 260964 Email: drjohnprior@compuserve.com — MB BChir 1975 Camb.; MA MB BChir (Hons.) Camb. 1974; MD Camb. 1984; FRCP Lond. 1994; MRCP (UK) 1976. (Univ. Camb. & Guy's Hosp. Lond.) Cons. Phys. (Thoracic & Gen. Med.) Glos. Roy. NHS Trust. Socs: Brit. Thorac. Soc.; Eur. Respirat. Soc.; Amer. Thoracic Soc. Prev: Sen. Regist. (Thoracic & Gen. Med.) Guy's Hosp. Lond.; Sir Philip Oppenheimer Research Fell. (Med.) Guys Hosp. Lond.; Ho. Phys. Brompton Hosp. Lond.

PRIOR, John Joseph (retired) The Mansion, Albury Park, Albury, Guildford GU5 9BB Tel: 01483 202702 — MB BS 1954 Lond.; DMRD Eng. 1957. Prev: Cons. Radiol. & Head Dept. Radiol. E.man Dent. Hosp. Lond.

***PRIOR, Kate Rebecca Edna Jane** 1 Highbridge Court, Farrow Lane, London SE14 5EB — MB BS 1996 Lond.

***PRIOR, Katherine Moncrieffe** 9 Goose Pasture, Yarm TS15 9EP — MB BS 1997 Newc.

PRIOR, Keith Sidney, Air Commodore RAF Med. Br. (retired) Tanpenygarnedd, Penybontfawr, Oswestry SY10 0PE — MB BS 1966 Lond.; MRCS Eng. LRCP Lond. 1966; FRCGP 1981, M 1971; MFOM RCP Lond. 1981; DAvMed Eng. 1977. Prev: Princip. Adviser (Gen. Pract.) RAF.

PRIOR, Kenneth Gordon (retired) 68 South Street, Warminster BA12 8DS Tel: 01985 215511 — MB BS 1950 Lond.; MRCS Eng. LRCP Lond. 1949; AKC. Med. Off. E. Knoyle.

PRIOR, Michael Bushmead Avenue Medical Centre, 21 Bushmead Avenue, Bedford MK40 3QJ Tel: 01234 267797 Fax: 01234 269649; 21 Bushmead Avenue, Bedford MK40 3QJ Tel: 01234 267797 — MB BS 1970 Lond.; MRCS Eng. LRCP Lond. 1970. (St Georges)

***PRIOR, Natasha Giselle** 3 Kent Drive, Congleton CW12 1SD — MB BS 1998 Lond.; MB BS Lond 1998.

PRIOR, Pamela Frances Department of Clinical Neurophysiology, St. Barts Hospital, West Smithfield, London EC1A 7BE Tel: 020 7601 8859 Fax: 020 7601 7875 — MD 1972 Lond.; MB BS 1958; FRCP Lond. 1990; MRCP (UK) 1985. (Lond. Hosp.) Cons. Clin. Neurophysiol. St. Bart. Hosp. Lond. Socs: Fell. Roy. Soc. Med.; Brit. Soc. Clin. Neurophysiol. Prev: Extern. Staff MRC Laborats. Carshalton; Med. Asst. EEG Dept. Lond. Hosp.; Ho. Surg. Roy. Devon & Exeter Hosp.

PRIOR, Roderick Clive Glendower Road Surgery, 54 Glendower Road, Peverell, Plymouth PL3 4LD Tel: 01752 673336 Fax: 01752 267130 — MB ChB 1977 Manch.; BSc (Med. Sci.) St. And. 1974. Prev: SHO (Anaesth.) Hope Hosp. Salford; SHO (Psychiat.) Prestwich Hosp. Manch.; SHO (Obst.) Hope Hosp. Salford.

PRIOR, Mr Roger James Yew Hedge House, Child Okeford, Blandford Forum DT11 8EF — MB BS 1970 Lond.; FRCS Eng. 1975; MRCP (UK) 1977; MRCS Eng. LRCP Lond. 1970; MRCGP 1983. (Char. Cross)

PRIOR, Tova Two Elms, Chobham Road, Knaphill, Woking GU21 2QF — MB BS 1990 Lond.

PRISCOTT, Robin Beverley, MBE Dr. Ghassan N. Pharaon Hospital, PO Box 4553, Jeddah, Saudi Arabia Tel: 00 966 02 6823200 Fax: 00 966 02 6972510; 67 St Mark Drive, Colchester CO4 4LP Tel: 01206 842338 Fax: 01206 842338 — MB BS 1960 Lond. (St. Bart.) Med. Dir. Dr Ghassan N. Pharaon Gen. Hosp., Jeddah, KSA.

PRISK, Adrian John Central Milton Keynes Medical, 1 North Sixth Street, Central Milton Keynes, Milton Keynes MK9 2NR Tel: 01908 605775 Fax: 01908 676752 — MB BS 1972 Lond.; MRCS Eng. LRCP Lond. 1972; MRCGP 1976; DObst RCOG 1975. (Guy's) Prev: Princip. GP LoW.oft; Trainee GP Livingston VTS.

PRITCHARD, Adrian John 21 Stuart Way, Market Drayton TF9 3TT — BM BS 1994 Nottm.

***PRITCHARD, Alison Louise** 3 Beech Avenue, East Leake, Loughborough LE12 6NU — MB BS 1998 Newc.; MB BS Newc 1998.

PRITCHARD, Ann Strawberry Place Surgery, 5 Strawberry Place, Morriston, Swansea SA6 7AQ Tel: 01792 522526 Fax: 01792 411020 — MB BS 1987 Lond. (St George's London)

PRITCHARD, Carl Nicholas Shakleton Department of Anaesthetics, Southampton General Hospital, Tremona Road, Southampton SO16 6YD Tel: 0410 416634 Email: carlpritchard@msn.com — MB ChB 1992 Birm.; DCH RCP Lond. 1998. SHO (Anaesth.) Soton. Gen. Hosp. Socs: Assn. Anaesths.

PRITCHARD, Caroline Anne 10 Wingrave Road, London W6 9HF — MB BS 1994 Lond.; MA Camb. 1995. Prev: Ho. Phys. St. Richards Hosp. Chichester; Ho. Surg. Char. Cross Lond.

PRITCHARD, David Arnold Rees (retired) 12 Gerddi Menai, Bangor Road, Caernarfon LL55 1LN — MRCS Eng. LRCP Lond. 1935. Prev: Anaesth. Caern. & Anglesey Hosp. Gp.

PRITCHARD, David Mark 8 Blackburn Gardens, Palatine Road, Manchester M20 3YH Tel: 0161 438 0385 Email: dpritch@fs1.scg.man.ac.uk — MB ChB 1991 Manch.; MB ChB (Hons.) Manch. 1991; BSc (Hons.) Manch. 1988; MRCP (UK) 1994; PhD Manch. 1999. (Manch.) Specialist Regist. (Gen. Med./Gastro.) Roy. Preston Hosp. Preston on NW Rotat. Socs: Train. Mem. Amer. Gastroenterol. Assn. Prev: MRC Clin. Train. Fell. Manch. Univ.; Brit. Digestive Foundat. Research Train. Fell. Manch. Univ.; Lect. (Med.) Manch. Univ. & Hon. Regist. (Med. & Gastroenterol.) Hope Hosp. Salford.

PRITCHARD, Deborah Susan East Herts Hospital, Stanstead Road, Hertford SG13 7JA; 6 The Old Drive, Welwyn Garden City AL8 6TB Tel: 01707 321297 — MB BS 1987 Lond.; DCH RCP Lond. 1989. Clin. Med. Off. E. Herts. Hosp.

PRITCHARD, Dewi Bryn — MB BCh 1992 Wales; BMedSci (Hons.) Wales 1992; MSc Wales 1998. (Cardiff) Specialist Regist. Roy. Free Hosp. Rotat. St Ann's Hosp. Lond. Socs: Roy. Coll. Psychiats.

PRITCHARD, Emma Louise 59 Mooreland Road, Bromley BR1 3RD — MB ChB 1997 Birm.

PRITCHARD, Gillian Pfizer Central Research (130), Ramsgate Road, Sandwich CT13 9NJ Tel: 01304 648192 Fax: 01304 658510; Hope Villa, 236 Couper Angus Road, Muirhead of Liff, Dundee DD2 5QN Tel: 01382 580129 — MB ChB 1985 Liverp.; MSc Aberd. 1989; MRCP (UK) 1992; AFPM RCP Lond. 1995; MBA Dundee 1998. (Liverp.) Clin. Project Manager, Pfizer Centr. Research. Prev: Asst. Med. Dir. Scotia Pharmaceut. Ltd. Stirling; Dep. Med. Dir. Drug Developm. (Scotl.) Ltd. Dundee; Clin. Research Fell. (Med. & Therap.) Univ. Aberd.

PRITCHARD, Mr Graham Arthur Department of Surgery, Princess of Wales Hospital, Coity Road, Bridgend CF31 1RQ Tel: 01656 752752 Fax: 01656 752593; Caegarw, Court Colman, Bridgend CF31 4NG — BM BS 1979 Nottm.; BMedSci (Hons.) Nottm. 1977; DM Nottm. 1989; FRCS Eng. 1983. Cons. Surg. Gen. Surg. & Gastroenterol. P.ss of Wales Hosp. Bridgend. Socs: Assn. Surg.;

Assn. Coloproctol.; Assn. Endoscopic Surgs. Prev: Sen. Regist. (Gen. Surg.) Singleton Hosp. Swansea; Research Fell. (Surg.) Univ. Wales Coll. Med. Cardiff; Regist. (Surg.) Glam. & Gwent HAs.

PRITCHARD, Mr Graham Cleverly (retired) Shawkbottom Cottage, Cumdivock, Dalston, Carlisle CA5 7JH Tel: 01228 710854 Email: pritchard@cumdivock.fsnet.co.uk — MB BChir 1939 Camb.; FRCS Eng. 1953; DOMS Eng. 1942. Prev: Cons. Ophth. Surg. King's Coll. Hosp. & Kensington, Chelsea & W.m. AHA (T).

***PRITCHARD, Guy Marcus** 3 Towers Close, Poynton, Stockport SK12 1DH — MB ChB 1996 Birm.

PRITCHARD, Gwenda Rosamond Grace (retired) Church Court, Hillside, Tingewick, Buckingham MK18 4QY Tel: 01280 848265 — MB BS 1963 Lond.; DRCOG 1965. Clin. Asst. (Genitourin. Med.) Radcliffe Infirm. Oxf. & Milton Keynes Hosp. Prev: Clin. Asst. (Genitourin. Med.) Radcliffe Infirm. Oxf. & Milton Keynes Hosp.

***PRITCHARD, Harri Robert Owen** Siop Isaf, Tudweiliog, Pwllheli LL53 8NF — MB BCh 1994 Wales; BSc (Hons.) Wales 1991, MB BCh 1994.

PRITCHARD, Hefin Wyn The Willow Surgery, 50 Heath Hill Avenue, Lower Bevandean, Brighton BN2 4FH Tel: 01273 606391 Fax: 01273 684880; October Cottage, 5 Withdean Crescent, Brighton BN1 6WG Tel: 01273 555625 — MB BS 1979 Lond. Socs: Soc. Apoth. Lond.; Sussex M-C Soc.

PRITCHARD, Hugh Malcolm Clarence House, 14 Russell Road, Rhyl LL18 3BY Tel: 01745 350680 Fax: 01745 353293; White Lodge, 35 Brighton Road, Rhyl LL18 3HL — MB ChB 1974 Manch.; DRCOG 1977.

PRITCHARD, Ian Paul Birbeck Medical Group, Penrith Health Centre, Bridge Lane, Penrith CA11 8HW Tel: 01768 245200 Fax: 01768 245295 — MB BS 1986 Lond.; MRCGP 1993; DA (UK) 1997; DCCH RCP Ed. 1992; DCH RCP Lond. 1992; DRCOG 1991. GP. Prev: SHO (Anaesth.) Cumbld. Infirm.; Dist. Med. Off. Forteau, Canada.

PRITCHARD, Jane Department of Neuroimmunology, Guy's King's & St. Thomas' School of Medicine, Hodkin Builiding, Guy's Hospital, London SE1 1UL Tel: 020 7848 6126 Fax: 020 7848 6123 Email: jane.pritchard@kcl-ac.uk; c/o 1 Roman Way, Coventry CV3 6RD Tel: 024 76 416118 — BM BCh 1993 Oxf.; MRCP 1996 (UK); BA Camb. 1990. MRC Fell., Dept of NeuroImmunol., Guy's, King's & St Thomas' Sch. of Med. Socs: Roy. Coll. Phys. (UK) 1996; Assoc. Mem. Assn. Brit. Neurol. Prev: Specialist Regist. (Neurol.) Nineweus Hosp., Dundee.

PRITCHARD, Jillian Margaret Huntersfield, Highlands Road, Reigate RH2 0LA Tel: 01737 244029 — BM BCh 1975 Oxf.; MA Oxf. 1976; MRCOG 1982, D 1977; DCH Eng. 1979. Cons. Genitourin. Med. St. Peter's Hosp. Chertsey. Socs: BMA; Med. Soc. Study VD; AGUM. Prev: Sen. Regist. (Genitourin. Med.) St. Mary's Hosp. Lond.

PRITCHARD, John Arthur Wyndrush, Newlands Road, Leominster HR6 8PS Tel: 01568 613586 — BM 1987 Soton.; MRCP (UK) 1991. SHO (O & G) Taunton & Som. Hosp. Prev: SHO (.Med.) St. Mary's Hosp. Portsmouth.

PRITCHARD, John Guthrie (retired) 15 Monastery Street, Canterbury CT1 1NJ — LMSSA 1956 Lond.; MD Lond. 1968, MB BS 1958. Prev: Cons. Phys. (Geriat. Med.) St. Lukes Hosp. Huddersfield.

PRITCHARD, Jonathan Institute of Child Health, Guilford St., London WC1N 1EH Tel: 020 7242 9782 Fax: 020 7404 6181; 12 Richborne Terrace, London SW8 1AU Tel: 020 7582 4582 — MB BChir Camb. 1967; BA Camb. 1967; FRCP Lond. 1981, M 1970. (Camb. & St. Thos.) Sen. Lect. (Paediat. Oncol.) Inst. Child Health & Cons. Hosp. for Childr. Gt. Ormond St. Lond.; Vis. Prof. Paediat. Perth, W Australia 1999 & MacDonald Orator; Vis. Prof. Paediat. Delhi, Chandigarh 1993. Socs: Hon. Fell. Amer. Acad. Pediat.; Fell. Roy. Coll. Paeds. & Child Health; Amer. Soc. Clin. Oncol. Prev: Leukaemia Research Fell. (Haemat.) Univ. Liverp.; MRC Trav. Fell. Childr. Hosp. Boston, USA 1974-5; (Founder) Cons. Oncol. Unit Gt. Ormond St. Hosp. Lond. 1978-98.

PRITCHARD, Kathryn Amelia Bideford Medical Centre, Abbotsham Road, Bideford EX39 3AF Tel: 01237 476363 Fax: 01237 423351; Gables, First Raleigh, Bideford EX39 3NJ — MB BS 1983 Lond.; MRCGP 1987; DGM RCP Lond. 1987. GP Bideford.

PRITCHARD, Keith (retired) 2 Honeythorn Close, Hempsted, Gloucester GL2 5LU Tel: 01452 303018 — MB BS 1956 Lond.; LMSSA Lond. 1956. Prev: GP Gloucester.

PRITCHARD, Lucinda Jane Humphris South Point, Berkeley Road, Cirencester GL7 1TX Tel: 01285 652260 — MRCS Eng. LRCP Lond. 1965. Med. Dir. of Prospect Hospice Swindon.; Clin. Asst. (Chest Dis.) P.ss Margt. Hosp. Swindon. Socs: Brit. Thorac. Soc.; Assn. Palliat. Med.

PRITCHARD, Mark Christopher Broadreach, Magpie Close, Ewshot, Farnham GU10 5TF — MB BS 1987 Lond.

PRITCHARD, Mr Mark Gawain St. Anns, Charles St., Tredegar NP22 4AF — MB BS 1992 Lond.; FRCS (Eng.) 1996. Specialist Regist. (Trauma & Orthop.) W. Midl. Deanery.

PRITCHARD, Meira (retired) Penygroes, Gorllwyn County Road, Caernarfon LL54 6EY Tel: 01286 881971 — MB ChB 1947 Liverp. Prev: Ho. Surg. & Ho. Phys. Co. Hosp. Bangor.

PRITCHARD, Michael Hugo Department of Rheumatology, University Hospital of Wales, Heath Park, Cardiff CF14 4XW Tel: 029 2074 2626 Fax: 029 2074 4388; East Barn, White Farm, Leckwith, Cardiff CF11 8AS Tel: 029 2051 4753 Fax: 01222 744388 Email: eastbarn@globalnet.co.uk — MB BCh BAO 1970 Belf.; BA Oxf. 1964; FRCP Lond. 1988. Cons. Rheumat. Univ. Hosp. Wales Cardiff.

PRITCHARD, Michael John 3 Great Spilmans, London SE22 8SZ — MB BChir Camb. 1953; FRCP Lond. 1977, M 1958; FRCPsych 1974, M 1971; DPM Lond. 1961. (St. Thos.) Emerit. Reader (Psychiat.) United Med. & Dent. Sch. Guy's & St. Thos. Hosp. Lond. Prev: Reader (Psychiat.) United Med. & Dent. Sch. Guy's & St. Thos. Hosp. Lond.; Sen. Lect. & Asst. Dir. (Psychiat.) Lond. Hosp. Med. Coll.; Sen. Regist. Maudsley Hosp. Lond.

PRITCHARD, Nicholas Charles Bromley Moorfields Eye Hospital, City Rd, London EC1V 2PD Tel: 020 7253 3411 — MB BS 1989 Lond.; BSc Lond. 1988; FRCA 1995. (St. Mary's Hosp. Lond.) Cons. Anaesth., Moorfields Eye Hosp., Lond. Socs: Anaesth. Assn.; Brit. Ophth. Anaesthetic Soc. Prev: Sen. Regist. (Anaesth.) Hammersmith Hosp.; Regist. (Anaesth.) Marsden & Hammersmith Hosp. Lond.; SHO (Anaesth.) Hammersmith Hosp. & St. Mary's Hosp. Lond.

PRITCHARD, Peter Michael Maddock (retired) 31 Martins Lane, Dorchester-on-Thames, Wallingford OX10 7JF Tel: 01865 340008 Fax: 01865 341593 — MB BChir 1942 Camb.; MA Camb. 1942; FRCGP 1978, M 1957; DCH Eng. 1947. Sen. Med. Adviser Advanced Computation Laborat. ICRF; Hon. Sec. UK - Nordic Med. Educat. Trust. Prev: Regist. (Paediat.) Univ. Coll. Hosp. Lond.

PRITCHARD, Philip Leslie James The Culverhay Surgery, Culverhay, Wotton-under-Edge GL12 7LS Tel: 01453 843252 — MB BS 1982 London; MB BS 1982 Lond; MRCS Eng LRCP Lond 1981. (London) GP Wotton-under-Edge, Glos.

PRITCHARD, Richard Michael Shotton Lane Surgery, 38 Shotton Lane, Shotton, Deeside CH5 1QW Tel: 01244 812094 Fax: 01244 811728 — MB ChB 1972 Liverp.; DObst RCOG 1974.

PRITCHARD, Robert Ifor Siop Isaf, Tudweiliog, Pwllheli LL53 8NF Tel: 01758 770277; Siop Isaf, Tudweiliog, Pwllheli LL53 8NF Tel: 01758 770277 — MB ChB 1967 Liverp.

PRITCHARD, Stephen John Rozel, Arleston Hill, Telford TF1 2JY — MB BS 1987 Lond.

PRITCHARD, Stephen Robert Ty'r Felin Surgery, Cecil Road, Gorseinon, Swansea SA4 4BY Tel: 01792 898844 — MB BCh 1974 Wales.

PRITCHARD, Susan Ann 18 The Street, Cherhill, Calne SN11 8XP — MB ChB 1989 Sheff.

PRITCHARD, Susan Clare c/o Brook Cottage, 233 Priests Lane, Shenfield, Brentwood CM15 8LE — MB ChB 1991 Birm.; ChB Birm. 1991; BSc (Hons) Birm. 1990; MBChB Birm. 1991; Dip. Child Health 1995; Dip. Of Obs. & Gynae. 1996; MRCGP 1998; DFFP 1998.

PRITCHARD, Terence Rodney The Surgery, 30 Westfield Road, Acocks Green, Birmingham B27 7TL Tel: 0121 706 5131 Fax: 0121 706 7593 — MB ChB 1976 Birm.; BSc Aston 1967.

PRITCHARD, Violet Gladys (retired) Taintree House, Heathfield Road, Audlem, Crewe CW3 0AU Tel: 01270 811833 Email: vipritchard@lineone.net.uk — MB BS 1953 Lond.; MRCS Eng. LRCP Lond. 1953; DCH Eng. 1956. Prev: SCMO Crewe HA.

PRITCHARD-HOWARTH, Martin Roy Wilowbank, 64 Barnston Road, Heswall, Wirral CH60 2SU — MB ChB 1993 Liverp.; BSc

PRITCHARD-JONES

Liverp. 1990; MRCP (UK) 1997. (Liverpool) Specialist Regist. Arrowe Pk. Hosp.

PRITCHARD-JONES, Kathryn Department of Paediatric Oncology, Royal Marsden Hospital, Downs Road, Sutton SM2 5PT Tel: 020 8642 6011 Fax: 020 8661 3617 Email: kpj@icr.ac.uk — BM BCh 1983 Oxf.; PhD CNAA 1992; MA Oxf. 1984; MRCP (UK) 1986; FRCP Ed. 1998. (Oxford) CRC Sen. Lect. & Hon. Cons. Paediat. Oncol. Inst. Cancer Research Roy. Marsden Hosp. Sutton.

*PRITCHARD JONES, Rowan Oliver 7 The Firs, Chester Rd, Whitchurch SY13 1NL — MB ChB 1997 Bristol.

PRITCHETT, Andrew Harold James New Hall Lane Practice, The Health Centre, Geoffrey Street, Preston PR1 5NE Tel: 01772 401730 Fax: 01772 401731; 10 Sharoe Green Park, Fulwood, Preston PR2 8HW — MB BS 1974 Lond.; MRCGP 1979; DRCOG 1977.

PRITCHETT, Mr Christopher Julian Ellengowam, Preston Park, North Shields NE29 9JL — MD 1983 Bristol; BSc Bristol 1971, MD 1983, MB ChB 1974; FRCS Eng. 1978. Cons. Gen. Surg. S. Shields Gen. Hosp. Prev: Lect. Univ. Hong. Kong.

*PRITCHETT, Jane Kathleen 25 Hendre Park, Llangennech, Llanelli SA14 8UP — MB BCh 1998 Wales.

PRITLOVE, Janice Carlton Gardens Surgery, 27 Carlton Gardens, Leeds LS7 1JL Tel: 0113 295 2678 Fax: 0113 295 2679; 9 West Pasture Close, Horsforth, Leeds LS18 5PB Tel: 0113 258 0116 — MB ChB 1971 Manch.; MRCGP 1975.

PRITTY, Mr Paul Edmund Accident & Emergency Department, Derbyshire Royal Infirmary NHS Trust, London Road, Derby DE1 2QY Tel: 01332 254925 Email: paul.pritty@sdah-tr.trent.nhs.uk — MB 1971 Camb.; MB BChir Camb. 1971; FRCS Eng. 1978; FFAEM 1994. (St. George's London) Cons. Accid. Roy. Infirm. Derby.; Train. Progr. Director (A & E), Trent. Prev: Ass Post Grad. Dean mid Trent; Sen. Regist. (Accid.) Univ. Hosp. Nottm.; Regist. (Accid.) Chester Hosp.

PRIVETT, James Thomas John 4 Windmill Croft, Windmill Hill, Cubbington, Leamington Spa CV32 7JU — MB ChB 1964 Bristol; DMRD Eng. 1971; FFR 1973.

PRIVONITZ, Dorothea Magdalena Little Harwood Health Centre, Plane Tree Road, Blackburn BB1 6PH Tel: 01254 580931 Fax: 01254 695794 — State Exam Med 1987 Mainz; State Exam Med 1987 Mainz.

*PRIYADARSHI, Saket 7 Parklands, Broxburn EH52 5RB — MB ChB 1994 Glas.

PRIYADHARSHAN, Rajasingham Victoria Road Surgery, 129A Victoria Road, Kirkcaldy KY1 1DH Tel: 01592 263332 Fax: 01592 644288 — MB BS 1985 Peradeniya. (Peradeniya) GP Kirkcaldy, Fife.

PROBERT, Christopher Simon John Rose Holding, Latteridge Road, Iron Acton, Bristol BS37 9TW — MB ChB 1985 Birm.; MRCP (UK) 1988.

PROBERT, Clive Barrington Redlam Surgery, 62 Redlam, Blackburn BB2 1UW Tel: 01254 260051 Fax: 01254 691937; Bentham Road Health Centre, Bentham Road, Blackburn BB2 4QD Tel: 01254 209918 — MB ChB 1962 Liverp. Med. Adviser Akzo-Nobel Ltd., St. Regis Paper Company, SCA Ltd. & Secto Ltd Blackburn; Local Med. Adviser Civil Serv.

PROBERT, Doris Evelyn (retired) 33 Cefn Coed Avenue, Cyncoed, Cardiff CF23 6HF Tel: 01222 759764 — MB ChB 1959 Manch.; Cert FPA 1963. Prev: Clin. Med. Off. S. Glam. AHA (T).

*PROBERT, Joanne Lisa 15 Sunningdale, Clifton, Bristol BS8 2NF — MB ChB 1998 Bristol.

PROBERT, Mr John Llewellyn — BM BS 1991 Nottm.; FRCS UROL 2001; BMedSci (Hons.) Nottm. 1989; FRCS Ed. 1995. (Univ. Nottm.) Specialist Regist. (Urol.) Bristol; Tutor (Surg.) Univ. Bristol. Socs: Brit. Assoc. of Urological Surgs. Prev: Specialist Regist. (Urol.) Roy. Cornw. Hosp. Truro; Research Regist. (Urol.) S.mead Hosp. Bristol & Bristol Roy. Infirm.; SHO (Urol.) W.on Gen. Hosp.

PROBERT, Winifred Evelyn (retired) 14 Llandaff Close, Penarth CF64 3JH — MRCS Eng. LRCP Lond. 1926; DPH Eng. 1928. Prev: Asst. MOH Aberdare & Mt.ain Ash Div. & Mon. Co. & Co. BreCons.

PROBST, Avalon Fey 130 Stepney Way, Whitechapel, London E1 3BG Tel: 020 7790 0381 — MB BS 1990 Lond.

PROBY, Charlotte Mary Centre for Cutaneous Research, St Bartholomews & Royal London School of Med. & Dentistry, 2 Newark St., London E1 2AT Tel: 020 78827160 Ext: 7173 Fax: 020 78827171 Email: charlotte.proby@cancer.org.uk — MB BS 1982 Lond.; BA Oxf. 1979; MRCP (UK) 1986. p/t Sen. Lect. (Hon. Cons.) (Dermat.) St Bart. & The Roy. Lond. Sch. of Med. & Dent., Qu. Mary & W.field Coll. Lond. Socs: Fell. Roy. Soc. Med. (Sect. of Dermat.); Brit. Assn. Dermat.; Brit. Soc. Investig. Dermat. Prev: Sen. Regist. (Dermat.) St John's Inst. Dermat. St Thomas' Hosp. Lond.; Wellcome Research Fell. Experimen. Dermatol. Lond. Hosp.; Regist. (Dermatol.) St. Geo. Hosp. Lond.

PROBYN, John (retired) Honey Farm, Wrantage, Taunton TA3 6DB — LAH Dub. 1949.

PROCTER, Andrew James McGill 3 Cherry Tree Lane, Great Houghton, Northampton NN4 7AT Tel: 01604 702268 — MRCS Eng. LRCP Lond. 1967; FFA RCS Eng. 1976. (Guy's) Prev: Cons. Anaesth. N.ampton Gen. Hosp.; Sen. Regist. (Anaesth.) Radcliffe Infirm. Oxf.; Anaesth. Regist. Addenbrooke's Hosp. Camb.

PROCTER, Andrew Markham (retired) Ropery Road Surgery, 2A Ropery Road, Gainsborough DN21 2NL Tel: 01427 612895 Fax: 01427 811763 — MB ChB 1979 Manch.; BSc St. And. 1976; MRCGP 1984; FRCGP 1998. Mem. Med. Pract.s Comm. Lond.; Clin. Governance Lead NW Lincs PCG; Mem. Regional Task Force on Waiting Lists, Trent. Prev: Lect. (GP) Univ. Manch.

PROCTER, Andrew William Rawnsley Building, Manchester Royal Infirmary, Oxford Road, Manchester M13 9BX — MB BS 1981 Lond.; MA Camb. 1982; PhD Lond. 1992, MB BS 1981; MRCPsych 1985; FRCPsych 2000. Cons. Psychiat. Manch. Roy. Infirm. & Hon. Clin. Sen. Lect. Univ. Manch. Prev: Sen. Lect. (Psychiat.) United. Med. & Dent. Sch. Guy's Hosp. Lond.

PROCTER, Ann Marie 12 Windermere Avenue, Roath Park, Cardiff CF23 5PQ — MB BCh 1985 Wales; MRCP (UK) 1990.

PROCTER, Anne Elisabeth X-Ray Department, Northern General Hospital, Herries Road, Sheffield S5 7AU Tel: 0114 243 4343 — MB ChB 1979 Sheff.; FRCR 1986. Cons. Diag. Radiol. N. Gen. Hosp. NHS Trust Sheff.

PROCTER, Claire Nicola Netherhouses, Rochester, Newcastle upon Tyne NE19 1RX Tel: 01830 20411 — MB BS 1983 Newc.

PROCTER, David Brian, Squadron Ldr. RAF Med. Br. Station Medical Centre, Royal Air Force BFPO 43 — MB BCh 1990 Wales; MRCGP 1995; DRCOG 1995; DFFP 1995. Dep. Sen. Med. Off. RAF Laarbruch. Prev: SHO (Psychiat.) P.ss Alexandra Hosp. Wroughton; SHO (O & G) Roy. United Hosp. Bath; Trainee GP & Unit Med. Off. RAF St Athan.

PROCTER, Denis 15 Ilton Garth, Clifton, York YO30 4XJ Tel: 01904 693240 — LMSSA Lond. 1955; MRCS Eng. LRCP Lond. 1957; DA Eng. 1958; DPM Eng. 1964; MRCPsych 1973; FRANZCP 1983, M 1968. (Liverp. & Cardiff) Hon. Cons. (Psychiat.) Birch Hill Hosp. Rochdale. Prev: Cons. (Psychiat.) Birch Hill Hosp. Rochdale.

PROCTER, Elizabeth Ann Canada House, Barnsole Road, Gillingham ME7 4JL Tel: 01634 583000 Fax: 01634 583048 — MB ChB 1976 Bristol; MMedSci Leeds 1994; BSc (Hons.) Psychol. Bristol 1973; MRCPsych 1994. p/t Cons. Child Adolesc. Psychiat., Canada Ho., Gillingham.

PROCTER, Gillian Sarah Ropery Road Surgery, 2A Ropery Road, Gainsborough DN21 2NL Tel: 01427 612895 Fax: 01427 811763 — MB ChB 1980 Manch.; Dip. Occ. Med. Manch. 1996; DFFP. RCOG 1995; L.F.Hom 1998. (Manch.) Socs: Soc. Occupat. Med.; Roy. Soc. Med.

PROCTER, Heather Mary Clarendon Medical Practice, Clarendon Street, Hyde SK14 2AQ Tel: 0161 368 5224 Fax: 0161 368 4767 — MB ChB 1981 Leeds; MRCGP 1994; MFFP 1994; DLO RCS Eng. 1986. Clin. Asst. (ENT) Tameside Gen. Hosp. Prev: Trainee GP HildenBoro.

*PROCTER, James Jason 29 Parkland Terrace, Meanwood, Leeds LS6 4PW — MB ChB 1998 Leeds.

PROCTER, Julian Christopher Hollies Surgery, 83 Birch Lane, Dukinfield SK16 4AJ Tel: 0161 330 2039 Fax: 0161 330 5149; 440 Huddersfield Road, Carrbrook, Stalybridge SK15 3JP — MB ChB 1981 Liverp.

PROCTER, Laura 78 Southborough Road, Bickley, Bromley BR1 2EN — MB BS 1981 Lond.

PROCTER, Malcolm Scott The Surgery, 1 Crawley Lane, Pound Hill, Crawley RH10 7DX Tel: 01293 549916 Fax: 01293 615382 — MB BS 1983 Lond.; MRCGP 1988; DRCOG 1987.

PROCTER, Robbyn Simone A&E, Wronswood Branch, Newtown Road, Worcester WR1; 21 Himbleton Road, St Johns, Worcester

WR2 6BA Tel: 01905 428450 — BM 1991 Nottm.; BM BS Nottm. 1991; DCH; DRCOG; DFFP. Sen. Trust Dr. (A&E). Prev: GP Locum Worcester; Worcester VTS Scheme.

***PROCTOR, Andrew James** Hill House, Melbury Rd, Newcastle upon Tyne NE7 7DE — BM BS 1997 Nottm.

PROCTOR, David Wilson Howeburn, Auchattie, Banchory AB31 6PT Tel: 0133 022205 — MB ChB 1961 Aberd.; FFA RCS Eng. 1968; DObst RCOG 1963. (Aberd.) Anaesth. Regist. Aberd. Roy. Infirm. Prev: Med. Regist. Aberd. Roy. Infirm.

PROCTOR, Mr Edward The Cottage, Penbidwal Lane, Pandy, Abergavenny NP7 8EA Tel: 01873 890269 — MB BS Lond. 1960; BA Keele 1954; MD Lond. 1974; FRCS Eng. 1986; MRCS Eng. LRCP Lond. 1960. (Westm.) Linder Foundat. Research Fell. RCS Unit Biophysics Inst. Child Health Lond. Socs: BMA; Roy. Soc. Med. Prev: Surg. Research Fell. (Thoracic Surg.) Guy's Hosp. Lond.; Ho. Surg. & Ho. Phys. St. Chas. Hosp. Lond.

PROCTOR, Edward Andrew Elm Tree Farm, Grove, Canterbury CT3 4BN Tel: 01227 722280 — MB BS 1968 Lond.; MRCS Eng. LRCP Lond. 1967; FFA RCS Eng. 1976. (Roy. Free) Anaesth. Canterbury & Thanet Health Auth. Prev: Sen. Regist. (Anaesth.) Soton. Gen. Hosp.; Med. Regist. Roy. Devon & Exeter Hosp.; Regist. Renal Unit. Gen. Infirm. Leeds.

***PROCTOR, Gillian** 22 Sunniside Drive, South Shields NE34 8DH — MB ChB 1997 Glas.

PROCTOR, Harold Leslie, RD (retired) Rosecroft, Furzeley Corner, Denmead, Waterlooville PO7 6TS Tel: 023922 262192 — MB ChB Leeds 1959. Prev: Ho. Surg. (Obst.) St. Mary's Hosp. Portsmouth.

PROCTOR, Mr Henry (retired) 7 Tudor Grove, Sutton Coldfield B74 2LL Tel: 0121 353 9855 — MB BS 1938 Durh.; FRCS Ed. 1948. Hon. Cons. Birm. AHA (T). Prev: Cons. Surg. Birm. Accid. Hosp.

PROCTOR, Iain Lochee Health Centre, 1 Marshall Street, Lochee, Dundee DD2 3BR Tel: 01382 611283 Fax: 01382 624480; 9 Campfield Gardens, Broughty Ferry, Dundee DD5 2NH Tel: 01382 770018 — MB BCh BAO 1988 Belf.; MRCGP 1993; DRCOG 1991. (Qu. Univ. Belf.) GP Lochee Health Centre Dundee. Socs: MDDUS. Prev: Locum GP; Staff Grade (Med.) Coleraine Hosp.; SHO (Paediat. & Med.) Coleraine Hosp.

PROCTOR, Ian Reginald Davidson (retired) Terwwnnack, Budock Vean Lane, Mawnan Smith, Falmouth TR11 5LH Tel: 01326 250253 Fax: 01326 250253 — MB BChir Camb. 1947; BA Camb. 1944; MRCS Eng. LRCP Lond. 1947; MRCGP 1957. Prev: Flight Lt. RAFVR 1947-50.

PROCTOR, Isobel Stewart Proctor and Partners, Doctors Surgery, 42 Heaton Road, Heaton, Newcastle upon Tyne NE6 1SE Tel: 0191 265 5911 Fax: 0191 265 6974; 6 Dene Crescent, Whitley Bay NE26 3AL — MB ChB 1976 Dundee; MRCGP 1981; DRCOG 1981. GP Newc. u. Tyne.

PROCTOR, Janet Louise Chapel Lane Surgery, 13 Chapel Lane, Formby, Liverpool L37 4DT; Alt Road, Hightown, Liverpool L38 3RH — MB ChB 1988 Liverp.

PROCTOR, John Charles Christopher Stag Medical Centre, 162 Wickersley Road, Rotherham S60 4JW Tel: 01709 379285 Fax: 01709 820431; Wildfell, York Cane, Morther, Rotherham S66 9JH Tel: 01709 703521 — MB ChB 1982 Sheff.; DRCOG 1986. (Sheffield) Hosp. Practitioner, Dermat. Rotherham Gen. Hosp., Rotherham. Prev: SHO (Med.) Roy. Hallamsh. Hosp. Sheff.; SHO (O & G) Nether Edge Hosp. Sheff.; SHO (Paediat. & A & E) Childr. Hosp. Sheff.

PROCTOR, Kenneth George Fraser Calsayseat Medical Group, 2 Calsayseat Road, Aberdeen AB25 3UY Tel: 01224 634345 Fax: 01224 620210; 38 Camperdown Road, Aberdeen AB15 5NU — MB ChB 1980 Aberd.; MRCGP 1984.

PROCTOR, Kenneth Stanley Riverside Surgery, Barnard Avenue, Brigg DN20 8AS Tel: 01652 650131 Fax: 01652 651551 — MB ChB 1969 Liverp.

PROCTOR, Mr Mark Timothy Department of Orthopaedic Surgery, Kingston General Hospital, Galsworthy Road, Kingston upon Thames KT2 7 Tel: 020 8546 7711 Ext: 3242 — MB BS 1983 Lond.; MA Camb. 1984; FRCS (Orth.) 1994; FRCS Eng. 1987. Cons. Orthop. Surg. Qu. Mary's Hosp. Lond. Socs: Assoc. Mem. Brit. Orthopaedic Assn.; Roy. Soc. Med.; Brit. Elbow & Shoulder Soc. Prev: Sen. Regist. & Regist. (Orthop.) Roy. Lond. Hosp. & Roy. Nat. Orthop. Hosp. Stanmore.

PROCTOR, Martyn Charles Davidson Lemon Street Surgery, 18 Lemon Street, Truro TR1 2LZ Tel: 01872 273133 Fax: 01872 260900; Boscolla Farm, Kenwyn, Truro TR4 9EB Tel: 01872 264268 Fax: 01872 260900 — MB BS 1976 Lond.; MRCS Eng. LRCP Lond. 1976; D.Occ.Med. RCP Lond. 1996; DRCOG 1979; Cert. Family Plann. JCC 1979. (St. Bart.) Med. Off. Truro High Sch. For Girls. Socs: BMA; Soc. Occupat. Med. Prev: Trainee GP Cornw. & Is. Scilly VTS.

PROCTOR, Shirley Joyce Rennet Alloa Health Centre, Marshill, Alloa FK10 1AQ Tel: 01259 216476 — MB ChB 1987 Aberd.

PROCTOR, Stephen 58 Hazelwood Avenue, Newcastle upon Tyne NE2 3HX — MB BS 1993 Newc.

PROCTOR, Stephen Clifford Clarendon Medical Practice, Clarendon Street, Hyde SK14 2AQ Tel: 0161 368 5224 Fax: 0161 368 4767 — MB ChB 1979 Sheff.; DObst RCOG 1982. Prev: GP Doncaster VTS; Ho. Off. (Med.) Lodge Moor Hosp. Sheff.; Ho. Off. (Surg.) Lincoln Co. Hosp.

PROCTOR, Professor Stephen John Department of Haematology, Royal Victoria Infirmary, Queen Victoria Road, Newcastle upon Tyne NE1 4LP Tel: 0191 222 7632 Fax: 0191 222 7632; Hill House, Melbury Road, Newcastle upon Tyne NE7 7DE — MB BS Newc. 1970; FRCP Lond. 1985; MRCP (UK) 1973; FRCPath 1989, M 1978. (University Newcastle upon Tyne) Prof. Haemat. Med. Roy. Vict. Infirm. Newc.; Dir. Leukaemia Research Fund Remission Unit.; Head of Sch. - Clin. & Laborat. Scis.

PROCTOR, Susan Elizabeth St. George's Hospital, Morpeth NE61 2NU Tel: 01670 512121 — MB BS 1970 Newc.; FRCPsych 1996, M 1979. Cons. Psychiat. St. Geo. Hosp. Morpeth. Prev: Sen. Regist. (Psychiat.) Newc. Gen. Hosp.

PROCTOR, Thomas Augustus Pugh (retired) 11 Oakhill Drive, Prestatyn LL19 9PU Tel: 0174 562522 — LMSSA 1928 Lond.

PRODHAN, Chitta Ranjan 2 Greenstone Place, Dundee DD2 4XB Tel: 01382 641725 — MB BS 1957 Calcutta. (R.G. Kar Med. Coll.)

PRODHAN, Masud Salam Gloucester House Medical Centre, 17 Station Road, Urmston, Manchester M41 9JS Tel: 0161 748 7115 Fax: 0161 749 8032; Pinecroft, 38 Gibwood Road, Northenden, Manchester M22 4BS Tel: 0161 998 2451 — MB ChB 1992 Manch.; MRCGP 1996. (Manch.) GP Princip. Urmston; GP Locum. Socs: BMA; (Dep. Chairm.) Gt.er Manch. Locum Gp. Prev: SHO (Psychogeriat.) Roy. Oldham Hosp. Trust; GP/Regist. Brooklands Med. Pract. Manch.

PRODROMOU, Salima Barnet & Enfield Health Authority — MB BS 1993 Lond.; DCH 1996; DRCOG 1996. (University College London) Socs: Roy. Coll. Gen. Pract.

PROFFITT, Catherine Mary St Michaels Surgery, Walwyn Close, Twerton-on-Avon, Bath BA2 1ER Tel: 01225 428277 Fax: 01225 338484 — BM BS 1978 Nottm.; MRCGP 1983; DRCOG 1984; DCH RCP Lond. 1983; MFFP 1996.

PROFFITT, Dorothy 229 Leesons Hill, Chislehurst BR7 6QJ Tel: 01689 818277; 84 Long Lane, Grays RM16 2PL Tel: 01375 384246 — MCRS Eng. LRCP Lond. 1983; DCH RCP Lond. 1987. (Sheffield) Staff Grade (Paediat.) Greenwich Healthcare Trust. Socs: BACDA; Assoc. of Brit. Paed. Soc. For CME; BACCH (Comm. CH). Prev: Clin. Med. Off. Optimum Trust Lond.; Clin. Med. Off. & Trainee Clin. Med. Off. Basildon & Thurrock HA; Ho. Off. Grimsby HA.

PROKOP, Renate 82 Ninian Road, Roath Park, Cardiff CF23 5EP — MB BCh 1996 Wales.

PROKOP, Stanislaw (retired) 16 Camborne Road, Sutton SM2 6RH Tel: 020 8642 4602 — MB BS 1975 Lond.; BSc (Hons.) (Pharmacol.) Lond. 1972, MB BS 1975; MRCPsych 1980. Prev: Cons. Child & Adolesc. Psychiat. Croydon Child Guid. Clinic.

PROLL, Sabine Accident & Emergency Department, Charing Cross Hospital, Fulham Palace Road, London W6 8RF; Flat 8, Lister Court, Pasteur Close, London NW9 5HZ — State Exam Med 1993 Aachen.

PRONER, Barry David 83 Strand-on-the-Green, London W4 3PU Tel: 020 8995 8319 Fax: 020 8995 8319 — MD 1967 Wayne State; BA Cornell 1962. (Wayne State Univ. Detroit) Indep. Jungian Psychoanal. Adults & Childr. Lond.; Co-Dir. Child Analytic Train. Soc. Analyt. Psychol.; Train. Analyst Soc. Analyt. Psychol. (Adult & Child Anal.); Train. Therapist. Brit. Assn. Psychother. & Lond. Centre for; Psychother. Prev: Med. Dir. C.G. Jung Childr. Clinic; Cons. Child Psychiat. Hounslow Child Guid. Clin.; Clin. Asst. (Child & Family Psychiat.) W. Lond. & Char. Cross Hosps.

PRONGER

***PRONGER, Elizabeth Ann** 13 Ashburnham Road, Hastings TN35 5JN — MB BS 1996 Lond.

PRONK, Apollo Department of Colorectal Surgery, The North Hampshire Hospital, Aldermaston Road, Basingstoke RG24 9NA — Artsexamen 1986 Utrecht; Artsexamen Utrect 1986.

PROOPS, Mr David William 49 Moor Green Lane, Moseley, Birmingham B13 8NE Tel: 0121 449 2764 Email: david.proops@talk21.com — MB ChB 1975 Birm.; BDS (Hons.) Birm. 1969, MB ChB 1975; FRCS Eng. 1980. Cons. ENT Surg. Qu. Eliz. Hosp. & Childr. Hosp. Birm.

PROPHET, Lynne Elizabeth 3 Dalrymple Place, Dundee DD2 2DN Tel: 01382 566679 — MB ChB 1992 Ed.; BSc (Med. Sci) Hons. Human Genetics Ed. 1991. SHO (Anaesth.) Vict. Hosp. Kirkcaldy. Prev: SHO (Med.) Qu. Margt. Hosp. Dunfermline; SHO (Med.) W.. Gen. Hosp. & Renal Unit Roy. Infirm. Edin.

PROPHET, Michael John (retired) Rose Cottage, Camp Road, Oldbury on Severn, Bristol BS35 1PR Tel: 01454 411154 Fax: 01454 411154 Email: mprophet@msn.com — MB BS 1955 Lond.; MRCS Eng. LRCP Lond. 1955. Prev: Sen. Med. Off. Dept. Health & Social Security.

PROPPER, David John Department of Medical Oncology, St. Bart's. Hospital, London EC1A 7BE Tel: 020 7601 7460 Email: d.j.propper@mds.pmw.ac.uk — MB ChB 1982 Liverp.; MD Aberd. 1993; MRCP (UK) 1985. Cons. Med. Onc. St. Bart's. Hosp. Lond. Prev: ICRF Sen. Regist. (Med. Oncol.) Ch.ill Hosp. Oxf.; MRC Clin. Research Fell. Univ. Aberd.; Sen. Regist. Research Unit Univ. Leeds.

PROSSER, Alison Sarah Jane c/o Anaesthetic Department, Queen Alexandra Hospital, Cosham, Portsmouth PO6 3LY Tel: 023 92 286000 Ext: 6279 — MB BS 1980 Newc.; FFA RCS Eng. 1989; DA Eng. 1982. Cons. Anaesth. & Pain Relief Portsmouth Trust Hosps. Prev: Gen. Med. Off. Holy Cross Hosp. Transkei.

PROSSER, Barbara Mary (retired) 85 Winterbourne Close, Hastings TN34 1XQ Tel: 01424 425134 — MB BChir 1951 Camb.; MA Camb. 1951; MRCS Eng. LRCP Lond. 1948. Prev: SCMO Hastings HA.

PROSSER, Dacre John Herbert (retired) The Vinery, The Hill, Swanton Abbott, Norwich NR10 5EA Tel: 01692 538458 — MRCS Eng. LRCP Lond. 1955; MB Camb. 1955, BChir 1954; DObst RCOG 1960. Prev: Ho. Surg. St. Geo. Hosp. Lond.

PROSSER, David Keith Lloyd Maudsley Hospital, Denmark Hill, London SE5 — MB BChir 1989 Camb.; MRCS Eng LRCP Lond. 1988.

PROSSER, Donald Ivor Flat 1, Mystole House, Chartham, Canterbury — MB BS 1961 Lond.; FRCP Lond. 1984, M 1968. (St. Bart.) Cons. Phys. (Renal & Gen. Med.) Kent & Canterbury Hosp. Prev: Lect. (Med.) W.m. Hosp. Lond.

PROSSER, Elizabeth Joan Shrubbery Avenue Surgery, 13 Shrubbery Avenue, Worcester WR1 1QN Tel: 01905 22888 — MB BS 1962 Lond.; MFFP 1993; DObst RCOG 1964. (Char. Cross) Sen. Clin. Med. Off. (Family Plann.) Worcester Community Trust; Clin. Asst. Worcester Dist. Hosp. Trust. Socs: Midl. Ophth. Soc.; W Midl. Menopause Soc. Prev: Med. Off.(Family Plann.) Cardiff; SHO (O & G) Centr. Middlx. Hosp. Lond.

PROSSER, Gareth Harding 118 Park Hill Road, Birmingham B17 9HD — MB ChB 1994 Manch.

PROSSER, Ingrid May Royal Gwent Hospital, Newport NP20 2UB; Pen-y-Bont, Llanbedr, Crickhowell NP8 1ST Tel: 01873 812124 — MB BChir 1993 Camb.; BSc (Hons.) Lond. 1991; DCH 1997; MRCGP 1998. (Univ. Camb. Sch. Clin. Med.) Specialist Regist. Paediat., All Wales Train. Progr. Prev: Sen. SHO Paediat., Nevill Hall Hosp., Abergavenny, Gwent; SHO (Paediat. & Neonatol.) Roy. Gwent Hosp. Newport. Gwent GP Regist. GP Regist. N. Gwent VTS Nevill Hall Hosp. Gwent; SHO (Cardiol.) Groote Schuur Hosp. Cape Town, S. Africa.

PROSSER, John Allen Croft House, 32 Albany Terrace, Worcester WR1 3DY Tel: 01905 20387 Fax: 01905 20387; Croft house, 32 Albany Terrace, Worcester WR1 3DY Tel: 01905 20387 Fax: 01905 20387 — MB BS 1963 Lond.; FFA RCS Eng. 1967; DA Eng. 1965. (Char. Cross) Cons. Anaesth. Worcester Roy. Infirm.; Curator of Med. museum, Worcester. Socs: Assn. Anaesths.

PROSSER, John Keith, MBE The Surgery, 6 College Road, Eastbourne BN21 4HY Tel: 01323 735044 Fax: 01323 417705; 15 Milton Crescent, Eastbourne BN21 1SP Tel: 01323 639881 — MB ChB Ed. 1968; MRCGP 1982; DTM & H Ed. 1970. GP. Prev: Regional Med. Off. S.A.M.S. Paraguay, S. America.

PROSSER, Jonathan George Stenson Osborn Clinic, Osborn Road, Fareham PO16 7ES Tel: 01329 822220 — MB BS 1988 Newc.; MRCPsych 1993; CCST Child & Adol. Psychiat 1998. (Newcastle) Cons. (Child & Adol. Psychiat.) Fareham & Gosport, Hants. Prev: Sen. Regist. Rotat. (Child Psychiat.) Newc.

PROSSER, Lyn Julia Upwell Street Surgery, 91 Upwell Street, Sheffield S4 8AN Tel: 0114 261 8608 — MB ChB 1981 Sheff.

PROSSER, Oswald Andrew (retired) Hazeldene, 103 Hardhorn Road, Poulton-le-Fylde FY6 8AY — MB BCh 1950 Witwatersrand; BSc Witwatersrand 1941; DPH Eng. 1966; DCH Eng. 1953. Prev: PMO DHSS.

PROSSER, Patricia Delphine Nuffield Health Centre, Welch Way, Witney OX28 6JQ Tel: 01993 703641 — MB BCh BAO 1975 Dub.; MB BCh Dub. 1975, DCH 1979; MRCGP 1983; MRCOG 1982; MFFP 1993; DObst RCPI 1980. (Trinity Coll. Dub.) Prev: Med. Off. Donald Fraser Hosp. Rep. Venda, N. Transvaal, S. Africa; Ho. Off. Nat. Childr. Hosp. Dub.; Ho. Off. Rotunda Hosp. Dub.

PROSSER, Ruth Ellen 13 Twyford Abbey Road, London NW10 7HH — MB BS 1992 Lond. SHO (A & E) St. Richard's Hosp. Chichester W. Sussex. Prev: Ho. Off. (Surg.) St. Richard's Hosp. Chichester; Ho. Off. (Med.) Worthing Dist. Hosp.

PROSSER, Susan Elizabeth Abbey Medical Centre, 42 Station Road, Kenilworth CV8 1JD Tel: 01926 852576 Fax: 01926 851746 — MB BCh 1982 Wales.

PROSSER, Yvonne Ingrid Jennifer Cherry Hayes, Newtown Road, Awbridge, Romsey SO51 0GG — MB BS 1989 Lond.; MRCGP 1994; T(GP) 1994. (Charing Cross & Westminster) GP, Stockbridge, Hants.

PROSSOR, Irene Mackenzie 12 Moray Place, Edinburgh EH3 6DT Tel: 0131 225 2835 — MB BS 1967 Lond.; FRCS Ed. 1985; MRCS Eng. LRCP Lond. 1967; FRCR 1975; FFR 1973; DMRD Eng. 1971. (Westm.) Cons. Radiol. Roy. Infirm. Edin.; Clin. Dir. (Radiol.) Roy. Infirm. Edin. NHS Trust; Hon. Sen. Lect. Univ. Edin. Prev: Cons. Radiol. Roy. Infirm. & Margt. Rose Orthop. Hosp. Edin.; Sen. Regist. (Radiol.), SHO (Path.) & Ho. Phys. W.m. Hosp. Lond.

PROSSOR, John Eckford 173 Ashley Road, Parkstone, Poole BH14 9DL; The Croft, 5 Ravine Road, Canford Cliffs, Poole BH13 7HS — MB ChB 1984 Leic.; MRCGP 1989; DRCOG 1987; DCH RCP Lond. 1986.

PROTHERO, David Priory Hospital North London The Bourne, Southgate, London N14 6RA Tel: 020 8882 8191 Fax: 020 8447 8138; Four Elms, Spring Lane, Lower Ufford, Woodbridge IP13 6EF — MB BS 1960 Lond.; MRCS Eng. LRCP Lond. 1960; FRCPsych 1985, M 1971; DPM Eng. 1964. (Univ. Coll. Hosp.) Cons. Psychiat. Priory Hosp. N. Lond. Prev: Cons. Psychiat. Claybury Hosp. & St. Margt. Hosp. Epping.

***PROTHERO, Joanna Dawn** 71 Durham Road, Rainham, Gillingham ME8 0JJ — BM 1995 Soton.

PROTHERO, William Bernard Francis 51 Benhurst Court, Streatham Common N., London SW16 — MB BCh 1978 Wales; MRCPsych 1982. Sen. Regist. W.m. Hosp. Lond. Prev: Regist. Guy's Hosp. Lond.

PROTHEROE, Andrew Simon 7 Falcon Close, Otley LS21 3EG — MB BS 1990 Lond.; MRCP (UK) 1994. SHO (Med.) King's Coll. Hosp. Lond.

PROTHEROE, Clement Keith Armada Surgery, 28 Oxford Place, Plymouth PL1 5AJ Tel: 01752 665805 Fax: 01752 220056; Little Court, St. Ive, Liskeard PL14 3ND Tel: 01579 362509 — MB ChB 1956 Bristol. (Bristol) Prev: Ho. Surg. Cossham Hosp. Kingswood; Ho. Phys. Scott Isolat. Hosp. Plymouth.

PROTHEROE, Colin (retired) 20 Adeline Gardens, Kenton, Newcastle upon Tyne NE3 4JQ Tel: 0191 285 3080 — MD Sheff. 1965, MB ChB 1953; MRCS Eng. LRCP Lond. 1953; FRCP Ed. 1973, M 1960; FRCPsych 1974, M 1972; DPM Durham. 1959. Prev: Cons. Psychiat. Newc. HA.

PROTHEROE, David Nicholas 8 Hampton Lane, Solihull B91 2PS — MB ChB 1987 Leeds.

PROTHEROE, David Trevelyan Long Barn, Charlton, Kilmersdon, Bath BA3 5TN Tel: 01761 32326 — BM BCh 1963 Oxf.; MA Oxf., BM BCh 1963; FFA RCS Eng. 1969. (Oxf.) Cons. Anaesth. Bath Clin. Area.

PROTHEROE, Dinah Elizabeth Drumhar Health Centre, North Methven St., Perth PH1 5PD Tel: 01738 564215 Fax: 01738 444410 Email: dinah.protheroe@tuht.scot.nhs.uk; Bellfield, Dalguise, Dunkeld PH8 0JU Tel: 01350 727380 Fax: 01350 727453 — MB BChir (Cantab); MB BChir Camb. 1975; MA Camb. 1975; MRCP (UK) 1978; Cert. Prescribed Equiv. Exp. JCPTGP 1990; DCH RCP Lond. 1979; DRCOG 1977; FRCPCH 1997. (Univ. Camb. Girton Coll. & Univ. Oxf. Med. Sch.) Cons. Community Paediat. Tayside Univ. Hosp.s NHS Trust; Med. Adviser, Perth & Kinross Fostering and Permanence Panel. Prev: SCMO Perth & Kinross Healthcare NHS Trust; Assoc. GP Hong Kong.

PROTHEROE, Mr Keith (retired) 13 Arden Drive, Giffnock, Glasgow G46 7AF Tel: 0141 638 4185 — MB ChB Ed. 1956; FRCS Ed. 1964. Prev: Cons. Orthop. Surg. Glas. Roy. Infirm.

PROTHEROE, Mark Christopher Nettleham Medical Practice, 14 Lodge Lane, Nettleham, Lincoln LN2 2RS Tel: 01522 751717 Fax: 01522 754474 — BM 1991 Soton.; BSc Wales 1986; DFFP 1996. (Soton.) GP Princip. Nettleham. Socs: BMA; Soc. Wessex Grad.s; Christ. Med. Fell.sh. (Regional Represen.) Prev: SHO (O & G) Roy. Bournemouth Hosp.; SHO (Paediat. & ENT) Poole Gen. Hosp.; SHO (Palliat. Care & Rheum.) ChristCh. Hosp. Dorset.

***PROTHEROE, Rachel Elizabeth** The Maples, 157 Vicarage Road, Morriston, Swansea SA6 6DT — MB BS 1998 Lond.; MB BS Lond 1998.

PROTHEROE, Richard Trevelyan Intensive Care Unit, Hope Hospital, Stott Lane, Salford M6 8HD Tel: 0161 789 7373; Brier Cottage, 15 Arthog Road, Hale, Altrincham WA15 0NA Tel: 0161 980 2864 — MB BS 1988 Lond.; MRCP (UK) 1993; MRCS Eng LRCP Lond. 1988; FRCA 1996; DA (UK) 1995. (St Thomas's) Cons. Anaesth. With interest in Critical Care, Hope Hosp. Salford. Socs: BMA; Assn. Anaesth.; Intens. Care Soc. Prev: Sen. Clin. Fell. In Anaesth. Bristol Roy. Infirm.; Sen. Regist. ICU, Roy. Adelaide Hosp. Adelaide, S.Australia; Specialist Regist. Rotat. (Anaesth.) Bristol.

PROTHEROE, Roger Henry Bertram (retired) 4 Riverside Drive, Solihull B91 3HH — MA, MD Camb. 1956, MB BChir 1947; FRCPath 1972, M 1964. Prev: Cons. Pathol. E. Birm. & Solihull Hosps.

PROTHEROE, Susan Alison Boultham Park Medical Practice, Boultham Park Road, Lincoln LN6 7SS Tel: 01522 874444 Fax: 01522 874466 — BM Soton 1984; DRCOG 1988. (Univ. Soton.) GP Partner. Socs: BMA; Christ. Med. Fell.sh. Prev: Staff Psychiat. Addic. Serv. E. Dorset; Regist. (Psychiat.) St. Ann's Hosp. Poole; Trainee GP/SHO Highcliffe & Poole Gen. Hosp.

PROTHEROE, Susan Margaret 51 Thorndon Gardens, Ewell, Epsom KT19 0QB Tel: 020 8393 7894 — MB ChB 1986 Bristol; MRCP (UK) 1989. Research Fell. (Paediat.) Univ. Birm. Prev: Regist. (Paediat.) Leics. Roy. Infirm.; SHO (Paediat.) Univ. Hosp. Qu. Med. Centre Nottm.; SHO (Paediat.) St. Jas. Univ. Hosp. Leeds.

PROTOPAPAS, Michael dept of anaesthetics, Darent Valley hospital, Darenthwood road, Dartford DA2 8DA Tel: 01322 428100 Fax: 01322 428652 — MB BS 1988 Lond.; BSc Lond. 1985; FRCA 1993; DA (UK) 1990. (St Marys Hospital medical school) Socs: MRCAnaesth. & Assn. Anaesth.; Intens. Care Soc.; BMA. Prev: Regist. anaesthetics Guys Hosp. Lonodn; Sen. Regist. ITU Guys Hosp.; Specialist Regist. (spr) anaesthetics UCH/Roy. free Rotat.

PROUD, Angela May Ystradgynlais Community Hospital, Glanrhyd, Ystradgynlais, Swansea SA9 1AU Tel: 01639 844777 Ext: 3571; Tegfan, Pen-y-Pentre, Llanfihangel, Talyllyn, Brecon LD3 7TG Tel: 01874 658518 — MB BCh 1977 Wales. (Univ. Hosp. Wales) Staff Grade (Psychiat.) Community Ment. Health Team Ystradgynlais. Prev: Clin. Asst. Community Ment. Health Team Ystradgynlais.

PROUD, Mr George Royal Victoria Infirmary, Queen Victoria Road, Newcastle upon Tyne NE1 4LP Tel: 0191 232 5131 Fax: 0191 232 5278; 3 Westfield, Gosforth, Newcastle upon Tyne NE3 4YE Tel: 0191 285 3335 Fax: 0191 285 7177 Email: george@g-proud-frcs.demon.co.uk — MB BS 1971 Newc.; MD Newc. 1980; BDS Durham. 1966; FRCS Eng. 1976. Cons. Surg. (Endocrine & Vasc. Surg.) Newc. AHA (T); Sen. Lect. (Surg.) Newc. Univ.; Ct. Examr. RCS Eng.; Regional Adviser RCS Eng.; Mem. Train. Bd. & the Hosp. Recognition Comm. RCS. Socs: Surg. Research Soc.; (Ex-Sec.) Brit. Transpl. Soc.; Assn. Surg. Prev: 1st Asst. Dept. Surg. Univ. Newc.; Sen. Research Assoc. Univ. Newc. Dept. Surg.; Regist. (Gen. Surg.) Newc. AHA (T).

PROUD, Jeremy Jon North House Surgery, North House, Hope Street, Crook DL15 9HU Tel: 01388 762945 Fax: 01388 765333; 33 Castle View, Witton-le-Wear, Bishop Auckland DL14 0DH — MB ChB 1976 Sheff.; DRCOG 1983. Gen. Med. Practitioner; Clin. Asst. Old Age Psychiat. Prev: SHO (O & G) & (Ophth.) Leic. Roy. Infirm.; Trainee GP Glos. VTS.

PROUD, Rena Danae (retired) 1 Kidbrooke Gardens, London SE3 0PD — MB BS 1957 Lond.; MRCPsych 1973; DPM Eng. 1963. Cons. Psychiat. Greenwich Dist. Hosp.

PROUDFOOT, Alexander Thompson (retired) Royal Infirmary, Lauriston Place, Edinburgh EH3 9YW Tel: 0131 536 2303 Fax: 0131 536 2304 — MB ChB 1962 Ed.; BSc (Hons.) Ed. 1959, MB ChB 1962; FRCP Lond. 1994; FRCP Ed. 1974, M 1965. Cons. Phys. Roy. Infirm. Edin.; Dir. Scott. Poisons Informat. Bureau.

PROUDFOOT, David James Hillbank Health Centre, Flat 1A, 1 Constitution Street, Dundee DD3 6NF Tel: 01382 221976 Fax: 01382 201980; 1 Glamis Terrace, Dundee DD2 1NA — MB ChB 1983 Dundee; DRCOG 1986.

PROUDFOOT, Elizabeth McGruther 21 Inverary Terrace, Dundee DD3 6BR Tel: 01382 224490 — MB ChB 1948 Glas. (Univ. Glas.) Prev: Princip. GP Tayside HB; Clin. Asst. Dept. Surg. Tayside HB; Hon. Tutor Dept. Gen. Pract. Univ. Dundee.

PROUDFOOT, Frederick Buchan (retired) 21 Inverary Terrace, Dundee DD3 6BR Tel: 01382 224490 — MD 1979 Glas.; MB ChB 1947; FRCGP 1981, M 1967. Prev: Princip. GP Tayside HB.

PROUDFOOT, Michael Crawford Hospital Hill Surgery, 7 Izatt Avenue, Dunfermline KY11 3BA Tel: 01383 731721 Fax: 01383 623352; Fernbank, 2 Bruccharen Road, Limekilns, Dunfermline KY11 3YZ — MB ChB 1976 Dundee.

PROUDFOOT, Ronald Thomas Calabar, Pica, Workington CA14 4PZ — MB ChB 1974 Glas.; FFA RCSI 1980.

PROUDLOVE, Derek Allan Paediatric Liaison, Mulberry House, Alder Hey Hospital, Eaton road, Liverpool L12 2AP Tel: 0151 252 5586 Email: derek.proudlove@rlch-tr.nwest.nhs.uk — MB ChB 1988 Leeds; MA Sheff. 1995; MRCPsych 1994. Cons child & Adolesc. Psychiat. Prev: Sen. Regist. Rotat. (Child & Adolesc. Psychiat.) Sheff.

PROUDLOVE, Robert Forth View Practice, Dean Road, Bo'ness EH51 0DQ Tel: 01506 822466 Fax: 01506 826216; 47 Green Tree Lane, Bo'ness EH51 0PH — MB ChB 1978 Manch.; MRCGP 1982.

PROUT, Elizabeth Jane Whitehaven, Bissoe Road, Carnon Downs, Truro TR3 6JA Tel: 01872 863015 — MB BS 1959 Lond.; BSc Lond. 1956; DCH Eng. 1962. (Univ. Coll. Hosp.) Prev: Research Regist. (Hypertens.) Roy. Cornw. Hosp. Truro; Med. Asst. Horton Hosp. Banbury; SHO St. Mary's Hosp. Childr. Annexe Lond.

PROUT, Mr Jeremy Robert 27B The Ridgeway, Enfield EN2 8PB — MB BS 1991 Lond.; MB BS (Distinc. Path & Surg.) Lond. 1991; BSc (1st. cl. Hons. Pharmacol.) Lond. 1988; MRCP (UK) 1995; FRCS Eng. 1996. (Middlx. Hosp. Med. Sch.) SHO Rotat. (Anaesth. / IC) Univ. Coll. / Roy. Free Hosps. Lond. Prev: SHO (Cardiothoracic Surg.) Roy. Brompton Hosp. Lond.; SHO Rotat. (Surg.) St. Mary's Hosp. Lond.; Ho. Surg. Middlx. Hosp. & Univ. Coll. Hosp. Lond.

PROUT, John Warwick, CStJ (retired) 9 Crownfields, Sevenoaks TN13 1EF Tel: 01732 454768 — MRCS Eng. LRCP Lond. 1953; MFOM RCP Lond. 1978; DIH Eng. 1965. Prev: Sen. Med. Off. Ford Motor Co. Warley.

PROUT, Muriel Frances (retired) 87 Chevening Road, Chipstead, Sevenoaks TN13 2SA — MD Lond. 1928, MB BS 1926. Prev: Ho. Phys. & Res. Asst. Pathol. Roy. Free Hosp.

***PROUT, Rachel** 22 Ermin Close, Baydon, Marlborough SN8 2JQ — MB ChB 1998 Bristol.

PROUT, Mr William Geoffrey The White Cottage, 39 Blackbrook Park Avenue, Fareham PO15 5JN Tel: 01329 280455 Fax: 01329 280455 — MB BS Lond. 1961; FRCS Eng. 1965. (St. Thos.) Cons. Surg. Portsmouth Hosp. Gp. Socs: Fell. Roy. Soc. Med. Prev: Sen. Surg. Regist. St. Thos. Hosp. Lond.; Surg. Regist. Wolverhampton Hosp. Gp.; Ho. Surg. Renal Unit Roy. Postgrad. Med. Sch. Lond.

PROVAN, Alison Anne Community Child Health Offices, Aros, Lochgilphead Tel: 01546 2323; Ashfield Old School House, Achnamara, Lochgilphead PA31 8PT Tel: 01546 850245 Fax: 01546 850302 — MB ChB 1982 Leic. Staff Grade (Comm. Child Health) Aros Lochgilphead. Prev: Clin. Asst. (Psychiat.) Argyll & Bute Hosp. Lochgilphead.

PROVAN

PROVAN, Andrew Benjamin Haematology Department, Royal United Hospital, Bath BA1 3NG Tel: 01225 428331 Fax: 01225 461044; 79 Roselands Gardens, Highfield, Southampton SO17 1QJ Tel: 01703 550262 — MB ChB 1984 Leic.; BSc Leic. 1979, MB ChB 1984; MRCP (UK) 1988; MRCPath 1992. Sen. Regist. (Haemat.) Roy. S. Hants. Hosp. Soton. Prev: LRF Research Fell. Roy. S. Hants. Hosp. Soton.; Regist. (Haemat.) Stobhill Hosp. Glas.; Regist. (Med.) Bradford Roy. Infirm. Bradford.

PROVAN, Christopher David Elmbank Group, Foresterhill Health Centre, Westburn Road, Aberdeen AB25 2AY Tel: 01224 696949 Fax: 01224 691650; 32 Burns Road, Aberdeen AB15 4NS Tel: 01224 317644 — MB ChB 1989 Aberd. (Aberd.) Socs: Roy. Coll. Gen. Pract. Prev: Trainee GP Aberd. VTS; Ho. Off. (Surg.) Aberd. Roy. Infirm.; Ho. Off. (Geriat.) Woodend Gen. Hosp. Aberd.

PROVAN, David Hart (retired) 66 St Michaels Drive, Cupar KY15 5BS — MB ChB 1944 St. And.; DMRD Eng. 1958. Prev: Cons. Radiol. E. Surrey HA.

PROVAN, Donald Alexander 28 Hen Parc Avenue, Upper Killay, Swansea SA2 7HA — MB ChB 1981 Birm.

PROVAN, Janice 32 Burns Road, Aberdeen AB15 4NS — MB ChB 1984 Dundee; FRCS Glas. 1992. Staff Grade Surg. (ENT) Aberd. Roy. Infirm.

PROVERBS, Allan Graham (retired) 28 Beechwood Crescent, Chandlers Ford, Eastleigh SO53 5PA — MB ChB Ed. 1935. Prev: Ho. Phys. & Ho. Surg. St. Luke's Hosp. Bradford.

PROVOST, Gillian Claire The Surgery, 67 Vineyard Hill Road, London SW19 7JL Tel: 020 8947 2579 — MB BS 1978 Lond.; BSc (2nd cl. Hons.) Immunol. Lond. 1978, MB BS 1981; MRCGP 1988; DRCOG 1987.

PROWSE, Alan David 46 Badingham Drive, Leatherhead KT22 9HA Tel: 01372 373798 — MB BCh 1956 Wales; BSc Wales 1952; DObst RCOG 1957. (Cardiff) Med. Adviser Lond. Country Bus Serv. Ltd., Lond. Links, Speed Link, Rawlinson, Hunter & Silvertech Ltd; Med. Examr. Min of Transport. Socs: Soc. Occupat. Med.; BMA. Prev: Ho. Phys. Bridgend Gen. Hosp.; Ho. Surg. (O & G) Neath Gen. Hosp.

PROWSE, Graham David Windsor The Limes Medical Centre, 65 Leicester Road, Narborough, Leicester LE9 5DU — MB BS 1979 Lond.; MA Camb. 1980, BA 1976; MRCGP 1983; DRCOG 1981. (Westm.) GP Leicester; GP Trainer Leicester VTS; Clin. Teach. Leicester Univ. Med. Sch.; Clin. Asst. UHL BrE. Care Centre; Forens. Med. Examr. Leics. Police. Socs: Leic. Med. Soc.; SW Leicester GP Gp.; Anplo French Med. Soc. Prev: SHO Leicester Roy. Infirm.; SHO Geo. Eliot Hosp. Nuneaton; Ho. Off. St. Stephens Hosp. Chelsea & Walsgrave Hosp. Coventry.

PROWSE, Keith Department of Respiratory Medicine, North Staffordshire Hospital, City General, Newcastle Road, Stoke-on-Trent ST4 6QG Tel: 01782 552328 Fax: 01782 552323; Kyriole, Pinewood Road, Ashley Heath, Market Drayton TF9 4PP Tel: 01630 672879 — MB ChB 1962 Birm.; BSc Birm. 1959, MD 1971; FRCP Lond. 1979, M 1966; MRCS Eng. LRCP Lond. 1962. (Birm.) Cons. Phys. (Respirat. Med.) N. Staffs Hosp. Stoke-on-Trent; Dir. RCP Int'l. Office. Socs: Eur. Respirat. Soc.; (Chairm. & Pres.) Brit. Thoracic Soc.; (Pres.) Eur. Bd. Pnenmology. Prev: Med. Dir. N. Staffs. Hosp. 1993-2001; Sen. Regist. & Lect. (Med.) Univ. Birm.; Research Fell. Unité 14, France.

PROWSE, Margaret Judith (retired) 46 Badingham Drive, Leatherhead KT22 9HA Tel: 01372 373798 — MB BCh 1955 Wales; BSc Wales 1952, MB BCh 1955. Prev: Clin. Asst. (Psychiat.) W. Pk. Hosp. Epsom.

PROWSE, Mary-Jane Clare 10 Mallorie Park Drive, Ripon HG4 2QD — MB ChB 1985 Leeds; DRCOG 1988.

PROWSE, Roger Beresford 1 The Orchard, South St., Uley, Dursley GL11 5ST — MB BChir 1950 Camb.; DObst RCOG 1952.

PROZESKY, Detlef Richard 11 Garth Boulevard, Wirral CH63 5LS — MB ChB 1974 Pretoria; BSc Pretoria 1971, MB ChB 1974; MCommH Liverp. 1983.

PRUDHOE, Kenneth Glenpark Medical Centre, Ravensorth Road, Dunston, Gateshead NE11 9AD Tel: 0191 460 4300, 0191 461 0106 Email: kenneth.prudhoe@gp-a85006nhs.uk — MB BS 1979 Newc.; PhD Newc. 1971, BSc 1968; FRCGP 1991, M 1983; AFOM RCP Lond. 1990; CChem MRSC 1991. (Newcastle upon Tyne) Trainer (Gen. Pract.) N.umbria VTS; BMA Occupat. Health Advis. Comm. Socs: RCGP (Dep. Mem. Counc.). Prev: Trainee GP N.d. VTS.

PRUDHOE, Rosemary Houghton Houghton Health Centre, Church Street, Houghton-le-Spring DH4 4DN Tel: 0191 584 2106 Fax: 0191 584 9493; 29 L'Arbre Crescent, Whickham, Newcastle upon Tyne NE16 5YQ Tel: 0191 488 6273 Email: rosiprudho@aol.com — MB BS 1974 Newc.; BSc Newc. 1971; MRCP (UK) 1977; MRCGP 1984. (Newcastle-upon-Tyne) Princip. GP (Reduced Committment) Houghton-le-Spring; Clin. Asst. Bone Metab. Freeman Hosp. Newc.-upon-Tyne. Prev: GP Jarrow; Regist. (Gen. Pract.) Cruddas Pk. & Felling N.umbria VTS; Regist. (Paediat.) Newc. Gen. Hosp.

PRUDO-CHLEBOSZ, Raymond Richard Zbigniew 71 Shepherds Hill, London N6 5RE — MB BS 1970 Lond.; MRCPsych 1973; MRCS Eng. LRCP Lond. 1969; FRCPC 1979. Dir. (Outpats. & Community Psychiat.) McMaster Univ. Med. Centre Hamilton Ontario, Canada; Prof. Dept. Psychiat. McMaster Univ. Hamilton Ontario, Canada. Prev: Sen. Regist. Bethlem Hosp. & Maudsley Hosps. Lond.

PRUNTY, Mark John 110 Bedford Avenue, Hayes UB4 0DU — MB ChB 1983 Leeds.

PRUSS, Anthony Ewen Tel: 020 8590 6600 Fax: 020 8983 8992; 607 Green Lane, Goodmayes, Ilford IG3 9RN Tel: 020 8597 3054 — MB BS 1970 Lond.; BSc Lond. 1967; MRCS Eng. LRCP Lond. 1970; AFOM RCP Lond. 1981. Gen. Practitioner; Princip. Forens. Med. Examr. Metrop. Police. Socs: Assn. Police Surg.; BMA. Prev: SHO (Gen. Med. & Paediat.) King Geo. Hosp. Ilford.

PRUSSIA, Celia Mary Hoseley Bank Cottage, Park Lane, Rossett, Wrexham LL12 0BL — MB ChB 1967 Liverp.; Dip. Psychother. 1994; DPhysMed Eng. 1972; DA Eng. 1970. (Liverpool) Clin. Asst. Psychoth.Maelor Gen Hosp.Wrexham; Private Psychoth. BUPA Yale Hosp.Wrexham; Vol. Counsellor. Stepping stones Wrexham. Socs: BMA.

PRUST, Alison Jane 113 Tippings Lane, Woodley, Reading RG5 4RY — MB BS 1996 Lond.

PRVULOVICH, Elizabeth Mary Institute of Nuclear Medicine, Middlesex Hospital, London W1N 8AA Tel: 020 7380 9387 Fax: 020 7637 0578 Email: l.prvulovich@nucmed.ucl.ac.uk — MB ChB 1985 Manch.; MSc (Nuclear Med.) Lond. 1995; MD Manch. 1993; MRCP (UK) 1988. (manchester) p/t Cons. Phys. in Nuclear Med. Middlx. Hosp. Lond. Socs: Brit. Cardiac Soc.; Amer. Soc. Nuclear Cardiol.; Soc. Of Nuclear Med. Prev: Sen. Regist. (Nuclear Med.) Middlx. Hosp. Lond.; Regist. (Cardiac & Research Cardiac) Kings Coll. Hosp. Lond.

PRYCE, Andrew Charles William Dinas Lane Medical Centre, 149 Dinas Lane, Huyton, Liverpool L36 2NW Tel: 0151 489 2298 — MB BS 1985 Lond. Prev: Trainee GP W. Suff. Hosp. Bury St. Edmunds VTS.

PRYCE, Damian William Taunton & Somerset Hospital, Musgrove Park, Taunton TA1 5DA Tel: 01823 342789 Fax: 01823 336877; Rooks House, Bishopswood, Chard TA20 3RZ — MB BS 1978 Lond.; MA Camb. 1979; MRCP (UK) 1983; MFOM RCP Lond. 1989; DIH 1988; FRCP 1999. (St. Bart.) Cons. Dermat. Taunton & Som. NHS Trust. Prev: Sen. Regist. (Dermat.) Roy. Liverp. Hosp.; Occupat. Phys. BP Research; Hon. Clin. Asst. St. John's Hosp. for Dis. of Skin Lond.

PRYCE, Douglas Paul Beech Hurst, 28 Queens Road, Waterlooville PO7 7SB — MB BS 1968 Lond.; MRCS Eng. LRCP Lond. 1968; MRCGP 1975; DRCOG 1981.

PRYCE, Elizabeth Mary — MB BS 1989 Lond.; MRCGP (Distinc.) 1994; BSc Pharm. Lond. 1986; DRCOG 1996; DFFP 1994. (Charing Cross and Westminster)

PRYCE, Heather Anne 14 Castlemaine Avenue, Ewell, Epsom KT17 2RA — MB BS 1981 Lond.; BSc Lond. 1978; MRCGP 1986; DRCOG 1984; Cert. Family Plann. JCC 1984.

PRYCE, Ivor Gwyndaf (retired) 5 The Close, Llanishen, Cardiff CF14 5NG — MB BS 1951 Lond.; MD Lond. 1961; MRCS Eng. LRCP Lond. 1951; FRCPsych 1981, M 1971; DPM Eng. 1957. Prev: Cons. Psychiat. WhitCh. Hosp. Cardiff.

PRYCE, John Charles The Surgery, Limes Avenue, Alfreton, Derby DE55 7DW Tel: 01773 832525 — MB BS 1983 Lond.; DRCOG 1987. (Univ. Coll. Hosp.) Prev: Trainee GP Avon VTS; SHO (Orthop.) Qu. Eliz. II Hosp. Welwyn Garden City; Ho. Off. (Surg.) N.ampton Gen. Hosp.

PRYCE, Linda Susan Moordown Medical Centre, 2A Redhill Crescent, Bournemouth BH9 2XF Tel: 01202 516139 Fax: 01202 548525 — MB ChB 1974 Bristol. GP Bournemouth.

PRYCE, Rebekah Anne Brynawel, Mary St., Treharris CF46 5LH; 17 Oakfield Close, Potters Bar EN6 2BE — BM BCh 1998 Oxf.; BM BCh Oxf 1998.

***PRYCE, Sarah Elizabeth** White Gables, Marsh Lane, North Cove, Beccles NR34 7QQ — BM BS 1998 Nottm.; BM BS Nottm 1998.

PRYCE-JONES, Elizabeth (retired) 73 Temple Sheen Road, London SW14 7RS Tel: 020 8876 5070 — MB ChB 1948 Leeds; FRCPCH 1997; DCH RCP Lond. 1955. Prev: Princip. Phys. (Child Health), Merton & Sutton HA.

PRYCE THOMAS, Rachel Louise Neuadd, Cwmdu, Crickhowell NP8 1RY Tel: 01874 730253 — MB BCh 1993 Wales. Staff Grade Community Padiat. E Surrey Healthcare NHS Trust. E Surrey Hosp. Redhill Surrey. Prev: Locum CMO Community Paediat. (Ashford); SHO Accid & Emerg. Caboolture Australia; SHO Med. Caboolture Australia.

PRYDAL, Jeremy Ikley Leicester Royal infirmary, Infirmary Square, Leicester LE1 5WW Tel: 0116 258 6964 Email: jip@elmc.demon.co.uk; Elm Cottage, Main Street, Keyham, Leicester LE7 9JQ Tel: 0116 259 5389 Fax: 01223 464969 Email: j.prydal@elmc.demon.co.uk — MB BS 1982 Lond.; PhD Camb. 1991; FRCOphth 1993; MD Lond. 1995.

PRYDE, Alan Neil Morton Howe of Fife Medical Practice, 27 Commercial Road, Ladybank, Cupar KY15 7JS Tel: 01337 830765 Fax: 01337 831658 — MB ChB 1982 Ed.; MRCGP 1986; DRCOG 1986. (Edinburgh) Clin. Asst. (A & E) Perth Roy. Infirm.; Med. Off. Knockhill Racing Circuit Fife.

***PRYDE, Iain** 29 Auchmithie Place, Finglassie, Glenrothes KY7 4TY — MB ChB 1996 Ed.

PRYDE, Louise Anne HMP Perth, 3 Edinburgh Road, Perth PH2 8AT Tel: 01738 622293 — MB ChB Dundee 1989; MRCGP 1995. Med. Practitioner HMP Perth.

PRYER, Anthony Alastair Wells City Practice, 22 Chamberlain Street, Wells BA5 2PF Tel: 01749 673356 Fax: 01749 670031 — BM BCh 1983 Oxf.; MA Camb. 1983; MRCGP 1987; DCH RCP Lond. 1987; DRCOG 1986. Prev: Trainee GP Bath VTS.

PRYER, Michael Phillip Lorimer Clarkson Surgery, De-Havilland Road, Wisbech PE13 3AN Tel: 01945 583133 Fax: 01945 464465 — MB BS 1980 Lond.

PRYKE, David Simon Ewart Churchfields Surgery, Recreation Road, Bromsgrove B61 8DT Tel: 01527 872163; Ingewood, 38 New Road, Bromsgrove B60 2JJ Tel: 01527 575610 — MB BS 1987 Lond.; MRCGP 1994.

PRYKE, Gillian Rachel Winyates Health Centre, Winyates, Redditch B98 0NR Tel: 01527 525533 Fax: 01527 517969 — MB BS 1989 Lond.; MRCGP 1994.

PRYKE, Jason Russell 41B Echo Barn Lane, Wrecclesham, Farnham GU10 4NG — MB BS 1994 Lond.; DRCOG 1999 Lond.; MRCGP 2000; DCH RCP Lond. 1998. (London)

PRYLE, Belinda Jane Anaesthetic Department, Gloucestershire Royal Hospital, Gloucester GL1 3NN Tel: 01452 528555; 6 College Lawn, Cheltenham GL53 7AE Tel: 01452 864673 — MB BS 1983 Lond.; FRCA 1990. (Middlx. Med. Sch.) Cons. Anaesth. Gloucester Roy. Hosp. Socs: Pain Soc.; Assn. Anaesth.; Obst. Anaesth. Soc.

PRYN, Robert Brian The Surgery, Station Road, Great Massingham, King's Lynn PE32 2JQ Tel: 01485 518336 Fax: 01485 518725; Parsley Barn, Weasenham Road, Great Massingham, King's Lynn PE32 2EY Tel: 01485 520104 — MB BS 1980 Lond.

PRYN, Stephen John Sir Humphrey Davy Department Anaesthetics, Bristol Royal Infirmary, Bristol BS2 8HW Tel: 0117 928 2163 Fax: 0117 928 2098; 45 Logan Road, Bishopston, Bristol BS7 8DS Tel: 0117 924 7942 — MB BChir 1981 Cam.; MA Camb. 1983; ECFMG Cert. 1987; FFA RCS Eng. 1988; DCH RCP Lond. 1985. (Cambridge University Addenbrookes Hospital) Cons. Anaesth. Bristol Roy. Infirm. Prev: Sen. Regist. (Anaesth.) Oxf. RHA; Regist. (Anaesth.) S.ampton. Gen. Hosp.; Instruc. (Anaesth.) Univ. Michigan, USA.

PRYOR, Antony Damian 228 Olney Road, London SE17 3HU — MB BS 1987 Lond.

PRYOR, Caroline Virginia Chitterne House, Chitterne, Warminster BA12 0LG — MB BS 1996 Lond.; BSc Lond. 1995. (St. Bart's Hosp. Lond.)

PRYOR, Mr Glyn Alan Orthopaedic Department, Edith Cavell Hospital, Bretton Gate, Peterborough PE3 9GZ; Autumn Lodge, Main St, Cotterstock, Peterborough PE8 5HD — MB BS 1978 Lond.; MS Lond. 1990; FRCS Eng. 1983. (Kings College Hospital) Cons. Orthop. Surg. Edith Cavell Hosp. P'boro. Socs: Fell. BOA; Nat. Osteoporosis Soc. Prev: Sen. Regist. (Orthop.) Addenbrooke's Hosp. Camb.

PRYOR, Mr John Pembro The Lister Hospital, Chelsea Bridge Road, London SW1W 8RH Tel: 020 7730 3417 Fax: 020 7824 8867; The Beacon, Channel Way, Fairlight TN35 4BP Tel: 01424 814945 — MB BS 1961 Lond.; MS Lond. 1971; FRCS Eng. 1967; MRCS Eng. LRCP Lond. 1961; AKC. (King's Coll. Hosp.) p/t Emerit. Reader Inst. Urol. Univ. Coll. Lond. Socs: Past Pres. Europ. Soc. Impotence Research; (Hon. Pres.) Europ. Assn. Gen. Surgs.; (Ex-Chairm.) Europ. Assn. Gen. Microsyrgs. Prev: Cons. Uroandrol. King's Coll. & St. Peter's Hosps. Lond.; Dean Inst. Urol. Univ. Coll. Lond.; Pres. ESSIR.

PRYS-JONES, David Robert Vaughan (retired) 65 West End Avenue, Nottage, Porthcawl CF36 3NH Tel: 01656 771526 — MRCS Eng. LRCP Lond. 1947. Prev: Regional Med. Admiss. Off. S.E. Thames RHA.

PRYS-JONES, Oliver Edmund Plas Meddyg Surgery, Station Road, Ruthin LL15 1BP Tel: 01824 702255 Fax: 01824 707221 — MB ChB 1987 Liverp.; MB ChB (Hons.) Liverp. 1987; PhD Camb. 1982; BSc (Hons.) St. And. 1976; MRCGP 1992; T(GP) 1992; DRCOG 1990. Socs: BMA. Prev: Trainee GP/SHO (Paediat. & O & G) Ysbyty Glan Clwyd Bodelwyddan VTS; Ho. Off. (Med. & Surg.) BRd.green Hosp. Liverp.

PRYS-ROBERTS, Cedric Foxes Mead, Cleeve Hill Road, Cleeve, Bristol BS49 4PG Tel: 01934 834267 — MB BS 1959 Lond.; PhD Leeds 1968; MA Oxf. 1967, DM 1975; FFA RCS Eng. 1964; DA Eng. 1962. (St. Bart.) Prof. Anaesth. Univ. Bristol; Hon. Cons. Anaesth. Bristol Roy. Infirm. & Bristol Roy. Hosp. Sick Childr; Edit. Bds. Brit. Jl. Anaesth., Europ. Jl. Anaesth. & Analgesia. Socs: Anaesth. Research Soc. (Chairm.); Europ. Acad. Anaesth. (Senator). Prev: Clin. Reader Nuffield Dept. Anaesth. Univ. Oxf.; Prof. Anaesth. Univ. Calif. USA.; Research Fell. in Anaesth. Univ. Leeds.

PRYS-ROBERTS, Curig Owen Foxes Mead, Cleeve Hill Road, Cleeve, Bristol BS49 4PG — MB BS 1993 Lond.

PRYSE, Jonathan Grant Oakfield Surgery, Oakfield Road, Aylesbury HP20 1LJ Tel: 01296 423797 Fax: 01296 399246; 12 Highfield Road, Winslow, Buckingham MK18 3DU Tel: 01296 712582 — MB BS 1992 Lond.; DFFP 1996; DRCOG 1995; DCH RCP Lond. 1995. (Guy's Hosp. Lond.) GP; Clin. Asst. (A & E) Stoke Mandeville Hosp. Aylesbury. Prev: GP/Regist. Chesterfield VTS; Ho. Off. (Surg.) Kingston upon Thames; Ho. Off. (Med.) E.bourne.

PRYSE, Rebecca Diane Whitehill Surgery, Oxford Road, Aylesbury HP19 8EN Tel: 01296 432742 Fax: 01296 398774 Email: whitensurg@aol.com; 12 Highfield Road, Winslow, Buckingham MK18 3DU Tel: 01296 712582 Email: drs.pryse@virgin.com — MB BS 1992 Lond.; DRCOG 1995; DCH RCP Lond. 1994. (UMDS Lond.) GP. Prev: GP/Regist. Sheff. VTS; Ho. Surg. Greenwich Dist. Hosp. Lond.; GP Asst.

PRYSOR-JONES, Ann 22 Bishop Kirk Place, Oxford OX2 7HJ — MB ChB 1942 Liverp.; DPH 1947; DObst RCOG 1945. (Liverp.) Assoc. Specialist Psychiat. Sefton Gen. Hosp. Liverp. Prev: Asst. Med. Off. Liverp. Corp.

PRZEMIOSLO, Robert Tadeusz Department of Gastroenterology, Frenchay Hospital, Bristol BS16 1LE Tel: 0117 970 2290 Email: rprzemioslo@compuserve.com; 36 Rivers Street, Bath BA1 2QA Tel: 01225 480502 — MB BS 1988 Lond.; MD Lond. 1995; MRCP (UK) 1991. (St. Geo. Hosp. Lond.) Cons. (Gastro.) Frenchay Hosp. Bris.; Hon. Sen. Lect. Univ. Bristol. Socs: Brit. Soc. Gastroenterol.; Cossham Med. Soc. Prev: Sen. Regist. (Gastroenterol. & Hepatol.) Inst. Liver Studies King's Coll. Lond.; Hon. Sen. Regist. St Mark's Hosp. Harrow; Hon. Regist. (Gastroenterol.) Rayne Inst. St. Thos. Hosp.

PRZYSLO, Francis Richard Hanley Street Medical Centre, Hanley Street, Hanley, Stoke-on-Trent ST1 3RX Tel: 01782 212305 Fax: 01782 201326 — BM BS 1980 Nottm.; MRCGP 1989; DRCOG 1985.

PSAILA, Mr Joseph Victor Doncaster Royal Infirmary, Armthorpe Road, Doncaster DN2 5TL Tel: 01302 366666; 7 St. Wilfrid's Road, Bessacarr, Doncaster DN4 6AA Fax: 01302 370610 Email:

PSARRA

sailajv@cs.com — MD 1971 Malta; MCH Wales 1981; FRCS Eng. 1976. Cons. Surg. Doncaster & Bassettlaw Hosp.s Trust; Lead Union BrE. Serv., Doncaster & Bassett Law Hosp. Trust. Socs: Brit. Soc. & Assn. Surgs.; Brit. Assn. of Surgic. Encology. Prev: Lect. (Surg.) Welsh Nat. Sch. Med.; Research Off. (Clin. Surg.) Welsh Nat. Sch. Med. Cardiff; Regist. (Surg.) Univ. Hosp. Wales Cardiff.

PSARRA, Anastasia 63 New Concordia Wharf, Mill St., London SE1 2BB — Ptychio latrikes 1989 Thessalonika.

PSIACHOU-LEONARD, Elene 79 Woolmer Gardens, Edgware HA8 8QH Tel: 020 8958 7491 Email: epsiachou@otenet.gr; 79 Woolmer Gardens, London HA8 8QH Email: epsiachou@hotmail.com — Ptychio latrikes 1984 Athens; MRCPI 1996; MRCPCH 1997. (Univ. Athens Sch. Med.) Cons. (Paediat. Haemat. Oncol.) Agia Sophia Childr.'s Hosp. Athens Greece. Socs: Fell. Greek Paediat. Assn. (Athens Prefecture); SIOP; Brit. Soc. Haematol. Prev: SHO (Haemat. & Oncol.) Gt. Ormond St. Hosp. Lond.; Hon. Clin. Asst. (Paediat. Haemat. & Oncol.) Gt. Ormond St. Hosp. Lond.; SHO (Paediat.) St Geo. Hosp. Lond. & W.m. Childr. Hosp.

PSIMENOU, Erasmia 8 Lyndhurst Gardens, London NW3 5NR — Ptychio latrikes 1985 Athens.

PSWARAYI, Ruveneko Zwirimumwoyo Tapiwa T 4 Romanny Road, West Norwood, London SE27 — MB BS 1980 Lond.

PSYCHARI, Stavroula Queen Marys House, PO Box 426, St Bartholomews Hospital, West Smithfield, London EC1A 7BE Tel: 020 7601 8888 — Ptychio latrikes 1988 Thessalonika. (Univ. Thessalonika) Hon. Clin. Asst. (Cardiol.) St. Bart. Hosp. Lond.; Cardiol. Speciality Bds. Athens Univ. 1996. Socs: Hellenic Soc. Cardiol. Prev: Regist. (Cardiol.) Athens Gen. Hosp. & Onassis Cardiac Surg. Center Athens; SHO (Internal Med.) St. Andreas Hosp. Patras, Greece.

PUCCI, Martin John Ellon Group Practice, Health Centre, Schoolhill, Ellon AB41 9AH Tel: 01358 720333 Fax: 01358 721578 — MB ChB 1979 Aberd.

PUCKETT, John Rees Whitstable Health Centre, Harbour Street, Whitstable CT5 1BZ Tel: 01277 263033 Fax: 01277 771474; The Horseshoes, Share & Coulter Road, Chestfield, Whitstable CT5 3LE — MB BS Lond. 1970; DA Eng. 1978; DCH Eng. 1974; DObst RCOG 1974. (King's Coll. Hosp.) Prev: SHO (Paediat.) & SHO (Obst.) Kent & Canterbury Hosp.; SHO (Med. & Geriat.) Luton & Dunstable Hosp.

***PUCKETT, Mark Anthony** 43 East Wynd Road, Weymouth DT4 0RP — BM 1996 Soton.

PUDDY, Bernard Reginald Department of Anaesthasia, Royal Oldham Hospital, Rochdale Road, Oldham OL1 2JH — MB ChB 1963 Manch.; FFA RCS Eng. 1969; DA Eng. 1967. (Manch.) Cons. Anaesth. Oldham AHA. Prev: Asst. Resid. Surg. Off. & SHO Orthop. Dept. Salford Roy. Hosp.; Sen. Regist. Manch. Roy. Infirm.

PUDDY, Elizabeth Helen 2 Enfield Road, Eccles, Manchester M30 9NF — MB ChB 1994 Sheff.

PUDDY, Mark Richard The New Surgery, Victoria Road, Wargrave, Reading RG10 8BP Tel: 0118 940 3939 Fax: 0118 940 1357; The Little House, 65 High St, Wargrave, Reading RG10 8BU Tel: 01189 402028 — BM BCh 1985 Oxf.; BA Camb. 1982; MA Oxf. 1989, BM BCh 1985; MRCGP 1989; DCH RCP Lond. 1989; DRCOG 1988. Prev: Trainee GP Hereford VTS.

PUDDY, Victoria Fielding 2 Enfield Road, Eccles, Manchester M30 9NF — MB ChB 1992 Leic.

PUDNEY, Delia Mary 38 Caburn Heights, Southgate West, Crawley RH11 8QX — MB ChB 1997 Birm.

PUE, Philip Farfield Group Practice, St. Andrew's Surgeries, West Lane, Keighley BD21 2LD Tel: 01535 607333 Fax: 01535 611818; 2 Hall Court, Sutton-in-Craven, Keighley BD20 7NF — MB ChB 1983 Leeds; MRCGP 1987; DRCOG 1987; DCH RCP Lond. 1986.

PUEBLA ALONSO, Maria Angeles 53 Draycott Place, London SW3 3DB — LMS 1985 Cantabria.

PUFFETT, Alison Ruth Invicta Community Care NHS Trust, Kingswood Mental Health Centre, 180-6 Union St., Maidstone ME14 1EY Tel: 01622 692686 — MB BS 1986 Lond.; MRCPsych 1992; DRCOG 1988. Cons. (Psychiat.) W. Kent; Hon. Sen. Lect. Inst. Psychiat. Prev: Sen. Regist. (Psychiat.) SE Thames Region.

PUGH, Alan Charles Old Road Surgery, Old Road, Abersychan, Pontypool NP4 7BH Tel: 01495 772239 Fax: 01495 773786; Pentwyn Farm, Llanddewi Fach, Croesyceiliog, Cwmbran NP44 2DB Tel: 0163 333062 — MB ChB 1958 Sheff.; MRCS Eng. LRCP Lond. 1958. (Sheff.)

PUGH, Angela Mill Street Health Centre, Mill Street, Crewe CW2 7AQ Tel: 01270 212725 Fax: 01270 216323; Willow Farm, Whitehouse Lane, Nantwich CW5 6HQ — MB ChB 1971 Leeds; MRCGP 1988; DCH Eng. 1974. (Leeds) Prev: Clin Asst. Crewe HA; Clin. Med. Off. Gtr. Glas. HB; SHO (Paediat. & Med.) Pontefract Gen. Infirm.

PUGH, Catrin Non 36 Cefn Coed Road, Cardiff CF23 6AR — BChir 1992 Camb.

***PUGH, Cerys Ann** 50 Lytton Road, Leicester LE2 1WJ — MB ChB 1998 Leic.; MB ChB Leic 1998.

PUGH, Charles James The Forest Group Practice, The Surgery, Bury Road, Brandon IP27 0BU Tel: 01842 813353 Fax: 01842 815221; Hartley Place, Nursery Lane, Hockwold, Thetford IP26 4ND — MRCS Eng. LRCP Lond. 1975; BSc (Hons. Physiol.) Lond. 1972, MB BS 1975; DRCOG 1979.

PUGH, Charles Robert Hellesdon Hospital, Drayton High Road, Norwich NR6 5BE Tel: 01603 421487 — MB BS 1974 Lond.; FRCPsych 1992, M 1978. (St. Mary's) Cons. Norf. Ment. Health Trust Norwich; Hon. Sen. Policy Adviser DOH; Hon. Sen. Lect. Univ. E. Anglia. Prev: Hon. Sen. Lect. Univ. Coll. Lond.; Cons. Middlx. & St. Luke's Hosps. Lond.; Cons. Shenley Hosp. & Centr. Middlx. Hosp. Lond.

PUGH, Christopher Edward The Steadings, Laigh of Rossie, Whitemon Road, Dunning, Perth PH2 0QY — MB ChB 1981 Liverp.; MRCS Eng. LRCP Lond. 1981; MFOM RCP Lond. 1990; Spec. Accredit. Occupat. Med. JCHMT 1991; FFOM 1999. Cons. (Occupat. Med.) Fife Healthcare NHS Trust; Med. Adviser Fife Counc. Socs: Soc. Occupat. Med. Prev: Chief Med. Off. Translink Jt. Venture Channel Tunnel Construction.

PUGH, Christopher William Institute of Molecular Medicine, John Radcliffe Hospital, Headington, Oxford OX3 9DU Tel: 01865 222382 Fax: 01865 222500 Email: cwpugh@molbiol.ox.ac.uk; 6 The Green, Horton cum Studley, Oxford OX33 1AE — BM BCh Oxf. 1985; DPhil Oxf. 1981, MA 198; MRCP (UK) 1990. (Oxf.) MRC Sen. Clin. Fell. Nuffield Dept. Clin. Med. & Hon. Cons. Renal Unit Oxf. Prev: MRC Train. Fell. Nuffield Dept. Clin. Med. & Hon. Sen. Regist. Renal Unit Oxf.; Regist. Nuffield Dept. Clin. Med. John Radcliffe Hosp. Oxf.; Deptm. Demonstr. Sir William Dunn Sch. Path. Univ. Oxf.

PUGH, David Alexander Elstree Aeromedical Centre, Elstree Aerodrome, Borehamwood WD6 3AW Tel: 020 8953 1882 Fax: 020 8953 2775 Email: pughelstree@aol.com — MB BS 1972 Lond.; MRCS Eng. LRCP Lond. 1972; MRCGP 1979; Cert. Av Med. MoD (Air) CAA 1980; Cert. JCC Lond. 1976. (St. Bart.) Authorised Med. Examr. Civil Aviat. Auth.; Private Gen. Pract.; Indust. Med. Off.

PUGH, David Henry Owen 36 Heol St Denys, Lisvane, Cardiff CF14 0RU Fax: 01443 217775; Wrangbrook, Lisvane Road, Llanishen, Cardiff CF14 0SE Tel: 01222 750263 — MB BCh 1972 Wales; MRCOG 1980. Cons. O & G E. Glam. Gen. Hosp. Prev: Sen. Regist. (O & G) Univ. Hosp. Wales Cardiff.; Sen. Regist. (O & G) Morriston Hosp. Swansea; Regist. (O & G) Univ. Hosp. Wales Cardiff.

PUGH, David Robert (retired) 8 Parkmead, London SW15 5BS — MB BChir 1950 Camb.; MA, MB BChir Camb. 1950. Prev: Ho. Surg. & Res. Obst. Guy's Hosp. Lond.

PUGH, Edwin John Wellhouse, East View, Sadberge, Darlington DL2 1SF Tel: 01325 333134 — MB BS 1977 Newc.; Diploma in Palliative Medicine 1998; MRCGP 1984; MFPHM 1989; MFCM 1986; FFPHM 1994. (Newcastle upon Tyne) Cons. in Palliat. Med.; Tutor for Med. Educat. Progr. run by Postgrad. Inst. for Med. and Dent., Univ. of Newc. Prev: Dir. Pub. Health Co. Durh. HA; Cons. Epidemiol. & Specialist (Community Med.) N. RHA.; Med. Dir. & Cons. (Palliat. Med.).

PUGH, Elizabeth March Granville 9 Russel Drive, Christchurch BH23 3PA — BM 1996 Soton.

PUGH, Elizabeth Wyn Nth. Manchester Gen. Hospital, Crumpsall, Manchester M8 5RL Tel: 0161 720 2038 Fax: 0161 720 2073 — MB BS 1967 Lond.; MRCS Eng. LRCP Lond. 1967; FRCOG 1992, M 1971; FRCPsych 1996. (Roy. Free) Cons. Psychiat. N. Manch. HA.; Regional Adviser, RCPSYCH, N. W.ern Region. Prev: Sen. Regist. & Regist. (Psychiat.) Manch.; Research Med. Off. Nuffield Inst. Oxf. Univ.

PUGH, Emma Caroline The Surgery, Margaret Street, Thaxted, Dunmow CM6 2QN Tel: 01371 830213 Fax: 01371 831278; The Old White Horse, High St, Great Chesterford, Saffron Walden CB10 1PL Tel: 01799 530450 — MB BChir 1993 (Bchir 1992, Mb 1993) Camb.; MRCGP 1997; DCH 1996; DFFP 1995; DRCOG 1994. (Qu. Coll. Camb. & Lond. Hosp. Med. Coll.) p/t GP Princip. The Surg. Margt. St. Thaxted, Essex. Socs: Worshipful Soc. Apoth. Prev: Trainee GP/SHO P.ss Alexdra Hosp. Harlow VTS; Ho. Off. (Gen. Surg.) Whipps Cross Hosp. Lond.; Ho. Off. (Gen. Med.) OldCh. Hosp. Romford.

PUGH, Felicity Venn 49 Parc-yr-Irfon, Golf Link Road, Builth Wells LD2 3NG — MB BCh 1980 Wales; FFARCS Eng. 1985.

PUGH, Geoffrey Hall Grove Surgery, 4 Hall Grove, Welwyn Garden City AL7 4PL Tel: 01707 328528 Fax: 01707 373139; 16 The Valley Green, Welwyn Garden City AL8 7DQ Tel: 01707 324760 — MB BS 1974 Lond.; BSc Lond. 1971; MRCGP 1979. (King's Coll. Hosp.)

PUGH, Gilbert Geoffrey 44 Groombridge Road, Hackney, London E9 7DP — MB BS Lond. 1968; MRCS Eng. LRCP Lond. 1968. (Guy's) Psycho-Therap. Lond.; Clin. Asst. Psychotherap. King Geo. Hosp. Ilford. Prev: GP Princip.

PUGH, Gordon Cameron 129 Morningside Drive, Morningside, Edinburgh EH10 5NR — MB ChB 1975 Birm.; BSc (1st cl. Hons.) CNAA 1970; FFA RCS Eng. 1984; MRCGP 1979; DA (UK) 1980; DRCOG 1977. Cons. Anaesth. City Hosp. Edin.

PUGH, Hadyn William 273 London Road, Horns Cross, Dartford — LMSSA 1963 Lond.

PUGH, Mrs Helen Ashcroft House, Ashton Road, Ashton-with-Stodday, Lancaster LA2 0AA Tel: 01524 35274 — MB ChB 1974 Manch.; DRCOG 1977. GP Asst. Rosebank Surg. Ashton Rd. Lancaster.

PUGH, Helen Mary Brentford Health Centre, Albany Road, Brentford TW8 0NE Tel: 020 8569 8888; 100 St. Ann's Hill, London SW18 2RR — MB BCh 1979 Wales.

PUGH, Henry Edward John The Flat, 16 Dawes Road, Fulham, London SW6 7EN — MB ChB 1991 Bristol. SHO (O & G & Urol.) City Hosp. Nottm.; SHO (Gyn.) UCH Lond. Prev: Ho. Off. (Med.) Derriford Hosp.; Ho. Off. (Surg.) S.mead Hosp.

PUGH, James Kendrick, MC (retired) Cedar Lodge, Parc-yr-Irfon, Builth Wells LD2 3NG Tel: 01982 553286 — LRCP LRCS Ed. LRFPS Glas. 1940; MRCGP 1963.

PUGH, Jennifer Leslie (retired) 5 Steele's Road, London NW3 4SE Tel: 020 7586 0966 Fax: 020 7722 0571 Email: mike-jenn@pughpill.freeserve.co.uk — BM BCh 1957 Oxf.; MA Oxf. 1957; DA Eng. 1960; FFA RCS Eng. (Nuffield Prize) 1963. Prev: Hon. Cons. Anaesth. St. Luke's Hosp. for the Clergy Lond.

PUGH, Jill Kathryn St Margaret's Practices, 237 St. Margarets Road, Twickenham TW1 1NE Tel: 020 8892 1986 Fax: 020 8891 6466; 26 Cranes Park, Surbiton KT5 8AD Tel: 020 8399 8008 — MB BS 1977 Lond.; MRCS Eng. LRCP Lond. 1977. (St. Mary's)

PUGH, Katherine Jane 64 Henderson Row, 2nd Floor Flat, Edinburgh EH3 5BJ — MB ChB 1986 Leic.

PUGH, Kathryn Elizabeth Gordon Hospital, Bloomburg Street, London SW1V 2RH Tel: 020 8746 8714; 4 Village Way, London SE21 7AW Tel: 0207 274 6150 Email: kate@katepugh.fsnet.co.uk — MB BS 1985 Newc.; BMedSci Newc. 1982; MRCPsych 1989. p/t Cons. Psychiat. in Psychother., Lond. Hosp., BKCW Ment. Health Trust. Socs: Roy. Coll. Psychiat. (Psychother. Sect.). Prev: Clin. Research Fell. Char. Cross & W.m. Med. Sch. Lond.; Regist. Rotat. (Psychiat.) St. Geo. Hosp. Lond.; Sen Regis Psychother. Maudsley Hosp Lond.

PUGH, Kim Childrens Services, South Durham NHS Trust, Escombe Road Health Centre, Bishop Auckland DL14 6AB; Well House, Sadberge, Darlington DL2 1SF — MB BS 1978 Newc.; MRCPsych 1986; DCCH RCP Ed. 1994; MMedSci Leeds 1998. Staff Grade (Comm. Paeds) Part0Time.

PUGH, Laura Joan Loveday 93 Westhill Road, Birmingham B38 8SX — MB ChB 1988 Birm.; MRCGP 1993.

PUGH, Mark David 47 Old Hall Drive, Ashton-in-Makefield, Wigan WN4 9NA — MB ChB 1992 Leeds.

PUGH, Mark Timothy Department of Rheumatology, Birmingham Heartlands Hospital, Bordesley Green E., Birmingham B9 5SS Tel: 0121 424 2000 Fax: 0121 424 2496; 120 Old Station Road, Hampton in Arden, Solihull B92 0HF — MB BCh BAO 1985 NUI; MRCPI 1990, L 1985; DCH NUI 1986; DTM RCSI 1985; Md - 1996 NUI. (Royal College Surgery in Ireland) Cons. & Hon. Sen. Lect. Birm. Heartlands & Solihull NHS Trust (Teachg.) Birm. Socs: Brit. Soc. Rheum.; Irish Soc. Rheum.; BMA. Prev: Sen. Regist. (Rheum.) Qu. Eliz.'s Hosp. Birm.; Research Fell. & Clin. Lect. (Rheum.) Birm. Univ.; Regist. (Rheum.) Walsgrave Hosp. Coventry.

PUGH, Mr Michael Arthur, AE St. Luke's Hodp. For the Clergy, Fitzroy Square, London W1P 6AH Tel: 01923 856200 Fax: 01923 857962 Email: pughs@mikejenn.com; 5 Steele's Road, Hampstead, London NW3 4SE Tel: 020 75 860966 Fax: 020 7722 0571 Email: mike-jenn@pughpill.freeserve.co.uk — MB BS Lond. 1953; FRCS Eng. 1962; FRCOG 1971, M 1959. (St. Bart.) Emerit. Cons.Gyn.Whittington Hosp.Wom.&Eliz.Garrett Anderson hosp for Wom.; Hon. Cons. Gynaeolgist St Lukes Hosp. for the Clergy, Lond.; Hon. Sen. Lect. ULC Hosps (O&G); Emerit. Cons. UCL Hosps. & Whittington Hosp. The Hosp. For Wom., Soho. Socs: Fell. Roy. Soc. Med.; Ct. Assoc. Soc. Apoth. Master 1997-8; Counc. Med. Soc. Lond. Prev: Sen. Regist. (O & G) Radcliffe Infirm. Oxf.; Examr. (O & G) ConJt. Bd., Univ. Lond. Soc. Apoth. & RCOG; Demonst. (Anat.) St. Bart. Hosp. Med. Coll.

PUGH, Peter John Frimley Park Hospital, Portsmouth Road, Frimley, Camberley GU16 7UJ Tel: 01276 692777; Westbury Cottage, Westbury, Sherborne DT9 3EL — MB BS 1994 Lond. SHO (A & E) Frimley Pk. Hosp. Surrey. Prev: Ho. Off. (Med.) Kent & Canterbury Hosp.; Ho. Off. (Surg.) Frimley Pk. Hosp. Surrey.

***PUGH, Richard James** 33A St Winifreds Road, Biggin Hill, Westerham TN16 3HP — MB ChB 1997 Bristol.

PUGH, Richard John Philip (retired) Thirley Cottage, Harwood Dale, Scarborough YO13 0DP — MB ChB 1944 Birm.; FRCP Lond. 1971, M 1946; MRCS Eng. LRCP Lond. 1944; DCH Eng. 1945. Prev: Cons. (Paediat.) Hull & Beverley HAs.

PUGH, Richard Nicholas Hinsley 18 Bluebell Drive, Newcastle ST5 3UD Tel: 01782 617634 Fax: 01782 627441 — MB BChir 1971 Camb.; MA Camb. 1971, MD 1992; FRCP Lond. 1992; MRCP (UK) 1974; MFPHM RCP (UK) 1994; DTM & H Liverp. 1975; FFPHM RCP (UK) 1999. (Camb. & King's Coll. Hosp.) Cons Pub. health med & communicable Dis. control Walsall HA W. Midl.s NHS. Socs: Fell. Roy. Soc. Hyg. & Trop. Med.; BMA; Internat. Soc. Infec. Dis. Prev: Assoc prof. Fac. Med. & Health Sci. UAE Univ. Al Ain United Arab Emirates; Lect. (Clin. Epidemiol.) Liverp. Sch. Trop. Med. (seconded Nigeria & Malawi); SHO Chest Clinic Roy. Postgrad. Med. Sch. Hammersmith Hosp. Lond.

PUGH, Robert Eric Willow Farm, Whitehouse Lane, Nantwich CW5 6HQ Email: pughre@aol.com — MB ChB 1971 Leeds; FRCP Lond. 1991; MRCP (UK) 1974; FRCPCH. (Leeds University) Cons. Paediat. Leighton Hosp. Crewe; Hon. Clin. Lect. (Child Health) Univ. Liverp. Socs: Brit. Paediat.y Assoc. Prev: Sen. Regist. & Honoray Tutor Child Health Roy. Liverp. Childr.'s Hosp.; Regist. Dept. Child Health Roy. Hosp. Sick Childr. Glas.; Fell. Roy. Coll. of Paediat. & Child Health.

PUGH, Roderick Morris Portland Road Surgery, 31 Portland Road, Kilmarnock KA1 2DJ Tel: 01563 522118 Fax: 01563 573562; 9 Howard Street, Kilmarnock KA1 2BP — MB ChB 1979 Glas.; MRCGP 1983; DRCOG 1982.

PUGH, Rosamund Joy Macmillan Unit, Christchurch Hospital, Fairmile Road, Christchurch BH23 2JX Tel: 01202 705208 Fax: 01202 705213 — MB BS 1986 Lond.; MRCGP 1992. Cons. (Palliat. Med.) Bournemouth & ChristCh. Hosps. NHS Trust. Prev: Sen. Regist. (Palliat. Med.) Poole Hosp. NHS Trust & Roy. Bournemouth & ChristCh. Hosps. NHS Trust.; Trainee GP Crawley; SHO (Palliat. Care) St. Catherine's Hosp. Crawley.

PUGH, Sara Ellis Department of Medicine, Sunderland Royal Hospital, Sunderland SR4 7TP; Linwood, Ashbrooke Range, Sunderland SR2 9BP — MB BCh 1974 Wales; MD Wales 1990, MB BCh 1974; FRCP Ed. 1994; MRCP (UK) 1977; FRCP Lond. 1995. Cons. Cardiol. & Phys.City Hosps Sunderland. Socs: Brit. Cardiac Soc. Prev: Lect. & Hon. Sen. Regist. (Med. Cardiol.) Char. Cross Hosp. Med. Sch.; Clin. Research Asst. (Clin. Pharmacol.) Oxf.; Regist. (Cardiol.) Univ. Hosp. Wales Card.

PUGH, Simon Francis 10 Coniger Road, Fulham, London SW6 3TA — MB BS 1969 Lond.; MRCP (UK) 1974.

PUGH, Stephen Charles Department of Aanesthetics, University Hospital of Wales, Heath Park, Cardiff CF14 4XW Tel: 029 2074 3107 — MB BS 1983 Lond.; FRCA 1992; DA (UK) 1988. Cons.

PUGH

Anaesth. Univ. Hosp. Wales Cardiff. Prev: Sen. Regist. (Anaesth.) Guy's Hosp. Lond.

PUGH, Stirling Taunton & Somerset NHS Hospital Trust, Musgrove Park Hospital, Taunton Tel: 01823 342720 Fax: 01823 342721; Croft Orchard, Curry Mallet, Taunton TA3 6TD — MRCS Eng. LRCP Lond. 1979; PhD Lond. 1989; MRCP (UK) 1982; FRCP (Eng) 1999. Cons. Phys. Gastroenterol. Taunton & Som. NHS Hosp. Trust; Clin. Dir. Med. Directorate Taunton & Som. NHS Hosp. Trust. Socs: Brit. Soc. Gastroenterol. Prev: Sen. Regist. (Gen. Med.) Univ. Hosp. Wales Cardiff; Regist. (Gen. Med.) Whittington Hosp. Lond.

PUGH, Susan Jane 4 Woodpecker Close, Kenton Lane, Harrow Weald, Harrow HA3 6FD — MB BS 1991 Lond.

PUGH, Venn Tannahill (retired) 49 Parc-Yr-Yrfon, Builth Wells LD2 3NG Tel: 01982 552220 — MB ChB 1941 Ed. Prev: Ho. Surg. Derby Roy. Infirm.

PUGH, Victor William 9 Knighton Road, Leicester LE2 3HL Tel: 0116 706994; Department of Pathology, Royal Infirmary, Leicester LE1 5WW Tel: 0116 541414 — MRCS Eng. LRCP Lond. 1943; MD Lond. 1951, MB BS 1947; FRCPath 1963. (Lond. Hosp.) Cons. Pathol. Leicester Area Path. Serv. Leicester Roy. Infirm.; Home Office Path.; Clin. Teach. Fac. Med. Univ. Leicester. Socs: Fell. Med. Soc. Lond.; Assn. Clin. Pathols. Prev: Asst. Pathol. Gp. Laborat. Mile End Hosp.; Supernum. Regist. Dept. Path. Lond. Hosp.; Surg. Lt. RNVR.

PUGH, Virginia Linda Tilstock, 2 Ashdale Close, Aldsworth, Cheltenham GL54 3QT — MB BCh 1994 Wales; DRCOG; DFFP; MRCGP 1998. (University of Wales College of Medicine) GP Partner. Socs: BMA; Fam. Plann. Assn. Prev: GP Locum; GP Regist. Riversdale Ho. Bridgend; SHO (Paediat.) P.ss of Wales Hosp. Bridgend.

PUGH, Wendy Anne Berwyn House Surgery, 13 Shrubbery Avenue, Worcester WR1 1QW Tel: 01905 22888 Fax: 01905 617352; Saint Hill, Northwick Close, Worcester WR3 7EF — MB ChB 1981 Birm.; MRCGP 1986; DRCOG 1984.

PUGH, William Vernon Norman Glendorgal, Buffs Lane, Heswall, Wirral L60 — MB ChB 1954 Liverp.

PUGH WILLIAMS, Sally 34 Millfield Drive, Cowbridge CF71 7BR — MB BCh 1978 Wales; MRCP (UK) 1982. Occupat. Health Phys. INCO (Ewgre) Clydach, Swansea. Prev: SHO (Cardiac) Riyadh Milit. Hosp. Saudi Arabia; Regist. Rotat. (Med.) S. Glam. AHA (T)/Mid Glam. AHA.

***PUGHE, Christopher Thomas** 3 Hockenhull Lane, Tarvin, Chester CH3 8LA — MB ChB 1995 Manch.

PUGSLEY, Angela Denise Lyme Valley Medical Centre, Lyme Valley Road, Newcastle ST5 3TF Tel: 01782 615367 Fax: 01782 713355 — BM 1986 Soton.; T(GP) 1991.

PUGSLEY, Robin Frederick 69 High Street, Harlaxton, Grantham NG32 1JA — BM BS 1976 Nottm. Prev: Med. Dir. St. Joseph's Hospice Hackney; Med. Regist. Derbysh. Roy. Infirm.

PUGSLEY, Mr Wilfred Bernard The Cardiothoracic Unit, Millenium Wing, The Royal Sussex County Hospital, Brighton BN2 5BE Tel: 01273 696955 Email: wpugsley@hotmail.com; Tel: 01273 605162 Fax: 020 7277 2222 Email: wpugsley@hotmail.com — MB BS 1978 Lond.; BA Camb. 1975; FRCS Ed. 1983. (Cambridge St Mary's) Cons. Cardiothoracic Surg. The Roy. Sussex Co. Hosp. Brighton; Squadron Ldr., Cons. Surg. R. Aux. A.F. Socs: Of the Soc. Of Cardiothoracic Surg.s of GB. & Irel.; Roy. Soc. Med. Prev: Cons. Cardiothoracic Surg. UCLH Middlx. Hosp. Lond.; Sen. Regist. (Cardiothoracic Surg.) Lond. Chest & Nat. Heart Hosps.; BHF Research Fell. Middlx. Hosp. 1987-88.

PUJARA, Bakulesh Kumar Prataprai 191 Portland Crescent, Stanmore HA7 1LP — MB ChB 1979 Manch.

PUJARA, Manpreet Singh Wrythe Green Surgery, Wrythe Lane, Carshalton SM5 2RE Tel: 020 8669 3232/1717 Fax: 020 8773 2524 — BM 1984 Soton.; MRCGP 1989; DRCOG 1988. (Univ. Soton.) Mem. EMIS Nat. User Gp. (Vice-Chairm. & Conf. Chair). Socs: Sutton & Dist. Med. Soc. Prev: Trainee GP St. Helier VTS.

PULESTON, Brenda Mary 21 Beaver Close, Winterbourne, Bristol BS36 1QU Tel: 01454 772720 — MB BS Lond. 1964; MRCS Eng. LRCP Lond. 1964; DO Eng. 1979; Cert. Family Plann. JCC 1970. (St. Bart.) Clin. Asst. Roy. United Hosp. Bath. Socs: MRCOphth. Prev: Clin. Asst. Soton. Eye Hosp.; SHO (Ophth.) Soton. Eye Hosp., Roy. Hants. Co. Hosp.

PULESTON, Joanne Mary 23 St Lawrence Forstal, Canterbury CT1 3PA — MB BS 1992 Lond.

PULESTON, Richard Lewellyn Birmingham Childrens Hospital, Ladywood Middleway, Five Ways, Birmingham B4 6 Tel: 0121 454 4851; 40 Witherford Way, Selly Oak, Birmingham B29 4AX — MB ChB 1992 Birm.; MRCGP 1996; DCH RCP Lond. 1995. SHO (Paediat.) Birm. Childr. Hosp. Prev: Trainee GP/SHO (Paediat.) Birm.

PULFORD, Elizabeth Claire Bolingbroke Hospital, Wandsworth, London SW11; 16 Russell Close, London W4 2NU — MB ChB 1990 Manch.; MRCP 1993; BA (Cantab) 1987. Specialist Regist. (Geriat. Med.). Socs: Brit Thor. Soc.; Brit. Geriat. Soc.

PULHAM, Nicola Lesley The Orchard Medical Centre, Heath Road, Coxheath, Maidstone ME17 4PL Tel: 01622 744994 Fax: 01622 741162; Durrants House, West St, Hunton, Maidstone ME15 0RY — MB BS 1987 Lond.

PULIYEL, Jacob Mammen 1 Cavendish Gardens, Manchester M20 1LA — MB BS 1989 Jabalpur, India; MD Jabalpur, India 1981; MRCP (UK) 1995. Prev: Cons. Paediat. Med. Trust Hosp. Cochin, India.

PULLAN, Alistair David Furlong Medical Centre, Furlong Road, Tunstall, Stoke-on-Trent ST6 5UD Tel: 01782 577388 Fax: 01782 838610; 38 Saint Georges Avenue N., Wolstanton, Newcastle ST5 8DF — MB ChB 1985 Aberd.; MRCGP 1990; DRCOG 1989.

PULLAN, Cedric William Alderson (retired) Borden Wood Lodge, Milland, Liphook GU30 7JY Tel: 0142 876369 — MRCS Eng. LRCP Lond. 1945; MA, MB BChir Camb. 1946. Prev: Med. Off. RAF.

PULLAN, Constance Ruth Children's Services, Gedling Office, 61 Burton Road, Carlton, Nottingham NG4 3DQ Tel: 0115 987 7043 Fax: 0115 961 3268 — MB BS 1970 Newc.; MD Newc. 1985; MRCP (UK) 1973. Cons. Community Paediat. Nottm. HA. Prev: Sen. Regist. (Child Health) Univ. Hosp. Nottm.; Sen. Resid. Assoc. (Virol. & Child Health) Roy. Vict. Infirm. Newc.; Regist. (Paediat.) Newc. Gen. Hosp.

PULLAN, Mr David Mark Cardiothoracic Centre, Thomas Drive, Liverpool L14 3PE Tel: 0151 228 1616 — MB BS 1988 Lond.; FRCS 1999 (CTh); FRCS Eng. 1992; FRCS Ed. 1992. Cons. Cardiac Surg., The Cardiotherpaic Centre, Liverp. Prev: SHO (Cardiothoracic Surg.) Leeds Gen. Infirm.

PULLAN, David Sebastian Bratby 32 Twatling Road, Barnt Green, Birmingham B45 8HT — MB BS 1993 Lond.

PULLAN, Mr Rupert Derek Torbay Hospital, Lawes Bridge, Torquay TQ2 7AA Tel: 01803 654982 Fax: 01803 654996 Email: rupert.pullan@sdevonhc-tr.swest.nhs.uk; Wylam Mount, 37 St Matthews Road, Chelston, Torquay TQ2 6JA Tel: 01803 406085 Fax: 01803 406085 Email: pullan@wylammount.freeserve.co.uk — BM BCh 1984 Oxf.; MA Oxf. 1987, DM 1994; FRCS (Gen. Surg.) 1996; FRCS Eng. 1989; FRCS Ed. 1989. (University of Oxford) Cons. Gen. & Colorectal Surg. Torbay Hosp. Torquay. Socs: Assn. of ColoProctol. of GB & Irel.; Assn. of Surg.s of GB & Irel. Prev: Sen. Regist. (Colorectal Surg.) Singleton Hosp. Swansea; Sen. Regist. Rotat. (Gen. Surg.) Ysbyty Gwynedd Bangor; Hunt Prof. RCS Eng.

PULLAPERUMA, Sunil Palitha 4 Curtis Drive, London W3 6YL — MB BS 1980 Colombo; MRCPI 1990.

PULLAR, Prudence Mary 22 Shelley Court, Glasgow G12 0XD — MB ChB 1980 Otago.

PULLAR, Thomas Ninewells Hospital Medical School, Dundee DD1 9SY Tel: 01382 60111 — MB ChB 1978 Glas.; MD Glas. 1986; FRCP ED. 1992; FRCP Glas. 1992; MRCP (UK) 1980. Cons. Phys. (Rheum.) Dundee Teach. Hosp. NHS Trust; Mem. Edit. Bd. Brit. Jl. Rheum.; Regional Adviser Tayside Roy. coll of Phys.s of Edin. Socs: Brit. Soc. Rheum. Prev: Sen. Lect. (Clin. Pharmaol.) & Hon. Cons. Phys. (Med.) Gen. Infirm. Leeds; Lect. & Hon. Sen. Regist. (Clin. Pharmacol.) The Gen. Infirm. Leeds.; Regist. & SHO (Med. & Rheum.) Glas. Roy. Infirm.

***PULLEN, Andrew John** Flat 2, 324 Lordship Lane, London SE22 8LZ — MB BS 1998 Lond.; MB BS Lond 1998.

PULLEN, Brian Walter Brook House, Harlton, Little Eversden, Cambridge CB3 7HB Tel: 01223 262579 — MB BS 1961 Lond.; MRCS Eng. LRCP Lond. 1961; DObst RCOG 1965. (King's Coll. Hosp.) Prev: Regist. (Gen. Med.) Plymouth Clin. Area; Ho. Surg. ENT Dept. & Ho. Phys. Neurol. & Dermat. Depts. King's Coll.; Hosp.

PULLEN, Denise Alma 11 Arlington Close, Goring-by-Sea, Worthing BN12 4ST Tel: 01903 505626 — MB BS Lond. 1943; MRCS Eng. LRCP Lond. 1943; MFFP 1993. (Lond. Sch. Med. Wom.) JP; Assoc. Specialist Worthing Hosp. & S.lands Hosp. Shoreham;

Med. Off. Family Plann. Worthing HA.; Mem. Fac. Family Plann. & Reproductive Health Care RCOG. Prev: Asst. Path. New Sussex Hosp. Brighton; Resid. Path. Roy. Free Hosp.; Med. Off. Clare Hall Hosp.

PULLEN, Frances Jill Vauxhall Surgery, Vauxhall Lane, Chepstow NP16 5PZ Tel: 01291 623246 Fax: 01291 627975; New House, Garway Hill, Hereford HR2 8EZ Tel: 01981 240032 — MB ChB Birm. 1976; DA Eng. 1978. (Birm.)

PULLEN, Geoffrey Peter Tel: 01865 223531 Fax: 01865 223530; Fairlight House, Brightwell-cum-Sotwell, Wallingford OX10 0RU — MB BChir 1972 Camb.; MA, MB Camb. 1972, BChir 1971; MRCPsych 1975; DPM Eng. 1975. (Camb. & Middlx.) Cons. Psychiat. Littlemore Hosp. Oxf. Prev: Clin. Dir., Dept. of Rehabil. & Forens. Servs. Oxf.; Sen. Regist. (Adult Psychiat.) Cambs. AHA (T); Regist. (Psychol. Med.) Middlx. Hosp. Lond.

PULLEN, Herbert (retired) 8 Whitechapel Close, Leeds LS8 2PT Tel: 0113 232 3038 — MB ChB 1957 Ed.; FRCP Ed. 1978, M 1964; DTM & H. Eng. 1960. Prev: Cons. Infec. Dis. Seacroft Hosp. Leeds.

PULLEN, Ian Michael BordersPrimary Care NHS Trust, Huntlyburn House, Melrose TD6 9BD Tel: 01896 827157 Fax: 01896 827154 Email: ian.pullen@borders.scot.nhs.uk — MB BS 1970 Lond.; FRCPsych 1990, M 1977. (Lond. Hosp .) Cons. Psychiat. Borders Care Trust, Melrose; Borders Primary Care NHS Trust,Melrose; Assoc. Med. Director (Ment. Health & Learning Disabil.); Hon. Fell. Univ. Edin. Socs: Fell. Roy. Coll. Psychiat. Prev: GP Aylsham, Norf.; Cons. Psychiat. Roy. Edin. Hosp. & Hon. Sen. Lect. Univ. Edin.

PULLEN, Joanna Eve Southbroom Surgery, 15 Estcourt Street, Devizes SN10 1LQ Tel: 01380 720909 — MB BS 1987 Lond.; BSc Lond. 1984; MRCGP 1992. (St George's Hospital Medical School)

PULLEN, Michael Dahlbom The Surgery, Stock Hill, Biggin Hill, Westerham TN16 3TJ; 6 Trinity Close, South Croydon CR2 0EP Tel: 020 8657 7344 — BSc (Hons. Physiol.) Lond. 1985, MB BS 1987; MRCGP 1993; DFFP 1993; DRCOG 1992; DCH RCP Lond. 1991; DGM RCP Lond. 1990; DA (UK) 1989. SHO Duke of Cornw. Spinal Injuries Unit Salisbury Dist. Hosp. Prev: SHO (Anaesth.) Greenwich Dist. Hosp.

PULLEN, Michael John (retired) Isbury Farm, Sheepdrove, Lambourn, Hungerford RG17 7UR Tel: 01488 71463 — MB ChB 1960 Glas. Prev: Ho. Surg., Ho. Phys. & SHO (Obst.) Derby City Hosp.

PULLEN, Peter Horace (retired) 51 High Street, Dilton Marsh, Westbury BA13 4DW — MB BChir 1953 Camb.; DObst RCOG 1954. Prev: Obst. Ho. Phys. Lambeth Hosp.

PULLETZ, Mark Christopher Karl 7 Longmoor Street, Poundbury, Dorchester DT1 3GN Tel: 01305 261485 — MB BS 1992 Lond.; BSc Lond. 1989; MRCP (UK) 1996; DCH RCP Lond. 1997. (UCMSM) SHO (Anaesth.) Yeovil Hosp. NHS Trust Higher Kingston Yeovil.

PULLEY, Melanie Susan 12 Shornefield Close, Bickley, Bromley BR1 2HX — MB ChB 1975 Liverp.

PULLIN, Allan Vincent (retired) 21 Walmoor Park, Sandy Lane, Chester CH3 5UT Tel: 01244 348846 Fax: 01244 351057 — MB ChB Liverp. 1961. Prev: Hosp. Practitioner (Orthoptics) Chester Roy. Infirm.

PULLIN, Jacqueline Anne Tarr House, Kingston St Mary, Taunton TA2 8HY — MB BS 1984 Lond.; FCAnaesth. 1989. (Guy's) Clin. Asst. (Anaesth.) Taunton & Som. Hosps. Socs: Harveian Soc. Prev: Clin. Asst. Pain Relief Unit. King's Coll. Hosp. Lond.; Regist. (Anaesth.) King's Coll. Hosp. Lond.; SHO (Anaesth.) St. Thos. Hosp. Lond.

PULLINGER, Richard Malone 30 Geoffreyson Road, Caversham, Reading RG4 7HS — MB BS 1989 Lond.; MA Oxf. 1988; MRCP 1993; FFAEM 1997. Cons. (A & E Med.) John Radcliffe Hosp. Oxf..

PULLINGER, Roland Hugh Brunswick Surgery, Oak Hill Health Centre, Oak Hill Road, Surbiton KT6 6EN Tel: 020 8390 5321 Fax: 020 8390 5321; 19 Werter Road, Putney, London SW15 2LL Tel: 020 8788 0792 Email: roland.pullinger@dial.pipex.com — MB BS Lond. 1968; MRCS Eng. LRCP Lond. 1968; DObst RCOG 1970. (St. Mary's) Prev: SHO A & E Unit W. Middlx. Hosp. Isleworth; Ho. Phys. Hillingdon Hosp. Uxbridge; Ho. Surg. Profess. Surg. Unit St. Mary's Hosp. Lond.

PULLINGER, Stephen (Surgery), 15 Winters Lane, Long Bennington, Newark NG23 5DW Tel: 01400 281220 Fax: 01400 282551 — BM BS 1983 Nottm.; BMedSci Nottm. 1981; MRCGP 1988; DRCOG 1986. Prev: Trainee GP Nottm. VTS.

PULLON, Hilary Ruth (retired) 18 Georges Wood Road, Brookmans Park, Hatfield AL9 7BT Tel: 01707 657437 — MB ChB 1949 Ed.; DObst RCOG 1952. Prev: Ho. Phys. Barnet Gen. Hosp. & Brook Gen. Hosp. Lond.

PULLYBLANK, Miss Anne Marie Tel: 0117 924 6964 Email: apullyblank@lineone.net — MB BS 1990 Lond.; BSc 1990 (Hons.) Lond.; FRCS Eng. 1995; MD Lond. 1998. Specialist Regist. S.W. Rotat.

PULMAN, Nicholas Robert The Surgery, 99 Belvoir Road, Coalville, Leicester LE67 3PH; 11 Marsden Close, The Limes, Ravenstone, Leicester LE67 2JU — MB ChB 1983 Leic.; MRCGP 1988; DRCOG 1983.

PULSFORD, David Robert The Surgery, 9 Godstow Road, Abbey Wood, London SE2 9AT Tel: 020 8310 7066 Fax: 020 8311 8867 — MB BS 1970 Lond.

PULVERTAFT, Robert James Valentine, OBE (retired) Stapeley House, Presteigne Road, Knighton LD7 1HY — MD 1933 Camb.; FRCP Lond. 1938; MRCS Eng. LRCP Lond. 1923; FCPath 1963. Prev: Vis. Prof. Univ. Coll. Ibadan & Makerere Univ. Coll. Kampala Uganda.

PULVERTAFT, Mr Roger William (retired) Kent House, High Street, Swaffham Prior, Cambridge CB5 0LD Tel: 01638 741443 — MB BS 1967 Lond.; BSc Lond. 1964, MB BS 1967; FRCS Eng. 1973; FRCR 1985. Prev: Cons. (Diag. Radiol.) Newmarket Gen. Hosp.

PUMFORD, Neil Andrew 16 Hepburn Gardens, St Andrews KY16 9DD — MB ChB 1988 Ed.; MRCGP 1992.

PUMFORD, Stanley (retired) 16 Hepburn Gardens, St Andrews KY16 9DD — MB BS 1964 Durh.; BSc, MB BS Durh. 1964; MFOM RCP Lond. 1980; DIH Soc. Apoth. Lond. 1971. Prev: Med. Dir. E. Scotl. Occupat. Health Serv. Ltd.

PUMPHREY, Charles Walter St. Georges Hospital, London SW17 0QT Tel: 020 8672 1255 — BM BCh 1973 Oxf.; DM Oxf. 1982; FRCP Lond. 1990; MRCP (UK) 1976. Cons. Cardiol. St. Geo. Hosp. Lond. Prev: Sen. Regist. Lond. Hosp.; Regist. (Med.) Nat. Heart Hosp. Lond.; Brit. Amer. Travel. Fell. Mayo Clinic, USA.

PUMPHREY, Judith Harries 4 Portland Road, Bowdon, Altrincham WA14 2NY Tel: 0161 928 7334 — MB BS 1968 Lond.; MRCS Eng. LRCP Lond. 1968; MFFP 1993; Cert. Family Plann. JCC 1974. (St. Bart.) SCMO (Adult Health inc. Family Plann. & Genitourin. Med.) Trafford HA & Univ. S. Manch. Withington Hosp. Prev: Ho. Surg. Whittington Hosp. Lond.; Ho. Phys. Qu. Mary's Hosp. for E. End Lond.

PUMPHREY, Richard Stephen Hugh Regional Immunology Service, St. Marys Hospital, Manchester M13 0JH Tel: 0161 276 6452 Fax: 0161 276 6439 Email: richard.pumphrey@man.ac.uk; 4 Portland Road, Bowdon, Altrincham WA14 2NY — MB 1971 Camb.; BChir 1970; FRCPath 1988, M 1976. (St. Bart.) Cons. Immunol. N. W.. Regional Immunol. Serv. St. Mary's Hosp. Manch. Socs: Brit. Soc. Immunol.; Coun. Mem. Brit. Soc. Allergy & Clin. Immunol. Prev: Sen. Regist. (Clin. Immunol.) Glas. Roy. Infirm.; Asst. Pathol. Addenbrooke's Hosp. (Univ. Camb.).

PUNCH, David Michael The Surgery, 221 Whaddon Way, Bletchley, Milton Keynes MK3 7EA Tel: 01908 373058 Fax: 01908 630076; 22/24 The Green, Stoke Hammond, Milton Keynes MK17 9BX — MB BS 1978 Lond. (St. Geo.) Med. Dir. Bletchley Community Hosp. Milton Keynes.

PUNCHIHEWA, Veerasiri Gardiye Department of Anaesthesia, Basildon Hospital, Basildon SS16 5NL Tel: 01268 533911; 24 Crescent Drive, Shenfield, Brentwood CM15 8DS — MB BS 1970 Ceylon; FFA RCS Eng. 1977. (Peradeniya) Cons. Anaesth. Basildon & Thurrock HA. Socs: Assn. Anaesth.; Brit. Assn. Day Surg.; Sri-Lankan Doctors' Assn. Prev: St. Chas. Hosp. Lond.; Qu. Charhottes Hosp. Lond.; Sen. Regist. (Anaesth.) Hammersmith Hosp. Lond. & Odstock Hosp. Salisbury.

PUNDIT, Mahesh 13 Hartgrove Court, Elmwood Crescent, London NW9 0NN — MB BS 1984 Lond. (Char. Cross) Research Schol. (Anaesth.) Chicago, Ill., USA.

PUNJA, Ali Nazim The Surgery, 118/120 Stanford Avenue, Brighton BN1 6FE Tel: 01273 506361 Fax: 01273 552483 — MB BS 1989 Lond.; MRCGP 1994; DRCOG 1994. (St. Thos.) GP Princip.

PUNT

Prev: Trainee GP/SHO Brighton HA; SHO (A & E) St. Peters Hosp. Chertsey; Ho. Surg. (Surg. & Orthop.) St. Thos. Hosp. Lond.

PUNT, Mr Jonathan Arthur Gilbert P.O. Box 6016, Keyworth, Nottingham NG12 5PR Tel: 01509 880445 Fax: 01509 881955 Email: j.punt@doctors.org.uk; Email: jpunt@doctors.org.uk — MB BS 1971 Lond.; FRCS Eng. 1976; FRCPCH 1996. (Guy's) Cons. Paediat. Neurosurg. Socs: Fell. Roy. Soc. Med.; Soc. Brit. Neurol. Surgs.; Eur. Soc. Paediat. Neurosurg. (Mem. of Counc. & Chairm. Scientif. & Pub.ations Comm.). Prev: Sen. Lect. (Paediat. Neurosurg.) Univ. of Nottm; Cons. (Paediat. Neurosurg.) Univ. Of Nottm. & Leicester Roy. Infirm.; Sen. Regist. (Neurosurg.) Wessex Neurol. Centre Soton.

PUNT, Lydia Flat 9, Ivy Lane, Headington, Oxford OX3 9DT — MB ChB 1992 Stellenbosch.

PUNTAMBEKAR, Sulabha (retired) Erinor, Gresham Avenue, Hartley, Longfield DA3 7BT — MB BS 1961 Bihar; MRCOG 1967, DObst 1965. Cons. (O & G) Dartford & Gravesham Health Dist. Prev: Clin. Asst. (O & G) Dartford & Gravesham Health Dist. & Medway.

PUNTER, Jale Psychotherapy Department, Villiess House, Tolworth Hospital, Red Lion Road, Surbiton KT6 7QU Tel: 020 8390 0102 Fax: 020 8390 3877 Email: jale.punter@kdc-tr.sthames.nhs.uk — BM 1986 Soton.; 2000 MInst.GA; MRCPsych .1991. p/t Cons. Psychiat. in Psychother., Tolworth Hosp., Surbiton, Surrey. Prev: Regist. (Psychiat.) & SHO Soton. Hosps.; SHO (Orthop., A & E, Neurol. & Neurosurg.) Soton. Gen. Hosp.; Sen. Regist. (Psychother.) St. Geo. Hosp. Lond.

PUNTIS, Hilary Selly Oak Health Centre, Katie Road, Selly Oak, Birmingham B29 6JG; 52 Rookery Road, Selly Oak, Birmingham B29 7DQ — BM 1980 Soton.; BM (Hons.) Soton. 1980; MRCP (UK) 1983. Prev: Regist. (Med.) Sandwell Dist. Gen. Hosp. W. Bromwich; SHO (Med.) Qu. Eliz. Hosp. Birm.

PUNTIS, John William Lambert Neonatal Unit, Clarendon Wing, The General Infirmary at Leeds, Belmont Grove, Leeds LS2 9NS Tel: 0113 392 3828 Fax: 0113 392 6068 Email: 100677.2423@compuserve.com; 6 The Avenue, Roundhay, Leeds LS8 1DW Tel: 0113 266 2739 — BM 1977 Soton.; BM (Hons.) Soton. 1977; DM Soton. 1996; FRCP Lond. 1996; MRCP (UK) 1980; FRCPCH 1996. (Soton.) Sen. Lect. (Paediat. & Child Health) Univ. Leeds; Cons. Paediat. (Gastroenterol.) Leeds Gen. Infirm. Prev: Lect. (Paediat. & Child Health) Univ. Birm.

PUNTIS, Mr Malcolm Colin Albert University Department of Surgery, University of Wales College of Medicine, Heath Park, Cardiff CF14 4XN Tel: 029 2074 3268 Fax: 029 2074 4709 Email: puntis@cf.dc.uk — MB BCh 1972 Wales; PhD Camb. 1981; FRCS Eng. 1981; FRCS Ed. 1980. (Wales) Hon. Cons. Surg. & Sen. Lect. Univ. Hosp. Wales NHS Trust; Edr.-in-Chief Hepato-Pancreato-Biliary Surg. Jl. Socs: Internat. Hepato-Pancreato-Biliary Assn.; Surgic. Research Soc.; Brit. Soc. Gastroenterol.

PURANDARE, Mr Arunkumar Shantaram 3 Bakers Farm Road, Verwood, Wimborne BH21 6QF Tel: 01202 825197 — MB BS 1966 Bombay; MS Bombay 1969; FRCS Ed. 1973; Dip. Med. Acupunc. BMAS 1997. (Topiwala Nat. Med. Coll.) Socs: Brit. Med. Acupunct. Soc.; BMA; Brit. Blood Transfus. Soc. Prev: Regist. (Surg.) Doncaster Roy. Infirm.; Cook Co. Hosp. Chicago Illinois, USA; LTM Gen. Hosp. Bombay, India.

PURANIK, Ananth Southlands, Keycol Hospital, Newington, Sittingbourne ME9 8NG — MB BS 1981 Osmania; MRCPsych 1988.

PURANIK, Mr Indudhar Northallerton Health Trust, Department of Orthopaedics, Friarage Hospital, Northallerton DL6 1SE Tel: 01609 779911 Fax: 01609 764638 Email: indudhar.puranik@btinternet.com — MB BS 1973 Mysore; MS (Gen. Surg.) Karnatak 1976. (Kasturba Med. Coll.) Assoc. Specialist (Orthop.) Friarage Hosp. N.allerton. Prev: Trust Med. Off. (Orthop.); Regist. (Orthop.).

PURBEY, Badri Narayan The Park Canol Group Practice, Park Carnol Surgery, Central Park, Church Village, Pontypridd CF38 1RJ Tel: 01443 203414 Fax: 01443 218218; 3 Pen-y-Waun, Efailisaf, Pontypridd CF38 1AY Tel: 01443 201337 Fax: 01443 400283 — MB BS 1971 Bihar; DCH NUI 1979; DCH Darbhanga 1974. (Darbhanga Med. Coll. Laheriasarai) GP Pontypridd. Prev: SHO (O & G) Gen. Hosp. Aberdare; SHO (Gen. Med.) Co. Hosp. HaverfordW.; SHO (Paediat.) Withybush Gen. Hosp. HaverfordW..

***PURBICK, Andrew** 1 Highfield Avenue, Alconbury Weston, Huntingdon PE28 4JS — MB BS 1996 Lond.

PURBRICK, Susan Attenborough Surgery, Bushey Health Centre, London Road, Bushey, Watford WD23 2NN Tel: 01923 231633 Fax: 01923 818594 Email: susan.purbrick@gp-e82124.nhs.uk; 84 Coldharbour Lane, Bushey WD23 4NX Tel: 020 8950 2989 Email: suepurbrick@yahoo.co.uk — MB ChB; DRCOG 1976; MRCGP 1980. (Liverpool) Gen. Practitioner Bushey Health Centre, Bushey. Socs: W. Herts & Watford Med. Soc.

PURCE, Elizabeth Jill Ballymena Health Centre, Cushendall Road, Ballymena BT43 6HQ Tel: 028 2564 2181 Fax: 028 2565 8919; 3 Leighinmohr Avenue, Ballymena BT42 2AT — MB BCh BAO 1981 Belf.; MRCGP 1985; DRCOG 1984.

***PURCELL, Anna Marie** Almaur, Grove Park, Pontnewydd, Cwmbran NP44 1RW — BM 1995 Soton.

PURCELL, Bernadette Louise Wiltshire Health Authority, Southgate House, Pans Lane, Devizes SN10 5EQ Tel: 01380 728899 Fax: 01380 722443 Email: bernadette.purcell@exchange.wilts-ha.swest.nhs.uk; 2nd Floor Flat, 27 Park St, Bath BA1 2TF Email: blpurcell@breathe.co.uk — MB BS 1992 Lond.; BA Oxf. 1989; MRCP (UK) 1997; MSc 1998. (Oxford and St Bartholomews Medical School London) Specialist Regist. (Pub. Health Med.) Wilts. HA.

***PURCELL, Colin** 7 Rosepark, Belfast BT5 7RG — MB BCh 1998 Belf.; MB BCh Belf 1998.

PURCELL, Daniel Joseph (retired) 13 Windermere Road, West Wickham BR4 9AN Tel: 0208 776 2501 — 1948 MB BCh BAO NUI 1948. Prev: GP, Thornton Heath, Surrey.

PURCELL, Graham Roger Gillies The Grange, Leigh, Sherborne DT9 6HL Tel: 01935 872404 — MB BChir 1970 Camb.; MA, MB Camb. 1970, BChir 1969; MRCS Eng. LRCP Lond. 1969; FFA RCS Eng. 1975. (Camb. & St. Bart.) Cons. Anaesth. Yeovil Dist. Hosp. Prev: Sen. Regist. (Anaesth.) Soton., S.W. Hants Health Dist. & W.m. Hosp. Lond.; Regist. (Anaesth.) Hosp. Sick Childr. Lond. & Salisbury Gen. Hosp.

PURCELL, Ian Findlay Cardiac Medicine, National Heart and Lung Institute, Dovehouse St., London SW3 6LY Tel: 020 7352 8121 Fax: 020 7823 3392 Email: i.purcell@ic.ac.uk — MB ChB 1990 Ed.; BSc (Hons.) Ed. 1988, MB ChB (Hons.) 1990; MRCP (UK) 1993. (Ed.) Research Fell. (Cardiol.) Nat. Heart & Lung Inst. Socs: Internat. Soc. Heart Research; Brit. Soc. Heart Failure. Prev: Regist. (Cardiol.) Freeman Hosp. Newc.; SHO Rotat. (Med.) Newc. HA; Regist. (Med. & Surg.) Roy. Infirm. Edin.

PURCELL, Michael Thornleigh, Old Road, Stalybridge SK15 2RG — MB BChir 1964 Camb.; MB Camb. 1964, BChir 1963; FRCP Lond. 1986; MRCP (UK) 1970; MRCS Eng. 1964, LRCP Lond. 1963; DCH Eng. 1969. (St. Mary's) Cons. (Paediat.) Tameside Gen. Hosp.

PURCELL, Patricia Mary Jennifer Ringing Stones, Mayals Road, Mayals, Swansea SA3 5DH Tel: 01792 405700 — BM 1985 Soton.; BSc (Hons.) Soton. 1975; MSc Lond. 1977; MRCGP 1990; Dip. Palliat. Med. 1993; Cert. Family Plann. JCC 1990; T(GP) 1990. Assoc. Specialist Ty Olwen Palliat. Care Serv. Morriston Hosp. Swansea. Socs: BMA & Assn. Palliat. Med. Prev: Clin. & Research Regist. (Palliat. Med.) Holme Tower Marie Curie Centre Cardiff; Asst. Prof. Nursing W. Virginia Wesleyan Coll.

PURCELL, Patrick 81 Pickhurst Lane, Bromley BR2 7JP Tel: 020 8462 4597 — MB BCh BAO 1948 NUI; DMRD Eng. 1951; DMRD Lond 1951. Cons. Radiol. Bromley, Beckenham & FarnBoro. Hosps. Prev: Regist. Char. Cross Hosp.; Sen. Regist. Guy's Hosp. Lond.; Sen. Specialist Radiol. RAMC.

PURCELL, Patrick Francis Tanglewood, 21A Old Bath Road, Sonning upon Thames, Reading RG4 6SY Tel: 0118 969 8128 Fax: 0118 969 2672; Clarkes Hill, Rochestown, Republic of Ireland Tel: 00 353 21 893632 Fax: 00 353 21 893632 — MB BCh BAO 1984 NUI. (Univ. Coll. Cork Med. Sch.) Locum Cons. Dept. Psych. Surrey Hants. Borders NHS Trust. Prev: Intern. Cork Regional Hosp. Cork; Resid. Dept. Intern. Med. St. Luke's Roosevelt Hosp., Columbia Univ. Med. Sch. New York, USA.

PURCELL, Rodney Thomas Gordon and Partners, 1 North Street, Peterborough PE1 2RA Tel: 01733 312731 Fax: 01733 311447 — MB ChB 1972 Ed.; MRCGP 1987; DA Eng. 1976; DObst RCOG 1974.

PURCELL, William Wadsley Hall, Hillsborough, Sheffield S6 4FD Tel: 0114 232 5767 — MB ChB 1964 Glas.; DObst RCOG 1966.

Socs: BMA. Prev: Ho. Off. (Med.) Glas. Roy. Infirm.; Ho. Off. (Surg.) E. Dist. Hosp. Glas.; Ho. Off. (Obst.) Robroyston Hosp. Glas.

PURCELL-JONES, Gari Department Anaesthesia General Hospital, Gloucester St., St Helier, Jersey JE2 3 Tel: 01534 622000 Fax: 01534 622633; Les Prés, La Rue des Prés, St Lawrence, Jersey JE3 1EH Tel: 01534 862829 — MRCS Eng. LRCP Lond. 1977; BSc (Hons.) (Biochem.) Lond. 1974, MB BS 1977; MRCP (UK) 1981; FRCA Eng. 1984; FRCP 2000 UK. (Char. Cross) Cons. Anaesth. & Pain Relief Gen. Hosp. St. Helier, Jersey. Socs: Intractable Pain Soc.; Internat. Assn. Study of Pain. Prev: Sen. Regist. (Anaesth.) St. Thos. Hosp. Lond.; Regist. (Anaesth.) Hosp. Sick Childr. Lond.; Regist. (Anaesth.) St. Bart. Hosp. Lond.

PURCHAS, Simon Francis Uthnoe Veor, Churchtown, Perranuthnoe, Penzance TR20 9NH Tel: 01736 711487 — MB ChB 1993 Bristol; BSc (Pharmacol.) Bristol 1990; MRCP (UK) 1997. (Bristol) SHO (A&E) Derriford Hosp. Plymouth. Socs: BMA; MDU. Prev: SHO (O & G) Roy. United Hosp. Bath; SHO Anaesth. Roy. Cornw. Hosp. Truro, Cornw.; SHO (Gen. Med.) Kingston Hosp. Kingston upon Thames Surrey.

PURCHASE, Mrs Sheila Marshall (retired) 232 Dyke Road, Brighton BN1 5AE Tel: 01273 550039 — MB ChB 1951 Aberd.; DObst RCOG 1954. Prev: Ho. Surg. Roy. Hosp. Sick Childr. Aberd. & Mothers' Hosp. Clapton.

PURCHES, Anthony Charles Warley Hospital, Brentwood CM1 5HQ Tel: 01708 465000 — MB BChir 1974 Camb.; MB Camb. 1974, MA, BChir 1973; MRCPsych 1978; DPM Eng. 1977. (Camb. & Lond. Hosp.) Cons. Psychiat. Warley Hosp., Brentwood & OldCh. Hosp. Romford. Prev: Sen. Regist. Maudsley & St. Mary's Hosps. Lond.; Ho. Surg. (Urol.) & Regist. (Psychiat.) Lond. Hosp.; Ho. Phys. St. Martins Hosp. Bath.

PURDAY, Jonathan Paul Department of Anaesthesia, Royal Devon and Exeter Hospital, Barrack Road, Exeter EX2 5DW Tel: 0117 402474 Fax: 0117 402472; Knowlfield, Exton Lane, Exton, Exeter EX3 0PP Tel: 01392 873762 Fax: 01392 873762 Email: jpurday@aol.com — MB BS 1983 Lond.; MRCP (UK) 1986; FRCA 1991. (St Mary's Hospital London) Cons. Anaesth. Roy. Devon & Exeter Hosp. Socs: BMA; Intens. Care Soc.; Assn. Anaesth. Prev: Sen. Regist. Rotat. (Anaesth.) Exeter & Bristol; Clin. Fell. (Paediat. Anaesth.) BC's Childr. Hosp. Vancouver BC, Canada; Regist. (Anaesth.) Guy's Hosp. Lond.

***PURDELL-LEWIS, Nicola Jane** Redstone, 16 Tower Road N., Wirral CH60 6RT — MB ChB 1998 Leeds.

PURDIE, Alasdair Thomas Flat 2/1, 110 Brunswick St., Glasgow G1 1TF — MB ChB 1990 Aberd.

PURDIE, Anne Veronica St Lawrence Medical Centre, 4 Bocking End, Braintree CM7 9AA Tel: 01376 552474 Fax: 01376 552417 — MB BS 1985 Lond.; MRCGP 1990; DRCOG 1989; DCH RCP Lond. 1989; DGM RCP Lond. 1987. Prev: Trainee GP Fulwell VTS.

PURDIE, Colin Alexander Department of Pathology, Ninewells Hospital and Medical School, Dundee DD1 9SY Tel: 01382 660111 Fax: 01382 640966 Email: colinp@tuht.scot.nhs.uk — MB ChB 1985 Ed.; PhD Ed. 1994, BSc (Hons.) Med. Sci. 1986, MB ChB 1985; MRCPath 1997. (Edinburgh University) Cons. Histopath./cytopathologist Path. Dept. Dundee; Hon. Sen. Lect. Dept. of molecular and cellular Path. Dundee Univrdity. Socs: Roy. Soc. Pathol.; Pathol. Soc.; Assn. Clin. Pathol. Prev: Sen. Regist., Univ. Dept. of Path. Edin.; Career Regist. Glas. Roy. Infirm.; Regist. (Med.) Roy. Infirm. Edin.

PURDIE, Professor David Wilkie Centre for Metabolic Bone Disease, Hull Royal Infirmary, Anlaby Road, Hull HU3 2JZ Tel: 01482 675302 Fax: 01482 675301 Email: d.w.purdie@medschool.hull.ac.uk; The Old Rectory, Rowley, Little Weighton, Cottingham HU20 3XR Tel: 01482 875987 — MB ChB 1969 Glas.; MD Leeds 1990; FRCP Ed. 1997; FRCOG 1988, M 1976. (Univ. Glas.) Prof. and Head of Clin. Research, Centre for Metab. Bone Dis., Hull Univ.; Hon. Cons. gynaecologist, The P.ss Roy. Hosp.; Mem., Scientif. Advisery Gp., The Nat. Osteoporosis Soc.; Mem., Expert Advisery Gp. O.N.H.R.T, Comm. on safety of Med.s. Socs: Nat. Osteoporosis Soc.; Brit. Endocrine. Soc; Fell., Roy. Soc. Med. Prev: Lect. (O & G) Univ. Dundee; Sen. Lect. (O & G) Univ. Leeds; Dean Postgrad. Med. Sch. Univ. Hull.

PURDIE, Erica Margaret Gertrude Helen (retired) Shearwater, Popes Lane, Colyford, Colyton EX24 6QR Tel: 01297 553206 — MB BCh 1941 Wales; MTh Lond. 1978, BD 1974; BSc Wales 1938;

DObst RCOG 1943. Prev: Resid. Surg. Off. St. Helier Co. Hosp. Carshalton.

PURDIE, Gregor Castle Douglas Medical Group, Castle Douglas Health Centre, Academy Sreett, Castle Douglas DG7 1EE Tel: 01556 503888 Fax: 01556 504302; The Auld Kirk, Hardgate, Haugh of Urr, Castle Douglas DG7 3LD Tel: 01556 660286 Fax: 01556 660415 — MB ChB 1978 Ed.; DRCOG 1982. (Edinburgh) GP Adviser Dumfries & Galloway Health Bd.; Chairm. Scott. Area Med. Comms. Chairm. Gp. Socs: Sec. Dumfries & Galloway Local Med. Comm. Prev: Trainee GP Castle Douglas; SHO (O & G) Simpson Memor. Matern. Pavilion & Roy. Infirm. Edin.; Ho. Surg. & Ho. Phys. Dumfries & Galloway Roy. Infirm.

PURDIE, Helen Rose Mary Basildon & Thurrock NHS Trust, Nether Mayne, Basildon SS16 5NL Tel: 01268 533911; 54 Priests Lane, Brentwood CM15 8BY Tel: 01277 261841 — MB BS 1979 Lond.; Dip. Pract. Dermat. Cardiff 1993; DRCOG 1983; DA Eng. 1981. (Middlx.) Assoc. Specialist (Dermat.) Basildon & Thurrock NHS Trust; Examr. for Dip. In Practical Derm., Univ. of Wales Coll. Of Med. Prev: GP Chelmsford.

PURDIE, Niall Lachlan Lochindaal, Mary Avenue, Aberlour AB38 9QN — MB ChB 1991 Dundee.

PURDIE, Sonia Anne (retired) 15 Brudenell Avenue, Poole BH13 7NW Tel: 01202 708427 — MRCS Eng. LRCP Lond. 1947; DObst RCOG 1949; DA Eng. 1953.

PURDOM, Deborah Jane Dept. of Nuclear Med, Glenfield Hospital, Groby Road, Leicester LE3 9QP Tel: 0116 287 1471; 27 Burton Street, Loughborough LE11 2DT Tel: 01504 219497 — BM BS 1983 Nottm.; BMedSci Nottm. 1981. Med. Off.

PURDUE, Basil Nigel Forensic Medicine Unit, Department of Pathology, University Medical School, Teviot Place, Edinburgh EH8 9AG Tel: 0131 650 4518 Fax: 0131 650 6529 Email: basil.purdue@ed.ac.uk — MB ChB 1976 Manch.; BSc St. And. 1973; FRCPath 1996, M 1986; DMJ(Path) Soc. Apoth. Lond. 1985. Sen. Lect. (Forens. Med.) Univ. Edin. Socs: Brit. Assn. Forens. Med.; Medico-Legal Soc.; Brit. Acad. Forens. Sci. Prev: Sen. Lect. Univ. Dundee; Lect. (Forens. Med.) St. Thos. Hosp. Lond. & Univ. Leeds.

PURDY, Brian 42A Lee Park, Blackheath, London SE3 9HZ Tel: 020 8852 7168 — MB ChB Birm. 1953; DPH (Distinc.) Lond. 1963; DObst RCOG 1963. Prev: Princip. Med. Off. DHSS.

PURDY, David Robert Pepperman and Partners, The Cottons, Meadow Lane, Raunds, Wellingborough NN9 6YA Tel: 01933 623327 Fax: 01933 623370 — MB BS 1984 Lond.; MSc Warwick; MRCGP Lond. 1988. Prev: SHO (Paediat. & Psych.) Joyce Green Hosp. Dartford; SHO (Infect. Dis.) Joyce Green Hosp. Dartford.

PURDY, Gerard Michael 5 Vicarage Gardens, Elloughton, Brough HU15 1JB — MB BCh BAO 1982 NUI; MRCP (UK) 1987; FFA RCSI 1986.

PURDY, Robert Hedley Dykes Hall Medical Centre, 156 Dykes Hall Road, Sheffield S6 4GQ Tel: 0114 232 3236 — MRCS Eng. LRCP Lond. 1975; MRCGP 1979; DRCOG 1979; Cert JCC Lond. 1979.

PURDY, Sarah Tel: 0191 222 8761 Fax: 0191 222 7892 — MB BS 1987 Lond.; MD London 1998; BSc (Hons.) Lond. 1984; MPH Harvard Univ. 1996; MRCGP (Distinc.) 1991. (Med. Coll. St. Bart. Hosp.) Hon. Sen. Lect..(Primary Health Care) Ubiv.Newc. Prev: Vis. Fell. Harvard Med. Sch.; Health Policy Analyst Jackson Hole Gp. USA; Trainee GP (Gen. Pract.) Exeter VTS.

PURDY, Vivienne Lesley Birbeck Medical Group, Penrith Health Centre, Bridge Lane, Penrith CA11 8HW; Boxwood House, Plumpton, Penrith CA11 9PA Tel: 01768 885100 — BM BS 1990 Nottm.; BMedSci Nottm. 1988; MRCGP 1996; DRCOG 1994. (Nottm.) GP Princip. Birbeck Med. GP Penrith. Prev: Trainee GP/SHO (Med.) Cumbld. Infirm. Carlise; SHO (O & G) City Gen. Hosp. Carlise; SHO (Rheum., Paediat. & A & E) Cumbld. Infirm. Carlisle.

PUREWAL, Tejpal Singh Link 6Z, Royal Liverpool University Hospital, Prescott St., Liverpool L7 8XP Tel: 0151 706 3561 Fax: 0151 706 5928 Email: tpurewal@flbuh-tr.nwest.nhs.uk — MB ChB 1987 Leeds; MD (Leeds) 1999; FRCP (UK) 2000; MBChB (Hons.) 1987; BSc (Hons.) Physiol. 1984; MRCP (UK) 1990. (Leeds) Cons. Phys. (Diabetes & Endocrinol.) Roy. Liverp. Univ. Hosp.; Cons phys Liverp. Wom.s' Hosp. Prev: Sen. Regist. Roy. United Hosp. Bath; Regist. Roy. Vict. Infirm. Newc. u. Tyne; Research Fell. (Diabetic) Kings Coll. Hosp. Lond.

PURI

PURI, Basant Kumar MRI Unit, Imperial College School of Medicine, Hammersmith Hospital, Du Cane Road, London W12 0HS Fax: 020 8383 3038 Email: bbasant.puri@csc.mrc.ac.uk; 63 Caraway Road, Fulbourn, Cambridge CB1 5DU — MB BChir 1985 Camb.; MA Camb. 1986; MRCPsych 1989; BSc (Hons.) Open Univ. 2001; DipMath 2000; DipStat 2001. (Univ. Camb.) Cons. (Psychiat.) MRI Unit, Imperial Coll. Sch. Med. Hammersmith Hosp. Lond.; Sen. Lect. (Neuroimaging); Sen. Clin. Scientist MRC Clin. Scis. Centre Hammersmith Hosp. Lond.; Hon. Cons. Dept. of Radiol. Hammersmith Hosp. Lond. Socs: Roy. Coll. Psychiat. Prev: Sen. Research Fell. (Neuroimaging) Roy. Postgrad. Med. Sch. Univ. Lond.; Sen. Regist. & Hon. Lect. (Psychiat.) Char. Cross & W.m. Hosps. Lond.; Hon. Regist., Regist. & SHO (Psychiat.) Addenbrooke's Hosp. Camb.

PURI, Sundeep c/o Three Trees, 202 College Road, Whalley Range, Manchester M16 0AA — MB ChB 1986 Manch.

PURITZ, Rupert 13 Clifton House Close, Clifton, Shefford SG17 5EQ Tel: 01462 812246 Fax: 01462 851858; 109 Station Road, Lower Stondon, Henlow SG16 6JJ Tel: 01462 850305 Fax: 01462 851858 — MB BS 1970 Lond.; MRCP (UK) 1975; MRCS Eng. LRCP Lond. 1970. (Roy. Free) Prev: Research Regist. (Cardiol.) Roy. Sussex Co. Hosp. Brighton; Rotat. Regist. (Med.) King's Coll. Hosp. Lond.; Ho. Phys. Roy. Free Hosp. Lond.

PURKAIT, Sudhir Kumar 8 Jutland Place, Mullens Road, Egham TW20 8AQ Tel: 01784 438297 — MB BS 1957 Calcutta. (Calcutta) GP Egham. Socs: Fell. Roy. Soc. Med.; BMA. Prev: Regist. (Gen. Psychiat.) St. Mary's Hosp. Stannington; Med. Asst. (Gen. Psychiat.) Morganwag Hosp. Bridgend, Wales; Trainee GP Pontypool, Wales VTS.

PURKAYASTHA, Bana Behari Royal Surrey County Hospital, Egerton Road, Guildford GU2 7XX — MB BS 1966 Calcutta; MRCOphth. 1988; DOMS Calcutta 1969; DO RCPSI 1975; DO Eng. 1975. (Calcutta Med. Coll.) Clin. Asst. (Ophth.) Farnham Rd. Hosp., Guildford & Haslemere Dist. Hosp. & Roy. Surrey Co. Hosp. Guildford.; Vis. Ophth. Univ. Surrey Guildford. Socs: BMA. Prev: Regist. (Ophth.) Regional Eye Unit, Herts & Essex Gen. Hosp. Bishops Stortford; SHO (Ophth.) Midl. Counties Eye Infirm. Wolverhampton.

PURKIS, Albert Edward 22 Westminster Gardens, Barking IG11 0BJ — MB BS 1957 Lond.; LMSSA Lond. 1956. (St. Mary's)

PURKIS, Jethro John McDonald 5 Richmond Park Crescent, Bournemouth BH8 9BU — MB ChB 1995 Birm.; ChB Birm. 1995. (Univ. Birm.)

PURKISS, Muriel Edith 23 St Agnes Close, Victoria Park Road, London E9 7HS Tel: 020 8533 5979 — MB BS 1954 Lond.; MFCM 1983.

PURKISS, Ruth Heather 24 Manor Park, Bristol BS6 7HH — MB ChB 1987 Bristol.

PURNACHANDRA RAO, Vuyyuru Rydal Mount, 30 Dinting Road, Glossop SK13 7DT — MB BS 1971 Andhra.

PURNELL, David Dept. Pathology, UHL Leicester Royal Infimary, Infirmary Square, Leicester LE1 5W Email: davep@doctors.org.uk — MB ChB 1996 Leic.; BSc Sheff. 1991. Specialist Regist. (Histopath.) Leicester. Prev: SpR (Histopath.) W. Midl.s; SHO (Histopath.) Roy. Free Hosp. Lond.; Ho. Off. (Med.) Leicester Roy. Infirm.

PURNELL, Elizabeth Mary (retired) Carr Hill, Shawclough Road, Rochdale OL12 6LG — MB BS 1959 Lond.; BSc Lond. 1952, MB BS 1959.

PURNELL, Kenneth Leslie (retired) Treetops, Wiswell Lane, Whalley, Clitheroe BB7 9AF Tel: 01254 824524 — MB ChB 1950 Manch. Prev: GP Accrington.

PURNELL, Leslie William (retired) Carr Hill, Shawclough Road, Rochdale OL12 6LG — MB BS Lond. 1959; FRCOG 1977, M 1964; DObst RCOG 1961. Prev: Cons. O & G Rochdale Healthcare NHS Trust.

PURNELL, Nicola Windsor Cottage, Windsor Lane, Little Kingshill, Great Missenden HP16 0DP — BM 1995 Soton.

***PURNELL, Richard Mark** Quantos, St Mary Church, Cowbridge CF71 7LT — BM BS 1998 Nottm.; BM BS Nottm 1998.

PURNELL, Robin John (retired) 6 Taylor Avenue, Cringleford, Norwich NR4 6XY Tel: 01603 454491 — MB BS Lond. 1959; FFA RCS Eng. 1963. Prev: Cons. & Sen. Regist. (Anaesth.) Norf. & Norwich Health Care NHS Trust.

PURNELL, Simon Leslie Ilkeston Health Centre, South Street, Ilkeston DE7 5PZ Tel: 0115 932 2968 — BM BCh 1988 Oxf.; MA Camb. 1985; MRCGP 1992; DRCOG 1991; DCH RCP Lond. 1990.

PURNELL-MULLICK, Samir 55 Arden Street, Coventry CV5 6FB — MB BS 1989 Lond.; BSc Physiol. Lond. 1986; MRCP (UK) 1992. Regist. (Radiol.) Leicester Roy. Infirm.

PUROHIT, Nimischandra Natverlal 242 The Fairway, New Moston, Manchester M40 3NH — MB BS 1979 Baroda; MRCPsych 1992; DPM RCPSI 1986.

PUROHIT, Shyamsundar Jagannath Spinney Hill Medical Centre, 143 St. Saviours Road, Leicester LE5 3HX Tel: 0116 251 7870 Fax: 0116 262 9816; 4 Meadowcourt Road, Oadby, Leicester LE2 2PB — MB BS 1973 Nagpur; MD Nagpur 1978. (Govt med Coll Nagdur)

PURR, Julia Margaret Haigh and Partners, 11 Church Street, Harston, Cambridge CB2 5NP Tel: 01223 870250 Fax: 01223 872741; The Surgery, 11 Church St, Harston, Cambridge CB2 5NP Tel: 01223 870250 Fax: 01223 872741 — MB BChir 1981 Camb.; MA Camb. 1981. (Camb. (New Hull and Addenbrookes))

PURRY, Nigel Angold (retired) 17 Chewton Common Road, Highcliffe, Christchurch BH23 5LX — MB BS Lond. 1959; FRCS Eng. 1970; DObst RCOG 1961. Prev: Cons. Rehabil. Med. Roy. Bournemouth & ChristCh. Hosp. NHS Trust.

PURSE, Pamela Ann (retired) Fieldgate House, Lock Lane, Birdham, Chichester PO20 7BA Tel: 01243 513617 — MB ChB Birm. 1955.

PURSER, James Randolph 1A Marlborough Road, Chiseldon, Swindon SN4 0NR Tel: 01793 741150 Fax: 01793 741150 — MB BCh BAO 1953 Belf. (Belf.) Prev: Med. Off. Colon. Med. Serv. Nigeria; Ho. Off. Moyle Hosp. Larne.

PURSER, John Hedley Springfield House, New Lane, Patricroft, Eccles, Manchester M30 7JE; Woodend, 44 Woodstock Drive, Worsley, Manchester M28 2WW Tel: 0161 794 4540 — MB ChB 1976 Manch. Clin. Asst. (Plastic Surg.) Withington Hosp.; Clin. Asst. (Gastroenterol.) Hope Hosp. Prev: SHO Rotat. (Surg.) Univ. Hosp. S. Manch.

PURSER, Mr Nicholas John Saltway Cottage, 28 Droitwich Road, Feckenham, Redditch B96 6HX — MB ChB 1990 Birm.; ChB Birm. 1990; FRCS Glas. Specialist Regist. (Gen. Surg.).

PURSER, Paul Cyril David and Partners, Clee Medical Centre, 363 Grimsby Road, Cleethorpes DN35 7XE Tel: 01472 697257 Fax: 01472 690852; 16 Abbey Drive W., Grimsby DN32 0HH Tel: 01472 352541 Fax: 01472 352541 Email: paulpurser@aol.com — MB ChB 1976 Leeds. p/t Med. Dir. St Andrews Hospice, Peaks Ln. Grimsby, N E Lincs; Macmillan Lead G.P. In Palliat. Care.

PURSER, Stanley Hubert (retired) Anvil House, Durlston Road, Swanage BH19 2DL Tel: 01929 3574 Fax: 01929 421072 — MA, MB BChir Camb. 1942. Prev: Anaesth. Swanage Gen. Hosp. & Swanage Cott. Hosp.

PURSSELL, Neville Richard Paddington Green Health Centre, 4 Princes Louise Close, London W2 1LQ Tel: 020 7887 1600 Fax: 020 7887 1635 — MB BS 1989 Lond.; MA Camb. 1982; DCH RCP Lond. 1992; DRCOG 1992; MRCGP 1995. (UMDS (Guys))

PURUSHOTHAM, Mr Anand David Cambridge Breast Unit, Addenbrookes Hospital, Cambridge CB2 2QQ Tel: 01223 586627 Fax: 01223 586932 — MB BS 1982 Madras; FRCS 2001 England; MD Glas. 1992; FRCS (Gen.) 1995; FRCS Ed. 1987; FRCS 1999 Glasgow. Cons. Surg. Addenbrookes Hosp. Camb.

***PURUSHOTHAMAN, Hema Nandini** 2 Kingsley Drive, Worcester Park KT4 7HB — MB BS 1998 Lond.; MB BS Lond 1998; BSc 1995.

***PURUSHOTHAMAN, Sunil** 17 Aintree Avenue, London E6 1PA — MB BS 1998 Lond.; MB BS Lond 1998.

PURUSHOTHMAN, Girija 4 Benrek Close, Ilford IG6 2QL — MB BS 1991 Madras, India; MRCS Eng. LRCP Lond. 1989.

PURVES, Alistair Martin kings College Hospital, Denmark Hill, London SE5 9RS Tel: 020 7848 5151 — MB BChir 1981 Camb.; MD Camb. 1994; MRCP (UK) 1985. Cons. In Clin. NeuroPhysiol. Prev: Sen. Regist. (Clin. Neurophysiol.) Hosp. for Childr. Gt. Ormond St. Lond.; Hon. Clin. Asst. (Clin. Neurophysiol.) Nat. Hosp. Neurol. & Neurosurg.Lond.

PURVES, George Fraser (retired) 14 Roker Park Road, Sunderland SR6 9PF Tel: 0191 548 3951 — MB BChir 1942 Camb.; MA MB

BChir Camb. 1942; MRCS Eng. LRCP Lond. 1942; FFA RCS Eng. 1954; DA Eng. 1947. Prev: Anaesth. City Gen. Hosp. Sheff.

PURVES, Hilda Jean (retired) 7 Worcester Crescent, Clifton, Bristol BS8 3JA Tel: 0117 973 6129 — MB BS 1953 Lond. Clin. Med. Off. (Child Health) Avon AHA; Instruc. Doctor (Family Plann.) Bristol & W.on HAs. Prev: SCMO Family Plann. & reproductive health.

PURVES, Professor Ian Nicholas 45 Western Way, Ponteland, Newcastle upon Tyne NE20 9AS; Sowerby Centre for Health Informatics at Newcastle, University of Newcastle, Newcastle upon Tyne NE4 6BE Tel: 0191 256 3141 Fax: 0191 256 3099 Email: ian.purves@ncl.ac.uk — MB BS 1985 Newc.; MRCGP 1989; DRCOG 1989; DCCH RCGP & FCM 1988; MD Newc. 1998. Head of Sowerby Centre for Health Informatics, Newc. Univ., Newc. u. Tyne; Prof. (Health Informatics) Newc. Univ. Socs: BMA; RCOGP; Chair RCGP Health Informatics Task Gp. Prev: GP Blaydon; Trainee GP N.d. VTS.

***PURVES, Jonathan David** 199 Dowson Road, Hyde SK14 5BR Tel: 0161 368 1947 Email: jopurves@hotmail.com; 199 Dowson Road, Hyde SK14 5BR Tel: 0161 368 1947 — MB ChB 1997 Birm.

PURVIS, Christopher Raymond (retired) Purvis and Partners, The Hart Surgery, York Road, Henley-on-Thames RG9 2DR Tel: 01491 843200 Fax: 01491 411296 — MRCS Eng. LRCP Lond. 1964. Prev: SHO (Obst.) Gen. Lying-In Hosp. Lond.

PURVIS, Diana Joan Avenue Medical Centre, Wentworth Avenue, Slough SL2 2DG Tel: 01753 524549 Fax: 01753 552537; 2 Rambler Close, Taplow, Maidenhead SL6 0JT — MB ChB 1983 Sheff.; MRCGP 1987; DRCOG 1986. (Sheffield)

PURVIS, Jane Torridon, Barmoor Lane, Ryton NE40 3AA — MB BS 1976 Newc.

PURVIS, John Arthur Department of Cardiology, Altnagelvin Area Hospital, Glenshane Road, Londonderry BT47 6SB Tel: 01504 451711 Fax: 01504 311020; 2 Cross Na Downell Park, Greystone Road, Limavady BT49 0TP Tel: 015047 69113 — MB BCh BAO 1985 Belf.; MD Belf. 1992; MRCP Glas. 1988; FRCP Glas. 1998. Cons. Phys. (Cardiol.) Altnagelvin Area Hosp. Socs: Amer. Heart Assn. (Counc. Clin. Cardiol.); Internat. Soc. Fibrinolysis & Thrombolysis.; Brit. Cardiac Soc. Prev: Sen. Regist. (Cardiol.) Roy. Vict. Hosp. Belf.; Sen. Regist. (Med.) Ulster Hosp. Dundonald; Regist. (Cardiol.) Belf. City Hosp. Belf.

PURVIS, Margaret Stewart (retired) 3 Gordon Street, Barnhill, Dundee DD5 2RA — MB ChB 1944 St. And.

PURVIS, Mark Julian 17 Uppertown, Pxenhope, Keighley BD22 9LL — MB ChB 1984 Leeds.

PURVIS, Richard John Childrens Centre, Damers Road, Dorchester DT1 2LB Tel: 01305 251150 Fax: 01305 254737; 2 Queens Avenue, Dorchester DT1 2EW Tel: 01305 262670 Email: richard.purvis@nationwideasp.net — MB ChB 1964 Ed.; FRCP Lond. 1986; FRCP Ed. 1983, M 1967; DCH Eng. 1966. (Ed.) Cons. Paediat. W. Dorset Gen. Hosps. NHS Trust; Med. Dir. W.Dorset Gen. Hosps. NHS Trust. Prev: Lect. (Child Life & Health) Univ. Edin.; SHO (Paediat.) Edin. Roy. Infirm. & Internat. Grenfell Assn. St. Anthony, Newfld.

PURWAR, Rajiv 48 Goddington Lane, Orpington BR6 9DS Tel: 01689 26638 — MB BS 1983 Lond.; BA Camb. 1980; MRCGP 1987; DCH RCP Lond. 1987; DRCOG 1986. Princip. GP Lond.

PURWAR, Shri Ram Ravenswood, 48 Sevenoaks Road, Orpington BR6 9JR Tel: 01689 821179 — MB BS Lucknow 1952. (Lucknow) Clin. Asst. Orpington Hosp. Prev: Cas. Off. & Sen. Ho. Surg. Roy. Alexandra Hosp. Rhyl; Res. Surg. Off. Gen. Hosps. Margate & Ramsgate.

PURWAR, Simon 48 Sevenoaks Road, Orpington BR6 9JR Tel: 01689 824500; 4 Nursery Gardens, Chislehurst BR7 5BW Tel: 020 8456 7925 — MB BS 1992 Lond.; MA Oxf. 1989.

PURWAR, Vijay Station Road Surgery, 74 Station Road, West Wickham BR4 0PU Tel: 020 8777 8245; 144 Wickham Way, Park Langley, Beckenham BR3 3AR Tel: 020 8658 9070 — MB ChB 1985 Bristol; MRCGP 1989; DCH RCP Lond. 1990.

PUSAVAT, Lilian Tharntip Department of Psychiatry, West Middlxsex University Hospital, Twickenham Road, Isleworth TW7 6AF Tel: 020 8565 5178 — MB BS 1979 Hong Kong; MRCPsych 1985. Cons. Psychiat. W. Middlx. Univ. Hosp.

PUSEY, Professor Charles Dickson Renal Section, Division of Medicine, Faculty of Medicine, Imperial College, Hammersmith Hospital, Du Cane Road, London W12 0NN Tel: 020 8383 3152 Fax: 020 8383 2062 Email: c.pusey@ic.ac.uk — MB BChir 1972 Camb.; MSc Lond. 1983; MA 1973; BA Camb. 1969; FRCP Lond. 1989; MRCP (UK) 1974; FRCPath Lond. 1997. (Guy's) Cons. Phys. Hammersmith Hosp. Lond. Socs: Renal Assn.; Assn. Phys.; Brit. Soc. Immunol. Prev: Reader (Renal Med.) & Sen. Lect. (Med.) Roy. Postgrad. Med. Sch. Lond.; Cons. Phys. Hammersmith Hosp. Lond.

PUSEY, Clare Tonna Hospital, Tonna, Neath SA11 3AX Fax: 01639 635404 — MB BCh 1992 Wales; MRC Psych 1996. (University of Wales Cardiff) Staff Grade (Psychiat.) Tonna Hosp. Neath. Prev: Regist. (Psychiat.) Cefn Coed Hosp. Swansea; SHO (Med.) P. Philip Hosp. Lla.lli; Ho. Off. (Med.) P.ss of Wales Hosp. Bridgend.

PUSEY, Johanna Mary 2 Willow Grove, Goosnargh, Preston PR3 2DE; Mill Top Farm, Mill Lane, Goosnargh, Preston PR3 2JX — MB BS 1975 Lond.; MRCS Eng. LRCP Lond. 1975; MRCOG 1981. (Roy. Free)

PUSEY, Judith Mary Southend Road, Stanford-le-Hope SS17 0PH; 12 Appleby Drive, Laindon, Basildon SS16 6NU — MB BS 1970 Lond.; DObst RCOG 1972. (Lond. Hosp.) Princip. GP Stanford le Hope. Prev: Lect. (Gen. Pract.) Welsh Nat. Sch. Med. Cardiff.

PUSEY, Mr Richard John, TD Basildon Hospital, Nether Mayne, Basildon SS16 5NL Tel: 01268 592284 — MB ChB 1970 Birm.; FRCS Eng. 1975. Cons. Orthop. Surg. Basildon & Thurrock NHS Trust. Socs: World Orthop. Concern. Prev: Sen. Regist. (Orthop.) Addenbrookes Hosp. Camb.; Regist. (Orthop.) St. Thos. Hosp. Lond.

PUSHPANATHAN, Mr Rajadurai Joseph 1 Elvington Gayton Road, King's Lynn PE30 4TB — MB BS 1975 Sri Lanka; FRCS Glas. 1985; LMSSA Lond. 1984; FCOphth 1989; DO RCS Eng. 1984. Cons. Ophth. Qu. Eliz. Hosp. King's Lynn. Prev: Ass. Specialist Ophth.

PUSHPANGADAN, Majnu 2 Woodlands Court, Longwood Avenue, Bingley BD16 2SW — MB ChB 1990 Leeds; MRCP (UK) 1994. Regist. (Gen. Med. & Med. for Elderly) Yorks. Prev: SHO Rotat. (Med.) Bradford.

PUSHPARAJAH, Christeta Ratnakumari The Surgery, 1 Knoll Rise, Orpington BR6 0EJ Tel: 01689 824563 Fax: 01689 820712 — MB BS 1982 Sri Lanka.

***PUSHPARAJAH, Savitha** 91 Beeston Road, Dunkirk, Nottingham NG7 2JQ — BM BS 1996 Nottm.

PUSZET, Jozef, Lt.-Col. RAMC Retd. Willowtree Bungalow, 19 Bicester Road, Long Crendon, Aylesbury HP18 9BP — MB BS 1962 Lond.; FRCOG 1990, M 1975; DObst 1964. (King's Coll. Hosp.) Sen. Cons. O & G Sultan Qaboos Univ. Hosp. Muscat, Oman. Prev: Cons. O & G King Khalid Nat. Guard Hosp. Jeddah, Saudi Arabia; Cons. O & G RAMC; Regist. (Gyn.) Roy. Berks. Hosp. Reading.

PUSZTAI, Edit Esther — MB ChB 1988 Glas.; MRCPsych 1993; Dip Cog Psych Dund 1997. (Glasgow) Sen. Regist. (Gen. Psychiat. & Learning Disabilities); Locum Cons. in Gen. Adult Psychiat., Pk.head Hosp., Salamanca St., Glas. Socs: BMA; Roy. Coll. Psychiat.; Brit. Assn. Cognitive and Behaviour Psychotherapists. Prev: SR Gen. Psychiat. and LD, Ment. Welf. Commiss., Edin.; SR Gen. Psychiat. and LD Strathlea Resource Centre, Kilmarnook; SR Gen. Psychiat. and LD, Roy. Scott. Nat. Hosps.

PUTHUCHEARY, Zudin Amilka 15 Victoria Road, West Bridgford, Nottingham NG2 7JW — BM BS 1997 Nottm.

PUTLAND, Anthony John 5 The Driveway, Shoreham-by-Sea BN43 5GG — BM BS 1990 Nottm.

PUTMAN, Helen Rose 14 Belgrave Street, Ossett WF5 0AD — MB ChB 1985 Leeds.

PUTMAN, Janet Margaret (retired) 33 Whitefields Gate, Solihull B91 3GE — MB BS 1976 Lond. Prev: Sen. Regist. Leics. HA & Cardiff.

PUTNAM, Elizabeth Ann Druids, Chilworth Ring, Chilworth, Southampton SO16 7HW — MB ChB 1975 Birm.; FFA RCS Eng. 1979. Cons. Anaesth. Soton. & S.W. Hants. Health Dist. Prev: Sen. Regist. (Anaesth.) Soton. & S.W. Hants. Health Dist.; Regist. (Anaesth.) Soton. Gen. Hosp.; SHO (Anaesth.) Roy. Devon & Exeter Hosp. (Wonford) Exeter.

PUTNAM, Mr Graham Douglas Cumberland Infirmary, Newtown rd, Carlisle CA2 7HY Email: graham.putnam@carlh-tr.demon.co.uk; Grayson House, Great Salkeld, Penrith CA11 9NB Tel: 01768 898080 — MB BCh 1988 Wales; BDS 1980; FDS RCS Eng. 1983; FRCS Ed. 1991. (University of Wales College of Medicine) Cons. Oral & Maxillofacial Surg. Carlisle Hosps. NHS Trust. Socs: Fell. Brit.

PUTRIS

Assn. Oral & Maxillofacial Surg. Prev: Sen. Regist. Bristol S.W. Regional HA; Regist. N.E. Rotat. Newc., Sunderland, Middlesbrough.

PUTRIS, Samera Haseeb Grosvenor Road Surgery, 23 Grosvenor Road, Muswell Hill, London N10 2DR Tel: 020 8883 5600 Fax: 020 8883 3324 — MB ChB 1972 Mosul, Iraq; T(GP) 1991.

PUTT, Christopher Mark New Road Surgery, 109 York Road, Chingford, London E4 8LF Tel: 020 8524 8124 Fax: 020 8529 8655 — MB ChB 1983 Leeds; MRCGP 1988; DRCOG 1986.

PUTTA GOWDA, Hethur M Duffrn Street Medical Centre, 8 Cardiff Road, Newtown, Mountain Ash CF45 4EY Tel: 01443 476505 Fax: 01443 473219.

PUTTAGUNTA, Balaji Park Grove Surgery, 94 Park Grove, Barnsley S70 1QE Tel: 01226 282345 — LRCP LRCS 1980 Ed.; LRCP LRCS Ed. LRCPS Glas. 1980.

PUTTERILL, Janet Sinclair 87B Sandpit Lane, St Albans AL1 4EY — MB ChB 1993 Stellenbosch.

PUTTICK, Michael Ian 62 Saltram Crescent, London W9 3HR Tel: 020 8969 8482 Email: m.puttick@bigfoot.com — MB BS 1996 Lond.; BSc 1995. (St. Mary's Lond.) SHO (A&E) St. Mary's Hosp. Leeds; Hon. Res. Fell. (Acad. Surg. Unit) St. Mary's Hosp. Lond. Socs: Roy. Soc. Med.; St. Mary's Assn. Prev: Research Fell. St. Mary's Hosp. Lond.

PUTTICK, Nigel 10 The Dorkings, Great Broughton, Middlesbrough TS9 7NA — MB 1979 Camb.; MA Camb. 1979, MB 1979, BChir 1978; FFA RCS Lond. 1983; Dip. Obst. Auckland 1980. Cons. Anaesth. S. Cleveland Hosp. Middlesbrough. Prev: Lect. Dept. Anaesth. Univ. Wales Coll. Med.

PUVANACHANDRA, Mr Kathir HM Stanley Hospital, Directorate on Ophthalmology, St Asaph LL17 0RS Tel: 01745 583275; Bryn Sai, 4 Hayden Close, Old Colwyn, Colwyn Bay LL29 9PB Tel: 01492 516510 — MB BS 1971 Ceylon; FRCS Ed. 1981; FRCOphth. 1993; DO Eng. 1981. (Colombo) Cons. Ophth. HM Stanley Hosp. St. Asaph; Ext. Examr. FRCS Ophth. RCS Glas.; Pant 3 MRCOpyth. RCOphth. Chairm. Overseas Doctors Train. Comm. RCOphth. Prev: Hon. Lect. Univ. Glas. & Sen. Regist. (Ophth.) W.. Infirm. Glas.

PUVANENDRAN, Kanagasabai 600 Rayleigh Road, Hutton, Brentwood CM13 1SG — MB BS 1978 Sri Lanka; MRCP (UK) 1987.

PUVANENDRAN, Priyadharshini 9 Rochester Gardens, Croydon CR0 5NN — MB ChB 1993 Dundee.

PUVANENDRAN-THOMAS, Rukshini 85B Walton Street, Oxford OX2 6EA — MB BS 1989 Singapore.

PUVI, Nirmalan 76 Rating Lane, Barrow-in-Furness LA13 9LD Tel: 01229 821621 — MB ChB 1993 Dundee; DRCOG 1997. (Dundee) GP Regist. Caereinion Health Centre Llanfair Caereinion. Prev: SHO (Opthalmol.)/ENT Furness Gen. Hosp.

PUVINATHAN, Himasalakumari The Surgery, 119 Northcote Road, Battersea, London SW11 6PW Tel: 020 7228 6762 — LMSSA 1995 Lond.

PUVINATHAN, Sinnathamby Arumugam 94 Springfield Avenue, London SW20 9JU — LRCP LRCS Ed. LRCPS Glas. 1994.

PUVIRAJASINGHAM, Shivani 76 Rating Lane, Barrow-in-Furness LA13 9LD — MB ChB 1993 Leeds; DCH 1997.

PUVIRAJASINGHAM, Suppiah 76 Rating Lane, Barrow-in-Furness LA13 9LD Tel: 01229 821621 — MB BS 1962 Ceylon; DPH Otago 1971. (Colomo Sri Lanka) Med. Off. Staff Grade, Bay Community Trust, Lancaster. Socs: Soc. Pub. Health. Prev: Clin. Med. Off. S. Cumbria HA; Med. Off. Of Health, Sri Lanka.

***PUXLEY, Deborah Mollie** 13 Cunningham Avenue, St Albans AL1 1JJ — MB ChB 1996 Liverp.

PUXON, Christine Margaret 19 Clarence Gate Gardens, Glentworth St., London NW1 6AY Tel: 020 7723 7922 Fax: 020 7258 2038 Email: margaretpuxon@dial.pipex.com — MB ChB (Hons.) Birm. 1942; MD (Obst.) Birm. 1947; MRCS Eng. LRCP Lond. 1941; FRCOG 1979, M 1946. (Birm.) Cons. Med. Legal Consult. Lond.; QC; Chairm. (Ethics Comm.) IVF Unit Lister Hosp. Socs: Fell. Roy. Soc. Med.; Medico-Legal Soc.; Soc. Of Doctors in Law (Chairm.). Prev: Crown Ct. Recorder; Dep. Circuit Judge; Regist. (Gyn.) Qu. Eliz. Hosp. Birm.

PUZEY, Angela Jane Southwell House Surgery, Southwell House, Back Lane, Rochford SS4 1AY Tel: 01702 545241 Fax: 01702 546390; The Old Post Office, Church End, Paglesham, Rochford SS4 2DJ — MB ChB 1965 Bristol. (Bristol) Prev: Cas. Off., Ho. Surg. & Ho. Phys. Stratford-on-Avon Hosp.; Sch. Med. Off. S.end.

PUZEY, Susan Hermione 1 Hillfield Road, Redhill RH1 4AP Tel: 01737 763888 — MB BS 1984 Lond.; MRCGP 1988; DRCOG 1987.

PYATT, Jason Robert The Cardiothoracic Centre, Thomas Drive, Liverpool L14 3PE Tel: 01942 523963 Email: jason.pyatt@ccl-tr.nwest.nhs.uk; 26 Nevada Close, Great Sankey, Warrington WA5 8WW Tel: 01925 650605 — MB ChB 1990 Manch.; MRCP (UK) 1995; BSc Hons Manchester 1987. (Manch.) Specialist Regist. (Cardiol.) Mersey Deanery; Res. Fell. (Cardio.). Prev: SHO (Med.) Hope Hosp. Salford; SHO (Med.) Wigan Infirm. Wigan.

PYATT, Richard Niel Kirkton Manor, The School House, Peebles EH45 9JN — MB BChir 1994 Camb.

PYBURN, Rachel Elizabeth Room 11 Redhouse, Tameside General Hospital, Ashton-under-Lyne OL6 8BJ — MB BS 1989 Newc.; MRCP (UK) 1993. Regist. (Gen. Med. & Cardio.) Tameside Hosp. Ashton under Lyme.

PYCOCK, Christopher John Department Medicine, Worcester Royal Infirmary, Newtown Road, Worcester WR5 1JG Tel: 01905 763333 Fax: 01905 760373 — MB ChB 1985 Bristol; PhD CNAA 1972; DSc Bristol 1984; BSc Soton. 1969; MRCP (UK) 1988; FRCP (UK) 1999. (Bristol) Cons. Phys. Worcester Roy. Infirm.; PostGrad. Clin. Tutor; Regional Coll. Tutor. Socs: Pharmacol. Soc.; BMA; Brit. Geriat. Soc. Prev: Lect. (Neuropharmacol.) Bristol; Res. Fell. Pk.inson's Dis. Soc.

PYCOCK, Julie Elizabeth Hackenthorpe Medical Centre, Main Street, Hackenthorpe, Sheffield S12 4LA Fax: 0114 251 0539 — MB ChB 1984 Sheff.

PYE, Anne Margaret (retired) 25 Whinmoor Road, Sandfield Park, Liverpool L12 2AU Tel: 0151 228 3038 — MB BCh BAO NUI 1949; LM Nat. Matern. Hosp. 1952. Prev: Ho. Surg. Wrexham War Memor. Hosp. & Ulster Hosp. Wom. & Childr. Belf.

PYE, David Charles 1 Carr Manor, Garth, Leeds LS17 5AS — MB ChB 1976 Dundee.

PYE, Eleanor Mary 3 Knighton Road, Stoneygate, Leicester LE2 3HL — MB ChB 1996 Leeds.

PYE, Mr Geoffrey Weston General Hospital, Uphill, Weston Super Mare BS23 4TQ Tel: 01934 647175 Fax: 01934 647018 — BM 1981 Soton.; FRCS 2001; MSc Aberd. 1975; BSc Leeds 1974; DM Nottm. 1988; FRCS Ed. 1985. (Soton.) Cons. Gen. & Colorectal Surg. W.on Area Health Trust. Socs: Assn. Coloproctol.; Brit. Soc. Gastroenterol. Prev: Lect. (Surg.) Univ. Nottm.

PYE, Geoffrey Francis Calcot Medical Centre, Hampden Road, Chalfont St Peter, Gerrards Cross SL9 9SA Tel: 01753 887311 Fax: 01753 891933; Kersham House, Bridge Reeve, Chulmleigh EX18 7BD Tel: 01769 581241 — MB BChir 1963 Camb.; BA Camb. 1959; MRCGP 1978. (King's Coll. Hosp.) Course Organiser i/c GP VTS Scheme Wycombe Dist.

PYE, Ian Frederick 3 Knighton Road, Stoneygate, Leicester LE2 3HL Tel: 0116 270 8536 — MD Camb. 1980, MB 1967,; BChir 1966; FRCP Lond. 1984; MRCP (U.K.) 1970; DObst RCOG 1969. (Camb. & Lond. Hosp.) Cons. Neurol. Leicester Roy. Infirm. Socs: Mem. Assn. Brit. Neurol.; Midl.s Neurol. Soc. Prev: Sen. Regist. (Neurol.) Univ. Hosp. Wales Cardiff; Regist. (Neurol.) N. Staffs. Hosp. Centre Stoke-on-Trent; Ho. Surg. & Ho. Phys. Lond. Hosp.

PYE, Mr Jonathan Kellow Department of Surgery, Wrexham Maelor Hospital, Croesnewydd Road, Wrexham LL13 7TD; Claremont Cottage, 29 Stansty Road, Wrexham LL11 2HR — MB BS 1974 Lond.; MS Lond. 1987; FRCS Eng. 1979; MRCS Eng. LRCP Lond. 1974; Cert. Higher Surg. Train. RCS Eng. 1988. Cons. Surg. Wrexham Maelor Hosp. Prev: Sen. Regist. (Surg.) S. Glam. & Clwyd HAs; 1 Year Secondment Qu. Mary Hosp. Hong Kong; Clin. Research Off. (Surg.) Univ. Wales Sch. Med.

PYE, Maryan Jennifer 2 Wingate Close, Trumpington, Cambridge CB2 2HW Tel: 01223 846463 Fax: 01223 847006; 2 Wingate Close, Trumpington, Cambridge CB2 2HW Tel: 01223 846463 Fax: 01223 847006 — MB BS Lond. 1970; MRCS Eng. LRCP Lond. 1970; FFPHM RCP (UK) 1993, M 1989; MFCM RCP (UK) 1984; DA Eng. 1972. (Char. Cross) Pub. Health Cons. Socs: Soc. Social Med.; Pub. Health & Primary Care Gp.; Inst. Healthcare Man. Prev: Sen. Cons. Dearden Consg.; Cons.Pub.Health Med.NHSE-E.ern; Cons. Pub. Health Med. Camb. & Huntingdon Health Auth.

PYE, Maurice Anthony Matthew Department of Cardiology, York District Hospital, York YO31 8HE Tel: 01904 631313 — MD 1992

Wales; BSc 1979; MB BCh 1982; MRCP (UK) 1985; FCP Lond. 1998; FRCP FRCP. (Cardiff) Cons. Cardiol. York Dist. Hosp. Socs: York Med. Soc.; Brit. Cardiovasc. Interven. Soc.; Brit. Cardiac Soc. Prev: Sen. Regist. (Cardiol.) St. Geo. Hosp. Lond.; Brit. Heart Foundat. Research Fell. Roy. Infirm. Glas.; Regist. (Cardiol.) Roy. Infirm. Glas.

PYE, Richard James 2A Wingate Close, Trumpington, Cambridge CB2 2HW Tel: 01223 843373 Fax: 01223 847006 Email: rjpye@dial.pipex.com — MB BS Lond. 1969; MA Camb. 1982; MD Lond. 1979; FRCP Lond. 1989; MRCP (UK) 1973; MRCS Eng. LRCP Lond. 1969. (Char. Cross) Cons. Dermat. Addenbrooke's Hosp. Camb. Socs: Brit. Assn. Dermat.; Eur. Soc. Micrographic Surg.; Amer. Acad. of Dermat. Prev: Sen. Regist. & Tutor (Dermat.) St. John's Hosp. Dis. Skin Lond.; Regist. (Dermat.) Bristol Roy. Infirm.

PYE, Seonaid Marie Queen's Medical Centre, University Hospital, Nottingham NG7 2UH; Flat 2, 40 Magdala Road, Mapperley Park, Nottingham NG3 5DF — BM BS 1995 Nottm. SHO (Gen. Med.) Qu.'s Med. Centre Nottm.

PYGOTT, Yvette Marie The Surgery, 4 Stoke Road, Bishops Cleeve, Cheltenham GL52 8RP Tel: 01242 672007 — MB ChB 1988 Birm.; DCH RCP Lond. 1992.

PYKE, Mark Richard 38 High Street, Milton Malsor, Northampton NN7 3AS — MB BS 1993 Lond.; BSc (Physiol.) Lond. 1990, MB BS 1993. Specialist Regist. Bristol Sch. Of Anaesth. Prev: SHO (A & E) Freemantle Hosp. Aust.; SHO Qu. Mary's Hosp. Roehampton; SHO King Edwd. vii Hosp. Midhurst.

PYKE, Mr Robert Consulting rooms, Three Shires Hospital, Northampton NN1 5DR — MB 1965 Camb.; BChir 1964; FRCS Eng. (Orl.) 1971; FRCS Ed. 1969. Cons. (Otolaryngol.) BMI Three Shires InDepend. Hosp. Prev: Sen. Regist. (Otolaryngol.) United Bristol Hosps.

PYLE, David Ian Llys Steffan, Temple Terrace, Lampeter SA48 7BJ Tel: 01570 422577 — MB BChir 1993 Camb. Assoc. Psychiat. Pembrokesh. & Derwen NHS Trust.

PYLE, Elizabeth Joy 81 Penland Road, Haywards Heath RH16 1PJ Tel: 01444 416303 Email: h2@ejpyle.freeserve.co.uk — MB BS 1994 Lond.; DRCOG 1997; DFFP 1999. (Kings College London) GP Regist, W. Sussx. Prev: SHO (Psychiat.) P.ss Roy. Hosp. Haywards Heath; SHO (Med.) P.ss Roy. Hosp. Haywards Heath; SHO (A & E) P.ss Roy. Hosp. Haywards Heath.

PYLE, Peter Owen (retired) Southlands, Hawkcombe Lane, Compton Abbas, Shaftesbury SP7 0NN Tel: 01747 811575 — MB BS Lond. 1955; FFA RCS Eng. 1966; DA Eng. 1957.

PYLE, Ronald Leslie Strathmore Surgery, 19 Jessie Street, Blairgowrie PH10 6BT Tel: 01250 872552 Fax: 01250 874504; Stapleton, Rosemount, Blairgowrie PH10 6LA Tel: 01250 872898 — MB ChB 1958 Aberd.; DObst RCOG 1960. (Aberd.) Prev: Med. Off. Trucial Oman Scouts; Obst. Brit. Milit. Hosp. Taiping, Malaya.

PYLE, Simon John 23 Broad Lane, Wilmington, Dartford DA2 7AQ — MB BS 1980 Lond.; DRCOG 1984.

PYLE, William Dryden Bayview Surgery, Bayview, Longhope, Stromness KW16 3NY Tel: 01856 701209 Fax: 01856 701224 — MB ChB 1958 Aberd.; MRCGP 1968; DObst RCOG 1962. (Aberd.) Socs: BMA. Prev: Ho. Surg. Roy. Infirm. Inverness; Ho. Surg. (Obst.) Aberd. Matern. Hosp.; Ho. Phys. (Paediat.) Roy. Hosp. Sick Childr. Glas.

PYM, Jenny (retired) 36 The Horsefair, Malmesbury SN16 0AP — MB ChB 1948 Bristol; DObst RCOG 1954. Prev: Internat. Planned Parenth. Federat. Organiser Family Plann. Train.

PYMONT, Frederick Edward Health Centre, Greenyard, Waltham Abbey EN9 1RD Tel: 01992 714088 Fax: 01992 763866; 162 Honey Lane, Waltham Abbey EN9 3BE Tel: 01992 711897 — MB BS 1968 Lond. (Roy. Lond. Hosp.)

PYNE, Andrew 7 Royal Chase, Tunbridge Wells TN4 8AX — BM 1980 Soton.; FRCA 1984. Cons. Anaesth. Kent & Sussex Weald NHS Trust Tunbridge Wells.

PYNE, Mr John Robin Stoke House, Stoke Holy Cross, 140 Norwich Road, Norwich NR14 8QJ Tel: 01508 493931 Email: john.pyne@lineone.net — MB BS Lond. 1965; FRCS Eng. 1971; MRCS Eng. LRCP Lond. 1965; FRCOphth 1991; DO Eng. 1969. (Char. Cross) Cons. Ophth. Norf. & Norwich Hosp. Socs: Fac. Ophth.; (Ex-Sec.) Norf. & Norwich M-C Soc. Prev: Sen. Regist. Lond. Hosp.; Sen. Lect. Moorfields Eye Hosp.; Ho. Phys. & Ho. Surg. Char. Cross Hosp.

PYNE, Tessa Mary 11 Muirfield Crescent, Gullane EH31 2HN Tel: 01620 842415 — MB BS 1975 Lond.; MRCS Eng. LRCP Lond. 1975; MRCGP 1983; MFFP 1992; DRCOG 1982; DCH RCPS Glas. 1978; Dip. GU Med. 1996. GP Asst.; CMO Family Plann.

PYONE LWIN MAUNG, Dr 106 Atlantic Avenue, Apartment 3B, Brooklyn NY 11201, USA; 7 The Windmills, Court Road, Chelmsford CM1 7HL Tel: 01245 514362 — MB BS 1983 Mandalay, Burma; MRCP (UK) 1993; DGM Glas. 1994.

PYONE PYONE MYINT, Dr 4 Eriksay Crescent, Newron Mearns, Glasgow G77 6XE — MB BS 1978 Med.; MB BS Med. Inst (II) Rangoon 1978.

PYOTT, Mr Andrew Anthony Edward 21 Wilmot Road, Glasgow G13 1XL Tel: 0141 959 6237 — MB ChB 1986 Glas.; BSc St. And. 1981; FRCS Glas. 1991; FCOphth 1991. Sen. Regist. (Ophth.) W.. Infirm. Glas. Prev: Regist. (Ophth.) S.. Gen. Hosp. Glas.

*****PYOTT, Jonathan James** Aylesbury Vales Healthcare NHS Trust, Aylesbury HP 1EG; 85 St Andrews Crescent, Stratford-upon-Avon CV37 9RP — BM 1995 Soton.

PYPER, Andrew James Unthank Road Surgery, 38 Unthank Road, Norwich NR2 2RD Tel: 01603 766815; Oakmead, 7 Stratford Crescent, Norwich NR4 7SF Email: pyper@lineace.net — MB ChB 1980 Aberd.; MRCGP 1987. Gen. Practitioner Norwich.

PYPER, Mr Patrick Charles Mid Ulster Hospital, Magherafelt BT45 5EX Tel: 028 7963 1031; 60 Coolshinney Road, Magherafelt BT45 5JF Tel: 028 7963 1628 Email: pyperpc@aol.com — MB BCh BAO 1975 Belf.; FRCS Ed. 1980. Cons. Surg. Mid Ulster Hosp. Magherafelt. Prev: Sen. Regist. Roy. Vict. Hosp. & City Hosp. Belf. & Roy. N. Shore Hosp Sydney, Austral.

PYPER, Mr Richard Julian David Department of Gynaecology, Worthing Hospital, Park Avenue, Worthing BN11 2DH Tel: 01903 285193 Fax: 01903 285191 — MB BChir 1978 Camb.; FRCOG 1999; MA Camb. 1979; FRCS Ed. 1984; MRCOG 1987. (Cambridge and The Middlesex) Cons. O & G Worthing Hosp. & S.lands Hosp. Shoreham-by-Sea; Chairm., Labour Ward Standing Comm. Socs: Brit. Soc. Gyn. Endoscopy; Brith. Pelvic Floor Soc. Prev: Sen. Regist. (O & G) St. Bart. Hosp. & N. Middlx. Hosp. Lond.; Lect. (O & G) Guy's Hosp. United Med. & Dent. Sch. Lond.; Regist. (Gen. Surg. & Urol.) St. Mary's Hosp. Lond.

PYRAH, Roger Dale (retired) Raikes Head, 90 Raikes Road, Skipton BD23 1LU Tel: 01756 792642 — MB BChir 1961 Camb.; FRCPath 1980, M 1968. Prev: Cons. Histopath. Airedale Gen. Hosp. Keighley.

PYRGOS, Nicos Accident & Emergency Department, County Hospital, Lincoln LN2 5QY Tel: 01522 573382 Fax: 01522 560334; 52 Hawthorn Road, Reepham, Lincoln LN3 4DU Tel: 01522 595728 — Ptychio latrikes 1966 Athens; Dip. Surg. DSS Athens 1973; FFAEM 1993. (Athens) Cons. A & E Lincoln Co. Hosp. Socs: Lincoln Med. Soc.

PYRGOS, Vassiliki 52 Hawthorn Road, Reepham, Lincoln LN3 4DU — Ptychio latrikes 1966 Athens.

*****PYSDEN, Karen Suzanne** Whitegate, Macclesfield Road, Alderley Edge SK9 7BH; Whitegate, Macclesfield Road, Alderley Edge SK9 7BH — MB ChB 1998 Sheff.; MB ChB Sheff 1998.

PYSZORA, Natalie Mary 94B Bourne Road, Bexley DA5 1LU — MB ChB 1993 Birm.

PYVES, Catherine Anne Corner House, Priory Gardens, Bridgend CF31 3LB — MB BS 1989 Lond.

QADAN, Hasan Muhammad Ahmad The Surgery, 128 Dormers Wells Lane, Southall UB1 3JB; 3 Crossmead Avenue, Greenford UB6 9TY Tel: 020 8813 1155 — DFFP; MD Istanbul 1968; Specialist in Internal Med. Univ. of Istanbul. (Istanbul) Princip. in Gen. Pract., Ealing, Hammersmith and Hounslow Health Auth., S.all, Middlx. Socs: BMA (Hon. Sec. Ealing Div.).; Med. Protec. Soc. Prev: Regist. (Gen. Med.) N.gate Hosp. Gt. Yarmouth & Scunthorpe Gen. Hosp.; Regist. (Diag. Radiol.) Centr. Middlx. Hosp.

QADIR, Mr Muhammad County Hospital, Louth LN11 9EU Tel: 01507 600100; 30 St. Mary's Park, Louth LN11 0EF Tel: 01507 608129 — MB BS 1968 Bangladesh; FRCS Ed. 1982; FICS 1991. Assoc. Specialist Co. Hosp. Louth.

QADIR, Nusrat 10 Whittagreen Court, Carfin Road, Newarthill, Motherwell ML1 5SN Tel: 01698 733662 — MB BS 1984 Karachi; MSc (Anaesth.) Glas. 1991; DA (UK) 1992; FFA RCSI 1994.

QADIRI, Mohammed Rida Radi Yeovil District Hospital, Higher Kingston, Yeovil BA21 4AT Tel: 01935 75122 Fax: 01935 707446

QADRI

Email: hillj@msmail.esomerset_tr.s.west.nhs.uk; 25 Laneside, Edgware HA8 9PL Tel: 020 8906 8854 Fax: 020 8906 8854 Email: mohammed@mrq@doctordoctor.co.uk — MB ChB 1975 Baghdad; MRCP (UK) 1980; FRCP Lond. Cons. Phys. Yeovil Dist. Hosp. Socs: Arab-African Soc. Gastroenterol. & Endoscopy; Brit. Geriat. Soc. Prev: Med. Specialist Ahmadi Hosp. Kuwait; Research Fell. Acad. Dept. Med. Roy. Free HSM Univ. Lond.

QADRI, A Q The Surgery, 157 Leytonstone Road, Stratford, London E15 1LH Tel: 020 8534 1026 Fax: 020 8534 4415 — MB BS 1974 Kashmir; MB BS 1974 Kashmir.

QAIYUM, Mansoor-Ui 1 Belgrave Road, Halesowen B62 9HA — MB ChB 1991 Leeds.

QAMAR, Arshad c/o Mr Ali Noorani, 119 Clarancegate Gardens, Glentworth St., London NW1 6AL — MB BS 1986 Karachi, Pakistan.

QAMAR-UZ-ZAMAN, S Sheffield Medical Centre, 21 Spital Street, Sheffield S3 9LB Tel: 0114 272 5552.

QAMRUDDIN, Ahmed Omer 63 Kestrel Park, Skelmersdale WN8 6TA — MB ChB 1992 Manch.

QAMRUDDIN, Mr Mohamed Ashurst Health Centre, Lulworth, Ashurst, Skelmersdale WN8 6QS Tel: 01695 732468 Fax: 01695 555365; 63 Kestrel Park, Ashurst, Skelmersdale WN8 6TA Tel: 01695 725887 Fax: 01695 725887 — MB BS 1965 Osmania; FRCS Ed. 1972; MRCS Eng. LRCP Lond. 1973. GP Skelmersdale. Socs: Assoc. Mem. Fac. Homoeop. Prev: Cons. Surg. Gen. Hosp. Kabwe, Zambia; Sen. Regist. & Tutor (Surg.) Meath Hosp. Dub.

QARSHI, Ahmed Ali The Surgery, 46 Montague Street, Wakefield WF1 5BB Tel: 01924 251811 Fax: 01924 242140 — MB BS 1961 Bihar. (Bihar) GP Wakefield, W. Yorks.

***QASIM, Asif** 1 Higher Downs, Bradford BD8 0NA — BChir 1995 Camb.

QASIM, Faieza Jabeen Renal Unit, Manchester Royal Infirmary, Oxford ST, Manchester Tel: 0161 276 4454 — LMSSA 1986 Lond.; BA (Hons.) Camb. 1983, MB BChir 1985; MRCP (UK) 1989; PHD 1995 Camb. (Cambridge) Sen. Regist. Camb. Socs: Renal. Assn; Brit Soc Immunol; Brit. Implantation soc. Prev: Regist. Rotat. (Med.) Newc. u Tyne; SHO (Neurol.) Addenbrooke's Hosp. Camb.; SHO (Med.) Leeds Gen. Infirm.

QAYYUM, Abdul 16 Douglas Road, Ilford IG3 8UX — MB BS 1972 Punjab; MRCPI 1989.

QAYYUM, Nadia Flat 12, Palatine Mansions, 124-126 Palatine Road, Manchester M20 3ZA — MB ChB 1993 Manch.

QAZI, Mr Abdul Aziz (retired) 2 Croft Gardens, Dalton-in-Furness LA15 8BS Tel: 01229 62157 — MB BS 1951 Punjab; MB BS Punjab (Pakistan) 1951; FRCS Ed. 1960; FRCS Eng. 1965; MChOrth Liverp. 1968. Cons. Orthop. Surg. Barrow & Furness Dist. Hosps.

QAZI, Fazle Azim 1 Foxhome Close, Chislehurst BR7 5XT; 6 Woodplace, Chislehurst Road, Sidcup DA14 6BG Tel: 020 8300 9258 — MB BS 1962 Karachi.

QAZI, Hamid Shafi (retired) 206 Roderick Avenue, Peacehaven, Newhaven BN10 8JG Tel: 01273 588300 — MB BS 1942 Punjab; MB BS Punjab (Pakistan) 1942; DPM Eng. 1973. Prev: Cons. Psychiat. Greenwich Health Dist.

QAZI, Nadeem Ahmad 308 Cavendish Road, London SW12 0PJ Tel: 020 8675 0506 Email: nqazi@hotmail.com — MB BS 1994 Lond.; LRCP 1997; LRCS Ed. 1997; LRCPS 1997; DGM.Glas 1998. (Char. Cross & Westm. Med. Sch.) Clin. Research Fell & Hon Regist in HIV Med. Univ. Lond. Prev: SHO. HIV/GUM, Chelsea & W.minster Hosp. Lond; SHO. Rotat.(Med.) Kings Coll. Hosp. Lond.

QAZI, Rafiz Ahmad Arthur Street Health Centre, Arthur Street, Brierfield, Nelson BB9 5SN Tel: 01282 615175 — MB BS 1968 Delhi; MB BS 1968 Delhi.

***QAZI, Shahjehan** 222 Brasenose Avenue, Gorleston-On-Sea, Great Yarmouth NR31 7ED — MB ChB 1998 Sheff.; MB ChB Sheff 1998.

QIDWAI, Aliya 29 Highfield Gardens, Westcliff on Sea SS0 0SY — MB BS 1992 Lond.

QIZILBASH, Nawab Academic Division of Geriatric Medicine, University of Oxford, Radcliffe Infirmary, Oxford OX2 6HE Tel: 01865 224975 Fax: 01865 224815 — MB ChB 1980 Manch.; DPhil Oxf. 1988; MSc Lond. 1985; BSc St. And. 1977; MRCP (UK) 1983. Clin. Lect. (Geriat. Med.) Univ. Oxf. Prev: Wellcome Research Train. Fell.sh. Madrid; Regist. (Med.) Leeds Gen. Infirm.

QUABA, Mr Awf-Abdul-Rahman Ali BUPA Hospital, 122 Corstorphine Road, Edinburgh EH12 6UD Tel: 0131 334 0363 Fax: 0131 334 7338; Williamcraigs House, Linlithgow EH49 6QF Tel: 01506 846244 Fax: 01506 846244 — MB ChB 1973 Mosul; FRCS Ed. (Plast) 1986; FRCS Ed. 1979. Cons. Plastic Surg. Lothian Plastic & Oral Surg. Serv. St. John's Hosp. Howden & Roy. Hosp. for Sick Childr. Edin. Socs: Brit. Assn. Plastic Surg. & Brit. Assn. Aesth. Plastic Surg.; Brit. Soc. Surg. Hand. Prev: Sen. Regist. NE Thames Regional Centre Billericay; Regist. Lond. Hosp. Whitechapel; SHO St. Lawrence's Hosp. Chepstow.

QUABECK, Gabriele c/o Arno Klefisch, 108 Church Lane, Coventry CV2 4AJ — State Exam Med 1990 Frankfurt.

QUADER, Keya 84c St Georges Terraces, Jesmond, Newcastle upon Tyne NE2 2DL Tel: 0191 281 2201 Email: kquader@hotmail.com — BM BS 1990 Nottm.; FFARCSI 1998. (Nottingham University) Specialist Regist. (Anaesth.) Newc.u.Tyne. Prev: SHO (A & E) Roy. Shrewsbury Hosp.

QUADER, Mohammad Abdul 22 Wilton Drive, Darlington DL3 9PS Tel: 01325 351010 — MB BS 1964 Dacca; FFA RCS Eng. 1972; DA Eng. 1970. (Chittagong Med. Coll.) Cons. Anaesth. Darlington Memor. Hosp. Socs: Obst. Anaesth. Assn.; BMA; Assn. Anaesth.

QUADER, Syed Eqbal 1 Long Meadow, The Pippins, Moss Pit, Stafford ST17 9DP Tel: 01785 41265 — MB BS 1967 Osmania; MRCPsych 1974; DPM Eng. 1972. (Osmania) Cons. Psychiat. (Adult) St. Geo. Hosp. Stafford.

***QUADHIR, Mohamed Jawfer Ahamed** 104 (Top Left), Great Northern Road, Aberdeen AB24 3QB — MB ChB 1994 Aberd.

QUADRI, Amal Fatima 39 Sweetcroft Lane, Uxbridge UB10 9LE — MB BS 1993 Lond. (Char. Cross & Westm.) SHO (Paediat.) Centr. Middlx. Hosp. Lond. Prev: SHO (Neonat. & Paediat.) St. Geo. Hosp. Lond.

QUADRI, F R Church Road Surgery, 296 Church Road, Northolt UB5 5AP Tel: 020 8248 2609 — MB BS 1962 Vikram; MB BS 1962 Vikram.

QUADRI, Syed Arif Lansbury Drive Practice, 166 Lansbury Drive, Hayes UB4 9NS Tel: 020 8848 3858 Fax: 020 8573 2082; 39 Sweetcroft Lane, Hillingdon, Uxbridge UB10 9LE — MB BS 1967 Bangalor; MB BS Bangalore 1967. (Bangalore) Socs: BMA; Affil. RCPsych. Prev: Ho. Phys. (Gen. Med.) Manor Hosp. Walsall; Regist. & SHO (Psychiat.) Runwell Hosp. Wickford.

QUADRI, Mr Syed Arifulla 160 Manor Court Road, Nuneaton CV11 5HG — MRCS Eng. LRCP Lond. 1935; FRCS Glas. 1962; FRFPS Glas. 1938.

QUAGHEBEUR, Gerardine Marie-Marthe Department of Neuroradiology, Radcliffe Infirmary, Woodstock Road, Oxford OX2 6HE Tel: 01865 224512 Fax: 01865 224689 Email: gqbeur@doctors.org.uk; Conifer House, Lamborough Hill, Wooton, Oxford OX13 6BY Tel: 01865 736862 Fax: 01865 730760 — MB BCh 1982 Witwatersrand; FRCS Eng. 1988; FRCS Ed. 1987; FRCR 1993. Cons. Neuroradiol. Radcliffe Infirm. Oxf. Prev: Sen. Regist. (Neuroradiol.) Nat. Hosp. Neurol. & Neurosurg. Lond.

QUAH, Say Pheng 19 The Crescent, Belfast BT10 0GJ Tel: 01232 586729 Email: pheng@l-neons.net — MB BCh BAO 1996 Belf.

QUAIFE, John Benenden Chest Hospital, Goddards Green Road, Benenden, Cranbrook TN17 4AX — MB BChir 1978 Camb.; MA Camb. 1977; LMSSA Lond. 1976. Cons. Anaesth. Benenden Hosp. Cranbrook.

QUAITE, Thomas James, TD Newtownards Health Centre, Frederick Street, Newtownards BT23 4LS Tel: 028 9181 7239; 45 Ballyrainey Road, Newtownards BT23 5AD — MB BCh BAO 1969 Belf.; MRCGP 1977; DObst RCOG 1974.

QUALTROUGH, John Edward Over Wyre Medical Centre, Pilling Lane, Preesall, Blackpool FY3 Tel: 01253 810722 — MB ChB 1975 Manch.

QUAN, Virginia Anne 40 Rowfant Road, London SW17 7AS — MB BChir 1989 Camb.; PhD 2000 (Lond.); MRCP (UK) 1992. p/t SpR Renal & Gen. Med. St Geo.'s Hosp.

QUANCE, Ian Michael 67 Cheyne Garth, Hornsea HU18 1BF — MB ChB 1986 Birm.

QUANSAH, Benjamin Bassaw Halbutt Surgery, 2 Halbutt Street, Dagenham RM9 5AS Tel: 020 8592 1544 Fax: 020 8596 9833 — Vrach Kiev Med Inst 1968; Dip. Practical Deramtology Univ. of Wales Med. School 1997.

QUANTEN, Patrick Paul Leonard Eagle Medical Practice, Stefan House, Olivier St, Alderney, Guernsey GY9 3TD Tel: 01481 822494 Fax: 01481 823892 — MD 1983 Brussels.

QUANTRILL, John (retired) The Furlong, Tinwell Road, Stamford PE9 2QQ Tel: 01780 763171 — MB BS Lond. 1956; MRCS Eng. LRCP Lond. 1956; DObst RCOG 1958. Prev: GP Stamford.

QUANTRILL, Simon John 12 Hyndman Court, Sheader Drive, Salford M5 2BX — MB ChB 1989 Manch. SHO (Endocrinol. & Ment. Oncol.) Christie Hosp. Manch. Prev: SHO (Geriat. & Gen. Med.) Trafford Gen. Hosp. Manch.; Ho. Off. (Renal & Gen. Med.) Manch. Roy. Infirm.; Ho. Off. (Gen. Surg.) Birch Hill Hosp. Rochdale.

QUARCOO, Samuel Tetteh 125 Stratton Road, Brighouse HD6 3UA Email: stquarcoo@hotmail.com — Lekar Nov Sad, Yugoslavia 1967; MD. Hosp. Specialist O & G Kirkcaldy Fife. Socs: BMA; Med. Protec. Soc. Prev: Regist.

QUARCOOPOME, Mr Wilfred Nii Sackey Manor Hospital, Manor Court Avenue, Nuneaton CV11 5SP Tel: 01203 351251; 11 Abingdon Way, St. Nicholas Park Est., Nuneaton CV11 6DX Tel: 01203 371230 — MB ChB 1975 Ghana; FRCS Ed. 1984. Regist. (Trauma & Orthop.) Manor Hosp. Nuneaton. Socs: BMA.

*****QUARISHI, Nasir Ali** 263 Greenford Road, Greenford UB6 8QZ — MB ChB 1996 Manch.

QUARMBY, Mr John Winston 86A East Hill, Wandsworth, London SW18 2HG — MB BS 1987 Lond.; BSc Lond. 1984, MB BS 1987; FRCS Ed. 1992. Regist. (Gen. Surg.) St. Thos. Hosp. Lond. Prev: Regist. (Gen. Surg.) Worthing Gen. Hosp.; Regist. (Gen. Surg.) St. Geos. Hosp. Lond. & Epsom Dist. Hosp.

QUARRELL, Oliver William John Dept. Clinical Genetics, Sheffield children's hosp, Sheffield S10 2TH Tel: 0114 271 7025 Fax: 0114 273 7467; 68 Woodholm Road, Sheffield S11 9HT — MB BS 1980 Lond.; BSc Lond. 1977, MD 1988; FRCP Ed. 1993; FRCP Lond. 1994. (St. Mary's Hospital London) Cons. Clin. Genetics Sheff. Childr.'s Hosp. Prev: Sen. Regist. (Med. Genetics) Univ. Hosp. Wales Cardiff.

QUARRIE, John (retired) 5 Broad Oak, Groombridge, Tunbridge Wells TN3 9SD — MB ChB 1970 Leeds; BSc (Pharmacol.) Leeds 1968, MB ChB 1970; MRCP (U.K.) 1973; MRCGP 1976. Prev: GP Maidstone.

QUARRY, Daniel Peter 435 Warsash Road, Fareham PO14 4JT — MB BCh 1989 Wales.

QUARRY, Samantha Jayne (Griffiths) 52 Mortimer Road, Pontcanna, Cardiff CF11 9LA Tel: 07976 309022 Email: samanthagriffith@hotmail.com — MB ChB 1994 Birm.; MRCGP (dist)2000 (UK); DRCOG 1997 Bristol; DFFP 1999 UK. (Univ. Birm.) GP Non Princip., S. Wales (various Pract.s); Clin. Med. Off. for Rhondda & Pontypridd, NHS Trust (community family Plann. clinics). Socs: Med. Defence Union; BMA. Prev: Psychiat. Regist. Gold Coast Hosp. Qu.sland Australia feb 98- Oct98; SHO Med. Jersey Gen. Hosp., Cl Aug 97 - feb98; GP Trainee Parcanol Gp. Pract. Ch. Village, Mid Glam Jan99-Aug99.

QUARTERMAN, Elizabeth Ann 19 Langdale Crescent, Bexleyheath DA7 5DZ — MB BS 1989 Lond.; BSc Lond. 1986, MB BS 1989. SHO (Cas.) Watford Gen. Hosp. Prev: SHO (O & G) QECH Blantyre Malawi; Ho. Phys. King Edwd. VII Hosp. Windsor; Ho. Surg. Watford Gen. Hosp.

QUARTEY, Mr Paul Kelvin Schering-Plough, Shire Park, Welwyn Garden City AL7 1TW Tel: 01707 363756 Fax: 01707 363692; 112 Chipperfield Road, Kings Langley WD4 9JD Tel: 01923 265565 Fax: 01707 363692 — MB ChB 1982 Univ. Ghana; FRCS Ed. 1987; Dip. Pharm Med. RCP (UK) 1994. Med. Dir. Schering-Plough Welwyn Gdn. City. Socs: BMA & BRAPP. Prev: Head Clin. Research & Med. Advisor Schering-Plough; Regist. (Surg.) Leeds Gen. Infirm.

QUARTLEY, Roger Graham Stuart The White Rose Surgery, Exchange Street, South Elmsall, Pontefract WF9 2RD Tel: 01977 642412 Fax: 01977 641290 — MB ChB 1984 Sheff.; DA (UK) 1987.

*****QUARTLEY, Tobias Penruddocke** 26 Cecilia Road, Leicester LE2 1TA Tel: 0116 270 4457 — MB ChB 1997 Leic.

QUARTLY, Christopher Francis West Street Surgery, 89 West Street, Dunstable LU6 1SF Tel: 01582 664401 Fax: 01582 475766 — MB BS 1982 Lond.; DMJ(Clin) Soc. Apoth. Lond. 1993; DRCOG 1984; DCH RCP Lond. 1983. GP Dunstable.

QUARTSON, Joseph Kwamina Harrogate General Hospital, Knaresborough Road, Harrogate HG2 7NG — MB BS 1964 Lond.

QUASEM, Mohammad Abul Tel: 01207 232696/99 Fax: 01207 239066 — MB BS 1966 Dacca. (Dacca Med. Coll.) Socs: MDU. Prev: Regist. (Diag. Radiol.) Leicester Roy. Infirm.

QUASIM, Isma Flat 2/R, 74 Dundrennan Road, Glasgow G42 9SG — MB ChB 1990 Glas.

QUASIM, Mohammad South Hetton Surgery, Front Street, South Hetton, Durham DH6 2TH Tel: 0191 517 1055 Fax: 0191 526 0001 — MB BS 1963 Dacca.

QUASIM, Mohammed 239 Lutterworth Road, Nuneaton CV11 6PX — MB BS 1958 Karachi.

QUASIM, Mohammed Nayar Iqbal Arundel House, 120 Wingrove Road, Newcastle upon Tyne NE4 9BT Tel: 0191 245 1488 Fax: 0191 245 1488 Email: nquasim@compuserve.com; Thornaby Healthcare Practice, The Health Centre, Trenchard Avenue, Thornaby, Stockton-on-Tees TS17 0DD Tel: 01642 762636 Fax: 01642 766464 — MB BS 1992 Newc.; MRCGP 1996; DRCOG 1995; DFFP 1995.

QUASIM, Tara 39 Herries Road, Pollockshields, Glasgow G41 4AH — MB ChB 1994 Glas.

QUASTEL, Anthony Stephen 204-206 High Street, Bromley BR1 1PW Tel: 020 8464 4599 Fax: 020 8464 3471; Rome Cottage, Rome Road, New Romney TN28 8DN Tel: 01797 362493 Fax: 01797 973 1417 Email: tonyquast@aol.com — MB BS 1980 Lond. (Middlx. Hosp.) Indep. GP Bromley Kent. Socs: Fell. Roy. Soc. Med. Prev: SHO (Psychiat.) Middlx. Hosp. Lond.; Ho. Phys. Benenden Chest Hosp.; Ho. Surg. Croydon Gen. Hosp.

*****QUATAN, Nadine** The Gables, 13 Houghton Avenue, Hempstead, Gillingham ME7 3RY — MB BS 1998 Lond.; MB BS Lond 1998.

QUATAN, Mr Saadon Mohamad Hassan The Gables, Houghton Avenue, Hempstead, Gillingham ME7 3RY — MB ChB 1961 Baghdad; FRCS Eng. 1974; MRCS Eng. LRCP Lond. 1978. (Coll. Med. Baghdad) Socs: BMA. Prev: Regist. (Gen. Surg.) & SHO (Gen. Surg.) St. Bart. Hosp. Rochester; SHO (Paediat. Surg.) Roy. Manch. Childr. Hosp. Pendlebury.

*****QUATE, Leza Zarrine** 4 Harland Cottages, Glasgow G14 0AS — MB ChB 1997 Glas.

*****QUATTAINAH, Mohammed Anwar** Flat 33, Windmill Court, Claremont Rd, Newcastle upon Tyne NE2 4BA — MB BS 1996 Newc.

QUAYLE, Mr Andrew John McMullan Church Street Surgery, Church Street, Martock TA12 6JL Tel: 01935 822541 — MB BChir 1978 Camb.; MA Camb. 1978; FRCS Eng. 1982; MRCGP 1984. GP Princip., Ch. St. Surg., Martock. Prev: Med. Off. Bethesda Hosp, Ubombo, Kwazulu; Regist. (Surg.) Edendale Hosp. Nr. Pietermaritzburg Kwazulu, S. Afr.

QUAYLE, Mr Anthony Robert Macclesfield District Hospital, Victoria Road, Macclesfield SK10 3BL Tel: 01625 421000 — MB ChB 1975 Sheff.; ChM Sheff. 1987, MB ChB 1975; FRCS Eng. 1980. Cons. Gen. Surg. Macclesfield Dist. Gen. Hosp. Prev: Lect. (Surg.) Roy. Hallamsh. Hosp. Sheff.

QUAYLE, Mr John Bryant Princess Royal Hospital, Telford Tel: 01952 641222; The River House, Isle Lane, Bicton, Shrewsbury SY3 8ED Tel: 01743 850646 Fax: 01743 850639 — MB BChir 1970 Camb.; MS Camb. 1982, MB BChir 1970; FRCS Eng. 1974. (St. Geo.) Cons. Gen. & Colerectal Surg. P.ss Roy. Hosp. Telford. Socs: Roy. Soc. Med. & Assn. of Surgs.; Assn. Coloproctol.

QUAYLE, Susan Elizabeth Netherfield House, Station Road, Seghill, Cramlington NE23 7EF Tel: 0191 237 0643 Fax: 0191 237 1091 — MB BS 1983 Newc. GP Cramlington, N.d.

QUBATY, Mr Mohamed Abdul-Mageed Ground Floor, 25 Birchington Road, London NW6 4LL; 14 Berkeley Court, Neasden Lane, Neasden, London NW10 1PX Tel: 020 8450 4998 — MB BS 1979 Lond.; FRCS Ed. 1989; MRCS Eng. LRCP Lond. 1979. (King's Coll. Hosp.) Sen. Lect. (Surg.) Univ. Sana'a & Cons. Surg. Sana'a Univ. Teach. Hosp. Prev: Regist. (Gen. Surg.) Manor Hse. Hosp. Lond.; Regist. (Urol.) Broomfield Hosp. Chelmsford; Regist. (Surg.) Al-Gamhooriya Teach. Hosp. Univ. Aden.

QUDDUS, Siraj Fatima 1A Denison Road, Manchester M14 5PW — MB BS 1950 Punjab; MB BS Punjab (Pakistan) 1950. Prev: Regist. ENT Manch. N.. Hosp., Booth Hall Hosp. Manch. & Manch.; Vict. Memor. Jewish Hosp.

QUEEN, Jane Karen 11 Antonine Gate, Verulam, St Albans AL3 4JA — MB BS 1987 Lond.; MRCP (UK) 1991.

QUEEN

QUEEN, Mr Kenneth Brodie Department of General Surgery & Urology, Nevill Hall Hospital, Brecon Road, Abergavenny NP7 7EG — MB ChB 1970 Glas.; LLM Wales 2000; FRCS Ed. 1977.

QUEEN, Scott Patrick 63a Dowanside Road, Glasgow G12 9DL — MB ChB 1996 Glas.

QUEENAN, Maria Bernadette The Old Beer House, Chilson, Chipping Norton OX7 3HU — BM BCh 1987 Oxf.; MSc York 1978; BSc Lond. 1977. Regist. (A & E) St. Peters Hosp. Chertsey. Prev: SHO (A & E) Hammersmith Hosp. Lond.; Tutor (Surg.) Univ. Liverp.

QUEENAN, Paul John Princes Avenue Surgery, 137 Princes Avenue, Hull HU5 3HH Tel: 01482 342473 Fax: 01482 493382 — MB ChB 1986 Leeds. GP Princip., 137 P.s Avenue, Hull; Clin. Asst. NeuroPhysiol., Hull Roy. Infirm., Hull.

QUEENBOROUGH, Robert Wigan and Bolton Health Authority, Bryan House, 61 Standishgate, Wigan WN1 1AH Tel: 01942 772763 Fax: 01942 496567 — MB ChB 1979 Birm.; MRCGP 1991; MHSM 1994; DRCOG 1983. Med. Dir. Wigan & Bolton HA.

QUEIPO DE LLANO TEMBOURY, Alfonso Residences Pasteur B31 No. 45, Queens Medical Centre, University Hospital NHS, Nottingham NG7 2UH — LMS 1991 Malaga.

QUEIROZ, Jane Elizabeth 64 Woodhall Road, Wollaton, Nottingham NG8 1LE — MB ChB 1992 Birm. Staff Grade Community Paediat.

QUEK, Fui Mee — MB BS 1988 Lond.; DRCOG 1992. p/t Gen. Practitioner.

QUEK, Selina Li Gek The Orchard Surgery, Constable Road, St Ives, Huntingdon Tel: 01480 466611; 209 High Street, Chesterton, Cambridge CB4 1NL Tel: 01223 500851 — MB ChB 1987 Leic.

QUEKETT, James Thomas Scott Top Floor Flat, 23 Suffolk Square, Cheltenham GL50 2EA Tel: 01242 529543 — MB ChB 1994 Bristol; BSc Bristol 1991; DRCOG 1999. (Bristol) GP Regist. Rosebank Surg., Gloucester. Prev: SHO (Paediat.) Glos. Roy. Hosp.; SHO (Obst & Gyn.) Glos.Roy. Hosp; Ho. Off. (Surg.) Yeovil Dist. Hosp.

QUENAULT, Sandra Lesley Les Saisons Surgery, 20 David Place, St Helier, Jersey JE2 4TD Tel: 01534 720314 Fax: 01534 733205; 2 New Road, Gorey Village, St Martin, Jersey JE3 6UN Tel: 01534 858678 Email: sdore@doctors.org.uk — MB BS 1986 Lond.; MRCGP 1990; DCH RCP Lond. 1988; DPM Cardiff 1997. (Roy. Free Hosp. Sch. Med.) GP. Prev: Trainee GP Torbay Hosp. Torquay VTS.

QUENBY, Siobhan Mary Faculty of Medicine & Health Sciences, Division of Obstetrics & Gynaecology, Nottingham City Hospital, Hucknall Road, Nottingham NG5 1PB Tel: 0115 962 7914 Fax: 0115 962 7670 — MB BS Lond. 1988; MRCOG 1994; MD 1998 Liverpool; CCST 1998 St Bart. (St. Bartholomew's) Sen. Lect. Hon. Cons. Univ. Liverp. & Liverp. Wom. Hosp.; Lect. & Hon. Sen. Regist. Univ. Liverp. & Liverp. Wom. Hosp.; Sen Lect. Prev: Regist. Rotat. (O & G) Merseyside Region.

QUERCI DELLA ROVERE, Mr Guidubaldo Royal Marsden Hospital NHS Trust (London & Surrey), Downs Road, Sutton SM2 5PT Tel: 020 8661 3118 Fax: 020 86613126 Email: ggercidellqzovece@doctors.org.uk; 12 Minehead Road, Streatham, London SW16 2AW Tel: 020 8677 7244 Fax: 020 8677 7244 Email: gquercidellarovere@doctors.org.uk — MD 1971 Padua; State DMS 1976; FRCS Eng. 1982; FRCS Ed. 1981. Cons. Surg. Roy. Marsden Hosp. Lond. & Surrey. Socs: Fell. Roy. Soc. Med.; Eur. Soc. Surg. Oncol.; Eur. Soc. Mastol. Prev: Clin. Asst. BrE. Clinic St Margt. Hosp. Epping, Essex; Lect. (Gen. Surg.) Padua Univ.; Regist. (Gen. Surg.) Roy. Marsden Hosp. Lond.

QUEREJETA, Izaskun Grantham & Kesteven General Hospital, 101 Manthorpe Road, Grantham NG31 8DG — LMS 1992 Basque Provinces.

QUERO HEREDIA, Farncisco Javier 47 Moorland Rise, Haslingden, Rossendale BB4 6AU — LMS 1986 Saragossa.

QUEST, Ivor Myer 50 Hallam Street, London W1W 6DE Tel: 020 7637 0541 Fax: 020 7323 1768 — MB ChB 1951 Liverp.; MRCGP 1968; DObst RCOG 1953. (Liverp.) Regional Sec. Med. Protec. Soc. Socs: Med.-Leg. Soc. Prev: Med. Off. Cowley Hill Matern. Hosp. St. Helens; Ho. Phys. Walton Hosp. Liverp.; Med. Off. RAF Hosp. Cosford.

QUEST, Laura Jane 6 Marlfield Lane, Barnston, Wirral CH61 1AJ — MB ChB 1986 Leeds.

QUESTED, Digby John Littlemore Hospital, Littlemore, Oxford OX4 4XN Tel: 01865 778911; 7 Burra Close, Sandford-on-Thames, Oxford OX4 4YE — MB ChB 1983 Cape Town; MRCPsych 1993.

QUEW, Rachel Ann 11 The Crescent, North Hampshire Hospital, Aldermaston Road, Basingstoke RG24 9NA; Oak Lodge, 39 Pyotts Copse, Old Basing, Basingstoke RG24 8WE — MB BCh 1987 Wales; BSc Wales, 1984, MB ChB 1987; MRCGP 1991; DCH RCP Lond. 1990. Clin. Med. Off. (Community Paediat.) E. Lothian.

QUIBELL, Ernest Philip, OBE (retired) 9 Adastra Avenue, Hassocks BN6 8DP Tel: 0179 183812 — MRCS Eng. LRCP Lond. 1937; BA Camb.; DCH Eng. 1947. Med. Cons. Thalidomide Trust. Prev: Med. Adminis. & Cons. Paediatr. Chailey Heritage (Craft Sch. & Hosp.).

QUIBELL, Rachel Mary 56 High View, Wallsend NE28 8SS Tel: 0191 287 3867 — MB BS 1992 Newc. SHO (Gen. Med.) St. Oswalds Hospice Newc.-u-Tyne. Prev: SHO (Gen. Med.) Marie Curie Centre, Newc.-u-Tyne; SHO (Oncol.); SHO (Gen. Med.) Sunderland Dist. Gen. Hosp.

QUICK, Mr Cedric Albert 3 Austin Avenue, Laleston, Bridgend CF32 0LG — MB BCh 1967 Wales; MB BCh Wales 1961; FRCS Ed. 1967.

QUICK, Mr Clive Robert Groves Hinchingbrooke Hospital, Huntingdon PE29 6NT Tel: 01480 416008; Brooklyn, Holywell, Huntingdon PE27 4TG Tel: 01480 468177 Fax: 01480 460275 — MB BS 1969 Lond.; MA Camb. 1994; MS Lond. 1982, BDS 1963; FRCS Eng. 1973; MRCS Eng. LRCP Lond. 1969; FDS RCS Eng. 1966, LDS 1963. Cons. Gen. & Vasc. Surg. Hinchingbrooke Hosp. Huntingdon & Addenbrooke's Hosp. Camb.; Course Organiser Camb. Anastomosis Workshop; Assoc. Lect. Univ. Camb. Socs: Fell. Assn. Surgs.; Vasc. Surg. Soc. Prev: Research Fell. (Biomed. Engin.) KCH Lond.; Sen. Regist. Leicester Gen. Hosp.; Regist. King's Coll. Hosp. Lond.

QUICK, David Gordon Chase 13 Cowper House, Browning St., London SE17 1DD Tel: 020 7708 2843 — MB BS 1990 Lond. SHO (Anaesth.) Lond.

QUICK, Felicity Jane Chelsea and Westminster Hosp, Fulham Rd, London SW10; 31 Queensmill Road, Fulham, London SW6 6JP Tel: 020 7386 7935 — MB BS 1996 Lond.; DCH, UMDS. Lond. 1997.

QUICK, Sarah Jayne Bridge House, Shalford Road, Guildford GU4 8BL Email: sjwolfenden@compuserve.com — BM BCh 1991 Oxf.; MRCGP 1996; DRCOG 1996; DFFP 1995; MA Camb. 1994, BA 1988. Clin. Asst. Drug & Alcohol; Med. Off. Family Plann.; Clin. Asst. GUM. Prev: GP Princip.

QUICKE, John Venny Cleave, Newton St Cyres, Exeter EX5 5BT Tel: 01392 851627 — MB ChB 1978 Bristol; MRCGP 1983; DRCOG 1982; DA (UK) 1981. Clin. Asst. (Cardiol.) Roy. Devon & Exeter Hosp. Devon.

QUICKENDEN, David Richard James 11 Sandhurst Road, Sidcup DA15 7HL Tel: 020 8302 2339 — MRCS Eng. LRCP Lond. 1965; MB Camb. 1970, BChir 1969; DObst RCOG 1969. (Guy's) Prev: SHO (Paediat.) Qu. Mary's Hosp. Sidcup.

QUIERY, Aidan Francis John Coleraine Health Centre, Castlerock Road, Coleraine BT51 3HP Tel: 028 7034 4834 Fax: 028 7035 8914; 12 Tullybeg Avenue, Coleraine BT51 3NG — MB BCh BAO 1979 Belf.; DRCOG 1982. Hosp. Pract. (Genitourin. Med.) Coleraine Hosp. Co. Derry.

***QUIGG, Jennifer Lucianne** 4 Willow Close, Woodham Park Way, Addlestone KT15 3SB — MB ChB 1998 Ed.; MB ChB Ed 1998.

QUIGLEY, Arthur James Rutherglen Health Centre, Stonelaw Road, Rutherglen, Glasgow G73 2PQ Tel: 0141 647 7171; 1 Thorn Drive, Burnside, Glasgow G73 4RH Tel: 0141 634 6114 — MB ChB 1958 Glas. (Glas.) Socs: BMA. Prev: Ho. Phys. Kilmarnock Infirm.; Ho. Surg. Glas. Roy. Infirm.

QUIGLEY, Brian Michael Riverside Practice, Upper Main Street, Strabane BT82 8AS Tel: 028 7138 4100 Fax: 028 7138 4115; Radharc na Finne, 83 Urney Road, Strabane BT82 9RT — MB BCh BAO 1974 NUI; DRCOG 1977. (Univ. Coll. Dub.) Prev: SHO (Med.) W.. Infirm. Glas.; SHO (Psychiat.) Leverndale Hosp. Glas.; Ho. Off. Altnagelvin Hosp. Lond.derry.

QUIGLEY, Mrs Bridget Mary Agnes (retired) The Knoll, Barmoor, Morpeth NE61 6LB Tel: 01670 512880 — MB BCh BAO 1949 NUI; DPM Eng. 1957. Prev: Cons. Psychiat. St. Geo. Hosp. Morpeth.

QUIGLEY, Catherine Sefton Health Authority, Burlington Hosue, Crosby Rd North, Waterloo, Liverpool L22 0QB Tel: 0151 478 1234 Fax: 0151 949 0799; 13 Crescent Road, Hale, Altrincham WA15 9NB — MB BCh BAO 1980 NUI; MSc Manch. 1987; MFPHM 1989. Consultant in Communicable Dis. Control, Liverp. & Sefton Health Authorities. Socs: Manch. Med. Soc. Prev: Cons. Communicable Dis. Control N. Chesh. HA & Wirral HA; Cons. Pub. Health Med. Salford & Trafford HA; Sen. Regist. (Pub. Health Med.) NW RHA.

QUIGLEY, Columba Sheila Mary Department of Medical Oncology, Barry Reed Laboratory, St Bartholomews Hospital, London EC1A 7BE; 7 Cleveland Gardens, Barnes, London SW13 0AE — MB BCh BAO 1985 NUI; MRCP Lond. 1990. Clin. Research Fell. St. Bart. Hosp. Lond. Prev: Sen. Regist. (Palliat. Med.) St. Barts. Hosp. Lond.; Regist. (Palliat. Med.) St. Christopher's Hospice Lond.; SHO (Oncol. & Palliat. Med.) Roy. Marsden Hosp. Sutton.

QUIGLEY, Conor Nial Department of Psychiatry, Lagan Valley Hospital, Lisburn — MB BCh BAO 1985 Belf.; MRCPsych 1992; MRCGP 1989.

***QUIGLEY, David Gavin** 64 Thornleigh Drive, Lisburn BT28 2DS — MB ChB 1996 Dundee.

QUIGLEY, Ian Graeme 24 Jasper Road, London E16 3TR Tel: 020 7511 460 — MB BS 1989 Lond. SHO (Gen. Med.) OldCh. Hosp. Romford. Prev: Ho. Phys. (Oncol. & Haemat.) OldCh. Hosp. Romford; Ho. Surg. (Urol. & Orthop.) Newham Gen. Hosp. Plaistow.

QUIGLEY, Margaret Garden 7 The Hawthorns, Gullane EH31 2DZ Tel: 01620 843359 — MB ChB 1944 Aberd. (Aberd.) Fell. Brit. Soc. Med. & Dent. Hypn.

QUIGLEY, Mary Concepta Birling Avenue Surgery, 3 Birling Avenue, Rainham, Gillingham ME8 7HB Tel: 01634 360390/361843 Fax: 01634 264061; 1 Hoath Close, Hempstead, Gillingham ME8 0SH Tel: 01634 362772 — MB BCh BAO 1976 NUI; MRCGP 1985; DCH NUI 1978. Asst. GP Kent. Socs: BMA. Prev: Regist. (Gen. Med. & Paediat.) Mt. Vernon Hosp. N.wood.

QUIGLEY, Mary Martha The Royal Marsden Hospital, Downs Road, Sutton SM2 5PT; 17 Owen Mansions, Queens Club Gardens, London W14 9RS — MB BCh BAO 1978 NUI; MRCP (UK) 1982; FFR RCSI 1986.

***QUIGLEY, Maureen** 5 Hollier Court, French Horn Lane, Hatfield AL10 8BX — MB BS 1994 Lond.

QUIGLEY, Michael Anthony The Brae, Craig Road, Rhonehouse, Castle Douglas DG7 1UB — MB ChB 1991 Ed.

QUIGLEY, Michele Paula 34 Thornleigh Road, Newcastle upon Tyne NE2 3ET — MB BS 1987 Newc.

QUIGLEY, Mr Peter James Laurence 3 Fernwood Grove, Hamsterley Mill, Rowlands Gill NE39 1HJ Tel: 01207 542723 — MB BS Newc. 1968; FRCS Ed. 1974; MRCGP 1978. (Newc.)

QUIGLEY, Philip Joseph Gerard 18 Castle Street, Newry BT34 2BY Tel: 02748 283026 — MB BCh BAO 1954 NUI; Dip. Amer. Bd. Path. 1961. p/t Asst. Inter-Co. Med. Examr. (State Pathologist), Cape May & Cumbld. Counties, New Jersey. Socs: Fell. Coll. Amer. Pathols.; Med. Soc. New Jersey. Prev: Clin. Asst. Prof. Path. New Jersey Coll. Med. & Dent. Newark, USA; Chief Med. Exam. (State Path.) State of Delaware, USA.; Path. & Dir. Laborat. Alexian Brothers Hosp. Eliz., USA.

QUILLIAM, Penelope Sally Anne Regent Road Surgery, 10/12 Regent Road, Lowestoft NR32 1PA Tel: 01502 565252; The Red House, North Cliff, Kessingland, Lowestoft NR33 7RA — MB BS 1976 Lond.; MRCGP 1983; DRCOG 1980. (St. Bart.) Prev: Ho. Phys. Newmarket Hosp. Ho. Surg. St. Bart. Hosp. Lond.; Ho. Off. Norf. & Norwich Hosp.

QUILLIAM, Professor Peter, OBE Hornbeams, 34 Totteridge Common, Totteridge, London N20 8NE Tel: 020 8959 3363 — MB BS Lond. 1941; DSc Lond. 1969, MSc 1938; FRCP Lond. 1975, M 1971; MRCS Eng. LRCP Lond. 1941. (Univ. Coll. Hosp.) Emerit. Prof. Pharmacol. Univ. Lond.; Chairm. Bd. of Dirs. Help the Hospices; Mem. Grants Counc. Charities Aid Foundat.; Trustee Univ. Lond. Convocation Trust; Vice-Pres. BMA. Socs: Acad. Med. Gp. Prev: Gresham Prof. of Physic; Sharpey Schol. Univ. Coll. Lond.; Univ. Lond. Trav. Fell.

QUILLIAM, Robert Paul New Elgin Practice, 44 Chippenham Road, London W9 2AF Tel: 020 7266 2431 Fax: 020 7289 6275 — MB BCh 1976 Wales; BSc (Hons.) Wales 1973, MB BCh 1976; MRCGP 1982. Prev: Regist. (Gastroenterol.) Lond. Hosp.

Whitechapel; Regist. (Med.) Basildon Hosp.; SHO (Med.) Lond. Hosp. Whitechapel.

QUILLIAM, Steven Juan Castle Surgery, Kepwell Bank Top, Prudhoe NE42 5PW Tel: 01661 832209 Fax: 01661 836338; West House, Hagg Farm, Wylam NE41 8JY Tel: 01661 852187 Email: stevenquilliam@hotmail.com — MB BS 1981 Newc.; MRCGP 1985; DRCOG 1984. Clin. Asst. (Ment. Handicap) Prudhoe Hosp. N.d. Prev: Trainee GP N.d. VTS; SHO (Psychiat.) St. Mary's Hosp. Stannington.

QUILLIAM, Thomas Andrew — MB BS 1943 Lond.; DSc Lond. 1983, PhD 1954; MRCS Eng. LRCP Lond. 1943; DLO Eng. 1946. (Univ. Coll. Hosp.) p/t Research Fell. Centre for Neurosc. Univ. Coll. Lond.; Med. Dir. Charity Heart Haven Lond.; Hon. Lect. St. Mary's Hosp. Med. Sch. Lond. & Lond. Foot Hosp.; Hon. Assoc. W.m. Univ. Socs: Anat. Soc., Physiol. Soc. & Genetic Interest Gp.; Emerit. Mem. Amer. Assn. of Anatomists. Prev: Vis. Prof. Dept. Anat. Univ. Calif. Los Angeles, USA; Hon. Research Fell. Univ. Minn., USA; Trav. Fell. of Postgrad. Med. Federat., Univ. Lond.

QUILTY, Brian Michael 185 Henley Road, Caversham, Reading RG4 6LH — MB BS 1987 Lond.; MRCP (UK) 1993.

QUIN, Charles Edward (retired) 31 Prince Edwards Road, Lewes BN7 1BL — MB BS 1939 Lond.; MD Lond. 1947; FRCP Lond. 1972, M 1947; MRCS Eng. LRCP Lond. 1939. Prev: Cons. Phys. (Rheum.) Roy. Sussex Co. Hosp.

QUIN, Jennifer Anne 3 Hamilton Avenue, Pollokshields, Glasgow G41 4JG Tel: 0141 427 3711 — MB ChB 1967 Glas. Socs: Brit. Med. Acupunct. Soc. Prev: GP Glas.; SHO (Anaesth.) Roy. Infirm. Glas.; Supernum. Regist. (Psychiat.) Leics. AHA (T).

QUIN, Leslie Murray Mearns Medical Centre, 3 Eaglesham Road, Newton Mearns, Glasgow G77 5BE Tel: 0141 639 2753 Fax: 0141 616 2403 — MB ChB 1970 Glas.; DObst RCOG 1972.

QUIN, Margaret Moira 3 Magpie Close, Ewshot, Farnham GU10 5TF — MB BS Durh. 1964; DA Eng. 1969; DObst RCOG 1966. (Durh.)

QUIN, Norman Edward, Col. late RAMC (retired) 3 Magpie Close, Ewshot, Farnham GU10 5TF — MB ChB 1949 Manch.; MFCM 1974.

QUIN, Mr Roger Owen 3 Hamilton Avenue, Pollokshields, Glasgow G41 4JG Tel: 0141 427 3711 Email: rogerquin@compuserve.com — MB ChB 1967 Glas.; MPhil Glas. 1992, BSc (Hons.) 1964, MD (Hons.) 1976; FRCS Eng. 1972; FRCS Glas. 1972. (Glas.) Cons. Vasc. Surg. W.. Glas. Hosps. Univ. NHS Trust; Hon. Clin. Sen. Lect. Univ. Glas. Socs: Vasc. Soc. GB & Irel.; Surgic. Research Soc.; Assn. Surg. Prev: Lect. (Surg.) Univ. Leicester; Lect. (Surg.) & Regist. W.. Infirm. Glas.

QUINBY, Mrs Janice Mary Freeman Hospital, Newcastle upon Tyne NE7 7DN Tel: 0191 284 3111 Fax: 0191 213 1968; Black Close House, Black Close Bank, Ashington NE63 8TF Tel: 01670 811480 — MB ChB 1975 Liverp.; FRCS Eng. 1982; FRCS Ed. 1981. Cons. Childr.s Orthop. Surg. Newc. Hosps. NHS Trust; Hon. Lect. Newc. Univ. Socs: Brit. Orthop. Assn.; Brit. Soc. Childr. Orthop. Surg.

QUINCEY, Caroline Histopathy Dept, Barsley District Hospital NHS Trust, Gawber Rd, Barnsley S75 2EP; 146 Dobercroft Road, Sheffield S7 2LU — MB ChB 1988 Sheff.; DRCPath 1993; MRCPath 1997. Cons.(Histopath.)and (Cytol.) Barsley Dist. Hosp. Prev: Sen. Regist. (Histopath.) Roy. Hallamsh. Hosp. Sheff.

***QUINE, David Juan** 122 Sandal Street, Manchester M40 7EF — MB ChB 1997 Manch.

QUINE, Mary Amanda Queen Alexandra Hospital, Portsmouth PO6 1HH; 5 Solent Road, Drayton, Portsmouth PO6 1HH — MB BS 1986 Lond.; MD 1998; MRCP (UK) 1990. (St. Bartholomews Medical College) Cons. (Gastroenterol.) Qu. Alexandra Hosp. Portsmouth. Prev: Regist. NW Thames HA; Research Fell. (Gastroenterol.) Roy. Coll. Surg. Lond.; Regist. (Med.) Frimley Pk. Hosp. Surrey.

QUINE, Mr Stuart Miles 41 Amesbury Road, Penylan, Cardiff CF23 5DX — BM BS 1987 Nottm.; BMedSci (Hons.) Nottm. 1985; FRCS (Orl.) 1995; FRCSI 1994; DRCOG 1991. Regist. (ENT Surg.) Univ. Hosp. Wales Cardiff.

QUINEY, Iain Donald Washington House Surgery, 77 Halse Road, Brackley NN13 6EQ Tel: 01280 702436 Fax: 01280 701805; Hill House, Wrightons Hill, Helmdon, Brackley NN13 5UF Tel: 01295 768168 — MB BS 1981 Lond.; DA (UK) 1985.

QUINEY

QUINEY, Jeremy Roderick Department of Clinical Chemistry, St. Richards Hospital, Spitalfield Lane, Chichester PO19 4SE Tel: 01243 788122 — MB BS 1976 Lond.; BSc Sussex 1971; MRCPath 1984. Cons. Path. St. Richard's Hosp. Chichester.

QUINEY, Marion Joan Gatehampton, Mill Lane, Gerrards Cross SL9 8AY — MB BS 1985 Lond.; DRCOG 1989.

QUINEY, Nial Francis The Old Dairy, Home Farm Court, Shillinglee, Chiddingfold, Godalming GU8 4SY Tel: 01428 708180 — MB BS 1985 Lond.; BSc Lond. 1982; FCAnaesth 1991; DCH RCP Lond. 1989; DRCOG 1987. Cons. Anaesth. Surrey. Prev: Sen. Regist. SW Regional Scheme.; Regist. Rotat. (Anaesth.) Bristol & W.on HA.

QUINEY, Mr Robert Edward 55 Harley Street, London W1N 1DD Tel: 020 7580 2426 Fax: 020 7436 1645; Russets, Orchehill Avenue, Gerrards Cross SL9 8QE Tel: 01753 891336 — MRCS Eng. LRCP Lond. 1980; BSc (Hons.) Lond. 1977, MB BS 1980; FRCS Eng. 1986; FRCS Ed. 1986; T(S) 1991. (Char. Cross) Cons. ENT Surg. Roy. Free Hosp. & Barnet & Edgware Hosp. Lond.; Sen. Lect. Roy. Free Hosp. Sch. Med. Prev: Sen. Regist. (ENT Surg.) Roy. Sussex Co. Hosp. Brighton; Sen. Regist. (ENT) Roy. Nat. Throat, Nose & Ear Hosp. Lond.

***QUINLAN, Jonathan Mark** 122 Pound Road, East Peckham, Tonbridge TN12 5BL — MB ChB 1994 Bristol.

QUINLAN, Margaret Helen Magda House Medical Centre, 257 Dialstone Lane, Great Moor, Stockport SK2 7NA Tel: 0161 483 3175 Fax: 0161 483 4992; Dover Beck House, 4 Parsonage Gardens, Marple, Stockport SK6 7NB — MB ChB 1971 Liverp.; DObst RCOG 1973; Cert. Family Plann. JCC 1982. Socs: BMA. Prev: GP Nottm.; SHO City Hosp. Nottm.; Ho. Phys. & Ho. Surg. BRd.green Hosp. Liverp.

QUINLAN, Mary Jane Dept. Of Anaesthetics, John Radcliffe Hospital, Headley Way, Oxford OX3 9DU — MB BS 1990 Lond.; FRCA 1995. (St. Thos.) Cons. Anaesth., John Radcliffe Hosp., Oxf.

QUINLAN, Mr Michael The Guest Hospital, Tipton Rd, Dudley DY1 4SE Tel: 01384 456111 — MB ChB 1984 Sheff.; FRCS Glas. 1989; DO RCS Eng. 1989. Cons. Dudley Gp. & Sandwell Healthcare, NHS Trust. Prev: Regist. (Ophth.) W. Norwich Hosp.; Specialist Regist. E. Anglian Rotat.

QUINLAN, Raymond Michael Business Healthcare, The Occupational Health Centre, Leeming Lane S., Mansfield NG19 9AG Tel: 01623 657446 Fax: 01623 423378 Email: rq@business-healthcare.co.uk; 11 Badgers Chase, Retford DN22 6RX Tel: 01777 708393 Email: ray.quinian@btopenworld.com — MB BCh BAO 1986 NUI; BSc NUI 1981; MRCP (UK) 1989; MFOM RCP Lond. 1996, AFOM 1993; DA (UK) 1991; MIOSH 1999. (University College Dublin) Med. Director Occupat. Med. Business Healthcare, Mansfield, WoodHo. Socs: Soc. Occupat. Med. (Ex-Sec. E. Midl. Gp.); Brit. Occupat. Hyg. Soc.; Mem. Inst. Occup. safety & health. Prev: Sen. Regist. (Occupat. Med.) Brit. Coal Corp. Mansfield WoodHo.; SHO (Gen. Med., Intens. Care & Anaesth.) Derbysh. Roy. Infirm.; Safety, Health & Environm. Manager & Occupat. Phys. Zeneca, Huddersfield Works.

QUINLIVAN, Rosaline Christina Mary Hillcrest, Sandford Avenue, Church Stretton SY6 7AB — MB BS 1985 Lond.; MRCP UK) 1990.

QUINN, Alice Nora Kennedy 64 Craiglea Drive, Morningside, Edinburgh EH10 5PF — MB BCh BAO 1990 NUI; MRCGP 1944.

***QUINN, Andrew Charles** 22 Mountford Close, Wellesbourne, Warwick CV35 9QQ — MB ChB 1995 Leeds.

QUINN, Andrew James Royal Alexandra Hospital, Corsebar Road, Paisley PA2 9P; 5 Newlands Road, Newlands, Glasgow G43 2JB — MB BCh BAO 1986 Belf.; MRCOG 1991. Cons. Obst. Roy. Alexandra Hosp. Paisley.

QUINN, Anne Marie 71 Barnards Hill, Marlow SL7 2NX — MB BCh BAO 1975 NUI.

QUINN, Professor Anthony Gerard Experimental Medicine, Astrazeneca R+D, Bakewell Road, Loughborough LE11 5RH Tel: 44 1509 644109 Fax: 44 1509 645514; 7 Blacksmiths Close, Thrussington, Leicester LE7 4UJ — MB ChB 1985 (Commend) Dundee; PhD Newc. 1995; BMSc (1st cl. Hons. Gen. Path.) Dundee 1982; MRCP (UK) 1988; FRCP 2000 London. Global Clin. Expert, Experim. Med., R+D Astrazenenca PLC. Socs: Brit. Assn. Dermatol.; Brit. Soc. Investig. Dermat.; Roy. Soc. Med. Prev: Prof. of Dermat.,

Bart's & The Roy. Lond. Hosp.; MRC Trav. Fell.sh. UCSF, Calif.; MRC Train. Fell. Dept. Dermatol, NEWC.

QUINN, Audrey Catherine 28 Briar Road, Newlands, Glasgow G43 2TX — MB ChB 1987 Glas.

QUINN, Benedict Noel Eugene 50 Wallasey Vill., Wallasey Tel: 0151 691 2088 — MB BCh BAO 1979 NUI.

QUINN, Christopher Anthony 91 Dixon Road, Glasgow G42 8AT — MB BS 1991 Lond.; PhD Biochem. Lond. 1983; BSc Biochem. Pharmacol. (Hons.) Glas. 1979. SHO (Paediat.) Roy. Liverp. Childr. Hosp. Alder Hey Liverp. Socs: BMA. Prev: SHO (Paediat.) Addenbrookes Hosp. Cambs.; SHO (Neonat.) Rosie Matern. Hosp. Camb.; SHO (Paediat.) Qu. Eliz. Hosp. King's Lynn.

QUINN, David Warwick 35 St John's Wood Terrace, London NW8 6JL — MB BS 1991 Lond.

QUINN, Deborah Catherine 54 Waveney Road, Harpenden AL5 4QY Tel: 01582 767794 — MB BS 1988 Lond.; MRCGP 1994; DFFP 1994; DCH RCP Lond. 1992. (Middlesex Hosp. Medical School) Med. Off. (Palliat. Med.) Isabel Hospice Welwyn Garden City. Socs: BMA; Assn. Palliat. Med.

QUINN, Elizabeth Ann 62 Corrour Road, Glasgow G43 2ED — MB ChB 1986 Glas.

QUINN, Fiona Mary 44 King's Road, Belfast BT5 6JJ Tel: 01232 656335 — MB BCh BAO 1992 Belf.; MRCGP 1996; DFFP 1997; DCH RCPSI 1995; DRCOG 1995. (Qu. Univ. Belf.)

QUINN, Fiona Michele 44 Rathfriland Road, Newry BT34 1LD — MB BCh BAO 1992 Belf.

QUINN, Gregory Francis 7 Canford Road, Poole BH15 2LE — MB BCh BAO 1984 NUI.

QUINN, Jean Community Studies Unit, Dept. of Primary Care, University of Liverpool L69 3BX Tel: 0151 794 5619 Fax: 0151 794 4907 Email: quinn@liv.ac.uk; 84 Black Horse Hill, West Kirby, Wirral CH48 6DT Tel: 0151 625 9547 Email: quinn@clava.ac.uk — MB ChB 1970 Liverp.; FRCGP 2001; ILTM 2001; MRCGP 1995. Clin Teach. Univ Liverp. Prev: Mem. FHSA; Chairm. Wirral LMC; Mem. GP Dist. Managem. Bd.

QUINN, Josiette Suzanne St. Georges Hospital, Northumberland Mental Health NHS Trust, Morpeth NE61 2NU Tel: 01670 512121 — MB ChB 1984 Glas.; MRCPsych. 1989. (Glasgow) Cons. Psychiat. St. Geo. Hosp. Morpeth. Prev: Sen. Regist. St. Nicholas Hosp. Newc. u Tyne; Regist. Gartnaval Roy. Hosp. Gt. Glas. HB.

QUINN, Kathleen 24J Constitution Road, Dundee DD1 1LD — MB ChB 1978 Dundee. SHO (Psychiat.) Roy. Dundee Liff Hosp.

QUINN, Kathleen Susan Craig Dunain Hospital, Inverness IV3 8JU Tel: 01463 234101; 6 Newtonhill, Lentran, Inverness IV3 8RN Tel: 01463 831364 — MB ChB 1968 Aberd.; MRCPsych 1980; DCH Eng. 1971; DObst RCOG 1970. Specialist Psychiat. (Ment. Health) Highland Communities NHS Trust.

***QUINN, Kealan Murray** Straidarran House, Claudy, Londonderry BT47 4DB — MB ChB 1996 Ed.

QUINN, Louise Anne Lowther Unit, St Andrews Hospital, Billing Rd, Northampton NN1 5DG Tel: 01604 661000 — MB ChB 1987 Sheff.; MRCPsych 1991. p/t Cons. Child & Adolesc. Psychiat. St Andrews Hosp., N.ampton. Prev: Sen. Regist. Train. Scheme Wessex; Cons. Child & Adolesc. Psychiat. Hosp. Campus Milton Keynes.

QUINN, Mark Alexander Dept. (Rhemat.) Leeds General Infirmary, Great George St, Leeds LS1 3EX Tel: 0113 392 3804; Saffron Cottage, 16 Moor Lane, Arkendale, Knaresborough HG5 0QU Tel: 01423 340470 — MB ChB 1994 Manch.; MRCP 1998. Research Fell. (Rheumat.); SDDD. Prev: SHO (Gen. Med.); Ho. Off. (Surg. & Med.) Macclesfield Dist. Gen. Hosp.

QUINN, Mark Edward The Grange, Owenbeg, Dungiven, Londonderry — MB BCh BAO 1988 Belf.

QUINN, Martin John 6 Cavendish Gardens, Sneyd Park, Bristol BS9 1RQ — MB ChB 1980 Bristol; MD Bristol 1994; MRCOG 1987. Sen. Regist. (O & G) Univ. Hosp. Wales NHS Trust. Prev: Lect. (O & G) Univ. Bristol.

QUINN, Mary Bridget Diabetes and Endocrinology, 5th Floor, Windsor Building, Leicester Royal Infirmary, Leicester LE1 5WW Tel: 0116 254 1414 — MB ChB 1986 Leic.; BSc (1st cl. Hons.) Leic. 1984; Cert. Family Plann. JCC 1992; T(GP) 1992; DFFP 1996. p/t Hosp. Practitioner in Diabetes Leicester Roy. Infirm. Leicester. Prev: GP Rushey Mead Leic.

QUINTON

QUINN, Mary Clare Tel: 01664 420131 — MB ChB 1985 Dundee; MRCGP 1992; DRCOG 1991. Prev: Princip. GP, Grange St Surg., St Albans; Princip. GP, Prospect Ho. Surg., Newc. upn Tyne.

QUINN, Mary Gerardine Herrington Medical Centre, Philadelphia Lane, Houghton-le-Spring DH4 4LE Tel: 0191 584 2632; 130 Benfieldside Road, Blackhill, Consett DH8 0RT — MB ChB 1981 Leeds. Prev: Trainee GP Doncaster Roy. Infirm.; Ho. Phys. Leeds Gen. Infirm.; Ho. Surg. St. Jas. Hosp. Leeds.

QUINN, Mary Margaret Cornmarket Surgery, Newry Health Village, Monaghan, Newry BT35 6BW Tel: 028 3026 5838 Fax: 028 3026 6727; 55 Crieve Court, Rathfriland Road, Newry BT34 2PE — MB BCh BAO 1983 NUI; MRCGP 1988; DRCOG 1987; DGM RCP Lond. 1986. Prev: Trainee GP Sandhead VTS; Clin. Med. Off. (Child Health & Family Plann.) Lurgan Co. Armagh.

QUINN, Michael (retired) Highlands, 25 Sheeplands Lane, Sherborne DT9 4BW Tel: 01935 813427 — MB BCh BAO 1952 NUI; MRCPsych 1971; DPM Eng. 1962; LM Nat. Matern. Hosp. Dub. 1955. Prev: Cons. Psychiat. (Ment. Handicap) Dorset AHA.

***QUINN, Michael Francis** 6 Greenan Road, Newry BT34 2PJ — MB BCh BAO 1995 Belf.

QUINN, Mr Michael Joseph 4 Breda Avenue, Belfast BT8 6JS — MB BCh BAO 1981 Belf.; FRCSI 1994.

***QUINN, Michelle Claire** 74 Ash Grove, Wavertree, Liverpool L15 1ET — MB ChB 1996 Liverp.

QUINN, Professor Niall Patrick Division of Clinical Neurology, Institute of Neurology, Queen Square, London WC1N 3BG Tel: 020 78373611 Ext: 4253 Fax: 020 7278 5616 Email: n.quinn@ion.ucl.ac.uk — MB BChir 1974 Camb.; MA Camb. 1976, MD 1988; FRCP Lond. 1994. (Lond. Hosp.) Prof. (Neurol.) & Clin. Sub-Dean Inst. Neurol. Lond.; Hon. Cons. Neurol. Nat. Hosp. Neurol. & Neurosurg. & Gt. Ormond St. Hosp. for childr. Lond. Socs: Hon. Foreign Mem. Soc. Francaise De Neurol.; Sec.Movement Disorder Soc.; Assoc. Brit. NeUrol.s. Prev: Reader & Sen. Lect. (Neurol.) Inst. Neurol. Lond.; Lect. (Neurol.) King's Coll. Hosp. Med. Sch. Lond.; Med. Resid. Neurol. Serv. Hôp. de la Salpêtrière Paris.

QUINN, Nicholas David 28 Eskdale Road, Hartlepool TS25 4AU — MB BS 1992 Lond.

QUINN, Patrick Henry Martin Omagh Health Centre, Mountjoy Road, Omagh BT79 7BA Tel: 028 8224 3521 — MB BCh BAO 1989 Belf.

QUINN, Patrick McDara 6 Fairfield Close, Exmouth EX8 2BN — MB BCh BAO 1980 Dub.; MRCPsych 1986. Sen. Regist. (Child & Adolesc. Psychiat.) Swindon.

QUINN, Philip Wyndham Blackburn Road Surgery, 257 Blackburn Road, Accrington BB5 0AL Tel: 01254 233048; High Lawn, Whins Lane, Read, Burnley BB12 7QY Tel: 01282 772802 — MRCS Eng. LRCP Lond. 1956; MRCGP 1965; DFFP 1993; Cert. Contracep. & Family Plann. RCOG & RCGP &; Cert FPA 1975; DObst RCOG 1957. (Sheff.) SCMO (Occupat. Health) Blackburn Health Dist.; Med. Dir. Communicare NHS Trust. Socs: Blackburn & Accrington Med. Soc. Prev: Mem. Dist. Managem. Team Blackburn Health Dist.; Chairm. E. Lancs. HC.

***QUINN, Rebecca** 13 Williams Way, Fleet GU51 3EU — MB BS 1998 Lond.; MB BS Lond 1998.

QUINN, Robert James Murray Straidarran House, Claudy, Londonderry BT47 4DB Email: rjmquinn@btinternet.com — MB BCh BAO Belf. 1970; FRCP Glas. 1986; MRCP (UK) 1973; DCH RCPS Glas. 1972; FRCP (Lon.) 1996; FRCP (Ed.) 1996; FRCP&CH 1997. (Belf.) Cons. Paediatr. Altnagelvin Hosp. Lond.derry. Socs: Brit. Paediat. Assn. Prev: Sen. Regist. & Sen. Tutor (Paediat.) Roy. Belf. Hosp. Sick Childr.; Sen. Regist. (Paediat.) King Edwd. VIII Hosp. Durban, S. Africa & Ulster Hosp. Dundonald.

QUINN, Ruadhri Paul Newtownhamilton Health Centre, 2A Markethill Road, Newtownhamilton, Newry BT35 0BE Tel: 028 3087 8202/8223 Fax: 028 3087 9043 — MB BCh BAO 1989 Belf.; MRCGP 1995; DCH Dub. 1992.

QUINN, Sally Jane Flat 4, 182 Drake St., Rochdale OL16 1UP — MB BS 1990 Newc.

QUINN, Siobhan Rosemarie 85 Baronscourt Road, Carryduff, Belfast BT8 8BQ — MB BCh BAO 1988 Belf.; MB BCh BAO Belf. 1989.

QUINN, Mr Steven James Apt. 13, Scotia West, 5 Jardine Road, London E1W 3WA — MB BS 1987 Lond.; FRCS Eng. 1992. Regist. (Otolaryngol.) Addenbrooke's Hosp. Camb.

QUINN, Teresa Josephine Dalkeith Road Medical Practice, 145 Dalkeith Road, Edinburgh EH16 5HQ Tel: 0131 667 1289 — MB BCh BAO 1985 Belf.; MRCGP 1990; DGM Lond. 1987. (Qu. Univ. Belf.) Gen. Practitioner, Dalkeith Rd. Med. Pract.,145 Dalkeith Rd., Edin. Prev: Staff Grade & Clin. Med. Off. (Community Paediat.) Edin.; SHO (Rehabil. Med.) Astley Ainslie Hosp. Edin.; Trainee Community Paediat. Howden Health Centre Livingstone.

QUINN, Tiernan George (retired) Wardlaw, 81 Winshields, Cramlington NE23 6JD Tel: 01670 712020 — MB BS 1951 Durh. Prev: Ho. Surg. P.ss Mary Matern. Hosp. Newc., Fleming Memor. Hosp. Sick Childr. & Roy. Vict. Infirm.

QUINN, Vincent Philip c/o Fr. B. Curley, 250 Chapel St., Salford M3 5LL — MB BCh BAO 1950 Dub.; MA Dub. 1953, MB BCh BAO 1950. Prev: Community Med. Off. Salford.

QUINN, Mrs Zandra Elizabeth 16 Waterford Drive, Coleraine BT52 1NQ Tel: 01265 44885; Saffron Cottage, 16 Moor Lane, Arkendale, Knaresborough HG5 0QU Tel: 01423 340470 — MB ChB 1995 Dundee; BMSc (Hons. Forens. Med.) Dund 1992; DRCOG 1997 RCObst&Gyn.; DFFP 1997 Roy. Coll. (Dundee Univ.) GP Regist. Socs: BMA; (GP Regist. Represen.) Local Med. Sub-Comm.; Med. Sickness Soc. Prev: SHO (Paediat.) Harrogate Dist. Hosp.; SHO (A & E) Harrogate Dist. Hosp.; GP Regist. Leeds Rd. Surg. Harrogate.

QUINNELL, Anthony John Drugs North West Mental Health Services of Salford, Prestwich Hospital, Bury New Road, Manchester M25 3BL Tel: 0161 773 9121 Fax: 0161 772 3595 Email: tonyq@clara.net; Stockport C.D.T, 129 Wellington Road S., Stockport SK1 3TS Tel: 0161 476 2533 Fax: 0161 476 1038 — MB ChB 1982 Aberd. (Aberdeen) Staff Psychiat. Regional Drug Dependance Serv. Prestwich Hosp.; Sen. Clin. Med. Off. Bolton Community Drug Team.

QUINNELL, George Alfred Fiske (retired) Llys Meddyg, New Road, Teignmouth TQ14 8UF Tel: 016267 73114 — MB ChB 1934 Glas. JP. (Supplm.. List).

QUINNELL, Philip Meyrick The Croft Surgery, Barnham Road, Eastergate, Chichester PO20 6RP Tel: 01243 543240 Fax: 01243 544862; Spitchwick, Church Lane, Oving, Chichester PO20 6DG Tel: 01243 779898 — MB BS 1965 Lond.; LMCC 1979; DA (UK) 1968; DObst RCOG 1967. (Lond. Hosp.) Prev: Chairm. W. Sussex LMC.

QUINNELL, Mr Richard Charles Little Orchard, 2 Ashbourne Road, Kirk Langley, Derby DE6 4NS Tel: 01332 824408 — MB BS Lond. 1969; FRCS Eng. 1975; MRCS Eng. LRCP Lond. 1969. (Guy's.) Cons. Orthop. Surg. S. Derbysh. Gp. Hosps.

QUINNELL, Timothy George Spitchwick, Church Lane, Oving, Chichester PO20 6DG Tel: 01243 779898 — MB BS 1993 Lond.; BSc (Hist. Med. & Basic Med. Scis.) Lond. 1990; MRCP (Lond.) 1997. (The London Hospital Medical College)

QUINTON, Anthony Arthur Greves Suite D, Metropolitan House, The Millfields,, Stonehouse, Plymouth PL1 3JX Tel: 01752 229116 Fax: 01752 269098; Higher Quither, Milton Abbot, Tavistock PL19 0PZ Tel: 01822 860284 — MRCS Eng. LRCP Lond. 1966; AFOM DCP Lond. 1980; DAvMed Eng. 1976. Occupat. Phys.; Authorised Med. Examr. Civil Aviat. Auth. Socs: Soc. Occupat. Med. & Assn. Aviat. Med. Examrs.

QUINTON, Catherine Frances c/o Mr. R.F. Quinton, 21 The Warren, Carshalton SM5 4EQ — MB BS 1988 Lond.; BSc Lond. 1985, MB BS 1988; MRCPsych 1993. Cons. Old Age Psychiat. Centr. Worthing Sussex.

QUINTON, Mr David Neil Accident & Emergency Department, Leicester Royal Infirmary, Infirmary Square, Leicester LE1 5WW Email: dnq@doctors.org.uk; 24 Church Lane, Thrussington, Leicester LE7 4TE — MB BS 1976 Lond.; FRCS Ed. 1981. (Middlesex London) Cons. A & E Leicester Roy. Infirm. Socs: Hand Soc. Gt. Brit.

QUINTON, Laura 55A Penn Road, London N7 9RE Tel: 020 7607 9673 — MB BS 1991 Lond.; BSc Lond. 1988. SHO (Gyn.) Univ. Coll. Hosp. Lond. Prev: Trainee GP/SHO Chase Farm Hosp. Enfield VTS; Ho. Off. (Orthop. & Gen. Surg.) P.ss Alexandra Hosp. Harlow; Ho. Off. (Med.) Wycombe Gen. Hosp.

QUINTON, Paul John 281A Old Birmingham Road, Bromsgrove B60 1HQ — MB BS 1991 Lond.

QUINTON, Peter John Orchard House, Lower Fold, Dorrington, Shrewsbury SY5 7JG — MB 1968 Camb.; BChir 1967.

QUINTON, Richard Dept. of Endocrinol, Roy. Victoria Infirm., Ward 23, Claremont Wing, Newcastle upon Tyne NE1 4LP Tel: 0191 282

QUINTON-TULLOCH

4635 Fax: 0141 227 5279 Email: cheree.collins@northy.nhs.uk — MB BChir 1988 Camb.; MA Camb. 1989; MRCP (UK) 1992; MD Camb. 2000. (Univ. Camb.) Cons.(Endocrinol.) Roy. Vict. Infirm. Newc.; Sen. Lect. (Med.), Univ. of Newc., Newc. Socs: Soc. Endocrinol.; Endocrine Soc.; BMA. Prev: Lect. & Hon.Sen. Regist. (Endocrinol); U.C.L. & Roy. Free Hosp. Med. Sch. Lond.

QUINTON-TULLOCH, John Charles Fremington Medical Centre, Barnstaple EX31 2NT Tel: 01271 376655 Email: jonyqq@aol.com; The Verne, Instow, Bideford EX39 4JX — MB ChB 1987 Bristol.

QUIRK, Jennifer Anne Bromley Hosp, Cromwell Avenue, Bromley BR2 9AJ Tel: 020 8289 7000 — MB BS 1981 Western Australia; FRACP 1989. Cons. (Neurol.) Bromley Hosp.; Hon. Cons. (Neurol.) KCL. Socs: BMA; ABN; AAN.

QUIRK, Patricia Ann (retired) Doctors Surgery, 79-81 Bowman Street, Glasgow G42 8LF Tel: 0141 423 1398 Fax: 0141 423 1845 — MB ChB 1966 Glas.

QUIRKE, James Joseph Room 1, 66 St Stephens Road, Norwich NR1 3RE — MB BCh BAO 1994 NUI.

QUIRKE, Professor Philip Division of Clinical Sciences, School of Medicine, Algernon Firth Institute of Pathology, Leeds LS2 9JT Tel: 0113 233 3412 Fax: 0113 233 3404 Email: philq@pathology.leeds.ac.uk; The Old Granary, Main St, Linton, Wetherby LS22 4HT Tel: 01937 587797 Fax: 01937 587797 Email: philip.quirke@cqw.net — BM 1980 Soton.; PhD Leeds 1987; FRCPath 1997; MRCPath 1988. (Soton.) Prof. Univ. Leeds; Hon. Cons. & Head Histopath. & Molecular Path. Leeds Gen. Infirm. Teachg. Hosp NHS Trust.

QUIRKE, Richard Joseph Ty Morlais, Berry Square, Merthyr Tydfil CF48 3AL Tel: 01685 722782 Fax: 01685 722951 — MB BCh BAO 1982 NUI.

QUIROGA GIRALDEZ, Isabel Southampton General Hospital, Tremona Road, Southampton SO16 6YD — LMS 1993 U Complutense Madrid.

QUIYUM, S A Handsworth Grange Medical Centre, 432 Handsworth Road, Sheffield S13 9BZ Tel: 0114 269 7505 Fax: 0114 269 8535.

***QULI, Xavier Haider** 13 Joinings Bank, Oldbury, Oldbury B68 8QJ — MB ChB 1997 Sheff.

QUORAISHI, Abu Hashem Muhammad Ali Haider Public Health Laboratory Service, Llandough Hospital & Community NHS Trust, Penlan Road, Penarth CF64 2XX Tel: 01222 715298 Fax: 01222 715134 Email: llanbact@celtic.co.uk — MB BS 1963 Dacca; MPhil Karachi 1966; FRCPath 1988, M 1977; Dip. Bact. (Distinc.) Manch. 1972. (Dacca Med. Coll.) Cons. Med. Microbiol. S. Glam. AHA (T).

***QURAISHI, Asifa** 43 Whalley Range, Blackburn BB1 6DX — MB ChB 1997 Ed.

QURAISHI, Mohammad Aslam Castleton Road Surgery, 19-21 Castleton Road, Goodmayes, Ilford IG3 9QW Tel: 020 8599 9951 Fax: 020 8597 9974 — MB BS 1962 Karachi; BSc Karachi 1955; DTM & H Eng. 1965. (Dow Med. Coll.) Prev: SHO (Paediat.) Univ. Hosp. S. Manch.; SHO (Gen. Med.) W. Wales Gen. Hosp. Carmarthen; Ho. Phys. St. Mary's Hosp. Plaistow.

QURAISHI, Mr Muhammad Shahed 11 Florey Court, University Hospital, Nottingham NG7 2UH Tel: 0115 970 4045 — MB BS 1985 Karachi; FRCSI 1992.

QURAISHY, Ehsanullah Stepping Hill Hospital, Stockport SK2 7JE Tel: 0161 483 1010; 303 Bramhall Lane S., Bramhall, Stockport SK7 3DN Tel: 0161 439 5272 Fax: 0161 440 0189 — MB BS 1977 Lucknow; BSc Gorakhpur 1961; MB BS Lucknow 1967; MRCPsych 1976; DPM Eng. 1975; Dip. Dermat. Lond 1971. Cons. Psychiat. Stepping Hill Hosp. Stockport. & Clin. Dir. Ment. Health. Socs: BMA. Prev: Sen. Regist. (Psychiat.) Sefton & Roy. Liverp. Hosps.; Regist. (Psychiat.) Mid-Wales Hosp. Talgarth; Regist. (Dermatol.) Manch. & Salford Skin Hosps.

QURAISHY, Muhammad Muneer 20A Long Lane, Stanwell, Staines TW19 7AA — MB BS 1987 Karachi; FCOphth 1991.

***QURASHI, Intikhab** 241 Manchester Road, Bury BL9 9HJ — MB ChB 1996 Dundee.

QURESHI, Aamir Mahmood c/o D.O.M.E. Office, Woodend Hospital, Eday Road, Aberdeen AB15 6JP; Woodbine Cottage, Grandholm Vill., Persley Den, Aberdeen AB22 8AJ — MB BS 1983 Karachi; MRCP (UK) 1993. Regist. (Med. for Elderly) Woodend Hosp. Aberd. Socs: Brit. Geriat. Soc. Prev: Regist. (Geriat. & Gen.

Med.) Maelor Gen. Hosp. Wrexham.; Regist. (Med.) Cumbld. Infirm. Carlisle; SHO (Gen. Med. & Elderly Care) Llandudno Gen. Hosp.

QURESHI, Akhtar Hussain 'Akhtar Lodge', 148 High Road, Chigwell IG7 5BQ Tel: 020 8501 0566 — MB BS 1958 Sind; LRCP LRCS Ed. LRFPS Glas. 1962. (Liaquat Med. Coll.) Socs: Assoc. MRCGP.

QURESHI, Amer Mehmood 42 Ancaster Crescent, New Malden KT3 6BE — MB ChB 1993 Manch.; BSc (Hons.) 1990; MRCP (UK) 1997. (Manch.) SHO (Anaesth.) St. Helier's Hosp. Carshalton.

***QURESHI, Amir Ali** 22 Priestley Gardens, Romford RM6 4SP — MB BCh 1997 Wales.

QURESHI, Anser Suhail Broomfield Hospital, Gorleston, Chelmsford CM1 7ET; 265 Campkin Road, Cambridge CB4 2LE Email: answerqueshi@aol.com — MB BS 1984 Punjab; MRCP (UK) 1994; CCST Gen. Med for Elderly 1999. Cons. Gen. Med. c/o Elderly, Broomfield Hosp. Chelsford; SR. Med. Bedford Hosp.; SR. Med.c/o elderly Camb. Hosp.; Sen. Regist. Med. James Paget Hosp.Gt. Yarmonth. Socs: BMA; RCP; Brit. Geriat.s Soc. Prev: Regist. (Med. for Elderly) W. Norwich Hosp.; SHO (Cardiol.) Papworth Hosp. Huntingdon; SHO (Med. for Elderly & Gen. Med.) Bedford Gen. Hosp.

QURESHI, Ashfaq Husain St Catherine Surgery, 19 St. Catherines, Lincoln LN5 8LW Tel: 01522 871771 Fax: 01522 871773.

QURESHI, Asjid Iqbal 83 Ballards Road, London NW2 7UE — MB ChB 1992 Ed.

***QURESHI, Ayesha Salma** Springhill House, Springhill Lane, Lower Penn, Wolverhampton WV4 4TJ — MB ChB 1995 Birm.; ChB Birm. 1995.

QURESHI, Bashir Ahmed Al-Bashir, 32 Legrace Avenue, Hounslow TW4 7RS Tel: 020 8570 4008 Fax: 020 8570 4008 — MB BS Punjab (Pakistan) 1961; DCH RCPSI 1976; DHMSA Lond. 1974; Cert. Family Plann. JCC 1974; Hon. MAPHA 1998; Hon. FRSH 1998; Hon. M GP Sec. RSM 1998; LRCP LRCS Ed. LRCPS Glas. 1975; LMSSA 1970; ECFMG Cert. 1976; MFFP 1993; FRCGP 1984, M 1976; MICGP 1984; AFOM RCP Lond. 1978; DPMSA Lond. 1980. (Nishtar Med. Coll., Multan) GP Hounslow, S.all & Boston Manor Lond.; Expert Witness Transcultural Medico-Legal Cases; Examr. Brit. Red Cross Soc. Ealing & Dep. Med. Adviser Lond. Br. Brit. Red. CrossS; Regular Book Reviewer of Jl. Roy. Soc. Hlth.; URDU-English Translator. Socs: FRSH (Ex-Vice Pres.); FRIPHH; Fell. Roy. Soc. Med. (Vice Pres. Counc. Gen. Pract. Sect.). Prev: Med. Off. W. Lond. Healthcare NHS Trust; SHO Nat. Hosp. Qu. Sq. Lond.; Ho. Phys. Whittington Hosp. Lond.

QURESHI, Mr Hamidullah Rotherham District General Hospital, Moorgate Road, Rotherham S60 2UD Tel: 01709 820000 Fax: 01709 824282 — MB BS 1958 Sind; MB BS Sind. 1958; FRCS Eng. 1972; FRCS Ed. 1971; MRCS Eng. LRCP Lond. 1975. (Liaquat Med. Coll. Hyderabad) Cons. A & E Dept. Rotherham Hosp. Prev: Regist. (Orthop.) Rotherham Hosp. & Roy. Orthop. Hosp. Birm.; Med. Off. Pakistan Army Med. Corps.

***QURESHI, Idris Fouad** 27 Lucknow Drive, Nottingham NG3 5EU — MB BS 1994 Lond.

***QURESHI, Irum** Flat 40, Block 3, 5 Beech Hill Road, Sheffield S10 2RA — MB ChB 1995 Sheff.

***QURESHI, Isaque D'Almendra** 26 Downhurst Avenue, London NW7 3QA — MB BS 1996 Lond.

QURESHI, Khalda Nasreen Maidstone Road Surgery, 262 Maidstone Road, Chatham ME4 6JL Tel: 01634 842093 Fax: 01634 842151; 71 College Avenue, Gillingham ME7 5HY Tel: 01634 578016 — MB ChB 1974 Manch.; DRCOG 1976. (Manch.)

QURESHI, Khalid Masood 46 Selkirk House, Bemerton St., Kings Cross, London N1 0AB Tel: 020 7607 2577 — MB BS 1969 Sind; FRCR 1986; DMRD Eng. 1981.

QURESHI, Khalida 43 Athol Road, Whalley Range, Manchester M16 8QW — MB BCh 1977 Wales.

QURESHI, Mr Khaver Naseer 46 Harley Terrace, Gosforth, Newcastle upon Tyne NE3 1UL — MB BS 1992 Lond.; BSc (Hons.) Lond. 1989; FRCS Eng. 1996. (St. Bart.) Clin. Research Assoc. (Surg.) Med. Sch. Univ. Newc. Prev: SHO (Gen. Surg.) Wansbeck N.umberland; SHO (Urol.) Freeman Hosp. Newc.; SHO (Gen. Surg.) Walsgrave Hosp. Coventry.

QURESHI, Mahmooda 79 Carlton Mansions, Randolph Avenue, London W9 1NS — MB BS 1992 Lond.

QURESHI, Mansur (retired) 16 Broxholm Road, Heaton, Newcastle upon Tyne NE6 5RL Tel: 0191 265 4516 — MB BS 1962 Punjab; FRCPath 1984, M 1972. Cons. Haemat. Freeman Hosp. Newc. Prev: Sen. Regist. (Haemat.) Newc. Gen. Hosp.

QURESHI, Mariam Amatullah 15 Fernbank Road, Bradford BD3 0PJ Tel: 01274 637754 — MB ChB 1993 Manch.; DRCOG 1996 RCOG; DFFP 1995 RCOG. GP Regist. The Gables Surg. Pudsey. Prev: Gen. Pract. VTS; Centr. Manch. Healthcare Trust.

QURESHI, Mazhar Uddin 34 Greaves Road, Walsall WS5 3QG — MB BS 1967 Punjab.

QURESHI, Mr Mohammad Akhtar Cromwell Hospital, Cromwell Road, London SW5 0UT Tel: 020 7460 5577 Fax: 020 7460 5709 Email: akhtarqureshi@cromwell-hospital.co.uk; Fax: 01372 277796 — MB BS 1964 Karachi; BSc; FRCS Glas. 1975; SpR Orthop. & Trauma Surg. (Dow Med. Coll.) Cons. Orthop. Surg. Cromwell & Ashtead Hosps. Socs: Fell. Brit. Orthop. Assn.; Int. Musculoskeletal Laser Soc. (IMLAS); AO. Alumni Switz. (Study of Internal Fixation). Prev: Cons. Orthop. & Traum. Surg. Qu. Eliz. Milit. Hosp. Lond.; Sen. Regist. (Orthop.) St. Mary's Hosp. Lond. W9; Regist. (Surg.) Qu. Mary's Hosp. Sidcup.

QURESHI, Mr Mohammad Iqbal Blackburn Street Health Centre, Blackburn Street, Radcliffe, Manchester M26 1WS; 51 Hillsborough Drive, Unsworth, Bury BL9 8LF Tel: 0161 766 6089 — MB BS 1965 Punjab; BSc Punjab (Pakistan) 1962, MB BS 1965; FRCS Glas. 1971. (King Edwd. Med. Coll. Lahore) Mem. Bury LMC; Chairm. Bury Fund Holding Pract. Socs: Local BMA; Pres. Pakistan Med. Assn. (UK). Prev: Surg. Specialist Ahmadi Hosp. Kuwait, Gulf.

QURESHI, Mohammad Sarfraz Akhtar The Calderdale Royal Hospital, Dudwell Lane, Halifax HX3 0PW Tel: 01422 357222 Ext: 4298; 8 Smithfield Avenue, Hipperholme, Halifax HX3 8HZ Tel: 01422 201888 — MB BS Punjab (Pakistan) 1964; FRCP Lond. 1987; MRCP (UK) 1971; DCH Eng. 1970; DCH RCPS Glas. 1968. (King Edwd. Med. Coll. Lahore) Cons. Phys. Gastroenterol. Halifax Gen. Hosp.; Sen. Clin. Lect. Univ. of Leeds Sch. of Med.

QURESHI, Mohammed Abdul Hai Oldhill Medical Centre, 19-21 Oldhill Street, London N16 6LD Tel: 020 8806 6993 Fax: 020 8806 6008; 95 Langford Court, London NW8 9DP Tel: 020 7266 3225 Fax: 020 7266 3225 — MB BS 1955 Osmania. (Osmania) Vis. Prof. Surg. Univ. La Paz, Bolivia. Socs: Fell. Roy. Soc. Med.; BMA & German Med. Assn.; Assoc. Mem. Brit. Assn. Plastic Surgs. Prev: Sen. Cas. Off. Farnham Hosp. Surrey; JHMO Booth Hall Hosp. Manch.; SHO Salford Roy. Hosp.

QURESHI, Mohammed Hasan Sharif The Surgery, 193 Lozells Road, Lozells, Birmingham B19 1RJ Tel: 0121 523 5089 — MB BS 1962 Karachi.

QURESHI, Mohammed Shafi 13 Parkwood Road, London SW19 7AQ — MB BS 1962 Karachi.

QURESHI, Mohammed Tahir St Paul's Road Surgery, 50 St Paul's Road, Bradford BD8 7LP Tel: 01274 543684 Fax: 01274 487674; 50 St Paul's Road, Manningham, Bradford BD8 7LP Tel: 01274 543684 Fax: 01274 487674 — MB BS 1956 Karachi. (Dow Med. Coll.)

QURESHI, Mohammed Zubair 97 Granson Way, Washingborough, Lincoln LN4 1HH Email: zqureshi@granson97.freeserve.co.uk — BM BS 1997 Nottm.; BMedSci, Nottm, 1995.

QURESHI, Muhammad Akram 46 Stonehall Avenue, Ilford IG1 3SH — MB BS 1961 Punjab; MB BS Punjab Pakistan 1961; DRCOG 1967; DA Eng. 1965. (Nishtar Med. Coll.) Clin. Asst. (Anaesth.) Qu. Mary's Hosp. Lond. Socs: BMA. Prev: SHO (O & G) St. Mary's Hosp. Leeds; Regist. (Anaesth.) Preston Hall Hosp. Maidstone & W. Kent. Gen. Hosp.; Maidstone.

*****QURESHI, Muhammad Ali** Flat 6, 26 Brunswick Square, Hove BN3 1EJ Email: dr@maqmaq.force9.co.uk — MB BS 1995 Lond.; BSc Hons, Univ. of St Andrews, 1992; FRCSEd, Royal Coll. Surgeons, Edinburgh, 2000.

QURESHI, Muhammad Aslam 8 Watery Lane, Walsall WS1 4HS — MB BS 1986 Karachi; MRCP (UK) 1993.

*****QURESHI, Muna Bashir** 84 Turnpike Link, Parkhill, Croydon CR0 5NY — MB ChB 1996 Manch.

QURESHI, Munir-ud-Din Nelson Road Surgery, 126 Nelson Road, Gillingham ME7 4LL Tel: 01634 571740 Fax: 01634 575024; 3 Bellwood Court, St Mary Hoo, Rochester ME3 8RT Tel: 01634 271425 — MB BS Punjab (Pakistan) 1964. (Nishtar Med. Coll. Multan)

*****QURESHI, Nadeem** Patrick and Partners, Rise Park Surgery, Revelstoke Way, Nottingham NG5 5EB Tel: 0115 927 2525 Fax: 0115 979 7056 — MB BS 1986 Lond.

QURESHI, Naeem Akhtar 58 New Way Road, London NW9 6PG — MB BS 1987 Punjab; LRCP LRCS Ed. LRCPS Glas. 1994.

QURESHI, Nagmi Riaz The Chantry, Hardwick, Worksop S80 3PB — MB ChB 1996 Liverp.

QURESHI, Najmi Riaz 1 Howard Place, St Andrews KY16 9HL; Golda Meirstraat 21, Groningen 9728 TB, Netherlands Tel: 00 31 50 5262924 Fax: 00 31 50 5262924 — MB ChB 1986 Dundee; MRCP (UK) 1990.

QURESHI, Mr Navid Sadiq 40 Rowland Lane, Thornton-Cleveleys FY5 2QU — MB BS 1977 Punjab; FRCS Ed. 1987.

QURESHI, Nazar Mohammad 38 Aylmer Road, Hampstead, London N2 0BX Tel: 020 8348 8642; 153 Copenhagen Street, London N1 0SR Tel: 020 7833 4981 — MB BS 1955 Punjab; DPath Eng. 1966. Gen. Phys. Lond.

QURESHI, Nubeel 4 Pinfold Court, Station Road, Barnby Dun, Doncaster DN2 5EQ — MB BS 1989 Newc.; MRCP (UK) 1993. Regist. (Gen. Med.) Doncaster.

QURESHI, Mr Rashid The Clementine Churchill Hospital, Sudbury Hill, Harrow HA1 3RX Tel: 020 8872 3872; Cessnock, Courtland Avenue, Mill Hill, London NW7 3BG Tel: 020 8906 3049 — MB BS 1964 Karachi; FRCS Eng. 1970. Cons. BrE. Surg. BrE. Unit Edgware & Barnet Gen. Hosps.; Sen. Lect. Middlx. & UCH. Lond.; Surg. Tutor RCS Eng.; Lead Surg. N.Lond BrE. Cancer Screening Unit. Socs: Fell. Roy. Soc. Med.; Brit. Assn. Surg. Oncol (Regional Co-ordinator BrE. Gp.); Assn. of Surg. of GB & Irel. Prev: Hon. Sen. Lect. Guy's Hosp. Lond.; Sen. Regist. BrE. Unit Guy's Hosp. Lond.

QURESHI, Ruby Nazar Medical Practice, 153 Copenhagen Street, London N1 0SR Tel: 020 7833 4981 Fax: 020 7837 2197; 38 Aylmer Road, London N2 0BX Tel: 020 8348 8642 — MB BS 1956 Punjab; MB BS Punjab Pakistan 1956; DA Eng. 1964 DGO Dub. 1962; DObst RCPI 1962. (F.J. Med. Coll. Lahore) GP Lond.

QURESHI, Saghir Ahmed Staff Grade Ophthalmologist, Staff Village, Royal Preston Hospital, Sharoe Green Lane, Preston PR2 9QF — MB BS 1965 Sind.

QURESHI, Sajid Ali 53 Muirhead Gardens, Perth PH1 1JR — MB BS 1979 Punjab, Pakistan; LMSSA Lond. 1985; FFARCSI 1992. (King Edwards Medical College Lahore, Pakistan) Cons. Anaesth. King Fahd Milit. Med. Complex Dhahran, Saudi-Arabia; Cons. Intensivist, Dewsbury & Dist. Hosp. Prev: Sen. Regist. (Anaesth.) Riyadh Milit. Hosp. Riyadh, Saudi Arabia; Regist. (Anaesth.) Roy. Free Hosp. Hampstead Lond.

QURESHI, Sardar Mohammad, MBE Sherwood Rise Surgery, 31 Nottingham Road, Sherwood, Nottingham NG7 7AD Tel: 0115 962 3080 Fax: 0115 985 6522; 27 Lucknow Drive, Mapperley Park, Nottingham NG3 5EU Tel: 0115 962 5706 Fax: 0115 962 5706 — MB BS 1965 Karachi; Dip. Ven. Liverp. 1969; DTM & H Liverp. 1968. (Dow Med. Coll.) GP Nottm.; Edr. Medicos. Socs: Chairm. DADA; Dir. AAAP UK. Prev: Clin. Asst. Univ. Nottm. Med. Sch. Venereol. Dept. (Genitourin. Med.) City Hosp. Nottm.

QURESHI, Shabbeer Ahmad Somerset Medical Centre, 64 Somerset Road, Southall UB1 2TS Tel: 020 8578 1903 Fax: 020 8578 0292; 113 Sudbury Court Drive, Harrow HA1 3SS Tel: 020 8922 6282 — BSc Punjab 1965, MB BS 1972; Cert. Av. Med. 1988; DLO Eng. 1979. (Nishtar Medical College Pakistan) Indep. Med. Pract. Lond. Prev: Regist. (ENT Surg.) Highlands Hosp. Lond.; Assoc. Specialist ENT Ealing Hosp. Middlx.

QURESHI, Shahida Munir Nelson Road Surgery, 126 Nelson Road, Gillingham ME7 4LL Tel: 01634 571740 Fax: 01634 575024; 3 Bellwood Court, St Mary Hoo, Rochester ME3 8RT Tel: 01634 271425 — MB BS 1964 Punjab; MB BS Punjab (Pakistan) 1964. (Nishtar Med. Coll. Multan & Fatima Jinnah Med. Coll. Lahore)

QURESHI, Shakeel Ahmed Department of Paediatric Cardiology, Guy's Hospital, 11th Floor Guy's Tower, St Thomas St., London SE1 9RT Tel: 020 7955 4616 Fax: 020 7955 4614 Email: s.a.qureshi@umds.ac.uk; 41 Beechwood Gardens, Clayhall, Ilford IG5 0AE Tel: 020 8252 0269 — MB ChB 1976 Manch.; FRCPCH 1997; FRCP Lond. 1995; MRCP (UK) 1979. Cons. Paediat. Cardiol. Guy's Hosp. Lond. Socs: Brit. Paediat. Cardiac Soc.; Assn. Europ. Paediat. Cardiol.; Roy. Coll. Paediat. and Child Health. Prev: Cons.

QURESHI

Paediat. Cardiol. & Sen. Regist. Roy. Liverp. Childr. Hosp.; Regist. (Cardiol.) Harefield Hosp. Harefield.

QURESHI, Shameem 3 Blackthorne Close, Solihull B91 1PF Tel: 0121 356 7310 — MD 1961 Osmania; MB BS 1955; DObst RCOG 1973. (Osmania Med. Coll. Hyderabad)

***QURESHI, Shazia** 157 Norval Road, Wembley HA0 3SX — BM 1997 Soton.

QURESHI, Siddiqua 4 Wheat Knoll, Hayes Lane, Kenley CR8 5JT — MB BS 1964 Karachi.

QURESHI, Sumbal 25 Firecrest Road, Chelmsford CM2 9SN — MB ChB Birm. 1995; MRCP Lond. 1998.

QURESHI, Tahseen Iftikhar 76 Byrefield Road, Guildford GU2 9UA — MB BS 1992 Lond.

QURESHI, Tariq Mahmud Flat 19, Frans Hals Court, 87 Amsterdam Road, London E14 3UX — MB BS 1995 Lond.

***QURESHI, Tipo Riaz** 1 Howard Place, St Andrews KY16 9HL — MB BS 1996 Lond.

QURESHI, Zafar Ahmad Arthur Street Health Centre, Arthur Street, Brierfield, Nelson BB9 5SN Tel: 01282 615175; 35 Fairfield Drive, Burnley BB10 2PU — MB BS 1962 Karachi; DCH Eng. 1967. (Dow Med. Coll. Karachi) Socs: BMA. Prev: Regist. (Gen. Med.) Altrincham Gen. Hosp.; Regist. (Paediat.) Childr. Hosp. Nottm.; SHO (Gen. Med.) Roy. Hosp. Sheff.

QURESHI, Zarrin The Garden Hospital, 46-50 Sunny Gdns. Road, London NW4 1RX Tel: 020 8457 4500; Cessnock, Courtlands Avenue, Mill Hill, London NW7 3BG Tel: 020 8906 1881 — MB BS 1964 Karachi; BSc Karachi 1960; FFA RCS Eng. 1971; DA Eng. 1969. Cons. Anaesth. Barnet & Edgware Gen. Hosps. Socs: Roy. Soc. Med.; Assn. Anaesth. Prev: Regist. (Anaesth.) Greenwich Dist. Hosp. Lond.

RAABE, Hans-Christian Emergency Department, Derbyshire Royal Infirmary, London Road, Derby DE1 2QY — State Exam Med 1992 Heidelberg; MD Heidelburg 1993.

RAAFAT, Faro The Children's Hospital, Steelhouse Lane, Birmingham B4 6NH Tel: 0121 333 9836 Fax: 0121 333 9831 — MD Geneva 1968; MRCPath 1983. Cons. Histopath. Birm. Childr.s Hosp.; Hon. Sen. Lect. Birm. Univ. Socs: RCPath; Brit. Paediat. Assn.; Paediat. Path. Soc. Prev: Lect. Histopath. Gt. Ormond St. Lond.

RAAFAT, Laura 11 Ferndale Cl, Hagley, Stourbridge DY9 0QA — MB ChB 1997 Birm.

RAASHED, Muhammad Llandough Hospital, Penarth CF64 2XX — MB BS 1986 Punjab; MRCP (UK) 1994.

RABAN, John Salisbury (retired) Woodcock Cottage, Woolhampton, Reading RG7 5QG Tel: 0118 971 3374 Fax: 0118 971 3374 — MB BS Lond. 1955; DObst RCOG 1959. Prev: Ho. Surg. Bedford Gen. Hosp. & Mill Rd. Matern. Hosp. Camb.

RABAN-WILLIAMS, Adrian (retired) Brook Farm, Bayham Road, Tunbridge Wells TN3 9BP Tel: 01892 529287 — MRCS Eng. LRCP Lond. 1951. JP. Prev: ENT Specialist HMHS Maine.

RABB, Leigh Michael Heartlands Hospital NHS Trust, Birmingham B9 5SS Tel: 0121 424 2685 — MB BS 1975 Lond.; MD 1986; MRCP (UK) 1978. (Community Paediat.) N.ern Birm.

RABBANI, Abu Adib Mohamed Zille 54 Hallam Road, Rotherham S60 3DA — MB BS 1965 Bihar; DPM Eng. 1981. (Darbhanga Med. Coll.) Assc. Specialist (Psychogeriat.) Rotherham Dist. Gen. Hosp. Prev: Clin. Asst. (Psychiat.) Rotherham Dist. Gen. Hosp.; Regist. (Psychiat.) Hartwood Hosp. Shotts.

RABBETT, Helen Louise Moorside Hall, Wyresdale Road, Lancaster LA1 3DY — MB ChB 1994 Manch.

RABBIN, David Cecil 55 Somerset Road, Wimbledon, London SW19 5HT — MB BS 1949 Lond.; MRCS Eng. LRCP Lond. 1949. (Middlx.) Temple Frere Obst. Prize, Middlx. Hosp. Prev: Flight Lt. RAF Med. Br.; Ho. Phys. St. Stephen's & Gordon (W.m.) Hosps.

RABBITT, Caroline Jayne Groby Road Medical Centre, 9 Groby Road, Leicester LE3 9ED Tel: 0116 253 8185 — MB ChB 1984 Leic. Prev: Trainee GP Huntingdon HA VTS.

RABBS, Jonathan Mark 20 Colbourne Road, Hove BN3 1TB — MB ChB 1989 Birm.

RABETT, Robert John (retired) Parfitt House, 8 Hovells Lane, Northwold, Thetford IP26 5NA Tel: 01366 727050 — MRCS Eng. LRCP Lond. 1945; MFOM RCP Lond. 1978; DObst RCOG 1950. Prev: Med. Dir. Occupat. Health Centre Char. Cross. Hosp. NW Thames HA.

RABEY, Graham Peter 14 Auckland Road, Cambridge CB5 8DW — PhD Manch. 1983; MB BS Lond. 1961; MRCS Eng. LRCP Lond. 1961; BDS Sydney 1955; FRACDS 1966. (Lond. Hosp.) Cons. Clin. MorphAnal. Stoke Mandeville Hosp. Aylesbury. Socs: (Ex-Pres.) Craniofacial Soc. Prev: Vis. Prof. Plastic Surg. (Research) Univ. Pittsburgh, USA; Sen. Lect. (Anat.) Univ. Manch.; Lect. Human Morphol. Centre for MorphAnal. Dept. Human Morphol. Univ. Soton.

RABEY, Peter George Department of Anaesth., University Hospital Of Leicester, Leicester General Hospital, Gwerdoler Road, Leicester LE4 5PW Tel: 01664 258 4661 — MB ChB 1984 Aberd.; FRCA 1991. Cons. Anaesth. Leicester Gen. Hosp.

RABIE, Sabah Merzi Mahmoud Kidsgrove Medical Centre, Mount Road, Kidsgrove, Stoke-on-Trent ST7 4AY Tel: 01782 784221 Fax: 01782 781703 — MB ChB 1972 Alexandria; MB ChB 1972 Alexandria.

RABIN, Neil Keith 17 Widecombe Way, London N2 0HJ — MB BS 1996 Lond.

RABINDRA, Buwaneswary 14 Waverely Avenue, Sutton SM1 4JY — MB BS 1975 Ceylon; MRCS Eng. LRCP 1986; DO RCS Eng. 1983.

RABINDRA-ANANDH, Ketheeswary Petersfield Surgery, 70 Petersfield Avenue, Harold Hill, Romford RM3 9PD Tel: 01708 343113 Fax: 01708 384672; 71 Camlet Way, Hadley Wood, Barnet EN4 0NL Tel: 020 8449 4348 — MB BS 1978 Sri Lanka; MRCP (UK) 1985; LMSSA Lond. 1985; DMedRehab RCP Lond. 1987. Prev: Regist. (Geriat. Med.) Char. Cross Hosp. Lond.; Regist. (Gen. Med.) Highlands Hosp. Lond.; SHO (Med. & Geriat.) OldCh. Hosp. Romford & St. Geo. Hosp. Lond. HornCh.

RABINOWICZ, Nathan David Health Centre, Durrow, Portlaoise, County Laois, Republic of Ireland; 31 Sherwood Road, London NW4 1AE — MB BChir 1985 Camb.; MRCGP 1991; DCH RCP Lond. 1990; DRCOG 1987. Prev: Trainee GP/SHO (Paediat.) Hillingdon Hosp. VTS; SHO (Geriat.) Manor Pk. Hosp.; SHO (Obst. & Gyn., Accid. & Emerg. & Orthop.) Roy. Sussex Co. Hosp.

RABSON, Doreen 7 Village Close, Belsize Lane, London NW3 5AH — MB BS 1956 Lond.; MRCS Eng. LRCP Lond. 1956; DCH Eng. 1959. (Westm.) Sessional Med. Off. BUPA & DSS. Socs: Brit. Paediat. Assn.; Fac. Comm. Health. Prev: Med. Adviser Dr. Barnardo's; Med. Adviser BUPA Childr. Assessm. Unit Lond.; Princip. Phys. (Child Health) S. Camden Dist. Bloomsbury HA.

RABUSZKO, Julian Paul 31 Sussex Garden, East Dean, Eastbourne BN20 0JF Tel: 01323 422466 — MB BS 1989 Lond.; DRCOG 1996. (St. Georges Hosp. Med. Sch.) Prev: VTS E.bourne 1993-1996.

RABY, Adrian Mark 34 Riffel Road, London NW2 4PH — MB BS 1993 Lond.

RABY, Christine Leahurst, Walton Hospital, Chesterfield S40 3HN Tel: 01246 277271; 18 Newbold Avenue, Chesterfield S41 7AR — MB ChB 1976 Sheff. Clin. Asst. (Psychogeriat.) Walton Hosp. Chesterfield.

RABY, James Roger (retired) 90 Station Road, Scholar Green, Stoke-on-Trent ST7 3JW Tel: 01782 783905 — MB ChB 1952 Manch.; DObst RCOG 1956. Prev: Ho. Off. N. Staffs. Roy. Infirm. & Glenroyd Matern. Hosp. Blackpool.

RABY, Michael Bruce The Health Clinic, Weeping Cross, Stafford ST17 0HE Tel: 01785 662505 Fax: 01785 661064; Woodgate, 66 Brocton Road, Milford, Stafford ST17 0UH Tel: 01785 661979 Email: woodgate@easicon.com — MB ChB 1950 Manch.; DObst RCOG 1956. (Manchester) Socs: Mid Slep Med. Soc.

RABY, Paul Richard Ashcombe Barton, Ashcombe, Dawlish EX7 0QE — MB ChB 1978 Birm.

RACE, (Alice) Catherine 11 Colletts Close, Corfe Castle, Wareham BH20 5HG — MB BS Lond. 1968; MRCPath 1976. Assoc. Specialist (Haemat.) Poole Hosp.

RACE, Jacqueline 6 Kennedy Place, Elgin IV30 4EL — MB ChB 1986 Aberd.

RACE, John William 86 Chelmsford Road, Brentwood CM15 8RL Tel: 01227 218389 — BSc (Hons.) Lond. 1959, MB BS 1962. (Lond. Hosp.) Socs: Past Chairm. Essex Local Med. Comm.; BMA. Prev: GP; Research Asst. Inst. Ophth. Lond.; Regist. (Venereol.) & Res. Accouch. Lond. Hosp.

RACE, Julian Hilton Hafan Wen Drug and Alcohol Treatment Unit, Watery Road, Wrexham LL13 7NQ Tel: 01978 313904 — MB ChB 1980 Liverp.; MRCS Eng. LRCP Lond. 1980; MRCPsych 1990; MRCGP 1988; Cert. Family Plann. JCC 1986; Cert. Prescribed Equiv. Exp. JCPTGP 1986. Cons. Psychiat. (Addic.) Hafa Wen, Wrexham. Prev: Sen. Regist. (Psychiat.) N. Wales Hosp. Denbigh Clwyd.; Hon. Sen. Regist., Rhondda NHS Trust; Hon. Sen. Regist., Cardiff Community Drug Serv.

RACE, Rebecca Louise The Corner House, 1 New St., Shipston-on-Stour CV36 4EJ; Manderley, 2 Bethell Road, Dairy Fields, Sneyd Green, Stoke-on-Trent ST1 6XL — BM 1996 Soton. (Southampton) Surg. Rotat. N. Staffs. Roy. Infirm. Stoke on Trent Staffs. Prev: SHO (Orthop.) N. Staffs. Roy. Infirm.; SHO (Surg.) Horton Gen. Hosp. Banbury Oxon.; SHO (Med.) Horton Gen. Hosp. Banbury Oxon.

RACHED, Sami Toufic Ferryview Health Centre, 25 John Wilson Street, Woolwich, London SE18 6PZ Tel: 020 8319 5400 Fax: 020 8319 5404 — MB ChB 1977 Ain Shams; MB BCh 1977 Ain Shams; MRCS Eng. LRCP Lond. 1981 London.

RACHMAN, Sandra Carole Fernlea Surgery, 114 High Road, London N15 6JR Tel: 020 8809 6445 Fax: 020 8800 4224 — MB ChB 1983 Bristol; DTM & H RCP Lond. 1987. Socs: BMA; MPS. Prev: GP Forest Gate; Trainee GP Islington; SHO (Gyn.) Redruth Hosp. Cornw.

RACK, Philip Horsman (retired) Rivulet Court, High Street, Pateley Bridge, Harrogate HG3 5JU Tel: 01423 712305 — MB 1958 Camb.; MB BChir Camb. 1958; MA Camb. 1957; FRCPsych 1980, M 1971; DPM Eng. 1962. Prev: Cons. Psychiat. Lynfield Mt. Hosp. & Bradford Roy. Infirm.

RACKHAM, Alison Joy 107 Chilternn Avenue, Bushey, Watford WD23 4QE — MB BS 1987 Lond.; MRCGP 1992.

RACKHAM, Jonathan Paul Caldicot Medical Group, Gray Hill Surgery, Woodstock Way, Caldicot, Newport NP26 4DB Tel: 01291 420282 Fax: 01291 425853 — MB ChB 1991 Leeds; MRCGP 1995; DRCOG 1994; DCH RCP Lond. 1995.

RACKHAM, Kenneth Thomas (retired) Pasley Road Health Centre, Pasley Road, Leicester LE2 9BU — MB ChB 1957 Bristol; DCH Eng. 1959. Prev: Med. Off. Duncan Hosp. Raxaul, Bihar.

RACKHAM, Mary Miles (retired) The Central Surgery, Oadby, Leicester LE2 5AA Tel: 0116 271 2175 — MB BS 1957 Lond.; DObst RCOG 1959. Prev: Med. Off. (Community Med.) Leicester AHA (T).

RACKHAM, Oliver James Alder Hey Childrens Hospital, Egton Road, Liverpool L12 2 AP; 68 Sefton Road, Hoole, Chester CH2 3RS Tel: 01244 346123 Email: ojrackham@talk21.com — MB BS 1994 Lond.; 1999 MRCPCH; MA Camb. 1995, BA (Hons.) 1991. (St Bartholomews Hospital) Specialist Regist. in Paediat., Mersey Deanery. Socs: RCPCH, Roy. Coll. of Paediat. and Child Health, Mem.

RACKOW, Francis Isidore (retired) 7 Chiswick Square, Burlington Lane, London W4 2QG Tel: 020 8747 5039 — MB BS Lond. 1943; MD (Distinc.) Lond. 1950; FRCP Ed. 1994, M 1959; FRCP Lond. 1976, M 1948; FRCPC 1959. Prev: Cons. Phys. St. Helier & Sutton Hosps.

RACKSTRAW, Simon Andrew 28 Old Market Square, London E2 7PQ — MB BS 1994 Lond.

RACTLIFFE, Donald Stuart (retired) Tolcarne House, The Green, Oscroft, Tarvin, Chester CH3 8NQ Tel: 01829 741204 — MB BS Lond. 1952; FRCGP 1977, M 1960; DObst RCOG 1954. Prev: SHO (O & G) N. Herts. Hosp. Hitchin.

RACZKOWSKI, Richard Matthew Marchmont Surgery, 10 Warrender Park Terrace, Edinburgh EH9 1JA — Lekarz 1981 Krakow; LEKARZ Krakow, Poland 1981.

RADATZ, Seemeen 30 Isis Avenue, Bicester OX26 2GS — MB ChB 1993 Sheff.

RADBOURNE, Barbara Mary (retired) Akrotiri, 18 Springfield, Bourton on the Water, Cheltenham GL54 2DF Tel: 01451 820475 — MB BCh Wales 1946; BSc Wales 1943; FFA RCS Eng. 1954; DA Eng. 1950. Prev: Wing Cdr. RAF Med. Br., Anaesth. Specialist.

RADCLIFFE, Mr Andrew Grieg Llandough Hospital, Cardiff & Vale NHS Trust, Penlan Road, Penarth CF64 2XX Tel: 029 2071 5416 Fax: 029 2071 5416 Email: clorectal.inct@incttr.wales.nhs.uk — MB BS 1971 Lond.; BSc (Hons.) Lond. 1968; MS Lond. 1984; FRCS Eng. 1976; MRCS Eng. LRCP Lond. 1971. (University College London) Cons. Gen. Colorectal Surg, Llandough Hosp. Penarth,

Vale of Gamorgan CF64 2XX Univ. Hosp. Of Wales; Hon. Sen. Lect Univ. of Wales Coll. of Med. Socs: Counc. Assn. Surgs.; Mem. Ct. Examr.ss Roy. Coll. Surg. Eng.; Counc. Assn. Coloproc. GB & Irel. Prev: Lect. (Surg.) St. Mary's Hosp. Med. Sch. Lond.; Regist. (Surg.) Addenbrooke's Hosp. Camb.; Research Fell. Harvard Med. Sch.

RADCLIFFE, Mr Anthony 135 Harley Street, London W1N 1DJ Tel: 020 7935 8793 — MB BCh BAO 1930 Dub.; FRCS Eng. 1938; DLO Eng. 1932. (T.C. Dub.) Hon. Consg. Surg. Roy. Nat. Throat, Nose & Ear Hosp. Socs: Fell. Roy. Soc. Med. Prev: Lect. Otolaryng. Univ. Lond.; Lect. Inst. Laryng. & Otol.; Ho. Surg. W. Lond. Hosp.

RADCLIFFE, Deborah 8 East Downs Road, Cheadle Hulme, Cheadle SK8 5ES — MB ChB 1982 Liverp.

RADCLIFFE, Douglas William John (retired) Compton Lodge, Egerton Road, Kearnsey, Dover CT16 3AF Tel: 01304 822443 — MB BS 1937 Lond.; MRCS Eng. LRCP Lond. 1937; MRCGP 1963. Prev: Med. Off. Dover Harbour Bd.

RADCLIFFE, Gordon Glodwick Health Centre, Glodwick Road, Oldham OL4 1YN Tel: 0161 652 5311 — MB ChB 1961 Manch.

RADCLIFFE, Mr Graham Stuart 1 Malvern Mews, Monk Fryston, Leeds LS25 5DX Tel: 01977 680058 Email: bev&gra@wilstonradcliffe.freeserve.co.uk — BM BCh 1990 Oxf.; FRCS Eng. 1994; MA Camb. 1987. (Oxford) Specialist Regist. Yorks. Orthop. Rotat.

RADCLIFFE, Mr Grant Jeremy 135 Harley Street, London W1N 1DJ Tel: 020 7935 8827 Fax: 020 7224 0732 Email: gradcliffe@harleystreetw1.com — MB BS 1970 Lond.; FRCS Eng. 1977; MRCS Eng. LRCP Lond. 1970. (St. Bart.) p/t Cons. Otolaryngol. Roy. Free, Edgware & Barnet Hosps. Socs: Brit. Assn. Otol.; Joseph Soc.; Fell. Roy. Soc. Med. - Counc. Sect. Gargnology & Rhinology. Prev: Sen. Regist. Rotat. Char. Cross Hosp.; Chief Resid. Head & Neck Profess. Unit Toronto Gen. Hosp. Canada; Regist. Rotat. Roy. Nat. Throat Nose & Ear Hosp. Lond.

RADCLIFFE, Hilary 4 Corner Green, Blackheath, London SE3 9JJ — MB 1977 Camb.; BChir 1976; MRCGP 1981; DCH Eng. 1981; DRCOG 1980.

RADCLIFFE, Jeremy John 20 Finchley Court, Ballards Lane, London N3 1NH — MB ChB 1988 Liverp.

RADCLIFFE, John Colin Meadowlands Surgery, Newry Health Village, Monaghan Street, Newry BT35 6BW Tel: 028 3026 7534; 36 Greenan Lough Road, Newry BT34 2PX Tel: 016937 53348 — MB BCh BAO 1987 Belf.; MRCGP (Distinc.) 1991; DCH Dub. 1992; DRCOG 1989. Prev: Trainee GP Armagh Health Centre.

RADCLIFFE, Keith William Department of GU Medicine, Whittall Street Clinic, Whittall St., Birmingham B4 6DH Tel: 0121 237 5719 Fax: 0121 233 5729 Email: k.w.tadcliffe@bhan.ac.uk; 49 Wellington Road, Bromsgrove B60 2AX Email: k.w.radcliffe@bham.ac.uk — MB BS 1983 Lond.; MB BS (Hons.) Lond. 1983; MA Camb. 1984, BA (Hons.) 1980; MRCP (UK) 1987; DFFP 1993; FRCP 1997. (Kings) Cons. Genitourin. Med. S. Birm. Community Health NHS Trust; Hon. Cons. Univ. Hosp. Birm. NHS Trust; Hon. Sen. Lect. (Genitourin. Med.) Univ. Birm. Socs: Internat. Union Against VD & Treponematoses; Med. Soc. Study VD; Assn. Genitourin. Med. Prev: Sen. Regist. (Genitourin. Med.) Char. Cross Hosp. Lond.; Regist. (Genitourin. Med.) Middlx. Hosp. Lond.

RADCLIFFE, Marion Elaine Davenal House Surgery, 28 Birmingham Road, Bromsgrove B61 0DD Tel: 01527 872008; 49 Wellington Road, Bromsgrove B60 2AX — BM BS 1985 Nottm.; BMedSci Nottm. 1983; MRCGP 1989; DRCOG 1989. Tutor (Gen. Pract.) BromsGr.

RADCLIFFE, Mark Harry 49 Poleacre Lane, Woodley, Stockport SK6 1PH — MB ChB 1988 Sheff.

RADCLIFFE, Michael John Sarum Road Hospital, Sarum Road, Winchester SO22 5HA Tel: 01962 826148 Fax: 023 8067 1677 Email: michael@radcliffe.net; 1 Leigh Road, Highfield, Southampton SO17 1EF Email: michael@radcliffe.net — MB ChB 1968 Birm.; MRCGP 1976. (Birmingham) p/t Con. Clin. Allergist.Roy. Free Hampstead NHS Trust; Hon. Clin. Research Fell., Div. of Infec. Inflammation and repair, Sch. of Med., Univ. S.ampton. Socs: Fell. Amer. Acad. Environm. Med.; Brit. Soc. Allergy & Clin. Immunol.

RADCLIFFE, Shirley Anne 10 Norland Square, London W11 4PX Tel: 020 7727 5501 — MB BS 1979 Lond.; LLB (Hons.) 1996; MRCGP 1984. (Char. Cross) Socs: Medico-Legal Soc. Prev: GP 1984-1994 Lond.

RADCLIFFE

*RADCLIFFE, **Mr Simon Neil** 40 Brockholme Road, Liverpool L18 4QQ — MB ChB 1986 Liverp.; FRCS Ed. 1991.

RADCLYFFE, Vivian Gerald 77/9 Falmouth Road, Southwark, London.SE1 4JW Tel: 020 7407 4101; 116 Wimbledon Hill Road, Wimbledon, London SW19 7QU Tel: 020 8946 6670 — MB BS 1948 Lond.; MRCGP 1965. (Middlx.) Hon. Maj. RAMC.

RADEMAKER, Johan Willem Ringlettes Farm, Whatlington Road, Battle TN33 0NA Tel: 01424 774349 — MB BCh BAO 1983 NUI; LRCPI & LM, LRCSI & LM 1983; MRCP (UK) 1987. Cons. Phys. Gastroenterol. Conquest Hosp. The Ridge, St Leonards on Sea, E. Sussex. Socs: Nutrit. Soc.; Brit. Soc. Gastroenterol. Prev: Sen. Regist. (Med. Gastroenterol.) Roy. United Hosp. Bath; Regist. (Gen. Med & Gastroenterol.) Qu. Alexandra Hosp. Portsmouth & Soton Gen. Hosp.; Research Fell. McMaster Univ. Hamilton, Canada.

RADEMAKER, Linda c/o Rademaker, 50 Lake Crescent, Hamilton, New Zealand; Overhall, Sandford, Strathaven ML10 6PL — MB ChB 1980 Ed.; BSc MedSci Ed. 1977; MRCGP 1984; DRCOG 1983. Clin. Asst. (Geriat. Med.) St. John's Hosp. at Howden.

RADEMEYER, Ivan Keith c/o Dr Peter Evans, 25 Blandy Road, Henley-on-Thames RG9 1QB — MB ChB 1975 Pretoria.

RADERSCHADT, Emma Louise Les Lohiers, La Grande Lande, St Saviours, Guernsey GY7 9YZ — MB BS 1996 Lond.; BSc (Hons.) Lond. 1993. (King's College School of Medicine & Dentistry London) Socs: BMA. Prev: Pre-regist. Ho. Off. (Surg.) Conquest Hosp. St. Leonards-on-Sea; Pre-regist. Ho. Off. (Med.) Warwick Hosp.

RADFORD, Allan Philip (retired) Crossways Cottage, West Bagborough, Taunton TA4 3EG Tel: 01823 432526 — MB ChB 1944 Bristol; DCH Eng. 1948. Prev: Capt. RAMC.

RADFORD, Anne Mary 1 Tanyfron Street, Llanllechid, Bangor LL57 3HL; 1 Tanyford Street, Llanllechid, Bangor LL57 3HL — MB BS 1984 Lond.; BSc Lond. 1981; DRCOG 1989.

RADFORD, Bryan James (retired) Health Centre, Broadfield, Crawley Tel: 01293 531951 — MB BS 1961 Lond.; BSc Lond. 1958; MRCS Eng. LRCP Lond. 1961; DObst RCOG 1964. Prev: Ho. Phys. & Cas. Off. (Surgic.) St. Geo. Hosp. Lond.

*RADFORD, **Dominic Herwin** 123 Alresford Road, Winchester SO23 0JZ — MB ChB 1996 Birm.; ChB Birm. 1996.

RADFORD, Ian Stanley The Upper Surgery, 27 Lemon Street, Truro TR1 2LS Tel: 01872 74931 Fax: 01872 260339; Kernou Veor, Greenbottom, Truro TR4 8QH — MB BS 1978 Lond.; DRCOG 1981. (St. Thos.)

RADFORD, Professor John Anthony CRC Department of Medical Oncology, Christie Hospital NHS Trust, Wilmslow Road, Manchester M20 4BX Tel: 0161 446 3753 Fax: 0161 446 3299 — MB ChB 1978 Sheff.; MD Sheff. 1993; MRCP (UK) 1982; FRCP 1998. (Sheff.) Prof. of Med. Oncol., Christie Hosp. NHS Trust Manch. Prev: Gordon Hamilton Fairley Fell. (Med. Oncol.) Christie Hosp. Manch.; Leukaemia Research Fund Fell. (Med. Oncol.) Christie Hosp. Manch.; Imperial Cancer Research Fund Fell. (Med. Oncol.) Guy's Hosp.Lond.

RADFORD, John Michael Chantrell 459 Whirlowdale Road, Sheffield S11 9NG — MB ChB 1980 Sheff.; MRCGP 1986; DRCOG 1985.

RADFORD, Martin Wootton House, The Crescent, Romsey SO51 7NG Tel: 01794 515220 — MRCS Eng. LRCP Lond. 1966; MD Lond. 1977, MB BS 1966; MRACP 1971; FRCP (UK) 1982, M 1971. (Univ. Coll. Hosp.) Sen. Lect. Dept. Child Health Soton. Gen. Hosp.

RADFORD, Michael James 20 West End Gardens, Esher KT10 8LD; 4 The Green, Horspath, Oxford OX33 1RP Tel: 01865 876432 — MB BS 1992 Lond.; FRCS (Ed). (Charing Cross & Westminster) Specialist Regist., Orthop. Rotat., Oxf. Socs: BOA; BOTA.

RADFORD, Nicola Margaret 4 Woodcote Green, Wallington SM6 9NN — MB ChB 1998 Bristol.

RADFORD, Patrick Department of Anaesthesia, St. Helier Hospital, Wrythe Lane, Carshalton SM5 1AA Tel: 020 8296 2444 Fax: 020 8296 2951 Email: spinder@sthelier.sghms.ac.uk; 4 Woodcote Green, Wallington SM6 9NN Tel: 020 8669 3472 Email: patrick@woodcote.free-online.co.uk — MB BS 1969 Lond.; FRCA 1975; DA Eng. 1971. (Univ. Coll. Hosp.) Cons. Anaesth. Epsom and St Helier NHS Trust; Sen. Lect. (Anaesth.) St. Geo. Hosp. Med. Sch.; Instruc. for ATLS, ALS and PALS. Socs: BMA; Assn. Paediat. Anaesth.; Obst. Anaesth. Assn.. Prev: Sen. Regist. (Anaesth.) St. Geo. Hosp. Lond. & Hosp. Sick Childr. Gt. Ormond St. Lond.

RADFORD, Mr Philip John Department of Trauma & Orthopaedics, University Hospital, Queen's Medical Centre, Nottingham NG7 2UH Tel: 0115 924 9924 Fax: 0115 919 4468 Email: pjradford@doctors.org.uk — BM BCh 1983 Oxf.; MA Camb. 1984, BA 1980; FRCS (Orth.) 1993; FRCS Eng. 1988. (Oxford) Cons. Orthop. Surg. Univ. Hosp. Qu. Med. Centre Nottm. Cons. Trauma & Orthopaedic Surg., Uni Hosp., Qu.s Med. Centre, Notts. Socs: Brit. Trauma Soc., Mem.; Skeletal Dyspasia Soc., Mem.; Brit. Med. Assn. Prev: Sen. Regist. & Regist. (Orthop.) Harlow Wood Hosp. & Nottm. Univ. Hosp.; Regist. (Surg.) Addenbrooke's Hosp. Camb.

RADFORD, Rafe The Coach House, Wren Park, Hitchin Road, Shefford SG17 5JD — BM 1984 Soton.

RADFORD, Raymond 43 Victoria Park Avenue, Leyland, Preston PR25 1UG — MB ChB 1990 Manch.

RADFORD, Raymond, CBE 3 Lakeside, Lee-on-the-Solent PO13 9AP Tel: 023 9255 1060 — MB BS 1955 Lond.; BSc (Physiol.) Lond. 1952; FFA RCS Eng. 1968; DA Eng. 1966. (Univ. Coll. Hosp.) Cons. Anaesth. Roy. Hosp. Haslar Gosport. Prev: Surg. Commodore RN; Med. Off. i/c & Cons. Anaesth. RN Hosp. Haslar; Hon. Surg. HM Qu..

RADFORD, Miss Rita Christine A & E Department, Bromley Hospital, Cromwell Avenue, Bromley BR2 9AJ Tel: 020 8289 7000 — MB BS 1967 Lond.; FRCS Eng. 1972; MRCS Eng. LRCP Lond. 1967. (Guy's) Cons. in A & E Bromley Hosp. Prev: Surg. Regist. Guy's Hosp. Lond.; Res. Surg. Off. Bolingbroke Hosp. Lond.; SHO (A & E) FarnBoro. Hosp., Kent.

RADFORD, Rosemary Jane Emily 4 Westfield, Loughton IG10 4EB Tel: 020 8502 1156 — MB ChB 1972 Manch. Med. Off. Marks & Spencers Ltd., Lond.

RADFORD, Sean Richard 14 Parry Close, Southdown, Bath BA2 1JR Tel: 01225 471374 Email: sean@bladesys.demon.co.uk — MB BS 1995 Lond. Prev: Surgic. SHO, Greenwich Dist. Hosp.

RADHA, Ramamoorthy Leighton Hospital, Crewe CW1 4QJ — MB BS 1982 Madras; MRCP (UK) 1992.

RADHA KRISHNA, Lalit Kumar Flat 201, Minster Court, Liverpool L7 3QH — MB ChB 1995 Liverp.

RADHAKRISHNA, Ganesh 69 Brampton Drive, Liverpool L8 7SU — MB ChB 1998 Liverp.; MB ChB Liverp 1998.

RADHAKRISHNAN, Gopi Rampton Hospital, Retford DN22 0PD; Mount Pleasant, Alltwen, Pontardawe, Swansea SA8 3AH — MB BS 1979 Poona; MRCPsych 1988. Lect. Dept. Psychol. Med. (Ment. Handicap) Univ. Wales Coll. of Med. Ely Hosp. Cardiff. Prev: Regist. (Psych.) Hensol Hosp. Pontyclun; Regist. (Psych.) St. Edwd.s Hosp. Leek.

RADHAKRISHNAN, Mr Subbiah 27 Streatfield Road, Kenton, Harrow HA3 9BP Tel: 020 8907 0038 — MB BS 1984 Madras; BSc Madras 1977, MB BS 1984; FRCSI 1990.

RADHAKRISHNAN, Suganthamala St Georges Avenue, 21 St Georges Avenue, Southall UB1 1PZ Tel: 020 8813 8122 — LRCP LRCS 1978 Ed.; LRCP LRCS Ed. LRCPS Glas. 1978.

RADHAKRISHNAN, Thambiah The Hamilton Practice, Keats House, Bush Fair, Harlow CM18 6LY Tel: 01279 692700 Fax: 01279 692719; 4 Arrow Head House, Hertfordshire & Essex Hospital, Haymeade Lane, Bishop's Stortford CM23 6NS — MB BS 1981 Sri Lanka; MRCS Eng. LRCP Lond. 1988; MRCGP 1992; T(GP) 1992; DLO RCS Eng. 1990. Prev: Trainee GP Bolton; SHO (Plastic Surg., ENT & O & G) Manch.

RADIA, Deepti Himantlal Ranchhoddas 130 Harrowdene Road, Wembley HA0 2JF — MB BS 1992 Lond.

RADIA, Krishnakant The Surgery, 21 Beaconsfield Road, Hastings TN34 3TW Tel: 01424 422389 Fax: 01424 431500; Kebuca, Winchelsea Road, Guestling, Hastings TN35 4LW — MRCS Eng. LRCP Lond. 1977; MBA 2000 (Strategic Health Management)(Univ. of Kent); MRCGP 1981; DRCOG 1979.

RADIX, Joan Cecelia Agatha 41 Grosvenor Court, London E10 6RH — MB BCh BAO 1968 NUI.

RADLEY, David James Malvern Health Centre, Victoria Park Road, Malvern Link, Malvern WR14 2JY Tel: 01684 612703 Fax: 01684 612779 — MB BS 1976 Lond.; MRCGP 1980; DRCOG 1980. Prev: GP Trainee Bath VTS; Ho. Surg. St. Bart. Hosp. Lond.; Ho. Phys. St. Richard's Hosp. Chichester.

RADLEY, Hazel Mary 67 Stumperlowe Crescent Road, Sheffield S10 3PR — MRCS Eng. LRCP Lond. 1959; MB Camb. 1960, BChir 1959.

RADLEY, Jacqueline Rita St. John's House, 28 Bromyard Road, Worcester WR2 5BU; 5 Lansdowne Court, Worcester WR3 8JE Tel: 01905 53989 — BSc Lond. 1986, MB BS 1988; DCH RCP Lond. 1992. Socs: BMA. Prev: Trainee GP Worcester; SHO (Paediat. & O & G) Worcester & Dist. HA.

RADLEY, Mr Simon 43 Malbet Park, Edinburgh EH16 6WB — MB ChB 1985 Birm.; FRCS Eng. 1989. Clin. Research Fell. Univ. Birm. Qu. Eliz. Hosp. Prev: SHO (Surg.) Worcester Roy. Infirm.; Lect. (Anat.) Univ. Birm.; Ho. Off. Selly Oak & Dudley Rd. Hosps. Birm.

RADLEY, Mr Stephen Christopher 21 Brighton Terrace Road, Crookes, Sheffield S10 1NT Tel: 0114 266 0445 — MB BS 1987 Lond.; FRCS Ed. 1991; MRCOG 1993. Sen. Regist. (O & G) Jessop Hosp. Wom. Sheff. Prev: Lect. (Urol.) N.. Gen. Hosp. Sheff.; Regist. (O & G) Rotherham & N.. Gen. Hosps. Sheff.; SHO (O & G) Jessop & N.. Gen. Hosps. Sheff.

RADLEY, William Henry (retired) 96 Barnfield Wood Road, Park Langley, Beckenham BR3 6SX Tel: 020 8658 9398 Fax: 020 8658 9398 — MB BCh BAO 1949 NUI; MB BCh BAO (1st Pl. & 1st Cl. Hnrs.) NUI 1949. Prev: Med. Asst. Profess. Unit NUI.

RADLEY SMITH, Rosemary Claire Harefield Hospital, Harefield UB9 6JH; Old Vicarage, Langrish, Petersfield GU32 1QY — MB BS 1963 Lond.; FRCP Lond. 1980, M 1968; FRACP 1976; MRCS Eng. LRCP Lond. 1963; FRCPCH 1997. (Roy. Free) Cons. (Paediat. Cardiol.) Roy. Brompton & Harefield Hosp. Gt. Ormond St. Hosp.; Hon. Cons. Roy. Free Hosp. Socs: Brit. Cardiac Soc. & Assn. Europ. Paediat. Cardiols.; Roy. Soc. Med. Prev: Ho. Phys. Roy. Free & Brompton Hosps. Lond.; Med. Regist. Roy. Melb. Hosp. Australia.

RADOMSKI, Jerzy Waclaw Child & Family Psychiatric Service, Ashvilla, Rauceby Hospital, Sleaford NG34 8PP — Lekarz 1970 Warsaw.

RADSTONE, David John Weston Park Hospital, Whitham Road, Sheffield S10 2SJ Tel: 0114 226 5000 Fax: 0114 226 5512; 34 Riverdale Road, Sheffield S10 3FB Tel: 0114 266 1260 Fax: 0114 266 1260 Email: dradstone@aol.com — MB BS 1976 Lond.; BA (Hons.) Keele 1968; FRCR 1984; DMRT Eng. 1981. (Lond. Hosp.) Cons. Radiother. & Oncol. Sheff. HA; Hon. Clin. Lect. Univ. Sheff.; Solicitor Supreme Ct. of Judicature Eng. 1971; Examr. Roy. Coll. of Radiols. Socs: Fell. Roy. Soc. Med.; Assn. Palliat. Care & Hospice Doctors. Prev: Sen. Regist. (Radiother. Oncol.) Oxf. RHA; Regist. (Radiother. & Oncol.) & Ho. Surg. Lond. Hosp.

RADULA SCOTT, Teodor (retired) 5 Knighton Road, Leicester LE2 3HL Tel: 0116 270 6891 — MB ChB 1943 Polish Sch. of Med. Prev: Ho. Surg. Whipps Cross Hosp.

RADVAN, Johannes 558 Welford Road, Leicester LE2 6EP — BM BS 1985 Nottm.; MRCP Lond. 1988.

RADVANYI, Miklos Carnegie Institute, Hunters Road, Hockley, Birmingham B19 1DR Tel: 0121 554 9920 Fax: 0121 456 5874; The Follies, 18 Hermitage Road, Edgbaston, Birmingham B15 3UR — MB BS 1962 Durh.; Cert. Family Plann. JCC 1976. (Durh.) Prev: SHO (O & G) & Ho. Surg. & Ho. Phys. Bensham Gen. Hosp.

RADWAN, Ahmed Fawzy Mohamed Kettering & District General Hospital, Rothwell Road, Kettering NN16 8UZ Tel: 01536 492243; 10 Westway, Kettering NN15 7LE Tel: 01536 522750 — MB BCh 1955 Cairo; LMSSA Lond. 1966; FRCP Lond. 1994; FRCP Ed. 1986. (Cairo) Cons. Phys. Gen. Med. & Geriat. Oxf. RHA. Socs: BMA & Brit. Geriat. Soc. Prev: Sen. Regist. (Geriat.) Manch. RHB; Regist. (Geriat.) Ipswich & E. Suff. Hosp. Gp.

RADWAN, Raouf Radwan Mohamed Ibrahim 11 Cooden Drive, Bexhill-on-Sea TN39 3DB Tel: 01424 222932 — MB ChB 1962 Cairo; DLO RCS Eng. 1974. Assoc. Specialist (ENT) Hastings HA.

RADWAN, Tarek Ahmed Hassan Dept. of Paediatrics, The Whittington Hospital, Highgate Hill, London N19 5NF; The Rosery, 3 Ness Road, Burwell, Cambridge CB5 0AA Tel: 01638 603976 Fax: 01638 603976 — BChir 1997 Camb.; BMedSci Nottm. 1994; MB Bchir 1997; AFRCS Ed Part 1 1998; MRCP PAED Part 1 1999. (Camb. & Nottingham.) SHO Rotat. (Paediat.), Whittington Hosp. & Gt. Ormond St. Hosp., Lond. Socs: MPS; MDU; BMA. Prev: SHO Rotat. (Surg.) Leicester Roy. Infirm.

RADWAY, Cecil John (retired) 10 Cottenham Place, Wimbledon, London SW20 0NF Tel: 020 8946 7846 — BM BCh 1945 Oxf.; MA Oxf. 1945; MFCM 1974; DPH Lond. 1954. Prev: Area Specialist in Community Med. (Child Health) Surrey HA.

RADY, Mr Aly Mohamed Flat 8, Winn Court, Winn Road, Highfield, Southampton SO17 1UZ Tel: 02380 559631 — MRCS Eng. LRCP Lond. 1976; FRCS Eng. 1966; FRCSI 1965; FRCS Glas. 1964. Hon. Cons. (Gen. Surg.) Roy. S. Hants. Hosp. Soton. Prev: Chairm. Dept. Surg., Kuwait.

RADY, Neveen A Convent Garden Medical Centre, 47 Shorts Gardens, London WC2H 9AA Tel: 020 7379 7209 Fax: 020 7379 7224 — BM 1991 Soton.; BSc (Hons.) Lond. 1987; T(GP) 1996; DFFP 1993. (Univ. Soton.) Socs: Assoc. RCGP; BMA; MPS.

RAE, Alan Philip Department of Medical Cardiology, Royal Infirmary, Glasgow G31 2ER Tel: 0141 211 4000 Fax: 0141 211 1124 Email: apr3f@clinmed.gla.ac.uk; 11 Glasgow Road, Uddingston, Glasgow G71 7AU — MB ChB 1975 Glas.; BSc (Hons.) Glas. 1971, MD 1987; FRCP Glas. 1988; MRCP (UK) 1978. Cons. Cardiol. Roy. Infirm. Glas.

RAE, Alison Ruth Margaret 3F2, 12 Viewforth Terrace, Edinburgh EH10 4LH; 10 Stuart Place, Cowdenbeath KY4 9BN — MB ChB 1996 Ed.

RAE, Alistair Sutherland Livingston (retired) 1 Collingwood Place, Barnhill, Dundee DD5 2UG — MD Ed. 1951, MB ChB 1935; DPH Ed. & Glas. 1938; DPM Eng. 1948.

RAE, Allan James Health Clinic, Main Street, Lennoxtown, Glasgow G66 7DD Tel: 01360 310357 Fax: 01360 311740; Ballag'an House, Strathblane, Glasgow G63 9AE Tel: 01360 771217 — MB ChB Glas. 1962; LM Rotunda 1972. Prev: Ship's Surg. Blue Star Line; Med. Dir. Dubai Petroleum Co., Dubai; Head Med. Servs. SSC N.E. Nigeria, W. Afr.

RAE, Catherine Anne Kenilworth Medical Centre, 1 Kenilworth Court, Greenfields, Cumbernauld, Glasgow G67 1BP Tel: 01236 727816 Fax: 01236 726306 — MB ChB 1987 Aberd.; MRCGP 1991.

RAE, Colin Kennedy The Surgery, 77 John Street, Stromness KW16 3AD — MB ChB 1971 Aberd.; DA Eng. 1979. GP (Anaesth.) Balfour Hosp. Kirkwall.

RAE, Colin Peter 155 Dames Drive, Scotstown, Glasgow G14 9GD — MB ChB 1990 Glas.; FRCA Lond. 1994. Specialist Regist. (Anaesth.) W.. Infirm. Glas.

RAE, Diana Elizabeth Tonglewood, Pump Hollow Lane, Mansfield NG18 3DU; Tonglewood, Pump Hollow Lane, Mansfield NG18 3DU Email: briggella@cs.com — MBBS Lond. 1986; DRCOG Lond. 1990; FP Cert. Lond. 1990. (Charing Cross Hospital London) GP Non-Princip. Locum; Clin. Asst. (Oncol.) Kingsmill Hosp. Mansfield. Prev: Clin. Asst. (Diabetes) Doncaster Roy. Infirm.

RAE, Eleanor Ruth 33 Meiklewood Avenue, Prestwick KA9 2JR — MB ChB 1994 Glas.

RAE, Fiona Campbell 14 Eastern Road, Willaston, Nantwich CW5 7HT — BM 1991 Soton.

RAE, George Beaumont Park Surgery, 35 Hepscott Drive, Beaumont Park, Whitley Bay NE25 9XJ Tel: 0191 251 4548 — MB ChB 1971 Ed.; BSc 1968. Gen. Med. Servs. Comm. (N.ern Region) N. Tyneside; Sec. Local Med. Comm.

RAE, George Buik Lochee Health Centre, 1 Marshall St., Lochee, Dundee DD2 3BR Tel: 01382 611283 — MB ChB 1957 St. And.

RAE, Hazel Heather 70 Findhorn Place (2FL), The Grange, Edinburgh EH9 2NW — MB ChB 1994 Ed.

RAE, Helen Elizabeth 66 Parkside Drive, Watford WD17 3AX Tel: 01923 241601 — MB BS 1989 Lond.; MRCGP 1994. (St. Georges Hosp. Med. Sch.)

RAE, Ian Frank Squire Kintail, Chestnut Hill, Keswick CA12 4LR Tel: 017687 73657 — MB BS 1953 Lond. Prev: Ho. Phys. & Ho. Surg. Vict. Hosp. Blackpool.

RAE, Isobel Watson (retired) 55 Hamilton Drive, Elgin IV30 4NL Tel: 01343 542210 — M.B., Ch.B. Aberd. 1944. Prev: Asst. Med. Off. Qu. Mary's Hosp. Childr. Carshalton, Gr. (Fev.).

RAE, James Wright (retired) Screel House, Auchencairn, Castle Doveras DE73 1QL Tel: 01556 640220 — MD 1947 Ed.; MD (Commend.) Ed. 1947, MB ChB 1936; FRCP Ed. 1952, M 1947. Prev: Hon. Cons. (Neurol.) Bradford HA.

RAE, Jaqueline Louise 10 Wirral Gardens, Wirral CH63 3BQ — MB ChB 1995 Sheff.

RAE

RAE, Mr Paul Jonathan Braeside, Markland Hill, Bolton BL1 5AL — MB ChB 1980 Manch.; FRCS Eng. 1984. Sen. Regist. (Orthop.) NW. Region. HA.

RAE, Peter Gordon (retired) 3 The Rowans, Ormskirk L39 6TD Tel: 01695 423518 — MB ChB 1958 Liverp.; FRCOG 1981, M 1968, DObst. 1960. Prev: Dir. Med. Manpower Plann. Mersey RHA.

RAE, Mr Peter Scott 26 Craigstewart Crescent, Doonbank, Ayr KA7 4DB — MB ChB 1972 Glas.; FRCS Glas. 1977. Cons. Orthop. Surg. Ayrsh. & Arran Health Bd. Socs: Fell. Brit. Orthop. Assn.; Assoc. Brit. Soc. Surg. of Hand.

RAE, Peter William Hamley Department of Clinical Biochemistry, Western General Hospital, Crewe Road, Edinburgh EH4 2XU Tel: 0131 537 1890 Fax: 0131 537 1023 — MB ChB 1984 Ed.; BA Oxf. 1976; PhD Ed. 1979; MRCP (UK) 1987; MRCPath 1994; FRCP Ed. 1999. Cons. Clin. Biochem. W.. Gen. Hosp. Edin.; Hon. Sen. Lect. Univ. Edin.

RAE, Robert MCalpine Campbeltown Health Centre, Stewart Road, Campbeltown PA28 6AT Tel: 01586 552105 Fax: 01586 554997 — MB ChB 1980 Glas.

RAE, Ruth 155 Danes Drive, Scotstoun, Glasgow G14 9GD — MB ChB 1990 Glas.; FRCA 1994. (Glas.) Career Regist. (Anaesth.) Glas. Roy. Infirm. Socs: Assn. Anaesth.; BMA; Scot. Soc. Anaesths. Prev: SHO (Anaesth.) W.. Infirm. & Stobhill Hosp. Glas.; SHO (Geriat.) Lightburn Hosp. Glas.

RAE, Sarah Alison Bedford Hospital, Bedford MK42 9DL Tel: 01234 792259 Fax: 01234 792260; 12 Chaucer Road, Bedford MK40 2AJ Tel: 01234 217977 — MB BS Lond. 1975; MRCP (UK) 1978; MRCS Eng. LRCP Lond. 1975. Cons. & Sen. Lect. Rehabil. Med. & Rheum. Roy. Devon & Exeter Hosp. Prev: Sen. Regist. Rotat. (Gen. Med. & Geriat.) Roy. Devon & Exeter Hosp.; Regist. & Sen. Regist. (Rheum.) Kings Coll. Hosp. Lond.

RAE, Stewart (retired) Craiginch, Tidmarsh Village, Reading RG8 8ER Tel: 0118 984 2998 — MB ChB Ed. 1944; FRCP Ed. 1968, M 1949; FFCM 1976, M 1974. Prev: Med. Adviser Nat. Radiol. Protec. Bd. Harwell.

RAE, Susan Jane Postern Gate Surgery, Cinque Port St., Rye TN31 7AP Tel: 01797 223333 Fax: 01797 227464; The Coach House, Flackley Ash, Peasmarsh, Rye TN31 6YH — MB ChB 1982 Ed.

RAE, Susan Marjorie 13 Newmills Crescent, Balerno EH14 5SX — MB ChB 1989 Ed.

RAEBURN, Andrew Lindsay 49 Hellath Wen, Nantwich CW5 7BB — MB ChB 1977 Glas.; MRCGP 1981; DRCOG 1980.

RAEBURN, Henry Brian (retired) 12 Willow Court, Pool in Wharefdale, Otley LS21 1RX Tel: 0113 284 2948 — MB BS Lond. 1958; MRCS Eng. LRCP Lond. 1958; MRCGP 1968. Prev: Med. Off. DHSS Leeds.

RAEBURN, Janine Ruth Flat 1, Palm Court, 11-13 Fellows Road, Chalk Farm, London NW3 3LT — MB BS 1994 Lond.

RAEBURN, Joanna Nest 31A Alleyn Park, Dulwich, London SE21 8AT — BM BCh 1973 Oxf.; MA Oxf. 1973; FRCP (Lond.) 1977; MFFP 1993. (Middlx.) Assoc. Specialist (Diabetes) King's Coll. Hosp. Lond.; Sessional Clin. Med. Off. (Family Plann. & Instruc.) Lond.

RAEBURN, Professor John Alexander, TD Centre for Medical Genetics, City Hospital, Hucknall Road, Nottingham NG5 1PB Tel: 0115 962 7712 Fax: 0115 962 7711; Tighlagan, 3 Grove Farm, Lambley Road, Lowdham, Nottingham NG14 7AY Tel: 0115 966 4793 — MB ChB 1964 Ed.; PhD Ed. 1976, MB ChB 1964; FRCP Ed. 1976, M 1968. (Ed.) Prof. Clin. Genetics Univ. Nottm. Socs: Fell. Roy. Med. Soc. Edin.; Clin. Genetics Soc. Prev: Sen. Lect. (Human Genetics) Univ. Edin.; Lect. (Therap.) Univ. Edin.; Research Fell. Univ. Leiden.

RAEBURN, Rhona Margaret 101 Auchinairn Road, Glasgow G64 1NF Tel: 0141 772 1808 Fax: 0141 762 1274; 23 Kennedy Drive, Airdrie ML6 9AN — MB ChB 1977 Glas.

RAEBURN, Stewart 61 Osprey Drive, Uddingston, Glasgow G71 6HU — MB ChB 1982 Glas.

RAESIDE, David Alexander 32 Jews Walk, London SE26 6PL — MB ChB 1986 Glas.; MRCP (UK) 1992. Regist. (Palliat. Med.) St. Christopher's Hospice Sydenham, Lond. Prev: SHO (Respirat. Med.) Glas. Roy. Infirm.

RAESIDE, John Apsley Street Surgery, 14 Apsley Street, Glasgow G11 7SY Tel: 0141 339 2960; Tregileen, 73 South Mains Road, Milngavie, Glasgow G62 6DE Tel: 0141 956 6722 — MB ChB 1981 Glas.; BSc (Hons. Pharamacol.) Glas. 1978; MRCGP 1989; DFM Glas. 1992; DRCOG 1989.

RAETZ, Hans Peter Sycamore House, Sycamore Terrace, Haswell, Durham DH6 2AG — State Exam Med 1990 Essen.

RAFF, Peter Franz 13B Scotland Street, Stornoway HS1 2JN — State Exam Med 1977 Tubingen; MD Tubingen 1980.

RAFFAELLI, Professor Philip Iain, Surg. Cdr. RN SO1 (Med) (NATO), D.Med. Prog. & Plans, Room 8121, Main Building, MoD, Whitehall, London SW1A 2HB Tel: 020 7807 0365 Fax: 020 7807 8834 Email: dmedops@gtnet.gov.uk; 9 Thorndyke Court, Hatch End, Pinner HA5 4JB Tel: 020 8421 6370 Email: piraffaelli@raftaeth.softnet.co.uk — MB ChB 1979 Ed.; BSc Ed. 1976; MSc (Occupat. Med.) Lond. 1987; MFOM RCP Lond. 1989, AFOM 1987; MRCGP 1984; FFOM 1997. (Edinburgh) Naval Med. Off. Med. Operats. & Plans (NATO) MoD; Prof. Naval Occupat. Med. Socs: Fell. Roy. Soc. Med.; Soc. Occupat. Med. Prev: Submarine Flotilla Med. Off. & Cons. Occupat. Med. N.wood; Naval Med. Off. Health (Flag Off. Portsmouth) & Princip. Med. Off. HM Naval Base; Princip. Med. Off. HMS Neptune.

RAFFAN, Alfred William, TD (retired) 24 Rubislaw Den S., Aberdeen AB15 4BB Tel: 01224 315660 — MB ChB Aberd. 1938; FFA RCS Eng. 1954; DA Eng. 1946. Hon. Cons. Anaesth. Grampian HB. Prev: Hon. Cons. Anaesth. Grampian HB.

RAFFEEQ, Parakkal Mohommed PICU, City General Hospital, Stoke-on-Trent ST4 6OG — MB BS 1988 Madras; MRCP (UK) 1993. Cons. Paediat., Intens. Care.

RAFFERTY, Ann Margaret Abraham Cowley Unit, Bournewood NHS Trust, Holloway Hill, Lyne, Chertsey KT16 0AE Tel: 01932 872010; 6 Shorland Oaks, Priory Lane, Warfield, Bracknell RG42 2JZ — MB BS 1982 Lond.; MRCPsych 1988. (Charing Cross Hosp. Medical School) Staff Grade (Gen. Psychiat.) Abraham Cowley Unit Chertsey.

RAFFERTY, Ciaran Vincent 44 Watermill Avenue, Kirkintilloch, Glasgow G66 5QS — MB BCh BAO 1985 Belf.; FFA RCSI 1989. Sen. Regist. (Anaesth.) WHSS Bd. Prev: Research Fell. (Anaesth.) Univ. Glas.

RAFFERTY, Claire Marie 7 Spelga Av, Newcastle BT33 0DR — MB BCh BAO 1997 Belf.

RAFFERTY, Colm Gerard 67 Sandhurst Drive, Belfast BT9 5AZ — MB BCh BAO 1987 Belf. SHO (Med.) Moyle Hosp. Larne.

RAFFERTY, Mary Sheila 169 Ballycoan Road, Belfast BT8 8LN — MB BCh BAO 1985 Belf.; MRCGP 1990; DRCOG 1988. (The Queen's University of Belfast)

RAFFERTY, Patrick Gerard 6 Rowlls Road, Kingston upon Thames KT1 3ET — MB BCh BAO 1989 NUI.

RAFFERTY, Patrick James 54 High Street, Dorchester-on-Thames, Wallingford OX10 7HN — LRCP LRCS 1962 Ed.; LRCP LRCS Ed. LRFPS Glas. 1962.

RAFFERTY, Paul Dumfries & Galloway Royal Infirmary, Bankend Road, Dumfries DG1 4AP Tel: 01387 46246; 2 Nunholm Place, Dumfries DG1 1JR — MB ChB 1977 Sheff.; DM Soton. 1990; FRCP Ed. 1995; MRCP (UK) 1980. Cons. Phys. Dumfries & Galloway Roy. Infirm. Prev: Sen. Regist. (Respirat. Med.) W.. Infirm. Glas.

RAFFERTY, Rosemary 48 Riverdale Road, Sheffield S10 3FB — MB ChB 1985 Leic.; MRCGP 1990; DRCOG 1988.

RAFFETY, Richard Charles The Surgery, Madams Paddock, Chew Magna, Bristol BS40 8PP Tel: 01275 332420 Fax: 01275 333860 — MB BS 1971 Lond.; MRCGP 1977.

RAFFLE, Angela Elizabeth — MB ChB 1980 Birm.; BSc (Hons.) Birm. 1977; FFPHM RCP (UK) 1996; MFPHM 1989. Cons. Pub. Health Med. Avon HA.

RAFFLE, Edmund James (retired) 10 Skene Street, Broughty Ferry, Dundee DD5 3ET Tel: 01382 477080 — MB ChB 1953 Liverp.; FRCP Ed. 1971, M 1958; DCH Eng. 1955. Cons. Dermatol. Tayside Health Bd. Prev: Sen. Regist. Dept. Dermat. Dundee Roy. Infirm.

RAFFLE, Jean Alison 153 Kew Road, Richmond TW9 2PN Tel: 020 8940 7727 — MB ChB Liverp. 1950. (Liverp.) Indep. Analytic Psycother. Richmond; Assoc. Mem. Lincoln Clinic &centre fro Psychother.

RAFFLE, Philip Andrew Banks, OBE, KStJ 3 Kings Stile, Middleton Cheney, Banbury OX17 2QZ Tel: 01295 710142 Fax: 01295 710142 — MB BS Lond. 1941; MD Lond. 1948; FRCP Lond. 1974, M 1967; FRCS Eng. 1982; MRCS Eng. LRCP Lond. 1941;

FFOM RCP Lond. 1978; DIH Eng. 1949; DPH Lond.1948. (Middlx.) Trustee (Ex-Chairm.) Med. Commiss. on Accid. Preven. Socs: Hon. Fell. (Ex-Vice Pres.) Roy. Soc. Med.; Fell. BMA (Ex-Dep. Chairm. Occupat. Health Comm.); Hon. Mem. (Ex-Pres.) Soc. Occupat. Med. Prev: Chief Med. Off. Lond. Transport Exec. & St. John Ambul. Assn.; Convenor Examrs. DIH. Soc. Apoth. Lond.

RAFFLES, Andrew Keith Mark Child Health Directorate, Queen Elizabeth II Hospital, Howlands, Welwyn Garden City AL7 4HQ Tel: 01707 365041 Fax: 01707 373357; 14 Bradmore Way, Brookmans Park, Hatfield AL9 7QX Tel: 01707 647213 Email: rafflesdr@btinternet.com — MB BS 1978 Lond.; FRCP Lond. 1995; MRCP (UK) 1982; DCH Eng. 1981. (St. Mary's) Cons. Gen. Paediat. NW Thames RHA. Socs: Roy. Coll. Paediat. & Child Health. Prev: Lect. & Sen. Regist. Jt. Acad. Dept. Child Health Qu. Eliz. Hosp. for Childr. Lond.; Sen. Regist. Roy. Alexandra Hosp. for Childr. Camperdown, Sydney, Austral.; Regist. (Paediat.) Hammersmith Hosp. Lond.

RAFI, Imran 20 Pembroke Road, Crawley RH10 3TL Tel: 01293 883158 Fax: 01293 883158 Email: imran_rati@compuserve.com; 94 Worcester Road, Sutton SM2 6QJ Tel: 020 8661 7913 — MB BS 1988 Newc.; BSc (Hons.) Computer Sc. Newc. 1983, MB BS 1988; MRCPI 1997. (Newcastle upon Tyne) Clin. Research Fell. Cancer Research Unit. Med. Sch. Univ. Newc. u Tyne. Socs: Assoc. Mem. Roy. Coll. Gen. Pract. Prev: SHO (Oncol.) Roy. Marsden Hosp. Sutton.; SHO Med. Rotat. Newc. Teachg. Hosps.

RAFI, Muhammed Amir Flat 1, 2 Marchmont Road, Edinburgh EH9 1HZ — MB ChB 1998 Ed.; MB ChB Ed 1998.

***RAFIQ, Idrees** 11 Hurstwood Road, London NW11 0AS — MB BS 1986 Newc.

RAFIQ, Mohammed 53 St Oswalds Road, Birmingham B10 9RB — MB BS 1989 Newc.; BSc (Hons.) Newc. 1984, MB BS 1989. Lect. (Anat.) Univ. Birm. Prev: Ho. Surg. Newc. Gen. Hosp.

RAFIQ, S S The Surgery, 162 Boleyn Road, London E7 9QJ Tel: 020 8503 5656 Fax: 020 8586 9028 — MB BS 1981 Karachi; MB BS 1981 Karachi.

RAFIQ, Mr Shahid Mentisbury, 25 Abbey Road, West Kirby, Wirral CH48 7EN — MB BS 1977 Punjab; FRCS Glas. 1984.

RAFIQ, Mr Shamoudeen Mohammed 2 Hunters Way, Enfield EN2 8NL Tel: 020 8342 0725; 11 Cairngorm Crescent, Paisley PA2 8AR — MB BS 1987 Madras; FRCS Glas. 1994. Staff Grade (ENT) Chase Farm Hosps. NHS Trust Enfield. Prev: Regist. (ENT) Roy. Alexandra Hosp. Paisley.

RAFIQI, Mohamad Aslam (retired) 20 Batsford Close, Redditch B98 7TF Tel: 01527 853870 Fax: 01527 857581 — MB BS 1950 Punjab; MB BS Punjab (Pakistan) 1950. Med. Off. HMP Blakenhurst, Redditch. Prev: ed OH. Hosp Blakenhurst Redditch.

RAFIQUE, Abdul 16 Briarswood Close, Poundhill, Crawley RH10 7TJ Tel: 01293 883014 — MB BS 1964 Punjab; MB BS Punjab (Pakistan) 1964; DA Eng. 1970. (Punjab) Assoc. Specialist (Anaesth.) Mid Downs & E. Surrey HAs. Prev: Intern Holy Family Hosp. Rawalpindi Pakistan; Res. Anaesth. Nelson Hosp. Lond.; Regist. (Anaesth.) Redhill & Netherne Hosp. Gp.

RAFIQUE, Arshad 85 Napier Street, Burton-on-Trent DE14 3LL — MB BS 1994 Lond.

RAFIQUE, Farooq 66 Hall Road, London E6 2NQ — MB BS 1992 Lond.; BSc (Hons.) Lond. 1989; MRCP (UK) 1995; DCH RCP Lond. 1994. Prev: SHO (Med., Obst., Psychiat. & Paediat.) St. Mary's Hosp. Lond.

RAFIQUE, Mohammad Akkib 249 Hook Rise S., Tolworth, Surbiton KT6 7LT — MB BS 1998 Lond.; MB BS Lond 1998.

RAFIQUE, Mr Muhammad 21 New Medical Residences, City General Hospital, Stoke-on-Trent ST4 6SE Tel: 01782 621133 ext. 2541 — MB BS 1981 Punjab; FRCS Ed. 1988; FRCS Glas. 1988.

RAFIQUE, Mustafa South Quay Surgery, 35-36 South Quay, Great Yarmouth NR30 2RG Tel: 01493 843196 — MB BS 1963 Dacca; MB BS 1963 Dacca.

RAFIQUE, Syed Firoz Alfred (retired) 19 Foreshore, London SE8 3AQ — MB BS 1959 Durh. Asst. to GP, Lond. Prev: Clin. Asst. (Dermat.) Greenwich Dist. Hosp. Lond.

RAFLA, Mary Felder Lodge, Deal Road, Worth, Deal CT14 0BD — MB BCh BAO 1978 Dub.; MRCGP 1982; DRCOG 1981; DCH Eng. 1980. (TC Dub.) Prev: GP Trainee Stirling; SHO (Med.), (Psychiat.) & (O & G) Crawley Hosp.

RAFLA, Nagy Marcos Infection Control And Surveilance Unit, Gateway House, Picadilly Approach, Manchester M60 7LP Tel: 0161 236 2400 Fax: 01227 864055; Felder Lodge, Deal Road, Deal CT14 0BD Tel: 0161 236 2400 Fax: 01227 864055 — MB ChB 1974 Alexandria; MRCOG 1986; MObstG Liverp. 1988; T(OG) 1991; DObst RCPI 1981. (Univ. Alexandria) Cons. (O & G); Dist. Tutor Roy. Coll. of Obst.s & Gyn. Socs: Beckett Med. Soc.; BMA; Brit. Ultrasound Soc. Prev: Dir. IVF unit at BMI Chaucer Hosp.; Sen. Regist. Univ. Coll. Hosp. Galway; Research Assoc. (O & G) Roy. Liverp. Hosp.

RAFTER, Martin James Shannon, Ty-Llwyd Road, Lisvane, Cardiff CF14 0SG — MB BCh BAO 1945 NUI.

RAFTERY, Mr Andrew Thomas Sheffield Kidney Institute, Northern General Hospital, Herries Road, Sheffield S5 7AU Tel: 0114 271 5316; Carnbrea, 280 Ecclesall Road S., Sheffield S11 9PS — MB ChB 1969 (Hons) Leeds; BSc (Hons.) Leeds 1966, MD 1973; FRCS Eng. 1976. Cons. Gen. Surg. & Transpl. N. Gen. Hosp. Sheff.; Mem. Ct. Examrs. RCS Eng.; Mem. Of Counc. RCS Eng. Socs: (Pres.) Counc. Brit. Assn. Clin. Anat.; Brit. Transpl. Soc.; Surgic. Research Soc. Prev: Cons. Gen. Surg. & Transpl. Addenbrooke's Hosp. Camb.; Lect. (Surg.) Manch. Roy. Infirm.; Regist. Rotat. (Surg.) Pontefract. Gen. Infirm.

RAFTERY, Martin John Renal Unit, The London Hospital, Whitechapel, London E1 1BB Tel: 020 7377 7368 Fax: 020 7377 7003; 19 Asmara Road, West Hampstead, London NW2 3SS Tel: 020 7435 3101 — MB BCh BAO 1975 NUI; MD 1987; MRCPI 1977; FRCP (UK) 1995. Cons./Sen. Lect. Nephrol. Lond. Hosp. Prev: Sen. Regist. Renal Unit Guy's Hosp. Lond.; Regist. (Nephrol./Transpl.) Roy. Free Hosp. Lond.; SHO (Chest Med.) Brompton Hosp. Lond.

RAFTERY, Patricia 7 Peel Moat Road, Heaton Moor, Stockport SK4 4PL — LRCPI & LM, LRSCI & LM 1964; LRCPI & LM, LRCSI & LM 1964.

RAFTERY, Stephen Mark Department of Anaesthesia, Whiston Hospital, Prescot L35 5DR — MB BCh BAO 1983 NUI; FFA RCSI 1988. Cons. (Anaesth.) Whiston Hosp., Prescot. Prev: Sen. Regist. (Anesth) S.W. RHA; Clin. Research Fell. Univ. Bristol.

RAGAB, Suzanne 27 Brambletyne Avenue, Saltdean, Brighton BN2 8EL — BM 1993 Soton.; MRCP (UK) 1996. Regist. (Med.) Jersey Gen. Hosp. Prev: SHO Rotat. & Ho. Off. (Med.) St. Mary's Hosp. Portsmouth; Ho. Surg. Bournemouth Gen. Hosp.

RAGBIR, Mr Maniram Department of Plastic & Reconstructive Surgery, Royal Devon & Exeter Hospital (Wonford), Barrack Road, Exeter EX2 5DW Tel: 01392 411611; 102 Jerningham Junction Road, Charlieville Chaduanas, Trinidad & Tobago Tel: 00 1 809 6651732 — MB BS 1989 West Indies; FRCS Glas. 1995. SHO (Plastic & Reconstruc Surg.) Roy. Devon & Exeter Hosp. Prev: Welsh Regional Centre Burns & Plastic Surg. Morriston Hosp. Swansea.

RAGBIR, Rai 28 Earlsmead, Harrow HA2 8SP — MB BS 1990 West Indies.

RAGGATT, Stephen Huw 114 Station Road, Cogenhoe, Northampton NN7 1LU Tel: 01604 890120 — MB ChB 1991 Bristol; MRCPsych 1996. Regist. (Psychiat.) Bucks. Socs: Roy. Coll. Psychiat.

RAGGE, Nicola Karyn Western Eye Hospital, Marylebone Road, London NW1 5YE Tel: 020 7402 4211 Fax: 020 7723 8726; 37 Langdon Park Road, Highgate, London N6 5PT — BM BCh 1984 Oxf.; MA Camb. 1985; MRCP (Paediat.) (UK) 1987; FRCOphth. 1989; DO 1989. Sen. Regist. (Ophth.) W.. Eye Hosp. Lond. Prev: Fell. (Paediat. & Developm. Ophth. & Molecular Genetics) Childr. Hosp. Los Angeles, Univ. S.. Calif.; Fell. (Paediat. & Neuro-ophth.) Univ. Calif., San Francisco; Regist. (Ophth.) Bristol Eye Hosp.

RAGGOO, Michel David Richard Latchets, Hackford Road, Hardingham, Norwich NR9 4ED — BM BS 1997 Nottm.

RAGHAVAIAH, Lingi Setty Dunoon General Hospital, Dunoon PA23 7RL — MB BS 1973 Andhra.

RAGHAVAN, Manoj 2 Witley Court, 68 Worple Road, London SW19 4HX — MB BS 1994 Lond.

RAGHAVAN, Ravi 14 The Firs, Salters Road, Gosforth, Newcastle upon Tyne NE3 4PH Tel: 0191 284 8250 — MD 1985 Madras; MB BS Calicut India 1980.

RAGHAVAN, Shiverdorayi 22 Sandhills Crescent, Solihull B91 3JE Tel: 0121 705 9139 — BM 1984 Soton.; MSc Newc. 1980; BSc

RAGHAVENDRA

(Hons.) E. Anglia 1979. Trainee GP/SHO E. Birm. Hosp. VTS. Prev: SHO (Med. & Geriat.) Birm. HA.

RAGHAVENDRA, Kulkarni 15 Linnburn Terrace, Ardrossan KA22 8NR Tel: 01294 61509 — MB BS 1964 Karnatak; DObst RCOG 1972. (Karnatak Med. Coll. Hubli)

RAGHAVJEE, Indira Vaghjee 10 Kensington Street, Leicester LE4 5GL — MB BS 1973 Bombay.

RAGHEB, Essam Abdel Aziz HM Prison Bullingdon, PO Box 50, Bicester OX25 1WD Tel: 01869 322111 Fax: 01869 323029 — MB BCh 1972 Cairo. Dir. Health Care HM Prison Bullingdon; Dip. Addic. Behaviour. Prev: Head Med. Servs. HM Prison Stafford; Med. Off. HM Prison Birm.; Assoc. Specialist (Psychiat.) Bassetlaw Dist. Gen. Hosp. Worksop.

RAGHEB, Mr Sherif Wasfy 37 Scafell Close, Taunton TA1 4LG — MB BCh 1982 Ain Shams; FRCS Ed. 1994.

RAGHU, Mr Cheruvalli Gopalan General Hospital, St Helier, Jersey JE2 3QS — MB BS 1982 Ranchi; FRCS Ed. 1991; FRCS Glas. 1991.

RAGHUNATH, Joanne Vernita 19 Pollards Hill E., London SW16 4UX — BM BS 1998 Nottm.; BM BS Nottm 1998.

RAGHUNATH, Nigel John 20 Hitherfield Road, London SW16 2LN — MB BCh 1996 Wales.

RAGHUNATHAN, Mr Krishnan 31 Millwood, Lisvane, Cardiff CF14 0TL Tel: 029 2075 2971 — MB BS 1960 Kerala; FRCS Eng. 1970. Orthop. Consult. Caerphilly Hosp. Prev: Ho. Surg. Copthorne Hosp. Shrewsbury; Trauma Regist. E. Glam. Hosp. Ch. Village; Orthop. Regist. P. of Wales Hosp. Rhydlafar.

RAGHUPATI, Rajan Flat 26, Halliard Court, Barquentine Place, Cardiff CF10 4NJ — MB BCh 1994 Wales.

RAGHUPATI RAJU, Alluri Sathyanarayana 34 Railton Avenue, Prescot L35 0QB — MB BS 1962 Andhra.

RAGI, Elias Fouad Elias Department of Clinical Neurophysiology, Royal Devon & Exeter Hospital (Wonford), Barrack Road, Exeter EX2 5DW Tel: 01392 402456 Fax: 01392 402721; 11 Lamacraft Drive, Exeter EX4 8QS Tel: 01392 426629 Fax: 01392 671282 Email: er@medix-uk.com — MB ChB 1972 Baghdad; DPhil Oxf. 1986. Cons. Clin. Neurophysiol. Roy. Devon & Exeter Hosp.; Cons. Clin. Neurophysiologist Taunton & Som. Hosps. Prev: Sen. Regist. (Clin. Neurophysiol.) Birm.

RAGLAN, Mrs Ewa Maria Institute of Laryngology & Otology, University College London, 330/332 Gray's Inn Road, London WC1X 8EE Tel: 020 7915 1630 Fax: 020 7278 8041 Email: ewaraglan@ucl.ac.uk; 172 Cottenham Park Road, London SW20 0SX Tel: 020 8947 2648 Fax: 020 7278 8041 — Med. Dipl. 1973 Warsaw; Med. Dip. (Distinc.) Warsaw 1973; FRCS Eng. (Orl.) 1981; MRCS Eng. LRCP Lond. 1978; DLO Eng. 1975. (Med. Acad. Warsaw) Sen. Lect. (Audiological Med.) Inst. Laryngol. & Otol. Univ. Coll. Lond.; Cons. (Audiological Med.) St. Geos. Hosp. Lond.; Govenor Sch. for Deaf Oak Lodge Lond. & Med. Represent. to BAOL; Invited Lect. 5th Polish - Amer. Symp. Warsaw, Poland, September 1997; MSc Audiological Med. Lond. Course Tutor; Expert witness in Audiological Med. Socs: Fell. Roy. Soc. Med.; BMA & Mem. Brit. Soc. Audiol.; BAAP & JAPA. Prev: Cons. Audiol. Phys. & Neurootol. St. Geo. Hosp. Lond.; Sen. Regist. (Audiol. Med.) Roy. Nat. Hosp. Neurol. Dis. Lond.; Regist. (ENT) St. Thos Hosp. Lond.

RAGOOWANSI, Rajesh Hiranand Flat 33, 35 Buckingham Gate, London SW1E 6PA — MB BS 1992 Lond.

RAGU, Mr Hiremagalur Keshavadas Sethuraghavan 5 The Birches, Townsend, Soham, Ely CB7 5FH — MB BS 1986 Karnatak; FRCS Ed. 1993.

RAGUNATHAN, Pakiyaluxmi 17 Dale View, Ilkley LS29 9BP — MB BS 1977 Sri Lanka.

RAGUPATHY, Markandu The Surgery, 80 Torridon Road, London SE6 1RA Tel: 020 8698 5281 Fax: 020 8695 1841 — MB BS 1976 Sri Lanka; DPM Eng. 1983; MRCGP 1997; DFFP 1998. GP; Clin. Asst. (Psychiat.) FarnBoro. Hosp. Orpington. Socs: Med. Inst. of Tamils; BMA; RCGP. Prev: Regist. (Psychiat.) FarnBoro. Hosp. Orpington.

RAHA, Arun Kumar The Medical Centre, 78 Oswald Road, Scunthorpe DN15 7PG Tel: 01724 843168 — MB BS 1961 Calcutta.

RAHA, H D Wath Health Centre, Church Street, Wath-On-Dearne, Rotherham S63 7RF Tel: 01709 873233 — MB BS 1973 Dacca; MB BS 1973 Dacca.

RAHA, Sandip Kumar Princess of Wales Hospital, Coity Road, Bridgend CF31 1RQ Tel: 01656 752746 Fax: 01656 752038; 24 Fieldway, Cambridge CB1 8RW Tel: 01223 523623 Email: sky@kumarraha.freeserve.co.uk — MB BS 1978 Bhagalpur; BSc (Hons.) Ranchi 1971. (Bhagalpur Med. Coll., India) Assoc. Specialist Dept. of Integrated Med. Bromorgannwg NHS Trust; Locum Cons. Phys. Bromorgannwg NHS Trust, Bridgend. Socs: Med. Soc. Bridgend; Soc. for Research & Rehabil.; Brit. Geriat. Soc. Prev: Sen. Clin. Med. Off. P.ss of Wales, Bridgend; Regist. (Geriat.) Cardiff Roy. Infirm.; Regist. (Med.) P.ss Roy. Hosp. Haywards Heath.

RAHAMAN, Andrew Edward 190 Aragon Road, Morden SM4 4QN — MB BS 1997 Lond.

RAHAMIM, Yousif Hyperion, Seymour Road, Mannamead, Plymouth PL3 5AU Tel: 01752 225198 — MB ChB 1973 Iraq. Cons. Thoracic Surg. Plymouth HA. Prev: Assoc. Specialist (Thoracic Surg.) Plymouth HA.

RAHBER, Mohammad S Mabarak Health Centre, 8-12 Cannon Hill Road, Balsall Heath, Birmingham B12 9NN Tel: 0121 440 4666 Fax: 0121 446 5986 — MB BS 1974 Patna; MB BS 1974 Patna.

RAHEJA, Sunil Kumar 13 Mallard Close, Hanwell, London W7 2PX Tel: 020 8579 5365 Email: sunil-raheja@lineone.net — BM 1989 Soton.; MRCPsych 1994. (Soton.) Flexible Trainee Char. Cross Higher Psychiat. Train. Scheme. Prev: Regist. Rotat. (Psychiat.) Solent; SHO (Psychiat.) St. Jas. Hosp Portsmouth & Roy. S. Hants. Hosp. Soton.

RAHEMTULLA, Aminmohamed Nuffield Department of Clinical Medicine, University of Oxford, John Radcliffe Hospital, Oxford OX3 9DU Tel: 01865 221347 Fax: 01865 221327 Email: amin.rahemtulla@ndm.ox.ac.uk; 21 Oakthorpe Road, Summertown, Oxford OX2 7BD — MB BS Lond. 1981; PhD Toronto 1994; BSc Lond. 1978; MRCP (UK) 1984. (Univ. Coll. Hosp.) Wellcome Sen. Clin. Research Fell. & Hon. Cons. Phys. John Radcliffe Hosp. Prev: Terry Fox Research Fell. Ontario Cancer Inst. Toronto, Canada; Regist. (Haemat.) Roy. Postgrad. Med. Sch. Hammersmith Hosp. Lond.

RAHI, Jugnoo Sangeeta Dept of Epidemiology, GOS NHS Trust, Institute of Child Health, London WC1N 1EH Tel: 020 7905 2250 Fax: 020 7242 9789; Flat 59, Anchorage Point, Westferry Road, London E14 8NF Tel: 020 7537 7500 — MB BS 1986 Lond.; MSc (Epidemiol.) Lond. 1994; FCOphth 1992; DO RCS Eng. 1990; DCH RCP Lond. 1989; PhD, Epidiol. Univ. Lond. 1998. Clin. Lect., Ophth. Epidemiol., GOS/ Inst. of Child Health & Inst. of Ophth. Socs: Fell. Roy. Soc. Med.; BMA.

RAHI, Swarn Lata (retired) Flat 59, Anchorage Point, Westferry Road, London E14 8NF Tel: 020 7537 7500 — MB BS 1962 Bihar; MS (Ophth.) Bihar 1964; MRCPath 1987; DO Eng. 1971. Med. Off. Moorfields Eye Hosp. (City Rd. Br.) Lond.; Assoc. Specialist (Ophth.) OldCh. Hosp. Romford. Prev: Regist. (Ophth.) Inst. Ophth. Aligarh Univ. India.

RAHIL, Hussein Mohammad Old Whint Road Surgery, 21A Old Whint Road, Haydock, St Helens WA11 0DN Tel: 01744 612555 Fax: 01744 454619; 42 Avery Road, Haydock, St Helens WA11 0XA Tel: 01744 616420 Fax: 01744 454619 — MB BCh 1971 Assuit, Egypt; DFFP 1995; DTM & H Liverp. 1983. (Assuit Med. Sch.) Clin. Asst. (Psychiat.) Warrington HA. Prev: Resid. Surg. Milit. Hosp., Abu Dhabi; Med. Off. UNRWA, Lebanon; Regist. (Cardiothoracic Surg.) Roy. Hallamsh. Hosp. Sheff. & Walsgrave Hosp. Coventry.

RAHILL, Mary Theresa Carmel (retired) 1 Fairfield Walk, Cheltenham GL53 7PF Tel: 01242 583409 — LRCPI & LM, LRSCI & LM 1951; LRCPI & LM, LRCSI & LM 1951.

RAHILLY, David Maurice (retired) The Old School House, Broadway, Ilminster TA19 9RE — MRCS Eng. LRCP Lond. 1947. Prev: Flight Lt. RAF Med. Br.

RAHILLY, Maeve Anne Pathology Dept, Victoria Hospital, Hayfield road, Kirkcaldy KY2 5AH — MB BCh BAO 1987 NUI; 2001 Dip FM; MD NUI 1995; MRCPath 1993. Cons. Histopath. Fife Acute Hosps. Trust. Prev: Sen. Regist. (Histopath.) Dept Path. Univ. Edin.; Cons. Histopath. N. Glas. Univ. Hosp. Trust.

RAHIM, Abdur Merthyr Tydfil Health Centre, Merthyr Tydfil CF47 0AY Tel: 01685 350035 Fax: 01685 723345 — MB BS 1967 Dacca. (Dacca) GP Merthyr Tydfil.

RAHIM, Asad 29 Swanage Road, Small Heath, Birmingham B10 9ER — MB ChB 1991 Leeds.

RAHIM, George Faradj 4 Burcott Road, Purley CR8 4AA Tel: 020 8660 9327 — MB BS 1943 Baghdad; PhD Ed. 1948. (Baghdad) Prev: Cons. Dermat. Birm. Walsall HAs.

RAHIM, Mr Md Abdur District General Hospital, Lovely Lane, Warrington WA5 1QG Tel: 01925 35911; 14 Teddington Close, Dudlows Green, Appleton, Warrington WA4 5QG — MB BS 1968 Dacca; FRCS Eng. 1981; FRCS Ed. 1981.

RAHIM, Mohamed Hanif Curacao, Grifon Road, Chafford Hundred, Grays RM16 6NP Tel: 01375 482156 — MB BCh 1990 Wales. (Univ. Wales Coll. Med.) Regist. (O & G) Whipps Cross Hosp. Lond. Prev: Regist. (O & G) S.end; Regist. (O & G) Portsmouth; SHO (O & G) Portsmouth.

RAHIM, Mustafa Sherali Warren Medical Centre, Uxbridge Road, Hayes UB4 0SG Tel: 020 8573 1781 Fax: 020 8561 3461 Email: drmrahim@dincon.co.uk; 17 St. Edmunds Drive, Stanmore HA7 2AT Tel: 020 8930 4291 Email: drmrahim@dincon.co.uk — MB ChB 1971 Makerere; CHS (Harrow & Hillingdon); DFFP; DFFP (RCOG); Cert. Equiv. Registration JCPT GP; Minor Surgery (Hillingdon). (Makerere) GP, Warren Med. Centre, Hayes. Socs: BMA; MPS.

RAHIM, Naeed Sadrudin Whispering Oaks, Broaldlands Close, Calcot, Reading RG31 7RP — MB BCh 1977 Wales; FRCR 1983.

RAHIM, Owais 84 York Avenue, Whalley Range, Manchester M16 0AG — MB BS 1990 Punjab; MRCP (UK) 1994. Regist. (Gen. Med.) Middlx. Hosp. Lond. Prev: Regist. (Med.) Colchester Gen. Hosp.; SHO (Med.) Jas. Paget Hosp. Gt. Yarmouth.

RAHIM, Sleem 69 Benton Road, Ilford IG1 4AS — MB BS 1994 Lond.

RAHMAAN, Abdur Kinsgway Surgery, 17 Kingsway, Hayes UB3 2TT Tel: 020 8573 3934 Fax: 020 8813 7034 — LAH 1960 Dublin; LAH 1960 Dublin.

RAHMAAN, Gillian 212 Swakeleys Road, Uxbridge UB10 8AY — MB BS 1962 Durh.; MRCOG 1967, D 1964. (Durh.) Clin. Asst. (Obst.) Hillingdon Hosp. Uxbridge.

RAHMAN, Mr Abdul Panteg Health Centre, Kemys Street, Griffithstown, Pontypool NP4 5DJ Tel: 01495 763608 Fax: 01495 753925 — MB BS 1977 Punjab; LMSSA 1990; FRCS Glas. 1993; MRCS 1990; LRCP 1990.

RAHMAN, Abdul Quader Mohammed Hamidir Clydebank Health Centre, Kilbowie Road, Clydebank G81 2TQ Tel: 0141 531 6400 Fax: 0141 531 6419; 17 Carse View Drive, Bearsden, Glasgow G61 3NJ — MB BS 1970 Dacca. (Dacca) GP Clydebank, Dunbaronsh.

RAHMAN, Abu Bazal Mohammad Shamsur 49 South Park Avenue, Mansfield NG18 4PJ — MB BS 1958 Dacca; FRCP Lond. 1994; MRCP (UK) 1970; FRCP Ed. 1983, M 1969; DTM & H Eng. 1965. Geriat. Centr. Notts. Healthcare NHS Trust. Socs: Brit. Geriat. Soc. & BMA. Prev: Sen. Regist. (Geriat.) St. Jas. Hosp. Leeds; Regist. (Gen. Med.) Sedgefield Gen. Hosp. Stockton-on-Tees; Med. Off. Govt. of N.. Nigeria.

RAHMAN, Abu Faiz Mohammad Shafiqur (retired) 40 Highfield, Letchworth SG6 3PZ Tel: 01462 676235 — MB BS Dacca 1956; FRCPath 1980, M 1968; DPH Punjab (Pakistan)1961; DTM & H Eng. 1963; Dip. Bact. Manch. 1965; LMSSA Lond. 1969. Prev: Cons. Microbiol. Lister Hosp. Stevenage.

RAHMAN, Abu Fakhr Muhammad Mustafizur (retired) 27 Dunstarn Drive, Adel, Leeds LS16 8EH Tel: 0113 225 7048 — MB BS 1961 Dacca; MB BS Dhaka 1961; DTM & H Ed. 1966. Prev: Assoc. Specialist (Geriat.) Leeds Gen. Infirm.

RAHMAN, Abu Saleh Mohammad Matinur The Surgery, Sundial Lane, Great Barr, Birmingham B43 6PA Tel: 0121 358 0082 — MB BS 1969 Dacca. (Dacca Med. Coll.)

RAHMAN, Abu Taher Mohammed Latifur 61 Applegrove, Enfield EN1 3DA Tel: 020 8366 5248 — MB BS 1964 Rajshahi; MB BS Rajshahi Bangladesh 1964.

RAHMAN, Mr Abu Zafar Mohammad Mafizur The Parc, Litchard Hill, Bridgend CF31 1QQ Tel: 01656 657734 — MB BS Dhaka 1969; FRCS Ed. 1980. (Dhaka) Cons. Gen. Surg. Ealing Hosp. Lond. Prev: Cons. Gen. Surg. Ealing Hosp. Lond; Cons.Gen.surg.King Khalid Univ.Hosp.Riyadh Saudi Arabia; Sen.Reg.Gensurg.King Khalid Univ.Hosp.Riyadh Saudi Arabia.

RAHMAN, Abul Kalam Mohammed Raziur, TD Marshall Street Surgery, 45-46 Marshall Street, Smethwick B67 7NA Tel: 0121 558 4446 Fax: 0121 555 5832 Email: raziurrahman@g.p.m88637.nhs.uk — LRCP LRCS Ed. LRCS Glas.

RAHMAN, Altaf-Ur (Surgery), 156 Crankhall Lane, Friar Park, Wednesbury WS10 0EB Tel: 0121 556 3412 — MB BS 1964 Peshawar.

RAHMAN, Amina 24A Tutbury Avenue, Coventry CV4 7BJ — BM BS 1997 Nottm.

RAHMAN, Arindam Rafiqur The Surgery, 69 Water Lane, London E15 4NL; 97 Burges Road, East Ham, London E6 2BJ Tel: 020 8470 0853 — MB BS 1970 Dacca.

RAHMAN, Asia 49 South Park Avenue, Mansfield NG18 4PJ Tel: 01623 29716 — MB BS 1960 Dacca; DA Eng. 1970. (Dacca Med. Coll.) Assoc. Specialist (Anaesth.) Kings Mill Hosp. Sutton-in-Ashfield. Socs: BMA. Prev: Clin. Asst. (Anaesth.) Mansfield Gp. Hosp.; Regist. (Anaesth.) Mansfield & Newark Health Dist.

RAHMAN, Faiza Amal 17 St Paul's Way, Finchley, London N3 2PP — MB BS 1984 Lond.; MRCOG 1991. (St. Thos.) Regist. St. Bart. Hosp. Lond. Prev: SHO (Obst.) Qu. Charlotte's Matern. Hosp. Lond.

RAHMAN, Faizur (retired) 58 Fountain Road, Birmingham B17 8NR Tel: 0121 429 9769 — MB BS 1951 Patna; DPM Eng. 1968; DCH Eng. 1959; TDD Calcutta 1955; DTM Sch. Trop. Med. Calcutta 1953. Med. Pract. Addic. Unit All St.s Hosp. Birm. Prev: Sen. Med. Off. H.M. Prisons, Winson Green Birm.

RAHMAN, Farida Khatoon Health Promotion Centre, 57 Lady Margaret Road, Southall UB1 2PH Tel: 020 8547 5186; WAFA House, Hillcrest Waye, Gerrards Cross SL9 8DN — MB BS 1958 Dacca; DObst RCOG 1965; DTM & H Eng. 1962. (Dacca Med. Coll.)

RAHMAN, Farooq Ziaur 3 Brentfield Gardens, London NW2 1JP — MB BS 1997 Lond.

RAHMAN, Fauzia Staplegrove House, Berghers Hill, Woodburn Common, High Wycombe HP10 0JP — MB BS 1986 Lond.; LMSSA Lond. 1985.

RAHMAN, Fawzia Rafat CHS NHS Trust Southern Derbyshire, Wilderslowe, 121 Osmastun Road, Derby DE1 2GA Tel: 01332 363371 — MB BS 1977 All India Inst. Med. Sci.; MRCP (UK) 1986; MRCS Eng. LRCP Lond. 1987; DCH, Lond. 1986; MD 1980 MD (poc)All India Insitit Med Sc. Cons., Pediatrician, Community Child Health, Community Health Servs. Trust, S.ern Derbysh. Socs: FRCPCh; BACCH.

RAHMAN, Habib Ur Canvey Village Surgery, 391 Long Road, Canvey Island SS8 0JH Tel: 01268 510520 Fax: 01268 684083; 205 Long Road, Canvey Island SS8 0JE Tel: 01268 680947 — MB BS 1975 Punjab; LRCP LRCS Ed. LRCPS Glas. 1982.

RAHMAN, Mr Habib Ur Orthopaedic Department, Birmingham Heartlands Hospital, Bordesley Green E., Birmingham B9 5SS — MB BS 1981 Punjab; FRCS (Orth.) 1995; FRCSI 1987. Cons. Orthop. Surg. Birm. Heartlands Hosp.

RAHMAN, Imran 318 Pershore Road, Edgbaston, Birmingham B5 7QY — MB BS 1998 Lond.; MB BS Lond 1998.

RAHMAN, Jarjis Springfield House, New Lane, Eccles, Manchester M30 7JE; Fax: 0161 789 2556 — MB BS 1962 Dacca; DTM & H Eng. 1966. (Dacca Med. Coll.)

***RAHMAN, Junia,** Surg. Lt. RN 40 Highfield, Letchworth SG6 3PZ Tel: 01462 676235; 117 Myddleton Avenue, Green Lanes, London N4 2FP Tel: 020 8880 1539 — MB BS 1996 Lond.

RAHMAN, Kazi Ataur 94 Lewisham Road, Smethwick, Warley B66 2DD Tel: 0121 555 5635 Fax: 0121 565 0293 — MB BS 1970 Dacca; MB BS 1970 Dacca.

RAHMAN, Khandaker Masihur Station Road Medical Centre, 53 Station Road, Brynamman, Ammanford SA18 1SH Tel: 01269 823210; 10 James Griffiths Road, Ammanford SA18 2AS Tel: 01269 592078 — MB BS 1958 Dacca; MB BS (Hons.) Dacca 1958; MRCP (UK) 1970. (Dacca) Family Phys. Brynamman. Prev: Med. Specialist Pakistan Army (1962-69).

RAHMAN, Khondker Mahfuzar 26 Ravensdale Gardens, Eccles, Manchester M30 9JD Tel: 0161 789 3649 — MB BS Dhaka 1961; FRCOG 1989, M 1972. Cons. O & G Ashton-Under-Lyne.

RAHMAN, Mr Mahfuzer 27 Rodney Road, New Malden KT3 5AB Tel: 020 8949 5352 — FRCS Glas. 1981.

RAHMAN, Mr Mahfuzur The Child Health Directorate, Royal Bolton Hospital, Minerva Road, Fanworth BL4 0JR Tel: 01204

RAHMAN

390537, 0208 894 3742 Fax: 01204 390657, 0208 894 3768 — MB BS 1958 Dacca; FRCS Eng. 1969; FRCS Ed. 1969; FRCOphth 1988; DO Eng. 1965. (Dacca Med. Coll.) Cons. Ophth. W. Middlx. Univ. Hosp. Socs: Fell. Roy. Soc. Med.; Oxf. Ophth. Congr.; United Kingdom & Irel. Soc. of Cataract and Refractive Surg.s. Prev: Sen. Regist. (Ophth.) Aberd. Teachg. Hosps.; Regist. (Ophth.) Roy. Eye Hosp. Lond.; SHO (Ophth.) Roy. Infirm. Sheff.

RAHMAN, Manibur 16 Sainfoin Road, London SW17 8EP Tel: 020 8672 5388 Email: t.rahman@rpms.ac.uk — BM BCh 1992 Oxf.; BA (Hons.) Physiol. Oxf. 1989; MRCP (UK) 1995. (Oxf.) Research Fell. (Gastroenterol.) Hammersmith Hosp. Lond. Socs: Roy. Soc. Med. Prev: Regist. (Med.) Inst. Liver Studies King's Coll. Hosp. Lond.; Regist. (Med.) Medway Hosp. Gillingham, Kent; SHO Rotat. St. Geo. Hosp. Lond.

RAHMAN, Mazin Khalid Abdul c/o Frimley Park Hospital, Portsmouth Road, Frimley, Camberley GU16 7UJ Tel: 01276 692777; 89 Thrale Road, London SW16 1NU — MB ChB 1976 Baghdad; MRCOG 1990. Regist. (O & G) Frimley Pk. Hosp. Surrey.

RAHMAN, Mobinur 178 Cropston Road, Anstey, Leicester LE7 7BN Tel: 0116 236 5174 — MB BS 1962 Dacca; DPM Eng. 1973. (Dacca Med. Coll.) Assoc. Specialist (Psychiat.) Towers Hosp. Leicester.

RAHMAN, Mohamed Abdur Ashmore Park Clinic, Griffiths Drive, Ashmore Park, Wolverhampton WV11 2LH Tel: 01902 732442 Fax: 01902 729048; 18 Corfton Drive, Tettenhall, Wolverhampton WV6 8NR Tel: 01902 732442 Fax: 01902 729048 — MBBS 1962 Dacca. (Dacca Med. Coll.) Socs: Fell. Overseas Doctors Assn.; BMA; Fell. Roy. Soc. Med. Lond.

RAHMAN, Mohamed Altafur Great Harwood Health Centre, Water Street, Great Harwood, Blackburn BB6 7QR Tel: 01254 886400 Fax: 01254 877360; The Bungalow, Mill Lane, Great Harwood, Blackburn BB6 7UQ Tel: 01254 885787 — LAH 1971 Dub. Div. Police Surg. Lancs.; Pres. Bangladesh Med. Assn. (UK).

RAHMAN, Mohammad Balmoral Road Surgery, 12 Balmoral Road, Gillingham ME7 4PG Tel: 01634 854933 — MB BS 1962 Peshawar.

RAHMAN, Mohammad Azizar The Surgery, 38-46 Bradley road, Patchway, Bristol BS34 5LD Tel: 0117 969 2040 Fax: 0117 947 0440 — MB BS 1959 Dacca. (Dacca) Prev: Regist. Bristol Roy. Infirm.; Ho. Phys. Whittington Hosp. Lond.

RAHMAN, Mohammad Bazlur c/o Drive S.M.S. Rahman, 16 Lynwood Avenue, Lowton, Warrington WA3 1HJ Tel: 01942 6649 — MB BS 1963 Dacca; BSc (Hons.) Dacca 1957, MB BS 1963; DTM & H Liverp. 1967. Regist. (O & G) Ayrsh. Gen. Hosp. Irvine. Socs: BMA. Prev: SHO (Gyn.) Roy. Samarit. Hosp. Wom. Glas.; SHO (Obst.) Bellshill Matern. Hosp.; SHO (O & G) Falkirk & Dist. Roy. Infirm.

RAHMAN, Mohammad Habibur Aston Health Centre, 175 Trinity Road, Aston, Birmingham B6 6JA Tel: 0121 328 3597 Fax: 0121 327 1674 — MB BS 1963 Dacca; LMSSA Lond. 1969. (Chittagong) Regist. Dept. Geriat. Med. St. Mary's Hosp. & St. Chas. Hosp. Lond. Socs: BMA. Prev: SHO Gen. Med. Newsham Gen. Hosp. Liverp.; Ho. Phys. All St.s' Hosp. Chatham; Ho. Phys. Manor Hosp. Nuneaton.

RAHMAN, Mohammad Khaledur Cross Lane Surgery, 148 Cross Lane, Prescot L35 5DU Tel: 0151 426 5345 Fax: 0151 426 6017 — MB BS 1963 Dacca; DTM & H Liverp. 1966. (Dacca Med. Coll.)

RAHMAN, Mr Mohammad Lutfor 1 Pattiswick Square, Basildon SS14 2R Tel: 01268 20772 — MB BS 1965 Dacca; FRCS Ed. 1972.

RAHMAN, Mohammad Masudur Stanley Health Centre, Clifford Road, Stanley DH9 0XE Tel: 01207 232696 Fax: 01207 239066 — MB BS 1968 Dacca. (Dacca) GP Stanley, Co. Durh.

RAHMAN, Mr Mohammad Matiur Department of Surgery, Erne Hospital, Enniskillen BT74 6AY — MB BS 1972 Dacca; FRCSI 1990.

RAHMAN, Mohammad Shamsur 190 Maidstone Road, Rochester ME1 3EJ Tel: 01634 814368 — MB BS 1967 Dacca.

RAHMAN, Mohammad Zalilur Woodilee/Stoneytts/Ruchill Hospital, Glasgow G66 3UG Tel: 0141 776 2451; Lyndoch, Larch Avenue, Lenzie, Glasgow G66 4HT — MB BS 1957 Dacca; FRCPsych 1986, M 1976; DTM & H Ed. 1969. (Dacca Med. Coll.) Cons. Psychiat. Gtr. Glas. HB; Hon. Sen. Clin. Lect. (Psychol. Med.) Univ. Glas. Socs: Fell. Roy. Coll. Psychiat.; BMA.

RAHMAN, Mohammed Abbas Anisur 172 Brunswick Quay, London SE16 7PT Tel: 020 7231 3558 — BM BCh 1988 Oxf.; BA Oxf. 1985, BM BCh 1988; MRCP (UK) 1991. Regist. (Med.) King Geo. Hosp. Ilford. Prev: Regist. (Rheum.) Roy. Free Hosp. Lond.; Regist. (Med.) St. Thos. Hosp. Lond.; SHO (Renal Med.) Hammersmith Hosp. Lond.

RAHMAN, Mohammed Arif-Ur 2 Blair Place, Kirkcaldy KY2 5SQ — MB ChB 1994 Dundee.

RAHMAN, Mohammed Atiqur The Health Centre, Wallsgreen Road, Cardenden, Lochgelly KY5 0JE Tel: 01592 722441 — MB BS 1960 Dacca. (Dacca) GP Lochgelly. Fife.

RAHMAN, Mohammed Fazlur Dewsbury District Hospital, Healds Road, Dewsbury WF13 4HS Tel: 01924 465105; Carr Lodge, Beckett Road, Dewsbury WF13 2DB — MB BS 1972 Rajshahi.

RAHMAN, Mohammed Haseebur Ashmore Park Clinic, Griffiths Drive, Ashmore Park, Wolverhampton WV11 2LH Tel: 01902 732442 Fax: 01902 729048 — MB ChB 1992 Dundee.

RAHMAN, Mohammed Lutfor Exmoor Surgery, Exmoor St., North Kensington, London W10 6DZ Tel: 0208 962 4245 Fax: 020 8962 4252; 18 Chestnut Drive, Harrow HA3 7DJ Tel: 020 8954 3935 Fax: 020 8954 3935 — MB BS Dacca 1969. (Dacca Med. Coll.) Socs: MDU.

RAHMAN, Mohammed Meshbahur St Mary's Hospital NHS Trust, Newport PO30 5NW — MB BS 1986 Dacca; MB BS Dacca, Bangladesh 1986; MRCP (UK) 1994.

RAHMAN, Mohammed Shafiqur 33 The Cedars, Burghley Close, Stevenage SG2 8SZ — MB ChB 1986 Aberd.

RAHMAN, Motiur Md 13 Winwood Road, E. Didsbury, Manchester M20 5PE — MB BS 1968 Rajshahi; DLO RCS Eng. 1981.

RAHMAN, Muhammad Abdur Tonypandy Health Centre, Winton Field, Tonypandy CF40 2LE Tel: 01443 433284 Fax: 01443 436848 — MB BS 1960 Dacca. (Dacca) GP Tonypandy, Mid Glam.

RAHMAN, Muhammad Khalilur Church Road Surgery, 113a Church Road, Burgess Hill RH15 9AA Tel: 01444 244294 — MB BS Karachi 1964. GP Burgess Hill, W. Sussex.

RAHMAN, Muhammad Mahbubur The Surgery, 482 Southend Road, Hornchurch RM12 5PA Tel: 01708 476036 Fax: 01708 471330 — MB BS 1970 Dacca, Bangladesh.

RAHMAN, Muhammad Rezaur 62 St Michael's Avenue, Margate CT9 3UH — MB BS 1981 Karachi; MRCP (UK) 1993; MRCPI 1993.

RAHMAN, Muhammad Shafiquer 5 Gosberton Road, London SW12 8LE Tel: 020 8673 5309 — MB BS 1958 Dacca. (Dacca)

RAHMAN, Muhammed Maerdy Surgery, North Terrace, Maerdy, Ferndale CF43 4DD Tel: 01443 733202 Fax: 01443 733730.

RAHMAN, Mushtaqur 13 Hanover Road, Norwich NR2 2HD — MB BS 1989 Newc.; MRCP (UK) 1993. Specialist Regist. in Diabetes & Endocrinol. the Norf. & Norwich Hosp. NHS Trust. Prev: SHO (Paediat.) City Hosp. Birm.; SHO (Med.) Lodge Moor Hosp. Sheff.; Resid. Med. Off. Good Hope Hosp. Sutton Coldfield.

RAHMAN, Mustafizur Blackburn Royal Infirmary, X-Ray Department, Infirmary Road, Blackburn BB2 2LR; 210 Preston Road, Chorley PR6 7BA — MB BS Dacca 1966; FRCS Ed. 1974; FRCR 1979; DMRD Eng. 1977. (Dacca Med. Coll.) Cons. Radiol. Blackburn Roy. Infirm. Socs: Brit. Soc. Interven. Radiol.; Brit. Nuclear Med. Soc. Prev: Sen. Regist. (Radiol.) Manch. Roy. Infirm.; Regist. (Gen. Surg.) Burnley Gen. Hosp.

RAHMAN, Mustafizur Department of Microbiology, King's Mill Hospital, Sutton-in-Ashfield NG17 4JL Fax: 01623 672304; 2 Chartwell Grove, Mapperley Plains, Nottingham NG3 5RD Tel: 0115 920 7403 — MB BS 1967 Dacca; FRCPath 1987, M 1975; Dip. Bact. Lond 1972. (Dacca Med. Coll.) Cons. Med. Microbiol. King's Mill Hosp. Trust, Near Mansfield, Notts.; Hon. Clin. Teach. Nottm. Univ. Med. Sch. Nottm. Socs: Brit. Soc. Antimicrob. Chem.v; New York Acad. Sci.; Path. Soc. of GB & Irel. (Comm. Mem. 1997-2000). Prev: Sen. Regist. (Microbiol.) St. Geo. Hosp. Lond.; Regist. (Path.) St. Bart. Hosp. Lond.; Demonst. (Path.) Mymensingh Med. Coll., Bangladesh.

RAHMAN, Nasima Akhtar The Parc, Litchard Hill, Bridgend CF31 1QQ Tel: 01656 657734 — MB BS 1969 Dacca; DObst Dub. 1981. (Dhaka Med. Coll.) Clin. Asst. (Psychiat.) Glanrhyd Hosp. Bridgend. Prev: Clin. Asst. (O & G) P.ss of Wales Hosp. Bridgend.

RAHMAN, Natasha 48 Norfolk Street, Norwich NR2 2SN — MB BS 1996 Lond.

RAHMAN, Nurun Nahar 53 St James Road, Rainhill, Prescot L35 0PE — LMSSA 1993 Lond.

RAHMAN, Rezaur Medical Centre, 3 Strouts Place, London E2 7QU Tel: 020 7739 1972; 10 Forest Close, Snaresbrook, London E11 1PY Tel: 020 8989 1411 Fax: 020 7739 6906 Email: rezaurrahman72@hotmail.com — MB BS 1961 Dacca; MRCS Eng. LRCP Lond. 1975; MRCPsych 1972; DPM Eng. 1966. (Dacca Med. Coll.) Prev: Asst. Prof. Psychiat. Med. Coll. & Hosp. Rajshahi, Bangladesh; Consult. Ment. Hosp. Pabna, Bangladesh.

RAHMAN, Sabera Nazneen 4 Sates Way, Bristol BS9 4SD — BM BCh 1991 Oxf.; BA Oxf. 1988.

RAHMAN, Sadequr Flat 5, Queens Court, 6 Grove Park, London SE5 8LS — MB BS 1998 Lond.; MB BS Lond 1998.

RAHMAN, Sally-Anne The Surgery, Sundial Lane, Great Barr, Birmingham B43 6PA Tel: 0121 358 0082 — BM BCh 1970 Oxf.; MRCGP 1975.

RAHMAN, Samantha 14 Railey Mews, London NW5 2PA — MB BS 1993 Lond.

***RAHMAN, Shabana** 318 Pershore Road, Edgbaston, Birmingham B5 7QY Tel: 0121 440 8598 — MB ChB 1996 Sheff.

RAHMAN, Shah Mohammed Lutfur 7 Begbie Road, Blackheath, London SE3 8BY Tel: 020 8856 2025 — MB BS 1959 Dacca; DLO Eng. 1979. (Dacca Med. Coll.) Prev: Regist. (ENT) Walsall Gp. Hosps.

RAHMAN, Shah Mohammed Siddiqur Shalimar, 131 Stonecross Lane, Lowton, Warrington WA3 1JT — MB BS 1962 Dacca.

RAHMAN, Shaikh O Cwmaman Health Centre, 6-14 Glanaman Road, Aberdare CF44 6HY Tel: 01685 873002 Fax: 01685 872179.

RAHMAN, Shakil Ur M Floor Reception, Respiratory Medicine, Royal Hallamshire Hospital, Glossop Road, Sheffield S10 2JF Tel: 01742 766222; 36 Timbercroft, Ewell, Epsom KT19 OTD — MB BS 1983 Karachi; MRCP (UK) 1991. Lect. & Sen. Regist. (Gen. Med.) Roy. Hallamsh. & N. Gen. Hosp. Sheff. Prev: Regist. (Teach.) Sheff. Univ. Hosp.; Regist. Doncaster Roy. Infirm.

RAHMAN, Shamima BEM Unit, Institute of Child Health, 30 Guilford Street, London WC1N 1EM Tel: 020 7404 6191, 020 7905 2134 Email: s.rahman@ich.ucl.ac.uk — BM BCh 1988 Oxf.; BA (Hons.) Oxf. 1985; MRCP (UK) 1991. (Oxford University) Clin. Lect. in Paediat. Metab. Med., Inst. of Child Health, Lond.; Hon. Specialist Regist. in Paediat. Metab. Med., Gt. Ormond St. Hosp., Lond. Prev: Regist. (Paediat.) John Radcliffe Hosp. Oxf. MRC Clin. Train. Fell. Inst. Child Health Lond. & Hon. Regist. Gt. Ormond St. Hosp. Childr. Lond.; Clin. Research Fell. Roy. Childr. Hosp. Melbourne, Austral.; Regist. (Paediat.) St. Mary's Hosp. Paddington.

RAHMAN, Shanim Ara 8 Willerby Drive, Whitebridge Park, Gosforth, Newcastle upon Tyne NE3 5LL — MB ChB 1996 Liverp.

RAHMAN, Mr Sheikh Mohammad Jamalur 2 Llandennis Road, Cardiff CF23 6EF Tel: 029 2074 7525 Fax: 01222 747525 — MB BS Dacca 1968; FRCS Ed. 1986; DLO RCS Eng. 1978. (Dacca Medical Coll.) Locum Cons. ENT.

RAHMAN, Shelley Louise Flat 116, Albany House, 41 Judd St., London WC1H 9QS — BChir 1994 Camb.

RAHMAN, Shewli 2 Glyncornel Close, Tonypandy CF40 2JT Tel: 01443 431045 — MB ChB 1993 Birm. SHO (Gen. Med.) Derby Roy. Infirm.

RAHMAN, Shupa Gitika 93 Boundary Road, London SW19 2DE — MB BS 1992 Lond.

RAHMAN, Snigdha 23 Byron Close, Ouston, Chester-le-Street DH2 1JR Tel: 0191 410 3901 — MB BS 1970 Dacca.

RAHMAN, Syed Irfanur 131 Touchwood Hall Close, Solihull B91 2UE — MB BS 1971 Patna; MRGOG 1981.

RAHMAN, Tahmina 18 Fairlie Avenue, Mansfield NG19 6RH — MB ChB 1996 Ed.

RAHMAN, Tariq Akhtar Cecil Square Surgery, 1 Cecil Square, Margate CT9 1BD Tel: 01843 232222 Fax: 01843 232205 — MRCS Eng. LRCP Lond. 1981; MRCS Eng LRCP Lond 1981; MBBS.

RAHMAN, Tracey Showkatara 3 Knight Street, Didsbury, Manchester M20 6WG — MB ChB 1993 Manch.

RAHMAN, Waheed 28 Kelvin Road, Cardiff CF23 5ET — MB BCh 1997 Wales.

RAHMAN, Yorick 83 Ribblesdale Road, London SW16 6SF — MB BS 1991 Lond.

RAHMAN, Ziaur 187 Ecclesall Road S., Sheffield S11 9PN — MB BS 1962 Gauhati; DTCD Wales 1970; DTM & H Eng. 1968. (Assam Med. Coll. Dibrugarh) Med. Advis. DHSS. Socs: Pneumoconiosis Med. Panel Sheff.; Trent Regional Thoracic Soc. & Occupat. Soc. Prev: Med. Off. DHSS; Med. Asst. Lodge Moor Hosp. Sheff. & Chest Clinic Roy. Infirm. Sheff.; SHO (Chest Med. & Gen. Med.) Lodge Moor Hosp. Sheff.

RAHMANIE, Nooria 7 Claydon House, Holders Hill Road, London NW4 1LS — MD 1971 Kabul.

RAHMANOU, Philip PO Box 20, Altrincham WA14 1BJ — MB ChB 1997 Liverp.

RAHMAT POUR MONFARED, Marjan 28 Sand's Wharf, Ferryman Quay, London SW6 2UT — MB BS 1993 Lond. (King's Coll. Sch. Med. & Dent.) Socs: BMA; RSM.

RAHMATHUNISA, Abdul Azeez c/o B.S.A. Rahman, East International Ltd., 2nd Floor Langham House, Regent St., London W1R 5AL — MB BS 1970 Madras.

RAHMATI, Margaret Anne (Spittle) 1 Berkeley Close, Moor Lane, Staines TW19 6ED Tel: 01784 462352 — MB BChir 1993 Camb.; MA Camb. 1995, BA 1991; MRCP (UK) 1996. (Camb. Univ.) Specialist Regist. (Nephrol.) W Mid. Rotat. Prev: Research Fell., Renal Research Inst., New York, USA.

RAHMATULLAH KHAN, Dr 51 Fair Cross Avenue, Barking IG11 8RD — MB BS 1961 Punjab; MB BS Punjab (Pakistan) 1961; FRCR 1975. (King Edwd. Med. Coll. Lahore)

RAHUJA, Saika Parveen 16 Abingdon Road, Urmston, Manchester M41 0GG Tel: 0161 748 2119; Flat 7, Foresterhill Court, Aberdeen AB25 2WA Tel: 01224 662314 — MB ChB 1993 Liverp.

RAHUJA, Shabbir Ahmed S King's Medical Centre, 7 Kings Road, Old Trafford, Manchester M16 7RT Tel: 0161 226 1288 Fax: 0161 232 1575; 11 Rivers Hill, Gdns., Hale, Altrincham WA15 0AZ Tel: 0161 980 1993 — MB BS 1965 Punjab; BSc Karachi 1959; MB BS Punjab (Pakistan) 1965; DLO Eng. 1973. (Nishtar Med. Coll. Multan) Gen. Med. Practitioner; Clin. Asst. ENT Dept. Wyntheshaw Hosp. Manch. Socs: Med. Protect. Soc.; Pakistan Med. Assn.; Sindhi Doctors Assn.

RAI, Amarjit Singh 148 Warren Crescent, Shirley, Southampton SO16 6AX — BM 1990 Soton.

RAI, Ashok Worcester Royal Infirmary, Dept. of Rheumatology, Newtown Branch, Newtown Rd, Worcester WR5 1HN; Clearview, 1 Chiltern Close, Great Witley, Worcester WR6 6HL — MB ChB 1985 Birm. Cons. Rheumatologist acute Worcs. NHS Trust. Socs: Fell.Roy. Soc. of Med. .

RAI, Gurcharan Singh Tel: 020 7288 5326 Fax: 020 7288 3008; 22 Northwick Circus, Kenton, Harrow HA3 0DY — MD 1978 Newc.; MSc Lond. 1977; MB BS 1971; FRCP Lond. 1988; MRCP (UK) 1974. (Newcastle-upon-Tyne) Cons. Phys. (Geriat. Med.) Whittington Hosp. Lond. Socs: FRSM (Sec. of Sect. of Geriat.s & Gerontology); Brit. Geriat. Soc.; Amer. Geriat. Soc. Prev: Sen. Regist. (Geriat. Med.) Cambridge; Sen. Research Fell. Universisty Newc.; Regist. Newc. Univ. Hosps.

RAI, Harjeev Singh 18 Alum Cl, Coventry CV6 5TQ — MB BCh 1997 Wales.

RAI, Harnek Singh 16 Warstone Terrace, Birmingham B21 9NE — MB ChB 1989 Dundee.

RAI, Jagjit 62 Homeway Road, Leicester LE5 5RG — MB ChB 1992 Sheff.

RAI, Jagjit Singh 43 Avenue Road, Southall UB1 3BW — MB ChB 1993 Aberd.

RAI, Jasdev Singh 32 Manor Avenue, Hounslow TW4 7JL — MB ChB 1979 Liverp.

RAI, Jatinder 46 Ednam Road, Wolverhampton WV4 5BP — MB BS 1998 Lond.; MB BS Lond 1998.

RAI, Kalwant 4 Pippin Close, Bury St Edmunds IP32 7HH — BM 1987 Soton.

RAI, Kundadka Divaker Honicknowle Green Medical Centre, Honicknowle, Plymouth PL5 3PY Tel: 01752 777207 Fax: 01752 775556; 91 Dunraven Drive, Derriford, Plymouth PL6 6AT — MB BS 1974 Mysore. (Mysore Medical College)

RAI, Nalini Rai and Duke, Bingley Health Centre, Myrtle Place, Bingley BD16 2TL Tel: 01274 566617 Fax: 01274 772345; Fieldhead Barn, Street Lane, West Morton, Keighley BD20 5UP Tel: 01535 609696 — MB BS 1973 Delhi; DCH RCPS Glas. 1976. (Maulana Azad Med. Coll. New Delhi) Clin. Asst. Bingley Hosp. Prev: Clin. Med. Off. Leeds AHA; Clin. Med. Off. N.ants. AHA.

RAI

RAI, Neerja 11 Chafinch Close, Scunthorpe DN15 8EL — MB BS 1981 Lucknow; MD India 1985; MRCOG 1993. (King Geo. Med. Coll. Lucknow, India) Specialist Regist. (O & G) Hull Matern. & P.ss Roy. Hosp. Hull. Prev: Regist. (O & G) P. Chas. Hosp. Merthyr Tydfil; Regist. (O & G) Glas. Roy. Infirm.

RAI, Rajendra Singh 105 Highview Road, London W13 0HL — MB BS 1988 Lond.; BSc (Hons.) Lond. 1985, MB BS 1988. Research Regist. Samarit. Hosp. for Wom. Lond. Prev: SHO (Gyn.) Samarit. Hosp. for Wom. Lond.; SHO (O & G) Lond. Hosp. Whitechapel; Ho. Phys. Med. Unit. St. Thos. Hosp. Lond.

RAI, Sanjey 7 Birch Hill Crescent, Wardle, Rochdale OL12 9QF — MB ChB 1993 Manch.

RAI, Santoch Singh Dove House, 15 Bakery Drive, Stockton-on-Tees TS19 0SN — MB ChB 1987 Manch.

RAI, Satya Kumar 21 The Green, St Leonards-on-Sea TN38 0SU — MB BS 1979 Punjabi, India.

RAI, Vikram Singh University College Hospital, Gower St., London WC1E 6AU; 9 Samels Court, South Black Lion Lane, Hammersmith, London W6 9TL — MB BS 1990 Lond.; BSc (Hons.) Lond. 1986, MB BS 1990. SHO (Obst.) Univ. Coll. Hosp. Lond. Prev: SHO (Gyn.) Univ. Coll. Hosp. Lond.

RAI CHOUDHURY, Krishna Bransholme Health Centre, Goodhart Road, Bransholme, Hull HU7 4DW Tel: 01482 825496; 4 Pine Meadows, Kirkella, Hull HU10 7NS — MB BS 1975 Dacca; DCH RCP Lond. 1981; DFFP 1997. Assoc. Community Paediat. Childr.'s Centre Hull. Socs: Hull Med. Soc. Prev: Clin. Med. Off. (Community Med.) Hull; Trainee GP Hull VTS; Regist. (Paediat.) Luton & Dunstable Hosps.

RAI CHOWDHURY, Saroj Lal 208 Mill Lane, Liverpool L15 8LJ — MB BS 1952 Calcutta; MRCOG 1964. (R.G. Kar Med. Coll.)

***RAICAR, Sheila** 45 Corringham Road, Wembley HA9 9PX — MB BS 1961 Karachi.

RAICHOUDHURY, Benjamin Sailen 1 Ffynnon-y-Coed, Clydbach, Abergavenny NP7 0LN — MB BCh 1974 Wales; MRCGP 1978.

RAICHURA, Manilal Madhavji The Surgery, 95 Grasmere Avenue, Wembley HA9 8TF Tel: 020 8904 8045 Fax: 020 8908 5363; 13 Sidney Road, Harrow HA2 6QE — MB ChB 1963 Birm.; MRCP (UK) 1971; LMCC Canada 1975.

RAICHURA, Naresh Hodnet Medical Centre, Drayton Road, Hodnet, Market Drayton TF9 3NF Tel: 0163 084230 Fax: 0163 084770; The Old Vicarage, Cheswardine, Market Drayton TF9 2RN Tel: 01630 685230 Fax: 01630 685770 — MB ChB 1978 Liverp.; MSc Lond. 1985.

RAICHURA, Vijay Kumar University Medical Practice, Elms Road, Off Pritchatts Road, Edgbaston, Birmingham B15 2SE Tel: 0121 414 5111 Fax: 0121 414 5108 — MB BS 1982 Lond.; MRCGP 1986; DRCOG 1986. (Guy's) Med. Off. Univ. Birm. Prev: Trainee GP St. Bart. Hosp. VTS; Ho. Phys. Guy's Hosp. Lond.

RAIJIWALA, Nipun Tarunkumar House F11, Residences, Princess of Wales Hospital, Coity Road, Bridgend CF31 1RQ; 50 Tremains Court, Brackla, Bridgend CF31 2SR — MB BCh BAO 1986 Belf.

RAIKES, Annette Sylvia (retired) 9 Wychwood Drive, Bournemouth BH2 6JG Tel: 01202 290777 — FRCP Lond. 1985, MRCP (UK) 1977; MRCS Eng. LRCP Lond. 1961. Prev: Cons. Paediat.

RAIL, John Frederick Whitburn (retired) 1 Ruston Avenue, Rustington, Littlehampton BN16 2AP Tel: 01903 786522 — MRCS Eng. LRCP Lond. 1952. Prev: Local Civil Serv. Med. Off.

RAILTON, Angela Department of Obstetrics and Gynaecology, Hope Hospital, Salford M6 — MD 1988 Cape Town; MB BCh Wales 1977; FRCOG 1995; MRCOG 1982. Cons. O & G Hope Hosp. Salford.

RAILTON, Mr Gilbert Taylor Kingston Hospital, Wolverton Avenue, Kingston upon Thames KT2 7Q Tel: 020 8546 7711; Bell House, Fairmile Pk Road, Cobham KT11 2PP — MB BCh 1977 Wales; FRCS Eng. 1982. Cons. Orthop. Surg. Kingston. Prev: Sen. Regist. (Orthop.) Lond. Hosp. Whitechapel.

RAILTON, Katherine Louise 3 The Brackens, Locks Heath, Southampton SO31 6TU — MB BS 1997 Lond.

RAIMAN, Alistair Charles Northbourne Medical Centre, Eastern Avenue, Shoreham-by-Sea BN43 6PE Tel: 01273 464640 Fax: 01273 440913; 16 Windlesham Gardens, Shoreham-by-Sea BN43 5AD Tel: 01273 273748 — MB BS 1985 Lond.; BSc (Hons.) Lond. 1982, MB BS 1985; MRCGP 1989. (The Royal London Hospital) Clin. Asst. DOME Worthing Hosp.; Med. Off. Brighton Hove Albion Football Club. Socs: BMA & Med. Protect. Soc.; Brit. Med. Acupunct. Soc. Prev: Occupat. Health Phys. Worthing Priority Care Hosp. Trust; GP Kawerau. NZ; GP Lond.

RAIMAN, John Draper The Health Centre, Handsworth Avenue, Highams Park, London E4 9PD Tel: 020 8527 0913; The Park House Surgery, 1 Cavendish Road, Highams Park, London E4 9NQ Tel: 020 8523 1401 — MB BS 1957 Lond.; FRCGP 1985, M 1965; DObst RCOG 1960. (Lond. Hosp.) Course Organiser Whipps Cross VTS. Prev: Ho. Surg. & Ho. Phys. St. Mary's Hosp. E.bourne; Cas. Off. & Sen. Ho. Off. (O & G) St. Margts. Hosp. Epping.

RAIMAN, Julian Andrew Jonathon 35 Castle Avenue, London E4 9PY Email: raiman@globalnet.co.uk — MB BS 1992 Lond.; MRCP (Paediat.) Lond. 1996. Specialist Regist. (Paediat.) S. E. Thames Region. Socs: MRCPCH.

RAIMES, Mr Simon Aylwin Department of Surgery, Cumberland Infirmary, Carlisle CA2 7HY Tel: 01228 814144 Email: susan.pedrosa@ncumbria-acute.nhs.uk — MD 1990 Newc.; FRCS Eng. 1983. Cons. Gen. Surg. & Gastroenterol. Cumbld. Infirm. Socs: Brit. Soc. Gastroenterol.; Assn. Upper G.I. Surg.; Assn. of Surg.s of Gt. Britain and Irel. (Counc. Mem.). Prev: Sen. Regist. (Gen. Surg.) Freeman Hosp. Newc. u Tyne; Lect. (Surg.) Chinese Univ., Hong Kong.

RAIMONDO, Carmelo 32 Windmill Rise, Kingston upon Thames KT2 7TU — State Exam Bologna 1983.

RAINA, C P The Surgery, 57 Gladstone Avenue, Manor Park, London E12 7NR Tel: 020 8471 4764 Fax: 020 8472 3378 — MB BS 1972 Jammu & Kashmir; MB BS 1972 Jammu & Kashmir.

RAINBOW, Daniel James 29 Riffel Road, London NW2 4PB — MB BS 1996 Lond.

RAINBOW, Josephine Ruth 6 Monkton Way, Speen, Princes Risborough HP27 0RZ Tel: 01494 488658 — BM BCh 1993 Oxf.; MRCP (Paeds.) Lond. 1996. Paediat. Regist. New Childr.'s Hosp. Sydney, Australia.

RAINE, Anne Ward 15, Medical Oncology Unit, Bradford Royal Infirmary, Bradford BD9 6RJ Tel: 01274 364095 Fax: 01274 366745; Cleughend, 1 The Bullfield, Harden, Bingley BD16 1HN Tel: 01535 272780 Fax: 01535 274699 — MB BS 1977 Newc.; MRCGP 1981; DRCOG 1980; Dip. Palliat. Med. Wales 1997. Staff Grade in Oncol. Prev: Staff Grade in Palliat. Care; GP.

RAINE, Cameron Plastic Surgery, Shotley Bridge Hospital, Consett DH9 0NB — MB ChB 1990 Ed.

RAINE, Mr Christopher Howard ENT Department, Bradford Royal Infirmary, Duckworth Lane, Bradford BD9 6RJ Tel: 01274 542200 — MB BS 1976 Newc.; ChM Liverp. 1987; BSc (Hons.) Newc. 1973, MB BS 1976; FRCS Eng. 1980. Cons. ENT Surg. Bradford Roy. Infirm. Prev: Sen. Regist. W. Midl. Rotat.; Rotat. Regist. Liverp. HA.

RAINE, Geoffrey James 24B Beaconsfield Road, Bexley DA5 2AE; 6 Apton Road, Bishop's Stortford CM23 3SN Tel: 01279 758574 — MB ChB 1984 Bristol; FRCA 1993. Cons. Anaesth. P.ss Alexandra Hosp. Harlow. Socs: OAA; ICS; Assn. Anaesth.

RAINE, Mr George Edward Thompson 144 Harley Street, London W1G 7LE Tel: 020 7935 0023 Fax: 020 7935 5972; 32 Pelhams Walk, Esher KT10 8QD Tel: 01372 466656 Fax: 01372 470265 Email: georgeraine@paedic.demon.co.uk — MB BChir Camb. 1958; MA Camb. 1959; FRCS Eng. 1966. (Camb. & St. Thos.) p/t Cons. Orthop. Surg. Teddington Memor. Hosp. & New Vict. Hosp. Kingston; Orthop. Adviser Various Sporting Bodies. Socs: Fell. BOA; BOSTA; Fell. Roy. Soc. Med. Prev: Cons. Orthop. Surg. W. Middlx. Univ. Hosp.; Orthop. Adviser Ballet Rambert Sch.; Sen. Regist. (Orthop.) St. Geo. Hosp. Lond., Rowley Bristow Orthop. Hosp. Pyrford & Centre for Hip Surg. Wrightington.

RAINE, John (retired) Mar House, Arkendale, Knaresborough HG5 0RG — MB ChB 1953 Leeds; MRCGP 1964. Prev: Ho. Surg. Gen. Infirm. Leeds.

RAINE, Joseph Dept Paediatrics, Whittington Hospital, Highgate Hill, London N19 — MB ChB 1983 Manch.; MD Manch. 1995; MRCP (UK) 1986; DCH RCP Lond. 1986. Cons. Paediat. Whittington Hosp. Hon. Sen. Lect., Univ. Coll., Lond. Socs: Brit. Soc. of Paediatric Endocrinol. and Diabates. Prev: Sen. Regist. (Paediat.) Addenbrooke's Hosp. Camb.; Cons. Paediat. Whipps Cross Hosp.; Research Fell., Nat. Heart & Lung Inst.

RAINE, June Munro 177 Hadham Road, Bishop's Stortford CM23 2QA — BM BCh 1978 Oxf.; MA, MSc, BM BCh Oxf. 1978; MRCP (UK) 1980; MRCGP 1982; DRCOG 1982. Sen. Med. Off. Meds. Div. DoH Lond. Prev: GP Oxf.; Research Regist. (Endocrinol. & Metab.) John Radcliffe Hosp. Oxf.; SHO (Med.) John Radcliffe Hosp. Oxf.

RAINE, Nicola Meriel Noble 19 Beaumont St, Oxford OX1 2NA Tel: 01865 240501; 40 Ash Grove, Headington, Oxford OX3 9JL Tel: 01865 762458 — MB BS 1989 Lond.; MA Oxf. 1990; FRCS Ed. 1994. p/t GP Princip.

RAINE, Mr Peter Alan Malden Royal Hospital for Sick Children, Yorkhill, Glasgow G3 8SJ Tel: 0141 201 0000 Fax: 0141 201 0865; 5 Westbourne Drive, Bearsden, Glasgow G61 4BD Tel: 0141 942 8881 — MB BChir 1967 Camb.; MA Camb. 1967; FRCS Glas. 1984; FRCS Ed. 1973; MRCS Eng. LRCP Lond. 1967. (Camb. & St. Bart.) Cons. Paediat. Surg. Roy. Hosp. Sick Childr. Glas.; Barclay Lect. (Paediat. Surg.) Univ. Glas. Socs: Brit. Assn. Paediat. Surg.; Brit. Soc. Paediat. Gastroenterol.; Craniofacial Soc. Prev: Regist. Roy. Childr. Hosp. Melbourne, Austral.; Lect. (Paediat. Surg.) Univ. Glas.; Regist. (Surg.) Lothian (Edin.) HB.

RAINE, Philip Mark 7 Vale View Close, Llandough, Penarth CF64 2QB — MB BCh 1977 Wales; DRCOG 1979.

RAINE, Richard Andrew 64 Oakham Road, Harborne, Birmingham B17 9DG — MB ChB 1987 Birm.

RAINE, Rosalind Ann Health Services Research Unit, London School of Hygiene & Tropical Medicine, Keppel St., London WC1E 7HT Tel: 020 7927 2395 Fax: 020 7580 8283 Email: r.raine@lshtm.ac.uk; 2 Upper Terrace, London NW3 6RH Tel: 020 7432 8107 — MB BS 1989 Lond.; BSc (1st cl. Hons.) Lond. 1986; MSc (Distinc.) Lond. 1994; MFPHM 1997. (University College London) MRC & N. Thames Lect. (Health Servs. Research) LSHTM Lond.; Hon. Cons. in Pub. Health Lambeth, S.wark & Lewisham HA.

RAINE, Wendy Jane Bailey D.C.F.P. Old Mill Studios, 187 Old Rutherglen Road, Gorbals, Glasgow G5 0RE Tel: 0141 300 6360 Fax: 0141 300 6399; 5 Westbourne Drive, Bearsden, Glasgow G61 4BD Tel: 0141 942 8881 — MB ChB 1970 Ed.; BMedSci 1968 Ed.; MRCPsych 1975. (Edin.) Cons. Child Psychiat. Yorkhill NHS Trust Glas. Prev: Cons. Child & Adolesc. Psychiat. Roy. Hosp. Sick Childr. Glas.; Sen. Regist. (Child & Family Psychiat.) Roy. Hosp. Sick Childr. Glas.; Regist. (Child Psychiat.) Roy. Childr. Hosp. Melbourne, Austral.

RAINE-FENNING, Nicholas John 10 Westfield Hall, Hagley Road, Edgbaston, Birmingham B16 9LG — MB ChB 1992 Birm.

RAINER, Mr Ernest Hermann (retired) 5 Marlings Close, Marlings Park, Chislehurst BR7 6RL Tel: 01689 602045 — LRCP LRCS Ed. LRFPS Glas. 1941; FRCS Ed. 1948. Prev: ENT Surg. Dartford & Sevenoaks Hosps.

RAINES, Julia Elizabeth 37 Regent Road, Horsforth, Leeds LS18 4NP — MB ChB 1988 Leeds; MRCP (UK) 1991; MPH Leeds 1994.

RAINES, Karen Patricia Whispering Pines, Holmefield Avenue, Thornton-Cleveleys FY5 2QP — MB ChB 1980 Sheff.; DRCOG 1982.

RAINES, Mr Michael Francis Department of Ophthalmology, Victoria Hospital, Blackpool FY3 8NR Tel: 01253 303472 Fax: 01253 306743; 8 Church Road, Lytham St Annes FY8 5LH Tel: 01253 730302 Fax: 01253 730304 — MB ChB 1980 Sheff.; FRCOphth 1989; FRCS Ed. 1985; DO RCS Eng. 1984. Cons. Ophth. Surg. Vict. Hosp. Blackpool; Hon. Sen. Lect., Univ. of Centr. Lancs., Preston. Socs: FRSM; U.K. & N. Ire. Soc. Of Cataract & Refractive Surg.; Amer. Acad. Of Opthalmology. Prev: Sen. Regist. (Ophth.) Birm. & Midl. Eye Hosp.

RAINES, Reginald John Hall 270 Woodchurch Road, Birkenhead CH43 5UU Tel: 0151 608 3475 Fax: 0151 608 9535; Point House, Ferry Lane, Sealand Road, Chester CH1 6QF Tel: 01244 372787 — MRCS Eng. LRCP Lond. 1950. (St. Bart.) Prev: Capt. RAMC TA.

RAINEY, Mr Albert Edmund Simpson Iorama, 3 Sandal Avenue, Sandal, Wakefield WF2 7LP Tel: 01924 56971 — MB BCh BAO 1960 Belf.; FRCSI 1965; FRCS Ed. 1966. (Qu. Univ. Belf.) Cons. Orthop. Surg. Pinderfields Gen. Hosp. & Clayton Hosp. Wakefield. Socs: BMA; Brit. Orthop. Assn. Prev: Ho. Off. Roy. Vict. Hosp. Belf.; Orthop. Regist. Belf. City Hosp.; Sen. Orthop. Regist. Musgrave Pk. Hosp. Belf. & N.. Irel. Orthop.

RAINEY, Andrew John 38 Concanon Road, Brixton, London SW2 5TA; 75 Tilchouse Street, Hitchin SG5 2DY — MB BS 1984 Newc.; BMedSc Newc. 1981; MRCPath 1995. Cons. (Histopath.) Lister Hosp. Stevenage Herts. Prev: Sen. Regist. (Histopath.) Roy. Sussex Co. Hosp. Brighton; Sen. Regist. (Morbid Anat.) King's Coll. Hosp. Lond.; Regist. (Histopath.) John Radcliffe Hosp. Oxf.

RAINEY, David Selbert Neillsbrook Road Surgery, 5 Neillsbrook Road, Randalstown, Antrim BT41 3AE Tel: 028 9447 2575 Fax: 028 9447 3653; Connors Wood, Randalstown, Antrim BT41 3LB — MB BCh BAO 1964 Belf.; FRCGP 1986, M 1971; MICGP 1987.

RAINEY, Garrett John 5 Thornhill Malone, Belfast BT9 6SS — MB ChB 1998 Dund.; MB ChB Dund 1998.

RAINEY, George Wesley Ballysillan Group Practice, 321 Ballysillan Road, Belfast BT14 6RD Tel: 028 9071 3689/7843 Fax: 028 9071 0626 — MB BCh BAO 1975 Belf.

RAINEY, Mr Henry Adrian Woodram Mead, Corfe, Taunton TA3 7AP — MB BCh BAO 1958 Belf.; FRCSI 1967. Cons. Orthop. & Traum. Surg. Som. AHA. Prev: Ho. Off. Belf. City Hosp.; Surg. Regist. Roy. Vict. Hosp. Belf.; Sen. Regist. P.ss Eliz. Orthop. Hosp. Exeter.

RAINEY, Jill Catherine Anne 61 Shore Road, Greenisland, Carrickfergus BT38 8TZ — MB ChB 1995 Glas.

RAINEY, Lynne The Hemmel, Great Whittington, Newcastle upon Tyne NE19 2HP — MB ChB 1983 Dundee; MRCP (UK) 1987.

RAINEY, Mervyn Glenn Argyll & Clyde Acute Hospitals NHS Trust, Inverclyde Royal Hospital, Greenock PA16 0XN Tel: 01475 633777 Email: mg.rainey@vol.scot.nhs.uk — MB ChB 1982 Ed.; MA Camb. 1983, BA 1979; MRCP (UK) 1987; MRCPath 1997. Cons. Haematologist, Argyll & Clyde Acute Hosps. NHS Trust. Prev: Sen. Regist. (Haemat.) Plymouth; Sen. Regist. (Haemat.) Bristol.; Research Fell. (Haemat.) S.mead Hosp. Bristol.

RAINEY, Norman Alexander Ballysillan Group Practice, 321 Ballysillan Road, Belfast BT14 6RD Tel: 028 9071 3689/7843 Fax: 028 9071 0626 — MB BCh BAO Belf. 1970. (Queen's Belfast)

RAINEY, Robert Stephen Chapman and Partners, 370-372 Cregagh Road, Belfast BT6 9EY Tel: 028 9049 2214 Fax: 028 9049 2214 — MB BCh BAO 1982 Belf.; MRCGP 1986; DRCOG 1985; DCH Dub. 1984. (Belf.) GP Belf. Socs: BMA.

RAINEY, Veronica 50 Barnhill Road, Dumbarton G82 2SN — MB ChB 1998 Glas.; MB ChB Glas 1998.

RAINFORD, Alison Beighton Health Centre, Queens Road, Beighton, Sheffield S20 1BJ Tel: 0114 269 5061; 25 Ranmoor Crescent, Sheffield S10 3GW Tel: 0114 230 7274 — MB ChB 1986 Sheff.; MRCGP 1993; DRCOG 1990; DCH RCP Lond. 1990. Prev: SHO (Psychiat.) Derby Ment. Health Unit Pastures Hosp.; Trainee GP Retainer Scheme Bolsover.

RAINFORD, David John, MBE, OStJ, QHS, Air Commodore RAF Med. Br. Scotsford Close, 23 Bates Lane, Weston Turville, Aylesbury HP22 5SL Tel: 0129 661 3707 Email: david@rainford.clara.net — MB BS 1969 Lond.; FRCP Lond. 1985; MRCP (UK) 1972; MRCS Eng. LRCP Lond. 1969; FFOM (Hon.) 1999; FRAeS 1998. (Char. Cross) Chief Exec., Defence secondary Care agency; Cons. Adviser Med. to Roy. RAF, Oman; Cons. Civil Aviat. Auth.; Hon. Sen. Lect. (Renal. Med.) Roy. Postgrad. Med. Sch. Hammersmith Hosp. Socs: Fell. Roy. Soc. Med.; Renal Assn.; Eur. Dialysis & Transpl. Assn. Prev: Clin. Dir., Roy. Air Force; Commanding Off. P.ss Mary's RAF Hosp. Halton; Sen. Regist. (Med.) Char. Cross Hosp. Lond.

RAINFORD, Frederick Alan (retired) 6 Victoria Road, Aughton, Ormskirk L39 5AU Tel: 01695 422931 — MB ChB Manch. 1947; MRCS Eng. LRCP Lond. 1948. Prev: Ho. Surg. (Orthop.) & Ho. Surg. Withington Hosp. Manch.

RAINFORD, Paul Jeremy Pilgrim Hospital, Sibsey Road, Boston PE21 9QS Tel: 01205 364801; 47 Spilsby Road, Boston PE21 9NX Tel: 01205 369873 — MB BS 1979 Lond.; MRCPsych 1983. Cons. Psychiat. Pilgrim Hosp. Boston.

RAINFORD, Peter Anthony Parkway Medical Centre, 2 Frenton Close, Chapel House Estate, Newcastle upon Tyne NE5 1EH Tel: 0191 267 1313 Fax: 0191 229 0630; 27 The Chesters, West Denton, Newcastle upon Tyne NE5 1AF Tel: 0191 267 9944 — MB ChB 1960 Liverp.; DObst. RCOG 1965. (Liverp.) Prev: SHO (O & G) MusGr. Pk. Hosp. Taunton; SHO (Med.) Bridgwater & Dist. Hosp.; Ho. Phys. & Ho. Surg. David Lewis N.. Hosp. Liverp.

RAINIER-POPE

RAINIER-POPE, Nicholas David 7 Lordswood Court, Coxford Road, Southampton SO16 5PD — MB ChB 1992 Cape Town; DCH RCP Lond. 1995.

RAINS, Professor Anthony John Harding, CBE 39A St.Cross Road, Winchester SO23 9PR Tel: 01962 869419 — MB BS Lond. 1943; MS Lond. 1952; FRCS Eng. 1948; MRCS Eng. LRCP Lond. 1943. (St. Mary's) Prev: Edr. Jl. Roy. Soc. Med.; Prof. Surg. Char. Cross Hosp.; Asst. Dir. & Regional Postgrad. Dean SW Thames RHA.

RAINS, Kathleen Maude (Fawcitt) 12 Leegate Gardens, Heaton Mersey, Stockport SK4 3NR — MRCS Eng. LRCP Lond. 1942; FFA RCS Eng. 1954; DA Eng. 1945. (Manch.) Cons. Anaesth. N. Manch. Hosps. Prev: Cons. Anaesth. Lancaster & Kendal Hosp. Gp.; Asst. Anaesth. S. Manch. Hosp. Gp.; Sen. Regist. Manch. Roy. Infirm.

RAINS, Simon George Harding Church Street Surgery, Church Street, Starcross, Exeter EX6 8PZ Tel: 01626 890368 Fax: 01626 891330; Tel: 01626 891311 — MB BS 1979 Lond.; BA (Hons.) Oxf. 1976; MRCP (UK) 1982; MRCGP 1988. (St. Thos.) Prev: Regist. (Gen. Med.) St. Mary's Hosp. Lond.; SHO (Gen. Med.) Taunton & Som. Hosps.; Ho. Surg. St. Thos. Hosp. Lond.

RAINSBURY, Mr Paul Albert BUPA Medical Director, IVF Unit, BUPA Roding Hospital, Roding Lane S., Ilford IG4 5PZ Tel: 020 8551 7107 Fax: 020 8551 7486; 2 Woodedge Close, Chingford, London E4 6BB Tel: 020 8523 9171 Fax: 020 8529 1109 Email: prainsbury@doctors.org.uk — MB BCh BAO 1969 Dub.; MA Dub. 1969; FRCOG 1990, M 1974. (TC Dub.) Med. Dir. (IVF) BUPA Roding Hosp., Ilford. Socs: Fell. Roy. Soc. Med.; Brit. Fertil. Soc.; Eur. Soc. Human Reprod. & Embryol. Prev: Med. Dir. Hallam Med. Centre Lond.; Dep. Med. Dir. Bourn Hall Clinic Camb.; Cons. Gyn. Fertil. & IVF Unit Humana Hosp. Lond.

RAINSBURY, Mr Richard Myles Surgical Unit, Royal Hampshire County Hospital, Romsey Road, Winchester SO22 5DG Tel: 01962 825146 Fax: 01962 824640 Email: breastunit@weht.swest.nhs.uk; Bridge House, Twyford, Winchester SO21 1QF Tel: 01962 712145 Fax: 01962 712145 Email: rrainsbury@aol.com — MB BS 1974 Lond.; MS Lond. 1984, BSc (Hon. Pharmacol.) 1971; FRCS Eng. 1979. (Univ. Collee Hosp. Med. Sch.) Cons. Gen. Surg. Roy. Hants. Co. Hosp. Winchester.; Hill Skills Tutor, Raven Dept. of Educat., Roy. Coll. of Surg.s of Eng., Lond. Socs: Brit. BrE. Gp.; BrE. Specialty Gp. of Brit. Assn. of Surgic. Oncol.; Fell. Roy. Soc. of Med. Prev: Sen. Regist. St. Geo. Hosp. Lond.; Hon. Sen. Regist. Roy. Marsden Hosp. Sutton; Regist. (Surg.) St. Jas. Hosp. Lond.

RAINSBURY, Sherwood George William (retired) 225 Manchester New Road, Middleton, manchester M24 1JT — MRCS Eng. LRCP Lond. 1943. Prev: Surg. Lt. RNVR.

RAISON, Helen Elizabeth 53 Down Road, Guildford GU1 2PZ — MB BS 1996 Newc.; BSc, Soton. 1989.

RAISON, John Charles Anthony (retired) 15 The Woodlands, Church Lane, Kings Worthy, Winchester SO23 7QQ Tel: 01962 885722 Email: jonrai@aol.com — MB BChir Camb. 1950; MD Camb. 1963; ECFMG Cert. 1966; FFPHM 1989; FFPHM 1987, M 1974. Prev: Cons. Clin. Physiol. Birm. RHA (Intens. Care).

RAISTRICK, Duncan Stuart 19 Springfield Mount, Leeds LS2 9NJ Tel: 0113 295 1305 Fax: 0113 295 1310 — MB ChB 1971 Leeds; MPhil Lond. 1978; MB ChB Leeds. 1971; FRCPsych 1977. Cons. Psychiat. Leeds Addic. Unit; Cons. Adviser to the Chief Med. Off. (Alcohol Misuse); Sen. Lect. Univ. of Leeds. Socs: Soc. Study Addic. Alcohol & other Drugs.

RAISTRICK, Eleanor Ruth (retired) 8 Southfield Road, Westbury-on-Trym, Bristol BS9 3BH Tel: 0117 962 9242 — MB ChB 1943 Leeds; DObst RCOG 1948. Prev: Med. Asst. Bristol Eye Hosp.

RAIT, David Ernest Student Health Service, University of Aberdeen, Block E, Taylor Buildings, Old Aberdeen, Aberdeen AB24 3UB Tel: 01224 276655 Fax: 01224 272463 — MB ChB 1977 Aberd.

RAIT, Elizabeth Anne East Donnington Street Clinic, East Donnington Street, Darvel KA17 0JR Tel: 01560 320205 Fax: 01560 321643 — MB ChB 1984 Ed.

RAIT, Greta 23 Vesper Rise, Leeds LS5 3NJ — MB ChB 1991 Manch.

RAIT, Robert Bain (retired) Balgray, Springwood Terrace, Peebles EH45 9ET Tel: 01721 721481 — MB ChB 1935 Aberd.

RAITHATHA, Hasmukh Haridas Doncaster Royal Infirmary, Armthrop Road, Doncaster DN2 5LT Tel: 01302 366666 Fax: 01302 320098; 6 Grange Road, Bessacarr, Doncaster DN4 6SA Tel: 01302 532788 — MRCS Eng. LRCP Lond. 1973; T(Anaesth.) 1991; FFA RCSI 1980. (Lond. Hosp.) Cons. (Anaesth.) Doncaster Roy. Infirm. Socs: Coll. Tutor - The Roy. Coll. of Anaesthetics 1992-1998; Linkman - Assn. of Anaesthetics of G.B. & Irel. 1999-to date; Local Negotiating Chairm. - Doncaster & Bassetlaw Hosps. Prev: Sen. Regist. Sheff. Gp. of Hosps.; Regist. (Anaesth.) Roy. Cornw. Hosp. Truro; Ho. Phys. Lond. Hosp.

RAITHATHA, Meera Mahendra 59 Kensington Avenue, Watford WD18 7RZ Tel: 01923 240462 — MB ChB 1995 Bristol. (Bristol) SHO Rotat. (Paediat.) Nottm. QMC. Prev: SHO (Paediat.) Smithmead Bristol Cheltenham.

RAITHATHA, Nitesh University of East Anglia Health Centre, University of East Anglia, Earlham Road, Norwich NR4 7TJ Tel: 01603 592172; Rivendell Cottage, The St, Colton, Norwich NR9 5AB Tel: 01603 880713 — MB BS 1987 Lond.; BSc Lond. 1984; MRCGP 1991; DRCOG 1991. Prev: Trainee GP Taunton VTS.

RAITHATHA, Raju 1 Woodberry Avenue, Winchmore Hill, London N21 3LE Tel: 020 8886 2751 Fax: 020 8882 2891; 40 Freston Gardens, Barnet EN4 9LY — MB BS 1983 Lond.; BSc (Immunol. Physiol.) Lond. 1980; LMSSA Lond. 1983; LMCC 1990; DRCOG 1986. (St. Bart.) Chairm. Enfield S.gate PCG.

RAITT, David Gordon Directorate of Anaesthesia, Leicester General Hospital, Gwendolen Road, Leicester LE5 4PW — MB ChB 1969 Aberd.; FFA RCS Eng. 1976; DA Eng. 1973. (Aberd.) Cons. & Clin. Dir. (Anaesth.) Univ. Hosp.s of Leicester NHS Trust. Prev: Sen. Specialist (Anaesth.) RAF Med. Br.; Med. Director, Leicester Gen. Hosp..

RAITT, Elspeth Jane 52 Painswick Road, Cheltenham GL50 2ER — MB ChB 1991 Leic.; MRCGP 1996. GP Locum, Chesh.

RAITT, George Price 76 Warwick Road, Carlisle CA1 1DU Tel: 01228 24477 — MB ChB 1963 St. And.; MRCGP 1973; DObst RCOG 1965. (St. And.) Mem. Cumbria LMC. Socs: Assur. Med. Soc. Prev: Scheme Organiser E. Cumbria VTS; Ho. Phys. & Ho. Surg. Roy. Infirm. Perth.; Ho. Off. (O & G) Daisy Hill Hosp. Newry.

RAITT, Neil Woodroffe, Dixon and Raitt, Ravenswood Surgery, New Road, Forfar DD8 2AE Tel: 01307 463558 Fax: 01307 468900 — BM BS 1988 Nottm.; MRCGP 1992; DRCOG 1991.

RAJ, Anita Aruna Dilmuir, Penstraze, Chasewater, Truro TR4 8PN — MB ChB 1996 Leeds.

RAJ, Mr Dev Eye Department, Queen's Medical Centre, Derby Road, Nottingham NG7 2QH Tel: 0115 924 9924 Fax: 0115 970 4008; 5 Kindlewood Drive, Chilwell, Beeston, Nottingham NG9 6NE Tel: 0115 973 2288 Fax: 0115 973 2288 — MB BS 1972 Delhi; FRCS Ed. 1980; FRCS Glas. 1980. Staff Grade (Ophth.) Qu. Med. Centre Nottm. Prev: Regist. Midl. Eye Hosp. Birm.

RAJ, Geeti Ramachandram 9 Elizabeth Road, Birmingham B13 8QH; Tel: 01614 748404 — MB ChB 1986 Leeds; BSc (Hons.) Microbiol. Lond. 1981; MRCGP 1999; DRCOG 1991.

RAJ, Inderjeet 32 Baylis Road, Slough SL1 3PJ Tel: 01753 538328 — MB BS 1993 Lond. SHO (Geriat. Med.) Hillingdon Hosp.

RAJ, Latha St Martins Medical Centre, 21 Eastcote Road, Ruislip HA4 8BE Tel: 01895 632410 Fax: 01895 675058; 108 Aylesham Drive, Ickenham, Uxbridge UB10 8UD — MB BS 1973 Bangalor; BSc Bangalore 1966, MB BS 1973. (Bangalore Med. Coll.) Socs: Med. Protec. Soc.

RAJ, Mani Whitfield Surgery, 123 Whitfield Drive, Dundee DD4 0DX Tel: 01382 508410 Fax: 01382 509808 — MB BS 1969 Osmania. (Osmania) GP Dundee.

RAJ, Nag St Martins Medical Centre, 21 Eastcote Road, Ruislip HA4 8BE Tel: 01895 632410 Fax: 01895 675058; 108 Aylsham Drive, Ickenham, Uxbridge UB10 8UD Tel: 01895 637800 Fax: 01895 675058 — MB BS 1967 Bangalor; MB BS Bangalore 1967. (Bangalore Med. Coll.) GP Princip. Socs: Med. Protec. Soc.; MPS.

***RAJ, Sanjay Prem** Dilmuir, Penstraze, Chacewater, Truro TR4 8PN — MB BS 1998 Lond.; MB BS Lond 1998.

RAJ, Shivanee Jayanthi 26 Stonor Road, London W14 8RZ Tel: 020 7371 6495 — MB BS 1993 Lond.; BA Oxf. 1990.

RAJ, Sunita 23 Glebe Crescent, Rugby CV21 2HG — MB ChB 1997 Leeds. SHO A & E, Dewsbury. Prev: SHO Med. For Elderly, Dewsbury; Ho. Off. (Surg.) ScarBoro.; Ho. Off. (Med.) Airedale.

RAJ, Suresh Kumar Union Hall Road Surgery, 55 Union Hall Road, Lemington, Newcastle upon Tyne NE15 8BP Tel: 0191 267 4894 — MB BS 1965 Agra.

RAJ, Venkatachalum Babu 37 Orient Road, Salford M6 8LE Tel: 0161 789 3029; Tel: 0161 976 2043 — MB BS 1982 Madras; MRCP (UK) 1991; MRCPI 1990; LMSSA Lond. 1988; DRCOG 1994. Socs: Manch. Med. Soc.; BMA. Prev: Trainee GP Rotat. Liverp. VTS; Regist. (Geriat. Med.) BRd.green Hosp. Liverp.

RAJA, Aman Ullah Khan Cheshunt Medical Centre, 11 Cromwell Avenue, Cheshunt, Waltham Cross EN7 5DL Tel: 01992 624732.

RAJA, Apoorvaa Surendra 3 Teasel Close, Narborough, Leicester LE9 5DZ — MB BS 1998 Lond.; MB BS Lond 1998.

RAJA, Freny Anwar B'Nai, 58 Snakes Lane W., Woodford Green IG8 0DF Tel: 020 8504 1866; 32 Burghley Road, Leytonstone, London E11 4QP Tel: 020 8539 5149 Fax: 020 8556 0372 — MB BS 1951 Bombay; DObst RCOG 1957.

RAJA, Jowad Hussan 50 Gibson Road, Birmingham B20 3UE — MB ChB 1996 Ed.

RAJA, Mr Mohammad Ashraf Khan 6 Harman Drive, London NW2 2EB Email: rajamak@yahoo.com — MB BS 1984 Punjab; FRCS Eng. 1992; FRCSI 1991; BSc Punjab 1981; FCPS Pakistan 1991; MSc (Surg. Sci.) Lond. 1996; Dip. Med. Educat. (Gen. Surg.) 1998, (Med.) 1997; FRCS (Gen) 1998. (King Edward Medical College, Lahore, Pakistan) Specialist Regist. (Gen. Surg.) St. Geo.'s Hosp. Lond. Socs: Roy. Soc. Med.; ASME. Prev: Specialist Regist. Worthing Hosp.; Specialist Regist. St Peter's Hosp. Chertsey; Research Fell. Univ. of Lond.

RAJA, Rakesh Clinical Microbiology, Box 236, Addenbrooke's Hospital, Cambridge CB2 22W Tel: 01787 370011; Forge Cottage, The Street, Horringer, Bury St Edmunds IP29 5RY — MB ChB 1992 Birm.; MRCP 1998 UK; MRCGP 1999; BSc (Hons.) Med. Biochem. Birm. 1989. Gp, Sudbury, Suff.; Pharmaceutical Cons.

RAJA, Rameshchandra Shamalji X Ray Department, Rochdale Infirmary, Rochdale OL12 0NB Tel: 01706 517406 Fax: 01706 755344; 7 Beaumonds Way, Bamford, Rochdale OL11 5NL Tel: 01706 639355 Fax: 01706 639355 — MB ChB 1971 Makerere; FRCR 1977; DMRD Lond. 1977. Cons. Radiol. Rochdale Infirm.; Clin. Dir. (Surg.); Managing Dir. MRI Highfield Scanning Unit. Socs: Roy. Coll. Radiol. & Brit. Inst. Radiol.; BMA. Prev: Chairm. & Sen. Lect. (Diagn. Radiol.) Univ. Nairobi.

RAJA, Uma Department Histopothology, St James's University Hospital, Beckett St., Leeds LS9 7TF Tel: 0113 206 4410; 51 Shelley Crescent, Oulton, Leeds LS26 8ER — MB BS 1982 Bangalore; MRCPath cond. (St. John's Med. Con.) Cons. Path. (Histopath.) St. Jas. Hosp. Leeds. Socs: Brit. Soc. Cervical Cyno. Prev: Sen. Regist. Rotat. Leeds.

RAJA LOPE, Raja Juanita 47 Chantry Road, Moseley, Birmingham B13 8DN — BM BS 1995 Nottm.

RAJAB, Hedjaz c/o 240A Edgware Road, London W2 1DW; 18 Beaulieu Close, Frampton Road, Hounslow TW4 5EN — MB BS 1983 West Indies; DTM RCSI 1992; MCH 1997; FRCS 1997; Cert Av Med 1998. Research Fell.

RAJABALI, Shaheen 2 Manor Road, Harrow HA1 2PB Tel: 020 8861 1598; Flat 15, 2A Addington Road, Reading RG1 5PH Tel: 01734 878601 — MB BS 1995 Lond.; BSc (Hons.) Lond. 1992. (Univ. Coll. Lond.) Trainee GP/SHO Reading VTS. Prev: Ho. Off. (Surg.) Thanet NHS Healthcare Trust; Ho. Off. (Med.) Mayday Healthcare NHS Trust.

RAJACK, Sacha Marie c/o Flat 2F2, 42 Spottiswoode Road, Edinburgh EH9 1DB — MB ChB 1998 Ed.; MB ChB Ed 1998.

RAJADURAI, Veeravagu (retired) 40 Etonville Road, London SW17 7SL — MB BS 1943 Ceylon; DTM & H Ceylon 1952. Asst. in Psychiat. Darenth Pk. Hosp. Dartford. Prev: Asst. Med. Off. Lond. Boro. Bexley.

RAJAGOPAL, Rajavalse Venkateshan 16 Warrington Spur, Windsor SL4 2NF Tel: 01753 864784 — MB BS 1968 Mysore; BSc Mysore 1960. (Govt. Med. Coll. Mysore) Clin. Asst. (Psychiat.) St. Peters Hosp. Chertsey.

RAJAGOPAL, Ramesh Flat 11, Park House, 150 Palatine Road, Manchester M20 2QH — MB ChB 1994 Liverp.

RAJAGOPALAN, Bheeshma Nuffield Dept of Clinical Medicine, John Radcliffe Hospital, Oxford OX3 1UT Tel: 01865 64711 — BM BCh 1968 Oxf.; DPhil Oxf. 1977, BA 1964, MA, BM BCh 1968; MRCP (UK) 1971. (Oxf.) Clin. Sci. Med. Research Counc. & Hon. Cons. Phys. John Radcliffe Hosp. Oxf.; Reader (Med.) Univ. of Oxf.; Reader Med. 1997. Socs: Brit. Cardiac Soc. & Assn. Phys. Gt. Brit. & Irel. Prev: Med. Tutor Univ. Oxf.; Lect. (Med.) Univ. Oxf. & Hon. Sen. Regist. Oxon AHA (T); Med. Tutor Univ. Manch. & Hon. Regist. Manch. Roy. Infirm.

RAJAGOPALAN, Narayanan (retired) 3 The Limes, Water Lane, Castor, Peterborough PE5 7BH Tel: 01733 380709 Email: rajagoplan@lineone.net — MB BS 1954 Madras; BSc Madras 1948. Prev: GP P'boro.

RAJAH, Abid 41 Prospect Lane, Harpenden AL5 2PL — MB ChB 1977 Liverp.

RAJAH, Christine Savitri 355 Street Lane, Leeds LS17 6RU — MB BS 1983 Lond.

RAJAH, Moossajee Ibrahim I (retired) c/o Drive I. Barmania, 318 High Road, Leytonstone, London E11 3HS — LRCP LRCS 1940 Ed.; LRCP LRCS Ed. LRFPS Glas. 1940.

RAJAH, Prins Arumugam Neelaranjitha 5 Cypress Close, Blackwell, Darlington DL3 8QR Tel: 01325 380300 — MB BS 1966 Ceylon; MRCOG 1977; MRCS Eng. LRCP Lond. 1979; Dip. Ven. Soc. Apoth. Lond. 1982; FRCOG 1998. Cons. Genitourin. Med. Darlington Memor. Hosp.

RAJAH, Vignesh 13A Fairview Road, Chigwell IG7 6HN — MB BS 1990 Lond.; DCH Lond. 1995; MRCP (UK) Lond. (UMDS Guy's and St Thomas's) Specialist Regist. (Paediat.) All St.'s Hosp. Medway NHS Trust Kent. Prev: Resid. (Paediat. IC) Guy's Hosp. Lond.; SHO (Paediat.) Lewisham Hosp. Lond.

RAJAKARIAR, Ravindra Flat 4, 26 Pelham Road, London SW19 1SX — MB ChB 1995 Leic.

RAJAKARUNA, Chanaka Sandaruwan Postgraduate Deans Office, Faculty of Medicine, Robert Kilpatrick Clinical Sciences Building, Leicester Royal Infirmary, PO Box 65, Leicester LE2 7LX — MB ChB 1998 Leic.; MB ChB Leic 1998.

RAJAKARUNA, Mr Mahasen Lakshman (retired) 11 Park Avenue, Woodthorpe, Nottingham NG5 4HS Tel: 0115 920 3667 — MB BS 1950 Ceylon; MChOrth Liverp. 1959; FRCS Eng. 1958. Prev: Surg. DHSS Artific. Limb. & Appliance Centre Nottm.

RAJAKULASINGAM, Karalasingam Department of Respiratory Medicine, Homerton Hospital, Homerton Row, London E9 6SR — MB BS 1982 Colombo; FRCP 2001; FACP 2001; MRCP (UK) 1988; DM Soton 1996. Cons. Respirat. Physician & Hon. Sen. Lect. Socs: Amer. Coll.of Phys.s. & Brit. Thoracic Soc.; Bma. Prev: Sen. Regist. (Allergy, Immunol. & Thoracic Med.) Roy. Brompton Hosp. Lond.; Clin. Research Fell. & Hon. Regist. (Med.) Soton. Gen. Hosp.; Regist. (Gen. & Chest Med.) Hope Hosp. Salford.

RAJAKULENDRAN, Thambimuthu Woodfarm Health Centre, Leiden Road, Headington, Oxford OX3 8RZ Tel: 01865 762 500 — MB BS 1973 Ceylon; MRCS Eng. LRCP Lond. 1981; MRCOG 1985. (University of Ceylon Colombo, Sri Lanka) GP. Prev: Regist. (O & G) Univ. Hosp. of Wales Cardiff; Locum Cons. (O & G) S. Wales.

RAJAKUMAR, Rajaratnam Genitourinary Medicine Department, Derbyshire Royal Infirmary, London Road, Derby DE1 2QY Tel: 01332 347141; 83 Derwent Avenue, Allestree, Derby DE22 2DP Tel: 01332 541114 — MB BS 1972 Sri Lanka; MRCP (UK) 1983; LRCP LRCS Ed. LRCPS Glas. 1983. Cons. Genitourin. Med. Derbysh. Roy. Infirm. Socs: BMA; Med. Soc. Study VD; Assn. Genitourin. Med.

RAJAKUMAR, Ratnasabapathy 22 Owen Gardens, Woodford Green IG8 8DJ — MB BS 1974 Sri Lanka; LMSSA Lond. 1986.

RAJALINGAM, Usha Pavalalochana 45 Franciscan Road, London SW17 8EA — BM BS 1993 Flinders.

RAJAMENON, Anusha 6 Hathaway Close, Bromley BR2 8RD — LRCP LRCS LRCPS 1998 Ed., Glas.; LRCP Ed LRCS Ed LRCPS Glas 1998.

RAJAN, Govindan 83 Chevet Lane, Sandal, Wakefield WF2 6JE Tel: 01924 256342 — MB BS 1950 Madras; BSc Madras 1944, MB BS 1950; FRCP Glas. 1981, M 1966. (Madras) Cons. Paediatr. Yorks. RHA; Hon. Lect. Paediat. Univ. Leeds. Socs: BMA & Brit. Paediat. Assn. Prev: Sen. Regist. & Regist. Childr. Hosp. Stockton-on-Tees; Regist. (Paediat.) Inst. Paediat. Madras Med. Coll. Gen. Hosp.; India.

RAJAN, Karikkassery Thomas Joseph The Surgery, Felmores Centre, Felmores, Basildon SS13 1PN Tel: 01268 728142 — MB BS 1964 Karnatak.

RAJAN, Kunnathur Thiruvenkatachari East Glamorgan General Hospital, Church Village, Pontypridd CF38 1AB Tel: 01443 216345 Fax: 01443 21775; ty Gornel, 11 Y Parc, Groesfaen, Pontyclun CF72 8NP Tel: 01222 890205 — PhD Camb. 1970; BSc Madras —

RAJAN

1951, MB BS 1958; DTCD Wales 1962. (Christian Med. Coll. Vellore) Cons., E. Glam. Gen. Hosp. Ch. Village. Socs: Brit. Soc. of Rheumatol.; Amer. Soc. Bone Mineral Research; Bone & Tooth Soc. Prev: Scientif. Staff - MRC Llandough Hosp., Penarth; Research Fell. Stoke Mandeville Hosp. Aylesbury.; Regist. Roy. Berks. Hosp. Reading.

RAJAN, Shanti 6 Silvanus Close, West Lodge Road, Colchester CO3 3NL Tel: 01206 540568 — MB BS 1977 Madras; DA (UK) 1986.

RAJANATHAN, Ehamparanathan Irvine Unit, Bexhill Hospital, Holliers Hill, Bexhill-on-Sea TN40 2DZ Tel: 01424 755255 Ext: 5312; 32A Parkhurst Road, Bexhill-on-Sea TN40 1DE — MB BS Sri Lanka 1962; DPH Liverp. 1972. Clin. Med. Off. (Med. for Elderly) Bexhill Hosp. E. Sussex.

RAJANI, Bhavesh 7 Limetree Walk, Chorleywood, Rickmansworth WD3 4BX — MB ChB 1989 Manch. Trainee GP Edgware VTS.

RAJANI, Kanesh Keshavlal Ruh's Corner, 4 Potters Heights Close, Pinner Hill, Pinner HA5 3YW — MB ChB 1992 Manch.

RAJANI, Mukeshkumar Haridas Lister Medical Centre, Lister House, Staple Tye, Harlow CM18 7LU Tel: 01279 414882 Fax: 01279 439600 — MB BS 1976 Lond.; MRCS Eng. LRCP Lond. 1976; MRCGP 1980; DRCOG 1979. (Westminster Medical School)

RAJANI, Ronak 24 Malcolm Drive, Surbiton KT6 6QS — BM 1998 Soton.; BM Soton 1998.

RAJANI, Vakesh 7 Lime Tree Walk, Rickmansworth WD3 4BX — MB BS 1993 Lond.

RAJAP, Tuan Ilan 48 Ernest Grove, Beckenham BR3 3JF — MB BS 1994 Lond.

RAJAPAKSA, Mr Pathirannahelage Nima 20 Colts Road, Rownhams, Southampton SO16 8JX — MB BS 1980 Colombo; FRCS Glas. 1990.

RAJAPAKSA, Rajapska A M Abercynon Health Centre, Abercynon, Mountain Ash CF45 4SU Tel: 01443 740447 Fax: 01443 740228.

RAJAPAKSA, Tusevnambi Jayatissa 211 Stoke Road, Slough SL2 5AX — MB BS 1952 Ceylon; MRCPsych 1976. (Ceylon) Cons. Psych. Med. St. Edwd.'s Hosp. Cheddleton.

RAJAPAKSE, Alujjage Dona Padma 3 Farnham Way, Bedford MK41 8RE — MB BS 1966 Ceylon.

RAJAPAKSE, Dayananda New Possibilities Trust, New Possibilities House, Turner Village, Turner Road, Colchester CO4 5JP — MB BS 1966 Ceylon; MRCPsych 1976; DPM Eng. 1974. (Ceylon) Cons. Psychiat. & Med. Dir. New Possibilities Trust Colchester. Prev: Cons. Psychiat. Essex Hall Hosp. Colchester.

RAJAPAKSE, Yasa Siri Bedfordshire Health, Charter House, Alma St., Luton LU1 2PL Tel: 01582 744898; 3 Farnham Way, Bedford MK41 8RE Tel: 01236 212107 — MB BS 1963 Ceylon; FFPHM RCP (UK) 1991; MFCM RCP (UK) 1974; DTPH 1971. Cons. Pub. Health Med. Beds. Health Luton. Prev: SCMO N. Beds. HA; Med. Off. Health Anti Filariasis Campaign Colombo, Sri Lanka.

RAJAR, Ramzi Mark 1818 Great Western Road, Glasgow G13 2TN — MB ChB 1998 Dund.; MB ChB Dund 1998.

RAJARATHNA SETTY, Raja Seetharamaiah Kiran, 47 Fairfield Drive, Burnley BB10 2PU Tel: 01282 425447 — MB BS Mysore 1966; DA Eng. 1972. (Kastruba Med. Coll.) Med. Asst. (Anaesth.) Burnley Gen. Hosp.

RAJARATNAM, Abharani 77 Ecton Avenue, Macclesfield SK10 1RA — MB BS 1978 Madras, India.

RAJARATNAM, David Vinaya West Drive, Whalley Lane, Uplyme, Lyme Regis DT7 3UP — MRCS Eng. LRCP Lond. 1977; BSc (Hons.) Lond. 1974, MB BS 1977.

RAJARATNAM, Giridharan Department of Public Health Medicine, Bradford Health Authority, New Mill, Victoria Road, Shipley BD18 3LD Tel: 01274 366080 Fax: 01274 366060 — MB BS 1981 Lond.; MSc Lond. 1986; MFCM 1989. Cons. Pub. Health Med. Bradford HA. Prev: Lect. (Epidemiol. & Community Med.) Univ. Wales Coll. Med.; Trainee (Community Med.) NW Thames RHA.

RAJARATNAM, Mr Koppada Department of Orthopaedics, Macclesfield District General Hospital, Victoria Road, Macclesfield SK10 3BL Tel: 01625 661316 Fax: 01625 663153; Ashramam, 77 Ecton Avenue, Macclesfield SK10 1RA Email: kiranraj@compuserve.com — MB BS 1975 Sri Venkateswara; DOrth 1979; MS (Orth) 19831; MChOrth Liverp. 1991. (Kurnool Med. Coll., India) Assoc. Specialist (Orthop. & Trauma) Macclesfield Dist. Gen. Hosp. Socs: Brit. Orthop. Assn.; BMA; World Orthop. Concern.

RAJARATNAM, Saroja Thavapalan and Partners, 55 Little Heath Road, Bexleyheath DA7 5HL Tel: 01322 430129 Fax: 01322 440949 — MB BS 1978 Sri Lanka; MB BS 1978 Sri Lanka; LRCP LRCS Ed. LRCPS Glas. 1983 Edinburgh & Glasgow.

RAJASANSIR, Jagatjit Gurjeet Singh The Surgery, Block Lane, Chadderton, Oldham OL9 7SG Tel: 0161 620 2321 — MB ChB 1985 Manch.; BSc St. And. 1982. Trainee GP/SHO GP Oldham HA VTS.

RAJASEKARAN, Mr Jeyachandran 11 Tunnel Wood Road, Watford WD17 4SN; 43 Rainford Road, Edison NJ 08820, USA Tel: 00 1 732 767 1444 Fax: 00 1 732 767 1444 — MB BS 1974 Madurai; FRCS Eng. 1981; FRCS Ed. 1981; FRCS Glas. 1981. Pres. Jersey City Med. Center New Jersey, USA.

RAJASEKHARA, Kori Siddabasappa (Surgery), 259 Hainton Avenue, Grimsby DN32 9JX Tel: 01472 342570 Fax: 01472 250404 — MB BS 1960 Karnatak; DOMS 1996 Karnatak; 1970 DO RCS Lond. Hosp. Pract. (Ophth.) Grimsby.

RAJASINGAM, Daghni 42 Almorah Road, Hounslow TW5 9AD — MB BS 1990 Lond. Research Fell. Qu. Charlottes Hosp. Lond.

RAJASINGHAM, Ponnuduray 6 Romney Road, New Malden KT3 5NN — MB BS 1962 Ceylon. SCMO (Psychiat. Ment. Handicap) Barnsley HA. Prev: SHO (Psychiat.) Napsbury Hosp. St. Albans Herts & Watford Gen. Hosp.

RAJASOORIYAR, Wijenathan Department Anaesthesia, Ward 7, General Hospital, Bishop Auckland DL14 6AD Fax: 01388 604040; 5 Ashcroft Gardens, Bishop Auckland DL14 6HF — MB BS 1967 Colombo; FFA RCS Eng. 1977; FFA RCSI 1976; DA (UK) 1976.

RAJASUNDARAM, S Tudor Way Surgery, 42 Tudor Way, Orpington BR5 1LH Tel: 01689 820268 Fax: 01689 839414.

RAJATHURAI, Alvappillai Doncaster Royal Infirmary, Armthorpe Road, Doncaster DN2 5NL Tel: 01302 366666; 3 Riding Close, Bessacarr, Doncaster DN4 6UZ — MB BS 1971 Ceylon; FRCP Lond. 1994; MRCP (UK) 1979; MRCS Eng. LRCP Lond. 1979. Cons. Phys. (c/o the Elderly) Doncaster Roy. Infirm. Socs: Brit. Geriat. Soc.

RAJATHURAI, Thirumaran 3 Ridings Close, Doncaster DN4 6UZ — BM BS 1998 Nottm.; BM BS Nottm 1998.

RAJAYOGESWARAN, Srirangini 80 Tyron Way, Sidcup DA14 6AZ Tel: 020 8300 8590 — MB BS 1971 Ceylon; DCH RCP Lond. 1990. (Med. Coll. Peradenia) Clin. Med. Off. (Child Health) Greenwich HA. Socs: BMA & Nat. Assn. Family Plann. Doctors. Prev: SHO (Neonat. Paediat. & Gen. Paediat.) Gloucester Roy. Hosp.; Ho. Off. (Surg.) & Ho. Off. (Gen. Med.) Base Hosp. Gampaha, Ceylon.

RAJBEE, Faisal Tariq 38 Little Ridge Avenue, St Leonards-on-Sea, St Leonards-on-Sea TN37 7LS — MB BS 1997 Lond.

RAJBEE, Tariq Yusuf The Surgery, 38 Little Ridge Avenue, St Leonards-on-Sea TN37 7LS Tel: 01424 755355 Fax: 01424 755560 — DAB, Lond. 2000; MB BS 1965 Bihar. (Darbhanga Med. Coll.) Princip. GP Hastings; Police Surg. Prev: Regist. (Surg.) JLN Med. Coll. Aligarh, India; SHO (Cas.) Staffs. Gen. Infirm. Stafford; SHO (Orthop.) Cumbld. Infirm. Carlisle.

RAJBHANDARI, Satyan Man 5 High Leys Drive, Priory Wood, Ravenshead, Nottingham NG15 9HQ; 17D Highnam Crescent Road, Sheffield S10 1BZ — MB BS 1989 Sambalpur; MRCP (UK) 1993. Regist. (Gen. Med., Diabetes & Endocrinol.) Roy. Hallamsh. Hosp. Sheff. Prev: Regist. (Gen. Med., Diabetes & Endocrinol.) Chesterfield Roy. Hosp. N. Derbysh.

RAJENDRA, Barathi 35 Greenfield Street, Dunkirk, Nottingham NG7 2JN — BM BS 1995 Nottm.

RAJENDRA, Malathi 2A Medical Mess, Law Hospital, Carluke ML8 5ER — MB ChB 1993 Dundee.

RAJENDRA, Shanmugarajam Flat 17, Brodie House, District General Hospital, Kings Drive, Eastbourne BN21 2YE — MB BCh BAO 1988 NUI; MRCP (UK) 1993; LRCPSI 1988.

RAJENDRAM, Ranjan 41 Aelxandra Road, Hounslow TW3 4HW — MB BS 1996 Lond.

RAJENDRAM, Saddanather Doctors Mess, Tameside General Hospital, Fountain St., Ashton-under-Lyne OL6 9RW — MB BS 1971 Ceylon.

RAJENDRAN, Sasha 4 Windsor Place, Dundee DD2 1BG — MB ChB 1992 Leic. SHO (O & G) Leicester Gen. Hosp. Prev: SHO (O & G) Leicester Roy. Infirm.; SHO (Neonat.) Leicester Gen. Hosp. & Leicester Roy. Infirm.

RAJENDRAN, Vijayaraghavan 9 Alford Road, High Wycombe HP12 4PT Tel: 01494 450827 — MB BS Madras 1977; MD Madras 1981; MRCP (UK) 1983.

RAJESH, Mr Pala Babu Regional Department of Thoracic Surgery, Birmingham Heartlands Hospital, Bordesley Green E., Birmingham B9 5SS Tel: 0121 424 2000 Fax: 0121 766 5823; 56 Arthur Road, Edgbaston, Birmingham B15 2UN Tel: 0121 440 1027 — MB BS 1974 Madras; FETCS 2001; FRCS (Cth.) 1994; FRCS Ed. 1982. (Madras Med. Coll.) Cons. Thoracic. Surg. Birm. Heartlands Hosp. Socs: Eur. Assn. for Cardiothoracic Surg.; Soc. Cardiothoracic Surg. GB & Irel. Prev: Hon. Sen. Regist. (Cardiothoracic Surg.) N.. Gen. Hosp. Sheff.; Regist. N. Gen. Hosp. Sheff.; Regist. (Cardiothoracic Surg.) Castle Hill Hosp. Cottingham.

RAJESHWAR, Kasam The Surgery, New Road, Brownhills, Walsall WS8 6AT Tel: 01543 373214 Fax: 01543 454591 — MB BS 1965 Osmania.

RAJESHWAR, Mahesh Honeywood, 3 The Fordrough, Sutton Coldfield B74 2XS — MB ChB 1997 Manch.

RAJGOPAL, Jairam Madura Southmoor Surgery, Southmoor Road, Hemsworth, Pontefract WF9 4DP Tel: 01977 615153 — MB BS 1965 Madras. (Madras) GP Pontefract, W. Yorks.

RAJGOPAL, Y (retired) Tel: 01226 752361 Fax: 01226 341577 — MB BS 1970 Madras; MB BS 1970 Madras.

RAJI, Adil Mahmud 139 Harley Street, London W1G 6BG; 20 Alexandra Road, Hornsey, London N8 0PP — MB ChB 1967 Baghdad. Gen. & Orthop. Surg. Lond.

RAJIV, Kumar 111 Thorpe Road, Peterborough PE3 6JQ.

RAJJAYABUN, Mr Paul Hosie 2A Vine Close, Clifton, Brighouse HD6 4JS Tel: 01484 719972 — MB ChB 1994 Birm.; ChB Birm. 1994; FRCS Ed. 1998. SHO Rotat. (A & E) Worcester Roy. Infirm.; SHO (Urol.) City Hosp. Sunderland; SHO Rotot. (Surgic) S. Midl. Socs: BMA; MPS. Prev: SHO (Orthop. Trauma) Worc. Roy. Infirm.; SHO (Cardiac Surg.) Walsgrave Hosp.; SHO (Gen. Surg.) Walsgrave Hosp.

RAJKHOWA, Madhurima 39 Plantation Gardens, Leeds LS17 8SX — MB BS 1982 Gauhati; MB BS Gauhati, India 1982; MRCOG 1993.

RAJKUMAR, Shivnathram The Medical Centre, 78 Oswald Road, Scunthorpe DN15 7PG Tel: 01724 843168 — MB BS 1975 Bombay.

RAJKUMAR, Mr Vellore Jayachandran 159 Ridgewood Gardens, Neath SA11 3QX Tel: 01639 646840 — MB BS 1977 Madras; MS (Gen. Surg.) Madras 1981, MB BS 1977; FRCS Glas. 1986; FRCSI 1985. Assoc. Specialist (Gen. Surg.) Neath Gen. Hosp.

RAJLAWOT, Ganesh Pratap Flat 3, 22 Falkner Square, Liverpool L8 7NY Tel: 0151 708 8153 — MB BS 1961 Agra; DCH RCPSI 1981; DA Copenhagen 1972; DA Agra 1963. (Sarojini Naidu Med. Coll.) Prev: SHO (Paediat. Med.) Leicester Gen. Hosp., Bradford Gp. Hosps. & Alder; Hey Childr. Hosp. Liverp.

RAJPURA, A I Earlsheaton Surgery, 252 Wakefield Road, Earlsheaton, Dewsbury WF12 8AH Tel: 01924 465511 — MRCS Eng. LRCP Lond. London; MB BS 1972 Gujarat; MB BS 1972 Gujarat.

RAJPURA, Anjum 79 Track Road, Batley WF17 7AB — MB ChB 1992 Birm.

RAJPURA, Arif Cheriton, 79 Track Rd, Batley WF17 7AB — MB ChB 1996 Manch.

***RAJPUT, Karim Sultan** 55 Portland Road, Edgbaston, Birmingham B16 9HS — MB ChB 1995 Manch.

RAJPUT, Mrs Kaukab Mufti Dept. of Audiological Medicine, Great Ormond Street Hospital, Great Ormond St., London WC1 3JH Tel: 0207 813 8316 Fax: 0207 833 2208 Email: kaukab.rajput@gosh-trnthames.nhs.uk; Lynfield House, Wexham St, Stoke Poges, Slough SL3 6PA Tel: 01753 663576 Fax: 01753 663576 Email: kaukab@globalnet.co.uk — MB BS 1982 Sind, Pakistan; LRCP LRCS Ed. LRCPS Glas. 1987 Glas.; FRCS 1992 Glas.; MSc 1995 Lond.; FRCS Glas. 1992; LRCP LRCS Ed. LRCPS Glas. 1987; MSc Lond. 1995. Cons. Socs: Btritish Assoc. of Audiological Phys.; Brit. Cochlear Implant Gp.; Internat. Assoc. of Audiological Phys.

RAJPUT, Pranjivandas Bhagwandas 361 Chingford Road, Walthamstow, London E17 5AE Tel: 020 8925 4229 — MB BS 1958 Bombay; DLO RCS Eng. 1967.

RAJPUT, Rais Ahmed Wilnecote Street Surgery, Parson Street, Wilnecote, Tamworth B77 5BD Tel: 01827 280800 Fax: 01827 261569; 22 Orchard Close, Dosthill, Tamworth B77 1ND — MB BS 1971 Sind.

RAJPUT, Ranbir Singh 27 Daventry Road, Coventry CV3 5DJ — BM BS 1993 Nottm.; BMedSci. Nottm. 1991.

RAJPUT, Satpal Springfield Medical Practice, 739-741 Stratford Road, Springfield, Birmingham B11 4DG Tel: 0121 778 4321 Fax: 0121 702 2662 — MB ChB 1984 Leic.; DRCOG 1989; Cert Family Plann. JCC 1987. Prev: SHO (O & G, Gen. Med., Gen. Paediat.) Coventry HA.

RAJPUT, Vijay Kumar Springfield Medical Practice, 739-741 Stratford Road, Springfield, Birmingham B11 4DG Tel: 0121 778 4422 Fax: 0121 702 2662; 36 Inverclyde Road, Handsworth Ward, Birmingham B20 2LJ Tel: 0121 554 6741 — MB ChB 1983 Leic.; MRCGP 1989; Cert. JCPTGP 1988; DRCOG 1987; Cert. Family Plann. JCC 1986. (Univ. Leic.) Med. Assessor SSAT; Mem. Disabil. Appeals Tribunal. Prev: Clin. Asst. (Diabetes & Endocrinol.) Dudley Rd. Hosp.; Clin. Asst. (Psychiat.) All St.s Hosp.; Clin. Asst. (ENT) Heartlands Hosp.

RAJPUT, Vije Kumar 95 Redwood Road, Kings Norton, Birmingham B30 1AE — MB ChB 1984 Manch.; MRCGP 1988; DObst. RCOG 1987.

RAJSHEKHAR, Math Sangaya 19 Crooklog, Bexleyheath DA6 8DZ Tel: 020 8304 3025 — MB BS 1953 Osmania. (Osmania Med. Coll. Hyderabad)

RAJU, Chintalapati Sanyasi Woodley Health Centre, Hyde Road, Woodley, Stockport SK6 1ND Tel: 0161 430 2466 Fax: 0161 406 8218 — MB BS 1967 Andhra; MB BS 1967 Andhra.

RAJU, Katari Singa Department of Psychiatry, Pembury Hospital, Tonbridge Road, Pembury, Tunbridge Wells TN2 4RT; 98 Headcorn Drive, Canterbury CT2 7TR — MB BS 1969 Andhra; MB BS Andhra India 1969; DCH RCP Lond. 1976.

RAJU, Sushila Warneford Hospital, Warneford Lane, Headington, Oxford OX3 7JX — MB ChB 1985 Glas.; MRCPsych 1991. Prev: Regist. Rotat. (Psychiat.) Warneford Hosp. Univ. Oxf.; SHO (Geriat.) Poole Gen. Hosp.; SHO (Gen. Med. & Haemat.) Barnsley Dist. Gen. Hosp.

RAJU, Mr Thakur Das Yeading Court Practice, 1-2 Yeading Court, Masefield Lane, Hayes UB4 5AJ Tel: 020 8845 1515 Fax: 020 8841 1171 — LRCP LRCS 1986 Ed.; MB BS Guru Nanak Dev 1977; FRCS Ed. 1990; LRCP LRCS Ed. LRCPS Glas. 1986; MRCS Eng. LRCP Lond. 1986.

RAJVANSHI, Reeta 1A Bexley Lane, Sidcup DA14 4JW — MB BS 1966 Lucknow.

RAKE, Mark Oliver The Barn, Pontus Farm, Molash, Canterbury CT4 8HW Tel: 01233 740728 — MB BS 1963 Lond.; BSc (Anat.) Lond. 1960; FRCP Lond. 1979, M 1968; MRCS Eng. LRCP Lond. 1963. (Guy's) Dean Kent Inst. Med. & Health Sci. Socs: Brit. Soc. Gastroenterol. & Brit. Soc. Digestive Endoscopy.; ASME; AMEE. Prev: Cons. Phys. Kent & Canterbury Hosp.; Sen. Regist. Guy's Hosp. Lond.; Research Fell. Liver Unit King's Coll. Hosp.

RAKHIT, Anita 65 Hall Drive, London SE26 6XL — MB BS 1998 Lond.; MB BS Lond 1998.

RAKHIT, Apurba Kumar 76 Market Street, Droylsden, Manchester M43 7UD Tel: 0161 370 2626; 12 Thornley Lane, Grotton, Oldham OL4 5RP Tel: 0161 624 6800 — MB BS 1959 Calcutta; DPH Manch. 1964. (Calcutta Nat. Med. Inst.) Sec. Tameside LMC Ashton-under-Lyne. Socs: BMA. Prev: Ho. Surg. Oldham Dist. Hosp.; Dep. MOH Saddelworth UD; Asst. Phys. Gen. Hosp. Ashton-under-Lyne.

RAKHIT, Dhrubo Jyoti Chelsea & Westminster Hospital, 369 Fulham Road, Fulham, London SW10 9NH Tel: 0208746 8039 Fax: 020 8746 8040 Email: drakhit@hotmail.com; Top Flat, 646 Fulham Road, Fulham, London SW6 5RT — MB BS 1993 Lond.; MRCP (UK) 1997. Research Fell., Cardiol. Chelsea & W.minster & Roy. Brompton Hosp. Prev: Specialist Regist. Bromley Hosp. NHS Trust.

RAKHIT, Durgadas Inverclyde Royal Hospital, Larkfield Road, Greenock PA16 0XN; 4 Exmouth Place, Gourock PA19 1JE Tel: 01475 796714 — MB BS 1967 Calcutta; MD Calcutta 1975; DRCOG Lond. 1984; MRCOG Lond. 1984. Assoc. Specialist (O & G) Inverclyde Roy. Hosp. Greenock.

RAKHIT

RAKHIT, Moona Kaberi 42 Copthall Lane, Gerrards Cross SL9 0DG; Kingscliffe, Bull Lane, Gerrards Cross SL9 8RF — MB BS 1989 Lond.; MRCGP 1996. (Charing Cross and Westminster)

RAKHIT, Roby Devasish Department of Cardiology, The Rayne Institute, St Thomas's Hospital, Lambeth Palace Road, London SE1 7EH; 7 Cyprus Avenue, Finchley, London N3 1SS — MB BS 1991 Lond.; BSc (Hons.) Pharmacol. Lond. 1989; MRCP (UK) 1995. (Char. Cross & Westm.) Research Regist. (Cardiol.) St. Thomas's Hosp. Lond. Socs: Brit. Soc. Cardiovasc. Research; BMA; Brit. Soc. Echocardiogr. Prev: Regist. (Cardiol.) Roy. Brompton Hosp. Lond.; Regist. (Cardiol.) Hammersmith Hosp. Lond.; SHO (Neurol.) Nat. Hosp. Qu. Sq. Lond.

RAKHIT, Sreeharsha Arghya, 3 Squires Croft, Woodway Park, Coventry CV2 2RQ Tel: 024 76 612258 — MB BS 1962 Calcutta; FRSH 1996; BSc Calcutta 1956, MD (Alternative Med.) 1990; DFFP 1993; DA Eng. 1974; DObst RCOG 1972; DGO Calcutta 1964. (R.G. Kar Med. Coll.) Socs: Roy. Soc. Health.

RAKHIT, Tuhina 6 Langstrath Drive, West Bridgford, Nottingham NG2 6SD — BM BS 1995 Nottm.

RAKICKA, Helena Tameside General Hospital, Fountain Street, Ashton-under-Lyne OL6 9RW — MUDr 1969 Univ. Safarikova Czechoslovakia; MUDr Univ. Safarikova, Czechoslovakia 1969; MRCP (UK) 1992. Cons. Phys. (c/o Elderly) Tameside Gen. Hosp. Ashton-under-Lyne. Prev: Regist. (Gen. & Geriat. Med.) Tameside Gen. Hosp. Ashton-under-Lyne.

RAKOWICZ, Anna Stefania Acorn Surgery, 136 Meeting House Lane, London SE15 2TT Tel: 020 7639 5055 Fax: 020 7732 4225; 102 Wood Vale, London SE23 3ED Tel: 020 8693 4732 — MB BS 1962 Lond. (Roy. Free) Socs: BMA. Prev: Ho. Surg. Eliz. G. Anderson Hosp. Lond.; Ho. Phys. S. Lond. Hosp. Wom. Clapham.

RAKOWICZ, Stefan Pawel Dysart House Surgery, 13 Ravensbourne Road, Bromley BR1 1HN Tel: 020 8464 0718; 102 Wood Vale, London SE23 3ED — MB BS 1990 Lond.; BSc Lond. 1987; MRCGP 1994. (King's Coll. Sch. Med. & Dent.) Socs: Chairm. Polish Med. Assn.; BMA. Prev: Trainee GP Bromley & FarnBoro. Hosp. Kent.

RAKOWICZ, Wojciech Piotr Dept. of Neurology, Washington University School of Medicine, Box 8228, 660 S.Euxlid Ave, St Louis MO 63110, USA Email: rakoviczw@neuro.wustl.edu; 102 Wood Vale, London SE23 3ED — MB BS 1990 Lond.; BSc (Hons.) Lond. 1987, MB BS 1990; MRCP (UK) 1993; AKC Lond. 1990. Research Fell.(Neurol), Univ. of Camb. Socs: MDU; BMA. Prev: Regist. (Psychiat.) Maudsley Hosp. Lond.; Regist. (Med.) Poole Hosp.; SHO (Neurol.) Nat. Hosp. for Neurol. & Neurosurg. Lond.

RAKOWSKI, Jane Helene 94 Victoria Road, Formby, Liverpool L37 1LP Tel: 01704 872293 — MB ChB 1979 Liverp.; DRCOG 1984; DCH Eng. 1981; DPD Cardiff 1997. (Liverpool) GP Formby; Clin. Asst. in Dermat., Roy. Liverp. Hosp. Prev: GP S.port, Cardiff & Liverp.

RAKSHI, Jimmy Sajal 24 Westbere Road, London NW2 3SR — MB ChB 1988 Aberd.

RAKSHIT, Ashok Kumar The Surgery, 170 Lower Clapton Road, London E5 0QA; F-74 Residential Apartment, Dakshinapan, 2 Gariahat Road (Sth.), Calcutta 700068, India Tel: 00 91 33 4731639 — MB BS 1955 Calcutta; LLB Calcutta 1956, BSc 1948, MB BS 1955. (Med. Coll. Calcutta) Socs: Fell. Roy. Inst. Pub. Health & Hyg.; Fell. Roy. Soc. Med. & Fell. Acad. of Sci. NY; Medico-Legal Soc. Prev: SHO (Radiother.) Postgrad. Med. Sch. Hammermsith Hosp. Lond.

RAKSHIT, Bhim Chandra Kings Road Surgery, 133 Kings Road, Blackburn BB2 4PY Tel: 01254 201269 Fax: 01254 200717 — MB BS 1969 Calcutta.

RAKUS, Marguerita Roma Flat A, 34 Hans Road, London SW3 1RW Tel: 020 7225 2016 — MB BS 1985 Sydney.

RALEVIC, Danica 45 Mawson Road, Cambridge CB1 2DZ — MB BS 1986 Lond.; BA (Natural Scs.) Camb. 1981.

RALFE, Simon William Huntersmoon, School Road, Riseley, Reading RG7 1XN — MB ChB 1996 Birm.; ChB Birm. 1996; BSc 1993; MBChB Birm 1996. Med. Rotat., Qu.'s Hosp. Burton-upon-Trent. Socs: Roy. Coll. Phys.s.

RALFS, Ian George William Harvey Hospital, Kennigton Road, Willesborough, Ashford TN2 0LZ — MB ChB 1970 Liverp.; MSc (Immunol.) Birm. 1976; FRCP Lond. 1996; MRCP (UK) 1974; FRCP. (Liverp.) Cons. Dermat. William Harvey Hosp. Ashford.

RALHAN, Rekha 77 Coleraine Road, Portrush BT56 8HN — MB ChB 1989 Dundee; DRCOG 1993.

RALL, Mathias Herbert 14 Firs Crescent, Kings Worthy, Winchester SO23 7NF Email: mathiasrall@cs.com — State Exam Med 1990 Freiburg; State Exam Med. Freiburg 1990; DFFP 1995.

RALLEIGH, Gita 42 Farm Avenue, Harrow HA2 7LR — MB BS 1993 Lond.

RALLI, Roger Alexander Medical Centre, HMYOI Glen Parva, Leicester LE18 4TN Tel: 0116 264 3101 Fax: 0116 264 3383 — MB ChB 1976 Dundee. Princip. Med. Off. Prison Dept. Home Off. Prev: Trainee GP Foyers VTS; Regist. (Psychiat.) Mapperley Hosp. Nottm.; Regist. (Anaesth.) Pinderfields Hosp. Wakefield.

RALPH, Catherine Janet Oral & Maxillofacial Unit, North Manchester General Hospital, Selaunays Road, Manchester M8 5RB — MB BS 1987 Lond.; FRCA 1995; DA (UK) 1992. (CXWMS) Cons. (Anaesthetics) Truro, Cornw. Prev: Regist. (Anaesth.) Qu.sland, Austral.; SHO (Anaesth.) Cornw. & I. of Scilly HA.; Regist. (Anaesth.) Auckland New Zealand.

RALPH, Mr David John The Institute of Urology, 48 Riding House St., London W1P 7PN Tel: 020 7823 5354 Fax: 020 7823 6525 Email: dralph@andrology.co.uk; Mulberry House, Beech Way, Gerrards Cross SL9 8BL — MB BS 1984 Lond.; BSc Lond. 1980; MS Lond. 1996; FRCS (Urol.) 1994; FRCS Ed. 1988; FRCS Eng. 1988. (St. Bart.) Cons. (Urol.) St. Peter's Hosps. & Inst. Urol. Lond. Socs: Brit. Assn. Urol. Surgs.; Internat. Soc. Impotence Research; Eur. Soc. Impotence Research.

RALPH, Debra Jane The Surgery, 22 St. Anne's Terrace, London NW8 6PH Tel: 020 7722 7389 — MB BS 1989 Lond.; DFFP 1994; DCH RCP Lond. 1992; DRCOG 1991. (St. Mary's Hosp.)

RALPH, Ian 59A Melrose Avenue, Portslade, Brighton BN41 2LT — MB BS 1990 Lond.

RALPH, Ian Fraser Longacre, 193 Moorgate Road, Rotherham S60 3BA Tel: 01709 378407 — MB ChB 1953 Aberd.; MFCM 1974; DPH Ed. 1959. Dist. Med. Off. Rotherham HA. Prev: Area Med. Off. Rotherham AHA; MOH & Princip. Sch. Med. Off. Co. Boro. Rotherham; Dep. MOH Co. Boro. Stockport.

RALPH, James Kelvin 10 Longaston Close, Slimbridge, Gloucester GL2 7BA — MB ChB 1991 Bristol.

RALPH, Michelle Dawn 14 Maple Road, Strood, Rochester ME2 2JW — MB BS 1991 Lond.

RALPH, Stanley James Derbyshire Royal Infirmary, London Road, Derby DE1 2QY; Tel: 023 8028 3084 — MB BS 1982 Nottm.; FFA RCS Eng. 1987. Cons. Anaesth. Derbysh. Roy. Infirm. Derby. Prev: Sen. Regist. (Anaesth.) Sheff.; Fell. Inten. Care Univ. Hosp. Groningen Netherlands; SHO (Anaesth.) Nott.

***RALPH, Stuart John** 29 Hillside, Horsham RH12 1NE — MB BS 1998 Lond.; MB BS Lond 1998.

RALPH, Susan Gwenda Department of Genitourinary Medicine, Sunny Bank Wing, Leeds General Infirmary, Great George St., Leeds LS1 2EX Tel: 0113 292 6762 Fax: 0113 292 6387; 1 Richmondfield Garth, Barwick in Elmet, Leeds LS15 4EP — MB ChB 1988 Sheff.; MRCP (UK) 1993; Dip. GU Med. Soc. Apoth. Lond. 1995; DFFP 1995. Specialist Regist. (Genitourin. Med.) Leeds Gen. Infirm.

RALPH, William Henry c/o Lynfield Mount Hospital, Heights Lane, Bradford BD9 6DP — MB BCh BAO 1994 Dub. (Univ. Dub., Trinity Coll.) Demonst. (Anat.) Roy. Coll. Surgs. Irel., Dub. Socs: BMA.

RALPHS, Alwyn Thomas Raynor 15 Warwick Road, Stafford ST17 4PD Tel: 01785 57674 — MB ChB 1987 Birm.; DRCOG 1991. Trainee GP Staffs.

RALPHS, Mr David Neil Lincoln 218 Unthank Road, Norwich NR2 2AH Tel: 01603 505463 Fax: 01603 505449 Email: ralphs@norwich.com — MB BChir 1966 Camb.; FRCS 1970 Eng.; MA 1966 Camb. (Middlx.) p/t Cons. Surg. Norf. & Norwich Hosp.; Mem. Ct. Examrs. & Regional Adviser (Surg.) RCS Eng.; Pres. Elect. Brit. Assn. Of Day Surg. Socs: Brit. Soc. Gastroenterol. & Brit. Assn. Surg. Oncol.; Brit. Assn. Day Surg.; Brit. Assn. Surg. Oncolo. Prev: Sen. Lect. & Hon. Cons. Middlx. Hosp.; Regist. (Surg.) Kettering Gen. Hosp.; Demonst. (Anat.) Univ. Camb.

RALPHS, Glenn John Gareth Abbotswood Medical Centre, Defford Road, Pershore WR10 1HZ Tel: 01386 552424 — MB ChB 1976 Birm.; DRCOG 1979. (Birm.) Chairm. Wychavon PCG.

RALSTON, Anthony James Withington Hospital, Nell Lane, Manchester M20 2LR — MB ChB 1956 Manch.; FRCP Lond. 1974, M 1961. Cons. Phys. Withington Hosp. Manch.

RALSTON, Charles Scott 166 Harborne Park Road, Birmingham B17 0BP — MB BS 1980 Lond.; FFA RCS Eng. 1986. Cons. Paediat. Anaesth. & Intens. Care Birm. Childr. Hosp.; Hon. Sen. Lect. Birm. Univ. Socs: Assn. Anaesth.; Assn. Paediat. Anaesth.; Paediat. Intens. Care Soc. Prev: Sen. Regist. (Anaesth.) W. Midl. Area Train. Scheme.

RALSTON, Mr David Robert Dept. Of Plastic & Reconstruc. Surg., Northern General Hospital, Sheffield S5 7AV — MB ChB 1986 Manch.; MD 1999 Univ. Of Sheff.; FRCS 1999; FRCS Eng. 1991. Cons. Plastic & Reconstruc. Surg., N.. Gen. Hosp., Sheff..; Hon. Sen. Lect., Univ. Of Sheff. Socs: Brit. Burn Assoc.

RALSTON, Mr Gavin James 67 Dundonald Road, Kilmarnock KA1 1TQ Tel: 01563 25225 — MB ChB 1939 Ed.; MA Ed. 1932, LLB 1935, MB ChB 1939; FRCS Glas. 1971; FRCS Ed. 1946. (Univ. Ed.) Prev: Cons. Surg. Kilmarnock Infirm.

RALSTON, Gavin Robert Duthie Lordswood House, 54 Lordswood Road, Harborne, Birmingham B17 9DB Tel: 0121 426 2030 Fax: 0121 428 2658 — MB ChB 1984 Birm.; MRCGP 1991; DRCOG 1990; DA (UK) 1986. Hon. Sen. Lect. (Gen. Pract.) Birm. Univ.

***RALSTON, Safdar James** The Beeches, 142 Caldy Road, Wirral CH48 1LN — MB ChB 1986 Aberd.

RALSTON, Stuart Hamilton Department of Medicine & Therapeutics, University of Aberdeen Medical School, Foresterhill, Aberdeen AB25 27D Tel: 01224 681818 Fax: 01224 699884 Email: s.ralston@abdn.ac.uk — MB ChB 1978 Glas.; MD Glas. 1987; MRCP (UK) 1980; FRCPS Ed. 1994; FRCPS Glas. 1991; Fmedsci 1999. Prof. Med. & Hon. Cons. Phys. Univ. Aberd. Med. Sch. Socs: (Past. Pres. Elect) Bone & Tooth Soc, 1999-2000, Pres., Europ. calcified tissues Soc.. Prev: Wellcome Sen. Research Fell. (Clin. Sci.) Univ. Edin.

RAM, Alison Jean The Medical Centre, 12 East King Street, Helensburgh G84 7QL Tel: 01436 672277 Fax: 01436 674526; Upper Rossland, 19A East Montrose St, Helensburgh G84 Tel: 01436 676914 — MB ChB 1986 Glas.; MRCGP 1990; DRCOG 1990. GP Helensburgh.

RAM, Mr Shatrughna c/o Dr S. N. Prasad, 25 Poppleton Road, Tingley, Wakefield WF3 1UX — MB BS 1974 Patna; MChOrth Liverp. 1990; FRCSI 1985.

RAM NATH, Krishnaswamy 35 The Archers, Archers Rd, Southampton SO15 2ND — BM 1996 Soton.

RAMA MOHANA RAO, D Sorsby Health Centre, 3 Mandeville Street, London E5 0DS Tel: 020 8986 5613 Fax: 020 8986 8072 — MBBS 1974 Andhra, India; BSc. (Guntur Medical College) Gen. Practitioner. Socs: BMA.

RAMACHANDER, Chelluri Baburao 28 Top Cross Road, Bexhill-on-Sea TN40 2RT — MB BS 1965 Madras.

RAMACHANDRA, Mr Channarayapatna Ramakrishna Setty Preston Hospital, Preston Road, North Shields NE29 0LR — MB BS 1959 Mysore; FRCS Eng. 1966; DLO Eng. 1973. Cons. (OtolaryngOL.) Preston Hosp. N. Shields. Prev: Sen. Regist. (Otolaryngol.) W. Midl. RHA; Regist. (Otolaryngol.) Singleton Hosp. Swansea; Surg. Regist. Moorgate Gen. Hosp. Rotherham.

RAMACHANDRA, Rattehalli Rangappa Consultant Radiologist, Walsgrave Hospital, Clifford Bridge Road, Coventry CV2 2DX Tel: 024 76 602020 Fax: 024 76 844150 Email: ratwhalll@hotmail.com; 4 Broadwells Court, Westwood Heath, Coventry CV4 9JX Tel: 024 76 471988024 764658165 Fax: 01203 471988 Email: rattehalli@hotmail.com — MB BS 1974 Mysore; MD Mysore 1977; DMRD UK 1981; FFR RCSI 1983. (Kasturba Medical College) Cons. (Radiol.) Walsgrave Hosp. Coventry. Socs: BMA Mem.; Roy. Coll. Radiol.; Roy. Coll. Surg. Irel. Fac. of Radiol. (Fell.). Prev: Cons. (Radiol.) Riyadh Nat. Hosp. Riyadh; Sen. Regist. Leicester Roy. Infirm. (Teachg.) Leicester.

RAMACHANDRA, Suvendrini Department of Clinical Microscopy, 2nd Floor, New Guy's House Guy's Hospital, St Thomas St., London SE1 9RT — MB BS 1981 Sri Lanka; MRCPath (Histopath.) 1991. Sen. Regist. (Histopath.) Guy's & Lewisham Hosps. Lond.

RAMACHANDRA, Vinodhini c/o Directorate of AnaesthesiaThe North West London Hospitals NHS Trust, Northwick Park & St Mark's Hospitals, Harrow HA1 3UJ — MB BS 1980 Colombo; FFA RCS Eng. 1986; DA RCS Eng. 1985. Cons. Anaesth. N.wick Pk. & St Mark's Hosp.s,Harrow. Prev: Sen. Regist. (Anaesth.) Char. Cross Hosp. Lond., Hosp Sick Childr. Gt. Ormond St. & Roy. Surrey Co. Hosp. Guildford.

RAMACHANDRA RAJU, Kalidindi Westbrook Centre, 150 Canterbury Road, Margate CT9 5DD Tel: 01843 224541; 98 Headcorn Drive, Canterbury CT2 7TR — MB BS 1973 Mysore. (Kasturba Med. Coll.) Assoc. Specialist (Psychiat.) Thanet Ment. Health Unit Margate; Locum Cons. Psychiat. Prev: Clin. Asst. (Psychiat.) St. Augustine's Hosp. Chartham; Regist. (Psychiat.) Cherry Knowle Hosp. Ryhope.

RAMACHANDRA RAO, Vinnakota 24 Petersham Drive, Appleton, Warrington WA4 5QF — MB BS 1972 Andhra.

RAMACHANDRAM, Raja Segar Moor Green Lane Medical Centre, 339 Moor Green Lane, Moseley, Birmingham B13 8QS Tel: 0121 472 6959 — MB BCh 1983 Wales; MRCGP 1988; DRCOG 1987. GP Birm. Prev: Trainee GP Cardiff VTS.

RAMACHANDRAN, Mr Kannan 22 Cumberland Drive, Royton, Oldham OL2 5AX — MB BS 1980 Madras; FRCSI 1996.

RAMACHANDRAN, Kumuthini Jenner House Surgery, 159 Cove Road, Farnborough GU14 0HH Tel: 01252 548141 Fax: 01252 371516 — LRCP LRCS Ed. LRCPS Glas. 1989.

RAMACHANDRAN, Mannath Kulangara The Haven, Sandown Road, Orsett, Grays RM16 4BB — MB BS 1970 Mysore.

RAMACHANDRAN, Manoj 74 Station Road, London N3 2SA — MB BS 1996 Lond.

RAMACHANDRAN, Mr Nagalingam Department of Accident & Emergency, Watford General Hospital, Vicarage Road, Watford WD18 0HB — MB BS 1959 Ceylon; FRCS Ed. 1971; MRCOG 1971.

RAMACHANDRAN, Nantha Kumaran 70 Peddie Street, Top Floor Flat, Dundee DD1 5LY — MB ChB 1992 Dundee.

RAMACHANDRAN, Sreenivasa 23 Bolton Road, Salford M6 7HL Tel: 0161 736 1616; 9 Victoria Road, Salford M6 Tel: 0161 789 3722 — MB BS 1964 Kerala. (Med. Coll. Trivandrum) Regist. Monsall Hosp. & Manch. Chest Clinic. Prev: Regist. Clare Hall Hosp. S. Mimms, Hartwood Hosp. Shotts & St.; Helen's Hosp. Ipswich.

RAMACHANDRAN, Sudarshan North Staffordshire Hospital Trust, North Staffordshire Hospital, Stoke-on-Trent ST4 6QG; 70 Sir Alfreds Way, Sutton Coldfield B76 1ET — MRCS Eng. LRCP Lond. 1990. Sen. Regist., Chem. Neurol., N. Staffs. Hosp. Trust.

RAMACHANDRAN, Sunita 20 Salcombe Lodge, Lissenden Gardens, London NW5 1LZ — MB ChB 1993 Glas.

RAMACHANDRAN, Vengatasamy 6 The Dell, Bishop Auckland DL14 7HJ; c/o General Hospital, Bishop Auckland DL14 6AD — MB BS 1965 Osmania.

RAMACHANDRAPPA, Mr Govindappa 31 Peldon Close, Vicars Lane, Newcastle upon Tyne NE7 7PB Tel: 0191 270 2738 — MB BS 1973 Madras; FRCSI 1990.

RAMADAN, Abdo Mohamed Newland House, 329 Gower Road, Killay, Swansea SA2 7AE — MB BCh 1974 Alexandria, Egypt.

RAMADAN, Mr Mohamed Fouad 28 Rodney Street, Liverpool L1 2TQ Tel: 0151 708 6137 Fax: 0151 932 9239; 44 Warren Road, Blundellsands, Liverpool L23 6UF Tel: 0151 931 4238 Fax: 0151 932 9239 — MB BCh Cairo 1968; FRCS Ed. 1976; DLO Eng. 1975; DA Cairo 1971. (Mansoura Fac. Med.) Cons. (ENT Surg.) Walton & Univ. Hosp. Aintree; Clin. Lect. (Otolaryng.) Univ. Liverp. Socs: Brit. Assn. Otol.; BMA; Roy. Soc. Med. Prev: Sen. Lect. (Otolaryng.) Univ. Liverp. & Mersey RHA.

RAMADAS, Ranjitharatnam Bungalow 3, Brighton General Hospital, Elm Grove, Brighton BN2 3EW — MB BS 1973 Sri Lanka; LMSSA Lon. 1984.

RAMAGE, Alison Elizabeth Renfrew Health Centre, 103 Paisley Road, Renfrew PA4 8LL Tel: 0141 886 2455 Fax: 0141 855 0457; 1340 Pollokshaws Road, Glasgow G41 3RF Tel: 0141 649 2662 — MB ChB 1981 Glas.; DRCOG 1984. (Glas.)

RAMAGE, Christina McCallum Hamilton Middlesex Hospital, Martimer St., London W1T 3AA Tel: 020 7636 8333; 30 Mayford Road, London SW12 8SD Tel: 020 8675 4689 Fax: 020 8675 4689 — MB BS 1983 Lond.; BSc Lond. 1980, MB BS 1983; FFA RCS Eng. 1988. Cons. (Anaesth). Middlx. Hosp. Lond. Socs: RCA; Brit. Assoc. of Day Surg. Prev: Sen. Regist. (Anaesth.) Middlx. Hosp. Lond.; Regist. (Anaesth.) Roy. Free. Hosp. Lond.; SHO (Anaesth.) St. Mary's & Kings Coll. Hosp. Lond.

RAMAGE, Ian (retired) Glebe Cottage, Old Back Lane, Wiswell, Clitheroe BB7 9BS Tel: 01254 823231 — MB ChB 1954 Manch.; BA Open 1995; FRCGP 1983, M 1965; DCH RCP Lond. 1957.

RAMAGE

RAMAGE, Ian John Flat 1st Left, 63 Gardner St., Glasgow G11 5BZ — MB ChB 1989 Dundee.

RAMAGE, John Keith North Hampshire Hospital, Aldermanston Rd, Basingstoke RG24 9NA Email: dr.ramage@bas.sweet.nhs.uk — MD 1989 Lond.; MB BS 1978; MRCP (UK) 1984; FRCP 1999. (Westm.) Cons. Phys. & Hepat. Gen. Med. & Gastroenterol. N. Hants. Hosp. Basingstoke Hants; Cons. Phys. Inst. of Liver Studies, Kings Coll. Hosp. Socs: Brit. Soc. Gastroenterol.; Amer. Gastroenterol. Assn.; BASL. Prev: Sen. Regist. (Gastroenterol. & Gen. Med.) Roy. Sussex Co. Hosp. Brighton; Research Fell. (Gastroenterol.) McMaster Univ. Med. Centre, Ontario; Sen. Reg. Inst. of liver Studies, King's Coll. Hosp.

RAMAGE, Lynn 33 Dornie Place, Dundee DD2 4UD — MB ChB 1983 Aberd.; MRCP (UK) 1987.

RAMAGE, Mary Muriel (retired) 8 St Johns Way, Ashley, Market Drayton TF9 4LB Tel: 01630 672685 — MB BS 1928 Lond.; MRCS Eng. LRCP Lond. 1928. Prev: Anaesth. N. Staffs. Roy. Infirm.

RAMAGE, Patrick Algernon James (retired) The Rowans, Fownhope, Hereford HR1 4PJ Tel: 01432 860307 Fax: 01432 860307 — MB BS 1962 Lond. Prev: GP Hereford.

RAMAGE, Philip Charles Vincent Limpsfield Road Surgery, 515 Limpsfield Road, Warlingham CR6 9LF Tel: 01883 265262 Fax: 01883 627893 — MRCS Eng. LRCP Lond. 1968; MRCP (UK) 1974. (Guy's) Dir. Interaction Systems Software; Application Cons. MFB Computers. Socs: Primary Care Spec. Gp. of Brit. Computer Soc. Prev: Specialist (Med.) P.ss Mary's Hosp. Halton.

RAMAGE, Victoria Mary Wallingford Medical Practice, Reading Road, Wallingford OX10 9DU Tel: 01491 835577 — MB BS Lond. 1990, BSc (Psychol. & Basic Med. Sci.) 1987; DCH RCP Lond. 1992. Trainee GP Reading VTS. Prev: SHO (A & E) W. Middlx. Univ. Hosp. Isleworth.

RAMAIAH, Mr Devajana Appacha Withybush General Hospital, Haverfordwest — MB BS 1960 Madras; FRCS Glas. 1976. (Madras) Regist. (Surg.) Withybush Gen. Hosp. HaverfordW..

RAMAKRISHNA, Gupta Mudalagiri Dasappagupta The Surgery, Bevan Close, Shotton Colliery, Durham DH6 2LQ Tel: 0191 526 1643 Fax: 0191 517 2746 — MB BS 1970 Mysore. (Mysore) GP Durh.

RAMAKRISHNA GUPTA, Mudalagiri Dasappagupta 17 Barnard Wynd, Oakerside Park, Peterlee SR8 1LT — MB BS 1969 Mysore. (Mysore) Prev: SHO (Med.) Ruchill Hosp. Glas.; SHO (O & G) Robroyston Hosp. Glas.

RAMAKRISHNAN, Kattukandy Patiyeri Chipstead Valley Road Surgery, 37 Chipstead Valley Road, Coulsdon CR5 2RA Tel: 020 8660 9400; (resid.) 127 Cheam Road, Sutton SM1 2EB Tel: 020 8642 2600 — MB BS 1954 Madras. (Madras Med. Coll.) Princip. GP Sutton.

RAMALINGAM, Dr Middlehouse, High St., Harby, Newark NG23 7EB — MB BS 1993 Lond.

RAMAMOORTHY, Sidha Naidu 2 Wirral View, Liverpool L19 0PU — MB BS 1976 Madras; MRCS Eng. LRCP Lond. 1986.

RAMAMURTHY, Anantapur Bache 156 Roe Lane, Southport PR9 7PN — MB BS 1964 Karnatak. (Kasturba Med. Coll. Mangalore) Prev: Regist. (Anaesth.) S.. Gen. Hosp. Glas.

RAMAMURTHY, Laxmi 60 Ashstead Road, Brooklands, Sale M33 3PX Tel: 0161 976 3289 — MB BS 1986 Madras; FRCS Ed. 1991.

RAMAN, Ashok 9 Hurst Park Road, Twyford, Reading RG10 0EZ — MB BS 1996 Lond.

RAMAN, Mr Chidambaram Medical Records Building, Barnet General Hospital, Wellhouse Lane, Barnet EN5 3DJ — MB BS 1976 Madras; FRCS Ed. 1986.

RAMAN, Sucharita Buckland Hospital, Coombe Valley Road, Dover CT17 0HD Tel: 01304 201624; 70 Hither Green Lane, Redditch B98 9BW — MB BS 1981 Madras; FRCS Ed. 1990. Regist. (Surg.) Buckland Hosdp. Dover. Prev: SHO (Paediat. Surg.) Gt. Ormond St. Hosp. Lond.; SHO (Gen. Surg.) Childr. Hosp. Madras.

RAMAN, Thirumalappa Sampangi Pallion Health Centre, Hylton Road, Sunderland SR4 7XF Tel: 0191 657 1319; 10 Thornfield Grove, Sunderland SR2 7UZ Tel: 0191 551 6257 — MB BS 1970 Bangalor, T (GP). (Bangalore Med. Coll.) Princip. GP. Prev: Princip. GP S.grange Med. Centre Trunk Rd. Eston Middlesbrough; Clin. Asst. (Psychiat.) St. Lukes Hosp. Middlesbrough.

RAMAN, Vivek 9 Hurst Park Road, Twyford, Reading RG10 0EZ — MB BS 1996 Lond. SHO Med. Rotat. Qu. Mary's Hosp. Sidcup, S. Lond. Prev: SHO (A & E) Univ. Hosp. Lewisham S. Lond.

RAMANADEN, David Niranjen 19 Tyle'r Hendy, Miskin, Pontyclun CF72 8QU — MB BCh 1992 Wales.

RAMANAN, Mr Ramaswami 103 Princes Avenue, London NW9 9JN — MB BS 1981 Calcutta; FRCSI 1989.

RAMANANANDAN, Avvai 17 Fraser Close, Nythe, Swindon SN3 3RP — MB BS 1996 Lond.

RAMANATHAN, Mr Chakkedath Royal Halifax Infirmary, Free School Lane, Halifax HX1 2YP Tel: 01422 357222 — MB BS 1969 Kerala; FRCS Glas. 1980; DLO Eng. 1978; DLO Mysore 1972. (Med. Coll. Calicut) Assoc. Specialist (ENT) Roy. Halifax Infirm. Socs: BMA; Semon Club.

RAMANATHAN, Jai Shankar 92 Hitchings Way, Reigate RH2 8ER — MB BS 1993 Lond.; BSc (Hons) Lond. 1989. SHO (Anaesth.) King Geo. Hosp. Redbridge. Prev: SHO (Elderly Care) Mayday Univ. Hosp.; SHO (Med.) Norf. & Norwich Hosp.

RAMANATHAN, Manickavasagar (retired) 92 Hitchings Way, Reigate RH2 8ER Tel: 01737 244818 — MB ChB 1961 Aberd.; FRCPath 1988, M 1977; DCP Lond 1974; DPath Eng. 1974.

RAMANATHAN, Mr Narayanaswami, OStJ Narayana, 23 Pincroft Wood, New Barn, Longfield DA3 7HB Tel: 01474 770 6473 Fax: 01474 705279 Email: narayanasamiramu@aol.com — Dip in Med. Acupunc. (British Med. Acupunc. Society); MB BS Madras 1959; BSc Madras 1952; FRCS Ed. 1975. (Madras Med. Coll.) Indep. Med. Pract. & Hyperbaric Phys. Lond.; Med. Adviser Port of Lond. Auth. Socs: Fell. Roy. Soc. Med.; Eur. Undersea Biomed. Soc.; Undersea Hyperbaric Med. Soc. USA. Prev: Chief Med. Off. Nat. Dock Labour Bd. Lond.

RAMANATHAN, Ponnambalam 24 Trinty Avenue, Bush Hill Park, Enfield EN1 1HS — MB BS 1973 Sri Lanka; MRCP (UK) 1983; MRCS Eng. LRCP Lond. 1984.

RAMANATHAN, Ramachandra Gary Ramanathan, McKay and Kearney, The Health Centre, 2-4 Bay Street, Port Glasgow PA14 5EW Tel: 01475 745321 Fax: 01475 745587 — LMSSA 1978 London. (London) GP Port Glas., Renfrewsh.; Hosp. Med. practitioner in obstetnic & gynaecological ultrasonography at the Inner chyler Roy. Hosp. IRN, Greenwich.

RAMANATHAN, Rasiah Fairfield Hospital, Hitchin Road, Stotfold, Hitchin SG5 4AA — MB BS 1978 Colombo.

RAMANATHAN, Ravi Shankar 92 Hitchings Way, Reigate RH2 8ER — MB ChB 1991 Glas.

RAMANATHAN, Satyavathi Narayana, 23 Pincroft Wood, New Barn, Longfield DA3 7HB Tel: 01474 706473 Fax: 01474 709303 Email: ramu@mcmail.com — MB BS Madras 1959; MFCH 1989; FRIPHH 1997. (Madras Med. Coll.) Socs: Fell. Soc. Community Med.; Fell. Roy. Soc. Med.; Brit. Paediat. Assn. & Kent Paediat. Soc. Prev: Cons. Community Paediat. Qu. Mary's Sidcup NHS Trust.

RAMANATHAN, Mr Uthaya Shankar 9 Juniper Drive, Sutton Coldfield B76 1GX Tel: 0121 240 5243 — MB BS 1990 Lond.; BSc (Hons.) Lond. 1986, MB BS 1990; FRCOphth 1995. (Charing Cross and Westminster Medical School) Specialist Regist. (Ophth.) Birm. & Midl. Eye Infirm. Prev: SHO Rotat. (Ophth.) St. Jas. Hosp. Leeds & Bradford Roy. Infirm.; SHO (Neurosurg.) Hull Roy. Infirm.; SHO (A & E) Char. Cross Hosp.

RAMANI, Pramila Consultant Pathologist, Childrens Hospital, Steelhouse Lane, Birmingham B4 6NH — MB BS 1979 Utkal; PhD Lond. 1987; FRCPath 1998. Cons. Histopath. Childr.'s Hosp. Birm. Socs: Paediatric Pathol. Soc.; Brit. Paediatric Path. Assn. Prev: Cons. (Histopath.) Hosp. Sick Childr. Lond.; Clin. Lect. Univ. Coll. Lond.; Clin. Research Fell. ICRF.

RAMANI, Ratilal Muljibhai 10 Deer Park Way, West Wickham BR4 9QQ Tel: 020 8462 6657 — MB BS 1970 Gujarat; DO Eng. 1979; DOMS Saurashtra 1972. (M.P. Shah Med. Coll. Jamnagar) Med. Pract. (Ophth.) Kent. Prev: Clin. Asst. (Ophth.) Centr. Middlx. Hosp. Lond.; SHO (Ophth.) St. Paul's Eye Hosp. Liverp.

RAMANNA, Marigowda (Surgery) 40 Old Hill Street, Stamford Hill, London N16 6LU Tel: 020 8802 3344; Flat 10, Caldew Court, 1 Bunns Lane, London NW7 2AW — MB BS 1970 Mysore; Dip. Pract. Dermat. Wales 1992. (Mysore Med. Coll.) Socs: Med. Protec. Soc. Prev: SHO (Gen. Med.) Downe Hosp. Downpatrick; SHO (Infec. Dis.) Seacroft Hosp. Leeds.

RAMARAO, Mallela Venkata Ramarao, Sparkbrook Health Centre, 32 Farm Road, Sparkbrook, Birmingham B11 1LS Tel: 0121 773 2104 Fax: 0121 766 7287 — MB BS Osmania 1969; DO; DPM Lond. 1980.

RAMARAO, Paidsetty Patel and Partners, Thornley Road Surgery, Thornley Road, Wheatley Hill, Durham DH6 3NR Tel: 01429 820233 Fax: 01429 823667 — MB BS 1969 Andhra. (Andhra) GP Durh.

RAMASAMY, Nirmalan The Surgery, 12-14 Golborne Road, London W10 5PG Tel: 020 8969 2058 Fax: 020 8964 4156 — MB ChB 1980 Birm.; MB ChB. Birm. 1980; MRCP (UK) 1985; MRCGP 1988.

RAMASUBBU, Mr Krishnamurthy Flat 2, 243 Addiscombe Road, Croydon CR0 6SQ — MB BS 1972 Mysore; FRCS Glas. 1980; FRCS Ed. 1980.

RAMASUBRAMANIAN, Navaneethakrishnan 10 Dukes Avenue, Northolt UB5 5DA — MB BS 1975 Madurai.

RAMASWAMI, Perinkulam Krishnasamy (retired) Kalpana, 1 Lovaine Grove, Sandal, Wakefield WF2 7NF Tel: 01924 250121 Fax: 01924 250121 — BSc Madras 1945, MB BS 1952; FRCP Glas. 1981, M 1962; DCH Bombay 1955. Cons. Phys. Barnsley Hosp. Gp. Prev: Regist. Hull (A) Hosp. Gp.

RAMASWAMI, Radha (retired) Kalpana, 1 Lovaine Grove, Sandal, Wakefield WF2 7NF Tel: 01924 250121 Fax: 01924 250121 Email: ramnad@talk21.com — BA Madras 1941, MB BS 1952; DCH Bombay 1955. Specialist in Community Med. (Child Health) Barnsley AHA. Prev: SCMO Barnsley AHA.

RAMASWAMI, Ravi Aravindan Cathey Pacific Airways, Aviation Medicine Office, h/f Cathay Pacific City, Hong Kong Intntl Airport Lantau, Hong Kong Tel: 00 852 27472922 Fax: 00 852 20624636 Email: ravi-ramaswami@cathaypacific.com; 1 Lovaine Grove, Wakefield WF2 7NF — MB BS 1985 Lond.; MSc (Occupat. Health) Aberd. 1995; MFOM(RCP Ireland) 1997; Dip Av Med 2000 Otago. (Royal Free Hospital) Company Med. Off.. Aviat. Med. Dept. Cathay Pacific Airways. Hong Kong.; Adjunct Ass. Prof. Dept. of Surg., Fac. of Med., Chinese Uni of Hong Kong, Shatin Hong Kong. Socs: Soc. Occupat. Med. & Europ. Undersea Biomed. Soc.; Underwater & Hyperbaric Med. Soc.; Aviat. Med. Soc. of Australia & New Zealand. Prev: Employm. Med. Adviser Health & Safety Exec. Scotl. E..; Med. Off. (Undersea Med.) Inst. Naval Med. Alverstoke,; Sen. Med. Off. (Underwater Med.) DoH, Hong Kong.

RAMASWAMI, Uma 99 North Road, Hertford SG14 2BU — MB BS 1987 Madras; MRCPI 1993.

RAMASWAMY, A Bridge Road Surgery, 25 Bridge Road, Stockton-on-Tees TS18 3AA Tel: 01642 604117 Fax: 01642 604602 — MB BS 1971 Madras; MB BS 1971 Madras.

RAMASWAMY, Aylam Chandran 8 Hatton Road, Croydon CR0 3LX — MB BS 1982 Lond.; DA (UK) 1986. SHO (ENT) Orsett Hosp. Prev: SHO (Anaesth.) Arrowe Pk. Hosp. Upton.

RAMASWAMY, Saroja 21 The Warren Drive, Wanstead, London E11 2LR Tel: 020 8989 0966 — MB BS 1954 Calcutta; DGO 1956; FRCOG 1976, M 1959. (Calcutta Med. Coll.) Mem. HQ Staff MRC. Socs: Fell. Roy Soc. Med.; Soc. Study Fertil. Prev: Dir. Med. Train. & Research Family Plann. Assn.; Research Assoc. Dept. Human Metab. St. Mary's Hosp. Med. Sch. Lond.; Edr. Family Plann. Assn. Med. Newsletters.

RAMAYYA, Anjali 35 Aytoun Road, Pollokshiels, Glasgow G41 5HW — MB BS 1981 Osmania; MRCPsych 1988.

RAMAYYA, Pradeep Department of Anaesthesia, Health Care International, Clydebank G81 4DY Tel: 0141 951 5606 Fax: 0141 951 5603; 35 Aytoun Road, Pollokshields, Glasgow G41 5HW Tel: 0141 423 6201 — MB BS 1979 Osmania; FFA RCS Eng. 1984. Vice-Chairm. & Cons. Anaesth. Health Care Internat. Clydebank. Socs: (Chairm.) Soc. Computing & Technol. in Anaesth. Prev: Cons. & Sen. Regist. (Anaesth.) Aberd. Roy. Infirm.; Sec. Intens. Care Computer Gp.; Regist. Prize NE Scotl. Soc. Anaesth.

RAMBIHAR, Brian Vishnu Sandy Lane Surgery, Sandy Lane, Leyland, Preston PR25 2EB Tel: 01772 909915 Fax: 01772 909911; 5 Old Oak Gardens, Walton-Le-Dale, Preston PR5 4BF Tel: 01772 620593 Email: bvram@compuserve.com — MB BS 1986 Lond.; BSc (Hons.) Lond. 1984; MRCGP 1992; MFFP 1992; Dip. Occ. Med. 1996. (Char. Cross & Westm.) GP Sandy La. Surg. Leyland & Trainer in Gen. Pract.; GP Postgrad. Tutor, Chorley & S. Ribble; Trainer in Gen. Pract.; Mem. Clin. Governance SubComm., Chorley & S. Ribble PCG. Socs: BMA. Prev: Trainee GP Aldergate Med. Pract. Tamworth;

Trainee GP/SHO (O & G) Derby City Hosp.; SHO Rotat. (Paediat.) Dudley Rd. Hosp. Birm.

RAMCHANDANI, Mr Mahesh 39 Bankside, Westhoughton, Bolton BL5 2QP — MB ChB 1993 Manch.; FRCS Ed. 1998.

RAMCHANDANI, Mohanlal Leigh Infirmary, The Avenue, Leigh WN7 1HS Tel: 01942 672333; The Gables, 39 Bankside, Westhoughton, Bolton BL5 2QP Tel: 01942 840126 — MB BS 1962 Karachi; MRCS Eng. LRCP Lond. 1977. (Dow Med. Coll. Karachi) Assoc. Specialist (Geriat. Med.) Wigan HA. Socs: Fell. Roy. Soc. Med.; Brit. Geriat. Soc.; BMA.

RAMCHANDANI, Parkash The Gables 39 Bank Side, Westhoughton, Bolton BL5 2QP — MB BS 1997 Manch.; MB BS Manc 1997.

RAMCHANDANI, Paul Gulab Child & Family Psychiatric Service, Sue Nicholls Centre, Manor House, Aylesbury HP20 1EG — BM 1991 Soton. Specialist Regist. Child & Family Psych. Serv. Sue Nicholls Centre Aylesbury.

RAMCHANDRA, Kanakam (retired) 44 Bakers Field, Crayford Road, London N7 0LT Tel: 020 7607 2546 — MB BS 1950 Madras; DPH Newc. 1966; DCH Madras 1962; DGO Madras 1952. Prev: Prison Med. Off. HM Prison Holloway.

RAMCHARITAR, Steve Harrinarine Linacre College, St Cross Road, Oxford OX1 3JA — BM BCh 1998 Oxf.; BM BCh Oxf 1998.

RAMDAHEN-GOPAL, Sangeeta The Medical Centre, 144-150 High Road, Willesdon Green, London NW10 2PE Fax: 0208 561 1128 — BSc 1991; MBBS 1991; MRCGP 1999; DFFP 1999. (Fatima Jinnah / Punjab Univ. Lahore, Pakistan) Gen. Practitioner. Socs: MRCGP; BMA.

RAMDEEHUL, Amal Raj 7 Dean Park Street, Stockbridge, Edinburgh EH4 1JN — MB BCh BAO 1990 NUI.

RAMDENEE, Radhayshyam 116 Manor Drive, Upton, Wirral CH49 4PJ Tel: 0151 677 0064; 81 Leasowe Road, Wallasey, Wirral CH46 Tel: 0151 639 8271 — LRCPI & LM, LRSCI & LM 1967; LRCPI & LM, LRCSI & LM 1967. (RCSI) Socs: Wallasey Med. Soc. Prev: Regist. (Anaesth.) Qu. Mary's Hosp. Sidcup; Ho. Off. (Surg.) Vict. Hosp. Blackpool; Ho. Off. (Med.) St. Lawrence's Hosp. Dub.

RAMDEO, Anil 54 Sleapshyde Lane, Smallford, St Albans AL4 0SB — MB BCh BAO 1981 NUI.

RAMDIN, Leeanne Sukrania 253 Prittlewell Chase, Westcliff on Sea SS0 0PW — MB ChB 1998 Manch.; MB ChB Manch 1998. SHO (A&E), Med., UHSM, Manch. Prev: PRHO Surg., Bury Dist. Gen. Hosp.; PRHO Med.

RAMELL, Michael David Barnfield Hill Surgery, 12 Barnfield Hill, Exeter EX1 1SR Tel: 01392 432761 Fax: 01392 422406 — MB BS 1983 Lond.

RAMESAR, Keith Christopher Robert Blair Pathology Department, St. John's Hospital, Livingston EH54 6PP — MB ChB 1981 Dundee; MB ChB (Hons.) Dundee 1981, BMSc (Hons.) 1978; MRCPath 1987. Cons. Histopath. W. Lothian Trust.

RAMESH, Chandakacharla Narasimha 21 Beamsish View, Stanley DH9 0XB — MB BS 1987 Sri Venkateswara.

RAMESH, Chaniyil Ayyappan St. Mary's Hospital, Whitworth Park, Manchester M13 0JU Tel: 0161 276 6200; c/o Drive S. Ramesh, Department of Paediatrics, Glan Clwyd Hospital, Bodelwyddan, Rhyl LL18 5UJ Tel: 01745 583910 — MB BS Kerala 1980; MRCP (UK) 1993; DCH RCP Glas. 1990. Regist. & Tutor (Paediat.) St. Mary's Hosp. Manch.

RAMESH, Cobarsanellore Belle Vue Surgery, 419 Poulton Road, Fleetwood FY7 7JY Tel: 01253 779113 Fax: 01253 770707 — MB BS 1971 Madras; MB BS 1971 Madras.

RAMESH, Girija c/o Dr K. P. Gopinathan, 1 Goodwood Close, Stratford-upon-Avon CV37 9FP — LRCP LRCS Ed. LRCPS Glas. 1983.

RAMESH, Mr Nadarajah 87 Gold Smith Avenue, London E12 6QB; 26 Lily Avenue, Colombo 6, Sri Lanka Tel: 010 941 586513 — MB BS 1986 Colombo; FRCS Ed. 1993; FRCS Glas. 1992; MRCS Eng. LRCP Lond. 1991. Cons. Emerg. Phys. King Fahad Nat. Guard Hosp. Riyadh, Saudi Arabia. Socs: Founder Mem. Brit. Assn. Day Case Surg.; Brit. Assn. Accid. & Emerg. Med.; Brit. Assn. Immed. Care Schemes. Prev: Sen. Regist. Fell. Emerg. Med. John Hunter Hosp. Newc. Austral.

RAMESH, Venkateswaran Newcastle General Hospital, Newcastle upon Tyne NE4 6BE Tel: 0191 273 8811; 6 Elmfield Park, Gosforth, Newcastle upon Tyne NE3 4UX — MB BS 1980 Madras; MRCP

RAMESSAR

(UK) 1985; MRCS Eng. LRCP Lond. 1986; DCH Eng. 1983; FRCP 1998 CH; FRCP 1996. Cons. Paediat. Neurol. Newc. Gen. Hosp. Prev: Sen. Regist. (Paediat. Neurol.) Booth Hall Childr. Hosp. Manch.; Research Fell. (Child Health) Dept. Child Health Med. Sch. Univ. Newc.; Hon. Regist. (Paediat.) Newc. Gen. Hosp.

RAMESSAR, John Abdul Sattar 8 Hill Farm Road, Southampton SO15 5SP — MB BS 1977 West Indies.

RAMGOOLAM, Mohit Department of Psychiatry, Doncaster Royal Infirmary, Armthorpe Rd, Doncaster DN2 5LT Tel: 01302 366666 Ext: 4084 Fax: 01302 761317 — BM 1980 Soton.; PhD Wales 1974, BPharm (1st cl. Hons.) 1970; MRCGP 1987; MRCPsych 1987. (Soton.) Cons. Old Age Psychiat. Doncaster & S. Humberside NHS Trust. Socs: Roy. Coll. of Psychiat., Mem. Prev: Cons. Old Age Psychiat. Dudley Priority Health; Cons. Old Age Psychiat. Cardiff; Sen. Regist. (Psychiat.) S. Devon.

RAMGOOLAM, Navinchandra 185 Inderwick Road, London N8 9JR — LRCPI & LM, LRSCI & LM 1975; LRCPI & LM, LRCSI & LM 1975. (RCSI) Clin. Med. Asst. Cardiac Dept. Univ. Coll. Hosp. Lond. Prev: Res. Med. Off. Civil Hosp. Port Louis, Mauritius.

RAMI REDDY, Sanampudi The Surgery, 522 Queslett Road, Great Barr, Birmingham B43 7UB Tel: 0121 360 8560 Fax: 0121 360 6833; 33 Carpenter Road, Edgbaston, Birmingham B15 2JH Tel: 0121 440 2580 — MB BS 1972 Sri Venkateswara. (Kurnool Med. Coll.) Prev: SHO (Anaesth.) Univ. Hosp. S. Manch.; SHO (Anaesth.) Burnley Gen. Hosp.

RAMIREZ, Professor Amanda Jane Department of Liaison Psychiatry & ICRF Psychosocial Oncology, 3rd Floor, Riddell House, St Thomas' Hospital, Lambeth Palace Road, London SE1 7EH Tel: 020 7960 5734 Fax: 020 7960 5719 Email: a.ramirez@umds.ac.uk; 7 College Road, Dulwich Village, London SE21 7BQ Tel: 020 8693 3657 Fax: 020 8693 3657 — MB BS 1998 London University; BSc Hons Human Genetics London University; FRCPsych 1987; MB BS London University 1982; MRCPsych 1987; MD London University; FRCPsych 1998. (Guy's, King's and St Thomas') Prof. of Liaison Psychiat. Guy's & St Thomas's Hosp. Trust; Prof. Liaison Psychiat. Guy's & St. Thomas' Hosp. Trust; Dir. of the Richard Dimbleby Cancer Informat. & Support Serv. Guy's & St. Thomas' Cancer Centre; Dir. for Liaison Psychiat. Guy's & St. Thomas' Hosp. Trust. Socs: Exec. Comm. Liaison Psychiat. Gp. of Roy. Coll. of Psychiat.; Coun. Mem. of the Soc. for Psychosomatic Research. Prev: Sen. Lect. & Hon. Cons. in Liaison Psychiat., Imperial Cancer Research Fund, Clin. Oncol. Unit & Div. of Psychiat., Guy's Hosp.

RAMIREZ RODRIGUEZ, Jose Manuel 6 Anderton Way, Garstang, Preston PR3 1RF — LMS 1983 Zaragoza.

RAMISHVILI, Akaki 188 Cromwell Road, London SW5 0SJ — MRCS Eng. LRCP Lond. 1949; MRCP Lond. 1961; MRCP Ed. 1961.

RAMJOHN, Mohamed Ally Ward End Medical Centre, 794A Washwood Heath Road, Ward End, Birmingham B8 2JN Tel: 0121 327 1049 Fax: 0121 327 0964; 4 Poundley Close, Castle Bromwich, Birmingham B36 9SZ — MB BCh BAO 1976 Dub.; MA Dub. 1993, BA 1976; DFFP 1993; DRCOG 1979. (Univ. Dub.)

RAMJOORAWON, Manilall Craven Park Health Centre, Knatchbull Road, London NW10 8XQ — LRCPI & LM, LRSCI & LM 1970; LRCPI & LM, LRCSI & LM 1970.

RAMKHALAWON, Meghraj 52 St Mary's Park, Louth LN11 0EF — MB BCh BAO 1986 NUI; LRCPSI 1986.

RAMKISSOON, Anand Mikhail Regional Clinical Virology Laboratory, City Hospital, Edinburgh Tel: 0131 536 6334 Fax: 0131 536 6123 — MB ChB 1988 Manch.; BSc (Hons.) St. And. 1983; DRCPath 1994. Regist. Reg. Clin. Urol. Laborat. Prev: Regist. (Microbiol.) Leicester Roy. Infirm.; SHO (Path.) Roy. Preston Hosp.

RAMLEE, Norsurainah Norashlinah Haji House 17, Dame Elizabeth Court, Puddings Wood Lane, Broomfield, Chelmsford CM1 7WE — MB ChB 1996 Manch.

RAMLI, Anis Safura Flat 4 NMA, South Tyneside District Hospital, Harton Lane, South Shields NE34 0PL — MB BS 1997 Newc.

RAMLI, Norlina 55 Doncaster Road, Newcastle upon Tyne NE2 1RB; 33 Grosvenor Place, Jesmond, Newcastle upon Tyne NE2 2RD Tel: 0191 2816 654 — MB BS 1997 Newc.

***RAMNANI, Suneil Mark** 8 Ambelside Drive, Walton, Wakefield WF2 6TJ Tel: 01924 258448 — MB BS 1996 Lond.

RAMNARINE, Vishan Dimitri Flat 11, Block 13, Good Hope Hospital, Rectory Road, Sutton Coldfield B75 7RR — MB BS 1991 West Indies.

RAMO, Marja Pauliina Department of Cardiology, Western General Hospital, Crewe Road, Edinburgh EH4 2XU — Lic Med Oulu 1985.

RAMON, Amos Jehoshua High Street Surgery, 69 High Street, Coningsby, Lincoln LN4 4RB Tel: 01526 344544 Fax: 01526 345540.

RAMON VALCARCEL, Benilde 13 Cavalry Gardens, London SW15 2QQ — LMS 1982 La Laguna.

RAMPA, Balarami Reddy Radhika, School Lane, Trinant, Crumlin, Newport NP11 3LQ — MB BS 1964 Andhra. (Guntur Med. Coll.)

RAMPERSAD, David Steve John 30 Grange, Furzehill, Wimborne BH21 4HX Tel: 01202 848981 — BM BCh 1991 Oxf.; MA Camb. 1989; MRCP (UK) 1995. SHO (Paediat.) Poole Hosp. Dorset. Prev: Regist. (Med.) Bundaberg Hosp. Australia; Regist. (Med.) S.land Hosp. Invercargill, NZ; SHO Med. Roy. Bournemouth Hosp.

RAMPERSAD, Randolph Frederick Flat 2, 211 Gipsy Road, West Norwood, London SE27 9QY — LRCPI & LM, LRSCI & LM 1958; LRCPI & LM, LRCSI & LM 1958. (RCSI) Prev: Ho. Surg. New Cross Hosp. Wolverhampton; Ho. Phys. Roy. Huddersfield Infirm.; SHO Cas. Derbysh. Roy. Infirm. Derby.

RAMPES, Hagen West London Mental Health NHS Trust, John Conolly Wing, Uxbridge Road, Southall UB1 3EU Tel: 020 8354 8014 Fax: 020 8354 8887 — MB ChB 1987 Ed.; BSc MedSci. (Biochem.) Ed. 1985; MRCPsych 1993. (Edinburgh) Cons., Gen. Adult Psychiat. Prev: Sen. Regist. Char. Cross Higher Psychiat.

RAMPHAL, Paul Shridath 57 Farm Avenue, Swanley BR8 7HZ — MB BS 1989 West Indies.

RAMPHUL, Neelmanee North Tees General Hospital, Hardwick, Stockton-on-Tees TS19 8PE Tel: 01642 617617; 9 Redall Drive, Cochrane Park, Newcastle upon Tyne NE7 7LH Tel: 0199 266 9141 — MB BS 1997 Newc. SHO (Paediat.) N. Tees. Socs: Med. Defence Union; BMA. Prev: Ho. Off. Med. S. Cleavland; Ho. Off. Surg. N. Tees.

RAMPHUL-GOKULSING, Shishana Kali 48 Montpelier Rise, London NW11 9DX — MB BS 1993 Lond.

RAMPLING, Alec Edwin, Surg. Cdr. RN (retired) Lisnamandra, Fort Road, Alverstoke, Gosport PO12 2DT Tel: 01705 583425 — MRCS Eng. LRCP Lond. 1957; DO Eng. 1965.

RAMPLING, Anita Margaret (retired) East Farm, Toller Whelme, Beaminster DT8 3NU Tel: 01308 862468 — MB ChB 1977 Birm.; MA Camb. 1979; PhD Birm. 1973; FRCPath 1992, M 1981. Cons. Med. Microbiol. & Dir. Pub. Health Laborat. Dorchester. Prev: Cons. Med. Microbiol. Pub. Health Laborat. Camb.

RAMPLING, Constance Mary (retired) 69 Townfield Gardens, Altrincham WA14 4DT Tel: 0161 941 5809 — MB ChB Liverp. 1937, CPH 1946; MRCS Eng. LRCP Lond. 1937.

RAMPLING, Kathleen 1-3 Morrowfield Avenue, Hightown, Manchester M8 9AR — MB ChB 1946 Manch. (Manch.)

RAMPLING, Michael John 38 Durham Road, London W5 4JP — MB ChB 1990 Dundee.

RAMPLING, Professor Roy Peter Beatson Oncology Centre, Western Infirmary, Glasgow G11 6NT Tel: 0141 211 2627 Fax: 0141 211 6356 Email: r.rampliong@udcf.glu.ac.uk — MB BS 1979 Lond.; PhD (Phys.) Lond. 1971; FRCP Glas. 1992; MRCP (UK) 1982; FRCR 1984. (University College London) Prof. of Neuro Oncol. Univ. Glas. And Hon. Cons. W.. Informary; Hon. Cons. (Radiother.) W.. Infirm. Glas. Socs: Fell. Roy. Coll. Phys.; Roy. Coll. Radiol. Prev: Sen. Regist. (Radiother.) Ch.ill Hosp. Oxf.; Regist. (Radiother.) Hammersmith Hosp. Lond.

RAMPTON, Anthony John William Harvey Hospital, Kennington Road, Willesborough, Ashford TN24 0LZ — MB BS 1980 Lond.; BSc Lond. 1977, MB BS 1980; FFA RCS Eng. 1986. Cons. Anaesth. William Harvey Hosp. Ashford.

RAMPTON, David Stephen Department of Gastroenterology, Royal London Hospital, London E1 1BB Tel: 020 7377 7442 Fax: 020 7377 7441 Email: drampton@mds.qmw.ac.uk — BM BCh 1973 Oxf.; MA, DPhil Oxf. 1970; FRCP Lond. 1989; MRCP (UK) 1975. (Oxf. & Univ. Coll. Hosp.) Cons. Gastroenterol. Roy. Lond. Hosp. & St Bart. Hosp.; Reader St Bartholomews & Roy. Lond. Sch. of Med. & Dent. Univ. Lond. Socs: Brit. Inflammatory Research Assn.; Brit. Soc. Gastroenterol.; Fell. Roy. Soc. Med. Prev: Cons. Phys. & Gastroenterol. Newham Gen. Hosp. & St. And. Hosp. Lond.; Lect. (Med.) Univ. Coll. Hosp. Lond.; Research Fell. (Gastroenterol.) Guy's Hosp. Lond.

RAMRAKHA, Punit Satyavrat Department of Clinical Pharmacology, Hammersmith Hospital, Du Cane Road, London W12 0NN Tel: 020 8383 3219 Fax: 020 8383 2066 Email: p.ramrakha@rpms.ac.uk; c/o Mrs. R. Sondhi, 54 Gilmore Close, Langley, Slough SL3 7BD Tel: 01753 539288 — BM BCh 1990 Oxf.; BA Camb. 1987; MRCP (UK) 1993. (Univ. Oxf.) MRC Train. Fell. & Hon. Sen. Regist. (Clin. Pharmacol. & Cardiol.) Imperial Coll. Hammersmith Hosp. Lond. Prev: Regist. (Clin. Pharmacol. & Cardiol.) Roy. Postgrad. Med. Sch. Hammersmith Hosp. Lond.

RAMSAHOYE, Bernard Harcourt 7 Teilo Street, Cardiff CF11 9JN — MB ChB 1988 Bristol; MRCP (UK) 1991.

RAMSAMY, Teygaraj 193 Windmill Road, London W5 4DH — MRCS Eng. LRCP Lond. 1958.

RAMSAY, Alan 18 Marchbank Gardens, Ralston, Paisley PA1 3JD Tel: 0141 810 3198 — MB ChB 1982 Aberd.; FRCR 1990. Cons. Radiol. Inverclyde Roy. NHS Trust Greenock; Clin. Director; Diagnostic Serv.s. Socs: Scott. Radiol. Soc.

RAMSAY, Alan Drummond Hiscopathology Department, Great Ormond Street Hospital For Children, Great Ormond St., London WC1N 3JH Tel: 020 7829 8663 Fax: 020 7813 1170 Email: a.ramsay@ich.ucl.ac.uk — MB BS 1976 Lond.; BSc (Anat.) (1st cl. Hons.) Lond. 1976, MB BS 1979; MRCPath 1985; FRCPath 1996; D.M. Soton 1997. Cons. Histopath. Gt. Ormond St. Hosp. for Childr. Prev: Lect. (Histopath.) Inst. Otol. & Laryngol. Lond.; Graham Schol. Dept. Histopath. Univ. Coll. Lond.; Cons. & Sen. Lect. Histopath. Soton. Gen. Hosp.

RAMSAY, Alan Livingstone 29 Church Street, Kilbarchan, Johnstone PA10 2JQ — MB ChB 1989 Glas.

RAMSAY, Andrew (retired) Ravenscraig, Frankscroft, Peebles EH45 9DX Tel: 01721 720420 Email: eahramsay@freenet.co.uk — MB ChB Ed. 1959; DObst RCOG 1966. Prev: GP Peebles.

RAMSAY, Andrew Miller (retired) Prospect House, 31 Station Road, Ossett WF5 8AY Tel: 01924 274053 — MB ChB 1929 Glas.

RAMSAY, Andrew Steven 14 Stratheden Road, London SE3 7TA — MB BS 1991 Lond.; BSc (Psychol.) Lond. 1988, MB BS 1991. SHO (Ophth.) W.. Infirm. Glas.

RAMSAY, Anne Elizabeth 10 Robertson Street, Dundee DD4 6EL Tel: 01382 461588 Fax: 01382 452121 Email: aeramsay@taybank.finix.org.uk; Tel: 01382 380547 — MB ChB 1983 Dundee; FRCGP 1998; MRCGP 1987. Hon. Lect. (Gen. Pract.) T.C.G.P. Dundee; Adviser to Postgrad. Dean in Career Counselling in Wom.; Mem. LMC. Socs: BMA. Prev: Trainee GP Dundee VTS; SHO (Psychiat., ENT & Geriat. Med.) Tayside HB.

RAMSAY, Bruce 14 Green Walk, Berkhamsted HP4 2LW — BM 1987 Soton.; MRCOG 1992. Sen. Regist. (O & G) Glos. Roy. Hosp.

RAMSAY, Colin Ninian Scottish Centre for Infection & Environmental Health, Clifton House, Clifton Place, Glasgow G3 7LN Tel: 0141 300 1100 Fax: 0141 300 1170 Email: colin.ramsay@scieh.csa.scot.nhs.uk; 22 Netherbank, Edinburgh EH16 6YR Tel: 0131 672 1101 Fax: 0131 672 1101 — MB ChB 1980 Dundee; MSc Ed. 1985; MFCM 1987; DRCOG 1983; FFPHM 1998. Cons. Epidemiologist (Environm. Health).

RAMSAY, Crichton Forbes Department of Respiratory Medicine, Norfolk and Norwich University Hospital, Norwich Coloney Lane, Norwich NR4 7UY Tel: 01603 289640 Email: chichton.ramsay@norfolk_norwich.thenhs.com — MB ChB 1986 Ed.; MRCP (UK) 1991. Cons. Phys., Respirat. and Gen. Med. Norf. and Norwich Univ. Hosp., Norwich. Prev: Regist. (Respirat. & Gen. Med.) Edin. Teach. Hosps.; Research Regist. (Thoracic Med.) Lond. Chest Hosp.; Specialist Regist. (Thoracic Med.) Whittingham Hosp., Roy. Lond. Hosp., St. Bart. Hosp., Lond.

RAMSAY, Deborah Ann 8 Rosebank Cottages, Edinburgh EH3 8DA — MB ChB 1993 Ed.

RAMSAY, Doris (retired) Fullerton, Hill of Forss, Janetstown, Thurso KW14 7XQ Tel: 01847 893896 — MB ChB Aberd. 1945. Prev: Regist. (Ophth.) Aberd. Roy. Infirm.

RAMSAY, Dorothy Hilda Elizabeth (retired) 133 Russell Road, Moseley, Birmingham B13 8RS — LRCP LRCS 1950 Ed.; LRCP LRCS Ed. LRFPS Glas. 1950; DObst RCOG 1953; DCH Eng. 1958. Prev: Sessional Clin. Med. Off. Sandwell HA.

RAMSAY, Douglas McNab The Tors, 2 Slamannan Road, Falkirk FK1 5LG Tel: 01324 20877 — MB ChB 1965 Ed.; FRCPath 1985, M 1973. (Ed.) Cons. Haemat. Falkirk & Stirling Roy. Infirm. Socs: Brit. Soc. Haematol.

RAMSAY, Duncan Winson 60 Lorne Road, Clarendon Park, Leicester LE2 1YG Tel: 0116 270 2159 — MB BS 1989 Lond.; FRCR 1997; MRCP (UK) 1993. (Middlx. Hosp.) Regist. (Radiol.) Leicester Roy. Infirm.

RAMSAY, Esther Margaret Elizabeth (retired) 24 Lynmouth Road, Liverpool L17 6AN Tel: 0151 427 5904 — MB ChB 1951 Liverp.; DPH 1956; FFCM 1981, M 1975. Prev: SCM (Med. Manpower & Postgrad. Educat.) Mersey RHA.

RAMSAY, Fiona Mary Horsham Hospital, Hurst Road, Horsham RH12 2DR; Little Duxford, 19 Langley Lane, Ifield, Crawley RH11 0NB Tel: 01293 539344 — MB BS 1977 Lond.; FRCP Lond. 1995; MRCS Eng. LRCP Lond. 1977; MRCP (UK) 1982. (St. Bart.) Cons. Phys. (c/o Elderly) Surrey & Sussex Healthcare Crawley & Horsham Hosps. Prev: Cons. Phys. (Geriat. Med.) The Roy. Lond. Hosp.; Sen. Regist. (Geriat. Med.) St. Geo. Hosp. Lond.

RAMSAY, Helen Mary 85 Redmires Road, Sheffield S10 4LB Tel: 01142 303 6159; 3 Taverners Drive, Stone ST15 8QF Tel: 01785 286406 — MB ChB 1993 Birm.; ChB Birm. 1993; MRCP (UK) 1996. (Birm.) Specialist Regist. (Dermat.) N Staffs. Hosp. Centre Stoke-on-Trent. Socs: Train. Brit. Assn. Dermat. Dowling Club & Midl.s Dermat. Soc.

RAMSAY, Hilary Vanessa Baddow Road Surgery, 115 Baddow Road, Chelmsford CM2 7PY; 57 Well Lane, Stock, Ingatestone CM4 9LZ Tel: 01277 841566 — MB BS 1991 Lond.; BSc Lond. 1988; MRCGP 1995; DRCOG 1994. (King's Coll. Sch. Med. & Dent. Lond.) Prev: Trainee GP/SHO Mid Essex Hosps. Chelmsford VTS; SHO (ENT) Orsett Hosp. Essex.

RAMSAY, Ian The Health Centre, 2 The Tanyard, Cumnock KA18 1BF Tel: 01290 422723 Fax: 01290 425444; 30 Oakbank Drive, Cumnock KA18 1BD Tel: 01290 420469 Email: ian.ramsay@talk21.com — MB ChB 1971 Glas. (Glasgow) Princip. GP Cumnock Ayrsh.; Med. Asst. (Geriat.) Holmhead Hosp. Ayrsh.; Exam. Med. Practit. Benefits Agency; Med.Asst. Socs: MDDUS. Prev: SHO (Paediat.) Hawkhead Hosp. Paisley; SHO (O & G) Paisley Matern. Hosp.; Ho. Off. (Med. & Surg.) Roy. Alexandra Infirm. Paisley.

RAMSAY, Ian Douglas (cons. rooms), The Cromwell Hospital, Cromwell Road, London SW5 0TU Tel: 020 7460 5700 Fax: 020 7460 5555; (cons. rooms), Kings Oak Hospital, Chase Farm North Side, The Ridgeway, Enfield EN2 8SD Tel: 020 8370 9505 Fax: 020 8370 9551 — MB ChB Ed. 1959; MD Ed. 1964; FRCP Ed. 1982, M 1963; FRCP Lond. 1979, M 1966. (Ed.) Cons. Endocrinol. Cromwell Hosp. Lond.; Hon. Lect. (Med.) Roy. Free Hosp. Sch. Med. Lond.; Prof. Med. St. Geo. Univ. Sch. Med. Grenada, WI. Socs: Fell. Roy. Soc. Med.; Brit. Thyroid Assn.; Ovarian Club. Prev: Cons. Endocrinol. N. Middlx. Hosp. Lond.; Lect. (Med.) King's Coll. Hosp. Med. Sch. Lond.; Research Fell. Roy. Vict. Hosp. Belf.

RAMSAY, Ian Duncan The Portland Practice, St Paul's Medical Centre, 121 Swindon Road, Cheltenham GL50 4DP Tel: 01242 707792; Westaway, Stockwell Lane, Cleeve Hill, Cheltenham GL52 3PU — MB ChB 1975 Liverp.; DRCOG 1978.

RAMSAY, Ian Nairn Department of Gynaecology, Southern General Hospital, Govan Road, Glasgow G51 4TF Tel: 0141 201 1100 Fax: 0141 201 2994; Westlodge, Erskine PA8 6AW Tel: 0141 812 1378 Email: ramsayinr@aol.com — MB ChB 1981 Dundee; MRCOG 1987. Cons. O & G S.. Gen. Hosp. Glas. Socs: Internat. Continence Soc. & Glas. Obst. Soc.; Sec./Treasurer of Internat. Continence Soc. (U.K.) Sect. Prev: Sen. Regist Rotat. (O & G) W. Scotl.; Clin. Research Assoc. Dept. O & G Univ. Newc. u Tyne; Regist. Rotat. (O & G) W. Scotl.

RAMSAY, Mr James Hamilton Hawthorn Cottage, Mildenhall, Marlborough SN8 2LR Tel: 01672 516281 — MB 1971 Camb.; MA; BChir 1970; FRCS Eng. 1976. Cons. Ophth. P.ss Margt. Hosp. Swindon & Ridgeway Hosp. Prev: Sen. Regist. Guy's Hosp. Lond. Sen. Resid. Surg. Off. Moorfields Eye; Hosp. Lond. Research Fell. Hosp. Sick Childr. Lond.

RAMSAY, James Richard 3 Green Acres, Lilley, Luton LU2 8LS — MB ChB 1997 Leeds.

RAMSAY, Jane Elizabeth 14 Woodend Drive, Jordanhill, Glasgow G13 1QS — MB ChB 1991 Glas.; MRCOG 1997. Specialist Regist. (O & G).

RAMSAY, Jock Watson 15 Cameron Avenue, Balloch, Inverness IV2 7JT Tel: 01463 798912 Fax: 01463 798912 Email: jock@hqhq.org — MB ChB 1984 Ed.; BSc MedSci Ed. 1981;

RAMSAY

MRCGP 1990; DRCOG 1989. (Ed.) Professional GP. Locum Highlands & W.ern Isles; Assoc. Adviser in Gen. Pract., NOS Instit. of Postgrad. Educat. Raigmore Hosp., Inverness; Exec. Dir. HQHQ Ltd, Peebles, Scotl.

RAMSAY, John Henry Rolland, OBE (retired) — MB ChB 1946 Glas.; FRCP Glas. 1981, M 1962; FRFPS Glas. 1953. Prev: Med. Dir. St. Benedicts Hospice Sunderland.

RAMSAY, John Laurence (retired) 25 Allerton Park, Leeds LS7 4ND Tel: 0113 268 4014 — MB ChB 1956 Leeds; DObst RCOG 1959. Prev: Dep. Resid. Med. Off. & Ho. Phys. St. Jas. Hosp. Leeds.

RAMSAY, Jonathan Robert Spencer Willow Cottage, Baunton, Cirencester GL7 7BB — MB ChB 1978 Bristol; MSc Lond. 1979; MRCP (UK) 1983; FRCR 1988. Cons. Div. Oncol. Roy. Brisbane Hosp., Austral. Prev: Sen. Regist. Addenbrooke's Hosp. Camb.; Fell. Harvard Med. Sch. Boston.

RAMSAY, Mr Jonathan William Alexander 15th Floor, Charing Cross Hospital, Fulham Palace Road, London W6 8RF Tel: 020 8846 7669 Fax: 020 8846 7696; Yew Trees, Southlea Road, Datchet, Slough SL3 9BY Tel: 020 7935 4444 — MB BS 1977 Lond.; MS Lond. 1987; FRCS Eng. 1982; FRCS (Urol.) Eng. 1988; FEBU 1992. (St. Bart.) Cons. Urol. Char. Cross Hosp., W. Middlx. Univ. Hosp. & Chelsea W.minster Hosp. Lond.; Hon. Cons. Urol. St. Lukes Hosp. for Clergy & UCH Lond.; Hon. Cons. (Urol.) King Edwd. VII Hosp. Lond.; Mem. Ct. Examrs. RCS Eng 1997; Regional adviser in Surg. (RCS 1999). Socs: Fell. Roy. Soc. Med. (Pres. Clin. Sect. & Counc. Sect. Urol.); Brit. Assn. Urol. Surg. & Europ. Intrarenal Surg. Soc. Prev: Sen. Regist. (Urol.) St. Bart. Hosp. Lond.; Brackenbury Schol. St. Bart. Hosp.; Hon. Lect. (Lithotripsy) St. Pauls Hosp. Lond.

RAMSAY, Kirsten 59 Taymouth Road, Polmont, Falkirk FK2 0PF — MB ChB 1997 Ed.

RAMSAY, Lawrence Eccles 85 Redmires Road, Lodge Moor, Sheffield S10 4LB Tel: 0114 230 3669 — MB ChB 1967 Glas.; MRCP (UK) 1970; FRCP Lond. 1983; FFPM RCP (UK) 1989. Cons. Phys. Hallamsh. Hosp. Sheff.; Reader Clin. Pharmacol. & Therap. Univ. Sheff.; Mem. Brit. Pharmacopoeia Commiss.; Mem. Comm. on Review of Med. Socs: Sec. Brit. Hypertens. Soc.; Clin. Pharmacol. Sect. Brit. Pharmacol. Soc. Prev: Lect. (Med.) Univ. Glas.

RAMSAY, Lorna Jane Information Statistics Division, Common Services Agency, Trinity Dark House, South Trinity Road, Edinburgh EH5 — MB ChB 1991 Glas.; MB ChB (Commend.) Glas. 1991; MPH Glas. 1997; DCH RCPS Glas. 1994. (Glasgow Uni) Clin. Adviser to Scott. Clin. Coding Centre, ISD, Edin.

RAMSAY, Louise Mary 1 Erskine Avenue, Glasgow G41 5AL; The Douglas Inch Centre, 2 Woodside Terrace, Glasgow G3 7UY Tel: 0141 211 8000 Fax: 0141 211 8005 — MB ChB 1988 Glas.; DRCOG 1991; MRCGP 1993; MRCPsych 1995. Sen. Regist. (Forens. Psychiat.) The Douglas Inan Centre Glas. Prev: Cons. (Forens. Med.), Dougla Inch Centre.

RAMSAY, Margaret Mary Department of Obstetrics & Gynaecology, Queen's Medical Centre, Nottingham NG7 2UH Tel: 0115 924 9924 Fax: 0115 970 9776 Email: margaret.ramsay@nottingham.ac.uk; The Hayloft, Town End Court, Main Street, West Leake, Loughborough LE12 5RF Tel: 01509 852651 — MA Camb. 1985, BA 1981, MD 1993, MB 1984, BChir 1983; MRCP (UK) 1987; MRCOG 1989. (Camb.) Sen. Lect. (FetoMatern. Med.) Qu. Med. Centre Nottm. Socs: Internat. Soc. Study Hypertens. in Pregn.; MacDonald Club. Prev: Vis. Asst. Prof. Physiol. Cornell Univ., USA; Train. Fell. (FetoMatern. Med.) Nottm.; Sen. Regist. (O & G) Derby City Gen. Hosp.

RAMSAY, Mary Elizabeth Booth 60 Harford Drive, Watford WD17 3DG — MB BS 1985 Lond.

RAMSAY, Mary Helen Granville Road Surgery, 296 Granville Road, Sheffield S2 2RT Tel: 0114 272 3638 — MB ChB 1967 Glas.; FFA RCS Eng. 1969; Cert. Equiv. Exp. Gen. Pract. JCPTGP 1981.

RAMSAY, Maureen Wilson The Priory Consulting Rooms, 2 Clarendon Road, Bournemouth BH4 8AH Tel: 01202 760079 — MB ChB 1979 Ed.; BSc (Med Sci.) 1976 Ed.; MRCPsych 1988; MRCGP 1987; BSc (Med Sci.) Ed. 1976; MRCPsych 1988; MRCGP 1987. Cons. Psychiat. Marchwood Priory Hosp. Hythe Soton. Prev: Cons. Psychiat. Roy. S. Hants Hosp. Soton.

RAMSAY, Peter Denis Bewick Crescent Surgery, 27 Bewick Crescent, Newton Aycliffe DL5 5LH Tel: 01325 313289 Fax: 01325 301428 — BM BCh 1982 Oxf.; MRCGP 1986; DRCOG 1986; DCCH RCP Ed. 1985. GP Newton Aycliffe.

RAMSAY, Robert Greig 15 March Road, Edinburgh EH4 3TD — MB ChB 1985 Aberd.

RAMSAY, Roger Barrington The Surgery, Scotland Street, Llanrwst LL26 0AL Tel: 01492 640411 Fax: 01492 641402; Garreg Wen, Llanddoged, Llanrwst LL26 0BJ — MB ChB 1982 Manch.; FRCGP 1995, M 1986; DObst RCOG 1985.

RAMSAY, Rosalind Louisa Scutari, St Thomas' Hospital, London SE1 7EH Tel: 020 7928 9292 Fax: 020 7922 8294 — MB BS Lond. 1986; MRCPsych 1990. Cons. Psychiat. St. Thos. Hosp. Lond. Prev: Sen. Regist. (Psychiat.) Maudsley & Bethlem Hosp.

RAMSAY, Rosemary 3 Mons Close, Harpenden AL5 1TD Tel: 01582 715839 — MB ChB 1986 Ed.

RAMSAY, Sarah Jane Top Floor Flat, Flat C, 73 Malvern Road, London NW6 5PU Tel: 020 7625 9306 — MB BS 1991 Lond.; MB BS (Hons.) Lond. 1991; BSc Lond. (Hons.) 1988; FRCA 1995.

RAMSAY, Scott Gordon 95 Kettil'stoun Mains, Linlithgow EH49 6SJ — MB ChB 1991 Glas.; MB ChB (Commend.) Glas. 1991; BSc (1st cl. Hons.) Anat. Glas. 1988; MRCP (UK) 1994; MD Glas. 1999. (Univ. Glas.) Specialist Regist. (Geriat. Med.) & Gen. Medicene Glas. Roy. Infirm. Socs: RCPS Glas.; Brit. Thorac. Soc.; Brit. Geriat. Soc. Prev: Career Regist. (Gen. Med.) StoneHo. Hosp. Lanarksh.; Research Fell. (Respirat. Med.) Gartnavel Gen. Hosp. Glas.; SHO Rotat. (Med.) W.. Infirm. Glas.

RAMSAY, Timothy Merle 1 Bollinwood Chase, Wilmslow SK9 2DF Tel: 01625 522390 — MB ChB 1982 Dundee; FFA RCS Eng. 1988; DRCOG 1986; DA (Eng.) 1984. Cons. Anaesth. Stepping Hill Hosp. Stockport.

RAMSAY, Mr William Mauchline Mains, Mauchline KA5 6LL — MB ChB 1977 Ed.; BSc (Hons.) Med. Sci. 1974; FRCS Ed. 1982.

RAMSAY, William Leslie (retired) Eastcourt Oast, Church Lane, Chalk, Gravesend DA12 2NL — MB ChB 1926 Aberd. Prev: Med. Off. Gravesend & N. Kent Hosp.

RAMSAY, William Wallace (retired) 2 The Firs, Portadown, Craigavon BT63 5TA Tel: 028 3833 3597 Email: williamramsay@compuserve.com — MB BCh BAO 1953; MD 1967 Belf.; FRCGP 1982, M 1965; DPH 1958; DObst RCOG 1956.

RAMSAY-BAGGS, Mr Peter Department Oral & Maxillo Facial Surgery, The Ulster Hospital, Dundonald, Belfast BT16 0RF Tel: 01232 484511 Fax: 01232 561388 Email: ramsayb@enterprise.net; 3 Plas Merdyn, Church Road, Holywood BT18 9DF Tel: 01232 426761 Fax: 01232 561388 Email: omfs@compuserve.com — MB BCh BAO 1985 Belf.; FRCS Ed. 1989; BDS Lond. 1976; FDS RCS Eng. 1987; FFD RCSI 1986. (Queens Univ. Belfast) Cons. (Oral & Maxillofacial Surg.) Ulster Hosp. Dundonald & Roy. Vict. Hosp. Belf.; Cons. (Oral & Maxillofacial Surg.) Antrim Area Hosp.; Cons. (Oral & Maxillofacial Surg.) Daisy Hill Hosp. Newry. Socs: BMA & Brit. Assn. Oral. & Maxillofacial Surg. Prev: Sen. Regist. Regional Oral & Maxillofacial Unit N. Irel.; Regist. (Maxillofacial) Ulster Hosp. Dundonald & Monklands Hosp. Airedrie; Regist. (Maxillofacial) Univ. Coll. Hosp. Lond.

RAMSAY SMITH, Mr Samuel Richard Department of Surgery, Victoria Hospital, Nevill Road, Lewes BN7 1PE Tel: 01273 474153 Fax: 01273 473362; 15 Arundel Street, Brighton BN2 5TG Tel: 01273 680386 — MB ChB 1971 Liverp.; MSc Lond. 1985; FRCS Eng. 1976; DCH RCP Lond. 1974. Assoc. Specialist & Resid. Surg. Vict. Hosp. E. Sussex; Cons. Pub. Health E. Sussex HA. Socs: Fell. Roy. Soc. Trop. Med. & Hyg.; Assn. Med. Educat. Europ.; Assn. Surg.. E. Afr. Prev: Health of the Nation Co-ordinator Brighton; GP Hailsham E. Sussex; Safari Surg. E. Afr. Flying Doctors.

RAMSBOTHAM, Simon Edward Thornton Heath Health Centre, 61A Gillet Road, Thornton Heath CR7 8RL Tel: 020 8689 5797 Fax: 020 8665 1195; 36 Bensham Lane, Croydon CR0 2RQ Tel: 020 8689 2916 — MB BS 1973 Lond.; MRCGP 1980; DCH Eng. 1976. (St. Thos.) GP Croydon. Socs: BMA. Prev: SHO (Gen. Surg.) St. Jas. Hosp. Balham; Regist. (A & E) May Day Hosp. Thornton Health; SHO (Paediat.) Childr. Hosp. Sydenham.

RAMSBOTTOM, Norman 22 Harley Street, London W1N 1AP Tel: 020 7580 2946 Fax: 020 7637 4983; 90 Langton Way, Blackheath, London SE3 7JU Tel: 020 8858 3555 — MB BS 1964 Lond.; MRCS Eng. LRCP Lond. 1964. Socs: Brit. Soc. Gastroenterol. & Physiol. Soc. Prev: Lect. (Physiol.) Guy's Hosp. Med. Sch. Lond.; Asst. Ho. Phys. & Ho. Surg. Guy's Hosp. Lond.

RAMSBOTTOM, Timothy James The Surgery, Nevells Road, Letchworth SG6 4TS Tel: 01462 675526; Tel: 01462 624323 — BM BCh 1993 Oxf.; MA Oxf. 1990; DRCOG 1997; DFFP 1997; DCH RCP Lond. 1995. GP Princip. Socs: Christ. Med. Fell.sh. Prev: SHO (Paediat.) Roy. United Hosp. Bath; Ho. Off. (Gen. Med.) John Radcliffe Hosp. Oxf.; Ho. Off. (Gen. Surg.) Milton Keynes Gen. Hosp.

RAMSDALE, David Roland 28 Beech Avenue, Whitefield, Manchester M45 7EW — MB ChB 1975 Manch.; BSc (Hons.) (Anat.) Manch. 1971, MB ChB 1975; MRCP (UK) 1978.

RAMSDALE, Dinah 2 The Crescent, Northampton NN1 4SB — MRCS Eng. LRCP Lond. 1964.

RAMSDALE, James Edward Elms Medical Centre, 31 Hoole Road, Chester CH2 3NH Tel: 01244 351000 — MB ChB 1976 Liverp.

RAMSDEN, Alexander John 15 Hazelwood Avenue, Newcastle upon Tyne NE2 3HU — MB ChB 1996 Glas.

RAMSDEN, Alistair Richard Lake House, Legh Road, Knutsford WA16 8LP; 3 Travellers Rest, Pickwick, Corsham SN13 0PP Tel: 01249 715410 Email: kll23@dial.pipex.com — MB ChB 1997 Ed.

RAMSDEN, Arthur Tapstone House, Hud Hey Road, Haslingden, Rossendale BB4 5JL — MB ChB Liverp. 1953. Prev: GP Haslingden; Ho. Phys. & Ho. Surg. Bury Gen. Hosp.; Med. Ref. Benefits Agency.

RAMSDEN, Clive Stuart Spring Grove House, Chapel Hill, Clayton West, Huddersfield HD8 9NH — MB ChB 1979 Manch.; MD Manch. 1989; MRCOG 1985. Sen. Regist. (O & G) Leeds.

RAMSDEN, George Deryk (retired) Aberdwyafon, Arthog LL39 1BQ — MB BS 1954 Lond.

RAMSDEN, Gordon Hugh Clifflands, Whitbarrow Road, Lymm WA13 9AG — MD 1991 Manch.; MB ChB Manch 1979; MRCOG 1987; DRCOG 1983. Cons. O & G Chesh.

RAMSDEN, Karen Lesley Department of Histopathology, Walsgrave Hospitals NHS Trust, Clifford Bridge Road, Coventry CV2 2DX — MB ChB 1983 Sheff.; MRCPath 1991. Cons. Histopath. & Cytopath. Walsgrave Hosps. NHS Trust. Prev: Cons. in Histopath. & Cytopath. Bury Health Care NHS Trust; Sen. Regist. & Regist. (Histopath.) W. Midl. RHA; SHO (Path.) N. Manch. Gen. Hosp.

RAMSDEN, Michael John (retired) 7 Chevet Lane, Wakefield WF2 6HN Tel: 01924 255356 — MA, MB Camb. 1959, BChir 1958; MRCS Eng. LRCP Lond. 1958; DObst RCOG 1962. Prev: Ho. Surg. & Ho. Phys. Clayton Hosp. Wakefield.

RAMSDEN, Peter Andrew Mayford House Surgery, East Road, Northallerton DL6 1NP Tel: 01609 772105 Fax: 01609 778553 — MB BS 1987 Lond.; DRCOG 1991.

RAMSDEN, Mr Peter David Carr House, Great Bavington, Newcastle upon Tyne NE19 2BN — MB BS 1968 Lond.; FRCS Eng. 1975; MRCS Eng. LRCP Lond. 1968. Cons. (Urol. Surg.) Freeman Hosp. Newc. Upon Tyne.

RAMSDEN, Peter George (retired) — MB BS 1970 Lond.; MRCS Eng. LRCP Lond. 1970. p/t Appeals Serv. Med. Tribunal Mem. Prev: Gen. Practitioner.

RAMSDEN, Professor Richard Thomas Anson Medical Centre, 23 Anson Road, Manchester M14 5BZ Tel: 0161 248 2022 Fax: 0161 248 2025; Brick Bank, Brick Bank Lane, Allostock, Knutsford WA16 9LY Tel: 01477 544838 — MB ChB St. And. 1968; FRCS Eng. 1973; FRCS 2000 (ED) (ad. Hominem). (St. And.) Clin. Dir. (Otolaryngol. & Head & Neck Surg.) Manch. Roy. Infirm.; Cons. Otolaryngol. Manch. Roy. Infirm.; Hon. Prof. Otolaryngol. Univ. Manch.; Edit. Bd. Jl. Laryngol. - Otol., Amer. Jl. Otol., ENT Jl. & Revue de Laryngologie Otologie & Rhinologie; Hon. Lect. Centre for Audiol., Educat. of the Deaf & Speech Path. Univ. Manch.; Examr. Otolaryngol. RCPS Glas.; Mem., SAC OtoLaryngol. Socs: Fell. Roy. Soc. Med. (Pres, Treas. & Hon. Sec. Sect. Otol.); Brit. Assn. Otol. & Head & Neck Surg.; Corr. Mem. Die Deutsche Gesellschaft fur Hals Nasen Ohren Heilkunde. Prev: Sen. Regist. (Otolaryngol.) Lond. Hosp.; Sen. Regist. & Regist. Roy. Nat. Throat, Nose & Ear Hosp. Lond.

RAMSDEN, Simon Steve The Surgery, 45A Pembridge Villas, London W11 3EP Tel: 020 7727 2222 Fax: 020 7792 2867; 45A Pembridge Villas, London W11 3EP Tel: 020 7727 2222 — MD 1994 Lond.; MA Oxf. 1987; MB BS 1984; MRCP (UK) 1987; MRCGP 1988. Socs: ICI Prize 1984.; Chairm. KCW Local Med. Comm. Prev: SHO (Med.) St. Mary's Hosp. Lond.; SHO (Paediat.) Univ. Coll. Hosp. Lond.

RAMSDEN, Valerie Marie Bollington Medical Centre, Wellington Road, Bollington, Macclesfield SK10 5JL Tel: 01625 572481 — MB ChB 1982 Manch.; MRCP (UK) 1986; MRCGP 1990; DRCOG 1988. p/t GP Chesh.; Clin. Asst. in Dermat., Buxton Hosp. Prev: Trainee GP Handforth Health Centre Chesh.; SHO (O & G) Fairfield Hosp. Bury; Regist. (Haemat.) Manch. Roy. Infirm.

RAMSDEN, Walter Norman (retired) 42 Repton Drive, The Westlands, Newcastle ST5 3JF Tel: 01782 617651 — MB BChir 1963 Camb.; BA Camb. 1959; MRCS Eng. LRCP Lond. 1962; FFA RCS Eng. 1967. Prev: Cons. Anaesth. N. Staffs. Hosp. Trust.

RAMSDEN, William Hugh Department of Clinical Radiology, St. James's University Hospital, Beckett St., Leeds LS9 7TF Tel: 0113 243 3144 Ext: 65331 — BM 1984 Soton.; FRCS Ed. 1989; FRCR 1993; T(R) (CR) 1994. Cons. Radiol. St. Jas. Univ. Hosp. Leeds. Prev: Sen. Regist. (Radiol.) Yorks. RHA.

RAMSEEBALUCK, Bhimduth Kempton House, Main Rd, Fleggburgh, Great Yarmouth NR29 3BA — LRCPI & LM, LRSCI & LM 1971. Socs: BMA.

RAMSELL, Nicola Jane Gosford Hill Medical Centre, 167 Oxford Road, Kidlington OX5 2NS Tel: 01865 374242 Fax: 01865 377826; 4 Heath Lane, Bladon, Woodstock OX20 1SB Tel: 01993 811318 — MB BS 1988 Lond.; MRCGP 1992; DCH RCP Lond. 1991. (Roy. Free Med. Sch.) Prev: Trainee GP N.wick Pk. Hosp. VTS.

RAMSELL, Susan Elizabeth Grasmere House, Dugdale Hill Lane, Potters Bar EN6 2DB — MB BS 1988 Lond.; MRCGP 1993; DRCOG 1991; DCH RCP Lond. 1990.

RAMSEY, Andrew Shannon, MBE 1A Magheralave Road, Lisburn BT28 3BE Tel: 01846 663034 — MD 1947 Belf.; MB BCh BAO 1939; FRCP Lond. 1971, M 1948; FRCPI 1979, M 1977. (Qu. Univ. Belf.) Cons. Phys. Lagan Valley Hosp. Lisburn. Socs: Fell. Ulster Med. Soc. Prev: Cas. Phys. & Med. Regist. Roy. Vict. Hosp. Belf.; RAMC 1940-46, Lt.-Col. O.C. Field Ambul. (Mentioned in Despatches).

RAMSEY, Deborah Jennifer Caroline The Garden House, Eyhurst Close, Kingswood, Tadworth KT20 6NR Tel: 01737 832678 — MB BS 1996 Lond.; MA Cantab. 1997. (Char. Cross & Westm. Med. Sch. Lond.) SHO (Elderly Care) Guy's Hosp. Lond. Prev: SHO (Med.) Lewisham Hosp,. Lond.; SHO (Haemat.) Guy's Hosp. Lond.; SHO (Med.) Guy's Hosp. Lond.

RAMSEY, Hugh Cameron Holywood Arches Health Centre, Westminster Avenue, Belfast BT4 1NS Tel: 028 9056 3354 Fax: 028 9065 3846; 14 Massey Court, Belfast BT4 3GJ — MB BCh BAO 1967 Belf.; DCH RCPS Glas. 1971. (Belf.)

RAMSEY, James Kenneth Banbridge Medical Group Centre, Linenhall Street, Banbridge BT32 3EG — MB BCh BAO 1970 Belf.

RAMSEY, Joan Atkinson 14 Massey Court, Belfast BT4 3GJ — MB BCh BAO Belf. 1967. Med. Off. Cytopath., Belf. City Hosp.

RAMSEY, John Charles Patrick 59 Eglantine Avenue, Belfast BT9 6EW Tel: 01232 280167 — MB BCh BAO 1985 Dub.; FRCR 1991. Cons. Radiol. Belf. City Hosp.

RAMSEY, John M 22 Shirley Avenue, Cheam, Sutton SM2 7QR Tel: 020 8642 3452 — MD 1959 Tehran; MRCS Eng. LRCP Lond. 1974. (Tehran)

RAMSEY, Marianne Clare 53 Englands Lane, Loughton IG10 2QX — MB BS 1987 Lond.

RAMSEY, Mark William Regional Cardiac Centre, Morriston Hospital NHS Trust, Swansea NHS Trust, Swansea SA6 6NL Tel: 01792 704123 Fax: 01792 704140 Email: mark.ramsey@swansea-tr.wales.nhs.uk — BM BS 1984 Nottm.; FRCP 2001; BMedSci 1982; DM Nottm. 1997; MRCP (UK) 1987. (Univ. of Nottingham) Cons. Cardiol. Morriston Hosp. Swansea NHS Trust. Socs: Brit. Cardiac Soc.; Brit. Cardiovasc. Interven. Soc.; Brit. Soc. Echocardiogr. Prev: Lect. & Hon. Sen. Regist. Univ. Wales Coll. Med. & Univ. Hosp. Wales Cardiff.; Regist. (Med.) Newc. Gp. Hosps.

RAMSEY, Pamela May Allendale, 22 Shirley Avenue, Cheam, Sutton SM2 7QR Tel: 020 8642 3452 — MB BS 1966 Durh. (Durh.)

RAMSEY, Peter Jerry 11A Ballymoney Road, Banbridge BT32 4DS — MB ChB 1997 Aberd.

RAMSEY, Thomas Linton Knockan Road, Broughshane, Ballymena BT42 Tel: 01648 2233 — MRCS Eng. LRCP Lond. 1970. SHO (Med.) Mid-Ulster Hosp. Magherafelt. Prev: Ho. Surg., Ho. Phys. & SHO (O & G) Mid-Ulster Hosp.

RAMSHAW

RAMSHAW, Andrew Lilwall The Park Medical Group, Fawdon Park Road, Newcastle upon Tyne NE3 2PE Tel: 0191 285 1763 Fax: 0191 284 2374; Park Medical Group, Kingston Pk Avenue, Kingston Park, Newcastle upon Tyne NE3 2HB Tel: 0191 286 0022 Fax: 0191 271 2544 — MB BS 1988 Newc.; MRCGP 1993; DFFP 1993; DRCOG 1993. Prev: Trainee GP Newc.

RAMSIS, Helen Elizabeth 44 Lindley Road, London E10 6QT — MRCS Eng. LRCP Lond. 1978; FCOphth 1990; DO RCS Eng. 1986. (Liverp.) Socs: Christ. Med. Fell.sh. Prev: Eye Bank Off. Moorfields Eye Hosp. Lond.; SHO (Ophth.) N. Middlx. Hosp. Lond. & York Dist. Hosp.; SHO (Ophth.) Myland Hosp. Colchester & Eye, Ear & Throat Hosp. Shrewsbury.

RAMSTEAD, Mr Keith Douglas 20 Gilleney Grove, Whiston, Prescot L35 7NL Tel: 0151 431 0252 Fax: 0151 431 0700 — MB ChB 1976 Manch.; BSc (2nd cl. Hons.) (Anat.) Manch. 1973; FRCS Eng. 1981; FRCS Ed. 1980; FRCS (Cardiothor Surg.) Ed. 1985; T(S) 1991. (Manch.) Staff Grade (A & E) Rochdale Healthcare NHS Trust. Prev: Sen. Regist. Cardiothoracic Surg. S.E. Thames RHA; Regist. Cardiothoracic Surg. Wythenshawe Hosp. Manch.; Ho. Surg. Profess. Unit Withington Hosp. Manch.

RAMSTER, David Guy 33 Welshwood Park Road, Colchester CO4 3HZ Tel: 01206 861191 — MB BChir 1971 Camb.; MA Camb. 1972, MB BChir 1971; MRCPsych 1976. Opinion Apptd. Doctor Ment. Health Act Commiss. Prev: Cons. Psychiat. NE Essex Ment. Health Servs. Colchester.; Sen. Regist. (Psychiat.) Old Manor Hosp. Salisbury; Regist. (Psychiat.) E. Anglian RHB.

RAMTOOLA, Shenaz 5 Eskdale Drive, Nottingham NG8 5GZ — MB ChB 1981 Bristol; BSc (Hons.) Bristol 1978, MB ChB 1981; MRCP (UK) 1984.

RAMU, V K Crescent Surgery, 8 The Crescent, Halfway, Sheerness ME12 3BQ Tel: 01795 662941 — MB BS 1973 Kerala; MB BS 1973 Kerala.

RAMUS, Mr Neville Ian Taunton & Somerset Hospital, Musgrove Park, Taunton TA1 5DA Tel: 01823 342104 Fax: 01823 323691; Thomas's House, Oake, Taunton TA4 1AR Tel: 01823 461974 Fax: 01823 461974 — MB BS Lond. 1969; MD Lond. 1978; FRCS Eng. 1973. (St. Mary's) Cons. Surg. Som. HA; Mem. Ct. Examrs. RCS Eng.; Surg. Tutor to RCS Eng.; Chairm. SW Regional BST Comm.; Mem.Counc. Surgic. Sect. RSM. Socs: Internat. Assn. Endocrine Surgs.; Brit. Assn. Surg. Oncol.; Brit. Soc. Gastroenterol. Prev: Sen. Regist. (Surg.) Bristol Roy. Infirm.; Research Fell. (Surg.) Univ. Tex. Med. Br. Galveston, USA.

RAMWELL, John Department of Anaesthesia, Cheriton House, South Cleveland Hospital, Marton Road, Middlesbrough TS4 3BW Tel: 01642 854600; 87 Davenport Road, Yarm on Tees, Yarm TS15 9TN Tel: 01642 790372 — MB BS 1980 Newc.; DA (UK) 1988. Assoc. Specialist Anaesth. S. Tees Acute Hosps. Trust.

RAMZAN, Asif Yusif Newton Lodge, Regional Secure Unit, Ouchthorpe Lane, Wakefield WF1 3SP — MB ChB 1993 Sheff.; MRCPsych 1998. Specialist Regist., Forens. Psychiat. Newton Lodge Regional. Secure Unit. Wakefield.

RAMZAN, Mohammed Ascot Medical Centre, 690 Osmaston Road, Derby DE24 8GT Tel: 01332 348845 — MB ChB 1981 Manch.; DRCOG 1985.

RAMZI, Nabil 4 Leggett Grove, Stevenage SG1 3RL — MB BCh 1972 Cairo.

RANA, Arup Kumar 122 High Street, Hook, Goole DN14 5PJ — MB BS 1972 Calcutta. (R.G. Kar Med. Coll.) Assoc. Specialist (Orthop.) Pontefract Gen. Infirm. Prev: SHO (A & E) Weymouth & Dist. Hosp.; SHO (Urol.) Bart. Hosp. Lond.; SHO (Med.) Elderly St. John Hosp. Goole.

RANA, Ashok Kumar Joyce Green Hospital, Dartford DA1 5PL — MB BS 1970 Agra; DLO Eng. 1979. (S.N. Med. Coll.) SHO (ENT) Joyce Green Hosp. Dartford.

RANA, Athar Mushtaq Weeks and Rana, 2 Deanhill Road, London SW14 7DF Tel: 020 8876 2424 Fax: 020 8876 3249 — MB BS 1981 Lond.; MRCGP 1992; DObst RCPI 1991. (Lond. Hosp.) Prev: Ho. Surg. St. Andrews Hosp. Lond.; Ho. Phys. The Lond. Hosp. Whitechapel.

RANA, Brijender Singh West Kent Health Authority, Preston Hall, Aylesford ME20 7NJ Tel: 01622 710161 Fax: 01622 719802; 9 College Drive, Tunbridge Wells TN2 3PN — MB ChB 1975 Dundee; MRCP (UK) 1981; MFPHM RCP (UK) 1991; DTM & H Liverp. 1978. Cons., Pub. Health Med.

RANA, Bushra Shahida 67A Stour Road, Christchurch BH23 1LN — MB BS 1993 Lond.

RANA, Dur-E-Sameen 63 Woodlands Road, Ilford IG1 1JN — MB BS 1994 Lond.

RANA, Hilla Hormusji 21 Industry Road, Sheffield S9 5FP Tel: 0114 41968; 363 Hall Road, Sheffield S9 4AF Tel: 0114 41755 — MB BS 1954 Bombay; BSc Bombay 1945, MB BS 1954. (Grant Med. Coll. Bombay) Socs: BMA. Prev: Ho. Off. Parsee Gen. Hosp. Bombay; SHO Childr. Hosp. Nottm.; SHO Lodge Moor Hosp. Sheff.

RANA, Kamlesh 23 Prestbury Road, Aston, Birmingham B6 6EP — BM BS 1991 Nottm.

RANA, Muhammad Zubair Khan 67A Stour Road, Christchurch BH23 1LN; Royal Bournemouth Hospital, Bournemouth BH7 7DW Tel: 01202 704590 Fax: 01202 704589 — BSc, MB BS Panjab (Pakistan) 1965; FRCP Glas. 1994; FRCP Lond. 1985; FRCP Ed. 1985; MRCP (UK) 1975. (Nishter Med. Coll. Multan) Cons. Phys. (Geriat. Med.) Wessex RHA. Socs: Fell. Internat. Coll. Angiol.; Brit. Soc. Digestive Endoscopy.; Brit. Soc. Geriat.s. Prev: Sen. Regist. (Geriat. Med.) Soton. Gen. Hosp.; Regist. (Med.) Liaquat. Med. Coll. Hosp. Hyderabad, Pakistan; Regist. (Geriat. Med.) Battle Hosp. Reading.

RANA, Mr Pradip Shumshere St. Peter's District General Hospital, Guildford Road, Chertsey KT16 0PZ Tel: 0193 287 2000 Fax: 01276 858290, 01932 873352 Email: prana@doctors.org.uk; 31 Red Lion Road, Chobham, Woking GU24 8RG Tel: 01276 857001 Fax: 01276 858290 — FRCS Ed. 1976. (Calcutta Medical College) Cons. Surg. A & E Dept. St. Peter's Dist. Gen. Hosp. Chertsey. Socs: FFAEM (Founding Fell.).

RANA, Pratap S Geriatric Medicine (Wd. 6/7), Huddersfield Royal Infirmary, Huddersfield HD3 3EA Tel: 01484 342704; 64 Ridge View Drive, Birkby, Huddersfield HD2 2EX Tel: 01484 545649 Email: pratasanguta@aol.com — MRCP (Uk) 1992 Edin.; MD (Medicine) 1989 Delhi; MBBS. (Maulawa Azad Medical College, N. Delhi, India) Cons. Phys., Geriat./ Stroke Med., Huddersfield Roy. Infirm., Huddersfield. Socs: Brit. Geriat.s Soc.; Brit. Soc. of Gastroenterol.; Roy. Coll. of Phys.s, Lond. Prev: Specialist Regist., Geriat. Med., Soton. Gen. Hosp.

RANA, Sangeeta 294 Bexley Lane, Sidcup DA14 4JG — MB ChB 1994 Leic.

RANA, Sanjeev Kumar 42 Hartington Road, Manchester M21 8UY — MB BS 1995 Lond.

RANA, Sunita 27 Whitton Street, Wednesbury WS10 8BA — MB ChB 1995 Leic.

RANA, Tanvir Ahmad 21 McKenzie Court, Northern Birmingham Community NHS Trust, All Saints Hospital, Lodge Road, Hockley, Birmingham B18 5SD; 37 Limetree Road, Sutton Coldfield B74 3SG — MB BS 1985 Punjab.

RANA, Tasneem 235 Crookesmoor Road, Sheffield S6 3FQ — MB ChB 1994 Sheff.

RANABOLDO, Mr Charles Jean Salisbury District Hospital, Salisbury SP5 8BJ Tel: 01722 425290 Email: cranaboldo@compuserve.com — BM 1984 Soton.; FRCS 1989 Eng; FRCS 1996 Gen; MS 1997 Soton. Cons. (Gen. & Vasc. Surg.) Salisbury Dist. Hosp. Socs: Assn. Surg. GB & Irel.; Assoc. Endoscopic Surg.; Europ. Vasc. Surg. Soc. Prev: Sen. Regist. Roy. United Hosp. Bath; Regist. (Surg.) Portsmouth Hosps.; Research Fell. (Vasc.) Soton. Univ. Hosps.

RANADE, Joothica Ulhas The Surgery, 25 Chichele Road, London NW2 3AN Tel: 020 8452 4666 Fax: 020 8450 3680 — MB BS 1970 Bombay.

RANAGHAN, Elizabeth Anne 55 Maryville Park, Belfast BT9 6LP — MB BCh BAO 1985 Belf.

RANASINGHE, Aaron Matthew 1 Westend Villas, Newbury Park, Ledbury HR8 1AX — MB ChB 1997 Birm.

RANASINGHE, Charles Lionel 2 Willow Lea, Oxton, Birkenhead L43 2GO — MB BS 1959 Lond.

RANASINGHE, David Nihal Essex Rivers Healthcare NHS Trust, Colchester General Hospital, Turner Road, Colchester CO4 5JL Tel: 01206 853535 — MB BS 1980 Colombo; FFA RCS Eng. 1989; DA (UK) 1986; DEAA 1995. (University of Colombo, Sri Lanka) Cons. Anaesth. Essex Rivers Healthcare NHS Trust Colchester Gen. Hosp. Prev: Cons. Anaesth. St. Albans & Hemel Hempstead NHS Trust; Sen. Regist. Rotat. (Anaesth.) Roy. Free Hosp. Lond.; Post-Fell.sh. Regist. Harefield Hosp. Middlx.

RANASINGHE, Don Upali Church House Surgery, 3 Church Passage, Barnet EN5 4QS Tel: 020 8449 9622; Church House Surgery, 3 Church Passage, Wood St., Barnet EN5 4QS Tel: 020 8449 9622 — MB BS 1975 Sri Lanka; MRCOG 1989. (Kandy, Sri Lanka) GP Ch. Ho. Surg.

RANASINGHE, Dulmini Piyawandi 106 Poverest Road, Orpington BR5 2DQ — MB ChB 1998 Liverp.; MB ChB Liverp 1998.

RANASINGHE, Hapu Arachchillage Newton 14 Clifton Avenue, Culcheth, Warrington WA3 4PD Tel: 01925 763067; Hollins Park Hospital, Hollins Lane, Winwick, Warrington WA3 Tel: 01925 664000 Email: hq@warington_health.co.uk — MB BS Ceylon 1969; MRCPsych 1982; DPM Lond. 1981. (Ceylon) Cons. Psychiat. Hollins Pk. Hosp. Warrington; Cons. Psychiat. Winwick Hosp. Warrington. Prev: Cons. Psychiat. NewCh. Hosp. Warrington; Staff Psychiat.. Lakehead Psychiat. Hosp. Thunderbay, Ontario, Canada; Cons. Psychiat. Winwick Hosp. Warrington.

RANASINGHE, Harischandra 71 Montagu Avenue, Gosforth, Newcastle upon Tyne NE3 4JN — MB BS 1955 Ceylon; FRCP Ed. 1975, M 1960; DMJ (Clin. & Path.) Soc. Apoth. Lond. 1968. (Colombo) Sen. Lect. (Forens. Path.) Univ. Newc.; Hon. Cons. Newc. AHA (T).

RANASINGHE, Nalini Church House Surgery, 3 Church Passage, Barnet EN5 4QS Tel: 020 8449 9622; 14 Ashurst Road, Barnet EN4 9LF — MB BS 1975 Sri Lanka; MRCP (UK) 1987. (Colombo Sri Lanka) GP Ch. Hse. Surg. Barnet.

RANASINGHE, Pandikoralalage Nilamani Ianthi 35 Hollymead Close, Colchester CO4 5JU — MB BS 1980 Colombo.

RANASINGHE, Renuka Sharon 15 Marshall Road, Cambridge CB1 7TY — MB BS 1990 Colombo; MRCS Eng. LRCP Lond. 1990; MRCGP 1995; DRCOG 1995; DFFP 1995; DCH RCP Lond. 1994. (Roy. Free Hosp. Sch. Med.) Clin. Asst. Renal Dialysis Unit Addenbrooke's Hosp. Camb. Prev: Trainee GP/SHO Addenbrooke's Hosp. Camb. VTS; Ho. Phys. (Med.) Roy. Free Hosp. Lond.

RANASINGHE, Mr Suraj Elsham House, Cliff Gardens, Scunthorpe DN15 7BH — MB BS 1986 Colombo; FRCS Ed. 1993. Staff Grade (A & E) Roy. Lancaster Infirm.

RANASINGHE, Wijesundara Appuhamillage Edmund Peiris National Blood Service, East Anglia Blood Centre, Long Road, Cambridge CB2 2PT Tel: 01223 548030 Fax: 01223 548136 Email: edmund.ranasinghe@nbs.nhs.uk; 44 Tomlyns Close, Hutton, Brentwood CM13 1PU Fax: 01277 201850 Email: edmund.ranasinghe@btinternet.com — MB BS Ceylon 1967; MSc (Immunol.) Lond. 1989; FRCPath 1992, M 1980. Cons. Haemat. Nat. Blood Serv. E. Anglia Blood Centre. Socs: Brit. Soc. Immunol.; Brit. Blood Transfus. Soc. Prev: Cons. Haemat. Nat. Blood Serv. Brentwood; Research Fell. N. Lond. Blood Transfus. Centre Edgware, Middlx.; Cons. Haemat. & Chief of Path. Abdulla Fouad Hosp. Dammam, Saudi Arabia.

RANASINHA, Kingsley Woodward Department of Medicine, Epsom General Hospital, Dorking Road, Epsom KT18 7EG Tel: 01372 735104 Fax: 01372 735261; Wedgwood, Woodcote Pk Road, Epsom KT18 7EY Tel: 01372 720240 — MD 1970 Ceylon; FCCP 1986 Ceylon; MBBS 1960 Ceylon; FRCP Lond. 1981, M 1967; FRCP Ed. 1982, M 1966. (Colombo) Cons. Phys. Epsom Gen. Hosp., Epsom & St. Helier Health Care Trust Gen. Med. & Elderly Care. Socs: Brit. Geriat. Soc. & Brit. Soc. Digestive Endoscopy; Sri Lanka Med. Assoc; Fell. of the Ceylon Coll. of Phys.s University of Ceylon M 1980. Prev: SHO (Gen. Med.) & Regist. (Gen. Med.) Epsom Dist. Hosp.; Sen. Lect. in Med. Univ. Ceylon Peradeniya.

RANAWAT, Nitranjan Singh Colchester General Hospital, Colchester CO4 5JL Tel: 01206 853535; 9 Lexden Court, Lexden, Colchester CO3 3QP Tel: 01206 563233 — MB BS 1966 Indore. Assoc. Specialist (Surg.) Colchester Gen. Hosp. & Black Notley Regional Orthop. Centre NE Thames RHA. Socs: Fell. BOA. Prev: Research Fell. (Orthop.) Hosp. Special Surg. New York; Regist. (Orthop.) Warwick Hosp.

RANCE, Bernard Harry Melide, Hallgate, Gedney, Spalding PE12 0AH — MB ChB 1956 Leeds; MFOM RCP Lond. 1982. (Leeds) Socs: Aerospace Med. Assn.; Soc. Occupat. Med.; Ergonomics Soc.

RANCE, David Baskerville Liquorpond Street Surgery, 10 Liquorpond Street, Boston PE21 8UE Tel: 01205 362763 Fax: 01205 358918; 63 Linden Way, Boston PE21 9DT Tel: 01205 353649 — MRCS Eng. LRCP Lond. 1979; MRCGP 1986; DRCOG 1984; DCH RCP Lond. 1983. (St. Mary's) Prev: Clin. Asst. (Paediat.) Pilgrim Hosp. Boston Lincs.

RANCE, Jacqueline Margaret St Neots Surgery, 47 Wolseley Road, Plymouth PL2 3BJ Tel: 01752 561305 Fax: 01752 605565 — MB ChB 1976 Manch.

RAND, Mr Christopher Consultant Orthopaedic Surgeon, Farnborough Hospital, Farnborough Common, Orpington BR6 8ND Tel: 01689 814228 Fax: 01689 814058; 45 Constance Crescent, Hayes, Bromley BR2 7QH Tel: 020 8462 3184 — MB BS 1977 Lond.; BSc Leicester 1969; FRCS Ed. 1982; FRCS Ed. (Orth.) 1988. (Lond. Hosp.) Cons. Orthop. Surg. Medway Hosp. Kent. Socs: Fell. Brit. Orthop. Assoc. Prev: Sen. Regist. Guy's & St. Thos. Hosp. Lond.; Anat. Demonst. Lond. Hosp. Med. Coll.; SHO (Neurosurg.) Brook Hosp. Lond.

RAND, David Freeman 2 The Barn, Mount's Court Farm, Acrise, Folkestone CT18 8LQ — MB ChB 1981 Cape Town.

RAND, Julia Irene 4 Meadow Way, Hitchin SG5 2BN — MB BS 1990 Newc.

RAND, Mr Roger John Bradford Royal Infirmary, Duckworth Lane, Bradford BD9 6RJ Tel: 01274 364891 Fax: 01274 366690 Email: roger.rand@bradfordhospitals.nhs.uk; Ghyll Crest, 30 Ghyllwood Drive, Bingley BD16 1NF Tel: 01274 564190 — MB ChB 1968 Leeds; MD Leeds 1980; FRCOG 1986, M 1974; DCH Eng. 1971; DObst RCOG 1970. (Leeds) p/t Cons. O & G Bradford Hosps. Trust. Socs: BMA; BSCCP; Fell. N. Eng. Obst. & Gyn. Soc.-Pres. Prev: Sen. Regist. (O & G) Yorks. RHA; Research Fell. (Oncol.) Leeds HA; Regist. (O & G) Bradford Gp. Hosps.

RAND, Walter (retired) Riftswood, 6 The Paddock, Walbottle Village, Newcastle upon Tyne NE15 8JG Tel: 0191 267 3238 — MB BS 1954 Durh.

RANDALL, Anthony Alexander Stephen South Oxford Health Centre, Lake Street, Oxford OX1 4RP Tel: 01865 244428 Fax: 01865 200985 — MB BS 1976 Lond.; MA Oxf. 1976; MRCGP 1982; Cert. Family Plann. JCC 1982. (St. Bart.) GP Tutor (Pub. Health & Primary Care) Univ. Oxf. Prev: Trainee GP Oxf. VTS; Ho. Phys. Profess. Med. Unit Addenbrooke's Hosp. Camb.; Ho. Surg. St. Bart. Hosp. Lond.

RANDALL, Barbara Joy Dept. of Cellular Pathology, Medway Maritime Hospital, Gillingham ME7 5NY Tel: 01634 830000 — MB BChir 1979 Camb.; 1997 FRCPath; MA Camb. 1981, BA 1976; MRCPath 1989. Cons. Histopath. Medway HA. Socs: Assn. Clin. Path. & Internat. Acad. Path.; Brit. Soc. for Clin. Cytol. Prev: Sen. Regist. (Histopath.) Middlesbrough Gen. Hosp. & Roy. Vict. Infirm. Newc.; Regist. (Histopath.) Leicester Roy. Infirm. & Roy. Hants. Co. Hosp. Winchester; SHO (Path.) Brook Gen. Hosp. Lond.

RANDALL, Christine Elms Surgery, 5 Derby Street, Ormskirk L39 2BJ — MB ChB 1985 Liverp.; BSc (Hons.) Biochem. Liverp. 1982; MRCP (UK) 1988; MRCGP 1992. (Liverpool) p/t GP. Socs: RCP; RCGP. Prev: SHO Med. Walton Hosp. Liverp.; SHO (O & G) Wellington, NZ.

RANDALL, Mr Christopher John Woodhays, 36 Northerwood, Swan Green, Lyndhurst SO43 7DU Tel: 0142 128 3493 — MB BS 1976 Lond.; FRCS Eng. 1980. Cons. ENT Surg. Soton. Univ. Hosp. Prev: Sen. Regist. (ENT) St. Mary's Hosp. & Roy. Marsden Hosp. Lond.; Regist. (ENT) St. Mary's Hosp. Lond.; SHO (Surg.) Bristol Roy. Infirm.

RANDALL, Colin Frederick (retired) 7 Higher Port View, Saltash PL12 4BU — MB BS 1968 Lond.; MRCP (UK) 1972; MRCS Eng. LRCP Lond. 1968; MRCGP 1974; DCH Eng. 1970. Postgrad. Research Stud.; Hon. Lect. Plymouth Postgrad. Med. Sch. Plymouth Univ.; Course Organiser Plymouth VTS; Teach. (Gen. Pract.) Bristol Univ. Prev: Princip. Trainer (Gen. Pract.) Saltash.

RANDALL, David George Stewart 16 Ravensbourne Gardens, London W13 8EW Tel: 020 8997 7227 — MB BS 1954 Lond. (Lond. Hosp.) Phys. USAF Hosp. S. Ruislip. Socs: Fell. Roy. Soc. Med. Prev: Ho. Phys. King Edwd. Memor. Hosp. Ealing; Ho. Surg. Hillingdon Hosp. Uxbridge.

RANDALL, Mr Derrick Henry (retired) 20 Stradbroke Road, Southwold IP18 6LQ Tel: 01502 723944 — MB BS 1951 Lond.; MB BS (Univ. Medal) Lond. 1951; FRCS Eng. 1948; MRCS Eng. LRCP Lond. 1943. Prev: Cons. Surg. Roy. Hallamsh. Hosp. Sheff.

RANDALL, Elizabeth Mary The Health Centre, 68 Pipeland Road, St Andrews KY16 8JZ Tel: 01334 473441 Fax: 01334 466508;

RANDALL

Tosh, Dunino, St Andrews KY16 8LT — MB ChB 1977 Leeds; DRCOG 1979.

RANDALL, Fiona Maria The Macmillan Unit, Christchurch Hospital, Fairmile Road, Christchurch BH23 2JX Tel: 01202 705375 Fax: 01202 705213; Beechwood, Beechwood Lane, Burley, Ringwood BH24 4AS Tel: 01425 403655 — MB BS 1977 Lond.; FRCP Lond. 1993; PHd Glasgow 2000. Cons. Palliat. Med.Roy. Bournemouth & ChristCh., Hosp.s trust.

RANDALL, Grahame Robert Haslemere Health Centre, Haslemere GU27 3BQ Tel: 01428 653881 Fax: 01428 645068 — MB BS 1963 Lond.; MRCS Eng. LRCP Lond. 1963; DObst RCOG 1967. (King's Coll. Hosp.) Hosp. Pract. Haslemere & Dist. Hosp. Prev: Med. Off. S. Pacific Health Serv.; Ho. Surg. (Orthop. & Urol.) King's Coll. Hosp. Lond.

RANDALL, Jean Margaret The Old Vicarage, Iford, Lewes BN7 3EH — MB BS 1948 Lond.; MRCS Eng., LRCP Lond. 1948. (Roy. Free) Clin. Asst. Nuclear Med. Dept. Roy. Sussex Co. Hosp. Prev: Anaesth. Regist. Edgware Gen. Hosp.; Res. Anaesth. Addenbrooke's Hosp. Camb.; Ho. Phys. Roy. Free Hosp.

RANDALL, Jill Mary Friarage Hospital, Northallerton DL6 1JG — MB BS 1986 Newc.; FRCR 1992. Cons. in Radiol.

RANDALL, Joanne Clair Southampton General Hospital, Tremona Road, Southampton SO16 6YD; 21 Armada Close, Rownhams, Southampton SO16 8JY Tel: 01703 737636 — MB BS 1996 Lond. (Royal London and St. Bartholomew's) SHO (Gen. Med.) Soton. Gen. Hosp. Prev: HS Broomfield Hosp. Chelmsford HP Roy. Lond. Hosp.

RANDALL, John Charles Montague Health Centre, Oakenhurst Road, Blackburn BB2 1PP Tel: 01254 268436 Fax: 01254 268440; 7 Willowfield Chase, Hoghton, Preston PR5 0SW — MB ChB 1988 Manch.; MRCGP 1992; DRCOG 1991. (Manch.) Company Med. Adviser Sappi, Europe & Paper Mill Blackburn; Company Med. Adviser Akzo Nobel Decorative Coatings Darwen, Lancs.; Mod. Adviser St. Wilfrids Sch. Blackburn. Prev: Trainee GP Blackburn, Hyndburn & Ribble Valley HA VTS.

RANDALL, John Martin Peterborough District Hospital, Thorpe Road, Peterborough PE3 6; The Cedars, 82 Church St, Market Deeping, Peterborough PE6 8AL — MD 1990 Manch.; MB ChB 1980; MRCOG 1987. Cons. O & G P'boro. Dist. Hosp. Prev: Sen. Regist. (O & G) St. Jas. Hosp. & Gen. Infirm. Leeds; Clin. Research Fell. (O & G) Univ. Aberd.; Regist. Newc. Gen. Hosp.

RANDALL, Mr Julian Brook Street Surgery, 7 Brook Street, Woodsetton, Dudley DY3 1AD; Acre-Rise Cottage, Upper Ludstone, Claverley, Wolverhampton WV5 7DH Tel: 01746 710634 — MB BCh 1978 Wales; FRCS Eng. 1983. (Wales) GP Dudley W. Midl.; Clin. Med. Off. Family Plann. Clinic Dudley. Socs: GPs Writer's Assn.

RANDALL, Keith John (retired) Red Tree House, Pine Glade, Keston Park, Orpington BR6 8NT Tel: 01689 853054 — MRCS Eng. LRCP Lond. 1943; MD (Path.) Lond. 1947, MB BS 1944; FRCPath 1964. Hon. Cons. Path. Bromley & Tunbridge Wells HAs. Prev: Sen. Regist. Path. St. Alfege's Hosp. Lond.

RANDALL, Kristen Anaesthetic Department, Worthing & Southlands Hospital, Worthing Hospital, Lyndhurst Road, Worthing BN11 2DH — MB BS 1990 Melbourne.

RANDALL, Lisa Sarah, Surg. Lt. RN Retd. 6 Castlemans Lane, Hayling Island PO11 0PZ — BM 1991 Soton.; 1998 DOCGMeds.; DFFP 1997; MRCGP 1998; DRCOG 1997. GP Portsmouth; GP non-Princip. Prev: Trainee GP RNH Haslar; Med. Off. HMS Osprey & HMS Endurance.

***RANDALL, Marc Stewart** Leeds General Infirmary, Great George St., Leeds LS1 3EX; 58 St Johns Road, Penn, High Wycombe HP10 8HU Tel: 01494 812530 — MB ChB 1998 Leeds.

RANDALL, Michaela Elizabeth Helen 31 Elmlea Avenue, Stoke Bishop, Bristol BS9 3UU Tel: 0117 982 3706 — MB BS 1982 Nottm.; BMedSci (Hons.) Nottm. 1980; DRCOG 1986. Prev: Asst. GP BedGr. Health Centre Aylesbury; Civil. Med. Off. Kowloon Gp. Pract. Brit. Milit. Hosp. Hong Kong.

RANDALL, Nigel Peter Crispian c/o Department of Anaesthesia, Victoria Hospital, Whinney Heys Road, Blackpool FY3 8NR — BM 1979 Soton.; FFARCS Eng. 1984. Cons. Anaesth. Vict. Hosp. Blackpool. Prev: Sen. Regist. (Anaesth.) N. W.. RHA.

RANDALL, Peter Graham Sandown Medical Centre, Melville Street, Sandown PO36 8LD Tel: 01983 402464 Fax: 01983 405781 Email: peter.randall@gp-j84013.nhs.uk; Spring Chase, Westhill Manor, Westhill Road, Shanklin PO37 6QB Tel: 01983 863962 Fax: 01983 405781 — BM 1979 Soton.; DMS Med. Soc. Apoth. Lond. 1995; MRCGP 1983; DCH RCP Lond. 1982; DRCOG 1981; DFFP 1990. (Soton.) Exec. Bd. Mem., Isle of Wight PCT; GP Trainer.

RANDALL, Peter John 104 Chapel Lane, Ravenshead, Nottingham NG15 9DH Tel: 01623 795606 — BM BS 1976 Nottm.; PhD Nottm. 1972, BM BS 1976, BMedSci 1973; FFA RCS Eng. 1983. Cons. Anaesth. Centr. Nottm. HA.

RANDALL, Mr Philip Edward North Manchester Hospital, Delauney Road, Manchester M20 4QP; 9 Ashwood, Oldham OL9 9TR — MB ChB 1973 Bristol; BSc (Anat. 1st cl. Hons.) Bristol 1971; FRCS Eng. 1978; FFAEM 1993. Cons. A & E N. Manch. Gen. Hosp. Trust Med. Director. Prev: Lect. Surg. (A & E) & Hon. Sen. Regist. Univ. Manch.

RANDALL, Raymond 22 Ethelbert Gardens, Ilford IG2 6UN Tel: 020 8551 3134; 2 Savoy Court, Firecrest Drive, West Heath Road, Hampstead, London NW3 7NF Tel: 020 7431 2422 Fax: 020 7431 2422 Email: rrandall@netcomuk.co.uk — LRCP LRCS Ed. LRFPS Glas. 1959; DObst. RCOG 1961. (RCSI & W. Lond.) Socs: BMA. Prev: Ho. Phys. W. Lond. Hosp.; Ho. Surg. New End Hosp. Hampstead; Ho. Surg. (Obst.) Whittington Hosp. Lond.

RANDALL, Reginald John (retired) 3 Georgian Close, Ringwood BH24 1SA Tel: 01425 475412 — MRCS Eng. LRCP Lond. 1946. Prev: GP Totton.

RANDALL, Richard Isidore (retired) Flat1, 15 Heath Drive, London NW3 7SN Tel: 020 7435 0736 — MRCS Eng. LRCP Lond. 1941. Prev: Capt. RAMC.

RANDALL, Sally Jane 4 Chantry Mews, Lower St., Merriott TA16 5NL — MB BS 1993 Lond.

RANDALL, Sarah Ella Gordon Unit, St. Mary's Hospital, Milton Road, Portsmouth PO3 6AD Tel: 023 92 866304 Fax: 023 92 866311 — MB ChB 1973 Manch.; MD Manch. 1983; FRCOG 1993, M 1978; MFFP 1993. Cons. Community Gyn. Portsmouth Healthcare Trust; Chairm. Workforce Plann. Commitee. Socs: Brit. Menopause Soc. Prev: Hon. Sec. Fac. Family Plann. & Reproductive Health Care; Vice Chairm. Fac. of Family Plann. & Reproductive Health Care.

RANDALL, Susan Carol 37 Orient Road, Salford M6 8LE Fax: 0161 789 3029 — MB ChB 1973 Bristol; Cert. Family Plann. JCC 1978. GP Salford FPC.

RANDALL, Tania Mia Kristin 168 High Street, Harston, Cambridge CB2 5QD — MB ChB 1993 Leeds; MRCP (UK) 1998. Specialist Regist. (Paediat.) S.mead Hosp. Bristol.

RANDALL, Vivienne Rosemary Shrivastva and Partners, 24 Gamble Road, Portsmouth PO2 7BN Tel: 023 9266 0910 Fax: 023 9267 8175 — MB ChB 1983 Sheff.; MRCGP 1988. (Sheff.) Trainer (Gen. Pract.) Portsmouth.

RANDALLS, Peter Bryce 27 Woodland Avenue, Teignmouth TQ14 8UU Tel: 01626 770848 — MB ChB 1983 Glas.; BSc (1st cl. Hons.) Glas. 1978; FFA RCS 1988. Cons. Anaesth. & Intens. Care Torbay Hosp. Torquay.

RANDELL, David Thomas Henry Ty Darren, 38 Nant y Felin, Efail Isaf, Pontypridd CF38 1YY — MB ChB 1960 Bristol; DObst RCOG 1962. (Bristol) Prev: Ho. Surg. (Obst.) S.mead Hosp. Bristol; Sen. Ho. Off. Anaesth. United Bristol Hosps.; Ho. Surg. & Ho. Phys. Bristol Roy. Infirm.

RANDELL, Justin Miles 25 Yew Tree Road, Rosliston, Swadlincote DE12 8JF — MB BS 1994 Lond.

RANDELL, Margaret (retired) Combe Orchard, 1A Bristol Road, Radstock, Bath BA3 3EF Tel: 01761 434641 — MB BCh 1943 Wales; BSc MB BCh Wales 1943; DObst. RCOG 1947. Prev: GP Elstree.

RANDELL, Peter 24 Rosebery Avenue, Goring-by-Sea, Worthing BN12 4EU Tel: 01903 242402 — MB BChir 1967 Camb.; MRCPsych 1974; DPM Eng. 1972. Lect. Brit. Coll. Naturopathy & Osteop. Lond.

RANDELL, Richard Arthur Newstone House, High St., Scaldwell, Northampton NN6 9JS Tel: 01604 881595 — MB BChir 1960 Camb.; MA Camb. 1986, BA 1957; AFOM RCP Lond. 1978; DIH Soc Apoth. Lond. 1972. (Camb. & Univ. Coll. Hosp.) Occupat. Health Phys. (Occupat. Health) N.ampton Gen. Hosp.; Cons. Occupat. Health Phys. Various Companies. Socs: Fell. Roy. Soc. Med.; Soc. Occupat. Med. Prev: Emplym. Med. Advisor Health & Safety Exec.

RANDELL, Roy 341 Broomfield Road, Chelmsford CM1 4DX Tel: 01245 57595 — MB BChir 1946 Camb.; MRCS Eng. LRCP Lond. 1945. (Camb. & Char. Cross) Prev: Dept. Demonst. Anat. Camb. Univ.; Ho. Surg. O & G Ashridge E.M.S. Hosp.

RANDELL, Tabitha Louise North Staffordshire NHS Trust, Stoke-on-Trent ST4 7LD; 17 Eastlands Close, Stafford ST17 9BD — MB ChB 1992 Manch.; MRCP (UK) 1996. Specialist Regist. (Paediat.) N. Staffs. NHS Trust. Prev: SHO (Paediat.) N. Staffs. NHS Trust, Booth Hall Childr. Hosp. Manch. & Macclesfield Dist. Gen. Hosp.; SHO (A & E & Gen. Med.) Bolton Roy. Infirm.

RANDELL, Wendy Denise Hope House Surgery, The Street, Radstock, Bath BA3 3PL Tel: 01761 433157 Fax: 01761 431880; Combe Orchard, 1A Bristol Road, Radstock, Bath BA3 3EF Tel: 01761 436301 — MB BS 1973 Lond.; DObst RCOG 1975. (Char. Cross) Prev: Surg. Lt. RN.

RANDERSON, Jonathan Michael Dewar and Randerson, The Health Centre, 1 Bridgeway Centre, Meadows, Nottingham NG2 2JG; Rothsay House, 1 Trevelyan Road, West Bridgford, Nottingham NG2 5GY — BM BS 1984 Nottm.; BMedSci Nottm. 1982, BM BS 1984. GP Notts. Prev: Trainee GP Mansfield.

RANDEV, Barkha 44 Church Road, Wavertree, Liverpool L15 9EF — MB ChB 1998 Liverp.; MB ChB Liverp 1998.

RANDEV, Mrs Parveen 8 Benenden Way, Ashby-de-la-Zouch LE65 2QS — MB ChB 1989 Leeds; DRCOG 1996. (Leeds)

RANDEV, Pawan Kumar 8 Benenden Way, Ashby-de-la-Zouch LE65 2QS — MB ChB 1986 Sheff.; BMedSci (Hons.) Sheff. 1985; MRCP (UK) 1991; MRCS Eng. LRCP Lond. 1986; MRCGP 1994; DCH RCP Lond. 1994; DRCOG 1993. (Sheff.)

RANDFIELD, Helen Ferrars Dollar Health Centre, Park Place, Dollar FK14 7AA Tel: 01259 742120 Fax: 01259 743053; 23 Ladysneur Road, Cambuskenneth, Stirling FK9 5NN Tel: 01786 462206 Email: simon@randfield.freeserve.co.uk — MB ChB 1990 Birm.; MRCGP (Distinc.) 1996; DRCOG 1995; DFFP 1995. (Birmingham) p/t GP. Prev: GP/Regist. DunbLa. Health Centre; Ho. Off. (Med.) Selly Oak Hosp.; Ho. off. (Surg.) Kidderminster Gen. Hosp.

RANDFIELD, Richard Simon c/o Crieff Health Centre, King St., Crieff PH7 3SA Tel: 01764 656283 — MB ChB 1990 Birm.; DRCOG 1996. (Birm.) GP Regist. Crieff H/L Crieff. Prev: Med. Off. Hlabisa, Kwazulu, Natal; Trainee GP/SHO Stirling Roy. Infirm.

RANDHAWA, Brijinder 21 Belbush Avenue, Sandhills, Oxford OX3 8EA — MB BS 1988 Sydney.

RANDHAWA, Joginder Singh 283 Hollyhedge Road, Wythenshawe, Manchester M22 4QR Tel: 0161 428 9411 — MBBS 1967 Panjab Univ. (Medical College Amritsar, India) GP.

RANDHAWA, Neil Andrew 13 Westbury Close, Chilwell, Nottingham NG9 5FP — MB ChB 1991 Birm.; ChB Birm. 1991.

RANDHAWA, Rajbir Singh 119 Oswald Road, Southall UB1 1HJ — MB BS 1982 Lond.

RANDHAWA, Samarjit Singh Regional Medical Centre, RAF Wyton, Huntingdon PE17 2EA Tel: 01480 52451; 11 Warren Road, St. Ives, Huntingdon PE27 5NX — MB BS 1975 Newc.; FRCS Eng. 1980; DRCOG 1982; DFPP 1996. (Newcastle upon Tyne) Civil. Med. Pract. Huntingdon.

RANDHAWA, Veena 269 Gillott Road, Birmingham B16 0RX — MB ChB 1997 Leeds.

RANDLE, Martin Philip The Surgery, 131 Goldsmith Avenue, Milton, Portsmouth PO4 8QZ — MB ChB 1975 Leeds. Socs: N. Eng. Obst. Soc.

RANDLE, Professor Sir Philip John, KBE Department of Clinical Biochemistry, Radcliffe Infirmary, Oxford OX2 6HE Tel: 01865 224001 Fax: 01865 224000; 11 Fitzherbert Close, Iffley, Oxford OX4 4EN Tel: 01865 773115 — MB BChir 1951 Camb.; FRS 1983; PhD 1955, MA 1951, MD 1964, Camb.; FRCP Lond. 1972, M 1964. (Univ. Coll. Hosp.) Emerit. Prof. Clin. Biochem. Univ. Oxf.; Fell. Hertford Coll. Oxf. Socs: (Ex.Pres.) Biochem. Soc.; (Ex-Pres.) Europ. Assn. Study Diabetes. Prev: Prof. Biochem. Univ. Bristol; Lect. (Biochem.) Univ. Camb.; Ho. Phys. & Ho. Surg. Univ. Coll. Hosp.

RANDS, Catherine Elizabeth Department of Child Health, University Hospital, Clifton Boulevard, Nottingham NG7 2UH Tel: 0115 924 9924 Fax: 0115 970 9255 — MB BCh 1989 Wales; MRCP (UK) 1994. Lect. (Community Child Health) Univ. Nottm. Socs: Brit. Assn. Community Child Health; RCPCH. Prev: Regist. (Paediat.) Lincoln Co. Hosp. & Nottm. City Hosp. Trust; SHO (Community Paediat.) S. Birm. HA; SHO (Paediat.) Selly Oak Hosp. Birm.

RANDS, David Allan (retired) Frenches Hill, The Frenches, Romsey SO51 6FE Tel: 01794 518727 — MB BS Lond. 1952; MRCS Eng. LRCP Lond. 1952; MRCGP 1969. Prev: Ho. Phys. Univ. Coll. Hosp.

RANDS, Gianetta Susan Jane Camden and Islington Community Services NHS Trust, The Whittington Hospital, A8, Archway Wing, 4th Floor, Highgate Hill, London N19 5NF Tel: 020 7530 2306 Fax: 020 7530 2304 — MB BS 1981 Lond.; BA Oxf. 1976; MRCPsych. 1988; MRCGP 1985; DRCOG 1983. (Royal Free Hospital London) Cons. Psychiat. Old Age Camden & Islington Community Health Servs. NHS Trust; Assoc. Clin. Tutor & Specialty Tutor in Psychiat. Camden & Islington Community Serv. NHS Trust; Hon. Sen. Lect., VCLMS; Progr. Dir. N. Thames Teachg. Hosps. Psychiat. Rotat. Prev: Sen. Regist. Maudsley Hosp. Lond.

RANDTE, Sandeep 8 Pexwood, Chadderton, Oldham OL1 2TS — MB ChB 1996 Manch.

RANE, Mr Abhay Muralidhar Dept. of Urology, East Surrey Hospital, Redhill RH1 5RH — MB BS 1983 Poona; FRCS 1999 (Urol.); FRCS Glas. 1993; Dip. Urol. Lond 1995. (Poona, India) Cons. Urol., Surrey and Sussex Healthcare. Socs: Full Mem. BAUS.

RANE, Vasudha Ajay c/o University Department of Obstetrics & Gynaecology, Level 19, Gledhow Wing, St James' Hospital, Beckett St., Leeds LS9 7TF; 16 Eversley Court, Sherburn in Elmet, Leeds LS25 6BP — MB BS 1989 Poona.

RANG, Elizabeth Harvey Merton sutton Wandsworth HA, Cranmer Road, Mitcham CR4 4TP Tel: 020 8648 3021; 1 Belvedere Drive, Wimbledon, London SW19 7BX Tel: 020 8947 7603 — MB BS 1959 Lond.; MB BS (Hons.) Lond. 1959; FFPHM RCP (UK) 1993; MFCM 1987; DObst RCOG 1962. (Univ. Coll. Hosp.) Cons. Pub. Health Med. Merton & Sutton & Wandsworth Health. Socs: BMA (Treas. Merton & Sutton Div.); Roy. Soc. Med. Prev: Clin. Asst. Roy. Marsden Hosp. Lond.; Clin. Research Fell. St. Geo. Hosp. Lond.; Lect. Nuffield Dept. Med. Oxf.

RANGA RAO, Nimmagadda Sandwell Health Care NHS Trust, Room 36C Black 2, Hallam Close, West Bromwich B71 4HU — MB BS 1975 Andhra.

RANGANATH, Lakshminarayan Rao Department of Chemical Pathology, Epsom District Hospital, Dorking Road, Epsom KT18 7EG Tel: 013727 26100 — MB BS 1976 Madras; MSc Clin. Biochem. Surrey 1987; MRCP (UK) 1988.

RANGANATHAN, Sarath Chandra First Floor Flat, 36 Hemstal Road, London NW6 2AL — MB ChB 1990 Sheff.; MRCP (UK) 1994.

RANGANATHAN, Srinivasan 301 Birmingham Road, Redditch B97 6EH — MD 1979 Mysore; MB BS 1974. (Kasturba Med. Coll.) SHO (Gen. Med.) Withybush Hosp. HaverfordW..

RANGANATHAN, Sudha 110 Shaftesbury Avenue, Kenton, Harrow HA3 0RF Tel: 020 8909 2967 Fax: 020 8930 2259 — MB BS 1967 Madras. Socs: Singapore Med. Assn.; BMA; Med. Protec. Soc. Prev: GP Singapore.

RANGARAJAN, Thangaperumal Prince Charles Hospital, Merthyr Tydfil CF47 9DT — MB BS 1975 Madras; MRCP (UK) 1986.

RANGASAMI, Jayanti Jairaj Paediatric Department, West Middlesex University Hospital, Twickenham Road, Isleworth TW7 6AF Tel: 020 8565 5662 Fax: 020 8321 6410 Email: jayanti.rangasami@wmuh-ten.nthames.nhs.net; 255B Jersey Road, Isleworth TW7 4RF Tel: 020 8569 7840 Fax: 020 8569 7840 Email: jayantirangasami@hotmail.co — MB BS 1978 Sambalpur; DCH 1980; MRCP (UK) 1990; MRCPCH 1997. (V.S.S. Medical College, BURLA, SAMBALPUR, INDIA.) Cons. Paediat. Middlx. Univ. Hosp. Socs: BMA; Brit. Soc. Paediat. Endocrinol.; MRCPCH. Prev: Lect. & Sen. Regist. (Child Health) Univ. Aberd.; Regist. Merton & Sutton HA; Hon. Sen. Regist. & Lect. (Child Health) Univ. Nottm.

RANGASWAMY, Venkataiah 23 Melbourne Road, Christchurch BH23 2HY — MB BS 1968 Mysore.

RANGE, Simon Paul Department Respiratory Medicine, Glenfield Hospital, Groby Rd, Leicester LE3 9QP; 1 Tansley House Gardens, Tansley, Matlock DE4 5HQ — MB ChB 1990 Birm.; DM (Nottingham) 2000; MRCP (UK) 1993. (Birmingham) Cons. Respirat. Phys., Glenfield Hosp., Leicester. Socs: Brit. Thoracic Soc.; BMA; Amer. Coll. Chest Phys.s.

RANGECROFT, Mr Laurence Department of Paediatric Surgery, The Royal Victoria Infirmary, Queen Victoria Road, Newcastle upon

RANGECROFT, Tyne NE1 4LP Tel: 0191 282 4711 Fax: 0191 227 5276; 17 The Poplars, Gosforth, Newcastle upon Tyne NE3 4AE Tel: 0191 285 0275 Email: lrc45@aol.com — MB BS Newc. 1970; FRCS Eng. 1975. (Newc. u. Tyne) Cons. Paediat. Surg. & Urol. Roy. Vict. Infirm. Newc. u. Tyne. Socs: Assoc. Mem. BAUS; Eur. Soc. Paediat. Urol.; Hon. Sec. And Treas.. Brit. Assn. Paediat. Surgs. Prev: Sen. Regist. (Paediat. Surg.) Alder Hey Childr. Hosp. Liverp.; Sen. Regist. (Paediat. Surg.) Hosp. Sick Childr. Dub.; Regist. (Paediat. Surg.) Roy. Childr. Hosp. Melbourne, Austral.

RANGECROFT, Margaret Ellen Haslam Regional Department of Psychotherapy, Claremont House, off Framlington Place, Newcastle upon Tyne NE1 4AA Tel: 0191 282 4542 Fax: 01912824542 Email: claremontpu@yahoo.com — MB BS Newc. 1970; MRCPsych 1990; TQAP 1997. (Newcastle upon Tyne) p/t Cons. Psychotherapist Regional Dept. Psychother. Claremont Ho. Newc. Socs: MRCPsych; Brit. ConFederat. of Psychotherapists; NEAPP. Prev: GP Sefton FPC; Ho. Phys. & Ho. Surg. Roy. Vict. Infirm. Newc.; Med. Off. Univ. Newc.

RANGECROFT, Ronald George (retired) East of Eden, 62 Victoria Place, Carlisle CA1 1LR Tel: 01228 522699 — MB ChB 1959 Ed.; LMCC 1961; FRCOG 1979, M 1966. Cons. Gyn. City Gen. Hosp. Carlisle.

RANGEDARA, Don Chandrasiri Epsom General Hospital, Dorking Road, Epsom KT18 7EG; 91 Holmwood Road, Cheam, Sutton SM2 7JP — MB BS 1971 Ceylon; MRCP (UK) 1979; FRCP 1977. (Colombo) Sen. Regist. Dept. Geriat. & Gen. Med. Guy's Hosp. Lond.; Cons. Phys., Epsom Gen. Hosp.

RANGEL, Richard Lawrence Caerleon Surgery, Dover Street, Bilston WV14 6AN Tel: 01902 493426 Fax: 01902 490096; 7 Wightwick Hall Road, Wightwick, Wolverhampton WV6 8BZ Tel: 01902 765486 — MB BS 1970 Bombay. (Topiwala Nat. Med. Coll.)

RANGER, Alistair Frank The Surgery, Lorne Street, Lochgilphead PA31 8LU Tel: 01546 602921 Fax: 01546 606735 Email: administrator@gp84415.ac-hb.scot.nhs.uk; Tigh an Inis, Kilmichael Glassary, Lochgilphead PA31 8QA Tel: 01546 605229 — MB ChB 1977 Dundee; DRCOG 1979. Sen. Partner in Gen. Pract. Socs: Chairm. Area Med. Comm. Prev: SHO (Gen. Med.) Co. Hosp. Oban.

RANGER, Mr Ian 15 Colney Lane, Norwich NR4 7RE Tel: 01603 54968 — MB BS 1947 Lond.; MS Lond. 1963, MB BS 1947; FRCS Eng. 1952. (Middlx.) Prev: Chief Asst. Dept. Surg. Studies, Asst. Bland. Sutton Inst. Path. & Ho. Surg. Middlx. Hosp. Lond.

RANGER, Michael White Lodge, 330 Prestbury Road, Prestbury, Cheltenham GL52 3DD — MB BS 1973 Lond.; AFOM RCP Lond. 1982; DAvMed RCP Lond. 1982; MRAeS Lond. 1988.

RANGI, Permjit Singh 21 Everton Road, Sheffield S11 8RY — MB ChB 1995 Sheff.

RANGR, Priya 2 Queen Victoria Avenue, Wembley HA0 4RW — MB BS 1996 Lond.

RANGWALA, Goolamali Dawoodbhai Mizzen Road Surgery, 5 Mizzen Road, Hull HU6 7AG Tel: 01482 854574 Fax: 01482 854576 — MB BS 1968 Ranchi; DLO Eng. 1977. (Mahatma Gandhi Memor. Med. Coll. Jamshedpur)

RANGWANI, Pushpa M (Surgery) 226 Derby Road, Lenton, Nottingham NG7 1PR Tel: 0115 941 1208; 6 Rectory Gardens, Wollaton Village, Nottingham NG8 2AR Tel: 0115 928 4687 — MB BS 1968 Sind; DObst RCOG 1970. (Liaquat Med. Coll. Hyderabad)

RANI, Raj 173 Hill Lane, Southampton SO15 7UA — MB ChB 1996 Leic.

RANIWALLA, Joher 27 Lydney Park, West Bridgford, Nottingham NG2 7TJ — BM 1984 Soton.

RANJADAYALAN, Kulasegaram Glen Road, Plaistow, London E13 Tel: 020 7363 8039; 59A Lord Avenue, Clayhall, Ilford IG5 0HN — MB BS 1979 Sri Lanka; FRCP 1999 Lond.; MPhil Lond. 1994; MD Sri Lanka 1985; FRCP Ed. 1997, MRCP 1987. Cons. Phys. (Cardiol.) Newham Gen. Hosp.; Examr. Dent. Studs. 1995. Socs: BMA; Brit. Cardiac Soc.; Brit. Soc. Echocardiogr. Prev: Staff Phys. (Cardiol. & Chest Med.) Newham HA.

RANJAN KUMAR, Pejaver Department of Paediatrics, Armed Forces Hospital, Tabuk, Saudi Arabia Tel: 00 966 4 4234426 Fax: 00 966 4 4222324; c/o Dr N. Subash, 46 Church St, Wootton, Ryde PO33 4PY — MB BS 1980 Bangalore; MRCPI 1991. Cons. Paediat. Armed Forces Hosp. Tabuk, Saudi Arabia. Socs: Fell. Neonat. Soc.; Fell. Roy. Soc. Trop. Med. & Hyg. Prev: Cons. Paediat. NW Armed Forces Hosp. Tabuk, Saudi Arabia.

RANJIT, Rajalingam Dainton Cross, Marldon Road, Ipplepen, Newton Abbot TQ12 5TY — MB BS 1979 Peradeniya; MRCOG 1988. Assoc. Specialist (O & G) Torbay Hosp. Torquay. Prev: Regist. (O & G) Ipswich Hosp.; Regist. (O & G) Basildon Hosp. Essex; SHO (O & G) Norf. & Norwich Hosp.

RANJITHAKUMAR, Subathira 111 The Avenue, Sunbury-on-Thames TW16 5HZ — MB BS 1976 Sri Lanka; MRCS Eng. LRCP Lond. 1986. Socs: MDU. Prev: Trainee GP Lightwater; SHO (A & E) King Geo. Hosp. Ilford; SHO (Geriat. Med.) Qu. Eliz. Hosp. Welwyn Gdn. City.

RANJITKUMAR, Sumathi 5 Heathercroft, Roxholme Gardens, Leeds LS7 4HF — MB BS 1988 Madras.

RANK, Katherine Margaret 19 East Street, Salisbury SP2 7SF — MB BS 1997 Lond.

RANK, Timothy John 2 Hailey Lane, Hertford SG13 7NX — MB BS 1996 Lond.

RANKEN, Anne Muriel 49 Little Dippers, Pulborough RH20 2DB — MB BS Lond. 1952; MRCS Eng. LRCP Lond. 1952. (Roy. Free) Prev: Assoc. Specialist Haemat. & Histol. Depts. St. Richards Hosp. Chichester.

RANKIN, Andrew Coats Department of Medical Cardiology, Royal Infirmary, 10 Alexandra Parade, Glasgow G31 2ER Tel: 0141 211 4833 Fax: 0141 552 4683; Glen Hall, 14 Cairns Drive, Milngavie, Glasgow G62 8AJ — MB ChB 1977 Glas.; BSc (Hons.) Glas. 1975, MD 1985; FRCP Glas. 1994; MRCP (UK) 1980; DRCOG 1979. Sen. Lect. (Med. Cardiol.) Roy. Infirm. Glas.

RANKIN, Angela 22 Queen Edith's Way, Cambridge CB1 7PN — MB ChB 1972 Sheff.; BSc Sheff. 1969, MB ChB 1972; MRCPath 1979. Assoc. Specialist Regional Transfus. Centre Camb. Prev: Sen. Regist. (Haemat.) Hosp. Sick Childr. Lond.; Sen. Regist. Dept. Haemat. Lond. Hosp. (Whitechapel); Regist. (Haemat.) Univ. Dept. Haemat. Sheff.

RANKIN, Archibald Macpherson (retired) Hill House, Aspatria, Wigton CA7 3HG Tel: 016973 20607 — MB ChB 1950 Glas.; FRCGP 1986, M 1972. Prev: Chairm. Cumbria Family Pract. Comm.

RANKIN, David Craig Turnbull (retired) 3 Westwinds, 27 Bowleaze Coveway, Weymouth DT3 6PL Tel: 01305 834374 — MB ChB Glas. 1948. Prev: GP Dorchester.

RANKIN, Donald Watson (retired) 58 Bennochy Road, Kirkcaldy KY2 5RB Tel: 01592 267847 — MB ChB 1963 Ed.; MPhil Ed. 1981; FRCPsych 1990, M 1979; DObst RCOG 1966. Prev: Dir. Scott. Health Advis. Serv.

RANKIN, Professor Elaine Mary Department of Cancer Medicine, University of Dundee, Ninewells Hospital and Medical School, Dundee DD1 9SY Tel: 01382 632863 Fax: 01382 632885 Email: erankin@dth.scot.nhs.uk — MB ChB 1976 Manch.; MB ChB (Hons.) Manch. 1976; BSc (Med. Sci.) St. And. 1973; MD Manch. 1984; FRCP. (Univ. Manch. & Univ. St. And.) Prof. Cancer Med. Univ. of Dundee; Hon. Cons. (Cancer Med.) Ninewells Hosp. Dundee Teachg. Hosps. Trust. Socs: Brit. Assn. Cancer Research; Eur. Working Gp. Gene Ther.; Bd. Mem.: Biological Therap. Developm. Gp. of Europ. Organisation for Treatm. of Cancer. Prev: Cons. (Med. Oncol.) Netherlands Cancer Inst., Amsterdam, The Netherlands; Sen. Lect. & Hon. Cons. Phys. Univ. Glas. & CRC Dept. Med. Oncol. Glas.; Lect. (Med. Oncol.) Guy's Hosp. Lond.

RANKIN, Elizabeth Catherine Cameron Department of Rheumatology, University Hospital Birmingham NHS Trust, Selly Oak, Birmingham B29 6JF Tel: 0121 627 1627 Fax: 0121 627 8480 — BM BCh 1988 Oxf.; PhD Lond. 1995; MA Oxf. 1986; MRCP (UK) 1991. Cons. Rheum. Univ. Hosp. Birm. HHS Trust. Prev: Sen. Regist. (Rheum.) Bristol Roy. Infirm.; Research Regist. & Regist. (Med.) Middlx. Hosp. Lond.; SHO (Gen. Med.) City Gen. Hosp. Stoke on Trent.

RANKIN, Elizabeth Margaret 15 Burnside Road, Burnside, Glasgow G73 4RL — MB ChB 1974 Glas.

RANKIN, George Lloyd Sinnett (retired) Herons, Barnston, Dunmow CM6 3PP — MB BChir Camb. 1953; MA Camb. 1953; MRCS Eng. LRCP Lond. 1952; FRCOG 1973, M 1960, DObst 1957. Prev: Hon. Cons. Gyn. Chelmsford Gp. Hosps.

RANKIN, Henry Alexander (retired) 8 Margaret's Lane, Larkhall ML9 2HQ Tel: 01698 883036 — MB ChB 1944 Glas.

RANKIN, James Sinnett Pershore Health Centre, Priest Lane, Pershore WR10 1RD Tel: 01386 502030 Fax: 01386 502058; Butts Bank, Great Comberton, Pershore WR10 3DP Tel: 01386 710018 — MB BS 1982 Lond.; MRCS Eng. LRCP Lond. 1982; DRCOG 1990. (Guy's)

RANKIN, John (retired) 38 Glasgow Road, Dennyloanhead, Bonnybridge FK4 1QG Tel: 01324 813471 — MB ChB 1952 Glas.

RANKIN, John Aird (retired) 269 Shinfield Road, Reading RG2 8HF Tel: 0118 871442 — MB ChB Glas. 1934; DMRD Eng. 1950. Prev: Cons. Radiol. Oxf. RHA.

RANKIN, John Graham Dovercourt Health Centre, 407 Main Road, Dovercourt, Harwich CO12 4ET Tel: 01255 506451; Millbank, 119 Fronks Road, Dovercourt, Harwich CO12 4EF Tel: 01255 503835 — MB BS Lond. 1963; MRCS Eng. LRCP Lond. 1963; MRCGP 1980; DObst RCOG 1966. (St. Geo.) Med. Staff Harwich Dist. Hosp. Socs: Colchester Med. Soc.

RANKIN, John Nestor (retired) Nia-Roo, 33 Crosshill Road, Strathaven ML10 6DS Tel: 01357 521580 — LRCP LRCS Ed. LRFPS Glas. 1946.

RANKIN, John Nestor Edgar Park Avenue Medical Centre, 9 Park Avenue, Stirling FK8 2QR Tel: 01786 473529; 1 Anne Drive, Bridge of Allan, Stirling FK9 4RE — MB ChB 1973 Glas.; DFM Glas. 1990.

RANKIN, Julia Dept. Medical Genetics, Box 134, Addgnbrooke's Hospital, Cambridge CB2 2QQ Email: jrankin@mrc.ac.uk; 11 Argyle Street, Cambridge CB1 3LR — MB ChB 1990 Manch.; BSc (Hons.) Pharmacol. 1987; MRCP (UK) 1993; PhD 1998. (Manchester) Clin. Lect., Medial Genetics, Addgnbrooke's Hosp., Camb. Prev: MRC Clin. Train. Fell. (Clin. Genetics) Univ. Newc.

RANKIN, Lisa Cherry Grantham North Lodge, Minnetts Hill, Syston Park, Grantham NG32 2BU — MB ChB 1997 Glas.

RANKIN, Margaret Gillian 72 Deramore Park S., Belfast BT9 5JY — MB BCh BAO 1977 Belf.; MRCGP 1981; DCH NUI 1980. Dir. of Serv. Developm. S. & E. Belf. Health & Social Servs. Trust. Prev: SCMO (Child Health) Med. Servs. Manager E. HSSB & SE Belf. Community Unit.

RANKIN, Marion Tigh Sona, Neilston Walk, Kilsyth, Glasgow G65 9PL — MB 1977 Glas.; FRCS Ed. 1981. Clin. Asst. Stobhill NHS Trust Glas. Socs: Med. Wom. Internat. Assn.; Med. Wom. Federat.; Brit. Menopause Soc.

RANKIN, Nicol Elliot (retired) 22 Queen Ediths Way, Cambridge CB1 7PN — MB BS 1945 Lond.; MRCS Eng. LRCP Lond. 1944; DPath Eng. 1955; FRCPath 1970, M 1963. Prev: Cons. Path. Yeovil Dist. Hosp. & Boston Hosp. Gp.

RANKIN, Paul Vincent 97 Mayogall Road, Magherafelt BT45 8PJ — MB BCh BAO 1987 Belf.

RANKIN, Philip Michael Kilsyth Medical Partnership, Kilsyth Health Centre, Burngreen Park, Kilsyth, Glasgow G65 0HU Tel: 01236 822081 Fax: 01236 826231 — MB ChB 1977 Glas.; MRCGP 1981; DRCOG 1980.

RANKIN, Rosslyn Department of Pathology, Raigmore Hospital, Inverness IV2 3UJ — MB ChB 1978 Glas. Cons. Path. Raigmore Hosp. Inverness. Socs: Roy. Coll. Path. Prev: Cons. Histopath. Univ. Aberd.

RANKIN, Sheila Campbell X-Ray Department, 2nd Floor Guy's Tower, Guy's Hospital, London SE1 9RT Tel: 020 7955 4258 — MB BS 1972 Lond.; MRCS Eng. LRCP Lond. 1972; FRCR 1981; DCH Eng. 1974; DMRD Eng. 1977; Amer. Bd. of Radiol. 1980. Cons. Radiol. Guy's Hosp. Lond. Prev: Sen. Research Fell. (Computerised Tomography) St. Thos. Hosp. Lond.; Resid. (Radiol.) Tufts, New. Eng. Med. Centre Boston, USA; Regist. (Radiol.) King's Coll. Hosp. Lond.

RANKIN, Mr Simon James Adrian 9 St Ellen's, Edenderry, Belfast BT8 8JN — MB BCh BAO 1985 Belf.; FRCS Ed. 1990; FCOphth 1990.

RANKIN, Susan Miriam 50 West End, Langtoft, Peterborough PE6 9LU — MB BS 1987 Lond.; MRCGP 1996; DRCOG 1991. (Royal Free Hosp.)

RANKIN, Wendy Joan Wythenshawe Health Care Centre, Stancliffe Rd, Manchester M22 4PJ Tel: 0161 946 9415 Fax: 0161 946 9417 Email: wendy.rankin@mch-tr.nwest.nhs.uk; Wood Lea, 229 Mottram Road, Stalybridge SK15 2RF — MB ChB 1979 Manch.; FRCP Lond. 1996; MRCP (UK) 1983. (Manch.) Cons. Paediat. (Community Child Health) Manch. Health Trust; Lect. Manch. Univ. Prev: Sen. Regist. (Community Paediat.) Salford HA.

RANKIN, William Thomas (retired) 19 Gloucester Avenue, Clarkston, Glasgow G76 7LH — MB ChB 1926 Glas.

RANKINE, Anne Eleanor 17 Queensferry Road, Edinburgh EH4 3HB Tel: 0131 332 3230 — MB ChB 1949 Ed.; DRCOG 1952. Prev: Ho. Phys. Tynemouth Infirm.; Ho. Surg. Ingham Infirm.; Ho. Off. (O & G) E.. Gen. Hosp. Edin.

RANKINE, George (retired) The Barn, 106A The Causeway, Petersfield GU31 4LL Tel: 01730 267538 Fax: 01730 267538 — MB ChB 1944 St. And.; BSc St. And. 1941; MD Duke Univ. 1944; MRCGP 1952. Prev: Maj. RAMC.

RANKINE, James Julian St James's Univ. Hospital, Beckett SL, Leeds LS9 7TF Tel: 0113 206 4807 Fax: 0113 2064 587 — MB ChB 1986 Ed.; MRad(D) Aberd. 1993; MRCP (UK) 1991; FRCR 1994; MD (Manchester) 1998. Cons. (Diagn. Radiol), St Jas. Univ. Hosp., Leeds.; Hon. Clin. Sen. Lect., Univ. of Leeds. Socs: Mem. Brit. Soc. Skeletal Radiol.; Mem. Europ. Soc. Skeletal Radiol. Prev: Lect. (Diagn. Radiol.) Univ. Manch.; Sen. Regist. Univ. Hosps. S. Manch.; Regist. (Radiol.) Aberd. Roy. Infirm.

RANKINE, Susan Elizabeth Victoria Medical Centre, Victoria Medical Centre, 7-11 Longmoore Street, London SW1V 1JH Tel: 020 7821 1531 Fax: 020 7233 5995; 12 Bloomfield Terrace, London SW1W 8PG Tel: 020 7730 4820 — MB BS 1983 Lond.; MRCGP 1989; DCH RCP Lond. 1989; DRCOG 1988; RCOG 1988. (Univ. Coll. Hosp.)

RANMUTHU, Anoma Hemantha Charlton House Medical Centre, 581 High Road, Tottenham, London N17 6SB Tel: 020 8808 2837 Fax: 020 8801 4179; 5 The Leys, Hampstead Garden Suburb, London N2 0HE — MB BS 1979 Colombo; LRCP LRCS Ed. LRCPS Glas. 1986.

RANMUTHU, Piyadasa North Middlesex Hospital, London N18 1QX Tel: 020 8887 2000; 5 The Leys, Hampstead Garden Suburb, London N2 0HE — MB BS 1961 Ceylon; FRCP Lond. 1992; MRCP (UK) 1975. (Colombo) Cons. Phys. N. Middlx. Hosp. Lond. & St. Ann's Hosp. Lond. Socs: Brit. Geriat. Soc. Prev: Hon. Lect. (Med.) Middlx. Hosp. Med. Sch. Lond.; Sen. Regist. Middlx. Hosp. Lond. & N.wick Pk. Hosp. Harrow.

RANN, Sarah Frances Great Shelford Health Centre, Ashen Green, Great Shelford, Cambridge CB2 5EY Tel: 01223 843661 Fax: 01223 844569; 19 High Green, Great Shelford, Cambridge CB2 5EG Tel: 01223 845009 — MB BS 1982 Lond.; DFFP 1994; DCH RCP Lond. 1985; DRCOG 1985; Cert. Family Plann. JCC 1985. Prev: GP Cambs. Retainer Scheme; Haemophilia Centre RCH & Alfred Hosp. Melbourne, Austral.

RANNAN-ELIYA, Ronald Walter Daniel Gomes 7 Stow Gardens, Withington, Manchester M20 8HT — MRCS Eng. LRCP Lond. 1960; LMSSA Lond. 1960.

RANNAN-ELIYA, Mr Sahan Viraj Dept. of Plastic and Reconstructive Surgery, Radcliff Infirmary, Oxford; 20 Orchard Rise, Croydon CR0 7QY Tel: 020 8776 1583 — BM BCh 1994 Oxf.; MA Camb. 1995; FRCS (Enl) 1998. (PreClinical- Cambridge, Clinical-Oxford) SHO Rotat. (Surg.) Oxf.

RANNIE, Gordon Hugh The Surgery, The Meads, Kington HR5 3DQ Tel: 01544 230302 Fax: 01544 230824; Sharkham, Lyonshall, Kington HR5 3HT Tel: 01544 340449 — BM BCh 1971 Oxf.; PhD Ed. 1978; BA (Physiol.) Oxf. 1967, BM BCh 1971. (Oxford) Prev: Lect. & MRC Jun. Research Fell. (Path.) Univ. Manch.; MRC Research Fell. (Path.) Univ. Edin; Regist. (Path.) Dept. Med. Sch. Edin. Univ.

RANNIE, Ian (retired) Ian Rannie, Apartment G, 8 Osborne Villas, Newcastle upon Tyne NE2 1JU Tel: 0191 281 3163 — MB ChB 1938 Glas.; BSc (Hons. Path. & Bact.) 1939; BSc (Pure Sci.) Glas. 1935; FRCPath 1963; FIBiol 1963. Prev: Prof. Path. Dent. Sch. Univ. Newc.

RANOLE, Anna-Lisa Gwynton (Williams) Pendre Surgery, Clayton Road, Mold, Flintshire CH7 1SS; 3 Church Farm Cottages, Church Lane, Guilden Sutton, Chester CH3 7EW Tel: 01244 301841 — MB ChB 1994 Liverp.; DRCOG 1997; DFFP 1997. (Liverp) Asst. in Gen. Pract. Prev: GP Locum; GP Reg; SHO paediat.

RANOTE, A S Harpurhey Health Centre, 1 Church Lane, Harpurhey, Manchester M9 4BE Tel: 0161 205 1541 Fax: 0161 202 3700 — MB BS 1965 Punjabi U; MB BS 1965 Punjabi U.

RANOTE, S R Harpurhey Health Centre, 1 Church Lane, Harpurhey, Manchester M9 4BE Tel: 0161 205 1541 Fax: 0161 202 3700 — MB BS 1968 Panjab; MB BS 1968 Panjab.

RANPURA

RANPURA, Niksha 28 Hayfield Close, Glenfield, Leicester LE3 8RH — MB ChB 1994 Manch.

RANSCOMBE, Brian John The Health Centre, Skimped Hill, Bracknell RG12 1LH Tel: 01344 485333 Fax: 01344 890429; Highlands, Locks Ride, Chavey Down, Ascot SL5 8RA Tel: 01344 884833 Fax: 01344 300137 — MB BS 1960 Lond.; MRCS Eng. LRCP Lond. 1959; MRCGP 1980; Cert. Av. Med. 1986; DObst RCOG 1962. (Westm.) Hosp. Pract. (Psychiat.) Ch.ill Ho. Hosp. Bracknell; Extern. Advis. to Ombudsman. Socs: (Ex-Pres.) Windsor Med. Soc.; Appeals Serv.s. Prev: SHO (Obst.) Lambeth Hosp.; Ho. Surg. W.m. Childr. Hosp.; Ho. Phys. W.m. Hosp.

RANSFORD, Mr Andrew Oliver 5 Fordington Road, London N6 4TD Tel: 020 8883 3317 Fax: 020 8374 3936 — MB BChir 1966 Camb.; BA Camb. 1966; FRCS Eng. 1970. (Univ. Coll. Hosp.) Medics legal Pract. Socs: Pres. Brit. Cervical Spine Soc.; Pres. Brit. Scolosis Soc. Prev: Cons. Orthop. Surg. Roy. Nat. Orthop. Hosp. Lond.; Cons. Orthop. Surg. Univ. Coll. Hosp. Lond.; Sen. Regist. Roy. Nat. Orthop. Hosp. Lond.

RANSFORD, Jacques 40 West Bank Avenue, Mansfield NG19 7BP — MB ChB 1998 Liverp.; MB ChB Liverp 1998.

RANSFORD, Rupert Alistair Joseph County Hall, Union Walk, Hereford HR1 2ER Tel: 01432 364064; Pithouse Farm, Coddington, Ledbury HR8 1JH — MB BS 1988 Lond.; MRCP (UK) 1992; MRCGP 1994; DRCOG 1993. Specialist Regist. (Gastroenterol.) Hereford Co. Hosp.s. Socs: BMA; (Dinner Sec.) Herefordsh. Med. Soc.; Roy. Coll. Phys.s. Prev: Staff Phys. Co. Hosp. Hereford; GP/Regist. Hereford; Regist. (Med.) Hereford.

RANSLEY, Mr Philip Goddard 234 Gt. Portland Street, London W1W 5QT Tel: 020 7390 8323 Fax: 020 7390 8324 Email: pgr2@doctors.org.uk; 30 Orde Hall St, London WC1N 3JW Tel: 020 7831 5078 — MA, MB Camb. 1967, BChir 1966; FRCS Eng. 1971. p/t Cons. Surg. Urol. Hosp. Sick Childr. Gt. Ormond St. Lond.; Sen. Lect. (Paediat. Urol.) Inst. Child Health Univ. Lond.; Cons. Surg. Urol. Guy's Hosp. Socs: Fell. Roy. Soc. Med.; Assoc. Mem. BAUS; Europ. Soc. for Paediatric Urol. (Pres. 1995 - 1999) Prev: Cons. Surg. (Urol) St Peter's Hosp.s Lond.; Sen. Regist. (Surg.) Hosp. Sick Childr. Gt. Ormond St. Lond.; Sen. Regist. St. Peter's Hosps. Lond.

RANSLEY, Yvonne Florence (retired) 119 Greenway, The Wells, Epsom KT18 7HY Tel: 01372 725025 — MB BS 1960 Lond.; FRCP Lond. 1985; MRCP (UK) 1971; DCH Eng. 1964; DObst RCOG 1964; FRCPCH 1990. Cons. Paediat. Epsom Health Care Trust; Hon. Sen. Lect. St. Geo. Hosp. Med. Sch. Univ. Lond. Prev: Sen. Regist. (Paediat.) Qu. Mary's Hosp. Childr. Carshalton.

RANSOM, Margaret Jane Brough Hammonds Farm, Pirton, Hitchin SG5 3QN — MB BChir 1962 Camb.; MA Camb. 1971. (St. Thos. & Addenbrooke's Hosps.) Clin. Asst. (Orthop. Fract.) Lister Hosp. Stevenage. Socs: BMA. Prev: Clin. Asst. (Diabetes) Lister Hosp. Stevenage.

RANSOM, Paul Alan 32 St Luke's Road, Brighton BN2 2ZD — MB ChB 1993 Manch.

RANSOM, Ruth Mary (retired) Armingland, Church St., Stiffkey, Wells-next-the-Sea NR23 1QJ Tel: 01328 830581 — MB BCh BAO 1951 Dub.; BSc Lond.; MD Dub. 1956, BA, MB BCh BAO 1951; FRCPath 1975, M 1964. Prev: Cons. (Morbid Anat.) Watford Gp. Laborat. N.W. Thames RHA.

RANSOM, Mr William Thomas McLean 13 Hampton Grove, Epsom KT17 1LA Tel: 0 7020 991144 Fax: 0 7020 991166 Email: mac@macran.demon.co.uk — MB ChB 1979 Bristol; FRCS Eng. 1983; MRCGP 1987; DMJ(Clin) Soc. Apoth. Lond. 1996; DRCOG 1986; PgDipL University West England 1996. (Univ. Bristol) Indep. Forens. Phys. Metrop. Police & HM Customs & Excise; HM Asst. Dep. Coroner St Pancras. Socs: FRSM (Coun. Clin. Forens. Med. Sector). Prev: GP Epsom.

RANSOME, Claire Tiffany 1 & 2 Parsonage Road, Newton Ferrers, Plymouth PL8 1AS — MB BS 1985 Monash.

RANSOME, Jennifer Anne Stonefield Street Surgery, 21 Stonefield Street, Milnrow, Rochdale OL16 4JQ Tel: 01706 46234 Fax: 01706 527946 — MB ChB 1987 Manch.; BSc Manch. 1984; MRCGP 1991; DRCOG 1991. Prev: Ho. Off. (Surg. & Med.) Birch Hill Hosp. Rochdale.

RANSOME, Peter John 520 Burnley Road, Todmorden OL14 8JF — MB BS 1963 Durh.

RANSOME (MRS HERON), Joselen 10 Rushmere Place, London SW19 5RP — MB BS 1949 Lond.; FRCS Eng. 1958; MRCS Eng. LRCP Lond. 1949. (Roy Free) Hon. Cons. Otolaryngol. Char. Cross Hosp. Lond. Socs: Fell. Roy. Soc. Med.; Hon. Life Mem. (Ex-Hon. Sec.) Brit. Assn. Otolaryngol. Prev: Cons. Otolaryngol. Metrop. ENT Hosp. & Char. Cross Hosp. Lond.; Sen. Regist. (ENT) Roy. Free Hosp.; Regist. Roy. Nat. Throat, Nose & Ear Hosp. Lond.

RANSON, Malcolm Richard Department of Medical Oncology, Christie Hospital and Holt Radium Inst., Manchester; 140 Woodsmoor Lane, Woodsmoor, Stockport SK2 8TJ — MB ChB 1982 Manch.; PhD Manch. 1990; BSc (Hons.) Manch. 1979; MRCP (UK) 1985. Sen. Lect. (Med. Oncol.) Christie Hosp. Manch. Prev: EORTC/NCI Exchange Fell.sh. Award; CRC Clin. Research Fell.

RANSON, Rosalind Woodside Health Centre, 3 Enmore Road, London SE25 Tel: 020 8655 1223; Ash Tree Cottage, Mount Gardens, Sydenham, London SE26 4NG Tel: 020 8699 6976 — MB BS 1988 Lond.; MRCGP 1994; MA Med. Ethics & Law, Kings Coll. Lond. Partner. Prev: SHO (A & E) W.m. Hosp. Lond.; SHO (Paediat.) W.m. Childr. Hosp. Lond.; SHO (Psychiat.) St. Mary Abbotts Hosp. Lond.

RANSON, Sarah Ann Sherries, Upper Warren Avenue, Caversham, Reading RG4 7ED — MB BS 1994 Lond.

RANU, Amandeep Singh 8 Aldington Close, Chadwell Heath, Dagenham RM8 1YQ — MB ChB 1993 Manch.; DRCOG, 1997; DFFP 1997; DCH 1998; MRCGP, 1998. (Manchester)

RANU, Harpal Kaur The Surgery, 406 Lobley Hill Road, Gateshead NE11 0BS Tel: 0191 604380; 44 Gresham Road, Osterley, Isleworth Tel: 020 8570 8319 — MRCS Eng. LRCP Lond. 1975; MD Panjab (India) 1971, MB BS 1963; MRCGP 1976; DObst RCOG 1974; Cert. Family Plann. & IUD Family Plann. Assn 1972. (Med. Coll. Amritsar) Local Med. Off. Civil Serv.; Mem. Gateshead Local Med. Comm. Socs: BMA. Prev: SHO (O & G) N.wick Pk. Hosp. & Clin. Research Centre; Harrow; Ho. Off. (Surg.) Roy. E. Sussex Hosp. Hastings.

RANU, Navjot Singh 34 Gregory Avenue, Stivichall, Coventry CV3 6DL — BM 1993 Soton.; DRCOG 2001.

RAO, Abbaraju Mohan 25 Dibbins Green, Bromborough, Wirral CH63 0QF Tel: 0151 334 1580 Fax: 0151 334 1580 Email: mohan@netcomuk.co.uk; 25 Dibbins Green, Bromborough, Wirral CH63 0QF Tel: 0151 334 1580 Fax: 0151 334 1580 — MB BS 1979 Osmania; FFA RCSI 1989. Cons. (Anaesth.) Arrowe Pk. Hosp. Wirral. Socs: Obst. Anaesth. Assn.; Soc. Computing & Tech. Anaesth. Prev: Sen. Regist. (Anaesth.) Mersey RHA; Staff Grade (Anaesth.) N. Tees Gen. Hosp. Stockton-on-Tees; Regist. (Anaesth.) Hull Roy. Infirm.

RAO, Amirchetty Rajeshwar The Surgery, 112 Watnall Road, Hucknall, Nottingham NG15 7JP Tel: 0115 963 2184 Fax: 0115 955 6311.

RAO, Anupama Len Valley Practice, Tithe Yard, Church Square, Lenham, Maidstone ME17 2PJ Tel: 01622 858341 Fax: 01622 859659 — MB BS 1989 Lond.; MRCGP 1994; DCH RCP Lond. 1992. (St George's Hospital Medical School) Clin. Asst. (Dermat.) Maidstone; Mem. Steering Gp. Maidstone PCG; Young Practitioners Represen. Kent Trainers Selection Comm. Prev: Trainee GP/SHO (Med.) Maidstone Hosp.

RAO, Bangalore Vinayak (Surgery), 47 Russell Road, Rhyl LL18 3DA Tel: 01745 50666; 27 Llys Brenig, Rhyl LL18 4BX — MB BS 1963 Mysore. (Mysore Med. Coll.) Prev: Regist. (ENT Surg.) Beaumont Hosp. Lancaster; Ho. Surg. (Gyn. & Obst.) Whiston Hosp. Prescot.

RAO, Bethapudy Ratna Sunder 13A Lime Tree Road, Norwich NR2 2NQ — MB BS 1972 Mysore. (Kasturba Med. Coll. Mangalore) SHO N.-E. Health Bd. Irel. Prev: Med. Off. Leprosy Miss. Hosp. Vilianagaram, India; SHO Sligo Gen. Hosp. & Co. Surg. Hosp. Cavan.

RAO, Chandini 29 Stoney Butts, Lea, Preston PR2 1RT — MB BS 1993 Newc.

RAO, Mr Chirivella Screenivasa A3 Main Residences, Shotley Bridge General Hospital, Consett DH8 0NB — MB BS 1977 Sri Venkateswara; FRCS Glas. 1993.

RAO, Professor Chitaldroog Ramachandra (retired) 18 Daryngton Avenue, Birchington CT7 9PS Tel: 01843 845540 Email: ram.rao@btinternet.com — MB BS 1958 Mysore; FRCP Ed. 1974, M 1959; FCCP 1975; DTM & H Liverp. 1959. Prev: Cons. Phys. Thanet Dist. Gen. Hosp. Kent.

RAO, Gita Satish Ida Darwin Hospital, Fulbourn, Cambridge CB1 5EE Tel: 01223 884000 Fax: 01223 884003; 245 Hills Road,

RAO

Cambridge CB2 2RP Tel: 01223 240970 Fax: 01223 240970 — MB BS 1966 Bombay. Psychiat. Ida Darwin & Fulbourn Hosps. Camb. Prev: Research Fell. (Path. & Cancer Research) Addenbrooke's Hosp. Camb.

RAO, Gutta Hanumanta Rao and Partners, 90 Darnley Road, Gravesend DA11 0SW Tel: 01474 355331 Fax: 01474 324407 — MB BS 1967 Bangalor; MB BS Bangalore 1967. (Bangalore) Community Family Plann. Doctor Thameslink Healthcare Servs. NHS Trust Gravesend. Prev: Clin. Asst. (Orthop.) Dartford & Gravesham HA.; Regist. (Orthop.) Medway & Gravesend Gp. Hosps.

RAO, Hindnavis Sudhakar Dipple Medical Centre, Wickford Avenue, Pitsea, Basildon SS13 3HQ Tel: 01268 583288 Fax: 01268 581586 — MB BS 1972 Osmania.

RAO, Ivatury Venkata c/o Drive V. R. Mamilla, 42 Heath Road, Barming, Maidstone ME16 9LG — MB BS 1967 Andhra.

RAO, Jammi Nagaraj Sandwell Health Authority, 438 High St., West Bromwich B70 9LD Tel: 0121 500 1615 Fax: 0121 500 1500 Email: jammi.rao@sandwell-ma.wmidj.nhs.uk-; Tel: 01992 724049 — MB BS 1975 Nagpur; BA Open 1990; MD Nagpur 1978; MRCP (UK) 1984; MFPHM 1990; DCH RCP Lond. 1985; FRCP 1998; FFPHM 1999. (Nagpur) Cons. Pub. Health Sandwell HA; Assoc. Fell. Sch. Postgrad. Med. Educat. Univ. Warwick; Hon. Sen. Clin. Lect. (Pub. Health & Epidemiol.) Univ. of Birm. Prev: Sen. Regist. (Pub. Health Med.) Sandwell HA; Regist. (Paediat.) E. Birm. Hosp.; SHO (Neonat.) Bristol Matern. Hosp.

RAO, Mr Janardhan 12 Burnside Close, Stalybridge SK15 2TW — MB ChB 1991 Manch.; FRCS (Orth & Trauma) 2001; BSc (Hons.) St. And. 1988; FRCS Ed. 1995. (St Andrews) Orthop. Specialist Regist. E. Anglia Orthop. Rotat. Prev: SHO (Burns & Plastic Surg.) Withington Hosp. Manch.; SHO (Orthop., A & E & Neurosurg.) Addenbrooke's Hosp. Camb.

RAO, Kanangi Srinivasa 6 Roman Way, Sandbach CW11 3EN — MB BS 1968 Madras. (Kilpauk Med. Coll.) Cons. Psychiat. Leighton Hosp. Crewe. Prev: SHO Leighton Hosp. Crewe.

RAO, Kandukuri Rajeshwar University of Child Health, Level G, Centre Block, Southampton General Hospital, Southampton SO16 6YD Tel: 02380 796691; 9 Brickfield Road, Portswood, Southampton SO17 3AF Tel: 02380 554304 — MB BS 1981 Delhi; MRCP (UK) 1991. Research Fell. (Child Health) Soton. Univ. Socs: BMA. Prev: Clin. Tutor & Hon. Regist. Univ. Manch.; Regist. Ipswich Gen. Hosp.

RAO, Karra Arjun 9 College Heights, 246-252 St John St., London EC1V 4PH — MB ChB 1987 Dundee; BMSc Dund 1984, MB ChB 1987. SHO (O & G) Singleton Dist. Hosp. Sketty. Prev: Ho. Off. (Gen. Surg.) Singleton Dist. Hosp.; SHO P.ss of Wales Hosp. Bridgend; Trainee GP Bridgend VTS.

RAO, Kavery Psychiatric Unit, Derby City General Hospital Trust, Uttoxeter Road, Derby DE22 3NE — MB BS 1975 Mysore.

RAO, Kusumeswara Chittajallu Audley Surgery, 2-4 Lincoln Close, Audley Range, Blackburn BB1 1NY Tel: 01254 671560 Fax: 01254 696679 — MB BS 1962 Andhra; DCH Andhra 1964. (Andhra Med. Coll.)

RAO, M S Princes Road Surgery, 116 Princes Road, Liverpool L8 2UL Tel: 0151 727 3434.

RAO, Madduri Joadadish Bulwell Health Centre, Main St., Bulwell, Nottingham NG6 8QJ.

RAO, Madipalli Venkateswara Glen Road Medical Centre, 1-9 Glen Road, London E13 8RU Tel: 020 7476 3434 Fax: 020 7473 6092; Bratton, 10 Bressey Grove, South Woodford, London E18 2HP — MB BS 1972 Andhra. (Andhra Med. Coll. Visakhapatnam) GP Princip. Socs: BMA; MPS; ODA. Prev: Trainee GP Asst.; GP Princip.

RAO, Mala Langley Mill Cottage, Colne Engaine, Colchester CO6 2JL Tel: 01787 472642 — MB BS 1977 Delhi; MSc Community Med. Lond. 1983; FFPHM RCP (UK) 1993; MFCM 1986; DA Eng. 1981. Dir. Pub. Health S. Essex HA. Prev: Cons. Pub. Health NE Essex HA Dist. Off. Cochester.

RAO, Mannige Rahul South London & Maudsley NHS Trust, Job Ward, GUY's Hospital, London SE1 9RT — MB BS 1989 Lond.; BSc Lond. 1986; MRCPsych 1994; MD Lond. 1999. Cons./Sen Lect., GUY's Hosp. Lond. Socs: Brit. Neuropsychiat. Assn.; Train. Mem. Brit. Assn. Psychopharmacol.; Brit. Geriat.s Soc. Prev: Sen. Regist. (Psychiat.) Maudsley Hosp. Lond.; Regist. (Psychiat.) Fulbourn Hosp.

Camb. & W. Suff. Hosp. Bury St. Edmunds; SHO (Psychiat.) Fulbourn Hosp. Camb.

RAO, Mannige Sateesh Edith Covell Hospital, Peterborough PE3 9QZ Tel: 01733 874854 Fax: 01733 875719; 245 HILLS Road, Cambridge CB2 2RP Tel: 01223 240970 — MB BS 1957 Agra. (Indore, India) Cons. Phys. Med. for Elderly/Integrated Med. Edith Cavell Hosp. Socs: BMA; Brit. Geriat.s Soc. Prev: Geriat. Newmarket Gen. Hosp. E. Anglian RHA; Regist. (Med.) Chesterton Hosp. Camb.

RAO, N. Mukunda — MBBS 1974 Bangalore.

RAO, Mr Nagesh Gadiyar Solway, Willowmead Drive, Prestbury, Macclesfield SK10 4BU 67 Chew Valley Road, Greenfield, Oldham OL3 7JG Tel: 01233 633331 Ext: 86693, 01303 851220, 01457 873100, 01625 828717, 01233 616019 Email: nagesh.rao@virgin.net, tomsinclair@doctors.org.uk — MBBS 1981 Madras Univ.; FRCS RCPS (Glasgow), 1986 May, Glasgow; MD (Univ. Of Hull) 1997 Dec., Univ. Of Hull; FRCS (Edin.) Gen. Surgery, 1986 May, Edinburgh, 2000 June, Intercollegiate board. (Jipmer, Pondicherry, India) Cons. Colorectal Surg., E. Kent NHS Trust, Ashford, Kent; Cons. Colorectal Surg., BUPA St Saviour, Hythe, Kent; Cons. Coloutal Surg., Chaucer Hosp., Nackingon Rd., Canterbury. Socs: Assoc. Of ColoProctol. of GB and I, Full Fell.s; Assn. of Surg.s of GB and I, Full Fell.s; Roy. Soc. of Med., Full Fell. Prev: Special Regist. Gen. Surg., All Wales HST, S. Wales - Swansea, Cardiff, Pontypridd and Newport.

RAO, Narayan 33 Penrose Street, London SE17 3DW Tel: 020 7703 3677 — MB BS 1958 Osmania. (Osmania Med. Coll. Hyderabad)

RAO, Nikhil Ramananda 22A Tudor Drive, Romford RM2 5LH — MB BS 1987 Lond. SHO (A & E) P.ss Alexandra Hosp. Harlow. Prev: Ho. Surg. P.ss Alexandra Hosp. Harlow; Ho. Phys. Harold Wood Hosp.

RAO, Padma Royal Victoria Hospitals Trust, Victoria Road, Newcastle upon Tyne Tel: 0191 232 5131; 180 Hollywood Avenue, Gosforth, Newcastle upon Tyne NE3 5BU Tel: 0191 285 1390 — MB BS 1989 Lond.; BSc (1st. cl. Hons.) Lond. 1986; MRCP (UK) 1993; FRCR (UK) 1996. (St Mary's Hosp.) Lect. (Paediat. Radiol.) Roy. Liverp. Childr. Hosp. Socs: Roy. Coll. Radiol.; Roy. Coll. Phys. Edin.; BMA. Prev: Sen. Regist. (Diagn. Radiol.) Newc. Hosps.; Regist. (Diag. Radiol.) Newc. Hosp.; SHO Rotat. (Gastroenterol. & Gen. Med.) N.wick Pk. Hosp. Harrow.

RAO, Pappu Bhogeswara Roper Street Surgery, 11 Roper Street, Workington CA14 3BY Tel: 01900 602997 Fax: 01900 870142 — MB BS 1971 Andhra; MB BS 1971 Andhra. (Andhra) GP Workington, Cumbria.

RAO, Poduri Jaya 31A Willows Drive, Failsworth, Manchester M35 0PZ Tel: 0161 682 4437 — MB BS 1973 Andhra. Staff Grade Roy. Oldham Hosp.

RAO, Ponnaganti Chandrasekhara 17 Staverton Leys, Rugby CV22 5RD — MB BS 1972 Sri Venkateswara; DA Eng. 1979. Staff Grade (Anaesth.) Hosp. St Cross Rugby. Prev: Regist. (Anaesth.) Roy. Infirm. Dumfries, Qu. Eliz. Hosp. Gateshead & Neath Gen. Hosp.

RAO, Premanand Bhaskeranand Kenley Parade Surgery, 4-6 Kenley Parade, Sheil Road, Liverpool L6 3BP Tel: 0151 263 6588 Fax: 0151 263 4723; 8 Hayles Grove, Gateacre, Liverpool L25 4SL — MB BS 1963 Karnatak. (Kasturba Med. Coll. Mangalore)

RAO, Puvvada Jagadishwara Birkdale Practice, 147 Liverpool Road, Birkdale, Southport PR8 4NT Tel: 01704 566277 Fax: 01704 563007.

RAO, Ravi Madduri 76 Comeragh Road, London W14 9HR — MB BChir 1993 Camb.; MA Camb. 1993; MRCP (UK) 1995. Regist. Rheum. Unit Hammersmith Hosp. Lond.

RAO, Sharon Vinnakota 24 Petersham Drive, Appleton, Warrington WA4 5QF — MB ChB 1998 Dund.; MB ChB Dund 1998.

RAO, Sheela 13 Padstow Drive, Bramhall, Stockport SK7 2HU — MB BS 1993 Lond.

RAO, Sridevi Kamma 13 Farnham House, Harewood Avenue, London NW1 6NT — MB BS 1996 Lond.

RAO, Sudha 15 Battersby Close, Yarm TS15 9RX Tel: 01642 879754 Fax: 01642 879754 Email: sudha@tinyonline.co.uk — MB BS 1974 Madras; MRCOG 1990.

RAO, Mr Sudhir Gururaja Queen Mary's Hospital, Sidcup BR5 2RH; 46 Spring Shaw Road, Orpington BR5 2RH Tel: 0958

RAO

632831 Fax: 020 8300 9294 Email: sudhir.rao@virgin.net — MB BS 1985 Bombay; MChOrth. Liverp. 1991; FRCS Glas. 1989; FRCS Ed. 1989; FRCS (Orth.) 1996; FRCS (Eng.) 1998. Cons. Orthopaedic Surg. Qu. Mary's Hosp. Sidcup; Cons. Orthopaedic Surg. The Blackheath Hosp., Lond. Bridge Hosp. & Chelsfield Pasrk Hosp., Kent; Cons. Orthopaedic Surg. Lond. Bridge Hosp.; Cons. Orthopaedic Surg. Chelsfield Pk. Hosp. Chelsfield, Kent. Socs: Fell. BOA; Brit. Assn. Surg. Knee; BMA. Prev: Cons. Orthopaedic Surg. Univ. Hosp. Lewisham; Sen. Regist. (Orthop.) N. W. Region Train. Progr.

RAO, Sumant Kogganna Damien's Mill, Datchet Road, Windsor SL4 Tel: 0175 35 52303 — MB BS 1958 Bombay; MRCP Lond. 1969; MRCP Glas. 1969. (Seth G.S. Med. Coll.) Cons. Phys. Canad. Red Cross, Maidenhead, Slough & Windsor Hosps. Socs: Fell. Amer. Coll. Chest Phys.; Brit. Pharmacol. Soc. Prev: Sen. Regist. (Geriat. Med.) Centr. & Middlx. Hosps. Lond.; Hon. Sen. Regist. Hammersmith Hosp. & Roy. Postgrad. Med. Sch.; Hon. Research Asst. Dept. Cardiol. N.wick Pk. Hosp. Harrow.

RAO, Suryadevara Yadu Purna Chandra Prasada Belgrave Medical Centre, 116 Belgrave Road, Dresden, Stoke-on-Trent ST3 4LR Tel: 01782 593344 Fax: 01782 593305 Email: prasad.rao@nshawebmail.nhs.uk; Fairfield House, 169 Barlaston Old Road, Trentham, Stoke-on-Trent ST4 8HJ Tel: 01782 646099 Fax: 01782 659125 Email: prasadraos@aol.com — MB BS Andhra 1973. (Andhra Med. Coll. Visakhapatnam) Clin. Exec. Chair S. Stoke PCT. Socs: Sec. Nat. Assn. Co-op.; Chairm. Doctors Co-op. N. Staffs. Prev: SHO (Gen. Surg.) Guest Hosp. Dudley; SHO (Orthop.) Gloucester Roy. Hosp. & Standish Hosp. StoneHo..

RAO, Tadepalli Lakshmi Narasimha 40-42 Atherstone Avenue, Netherton, Peterborough PE3 9TY Tel: 01733 333788 Fax: 01733 333788 Email: trao266233@aol.com — MB BS 1972 Osmania; MCOphth 1988; DO RCPSI 1978. Ophth.Med. Practitioners. Socs: RCOphth; Brit. Contact Lens Assoc; Brit. Excimer Laser Soc. Prev: Regist. (Ophth.) N.ampton Gen. Hosp.; SHO (Ophth.) P'boro. Hosp.; Laser Ophth., Optimax laser eye clinic, Manch.

RAO, Valluri Ranganadha 42 Landseer Avenue, Tingley, Wakefield WF3 1UE Tel: 0113 253 2278 Email: rvalluri@aol.com — MB BS Andhra 1953; BSc Andhra 1953; MFPHM 1989; MFCM 1974; FRSH 1970; Cert FPA 1968; DPH Liverp. 1967. Socs: Fac. Community Health; BMA. Prev: SCM Wakefield & Sandwell HA; Med. Off. Environm. Health Sandwell DC.

RAO, Vasanampalli Meena Kamalakshi 59 The Broadway, Dudley DY1 4AP — MB BS 1996 Lond. Dept.of Paed.Neorology,Birm. Childr.s Hosp.k, Birm. B4 6NH.

RAO, Vibha Rohit 7 Tapley Road, Chelmsford CM1 4XY Tel: 01245 441370 — MB BS 1972 Bombay; FRCS Ed. 1978. (Grant Med. Coll.) Clin. Asst. (Ophth.) Lond. Hosp.

RAO, Mr Victor Moor Green Lane Medical Centre, 339 Moor Green Lane, Moseley, Birmingham B13 8QS Tel: 0121 472 6959 — MB BS 1952 Calcutta; MS Calcutta 1962, MB BS 1952; FRCS Eng. 1957. (Calcutta) Clin. Asst. Migraine Research Clinic Birm.

RAO, Vidya Digambar Gorway Cottage, Gorway Road, Walsall WS1 3BB — MD (Paediat.) Osmania 1979, MB BS 1974; MRCP (UK) 1990; DCH RCP Lond. 1984. Staff Grade Paediat. Good Hope Hosp. Walsall. Prev: Clin. Med. Off. N. Birm. & BromsGr. & Redditch HAs; Regist. (Paediat.) Manor Hosp. Walsall.

RAO, Vuppala Radha Kishan 34 Albyfield, Bromley BR1 2HZ — MB BS 1969 Osmania.

RAO, Vyakaranam Padmavathi Halling Medical Centre, Ferry Road, Halling, Rochester ME2 1NP Tel: 01634 240238; 62 Rochester Road, Halling, Rochester ME2 1AH — MB BS 1965 Osmania; DA Eng. 1976. (Gandhi Med. Coll. Hyderabad) Prev: Clin. Asst. (Anaesth.) Epsom Dist. Hosp.; SHO (O & G) All St.s Hosp. Chatham; Capt. IAMC.

RAO, Mr Yella Veera Venkata Satya Greenfields Medical Centre, 12 Terrace Street, Hyson Green, Nottingham NG7 6ER Tel: 0115 942 3582 Fax: 0115 900 2330; 9 Pavilion Road, Nottingham NG5 8NL Tel: 0115 926 0274 — MB BS 1967 Andhra; FRCS Eng. 1976. (Andhra) p/t Med. Bd.ing Off. DHSS Nottm.; Med. Off. (Disabil. Med.) City Hosp. Nottm. Prev: SHO (Gen. Surg.) Corbett Hosp. Stourbridge; Cas. Off. King Edwd. VII Hosp. Windsor; SHO (Orthop.) Good Hope Gen. Hosp. Sutton Coldfield.

RAOOF, Abdur 5 Groveside Crescent, Clifton Village, Nottingham NG11 8NT Tel: 0115 984 2959 Email: raoof@btinternet.com — MRCS Eng. LRCP Lond. 1969; BSc, MB BS Punjab 1958; MFOM RCP Lond. 1978; DIH Soc. Apoth. Lond. 1973. (Nishtar Med. Coll.) Indep. Cons. Occupat.al Med.. Socs: Soc. Occupat. Med.; Brit. Occupat. Hyg. Soc. Prev: Occupat. Health Phys. Nottm. CC; Med. Off. Nat. Coal Bd. (NE Area), Roy. Ordnance Fact. Nottm. & COD Chilwell MOD.

RAOOF, Mr Hikmat Yousif 9 St Leonards Close, Welling DA16 2DN — MB ChB 1973 Mosul; FRCS Glas. 1987.

RAOUF, Ali Hameed 32 Middlemore, Southfields, Northampton NN3 5DE — MB ChB 1973 Baghdad; MRCP (UK) 1983.

RAPEPORT, William Garth GlaxoWellcome RID, Greenford Road, Greenford UB6 Tel: 020 8966 3073 Fax: 020 8966 2757 Email: gr45271@glasowellcome.co.uk — MB BCh 1977 Witwatersrand; MRCP (UK) 1979; FFPM RCP (UK) 1995. Worldwide Dir. (Clin. Pharmacol.) Glaxo Wellcome Greenford; Vis. Prof. Dept. Pharmacol. & Therap. Univ. Liverp. Socs: Brit. Pharm. Soc. Prev: Dir. Early Clin. Research Gp. Pfizer Centr. Research Sandwich Kent; Hon. Sen. Regist. & MRC Clin. Scientist MRC Univ. Dept. Clin. Pharmacol. Radcliffe Infirm. Oxf.; Regist. Univ. Dept. Med. Gardiner Inst. W.. Infirm. Glas.

RAPER, Joan Marjorie 12 ladywood Mead, Asket Hill, Leeds LS8 2LZ — MB ChB 1937 Leeds.

RAPER, John Malcolm (retired) Hilltop, 13 Meadow Croft, Draughton, Skipton BD23 6EG Tel: 01756 710367 — MB ChB 1961 Leeds; FFA RCS Eng. 1967. Prev: Cons. Anaesth. Airedale Gen. Hosp. E.burn.

RAPER, Joyce Agnes (retired) Owl End, 64 Stoughton Lane, Stoughton, Leicester LE2 2FH Tel: 0116 271 3331 — MB ChB 1952 Manch.; DCH Eng. 1955.

RAPER, Sally Clair 80 Clough Road, Golcar, Huddersfield HD7 4JX — MB BS 1997 Newc.

RAPERPORT, Gerald (retired) 46 The Little Green, Gosport PO12 2EX — MB BChir 1947 Camb.; MA, MB BChir Camb. 1947.

RAPHAEL, Alison Mary Cherryvalley Health Centre, Kings Square, Belfast BT5 7AR; 8 Wandsworth Drive, Belfast BT4 2BJ Tel: 653874 — MB BCh BAO 1973 Belf.

RAPHAEL, Frances Jane Springfield Hospital, Glenburnie Road, Tooting, London SW17 — MB BS 1987 Lond.; MRCPsych 1991; MD 1999 Llondon. Cons. Psychiat. S. W. Lond. and St Geo.s , NHS Trust, Tooting Lond.. Prev: Lect. (Community Psychiat.) St. Geo. Hosp. Med. Sch.; Lect. (Gen. Psychiat.) Lond.; Regist. Rotat. (Psychiat.) St. Geo. Hosp. Lond.

RAPHAEL, George Anton Jayaseelan 1 Marsden Road, Cleadon Village, Sunderland SR6 7RA Tel: 0191 537 2198 — MB BS 1969 Ceylon; FFA RCSI 1988; DA (UK) 1979. Locum Cons. & Assoc. Specialist (Anaesth.) S. Tyneside Health Care Trust. Prev: Staff Grade (Anaesth.) Freeman Hosp. Newc.

RAPHAEL, Helen Mary 51 Park Road, Hagley, Stourbridge DY9 0QQ — MB ChB 1988 Leic.; MRCGP 1994; DRCOG 1991.

RAPHAEL, J A G Mounts Medical Centre, Campbell Street, Northampton NN1 3DS Tel: 01604 631952 Fax: 01604 634139; Windycroft, Monlton Lane, Bonghton, Northampton NN2 8RG Tel: 01604 845030 Email: raphael@tinyworld.co.uk — LRCPI & LM, LRSCI & LM 1977. (RCSI) p/t Ruby Club Doctor to N.ampton RFC. Prev: SHO (O & G) N.ampton Gen. Hosp.; SHO (Gen. Paediat. Surg.) Our Lady's Hosp. Sick Childr. Crumlin; Ho. Surg. & Ho. Phys. Jervis St. Hosp. Dub.

RAPHAEL, Jonathan Howard 51 Park Road, Hagley, Stourbridge DY9 0QQ — MB ChB 1984 Glas.

RAPHAEL, Julian Morris Cuthbert 447 Wellingborough Road, Northampton NN1 4EZ Tel: 01604 30291; 20 The Avenue, Spinney Hill, Northampton NN3 6BA Tel: 01604 642848 — MB BCh BAO 1981 NUI. Socs: BMA (Hon. Sec. N.ampton Div.).

RAPHAEL, Maurice John 126 Harley Street, London W1N 1AH Tel: 020 7935 4072; 37 Rotherwick Road, London NW11 7DD Tel: 020 8201 9065 — MD Camb. 1971, MB 1959, BChir 1958; FRCP Lond. 1978, M 1961; FFR 1964; DMRD Eng. 1961; DObst RCOG 1960. Cons. Radiol. Middlx. Hosp. Lond. Socs: Fell. Roy. Soc. Med.; Brit. Inst. Radiol.

RAPHAEL, Montague, MBE 20 Bordeaux Close, Northfield Green, Sunderland SR3 2SR Tel: 0191 528 0784 — LRCP LRCS Ed. LRFPS Glas. 1950 Ed.; MRCGP 1958. (Roy. Colls. & Univ. Ed.) Med. Off. Remploy Sunderland; Med. Adviser Benefits Agency Sunderland.

Prev: Clin. Asst. Gen. Hosp. & Roy. Infirm. Sunderland; Ho. Surg. N. Ormesby Hosp.

RAPHAEL, Nabil St Marks Medical Centre, 24 Wrottesley Road, Plumstead, London SE18 3EP Tel: 020 8854 6262 Fax: 020 8317 3098 Email: nabilraphael@cs.com — MRCS Eng. LRCP Lond. 1979; MRCOG 1983.

RAPHAEL, Olga Rachel (retired) Briar Cottage, 154 Tilt Road, Cobham KT11 3HR Tel: 01932 867370 — MB ChB Sheff. 1951. Prev: Clin. Med. Off. Kingston & Esher HA.

RAPLEY, David Michael The Castle Medical Centre, 22 Bertie Road, Kenilworth CV8 1JP Tel: 01926 857331 Fax: 01926 851070; 2 Amherst Road, Kenilworth CV8 1AH Tel: 01926 512192 Email: dave@ruple.freeserve.co.uk — MB ChB 1980 Birm.; MRCGP 1984; Cert. Family Plann. JCC 1984. (Birmingham) Course Organiser Coventry & Warks.; Mem. Warks. MAAG; Hon. Sen. Clin. Lect. (Gen. Pract.) Warwick Univ. Socs: (Hon. Sec.) Midl. Fac. RCGP. Prev: GP Postgrad. Tutor S. Warks.

RAPOPORT, Arron, MBE (retired) 25 Upfield, Croydon CR0 5DR Tel: 020 8654 3741 — LRCP LRCS 1938 Ed.; LRCP LRCS Ed. LRFPS Glas. 1938.

RAPOPORT, Jill Wirksworth Health Centre, St. Johns Street, Wirksworth, Matlock DE4 4DT Tel: 01629 822434; 7 Yokecliffe Hill, Wirksworth, Derby DE4 4PE Tel: 01629 823515 — BM BS 1975 Nottm.; BMedSci Nottm. 1973, BM BS 1975; MRCGP 1979; DRCOG 1978; Cert JCC Lond. 1979; LF HOM 1997. (Nottm.)

RAPP, D A Simmons and Partners, Chalkhill Health Centre, Chalkhill Road, Wembley HA9 9BQ Tel: 020 8904 0911 Fax: 020 8908 6945 — MB BS 1977 London; MB BS 1977 London.

RAPPAPORT, Ruth Alison (retired) 7 Howard Walk, London N2 0HB Tel: 020 8455 4813 — MB ChB Glas. 1946; DPM Lond. 1950. Prev: Cons. (Child & Adoles. Psychiat.) Redbridge Child Guid.

RAPPORT, Henry Maurice, MBE (retired) Kockmaroon, 37 Brandreth Road, Penylan, Cardiff CF23 5NW Tel: 01222 460255 — MRCS Eng. LRCP Lond. 1937; FRCGP 1975, M 1956. Clin. Asst. Marie Curie Hospice Penarth S. Glam. Prev: Ho. Surg., Ho. Phys. & Cas. Surg. Off. Cardiff Roy. Infirm.

RAPTOPOULOS, Paul 5 Ellesmere Place, Queens Road, Walton-on-Thames KT12 5AE Tel: 020 7273 0419 — MD 1967 Thessalonika; FFPM RCP (UK) 1996, MFPM 1990; MRCPsych 1976; MFPM rcp (UK) 1990; FFPM RCP (UK) 1996. (Thessaloike) Sen. Med. Off. Meds. Control Agency DoH Lond. Prev: Clin. Projects Manager, Pharmaceutical Industry; Research Sen. Regist. & Hon. Lect. St. Mary's Hosp. Med. Sch. Lond.

RARATY, Mrs Catherine Carmel Westford Lodge, Merrill's Lane, Upton, Wirral CH49 0UA Tel: 0151 605 0205 Email: c.raraty@virgin.net — MB ChB 1989 Leeds; FRCS Ed. 1997.

RARATY, Mr Michael Godwin Thomas Westford Lodge, Merrill's Lane, Upton, Wirral CH49 0UA Tel: 0151 605 0205 Email: m.raraty@virgin.net — MB BS 1989 Newc.; FRCS Eng. 1994. (Newc. u tyne) Clin. Research Fell. (Dept. Surg.) Univ. of Liverp. Prev: Regist. (Gen. Surg.) Arrowe Pk. Hosp. Wirral.

RARITY, Russell Alexander Gilbert Bain Hospital, Lerwick ZE1 0TB Tel: 01595 743007 Email: russel.rarity@shetland-hb.scot.nhs.uk; 1 Hayfield Court, Commercial St, Lerwick ZE1 0AN Tel: 01595 692589 — MB BChir 1988 Camb.; MA Camb. 1992; FRCA 1994. Cons. Anaesth., Gilbert Bain Hosp., Shetland Is.s.; Med. Serv.s Manager-Shetland Health Bd.. Socs: FRSM; Mem. Intens. Care Soc.; Mem. Assn. Anaesth. GB & Irel. Prev: Sen. Regist. (Anaesth.) Roy. Berks. Hosp. Reading & Anglia & Oxf. RHA; Regist. Rotat. (Anaesth.) Oxf. RHA & Aylesbury Vale HA.

RASAIAH, Dorairetnam (retired) The Paddock, Leigh, Sherborne DT9 6HW Tel: 01935 873229 — MB ChB 1963 St. And. Prev: SHO (Fract. & Orthop.) Dundee Roy. Infirm.

RASAIAH, Karen Higher Stert, Stert Barton, Diptford, Totnes TQ9 7NB — MB ChB 1984 Manch.

RASAIAH, Selva Arden House, 9-10 Launceton Close, Winsford CW7 1LY Tel: 01606 861200 — MB ChB 1987 Manch. Trainee GP Sandbach.

RASAMUTHIAH, Thuraiappah Calnwood Court, Calnwood Road, Luton LU4 0LX Tel: 01582 709150 Fax: 01582 709151; 11 Hayton Close, Luton LU3 4HD Tel: 01582 596710 — MBBS 1968 Colombo. (University of Ceylon, Colombo, Srilanka) Assoc. Specialist Psychiat. Dept., Beds & Luton Community NHS Trust, Luton. Socs: Affil. Mem., Roy. Coll. of Psychiat.s.

RASANAYAGAM, Stephen Romesh 36A Atherston, Warmley, Bristol BS30 8YB Tel: 0117 947 5072 — MB BS 1987 Lond.

RASARATNAM, Renuga Harperbury, Harper Lane, Shenley, Radlett WD7 9HQ Tel: 01923 427222; 7 Tithe Farm Close, South Harrow, Harrow HA2 9DP Tel: 01273 555382, 020 8933 2284 Fax: 01273 556093 Email: hempling@cwcom.net, renuga@lineone.net — MB BS 1972 Columbo; BC Psych 1995; MRC Psych 1996. Specialist Regist. (Psychiat. of Learning Disabilities) Horizon NHS Trust Shenley. Prev: Staff Grade Psychiat. (Acute Adult Psychiat.) N.wick Pk. Hosp. Harrow; Regist. Rotat. (Psychiat.) S. Essex Train. Scheme.

RASBURN, Barbara 27 Grayling Road, London N16 0BL; 92A Lordship Park, London N16 5UA — MB BS 1991 Lond.

RASCHID, Muhammad Salman 15 Hillfield Mansions, Haverstock Hill, Hampstead, London NW3 4QR — MB 1964 Camb.; BChir 1963.

RASCHKES, Beena Jacqueline Hatton Farm, Abernethy, Perth PH2 9LN — MB ChB 1982 Manch.; BSc (Med. Sci.) St. And. 1979; DFFP 1994; DCH RCP Lond. 1984; DRCOG 1984. Prev: Trainee GP Timperley; SHO (O & G) Wythenshawe Hosp. Manch.; SHO (Paediat.) Booth Hall Childr. Hosp. Manch.

RASDALE, Paul Ferry Road Health Centre, Ferry Road, Dingwall IV15 9QS Tel: 01349 863034 Fax: 01349 862022 — MB ChB 1977 Glas.; FRCP Glas. 1994; MRCP (UK) 1980.

RASH, Amar 46 Leegate Road, Stockport SK4 4AX — MB ChB 1994 Sheff.; MRCP (UK) 1998. (Sheffield) SHO (Med.) Chesterfield & N. Derbysh. Roy. Hosp.

RASH, Guy James Eric Lawson Road Health Centre, Lawson Road, Norwich NR3 4LE Tel: 01603 427096 Fax: 01603 403074 Email: tilfordptn@aol.com; 23 Hanover Road, Norwich NR2 2HD — MB BS 1990 Lond.; MRCP (UK) 1994; MRCGP (Dist.) 1998. (St Bartholomew's Med. School)

RASH, Ramakant Maganlal (retired) 46 Leegate Road, Heaton Moor, Stockport SK4 4AX Tel: 0161 432 1085 — MB ChB 1962 Manch.; BSc (Hons. Anat.) Manch. 1959, MB ChB 1962; FRCP Lond. 1984, M 1967. Prev: Cons. Phys. (Geriat. Med.) Wythenshawe Hosp. Manch.

RASHAD, Shawky Youssef Flat 3, 18 Langley Avenue, Surbiton KT6 6QL Tel: 020 8399 3131 — MB BCh 1968 Cairo. Clin. Asst. (Orthop.) Hip Research Unit W. Middlx. Univ. Hosp.

RASHBASS, Barbara Joan 48 High View, Pinner HA5 3PB — MB BS Lond. 1958; FRCP Lond. 1995; DPH Eng. 1968; DCH Eng. 1961. (Univ. Coll. Hosp.) Barrister-at-Law; Non-Exec. Dir. Harrow & Hillingdon Healthcare Trust. Socs: Medico-Legal Soc.; Roy. Soc. Med. Prev: Dir. & Sec. Wolfson Foundat. & Family Charitable Trust; PMO H.Q. Staff Med. Research Counc.

RASHBASS, Jeremy Lewis Clinical and Biomedical Computing Unit, Addenbrooke's Hospital, Cambridge CB2 2SP Tel: 01223 762034 Fax: 01223 400060 Email: jem@cbcu.cam.ac.uk — MB BS 1987 Lond.; PhD Camb. 1991; BSc (Hons.) Anat. Lond. 1983; MRCPath 1995. (Univ. Coll. Lond.) Dir. BioMed. Computing Camb. Univ. Camb.; Hon. Cons. Haemat. Histopath.; Non-Exec. Dir. NHS Informat. Auth. Prev: Clin. Research Fell. Cancer Research Campaign Camb.

RASHBASS, Penelope MRC Human Genetics Unit, Western General Hospital, Crewe Road, Edinburgh EH4 2XU Tel: 0131 332 2471 — MB BChir 1989 Camb.; PhD Ed. 1994; MA Camb. 1989, MB BChir 1989. (Camb.)

RASHBROOK, Patricia Sybil 26 Friars Walk, Lewes BN7 2LF — MB ChB 1967 Sheff.; MSc Lond. 1972; MRCPsych 1985.

RASHED, Khalid Areef Mustafa Yeovil District Hospital, Yeovil BA21 4AT Tel: 01935 707344 Email: rashed@clara.net; Al-Gazal, Queen St, Tintinhull, Yeovil BA22 8PG Tel: 01935 825253 — MB ChB 1979 Mosul; MRCP (UK) 1987; MRCPI 1986. Cons. Gen. & Geriat. Med. E. Som. NHS Trust Yeovil. Socs: Brit Geriat. Soc. Prev: Sen. Regist. (Gen. & Geriat. Med.) SE Thames RHA; Regist. (Geriat.) Ealing Hosp. Middlx.; Research Regist. (Cardiol.) Bath.

RASHED, Mr Mohamed Daw Kettering General Hospital, Rothwell Road, Kettering NN16 8UZ Tel: 01536 492000 Fax: 01536 493570; 3 Keating Close, Barton Sea Grave, Kettering NN15 5JA Tel: 01536 312953 — MB BCh Tripoli 1981; FRCS Ed. 1989; FRCS (Gen.) 1998; FRCS Ed (Gen) 1998. Cons. Surg. Socs: Mem. Assn. Cloproctol. GB & Irel.; Assoc of Surg.s of Gt. Brit. Irel..

RASHED

RASHED, Nabil Fathalla Psychiatric Department, Queens Park Hospital, Blackburn BB2 3HH Tel: 01254 63555; 23 Walton Crescent, Blackburn BB2 3TQ Tel: 01254 665060 — MB ChB 1967 Alexandria; DPM Eng. 1978. Socs: BMA. Prev: Med. Asst. (Psychiat.) Qu.'s Pk. Hosp. Blackburn.

RASHED, Ali SEBDOC Night Centre, Heatherwood Hospital, Ascot SL5 8AA Tel: 01344 877447 Fax: 01344 877073; 257 Arethusa Way, Bisley, Woking GU24 9BU Tel: 01483 480097 — MB ChB 1969 Ed.; BSc Ed. 1966; T(GP) 1992; DTM & H RCP Lond. 1971; AMP (Aerospace Medicine Primary) Air Univ. Texas 1996. (Edinburgh University) Duty Primary Care Practitioner SEBDOC Berks. (GP Co-op). Socs: Roy. Coll. Gen. Pract.; Nat. Assn. Non-Princip.; Roy. Soc. Med. Prev: GP Princip. Camberley Surrey; Med. Off. Govt. of Malaysia; U.N. Exam. Phys. RePub. of Maldives.

RASHEED, Farhat 7 Woodfield Road, Middleton, Manchester M24 1NF — MB ChB 1997 Manch.

RASHEED, Mohamed Haroon The Surgery, 77 Sandy Lane, Mansfield NG18 2LT Tel: 01623 656055 Fax: 01623 424898 — MB BS 1967 Madras.

RASHEED, Mr Sohail 10 Lenten Grove, Hopwood, Heywood OL10 2LR — MB BS 1988 Punjab; FRCSI 1993.

***RASHEED, Sultana Amtul Ahad** 18 Wessex Gardens, London NW11 9RT Tel: 020 8445 3496 — MB ChB 1994 Sheff.

RASHID, Abdul Azeem Waqar 3 Ambleside Avenue, Bradford BD9 5NX — MB ChB 1995 Leeds.

RASHID, Abutaleb Muhammed Fazlur Pathology Laboratory, Darent Valley Hospital, Dartford DA2 8DA Tel: 01322 428489 Fax: 01322 428493 — MB BS 1961 Dacca; MSc (Path.) Dacca 1967; FRCPath 1990, M 1978. (Dacca Med. Coll.) Cons. Histopath. Darent Valley Hosp. Socs: Clin. Path. Assn.; Brit. Clin. Cytol. Soc.; Roy. Soc. Med. Prev: Sen. Regist. (Histopath. & Morbid Anat.) Soton. Gen. Hosp.; NHS Trust -1992-1997.; Regist. in Path., Roy. Sussex Co. Hosp., Brighton.

RASHID, Ahmad Yusafi 90 North Hyde Road, Hayes UB3 4NF Tel: 020 8573 8560 Fax: 020 8569 0551; 11 Youlden Drive, Camberley GU15 1AL Tel: 01276 20750 — MB BS Punjab 1962; BSc Punjab (Pakistan) 1955. (King Edwd. Med. Coll. Lahore) GP Clin. Asst. (Ophth.) Hillingdon Hosp. Uxbridge. Socs: BMA. Prev: Clin. Asst. (Ophth.) Hillingdon Hosp. Uxbridge; Staff Phys. Horton Hosp. Epsom; Clin. Asst. (Ophth.) St. And. Hosp. Bow.

RASHID, Alan Hasnat 33 Hervey Close, London N3 2HG — MB BS 1994 Lond.

RASHID, Aly Central Street Health Centre, Central Street, Countesthorpe, Leicester LE8 5QJ Tel: 0116 277 6336 — MB ChB 1982 Manch.; MD Manch. 1995; FRCGP 191991, M 1986; DRCOG 1985. (Manch.) GP Leics.; Assoc. Adviser (Gen. Pract.) Univ. Leicester. Prev: Nat. Chairm. (Educat.) RCGP.

RASHID, Asrar Dept of Paediatrics, Birmingham Heartlands Hospital, Birmingham B9 5SS Email: drasrak@lineone.net; 55 Leicester Road, Luton LU4 8SF — MB ChB 1992 Aberd. Specialist Regist. Paediat. Birm. Heartlands. Hosp.

RASHID, Attiya 90B Plaistow Lane, Bromley BR1 3JE — MB BS 1998 Lond.; MB BS Lond 1998.

RASHID, Badr Ur 28 Corringham Road, Wembley HA9 9PY — MB BS 1971 Karachi; DTM & H RCP Lond. 1981.

RASHID, Mr Hisham Ikram Lewisham Hospital, Lewisham High St., Lewisham, London SE13 6LH Tel: 020 8333 3166 Fax: 020 8333 3166; 59 Heath Lane, Dartford DA1 2QE Tel: 01322 275128 Fax: 01322 275128 Email: hirashid@aol.com — MB BCh 1984 Cairo; MsC Cairo 1991; FRCS Eng. 1993. Specialist Regist./Research Fell. (Vasc. Surg.). Socs: Affil. Mem. Assn. Surgs. of GB & Irel.; Assn. Surg. Train. Prev: Specialist Regist. Joyce Green Hosp., Dartford; Specialist Regist. Lewisham Hosp. Lond.

RASHID, Irme 23 Cottrell Road, Bristol BS5 6TH — MB BS 1993 Lond.

RASHID, Khalid 42 Fairfield Road, Scunthorpe DN15 8DQ — MB BS 1984 Bahauddin Zakariya Univ. Pakistan; MB BS Bahauddin Zakariya U Pakistan 1984.

RASHID, Masoud 39 Froghall Terrace, Aberdeen AB24 3JP — MB ChB 1997 Aberd.

RASHID, Mohammed Abdur 41 Sutherland Grove, London SW18 5QP Tel: 020 8788 6047 — MB BS 1961 Karachi; DTM & H Liverp. 1963. (Dow Med. Coll.)

RASHID, Mr Najam Zafar Accident & Emergency Department, Manor Hospital, Moat Road, Walsall WS2 9PS Tel: 01922 721172 Fax: 01922 611902 Email: rashidn@wht.walsallh-tr.wmids.nhs.uk — MB ChB 1987 Birm.; FRCS Ed. 1993; FFAEM 1997. (Birmingham University) Cons. (A & E).

RASHID, Nasim Akhtar 117 Bawtry Road, Tinsley, Sheffield S9 1UF — MB ChB 1996 Sheff.

RASHID, Parveen Akhtar 86 Clifton Avenue, Leeds LS9 6EX — MB ChB 1993 Sheff.

RASHID, Rafaqut 9 Thorn Grove, Heaton, Bradford BD9 6LT — MB ChB 1996 Liverp.

RASHID, Rajeeb Flat 1, 28 Northumberland Road, Bristol BS6 7BB — MB ChB 1995 Glas.

RASHID, Raza-Ullah 4 Selwyn Road, London E3 5EA — MB BS 1996 Lond.

RASHID, Regina 10 Chelmsford Drive, Glasgow G12 0NA — MB ChB 1993 Glas.

RASHID, S Deepcar Medical Centre, 241-245 Manchester Road, Deepcar, Sheffield S36 2QZ Tel: 0114 288 2146.

RASHID, Sakina Department of Genitourinary Medicine, District General Hospital, Sunderland SR4 7TP Tel: 0191 569 9021 Fax: 0191 569 9244; 5 Eastfield, Peterlee SR8 4SS Tel: 0191 586 7917 — MB BS 1965 Punjab; MB BS Punjab (Pakistan) 1965; MMed Makerere 1971; FRCOG 1989, M 1972; DObst E. Afr. 1970. Cons. Genitourin. Med. City Hosps. Sunderland & S. Tyneside Dist. Hosp. Prev: Cons. Venereol. Sunderland & S. Tyneside AHA's & Newc. AHA (T).

RASHID, Shah Mohammad 32 Woodlands Road, Stalybridge SK15 2SQ Tel: 0161 338 3996 — MB BS 1957 Karachi; DA Eng. 1964.

RASHID, Sheikh Abdur Rashid and Partners, Havercroft Health Centre, Cow Lane, Ryhill, Wakefield WF4 2AX Tel: 01226 725555 Fax: 01226 700051; 6 Chevet Croft, Sandal, Wakefield WF4 2AX — MB BS 1969 Jammu & Kashmir; MD Kashmir 1974; DFFP 1996; Dip. Thoracic Med. Lond 1988. Socs: Brit. Thorac. Soc.

RASHID, Sheikh Tawqeer 6 Chevet Croft, Sandal, Wakefield WF2 6QR — BChir 1996 Camb.

RASHID, Waqar 110 Brunswick Road, Ealing, London W5 1AW — MB BS 1996 Lond. SHO (Med.) S. Cleveland Hosp. Middlesbrough. Socs: Med. Protec. Soc. Prev: Ho. Off. (Gen. Surg.) S. Cleveland Hosp. Middlesbrough; Med. Ho. Off. Watford & Mt. Vernon Trust Middlx.

RASHID, Yousef 277 Shrewsbury Road, London E7 8QU — MB BS 1992 Lond.

RASHID, Zafar Iqbal 21 Creslow Way, Stone, Aylesbury HP17 8YN Tel: 01296 748461 Fax: 01296 748461 — BChir 1985 Camb.; BMSc (Pharmacol.) Dund 1983; FRCA 1994; DRCOG 1991. (Cambridge) Cons., (Anaesth. & IC) Med. Stoke Mandeville Hosp. Aylesbury. Socs: Assn. Anaesth.; Intens. Care Soc.; BMA. Prev: Specialist Regist. Rotat. (Anaesth.) Nuffield Dept. Anaesth. Oxf.; SHO (Anaesth.) Roy. Berks. Hosp. Reading; Trainee GP Centr. Milton Keynes Med. Centre VTS.

RASHID, Zahid 43 Shorwell Close, Lingby Green, Great Sankey, Warrington WA5 3JY — MB BS 1987 Punjab; MRCP (UK) 1993.

RASHIQ, Hunaid Noorudin 55 Broadlands Avenue, Chesham HP5 1AL — MB BChir 1992 Camb.

RASIAH, Norbert Jagadeesan 102 Queen Elizabeth Drive, London N14 6RE — MB BS 1974 Sri Lanka; LRCP LRCS Ed. LRCPS Glas. 1986.

RASLAN, Mr Fateh West Middlesex University Hospital, Twickenham Rd, Isleworth TW7 6AF Tel: 0208 565 5427; Email: rassyr@aol.com — MB BCh 1984 Cairo; MRCOG 1992. Regist. (Obst.& Gyn.) John Radcliffe Hosp. Oxf.; Cons. at W.b Middx, Uni. Hosp - Isleworth. Socs: Brit. Soc. Gyn. Endoscopy; Brit. Assn. Day Surg.

RASMUSSEN, Jill Galloway Chisnall Psynapse, Arlington Cottage, Spook Hill, North Holmwood, Dorking RH5 4HH Tel: 01306 883272 Fax: 01306 740911 — MB ChB 1972 Manch.; MFPM RCP (UK) 1991; MRCGP 1976; DRCOG 1976; Dip. Ther. 1997; FFPMRCP1999. Indep. Cons. Dorking; Ment. Health Lead E. Surrey; Salaried GP. Socs: Collegium Internat.e Neuropsycho Pharmacologicum (CINP); Eur. Coll. Neuropsychopharm.; Brit. Assn. Psychopharmacol. Prev: Head (Clin. Operats.) Wellcome Research Laborat. Beckenham; Head (Med. & Scientif. Affairs) & Dir. Clin.

RATCLIFFE

Research, Lundbeck; Controller Developm. Project Managem. & Dir. Strategic Product Developm. SmithKline Beecham Pharmaceut.

RASOOL, Hufrish 102 Valley Drive, Kirkella, Hull HU10 7PW — MB BS Karachi 1978; MRCPsych 1990. Cons. Child & Adolesc. Psychiat. W.-End Child, Adolesc. & Family Serv. Hull. Prev: Sen. Regist. Rotat. (Child & Adolesc. Psychiat.) St. Jas. Univ. Hosp. Leeds.

RASOOL, Iftikhar 41 Hollymead Close, Colchester CO4 5JU — MB BS 1975 Punjab; MRCP (UK) 1988.

RASOOL, Mushtaq Abdul 102 Valley Drive, Kirkella, Hull HU10 7PW Email: mushtaq@rasool.5.freeserve.co.uk — MB BS 1978 Karachi; DO RCPSI 1986. Med. Pract. (Ophth.) Humberside.

RASOOL, Shafquth South Grange Medical Centre, Trunk Road, Eston, Middlesbrough TS6 9QG Tel: 01642 467001 Fax: 01642 463334 — MB BS 1985 Bahauddin Zakariya Univ. Pakistan; MB BS Bahauddin Zakariya Pakistan 1985; MRCP (UK) 1992.

RASOOL, Tahira Parveen 81 Ferryfield, Edinburgh EH5 2PS — MB ChB 1990 Glas.; MRCGP 1994; DRCOG 1993.

RASOOLY, Mr Raphael 47 Love Lane, Pinner HA5 3EY Tel: 020 8429 3453 — MD 1987 Israel; FRCS Glas. 1994.

RASOR, Mr Paul Andrew, Lt.-Col. RAMC Retd. Rectory Road Surgery, 7 Rectory Road, Rowhedge, Colchester CO5 7HP Tel: 01206 728585 Fax: 01206 729262; 14 Green Lane, Colchester CO4 4JA — MB BS 1975 Lond.; BSc Hull 1967; FRCS Ed. 1984; MRCS Eng. LRCP Lond. 1975. (Char. Cross) Socs: BMA; MRCS (Ed.); Colchester Primary Care Trust Developm. Sub Comm. Chairm. Prev: Sen. Specialist (Orthop.) Qu. Eliz. Milit. Hosp. Lond.; Ho. Surg. & Ho. Phys. Char. Cross Hosp. Lond.; Regtl. Med. Off. RAMC 2/2 Gurkha Rifles.

RASOUL, Mustafa Salim Laburnum Medical Group, 14 Laburnum Terrace, Ashington NE63 0XX Tel: 01670 813376 Fax: 01670 854346 — MB BS 1973 Newc.; BSc Newc. 1971.

RASSAM, Saad Munir Bashir Queen Mary's Hospital, Sidcup DA14 6LT Tel: 020 8308 3023 Fax: 020 8308 3153 Email: saad.rassam@qms-tr.sthames.nhs.uk — MB ChB 1980 Baghdad; FRCP Lond. 1997; MRCP (UK) 1989; MRCPath 1991; FRCPath 1999. (Baghdad) Cons. Haemat. & Oncol. Qu. Mary's Sidcup NHS Trust. Socs: Brit. Soc. Haematol.; Amer. Soc. of Haemat.; Amer. Soc. Of Clin. Oncol. Prev: Lect. & Hon. Sen. Regist. (Haemat. & Oncol.) Hosp. for Sick Childr. Gt. Ormond St. & Univ. Coll. Hosp. Lond.; Regist. (Haemat.) Edgware Gen. Hosp.

RASSAM, Salwan Munir Bashir Eye Department, Worthing Hospital, Lyndhurst Road, Worthing BN11 2DH Tel: 01903 205111 Ext: 4039 Email: sal.rassam@washtr.sthames.nhs.uk — MB BCh BAO 1985 NUI; MD NUI 1994; LRCPI & LM LRCSI & LM 1985; FRCOphth 1992, M 1990; DO RCS Eng. 1990. (Roy. Coll. of Surgeons in Irel.) Cons. Opthalmologist, Worthing Hosp, Worthing, W. Sussex.; Dir. of Research, Worthing Hosp. Socs: BMA; Research Vision & Ophth. Prev: Hon. Regist. Hammersmith Hosp. Lond.

RASSL, Doris Monika The Homestead, Grove, Retford DN22 0RJ — MB BS 1990 Lond.

RASTALL, Mark Peter Station Road Surgery, Station Road, Sowerby Bridge HX6 3AB Tel: 01422 831453; 95 Zetland Road, Town Moor, Doncaster DN2 5EH — MB ChB 1989 Sheff. Trainee GP/SHO (Paediat.) Doncaster VTS.

***RASTALL, Sarah Jane** 101 Upper Gungate, Tamworth B79 8AX — MB ChB 1996 Birm.; ChB Birm. 1996.

RASTOGI, Amit 17 The Moorlands, Sutton Coldfield B74 2RF — MB ChB 1994 Leic.

RASTOGI, Gulab Chand Paediatrics Department, Wycombe General Hospital, Queen Alexandra Road, High Wycombe HP11 2TT Tel: 01494 526161 Fax: 01494 425007; 8 Victoria Gardens, High Wycombe HP11 1SY Tel: 01494 444869 — MB BS 1974 Lucknow; MD (Paediat.) Lucknow 1978; DCH Lucknow 1976; MRCP (UK) 1987; FRCPCH 1997. (King George Medical College, Lucknow India) Cons. Paediat. Wycombe Gen. Hosp. Prev: Cons. Paediat. P.ss Roy. Hosp. NHS Trust Telford; Staff Grade (Paediat.) Ealing Hosp. Middlx.; Regist. (Paediat.) W. Middlx. Hosp.

RASTOGI, Navin Chandra Horsefair Practice, Horse Fair, Rugeley WS15 2EL Tel: 01889 582244 Fax: 01899 582244; 24 Elm Close, Bolsover, Chesterfield S44 6EA Tel: 01246 823283 — MB BS 1972 Calcutta; DA (UK) 1976.

RASTOGI, Robin 127 Longwood Gardens, Clayhall, Ilford IG5 0EG — MB BS 1998 Lond.; MB BS Lond 1998.

RASTOGI, S Kensington Medical Centre, 17 Fielding Street, Liverpool L6 9AP Tel: 0151 263 3085.

RASTOGI, Sudhir Chandra St. Ann's Hospital, Haven Road, Canford Cliffs, Poole BH13 7LN Tel: 01202 708881 Fax: 01202 707628; 8 Roslin Road S., Talbot Woods, Bournemouth BH3 7EF Tel: 01202 532924 — MB BS 1970 Kanpur; FRCPsych. 1992, M 1977; DPM Eng. 1978. (G.S.V.M. Med. Coll. Kanpur) Cons. Psychiat. E. Dorset HA. Prev: Sen. Regist. (Psychiat.) St. Ann's Hosp. Poole; Regist. (Psychiat.) Airedale Gen. Hosp. Steeton.

RASTOGI, Tej Krishan Gillmoss Medical Centre, 48 Petherick Road, Liverpool L11 0AG Tel: 0151 546 3867 — MB BS 1972 Lucknow.

RASTOMJEE, Cawas Dirk 33 Brockenhurst Close, Rainham, Gillingham ME8 0HD — MB BS 1996 Lond.

RASUL, Ameen Email: arasul@bradford-ha.nhs.uk — MB ChB 1989 Liverp.; DRCOG 1993. Gen. Practitioner.

RASUL, Shahid Rosevale, Hilton Rd, Alloa FK10 3SG — MB ChB 1997 Dundee.

RATAN, Dev Anand Leicestershire Mental Health Service, Bradgate Mental Health Unit, Leicester LE3 9EJ Tel: 0116 250 2661 — MB BS 1983 West Indies; MRCPsych 1993. Cons. Psychiat. (Adult & Gen. Psychiat.).

RATAN, Hari Lakshmi 34 Melrose Road, Upper Shirley, Southampton SO15 7PA — BM BS 1998 Nottm.; BM BS Nottm 1998.

RATANI, Tajbano Hassanali 156 Prestonfield, Milngavie, Glasgow G62 7QA — MB BS 1962 Karachi.

RATCHFORD, Andrew Habost Clinic, Habost, Ness, Isle of Lewis HS2 0TG Tel: 01851 810689 — MB ChB 1977 Ed.

RATCHFORD, Mr Andrew Martin 62 Bates Lane, Helsby, Warrington WA6 9LF — MB BS 1992 Newc.; FRCS Eng. 1996. (Newc.) Specialist Regist. (A & E) N.n. Deanery Rotat. Prev: SHO (A & E) Newc. Gen. Hosp.

RATCHFORD, Joseph Anthony (retired) 24 Brock Mill Lane, Wigan WN1 2NZ — MB ChB 1962 Liverp. Hon. Med. Off. Liverp. St. Helens Rugby Club; Mem. Guild of Catholic Doctors. Prev: Ho. Off. Ormskirk & Dist. Gen. Hosp.

RATCLIFF, Alison Jane 23 Wain Park, Plymouth PL7 2HX — MB BS 1993 Lond.

RATCLIFF, Arthur Jamieson Department of Anaesthetics, Perth Royal Infirmary, Perth PH1 1NX Tel: 01738 623311; Easter Hill, 16 Gannochy Road, Perth PH2 7EF — MB ChB 1981 Ed.; FRCA 1985. Cons. Anaesth. Perth Roy. Infirm. Prev: Sen. Regist. (Anaesth.) Manch. Roy. Infirm.; Clin. Fell. Roy. Vict. Hosp. Montreal; SHO (Anaesth.) Aberd. Infirm.

RATCLIFF, Raymond Alfred William (retired) 9 Inverleith Terrace, Edinburgh EH3 5NS — LRCP LRCS 1952 Ed.; FRCP Ed. 1979, M 1956; LRCP LRCS Ed. LRFPS Glas. 1952; FRCPsych 1979, M 1971; DPM Eng. 1960; Dip. Med. Servs. Admin. Ed. 1961. Prev: PMO Scott. Home & Health Dept.

RATCLIFFE, Andrew Brian 4 Old Church Close, Quarndon, Derby DE22 5JF — MB ChB 1997 Leic.

RATCLIFFE, Brendan Laurence 17 Welbeck Close, Middlewich CW10 9HX — MB ChB 1980 Manch.; BSc Manch. 1977, MB ChB 1980; MRCGP 1985; FFA RCS Eng. 1984. GP Knutsford. Prev: Clin. Asst. (Anaesth.) Warrington Dist. Gen. Hosp.; Regist./Tutor (Anaesth.) Aberd. Hosp.; SHO (Anaesth.) Manch. Roy. Infirm.

RATCLIFFE, Charles George Old Peppard Farm House, Church Lane, Rotherfield Peppard, Henley-on-Thames RG9 5JU Tel: 01491 628698 Fax: 01491 628094 — MB ChB 1984 Sheff.; MSc (Solid State Physics) Manch. 1973, BSc (Electronics) 1972.

RATCLIFFE, Christopher Alan Churchtown Medical Centre, 137 Cambridge Road, Southport PR9 7LT — MB ChB 1978 Manch.

RATCLIFFE, David Malcolm Fort House Surgery, 32 Hersham Road, Walton-on-Thames KT12 1JX Tel: 01932 253055 Fax: 01932 225910; Stretton House, 63 Winchester Road, Walton-on-Thames KT12 2RH — MB BS 1980 Lond.; MRCP Lond. 1984; MRCGP 1988; DRCOG 1987; BSc 1997. (Charing Cross) Prev: Chas. Wolfson Research Fell. City of Lond. Migraine Clinic; Regist. (Nephrol.) John Ratcliffe Hosp. Oxf.

RATCLIFFE, David Stephen Chorlton Health Centre, 1 Nicolas Road, Chorlton, Manchester M21 9NJ Tel: 0161 860 4545 Fax: 0161 860 4565; 25 Westfield Road, Chorlton, Manchester

RATCLIFFE

M21 0SW — MB ChB 1992 Manch.; MRCGP 1997; DCH 1994. (Manchester) GP; Clin. Asst. A & E.

RATCLIFFE, Francis Hubert 3 Woodsleigh Coppice, Bolton BL1 5XR — MB ChB 1960 Manch.; DObst RCOG 1962. (Manch.) Socs: Bolton Med. Soc. Prev: SHO Crumpsall Hosp. Manch.; Ho. Phys. & Ho. Surg. Ancoats Hosp. Manch.

RATCLIFFE, Guy Edmund, Brigadier late RAMC The Medical Council on Alocohol, 3 St Andrew's Place, London NW1 4LB Tel: 0207 487 4445 Fax: 0207 935 4479 Email: mca@medicouncilalcol.demon.co.uk; Tel: 01985 840405 Email: guyratcliffe@compuserve.com — MB BS Lond. 1966; MSc (Nuclear Med.) Lond. 1990; FRCP Lond. 1993; MRCP (UK) 1988; MRCPI 1980; MRCS Eng. LRCP Lond. 1966. (Guy's) p/t Exec. Direc. The Med. Counc. on Alcoholism.; Represen. Col. Commandant RAMC; HQ Army Med. Serv.s, Slim Rd., Camberley, Surrey GU15 4NP. Socs: BAMM; Med. Counc. on Alcohol. Prev: Commanding Off. Qu. Eliz. Milit. Hosp.; Cons. Phys. & Clin. Tutor Qu. Eliz. Milit. Hosp.; Sen. Med. Off. & Cons. Phys. BMH Dharan., Nepal.

RATCLIFFE, Helen Diane 13 Bonnytoun Avenue, Linlithgow EH49 7JR — MB ChB 1997 Aberd.

RATCLIFFE, Jane Margaret Royal Liverpool Children's NHS Trust, Alder Hey, Eaton Road, Liverpool L12 2AP Tel: 0151 228 4811 Fax: 0151 252 5771 Email: jane.ratcliffe@rlch-tr.nwest.nhs.uk — MB ChB 1977 Manch.; FRCP Lond. 1995, M Glas. 1980; FRCPCH 1997. Cons. Paediat. (Intens. Care) Roy. Liverp. Childr. Hosp. Socs: Roy. Coll. Paediat. & Child Health; Paediat. Intens. Care Soc. Prev: Sen. Regist. (Paediat.) The Hosp. for Sick Childr. Lond.; ICU Fell. Hosp. Sick Childr. Toronto, Canada; Brit. Heart Foundat. Research Fell.

RATCLIFFE, Professor John Graham Carreg Pen-Las, Dinas, Newport SA42 0SD Tel: 01348 811568 Fax: 01348 811568 Email: jgratcliffe@aol.com — BM BCh 1963 Oxf.; MSc Lond. 1968; DM Oxf. 1972; FRCP Glas. 1982, M 1979; FRCPath 1985, M 1975. Emerit. Prof. Clin. Chem. Univ. Birm. Med. Sch.; Hon. Sen. Research Fell. Univ. Birm. Med. Sch. Socs: Internat. Fed. of Clin. Chem. (IFCC) (V. Chair., Scientif. Div.). Prev: Prof. Chem. Pathol. Univ. Manch. Med. Sch.; Cons. Clin. Biochem. & Hon. Lect. Glas. Roy. Infirm.; Lect. (Chem. Path.) St. Bart. Hosp. Lond.

RATCLIFFE, Joy York House, Manchester Royal Infirmary, Oxford Road, Manchester M13 9WL Tel: 0161 276 5317 — MB ChB 1988 Manch.; MRCPsych 1993; MSc 1996. (Manchester)

RATCLIFFE, Marcia Alexandra Ward 16, Aberdeen Royal Infirmary, Aberdeen — MB BS 1975 Newc.; FRCP 1999 UK; MD Newc. 1993; MRCP (UK) 1980.

RATCLIFFE, Mary Jean Rhoslan Surgery, 4 Pwllycrochan Avenue, Colwyn Bay LL29 7DA — MB ChB 1983 Manch.; DCH RCP 1987; DRCOG 1986.

RATCLIFFE, Mary Jennine Helen 148 Hammersmith Grove, London W6 7HE — MB BS 1994 Lond.

RATCLIFFE, Norman Arthur 7 Onslow Way, Pyrford, Woking GU22 8QX Tel: 0193 23 42832 — MB 1970 Camb.; BChir 1969; MRCPath 1976. (Univ. Coll. Hosp.) Cons. Path. St. Peter's Hosp. Chertsey. Prev: Lect. Dept. Histopath. St. Geo. Hosp. Lond.

RATCLIFFE, Mr Peter John Hucks Farmhouse, Willow Road, Martley, Worcester WR6 6PS — MB BS 1981 Lond.; FRCS Eng. 1986.

RATCLIFFE, Peter John Institute of Molecular Medicine, John Radcliffe Hospital, Oxford OX3 9DU Tel: 01865 222382 Fax: 01865 222500; Sumner House, 108 Mill St, Kidlington, Oxford OX2 0 — MD 1986 Camb.; MB 1979, BChir 1978; MRCP (UK) 1980. Prof. Renal Med. & Hon. Cons. Phys. Inst. Molecular Med. John Radcliffe Hosp. Oxf. Prev: Wellcome Sen. Fell. (Clin. Sci.) Nuffield Dept. Med. John Radcliffe Hosp. Oxf.

RATCLIFFE, Peter Wilfred 74 Thurleigh Road, London SW12 8UD Tel: 020 8675 3128 — MSc Lond. 1980; MB BS Sydney 1962; DMRD Eng. 1966. Med. Adviser Dept. Social Security Lond. Socs: Soc. Occupat. Med.; Roy. Coll. Radiol.; Assoc. Mem. Austral. Fac. Occupat. Med.

RATCLIFFE, Rosalind Margaret Hall 102 Onslow Gardens, Wallington SM6 9QG Tel: 020 8647 5997 — MB BS 1964 Lond.; LMSSA Lond. 1964; FFA RCS Eng. 1973; DA Eng. 1966. (St. Bart.) Cons. Anaesth. E. Surrey Health Dist. Prev: Sen. Regist. (Anaesth.) Char. Cross. Hosp. Lond.; Regist. (Anaesth.) E.man Dent. Hosp.; Regist. (Anaesth.) St. Helier Hosp. Carshalton.

RATCLIFFE, Shirley Geraldine (retired) Medical Unit, Institute of Child Health, 30 Guilford St., London WC1N 1EH Tel: 020 7242 9789 Fax: 020 7831 1481 — MB BS 1956 Lond.; FRCP Ed. 1977, M 1960; MRCS Eng. LRCP Lond. 1956; DCH Eng. 1958. Mem. Scientif. Staff & Hon. Cons. Paediat. MRC Human Genetics Unit W.. Gen. Hosp. Edin.; Hon. Sen. Lect. Inst. Child Health Lond. Prev: Lect. (Child Life & Health) Univ. Edin.

RATCLIFFE, Stuart Harry Richard Commonwood Farm, Holt, Wrexham LL13 9TA Tel: 01829 270824; Grünenthal Gmbh, Stolberg, 2 Steinfeldstrass, Rheinland D-5190, Germany Tel: 012402 103264 — MB ChB 1985 Manch. Pharm. Phys. (Internat. Med. Dept.).

RATCLIFFE, Victoria Ann 38 Hedingham Way, Mickleover, Derby DE3 5NX — BChir 1996 Camb.

RATE, Mr Anthony John 10 Churchston Avenue, Bramhall, Stockport SK7 3DA Tel: 0161 440 8062 — MB ChB 1987 Manch.; FRCS Eng. 1991; MD Manchester 1995 (Gold Medal); FRCS (Gen Surg.)1998. Cons. Gen Surg, The Roy. Odham Hosp. Socs: Assoc of Coloproculogists, GB & Ire. Prev: Specialist Regist. Hope Hosp. Salford, The Christie Hosp.

RATH, Sucheta 5 Frankton Avenue, Haywards Heath RH16 3QX Tel: 01444 459390; Ashoak Nivans, 106 Folders Lane, Burgess Hill RH15 0DX Tel: 01444 230504 Fax: 01444 230504 — MB BS 1972 Berhampur; MB BS Berhampur, India 1972. Clin. Asst. (Psychiat. & Subst. Misuse) S. Downs Health NHS Trust Brighton.

RATHAKRISHNAN, Rahul 24 Malcolm Drive, Surbiton KT6 6QS — BM 1998 Soton.; BM Soton 1998.

RATHBONE, Anthony Reynolds Shropshire Health Authority, William Farr House, Mytton Oak Road, Shrewsbury SY3 8XL Tel: 01743 261300 Fax: 01743 261303; 8 Station Road, Madeley, Telford TF7 5BA Tel: 01952 586103 — MB BS 1976 Lond.; BA Oxf. 1968; MRCGP 1980; DRCOG 1989. (Middlx.) Med. Adviser (Primary Care) Shrops. HA. Prev: GP Telford.

RATHBONE, Barrie John Leicester Royal Infirmary, Infirmary Square, Leicester LE1 5WW Tel: 0116 254 1414 Fax: 0116 258 6985; Claremont House, 20 Nether Hall Lane, Leicester LE4 4DT Email: bjrathbone@aol.com — MB BS 1978 Lond.; MD Lond. 1990; FRCP Lond. 1993; MRCP (UK) 1983. Cons. Phys. & Gastroenterol. Leicester Roy. Infirm. Socs: Brit. Soc. Gastroenterol. Prev: Sen. Regist. Leeds.

RATHBONE, Elizabeth Ironbridge Medical Practice, Trinity Hall, Dale Road, Coalbrookdale, Telford TF8 7DT Tel: 01952 432568; 8 Station Road, Madeley, Telford TF7 5BA — MB BS 1976 Lond.; MRCGP 1980.

RATHBONE, Gillian Valerie The Leicestershire Hospice, Groby Road, Leicester LE3 9QE Tel: 0116 231 3771 Fax: 0116 232 0312; Claremont House, 20 Nether Hall Lane, Birstall, Leicester LE4 4DT Email: bjrathbone@aol.com — MB BS Lond. 1979; MRCGP 1983; DRCOG 1984; Cert. FPA 1985. Cons. Phys. (Palliat. Med.) Leics. Hospice. Prev: Med. Dir. Sye Ryder Hospice Staunton.

RATHBONE, Nia 39 North Street, Sandycroft, Deeside CH5 2PP — MB BCh 1996 Wales.

RATHBONE, Philip Sean The Welby Practice, The Woll Surgery, Walford Close, Bottesford, Nottingham NG13 0AY; Ash Gables, 16 Scalford Road, Eastwell, Melton Mowbray LE14 4EJ — MB ChB 1991 Sheff.; BMedSci Sheff. 1989; MRCGP 1996'. (Sheff.)

RATHBONE, Richard George Elm Lodge Surgery, 2 Burbage Road, London SE24 9HJ Tel: 020 7274 6138 Fax: 020 7924 0710; 31 Hitherwood Drive, London SE19 1XA Tel: 020 8670 5806 — MB BS Lond. 1961; MRCS Eng. LRCP Lond. 1961; MRCGP 1975; DObst RCOG 1963. (King's Coll. Hosp.) Partially Retd. Prev: Med. Off. Baptist Miss. Soc.

RATHBORNE, Andrew Charles Springfield Surgery, Springfield Way, Brackley NN13 6JJ Tel: 01280 703431 Fax: 01280 703241 — MB BS 1993 Lond.; MRCGP 1997; DCH RCP Lond. 1996; DRCOG 1995. (Roy. Free Hosp. Sch. Med.) GP Princip. Springfield Surg.

RATHE, Mark Penketh Health Centre, Honiton Way, Penketh, Warrington WA5 2EY Tel: 01925 725644 Fax: 01925 791017; 3 Rawcliffe Close, Balmoral Park, Widnes WA8 9FZ — MB ChB 1984 Liverp.; DRCOG 1987; Dip. Occ. Med. 1996.

RATHER, Mr Ghualam Mohammed 19 Wordsworth Avenue, London E18 2HD — MB BS 1972 Jammu & Kashmir; FRCS Ed. 1983; FRCS Glas. 1981.

RATHI, Ashok Kumar The Surgery, 5 Rupert Street, Biddulph, Stoke-on-Trent ST8 6EB Tel: 01782 514674 Fax: 01782 523044 — MB BS 1974 Jiwaji; MB BS 1974 Jiwaji.

RATHI, Rajendra Kumar Atkinson Health Centre, Market Street, Barrow-in-Furness LA14 2LR Tel: 01229 821030 Fax: 01229 827171 — MB BS 1972 Indore. (Indore) GP Barrow-in-Furness, Cumbria.

RATHMELL, Adrian John South Cleveland Hospital, Marton Road, Middlesbrough TS4 3BW Tel: 01642 850850 Fax: 01642 824877 — MB ChB 1981 Leeds; MRCP (UK) 1984; FRCR 1989. Cons. Radiother. & Oncol. S. Cleveland Hosp. Middlesbrough.

RATHNAVARMA, Mr Chintalapati Venkata Rama c/o Drive L. Chandrasekaran, 6 Ashenden Road, Guildford GU2 7UU — MB BS 1985 Poona; FRCS Glas. 1990.

RATHOD, Bhupendra Kumar Older Persons CMHT, Plank Lane, Leigh WN7 4QE — MB BS 1966 Jabalpur; BSc Jabalpur 1960, MB BS 1966; FRCPsych 1992, M 1975; DPM Eng. 1972. (Govt. Med. Coll.) Cons. Psychiat. Leigh Infirm.

RATHOD, Nehkant Hamermall (retired) Corsletts Farm, Broadbridge Heath, Horsham RH12 3LD Tel: 01403 60176 — MB BS 1948 Bombay; FRCP Lond. 1978, M 1963; FRCPsych 1973, M 1971; DPM Lond. 1956. Cons. Psychiat. Cuckfield & Crawley Health Dist. Prev: Cons. to WHO.

RATHOD, Ramniklal Chimanlal 18 Quarry Park Road, Cheam, Sutton SM1 2DN — MB BS 1970 Gujarat.

RATHOD, Shanaya — MBBS 1992; 2000 Cert. in Health Servs. Managem., Inst. Of Health Care Managem.; MRCPsych 1998 Lond. (Mahatma Ghandi Inst. of Med. Sci., India) Specialist Regist. Psychiat., Moorgreen Hosp. Soton. Socs: Roy. Coll. Psychiat.s. Prev: SpR. Psychiat., Pk.lands Hosp, Basingstoke; Lect./SpR, Roy. S. Hants Hosp., Soton.; SpR., Seymore Clinic, Swindon.

RATHOD, Sunil Lal Bramblys Grange Health Centre, Bramblys Drive, Basingstoke RG21 8UW Tel: 01256 467778 Fax: 01256 814190 — MB BS 1988 Saurashtra.

RATHORE, Mr Chandra Kishore 6A Elm Park Road, London N3 1EB — MB BS 1961 Agra; MS Agra 1964, MB BS 1961; FRCS Ed. 1970; FICS 1971. (S.N. Med. Coll.)

RATHORE, Jaswant Singh 2 Ploughmans Walk, Heathbrook Farm, Wall Heath, Kingswinford DY6 0DX — MB ChB 1980 Manch.; MRCGP (Distinc.) 1985; DRCOG 1983.

RATHWELL, Claire Alison 13 Campion Close, Croydon CR0 5SN — MB BS 1992 Lond.

RATI, Naresh The Laurie Pike Health Centre, 95 Birchfield Road, Handsworth, Birmingham B19 1LH Tel: 0121 554 0621 Fax: 0121 554 6163 — MB ChB 1993 Manch. GP Regist. The Dow Surg. William St. Redditch.

***RATIB, Karim** 56 Clarence Road, Kings Heath, Birmingham B13 9UH — MB ChB 1996 Birm.; ChB Birm. 1996.

RATIP, Siret 34 Sutherland Avenue, London W9 2HQ — MB BS 1987 Lond.

RATLIFF, Mr Anthony Hugh Cyril (retired) 2 Clifton Park, Bristol BS8 3BS Tel: 0117 973 4500 Fax: 0117 973 0887 — MB ChB 1945 Manch.; MB ChB (Distinc. Surg.) Manch. 1945; ChM Bristol 1968; FCPSP (Hon.) 1991; FRCS Eng. 1951; MRCS Eng. LRCP Lond. 1945. Special Lect. (Orthop. Surg.) Univ. Bristol. Prev: Cons. Orthop. Surg. Avon HA.

RATLIFF, Mr David Anthony Northampton General Hospital NHS Trust, Cliftonville, Northampton NN1 5BD Tel: 01604 634700 Fax: 01604 544312 Email: davidratcliff@ngh-tr.anglox.nhs.uk; 15 Mears Ashby Road, Earls Barton, Northampton NN6 0HQ Tel: 01604 812731 Fax: 01604 812731 — MB ChB 1977 Birm.; FRCP 2001; MD Birm. 1985; FRCS Eng. 1982; FRCS Ed. 1982; MRCP (UK) 1980. Cons. Surg. (Gen. & Vasc. Surg.) N.ampton Gen. Hosp. NHS Trust. Socs: Vasc. Surg. Soc.; Assn. Surg.; Brit. Assn. Endocrine Surgs. Prev: Sen. Lect. & Hon. Cons. Surg. Leicester Roy. Infirm. & Univ. Leicester; Clin. Fell. (Vasc. Surg.) Univ. Brit. Columbia, Vancouver, Canada; Sen. Regist. (Gen. Surg.) W. Midl. RHA.

RATNAIKE, Mr Nimal Dushyantha Anthony Commonfield Road Surgery, 156 Commonfield Road, Woodchurch, Birkenhead CH49 7LP Tel: 0151 677 0016 — MB BS 1988 Lond.; FRCS Eng. 1993; DFFP 1995; DRCOG 1995. (St. Mary's) Prev: GP/Regist. Rugby VTS; SHO (O & G) Hosp. of St Cross Rugby.; SHO (Surg.) Medway Hosp. Gillingham.

RATNAKUMAR, Mr Kandiah 5 Abbotswood Gardens, Ilford IG5 0BG — MB BS 1976 Sri Lanka; MRCS Eng. LRCP Lond. 1984; FRCS RCPS Glas. 1987.

RATNAKUMAR, Sarojinidevi 5 Abbotswood Gardens, Ilford IG5 0BG — MB BS 1976 Sri Lanka.

RATNALINGAM, Rishya Anand Doctors Accommodation, St James University Hospital, Leeds LS9 7TF — MB ChB 1997 Leeds.

RATNAM, Dharshini Sumitha John Howard Centre, 2 Crozier Terrace, Hackney, London E9 6AT Tel: 020 8919 8084 — MB BS 1992 Lond.; MRCPsych 1996. (St Bartholomews Medical School) Specialist Regist. (Forens. Psychiat.), John Howard Centre.

RATNARAJAH, Christine Rukma 1 Tarragon Way, Shoreham-by-Sea BN43 6JG — MB BS 1974 Sri Lanka.

RATNARAJAH, Karunadevy 7 Elmer Close, Enfield EN2 7EZ Tel: 020 8364 4566 Fax: 020 8364 4566 — MB BS 1980 Peradeniya; MRCS Eng. LRCP Lond. 1988; DA (UK) 1986. Clin. Asst., (A&E), Dept. (p/t); GP. Prev: SHO (O & G), Pediatrics, Psychiat.

RATNARAJAH, Mark Rauindran 128 Osward Road, Courtwood Lane, Croydon CR0 9HD — BM BCh 1996 Oxf.

RATNARAJAN, Nadarajan Woodlands Surgery, Woodlands Walk, Off Trafalgar Road, London SE10 9UB Tel: 020 8858 0689 Fax: 020 8293 9615 — MB BS 1975 Sri Lanka; MRCS Eng LRCP Lond 1986.

RATNARAJAN, Subathira Thevy Woodlands Surgery, Woodlands Walk, Off Trafalgar Road, London SE10 9UB Tel: 020 8858 0689 Fax: 020 8293 9615 — MB BS 1975 Sri Lanka; MRCS Eng LRCP Lond 1985.

RATNASABAPATHY, Lawrence 22 Elmcroft Avenue, London NW11 0RR Tel: 020 8449 5707 Fax: 020 8732 4617 Email: ratna@msn.com — MB BS 1966 Ceylon; MRCPsych 1972; DPM Eng. 1970. (Ceylon) Cons. Psychiat. Barnet Gen. Hosp. & Napsbury Hosp. St. Albans; Hon. Cons. Lond. Hosp.; Clin. Tutor Univ. Lond.; Lead Clin. Barnet Healthcare Trust.

RATNASABAPATHY, Urmila 8 Simpson Street, Crosshouse, Kilmarnock KA2 0BD — MB BCh BAO 1993 Belf.

RATNASINGAM, Latha 178 Queens Road, London SW19 8LX — MB BCh BAO 1993 NUI.

RATNASINGHAM, Priyan 3 Beech Grove, Cliffsend, Ramsgate CT12 5LD — MB BS 1998 Lond.; MB BS Lond 1998.

RATNASINGHE, Damitha Deshapriya 22 Leyburn Gardens, East Croydon, Croydon CR0 5NL — MB BS 1988 Ibadan, Nigeria; MRCP (UK) 1993.

RATNATUNGA, Mr Chandana Premukh Oxford Heart Centre, John Radcliffe Hospital, Headley Way, Oxford OX3 9DU Tel: 01865 220442 Fax: 01865 220244 Email: alison.homer@orh.nhs.uk; 27 Lansdowne Road, London W11 3AG Tel: 020 7229 5065 — MB BS 1980 Lond.; BSc Lond 1977; MS Lond. 1991; FRCS (Cth) 1994; FRCS Eng. 1986; FRCS Ed. 1984. (St Bartholomew's Hospital London) Cons. Cardiothoracic Surg. John Radcliffe Hosp. Oxf.

RATNAVAL, Nandiran 20 Addison House, Grove End Road, London NW8 9EH — MB BS 1995 Lond.

RATNAVEL, Chenji Dakshinamurthi Flat 3, 29 New Walk, Beverley HU17 7DR — MB BS 1982 Madras; LMSSA Lond. 1989.

RATNAVEL, Kathir Khanta 3 Molly Road, Jonesborough, Newry BT35 8HY — MRCS Eng. LRCP Lond. 1970; MA, MD Sri Lanka 1988; FFA RCSI 1975; DA Eng. 1973. (Oxf.) Cons. Anaesth. Our Lady's Hosp. Navan Eire. Socs: Fell. Roy. Soc. Med.; Brit. Med. Acupunct. Soc.; Assn. Anaesth. Prev: Cons. Anaesth. Co. Hosp. Wexford Eire & St. Catherine's Co. Hosp. Tralee Eire; Regist. St. Bart. Hosp. Lond.

RATNAVEL, Rathini St. Philips Health Service, London School of Economics & Political Science, Sheffield St., London WC2 2AE Tel: 020 7955 7016 Fax: 020 7955 6818 Email: rratanvel@lse.ac.uk; Tel: 020 7503 5265 — MB BS 1989 Lond.; DFFP 1993; MRCGP 1993; DRCOG 1992; BA 1986 Oxf.; BA Oxf. 1986; MRCGP 1993; DFFP 1993; DRCOG 1992. (UCL Hosps. Med. Sch.) Gen. Practitioner, St. Philips Med. Centre. Prev: Partner, Taylor Pract. Hornsey Rise 1994-1996; Trainee GP Edgware VTS.

RATNAVEL, Ravi Chandran Stoke Mandeville NHS Trust, Mandeville Road, Aylesbury HP21 8AL Tel: 01296 315551 Fax: 01296 315296 Email: ratnavel@talk21.com; Downhurst, Manor Drive, Chesham Bois, Amersham HP6 5NH Tel: 01494 725905 Email: ratnavel@epulse.net — MB BS 1988 Lond.; BA 1985; DM Oxf. 1997; MRCP (UK) 1991. Cons. Dermatol. Stoke Mandeville NHS Trust & S. Bucks NHS Trust; Hon. Cons. (Dermat.) Ch.ill Hosp.

RATNAVEL

Oxf. Socs: FRSM; Soc. Worshipful Apoth.; Brit. Assn. of Dermatol. Prev: Sen. Regist. St. John's Inst. of Dermat. Lond.; Hon. Sen. Regist. & MRC Train. Fell. Roy. Lond. Hosp. Med. Coll.; Regist. (Dermat.) Addenbrooke's Hosp. Camb.

RATNAVEL, Saravanamuttu (retired) 47 Grove Court, Grove End Road, London NW8 9EP — MB BS Ceylon 1957; FFA RCS Eng. 1967; DA Eng. 1963. Prev: Cons. Anaesth. Rotherham & MexBoro. Gp. Hosps.

RATNAVEL, Thambipillai Upton Road Surgery, 30 Upton Road, Watford WD18 0JS Tel: 01923 226266 Fax: 01923 222324; 20 Langley Way, Watford WD17 3EQ Tel: 01923 225850 — MB BS 1961 Ceylon; DIH Eng. 1970; DIH Soc. Apoth. Lond. 1970. (Ceylon)

RATNAYAKA, Bethmage Dona Malkanthi Childrens Hospital, Uttoxeter Road, Derby DE22 3NE Email: mratnayaka@yahoo.com; 34 Tawny Way, Littleover, Derby DE23 7XG Tel: 01332 510502 — MB BS 1986 Colombo; MMed Sc 1999 (Keele Univ.); MRCP (UK) 1994. Specialist Regist. (Paediat.) Childr.s Hosp. Derby. Socs: Roy. Coll. of Paediat.s.

RATNAYAKE, Bernadette Chandrika Nilmini RTR Healthcare NHS Trust, Queen Marys University Hospital, Roehampton Lane, London SW15 5PN — MB BS 1985 Sri Lanka; FRCA 1992.

RATNAYAKE, Ivan Bertram Maxwell 10 Collingwood Road, Sutton SM1 2RZ Tel: 020 8643 6753 Email: ibmraatnayake@doctors.net.uk — MB BS 1993 Lond.; FRCS Lond. 1999. (Charing Cross and Westminster) Socs: BMA; MPS.

RATNESWARAN, Mrs Dhiyaki Highfield Surgery, Jupiter Drive, Hemel Hempstead HP2 5NU; 10 Filmer Road, Leagrave, Luton LU4 9BX — MB BS 1978 Andra; BA Madras 1970; Cert. Family Plann. JCC 1990; DObst. RCPI 1988. Socs: Med. Protec. Soc. Prev: SHO (Psychiat.) Luton Hosp.; Trainee GP Hemel Hempstead; SHO (Paediat.) W. Herts. Hosp. Hemel Hempstead.

RATNESWAREN, Nageswary 32 Albyfield, Bickley, Bromley BR1 2HZ Tel: 020 8467 8453 — MB BS 1981 Colombo; MRCS Eng. LRCP Lond. 1986; DCH RCP Lond. 1989; DRCOG 1988. SHO (Paediat. Med.) Edgware Gen. Hosp. Middlx. Prev: SHO (O & G) Edgware Gen. Hosp.; SHO (Geriat./Gen. Med.) Bedford Gen. Hosp.

RATNESWAREN, Suppiah The Surgery, 145 White Horse Hill, Chislehurst BR7 6DH Tel: 020 8857 4546 Fax: 020 8857 7778; 32 Albyfield, Bickley, Bromley BR1 2HZ Tel: 020 8295 1982 — MRCS Eng. LRCP Lond. 1978. Socs: MRCGP; MRCP (UK). Prev: Regist. (Cardiol. & Chest Med.) Watford Gen. Hosp.; Regist. (Med., Diabetes, Endocrin., Gastroenterol. & Chest Med.) Roy. Infirm. Stirling.

RATOFF, Jonathan Charles 1 Brick Kiln Lane, Rufford, Ormskirk L40 1SY — MB BS 1994 Lond.

RATON LUNN, Sara Maria 26 Holywell Close, Bury St Edmunds IP33 2LS — LMS 1992 U Complutense Madrid.

RATRA, Surjan Singh Wolverhampton Health Care NHS Trust, Red Hill Street Clinic, Red Hill St., Wolverhampton WV1 1NR Tel: 01902 444325; White House, 559 Birmingham Road, Marlbrook, Bromsgrove B61 0HY Tel: 0121 445 1165 Fax: 0121 447 8363 — MB BS 1969; MB BS Agra 1969; BSc Agra 1963; DPM Eng. 1979; Cert. Community Paediat. Warwick 1981. (S.N. Med. Coll.) SCMO Wolverhampton HA; Sen. Med. Off. HMP Redditch. Socs: MRCPCH; Fac. Comm. Health & Med.

RATSEY, David Hugh Kerr 2 Harley Street, London W1N 1AA Tel: 020 7589 2776 Fax: 020 7323 5743; 204 Raleigh House, Dolphin Square, London SW1V 3NP Tel: 020 7798 8800 — MB BS 1967 Lond.; FFHom 1992, M 1980. (St. Bart.) Homoeop. Phys. Lond.; Cons. Homoeop. Phys. Kent & Sussex Weald NHS Trust. Socs: BMA; Fell. Med. Soc. of Lond. Prev: Clin. Asst. Roy. Lond. Homoeop. Hosp.

RATTAN, Dapinder Singh Allum Medical Centre, Fairlop Road, Leytonstone, London E11 1BN Tel: 020 8539 2513 Fax: 020 8558 0525 — MRCS Eng. LRCP Lond. 1989.

RATTI, Bandna Moona 23 St Marks Road, Maidenhead SL6 6DG — MB ChB 1993 Liverp.

RATTI, Naveen 2 Siskin Green, Liverpool L25 4RY — MB ChB 1990 Liverp.

RATTIGAN, Siobhan Mary Ophthalmology Department, Unversity Hospital Wales, Heath Park, Cardiff CF4 4XW; 4 Great Burnet Close, St Mellons, Cardiff CF3 0RJ — MB BCh BAO 1989 NUI.

RATTNER, Gil Jonathan c/o Thorpe Health Centre, St. Williams Way, Thorpe St Andrew, Norwich NR7 0AJ Tel: 01603 701010 Fax: 01603 701942 — MB ChB 1987 Glas.; BSc (Hons.) St. And. 1983.

RATZER, Maria Alexandra (retired) Flat 3, 71 Terregles Crescent, Glasgow G41 4RL — MD 1961 Glas.; MB ChB 1953. Prev: Cons. Dermat. & Hon. Clin. Lect. (Dermat.) W.. Infirm. & Assoc.

RAU, Donald (retired) 29 Downside Crescent, London NW3 2AN Tel: 020 7794 3636 Fax: 01793 750800 — MB BS Lond. 1960.

RAU, Udipi Badri Narayana Trent Meadows Medical Centre, 87 Wood Street, Burton-on-Trent DE14 3AA Tel: 01283 845555 Fax: 01283 845222; Anand, Craythorne Road, Stretton, Burton-on-Trent DE13 0AZ Tel: 01283 564168 — MB BS Madras 1966; DLO Eng. 1973; DLO Madras 1968. (Madras Med. Coll.) GP Burton-on-Trent. Prev: Clin. Asst. (ENT) Dist. Hosp. Burton on Trent & Roy. Infirm. Derby.

RAUBITSCHEK, Eugene The Surgery, 103 Main Street, Addingham, Ilkley LS29 0PD Tel: 01943 830367 Fax: 01943 831287 — MB ChB Manch. 1965; DMRT Eng. 1969. (Manch.) Clin. Asst., Gastroenterol., Chemother. Socs: Roy. Soc. Med.

RAUCHENBERG, Peter Michael The Caludon Centre, Walsgrave General Hospital, Clifford Bridge Road, Coventry CV2 2TE Tel: 024 76 602266 Fax: 024 76 538920 — MRCS Eng. LRCP Lond. 1971; MRCPsych 1975. (Prague & Oxf.) Cons. Psychiat. The Caludon Centre Coventry. Prev: Cons. Psychiat. Highcroft Hosp. Birm.; Sen. Regist. (Psychiat.) Birm. AHA; Hon. Clin. Lect. (Psychiat.) Birm. Univ.

RAUDNITZ, Leslie Camill Bradley The Chestnuts, Green End Road, Boxmoor, Hemel Hempstead HP1 1 — MB BS 1970 Lond.; MA Camb. 1964; MRCS Eng. LRCP Lond. 1966.

RAUF, Mr Abdul Ophthalmology Department, Queens Hospital, Belvedere Road, Burton-on-Trent DE13 0RB Tel: 01283 566333 ext 5260 Fax: 01283 593014 Email: arauf@doctors.org.uk; Garden Cottage, Newton Road, Burton-on-Trent DE15 0TF — MB BS 1983 Lond.; FRCS Glas. 1990; FRCOphth 1990. (Roy. Free Hosp. Sch. Med.) Cons. Ophth., Qu.'s Hosp., Burton-Upon-Trent; Cons. Opthalmologist at both : E. Midl.s Nuffield Hosp., Derby; BUPA Hopsital, Sutton Coldfield. Socs: Brit. Med. assoc.; Roy. Coll. Ophth. Prev: Fell. in Strabismus, Moorfields Eye Hosp.; Fell. in Med. Retina, Moorfields Eye Hosp.; Specialist Regist. Moorfields Eye Hosp.

RAUF, Abdul Healey Surgery, Whitworth Road, Rochdale OL12 0SN — MB BS 1964 Sind.

RAUF, Mr Khawaja Gulraiz Lenham, Maybury Hill, Woking GU22 8AL — MB BS 1982 Punjab; FRCS Eng. 1988.

RAUH, Peter Braxton Chinthurst Lodge, Wonersh, Guildford GU5 0PH Tel: 01483 458317 — MB BS 1992 Lond.; MSc Biochem. Endocrinol. Sussex 1986; FRCS Lond. 1996. (St Georges) Specialist Regist. (Orthop.) S.W. Thames. Socs: Soc. for the Relief of Widows and Orphans of Med. Men.

RAULT, John Peter Richard 32 Balfour Road, Bromley BR2 9SL — MB BS 1986 Lond.; MRCGP 1991; Cert. Family Plann. JCC 1990.

RAUNIAR, Arun Kumar 19 Leicester Close, Ipswich IP2 9EX — MB BS 1978 Calcutta.

RAURELL ROSIQUE, Anna c/o Fitzroy College, Northdown House, Margate CT9 3TP — LMS 1988 U Autonoma Barcelona.

RAUT, Rajeev 10 Allderidge Avenue, Hull HU5 4EQ — MB ChB 1989 Dundee.

RAUT, Suresh Laxman 21 Colebourne Road, Birmingham B13 0EZ Tel: 0121 65746 — MB BS 1979 Bombay; PhD Lond. 1971; MSc Bombay 1966, BSc (Hons.) 1963, MB BS 1979; LMSSA 1982.

RAUT, Mr Videshnandan Vijayanand Centre for Hip Surgery, Wrightington Hospital, Hall Lane, Appley Bridge, Wigan WN6 9EP Tel: 01257 256304; Foxgloves, Wood Lane, Parbold, Wigan WN8 7TH — MB BS 1980 Bombay; MS (Orthop.) Bombay 1984; DNBOrth. New Delhi 1985; MChOrth. Liverp. 1992; FRCS (Orth.) Ed. 1996. Cons. Orthop. Surg. Wrightington Hosp. & Chorley Hosp. Lancs. Socs: Brit. Hip Soc. Prev: Sen. Orthop. Regist. Birm. Rotat.; Sen. Surg. Fell. (Revision Surg.) Wrightington Hosp.

RAUT, Mr Vivek Vijayanand 12 Calnewood Road, Luton LU4 0ET — MB BS 1986 Bombay; FRCSI 1996.

RAUTRAY, Ramesh Chandra Primrose Bank Medical Centre, Larkhill, Blackburn BB1 5ER Tel: 01254 672132 Fax: 01254 699189; Utkalika, Park Crescent, Blackburn BB2 6DQ Tel: 01254 672132 Fax: 01254 672132 — MB BS 1970 Utkal; Hon. Fell. Internat. Coll. Angiol. 1977; MD Patna 1971; DRCOG 1993; DFFP

1993; Dip. Pract. Dermat. Wales 1992; DCH RCP Lond. 1985; Dip. Ven. Apoth. Lond. 1985; Dip. Acupunc. Liverp. 1983; Cert. Family Plann. JCC 1981. (S.C.B. Med. Coll. Cuttack) Clin. Asst. (Med.) Blackburn Roy. Infirm. Socs: Overseas Doctors Assn. (Sec. Blackburn Div.); (Chairm.) BMA; Indian Med. Assn. Prev: Regist. (Med.) Monklands Dist. Gen. Hosp. Airdrie; Regist. (Med.) Leicester Gen. Hosp.; SHO (Gen. & Geriat. Med.) Isebrook Hosp. WellingBoro.

RAUTRAY, Reena Mount Pleasant, Blackburn BB1 5BJ — MB BS 1971 Utkal.

RAUZ, Rooh-ul-Amin 13 Brunswick Gardens, Dover CT16 2AP — MB BS 1956 Punjab; MB BS Punjab (Pakistan) 1956; MRCS Eng. LRCP Lond. 1975.

RAUZ, Saaeha 11 Malvern Meadow, Temple Ewell, Dover CT16 3AH — MB BS 1990 Lond.; FRCOphth 1995. (UMDS Guy's & St. Thos. Hosps. Lond.) Specialist Regist. (Ophth.) Birm. & Midl. Eye Centre; Clin. Lect. (Ophth) Birm. Univ.

RAVAGO, Eranio 467 Kingston Road, Epsom Ewell, Epsom KT19 0DJ — MD 1970 Far East. Univ. Philippines. Staff Grade (Anaesth.) Epsom Health Care & Trust.

RAVAL, Jayantkumar Kantilal Walderslade Village Surgery, 62A Robin Hood Lane, Walderslade, Chatham ME5 9LD Tel: 01634 687250; 12 Fernbank Close, Chatham ME5 9NH Tel: 01634 865232 — MB BS 1972 Bombay.

RAVAL, Manish Pradyumna Flat 1, 21 Hesketh Place, London W11 4HW — MB BS 1994 Lond.

RAVAL, Mark Mukund The Surgery, 24 Broadwater Road, Worthing BN14 8AB Tel: 01903 231701 — BM 1986 Soton.

RAVAL, Pradyumna Bhuralal Stonecross Surgery, 25 Street End Road, Chatham ME5 0AA Tel: 01634 842334 — MB BS Indore 1966; MRCS Eng. LRCP Lond. 1974. (M.G.M. Med. Coll.) GP Princip. Socs: MPS; BMA.

RAVAL, Veena Pradyumna Blue Bell Hill Village, 82 Common Road, Chatham ME5 9RG Tel: 01634 670630 — MB BS Indore 1966; DRCOG 1974; MRCS Eng. LRCP Lond. 1975; DCCH 1983; MFCH 1989. (M.G.M. Med. Coll.) SCMO Community Child Health Dept. Kent. Socs: Fac. Comm. Health.

RAVALIA, Abdulsatar Department of Anaesthesia, Kingston Hospital, Kingston upon Thames KT2 7QB Tel: 020 8546 7711; 69 Bodley Road, New Malden KT3 5QJ Tel: 020 8949 1268 — MB ChB 1978 Zimbabwe; FFA RCS Eng. 1986. Cons. Anaesth. Kingston NHS Trust. Socs: MDUn & Intens. Care Soc. Prev: Cons. Anaesth. Walsgrave Hosp. Coventry; Sen. Regist. (Anaesth.) Middlx. Hosp. Lond.; SHO (Anaesth.) Harari Zimbabwe.

RAVAT, Farhana Esmail 7 Greenhead Avenue, Little Harwood, Blackburn BB1 5PR — MB BS 1996 Lond.

RAVAT, Sangita Wigston Central Surgery, 48 Leicester Road, Wigston LE18 1DR — MB ChB 1990 Glas.; MRCGP 1994.

RAVEENTHIRANATHAN, Chandraprabha 14 Thorndene, Elderslie, Johnstone PA5 9DA — MB BS 1972 Ceylon; LRCP LRCS Ed. LRCPS Glas. 1975; DObst RCOG 1975. Clin. Med. Off. Forth Valley Health Bd. Prev: Clin. Med. Off. Gtr. Glas. Health Bd.; Regist. (O & G) Falkirk & Dist. Roy. Infirm.; Regist. (O & G) Rankin Memor. Hosp. Greenock.

RAVEN, Peter William Dept. of Psychiatry & Behavioural Sciences, Royal Free & Univ. Coll. Medical School, UCL Royal Free Campus, Rowland Hill St., London NW3 2PF Tel: 0207 830 2280 — MB BS 1985 Lond.; PhD(Endocrinology), Lond. 1983, BSc (Hons. Biochem.) 1979; MRCP (UK) 1989; MRCPsych 1992. (St. Bartholomews Hospital Medical College) Sen. Lect. Psychiat. Hon. Cons. Psychiat. UCL, Lond. Prev: Regist. (Psychiat.) Bethlem Roy. & Maudsley Hosp. Lond.; Hon. Sen. Regist. (Psychiat.) Bethlem Roy. & Maudsley Hosp. Lond.; Lect. (Affective Disorders) Inst. Psychiat. Lond.

RAVEN, Sarah Clare Perch Hill Farm, Brightling, Robertsbridge TN32 5HP — MB BS 1992 Lond.

RAVENSCROFT, Andrew John Flat 4, Ashfield House, 8 Grove Road, Leeds LS6 2EQ — MB ChB 1988 Leeds; DA (UK) 1991.

RAVENSCROFT, Mrs Ann (retired) Bosvran, 5 Trelinnoe Close, South Petherwin, Launceston PL15 7JX — MB ChB 1956 Leeds. JP.

RAVENSCROFT, Jane Catherine 11 Caythorpe Road, West Park, Leeds LS16 5HW Tel: 0113 275 5432 — MB ChB 1988 Leeds; MB ChB (Hons.) Leeds 1988; MRCP (UK) 1991. Regist. (Dermat.) Leeds. Gen. Infirm. Leeds. Prev: Trainee GP Leeds VTS.

RAVENSCROFT, Peter James Staplegrove Anaesthetic Group, Somerset Nuffield Hospital, Staplegrove Elm, Taunton TA2 6AN Tel: 01823 353575 Fax: 01823 353576 Email: dr.r@sag.org.uk; 5 Elm Grove, Taunton TA1 1EG Tel: 01823 272400 Fax: 01823 251370 Email: peter@ravenscroft.org.uk — MB BS 1974 Lond.; MRCS Eng. LRCP Lond. 1974; LMSSA Lond. 1974; FFA RCS Eng. 1979; DRCOG 1978. (St. Bart.) Cons. Anaesth. Taunton & Som. NHS Trust; Cons. Anaest. StapleGr. Anast. Gp. Socs: Assn. Anaesth. Gt. Brit. & Irel.; W Som. Med. Soc. Sec.; Soc. Anaesth. S. W.. Region. Prev: Cons. Anaesth. Som. HA; Sen. Regist. Nuffield Dept. Anaesth. Oxf. & Wycombe HAs; Regist. (Anaesth.) Centr.lasarettet Västerås Sweden.

RAVENSCROFT, Sarah Jane Kingley Cottage, 6 Downs Road, West Stoke, Chichester PO18 9BH — MB BS 1996 Lond.

RAVETTO, Marc Peter Celestine 83 Carlton Towers, North St., Carshalton SM5 2EH Tel: 020 8647 1386 — MB BS 1991 Lond.; DRCOG 1994; MRCGP 1996. Trainee GP/SHO (O & G) E. Surrey Hosp. VTS.; GP Non Princip.

RAVETTO, Savino 42 Graham Road, Mitcham CR4 2HA Tel: 020 8648 2432 Fax: 020 8646 8249; 57 All Saints Road, Sutton SM1 3DQ Tel: 020 8644 1974 — MB BS Lond. 1957; MRCS Eng. LRCP Lond. 1957. (Univ. Coll. Hosp.) Prev: Regist. (Med.) E. Birm. Hosp.; Ho. Phys. St. Jas. Hosp. Balham; Ho. Surg. (O & G) Nelson Hosp. Merton.

RAVEY, Moira 29 Menlove Mansions, Menlove Gardens W., Woolton, Liverpool L18 2HY — MB ChB 1961 Liverp.; MRCPsych 1972; DPM Eng. 1966. Cons. Psychiat. Whiston Hosp.

RAVI, Asha New Street Health Centre, Upper New Street, Barnsley S70 1LP Tel: 01226 730000 Email: asharavi@doctors.org.uk — MB BS 1979 Nagpur; 1992 Dip. Community Child Health, Sheffield University; MD (Gen. Med.) Nagpur Univ. 1982; MRCPI 1990; M.Med,sc Leeds Univ. 1998. Cons.Paediat. (Community) Barnsley Communjity & Priority Serv.s (NHS) Trust, Barnsley. Socs: Roy. Coll. of Paediat. & Clin. Health (Fell.); Brit. Paediatric Neurol. Assn.; Brit. Assn. of Community Child Health. Prev: Clin. Med. Off. (Child Health) Pontefract Gen. Infirm.; Regist. & SHO (Paediat.) Barnsley Dist. Gen. Hosp.; Sen. Regist. (Community Paediat.) Leeds Community & Ment. Health Trust Leeds.

RAVI, Kambhammettu West Leeds Medical Practice, 289 Lower Wortley Place, Lower Wortley, Leeds LS12 4PZ Tel: 0113 279 9190 Fax: 0113 279 9204 — MB BS 1972 Andhra. Medico Legal Servs. to Solicitors; Police Surg. Leeds & Bradford Cities. Socs: Fell. Roy. Soc. Med.; Amer. Acad. Forens. Scis.; Assn. Police Surg.

RAVI, Mr Manoharan 27 Lady Lane, Chelmsford CM2 0TG — MB BS 1987 Karnatak; FRCS Ed. 1991.

RAVI, Mr Srinivasan Blackpool Victoria Hospital, Blackpool FY3 8BD Tel: 01253 300000; Baliyeur, The Oaks, Poulton-le-Fylde FY6 7HG — MB BS 1977 Mysore; MS (Gen. Surg.) Madras 1979; FRCS Ed. 1982; FRCS (Eng.) 1996. Cons. Gen. Surg. Blackpool Vict. Hosp.; Surgic. Tutor - Roy. Coll. of Surg.s; Lead Clinician, Coloreefal cancer. Socs: Assn. of Surg.s of Eng.; Assn. of ColoProctol.; Assn. of Endoscopic Surg.s. Prev: Sen. Regist. Leicester Roy. Infirm.; Regist. Lincoln Co. Hosp.; Regist. Newham & St. And. Hosp. Lond.

RAVI, Swaminathan Oakdale, Worsbrough Dale, Barnsley S70 3EG Tel: 01226 204404 Fax: 01226 779669; 1 Church Heights, Hoylandswaine, Sheffield S36 7LX — MB BS 1974 Madras. (Madras) GP Barnsley, S. Yorks.

RAVICHANDRAN, Mr Duraisamy Addenbrooke's Hospital, Cambridge CB2 2QQ Tel: 01223 245151; 4 Greenlands, Cambridge CB2 2QY Tel: 01223 210144 — MB BS 1986 Colombo; FRCS Eng. 1991. Regist. (Surg.)Addenbrooke's Hosp. Camb.; Research Fell. Univ. of Soton.

RAVICHANDRAN, Mr Ganapathiraju Princess Royal Spinal Injuries Unit, Osborn Building, Northern General Hospital, Sheffield S5 7AU Tel: 0114 271 5647 Fax: 0114 271 5649 Email: ravichandran@btinternet.com — MB BS 1972 Madras; BSc Annamalai 1964; FRCS Ed. 1976; T(S) 1994. (Jawaharlal Inst. Postgrad. Med. Pondicherry) Cons. Spinal Injuries Osborn Bldg., N. Gen. Hosp. Socs: Internat. Med. Soc. Paraplegia; Eur. Tissue Repair Soc.; Brit. Soc. Rehab.Med. (BSRM). Prev: Cons. Spinal Injuries Lodge Moor Hosp.; Sen. Regist. (Spinal Injuries) Stoke Mandeville Hosp. Aylesbury; Back Research Fell. Harlow Wood Orthop. Hosp. Mansfield.

RAVICHANDRAN, Subbiah Sadhashivan 6 Woodbridge Road, Newcastle ST5 4LA — MB BS 1986 Madras.

RAVIKUMAR, Mr Aloor 9 Fenton Place, Monifieth, Dundee DD5 4SE Tel: 01382 534000 — MB BS 1979 Osmania; FRCS Glas.

RAVIKUMAR

1989. Regist. (Orthop. & Trauma) Law Hosp. Lanarksh. Prev: SHO (Surg. & Urol.) S.lands Hosp. Sussex; SHO (Surg. & Orthop.) Worthing Hosps. Sussex; SHO (Orthop.) St. Jas. Hosp. Lond.

RAVIKUMAR, Mr Rathinam 24 Chockley's Meadow, Leegomery, Telford TF1 6TL; 4 Compton Road, Worcester WR5 1DY — MB BS 1984 Madras; MSc (Surg. Scs.) 1997; FRCS Ed. 1991. Research Regist. - Roy. Free Hosp. Dept. Neuroanat., Hampstead; Regist. Surg. Newcross Hosp., Wolverhampton; Regist. Surg. P.ss Roy. Hosp. Telford; Regist. Surg. Manor Hosp. Walsall.

RAVIKUMAR, Ratukondla 50A Anmersh Grove, Stanmore HA7 1PA — MB BS 1980 Madras.

RAVIKUMAR, Velupillai 67 Welbeck Road, Harrow HA2 0RU — LMSSA 1995 Lond.

RAVINDRA BOSE, Mr Sowdi Sundara Bharathy Bridlington District Hospital, Bessingby Road, Bridlington YO16 4QP Tel: 01262 606666 — MB BS 1984 India; FRCS Glas. 1993.

RAVINDRA NATH, Arepalli Accident & Emergency Department, County Hospital, Louth LN11 0EU Tel: 01507 600100; 6 Blue Stone Rise, Louth LN11 9XZ Tel: 01507 609037 — MB BS 1975 Andhra; MS Delhi 1980. Staff Grade A & E Co. Hosp. Louth. Socs: BMA.

RAVINDRABABU, Gottipati 61 Hagley Road W., Birmingham B17 8AE — MB BS 1972 Karnatak.

RAVINDRAN, Anchery Health Centre, Welbeck St., Castleford WF10 1DP Tel: 01977 552041 Fax: 01977 519342; 6 Manor Garth, Ledsham, South Milford, Leeds LS25 5LZ Tel: 01977 682876 Fax: 01977 685970 — MB BS Madras 1953; BSc Madras 1953. (Madras) Hosp. Pract. (Thoracic. Med.) Gen. Infirm. Pontefract. Socs: Fell. Roy. Soc. Med.; BMA, RSM & RCGP. Prev: Regist. (Med.) Roy. Infirm. Halifax; SHO Warrington Infirm.; Ho. Phys. Gen. Hosp. Dewsbury.

RAVINDRAN, Arumugavadivelu 54 Bursland Road, Enfield EN3 7EX Tel: 020 8804 6186 — MB BS 1971 Ceylon. (Ceylon) SHO Psychiat. Unit N.wick Pk. Hosp. Harrow.

RAVINDRAN, Thambar Sabaratnam Ravindran, East Park Medical Practice, Jonesfield Crescent, Wolverhampton WV1 2LW Tel: 01902 455422 Fax: 01902 454131; Longwood, 26 Wergs Road, Tettenhall, Wolverhampton WV6 8TD Tel: 01902 579228 — MB BS 1973 Sri Lanka; MSc (Dermat.) Oxf. 1995; MRCP (UK) 1981; MRCS Eng. LRCP Lond. 1979; MRCGP 1983; DCH RCP Lond. 1990; FRCP (UK) 1998. Clin. Asst. (Dermat.) Wolverhampton & Dudley.

RAVINDRANE, Arumugam 3 Lansdowne Court, Lansdowne Road, Worthing BN11 5HD — MB BS 1988 Madras; MRCP (UK) 1992.

RAVINE, David Medical Genetics Service for Wales, University Hospital of Wales, Heath Park, Cardiff CF14 4XW Tel: 029 2074 5008 Fax: 029 2074 7603 Email: ravine@cardiff.ac.uk — MB BS 1980 Western Australia; MS Melbourne 1994; BMedSc (Hons.) 1980; FRACP 1990; DRCPath 1998; MRCP 2000. (University Western Australia) Cons. Molecular Genetic Med. (Med. Genetics & Med. Biochem.ry) Univ. Hosp. Wales Cardiff. Socs: Brit. Soc. Human Genetics; Amer. Soc. Human Genetics; Human Genet. Soc. of Austral.

RAVISEKAR, Mr Oduru 24 Ravelrig Park, Balerno, Edinburgh EH14 7DL — MB BS 1977 Madras; FRCSI 1991.

RAVISHANKAR, Guhendran 14A The Drive, Coulsdon, Croydon CR5 2BL — MB BS 1979 Madras; MB BS Madras, India 1979; LRCP LRCS Ed., LRCPS Glas. 1987; DMedRehab RCP Lond. 1984.

RAVISHANKAR, Mr Ramachandran Royal Oldham Hospital, Rochdae Road, Oldham OL1 2JH Tel: 0161 624 0420 Fax: 0161 627 8498 Email: rshankar@ukonline.co.uk; 206 Oldham Road, Royton, Oldham OL2 5AA Tel: 0161 652 3735 Fax: 0161 652 3735 — MB BS 1981 Mysore; MS (Orth) Madras 1985; MChOrth Liverp. 1994; DOrth Madras 1983. (Mysore Med. Coll., India) Assoc. Specialist (Orthop.) Roy. Oldham Hosp. Socs: Brit. Orthop. Assn.; BMA; Internat.l Affil. Mem. Prev: Sen. Regist. (Orthop.) Bradford Roy. Infirm.; Regist. (Orthop.) Russells Hall Hosp. Dudley, Corbett Hosp. Stourbridge, Alder Hey Childr. Hosp. Liverp. & Roy. Albert Edwd. Infirm. Wigan.

RAW, Anthony John Askham, RD Farnham Health Centre, East Street, Farnham GU9 7SA Tel: 01252 723122 Fax: 01252 728302; Ridgewood House, Highlands Close, Farnham GU9 8SP — MB BS 1968 Lond.; MRCS Eng. LRCP Lond. 1968. (Westm.) Prev: Ho. Surg. W.m. Hosp. Lond.; Ho. Phys. Soton. Gen. Hosp.

RAW, David Stuart Sunnyside Doctors Surgery, 150 Fratton Road, Portsmouth PO1 5DH Tel: 023 9282 4725 Fax: 023 9286 1014; 16 St. Edwards Road, Southsea PO5 3DJ Tel: 023 92 731481 Email: thefamily@raws99.freeserve.co.uk — MB BS 1973 Lond.; MRCS Eng. LRCP Lond. 1973; FRCGP 1996; DCH Eng. 1976; DObst RCOG 1975; MA Portsmouth Univ. 1998. (St. Mary's) GP; Assoc. Sen. Lect. Sch. of Postgrad. Med. Portsmouth Univ. Prev: Trainee GP Bristol; SHO (Psychiat.) Barrow Hosp.; SHO (A & E) Bristol Roy. Infirm.

RAW, Jason Michael 11 Shadwell Park Av, Leeds LS17 8TL — MB ChB 1997 Dundee.

RAW, John Page (retired) 3 West Dene, Park Lane, Cheam, Sutton SM3 8BW Tel: 020 8642 3050 — MB BS 1943 Lond.; MRCS Eng. LRCP Lond. 1942. Prev: Med. Off. EBS (Lond.).

RAW, Theodore Robert Foster (retired) Poptts Farmhouse, Chennell Park Road, Tenterden TN30 6XA Tel: 01580 765525 — MRCS Eng. LRCP Lond. 1934. Prev: Hon. Med. Off. Horley & Dist. Hosp.

RAWAL, Bandhana Kumari Medical Department, Glaxo Wellcome UK Ltd., Stockley Park W., Uxbridge UB11 1BT — MB BS 1985 Lond.; MSc (Distinc.) Lond. 1989, BSc (1st cl. Hons.) 1982; MRCPath 1992. Sen. Med. Adviser Glaxo plc Uxbridge. Prev: Clin. Research Fell. (Virol.) St. Geo. Hosp. Lond.

RAWAL, Jewan Lal 39 Nelmes Crescent, Hornchurch RM11 2PX Tel: 01708 621179 Fax: 01708 782308 Email: jeewarn l @hotmail.com — MB BS 1975 Delhi; MRCPCH; MD; MRCPI. Cons. Pediatrician; Med. Dir. Socs: RCDH; BMA.

RAWAL, Krishna Mark, Surg. Lt.-Cdr. RN 52 Guildown Road, Guildford GU2 4EY Tel: 01483 538560 — MB BS 1990 Lond.; Dip RHC Aberdeen Nov 1993. (GUYs Hosp. Med. School) Med. Off., Roy. Navy. Prev: Med. Off. RN; SHO (A & E) Poole Hosp. Trust Dorset; Med. Off. Brit. Antarctic Survey.

RAWAL, Om Prakash 185 Ladybank Road, Mickleover, Derby DE3 5QL Tel: 01332 518918; 132 Station Road, Derby DE3 5FN Tel: 01332 512766 — MB BS 1952 Calcutta. (Lake Med. Coll.) Socs: BMA. Prev: Asst. Phys. (Geriat.) Pk. Hosp. WellingBoro.; SHO (Med.) Dorking Gen. Hosp.; SHO (Geriat.) St. Mary's Hosp. Colchester.

RAWAL, Parmjit 110 Bakers Lane, Sutton Coldfield B74 2BA — MB ChB 1997 Leeds.

RAWAL, Punam 50 Burlingham Avenue, Wirral CH48 8AR — MB ChB 1993 Leeds.

RAWAL, Ram Swarup (retired) 31 Riffel Road, London NW2 4PB Tel: 020 8450 7455 Fax: 020 8450 1353 Email: rsrawal@yahoo.com — MB BS 1954 Lucknow; MD Anaesth. Panjab 1958; Lucknow 1954; MFHom Lond. 1972; LCPS Bombay 1951; Dip. Ven. Liverp. 1971; DA Eng. 1966. Prev: Cons. Anaesth. N.W. Metrop. Bd. Hosp. & Wembley Hosp.

RAWAL, Rama Rajnikant (Surgery) Stuart Crescent Centre, Bounds Green, London N11; 60 Maidstone Road, Bounds Green, London N11 2JR Tel: 020 8361 1391 — MB BS 1973 Rajasthan. (R.N.T. Med. Coll.)

RAWAL, Miss Shashi Bala 'Bow Green', Prestbury Road, Wilmslow SK9 2LL — MB BS 1972 Delhi; FFA RCSI 1977; DA Eng. 1976; DObst RCOG 1974. (Lady Hardinge Med. Coll.) Cons. Anaesth. Macclesfield Dist. Chesh. Socs: BMA & Assn. Anaesth. Gt. Brit. & Irel. Prev: Cons. Anaesth. Qu. Eliz. Hosp. Barbados, W. Indies; Sen. Regist. Yorks. RHA.

RAWBONE, Roger Geoffrey Health & Safety Executive, Magdalen House, Stanley Precinct, Bootle L20 3QZ Tel: 0151 951 4555 Fax: 0151 951 3180 Email: roger.rawbone@hse.gsi.gov.uk; 38 South Parade, Bramhall, Stockport SK7 3BJ — MB BS 1969 Lond.; FFOM (Hon.) 2001; MA Manc. 2001; MD Lond. 1995; MRCS Eng. LRCP Lond. 1969. (Char. Cross) Head of the Med. Unit Health & Safety Exec. Bootle. Prev: Sen. Manager R & D/Occupat. Health Servs. Gallaher Ltd.; Research Fell. Cardiopulm. Laborats. Dept. of Med. Char Cross Hosp. Med. Sch. Lond.; Cons. Adviser to Nat. Childr. Bureau.

RAWCLIFFE, Debra Samantha The Surgery, Marsh Gardens, Honley, Huddersfield HD9 6AG Tel: 01484 303366 Fax: 01484 303365 — MB ChB 1987 Leeds.

RAWCLIFFE, Jacqueline Anne The Health Centre, Bailey Street, Old Basford, Nottingham NG6 0HD Tel: 0115 978 1231 Fax: 0115 979 0419; 18 Villiers Road, West Bridgford, Nottingham NG2 6FR Tel: 0115 923 2560 — MB ChB 1988 Manch.; MRCGP 1993; DRCOG 1992; DCH RCP Lond. 1991.

RAWCLIFFE, John Francis Xavier 10 Downs Avenue, Dartford DA1 1SU — MB BS 1983 Lond.

RAWCLIFFE, Peter Morgan Botley Medical Centre, Elms Road, Botley, Oxford OX2 9JS Tel: 01865 248719 Fax: 01865 728116 — MB 1974 Camb.; MA Camb. 1970, MB 1974, BChir 1973. (Lond. Hosp.) GP Oxf. Prev: MRC Research Fell. Gastroenterol. Unit Radcliffe Infirm. Oxf.; Coeliac Trust Research Fell. & Hon. Regist. Nuffield Dept. Clin. Med. Radcliffe Infirm. Oxf.; SHO (Gastroenterol.) Hammersmith Hosp. Lond.

RAWCLIFFE, Philip John 6 Wellington Road, Ombersley, Droitwich WR9 0DZ — MB ChB 1974 Liverp.

RAWDEN, Alison Margaret Birchwood Medical Practice, Jasmin Road, Lincoln LN6 0QQ Tel: 01522 501111; Rustaley, Fen Lane, Owmby-by-Spital, Market Rasen LN8 2HP — MB ChB 1990 Leic.; MRCGP 1994.

RAWDON SMITH, Henry Stewart Russets, 9c Irving Burgess Close, Whittlesey, Peterborough PE7 1QB Tel: 01733 206664 — MB BS Lond. 1959; DObst RCOG 1964. (Middlx.) Prev: GP Newton Abbot.

RAWES, Geoffrey Douglas Dr Geoff Rawes Surgery, The Harbour Suite, Blyth Hospital, Blyth NE24 1DX Tel: 01670 396550 Fax: 01670 396556; 1 Holywell Avenue, Whitley Bay NE26 3AH Tel: 0191 252 5728 — MB BS 1968 Newc.; MRCGP 1974; DObst RCOG 1970.

RAWES, James Charteris Lea (retired) Falcons, Little Easton, Dunmow CM6 2JH Tel: 01371 872640 — MB BChir 1954 Camb.; DCH Eng. 1960; DObst RCOG 1959. Prev: GP Dunmow. Essex.

RAWES, Mr Malcolm Lindsay Department of Orthopaedic Surgery, Pinderfields General Hospital, Aberford Road, Wakefield WF1 4DG Tel: 01924 212546 Fax: 01924 212614 — MB ChB 1986 Leeds; BSc (Hons.) Leeds 1983; MCh (Orth.) Liverp. 1995; FRCS (Orth.) 1996; FRCS Eng. 1990. (Univ. Leeds) Cons. Orthop. Surg. Pinderfield Gen. Hosp. Aberford Rd. Wakefield W. Yorks.; Hon. Sen. Lect., Univ. of Leeds. Socs: Brit. Orthop. Research Soc.; Brit. Trauma Soc.; Fell. BOA. Prev: Lect. (Clin.) & Hon. Sen. Regist. Univ. Liverp.; Career Regist. Rotat. (Orthop.) Leicester & Lincoln Train. Scheme; Tutor (Surg.) Gen. Infirm. Leeds.

RAWKINS, Montague David 'Whitecroft', 21 Connaught Road, Sidmouth EX10 8TT — MRCS Eng. LRCP Lond. 1925; MD Lond. 1933, MB BS 1925. (St. Bart.) Prev: Temp. Wing Cdr. RAF Med. Serv.; Specialist in Neurol. Min. of Pens. & Nat. Insur.

RAWLE, Diane Premier Health Trust HQ, St Michael's Hospital, Trent Valley Road, Lichfield WS13 6EF Tel: 01543 441400 Fax: 01543 441430 — MB ChB Sheff. 1978; MRCGP 1982.

RAWLE, Michael Stirling Mill Bank Surgery, Water Street, Stafford ST16 2AG Tel: 01785 258348 Fax: 01785 227144; 16 White Oaks, Wildwood, Stafford ST17 4SL — MB BS 1977 Lond.; MRCS Eng. LRCP Lond. 1976. (St. Mary's) Clin. Asst. Cardiol. Stafford Day.

RAWLE, Peter Royston Anaesthetic Department, Frimley Park Hospital NHS Trust, Frimley, Camberley GU16 5UJ — MB BS 1978 Lond.; MRCS Eng. LRCP Lond. 1978; FFA RCS Eng. 1985. Cons. Anaesth. Frimley Pk. Hosp. Camberley.

RAWLENCE, Patrick Donnithorne (retired) The Close, Station Road, Pulham Market, Diss IP21 4TD Tel: 01379 676285 — MB BS Lond. 1940. Prev: GP Pulham Market.

RAWLES, John Michael (retired) Brunnion Minor, Lelant Downs, Hayle TR27 6NT Tel: 01736 740983 Fax: 01736 740067 Email: john.rawles@btinternet.com — MB BS 1964 Lond.; BSc Lond. 1960, MB BS 1964; FRCP Ed. 1989; FRCP Lond. 1982, M 1969. Prev: Hon. Sen. Lect. (Med.) Univ. Aberd.

RAWLIN, Michael Eyre Medical Centre, New St., Dinnington, Sheffield S25 2EX Tel: 01909 562207 — MB ChB 1959 Sheff.; MRCGP 1990. (Sheff.)

RAWLING, Angela Heather Springs Medical Centre, Springs Lane, Ilkley LS29 8TH Tel: 01943 604455 Fax: 01943 604466; Maxwell House, Maxwell Road, Ilkley LS29 8RP Tel: 01943 816588 Email: angela@rawling.force9.co.uk — MB ChB 1970 Manch.; DObst RCOG 1972. Prev: Clin. Asst. (ENT Surg.) Airedale HA.

RAWLING, Keith Gordon Kintyre, Dene Road, Dalton-on-Dale, Seaham — MB BS 1976 Lond.

RAWLING, Roger Graham Springs Medical Centre, Springs Lane, Ilkley LS29 8TH Tel: 01943 604455 Fax: 01943 604466 Email: rawlingpartner@hotmail.com; Maxwell House, Maxwell Road, Ilkley LS29 8RP Tel: 01943 816588 Email: graham@rawling.force9.co.uk — MB ChB 1970 Manch.; MRCGP 1975; DObst RCOG 1973. Socs: Soc. Occupat. Med.

RAWLINGS, David Medical Imaging Deot, Cross house Hospital, Kilmarnock KA2 0BE Email: david.rawlings@aaaht.scot.nhs.uk; 34 Castlehill Road, Ayr KA7 2HZ — MB ChB 1982 Ed.; FRCR; DMRD Aberd. 1987. Cons. Radiol. CrossHo. Hosp. Kilmarnock. Prev: Sen. Regist. (Radiol.) Newc. Roy. Vict. Infirm.

RAWLINGS, Elizabeth Lexden, Hartley Avenue, Mannamead, Plymouth PL3 5HR Tel: 01752 662323 — MB BCh 1968 Wales; BSc Wales 1965; FFA RCS Eng. 1972. Cons. Anaesth. Plymouth Gen. Hosp.

RAWLINGS, Mr Ian David Mount Gould Hospital, Plymouth PL4 — MB BS 1969 Lond.; FRCS Eng. 1974. Cons. Orthop. Surg. Plymouth Health Auth.

RAWLINGS, Kate 6 Lincombe Avenue, Bristol BS16 5UD — MB ChB 1998 Leic.; MB ChB Leic. 1998.

RAWLINGS, Keith Leonard Balmoral Surgery, 1 Victoria Road, Deal CT14 7AU Tel: 01304 373444; 19 Archery Square, Walmer, Deal CT14 7JA — MB ChB 1976 Sheff. (Sheff.) Clin. Asst. (Dermat.) SE Kent Hosps. Trust. Prev: Surg. Lt.-Cdr. RN.

RAWLINGS, Kenneth Owen 2 North Close, Lymington SO41 9BT Tel: 01590 671563 — MB BS 1940 Lond.; MD Lond. 1948; FRCP Lond. 1965, M 1943; MRCS Eng. LRCP Lond. 1940. (Guy's) Hon. Cons. Phys. Bromley Hosp. Gp. Prev: Maj. RAMC, Specialist Phys.; Chief Asst. (Endocrine) Guy's Hosp. Lond.; Ho. Phys. Guy's Hosp.

RAWLINGSON, Christopher John 43 Tavistock Road, Basildon SS15 5QF — MB BS 1994 Lond.

RAWLINS, David Charles Green Farm, Chantry, Frome BA11 3LY Tel: 01373 836252 — MB BS Lond. 1959. (Lond. Hosp.) Socs: Fell. Roy. Soc. Med. Prev: Receiv. Room Off. Lond. Hosp.; Med. Regist. Barnet Gen. Hosp.; Regist. (VD) St. Mary's Hosp. Lond.

RAWLINS, Dawn Betty Westrop Surgery, Newburgh Place, Highworth, Swindon SN6 7DN Tel: 01793 762218; 42 The Willows, Highworth, Swindon SN6 7PH Tel: 01793 763494 — MB ChB 1982 Leeds. GP Highworth, Swindon.

RAWLINS, Sir John Stuart Pepys, KBE, OBE, MBE, Surg. Vice-Admiral Little Cross, Holne, Newton Abbot TQ13 7RS Tel: 01364 631249 Fax: 01364 631400 — BM BCh Oxf. 1946; MA Oxf. 1946; FRCP Lond. 1978, M 1973; MFOM 1975. (Oxf. & St. Bart.) Hon. Fell. Univ. Coll. Oxf.; Hon. Research Fell. Univ. Lancaster; Hon. Doctor Technol. Robt. Gordon's Inst. of Technol. Socs: Fell. Aerospace Med. Soc.; Hon. Fell. (Ex-Pres.) Soc. Underwater Technol.; (Ex-Vice-Pres.) Underwater and Hyperbaric Med. Soc. Prev: Hon. Phys. to HM the Qu.; Med. Dir.-Gen. (Naval) MoD; Ho. Surg. Roy. Hants. Co. Hosp. & Lond. Chest Hosp.

RAWLINS, Professor Sir Michael David National Institute for Clinical Excellence, London WC2N 5HR — MB BS Lond. 1965; BSc Lond. 1962, MD 1973; FRCP Ed. 1987; FRCP Lond. 1977, M 1968; FFPM RCP (UK) 1989. (St. Thos.) Chairm. Nat. Inst. Clin. Excellence; Prof. Clin. Pharmacol. Univ. Newc.; Hon. Cons. Clin. Pharmacol. Freeman Hosp. & Roy. Vict. Infirm. Newc. Socs: Brit. Pharm. Soc.; Assn. Phys.; Chair, Nat. Inst for Clin. Excellence. Prev: Sen. Regist. (Clin. Pharmacol.) Hammersmith Hosp. Lond.; Lect. (Med.) St. Thos. Hosp. Med. Sch. Lond.; Ho. Phys. & Ho. Phys. (Neurol.) St. Thos. Hosp. Lond.

RAWLINS, Mr Richard Duddingston The Manor Hospital, Biddenham, Bedford MK40 4AW Tel: 01234 364252 Fax: 01234 325001 Email: richardr@awlins.demon.co.uk; 13 Pemberley Avenue, Bedford MK40 2LE Tel: 01234 211882 Fax: 01234 217520 — MB BS 1968 Lond.; MBA Keele 1996; FRCS Eng. 1975; Spec. Accredit. Orthop. RCS Eng. 1981. (Middlx.) Cons. Orthop. Surg. Bedford Gen. Hosp.; Mem. Jt. Cons. Comm.; Mem. Chiropodists Bd. CPSM Policy Bd. Nat. Centre for Clin. Audit; Chairm. Clin. Audit Commit. BMA; Mem. Policy. Bd. Nat. Centre for Clin. Audit; Chairm., Advisery Counc. Health Quality Serv. Socs: (Ex-Pres.) Brit. Orthop. Trainees Assn.; Brit. Assn. for Surg. of Knee; Brit. Hip Soc. Prev: Sen. Regist. (Orthop.) Guy's Hosp. Lond.; Lect. King's Coll. Lond.

RAWLINSON, Alicia Community Child Health Paediatrics, Royal Gwent Hospital, Newport NP20 2UB Tel: 01633 238999 Fax: 01633 656309 Email: alicia.rawlinson@gwent wales.nhs.uk — MB ChB 1976 Sheff.; MRCP (UK) 1982; MRCGP 1984; LMCC 1980; DCH RCP Lond. 1982; FRCPCH 1997. (Sheff.) Cons. Community Paediat. Glan Hafren NHS Trust. Socs: Brit. Paediat. Assn.; Brit.

RAWLINSON

Assn. Community Child Health. Prev: SCMO (Community Paediat.) S.mead Hosp. Bristol; Regist. Childr. Hosp. Sheff.

RAWLINSON, Andrew John Yarm Medical Centre, 1 Worsall Road, Yarm TS15 9DD Tel: 01642 786422 Fax: 01642 785617; 684 Yarm Road, Eaglescliffe, Stockton-on-Tees TS16 0DP Tel: 01642 784313 — MB ChB 1973 Bristol. Prev: Trainee GP Shrewsbury VTS.

RAWLINSON, Fiona Mary Velindre Hospital, Cardiff CF14 2TL Tel: 029 2061 5888; Brynlea Hey, The Downs, St. Lythan's, Cardiff CF5 6SB — MB BChir 1988 Camb.; MRCGP 1993; Dip Palliat. Med. Wales 1995; DRCOG 1992. p/t Sen. Regist. (Palliat. Care) Allwalts Pallialine Med. Train.; Course Tutor Diploma in Palliat. Med. (UWCM). Prev: SR. Bridgend & Dist. NHS Trust; Staff Grade (Palliat. Care) Ybwthyn Palliat. Care Unit Pontypridd; Trainee GP Essex.

RAWLINSON, Graham Vaughan Lodgeside Surgery, 22 Lodgeside Avenue, Kingswood, Bristol BS15 1WW Tel: 0117 961 5666 Fax: 0117 947 6854; 328 Canford Lane, Westbury-on-Trym, Bristol BS9 3PW — MB ChB 1976 Sheff.; LMCC 1980; MRCGP 1982; DRCOG 1982. (Sheff.) Course Organiser Univ. Bristol VTS; Assoc. Regional Adviser Gloucester, Avon & Som; Examr. Roy. Coll. Gen. Pract. Socs: Cossham Med. Soc. Prev: Clin. Asst. (Orthop. Med.) S.mead Hosp. Bristol; GP Trainer S.mead Hosp. Bristol.

RAWLINSON, Howard Rowan Duncan (retired) Bryn-yr-eds Cottage, Whitehurst, Chirk, Wrexham LL14 5AS — MRCS Eng. LRCP Lond. 1967. Prev: Ho. Phys. Hope Hosp. Salford.

RAWLINSON, Mr James Keith McClure Glenburn, 6 Oldfield Road, Heswall, Wirral CH60 6SE Tel: 0151 342 2232 — MB ChB 1947 Liverp.; ChM Liverp. 1960, MB ChB 1947; FRCS Eng. 1951. Prev: Cons. (Urol.) Walton Hosp. Liverp.

RAWLINSON, Rev. James Nigel Accident and Emergency Department, Bristol Royal Infirmary, Marlborough St., Bristol BS2 8HW Tel: 0117 928 2713; Glen Boyd House, 38 Court View, Wick BS30 5QP — MB BChir 1980 Camb.; Dip. Applied Theology 1999; BA Camb. 1980; FRCS Ed. 1986; FFAEM 1998. Cons., (A & E) Bristol Roy. Infirm.; Priest, Bath & Wells Diocese All St.s Ch. W.on Bath & Bristol Roy. Infirm.; Clin. Sub. Dean HBHT Brit. Med. Sch. Prev: Hon. Sen. Regist. (Neurosurg.) Frenchay Hosp. Bristol; SHO Rotat. (Gen. Surg.) Roy. United Hosp. Bath.; Demonst. (Anat.) Emmanuel Coll. & Dept. Anat. Univ. Camb.

RAWLINSON, John Hunters Way Medical Centre, Hunters Way, Kimbolton, Huntingdon PE18 0HY Tel: 01480 860205 Fax: 01480 861590 — MRCS Eng. LRCP Lond. 1971; BSc Lond. 1967, MB BS 1971. (Guy's) Clin. Asst. (Ophth.) Hinchingbrooke Hosp. Huntington. Prev: Med. Off. Save Childr. Fund Yemen; Demonst. Anat. Aberd. Univ.; SHO (O & G) Raigmore Hosp. Inverness.

RAWLINSON, John Robert Radnor House Practice, 25 London Road, Ascot SL5 7EN Tel: 01344 874011 Fax: 01344 28868; 6 Froghall Drive, Wokingham RG40 2LF Email: jrawlin925@aol.com — BM BCh 1979 Oxf.; MA Oxf. 1979; Cert. Family Plann. JCC 1984; Cert. Managem. 1996; O.U. (Oxf.) GP Princip. Ascot; Mem. Winder & Ascot PCG; Mem. (Chairm.) LMC; Mem. (Chairm.) Regional Gen. Pract. Advis. Comm. Socs: Roy. Soc. Med. Prev: Mem. GMSC.

RAWLINSON, Marmaduke Peter Goodwin 63 Melton Crt., Old Brompton Road, London SW7 3JH Tel: 020 7589 0225 — MRCS Eng. LRCP Lond. 1940; MA (Hnrs.) Camb. 1941; DPH Lond. 1947. (Camb. & Westm.) Prev: Med. Off. i/c U.K. Canad. High Commiss.; Sen. Cas. Off. W.m. Hosp. Lond.; MOH Mt.ain View Health Unit Calgary, Alta.

RAWLINSON, Peter Samuel Marshall Hatton Farm House, Abernethy, Perth PH2 9LN — MB ChB Manch. 1982; BSc (Med. Sci.) St. And. 1979; MRCP (UK) 1986; MRCPath 1993. Cons. Haemat. E. of Scotl. Blood Transfus. Ninewells Hosp. Dundee. Prev: Cons. Haemat. Army Blood Supply Depot Aldershot; Sen. Regist. (Haemat. & Blood Transfus.) Yorksh. Blood Transfus. Serv.; Regist. (Haemat.) Glas. Roy. Infirm.

RAWLINSON, Sarah Meregan Basement Flat, 6 Miles Road, Bristol BS8 2JN — MB BS 1990 Lond.

RAWLINSON, William Arnold Lewin Oaklands Park, High Hatch Lane, Hurstpierpoint, Hassocks BN6 9LH Tel: 01273 832404 Fax: 01444 441528 Email: wrawlina@mid-sussex.sthames.nhs.uk — BM BCh 1971 Oxf.; MA Oxf. 1973; FRCA. 1976. (Lond. Hosp.) Cons. Anaesth. P.ss Roy. Hosp. Haywards Heath; Med. Dir. Mid. Sussex

NHS Trust. Socs: Brit. Assn. Med. Managers & Neuroanaesth. Soc.; Assn. Anaesth. Prev: Gen. Manager Mid-Downs E. Unit; Sen. Regist. Nuffield Dept. Anaesth. Oxf.; Ho. Surg. & Ho. Phys. Lond. Hosp.

RAWLINSON, Zoe Louise Heatherlea, Pitmore Lane, Sway, Lymington SO41 6BW — MB BS 1998 Lond.; MB BS Lond 1998.

RAWLL, Christopher Charles Gadsdon, OStJ British Airways Health Services, Speed Bird House, PO Box 10, London Airport, Hounslow TW6 2JA Tel: 020 8562 5671 Fax: 020 8562 9992; 3 Cavendish Court, Cardigan Road, Richmond TW10 6BL Tel: 020 8948 2838 — MB ChB 1953 Birm.; FFOM RCP Lond. 1988, MFOM 1978; DTPH Lond 1965; CIH St. And. 1964, (Birm.) Cons. Occupat. Phys. Brit. Airways Health Servs.; Mem. Internat. Commiss. on Occupat. Health, Socs: Soc. Occupat. Med. Prev: Cons. Occupat.al Phys. Brit. Airways Health Serv..; Wing Cdr. RAF Med. Br..

RAWNSLEY, Anne Helen 6 Hudson View, Tadcaster LS24 8JE Tel: 01937 531673 Email: scbuckle@globalnet.co.uk — MB ChB 1996 Manch. (Manchester) SHO, Basic Surgic. Train. Rotat., Huddersfield Roy. Infirm.

RAWORTH, Ronald Eric (retired) 20 Lodges Grove, Bare, Morecambe LA4 6HE — MB ChB Manch. 1950; MFCM 1977; DObst RCOG 1963; DPH (Distinc.) Liverp. 1973. Prev: SCM Burnley DHA.

***RAWSE, Helen Elizabeth Louise** Flat 2/1, 70 Fergus Drive, Glasgow G20 6AP — MB ChB 1998 Glas.; MB ChB Glas 1998.

RAWSON, Aneil Flat 8, Tall Trees, 8 Mersey Road, Manchester M20 2PE — MB ChB 1991 Sheff.

RAWSON, Anjali 46 Quarry Lane, Sheffield S11 9EB — MB BS 1990 Lond.

RAWSON, Annette Barbara, OBE (retired) 6 Cecil Close, Mount Avenue, Ealing, London W5 2RB — MB BS Lond. 1953; FRCP Lond. 1976, M 1955; MRCS Eng. LRCP Lond. 1953; MFCM 1974. Prev: Sen. Med. Off. DHSS.

RAWSON, Donald Alexander (retired) Kavalla, Mauchline KA5 5AN Tel: 01290 550268 — MB ChB Glas. 1943. Prev: Hon. Capt. RAMC.

RAWSON, Isabel Anne 145 Almsford Drive, Harrogate HG2 8EE — MB ChB 1979 Sheff.; MRCGP 1985.

RAWSON, Lucy Elisabeth The Surgery, Tanners Meadow, Brockham, Betchworth RH3 7NJ Tel: 01737 843259 Fax: 01737 845184; Greenbanks, Old Road, Buckland, Betchworth RH3 7DU — BSc (Hons.) Lond. 1986, MB BS 1989; MRCGP 1993; Cert. Prescribed Equiv. Exp. JCPTGP 1993; DCH RCP Lond. 1993; DRCOG 1992. Prev: Trainee GP E. Surrey VTS.

RAWSON, Malcolm David 19 The Paddocks, Kirk Ella, Hull HU10 7PF Tel: 01482 655351 — MD Leeds 1976, MB ChB 1956; FRCP Lond. 1977, M 1959; MRCS Eng. LRCP Lond. 1956; FRCR 1975; FFR 1963; DMRD Eng. 1961. Cons. Neurol. The Nuffield Hosp. Hull. Prev: Sen. Regist. Univ. Dept. Neurol. Manch. Roy. Infirm.; Sen. Research Fell. Yale Univ. Med. Sch. New Haven, USA; Ho. Surg. & Ho. Phys. Leeds Gen. Infirm.

RAWSON, Theresa Mary Sinead 8 Ashfordby Street, Leicester LE5 3QG — MB ChB 1997 Leic.

RAWSON, Wendy Christine Peterborough District Hospital, Thorpe Road, Peterborough PE3 6DA — MB ChB 1984 Leic.

RAWSTHORNE, Anne Margaret The Crofts, Wrenbury Road, Aston, Nantwich CW5 8DQ Tel: 01270 780244 — MB ChB Aberd. 1965. (Aberd.) Clin. Asst. (Psychiat.) Leighton Hosp. Crewe. Prev: SHO (Psychiat.) Ross Clinic Aberd.; Ho. Surg. (Gyn.) Aberd. Roy. Infirm.; Ho. Phys. (Gen. Med.) Roy. N.. Infirm. Inverness.

RAWSTHORNE, Mr George Brian The Crofts, Wrenbury Road, Aston, Nantwich CW5 8DQ — MB ChB 1965 Aberd.; FRCS Eng. 1973; FRCS Ed. 1970. (Aberd.) Cons. Surg. Leighton Hosp. Crewe. Prev: Sen. Regist. (Surg.) Liverp. RHB; Regist. Merseyside RHA; SHO Woodend Hosp. Aberd.

RAWSTORNE, Steven Well Lane Surgery, Well Lane, Stow on the Wold, Cheltenham GL54 1EQ Tel: 01451 830625 Fax: 01451 830693 Email: rawstorne@rcsed.ac.uk — MB BS 1982 Lond.; BSc (Hons.) Biochem. Lond. 1979; FRCP 2001; MRCGP 1986; FIMC RCS (Ed.) 2001; DRCOG 1986; DCH RCP Lond. 1984. (Guy's Hosp.) Prev: Trainee GP Chipping Norton Oxon.; Ho. Surg. Guy's Hosp. Lond.; Ho. Phys. Lewisham Hosp. Lond.

RAWSTRON, John Roberts, TD (retired) 5 HighStreet, Watlington OX49 5PZ Tel: 01491 613108 Email: jrrawstron@ibm.net — MRCS Eng. LRCP Lond. 1954; MD Lond. 1964, MB BS 1954; FRCPath

RAY

1976, M 1964; DPath Eng. 1960. Cons. Clin. Pathol. Amersham & High Wycombe Area Dept. of Path.; Maj. RAMC (TA). Prev: Sen. Lect. in Clin. Path. King's Coll. Hosp. Med. Sch.

RAY, Amar Kumar (retired) Hollybank, Rectory Lane, Heswall, Wirral CH60 4RZ Tel: 0151 342 5868 — MB BS Calcutta 1957; FFA RCS Eng. 1965. Cons. Anaesth. Mersey RHA. Prev: Sen. Regist. United Liverp. Hosps. & Liverp RHB.

RAY, Mr Amares Chandra 30 Havenwood Road, Whitley, Wigan WN1 2PA — MB BS 1965 Calcutta; FRCS Eng. 1971; FRCS Ed. 1971.

RAY, Aparna 2c Sandy Lane, Hampton Wick, Kingston upon Thames KT1 4BB — MB BS 1998 Lond.; MB BS Lond 1998.

RAY, Mr Arup Kumar Department of Plastic Surgery, Canniesburn Hospital, Switchback Road, Bearsden, Glasgow G61 1QL Tel: 0141 211 5845; 32 Westbourne Gardens, Glasgow G12 9PF — MB BS 1978 Madras.

RAY, Mr Ashoke Kumar 32 Monkhams Drive, Woodford Green IG8 0LE Tel: 020 8504 0179 — MB BS 1958 Calcutta; FRCS Canada 1968; MRCOG 1964; DGO Calcutta 1960. (Calcutta Med. Coll.)

RAY, Mr Atanu Dept. of Surgery, Whiston Hospital, Prescot L35 5DR Tel: 0151 426 1600 — MB ChB 1983 Zambia; BSc Zambia 1980; FRCS Glas. 1990.

RAY, Bibhas Chandra Braidholm, 3 Kenmure Road, White Craigs, Glasgow G46 6TU Tel: 0141 639 7055 — MB BS 1974 Calcutta; MD Calcutta 1977; MFFP 1993; MRCOG 1988; DObst RCPI 1988. Staff (Obst. & Gyn.) Roy. Alexandra Hosp. & Paisley Matern. Unit. Socs: Brit. Colposcopy Soc. & Brit. Ultrasound Soc. Prev: Regist. (O & G) Inverclyde Roy. Hosp. Greenock; Regist. (O & G) Jersey Gen. Hosp. CI.

RAY, Carol Kanti 64 Sandringham Gardens, London N12 0PJ — MB ChB 1997 Birm.

RAY, Coralie Sunanda 4 Cairns Drive, Beaconside, Stafford ST16 3PW Tel: 01785 245352 — MB BS 1981 Lond.; MSc (Community Health in Developing Countries) Lond. 1983, BSc (Basic. Med. Sci.; with Med. Sociol.) 1978; MPH Birm. 1997. (Char. Cross Hosp. Med. Sch.) Specialist Regist. (Pub. Health Med.) S. Staffs. HA; Edit. Bd. Reproduc. Health Matters (Lond.); Edit. Bd. AIDS Action (Lond.). Prev: Research Fell. & Lect. (Community Med.) Univ. Zimbabwe; Med. Off. Harare City Health, Zimbabwe; Oxfam-UK Community Health, Zimbabwe.

RAY, David Charles Department of Anaesthetics, Royal Infirmary, Lauriston Place, Edinburgh EH3 9YW Tel: 0131 536 3651 Fax: 0131 536 3672 Email: david.ray@ed.ac.uk; Easterhill, 13 Galachlaw Shot, Edinburgh EH10 7JF — MB ChB 1983 Ed.; MD Ed. 1992; FRCA 1989. Cons. Anaesth. & Intens. Care Roy. Infirm. Edin.; Clin. Dir. (Anaesth./Theatres) Roy. Infirm. of Edin. NHS Trust. Socs: Assn. Anaesth.; Intens. Care Soc.; (Hon. Sec.) Edin. & E. Scotl. Soc. Anaesth. Prev: Sen. Regist. (Anaesth.) Roy. Infirm. Edin.; Sen. Regist. (Anaesth.) Christchuch, NZ; Regist. (Anaesth.) Roy. Infirm. Edin. Train. Scheme.

RAY, David William 270 Brooklands Road, Manchester M23 9HD Tel: 0161 962 6049 Fax: 0161 275 5958 Email: dray@fsi.scg.man.ac.uk — MB ChB 1987 Manch.; PhD Manch. 1994; MRCP (UK) 1990. (Manch.) Research Fell., Manch. Univ. Socs: N. W. Eudocrae Soc.; Soc. Eudocreuology. Prev: Lect. (Med.) Manch. Univ.; Vis. Fell. Cedars-Sinai Med., Center, Los Angeles, USA.

RAY, Debendra 157 Cambridge Road, Seven Kings, Ilford IG3 8LZ — MB BS 1967 Utkal; MRCPsych 1974.

RAY, Debi 32 Monkhams Drive, Woodford Green IG8 0LE — MB BS 1998 Lond.; MB BS Lond 1998.

RAY, Mr Dilip Kumar 3 Regpree Court, 45-47 South Park Road, Wimbledon, London SW19 8RS Email: dkray@resed.ac.uk — MB BS 1972 Calcutta; FRCS Ed. 1984. (Calcutta Nat. Medical Coll., INDIA)

RAY, Dipak Kumar 36 Lilian Road, Blackwood NP12 1DN Tel: 01495 224267 — MB BS 1955 Calcutta; MRCGP 1971.

RAY, Dominic Andres Anthony HCI International Medical Centre, Beardmore St., Clydebank G81 4HX — MB ChB 1982 Birm.; MSc Birm. 1991; FRCA 1987; DA (UK) 1985. (Birm.) Dir. of Cardiac Anaesth. Health Care Internat. Glas. Socs: Soc. Computing & Technol. in Anaesth.; UK Assoc. Cardiothoracic Anaesth.; Eur. Assoc. Cardiothoracic Anaesth. Prev: Sen. Regist. (Anaesth.) W.

Midl. Train. Scheme; Regist. (Anaesth.) Centr. Birm.; Regist. (Anaesth.) Russells Hall Hosp. Dudley.

***RAY, Elizabeth Helen** 12 St Gerards Road, Solihull B91 1TZ; 7 Canons Way, Tavistock PL19 8BJ Tel: 01822 614775 — MB ChB 1995 Leic.

RAY, Gautam 13 Abbots Lane, Kenley CR8 5JB — MB BS 1989 Lond.

RAY, J N The Medical Centre, Gun Lane, Strood, Rochester ME2 4UW Tel: 01634 727888 — MB BS 1973 Patna; MB BS 1973 Patna.

RAY, Jacqueline Anne Adam Practice, Upton Health Centre, Blandford Road North, Poole BH16 5PW Tel: 01202 622339; Elisir, 231 Sandbanks Road, Lilliput, Poole BH14 8EY — BM 1988 Soton.; MRCGP 1992; DRCOG 1991. Clin. Asst. (A & E) Poole Hosp. Trust. Socs: MDU; MSS. Prev: Trainee GP Lymington Hants.; SHO (A & E) Soton. Gen. Hosp.; SHO (Med.) Lymington Hosp.

RAY, Jagadis Chandra (Surgery), 117 Fulbourne Road, Walthamstow, London E17 4HA Tel: 020 8527 6373 — MB BS 1958 Calcutta.

RAY, Julian Lincoln Dept. of Clinical Neurophysiology, Box 124, Addenbrooke's Hospital, Cambridge CB4 1DG Tel: 01223 217136 Fax: 01223 336941 Email: j.l.ray@medscl.cam.ac.uk; 40 Newmarket Street, Norwich NR2 2DW Tel: 01603 665815 Email: julianray@hotmail.com — MB BS 1994 Lond.; BSc, physilogy, 1991; MRCP U.K. 1999. Specialist Regist., Clin. Neuropath., Addenbrooke's Hosp. Camb. Prev: SHO, Med. Rotat., Norf. & Norwich Hosp.

RAY, Kamala Braidholm, 3 Kenmure Road, Glasgow Whitecraigs, Glasgow G46 6TU Tel: 0141 639 7055 — MB BS 1974 Patna; MRCPI 1985; DCH Eng. 1980; DCH RCPSI 1980. (P. of Wales Med. Coll.) Regist. (Med. Paediat.) Inverclyde Roy. Hosp. Greenock; Clin. Med. Off. Lanarksh.; Assoc. Specialist (Community Child Health) Lanarksh. Socs: Ordinary Mem. Roy. Coll. Paediat. & Child Health; Roy. Coll. Phys. of Irel.; Fell. Soc. Pub. Health. Prev: Regist. (Med. Paediat.) Roy. Liverp. Childr. Hosp. Heswall; SHO (Med. Paediat.) Marston Green Hosp., E. Birm. Hosp. & Sydenham Childr. Hosp. Lond.

RAY, Mr Kartik Chandra Sai Medical Centre, 10 Moat Road, Walsall WS2 9PJ Fax: 01922 614088; 10 Moat Road, Walsall WS2 9PJ Tel: 01922 647353 Fax: 01922 614088 — MB BS 1966 Calcutta; MS Bihar 1969; DGO 1968; MRCOG 1976; FICS 1978; MD Act Medicine; Dip. Med. Acupunc. Vis. Gyn. Colthorpe Nursing Home Birm. Socs: Med. Protec. Soc.; Brit. Accupunc. Soc. Prev: Cons. Gyn. Leeds Private Hosp.

RAY, Kausik Kumar Cardiology Department, Northern General Hospital, Herries Road, Sheffield S5 7AU Email: kausk@optocardio.demon.co.uk; 18 Monteney Gardens, Ecclesfield, Sheffield S59DY Tel: 0114 2570587 — MB ChB 1991 Birm.; BSc (Hons. Pharm.) Birm. 1988; MRCP (Ed.) 1994. (Birmingham) Spr Cardiol., N. trent. Socs: BMA; Fell. Roy. Soc. Med. Prev: Ho. Phys. E. Birm. Hosp.; Ho. Surg. Good Hope Dist. Gen. Hosp. Sutton Coldfield.; Career SHO Rotat. (Med.) Dudley Rd. Hosp. Birm.

RAY, Lesley Carol Windyridge, Forge Lane, Little Aston, Sutton Coldfield B74 3BE — MB BS 1993 Lond.

RAY, Mary 5 St Margaret's Close, Shady Bower, Salisbury SP1 2RY Tel: 01722 336967 — MB BS 1980 Poona; MRCP Ed. 1986.

RAY, Nandini Whipps Cross Hospital, Leytonstone, London E11 1NR Tel: 020 8539 5522 — MB BS 1984 Calcutta; FCOphth 1991; MCOphth 1990.

RAY, Narendra Kumar Victoria Road Health Centre, Victoria Road, Washington NE37 2PU Tel: 0191 415 5656; 1 Dalmahoy, Washington NE37 1SF — MB BS 1972 Utkal. (Utkal) GP Washington, Tyne & Wear.

RAY, Natasha Ground Floor Flat, 264 Camden Road, London NW1 9AB — MB BS 1998 Lond.; MB BS Lond 1998.

RAY, Nicolette Louise Flat 13, Arnhem Wharf, 2 Arnhem Place, London E14 3RU — MB BS 1996 Lond.

RAY, Paramita 28 Whitwell Acres, High Shincliffe, Durham DH1 2PX — MB ChB 1994 Dundee; DRCO 1997. SHO. Socs: MPS.

RAY, Patricia Jane 319 Chapeltown Road, Leeds LS7 3JT Tel: 0113 262 1013; Stable Cottage, Steep, Petersfield GU32 1AE — MB BS 1975 Lond.; MRCP (UK) 1976; MRCGP 1984.

RAY, Mr Prabhat Kumar 3 Balfron Place, Aberdeen AB15 6HW Tel: 01224 314034 — MB BS 1949 Calcutta; FRCS Ed. 1964; DO

RAY

Eng. 1953. (Calcutta) Cons. Ophth. Aberd. Teach. Hosps.; Sen. Clin. Lect. in Ophth. Aberd. Univ. Prev: Regist. Glas. Eye Infirm.; Clin. Tutor in Ophth. Aberd. Univ. & Sen. Regist. Aberd. Gen. Hosps.; Cons. Ophth. Lanarksh. Area.

RAY, Roberta Jane Department of Anaesthetics, Salisbury District Hospital, Salisbury Tel: 01722 336262; Awbridge Farm, Dunbridge Lane, Awbridge, Romsey SO51 0GQ Tel: 01794 340095 — MB ChB 1978 Leeds; FFA RCSI 1984. (Leeds) p/t Cons. Anaesth. Salisbury Dist. Hosp.

RAY, Ronnie Aurun 12 Wildwood Gardens, Apartment F/2, Port Washington, New York NY 11050, USA; 20 Heathfielde, Lyttelton Road, London N2 0EE — MB BS 1984 Lond.; BSc Lond. 1980; US Boards in Anat. Clin. Path. 1990. Attend. Pathologist St. Vincents Hosp. Richmond, USA. Socs: Univ. Lond. Convocation & NY Path. Soc. Prev: Attend. Pathologist Glen Core, NY, USA; Sen. Regist. Roy. Free Hosp. Lond.; Fell. Gastrointestinal & Surg. Path. New Eng. Deacones Hosp. Boston, USA.

RAY, Ruth Elaine Easterhill, Galachlaw Shot, Edinburgh EH10 7JF Tel: 0131 445 5676 — MB ChB 1982 Ed.; BSc Med. Sc. Ed. 1979, MB ChB 1982; MRCGP 1986; DRCOG 1986. Staff Grade (Dermat.) Edin.

RAY, Sarbani 30 Colin Gardens, London NW9 6EJ — MB ChB 1993 Birm.

RAY, Simon Guy Department of Cardiology, Wythenshawe Hospital, Southmoor Road, Manchester M23 9LT Tel: 0161 291 2402 Fax: 0161 291 2389 — MB ChB 1983 Bristol; 2001 FESC; MD Bristol 1993, BSc (Hons.) 1980; MRCP (UK) 1986; FACC 1996; FRCP 1999. Cons. Cardiol. Regional Cardiothoracic Centre Wythenshawe Hosp. Manch. Prev: Sen. Fell. (Cardiol.) Vancouver Hosp. Vancouver, Canada; Sen. Regist. (Cardiol.) Cardiothoracic Centre Liverp.; Regist. (Cardiol.) Freeman Hosp. Newc. u. Tyne.

RAY, Sisir Beaufort Gardens Surgery, 2 Beaufort Gardens, Hendon, London NW4 3QP Tel: 020 8202 2141 Fax: 020 8203 3638 Email: harleystmedicare@yahoo.co.uk — MB BS 1961 Calcutta. (Medical coll. Calcutta)

RAY, Subal Chandra Walton Hospital, Chesterfield S40 3HN Tel: 01246 277271; 28 Carnoustie Avenue, Walton, Chesterfield S40 3NN Tel: 01246 204852 — MB BS 1968 Calcutta; FCCP USA 1991; DTM & H Liverp. 1985; DCH Calcutta 1970. Staff Grade Phys. (Med. for Elderly) Walton Hosp. Chesterfield. Prev: Indep. Pract. India; SHO (Acute Med. for Elderly) Luton & Dunstable Hosp. & St. Lukes Hosp. Huddersfield; SHO (Rheum. & Rehabil. & Gen. Med.) Morriston Hosp. Wales.

RAY, Subrata Newtown Health Centre, 171 Melbourne Avenue, Newtown, Birmingham B19 2JA Tel: 0121 554 7541 Fax: 0121 515 4447; 20 Heaton Drive, Edgbaston, Birmingham B15 3LW Tel: 0121 454 0395 — MB BS 1964 Calcutta; MFFP 1993; DObst RCOG 1971. (R.G. Kar Med. Coll.)

RAY, Mr Sudip Abhijit Boughton House, Coalecroft Road, London SW15 6LP Tel: 020 8878 5745 Fax: 020 8878 8113 Email: sudip_a_ray@hotmail.com — MB BS 1986 Lond.; MA 1987 Oxf.; MS Lond. 1996; FRCS Lond. 1990; FRCS (Gen.) 1997. (Westm.) Cons. Vasc. & Gen. Surg. Kingston, Roehampton & Char. Cross Hosp. Prev: Sen. Regist. (Surg.) St. Geo. Hosp. Lond.; Sen.Regist.(Surg) St.Thos.Hosp.Lond.

RAY, Sukamal 51 Golders Gardens, London NW11 9BS Tel: 020 8458 6093 — MB BS 1956 Calcutta; FFA RCS Eng. 1969; DA Eng. 1962. Socs: Assn. Anaesths. Gt. Brit. Prev: Anaesth. Regist. Derbysh. Roy. Infirm., Centr. Middlx. Gp. Hosps. & Roy. Nat. Throat, Nose & Ear Hosp.

RAY, Susmita c/o Mrs R. Rose, 6 Wolsey Court, Harben Road, London NW6 4RG — MB BS 1967 Calcutta; DGO Calcutta 1968. (Calcutta Med. Coll.) Prev: SHO (Gyn.) N. Tees-side Gp. Hosps.; SHO (Gyn. & Obst.) Norf. & Norwich Hosp. & Friarage Hosp.; N.allerton.

RAY-CHAUDHURI, Dominic Sunay 8 Elsee Road, Rugby CV21 3BA — MB BS 1990 Lond.; MRCP (UK) 1993. Regist. (Radiol.) Roy. Hallamsh. Hosp. Sheff.

RAY CHAUDHURI, Kallol 42 Minet Avenue, London NW10 8AH Tel: 020 8965 8937; 8 Williams Lane, Calcutta 700009, India Tel: 50 0669 — MB BS 1983 Calcutta; MRCP (UK) 1986, Lect. & Hon. Sen. Regist. (Neurol.) King's Coll. Hosp. & Maudsley Hosp. Lond. Socs: Clin. Autonomic Res. Soc. & Lond. Hypertens. Soc. Prev: Lect. Leicester Univ.; Research Fell. Inst. Neurol. & Nat. Hosp. Neurol. &

Neurosurg. & St. Mary's Hosp. Med. Sch. Lond.; Regist. (Neurol.) Hammersmith Hosp. Lond.

RAY CHAUDHURI, Rita 96 Moorland View Road, Walton, Chesterfield S40 3DF — MB BS 1976 Mysore. Sessional Med. Off. Blood Transfus. Trent Region Sheff..

RAY-CHAUDHURI, Simon Bibek 8 Elsee Road, Rugby CV21 3BA — MB BS 1990 Lond.

RAY-CHAUDHURI, Subrata Moultrie House, 6 Moultrie Road, Rugby CV21 3BD Tel: 01788 61313; 8 Elsee Road, Rugby CV21 3BA — MB BS 1960 Calcutta.

RAYANI, Ashok Patel Grove Medical Centre, 6 Uplands Terrace, Uplands, Swansea SA2 0GU Tel: 01792 643000 Fax: 01792 472800; The Paddock, Gowerton Road, Three Crosses, Swansea SA4 3PX — MB BCh 1982 Wales; MRCGP 1986. (Welsh Nat. Sc. Med.) GP Walter Rd. Med. Gp.

RAYANI, Atual Jayantilal 1 Heol-y-Parc, Pontardawe, Swansea SA8 3BN Tel: 01792 830307 — BM BS 1985 Nottm.; MRCGP 1994. (Nottm.) Hosp. Pract. (Rheum.) Swansea.

RAYAT, Salinder Theobald Centre, 119-121 Theobald Street, Borehamwood WD6 4PU Tel: 020 8953 3355 — MB BS 1985 Lond.; AKC.

RAYATT, Mr Sukhbir Singh Dept of Plastic Surgery, Sandwell Healthcare NHS Trust, West Bromwich B71 4HJ; 163 Horsenden Lane South, Perivale, Greenford UB6 7NR — MB BS 1993 Lond.; BDS Lond. 1984; FRCS Eng. 1996; LDS RCS Eng. 1985; FDS RCS Eng. 1992. (UMDS St. Thos.)

RAYBOULD, Adrian David University College Hospital of Wales, Heath Park, Cardiff CF14 4XN — MB BS 1993 Lond.; BSc Lond. 1990; MRCP (UK) 1997. Specialist Regist. (Cardiol.) Univ. Hosp. of Wales Cardiff.

RAYBOULD, Ronald Henry (retired) 3 Wharfedale Rise, Bradford BD9 6AU Tel: 01274 543493 — MB ChB Leeds 1958. Prev: GP Bradford.

RAYBOULD, Sarah Anne John Tasker House Surgery, 56 New Street, Great Dunmow, Dunmow CM6 1BH Tel: 01371 872121 Fax: 01371 873793 — BSc Wales 1978, MB BCh 1981; MRCP (UK) 1984; DCH RCP Lond. 1988; DRCOG 1988.

RAYCHAUDHURI, Debnarayan 187 Brentwood Road, Romford RM1 2SJ Tel: 01708 61442 — MB 1943 Calcutta; TDD Wales 1954; FCCP 1956. (Carmichael Med. Coll. Calcutta) Socs: BMA. Prev: Med. Off. i/c Gp. of Chest Clinics Calcutta Corp.; Sen. Consult. Tuberc. & Chest Dis. Govt. N.. Nigeria; Mem. Advis. Bd. Tuberc. Federal Govt. Nigeria.

RAYCHAUDHURI, Mr (Ray) Kaustabh 7 Albert Road, Reading RG4 7AN Riverside Farm, Huddersfield Road, Barnsley S75 4DE, 01226 777739 — MRCS 1989 Lond.; MRCOG 1993 UK; LRCP 1989 Lond. Cons., OBS & Gyn., Barnsley Dist. Gen. Hosp. Socs: Roy. Coll. of OBS & Gym; Brit. Soc. of Gyn. Endoscopy; Brit. Soc. of Fetal & Matern. Med.

RAYCHAUDHURI, Sujay c/o Mr J.P. Sinha, 71 Sussex Road, Watford WD24 5HR — MB BS 1988 Calcutta.

RAYCHOWDHURI, Mr Rajendranarayan 7 Marine Crescent, Liverpool L22 8QP — MB BS 1958 Calcutta; FRCS Ed. 1972.

RAYMAKERS, Katharine Lois Maria The Health Centre, Madeira Road, West Byfleet, Weybridge Tel: 01932 340411; Summerhill Cottage, 9 Crawley Hill, Camberley GU15 2DA — MB BS 1986 Lond.; MRCGP 1996; DRCOG 1989.

RAYMAKERS, Mr Roeland Leonard Nuffield Hospital Leicester, Scaptoft Lane, Leicester LE5 1HY Tel: 0116 276 9401 Fax: 0116 246 1076; Wheelwrights, 5 Top Yard Farm, Burnmill Road, Great Bowden, Market Harborough LE16 7JB Tel: 01858 466605 — MB BS Lond. 1957; FRCS Eng. 1965; MRCS Eng. LRCP Lond. 1957. (Westm.) Emerit. Cons. Orthop. Surg. Leicester AHA; Cons. Orthop. Surg. Private Pract. Nuffield Hosp. Leicester. Socs: Fell. BOA (Fell.Brit. Orthopaedic Assoc.; BMA; Hosp. Cons. & Spec. Assn. Prev: Clin. Head Orthop. Serv. Leic. Roy. Infirm.; Sen. Regist. Harlow Wood Orthop. Hosp.; Regist. Roy. Nat. Orthop. Hosp.

RAYMAN, Gerrard Diabetic Centre, Ipswich Hospital, Ipswich IP4 5PD Tel: 01473 704183 Fax: 01473 704197 — MB BS 1976 Lond.; MD Lond. 1992; MRCP (UK) 1979; FRCP Lond 1998. (Middlesex Hosp) Cons. Phys. (Gen. Med., Diabetes & Endocrinol.) Ipswich Hosp.

RAYMENT, Alan Overdale Medical Practice, 207 Victoria Avenue, Borrowash, Derby DE72 3HG Tel: 01332 280800 Fax: 01332

669256 — MB ChB 1969 Manch.; DObst RCOG 1971. (Manch.) Socs: BMA. Prev: Ho. Off. Dept. Med. & Ho. Surg. Manch. Roy. Infirm.; SHO (Anaesth. & O & G) Nott. City Hosp.

RAYMOND, Christopher John Parkfield Health Centre, Sefton Road, New Ferry, Wirral CH62 5HS Tel: 0151 644 0055 Fax: 0151 643 1679; Redwynde, 4 North Close, Bromborough, Wirral CH62 2BU Tel: 0151 334 5206 — MB ChB 1979 Liverp.; DRCOG 1982. Prev: Trainee GP/SHO Clatterbridge Hosp. Bebington VTS; Ho. Off. Roy. Liverp. Hosp.

RAYMOND, Frances Lucy Dept. Medical Genetics, Cambridge Inst. Of Medical Research, Addenbrookes Hospital, Cambridge CB2 2XY — MB BS 1989 Lond.; MA Oxf. 1981, DPhil 1984; MRCP (UK) 1992.

RAYMOND, Frank Damian 230 Cambridge Road, Hitchin SG4 0JW Tel: 01462 53159 — MB BS 1988 Lond.; PhD Lond. 1981, MSc 1976, BSc (Hon) 1974.

RAYMOND, George Philip Maurice 21 Brampton Grove, London NW4 4AE — MB ChB 1951 Ed.; DA Eng. 1957. (Ed.) Prev: Regist. (Anaesth.) Poplar Hosp.; SHO (Surg. & Orthop.) Ipswich & E. Suff. Hosp.; SHO (O & G) W.wood Hosp. Beverley.

RAYMOND, Martin Paul Chatsworth, Flat 6, 5 Wollaston Road, Bournemouth BH6 4AR — MB BS 1998 Lond.; MB BS Lond 1998.

RAYMOND, Mr Santhiapillai Paulpillai 11 Faircross Way, St Albans AL1 4RT — MB BS 1972 Sri Lanka; FRCS Ed. 1983.

RAYMOND, Thomas Michael James Richard Low Green Farm, Lindale, Grange-over-Sands LA11 6ND — MB BS 1996 Lond.

RAYMOND-JONES, John Graham 21 Barn Close, Camberley GU15 2HW — MB BS 1963 Lond.

RAYMONT, Vanessa 139 St Josephs Vale, London SE3 0XQ — MB ChB 1993 Birm.; MRCPsych 1998. Specialist Regist. Psychiat. Maudsley Hosp, Lond. Prev: Regist. Rotat. & SHO Rotat. (Psychiat.) St. Geo. Hosp. Lond.; Ho. Off. Medway Hosp. Gillingham & Bromley Hosp. Kent.

RAYNAL, Anne Louise EMAS, HSE, Intercity House, Mitchell Lane, Bristol BS1 6AN Tel: 01179 886003 — MB ChB 1979 Cape Town; MSc Lond. 1982; MFOM RCP Lond. 1994, AFOM 1992; MFPHM RCP (UK) 1989; DPH RIPHH 1982. Her Majesty's Insp. of Health & Safety (Med.) Wales & W.Region, Bristol. Socs: Soc. Occupat. Med. (SW Br.). Prev: Cons. Occupat. Phys. NHS Gloucestershire; Regional Med. Advisor Brit. Gas W. Midl.; Mine Med. Off. E. Rand Proprietary Mine S. Afr.

RAYNE, David Saint Hildas Surgery, 50 St Hildas Street, Sherburn, Malton YO17 8PH; 5 Saint Hilda's Crescent, Sherburn, Malton YO17 8PJ Tel: 01944 710175 Email: david@healthcare.org.uk — MB BS 1977 Lond. (Univ. Coll. Hosp.) Hosp. Practitioner (Gastroenterol.) ScarBoro. HA.

RAYNE-DAVIS, Clement Walter Richard 21 Galton Road, Westcliff on Sea SS0 8LE — MRCS Eng. LRCP Lond. 1937; MA, BM BCh Oxon. 1938. (Middlx.) Squadron Ldr. RAFVR. Socs: BMA. Prev: Ho. Surg. Roy. W. Sussex Hosp. Chichester.

RAYNER, Caroline Ann Longshoot Health Centre, Scholes, Wigan WN1 3NH Tel: 01942 242610 Fax: 01942 826612; 31 Riversmeade, Leigh WN7 1JA — MB ChB 1986 Manch.; MRCGP 1992; DCH RCP Lond. 1991. Trainee GP/SHO Bolton Gen. Hosp. VTS.

RAYNER, Charlotte Frances Jessica Chest Clinic, St Georges Hospital, Blackshaw Road, London SW17 0QT Tel: 020 8725 1262 Fax: 020 8725 3369; 12 Clairview Road, London SW16 6TX — MB BS 1985 Lond.; MD Lond. 1995; MRCP (UK) 1988; FRCP 2000. (St. Thos.) Cons. Thoracic & Gen. Med. St. Geo. Hosp. Lond. Prev: Sen. Regist. Roy. Brompton & St. Geo.'s Hosp.

RAYNER, Christopher Martin 6 White House Drive, Guildford GU1 2SU — MB BS 1972 Lond.; MRCGP 1976; DObst RCOG 1974.

RAYNER, Clare Rachel North Manchester General Hospital, Delaunay's Road, Manchester M8 — MB ChB 1990 Manch.; MRCGP 1994. Specialist Regist. Occupat. Health N. W. Region.

RAYNER, Mr Colin Robert Wilfred BUPA Parkway Hospital, 1 Damson parkway, Solihull B91 2PP; 64 Wellington Road, Edgbaston, Birmingham B15 2ET Tel: 0121 244 8566 — MB BS Lond. 1964; MS Lond. 1978; FRCS Ed. 1982; FRCS Eng. 1969. (Middlx.) Cons. Plastic SurgBupa Pk.way Hosp; Clin. Dir. Burns & Plastic Surg. Birm.; BUPA S. Bank Hosp Worcester. Prev: Cons.

Plastic Surg. S. Birm. HA; Cons. Plastic Surg. Grampian HB; Clin dir.Burns & Plastic Surg. Univ.Hosp.Birm.

RAYNER, Helen Catherine Anne 291 Milkwood Road, Herne Hill, London SE24 0HE — MB BS 1986 Lond.

RAYNER, Hugh Clive Birmingham Heartlands Hospital, Bordesley Green E., Birmingham B9 5SS Tel: 0121 424 2158 Fax: 0121 424 1159 — MB BS 1981 Lond.; MA Camb. 1982; MD Leic. 1990; MRCP (UK) 1984; Dip. Med. Educat. Dund 1996; FRCP 1998. Cons. Renal. Med. Birm. Heartlands Hosp.; Hon. Clin. Sen. Lect. Univ. Birm.; Med. Director (Med.Serv.s) Birm. Heartlands and Solihull NHS Trust (Teachg.). Socs: Assn. for Study of Med. Educat.; Renal Assn.; Amer. Soc. Nephrol. Prev: Sen. Regist. (Nephrol. & Gen. Med.) Leeds Gen. Infirm. & St. Jas. Univ. Hosp. Leeds; Renal Fell. P. Henry's Hosp. Melbourne, Austral.; NKRF Research Fell. (Renal Med.) Leic.

RAYNER, Ian Robert Bridge House, 509 Aldridge Road, Birmingham B44 8NA Tel: 0121 685 6730 Fax: 0121 344 4645; 5 Oakwood Close, Shenstone, Lichfield WS14 0JJ Email: irayn@aol.com — MB ChB 1983 Birm.; MRCPsych 1990. (Birm.) Cons. Old Age Psychiat. N. Birm. Ment. Health NHS Trust. Prev: Regist. Rotat. (Psychiat.) Birm.

RAYNER, Jane Ann The White House, Stoney Lane, Coleorton, Leicester LE67 8JJ — MB ChB 1987 Sheff.; MRCGP (Distinc.) 1992; DRCOG 1992. Staff Grade Phys. (Diabetes & Med.) Derbysh. Roy. Infirm. Derby; Med. Assessor for Indep. Tribunal Serv.

RAYNER, Jonathan Machan Hockin Ramsbury Surgery, High Street, Ramsbury, Marlborough SN8 2QT Tel: 01672 520366 Fax: 01672 520180; Yew Tree House, South St, Aldbourne, Marlborough SN8 2DW Tel: 01672 541418 Fax: 01672 541419 Email: raynerjmh@hotmail.com — MB BS 1983 Lond.; D. Occ. Med. 2001; DCH RCP Lond. 1988.

RAYNER, Juliet Mary The Surgery, Elsenham, Bishop's Stortford CM22 6LA Tel: 01279 814730 Fax: 01279 647342; Blythwood Lodge, 68 Silver St, Stansted Mountfitchet, Stansted CM24 8HD Tel: 01279 812271 — MB ChB 1972 Birm.; DObst RCOG 1974. (Birm.)

***RAYNER, Kirsty Elizabeth** Ballaghy, Bovingdon Green, Marlow SL7 2JQ Tel: 01628 486895 — MB ChB 1997 Birm.

RAYNER, Linda Dawn — MB ChB 1977 Bristol; DRCOG 1980. p/t Asst. GP, Badewell Med. Centre, Bristol. Prev: Clin. Med. Off. (Disabelm. Serv.) S.mead Hosp. Bristol.; Clin. Asst. Psychiat. Barrow Hosp. Bristol.; Clin. Med. Off. (Family Plann.) S.mead Hosp. Bristol.

RAYNER, Lisa White House, Bardsea, Ulverston LA12 9QT — MB ChB 1993 Leeds.

RAYNER, Mary Millicent The White House, 33 Meadow Hill Road, King's Norton, Birmingham B38 8DF Tel: 0121 458 6595 Fax: 0121 458 6595 Email: 101551.3354@compuserve.com — MRCS Eng. LRCP Lond. 1947; MRCGP 1973. (Birm.) Socs: Fac. Homoeop. (Sec. Midl. Br.). Prev: Med. Off. Bournville Trust AlmsHo.s; Med. Off. Monyhull Hosp. Birm.; Med. Off. St. Francis Sch.

RAYNER, Nigel 1 Rose Cottages, Bissoe Road, Carnon Downs, Truro TR3 6JA — MB ChB 1990 Leic.

RAYNER, Paul Henry Walter Institute of Child Health, Clinical Research Block, Whittall St., Birmingham B4 6NH Tel: 0121 333 9999 Fax: 0121 333 8701; 219 Harborne Park Road, Harborne, Birmingham B17 0BQ Tel: 0121 426 5870 Fax: 0121 428 4414 — MB ChB Birm. 1960; BSc (Hons.) Birm. 1957; FRCP Lond. 1978, M 1964; FRCPCH 1997. (Birm.) Hon. Sen. Research Fell. & Hon. Cons. Paediat. Childr. Hosp. Birm. Prev: Sen. Lect. (Paediat.) Univ. Birm.

RAYNER, Philip Michael Charles The Surgery, 2A St. Wilfrids Square, Calverton, Nottingham NG14 6FP Tel: 0115 965 2294 Fax: 0115 965 5898; 11 Beaumont Avenue, Southwell NG25 0BB — MB ChB 1985 Leeds; MB ChB (Hons.) Leeds 1985; MRCP (UK) 1989; MRCGP 1995. (Univ. Leeds) Prev: Regist. Adelaide Childr. Hosp. S. Austral.

RAYNER, Philip Robert 5 Priory Close, Walton, Chesterfield S42 7HQ — MB ChB 1975 Sheff.; BSc (Hons.) Lond. 1972; FFA RCSI 1980; FFA RCS Eng. 1980. Cons. Anaesth. N. Derbysh. HA.

RAYNER, Robin Arthur Manor Farm Medical Centre, Mangate Street, Swaffham PE37 7QN Tel: 01760 721786 Fax: 01760 723703; Hill House, North Pickenham, Swaffham PE37 8JZ Tel: 01760 440679 — MB BS 1971 Lond.; MRCS Eng. LRCP Lond. 1971; Cert. JCC Lond. 1977; DObst RCOG 1973. (St. Bart.) Socs:

RAYNER

BMA. Prev: Med. Off. DoH Bermuda; SHO (Paediat.) Pembury Hosp. Kent.; SHO (O & G) Freedom Fields Hosp. Plymouth.

RAYNER, Rosemary Jane Department of Paediatrics, New Cross Hospital, Wolverhampton WV10 0QP Tel: 01902 307999 Fax: 01902 643051 Email: drrayner@rwh-tr.wmids.nhs.uk; 100 Streetly Lane, Four Oaks, Sutton Coldfield B74 4TB Tel: 0121 353 0854 Fax: 01902 643051 — MB BS 1981 Lond.; MA Camb. 1982; DM Nottm. 1991; MRCP (UK) 1984; FRCPCH 1997; DCH RCP Lond. 1983. (Cambridge/London Hospital) Cons. Paediat. Wolverhampton; Clin. Dir. Child. Servs. Roy. Wolverhampton Hosps. NHS Trust; Hon. Sen. Lect. Univ. Birm. Med. Sch. Socs: MDU; BMA & Brit. Paediat. Respirat. Gp.; Roy. Coll. Paeds. & Child Health - Clin. Directors Gp.. Prev: Research Fell. (Cystic Fibrosis) City Hosp. Nottm.; Sen. Regist. (Paediat.) Leeds; Regist. (Paediat.) City Hosp. Nottm.

RAYNER, Sandra Anne Immunology Department, ICSM, Hammersmith Hospital, Du Cane Road, London W12 0NN Tel: 020 8383 8174 Fax: 020 8383 2788 Email: srayner@ic.ac.uk; Flat 2, 17 Adamson Road, London NW3 3HV Tel: 020 7586 7920 — MB BChir 1988 Camb.; MA Camb. 1990, BA 1986; FRCOphth 1994. Research Regist. (Immunol.) Hammersmith Hosp. Lond.

RAYNER, Sarah Ann Louise 45 Malvern Avenue, Fareham PO14 1QB — MB ChB 1998 Bristol.

RAYNER, Shaun Price and Partners, The Surgery, Park Road, Holbeach, Spalding PE12 7EE Tel: 01406 423288 Fax: 01406 426284; White House, Bardsea, Ulverston LA12 9QT Tel: 01229 88542 — MB ChB 1985 Leeds. Trainee GP Hull VTS. Prev: Ho. Off. (Med. & Surg.) Airedale Gen. Hosp. Steeton.

RAYNER, Mr Simeon Sharratt Lister House Surgery, Lister House, 53 Harrington Street, Pear Tree, Derby DE23 8PF Tel: 01332 271212 Fax: 01332 271939; 26 Stourport Drive, Chellaston, Derby DE73 1PX Tel: 01332 705440 — MB BS 1985 Lond.; MA Oxf. 1986; FRCS Ed. 1989; FRCS Eng. 1989; MRCGP 1992; DRCOG 1992. Prev: Trainee GP Midway; SHO (Geriat. Med.) Derbysh. Roy. Infirm.

RAYNER, Thomas William (retired) The Cedars, Kenninghall, Norwich NR16 2ED Tel: 0195 388 8242 — MB BChir 1952 Camb.; MRCGP 1968.

RAYNER, Tiina Alexandra 35 Tithebarn Street, Poulton-le-Fylde FY6 7BY — MB ChB 1994 Liverp. SHO (Med.) Blackpool Vict. NHS Trust. Prev: Ho. Off. Aintree Hosps. Trust Liverp.

RAYNES, Richard Hollings (retired) Dolphins Leap, St. Margarets Bay, Dover CT15 6HP — MB BS Lond. 1958; MFCM 1974; DPH London 1968. Prev: Med. Off. DHSS.

RAYNOR, Katherine Louise 9 Northeron, West Cross, Swansea SA3 5PJ Tel: 01792 401175 — MB BCh 1997 Wales. (Cardiff) SHO Paediat., Singleton Hosp., Swansea. Socs: MPS; BMA. Prev: SHO O & G - Singleton; SHO ENT - Singleton; SHO Ophth. - Singleton.

RAYNOR, Mathew Keith 18 Woodlands Drive, Sale M33 3PQ — MB ChB 1994 Manch. SHO (Ophth.) Soton. Eye Unit.

RAYNOR, Yvonne Margaret Marsh Street Surgery, 25A Marsh Street, Rothwell, Leeds LS26 0AG Tel: 0113 282 1571 Fax: 0113 282 4720 — MB ChB 1979 Leeds; DRCOG 1982; Cert. Family Plann. JCC 1982.

RAYNSFORD, Andrew David Singleton Hospital, Swansea SA2 8QA — MB ChB 1986 Birm.

RAYTER, Mr Zenon Department of Surgery, Level 4, Bristol Royal Infirmary, Bristol BS2 8HW Tel: 0117 928 2883; 3 Royal York Mews, Royal York Crescent, Bristol BS8 4LF — MB BS 1977 Lond.; BSc (Hons.) Lond. 1972, MS 1988; FRCS Eng. 1981. (St. Geo.) Cons. Surg. Bristol Roy. Infirm.; Hon. Sen. Lect. (Surg.) Bristol. Socs: Brit. Assn. Surgic. Oncol.; Brit. Assn. Cancer Research; Roy. Soc. Med. (Counc. Mem. Sect. Surg.). Prev: Sen. Regist. (Surg.) & Regist. St. Geo. Hosp. Lond.; Regist. (Surg.) St. Jas. Hosp. Lond.; Research Fell. Roy. Marsden Hosp.

RAYTON, Edgar Leo The Surgery, 1 Manor House Lane, Yardley, Birmingham B26 1PE Tel: 0121 743 2273 Fax: 0121 722 2037 — MB ChB 1960 Sheff. Prev: Asst. Cas. Off. Roy. Hosp. Sheff.; Sen. Ho. Off. O & G Moorgate Gen. Hosp. Rotherham; Sen. Ho. Off. Paediat. City Gen. Hosp. Sheff.

RAZA, Asif 4 Lochview Drive, Hogganfield Park, Glasgow G33 1QF — MB ChB 1991 Glas.

RAZA, Karim MRC Centre for Immune Regulation, Division of Immunity & Infection, University of Birmingham, Birmingham B15 2TT — BM BCh 1993 Oxf.; MRCP (UK) 1996. (Oxf.) ARC Clin. Research Fell., Rheum. Univ. of Birm., Birm. Prev: Research Fell. (Rheum.) Roy. Nat. Hosp. Rheumatic Dis.; SHO Rotat. (Med.) Qu. Med. Centre Nottm.; Rhematology Specialist Regist., City Hosp., Birm.

RAZA, Kazmi 58 Highfield Avenue, London NW11 9UD — MB BS 1958 Patna; MS Patna 1965, MB BS 1958, DGO 1963; FRCS Eng. 1989; FRCOG 1988, M 1970; DRCOG 1969.

RAZA, Mr Masood 155 Albert Road, London N22 7AQ — MB BS 1983 Karachi; FRCS Glas. 1991.

RAZA, Mohsin Primary Health Care Medical Centre, 31 Wargrave Road, Newton-le-Willows WA12 9QN Tel: 01925 220469 — MB BS 1967 Punjab; MB BS Punjab (Pakistan) 1967; DA Eng. 1969. (King Edwd. Med. Coll. Lahore) Prev: Regist. (Anaesth.) Lincoln Co. Hosp., St. Geo. Hosp. Lincoln & Vict. Hosp. Kirkcaldy.

RAZA, Muhammad Naeem Dorset Renal Unit, Dorset County Hospital, Williams Avenue, Dorchester DT1 2JY Tel: 01305 251150 Fax: 01305 254756; Fax: 01305 254756 — MB BS 1988 Punjab; MRCP (UK) Roy. Coll. of Physicians Lond. (Punjab Med. Coll. - Faisalabad, Pakistan) Staff Nephrologist, Dorset Renal Unit, Dorset Co. Hosp. Prev: Regist. (Renal Med.) Dorset Renal Unit Dorchester; SHO Med. Rotat., Dorchester.

RAZA, Mr Naeem 82 Salmon Street, London NW9 8PU — MB BS 1984 Karachi; FRCS Eng. 1991.

RAZA, Mr Syed Asghar 179 Burges Road, Southend-on-Sea SS1 3JP — MB BS 1983 Karachi; FRCS Ed. 1991.

RAZA, Syed Safdar St Nicholas Health Centre, Saunder Bank, Burnley BB11 2EN Tel: 01282 423677 Fax: 01282 832945 — MB BS 1969 Bihar; MB BS 1969 Bihar.

RAZA, Tanzeem Haider Acute Medicine, Royal Bournemouth Hospital, Bournemouth BH7 7DW Tel: 01202 704416 Fax: 01202 704435 Email: tanzeem.raza@rbch-tr.swestnhs.uk; Email: tanzeem@doctors.org.uk — FRCP 1999 London; MCPS 1982 Karachi; BSc 1985 Lahore; MBBS Punjab, Pakistan; FRCP 1996 Edin. (King Edward Medical College, Lahore) Cons. Phys. Gen. Med. Socs: Brit. Med. Assn.; Soc. for Acute Med.; Assn. for Study of Med. Educat. Prev: Assoc. Prof. Of Med., King Edwd. Med. Col.; Assist. Prof. of Med.; Senior Regist.

RAZA, Mr Zahid 19 Middlewood Park, Deans, Livingston EH54 8AZ Tel: 01506 412033 Fax: 01506 491147 Email: rdocvasc@aol.com — MB ChB 1990 Dundee; FRCS (Gen. & Vasc.) 20001 (Intercollegiate Exam); FRCS Ed. 1994. Specialist Regist. (Vasc. Surg.) S. E. Scot. (Ed.) HST Rotat. Prev: SHO Rotat. (Gen. Surg.) Ninewells Hosp. & Med. Sch. Dundee; Research Regist. (Vasc. Surg.) Ninewells Hosp. Dundee.

RAZACK, Mr Azad Hassan Bin Abdul 43 Daley House, Du Cane Road, London W12 0UE — MB BS 1986 Malaya; FRCS Ed. 1991.

RAZAK, Dr 26 Apple Close, Tilehurst, Reading RG31 6UR Tel: 01734 423916 Fax: 01734 423916 — MB BS 1965 Karachi; MRCPsych 1973; T(Psych) 1991; DPM Eng. 1970. (Karachi) Hon. Cons. Trans-Cultural Psychiat. Oxf. RHA. Socs: BMA. Prev: Sen. Regist. (Psychiat.) Barnet Gen. Hosp.; Sen. Regist. (Psychiat.) Napsbury Hosp.; Regist. (Psychiat.) Tooting Bec Hosp. Lond.

RAZAK, Ali Abdul Martin Roth Unit, St Marys Hospital, London Rd, Kettering NN15 7PW Tel: 01536 410141; 35 Saxon Dale, Kettering NN16 9JN — MB ChB 1975 Baghdad; DPM RCPSI 1991. Staff Grade Doctor St. Mary's Hosp. Kettering. Socs: MDU. Prev: Regist. (Psychiat.) Pk.side Hosp. Macclesfield; SHO (Psychiat.) Runwell Hosp. & Countess of Chester Hosp.

RAZAVI, Lawrence Michael c/o Royal Society of Medicine, 1 Wimpole St., London W1G 0AE — MB BS 1960 Lond.; MRCS Eng. LRCP Lond. 1960; MPH Harvard 1962. Adviser (Genetics) WHO. Socs: Fell. Roy. Soc. Med.; Harv. Med. Alumni Assn. Prev: Acad. (Med.) Oxf., Stanford & Harvard.

RAZAY, George Salim Torbay Hospital, Lawes Bridge, Newton Road, Torquay TQ2 7AA Tel: 01803 64567 — MD 1980 Aleppo; MRCP (UK) 1987.

RAZIS, Platon Anthony Department of Anaesthesia, St. George's Healthcare NHS Trust, Blackshaw Road, Tooting, London SW17 0QT Tel: 020 8725 3316 Fax: 020 8767 5216 Email: raz@windward.freeserve.co.uk — MB ChB 1979 Rhodesia; LRCP LRCS Ed. LRCPS Glas. 1979; FFA RCS Eng. 1985. Cons. Anaesth. St. Geo. & Atkinson Morley's Hosp. Lond. Socs: Assn. Anaesth.; Neuroanaesth. Soc.; Intens. Care Soc. Prev: Sen. Regist. (Anaesth.)

Univ. Coll. Hosp. Lond.; Regist. (Anaesth.) St. Geo. Hosp. Lond.; SHO (Anaesth.) Whittington & Univ. Coll. Hosps. Lond.

RAZOUQI, Bashar Mikail 5 Piper Close, Danes Court, Cardiff CF5 2RB — MB ChB 1985 Baghdad.

RAZVI, Freda Miriam 15 Beresford Park, Sunderland SR2 7JU; 21 Brandling Park,, Jesmond, Newcastle upon Tyne NE2 4RR Tel: 0191 281 1133 Email: freda@chtciu.demon.co.uk — MB ChB 1993 Dundee; MRCP UK 1997. Research Fell. (Diabetes & Endocrinol.) City Hosps. NHS Trust Birm. Socs: BMA; MDU; BDA. Prev: SHO Rotat. (Gen. Med.) S. Tees Acute NHS Trust Middlesbrough.

RAZVI, Syed Ahmed Hussain Walton Village Medical Centre, 172 Walton Village, Liverpool L4 6TW Tel: 0151 525 8254 Fax: 0151 525 6448 — MB BS 1970 Bangalore; DTM & H Liverp. 1983. Socs: Med. St Pauls. Prev: GP Saudi Arabia & Iran; Asst. Surg. Minto Eye Hosp., Bangalore.

RAZVI, Syed Omar (retired) 15 Beresford Park, Sunderland SR2 7JU Tel: 0191 565 3486 — MB BS Osmania 1955, DCP 1961. Prev: Haemat. S. Shields Gen. Hosp.

RAZZAK, Abdul 5 Heycroft, Whitefield, Manchester M45 7HX Tel: 0161 796 7063 — MB BS 1965 Karachi; BSc Karachi 1959, MB BS 1965; FFA RCS Eng. 1971; DA Eng. 1967. (Dow Med. Coll. Karachi) Cons. Anaesth. Manch. AHA (T).

RAZZAK, Abdul Haji Moosa Haji Wali Muhammad Department of Psychiatry, Charing Cross Hospital, Fulham Palace Road, London W6 8RP Tel: 020 8846 1513 — MB BS 1981 Karachi; MRCPsych 1988. Research Asst. (Psychiat.) Char. Cross & W.. Med. Sch. Lond. Prev: Regist. & Lect. Acad. Unit Horton Hosp. Epsom; Regist. Crichton Roy. Hosp. Dumfries.

RAZZAK, David (retired) Bas Séjour, Ruette des Fries, Cobo GY5 7PW Tel: 01481 57456 — BM BCh 1948 Oxf.; MA Oxf. 1951, BM BCh 1948; DA Eng. 1972; DObst RCOG 1950. Prev: GP & Chairm. Med. Staff Comm. P.ss Eliz. Hosp. Guernsey.

RAZZAK, Mr Fadhil Abdul 14 Brome Way, Spital, Bebington, Wirral CH63 9ND — MB ChB 1970 Baghdad; FRCS Glas. 1981.

RAZZAK, John Nicholas Queens Road Medical Practice, The Grange, St. Peter Port, Guernsey GY1 1RH Tel: 01481 724184 Fax: 01481 716431; Mill Lane Cottage, La Rue Des Grantez, Castel, Guernsey GY5 7QD — MB BS 1984 Lond.; MRCS Eng. LRCP Lond. 1985; MRCGP 1988; DRCOG 1990; DLO RCS Eng. 1989. (Lond. Hosp.) Socs: BMA. Prev: Trainee GP/SHO Plymouth HA VTS.

RAZZAK, Muna Salih Abdul Parkside Surgery, Tawney Street, Boston PE21 6PF Tel: 01205 365881 Fax: 01205 357583; The Burrows, Hall Lane, Frampton, Boston PE20 1AB Tel: 01205 722129 — MB ChB Baghdad 1978. (University of Baghdad) GP Boston Lincs.; Clin. Asst. Oncol.

RAZZAQ, Abdur Baillie Street Health Centre, Baillie Street, Rochdale OL16 1XS Tel: 01706 525322; 17 Norford Way, Bamford, Rochdale OL11 5QS Tel: 01706 525322 — MB BS 1959 Punjab; DTM & H RCP Lond. 1965.

RAZZAQ, Furhan 17 Norford Way, Rochdale OL11 5QS — MB ChB 1995 Manch.; MRCP (UK) 1999. (Manchester)

RAZZAQ, Ghizala Flat 3, 19 Leamington Terrace, Edinburgh EH10 4JP — MB ChB 1990 Manch.

RAZZAQ, Isma 51 Talbot Crescent, Leeds LS8 1AL — MB ChB 1993 Leeds.

RAZZAQ, Nasrin 17 Park Road, London NW4 3PT — MB ChB 1993 Manch.

RAZZAQ, Mr Quaisar Mahmood 67 Longspring, Watford WD24 6QA Tel: 01923 441274 Fax: 01923 336648 — MB ChB 1985 Aberd.; FRCS Glas. 1991; FMGEMS 1992. Cons. (A & E) N. Hants. Hosp. Basingstoke. Prev: Regist. (A & E) Good Hope Hosp. Birm.; Regist. (Cardiothoracic Surg.) W. Midl. RHA; SHO & Regist. (Cardiothoracic Surg.) St. Thos. Hosp. Lond.

RAZZAQ, Rubeena 17 Norford Way, Rochdale OL11 5QS Tel: 01706 32827 — MB ChB 1988 Manch.; FRCR (UK) 1995, MRCP (UK) 1991. Cons. Radiol., Bolton Hosp. Bolton. Prev: Regist. (Diagnostic Radiol.) Manch.; SHO (Med. Oncol. & Radiotherap.) Christie Hosp. Manch.; SHO (Med.) Burnley Gen. Hosp. & Wythenshawe Hosp. Manch.

RAZZAQ, Zohra Bano 20 Ferrers Avenue, Wallington SM6 8HD — MB BS 1966 Dacca; MB BS Dacca 1066.

RAZZAQUE, Mira Flat 37 Penthouse, Matheson Lang House, Baylis Road, Waterloo, London SE1 7AN Tel: 020 7928 5690 Email: nigel_mira@msn.com — MB BS 1990 Lond.; MRCP 1992; FFA &

Dub. 1997. (Middlx. Hosp. Univ. Coll. Med. Sch.) Specialist Regist. Rotat. (Anaesth.) NW Thames Middlx. Hosp. & Univ. Coll. Hosp. Socs: Med. Protec. Soc.; MRCAnaesth. & Dub./Lond.

RAZZAQUE, Mohammed Abdur Calderstones NHS Trust, Mitton Road, Whalley, Clitheroe BB7 9PE Tel: 01254 821312 Fax: 01254 823023; Silverley, Whitehall Terrace, Darwen BB3 2LL Tel: 01254 775808 — 1965 MB BS Rajshahi; FRCPsych Lond.; Registered on Specialist Register, Forensic Psychiatry General Medical Council, London; Registered on Specialist Register, Mental Handicap General Medical Council, Lond.; Annual Certificate of Completion of CPD, Royal College of Psychiatrists.; DFFP 1980 Lond.; Dip. Psychol. Med. RCP Lond. RCS Eng. 1973; Cert. Psychosexual Counselling Manch. 1982. (Rajshahi) Cons. Psychiat. (Ment. Handicap) N. W.. RHA & Med. Dir. Calderstone NHS Trust. Socs: Fell. Roy. Soc. Health. Prev: Sen. Regist. (Ment. Health & Develop. Paediat.) Regist. (Psychiat.).

RAZZELL, Philip John Town Medical Centre, 25 London Road, Sevenoaks TN13 1AR Tel: 01732 454545 — MB BS 1980 Lond.; BSc (Hons.) Lond. 1977; MRCS Eng. LRCP Lond. 1980; DGM RCP Lond. 1996; DRCOG 1982. (Guy's) p/t Hosp. Pract. (Geriat. Med.) S.W. Kent PCT, Sevenoaks Hosp. Kent; Hosp. Pract.(Ment. Health Serv.s for Older People) INVICTA NHS Trust, Darent Ho. Sevenoaks Hosp. Kent.

REA, Anthony James County Hospital, Greetwell Road, Lincoln LN2 5QY Tel: 01522 512512 — MB BS 1988 Lond.; BSc (Hons.) Pharmacol. & Therap. Lond. 1984; MRCP (UK) 1993; MRCS Eng. LRCP Lond. 1988. Cons. Genitourin. Med. Co. Hosp. Lincoln. Socs: Young Fell. Roy. Soc. Med. Prev: Lect. (HIV & Genitourin. Med.) Kings Coll. Hosp.; Regist. (HIV & Genitourin. Med.) Roy. Lond. Hosp.; Ho. Off. (Med.) St. Stephens Hosp. Fulham.

REA, Daniel William 7 Serpentine Road, Selly Park, Birmingham B29 7HU; 4 Queens Gate Villas, Victoria Pk Road, London E9 7BU — MB BS 1986 Lond.; BSc (Hons.) Bristol 1981; MRCP (UK) 1990.

REA, Duncan Patrick Alconbury and Brampton Surgeries, The Surgery, School Lane, Alconbury, Huntingdon PE28 4EQ Tel: 01480 890281 Fax: 01480 891787; The Haven, Horningtoft, Dereham NR20 5DP Tel: 01480 830760 Email: duncan.rea@btinternet.com — BM BCh 1992 Oxf.; MA Camb. 1993; MRCGP 1996; DRCOG 1995. Partner GP Pract. Sch. La. Alconbury Huntingdon.

REA, George Rupert Albertville Drive Surgery, 16 McCandless Street, Crumlin Road, Belfast BT13 1RU Tel: 028 9074 6308 Fax: 028 9074 9847; 69 Broadacres, Temple Patrick, Ballyclare BT39 0AY — MB BCh BAO Belf. 1966; MRCGP 1972; DObst RCOG 1970. (Queens University of Belfast) Socs: Fell. Ulster Med. Soc.; BMA (Ex-Chairm. E.. Div. N. Irel.).

REA, Irene Maeve Department of Geriatric Medicine, Queens University of Belfast, Whitla Medical Building 97 Lisburn Road, Belfast BT9 7BL Tel: 01232 245133 Fax: 01232 438346 — MB BCh BAO 1972 Belf.; MD Belf. 1986 BSc 1969; FRCP Lond. 1993; FRCP Ed. 1991; MRCP (UK) 1979. Cons. Phys. (Geriat. Med.) Belf. City Hosp.; Sen. Lect. Qu. Univ. Belf.

REA, Rt. Hon. Lord John Nicolas (retired) 11 Anson Road, London N7 0RB Tel: 020 7607 0546 Fax: 020 7687 1219 Email: reajn@parliament.uk — MB BChir Camb. 1955; MD Camb. 1969; FRCGP 1989, M 1971; DPH Lond. 1966; DCH Eng. 1957; DObst RCOG 1956. Prev: Princip. GP Lond.

REA, Margaret Alice Skeoge House, Brookeborough, Enniskillen BT94 4GN — MB BCh BAO 1993 Belf.

***REA, Melanie Jane** St. Peter's Hospital, Chertsey KT16 0PZ; 425 Fulham Palace Road, Fulham, London SW6 6SU Tel: 020 7731 5763 — MB BS 1998 Lond.; MB BS Lond 1998.

REA, Michael John 1 Airlie Street, Glasgow G12 9RH — MB ChB 1995 Glas.

REA, Owen Henry The Terrace Surgery, 2 Dhu Varren Park, Portrush BT56 8EL Tel: 028 7082 4637 Fax: 028 7082 4637 — MB BCh BAO 1984 Belf.

REA, Mr Peter Anthony The Royal National Throat, Nose and Ear Hospital, Gray's Inn Road, London WC1X 8DA Tel: 0208 562800; 4 Waldron Road, Harrow HA2 0HU Tel: 020 8422 6388 Email: peter@rea999.freeserve.co.uk — BM BCh 1991 Oxf.; MA Camb. 1988; FRCS Eng. 1995; FRCS (OTO) 1997. (Oxf.) Specialist Regist. in Otolarynogology, N. Thames Rotat. Prev: SHO Rotat. (ENT) Roy. Nat. Throat Nose & Ear Hosp. Lond.

REA, Richard Ernest Ballymena Health Centre, Cushendall Road, Ballymena BT43 6HQ Tel: 028 2564 2181 Fax: 028 2565 8919 —

REA

MB ChB 1969 Ed.; BSc Ed. 1966, MB ChB 1969; FRCGP 1991, M 1975; MICGP 1987.

REA, Rustam Denzil 69 BRoadacres, Templepatrick, Ballyclare BT39 0AY; 71 Latimer Drive, Bramcote, Nottingham NG9 3HT — BM BCh 1996 Oxf. SHO (Gen. Med.) Qu.'s Med. Centre Nottm.

REA, Shelagh Mary Ardvilla, 9 Victoria Park, Londonderry BT47 2AD Tel: 02871 348563 — MB BCh BAO 1974 Belf.; MRCPsych 1978. Cons. Psychiat. (Old Age Psychiat.) Foyle Health and Social Serv.s Trust. Socs: Mem. Roy. Coll. Psychiatr.; Ulster Med. Soc.; Brit. Feriatric Soc.

REA, Vanree Alne Cross, Alne, York YO61 1SD — MB BCh BAO 1964 Belf.; DA RCPSI 1968. (Belf.)

REA, William Edward Flat 10, Grenofen House, Grenofen, Tavistock PL19 9ES — MB BS 1996 Lond.

REACHER, Mr Mark Henry 58 Eltisley Avenue, Cambridge CB3 9JQ — MD 1995 Lond.; MB BS 1976; FRCS (Ophth.) Glas. 1984; FRCS (Gen. Surg.) Eng. 1981; MPH Johns Hopkins Univ. 1988; DO RCS Eng. 1984. (Westm.) Socs: Ophth. Soc. UK.

READ, Andrew Mabyn (retired) 26 Magdala Road, Cosham, Portsmouth PO6 2QG Tel: 01705 378185 — MRCS Eng. LRCP Lond. 1942. Prev: Asst. Phys. Chest. Clinic Portsmouth.

READ, Annette Catherine Plymouth Community Drugs Service, Plymouth Primary Care Trust, Damerel House, Damerel Cl., off Madden Road, Devonport, Plymouth PL1 4JZ Tel: 01752 56670 Fax: 01752 56670 — MB BS 1973 Lond.; BSc (Anat.) Lond. 1970; MRCPsych 1978; FRCPsych 1999. (London Hospital) Cons. Psychiat. Plymouth Comm.NHS Trust. Prev: Sen. Regist. (Psychiat.) Roy. United Hosp. Bath; Sen. Research Assoc. Avon Drug Research & Rehabil. Project Bristol; Sen. Regist. (Psychiat.) Glenside Hosp. Bristol.

READ, Bruce Alfred Norman 4 Lllington Close, Lichfield WS13 7AL Tel: 01543 262843 Email: bamyread@aol.com — MB BS 1966 Lond.; MRCS Eng. LRCP Lond. 1965. (Lond. Hosp.) Prev: Regist. (Clin. Path,) Guy's Hosp. Lond.; Regist. (Path.) Groote Scheur Hosp., Cape Town.

READ, Catherine Anne Fairways, Saltergate Lane, Bamford, Hope Valley S33 0BE — MB ChB 1983 Sheff.

READ, Colin Andrew Dept of A&E, Leicester Royal Infirmary, Leicester LE1 5WW — MB ChB 1992 Leic.

READ, David Edward The Wistaria Practice, 32 St. Thomas' Street, Lymington SO41 9NE Tel: 01590 672212 Fax: 01590 679930 — MB BS 1975 Lond.; MRCS Eng. LRCP Lond. 1975; MRCGP 1994; DRCOG 1984; FRCA. 1982. (Char. Cross) Prev: Regist. (Anaesth.) Soton HA; Trainee GP Soton VTS.

READ, David Henry Princess Royal Hospital, Lewes Road, Haywards Heath RH16 4EX — MB ChB 1973 Bristol; BSc (Hons.) Bristol 1970, MB ChB 1973; FFA RCS Eng. 1979. Cons. Anaesth. S.W. Thames RHA P.ss Roy. Hosp.

READ, David John District General Hospital, Turner Road, Colchester CO4 — BM BCh 1971 Oxf.; MRCP (U.K.) 1974.

READ, Lady (Frances Edna) 173 Bickenhall Mansions, Baker St., London W1H 3DF Tel: 020 7935 3629 — MB BCh BAO 1929 Dub.; BA, MB BCh BAO Dub. 1929; FFA RCSI 1960. (T.C. Dub.) Hon. Cons. Anaesth. Samarit. Hosp. Wom.; Hon. Anaesth. Chelsea Hosp. Wom. Prev: Sen. Res. Anaesth. Char. Cross Hosp.; Dep. Anaesth. Roy. Nat. Orthop. Hosp.; Hon. Anaesth. All St.s' Genitourin. Hosp.

READ, Gordon Alistair The Rectory Close, Hadley Common, Barnet EN5 5QD Tel: 020 8449 2679 Fax: 020 8364 8787 Email: gordonread@aol.com — MB ChB Birm. 1966; FRCR Lond. 1980; DMRT Liverp. 1977. (Birmingham) Med. Adviser,Oncol.Internat. DC Ltd; Hon. Cons. Clin. Oncol. & Radiat. Ther. Trent RHA; Cons. Clin. Oncol. Hosp. St. John & St. Eliz. Lond.; PPP/Columia Gp. of Hosps., The Lond. Clinic, The Cromwell Hosp. The Lond. Bridge. Socs: Fell. Roy. Coll. Radiologists; Brit. Inst. Radiol.; Roy. Soc. Med. Prev: Cons. Radiother. & Oncol. Lincs.; Sen. Regist. (Radiother.) W.. Gen. Hosp. Edin.; Med. Supt. Trinity Hosp. Chiromo, Malawi.

READ, Graham Royal Preston Hospital, Sharoe Green Lane N., Fulwood, Preston PR2 9HT Tel: 01772 522089 Fax: 01772 522178 Email: graham.read@patr.nhs.uk; 2 Duddon Drive, Uplands, Standish, Wigan WN6 0UJ Tel: 01257 422662 Fax: 01257 422727 Email: drgrahamread@cs.com — MB BChir 1972 Camb.; FRCP 2001; MA Camb. 1972; MRCP (UK) 1974; FRCR 1978. (Cambridge) Dir. Cancer Servs. Roy. Preston Hosp.; Director, Div. of Specialist Serv.s Roy. Preston Hosp.; Med. Director, Lanc & S.Cumbria cancer network. Socs: Amer. Soc. Clin. Oncol.; Brit. Assn. Cancer Research; Amer. Soc. Therapeutic Radiol. & Oncol. Prev: Cons. Clin. Oncol., Christie Hosp. Manch.; Sen. Regist. (Radiother.) & Regist. (Radiother.) Christie Hosp. Manch.; Sen. Health Off. (Gastroenterol.) Manch. Roy. Infirm.

READ, Gregory Martin Fressingfield Medical Centre, New Street, Fressingfield, Eye IP21 5PJ Tel: 01379 586227 Fax: 01379 588265; Old Leaf Cottage, Earsham Road, Hedenham, Bungay NR35 2DF Tel: 01508 482581 Email: greg@paston.co.uk — MB ChB 1979 Manch.; DRCOG 1984. (Univ. Manch.) Socs: BMA. Prev: SHO (Neonat. Paediat.) Bristol Matern. Hosp.; SHO (Radiother. & Oncol.) Cheltenham Gen. Hosp.; SHO (Ophth.) Leighton Hosp.

READ, Heather Susan 8 Bryce Avenue, Edinburgh EH7 6TX — MB ChB 1991 Ed.; BSc (Med. Sci.) St. And. 1987; FRCS Ed. 1995. Regist. (Orthop.) P.ss Margt. Rose Hosp. Edin. Prev: SHO Rotat. (Surg.) SE Scotl.

READ, James Adam Poole Gatton Surgery, Sutton Scotney, Winchester SO21 3LE — MB BS 1993 Lond.; MRCGP 1997; MRCGP 1997; MA Camb. 1990; DCH RCP Lond. 1996; DRCOG 1995. (Guy's Hosp. Lond.)

READ, James Dudley, OBE Tannery Buildings, 50-60 Woodgate, Loughborough LE11 2TQ Tel: 01509 611006 Fax: 01509 235560 Email: james@cams.co.uk; Greystones, 298 Forest Road, Loughborough LE11 3HX Tel: 01509 260054 Fax: 01509 260074 — MB ChB 1971 Liverp.; FRCGP 1990, M 1975; DObst RCOG 1974. Managing Dir., Lernout & Hauspie Healthcare Terminology Solutions, LoughBoro.; Dir. NHS Centre for Coding & cl.ification, LoughBoro. Prev: Med. Dir. Abies Informatics Ltd Lond.; Stuart Research Assoc. Dept. Gen. Pract. Univ. Liverp.; GP LoughBoro..

READ, James Michael 5 Strathavon Close, Cranleigh GU6 8PW — BM BS 1998 Nottm.; BM BS Nottm 1998.

READ, Jason Matthew 12 Bramber Way, Burgess Hill RH15 8JX — MB ChB 1996 Liverp.

READ, Jennifer Mary 24 Beck Road, London E8 4RE — MB BS 1991 Lond.

READ, Joan Margaret 1 Jacklyns Close, Alresford SO24 9LL — MB BS 1957 Lond.

READ, Mr John Lewis (retired) Wroxham, 196 North Road, Hertford SG14 2PJ Tel: 01992 586820 — MB BS 1954 Lond.; FRCS Ed. 1966. Prev: Cons. Orthop. Surg. P.ss Alexandra Hosp. Harlow, Co. Hosp. Hertford & Qu. Eliz. II Hosp. Welwyn Gdn. City.

READ, John Robert Montresor Anaesthetics Department, Aberdeen Royal Infirmary, Aberdeen — MB ChB 1983 Dundee; BSc 1979 Dund.; FCAnaesth. 1991; DA (UK) 1991. Sen. Regist. (Anaesth.) Aberd. Roy. Infirm. Prev: Regist. (Anaesth.) Roy. Infirm. Edin.

READ, John Roderick Dept of Histopathology, Hull Royal Infirmary, Anlaby Rd, Hull HU3 2JZ Tel: 01482 607711; 3 St. Matthew's Court, Minster Moorgate, Beverley HU17 8JH Tel: 01482 864051 — MB ChB 1969 Birm.; BSc 1966 Birm.; FRCPath 1988, M 1976. Cons. Histopath. Prev: Sen. Regist. (Morbid Anat.) King's Coll. Hosp. & Kingston-on-Thames; Hosp.; Regist. (Path.) Bristol Roy. Infirm.

READ, Jonathan Asher Jason Marcus 86 Stopples Lane, Hordle, Lymington SO41 0GL — MB BS 1998 Lond.; MB BS Lond 1998.

READ, Juliette Helen Mary The Oak House, St Ann's Hospital, St Ann's Road, London N15 3TH Tel: 020 8442 6000 — MB ChB 1990 Liverp. SHO (Psychiat.) St Anns Hosp. Lond.

READ, Katherine Gwenda 3 Arlington Villas, Bristol BS8 2ED — MB ChB 1998 Bristol.

READ, Kathleen Margaret Long View, Castle Rise, Spittal, Haverfordwest SA62 5QW — MB ChB 1971 Liverp.

READ, Mr Laurence Droitwich Private Hospital, St Andrew's Road, Droitwich WR9 8DN Tel: 01905 794793 — MB BS 1971 Lond.; BSc (Zool., Hons.) Lond. 1960, MB BS 1971; FRCS Eng. 1977; MRCS Eng. LRCP Lond. 1971. (St. Bart.) Cons. Orthop. & Traum. Surg. Alexandra Hosp., BromsGr. & Redditch HA. Socs: Brit. Orthop. Assn. & Orthop. Foot Soc. Prev: Clin. Lect. (Orthop.) & Hon. Sen. Regist. Univ. Dept. Orthop. Surg.; Hope Hosp. Salford, Lancs.; Regist. (Orthop.) Nuffield Orthop. Centre Headington.

READ, Lucien (retired) 20 Pleck Farm Avenue, Blackburn BB1 8PE Tel: 01254 53789 — MB BChir 1941 Camb.; MRCS Eng. LRCP

Lond. 1940. Hon. Cons. Venereol. Blackburn, Burnley, Chorley & Bury Hosp. Gps. Prev: Venereol. Co. Boro. Oldham.

READ, Malcolm Trevor Fitzwalter 7 Waterden Road, Guildford GU1 2AN Tel: 01483 566442 Fax: 01483 566442; Barbican Health, 3 White Lyon Court, The Barbican, London EC2Y 3EA Tel: 020 7588 3146 Fax: 020 7628 1831 — MB Camb. 1967, BChir 1966; MA Camb. 1966; DMS Med. Soc. Apoth. Lond. 1994; MRCGP 1977; DObst RCOG 1969; FISM 1999. (Camb. & St. Thos.) Orthop. & Sport Phys. Barbican Health Clinic & Guildford; Lect. & Examr. MSc Course Sports Med. Lond. Hosp. & Soc. Apoth. Socs: Brit. Assn. Sport & Med. (Chairm. SE Div.); Roy. Soc. Med.; Brit. Inst. Musculoskeletal Med. Prev: Med. Off. English Commonw. & Brit. Olympic Teams.

READ, Maria Grazyna, MBE Tel: 0114 270 0997 Fax: 0114 276 6786 Email: m.g.read@sheffield.ac.uk — MB ChB 1972 Sheff.; DCH Eng. 1974. (Sheffield) Sernor Partner, DoverCt. Surg. Prev: Research Fell. (Gastroenterol.) Roy. Hallamsh. Hosp. Sheff.; Research Fell. Univ. Texas Dallas, USA.

READ, Martin Samuel, Wing Cdr. RAF Med. Br. Retd. British Gas plc, East Midlands, PO Box 145, De Montfort St., Leicester LE1 9DB Tel: 0116 253 5638; 8 Chestnut Close, Uppingham, Oakham LE15 9TQ Tel: 01572 823309 — MB ChB 1965 Leeds; MFOM RCP Lond. 1981; DAvMed Eng. 1973; MRAeS 1981. Regional Med. Adviser Brit. Gas. plc E. Midl. Socs: Soc. Occupat. Med. & Anglo-Amer. Med. Soc. Prev: RAF Exchange Flt. Surg. HQ AFSC Andrews AFB, Washington DC, USA; Staff. Med. Off. Defence Med. Servs. Directorate MoD; DPMO HQ RAF, Germany.

READ, Martyn Sinclair Department of Anaeshetics, University Hospital of Wales, Heath Park, Cardiff CF14 4XW Tel: 029 2074 3107 Fax: 029 2074 7203 — MB BS 1981 Lond.; FFA RCS Eng. 1986. Cons. Anaesth. & ITU Univ. Hosp. Wales Cardiff. Prev: Sen. Regist. (Anaesth.) Morriston Hosp. Swansea & Univ. Hosp. Wales Cardiff; Research Asst. (Anaesth.) Univ. Hosp. Wales Cardiff; Regist. & SHO (Anaesth.) St. Mary's Hosp. Lond.

READ, Mr Michael David Maternity Department, Gloucestershire Royal Hospital, Great Western Road, Gloucester GL1 3NN Tel: 01452 528555 Fax: 01452 395556 — MD 1981, MB ChB Manch. 1970; FRCS Ed. 1976; FRCOG 1991, M 1976; FRACOG 1981, M 1981. Cons. O & G Glos. Roy. Hosp.

READ, Moira Yvonne 4 Lillington Close, Lichfield WS13 7AL Tel: 01543 262843 — MB ChB 1962 Cape Town. (Cape Town) Med. Off. MoD. Prev: Med. Off. Red Cross Childr. Hosp. Rondebosch, S. Afr. & E. Hosp. Lond.

READ, Nathanael Peter (retired) Meadow Lea, Herne Common, Herne Bay CT6 7LB Tel: 01227 375569 — MRCS Eng. LRCP Lond. 1942; FFA RCS Eng. 1954; DA Eng. 1949. Prev: Cons. Anaesth. Canterbury & Isle of Thanet Hosp. Gps.

READ, Neil Edward Sandpiper, Turvey Mill, Turvey, Bedford MK43 8ET — MB BS 1997 Lond.

READ, Nicholas John Blackmore Health Centre, Blackmore Drive, Sidmouth EX10 8ET Tel: 01395 512601 Fax: 01395 578408; 41 Woolbrook Park, Sidmouth EX10 9DX — MB BS 1984 Lond.; MRCGP 1988; DRCOG 1990. (Middlx. Hosp. Med. Sch.) Prev: GP Melbourne, Austral.; Trainee GP Exeter VTS; SHO (O & G) Odstock Hosp. Salisbury.

READ, Professor Nicholas Wallace Centre for Human Nutrition, Northern General Hospital, Sheffield S5 7AU Tel: 0114 242 1528 Fax: 0114 261 0112 Email: n.w.read@sheffield.ac.uk; 74 Nairn Street, Crookes, Sheffield S10 1UN Tel: 0114 267 8633 Email: N.W.Read@sheffield.ac.uk — MB BChir 1971 Camb.; MA Sheffield 1997; MA Camb. 1975, MD 1981; FRCP Lond. 1985; MRCP (UK) 1972. (Camb. & Lond. Hosp.) p/t Cons. Phys. Psychoanal. Psychotherapist N.. Gen. Hosp. Sheffield, Comm. Helth Sheff. Trust; Hon. Cons. Gastroenterol. Trent RHA 1981; Analyt. Psychotherapist 1993. Socs: Brit. Soc. Gastroenterol.; UK Counc. for Psychother.; Amer. Gastroenterol. Assoc. Prev: Dir. Sheff. Univ. Centre for Human Nutrit. 1990; Prof. Integrated Med. Univ. Sheff.1998-2001; Prof. Gastrointestinal Physiol. & Nutrit. Univ. Sheff. 1988-1990.

READ, Peter (retired) 15 Testwood Court, Clifton Gardens, Folkestone CT20 2EF Tel: 01303 210090 — MRCS Eng. LRCP Lond. 1947. Prev: Receiv. Room Off. Poplar Hosp.

READ, Peter Brydon (retired) Lane's End, Bowling Green Lane, Hanley Castle, Worcester WR8 0BP Tel: 01684 592776 — MB BS

Lond. 1954; DPM Eng. 1965; DObst RCOG 1960. Indep. Psychother. Worcs. Prev: Regist. Psychiat. Shenley Hosp.

READ, Peter Robert Marchfields, 6 Ashley Hill Place, Cockpole Green, Wargrave, Reading RG10 8NL Tel: 01189 401277 Fax: 01189 404287 — MB BS Lond. 1964; DSc (Hon.) De Montfont 1994; FRCP Lond. 1996; FFPM RCP (UK) 1989; DObst RCOG 1967. (Char. Cross) Chairm. Behring Diagn. UK Ltd.& Hoechst; Marion Roussel Ltd., & Hoechst Roussel Vet Ltd.; Dir. Datapharm. Pub.ats. Ltd.; Non-Exec. Dir. Hoechst Schering Agrevo UK Ltd.; Non-Exec. Dir. Vanguard Medica PLC. Prev: SHO, Ho. Phys. & Ho. Surg. Char. Cross Hosp. Lond.

READ, Mrs Priscilla Elise Smithy Hall, Cookridge Lane, Leeds LS16 7NE — BM BCh 1971 Oxf.; DCH Eng. 1974.

READ, Mr Richard Fitzwalter (retired) 3 Moyleen Rise, Marlow SL7 2DP Tel: 01628 483765 — MB BS Melbourne 1939; FRCS Eng. 1946. Prev: Cons. Gen. Surg. Hackney Hosp. Homerton. Clin. Asst. St. Peters Hosp. Lond.

READ, Robert Charles Infectious Diseases Unit, Royal Hallamshire Hospital, Sheffield S10 2JF Tel: 0114 271 3561 Fax: 0114 275 3061 Email: r.c.read@sheffield.ac.uk; Fairways, Saltergate Lane, Bamford, Hope Valley S33 0BE — MB ChB 1982 Sheff.; MD Sheff. 1992, BMedSci 1980; MRCP (UK) 1985; FRCP 1998. Cons. Phys. & Reader (Infec. Dis.) Centr. Sheff. Univ. Hosps. Socs: Infect. Dis. Soc. Amer.; Brit. Infect. Soc. (Meetings Sec.). Prev: Peel Trav. Fell. San Francisco Gen. Hosp. USA; Clin. Research Fell. Nat. Heart & Lung Inst. Roy. Brompton Hosp. Lond.; Regist. & Hon. Lect. (Med.) N.wick Pk. Hosp. & Clin. Research Centre Harrow.

READ, Sheila Mary Church View Surgery, Burley House, 15 High Street, Rayleigh SS6 7DY Tel: 01268 774477 Fax: 01268 771293 — MB ChB 1965 Leeds; DA Eng. 1972; DObst RCOG 1972.

READ, Simon Mihill The Old Vicarage, Spilsby Road, Horncastle LN9 6AL Tel: 01507 522477 Fax: 01507 522997; 40 Elmhurst Road, Horncastle LN9 5LU Tel: 01507 527108 Email: simonread@callnetuk.com — MB ChB 1982 Leeds; BSc Leeds 1979, MB ChB 1982; DRCOG 1987. (Leeds) Princip. GP Horncastle.

READ, Professor Stephen Geoffrey University of Huddersfield, Ramsden Building, Queensgate, Huddersfield HD1 3DH Tel: 01484 473498 Fax: 01484 472794 Email: s.read@hud.ac.uk; Tel: 01422 831320 — MB BS 1975 Lond.; MRCS Eng. LRCP Lond. 1975; MRCPsych. 1981; FRCPsych 1997; MD (Leeds) 1997. Prof. of Psychiat. & Cons. in Psychiat. in Learning Disabil. Leeds Community and Ment. Health Serv.s Trust and Huddersfield NHS Trust. Prev: Sen. Lect. & Cons. in Psychiat. in Learning Disabil., Univ. of Leeds & Leeds Community & Ment. Health Servs. (Teachg.) Trust.

READ, Timothy Rupert Charles Department Psychiatry, Royal London Hospital, Whitechapel, London E1 1BB Tel: 020 7375 1052 — MB BS 1982 Lond.; BSc (Hons.) Lond. 1979, MB BS 1982; MRCPsych. 1988. (Westm.) Cons. Psychiat. Roy. Lond. Hosp. Trust. Socs: Inst. Gp. Anal.; Gp. Analyt. Soc.; Assoc. Mem. Gp. Anal. Pract. Prev: Sen. Regist. (Psychiat.) Univ. Coll. Hosp. Lond.; Clin. Lect. (Psychiat. Middlx. Hosp. Lond.; Regist. (Psychiat.) St. Geo. Hosp. Lond.

READ, Zoe Helen 40 Lindford Chase, Lindford, Bordon GU35 0TB — MB BS 1998 Lond.; MB BS Lond 1998.

READE, David William The Orrell Park Surgery, 46 Moss Lane, Orrell Park, Liverpool L9 8AL Tel: 0151 525 2736 Fax: 0151 524 1037; 6 Rose Place, Aughton, Ormskirk L39 4UJ Tel: 01695 422129 — MB ChB 1986 Liverp.; MRCGP 1991. (Liverpool) Hosp. Pract. (Thoracic Med.) Aintree Chest Centre Fazakerley Hosp. Liverp.; Treas. Continuing Educat. Support Gp.; Chairm. Liverp. MAAG. Prev: Trainee GP Maghull Liverp.; SHO (A & E) Walton Gen. Hosp. Liverp.; SHO (Anaesth.) Walton Gen. Hosp. Liverp.

READE, Sophia Kathryn 10 Winsu Avenue, Paignton TQ3 1QF — MB ChB 1995 Leeds.

READER, Andrew Graham Maxwell Tel: 01444 457666 Fax: 01444 483887 — MB BS 1982 Lond.; MRCGP 1986; Cert. Family Plann. JCC 1987; DRCOG 1986. (Lond. Hosp.) Prev: Trainee GP Shoreham-by-Sea W. Sussex VTS & Worthing VTS; SHO (Psychiat.) Brighton HA.

READER, Antony Maxwell (retired) 5 The Saltings, Birdham, Chichester PO20 7JA Tel: 01243 514853 — MB BS 1950 Lond.; MRCS Eng. LRCP Lond. 1950; DObst RCOG 1955. Prev: Med. Staff Horsham Hosp.

READER

READER, Carole Alison Stanton House, Hyde Lane, Newnham GL14 1HQ — MB BCh 1984 Wales; BPharm (Hons.) Wales 1974, MB BCh 1984. GP Glos. Asst.; Sen. Clin. Med. Off. (Family Plann.).

READER, Claire Elizabeth 27 Coral Drive, Ipswich IP1 5HP — BM BS 1997 Nottm.

READER, David Cedric, Group Capt. RAF Med. Br. (retired) Kingsmede, Crondall Road, Crookham Village, Fleet GU51 5SU — MB BS Lond. 1961; PhD Lond. 1975, BSc (Physiol.) 1958; MRCS Eng. LRCP Lond. 1961. Prev: Commanding Off. Aviat. Med. Train. Centre.

READER, Frances Clare Ipswich Hospital NHS Trust, Heath Road, Ipswich IP4 5PD Tel: 01473 703016 Fax: 01473 703015 — MB BS 1973 Lond.; MFFP 1993; FRCOG 1995, M 1982. (Univ. Coll. Hosp.) Cons. Family Plann. & Reproduc. Health Ipswich Hosps. NHS Trust. Socs: Fac. Fam. Plann. & Reproduc. Health; Hon. Edr. Jl. of family Plann. and reproductive health care. Prev: Sen. Lect. (Human Sexuality) St. Geo. Hosp. Med. Sch.; Hon. Cons. Well Wom. Serv. Tower Hamlets HA.

READER, John Granville (retired) International Christian Medical & Dental Association, 82-88 Hills Road, Cambridge CB2 1LQ Tel: 01223 321715 Fax: 01223 321715 — MB ChB Liverp. 1957. Prev: GP Marple Chesh.

READER, Peter Mark Suthergrey House Surgery, 37A St. Johns Road, Watford WD17 1LS Tel: 01923 224424 Fax: 01923 243710; 24 Bisham Gardens, Highgate, London N6 6DD — MB BS 1988 Lond.; MRCGP 1992; DCH RCP Lond. 1990. (Roy. Free Hosp.) Pract. Partner Watfert Herts.; Chairm. Watford & Three Rivers PCG. Prev: Trainee GP N.wick Pk. Hosp. Harrow VTS.

READETT, David Robert John Eli Lilly and Company Ltd., Dextra Court, Chapel Hill, Basingstoke RG21 5SY; 29 Cranesfield, Sherborne St. John, Basingstoke RG24 9LN — BM BS 1980 Nottm.; BMedSci Nottm. 1978; MRCP (UK) 1984. (Nottm.) Oncol.Clin. Research Phys., Eli Lilly & Company, Basingstoke. Prev: Sen. Regist. (Paediat. Oncol.) Sheff. Childr. & Qu. Med. Centre Nottm.; Fell. (Paediat., Haemat. & Oncol.) Coll. Phys. & Surgs. Columbia Univ. NY; Regist. (Paediat.) Perth W.. Austral.

READETT, Elizabeth Jane 5 Digby Road, Sutton Coldfield B73 6HG — BM BS 1985 Nottm.; BMedSci Nottm. 1983, BM BS 1985.

READING, Mr Alexander David The Alexandra Hospital, Woodrow Drive, Redditch B98 7UB Tel: 01527 503030 Fax: 01527 517432; Camelot Cottage, Illington, Worcester WR7 4DH Email: alexreading@hotmail.com — MB ChB 1990 Glas.; MD 2001 Leicester; FRCS 2000; FRCS Eng. 1994. (Glas.) Cons. Orthop. & Truama. Socs: BORS; BOA (Ass). Prev: HIP Fell. Bristol; Specialist Regist. Rotat. (Orthop.) W. Scotl.; Clin. Research Fell. (Orthop.) Leicester & Rugby.

READING, Catherine Althea The Priory Surgery, 326 Wells Road, Bristol BS4 2QJ Tel: 0117 949 3988 Fax: 0117 778250 — MB BS 1975 Lond.; MRCP (UK) 1980; DRCOG 1979; DCH Eng. 1978. (Middlx.) Prev: SHO (Paediat.) Roy. United & St. Martins Hosp. Bath; SHO (Obst.) S.mead Hosp. Bristol; SHO (Paediat.) Freedom Fields Hosp. Plymouth.

READING, James Henry Medical Centre, Rushden NN10 9TU Tel: 01933 314836 — MB BS 1950 Lond.; MRCS Eng. LRCP Lond. 1950; DTM & H Eng. 1963; DTM & H Lond 1963. (St. Bart.) Local Treasury Med. Off.; Med. Off. Shaftesbury Soc. Homes for Disabled. Prev: Specialist in Med. RAF Hosp. Uxbridge; Ho. Phys. & Ho. Surg. St. John's Hosp. Lewisham; Ho. Surg. (Obst.) Lewisham Gen. Hosp.

READING, Jane Maralyn Grasmere, 110 High St., Cottenham, Cambridge CB4 8RX — MB BS 1978 Lond.; MRCS Eng. LRCP Lond. 1978; Cert FPA. 1981.

READING, Jonathan Graham Ryders Farm, Manchester Rd, Kearsley, Bolton BL4 8RU — MB ChB 1997 Ed.

READING, Nicholas Graham Whipps Cross Hospital, Whipps Cross Road, London E11 1NR Tel: 020 8535 6652 Fax: 020 8535 6719; 48 Inderwick Road, London N8 9LD Tel: 020 8341 9726 — MB BChir 1979 Camb.; MA 1982 Camb.; MRCP (UK) 1982; FRCR 1985. (Middlx.) Cons. Radiol. Whipps Cross Hosp. Lond. Prev: SHO (Neurol.) Nat. Hosp. Nerv. Dis. Qu. Sq. Lond.; SHO (Med.) Whittington Hosp. Lond.; SHO (Clin. Pharmacol.) Hammersmith Hosp. Lond.

READING, Paul James 64 Gayton House, Knapp Road, Bow, London E3 4BX — MB BChir 1986 Camb.

READING, Richard Fletcher 7 Lodge Place, Thunder Lane, Norwich NR7 0LA — MB BChir 1979 Camb.; MRCP (UK) 1983.

READINGS, Stella Madeleine Four Oaks, Billingbear Lane, Binfield, Bracknell RG42 5PS Tel: 01344 421911 — MB BS 1957 Lond. (St. Geo.)

REAH, Gary Old Belmont, 26 Rochdale Road, Sowerby Bridge HX6 3BL — MB ChB 1986 Ed.

REAICH, David Renal Unit, South Cleveland Hospital, Middlesbrough TS4 3BN; 12 Cringle Moor Chase, Great Broughton, Middlesbrough TS9 7HS — MB ChB 1986 Aberd.; FRCP 2000 London; MD Aberd. 1996; MRCP (UK) 1989. Cons. Nephrol. James Cook Univ. Hosp. Middlesbrough.

REAKES, Ruth Elisabeth May The Straw House, Roundabout Lane, Winnersh, Wokingham RG41 5AD — MB BS 1985 Lond.

REAM, Janet Elizabeth Fender Way Health Centre, Fender Way, Birkenhead CH43 9QS Tel: 0151 677 9103 Fax: 0151 604 0392 — MB ChB 1980 Liverp.

REAM, Judith Ann 58 Branksome Drive, Heald Green, Cheadle SK8 3AJ — MB ChB 1977 Glas.

REAN, Yvette Maria 36 Lytton Road, Barnet EN5 5BY — MB BS 1992 Lond.

REANEY, Elizabeth Ann 3 Linsey's Hill, Armagh BT61 9HD — MB BCh BAO 1980 Belf.; DCCH RCP Ed. Staff Grade Paediat. (Community Child Health) Armagh & Gungannon Health & Social Servs. Trust, based in Armagh. Socs: BACCH; BACDA.

REANEY, Susan Margaret York District Hospital, Wigginton Road, York YO31 8HE — MB ChB 1983 Liverp.; FRCR 1990; DMRD Liverp. 1988. Cons. Radiologist, York Dist. Hosp. from Jan. 2002. Prev: Cons. Radiologist, S. Winchester Univ. Hosps. Trust 1995-2001.

REARDON, Jeffrey Allan Mayday Hospital, Thornton Heath Tel: 020 8401 3010 Fax: 020 8401 3009; 4 Selwyn Road, New Malden KT3 5AT Tel: 020 8949 3263 Fax: 020 8715 Email: 4603 — MB BS Queensland. 1970; MRCP (UK) 1975. (Queensland) Cons. Croydon HA. Prev: Sen. Regist. Kennedy Inst. Rheum. Lond.

REARDON, Michael Francis Department of Geriatric Medicine, Worthing and Southlands Hospital, Worthing BN11 2DH Tel: 01903 205111 — MB BCh BAO 1989 NUI; MRCPI 1992. Cons. Geriat. Med. Worthing Hosp. W. Sussex. Socs: Brit. Geriat. Soc.; Irish Gerontol. Soc. Prev: Sen. Regist. (Geriat. Med.) St. Richards Hosp. Chichester.

REARY, Stuart Flat 18, Cedar Court, Ashgrove Road, Aberdeen AB25 3BJ Tel: 01224 276095 Email: stureary@hotmail.com — MB ChB 1997 Aberd.; BSc Med.Sci1995. GP Rotat. Aberd.Roy.Infirm.

REASBECK, Mr Philip George Lincoln County Hospital, Greenwell Road, Lincoln LN2 5QY Tel: 01522 512512 Fax: 01522 573629; The Grove, Ramsgate Road, Louth LN11 0NH Tel: 01507 607525 Fax: 01507 607525 Email: teasbeck@globalnet.co.uk — MD 1985 Camb.; MA Camb. 1975, MD 1985, MB 1975, BChir 1974; FRACS 1982; FRCS Eng. 1978; MRCP (UK) 1976. (Guy's) Cons. Surg. Lincoln Co. Hosp. Trent RHA. Socs: Assn. Surg.; Assn. ColoProctol.; Assn. Upper G.I. Surg. Prev: Sen. Lect. (Surg.) Univ. Qu.sland & Cons. Surg. P.ss Alexandra Hosp. Brisbane, Austral.; Sen. Lect. (Surg.) Univ. Otago Med. Sch. & Cons. Surg. Dunedin Hosp., NZ; Sen. Lect. (Surg.) Univ. Hong Kong & Cons. Surg. Qu. Mary Hosp., Hong Kong.

***REAVELEY, Anne Mary** 4 Parklawn Avenue, Epsom KT18 7SQ Tel: 01372 725054 — BM BS 1998 Nottm.; BM BS Nottm 1998.

REAVES, Charles Stuart Charters Surgery, 38 Polsloe Road, Exeter EX1 2DW Tel: 01392 273805 — MRCS Eng. LRCP Lond. 1971.

REAVES, Elizabeth Chance Charters Surgery, 38 Polsloe Road, Exeter EX1 2DW Tel: 01392 273805; Deep Dene House, Deep Dene Park, Wonford Road, Exeter EX2 4PH — MB ChB St. And. 1970.

REAVEY, James 6 Argyle Terrace, Dunblane FK15 9DN — MB ChB 1970 Glas.

REAVLEY, Caroline Mary Three Ways, The Saltway, Astwood Bank, Redditch B96 6NE — MB BS 1987 Lond.; BSc (Hons.) Lond. 1981; MRCP (UK) 1991; FRCA 1995.

REAVLEY, Paul David Alexander Barmoor Ridge, Berwick-upon-Tweed TD15 2QD — MB ChB 1998 Dund.; MB ChB Dund 1998.

REAVLEY, Saffron Beryl 8 Berkeley Road,, Westbury Park, Bristol BS6 7PJ — MB ChB 1995 Manch.

REAY, Barbara Ann 10 Meadowview Drive, Inchture, Perth PH14 9RQ — MB ChB 1980 Dundee. Staff Grade (Anaesth.) Perth Roy. Infirm. Prev: Regist. (Anaesth.) Ninewells Hosp. & Med. Sch. Dundee.

REAY, Sir (Hubert) Alan (John), KBE (retired) 63 Madrid Road, Barnes, London SW13 9PQ Tel: 020 8748 2482 Fax: 020 8748 2482 — MB ChB Ed. 1948; FRCP Lond. 1973, M 1955; FRCP Ed. 1968, M 1955; FRCPCH 1996; FRCGP 1985; DCH RCP Lond. 1957; DTM & H 1954. Pres. Friends St. Thos. Hosp.; Chairm. Lambeth ClubHo. for Ment.ly Ill People. Prev: Chairm. Lambeth Health Care NHS Trust.

REAY, John Mark Ridley The Surgery, Pickering Road, West Ayton, Scarborough YO13 9JF Tel: 01723 863100 Fax: 01723 862902 Email: john.reay@gp-b82063.nhs.uk — MB BChir 1986 Camb.; MRCGP 1990; DRCOG 1990. Prev: SHO (Paediat.) York Dist. Hosp.; Trainee GP York Dist. Hosp. VTS; Ho. Surg. W. Suff. Hosp. Bury St. Edmunds.

REAY, Katherine Annette Park Parade Surgery, 69 Park Parade, Whitley Bay NE26 1DU Tel: 0191 252 3135 Fax: 0191 253 3566 — MB BS 1989 Newc.; MRCGP 1993; DRCOG 1993. Socs: Brit. Med. Acupunct. Soc. Prev: Trainee GP/SHO N.umbria VTS Newc.

REAY, Lewis Mackay Department of Public Health, Argyll & Clyde Health Board, Ross House, Paisley PA2 7BN Tel: 0141 842 7207 Fax: 0141 848 0165 Email: lewis.reay@achb.scot.nhs.uk; 3 Sinclair Lane, Helensburgh G84 9DB Tel: 01436 674170 — MB ChB St. And. 1969; MPH Glas. 1986; FRCGP 1994, M 1977; FFPHM 1998; M 1988; DObst RCOG 1975. (St. And.) Cons. Pub. Health Med. Argyll & Clyde HB; Hon. Clin. Sen. Lect. Univ. Glas. Prev: GP Strachur; GP Tadcaster.

REAY, Pamela Livingstone 3 Sinclair Lane, Helensburgh G84 9DB — MB ChB 1969 St. And. (St. And.)

REAY, Stephen 47 Crown Road, Belle Vue, Carlisle CA2 7QQ — MB ChB 1978 Liverp.; MRCGP 1982.

REAY, William Anthony (retired) Caroltina Lodge, The Spinney, Kenilworth Road, Coventry CV4 7AG Tel: 024 76 418855 — MB BS 1957 Durh.; MRCGP 1977; DObst RCOG 1969. p/t GP Coventry. Prev: Regtl. Med. Off. 1/2Nd K.E.O. Goorkhas.

REAY-JONES, Martin Henry Havelock Caterham Valley Medical Practice, Eothen House, Eothen Close, Caterham CR3 6JU Tel: 01883 347811 Fax: 01883 342529; Dukes Mount, Lunghurst Road, Woldingham, Caterham CR3 7HE Tel: 01883 652374 — MB BS Lond. 1962. (St. Thos.) Phys. Caterham & Dist. Hosp. Prev: Squadron Ldr RAF Med. Br.; Cas. Off. & Ho. Surg. St. Thos. Hosp. Lond.; Ho. Phys. St. Helier Hosp. Carshalton.

REAY-JONES, Mr Nicholas Havelock John 23 Talbot Street, Hitchin SG5 2QU Tel: 01462 435656 Email: nreayjones@aol.com — MB BS 1990 Lond.; BSc Lond. 1989; FRSC. Eng. 1995. Specialist Regist., Gen. Surg., N. Thames, (W.).

REBEL, David John Kent House Surgery, 36 Station Road, Longfield DA3 7QD Tel: 01474 703550 — MB BS 1973 Lond.; DObst RCOG 1975. Prev: Ho. Phys. King's Coll. Hosp. Lond.; Ho. Surg. Joyce Green Hosp. Dartford; SHO (Obst.) W. Hill Hosp. Dartford.

REBELLO, Alan Joseph Anthony (retired) Silsden, Gib Lane, Houghton, Preston PR5 0RU Tel: 0125 485 4498 — MB BS 1950 Bombay. Prev: Regist. Wakefield A & B Hosp. Gps.

REBELLO, Gemma Department of CYTO Pathology, Forth Park Hospital, 30 Bennochy Road, Kirkcaldy KY2 5RA Tel: 01592 643355 Ext: 2783 Fax: 01592 642376; 9 Blackford Hill View, Edinburgh EH9 3HD Tel: 0131 667 2428 — MB BS 1966 Madras; FRCPath 1990, M 1978; Dip RC Path. 1996. (Christian Med. Coll., Vellore, Tamilnadu, S. India) Cons. Cytopath. & Head of Dept. of Cytopath. Fife Acute Hosps. NHS Trust. Forth Pk. Hosp. 30 Bennochy Rd. Kirkaldy KY2 5RA; Assoc. Specialist Lothian Colposcopy Clinic, Elsie Inglis Suite Roy. Infirm Edin NHS Trust. Socs: Brit. Soc. Colpos. & Cerv. Path. Prev: Lect. & Assoc. Specialist (Path. Cervical Cytol.) Univ. Edin.; Sen. Regist. (Path.) Roy. Infirm. Edin.; Regist. (Path) & Regist. (Neuropath.) Roy. Infirm. Edin.

REBMANN, Claudia Shiren 2 Calder Drive, Mossley Hill, Calder Stones, Liverpool L18 3HX — State Exam Med 1992 Bonn.

REBSTEIN, Julia Water Lanes Cottage, Ville Amphrey, St Martin's, Guernsey GY4 6DT — MB BS 1997 Lond.

RECALDIN, Stephen 137 Westley Road, Bury St Edmunds IP33 3SE — BSc Lond. 1980, MB BS 1983; MRCGP 1988; DRCOG 1988; DCH RCP Lond. 1986. Civil. Med. Pract. 48 MG Hosp. RAF Lakenheath Suff.

RECKLESS, Helena Marigold (retired) Pembroke House, Mullion, Helston TR12 7HN Tel: 01326 240159 — MB BS Lond. 1946; DCH Eng. 1948. Prev: Jun. Specialist in Med. Brit. Milit. Hosp. Singapore.

RECKLESS, John Phillip David Royal United Hospital, Combe Park, Bath BA1 3NG Tel: 01225 428331 Fax: 01225 824529; Manor Farm House, Buckland Dinham, Frome BA11 2QS Tel: 01373 461841 — MB BS 1968 Lond.; MD Lond. 1977; FRCP Lond. 1985; MRCP (UK) 1972; MRCS Eng. LRCP Lond. 1968. (St. Bart.) Cons. Phys. Roy. United Hosp. Bath; Hon. Reader Dept. Med. Sci. Med. Univ. Bath; Hon. Reader (Biochem.) Univ. Bath. Socs: Fell. Roy. Soc. Med.; Diabetes UK; Nat. Osteop. Soc. Prev: Sen. Regist. (Med.) Hallamsh. Hosp. Sheff.; MRC Trav. Fell. Div. Metab. Dis. Univ. Calif. San Diego, USA; Hon. Sen. Regist. (Med.) & Research Fell. St. Bart. Hosp. Lond.

RECORD, Carol Stoke Mandeville Hospital, Mandeville Road, Aylesbury HP21 8AL Tel: 01296 316918 Fax: 01296 316919 Email: carol.record@smh.nhs.uk; Western House, West St, Marlow SL7 2BS — MB BS 1978 Lond.; BA Oxf. 1975; MRCP (UK) 1982; FRCR 1985. p/t Cons. Radiol. Stoke Mandeville Hosp. Aylesbury. Prev: Sen. Regist. (Radiol.) N.wick Pk. Hosp. Lond.

RECORD, Charles Anthony Flat 1, Essendene House, Bartlett Court, Clifton, Bristol BS8 3HG — MB BS 1989 Lond.; DRCOG 1995; MRCGP 1997; MRCP (UK) 1993. (St. Thos. Hosp. Lond.) GP Locum.

RECORD, Christopher Oswald 26 The Grove, Gosforth, Newcastle upon Tyne NE3 1NE Tel: 0191 284 2273 — MB BS 1966 Lond.; DPhil Oxf. 1973; FRCP 1981, M 1968; DCC (Biochem.) Chelsea Coll. Sc. & Technol. 1968. (Lond. Hosp.) Cons. Phys. Roy. Vict. Infirm. Newc. Socs: Assn. Phys.& Brit. Soc. Gastroenterol. Prev: Sen. Regist. (Med.) Lond. Hosp.; Research Fell. Nuffield Dept. Clin. Med. Univ. Oxf.; Hon. Lect. King's Coll. Hosp. Med. Sch. Lond.

RECORD, Dorothy Maud Hope Cottage, Twitchen, Craven Arms SY7 0HN Tel: 0158 87 334 — MB ChB 1945 Birm. (Birm.) Prev: Res. Med. Off. Little Bromwich Isolat. Hosp. Birm.

RECORD, Jane Louise 9 Cillocks Close, Hoddesdon EN11 8QT — MB ChB 1991 Leeds.

RECORD, Marion Eva St. Hildas Priory, Sneaton Castle, Whitby YO21 3QN Tel: 01947 602079 — MRCS Eng. LRCP Lond. 1950; FFA RCS Eng. 1957; DA Eng. 1955. (Leeds) Prev: Med. Off. Martin Hse. Childr. Hospice; Cons. Anaesth. York 'A' Hosp. Gp.

RECORDON, John Piers (retired) 3 Vicarage Drive, Grantchester, Cambridge CB3 9NG Tel: 01223 841342 — MA, MB Camb. 1961, BChir 1960.

REDA, Fotna Elmottassem 3 Woodlands Lane, Shirley, Solihull B90 2PX Tel: 0121 745 1597 — MB BCh 1976 Cairo.

REDD, Reginald Alfred Stanley (retired) Woodlands, South Close Green, Redhill RH1 3DU Tel: 01737 643179 Email: roger@segmer.freeserve.co.uk — MB BS 1952 Lond. Prev: Med. Off. Roy. Earlswood Hosp. Redhill.

REDDEN, Mr Jonathan Francis Tofield House, Carr Lane, Wadworth, Doncaster DN11 9AR Tel: 01302 853829 — MB BS 1970 Lond.; FRCS Ed. (Orth.) 1980; FRCS Eng. 1975; MRCS Eng. LRCP Lond. 1970. Cons. Orthop. Surg. Doncaster Roy. Infirm.; Hon. Cons. Orthop. Surg. Dandong No.2 Hosp. Liaoning Peoples RePub. of China; Vis. Prof. Orthop. Surg. Beijing Med. Univ. Prev: Lect. (Orthop.) Surg. Wellington, NZ; Sen. Regist. (Orthop. Surg.) Edin.

REDDIE, Ethel Mary The Landscape, 41 East Road, Bromsgrove B60 2NW Tel: 01527 872055 — MB BS 1953 Lond.; MRCPsych 1978. Indep. Psychother. BromsGr. Prev: Cons. Psychiat. Kidderminster Gen. Hosp.

REDDING, Georgina Anne Catling, Rosehill, Ladock, Truro TR2 4PQ — MB BChir 1972 Camb.; MB Camb. 1972, MA, BChir 1971; MRCPsych 1976; DPM Eng. 1976; DCH Eng. 1974. Cons. (Child Psychiat.) Cornw. DHA. Prev: Sen. Regist. (Child Psychiat.) Guy's Hosp. Lond.

REDDING, Helen Louise 69 Ryegate Road, Sheffield S10 5FB — MB ChB 1995 Sheff.

REDDING, Penelope Jane Lea Rig, 133 Maxwell Drive, Pollokshields, Glasgow G41 5AE Tel: 0141 427 0149 — MB BS 1974 Lond.; MRCS Eng. LRCP Lond. 1974; FRCPath 1995, M 1983. Cons. in Admin. Charge Bacteriol. Vict. Infirm. Glas.; Hon. Clin. Lect. Univ. Glas. Prev: Sen. Regist. & Regist. (Microbiol. &

REDDING

Immunol.) W.. Infirm. Glas.; Asst. Lect. (Microbiol.) St. Thos. Hosp. Lond.

REDDING, Vincent Joseph The Grange, Cossington, Leicester LE7 4UZ Tel: 01509 812810 — MD Lond. 1974, MB BS 1952. (St. Thos.) Emerit. Cons. Cardiol. Leicester HA. Socs: Brit. Cardiac Soc. Assoc mem. Prev: Cons. Cardiol. Leicester Regional Cardiac Unit Groby Rd. Hosp.

REDDING, Warren 5 Holroyd Road, Putney, London SW15 6LN Tel: 020 8788 7190 — MRCS Eng. LRCP Lond. 1956. (Westm.)

REDDING, Mr Warren Howard Tennyson House, 2 High St., Thurlby, Bourne PE10 0EE — MB BS 1976 Lond.; FRCS Eng. 1980.

REDDINGTON, Jacqueline Anne The Village Surgery, Elbow Lane, Liverpool L37 4AW Tel: 01704 878661 Fax: 01704 832488 — MB ChB 1989 Liverp.

REDDY, Dr Hodge Road, 56 Hodge Road, Walker Worsley, Manchester M28 3AU.

REDDY, Annaparreddy Venkata Gurava c/o Drive K. Sastrulu, 18 Hornby Lane, Calderstones, Liverpool L18 3HH Tel: 0151 722 5832 — MB BS 1984 Nagarjuna.

REDDY, Ayalam Nandini Copperfield, Church St., Tempsford, Sandy SG19 2AN — MB BS 1977 Osmania.

REDDY, C Narayana Deneside Medical Centre, The Avenue, Deneside, Seaham SR7 8LF Tel: 0191 513 0202 Fax: 0191 581 6764; 39 Middleton Close, Seaton, Seaham SR7 0PQ Tel: 0191 581 9515 — MB BS 1972 Bangalore; MB BS 1972 Bangalore. (Bangalore) GP Seaham, Co. Durh.

REDDY, Challa Prabhakar The Vale Surgery, 97 The Vale, Acton, London W3 7RG Tel: 020 8743 4086 — MB BS 1964 Osmania. (Gandhi Med. Coll. Hyderabad) Socs: BMA. Prev: SHO Geriat. Mt. Pleasant Hosp. Chepstow. Regist. (Gen. Med.) Dist.; Gen. Hosp. W. Bromwich.

REDDY, Mr Chandrashekar Kuppireddygari c/o Dr Bhagya Munishankar, 42 Hamilton Drive, Dundee — MB BS 1990 Gulbarga, India; FRCS Ed. 1992.

REDDY, Chillakuru Rajasekhara Flat 77, J Block, William Harvey Hospital, Ashford; 6 Boys Hall Road, Willesborough, Ashford TN24 0LA — MB BS 1983 Mysore.

REDDY, Diggireddy Pratap 66 Rhydelig Avenue, Heath, Cardiff CF4 4DE Tel: 029 2061 7598 — MB BS Osmania 1960. (Osmania Med. Coll. Hyderabad) Assoc. Specialist (Trauma & Orthop.) E. Glam. Health Trust.

REDDY, Eileen 76 Rosemary Hill Road, Little Aston, Sutton Coldfield B74 4HJ — LRCP LRCS LRFPS 1952 Glas.; DPH Ed. 1954. (RCS Ed.) Prev: Asst. Med. Off. Midlothian & Peebles Cos.; Asst. Div. Med. Off. Lancs. CC; Ho. Surg. & Ho. Phys. Warrington Gen. Hosp.

REDDY, Gaddam Madhusudan Red House Surgery, Renfrew Road, Hylton Red House, Sunderland SR5 5PS Tel: 0191 548 1269 Fax: 0191 549 8998 — MB BS 1965 Osmania. (Osmania) GP Sunderland.

REDDY, Mr Geetla Vijender Snow Hill Medical Centre, Shelton, Stoke-on-Trent ST1 4LT Tel: 01782 219906 — MB BS 1971 Osmania; FRCS Ed. 1985; T(GP) 1992; DLO RCS Eng. 1984. Prev: Trainee GP Swindon VTS; Regist. (ENT) Stoke Mandeville Hosp. Aylesbury; SHO (A & E) Milton Keynes Hosp.

REDDY, Mr Gopinath 129 Clarence Road, Wimbledon, London SW19 8QB Tel: 020 8543 3143 — MB BS 1992 Lond.; BSc (Clin. Pharmacol.) Lond. 1989; FRCOphth 1996. (Guy's Hosp. Lond.) Specialist Regist. (Ophth.) Soton. Gen. Hosp. Prev: SHO (Ophth.) Kingston Hosp. Lond.; SHO (Ophth.) St Geo.s Hosp. Lond.

REDDY, Mr Gudimetla Adi Narayana c/o Mr N.R. Padala, 6 Fitzgerald St., Preston PR1 5EN — MB BS 1984 Andhra; FRCS Glas. 1993.

REDDY, Gundala Suryanarayana 272 Lister House, District General Hospital, Kings Drive, Eastbourne BN21 2YP — MB BS 1983 Sri Venkateswara.

REDDY, Jason, Commander, British Merchant Navy 25 Fountains Road, Bedford MK41 8NU Tel: 01234 351304 Fax: 01234 351304 Email: dr.jason.reddy@dial.pipex.com — MB BS 1990 Lond.; DRCOG 1996; DFFP 1994; DCH RCP Lond. 1993. (Univ. Coll. Hosp. Lond.) p/t Sen. Ship's Doctor P & O/P.ss Cruises Ltd. Socs: Mem. of the Fac. of pre-Hosp. c/o the Roy. Coll. of Surg.s (Edin.). Prev: Trainee GP/SHO (Gen. Med.) Milton Keynes Gen. Hosp.; Ho. Surg.

(ENT, Vasc. & Gen. Surg.) Middx. & Univ. Coll. Hosp. Lond.; Ho. Phys. (Radiother., Oncol., Haemat. & Gen. Med.) S.end Gen. Hosp.

REDDY, Jayendravadan Y. J. Child & Adolescent Mental Health Service, Queen's Park Hospital, Haslingden Road, Blackburn BB2 3HH Tel: 01254 293346 Fax: 01254 293351; Springhill House, 112 Mancester Rd, Burnley BB11 4HS Tel: 01282 429779 Fax: 01282 429779 Email: reddy-jyj@talk21.com — MB BS 1971 Osmania, India.; DMR 1972 Osmania, India; MSc 1964 (Entomology) India; MSc 1998 (Gen Psyciatry) Keele; DPM Dublin; BSc 1962 India; DPIP (Inst. Of Psychiatry) Lond; DCP (RCP&S) Ireland. Cons. Psychiat., Qu.'s Pk. Hosp. Prev: Sen. Clin. Med. Off. Child & Adolesc. Ment. Health Serv. Burnley Gen. Hosp. Burnley.

REDDY, Mr Kamireddy Marcus Flat 12, Lantern Court, 99 Worple Road, Wimbledon, London SW20 8HB Tel: 020 8286 1797 Fax: 079 3221 0837 Email: marcusreddy@hotmail.msn.com — MB BS 1992 Lond.; BSc Basic Med. Scs. & Pharmacol. Lond. 1989; FRCS (Eng.) 1997. (St. George's Hospital Medical School London) Hon. Research Fell. & Specialist Regist., (Gen. Surg.) St. Geo. Hosp. Med. Sch. Lond.& Kingston Hosp.,Kingston-Upon-Thames. Socs: Assoc. Mem. Assn. Surg. GB & Irel.; Assoc. Mem. Brit. Assn. Surg. Oncol.

REDDY, Kamireddy Prema Elm House Surgery, 29 Beckenham Road, Beckenham BR3 4PR Tel: 020 8650 0173 Fax: 020 8663 3911; Marley Hayes, Oldfield Road, Bromley BR1 2LE — MB BS 1989 Lond. (GUYS (UNDS))

REDDY, Kaukutla Venkat Deneside Medical Centre, The Avenue, Deneside, Seaham SR7 8LF Tel: 0191 513 0202 Fax: 0191 581 6764; 11 Lodgeside Meadow, Burdon, Sunderland SR3 2PN — MB BS 1971 Osmania; MB BS 1971 Osmania. (Osmania) GP Seaham, Co. Durh.

REDDY, Kishore Department of Radiology, Medway Hospital, Windmill Road, Gillingham ME7 5NY Tel: 01634 830000 Fax: 01634 401177; 119 Wigmore Road, Gillingham ME8 0TH — MB BS 1976 Mysore; FRCR 1986; DMRD Eng. 1984. Cons: Radiol. Medway Hosp. Gillingham.

REDDY, Kokkanda S P Joshi and Reddy, Aston Health Centre, 175 Trinity Road, Aston, Birmingham B6 6JA Tel: 0121 327 0144 Fax: 0121 326 9784 — MB BS 1971 Osmania; MB BS 1971 Osmania.

REDDY, Kothur Suresh Health Centre, Cramlington NE23 6QN Tel: 01670 714581 — MB BS 1961 Osmania; DTCD Wales 1971. (Osmania Med. Coll. Hyderabad)

REDDY, Mr Lankola Chandra Shekhar Department of Cardiac Surgery, Clinical Sciences Centre, Northern General Hospital, Herries Road, Sheffield S5 7AU Tel: 0114 243 4343 — MB BS 1983 Osmania; FRCS Ed. 1992.

REDDY, Mr Maddy Ashwin 13 Mill Close, Nuneaton CV11 6QD — BChir 1992 Camb.; MA (Cantab) 1990. (Cambridge University) Specialist Regist., E. Anglican Rotat.

***REDDY, Mr Majjiga Rajashekar** House 5, The Green, Wylde Green Road, Sutton Coldfield B72 1JB — MRCS Eng. LRCP Lond. 1987; FRCS Glas. 1993.

REDDY, Mamatha St Thomas' Hospital, Department of Radiology, Lambeth Wing, Lambeth Palace Rd, London SE1 7EH Tel: 0207 928 9292; Tel: 0208 767 3380 Email: mamathareddy14@hotmail.com — MB BS 1993 Lond.; BSc (1st cl. Hons.) Lond. 1990; MRCP (Lond.) 1997; FRCR Lond. 1998. Specialist Regist. Radio. Guys & St Thos. Hosp. NHS Trust Lond. SEI. Prev: SHO Gen. Med. St. Geos. Hosp. Tooting, Lond.

REDDY, Nallamilli Somasekhara Research & Teaching Centre, Royal Orthopaedic Hospital, The Woodlands, Northfield, Birmingham B31 2AP — MB BS 1984 Andhra.

REDDY, Mr Nallapareddy Surendranath 24 Petersham Drive, Appleton, Warrington WA4 5QF — MB BS 1973 Andhra; FRCS Ed. 1983.

REDDY, Nivedita 119 Wigmore Road, Gillingham ME8 0TH — MB BS 1972 Madras.

REDDY, Paul Joseph Hill Farm Oast, Yalding Hill, Yalding, Maidstone ME18 6AN; Mid Kent Trust, Hermitage Lane, Maidstone ME16 9QQ Tel: 01622 729000 — LRCPI & LM, LRSCI & LM 1977; FRCSI 1981; FRCS 1983. (Royal College Surgeons Ireland) Cons. Urol. Socs: BAUS; R.S.M.

REDDY, Prashanthi 41A Guilford Road, Stoneygate, Leicester LE2 2RD — MB ChB 1997 Leic.

REDDY, Ramchandra (retired) 13 Mill Close, Nuneaton CV11 6QD — MB BS 1964 Osmania. Prev: GP Bedworth.

REDDY, Regina 47 Manor Court, Monument Hill, Weybridge KT13 8RG Tel: 01932 41249 — MB BS 1965 Bangalor; MB BS Bangalore 1965; MRCOG 1974, DObst 1969. (Bangalore) Clin. Asst. (O & G) Frimley Pk. Hosp. Prev: Ho. Off. (Obst.) & Ho. Off. (Surg.) Edgware Gen. Hosp.; SHO (Gyn.) Amersham Gen. Hosp.

REDDY, Roopa Flat 4, 44 Woodville Gardens, London W5 2LQ — MB BS 1993 Lond.

REDDY, Sathineni Venkateshwar Wickersley Health Centre, Poplar Glade, Wickersley, Rotherham S66 2JQ Tel: 01709 549610 Fax: 01709 702470 — MB ChB 1996 Leic.

REDDY, Soma Sudershan Newmains Health Centre, 18 Manse Road, Newmains, Wishaw ML2 9AX Tel: 01698 383296 Fax: 01698 387157.

REDDY, Subbalekshmi Runwell Hospital, Wickford SS11 7XX; Oakdene, Bicknacre, Chelmsford CM3 4HA — MB BS 1970 Kerala; MRCPsych 1983; DPM Eng. 1982. (Trivandrum Med. Coll.) Cons. Psychiat. Mid. Essex HA; Cons. Psychiat. S.end Community Care Trust. Prev: Regist. (Psychiat.) Runwell Hosp. Wickford; Regist. (Psychiat.) City Gen. Hosp. Stoke-on-Trent; SHO (Gen. Med.) Preston Hosp. N. Shields.

REDDY, Mr Thimmareddy Narayana Staffs District General Hospital, Weston Road, Stafford ST16 3SA Tel: 01785 57731 & 58251; 34 Museum Road, Bangalore, India — MB BS 1970 Mysore; BSc Mysore 1962, MB BS 1970; FRCS Glas. 1981; DLO Eng. 1973. (Mysore Med. Coll.) Cons. ENT Surg. Mid Staffs. HA. Prev: Regist. (ENT) Dartford & Gravesham HA & Barking & Havering HA; Regist. (ENT) Rochdale HA; Sen. Regist. (ENT) W. Midl. RHA.

REDDY, Vatrapu Laxmi Narayana Stantonbury Health Centre, Purbeck, Stantonbury, Milton Keynes MK14 6BL Tel: 01908 316262 — MB BS 1965 Andhra. (Andhra Med. Coll.) Prev: Regist. Mapperley Hosp. Nottm.

REDDY, Veena 3 Forge Road, Naphill, High Wycombe HP14 4ST — MB ChB 1993 Leeds.

REDDY, Veena 114 Cherry Crescent, Rossendale BB4 6DS — MB BS 1998 Lond.; MB BS Lond 1998.

REDDY, Vuchuru Anila Prem 2 Horton Grove, Monkspath, Solihull B90 4UZ — MB ChB 1984 Aberd.

REDELINGHUYS, Johan 50 Clonmore Street, Southfields, London SW18 5EY — MB ChB 1992 Pretoria.

REDENHAM, Antonio Jay 50 Thorpewood Avenue, Sydenham, London SE26 4BX — MRCS Eng. LRCP Lond. 1950. (St. Geo.) Prev: Ho. Off. Lambeth Hosp. Lond.

REDER, Peter Child & Family Consultation Centre, 1 Wolverton Gardens, London W6 7DY Tel: 020 8846 7806 Fax: 020 8846 7817; 20 Devereux Lane, Barnes, London SW13 8DA Tel: 020 8748 9805 — MB ChB 1969 Birm; FRCPsych 1993, M 1975; DPM Eng. 1974; DCH Eng. 1972; DObst RCOG 1971. Mem. Teachg. Staff Inst. Family Ther. Lond.; Dir. Centre for Relationship Studies Lond. Prev: Cons. Child Psychiat. Newham Child Guid. Clin. Lond.; Sen. Regist. (Psychiat.) Dept. Childr. & Parents Tavistock Clinic Lond.

REDFERN, Anabel Blyth Health centre, Blyth — MB BS 1987 Newc.; MRCP (UK) 1991. (Newcastle upon Tyne) Cons. Paediat. with an interest in Community Child Health, N.umberland, N.umbria & N. Tyneside Trust, based at Blyth. Socs: MRCPCH; MDU; CPRG. Prev: Regist. (Paediat.) N.. Region; Sen. Regist. (Community Child Health) Newc. u. Tyne Flexible Train Scheme.

REDFERN, Auberon Emergency Bed Service, Fielden House, 28 London Bridge St., London SE1 9SG Tel: 020 7407 7181 Fax: 020 7357 6705; 11 Glossop Road, Sanderstead, South Croydon CR2 0PW Tel: 020 8657 6039 — MB BChir 1976 Camb.; MA Camb. 1959. SCMO Emerg. Bed. Servs. Lambeth, S.wark & Lewisham FHSA Lond. Socs: Camb. Univ. Med. Soc.; St. Bart. Hosp. Med. Coll. Alumni Assn. Prev: Regist. (Chem. Path.) St. Geo. Hosp. Lond.; Regist. (Chem. Path.) & SHO (Path.) Mayday Hosp. Croydon.

REDFERN, Damian Paul 99 St Leonard's Road, Leicester LE2 1WT — MB ChB 1993 Leic.

REDFERN, Edward 11 The Vale, MacKenzie Road, Birmingham B11 4EN Tel: 0121 449 3903 — MB 1955 Camb.; BA Camb. 1951, MB 1955, BChir 1954; DObst RCOG 1957. (Camb. & Middlx.) Founder Mem. Lect. (Ex-Chairm.) Brit. Med. Accupunc. Soc. Prev: Ho. Phys. & Ho. Surg. Middlx. Hosp.

REDFERN, Joseph William Thorpe London House, 90/92 High St, Brightlingsea, Colchester CO7 0EG Tel: 01206 305374 — MB BChir Camb. 1946; MA Camb. 1945, MD 1956; MD Camb. 1957MD Camb. 1957; MD Johns Hopkins Univ. 1946; MRCS Eng. LRCP Lond. 1945; MRCPsych 1971; DPM Lond. 1948. (Univ. Camb. & Johns Hopkins Univ.) Train. Analyst Soc. Analyt. Psychol. Prev: Psychotherap. Middlx. Hosp.; on Extern. Scientif. Staff. Med. Research Counc.; Head of Physiol. Sect. Army Operat. Research Gp.

REDFERN, Peter Matthew The Grange Road Practice, 108 Grange Road, London SE1 3BW Tel: 020 7237 1078 Fax: 020 7771 3550 — MB BS 1988 Lond. (Univ. Lond., King's Coll. Sch. Med. & Dent.) Socs: BMA.

REDFERN, Simon William Birchwood Medical Centre, 15 Benson Road, Birchwood, Warrington WA3 7PJ Tel: 01925 823502 Fax: 01925 852422; 9 Pool Lane, Lymm WA13 9BJ Tel: 01925 754345 — MB ChB 1979 Liverp.; MRCP (UK) 1982; MRCGP 1986; DRCOG 1983. Prev: SHO (Paediat.) Alder Hey Childr. Hosp. Liverp.; SHO (O & G) Liverp. Matern. Hosp.; SHO (Gyn.) & (Med.) Rotat. Roy. Liverp. Hosp.

REDFERN, Andrew Christopher Home Farm Cottage, Barton Road, Market Bosworth, Nuneaton CV13 0LQ — BChir 1990 Camb.

REDFERN, Clare Elizabeth 17 Ascham Road, Cambridge CB4 2BD — MB ChB 1988 Manch.; BA Camb. 1985.

REDFERN, Mr Daniel Richard Malachy Hammersmith Hospital, Du Cane Road, London W12 0HS Tel: 020 8743 2030 Email: dredfern@rpms.uk; 13 Canopus Way, Stanwell, Staines TW19 7TA — MB BS 1988 Lond.; MA (Hons.) Oxf. 1985; FRCS Eng. 1992. (St. Barts. Lond.) Specialist Regist. (Orthop.) Hammersmith Hosp. Lond. Socs: BMA; BOTA. Prev: Laming Evans Fell.; Regist. (Orthop.) Hammersmith Hosp. Lond.; SHO (Orthop.) Ashford Hosp. Middlx.

***REDFERN, Emma** 18 Ulviet Gate, High Legh, Knutsford WA16 6TT Tel: 01925 754 4356 — MB ChB 1997 Sheff.

REDFERN, Hyla Mary (retired) Swallow Barn, Andrew House, Stainton, Penrith CA11 0ES — MRCS Eng. LRCP Lond. 1950; MFCM 1974; DPH Eng. 1969. Prev: SCMO Notts. AHA (T).

REDFERN, John North, TD (retired) Greenacre, Kemp Road, Swanland, North Ferriby HU14 3LZ — MB BChir 1950 Camb.; BA Camb. 1948, MB BChir 1950; DObst RCOG 1951. Prev: Ho. Surg. Hull Matern. Hosp.

REDFERN, Lisa 22 Noel Gate, Aughton, Ormskirk L39 5EG Tel: 01695 421606 — MB ChB 1994 Manch.; BSc (Hons.) Manch. 1991; MRCP (Edin) 1998. Regist. (Paediat.) Alder Hey Childr.'s Hosp. Prev: SHO (Paediat.) Stepping Hill Hosp.; SHO (Paediat.) Countess of Chester Hosp.; SHO (Paediat.) Alder Hey Childr.'s Hosp.

REDFERN, Mark Adrian Ashfield House, Forest Road, Annesley Woodhouse, Kirkby in Ashfield, Nottingham NG17 9JB Tel: 01623 752295/153 — BM BS 1980 Nottm.

REDFERN, Michael 9 Pacific Court, Riverside, Shoreham-by-Sea BN43 5RW Tel: 01273 703157 — MB BS Lond. 1969; MA Soton. 1994; MRCS Eng. LRCP Lond. 1969; MRCGP 1979. Socs: Rowhook Med. Soc. Prev: GP N.bourne Med. Centre Shoreham-by-Sea.

REDFERN, Nancy Royal Victoria Infirmary, Queen Victoria Road, Newcastle upon Tyne NE1 4LP Tel: 0191 273 8811 — MB BS 1979 Lond.; BSc Lond. 1977; FRCA 1983. Cons. Anaesth. Roy. Vict. Infirm.; Assoc. Postgrad. Dean Newc.

REDFERN, Richard Fort House Surgery, 32 Hersham Road, Walton-on-Thames KT12 1JX Tel: 01932 253055 Fax: 01932 225910; 17 Connaught Drive, Weybridge KT13 0XA — MB BS 1989 Lond.; MRCGP 1994. (Char. Cross & West. Med. Sch.)

REDFERN, Mr Robert Michael Department of Neurosurgery, Morriston Hospital, Swansea SA6 6PN Tel: 01792 703382 Fax: 01792 703455; Glyncasnod Farm, Felindre, Swansea SA5 7PU Tel: 01269 592145 Email: glyncasnod@aol.uk — MB BS 1977 Lond.; FRCS Eng. 1983. (Lond. Hosp.) Cons. Neurosurg. Directorate of Neurosci. Morriston Hosp. Swansea. Socs: BMA; Soc. Brit. Neurol. Surgs. Prev: Sen. Regist. (Neurosurg.) Brook Hosp. & Maudsley Hosp.; Regist. (Neurosurg.) Walton Hosp. Liverp.

REDFERN, Suzanne Jane 7A Monsell Dr, Leicester LE2 8PP — MB ChB 1997 Birm.

REDFERN, Mr Thomas Roberton Department of Orthopaedic Surgery, Leighton Hospital, Middlewich Road, Crewe CW1 4QJ Tel: 01270 612258 Fax: 01270 612043; The Grange, Wrenbury, Nantwich CW5 8HA Tel: 01270 780873 Fax: 01270 780873 Email:

REDFERNE

t.redfern@virgin.uk — MB ChB 1976 Manch.; MChOrth. Liverp. 1984; FRCS Ed. 1981. Cons. Surg. Orthop. Leighton Hosp. Prev: Sen. Regist. (Orthop. Surg.) Mersey RHA.

REDFERNE, Jennifer Halina The Residence, 3 Church Lane, Osgathorpe, Loughborough LE12 9SY — MB BS 1988 Lond.; DFFP 1993; DGM RCP Lond. 1992; DRCOG 1990; MRCGP 1997. (St. Mary's)

REDFORD, Anthony (retired) 11 Malvern Road, Knutsford WA16 0EH Tel: 01565 634600 — MB ChB 1961 Manch. Prev: Sen. Partner Manch. Rd. Med. Centre, Knutsford Chesh.

REDFORD, Mr David Humphrey Alexander 11 Kennedy Road, Shrewsbury SY3 7AD Tel: 01743 353541 — MB ChB 1972 Bristol; FRCS Eng. 1977; FRCOG 1993, M 1978. Cons. O & G Roy. Shrewsbury Hosp. NHS Trust. Prev: Sen. Regist. (O & G) Gtr. Glas. HB; Lect. (O & G) Univ. Bristol.

REDGMENT, Christopher John 112A Harley Street, London W1N 1AF Tel: 020 7224 0707 Fax: 020 7224 3102 — MB ChB 1983 Zimbabwe; MRCOG 1991.

REDGRAVE, Allan Paul Public Health Department, Rotherham Health Authority, 220 Badsley Moor Lane, Rotherham S65 2QU Tel: 01709 302164 Fax: 01709 302175 Email: paul.redgrave@sheffield.ac.uk; 108 Carr Road, Walkley, Sheffield S6 2WZ Tel: 0114 233 6020 — MB ChB 1975 Bristol; MRCGP 1987; MFPHM RCP (UK) 1995; DRCOG 1979. Cons. Pub. Health Med. Rotherham HA. Prev: GP Sheff.

REDGRAVE, Elizabeth Ann Casitas, Goodwood Rise, Marlow Bottom, Marlow SL7 3QE Tel: 01628 483021 Fax: 01628 474322 — MB BS 1985 Lond.; BSc Lond. 1981. (Char. Cross Hosp. Med. Sch.) Orthop. Phys. Redgrave Clinic Bucks. Socs: Brit. Assn. Sport & Med.; Brit. Med. Acupunct. Soc. Prev: SHO (Surg.) Char. Cross Hosp. Lond.; Chief Med. Off. GB Rowing Team; Regional Med. Off. LTA.

REDHEAD, Doris Nicol Department of Radiology, Royal Infirmary, Edinburgh EH3 9YW Tel: 0131 536 2900 Fax: 0131 536 2920; 10B Ettrick Road, Edinburgh EH10 5BJ Tel: 0131 228 3177 Fax: 0131 228 3177 — MB ChB Ed. 1966; FRCR 1978; DMRD Ed. 1975. (Ed.) Cons. (Radiol.) Roy. Infirm. Ed. Socs: BMA; Roy. Coll. Radiol.; Soc. Minimal Invasive Ther.

REDHEAD, Ian Hugh (retired) Swallowfield, Norman Cross, Peterborough PE7 3TB Tel: 01733 240544 — MB ChB St. And. 1949; MD (Commend.) St. And. 1959; FRCGP 1979, M 1962. Prev: Provost E. Anglian Fac. RCGP.

REDHEAD, Julian Bladen Gonne 34 Coniger Road, London SW6 3TA — MB BS 1991 Lond.

REDHEAD, Keith Andrew St James House Surgery, County Court Road, King's Lynn PE30 5SY Tel: 01553 774221 Fax: 01553 692181 Email: sjmp@globalnet.co.uk — MB ChB 1979 Manch.; MFFP 1993; MRCGP 1987; DRCOG 1986. Princip. in Gen. Pract., St James' Ho. Surg. Kings Lynn.; Instruc. Doctor (Family Plann.) King's Lynn; Course Organiser, Kings Lynn Gen. Pract. Train. Scheme. Prev: Trainee GP King's Lynn VTS; Dist. Med. Insp. S. Sudan.; Clin. Assist. Andrology 1997-1999 Qu. Eliz. Hosp., Kings Lynn.

REDHEAD, Robert Gonne (retired) 3 Ashfield Close, Petersham, Richmond TW10 7AF Tel: 020 8940 9336 — MB BS Lond. 1951; PhD Surrey 1974; MRCS Eng. LRCP Lond. 1951. Cons. Rehabit. Qu. Mary's Univer. Hosp. Lond. Prev: Sen. Med. Off. (Limb Fitting) DHSS.

REDINGTON, Alan Norton Tregony Road Surgery, Tregony Road, Probus, Truro TR2 4JZ; Trencreek Barn, Tregony, Truro TR2 5SY Tel: 01872 530880 — MB ChB Birm. 1968; MRCGP 1974; DCH Eng. 1972; DObst RCOG 1970. (Birm.)

REDINGTON, Professor Andrew Nicholas Great Ormond Street Hospital for Children, Great Ormond St., London WC1N 3JH Tel: 020 7405 9200 Fax: 020 7813 8263 Email: reding@attglobal.net; 3 West Park Road, Kew, Richmond TW9 4DB Tel: 020 8876 3635 Email: reding@ibm.net — MB BS 1981 Lond.; MD Lond. 1988; FRCP Lond. 1994; MRCP (UK) 1984. Cons. Paediat. (Cardiol.) Gt. Ormond St. Hosp. for Childr. Prev: Cons. Paediat. (Cardiol.) Roy. Brompton Hosp., Lond.; Prof. Congen. Heart Dis. Nat. Heart & Lung Inst. Imperial Coll. of Sci., Technolgy & Med., Lond.; Sen. Regist. (Paediat. Cardiol.) Brompton Hosp. Lond.

REDINGTON, Anthony Edward Academic Department of Medicine, Castle Hill Hospital, Cottingham HU16 5JQ Tel: 01482 624067 Fax: 01482 624068 Email: a.e.redington@hull.ac.uk; 55a Gubyon Avenue, Herne Hill, London SE24 0DU Tel: 020 7737 6050 — MB BS 1984 Lond.; BA Oxf. 1981; MRCP (UK) 1988; DM Soton. 1997; MA Oxf. 1997. (Oxf./King's Coll. Hosp.) Sen. Lect., Univ. of Hull; Hon. Cons. Phys., Hull & E. Riding Hosp. NHS Trust. Socs: Amer. Thoracic Soc.; Brit. Thorac. Soc.; Brit. Soc. Allergy & Clin. Immunol. Prev: Lect. & Hon. Sen. Regist. Guy's Hosp. Lond.; Postdoctoral Research Fell. (Pathol.), McMaster Univ. Ontario, Canada.

REDKAR, Mr Rajeev Gurunath 34 Bavent Road, London SE5 9RY — MB BS 1988 Bombay; FRCS Ed. 1996.

REDLAFF, Leszek Vicarage Road Medical Centre, Vicarage Road, Mickleover, Derby DE3 5EB Tel: 01332 513283 Fax: 01332 518569 — MB ChB 1991 Manch.; MRCGP 1995; Cert. Prescribed Equiv. Exp. JCPTGP 1995; DFFP 1994; DRCOG 1994. Prev: Trainee GP Stockport VTS.

REDLICH, Lisbeth Angela Henrietta (retired) 11A Buchanan Road, Walsall WS4 2EW Tel: 019220 20389 — MD 1935 Vienna. Prev: Capt. RAMC 1945-7.

REDLICH, Martha Josefa Hilda 257A Rotton Park Road, Birmingham B16 0LS Tel: 0121 429 7464 — MD 1933 Vienna. (Vienna)

REDMAN, Alan Geddis Oscar 52 Morris Lane, Bath BA1 7PS — MB BS 1994 Lond.

REDMAN, Carol Elizabeth 15 Pont View, Ponteland, Newcastle upon Tyne NE20 9UZ — MB BS 1993 Lond.

REDMAN, Mr Charles William Everett Maternity Building, North Staffs Hospital, Newcastle Road, Stoke-on-Trent ST4 6QG Tel: 01782 553460 Fax: 01782 553460 Email: credman@netcentral.co.uk; South Wing, The Old Rectory, Dalbury DE6 5BR Tel: 01283 734173 — MD 1989 Manch.; MB ChB 1978; FRCS Ed. 1984; MRCOG 1983; FRCOG 1997. (Manchester) Cons. O & G N. N. Staffs Hosp. Socs: Liveryman Worshipful Soc. Apoth.; Asst. Sec. Brit. Soc. Colposcopy & Cervical Path. Prev: Sen. Lect. (O & G) Sch. of Physiol. Sci.s & Postgrad. Med. Univ. Keele; Lect. Univ. Birm.; CRC Research Fell. Univ. Birm.

REDMAN, Christopher Willard George Nuffield Department of Obstetrics & Gynaecology, John Radcliffe Hospital, Oxford OX3 9DU Tel: 01865 221009 Fax: 01865 69141 — MB BChir 1967 Camb.; FRCP Lond. 1981, M 1971; FRCOG 1993. Clin. Prof. & Cons. Obst. Med. John Radcliffe Hosp. Oxf. Prev: Lect. Dept. Regius Prof. Med. Radcliffe Infirm. Oxf.

REDMAN, David Robert Oscar Anaesthetic Department, Watford General Hospital, Watford WD18 0HB Tel: 01923 217604; Sundial Cottage, The Green, Croxley Green, Rickmansworth WD3 3HT Tel: 01923 711053 Fax: 01923 896767 — MB BS 1976 Lond.; FFA RCS Eng. 1981. (Middlx.) Cons. Anaesth. Watford Gen. Hosp. Herts. Socs: FRCA; Assn. Anaesth. Prev: Sen. Regist. Rotat. (Anaesth.) St. Mary's Hosp. Lond. Nat. Hosp. Nerv. Dis. Edgware Gen. Hosp. & Roy. Marsden Hosp. Lond.; Regist. (Anaesth.) Roy. Free Hosp. Lond.; SHO (Anaesth.) St. Thos. Hosp. Lond.

REDMAN, Deveda Antoinette The Surgery, High Street, Heathfield TN21 8JD Tel: 01435 864999 Fax: 01435 867449 Email: deveda.redman@tesco.net; Fair Meadow Farm, Fir Toll Road, Mayfield TN20 6NA Tel: 01435 872558 Fax: 01435 872189 Email: deveda.redman@tesco.net — MB ChB 1968 Sheff. (Sheff.) GP Heathfield E. Sussex; Chair High Weald Primary Care Gp. Socs: E.bourne Med. Soc. Prev: GP Old Coulsdon; Ho. Phys. St. Luke's Hosp. Guildford; Ho. Surg. (Gyn.) Redhill Hosp.

REDMAN, Helen Kathleen Anne Kingsfield Medical Centre, 146 Alcester Road South, Kings Heath, Birmingham B14 6AA Tel: 0121 444 2054 Fax: 0121 443 5856; 43 Chantry Road, Moseley, Birmingham B13 8DN — MB ChB 1991 Birm.; MRCGP 1995; DGM RCP Lond. 1994. GP Princip. BromsGr. Prev: Clin. Asst., (GP) BromsGr.; Trainee GP Redditch VTS.

REDMAN, James Houston 1 The Gatehouse, Rochester ME1 1QP Tel: 01634 848202 Fax: 01634 847808; Elphicks Farmhouse, Hunton ME15 0SB — MB ChB 1982 Sheff.; DMJ 2000 (Clin); AFOM RCP (UK) 1994; MRCGP 1987. GP & Occupat. Phys. Rochester; Forens. Med. Examr., Kent Co. Constab. Socs: Occupat. Med. Soc. Prev: Army Med. Off.

REDMAN, Jonathan Warwick Rosslyn Cottage, Sinderby, Thirsk YO7 4JD — MB ChB 1993 Ed. (Ed.) Socs: Scott. Soc. Anaesth.; SE Scotl. Soc. Anaesth.

REDPATH

REDMAN, Karen Northern General Hospital, Hermes Road, Sheffield S5; 43 Truswell Avenue, Sheffield S10 1WJ — MB ChB 1997 Sheff. SHO Med.

REDMAN, Leonard Rountree (retired) 52 Morris Lane, Bathford, Bath BA1 7PS Tel: 01225 858202 — MB BCh BAO Dub. 1957; FFA RCS Eng. 1963; DA Eng. 1960; DObst RCOG 1960. Cons. Anaesth. Bath Clin. Area. Prev: Jt. Sen. Regist. Anaesth. St. Thos. Hosp. & Nat. Heart Hosp. Lond.

REDMAN, Pamela Joan Ulverston Health Centre, Victoria ROAd, Ulverston LA12 0EW Tel: 01229 582588 — MB ChB 1984 Ed.; MRCGP 1989. p/t GP. Prev: SHO (Haemat.) Memor. Hosp. Darlington; Trainee GP Durh. & Gateshead.; Clin. Asst. (Obst. & Gyn.) Furness Hosp. Trust Barrow in Furness.

REDMAN, Paul Alexander 43 Truswell Avenue, Crookes, Sheffield S10 1WJ Tel: 0114 267 8262 — MB ChB 1996 Sheff. (Sheffield University)

REDMAN, Richard Carlyle Burnham Market Surgery, Church Walk, Burnham Market, King's Lynn PE31 8DH Tel: 01328 737000 Fax: 01328 730104 — MB Camb. 1971, BChir 1970; MRCGP 1975. Mem. Core Gp. GP Working Party Read Codes (CCC LoughBoro.); Treas. EMIS NUG.

REDMAN, Sarah Patricia 52 Morris Lane, Bath BA1 7PS; 45 Woodlaw Road, Condon, London SW6 6NQ Tel: 020 7385 3539 — MB BS 1993 Lond.; DCH 1995; DRCOG 1998. (Charing Cross & Westminster)

REDMAN, Susan Deborah Dingle Cottage, North Drive, Angmering, Littlehampton BN16 4JJ — MB ChB 1998 Bristol. (Bristol) SHO, Med., MusGr. Pk. Hosp., Taunton, Som.

REDMAN, Mr Theodore Francis, TD (retired) 5 Mayo Close, Leeds LS8 2PX Tel: 0113 293 1563 Email: theor@onetel.net.uk — MB ChB 1940 Manch.; FRCS Ed. 1952; FRCOG 1959, M 1948. Prev: Cons. Obst. Gyn. St. Jas. Hosp. Leeds & Sen. Clin. Lect. Univ. Leeds.

REDMAN, Thomas Malcolm Walker Health Centre, Warrenpoint, Newry BT34 3JD; 42 Seaview, Warrenpoint, Newry BT34 3NJ — MB BCh BAO 1948 Dub. (Dub.) Prev: Ho. Phys. Chase Farm Hosp. Enfield; Ho. Surg. Clacton & Dist. Hosp.

REDMAN, Victor Leonard (retired) Cedarwood, Smith Lane, Snitterfield, Stratford-upon-Avon CV37 0JY — MRCS Eng. LRCP Lond. 1939. Prev: Med. Off. DHSS.

REDMEN, J Ebejer (retired) Dormers, Heath Lane, Munstead, Godalming GU7 1UN Tel: 01483 415693 — MD 1955 Malta; BPharm 1953; FFA RCS Eng. 1967; DA Eng. 1962. Prev: Cons. Anaesth. Guildford & Godalming Gp. Hosps.

REDMILL, Brian Sidney Department of Ophthalmology, St George's Hospital, Blackshaw Road, London SW17 0QT Tel: 020 8672 1255 Fax: 020 8725 3026; 29 Kenley Walk, North Cheam, Sutton SM3 8ES Tel: 020 8644 9288 — MB BChir 1987 Camb.; FRCOphth 1991. (Camb.) Specialist Regist. (Ophth.) St. Geos. Hosp. Lond. Prev: Research Fell. Univ. Aberd.; Sen. Regist. St. John Ophth. Hosp., Jerusalem.

REDMILL, Duncan Allen 30 Princeton Road, Bangor BT20 3TA — MB BCh BAO 1994 Belf. Prev: SHO (Surgic.) Whiteabbey Hosp. Belf.; SHO (Surgic. & A & E) Antrim Area Hosp.

REDMOND, Professor Anthony Damien, OBE Emergency Department, Windsor House, North Staffordshire Hospital, Stoke-on-Trent ST4 7LN Tel: 01782 554768 Fax: 01782 747179 Email: profadr@aol.com; 27 Byrom Street, Manchester M3 4PF Tel: 0161 832 9935 — MB ChB 1975 Manch.; MD Manch. 1979; FRCPS Glas. 1991; FRCS Ed. 1982; MRCP (UK) 1981; Dip IMC 1995; FFAEM 1993. (Manchester) Prof. Emerg. Med. Keele Univ.; Cons. Emerg. Med. N. Staffs. Trauma Centre; Mem. Internat. Counc. on Alcohol & Addic.; Mem. Fontmell Gp. for Disaster Relief.; Chief Exec. UK-Med. Socs: Fell. Roy. Soc. Med.; N. Staff. Med. Inst.; Manch. Med. Soc. Prev: Cons. A & E Med. Univ. Hosp. S. Manch.; Sen. Regist. (A & E Med.) Hope Hosp. Manch.; Lect. (Surg.) MRC Trauma Unit Univ. Manch.

REDMOND, Brian 10 Hollins Drive, Middleton, Manchester M24 5LN Tel: 0161 643 3314 — MB BCh BAO 1946 Dub. (T.C. Dub.) Mem. Frank Lord Postgrad. Centre Oldham. Socs: BMA. Prev: Cas. Off. Sir P. Dun's Hosp. Dub.; Ho. Surg. (Orthop. & Anaesth.) Mansfield Hosp.

REDMOND, Elizabeth Jane 61 Pool Bank, Wirral CH62 5EX — MB ChB 1985 Liverp.

REDMOND, Ian Thomas 273 Loughborough Road, West Bridgford, Nottingham NG2 7EG — BChir 1991 Camb.

REDMOND, John V Elm Lodge Surgery, 43 Gloucester Road North, Bristol BS7 0SN Tel: 0117 969 0909 Fax: 0117 983 9969; 22 Malmains Drive, Frenchay, Bristol BS16 1PQ Tel: 0117 956 7909 — MB BCh BAO 1975 Dub.; MRCGP 1981; DRCOG 1980; DCH Dub. 1979. (Univ. Coll. Dub.) GP; Med. Bristol Rugby Club & St Mary's O.B. Rugby football Club. Socs: Frenchay Hosp. Med. Postgrad. Soc.; Cossham Med. Soc.; Brit. Assn. Sport & Med. Prev: Trainee GP Bedford VTS; SHO (Med.) Regional Hosp. Galway; SHO (Med.) St. Jas. Hosp. Dub.

REDMOND, Maureen Joan 22 Eastlands Crescent, London SE21 7EG — MB ChB 1976 Liverp.

REDMOND, Michael Robert Broughshane Medical Practice, 76 Main Street, Broughshane, Ballymena BT42 4JP Tel: 028 2586 1214 Fax: 028 2586 2281 — MB ChB 1991 Dundee.

REDMOND, Oonagh Aileen Beatrice (retired) Royal Belfast Hospital for Sick Children, Falls Road, Belfast BT12 6BE Tel: 01232 240503 — MB BCh BAO Dub. 1959; FRCPI 1981, M 1964; DCH Eng. 1961; FRCPCH. Cons. Paediatr. Roy. Belf. Hosp. Sick Childr. Prev: Sen. Research Fell. Dept. Paediat. Univ. Cape Town S. Afr.

REDMOND, Peter Vincent Stephen Lewisham Medical Centre, 158 Utting Avenue East, Liverpool L11 1DL Tel: 0151 256 9800 Fax: 0151 256 5765 — MB ChB 1981 Liverp.

REDMOND, Mr Richard Maguire c/o Department of Ophthalmology, Scarborough Hospital, Scarborough YO12 6QL Tel: 01723 368111 Email: rmri@ntlworld.com — MB ChB 1981 Bristol; MSc (Med. Sci.) Glas. 1984; FRCS (Ophth.) Lond. 1987; DO RCS Eng. 1987. Cons. Ophth. Surg. ScarBoro. Hosp. Prev: Sen. Regist. Moorfields Eye Hosp. Lond.; SHO Bristol Eye Hosp.; SHO (Neurosurg.) Frenchay Hosp. Bristol.

REDMOND, Robert Anthony Alexander Broughshane Medical Practice, 76 Main Street, Broughshane, Ballymena BT42 4JP Tel: 028 2586 1214 Fax: 028 2586 2281 — MB BCh BAO 1964 Belf.; MRCGP 1975; DCH RCPSI 1975; DObst RCOG 1966. (Belf.) Socs: BMA. Prev: Ho. Off. Belf. City Hosp.; SHO (Midw.) Ards Hosp.; SHO Ulster Hosp. Sick Childr.

REDMOND, Stephen James Lewisham Medical Centre, 158 Utting Avenue East, Liverpool L11 1DL Tel: 0151 256 9800 Fax: 0151 256 5765; 95 Queens Drive, Liverpool L15 7ND Tel: 0151 737 1719 — MB BS 1978 Lond.; DCH RCP Lond. 1983.

REDMOND, Timothy Kevin 33 Score Lane, Childwall, Liverpool L16 6AN Tel: 0151 722 6312 — MB BS 1978 Lond.; MA Camb. 1979; MB BS (Hons._Distinc. Surg.) Lond. 1978; MRCP (UK) 1981; DCH Eng. 1981. (Lond. Hosp.)

REDMOND, Vera Alexandra Broughshane Medical Practice, 76 Main Street, Broughshane, Ballymena BT42 4JP Tel: 028 2586 1214 Fax: 028 2586 2281 — MB BCh BAO 1965 Belf. (Belf.) Princip. Gen. Pract. & Community Family Plann. Dr. Socs: Mem. Fac. of Family Plann. and Reproductive Health Care. Prev: Ho. Off. Ards Hosp. Newtownards.

REDMORE, Michael John The Grange Clinic, Westfield Avenue, Malpas, Newport NP20 6EY Tel: 01633 855521 Fax: 01633 859490; 103 Ringwood Hill, Newport NP19 9EA — MB BS 1982 Nottm.; MRCGP 1986; DRCOG 1985.

REDONDO CAMPOS, Agustin Rafael 306 Osler House, Eastbourne District General Hospital, Kings Drive, Eastbourne BN21 2UD — LMS 1986 Cordoba.

REDPATH, Abigail Jane Ninewells Mains, Chirnside, Duns TD11 3JU — MB ChB 1998 Aberd.; MB ChB Aberd 1998.

REDPATH, Alexander 5 Woodside, Hexham NE46 1HU — MB ChB 1975 Dundee; FFA RCS Eng. 1980. Cons. Anaesth. Hexham Gen. Hosp.

REDPATH, Anne Margaret Abbey House Medical Practice, Golding Close, Daventry — MB ChB 1995 Birm.; DFFP 2000; BDS Lond. 1987; DRCOG 1997. GP Partner; Clin. Asst., Maxillofacial Surg., Univ. Hosps. Coventry & Warks. NHS Trust, Coventry & Warks. Hosp., Stoney Stanton Rd, Coventry. Socs: BMA; Rugby & Dist. Med. Soc. Prev: GP Regist. N.ampton Gen. Hosp. VTS; SHO (Oral Surg.) Soton. Gen. Hosp.; Ho. Off. (Surg. & Med.) N.ampton Gen. Hosp.

REDPATH, Calum Jon 29 Stevenson Road, Edinburgh EH11 2SH — MB ChB 1997 Glas.

REDPATH

REDPATH, Douglas (retired) Nuthatch, Low St., Burton-in-Lonsdale, Carnforth LA6 3LF — LMSSA 1949 Lond.; MRCGP 1958.

REDPATH, Douglas Alexander Waterside, Bar Creek, Malpas, Truro TR1 1SS — MB BS 1985 Melbourne.

REDPATH, James Barron Scott 11 Orion Way, Carluke ML8 5TP — MB ChB 1971 Ed.; FFA RCS Eng. 1978.

REDPATH, Marion 28 Hayfield Road, Kirkcaldy KY2 5DG — MB ChB 1979 Dundee.

REDPATH, Sharon Carlisle House, 53 Lagland Street, Poole BH15 1QD Tel: 01202 678484 Fax: 01202 660507; Tel: 01202 708719 Email: redhotdoc@aol.com — MB BS 1981 Lond.; MRCGP 1986; DCH RCP Lond. 1985; DRCOG 1983.

REDPATH, Trevor Henry Headbourne Worthy Grange, Winchester SO23 7JX Tel: 01962 880297 Fax: 01962 880297 — MRCS Eng. LRCP Lond. 1964; FDS RCS Eng. 1967, LDS 1958. (Guy's) Cons. Oral & Maxillofacial Surg. Soton. Univ. Teach. Hosp. & N. Hants. Dist. HA. Socs: Fell. Brit. Assn. Oral Surgs.; EAMFS; BMA.

REDSHAW, Gillian Wendy 10 Fall Lane, Hartshead, Liversedge WF15 8AR — MB ChB 1983 Sheff.; DGM RCP Lond. 1985.

REDSTONE, Clare Diana 14 Biscay House, Mile End Road, London E1 4QU Tel: 020 7790 4151 Fax: 020 7423 9889 — MB ChB 1982 Bristol; BSc (Hons.) Anat. Bristol 1979; MRCGP 1988. (Univ. Bristol)

REDSTONE, David 7 Charlotte Road, London SW13 9QJ — MB ChB 1955 St. And.; DCH Eng. 1960. (St. And.) Lect. Paediat. & Hon. Lect. Chem. Path. St. Mary's Hosp. Med. Sch. Lond. Prev: RAF Med. Br.; Regist. in Clin. Path. St. Mary's Hosp. Lond.

REDSTONE, Isidore Flat 1, 35 Bryanston Square, London W1H 2DZ — MB BS 1948 Lond. (Lond. Hosp.) Prev: Emerg. Med. Off. Lond. Hosp.; Ho. Phys. St. Mary's Hosp. Portsmouth.

REDVERS, Amanda 88 Gascoigne Road, New Addington, Croydon CR0 0NE — MB BS 1996 Lond.

REDWOOD, David Robert St. Anthony's Hospital, North Cheam, Sutton SM3 9DW Tel: 020 8337 6691; Oakwood Cottage, Ide Hill Road, Ide Hill, Sevenoaks TN14 6JY — MB BChir 1961 Camb.; MA Camb. 1962; FRCP Lond. 1979, M 1963. Cons. Cardiol. St. Anthony's Hosp. N. Cheam. Prev: Cons. Cardiol. SW Thames Regional Cardiothoracic Unit; Hon. Sen. Lect. St. Geo. Hosp. Med. Sch. Lond.; Vis. Scientist & Chief Cardiovasc. Diag. Nat. Inst. of Health Bethesda, USA.

REDWOOD, Michael David Tobin, Redwood and Lalli, 25 Alms Hill, Bourn, Cambridge CB3 7SH Tel: 01954 719313 Fax: 01954 718012 — MB BS 1987 Lond.; MRCGP 1993; T(GP) 1993; DRCOG 1992; DCH RCP Lond. 1991. (St. Thos.)

REDWOOD, Mr Nicholas Frederick Wakerley Dept of Surgery, The Queen Elizabeth Hospital, Gayton Road, King's Lynn PE30 4ET — MB BS 1984 Lond.; FRCS Eng. 1990. Cons. Gen. & Vasc. Surg. Prev: Sen. Regist., N.ern Region Vasc. Unit, Newc.

REDWOOD, Rebekah 183 Cator Lane N., Chilwell, Nottingham NG9 4BL — BM BS 1998 Nottm.; BM BS Nottm 1998.

REDWOOD, Simon Robert Cardiothoraci Centre, St Thomas's Hospital, Lambeth Palace Road, London SE1 7EH Tel: 020 7922 8191 Fax: 020 7960 5680 — MB BS 1987 Lond.; MD Lond. 1996; MRCP (UK) 1990. (St. Geo. Hosp. Med. Sch.) Sen. Lec./Cons Cardiol St. Thos. Hosp. Lond. Prev: Interven. Fell. (Cardiol.) Washington Cardiol. Center Washington, DC, USA; Clin. Research Regist. (Cardiol.) St. Geo. Hosp. Med. Sch.; Regist. (Cardiol.) Roy. Free Hosp. Lond.

REDZISZ, Boleslaw 57 Queens Road, Leicester LE8 4EH — MD 1946 Beirut.

REE, Christopher James Brooklea Clinic, Wick Road, Bristol BS4 4HU Tel: 0117 971 1211 Fax: 0117 972 3370; Ivy Cottage, Woollard, Pensford, Bristol BS39 4HY Tel: 01761 490860 — MB ChB 1983 Bristol; MA Oxf. 1980; MRCGP 1987; DCH RCP Lond. 1988; DRCOG 1987.

REEBACK, Jane Susan Department of Rheumatology, Edgware General Hospital, Edgware; 40 St Marys Avenue, Northwood HA6 3AZ — MB BS 1972 Lond.; BSc (Hons.) Lond. 1969, MB BS (Hons.) 1972; MRCP (UK) 1975. (Lond. Hosp.) Clin. Asst. (Rheum.) Edgware Gen. Hosp. Socs: Brit. Soc. Rheum. Prev: Sen. Regist. (Rheum.) Lond. Hosp.; Regist. Guy's Hosp. Lond.; SHO (Med.) & Ho. Phys. Lond. Hosp.

REECE, Alastair Hugh Mackintosh Wexham Park Hospital, Slough SL2 4HL Tel: 01753 633000; 1 Hockley Lane, Stoke Poges, Slough SL2 4QF Tel: 01753 663480 — MB ChB 1975 Dundee; MSc Cardiff 1999. Hosp. Pract. Chronic Pain Clinic.

REECE, Mr Anthony Thomas Christopher Freeman Hospital, High Heaton, Newcastle upon Tyne NE7 7DN; 117 Glenthorn Road, Jesmond, Newcastle upon Tyne NE2 3HJ — MB ChB 1983 Dundee; FRCS Eng. 1988. Sen. Regist. Rotat. (Orthop.) Newc. & Sunderland N. RHA. Prev: Smith & Nephew Trauma Research Fell. Univ. Dept. Orthop. Glenfield Gen. Hosp. Leic.; W. Scotl. Surg. Rotat. Glas. Roy. Infirm.; Regist. (Orthop.) Leicester Roy. Infirm.

REECE, Ashley 37 Kingfisher Way, Leeds LS17 8XA — MB ChB 1995 Leeds.

REECE, Dorothy Ann Moor House, Friar Terrace, Hartlepool TS24 0PF Tel: 01429 66803 — MB BS 1958 Durh. Prev: SHO Sunderland Childr. Hosp.; Ho. Phys. Roy. Vict. Infirm. Newc.; Ho. Surg. Newc. Gen. Hosp.

REECE, Elizabeth Victoria The Old Hall, Billington Lane, Derrington, Stafford ST18 9LR Tel: 01785 251550; 5 Cedric Road, Bath BA1 3PD Tel: 0122 5427 435 — MB BCh 1992 Wales; DCH; DRCOG; DFFP; MRCGP (merit) 1999. GP VTS Bath.

REECE, Gillian June Kenmure Medical Practice, 7 Springfield Road, Bishopbriggs, Glasgow G66 7PJ Tel: 0141 772 6309 Email: gillian.reece@gp43171.glasgow-hb.scot. nhs.uk; 3 Kirklee Quadrant, Kelvinside, Glasgow G12 0TR — MB ChB 1985 Glas.; MRCGP 1992; DCH RCP Lond. 1992; DRCOG 1992; DA (UK) 1989; DFFP 1997. (Glas.) p/t GP Retainer Kenmure Med. Pract. 7 Springfield Rd. Bishopbriggs.

REECE, Michael Frederick (retired) Moor House, Friar Terrace, Hartlepool TS24 0PF Tel: 01429 266803 — MB BS 1958 Durh.; MRCGP 1967. Hosp. Pract. (Med.) Hartlepool Gen. Hosp.; Clin. Tutor Univ. Newc. Prev: GP Hartlepool.

REECE, Mr Michael William (retired) September Cottage, Yeoland Down, Yelverton PL20 6BY Tel: 01822 852037 Email: mwreece@globalnet.co.uk — MB BS Lond. 1948; FRCS Eng. 1953. Prev: Cons. Surg. Plymouth HA.

REECE, Richard John Department of Rheumatology, Faculty of Medicine & Dentistry, University of Birmingham, Edgbaston, Birmingham B15 2TT; 46 Corbett Avenue, Droitwich Spa, Droitwich WR9 7BE — MB BCh 1987 Wales; MRCP (UK) 1992. Research Regist. (Rheum.) Fac. Med. & Dent. Univ. Birm. Socs: Brit. Soc. Rheum. Prev: Regist. (Renal & Gen. Med.) Roy. Devon & Exeter Hosp.; Regist. Roy. Devon & Exeter Hosps.; SHO (Gen. Med.) N.ampton Gen. Hosp.

REECE, Mr Victor Alan Cyril, RD Accident & Emergency Department, South Tyneside District Hospital, South Shields NE34 0P6 Tel: 0191 454 8888 Fax: 0191 202 4179 Email: alan.reece@eem.sthet.northy-nhs.uk; 72 Moorfield Gardens, Ceadon, Sunderland SR6 7TP Tel: 0191 537 4817 Email: reece.alan@virgin.net — MB BS Newc. 1970; BSc Newc. 1967; FRCS Eng. 1975; FFAEM 1993. (Newc. u. Tyne) Cons. A & E S. Tyneside Dist. Hosp. S. Shields. Socs: Assoc. Mem. Brit. Hyperbaric Assn.; Brit. Assn. Accid. & Emerg. Med.; Fell. Roy. Soc. Med. Prev: Surg. Cdr. RNR; Chairm. Med. Advis. Gp. N.umbria Ambul. Serv.; Cons. A & E Qu. Eliz. Hosp. Gateshead.

REECE-SMITH, Mr Howard 72 Berkeley Avenue, Reading RG1 6HY Tel: 01189 553454 Fax: 01189 553478/01189 588110; St Anthonys, 95 Reading Rd, Finchampstaed, Wokingham RG40 4RD — MB BS 1973 Lond.; MS Lond. 1981; FRCS Eng. 1978. (Lond. Hosp.) Cons. Surg. Reading Hosp.s. Prev: Sen. Surg. Regist. Roy. United Hosp. Bath; Hanson Trust Surg. Research Fell. John Radcliffe Hosp. Oxf.; Cons. Surg. Battle Hosp. Reading.

REED, Alice 2 The Woodlands, Slad Road, Stroud GL5 1QE — MRCS Eng. LRCP Lond. 1945; MRCS Eng., LRCP Lond. 1945. (Leeds) Prev: Leeds & Matern. Hosp. Leeds.

REED, Alison The Reaside Clinic, Birmingham Great Park., Bristol Road South, Birmingham B45 9BE Tel: 0121 678 3014, 0121 678 3052 — MB BS 1983 Lond.; MRCP (UK) 1987; MRCPsych 1989. Sen. Lect. in Forens. Psychiat. Uni. Of Birm., Hon. Cons. Readside clinic, Birm.. Prev: Research Worker Inst. Psychiat. & Hon. Sen. Regist. Maudsley Hosp.; Sen.Regist. Rotat. (Forens.Psychiat.) Maudsley Hosp.; Sen. Regist. (Forens. Psychiat)Readside Clinic.

REED, Andrew John Cantilupe Surgery, 49-51 St. Owen Street, Hereford HR1 2JB Tel: 01432 268031 Fax: 01432 352584 — MB BS 1961 Lond.; DObst RCOG 1968. (Westm.) Socs: Past-Pres. Herts. Med. Soc. Prev: Ho. Surg. Gordon Hosp. Lond.; Surg. Lt.-Cdr. RN.

REED, Andrew Mark 143 Butchers Lane, Mereworth, Maidstone ME18 5QD — MB BS 1997 Lond.

REED, Anne Elisabeth Ryder Taunton Road Medical Centre, 12-16 Taunton Road, Bridgwater TA6 3LS Tel: 01278 444400 Fax: 01278 423691; 78 Wembdon Hill, Bridgwater TA6 7PZ — MB BS 1974 Lond. (Lond. Hosp.)

REED, Anne Mary 7 Rede Place, London W2 4TU — MB BS 1988 Lond.

REED, Anthony Birbeck Medical Group, Penrith Health Centre, Bridge Lane, Penrith CA11 8HW Tel: 01768 245200 Fax: 01768 245295; Ellangowan, Pooley Bridge, Penrith CA10 2NG Tel: 01768 486256 Fax: 01768 486256 — MB BS 1968 Newc.; FRCGP 1984, M 1972; DObst RCOG 1972. Examr. RCGP. Prev: Trainee GP Newc. VTS; Ho. Phys. & Ho. Surg. Roy. Vict. Infirm. Newc.; chairm.eden valley Pcg.

REED, Anthony Bridge Cottage Surgery, 41 High Street, Welwyn AL6 9EF Tel: 01438 715044 Fax: 01438 714013; The Old Rectory, 2 Walkern Road, Benington, Stevenage SG2 7LP Tel: 01438 869125 Email: areeddoc@aol.com — MB BS 1981 Lond.; DRCOG 1985. (St. Mary's) GP Welwyn.; Med. Cons. Ship Managem. Ltd. Lond. Prev: Ship's Phys. Wind Star Miami; SHO Qu. Eliz. II Hosp. Welwyn Garden City; Trainee GP Welwyn Garden City VTS.

REED, Anthony Raddon 2 Wanstead Place, London E11 2SW — MB ChB 1989 Cape Town.

REED, Antonia Lucy — MB ChB 1996 Leeds; DCH 2001 Lond.

REED, Derwyn Huw Nevill Hall And District Hospital Trust, Abergavenny NP7 7EG — MB BS 1982 Lond.; MA Camb. 1982, BA 1979; MRCP (UK) 1985; FRCR 1988. Cons. Diag. Radiol. Nevill Hall Hosp. Abergavenny. Prev: Sen. Regist. (Diag. Radiol.) Univ. Hosp. Wales Cardiff; Regist. (Diag. Radiol.) Addenbrooke's Hosp. Camb.; SHO (Gen. Med.) Univ. Coll. Hosp. Lond.

REED, Dianna Tracy 1 Sandfield Avenue, Milngavie, Glasgow G62 8NR Tel: 0141 956 2004 — MB ChB 1993 Aberd.; DFFP, DRCOG, MRCGP. CMO Family Plann., Arbroath / Staff Grade Community Paediat.(SO/SG split), Angus. Socs: MRCGP; DFFP; DRCOG. Prev: Trainee GP Dumfries VTS.; GP Trainee.

REED, Elizabeth Alice Glan Clwyd Hospital, Bodelwyddan, Rhyl LL18 5UJ — MB ChB 1983 Ed.; BSc (Med. Sci.) Ed. 1980, MB ChB 1983; MRCP)UK) 1988. (Edinburgh) Locum cons Geriat. med. Socs: Brit Geriat. soc. Prev: Sen Reg gen & Geriat. med, Glan clwyd hosp & Roy. Liverp. Hosp; Research Regist. (Med. for Elderly) Woodend Hosp. Aberd.; Regist. (Med.) Rotherham Dist. Gen. Hosp.

REED, Enid Ann Southgate, 40 St Michael's Road, Llandaff, Cardiff CF5 2AP — MB BCh 1945 Wales; DCH Eng. 1948. (Cardiff)

REED, Freda Susanne (retired) Castle Cottage, Chilham, Canterbury CT4 8DB Tel: 01227 730330 — MB BS 1946 Lond.; MRCS Eng. LRCP Lond. 1946; FRCPsych 1979, M 1973; DPM Eng. 1962. Vis. Psychiat. H.M. Prison Canterbury; Hon. Cons. Psychiat. Maidstone HA. Prev: SCMO (Child & Family Psychiat.) Dover.

REED, George Patterson (retired) The Mews, Shard Lane, Hambleton, Blackpool Tel: 01253 700492 — MB ChB 1945 Liverp.; DPH 1949.

REED, Hilary Willow Tree House, Westleigh Drive, Bromley BR1 2PN — MB BS 1956 Lond.; MRCS Eng. LRCP Lond. 1956; DCH Eng. 1958; DObst RCOG 1958. (Guy's) SCMO (Audiol.) Bromley HA.

REED, Ian Alan Albion House Suegery, Albion Street, Brierley Hill DY5 3EE Tel: 01384 70220 Fax: 01384 78284; 269 Hagley Road, Stourbridge DY9 0RJ Email: ian_reed@bigfoot.com — MB BCh 1987 Wales; MRCGP 1994; T (GP) 1991; Cert. Family Plann. JCC 1990; DRCOG 1990. (University Wales) Princip. GP. Socs: BMA & Roy. Coll. GPs.

REED, Isabel Therese Delma Bushyfields Hospital, Russell Hall, Dudley DY1 2LZ; 269 Hagley Road, Stourbridge DY9 0RJ — MB BCh 1987 Wales. Clin. Asst. (Psychiat.) Lucy Baldwin Hosp. Stourport-on-Severn. Socs: BMA.

REED, Joanna Bell 1 Northumberland Terrace, North Shields NE30 4BA — BM BS 1987 Nottm.; BMedSci (Hons.) Nottm. 1985; FRCS Eng. 1992. Specialist Regist. (Gen. Surg.) N. Region. Prev: Sen. Research Assoc. (Surg.) Univ. Newc.

REED, John (retired) Trenhale, Treseders Gdn, Truro TR1 1TR Tel: 01872 278612 — BSc (Hons. Physiol.) Sheff. 1936, MB ChB 1939; DPH Manch. 1948.

REED, John Langdale, CB HM Inspectorate of Prisons, Home Office, 50 Queen Anne's Gate, London SW1H 9AT Tel: 020 7273 2305 Fax: 020 7273 4087; Willow Tree House, Westleigh Drive, Bromley BR1 2PN Tel: 020 8467 1452 Fax: 020 8249 4940 Email: 106124.342@compuserve.com — MB BChir 1957 Camb.; MB Camb. 1957, BChir 1956; FRCP Lond. 1974; M 1958; FRCPsych 1974, M 1971; DPM Lond. 1964. (Guy's) Med. Insp. HM Insp.ate of Prisons Lond. Prev: Special Adviser Ment. Health & Community Care Div. DoH; Qu. Hon. Phys.; Sen. Princip. Med. Off. Health Care Div. (Med.) DoH.

REED, John Matheson Heathfield, Collinswood Road, Farnham Common, Slough SL2 3LH Tel: 01753 5316 — MRCS Eng. LRCP Lond. 1945. (St. Thos.)

REED, John Paul Front Street Surgery, 14 Front Street, Acomb, York YO24 3BZ Tel: 01904 794141 Fax: 01904 788304 — MB BS 1991 Newc.

REED, John Richard 26c Nassington Road, London NW3 2UD — MB BS 1991 Lond.; MRCP (UK) 1996.

REED, Jonathan Mark Liberty Occupational Health, Sunnybank Road, Aberdeen AB24 3NG Tel: 01224 492884 Fax: 01224 487812 Email: jonnyreed@libertyhealth.co.uk; 6 Thomas Glover Place, Bridge of Don, Aberdeen AB22 8JR Tel: 01224 705061 — MB ChB 1990 Ed.; AFOM RCP Lond. 1997. (Ed.) Occupat. Phys. Liberty Occupat. Health Aberd.

REED, Laurence John 12 Trinity Church Square, London SE1 4HU; Department of Psychological Medicine, Institute of Psychiatry, De Crespigny Park, Denmark Hill, London SE5 8AF — MB BS 1994 Lond.

REED, Lesley 3 Lower Hall Road, Lascelles Hall, Huddersfield HD5 0AZ — MB ChB 1984 Leeds.

REED, Linda 27 Lilburn Close, East Boldon NE36 0TZ — BM BS 1986 Nottm.; MRCGP 1990; DCH RCP Lond. 1990.

REED, Professor Malcolm Walter Ronald Academic Surgical Oncology Unit, University of Sheffield, K Floor, Royal Hallamshire Hospital, Sheffield S10 2JF Tel: 0114 271 3326 Fax: 0114 271 3314 Email: m.w.reed@shef.ac.uk — MB ChB 1981 Sheff.; BMedSci Sheff. 1979, MD 1990; FRCS Eng. 1986. Prof. Surg. Oncol./ Hon. Cons. Surg, Univ. of Sheff., Roy. Hallamshire Hosp. Prev: Cons. Surg. Roy. Hallamshire Hosp. Sheff.; Sen. Lect. (Surg.) Univ. Sheff.; Regist. Sheff. & Lincoln HAs.

REED, Margaret Geraldine Phoebe (retired) Meadowcroft, 16 Trumpington Road, Cambridge CB2 2EX Tel: 01203 352367 — MB BChir 1927 Camb.; MRCP Lond. 1930; MRCS Eng. LRCP Lond. 1926. Prev: Med. Off. Ely Diocesan Matern. Home & Girton Infant Welf. Centre.

REED, Mark Geoffrey 30 Crescent Road, Kingston upon Thames KT2 7RG — BM BCh 1998 Oxf.; BM BCh Oxf 1998.

REED, Mr Michael Richard Long Byre, Highcliff Farm, Winston, Darlington DL2 3PJ Email: mike.reed@sheffield.ac.uk — MB BS 1992 Newc.; FRCS Ed. 1996. Specialist Regist. (Orthop.) N.ern Deanery. Socs: Brit. Orthop. Research Soc.

REED, Michelle 52 Commercial Road, Machen, Newport CF83 8PG — MB BS 1998 Lond.; MB BS Lond 1998.

REED, Natasha Jane Hunter 15 Kings Road, Cambridge CB3 9DY — MB BS 1994 Lond.

REED, Nicholas Guy Gold Street Medical Centre, 106 Gold Street, Wellingborough NN8 4BT Tel: 01933 223429 Fax: 01933 229240; Tel: 01933 442261 — BM BS 1983 Nottm.; BMedSci Nottm. 1981; MRCGP 1987; DRCOG 1985. GP; Chairm. WellingBoro. PCG. Socs: Soc. Occupat. Med.; N.ants. Medico-legal Soc. Prev: Trainee GP Croydon HA VTS; Ho. Phys. Edgware Gen. Hosp.; Ho. Surg. Mayday Hosp. Croydon.

REED, Nicholas Laurence 27 Arthur Road, Wokingham RG41 2SS — BM 1995 Soton.

***REED, Nicholas Norman** Stone House, West Felton, Oswestry SY11 4EH — BM BS 1986 Nottm.

REED, Nicholas Simon Ephraim 3 Lancaster Crescent, Glasgow G12 0RR Tel: 0141 334 7543 — MB BS 1976 Lond.; FRCP Glas. 1988; MRCP (UK) 1979; MRCS Eng. LRCP Lond. 1976; FRCR 1982. (Roy. Free) Cons. Clin. Oncol. Beatson Oncol. Centre W.. Infirm. Glas.; Hon. Sen. Clin. Lect. Univ. Glas. Prev: Sen. Regist. (Radiother. & Oncol.) Wessex Radiother. Centre Soton.; Regist. (Radiother. & Oncol.) Hammersmith Hosp. Lond.

REED

REED, Paul Francis Queens Park Hospital, Haslington Rd, Blackburn BB2 3HH Tel: 01254 293403 Fax: 01254 293856 — MB ChB 1984 Manch.; MSc Manch. 1993; MRCPsych 1989. Cons. Psychiat. Blackburn Hyndburn and Ribble Valley NHS Trust. Socs: Roy. Coll. Psychiat.; Brit. Med. Assoc.; Brit. Assn. Of PsychoPharmacol. Prev: Cons (Psychiat.) Roy. Bolton Hosp.; Cons. (Psychiat.) Ment. Health Serv.s of Salford NHS Trust.

REED, Paul Nicholas 19 Regency Way, Peterborough PE3 6HJ — MB BS 1977 Lond.; MRCS Eng. LRCP Lond. 1977; FFA RCS Eng. 1983. (St. Mary's) Cons. Anaesth. P'boro. NHS Trust. Socs: Assn. Anaesth.; Brit. Hyperbaric Assn.; (Hon. Sec.) Sheff. & E. Midl. Soc. Anaesth. Prev: Sen. Regist. (Anaesth.) Leic. HA; Sen. Specialist Anaesth. RAMC; Regtl. Med. Off. 3rd Roy. Ang./2nd RRF.

REED, Peter Austin The Lodge, Newton Road, Emberton, Olney MK46 5JJ Tel: 01234 241925 — BM BS 1976 Nottm.; FFA RCS Eng. 1981. Cons. Anaesth. Milton Keynes Gen. Dist. Hosp.

REED, Peter Dennis Taunton Road Medical Centre, 12-16 Taunton Road, Bridgwater TA6 3LS Tel: 01278 444400 Fax: 01278 423691 — MB BS 1974 Lond.; DA Eng. 1978. (Lond. Hosp.)

REED, Peter Ivan HRH Princess Christian's Hospital, Clarence Rd, Windsor SL4 5AG — MB BS 1953 Lond.; FRCP Lond. 1976, M 1963; FRCP Canada 1972; MRCS Eng. LRCP Lond. 1953; CRCP Canada 1959; LMCC 1957. (King's Coll. Hosp.) Hon. Dir. UK Nat. Barrett's Oesophagus Registry. Socs: Fell. Roy. Soc. Med. (Ex-Mem. Counc.Clin. Sect.); Brit. Soc. Gastroenterol. (Mem. Oesoph. Comm.); Fell. (Past Vice Pres.) Hosp. Cons. & Specialists Assn. Prev: Cons. Phys. Hammersmith Hosp. & Heatherwood & Wexham Pk. Hosp. Trust; Sen. Regist. (Med.) St. Thos. Hosp. Lond.; Instruc. (Med.) & Trainee (Gastroenterol.) Univ. Chicago, USA.

REED, Phillip David Barnsley District General Hospital NHS Trust, Pogmore Road, Barnsley S75 2EP — MB ChB 1992 Sheff.

REED, Richard William Holland House, 31 Church Road, Lytham, Lytham St Annes FY8 5LL Tel: 01253 794999 Fax: 01253 795744; 12 Eden Avenue, Lytham, Lytham St Annes FY8 5PS Tel: 01253 730500 — MB ChB 1975 Manch.; MRCGP 1982. Clin. Asst. (Cardiol.) Vict. Hosp. Blackpool. Prev: SHO (Obst.) & SHO (Paediat.) Vict. Hosp. Blackpool.

REED, Roderick Alan The Health Centre, Aylesbury Road, Wendover, Aylesbury HP22 6LD Tel: 01296 623452 — MB BS 1983 Lond.; MRCGP 1995; DRCOG 1990. (King's Coll. Lond.)

REED, Ruth Catherine Dalston Medical Group, Townhead Road, Dalston, Carlisle CA5 7PZ — MB BS 1980 Newcastle; MRCGP 1984. (Newcastle) GP Carlisle.

REED, Susan Margaret Quarry Dene, Owl Lane, Gawthorpe, Ossett WF5 9AU Tel: 01924 270749 — MB ChB 1975 Manch.; BSc St. And. 1972. Med. Off. DSS. Prev: Trainee GP Leeds VTS; Sen. Med. Off. (Child Health) Bradford HA; Ho. Phys. & Ho. Surg. Derby City Hosp.

REED, Sylvia Elsie (retired) 57 Watford Road, St Albans AL1 2AE — MB BChir 1954 Camb.; FRCPath 1978, M 1972. Prev: Mem. Scientif. Staff MRC.

REED, Timothy John Haven Health Surgery, Grange Farm Avenue, Felixstowe IP11 2FB Tel: 01394 670107 Fax: 01394 282872 — MB BS 1985 Lond.; MA Camb. 1980; MRCGP 1990; DCH RCP Lond. 1989; DRCOG 1988.

REEDER, Judith Alison Dr A Willis and Partners, King Edward Road Surgery, Christchurch Medical Centre, King Edward Road, Northampton NN1 5LY Tel: 01604 633466 Fax: 01604 603227; 45 Thorburn Road, Weston Favell, Northampton NN3 3DA Tel: 01604 401426 — MB ChB 1985 Leeds; MRCGP 1990; DRCOG 1989; DCH RCP Lond. 1988. (Leeds) Prev: Ho. Phys. Chapel Allerton Hosp. Leeds; Ho. Surg. Wycombe Gen. Hosp.

REEDER, Martin Kingston 9 East Cottages, Shipton Road, Clifton, York YO30 5RH — MB BS 1979 Lond.; BSc Lond. 1976, MB BS 1979; MRCP (UK) 1983; FFA RCS 1987. (St. Bart.)

REEDER, Sally Ann 18 Kendal Green, Kendal LA9 4SPN Tel: 01539 720241 Fax: 01539 725048 — MB ChB 1986 Dundee. p/t Salaried Gen. Practitioner; Clin. Asst. Geriat. Med., W.morland, Gen. Hosp., Kendal, Cumbria.

REEDER, Sarah-Jane 118 Whatton Road, Kegworth, Derby DE74 2DT — BM BS 1988 Nottm. Prev: SHO (Paediat.) City Hosp. & Qu. Med. Centre Nottm.; Ho. Surg. Qu. Med. Centre Nottm.; Ho. Phys. FarnBoro. Hosp.

REEK, Christine Radiology Department, Glenfield Hospital, Groby Road, Leicester LE3 9QP Tel: 0116 287 1471 Fax: 0116 232 0368; York Cottage, 2 Church Lane, Thorpe Satchville, Melton Mowbray LE14 2DF Tel: 01664 840766 — MB ChB 1979 Manch.; BSc (Hons.) Manch. 1976, MB ChB 1979; FRCR 1985. Cons. Radiol. (Cardiac Radiol.) Glenfield Hosp. Leics. Prev: Fell. (Cardiovasc. Radiol.) Green La. Hosp. Auckland, NZ; Sen. Regist. (Cardiac. Radiol.) Groby Rd. Hosp. Leics.; Sen. Regist. (Diag. Radiol.) Leics.

REEKIE, Alexander Euan Mackay (retired) Birchwood House, Sandyloan Crescent, Laurieston, Falkirk FK2 9NG Tel: 01324 623860 — MB ChB 1951 Ed. Prev: Res. Med. & Orthop. Ho. Off. Law Hosp. Carluke.

REEKIE, Elizabeth Heather (retired) Birchwood House, Sandyloan Crescent, Laurieston, Falkirk FK2 9NG Tel: 01324 623860 Email: hreekie@aol.com — MB ChB 1955 Ed. Prev: GP Falkirk.

REEKIE, Ian (retired) Mann Cottage, Moreton-in-Marsh GL56 0LA Tel: 01608 650764 Fax: 01608 650996 — MB BS Lond. 1964; MRCS Eng. LRCP Lond. 1966; DObst RCOG 1969. Prev: Cas. Off. Guy's Hosp.

REEKIE, Robert Andrew, OBE Ash Tree House, Hyde Lane, Marlborough SN8 1JN Tel: 01672 512083 Email: andrewreekie@hotmail.com — MB BChir 1966 Camb.; MA Camb. 1966; MRCS Eng. LRCP Lond. 1966; MRCGP 1977; DPD Wales 1990; DTM & H Liverp. 1988; DCH Eng. 1976; DObst RCOG 1970. (Camb. & St. Geo.) Socs: Fell. of the Roy. Soc. of Trop. Med. and Hyg.

REEKIE, Robert Morris ClinTrials Research Ltd, 1 Cadogan Square, Cadogan St., Glasgow G2 7HF Tel: 0141 222 5500 Fax: 0141 222 5511; Robertloan House, 32 Main St, Loans, Troon KA10 7EX Email: robert@mreekie.freeserve.co.uk — MB ChB 1982 Ed.; MBA Nottm. 1995; BSc (Hons.) St. And. 1979; Dip. Pharm. Med. RCP 1988; MFPM 1990. Sen. Dir., Med. & Regulatory Clin. Trials Research Ltd Glas. Prev: Med. Dir. DAR Ltd.; Head Clin. Developm. & Internat. Managem. Boots Pharmaceut. Nottm.

REEKS, John Lionel 2 East Campbell Court, Longniddry EH32 0NW Tel: 01875 52606 — MB ChB 1973 Dundee. (Dundee)

REES, Alan Martin Y Delyn, Llangan, Bridgend CF35 5DR — MB BCh 1976 Wales.

REES, Alexandra Elizabeth Joy Department of Obstetrics & Gynaecology, Llandough Hospital, Penlan Road, Penarth CF64 2XX Tel: 01222 716068 — MB ChB 1981 Liverp.; MRCOG 1987; Dip. Obst. (Liverp.) Cons. O & G Llandough Hosp. Cardiff. Prev: Sen. Regist. Morriston Hosp. Swansea & Llandough Hosp. Cardiff; Regist. (O & G) Derby & Nottm. City Hosps.; Perinatal Fell. (Reproduc. Med.) Groote Schurr Hosp. Cape Town.

REES, Alice Mary 38 Church Street, Lenton, Nottingham NG7 2FF — BM BS 1998 Nottm.; BM BS Nottm 1998.

REES, Allison Noreen Waterloo Road Surgery, 178 Waterloo Road, Blackpool FY4 3AD Tel: 01253 348619 Fax: 01253 404330 — MB ChB 1990 Manch.; BSc (Med. Sci.) Manch. 1987; MRCGP 1994; DCH RCP Lond. 1995; DRCOG 1993. (St. And. & Manch.)

REES, Alun (retired) Combedene, Broadwell Close, Combe St Nicholas, Chard TA20 3PB — MRCS Eng. LRCP Lond. 1942.

REES, Mr Alun 25 Lakeside Drive, Lakeside Est., Cyncoed, Cardiff CF23 6DF — MB BCh 1963 Wales; FRCS Eng. 1970.

REES, Alun David Meddygfa Pengorof, Gorof Road, Ystradgynlais, Swansea SA9 1DS Tel: 01639 843221 Fax: 01639 843790 — MB BCh 1978 Wales.

REES, Alyson Frances Park Medical Centre, Ball Haye Road, Leek ST13 6QP; Luxmore, Buxton Road, Leek ST13 6NE — MB ChB 1982 Liverp.; MRCGP 1986.

REES, Amanda Jane Severne Rotherham General Hospital, Moorgate Road, Rotherham S60 2UD Tel: 01709 824581 — MB BChir 1983 Camb.; FRCS (Orth.) 1993; FRCS Eng. 1986. Cons. Orthop. Rotherham Gen. Hosp. Prev: Clin. Lect. (Orthop.) Sheff.

REES, Amanda Jayne 45a Turner Street, London E1 2AU — MB BS 1996 Lond.

REES, Andrew Hugh The Surgery, 113 Church Lane, Stechford, Birmingham B33 9EJ Tel: 0121 783 2861 — MB ChB 1965 Birm.; DObst RCOG 1968.

REES, Andrew Jackson 20 The Chanonry, Aberdeen AB24 1RQ — MB ChB 1969 Liverp.; MSc Lond. 1979; FRCP Lond. 19832; MRCP (UK) 1972. Prof. Nephrol. Roy. Postgrad. Med. Sch. Hammersmith Hosp. Lond.; Hon. Sen. Lect. Roy. Postgrad. Med.

Sch. Lond. Socs: Assn. Phys. & Internat. Soc. Nephrol. Prev: Cons. Phys. (Nephrol.) Hammersmith Hosp. Lond.

REES, Angela Lynn 23 Denby Drive, Cleethorpes DN35 9QQ — MB BS 1996 Lond.

REES, Ann Old Oaks, Nantgaredig, Carmarthen SA32 7LJ — MB BCh 1965 Wales.

REES, Anne Margaret Deparment of Community Child Health, Trinity Buildings, 21 Orchard St., Swansea SA1 5AT Tel: 01792 651501 — MB BCh 1978 Wales; MRCGP 1984; DCH RCP Lond. 1982. Staff Grade Community Paediat.

REES, Bethan Margaret Penylan Surgery, 74 Penylan Road, Cardiff CF23 5SY Tel: 029 2049 8181 Fax: 029 2049 1507; 1 St. Edeyrn's Close, Cyncoed, Cardiff CF23 6TH Tel: 029 2076 3153 — MB BCh 1972 Wales; DObst RCOG 1974.

REES, Bethan Wyn 14 Mylne Close, Upper Mall, London W6 9TE — MB BCh 1994 Wales.

REES, Betty 9A Fulwood Park, Liverpool L17 5AA — MB ChB 1942 Liverp.

REES, Mr Brian Idris St. David's, The Avenue, Llandaff, Cardiff CF5 2L Tel: 029 2056 3109 — MB BChir 1970 Camb.; MA, MB Camb. 1970, BChir 1969; FRCS Eng. 1974; MRCS Eng. LRCP Lond. 1969. (Camb. & St. Bart.) Cons. Surg. Univ. Hosp. Wales Cardiff. Prev: Sen. Regist. Hosp. Sick Childr. Lond.; Sen. Regist. (Surg.) Univ. Hosp. Wales Cardiff; Regist. (Rotat.) Univ. Hosp. Wales.

REES, Bryn Spencer James Melville Street Surgery, 17 Melville Street, Ryde PO33 2AF Tel: 01983 811431 Fax: 01983 817215 — MB BS 1975 Lond.; MRCS Eng. LRCP Lond. 1975; MRCGP 1980.

REES, Catherine Mary Evans (retired) Pant-Y-Castell, Solva, Haverfordwest SA62 6XB Tel: 01437 721381 — MB BChir 1946 Camb.; MA Camb. 1950 MB BChir 1946; MRCS Eng. LRCP Lond. 1946. Prev: Clin. Med. Off. Dyfed AHA.

REES, Charles Robert Penny's Hill Practice, St Mary's Road, Ferndown BH22 9HB Tel: 01202 897200 Fax: 01202 877753; 13A Pine Vale Crescent, Redhill, Bournemouth BH10 6BG Tel: 01202 251737 Email: 106207.2102@compuserve.com — MB ChB 1968 Leeds; MRCGP 1976; DObst RCOG 1970. GP Tutor E. Dorset. Prev: SHO (Cas. & Orthop.) Poole Gen. Hosp.; SHO (Obst.) Leeds Matern. Hosp.; Ho. Surg. Leeds Gen. Infirm.

REES, Charlotte Nicola 24 Chivalry Road, London SW11 1HT — MB BS 1990 Lond.; BSc Lond. 1987, MB BS 1990; MRCP (UK) 1994.

REES, Cheryl (retired) 2 Bryning Avenua, Wrea green, Preston PR4 2WL Tel: 01772 684037 Email: cheryl.rees@btinternet.com — MB ChB 1976 Manch.; DCCH RCP Ed. 1987.

***REES, Clare Miranda** 17 Miles Road, Bristol BS8 2JW Tel: 0117 973 4331 Fax: 0117 973 4331 Email: cmrees@btinternet.com — MB ChB 1997 Bristol.

REES, Colin John Royal Victoria Infirmary, Newcastle upon Tyne NE1 4LP Tel: 0191 232 5131; 46 Wolseley Gardens, Jesmond Vale, Newcastle upon Tyne NE2 1HR Tel: 0191 281 3359 — MB BS 1990 Newc.; MRCP (UK) 1993. Research Fell. Roy. Vict. Infirm. Newc. u. Tyne. Prev: Regist. (Gastroenterol. & Gen. Med.) N.. Region; SHO (Hepatol.) St. Jas. Hosp. Leeds.

REES, Constance Margaret Pascal Nuffield Department of Obstetrics & Gynaecology, John Radcliffe Hospital, Oxford OX3 9DU — MB BS 1975 Lond.; DPhil Oxf. 1984, MA 1988; BSc (1st cl. Hons.) Lond. 1972; MRCOG 1985. (St George's Hosp. Lond.) Hon. Sen. Clin. Lect. (O & G) John Radcliffe Hosp. Oxf.; Edr. in Chief Jl. Brit. Menopause Soc. Socs: (Counc.) Brit. Menopause Soc.; Endocrine Soc.; Soc. Study of Fertil. Prev: MRC Train. Fell. 1979-1983.

REES, Corinne Alison 46 Clifton Park Road, Bristol BS8 3HN — MB ChB 1976 Bristol; MA Oxf. 1977; MRCP (UK) 1979. Assoc. Specialist (Community Paediat.) & Med. Adviser to Avon AdoptionAgency, United Bristol Healthcare NHS Trust. Prev: Sen. Regist. (Paediat. with Interest in Community Child Health) SW RHA; Regist. (Paediat.) Sheff. Childr. Hosp. & Birm. Childr. Hosp.

REES, Dafydd Aled Cerdd-y-Don, Feidr Brenin, Newport SA42 0RZ — MB BCh 1993 Wales.

REES, Mr David Department of Orthopaedic Surgery, Robert Jones & Agnus Hunt Orthopaedic Hospital, Oswestry Tel: 01691 404167; Springfields, Kidderton Lane, Brindley, Nantwich CW5 8JD — MB BS 1976 Lond.; MChOrth Liverp. 1985; FRCS Eng. 1982; FRCS Ed. 1981. Cons. Surg. (Orthop.) Orthop. Hosp. OsW.ry. Prev: Cons.

Surg. (Orthop.) Leighton Hosp. Crewe; Sen. Regist. (Orthop.) Roy. Liverp. Hosp.; Ho. Surg. St. Bart. Hosp. Lond.

REES, David Alun 44 College Street, Bury St Edmunds IP33 1NL — MRCS Eng. LRCP Lond. 1962; MA, MB BChir Camb. 1962; FRCOG 1981, M (Gold Medal) 1968. (Camb. & Guy's) Cons. (O & G) W. Suff. Hosp. Socs: E. Anglian Obst. & Gyn. Soc. Prev: Sen. Regist. O & G St. Mary's Hosp. Lond. & United Camb.; Hosps.; Res. Med. Off. Qu. Charlotte's Hosp.

REES, David Alun Wordsley Green Health Centre, Wordsley Green, Wordsley, Stourbridge DY8 5PD Tel: 01384 277591 Fax: 01384 401156 — MB BCh 1968 Wales.

REES, David Charles 10 Vicarage Road, Silsoe, Bedford MK45 4ED — MB BS 1987 Lond.; MRCP (UK) 1990.

REES, Mr David Christopher 11 Greenes Court, Lower Kings Road, Berkhamsted HP4 2JU Tel: 01442 876233; 1419 Lakeshore Boulevard, Lake Orion MI 48362, USA Tel: 00 1 248 814 0582 — MB BS 1994 Lond.; BSc (Clin. Sci.) Lond. 1992, MB BS 1994; FRCS Lond. 1998. (Royal Free Hospital School of Medicine) SHO (Orthop.) Roy. Nat. Orthop. Hosp. Stanmore Middlx. Prev: SHO (Gen. Surg.) N.wick Pk. Hosp. Middlx.; SHO (Neurosurg.) Nat. Hosp. for Neurol. & Neurosurg. Lond.; SHO (Cardiac Surg.) Roy. Brompton Hosp. Lond.

REES, David Garfield Panty Scallog Farm, Sennybridge, Brecon LD3 8PT Tel: 01874 636427 — MB BCh Wales 1965. SCMO Powys HA.

REES, David Geraint The Valley, Narberth SA67 8BS — MB BCh 1965 Wales.

REES, David Henry Everard Tel: 01432 364097 Fax: 02432 364449; Bearwood House, Pembridge, Leominster HR6 9EE Tel: 01544 388613 — MB BS 1986 Lond.; FRCP 2001; MRCP (UK) 1990. Cons. Rheumatologist. Prev: Sen. Regis. Char. Cross, W.minster & Chelsea & St Mary's Hosp. Lond.; Research Regist., Dept of Immunol. St Geo.s Hosp., Lond..; SHO in Nephetologist, Cardiol., Endocrinol. W.minster Hosp. & Char. Cross Hosp., Lond.

REES, David Rhydian The Ashgrove Surgery, Morgan Street, Pontypridd CF37 2DR Tel: 01443 404444 Fax: 01443 480917; 50 Summerfield Drive, Llantrisant, Pontyclun CF72 8QF Tel: 01443 237886 — MB BCh 1984 Wales; BSc Wales 1979, MB BCh 1984.

REES, Dawn Elizabeth 24 Fleurs Avenue, Glasgow G41 5AP — MB ChB 1990 Glas.

REES, Diana Gillian Department of Anaesthesia, Whipps Cross University Hospital, Whipps Cross Road, London E11 Tel: 020 8535 6614 Fax: 0208 535 6467; Parnassus, Park Hill, Loughton IG10 4ES Tel: 020 8508 8673 Fax: 020 8508 8673 — MB BS 1972 Lond.; MRCS Eng. LRCP Lond. 1972; FFA RCS Eng. 1977. (St. Bart.) Cons. Anaesth. Whipps Cross Univ. Hosp. Clin. Director, Critical Care, Whipps Cross Univ. Hosp. Socs: BMA; Assn. Anaesth. Prev: Sen. Regist. (Anaesth.) St. Bart. Hosp. Lond.; Regist. (Anaesth.) Hosp. Sick Childr. Lond.

REES, Edgar Lowell Cross Cottage, Rushlake Green, Heathfield TN21 9QG — MB BS 1955 Lond.

REES, Elizabeth Napier 5 Sundbury Rise, Birmingham B31 2EZ — MB ChB 1987 Birm.

REES, Ernest Gwyn (retired) 12 Mill Road, Salisbury SP2 7RZ Tel: 01722 334944 — MB BS 1948 Lond.; FRCP Lond. 1988, M 1950; MRCS Eng. LRCP Lond. 1948; FRCPath 1972. Prev: Cons. Haemat. Salop AHA.

REES, Esther Hughes (retired) High Ridge, Mathern, Chepstow NP16 6JD — MB BCh 1950 Wales; MFCM 1974; DPH Wales 1971. JP. Prev: SCM Gwent HA.

REES, Evan Glyn (retired) Sycharth, Feidr Henffordd, Cardigan SA43 — MB BCh 1948 Wales.

REES, Gareth Bowen 21 Ogmore Drive, Nottage, Porthcawl CF36 3HR — MB BChir 1977 Camb.; MA, MB Camb. 1977, BChir 1976; DM Nottm. 1989; MRCOG 1986.

REES, Gareth John Glyn 46 Clifton Park Road, Clifton, Bristol BS8 3HN Tel: 0117 973 7712 Email: gareth.rees@ubht.swest.nhs.uk — MB BCh 1972 Cymru; MRCP (UK) 1975; FRCR 1981; FRCP 1998. (Ysgol Feddygol Cymru) Cons. Clin. Oncol. Bristol Oncol. Centre & Roy. United Hosp. Bath. Socs: Founder Mem. Brit. Oncol. Assn. Prev: Sen. Regist. (Radiotherap. & Oncol.) W.on Pk. Hosp. Sheff.; Med. Off. Montebello Mission Hosp. Natal, S. Afr.

REES, Mr Gareth Mervyn Flat 1, 21 Devonshire Place, London W1G 6HZ Tel: 020 7487 3598; 23 Church Row, Hampstead,

REES

London NW3 6UP — MS Lond. 1972, MB BS (Hons.) 1960; FRCP Lond. 1983, M 1963; FRCS Eng. 1966. (St. Mary's) Emerit. Cons. Cardiothoracic Surg. St. Bart. Hosp. Lond.; Cons. Cardiac Surg. Harley St. Clinic; Cons. Cardiac Surg. Wellington Hosp. Socs: Assn. Thoracic Surgs.; Cardiac Soc. Prev: Ho. Phys. St. Mary's Hosp. Lond.; Internat. Research Fell. (Cardiac Surg.) Univ. Oregon, Portland, USA; Sen. Regist. (Surg.) Brompton & Nat. Heart Hosps. Lond.

REES, Geraint Ellis Wellcome Department of Cognitive Neurology, 12 Queen Square, London WC1N 3BG Tel: 020 7833 7472 Fax: 020 7813 1420 Email: g.rees@fil.ion.ucl.ac.uk; 51 Brompton Park Crescent, London SW6 1SW Tel: 020 7381 8258 — BM BCh 1991 Oxf.; BA Camb. 1988; MRCP (UK) 1994. Research Fell. (Cognitive Neurol.) Inst. Neurol. Lond. Prev: Regist. (Med. & Neurol.) Qu. Mary's Univ. Hosp. Lond.; SHO Nat. Hosp. Neurol. & Neurosurg. Lond.; SHO (Intens. Ther.) St. Thos. Hosp. Lond.

REES, Gerwyn 5 Brookes Lane, Whalley, Clitheroe BB7 9RG — MB ChB 1996 Aberd. SHO Anaesth., S. Warks. Hosp. NHS. Aug 99 - Aug 00.

REES, Geryl Anne 22 Pine Road, Didsbury, Manchester M20 6UZ — BM BS 1975 Nottm.; BMedSci Nottm. 1973, BM BS 1975; MRCGP 1979; DRCOG 1977.

REES, Gillian Frances Margaret 48 The Drive, Northwood HA6 1HP Tel: 01923 822004 — MB ChB 1972 Liverp.; DRCOG 1974. Clin. Asst. (Rheum.) N.wick Pk. & Mt. Vernon Hosps. Prev: Asst. GP N. Lond.

REES, Gillian Lesley 154 Ravenhurst Road, Birmingham B17 9HS — MB ChB 1986 Birm.; DRCOG 1988.

REES, Gwyneth Lodwick 36 Macfarlane Road, Bearsden, Glasgow G61 2LZ — MB ChB 1990 Glas. Prev: Ho. Off. (Med.) Heathfield Hosp. Ayr; Ho. Off. (Surg.) Monklands Hosp. Airdrie.

REES, Mr Harland (retired) Kensworth Gorse, Kensworth Road, Dunstable LU6 3RF Tel: 01582 872411 — BM BCh 1936 Oxf.; MA, MCh 1941, BA, BM BCh Oxf. 1936; FRCS Eng. 1941. Prev: Lt.-Col. RAMC, OC Surg. Div. 53 I.G.H.(C.).

REES, Harry Alan 3 Vensland, Bishopston, Swansea SA3 3ET Tel: 0144 128 3049 — MB BCh 1953 Wales; BSc Wales 1950, MB BCh 1953; FRCP Lond. 1977, M.1961. (Cardiff) Cons. Phys. W. Glam. AHA. Socs: Thoracic Soc.; Brit. Cardiac Soc. Prev: Sen. Regist. Univ. Dept. Med. Roy. Infirm. Edin.; Hon. Lect. & Research Fell. Univ. Dept. Edin.; Research Fell. in Cardiol. Llandough Hosp. Cardiff.

REES, Harvey James Grove Road Day Hospital, 12 Grove Road, Clifton, Bristol BS6 6UJ Tel: 0117 973 0225 — MB BCh 1989 Wales; MRCPsych 1995. (Wales) Cons. Adult Psychiat.

REES, Haydn Griffith 24 Fernhill Close, Mayals, Swansea SA3 5BX — MB BCh 1967 Wales. Prev: GP Swansea.

REES, Helen Louise Flat 96 Finchley Court, Ballards Lane, London N3 1NJ — MB BS 1991 Lond.

REES, Helen Mary Church Lane Surgery, Church Lane, Boroughbridge, York YO51 9BD Tel: 01423 322309 Fax: 01423 324458; Coverpoint, Scarah Lane, Burton Leonard, Harrogate HG3 3SZ Tel: 01765 676566 — BM BS (Hons.) Nottm. 1989; BMedSci Nottm. 1987; MRCGP 1993; DCH RCP Lond. 1991. Princip. in Gen. Pract. Prev: SHO (Cas.) Harrogate Dist. Hosp.; SHO (O & G & Geriat.) Harrogate Gen. Hosp.

REES, Helene Ceredwyn Hammersmith Hospitals NHS Trust, Dept. of Histopathology, Charing CrossHospital, Fulham Palace Road, London W6 8RF Tel: 020 8846 7150 Email: helen.rees@ic.ac.uk; 72 Mortlake Road, Kew, Richmond TW9 4AS — MB BS 1972 Melbourne; LLB 1996; FRCPath 1996; FRCPA 1980; MRCPath 1984. Cons. Histopath. Char. Cross Hosp. Socs: (Vice-Pres.) Med. Soc. Lond. (Ex-Sen. & Jun. Sec.); Liveryman Soc. Apoth.; Soc. of Doctors in Law. Prev: Sen. Lect. & Hon. Cons. Histopath. St. Bart. & Homerton Hosps. Lond.; Sen. Regist. (Histopath.) Hammersmith Hosp. Lond.

REES, Hilary Margaret The Caxton Surgery, Oswald Road, Oswestry SY11 1RD Tel: 01691 654646 Fax: 01691 670994; Pentlands, 93 Oakhurst Road, Oswestry SY11 1BL — MB BChir 1975 Camb.; DCH Eng. 1981; DRCOG 1979.

REES, Howard William (retired) Cedar Ridge, Gate Burton, Gainsborough DN21 5BG Tel: 0142 771207 — MRCS Eng. LRCP 1936 Lond.; MRCS Eng LRCP Lond. 1936. Prev: Ho. Phys. Middlx. Hosp. & Brompton Hosp. Sanat. Frimley.

REES, Hugh Edward Gordon London Road Medical Centre, 2 London Road, Uppingham LE15 9TJ Tel: 01572 823531 Fax: 01572 821145; Carey's House, 4 Church Lane, Barrowden LE15 8ED Tel: 01572 747420 — MB BS 1966 Lond.; MRCS Eng. LRCP Lond. 1966; DObst RCOG 1968. (Guy's) Prev: Clin. Asst. (Orthop.) Rutland Memor. Hosp. Oakham; Ho. Surg. (Obst.) Brighton Gen. Hosp.; Ho. Surg. & Ho. Phys. (Cas. & Orthop.) Roy. Sussex Co. Hosp. Brighton.

REES, Huw Garwood UWCM Therapeutics & Toxicology Centre, Academic Centre, Llandough Hospital, Cardiff CF64 2XX Tel: 029 2071 6944 Fax: 029 2070 3454 — MB BCh 1979 Wales; MFOM RCP Lond. 1993, AFOM 1991; MRCGP 1985; DRCOG 1983; Cert. Family Plann. RCOG 1982; FFOM 1999. (Welsh Nat. Sch. Med.) p/t Hon. Sen. Lect. Occupat. Med. & Toxicology, UWCM, Cardiff; Hon. Cons. (Occupat. Med.). Socs: BMA & Soc. Occupat. Med.; BOHS. Prev: Cons. Occupat. Med., Univ. Hosp. of Wales, Cardiff; Sen. Clin. Med. Off. (Occupat. Health) Glan Hafren NHS Trust; GP Glynneath W. Glam.

REES, Ian Walter James Winstanley Drive Surgery, 138 Winstanley Drive, Leicester LE3 1PB Tel: 0116 285 8435 Fax: 0116 275 5416; 17 Wentworth Green, Kirby Muxloe, Leicester LE9 2EQ Tel: 0116 238 7256 — MB ChB 1982 Leic.; DCH RCP Lond. 1989; DRCOG 1985. Forens. Med. Examr. Leics. Constab. Socs: Brit. Assn. Sport & Med. Prev: Clin. Asst. (Rheum.) Leicester; SHO (Obst. Gyn.) Leicester Gen. Hosp.; SHO (Paediat.) Leicester Gen. Hosp.

REES, Jacqueline Emma Ford House, Ford Road, Ashford TW15 2RF — MB BS 1998 Lond.; MB BS Lond 1998.

REES, Jane Susan 9 Kensinton Drive, Willaston, Nantwich CW5 7HL Fax: 01270 664930 Email: jane@reesjs.freeserve.co.uk — MB BS 1970 Lond.; MRCGP 1984; DObst RCOG 1973; MA Med. Ethics. Keele Uni 2000. Med. Adviser to Shrops. Primary Care Audit Gp.; Occupat.al Health -Sema Gp. Vibreation white Fincter Scheme.; Assoc. Lect. open Uni. Prev: GP Llanfyllin, Powys.

REES, Jeni 11 Birch Grove, Hook RG27 9RJ — BM 1992 Soton.; MRCGP 1996; DRCOG 1994. (Soton.)

REES, Jennifer Ann (retired) Yaffle Lodge, Bleasby Road, Thurgarton, Nottingham NG14 7FW — MB BS 1963 Lond.; MRCS Eng. LRCP Lond. 1963; DObst RCOG 1965. Prev: GP Thurgarton.

REES, Jeremy Harry Institute of Neurology, National Hospital for Neurology & Neurosurgery, London WC1N 3BG Tel: 020 7837 3611 Fax: 020 7278 7894 Email: j.rees@ion.ucl.ac.uk — MB BS 1988 Lond.; MRCP 1991 UK; BSc 1985 Lond.; PhD 1995 Lond. (University coll. & Middx) Sen. Lect., Neuro-onclogy, Inst. of Neurol., UCL; Hon. Cons. Neurol., Nat. Hosp. For Neurol. & Neurosurg., Roy. Marsden Hosp. Middlx. Univ. Coll. Hosp. Trust. Socs: Brit. Neuro-Oncol. Gp.; Mem. Assn. Brit. Neurol.; Europ. Assn Neuro-Oncol. Prev: Regist. (Neurol.) St. Thos. Hosp. Lond.; Regist. (Neurol.) Nat. Hosp. Neurol. & Neurosurg. Lond.; Regist. (Neurol.) Roy. Free Hosp. Lond.

REES, Joanna Deborah Suzanne 84 Sevington Road, London NW4 3RS Tel: 020 8202 0248 — MB BS 1994 Lond.; MRCGP with merit 2001. Gen. Practitioner. Prev: Ho. Off. (Med. & Radiother.) Mt. Vernon Hosp. N.wood.; Ho. Off. (Surg. & Urol.) Luton & Dunstable Hosp.; GP Regist. - Challihill Med. Centre.

REES, John Pomeroy, Chineham Lane, Sherborne St John, Basingstoke RG24 9LR — MB BS 1980 Lond.

REES, John Alan Evan Fferm Llwyn-onn, 67 Pant Mawr Rd, Whitechurch, Cardiff CF14 7TB Tel: 029 2061 7178 Fax: 029 2074 4581 — MD 1986 Wales; BSc (Hons.) Liverp. 1973; MB BCh 1978; FRCP Lond. 1993; MRCP (UK) 1981. Cons. Phys. Univ. Hosp. Wales Cardiff. Socs: Fell. Roy. Soc. Med.; Comm. Mem. Brit. Hyperlipidaemia Assn.; Chairm., welsh Endocrine & Diabetes Soc. Prev: Wellcome Sen. Research Fell. Clin. Med. Univ. Wales Coll. Med. Cardiff; Lect. (Med.) Univ. Wales Coll. Med. Cardiff; Research Fell. St. Bart. Hosp. Lond.

REES, John Andrew 9 Castle Quay, Castle Boulevart, Nottingham NG7 1FW — MB BS Lond. 1967. (St. Geo.)

REES, John Donald George Woodbridge Hill Surgery, 1 Deerbarn Road, Guildford GU2 8YB Tel: 01483 562230 Fax: 01483 452442; 10 Woodlands Road, Loughor, Swansea SA4 6PS — MB BS 1986 Lond.; Dip Occupational Health R. C. P. Lond. 1996; DRCOG 1990; DCH RCP Lond. 1989; MRCGP 1992. (St Georges Hospital) Prev: Trainee GP Milton Keynes Gen. Hosp. VTS.; Ho. Off. (Med.) Frimley Pk. Hosp.; Ho. Off. (Surg.) St. James'. Hosp. Lond.

REES

REES, John Edward Peter 11 Northmead, Narberth SA67 7DN; Rosebank, Upper Cynor Place, off Cae Siriol, Ynyshir, Porth CF39 0NW — MB BCh 1981 Wales.

REES, John Eric 45 Heol Ebrandy, Pontyberem, Llanelli SA15 5DG — MRCS Eng. LRCP Lond. 1978.

REES, John Esmond (retired) Nuffield Hospital, 55 New Church Road, Hove BN3 4BG Tel: 01273 720217 Fax: 01273 220919 — MA, MD Camb. 1973, MB 1966, BChir 1965; FRCP Lond. 1982, M 1968. Hon. Cons. Neurol. Brighton & Mid Sussex NHs Trust; Vis. Research Fell. Sussex Univ. Prev: Sen. Regist. (Neurol.) King's Coll. Hosp. Lond.

REES, John Francis (retired) Pant-y-Castell, Solva, Haverfordwest SA62 6XB Tel: 01437 721381 — MB BCh 1943 Wales; BSc, MB BCh Wales 1943. Clin. Med. Off. Dyfed AHA. Prev: Ho. Surg. M. Glam Co. Hosp. Bridgend.

REES, John Henry Thomas (retired) Kings Park, St. Clears, Carmarthen SA33 4AX Tel: 01994 230420 — MRCS Eng. LRCP Lond. 1944. Prev: Med. Off. Min. of Supply Experim. Establishm. Pendine.

REES, John Howell Norfolk Health,Norfolk Health Authority, St Andrew's House, Northside, St Andrews, Business Park, Thorpe St Andrew, Norwich NR7 0HT Tel: 01603 300600; 15 Coniston Close, South Wootton, King's Lynn PE30 3NL Tel: 01553 679304 Fax: 01553 679304 — MB ChB 1975 Manch.; MFPHM RCP (UK) 1989; MRCGP 1981. Cons. Pub. Health, Norf. HA & PH Exec. Mem. W. Norf PCT. Prev: Sen. Med. Off. DoH HCD-PH Div. Leeds; Dir. Pub. Health W. Norf. & Wisbech HA; Sen. Regist. (Community Med.) E. Anglian RHA.

REES, John Howell Martyn 10 The Orchard, Aberthin, Cowbridge CF71 7HU — MB BCh 1987 Wales; MRCP (UK) 1994; MRCGP 1992; DCH RCP Lond. 1992. Regist. (Paediat.) E. Glam. Gen. Hosp. & Llandough Hosp. Cardiff. Prev: SHO (Paediat.) P.ss of Wales Hosp. Bridgend.

REES, John Hywel (retired) 15 Northanger Court, Grove St., Bath BA2 6PE Tel: 01225 469728 — MB BS 1950 Lond.; MRCS Eng. LRCP Lond. 1950; MRCGP 1965.

REES, John Idwal Stephen Department of Radiology, University Hospital of Wales, Heath Park, Cardiff CF14 4XW — MB BCh 1984 Wales; BSc Wales 1979, MB BCh 1984; FRCR 1989. Cons. Radiol. Univ. Hosp. Wales Cardiff.

REES, John Kempton Harold Department of Haematological Medicine, MRC Centre, University of Cambridge, Hills Road, Cambridge CB2 2QH Tel: 01223 336836 Fax: 01223 336827 — MB BCh 1963 Wales; Hon. MA Camb. 1974; MRCP (UK) 1970. (Cardiff) Socs: Brit. Soc. Haematol.; Eur. Haematol. Assn.; Amer. Soc. Haemat. Prev: Lect. (Haemat.) St. Thos. Hosp. Lond.

REES, John Kenneth (retired) Cleveland Lodge, The Strand, Ryde PO33 1J — MRCS Eng. LRCP Lond. 1960; DA Eng. 1963. Prev: Dep. Police Surg. I. of Wight.

REES, John Llewelyn Rees, Hoe, Rostron and James, Lister House Surgery, Bollams Mead, Wiveliscombe, Taunton TA4 2PH Tel: 01984 623471 Fax: 01984 624357; Hartswell House, Wiveliscombe, Taunton TA4 2NF Tel: 01984 623343 — MB BChir Camb. 1964; DObst RCOG 1965. (St. Thos.) Prev: Ho. Off. (Paediat.) Cardiff Roy. Infirm.; Ho. Off. (Obst.) & Ho. Surg. (ENT) St. Thos. Hosp. Lond.

REES, John Russell Litfield House, Litfield Place, Clifton Down, Bristol BS8 3LS Tel: 0117 973 1323; Friars Halt, St. Mary's Road, Leigh Woods, Bristol BS8 3PY Tel: 0117 973 5049 — MB BChir Camb. 1951; MA, MD Camb. 1959, BA 1951; FRCP Lond. 1973, M 1956. (Guy's) Emerit. Cons. Cardiol. United Bristol Healthcare NHS Trust; Chief. Med. Off. Clerical Med. Investment GP. Socs: Med. Res. Soc.; Brit. Cardiac Soc. Prev: Cons. Cardiol. Bristol Roy. Hosp. & S. W.. RHA; Sen. Regist. (Med.) W.m. Hosp. Lond.; Regist. (Med.) Guy's Hosp. Lond.

REES, John Sebastian Corbett House Surgery, Avondale Road, Bristol BS5 9QX Tel: 0117 955 7474 Fax: 0117 955 5402 — BM BCh 1973 Oxf.; MRCS Eng. LRCP Lond. 1973; MRCGP 1979; DObst RCOG 1975. (Oxf. & St. Thos.) Prev: SHO (A & E) & SHO (O & G) Plymouth Gen. Hosp.

REES, John Wilson The Health Centre, 118 Ravenhill Road, Fforestfach, Swansea SA5 5AA Tel: 01792 581666; 2 Somerville Court, Sketty, Swansea SA2 0RY — MB BS 1976 Lond.; MRCGP 1983; DCH RCP Lond. 1981.

REES, Jonathan Clifford 17 Brislee Avenue, North Shields NE30 2SQ — MB BS 1992 Lond.; BSc Lond. 1989.

REES, Jonathan Edward Gooderid 8 Meadowbrook Close, Exeter EX4 2NN — MB ChB 1995 Bristol.

REES, Professor Jonathan Laurence Department Dermatology, Medical School, Framlington Place, Newcastle upon Tyne NE2 4HH Tel: 0191 222 8936 Fax: 0191 222 7094 Email: jonathan.rees@newcastle.ac.uk; 19 Carr Field, Eland Haugh, Ponteland, Newcastle upon Tyne NE20 9XR Tel: 01661 825782 — MB BS 1982 Newc.; MB BS (Hons.) Newc 1982; BMedSc (1st. cl. Hons.) Newc. 1981; MRCP (UK) 1985; FRCP 1993. Prof. & Hon. Cons. Dermat. Roy. Vict. Infirm. Newc. u. Tyne. Prev: MRC Clinician Scientist Univ. Newc.; Vis. Scientist Univ. Strasbourg; Regist. (Dermat.) Allgemeines Krankenhaus, Vienna.

REES, Jonathan Lloyd Fronhaul, Pentwyn Deintyr, Treharris CF46 5EA — MB BS 1992 Lond.

REES, Jonathan Richard Edward United Bristol Health Care Trust, Bristol Royal Infirmary, Upper Maudlin St., Bristol BS2 8UW Tel: 0117 923 0000; Fairways, 11 Cecil Road, Gowerton, Swansea SA4 3DF Tel: 01792 873275 — MB ChB 1997 Bristol. Demonst. (Anat.) & SHO (A & E) Bristol Roy. Infirm. Prev: Ho. Surg. (Gen. Surg.) Bristol Roy. Infirm.; Ho. Phys. (Cardiol.) Roy. Devon & Exeter Hosp.

REES, Joseph Philip Mervyn 13 Second Cross Road, Twickenham TW2 5QY — MB BS 1989 Lond.

REES, Judith Elizabeth 78 Herongate Road, Wanstead, London E12 5EQ — MB BS 1974 Lond.; BSc Lond. 1971, MB BS 1974; DCH Eng. 1977. (Lond. Hosp.)

REES, Julia Alison Occupational Health Department, Epsom General Hosptial, Dorking Road, Epsom KT18 7EG Tel: 01372 735377 Fax: 01372 743421; One Northweald Lane, Royal Park Gate, Kingston upon Thames KT2 5GL Tel: 020 8549 4586 — BM 1981 Soton. (Soton.) Clin. Asst. (Occupat. Health) Epsom Healthcare NHS Trust. Prev: Med. Off. Lond. Boro. Ealing; Med. Off. Thos. Cook Ltd.; Clin. Asst. (Occupat. Health) W. Dorset HA.

REES, Julia Anne Department of Histopathology, North Middlesex Hospital, Sterling Way, London N18 1QX Tel: 020 8887 2275 Fax: 020 8887 2569 — MB BS 1990 Lond.; BSc (Hons.) Pharmacol. Lond. 1986; MRCPath 1999. Cons. Histocytopathologist, Dept Histopath., N. Middlx Hosp. Lond..

REES, Julian Charles 7 Margaret Street, Ammanford SA18 2NP — BM 1998 Soton.; BM Soton 1998.

REES, Katharine Sophia 17 Brislee Avenue, Tynemouth, North Shields NE30 2SQ — MB BS 1994 Lond.; MA Camb. 1991; MRCP (UK) 1998. SHO (Psychiat.).

REES, Katherine Sian Plas Caer Pwsan, Clynnog Fawr, Caernarfon LL54 5PF — MB BS 1995 Lond.

REES, Lesley Renal Unit, Gt Ormond St Hospital fro Children, NHS Trust, London WC1N 3JH Tel: 020 7813 8346 Email: l.rees@ich.ucl.ac.uk; 65 Shepherds Hill, Highgate, London N6 5RE Tel: 0208 348 6804 Email: l.rees@ich.ucl.ac.uk — MB ChB 1974 Manch.; MD Manch. 1982; FRCP Lond. 1994; MRCP (UK) 1977; T(M) 1991; FRCPH 1998. Cons. Paediat. Nephrol. Gt. Ormond St. NHS Trust Lond. Socs: Roy. Coll. Paediat. & Child Health; (Exec. Mem.) Brit. Assoc. Paediatric Nephrol.; Coun.lor Internat. Paediatric Nephrol. Assoc. Prev: Cons. Paediat. Nephrol. Roy. Free Hosp. & Hosp. for Sick Childr. Lond.; Lect. (Paediat.) Guy's Hosp. Lond.

REES, Lesley Howard 23 Church Row, Hampstead, London NW3 6UP Tel: 020 7794 4936 — MB BS 1965 Lond.; MB BS (Hons.) Lond. 1965; MSc Lond. 1974, DSc 1989, MD 1972; FRCP Lond. 1979, M 1968; FRCPath 1988, M 1976. (St. Bart.) Prof. Chem. Endocrinol. St. Bart. Hosp. Med. Coll. Lond.; Hon. Cons. St. Bart. Hosp. Lond. Socs: Fell. Roy. Soc. Med.; Soc. Endocrinol.; (Sec. Gen.) Internat. Endocrine Soc. Prev: Ho. Phys. St. Bart. Hosp. Lond. & Hammersmith Hosp. & Roy. Postgrad. Med. Sch. Lond.; Clin. Research Fell. Endocrine Unit Univ. Oregon Med. Sch. Portland, USA.

REES, Lynne Justine Brynhyfryd Surgery, Brynhyfryd, Swansea SA1 9EB Tel: 01792 655083; 12 Pennard Road, Kittle, Swansea SA3 3JS Tel: 01792 233645 Email: rees.etal"zoom.co.uk — MB BCh 1991 Wales; Dip Pract Derm 1997; BSc (Hons.) Cardiff 1988; MRCGP 1995; DRCOG 1994; DCH RCP Lond. 1994. Gen. Pract. Half Time Princip.; Clin. Asst. (A & E) Morriston Hosp. Swansea. Prev: Trainee GP Swansea VTS.

REES

REES, Mandy Flat 10, 118 Kingston Road, London SW19 1LY Tel: 020 8542 2020 Email: simonandmandy@horahoplace.u-net.com — MB BS 1991 Lond.; FRCA 1997. (St. Bartholomews) Specialist Regist. Anaesth., St Geo.s Hosp. Lond.

REES, Mary Aldery Hey Childrens Hospital, Department of Community Paediatrics, Eaton Road, West Derby, Liverpool L12 2AP Tel: 0151 228 4811 Fax: 0151 252 5120 — MB BS 1967 Lond.; MRCS Eng. LRCP Lond. 1967; Cert. JCC Lond. 1977; DObst RCOG 1969. (St. Bart.) Cons. Community Paediat. Alder Hey Childr. Hosp. Liverp. Socs: Inst. Psychosexual Med.; Brit. Paediat. Assn. Prev: SCMO (Family Plann., Genitourin. Med. & Community Paediat.) Hastings Dist HA.

REES, Mary Carol 21A West Heath Road, London NW3 7UU — MB 1962 Camb.; BChir 1961.

REES, Mary Patricia Pen-y-Bryn, Danesfield Drive, Leominster HR6 8HW — MB BCh 1965 Wales; DObst RCOG 1967. (Cardiff) Clin. Asst. Genitourin. Med. Hereford Co. Hosp.; Clin. Med. Off. Herefordsh. HA. Prev: Med. Off. Family Plann. Assn.; Ho. Surg. Roy. Gwent Hosp. Newport & Hillingdon Hosp.; Ho. Phys. St. Luke's Hosp. Guildford.

REES, Menna Stockton Heath Medical Centre, The Forge, London Road, Stockton Heath, Warrington WA4 6HJ Tel: 01925 604427 Fax: 01925 210501; 51 Pepper Street, Lymm WA13 0JG Tel: 0192 575 4069 — MB BCh 1972 Wales; MRCGP 1976; DObst RCOG 1974. GP Warrington; Clin. Asst. (Colposcopy) Warrington Hosp. Socs: (Comm. Mem.) NW Soc. Study Sexual Med. Prev: Phys. Rochester State Hosp., USA.; SHO (O & G & Paediat.) Univ. Hosp. Wales Cardiff.

REES, Mr Myrddin North Hampshire Hospital, Aldermaston Road, Basingstoke RG24 9NA Tel: 01256 473202 Fax: 01256 313512; Old Rectory, Church Lane, Worting, Basingstoke RG23 8PX Tel: 01256 320208 Fax: 01256 350818 — MB BS 1973 Lond.; MS Lond. 1983; FRCS Eng. 1977; MRCS Eng. LRCP Lond. 1973. (Westm.) Cons. Surg. N. Hants. Hosp. Socs: Roy. Soc. Med. (Vice-Pres. Surg. Sector); RSM Pres. Surg. Sect. (Past); AUGIS Mem. of Educat. Comm. (Past). Prev: Sen. Regist. St. Geo. Hosp. Lond.; Research Fell. Ochner Med. Inst. New Orleans, USA.

REES, Mr Neville Clark (retired) Scarlets Acre, Plastow Green, Headley, Newbury Tel: 01635 268737 — MB BS 1945 Lond.; FRCS Eng. 1954; MCRS Eng. LRCP Lond. 1945. Med. Dir. Saudi Medicare; Lt. Col.RAMC. Prev: Med. Supt. Roy. Perth Hosp. W.. Austral.

REES, Olwen Vivien (retired) 52 Southlands Drive, West Cross, Swansea SA3 5RA Tel: 01792 404144 — MB BCh 1945 Wales; BSc Wales 1941; DPhysMed. Eng. 1961. Cons. Rheum. & Rehabil. W. Glam. AHA. Prev: Asst. Med. Off. W. Glam. AHA.

REES, Paul Ash Tree House, Church Street, Kirkham, Preston PR4 2SE Tel: 01772 686688 Fax: 01772 672054; 2 Bryning Avenue, Wrea Green, Preston PR4 2WL — MB ChB 1976 Manch.

REES, Paul Stuart Chadwick 66 Heol Maengwyn, Machynlleth, Meifod — MB BS 1996 Lond.

REES, Peter John Guy's Hospital, London SE1 9RT Tel: 0207 955 4479 Fax: 0207 955 2766 Email: john.rees@kcl.ac.uk — MB BChir 1974 Camb.; MA Camb. 1974, MD 1982; FRCP Lond. 1988, M 1975. Cons. Phys. Guy's Hosp. Lond.; Sen. Lect. (Med.) UMDS Guy's Campus Lond.

REES, Philip Grufydd Great Ormond Street Hospital for Children, Great Ormond St., London WC1 3NT Tel: 020 7829 8839 Fax: 020 7829 8673 — MB BCh 1969 Wales; BSc Wales 1966; FRCP Lond. 1987; MRCP (UK) 1973; DCH RCP Lond. 1974; DRCOG 1971. Cons. Paediat. Cardiol. Gt. Ormond St. Hosp. Childr. Lond.; Hon. Cons. Wexham Pk., Heatherwood, Luton & Dunstable, Lincoln, N.ampton, Roy Surrey; Qu. Eliz. Hackney, Ealing Gen. & St. Luke's (Malta) Hosps.

REES, Philip Howell, OBE 21A West Heath Road, London NW3 7UU — MB 1962 Camb.; BChir 1961; FRCP Lond. 1980; FRCP Ed. 1980.

REES, Philip John Richards and Partners, Llanfair Surgery, Llanfair Road, Llandovery SA20 0HY Tel: 01550 720648 Fax: 01550 721428; Ty-Cerian, Llandovery SA20 0YF Tel: 01550 721428 — MB BS 1982 Lond.; MRCGP 1990; DRCOG 1984. (St. Bart.) Hosp. Pract. Llandovery Cottage Hosp. Prev: Trainee GP St. Albans & Llandovery VTS; SHO (Radiother.) St. Bart. Hosp. Lond.; Ho. Off. St. Bart. Hosp. Lond.

REES, Philippa Helen Buckland 8 Glebeland Close, West Stafford, Dorchester DT2 8AE — MB ChB 1984 Zimbabwe; LRCP LRCS Ed. LRCPS Glas. 1987; MRCGP 1991; DA (UK) 1990.

REES, Richard Gwyn Department of Rheumatology, St. Mary's Hospital, Praed St., London W2 1NY Tel: 020 7886 1046 Fax: 020 7886 6083 — MB BCh 1980 Wales; FRCP 1997; MRCP (UK) 1985. Cons. Rheum. St. Mary's Hosp. NHS Trust Lond.; Hon. Clin Sen. Lect. Imperial Coll. Sch. of Med. Socs: Fell. Roy. Soc. Med.; Brit. Soc. Rheum.; Fell. Med. Soc. Lond. Prev: Sen. Regist. (Med. & Rheum.) Char. Cross Hosp. & Qu. Mary's Hosp. Roehampton; Arthritis & Rheum. Counc. Research Fell. (Rheum.) W.m. Hosp. Lond.; Resid. Med. Off. & Regist. (Med.) W.m. Hosp. Lond.

REES, Richard John, RD London Road Surgery, 31 London Road, Sittingbourne ME10 1NQ Tel: 01795 472534/425439 — MB BS 1970 Lond.; AKC. (Westm.) Police Surg.; Admiralty Surg. & Agent. Prev: SHO (O & G) Soton. Gen. Hosp.; SHO (A & E) St. Stephens Hosp. Lond.; Surg. Lt.-Cdr. RNR.

REES, Richard John William, CMG (retired) 10 Home Farm Court, Greenway Lane, Charlton Kings, Cheltenham GL52 6LA Tel: 01242 574953 — MB BS 1942 Lond.; BSc Lond. 1939; FRCP Lond. 1983; MRCS Eng. LRCP Lond. 1941; FRCPath 1964, M 1963. Vice-Chairm. Edr. Bd. Leprosy Review; WHO Expert Advis. Panel on Leprosy. Prev: Head Laborat. Leprosy Mycobacterial Research Nat. Inst. Med. Research.

REES, Mr Richard Lestrem (retired) Penrhos, Maes y Ffynnon, Carmarthen SA31 1DZ — MRCS Eng. LRCP Lond. 1941; FRCS Eng. 1953. Hon. Cons. (Orthop. & Traum. Surg.) Dyfed AHA. Prev: Prof. Orthop. Surg. Univ. Riyad Med. Sch., Saudi Arabia.

REES, Mr Richard Wellesley Morgan (retired) Caer Wigau Isaf Farm, Nr. Pendoylan, Cowbridge CF71 7UJ Tel: 01446 760227 — MB ChB 1957 Birm.; FRCS Ed. 1966; FRCS Eng. 1966. Cons, Urol. Dept. Urol. Univ. Hosp. of Wales, Cardiff; Hon. Clin. Teach. Univ. Wales Coll. Med. Prev: Ho. Surg. United Birm. Hosps.

REES, Robert Griffiths West Winds, 44 Great Lane, Frisby-on-the-Wreake, Melton Mowbray LE14 2PB Tel: 01664 434874 — MB BS 1942 Lond.; MRCS Eng. LRCP Lond. 1942. (St. Bart.) Socs: Auth. Examr. U.K. Civil Aviat.; Leic. Med. Soc. Prev: Ho. Surg. Mt. Vernon Hosp. & Radium Inst. N.wood; Temp. Surg. Lt. RNVR; SHO (Surg.) Roy. Cripples Hosp. Birm.

REES, Robert Simon Owen (retired) Rubbin Cottage, Treyford, Midhurst GU29 0LD Tel: 01730 825444 — MA, MB Camb. 1958, BChir 1957; FRCP Lond. 1975, M 1963; MRCS Eng. LRCP Lond. 1957; FRCR 1975; FFR 1965; DMRD Eng. 1962. Prev: Dir. Radiol. Roy. Brompton Lond.

REES, Robin James Buckfield House, Barons Cross Road, Leominster HR6 8QX — MB ChB 1993 Birm.

REES, Roger Thomas Norfolk And Norwich University Hospital NHS Trust, Colney Lane, Norwich NR4 7UY Tel: 01603 286286 Fax: 01603 550431; 9 The St, Brooke, Norwich NR15 1JW Tel: 01603 550431 Fax: 01603 550431 — MB BS 1971 Lond.; BDS 1967; MRCS Eng. LRCP Lond. 1971; FDS RCS Eng. 1974, LDS 1968. (Roy. Dent. & St. Bart.) Cons. Oral & Maxillofacial Surg. Norf. & Norwich NHS Trust & Jas. Paget NHS Trust. Socs: Fell. Brit. Assn. Oral & Maxillofacial Surg. Prev: Sen. Regist. (Oral Surg.) King's Coll. Hosp. Dent. Sch. & Qu. Vict. Hosp. E. Grinstead.

REES, Romilly Whitchurch Health Centre, Armada Road, Bristol BS14 0SU Tel: 01275 832285 Fax: 01275 540035; 5 Walnut Close, Bristol BS31 2RP — MB ChB 1987 Manch.; MRCGP 1991; DGM RCP Lond. 1992; DRCOG 1991; DCH RCP Lond. 1990. Socs: Brit. Geriat. Soc.; BMA. Prev: Staff Grade Geriat. St. David's Hosp. BreCons.

REES, Ruth Margaret Westerhope Medical Group, 377 Stamfordham Road, Westerhope, Newcastle upon Tyne NE5 2LH Tel: 0191 243 7000 Fax: 0191 243 7006 — MB BS 1993 Newc. GP Regist. Longrigg Med. Centre Gateshead. Prev: SHO (Gen. Med. & Elderly Care) N. Tees Gen. Hosp. Stockton on Tees.

***REES, Samantha Jane** Beechfield House, 30 Parrys Lane, Stoke Bishop, Bristol BS9 1AA — MB BS 1998 Lond.; MB BS Lond 1998; BSc (Hons) London 1995.

REES, Sheridan Giles Oliver — Cert AvMed 2002 Dundee; FRCA 1996. (St Bart's London) Cons. (Full Time) Anaesth. Cheltenham Gen. Hosp. (Gloucestershire Hosps. N.H.S. Trust). Socs: Assoc of Anaesth.s (AAGBI) Mem.; Obstetric Anaesth.s Assn. (OAA) (Mem.); Soc. of Anaesth.s of The S.-W. Region (SASWR) Mem.

REES, Sian 16 High Street, Caerleon, Newport NP18 1AG — MB BS 1985 Lond.; BA Oxf. 1982.

REES, Sonja 104 Oxclose Lane, Arnold, Nottingham NG5 6FX — State Exam Med. Frankfurt 1991.

REES, Stephen Osborn Glaslyn, 7 Cilonen Road, Three Crosses, Swansea SA4 3PH — MB BCh 1985 Wales.

REES, Timothy Seaborn The Redcliffe Surgery, 10 Redcliffe St., Chelsea, London SW10 9DT Tel: 020 7460 2222 Fax: 020 7460 0116 Email: redcliffe.surgery@mcmail.com; 24 Querrin Street, Fulham, London SW6 2SJ Tel: 020 7731 7264 Fax: 020 7731 7264 Email: tim.rees@btinternet.com — MB BS 1986 Lond.; BSc Lond. 1983; MRCGP 1992; Cert. Family Plann. JCC 1991; DRCOG 1990. (Char. Cross & Westm.) Prev: Clin. Asst. (Genitourin. Med.) Jas. Pringle Hse. Lond.; SHO (O & G) W. Lond. & Char. Cross Hosps. Lond.; Research Regist. (MRC HIV Trials) Char. Cross Hosp. Lond.

REES, Trevor Percival Greensward Surgery, Greensward Lane, Hockley SS5 5HQ Tel: 01702 202353 Fax: 01702 204535; Greenacre, Mayes Lane, Danbury, Chelmsford CM3 4NJ Tel: 01245 222016 Fax: 01245 222016 — MB BS 1973 Lond.; DObst RCOG 1975; Cert. Av Med. MoD (Air) & CAA. 1980; Cert. Family Plann. JCC Lond. 1976. (Lond. Hosp.) Sen. Med. Off. HM Prison & Youth Custody Centre Hockley; GP Tutor St. Bart. Hosp. & Lond. Hosp.; Examr. Brit. Red Cross. Socs: Brit. Soc. Med. & Dent. Hypn. (Metrop. Br.). Prev: SHO (O & G), Ho. Phys. & Ho. Surg. Rochford Gen. Hosp.

REES, Trevor William Hawthorns Surgery, 331 Birmingham Road, Sutton Coldfield B72 1DL Tel: 0121 373 2211 Fax: 0121 382 1274; 30 Beech Hill Road, Wylde Green, Sutton Coldfield B72 1DT Tel: 0121 382 0090 — MB ChB 1979 Birm.

REES, Tudor Williams (retired) Llys Deri, Heol Henfwlch, Carmarthen SA33 6AJ — MB BCh Wales 1963; MRCPsych 1973; DPM Eng. 1972. Prev: Indep. Psychiat. Servs. Carmarthen.

REES, William David Wynne Department Gastroenterology, Hope Hospital, Salford M6 8HD Tel: 0161 789 7373 Fax: 0161 787 5366 Email: wynne.rees@srht.nhs.uk; Email: wowrees@cs.com — MD 1978 Wales; MB BCh 1972; FRCP Lond. 1992; MRCP (UK) 1974. (University of Wales School of Medicine) Cons. Phys. & Gastroenterol. Univ. Manch. Sch. Med. Hope Hosp. Salford; Dep. Regional Adviser, Roy. Coll. of Phys.s, Lond.; Hon. Reader (Med.) Univ. Manch. Med. Sch. Socs: Brit. Soc. of Gastroenterol. - Mem.; Amer. Gastroenterol. Assn. Mem.; Brit. Assn. of Med. Managers - Meb. Prev: Wellcome Research Fell. & Lect. (Med.) Univ. Manch.; Hon. Cons. Phys. Salford HA; Research Fell. (Gastroenterol.) Mayo Clin. Rochester, USA.

REES, William Dewi (retired) Plott Cottage, Plott Lane, Stretton-on-Dunsmore, Rugby CV23 9HL Tel: 02476 544363 — MB BS 1956 Lond.; MD Lond. 1971; FRCGP 1974, M 1966. Prev: Med. Dir. St. Mary's Hospice Birm.

REES, William Euros Lloyd 42 Church Road, Tonteg, Pontypridd CF38 1EL Tel: 01443 202629 — MB ChB 1957 St. And.; FCOphth 1990; DO RCS Eng. 1960. Surg. (Ophth.) E. Glam. Hosp. & Bridgend Gen. Hosp.; Dir. Ophth. Treatm. Centre Bridgend.

REES, William Henry Russell The Mynde House, Caerleon, Newport NP18 1AG — MB BS 1949 Lond.

REES, Professor William Linford Llewelyn, CBE Charter Nightingale Hospital, 11-19 Lisson Grove, London NW1 6SH Tel: 020 7935 0640; Penbryn, 62 Oakwood Avenue, Purley CR8 1AQ — MD 1943 Wales; LLD (Hon.) Wales 1981; DSc Lond. 1978; BSc Wales 1935, MD 1943, MB BCh 1938; FRCP Lond. 1960, M 1942; FRCPsych 1971, Hon. F 1978; Hon. FACPsych 1977; DPM Eng. 1940. (Cardiff) Emerit. Prof. Psychiat. Univ. Lond.; Cons. Phys. St. Bart. Hosp. Lond.; Distinguished Fell. Amer. Psychiat. Assn. Socs: Hon. Mem. Swedish Psychiat. Assn. Prev: Regional Psychiat. For Wales & Cons. Psychiat. E. Glam. & St. David's Hosp.; Pres. RCPsych & BMA Mem. Review of Med. Comm. & Safety of Med.; Phys. Maudsley & Bethlem Roy. Hosps.

REES, William Michael Thomas (retired) Ty Petroc, Little Petherick, Wadebridge PL27 7QT — MRCS Eng. LRCP Lond. 1963. Maj. RAMC RARO. Prev: Hon. Med. Adviser RNLI.

REES, Yvonne Afallon, New Quay SA45 9TY — MB BCh 1978 Wales; FRCR 1984; DMRD Wales 1983. Cons. Radiol. Leicester Roy. Infirm. & Leicester Gen. Hosp.

REES-JONES, Mrs Adrienne Camois Court, Barcombe, Lewes BN8 5BH Tel: 01273 400507 Fax: 01273 401901 — MB BCh BAO 1967 Belf.; Dip. Sports Med. Scotl. 1991. Assoc. Specialist (Rheum.) E.bourne Dist. Gen. Hosp. Socs: BIMM; BASM; BMA.

REES-JONES, Elizabeth Corinne Ty'r Felin Surgery, Cecil Road, Gorseinon, Swansea SA4 4BY Tel: 01792 898844 — MB BS 1975 Lond.; MRCS Eng. LRCP Lond. 1974; DCH Eng. 1977; DRCOG 1976. Prev: Ho. Surg. Char. Cross Hosp. Lond.; Ho. Phys. Canad. Red Cross Memor. Hosp. Taplow.

REES-JONES, Susan Victoria West End Surgery, Moorgreen Road, West End, Southampton SO30 3PY Tel: 023 8047 2126/8039 9200 Fax: 023 8039 9201; Shirral House, Shedfield, Southampton SO32 2HY Tel: 01329 832137 — MB BS 1973 Lond.; MRCS Eng. LRCP Lond. 1973. (Char. Cross Hosp. Lond.) Prev: Ho. Phys. & Ho. Surg. & SHO (A & E) Basingstoke & Dist.; Hosp.

REES-JONES, Thomas Glyn, Col. late RAMC (retired) 70 Bouverie Avenue, Salisbury SP2 8DX Tel: 01722 335041 — MRCS Eng. LRCP Lond. 1952; MRCGP 1971; DCH Eng. 1972; DObst RCOG 1964. Prev: Sen. Med. Off. Med. Centre Army Air Corps. Middle Wallop.

REESE, Alan John Morris, TD, OStJ (retired) 9 Hopping Lane, Canonbury, London N1 2NU Tel: 020 7226 2088 — MB BS Lond. 1943; MD Lond. 1951; LMSSA Lond. 1943; FRCPath 1968, M 1963. JP.; Barrister-at-Law, Middle Temple; Lt.-Col. RAMC RARO. Prev: WHO Prof. Path. Univ. Mandalay, Burma.

REESE, Christopher David 27 St Lukes Place, Cheltenham GL53 7JL — MB BCh 1992 Wales; MRCP (UK) 1998. (Univ. of Wales Coll. Of Med.) Clin. Fell. Paediat. IC, Bristol Childr.s Hosp. Prev: Regist. (Paediat.) Cheltenham Gen. Hosp.; Regist. (Paediat.) Wom.s & Child. Hosp. Adelaide.

REESE, John Mansel, CB, OBE, CStJ, Surg. Rear-Admiral Retd. 4 Meldon Court, East Budleigh Road, Budleigh Salterton EX9 6HE — MRCS Eng. LRCP Lond. 1930; DPH Eng. 1934. (St. Mary's) Mem. Grays Inn. Socs: Fell. Roy. Soc. Trop. Med. & Hyg. Prev: Hon. Phys. to HM The Qu. 1960-63.

REEVE, Abigail Amelia 8 Oates Way, Ramsey, Huntingdon PE26 1UX — MB ChB 1997 Leic. Pre-registrat. Ho. Off. (Gen. Surg.) Pilgrim Hosp. Boston. Socs: BMA; MDU.

REEVE, Anne Catherine 97 Boundary Road, Walthamstow, London E17 8NQ — MB ChB 1983 Sheff.; MRCPsych 1988. Sen. Regist. (Child & Adolesc. Psychiat.) Child & Family Consultation Serv. Waltham Forest HA. Socs: BMA; Roy. Coll. Psychiat. (E. Anglian CTC Rep.). Prev: Regist. (Psychiat.) Whipps Cross, Claybury & Chase Farm Hosps.

REEVE, Anne Patricia Mary The Surgery, 82 St Ann St., Salisbury SP1 2PT Tel: 01722 322624 — MB BS 1975 Lond.; MA (Physiol. Scs.) Oxf. 1976; DCH Eng. 1982. GP. Prev: SHO (Paediat.) Norf. & Norwich Hosp.; SHO (O & G) W. Suff. Hosp. Bury St. Edmunds; Partner Gen. Pract. Cotswolds.

REEVE, Brian John Norton Brook Medical Centre, Cookworthy Road, Kingsbridge TQ7 1AE Tel: 01548 853551 Fax: 01548 857741 — MB BS 1976 Lond.; MRCGP 1980; DCH RCP Lond. 1982; DRCOG 1980. (Lond. Hosp.)

REEVE, Howard Sydney (retired) Netherton, Leeks Hill, Melton, Woodbridge IP12 1LW Tel: 01394 382727 — MSc (Med.) Lond. 1982, MB BS 1952; MFOM RCP Lond. 1983, AFOM 1981; MRCGP 1959; DIH Eng. 1980. Cons. Phys. Occupat. Med. RCP. Prev: Med. Adviser (Occupat. Health) Felixstowe Dock & Railway Co.

REEVE, Hugh Anthony Brinnington Health Centre, Brinnington Road, Stockport SK5 8BS Tel: 0161 430 4002 Fax: 0161 430 7918; 28 Amherst Road, Withington, Manchester M20 4NS Tel: 0161 286 2271 — MB ChB 1981 Manchester; MBCHB Manchester 1981; MRCGP (London RCGP) 1985. (Manchester) Princip. Gen. Pract.; Course Organiser Stockport GP VTS; Chairm. Stockport PCG Clin. Governance Comm. Prev: Med.Advis.Stockport HA (1993-1996); Lect. GP. Univ. Manch. (1986-1993).

REEVE, Jeanne Daphne (retired) 2 Norland Square Mansions, London W11 4PY Tel: 020 7602 1066 — MB BS 1957 Lond.; FRCPath 1976, M 1964. Prev: Cons. Haemat. Haringey HA.

REEVE, Joanne Lucy 2 Dodford Court, Fockbury Road, Dodford, Bromsgrove B61 9AP Tel: 01527 878694; 25 Bryanston Road, Liverpool L17 7AL Tel: 0151 727 3418 — MB ChB 1997 Liverp.; MB ChB (Hons.) Liverp. 1997; BClinSci, (Hons) Liverp. 1994.

REEVE, Jonathan 38 Hugh Street, London SW1V 1RP Tel: 020 7834 5166 — BM BCh 1968 Oxf.; MSc Lond. (Nuclear Med.) 1972; DM Oxf. 1976, BM BCh 1968; FRCP Lond. 1983; MRCP (UK)

REEVE

1970; DSc Oxf. 1984. MRC Clin. Scientif. Staff Clin. Research Centre; Hon. Cons. Phys. N.wick Pk. Hosp. Harrow.

REEVE, Marjorie 592 Wells Road, Bristol BS14 9BD Tel: 01275 832102 — MB ChB 1940 Bristol.

REEVE, Norman Leonard Department of Pathology, Stepping Hill Hospital, Poplar Grove, Stockport SK2 7JE Tel: 0161 419 5605 Fax: 0161 419 5668; Kingsley, 64 Woodford Road, Bramhall, Stockport SK7 1PA — MB ChB 1973 Manch.; BSc (Anat.) Manch. 1970; FRCPath 1992, M 1979. (Manch.) Cons. Histopath. Stepping Hill Hosp. Stockport; Clin. Dir. Pathol.Lab.Med.Stockport NHS Trust. Prev: Lect. (Path.) Univ. Manch.; Ho. Surg. Manch. Roy. Infirm.; Ho. Phys. Withington Hosp. Manch.

REEVE, Robert George X Ray Department, Kettering & Dist. Gen Hospital, Rothwell Road, Kettering NN16 8UZ Tel: 01536 492000; The Coach House, Glendon Hall, Kettering NN14 1QE — MB ChB 1979 Liverp.; FRCR 1986; DMRD Liverp. 1984. Cons. Radiol. Kettering & Dist. Gen. Hosp. Prev: Sen. Regist. Mersey RHA.

REEVE, Roy Stephen Histopathology Department Hope Hospital, Eccles Old Road, Salford M6 8HD — MB BChir 1977 Camb.; MA Camb. 1979; FRCPath 1992, M 1982. Cons. Histopath. Hope Hosp. Salford. Prev: Sen. Regist. (Histopath.) Nottm.

REEVE, Samantha 67 Acacia Grove, New Malden KT3 3BU — MB BS 1997 Lond.

REEVE, Sandra Dawn 24 Amberwood Drive, Christchurch BH23 5RU — MB BS 1993 Lond.

REEVE, William Grant Glasgow Royal Infirmary, Glasgow G4 0SF; 16 South Erskine Park, Bearsden, Glasgow G61 4NA — BM 1981 Soton.; FFARCS Eng. 1988; DRCOG 1983. Cons. Anaesth. Glas. Roy. Infirm.

REEVES, Alfred (retired) 5 Norwich Close, Scalby, Scarborough YO13 0PP Tel: 01723 369267 — MRCS Eng. LRCP Lond. 1936. Prev: Capt. RAMC 1940-45.

REEVES, David Bath Road Surgery, Buxton SK17 6HL Tel: 01298 23298 Fax: 01298 73227; Castlemaine, 25 Macclesfield Road, Buxton SK17 9AH Tel: 01298 23071 — MB BS 1964 Durh. (Newc.) Prev: Regist. (Path.), SHO (Surg. & Obst.) & Ho. Off. (Med. & Surg.) SteppingHill Hosp. Stockport.

REEVES, David Mark 25 Lon-y-Dail, Cardiff CF14 6DZ — MB ChB 1992 Bristol.

REEVES, Professor David Sims 4 Parkfield Road, Pucklechurch, Bristol BS16 9PN Tel: 0117 937 3241 Fax: 0117 937 4024 Email: davidreeves2@cs.com — MB BS (Hons.) Lond. 1961; MD Bristol 1989; MRCS Eng. LRCP Lond. 1961; FRCPath 1982, M 1970; DA Eng. 1963. (Westm.) Hon. Prof, Univ. Bristol.; Edr.-in-chief, Jl. of Antimicrobiol chemolTher.; Hon. Emerit. Cons.N. Bristol NHS Trust. Socs: Hon. Life Mem. Brit. Soc. Antimicrobial Chemother.; Past Pres., Assn. Med. Microbiol. Prev: Med. Dir. & Cons. Microbiol. S.mead Health Servs. NHS Trust Bristol; Lect. (Bact.) St. Mary's Med. Sch. Lond.

REEVES, Diana Mary 50 Dore Avenue, North Hykeham, Lincoln LN6 8LW — MB ChB 1965 Aberd.; DCH RCPS Glas. 1980.

REEVES, Edward Rupert James Rose Cottage, Tutts Clump, Bradfield, Reading RG7 6LL Tel: 01734 744520 — MB BS 1991 Lond.; MA (Hons.) Oxf. 1993.

REEVES, Elizabeth Mary 32 Listley Street, Bridgnorth WV16 4AW — MB ChB 1992 Birm.

REEVES, Graham Edgar 220 Redland Road, Bristol BS6 6YR Tel: 0117 973 2800 — MRCS Eng. LRCP Lond. 1962. (Lond. Hosp.)

REEVES, Helen Louise 98 The Avenue, Stoke-on-Trent ST4 6BZ; Flat 3, 16 Tankerville Terrace, Jesmond, Newcastle upon Tyne NE2 3AH Tel: 0191 281 5125 Email: h.l.reeves@newcastle.ac.uk — BM BS 1990 Nottm.; BMedSci. Nottm. 1988. Specialist Regist. (Gastro enterol.) Newc.-upon-Tyne. Prev: Wellcome Trust Clin. Research Fell.

REEVES, Iain Christopher 2F2 15 Spittal Street, Edinburgh EH3 9DY — MB ChB 1998 Ed.; MB ChB Ed 1998.

REEVES, Ian Gareth 150 Fergus Drive, Glasgow G20 6AX Tel: 0141 945 5261 — BM 1991 Soton.; MRCP (UK) 1996. Clin. Lect. (Pub. Health) Lond. Sch. Hyg. & Trop. Med. Prev: Regist. (Med.) Newc., Austral.; SHO (Med.) Glas.

REEVES, Iris Agnes 86 Holland Road, Maidstone ME14 1UT Tel: 01622 661980 — MRCS Eng. LRCP Lond. 1950. (Roy. Free) Prev: Research Clin. Epidemiol. Unit Univ. Oxf.; Research Asst. Radiobiol. Laborat. & SHO Radiother. Dept. Ch.ill Hosp. Oxf.

REEVES, James Hargrave Kirk (retired) Chapel Row Surgery, The Avenue, Bucklebury, Reading RG7 6NS Tel: 01734 713252 Fax: 01734 714161 — MB BS 1960 Lond.; MRCS Eng. LRCP Lond. 1960. Prev: Resid. Med. Off. Mersey Gen. Hosp. Tasmania.

REEVES, Jane Philippa Well House, Well Lane, Upper Broughton, Melton Mowbray LE14 3BL — MB BS 1984 Lond.

REEVES, Joanna Appledown, Petrockstow, Okehampton EX20 3HQ Tel: 01837 810571 — BM 1993 Soton.

REEVES, Kenneth Edgar Gabriel Clanricarde House Surgery, Clanricarde Road, Tunbridge Wells TN1 1PJ Tel: 01892 546422 Fax: 01892 533987 — MB BS 1972 Lond.; MRCGP 1977; DObst RCOG 1976. (King's Coll. Hosp.) G. P. Represen., W. Kent Area Health Auth.; Osteoporosis Comm.

REEVES, Malcolm Thomas Newington Road Surgery, 100 Newington Road, Ramsgate CT12 6EW Tel: 01843 595951 Fax: 01843 853387 — MB ChB 1969 Liverp.

REEVES, Mark Andrew Trescobeas Surgery, Trescobeas Road, Falmouth TR11 2UN Tel: 01326 434888 Fax: 01326 434899; Holyrood, 43 Wood Lane, Falmouth TR11 4RB — MB BS 1983 Lond.; BSc (Biochem.) Lond. 1980, MB BS 1983; MRCGP 1988; DCH RCP Lond. 1987; DRCOG 1985; AKC 1983.

REEVES, Nicola Ann 154 Howard Drive, Maidstone ME16 0QB Tel: 01622 757185 — MB BS 1993 Lond. (Lond. Hosp. Med. Coll.) SHO (Paediat.) Luton & Dunstable Hosp. Luton Beds. Socs: BAEM Full Mem.ship. Prev: SHO (Neurosurg.) Old Ch. Hosp. Romford Essex; SHO (A & E) Basildon Hosp. Essex; SHO (Orthop. & Trauma) Qu. Mary's Hosp. Sidcup.

REEVES, Peter (retired) Ash Tree Cottage, Chapel Lane, Caunton, Newark NG23 6AN Tel: 01636 636209 — MB ChB 1956 Sheff.; Cert Contracep. & Family Plann. RCOG, RCGP &; Cert FPA 1975.

REEVES, Peter Olaf Longacre, Wyke Lane, Farndon, Newark NG24 3SP — MRCS Eng. LRCP Lond. 1955; FRCPsych 1984, M 1971; DPM Eng. 1962. Cons. (Foren. Psychiat.) Rampton Hosp. Prev: Cons. Psychiat. Balderton Hosp. Newark.

REEVES, Richard George William (retired) Holyrood House, Chard TA20 2DN Tel: 0146 063333 — MB ChB 1944 Birm.

REEVES, Robert Walter Kingham The Priory Hospital Bristol, Heath House Lane, Bristol BS16 1EQ — MB BS 1959 Lond.; FRCPsych 1987, M 1972; DPM Eng. 1965. (Roy. Lond. Hosp.) Cons. Forens. Psychiat. The Priory Hosp. Bristol. Prev: Mem. Parole Bd.; Med. Dir. Fromeside Clinic Bristol (Sub-Regional Secure Unit); Cons. Psychiat. BRd.moor Hosp. Med. Off. HM Remand Centre, PuckleCh. & HM Prison Bristol.

REEVES, Simon David Fenton and Partners, Medical Centre, Burgage Green, Southwell NG25 0EW; 1 Lambs Meadow, Mansfield Road, Edingley, Newark NG22 8BG Tel: 01623 882611 — BM BS 1988 Nottm.; BMedSci (Hons.) Nottm. 1986; MRCP (UK) 1992; MRCGP 1994. (Nottm.)

REEVES, Susan Elizabeth Shropshire Health Authority, District HQ., Cross Houses, Shrewsbury SY5 6JN Tel: 01743 761242 — MB BS 1982 Lond.; MA Camb. 1983; DRCOG 1986. Clin. Med. Off. Shrops. HA.

REEVES, Susan Mary Manchester Road Medical Centre, 27 Manchester Road, Knutsford WA16 0LZ Tel: 01565 633101 Fax: 01565 750135; 22 Comber Way, Knutsford WA16 9BT Tel: 01565 755286 — MB BS 1987 Lond.; MRCGP 1993; DRCOG 1991. (Char. Cross & Westm.) Gp. Socs: BMA. Prev: Trainee GP Macclesfield; SHO (Psychiat., Paediat. & O & G) Qu. Eliz. II Hosp. Welwyn Gdn. City.

REEVES, Suzanne Jane Hey Tor Oakfield, Huddersfield Road, Stalybridge SK15 3PY — MB ChB 1992 Manch.

REEVES, Wendy Jane Tadcaster Medical Centre, Crab Garth, Tadcaster LS24 8HD Tel: 01937 530082 Fax: 01937 530192 — BSc (Hons.) Sheff. 1982, MB ChB 1986; MRCGP 1990; DCH RCPS Glas. 1989; DRCOG 1988. (Sheff. Univ.) Prev: Trainee GP Leeds VTS; Ho. Off. (Gen. Surg.) Huddersfield Roy. Infirm.; Ho. Off. (Gen. Med. & Dermat.) Rotherham Dist. Gen. Hosp.

REEVES, Professor William Gordon Court Cottage, Cricket Malherbie, Ilminster TA19 0PW Tel: 01460 53080 Fax: 01460 53080 — MB BS 1964 Lond.; BSc (1st cl. Hons.) Lond. 1961; FRCP Lond 1978, M 1966; MRCS Eng. LRCP Lond. 1964; FRCPath 1985. (Guy's) Author, Edr. & Cons. Socs: Brit. Soc. Immunol.; Eur. Assn. of Sci. Edrs. Prev: Prof. Immunol. & Head Dept. Microbiol. & Immunol. Coll. Med. Sultan Qaboos Univ., Oman; Edr. The Lancet; Prof. &

Cons. Immunol. Univ. Hosp. Qu. Med. Centre Nottm. & Nottm. Univ. Med. Sch.

REFAAT, Refaat Faiq Eye Dept, Pilgrim Hospital, Boston PE21 9QS — MB ChB 1970 Alexandria; DO RCPSI 1986.

REFFITT, David Michael 16 Park Edge, Harrogate HG2 8JU — MB ChB 1990 Bristol.

REFSON, Alicia Rebekah Garden Flat, 6 Phillimore Gardens, London W8 7QD — MB BS 1998 Lond.; MB BS Lond 1998.

REFSON, Mr Jonathan Simon 15 Hanover Steps, St. Georges Fields, London W2 2YG — MB BS 1988 Lond.; FRCS Eng. 1992.

REFSUM, Mr Erling 142 Humber Road, London SE3 7LY — MB BS 1978 Lond.; FRCS Ed. 1983. (Guy's)

REFSUM, Miss Sigrid Elisabet 2 Malone Hill Park, Belfast BT9 6RD Tel: 01232 666613 Fax: 01232 664667 Email: srefsum@aol.com — MB BCh BAO 1985 Belf.; BSc (Hons.) Manch. 1980; MD Belf. 1997MD Belfast 1997; FRCS Ed. 1989. Socs: Ulster Med. Soc.; BMA; BASO.

REGAN, Alison Fiona Margaret National Blood Service, North London Centre, Colindale Avenue, London NW9 5BG Email: fiona.regan@nbs.nhs.uk — MB BS 1987 Lond.; MRCP (UK) 1991; MRCPath 1998. (Middlesex Hospital Medical School (82-87)) Jt. Post Cons. Haeratologist - Nat. Blood Serv. and Hammersmith Hosps. NHS Trust. Prev: Research Fell. N. Lond. Blood Transfus. Centre.; Regist. (Haemat.) Soton. Gen. Hosp.; SHO Rotat. (Med.) Soton. Gen. Hosp.

REGAN, Christopher Martyn 16 Hardmans, Bromley Cross, Bolton BL7 9XR — MB ChB 1981 Liverp.

REGAN, Ciaran Campbell TFR, 41A Broughton St., Edinburgh EH1 3JU — MB ChB 1996 Ed.

REGAN, Dermot Martin 54 St Mark's Road, Sale M33 6SA — MB BCh 1984 Wales.

***REGAN, Fiona Mary** 116 Pennard Drive, Southgate, Swansea SA3 2DP — MB ChB 1994 Leic.

REGAN, Joanna Margaret The Old Farmhouse, Pinn Lane, Exeter EX1 3RG; The Old Farmhouse, Pinn Lane, Exeter EX1 3RG Tel: 01392 464816 — MB BS 1992 Lond.; DPD 2000; DFFP 1997; MRGP 1997; DRCOG 1996; DCH RCP Lond. 1995. (St. Geo. Hosp. Lond.) p/t Clin. Asst. in Dermat. Roy. Devon & Exeter Hosp.; GP Non-Princip. Exeter; CMO Family Plann. Prev: GP/Regist. Newport; SHO (Gen. Adult Psychiat.) St. Cadoc's Hosp. Caerleon Gwent; SHO (O & G) Roy. Gwent Hosp. Newport.

REGAN, Judith Louise 9 Frognal Court, Finchley Road, London NW3 5HL — MB BS 1998 Lond.; MB BS Lond 1998.

REGAN, Kathryn Jane Trevose, Oakland Av, Farnham GU9 9DX — BM BCh 1997 Oxf.

REGAN, Professor Lesley Imperial College School of Medicine at St Mary's, Norfolk Place, London W2 1PG Tel: 020 7886 1050 Fax: 020 7886 6054 Email: l.regan@ic.ac.uk — MB BS 1980 Lond.; MD Lond. 1989; MRCOG 1985; FRCOG 1998. (Royal Free, Lond.) Prof. & Head of Dept. O & G ICSM at St. Mary's; Hon. Cons. (Obst. & Gyn.) at St. Mary's. Socs: Soc.for Gyn. Investig.; Gyn. Vis. Soc.; Expert (Reproduc. Med.) Fed. of Int. Obst. & Gyn. Prev: Sen. Lect. (O & G) St. Mary's; Sen. Regist. (O & G) Addenbrooke's Hosp. Camb.; Fell. & Dir. Med. Studies Girton Coll. Camb.

REGAN, Margaret Mary (retired) 88 Bramcote Drive, Beeston, Nottingham NG9 1DU Tel: 0115 925 6205 — MB BCh BAO 1943 NUI. Prev: Ho. Surg. & Ho. Phys. Richmond Hosp. Dub.

REGAN, Marian Rose Derbyshire Royal Infirmary, London Road, Derby DE1 2QY Tel: 01332 347141 Fax: 01332 254989 Email: marian.regan@sdaht-tr.trent.nhs.uk; Tel: 01332 346175 — MB BCh BAO 1984 NUI; FRCP. (University College Dublin) Cons. Rheum. Derbysh. Roy. Infirm.

REGAN, Millicent Maire Corban 83 Cambridge Road, Gt Crosby, Liverpool L23 7TX — MB ChB Liverp. 1948, DPH 1962; MFPHM 1989; MFCM 1974. (Liverp.)

REGAN, Richard John Riva, 54 North Park, Gerrards Cross SL9 8JR Tel: 01753 887057 — MB BS 1965 Sydney; FRCP Lond. 1993; MRCP (UK) 1970. (Sydney) Cons. Phys. Gen. Med. & Geriat. Amersham Gen. Hosp. Oxf. RHA. Socs: Renal Assn. & Brit. Geriat. Soc. Prev: Sen. Regist. (Gen. Med. & Nephrol.) Hants; AHA (T); Regist. (Nephrol.) St. Jas. Univ. Hosp. Leeds.

REGE, Kanchan Pandurang 54 Haydon Park Road, London SW19 8JY — MB BChir 1990 Camb.; MRCP (UK) 1992; MRCPath 1997. (Camb.) Sen. Regist. (Haemat.) St. Geo. Hosp. Lond. Prev: Regist. (Haemat.) Hammersmith Hosp. Lond.

REGESTER, Percy Thomas Moor Park, Moor Lane, Croyde, Braunton EX33 1NU — MRCS Eng. LRCP Lond. 1951; MFCM 1974; DPH Eng. 1956. (Lond. Hosp.) DMO N. Devon Health Dist. Prev: MOH City of Gloucester & Cons. Phys. S. W.. RHB; Med. Off. Interior N. Borneo.

REGGLER, Jonathan Guy 7 School Close, High Wycombe HP11 1PH — MB BChir 1984 Camb.; MA Camb. 1986; MRCGP (Distinc.) 1989; T (GP) 1991.

REGINALD, Philip Wallace Department of Obstetrics & Gynaecology, Wexham Park Hospital, Slough Tel: 01753 34567 — MD 1989 Lond.; MB BS Bangalore 1976; MRCOG 1981. Cons. O & G Wexham Pk. Hosp. Slough. Prev: Lect. & Sen. Regist. (O & G) St. Mary's Hosp. Lond.

REGISTER, Paula Wendy Lyndale, Poundstock, Bude EX23 0AU — BM BS 1998 Nottm.; BM BS Nottm 1998.

REGLINSKI, Frank Andrew The Surgery, Anderson Drive, Leslie, Glenrothes KY6 3LQ Tel: 01592 620222 Fax: 01592 620553 — MB ChB 1983 Dundee. (Dundee) GP Glenrothes, Fife.

REGNARD, Claud Francis Bernard St. Oswalds Hospice, Regent Avenue, Gosforth, Newcastle upon Tyne NE3 1EE Tel: 0191 285 0063 Fax: 0191 284 8004 — MB ChB 1976 Dundee; BMSc (Hons.) Dund 1973; MRCP (UK) 1996; FRCP (UK) 1998. Cons. (Palliat. Med.) St. Oswald's Hospice & Newc. Hosps. Trust Newc.; Hon. Clin. Lect. (Pharmacol. Scis.) Univ. of Newc. Socs: Assn. Palliat. Med; Assoc. Mem. Europe Assoc. Palliat. Care; Internat. Assn. Study Pain. Prev: Macmillan Fell. (Palliat. Care) Ch.ill Hosp. Oxf..

REGUNATHAN, Ponniah The Surgery, 238 Headstone Lane, Harrow HA2 5EF Tel: 020 8428 1211 Fax: 020 8428 9434 — MB BS Ceylon 1959; PhD Ed. 1971. (Ceylon) Socs: BMA; Med. Protec. Soc.

REHANA, Hussain Akhter 8 Rhindmuir Grove, Baillieston, Glasgow G69 6NE — MB BS 1965 Punjab.

REHLING, Graham Hugh Psychotherapy Department, 2 Cossington Road, Canterbury CT1 3HU — MB BS 1977 Lond.; MSc Lond. 1985; MRCPsych 1981. Cons. Psychiat. & Psychotherapist E. Kent Community NHS Trust. Prev: Cons. Psychiat. SE Kent HA; Sen. Regist. Camb.; Regist. Guy's Hosp. Lond.

REHM, Andreas 4 Barham Close, Chislehurst BR7 6JA — State Exam Med 1991 Bonn; MD Bonn 1993.

***REHMAN, Abdul** 64 Park Road, Sparkhill, Birmingham B11 4HB — MB ChB 1998 Birm.; ChB Birm. 1998.

REHMAN, Afzal Mohammed The Bloomsbury Surgery, 1 Handel St., Bloomsbury, London WC1N 1PD Tel: 020 7837 8559 — MB ChB 1974 Otago; Dip Obst Auckland 1977.

REHMAN, Alim John 93 Harley Street, London W1N 1DF Tel: 020 7935 2079 Fax: 020 7487 2831 — MB BS 1985 Lond.; D.Occ.Med. RCP Lond. 1996. (St. Mary's Hosp. Med. Sch. Lond.) Chief Med. Off. Arcadia plc Debenhams plc & Nat. Hist. Museum; Occupat. Phys. StoreHo. plc. The Arcadia plc, Hypo Bank, Vivat Holding plc Lee Cooper Jeans & Star Mining, Siberia; Chief Med. Off. Marshalls plc, Hamptons, Internat. Socs: Fell. Roy. Soc. Med.; Soc. Occupat. Med.; Fell. Roy. Geogr. Soc. Prev: Chief Med. Off. Union Bank of Switz.; Med. Off. Boxing Bd. of Control.

REHMAN, Anib 186 Howbeck Road, Birchfields Arnold, Nottingham NG5 8QE — BM BS 1995 Nottm.

REHMAN, Faiz Ur Norfolk Square Surgery, 14 Aldwick Road, Bognor Regis PO21 2LJ Tel: 01243 821404 Fax: 01243 841404; The Rubens, 105 Marshall Avenue, Bognor Regis PO21 2TN Tel: 01243 822227 — MB BS 1965 Punjab; MB BS Punjab (Pakistan) 1965. (Nishtar Med. Coll. Multan) Cas. Surg. (GP) Bognor War Memor. Hosp. Socs: Fam. Plann. Doctors Assn.; (Jt. Sec.) BMA (W. Sussex Br.). Prev: Regist. (Orthop.) Nishtar Med. Coll. Hosp. Multan, Pakistan.

REHMAN, Humaira 15 Ruby Close, Slough SL1 9DZ — MB BS 1994 Lond.

REHMAN, Jahangir 3 Laisteridge Lane, Great Horton, Bradford BD7 1RD — MB BS 1998 Newc.; MB BS Newc 1998.

REHMAN, Mohammed Javed 224 Upper Woodlands Road, Bradford BD8 9JQ — MB ChB 1994 Manch.

REHMAN, Shafiq Ur 21 Well Garth Bank, Leeds LS13 1EW — MB ChB 1992 Aberd.

REHMAN

REHMAN, Mr Shafiq-Ur 93 South Street, Savile Town, Dewsbury WF12 9NG — MB BS 1978 Karachi; FRCS Glas. 1985.

REHMAN, Shamim-ur Salford Medical Centre, 194 Langworthy Road, Salford M6 5PP Tel: 0161 736 2651 Fax: 0161 745 8955 — MB BS 1966 Karachi.

REHMAN, Sheikh Abdul 2 Midfield, Langho, Blackburn BB6 8HF Tel: 01254 249994 — MB BS 1949 Punjab; FRCP Glas. 1990; MRCP (UK) 1973. (King Edwd. Med. Coll. Lahore) Cons. Phys. Geriat. Med. Blackburn Health Dist. Prev: Ho. Surg. (ENT) & Med. Off. Tuberc. Outpat. Dept. Mayo Hosp. Lahore; JHMO (Chest Dis.) Ladywell Hosp. Salford.

REHMAN, Mrs Zeb 4 Hillbury Road, London SW17 8JT — MB BS 1964 Punjab; MB BS Punjab (Pakistan) 1964.

REHMAN, Zia-ur Church Street Surgery, 112 Church Street, Flint CH6 5AF Tel: 01352 733194 Fax: 01352 763669 — MB BS 1962 Punjab; MB BS Punjab (Pakistan) 1962. (Nishtar Med. Coll. Multan)

REHMANY, Khalid Mahmood Avian Nook, Coleshill Heath Road, Marston Green, Birmingham B37 7HU — MB BS 1959 Karachi; DA Eng. 1965. (Dow Med. Coll.) Prev: Regist. Selly Oak Hosp. Birm.

REICHARDT, Ortrud Sabine 17 Grange Terrace, Edinburgh EH9 2LD — State Exam Med 1993 Berlin.

REICHHELM, Thomas 1 Boughton Church Cottages, South St., Boughton-under-Blean, Faversham ME13 9NB — State Exam Med 1992 Freiburg; DRCOG 1995. GP Regist. Canterbury VTS.

REICHL, Mr Michael Accident & Emergency Department, Poole Hospital, Longfleet Road, Poole BH15 2JB Tel: 01202 442660 Fax: 01202 448207 — MB BS 1978 Lond.; FRCS 1983 Ed.; FRCS Ed. 1983. (Univ. Coll. Hosp.) Cons. A & E Poole Hosp. NHS Trust & Roy. Bournemouth Hosp. Prev: Sen. Regist. (A & E) Soton. Gen. Hosp.; Regist. (Accid & Emerg.) Leic. Roy. Infirm.; Regist. (Surg.) Stepping Hill Hosp. Stockport.

REID, Abigail Simpson (retired) 36 Tinto Road, Newlands, Glasgow G43 2AP Tel: 0141 637 1790 — MB ChB 1956 Glas. Prev: Assoc. Specialist Cytol. Path. Dept. Roy. Alexandra Hosp. Paisley.

REID, Ainsley Well Street Surgery, Well Street, Montgomery SY15 6PF Tel: 01686 668217 Fax: 01686 668599; Upper Brynkin, Churchstoke, Montgomery SY15 6EN Tel: 01588 620332 Fax: 01588 £20690 — MB ChB 1976 Aberd.; MRCGP 1982; MFFP 1993; DRCOG 1980. (Aberd.) GP Princip.; Non-Exec. Dir. Dyfred-Powys HA. Socs: Montgomery Med. Soc.

REID, Alan Iain Tranent Medical Practice, Loch Road, Tranent EH33 2JX — MB ChB 1975 Glas.

REID, Alan Robert, TD Occupational Health Service, The Boots Company PLC, 1 Thane Road W., Nottingham NG2 3AA Tel: 0115 959 3656 Fax: 0115 959 4867 Email: alan.reid@boots_plc.com; 7 Wemyss Gardens, Wollaton Park, Nottingham NG8 1BJ Tel: 0115 970 8138 — MB ChB 1966 Aberd.; FRCP Lond. 1993; DIH Soc. Apoth. Lond. 1980; FFOM RCP Lond. 1987, M 1982. (Aberd.) Chief Med. Off. (Occupat. Health Serv.) The Boots Co. PLC; Lt.-Col. RAMC(V). Socs: Fell. Soc. Occupat. Med. Prev: Sen. Occupat. Phys. Centr. Electricity Generating Bd. Lond. HQ; Med. Off. ICI Petrochem. Div. Middlesbrough; Ho. Off. (Surg.) Roy. Hosp. Sick Childr. & (Med.) Woodend Hosp. Aberd.

REID, Alan Stuart 4 Wheatfields, Enfield EN3 5DW — MB ChB 1997 Birm.

REID, Alastair Gilmour 2 (TFL) Lauriston Park, Edinburgh EH3 9JA Tel: 0131 229 1665; TFL, 2 Lauriston Park, Edinburgh EH3 9JA — MB ChB 1991 Ed. Prev: Ho. Off. W.. Gen. Hosp. Edin.; Ho. Off. (Surg.) Orkney.

REID, Alastair Grant Parkfield Health Centre, Sefton Road, New Ferry, Wirral CH62 5HS Tel: 0151 644 6665; Plymyard Cottage, 48 Plymyard Avenue, Bromborough, Wirral CH62 6BW Tel: 0151 328 1007 — MRCS Eng. LRCP Lond. 1960; DObst RCOG 1963. (Liverp.) Chief Med. Off. Aintree Motor Cycle Club. Prev: Vis. Med. Off. Birkenhead Matern. Hosp.; Regist. (Cas.) Roy. Infirm. Liverp.; SHO (O & G) & Ho. Phys. (Paediat.) Clatterbridge Hosp.

REID, Alastair James Mayne Department of Child Health, Queen's University of Belfast, Institute of Clinical Science, Belfast BT12 6BJ — MB BCh BAO 1990 Belf.

REID, Alastair Norman Crawford c/o Director General Medical Services (Royal Air Force), Headquarters Personnel and Training Command, Royal Air Force Innsworth, Gloucester GL3 1EZ Tel: 01452 712612 Ext: 5853 Email: ancreid@doctors.org.uk; 4 Kingswood Road, Kingswells, Aberdeen AB15 8TD Tel: 01502 512851 Email: ancreid@doctors.org.uk — MB ChB 1983 Glas.; DAvMED 1998; MRCGP 1987; DRCOG 1986. (Glasgow) Specialist Regist. in Occupat.al Med.

REID, Alexander Colinton, St. Martin's Crescent, Caerphilly CF8 — MB ChB 1946 Ed. (Ed.)

REID, Alexander Graham Mayfield Road Surgery, 125 Mayfield Road, Edinburgh EH9 3AJ Tel: 0131 668 1095 Fax: 0131 662 1734; 2A Church Hill, Edinburgh EH10 4BQ Tel: 0131 447 5510 — MB ChB 1966 Glas.; MRCGP 1970.

REID, Alick Mitchell (retired) 108 Southbrae Drive, Glasgow G13 1TZ Tel: 0141 959 3083 — MB ChB Glas. 1949; FRCA Eng. 1955; DObst RCOG 1951. Prev: Cons. Anaesth.. Glas. Roy. Infirm.

REID, Allan William Department of Radiology, Glasgow Royal Infirmary, 16 Alexandra Parade, Glasgow G31 2ER Tel: 0141 211 4783 Fax: 0141 211 4781 Email: awr@gri.org.uk; 3/1, 17 Julian Avenue, Kelvinside, Glasgow G12 0RB Tel: 0141 334 9112 — MB ChB 1980 Glas.; FRCR 1986; DRCOG 1982. Cons. (Radiol.) Glas. Roy. Infirm.; Clin. Dir. Imaging Directorate Glas. Roy. Infirm.; Hon. Clin. Sen. Lect. Glas. Univ.; Cons. (Radiol.) Ross Hall Hosp. Glas. Socs: Hon. Treas. Scott. Radiological Soc.; Roy. Med. Chir. Soc. of Glas.

REID, Allison Anna Balmore Road Surgery, 138-142 Balmore Road, Glasgow G22 6LJ Tel: 0141 531 9393 Fax: 0141 531 9389 — MB ChB 1991 Glas.

REID, Allyn Costandine Cleveland Clinic, 12 Cleveland Road, St Helier, Jersey JE1 4HD Tel: 01534 722381/734121 — MB BS 1971 Lond.; DRCOG 1976.

REID, Andrew Hamilton The Cottage, Main St., Longforgan, Dundee DD2 5ET Tel: 01382 360247 — MD 1972 Dundee; MB ChB St. And. 1965; FRCP Ed. 1980, M 1970; FRCPsych 1980, M 1972; DPM Ed. & Glas. 1968. (St. And.) Cons. Psychiat. Dundee Psychiat. Servs. (Tayside HB.). Socs: Hon. Sen. Lect. (Psychiat.) Univ. Dundee; Fell. Roy. Soc. Med.; BMA. Prev: Lect. (Psychiat.) Univ. Dundee; Sen. Regist. (Psychiat.) Dundee Psychiat. Servs.; Ho. Surg. & Ho. Phys. Dundee Roy. Infirm.

REID, Andrew John Cheyne Doctors Residence, St Pancras Hospital, 4 St Pancras Way, London NW1 0PE — MB ChB 1983 Otago.

REID, Mr Andrew Peter 68 Gillhurst Road, Harborne, Birmingham B17 8PB — MB ChB 1978 Birm.; FRCS Ed. 1984. Cons. ENT Surg. Selly Oak Hosp. Birm.

REID, Angela Rosemary Community Paediatrics, Lawson Memorial Hospital, Golspie Tel: 01408 633157; The Old Manse of Creich, Bonar Bridge, Ardgay IV24 3AB Tel: 01863 766257 — MB ChB 1970 Ed.; BSc, MB ChB Ed. 1970. (Ed.) Community Paediat. Sutherland & E. Ross-sh. Prev: GP Tain Ross Shire.

REID, Anne Grampian Health Board, Summerfield House, 2 Eday Road, Aberdeen AB15 6RE Tel: 01224 404008 Fax: 01224 404014 Email: anne.reid@ghb.grampian.scot.nhs.uk; 22 Burns Road, Aberdeen AB15 4NS Tel: 01224 318130 Email: arjazz22@aol.com — MB ChB 1971 Aberd. Med. Off. (Communicable Dis.s) Grampian HB. Prev: Med. Edr. Gtr. Glas. HB; Regist. (Community Med.) Grampian HB; Research Off. (Biomed., Physics & Bioeng.) Univ. Aberd.

REID, Anne Cheyne 130 Novar Drive, Glasgow G12 9SY — MB ChB 1988 Glas.

REID, Anthony Donald Worden Medical Centre, West Paddock, Leyland, Preston PR5 5HA Tel: 01772 423555 Fax: 01772 623878; 5 Beechfield Court, Mayfield, Leyland, Preston PR25 3SA — MB ChB 1987 Manch.; MRCGP 1991; DRCOG 1990. Prev: Trainee GP Bury VTS.

REID, Basil Raymond 19 Burghley Avenue, New Malden KT3 4SW — MB BCh BAO 1964 Belf.; FRCR 1975; FFR 1972; DMRD Eng. 1969.

REID, Mr Brian Alexander, Wing Cdr. RAF Med. Br. Retd. (retired) Department Obstetrics & Gynaecology, Claydon Wing, Stoke Mandeville Hospital NHS Trust, Aylesbury HP21 8AL Tel: 01296 315201 Email: grian.reid@smh.nhs.uk — MB ChB 1980 Glas.; MFFP 1995; MRCOG 1990; MRCGP 1984; T(OG) 1994; DRCOG 1987; DCH RCP Lond. 1986. Cons O&G Stoke Mandeville Hosp. NHS Trust, Aylesbury; Cons. O & G Stoke Mandeville Hosp. NHS Trust. Prev: Hon. Sen. Regist. (O & G) Glas. Roy. Infirm.

REID, Carolyn Anne Department of Plastic Surgery, Royal Victoria Infirmary, Queen Victoria Road, Newcastle upon Tyne NE1 4LP Tel: 0191 232 5131; 6 Croft Park, Hepscott, Morpeth NE61 6LJ Tel: 01670 515308 — MB BS 1969 Newc.; FRCS Ed. 1975. Cons. Plastic Surg. Roy. Vict. Infirm. Newc. u. Tyne. Socs: Brit. Burns Assn. (Hon. Sec.).

REID, Catriona Mary 16 Darlington Place, Bath BA2 6BX — MB ChB 1968 Ed.; DObst RCOG 1970; MFFP 1993 RCOG. Manager Adult Health Servs. Bath & W. Community NHS Trust; Med. Off. Bath Univ.

REID, Cecil David Leo Meadway, Royston Grove, Hatch End, Pinner HA5 4HF — MB BS 1966 Lond.; BSc Lond. 1963; FRCP Lond. 1977; FRCPath 1981; DCH Eng. 1971. (Univ. Coll. Hosp.) Cons. Haemat. N.wick Pk. Hosp. Prev: Hon. Sen. Regist. (Haemat.) N.wick Pk. Hosp. Harrow.

REID, Charles Henry The Firs, Cross in Hand, Heathfield TN21 0LT Tel: 01435 862021 Fax: 01435 867522; 31 Frenches Farm Drive, Heathfield TN21 8BQ — BM BCh 1975 Oxf.; BA Oxf. 1972. Socs: Fell. Roy. Soc. Med. Prev: Regist. (Orthop.) E.bourne Dist. Gen. Hosp.

REID, Christopher John Douglas Department of Paediatric Nephrology & Urology, 9th Floor, Guy's Hospital, St Thomas St., London SE1 9RT Tel: 020 7955 5000 Email: christopher.reid@kcl.ac.uk; 244 Barry Road, East Dulwich, London SE22 0JS — MB ChB Liverp. 1983; MRCP (UK) 1987. Cons. Paediat. Nephrol. Guy's & St. Thos. NHS Trust Lond. Prev: Sen. Regist. (Paediat.) Guy's & St. Thos. NHS Trust Lond.

REID, Christopher Joseph 15 Shearwater, Whitburn, Sunderland SR6 7SF — MB BS 1992 Newc.

REID, Christopher Michael Barrett Holland House, 31 Church Road, Lytham, Lytham St Annes FY8 5LL Tel: 01253 794999 Fax: 01253 795744; Eden House, 1 Eden Avenue, Lytham, Lytham St Annes FY8 5PS Tel: 01253 730705 Fax: 01253 730705 Email: michaelreid@edenhouse100.freeserve.co.uk — MB BCh BAO 1969 Dub.; MA Dub. 1992; DObst RCOG 1971. (Trinity Coll. Dub.) Clin. Asst. (Cardiol.) Vict. Hosp. Blackpool; Hon. Med. Off. Lytham Lifeboat Station; Mem. (Vice-Chairm.) NW Lancs. LMC; Vice. Chairm. Fylde PCG. Socs: Brit. Hyperlipid. Assn.; Nat. Assn. Commiss. GP's. Prev: SHO (Med. & Surg.) Roy. Manch. Child. Hosp. Pendlebury; Ho. Phys. & Ho. Surg. Roy. City Dub. Hosp.; Ho. Off. Glenroyd Matern. Hosp. Blackpool.

REID, Clifford Gordon A & E Medicine, North Hampshire Hospital, Basingstoke RG24 9NA — BM 1991 Soton.; MRCP (UK) 1994. Specialist Regist. A&E Med. N. Hants. Hosp.

REID, Mr Clive Douglas Department of Plastic & Reconstructive Surgery, Frenchay Hospital, Bristol BS16 1LE Tel: 0117 970 1212 Fax: 0117 975 3846 Email: c.d.reid@ukonline.co.uk — MB ChB Dundee 1970; FRCS Glas. 1975. Cons. Plastic Surg. Frenchay Hosp. Socs: Brit. Assn. Plastic Surg.; Aesthetic Plastic Surgs.; Brit. Assn. Aesthetic Plastic Surgs.

REID, Colette Mary Countess Mountbatten House, Moorgreen Hospital, Botley Road, Westend, Southampton SO30 3JB Tel: 02380 477414; 1 Bankside Cottages, Church Lane, Owslebury, Winchester SO21 1LU — MB ChB 1989 Glas.; MRCGP 1995; DRCOG 1994. Staff Grade (Palliat. Med.) Countess Mounbatten Ho. Soton.

REID, Colin Flat N Melville Court, 75 Rose St., Aberdeen AB10 1UH Tel: 01224 637556 Fax: 01224 637556 Email: colin.reid@arh.grampian.scot.nhs — MB ChB 1990 Aberd.; FRCA 1994; DA (UK) 1992. Cons. Anaesth., Aberd. Roy. Infirm., Aberd. Prev: Clin. Fell. Cardiothoracic Anaesth., Roy. Brompton Hosp. Lond.; Specialist Regist. (Anaesth. & Intens. Care) Aberd. Roy. Infirm.; Regist. (Anaesth.) Raigmore Hosp. Inverness.

REID, Colin Brown The Charleston Surgery, 5 South Campbell Street, Paisley PA2 6LR Tel: 0141 889 4373 Fax: 0141 848 0648; 103 Arkleston Road, Paisley PA1 3TY — MB ChB 1975 Glas.; MRCGP 1980; DRCOG 1978. (Glasgow University) Clin. Asst. (Haemat.) Roy. Infirm. Glas.; Clin. Tutor, Univ. of Glas.

REID, Colin James Hunter Lodge, Oving, Chichester PO20 6BT Tel: 01243 532254 Fax: 01243 532254 Email: cjreid@ibm.net — MB BS 1973 Lond.; FRCP Lond. 1994; MRCP (UK) 1976; MRCS Eng. LRCP Lond. 1973. (St. Bart.) Cons. Phys. Cardiol. Roy. W. Sussex Hosp. Chichester. Socs: Brit. Cardiac Soc. Prev: Sen. Regist. (Cardiol.) Roy. Free Hosp. Lond. & Harefield Hosp.; Regist. (Med.) St. Thos. Hosp. Lond.; Regist. Nat. Heart Hosp. Lond.

REID, Crawford Russell Greenshields 20 Back Road, Dollar FK14 7EA — MB ChB 1979 Dundee.

REID, Damien Gerard 26 Lennox Avenue, Glasgow G14 9HG — MB ChB 1992 Glas.

REID, Professor Daniel, OBE (retired) 29 Arkleston Road, Paisley PA1 3TE Tel: 0141 889 4873 Email: daniel.ried@virgin.net — MB ChB 1958 Glas.; MD (Commend.) Glas. 1969; FRCP Ed. 1994; FRCP Glas. 1983, M 1980; FFPHM RCP (UK) 1978, M 1974; DPH Eng. 1967; FRS Ed. 1997. Prev: Dir. Scott. Centre for Infec. & Environm. Health Ruchill Hosp. Glas.

REID, Daniel Vaughan 7 Merganser Way, Kidderminster DY10 4EQ — MB ChB 1993 Birm.

REID, David Arthur Rowan House, Whyteman's Brae, Kirkcaldy KY1 2LS Tel: 01592 643355 — MB ChB 1985 Ed.; Dip. Cog. Psychol. Dund 1996; MRCPsych 1992; DRCOG 1990. (Ed.) Cons. Psychiat. Whyteman's Brae Hosp. Kirkcaldy. Prev: Lect. & Hon. Sen. Regist. (Psychiat.) Univ. Dundee.; Regist. Rotat. Roy. Dundee Liff Hosp.; Trainee GP Fife HB VTS:.

REID, David Coutts Tayside Health Screening Clinic, 313 Strath Martine Road, Dundee DD3 8ND Tel: 01382 832600 — MB ChB 1977 Dundee; T(GP) 1991. Med. Adviser for Benefits Agency; Health Screening & Occupat. Health Clinic. Socs: Fell. Roy. Soc. Med.; Brit. Soc. Med. & Dent. Hypn.; Brit. Med. Acupunct. Soc.

REID, David Graham Craigwood, 23 Old Edinburgh Road, Inverness IV2 3HJ — MB ChB 1964 St. And.; MRCPsych 1972; DPM Eng. 1969. (St. And.) Hon. Sen. Lect. (Psychiat.) Univ. Aberd. Prev: Cons. Psychiat. Craig Dunain Hosp. Inverness; Cons. Psychiat. Pk.side Hosp. Macclesfield; Sen. Regist. (Psychiat.) Uffculme Clinic Moseley, Qu. Eliz. Hosp. Birm.

REID, David Hamilton Struthers Medical Institute for Research into Child Cruelty, Step Rock House, St Andrews KY16 9AT Tel: 01334 473599 Fax: 01334 473599 — MD 1969 St. And.; MB ChB 1956; FRCP Ed. 1972, M 1963; FRCPCH 1997; CIH Dund 1981. (St. And.) Cons. Paediat. & Dir. MIRIC St. And. Socs: MRCPCH. Prev: Cons. Paediat. Mersey Regional HB; MRC Research Fell. (Child Health) Univ. Aberd.; Resid. Childr. Hosp. of Philadelphia, USA.

REID, David Howard 16 Masham Court, Shaw Lane, Leeds LS6 4DT — MB ChB 1971 Manch.

REID, Mr David Lauriston Lincoln 26 Foxborough Gardens, Bradley Stoke, Bristol BS32 0BT — BM 1987 Soton.; FRCS Ed. 1992.

REID, Professor David Macaulay Medical School, Foresterhill, Aberdeen AB25 2ZD Tel: 01224 681818; 25 Friarsfield Road, Cults, Aberdeen AB15 9LB Tel: 01224 867874 — MD 1985 Aberd.; MB ChB 1975; FRCP Ed. 1989; MRCP (UK) 1978. Prof. of Rheum., Univ. of Aberd.; Hon. Cons. Aberd. Roy. Hosps. NHS Trust. Socs: Brit. Soc. Rheum., Scott. Soc. Experim. Med. (Counc. Mem.); Treas. Natl. Osteoporosis Soc.; Scientif. Advis. Comm., ARC. Prev: Cons. Rheumatologist, Grampian HB; Sen. Regist. (Med. & Rheum.) Grampian HB; Lect. Med. (Rheum.) Univ. Edin.

REID, David Mark Rutherglen Health Centre, 130 Stonelaw Road, Rutherglen, Glasgow G73 2PQ Tel: 0141 531 6010 Fax: 0141 613 3460; 2 Victoria Lane, Mearnskirk Road, Newton Mearns, Glasgow G77 5TP — MB ChB 1978 Glas.; Dip. Forens. Med. Glas. 1992.

REID, David William Edward 23 Old Edinburgh Road, Inverness IV2 3HJ — MB ChB 1988 Manch.

REID, Mr Donald Alexander Highbird, The Turnpike, Halam, Newark NG22 8AE — MB ChB 1973 Dundee; FRCS Ed. 1979.

REID, Mr Donald Benjamin Vascular & Endovascular Institute, Wishaw Hospital, Wishaw — MB ChB 1983 Glas.; MD Glas. 1991; FRCS (Surg.) 1995; FRCS Glas. 1987. (Glas.) Cons., Vasc. & EndoVasc. Surg., Vasc. & EndoVasc. Inst., Wishaw Hosp. Scott.; Hon. Sen. Clin. Lect., Univ. of Glas. Socs: (Counc.) Roy. M-C Soc.; W Scotl. Surg. Assn.; Internat. Soc. EndoVasc. Specialists. Prev: Fell. (Cardiovasc.) Arizona Heart Inst. Phoenix, Arizona, USA; Regist. (Surg.) Univ. Dept. Surg. Roy. Infirm. Glas.; Clin. Fell. & Sen. Regist. (Surg.) Unit for Peripheral Vasc. Surg. Glas. Roy. Infirm.

REID, Mr Donald James (retired) (cons. rooms), The Ashdown Nuffield Hospital, Haywards Heath RH16 1UD Tel: 01273 842348 Fax: 01273 842348 Email: thereids@hemscott.net — BM BCh Oxf. 1954; MA Oxf. 1954, MCh 1967, DM 1967; FRCS Eng. 1960; FRCS Ed. 1960. Prev: Research fell. Mayo Clinic USA.

REID, Doreen Isobel Leslie Clinic, Anderson Drive, Leslie, Glenrothes KY6 3LG Tel: 01592 743388; Aviemore, 16 Largo Road,

REID

Lundin Links, Leven KY8 6DH Tel: 01333 320268 — MB ChB 1966 Aberd. SCMO (Community Child Health) Fife HB. Socs: Fac. Community Health; BMA; Soc. Pub. Health.

REID, Dorte Elisabeth Bjorchmar Hunter Lodge, Oving, Chichester PO20 6BT Fax: 01243 532254 — MD 1983 Odense. Med. Off. (Orthop.) King Edwd. VII Hosp. Midhurst.

REID, Mr Douglas Andrew Campbell (retired) Croft House, 6 Buxton Road, Eastbourne BN20 7LA Tel: 01323 732631 — MB BS 1943 Lond.; FRCS Eng. 1949; MRCS Eng. LRCP Lond. 1943. Hon. Cons. Plastic Surg. Sheff. HA. Prev: Cons. Plastic Surg. United Sheff. Hosps. & Sheff. HA & Trent RHA.

REID, Douglas Simpson Regional Cardiothoracic Centre, Freeman Hospital, Freeman Road High Heaton, Newcastle upon Tyne NE7 7DN Tel: 0191 284 3111 Fax: 0191 213 0174 Email: d.s.reid@ncl.ac.uk; 25 Moor Road S., Gosforth, Newcastle upon Tyne NE3 1NP Tel: 0191 284 7737 Fax: 0191 285 8824 — FRCP Lond. 1981, M 1968; FRCP Glas. 1980, M 1968. (Glas.) Cons. Cardiol. Regional Cardiothoracic Unit Freeman Hosp. Newc. Socs: Fell.Europ. Soc. Cardiol.; Brit. Cardiac Soc.; Scott. Cardiac Soc. Prev: Sen. Regist. (Cardiol.) Newc. Gen. Hosp.; Brit. Amer. Research Fell.; Regist. (Med.) Roy. Postgrad. Med. Sch. Hammersmith Hosp.

REID, Duncan Andrew Colinton Surgery, 296B Colinton Road, Edinburgh EH13 0LB Tel: 0131 441 4555 Fax: 0131 441 3963; 296B Colinton Road, Edinburgh EH13 0LB Tel: 0131 441 4555 — MB ChB 1987 Ed.; BSc Hons. (Path.) Ed. 1985, MB ChB 1987; MRCGP 1991. Trainee GP Gtr. Glas. VTS.

REID, Elspeth Kathleen 2 Bogton Avenue, Glasgow G44 3JJ — MB ChB 1988 Glas.; DA (UK) 1992. SHO (Anaesth.) Roy. United Hosp. Bath. Prev: SHO (A & E) Falkirk Roy. Infirm.; SHO (Anaesth.) Basildon Hosp. Essex; Ho. Off. (Med.) Edin. Roy. Infirm.

REID, Evan Arthur Leslie Department of Medical Genetics, Addenbrooke's NHS Trust, Addenbrooke's Hospital, Hills Road, Cambridge CB2 2QQ; 254 Queen Ediths Way, Cambridge CB1 8NL — MB ChB 1991 Glas.; MB ChB (Hons.) Glas. 1991; BSc (Hons.) Glas. 1988; MRCP (UK) 1994. Wellcome Research Train. Fell. & Hon. Sen. Regist. Camb. Univ. & Addenbrooke's NHS Trust Camb. Socs: Soc. Brit. Human Genetics. Prev: Clin. Lect. (Med. Genetics); Career Regist. (Med. Genetics) Yorkhill NHS Trust Glas.; SHO (Med.) Gtr. Glas. HB.

REID, Fergus Macdonald Hayfield, Rockcliffe, Carlisle CA6 4AA — MB ChB 1997 Glas.

REID, Fiona Margaret 68 Craigleith View, Edinburgh EH4 3JY — MB ChB 1993 Aberd.

REID, Fiona Mary Kantara, Chapel Lane, Elsham, Brigg DN20 0RN — MB ChB 1992 Manch.

REID, Frances Crowmere House, Broad Oak Crescent, Bayston Hill, Shrewsbury SY3 0NE Tel: 01743 873284 Fax: 01743 873284 Email: frankiereid@doctors.org.uk — MB ChB 1977 Birm. Clin. Asst. (Anaesth.) Roy. Shrewsbury Hosp.; Private Acupunc. Socs: Accred. Mem. Brit. Med. Acupunc. Soc.

REID, Gael Susan 66 Bonhard Road, Scone, Perth PH2 6QB — MB ChB 1978 Dundee.

REID, Gavin Desmond 11 Scrabo Road, Newtownards BT23 4NW — MB ChB 1998 Dund.; MB ChB Dund 1998.

REID, Geoffrey Donald c/o Heatherwood Hospital, Ascot SL5 8AA Tel: 01344 23333 — MB BS 1975 Monash; MRACOG 1985.

REID, Geoffrey Ewing, Group Capt. RAF Med. Br. Department of Community Psychiatry, RAF Brize Norton, Carterton OX18 3LX Tel: 01993 897999 Fax: 01993 897555 Email: geoffreid@beeb.net; 34B Belfast Square, Brize Norton, Carterton OX18 3TA Tel: 01993 842253 Email: geoffreid@beeb.net — MB ChB 1974 Manch.; MRCPsych 1981; DAvMed FOM RCP Lond. 1993; T(Psych) 1991; FRCPsych 1998. (Manch.) Cons. Adviser (Psychiat.) RAF. Socs: Fell. Roy. Soc. Med.; BMA. Prev: Head of Dept. RAF Psychiat. Centre Wroughton, Swindon; Cons. Psychiat. RAF Germany; Cons. Psychiat. (Community Psychiat.) RAF Nocton Hall.

REID, Mr Gordon Findlay Montague Medical Centre, Fifth Avenue, Goole DN14 6JD Tel: 01405 767600 Fax: 01405 726126 — MB ChB 1968 Aberd.; FRCS Ed. 1972. GP Goole.

REID, Hamish Andrew Harman Penicuik Health Centre, 37 Imrie Place, Penicuik EH26 8LF Tel: 01968 672612 Fax: 01968 671543 — MB ChB 1985 Dundee; MRCGP 1992; MCOphth 1990; DO RCS Eng. 1990; DRCOG 1988.

REID, Hamish La Mont Forest End Surgery, Forest End, Waterlooville PO7 7AH — MB BS 1981 Lond.; MRCGP 1988. (Westm.) Prev: Resid. Amer. Hosp., Paris; SHO (Gyn.) W.m. Med. Sch. Profess. Unit; Ho. Surg. W.m. Hosp. Surg. Unit.

REID, Helen Department of Pathological Sciences, Medical School, Oxford Road, University of Manchester, Manchester M13 9PT Tel: 0161 275 5297; 64 Heaton Road, Withington, Manchester M20 4GW — MB BS 1969 Newc.; FRCPath 1989, M 1977; DCH Eng. 1972. (Newc.) Lect. (Neuropath.) Univ. Manch.; Hon. Cons. Neuropath. Centr. Manch. HA. Socs: (Sec. Profess. Affairs Sub. Comm.) Neuropath. Soc. Prev: Resid. Clin. Pathol. & SHO (Paediat.) Roy. Manch. Childr. Hosp.; Ho. Off. (O & G) Oldham & Dist. Gen. Hosp.

REID, Helen Susanna 43 East End Lane, Ditchling, Hassocks BN6 8UP — MB BS 1991 Lond.; MB BS (Distinc.) Pharmacol. Lond. 1991; MRCP (UK) 1994; FRCR 1997. (Roy. Free) Regist. (Radiol.) John Radcliffe Hosp. Oxf.

REID, Hugh Aymer Stewart Department of Pathology, Enfield District Hospital, Chace Wing, The Ridgeway, Enfield EN2 8JL — MB BS 1965 Lond.; FRCPath 1986; DObst RCOG 1967. (St. Mary's) Cons. Histopath. Enfield Dist. Hosp. (Chace Wing). Socs: Assn. Clin. Path.; Internat. Acad. Path. (Brit. Div.). Prev: Sen. Regist. (Histopath.) St. Mary's Hosp. Lond.; Lect. Bland Sutton Inst. Path. Middlx. Hosp. Lond.

REID, Hugh Conn Dunure, 553 Upper Wortley Road, Thorpe Hesley, Rotherham S61 2SZ Tel: 0114 246 7952 — MB ChB 1955 Glas.; MRCGP 1965; MFHom 1984.

REID, Mr Hugh Conn (retired) 2 Machrie Drive, Newton Mearns, Glasgow G77 6LB — MB ChB 1944 Glas.; FRCS Ed. 1950. Cons. Surg. Vict. Infirm. Glas. Prev: Ho. Surg. Vict. Infirm. Glas.

REID, Iain Andrew Greystones, Quarry Cottages, Off Foel Road, Dyserth, Rhyl LL18 6AR Tel: 01745 571960 Email: ian.reid@xenocide.freeserve.co.uk — MB ChB 1993 Ed. GP Regist.

REID, Ian Cameron Templeton Farm, Newtyle, Blairgowrie PH12 8SQ — MB ChB 1983 Aberd.; BMedBiol 1983. Lect. Dept. Ment. Health Aberd. Univ. Prev: Regist. Psychiat. Ross Clin. Aberd.

REID, Ian Leslie Northcote Surgery, 2 Victoria Circus, Glasgow G12 9LD Tel: 0141 339 3211 Fax: 0141 357 4480 — MB ChB 1971 Glas.

REID, Ian Nicol Department of Histopathology, York District Hospital, Wiggington Road, York YO31 8HE Tel: 01904 453039 Fax: 01904 635823; Carlton Farm, Nun Monkton, York YO26 8EJ Tel: 01423 331014 — MB ChB 1973 Aberd.; FRCPath 1992, M 1980. Cons. Histopath. York Dist. Hosp. Prev: Cons. Histopath. York & N.allerton HAs; Lect. (Forens. Med.) Path. Leeds; Lect. (Path.) Univ. Aberd.

REID, Iona Margaret Victoria Infirmary, Langside Road, Glasgow G41 4NL Tel: 0141 201 5454 Fax: 0141 201 5117 — MB BCh BAO 1985 Dub.; MD Dub. 1994; FRCSI 1989. Sen. Lect./Hon. Cons. Surg. Univ. of Glas. & Vict. Infirm. Glas. Prev: Lect. & Sen. Regist. (Gen. Surg.) N. Gen. Hosp. Sheff.

REID, Irvine Raeburn Durie (retired) 20 Bath Road, Felixstowe IP11 7JW Tel: 01394 284595 — MB BChir 1953 Camb.

REID, Isabel Anne Claire Skegoneill Health Centre, 195 Skegoneill Avenue, Belfast BT15 3LL Tel: 028 9077 2471 Fax: 028 9077 2449; 28 Church Avenue, Jordanstown, Newtownabbey BT37 0PJ — MB BCh BAO 1961 Belf.

REID, Jacqueline Anne Neonatal Unit, Aberdeen Maternity Hospital, Cornhill Road, Aberdeen AB25 2ZL Tel: 01224 840660 Fax: 01224 404919; 142 Osborne Place, Aberdeen AB25 2DU — MB ChB 1973 Aberd. Assoc. Specialist (Med. Paediat.) Aberd. Matern. Hosp.

REID, Jacqueline Anneta 56 Peveril Road, Beeston, Nottingham NG9 2HU — MB ChB 1992 Leeds.

REID, James Edmund (retired) 4 Cranmore Park, Belfast BT9 6JG Tel: 01232 666238 — MB BCh BAO 1946 Belf.; DA Eng. 1952; DA RCPSI 1949. Prev: Cons. Anaesth. Belf. Gp. Hosps. & Craigavon/Banbridge Unit.

REID, James Paterson (retired) Belair, St. Mary St., Kirkcudbright DG6 4AH Tel: 01557331243 — MB ChB 1950 Glas.

REID, Jane Helen Whitefriars Surgery, Whitefriars Street, Perth PH1 1PP Tel: 01738 625842 Fax: 01738 445030 — MB ChB 1980 Aberd.; MRCGP 1986; DRCOG 1983; DCH RCPS Glas. 1985. Clin. Med. Off. Tayside Health Bd.

REID, Jean Perry Smellie 19 Humbie Lawns, Newton Mearns, Glasgow G77 5EA — MB ChB 1978 Glas.; MRCPsych 1990. Cons. Psychiat. Gartnavel Roy. Hosp. Glas.

REID, Jennifer Anne 15 Park Avenue, Crossgates, Leeds LS15 8EN — MB BS 1994 Newc.

***REID, Jennifer Susan** 27 Allesborough Drive, Pershore WR10 1JH — MB ChB 1998 Birm.; ChB Birm. 1998.

REID, Jeremy Michael Queen Alexandra Hospital, Southwich Hill Road, Cosham, Portsmouth PO6 3LY Tel: 02392 286279; 10, Five Elms Drive, Ramsey SO51 5RN Tel: 01794 522879 Email: jeremymreid@hotmail.com — BM 1992 Soton.; FRCA 2001; MRCP (UK) 1995. SpR in Anaesthetics, Portsmouth Hosp.s NHS Trust. Prev: SHO (Anaesth.) Soton. Univ. Hosp. Trust; Regist. (Cardiol.) Jersey Gen. Hosp.; Regist. (Cardiol.) W. Dorset Gen. Hosps. NHS Trust.

REID, Joan Elizabeth 16 Downview Park W., Belfast BT15 5HN Email: joanreid@ntlworld.com — MB BCh BAO 1992 Belf.; FFARCSI 1998. Specialist Regist. Roy. Vict.. Hosp. Belf., Specialist Regist., Ulster Hosp. Dundonald; Specialist Regist. (Anaesths.) Dept. of Anaesth. Qu.'s Univ. Belf.; Clin. Fell. in Chronic Pain, Ulster Hosp. Dundonald. Socs: N. Irel. Soc. Anaesth.; Assn. Anaesth.; Brit. Assn. Sport & Med. Prev: SHO (Anaesth.) Belf. City Hosp., SPR Ulster Hosp. Dundonald; SHO (Anaesth.) Altnagelvin Gp. Hosps. Lond.derry, SPR Roy. Vict. Hosp. Belf.; SHO (Gen. Med.) Ulster Hosp. Dundonald, SPR Dept. Of Anaesth., Qu.s Univ., Belf.

REID, Joan Maud Magill 25 Craigarogan Road, Mallusk, Newtownabbey BT36 4RA — MB BCh BAO 1957 Belf.

REID, John Forth Valley Acute Hospitals NHS Trust, Westbourne Ave, Falkirk FK1 5ST Tel: 01324 678506 Fax: 01324 678523 Email: john.reid@fvah.scot.nhs.uk; 7 Clarendon Place, Stirling FK8 2QW Email: drjohnreid@aol.com — MB ChB 1973 Ed.; BSc (Hons.) Ed. 1970, MB ChB 1973; FRCP Ed. 1989; MRCP (UK) 1977; DObst RCOG 1976. Med. Dir., Forth Valley Acute Hosp.s NHS Trust. Prev: Sen. Regist. Vict. Geriat. Unit Glas.; Lect. (Therap. & Clin. Phamacol.) Univ. Edin.; Cons. Phys. (Geriat. Med.) Stirling Roy. Infirm.

REID, John Bon Air Consulting Rooms, St Saviour, Jersey JE2 7LJ Tel: 01534 66127 Fax: 01534 864869; Hunters Moon, Route de la Trinite, Trinity, Jersey JE3 5JP Tel: 01534 863004 — MB ChB 1959 Aberd.; MD Aberd. 1967. (Aberd.) Cons. Dermat. Bon Air Nursing Home Jersey. Socs: Fell. Roy. Soc. Med. (Mem. Sect. Dermat.); Fell. Internat. Soc. Dermat. Surg. Prev: Squibb Research Fell. (Dermat.) & Hon. Regist. Manch. & Salford Hosps. Skin Dis.; Regist. (Dermat.) Leeds Regional Hosp. Bd. (Bradford Roy. & St. Lukes Hosp.).

REID, John David Posterngate Surgery, Portholme Road, Selby YO8 4QH Tel: 01757 700561 Fax: 01757 213295; Briarfields, Lordship Lane, Wistow, Selby YO8 3XE Tel: 01757 268473 Email: jreid@posterngate.co.uk — MB ChB 1979 Ed.; DRCOG 1981.

REID, John Henderson Radiology Department, Borders General Hospital, Melrose TD6 9BS Fax: 01896 662351 — MB ChB 1979 Glas.; FRCR 1984; DMRD Ed. 1983. Cons. Borders Gen. Hosp.; Asst. Med. Director, Borders Gen.Hosp. Socs: Roy. Coll. Radiol.; Brit. Inst. Radiol. Prev: Cons. (Radiodiagnostics) Edin. Roy. Infirm.; Sen. Regist. (Radiodiagnosics) Edin. Roy. Infirm.

REID, John Jeffrey Kiveton Park Primary Care Centre, Chapel Way, Kiveton Park, Sheffield S26 6QU Tel: 01909 770213 Fax: 01909 510108; Highfield House, 11B Common Road, Thorpe Salvin, Worksop S80 3JJ Tel: 01909 770000 — MB ChB 1984 Sheff.; DRCOG 1989. Prev: Trainee GP Bassetlaw VTS; SHO (Dermat.) Grimsby Dist. Gen. Hosp.; SHO (Rheum. & Rehabil.) Norwich HA.

REID, John Low University Department of Medicine & Therapeutics, Gardiner Institute, Western Infirmary, Glasgow G11 6NT Tel: 0141 211 2886 Fax: 0141 339 2800 — BM BCh 1967 Oxf.; FRSE 1995; BA Oxf. 1964, DM 1975; FRCP Irel. 1997; FRCP Lond. 1986; FRCP Glas. 1979; MRCP (UK) 1970. (Oxf.) Regius Prof. Med. & Therap. Univ. Glas.; Cons. Phys. W.. Infirm. Glas. Socs: Fell. Roy Soc. Edin.; Med. Res. Soc.; Brit. Pharm. Soc. Prev: Regius. Prof. Mat. Med. Univ. Glas.; Reader (Clin. Pharmacol.) & Cons. Phys. Roy. Postgrad. Med. Sch. Hammersmith Hosp. Lond.

REID, John Mark 55 Cedarwood Avenue, Newton Mearns, Glasgow G77 5LP Tel: 0141 639 1376 — MB ChB 1955 Glas.; FFA RCS Eng. 1962; DA Eng. 1959. (Glas.) Cons. (Anaesth.) & Pain Relief Clinic Roy. Infirm. Glas.; Hon. Clin. Lect. in Anaesth. Univ. Glas.; Chairm. Glas. Terminal Care Gp. Prev: Sen. Regist. Anaesth.

Glas. Roy. Infirm.; Regist. (Anaesth.) Stobhill Gen. Hosp. Glas.; Capt. RAMC.

REID, John Matheson (retired) 44 Eaglesham Road, Clarkston, Glasgow G76 7TW Tel: 0141 644 1069 — MB ChB 1949 Glas.; MD (High Commend.) Glas. 1957; FRCP Ed. 1969, M 1954. Prev: Cons. Phys. (Cardiol.) W.. Infirm. Glas. & Roy. Hosp. Sick Childr. Glas.

REID, John Priestley Grampian Health Board, Summerfield House, 2 Eday Road, Aberdeen AB15 6RE Tel: 01224 558605 Email: john.reid@ghb.grampian.scot.nhs.uk; 22 Burns Road, Aberdeen AB15 4NS Tel: 01224 318130 — MB ChB 1971 Aberd.; BA (OU) 1997; MRCGP 1975. Med. Prescribing Adviser Grampian Primary Care Trust. Prev: Region. Med. Off. Scott. Home & Health Dept., Glas.; Clin. Lect. (Gen. Pract.) Aberd.; GP Aberd.

REID, John Smith Hall Alford Medical Practice, 2 Gordon Road, Alford AB33 8AL Tel: 019755 62253 Fax: 019755 62613; West Lodge, Montgarrie Road, Alford AB33 8AE Tel: 019755 62978 — MB ChB 1976 Aberd.; MRCGP 1981; DRCOG 1980. Teach. Fell. (Gen. Pract.) Univ. Aberd.

REID, Mr John William 7 Gloucester Row, Bristol BS8 4AW — MB BS 1979 Cape Town; FRCS Ed. 1986; MRCGP 1991; T(GP) 1991.

REID, Joseph McKinstry George Street Surgery, 99 George Street, Dumfries DG1 1DS Tel: 01387 253333 Fax: 01387 253301; 9 Robertson Avenue, Dumfries DG1 4EY Tel: 01387 264463 — MB ChB 1979 Glas.; MRCGP 1983; DGM RCP Lond. 1986; DRCOG 1981.

REID, Joyce Allison 6 Hamilton Avenue, Glasgow G41 4JF — MB ChB 1978 Glas.; FFA RCS Eng. 1983; DRCOG 1980. Sen. Regist. (Anaesth.) W.. Infirm. Glas. Socs: BMA & W. Scotl. Soc. Anaesth. Prev: Regist. (Anaesth.) Vict. Infirm. Glas.; Research Regist. (Anaesth.) Univ. Dept. Glas. Roy. Infirm.

REID, Judith Eileen Infertility Clinic, Farnborough Hospital, Farnborough Common, Farnborough BR6 8ND Tel: 01689 814157; 2 April Close, Green Street Green, Orpington BR6 6NA Tel: 01689 857027 — MB ChB 1981 Manch. Clin. Asst. (O & G) Orpington & Beckenham Hosp. Prev: Regist. (O & G) FarnBoro. Hosp. & Whittington Hosp.

REID, Julie Ann 143 Old Ballymoney Road, Ballymena BT43 6SL Tel: 01266 413601 — MB BCh BAO 1997 Belf. (Queen's University, Belfast)

REID, Karen Wright The Coach House, Sandy Lane, Guildford GU3 1HF Tel: 01483 569125 — MB BChir 1985 Camb.; MA Camb. 1986; MRCGP 1991; DRCOG 1986. (Addenbrooke's Clin. Med. Sch.) Prev: GP Groombridge; SHO (ENT) Kent & Sussex Hosp. Tunbridge Wells; Trainee GP E. Grinstead.

REID, Kathleen Annie 6 Bartongate Avenue, Barnton, Edinburgh — MB ChB 1977 Glas.

REID, Kathleen May (retired) 17 Gallery Lane, Holymoorside, Chesterfield S42 7ER — MRCS Eng. LRCP Lond. 1954. Prev: Sen. Med. Off. (Family Plann.) N. Derbysh. HA.

REID, Keith 5 Blandfield Road, London SW12 8BQ — MB ChB 1990 Manch. Research Med. Off. (Applied Physiol.) Centre for Human Sci.s Dera FarnBoro.

REID, Kingsley, SBStJ Sunfield Medical Centre, Sunfield Place, Stanningley, Leeds Tel: 0113 257 0361 Fax: 0113 236 3261; Windrush, Apperley Lane, Rawdon, Leeds LS19 7DX — MB ChB 1964 Ed.; MRCGP 1978; DObst RCOG 1966. (Ed.) Clin. Asst. (Dermat.) Bradford Roy. Infirm.; Area Surg. St John Ambul. Prev: SHO (Anaesth.) St. Luke's Hosp. Bradford; Ho. Surg. Bangour Gen. Hosp. W. Lothian; Ho. Phys. W. Gen. Hosp. Edin.

REID, Kirsty Jane Dunadd, Tulloch Avenue, Dingwall IV15 9TU — MB ChB 1993 Glas.

REID, Lorna Kay 29 Roseworth Avenue, Gosforth, Newcastle upon Tyne NE3 1HS Tel: 0191 285 8035; Flat 18 Deneway, 17 Adderstone Crescent, Jesmond, Newcastle upon Tyne NE2 2HH Tel: 0191 281 1327 — BSc (Hons. Bact. & Immunol.) Brit. Columbia 1959, MD 1963; Lic. Newfld. Med. Bd. 1970. (Univ. Brit. Columbia) Guest Lect. (Microbiol.) Univ. Newc.

REID, Malcolm Fraser University Hospital, Nottingham NG7 2UH; 313 Wollaton Vale, Nottingham NG8 2PX — BM BS 1980 Nottm.; FFA RCS Lond. 1985. Cons. Notts. HA.

REID, Margaret 15 Sturdee Gardens, Jesmond, Newcastle upon Tyne NE2 3QU — MB BS 1984 Lond. Socs: MFHom.

REID

REID, Margaret Jarvie Gray Craigelvan, Elmira Road, Muirhead, Chryston, Glasgow G69 9EJ Tel: 0141 779 2366 — LRCP LRCS Ed. LRFPS Glas. 1949. (Glas.) Prev: Ho. Surg. Glas. Roy. Infirm.

REID, Margaret Mary Gateacre Brow Surgery, 1 Gateacre Brow, Liverpool L25 3PA Tel: 0151 428 1851 — MB ChB 1978 Liverp.; MRCGP 1986; DCH Eng. 1981.

REID, Marguerite Marion Wilson (retired) 108 Southbrae Drive, Glasgow G13 1TZ Tel: 0141 959 3083 — MB ChB Glas. 1963; DA Eng. 1966. Prev: Assoc. Specialist (Cytol.) Vale of Leven Hosp. Alexandria, Dunbaronsh..

REID, Marion Bernadette Department of Cellular Pathology, Stoke Mandeville Hospital, Aylesbury HP21 8AL Tel: 01296 315340; 22 Arnold Way, Thame OX9 2QA — MB ChB 1978 Manch.; MRCPath 1986. (St. And. & Manch.) Cons. (Cell. Path.) Stoke Mandeville Aylesbury Hosp. Prev: Sen. Regist. (Histopath.) Oxf. RHA; Regist. (Histopath.) Bradford HA; SHO (Histopath.) Withenshawe Manch.

REID, Mark Andrew 56 Upper Malone Gardens, Belfast BT9 6LY Tel: 01232 612986 — MB BCh BAO 1988 Belf.; MRCP (UK) 1992; FRCA 1995.

REID, Mark McClean Royal Belfast Hospital For Sick Children, Falls Road, Belfast BT12; 10 Kensington Gardens, Hillsborough BT26 6HP — MB BCh BAO 1962 Belf.; FRCP Ed. 1994; FRCP Glas. 1978, M 1967; FRCPI 1991, M 1990; DCH RCPS Glas. 1965. (Queen's Belf.) Cons. Neonat. Roy. Matern. Hosp. Sick Childr. & City Hosps. Belf.; Chairm. of Staff Roy. Matern. Hosp. Belf. & Roy. Belf. Hosp. Sick Childr. Socs: BMA; (Ex-Pres.) Irish Perinatal Soc.; (Counc.) RCP. Prev: Cons. Paediat. Craigavon Hosp., S. Tyrone Hosp. & Roy. Belf. Hosp. Sick Childr.; Resid. Fell. Toronto Hosp. Sick Childr., Canada; Regist. Roy. Belf. Hosp. Sick Childr.

REID, Maureen 23 South Street, St Andrews KY16 9QS — MB ChB 1977 Ed.; MRCPsych 1983; MRCGP 1982. (Edinburgh) GP Retainer Scheme. Prev: GP E. Lothian.; Regist. (Psychiat.) Rosslynee Hosp. Midlothian.

REID, Maurice Tel: 01942 831263; 45 Parsons Walk, Wigan WN1 1RU — MB ChB 1974 Manch.

REID, Merriel Victoria 67 Pogmoor Road, Barnsley S75 2DZ Tel: 01226 245179 — MB BS 1972 Newc.; MRCGP 1976; DObst RCOG 1975. Clin. Med. Off. (Child Health) Barnsley HA.

REID, Michael Macdonald Department Haematology, Royal Victoria Infirmary, Newcastle upon Tyne NE1 4LP Tel: 0191 232 5131; 33 St. George's Terrace, Jesmond, Newcastle upon Tyne NE2 2SU — MB BS 1971 Lond.; BSc (Physiol.) Lond. 1968, MD 1981; FRCP Lond. 1990, M (UK) 1977; FRCPath 1996, M 1983; FRCPCH 1997, M 1996; DCH RCPS Glas. 1973. (St. Thos.) Cons. Haemat. Roy. Vict. Infirm. Newc.; Hon. Sen. Lect. (Med. & Child Health) Univ. Newc. Socs: Brit. Soc. Haematol.; Brit. Paediat. Assn.; Assn. Clin. Path. Prev: Sen. Regist. (Haemat.) Roy. Vict. Infirm. Newc.; Research Fell. (Paediat. Oncol.) Sidney Farber Cancer Inst. Boston, USA; Research Assoc. (Child Health) Univ. Newc.

REID, Morag Marsaili MacColl 282 Ferry Road, Edinburgh EH5 3NP — MB ChB 1998 Bristol.

REID, Moyra Janette 22 Brines Orchard, Templecombe BA8 0JL — BM BCh 1997 Oxf.

REID, Muriel Hutchison Flat 6B, 14 Sutherland Avenue, Bearsden, Glasgow G61 3JW — MB ChB 1943 Glas.

REID, Neil Balfour (retired) Lealands, Staunton on Arrow, Leominster HR6 9HS Tel: 01544 388277 — MB ChB 1948 Birm.; MRCGP 1959. Med. Off. Kington Cottage Hosp. Prev: RAFVR.

REID, Nicholas Cunningham Green Lane Hospital, Devizes SN10 5DS Tel: 01380 731200 Fax: 01380 731308 Email: reidkn@bath-mhct.swest.nhs.uk — MB ChB 1978 Manch.; MPhil Ed. 1988; BSc St. And. 1975; MRCPsych 1986. Cons. Psychiat. Bath Ment. Health Care Trust. Prev: Sen. Regist. Roy. S. Hants. Hosp. Soton.; Regist. (Psychiat.) Roy. Edin. Hosp.; Area Med. Off. Kandrian W. New Brit. Papua New Guinea.

REID, Nigel Charles Ronald Wyman (retired) Reid, Broadlands Harbour, Stubb Lane, Broad Oak, Brede, Rye TN31 6BS Tel: 01424 882427 — MD 1969 Camb.; MA, MB BChir 1956; FRCP Lond. 1976, M 1962. Prev: Cons. Phys. (Gastroenterol.) Hastings HA.

REID, Nigel George Bruce Horse Fair Surgery, 12 Horse Fair, Banbury OX16 0AJ Tel: 01295 259484 Fax: 01295 279293 — MB BChir 1974 Camb.; MA Camb. 1974; MRCGP 1980. Prev: Hon. Med. Advis. Yarmouth Life Boat; RMO 1 Chesh.

REID, Patrick Julian 2 Harlands Grove, Orpington BR6 7WB — MB BS 1998 Lond.; MB BS Lond 1998.

REID, Paul John 6 Lamb Terrace, Arbroath DD11 4HD — MB ChB 1996 Aberd.

REID, Paul Vincent 284 Lees Road, Oldham OL4 1PA — MB ChB Manch. 1979; MRCGP 1983. Socs: Brit. Med. Acupunct. Soc.

REID, Paula Elizabeth 2/64 Edenderry Village, Belfast BT8 8LQ Tel: 01232 645523 — MB BCh BAO 1992 Belf. (Queens Univ. Belfast) Regis., Phys. Asst., Dermat. Prev: Lats Dermat.; SHO Dermat.

REID, Peter Cameron 1 Hawsley Road, Harpenden AL5 2BL Tel: 01582 763261 Email: pcre10@talk21.com — FRCOG 1998 Manch.; BSc (Hons.) (Anat.) Manch. 1976, MD 1989, MB ChB 1979; MRCOG 1985. Cons. Obst. Luton & Dunstable NHS Trust Hosp. Prev: Sen. Regist. N.. Gen. Hosp. Sheff.; Research Regist. N.. Gen. Hosp. Sheff.; Regist. Watford Gen. Hosp.

REID, Peter Geddes Countess of Chester Hospital, Liverpool Road, Chester CH2 1UL Tel: 01244 366305 Fax: 01244 366455; 48 Cinder Lane, Guilden Sutton, Chester CH3 7EN — MD 1991 Ed.; MB ChB 1979; FRCP UK 1997; MRCP (UK) 1982. (Ed.) Cons. Phys. Cardiol. Countess of Chester Hosp. NHS Trust.; Vis. Cardiol. Cardiothoracic Centre Liverp. Prev: Sen. Research Regist. (Cardiol.) Roy. Vict. Infirm. Newc.; Regist. (Cardiol.) Freeman Hosp. Newc. u. Tyne; Clin. Research Off. & Hon. Regist. S. Glam HA.

REID, Peter Trevor 3 Kinedar Crescent, Belmont, Belfast BT4 3LY — MB BCh BAO 1988 Belf.

REID, Philip John The Surgery, 45A Pembridge Villas, London W11 3EP Tel: 020 7727 2222 Fax: 020 7792 2867; 117 Sutherland Avenue, London W9 2QJ Tel: 020 7289 1978 Fax: 020 7266 1518 — MB BS 1989 Lond.; BA Oxf. 1986; MRCP (UK) 1992; MRCGP 1995; DRCOG 1993. (Oxford and St Mary's London) Sec. to Trustees & Vice-Princip. Wytham Hall. Prev: Trainee GP Lond. VTS; SHO (O & G) Hillingdon Hosp. Uxbridge; SHO Rotat. (Gen. Med.) St. Mary's Hosp. Lond.

REID, Miss Priscilla Margaret A&E Department, The Lister Hospital, Stevenage SG1 4AB Tel: 01223 217118; Tel: 01954 50412 — MB BCh 1976 Wales; FRCS 1982 Eng.; FFAEM 1996. Cons. A & E The Lister Hosp. Socs: BAEM; FRCS; Fell. FAEM. Prev: Regist. (A & E & Neurosurg.) Addenbrooke's Hosp. Camb.; Sen. Regist. (A & E) Addenbrooke's Hosp. Camb.

REID, Rachel Elizabeth Glen 144 Tile Cross Road, Tile Cross, Birmingham B33 0LU Tel: 0121 779 2711; 4 Scomerby Drive, Solihull B91 3YY — MB BChir 1990 Camb.; MA Camb. 1991. GP Partner; Clin. Asst. (Psychiat.).

REID, Richard David Bangor Health Centre, Newtownards Road, Bangor BT20 4LD Tel: 028 9146 9111; 148 Groomsport Road, Bangor BT20 5PE — MB BCh BAO 1985 Belf.; MRCGP 1989; DCH Dub. 1990; DRCOG 1987.

REID, Richard Ian Portsmouth Healthcare Trust, Department of Medicine for the Elderly, Queen Alexandra Hospital, Portsmouth PO6 3LY Tel: 023 92 286891 Fax: 023 92 200381; 6 Swanage Road, Lee-on-the-Solent PO13 9JW Tel: 023 92 550539 — MB ChB 1974 Glas.; FRCP Lond. 1992; FRCP Glas. 1990; MRCP (UK) 1978. (Glas.) Cons. Phys. (Elderly Med.) Portsmouth Healthcare Trust; Med. Dir. Portsmouth Healthcare Trust. Socs: Brit. Geriat. Soc. Prev: Sen. Regist. (Geriat. Med.) Portsmouth & SE Hants. & Soton. & SW Hants. Health Dists.; Regist. (Gen. Med.) Kilmarnock Infirm.; SHO (Med. Cardiol.) Glas. Roy. Infirm.

REID, Robert 55 Lucknow Drive, Mapperley Park, Nottingham NG3 5EJ Tel: 0115 960 6777 — MB BCh BAO 1939 Belf. (Qu. Univ. Belf.) Socs: BMA.

REID, Robert Alasdair Hlabisa Hospital, P/Bay X 5001, Hlabisa, Kwazulu, Natal 3937, South Africa Fax: 0358 381117 Email: alreid@iafrica.com; 18 West Harbour Road, Charlestown, Dunfermline KY11 3ET — MB ChB 1990 Aberd.; MRCP (UK) 1993; DTM & H Liverp. 1995. (Aberd.) Sen. Clin. Research Off. Liverp. Sch. Trop. Med.; Med. Off. Hlabisa Hosp., S. Afr. Prev: Regist. (Infec. Dis.) Fazakerley Hosp. Liverp.; SHO (Med.) Clwyd HA.

REID, Robert Pearson 19 Humbie Lawns, Newton Mearns, Glasgow G77 5EA — MB ChB 1978 Glas.; BSc Glas. 1975, MB ChB 1978; MRCPath 1984.

REID, Rosemary Anne Cholderton House, Cholderton, Salisbury SP4 0DW — MB BS 1982 Lond.; MRCOG 1989.

REID, Ross Paterson Glover Street Medical Centre, 133 Glover Street, Perth PH2 0JB Tel: 01738 639748 Fax: 01738 635133; 66 Bonhard Road, Scone, Perth PH2 6QB — MB ChB 1978 Dundee; MRCGP 1984.

REID, Sara Elizabeth 41 Eglantine Park, Hillsborough BT26 6HL Tel: 01846 688140 Fax: 0802 364559 — MB BCh BAO 1993 Belf.; DCH 1997; DRCOG 1997; DFFP 1998; MRCGP (distinction) 1998. (Queen's University Belfast) GP Locum. Socs: BMA; RCGP. Prev: GP Regist. HillsBoro. H.C. Co. Down; SHO (O & G); SHO (Paediat.).

REID, Sheilagh Vivienne 29 St. Thomas Road, Mount Merrion, Blackrock, County Dublin, Republic of Ireland; 2 Hayes Farm Court, Ticknall, Derby DE73 1JE Tel: 01332 864351 Email: mullreid@aol.com — MB BCh BAO 1992 Dub.; MB BCh Dub. 1992; FRCS Lond. 1997. Research Regist. Hallamshire Hosp. Sheff. Socs: BMA; Fell. Roy. coll. Surgs. Eng.

REID, Simon Alexander 43 East End Lane, Ditchling, Hassocks BN6 8UP Tel: 01273 842348 Fax: 01273 842348 — MB BS 1994 Newc.; DTM & H Liverp. 1997; MRCP, Uk 1998. SHO, (Anaesth.) Gwynedd Hosp. NHS Trust. Prev: Sen. H. Off. (Med.) Roy. Vict. Hosp. Blackpool, (Med); SHO Tamanaki Hosp. New Zealand. (Med).

REID, Simon Charles Radbrook Green Surgery, Bank Farm Road, Shrewsbury SY3 6DU Tel: 01743 231816 Fax: 01743 344099; Email: simon@bictonbarn.freeserve.co.uk — MB ChB 1977 Birm.; MRCGP 1986. (Birmingham) GP Princip.; Clin. Assist. - Procedural Dermatol., Roy. Shrewsbury Hosp., Shrewsbury.; Course Orginiser Shrops. VTS. Prev: Vis. Educat. Cons., Brit. Internat. Healthcare., Macedonia. 1999-2001.

REID, Simon Charles Thomas Stranraer Health Centre, Edinburgh Road, Stranraer DG9 7HG Tel: 01776 706566; Larg House, Larg Road, Stranraer DG9 0JN Tel: 01776 3228 — MB BCh BAO 1985 Belf.; LFHom RCP Lond. 1996; MRCGP 1991; DRCOG 1990. Prev: Trainee GP Girvan Ayrsh.; SHO (Gen. Med.) N.. Health & Social Serv. Bd. GP VTS; SHO (Cas.) Belf. City Hosp.

REID, Stephen Alastair 17 Devonshire Road, Hornchurch RM12 4LG Tel: 014024 51969 — MB BS 1989 Lond.; PhD Lond. 1986, BSc (Hons.) 1982, MB BS 1989. Regist. (Paediat.) Waitkato Area HB, New Zealand.

REID, Steven Fitzroy Clare House, St. George's Hospital, Blackshaw Road, London SW17 0DY — MB BS 1990 Lond.; MRCPsych 1994.

REID, Steven Patrick John Holland House, 31 Church Road, Lytham, Lytham St Annes FY8 5LL Tel: 01253 794999 Fax: 01253 795744 — MB BCh BAO 1971 Dub.; MB BCh BAO (Hons.) Dub. 1971; MA Dub. 1977, BA 1969; FRCS Eng. 1977; MRCGP 1979; LM Rotunda 1972. (T.C. Dub.) Clin. Asst. (Orthop. & Surg.) Lytham Hosp. Socs: Brit. Soc. Med. & Dent. Hypn. Prev: Tutor (Surg.) Univ. Manch.; Demonst. (Anat.) TC Dub.; Ho. Phys. & Ho. Surg. Dr. Steevens Hosp. Dub.

REID, Susan Rachel 98 Pilmuir Street, Dunfermline KY12 0ND — MB ChB 1985 Aberd.

REID, Suzanne 15 Beverley Gardens, London SW13 0LZ — MB BS 1990 Lond.

REID, Thomas Myles Sutherland Microbiology Department, Aberdeen Royal Infirmary, Aberdeen AB25 2ZD Tel: 01224 554954 Fax: 01224 662979 Email: thomas.reid@arh.grampian.scot.nhs.uk; 22 Gordondale Road, Aberdeen AB15 5LZ Tel: 01224 633665 — MB ChB 1972 Aberd.; BMedBiol (Immunol.) 1969; FRCP Ed. 1991; MRCP Ed (UK) 1988; FRCPath 1991, M 1979. Head of Serv. & Cons. Microbiol. Grampian Univ. Hopitals NHS Trust; Hon. Sen. Lect. (Bact.) Univ. Aberd. Socs: (Hon. Sec.) Aberd. M-C Soc. 1988-2002; Pres. Aberd. M-C Soc. 2002-2003. Prev: Lect. (Bact.) Aberd. Univ.

REID, Veronica Theresa Anaesthetic Department, Monklands Hospital, Airdrie ML6 Tel: 01236 748748 Email: thrys1205@yahoo.com — MB ChB 1970 Glasg.; FRCA 1975. (Glasgow) Cons. (Anaesth.) Monklands Dist. Gen. Hosp. Airdrie. Socs: BMA & Assn. Anaesth.; Chairm., Scott. LNC Forum; Mem. Scott. Counc. BMA. Prev: Sen. Regist. (Anaesth.) Roy. Infirm. Glas.; Regist. (Anaesth.) Stobhill Gen. Hosp. Glas.

REID, Wendy Margaret Neely The Royal Free Hosptial, London NW3 2QG Tel: 020 7794 0500; 2A Woodsome Road, London NW5 1RY — MB BS 1981 Lond.; MRCOG 1988. (Univ. Lond. Roy. Free Hosp. Sch. Med.) Cons. O & G Roy. Free Hosp. Lond.

REID, William Hayfield, Rockcliffe, Carlisle CA6 4AA Tel: 01228 74552 — MB ChB 1968 Ed.; FRCOG 1988, M 1975.

REID, William 20 Johnstone Drive, Rutherglen, Glasgow G73 2PT Tel: 0141 647 1786 — MD 1990 Glas.; MB ChB 1980; FRCP Glas. 1994; MRCP (UK) 1983. Cons. Phys. Med. for Elderly S.. Gen. Hosp. Glas. Prev: Sen. Regist. (Geriat. & Gen. Med.) S.. Gen. Hosp. Glas.

REID, Mr William (retired) 36 Tinto Road, Glasgow G43 2AP Tel: 0141 637 1790 — MB ChB Glas. 1933; FRCS Glas. 1962; FRCS Ed. 1946; FRFPS Glas. 1946. Hon. Cons. Surg. Glas. Roy. Infirm. Prev: Surg. i/c Unit for Peripheral Vasc. Surg., Glas. Roy. Infirm. & Belvidere Hosp.

REID, William Alexander Pathology Department, University of Edinburgh, Edinburgh EH8 2AG Email: sandy.reid@ed.ac.uk; 8 Strathfillan Road, Edinburgh EH9 2AG — MD 1988 Glas.; MB ChB Glas. 1972; MRCPath. 1980; Dip. Med. Ed. 1992. Sen. Lect. & Hon. Cons. Path. Univ. of Edin. Socs: Path. Soc.; Roy. Coll. Path. Prev: Lect. & Hon. Cons. Path. Univ. of Leeds; Lect. Univ. Glas.

REID, Mr William Henry 6 Sutherland Avenue, Glasgow G41 4JH Tel: 0141 427 1489 — MB ChB 1955 Glas.; FRCS Ed. 1959; FRFPS Glas. 1960; FRCS Eng. 1960. (Glas.) Vis. Prof. Bio-Engin. Strathclyde Univ. 1985; Cons. Plastic Surg. W. Scotl. Regional Plastic Surg. Serv.; Canniesburn Auxil. Hosp. Glas. Prev: Gen. Surg. Regist. Glas. Roy. Infirm.; Cas. Off. & Ho. Surg. W.. Infirm. Glas.; Ho. Phys. Roy. Alexandra Infirm. Paisley.

REID, William James 6 Barntongate Avenue, Edinburgh EH4 8BB — MB ChB 1977 Glas.; MRCP (UK) 1982.

REID-BRAIN, Hannah Euphemia (retired) c/o Mrs. C.L.D'Cruz, 37 Sarum Avenue, Melksham SN12 6BN Tel: 01225 703595 — MB BS 1929 Punjab. Prev: Orthop. Surg. Lady Harding Hosp., New Delhi.

REID MILLIGAN, David Alexander Wilson Forest Hall Medical Centre, Station Road, Forest Hall, Newcastle upon Tyne NE12 9BQ Tel: 0191 266 5823; Ovingham House, Main Road, Ovingham, Prudhoe NE42 6AG — MB ChB 1977 Dundee; MRCGP 1982.

REIDY, Anthony James The Surgery, Alexandra Road, Lowestoft NR32 1PL Tel: 01502 574524; 1 Church Lane, Swilland, Ipswich IP6 9NJ Tel: 01473 85716 — BM BS 1977 Nottm.; DRCOG 1983.

REIDY, John Quayside Medical Practice, 82-84 Strand Road, Londonderry BT48 7NN Tel: 028 7126 2790 Fax: 028 7137 3729 — LRCPI & LM, LRSCI & LM 1977; LRCPI & LM, LRCSI & LM 1977.

REIDY, John Francis Department of Radiology, Guy's Hospital, London SE1 9RT Tel: 020 7955 4117 Fax: 020 7955 4076 Email: john.reidy@gstt.sthames.nhs.uk; 19 Cumberland Street, London SW1V 4LS Tel: 020 7834 3021 — MB BS Lond. 1967; MRCS Eng. LRCP Lond. 1967; FRCP Lond. 1987; MRCP (UK) 1971; FRCR 1975; FFR 1974; DMRD Eng. 1972. (St. Geo.) Cons. Radiol. Guy's Hosp. Lond.; Hon. Sen. Lect. KCL; Hon. Cons. Radiol. Gt. Ormond St. Hosp. for Childr. Socs: Fell. (Treas.) Roy. Soc. Med. (Counc. Mem. Radiol. Sect.); Fell. Cardiovasc. & Interven. Soc. Europe. Prev: Lect. (Radiol. Teach. & Research) St. Geo. Hosp. Med. Sch. Lond.; Sen. Regist. (Radiol.) St. Geo. Hosp. Lond.; Vis. Asst. Prof. Bowman Gray Sch. Med. N. Carolina USA.

REIDY, Mr John Joseph Department of Surgery, Inverclyde Royal Hospital, Larkfield Road, Greenock PA16 0XN Tel: 01475 633777 Fax: 01475 656139 — MB BCh BAO 1981 NUI; MCh NUI 1992; FRCSI (Gen.) 1995; FRCSI 1986. (Univ. Coll. Cork) Cons. Surg. Inverclyde Roy. Hosp. NHS Trust; Hon. Clin. Sen. Lect. Univ. of Glas. Socs: Fell. Assn. Surgs.; Vasc. Surgic. Soc. GB & Irel. Prev: Sen. Regist. (Surg.) & Career Regist. W. Scotl. Higher Surg. Train. Scheme; Regist. Clin. Shock Study Gp. W.. Infirm. Glas.; Surg. Fell. Train. Rotat. Regional Hosp. Wilton Cork.

REIDY, Michael Basil Courtney (retired) Blounts, Vicarage Lane, Haslemere GU27 1LQ — BA Dub. 1953, MB BCh BAO 1955; MB BCH BAO Trinity College Dublin 1955. Clin. Asst. (Neurol.) Roy. Surrey Co. Hosp. Guildford; Res. Med. Off. Godwin Unit Haslemere Dist. Hosp. Prev: Med. Supt. Holy Cross Hosp. Haslemere.

REIDY, Michael Jason 14 Gallows Hill, Kings Langley WD4 8PQ — MB BS 1998 Lond.; MB BS Lond 1998.

REIDY, Richard Nicholas Desborough Avenue Surgery, 65 Desborough Avenue, High Wycombe HP11 2SD Tel: 01494 526006 Fax: 01494 473569; Woodbine Cottage, 81 Totteridge Lane, High Wycombe HP13 7QA Tel: 01494 527597 — MB BS 1977 Lond.

REIDY-BRADY, Nora Maria Ros Erne House, 8 Darling St., Enniskillen BT74 4TP — MB BCh BAO 1948 NUI.

REIFENBERG

REIFENBERG, Naomi Ann 22 St Leonard's Road, Bristol BS7 8SH — MB ChB 1990 Bristol. SHO (Anaesth.) ScarBoro. Hosp. Prev: Ho. Surg. ScarBoro. Hosp.; Ho. Phys. Worcester Roy. Infirm.

REIFF, Daniel Barnett Department of Radiology, Ashford Hospital, Ashford St Peters NHS Trust, London Road, Ashford TW15 3AA Tel: 01784 884552 Fax: 01784 884041; Stoneleigh, Acrefield Road, Gerrards Cross SL9 8NA Tel: 01753 884663 — MB ChB 1980 Cape Town; MRCP (UK) 1985; T(R) (CR) 1993; FRCR 1992. (Univ. Cape Town, S. Afr.) Cons. Radiol. Asford. Ashford St. Peter's NHS Trust. Socs: Amer. Roentgen Ray Soc.; RCR; BMA. Prev: Sen. Regist. & Regist. (Radiol.) St. Geo. Hosp. Lond.; Regist. (Med.) Hammersmith Hosp. Lond.

REILLY, Bernard Martin Aloysius Whitefriars Surgery, Whitefriars Street, Perth PH1 1PP Tel: 01738 625842 Fax: 01738 445030; 3 Tullylumb Terrace, Perth PH1 1BA Tel: 01738 643337 — MB ChB 1986 Aberd.; MRCGP 1990. Prev: GP Aberd.; Trainee GP/SHO Aberd. Hosps. VTS.

REILLY, Professor Charles Stewart Department of Surgical & Anaesthetic Sciences, University of Sheffield, Royal Hallamshire Hospital, Glossop Road, Sheffield S10 2JF Tel: 0114 271 2510 Fax: 0114 271 3771 Email: c.s.reilly@sheffield.ac.uk; 242 Millhouses Lane, Sheffield S11 9JA — MB ChB 1977 Glas.; MD Glas. 1989; FRCA 1982. Prof. of Anaesth. & Head of Div. of Surg. & Anaesth. Sci. Univ. Sheff.; Hon. Cons. Anaesth. Roy. Hallamsh. Hosp. Prev: Sen. Lect. & Head Dept. Anaesth. Univ. Sheff.

REILLY, David Glasgow Homoeopathic Hospital, 1053 Great Western Road, Glasgow G12 0XQ Tel: 0141 211 1621 Fax: 0141 211 1631 — MB ChB 1978 Glas.; FRCP Glas. 1993; MRCP Glas. 1981; FFHom RCP (UK) 1990, M 1983; MRCGP 1982. (Glas.) Cons. Phys. & Dir. Acad. Depts. Glas. Homoeop. Hosp.; Hon. Sen. Lect. (Clin. Med.) Univ. Dept. Med. Glas. Roy. Infirm. Socs: Brit. Soc. Med. & Dent. Hypn.; Brit. Med. Acupunct. Soc.; Fell. Fac. of Homeopathy. Prev: RCCM/MRC Fell.sh. Complementary Med. Dept. Med. Univ. Glas.; Sen. Regist. (Med.) Glas. Roy. Infirm.

REILLY, Mr David Tempest Wirral Hospital, Arrowe Park, Arrowe Park Road, Upton, Wirral CH49 5PE Tel: 0151 604 7054 Fax: 0151 604 1760 Email: reillydt@aol.com; 2 Upholland, New Hey Lane, Willaston, South Wirral CH64 2UU Tel: 0151 327 4668 — MB BChir 1972 Camb.; MD Leics. 1982; FRCS Eng. 1977; MRCS Eng. LRCP Lond. 1971. (St. Mary's Hosp. Lond.) Cons. Surg. Wirral Hosp. Merseyside. Socs: Eur. Soc. Vasc. Surg.; Vasc. Surg. Soc. GB & Irel.; Assn. Surg. Prev: Cons. Surg. Watford Gen. Hosp.; Sen. Regist. (Surg.) St. Mary's Hosp. Lond.; Research Fell. (Transpl. Surg.) Univ. Leicester.

REILLY, Desmond James (retired) 1 Castleton Drive, Newton Mearns, Glasgow G77 5JU Tel: 0141 639 8286 — MB ChB 1951 Glas.; DPH 1960; DPH 1960; FFPHM 1990; MFCM 1974; DIH St. And. 1966.

REILLY, Edwin Peter Young Peoples Centre, Mount Gould Hospital, Plymouth PL4 7QD — MB BS 1976 Lond.; DRCOG 1978. Staff Grade Psychiat., Young People's Centre, Mt. Gould Hosp. Prev: Princip. in Gen. Pract., Plymouth.

REILLY, Elizabeth Irene 2 Upholland, New Hey Lane, Willaston, South Wirral CH64 2UU Tel: 0151 327 4668 — MB BS 1971 Lond.; DCH Eng. 1973.

REILLY, Graham David St. Sampsons Surgery, Grandes Maisons Road, St Sampsons, Guernsey GY2 4; Cambrai, Le Bigard, Forest, Guernsey GY8 0HU — MB BChir 1978 Camb.; MA 1978, MB BChir Camb. 1978; MRCP (UK) 1981; DRCOG 1985. Prev: Regist. (Dermat.) Roy. Hallamsh. Hosp. Sheff.

REILLY, John Tennison 79 Devonshire Road, Dore, Sheffield S17 3NU Tel: 0114 236 6043 — MD 1986 Liverp.; BSc Biochem. Liverp. 1973, MB ChB 1976; FRCP (UK) 1996; MRCP (UK) 1980; FRCPath 1997; MRCPath 1987. Cons. Haemat. Roy. Hallamshire Hosp. Socs: BMA. Prev: Sen. Regist. (Haemat.) Roy. Liverp. Hosp.; Research Fell. (Haemat.) Roy. Liverp. Hosp.; Regist. (Haemat.) Roy. Liverp. Hosp.

REILLY, Joseph Gerard Parkside Community Mental Health Centre, Park Road N., Middlesbrough TS1 3LF Tel: 01642 230542 Fax: 01642 230542 — BM BS 1989 Nottm.; BMedSci Nottm. 1987; MRCPsych 1994; Dip. Med. Sci. Newc. 1995. Cons. (Adult Psychiat.) Tees and N. E. Yorks., NHS Trust; Lead Clinician for Research and Developm. Socs: Brit. Assn. Psychopharmacol. Prev: Sen. Regist. N. & Yorks. RHA; Research Regist. (Psychiat.) Roy. Vict. Infirm. Newc. u. Tyne; SHO Warlingham Pk. Hosp. Croydon.

REILLY, Margaret Catherine 34 King William Drive, Cheltenham GL53 7RP; 34 King William Drive, Cheltenham GL53 7RP. — MB BS 1984 Lond.

REILLY, Margaret Mary Hartland Way Surgery, 1 Hartland Road, Shirley, Croydon CR0 8RG Tel: 020 8777 7215 Fax: 020 8777 7648; 58 Barnmead Road, Beckenham BR3 1JE Tel: 020 8777 7215 — MB BCh BAO 1976 NUI; MRCGP 1981; DCH RCPSI 1980; DRCOG 1979. Socs: Croydon Medico-Legal Soc.

REILLY, Michael Patrick X-Ray Department, Altnagelvin Hospital, Londonderry BT47 6SB Tel: 01504 345171; 18 Palmerston Park, Londonderry BT47 6DJ — MB BCh BAO 1982 NUI; DMRD Aberd. 1988; FRCR 1988. Cons. Radiol. Altnagelvin Area Hosp. Prev: Sen. Regist. (Radiol.) Univ. Hosp. S. Manch.

REILLY, Paul Alexander Joseph Frimley Park Hospital, Portsmouth Road, Camberley GU16 7UJ Tel: 01276 604348 Fax: 01276 604846; Brackenwood, Hollybush Ride, Finchampstead, Wokingham RG40 3QP Tel: 01344 774028 Fax: 01344 774028 — MB ChB 1980 Aberd.; MRCP (UK) 1985; FRCP Ed. 1995; FRCP Glas. 1995; FRCP Lond. 1996. Cons. Rheum. Frimley Pk. NHS Trust Hosp. Camberley. Socs: Brit. Soc. Rheum.; Windsor Med. Soc. Prev: Sen, Regist. (Rheum. & Rehabil.) E. Dorset & Salisbury HA; Research Fell. (Rheum.) Monash Med. Centre Melbourne, Austral.; Regist. (Rheum.) Roy. Nat. Hosp. Rheum Dis. Bath.

REILLY, Peter Charles Gateacre Brow Surgery, 1 Gateacre Brow, Liverpool L25 3PA Tel: 0151 428 1851; 41 Park Road, Prescot L34 3LW Tel: 0151 430 6395 — MB ChB 1979 Liverp.; MRCGP 1987. GP Liverp. Prev: Ho. Off. Vict. Centr. Hosp. Wallasey; Trainee GP Whiston Hosp. VTS.

REILLY, Peter Gerard ENT Department, York District Hosptial, Wigginton Road, York YO31 8HE Tel: 01904 453900 Fax: 01904 453900 Email: pgr.york@virgin.net — MB BChir 1984 Camb.; BSc St. And. 1981; FRCS (Orl.) 1994; FRCS Ed. 1989. (cambridge) Cons. ENT Surg. York Dist. Hosp.; Cons. Ent Surg. Harrogate Dist. Hosp.. Prev: Sen. Regist. (ENT) Leicester Roy. Infirm.; Regist. (ENT) St. Bart. Hosp. Lond.; SHO (ENT) Qu. Med. Centre Nottm.

REILLY, Professor Philip Finaghy Health Centre, Department of General Practice, Queen's University, Dunluce Health Centre, Belfast BT9 7HR Tel: 028 9062 8211; 21 Wellington Park, Belfast BT9 6DL Tel: 01232 666023 — MB BCh BAO Belf. 1968; MD Belf. 1985; FRCGP 1986, M 1972. (Belf.) Prof. & Head of Dept. Qu. Univ. Belf. Socs: MICGP. Prev: UK Prescribing Fell. RCGP; Sen. Lect. (Gen. Pract.) Qu. Univ. Belf.; Lect. (Gen. Pract.) Univ. Liverp.

REILLY, Ruth Patricia Friary Surgery, Dobbin Lane, Armagh BT61 7QG Tel: 028 3752 3165 Fax: 028 3752 1514; 63 Main Street, Loughgall, Armagh BT61 8HZ — MB BCh BAO 1983 Belf.; DRCOG 1986.

REILLY, Sarah Jane Cambrai, Le Bigard, Forest GY8 0HU — MRCS Eng. LRCP Lond. 1985.

REILLY, Shaula Jane 70 Croydon Road, Reigate RH2 0NH — MB BS 1993 Lond.

REILLY, Sheena (retired) 24 Culme Road, Mannamead, Plymouth PL3 5BJ Tel: 01752664261 Email: she52edw@hotmail.com — MB BS 1976 Lond.; MB BS (Hons.) Lond. 1976; MSc (Hons.) Lond. 1979; FRCPath 1994, M 1982; Cert. Family Plann. JCC 1989. Prev: Cons. Med. Microbiol. Pub. Health Laborat. Serv. Plymouth.

REILLY, Sheila Mary 12 Papermill Road, Bromley Cross, Bolton BL7 9DF — MB ChB 1990 Leeds. Regist. (Paediat.) Mater Childr. Hosp. Prev: SHO (Paediat.) Bolton Gen. Hosp.; Trainee GP Hull HA VTS.

REILLY, Stephen Paul Bootham Park Hospital, York YO30 7BY Tel: 01904 610777 Fax: 01904 453794 — MB BS 1976 Lond.; MSc Manch. 1983; BSc (Hons.) Lond. 1973; MRCPsych 1982; 2000 FRCPsych. (Royal Free) Cons. Psychiat. (Psychother.) Bootham Pk. Hosp. York.; Sen. Clin. Lect. (Psychiat. & Behavioural Sc. in Relation to Med.) Univ. of Leeds Sch Med. Prev: Specialist Sen. Regist. (Psychother.) Manch. Roy. Infirm.; Psychiat. Heidelberg Clinic Melbourne, Austral.

REILLY, Tennison David (retired) Craigmin, Warren Road, Blundellsands, Liverpool L23 6 Tel: 0151 924 6464 — MB ChB 1950 Liverp. Prev: Ho. Surg. Liverp. Roy. Infirm.

REILLY, Terence Anthony Arthur Riversdale Surgery, Riversdale House, Merthyrmawr Road, Bridgend CF31 3NL Tel: 01656 766866

Fax: 01656 668659 — MB BCh 1969 Wales; FRCGP 1985, M 1973.

REILLY, Terence Michael c/o The Retreat Hospital, 107 Heslington Road, York YO10 5BN Tel: 01904 412551 Fax: 01904 430828 — MB ChB 1971 Glas.; MRCPsych 1975; DPM Eng. 1974; FRCPsych 1997. Cons. Psychiat. Retreat Hosp. York. Socs: FRSM; York Med. Soc.; BMA. Prev: Sen. Regist. Maudsley Hosp. Lond.; Sen. Regist. (Psychol. Med.) St. Mary's & Middlesex Hosp. Lond.; Regist. (Pyschiatry) Middlx. Hosp. Lond.

REILLY, Thomas, MC, KStJ (retired) Glenrig, Falkirk Road, Bonnybridge FK4 1BB Tel: 01324 812366 — MB ChB Glas. 1929. Prev: Regist. (Surg.) & Ho. Phys. Stobhill Hosp. Glas.

REILLY, Timothy Gilbert Glasgow Royal Infirmary, 16 Alexandra Parade, Glasgow G31 2ER Tel: 0141 211 4000 Fax: 0141 211 0468 Email: timreilly@clara.net; 1 May Terrace, Giffnock, Glasgow G46 6LD Tel: 0141 638 5769 Fax: 0141 638 5769 — MB ChB 1987 Bristol; MRCP (UK) 1992; MD Bristol 1998. (Bristol) Sen. Regist. (Gastroenterol.) Glas. Roy. Infirm. Socs: Brit. Soc. of Gastroenterol. Prev: Clin. Research Fell. (Gastroenterol.) Qu. Eliz. Hosp. Birm.; Regist. Rotat. (Med.) E. Birm.

REILY, Clive Michael The Health Centre, High Street, Bedworth, Nuneaton CV12 8NQ Tel: 024 7631 5827 Fax: 024 7631 0580 — MB BChir 1985 Camb.; MA Camb. 1985. (Cambridge University) Gen. Practitioner, Bedworh Health Centre; Clin. Asst. (Cardiol.) Geo. Eliot Hosp. Nuneaton. Prev: Regist. (Cardiol. & Gen. Med.) Walsgrave Hosp. Coventry.

REIMAN, Gunnar (retired) Saffron Lane Health Centre, 612 Saffron Lane, Leicester LE2 6TD Tel: 0116 291 1212 Fax: 0116 291 0300 — MB BS Lond. 1960; MRCS Eng. LRCP Lond. 1960; DObst RCOG 1962. Prev: SHO & Ho. Off. (Surg.) Leicester Roy. Infirm.

REIN, Howard Irving Village Surgery, Gillett Road, Talbot Village, Poole BH12 5BF Tel: 01202 525252 Fax: 01202 533956; Tel: 01202 514879 — MB ChB 1967 Leeds; DObst RCOG 1969. p/t Police Surg. Socs: Assn. Police Surg. Prev: Ho. Surg. (Obst.) Boscombe Hosp.

REINALD, Florian Nicolas Christian 112A West End Lane, London NW6 2LS — MB BS 1998 Lond.; MB BS Lond 1998.

REINBACH, Diana Helen Flat 2L, 26 Woodcroft Avenue, Glasgow G11 7HY Tel: 0141 334 0462 — MB BS 1983 Lond.; MS Lond. 1995; FRCS Eng. 1989; FRCS Ed. 1989. Higher Surg. Trainee W. Scotl. Surg. Train. Scheme. Prev: Research Regist. (Gastroenterol.) W.. Infirm. Glas.; Regist. (Surg.) W. Scotl. Train. Scheme Gtr. Glas. HB; SHO (Cas.) Chase Farm Hosp. Enfield.

REINDERS, Karel Stable Flat, Irton Manor, Moor Lane, Irton, Scarborough YO12 4RW — Artsexamen 1992 Amsterdam.

REINHARDT, Alistair Karl Centre For Respiratory Research, University College London, Rayne Institute, 5 University Street, London WC1E 6JJ Tel: 020 7679 6976, 0207 790 6418 Fax: 020 7679 6973 Email: a.reinhard@ucl.ac.uk, natwatt@fsmail.net — MB BChir 1993 Camb.; MB Camb. 1993.; MA (Hons.) Camb. 1993; MRCP (UK) 1995. Wellcome Trust Clin. Research Fell. Respirat. Med., Centre for Respirat. research, UCL Lond. Prev: SpR (Gen & Respirat. Med.) Roy. Lond. Hosp., Lond; Specialist Regist. (Gen. & Respirat. Med.) Broomfield Hospial Chelmsford Essex; Specialist Regist. (Gen. & Respirat. Med.) OldCh. Hosp.

REINHOLD, Piers Hayward Fakenham Medical Practice, The Fakenham Medical Centre, Greenway Lane, Fakenham NR21 8ET Tel: 01328 851321 Fax: 01328 851412; Holly Farm House, Wood Norton Road, Stibbard, Fakenham NR21 0EX Tel: 01328 829295 Fax: 01328 851412 Email: piersreinhold@hollyfm.force9.co.uk — MRCS Eng. LRCP Lond. 1970; MRCGP 1976; DObst RCOG 1975. (Guy's) Prev: SHO (Cas.) & Ho. Surg. (ENT) Guy's Hosp. Lond.; Med. Off. Brit. Milit. Hosp. Berlin.

REINSTEIN, Dan Zoltan 15 Sydney House, Woodstock Road, London W4 1DP Tel: 020 8994 2890 Fax: 020 8995 0915 Email: danreinstein@compuserve.com — MB BChir 1989 Camb.; MA Camb. 1988; FRCS (C). (Camb. Univ./ Univ. Coll. Lond. Medical School) Asst. Prof. of Ophth. Weill Med. Coll. Of Cosrell Univ. NY. USA; Professeur Associe Univ. de Paris France.

REIS, Julian Leonard (retired) 9 Combemartin Road, London SW18 5PP Tel: 020 8788 2462 — MD Lwow 1937; Med. Dip. 1934; DOMS Eng. 1948. Prev: SHO (Med.) W.. Ophth. Hosp. Lond.

REIS, Mrs Miriam (retired) 9 Combemartin Road, London SW18 5PP Tel: 020 8788 2462 — MD Lwow 1936.

REISER, Jan Lister Hospital, Corey's Mill Lane, Stevenage SG1 4AB Tel: 01438 781010 Email: dr.reiser@lister.org.uk; 24 Chiltern Road, Hitchin SG4 9PJ Tel: 01462 452765 Email: reiserjan@hoymail.com — MB BS 1975 Lond.; MD Lond. 1994; MRCP (UK) 1980; MRCS Eng. LRCP Lond. 1975; DCH Eng. 1978; FRCP (L) 1996; FRCPCH 1996. (Charing Cross Hospital London) Cons. Paediat. Lister Hosp. Stevenage. Socs: Brit. Paediat. Respirat. Soc.; Brit. Soc. Allergy & Clin. Immunol.

REISIG, Veronika Maria Theresia 44 Denholme Road, Oxenhope, Keighley BD22 9SJ — State Exam Med 1993 Marburg; MRCP (UK) 1996; MD Marburg 1994; MPH 1998. Specialist Regist. (Pub. Health Med.) N. & Yorks. Region.

REISLER, Ronald AVRO International Aerospace, Chester Road, Woodford, Stockport SK7 1QR Tel: 0161 955 4185 Fax: 0161 955 4101; 11 Wicker Lane, Hale Barns, Altrincham WA15 0HG Tel: 0161 980 2024 — MB ChB 1950 Leeds. (Leeds) Med. Examr. Min. of Aviat. CAA Lond., Federal Aviat. USA, Austral. CAA & Canad. CAA; Sen. Aviat. Med. Examr. Federal Aviat. Auth.; Med. Off. Monarch Airlines; Med. Off. Brit. Aerospace AVRO Internat. Aerospace Woodford; Med. Off. Air 2000 Manch. & Airtours Manch.; Med. Off. Flying Colours Manch. Prev: GP Stockport.

REISNER, Colin Queen's Hospital, Burton-on-Trent DE13 0RB Tel: 01283 566333 — MB BChir 1972 Camb.; FRCP Lond. 1989; MRCP (UK) 1974. (St. Bart.) Cons. Phys. (c/o Elderly) Burton Hosp. Prev: Cons. Phys. (Geriat. Med.) Lond. Hosp.; Hon. Sen. Regist. (Med.) St. Bart. Hosp. Lond.; Interne des Hôp. de Paris, France.

REISS, David Dept. of Forensic Psychiatry (023), Institute of Psychiatry, KCL, De Crespigny park, Demark Hill, London SE5 8AF Tel: 020 7919 3123 Fax: 020 7919 3754 Email: d.reiss@iop.kcl.ac.uk — 1988 BChir Camb.; MB 1987 Camb.; MPhil Lond. 1994; MA Camb. 1987; MRCPsych 1992; Dip. Forens. Psychiat. Lond. 1996. Director Teachg. unit, dept. of Forens. Psychiat., KCL; Hon. Cons. Forens. Psychiat., Maudsley Hosp. Socs: Roy. Soc. Med. Prev: Clin. Lect. (Victimoclgy & Forens. Psychiat.) Inst. Psychiat.; Sen. Regist. (Forens. Psychiat.) Bethlem Maudsley Hosp. Lond; Regist. Rotat. (Psychiat.) Roy. Free & Friern Hosp. Postgrad. Train. Scheme.

REISS, Herbert Erik (retired) 67 Eversden Road, Harlton, Cambridge CB3 7ET Tel: 01223 262375 — BM BCh 1948 Oxf.; MA, BM BCh Oxf. 1948; FRCOG 1967, M 1956. Hon. Cons. O & G Homerton Hosp. Lond.; Examr. Univ. Lond., RCOG & Centr. Midw. Bd. Prev: Sen. Lect. (O & G) Univ. Hong Kong.

REISS, Janet Elizabeth Department of Child Life & Health, University of Edinburgh, 20 Sylvan Place, Edinburgh EH9 1UW Tel: 0131 536 4350 Email: reissj@telemedicine.clh.ed.ac.uk; 53 McDonald Road, Edinburgh EH7 4LY Tel: 0131 556 7534 — MB ChB 1991 Ed.; BSc (Hons.) Med. Sci. Pharm. Ed. 1989; MRCP (UK) 1995. (Univ. Ed.) Research Fell. (Child Life & Health) Univ. Edin. Socs: Roy. Coll. Paediat. & Child Health; BMA; RCP Edin. Prev: SHO III (Paediat.) SE Scotl.; SHO (Paediat., Neonates & Med.) Lothian HB.

REISS, Mary Catherine — MB ChB 1988 Leeds; MRCOG 1998. Regist. Rotat. (O & G) N. & Yorks. RHA. Prev: SHO (O & G) Bradford, St. Jas. Hosp. Leeds & York Dist. Hosp.

REISS, Stefan Horatio 31 Hull Road, Cottingham HU16 4PN — MRCS Eng. LRCP Lond. 1976.

REISS, Stephen Butts New Sheepmarket Surgery, Ryhall Road, Stamford PE9 1YA Tel: 01780 758123 Fax: 01780 758102 — BM BS 1983 Nottm.; MRCP (UK) Paediat. 1987; MRCGP 1991; DRCOG 1986. Prev: Exchange Regist. Roy. Childr. Hosp. Melbourne, Australia.

REISSIS, Mr Nikolaos 31 Sandy Lodge Way, Northwood HA6 2AR Tel: 01923 841228 Fax: 01923 841228 Email: nreissis@globalnet.co.uk — Ptychio latrikes 1981 Thessaloniki; Europ Accredit Orthop Surg 1994. Cons. Orthop. Surg., Mt. Vernon & Watford NHS Trust.

REITANO, Teresa Medical Centre, 12 East King Street, Helensburgh G84 7QL Tel: 01436 673366 Fax: 01436 679715 — MB ChB 1992 Glas.

REITER, Marianne Eva Karoline Penralltwen Cross Inn, Llandysul SA44 6LX — State Exam Med. Freiburg 1987.

***REITH, Christina Alison** Lecropt House, Bridge of Allan, Stirling FK9 4NB — MB ChB 1998 Glas.; MB ChB Glas 1998; BSc 1995.

REITH

REITH, Hellen Lind (retired) 4 Kenfield Crescent, Aberdeen AB15 7UQ Tel: 01224 318530 — MB ChB 1938 Aberd.; FRCOG 1971, M 1951. Prev: Cons. O & G Co. Renfrew.;

REITH, Sheila Baillie Mackenzie Stirling Royal Infirmary, Stirling FK8 2AU Tel: 01786 434000 Fax: 01786 434467; Lecroft House, Lecroft, Bridge of Allan, Stirling FK9 4NB — MB BS 1962 Lond.; BSc (Hons.) Lond. 1959; FRCP Lond. 1990; FRCP Glas. 1983; MRCP Lond. 1965; FRCP Ed 1998. (Univ. Coll. Hosp.) Cons. Phys. Stirling Roy. Infirm.; Hon. Sen. Lect. Univ. Glas. Socs: Eur. Assn. for Study Diabetes; Caledonian Endocrine Soc. Prev: Cons. Phys. St. Jas. & St. Geo. Hosp. Lond.; Hon. Sen. Lect. St. Geo. Hosp. Med. Sch. Lond.; Regist. (Med.) Univ. Coll. Hosp. Lond.

REITH, William Westburn Medical Group, Foresterhill Health Centre, Westburn Road, Aberdeen AB25 2AY Tel: 01224 696848 Fax: 01224 696753; 54 Gray Street, Aberdeen AB10 6JE Tel: 01224 326380 Fax: 01224 322098 — MB ChB 1974 Ed.; BSc (Med. Sci.) Ed. 1971; FRCP Ed. 1994; FRCGP 1991, M 1978. (Ed.) Princip. in Gen. Pract.; Hon. Clin. Sen. Lect. Univ. Aberd. Socs: Hon. Sec. (Counc.) RCGP. Prev: Regional Adviser Gen. Pract. NE. Scotl.; Special Adviser (Primary Care) SCPMDE.

REIVE, Alyson Ronald Southside Surgery, 17 Bernard Terrace, Edinburgh EH8 9NU Tel: 0131 662 1633, 0131 667 2240 — MB ChB 1984 Ed.; MRCGP 1988; DCH RCPS Glas. 1987. GP Princip. S.side surgy Edin.; Clin. Asst., Cardiol., Roy. Infirm. of Edin. Prev: GP Retainer, Grange Med. Gp., Edin.; GP Dhaka Bangladesh.

REJ, Edward Priory Fields Surgery, Nursery Road, Huntingdon PE29 3RL Tel: 01480 52361 Fax: 01480 434640 — MB BS 1989 Lond.; MRCGP 1995.

REJALI, Mr Stephen Dariush 58 Craigton Drive, Newton Mearns, Glasgow G77 6TD Tel: 0141 639 5527 — MB ChB 1992 Manch.; BSc (Hons.) Immunol Experim Oncol, 1989; FRCS CSiG (Eng.) 1996; FRCS CSiG with Otolarying (Eng.) 1998. (Manchester) Regist. (OtoLaryngol.) Monklanh Hosp. Airdric. Socs: Manch. Med. Soc.; BAO - HNS; ORS. Prev: Hope Hosp. Sa ENT SHO; Manch. Roy. Infirm. Manch. ENT Gen. Surg.

REJMAN, Andrzej Stefan Miroslaw, OStJ Eileen House, 80 Newington Causeway, London SE1 6EF; 15 Selwyn Road, New Malden KT3 5AU Tel: 020 8942 1767 — MB BS 1976 Lond.; MD Lond. 1984; FRCP Lond. 1996; MRCP (UK) 1979; FRCPath 1996, M 1986. Sen. Med. Off. DOH & Hon. Cons. Haemat. St. Thos. Hosp. Lond.; Area Surg. St. John Ambul. SW Area Lond. Socs: Brit. Soc. Haematol.; Assn. Clin. Path. Prev: Lect. (Haemat.) Guy's Hosp. Med. Sch. Lond.; Research Fell. & Hon. Sen. Regist. Inst. Urol. Lond.; Hon. Sen. Regist. (Haemat.) St. Thos. Hosp. Lond. & Asst. Lect. (Path.) St. Thos. Hosp. Lond.

RELF, Christine Marjorie Trevithick Surgery, Basset Road, Camborne TR14 8TT Tel: 01209 716721 Fax: 01209 612488; Rosevale Farm, Kerris Paul, Penzance TR19 6UX Tel: Penzance 731724 — MB BChir 1970 Camb.; DObst RCOG 1972. (St. Geo.) Police Surg. Devon & Cornw. Constab. Socs: BMA. Prev: Med. Off. Sanaa, Yemen Arab Rep.; Med. Off. Ascension Is.; SHO N. Staffs. Matern. Hosp. Stoke.

RELTON, Peter George Sparks Chadwick House, 127 York Road, Hartlepool TS26 9DN Tel: 01429 234646 Fax: 01429 861559; Parkmead, Elwick Road, Hartlepool TS26 0DW Tel: 01429 273628 Fax: 01429 273628 — MB BS 1960 Lond. (Westm.) Prev: Ho. Surg. (Obst.) N. Middlx. Hosp. Lond.; Ho. Surg. & Cas. Off. W.m. Hosp.

REMBACKEN, Bjorn Joakim 15 Wayland Close, Adel, Leeds LS16 8LT — MB ChB 1987 Leic.; MRCP (UK) 1990.

REMBERG, Doerte Cornelia 14 Albert Road, West Kirby, Wirral CH48 0RS — MB ChB 1991 Liverp.

REMEH, Bashir Sayed 25 Pearson Road, Ipswich IP3 8NL — MB BCh 1991 Al Fateh, Libya; MRCP (UK) 1990.

REMFRY, Christopher John Charles Hadwen Medical Practice, Glevum Way Surgery, Abbeydale, Gloucester GL4 4BL Tel: 01452 529933; The Coach House, Tewkesbury Road, The Leigh, Gloucester GL19 4BP — MB BChir 1989 Camb.; MA Camb. 1992; MRCGP 1993; DCH RCP Lond. 1992.

REMFRY, Rita Mariaselvi Rosebank Surgery, 153B Stroud Road, Gloucester GL1 5JQ Tel: 01452 522767; Rosebank Surgery, 1538 Stroud Road, Gloucester GL1 5JQ Tel: 01452 522767 — MB ChB 1990 Glas.; MRCGP 1995; DRCOG 1994. (Glasgow University) Socs: RCGP; BMA; Fac. Fam. Plann. Prev: Clin. Asst. (Diabetes).

REMINGTON, George Arthur 41 Sunnyfield, Mill Hill, London NW7 4RD — MB BS 1976 Lond.; MSc Lond 1984; BSc (Pharmacol.) Lond. 1973, MB BS 1976; MFOM RCP Lond. 1990; AFOM RCP Lond. 1984. (Univ. Coll. Hosp.) Sen. Med. Advis. Marks & Spencer. Prev: SHO (Paediat.) N.wick Pk. Hosp. Harrow; Ho. Surg. Univ. Coll. Hosp.; Ho. Phys. Barnet Gen. Hosp.

REMINGTON, Kathryn Naomi 41 Sunnyfield, Mill Hill, London NW7 4RD — MB BS 1978 Lond.; BSc (Hons.) (Pharmacol.) Lond. 1973, MB BS 1978. (Roy. Free) Prev: Ho. Phys. Roy. Free Hosp. Lond.; SHO (Cas. & Orthop.) & Ho. Surg. Barnet Gen. Hosp.

REMINGTON, Shirley Ann Mary Barrfield, Prescot Road, Hale, Altrincham WA15 9PZ — MB ChB 1979 Manch.; BSc (Med. Sci.) St. And. 1976; MB ChB (Hons. & Distinc.) Manch. 1979; FFA RCS Eng. 1984.

RENBOURN, Edward Tobias 8 Garrick Way, Frimley Green, Camberley GU16 6LY — MRCS Eng. LRCP Lond. 1931; MD Lond. 1934, MB 1931; MRCP Lond. 1932.

RENDALL, Charles Mark Shuttleworth Giffords Surgery, 28 Lowbourne, Melksham SN12 7EA Tel: 01225 703370 — MB BS 1966 Lond.; MRCS Eng. LRCP Lond. 1966; DObst RCOG 1973; DA Eng. 1970. (St. Bart.) Prev: Surg. Lt. RN.

RENDALL, David Charles Shuttleworth (retired) 12 West Quay, Abingdon Marina, Abingdon OX14 5TL Tel: 01235 520389 — MRCS Eng. LRCP Lond. 1937. Prev: Surg. Lt.-Cdr. RNVR.

RENDALL, Jacqueline Carole 22 Circular Road, Newtownabbey BT37 0RF — MB BCh BAO 1993 Belf.

RENDALL, Joan (retired) Firle, Peaslake, Guildford GU5 9PA Tel: 01306 730630 — MB BS 1948 Lond.; MRCS Eng. LRCP Lond. 1947. Prev: Ho. Phys. Vict. Hosp. Sick Childr. Hull.

RENDALL, Jonathan Richard Shuttleworth Hereford County Hospital, Union Walk, Hereford HR1 2ER Tel: 01432 364132 — MB BS 1969 Lond.; FRCP Lond. 1989; MRCP (UK) 1972; MRCS Eng. LRCP Lond. 1969. (St. Bart.) Cons. Dermat. Hereford Hosps. NHS Trust.

RENDALL, Mr Max (retired) 4 Ladbroke Square, London W11 3LX Tel: 020 7221 4878 — MB BChir 1960 Camb.; BA Camb. 1960; FRCS Eng. 1964; MRCS Eng. LRCP Lond. 1959. Prev: Clin. Supt. & Cons. Surg. Guy's Hosp. Lond.

RENDEL, Susan Elizabeth Halstead St Johns Road Surgery, 10 St. Johns Road, Newbury RG14 7LX Tel: 01635 40160 — MB BS 1975 Lond.; BA (Hons.) Oxf. 1972; MRCP (UK) 1978; DRCOG 1977.

RENDELL, Christine Muriel (retired) 1 The Crossway, Mottingham, London SE9 4JJ Tel: 020 8857 4071 — MB ChB Bristol 1941; FFA RCS Eng. 1954; DA Eng. 1943.

RENDELL, Jean Angus (retired) 88 Abbey Meadows, Kirkhill, Morpeth NE61 2YA Tel: 01670 514922 — MB BS Durh. 1945; DObst RCOG 1948. Prev: SCMO N. Tyneside HA.

RENDER, Christina Anne (retired) 7 Speckled Wood Road, Sherborne St John, Basingstoke RG24 9SR — MB ChB 1984 Ed.; FRCA 1993. Sen. Regist. (Anaesth.) Wessex Region. Prev: Regist. (Anaesth.) St. Geo. Hosp. Lond.

RENDLE, Derek Ernest Estover, Brynhafod, Cardigan SA43 1NS — MB BS 1956 Lond.; DA Eng. 1963; DObst. RCOG 1963. (St. Thos.)

RENE, Mr Cornelius Hinchinbrooke Hospital, Hinchinbrooke Park, Huntingdon PE29 6NT Tel: 01480 416561 — MB BS 1985 Lond.; FRCOphth 1992. (Middlesex Hospital Medical School) Cons. Ophth., Hinchinbrooke Hosp., Huntingdon; Cons. Ophth., Addenbrookes Hosp. Camb. Socs: BMA; British Oculoplastic Surgery Society; Fellow Royal Colege Of Ophthalmologists. Prev: Fell. Ocular Adnexal Surg., Moorfields EH, Lond.; Fell. In Ocular Adnexal Surg., Qu.s MC, Nottm.; Sen. Reg, Ophth., W Midl.s Rotat.

RENEHAN, Andrew Gerard 1 The Willows, Chorltonville, Manchester M21 8FQ — MB ChB 1995 Manch.; BDentSc. Dub. 1986; FDS RCS Ed. 1989; FRCS Eng. 1997. (Manch.) Research Fell. PhD Stud., Cheiste Hosp. Manch. Socs: Dent. Fell. RCS Edin.; Assn. of Colopeochology of GB & Ire (Assoc. Mem); Fell. Roy. Coll. Surg Eng (Gen. Surg.). Prev: research fell., Cheiste Hosp. Manch.; SHO Rotat. (Gen. Surg.) S. Manch.; Ho. Off. (Med. & Surg.) Withington Hosp. Manch.

RENFREW, Anne Catherine 27B The Gables, Haddenham, Aylesbury HP17 8AD — MB ChB 1975 Glas.; MRCOG 1981.

RENFREW, Christopher Charles Hermes Lodge, Bredons Norton, Tewkesbury GL20 7EZ — MB BS 1983 Lond.; MRCGP 1995; DRCOG 1986. (Roy. Free) Managing Dir. Montpellier Health Care Ltd. Cheltenham. Prev: Trainee GP Tewkesbury.

RENFREW, Craig William 2 Cherryvalley Gardens, Belfast BT5 6PQ — MB BCh BAO 1990 Belf.; FRCA 1994.

RENFREW, Dawn Margaret Burnhead Frm., Netherburn, Larkhall ML9 3DQ — MB ChB 1989 Ed.

RENFREW, Ian 112A Agar Grove, London NW1 9TY — MB BS 1994 Lond.

RENFREW, Margaret Addie East Lodge, Barnhill, Perth PH2 7AT Tel: 01738 21097 — MB ChB Glas. 1958; Mem. BMA. Prev: Ho. Surg. Greenock Roy. Infirm.; Ho. Phys. Larkfield Hosp. Greenock; Regist. Anaesth. Roy. Halifax Infirm.

RENFREW, Stewart (retired) 3 Heiton Park, Darnick by Melrose, Melrose TD6 9AU — MB ChB 1940 Glas.; BSc Glas. 1937; FRCP Lond. 1967, M 1945.

RENGAN, Mr Dhanakodi Chettiar No. 5 Sandiway, Chesterfield S40 3HG — MB BS 1983 Madras; FRCS Glas. 1989.

RENKEMA, Saskia Eva Blackthorn Medical Centre, St Andrews Road, Barming, Maidstone ME16 9AL — Artsexamen Utrecht 1989; DRCOG 1994. GP Maidstone Retainer Scheme.

RENNER, Norren Edward Awunor (retired) 13 Dalmeny Court, Duke St., St James's, London SW1 6BL — MB ChB 1949 Ed.; DO Eng. 1956; FDS RCS Eng. 1970, L 1965.

RENNER, Suzanne Louise Shipley Hill Farmhouse, Alnwick NE66 2LX — MB BS 1997 Newc.

RENNICK, Charles Burridge (retired) 8 Longbank Drive, Ayr KA7 4SB Tel: 01292 266458 — MB ChB 1953 Glas.; MRCGP 1976; DObst RCOG 1957. Prev: GP Ayr.

RENNICK, Michael John 44 Brixworth Way, Retford DN22 6TT — MB ChB 1993 Glas.

RENNIE, Agnes Lees 23 Lady Jane Gate, Bothwell, Glasgow G71 8BW — MB ChB 1968 Glas.; FFA RCS Eng. 1974; DA Eng. 1971; DObst RCOG 1970. Cons. Anaesth. Monklands Dist. Hosp. Prev: Cons. (Anaesth.) Rutherglen Matern. Hosp. & Vict. Infirm. Glas.; Sen. Regist. (Anaesth.) Dundee Teachg. Hosps.; Regist. (Anaesth.) Vict. Infirm. Glas.

RENNIE, Alan Nisbet Thornliebank Health Centre, Glasgow G46 8HY Tel: 0141 620 2222 Fax: 0141 638 7554; Glebe Capel, Newton Mearns, Glasgow G77 6JW Tel: 0141 639 5071 — MB ChB 1965 Glas.; MRCGP 1977; DObst RCOG 1967. Socs: BMA. Prev: Ho. Surg. Glas. Roy. Infirm.; Ho. Phys. Vict. Infirm. Glas.; Ho. Surg. Glas. Roy. Matern. & Wom. Hosp.

RENNIE, Mr Alexander Milne (retired) Place of Bridgefoot, Caskieben, Kinellar, Aberdeen AB21 0SY Tel: 0122 479273 — MB ChB 1933 Aberd.; MB ChB (Hnrs.) Aberd. 1933; FRCS Eng. 1937; FRCS Ed. 1959. Prev: Sen. Cons. (Orthop. Surg.) Min. Health Kuwait.

RENNIE, Alexander Stark 8 Douglas Tower, Regents Gate, Bothwell, Glasgow G71 8QU Tel: 0141 817351 — MB ChB 1940 Glas. (Glas.)

RENNIE, Alison Cunningham Dr Alison Rennie, Consultant Paediatrician, Southbank Child Centre, 207 Old Rutherglen Rd, Glasgow G5 0RE Tel: 0141 201 0908 — MB ChB 1989 Dundee; MRCP (UK) 1993; MRCPCH founder. Roy. Hosp. Sick Childr. Glas. Socs: Roy. Coll. Paediat. & Child Health.

RENNIE, Mr Alistair George Robert (retired) Altacraig, 26 Leighton Gardens, Ellon AB41 9BH Tel: 01358 720442 Fax: 01358 725236 — MB ChB 1966 Glas.; FRCS Ed. 1977; FCOphth 1989. Cons. Ophth. S. Grampian (Aberd.) Health Dist. Prev: Med. Off. Malaita Brit. Solomon Isls.

RENNIE, Andrew Robertson (retired) 20 Roman Road, Ayr KA7 3SZ — MB ChB 1941 Glas.; BSc Glas. 1938; DPM Eng. 1969. Prev: Assoc. Specialist (Psychiat.) Ailsa Hosp. Ayr.

RENNIE, Mr Christopher Douglas Droitwich Private Hospital, St. Andrews Road, Droitwich WR9 8DN Tel: 01905 794793; Copcot House, Salwarpe, Droitwich WR9 7JB Tel: 01905 796798 Fax: 01905 796772 — MB ChB 1972 Birm.; BSc (Hons.) (Anat.) Birm. 1969; FRCS Eng. 1977. Cons. Urol. Alexandra NHS Health Trust. Prev: Sen. Regist. Qu. Eliz. Hosp. Birm. & St. Peters Hosps. Lond.; Regist. N.wick Pk. Hosp. Harrow.

RENNIE, Elizabeth Medico-Legal Centre, Watery St., Sheffield S3 7ES Tel: 0114 273 8721; 23 Ashdell Road, Broomhill, Sheffield S10 3DA Tel: 0114 367 6304 — MB ChB 1977 Sheff.; Cert. Family Plann. JCC 1986; LLB Sheff. 1998. (Sheffield) Police Surg. S. Yorks. Police; Ext. Lect. (Anat.) Sheff. Hallam Univ.; Ext. Lect. (Med. Law) Sheff. Univ. Socs: Assn. Police Surg.; S. Yorksh. Medico-Legal Soc. Prev: Lect. (Anat.) Univ. Sheff.

RENNIE, Fay Margaret (retired) 65 Friary Park, Ballabeg, Castletown IM9 4EP — MB ChB St. And. 1952; MRCOG 1961. Prev: Cas. Off. Nobles. Hosp. Douglas Isle of Man.

RENNIE, Gordon Grant (retired) 48 Station Road, Carluke ML8 5AD Tel: 01555 771361 — MB ChB Aberd. 1953. Prev: Cons. Anaesth. Lanark Area HB.

RENNIE, Ian George 33 Shrublands Road, Berkhamsted HP4 3HX Tel: 0144 286 6016 — MRCS Eng. LRCP Lond. 1968; DIH Eng. 1981; FFOM RCP Lond. 1992, MFOM 1984; DObst RCOG 1969. Chief Med. Off. Kodak Ltd. Socs: Fell. Roy. Soc. Med.; BMA. Prev: Sen. Med. Off. Lucas CAV; Med. Off. Lucas Aerospace, Lucas CAV & Lucas Elec. Companies; Trainee GP Newport Isle of Wight.

RENNIE, Professor Ian George Department Ophthalmology and Orthoptics, University of Sheffield, Glossop Road, Royal Hallamshire Hospital, Sheffield S10 2JF Tel: 0114 276 6222 Fax: 0114 276 6381; Church Lane House, Litton, Buxton SK17 8QU Tel: 01298 871586 — MB ChB 1976 Sheff.; FRCS Ed. 1981; FCOphth 1989. Prof. Ophth. Univ. Sheff.; Edr. Oxf. Congr..; Hon. Cons. Ophth. Roy. Hallamsh. Hosp., Sheff.; Edr. Eye. Socs: Sen. Vice Pres. Roy. Coll. of Opthalmologists.

RENNIE, Ian Michael 16 Crawfordsburn Road, Bangor BT19 1BE — MB BCh BAO 1994 Belf.

RENNIE, Janet Mary 4th Floor Ruskin Wing, King's College Hospital, Denmark Hill, London SE5 9RS Tel: 020 7737 4000 Ext: 4344 Fax: 020 7582 8353 Email: janet.rennie@kcl.ac.uk — MB ChB Sheffield 1978; MA Cambridge 1994; MD Sheffield 1986; FRCP Lond 1994; MRCP (UK) 1981; DCH RCP Lond 1982; FRCPCH 1993. (Sheffield) p/t Cons. Neonat. Med. King's Coll. Hosp. Lond.; Chair CSAC, RCPCH, Acad. Bd. RCPCH. Socs: Neonat. Soc. (Comm. Mem.); Brit. Med. Ultrasound Soc.; Brit. Assn. Perinatal Med. Prev: Cons. Neonat. Med. Rosie Matern. Hosp. Camb.; Research Fell. (Neonat. Med.) Univ. Liverp.; Lect. (Paediat.) Univ. Camb.

RENNIE, Jean Ann The Kitchen, Cullen House, Cullen, Buckie AB56 4XW — MB ChB 1965 St. And.; DObst RCOG 1976. Self-Employed GP Non-Princip. Socs: BMA; Med. Wom. Federat.; Roy. Soc. Med. Prev: SHO Elsie Inglis Memor. Matern. Hosp. Edin.; Ho. Surg. (Gyn.) & Ho. Phys. Bruntsfield Hosp. Edin.

RENNIE, Jean Gibson (retired) Penchrise Peel, Hawick TD9 9UA Tel: 01450 375076 — MB ChB 1958 Glas.; MRCGP 1974. Prev: GP Gulla. E. Lothian.

RENNIE, Mr John Aubery 94 Burbage Road, London SE24 9HE Tel: 020 7274 0233 — MRCS Eng. LRCP Lond. 1970; MS Lond. 1984, MB BS 1970; FRCS Eng. 1975; DTM & H Liverp. 1974. (St. Bart.) Sen. Lect. & Hon. Cons. Surg. King's Coll. Hosp. Lond. Socs: Fell. Roy. Soc. Med. (Surg. & Coloproctocolectmy Sect.); Assn. Surgs. Prev: Lect. Char. Cross. Hosp. Lond.; Regist. St. Mark's Hosp. Dis. Colon & Rectum Lond. & Duncan Hosp.; Raxaul, India.

RENNIE, Kathleen Mary (retired) Westleigh Park View, Arrow, Alcester B49 5PN Tel: 01789 764160 — MB ChB 1943 Birm. Prev: Ho. Phys. Qu. Eliz. Hosp. Birm.

RENNIE, Louise Morag 192/3 Causewayside, Edinburgh EH9 1PN — MB ChB 1998 Ed.; MB ChB Ed 1998.

RENNIE, Mary (retired) 25 St Margaret's Road, Ruislip HA4 7NX Tel: 01895 639700 — MB ChB 1938 St. And.; MB ChB (Commend.) St. And. 1938, DPH 1940; DCH Eng. 1955. Prev: Asst. MOH (Matern. & Child. Welf.) Sheff.

RENNIE, Morag Lilian (retired) 48 Station Road, Carluke ML8 5AD Tel: 01555 771361 — MB ChB 1968 Glas.; FRCPsych 1996, M 1974; DPM Eng. 1972. Cons. Psychiat. & Psychiat. of Old Age Law Hosp. Lanarksh. Prev: Cons. Psychiat. Hartwood Hosp. Shotts.

RENNIE, Nichola Jane 15A Carlton Terrace, Edinburgh EH7 5DD — MB ChB 1989 Ed.

RENNIE, Peter Robertson Idle Medical Centre, 440 Highfield ROAd, Idle, Bradford BD10 8RU Tel: 01274 771999 Fax: 01274 772001; 23 Cleasby Road, Menston, Ilkley LS29 6JE Tel: 01943 874943 — MB ChB 1971 Ed.

RENNIE, Robert Alexander Jenner Health Centre, Turners Lane, Whittlesey, Peterborough PE7 1EJ Tel: 01733 203601 Fax: 01733

RENNIE

206210 — BSc (Hons. Anat.) Manch. 1965, MB ChB 1968; DObst RCOG 1971; DCH RCPS Glas. 1970.

RENNIE, Sandra Mary 28 Southey Street, Keswick CA12 4EF — MB ChB 1996 Ed.

RENNISON, John Neal Royal Devon and Exeter Hospital, (Heavitree), Gladstone Road, Exeter EX1 2ED Tel: 01392 405052 — MB ChB 1985 Manch.; MRCOG 1991; DA (UK) 1990. Cons. Roy. Devon & Exeter NHS Trust.

RENNISON, Claire Marie 1 Rothley Avenue, Ashington NE63 0LG — MB ChB 1998 Dund.; MB ChB Dund 1998.

RENNY, Francis Hugh Blakiston Shirley House, 186 Bridgnorth Road, Wollaston, Stourbridge DY8 3PN Tel: 0138 43 77257 — MB ChB 1969 Birm.; FRCR 1978; DMRD Eng 1977. Cons. Radiol. Dudley AHA.

RENNY, Mr Nicholas Michael Charles Dept. Maxillofacial surgery, Aberdeen Royal Infirmary, Foresterhill, Aberdeen AB25 2ZN Tel: 01330 860859 Fax: 01224 840925; Skene House, Lyne of Skene, Skene AB32 7BQ Tel: 01330 860859 Fax: 01330 860859 — MB BS 1988 Lond.; BDS Ed. 1981; FDS RCS Eng. 1990; FRCS Ed. 1991. (Charing Cross and Westminster) Head of Serv., Cons. & Hon. Sen.Lect. Oral & Maxillofacial Surg. Aberd.; Hon. Sen. Lect. Aberd. Univ. Socs: Fell. Brit. Assn. Oral & Maxillofacial Surg.; Craniofacial Soc. Prev: Sen. Regist. (Oral & Maxillofacial Surg.) N.. Region.; Regist. (Oral & Maxillofacial Surg.) Lothian & Borders HB; Regist. (Gen. Surg.) Roy. Infirm. Edin.

RENOUF, Adrian Charles Dominic Chapel Platt Surgery, 1901 Fore Street, Topsham, Exeter EX3 0HE Tel: 01392 875777 Fax: 01392 875777; Court Dairy Farm, Clyst St. George, Exeter EX3 0NP Tel: 01392 874854 — MB BS 1978 Lond.; MRCS Eng. LRCP Lond. 1978; DRCOG 1986. (St. Bart.) Princip. GP Clin. Asst. Cardiol. Dept. RD&E Exeter. Prev: Surg. Lt. RN. SMO D5.

RENSHAW, Anthony John Neil Werneth, 31 The Baulk, Worksop S81 0HU Tel: 01909 500990 — MRCS Eng. LRCP Lond. 1973; FFA RCS Eng. 1977. (Guy's) Cons. Anaesth. Bassetlaw Hosp. & Community Servs. NHS Trust. Socs: Obst. Anaesth. Assn.; Assn. Anaesth. Prev: Cons. Anaesth. Worksop & Retford Dist.; Sen. Regist. & Regist. (Anaesth.) Roy. Infirm. Edin.; SHO (Anaesth.) Salisbury Hosp. Gp.

RENSHAW, Joanne Claire 13 Rosemount Road, Alum Chine, Bournemouth BH4 8HB — MB ChB 1986 Birm.; MRCP 1991; DCH RCP 1990 Lond.; DRCOG 1989. Sen. Regis. Poole Hosp. NHS Trust, Cons., Paediat., Poole Hosp. NHS Trust. Socs: Roy. Coll. of Paedaitrisce Child Health. Prev: Sen. Regist. United Bristol Healthcare Trust; Regist. (Paediat.) Mersey RHA Liverp.

RENSHAW, Neil David Felixstowe Road Surgery, 235 Felixstowe Road, Ipswich IP3 9BN Tel: 01473 719112; 14 Glemham Drive, Rushmere, Ipswich IP4 5BH Tel: 01473 716357 — MB BS 1988 Lond.; BSc Lond. 1985; MRCGP 1992; DCH RCP Lond. 1992; DRCOG 1990. Prev: Trainee GP/SHO Ipswich VTS.

RENSHAW, Piers Robin 30 Thomson Street, Aberdeen AB25 2QQ — MB ChB 1991 Aberd.

RENSHAW, Stephanie Barbara Helen Dumbarton Health Centre, Station Road, Dumbarton G82 1PW Tel: 01389 602633 Fax: 10289 602623; Helenslee, 21 Suffolk St, Helensburgh G84 9PB Tel: 01436 74076 — MB ChB 1973 Manch.; DObst RCOG 1976. Prev: Trainee GP Helensburgh.

RENSHAW, Stephen Andrew 17 Marshall Drive, Bramcote, Nottingham NG9 3LE Tel: 0115 939 6760 — BM BCh 1994 Oxf.; MA Camb. 1994; MRCP (UK) 1997. Research Fell. (Molecular & Genetic Med.) Univ. of Sheff. Prev: Specialist Regist. (Respirat. Med.) RHH Sheff.; SHO (Med.) QMC Nottm.; SHO (Med.) Burton Hosp. Burton-on-Trent.

RENSHAW, Veronique (retired) — MD 1973 Bordeaux; CPEBH 1975; CES 1977. Cons. Anaesth. Furness Gen. Hosp. Barrow-in-Furness. Prev: Cons. Anaesth. C H Lourdes France.

RENTERIA, Nagore 9 Sherwood Court, High Road, Leavesden, Watford WD25 7PA — LMS 1994 Basque Provinces.

RENTON, Mr Charles James Crawford (retired) Mavis Holt, 35 Hampton Park Road, Hereford HR1 1TH Tel: 01432 268079 — MB ChB 1953 Glas.; FRCS Ed. 1958; FRFPS Glas. 1960; FRCS Eng. 1960. Cons. Surg. Co. Hosp. Hereford. Prev: Sen. Regist. (Surg.) Roy. Hosp. Sheff. & Hon. Clin. Tutor (Surg.) Univ. Sheff.

RENTON, Margaret Grant Mavis Holt, 35 Hampton Park Road, Hereford HR1 1TH — MB ChB 1955 Glas.; DObst RCOG 1958. (Glas.)

RENTON, Mary Collette Blaise Leah Islington Square Surgery, 3 Islington Square, Liverpool L3 8DD Tel: 0151 207 0848 — BM BCh 1975 Oxf.; BA Oxf. 1972, BM BCh 1975.

RENTON, Morag Carol Top Floor Right, 9 Viewforth, Bruntsfield, Edinburgh EH10 4JD — MB ChB 1992 Ed.

RENTON, Nicholas James Petersfield Hospital, Petersfield GU32 3LB Tel: 01730 263221 Fax: 01730 268218; St James' Hospital, Locksway Road, Portsmouth PO4 8LD Tel: 01705 822331 — MB BS Lond. 1970; MRCS Eng. LRCP Lond. 1970; MRCPsych 1976; FRCPsych 1997. (St Bartholomews Hospital) Cons. Psychiat. Portsmouth & S.E. Hants. HA.

RENTON, Peter 52 Ossulton Way, London N2 0LB — MB BS 1967 Lond.; MRCS Eng. LRCP Lond. 1967; FFR 1973; DMRD Eng. 1971. (King's Coll. Hosp.) Cons. Radiol. Univ. Coll. Hosp., Hosp. Trop. Dis. & Roy. Nat. Orthop. Hosp. Lond. Prev: Cons. Radiol. N.wick Pk. Hosp. Harrow; Sen. Regist. (Diag. Radiol.) St. Marks Hosp. Lond. & Hosp. Sick; Childr. Gt. Ormond St.

RENTON, Peter Heap (retired) Green Oaks, Chapel Road, Alderley Edge SK9 7DX Tel: 01625 583225 — MD 1949 Manch.; BSc Manch. 1940, MD 1949, MB ChB 1943; FRCPath 1964. Dep. Dir. Regional Blood Transfus. Centre Manch.

RENTON, Sophie Caroline Northwick Park Hosptial, Harrow HA1 3UJ Tel: 020 8864 3232 Fax: 020 8869 2571; 4 Somerset Road, London W13 9PB Tel: 020 8810 1473 Email: sophierenton@jahoo.co.uk — MB BS 1983 Lond.; MS Lond. 1994; FRCS (Gen.) 1996; FRCS Eng. 1988. Cons. Gen. Surg. & Vasc. Surg. N.wick Pk. Hosp. Harrow. Prev: Sen. Regist. St. Mary's, Hammersmith & Allied Hosps.; Career Regist. SW Thames; Research Fell. (Vasc. Surg.) E.cott St. Mary's Hosp. Med. Sch. Lond.

RENTOUL, James Woods (retired) Pine Cottage, 36 Fore St., Tregony, Truro TR2 5RN Tel: 0187 253233 — MRCS Eng. LRCP Lond. 1952. Prev: RAMC.

RENTOUL, Jocelyn Roelanda 25 Lawmarnock Crescent, Bridge of Weir PA11 3AS — MB ChB 1971 Glas. Socs: Soc. Occupat. Med. Prev: Regist. (Dermat.) W.. Infirm. Glas.; SHO (Dermat.) Vict. Infirm. Glas.; SHO (Dermat.) S.. Gen. Hosp. Glas.

RENVOIZE, Edward Bernard Lytham Hostpial, Warton St., Lytham, Lytham St Annes FY8 5EE — MB ChB 1971 Ed.; MB Ed. 1983, MB ChB 1971; FRCPsych 1996, M 1976; MFPHM RCP 1991; MPH Leeds 1988; DPM Leeds 1975. (Ed.) Cons. Psychiat. (Old Age Psych.) & Dir. Research & Developm., Blackpool Wyre & Fylde Comm. Health Servs. NHS Trust. Prev: Cons. in Clin. Audit, Leeds Gen. Inf.; Cons. Psych. Bootham Pk. Hosp. York.

RENWICK, Alexander Colquhoun Remore, Low Causeway, Culross, Dunfermline KY12 8HL Tel: 013830 880256 — MB ChB 1968 Glas.; DObst RCOG 1970. (Glas.)

RENWICK, Amanda Claire 7 Saracens Road, Chandlers Ford, Southampton SO53 2NT — MB ChB 1997 Birm; ChB Birm 1997.

RENWICK, Mr Andrew Austin Rookesbury, Findhorn Road, Forres IV36 3TR Tel: 01309 674046; 111 Balshagray Avenue, Jordanhill, Glasgow G11 7EG Tel: 0141 959 6809 — MB ChB 1991 Aberd.; FRCS Glas. 1995; FRCS Ed. 1995. Specialist Regist. Dept. of Gen. Surg.; Fell. Surg. RCP Surg. Glas. Coll. Counc. Socs: Med. & Defence Union Scotl.; BMA; RCPS Glas. (Counc.lor). Prev: CrossHo. Hosp. Kilmarnock; Monklands Hosp. Airdrie; Stirling Roy. Inf.

RENWICK, Caroline Joy Casse Airthrey Park Medical Centre, Hermitage Road, Stirling University, Stirling FK9 4NJ Tel: 01786 463831 Fax: 01786 447482; 3 The Yetts, Cambusbarron, Stirling FK7 9NJ Tel: 01786 461930 — MB ChB 1969 Ed.; MFFP 1992. (Ed.) Sen. Clin. Med. Off. (Family Plann. Servs.) Forth Valley HB.; Med. Off. (Family Plann. Servs.) HM Cornston Vale Inst. Prev: Clin. Asst. (Genitourin. Med.) Forth Valley HB; SHO (O & G) Simpson Memor. Matern. Pavil. & Roy. Infirm. Edin.; SHO (Paediat.) N.ampton Gen. Hosp.

RENWICK, Claire Alison 7 Holly Park, Huby, Leeds LS17 0BT — MB ChB 1989 Ed.

RENWICK, Colin Jeffrey Townhead Surgeries, Townhead, Settle BD24 9JA Tel: 01729 822611 Fax: 01729 892916 — MB ChB 1986 Leeds; MRCGP 1990; DGM RCP Lond. 1992.

RENWICK, Deborah Susan Department of Medicine for the Elderly, St. James's Hospital, Leeds; 83 Blackmoor Court, Alwoodley,

Leeds LS17 7RT — MB ChB 1987 Ed.; BSc (Med. Sci.) Ed. 1985, MB ChB 1987; MRCP (UK) 1990. Sen. Regist. (Med. & Med. for Elderly) Yorks. RHA. Socs: BMA & Brit. Geriat. Soc.

RENWICK, George Kerr 5 Roundwood Road, Baildon, Shipley BD17 7JZ — MRCS Eng. LRCP Lond. 1961. (W. Lond.) Sir Titus Salt's Hosp. Shipley. Prev: Ho. Phys. & Ho. Surg. Joyce Green Hosp. Dartford; Ho. Surg. N. Herts. & S. Beds. Hosp. Hitchin.

RENWICK, Jacqueline Rose Harlosh, Albert Hill, Settle BD24 9HE — MB ChB 1986 Leeds.

RENWICK, Jill Andrae Claughton Medical Centre, 161 Park Road North, Birkenhead CH41 0DD Tel: 0151 652 1688 Fax: 0151 670 0565; 5 Howbeck Road, Oxton, Prenton CH43 6TD Tel: 0151 652 7306 — MB ChB 1977 Liverp.; DRCOG 1980. (Liverp.) Clin. Asst. Wirral Drug Unit St. Catherines Hosp., Wirral. Socs: BMA.

RENWICK, Margaret Ivy (retired) 1 West Burnbank, Greenhaugh, Tarsat, Hexham NE48 1LY — MB BS 1939 Durh.

RENWICK, Mr Paul Malcolm 10 Glencoe Street, Anlaby Road, Hull HU3 6HS — BM BS 1983 Nottm.; FRCS Ed. 1992. Sen. Regist. (Vasc. Surg.) St. Jas. Univ. Hosp. Leeds. Prev: Career Regist. (Gen. Surg.) Scunthorpe Gen. Hosp.; Regist. (Gen. Surg.) Grimsby Dist. Gen. Hosp.; Regist. (Gen. & Vasc. Surg.) Hull Roy. Infirm.

RENWICK, Sally Jane Thorns, Cuddington Way, South Cheam SM2 7JE Email: milesrenwick@barclays.net — MB BS 1991 Lond.; DA (UK) 1994; FRCA (UK) 1997. (St George's Hospital Medical School London) Cons. Anaesth. Epsom & St Helier NHS Trust. Socs: Roy. Coll. of Anaethetists; Assoc. of Anaethetists; Obstetris Anaesth.s Assoc. Prev: Specialist Regist., (Anaesth./PICU), St Geo.'s Hosp.Lond; Specialist Regist., (Anaesth.), Frimley Pk. Hosp. Surrey; Specialist Regist., (Anaesth.) St Geo.s Hosp. Lond., St Helier NHS Trust, Surrey.

RENWICK, Sheila Jane Kerr Gilsyke House, 212A Selby Road, Halton, Leeds LS15 0LF Tel: 0113 295 2710 Fax: 0113 295 2713; 83 Parkside Road, Meanwood, Leeds LS6 4NA Tel: 0113 275 0291 — MB ChB 1985 Manch.; Cert. Family Plann. JCC 1991. GP. Prev: Clin. Asst. (A & E) Leeds Gen. Infirm.

RENWICK, Sonia Ruth Department of Anaesthetics, Royal Free Hospital, Pond Street, London NW3 2QG — MB BChir 1988 Camb.; MA Camb. 1989, MB 1988, BChir 1988; MRCP (UK) 1992; FRCA 1994. (Cambridge) Regist. (Anaesth.) Char. Cross Hosp. Lond.; Cons. (Anaesth.) Roy. Free Hosp. Lond. Prev: SpR Hammersmith Hosp.; Reg. (Anaesth.) Gt. Ormond St. Hosp. Lond.; Regist. Char. Cross & Chelsea W.m. Hosps.

RENYARD, Mr Harold Holmwood (retired) Holmwood, 15 The Spinney, Elston, Newark NG23 5PE Tel: 01636 525204 — MB BS 1940 Lond.; MS Lond. 1952; FRCS Eng. 1948; MRCS Eng. LRCP Lond. 1940. Prev: Cons. Surg. Nottm. & Newark Hosps.

REPPER, James Alexander Elmbank Group, Foresterhill Health Centre, Westburn Road, Aberdeen AB25 2AY Tel: 01224 696949 Fax: 01224 691650; Kings Lodge, 14 Kingsgate, Aberdeen AB15 4EJ — MB ChB 1980 Aberd.; FRCGP 1994, M 1984. Sen. Research Fell. (Gen. Pract.) Univ. Aberd.; Assoc. Regional Adviser N. E. Scot. Socs: M-C Soc. Aberd.; Brit. Med. Acupunct. Soc. Prev: Recertification Fell. Roy. Coll. Gen. Practs.

REQUENA DURAN, Maria del Mar Department of General Surgery, Royal Berkshire Hospital, London Road, Reading RG1 5AN Tel: 01734 875111; 16 Bradley Gardens, Ealing, London W13 8HF Tel: 020 8081 6561 — LMS 1992 La Laguna. SHO Rotat. (Gen. Surg.) Roy. Berks. Hosp. & Battle NHS Trust. Prev: SHO (Urol. & Orthop.) Roy. Berks. Hosp.

RERRIE, Mr John David (retired) 14A Green Lane, Leominster HR6 8QJ — MB BS Lond. 1960; FRCS Ed. 1972; FRCOphth 1988. Prev: Cons. Ophth. Surg. P'boro. Dist. & Stamford & Rutland Hosps.

RESEK, George Emile 135 Harley Street, London W1N 1DJ Tel: 020 7935 6032 Fax: 020 7935 3148 — MD 1976 Amer. Univ. Beirut; MRCPsych 1980. Med. Dir. (Psychol. Med.) Cromwell Hosp. Lond. Socs: Indep. Doctors Forum; RCPsych (Sect. Psychother. & Social & Community Psychiat.); Brit. Neuropsychiat. Assn. Prev: Lect. Univ. Coll. Hosp. Lond.; Sen. Regist. MRC Graylingwell Hosp. Chichester; Regist. Roy. Edin. Hosp.

RESHAMWALA, Niranjan Kantilal Doctors' Mess, Corbett Hospital, Amblecote, Stourbridge DY8 4JB Tel: 01384 456111; 18 Chawn Park Drive, Pedmore, Stourbridge DY9 0YG Tel: 01384 392960 — MB BS Bombay 1962; DA Eng. 1969; DA Bombay 1965. (Grant Med. Coll.) Clin. Asst. (Anaesth.) Corbett Hosp. Stourbridge.

RESHAMWALLA, Daulat Khanum Nooredin The Surgery, 277 Fore Street, Edmonton, London N9 0PD — MB BS 1965 Osmania.

RESHI, Sajjad Hussain c/o 40 Adelaide Avenue, Brockley, London SE4 1YR — MB BS 1973 Jammu & Kashmir; MRCP (UK) 1984. (Med. Coll. Srinagar)

RESNICK, Jeremy Victor Nottingham Healthcare NHS Trust, The Wells Road Centre, The Wells Road, Nottingham NG3 3AA Tel: 0115 955 5389 Fax: 0115 952 9420 Email: jresnick@nadt.org.uk — MB ChB 1981 Stellenbosch; MRCPsych 1989; DPM Dublin 1990; Dip Forens Psychother Lond 1994. Cons. Forens. Psychiatrist Nottm. Forens. Serv. Nottm. Healthcare Trust. Prev: Cons. Forens. Psychiatrist Rampton Hosp.

RESOULY, Mr Adel ENT Department, Queen Alexandra Hospital, Portsmouth NHS Trust, Portsmouth PO6 3LY Tel: 023 92 286377; Southlands, Prinsted Lane, Emsworth PO10 8HS Tel: 01243 373900 — MB ChB 1966 Bristol; FRCS (Orl.) Ed. 1971; FRCS Eng. 1998. (Bristol) Cons. Otolayngol., Head & Neck Surg. (ENT) Portsmouth NHS Trust; Hon. Civil Cons. Roy. Naval Hosp. Haslar. Socs: BMA; Roy. Soc. Med.; Brit. Assoc. of Head & Neck Surg.s. Prev: Sen. Regist. (ENT) Soton. Univ. Hosp. & Wessex RHB; Regist. (ENT) United Bristol Hosps. & S. W.. RHB; SHO Radcliffe Infirm. Oxf.

RESTALL, John, OStJ, Brigadier late RAMC Retd. Maple Lodge, Frimley Hall Drive, Camberley GU15 2BE Tel: 01276 62380 — MB BS 1958 Lond.; FFA RCS Eng. 1967. (St. Thos.) Cons. Anaesth. Heatherwood & Wexham Pk. Trust. Socs: BMA & Assn. Anaesth. Prev: Cons. Adviser Anaesth. & Resusc. to Army; Regist. & SHO (Anaesth.) St. Thos. Hosp. Lond.; SHO (Anaesth.) Soton. Gp. Hosps.

RESTELL, Carol Ann Burvill House Surgery, 52 Dellfield Road, Hatfield AL10 8HP Tel: 01707 269091; 16 Rodney Avenue, St Albans AL1 5SX Tel: 01727 845215 — MB BS 1979 Lond.; MRCGP 1983. Trainer (Gen. Pract.) Hatfield.

RESTON, Peter John James X-Ray Department, Ormskirk Hospital, Ormskirk L39 2AZ Tel: 01695 656571 Fax: 01695 656571; 20A Tower Hill, Ormskirk L39 2EF — MB ChB 1970 Liverp.; FRCR 1976; DMRD Liverp. 1974. Cons. (Radiol.) Ormskirk & Dist. Gen. Hosp.

RESTON, Samuel Craig Flat 4, 22 Crescent Road, Gosport PO12 2DH — MB ChB 1995 Glas.

RESTORICK, Helen Margaret 62 Barnmead Road, Beckenham BR3 1JE — MB BS 1994 Lond.; BSc Lond. 1990; DRCOG 1997.

RESTRICK, Louise Jane Department of Thoracic Medicine, The Whittington Hospital, Highgate Hill, London N19 5NF Tel: 020 7288 5353 Fax: 020 7288 5060; 292 Globe Road, Bethnal Green, London E2 0NS — MB BS 1986 Lond.; MRCP (UK) 1989; MD Lond. 1997; FRCP 2000. (Cambridge University London Hospital Medical School) p/t Cons. Phys. & Hon. Sen. Lect. Respirat & Gen. Med. Whitt. Hosp. Lond. Prev: Research Fell. (Thoracic Med.) King's Coll. Sch. Med. & Dent. Lond.; Sen. Regist. (Thoracic & Gen. Med.) Roy. Lond. Hosp. & Lond. Chest Hosp.

RETHINASAMY, Edward Lewis 12 Ophir Gardens, Belfast BT15 5EP — MB BCh BAO 1985 Belf.

RETI, Shane Raymond Heron Hill, Lower Road, One House, Stowmarket IP14 3BX — MB ChB 1988 Auckland.

RETSAS, Spyros Department of Medical Oncology, Charing Cross Hospital, Fulham Palace Road, London W6 8RF Tel: 020 8846 1234 Fax: 020 8746 8293 Email: s.retsas@ic.ac.uk; Parnassus, Park Hill, Loughton IG10 4ES Tel: 020 8508 8673 Fax: 020 8508 8673 Email: sretsas@msn.com — Ptychio Iatrikes Aristotle 1967; MD (Thesis) Athens 1979; FRCP Lond. 1994; MRCP (UK) 1975; MRCS Eng. LRCP Lond. 1972; LMSSA Lond. 1971. (Aristotle Univ. Thessaloniki) p/t Cons. Med. Oncol. Char. Cross & Chelsea & W.m. Hosp. Lond.; Mem. Edit. Bd. Melanoma Research; Mem. Edit Bd. Seminars in Oncol. Socs: Fell. Roy. Soc. Med.; Amer. Soc. Clin. Oncol.; Brit. Assn. Cancer Phys. Prev: Sen. Lect. (Med. Oncol.) & Hon. Cons. Phys. W.m. Med. Sch. Lond.; Regist. (Med.) Whipps Cross Hosp. Lond.; Sen. Ho. Phys. (Med. Oncol.) Roy. Marsden Hosp. Sutton.

RETTIE, George Kelly Cargill (retired) 58 Napier Court, Ranelagh Gardens, London SW6 3UX Tel: 020 7736 0921 Email: george.rettie@virgin.net — MB BS 1941 Lond.; MD Lond. 1948; MRCS Eng. LRCP Lond. 1941. Prev: Phys. Imperial Life Assur. Company of Canada.

RETTMAN

RETTMAN, Christopher Department of Pathology, North Tees General Hospital, Hardwick, Stockton-on-Tees TS19 8PE Tel: 01642 617617 Fax: 01642 624116 — Lekarz Warsaw 1966; MD Warsaw Med. Sch. 1975; FRCPath 1997, MRCPath 1986. (Warsaw, Poland) Cons. Histopath. N. Tees HA. Socs: ACP; BMA; BSCC. Prev: Dept. Path. Inst. Paediat. Warsaw, Poland; Dept. Path. Univ. of Jos; Dept. Path. Newc. Gen. Hosp.

RETZLAW, Elsa 47 Rutland Court, Denmark Hill, London SE5 8ED — MD 1937 Vienna. Prev: Med. Off. Epsom Co. Hosp. & St. Augustine's Hosp. Chartham Down.

REUBEN, Adam Dov 113 Kineton Green Road, Solihull B92 7DT — MB ChB 1997 Bristol.

REUBEN, Joselle Raymond 99 Regal Way, Kenton, Harrow HA3 0SG — MB ChB 1956 Cape Town.

REUBEN, Mark Jonathan Westcotes Health Centre, Fosse Road South, Leicester LE3 0LP Tel: 0116 254 1800 — MB BChir 1979 Camb.; BSc Pharm. Lond. 1976; DRCOG 1983.

REUBEN, Simon Francis Beverley, Brimstage Road, Heswall, Wirral CH60 1XG — MB ChB 1990 Manch.

REUBIN, Richard David Cassio Surgery, 62-68 Merton Road, Watford WD18 0WL Tel: 01923 226011 Fax: 01923 817342 — MB ChB 1973 Birm. Prev: Dir. Med. Servs. N.ants. FHSA; Ships Surg. P & O SN Company Lond.; Ho. Off. Birm. Gen. Hosp.

REUTER, Christopher William 50 Quarry Road, Headington, Oxford OX3 8NX — MB ChB 1998 Leeds. (university of Leeds) SHO Rotat., Glonfield Med., Glonfield Gen. Hosp., Glonfield, Leicester. Prev: PRMO, Leeds Gen. Infirm., General Med.; PRHO, Castle Hill Hosp., Hull, Gen. Surg.; PRHO, Hull Roy. Infirm., Hull Gen. Surg.

REUTER, Simone Chesterfield & North Derbyshire Royal Hospital, Hazel Court, Calow, Chesterfield S44 5BL; 12 Gladstone Road, Chesterfield S40 4TE — State Exam Med 1990 Frankfurt.

REVEL, Jean-Claude Ananda Medwyn, Moores Road, Dorking RH4 2BG Tel: 01306 882422 — MB BS 1974 Mysore; DObst. RCOG 1981. Med. Off. Harrowlands Rehabil. Unit Dorking; Clin. Asst. (Diabetes) Epsom Gen. Hosp. Socs: BMA. Prev: SHO (Med.) Dorking Gen. Hosp.; SHO (Obst.) Redhill Gen. Hosp.; SHO (A & E) E. Surrey Hosp. Redhill.

REVELEY, Adrianne Bethlem Royal Hospital, Monks Orchard Road, Beckenham BR3 3BY Tel: 020 8776 4418 Fax: 020 8776 4419; Maudsley Hospital, Denmark Hill, London SE5 8AT Tel: 020 8776 4418 Fax: 020 8776 4419 — MB BCh BAO 1972 Dub.; FRCPsych 1989, M 1978. Lead Cons. Psychosis Unit Bethlem Roy. & Maudsley Hosps. Lond.; Hon. Sen. Lect. Inst. Psychiat. Lond.

REVELEY, Colette Helen 89 Oakfield Road, Gateshead NE11 0AD — MB ChB 1997 Leic.

REVELEY, Professor Michael August Neuropsychpharmacology Unit, University Department of Psychiatry, Leicester General Hospital, Leicester LE5 4PW Tel: 0116 225 7924 Fax: 0116 225 7925 Email: rev@le.ac.uk — MD Univ. Texas 1970; PhD Lond. 1988; BA Univ. Texas 1966; FRCPsych 1989, M 1978. (Southwestern Med. Sch.) Socs: Brit. Assn. for Psychopharmacol.; Eur. Coll. Neuropsychopharm.; Collegium Internat. Neuropsychopharmacol. Prev: Sen. Lect. (Psychiat.) Lond. Hosp. Med. Coll. Lond. & Hon. Cons. (Psychiat.) Lond. Hosp.; Sen. Lect. (Psychiat.) Inst. Psychiat. Lond. & Hon. Cons. (Psychiat.) Bethlem Roy. & Maudsley Hosp. Lond.

REVELL, Vice Admiral Anthony Leslie, CB, Surg. Vice-Admiral (retired) 29 Little Green, Alverstoke, Gosport PO12 2EX Tel: 023 9258 8296 Fax: 01705 588296 — MB ChB Birm. 1959; Hon. MD Birm. 1996; FFA RCS Eng. 1969; DA Eng. 1965. Prev: Hon. Surg. to HM The Qu. (1992-97).

REVELL, Claire Pamela Brentford Health Centre, Albany Road, Brentford TW8 0NE Tel: 020 8568 0771; 47 Montholme Road, Battersea, London SW11 6HX Tel: 020 7228 8053 — MB BS 1985 Lond.; MRCGP 1991; DRCOG 1989; DCH RCP Lond. 1987.

REVELL, Edmund HM Prison Lewes, 1 Brighton Road, Lewes BN7 1EA Tel: 0273 405100; 10 First Avenue, Havant PO9 2QN — MB BS 1973 Lond.; BSc Lond. 1970, MB BS 1973. (Westm.) Sen. Med. Off. HM Prison Lewes. Prev: GP Havant; Regist. (Anaesth.) Glos. Roy. Hosp. Gloucester; Regist. (Anaesth.) Roy. Berks. Hosp. Reading.

REVELL, Paul Graeme Abbots Croft, Newport Road, Stafford ST16 1DH Tel: 01785 223240 — MB BS 1981 Lond.; BSc Lond. 1978; MRCP (UK) 1984; MRCPath 1992; FRCPCH 1997; DCH RCP Lond. 1986; FRCP FRCpath 2000. (Guy's Hospital Medical School University of London) Cons. Haemat. Mid Staffs. Gen. Hosps. NHS Trust. Staff. Gen. Hosp. & Cannock Chase Hosp. Prev: Sen. Regist. Rotat. (Haemat.) W. Midl. RHA; Lect. (Haemat.) United Med. & Dent. Schs. Lond.

REVELL, Professor Peter Allen Department of Histopathology, Royal Free and University College Medical School, Rowland Hill St., London NW3 2PF Tel: 020 7794 0500 Fax: 020 7435 3289 Email: parevell@rfhsm.ac.uk; 17 Willowdene Court, Warley, Brentwood CM14 5ET — MB BS Lond. 1967; PhD Lond. 1973, BSc 1964; FRCPath 1988, M 1975. (Lond. Hosp.) Prof. Dept. Histopath. Roy. Free & Univ. Coll. Med. Sch. Lond. Socs: Pres. Europ. Soc. Biomaterials; Path. Soc.; Internat. Acad. Path. Prev: Reader Inst. Path. Lond. Hosp.; Sen. Lect. Inst. Path. Lond. Hosp.; Lect. Inst. Path. Lond. Hosp.

REVESZ, Thomas Department of Neuropathology, Institute of Neurology, Queen Square, London WC1N 3BG Tel: 020 7837 3611 Fax: 020 7916 9546 Email: t.revesz@ion.ucl.ac.uk — MD 1972 Budapest; 1998 FRCPath; 1990 MRCPath. (Semmelweis Med. Sch. Budapest) Reader (Neuropath.) Inst. Neurol. Lond.; Hon. Cons. Nat. Hosp. Neurol. & Neurosurg. Lond. Prev: Sen. Regist. (Neuropath.) Maida Vale Hosp. Lond.

REVILL, Hugh The Dog Mills Cottages, Bride, Ramsey IM7 4AD Tel: 01624 814221 — MB ChB 1946 Glas. Socs: I. of Man Med. Soc. Prev: Med. Dir. St. Bridget's Hospice I. of Man; Ho. Phys. Glas. Roy. Infirm.

REVILL, John Greenhill Health Centre, 482 Lupton Road, Sheffield S8 7NQ Tel: 0114 237 2961; 212 Eckington Road, Coal Aston, Dronfield S18 3AZ Tel: Dronfield 412671 — MB BChir 1963 Camb.; MA, MB Camb. 1963, BChir 1962; DObst RCOG 1964. (St. Geo.) Socs: Camb. Univ. Med. Soc.; Brit. Hyperlipidaemia Assn. & Medac (UK). Prev: Res. Obst. Asst., Ho. Phys. & Cas. Off. St. Geo. Hosp. Lond.

REVILL, Susan Irene Llygad Yr Haul, Mountain West, Newport SA42 0QX — MB BCh 1987 Wales; PhD Wales 1980, MA 1973, MB BCh 1987.

REVINGTON, Mr Peter John Department of Maxillofacial Surgery, Frenchay Hospital, Bristol BS16 1LE Tel: 0117 975 3997 Fax: 0117 918 6650 Email: prev@classicfm.net; Honey Hall, Honey Hall Lane, Congresbury, Bristol BS49 5JX Tel: 01934 853197 Fax: 01934 853197 Email: prev@classicfm.net — MB BS 1991 Lond.; MScD 1980 Wales; BDS 1976; FRCS 1993 Eng; FDS 1981 RCS Eng. (charing cross/westminster) Cons. Maxillofacial Surg. Frenchay Hosp. Bristol; Hon. Sen. Lect., Univ. Bristol. Socs: Fell. Brit. Assn. Maxillofacial Surg. & BMA; Eur. Assn. Facial Plast. Surg.; BMA. Prev: Sen. Regist. (Oral Surg.) King's Coll. Hosp. Lond.; Regist. Bristol Roy. Infirm. & Frenchay Hosp.; SHO (Gen. Surg.) Kingston Hosp. Kingston-upon-Thames.

REVOLTA, Alexander David Castle Place Surgery, 9 Park Hill, Tiverton EX16 6RR Tel: 01884 252333 Fax: 01884 252152 — MB ChB 1970 Ed.; BSc Ed. 1968, MB ChB 1970; MRCGP 1982; DObst RCOG 1973; DCH Eng. 1977. (Ed.) GP Trainer Tiverton.

REW, Mr David Anthony, TD Breast & Endocrine Unit, Southampton University Hospitals, Southampton SO14 0YG Tel: 023 8082 5317 Fax: 023 8082 5148 Email: dr1@soton.ac.uk; Tel: 023 8025 8422 — MB BChir 1981 Camb.; MChir 1991; MA Camb. 1982, MChir 1991; FRCS Eng. 1985. (Cambridge University, Kings College Hospital) Cons. Surg. Hon. Sen. Lect. Soton. Univ. Hosps.; Jt. Edr. Europ. Jl. Surgic. Oncol.; Nat. Sec., Brit. Assn. of Surgic. Oncol. 2000-2002. Socs: Nat. Sec. Brit. Assn. Surg. Oncol.; Roy. Soc. Med. (Sect. Coloproctol.); Internat. Soc. Anal. Cytol. Prev: Dir. Leicester Laser Cytometry Facility Glenfield Univ. Hosp.; Sen. Lect. (Surg.) & Hon. Cons. Surg. Univ. Leicester; Sen. Regist. (Gen. Surg.) Soton. Univ. Hosp.

REW, Robert John (retired) Applegate, 10 Trump's Orchard, Cullompton EX15 1TW Tel: 01884 34096 Email: rjrew@aol.com — MRCS Eng. LRCP Lond. 1960; DMJ(Clin) Soc. Apoth Lond. 1979; DObst RCOG 1962. Non-Princip. Gen. Practitioner (p/t), Cullompton Area. Prev: Div. Police Surg. E.bourne.

REWHORN, Ian David 51 Heron's Way, Selly Oak, Birmingham B29 6TR — MB ChB 1980 Dundee; MRCP (UK) 1985.

REWILAK, Anna Teresa Eisner, Goldman and Ship, Shipley Health Centre, Alexandra Road, Shipley BD18 3EG Tel: 01274 589160 — MB BS 1984 Lond.

REYNOLDS

REX, Stephen Douglas Suilven, The Orpines, Wateringbury, Maidstone ME18 5BP — MB BS 1994 Lond.; BSc (Hons.) Lond. 1993, MB BS 1994; MRCP (UK) 1997. (Roy. Free Hosp. Lond.) Specialist Regist. (Cardiol.) N W Thames.

REY, Mr Charles Humphrey Jules (retired) Reyscourt, Rue Du Friquet, Castel GY5 7SS Tel: 01481 257980 — MB BS 1953 Lond.; FRCS Eng. 1952; MRCS Eng. LRCP Lond. 1939. Prev: Surg. P.ss Eliz. Hosp. Guernsey.

REYBURN, Hugh William 88 Copleston Road, London SE15 4AG — MB BS 1974 Lond.; MSc (Community Med.) Lond. 1981; MRCP (UK) 1979; MRCGP 1985; DTM & H RCP Lond. 1995.

REYES, Mr Richard John Queen Mary's Hospital, Sidcup DA14 6LT Fax: 020 8302 2698 Email: rick.reyes@qms-tr.sthames.nhs.uk — MB BS 1985 Lond.; FRCS (Gen.) 2000; FRCS Eng. 1989. Cons. BrE. & Gen. Surg.; Clin. Research Fell. (Surg.) Univ. Coll. Hosp. Lond.; SpR N. Thames. Socs: Roy. Soc. Med.; Brit. Assn. Surgic. Oncol. Prev: Regist. Rotat. (Surg.) Guy's Hosp. Lond.

REYNARD, Amanda Jane 17 Towncroft Lane, Heaton, Bolton BL1 5EN — MB ChB 1984 Liverp.

REYNARD, Anthony Laurence (retired) 36 Church Lane, Eaton, Norwich NR4 6NY Tel: 01603 452504 — MRCS Eng. LRCP Lond. 1939; FRCA Eng. 1953; DA Eng. 1949; Cert. Av. Med. 1972. Prev: Cons. Anaesth. United Norwich Hosps.

REYNARD, John Michael Department of Urology, 4th Floor Alexandra Wing, The Royal London Hospital, PO Box 59, London E1 1BB; Rosemary, Hardwick Road, Whitchurch on Thames, Reading RG8 7HH — MB BS 1987 Lond.

REYNARD, Kevin 9 Beech Walk, Adel, Leeds LS16 8NY — MB ChB 1987 Leeds.

REYNARD, Timothy James Wilkinson Stable Cottage, Broad Lane, Newdigate, Dorking RH5 5AT — MB BS 1989 Lond.

REYNELL, Peter Carew 12 Park View Road, Bradford BD9 4PA Tel: 01274 546585 — BM BCh 1942 Oxf.; DM Oxf. 1951; FRCP Lond. 1962, M 1947. (Oxf.) Cons. Phys. Roy. Infirm. & St. Luke's Hosp. Bradford. Socs: Assn. Phys. Gt. Brit. & Brit. Cardiac Soc. Prev: Med. Tutor Radcliffe Infirm. Oxf.; Rockefeller Trav. Fell. Clin. Med.; Graded Phys. RAMC.

REYNER, Lindsay Jill Toddington Medical Centre, Luton Road, Toddington, Dunstable LU5 6DE Tel: 01525 872222 Fax: 01525 876711; 38 Park Mount, Harpenden AL5 3AR Tel: 01582 462808 — MB BS 1985 Lond.; DRCOG 1988. (Univ. Coll. Lond.) GP. Prev: GP Harpenden.

REYNISH, William Patrick 14 Fettes Row, Edinburgh EH3 6RH — MB ChB 1992 Manch.

REYNOLDS, Mrs Anita 5 Kellett Mount, Leeds LS12 4AJ — MB BS 1989 Lond.; MMedSci 1997; FRCOphth 1995; MRCOphth 1993. (Middlx. & Univ. Coll. Lond.) Specialist Regist. Rotat. (Ophth.) W. Midl. Socs: Roy. Soc. Med.; BMA.

REYNOLDS, Ann Lea (retired) 24 Christchurch Close, Edgbaston, Birmingham B15 3NE Tel: 0121 454 4680 — MB ChB Birm. 1949; FRCS Ed. 1957; FRCOG 1972, M 1959. Prev: Cons. O & G Dudley Rd. Hosp. Birm.

REYNOLDS, Anthony Douglas West Lodge, West Drive, Sudbrooke, Lincoln LN2 2RA — MB BCh 1972 Wales; FFA RCS Eng. 1978. Cons. Anaesth. Co. Hosp. Lincoln.

REYNOLDS, Carol Ann Brent Area Medical Centre, Anvil House, Brent Road, East Brent, Highbridge TA9 4JD Tel: 01278 760313 Fax: 01278 760753 — BM 1983 Soton.; MRCGP 1989; DRCOG 1987. Prev: Trainee GP W.on-Super-Mare VTS.

REYNOLDS, Christopher Michael Norfolk Mental Health Care NHS Trust, Hellesdon Hospital, Norwich NR6 5BE Tel: 01603 421421 Fax: 01603 421563 Email: chris.reynolds@norfmhc-tr.anglox.nhs.uk; South Barn, Sea Palling Road, Ingham, Norwich NR12 0TW Tel: 01692 5880 540 — MB BS 1969 Lond.; MRCS Eng. LRCP Lond. 1969; FRCPsych 1993, M 1975; DPM Eng. 1973; DObst RCOG 1972. (Roy. Free) Cons. Psychiat. Hellesdon Hosp. Norwich. Prev: Sen. Regist. (Psychiat.) St. Geo. Hosp. Lond. & W. Pk. Hosp. Epsom; Regist. (Psychiat.) Friem Hosp. Lond.

REYNOLDS, Christopher William Knoll Pharmaceuticals, Clinical Development, E50, Evelyn St., Nottingham NG1 1GF Tel: 0115 912 4210 Fax: 0115 912 4162 Email: chris.reynolds@knoll.co.uk; 10c Hope Drive, The Park, Nottingham NG7 1DL — BM BS 1991 Nottm.; BMedSci (Hons.) Nottm. 1989; AFPM 1997; Dip. Pharm. Med. 1996; DA (UK) 1994. (Nottm.) Research Phys. (Clin. Developm.) Knoll Pharmaceut. Nottm.; Hon. Clin. Asst. (Anaesth.) Qu. Med. Centre Nottm. Socs: Brit. Assn. Pharmaceut. Phys.; Nottm. M-C Soc.; Roy. Coll. Anaesth. Prev: Med. Adviser CNS Clin. Investig. Boots Pharmaceut. Nottm.; SHO Rotat. (Anaesth.) Nottm.

REYNOLDS, Clare Elizabeth Hudson Drive, Health Centre, Hudson Drive, Burntwood WS7 Tel: 01543 674477 — MB BS 1989 Lond.; MRCGP 1994; DRCOG 1993; DFFP 1993. (St Bartholomews) Socs: BMA.

REYNOLDS, Colin David, Capt. RAMC 25 Holly Road, Poynton, Stockport SK12 1PA — LMSSA 1985 Lond.; MSc (Radiat. Biol.) Lond. 1975; BSc (Hons.) UPEI Canada 1973. (Middlx.)

REYNOLDS, Colin Peter (retired) Serjeant Bendlowes Cottage, Brook St., Great Bardfield, Braintree CM7 4RQ Tel: 01371 810515 — MB BS 1961 Lond.; FRCR 1979; DMRD Eng. 1977; DObst RCOG 1964. Prev: Sen. Regist. Radio-diag. Dept. & Ho. Surg. Lond. Hosp.

REYNOLDS, Darren 3 Pallotine Walk, Beechwood Gardens, Rochdale OL11 4LS Tel: 01706 341707 — MB ChB 1993 Manch.; MRCPsych 1998. Specialist Regist. Dual trainee in Gen. & Old Age Psychiat.

REYNOLDS, Mr David Arturo Albany House, 52 Ashley Park Avenue, Walton-on-Thames KT12 1EU Tel: 020 7928 9292 Fax: 020 7922 8019 — MB BS 1960 Lond.; FRCS Eng. 1965; MRCS Eng. LRCP Lond. 1960. (Guy's) Emerit. Cons. Orthop. Surg. Guys St. Thomas NHS Trust, Lond.; Emerit. Cons. Orthop. Surg. Qu. Vict. Hosp. E. Grinstead. Socs: Sen. Fell. BOA. Prev: Clin. Dir. & Sen. Surg. (Orthop. Surg.) Guys St. Thos. NHS Trust Lond.; Assoc. Prof. Orthop. Einstein Coll. Med., NY; Cons. Orthop Surg. Metrop. Police.

REYNOLDS, David Farmer (retired) 34 Galton Road, Westcliff on Sea SS0 8LA Tel: 01702 475775 — MB BS Lond. 1945; FRCR 1975; FFR 1956; DMRD Eng. 1950. Cons. Radiol. S.end Hosp. S.end on Sea. Prev: Sen. Regist. St. Mary's Hosp. Lond.

REYNOLDS, David John Morton The John Radcliffe, Oxford Radcliffe Trust, Headley Way, Oxford OX3 9DU Tel: 01865 220964 Fax: 01865 220972 Email: john.reynolds@clinpharm.ox.ac.uk — BM BCh 1981 Oxf.; DPhil Oxf. 1994, BM BCh 1981; MA Camb. 1981; MRCP (UK) 1984; FRCP 1998. (Oxford) Cons. Clin. Pharmacol. & Gen. Phys. Oxf. Radcliffe Trust; Hon. Sen. Clin. Lect. (Clin. Pharmacol.) Univ. Oxf. Prev: Clin. Lect. (Clin. Pharmacol.) Univ. Oxf.

REYNOLDS, Dorothy Jean Bridge Street Surgery, Bridge Street, Louth LN11 0DR Tel: 01507 603121 Fax: 01507 605916; 2 Crowtree Lane, Louth LN11 9LN Tel: 01507 603309 — MD 1991 Manch.; MB ChB 1974; DRCOG 1977; DCH Eng. 1977.

REYNOLDS, E. Mark R. Reynold, MBE Stockett Lane Surgery, 3 Stockett Lane, Coxheath, Maidstone ME17 4PS Tel: 01622 745585 Fax: 01622 741987 Email: edward.reynolds@gp-g82024.nhs.uk — MB BS 1981 Lond.; MRCGP 1993; BSc Lond. 1978; DRCOG 1983; DCH 1993. (St Thomas) GP Princip. Socs: Chairm. Nat. Assn. of GP coOperat.s; Med. Director Assn. of Maidstone, Doctors on Call (MAIDDOC). Prev: GP Tutor.

REYNOLDS, Edward Henry The Centre for Epilepsy, The Maudsley Hospital, Denmark Hill, London SE5 8AZ Tel: 020 7277 1985 Fax: 020 7703 6396; Buckles, Yew Tree Bottom Road, Epsom KT17 3NE Tel: 01737 360867 Fax: 01737 363415 — MB BCh 1959 Wales; MD Wales 1969; FRCP Lond. 1980, M 1963; MRCS Eng. LRCP Lond. 1959; FRCPsych 1985. (Cardiff) Cons. Neurol. Bethlem Roy., Maudsley & King's Coll. Hosps. Lond.; Chairm. Centre for Epilepsy Maudsley Hosp. Lond.; Dir. Inst. Epileptol. King's Coll. Lond.; Hon. Sen. Lect. Univ. Dept. Neurol. Inst. Psychiat. & King's Coll.Hosp Med Sch. Socs: (Pres.) Internat. League Against Epilepsy; (Pres.) Brit. Charter Internat. League Against Epilepsy. Prev: Vis. Asst. Prof. Neurol. Yale Univ. Med. Sch. New Haven USA; Regist. Nat. Hosp. Nerv. Dis. Lond. & MRC Neuropsychiat. Research Unit Carshalton.

REYNOLDS, Professor Edward Osmund Royle, CBE Department of Paediatrics, University College London, Rayne Institute, University St., London WC1E 6JJ; 72 Barrowgate Road, London W4 4QU Tel: 020 8994 3326 Email: reynolds@dircon.co.uk — MB BS 1958 Lond.; FMedSci (Founder) 1998; FRCPCH 1997 (Hons.); FRS 1993; BSc Lond. 1955, MD 1966; FRCP Lond. 1975, M 1966; FRCOG (ad eundem) 1983; DCH Eng. 1961. (St. Thos.) Emerit. Prof. Neonat. Paediat. Univ. Coll. Lond.; Emerit. Cons. Paediat. Univ. Coll. Hosp. Lond. Socs: Fell. Roy. Soc.; (Ex-Pres.) Neonat. Soc.; Roy. Soc. of Med. (Hon. Fell.). Prev: Prof. Neonat.

REYNOLDS

Paediat. Univ. Coll. Lond.; Cons. Paediat. Univ. Coll. Hosp. Lond.; Head Dept. Paediat. Univ. Coll. & Middlx. Sch. Med. Lond.

REYNOLDS, Elizabeth Ruth 95 Cinderhill Lane, Scholar Green, Stoke-on-Trent ST7 3HR Tel: 01782 782872; 6 Sycamore Grove, Sandbach CW11 1PJ — MB ChB 1986 Birm.; DCH RCP Lond. 1990. (Birm.)

REYNOLDS, Professor Felicity Jane Morten Department of Anaesthetics, St Thomas' Hospital, London SE1 7EH Tel: 020 7928 9292 Ext: 3215 Email: felicity.reynolds@btinternet.com; 40 Cleaver Square, London SE11 4EA Tel: 020 7735 9357 — MB BS 1960 Lond.; MD Lond. 1971; FRCOG (ad eundem) 1995; FRCA 1963. (St. Thos.) Emerit. Prof. (Obst. Anaesth.)KCL (St. Thomas'). Prev: Prof. Obst. Anaesth. United Med. & Dent. Sch. & Hon. Cons. Anaesth. St. Thos. Hosp. Lond.; Reader (Pharmacol. Applied to Anaesth.) United Med. & Dent. Sch. Lond.; Clin. Lect. (Pharmacol.) St. Thos. Hosp. Lond.

REYNOLDS, George Morton (retired) 131 Abergwili Road, Carmarthen SA31 2HG — BSc, MB BCh Wales 1948; FFCM 1978, M 1974; DPH Eng. 1952. Prev: Chief Admin. Med. Off. & Dir. Pub. Health Med. E. Dyfed HA.

REYNOLDS, Gerald Martin 115 Broomlands Road, Cumbernauld, Glasgow G67 2PT — MB ChB 1992 Dundee.

REYNOLDS, Ginette Elizabeth Ilmington House, Birmingham Road, Budbrooke, Warwick CV35 7DX — MB BS 1998 Newc.; MB BS Newc 1998.

REYNOLDS, Godfrey Alexander Market Cross Surgery, 7 Market Place, Mildenhall, Bury St Edmunds IP28 7EG Tel: 01638 713109 Fax: 01638 718615; Horne Lea, The St, Barton Mills, Bury St Edmunds IP28 6AA Tel: 01638 510241 — MB ChB 1983 Birm.; BSc (Hons.) Physiol. Birm. 1980, MB ChB 1983; MRCGP 1989; DRCOG 1988. Socs: BMA; RCGP. Prev: SHO Rotat. (Med.) Selly Oak Hosp. Birm.; Trainee GP/SHO E. Birm. Hosp. VTS.

REYNOLDS, Graham Collis Stephen Priory Fields Surgery, Nursery Road, Huntingdon PE29 3RL Tel: 01480 52361 Fax: 01480 434640 — MB BS 1966 Durh.; T(GP) 1990. (Durh. & Newc.) Treas. Huntsdoc (GP Night Co-op); Clin. Asst. (Cas.) Hinchingbrooke Hosp. Huntingdon; Asst. Police Surg. Camb. Constab; Med. Adviser Camb. Amateur Gymnastics Assn. Prev: Chairm. Huntingdon GP Forum; Hon. Vis. Phys. Centr. Gippsland Hosp., Austral.; Clin. Asst. (Obst.) Matern. Unit Primrose La. Hosp. Huntingdon.

REYNOLDS, Gregory William Tel: 0113 392 2185; 62 Gledhow wood Grove, Leeds LS8 1PA Tel: 0113 392 2185 — MB BS 1979 Lond.; FRCP UK. Cons. Cardiol. Leeds Gen. Infirm.

REYNOLDS, Mr Ian Stuart Russell Mouse Castle, Old Eign Hill, Hereford HR1 1TU Tel: 01432 69111 Fax: 01432 263499 — MB BChir 1969 Camb.; MA Camb. 1969; FRCS Eng. 1975; FRCS Ed. 1974; MRCS Eng. LRCP Lond. 1968. (St. Thos.) Cons. Orthop. Surg. Hereford Gen. & Co. Hosps. Socs: Brit. Orthop. Assn. & BMA. Prev: Sen. Regist. (Orthop.) Birm. AHA (T) & Coventry & Warks. Hosp.; SHO (Orthop.) Rowley Bristow Orthop. Hosp. Pyrford.

REYNOLDS, Jeffrey Hugh 8 Forge Row, Saleyard Bridge, Gilwern, Abergavenny NP7 0HA — MRCS Eng. LRCP Lond. 1971.

REYNOLDS, Jennifer Heather Kendrick Surgery, 10 Kendrick Road, Sutton Coldfield B76 1EG Tel: 0121 351 2020 Fax: 0121 351 7987; 90 Orchard Road, Erdington, Birmingham B24 9JD — MB ChB Birm. 1978; MRCGP 1982; DRCOG 1980.

REYNOLDS, Jeremy James 3 Broomlands, Wirral CH60 6TF — MB ChB 1997 Bristol.

REYNOLDS, John Beresford (retired) Alexandra Cottage, Dog Lane, Chlidrey, Wantage OX12 9UW — MRCS Eng. LRCP Lond. 1957; BA Camb. 1954.

REYNOLDS, John Clifford Lutterworth Health Centre, Gilmorton Road, Lutterworth LE17 4EB Tel: 01455 553531 — MB BS 1978 Lond.; BSc (Biol.) (1st cl. Hons.) Sussex 1973. Clin. Asst. (Ophth.) Leics. Roy. Infirm.

REYNOLDS, John Cyril Citisport House, The Chackpit, College Road, Epsom KT17 4JA Tel: 01372 743166 Fax: 01372 743538; 40 Bunbury, Epsom KT17 4JP Tel: 01372 741939 — MB BS 1975 Lond.; MRCP (UK) 1985; MRCS Eng. LRCP Lond. 1975. (Royal Free Hospital School of Medicine) Orthop. Phys. Breakspear Clinic Milton-under-Wychwood & 30A Wimpole St. Lond.; Cons. Rehabil. Med. to Metrop. Police; Cons. Sports Med. P.ss Margt. Hosp. Windsor; Cons. Rheum. To Mid Surrey PCG. Socs: Fell. Inst. Sports Med.; (Past Chairm). Brit. Med. Acupunc. Soc. Prev: Specialist (Rehabil. &

Rheum.) RAF MRU Headley Ct. Surrey.; Med. Dir. Brit. Paralympic Assn.

REYNOLDS, John Francis (retired) 51 Princes Road, Wimbledon, London SW19 8RA Tel: 020 8542 2827 — MRCS Eng. LRCP Lond. 1963. Prev: G.P. Trainer S.W.Thames.

REYNOLDS, John Haydn Department of Radiology, Birmingham Heartlands Hospital, Bordesley Green E., Birmingham B9 5ST Tel: 0121 766 6611 Fax: 0121 766 6919; 51 Glendon Way, Dorridge, Solihull B93 8SY Tel: 01564 775059 Email: jhaydnreynolds@msn.com — MB ChB 1983 Manch.; FRCR 1991; T(R)(CR) 1992; DMRD Aberd. 1989. Cons. Diag. Radiol. Birm. Heartlands & Solihull NHS Trust (Teachg.). Socs: Roy. Coll. Radiol.; Assn. Chest Radiologists. Prev: Sen. Regist. Rotat. (Diag. Radiol.) W. Midl. Train. Scheme; Regist. (Diag. Radiol.) Aberd. Roy. Infirm.; SHO (Gen. Med.) N. Manch. Gen. Hosp.

REYNOLDS, Mr Jonathan Richard Southern Derbyshire Acute Hospital Trust, Derby City General Hospital, Uttoxeter Rd, Derby DE22 3NE Tel: 01332 625548 Email: jrreynoldsfrcs@msn.com; The Tower, Hob Hill, Hazelwood, Belper DE56 4AL Tel: 01332 842898 Email: jrreynolds@rcsed.ac.uk — MB ChB 1978 Dundee; DM Nottm. 1988; FRCS Eng. 1982; FRCS Ed. 1982. (Dundee) Cons. Surg. S.ern Derbysh. Acute Hosp.s Trust; Arris & Gale Lect. RCS Eng. Socs: Assn. Surg. & Roy. Soc. Med.; Assn. Coloproctol.; Brit. Soc. Gastroenterol. Prev: Sen. Regist. (Surg.) Nottm. & Derby; Regist. (Surg.) Derbysh. Roy. Infirm.; Research Fell. (Surg.) Nottm.

REYNOLDS, Joseph M Cornmarket Surgery, Newry Health Village, Monaghan Street, Newry BT35 6BW — MB BCh BAO 1979 NUI; MRCGP 1984. GP Newry.

REYNOLDS, Karen Anne Child Development Centre, North Staffordshire Hospital (City General), Newcastle Road, Stoke-on-Trent ST4 6QG — MB BS 1981 Lond.; MRCP (UK) 1991; MRCGP 1985; FRCPCH 1997; DCH RCP Lond. 1985; DRCOG 1984. Cons. Community Paediat. N. Staffs. Hosp. Trust.

REYNOLDS, Karen Neilson 43 Brechin Road, Bishopsbriggs, Glasgow G64 1BH — MB ChB 1989 Glas.

REYNOLDS, Kate Margaret Dunchurch Surgery, Dunsmore Heath, Dunchurch, Rugby CV22 6AP Tel: 01788 522448 Fax: 01788 814609 — BM BS 1994 Nottm.; MRCGP 1999. Gen. Practitioner Princip. Socs: Roy. Coll. of Gen. Practitioners; BMA.

REYNOLDS, Kathleen Margaret Mary (Karina) The Department of Obstetrics, Gynaecology and Reproductive Healthcare, St Mary's Hospital, Whitworth Park, Manchester M13 0JH Tel: 0161 276 6278 Fax: 0161 276 6134 Email: kreynolds@central.cmht.nwest.nhs.uk; Brooklands, 446 Hale Road, Hale Barns, Altrincham WA15 8XR — MB BCh BAO 1982 Dub.; FRCS Ed. 1991; MRCOG 1988. Sen. Lect., Gyn. Oucology, Univ.of Manch.; Hon Cons. Gun. Oncol., St. Mary's & Clinstie Hosp. Manch. Socs: Brit. Gyn. Cancer Soc.; Brit. Assoc. of Cancer Research; BMA. Prev: Fell. in Gyn. Oucology Universties of Toronto & Nu Master, Ontario, Canada. 1994-1996.

REYNOLDS, Kevin Vaughan St Mary's Surgery, James Street, St Mary's, Southampton SO14 1PJ Tel: 023 8033 3778 Fax: 023 8021 1894; 168 Woodmill Lane, Bitterne Park, Southampton SO18 2PF — BM 1988 Soton.; MRCGP 1992; DGM RCP Lond. 1991; DRCOG 1990.

REYNOLDS, Laraine Collette 89 Manorbier Cr, Liverpool L9 1HF — MB ChB 1997 Ed. (Edinburgh) SHO.

REYNOLDS, Linda June The Brooke Surgery, 20 Market Street, Hyde SK14 1AT Tel: 0161 368 3312 Fax: 0161 268 5670; 19 Peel Moat Road, Heaton Moor, Stockport SK4 4PL — MB ChB 1974 Manch.

REYNOLDS, Lucy Jane 25 Court Road, Banstead SM7 2NQ — BM BS 1989 Nottm.; MRCP (UK) 1994; DTM & H RCP Lond. 1992. Socs: Roy. Coll. Paediat. & Child Health; Fell. Roy. Soc. Trop. Med. & Hyg.; Child Pub. Health Interest Gp. Prev: Specialist Regist. (Paediat. IC) St. Mary's Hosp. Lond.; SpR (Community Paeds) Roy. Hamp. Co. Hosp., Winchester.; SpR (Community Paeds.) E+ N Herts.

REYNOLDS, Margaret Mary The Medical Centre, Hadlow Old School, School Lane, Hadlow, Tonbridge TN11 0ET Tel: 01732 850248; Little Spitzbrook, Collier St, Tonbridge TN12 9RB Tel: 0189273 291 — MRCS Eng. LRCP Lond. 1965; MRCGP 1987. (Roy. Free) Prev: Clinic Med. Off. Family Plann. Servs. Kent AHA.

REYNOLDS, Mari Wyn Morden Hall Medical Centre, 256 Morden Road, London SW19 3DA Tel: 020 8540 0585 — MB BS 1985 Lond.; Dip. Pract. Dermat. Wales 1992; DRCOG 1989.

REYNOLDS, Martin Francis 10 Duns Crescent, Wishaw ML2 8SF — MB ChB 1980 Glas.; MRCGP 1988; DAvMed FOM RCP Lond. 1990; DRCOG 1987.

REYNOLDS, Martin Richard Finch (retired) — MB ChB 1966 Bristol; FRCP Lond. 1996; FFPHM RCP (UK) 1989; FFCM RCP (UK) 1980, M 1974; DPH Bristol 1969. Prev: Assoc. Dir. Health Policy & Pub. Health E. Riding HA.

REYNOLDS, Mary Angela Ladycroft, 118 Marsh Lane, Mill Hill, London NW7 4PE Tel: 020 8906 1401 — MB BS 1963 Lond.; FBIM 1979. (Char. Cross) Asst. Gen. Manager, Chief Underwriter & Chief Med. Off. Canada Life Assur. Co.; Chairm. Med Affairs Panel, Life Offices Assn. Socs: Fell. Roy. Soc. Med.; (Pres.) Assur. Med. Soc.; BMA. Prev: Med Adviser Amer. Embassy, Lond.; Ho. Surg. & Ho. Phys. St. Nicholas Hosp. Lond; Ho. Phys. Whittington Hosp. Lond.

REYNOLDS, Maureen Teresa Leeds Student Medical Practice, 4 Blenheim Court, Blenheim Walk, Leeds LS2 9AH Tel: 0113 295 4488 Fax: 0113 295 4499; 23 Shire Oak Road, Headingley, Leeds LS6 2DD Tel: 0113 275 4689 — MB ChB 1979 Bristol; BSc (Physiol. Biochem.) Soton. 1974; MRCP (UK) 1994; Dip. GU Med. Soc. Apoth. Lond. 1991; DRCOG 1982. (Bristol) Gen. Practitioner, Leeds Stud. Med. Pract. Prev: Cons. Genitourin. Med. Leeds Gen. Infirm.

REYNOLDS, Michael Anthony Buxton Health Centre, Bath Road, Buxton SK17 6HH Tel: 01298 79251; 21 Lansdowne Road, Buxton SK17 6RR Tel: 01298 23376 — MB ChB 1976 Sheff.; FRCPCH 1997; FRCP (Lond.) 1997; MRCP (UK) 1979. (Sheffield) Cons. Community Paediat. N. Derbysh. HA. Socs: Fell. Roy. Coll. Paediat. & Child Health; Brit. Assn. Community Child Health; BACCH. Prev: SCMO Halton HA; Regist. (Paediat.) Liverp. HA.

REYNOLDS, Michael John 50 Strouden Avenue, Queen's Park, Bournemouth BH8 9HX — MB BS 1996 Lond.; BSc (Med. Physics) Lond. 1993. Med. SHO, Old Ch. Hosp. Romford; Staff Christian Med. Fell.sh.

REYNOLDS, Michael Thomas Paul 9 Birdwood Gardens, Mathern, Chepstow NP16 6UF — MB BCh BAO 1989 NUI.

REYNOLDS, Muriel Primrose (retired) The White House, The Heath, East Malling, Maidstone ME19 6JL Tel: 01732 842549 — MB BS Lond. 1949.

REYNOLDS, Neil George Yarm Medical Centre, 1 Worsall Road, Yarm TS15 9DD Tel: 01642 786422 Fax: 01642 785617 — MB ChB 1976 Leeds; DRCOG 1979.

REYNOLDS, Nicholas John 1st Floor Flat, Kirkness House, 11 Edward St., Bathwick, Bath BA2 4DU — MB ChB 1994 Bristol.

REYNOLDS, Professor Nicholas John Department Dermatology, Medical School, University of Newcastle Upon Tyne, Newcastle upon Tyne NE2 4HH Tel: 0191 2227094 Email: n.j.reynolds@ncl.ac.uk — MB BS 1983 Lond.; BSc Lond. 1980, MD 1995; MRCP (UK) 1985; FRCP 1999. (Charing Cross Hospital Medical School) Prof. of Dermat. Univ. of Newc. and Hon. Cons. dermatologst Roy. Infirm. Newc. Prev: Sen. Regist. (Dermat.) Roy. Vict. Infirm. Newc.; Regist. Fell. & Lect. (Dermat.) Univ. Michigan, USA; Regist. (Dermat.) Bristol Roy. Infirm.

REYNOLDS, Nicholas John 46A Trevor Road, West Bridgford, Nottingham NG2 6FT — MB ChB 1995 Leeds.

REYNOLDS, Nicholas Mark Temple House Surgery, Temple House, Temple Street, Keynsham, Bristol BS31 1EJ Tel: 0117 986 2406 Fax: 0117 986 5695 — MB BCh 1987 Wales; MRCGP 1992; DCH RCP Lond. 1991; Dip. Ther. Wales 1998.

REYNOLDS, Nigel Ninewells Hosp., Dundee DD1 9SY; The Peah House, Easter Ballindean, Inchture, Perth PH14 9QS — MB ChB 1989 Dundee; MRCP Glas. 1993. Cons. Castroenterology Ninewells Hosp. Dundee.

REYNOLDS, Patricia Ann Department of Oral & Maxillofacial Surgery, Dental Institute, King's College Hospital, Denmark Hill, London SE5 9RW Tel: 020 7346 3474 Fax: 020 7346 3754 — MB BS 1984 Lond.; BDS Lond. 1977; FDS RCS Eng. 1986; PhD Lond. 1996. (UMDS Guy's Hospital) Sen. Lect. (Oral. & Maxillofacial Surg.) King's Coll. Lond. Socs: Hon. Sec. Craniofacial Soc. GB; Brit. Assn. of Oral & Maxillofacial Surg.s; Univ. Teach.s Oral & Maxillofacial Surg. Prev: Lect. (Oral & Maxillofacial Surg.) King's Coll. Lond.; Regist. (Oral Med. & Oral Surg.) Guy's Hosp. Lond.

REYNOLDS, Patricia Anne Mary Tamside General Hospital, Fountain St., Ashton-under-Lyne OL6 9RW Tel: 0161 331 6000; 9 Sunnyfield Road, Stockport SK4 3HS Tel: 0161 443 2193 — MB ChB 1991 Manch.; BSc (Med. Sci.) St. And. 1988; MRCP Ed. 1997. (St. And. & Manch.) Regist. (Paediat.) Tameside Gen. Hosp. Prev: Regist. (Paediat.) Stepping Hill Hosp.; Regist. (Paediat.) Roy. Oldham Hosp.; SHO (Paediat.) Stepping Hill Hosp.

REYNOLDS, Patricia Marianne Eye Department, Kings College Hospital, Denmark Hill, London SE5 9RS — MB BS Lond. 1963; MRCS Eng. LRCP Lond. 1963; MRCOphth 1989; DO Eng. 1965; AMQ 1968. (King's Coll. Hosp.) Hon. Lect. & Assoc. Specialist (Ophth.) King's Coll. Hosp. Sch. of Med. & Dent. Lond. Socs: BMA & S.. Ophth. Soc.

REYNOLDS, Paul Dominic 5 Kellett Mount, Leeds LS12 4AJ — MB BS 1986 Lond.; MRCP (UK) 1990. Specialist Regist. (Gastroenterol.) W. Yorks. Rotat. Prev: Research Regist. (Gastroenterol.) Addenbrooke's Hosp. Camb.

REYNOLDS, Paul Jonathan Pembury Hospital, Pembury, Tunbridge Wells TN2 4QJ — MB BS 1985 Lond.; BSc (Hons.) Lond. 1982; FRCP Ed. 1996; FRCP Lond. 1998. Cons. Phys. (Med. for Elderly) Pembury Hosp. Tunbridge Wells. Prev: Sen. Regist. (Gen. Med.) Soton. Univ. Hosps.; Sen. Regist. (Gen. Med.) Bournemouth & ChristCh. Hosps.; Regist. (Gen. Med.) Basingstoke Gen. Hosp.

REYNOLDS, Paul Joseph 38 Whitmore Road, Harrow HA1 4AD — MB BS 1992 Lond.

REYNOLDS, Peter Maxwell Gore 3 Alloway Park, Ayr KA7 2AW Tel: 01292 262730 Email: peter@psreynolds.demon.co.uk — MB BChir Camb. 1970; MA Camb. 1971; FRCP Glas. 1983; MRCP (UK) 1973. (Westm.) Cons. Phys. (Gen. Med. & Rheum.) The Ayr Hosp. Socs: Brit. Soc. Rheum.; Scott. Soc. Phys.; BMA. Prev: Sen. Regist. Leicester Roy. Infirm.; Regist. Aberd. Roy. Infirm. & Centre for Rheum. Dis. Glas.

REYNOLDS, Peter Robert 44 Arundel Road, Kingston upon Thames KT1 3RZ Tel: 020 8942 7102 — MB BS 1990 Lond.; MRCP (Paediat.) (UK) 1997; MRCGP 1993; DRCOG 1993. (St. Barths.) Paediat. Specialist Regist. (N. Thames).

REYNOLDS, Philip Alfred Purton Surgery, High Street, Purton, Swindon SN5 4BD — MB BS 1984 Lond.; 1999 (Dip. Trav. Med.) Royal Free Hosp.; BSc Lond. 1981; MRCGP 1989; DRCOG 1990. Clin. Asst. Dermat. Cirencester Hosp. Socs: Christ. Med. Fell.sh.; BMA; ISTM. Prev: Trainee GP Dorset VTS; SHO (Psychiat., A & E, Orthop. & Dermat.) E. Dorset HA; SHO (O & G) Shoreham.

REYNOLDS, Philip Arthur Padgate Medical Centre, 12 Station Road South, Padgate, Warrington WA2 0RX Tel: 01925 815333 Fax: 01925 813650; The Swallows, Cann Lane, Appleton, Warrington WA4 5NJ — MB ChB 1986 Manch.; MRCGP 1990; DRCOG 1989.

REYNOLDS, Rachel 9 Alexandra Road, Colwyn Bay LL29 7YB — BM BS 1978 Nottm.

REYNOLDS, Rebecca Mary MRC EE Unit, Southampton University Hospital NHS Trust, Tremona Road, Souton, Southampton SO16 6YD Tel: 02380 777624 Email: rmr@mrs.soton.ac.uk; The Coach House, Bicclescombe Pk Road, Ilfracombe EX34 8EU Tel: 01271 863686 — BM BCh 1992 Oxf.; MA Oxf. 1989; MRCP (UK) 1995. (Oxf.) Research Fell. (Med. Research Counc.) Soton. Univ. Hosps. Socs: Med. Defence Union; BMA. Prev: Regist. (Med.) Soton. Univ. Hosps.; SHO (Med.) Soton. Univ. Hosps.; Ho. Off. (Surg.) Oxf.

REYNOLDS, Robert Hugh (retired) White Briars, Slinfold, Horsham RH13 7RR Tel: 01403 790348 Email: mid7545@aol.com — MB BChir 1951 Camb.; MA Camb. 1982; FRCGP 1982, M 1963; DObst RCOG 1953. Prev: Nuffield Foundat. Trav. Fell. For GPs. 1964.

REYNOLDS, Mr Robert John 85A Pilton Street, Barnstaple EX31 1PQ Tel: 01271 372178 — MB ChB 1974 Ed.; FRCS Eng. 1980.

REYNOLDS, Mr Robert Philip The Health Centre, Queensway, Billingham TS23 2LA Tel: 01642 554967; 10 Crooks Barn Lane, Norton, Stockton-on-Tees TS20 1LW — MB ChB 1975 Sheff.; FRCS Eng. 1981; MRCGP 1991.

REYNOLDS, Sally May Luther Street Primary Care Ltd, Luther Street, PO Box 7, Oxford OX1 1TD Tel: 01865 726008 Fax: 01865 204133 — MB ChB 1972 Bristol; BA Camb. 1969. (Bristol) Med. Dir. Luther St. Med. Centre for Homeless Oxf.

REYNOLDS

REYNOLDS, Sarah Elizabeth (Wells) 10 Parkview Avenue, Burley, Leeds LS4 2LH; 22 Greenhill, Burgot, Bromsgrove B60 1BJ — MB ChB 1997 Leeds.

REYNOLDS, Mrs Sarah Frances Cygnet Wing, Bedford Hospital South Wing, Kempston Road, Bedford MK42 9DJ Tel: 01234 355122; 11 Prestwick Road, Biddenham, Bedford MK40 4FH — MB BS 1988 Lond.; MRCOG 1995. Cons. (O & G) Bedford Hosp. Bedford. Prev: Research Fell. (Urogyn.) St. Geo. Hosp. Lond.; SpR. (O & G) St. Thomas W. Region.

REYNOLDS, Sheila Mary 2 Langham Mount, Langham Road, Bowdon, Altrincham WA14 3NN Tel: 0161 928 7131 — MB ChB 1951 Manch.

REYNOLDS, Thomas (retired) Elm House, Warkworth, Morpeth NE65 0SP Tel: 01665 711261 — MB BS 1959 Durh.

REYNOLDS, Thomas Joseph UCLMS, Department of Psychiatry & Behavioural Sciences, 2nd Floor Woolfson Building, 48 Riding House St., London W1N 8AA Tel: 020 7323 1459 Email: t.reynolds@ucl.ac.uk; 59 Barry Road, London SE22 0HR — MB BCh BAO 1988 NUI; MMedSci NUI 1993; MRCPsych 1996. (Univ. Coll. Galway) Clin. Research Fell. & Hon. Specialist Regist. (Psychiat. Elderly) UCLMS.

REYNOLDS, Timothy David Richard The Malthouse Surgery, The Charter, Abingdon OX14 3JY Tel: 01235 524001 Fax: 01235 532197 — MB ChB 1972 Bristol; MRCGP 1978; DObst RCOG 1974. (Bristol)

REYNOLDS, Timothy Henry 417 Weedon Road, Duston, Northampton NN5 4EX — MB ChB 1969 Manch.

REYNOLDS, Professor Timothy Mark Clinical Chemistry Department, Queen's Hospital, Belvedere Road, Burton-on-Trent DE13 0RB Tel: 01283 566333 Ext: 4035 Fax: 01283 593064 Email: tim.reynolds@clinichem.demon.co.uk; 79 The Moorlands, Coleorton, Coalville LE67 8GG — MB ChB 1984 Leeds; BSc (Hons.) Leeds 1981, MD 1994; MRCPath 1991; FRCP 2000 (Path). Cons. Chem. Path. Qu.s Hosp., Burton on Trent; Prof. Chem. Pathol. Wolverhampton Univ. Socs: Assn. Clin. Biochem.s (Reg. Vice Chairm.); Assn. Clin. Path. (Vice Chairm. Clin. Chem. SAC). Prev: Sen. Regist. (Chem. Path.) Univ. Hosp. Wales & Roy. Gwent Hosp. Newport; Regist. Rotat. (Chem. Path.) W. Midl.

REYNOLDS, Valerie Joan Serjeant Bendlowes Cottage, 5 Brook St, Great Bardfield, Braintree CM7 4RQ Tel: 01371 810515 — MB BS 1961 Lond.; MRCS Eng. LRCP Lond. 1961; Dip. Ven. 1977. (Lond. Hosp.) Cons. Genitourin. Med. Suff. Socs: BMA. Prev: Sen. Regist. (Genitourin. Med.) Addenbrooke's Hosp. Camb.; Cons.Gv.Med.W. Suff.

REYNOLDS, William Henry Ladycroft, 118 Marsh Lane, Mill Hill, London NW7 4PE Tel: 020 8906 1401 — MRCS Eng. LRCP Lond. 1929. (Cardiff) Socs: BMA. Prev: Treasury Med. Off. & Admiralty Surg. & Agent; Chairm. Med. Bd., DHSS; Edr. Catholic Med. Quar.

REYNOLDS, Zsuzanna Maria Brannams Medical Centre, Brannams Square, Kiln Lane, Barnstaple EX32 8AP Tel: 01271 329004 Fax: 01271 346785; 85A Pilton Street, Barnstaple EX31 1PQ Tel: 01271 372178 — MD 1975 Debrecen Hungary; MFFP 1995; FFP &RHC, RCOG. 1995. SCHO, FP; GP. Prev: CHO, FP.

REZAUL-KARIM, Sheikh Muhammad The Surgery, 108 Victoria Road, Pinxton, Nottingham NG16 6NH Tel: 01773 810207 — MB BS 1969 Dacca.

REZK, Rezk Nicola 67 Lushington Hill, Wootton, Ryde PO33 4NR — MB BCh 1974 Cairo; MRCOG 1983.

REZVANI, Katayoun 63 Rosebank, Holyport Road, London SW6 6LJ — MB BS 1993 Lond.

RFIDAH, El Hussein Ibrahim East Kent Hospital Trust, Queen Elizabeth, the Queen Mother Hospital, St Peters Road, Margate CT9 4AN Tel: 01843 225544 Fax: 01843 234589; 10 Bridleway Gardens, Broadstairs CT10 2LG Tel: 01843 600139 — MB BCh 1981 Al Fateh, Libya; MRCPI 1988; DCH Dub. 1986; FRCPCH 1997. (Al Fateh, Libya) Cons. Paediatrist E. Kent Hosp. NHS Trust, QEQM Hosp., Margate. Socs: Roy. Coll. Paediatry and Childhealth; Internat. Paediatric Nephrol. Assn.; Brit. Assn. of Paediat. Nephrol. Prev: Cons. (long term locum) Paediat. Nephrol. Roy. Vict. Infirm. Newc.; Research Fell. & Regist. (Paediat.) Roy. Hosp. Sick Childr. Glas.; Regist. (Neonat..) Rutherglen Matern. Hosp.

RHATIGAN, Maire Caitriona Flat 6, Lansdowne House, Wilmslow Road, Manchester M20 6UJ — MB BCh BAO 1985 NUI; FRCOPhth 1992.

RHEAD, Emma 8B Fulwood Park, Liverpool L17 5AH — MB ChB 1994 Liverp.

RHEEM, Ju Yun 56 Rotherhithe Old Road, London SE16 2QD — MB BS 1997 Lond.

RHEIN, Helga Maria Muirhouse Medical Group, 1 Muirhouse Avenue, Edinburgh EH4 4PL Tel: 0131 332 2201; 37 Claremont Bank, Edinburgh EH7 4DR — State Exam Med 1978 Frankfurt.

RHIND, Elizabeth (retired) 26 Countisbury Drive, Childwall, Liverpool L16 0JJ — MB ChB Liverp. 1947. Anaesth Walton Prison Liverp. Prev: Anaesth. Deva, Mostyn & Leasowe Pk. Hosps.

RHIND, George Brown 26A Mansionhouse Road, Edinburgh EH9 2JD — MB ChB 1977 Glas.; FRCP Ed. 1990; MRCP (UK) 1980.

RHIND, Gordon Baird 23 Rubislaw Terrace, Aberdeen AB10 1XE Tel: 01224 643665; 32 Harlaw Road, Aberdeen AB15 4YY Tel: 01224 310129 — MB ChB 1965 Aberd.; MRCGP 1975. (Aberd.) Hosp. Pract. (Orthop.) Aberd. Roy. Infirm.; Police Surg. Grampian Police.

RHIND, Mr James Ronald Dryburn, North Road, Durham DH1 5TW Tel: 0191 333 2279; 41 Valley Drive, Hartlepool TS26 0AL Tel: 01429 236589 — MB ChB 1965 Leeds; FRCS Eng. 1972; Specialist Accredit (Urol.) RCS Lond. 1979. (Leeds) Cons. Urol. N. Durh. Acute Hosps NHS Trust. Socs: Brit. Assn. Urol. Surgs.; BMA; EAU. Prev: Cons. Urol. Hartlepool & Peterlee Trust; Sen. Regist. (Urol.) Leeds AHA (T); Regist. Inst. Urol. Lond.

RHIND, Robin Ann St. Helier Hospital, Wrythe Lane, Carshalton SM5 1AA Tel: 020 8644 4343; 33 The Crescent, Wimbledon Park, London SW19 8AW Tel: 020 8947 3233 — MB BS 1964 Queensland; FFA RCS Eng. 1971. (Queensld.) Assoc. Specialist in Anaesth.

RHIND, Thomas Peter Ferrari Morden Hall Medical Centre, 256 Morden Road, London SW19 3DA Tel: 020 8540 0585 Fax: 020 8542 4480; 33 The Crescent, London SW19 8AW Tel: 020 8947 3233 — MB BS 1969 Lond.; MRCS Eng. LRCP Lond. 1969; MRCP (UK) 1973; DA Eng. 1971. (Lond. Hosp.)

RHODEN, Frances Mary Rudrashetty and Partners, Mary Potter Health Centre, Gregory Boulevard, Hyson Green, Nottingham NG7 5HY; 2 Claremont Gardens, Carrington, Nottingham NG5 1BE — BM BS 1985 Nottm.; MRCGP 1989; Cert. Family Plann. JCC 1989. Socs: BMA. Prev: Clin. Med. Off. Memor. Hse. Nottm. Community Health NHS Trust.

RHODEN, Harold Michael (retired) 16 Insole Grove E., Llandaff, Cardiff CF5 2HP Tel: 029 2056 3731 — MB BCh 1955 Wales; ECFMG Cert. USA 1967. Adjudicating Med. Pract. for Indust. Injuries & Prescribed Dis. Prev: Sen. Asst. Resid. Gtr. Baltimore Med. Center, USA.

RHODEN, Walter Ernest Doctors' Mess, Royal Preston Hospital, Sharoe Green Lane, Fulwood, Preston PR2 9HT — MB ChB 1984 Manch.

RHODES, Mr Alan (retired) — MRCS Eng. LRCP Lond. 1959; BSc (Hons.) Birm. 1956, MB ChB (Hons.) 1959; FRCS Eng. 1966. Prev: Sen. Regist. (Surg.) United Birm. Hosps.

RHODES, Alison Jane Student Health Centre, De Montfort University, The Gateway, Leicester LE1 9BH Tel: 0116 257 7594 Fax: 0116 257 7614 — MB ChB 1977 Aberd.; DRCOG 1979. (Aberd.) GP De Montfort Surg. Socs: Brit. Assn. Health Servs. in Higher Ed. Prev: GP Leicester Stud. Health Serv.

RHODES, Andrew Department of Intensive Care, St George's Hospital, Blacksmaw Road, Tooting, London SW17 0QT Tel: 020 8672 1225 Email: arhodis@dial.pipex.com — MB BS 1990 Lond.; MRCP (UK) 1993; FRCA 1994. Cons., IC & Anaesth., St Geo.'s Hosp Lond. Prev: Regist. & SHO Rotat. (Anaesth.) St. Geo. Hosp. Lond.; SHO (Gen. Med.) St Heliers Hosp. Carshalton; SHO (Geriat. Med.) Soton. Gen. Hosp.

RHODES, Anita Izabela 12 Camel Grove, Kingston upon Thames KT2 5GR — MB BS 1991 Lond.; BSc (Hons.) Lond. 1988; MRCP (UK) 1995; FRCR Lond. 1999. (SGHTIS) Regist. (Radiol.) St. Mary's Hosp. Lond. Socs: Fell. RCR. Prev: Regist. (Gen. Med.) St. Heliers' Hosp. Carshalton; SHO (Radiother.) Roy. Marsden Hosp. Surrey; SHO (Cardiol.) St Geo. Hosp. Lond.

RHODES, Benjamin 65 Beauval Road, London SE22 8UH — MB BS 1998 Lond.; MB BS Lond 1998.

RHODES, Caroline Ann Mount Street Surgery, 69 Mount Street, Coventry CV5 8DE Tel: 024 7667 2277 Fax: 024 7671 7352; Stanmore, 15 Stoneleigh Road, Coventry CV4 7AB Tel: 024 76 414919 — MB ChB 1977 Birm.; BSc Birm. 1974; MRCP (UK) 1979; DRCOG 1981. (Birmingham) GP Coventry. Socs: LMC & BMA.

RHODES, Catharine Alison 3 Road 17 Flat 5, Maadi, Cairo, Egypt Email: stjohn1@mailexcite.com; 90 Kidbrooke Park Road, Blackheath, London SE3 0DX — MB ChB 1988 Bristol; MRCOG 1996. Research Fell. Egypt IVF-ET Centre, Cairo. Prev: p/t Specialist Regist. (Obst. & Gyn.) City Hosp. Trust Birm.

RHODES, Cecil David Patterson (retired) Tregare, Chagford, Newton Abbot TQ13 8AR Tel: 01647 433480 — MB BS 1958 Lond.; MRCS Eng. LRCP Lond. 1958; DCH Eng. 1966; DObst RCOG 1965. Prev: Regist. (Path.) St. Geo. Hosp. Lond.

RHODES, David James (retired) The Spinney, Hunts Lane, Felmersham, Bedford MK43 7JQ Tel: 01234 782460 Fax: 01234 782086 Email: countryheart@aol.com — MB BS Lond. 1966; FRCP 2000; MRCS Eng. LRCP Lond. 1966; MRCGP 1971; DObst RCOG 1968. Indep. GP & Phys. Co. Heart & Healthcare Clinic Bedford.; Med. Off. to Human Stud.s Unit, (Colworth Research), UNILEVER Plc Laboratories; Mem. of Edit. Bd. - Cardiabetes. Prev: Gen. Practitioner, Harrold, Bedford.

RHODES, Edith (retired) 42 Erskine Hill, London NW11 6HD — MRCS Eng. LRCP Lond. 1941; MD Camb. 1947, MB BChir 1942; FFA RCS Eng. 1955; DA Eng. 1944.

RHODES, Elizabeth Geraldine Helen Springfield, 34 Gorse Lane, West Kirby, Wirral CH48 8BH Tel: 01244 365377 — MD 1993 Lond.; MB BS 1976; FRCP (UK) 1978; FRCPath 1989. Cons. Haemat. Countess of Chester Hosp. Prev: Sen. Regist. (Haemat.) Qu. Eliz. Hosp. Birm.; Regist. (Haemat.) Roy. Free Hosp. Lond.; SHO (Med.) Roy. N.. Hosp. Lond.

RHODES, Ellen Linda (retired) 3 Pelhams Close, Esher KT10 8QB Tel: 01372 466127 — MB ChB 1944 Leeds; FRCP Lond. 1975, M 1960; DCH Eng. 1953. Prev: Cons. Dermat. St. Helier Carshalton & Kingston Hosps.

RHODES, Gerald Anthony Barn Surgery, Christchurch Medical Centre, Purewell Cross Road, Christchurch BH23 3AF Tel: 01202 486456 Fax: 01202 486678; 8 Island View Avenue, Friars Cliff, Christchurch BH23 4DS Tel: 0145 52 72674 — LRCPI & LM, LRSCI & LM 1972; LRCPI & LM, LRCSI & LM 1972; DObst RCOG 1975.

RHODES, Helen Louise — MB ChB 1992 Manch.; BSc (Hons.) 1990; MRCP (UK) 1995. (University of Manchester) Research Regis. Respirat. Paediat. Poole Hosp.; Specialist Regist. Respirat. Paediat. Soton. Gen. Hosp. Socs: MRCPCH. Prev: Specialist Regist. (Paediat.), Poole Gen. Hosp.; Regist. (Paediat.) Roy. Childr.'s Hosp. Melbourne Australia; Specialist Regist. Paedriatric Intens. Care Soton. Gen. Hosp.

RHODES, John (retired) 30 Netherfield Avenue, Eastbourne BN23 7BS Tel: 01323 769368 — MB BS 1954 Lond.; MRCS Eng. LRCP Lond. 1954; DMRD ENG 1975; FFR 1962; FRCR 1975. Prev: Cons. Radiol. E.bourne HA.

RHODES, Professor John (retired) 25 Nantfawr Road, Cyncoed, Cardiff CF23 6JQ Tel: 029 20 762734 Fax: 029 20 762734 Email: jjrhodes1@aol.com — BSc Manch. 1957, MD 1965, MB ChB 1960; FRCP Lond. 1974, M 1962. Prof. (Hon.) 1987 Univ. Hosp. Wales Cardiff. Prev: Cons. Gastroenterol. Univ. Hosp. Wales Cardiff.

RHODES, John David (retired) 33 Scott Lane, Riddlesden, Keighley BD20 5BU Tel: 01535 669551 — MB ChB 1958 Manch. Prev: GP Shipley, W. Yorks.

RHODES, Jonathan Kenneth James 1FR, 59 The Promenade, Edinburgh EH15 2BS — MB ChB 1990 Ed.

RHODES, Professor Jonathan Michael Department of Medicine, University of Liverpool, Liverpool L69 3GA Tel: 0151 706 4073 Fax: 0151 706 5802 Email: rhodesjm@liverpool.ac.uk — MB BChir 1974 Camb.; MD Camb. 1982, MA 1973; FRCP Lond. 1989; MRCP (UK) 1975. (St. Thos.) Prof. Gastroenterol. & Hon. Cons. Phys. Roy. Liverp. Hosp. Socs: Assn. Phys. Soc.; Fell. Acad. Med. Sci; Brit. Soc. Gastroenterol. (Chairm. Educat. Comm.). Prev: Sen. Regist. (Med.) Qu. Eliz. Hosp. Birm.; Hon. Lect. Med. Unit Roy. Free Hosp. Lond.; SHO Hammersmith Hosp. Lond.

RHODES, Juliet Elise 38 Ena Avenue, Nottingham NG2 4NB — BM BS 1989 Nottm.; MRCGP (Distinc.) 1994.

RHODES, Katharine Emma The Surgery, 30 Beeston Fields Drive, Beeston, Nottingham NG9 3DB; 11 Mossdale Road, Sherwood, Nottingham NG5 3GX — BM BS 1986 Nottm.; BMedSci Nottm. 1984; MRCGP 1990; DRCOG 1990; DGM RCP Lond. 1988. (Nottm.) Lect. (Gen. Pract.) Nottm. Socs: BMA. Prev: Trainee GP Nottm. VTS; SHO MacMillon Fell. Hayward Hse. Nottm.

RHODES, Kenneth Michael Bromley Hospitals NHS Trust, Academic Department of Elderly Medicine, Orpington Hospital, Sevenoaks Road, Orpington BR6 9JU — MB BS 1973 Lond.; MRCP (UK) 1978; FRCP. (Westm.) Cons. Phys. Bromley NHS Trust. Socs: Brit. Geriat. Soc. Prev: Cons. Phsyician James Paget Hosp. Gt. Yarmouth; Sen. Regist. (Health c/o Elderly) Nottm.; Specialist Phys. Vanuatu, S. Pacific.

RHODES, Leonaura Ursula Nicomis 11 Camberley Avenue, West Wimbledon, London SW20 0BG — MB ChB 1992 Manch.; DFFP 1995; DRCOG 1995. GP Regist. Wimbledon, Lond. Prev: SHO (O & G & A & E) Kingston; SHO (Paediat.) Bury.

RHODES, Lesley Elizabeth Department of Medicine, University Clinical Departments, University of Liverpool, Liverpool L69 3SA Tel: 0151 706 4030 Fax: 0151 706 5842 Email: lerhodes@liverpool.ac.uk; 315 The Colonnades, Albert Dock, Liverpool L3 4AB — MB BS 1982 Lond.; BSc (1st cl. Hons.) Lond. 1979; MD (Mechanisms of UVB-induced erythema) Liverp. 1995; MRCP (UK) 1985; AKC 1979; FRCP 1999. (Kings Coll. Hosp. Med. Sch. Lond.) Cons. Dermat. Roy. Liverp. Univ. Hosp.; Sen. Clin. Lect. (Med.) Univ. Liverp. Socs: Brit. Assn. Dermat. (Ex-Jun. Rep. Audit Sub. Comm.); Eur. Soc. Photobiol.; Comm. Mem. Brit. Photodermatol. Gp. Prev: Research Fell. Wellman Laborats. PhotoMed. Boston, Mass., USA; Sen. Regist. (Dermat. & Haemat.) Roy. Liverp. Hosp.

RHODES, Martin Moorlands Surgery, 139 Willow Road, Darlington DL3 9JP Tel: 01325 469168 — MB BS 1972 Newc.; MRCGP 1976.

RHODES, Martin John 20 Briar Road, Nether Edge, Sheffield S7 1SA — MB ChB 1993 Sheff.; MA Oxf. 1983. SHO, SCBU, N.ern Gen. Hosp. Sheff. Prev: SHO (Paediat.) Sheff. Childr. Hosp.; SHO (A & E) Roy. Hallamsh. Hosp. Sheff.

RHODES, Martin Trevor The Medical Centre, 45 Enderley Road, Harrow Weald, Harrow HA3 5HF Tel: 020 8863 3333; 140 Woodcock Hill, Kenton, Harrow HA3 0JN — MB BS 1973 Lond.; FRCGP 1990, M 1977; DObst RCOG 1975; MA Lond. 1997. GP Assoc. N.wick Pk. Hosp. Harrow; Assoc. Dean (Gen. Pract.) N. Thames; Mem. Panel of Assessors GMC. Prev: Trainee GP N.wick Pk. VTS; Course Organiser N.wick Pk. VTS.

RHODES, Mr Michael Department of General Surgery, Norfolk & Norwich NHS Trust, Norwich NR1 3SR Tel: 01603 286286 — BM BCh 1984 Oxf.; MA Camb. 1985; MD Newc. 1991; FRCS Eng. 1988. Cons. Surg. Gastroenterol. Norf. & Norwich NHS Trust; Hon. Reacher Surg., UEA. Socs: BSG; AESGBI; AGA.

RHODES, Michael John Yew Tree Cottage, Fen Road, Owmby-by-Spital, Market Rasen LN8 2HP — BM BS 1978 Nottm.; BMedSci (Hons.) Nottm. 1976; MPH Leeds 1984; MRCGP 1982; DRCOG 1981.

RHODES, Nicholas Duncan 3 Clarence Grove, Horsforth, Leeds LS18 4LA — MB ChB 1996 Leeds.

RHODES, Paul Charles Burnley Wood Medical Centre, 50 Parliament Street, Burnley BB11 3JX Tel: 01282 425521 Fax: 01282 832556; 3 Clover Crescent, Ightenhill, Burnley BB12 0EX Tel: 01282 454956 — MB ChB 1980 Manch.

RHODES, Paul Martin Scotstown Medical Centre, Cairnfold Road, Bridge of Don, Aberdeen AB22 8LD Tel: 01224 702149 Fax: 01224 706688 — MB ChB 1977 Aberd.; MRCGP 1981.

RHODES, Peter 25 Nant Fawr Road, Cyncoed, Cardiff CF23 6JQ Tel: 029 20 762 734 Fax: 01222 762734 — MB BChir 1989 Camb.; MA Camb. 1992; BA Camb. 1986; MD Camb. 1995; MRCP (UK) 1992; FRCA 1997. (Camb.) Specialist Regist. (Intens. Care/Anaesth.) Soton. Gen. Hosp. Soton. Prev: Resid./SHO (Intens. Care Med.) Univ. Hosp. Wales Cardiff; Brit. Heart Foundat. Research Fell. & Hon. Med. Regist. Wellcome Research Laborats. Beckenham; SHO Rotat. (Gen. Med.) Soton. Univ. Teachg. Hosps.

RHODES, Peter Llewellyn (retired) Station House, Little Hereford, Ludlow SY8 4LN Tel: 01584 711424 — MRCS Eng. LRCP Lond. 1945; MA Camb. 1946. Prev: GP Camb.

RHODES, Professor Philip (retired) 1 Wakerley Court, Wakerley, Oakham LE15 8NZ Tel: 01572 747871 — MB BChir 1946 Camb.;

RHODES

MA Camb. 1953; FRCS Eng. 1953; FRACMA 1976; FRCOG 1964, M 1956; FFOM RCP Lond. 1990. Prev: Postgrad. Dean Wessex RHA & Prof. Postgrad. Med. Educat. Univ. Soton.

RHODES, Richard Jonathan Richmond Group Medical Centre, 1 Albion Street, Ashton-under-Lyne OL6 6HF Tel: 0161 339 9161 Fax: 0161 343 5131; 7 Clifton Road, Heaton Moor, Stockport SK4 4DD — MB ChB 1971 Manch.; BSc (Hons.) (Elec. Engin.) Manch. 1964; MRCS Eng. LRCP Lond. 1971; MFFP 1993; FRCOG 1995, M 1978. (Manchester) GP Ashton-under-Lyne; Instruc. Doctor (Family Plann.) Tameside AHA. Socs: NW Soc. Study of Sexual Med. & Family Plann.; Chairm. W. Pennine LMC. Prev: Regist. (O & G) Tameside Gen. Hosp. Ashton-under-Lyne; Surg. Lt. RN.

RHODES, Richard Ronald Queensway Medical Centre, Doctors Surgery, Queensway, Poulton-le-Fylde FY6 7ST Tel: 01253 890219 Fax: 01253 894222; Hurstwood, 133 Carr Head Lane, Poulton-le-Fylde FY6 8EG — MB ChB 1982 Manch.; MRCGP 1986; DRCOG 1984; DCH RCP Lond. 1986.

RHODES, Simon 8 Emery Close, Altrincham WA14 1NJ — MB ChB 1998 Manch.; MB ChB Manch 1998.

RHODES, Simon Mitchell Edenfield Road Surgery, Cutgate Shopping Precinct, Edenfield Road, Rochdale OL11 5AQ Tel: 01706 344044 Fax: 01706 526882; 19 Passmonds Way, Rochdale OL11 5AN Tel: 01706 868810 Fax: 01706 868810 Email: s.m.rhodes@brinternet.com — MB ChB 1985 Manch.; BSc (Hons.) Med. Sci. St. And. 1982; DRCOG 1988. GP Princip. Rochdale. Prev: Trainee GP Rochdale VTS.

RHODES, Steven Myatt and Rhodes, Hermitage Surgery, Dammas Lane, Old Town, Swindon SN1 3EF Tel: 01793 522492 Fax: 01793 512520 — MB ChB 1982 Manch.; MRCGP 1986; DRCOG 1985.

RHYS, Anne Student Health Centre, 1 Marine Terrace, Aberystwyth SY23 2AZ Tel: 01970 622086 Fax: 01970 621914 Email: ahr@aber.ac.uk; Plas Bronmeurig, Ystrad Meurig SY25 6AA — MB BCh 1959 Wales; MB BCh (Distinc. Path. & Surg.) Wales 1959; MRCPsych 1984; MFCM RCP (UK) 1974; DPM Eng. 1967. (Cardiff) Cardiff Med. Soc. Prize 1959; Howell Rees Schol. Med. Univ. Wales; Sen. Clin. Med. Off. (Ment. Health) Ceredigion Health Dist.; Univ. Wales Psych. Socs: Y Gymdeithas Feddygol. Prev: Regist. Hensol Castle Psychiat. Hosp.; SHO Dept. Psych. Med. Middlx. Hosp. Lond.; Ho. Off. United Cardiff Hosps. Llandough.

RHYS, Gwion Gwyddfor, Bow Street SY24 5BJ — MB ChB 1996 Manch.

RHYS, Gwyneth Mared 9 Glynne Street, Cardiff CF11 9NS — MB BCh 1990 Wales; MRCGP 1997; DRCOG 1996. SHO (Med.) King Edwd. VII Hosp., Bermuda. Prev: SHO (Paediat.) Roy. Gwent Hosp. Newport; SHO (A & E) Univ. Hosp. Wales Cardiff; SHO (Med.) Llandough Hosp. Cardiff.

RHYS, Rhian Department of Radiology, Royal Glamorgan Hospital, Ynysmaerdy CF72 8YR Tel: 01443 443443; 12 Bloom Street, Pontcanna CF11 9QE — MB BCh 1985 Wales; FRCS Eng. 1990; FRCR 1996. (Welsch National School of Medicine) Cons. Radiol., Roy. Glam. Hosp., Cardiff. Socs: Roy. Coll. of Radiologists; Head and Neck Sect. of Roy. Soc. of Med. Prev: Specialist Regist. (Radiol.) Univ. Hosp. Wales Cardiff.; Regist. (ENT) Univ. Hosp. Wales Cardiff; SHO (Surg.) Roy. Marsden Hosp. Lond.

RHYS, William Joseph St Ervyl-Glyndwr, CStJ Plas Bronmeurig, Ystrad Meurig SY25 6AA Tel: 0197 45 650; Minffordd, Llangadog SA19 9BU Tel: 0155 03 496 — MB BS 1948 Lond.; MA Camb. 1950; BSc Wales 1945; MRCOG 1961, DObst 1950; MFCM 1974; DPH Wales 1966. (Cardiff & Guy's) High Sheriff Co. Dyfed; Dist. Community Phys. Ceredigion Health Dist.; Med. Adviser Environm. Health Ceredigion DC; Hon. Med. Adviser Welsh Nat. Water Developm. Auth. Socs: Fell. Soc. Community Med.; Nat. Assn. Community Phys. Prev: Squadron Ldr. Inst. Aviat. Med. FarnBoro.; Regist. (O & G) Welsh Nat. Sch. of Med. Cardiff; Ho. Surg. (O & G) Hammersmith Hosp. Lond.

RHYS-DAVIES, Mrs Harriet Emily, MBE (retired) Caledon Cottage, South St., Milborne Port, Sherborne DT9 5DH Tel: 01963 250355 — MB BCh BAO Belf. 1947; DObst RCOG 1951; DCH Eng. 1950.

RHYS-DAVIES, Nigel College Surgery, College Road, Cullompton EX15 1TG Tel: 01884 32373 Fax: 01884 35541; Hayes, Halberton Road, Willand, Cullompton EX15 2QF Tel: 01884 820411 — MB BChir 1967 Camb.; MA, MB Camb. 1967, BChir 1966; MRCGP

1976. Prev: Ho. Surg. & SHO Cas. Dept. Middlx. Hosp. Lond.; SHO Gyn & Obst. Chase Farm Hosp. Enfield.

RHYS-DAVIES, Simon Tudur Main Road Surgery, Main Road, Stickney, Boston PE22 8AA Tel: 01205 480237 Fax: 01205 480987; The Chestnuts, Royal Oak Lane, New Bolingbroke, Boston PE22 7LF — MB ChB 1976 Birm.; DCH Eng. 1980. Trainee Gen. Pract. Lincoln Vocational Train. Scheme. Socs: BMA. Prev: SHO (Obst., Med. & Cas.) Lincs. AHA.

RHYS-DILLON, Cristyn Ceril Glyn Plas Bronmeurig, Ystrad Meurig SY25 6AA Tel: 01974 831650; 23 Cressy Road, Cardiff CF23 5BE Tel: 01222 452686 Email: rhys-dillon@easynet.co.uk — BChir 1992 Camb.; MB BChir Camb. 1992; MA Camb. 1994; MRCP (Lond.) 1997. (Camb. Sch. Med.) Regist. Rheum. Univ. Hosp. Wales, Cardiff. Socs: Y Gymdeithas Feddygol. Prev: SHO (Rheum.) Roy. Lond. Hosp. Lond.; Asst. (Nephrol.) St. Luc., Brussels; SHO (Neurol.) Guy's Hosp. Lond.

RHYS EVANS, Gwilym, MC 2 Camperdown Avenue, Chester-le-Street DH3 4AB Tel: 0191 388 3173 — MB BS 1940 Lond.; DLO Eng. 1947. (St. Bart.) Hon. Surg. (Otolaryngol.) Sunderland HA. Prev: Sen. Regist. (ENT) Coventry & Warw. Hosp.; Regist. Roy. Nat. Throat, Nose & Ear Hosp.; Ho. Surg. (ENT) St. Bart. Hosp. Lond.

RHYS EVANS, Mr Peter Howell 106 Harley Street, London W1N 1AF Tel: 020 7935 3525; The Halt, Smugglers Way, The Sands, Farnham GU10 1NB Tel: 01252 782327 Fax: 01252 782327 Email: peterre@globalnet.co.uk — MB BS 1971 Lond.; FRCS Eng. 1978; MRCS Eng. LRCP Lond. 1971; Dip. Carcinol. Cervicofaciale Paris 1981. (St. Bart.) Cons. Otolaryngol. (Head & Neck Surg. Roy. Marsden & St. Mary's Hosps. Lond.; Vis. Cons. St. Bernards Hosp. Gibraltar; Hon. Cons. ENT RN; Leon Goldman Vis. Prof. Inst. Cape Town, S. Africa; Vis. Pres. Yale Univ. June 1999. Socs: FRSM (Counc.); Counc. Otolaryngol. Research Soc.; Fell. Amer. Head & Neck Soc. Prev: Sen. Regist. Roy. Nat. Throat, Nose & Ear Hosp. Lond. & W. Midl.; Sen. Lect. & Cons. OtyoLaryngol. Qu. Eliz. Hosp. Univ. Birmingham; Interne Etranger (OtorhinoLaryngol.) Gustave-Roussy Inst., Paris.

RIACH, Ian Charles Frazer Corronich, Boat of Garten PH24 3BU Tel: 01479 357; 16 Aignish, Point, Isle of Lewis HS2 Tel: 01851 870744 — MB ChB 1958 Ed.; DMRD 1963. Cons. Radiol. W.. Isles Hosp. Stornoway, I. of Lewis. Socs: BMA, Roy. Coll. Radiols. & Brit. Soc. Gastro-Enterol. Prev: Chief Radiol. Sultanate of Oman & Head Radiol. Roy. Hosp. Muscat; Cons. Radiol. N. Birm. Health Dist.; Sen. Regist. (Radiol.) Childr. & Dudley Rd. Hosps. Birm.

RIAD, Mr Hany Naim 22 Manor Park, Clyst St Mary, Exeter EX5 1BW — MB BCh 1973 Cairo; FRCS Glas. 1983.

RIAD, Mr Magdy Mohamed Amin ENT Department, Victoria Hospital, Hayfield Road, Kirkcaldy KY2 5AH — MB ChB 1979 Ain Shams; FRCS Ed. 1986; MSc (Otolaryngol.) 1983; MD (Otolaryngol.) 1986. Cons ENT Surg. & Head of Ear, Nose & Throat Dept.; Prof. (Otolalrygol.) Ain Shams Univ. Cairo, Egypt. Socs: Collegium Otorhinolaryng. Assn.; Scott. Otolaryngol. Soc.; Brit. Assn. Otol. & Head & Neck Surg.

RIAL, Susan Carolyn The Red Practice, Waterside Health Centre, Beaulieu Road, Hythe SO45 4WX Tel: 023 8084 5955 Fax: 023 8084 1292; Bowness, 1 Forest Front, Butts Ash, Hythe, Southampton SO45 3RG Tel: 02380 844712 — MB BS 1976 Lond. (Middlx.) Prev: SHO (O & G) Soton. Gen. Hosp.; SHO (Rheum.) & Ho. Surg. Middlx. Hosp. Lond.; Ho. Phys. Watford Gen. Hosp.

RIAZ, A Breckfield Road North Surgery, 141 Breckfield Road North, Liverpool L5 4QU Tel: 0151 263 6534.

RIAZ, Amjid The Surgery, 691 Coventry Road, Small Heath, Birmingham B10 0JL Tel: 0121 773 4931 Fax: 0121 753 2210 — MB ChB 1991 Leeds.

RIAZ, Muhammad 2/2, 41 Annette St., Glasgow G42 8EH — MB BS 1973 Punjab; MRCOG 1993.

RIAZ, Mr Nadeem Uddin 14 Condor Court, Guildford GU2 4BP — MB BS 1982 Punjab; FRCS Ed. 1990; FCOphth 1990; DO RCS Eng. 1989.

***RIAZ, Sabiha** 839 Finchley Road, Golders Green, London NW11 8NA Tel: 020 8458 4321; 89-B Hali Road, Gulberg II, Lahore, Pakistan Tel: 0142 874012 — MB BS 1975 Punjab; MRCPath. 1987.

RIAZ, Yasmin 124 St Dunstan's Road, London W6 8RA — MB BS 1995 Lond.

RIBBANS, Mr William John Northampton General Hospital, Cliftonville, Northampton NN1 5BD Tel: 01604 545943 Email: wjribbans@uk-consultants.co.uk — MB BS 1980 Lond.; FRCS 2001 Eng.; BSc (Hons.) Lond. 1977; MChOrth Liverp. 1990; FRCS Ed. (Orth.) 1990; FRCS Ed. 1985. (Roy Free) Cons. Orthop. Surg. N.ampton Gen. Hosp. Socs: Fell. BOA; BMA; BOFSS. Prev: Cons. Orthop. Surg. Roy. Free Hosp. Lond.; Clin. Fell. (Orthop. Surg.) Harvard; Sen. Regist. (Orthop. Surg.) Middlx. Hosp.

RIBBENS, Susara Cornelia 25 Staples Road, Loughton IG10 1HP — MB ChB 1995 Pretoria.

RIBBONS, Richard Michael Cyril Grove Road Surgery, 59-63 Grove Road, Eastbourne BN21 4TX Tel: 01323 720606 Fax: 01323 437444 — MB BS 1984 Lond.; MRCGP 1988; DRCOG 1988. (Guy's Hospital) GP E.bourne. Prev: Trainee GP Hemel Hempstead VTS; Ho. Surg. Orpington Hosp.; Ho. Phys. Joyce Green Hosp. Dartford.

RIBCHESTER, John Martin Whitstable Health Centre, Harbour Street, Whitstable CT5 1BZ Tel: 01277 263033 Fax: 01277 771474; The Oast House, Pean Hill, Whitstable CT5 3BH — MB BS 1975 Lond.; DCH Eng. 1979. (King's Coll. Hosp.) Chairm. Canterbury & Coastal PCG. Socs: Beckett Med. Soc. Prev: Clin. Asst. (Surg.) Qu. Vict. Memor. Hosp.; Jun. Lect. & Demonst. (Anat.) Middlx. Hosp. Med. Sch. Lond.; SHO Rotat. (Surg.) Kent & Canterbury Hosp.

RIBEIRO, Mr Alvin Anthony Hospital of St Cross, Barby Road, Rugby CV22 5PX Tel: 01788 572831; 132/134 Pytchley Road, Rugby CV22 5NG Tel: 01788 575009 — MB BS 1974 Univ. W. Indies; FRCS Ed. 1980. Staff Doctor (A & E) Hosp. of St. Cross Rugby.

RIBEIRO, Anthony 4 Erica Grove, Manor Park, Marton, Middlesbrough TS7 8RY — MD 1959 Lucknow; MB BS 1954, DMRE 1956; DMRT Eng. 1963; DMRD Eng. 1968. (King Geo. Med. Coll. Lucknow) Radiol. Duchess of Kent's Milit. Hosp. Catterick.

RIBEIRO, Mr Bernard Francisco (cons. rooms), The Essex Nuffield Hospital, Brentwood CM15 8EH Tel: 01277 695695 Fax: 01277 201158; Merivale, Howe Green, Sandon, Chelmsford CM2 7TQ Tel: 01245 472158 Fax: 01245 473137 Email: bernard.ribeiro@which.net — MB BS 1967 Lond.; FRCS Eng. 1972; MRCS Eng. LRCP Lond. 1967. (Middlx.) Cons. Surg. Basildon & Orsett Hosps.; Dir. Of UnderGrad. Educat. - Surg. Socs: Fell. Roy. Soc. Med.; Fell. Assn. Surgs. (Past-Pres.); Roy. Coll. Of Surg. Engl. (Counc. Mem.). Prev: Sen. Regist. (Surg.) Middlx. & Centr. Middlx. Hosps.; Lect. (Surg.) Ghana Med. Sch. Accra.

RIBEIRO, Cedric Albert Balham Health Centre, 120 Bedford Hill, London SW12 9HS Tel: 020 8673 1720 Fax: 020 8673 1549 — MB BS 1978 Mysore; BSc (Hons.) Bombay 1972; LRCP LRCS Ed. LRCP Glas. 1979; DTM & H Liverp. 1980. (Kasturba Med. Coll. Mangalore) Clin. Asst. EMI Unit Springfield Hosp. Lond. Prev: Asst. GP Lond.; SHO (A & E & O & G) Arrowe Pk. Hosp. Wirral; SHO (Paediat.) Birkenhead Childr. Hosp.

RIBEIRO, Charles Donald Public Health Laboratory, University Hospital of Wales, Heath Park, Cardiff CF14 4XW Tel: 029 2074 2046 Fax: 029 2074 6403 Email: don.ribeiro@phls.wales.nhs.uk — MB BCh Wales 1969; FRCPath 1988, M 1976; Dip. Bact. Manch. 1975. (Cardiff) Cons. Microbiol. & Ass. Dir. Cardiff Pub. Health Laborat.; Hon. Clin. Teach., Univ. of Wales Coll. of Med. Socs: Assn. Clin. Path.Past Sect, Cambrian Br..; Cardiff Med. Soc. (Past-Pres.); Brit. Infec. Soc. (Past Sect.) Eng. Br. Brit.Soc. Study of Infec. Dis.s. Prev: Sen. Regist. (Bact.) Manch. AHA (T); Regist. (Path.) Soton. Gen. Hosp.; Ho. Phys. Llandough Hosp. Penarth.

RIBEIRO, Maria Dulce Correia 2nd Floor, 126 Amhurst Road, London E8 2AG — MB BS 1986 Lond. SHO Rotat. (Gen. Med.) Kent & Canterbury Hosp.

RIBEIRO, Neil McLaren Northcroft Surgery, Northcroft Lane, Newbury RG14 1BU Tel: 01635 31575 Fax: 01635 551857 — BM 1981 Soton.; DRCOG 1985.

RIBERA CORTADA, Inmaculada 3 The Grange, Walton-on-Thames KT12 3HN — LMS 1994 Lleida.

RIBES PASTOR, Purificacion Anaesthetic Department, Stoke Mandeville Hospital, Mandeville Road, Aylesbury HP21 8AL Tel: 01296 315262 — LMS 1989 Valencia; LMS Valencia 1988; FRCA 1996; FFARCSI 1996; MSc 1989. (Valencia (Spain)) Cons., (Anaesth.) Stoke Mandeville Hosp. Aylesbury. Socs: BMA; AAGBI; OAA. Prev: Specialist Regist. (Anaesth.) Swansea, Moriton & Simpleton Hosps.; Regist. (Anaesth.) Cardiff & Wrexham.

RIBET, Lartigue Pierre Speranza, Turketel Road, Folkestone CT20 2PA Tel: 01303 242065 — MB BS 1944 Lond. (Guy's) Prev: ENT Regist. S.E. Kent Hosp. Gp.; Res. Surg. Off. Roy. Vict. Hosp. Folkestone.

RIBET, Philippe William Lartigue Old Court House Surgery, 27 Wood Street, Barnet EN5 4BB Tel: 020 8449 2388; 21 Camlet Way, Hadley Wood, Barnet EN4 0LH Tel: 020 8449 1120 — MB BS 1971 Lond.; MRCS Eng. LRCP Lond. 1971. (Guy's)

RIBET, Roisin Patricia Old Court House Surgery, 27 Wood Street, Barnet EN5 4BB Tel: 020 8449 2388; 21 Camlet Way, Hadley Wood, Barnet EN4 0LH Tel: 020 8449 1120 — MB BS 1969 Lond.; MRCS Eng. LRCP Lond. 1969; DCH Eng. 1971. (Char. Cross)

RICCIO, Massimo The Priory Hospital, Priory Lane, London SW15 5JJ Tel: 020 8392 4225 Fax: 020 8392 8995 Email: mriccio@roehampton.prioryhealthcare.co.uk — State DMS 1978 Milan; MRCPsych 1987; T(Psych) 1991; FRCPsych 1997. (Univ. Milan) Cons. Adult Gen. Psychiat. Priory Hosp. Lond.; Med. Dir.; Hon. Sen. Lect. Char. Cross & W.m. Med. Sch. Prev: Cons. Adult Gen. Psychiat. Chelsea & W.m. Hosp. Lond.; Lect. & Hon. Sen. Regist. (Psychiat.) Char. Cross Hosp. Lond.; Regist. & SHO Rotat. (Psychiat.) Char. Cross & W.m. Hosp.

***RICE, Alexandra Joan** Quains, Woodlands Road W., Virginia Water GU25 4PL — MB BChir 1994 Camb.; MA Camb. 1996, BA (Hons.) 1992.

RICE, Andrew Sven Cracroft Pain Research, Dept. Anaesthetics, Imperial College, Chelsea & Westminster Hospital Campus, 369 Fulham Road, London W2 1NY Tel: 020 87468156 Fax: 020 82375709 Email: a.rice@ic.ac.uk — MB BS 1982 Lond.; MD (St. Thomas's) Lond. 1991; FFA RCS Eng. 1987. (St. Mary's) Sen. Lect. (Anaesth.) Imperial Coll. Lond.; Hon. Cons. Chronic Pain Managem., Chelsea & W.minster Hosp. Lond. Socs: Pain Soc.; Physiol. Soc.; Soc. for Neurosci. Prev: Sen. Regist. (Anaesth.) Oxf.; Regist. (Anaesth.) & Research Fell. (Neurophysiol.) St. Thos. Hosp. Lond.; Hon. Cons. Pain Relief, St. Marys Hosp. Lond.

RICE, Christopher Paul 9 Meaford Road, Barlaston, Stoke-on-Trent ST12 9EE — MB ChB 1968 Birm.; FFA RCS Eng. 1972. Cons. Anaesth. City Gen. Hosp. Stoke-on-Trent.

RICE, Denis Fitzsimons (retired) 9 Buckingham Court, Westwood Road, Southampton SO17 1HD Tel: 01703 552172 — MB ChB Liverp. 1953. Prev: PMO DHSS.

RICE, Edward Alexander, OBE 31 Wallaford Road, Buckfastleigh TQ11 0AR Tel: 01364 643313 — MB BCh BAO Belf. 1926. Socs: BMA.

RICE, Edward Alexander 76 Park View, Cloughoge, Newry BT35 8LX — MB BCh BAO 1997 Belf.

RICE, Edward Francis 10 Hatchlands, Horsham RH12 5JX — MRCS Eng. LRCP Lond. 1955; DObst RCOG 1959. (Birm.) Div. Surg. St. John Ambul. Brig. Socs: BMA. Prev: Obst. Ho. Surg. Marston Green Matern. Hosp. Birm.; Med. Off. RAF; Ho. Phys. WillesBoro. Hosp. Ashford.

RICE, Elizabeth Daphne Fairmile Hospital, Wallingford OX10 9HH Tel: 01491 651281 Fax: 01491 651128 — MB BS 1975 Lond.; MRCS Eng. LRCP Lond. 1975; MRCPsych. 1981. (Westm.) Cons. Psychiat. of Old Age Fairmile Hosp. Wallingford.

RICE, Gillian Adele Dean Lane Family Practice, 1 Dean Lane, Bedminster, Bristol BS3 1DE Tel: 0117 966 3149 Fax: 0117 953 0699 — MB ChB 1980 Birm.; MPhil Camb. 1984; MRCP (UK) 1983; MRCGP 1985.

RICE, Mr Graham John (retired) The Coach House, Bitham Hall, Avon Dassett, Southam CV47 2AH Tel: 01295 690255 Email: rices@clara.co.uk — MB ChB 1952 Birm.; FRCS Ed. 1961; FRCS Eng. 1961. Prev: Cons. ENT Surg. Coventry Gp. Hosps.

RICE, Hugh Macan Three Gables, Nimms Meadow, Great Shefford, Hungerford RG17 7BZ Tel: 01488 648530 — MB BS 1939 Lond.; MD Lond. 1947; MRCS Eng. LRCP Lond. 1938; FRCPath 1963. (Westm.) Cons. Path. Emerit. Gen. Hosp. Nottm. Socs: (Ex-Vice Pres.) Assn. Clin. Path.; Path. Soc. Prev: Cons. Path. Gen. Hosp., Childr. Hosp. & Highbury Hosp. Nottm.; Maj. RAMC; Ho. Surg. W.m. Hosp. Lond.

RICE, Karl Joseph Lyndhurst, Eureka Place, Ebbw Vale NP23 6PN Tel: 01495 353700 Fax: 01495 353737 — MB BCh BAO 1983 Belf.; MRCPsych 1988. Cons. Psychiat. Ebbw Vale. Prev: Sen. Regist. Rotat. (Psychiat.) S. Wales.

RICE

RICE, Katherine Mary 34 Kings Road, Walton-on-Thames KT12 2RA — MB BS 1987 Lond.; BSc Lond. 1984, MB BS 1987; MRCP (UK) 1990. Specialist Regist. Rotat. (Haemat.) SW Thames. Prev: Regist. (Haemat.) St. Thos. Hosp. Lond., Roy. Hallamsh. & N.. Gen. Hosp. Sheff.

RICE, Katherine Victoria Romaine 17 Minster Road, West Hamstead, London NW2 3SE Tel: 020 842 1039 Email: kate_rice@hotmail.com — MB ChB 1997 Ed.; BSc. Pharm (Edinb) 1995. SHO, Renal Med., Roy. Free Hosp. Lond. Socs: BMA. Prev: SHO A & E; SHO Surg., Edinb. Roy. Infirm.; SHO Medium E.ern Gen Hosp. Edin.

RICE, Mary (retired) 18 Shepherds Way, Liphook GU30 7HF Tel: 01428 723618 — MB BS 1963 Lond.; BA (Hons.) (French) Lond. 1951; MRCS Eng. LRCP Lond. 1963; MRCPsych 1977; DPM Eng. 1966. Prev: Cons. Psychiat. (Psychogeriat.) & Sen. Regist. Graylingwell Hosp. Chichester.

RICE, Michael Hugh Cracroft (retired) River Lodge Surgery, Malling Street, Lewes BN7 2RD Tel: 01273 472233 Fax: 01273 486879 — MB BChir 1961 Camb.; MA Camb. 1961; DObst RCOG 1963. Prev: Med. Off. Brit. Antarctic Survey.

RICE, Neil Elliot Doctors Quarters, Chase Farm Hospital, The Ridgeway, Enfield EN2 8JL; 34 Waterman Way, Wapping, London E1W 2QN Tel: 020 7702 3785 Email: grierice@mc.mail — MB ChB 1990 Pretoria; DA 1996.

RICE, Mr Noel Stephen Cracroft (retired) The Hospitaller, The St John Ophthalmic Hospital, 1 Grosvenor Crescent, London SW1X 7EF Tel: 020 7235 5231 Fax: 020 7235 0796 — MB BChir Camb. 1957; MD Camb. 1965; FRCS Eng. 1966; FCOphth 1988; DO Eng. 1959. Prev: Cons. Surg. Moorfields Eye Hosp.

RICE, Paul DSH Chemical & Biological Sciences, Building 04, Porton Down, Salisbury SP4 0JQ Tel: 01980 613517 Fax: 01980 613741 Email: price1@dsh.gov.uk; 35 Cygnet Drive, Willow Mead, Amesbury, Salisbury SP4 8LQ Tel: 01980 653501 — BM 1982 Soton.; FRCPath 2002; MRCPath 1993. (Univ. Soton.) Prev: Med. Off. Chem. Defence Estab. Porton Down; Regist. (Histopath.) & SHO Soton. Gen. Hosp.; Ho. Off. (Med.) Basingstoke Dist. Hosp.

RICE, Paul Francis 12 Fortfield, Maypole Hill, Dromore BT25 1DD — MB BCh BAO 1992 Belf.

RICE, Peter Francis Leach Health Medical Centre, Leach Health Lane, Rubery, Birmingham B45 9BU Tel: 0121 453 3516 Fax: 0121 457 9256 Email: peter.rice@pc.birminghamha.wmids.nhs.uk; 9 Hewell Lane, Barnt Green, Birmingham B45 8NZ Tel: 0121 445 5014 Email: rice5birm@aol.com — MB ChB 1983 Birm.; MRCGP 1987; DRCOG 1986.

RICE, Peter Martin Sunnyside Royal Hospital, Montrose DD10 9JP Tel: 0167 483361; Keepers Cottage, Crow Wood, Meigle, Blairgowrie PH12 8RB — MB ChB 1981 Glas.; MRCPsych. 1986. Cons. Psychiat. Tayside HB; Hon. Sen. Lect. Univ. Dundee. Prev: Lect. (Psychiat.) Univ. Dundee; Regist. (Psychiat.) Murray Roy. Hosp. Perth; Regist. (Psychiat.) S.. Gen. Hosp. & Leverndale Hosp. Glas.

RICE, Philip Stuart Department of Virology, St Georges.Hosp., 1st Floor Jenner Wing Blackshaw Road, London SW17 0QT Tel: 020 8725 5734 Fax: 020 8725 5694 Email: p.rice@sghms.ac.uk; 34 Kings Road, Walton-on-Thames KT12 2RA Tel: 01932 888774 — MB BS 1987 Lond.; BSc (Hons.) Lond. 1984, MB BS 1987; DRCPath 1994; MRCPath 1998. (St Thomas' Hospital Medical School) Cons.Virol./Hon.Sen.Lect.St Geo.s Hosp. Socs: Soc. Gen. Microbiol.; Amer. Soc. for MicroBiol. Prev: Sen. Regist. (Virol.) St. Thos. Hosp. Lond.

RICE, Robert Harold Wynne Hill Surgery, 51 Hill Street, Lurgan, Craigavon BT66 6BW — MB BCh BAO 1970 Belf.; DRCOG 1979.

RICE-EDWARDS, Mr John Martin Charing Cross Hospital, Fulham Palace Road, London W6 8RF Tel: 020 8846 1182 Fax: 020 8846 7487; Ham House Stables, Ham, Richmond TW10 7RS Tel: 020 8940 6605 — MA, BM BCh Oxf. 1960; FRCS Eng. 1965. (Oxf.) Cons. Neurosurg. Dept. Neurosci. Char. Cross Char. Cross Hosp. Hammersmith Hosp. Trust. Prev: Ho. Phys. & Ho. Surg. Radcliffe Infirm. Oxf.; Sen. Regist. Nat. Hosp. Nerv. Dis. Lond.

RICE-EDWARDS, Susan Anne 41 George Street, Berkhamsted HP4 2EG Tel: 01442 873834 — MRCS Eng. LRCP Lond. 1966; DO Eng. 1975; DObst RCOG 1968. (St. Mary's) Socs: BMA. Prev: PMO Umtata Hosp. Transkei, S. Africa; Med. Off. Jane Furse Memor. Hosp. Sekhukhuneland, S. Africa.

RICE-EVANS, Elisabeth I (retired) 1 Tivoli Lawn, 8 Tivoli Road, Cheltenham GL50 2TG Tel: 01242 518498 — MRCS Eng. LRCP Lond. 1942. Ho. Surg. Roy. Free Hosp. Lond.; Ho. Surg. Roy. Kent & Sussex Hosp.

RICE-JONES, Matilda Claire The Surgery, 1 Glebe Road, Barnes, London SW13 0DR Tel: 020 8748 1065 Fax: 020 8741 8665 — MB BCh 1991 Wales; MRCGP 1996; DCH RCP Lond. 1994; DRCOG 1994.

RICE-OXLEY, Charles Patrick Martins Oak Surgery, 36 High Street, Battle TN33 0EA Tel: 01424 772263/772060; Lower Almonry Farm House, North Trade Road, Battle TN33 0HS — BM BCh 1973 Oxf.; MRCP (UK) 1977.

RICE-OXLEY, John Michael 9 Blyth Grove, Worksop S81 0JG Tel: 01909 472082 — BM BCh 1943 Oxf.; DM Oxf. 1950; MA Oxf. 1945; FRCP Lond. 1971, M 1948. (Oxf.) Emerit. Cons. Phys. Bassetlaw HA. Socs: Fell. Roy. Soc. Med.; E. Midl. Soc. Phys. Prev: Cons. Phys. Roy. Hosp. Chesterfield & Bassetlaw HA; Sen. Med. Regist. Radcliffe Infirm. Oxf.; Capt. RAMC.

RICE-OXLEY, Margaret The Royal West Sussex Trust, St Richards Hospital, Spitalfield Lane, Chichester PO19 4SE; Lower Almonry Farm House, 43 North Trade Road, Battle TN33 0HS — BM BCh 1973 Oxf.; FRCP Lond. 1996. (Oxf.) Cons. Rehabil. Med. St Richards Hosp. Chichester. Prev: Sen. Regist. (Rehabil. Med.) N.wick Pk.; Assoc. Specialist (Neurol.) Brighton & Worthing.

RICH, Mr Alan John Washington Hospiotal, Picktree Lane, Washington NE38 9JZ Tel: 0191 415 1272 Fax: 0870 168 9178 Email: a.j.rich@ncl.ac.uk — MD 1982 Newc.; MB BS 1968; FRCS Eng. 1974; FRCS Ed. 1974. (Newc. upon Tyne) Assoc Dean (Postgrad Inst. Med & dean) Uni Newc.U Tyne.; Assoc Dean (Postgrad. Inst. Med. & Dent.) Univ. Newc. u. Tyne; Cons. Sirgeon, Sunderland Roy Hosp. Socs: Surgic. Research Soc.; Brit. Soc. Gastroenterol.; Assn. for Study Med. Educat. Prev: Lect. (Surg.) Roy. Vict. Infirm. Newc.; Arris & Gale Lect. RCS Eng.; Director of Poatgrad Med. Educat. City Hosp.s, Sunderland.

RICH, Alison Elizabeth Department of Medicine, Royal Sussex County Hospital, Brighton BN2 5BE; 32 Victoria Road, Brighton BN1 3FS — BM BCh 1992 Oxf.; MA Camb. 1993; MRCP (UK) 1995. SHO (Med.) Brighton.

RICH, Delyth Ann 72 Hereford Road, Abergavenny NP7 6AB — MB BS 1990 Lond.; BSc Lond. 1987; MRCOG 1997. (St. Geos. Hosp.) Regist. (O & G) Wales. Prev: SGR Nevill Hall Hosp.; SpR Roy. Gwent Hosp.; SpR Llandough.

RICH, Elizabeth Margaret c/o National Westminster Bank plc, Kentish Town Branch, 170 Kentish Town Road, London NW5 2DG — MB ChB 1957 New Zealand; FRCPsych. 1986, M 1973; T(Psych.) 1991; DPM Eng. 1965. (Otago) Prev: SCMO (Ment. Health) City & Hackney (St. Bart.) Health Dist. (T).

RICH, Graham Francis Newcastle & North Tyneside Health Authority, Benfield Road, Newcastle upon Tyne NE6 4PF Tel: 0191 219 6046 Fax: 0191 219 6084 Email: graham.rich@nant-ha.northy.nhs.uk; 9 Osborne Avenue, Newcastle upon Tyne NE2 1JQ — MB BS 1985 Lond.; MBA Insead France 1992; BSc Lond. 1982; MRCGP 1991; DRCOG 1989; Dip. IMC RCS Ed. 1989; DCH RCP Lond. 1987. Dir. Commiss.ing & Primary Care Newc. & N. Tyneside HA. Socs: Brit. Assn. Med. Managers. Prev: Managem. Cons. Boston Consg. Gp. Inc., Mass., USA; Sen. Health Policy Analyst Jackson Hole Gp.; Sen. Med. Off. NHS Exec.

RICH, Jennifer Shay Lane Medical Centre, Shay Lane, Hale, Altrincham WA15 8NZ Tel: 0161 980 3835 Fax: 0161 903 9848; 4 Poppy Close, Brooklands, Manchester M23 9TF Tel: 0161 998 5194 — MB ChB Ed. 1962. (Ed.) Socs: Inst. Psychosexual Med. Prev: Ho. Surg. & Ho. Phys. Hope Hosp. Salford.

RICH, John Albert (retired) Curlew Cottage, 8 Heather Grove, Warkworth, Morpeth NE65 0YS Tel: 01665 712991 — MRCS Eng. LRCP Lond. 1940; DIH Soc. Apoth. Lond. 1975. Prev: Employm. Med. Adviser EMAS.

RICH, Kathleen Marian (retired) 18 Mulberry Lane, Cosham, Portsmouth PO6 2QU Tel: 01705 378295 — MB BS Lond. 1956; MRCS Eng. LRCP Lond. 1956. Prev: Gen.Med.Pract.Portsmouth.

RICH, Martin George 75 Collinson Road, Hartcliffe, Bristol BS13 9PH — BM 1979 Soton.

RICH, Patricia Mary (retired) 15 Southernhay E., Exeter Tel: 01392 54335 Fax: 01392 498172 — MB ChB 1959 Bristol; DCH

RCPS Glas. 1965; DObst RCOG 1962; Cert. FPA 1962. Prev: Ho. Surg. Bristol Gen. Hosp.

RICH, Paul Antony St Georges Hospital, Blackshaw Road, London SW17 0QT Tel: 020 8725 3316; 25 Cottenham Park Road, West Wimbledon, London SW20 0RX Tel: 020 8944 1778 Fax: 020 8725 3135 Email: paul-rich@gas.mailbox.co.uk — MB BS Lond. 1984; BSc (Hons.) (Immunol. & Genetics) Lond. 1981; FRCA. 1990. (Univ. Coll. Lond.) Cons. Anaesth. St. Geo.s's Hosp. Lond. Socs: Assn. Anaesth.; Difficult Airway Soc.; Soc. for Computing & Technol. in Anaesth. (SCATA). Prev: Sen. Regist. (Anaesth.) Middlesx Hosp. Lond.

RICH, Paula Naomi 43 Dawpool Drive, Bromborough, Wirral CH62 6DE — MB BS 1998 Lond.; MB BS Lond 1998.

RICH, Philip Malcolm Top Flat, 27 Warrington Crescent, London W9 1ED — MB BS 1989 Lond.; BSc (Hons.) Lond. 1986, MB BS 1989.

RICH, Mr Walter John Cecil Christopher (retired) Springfield House, Hensleigh Drive, Exeter EX2 4NZ Tel: 01392 259967 Fax: 01392 498172 — MB ChB Bristol 1960; FRCS Ed. 1967; FRCS Eng. 1967; FRCOphth 1989; DO Eng. 1964. Prev: Chairm. SAC Ophth.

RICHARD, Bella Lucy Day Hospital, Nevill Hall Hospital, Abergavenny NP7 7EG — MB BS 1988 Madras; MRCP (UK) 1993; Dip Geriatric Med 1996, RCOP. Staff Phsician in Adult Med., Gwent Health Care, NHS Trust, Abergavenny. Socs: BGS.

RICHARD, Christopher John Department of Anaesthetics, Borders General Hospital, Melrose TD6 9BS Tel: 01896 754333; Mertoun School House, Clintmains, St. Boswells, Melrose TD6 0DY Tel: 01835 823470 — MB ChB 1982 Manch.; BSc (Med. Sci.) St. And. 1979; FRCA 1992; DA (UK) 1986. Assoc. Specialist (Anaesth.) Borders Gen. Hosp. NHS Trust Melrose.

RICHARD, Mr Derek Randal (retired) Warwick House, Bumbles Green, Nazeing, Waltham Abbey EN9 2SD Tel: 01992 893501 — BM BCh 1948 Oxf.; MA Oxf. 1962, BM BCh 1948; FRCS Eng. 1955. Hon. Cons. Orthop. Surg. Whipps Cross Hosp. Prev: Cons. Orthop. Surg. Whipps Cross & Wanstead Hosps. Lond.

RICHARD, Helen Winifred Occupational Health Unit, Staffordshire County Council, 15 Tipping Street, Stafford ST16 2LN Tel: 01785 276282; Virginia Cottage, Brook End, Longdon, Rugeley WS15 4PD Tel: 01543 491161 — MB ChB 1972 Birm.; DObst RCOG 1975. (Birmingham Univ.) Med. Adviser, Occupat.al Health Unit, Staffs. Co. Counc..Socs: ALAMA; Soc. Occupat. Med. Prev: Med. Off. Marks & Spencer Plc W. Midl.; Gen. Practitioner, Sutton Coldfield.

RICHARD, Karen West Murray Royal Hospital, Perth PH2 7BH Tel: 01738 621151; Craigard, 14 Birkhill Avenue, Wormit, Newport-on-Tay DD6 8PX Email: karen.richard@btinternet.com — MB ChB 1982 Ed.; MRCPsych 1986. Cons. Forens. Psychiat. Murray Roy. Hosp. Perth; Hon. Sen. Lect. (Psychiat.) Univ. of Dundee.

RICHARDS, Mr Adrian Mark Plastic Surgery Department, Salisbury District Hospital, Salisbury Tel: 01722 336262; Valley Cottage, Princes Hill, Redlynch, Salisbury SP5 2HG Tel: 01725 511032 Fax: 01725 511032 — MB BS 1988 Lond.; FRCS Eng. 1992. (St. Thos.) Regist. (Plastic Surg.) Salisbury Dist. Hosp.

RICHARDS, Alison Judith The Cottage in the Tewer, Mill End, Chadlington, Oxford OX7 3NZ — MB ChB 1981 Aberd.

RICHARDS, Mr Andrew Barnett Glenthorn, Cleeve Road, Goring on Thames, Reading RG8 9BJ Tel: 01491 872296; (cons. room), 72 Berkeley Avenue, Reading RG1 6HY Tel: 01734 584711 — MRCS Eng. LRCP Lond. 1958; MB Camb. 1959, BChir 1958; FRCS (Ophth.) Eng. 1967; DO Eng. 1964. (Camb. & Guy's) Cons. Ophth. Roy. Berks. Hosp. Reading & Townlands Hosp. Henley. Socs: Ophth. Soc. & Oxf. Ophth. Congr. Prev: Lect. Profess. Unit Moorfields Eye Hosp. Lond.; Asst. Resid. in Neurol. Johns Hopkins Hosp. Baltimore, U.S.A.; Sen. Res. Moorfields Eye Hosp.

RICHARDS, Andrew Michael 64 West Cross Lane, Westcross, Swansea SA3 5LU — MB BS 1996 Lond.

RICHARDS, Andrew Philip X-Ray Department, Prince Philip Hospital, Llanelli SA14 8QF Tel: 01554 756567; 19 Old Road, Llanelli SA15 3HR Tel: 01554 774247 — MB ChB 1986 Leeds; BSc Leeds 1983; MRCP (UK) 1989; FRCR 1993. Cons. Radiol. P. Philip Hosp. LLa.lli. Socs: BMA. Prev: Sen. Regist. (Radiol.) Yorks. RHA.

RICHARDS, Anne Elizabeth Magdalen Medical Practice, Lawson Road, Norwich NR3 4LF Tel: 01603 475555 Fax: 01603 787210; 26 Carterford Drive, Norwich NR3 4DW — MB ChB 1983 Leeds;

DCH RCP Lond. 1989; DRCOG 1986. Prev: GP Kempston; Trainee GP/SHO Bedford Gen. Hosp. VTS; SHO (Ophth.) Newc. Gen. Hosp.

RICHARDS, Anthony Arthur (retired) 140A Doddington Road, Lincoln LN6 7HB — MB ChB 1960 Sheff. Prev: GP Lincoln.

RICHARDS, Mr Anthony Brynmor The North Hampshire Hospital, Aldermaston Road, Basingstoke RG24 9NA Tel: 01256 313556 Fax: 01256 313532; The Hampshire Clinic, Basing Road, Basingstoke RG24 7AL Tel: 01256 357111 — MB BChir 1962 Camb.; MChir Camb. 1966, MA 1962; FRCS Eng. 1966; MRCS Eng. LRCP Lond. 1961. (Camb. & Guy's) Cons. Urol. N. Hants. Hosp. Socs: Fell. Assn. Surgs.; Brit. Assn. Urol. Surgs. Prev: Sen. Regist. (Surg.) Guy's Hosp. Lond.; Regist. (Surg.) Roy. Surrey Co. Hosp. Guildford; Ho. Surg. Guy's Hosp. Lond.

RICHARDS, Mr Anthony Edwin Stewart ENT Department, Benenden Hospital, Cranbrook TN17 4AX Tel: 015802 40333; Headcorn Manor, Headcorn, Ashford TN27 9NP Tel: 01622 890907 — MB BS Lond. 1963; FRCS Ed. 1970; FRCS Eng. 1967; MRCS Eng. LRCP Lond. 1963. (Lond. Hosp.) Socs: Fell. Roy. Soc. Med. Prev: Cons. (ENT) Char. Cross Hosp. Lond.; Sen. Regist. (ENT) St. Mary's Hosp. Lond.; Sen. Regist. & Regist. Roy. Nat. Throat, Nose & Ear Hosp. Lond.

RICHARDS, Anthony John 30 The Heights, Worthing BN14 0AJ Tel: 01903 265372 Fax: 01903 265372 Email: tony.richards1@tesco.net — MB BS 1963 Lond.; MRCS Eng. LRCP Lond. 1963; FRCP Lond. 1986, M 1968; DPhysMed Eng. 1974. (Guy's) Cons. Rheum. Worthing & S.lands NHS Trust. Socs: Fell. Roy. Soc. Med.; BMA; Brit. Soc. Rheum. Prev: Sen. Regist. (Rheum. & Rehabil.) King's Coll. Hosp. Lond.; Asst. Prof. Med. McMaster Univ., Canada; Regist. (Med.) W.m. Hosp. Lond.

RICHARDS, Antony Lawrence — MB ChB 1987 Manch.; MRCP (UF), 1991; FRCA 1993. Cons., Anaesth. & IC, Roy. Oldham Hosp.

RICHARDS, Arthur David, Squadron Ldr. RAF Med. Br. Retd. Winch Lane Surgery, Winch Lane, Haverfordwest SA61 1RN Tel: 01437 762333 Fax: 01437 766912; Ty Newydd, Suttonfold, Sutton, Haverfordwest SA62 3LP Tel: 01437 769031 — MB BCh 1983 Wales; MRCGP 1988. Prev: Sen. Med. Off., Sen. Med. Off., RAF Brawdy.

RICHARDS, Arthur Forbister Park Surgery, Windsor Street, Trecynon, Aberdare CF44 8LL Tel: 01685 872040 Fax: 01685 883696; Nant Goch, Merthyr Road, Llwydcoed, Aberdare CF44 0UT Tel: 01685 872239 — MB ChB 1957 Sheff.; DObst RCOG 1961.

RICHARDS, Miss Aurelia ENT Department, Guys Hospital, St Thomas St., London SE1 9RT Tel: 020 7955 5000 Ext: 4349 or 4350; 4 Chadworth Way, Claygate, Esher KT10 9DB — MB ChB 1985 Aberd.; FRCS Eng. 1992; DLO RCS Eng. 1988; Mphi l(Univ. of Sussex), 1996; FRCS (Orlhns) 1998. (Aberdeen University) Sen. Regist. (ENT Surg.) SE Thames HA. Socs: Assoc. Mem. BAOL HNS; BAPO; ORS. Prev: Sen. Regist. (ENT Surg.) Lewisham Hosp.; Regist. (ENT Surg.) Brighton HA.; SPR (Ent Surg) Hosp. for Sick Childr. Gt. Ormond St.

RICHARDS, Barbara Anne 30 Park Road, Watford WD17 4QN Tel: 01923 241551 Fax: 01923 241551 — MB BS 1956 Lond.; MFFP 1993; DObst RCOG 1958. (Univ. Coll. Hosp.) SCMO (Family Plann.) W. Herts. Community Trust. Prev: Asst. Co. Med. Off. Herts. CC; Ho. Surg. (Obst.) & Ho. Phys. Univ. Coll. Hosp. Lond.

RICHARDS, Barry Wyndham (retired) 102B Effra Road, Wimbledon, London SW19 8PR — MRCS Eng. LRCP Lond. 1939; FRCPsych 1971 (Founder Fell.); DPM Lond.1948.

RICHARDS, Basil Francis Greystones, Beach Road, Llantwit Major CF61 9RF Tel: 014465 2607 — MRCS Eng. LRCP Lond. 1946.

RICHARDS, Mr Brian (retired) Higher Tale Farm, Higher Tale, Payhembury, Honiton EX14 3HJ Tel: 01884 277344 Email: brichathtf@aol.com — MD 1968 Camb.; MB 1959, BChir 1958; FRCS Eng. 1962. Prev: Cons. Urol. York Dist. Hosps.

RICHARDS, Bruce William (retired) 15 The Glade, Endcliffe Vale Road, Sheffield S10 3FQ Tel: 0114 266 8354 — MB BS 1948 Lond.; MRCS Eng. LRCP Lond. 1948; MRCGP 1973; MFCM RCP 1982; DObst RCOG 1954. Prev: Regional SCM (Health Care Plann.) Trent RHA.

RICHARDS, Catherine Amelia Lucy The Hollies, 4 St. Athans Walk, Harrogate HG2 9DU Tel: 01423 565264 — MB BCh 1987 Wales; MRCP (UK) 1990; MFPHM RCP (UK) 1996; MRCGP 1996; MPH Leeds 1993. (Univ. Wales Coll. Med.) GP, Leeds. Prev: Sen.

RICHARDS

Regist. (Pub. Health Med.) N. & Yorks. Region; Vis. Lect (Pub. Health) Nuffield Inst. for Health 1998.

RICHARDS, Mrs Catherine Anne 50 Lauderdale Mansions, Lauderdale Road, London W9 1NE — MB BChir 1989 Camb.; FRCS Eng. 1993. Specialist Regist., Roy. Lond. Hosp. Prev: Specialist Regist., (Paediat. Surg.), Lewisham; Specialist Regist., (Paediat. Surg.), St Geo.s.

RICHARDS, Catherine Jane 16 Ashtree Road, Cosby, Leicester LE9 1UA — BM BS 1990 Nottm.; BMedSci (Hons.) 1988. SHO (Histopath.) Leicester Roy. Infirm.

RICHARDS, Catherine Meredith 40 Birkenpale, Sheffield S6 3NJ Tel: 0114 234 8848 Email: 40birkendale@cw.com.net — MB BChir 1977 Camb.; DRCOG 1979.

RICHARDS, Celia Ann Beech House, Post Office Lane, Lyndon, Rutland, Oakham LE15 8TZ Tel: 01572 737718 — MB BS 1971 Lond.; MRCS Eng. LRCP Lond. 1971; DObst Auckland 1975. (Westm.) Med. Off. (Family Plann.) Market HarBoro.; Clin. Asst. (Ophth.) Leicester Roy. Infirm. Socs: Fac. Family Plann. Prev: GP Corby; Ho. Surg. (Radiother.) W.m. Hosp. Lond.; Ho. Phys. Putney Hosp.

RICHARDS, Christopher Graham Morgan Royal Victoria Infirmary, Queen Victoria Road, Newcastle upon Tyne NE1 4LP. Tel: 0191 232 5131; 25 Brandling Place S., Jesmond, Newcastle upon Tyne NE2 4RU Tel: 0191 281 2825 — MB BS 1985 Lond.; BA Oxf. 1982; MRCP (UK) 1988. (Oxford - Preclinical Lond. (BARTS) Clinical) Cons. Paediat., Roy. Vic. Infirm., Newc. Prev: Clin. Lect. (Paediat.) & Hon. Sen. Regist. John Radcliffe Hosp. Oxf.; Tutor (Child Heath) & Hon. Regist. (Paediat.) Roy. Manch. Childr. Hosp.; SHO (Paediat.) Newc. & N. Tyneside HAs.

RICHARDS, Christopher Mordaunt 4 St Ronans Avenue, Redland, Bristol BS6 6EP Tel: 0117 909 3474 Fax: 0117 909 3474 Email: cricha@globalnet.co.uk — MB ChB 1972 Bristol; MB ChB (Hons.) Bristol 1972; MRCGP 1976; DObst RCOG 1975; DCH Eng. 1974. (Bristol) Indep. Psychother. Bristol. Prev: GP Keynsham; Trainee GP Newc. VTS; Ho. Phys. & Ho. Surg. S.mead Hosp. Bristol.

RICHARDS, Clifford Brookvale Practice, Hallwood Health Centre, Hospital Way, Runcorn WA7 2UT Tel: 01928 718182 Fax: 01928 790716 — MRCS Eng. LRCP Lond. 1978; MRCGP 1984; DRCOG 1982.

RICHARDS, Clive Haskell Lister Medical Centre, Lister House, Staple Tye, Harlow CM18 7LU Tel: 01279 414882 Fax: 01279 439600 — MB BS 1970 Lond.; MRCS Eng. LRCP Lond. 1970; DObst RCOG 1973. Prev: Ho. Phys. & Ho. Surg. St. Margt.s Hosp. Epping; SHO (O & G) St. And. Hosp. Billericay; Resid. in Paediat. Univ. Alberta Hosp. Edmonton, Canada.

RICHARDS, Clive Wynford 8 Park Terrace, The Park, Nottingham NG1 5DN — MB ChB 1971 Bristol; MSc (Health Care) Exeter 1988; MFPHM RCP (UK) 1994; FRCGP 1985, M 1976; DA Eng. 1974; DObst RCOG 1973. Cons. Pub. Health Med. Nottm. Health; GP Nottm. Prev: GP Avon.

RICHARDS, Colin John Tychwyth, The Downs, St Nicholas, Cardiff CF5 6SB; Glamorgan House, Croescadarn Road, Pentwyn, Cardiff — MB BS 1963 Lond.; FRCOG 1983, M 1970. (St. Bart.) Cons. (O & G) Mid. Glam. AHA. Prev: Ho. Surg. St. Bart. Hosp. Lond.; Sen. Regist. (O & G) S. Glam. AHA; SHO (O & G) Hammersmith Hosp. Lond.

RICHARDS, Dafydd Gwilym X-Ray Department, Morriston Hospital, Swansea SA6 6NL; 19 Daphne Road, Penywern, Neath SA10 8DP — MRCS Eng. LRCP Lond. 1976; BSc (Hons.) Lond. 1973, MB BS 1976; MRCP (UK) 1980; FRCR 1984. (St. Mary's) Cons. Radiol. Morriston Hosp. Swansea. Prev: Sen. Regist. (Radiol.) Univ. Hosp. Wales Cardiff.; Regist. Rotat. (Med.) Univ. Hosp. Wales Cardiff; SHO (Med.) City Hosp. Nottm.

RICHARDS, Daphne Patricia (retired) 2 Harvest Bank Road, West Wickham BR4 9DJ Tel: 020 8325 8648 — MB BS Lond. 1961; MFCM 1974; DPH Eng. 1970; DCH Eng. 1965. Prev: SCM Croydon DHA.

RICHARDS, David c/o Mr G. Richards, 2 Moor Copse Close, Reading RG6 7NA — MB BS 1984 Lond.

RICHARDS, David Allan Public Health Laboratory, Leicester Royal Infirmary, Leicester LE1 5WW — MB BS 1985 Lond.

RICHARDS, David Anthony 278 Hills Road, Cambridge CB2 2QE Tel: 01223 247086 — MRCS Eng. LRCP Lond. 1966; MD Lond. 1977, MB BS 1966. (King's Coll. Hosp.) Vice-Pres. Clin. Operats.

Arigen Europ.; Hon. Research Fell. UCH Med. Sch. Lond. Socs: Brit. Pharmacol. Soc. & Soc. Drug Research.

RICHARDS, David Anthony (Main Surgery) North Cardiff Medical Centre, Excaliber Drive, Thornhill, Cardiff CF14 9BB Tel: 029 2075 0322 Fax: 029 2075 7705; 40 Mill Wood, Lisvane, Cardiff CF14 0TL Tel: 029 2075 0322 — MRCS Eng. LRCP Lond. 1959; MB Camb. 1960, BChir 1959; MRCGP 1974; DObst RCOG 1962. Prev: Clin. Asst. WhitCh. Hosp. Cardiff.

RICHARDS, David Brynmor (retired) 14 Main Road, Bryncoch, Neath SA10 7PD — MD Lond. 1951, MB BS 1945; MB BCh Wales 1944.

RICHARDS, David Edwin William McGregor Laserase, Laser Dermatological Clinic, Royal Liverpool University Hospital, Prescot St., Liverpool L7 8XP Tel: 0151 708 9994 Fax: 01244 677671; Mill Hill Cottage, Rake Lane, Eccleston, Chester CH4 9JN Tel: 01244 677445 Fax: 01244 677671 — MB BCh 1984 Wales; Cert. Family Plann. JCC 1990. Clin. Dir. Laserase, Laser Dermatological Clinic Roy. Liverp. Univ. Hosp. Prev: GP Birkenhead.

RICHARDS, Mr David Gwilym Department of Surgery, West Cumberland Hospital, Hensingham, Whitehaven CA28 8JG Tel: 01946 693181; Ghyll Head, Low Moresby, Whitehaven CA28 6RU — MB ChB 1970 Sheff.; FRCS Eng. 1974. Cons. Gen. Surg. W. Cumbld. Hosp. Prev: Lect. Surg. Univ. Sheff. N.. Gen. Hosp.

RICHARDS, Mr David Michael Salford Royal Hospitals Trust, Scott Lane, Salford M6 8HD Tel: 0161 789 7373; 21 Oulder Hill Drive, Bamford, Rochdale OL11 5LB Tel: 01706 712168 — MB ChB 1987 Manch.; MD Manch. 1996; FRCS Eng. 1992; FRCS Glas. 1989. (Manch.) Sen. Regist. (Gen. Surg.) Hope Hosp. Salford. Socs: Manch. Med. Soc. Prev: Sen. Regist. Blackburn Roy. Infirm.; Sen. Regist. Manch. Roy. Infirm.; Tutor (Research & Gen. Surg.) Hope Hosp. Manch.

RICHARDS, David Stephen Worcester Road Surgery, 74A Worcester Road, West Hagley, Stourbridge DY9 0NH Tel: 01562 882474 Fax: 01562 887185; 19 Woodland Avenue, Hagley, Stourbridge DY8 2XQ — MB ChB 1987 Birm. SHO Kidderminster & Dist. HA GP VTS. Prev: Ho. Off. (Gen. Med.) City Gen. Hosp. Stoke on Trent; Ho. Off. (Gen. Surg. & Urol.) Dudley Rd. Hosp. Birm.

RICHARDS, David William Lawson Department of Genitourinary Medicine, Woolman Hill, Aberdeen AB25 1 Tel: 01224 641104; Ambleside, 143 North Deeside Road, Milltimber, Milltimber AB13 0JS Tel: 01224 868855 — MB ChB 1965 Aberd.; MRCGP 1975; DObst RCOG 1967. Assoc. Specialist (Genitourin. Med.) Aberd. Roy. Infirm.; Clin. Lect. (Genitourin. Med.) Univ. Aberd. Socs: BMA & Scott. Comm. for Hosp. Med. Servs. Prev: Regist. (Med.) Aberd. Gen. Hosps.; SHO (Med.) City Hosp. Aberd.; Res. Ho. Off. (Surg. & Med.) Aberd. Gen. Hosp.

RICHARDS, Dawn 39 Kingsbury Road, London NW9 7HY; 59 Woodlands Road, Irchester, Wellingborough NN29 7BU — MB BS 1983 Lond.; BSc Lond. 1980, MB BS 1983; MRCGP 1987. (Guy's) GP Lond.

RICHARDS, Denis John Rushden Medical Centre, Adnitt Road, Rushden NN10 9TU Tel: 01933 412444 Fax: 01933 317666 — MB ChB 1979 Birm. Prev: Ho. Surg. (Profess. & Cardiothoracic Units) Qu. Eliz. Hosp.; Trainee GP N.ampton VTS.

RICHARDS, Mr Derek James (cons. rooms), 1 Arlington Road, Eastbourne BN21 1DH Tel: 01323 734030 Fax: 01323 734030; Clare Glen, Rock's Lane, High Hurstwood, Uckfield TN22 4BN Tel: 01825 733306 Fax: 01825 733306 — MB BChir 1959 Camb.; MA, MB Camb. 1959, BChir 1958; FRCS Eng. 1964; MRCS Eng. LRCP Lond. 1958. (Camb. & Guy's) Cons. Surg. Orthop. Horder Centre for Arthritis CrowBoro. Socs: Fell. BOA. Prev: Cons. Surg. Orthop. Dist. Gen. Hosp. E.bourne; Sen. Regist. (Orthop.) Univ. Coll. Hosp. Lond.; Regist. (Orthop.) & Ho. Surg. Guy's Hosp. Lond.

RICHARDS, Edward Michael Department Paediatric Haematology, St. James's Hospital, Leeds; 7 Rayleigh Road, Harrogate HG2 8QR — BM BCh 1987 Oxf.; BA Oxf. 1984; MRCP (UK) 1990; MRCPath 1997; DM Oxf. 1998. (Oxf.) Cons. Paediat. Haematologist St. Jas. Hosp. Leeds. Socs: Brit. Soc. Haematol. Prev: Sen. Regist. (Haemat.) Centr. Sheffild Univ. Hosps.; Regist. (Haemat.) Addenbrooke's Hosp. Camb.; SHO (Gen. Med.) Swansea.

RICHARDS, Emily Dorothy Jean (retired) The Mount, Rudry Road, Lisvane, Cardiff CF14 0SN Tel: 029 2075 2660 — MB ChB 1946 Ed. Clin. Med. Off. Mid Glam. AHA. Prev: Resid. Med. Off. E. Gen. Hosp. Edin.

RICHARDS

RICHARDS, Emma Rachel Donmall and Partners, 87 Albion Street, London SE16 7JX Tel: 020 7237 2092 Fax: 020 7231 1435 — BM BS 1991 Nottm.; MRCP (UK) 1994; DCH RCP Lond. 1995; DGM RCP Lond. 1993. GP Asst./Research Assoc. Prev: SLOUTS SHO.

RICHARDS, Eurfyl Lowesmoor Medical Centre, 93 Lowesmoor, Worcester WR1 2SA Tel: 01905 723441 Fax: 01905 724987; Linacre, 7 Lansdowne Crescent, Worcester WR3 8JE Tel: 01905 25127 — MB BCh Wales 1957; DCH Eng. 1962; DObst RCOG 1963. (Cardiff) Prev: SHO (Med. & Child Health), Ho. Phys. & Ho. Surg. Llandough Hosp. Penarth.

RICHARDS, Evan Huw (retired) 8 Fleetwood Avenue, Powick, Worcester WR2 4PY — MB BChir 1960 Camb.; MA, MB Camb. 1960, BChir 1959; FRCPsych 1988, M 1972; DPM Ed. & Glas. 1965. Prev: Cons. Psychiat. S. Worcs. Hosp. Gp.

RICHARDS, Evan Thomas Eric (retired) Biscovey, Trewithen Road, Penzance TR18 4LS — MB BS Lond. 1957; LMSSA Lond. 1956. Prev: Ho. Surg. & Ho. Phys. Harold Wood Hosp.

RICHARDS, F Gloria (retired) 9 Argyll Road, Exeter EX4 4RX — MRCS Eng. LRCP Lond. 1935; DObst RCOG 1939. Prev: Sen. Med. Off. Devon CC.

RICHARDS, Fiona Ann Hill Brow Surgery, Long Croft, Mapplewell, Barnsley S75 6FH Tel: 01226 383131 Fax: 01226 380100; 34 Albert Road, Clayton W., Huddersfield HD8 9NL — MB ChB 1988 Sheff.; MRCGP 1993; DRCOG 1992. (Sheff.) Socs: BMA. Prev: Trainee GP Sheff. VTS; Ho. Off. (Med. & Surg.) Rotherham Dist. Gen. Hosp.

RICHARDS, Miss Frances Helen Patricia (retired) Cedarcroft House, Broad Bush, Blunsdon, Swindon SN26 7DH — MB BS 1975 Lond.; FRCS Eng. (Ophth.) 1982; FCOphth. 1988; DO Eng. 1980; DRCOG 1977. Prev: Cons. Ophth. P.ss Margt. Hosp. Swindon.

RICHARDS, Frances Marie (retired) 3 Thompson Avenue, Cardiff CF5 1EX Tel: 02920 563771 — MB BCh 1948 Wales; BSc 1945; FFCM 1978, M 1974; DCH Eng. 1951; DObst RCOG 1950; DPH Wales 1969. Prev: Sen. Med. Off. Welsh Office, Cardiff. Jt. Med. Off. City of Cardiff.

RICHARDS, Francis James Abel Bay View, Cadgwith, Helston TR12 7JL Tel: 01326 290524; 4 Harriers Close, Ealing, London W5 3UA Tel: 020 8579 5499 Email: francisric@aol.com — MB BS 1996 Lond. (King's Coll.) GP VTS SHO Rotat. King Geo. Hosp. Ilford. Prev: Ho. Off. (Surg.) Bromley Hosp.; Ho. Off. (Med.) Bromley Hosp.

RICHARDS, Gareth David Huw The Surgery, 36 The Street, Capel St Mary, Ipswich IP9 2EE Tel: 01473 310203 Fax: 01473 311722; The Granary, Mill Lane, Upper Layham, Ipswich IP7 5JY Tel: 01473 824869 Email: gdhrichards@enta.net — MB BS 1984 Lond. (Roy. Free) Prev: Trainee GP Braintree; SHO (O & G) St. John's Hosp. Chelmsford.; SHO (Paediat. & Cas.) Colchester Gen. Hosp.

RICHARDS, Gareth Edward 66 Parkstowe Road, Poole BH15 2QE — MB BS 1986 Lond. Regist. (Anaesth.) W. Dorset Hosp. Dorchester. Prev: SHO (Anaesth.) Lond. Hosp. & Weymouth & Dist. Hosp.

RICHARDS, Gareth Justin 72 Forest Drive, Theydon Bois, Epping CM16 7EZ — MB BS 1993 Lond.

RICHARDS, Gareth Lloyd 6 Grange Crescent, Coychurch, Bridgend CF35 5HP — MB BCh 1996 Wales.

RICHARDS, Gillian Anne Corner Place Surgery, 46A Dartmouth Road, Paignton TQ4 5AH Tel: 01803 557458 Fax: 01803 524844; Millbrook, Saxon Meadow, Collaton St. Mary, Paignton TQ4 7DE Tel: 01803 525948 Email: gimkrich@aol.com — MB BS 1983 Lond.; MRCGP 1987; DRCOG 1986. (Guy's Hospital)

RICHARDS, Glenn Paul Ironbridge Medical Practice, Trinity Hall, Dale Road, Coalbrookdale, Telford TF8 7DT Tel: 01952 432568 Email: glenn.richards@gp-m82606.nhs.uk — MB BS 1979 Lond.; DRCOG 1983.

RICHARDS, Gwen Health Centre, New Street, Beaumaris LL58 8EL Tel: 01248 810818 Fax: 01248 811589; Godreddi Bach, Llanddona, Beaumaris LL58 8UY Tel: 01248 810330 Fax: 01248 810330 — MB BCh 1976 Wales; MRCGP 1980; DRCOG 1980.

RICHARDS, Gwyneth (retired) 21 Meadway, Rustington, Littlehampton BN16 2DD — LRCP LRCS 1949 Ed.; LRCP LRCS Ed. LRFPS Glas. 1949; MFCM 1974; DCH Eng. 1959; DObst RCOG 1951. Prev: Area SCM (Child Health) W. Sussex AHA.

RICHARDS, Hannah Catharine Mary 15 Forsyth Road, Newcastle upon Tyne NE2 3DB — MB BS 1998 Newc.; MB BS Newc. 1998.

RICHARDS, Mr Harold James (retired) 13 Green Street, Riverside, Cardiff CF11 6LN Tel: 029 20 224105 — MB BS 1938 Lond.; FRCS Eng. 1941; MRCS Eng. LRCP Lond. 1938; DA Eng. 1942. Cons. Orthop. Surg. Univ. Hosp. Wales & P. of Wales Orthop. Hosp. Cardiff. Prev: Res. Surg. Off. Robt. Jones & Agnes Hunt Orthop. Hosp.

RICHARDS, Harriet Jane (retired) 12 Grangewood Road, Wollaton, Nottingham NG8 2SH Tel: 0115 928 2011 — MB ChB Glas. 1937.

RICHARDS, Hayley Weavers Croft, Field Road, Stroud GL5 2HZ — MB ChB 1986 Bristol; MRCPsych 1993; MRCGP 1990; DRCOG 1988. Cons. Psychiat. Prev: Regist. (Psychiat.) SW RHA.

RICHARDS, Henry Hopkin (retired) 11 Osmond Gardens, Hove BN3 1TE — MB BS 1949 Lond.; MRCS Eng. LRCP Lond. 1949.

RICHARDS, Hilary (retired) 102 Fernedene Road, London SE24 0AA — MB BS 1955 Lond.; MRCPsych 1973; DPM Eng. 1960. Hon. Research Fell. Inst. Psychiat. Prev: Cons. Psychiat. Merton Child Guid. Serv. Lond.

RICHARDS, Iain McKay Portland Road Surgery, 31 Portland Road, Kilmarnock KA1 2DJ Tel: 01563 522118 Fax: 01563 573562 — MB ChB 1982 Glas.; BSc (Hons.) Glas. 1979; MRCP (UK) 1985; MRCGP 1990.

RICHARDS, Ian Michael Corner Place Surgery, 46A Dartmouth Road, Paignton TQ4 5AH Tel: 01803 557458 Fax: 01803 524844; Millbrook, Saxon Meadow, Collaton St. Mary, Paignton TQ4 7DE Tel: 01803 525948 Email: gimkrich@aol.com — MB BS 1983 Lond.; MRCGP 1987. (Middlesex Hospital)

RICHARDS, Professor Ifor David Gerald (retired) 7 Beech Grove Court, Beech Grove, Harrogate HG2 0EU Tel: 01423 565211 — MB ChB Wales 1953; PhD Wales 1971, MD 1965; FRCP Glas. 1973; FFPHM 1989; MFCM 1974; DPH Wales 1960; DObst RCOG 1957. Chairm. St Gemma's Hospice Leeds. Prev: Prof. Pub. Health Med. Univ. Leeds.

RICHARDS, Jane Elizabeth Crystals Peaks Medical Centre, Crystal Peaks, 15 Peaks Mount, Sheffield S20 7HZ Tel: 0114 251 0040 Fax: 0114 251 0954; 180 Tom Lane, Sheffield S10 3PG Tel: 0114 230 7901 Email: vertigo@globalnet.co.uk — MB BS 1986 Lond.; MRCGP 1991; DRCOG 1991. (The London Hospital)

RICHARDS, Janet Elizabeth Hamilton 19 Woodland Avenue, Hagley, Stourbridge DY8 2XQ — MB ChB 1989 Birm.

RICHARDS, Janice Gwendoline Milman Road Health Centre, Milman Road, Reading RG2 0AR Tel: 0118 968 2285 Fax: 0118 975 5033; Thornton, 117 Cockney Hill, Reading RG30 4EY — MB BS 1974 Lond.; MRCS Eng. LRCP Lond. 1974; DObst RCOG 1976; Cert JCC Lond. 1976. (King's Coll. Hosp.) Prev: Ho. Off. (Med.) Dulwich Hosp. Lond.; Ho. Surg. Brook Gen. Hosp. Woolwich; Ho. Off. (O & G) Whipps Cross Hosp. Leytonstone.

RICHARDS, Jean Margaret 62 Lauderdale Tower, Barbican, London EC2Y 8BY Tel: 07939 843231 — MB BS 1963 Lond.; MRCS Eng. LRCP Lond. 1963; FFCM 1982, M 1974. (Lond. Hosp.) Indep. Pub. Health Cons. Lond.; Hon. Lect. Lond. Hosp. Med. Coll. Prev: Dir. Pub. Health Tower Hamlets; Specialist in Community Med. (Child Health) City & E. Lond. AHA (T); PMO Lond. Boro. Tower Hamlets.

RICHARDS, Jeffrey Brereton Cumberland House, Jordangate, Macclesfield SK10 1EG Tel: 01625 428081 Fax: 01625 503128; 9 Henbury Rise, Henbury, Macclesfield SK11 9NW Tel: 01625 610547 — MB ChB 1977 Manch.; BSc (Hons.) (Chem. Engineering) Leeds 1967; MRCGP 1981; DCH RCPS Glas. 1980; Dip. Palliat. Med., Wales 1998. (Manchester) GP Macclesfield; Hospice Pract. E. Chesh. Hospice Macclesfield. Prev: Trainee GP Macclesfield Hosps. VTS.

RICHARDS, Joan Mary (retired) 38 Sitwell Way, Sandfields, Port Talbot SA12 6BL Tel: 01639 886683 — MB BCh 1954 Wales.

RICHARDS, Joanna Mary The Horns Hill Medical Group, 74 Horns Hill, London SE24 9QP Tel: 020 7274 3314; 1 Gainsborough Court, College Road, Dulwich, London SE21 7LT — MB BCh 1990 Wales; MRCGP 1996; DFFP 1995; DCH RCP Lond. 1994; DRCOG 1993. GP Asst./Research Assoc.

RICHARDS, Joanna Patricia 3/12 Silvermills, Stockbridge, Edinburgh EH3 5BF — MB ChB 1996 Ed. SHO (Psychiat.) S.ern

RICHARDS

Gen. Glas.. Prev: SHO (O & G) SMMP Edin.; SHO (A & E Med.) Edin. Roy. Infirm.; SHO (Geriat.) Gartnavel Hosp. Glas.

RICHARDS, John Desmond Morgan Parkfield Lodge, 30 Park Road, Watford WD17 4QN Tel: 01923 241551 Fax: 01923 241551 — MB BChir 1957 Camb.; MA Camb. 1955, MD (Raymond Horton-Smith prize & Sir Lionel Whitby Medal) 1965 Prize; FRCP Lond. 1987; FRCP Ed. 1971, M 1961; MRCS Eng. LRCP Lond. 1956; FRCPath 1975, M 1963. (Univ. Coll. Hosp.) Emerit. Cons. Haemat. & Phys. Univ. Coll. Hosp. Lond. Prev: Sen. Regist. Univ. Coll. Hosp. Lond.; Ho. Phys. & Ho. Surg. Univ. Coll. Hosp. Lond.

RICHARDS, John Lewis The Firs, Old Lane, Peterstow, Ross-on-Wye HR9 6LB — MRCS Eng. LRCP Lond. 1948; MRCPath 1971. (Middlx.) Prev: Ho. Phys. & Cas. Off. Hounslow Hosp. & Hertford Co. Hosp.; Ho. Surg. Roy. Gwent Hosp. Newport.

RICHARDS, John Llewellyn Richards and Partners, Llanfair Surgery, Llanfair Road, Llandovery SA20 0HY Tel: 01550 720648 Fax: 01550 721428 — MB BCh 1973 Wales; MRCGP 1977; DCH Eng. 1976; DRCOG 1975.

RICHARDS, Jonathan David Gwanwr-Fryn, Clydach Road, Ynysybwl, Pontypridd CF37 3LX — MB BS 1986 Lond.

RICHARDS, Professor Jonathan Philip Ty Morlais, Berry Square, Merthyr Tydfil CF48 3AL Tel: 01685 722782 Fax: 01685 722951; 20 The Grove, Merthyr Tydfil CF47 8YR Email: pagchair@dial.pipex.com — BSc (Hons.) Anat. Wales 1976, MB BCh 1979; MRCGP 1984; DRCOG 1983. (Wales) GP Merthyr Tydfil.; Ext. Prof. Prim. Care Sch. of Nurs. & Midw. Univ. Glam.; Chair/Bro Taf Prim. Care Aud. Gp. Prev: Lect. Univ. Wales Coll. Med.

RICHARDS, Josephine Anne 60 Hall Green, Malvern WR14 3QX — MB BCh 1986 Wales; MRCPsych 1992.

RICHARDS, Judit Public Health Laboratory, Bowthorpe Road, Norwich NR2 3TX Tel: 01603 611816; Lynden, Long St, Great Ellingham, Attleborough NR17 1LN Tel: 01953 453503 — Medico 1976 Buenos Aires; MRCPath 1988; T(Path.) 1991; FRCP 1998 (Path). Cons. Microbiologist Norwich Pub. Health Laborat.; Hon. Lect. Sch. Biological Sci. Univ. E. Anglia; Hon. Sen. Lect. Sch. of Health Policy & Pract., Univ. E. Anglia. Socs: Hosp. Infec. Soc.; Assoc. Med. MicroBiol. (Exec.Coun.). Prev: Sen. Regist. (Microbiol.) Newc.; Regist. (Microbiol.) Leicester Roy. Infirm. & Ipswich.

RICHARDS, Julia Marjorie 72 Forest Drive, Theydon Bois, Epping CM16 7EZ — MB BS 1995 Lond.

RICHARDS, Julie Louise Valentine House, 1079 Rochdale Road, Manchester M9 8AJ Tel: 0161 740 2524 Fax: 0161 795 2531; 21 Oulder Hill Drive, Bamford, Rochdale OL11 5LB Tel: 01706 712168 — MB ChB 1987 Manch. GP Princip. Manch. Prev: Trainee GP Falkirk Scotl. & Heywood Lancs.; SHO (Paediat.) Roy. Hosp. Sick Childr. Glas.

RICHARDS, Justin Paul DDS Medicines Research Ltd, Ninewells Hospital & Medical School, Dundee DD1 9SY — MB ChB 1984 Liverp.; FRCA 1994. Med. Dir.; Hon. Cons. Anaesth. Socs: Assn. Anaesth.; Fell. Roy. Coll. Anaesth. Prev: Sen. Regist. (Anaesth.) NW RHA.

RICHARDS, Keith Fforestfach Medical Centre, 118 Ravenhill Road, Fforestfach, Swansea SA5 5AA Tel: 01792 581666 Fax: 01792 585332; 8 Woodlands Terrace, Caerau, Maesteg, Bridgend CF32 7LB — MB BCh 1972 Wales; MRCGP 1976; DObst RCOG 1975.

RICHARDS, Kirsten Jayne Campbell 84 Hull Road, Hedon, Hull HU12 8DJ — MB ChB 1994 Sheff.

RICHARDS, Leslie Frisby (Surgery) Ravenscourt, Barry Tel: 01446 733515 & 734744; 63 The Parade, Barry CF62 6SG Tel: 01446 734973 — MRCS Eng. LRCP Lond. 1945; DObst RCOG 1947. (St. Mary's) Prev: Ho. Surg. & Ho. Surg. (O & G) Roy. Infirm. Cardiff.

***RICHARDS, Lorna Alison** 133 Overslade Lane, Rugby CV22 6EF — MB ChB 1995 Birm.; ChB Birm. 1995.

RICHARDS, Louise Eleanor Jane Burford House, 5 St Davids Drive, Cherry Orchard, Evesham WR11 6AS — BM 1998 Soton.; BM Soton 1998.

RICHARDS, Louise Marie Elaine 21 Bow Lane, Finchley, London N12 0JR — MB ChB 1992 Manch.; DCH RCP Lond. 1996. Regist. (Forens. Psychiat.) Roy. Free Hosp. Rotat. Prev: Regist. (Child & Adolesc. Psychiat.) Lond.; Regist. Rotat. (Psychiat.) Roy. Free Hosp. Lond.; Regist. (Psychiat. of Old Age) St. Anne's Hosp. Lond.

RICHARDS, Mair 96 Hunter House Road, Sheffield S11 8TW — MB ChB 1975 Bristol; MRCP UK 1981; DCH Eng. 1979. Cons.

Community Paediat. Community Health, Sheff. Socs: Brit. Paediat. Assn.; Brit. Soc. Audiol. Prev: Hon. Clin. Lect. Paediat. Univ. Sheff.; SCMO (Child Health) Sheff. HA.

RICHARDS, Margaret Anne 83 Sutton Heights, Albion Road, Sutton SM2 5TD — MB BS 1990 Lond.

RICHARDS, Margaret Cecil (retired) 5 Marston Lane, Norwich NR4 6LZ Tel: 01603 452505 Fax: 01603 452505 Email: 106313.1216@compuserve.com — MB BS 1949 Lond. Prev: Clin. Med. Off. Norf. AHA.

RICHARDS, Margaret Helen Jean (retired) 2 Heol-Y-Pavin, Llandaff, Cardiff CF5 2EG — MB BCh 1950 Wales; FRCGP 1975. Prev: Regist. (Med.) Min. of Pens. Hosp. Rookwood, Cardiff.

RICHARDS, Martyn James Penn Hill Surgery, St. Nicholas Close, Yeovil BA20 1SB Tel: 01935 74005 Fax: 01935 421841; 52 Grove Avenue, Yeovil BA20 2BE — MB BChir 1984 Camb.; BSc (Hons.) St. And. 1982; MA Camb. 1984; MRCGP 1990; Dip. Pract. Dermat. Wales 1994; DGM RCP Lond. 1988; DObst RCOG 1988; Cert. Av. Med. 1996. (St. And.) Trainer (Gen. Pract.) Yeovil. Socs: Brist. M-C Soc.; BMA. Prev: SHO (O & G, Cardiol. & Paediat.) S.mead Hosp. Bristol; Ho. Surg. Norf. & Norwich Hosp.

RICHARDS, Martyn William 47A Quaker Street, London E1 6SN — MB BS 1998 Lond.; MB BS Lond 1998.

RICHARDS, Mary Elizabeth (retired) 36 Le More, Four Oaks, Sutton Coldfield B74 2XY Tel: 0121 308 6314 — MB ChB Wales 1943; BSc Wales 1940; MRCOG 1949. Prev: Sen. Med. Off. (Family Plann. Serv.) Dudley, Sandwell & Walsall DHA's.

RICHARDS, Megan Branwen (retired) Norlands, Clytha Park Road, Newport NP20 4NA Tel: 01633 264535 — MB BCh Wales 1942; BSc Wales 1939. JP.; Chairm. Med. Bds. Min. of Social Security. Prev: GP Rhymney, Gwent.

RICHARDS, Professor Michael Adrian Department of Palliative Medicine, St. Thomas' Hospital, London SE1 7EH Tel: 020 7922 8009 Fax: 020 7922 8253; 42 Liberia Road, Highbury, London N5 1JR Tel: 020 7226 6808 Fax: 020 7226 6808 — MB BChir 1978 Camb.; MA Camb. 1987, MD 1988; FRCP Lond. 1993; MRCP (UK) 1979. Prof. Palliat. Med. & Clin. Dir. (Cancer Servs.) Guy's & St. Thos. Hosp. Lond.; Chairm. Div. of Oncol. & Palliat. Care Guy's, King's & St. Thomas' Med. Sch. Prev: Reader (Med. Oncol.) & Sen. Lect. (Med. Oncol.) Guy's & St. Thos. Hosp. Lond.; ICRF Research Fell. (Med. Oncol.) St. Bart. Hosp. Lond.; Regist. (Gen. Med.) Nottm. City Hosp.

RICHARDS, Michael John Albany Surgery, Albany Street, Newton Abbot TQ12 2TX Tel: 01626 334411 Fax: 01626 335663; Springbank, Croft Road, East Ogwell, Newton Abbot TQ12 6BA Tel: 01626 56261 — MB BS 1982 Lond.; MA Camb. 1982; MRCGP 1986; DRCOG 1986. (Guy's) Prev: SHO (Paediat., Psychiat., O & G & Med.) Taunton Hosp. VTS.

RICHARDS, Michael John c/o Anaesthetic Department, Cheltenham General Hospital, Sandford Road, Cheltenham GL53 7AN — MB BCh 1976 Wales; FFA RCS Eng. 1984. Cons. Anaesth. Cheltenham Gen. Hosp. Prev: Carey Coombs Research Fell. Bristol Roy. Infirm.; Cons. Anaesth. Middlemore Hosp. NZ.

RICHARDS, Michael John 60 Hall Green, Malvern WR14 3QX Tel: 01689 863942 — BM 1993 Soton. SHO (Cardiol.) Soton. Gen. Hosp. Prev: SHO (Gen. Med.) & Ho. Phys. Roy. S. Hants. Hosp.

RICHARDS, Michael Lindsay Richards and Partners, The Surgery, North Street, Langport TA10 9RH Tel: 01458 250464 Fax: 01458 253246; Croftlands, School St, Drayton, Langport TA10 0LW — MB ChB 1968 Bristol; DObst RCOG 1969. Prev: Med. Off. Roy. Flying Doctor Serv. Austral.

RICHARDS, Myrtle Vivien (retired) 29A Arlington Avenue, Leamington Spa CV32 5UD Tel: 01926 422485 — MB ChB 1946 Ed.; MFCM 1972; DCH Eng. 1951; DPH Lond. 1952. Specialist in Community Med. S. Warks. HA. Prev: PMO Warks. AHA.

RICHARDS, Nicholas Christopher Guyon, SBStJ Telford Occupational Health Service, Occupational Health Centre, Halesfield 13, Telford TF7 4PL Tel: 01952 581251 Fax: 01952 581251; 4 Cavendish Close, Bicton Heath, Shrewsbury SY3 5PG Email: nickrichards@doctors.org.uk — MB BS 1965 Lond.; MRCGP 1974; MFOM RCP Lond. 1997, A 1991; DObst RCOG 1972; DIH Soc. Apoth. Lond. 1971. (St. Bart.) Med. Dir. of Telford Occupat.al Health Serv. Socs: Soc. Occupat. Med.; BMA; FOM. Prev: Surg. Lt. Cdr. HMNB Portsmouth; GP S. Wales.

RICHARDS

RICHARDS, Nicholas Talbot Department of Nephrology, Queen Elizabeth Hospital, Edgbaston, Birmingham B15 2TH Tel: 0121 627 2528 Fax: 0121 627 2527 — MD 1992 Lond.; BSc Pharmacol. Lond. 1978, MB BS 1981; MRCP (UK) 1992; FRCP 1996. Cons. Nephrol. & Phys. Qu. Eliz. Hosp. Birm.

RICHARDS, Paul London Road Surgery, 64 London Road, Wickford SS12 0AH Tel: 01268 765533 Fax: 01268 570762 — MB ChB 1987 Manch.; MRCGP 1992; T(GP) 1992. (Manch.)

RICHARDS, Paul Rees Nant Goch, Merthyr Road, Llwydcoed, Aberdare CF44 0UT — MB ChB 1989 Sheff.

RICHARDS, Paula Jane North Staffordshire NHS Trust, X Ray Department, Royal Infirmary, Princes Rd., Heartshill, Stoke-on-Trent ST4 7LN; Fax: 01270 820331 — MB BS 1987 Lond.; BSc (Hons.) 1984 Path. & Med. Sci. Lond.; MRCP (UK) 1990; FRCR 1995. (Guy's Hospital) Cons. Musculoskeletal & Trauma Radilogist; Sen. Clin. Lect., Keele Univ. Staffs.. Socs: Brit. Trauma Soc.; Europ. Soc. of Skeletal Radiologists; Brit. Soc. Of Skeletal Radiologists. Prev: SHO (Renal) Guy's Hosp. Lond.; SHO Rotat. (Med.) Guy's & Lewisham Hosp. Lond.; Sen. Regist. (Diag. Radiol.) St. Bart. Hosp. Lond.

RICHARDS, Professor Peter Northwick Park Hospital, Watford Road, Harrow HA1 3UJ Tel: 020 8869 2609 Fax: 020 8869 2995 — MB BChir Camb. 1961; PhD Lond. 1966; MD Camb. 1971, BA 1957, MA 1961; FRCP Lond. 1976, M 1962. (Canb. & St. Geo.) Med. Dir. & Cons. Phys. N.wick Pk. & St. Mark's NHS Trust; Emerit. Prof. Med. Univ. Lond. (Imperial Coll.). Socs: Assn. Phys.; Elected Mem. GMC; Founder Fell. Acad. Med. Sci. Prev: ProRector (Med.) Imperial Coll.; Dean & Prof. (Med.) St. Mary's Hosp. Med. Sch. Lond.; Cons. Phys. & Sen. Lect. (Med.) St. Geo. Hosp. Lond.

RICHARDS, Mr Peter Gerald Department of Neurosurgery, The Radcliffe Infirmary, Woodstock Road, Oxford OX2 6HE Tel: 01865 228507 Fax: 01865 224898 Email: prichards@btinternet.com — MB BS 1977 Lond.; FRCS Ed. 1981; FRCPCH 1998; FRCS Eng 1999. (Middlx.) Cons. Paediat. Neurosurg. Radcliffe Infirm. Oxf. Prev: Cons. Neurosurg. Char. Cross Hosp. Lond.; Cons. Paediat. Neurosurg. Chelsea & W.m. Hosp. Lond.

RICHARDS, Peter Llewellyn Wickham Surgery, Station Road, Wickham, Fareham PO17 5JL Tel: 01329 833121 Fax: 01329 832443; Speedfield House, Ingoldfield Lane, Newtown, Fareham PO17 6LF Tel: 01329 833262 — MB BS 1975 Lond.; MRCP (UK) 1979; MRCS Eng. LRCP Lond. 1975; DRCOG 1980. Prev: Clin. Asst. (Rheum.) Portsmouth.

RICHARDS, Peter William Grandes Maison Road Surgery, St Sampsons, Guernsey; L'aumone & St. Sampsons Practice, Plaisance, Candie Road, Castel, Guernsey GY5 7BX — MB ChB (Hons.) 1983; MRCGP 1988; DCH RCP Lond. 1986; DRCOG 1986. Prev: Trainee GP Winchester VTS.

RICHARDS, Mr Philip Alfred Flemish House, Chapel Lane, Dudleston Heath, Ellesmere SY12 9LZ — MB ChB 1981 Ed.; FRCS Ed. 1986. Assoc. Specialist (Surg.) Wrexham Maelor Hosp.

RICHARDS, Philip Warren 113 Dunedin Road, Birmingham B44 9DL — MB ChB 1994 Leeds.

RICHARDS, Philippa Eloise Inez 4 Sylvan Drive, Coventry CV3 6AB — MB BS 1996 Lond.

RICHARDS, Polly Sara Mariabella Bristol Royal Infimary, Bristol BS2 8HW Tel: 0117 923 0000 — MB BS 1991 Lond.; BA Oxf. 1988; MRCP (UK) 1994. Regist. (Clin. Radiol.) Bristol Roy. Infirm.

RICHARDS, Rachel (retired) Amberley, Well-Meadows, Shaw, Newbury RG14 2DS — MRCS Eng. LRCP Lond. 1945; FRCOG 1989, M 1957, DObst 1947. Gyn. Asst. Newbury Dist. Hosp. Prev: Res. Obst. Off. Univ. Obst. Unit, S.mead Hosp. Bristol.

RICHARDS, Richard George North Nottinghamshire Health Authority, Rainworth, Mansfield NG21 0ER; The Old Rectory, 35 High St., Brant Broughton, Lincoln LN5 0SL — MB BS 1980 Newc. Cons., Pub. Health Med., Nth Nott. Health Auth..

RICHARDS, Richard Michael (retired) 2 Heol Y Pavin, Llandaff, Cardiff CF5 2EG Tel: 01222 563241 — MB BCh 1949 Wales; BSc, MB BCh Wales 1949; FRCGP 1976, M 1959. Prev: Ho. Surg. Obst. Dept. St. David's Hosp. Cardiff.

RICHARDS, Mr Robert Hargest Orthopaedic Department, Queen Alexandra Hospital, Cosham, Portsmouth PO6 3LY Tel: 023 92 286000; Corkallian, 10 Cold Harbour Close, Wickham, Fareham PO17 5PT Tel: 01329 834910 — BM BCh 1982 Oxf.; MA Camb. 1983, BA (Natural Sc.) 1979; FRCS Eng. 1986. Cons. Orthop. Surg.

Qu. Alexandra Hosp. Portsmouth. Socs: Fell. BOA; Brit. Soc. Childr. Orthop. Surg. Prev: Sen. Regist. (Orthop.) Soton. Gen. Hosp.; Regist. Rotat. (Orthop.) Lord Mayor Treloar Hosp. Alton.

RICHARDS, Robert Prideaux 45 Lisvane Street, Cathays, Cardiff CF24 4LH Tel: 029 2023 6669 — MB BCh 1990 Wales.

RICHARDS, Robert William Drayton Medical Practices, The Health Centre, Cheshire St., Market Drayton TF9 3BS Tel: 01630 652158 — MB ChB 1989 Aberd.; MRCGP 1994; DRCOG 1993.

RICHARDS, Rosemary Kyffin Severn NHS Trust, Child & Adolescent Services, Cleeve House, Horton Road, Gloucester GL1 3PX Tel: 01452 891312 — BM 1982 Soton.; 1982 BM (Hons.) Soton. 1982; 1979 PhD Nottm. 1979, MA Nottm. 1974; 1972 BSc (Hons.) Bristol 1972; 1994 MRCPsych 1994; 1984 DRCOG 1984; 1997 C. Psychol. 1997. Cons. Child, Adolesc. & Family Psychiat. Severn NHS Trust,(p/t). Socs: Brit. Psychol. Soc.; Asson. Child Psychol. & Psych. Prev: Sen. Regist. (Child Psychiat.) W. Midl.; Sen. Regist. (Child Psychiat.) United Bristol Hosps. Trust; Regist. & SHO (Psychiat.) Bristol & W.on HA.

RICHARDS, Sally Flat 5, 67 Pen-y-lan Road, Roath, Cardiff CF23 5HZ — MB BCh 1998 Wales.

RICHARDS, Sarah Caroline First Floor Flat, 7 Bradiston Road, Maida Vale, London W9 3HN — MB BCh 1996 Wales.

RICHARDS, Sarah Elizabeth Heathville Road Surgery, 5 Heathville Road, Gloucester GL1 3DP Tel: 01452 528299 Fax: 01452 522959 — MB ChB 1988 Sheff.

RICHARDS, Sarah Kathryn 6 Coppice View, Weavering, Maidstone ME14 5TX — MB ChB 1997 Bristol.

RICHARDS, Selwyn Charles Morgan Department of Rheumatology, Poole NHS Trust, Poole BH15 2JB Tel: 01202 448613 Fax: 01202 660147 Email: selwynrichards@lineone.net; 48 Pilford Heath Road, Colehill, Wimborne BU21 2NB Tel: 01202 888610 — BM BCh 1991 Oxf.; MA Camb. 1991; MRCP (UK) 1994; Dip. Sports Med. (Scot.) 1997. Cons. Rheumatologist. Socs: Brit. Soc. Rheum.; Brit. Pain Soc.; Chronic fatigue Network. Prev: NHS Research Train. Fell., Kings Coll. Hosp.; Specialist Regist., Rheum., S. Thames; SHO City Hosp. Nottm.

RICHARDS, Sheila Mary 133 Overslade Lane, Rugby CV22 6EF — MB BS 1993 Lond.; DRCOG 1997; MRCGP 1998; DFFP 1997. (St George's, Lond.)

RICHARDS, Shirley Jane, OBE (retired) Quarryfield House, Whitestone, Exeter EX4 2JS Tel: 01392 811492 Fax: 01392 811489 Email: dr_j_richards@compuserve.com — MB BS Lond. 1957; MRCS Eng. LRCP Lond. 1957; FRCGP 1978, M 1970; DCH Eng. 1961; DObst RCOG 1960. p/t Locum, Gen. Practitioner.

RICHARDS, Simon David Jackson, Knights, Richards and Hobbis, Thorney Medical Centre, Wisbech Road, Thorney, Peterborough PE6 0SA Tel: 01733 270219 Fax: 01733 270860; 7 The Willows, Glinton, Peterborough PE6 7NE Tel: 01733 253445 Fax: 01733 270860 — MB BChir 1983 Camb.; BSc St. And. 1980; MRCGP 1988; DRCOG 1991. Prev: Trainee GP/SHO Rotat. Camb. Milit. Hosp. VTS; Regtl. Med. Off. 17/21 Lancers (GP VTS); RMO 1 King's.

RICHARDS, Stella Jane Grandes Maison Road Surgery, St Sampsons, Guernsey Tel: 01481 45915; Plaisance, Rue De Candie, Castel, Guernsey GY5 7BX Tel: 01481 52038 — MB ChB 1983 Bristol; MRCGP 1988; DRCOG 1987. p/t GP. Socs: MDU. Prev: Trainee GP Bournemouth VTS; Trainee Year, Bishops Waltham; SHO (Cas.) W.on-Super-Mare.

RICHARDS, Stephen Andrew The Health Centre, Wayside Green, Woodcote, Reading RG8 0QL Tel: 01491 680686 Fax: 01491 682264; Yew Tree Farm House, Behoes Lane, Woodcote, Reading RG8 0PP — MB BChir 1982 Camb.; MA Camb. 1983, MB BChir 1982; MRCGP 1986; DRCOG 1985; DCH RCP Lond. 1984.

RICHARDS, Mr Stephen Higgs (cons. rooms) Glamorgan House, Bupa Hospial, Croescadarn Road, Pentwyn, Cardiff CF23 8XL Tel: 029 2073 6011; The Mount, Rudry Road, Lisvane, Cardiff CF14 0SN Tel: 029 2075 2660 — MB BS 1951 Lond.; FRCS Eng. 1959; MRCS Eng. LRCP Lond. 1951; DLO Eng. 1959. (Guy's) Mem. Ct. Examrs. RCS Eng. Socs: Welsh Assn. Otolaryngol.; (Ex-Pres.) S. W.. Laryngol. Assn.; Fell. Roy. Soc. Med. (Pres. Sect. Otol.). Prev: Cons. ENT Surg. Univ. Hosp. Wales Cardiff; 1st Asst. Dept. Otolaryng. Radcliffe Infirm. Oxf.; Grad. Fell. Henry Ford Hosp. Detroit, USA.

RICHARDS

RICHARDS, Stephen Miles 98 St Martins Road, Finham, Coventry CV3 6ER — MB BS 1980 Lond.; BSc Lond. 1976, MB BS 1980. (Univ. Coll. Hosp.)

RICHARDS, Stuart David 278 Hills Road, Cambridge CB2 2QE — BM BS 1997 Nottm.

RICHARDS, Sylvia Théone Mary 18 Rose Close, Hedge End, Southampton SO30 2GR Tel: 02380 554625 — MB ChB 1974 Liverp.

RICHARDS, Tessa Jane Louise 30 Dartmouth Row, Greenwich, London SE10 8AW — MB ChB 1973 Leeds; MRCP (UK) 1976; MRCGP 1982. (Leeds & Guy's) Asst. Edr. Brit. Med. Jl. Socs: BMA.

RICHARDS, Thomas Arthur (retired) 84 St George's Avenue, Northampton NN2 6JF Tel: 01604 714044 — MB BS 1945 Lond.; MD Lond. 1949; MRCP Lond. 1949; DObst RCOG 1954.

RICHARDS, Thomas David The Surgery, 52 Springfield Avenue, Mangotsfield, Bristol BS16 9BL Tel: 0117 937 2181; Harwood House, Castle Road, Pucklechurch, Bristol BS16 9RF — MB ChB 1953 Bristol; MRCGP 1968; Cert Family Plann. RCOG, RCGP & Family Plann; Assn. 1976. (Bristol & Vienna) Clin. Teach. (Gen. Pract.) Univ. Camb. Socs: Bristol M-C Soc. & Med.-Leg. Soc. Prev: Med. Off. Home Office; Res. Med. Off. Bristol Roy. Infirm.; SHO (Obst.) Bristol Matern. Hosp.

RICHARDS, Thomas Harold (retired) Ra-Mo-Ana, 8 Cwmbach Road, Llanelli SA15 4EP Tel: 01554 750429 — MB BS 1944 Lond.; MRCS Eng. LRCP Lond. 1944; MRCGP 1955. Prev: Ho. Phys. Brit. Postgrad. Med. Sch. Hammersmith & E. Suff. & Ipswich Hosp.

RICHARDS, Thomas Martin (retired) Turf Run, Bunch Lane, Haslemere GU27 1AE Tel: 01428 642582 Fax: 01428 642582 Email: tom@richardst.freeserve.co.uk — MB BS Lond. 1954; DObst RCOG 1956. Prev: Ho. Surg. Salisbury Gen. Hosp.

RICHARDS, Thomas Vincent Howells 44 Dinam Street, Nantymoel, Bridgend CF32 7PU — MRCS Eng. LRCP Lond. 1939.

RICHARDS, Veronica Jane Weir Cottage, Fladbury, Pershore WR10 2QA Tel: 01386 860668 — MB ChB 1962 Birm.

RICHARDS, Walter Charles Desmond (retired) Gable Cottage, Vicarage Lane, Laleham, Staines TW18 1UE — MB BS 1947 Lond.; MRCPath 1964. Prev: Cons. Morbid Anat. & Histol. Ashford Hosp. Middlx.

RICHARDS AFFONSO, Nicola Wokingham CAM HS, Wokingham Hospital, Barkham Road, Wokingham RG41 2RE Tel: 01189 49506 — MB ChB 1991 Bristol; MRCPsych 1997; MA Oxf. 1985. SPR. Rotat. (Psychiat.) Oxf. Regional Train. Scheme in Child and Adolesc. Psychiat.

RICHARDS-JONES, Margaret Carys (retired) Elanegys, 8 Stewart Drive, Ammanford SA18 3BH Tel: 01269 592768 — MB BCh 1965 Wales; DObst RCOG 1967. Prev: SCMO (Community Child Health, Special Needs) W. Glam. HA Swansea.

RICHARDSON, Rt. Hon. Lord, LVO Windcutter, Lee, Ilfracombe EX34 8LW — MA, MD Camb. 1940, BA, MB BChir 1936; Hon. FRCPI 1975; Hon. FRCGP 1980; FRCPS 1980; Hon. FRCPsych. 1979; Hon. FFCM 1977; Hon. FPS 1974; FRCP Ed. 1974 Glas. & Irel.; FRCP Lond. 1948, M 1937; MRCS Eng. LRCP Lond. 1935; Hon. LLD 1981 & 1983; Hon. DCL 1980 & 1981; Hon. DSc 1975; Hon. FRCP Ed. 1981; Hon. FRCS Eng. 1980. Hon. Fell. Trin. Coll. Camb. 1979 & KCL. 1998; Hon. Consg. Phys. St. Thos. Hosp. Lond. & King Edwd. VII Hosp. Offs. Lond.; Emerit. Cons. to the Army. Socs: Hon. Fell. (Ex-Pres.) Roy. Soc. Med.; Hon. Pres. Internat. Soc. Internal Med.; Hon. Fell. Med. Soc. Lond. Prev: Hon. Bencher Gray's Inn 1974; Pres Gen. Med. Counc.; Pres. BMA.

RICHARDSON, Abby Jane Wellside Surgery, 45 High St., Sawtry, Huntingdon PE28 5SU — MB ChB 1992 Leic.

RICHARDSON, Adrian Law Medical Group Practice, 9 Wrottesley Road, London NW10 5UY Tel: 020 8965 8011 Fax: 020 8961 6239; 10 Crooked Usage, Church End, Finchley, London N3 3HB Tel: 020 8349 3563 Email: ar@drick.ttech.co.uk — MB BS 1980 Lond.; MRCP (UK) 1984; MRCGP 1988; DCH RCP Lond. 1987. (Middlx.) Prev: Clin. Research Fell. King's Coll. Hosp. Lond.; Regist. (Med.) Hillingdon Hosp. Uxbridge.

RICHARDSON, Adrian Scott Fernville Surgery, Midland Road, Hemel Hempstead HP2 5BL Tel: 01442 213919 Fax: 01442 216433; 39A Sherwood, Pk Road, Sutton SM1 2SG Tel: 020 8661 6127 — MB ChB 1992 Ed.; BMedSci Ed. 1990; MRCP (UK) 1995; MRCGP 1997. (Edinburgh) Partner. Hemel Hempstead. Prev: SHO (Obst. & Gyn), St Heliers, Surrey; GP/Regist. Camb. St. Surg. Lond.; SHO (Dermat.) N.ampton Gen. Hosp.

RICHARDSON, Mr Alan Ernest 6 Southwood Avenue, Kingston upon Thames KT2 7HD Tel: 020 8942 6476 — MB BS 1949 Lond.; FRCS Eng. 1955; FRCS Ed. 1955; MRCS Eng. LRCP Lond. 1949. (Guy's) Hon. Cons. Neurosurg. St. Geo. Hosp. Lond. & SW Thames RHA; Teach. (Surg.) St. Geo. Hosp. Med. Sch. (Univ. Lond.); Vis. Surg. Mayday Hosp. Croydon & Accid. Centre St. Peter's Hosp. Chertsey; Hon. Cons Neurosurg. Wolfson Med. Rehabil. Centre. Socs: Fell. Roy. Soc. Med.; Soc. Brit. Neurol. Surgs.; Amer. Assn. Neurol. Surgs. Prev: Research Fell. (Neurosurg.) St. Geo. Hosp. Lond.; 1st Asst. (Neurosurg.) St. Geo. Hosp. Lond. & Nat. Hosp. Nerv. Dis. QuSq.

RICHARDSON, Alfred Ian, MBE (retired) Laggan, Mullach Na Beinne, Highland, Newtonmore PH20 1DT Tel: 01528 544240 — LRCP LRCS 1947 Ed.; LRFPS Glas. 1947. Prev: Med. Pract. Highlands & Is.s Med. Serv.

RICHARDSON, Alison Parkway Medical Centre, 2 Frenton Close, Chapel House Estate, Newcastle upon Tyne NE5 1EH Tel: 0191 267 1313 Fax: 0191 229 0630; 7 Sunnidale, Fellside Park, Whickham, Newcastle upon Tyne NE16 5TT Tel: 0191 488 4010 — MB BS 1980 Newc.; MRCGP 1984; DRCOG 1983.

RICHARDSON, Andrew Grant 59 Hillhead Parkway, Newcastle upon Tyne NE5 1DQ — MB ChB 1994 Leeds. Sen. Unified SHO. (Gen. Adult Psychiat.) Newc. Gen. Hosp. Prev: Sen. Unified SHO (Child & Adolesc. Psychiat.) Sunderland Roy. Infirm.; Sen. Unified SHO (Psychiat. in Learning Disabil.) Earls Ho. Hosp. Durh.; Sen. Unified SHO (Old Age Psychiat.) Chester-le-St. Hosp.

RICHARDSON, Andrew James Worcester & District HA, Isaac Maddox House, Shrub Hill Road, Worcester WR4 9RW — MB ChB 1985 Manch.; BSc St. And. 1982; MFPHM RCP (UK) 1992. Cons. Pub. Health Med. & Dir. Commiss.ing Worcs. Dist. HA. Prev: Sen. Regist. (Pub. Health Med.) Wessex RHA & Bath Dist. HA.

RICHARDSON, Andrew Julian 35 Hilltop Way, Salisbury SP1 3QY — MB BS 1997 Lond.

RICHARDSON, Andrew Mark Edward McLaughlin and Partners, 27-29 Derby Road, North End, Portsmouth PO2 8HW Tel: 023 9266 3024 Fax: 023 9265 4991; Bradley Cottage, Ogwell Mill Road, Newton Abbot TQ12 6LS — MB BS 1989 Lond.; BSc Lond. 1984, MB BS 1989.

RICHARDSON, Andrew Paul Cormer Place Surgery, 46A Dartmouth Road, Paignton TQ4 5AH Tel: 01803 557458; The Gables, 31 St. Matthews Road, Chelston, Torquay TQ2 6JA Tel: 01803 606161 — MB ChB 1984 Birm.; MRCGP 1989; DRCOG 1988; DCH RCP Lond. 1987; DA (UK) 1986.

RICHARDSON, Anna Mary Therese 18 Fords Lane, Bramhall, Stockport SK7 1DQ — MB ChB 1990 Manch.; BSc Path. (Hons.) Manch. 1988, MB ChB Manch. 1990; MRCP (UK) 1993. (Manchester) Regist. (Neurol.) Manch. Roy. Infirm. Prev: SHO (Gen. Med.) Trafford Gen. Hosp.; SHO (Cardiothoracic Med.) Wythenshawe Hosp.

RICHARDSON, Barbora 18 Comeragh Road, London W14 9HP — MB BChir 1989 Camb.; MSc 2001; DRCOG 1991; DCH 1992; MRCGP 1993; MRCPsych 1997. (St Anne's Coll. Oxf., Queen's Coll. & Addenbrooke's Hosp. Camb.) Specialist Regist., Dual Train., Old Age & Gen. Psychiat.; Hon. Sen. Lect.; Old Age Psychiat., Univ. Coll., Lond.

RICHARDSON, Benjamin Peter The Surgery, Ewyas Harold, Hereford HR2 0EU Tel: 01981 240320 Fax: 01981 241023; Merton Lodge, Ewyas Harold, Hereford HR2 0HU Tel: 01981 240320 Fax: 01981 241023 — MB ChB 1971 Birm.; MRCP (UK) 1974; DObst RCOG 1973.

RICHARDSON, Bernard William Thomas (retired) Stable Cottage, Chequers Lane, Watford WD25 0GP Tel: 01923 672238 — LRCP LRCS Ed. LRFPS Glas. 1946. Prev: Med. Off. Beckenham Hosp. & Leavesden Hosp. Abbot's Langley.

RICHARDSON, Brian David 23 Allenbys Chase, Sutton Bridge, Spalding PE12 9SY — MB ChB 1989 Leeds.

RICHARDSON, Bruce The Surgery, The Brooklands, Leek Road, Waterhouses, Stoke-on-Trent ST10 3HN — MB ChB 1971 Sheff.; DObst RCOG 1973.

RICHARDSON, Caroline Annie 23 Sandringham Road, Gosforth, Newcastle upon Tyne NE3 1QB — MB BS 1992 Newc.

RICHARDSON, Catherine Margaret The Old Stores Cottage, Weston Underwood, Ashbourne DE6 4PA — MB ChB 1996 Leic.

RICHARDSON, Charles Edward 21 Park Avenue, Mumbles, Swansea SA3 4DU — MB ChB 1989 Birm.; BSc (Hons.) Birm. 1986; MRCP (UK) 1992.

RICHARDSON, Clare Denise Pitsmoor Surgery, 151 Burngreave Road, Sheffield S3 9DL Tel: 0114 272 8228 — MB ChB 1983 Sheff.; MRCGP 1987; DCCH Sheff. 1989; DCH RCP Lond. 1987.

RICHARDSON, David 89 Bedford Road, Sutton Coldfield B75 6BG Tel: 0121 378 3374 — MB ChB 1975 Birm.; BSc (Hons.) Sheff. 1962. (Birmingham)

RICHARDSON, Mr David Maxillofacial Unit, Aintree Hospitals NHS Trust, Walton Hospital, Rice Lane, Liverpool L9 1AE Tel: 0151 529 4786 Fax: 0151 529 4358; Maxillofacial Unit, Chester Royal Infirmary, Nicholas St, Chester CH1 2AZ Tel: 01244 363056 Fax: 01244 363056 — MB BS 1987 Lond.; BDS Lond. 1979; FRCS Eng. 1991; FDS RCS Eng. 1990. Cons. Oral & Maxillofacial Surg. Aintree Hosps NHS Trust Liverp. & Countess of Chester NHS Trust. Socs: Fell. Brit. Assn. Oral & Maxillofacial Surg. Prev: Sen. Regist. & Regist. Rotat. (Maxillofacial Surg.) Mersey Region.

RICHARDSON, David Andrew Tel: 01290 551237 Fax: 01290 552784 — MB ChB 1977 Glas. GP Princip. Catrine.; Clin. Plann. Adviser Ayrsh. & Arran Health Bd., Ayr. Prev: Trainee Gen. Pract. Ayrsh. & Arran Vocational. Surgic. Ho. Off.; Med. Ho. Off. Ballochmyle Hosp.

RICHARDSON, David Andrew Cardiovascular Investigation Unit, Ward 15 Offices, Royal Victoria Infirmary, Newcastle upon Tyne NE1 4LP Email: david.richardson@ncl.ac.uk; 9 The Grange, Nedderton Village, Bedlington NE22 6BQ — MB ChB 1986 Leeds; MRCP (UK) 1993. Specialist Regist., Geriat. Med., Cumbld. Infirm., Carlisle; Research Assoc. (Hon.), Roy. Vict. Infirm., Newc.-Upon-Tyne. Socs: Brit. Geriat. Soc.; BMA.

RICHARDSON, David Edward Ryder, VRD (retired) 121 Quantock Road, Bridgwater TA6 7EJ Tel: 01278 429448 — MRCS Eng. LRCP Lond. 1947. Prev: Ho. Phys. & Ho. Surg. (Neurosurg.) Lond. Hosp.

RICHARDSON, David Leslie Department Diagnostic Radiology, Royal Victoria Infirmary, Queen Victoria Road, Newcastle upon Tyne NE1 4LP Tel: 0191 232 5131 Fax: 0191 227 5223; Fell View, 8 Deepdale Close, Whickham, Newcastle upon Tyne NE16 5SN Tel: 0191 488 4010 — MB BS 1980 Newc.; FRCR 1987. Cons. Radiol. Roy. Vict. Infirm. Prev: Cons. Radiol. Newc. Gen. & Freeman Hosps.; Sen. Regist. (Radiol.) Newc. u Tyne.

RICHARDSON, David Peter Mitchell Road Surgery, 9 Mitchell Road, Canferd Heath, Poole BH17 8UE Tel: 01202 672474 Fax: 01202 660926 — MB BS 1985 Lond.

RICHARDSON, Deborah Susan Southampton General Hospital, Dept. of Haematology, Tremona Road, Southampton SO16 6YD Tel: 02380 796164 Fax: 02380 794134 Email: deborah.richardson@suht.swest.nhs.uk — MB BChir 1989 Camb.; MA Camb. 1991, BA (Hons.) 1987; MRCP (UK) 1993; MRC Path 1999. (Univ. Camb.) Cons. Haemat.S.ampton Univ. Hosp..; Hon.Sen. Lect. Univ. of S.ampton, Sch. Of Med. Socs: Brit. Soc. Haematol.; Amer. Soc .Haemat.; Eur. Haematol. Assn. Prev: Sspecialist Regist. & Hon. Lect. St Barts & Roy. Lond. Hosps.

RICHARDSON, Dennis Martin Dunster, 47 Greenways, Haywards Heath RH16 2DT Tel: 01444 413039 — MRCS Eng. LRCP Lond. 1950; MFPHM 1989; MFCM 1974; DIH Eng. 1966; DPH Eng. 1957. (St. Geo.) Specialist (Pub. Health Med.) E. Sussex HA. Socs: FRIPHH; Fell. Roy. Soc. Med. Prev: Dir. Dept. Med. Illust. Inst. Neurol. Nat. Hosp. Qu. Sq. Lond.; MOH Mid. Sussex Area; Dep. Med. Adviser Lloyds Bank plc Hqrs.

RICHARDSON, Dominic James Jersey Cottage, Bashurst Hill, Itchingfield, Horsham RH13 7PA — BM 1995 Soton.

RICHARDSON, Donald Stockingwood Farmhouse, Hillesden, Buckingham MK18 4DE — MB ChB 1989 Leeds.

RICHARDSON, Donald Arthur 1 Cherry Tree Rise, Walkern, Stevenage SG2 7JL Tel: 01438 861349 Fax: 01438 861349 — MB BS Lond. 1956; FRCGP 1984, M 1964; DObst RCOG 1958. (Westm.) Med. Advis. NHS Direct.Beds.-Herts; Treas. Cameron Fund. Socs: BMA. Prev: GP St. Albans.; dir.Secretariat.Beds & hertsCRUCs.

RICHARDSON, Dorothy Evelyn Margaret Carradale, Whimple, Exeter EX5 2PL — MRCS Eng. LRCP Lond. 1938. (King's Coll. Lond. & Bristol) Prev: Ho. Surg. Res. Anaesth. & Sen. Ho. Phys. Roy. Infirm. Bristol.

RICHARDSON, Dunsford Leaf Foxfold, Gristhorpe, Filey YO14 Tel: 01723 513283 — MB ChB 1941 Leeds.

RICHARDSON, Edwin Ian 95 Gresley Close, Welwyn Garden City AL8 7QA Tel: 01707 377467 Email: edwinianrichardson@compuserve.com — MB 1976 Camb.; BChir 1975; MRCGP 1980; DRCOG 1979.

RICHARDSON, Elizabeth Margaret 24 Penlan Crescent, Uplands, Swansea SA2 0RL Tel: 01792 298516 — MB BCh 1982 Wales; MRCPsych. 1989. Sen. Regist. Cefn Coed Hosp. Swansea. Prev: Research Regist. WhitCh. Hosp. Cardiff.

RICHARDSON, Esther Joy Laura PO Box 13787, London N14 4WD Email: gpax@supanet.com — MB BChir 1992 Camb.; MRCGP 200. (Cambridge) Socs: Mem. of Roy. Coll. of Gen. Practitioners.

RICHARDSON, Ethel Anne (retired) 5 Colletts Close, Corfe Castle, Wareham BH20 5HG — MB ChB Leeds 1955; MRCS Eng. LRCP Lond. 1954; FRCPath 1986, M 1974; DCH Eng. 1959. Prev: Cons. Microbiol. (Pub. Health & Hosp. Microbiol. Laborat.) Poole Gen. Hosp.

RICHARDSON, Fiona Mary Millburn, 2 Milton of Straloch, Newmacher, Aberdeen AB21 0QE — MB ChB 1988 Aberd.; MRCGP 1993.

RICHARDSON, Mr Francis John Acident & Emergency Department, Royal Gwent Hospital, Cardiff Road, Newport NP20 2UB Tel: 01633 234065 Fax: 01633 238966 — MB ChB 1981 Liverp.; FRCS Ed. 1988; FFAEM 1996; DA (UK) 1990; Dip IMC RCS Ed. 1989; Dip Med Educ. 1999. Cons. (A & E Med.) Roy. Gwent Hosp. Newport S. Wales. Socs: Brit. Assn. Accid. & Emerg. Med.; BASICS; BMA. Prev: Sen. Regist. (A & E Med.) Cardiff Roy. Infirm.; Regist. (A & E) W. Midl. RHA; Sen. Med. Off. Johannesburg Trauma Unit.

RICHARDSON, Fraser Elmbank Group, Foresterhill Health Centre, Westburn Road, Aberdeen AB25 2AY Tel: 01224 696949 Fax: 01224 691650; 13 Earlswells Road, Fairacres, Cults, Aberdeen AB15 9NY Tel: 01224 867286 Fax: 01224 691650 — MB ChB 1968 Aberd. (Aberd.) Med. Off. Offshore Oil Indust.; Sen. Lect. (Gen. Pract.) Univ. Aberd. Socs: Aberd. M-C Soc. Prev: Regist. (Med.) Aberd. Roy. Infirm.

RICHARDSON, Gail 12 Nelson Street, King's Lynn PE30 5DY — MB BS 1990 Lond.; BSc (Hons.) Lond. 1987; MRCP (UK) 1994. Regist. Rotat. (Cardiol.) Chase Farm., Roy. Free & Lond. Chest Hosps. Prev: SHO Rotat. (Med.) St. Bart. Hosp. Lond.

RICHARDSON, Giles Lindley Flat 4, Pembroke Mansions, 1-3 Oakfield Road, Clifton, Bristol BS8 2AH Tel: 01177 973 4766 Email: gilesrich@hotmail.com — MB ChB 1994 Bristol. (Bristol)

RICHARDSON, Gillian Tel: 01722 336262, 020 2040 2402; Tel: 029 2040 2402 — MB BCh 1985 Wales; MPH 1997 Wales; 2001 MFPHMI Dublin; MRCGP (Distinc.) 1990. p/t Spcialist Pub. Health and policy BroTaf Health Auth., Cardiff, Wales. Socs: BMA; Christian Med. Fell.sh. Prev: SpR Pub. Health Med. BroTaf Health Auth.; SpR Pub. Health Med. Mid Glam. Health Auth.; Lect. Univ. Wales Coll. of Med.

RICHARDSON, Graham Andrew Bradley Cottage, Ogwell Mill Lane, Newton Abbot TQ12 6LS — MRCS Eng. LRCP Lond. 1958; MD Lond. 1969, MB BS 1958; MRCP (U.K.) 1970. (Univ. Coll. Hosp.) Cons. Phys. & Cons. Chest Phys. Torbay Hosp. Torquay. Socs: Fell. Med. Soc. Lond. Prev: Sen. Rgis.Univ. Coll. Hosp. Resid. Med Off. Univ Coll Hosp. Lond.. HO,Ssurg Univ. Coll Hosp.

RICHARDSON, Gregory James Ronald Lime Trees, Child Adolescent and Family Unit, 31 Shipton Road, York YO30 5RF Tel: 01904 652908 Fax: 01904 632893 — MB ChB 1971 Liverp.; MRCS Eng. LRCP Lond. 1971; FRCPCH 1997; FRCPsych. 1991, M 1977; DPM Leeds 1977; DCH Eng. 1975. Cons. Child Adolesc. & Family Psychiat. Lime Trees York; Hon. Lect. Child & Adolesc. Psychiat. Univ. Leeds.; Vis. Fell. Univ. York; Specialist Adviser to the health Advisery Serv. Socs: Fell. Roy. Coll. Psychiat.; Fell. Roy. Coll. Peadiat. & Child Health; BMA. Prev: Cons. Child & Adolesc. Psychiat. Harrogate & N.allerton HAs; Med. Off. Save the Childr. Fund Mother & Child Health Unit Torit, Sudan; Resid. (Child & Adolesc. Psychiat.) Hosp. Sick Childr. Toronto, Canada.

RICHARDSON, Hanora Bernadette Mary Thornley Street Surgery, 40 Thornley Street, Wolverhampton WV1 1JP Tel: 01902

RICHARDSON

26843 Fax: 01902 688500 — MB BCh BAO 1987 Dub.; MB BCh BAO (Dub) 1987.

RICHARDSON, Hazel Joan Richardson and Ilves, 351 Danebury Avenue, London SW15 4DU Tel: 020 8876 6666 Fax: 020 8878 2629; 58 Temple Sheen Road, London SW14 7QG — BM BCh 1968 Oxf.; MA Oxf. 1968; MRCGP 1981.

RICHARDSON, Heather Temple Ward, St Martins Hospital, Littlebourne Road, Canterbury CT1 1TD Tel: 01227 459371; Cambridge Cottage, Seawalk, Sandgate, Folkestone CT20 3AW Tel: 01303 220926 — MB BS Lond. 1961; FRCP Ed. 1987, M 1966; MRCP Lond. 1967; MRCS Eng. LRCP Lond. 1961; MFCH 1989; DCH Eng. 1964; MFCH by Distinction 1997; FRCPCH 1992. (Guy's) Cons. Paediat. E. Kent Community Trust, Canterbury; Designated Doctor Child Protec., E. Kent Health Auth. (S. E. Kent Canterbury & Thanet). Prev: Lect. Inst. Dis. Chest Lond.

RICHARDSON, Helen Diane Department of Diagnostic Radiology, Kingston Hospital NHS Trust, Galsworthy Road, Kingston KT2 7QB Tel: 0208 546 7711 — MB BS 1991 Lond.; FRCR 2000 UK; BSc Lond. 1988; MRCP (UK) 1995. (St. Geo. Hosp. Lond.) Cons. Radiol. Kingston Hosp. Surrey. Prev: Regist. (Toxicol.) Guy's Hosp. Lond.; SHO (Med.) Medway Hosp. Gillingham & King's Coll. Hosp. Lond.; Specialist Regist. (Clin. Radiol.) King's Coll. Hosp. Lond.

RICHARDSON, Ian Arthur Southbourne Surgery, 337 Main Road, Southbourne, Emsworth PO10 8JH Tel: 01242 372623 Fax: 01243 379936; Shamba, Cemetery Lane, Woodmancote, Emsworth PO10 8QB Tel: 01243 374367 Email: hilary.richardson@virgin.net — MB BS Lond. 1969; MRCS Eng. LRCP Lond. 1968; DObst RCOG 1970. (Roy. Free)

RICHARDSON, Ian Harold (retired) Hill Orchard, Blenheim Hill, Harwell, Didcot OX11 0DS Tel: 01235 835222 Fax: 01235 835222 — MRCS Eng. LRCP Lond. 1949. Prev: Jun. Regist., Ho. Surg. & Ho. Phys. (Paediat.) St. Helier Hosp. Carshalton.

RICHARDSON, Ian Milne (retired) Rockland, 9 Grampian Avenue, Auchterarder PH3 1NY Tel: 01764 63826 — MB ChB 1944 Ed.; MB ChB (Hons.) Ed. 1944; PhD Aberd. 1956; MD (High Commend.) Ed. 1953; FRCP Ed. 1956, M 1946; FRCGP 1973, M 1968; DPH Glas. 1948. Prev: James Mackenzie Prof. Gen. Pract. Univ. Aberd.

RICHARDSON, Ian Robert The Clinic, 4 Firs Entry, Bannockburn, Stirling FK7 0HW Tel: 01786 813435 Fax: 01786 817545 — MB ChB 1963 Glas.; DObst RCOG 1966. (Glas.) Hosp. Pract. Bannockburn Hosp. Socs: BMA. Prev: Ho. Off. Stirling Roy. Infirm. & Ayrsh. Centr. Matern. Hosp. Irvine; Ho. Surg. S. Gen. Hosp. Glas.

RICHARDSON, James Hackwood Partnership, Essex House, Worting Road, Basingstoke RG21 8SU; The Rose, Basingstoke Road, Ramsdell, Basingstoke RG26 5RB Tel: 01256 850345 — MB BS 1974 Lond.; MRCS Eng. LRCP Lond. 1974; Dip Occ. Med. 1996; DObst RCOG 1976; Cert JCC Lond. 1976. (Guy's)

RICHARDSON, Professor James Bruce Institute of Orthopaedics, Robert Jones and Agnes Hunt Orthopaedic & District Hospital NHS Trust, Oswestry SY10 7AG Tel: 01691 404386 Fax: 01691 404071 Email: jamet.main@rjahah.tr.wmids.nhs.uk — MB ChB 1977 Aberd.; MD Aberd. 1989; FRCS Ed. 1984. (Univ. Aberd.) Prof. Keele Univ. Socs: Brit. Orthop. Assn.; Assn. Prof.s of Orthop. Surg.; Knee Soc. Prev: Sen. Lect. & Hon. Cons. Leicester; RSO (Orthop.) OsW.ry.

RICHARDSON, Jane 8 Briarwood Close, Brynoch, Neath SA10 7UH — MB BCh 1983 Wales.

RICHARDSON, Jeanette Olga Concorde Cottage, Ellingstring, Ripon HG4 4PW — MB ChB 1997 Ed.

RICHARDSON, Jennifer Barbara Ladthorne Grange, Brownstow, Modbury, Ivybridge PL21 0SH — MB ChB 1978 Liverp.; DA Eng. 1982.

RICHARDSON, Jeremy Peter Allan Sutton Hill Medical Practice, Maythorne Close, Sutton Hill, Telford TF7 4DH Tel: 01952 586471 Fax: 01952 588029; 3 Grange Farm View, Telford TF3 1DX — MB BS 1977 Lond.; BSc Lond. 1974; MRCGP 1981. p/t Hosp. Practitioner Psychiat. Shrops. Community & Ment. Health Servs. Trust.

RICHARDSON, Jeremy Robert Millburn, 2 Milton of Staloch, Newmachar, Aberdeen AB21 0QE Email: j.r.richardson@abdn.ac.uk — MB ChB 1989 Aberd.; MRCP (UK) 1993. Specialist Regist. (A & E) Aberd. Roy. Hosps. NHS Trust. Prev: Career Regist. (Clin. Pharmacol.) Aberd. Roy. Hosps. NHS Trust & Raigmore Hosp. Inverness; Clin. Research Fell. (Med. & Therap.) Aberd. Univ.; SHO (Gen. Med.) Aberd. Hosps.

RICHARDSON, Joanna Rachel Island Health, 145 East Ferry Road, London E14 3BQ Tel: 020 7363 1111 Fax: 020 7363 1112 — MB BS 1984 Lond.; MRCP (UK) 1988; MRCGP 1989; DRCOG 1988; DCH RCP Lond. 1988. Princip. GP Lond. Prev: Trainee GP Roy. Free Hosp. Lond. VTS; SHO (Cardiol.) Hammersmith Hosp. Lond.; Ho. Off. Med. Unit Roy. Free Hosp. Lond.

RICHARDSON, Mr John 14 Drumoyne Close, Greenacres, E. Herrington, Sunderland SR3 3SD Tel: 0191 528 0704 — MB BS Durh. 1963; FRCS Eng. 1968; FRCOphth 1989; DO Eng. 1967. (Newc.) Cons. Ophth. Sunderland Eye Infirm. Socs: Fac. Ophthalmol.; N. Eng. Ophth. Soc. Prev: Sen. Regist & Regist. Eye Dept. Vict. Infirm. Newc.; SHO Oxf. Eye Hosp.

RICHARDSON, John Boundary Cottage, Foley Manor, Liphook GU30 7JF Tel: 01428 723111 — MB ChB 1937 Glas. (Glas.) Prev: RAMC 1940-46; Ho. Surg. & Ho. Phys. Stobhill Hosp. Glas.; Sen. Res. Med. Off. W.. Dist. Hosp. Glas.

RICHARDSON, John Newcastle Research Group, Bellevue, Grange Road, Ryton NE40 3LU Tel: 0191 413 2268 Fax: 0191 413 7332 — MB BS 1952 Durh. Clin. Tutor (Family Med.) Univ. Newc. u. Tyne. Prev: Ho. Phys. Newc. Gen. Hosp.

RICHARDSON, Mr John Anthony Rumwell Lodge, Rumwell, Taunton TA4 1EJ — MB ChB 1966 Bristol; FRCS Ed. 1973; MRCOG 1973, DObst 1966. (Bristol) Cons. (O & G) MusGr. Pk. Hosp. Prev: Lect. (O & G) Univ. Bristol; Regist. (O & G) S. W. RHB.

RICHARDSON, John Carter 1 Franklin Place, Chichester PO19 1BL Tel: 01243 780786 Fax: 01243 774667 Email: johncrichardson@hotmail.com — MB BChir 1968 Camb.; MA Camb. 1968; MSc (GP) Lond. 1990; MMedSc. (Occupat. Health) Birm. 1992; MRCS Eng. LRCP Lond. 1967; FFOM RCPI 1995; FRCGP 1996, M 1974; DRCOG 1977. (Camb. & St. Bart.) Defence Med. Servs. Prof. & GP, Roy. Defence Med. Coll. Socs: Fell. Roy. Soc. Med.; Soc. Occupat. Med.; Soc. Apoth. Lond. Prev: GP Brackley.

RICHARDSON, John Craig (retired) 56 Porth y Felin, Holyhead LL65 1BD Tel: 01407 760206 — MB ChB 1949 Liverp.; FFA RCS Eng. 1954; DA Eng. 1952. Prev: Cons. Anaesth. Liverp. Regional Cardiothoracic Surg. Centre & Mill Rd. Matern. Hosp. Liverp.

RICHARDSON, John Francis (retired) 12 Kings Hall Road, Beckenham BR3 1LU — MB BS 1963 Lond.; MRCP (U.K.) 1970. Prev: Ho. Surg. Lond. Hosp.

RICHARDSON, John Patrick Stuart Church Field Medical Centre, Church Field, Camelford PL32 9YT Tel: 01840 213894; The Old Farm House, Condolden, Tintagel PL34 0HJ Tel: 01840 212818 Email: condolden@aol.com — MB BS Lond. 1964; MRCS Eng. LRCP Lond. 1964.

RICHARDSON, John Pierre Ryder, VRD (retired) Westhill, Saxmundham IP17 1DT Tel: 01728 602376 — MRCS Eng. LRCP Lond. 1946. Prev: Ho. Phys., Ho. Surg. Lond. Hosp.

RICHARDSON, John Sherbrooke Mount Chambers, 92 Coggeshall Road, Braintree CM7 9BY Tel: 01376 553415 Fax: 01376 552451 — MB 1969 Camb.; BChir 1968; MRCGP 1974; DA Eng. 1971; DObst RCOG 1971. (Camb. & St. Thos.)

RICHARDSON, John Stuart Carradale, Whimple, Exeter EX5 2PL — M.B., Ch.B. Bristol 1938. (Bristol) Prev: Squadron Ldr. R.A.F. Med. Br.

RICHARDSON, John Warlow Holderness Road Surgery, 445 Holderness Road, Hull HU8 8JS Tel: 01482 374255 Fax: 01482 790301 — MB 1978 Camb.; BChir 1977; MRCP (UK) 1979; MRCGP 1984; DRCOG 1983.

RICHARDSON, Mr John Wilberforce, OBE, Surg. Capt. RN (retired) 1 Leep Lane, Clayhall Road, Alverstoke, Gosport PO12 2BE Tel: 01705 581543 Fax: 01705352366 — MB BS 1953 Lond.; FRCS Eng. 1961. Prev: Dean of Naval Med.

RICHARDSON, Jonathan Charles Willerton The Surgery, Mount Avenue, Shenfield, Brentwood CM13 2NL Tel: 01277 224612 Fax: 01277 201218; 27 Coombe Rise, Shenfield, Brentwood CM15 8JJ — MB 1983 Camb.; BChir 1982; PhD Ed. 1979; BSc (Hons.) Physiol. St. And. 1975. (Camb.) Socs: Assoc. RCGP; Fell. Amer. Soc. for Laser Med. & Surg. Prev: Regist. (Med.) Qu. Med. Centre Nottm.; SHO (O & G) Newmarket Gen. Hosp.; Ho. Phys. Addenbrookes Hosp. Camb.

RICHARDSON, Jonathan Paul 26 Ruthven Street, Glasgow G12 9BT — MB ChB 1997 Glas.

RICHARDSON, Joyce Elizabeth (retired) 11/2 Whistlefield Court, Canniesburn Road, Bearsden, Glasgow G61 1PX Tel: 0141 943 0678 — MB ChB Ed. 1957; FRCP Ed. 1979, M 1967; FRCP Glas. 1983, M 1980; DCH RFPS Glas. 1960; FRCP 1997. Cons. Med. Paediat. Lomond Healthcare NHS Trust & Roy. Hosp. Sick Childr. Glas. Prev: Sen. Regist. (Med. Paediat.) Roy. Aberd. Childr. Hosp.

RICHARDSON, Judith Anne Manchester Health Authority, Gateway House, Piccadilly S., Manchester M60 7LP Tel: 0161 237 2977 Fax: 0161 237 2813 Email: richardj@manchester.nwest.nhs.uk — MB BS 1986 Lond.; MRCGP 1996; MPH Leeds 1992; MFPHM RCP (UK) 1996. (Middlesex Hosp. Medical School) Cons., (Pub. Health Med.) Manch. Health Auth., (p/t).

RICHARDSON, Judith Mary University Health Service, University of Edinburgh, Richard Verney Health Centre, 6 Bristo Square, Edinburgh EH8 9AL Tel: 0131 650 2777 Fax: 0131 662 1813; Easter Walstone, Penicuik EH26 9LS Tel: 01968 677822 Email: judith.richardson@ed.ac.uk — MB ChB 1990 Ed.; MRCGP 1994; DRCOG 1993; DCH RCPS Glas. 1993. (Ed.)

RICHARDSON, Justin Charles 36 Westfield Close, Bath BA2 2EB — MB BS 1990 Lond.

RICHARDSON, Katie Louise Goodnight Cottage, 15 Peterville, St Agnes TR5 0QU — MB BS 1998 Lond.; MB BS Lond 1998. (UCL MS) SHO in Paediat. Roy. Cornw. Hosp. Treliske. Prev: SHO A& E. Med. Roy Cornw. Hosp.; PKHO Whittington Hosp. Lond.

RICHARDSON, Keith Alan The Health Centre, Smithy Green, Cheadle Hulme, Cheadle SK8 6LU Tel: 0161 485 7272 Fax: 0161 485 6567; 18 Fords Lane, Bramhall, Stockport SK7 1DQ — MB ChB 1987 Manch.; MRCGP 1992.

RICHARDSON, Madeleine Helen 51 Cossington Road, Canterbury CT1 3HX Tel: 01227 763377 Fax: 01227 786908 — MB BS 1974 Lond.; DA Eng. 1976.

RICHARDSON, Mark Lindeem Medical Practice, 1 Cabourne Court, Cabourne Avenue, Lincoln LN2 2JP Tel: 01522 569033 Fax: 01522 576713; 23 The Alders, Scothern, Lincoln LN2 2WD Tel: 01673 862052 Email: mark.scothern@lineone.net — MB ChB 1982 Liverp.

RICHARDSON, Martin Craig 2A Kingsborough Road, 55-59 Hyndland Road, Glasgow G12 9UX — MB ChB 1989 Ed.

RICHARDSON, Michael Ian Hadleigh House Medical Centre, 20 Kirkway, Broadstone BH18 8EE Tel: 01202 692268 Fax: 01202 658954 — MB ChB 1974 Bristol; MRCP (UK) 1977; DRCOG 1978.

RICHARDSON, Michael John Altrincham Medical Practice, Normans Place, Altrincham WA14 2AB Tel: 0161 928 2424; 2 Groby Road, Altrincham WA14 1RS Tel: 0161 929 6053 — MB ChB 1988 Manch.; BSc (Med Sci.) St. And. 1985; MRCGP 1992; DRCOG 1991.

RICHARDSON, Michael John North Brink Practice, 7 North Brink, Wisbech PE13 1JR Tel: 01945 585121 Fax: 01945 476423 — BM BS 1981 Nottm.; BMedSci Nottm. 1979, BM BS 1981; MRCGP 1987.

RICHARDSON, Michael Robert William Knott Day Hospital, Overdale, Westmount, St Helier, Jersey JE2 3LP Tel: 01534 623060 Fax: 01534 623098; Becquet House, Rue Du Becquet, Trinity, Jersey JE3 5BS Tel: 01534 866877 Fax: 01534 866899 — MB ChB 1982 Ed.; BSc (Med. Sci.) Ed; FRCP Lond. 1997, M 1986. (Edin.) Cons. Phys. Gen. Hosp. St. Helier, Jersey. Prev: Cons. Phys. S. Tyneside Dist. Hosp.

RICHARDSON, Mr Nigel George Boyd Broomfield Hospital, Court Road, Broomfield, Chelmsford CM1 7ET Tel: 01245 516064 Fax: 01245 514858; The Old School House, Little Dunmow CM6 3HT Tel: 01371 821303 Email: nigel.richardson@virgin.net — MB BS 1986 Lond.; MS Lond. 1995; FRCS Eng. 1991; FRCS (Gen.) 1998. (St George's Hospital Medical School) Cons. Colorectal & Gen. Surg. Socs: RSM; Assoc. of Surg.s of GB & Ire; Assoc. of CeroProctol. of GB & Ire. Prev: S. Thames (WNST), Surgic. Train. Schemes; S. Austral., Surgic. Train. Scheme - Hon. Clin. Lect.

RICHARDSON, Paul Millmead, 61 Hall Ing Lane, Honley, Huddersfield HD9 6QW Tel: 01484 667681 — MB ChB 1984 Leeds; MRCGP 1990. (Leeds) GP Huddersfield; Clin. Asst. (A & E) Huddersfield Roy. Infirm. Socs: BMA; RCGP; Brit. Med. Acupunct. Soc.

RICHARDSON, Paul 45 Yew Tree Lane, West Derby, Liverpool L12 9HG — MB BS 1990 Newc.; MRCP (UK) 1994.

***RICHARDSON, Paul Gerard Guy** 38 Fontarabia Road, Battersea, London SW11 5PF — MB BS 1986 Lond.

RICHARDSON, Paul Sebastian Department of Physiology, St. George's Hospital Medical School, London SW17 0RE; 45 Hazlewell Road, London SW15 6LS — BM BCh 1968 Oxf.; DM Oxf. 1974, MA, BM BCh 1968. (St. Geo.) Reader Physiol. St. Geo. Hosp. Tooting.

RICHARDSON, Paul Stuart The Surgery, Bengal Street, Leigh WN7 1YA Tel: 01942 605506 Fax: 01942 680109 — BSc, MB BS Lond. 1979; MRCGP 1983; DCH RCP Lond. 1983; DRCOG 1982; AKC.

RICHARDSON, Peter Craig 3 Kings Mill Road, Driffield YO25 6TT — BM BS 1983 Nottm.

RICHARDSON, Peter John Cardiac Department, King's College Hospital, Denmark Hill, London SE5 9RS Tel: 020 7346 3217 Fax: 020 7346 3489; 10 Girton House, Manor Fields, Putney Hill, London SW15 3LN Tel: 020 8788 6860 Fax: 020 7244 6429 — MB BS 1963 Lond.; MD (Cardiol.) Lond 1984; FRCP Lond. 1985, M 1969. (King's Coll. Hosp.) Cons. Cardiol. King's Coll. Hosp. Lond. Socs: Fell. Amer. Heart Assn. (Counc. Clin. Cardiol.); (Past Pres.) Internat. Med. Club; Brit. Cardiac Soc. Prev: Sen. Lect. (Cardiol.) & Hon. Cons. Phys. King's Coll. Hosp. Lond.; Sen. Regist. (Cardiol.) King's Coll. Hosp. Lond.; Regist. (Med.) Roy. Free Hosp. Lond.

RICHARDSON, Mr Peter Leslie c/o Department of Neurosurgery, Manchester Royal Infirmary, Oxford Road, Manchester M13 9WL; 22 York Street, Altrincham WA15 9QH — MB ChB 1973 Ed.; FRCS Eng. 1977; Specialist Accredit. Neurol. Surg. RCS Eng. 1983. Cons. Neurosurg. Roy. Infirm. Manch. Socs: Fell. Manch. Med. Soc.; Soc. Brit. Neurol. Surgs.; N. Eng. Neurolog. Assn. Prev: Sen. Regist. (Neurosurg.) Brook & Guy's-Maudsley Hosps. Lond.; Regist. (Neurosurg.) Brook. Hosp. Lond.; Ho. Surg. (Surg. Neurol.) Roy. Infirm. & W.. Gen. Hosps. Edin.

RICHARDSON, Richard James 7 Emlyn Road, London W12 9TF Tel: 020 8749 4411 Fax: 020 8749 4422 Email: rjrichardson@btinternet.com; 7 Bridgon Road, London W12 9TF Tel: 020 87461677 Fax: 020 87494422 Email: rjrichardson@btinternet.com — MB BS 1973 Lond.; BSc Lond. 1969; MRCP (UK) 1977; DTM & H Liverp. 1979; DCH Eng. 1977; FRCPCH; FRCP London. (Middlx.) Chairm. Richardson Cons. U.K. Ltd. 7 Emlyn Rd., Lond. W12 9TF; Cons. Paediat. Gt. Ormond St. Hosp. Childr. Lond.; Cons. Paediatr., Portland Hosp. fro Wom. and Childr..; Speech Language & Hearing Centre, Christopher Pl..; Chairm. Europ. Commiss.s Thematic Working Gp. on e-Health & TeleMed..; Chairm.- UK Tele Health assoc. Socs: Fell. Roy. Soc. Med.; Fell. Roy. Soc. Trop. Med.; Fell. Roy. Coll. Pead. OBO health. Prev: Sub-Dean & Sen. Lect. Centre for Internat. Child Health Inst. Child Health Lond.; Cons. Paediat. MoH Oman & Brunei.

RICHARDSON, Robert Galloway Apple Tree Cottage, French Street, Westerham TN16 1PW Tel: 01959 563942 Fax: 01959 563942 — BM BCh 1951 Oxf.; MA Oxf. 1951; LMSSA Lond. 1951. (Oxf. & Middlx.) Socs: Fell. Roy. Soc. Med.; Brit. Soc. Hist. of Med. Prev: Edt. Spectrum Internat.; Edr. Abbottempo; Med. Edr. Butterworth's Med. Pub.ats.

RICHARDSON, Robert John Ormeau Road Surgery, 137 Ormeau Road, Belfast BT7 1SN — MB BCh BAO 1965 Belf.; MRCGP 1971.

RICHARDSON, Robert Patrick Simon 1 Catchford View, Chesterfield S41 8XE — MB BS 1985 Lond.; BSc (Anat.) Lond. 1982, MB BS 1985; FCOphth 1992. Lect. & Hon. Sen. Regist. (Ophth.) Sheff.

RICHARDSON, Mr (Robert) Simon (retired) Braeburn, Eglingham, Alnwick Tel: 01665 578448 — MB BS 1960 Lond.; FRCS Eng. 1967; Specialist Accredit (Orthop.) RCS Eng. 1975. Prev: Sen. Regist. (Orthop.) St. Geo. Hosp. Lond.

RICHARDSON, Robert William Hartlepool Health Centre, Victoria Road, Hartlepool Tel: 01429 273191; 33 Parklands Way, Hartlepool TS26 0AP Tel: 01429 272593 — MB ChB 1956 Leeds. (Leeds) Socs: BMA. Prev: Ho. Surg. (Gen. Surg.) & Ho. Phys. (Obst. & Gen. Med.) St. Jas. Hosp. Leeds; Clin. Asst. (Occupat. Health) Hartlepool HA.

RICHARDSON, Rosalind Patricia c/o Lagan Valley Hospital, Hillsborough Road, Lisburn BT28 1JP — MB BCh BAO 1988 Belf.

RICHARDSON, Rosemary Launceston Health Office, Market St., Launceston PL15 8BY Tel: 01566 765700; The Old Farm House, Condolden, Tintagel PL34 0HJ Tel: 01840 212818 — MB BS Lond. 1966; MRCS Eng. LRCP Lond. 1966; DRCOG 1969; DCH RCP Lond. 1969. (Bart's) Staff Paediat. (Community Child Health) E. Cornw.

RICHARDSON

Socs: Fac. Community Health; Brit. Paediat. Assn. Prev: Staff Paediat. (Community Child Health) Moorland Rd. Health Clinic St. Austell.

RICHARDSON, Sally Ann Whitley Road Health Centre, Whitley Road, Whitley Bay NE26 2ND Tel: 0191 253 1113; 4 The Crossway, Morpeth NE61 2DA Tel: 01670 510382 — MB BS 1982 Newc.; MRCGP 1986; DRCOG 1986; DCCH RCGP & FCM 1985. (Newcastle-upon-Tyne)

RICHARDSON, Sharon Jane Keepers Gate, Hunstanton Road, Heacham, King's Lynn PE31 7JU — MB ChB 1984 Bristol; DA (UK) 1988. Staff Grade (Anaesth.) Qu. Eliz. Hosp. King's Lynn. Prev: Clin. Asst. (Anaesth.) Qu. Eliz. Hosp. King's Lynn.

RICHARDSON, Shona Murray Watson Homoeopathy Centre, 30 Salop Road, Oswestry SY11 2NU Tel: 01691 671171; 30 Salop Road, Oswestry SY11 2NU — MB ChB 1977 Glas.; MRCGP 1984. Socs: Coll. Pract. Homoeop. Lond.

RICHARDSON, Sian Margaret 22 Charlton-on-the-Hill, Charlton Marshall, Blandford Forum DT11 9NR — MB ChB 1984 Dundee.

RICHARDSON, Stephen 53 Red Scar Lane, Newby, Scarborough YO12 5RH — MB ChB 1979 Manch.; MRCGP 1984; DA UK 1982. Prev: Clin. Asst. (Anaesth.) ScarBoro. Gen. Hosp.

RICHARDSON, Stephen Andrew Child Health Directorate, Westgate House, Southmead Hospital, Bristol BS16 1WF Tel: 0117 959 5355 Fax: 0117 959 5363 Email: richardson-s@southmead.swest.nhs.uk; 1 Paxton, Stoke Park, Stapleton, Bristol BS16 1WF — MB BS 1975 Lond.; MSc Lond. 1990, BSc 1972; MRCPCH 1996; MRCGP 1983; DTM & H Liverp. 1980; DRCOG 1979; DCH RCP Lond. 1979; DLSHTM Lond. 1997; FRCPCH 1998; BSc (Physiology) London 1972. (St. Thos.) Socs: Christ. Med. Fell.sh.; BMA; Neonat. Soc. Prev: Tutor & Lect. (Paediat.) Lilongwe Sch. for Health Sci.s & Kamuzu Centr. Hosp. Lilongwe, Malawi; Cons. Paediat. N. Devon. Distict Hosp. Barnstaple (1992-1999); Cons. Paediat.,Roy. Naval Hosp., Gibralter (1999-2001).

RICHARDSON, Stephen Geoffrey Belfast City Hospital, Belfast BT9 7AB Tel: 01232 263834 Fax: 01232 263583 Email: geoff.richardson@bch.n-i.nhs.uk — MD 1987 Belf.; MB BCh BAO 1981; MRCP (UK) 1984; FRCP Lond 1997. Cons. Cardiol. Belf. City Hosp. Socs: Brit. Cardiac Soc.; Irish Cardiac Soc. Prev: Sen. Regist. (Cardiol.) Belf. City Hosp.

RICHARDSON, Stephen Guy Noel Haematology Department, Russells Hall Hospital, Dudley DY1 2HQ Tel: 01384 244158 — MB ChB 1966 Birm.; FRCP Lond. 1991; MRCP (UK) 1970; FRCPath 1988, M 1976. (Birm.) Cons. Haemat. Dudley AHA. Prev: Sen. Regist. (Haemat.) Qu. Eliz. Hosp. Birm.; Regist. (Med.) N. Staffs. Roy. Infirm. Stoke-on-Trent; Sen. Regist. (Haemat.) Univ. Hosp. W. Indies Kingston, Jamaica.

RICHARDSON, Stephen Stothard 293 Coniscliffe Road, Darlington DL3 8AA — MB ChB 1956 Leeds.

RICHARDSON, Susan Mary Family Planning Clinic, Keighley Health Centre, Oakworth Road, Keighley BD21 1SA Tel: 01535 606111; 37 Main Street, Farnhill, Keighley BD20 9BJ Tel: 01535 633205 Fax: 01535 295636 — MB ChB Liverp. 1966; MFFP 1993. Cons. (Family Plann. & Reproductive Health Care) Aredale NHS Trust; Research Assoc. Univ. Exeter; Chairm. UK FP Research Network. Socs: Fac. Fam. Plann. & Reproductive Health Care; Chairm. N.. InterBr. Drs. Gp. Affiliation to FFP RCOG. Prev: Sen. Med. Off. (Family Plann.) Airedale NHS Trust; Clin. Asst. (Paediat. Oncol.) Cookridge Hosp. Leeds; Regist. (Chemother.) Bradford Roy. Infirm.

RICHARDSON, Suzanne Margaret The Croft, Great Wymondley, Hitchin SG4 7EU Tel: 01438 354081 Fax: 01438 357005 — MB BS 1972 Lond.; MRCS Eng. LRCP Lond. 1972.

RICHARDSON, Sylvia 34 Linden Drive, Evington, Leicester LE5 6AH Tel: 0116 273 6302 — MB BS 1960 Durh. (Newc.) Med. Asst. (Anaesth.) Leicester Community Dent. Serv. Prev: Med. Asst. (Anaesth.) Harlow Wood Orthop. Hosp.; Anaesth. Regist. Hexham Gen. Hosp.

RICHARDSON, Theresa Anne 38 Methuen Park, London N10 2JS — MB BS 1991 Lond.

RICHARDSON, Thomas (retired) 20 Rivergrove Park, Rectory Road, Beckenham BR3 1HX Tel: 020 8650 5654 — MB BCh BAO 1926 NUI.

RICHARDSON, Thomas James 33 Kinghorn Road, Kirkcaldy KY1 1SU — MB ChB 1966 Ed.; DObst RCOG 1968. Socs: BMA.

Prev: Surg. Resid. City Hosp. Edin.; Med. Resid. Roodlands Hosp. Haddington; SHO Simpson Memor. Matern. Pavil. Edin.

RICHARDSON, Thomas Noel Anthony The Surgery, 10 Bolton Road, Eastbourne BN21 3JY Tel: 01323 730537 Fax: 01323 412759; 4 Ocklynge Avenue, Eastbourne BN21 2QD Tel: 01323 737092 — MB BS 1975 Lond. (Kings Coll. Hosp.)

RICHARDSON, Timothy Integrated Care Partnership, Alexandra Road, Epsom KT17 4BL Tel: 01372 724434 Fax: 01372 748171 Email: trichardson@oldcottagehopsital.co.uk; 3 Ladbroke Road, Epsom KT18 5BG Tel: 01372 722344 — MB BS 1979 Lond.; MRCGP 1983. Mem. E. Surrey LMC (Mid Surrey Represen.); Dir. Epsom Med. Serv. Ltd; Dir. Epsom Day Surg. Ltd. Prev: GP Trainer SW Thames; Exec. Partner; Bd. Mem. Mid Surrey PCG.

RICHARDSON, Tristan Ian Laurent 49 Whiteknights Road, Reading RG6 7BB — MB BS 1993 Lond.; BSc (Hons.) Lond. 1990; MRCP (UK) 1996. (Univ. Coll. Lond.) SHO (Med.) Derriford Hosp. Plymouth.

RICHARDSON, Wendy Lisa Pear Tree Surgery, 28 Meadow Close, Kingsbury, Tamworth B78 2NR Tel: 01827 872755; 14 Avon, Hockley, Tamworth B77 5QA — MB 1985 Camb.; MA Oxf. 1982; BChir 1984. Socs: DRCOG.

RICHARDSON, Wilfred Thomas University of Hull, 187 Cottingham Road, Hull HU5 Tel: 01482 465633 — MB BS 1949 Durh.; MFCM 1974; MFOM RCP Lond. 1978; DPH Lond. 1957; DTM & H Eng. 1956, DIH 1957. (Newc. upon Tyne) Dir. Univ. Health Serv. Prev: Lt.-Col. RAMC.

RICHARDSON, William 298 Lower Eastern Green Lane, Coventry CV5 7DT — MB ChB 1988 Sheff.

RICHARDSON, William Arthur Welburn 4 Summerhill, E. Herrington, Sunderland SR3 3NH Email: willrichardson@btinternet.com — MB BS 1986 Newc. Project Ldr. of the Pennywell Project; Clin. Lect. centre for Health Studies Durh. Univ. Socs: BMA; MDU.

RICHARDSON, William Nicholas 29 Park Road, Welton, Brough HU15 1NW — MB ChB 1980 Dundee; FFA RCSI 1985.

RICHARDSON, William Robert Dept. of Homoeop. Med., Old Swan Health Centre, St Oswalds St., Liverpool L13 2BY Tel: 0151 228 6808 Fax: 0151 228 8368 — MB BS Lond. 1967; FRCS Eng. 1972; MRCS Eng. LRCP Lond. 1967; MRCGP 1991; FFHom 1989, M 1985. (St. Thos.) Cons. Homoeop. Med. Liverp. Reg. Homoeop. Med. Dept. Socs: BMA; Brit. Med. Acupunct. Soc.; Liverp. Med. Inst. Prev: GP St. Asaph N. Wales; GP Beccles, Suff.

RICHARDSON, William Wigham Medical Acupuncture Clinic, The Old Orchard Surgery, South Street, Wilton, Salisbury SP2 0JU Tel: 01722 741314 Fax: 01722 746616; Manor Cottage, Durnford Road, Stratford Sub Castle, Salisbury SP1 3YP Tel: 01722 331239 — MB 1974 Camb.; MB BChir Camb. 1974; MA Camb. 1971; MRCP (UK) 1978. (Camb. & St. Bart.) Indep. Med. Acupunc. Salisbury; GP Asst. Wilton Salisbury. Socs: Brit. Med. Acupunct. Soc.; Brit. Soc. Allergy, Environm. & Nutrit. Med. Prev: GP Salisbury; Princip. Tutor & Hon. Sen. Regist. (Paediat.) Univ. Leeds & Leeds Gen. Infirm.

RICHENBERG, Jonathan Leonard Tel: 01273 676955 Email: jonathan.rickenberg@brighton-healthcare.nhs.uk — BM BCh 1990 Oxf.; MA Camb. 1989; MRCP (UK) 1993; FRCR (Lond.) 1997. Cons. Radiologist, RSCH, Brighton. Speciality: Uroradiologist & Interven.al Radiol., Fertil. Imaging. Prev: Fell., St Pauls Hosp., Vancouver BC Canada; Sen. Regist., UCLH Dept. of Radiol. Lond..

RICHENS, Alan Aylburton Lodge, Aylburton, Lydney GL15 6DX — MB BS 1962 Lond.; PhD Lond. 1968; BSc (Physiol.) 1964; FRCP Lond. 1979, M 1969. Prof. of Pharm. & Therap. Univ. Wales Coll. Med. Cardiff. Socs: Assn. Phys. & Assn. Brit. Neurols. Prev: Prof. of Clin. Pharmacol. Inst. Neurol. Lond.; Reader in Clin. Pharmacol. St. Bart Hosp. Lond.

RICHENS, Mr David Department of Cardiothoracic Surgery, Nottingham City Hospital, Hucknall Road, Nottingham NG5 1PB Tel: 0115 969 1169 Email: drichens@ncht.org.uk; 145 Musters Road, West Bridgford, Nottingham NG2 7AF Tel: 0115 981 3260 — MB BS 1981 Lond.; FRCS Glas. 1986; FETCS 1999. (Kings Coll. Hosp.) Cons. Cardiac Surg. Nottm. City Hosp.; Clin. Dir. Cardio. Surg. Notts. City Hosp. Socs: Soc. Cardiothoracic Surg. GB & Irel.; Eur. Assn. Cardiothoracic Surg. Prev: Cons. Cardiac Surg. Roy. Infirm. Glas.; Sen. Regist. (Cardiothoracic Surg.) Soton. Gen. Hosp.; Sen. Regist. (Cardiopulm. Transpl.) St. Vincents Hosp., Sydney.

RICHMOND

RICHENS, John Everard Department of Sexually Transmitted Diseases, The Mortimer Market Centre, Mortimer Market, off Capper St., London WC1E 6AU Tel: 020 7380 9660 Fax: 020 7380 9669 Email: j.richens@gum.ucl.ac.uk; 11 Barton Close, Cambridge CB3 9LQ Tel: 01223 324172 — MB BS 1979 Lond.; MSc Lond. 1983; MA Camb. 1978; FRCP Ed. 1990; MRCP (UK) 1983; MRCS Eng. LRCP Lond. 1978. Clin. Lect. Dept. STD's Univ. Coll. Lond. Socs: Fell. Roy. Soc. Trop. Med. & Hyg.; Med. Soc. Papua New Guinea; Med. Soc. Study VD. Prev: Clin. Lect. Lond. Sch. Hyg. & Trop. Med.; Specialist Med. Off. Goroka Base Hosp., Papua New Guinea; Regist. (Gen. Med.) N.ampton Gen. Hosp.

RICHER, Lorna Audrey (retired) Morcote, 6 Hawkmoor Parke, Bovey Tracey, Newton Abbot TQ13 9NL — MB BS Lond. 1961; MRCS Eng. LRCP Lond. 1961; FFA RCS Eng. 1970; DA Eng. 1964; DObst RCOG 1962. Prev: Cons. Anaesth. Roy. United Hosp. NHS Trust, Bath.

RICHER, Mr Reginald George (retired) Morcote, 6 Hawkmoor Parke, Bovey Tracey, Newton Abbot TQ13 9NL Tel: 01626 835422 Email: richer@morcote.fsnet.co.uk — MRCS Eng. LRCP Lond. 1961 Londres; FRCS Ed. 1970; FRCOphth 1989; DO Eng. 1968. Prev: Med. Off. Colombo Plan Med. Team Vientiane, Laos.

RICHES, Professor David John International Medical College, 21 Jalan Selangor, 46050 Petaling Jaya, Selangor, Malaysia Tel: 00 60 3 7584244 Fax: 00 60 3 7584239 Email: driches@imc.po.my; 8 Elsworth Place, Hills Road, Cambridge CB2 2RG Tel: 01223 241649 — MB BS 1969 Lond.; BSc Lond. 1964, PhD 1969; MRCS Eng. LRCP Lond. 1969. (St. Thos.) Dean Internat. Med. Coll. Kuala Lumpur, Malaysia; Emerit. Prof. Anat. Qu. Mary & W.field Coll. Lond. Socs: Fell. Roy. Soc. Med.; Fell. Brit. Assn. Clin. Anat.; Anat. Soc. Prev: Prof. Anat. Chinese Univ. Hong Kong; Sen. Lect. (Anat.) Char. Cross Hosp. Med. Sch. Lond.; Lect. (Anat.) St. Mary's Hosp. Med. Sch. Lond.

RICHES, Elizabeth Chatsworth Road Medical Centre, Chatsworth Road, Brampton, Chesterfield S40 3PY Tel: 01246 568065 Fax: 01246 567116; Newfield Cottage, Hemming Green, Brampton S42 7JQ — MB ChB 1991 Sheff.; DRCOG 1994; DFFP 1993; MRCGP 1995. GP Princip. Chesterfield.

RICHES, Harry Ralph Claude (retired) 2 South Approach, Moor Park, Northwood HA6 2ET Tel: 01923 823330 Fax: 01923 841421 Email: harry.riches@btinternet.com — MD Lond. 1956, MB BS 1948; FRCP Lond. 1974, M 1952; MRCS Eng. LRCP Lond. 1948. Hon. Cons. Phys. Harefield Hosp. Prev: Cons. Phys. Harefield, Mt. Vernon & Wembley Hosps.

RICHES, Helen Isobel Links Medical Centre, Restalrig Park Medical Centre, 40 Alemoor Crescent, Edinburgh EH7 6UJ Tel: 0131 554 2141 Fax: 0131 554 5363 — MB ChB 1992 Ed.

RICHES, Louise Anna Flat 1, 45 St John's Grove, London N19 5RP — MB BS 1990 Lond.

RICHES, Marilyn Celia The Surgery, 29 Derry Downs, Orpington BR5 4DU Tel: 01689 820036 Fax: 01689 819768; Holly Cottage, Chelsfield Lane, Orpington BR6 7RP Tel: 01689 837294 — MB BS 1966 Lond.; MRCS Eng. LRCP Lond. 1966. (Roy. Free)

RICHES, Susanna Marie-Therese Viewfield, Balmore, Torrance, Glasgow G64 4AE — MB ChB 1993 Ed.

RICHEY, Edmund Eric Lynden Lodge, 4 Algeo Drive, Derrychara, Enniskillen BT74 6JL Tel: 01365 322104 — MB BCh BAO 1962 Belf.; LAH Dub. 1964; FFA RCSI 1969.

*****RICHEY, Helen Claire** 4 Algeo Drive, Enniskillen BT74 6JL Tel: 01365 322104 Email: clairerichey@yahoo.com — MB ChB 1998 Dund.; MB ChB Dund 1998.

RICHEY, Ruth Elizabeth Margaret 4 Algeo Drive, Enniskillen BT74 6JL Email: ruthrichey@yahoo.com — MB BCh BAO 1994 Belf.; DCH Coll. Surgeons 1997; DRCOG RCObst&Gyn. UK 1998.

RICHI, Mohammed Nabil Mahmoud c/o Drive J.M. Feloy, Holmwood, Staverton, Totnes TQ9 6NX — LRCP LRCS 1985 Ed.; MD Aleppo 1976; MRCPI 1986; LRCP LRCS Ed. LRCPS Glas. 1985.

RICHINGS, Ceri Ian 47 Cartland Road, Stirchley, Birmingham B30 2SD — MB ChB 1989 Leic.

RICHINGS, Jane Carol Hinchliffe (retired) 65A Carlisle Mansions, Carlisle Place, London SW1P 1HZ Tel: 020 7828 1816 — MB BS 1957 Lond.; MRCP Lond. 1965; DCH Eng. 1961; 1991 BA.

RICHMAN, Deirdre Margot 45 Fairhazel Gardens, West Hampstead, London NW6 3QN — MB ChB 1992 Cape Town.

RICHMAN, Geoffrey 138 Fordwych Road, London NW2 3PA Tel: 020 8452 7646 — BM BCh 1956 Oxf.

RICHMAN, Naomi Shirley The Medical Foundation For The Care, 96-98 Grafton Road, London NW5 3EJ Tel: 020 7813 9999; 17 Holmesdale Road, London N6 5TH Tel: 020 8348 9497 — BM BCh 1958 Oxf.; MSc (Epidemiol.) Columbia Univ. New York 1969; FRCPsych 1981, M 1973. (Middlx.) Indep. Cons. Lond. Prev: Adviser (Child Ment. Health) Min. of Educat., Mozambique; Hon. Cons. Hosp. Sick Childr. Gt. Ormond St. Lond.; Reader Inst. Child Health Lond.

RICHMAN, Sharon Windmill Lodge Centre for Childrens Services, Hounslow and Spelthorne Community and Mental Health NHS Trust, Uxbridge Road, Southall UB1 3EU Tel: 020 8354 8862 Fax: 020 8354 8948 Email: sharon.richman@hscmh-tr.nthames.nhs.uk; 1 Winscombe Crescent, Ealing, London W5 1AZ — MB BS 1978 Lond.; MRCP (UK) 1985; DCH RCP Lond. 1983. (Middlx. Hosp. Med. Sch.) Cons. Paediat. (Community Child Health) Hounslow & Spelthorne community & Ment. Health NHS Trust. Prev: Lect. (Community Paediat.) St. Mary's Hosp. Med. Sch. Lond. Univ.

RICHMOND, Catherine Ellen Dept.of Anaesthetics, West Middlesex Ini. Hospital, Isleworth TW7 6AF Tel: 020 8997 1270; 48 Lynwood Road, Ealing W5 1JJ — MB ChB 1986 Manch.; MB ChB (Hons.) Manch. 1986; BSc (Hons.) Manch. 1984; MRCP (UK) 1989; FRCA 1991. Cons. Anaesth. W. Middlx. Univ. Hosp. Isleworth. Socs: MRCAnaesth.; Assn. Anaesth.; BMA. Prev: Sen. Regist. (Anaesth.) Univ. Coll. Lond. Hosps.; Regist. (Anaesth.) Gt. Ormond St. Hosp. for Sick Childr. Lond. & Middlx. Hosp. Lond.; Regist. Rotat. (Anaesth.) NW Region.

RICHMOND, Charles Steven Ashley The Old Brokes Farmhouse, Brokes, Hudswell, Richmond DL11 6DD; South Lodge, Heath Side, London NW3 1BL — MB BS 1996 Lond.

RICHMOND, David Hugh Liverpool Womens Hospital, Liverpool L8 7SS Tel: 0151 708 9988; Heatherlea, Welstone Lane, West Kirby, Wirral CH48 7HG Tel: 0151 248 7119 — MD 1988 Ed.; BSc Ed. 1974, MD 1988, MB ChB 1977; FRCOG 1995; MRCOG 1982. Cons. & Med. Dir. O & G Liverp. Wom. Hosp. Socs: Gyn. Club & Internat. Continency Soc. Prev: Sen. Lect. (O & G) Univ. Liverp.

RICHMOND, David John Hamilton Dept. of Anaesthetics, New Cross Hospital, Wolverhampton WV10 0QP Tel: 01902 367999; Greenways, StockwellEnd, Tettenhall, Wolverhampton WV6 9PH Tel: 01902 751448 Email: djhrichmond@lineone.net — MB BChir 1964 Camb.; MA Camb. 1963; MRCS Eng. LRCP Lond. 1963; FFA RCS Eng. 1969; DA Eng. 1966; DObst RCOG 1965. (Camb. & Guy's) Cons. Anaesth. Roy. Wolverhampton Hosps. NHS Trust. Socs: Fell. Birm. & Midl. Obst. & Gyn. Soc.; Obst. Anaesth. Assn. Prev: Sen. Regist. (Anaesth.) United Birm. Hosps.; Regist. (Anaesth.) St. Bart. Hosp. Lond. & St. Geo. Hosp. Lond.

RICHMOND, David William 22 Learmonth Terrace, Edinburgh EH4 1PG Tel: 0131 336 5419 — MB ChB 1982 Ed.; MRCGP 1986.

RICHMOND, Eunice Edith Upton Group Practice, 32 Ford Road, Wirral CH49 0TF Tel: 0151 677 0486 Fax: 0151 604 0635; 21 Manor Road, Upton, Wirral CH49 6JE — MB ChB 1981 Manch.; DRCOG 1986. GP Upton.

RICHMOND, Geoffrey Alan Limes Medical Centre, Limes Avenue, Alfreton DE55 7DW Tel: 01773 832749 Fax: 01773 832921 — MB ChB Sheff. 1967; MRCGP 1973; DObst RCOG 1969. (Sheff.) Chairm. Derby Obst. Gp. Socs: Derby Med. Soc. & Nott. M-C Soc. Prev: SHO Jessop Hosp. Wom. Sheff.; Ho. Off. (Med.) N.. Gen. Hosp. Sheff.; Ho. Off. (Surg.) Roy. Hosp. Sheff.

RICHMOND, Geoffrey Oliffe Claremont Medical Practice, Exmouth Health Centre, Claremont Grove, Exmouth EX8 2JF Tel: 01395 273666 Fax: 01395 223301 Email: claremont@eclipse.co.uk; Merrion House, 1 Merrion Avenue, Exmouth EX8 2HX Tel: 01395 279164 — MB BS 1974 Lond.; MRCS Eng. LRCP Lond. 1974; MRCGP 1979; DRCOG 1977. (Roy. Free) Prev: Trainee GP Exeter VTS; Ho. Phys. W. Kent Gen. Hosp. Maidstone; Ho. Surg. (Orthop.) Roy. Free Hosp. Lond.

RICHMOND, Helen Susan 6 Balmore Drive, Caversham, Reading RG4 8NL — MB BCh 1998 Wales.

RICHMOND, Hendry Gilmour (retired) Ridgeleigh, 50 Crown Drive, Inverness IV2 3QG Tel: 01463 232895 — MD 1958 Aberd.; MB ChB 1948; FRCPath 1971. Prev: Cons. Path. Highland HB.

RICHMOND, Henry Auld Nisbet Towerdene, 14 Langside Drive, Glasgow G43 2EQ — MB ChB 1946 Glas.; FRCP Glas. 1985;

RICHMOND

MRCP (UK) 1983; MFOM RCP Lond. 1982. (Univ. Glas.) Sen. Med. Off. Univ. Glas.; Princip. Med. Off. Scott. Mutual Assur. Soc. Socs: BMA. Prev: Res. Asst. (ENT & Phys.) W.. Infirm. Glas.

RICHMOND, Iain Miller Moreton Cross Group Practice, Ashton House, Chadwick Street, Moreton, Wirral L46 7US Tel: 0151 678 0993; 21 Manor Drive, Upton, Wirral CH49 6JE — MB ChB 1980 Manch.; BSc St. And. 1977; DRCOG 1986.

RICHMOND, Ian Department of Histopathology, Castle Hill Hospital, Cottingham HU16 Tel: 01482 623288 Fax: 01482 623290; Elm Cottage, 13 Mill St, Hutton, Driffield YO25 9PU Tel: 01377 270529 — MB ChB 1986 Manch.; MD Manch. 1996; MRCPath 1994. Cons. Histopath. Castle Hill Hosp. Cottingham; Hon. Clin. Sen. Lect. Fac. Health Hull Univ. Sch. Med. Prev: Sen. Regist. Rotat. (Histopath.) N. W.. RHA; Research Fell. (Path.) Freeman Hosp. Newc. u. Tyne; Regist. (Histopath.) Blackburn Roy. Infirm.

RICHMOND, James Brown 3 Bridge Street, Otley LS21 1BQ Tel: 01943 464001 Fax: 01943 850849; Creskeld Gardens, Bramhope, Leeds LS16 9EN — MB ChB 1955 Leeds. (Leeds)

RICHMOND, Jane Rowena Queen Mother's Hospital, Yorkhill, Glasgow G3 8SJ; 35 Scotland Street, Edinburgh EH3 6PY — MB ChB 1993 Ed.; MRCOG 1998. Specialist Regist. (O & G) Qu. Mother's Hosp. Glas.

RICHMOND, Jennifer Kay 24 Llantrisant Rise, Llandaff, Cardiff CF5 2PG Tel: 029 2057 8089 — MB BCh Wales 1968; DCH 1970; FFPHM RCP (UK) 1997; MFCM RCP 1989; FRCGP 1987, M 1976; MICGP 1987; T(GP) 1991; T(PHM) 1991; DObst RCOG 1972; DCH Eng. 1970. (Cardiff) Indep. Cons. Prev: Princip. Med. Off. Welsh Off. Cardiff; Sen. Med. Off. & Med. Off. Welsh Off.; GP Barry.

RICHMOND, Professor John, CBE 15 Church Hill, Edinburgh EH10 4BG Tel: 0131 447 2760 — MB ChB 1948 Ed.; FRACP (Hon.) 1990; FFPHM (Hon.) 1990; FFPM (Hon.) 1989; FACP (Hon.) 1989; FRSE 1992; MD Ed. 1963; FRCS Ed. 1990; FRCPI 1990; FRCP Lond. 1970, M 1957; FRCP Ed. 1963, M 1955; FRCPS 1988; FCP(SA) (Hon.) 1991. (Ed.) Emerit. Prof. Med. Univ. Sheff. Socs: Assn. Phys. Prev: Pres. RCP Edin.; Dean Fac. Med. & Dent. Univ. Sheff.; Sen. Vice-Pres. & Sen. Censor RCP Lond.

RICHMOND, John Paul 46 Devon Street, St Helens WA10 4HT — MB ChB 1998 Dund.; MB ChB Dund 1998.

RICHMOND, Mr Jonathan David P.O. Box 6779, Dundee DD1 9WN Tel: 01382 223189 — MB ChB 1977 Ed.; BSc (Hons.) Ed. 1974, MB ChB 1977; FRCS Ed. 1981. Govt. Servant Home Office.

RICHMOND, Kathleen Margaret (retired) 7 Calder Drive, Cambuslang, Glasgow G72 8NE Tel: 0141 641 1640 — MB ChB Glas. 1941; DCH Eng. 1945. Prev: SCMO Matern. & Child Health Gt.er Glas. Health Bd.

RICHMOND, Marion Laurel St Patrick Surgery, 4 Laurel St Patrick, Glasgow G3 6JB Tel: 0141 332 5553 Fax: 0141 332 5557 — MB ChB 1967 Glas.

RICHMOND, Mary McLean (retired) 9 Dean Road, Kilmarnock KA3 1RW Tel: 01563 523420 — MB ChB Glas. 1933, DPH 1936. Prev: Tuberc. Phys. Renfrewsh. & Bute Tuberc. Dept. Med. Supt. Darnley.

RICHMOND, Maureen Shannon 20 Kirby Park, Wirral CH48 7HJ — MB ChB 1979 Ed.; BSc Ed. 1976, MB ChB 1979. SHO (Paediat.) Wirral.

RICHMOND, Moses (retired) 66 Chatsworth Road, London NW2 4DD — MRCS Eng. LRCP Lond. 1933. Prev: Sen. Ho. Phys. & Cas. Off. Roy. Infirm. Oldham.

RICHMOND, Mr Paul John Murray 48 Lynwood Road, Ealing, London W5 1JJ Tel: 020 8997 1270 — MB ChB 1986 Aberd.; FRCS Ed. 1991. Cons.Urol., Durh. Hosp. Durh.. Socs: BMA; Brit. Assn. Urol. Surgs.; RCS Edin. Prev: Sen.Regist.(Urol) UCLH; Sen. Regist. (Urol.) Whipps Cross; Sen. Regist. (Urol.) Roy. Free Hosp. Lond.

RICHMOND, Mr Peter William Emergency Unit, University Hospital of Wales, Heath Park, Cardiff CF14 4XW Tel: 02920 748004 Fax: 02920 748062 Email: peter.richmond@uhw-tr.wales.nhs.uk — MB ChB 1977 Liverp.; FRCS Eng. 1982; FRCS Ed. 1981. Cons. Accid. Emerg. Med. Univ. Hosp. Of Wales.

RICHMOND, Peter William (retired) 74B Thorndon Gardens, Stoneleigh, Epsom KT19 0QJ Tel: 020 8393 6906 — MB ChB 1949 NZ; MRCP Lond. 1955; MRCPsych 1971; DPM Eng. 1960. Hon. Cons. Psychiat. Riverside HA. Prev: Cons. Psychiat. & Med. Admin. Banstead Hosp.

RICHMOND, Rhianne Mary Linwood Health Centre, Ardlamont Square, Linwood, Paisley PA3 3DE Tel: 01505 321051 Fax: 01505 383302; 18 Gryfewood Crescent, Houston, Johnstone PA6 7LY Tel: 01505 336660 — MB ChB 1986 Glas.; MRCGP 1992; DFFP 1993; DRCOG 1991. (Univ. Glas.) Clin. Med. Off. (Family Plann. & Well Wom. Servs.) Renfrewsh. Healthcare NHS Trust; Licenced Assoc. Fac. Homoeop. Socs: BMA. Prev: Trainee GP Glas.

RICHMOND, Robert (retired) Eliock Dower House, Sanquhar DG4 6LD Tel: 01659 50254 — MB ChB 1951 Glas. Prev: Ho. Phys. Stobhill Hosp. Glas.

RICHMOND, Ruth Borders Community Rheumatology Service, Kelso Hospital, Kelso TB5 7JP Tel: 01573 228126 Fax: 01573 228126 — MB BS 1989 Lond.; MRCP (UK) 1993. (St Mary's Hosp.) Cons. Rheumt., Borders Primary Care Trust.; Cons. Rheumatologist, Rheumatic Dis.s Unit, W.. Gen. Hosp., Crewe Rd, S. Edin.,EH4 2XU. Socs: Collegiate Mem. Roy. Coll. Of Phys.s; Brit. Soc. Rheum.; Scott. Soc. Phys.s. Prev: Specialist Regist. (Med & Rheum.) Edin.; SHO Rotat. (Med.) Roy. Lond. Hosp.

RICHMOND, Samuel William John Paediatrics, Northern Congenital Abnormality Survey, Maternity Service Office, Newcastle upon Tyne NE2 4AA; 28 Hedley Street, Gosforth, Newcastle upon Tyne NE3 1DL — MB BS 1972 Newc.; MRCP (UK) 1983.

RICHMOND, Shirley Jean (retired) Clinical Virology Manchester Central Laboratory Services, 3rd Floor, Clinical Services Building, Manchester Royal Infirmary, Oxford Road, Manchester M13 9WL — MD 1976 Camb.; MB 1960, BChir 1959. Prev: Reader (Med. Virol.) Univ. Manch.

RICHMOND, Susanna Mary 2 The Chase, Silverdale, Carnforth LA5 0UT — MB ChB 1988 Liverp.; FRCA 1994. Cons. Anaesth. Roy. Lancaster Infirm.

RICHMOND, Mr Thomas Randall Anderson (retired) 7 Calder Drive, Cambuslang, Glasgow G72 8NE Tel: 0141 641 1640 — MB ChB Glas. 1941; BSc Glas. 1938; FRFPS Glas. 1949; FRCS Glas. 1962. Prev: Regist. (Surg.) & Ho. Phys. Glas. Roy. Infirm.

RICHOLD, Jonathan Paul Garforth Medical Centre, Church Lane, Garforth, Leeds LS25 1ER Tel: 0113 286 5311 Fax: 0113 281 2679; 30 The Boyle, Barwick in Elmet, Leeds LS15 4JN Tel: 0113 281 2628 — MB BS 1978 Newc.; MRCGP 1982; DRCOG 1981. Clin. Asst. (Endoscopy) Seacroft Hosp. Leeds; GP Trainer Leeds. Prev: Trainee GP Airedale Gen. Hosp. Steeton VTS.

***RICHTER, Alex Gisela** 30 Gloucester Road, Kew, Richmond TW9 3BU — MB ChB 1996 Birm.; ChB Birm. 1996.

RICHTER, George 184 Nevill Avenue, Hove BN3 7NG Tel: 01273 821517 — MD 1971 Charles U Prague; Dip. Trop. Dis. UPDL Prague 1978. Staff Specialist (O & G) Crawley Hosp. E. Sussex. Prev: Sen. Regist. (O & G) St. Luke's Hosp. Malta.

RICHTER, Martin Bruce 162 New Cavendish Street, London W1 Tel: 020 7637 5515 — MB BS 1973 Sydney; FRACP 1980. (Sydney) Sen. Regist. (Rheum.) Middlx. Hosp. Lond. Socs: Heberden Soc.; Fell. Roy. Soc. Med. Prev: Research Fell. CRC N.wick Pk. Hosp. Harrow; Research Fell. & Hon. Sen. Regist. (Rheum.) Guy's Hosp. Lond.; Regist. (Rheum.) Middlx. Hosp. Lond.

RICKARD, Alison Jill Alton Health Centre, Anstey Road, Alton GU34 2QX Tel: 01420 84676 Fax: 01420 542975; 18 Beechlands Road, Medstead, Alton GU34 5EQ — BM BCh 1989 Oxf.; BA Oxf. 1986; MRCGP 1994; DRCOG 1994; Dip. Occ. Med. 1998. (Oxford University) Prev: SHO Spinal Unit Salisbury Dist. Hosp.; SHO (Med.) Derriford Hosp. Plymouth; Trainee GP Plymouth.

RICKARD, Anne Macleod Wellington Medical Centre, Bulford, Wellington TA21 8PW Tel: 01823 663551 Fax: 01823 660650 — MB BS 1979 Lond. (Royal London Hospital) GP; Skin Laser Specialist.

RICKARD, Rory Frederick c/o Royal Navy Hospital, Hasler, Gosport PO12 2AA — MB BCh BAO 1992 Belf.

RICKARD, Samantha Peggy Louise Reidfield Cottage, Budworth Heath, Northwich CW9 6NQ — MB ChB 1997 Sheff.

RICKARDS, Angela Frances Blomfield Practice, Nursery Lane Surgery, 150 Nursery Lane, Leeds LS17 7AQ Tel: 0113 293444 Fax: 0113 295 3440; 56 Larkfield Avenue, Rawdon, Leeds LS19 6EN — MB ChB 1990 Leeds; MRCGP 1994; DTM & H Liverp. 1994; DRCOG 1993. Princip. GP.

RICKARDS, Anthony Francis 47 Wimpole Street, London W1G 8SE Tel: 020 7573 8899 Fax: 020 7573 8898 Email: a.rickards@heart.org.uk — MB BS Lond. 1968; FRCP Lond. 1983; MRCP (UK) 1971; FESC 1988; FACC 1982. (Middlx.) Cons. Phys. Roy. Brompton & Nat. Heart Hosp. Lond.; Hon. Sen. Lect. Cardiothoracic Inst. Univ. Lond.; Recognised Teach. Fac. Med. Univ. Lond.; Hon. Cons. Cardiol. RAF. Socs: Fell. Amer. Coll. Cardiol.; Fell. Europ. Soc. Cardiol. Prev: Sec. Brit. Cardiac Soc.; Vice Dean Cardiothoracic. Inst. Univ. Lond.; Wellcome Sen. Research Fell. Inst. Cardiol. Lond.

RICKARDS, Christopher Morriston Hospital, Morriston, Swansea SA6 6NL Tel: 01792 702222 — MB ChB 1987 Manch.; MB ChB (Hons.) Manch. 1987; BSc (Hons.) Manch. 1985, MD 1994; MRCP (UK) 1990; MD Manchester 1994. Cons. Neurol.

RICKARDS, David Department of Radiology, University College London, London W1N 8AA Tel: 020 7380 9070 Fax: 020 7486 1084 Email: drick@aol.com; 136 Harley Street, London W1N 1AH Tel: 020 7637 8207 Fax: 020 7436 7059 — MRCS Eng. LRCP Lond. 1972; FRCR 1982; FFR (D) S. Afr. 1980. Cons. Uroradiol. Univ. Coll. Lond. Hosp. & Inst. Urol. Lond. Socs: (Counc.) Brit. Inst. of Radiol. Prev: Regist. (Radiol.) K. Edwd. VII Hosp. Congella, Roy. S. Afr.; Lect. (Radiol.) Univ. Manch.

RICKARDS, David Francis Tingle's Farm, 15 Wood Side Lane, Grenoside, Sheffield S35 8RW — MB ChB 1960 Sheff.; MRCGP 1969. Socs: Soc. Occupat. Med.

RICKARDS, Edward Hugh Galbraith 44 Franklin Road, Cotteridge, Birmingham B30 2HG Tel: 0121 627 2834 Email: wulfric@cix.compulink.co.uk — MB ChB 1988 Birm.; ChB Birm. 1988; MMedSci 1994; MRCPsych 1993. Cons. (Neuropsychiat. & Gen. Psychiat.) Qu. Eliz. Psychiat. Hosp. Birm.; Hon. Sen. Clin. Lect. (Psychiat.) Birm. Univ.; Hon. Clin. Asst. Nat. Hosp. Qu. Sq. Lond. Socs: Brain Res. Assn.; Huntington's Dis. Assn.; Tourette's Syndrome Assn. Prev: Sen. Regist. (NeuroPsychiat.) Qu. Eliz. Psychiat. Hosp. Birm.; Regist. (Psychiat.) Birm. VTS; Sen. Reg. (Psychiat.) W. Midl.

RICKARDS, Francis Sylvester (retired) 15 St Oswald's Close, Oswaldkirk, Helmsley, York YO62 5YH Tel: 01439 788661 Fax: 01439 788661 — MB ChB Liverp. 1941.

RICKARDS, Mabli Ann (retired) 27 Walton Park, Preston Village, North Shields NE29 9DA — MB BCh 1963 Wales; AFOM RCP Lond. 1983. Prev: Sen. Med. Off. (Radiol.) Brit. Coal Wath-on-Dearne S. Yorks.

RICKARDS, Manisha 77 Buxton Road, High Lane, Stockport SK6 8DX Tel: 01663 762551 Fax: 01663 763970 — MB ChB 1986 Manch.; DRCOG 1992. Prev: Trainee GP Cheadle Hulme.

RICKARDS, Mr Michael Queen Elizabeth Hospital, Sheriff Hill, Gateshead NE9 6SX Tel: 0191 482 0000 — MB BS 1989 Newc.; FRCS Ed. 1994; FFAEM 1998. Cons. (A&E) Med., Qu. Eliz. Hosp. Gateshead.

RICKARDS, Nigel Peter 38 Crewe Road, Alsager, Stoke-on-Trent ST7 2ET Tel: 01270 882004; Four Winds, 6 Dunnocksfold Road, Alsager, Stoke-on-Trent ST7 2TJ — MB ChB 1980 Ed.

RICKENBACH, Carol Ann Mary High Street Surgery, 75 High Street, Minster, Ramsgate CT12 4AB Tel: 01843 821333 Fax: 01843 823146 — MB BS 1989 Lond.; MRCGP 1995; DCH RCP Lond. 1993; DRCOG 1994. (Char. Cross & Westminster)

RICKENBACH, Mark Alan Park Surgery, Hursley Road, Chandlers Ford, Eastleigh SO22 5DH; West Deanery, Postgraduate Medical and Dental Education, Highcroft, winchester SO22 5DH Tel: 01962 863511 Ext. 545 Fax: 01705 866849 — MB BS 1984 Lond.; FRCGP 2000; BSc Lond. 1981; MRCP (UK) 1988; MRCGP 1992; T(GP) 1992; DFFP 1989; DCH RCP Lond. 1988. GP; Course Organiser for Hosp. Gen. Pract. Train. Scheme; Coordinator Wessex Research Club (WREc); Research Stud.ship NHS R&D (PHD); GP Trainer; Ass. Dir. GP SHO Educat.; Bd. Mem. E.leigh N. PCT; Ass. Dir. GP SHO Educat. Socs: BMA; RCGP (Mem. Research & Educat. Subcomm.) (Fell.); Roy. Coll. Phys.t (Mem.). Prev: Regist. (Med.) Sir Chas. Gairdner Hosp. Perth, W. Austral.; SHO (O & G) St. Richard's Hosp. Chichester; SHO (Ophth. & Med.) St. Mary's & Qu. Alexandra Hosps. Portsmouth.

RICKERBY, Elizabeth Jane Cumberland Infirmary, Carlisle CA2 7HY Tel: 0122 852 3444; Southwaite Park, Southwaite, Carlisle CA4 0LN Tel: 0169 74 73200 Email: rickerby@dial.pipex.com — MB ChB 1978 Dundee; DA 1982. p/t Clin. Asst. (Gyn.) Cumberld. Infirm. Carlisle. Prev: SHO & Regist. (Anaesth.) Cumberld. Infirm. Carlisle; SHO (O & G) City Gen. Hosp. Carlisle.

RICKERBY, John Dr A Willis and Partners, King Edward Road Surgery, Christchurch Medical Centre, King Edward Road, Northampton NN1 5LY Tel: 01604 633466 Fax: 01604 603227; 10 Trinity Avenue, Northampton NN2 6JJ — MB BS 1981 Lond.; BSc Lond. 1978; FRCGP 1995, M 1988; DCH RCP Lond. 1984; DRCOG 1983.

RICKETS, Mark Nightingale Practice, 10 Kenninghall Road, Clapton, London E5 8BY Tel: 020 8985 8388 Fax: 020 8986 6004; 32 Sidney Road, London N22 8LU Tel: 020 8829 9042 — MB BS 1988 Lond.; BSc (Physiol.) Bristol 1982; MRCGP 1994; DRCOG 1994; DGM RCP Lond. 1992. GP Princip.; Clincial Lect. St. Bartholomews & Roy. Lond. Hosp. Med. Sch.

RICKETT, Andrew Brian 37 Beechings Close, Countesthorpe, Leicester LE8 5PA — MB ChB 1985 Leic.; FRCR 1992. Cons. Radiol. Leicester. Prev: Sen. Regist. & Regist. (Radiol.) Leicester; SHO (Cardiol. & Neonates) Centr. Birm. HA; SHO (Paediat. & Neonates) Leics. HA.

RICKETT, Mr John William Stanley (retired) Mount Stuart Hospital, St. Vincents Road, Torquay TQ1 4UP Tel: 01803 313881 Fax: 01626 873148 — MB BChir 1966 Camb.; MB BChir Camb. 1960; MChir Camb. 1972; FRCS Eng. 1965; MRCS Eng. LRCP Lond. 1959. Prev: Sen. Regist. St. Geo. Hosp. Lond.

RICKETTS, Andrew Lester 5 Hookstone Chase, Harrogate HG2 7HH — MB BCh 1980 Wales; BSc St. And. 1977; FFA RCS Eng. 1986; FFA RCSI 1985; DRCOG 1982. Prev: Regist. (Anaesth.) & SHO (O & G) S. Glam. HA.

RICKETTS, Mr David Mark Princess Royal Hospital, Lewes Road, Haywards Heath RH16 4EX Tel: 01444 441881 — MB BCh 1982 Witwatersrand; FRCS Eng. 1988; FRCS (Orth.) 1995. Cons. Orthop. Surg. P.ss Roy. Hosp. Haywards Heath. Prev: Sen. Regist. Bristol Roy. Infirm.; Regist. St. Mary's & Char. Cross Hosps.

RICKETTS, Donald 3 South Row, London SE3 0RY — MB BS 1953 Lond.; LMSSA Lond. 1952; MRCS Eng. LRCP Lond. 1953.

RICKETTS, Karen Jane Norven, 19 Lutterworth Close, Bracknell RG42 2NW — MB ChB 1996 Leeds. SHO Med. Rotat. Wakefield Pinderfields Hosp.

RICKETTS, Nora Elizabeth Marjorie Tayview Medical Practice, 16 Victoria Street, Newport-on-Tay DD6 8DJ Tel: 01382 543251 Fax: 01382 542052; Wellgate House, 78 West Road, Newport-on-Tay DD6 8HP Tel: 01382 542851 — MB ChB 1975 Dundee; BSc St. And. 1972; DRCOG 1977. Prev: Regist. (Obst.) Ninewells Hosp. Dundee; Trainee GP Alyth VTS; SHO (Geriat.) Ashludie Hosp. Dundee.

RICKFORD, Mr Christopher Richard Keevil Pensylva, Kenwyn Close, Truro TR1 3DX Tel: 01872 272039 Fax: 01872 272039 Email: crrickford@tinyworld.co.uk — MB BChir 1967 Camb.; MA, Camb. 1967; FRCS Eng. 1970. (St. Thos.) Cons. Gen. Surg. Roy. Cornw. Hosp. Trust Truro. Socs: Fell. Roy. Soc. Med.; BMA. Prev: Sen. Regist. (Surg.) St. Thos. Hosp. Lond. & St. Helier Hosp. Carshalton; Regist. Rotat. (Surg.) St. Thos. Hosp. Lond.

RICKFORD, William Jeremy Keevil Department of Anaesthetics, Lister Hospital NHS Trust, Corey's Mill Lane, Stevenage SG1 4AB Tel: 01438 314333; Rushcroft, Green End, Weston, Hitchin SG4 7AL Tel: 01462 790323 Fax: 01462 790163 Email: drrickford@aol.col — MB BS Lond. 1973; FRCA 1981; FFA RCSI 1980. (St. Thos.) Cons. Anaesth. Lister Hosp. Stevenage. Socs: Fell. Roy. Soc. Med. Prev: Vis. Asst. Prof. (Anaesth.) Univ. Maryland Hosp. Baltimore, USA; Sen. Regist. (Anaesth.) Nat. Heart Hosp. & Hosp. for Sick Childr. Gt. Ormond St. Lond., Nat. Hosp. Nerv. Dis. Lond. & St. Thos. Hosp.

RICKHUSS, Mr Peter Kenneth Stracathro Hospital, Brechin DD9 7QA; 12 Balruddery Meadows, Invergowrie, Dundee DD2 5LJ Tel: 01382 360688 — MB ChB 1985 Dundee; FRCS Ed. Orth. 1996. Cons. (Orthop. Surg.) Stracathro Hosp. Brechin, Ninewcus Hosp., Dundee.

RICKINSON, John Derek (retired) Yew Court, Scalby, Scarborough YO13 0NN — MB BS 1950 Durh.; MRCGP 1963. Mem. Med. Bds. DHSS. Prev: Sec. Newc. Local Med. Comm.

RICKMAN, Angus James 66 Ridgeway Road, Timperley, Altrincham WA15 7HD — MB ChB 1994 Leic.

RICKMAN, Mark Sean 206 Hinde House Lane, Sheffield S4 8HD — MB ChB 1994 Sheff.

RICKUS

***RICKUS, Katherine Patricia Ann** 142 Cleveden Road, Glasgow G12 0LA Tel: 0141 339 6708 Email: katherine.rickus@doctors.org.uk — MB ChB 1998 Ed.; MB ChB Ed 1998; BSc (Med Sci) Psychology 1996; MBChB 1998.

RICKWOOD, Mr Anthony Michael Kent Royal Liverpool Childrens Hospital, Eaton Road, Liverpool L12 2AP Tel: 0151 228 4811; 51 Dudlow Lane, Liverpool L18 2EX Tel: 0151 737 1265 — BM BCh 1965 Oxf.; FRCS Eng. 1972. Cons. Paediat. Urol. Roy. Liverp. Childr. Hosp. Prev: Sen. Regist. (Surg.) Sheff. Childr. Hosp.; Cons. Spinal Injuries Unit Lodgemoor Hosp. Sheff.

RICKWOOD, Ellis Paul — MB ChB 1990 Leeds; MRCGP 1994; DRCOG 1993.

RIDD, Matthew John Ballaire, Goodleigh, Barnstaple EX32 7LZ Tel: 01271 372140 Email: mjridd@doctors.org.uk — MB ChB 1998 Birm.; ChB Birm. 1998; MBCLB, Birm. 1998; BMedSc (Hons) 1996. (Birm.) HO, Surg., Stoke-on-Trent. Socs: BMA; MES. Prev: HO, Med, Birm. Heartlands Hosp.

RIDDALL, Michael Walter 80 Riverside Close, Bridge, Canterbury CT4 5TN Tel: 01227 832375 Fax: 01227 832375 — MB 1958 Camb.; BChir 1957; MRCPsych 1972; T(Psych) 1991; DPM Eng. 1967. (Camb. & Univ. Coll. Hosp.) Cons Psychiat. Ramsgate, Canterbury & Thanet Healthcare Trust. Socs: BMA. Prev: Cons. Psychiat. HM Prison Canterbury; Sen. Regist. St. Geo. Hosp. Lond. & W. Pk. Hosp. Epsom; Ho. Surg. Univ. Coll. Hosp. Lond.

RIDDELL, Alastair James Pharmagene Laboratories Ltd, 2A Orchard Road, Royston SG8 5HD Tel: 01763 211600 Fax: 01763 211556 Email: alastair.riddell@pharmagene.com; Kia Ora, 64 Lymington Bottom, Four Marks, Alton GU34 5AH Tel: 01962 772667 Fax: 01962 773033 — MB ChB 1977 Birm.; BSc (Hons.) (Biol. Scs.) Aston 1971; MSc (Anat.) Birm. 1973; MFPM RCP (UK) 1992; MRCGP 1982. (Univ. Birm.) CEO Pharmagene Laborat. Ltd. Royston. Socs: Fell. Roy. Soc. Med.; Soc. Nuclear Med. Prev: Managing Dir. Caremark Ltd. Harlow; SHO (Med.) Brit. Milit. Hosp. Rinteln; SHO (O & G) Roy. Berks. Hosp. Reading.

RIDDELL, Angela Mary Department of Radiology, John Radcliffe Hospital, Headington, Oxford — MB BS 1994 Lond.; FRCR 2001; BSc Lond. 1991; FRCS Eng. 1998. (Univ. Coll. Lond.) Regist. Radiol.

RIDDELL, Anna Felicity 44 Coity Road, London NW5 4RY — MB BS 1994 Lond. Socs: Med. Wom. Federat.; BMA.

RIDDELL, Christopher William Grove Surgery, Grove Lane, Thetford IP24 2HY Tel: 01842 752285 Fax: 01842 751316; 63 Arlington Way, Thetford IP24 2DZ Tel: 01842 754928 — MB BS 1976 Lond.; MRCS Eng. LRCP Lond. 1976. (St. Mary's)

RIDDELL, Claire 15A Southbank Road, Kenilworth CV8 1LA — BM BCh 1993 Oxf.; MA Oxf.; FRCOphth. (Oxford)

RIDDELL, David Ian, MBE, Surg. Cdr. RN Retd. Dornoch Lodge, Glen Lyon, Aberfeldy PH15 2NH — MD 1984 Dundee; MB ChB 1974.

RIDDELL, David John Goyt Valley Medical Practice, Chapel Street, Whaley Bridge, High Peak SK23 7SR Tel: 01663 732911 Fax: 01663 735702; The Old Vicarage, 23 High St, Chapel-en-le-Frith, High Peak SK23 0HD Tel: 01298 812201 — MB ChB 1981 Sheff.; MRCGP 1986; DRCOG 1985.

RIDDELL, Elizabeth Mary 60 Lanton Road, Newlands, Glasgow G43 2SR Tel: 0141 633 2453 — MB ChB 1958 Glas.; FRCPath 1979, M 1967; DPath Eng. 1964; DObst RCOG 1960. (Glas.) Prev: Cons. Haematol. Vict. Infirm. Glas.; Cons. Pathol. St. James' Hosp. Lond.; Lect. Haematol. St. Geo. Hosp. Med. Sch.

RIDDELL, Gareth 42 Malone Hill Park, Belfast BT9 6RE Tel: 01232 668058 — MB BCh BAO 1996 Belf. (Queens Belfast) Resid. MO Tweed Heads Hosp. Qu.sland Australia. Prev: Resid. MO Roy. Brisbane Hosp. Brisbane, Australia; SHO Belf. City Hosp. Belf., N.ern Irel.

RIDDELL, James Gray Department of Therapeutics & Pharmacology, Whitla Medical Building, 97 Lisburn Road, Belfast BT9 7BL Tel: 01232 335774 Fax: 01232 438346; 42 Malone Hill Park, Belfast BT9 6RE Tel: 01232 668058 — MD 1979 Belf.; BSc 1964, MB BCh BAO 1972; MRCP (UK) 1975. Reader & Cons. Therap. & Pharmacol. Qu. Univ. Belf., City & Roy. Vict. Hosp. Belf. Prev: Ho. Off. Lagan Valley Hosp. Lisburn.

RIDDELL, John Alistair, OBE (retired) 27 Upper Glenburn Road, Bearsden, Glasgow G61 4BN Email: ajriddellsafiaser@binternet.com — MB ChB 1953 Glas.; FRCP 1996 Glas.; FRCGP 1983, M 1966. Prev: Med. Sec. Glas. Local Med. Comm.

RIDDELL, John Wilson Royal Victoria Hospital, Grosvenor Road, Belfast BT12 6BA Tel: 01232 240503 — MB BCh BAO 1994 Belf. (Qu. Univ. Belf.) SHO (Med.) Roy. Vict. Hosptial Belf. Socs: MRCP (Lond.). Prev: SHO (Med.) Erne Hosp. NI; Resid. MO, P. Cha. Hosp., Brisbane, Australia; Resid. MO, Caboolture Hosp, Qu.sland, Australia.

RIDDELL, Jonathan Douglas Highgate Group Practice, 44 North Hill, London N6 4QA Tel: 020 8340 6628 Fax: 020 8342 8428; 15 Park Avenue S., London N8 8LU Tel: 020 8341 1026 Email: riddfam@aol.com — MB BS 1975 Lond.; MRCGP 1980. GP Trainer Whittington Hosp. Lond. VTS.

RIDDELL, Margaret Anthea (retired) The Dale, Bayswater Farm Road, Headington, Oxford OX3 8BX Tel: 01865 750981 — MB BS Lond. 1955; MRCS Eng. LRCP Lond. 1954. Prev: GP Oxf.

RIDDELL, Michael James (retired) Dornoch Lodge, Glenlyon, Aberfeldy PH15 2NH Tel: 01887 877244 — MB BS 1941 Lond.; MB BS (Hons.) Lond. 1941; BSc (1st cl. Hons. Physiol.) Lond. 1938, MD 1951; FRCP Glas. 1970, M 1965; MRCP Lond. 1948; MRCS Eng. LRCP Lond. 1941.

RIDDELL, Niall Jervis Swallowfield Medical Practice, The Street, Swallowfield, Reading RG7 1QY Tel: 0118 988 3134 Fax: 0118 988 5759 — MB BChir 1977 Camb.; MA Camb. 1977; MRCP (UK) 1982; MRCGP 1984; DRCOG 1984. Hosp. Pract. (Gastroenterol.) Battle Hosp. Reading. Prev: Regist. (Med.) Camb. Milit. Hosp. Aldershot; Ho. Off. (Orthop.) St. Thos. Hosp. Lond.; Ho. Phys. Soton. Gen. Hosp.

RIDDELL, Philip Leslie 23 Gillhurst Road, Harborne, Birmingham B17 8QS Tel: 0121 682 4926 Email: riddell@the freeinternet.co.uk — MB ChB 1973 Aberd.; FFA RCS Eng. 1978; FRCA. p/t Cons. (Anaesth.) Selly Oak Hosp. Birm. Prev: Sen. Regist. (Anaesth.) Midl. Anaesth. Train. Scheme; Regist. (Anaesth.) Aberd. Roy. Infirm.

RIDDELL, Rebecca Ellen Westburn Medical Group, Foresterhill Health Centre, Westburn Road, Aberdeen AB25 2AY Tel: 01224 696848 Fax: 01224 696753; 75 Braemar Place, Aberdeen AB10 6EQ — MB ChB 1990 Aberd.; MRCGP 1994. Clin. Sen. Lect. Dept. GP Aberd.

RIDDELL, William Stuart The Health Centre, The Square, Whitwell, Worksop S80 4QR Tel: 01909 720236 Fax: 01909 720236 — MB ChB 1987 Sheff.; MRCGP 1993.

RIDDICK, Mr Antony Charles Paul 4 Orchard Street, Bury St Edmunds IP33 1EH — BM BS 1992 Nottm.; FRCS Ed. 1996. SHO (Urol.) Nottm. City Hosp. Prev: SHO (Gen. Surg.) Derby City Hosp. & Qu. Med. Centre Nottm.; SHO (Orthop.) Qu. Med. Centre Nottm.

RIDDICK, David George Bushman, Col. late RAMC Retd. (retired) Tudor Cottage, Church Lane, Flyford Flavell, Worcester WR7 4BZ Tel: 01386 462631 — MRCS Eng. LRCP Lond. 1948; MFCM 1974; DTM & H RCP Lond. 1962; DA Eng. 1954. Prev: Med. Off. DSS.

RIDDINGTON, David William Department Anaesthetics, Queen Elizabeth Hospital, Edgbaston, Birmingham B15 2TH Tel: 0121 472 1311 Fax: 0121 697 8359 Email: d.w.riddington@btinternet.com — MB ChB 1984 Birm.; FCAnaesth 1990; DA (UK) 1986. Cons. Anaesth. Univ. Hosps. Birm. NHS Trust. Prev: Sen. Regist. (Anaesth.) W. Midl. RHA.; Regist. (Anaesth.) P'boro. Hosps.; Regist. (Anaesth.) Leicester Hosps.

RIDDLE, Mr Andrew Forsyth Victoria Wing, Nuffield Hospital, Shores Road, Woking GU21 4BY Tel: 01483 227800; Tel: 01483 724076 Fax: 01483 724076 — MB BS 1977 Newc.; FRCOG 1998; MRCGP 1981. Cons. O & G Frimley Pk. Hosp. Camberley SurreyClin. director Obtetrics & Gyn.; Med. Dir. Assisted Conception Unit Woking Nuffield Hosp.; Chair, Clin. Audit, Frimley Pk. Hosp. Socs: Roy. Soc. Med.; Brit. Fertil. Soc.; Eur. Soc. Human Reproduc. & Embryol. Prev: Sen. Regist. (O & G) King's Coll. Hosp. Lond.; Clin. Research Fell. (Reproduct. Endocrinol. & Infertil.) King's Coll. Hosp. Lond.

RIDDLE, Fiona Jane The Village Green Surgery, The Green, Wallsend NE28 6BB Tel: 0191 295 8500 Fax: 0191 295 8519; 48 Elsdon Road, Gosforth, Newcastle upon Tyne NE3 1HY — MB BS 1985 Newc.; MRCGP 1989; Cert. Family Plann. JCC 1987. Prev: Trainee GP Newc. VTS.

RIDDLE, Graham Douglas Sunderland District General Hospital, Kayll Road, Sunderland SR4 7TP — MB ChB 1988 Aberd.

RIDDLE, Henry Francis Valentine Craigview, Chapelgreen, Earlsferry, Leven KY9 1AD Tel: 01333 330965 Fax: 01333 330965

Email: valentineriddle@aol.com — MB ChB 1959 Liverp.; PhD Liverp. 1957, BSc (Hons. Physiol.) 1952; MD Liverp. 1970; MRCGP 1968; FFOM RCP Lond. 1989, M 1983. Socs: Liverp. Med. Inst. & Thoracic Soc. Prev: Dir. Fife HB Occupat. Health Serv.; Sen. Regional Med. Off. Civil Serv. Med. Serv. Edin.; Regist. (Med.), Ho. Phys. & Ho. Surg. Liverp. Roy. Infirm.

RIDDLE, Ian Forsyth Department of Anaesthesia, The James Cook University Hospital, Marton Road, Middlesbrough TS4 3BW Tel: 01642 850850 Fax: 01642 824877 — MB BS 1974 Newc. Cons. Anaesth. S. Tees Acute Trust Middlesbrough.

RIDDLE, John Albert (retired) New Clee, St. Wilfrid's Green, Hailsham BN27 1DR Tel: 01323 841182 — MB BS 1943 Lond.

RIDDLE, Miles Andrew Rosemount, Jenny Brough Lane, Hessle HU13 0JX — MB ChB 1996 Ed.

RIDDLE, Peter Napier (retired) 4 Arnett Close, Rickmansworth WD3 4DB Tel: 01923 778010 — MB BS 1962 Lond.; BSc Lond. 1954. Prev: Cons. Applied Microscopy Laborat. Imperial Cancer Research Fund.

RIDDLE, Mr Peter Riversdale Fitz Farm, Dinton, Salisbury SP3 5DZ Tel: 01722 716255 — MB BS 1957 Lond.; MS Lond. 1968; FRCS Eng. 1963; MRCS Eng. LRCP Lond. 1957. (St. Geo.) Emerit. Surg. UCL Hosp. & St. Peters Hosp. Lond.; Hon. Cons. Urol. St. Geo. Hosp. Lond.; Hon. Cons. Surg. Urol. to the Army. Socs: Fell. & Med. Soc. Lond.; Brit. Assn. Urol. Surgs.; Mem.BMA. Prev: Resid. Surg. Off. St. Peter's Hosp. Lond.; Lect. (Surg.) St. Mary's Hosp. Med. Sch. Lond.; Ho. Surg. Surgic. Unit St. Geo. Hosp. Lond.

RIDDLE, Philippa Jane Radiotherapy Department, Churchill Hospital, Oxford OX3 7XG Tel: 01865 741841 Email: pipriddle@aol.com; 6 Murrayfield Gardens, Edinburgh EH12 6DF — BChir 1991 Camb.; MA Camb. 1992; MRCP (UK) 1994; FRCR May 1999. (Char. Cross & Westm.) Specialist Regist. (Clin. Oncol.) Ch.ill Hosp. Oxf.

RIDDLE, Robert Womack (retired) The Walled Garden, 21 Middle St., Shoreham-by-Sea BN43 5DP Tel: 01273 454262 — MB BS Durh. 1932, BHyg., DPH 1934. Prev: Ho. Surg. Roy. Vict. Hosp. Newc.

RIDDLE, William James Robert Herdmanflat Hospital, Haddington EH41 3BU Tel: 01031 536 8515 Fax: 0131 536 8500 — MB ChB 1982 Aberd.; MPhil Ed. 1995; MRCPsych 1991. Cons. Gen. Adult Psychiat. Herdmanflat Hosp. Haddington. Socs: Brit.Assoc. fro PsychoPharmacol., Mem.. Prev: Sen. Regist. Roy. Cornw. Hosp. Aberd.; Research Fell. MRC Brain Metab. Unit Edin.; Regist. Roy. Edin. Hosp.

RIDDOCH, Andrew James Cornwall Road Surgery, 15 Cornwall Road, Dorchester DT1 1RU Tel: 01305 251128; 166 Amersham Way, Little Chalfont, Amersham HP6 6SG — MB BS 1989 Lond.; DRCOG 1994; MRCGP 1998. (St Bartholomews London)

RIDDOCH, Donald 5 Davenport Road, Coventry CV7 6QA Tel: 024 7667 2997; 9 Alder Lane, Balsall Common, Coventry CV7 7DZ — MB ChB Birm. 1960; FRCP Lond. 1980, M 1964. p/t Cons. Neurol. Socs: BMA & Assn. Brit. Neurol. Prev: Sen. Regist. (Neurol.) United Birm. Hosps.

RIDDOCH, Margaret Elsie (retired) 33 Millfield, Kirkton, Livingston EH54 7AR Tel: 01506 493574 — MB ChB 1951 Ed.; MRCGP 1977; FFA RCS Eng. 1959. Prev: Cons. Anaesth. Bangour Gen. Hosp. & GP Howden Health Centre Livingston.

RIDDOLLS, Lucy Elizabeth (retired) Aislaby Lodge, Aislaby, Whitby YO21 1SY Tel: 01947 810419 — MB BS 1949 Lond.; MRCS Eng. LRCP Lond. 1949. Prev: SCMO (Child Health) ScarBoro. HA.

RIDEHALGH, Harry (retired) 176 Bramhall Moor Lane, Hazel Grove, Stockport SK7 5BE Tel: 0161 483 2267 — MB ChB (Commend.) St. And. 1958. Prev: Ho. Surg. & Ho. Phys. Co. Hosp. Lincoln.

RIDEN, Donald Keith dept. Oral & Maxillofacial Surgery, Derriford Hospital, Plymouth; 25 Easterdown Close, Plymstock, Plymouth PL9 8SR Fax: 01752 494155 Email: dkriden@rnhp.demon.co.uk — BM 1988 Soton.; FRCS 1996; FDS 1994; FRCS (OMFS0) 1998. Specialist. Regist. (Oral & Maxillofacial Surg.) Derriford Hosp. Plymouth.

RIDER, David (retired) 9 Richmond Avenue, Trench, Telford TF2 7ES Tel: 01952 411190 — MB ChB 1961 St. And.; DObst RCOG 1964. Div. Surg. St. John Ambul. Brig. Prev: Clin. Asst. (Orthop.) Roy. Hosp. Wolverhampton.

RIDER, Ian Atherton 529 Meanwood Road, Leeds LS6 4AW — MB ChB 1996 Leeds.

RIDER, James Gordon (retired) Ravensthorpe, Doctors Lane, Hutton Rudby, Yarm TS15 0EQ Tel: 01642 700143 Fax: 01642 700305 Email: gordon.rider@lineone.net — MB ChB 1951 Ed.; FRCGP 1980, M 1959; DObst RCOG 1953. Prev: Ho. Surg. Simpson Memor. Matern. Pavil. Edin.

RIDER, Jessica Charlotte Yew Trees, Bull Ring Farm Road, Harbury, Leamington Spa CV33 9HJ — BM 1992 Soton.

RIDER, Mr Mark Ainsley 13 Fulwith Drive, Harrogate HG2 8HW — MB ChB 1987 Dundee; FRCS Ed. 1993.

RIDER, Stella Jane Caldwell 71 West End Avenue, Harrogate HG2 9BX Tel: 01423 505948 — MB BS 1988 Lond. Ho. Off. (Surg./Med.) Harrogate GP VTS.

RIDGE, Alan Timothy Carlton House Surgery, 28 Tenniswood Road, Enfield EN1 3LL Tel: 020 8363 7575 Fax: 020 8366 8228; 207 Lavender Hill, Enfield EN2 8RW Fax: 020 8364 6100 Email: 106627.2004@compuserve.com — MB BS 1972 Lond.; MRCGP 1976; Cert FPA 1974. (Lond. Hosp.) Socs: BMA; (Vice-Chairm.) Doctor-Healer Network; Brit. Holistic Med. Assn. Prev: Trainee GP Ipswich VTS; Ho. Surg. (Gen. Surg. & Orthop.) Ipswich Hosp.; Ho. Phys. Ipswich Hosp. (Heath Rd. Wing).

***RIDGE, Anna Louise** The Limes, Randalls Green, Chalford Hill, Stroud GL6 8EE — MB ChB 1998 Birm.; ChB Birm. 1998.

RIDGE, Mr Jeremy Andrew Francis Hopton Hall, Mirfield WF14 8EL Tel: 01924 497272 Fax: 01924 497270 — MB BS 1981 Lond.; FRCS Ed. 1986; MRCS Eng. LRCP Lond. 1980; LMSSA Lond. 1980. Cons. Orthop. Surg. Dewsbury Dist. Hosp. Socs: Fell. BOA; BMA. Prev: Cons. Orthop. Surg. Manor Hse. Hosp.; Regist. (Orthop. Surg.) Barnet Gen. Hosp.; Regist. (Gen. Surg. & Orthop.) Mt. Vernon Hosp. N.wood.

RIDGE, John Martin Flat 1, Mount Stuart, Higher Woodfield Road, Torquay TQ1 2LB — MB ChB 1994 Bristol.

RIDGEWELL, Mark Charles Kings Road Surgery, 2- 6 Kings Road, Mumbles, Swansea SA3 4AJ Tel: 01792 360933 Fax: 01792 368930; 61 Hendrefoilan Road, Sketty, Swansea SA2 9LU — MB BS 1986 Lond.; Cert Family Planning 1990 JCC; Dip Sports Med 1999 RCPS, Glas.; DRCOG 1990; MRCGP 1990; MSc 2001 (Sport & Exercise Med.) Uni. Bath. (St. Mary's Hosp. Lond.) Socs: (Sec.) Brit. Assn. Sport & Exercise Med.; UK Assn. Of Doctors In Sport.

RIDGWAY, Mr Alan Edward Andrew Russell House, Russell Road, Manchester M16 8AR Tel: 0161 862 9568 Fax: 0161 227 9405; 10 Framingham Road, Brooklands, Sale M33 3SH Tel: 0161 973 9479 Fax: 0161 973 9479 Email: alan.e.ridgway@man.ac.uk — MB 1964 Cantab; FRCOphth; DO 1967 Eng; FRCS 1970 Eng; MRCS Eng. LRCP 1964 Lond.; BChir 1965 Camb. (Lond. Hosp.) p/t Hon. Cons. Surg. Manch. Roy. Eye Hosp.; Hon. Research Fell. Dept. Of Opthalmology, Uni. Manc. Socs: Fell. Roy. Soc. Med. (Ex Vice-Pres. Counc. Sect. Ophth.); (Ex-Pres.) N. of Eng. Ophth. Soc.; Delegue Britannique Soc. Francaise D'Ophtalmologie. Prev: Sen. Regist. Birm. & Midl. Eye Hosp.; Regist. (Ophth.) Cardiff Roy. Infirm.; SHO Oxf. Eye Hosp.

RIDGWAY, Brian Arthur Firth Park Surgery, 400 Firth Park Road, Sheffield S5 6HH Tel: 0114 242 6406 — MB ChB 1960 Sheff.; BSc (Hons. Biochem.) Sheff. 1963, MB ChB 1960; MRCGP 1970. Prev: Research Asst. Med. Profess. Unit Roy. Hosp. Sheff.; Ho. Surg. Roy. Infirm. Sheff.; Ho. Phys. Childr. Hosp. Sheff.

RIDGWAY, Daniel Mark Cobwebs, Elmdale, Barton-upon-Humber DN18 5EB — MB ChB 1997 Leic.

RIDGWAY, Elisabeth Jane Department of Microbiology, Royal Hallamshire Hospital, Glossop Road, Sheffield S10 2JF Tel: 0114 271 2610 Fax: 0114 278 9376 Email: elisabeth.ridgway@sth.nhs.uk — MB BS 1985 Lond.; BSc (Hons.) Lond. 1982, MB BS 1985; MD University of Liverpool 1999; MRCPath 1992; FRCPath 2000. (St Barts. Hosp.) Cons. Microbiol. Roy. Hallamshire Hosp. Sheff.; Hon. Sen. Clin. Lect. Univ. of Sheff. Socs: Hosp. Infec. Soc.

RIDGWAY, Elizabeth Susan 8 Monmouth Close, Chiswick, London W4 5DQ Tel: 020 8742 1386; 10 Nethercote,, Newton Burgoland, Leicester LE67 2ST Tel: 01530 272205 Email: esridgway@hotmail.com — MB BS 1994 Lond.; BSc (Hons.) Lond. 1992.

RIDGWAY, Geoffrey Lindsay Dept Clinical Microbiology, University College London Hospitals, Grafton Way,, London WC1E 6DB Tel: 0207 380 9914 Fax: 0207 388 8514 Email:

RIDGWAY

geoff.ridgeway@uclh.org; 23 Richmond Road, New Barnet, Barnet EN5 1SA Tel: 020 8441 1732 Fax: 020 8441 1732 Email: gl.ridg@dial.pipex.com — MB BS 1971 Lond.; BSc (Special Zool.) Lond. 1966, MD 1977; MRCP (UK) 1996; MRCS Eng. LRCP Lond. 1971; FRCPath 1989, M 1977; Hon Dip. Hic 1999; FRCP 2000. (Royal Free) Cons. Microbiologist Univ. Coll. Lond. Hosps.; Hon. Sen. Lect. UCL & Lond. Sch. of Hyg. & Trop. Med.; Hon. Cons. Microbiol. Roy. Nat. Heart & Brompton Hosp. Gp. Socs: Roy. Soc. Med. (Counc. Path.); Brit. Soc. Antimicrob. Chemother.; Hosp. Infec. Soc. Prev: Sen. Regist. (MicroBiol.) Univ. Coll. Lond. Hosps.; Ho. Off. Phys. St. Andrews Hosp. Bow; Ho. Off. Surg. Roy. Free Hosp. Lond.

RIDGWAY, John Charles Quinton Family Practice, 406 Quinton Road West, Birmingham B32 1QG Tel: 0121 421 6011; Chestnut Lodge, Court Road, Upper Strensham, Worcester WR8 9LP — MB ChB St. And. 1968. (St. And.) Prev: SHO (Obst.) N.ampton Gen. Hosp.; Ho. Off. Stratford Gen. Hosp.

RIDGWAY, Stephen David Flat 8, 2 Craddock Court, 30 Bodenham Road, Hereford HR1 2TS — MB BCh 1994 Wales.

RIDGWAY, Timothy John 53 West Coats Road, Cambuslang, Glasgow G72 8AE — MB ChB 1989 Ed.

RIDHA, Basil Hassan Room 810, Neuadd Meirionnydd, Heath Park, Cardiff CF14 4YS — MB BCh 1998 Wales.

RIDING, Blodwen Eleanor Joyce (retired) Merlyn Moelfre, Abergele LL22 9RH Tel: 01745 824435 — MB ChB 1950 Liverp.; MRCPsych 1973; DPM Eng. 1972; DA Eng. 1959. Prev: Cons. Psychiat. Fazakerley, Walton & Rainhill Hosps.

RIDING, Graham Stuart Garnett Victoria Hospital, Blackpool FY3 8NR Tel: 01253 300000; 39 South Road, Bretherton, Preston PR26 9AB — MB ChB 1991 Manch.; BSc (Physiol.) Manch. 1988. SHO (Gen. Surg.) Vict. Hosp. Blackpool. Prev: SHO (A & E) Roy. Preston Hosp.; Ho. Off. (Med.) Qu. Eliz. Hosp. Blackburn; Ho. Off. (Surg.) Roy. Preston Hosp.

RIDING, Mr John Edmund, CBE (retired) Merlyn, Moelfre, Abergele LL22 9RH Tel: 01745 824435 — MD 1959 Liverp.; MB ChB 1947; FRCS Eng. 1980; FFA RCS Eng. 1954; DA Eng. 1951; Hon. FFA RACS 1979. Prev: Cons. Anaesth. Liverp. HA.

RIDING, Katie Jane Sherwood House, Division Lane, Blackpool FY4 5DZ — MB ChB 1997 Manch.

RIDING, William Douglas Currajong, Avenue Farm Lane, Wilden, Bedford MK44 2PY Tel: 01234 771669 Fax: 01234 771669 Email: william-riding@msn.com — MB BChir Camb. 1960; MA Camb. 1961, BA 1957; FRCP Lond. 1983, M 1964; MRCS Eng. LRCP Lond. 1960. (Camb. & Liverp.) Cons. Phys. Bedford Hosp.; JP. Socs: Brit. Thorac. Soc.& BMA. Prev: Sen. Regist. (Med.) United Manch. Hosps.

RIDINGS, Philip Charles 95 Seaford Road, London W13 9HS — BM 1987 Soton.

RIDLER, Andrew Hughes Blackmore Health Centre, Blackmore Drive, Sidmouth EX10 8ET Tel: 01395 512601 Fax: 01395 578408; Rosemead, Hillside Road, Sidmouth EX10 8JF Tel: 01395 512601 — MB BChir 1973 Camb.; MA Camb. 1973; Cert Family Plann. RCOG RCGP & FPA 1976; DObst RCOG 1975.

RIDLER, Brigid Mary Fitzclarence Royal Devon & Exeter Hospital (Wonford), Exeter EX2 5DW Tel: 01392 411611 Fax: 01392 402067 Email: bmfridler@hotmail.com; 57 Elmside, Mount Pleasant, Exeter EX4 6LR Tel: 01392 433861 Fax: 01392 433861 — MB ChB 1972 Sheff.; Cert. Family Plann. JCC 1975; DObst RCOG 1974. (Sheff.) Research Assoc. (Vasc.) & Clin. Asst. Roy. Devon & Exeter Hosp. Prev: Trainee GP Wessex VTS.

RIDLER, Samantha Louise 1 Arrowfield Close, Bristol BS14 0UQ — BM BS 1994 Nottm.

RIDLER, Simon John Moorlands, Main St., Newburgh, Ellon AB41 6BE — MB ChB 1997 Manch.

RIDLEY, Alan Eastling 19 Hillsden Road, Whitley Bay NE25 9XF; 19 Hillsden Road, Whitley Bay NE25 9XF Tel: 0191 251 0091 — MB BS Durh. 1954; MRCGP 1967; DObst RCOG 1960. Indep. GP Whitley Bay. Prev: GP N. Shields Tyne & Wear.

RIDLEY, Alan Ridley (retired) Five Winds, 174 Pennsylvania Road, Exeter EX4 6DZ Tel: 01392 216679 — MB BS Durh. 1955; PhD Durh. 1962; MD (Distinc.) Newc. 1964; FRCP Lond. 1975, M 1959. Prev: Sen. Cons. Neurol. Lond. Hosp.

RIDLEY, Catherine Mary 34 Large Acres, Selsey, Chichester PO20 9BA — M.B., Ch.B. St. And. 1940. (St. And.)

RIDLEY, Colin Charles Sheridan The Regional Child & Adolescent Unit, Park View Clinic, 60 Queensbridge Road, Moseley, Birmingham B13 8QE Tel: 0121 243 2000 Fax: 0121 243 2010; Cornerstone, Cofton Church Lane, Cofton Hacket, Birmingham B45 8BB Tel: 0121 445 2515 — MB BS 1978 Lond.; AKC 1978; Dip. Psychoanal. Observat. Studies E. Lond. 1995; Dip. Social Learn Theory & Pract. in App Settings Leic. 1988. (St. Geo. Hosp. Lond.) Staff Grade Doctor Irwin Unit Pk. View Clinic Birm. Socs: Affil. Roy. Coll. Psychiat.

RIDLEY, David Curtis Greystoke Surgery, Kings Avenue, Morpeth NE61 1SA Tel: 01670 511393 — MB ChB 1980 Sheff.

RIDLEY, David Malcolm 52 Stangate, Royal St., London SE1 7EQ — MB ChB 1972 Aberd.; MRCOG 1978.

RIDLEY, Dennis Snow, OBE (retired) 32 Basildon Court, 28 Devonshire St., London W1G 6PR Tel: 020 7935 3507 — BSc (Hons.) Lond. 1939, MD 1950; MRCS Eng., LRCP Lond. 1942; FRCPath 1967, M 1963. Prev: Path. Hosp. Trop. Dis. Lond.

RIDLEY, Diane Melbourne Park Medical Centre, Melbourne Road, Aspley, Nottingham NG8 5HL Tel: 0115 978 6114 Fax: 0115 924 9334 — BM BS 1994 Nottm.; DFFP Loc Lut 1999; MRCGP 1998. Gen. Practitioner Nottm.

RIDLEY, John Graham Haltwhistle Health Centre, Greencroft Avenue, Haltwhistle NE49 9AP Tel: 01434 320077 Fax: 01434 320674 — MB ChB 1975 Bristol; BA Camb. 1965.

RIDLEY, Joy 27 Little Moor Hill, Smethwick B67 7BG — MB ChB 1998 Aberd.; MB ChB Aberd 1998.

RIDLEY, Malcolm Gavin Grove House Surgery, 80 Pryors Lane, Rose Green, Bognor Regis PO21 4JB Tel: 01243 265222/266413 Fax: 01243 268693 — MB BS 1967 Lond.; DA Eng. 1969. (St. Thos.) Prev: Ho. Off. St. Richard's Hosp. Chichester; Resid. (Anaesth.) St. Thos. Hosp. Lond.; Regtl. Med. Off. 21st S.A.S. Regt. (AVR).

RIDLEY, Martin Grant Tel: 01243 01243 Ext: 5214 Fax: 01243 831599 Email: martin.ridley@rwstr.nhs.uk; 35 Plainwood Close, Summersdale, Chichester PO19 4YB Tel: 01243 532164 Fax: 01242 532164 Email: martin.ridley@plainwood.demon.uk — MB BS 1978 Lond.; MRCP (UK) 1981; FRCP 1997. (King's Coll. Hosp.) Cons. Rheum. with interest Gen. Med. St. Richard's Hosp. Chichester; Med. Director Roy. W. Sussex Trust. Socs: Brit. Soc. Rheum. Prev: Sen. Regist. (Rheum.) St. Thos. Hosp. Lond.; Research Fell. Rheum. Dis. Unit Guy's Hosp. Med. Sch. Lond.; Regist. (Gen. Med.) Bath Health Dist.

RIDLEY, Nancye Mary (retired) 12 Brooklands Close, Fordwich, Canterbury CT2 0BT — MRCS Eng. LRCP Lond. 1942. Prev: Med. Off. Nixon Memor. Hosp. Sierra Leone.

RIDLEY, Mr Nicholas Harold Lloyd Keeper's Cottage, Stapleford, Salisbury SP3 4LT Tel: 01722 790209 — FRS 1986; Hon. DSc City 1990; MA 1927 Camb. (Nat. Sc. Trip.) 1927, MD 1945, MA, MB BChir 1931; FRCS Eng. 1932; MRCS Eng. LRCP Lond. 1930; FRCOphth. Hon. 1989; Hon. FICS. (Camb. & St. Thos.) Hon. Cons. Surg. Ophth. Dept. St. Thos. Hosp.; Hon. Cons. Moorfields Eye Hosp. Socs: Hon. Fell. Roy. Soc. Med.; Hon. Mem. Oxf. Ophth. Congr.; Hon. Life Pres. Internat. Intraocular Implant Club. Prev: Mem. Expert Advis. Panel on Parasitic Dis. (Filariasis) WHO; Temp. Maj. RAMC; Chief Asst., &c. St. Thos. Hosp. & Moorfields Eye Hosp.

RIDLEY, Nicholas Terence Francis The Green, Stratton Audley, Bicester OX27 9BJ — MB ChB 1983 Zimbabwe; MRCP (UK) 1988; LRCP LRCS Ed. LRCPS Glas. 1983; FRCR 1993.

RIDLEY, Nicola Anne Waverley, Hatchett Green, Hale, Fordingbridge SP6 2NB — MB BChir 1989 Camb.

RIDLEY, Patricia Graham Haltwhistle Health Centre, Greencroft Avenue, Haltwhistle NE49 9AP Tel: 01434 320077 Fax: 01434 320674; The Pikes, Haltwhistle NE49 9JL Tel: 01434 320346 — MB BS 1968 Newc. (Newc.)

RIDLEY, Paul Damien Chatswood, North Marine Road, Flamborough, Bridlington YO15 1LG — MB BS 1982 Lond.

RIDLEY, Philippa 13 Cotham Gardens, Bristol BS6 6HD — BM BS 1994 Nottm.

RIDLEY, Philippa Jane Brackendale, Parkside, Hale, Farnham GU9 0JP — MB BS 1998 Lond.; MB BS Lond 1998.

RIDLEY, Mr Robert Edward Wilson (retired) The Old Vicarage, Dinnington, Newcastle upon Tyne NE13 7AA Tel: 01661 24585 — MB BS 1963 Durh.; FRCS Ed. 1977; LMCC 1967; DO Eng. 1973. Prev: Cons. Ophth. Newc. Gen. Hosp. & Hexham Gen. Hosp.

RIDLEY, Saxon Alan Norfolk and Norwich Hospital, Brunswick Road, Norwich NR1 3SR Tel: 01603 286286 — MB BS 1981 Lond.; MD Lond. 1995; FFA RCS Eng. 1985. Cons. Anaesth. & Intens. Care Norf. & Norwich Hosp.; Hon. Sen. Lect. Univ. E. Anglia. Socs: Hon. Sec. Intens. Care Soc. Prev: Sen. Regist. (Anaesth.) W.. Infirm. Glas.; Clin. Research Fell. Clin. Shock Study in W.. Infirm. Glas.; Regist. (Anaesth.) The Hosp. for Sick Childr. Gt. Ormond St. Lond.

RIDOUT, Aileen Betty (retired) 4 Mulgrave Road, Croydon CR0 1BL Tel: 020 8688 5257 Email: brid.crioy@virgin.net — MB BS 1954 Lond.; MRCS Eng. LRCP Lond. 1954; FFCM 1978, M 1973; DPH Eng. 1961. Specialist in Community Med. (Med. Staffing & Postgrad. Med. Educat.) SE Thames RHA; Barrister-at-Law Gray's Inn 1972. Prev: Dep. Med. Off. Health Lond. Boro. S.wark.

RIDOUT, Dorothy Mary (retired) 36 Parkside Road, Leeds LS6 4QG Tel: 0113 275 2311 — MB BS Lond. 1943; FRCS Eng. 1952; FRCOG 1986, M 1951.

RIDOUT, Douglas Lyon Shutlers, Salt Grass Lane, Keyhaven, Lymington SO41 0TQ — MB BChir 1939 Camb.; MRCS Eng. LRCP Lond. 1938. (Camb. & Univ. Coll. Hosp.) Prev: Med. Off. Ripon & Dist. Hosp.; Ho. Phys. & Ho. Surg. Univ. Coll. Hosp.; Surg. Lt.-Cdr. R.N.

RIDOUT, Sally Marshall Long Meadow, Gravel Pit Road, Wooton Bridge, Ryde PO33 4RB — BM 1985 Soton.; MRCGP 1990; DRCOG 1989.

RIDOUT, Simon Scott Hawkmoor House, Tavistock PL19 8PA — MB BS 1976 Lond.; MSc (Human Appl. Physiol.) Lond. 1985; MFOM RCP Lond. 1994, AFOM 1987. (Middlx.) Company Med. Off., Devonport Roy. Dockyard Hsp. Prev: Employm. Med. Adviser Health & Safety Exec. Som.; RN Med. Off.; Ho. Surg. Middlx. Hosp. Lond.

RIDPATH, Joanne Homestead, 13 Hillside Walk, Brentwood CM14 4RA Tel: 01277 211802; Padstones, 7 Back Lane, Ripley, Harrogate HG3 3AE Tel: 01423 772271 — BM 1991 Soton.; MRCP (UK) 1996. (Southampton) SpR Leeds Liver Unit, St. Jas. Univ. Hosp. Prev: Specialist Regist. (Gastroenterol.) Yorks. Reg.; SHO St. Jas. Univ. Hosp. Leeds '93-'97.

RIDSDALE, Alison The Crookes Practice, 203 School Road, Sheffield S10 1GN Tel: 0114 266 0677 Fax: 0114 266 4526 — MB ChB 1993 Sheff.

RIDSDALE, Leone Lorna Dept. of Clinical Neuroscieces, Academic Dept, Guy's, King and St Thomas's School of Medicine, Bessemer Road, Denmark Hill,, London SE5 9RJ Tel: 020 848 5150 Fax: 020 848 5781 Email: l.ridsdale@iop.kcl.ac.uk — MD 1974 McMaster Univ. Canada; PhD Lond. 1994, MSc 1970; BA Kent 1969; FRCGP 1994, M 1981; FRCPC 1979. (McMaster Univ., Canada) Reader & Hon. Cons. (Gen. Pract.& Neurol.) Kings, & St. Thomas Sch. of Med.. Lond.; Sen. Lect. in Neurol. Guy's Kings and St Thomas Sch. of Med. Socs: Amer. Acad. Neurol.; Fell. Roy. Coll. Phys. Canada.; Fell. Roy. Coll. GPs. Prev: Sen. Regist., Nat. Hosp. for Neurol.; Chief Neurol. Resid. & Fell. The Montreal Neurol. Inst. Canada; Lect. Univ. Coll. & Middlx. Hosp.

RIDSDALE, Patricia Anne South Ham House, 96 Paddock Road, Basingstoke RG22 6RL Tel: 01256 324666 Fax: 01256 810849; 32 The Topiary, Lychpit, Basingstoke RG24 8YX Tel: 01256 473256 Email: trish@hawkeye.hiway.co.uk — MB ChB 1987 Birm.; MRCGP 1992; DRCOG 1992.

RIDSDILL SMITH, Geoffrey Patrick The Burwell Surgery, Newmarket Road, Burwell, Cambridge CB5 0AE Tel: 01638 741234 Fax: 01638 743948; The Abbey, Swaffham Bulbeck, Cambridge CB5 0NQ — MB 1977 Camb.; BChir 1976; DRCOG 1978; MA Cambridge 1966. (University of Cambridge) Trainer (Gen. Pract.) Camb. VTS.

RIDSDILL SMITH, Philip Anthony Haslemere Health Centre, Church Lane, Haslemere GU27 2BQ Tel: 01483 783023 Fax: 01428 645065 — MB BS 1993 Lond.; DCH RCP Lond. 1995; DFFP 1998; DRCOG 1998. GP Regist. St Clements Winchester, Bapdune Ho. Guildford. Prev: SHO Rotat. (Paediat.) Soton. Gen. Hosp.

RIDSDILL SMITH, Robin Michael 241 Woodlands Road, Aylesford, Aylesford ME20 7QF Tel: 01622 717324 Fax: 01622 882304 Email: robin.ridsdill.smith@which.net — MB BChir Camb. 1959; MRCS Eng. LRCP Lond. 1958; DObst RCOG 1960; FRCGP 1981, M 1968. (St. Bart.) Non. Exec. Dir. W. Kent HA. Socs: Roy. Coll. Gen. Pract. Prev: GP Thornhills Med. Gp.; Ho. Surg. (Obst.) Norf. & Norwich Hosp.; Ho. Phys. Jenny Lind Childr. Hosp. Norwich.

RIDSDILL-SMITH, William Patrick Mill House, Swaffham Bulbeck, Cambridge CB5 0NF — BChir 1993 Camb.

RIDYARD, John Bolton 9 The Meadows, Rainhill, Prescot L35 0PQ — MA Camb. 1966; MD Liverp. 1978, MB ChB 1968; FRCP Lond. 1986; MRCP (UK) 1972. Cons. Phys. Whiston Hosp. Prescot; Clin. Lect. Liverp. Univ. Socs: Liverp. Med. Inst. & Brit. Thoracic Soc. Prev: Lect. (Med.) Ahmadu Bello Univ. Hosp. Zaria, Nigeria; Sen. Med. Regist. BRd.green Hosp. Liverp.; Ho. Phys. & Ho. Surg. Roy. S.. Hosp. Liverp.

RIEBERER, Gabriela Clair Academic Unit, Royal London Homoeopathic Hospital, Great Ormond St., London WC1N 3HR Tel: 020 7833 7223 Fax: 020 7833 7212 — State Exam Med 1987 Gottingen; PhD Gottingen 1991; MFHom Lond. 1993. Specialist Homoeop. Phys. Bradford & Acad. Unit Roy. Lond. Homoeop. Hosp. Prev: Clin. Asst. Glas. Homoeop. Hosp.

RIECK, Jonathan 7 Mount Mews, High St., Hampton on Thames, Hampton TW12 2SH Tel: 020 8979 2262 — MB BS 1983 Lond.

RIEDEL, Mr John Adolf (retired) 1 Dovedale Road, Leicester LE2 2DN Tel: 0116 270 5068 — MB ChB 1948 Ed.; Med. Dipl. Amsterdam 1949; FRCS Ed. 1956; FRCOG 1973, M 1959. Cons. O & G Leicester Roy. Infirm. Prev: Resid. Simpson Matern. Pavil. Edin. Roy. Infirm.

RIEFFLIN, Axel Radcliffe Infirmary, Woodstock Road, Oxford OX2 6HE — State Exam Med. Hamburg 1991.

RIEGER, Christopher Andrew Cardiff Road Surgery, 12 Cardiff Road, Luton LU1 1QG Tel: 01582 722148 Fax: 01582 485721; 1 Wensleydale, Luton LU2 7PN Tel: 01582 735484 — MB BS 1975 Lond.; MRCGP 1981; DRCOG 1979. (Lond. Hosp.) Vis. Med. Off. Luton Day Centre for the Homeless. Socs: BMA.

RIELEY, Thomas Christopher Marna Cottage, Rosebank, Carluke ML8 5QD Tel: 01555 860287; The Knowe, 94 Midton Road, Ayr KA7 2TP Tel: 01292 288331 — MB ChB 1994 Glas. SHO (A & E) Vict. Infirm. Glas. Socs: BMA; MDU. Prev: SHO (Orthop.) Ayr Hosp.; Ho. Off. (Med.) Vict. Infirm. Glas.; Ho. Off. (Surg.) Ayr Hosp.

***RIEMERSMA, Gordon Remko** 36 Buckstone Loan, Edinburgh EH10 6UD — MB ChB 1998 Ed.; MB ChB Ed 1998.

RIETSEMA, Cornelius The Manor Hospital, Moat Road, Walsall WS2 9PS — Artsexamen 1988 Leiden.

RIEU, Edward Christopher Suthergrey House Surgery, 37A St. Johns Road, Watford WD17 1LS Tel: 01923 224424 Fax: 01923 243710; Merrowdown, Burtons Lane, Chalfont St Giles HP8 4BD — MB BS 1979 Lond.; MRCP (UK) 1987; DRCOG 1982.

RIFAI, Rami 42 Windsor House, Whiston Hospital, Prescot L35 5DR; 12 Kiltongue, Monkland District General Hospital, Monkscourt Avenue, Airdrie ML6 0JS — MD 1988 Aleppo.

RIFAT-GHAFFAR, Dr The Surgery, Abbey Square, Walsall WS3 2RH Tel: 01922 408416 Fax: 01922 400372; 418 Sutton Road, Walsall WS5 3BA Tel: 01922 614269 — MB BS 1974 Patna. (P. of Wales Med. Coll.) GP.

RIFKIN, Larry Maudsley Hospital, 103 Denmark Hill, London SE5 8AF Tel: 020 7740 5091 Fax: 020 7701 5092 — MB BCh 1984 Witwatersrand; MRCPsych 1991. Cons. Psychiat. Maudsley Hosp.; Hon. Sen. Lect. Inst. Isyemiat. IOP.

RIFKIN, Shelley 21 Woodfield Way, London N11 2NP — MB BCh 1986 Witwatersrand; MB BCh Witwatersrand 1986.

RIGBY, Andrew Neil Church Street Surgery, 77 Church Street, Tewkesbury GL20 5RY Tel: 01684 292343 Fax: 01684 274305; Upper Westcroft, Westmancote, Tewkesbury GL20 7ES Tel: 01684 772412 — MB BS 1973 Lond.; DRCOG 1978; DGM 1996. (Middlx.) Med. Off. Tewkesbury Hosp. Prev: Asst. Lect. (Path.) St. Thos. Hosp. Med. Sch. Lond.; Ho. Surg. W. Norwich Hosp.; Ho. Phys. Centr. Middlx. Hosp. Lond.

RIGBY, Anthony John Brundall Medical Partnership, The Dales, Brundall, Norwich NR13 5RP Tel: 01603 712255 Fax: 01603 712156; Alveston House, Yarmouth Road, Blofield, Norwich NR13 4LQ Tel: 01603 713904 — MB BS 1969 Lond.; DObst RCOG 1970; Univ. Coll. Hosp. Prev: SHO (O & G) Hillingdon Hosp. Middlx.; SHO (Paediat.) & Ho. Phys. Warwick Gen. Hosp.; Ho. Off. (Surg.) Univ. Coll. Hosp. Lond.

RIGBY, Carolyn Jane North Tees General Hospital, Stockton-on-Tees TS19 8PE — MB BS 1989 Newc. SHO (Gen. Med.) N. Tees Gen. Hosp.

RIGBY, Mr Christopher Colton (retired) Newvale, 7 Clyro Place, Sutton Cum Lound, Retford DN22 8PE Tel: 01777 700469 — MB

RIGBY

ChB 1960 Sheff.; FRCS Eng. 1967. InDepend. private Pract. - Gen. and Vasc. Surg. Prev: Sen. Regist. (Surg.) Nottm. Gen. Hosp. & Roy. Hosp. Sheff.

RIGBY, Christopher Harold Lester (retired) The Elms Medical Practice, Hoo, Rochester ME3 9AE Tel: 01634 250142 — MB BChir 1963 Camb.; MA, MB Camb. 1963, BChir 1962; DCH Eng. 1964. Prev: Regist. (Med.) Mayday Hosp.

RIGBY, David Jeffrey North Lochs Medical Practice, Gleann Mor, Lochs, Isle of Lewis HS2 9JP Tel: 01851 860222 Fax: 01851 860611 — MB ChB 1990 Dundee. SHO (O & G) Vale of Leven Dist. Gen. Hosp. Dunbartonsh.

RIGBY, Diana 57 Eastwood Road, Rayleigh SS6 7JF; 24 Kings Road, Westcliff on Sea SS0 8LL — MB BS 1979 Lond.; MRCP (UK) 1982. GP S.end.

RIGBY, George Vernon 2 The Grange, 85 High St., Iver SL0 9PN — MB BS 1971 Lond.; BSc (Special, Physiol., Hons.), MB BS Lond. 1971; MRCP (UK) 1977.

RIGBY, Mr Howard Seymour Department of Pathology, Frenchay Hospital, Bristol BS16 1LE — BM BS 1976 Nottm.; DM Nottm. 1986, BM BS 1976; FRCS Eng. 1980; MRCPath 1991. Cons. Histopath. Frenchay Hosp. Bristol.

RIGBY, John Anthony (retired) T. S. Hattersley & Son Ltd., 63 Weymouth Road, Eccles, Manchester M30 8TH Tel: 0161 789 1374 Fax: 0161 787 8632 — MB ChB 1954 Birm.; FFOM RCP Lond. 1992, MFOM 1983; DIH Soc. Apoth. Lond. 1976; DObst RCOG 1960. Chief. Exec. & Occupat. Phys. T.S. Hattersley & Son. Ltd. Eccles. Prev: Chief Med. Adviser VSEL plc Barrow-in-Furness.

RIGBY, John Christopher Hesketh Centre, Albert Road, Southport PR9 0LT; 9 Delamere Road, Aimsdale, Southport PR8 2RD — MB ChB 1977 Leeds; MMedSc Aberd.1986; MRCPsych 1984; DRCOG 1980; FRCPsych 1996. Cons. Psychiat. S.port; Med. Dir. Prev: Postgrad. Clin. Tutor; Specialist Scheme Organiser (Mersey Drantry); Sec. BMA.

RIGBY, John Gilbert (retired) 3 Bertram Drive, Meols, Hoylake, Wirral L47 — MB ChB 1951 Liverp.; DObst RCOG 1956. Prev: GP Hoylake.

RIGBY, John Martin 52 Towan Blystra Road, Newquay TR7 2RP — MB ChB 1992 Leic.

RIGBY, John Peter Vernon, TD Huntsmoor Weir, Old Mill Lane, Cowley, Uxbridge UB8 2JH Tel: 01895 234898 — BM BCh Oxf. 1942; BA (Hons. Physiol. & Nat. Sc.) Oxf. 1937; MA Oxf. 1942; MRCS Eng. LRCP Lond. 1942; Cert. FPA 1979. (Oxf. & St. Thos.) Emerit. Cons. Phys. Guy's Hosp. Lond.; Phys. (Approved Under Sect. 12 Ment. Health Act 1983). Socs: Harveian Soc.; Brit. Thorac. Soc.; Roy. Brompton Hosp. Soc. Prev: Cons. Phys. Deptford Chest Clinic Lond.; Ho. Phys. Brompton Hosp. Dis. Chest; Cas. Phys. and Med. Reg. St Mary's Hosp. Lond.

RIGBY, Kathryn Ann 34 Church Lane, Bessacarr, Doncaster DN4 6QA — MB ChB 1994 Leeds.

RIGBY, Marcus Thornburn (Surgery), 398 Ladywood, Middleway, Birmingham B1 2TP Tel: 0121 454 3426; Waterside, Haye Lane, Mappleborough Green, Studley B80 7BX Tel: 01527 852873 — MB ChB 1955 Birm.

RIGBY, Michael Charles Barn Acre, Bishops Frome, Worcester WR6 5AS — MB BS 1992 Lond.; FRCS 1996.

RIGBY, Michael Francis North Lakeland Health Care, Department of Psychotherapy, Beech Lodge, Carleton Clinic,, Carlisle CA1 3SX Tel: 01228 602392; High Barn, Boon Hill, Farlam, Brampton CA8 1LA Tel: 016977 46078 — MB BS 1982 Lond.; BSc (1st cl. Hons.) Lond. 1979; MRCPsych 1992; DA (UK) 1986. (Westm.) Cons. Psychotherapist, N. Cumbria Psychother. Serv. Prev: Sen. Regist. (Psychother.) St. Geo. Hosp. & Henderson Hosp. Lond.; Regist. (Psychiat.) Char. Cross Hosp. Lond.; Regist. (Anaesth.) Char. Cross & Roy. Brompton Hosp. Lond.

RIGBY, Michael Laurence Royal Brompton Hospital, Sydney St., London SW3 6NP Tel: 020 7351 8542 Fax: 020 7351 8547 Email: m.rigby@rbh.nthames.nhs.uk — MB ChB Leeds 1970; MD Leeds 1984; FRCP Lond. 1988; MRCP (UK) 1974; FRCPCH 1997. Dir. & Cons. Paediat. Cardiol. Roy. Brompton Hosp. Lond. Socs: Brit. Cardiac Soc. & Argentinian Soc. Cardiol. Prev: Canad. Heart Foundat. Fell. Hosp. Sick Childr. Toronto, Canada.

RIGBY, Paul Stockbridge Village Health Centre, Leachcroft, Waterpark Drive, Stockbridge Village, Liverpool L28 1ST Tel: 0151 489 9924; 8 Campsey Ash, Widnes WA8 9GP — MB ChB 1987 Liverp.; MRCGP 1995; DRCOG 1992.

RIGBY, Peter John Readesmoor Medical Group Practice, 29-29A West Street, Congleton CW12 1JP Tel: 01260 276161 Fax: 01260 297340; 67 Ennerdale Drive, Congleton CW12 4FJ — MB ChB 1985 Sheff.; MRCGP 1989; DRCOG 1989.

RIGBY, Philip (retired) 7 Azalea Road, Wick St Lawrence, Weston Super Mare BS22 9TN Tel: 01934 521964 Email: drrigby@globalnet.co.uk — MB ChB 1946 Birm.; DPhysMed Eng. 1970; DTM & H Liverp. 1960. Prev: Cons. Rehabil. Raigmore Hosp. Inverness.

RIGBY, Richard Christopher 36 Glengarvan Close, Lambton, Washington NE38 0DY Tel: 0191 416 1196 — MB BS 1990 Newc.; BMedSci. (Hons.) 1987. Trainee GP N.umbria VTS.

RIGBY, Shirley Patricia 20 Appleby Close, Twickenham TW2 5NA Tel: 020 8898 0945 — MB BS 1988 Lond.; BSc (Hons.) Lond. 1985, MB BS 1988; MRCP (UK) 1991. (Charing Cross & Westm. Med. Sch.) Specialist Regist. N.wick Pk. Hosp.

RIGBY-JONES, Timothy Grosvenor Medical Centre, Grosvenor Street, Crewe CW1 3HB Tel: 01270 256348 Fax: 01270 250786; Laburnum Cottage, Audlem Road, Hatherton, Nantwich CW5 7QT Tel: 01270 841251 — MB BChir 1968 Camb.; MA, MB Camb. 1968, BChir 1967; MRCS Eng. LRCP Lond. 1967; DCH Eng. 1970; DObst RCOG 1969. (Camb. & Westm.) Prev: Ho. Surg. Gordon Hosp. Lond.; Ho. Off. (Obst. & Med.) Crumpsall Hosp. Manch.; SHO Booth Hall Childr. Hosp. Manch.

RIGDEN, Brian Richard Queensview Medical Centre, Thornton Road, Northampton NN2 6LS; Home Close, Moulton Lane, Boughton, Northampton NN2 8RF Tel: 01604 847964 — MB ChB 1983 Leic.; DRCOG 1987. (Leicester)

RIGDEN, Jessica 1/6 Saxe Coburg Terrace, Edinburgh EH3 5BU — MB ChB 1992 Ed.; MRCGP 1996.

RIGDEN, Susan Patricia Alice Dept. of Paediatric Nephrology, 9th Floor Guys's Tower,, guy's Hospital,, London SE1 9RT Tel: 020 7955 5000 ext 3115 Fax: 0207 955 4971 Email: sue.rigden@gstt.sthames.nhs.uk; 205 john ruskin st, London SE5 0PT Tel: 0207 703 4860 Email: sue.rigden@virgin.net — MB BS Lond. 1972; FRCP Lond. 1990; MRCP (UK) 1976. (Roy. Free) Cons. Paediat. Nephrol. Guy's Hosp. Lond.

RIGG, Alastair William The Surgery, 46 Annan Road, Gretna DG16 5DG Tel: 01461 338317 Fax: 01461 337180; 3 The Meadow, Eaglesfield, Lockerbie DG11 3PH Tel: 01461 500565 — MB ChB 1980 Ed.; BSc (Med. Sci.) Ed. 1977; MRCGP 1985; DRCOG 1984. Socs: Christ. Med. Fell.sh.

RIGG, Christopher Donald Dept of Anaesth., Hull Royal Infirmary, Andhy Road, Kingston upon Thames; 5 St. Pauls Close, Northallerton DL7 8YN Tel: 01608 770814 Email: christopher.rigg@vigin.net — BSc (Hons.) Med. Sci. Ed. 1983, MB ChB 1985; FRCA 1994; DRCOG 1991; DCH RCP Lond. 1990; DA (UK) 1989. Cons. Anaesth., (Hull Roy. Infirm.).; Regist. (Anaesth.) Newc.; Specialist Regist, (Anaesth.) Newc. Socs: Roy. Soc. Med. (Edin. Br.); BMA. Prev: Trainee GP N.allerton VTS.

RIGG, Colin John The Coach House, The Old Stables, High Street, Whaddon, Milton Keynes MK17 0NA — BM BS 1985 Nottm.

RIGG, David Robert (retired) 10 Clinton Avenue, Hampton Magna, Warwick CV35 8TX Tel: 01926 491658 — MB ChB Sheff. 1931; LMSSA Lond. 1931; FFA RCS Eng. 1954; DA Eng. 1950. Prev: Sen. Lect. Univ. Coll. Ibadan.

RIGG, Emma Louise 41 The Valley, Comberton, Cambridge CB3 7DF — MB BS 1998 Lond.; MB BS Lond 1998.

RIGG, John Harvey White Lodge, 28 Waterloo Road, Birkdale, Southport PR8 2NG Tel: 01704 569619 Fax: 01704 569619; White Lodge, 28 Waterloo Road, Birkdale, Southport PR8 2NG Tel: 01704 569619 Fax: 01704 569619 — MB ChB Ed. 1966; DObst RCOG 1969. (Edinburgh) Med. Off. Roy. & Ancient Golf Club St. And.; Med. Off. Birkdale Sch. for Hearing Impaired Childr.; Chairm. S.port & Formby Fundholders Assn.; Chief Med. Off. Roy. and Ancient Golf Club of St. Andrews. Socs: (Ex-Pres.) S.port Med. Soc. Prev: Rotat. Intern. New Hanover Memor. Hosp. Wilmington, N. Carolina; Cas. Off. Roy. Albert Edwd. Infirm. Wigan; SHO (O & G) Roy. Infirm. Perth.

RIGG, Jonathan David 2 St Ann's Road N., Cheadle SK8 3SE — MB ChB 1985 Leic.

RIGG, Kathleen Jessie (retired) 14 Sherlock Close, Cambridge CB3 0HW — MB BS 1947 Lond.; MRCPath 1964; DCP Lond. 1956. Prev: Cons. Haemat. Salford AHA (T).

RIGG, Mr Keith Malcolm Nottingham City Hospital NHS Trust, Hucknall Road, Nottingham NG5 1PB Tel: 0115 969 1169 Fax: 0115 962 7678 Email: krigg@ncht.trent.nhs.uk; 2 Cragmoor Road, Burton Joyce, Nottingham NG14 5AR Tel: 0115 911 7832 — MB BS 1981 Newc.; MD Newc. 1991; FRCS Eng. 1986. City Hosp. Nottm. & Cons. Gen. Surg.. Prev: 1st. Asst. & Hon. Sen. Regist. (Transpl.) Univ. Newc. u Tyne; Regist. (Surg.) N. Tees Gen. Hosp.; Clin. Research Fell. Univ. Newc.

RIGG, Kenneth Stephen 11 Wade Park Avenue, Market Deeping, Peterborough PE6 8JH — MB ChB 1982 Leic.; MRCGP 1986; DRCOG 1984.

RIGG, Mark 112 Garmoyle Road, Liverpool L15 5AD — MB ChB 1997 Liverp.

RIGG, Nancy Dunlop 3 The Meadows, Eaglesfield, Lockerbie DG11 3PH — MB ChB 1981 Ed.; 1999 (Diploma Primary Care Rheumat. Soc.) Bath; BSc (Med. Sci.) Ed. 1978, MB ChB 1981. Staff Grade in Haemat. & Clin. Oncol., Dumfries & Galloway Roayl Infirm., Dumfries. Prev: Cas. Off. Cumbld. Infirm. Carlisle.; Clin. Asst. (Rheum.) Cumbld. Infirm. Carlisle; Clin. Med. Off. Family Plann., N.bank Dumfries.

RIGG, Philip Prospect Road Surgery, 174 Prospect Road, Scarborough YO12 7LB Tel: 01723 360178 — MB ChB 1975 Sheff.; FFA RCS Eng. 1980; DRCOG 1977; MRCGP 1997.

RIGG, Rita Charlotte The Hermitages Medical Practice, 5 Hermitage Terrace, Edinburgh EH10 4RP Tel: 0131 447 6277 Fax: 0131 447 9866; 30 Morningside Place, Edinburgh EH10 5EY — MB BCh BAO 1973 Dub.; MRCGP 1996. (Trinity Coll. Dub.) Princip.; Dip. Family Med. Chinese Univ. Hong Kong 1991. Socs: BMA & Assoc. Mem. Hong Kong Coll. Gen. Practs.; Roy. Coll. Gen. Pract. Prev: Med. Off. United States Consulate Bombay, India; Assoc. GP, Hong Kong.

RIGGS, Mary Alexandra Surgery, 2 Wellington Avenue, Aldershot GU11 1SD Tel: 01252 332210 Fax: 01252 312490; April Cottage, Portesbery Road, Camberley GU15 3TF Tel: 01276 21075 — BM BCh 1973 Oxf.; DCH Eng. 1976.

RIGLER, Malcolm Stuart Withymoor Village Surgery, Turners Lane, Brierley Hill DY5 2PG Tel: 01384 573670 — MB ChB 1971 Bristol; DObst RCOG 1973. Socs: Social Hist. Medico Social Soc. Prev: Regist. Community Med. S. W.. RHA.

RIGNEY, Anne Theresa Roysia Surgery, Burns Road, Royston SG8 5PT Tel: 01763 243166 Fax: 01763 245315; 7 Valley Rise, Royston SG8 9EY Tel: 01763 242686 — LRCPI & LM, LRSCI & LM 1972; LRCPI & LM, LRCSI & LM 1972; DRCOG 1977; DCH RCPSI 1975. (RCSI) Prev: Ho. Off. (Paediat.) Whipps Cross Hosp. Lond.; SHO (Med.) Jervis St. Hosp. Dub.; Ho. Off. (Obst.) Mother's Hosp. Lond.

RIHAN, Mr Robert Stanley (retired) Foxgloves, Foscot, Chipping Norton OX7 6RP Tel: 01608 658280 — MB ChB Birm. 1951; FRCS Eng. 1959; MRCS Eng. LRCP Lond. 1951. Prev: Cons. Surg. N. Birm. Dist. Hosp. Gp.

RIISNAES, Annette May Silverdale Drive Health Centre, 6 Silverdale Drive, Thurmaston, Leicester LE4 8NN — MB ChB 1979 Bristol; DRCOG 1985. (Bristol) Gen. Practitioner, Thurmaston, Leicester. Prev: GP Bedford.; Trainee GP Mansfield VTS.

RIKH, India 18 Forum Way, Sleaford NG34 7FF — MB BS 1972 Bangalor; BA Mysore 1964; MB BS Bangalore 1972; MRCPsych 1979; DPM Eng. 1977. (Bangalore)

RILEY, Adrian Patrick Queens Road Surgery, 8 Queens Road, Portsmouth PO2 7NX — MB ChB 1967 Birm.; DA Eng. 1972; DObst RCOG 1969.

RILEY, Professor Alan John, OStJ Lancs. Postgrad. School of Medicine and Health University of Central Lancs., Harrington Building, Preston PR1 2HE Tel: 01772 892791 Fax: 01772 892992 Email: a.j.riley2@uclan.ac.uk; 41 Maritime Way, Riversway Docklands, Preston PR2 2HT Tel: 01772 731500 Email: alanriley@doctors.org.uk — MB BS 1967 Lond.; MSc Manch. 1976; MRCS Eng. LRCP Lond. 1967; FFPM RCP (UK) 1992, M 1989; DObst RCOG 1969. (Char. Cross) Prof. of Sexual Med., Univ. of Centr. Lancs.; Cons. Pharmaceut. Med. Preston; Med. Edr. Sexual & Marital Ther. Socs: Fell. Roy. Soc. Med.; Assn. for Marital & Sexual Therapists; BMA. Prev: Edr. Brit. Jl. Sexual Med. & Jl. Sexual Health; Head New Chem. Entities Glaxo Gp. Research.

RILEY, Andrew Habergham 3 Brynteg, Beaumaris LL58 8HF; The Health Centre, New St, Beaumaris LL58 — MB ChB 1980 Liverp.; MRCGP 1986; DRCOG 1985. Prev: GP Trainee Bangor Gwynedd VTS; Ho. Phys. Halifax Gen. Hosp.

RILEY, Annette Department of Pathology, Stirling Royal Infirmary, Livilands, Stirling FK8 2AU Tel: 01786 434000 Fax: 01786 449233 — MB ChB 1985 Glas.; 2001 (DFMS) Glasgow; BSc (Hons.) Glas. 1982, MB ChB 1985; FRCPath 2000. Cons. (Path.) Stirling Roy. Infirm. Stirling. Socs: Assn. Clin. Path.; Internat. Acad. of Pathol.; Brit. Soc. for Clin. Cytol. Prev: Sen. Regist. (Path.) & Hon. Lect. W. Infirm. Glas.; Regist. (Path.) W.. Infirm. Glas.

RILEY, Anthony John Bellevue Surgery, Bellevue Terrace, Newport NP20 2WQ Tel: 01633 256337 Fax: 01633 222856 — MB BCh 1992 Wales; DCH 1996; MRCGP 1999. (Cardiff) GP Princip.

RILEY, Bernard, MBE Adult Intensive Care Unit, Queen's Medical Centre, University Hospital, Nottingham NG7 2UH Tel: 0115 924 9924 Fax: 0115 970 9910; The Corner House, 32 Browns Lane, E. Bridgford, Nottingham NG13 8PL — MB BS 1978 Lond.; BSc Lond. 1975; MRCS Eng. LRCP Lond. 1978; FFA RCS Eng. 1982. (St. Geo.) Cons. Anaesth. & Adult Intens. Care Qu. Med. Centre Univ. Hosp. NHS Trust Nottm. Prev: Cons. Anaesth. & Intens. Care Char. Cross & W.m. Hosp. Lond.; Sen. Regist. (Anaesth. & Intens. Care) Roy. Surrey Co. Hosp. Guildford.

RILEY, Christine Elizabeth Torrington Speedwell Practice, Health Centre, Torrington Park, London N12 9SS Tel: 020 8445 7261 Fax: 020 8343 9122; 2 The Grange, Grange Avenue, Totteridge, London N20 8AB Tel: 020 8445 5687 — MB BS Lond. 1960; MRCS Eng. LRCP Lond. 1960. (Univ. Coll. Hosp.) Socs: Roy. Soc. Med.; Brit. Med. Acupunct. Soc. Prev: Ho. Surg. New End Hosp. Hampstead; Ho. Phys. S. Lond. Hosp.

RILEY, Christopher John (retired) 4 Riverside Close, Halton on Lune, Lancaster LA2 6NA Tel: 01524 811513 Email: chris@halton80.freeserve.co.uk — MB ChB Manch. 1959; MRCP Lond. 1967; MRCP Glas. 1966; DObst RCOG 1961. Prev: GP Lancaster.

RILEY, Colin Christopher (retired) The Health Centre, Aylesbury Road, Wendover, Aylesbury HP22 6LD Tel: 01296 623452 — MB BS Lond. 1953; MRCGP 1966; DObst RCOG 1954. Prev: Ho. Surg. (Obst.) Univ. Coll. Hosp. Lond.

RILEY, Damian James 99 Harboro Road, Sale M33 6GH — MB ChB 1987 Manch.

RILEY, Mr David Orthopaedic Department, Pontefract General Infirmary, Pontefract WF8 1PL Tel: 01977 606469 Fax: 01977 606723 — MB ChB 1977 Leeds; FRCS Ed. 1982; FRCS Eng. 1982. (Leeds) Cons. Orthop. Surg. Pontefract Gen. Infirm. Socs: Fell. BOA; Brit. Soc. Childr. Orthop. Surg. Prev: Regist. (Orthop.) King's Coll. Hosp. Lond.; Ho. Surg. Chapel Allerton Hosp. Leeds; Ho. Phys. Leeds Gen. Infirm.

RILEY, David John Church Street Surgery, Church Street, Spalding PE11 2PB Tel: 01775 722189 Fax: 01775 712164; 6 Amsterdam Gardens, Spalding PE11 3HY — MB ChB 1978 Liverp.; DRCOG 1983. Prev: SHO (Med./Geriat., Paediat. & O & G) Whiston & St. Helen's; Hosps. Merseyside.

RILEY, Deborah Anne Grovelands Medical Centre, 701 Oxford Road, Reading RG30 1HG Tel: 0118 958 2525 Fax: 0118 950 9284 — BM BCh 1988 Oxf.; MA Camb. 1989; MRCGP 1996. Prev: Trainee GP Reading VTS.

RILEY, Diana Margaret The Red House, Wendover, Aylesbury HP22 6JQ Tel: 01296 622477 Fax: 01296 624727 Email: dmriley@cwcom.net; The Red House, Wendover, Aylesbury HP22 6JQ Tel: 01296 622477 Fax: 01296 624727 Email: dmriley@cwcom.net — MB BS 1953 Lond.; MRCS Eng. LRCP Lond. 1953; FRCPsych 1988, M 1974; DPM Eng. 1974. (Univ. Coll. Hosp.) p/t Indep. Cons. Chiltern Hosp. Gt. Missenden, Bucks. & Portland Hosp. Lond.; Trustee Bucks. Assn. for Ment. Health. Socs: Marcé Soc.; Roy. Soc. Med.; ISPOG. Prev: Sen. Regist. (Psychiat.) St. John's Hosp. Stone; Civil Med. Pract. RAF Halton; Ho. Phys. & Ho. Surg. Univ. Coll. Hosp. Lond.

RILEY, Donald Owen (retired) 44 Moat Road, Loughborough LE11 3PN Tel: 01509 266300 Email: don@doriley.demon.co.uk — MB ChB Sheff. 1959; MRCGP 1982; DObst RCOG 1962; DA Eng. 1962.

RILEY

RILEY, Esther Turner (retired) 118 Whitecrest, Great Barr, Birmingham B43 6EN Tel: 0121 357 5608 — MB ChB 1941 Ed.

RILEY, Gaynor Ann Caldbergh Cottage, Caldbergh, Middleham, Leyburn DL8 4RW — MB ChB 1990 Liverp.

RILEY, Genevieved Hannah Mary 135 Pasley Street, Plymouth PL2 1DT — MB ChB 1998 Liverp.; MB ChB Liverp 1998.

RILEY, Gillian A Girlington Road Surgery, 252 Girlington Road, Bradford BD8 9PB Tel: 01274 491448/9 Fax: 01274 483362; 10 Salisbury Avenue, Baildon, Shipley BD17 5AA — MB ChB 1973 Leeds; MRCGP 1977; DObst RCOG 1976.

RILEY, Jane Maria Flat 2, Straysyde House, Cavendish Avenue, Harrogate HG2 8HX — BM BS 1990 Nottm. Trainee GP/SHO W. Cumbld. Hosp. VTS.

RILEY, Janet Priscilla Mary Rowley Medical Practice, 65 Hawes Lane, Rowley Regis B65 9AJ Tel: 0121 559 2449 Fax: 0121 559 8579; 132 Barrs Road, Cradley Heath, Cradley Heath B64 7EZ Tel: 01384 560701 Email: jan@owdill.demon.co.uk — MB ChB Leeds 1966; DCH Eng. 1968. (Leeds) Hon. Med. Adviser City of Birm. Symphony Orchestra. Prev: Ho. Phys. (Paediat.) Selly Oak Hosp. Birm.; Ho. Phys. Med. Unit St. Mary's Hosp. Lond.; Ho. Surg. King Edwd. Memor. Hosp. Ealing.

RILEY, John Ernest The Old School Medical Centre, Horseman Lane, Copmanthorpe, York YO23 3UA; 16 Aintree Court, York YO24 1EW — MB ChB 1972 Leeds; MRCGP 1977; DObst RCOG 1974.

RILEY, John Lawson (retired) 4 Farnham Close, Baildon, Shipley BD17 6SF Tel: 01274 590080 — MB ChB 1954 Ed. Prev: Ho. Surg. St. Luke's Hosp. Bradford & Huddersfield Roy. Infirm.

RILEY, Kate Health Centre, Victoria Sq, Portishead, Bristol BS20 6AQ Tel: 01275 847474 Fax: 01275 817516; Email: kmj@cncom.net — BM 1981 Soton.

RILEY, Katharine Julia 8 Snab Wood Close, Little Neston, South Wirral CH64 0UP — MB ChB 1986 Manch.; MRCP (UK) 1990; MRCGP 1991.

RILEY, Katharine Julie Northwick Park Hospital, Watford Road, Harrow HA1 3UJ; 29 Talbot Road, Rickmansworth WD3 1HD — MB BS 1994 Lond.; MRCP UK 1997.

RILEY, Kevin Paul The Surgery, 4-6 High Street, kinver, Stourbridge DY7 6HG Tel: 01384 873311 Fax: 01384 877328 — MB BCh 1981 Wales.

RILEY, Lindsay Michael Garden Lane Medical Centre, 19 Garden Lane, Chester CH1 4EN Tel: 01244 346677 Fax: 01244 310094 — MB ChB 1976 Manch.; BSc (Med. Sci.) St. And. 1974.

RILEY, Louise 99 Harboro Road, Sale M33 6GH — MB ChB 1987 Manch.

RILEY, Lynne Catherine Flat 3, 5 Milton Avenue, London N6 5QF — MB BS 1992 Lond.

RILEY, Marshall Seth 20 Tullyhubbert Road, Moneyrea, Newtownards BT23 6BY — MB BCh BAO 1983 Belf.; BSc Belf. 1980, MD 1990; MRCP (UK) 1986.

RILEY, Martin 55 Borfa Green, Welshpool SY21 7QF — MB BCh 1971 Wales; BSc (Hons. Physiol.) Wales 1971, MB BCh (Hons.) 1974; MRCP (U.K.) 1976; DRCOG 1977.

RILEY, Neville Paul Sycamores, The Street, All Cannings, Devizes SN10 3PA — MB BS 1977 Newc.

RILEY, Pamela Margaret 5 Hoghton Close, Lancaster LA1 5UF; 2 South Barn, Burrow Rd, Lancaster LA1 0PG Tel: 01524 752355 — MB ChB 1994 Manch.; DFFP 1997. LOCUM GP; SHO Dermat. Qu Vict Hosp. Morecambe.

RILEY, Professor Patrick Anthony (retired) Gray Cancer Institute, Mount Vernon Hospital, Box 100, Northwood HA6 2RJ — MB BS Lond. 1960; PhD Lond. 1965, DSc 1990; FRCPath. 1985, M 1980. Edito, Melanoma Research, (Publ. by LWM,Lond.). Prev: Reader (Cell Path.) Univ. Coll. Sch. Med. Lond.

RILEY, Paul Adrian Fraser Le Pommier, La Rue Des Bordes, St Peter Port, Guernsey GY7 9PX Tel: 01481 65505 — MB ChB 1972 Dundee; FRCP Lond. 1994; DRCOG 1978. Phys. P.ss Eliz. Hosp. Guernsey.

RILEY, Paul Brook Rambleside, 94 Kingsway, Scunthorpe DN15 7ER Tel: 01724 840089 — MB BS 1942 Lond.; MRCS Eng. LRCP Lond. 1939. (St. Thos.) Prev: Ho. Phys. Roy. Hosp. Bristol; Regist. Bristol Matern. Hosp.; Capt. RAMC.

RILEY, Mr Peter Latham House Medical Practice, Sage Cross Street, Melton Mowbray LE13 1NX Tel: 01664 854949 Fax: 01664 501825 — MB ChB 1973 Manch.; FRCS Glas. 1987; MRCOG 1980; DA (SA) 1984; DObst RCOG 1975. Hosp. Pract. (Gen. & Plastic Surg.) War Memor. Hosp., Melton Mowbray. Prev: Trainee GP Measham Med. Unit Burton on Trent; Regist. (Plastic Surg.) Harare, Zimbabwe.

RILEY, Peter Andrew 94 Kingsway, Scunthorpe DN15 7ER — MB BS 1986 Lond.; MD Lond. 1993; MRCPath 1993. Lect. (Med. Microbiol.) Univ. Malaya Kuala Lumpur, Malaysia. Prev: Lect. (Med. Microbiol.) UMDS Lond.; Asst. Lect. (Path.) UMDS Guy's & St. Thos. Hosps. Lond.; Ho. Surg. (Orthop. & Gen. Surg.) St. Thos. Hosp. Lond.

RILEY, Peter David Shotley Bridge General Hospital, Shotley Bridge, Consett DH8 9TE — MB BS 1976 Newc.

RILEY, Peter Frederick Blagbrough (retired) Strawberry Farmhouse, Up Somborne, Stockbridge SO20 6RB Tel: 01794 388078 — MRCS Eng. LRCP Lond. 1949. Prev: Ho. Phys. & Ho. Surg. Lond. Hosp.

RILEY, Peter John The Hunting Clinic, 55 St Lukes Road, Maidenhead SL6 7DN Tel: 01628 622261 — MB BS Lond. 1968. (Middlx.) Med. Dir. Maidenhead Inst. Rotterdam, Holland; Med. Dir. Hunting Clinic Maidenhead.

RILEY, Peter Leslie Department of Radiology, University Hospital Birmingham, NHS Trust, Queen Elizabeth Hospital, Edgbaston, Birmingham B15 2TH Tel: 0121 472 1311; Email: peter.riley@university-b.nhs.uk — MB ChB 1984 Liverp.; MRCP (UK) 1991; FRCR 1998. Cons. Radiol. Qu. Eliz. Hosp. Univ. Hosp. Birm. NHS Trust Metchley Pk. Rd., Edgbaston.B15 2TH.

RILEY, Philip James Group Practise Centre, Bowring Road, Ramsey Tel: 01624 813881; Lytchett, Mount Auldyn, Ramsey IM8 3PJ — MB ChB 1984 Manch.; MRCGP 1988; DRCOG 1987.

RILEY, Raymond Eric 11 Tixover Park, Stamford PE9 3QN Tel: 01780 444454 — MB ChB Leeds 1944. (Leeds)

RILEY, Robert Michael Haverthwaite Surgery, Backbarrow, Ulverston LA12 8QF Tel: 01448 31619 — MB ChB 1961 Leeds; BSc (Physiol.) Leeds 1957. (Leeds) Socs: BMA.

RILEY, Sara Jane Gosbury Hill Health Centre, Orchard Gardens, Chessington KT9 1AG Tel: 020 8397 7019 — MB BS 1986 Lond.; DRCOG 1991. Prev: Trainee GP Brighton.

RILEY, Stephanie Elisabeth Glan-y-Mor, Manorbier, Tenby SA70 7TE — MB ChB 1988 Bristol.

RILEY, Stephen George 29 Wrens Avenue, Tipton DY4 8AF — MB BCh 1993 Wales; MRCP (UK) 1996. (Univ. Wales Coll. Med.) Regist. (Renal & Med.) Wrexham Maelor Hosp. Prev: SHO (Neurol.) Univ. Hosp. Wales Cardiff.

RILEY, Stephen Peter John Ryle Health Centre, Southchurch Drive, Clifton, Nottingham NG11 8EW Tel: 0115 921 2970 — BM BS 1983 Nottm.

RILEY, Steven Frederick Surrey Lodge Group Practice, 11 Anson Road, Victoria Park, Manchester M14 5BY Tel: 0161 224 2471 Fax: 0161 257 2264 — MB BS 1974 Lond.; MRCOG 1980. (Univ. Coll. Hosp.)

RILEY, Stuart Anthony 24 Sefton Road, Sheffield S10 3TP — MB ChB 1979 Leeds; FRCP 1996; MRCP (UK) 1983. Cons. Phys. & Gastroenterol. N. Gen. Hosp. Sheff.

RILEY, Susan Jennifer Hurst Farm Surgery, Chapel Lane, Milford, Godalming GU8 6HU Tel: 01483 415885 Fax: 01483 42006; 83 The Street, Puttenham, Guildford GU3 1AT — MB BS 1980 Lond.; DRCOG 1984. (Middlx.)

RILEY, Mr Timothy Brian Hugh Bedford Hospital NHS Trust, Kempston Road, Bedford MK42 9DJ Tel: 01234 792203 — MB BChir 1963 Camb.; BChir 1962; FRCS Eng. 1972; MRCS Eng. LRCP Lond. 1963. (Westm.) Cons. Surg. (Orthop. & Trauma) Bedford Hosp. NHS Trust. Prev: Sen. Regist. (Orthop.) S. Glam. AHA (T); Regist. (Orthop) & Ho. Surg. W.m. Hosp. Lond.

RILEY, Unell Barrington George 155 Shakespeare Road, Herne Hill, London SE24 0PY — MB BS 1986 Lond.

RILEY, Vincent Charles 3 Meadow Road, Woodhouse Eaves, Loughborough LE12 8SA — MB ChB 1970 Birm.; MRCGP 1981; Dip Ven Soc. Apoth, Lond. 1976; DTM & H Liverp. 1972. (Birm.) Cons. Genitourin. Med. Leics. AHA (T). Prev: Med. Off. (Gen. Duties) Govt. Seychelles; Sen. Regist. (Venereol.) Nottm. Gen. Hosp.; Med. Off. (Gen. Duties) Govt. St. Lucia.

RILEY, Walter Riddell (retired) The Old Rectory, Chapel Lane, Holcombe, Bury BL8 4NB Tel: 01706 822350 — MB ChB Manch. 1948; MRCS Eng. LRCP Lond. 1948. Prev: Ho. Phys. & Ho. Surg. Crumpsall Hosp. Manch.

RILSTONE, Francis William Borlase Barnhall Cottage, 40 High St., Stock, Ingatestone CM4 9BW Tel: 01277 840370 — MRCS Eng. LRCP Lond. 1939. (Guy's) JP. Prev: Surg. EMS S. Middlx. Fev. Hosp.; Out-pat. Off. Guy's Hosp.; ENT Ho. Surg. Kent Co. Ophth. & Aural Hosp. Maidstone.

RIMELL, Phillip John Steep Holm, Bronwydd Road, Carmarthen SA31 2A — MB BCh 1971 Wales; FFA RCS Eng. 1975. Cons. (Anaesth.) W. Wales Gen. Hosp. Carmarthen. Socs: Assn. Anaesth. Gt. Brit. & Irel. & Hosp. Cons. & Specialists Assn. Prev: Capt. RAMC (V); Sen. Regist. (Anaesth.) Univ. Hosp. Wales Cardiff; Clin. Fell. (Anaesth.) McGill Univ. Roy. Vict. Hosp. Montreal.

RIMINGTON, Jane Elizabeth 81 Leylands Lane, Bradford BD9 5PZ Tel: 01274 770771 — MB ChB 1984; MRCP 1989; 1997 (Dip. Family Medicine) Melbourne; DRCOG 1987. (Leeds) GP, Bradford. Socs: Roy. Coll. of GPs.

RIMINGTON, John 3 Ballakeyll, Colby, Castletown IM9 4AY Tel: 01624 834937 — MB ChB Manch. 1947; MD Manch. 1968; MFCH 1991. (Lond.) Socs: Assoc. Mem. Soc. Pub. Health; BMA & I. of Man Med. Soc.; Fell. Roy. Soc. Pub. Health and Hyg. Prev: Cons. Chest. Phys. & Med. Dir. Gtr. Manch. Mobile Chest X-Ray Serv. St. Thos. Hosp. Stockport; Regist. (Chest Dis.) Stockport, Macclesfield & Buxton Hosp. Gp.

RIMINGTON, Michael Robert 6 The Crescent, Basingstoke District Hospital, Aldermaston Road, Basingstoke RG24 9NA; 13 St Marys Lane, Speldhurst, Tunbridge Wells TN3 0PR — MB BS 1985 Lond.

RIMMER, Alison Sheffield Occupational Health Service, Northern General Hospital, Herries Road, Sheffield S5 7AU Tel: 0114 271 4161 Fax: 0114 244 4470; 10 Belgrave Road, Ranmoor, Sheffield S10 3LN — MB BCh 1978 Wales; FRCP Lond. 1994; FFOM RCP Lond. 1994, MFOM 1987. Cons. Occupat. Phys. & Dir. Occupat. Health Serv. Sheff. Occupat. Health Serv. N. Gen. Hosp. NHS Trust; Hon. Sen. Lect. (Pub. Health Med.) Univ. Sheff. Socs: (Sec.) Assn. of NHS Occupat. Phys.; Soc. Occupat. Med. Prev: Area Med. Off. Brit. Coal Corp.

RIMMER, Alison Jane 19 Great Burnet Close, St. Mellons, Cardiff CF3 0RJ — BM 1992 Soton.; DRCOG 1998.

RIMMER, Anthony Francis George Dapdune House Surgery, Wharf Road, Guildford GU1 4RP Tel: 01483 573336 Fax: 01483 306602 — MB ChB 1979 Liverp.; DRCOG 1984; DA Eng. 1981.

RIMMER, Anthony Joseph Bewsey Street Medical Centre, 40-42 Bewsey Street, Warrington WA2 7JE Tel: 01925 635837 Fax: 01925 630353 — MB ChB 1984 Leeds; MRCGP 1988; DGM RCP Lond. 1987. Socs: BMA. Prev: Trainee GP Grimsby VTS; Ho. Off. (Gen. Med. & Cardiol.) Leeds Gen. Infirm; Ho. Off. (Gen. Surg. & Orthop.) Pinderfields Gen. Hosp. Wakefield.

RIMMER, Brenda Kathleen c/o Barclays Bank, Smithfield Branch, 89 Charterhouse St., London EC1M 6HR — MB BS 1953 Lond.; DPH Eng. 1957, DA 1958. (St. Bart.)

RIMMER, Caroline Jeanie Fairfax House, 8 Montserrat Road, Putney, London SW15 2LA — MB ChB 1993 Liverp.

RIMMER, Caroline Susan Department of Genitourinary Medicine, Royal Infirmary, Edinburgh EH3 9YW Tel: 0131 536 1000; Woodhall Lodge, 162 Woodhall Road, Colinton, Edinburgh EH13 0PJ Tel: 0131 441 5044 — MB BS 1987 Lond.; BSc Lond. 1984; Cert. Family Plann. JCC 1990. Clin. Asst. (Genitourin.) Roy. Infirm. Edin. Prev: SHO (Genitourin. Med.) Roy. Infirm. Edin.; SHO (Family Plann. & Wom. Health) Lothian HB; SHO (Communicable Dis.) St. Geo. Hosp. Lond.

RIMMER, Catherine Sarah 84 Nether Edge Road, Sheffield S7 1RX — MB ChB 1998 Sheff.; MB ChB Sheff 1998.

RIMMER, Corinne Jayne 2 Elm Cottage, South Marston, Swindon SN3 4SR — MB BS 1993 Lond.

RIMMER, David Bernard Department of Pathology, Bedford Hospital, Kempston Road, Bedford MK42 9DJ Tel: 01234 792162 Fax: 01234 792161; 22 Biddenham Turn, Bedford MK40 4AZ — BM BCh 1970 Oxf.; MA Oxf. 1976; MRCS Eng. LRCP Lond. 1970; FRCPath 1988, M 1976. Cons. Histopath. Bedford Hosp. Prev: Lect. (Path.) Univ. Bristol Med. Sch.; Lect. (Histopath.) St. Bart. Hosp. Med. Coll. Lond.; SHO (Path.) N.wick Pk. Hosp. Harrow.

RIMMER, David Richard John Elliot Unit, Birch Hill Hospital, Rochdale; Lower Walls Farm, Wallsclough, Lumb, Rossendale BB4 9NE — BM BS 1985 Nottm.; BMedSci (Hons.) Nottm. 1985; MRCPsych 1993. Assoc. Specialist (Psychiat.) Birch Hill Hosp. Rochdale. Prev: Assoc. Specialist (Psychiat.) Bolton Gen. Hosp.

RIMMER, Diana Mary Duckworth 75 Creffield Road, London W3 9PS Tel: 020 8992 8857 — MB BS 1965 Lond.; FRCPath 1984, M 1972. (St. Thos.) Cons. Microbiol. Hillingdon Hosp. Uxbridge. Prev: Lect. Dept. Clin. Microbiol. Louis Jenner Laborat. St. Thos. Hosp.; Lond.

RIMMER, Elizabeth Mary Argyll and Clyde Health Board, Ross House, Hawkhead Road, Paisley PA2 7BN Tel: 0141 842 7327 Fax: 0141 848 0165; 18 Craigmillar Avenue, Milngavie, Glasgow G62 8AX Tel: 0141 956 4626 — MB ChB 1977 Liverp.; MD Liverp. 1987; FRCP Glas. 1996; MRCP (UK) 1979; MRCGP 1990. (Liverp.) Med. Prescribing Adviser Argyll & Clyde HB. Prev: Research. Fell. (Clin. Pharmacol.) Univ. Wales Coll. Med. Cardiff; Sen. Regist. (Clin. Pharmacol. & Gen. Med.) Univ. Hosp. Wales Cardiff.

RIMMER, Mr Martin Gerard 3 Woodford Road, Windle, St Helens WA10 6JA — MB BS 1983 Lond.; BSc (Hons.) Lond. 1980, MB BS 1983; FRCS Ed. 1989; DRCOG 1995. (Middlx.) GP Princip. Garden City Pract. Welwyn Garden City. Prev: SHO Rotat. (Surg.) Plymouth HA; Cas. Surg. Off. Middlx. Hosp. Lond.; Ho. Surg. Middlx. Hosp. Lond.

RIMMER, Martin Joseph 45 Goodwins Road, King's Lynn PE30 5QX Tel: 01553 775022 — MB 1977 Camb.; BChir 1976; MRCP (UK) 1979; FRCR 1983. Cons. (Radiol.) Qu. Eliz. Hosp. Kings Lynn. Prev: Sen. Regist. (Radiol.) Addenbrookes Hosp. Camb.

RIMMER, Maurus Euan Winterdyne, Flowers Hill, Pangbourne, Reading RG8 7BD Tel: 0118 984 4926 Fax: 0118 987 7067 Email: maurus.rimmer@hospital-doctor.net — MB BS Lond. 1965; MRCS Eng. LRCP Lond. 1965; FFA RCS Eng. 1974; DObst RCOG 1971. (St. Bart.) Cons. Anaesth. Roy. Berks. & Battle Hosps. NH Trust. Socs: BMA; Assn. Anaesth.; Soc. Computing & Technol. in Anaesth. Prev: Sen. Regist. (Anaesth.) Soton. Univ. Hosps.; Clin. Research Fell. Hosp. Sick Childr. Toronto, Canada; Regist. Rotat. (Anaesth.) W.m. Hosp. & Qu. Vict. Hosp. E. Grinstead.

RIMMER, Michael Alan 1 Pine Grove, Waterloo, Liverpool L22 2AQ — MB ChB 1997 Liverp.

RIMMER, Roger Osborne (retired) 75 Charlemont Avenue, West Bromwich B71 3BZ — MB ChB Birm. 1955. Prev: Ho. Phys. Ho. Surg. & O & G Ho. Surg. Hallam Hosp. W.

RIMMER, Stephen Flat 22/1, The Grassmarket, Edinburgh EH1 2HY — MB BS 1990 Sydney.

RIMMER, Sylvia Brownlands, Pleasington, Blackburn BB1 — MB ChB 1967 Manch.; FFR 1974; DMRD Liverp. 1971. Sen. Regist. Radiol. Manch. Roy. Infirm. Prev: SHO (Med.) Mossley Hill Hosp. Liverp. RHB; SHO (Radiol.) United Liverp. Hosps.; Regist. Radiol. BRd. Green Hosp. Liverp.

RIMMER, Mr Timothy John Eye Department, Peterborough District Hospital, Thorpe Road, Peterborough PE3 6DA Tel: 01733 874018 Fax: 01733 875281; 64 High Street, St. Martins, Stamford PE9 2LA Tel: 01780 756611 Email: timothy.rimmer@talk21.com — MB ChB 1979 Liverp.; PhD N. West. Univ. Evanston, Ill., USA 1991; FRCS Ed. 1987; FRCOphth 1989. (Liverp.) Cons. Ophth. P'boro. Dist. Hosp. Prev: Sen. Regist. (Ophth.) Leicester Roy. Infirm.; Research Assoc. Biomed. Engineer. Dept. N.W.. Univ. Illinois, USA; Sen. Regist. St. John Ophth. Hosp. Jerusalem.

RIMMER, Trevor William East cheshire NHS Trust, Macclesfield DGH, Victoria Rd, Macclesfield SK10 3BL Tel: 01625 663177 Fax: 01625 663177 Email: trevor.rimmer@echeshire-tr.nwest.nhs.co.uk — MB BCh 1979 Wales; MRCP (UK) 1983; DRCOG 1986; FRCP Ed. 1998. (Welsh National School Medicine) Macmillan Cons. In Pall. Med., E. Chesh. NHS Trust; Med. Dir. E. Chesh. Hospice. Socs: Assn. Palliat. Med.; BMA; Roy. Soc. Med. Prev: Cons. Palliat. Med. St. Catherine's Hospice ScarBoro.; Sen. Regist (Palliat Med) Michael Sobell Hse & Mt. Vernon Hosp. Middx; GP Seven Sisters, W. Glam.

RIMMER, Yvonne Louise 14a Birckbeck Avenue, London W3 6HX — MB BS 1996 Lond.

RINALDI, Christopher Aldo Cardiology Department, Medway Hospital, Gillingham ME7 5NY; 27 Smiths Road, Birchgrove, Swansea SA7 9DY — MB BS 1990 Lond.; MRCP (UK) 1993. (King's Coll. Hosp. Med. & Dent. Sch.) Specialist Regist. (Cardiol.) Guy's &

RINCON AZNAR

St. Thos. Healthcare Trust. Prev: Research Fell. (Cardiol.) Roy. Postgrad. Med. Sch.

RINCON AZNAR, Cristobal Department of Anaesthesia, West Wales General Hospital, Carmarthen SA31 2AF — LMS 1983 Valencia.

RING, Alistair Edward 50 Thorn Park, Mannamead, Plymouth PL3 4TF Tel: 01752 250765 — BM BCh 1997 Oxf.; MA (Hons.) Cantab. 1994. (Oxf. Clin. Sch.) SHO, Med, Roal Postgrad. Med. Sch., Hammersmith Hosp.; Ho. Off. (Surg.) Roy. United Hosp. Bath. Prev: SHO, (Med) Roy. Brompton Hosp.; Hse. Off. (Med.) Oxf. John Radcliffe Hosp.

RING, Helen Patricia (retired) Senacre Wood Surgery, Reculver Walk, Senacre, Maidstone ME15 8SW Tel: 01622 761963 — MB BCh BAO 1969 Dub.; DObst RCOG 1971; DCH Eng. 1972. Prev: Trainee Gen. Pract. King's Lynn Vocational Train. Scheme.

RING, Howard Anton Academic Department of Psychiatry, Barts and the London school of Medicine, Basic Medical science building, Mile end Road, London E1 4NS Tel: 020 78827550 Fax: 020 78827551 Email: h.a.ring@qmul.ac.uk — MB BS 1984 Lond.; BSc Lond. 1981, MD 1994; MRCPsych 1989. Sen. Lect. (Psychiat.) Barts and the Lond. Sch. of Med.; Hon. Cons. Psychiat. Roy. Lond. Hosp.; Hon. Sen. Lect. (Neuropsychiat.) Inst. Neurol. Lond. Socs: Hon. Sec. Assn. Univ. Teachs. of Psychiat.; Chairm.. Roy. Coll. of Psychiat.s, s/i grp in neuropsy chiatry. Prev: Sen. Regist. (Psychiat.) Maudsley Hosp. Lond.

RING, Jonathan Paul George High Street Surgery, High Street, Pewsey SN9 5AQ Tel: 01672 563511 Fax: 01672 563004; The Dairy House, Easton Royal, Pewsey SN9 5LZ Tel: 01672 810134 — MB ChB 1987 Bristol; BSc (Hons.) Bristol 1984; MRCGP 1991; DRCOG 1990. Prev: Trainee GP N. Wilts. VTS.

RING, Kathleen Patricia The Crescent Surgery, 38 Marion Crescent, St Mary Cray, Orpington BR5 2DD Tel: 01689 818696; 1 Greenwood Close, Petts Wood, Orpington BR5 1QG Tel: 01689 601015 — MB BS 1978 Lond.; MRCGP 1984. (Lond. Hosp. Med. Coll.) GP Tutor FarnBoro. Postgrad. Centre. Prev: Trainee GP Epsom Dist. Hosp. VTS.

RING, Nicholas John Department of Diagnostic Radiology, Derriford Hospital, Plymouth PL6 8DH Tel: 01752 792701 Fax: 01752 792853; 8 Venn Court, Hartley, Plymouth PL3 5NS Tel: 01752 795463 — MB BS 1970 Lond.; MRCS Eng. LRCP Lond. 1970; FRCR 1979; DMRD Eng. 1978; DObst RCOG 1973. (St. Bart.) Cons. Radiol. Plymouth Hosps. NHS Trust. Prev: Sen. Regist. (Radiol.) Bristol Roy. Infirm.

RING, Nicholas Paul The Surgery, 58 Pembroke Road, Clifton, Bristol BS8 3DT Tel: 0117 974 1452 Fax: 0117 923 8040 — MB ChB 1982 Bristol.

RING, Noreen Mary 32 Hawthorn Lane, Wilmslow SK9 5DG — MB BCh BAO 1983 NUI.

RING, Mr Peter Alexander (cons. rooms), Gatwick Park Hospital, Povey Cross Road, Horley RH6 0BB Tel: 01293 785511; Eversfield, Denne Park, Horsham RH13 7AY Tel: 01403 257424 Fax: 01403 261998 — MRCS Eng. LRCP Lond. 1945; MS Lond. 1956, MB BS 1945; FRCS Eng. 1948. (Univ. Coll. Hosp.) Cons. Orthop. Surg. Gatwick Pk. Hosp. Socs: Fell. BOA; Fell. Roy. Soc. Med. Prev: Cons. Orthop. Surg. E. Surrey; Laming Evans Sen. Orthop. Research Fell. RCS Eng.; Regist. (Surg.) Roy. Nat. Orthop. Hosp. & Univ. Coll. Hosp.

RING, Stella Muriel (retired) Courtlands House, Courtlands Lane, Exmouth EX8 3NZ Tel: 01395 274288 Fax: 01395 274288 — MB BS 1946 Lond.; MRCS Eng. LRCP Lond. 1946; DCH Eng. 1949, DPM 1965. Prev: Assoc. Specialist in Child & Adolesc. Psychiat. Croydon Child & Family Clinic.

RING, Susan Jane Central Street Health Centre, Central Street, Countesthorpe, Leicester LE8 5QJ Tel: 0116 277 6336; Straw Hall, Peatling Parva, Lutterworth LE17 5QB Tel: 0116 277 6336 — MB ChB 1984 Leic.; MRCGP 1990; DRCOG 1988. GP Countesthorpe.

RINGER, Wilbur Steven 131 Woodmansterne Road, Carshalton Beeches, Carshalton SM5 4AF Tel: 020 8395 0318 Email: wsr@sprynet.co.uk — MB BCh 1968 Wales; MB BCh (Distinc. Anat., Physiol. & Pharmacol.) Wales 1968; BSc (Hons. Physiol.) Wales 1965; MRNZCGP 1986. Sen. Med. Adviser Benefits Agency Med. Servs. DSS for SE Eng. Prev: GP Ystad Mynach; GP Auckland, NZ; Industr. Phys. Alex Harvey's Industries, Auckland, NZ.

RINGLAND, Raymond Alexander 7A Moneylane Road, Dundrum, Newcastle BT33 0NR Tel: 013967 51348 Email: u01rar@doctors.org.uk — MB ChB 1997 Aberd.; MB ChB Aberd. 1997(with comm.). (Univ. of Aberdeen) SHO, Med., Downe Hosp., Downpatrick, Co.down. Prev: SHO Med. Oncol. Belf. City Hosp.; Jun. Ho. Off. Gen. Med. Aberd. Roy. Infirm.; Jun. Ho. Off. Gen. Surg. Aberd. Roy. Infirm.

RINGROSE, Caroline Suzanne 2 Boyce Street, Walkley, Sheffield S6 3JS — MB ChB 1998 Sheff.; MB ChB Sheff 1998.

RINGROSE, David Karl 45 Somerford Way, Rotherhithe, London SE16 6QN — MB BS 1988 Lond.; FRCA 1993; DA (UK) 1990. (UMDS Guy's Campus) Sen. Regist. (Anaesth.) Guy's Hosp. Lond. Prev: Regist. (Anaesth.) St. Thos. Hosp. Lond.; SHO (Anaesth.) Char. Cross Hosp. Lond.; SHO (Neonat. Intens. Care) St. Geo. Hosp. Lond.

RINGROSE, Dora Winifred (retired) The Dovecote, Clay Lane, Newbridge, Yarmouth, Isle of Wight PO41 0UA — MB BChir 1950 Camb.; BA Camb. 1947. Prev: Regist. (Path.) United Sheff. Hosps.

RINGROSE, Timothy Richard 32 Valley View, Jesmond, Newcastle upon Tyne NE2 2JS — MB BCh 1990 Wales.

RINSLER, Albert Henry (retired) 9 Kingsley Way, London N2 0EH Tel: 020 8455 8864 — MRCS Eng. LRCP Lond. 1947; MRCGP 1965; DHMSA 1990. Prev: Ho. Phys. Pneumoconiosis Research Unit, MRC Llandough Hosp. Penarth.

RINSLER, Michael Gerald Royal College of Pathologists, 2 Carlton House Terrace, London SW1Y 5AF; 49 Wellington Court, Wellington Road, London NW8 9TB — MB BChir 1950 Camb.; MD Camb. 1958, MA, MB BChir 1950; FRCPath 1970, M 1964. (Camb. & King's Coll. Hosp.) Dir. of Studies Roy. Coll. Path. Socs: Fell. Roy. Soc. Med. Prev: Cons. Chem. Pathol. N.wick Pk. Hosp.; Cons. Chem. Pathol. Chelsea & Kensington Gp. Hosps.; Research Asst. Sect. Radiobiol., Radiother. Dept, Roy. Marsden Hosp.

RINTALA, Risto Juhana Institute of Child Health, Alder Hey Children's Hospital, Eaton Road, West Derby, Liverpool L12 2AP — Lic Med 1975 Helsinki; Lic Med. Helsinki 1975.

RINTOUL, Mr Andrew Johnstone, Surg. Capt. RN Retd. (retired) 9 Clayhall Road, Alverstoke, Gosport PO12 2BB Tel: 01705 582387 — MB ChB Glas. 1956; FRCS Eng. 1968; FCOphth 1989; DO Eng. 1962. Hon. Cons. Ophth. RNLI. Prev: Cons. & Adviser Ophth. MDG (Naval).

RINTOUL, Doreen Margaret Mary 15 Dunkeld Road, Talbot Woods, Bournemouth BH3 7EN Tel: 01202 317660 — MB BS 1961 Lond.; MRCS Eng. LRCP Lond. 1961. (St. Thos.)

RINTOUL, Robert Campbell Rayne Laboratory, Respiratory Medicine Unit, Medical School University of Edinburgh, Edinburgh EH8 9AG Tel: 0131 650 6947 Fax: 0131 650 4384 Email: rrintoul@ed.ac.uk; 6A Merchiston Avenue, Edinburgh EH10 4NX — MB ChB 1992 Ed.; BSc (Hons.) St. And. 1990; MRCP (UK) 1995. Clin. Research Fell. (Respirat. Med.) Univ. Ed. Prev: SHO (Med.) St. Thos. Hosp. Lond.; SHO (Med.) Hammersmith Hosp. Lond. & Roy. Infirm. Edin.

RINTOUL, Mr Robert Forbes (retired) — MB ChB Ed. 1960; FRCS Ed. 1964; FRCS Eng. 1965. Prev: Cons. Gen. Surg. Nevill Hall Hosp. Abergavenny.

RINTOUL, Russell Campbell (retired) The Cottage, Frostenden Corner, Frostenden, Beccles NR34 7JA Tel: 01502 578507 — MB BS 1957 Lond.; LMSSA Lond. 1955. Prev: SHO Leicester Roy. Infirm. Matern. Hosp.

RIORDAN, Daniel Christopher 127 Ashburton Avenue, Seven Kings, Ilford IG3 9EP — MB BS 1993 Lond.

RIORDAN, Denise Mary Child Health Directorate, Albion Road Resource Centre, Albion Road, North Shields NE29 0HG — MB BS 1987 Newc.; MRCPsych 1992. Sen. Regist. (Child & Adolesc. Psychiat.) Prestwich Hosp. Manch. Prev: Regist. (Psychiat.) N. W.. RHA; Regist. Rotat. (Psychiat.) N.. RHA Scheme; Ho. Surg. Roy. Vict. Infirm. Newc.

RIORDAN, Frederick Andrew Ian Department of Paediatrics, Birmingham Heartlands Hospital, Bordesley Green E., Birmingham B9 5SS Tel: 0121 424 0823 Fax: 0121 424 0827 Email: riordad@heartso.wmids.nhs.uk; 71 Ferndown Road, Solihull B91 2AX — BM 1984 Soton.; MD 1996 Liverp.; MRCP 1989 UK; MD Liverp. 1996; MRCP (UK) 1989; MRCPCH 1996; DTM & H Liverp. 1995. Cons. Paediat. Birm. Heartlands Hosp. Socs: Paediat. Research Soc.; Brit. Paediatric Allergy Immunity Infec. Gp. (Sec.).

Prev: Lect. (Paediat. & Child Health) Birm. Univ.; Research Fell. Liverp. Univ.

RIORDAN, John Finbar General Office, Central Middlesex Hospital NHS Trust, Acton Lane, London NW10 7NS Tel: 020 8453 2327 Fax: 020 8453 2091 Email: john.riordan@cmh-tr.nthames.nhs.uk; 36 Woodville Gardens, Ealing, London W5 2LQ Tel: 020 8997 2319 Fax: 020 8997 2319 — MB BCh BAO NUI 1963; FRCP Lond. 1982, M 1966. (Cork) Med. Dir. Centr. Middlx. Hosp. NHS Trust; Cons. Phys. Centr. Middlx. Hosp. & Willesden Chest Clinic; Hon. Clin. Sen. Lect. (Med.) Imperial Coll. Sch. of Med.; Cons. Phys. Clementine Ch.ill Hosp. Harrow. Socs: Fell. Roy. Soc. Med.; Brit. Thorac. Soc. Prev: Cons. Phys. Dudley Rd. Hosp. Birm.; Lect. (Med.) Middlx. Hosp. Med. Sch. Lond.

RIORDAN, Maureen Ethel Patricia (retired) 21 School Road, Killough, Downpatrick BT30 7QL — MB BCh BAO 1926 Belf.

RIORDAN, Michael Francis 162 Bournbrook Road, Selly Oak, Birmingham B29 7DD — MB ChB 1994 Leic.

RIORDAN, Patrick Michael Aloysius Mary St Davids Hospital, Jobswell Avenue, Carmarthen SA31 3HB — MB BCh BAO 1968 NUI.

***RIORDAN, Richard David** 25 Gorse Way, Ivybridge, South Hams, Ivybridge PL21 0GA — MB BS 1994 Lond.; BSc (Hons) Lond. 1991; MRCP (UK) 1998.

RIORDAN, Terence Public Health Laboratory, Royal Devon & Exeter Hospital, Church Lane, Exeter EX2 5AD Tel: 01392 402973; 5 Holm Hill, Wirral CH48 7JA Tel: 01404 814513 — MB 1976 Camb.; BChir 1975; MRCP (UK) 1978; MRCPath 1981. (King's Coll. Hosp.) Cons. Microbiol. Pub. Health Laborat. Roy. Devon & Exeter Hosp. Prev: Cons. Microbiol. Pub. Health Laborat. Withington Hosp. Manch.

RIORDAN, Thomas Prior Swn-y-Don, 15 Rotherslade Road, Langland, Swansea SA3 4QW — MD 1948 NUI; MB BCh BAO 1936; FRCPsych 1972; DPM Eng. 1939. (Cork) Prev: Cons. Psychiat. Hosp. Advis. Serv.; Med. Supt. Cefn Coed Hosp. Swansea; Specialist Psychiat. RAMC.

RIORDAN, Timothy Health Centre, Hinckley Tel: 01455 32277 — MB BCh BAO 1951 NUI.

RIORDAN EVA, Mr Paul Department of Ophthalmology, King's College Hospital, Denmark Hill, London SE5 9RS Tel: 020 7346 1524 Fax: 020 7346 3738 Email: paulreva@doctors.org.uk — MB BChir 1982 Camb.; MA Camb. 1984; FRCS Eng. 1988; FRCOphth 1989. (St Thomas' Hosp. Lond.) Cons. Ophth. King's Coll. Hosp. Lond.; Hon. Cons., Neuro-Ophth., Nat. Hosp. For Neurol. and Neurosurg., Lond.. Socs: FRSM; Corr. Mem. N. Amer. Neuro-Ophth. Soc. Prev: Cons. Ophth. W. Kent Eye Centre FarnBoro. Hosp. Kent; Cons. Neuro-Ophth. Nat. Hosp. Neurol. & Neurosurg. & Moorfields Eye Hosp. Lond.; Sen. Regist. (Neuro-Ophth.) Nat. Hosp. Neurol. & Neurosurg. Lond.

RIOU, Mr Peter John Accident & Emergency Department, Derriford Hospital, Derriford Rd, Plymouth PL6 8DH — MB BS 1991 Lond.; FFAEM 2001; BA (Physiol. Scs) Oxf. 1988; FRCS Eng. 1996. (Charing Cross and Westminster Hospital London) Specialist Regist. Derriford Hosp. Plymouth Devon. Prev: Sen. Clin. Fell. (A & E) Roy. Devon & Exeter Hosp. Wonford.

RIPLEY, Colin Stephen 3 Fitzroy Terrace, Perth PH2 7HZ — MB ChB 1996 Dundee.

RIPLEY, George Salvarani Bulwell Health Centre, Main Street, Bulwell, Nottingham NG6 8QJ Tel: 0115 977 1181 Fax: 0115 977 1377 — MB ChB 1974 Sheff.; MRCGP 1978.

RIPLEY, James Stuart Medical Centre, Caledonian Road, Perth PH2 8HH Tel: 01738 628234 Fax: 01738 624945; 3 Fitzroy Terrace, Perth PH2 7HZ Tel: 01738 624756 Email: hu52@dial.pipex.com — MB ChB 1968 St. And.

RIPLEY, Joan Ruth (retired) 1 Aldenham Grove, Radlett WD7 7BN Tel: 01923 854357 — MB BS 1954 Lond.; Cert Family Plann. JCC Lond. 1977; FRCPCH 1997. Med. Convocation Senator, Univ. Lond. Prev: Sen. Med. Off. (Child Health & Audiol.) Barnet HA.

RIPLEY, Linda Hilary 12 Farm Lane, Tonbridge TN10 3DG — MB ChB 1973 Ed.; BSc (Med. Sci.) Ed. 1970, MB ChB 1973; DObst RCOG 1975. Clin. Med. Off. S.E. Thames RHA. Prev: SHO (Obst.) Firs Matern. Hosp. Nottm.; Ho. Surg. Warrington Gen. Hosp.; Ho. Phys. Leighton Hosp. Crewe.

RIPLEY, Maurice Ian eThe Five Bells, Main St., Claypole, Newark NG23 5BJ — MB ChB 1976 Sheff.

RIPLEY, Pamela 48 Overstrand Road, Cromer NR27 0AJ Tel: 01263 513148 Fax: 01263 515264 — MRCS Eng. LRCP Lond. 1981 London; MRCS Eng. LRCP Lond. 1981 London.

RIPLEY, Peter 37/39 Lea Avenue, Neilston, Glasgow G78 3EQ — MB ChB 1997 Aberd.

RIPMAN, Mr Hujohn Armstrong (retired) Red House, Sproughton, Ipswich IP8 3AT Tel: 01473 253325 — MB BS 1942 Lond.; FRCS Eng. 1949; MRCS Eng. LRCP Lond. 1941; FRCOG 1961, M 1948. Prev: Cons. O & G Ipswich Hosp. Gp.

RIPPIN, Jouathan David Birmingham Heartlands Hospital., Bordesley Green E., Bondesley Green, Birmingham Tel: 0121 766 6611; Flat 1, 79 Springfield Road, Kings Heath, Birmingham B14 7DU — MB BS 1994 Lond.; BA Cantab . 1991; MRCP 1998. (Univ. of Cambridge & Charring Cross Med. School)

RIPPINGALE, Catherine 43 Liberty Avenue, London SW19 2QS — MB BS 1996 Lond.

RIPPON, Adrian George 2nd Up Left, 9 Bellefield Avenue, Dundee DD1 4NG — MB ChB 1998 Dund.; MB ChB Dund 1998.

RIPPON, Clare 2 Strand Road, Carlisle CA1 1NB — MB ChB 1994 Manch. SHO (O & G) The Roy. Oldham Hosp. Prev: Ho. Off. (Med., Neurol. & Rheum.) N. Manch. Gen. Hosp.; Ho. Off. (Gen. Surg.) The Roy. Oldham Hosp.

RIPPON, Doreen Aldebaran, 37 Carr Hill Lane, Sleights, Whitby YO21 1RS — MB ChB 1950 Liverp.

RIPPON, Lisa Maria 42 The Avenue, Durham DH1 4EB — MB BS 1992 Newc.

RIPPY, Elisabeth Ellen 176 Spixworth Road, Norwich NR6 7EQ — MB BS 1995 Lond.

RISDALL, Jane Elizabeth, Surg. Cdr. RN Institute of Naval Medicine, Alvestoke, Gosport PO12 2DL Fax: 02392 504823, 02392 768426 — MB BS 1984 Newc.; MA Camb. 1985; FFA RCSI 1992; DA (UK) 1989. (Newcastle upon Tyne) Cons. Anaesth. Roy. Navy; Hon. Cons. Soton. Gen. Hosp.; Sen. Med. Off., Hyperbaric Med., Inst. of Naval Med., Alverstoke, Gosport, Hants. Prev: Sen. Regist. (Anaesth.) RN Hosp. Haslar & Addenbrooke's Hosp. Camb.; Regist. (Anaesth.) Roy. Infirm. Edin.; SHO & Regist. (Anaesth.) S.. Gen. Hosp. Glas.

RISDON, Rupert Anthony Department Histopathology, The Hospital For Sick Children, Great Ormond St., London WC1N 3JH Tel: 020 7405 9200 Fax: 020 7813 1170; 4 Byfeld Gardens, London SW13 9HP Tel: 020 8748 7028 — MRCS Eng. LRCP Lond. 1962; MD Lond. 1972, MB BS 1962; FRCPath. 1980, M 1968. (Char. Cross) Prof. Histopath. Hosp. Sick Childr. Gt. Ormond St. Socs: Path. Soc. Gt. Brit. & Irel. & Assn. Clin. Pathol. Prev: Reader (Morbid Anat.) Lond. Hosp. Med. Coll.; Cons. (Histopath.) Addenbrooke's Hosp. Camb.; Lect. in Histopath. Char. Cross Hosp. Med. Sch.

RISEBURY, Michael John 77 Southwood, Coulby Newham, Middlesbrough TS8 0UF — MB BS 1998 Lond.; MB BS Lond 1998.

RISHI, Nand Prakash Gillingham Medical Centre, Woodlands Road, Gillingham ME7 2BU Tel: 01634 854431 — MB BS 1961 Vikram; MRCGP 1978; DCH Eng. 1971. (Gandhi Med. Coll. Bhopal)

RISHI, Naveen Acorn Cottage, Hartlip, Sittingbourne ME9 7TH — BChir 1996 Camb.

RISHKO, Alun John 39 Glenroy Street, Roath, Cardiff CF24 3JX — MB BCh 1997 Wales.

RISHTON, Patricia Haslingden Health Centre, Manchester Road, Haslingden, Rossendale BB4 5SL Tel: 01706 212518 Fax: 01706 218112; 1 Oak Mount, Haslingden Road, Rawtenstall, Rossendale BB4 6SH Tel: 01706 212480 — MB ChB 1979 Manch.; DRCOG 1982.

RISHWORTH, Ruth Hannah Friars Close, Goathland, York YO22 5JU — MB BS Durh. 1957.

RISHWORTH, Vivienne Cecilia The Health Centre, Brightwells, Farnham GU9 7SA Tel: 01252 712572 Fax: 01252 716336; Foxgreyden, Parkside, Farnham GU9 0JP Tel: 01252 724643 — MB BCh 1980 Wales; DObst RCOG 1984.

RISK, Ahmad Mahmoud Mohamed 3 Adelaide Crescent, Hove BN3 2JD Tel: 01273 724866 Email: risk@ehrad.com; 3 Adelaide Crescent, Hove BN3 2JD Tel: 01273 724866 Fax: 01273 774614 — MB BCh 1973 Univ. Ain Shams; MB BCh Ain Shams 1973. (Ain Shams) p/t Private Primary Care Phys.; Edr. Health Informatics Europe; Med. Dir. eHealth R+D Ltd. Socs: Chairm. Brit. Healthcare

RISK

Internet Assn.; Mem. Bd. Dir. Internet Healthcare Coalition. Prev: GP Reigate; Med. Off. Roy. Engineers; Med. Off. Mustique Co., W.I.

RISK, Winifred Jessie Hillside, 38 Back Road, Dollar FK14 7EA Tel: 01259 742176 — MB ChB Glas. 1938. (Univ. Glas.) Prev: Ho. Surg. & Ho. Phys. Glas. Roy. Infirm.; Squadron Ldr. RAF Med. Br.; Dep. Div. Moh Bucks. CC.

RISSIK, Kate Matrjorie Rock Robin, Underriver, Sevenoaks TN15 0SL — BM BCh 1998 Oxf.; BM BCh Oxf 1998.

RIST, Colin Leslie Department Haematology, Worthing Hospital, Worthing BN11 2DH — BM BCh 1971 Oxf.; MA,BM BCh Oxf. 1971; FRCP Lond. 1991; MRCP (UK) 1974; FRCPath 1990, M 1978. Cons. Haemat. Worthing & S.lands NHS Trust. Socs: Brit. Soc. Haematol. Prev: Sen. Regist. (Haematol.) Bristol Roy. Infirm.; Regist. Addenbrooke's Hosp. Camb.; SHO Radcliffe Infirm. Oxf.

RISTIC, Charles Dominic Haxby & Wigginton Health Centre, The Village, Wigginton, York YO32 2LL Tel: 01904 760125 — BM BS Nottm. 1983; MRCGP 1987.

RITCH, Alistair Edward Sutherland 3 Wyvern Road, Sutton Coldfield B74 2PS — MB ChB 1966 Ed.; MRCP (U.K.) 1974.

RITCH, Genevra Mary 7 Elmwood Manor, Bothwell, Glasgow G71 8EA — MB ChB 1959 Ed.; DA Eng. 1961. Assoc. Specialist (Rheum. & Rehabil.) Lanarksh. HB.

RITCHIE, Alan Kerr (retired) Upway, 12 Dark Lane, Astwood Bank, Redditch B96 6AS Tel: 0152 789 2323 — MRCS Eng. LRCP Lond. 1958.

RITCHIE, Alasdair Nicolson 140 Thurston Road, Glasgow G52 2AL Tel: 0141 883 8838 — MB ChB 1986 Glas.; MRCGP 1992; DRCOG 1992. (Glasgow)

RITCHIE, Mr Alastair William Scarth Urology Department, Gloucestershire Royal Hospital, Great Western Road, Gloucester GL1 3NN Tel: 01452 394902 Fax: 01452 386628 Email: ritchieandsons@compuserve.com; New Hall, Tibberton, Gloucester GL2 8EB Tel: 01452 790302 Fax: 01452 790763 — MB ChB 1976 Ed.; BSc (Med. Sci.) Ed. 1973, MD 1985; FRCS Ed. 1980. (Edinburgh) Cons. Urol. Surg. Glos. Roy. Hosp. Socs: Brit. Assn. Urol. Surgs.; Brit. Assn. Cancer Research. Prev: Sen. Lect. (Urol.) Univ. Edin.; Sen. Regist. (Urol.) Lothian HB; Regist. (Urol.) Liverp. HA.

RITCHIE, Alison Frances Parklands Surgery, Wymington Road, Rushden NN10 9EB Tel: 01933 396000; 2 Grange Farm, Church Road, Hargrave, Wellingborough NN9 6BQ Tel: 01933 460850 Fax: 01933 460850 — MB BS 1985 Lond.; BSc Lond. 1982; MRCGP 1989; DRCOG 1988. (Univ. Coll. Hosp. Lond.) Prev: Regist. (A & E) Monash Univ. Med. Centre Vict., Austral.

RITCHIE, Alison Morag The Viaduct Medical Practice, Denburn Health Centre, Rosemount Viaduct, Aberdeen AB25 1QB Tel: 01224 644744 Fax: 01224 627115; Westwinds, Fowlershill, Dyce, Aberdeen AB21 7AQ — MB ChB 1979 Aberd.; MFHom 1999; DRCOG 1982; MRCGP 1983. (Aberdeen) Clin. Sen. Lect. Dept. Gen. Pract. Aberd. Univ.

RITCHIE, Alyson Mary 5B Carden Terrace, Aberdeen AB10 1US — MB ChB 1980 Aberd.

RITCHIE, Andrew Ferrier The Health Centre, Lawson St., Stockton-on-Tees TS18 1HX Tel: 01642 607435 — MB ChB 1940 Glas.; DPH Eng. 1947. (Glas.) Socs: BMA & Assn. Indust. Med. Offs.

RITCHIE, Mr Andrew John Papworth Hospital NHS Trust, Papworth Everard, Cambridge CB3 8RE Fax: 01480 364740 Email: ritchie25@hotmail.com — MD 1992 Belf.; BSc (1st. cl. Hons.) Glas. 1979, MB ChB 1984; PhD Belf. 1993; FRCS Ed. 1989; FRCSI 1989. (Glasgow) Cons. Cardiothoracic & Transp. Surg. Papworth NHS Trust Camb. Socs: EACTA; ISHLT; Soc. & Cardiothoracic Surg.s. Prev: Cardiothoracic Surg. Sen. Regist. Freeman Hosp. Newc.; Cardiothoracic Surg. Regist. Aberd. Roy. Infirm.; Regist. (Surg.) Waveney Hosp. Ballymena.

RITCHIE, Arthur James 10 Aytoun Road, Glasgow G41 5RN — LRCP 1931 Ed.; LRCP, LRCS Ed. LRFPS Glas. 1931.

RITCHIE, Barbara Anne New Hall, Tibberton, Gloucester GL2 8EB — MB ChB 1976 Ed.; DO Eng. 1980; BSc (Med. Sci.) Ed. 1973, MB ChB 1976; MRCOphth 1989. Clin. Asst. (Ophth.) Glos. HA. Prev: Clin. Asst. (Ophth.) S.port Gen. Infirm.; Regist. (Ophth.) P.ss Alexandra Eye Pavil. (Roy. Infirm.) Edin.

RITCHIE, Brian William Drymen Road Surgery, 160 Drymen Road, Bearsden, Glasgow G61 3RD Tel: 0141 942 6644 — MB ChB 1980 Glas.; MRCGP 1990.

RITCHIE, Campbell James Cook University Hospital, Marton Rd, Middlesbrough TS4 3BW Tel: 01642 850850 ext5647 Email: c-ritchie@crse.fsnet.co.uk — MB BChir 1978 Camb.; MA Camb; MRCPath 1984. (Camb. & King's Coll. Hosp.) Cons. (Histopath./Cytopath.) James Cook Univ.. Hosp. Socs: Assn. Clin. Path. & Internat. Acad. Path. Prev: SHO Regist. & Sen. Regist. (Histopath.) Leicester Hosps, Qu. Med. Centre Nottm. & Kettering Gen. Hosp.; SHO (Path.) Univ. Hosp. Wales & Llandough Hosp. Penarth.

RITCHIE, Caroline Ann Margaret 568 Lanark Road W., Balerno EH14 7BN — MB ChB 1994 Aberd. SHO (Psychiat.) Falkirk & Dist. Roy. Infirm. Prev: SHO Rotat. (Psychiat.) N. Glas.; SHO (Rehabil. Med.) Astley Ainslie Hosp. Edin.

RITCHIE, Catherine Marian 171 Clare Road, Waringstown, Craigavon BT66 7SE — MD 1986 Belf.; MB BCh BAO 1978; MRCP (UK) 1981. Cons. Phys. Craigavon Area Hosp.

RITCHIE, Catriona Milne Davidson 4 Dudley Gardens, Edinburgh EH6 4PY — MB ChB 1997 Manch.

RITCHIE, Craig William 26 Beechgrove Avenue, Aberdeen AB15 5EJ — MB ChB 1991 Aberd.

RITCHIE, David Alfred Rattray (retired) 68 Bonhard Road, Scone, Perth PH2 6QB — MB ChB 1946 Aberd.; DMRD Ed. 1952. Prev: Cons. Radiol. Perth & Kinross Health Dist.

***RITCHIE, David Alistair** 3 Townfield Road, Wirral CH48 7EY — MB ChB 1981 Glas.

RITCHIE, Mr David Andrew William 1 Naseby Avenue, Broomhill, Glasgow G11 7JQ — MB ChB 1977 Aberd.; FRCS Ed. 1985. Cons. A & E Med. Glas.

RITCHIE, Derek Keith 43 Dura Street, Dundee DD4 6SW Tel: 01382 451100 Fax: 01382 453679 Email: dritchie@terra.finix.org.uk; 91 Camphill Road, Broughty Ferry, Dundee DD5 2NE — MB ChB 1978 Dundee; MRCGP 1982; DRCOG 1983. Princip. GP Dundee. Socs: (Treas.) Dundee Med. Chub; Forfarshire Med. Assn.; Scott. Heart & Arterial Risk Preven. Gp. (SHARP).

RITCHIE, Diana Margaret 14A Kirklee Circus, Glasgow G12 0TW — MD 1988 Glas.; MB ChB 1977; MRCP (UK) 1980; FRCR 1992. Cons. Clin. Oncol. Boston Oncol. Centre Glas.

RITCHIE, Elizabeth Lambie 12 Ravelston Park, Edinburgh EH4 3DX Tel: 0131 332 6560 — MB ChB 1940 Ed. (Edinburgh)

RITCHIE, Elizabeth Lorraine 1 Hamilton Way, Stonehouse ML9 3PU — MB ChB 1991 Glas.; MB ChB Glasgow 1991; DCH RCPS Glas 1994; MRCGP Glasgow 1995. (Glasgow) Sen. Health Off., Anaesth.

RITCHIE, Elizabeth Rosemary Joyce (retired) Springbank, Kilchattan Bay, Rothesay PA20 9NL Tel: 01700 831269 — MB ChB Glas. 1955; DObst RCOG 1958. Prev: GP Alexandria Dunbartonsh.

RITCHIE, Emma Catriona Pasley Road Health Centre, Pasley Road, Eyres Monsell, Leicester LE2 9BU Tel: 0116 278 2272 — MB ChB 1985 Ed.; MRCOG 1990; DCH RCP Lond. 1988. Regist. (O & G) Leic. Gen. Hosp. Prev: Regist. (O & G) Marston Green Hosp. Birm.

RITCHIE, Ewan Douglas Consultant in Anaesthesia, Department of Anaesthesia, Perth Royal Infirmary, Perth Tel: 01738 623311; 18 Corsie Avenue, Kinnoull Hill, Perth PH2 7BS Tel: 01738 625378 — MB ChB 1989 Aberd.; FRCA 1993. Cons. (Anaesth.) Perth Roy. Infirm. Perth. Prev: Clin. research fell. (Anaesth.) Toronto Hosp., Canada; Sen. Regist. (Anaesth.) Aberd. Roy. Infirm.

RITCHIE, Fiona Anne Albany Road Surgery, 5 Albany Road, Earlsdon, Coventry CV5 6JQ Tel: 024 7622 8606 Fax: 024 7622 9985; 14 Clive Road, Balsall Common, Coventry CV7 7DW — MB ChB 1978 Bristol; MRCGP 1986.

RITCHIE, Fiona Hilda 45 Denwood, Summerhill, Aberdeen AB15 6JE Tel: 01224 325936 — MB ChB 1994 Aberd.; MRCGP 1998. (Aberdeen)

RITCHIE, Gary Dunbar 71 Mile End Avenue, Aberdeen AB15 5PS — MB ChB 1987 Aberd.

RITCHIE, Grace Macfarlane (retired) The Anchorage, Burghead Road, Alves, Elgin IV30 8UY Tel: 01343 850274 — MB ChB Glas. 1945. Prev: Sen. Regist. (Path.) Glas. N.. Hosp. Gp. & W.. Dist. Hosp. Glas.

RITCHIE, Hugh Robert James (retired) 141 London Road, Luton LU1 3RL Tel: 01582 28547 — MB ChB 1943 St. And.; Cert Av Med MoD (Air) & CAA; Aviat. Auth. 1973. Med. Off. Britannia

Airways Ltd. Luton; Authorised Med. Examr. & Assessor Civil Aviat. Auth. (U.K.) & Hong Kong; Clin. Asst. (Ophth.) Luton & Dunstable Hosp. Luton. Prev: Ho. Phys. Roy. United Hosp. Bath.

RITCHIE, Ian (retired) 7 Grizedale Close, Grantham NG31 8QY — MB BCh BAO 1969 Dub.; BA, MB BCh BAO Dub. 1969; DObst RCOG 1971; DCH Eng. 1971; DTM & H Liverp. 1971. Locum work. Prev: Dist. Med. Off. Beaufort, Sabah.

RITCHIE, Mr Ian Kristensen Department of Orthopaedic & Trauma Surgery, Stirling Royal Infirmary, Stirling FK8 2AU Tel: 01786 434000 Fax: 01786 434432; 13 Abercromby Place, Stirling FK8 2QP Tel: 01786 474530 Fax: 01786 434432 Email: ian_ritchie@email.msn.com — MB ChB 1977 Aberd.; FRCS Ed. (Orth.) 1990; FRCS Ed. 1984. Cons. Orthop. Surg. Stirling Roy. Infirm. NHS Trust; Civil. Cons. Orthop. Surg. RN Scotl.; Clin. Sen. Lect. (Orthop.) Univ. Dundee; Convener of Educating Cons. Courses RCS Ed. Socs: Fell. BOA; Assoc. Brit. Soc. for Surg. of the Hand. Prev: Sen. Regist. (Orthop.) Aberd. Roy. Infirm.

RITCHIE, Ian Samuel Daniel 62 Maryville Park, Belfast BT9 6LQ — MB BCh BAO 1992 Belf.

RITCHIE, Ian William William Street Surgery, 67 William Street, Herne Bay CT6 5NR Tel: 01227 740000 Fax: 01227 742729; The Six Bells, Church Lane, Chiswet, Canterbury CT3 4OX — MB ChB 1972 Aberd.; MRCGP 1980; DObst RCOG 1975.

RITCHIE, Iris Margaret The Clinic, Drummore, Stranraer DG9 9QQ Tel: 01776 840205 Fax: 01776 840390 — MB BCh BAO 1984 Belf.; MRCGP 1989; DCH RCP Lond. 1990; DRCOG 1988. GP Drummore.

RITCHIE, James Morrison Garth, Strathmore Avenue, Kirriemuir — MB ChB 1919 Glas.; DPH 1920. (Glas.) Prev: Dir. Typhoid Research Laborat. Geo.town, Brit. Guiana & Pub.; Health Laborat. (Med. Research Counc.) Birkenhead.

RITCHIE, Jane Patricia Birling Ward, Preston Hall Hospital, Maidstone ME20 7NJ Tel: 01622 255642 Fax: 01622 225658 — MB ChB 1977 Ed.; MTrop. Paediat. Liverp. 1992; MRCP (UK) 1985; DCH RCPS Glas. 1980. (Edin.) Cons. Community Paediat. Maidstone and Tunbridge Wells NHS Trust. Socs: BACCH; ICHG; Fell. Roy. Coll. Paediat. & Child Health. Prev: Cons. Community Paediat. Medway Trust; Sen. Regist. (Community Paediat.) Roy. Liverp. Childr. NHS Trust; Paediat. Community Based Rehabil. Project, Jamaica.

RITCHIE, Janice 898 Govan Road, Glasgow G51 3DL — MB ChB 1995 Glas.

RITCHIE, Jean Katherine (retired) Angkor, 5 Park Avenue, Hutton, Brentwood CM13 2QL — BM BCh Oxf. 1946; DM Oxf. 1972; MRCP Lond. 1953; FFR 1955; DMRT 1950. Prev: Dir. of Research (Records) St. Marks Hosp. Lond.

RITCHIE, Jessie More Ramsay 21 Culbowie Crescent, Buchlyvie, Stirling FK8 3NH Tel: 01360 850406 — MB ChB 1950 Glas. (Glas.)

RITCHIE, Joan Moira Community Child Health, St. John's Hospital, Howden, Livingston EH54 6PP Tel: 01506 419666 Fax: 01506 416484; Green Gables, 9 Riselaw Crescent, Edinburgh EH10 6HN Tel: 0131 447 3192 — MB ChB 1976 Dundee; MRCGP 1982; DCCH RCP Ed. 1984; DCH RCP Glas. 1982. SCMO (Child Health) W. Lothian NHS Trust.

RITCHIE, John Matheson (retired) Oldways, Castle Road, Wellingborough NN8 1LL Tel: 01933 222130 — MB BS 1952 Lond.; FRCOG 1977, M 1964. Prev: Cons. (O & G) Kettering & Dist. Hosp. Gp.

RITCHIE, Keith Anthony Woodlands Surgery, 146 Halfway St., Sidcup DA15 8DF Tel: 020 8300 1680 Fax: 020 8309 7020; 7 Marlowe Close, Chislehurst BR7 6ND — MB BS 1980 Lond.; BSc Hons Lond. 1977; MRCS LRCP Lond. 1980; DRCOG 1985. (Guy's) GP.

RITCHIE, Kenneth Brian Inverkeithing Medical Group, 5 Friary Court, Inverkeithing KY11 1NU Tel: 01383 413234 Fax: 01383 410098; Fernbank, North Queensferry, Inverkeithing KY11 1HB Tel: 01383 413508 Fax: 01383 627527 Email: drkritchie@aol.com — MB ChB Aberd. 1967; DObst RCOG 1969. (Aberd.) GP Princip.; Adviser Fife Health Bd. Socs: Brit. Soc. Med. & Dent. Hypn.; Assoc. Fac. Homeopath. Prev: Ho. Surg. & Ho. Phys. Dumfries Roy. Infirm.; Ho. Surg. O & G Falkirk & Dist. Roy. Infirm.; SHO Seafield Childr. Hosp. Ayr.

RITCHIE, Kenneth Henry (retired) 112 Shirley Road, Southampton SO15 3FD Tel: 01703 221964 — MRCS Eng. LRCP Lond. 1949. Prev: Ho. Phys. Diabetic Dept. King's Coll. Hosp.

RITCHIE, Professor Lewis Duthie Health Centre, Forrest Road, Peterhead AB42 2TX Tel: 01779 474841 Fax: 01779 474651; Department of General Practice and Primary Care, University of Aberdeen, Westburn Road, Aberdeen AB25 2AY Tel: 01224 681818 Fax: 01224 840683 Email: l.d.ritchie@abdn.uk — MB ChB 1978 Aberd.; MB ChB (Commend.) Aberd. 1978; MSc Ed. (Comm. Med.) 1982, BSc (Chem.) 1978, MD 1993; FRCP Ed. 1995; FRCGP 1994, M 1982; FFPHM RCP (UK) 1993, M 1989; DRCOG 1980. (Aberd.) Mackenzie Prof. & Head Gen. Pract. Univ. Aberd.; Hon. Cons. Pub. Health Med. Grampian HB. Socs: Fell. Roy. Soc. Med.; Brit. Computer Soc. Prev: Cons. Pub. Health Med. Grampian HB; SHO (Gen. Med.) Aberd. Roy. Infirm.; SHO (Obst.) Aberd. Matern. Hosp.

RITCHIE, Neil Jonathan 61 Cavendish Road, Matlock DE4 3HD — MB ChB 1996 Leic.

RITCHIE, Peter Lowfield Farm, 18 Durham Road, Wolviston, Billingham TS22 5LP — MB ChB 1975 Dundee; FFA RCS Eng. 1981. Cons. Anaesth. N. Tees Gen. Hosp. Stockton-on-Tees.

RITCHIE, Peter Andrew Department of Anaesthesia, Cheltenham General Hospital, Sandford Road, Cheltenham GL53 7AN Tel: 01242 274143 Fax: 01242 273405 Email: peter.ritchie@egnhst.org.uk — MB BS 1977 Lond.; BSc (Hons.) (Pharmacol.) Lond., MB BS 1977; FRCA 1982. (King's Coll. Hosp.) Cons. Anaesth. Cheltenham NHS Trust.

RITCHIE, Rhoda Marjorie 466 Kilmarnock Road, Glasgow G43 2BS Tel: 0141 637 0701 — MB ChB 1950 Glas.

RITCHIE, Robert Tyrie (retired) Romney Lodge, 5 Panmure Terrace, Broughty Ferry, Dundee DD5 2QL Tel: 01382 779863 — MB ChB 1944 Ed.; FRCP Ed. 1966, M 1949. Prev: Cons. Phys. (Geriat.) Dundee & Angus Geriat. Serv.

RITCHIE, Robina Donaldson Skene Medical Group, Westhill Drive, Westhill AB32 6FY Tel: 01224 742213 Fax: 01224 744664; 9 Fallow Road, Westhill AB32 6PT — MB ChB Aberd. 1980.

RITCHIE, Sharon Anne The Surgery, John Street, Bellshill ML4 1RJ Tel: 01698 747195; East Belmont Orchard, By Overtown, Wishaw MC2 0RU — MB ChB 1992 Aberd.; MRCGP 1996; DRCOG 1997.

RITCHIE, Stuart Norman Parkview resource Centre, 152 Wellshot Road, Tollcross, Glasgow G32 7AX Tel: 0141 303 8818 — MB ChB 1988 Glas.; MD; MRCP MRCPsych. Cons. In old age Psychiat. Pk.ehead Hosp. Salamanca St, Glas. G32. Prev: Career Regist. (Psychiat.) Gartnavel Roy. Hosp. Glas.

RITCHIE, Vaughn Health Centre, Blackfaulds Place, Fauldhouse, Bathgate EH47 9AS Tel: 01501 70282 Fax: 01501 772515; Bouley, Main St, Longridge, Bathgate EH47 9AS Tel: 01501 71162 — MB ChB 1981 Dundee. GP FauldHo. Health Centre W. Lothian VTS.

RITCHIE, William Alan Howard 85 Galgorm Road, Ballymena BT42 1AA — MB BCh BAO 1971 Belf.; FRCOG 1990, M 1975. Cons. O & G Waveney Hosp. Ballymena. Socs: Irish Perinatal Soc.; Ulster Med. Soc.

RITCHIE, William Neil Dyfed Powys Health Authority, Department of Public Health, P.O. Box 13, St David's Hospital, Carmarthen SA31 3YH Tel: 01267 225225 Fax: 01267 223337 Email: william.ritchie@dyfrs-ha.wales.nhs.uk; The Old Rectory, Garthbrengy, Brecon LD3 9TD Tel: 01874 624372 Email: writchie@theoldrectory.prestel.co.uk — MB BS 1971 Lond.; FFPHM RCP Lond. 1994; MFCM 1987; DPH Sydney 1977. (Middlx.) Director of health Pohay and Pub. Health Dyfed Powys Health Auth. Socs: Soc. of Social Med. (Memb). Prev: SCM Powys HA; Sen. Regist. (Community Med.) Som. HA; Dist. Med. Off. N.. Territory Health Dept. Alice Springs, Austral.

RITCHIE, William Primrose 466 Kilmarnock Road, Glasgow G43 2BS Tel: 0141 637 0701 — MB ChB 1952 Glas.

RITSON, Anne Marie (retired) 12 Mayfield, Barnard Castle DL12 8EA Tel: 01833 638074 — MB ChB 1941 St. And.

RITSON, Edward Bruce Royal Edinburgh Hospital, Morninside Park, Edinburgh EH10 5HF Tel: 0131 537 6297 Fax: 0131 537 6108 Email: bruceritson@netscapeonline.co.uk; 4 McLaren Road, Edinburgh EH9 2BH Tel: 0131 667 1735 — MB ChB Ed. 1961; MD Ed. 1967; FRCP Ed. 1987; FRCPsych 1980, M 1971; Dip. Community Ment. Health Harvard 1967; DPM 1964, Dip. Psych 1964. (Ed.) Clin. Dir. & Cons. Roy. Edin. Hosp.; Sen. Lect. Edin. Univ.; Chairm. DVLA Alcohol Drugs Ment. Comm.; Mem. Alcohol Educat. Research Counc. Socs: Soc. Study of Addic.; (Chairm.) Med. Counc. Alcohol.; Roy. Coll. Psychiat. (Fac. Chairm. Subst. Misuse,

RITSON

Former Sect.). Prev: Dir. Sheff. Region Addic. Unit; Sen. Regist. Roy. Edin. Hosp.; Research Fell. Harvard Med. Sch. Boston, USA.

RITSON, Roger Harry Hailwood Medical Centre, 2 Hailwood Court, Governors Hill, Douglas IM2 7EA Tel: 01624 67544 Fax: 01624 616290; Ballafletcher, Poultry Farm Cottage, Ballafletcher Road, Braddan, Douglas IM4 4QL Tel: 01624 623219 — MB ChB 1966 Manch.; MRCS Eng. LRCP Lond. 1966. (Manch.) Approved under Sect. 28(2) Ment. Health Act. Socs: BMA. Prev: Ho. Phys. Ho. Off. (O & G) & Regist. Psychiat. Ashton Gen.; Hosp.

RITSOU-ZAVOLIA, Konstantina Cytopathology Department, Fourth Floor/Clarence Wing, St Mary's Hospital, Praed St., London W2 1NY — Ptychio latrikes 1986 Patras.

RITTER, Alison Clare Jarvis and Partners, Westbrook Medical Centre, 301-302 Westbrook Centre, Westbrook, Warrington WA5 8UF Tel: 01925 654152 Fax: 01925 632612; 83 Stonehill Close, Appleton, Warrington WA4 5QD Tel: 01925 265899 — MB ChB 1989 Birm.; DFFP 1993; DCH RCP Lond. 1992. Prev: Trainee GP Wirral HA VTS; SHO (Psychiat.) Arrowe Pk. Hosp. Liverp.

RITTER, Professor James Michael Department Clinical Pharmacology, St. Thomas' Hospital, Lambeth Palace Road, London SE1 7EH Tel: 020 7928 9292 ext 2250 Fax: 020 7401 2242 Email: james.ritter@kcl.ac.uk; 20 Vine Road, London SW13 0NE Tel: 020 8878 2381 Fax: 020 8878 9256 — BM BCh 1974 Oxf.; 1970 Dphill, (oxf); MA Oxf. 1970; FRCP Lond. 1994; MRCP (UK) 1976. (Oxford University) Prof. Clin. Pharmacol. GKT St. Thos. Hosp. Kings Coll. Lond.; Hon. Cons. Phys. Guy's & St. Thos. Hosps. Lond. Socs: Brit. Pharm. Soc.; Assn. Phys.; Med. Res. Soc. Prev: Sen. Lect. (Clin. Pharmacol.) Roy. Postgrad. Med. Sch. Lond.; Asst. Prof. Med. Case W.. Reserve Univ. Cleveland Ohio, OH, USA; Asst. Chief of Serv. (Med.) John Hopkins Hosp. Baltimore MD, USA.

RITTER, Juliet Maria Natasha 7 Louisa Street, London E1 4NF — MB BS 1994 Lond.

RITTEY, Christopher Donald Clement The Ryegate Childrens Centre, Tapton Crescent Road, Sheffield S10 5DD Tel: 0114 267 0237 Fax: 0114 267 8296; 45 Redmires Road, Sheffield S10 4LB Tel: 0114 230 2059 Fax: 0114 230 2671 Email: c.d.rittey@sheffield.ac.uk — MB ChB 1982 Ed.; FRCP 1997; FRCPch 1997. (Ed.) Cons. Paediat. Neurol. Ryegate Childr. Centre Sheff. Prev: Sen. Regist. & Regist. (Paediat.) Roy. Hosp. Sick Childr. Glas.; Regist. (Paediat.) Rutherglen Matern. Hosp. Glas.; SHO (Paediat.) Stobhill Gen. Hosp. & Roy. Hosp. Sick Childr. Glas.

RITTOO, Dev Bhuruth 8 Addison Close, Chorlton-on-Medlock, Manchester M13 9SB — MB ChB 1982 Manch.

RITTOO, Dylmitr Department of Cardiology, Arrowe Park Hospital, Upton CH49 5PE Tel: 0151 6785111 Email: drittoo@yahoo.co.uk; 14 Addison Close, Manchester M13 9SB Tel: 0161 272 6064 Fax: 0151 6047220 — MD 1993 Manch.; MB ChB 1984; MRCP (UK) 1988. (Manchester University) Lect. (Cardiol.) , Cons. Cardiologist Arrowe Pk. Hosp.; Regist. (Med.) Roy. Liverp. Hosp.; Fell. Interven.al Cardiol., Halifax, Nova Scotia; Research Fell. KCH Lond. Prev: Lect. (Cardiol) Manch. Roy. Infirm.; Research Fell. (Cardiol.) W.. Gen. Hosp. Edin.

RITTOO, Mr Dynesh 8 Addison Close, Chorlton on Medlock, Manchester M13 9SB — MB ChB 1991 Manch.; FRCS 1995. Research Fell. Selly Oak Univ. Hosp. Birm. Prev: Regist. (Surg.) Bury Gen. Hosp.; Regist. (Surg.) Blackburn Roy. Infirm.

***RITZEMA-CARTER, Jay Lynn Tamara** The Old Post House, Crazies Hill, Reading RG10 8LU Tel: 01189 403437 — BM 1998 Soton.; BM Soton 1998.

RIUSECH MAS, Ines Flat 11, Warehouse 13, Kingston St., Hull HU1 2DZ — LMS 1990 U Autonoma Barcelona.

RIVAS, Peter Hugh (retired) 57 Hemingford Road, Islington, London N1 1BY Tel: 020 7609 8717 — MRCS Eng. LRCP Lond. 1972; MB BS Lond. 1972, BDS 1967; FDS RCS Eng. 1975. Cons. Oral Surg. & Dent. Supt. Univ. Coll. Hosp. Lond. Prev: Sen. Regist. (Oral Surg.) Mt. Vernon Hosp. N.wood.

RIVERA DE ZEA, Antonio 21 Averon Rise, Oldham OL1 4NX — LMS 1993 Malaga.

RIVEROS HUCKSTADT, Maria del Pilar Flat 4, 71 Richmond Road, Worthing BN11 4AQ — LMS 1988 Seville.

RIVERS, Colin Michael 2 High Street, Castor, Peterborough PE5 7BB — MB BS 1967 Newc.

RIVERS, David (retired) 181 Cromwell Lane, Burton Green, Coventry CV4 8AN Tel: 01203 466198 — LMSSA Lond. 1946; MRCGP 1965. Prev: Pathol. Pneumoconiosis Research Unit Llandough Hosp.

RIVERS, David Somers Hastings House, Kineton Road, Wellesbourne, Warwick CV35 9NF Tel: 01789 840245 Fax: 01789 470993; Aldeen House, Lighthorne Rd, Kineton CV35 0JL Tel: 01926 640767 Email: drivers@netcomuk.co.uk — MB BChir 1973 Camb.; MA, MB BChir Camb. 1973; MRCGP 1979; DRCOG 1979. (Camb. & Middlx.)

RIVERS, Jane Ann The Park Medical Centre, Maine Drive Clinic, Maine Drive, Chaddesden, Derby DE21 6LA Tel: 01332 665522 Fax: 01332 678210 — MB ChB 1983 Leic.; MSc CNAA 1978; BPharm. Lond. 1974; MRCGP 1988; DRCOG 1986. (Leicester)

RIVERS, John Somers (retired) Homeland, Balscote, Banbury OX15 6JP Tel: 01295 730672 — MB BChir 1946 Camb.; MA Camb. 1947, MB BChir. 1946. Prev: GP Lincs.

RIVERS, John William Shanklin Medical Centre, 1 Carter Road, Shanklin PO37 7HR Tel: 01983 862245 Fax: 01983 862310; Apse Manor, Apse Manor Road, Shanklin PO37 7PN Tel: 01983 867677 — MB BS 1982 Lond.; BSc Lond. 1979; MRCGP (Distinc.) 1986; DRCOG 1986; DCH RCP Lond. 1984. Chairm. IDOC (Isle of Wight GP Co-op.). Prev: Trainee GP Crawley VTS.

RIVERS, Malcolm Derek 16 Oatlands, Crawley RH11 8EQ — MB ChB 1997 Sheff.

RIVERS, Nigel 26 Westholme Close, Woodbridge IP12 4BE Tel: 01394 383120 — MRCS Eng. LRCP Lond. 1949; DPM Eng. 1967; LMSSA Lond. 1948. (Middlx.) Assoc. Specialist (Psychiat.) St. Audry's Hosp. Woodbridge. Socs: Soc. Clin. Psychiat.; Assn. Behavioural Clinicians. Prev: JHMO (Psychiat.) Clifton Hosp. York; Regist. Mt. Vernon Hosp. N.wood & Harrow Chest Clinic; Ho. Surg. Middlx. Hosp.

RIVERS, Rodney Peter Aldridge Imperial College School of Medicine, St Mary's Campus, London W2 1PG Tel: 020 7886 6103 Fax: 020 7886 6284 Email: r.p.rivers@ic.ac.uk — MB 1966 Camb.; BChir 1965; FRCP Lond. 1980; MRCP (U.K.) 1970. Reader (Paediat.) Imperial Coll. Sch. of Med. Socs: Neonat. Soc. & Europ. Soc. Paediat. Research.

RIVETT, Anne Williton and Watchet Surgeries, Robert Street, Williton, Taunton TA4 4QE Tel: 01984 632701 Fax: 01984 633933; Chilcombe House, 30 Trendle Lane, Bicknoller, Taunton TA4 4EG Tel: 0198 46 56243 — MB ChB 1978 Bristol.

RIVETT, Geoffrey Christopher (retired) 173 Shakespeare Tower, Barbican, London EC2Y 8DR Tel: 020 7786 9617 Email: geoffrey@rivett.net — BM BCh 1956 Oxf.; MA (1st cl. Hons.) Oxf. 1957; FRCGP 1987, M 1965; DObst RCOG 1958. Prev: Sen. Princip. Med. Off. DoH.

RIVETT, James Frederick Manor Farm Close Surgery, 8 Manor Farm Close, Drayton, Norwich NR8 6DN Tel: 01603 867532 — MRCS Eng. LRCP Lond. 1977; BSc Lond. 1974, MB BS 1977; AFOM RCP Lond. 1994; MRCGP 1983. (Guy's)

RIVETT, Joan Dorothy (retired) 26 Whalley Drive, Bletchley, Milton Keynes MK3 6HP Tel: 01908 373222 — BM BCh 1957 Oxf.; MA Oxf. 1958, BM BCh 1957; FRCPath 1981, M 1969. Prev: Cons. Histopath. Stoke Mandeville Hosp. Aylesbury.

RIVETT, John Graham Martins Oak Surgery, 36 High Street, Battle TN33 0EA Tel: 01424 772263/772060 — MB BS 1985 Lond.; MA Oxf. 1986; MRCGP 1989; DCH RCP Lond. 1992; DRCOG 1990; DA (UK) 1988. Prev: Dist. Med. Off. Roddickton Newfld., Canada; Resid. Med. Off. The Childr. Hosp. Sydney, Austral.; Trainee GP Lostwithiel Cornw. VTS.

RIVETT, Katharine Alison 45 Paterson Close, Stocksbridge, Sheffield S36 1JQ — MB ChB 1997 Sheff. (Sheffield) SHO, A&E, N.ern Gen. Hosp., Sheff.; VTS Trainee. Prev: GP Reg., FarLa. Surg. Sheff.; Ho. Off. InMed., Rotherham Dist. Gen.; HO, Surg., Bassetlaw, Dist., Gen.

RIVETT, Paula Maria Catslide Cottage, Caldbec Hill, Battle TN33 0JS Tel: 01424 775673 — MB BS 1987 Lond.; DRCOG 1992; DGM RCP Lond. 1990. Prev: Trainee GP Taunton; Dist. Med. Off. Newfld., Canada; Resid. Med. Off. Childr. Hosp. Camperdown, Sydney, Austral.

RIVETT, Robert Stephen Williton and Watchet Surgeries, Robert Street, Williton, Taunton TA4 4QE Tel: 01984 632701 Fax: 01984 633933; Chilcombe House, 30 Trendle Lane, Bicknoller, Taunton TA4 4EG Tel: 01984 656243 Email: bob.rivett@doctors.net.uk — MB ChB 1978 Bristol; MRCP (UK) 1981; FRCGP 1996, M 1982;

DRCOG 1981; Dip. Med. Educat. Dund. RCGP Internat. Developm. Adviser Lebanon.

RIVLIN, Anne 21 Devonshire Place, London W1G 6HZ Tel: 020 7486 8557 Fax: 020 7224 0080; Wick Farm, Tisbury, Salisbury SP3 6NW Tel: 01747 870373 — MB BS 1974 Lond. (Westm.) Med. Pract. Lond.; Clin. Med. Off. Salisbury Health Dist. Socs: Chelsea Clin. Soc.; Salisbury Med. Soc. Prev: Chief Resid., Amer. Hosp. Paris.

RIVLIN, Ian 17 Dobcroft Close, Ecclesall, Sheffield S11 9LL — MB ChB 1984 Sheff. SHO (O & G) Rotherham Dist. Gen. Hosp. Socs: BMA & Med. Protec. Soc. Prev: SHO (Geriat.) Rotherham Dist. Gen. Infirm.; Ho. Off. (Gen. Med.) Rotherham Dist. Gen. Hosp.; Ho. Off. (ENT, Renal Transpl. & Gen. Surg.) Roy. Hallamsh. Hosp. Sheff.

RIVLIN, Joseph Joel (retired) Parkfield, Courtenay Road, Liverpool L25 4RL Tel: 0151 428 1203 Email: rivlin@cableinet.co.uk — MSc Liverp. 1997; MB ChB Liverp. 1943; MRCS Eng. LRCP Lond. 1943; MLCOM 1969. Prev: Cons. Osteop. Phys. Liverp.

RIVLIN, Mona Viviette (retired) Parkfield, Courtenay Road, Liverpool L25 4RL Tel: 0151 428 1203 Email: rivline@cableinet.co.uk — MB ChB 1950 Liverpool; BA Manch. 1996; MSc (Social Med.) Lond. 1975; FFCM 1976; MA Manch. 1999. Prev: Consulant (Community Med.) Mersey RHA.

RIVLIN, Rosa Sutton 9 Clarendon Court, Eastbury Avenue, Northwood HA6 3LN Tel: 01923 836713 — MRCS Eng. LRCP Lond. 1947; CPH Wales 1950. (Cardiff) Locum GP Middlx. Socs: BMA & Cardiff Med. Soc. Prev: GP Cardiff; Research Asst. (Social & Occupat. Med.) Welsh Nat. Sch. Med. Cardiff; Ho. Surg. (Radiother.) Brit. Postgrad. Med. Sch. Hammersmith.

RIVRON, Marilyn Joy 24 Station Road, Radyr, Cardiff CF15 8AA Tel: 029 20419 864 — MB BCh 1979 Wales; BSc Wales 1976; MRCGP 1983. (Wales) Community Paediat. Cardiff & Dist. NHS Trust. Prev: Clin. Med. Off. (Community Child Health) Lothian HB.

RIVRON, Mr Raymond Peter Royal Glamorgan Hospital, Ynysmaerdy, Llantrisant CF72 8XR Tel: 01443 443443 Fax: 01443 443248 — MB BCh 1979 Wales; BSc 1976 Wales; FRCS 1986 Eng.; MD 1995 Wales. Cons. Otolaryngol. Taff Ely Health Unit. Prev: Sen. Regist. (Otolaryngol.) Lothian HB Edin.; Regist. (Otolaryngol.) Leeds HA; Lect. & Hon. Regist. Dept. Clin. Surg. (Otolaryng.) Univ. Edin.

RIX, Bruce David The Ongar Health Centre, Great Bansons, Bansons Lane, Ongar CM5 9EF Tel: 01277 363028 Fax: 01277 365264; Coopers, Coopers Hill, Marden Ash, Ongar CM5 9EG Tel: 01277 362912 — MB BS 1974 Lond.; MRCS Eng. LRCP Lond. 1974; MRCGP 1981. Clin. Asst. (Rheum.) Broomfield Hosp. Chelmsford. Prev: SHO Broomfield Hosp. Chelmsford; Ho. Phys. Plumstead Hosp. Lond.; Ho. Surg. Guy's Hosp. Lond.

RIX, David Alan Antler Cottage, Dalton, Newcastle upon Tyne NE18 0AA — MB BS 1989 Newc.

RIX, Gerald Henner West Suffolk Hospital, Hardwick Lane, Bury St Edmunds IP33 2QZ; 8 Loch of Liff Road, Liff, Dundee DD2 5NE — MB BChir 1992 Camb.; BA (Hons.) Physiol. Sci. Oxf. 1989. (Addenbrooke's Hosp. Camb.) SHO Rotat. (Gen. Surg.) W. Suff. Hosp. Bury St. Edmunds. Prev: SHO Rotat.(A & E Trauma, Orthop. & Neurosurg.) Addenbrooke's Hosp. Camb.; Ho. Off. (Gen. Med.) Ipswich Hosp.; Ho. Off. (Gen. Surg.) Addenbrooke's Hosp. Camb.

RIX, Keith John Barkclay The Grange, 92 Whitcliffe Rd, Cleckheaton BD19 3DR Tel: 01274 878604 Fax: 01274 869898 — MB ChB 1975 Aberd.; MD Aberd. 1986, BMedBiol. (Hons.) 1972; MPhil Ed. 1980; FRCPsych 1992, M 1979; CBiol. 1986; MAE 1995; MEWI 1997. Cons. Forens. Psychiat. The Grange Consg. Rooms, Cleckheaton; Vis. Cons. Psychiat. HM Prison Leeds; Mem. Inst. Biol. & Inst. Health Educat. Socs: Acad. Experts; Fell. RSM; Med. Sec. Leeds & W. Riding Medico-Legal Soc. Prev: Cons. Forens. Psych., Leeds CMH Trust; Lect. (Psychiat.) Univ. Manch.; Regist. (Psychiat.) Roy. Edin. Hosp.

RIX, Robert Daren 24 Kennet Close, Upminster RM14 1ST — MB ChB 1989 Sheff.

RIX, Stephen Mark c/o 24 Hill View, Langthorpe, Boroughbridge, York YO51 9BE — MB BS 1996 Newc.

RIX, Susan Paula 38 Parsonage Street, Dursley GL11 4AA — MB BS 1989 Lond.

RIX, Thomas Elliott 12 Abinger Way, Eaton, Norwich NR4 6NA — BChir 1995 Camb.

RIXOM, James Andrew West Hallam Medical Centre, The Dales, West Hallam, Derby DE7 6GR Tel: 0115 932 5462 — MB BCh 1982 Wales; MRCGP 1989; DRCOG 1986.

RIXON, Peter Ernest (retired) Rosemary Cottage, Chillesford, Woodbridge IP12 3PU Tel: 01394 450512 — MB ChB 1949 Aberd.; MRCPsych 1971; DPM Eng. 1956. Prev: Cons. Psychiat. St. Audry's Hosp. Melton & St. Geo. Hosp. Morpeth.

RIXON, Rebekah Ann Limewood Farm, Ashford Hill Road, Ashford Hill, Thatcham RG19 8BB — MB ChB 1998 Leeds.

RIYAMI, Bazdawi Mohammed Said 202 Kirkintilloch Road, Bishopbriggs, Glasgow G64 2ND — MB ChB 1971 Baghdad; MRCP (UK) 1976; DTM & H Liverp. 1974; DTCD Wales 1975.

RIYAT, Manjeet Singh 20 Claymoor Park, Booker, Marlow SL7 3DL — MB ChB 1992 Leic.

RIZA, Mr Ibrahim Mohamed Department of Vascular Surgery, Manchester Royal Infirmary, Oxford Road, Manchester M13 9WL Tel: 0161 276 4525; 49 Calder Drive, Walmley, Sutton Coldfield B76 1YR Tel: 0121 313 0340 Email: viriza@btinternet.com — MB BS 1990 Mangalore; FRCS 1994 Glas.; FRCS Glas. 1994. (Kasturba Med. Coll. Manipal, India) Research Fell. Vasc. Surg. Manch. Roy. Infirm. Prev: SPR Gen. Surg. Roy. Infirm. Edin.; SPR Gen. Surg. Roy. Falkirk and Dist. Roy. Infirm.; SPR (Gen. Surg.) Roy. Infirm. Edin.

RIZK, Mr Mohib Samy Rosedale, West Ella Road, West Ella, Hull HU10 7SF — MB ChB 1967 Alexandria; FRCS Ed. 1981.

RIZK, Nader Fouad Tel: 01724 842415 Fax: 01724 271437; St. John's Well, 109 Manor Road, Bottesford, Scunthorpe DN16 3PT Tel: 01724 840404 Fax: 01724 271437 — MB BCh Cairo 1968; LRCP LRCS Ed. LRCPS Glas. 1974. (Cairo) Prev: Trainee GP Aberd. VTS; SHO (Obst.) Mayday Hosp. Thornton Heath; SHO (Orthop.) Roy. Nat. Orthop. Hosp. Stanmore.

RIZK, Mr Samir Nessim Morcos 51 Cropwell Road, Radcliffe-on-Trent, Nottingham NG12 2FQ Tel: 0115 933 6675 Fax: 0115 933 6775 — MB BCh Cairo 1956; FRCS Eng. 1963; LMSSA Lond. 1962; FRCOpth 1989; DO Eng. 1961. (Cairo) Cons. Ophth. Surg. Pk. Hosp. Nottm.; Nottm. Nuffield Hosp. Prev: Ho. Phys. & Ho. Surg. Univ. Hosp. Cairo; Sen. Regist. Roy. Hosp. & Roy. Infirm. Sheff.; Regist. Nottm. Eye Hosp.

RIZKI, Sabiha 134 Albury Drive, Pinner HA5 3RG — MB BS 1965 Osmania.

RIZVI, Fakhrul Hassan 3 Queen Anne Street, Stoke-on-Trent ST4 2EQ — MB BS 1975 Karachi; MRCS LRCP Lond. 1980.

RIZVI, Negheth 18 Church Path, London W4 5BJ — MB BS 1996 Lond.

RIZVI, Qasim Raza 3 Poplar Road, Manchester M19 1QH Tel: 0161 286 8658 Email: qrizvi@aol.com — MB ChB 1992 Dundee; MRCS (I & II) Eng. 1997. Specialist Regist. (Radiol.) Liverp. Prev: SHO (ENT) N. Manch. Gen. Hosp.; SHO (Neurosurg.) Manch. Roy. Infirm.

RIZVI, Syed Akhlaq Hussain Consultant Physician, Watford General Hospital, Vicarage Road, Watford WD1 8HB Tel: 01923 217768; 43 Marlings, Park Avenue, Chislehurst BR7 6RD Tel: 01689 608376 — MB BS 1979 Karachi; MRCP (UK) 1991; Dip. Cardiol. Lond 1992. (Dow Medical College, Karachi) Cons. Phys., Watford Gen. Hosp., Watford, Herts WP1 8HB. Socs: BMA; Brit. Geriat. Soc.

RIZVI, Mr Syed Ishtiaq Hussain 3 Lessingham Avenue, Clayhall, Ilford IG5 0BJ — MB BS 1979 Punjab; FRCSI 1990; BSc Principles 1975. (Nishtar Med. Coll. Mutan, Univ. of The Punjab, Lahore, Pakistan) Staff Grade Doctor, (A & E), King Geo. Hosp. Barley La., Good Mayes, Essex. Socs: Roy.Soc. of Med.; BMA; Pakistan Med. & Dent. Counc. Prev: Cons Surg., Rasheed Hosp, Lahore.; Asstt. Prof., Cons. Surg., Punjab Med. Coll. Faisalabad, Pakistan.

RIZVI, Syed Pervez Jamal 193 Homerton High Street, Hackney, London E9 6BB — MB BS 1978 Lucknow.

RIZVI, Syed Shakil Ahmed Flat 2, Block 7, St. Peter's District General Hospital, Guildford Road, Ottershaw, Chertsey KT16 0PZ — MB BS 1975 Punjab; MRCP (UK) 1991; DCH RCPS Glas. 1983. Prev: Regist. (Paediat.) Roy. Alexandra Hosp. Paisley.; Regist. (Paediat.) Bellshill Matern. Hosp., Law Hosp. Carluke & Vale of Leven Hosp. Dunbartonsh.

RIZVI, Mr Syed Tanveer Mustafa 8 Calside Place, Dumfries DG1 4AW — MB BS 1986 Sind; MB BS Sind Pakistan 1986; FRCS Glas. 1992.

RIZWAN

RIZWAN, Muhammad Raziuddin 26 Salisbury Avenue, Swanley BR8 8DG Tel: 01322 666693 — MB BS 1976 Karachi; DA (UK) 1987. SHO.

RIZWI, Mohammad Taher Ali Central Gateshead Medical Group, The Health Centre, Prince Consort Road, Gateshead NE8 1NR Tel: 0191 477 2243 Fax: 0191 478 6728 — MB BS 1963 Karachi.

RIZZA, Charles Rocco Carmine (retired) 24 Ickford Road, Tiddington, Oxford OX9 2LR Tel: 01844 339335 Email: crrizza@aol.com — MB ChB St. And. 1955; MD (Gold Medal) St. And. 1962; FRCP Ed. 1972, M 1964. Cons. Phys. Oxf. Haemophilia Centre Ch.ill Hosp.; Clin. Lect. (Haemat.) Univ. Oxf. Prev: Ho. Phys. Therap. Unit Maryfield Hosp. Dundee.

RIZZO-NAUDI, Joseph Louis Whitchurch Surgery, 49 Oving Road, Whitchurch, Aylesbury HP22 4JF Tel: 01296 641203 Fax: 01296 640021 — MRCS Eng. LRCP Lond. 1979; MRCP (UK) 1985; MRCGP 1991.

ROACH, Diana Louise 27 Grange Street, Port Talbot SA13 1EN — BM 1991 Soton.

ROACH, Emma 93 Octavia Terrace, Greenock PA16 7PY — MB ChB 1997 Aberd.

ROACH, Huw David Universtiy Hospital Of Wales, Heath Park, Cardiff CF4 4XW Tel: 029 2074 3030; 19 Clodien Avenue, Cardiff CF14 3NL Tel: 029 2052 1034 — MB BS 1994 Lond.; BSc (Hons.) Lond. 1991; MRCP (UK). (Univ. Coll. Lond. Med. Sch.) Specialist Regist. (Radiol.) Univ. Hosp. Wales Cardiff. Prev: SHO (Med.) Plymouth Hosps.; SHO (Elderly Care) Univ. Coll. Hosps. Lond.; SHO (A & E) S.mead Hosp. Bristol.

ROACH, Richard Tremayne Springhouse, St Marys Lane, Hertford SG14 2LF — MB BS 1994 Lond.

ROACH, Sue Claire Middle Flat, 27 Spath Road, Manchester M20 2QT — MB ChB 1995 Manch.

ROACH, Susan Mary 31 Leaway, Greasby, Wirral CH49 2PY — MB ChB 1987 Liverp. Trainee GP Neston S. Wirral. Prev: SHO (Paediat.) Warrington Dist. Gen. Hosp.; SHO (Med.) Warrington Dist. Gen. Hosp.; SHO (Geriat.) BRd.green Hosp. Liverp.

ROADS, Peter George (retired) Pasture Cottage, Dinton, Aylesbury HP17 8UZ Tel: 01296 748504 — MRCS Eng. LRCP Lond. 1943; MB BS Lond. 1948; MD Lond. 195; FFCM 1974; FFPHM 1989; DPH Lond. 1949. Med. Ref. for Cremat. Prev: Regional Med. Off. SW Thames RHA.

ROAF, Mr Robert 88 Upton Park, Chester CH2 1DQ Tel: 01244 376911 Email: robertroaf@aol.com — BM BCh Oxf. 1938; MA Oxf. 1938; MCh Orth. Liverp. 1946; FRCS Eng. 1942; FRCS Ed. 1939; MRCS Eng. LRCP Lond. 1937. (Oxf.) Cons. Orthop. Surg. United Liverp. Hosp. & Robt. Jones & Agnes Hunt Orthop. Hosp. OsW.ry; Hon. Acad.ian Acad. Med. Singapore; Emerit. Prof. Orthop. Surg. Univ. Liverp. Socs: Fell. BOA; Hon. Fell. Indian Orthop. Assn.; Hon. Fell. Singapore Orthop. Assn. Prev: Dir. of Clin. Studies & Research Robt. Jones & Agnes Hunt Orthop. Hosp. OsW.ry; Vis. Orthop. Surg. Irwin Hosp., New Delhi.

ROAN, Christian Anne MacGregor 2 Regent Square, Lenzie, Glasgow G66 5AE — MB ChB 1967 Glas.; DObst RCOG 1969. (Glas.) Prev: GP StenHo.muir.

ROBACK, Sharon Denise 11 Canterbury Close, Chigwell IG7 6HG — MB ChB 1989 Manch.; MRCGP 1994; DRCOG 1993; DCH RCP Lond. 1992. Socs: BMA; RCGP. Prev: Retainer GP Watford.

ROBAK, Krzystof Robert 10 Grove Court, Walton Road, East Molesey KT8 0DG — Lekarz 1973 Warsaw.

ROBARDS, Martin Frank Childrens Department, Pembury Hospital, Tunbridge Wells TN2 4QJ Tel: 01892 823535 Fax: 01892 825246 — MB BS 1967 Lond.; BSc (Physiol.) Lond. 1964; FRCPCH 1993. (St. Thos.) Cons. Paediat. Pembury Hosp. Kent. Socs: BMA; Roy. Coll. of Paediat. & Child Health. Prev: Sen. Regist. (Paediat.) Liverp. AHA (T); Regist. (Paediat.) Hosp. Sick Childr. Gt. Ormond St.; SHO (Paediat.) St. Thos. Hosp. Lond.

ROBARTS, James Herbert (retired) Cnoc Nan Caoraich, 233 Bruernish, Castlebay HS9 5UY Tel: 01871 890381 — MB ChB Ed. 1939. Prev: Res. Ho. Surg. & Ho. Phys. Deaconess Hosp. Edin.

ROBARTS, Philip James Barbers Orchard, Colam Lane, Little Baddow, Chelmsford CM3 4SY — MB ChB 1975 Ed.; FRCOG 1994, M 1981. Cons. O & G St. John's Hosp. Chelmsford.

ROBARTS, Mr William Martin 31 Sloane Avenue, London SW3 3JB Tel: 020 7589 6666 Fax: 020 7584 3871 — MB BChir 1968 Camb.; MA Camb. 1968; FRCS Eng. 1973. (Camb. & Middlx.) Prev: Regist. (Surg.) Middlx. Hosp. Lond. & Cheltenham Gen. Hosp.; Ho. Phys. Centr. Middlx. Hosp.

ROBAYO CASTILLO, Luisa Victoria 35 Helena Road, London NW10 1HY Tel: 020 8452 6251 — LMS 1985 Bilbao; MSc (Nutrit.) Lond. 1990.

ROBB, Agnes Kate (retired) 89 Westfield Road, Leicester LE3 6HW Tel: 0116 285 8056 — MB ChB 1932 Aberd. Prev: Med. Off. Leics. AHA (T) (Leicester).

ROBB, Alastair Keith 87 Anchorsholme Lane, Blackpool — MB ChB 1985 Liverp.

ROBB, Angela Garstang Road Surgery, 63-65 Garstang Road, Preston PR1 1LB Tel: 01772 253554 Fax: 01772 909131; Barnsfield, Eaves Green Lane, Goosnargh, Preston PR3 2FE — MB BChir 1987 Camb.; MA Camb. 1988; MFFP 1993; MRCGP (Distinc.) 1992; DRCOG 1992. Examr. RCGP; Family Plann. Instruc. Doctor. Socs: Brit. Med. Acupunct. Soc.

ROBB, Anne Gillespie 29 Hope Street, Lanark ML11 7NE Tel: 01555 662812; 33 Waterloo Road, Lanark ML11 7QH Tel: 01555 662405 — MB ChB Glas. 1970; MFHom 1990; DObst RCOG 1971; Dip. Med. Acupunc. - BMAS. Indep. Pract. (Homoeop. Acupunc.) Lanark. Socs: Brit. Med. Acupunct. Soc. Prev: Clin. Asst. Glas. Homoeop. Hosp.

ROBB, Anne Leslie (retired) Avalon, 12 Feddon Hill, Fortrose IV10 8SP — MB ChB 1961 Glas. Prev: Clin. Asst. (Cytol.) Dept. Path. Raigmore Hosp. Inverness.

ROBB, Curtis Alexander 12 Hightor Road, Liverpool L25 6DL — MB ChB 1997 Sheff.

ROBB, Dorothy Elizabeth (retired) Flat 1, 105 Marlborough Park S., Belfast BT9 6HT Tel: 01232 381053 — MB BCh BAO Belf. 1950; DObst RCOG 1958.

ROBB, Elaine Masonic House Surgery, 26 High Street, Buckingham MK18 1NU Tel: 01280 816450 Fax: 01280 823885; The Old School House, Shalstone, Buckingham MK18 5LT Tel: 01280 702476 — MB BS 1980 Lond.; MRCS Eng. LRCP Lond. 1980; DRCOG; MRCGP.

ROBB, Geoffrey Hugh Ashtead Hospital, Ashtead KT21 2SB Tel: 01372 276161 Fax: 01372 278704; Heath House, Headley, Epsom KT18 6NJ Tel: 01372 377227 Fax: 01372 377748 — MB ChB 1961 Bristol; FRCP Lond. 1982, M 1966; DObst RCOG 1963. (Bristol) Cons. Phys. Epsom Gen. Hosp.; Chief Med. Off Pension & Annuity Friendly Soc.; Chief Med. Off. Friends Provident Life Off.; Chief Med. Off. UNUM Ltd; Co-Edr. Med. Selection of Life Risks 4th Edition Macmillan; Chief Med. Off. R.G.A. (UK) Ltd. Socs: Soc. Occupat. Med.; Brit. Diabetic Assn. (Med. & Scientif. Sect); Assn. Study Obesity. Prev: Sen. Regist. (Cardiol.) Groote Schuur Hosp., Cape Town; Counc.lor RCP Lond.; Presidetn Assur. Med. Soc.

ROBB, Graeme Anthony Garstang Road Surgery, 63-65 Garstang Road, Preston PR1 1LB Tel: 01772 253554 Fax: 01772 909131; Barnsfield, Eaves Green Lane, Goosnargh, Preston PR3 2FE Tel: 01772 861188 — MB BChir 1985 Camb.; MB Chir Camb. 1985; MA Camb. 1987, BA 1983; MRCGP 1991; DRCOG 1988. (Camb.) Princip. GP; Course Oganiser Preston Hosp. VTS Preston; Exam. RCGP Trainer. Socs: BMA; Roy. Coll. Gen. Pract. Prev: Trainee GP Preston VTS; SHO (Obst. & Gen.) Sharoe Green Hosp. Preston; SHO (A & E & Psychiat.) Preston.

ROBB, Henry Morgan Falkirk & District, Royal Infirmary Trust, Falkirk FK1 Tel: 01324 624000; 10 The Glebe, Linlithgow EH49 6SG — MB ChB 1982 Dundee; MSc Glas. 1988; FFA RCS Eng. 1987. Cons. Anaesth. Falkirk. Prev: Sen. Regist. (Anaesth.) Glas.

ROBB, Mr James Eybers Princess Margaret Rose Orthopaedic Hospital, Edinburgh EH10 7ED Tel: 0131 536 4634 Fax: 0131 536 4601; 55 Nile Grove, Edinburgh EH10 4RE — MB ChB 1975 Dundee; BSc St. And. 1972; FRCS Ed. 1980; FRCS Glas. 1980. Cons. Orthop. Surg. P.ss Margt. Rose Orthop. Hosp. & Roy. Hosp. for Sick Childr. Edin.

ROBB, John Daniel 85 Charlotte Street, Ballymoney BT53 6AZ — MB BS 1996 Newc.

ROBB, Mr John Daniel Alexander Model Farm, Ballymoney BT53 6BX — MB BCh BAO 1957 Belf.; FRCS Eng. 1961. Cons. Surg. Route Hosp. Ballymoney. Prev: Sen. Lect. in Surg. Qu. Univ. Belf. & Roy. Vict. Hosp. Belf.

ROBB, John Joseph Braemar, 52 Belfast Road, Antrim BT41 1PB Tel: 01849 3376 — MB BCh BAO 1956 Belf.; FRCPI 1979, M

1967; LRCP LRCS Ed. LRFPS Glas. 1956; DCH RCPSI 1972; DPH Belf. 1958. (Belf.) Cons. Phys. Antrim & Ballymena Health Dist. Prev: Ho. Phys. & Ho. Surg. Lond.derry Gp. Hosps.; Med. Asst. Downe Hosp. Downpatrick & Belf. City Hosp.

ROBB, Katherine Hilary 83 Front Road, Drumbo, Lisburn BT27 5JX — MB BCh BAO 1996 Belf.

ROBB, Olive Jean 3 Lomond Drive, Carnoustie DD7 6DN — MB ChB 1978 Aberd.

ROBB, Patricia Marlowe (retired) 48 Montclair Drive, Liverpool L18 0HB Tel: 0151 475 0203 — MB ChB Ed. 1950; FRCP Ed. 1971, M 1954; FRCPath 1974, M 1963. Prev: Cons. Haemat. Walton Hosp. Liverp.

ROBB, Mr Peter John Epsom General Hospital, Epsom KT18 7EG; Ashtead Hospital, Ashtead KT21 2SB — MB BS 1981 Lond.; BSc (1st cl. Hons.) Lond. 1978, MB BS 1981; FRCS Eng. 1985; FRCS Ed. 1985. (Lond. Hosp.) Cons. ENT. Surg. Epsom Health Care. Hon. Cons. Ent Surg. The Childern's Trust, Tadworth. Socs: Fell. Roy. Soc. Med.; Brit. Assn. Paediat. Otol. Prev: Sen. Regist. (ENT) Guy's Hosp. Lond.; Research Fell. Univ. Washington, Seattle, USA; Fell. (Paediat. Laryngol.) Childr. Hosp. Sydney, Austral.

ROBB, Robert Cleghorn, OBE (retired) La Ferronerie, Sark, Guernsey GY9 0SA Tel: 01481 832128 — MB ChB Glas. 1946; DIH Eng. 1960; DPH Lond. 1959; DPhysMed. Eng. 1952. Prev: Med. Off. Sark.

ROBB, Sanghamitra Department of Anaesthetics, Dryburn Hospital, Durham DH1 5TW Tel: 0191 333 2333; 23 Westerdale, Penshaw, Houghton-le-Spring DH4 7SD Tel: 0191 415 0842 — MB BS 1981 Calcutta; DA (UK) 1991. (Calcutta Med. Coll.) Staff Grade Anesth., Dryburn Hosp. Durh. Socs: Med. Defence Union; BMA. Prev: Trust Grade Anaesth. Anaesth. Bishop Auckland Gen. Hosp.

ROBB, Stephanie Ann The Newcomen Centre, Guys Hospital, St Thomas St., London SE1 1RT Tel: 020 7955 4498 Fax: 020 7955 4950; Tel: 020 8994 5868 — MB BS 1977 Newc.; MD Newc. 1987; FRCP Lond. 1994; MRCP (UK) 1979; FRCP CH. Cons. Paediat. Neurol. Guy's Hosp. Lond. Prev: Sen. Regist. Hosp. Sick Childr. Lond.; Regist. Hammersmith Hosp. Lond.; MRC Train. Fell. (Neurol. Sci.) Roy. Free Hosp. Sch. Med. Lond.

ROBBE, Iain James University of Wales College of Medicine, Temple of Peace, Cathays Park, Cardiff CF10 3NW Tel: 029 2040 2480 Fax: 029 2040 2504 Email: robbe@cardiff.ac.uk; Whip's Cottage, Dawn of Day, Grosmont, Abergavenny NP7 8LT Tel: 01873 821331 — MB BS 1980 Lond.; BSc Lond. 1977, MSc (Community Med.) 1985; MRCS Eng. LRCP Lond. 1980; FFPHM RCP (UK) 1995, M 1987. (Westm.) Sen. Lect. (Pub. Health Med.) Univ. Wales Coll. Med. Cardiff. Prev: Sen. Regist. (Community Med.) Oxf. RHA; Regist. (Radiol.) Addenbrookes Hosp. Cambs.; SHO Rotat. (Paediat.) W.m. Chidr. Hosp. Lond.

ROBBIE, Douglas Stewart (retired) 6 Lilyville Road, London SW6 5DW — MB ChB Aberd. 1954; FFA RCS Eng. 1960. Prev: Cons. Anaesth. (i/c Pain Clinic) Roy. Marsden Hosp. Lond.

ROBBIE, Nicola Fax: 01924 334439; 37 Broad Oak Road, Worsley, Manchester M28 2TL — MB ChB 1989 Manch.; MRCP Paediat. (UK) 1994. GP Retainee, Manch. Prev: Regist. (Paediat.) Trafford Gen. Hosp. Manch.

ROBBIE, Rosalene Betsy RGIT Health, RGIT Ltd., 338 King St., Aberdeen AB24 5BQ Tel: 01224 619619 Fax: 01224 619519; 69 Woodend Place, Aberdeen AB15 6AP — MB ChB 1974 Aberd.; Dip. Occ. Med. RCP Lond. 1996. Occupat. Phys. RGIT Health Aberd.. Prev: Occupat. Phys. (Occupat. Health) RGIT Ltd Aberd.

ROBBINS, Aphra Giorgina Flat 3F3 96 Marchmont Road, Edinburgh EH9 1HR — MB ChB 1998 Ed.; MB ChB Ed 1998.

ROBBINS, Gerard Department of Haematology, Royal Surrey County Hospital, Egerton Road, Guildford GU2 7XX Tel: 01483 464122 Fax: 01483 464072 — MB BS 1976 Lond.; BSc Lond. 1973; MRCP (UK) 1978; MRCPath 1984. (Guy's) Cons. Haemat. Roy. Surrey Co. Hosp. Guildford; Med. Director Roy. Surrey Co. Hosp. Guildford. Prev: Co-ordinator Bone Marrow Transp. Progr. Roy. Free Hosp. Lond.; Sen. Regist. (Haemat.) Hillingdon Hosp. & Roy. Free Hosp. Lond.

ROBBINS, Graham Mark 24 Harwood Close, Tewin, Welwyn AL6 0LF — MB BS 1987 Lond.

ROBBINS, Judy Caroline Victoria House Surgery, 33 Victoria Road, Swindon SN1 3AW Tel: 01793 536515; Garden Cottage, Broadbush, Swindon SN26 7AJ Tel: 01793 728559 — MB BS 1985 Lond.; MRCGP 1993; DRCOG 1994; DFFP 1992; DGM RCP Lond. 1992. Prev: Trainee GP Twickenham; SHO (O & G) Wexham Pk. Slough; SHO (Gen. Med.) W. Middlx. Hosp.

ROBBINS, Justin Alexander Baird Church View Surgery, 30 Holland Road, Plymstock, Plymouth PL9 9BW Tel: 01752 403206 — MB BS 1966 Lond.; MRCP (U.K.) 1970; DObst RCOG 1968. (St. Thos.) Prev: Med. Regist. Hither Green Hosp. Lond.; Sen. Med. Regist. Kitwe Centr. Hosp. Zambia.

ROBBINS, Matthew Charles Oliver 80 Stratford Street, Upper Stoke, Coventry CV2 4NJ — MB BS 1994 Lond.

ROBBINS, Nancy Estelle (retired) Heacham Lodge, Lodge Road, Heacham, King's Lynn PE31 7AZ Tel: 01485 71582 — MRCS Eng. LRCP Lond. 1938.

ROBBINS, Professor Peter Alistair The University Laboratory of Physiology, Parks Road, Oxford OX1 3PT Tel: 01865 272490 Fax: 01865 282486 Email: peter.robbins@physiol.ox.ac.uk; 10 Summerhill Road, Summertown, Oxford OX2 7JY Tel: 01865 558450 Fax: 01865 558450 — BM BCh 1984 Oxf.; BA (Maths.) Open 1993; BA (Physiol.) Oxf. 1978; MA, DPhil Oxf. 1981. (Oxford) Prof. (Physiol.) & Fell. Qu.'s Coll. Oxf. Socs: BMA; Physiol. Soc.; Amer. Physiol. Soc.

ROBBINS, Peter Michael Harefield Hospital, Harefield, Uxbridge UB9; 50 Croftdown Road, London NW5 1EN — MB BS 1989 Lond.; FRCA 1994. Clin. Fell. (Anaesth.) Harefield Hosp. Middlx. Prev: Regist. (Anaesth.) Roy. Free Hosp. Lond.

ROBBINS, Sarah Anne 50 Croftdown Road, London NW5 1EN — MB BS 1989 Lond.; DRCOG 1992. Trainee GP Roy. Hants. Co. Hosp. Winchester VTS. Prev: SHO (A & E) Roy. Hants. Co. Hosp. Winchester; Ho. Surg. St. Mary's Hosp. Portsmouth.

ROBBINS, Sian Eryl 1 Tithe Barn, Main St., Merton, Bicester OX25 2NF — MB BS 1987 Lond.; MRCP (UK) 1990; FRCR 1995. Sen. Regist. (Radiol.) Bristol Roy. Infirm. Prev: Regist. (Med.) S.mead Hosp. Bristol & P.ss Margt. Hosp. Swindon; SHO (Renal Med.) S.mead Hosp. Bristol.

ROBBINS, Sonia Penelope Pelican Pit-Stop, Flat 7, 87 Amsterdam Road, London E14 3UX Tel: 020 7987 4175 — MB BS 1980 Lond.; DTM & H RCP Lond. 1987; FRCS Ed. 1988; MS Melbourne 1995; MSc Lond. 1996; MA Lond. 1997; Europ. Dip. of Hand Surg (FESSH) 1997. Fell. (Hand Surg.) Pulvertaft Hand Surg. Centre Derby. Socs: Fell. Roy. Soc. Med.; Assoc. Mem. Brit. Soc. Surg. Hand. Prev: Clin. Fell. (Plastic Surg.) St. Vincents Hosp., Melbourne, Austral.; Regist. (Plastic Surg.) St. And. Hosp. Billericay; Regist. (Surg.) Amersham Dist. Gen. Hosp.

ROBBINS-CHERRY, Anthony Martin Sturton Road Surgery, 12 Sturton Road, Saxilby, Lincoln LN1 2PG Tel: 01522 702791 Fax: 01522 704434; 43 Station Road, Thorpe-on-the-Hill, Lincoln LN1 2RR Tel: 01522 731591 — MB BS 1973 Lond.; BSc (Hons. 1st cl.) Lond. 1970; MRCS Eng. LRCP Lond. 1973. (St. Marys)

ROBERSON, Frances Elizabeth Delaforce Chaddle Wood Surgery, 128 Bellingham Crescent, Plympton, Plymouth PL7 2QP Tel: 01752 345317; Trematon Barton, NR Saltash, Saltash PL12 4RT Tel: 01753 633185 — MB BS 1979 Lond.; DCH Glasgow; DRCOG Lond. (St. Bart.) Gen. Practitioner Chaddlewood Surg. Plympton. Prev: Trainee GP Saltash VTS.

ROBERT, Pratima Shalini 24A Tutbury Avenue, Cannonhill, Coventry CV4 7BJ Tel: 024 76 415631 — MB BS 1965 Nagpur; DCH RCPS Glas. 1969. (Nagpur Med. Coll.) SCMO (Child Health) Coventry. Prev: Med. Off. Coventry AHA.

ROBERTON, Clare Jane Royal Edinburgh Hospital, 10 Morningside Terrace, Edinburgh EH10 5HG Tel: 0131 537 6000; Yetholm Mains, Kelso TD5 8DB Tel: 01573 420260 — MB ChB 1994 Glas. SHO (Psychiat.) Roy. Edin. Hosp. Prev: SHO (A & E) Monklands Hosp.; SHO (c/o Elderly) Liberton Hosp. Edin.; Ho. Off. (Med.) Gartnavel Hosp.

ROBERTON, Mary 24 Bertie Road, Cumnor, Oxford OX2 9PS Tel: 01865 862308 — MB BS 1963 Lond.; MRCS Eng. LRCP Lond. 1963; MRCPCH 1996. (King's Coll. Hosp.) Community Paediat. & Occupat. Phys. Oxf. Socs: Fac. Community Health; BPA; ANHOPSOM.

ROBERTON, Norman Reid Clifford (retired) Sea Cottage, Lower Harrapool, Broadford, Isle of Skye IV49 9AQ Tel: 01471 822467 Fax: 01471 822095 — MB BChir 1964 Camb.; MA, MB Camb. 1964, BChir 1963; FRCP Lond. 1979, M 1965. Prev: Cons. Paediat. Addenbrooke's Hosp. Camb. & Newmarket Gen. Hosp.

ROBERTON

ROBERTON, Pamela Ann 31 Colmere Drive, Thingwall, Heswall, Wirral L61 — MB ChB 1955 Liverp.; DObst RCOG 1959. Asst. MOH Birkenhead. Socs: Liverp. Med. Inst. Prev: Asst. MOH Liverp. Regist. Anaesth. United Liverp. Hosps.; Sen. Ho. Off. Liverp. Matern. Hosp.

ROBERTS, Adam Paul 73 Dacre Park, London SE13 5BX — MB ChB 1993 Manch.

ROBERTS, Adrian 102 Cyncoed Road, Cardiff CF23 5SJ Tel: 029 2048 3005 — MB BCh BAO Belf. 1968; FRCOG 1989, M 1973. Cons. O & G Llandough Hosp. NHS Trust Penarth. Prev: Lect. (O & G) Welsh Nat. Sch. Med. Cardiff.

ROBERTS, Adrian Bernard Government Buildings, Otley Road, Lawnswood, Leeds LS16 5PU — MB ChB 1973 Manch.; Cert. JCC Lond. 1977; DObst RCOG 1975. Med. Quality Manager, Sema Gp. Med Servs., Leeds. Prev: GP Leeds; SHO (O & G & Paediat.) Bolton Dist. Hosp.

ROBERTS, Adrian Brian Bowling Green Surgery, Bowling Green, Constantine, Falmouth TR11 5AP Tel: 01326 340666 Fax: 01326 340968 — MB ChB 1969 Bristol; BSc Bristol 1965; MRCP (UK) 1973; FRCGP 1993, M 1979; DTM & H Liverp. 1978; DCH RCP Lond. 1971. Course Organiser Cornw. VTS. Prev: Cons. Phys. Gilbert & Ellice Is.s & Solomon Is.s.

ROBERTS, Alan Grove Medical Centre, 27 Grove Road, Wallasey CH45 3HE Tel: 0151 691 1112 Fax: 0151 637 0266; Grosvenor, 14 Linksview, Wallasey CH45 0NQ Tel: 0151 691 1112 Fax: 0151 637 0266 — MB ChB 1975 Liverp. Forens. Med. Examr. & Locality Facilitator Merseyside.

ROBERTS, Aled Wyn 32 Corvette Court, Atlantic Wharf, Schooner Way, Cardiff CF10 4NL Tel: 02920 913394 Email: aledwynroberts@hotmail.com; 32 Corvette Court, Atlantic Wharf, Schooner Way, Cardiff CF10 4WL Tel: 02920 913394 Email: aledwynroberts@hotmail.com — MB BCh 1996 Wales; MRCP, (Lond). (UWCM) Specilaist Regist. in Diabetes/Endocrinol./Internal Med., All Wales Higher Train. Progr. in Diabetes and Endocrinol.

***ROBERTS, Alexandra Claire** 14 Eewrland, Barnton, Edinburgh EH4 6DH — MB ChB 1996 Birm.; ChB Birm. 1996.

ROBERTS, Alfred Edward (retired) 18 Riverview Crescent, Cardross, Dumbarton G82 5LT Tel: 01389 841007 — MB ChB 1957 Glas.

ROBERTS, Alice Mahala 8 Islivig, Wig, Isle of Lewis HS2 9HA — MB BS 1992 Newc.; MRCPsych 1998. SHO (Psychiat.) & Prof. Cook St Martins Hosp. Canterbury; Specialist Regist. in old age Psychiat., Lewisham Hosp. Prev: SHO (Psychiat.) Bexley Hosp.; SHO (Psychiat.) S.W.ern UMDS Psychiat. Rotat.

***ROBERTS, Alice May** 190 Henbury Road, Henbury, Bristol BS10 7AE; Flat 6, 152 Redland Road, Redland, Bristol BS6 6YD — MB BCh 1997 Wales; BSc (Hons) (Anat.) Wales 1995.

ROBERTS, Alison Claire 37 Elmwood Court, Pershore Road, Birmingham B5 7PE — MB ChB 1996 Birm.; ChB Birm. 1996.

ROBERTS, Alison Joan 121 Brookhouse Hill, Fulwood, Sheffield S10 3TE — MB ChB 1996 Sheff.

ROBERTS, Alison Margaret Idle Medical Centre, 440 Highfield ROAd, Idle, Bradford BD10 8RU Tel: 01274 771999 Fax: 01274 772001; 3 Beechwood Grove, Ilkley LS29 9AX Tel: 01943 600480 — MB BS 1981 Lond.; MRCPsych 1985; MRCGP 1987. GP Idle Bradford.

ROBERTS, Amanda Jane Cardiff & District NHS Trust, Lansdowne Hospital, Sanatorillm, Canton, Cardiff CF1 8TE Tel: 029 2037 2451; 25 Lon-y-Fro, Pentyrch, Cardiff CF15 9TE — MB BCh 1982 Wales; MRCGP 1986; DCH RCP Lond. 1996. (Univ. Wales Sch. Med.) SCMO (Audiol.) Cardiff Community Healthcare NHS Trust. Socs: Roy. Coll. Paediat. & Child Health.

ROBERTS, Amanda Jane 36 Queen Alexandra Mansions, Judd St., London WC1H 9DQ — MB BChir 1982 Camb.; MA Camb. 1983, MB BChir 1982. SHO (Gen. Med.) St. Stephens Hosp. Lond. Prev: Research Regist. (Genito-Urin. Med.) Middlx. Hosp. Lond.; SHO (Dermat.) Middlx. Hosp. Lond.; SHO (Genito-Urin. Med.) Middlx. Hosp. Lond.

ROBERTS, Mr Andrew Patrick Children's Unit, Robert Jones & Agnes Hunt Orthopaedic Hospital, Oswestry SY10 7AG Tel: 01691 404573 Fax: 01691 679471 Email: andrew.roberts@roberts-rtwmids.nhs.uk; Starlings Castle, Bron y Garth, Oswestry SY10 7NU Tel: 01691 718103 — MB ChB 1980 Birm.; DM Nottm. 1991; FRCS Ed. 1985; FRCS Eng. 1985. Cons. Orthop. Surg. Robt. Jones & Agnes Hunt Orthop. Hosp. OsW.ry. Socs: Fell. BOA; BMA; Eur. Soc. Movement Anal. in Childr. Prev: Sen. Regist. Rotat. (Orthop.) QMC Nottm.; Hon.Sen.Lect, Univ, Keele.

ROBERTS, Andrew Steven 18 Chantry Grove, Bristol BS11 0QH — MB ChB 1994 Liverp.; DRCOG 1996. Vocational Trainee (Gen. Pract.) S.port Merseyside.

ROBERTS, Angela Department of Dermatology, King Edward VII Hospital, Windsor SL4 3DP Tel: 01753 860441 Fax: 01753 636107; 111 Western Avenue, Woodley, Reading RG5 3BL — MB BS Lond. 1970; MRCP (UK) 1974; DObst RCOG 1972. (Lond. Hosp.) Cons. Dermat. King Edwd. VII Hosp. Windsor. Prev: Sen. Regist. (Dermat.) Char. Cross Hosp. Lond; Regist. (Dermat.) Roy. Berks. Hosp. Reading.

ROBERTS, Angela Judith Brent Child & Family Clinic, Warranty House, Dudden Hill Lane, London NW10 1DL Tel: 0208 208 7200 Fax: 0208 208 2635 — MB BS 1981 Lond.; MRCPsych 1990; DCH RCP Lond. 1983. (Char. Cross) Cons. (Child & Adolesc. Psychiat.) Brent, Kensington Chelsea & W.minister NHS Trust Brent Child & Family Clinic. Prev: Sen. Regist. (Child & Adolesc. Psychiat.) Tavistock Clinic Lond.; Regist. Rotat. (Psychiat.) St. Mary's Hosp. Lond.; SHO & Regist. (Paediat.) Qu. Eliz. Hosp. Sick Childr. Lond.

ROBERTS, Angus Murray, RD The Sycamores, Rectory Road, Padworth Common, Reading RG7 4JD Tel: 0118 970 0463 Fax: 0118 970 0463 Email: murray_roberts@msn.com — MB BS Lond. 1965; MRCS Eng. LRCP Lond. 1965; FFOM RCP Lond. 1993; FRCP 1999 London. (Guy's) p/t Cons. Occupat.al Phys.; Surg.Cdr. RNR. Socs: Fell. Roy. Soc. Med.; Fell. Amer. Coll. Occupat. & Environm. Med.; Soc. Occupat. Med. Prev: Chief Med. Off. ICL; Med. Adviser Atomic Weapons Research Establishm. Aldermaston; Sen. Med. Off. Brit. Nuclear Fuels Ltd.

ROBERTS, Ann Whyteleafe Surgery, 19 Station Road, Whyteleafe CR3 0EP Tel: 01883 624181 Fax: 01883 622498; 3 Wheat Knoll, Kenley CR8 5JT Tel: 020 8645 0272 Email: drann@saqnet.co.uk — MB BS 1980 Lond.; DRCOG 1983. (Guy's Hospital)

ROBERTS, Ann Gertrud Department of Psychiatry, Queen Elizabeth II Hospital, Howlands, Welwyn Garden City AL7 4HQ Fax: 01707 365169 — MB BS 1984 Lond.; BA Camb. 1981; MRCPsych 1993; MRCGP 1988; DRCOG 1988; DCH RCP Lond. 1987. Cons. Gen. Adult Psychiat. (Liaison Psychiat.) Qu. Eliz. II Hosp. Welwyn Garden City. Prev: GP Herts.

ROBERTS, Anna Izabela 12 Clay Street, Burton-on-Trent DE15 9BB — BM BS 1986 Nottm.

ROBERTS, Anne Elizabeth (Medill) Nursery Park Medical Group, Nursery Park, Ashington NE63 0HP; The Grange, Longhirst Road, Morpeth NE61 3LG — MB ChB 1980 Bristol; MB ChB 1980 (Hons) Bristol; MRCP (UK) 1983; DRCOG 1985; DA Eng. 1984; DCH RCP Lond. 1983. Prev: GP Retainer Morpeth.

ROBERTS, Anne Patricia 79 Kidbrooke Grove, London SE3 0LQ — MB BS 1960 Lond.; MRCS Eng. LRCP Lond. 1960; FRCOG 1979, M 1965. (Univ. Coll. Hosp.) Cons. Gyaenocologist, Lond. Indep. Hosp. Stepney Green; Honarary Specialist Dispensari Francais Oshe Combh Sq. WCI. Prev: Cons. O & G Newham Gen. Hosp. Lond.

ROBERTS, Anthony Deans Guthrie Kirby Holt, 22 Main St., Milton, Derby DE65 6EF Tel: 01283 702945 Email: anthony.roberts2@virgin.net — MB ChB 1977 Glas.; MD Glas. 1987; FRCOG 1995, M 1982. Cons. O & G Qu.s Hosp. Burton upon Trent; Hon. Clin. Sen. Lect. Univ. of Birm.; Clin. Teach. Univ. Leic. & Examr. Leics. Univ. Med. Sch.; RCOG Regional Adviser; Chairm. Med. Staff Comm.: Qu.s Hosp. Socs: Brit. Med. Assn.; Roy. Soc. Med. Prev: Sen. Regist. (O & G) Leicester Roy. Infirm.; Regist. (O & G) Qu. Mothers & Stobhill Hosps. Glas.

ROBERTS, Anthony Herber 74 Harley Street, London W1G 7HQ Tel: 020 7580 0731 — MB BS 1959 Lond.; PhD Lond. 1979, MD 1969; FRCP Lond. 1977, M 1964; MRCS Eng. LRCP Lond. 1959; DPM Eng. 1962. (St. Thos.) Cons. Neurol. Lond. Prev: Cons. Neurol. SE Thames Regional Neurol. Centre; Sen. Regist. (Neurol.) Lond. Hosp.; Regist. (Med.) St. Thos. Hosp. Lond.

ROBERTS, Mr Anthony Howard Norman Department of Plastic Surgery, Stoke Mandeville Hospital, Aylesbury HP21 8AL Tel: 01296 315116; The Old House, Whitchurch, Aylesbury HP22 4JX Tel: 01296 641232 Fax: 01296 641820 Email: roberts@harsleymanor.freeserve.co.uk — BM BCh 1972 Oxf.; BSc Leeds 1961; MA Camb. 1972, BA 1969; MA Oxf. 1971; FRCS Eng. 1976. (Cambridge/Oxford) Cons. Plastic & Hand Surg. Stoke

Mandeville Hosp. Aylesbury; Dir. Research Stoke Mandeville Burns & Reconstrvc. Surg. Research Trust; Civil.. Cons. Advis. Plastic Surg. RAF; Hon. Sen. Lect. Dept. Surg. UCL; Vis. Prof. Dept. Surg. Chinese Univ., Hong Kong. Socs: Brit. Soc. Surg. of Hand & Mem .Brit. Assn. Plastic Surgs.; Brit. Burn Assn. (Exec. Cttee); Chairm. Burn Preven. (Cttee). Prev: Sen. Regist. (Plastic Surg.) St. Luke's Hosp. Bradford & St. Jas. Hosp. Leeds; Research Fell. (Microsurg.) St. Vincent's Hosp. Melbourne, Austral.; Cons. Plastic & Hand Surg. Stoke Mandeville Hosp. Aylesbury.

ROBERTS, Anthony John Prestwood Surgery, 1-3 Chequers Drive, Prestwood, Great Missenden HP16 9DU Tel: 01494 863899; Hilden Hall, Hammersley Lane, Penn, High Wycombe HP10 8HE — MB BS 1968 Lond.; DObst RCOG 1970.

ROBERTS, Anthony Peter The Barn, Pen-Y-Fron, Trofarth, Abergele LL22 8BP — MB ChB 1982 Manch.; BSc Physiol. Manch. 1979, MB ChB 1982; MRCPsych 1987. Cons. Psychiat. Gwynedd HA.

ROBERTS, Anthony Philip Wyke Regis Health Centre, Portland Road, Weymouth DT4 9BE Tel: 01305 782226 Fax: 01305 760549; 2 Russell Avenue, Weymouth DT4 9RA — MB ChB 1979 Bristol; DRCOG 1982. Prev: Med. Superinten. Methodist Hosp. Semonkong Lesotho Africa.

ROBERTS, Anthony Waldron Moore Street Health Centre, 77 Moore Street, Bootle L20 4SE Tel: 0151 944 1066 Fax: 0151 933 4715 — MB ChB 1978 Dundee.

ROBERTS, Antony Paul 3 East Street, Wardle, Rochdale OL16 2EG — MB ChB 1984 Leeds. Trainee GP Stepping Hill Hosp. Stockport VTS.

ROBERTS, Archibald Peter (retired) 19 The Shimmings, Boxgrove Road, Guildford GU1 2NG — MB BS 1946 Lond.; FRCP Lond. 1975, M 1952; MRCS Eng. LRCP Lond. 1945; DCH Eng. 1946. Prev: Cons. Paediat. Bradford & Airedale Hosp. Gps.

ROBERTS, Arthur Bodowen Surgery, Halkyn Road, Holywell CH8 7GA Tel: 01352 710529 Fax: 01352 710784 — MB ChB 1969 Liverp. (Liverp.) Prev: SHO (Orthop.) Birkenhead Gen. Hosp.; Ho. Phys. & Ho. Surg. St. Catherine's Hosp. Birkenhead.

ROBERTS, Arthur John, Squadron Ldr. RAF Med. Br. 14 Barnby Road, Coltishall, Norwich NR10 5JN — MB BS 1985 Lond.; BSc Lond. 1981, MB BS 1985; MRCGP 1989; DAvMed 1993.

ROBERTS, Arthur Westwood (retired) The Surgery, 1 Ratcliffe Road, Atherstone CV9 1EY Tel: 01827 713664 Fax: 01827 713666 — MB BS 1950 Lond.; MRCS Eng. LRCP Lond. 1950. Prev: Cas. Off. & Ho. Surg. King's Coll. Hosp.

ROBERTS, Austin Parry Department of Mental Health, Friarage Hospital, Northallerton DL6 1JG Tel: 01609 763438 Fax: 01609 778066 — MB BChir 1987 Camb.; MA 1987 Camb.; MRCPsych 1992. Cons. Psychiat. for Older People Friarage Hosp. N.allerton. Socs: Roy. Coll. Psychiatr.; BMA. Prev: Sen. Regist. (Psychiat.) Univ. Coll. Hosp. & Middlx. Hosp Lond.; SHO & Regist. Rotat. (Psychiat.) N. Yorks. Train. Scheme; Ho. Off. (Gen. Surg. & Urol.) Newmarket Gen. Hosp.

ROBERTS, Barbara Cecily The Lodge, 8 Drysgol Road, Radyr, Cardiff CF15 8BT Tel: 029 2084 2469 — BSc Wales 1938, MB BCh 1941; FFA RCS Eng. 1953; DA Eng. 1945. (Cardiff) Cons. Anaesth. Univ. Hosp. Wales (Cardiff) Gp. Hosps. Socs: Assn. Anaesths.; Cardiff Med. Soc.; Fell. Roy. Soc. Med. Prev: Sen. Res. Anaesth. Co. Hosp. FarnBoro., Lond. Hosp. & Roy. Infirm.; Cardiff.

ROBERTS, Barbara Kathleen 2 Lesley Avenue, Canterbury CT1 3LF Tel: 01227 51072 — MB ChB 1944 Liverp.; MRCS Eng. LRCP Lond. 1944. (Liverp.)

ROBERTS, Beatrice Jane Gable House, 46 High Street, Malmesbury SN16 9AT Tel: 01666 825825; 3 Chedglow Manor Cottages, Chedglow, Malmesbury SN16 9EZ — MB BS 1987 Lond.; MRCGP 1992; DRCOG 1991. Socs: BMA. Prev: Trainee GP Bath VTS.

ROBERTS, Bernard Lyall 88 Corringham Road, London NW11 7EB — MB ChB 1973 Manch.; FRCPsych 19896, M 1979. (Manch.) Cons. Psychotherapist Brent Kensington Chelsea & W.minster Ment. NHS; Cons. Psychotherapist St Geo.s & SW Thames Ment. Health NHS Trust. Socs: Brit. Psychoanal. Soc. Prev: Sen. Regist. (Psychother.) Tavistock Clinic Lond. & Cassel Hosp. Richmond; Regist. (Psychiat.) Lond. Hosp.; Cons. Psychother. & Med. Dir. Kingston & Kingston & Dist. Community NHS Trust.

ROBERTS, Beryl Ann North Parade Surgery, 26 North Parade, Aberystwyth SY23 2NF Tel: 01970 624545 Fax: 01970 615612; Taleithin, Penglais Road, Aberystwyth SY23 2EU Tel: 01970 623321 — MB BCh Wales 1961. (Cardiff) Socs: Brit. Geriat. Soc. Prev: SHO (Anaesth.) W. Norf. & King's Lynn Gen. Hosp.; Ho. Phys. Llandough Hosp. Penarth; Ho. Surg. (Obst.) Annie McCall Hosp. Stockwell.

ROBERTS, Bethan Non 226 Caerphilly Road, Cardiff CF14 4NR — MB BCh 1991 Wales.

ROBERTS, Bryn Merllyn, Henllan, Denbigh LL16 5DF — MB BCh 1987 Wales.

ROBERTS, Mr Carl Jessamine House, Hamsterley, Bishop Auckland DL13 3QF — MB BS 1970 Newc.; FRCS Eng. 1975. (Newc.) Cons. Urol. Bishop Auckland Gen. Hosp. & Univ. Hosp. Of N. Durh.. Durh. Socs: BMA; Brit. Assn. Urol. Surgs. Prev: Sen. Regist. (Gen. Surg. & Urol.) Newc. Hosps.; Regist. (Gen. Surg.) Norwich Hosps.; Research Fell. Univ. Calif. San Francisco, USA.

ROBERTS, Caroline Anne Thorkhill Road Surgery, 115A Thorkhill Road, Thames Ditton KT7 0UW Tel: 020 8398 3141 Fax: 020 8398 7836 — MB BS 1977 Lond.; MRCGP 1982; DGM RCP Lond. 1986; DCH Eng. 1980. (St. Mary's)

ROBERTS, Caroline Evelyn Ann St Peter's Medical Centre, 30-36 Oxford Street, Brighton BN1 4LA Tel: 01273 606006 Fax: 01273 623896; 18 Tongdean Avenue, Hove BN3 6TL — MB BS 1968 Lond.; MRCS Eng. LRCP Lond. 1968; MFFP 1993. Tutor Family Plann. JCC. Prev: SHO (Paediat.) W. Middlx. Hosp. Isleworth; SHO (Gyn.) St. Olave's Hosp. Lond.; SHO (Obst.) Roy. Sussex Co. Hosp. Brighton.

ROBERTS, Catharine Helen 118 Old Ford Road, London E2 9PW — MB BS 1990 Lond.

ROBERTS, Catherine Elizabeth Patricia (retired) Clinton House, 31 Trefusis Road, Flushing, Falmouth TR11 5TZ — MB ChB 1943 Glas. Prev: Clin. Med. Off. Kent HA.

ROBERTS, Catherine Jane Riversdale Surgery, 51 Woodcroft Road, Wylam NE41 8DH Tel: 01661 852208 Fax: 01661 853779; 6 Village W., Ryton Old Village, Ryton NE40 3QD — BM BS 1985 Nottm.; BMedSci Nottm. 1983; MRCGP 1989; DRCOG 1988. (Nottm.)

ROBERTS, Catherine Jane 11 Holyhead Court, Caerphilly CF83 2UH — MB BCh 1981 Wales.

ROBERTS, Catherine Louise Dept. of Radiology, Huddersfield Royal Infirmary, Acre Street, Lindley, Huddersfield HD3 3EA — MB BS 1990 Newc. (Honours); MRCP (UK) 1993; FRCR 1996. (Newc. u. Tyne) p/t Cons. Radiol., Radiol. Dept. Huddersfield Roy. Infirm. Prev: Specialist Regist. (Radiol.) Leeds & Bradford Scheme; SHO Rotat. (Med.) Newc. HA.

ROBERTS, Ceinwen Jayne 4 Codrington Street, Newtown, Exeter EX1 2BU — BM 1988 Soton. SHO (Med.) Exeter HA.

ROBERTS, Mr Ceri Department of Otorhinolaryngology, Princess of Wales Hospital, Coity Road, Bridgend CF31 1RQ — MB BS 1978 Lond.; FRCS Ed. 1985.

ROBERTS, Charles Andrew Tel: 01270 764151 — MB ChB 1988 Manch.; MSc (Physiol.) Aberd. 1979; BSc (Hons.) (Physiol.) Wales 1977; MRCGP 1992; DRCOG 1992; DCH RCP Lond. 1990. Prev: Clin. Asst. (Dermat.) Leighton Hosp. Crewe.

ROBERTS, Charles Christopher Nicholson Sarum House Surgery, 3 St. Ethelbert Street, Hereford HR1 2NS Tel: 01432 265422 Fax: 01432 358440 — MB BChir 1966 Camb.; MA, MB Camb. 1966, BChir 1965; DObst RCOG 1968. (Middlx.) Socs: BMA. Prev: Res. Med. Off. King Edwd. VII Memor. Hosp. Bermuda; Ho. Surg. (Obst.) Whittington Hosp. Lond.; Ho. Surg. Middlx. Hosp. Lond.

ROBERTS, Charles Glyn 10 Priory Way, Hitchin SG4 9BH Tel: 01462 59559 — MB BS 1945 Lond. (Guy's) Prev: Ho. Phys. & Obst. Resid. Guy's Hosp.; Ho. Surg. EMS Hosp. Dartford.

ROBERTS, Charles Ian 16 Ethelbert Road, Canterbury CT1 3NE Tel: 01227 760294 Fax: 01227 781377 Email: charlesrob@lineone.net — BM BCh 1962 Oxf.; MA Oxf. 1965, DM 1972; FRCP Lond. 1980, M 1966. (Oxf. & Guy's) Prev: Clin. Tutor & Hon. Cons. Phys. Guy's Hosp.; Ho. Appts. Guy's Hosp.; Instruc. (Med. & Research Fell.) Univ. Rochester NY, USA.

ROBERTS, Christine 27A Shirley Drive, Hove BN3 6NQ — MB ChB 1985 Birm.; ChB Birm. 1985. GP Hove Retainer Scheme.

ROBERTS, Christopher David Palace Road Surgery, 3 Palace Road, London SW2 3DY Tel: 020 8674 2083 Fax: 020 8674 6040

ROBERTS

— MB BS 1971 Lond.; DObst RCOG 1973. Socs: BMA. Prev: SHO (O & G & Cas.) Whipps Cross Hosp. Lond.; SHO (Paediat.) Paddington Green Childr. Hosp. Lond.

ROBERTS, Christopher James Department of Anaesthesia, Gloucester Royal Hospital, Gloucester GL1 3NN Tel: 01452 528555 Fax: 01452 394249 — BM BCh 1980 Oxf.; BA Camb. 1977; FFA RCS Eng. 1988. Cons. Anaesth. & Intens. Care Glos. Roy. Hosp. Socs: Intens. Care Soc.; Assn. Anaesth. of GB & Irel.; BMA. Prev: Sen. Regist. Nuffield Dept. Anaesth. Oxf.; Regist. (Anaesth.) Bristol & W.on Hosps.; Anaesth. Project Orbis Inc. New York, USA.

ROBERTS, Christopher Mark 32D Udney Park Road, Teddington TW11 9BG — MB BS 1991 Lond.

ROBERTS, Christopher Michael Chest Clinic, Whipps Cross Hospital, London E11 1NR Tel: 020 8535 6782 Fax: 020 8535 6709 Email: michael.roberts@whippsx.nhs.uk — MB ChB 1980 Liverp.; MD Liverp. 1992; FRCP Lond. 1996; MRCP (UK) 1983. (Liverp.) Cons. Phys. Thoracic Med. Whipps Cross Hosp. Lond.; Hon. Sen. Lect. St. Bart Hosp. Med. Coll.; Dir. Med. Educat. Forest Healthcare Trust; Assoc. Director Clin. Effectiveness Unit, Roy. Coll. of Physicans of Lond.. Socs: Brit. Thorac. Soc.; Mem.Educat. & Train. Comm.; Mem. Audit Sub Comm. Prev: Sen. Regist. (Thoracic Med.) Univ. Coll. & Lond. Chest Hosps.; Sen. Regist. St Vincents Hosp. Sydney; Regist. (Thoracic Med.) Brompton Hosp. Lond.

ROBERTS, Christopher Michael The Surgery, Gaywood House, North St, Bedminster, Bristol BS3 3AZ Tel: 0117 966 1412 Fax: 0117 953 1250; Battens House, Jacklands Bridge, Tickenham, Clevedon BS21 6SG — MRCS Eng. LRCP Lond. 1973; LMSSA Lond. 1973. Prev: Trainee GP Bristol VTS; Regist. (Anaesth.) Bristol Roy. Infirm.; Chief Med. Off. Anguilla, W. Indies.

ROBERTS, Christopher Paul 14 Wimbish Road, Papworth Everard, Cambridge CB3 8XJ — MB BS 1992 Lond.; FRCS Eng. 1996. (UMDS)

ROBERTS, Clare Judith Southampton Eye Unit, Southampton General Hospital, Tremona Road, Southampton SO16 6YD; Flat 12 Pavillon Court, 74 Northlands Road, Southampton SO15 2NN — BM BCh 1991 Oxf.; MA Camb. 1992; FRCOphth 1995. Regist. Soton. Eye Unit Soton. Gen. Hosp.

ROBERTS, Clive John Charlton Clinical Dean's Office, Bristol Royal Infirmery, Bristol BS2 8HW Tel: 0117 928 2335 Fax: 0117 928 2151 Email: c.j.c.roberts@bristol.ac.uk; Clapton Wick Farm, Clevedon Lane, Clevedon BS21 7AG Tel: 01275 852403 — MD 1979 Bristol; MRCS Eng. LRCP 1969 Lond; 2001 MILT (Inst. Of Learning & Teaching); MRCP 1973 UK; FRCP 1987 Lond; MB BS 1969 Lond. (King's Coll. Hosp.) Sen. Lect. (Clin. Pharmacol.)/Clin. Dean Bristol Univ.; Hon. Cons. Phys. Bristol Roy. Infirm. Socs: Brit. Pharm. Soc.; Assn. For Med. Educat. In Europe. Prev: Regional Adviser (SW) Roy. Coll. Phys.; Asst. Lect. (Clin. Pharmacol.) Lond. Hosp. Med. Coll.; Regist. (Med.) Plymouth Gen. Hosp.

ROBERTS, Clive Julian Thornbury Health Centre, Eastland Road, Thornbury, Bristol BS35 1DP Tel: 01454 412599 Fax: 01454 41911 — MB ChB 1985 Bristol; BSc (Hons.) Bristol 1982, MB ChB (Hons.) 1985; MRCGP 1989; DRCOG 1987. Prev: Trainee GP Bristol VTS; SHO (Obst.) Bristol Matern. Hosp.; SHO (Psychiat. & Geriat.) Ham Green Hosp. Bristol.

ROBERTS, Professor Colin Level 6, Medical Micro biology, John Radcliffe Hospital, Oxford OX3 9DU Tel: 020 8200 1295 Fax: 020 8200 8130 — MB ChB 1963 Liverp.; BSc Liverp. 1960, MD 1968; FRCP (UK) 1999. M RCP 1996; FRCPCH (Hon.) 1996; FRCPath 1986, M 1973; Dip. Bact. Manch. 1972; FFPath (I) 2000; FFPHM. (Liverp.) Locum Cons. John Radcliffe Hosp. Oxf..; Vis. Prof. Univ. Strathclyde; Vis. Prof. Lond. Sch. of Trop. Med. and Hyg.. Socs: (Pres.) Assn. Med. Microbiol. Prev: Med. & Scientif. Postgrad.Deran Pub. Health Lab Serv. Lond; Dep. Dir. PHLS; Cons. Med. Microbiol. & Sen. Microbiol. Pub. Health Laborat. Liverp.

ROBERTS, Professor Colin John (retired) Department Epidemiology and Public Health, University of Wales, College of Medicine, Heath Park, Cardiff CF14 4XN Tel: 01222 750435 Fax: 01222 742898 — MRCS Eng. LRCP Lond. 1958; PhD Wales 1970; MD Birm. 1966, MB ChB 1958; FRCR 1984; FFPHM 1977, M 1974; DPH Wales 1964; DObst RCOG 1960. Prof. Epidemiol. & Pub. Health Univ. Wales Coll. Med. Cardiff; Hon. Cons. Pub. Health Med. S. Glam. HA (T). Prev: Sen. Lect. Univ. Wales Coll. Med. Cardiff.

ROBERTS, Dafydd Llewelyn Lloyd Singleton Hospital, Swansea SA2 8QA Tel: 01792 285324 Email: dafydd.roberts@swansea-tr.wales.nhs.uk — MB BS 1972 Lond.; FRCP Lond. 1994; MRCP (UK) 1975. (Lond. Hosp.) Cons. Dermatol. Swansea NHS Trust; Chairm. Welsh Skin Cancer Site Specific Gp.; Chairm. UK Skin Cancer Working Party. Prev: Sen. Regist. (Dermat.) N. Staffs. Hosp. Centre Stoke-on-Trent; Regist. (Dermat. & Gen. Med.) Univ. Hosp. Wales, Cardiff; Med. Off. King Edwd. VII Memor. Hosp. Bermuda.

ROBERTS, David Arthur Thomas Gwyninydd, Gorrig Road, Llandysul SA44 4LF — MB ChB 1973 Birm.

ROBERTS, David Blakeway Crugiau, Rhydyfelin, Aberystwyth SY23 4PT — MRCS Eng. LRCP Lond. 1940. (Camb. & Guy's) Prev: Ho. Surg. Guy's Emerg. Hosp. Orpington; Med. Off. Guy's Emerg. Hosp. Pembury; Res. Anaesth. W. Lond. Hosps.

ROBERTS, David Edward X-Ray Department, Morriston Hospital, Swansea SA6 6NL Tel: 01792 703636 — MB BCh 1986 Wales; FRCR 1993; DMRD Liverp. 1991. Cons. Radiol. Morriston Hosp. Swansea.

ROBERTS, David Frost St Mark's Dee View Surgery, Church Street, Connah's Quay, Deeside CH5 4AD Tel: 01244 812003 Fax: 01244 822609 — MB BCh 1977 Wales.

ROBERTS, David Gareth Vaughan Wendover, 170 Downend Road, Bristol BS16 5EB — MB BS 1976 Lond.; MRCP (UK) 1981. Cons. Paediat. Community Child Health Frenchay Health Care Trust Bristol. Prev: SCMO Frenchay HA; Lect. (Child Health) Univ. Bristol; Regist. Birm. Childr. Hosp.

ROBERTS, David Geoffrey St Thomas Road Surgery, St. Thomas Road, Featherstone, Pontefract WF7 5HF Tel: 01977 792212 Fax: 01977 600278 — MB ChB 1982 Sheff.

ROBERTS, David Griffith Ty Isa, Corwen LL21 9EF Tel: 01490 2412 — MRCS Eng. LRCP Lond. 1943.

ROBERTS, David Hesketh Dept. of Cardiology, Victoria Hospital, Whinney Heys Rd, Blackpool FY3 8NR Tel: 01253 303611 Fax: 01253 306941 — MD 1991 Liverp.; FACC 2000; FRCP 1999; 2000 FESC; FRCP 1998; FACC 2000; FESC 2000; MB BCh Wales 1978; MRCP (UK) 1981. Cons. Cardiol., Blackpool. Socs: Brit. Hypertens. Soc. & Brit. Pacing & Electrophysiol. Gp.; Mem. of Brit. Cardiac Soc.; Fell. of Amer. Coll. of Cardiol. Prev: Sen. Regist. (Cardiol.) Qu. Eliz. Hosp. Birm.; Regist. (Cardiol.) Regional Cardiac Unit BRd.green Hosp. Liverp.; Lect. (Clin. Pharmacol. & Therap.) Univ. Liverp.

ROBERTS, David Hywel Griffith Great Staughton Surgery, 57 The Highway, Great Staughton, St. Neots, Huntingdon PE19 5DA Tel: 01480 860770 Fax: 01480 861514; Tel: 01480 861682 Fax: 01480 861514 — MB ChB 1982 Manch.; BSc St. And. 1979; MRCGP 1986; DRCOG 1985. GP; Mem. Caring Professions Concern; Princip. Police Surg. Camb.shire. Socs: BMA. Prev: Princip. GP Altrincham Chesh.; Trainee GP Univ. Manch. Dept. Gen. Pract. VTS; Trainee GP Tameside Gen. Hosp. VTS.

ROBERTS, David John Molecular Parasitology Group, Institute of Molecular Medicine, John Radcliffe Hospital, Headington, Oxford OX3 9DU Tel: 01865 222302 Fax: 01865 222444 Email: droberts@immausl.jrl.ox.ac.uk; 3 Fulwell, Chipping Norton OX7 4EN Tel: 01608 677125 — MB ChB 1983 Liverp.; DPhil Liverp. 1994, MB ChB 1983; MRCP (UK) 1986; DTM & H Liverp. 1989. Hon. Sen. Regist. (Haemat.) John Radcliffe Hosp. Oxf.; Wellcome Fell.sh. Inst. of Molecular Med. John Radcliffe Hosp. Oxf. Prev: Regist. (Haemat.) Roy. Liverp. Hosp.; Ho. Off. (Profess. Med. & Surg. Units) Roy. Liverp. Hosp.; SHO (Gen. Med.) Walton & Fazakerley Hosps.

ROBERTS, David Lloyd Oak Hill Health Centre, Oak Hill Road, Surbiton KT6 6EN Tel: 020 8399 6622 Fax: 020 8390 4470; 18 The Ridge, Surbiton KT5 8HX — MB ChB 1961 Manch.; DObst RCOG 1967. (Manch.) Clin. Asst. Endoscopy Unit Kingsgton Hosp. Surrey. Prev: Clin. Asst. (Surg.) Surbiton Gen. Hosp.; SHO (Neurosurg. & Plastic Surg.) Frenchay Hosp. Bristol; Ho. Surg. (Orthop.) Manch. Roy. Infirm.

ROBERTS, Mr David Michael Stepping Stones, 9 Over Lane, Almondsbury, Bristol BS32 4BL — MB BS 1963 Lond.; FRCS Eng. 1970; MRCS Eng. LRCP Lond. 1963; MFOM RCP Lond. 1983, A 1982; DIH Eng. 1982; DObst RCOG 1965. (King's Coll. Lond. & Liverp.) Sen. Med. Off. Rolls-Royce Plc. Socs: Soc. Occupat. Med. & Brit. Occupat. Hyg. Soc. Prev: Sen. Med. Adviser Standard Telephones & Cables Plc.; Dep. Med. Dir. Harlow Indust. Health Serv.

ROBERTS, David Michael, Maj.-Gen. late RAMC Retd. (retired) Rose Cottage, New Road, Donhead St Andrew, Shaftesbury SP7 9EG — MB BS 1954 Lond.; MD Lond. 1971; FRCP Lond.

1985, M 1978; FRCP Ed. 1975, M 1965. Prev: Dir. of Army Med. & Cons. Phys. to Army.

ROBERTS, David Michael Rosebank Surgery, 153B Stroud Road, Gloucester GL1 5JQ Tel: 01452 543000 Fax: 01452 387807 Email: mike.roberts@gp-l84050.nhs.uk; 90 Hucclecote Road, Hucclecote, Gloucester GL3 3RU Tel: 01452 547566 — MB ChB 1982 Bristol; 1988 Family planning diploma; T(GP) 1991; DRCOG 1988. Gen. practitioner, Rosebank health; Chair Glos. + S. Tewkesbury PCG. Prev: SHO (Med. & Anaesth.) Glos. Roy. Hosp.

ROBERTS, David Michael 27 Huntsmans Corner, Wrexham LL12 7UE Tel: 01978 364307 — MB ChB 1963 Birm.; FFOM RCP Lond. 1994, MFOM 1986, AFOM 1984; DObst RCOG 1965. (Birm.) Prev: Ho. Surg., Ho. Phys. & Ho. Surg. (O & G) Manor Hosp. Walsall.

ROBERTS, Mr David Newton 55 Harley Street, London W1G 8QR Tel: 020 7580 1481 Fax: 020 7631 0807 Email: dr@easynet.co.uk — MB BS 1987 Lond.; BSc (Anat.) Lond. 1984, MB BS 1987; FRCS (Otol.) Lond. 1993; FRCS (Gen. Surg.) Lond. 1992; FRCS (Orl) 1996. (St. Thomas') Cons., Otorhubinolatyng., GUYs & St Thomas NHS Trust; Hon.Cons. King Edwd. V11's (Sister Agnes). Socs: Europ. Acad. of Facial Plastic Surg.. (Bd. Mem.); Europ. Rhinological Soc. (Mem.). Prev: Research Fell. Roy. Postgrad. Med. Sch. Hammersmith Hosp. Lond.; Fell. (Facial Plastic Surg.) The Europ. Acad. of Facial Plastic Surg.; Sen. Regist. (Otorhinolaryngol.) Roy. Nat. Throat, Nose & Ear Hosp. Lond.

ROBERTS, David Powys Wynn 8 Trefonwys, Bangor LL57 2HU — MB ChB 1952 Birm.; MRCS Eng. LRCP Lond. 1953; MFCM 1974; DObst RCOG 1955; DPH Liverp. 1957. Specialist in Community Med. Gwynedd AHA. Socs: BMA. Prev: MOH W.. Flints. CC; Dep. MOH Blackpool; Asst. MOH Chester.

ROBERTS, David Robert Ainsley Fenstanton Lodge, High St., Fenstanton, Huntingdon PE28 9LA — MB BS 1992 Lond.

ROBERTS, David Ronald Digby Freeman Hospital, High Heaton, Newcastle upon Tyne NE7 7DN Tel: 0191 223 1304 Fax: 0191 223 1337 Email: digby.roberts@tfh.nnth.northy.nhs.uk — MB ChB 1981 Manch.; BSc (Hons.) Physiol. Manch. 1978, MB ChB 1981; FRCA 1988. (Manchester) Cons. Anaesth. Freeman Hosp. Prev: Sen. Regist. Newc.; Regist. & SHO (Anaesth.) RN; Med. Off. Roy. Marines.

ROBERTS, Mr David St Clair (retired) Beechfield, 25 Bolnore Road, Haywards Heath RH16 4AB Tel: 01444 413507 — BM BCh 1945 Oxf.; MA, BM BCh Oxf. 1945; FRCS Eng. (Ophth.) 1956; FCOphth 1989. Mem. Oxf. Ophth. Congr. Prev: Mem. Ct. of Examrs. RCS Eng.

ROBERTS, David Thomas 282 Ladybrook Lane, Mansfield NG19 6QL — MB BS 1980 Lond.; MRCPsych 1988. (Lond.)

ROBERTS, David Trevor Southern General Hospital, 1345 Govan Rd, Glasgow G51 4TF Tel: 0141 201 1567 Fax: 0141 201 2990; 17c Mains Avenue, Glasgow G46 6QY Tel: 0141 638 8258 — MB ChB 1970 Glas.; FRCP Glas. 1984; MRCP (UK) 1973. Cons. Dermat. S.. Gen. Hosp. & Vict. Infirm. Glas.; Hon. Sen. Lect. Univ. Glas. Prev: Cons. Dermat. W.. Infirm. & Roy. Hosp. Sick Childr. Glas.; Sen. Regist. (Dermat.) Roy. Infirm. Glas.; Regist. (Dermat.) W.. Infirm. Glas.

ROBERTS, Derrick (retired) 340 Upper Richmond Road, Putney, London SW15 6TL Tel: 020 8788 0686 — MB BS 1954 Lond.; MRCS Eng. LRCP Lond. 1954. Prev: Ho. Surg. Vict. Hosp. Childr. Lond.

ROBERTS, Devender 12 Elmsdale Road, Liverpool L18 1LX — MB ChB 1989 Liverp.; MRCOG 1995. Lect., Univ. Dept. of (O & G), Univ. of Liverp., Liverp. Wom.'s Hosp. Prev: Specialist Regist., Mersey Rotat.; SHO Countess of Chester Hosp.

ROBERTS, Dewi Wyn (retired) Plas Newydd, Glynilifon Park, Caernarfon LL54 5ED — MB BChir 1965 Camb.; MA Camb. 1965; MRCS Eng. LRCP Lond. 1964. Med. Off. Cummins Engine Co. Prev: GP Daventry.

ROBERTS, Diana Mary Bron Heulog, Four Mile Bridge, Holyhead LL65 2HX — MB BS 1972 Newc.

ROBERTS, Dilys Yvonne 7 Fieldside, Hawarden, Deeside CH5 3JB — MB BCh 1977 Wales.

ROBERTS, Donald James (retired) Wild Acre, 15 Ashley Drive N., Ashley Heath, Ringwood BH24 2JL Tel: 01425 471624 — MB BChir Camb. 1956; MA Camb. 1956; MRCS Eng. LRCP Lond. 1954;

FFPHM 1989; FFCM 1980, M 1972; DPH Leeds 1959. Prev: DMO St. Helens & Knowsley HA.

ROBERTS, Doreen Jean South Manchester Health Authority, Mauldeth House, Mauldeth Road S., Manchester M21 7RL; 3 Linden Road, Manchester M20 2QJ Tel: 0161 445 4308 — MB ChB 1964 Manch.; MSc (Clin. Audiol.) Manch. 1987, BSc (Hons. Anat.) 1961. (Manch.) SCMO (Audiol. Med.) S. Mancunian Community Health NHS Trust. Socs: Fell. Manch. Med. Soc. Prev: SHO (Geriat.) Barnes Hosp. Manch.; Family Plann. Assn. Clinic Doctor.

ROBERTS, Dorothy Margaret Haver, OStJ (retired) Field Barn Farm, Hampton Poyle, Kidlington OX5 2PY Tel: 01865 374773 — MB BS 1955 Durh.; MRCS Eng. LRCP Lond. 1955; MFCM 1974; DPH Bristol 1968. Prev: PMO Oxf. Health Auth.

ROBERTS, Dubravka Stefica 19 Woodhall Lane, Balsham, Cambridge CB1 6DT — MB ChB 1980 Birm.; MRCP (UK) 1985. Prev: Sen. Regist. (Paediat.) Addenbrooke's Hosp. Camb.

ROBERTS, Edward Morgan Fairfield Medical Centre, Julian Terrace, Port Talbot SA12 6UQ Tel: 01639 890916; 7 Tenacre Wood, Margam, Port Talbot SA13 2SU Tel: 01639 897706 — MB BCh Wales 1970; MRCGP 1977; FRCGP 1996. (Welsh National School of Medicine Cardiff) Trust Practitioner (Geriat.) Glan Y Mor Trust; CME Tutor Neath Postgrad. Centre; Mem. Morgannwg LMC. Socs: BMA (Chairm. W. Glam. Div.). Prev: Chairm. & Sec. W. Glam. LMC (Ex. Mem. W. Glam. FPC).

ROBERTS, Edward Reginald 206 Hawthorn Drive, Ipswich IP2 0QQ Tel: 01473 685070 — MB 1957 Camb.; MA Camb. 1960, MB 1957, BChir 1956; DObst RCOG 1959. (St. Thos.) Socs: BMA. Prev: Ho. Surg. St. Mary's Hosp. Portsmouth; Ho. Phys. St. Richard's Hosp. Chichester; SHO Obst. Herts. & Essex Hosp. Bishop's Stortford.

ROBERTS, Edwin George Gerald (retired) Marford Gate, Marford, Wrexham LL12 8SF Tel: 01978 852217 — MRCS Eng. LRCP Lond. 1945; BSc (Distinc. Anat.) 1941, MB BCh Wales 1944; FRCP Lond. 1971, M 1947; FRCPCH 1997; DCH Eng. 1949. Cons. Paediat. Clwyd & Powys AHAs, Wrexham; Hon. Cons. Paediat. Robt. Jones & Agnes Hunt Orthop. Hosp. OsW.ry. Prev: Regist. (Paediat.) Roy. Infirm. Cardiff.

ROBERTS, Eilir Arwel Wyn Southport and Formby District General Hospital, Town Lane, Kew, Southport PR8 6PN Tel: 01704 547471 Fax: 01704 502054; Bryn Dedwydd, 8 Trefonwys, Bangor LL57 2HU Tel: 01248 352297 — MB ChB 1995 Liverp. (Univ. Liverp. Med. Sch.) SHO (Anaesth.) S.port & Formby Dist. Gen. Hosp.

ROBERTS, Eiry Wyn Lilly Research Centre Ltd., Erlwood Manor, Windlesham GU20 6PH — MB BS 1987 Lond.; BSc (Pharmacol.) Lond. 1983; MRCP (UK) 1990; Dip. Pharm. Med. RCP (UK) 1994. (St. Bart. Med. Coll.) Dir. Clin. Pharmacol. (Europe) Lilly Research Centre Ltd. Surrey. Socs: Roy. Soc. Med.

ROBERTS, Elaine Quarry Farm, Sandy Lane N., Irbymill Hill, Irby, Wirral L61 4XW — MB ChB 1986 Liverp. Clin. Med. Off. (Paediat.) Liverp. HA.

ROBERTS, Elisabeth Damaris (retired) 31 Park Gates Drive, Cheadle Hulme, Cheadle SK8 7DD Tel: 0161 485 4975 Email: roberts@dameris.treasure.co.uk — MB ChB Manch. 1956; DA Eng. 1959. Prev: Clin. Med. Off. S. Manch. HA.

ROBERTS, Elizabeth Jane Queen Marys Sidcup NHS Trust, Sidcup DA14 6LT Tel: 020 8302 2678 Fax: 020 8308 3052 Email: erobgas@aol.com; 2 Park Hill, Bickley, Bromley BR1 2JH Email: erebgas@aol.com — BM 1978 Soton.; FFA RCS Eng. 1985. (Univ. Soton.) Cons. Anaesth. Qu. Mary's Hosp. Sidcup; Assoc. Med. Director, Peri-Operat. Serv.s, Qu. Mary's Sidcup Trust. Socs: Obsteric Anaesthetics Assn.; H.C.S.A; B.M.A. Prev: Sen. Regist. Rotat. (Anaesth) Soton. Gen. Hosp. & Roy. Hants. Co. Hosp. Winchester.

ROBERTS, Elizabeth June Dunchurch Surgery, Dunsmore Heath, Dunchurch, Rugby CV22 6AP Tel: 01788 522448 Fax: 01788 814609; 7 Church Close, harborough Magna, Rugby CV23 0GA Tel: 01788 833250 Fax: 01788 814609 — BM 1987 Soton.; MRCGP 1991. (Southampton)

ROBERTS, Elizabeth Merryl Plains View Surgery, 57 Plains Rd, Mapperley, Nottingham NG3 5LB Tel: 0115 962 1717; 8 Highcroft, Woodthorpe, Nottingham NG3 5LP Tel: 0115 967 0613 — MB ChB 1989 Manch.; BSc St. And. 1986; MRCGP 1996. p/t GP Retainer, Plains View Surg. Nottm. Socs: Roy. Coll. of Gen. Practitioners. Prev: Trainee GP Stockport; SHO (O & G) Hope Hosp. Manch.

ROBERTS

ROBERTS, Elizabeth St Clair (retired) Beechfield, 25 Bolnore Road, Haywards Heath RH16 4AB Tel: 01444 413507 — BM BCh 1945 Oxf.; MA, BM BCh Oxon. 1945; DCH Eng. 1948. Prev: Clin. Asst. (Dermat.) Brighton & Cuckfield & Crawley Health Dists.

ROBERTS, Elved Bryn Flat 30, Glan Clwyd Hospital, Bodelwyddan, Rhyl LL18 5UJ Tel: 01745 583910 — MB ChB 1993 Liverp. SHO (Chest Med. & Rheum.) Abergele Hosp. Glan Clwyd Hosp. Trust. Socs: BMA. Prev: SHO (Elderly Med.) GLan Clwyd Dist. Gen. Hosp. Trust; SHO (Cardiol.) Aintree Hosps. Liverp.; SHO (Gen. Med.) Aintree Hosps.

ROBERTS, Elwyn Bron Derw, Garth Road, Bangor LL57 2RS Tel: 01248 370900; Cil-y-Bont, Treborth Road, Bangor LL57 2RJ Tel: 01248 353312 — MB BCh 1959 Wales; DPH 1962; DObst RCOG 1964. (Cardiff) Socs: BMA. Prev: Ho. Surg. ENT & Ophth. Depts. Cardiff Roy. Infirm.; SHO (Paediat.) & Ho. Surg. (Obst.) St. David's Hosp. Bangor.

ROBERTS, Emyr The New Surgery, 42 Duke Street, Formby, Liverpool L37 4AT Tel: 01704 876363 Fax: 01704 833808; 21 St. George's Road, Formby, Liverpool L37 3HH — MB BCh 1967 Wales; MRCOG 1974. Prev: Regist. (O & G) Liverp. Matern. Hosp. & Wom. Hosp. Liverp.; Regist. (O & G) Walton & Fazakerly Hosps. Liverp.; SHO (Gen. Surg.) Roy. Alexandra Hosp. Rhyl.

ROBERTS, Eric Lloyd (retired) Lower Hisley, Lustleigh, Newton Abbot TQ13 9SH Tel: 0164 77 389 — MB ChB 1923 Liverp. Prev: Ho. Surg. Roy. Liverp. Childr. Hosp. & Special Depts. Liverp. Roy.

ROBERTS, Eric Lloyd Kyle Firth, Lon-y-Bryn, Treardour Bay, Anglesey LL65 2BQ Tel: 01407 860619; Euron, 1 Garth Drive, Gaerwen LL60 6DH Tel: 01248 421683 — MB ChB 1962 Liverp. (Liverp.) Prev: SHO Radiol. Liverp. Roy. Infirm. Ho. Phys. Wiston Hosp. Prescot; Ho. Surg. Ormskirk & Dist. Gen. Hosp.

ROBERTS, Ernest Forbes (retired) 90 Park Road, London W4 3HL Tel: 020 8995 2583 — LMSSA 1944 Lond.; MA Camb. 1943; MRCGP 1953. Prev: GP Lond.

ROBERTS, Ernest Theodore (retired) The Torrs, 101 Havant Road, East Cosham, Portsmouth PO6 2JE Tel: 01705 379726 — MB BChir 1947 Camb.; BA Camb. 1944, MA 1949, MB BChir 1947. Prev: Cas. Off. & Ho. Phys. St. Thos. Hosp.

ROBERTS, Fiona 17 Kirklee Circus, Glasgow G12 0TW Email: froberts@cableinet.co.uk; f.roberts@spr.co.uk — MB ChB 1991 Glas.; BSc Glas. 1989, MB ChB 1991; MD 1998; MRCPath Glas.1998; Dip RCPath 1995. (Glasgow) Cons. Dept. Path. Vict. Infirm. Glas.

ROBERTS, Fiona Cookridge Hospital, Leeds LS16 6QB Tel: 0113 392 4428 — MB BS 1981 Lond.; MA (Hons.) Camb. 1981; MD Lond. 1994; MRCP (UK) 1985; FRCR 1990. Cons. Clin. Oncol. Cookridge Hosp. Leeds.

ROBERTS, Fiona Edith Vivian (retired) Whitchurch Surgery, 49 Oving Road, Whitchurch, Aylesbury HP22 4JF Tel: 01296 641203 Fax: 01296 640021 — MB BS 1968 Lond.; MRCS Eng. LRCP Lond. 1968; MRCGP 1975; DCH RCP Lond. 1973; DObst RCOG 1971.

***ROBERTS, Fleur Elizabeth** 157 Quinton Road, Harborne, Birmingham B17 0PY — MB ChB 1997 Birm.; ChB Birm. 1997.

ROBERTS, Francis Paul Washford House, Claybrook Drive, Redditch B98 0DU Tel: 01527 517747 Fax: 01527 525934 — MB ChB 1967 Birm.; MRCS Eng. LRCP Lond. 1967; FFOM RCP Lond. 1993, MFOM 1984; DIH Eng. 1979. (Birmingham) Director, Med. Serv.s, Marsh Heath Ltd (UK). Socs: Soc. Occupat. Med.; Fell., Roy. Soc. of Med. Prev: Sen. Employm. Med. Adviser to the Health & Safety Exec. W. Midl.; Company Med. Adviser Lucas Elec. Ltd. Birm.; Health Progr. Manager & Sen. Med. Adviser Lucas Varity plc Solihull.

ROBERTS, Freda Milner (retired) Fernlea, Grassendale Esplanade, Grassendale Park, Liverpool L19 0LL — MB ChB 1948 Liverp.; FRCOG 1985, M 1956; FRCPath 1984, M 1972. Prev: Dir. Mersey Regional Blood Transfus. Serv.

ROBERTS, Frederick David 5 Manor Farm Close, Gate Lane, Brouchton, Kettering NN14 1ND Tel: 01536 791515 Fax: 01536 791175 Email: drobertscda@compuserve.com; 5 Manor Farm Close, Gate Lane, Broughton, Kettering NN14 1ND Tel: 01536 791515 Fax: 01536 791175 Email: drobertscda@compuserve.com — MRCS Eng. LRCP Lond. 1967; DObst RCOG 1972. (Leeds) Indep. Dispensing Cons.; Edr. Non-Princip., Locum GP. Socs: (Counc.) BMA (Ex-Pres. Leics. Div.) GPC; Founder Mem. (Ex-Chairm.) Dispensing Doctors' Assn.; Founder Mem. Country Doctors Assn. Prev: SHO (Paediat.) Herts. & Essex Gen. Hosp. Bishop's Stortford; SHO (Obst.) St. John's Hosp. Chelmsford; Ho. Phys. Clayton Hosp. Wakefield.

ROBERTS, Frederick John (retired) Hilltop, 2 West Road, Prenton, Prenton CH43 9RP Tel: 0151 677 4087 Email: john.pam@tesco.net — MD 1974 Bristol; MB BS Lond. 1956; FRCP Ed. 1982, M 1961; MRCS Eng. LRCP Lond. 1956; FRCPsych. 1979; FRANZCP 1979; FRACP 1978; DPM Durham. 1960. Prev: Prof. Psychol. Med. Univ. of Otago, NZ.

ROBERTS, Frederick Leighton 18 Penleonard Close, Exeter EX2 4NY Tel: 01392 420077 — MB ChB 1978 Bristol; FFA RCS Eng. 1982. Cons. Anaesth. Roy. Devon & Exeter Hosp. Prev: Sen. Regist. (Anaesth.) Bristol; Regist. (Anaesth.) Cardiff; Vis. Asst. Prof. Anaesth. Madison Wisconsin.

ROBERTS, Gareth Endaf Wyn Bryn Dedwydd, 8 Trefonwys, Bangor LL57 2HU Tel: 01248 352297 — MB ChB 1994 Liverp.; BSc (Hons.) Physiol. Liverp. 1991, MB ChB 1994. Ho. Off. (Med. & Surg.) Aintree Trust Hosps. Liverp. Socs: Y Gymdeithias Feddygol.

ROBERTS, Gareth Rhys 3 Barras Terrace, Bedale DL8 2DD — MB ChB 1994 Manch.; BSc (Hons.) Manch. 1991, MB ChB (Hons) 1994. (Manch.) Socs: Roy. Coll. GP's.

ROBERTS, Geoffrey Cyril Stuart 4 Newhaven Road, New Brighton, Wallasey CH45 1HS — MB ChB 1952 Liverp. Prev: Orthop. Ho. Surg. & Cas. Off. David Lewis N.. Hosp.

ROBERTS, Geoffrey David Upper Gordon Road Surgery, 37 Upper Gordon Road, Camberley GU15 2HJ Tel: 01276 26424 Fax: 01276 63486; 2 Kingsley Avenue, Camberley GU15 2LZ Tel: 01276 27770 — MB ChB 1973 Manch.; MRCP (UK) 1980; FRCGP 1992, M 1978; DCH Eng. 1980. (Manchester University) Chairm. Surrey Heath PCG; Sen. Tutor & Hon. Sen. Lect. (Gen. Pract.) St. Geo. Hosp. Med. Sch. Lond.; Educat. Adviser W. Surrey HA. Socs: Fell.RCGP; Centre for Advancem. of Interprofessional Educat.; Commiss. on Primary Care. Prev: Cons. Primary Care MSW HA; Chairm. Anticipatory Care Teams; Educat.l Adviser RCGP.

ROBERTS, Geoffrey James 24 Springmeadow, Charlesworth, Glossop SK13 5HP Tel: 01457 867027 Fax: 01457 858048 — MB ChB 1972 Manch. Med. Dir. Warrington Community Health Care NHS Trust; Hon. Clin. Lect. Manch. Univ.; Chief Examr. Health Inst. Risk Managem.; Mem. Ment. Health ACT Commision. Socs: Manch. Med. Soc.; BAMM. Prev: Head Risk Managem. Med. Defence Union; Med. Dir. & Dir. Ment. Health Servs. Worthing Priority Care NHS Trust.

ROBERTS, Geoffrey Stafford (retired) 14 Stevens Road, Heswall, Wirral CH60 1XS Tel: 0151 342 8910 — MB ChB Liverp. 1953; MRCS Eng. LRCP Lond. 1953; FRCGP 1980, M 1965. Prev: Mem. Disabil. Appeal Tribunals Indep. Tribunal Serv.

ROBERTS, George Battersby Shuttleworth 10 Lochbroom Drive, Newton Mearns, Glasgow G77 5DY — MB ChB 1944 Glas.; BSc Glas. 1941, BSc (Hons. Path.) 1948, MD (Hons.) 1957; FRCP Glas. 1971, M 1962; FRCPath 1967, M 1963. (Univ. Glas.) Cons. Path. in Admin. Charge Vict. Infirm. Glas. & Assoc. Hosps.; Hon. Lect. Path. Univ. Glas. Socs: Path. Soc. Gt. Brit. & Assn. Clin. Pathol. Prev: Area Path. Ayrsh. Hosps.; Pathol. Ruchill Hosp. Glas. & W.. Infirm. Glas.; Sen. Lect. Univ. Glas.

ROBERTS, George David Dodd (retired) Department Oral & Maxillofacial Surgery, York District Hospital, Wigginton Road, York YO31 8HE Tel: 01904 631313 — MB ChB 1968 Sheff.; FDS RCS Eng. 1971; BDS Liverp. 1963. Cons. Oral & Maxillofacial Surg. York Dist. Hosp., ScarBoro. & Harrogate Hosps. Prev: Sen. Regist. (Oral Surg.) King's Coll. Hosp. & Qu. Vict. Hosp. E. Grinstead.

ROBERTS, Geraint 2 Penybanc, Tanerdy, Carmarthen SA31 2HA Tel: 01267 234099 — MB BCh 1964 Wales; FRCOG 1982, M 1969. (Cardiff) Cons. O & G W. Wales Gen. Hosp.; Hon. Clin. Teach. Univ. Wales Coll. Med. & Univ. Lond. Socs: Welsh Obst. & Gyn. Soc.; Eur. Obst. & Gyn. Soc. Prev: Sen. Regist. (O & G) Welsh Hosp. Bd. & Univ. Hosp. Wales Gp. Hosps.; Regist. United Cardiff Hosps.

***ROBERTS, Geraint Llion Wyn** 8 Trefonwys, Bangor LL57 2HU — MB ChB 1997 Liverp.

ROBERTS, Professor Geraint Meirwyn, CBE Department Radiology, University of Wales College of Medicine, Heath Park, Cardiff CF14 4XN Tel: 029 2074 3070 Fax: 029 2074 4726; 16 Ty Draw Road, Penylan, Cardiff CF23 5HB Tel: 029 2047 1680 — MB BS 1965 Lond.; MD Lond. 1978; FRCP Lond. 1987, M 1969; MRCS Eng. LRCP Lond. 1965; FRCR 1973; Hon. FRACR 1994; DMRD Eng.

1971. (St. Thos.) Prof. Med. Imaging & Dean of Med. Univ. Wales Coll. Med. Cardiff; Baker Prof. Roy. Australasian Coll. Radiol. 1994. Prev: Cons. Radiol. Univ. Hosp. Wales, Cardiff; Sen. Lect. (Radiol.) Welsh Nat. Sch. Med. Cardiff.

ROBERTS, Gerard William Madeira Road Surgery, 1A Madeira Road, Parkstone, Poole BH14 9ET Tel: 01202 741345; 14 Eaton Road, Branksome Park, Poole BH13 6DG Tel: 01202 757613 Fax: 01202 757613 Email: gerry.roberts@dial.pipex.com — MB ChB 1980 Bristol; MRCGP; FFARCS; DCH; MBA Bournemouth. GP Princip.; Lect. in Gen. Med. Diag. AngloEurop. Chirpractic Coll.; Dir. Poole Hyperbaric Centre Ltd. Socs: BMA; Undersea & Hyperbaric Med. Soc.

ROBERTS, Gillian Catherine 7 Hawick Avenue, Paisley PA2 9LD — MB ChB 1998 Glas.; MB ChB Glas 1998.

ROBERTS, Gillian Margaret 19 Mimosa Close, Birmingham B29 4DA Tel: 0121 476 1384 Fax: 0121 476 1384; Bryn Arlais, Llanaelhaearn, Caernarfon LL54 5AG — BM BCh 1960 Oxf.; MA, BM BCh Oxf. 1960; MRCOG 1967. (Oxf. & Univ. Coll. Hosp.) JP. Prev: Regist. (O & G) King's Coll. Hosp. Gp. Hosps.; SHO (O & G) Addenbrooke's Hosp. Camb.; Ho. Surg. Obst. Unit. Univ. Coll. Hosp. Lond.

ROBERTS, Glenn Anthony North Devon District Hospital, Raleigh Park, Barnstaple EX31 4JB Tel: 01271 22577 — MB ChB 1979 Bristol. Cons. Psychiat. N. Devon. Prev: Sen. Regist. (Adult Psychiat.) Wessex RHA.

ROBERTS, Glyn Hywel Plas Meddyg Surgery, Station Road, Ruthin LL15 1BP Tel: 01824 702255 Fax: 01824 707221; Plas Meddyg, Station Road, Ruthin LL15 1BP Tel: 01824 702255 — MB BS 1981 Lond.; BSc (Hons.) (Biochem.) Lond. 1978; MRCS Eng. LRCP Lond. 1981; DFFP 1994; DRCOG 1986; Cert. Family Plann. JCC 1986. (St. Bart.) Hon. Med. Advis. Welsh Wom's Hockey Assn. Prev: SHO (Orthop.) Roy. Nat. Orthop. Hosp. Lond.

ROBERTS, Graham Alexander 10 Garw-Wood Drive, Croesyceiliog, Cwmbran NP44 2QJ — MB BS 1991 Lond.

ROBERTS, Graham Colin 87 Victory Road, London SW19 1HP — BM BCh 1993 Oxf.; MA Oxf. 1996; MRCP (UK); MRCPCH. (Oxf.) Specialist Regist. (Paediat.) N. Thames. Prev: Regist. (Paediat.) St. Mary's Hosp. Lond.; SHO Rotat. St. Jas. Univ. Hosp. Leeds; Ho. Off. (Paediat. Surg.) Roy. Hosp. Sick Childr. Glas.

ROBERTS, Graham Ivor 18 Chantry Grove, Lawrence Weston, Bristol BS11 0QH Tel: 0117 982 7710 — LRCPI & LM, LRSCI & LM 1954; LRCPI & LM, LRCSI & LM 1954. (RCSI)

ROBERTS, Gregory Anthony Manor Road Surgery, 31 Manor Road, Folkestone CT20 2SE Tel: 01303 851122 Fax: 01303 220914 — MB BChir 1991 Camb. (Cambridge)

ROBERTS, Mr Griffith Ithel (retired) Rutherglen, 17 Wexham St., Beaumaris LL58 8HW Tel: 01248 810707 — MB ChB 1938 Liverp.; MChOrth. Liverp.1947; FRCS Ed. 1943. Prev: Ships Surg. Roy. Fleet Auxil.

ROBERTS, Griffith Wyn, OBE (retired) Greengates, Gwernaffield Road, Mold CH7 1RE Tel: 01352 756565 — MB BCh BAO Belf. 1941; FFCM 1974; DPH Belf. 1947. Prev: Area Med. Off. Clwyd AHA.

ROBERTS, Gwendolen Ellen (retired) Nursing & Residential Home, Westlecot House, Belmont Crescent, Swindon SN1 4EY — MRCS Eng. LRCP Lond. 1931; MD Lond. 1933; MB BS 1931. Prev: Clin. Asst. Burderop Hosp. Wroughton.

ROBERTS, Gwilym James (retired) 31 Cwnt y-Vil Road, Penarth Tel: 01222 708334 — MRCS Eng. LRCP Lond. 1931; BSc Wales 1925; MD Ed. 1932, MB ChB 1928; DPH Wales 1933; DPA Liverp. 1940. Prev: Med. Off. Welsh Bd. Health.

ROBERTS, Gwyn Elias Buckelands, 9 Station Road, Fulbourn, Cambridge CB1 5ER Tel: 01223 880738 — MB BCh 1956 Wales; MA Camb. 1977; FRCPsych 1984, M 1971; DPM Eng. 1961. (Cardiff) Emerit. Prof. Ment. Handicap Univ. Nottm. Med. Sch. Socs: Fell. Roy. Soc. Med.; Brit. Paediat. Assn. Prev: Cons. Psychiat. Camb. HA; Assoc. Lect. (Fac. Clin. Med.) Univ. Camb.; Sen. Regist. (Research) Hosp. Sick Childr. Gt. Ormond St.

ROBERTS, Gwyn Haydn Berllys, Penaber, Criccieth LL52 0ES — MB BCh 1993 Wales.

ROBERTS, Mr Gwyn Richard Ellis (retired) Beech Farm House, Sedlescombe, Battle TN33 0QS Tel: 01424 87 267 — MRCS Eng. LRCP Lond. 1955; MS Lond. 1973, MB BS 1955; FRCS Eng. 1960;

FRCS Ed. 1960. Prev: Cons. Surg. Roy. E. Sussex & St. Helen's Hosps. Hastings & Bexhill Hosp.

ROBERTS, Gwyneth Margaret (retired) 65 Beacon Way, Rickmansworth WD3 7PB Tel: 01923 897500 — MB ChB 1954 Manch. Prev: Ho. Phys. Crumpsall Hosp. Manch.

ROBERTS, Gwynfor Health Centre, Llanfairpwllgwyngyll LL61 5YZ Tel: 01248 714388 Fax: 01248 715826; Carreg Lwyd, Ffordd Pentraeth, Menai Bridge LL59 5HU Tel: 01248 712448 — MB BCh 1969 Wales; BSc Wales 1966.

ROBERTS, Gwynneth Ann 48 Redwood Road, Kinver, Stourbridge DY7 6JR Tel: 01384 877351; Midlands Occupational Health Service, 83 Birmingham Road, West Bromwich B70 6PX Tel: 0121 601 4041 — MB BCh 1981 Wales; BSc (1st cl. Hons.) Wales 1978; MRCP (UK) 1985; MFOM RCP Lond. 1995, AFOM 1990. (Welsh National School of Medicine) Med. Off. Midl. Occupat. Health Serv. W. Bromwich. Socs: Soc. Occupat. Med. (Treas. W. Midl.s Gp. 1998).

ROBERTS, Harold Edward Saltaire Medical Centre, Richmond Road, Shipley BD18 4RX Tel: 01274 593101 Fax: 01274 772588 — MB ChB 1968 Leeds. (Leeds) Socs: Bradford M-C Soc.

ROBERTS, Harold Ellison 20 Clifford Road, Sheffield S11 9AQ Tel: 0114 255 1473 Fax: 0114 255 4703 — BM BCh 1957 Oxf.; MRCS Eng. LRCP Lond. 1949. (Oxf. & Lond. Hosp.) Med. Off. Sheff. Regional Blood Transfus. Centre; Hon. Med. Off. Edale Mt.ain Rescue Team. Socs: Fell. Roy. Soc. Med.

ROBERTS, Helen Clare Elderly Care Unit, Level G, West Wing, Southampton General Hospital, Tremona Road, Shirley, Southampton SO16 6YD Tel: 02380 794354 Fax: 02380 796965 — MB ChB 1984 Birm.; BSc (Hons.) Birm. 1981; MRCP (UK) 1989; FRCP (UK) 1999. p/t Cons. Phys. (Elderly Care) Soton. Gen. Hosp. Socs: BMA; Brit. Geriat. Soc. Prev: Sen. Regist. (Geriat. Med.) Qu. Alexandra Hosp. Portsmouth & Soton. Gen. Hosp.; Regist. (Gen. Med.) Gen. Hosp. St. Helier Jersey & Roy. S. Hants. Hosp. Soton.

ROBERTS, Helen Judith Margaret Farnham Health Centre, Brightwells, Farnham GU9 7SA Tel: 01252 723122; 37 Weydon Hill Road, Farnham GU9 8NX Tel: 01252 733630 Fax: 01252 733630 — MB BS 1988 Lond. (Univ. Coll. Hosp. Med. Sch.) p/t SCMO Jarvis BrE. Screening Centre Guildford. Prev: Trainee GP Yeovil Dist. Hosp.

ROBERTS, Helen Louise 26 Oldacres, Maidenhead SL6 1XJ — MB ChB 1996 Sheff.

ROBERTS, Helen May Dinas, Port Dinorwic LL56 4RX — MB BCh 1973 Wales.

ROBERTS, Mr Henry (retired) 38 Greening Drive, Edgbaston, Birmingham B15 2XA Tel: 0121 454 7676 — MD 1951 Liverp.; MB ChB 1945; FRCS Ed. 1956; FRCOG 1961, M 1951. Cons. O & G United Birm. Hosps. Prev: Regist. (Obst.) & Tutor, Mill Rd. Matern. Hosp. Liverp.

ROBERTS, Henry Lomax, Col. late RAMC (retired) 11 Pendleton Close, Redhill RH1 6QY Tel: 01737 760669 — MB ChB 1954 Leeds; DTM & H Eng. 1964. Adviser Insur. Med. (UNUM). Prev: Dir. Med. Servs. Sultans' Armed Forces Oman.

ROBERTS, Honor Susan Anne Department of Microbiology, Farnborough Hospital, Farnborough Common, Orpington BR6 8ND Tel: 01689 814110 Fax: 01689 814031 Email: honor.roberts@bromleyhospitals.nhs.uk — MRCS Eng. LRCP Lond. 1979; MSc (Microbiol.) Lond. 1987, BSc (Hons. Path.) 1976, MB BS 1979; FRCPath 1986. p/t Cons. Microbiol. Bromley Hosp.s NHS Trust. Prev: Sen. Regist. (Microbiol.) Guy's Hosp. Lond. & Pub. Health Laborat. Serv. Ashford Kent.

ROBERTS, Howard Frederick 73, Onslow Gardens, London N10 3JY Tel: 020 8883 7473 Fax: 020 8883 7473 — MPhil Lond. 1973, MB BS 1963; MRCP Lond. 1969; MRCPsych 1974. (Lond. Hosp.) Cons. Child & Adolesc. Psychiat. S. Lond. and Maudsley NHS Trust. Socs: Assoc. Mem. Brit. Psychoanalyt. Soc. Prev: Regist. & Hon. Sen. Regist. Maudsley Hosp. Lond.; Research Worker Inst. Psychiat. Lond.

ROBERTS, Hugh Richard Sydney 18 Gosset Street, St Albans, Christchurch, New Zealand; 19 St. Thomas Road, London N4 2QH — MB BS 1987 Lond.; MD Lond. 1996; MRCP (UK) 1990; FRCR 1994. (Char. Cross & Westm.) Cons. Radiol. & Hon. Sen. Lect. ChristCh. Pub. Hosp. NZ. Prev: Sen. Regist. (Radiol.) Univ. Coll. Lond. Hosps.; Clin. Lect. (Surg.) Univ. Coll. Lond.; Regist. (Med.) Jersey Gen. Hosp.

ROBERTS

ROBERTS, Mr Humphrey Richard Medwyn (retired) 64 Chartfield Avenue, London SW15 6HQ Tel: 020 8789 1758 — MB BChir 1958 Camb.; MB Camb. 1958; BChir Camb. 1957; MA Camb. 1958; FRCS Eng. 1961, LRCP Lond. 1957; FRCOG 1978, M 1965. Prev: Cons. O & G W.m. Hosp. Lond.

ROBERTS, Huw Gruffydd Tenby Surgery, The Norton, Tenby SA70 8AB Tel: 01834 844161 Fax: 01834 844227; Ger-y-Rhyd, St. Florence, Tenby SA70 8LJ — MB BS 1973 Lond.; BSc Lond. 1973, MB BS 1973.

ROBERTS, Huw Lewis Liverpool House, Waunfawr, Caernarfon LL55 4YY Tel: 01286 650223 Fax: 01286 650714; Y Culfor, Bangor Road, Caernarfon LL55 1LN Tel: 01286 671067 — MB ChB 1971 Liverp.; MRCP (UK) 1974; MRCS Eng. LRCP Lond. 1971. (Liverp.) Socs: Gymdeithas Feddygol; BMA. Prev: Resid. & Fell. (Med.) Johns Hopkins Hosp. Baltimore, USA; Regist. David Lewis N.. Hosp. Liverp.; Ho. Off. Liverp. Roy. Infirm.

ROBERTS, Mr Hywel Griffith (retired) 2 Cadnant Court, Rating Row, Beaumaris LL58 8AT — MB BCh 1935 Wales; BSc Wales 1932, MB BCh 1935; FRCS Ed. 1939; DObst RCOG 1938. Prev: Sen. Surg. Regist., Ho. Surg., Roy. Infirm. Cardiff.

ROBERTS, Hywel Sion Ffrydlas, 4 Frondeg Crescent, Llanfairpwllgwyngyll LL61 5AX Tel: 01498 551308 — MB BCh Wales 1996; BSc (1st cl. Hons) Phys. Wales; BSc Hons - Physiology - 1st Class Univ. of Wales Coll. Cardiff, 1993. (University of Wales College of Medicine) SHO Cardiol. Ysbyty Gwynedd Bangor. Socs: BMA; MDU; Gymedithas Feddygol, Welsh Med. Soc. Prev: SHO Gastroenterol.; Ho. Off. Vasc./Gen. Surg.; Ho. Off. Respirat./Gen. Med.

ROBERTS, Ian Queens Hospital, Burton Hospitals NHS Trust, Belvedere Road, Burton-on-Trent DE13 0RB; 51 Main Street, Rosliston, Swadlincote DE12 8JW — MB ChB 1986 Leic.; FRCA 1995; DA (UK) 1988; M.Med Sci. (Distinction) 1998. (Leicester) Cons. Anaesth. Prev: Regist. (Anaesth.) N. Staffs. Hosps.

ROBERTS, Ian Station Road Health Centre, Station Road, Haydock, St Helens NA11 0JN Tel: 01744 22272; 6 Elmsfield Park, Aughton Green, Ormskirk L39 6TJ — MB ChB 1973 Liverp.; DCH Eng. 1976; Dip. Pract. Dermat. Wales 1990. GP St. Helens Merseyside. Socs: Fac. Community Health.

ROBERTS, Ian Cobtree Medical Practice, Southways, Sutton Valence, Maidstone ME17 3HG Tel: 01622 843800 Fax: 01622 844184; Gladstones, The Quarries, Boughton Monchelsea, Maidstone ME17 4NJ — MB BS 1971 Lond.; MRCP (UK) 1975; MRCS Eng. LRCP Lond. 1971; DRCOG 1976.

ROBERTS, Ian Ellis Meddygfa, Canolfan, Iechyd, Bala LL23 7BA Tel: 01678 520308 — MB ChB 1958 Liverp. (Liverp.) Socs: BMA. Prev: Ho. Phys., Ho. Surg. & Ho. Surg. (Obst.) Sefton Gen. Hosp.; Res. Med. Off. Colwyn Bay & W. Denbighsh. Hosp.

ROBERTS, Ian Forrest Chesterfield and North Derbyshire Royal Hospital, Calow, Chesterfield S44 5BL Tel: 01246 277271 Fax: 01246 552620 Email: ian.roberts@cndrh.tr.trent.nhs.uk; Cornerstone Cottage, 209 Walton Back Lane, Walton, Chesterfield S42 7LP Tel: 01246 569789 Email: ian@therobertshouse.f9.co.uk — MB BS Lond. 1966; FRCP Lond. 1991; MRCP (UK) 1969; MRCS Eng. LRCP Lond. 1966; FRCPCH 1997. (Guy's) Cons. Paediat. Chesterfield & N. Derbysh. Roy. Hosp. Socs: Hon. Sec. Chesterfield Med. Soc.; E. Mids. Med. Soc; Trent Regional Paediat. Soc. Prev: Sen. Regist. St. Geo. Hosp. Lond.; SHO Hammersmith Hosp. Lond.; Ho. Phys. Evelina Childr. Hosp. S.wark.

ROBERTS, Ian Gray Child Health Monitoring Unit, Department of Edipemiology & Biostatistics, Institute of Child Health, 30 Guildford St., London WC1N 1EH — MB BCh 1985 Wales.

ROBERTS, Ian Simon David Dept. of Cellular Pathology, John Radcliffe Hospital, Headington, Oxford OX3 9DU Tel: 01865 222889 Fax: 01865 220519 Email: iau.roberts@orh.nhs.uk — MB ChB 1985 Manch.; MRCPath 1993. Cons. Pathologist Oxf. Radcliffe. Hosp.; Hon. Sen. Lect. The Univ. of Oxf. Prev: Lect. (Path.) Univ. Manch.; Sen. Regist. (Histopath.) NW Region; Regist. (Histopath.) Merseyside Region.

ROBERTS, Ifor John Wynn 34 Balmore Drive, Caversham, Reading RG4 8NL — MB ChB 1966 Ed.

ROBERTS, Iorwerth, MM (retired) 209 Pitshanger Lane, Ealing, London W5 1RQ — MB BS 1956 Lond.; MRCS Eng. LRCP Lond. 1956; DObst RCOG 1958.

ROBERTS, Professor Irene Anne Graham Department of Haematology, Imperial College School of Medicine, Hammersmith Hospital, London W12 0HS Tel: 020 8383 3387 Fax: 020 8742 9335 — MB ChB 1978 Glas.; MD (Hons.) Glas. 1988; FRCP Lond. 1994; FRCP Glas. 1992; MRCP (UK) 1981; MRCPath 1987; T(M) 1991; T(Path) 1991; DRCOG 1980. Prof. of Paediatric Haemat., Imperial Coll. Sch. of Med., Hammersmith Campus; Hon. Cons. Paediat. Haemat. Hammersmith Hosp. Lond.; Hon. Cons. Paediat. Haemat. St. Mary's Hosp., Paddington, Lond. Prev: Sen. Lect. (Haemat.) Roy. Postgrad. Med. Sch. Univ. Lond.

ROBERTS, Irene Elizabeth Maesyrhedydd, Pencefn Road, Dolgellau LL40 2ET — MB BCh 1964 Wales. (Cardiff) Clin. Med. Off. Swynedd Aha. Prev: Ho. Phys., Ho. Surg. & SHO Paediat. Maelor Gen. Hosp.

ROBERTS, Mr Iwan Francis 45 Stroud Road, Wimbledon Park, London SW19 8DQ — MB BS 1987 Lond.; BA Oxf. 1984; FRCS Eng. 1991. Regist. (Radiol.) St. Geo. Hosp. Lond. Prev: Regist. (Paediat. Surg.) St. Geo. Hosp. Lond.; Demonst., SHO (Anat.) & Phys. (Accid. & Emerg.) St. Mary's Hosp. & Med. Sch. Lond.; SHO (Gen. Surg.) Bristol & W.on HA.

ROBERTS, Jack (retired) 28 Altar Drive, Bradford BD9 5QD Tel: 01274 226992 Email: jack.roberts@virgin.net — MA Oxf. 1947, BM BCh 1944. Prev: Res. Anaesth. Roy. Berks. Hosp. Reading.

ROBERTS, Jacqueline Mary Putneymead Medical Centre, 350 Upper Richmond Road, London SW15 6TL Tel: 020 8788 0686 — MB BS 1984 Lond. GP Princip. Prev: Trainee GP Richmond, Twickenham & Roehampton HA VTS; Ho. Phys. (Gen. Med. & Radiother.) Essex Co. Hosp. Colchester; Ho. Surg. (Gen. Surg. & Orthop.) & SHO (A & E) Qu. Mary's Hosp. Roehampton.

ROBERTS, James (retired) 459 Altrincham Road, Wythenshawe, Manchester M23 1AA Tel: 0161 998 3326 — MB ChB 1957 Manch.; FRCGP 1975, M 1965; DObst RCOG 1959. Prev: Regional Adviser (Gen. Pract.) Univ. Dept. Postgrad. Med. Studies Manch. Univ.

ROBERTS, James (retired) Orwell Cottage, 3 East Somerville Place, Dundee DD3 6JL Tel: 01382 213671 — MB ChB 1935 St. And.; DPH 1940; MRCGP 1960. Prev: Res. Med. Off. Arbroath Hosp. & Dundee Ment. Hosp.

ROBERTS, James Hugh Martiwdale, Bridgwater Road, Winscombe BS25 1NW — MB ChB 1989 Leeds. SHO (Orthop.) Norf. & Norwich Hosp. Prev: SHO (A & E) & Demonst. (Anat.) Leics. Roy. Infirm.; Ho. Off. Leeds Gen. Infirm. & St. Jas. Hosp. Leeds.

ROBERTS, James Hugh Medwyn 64 Chartfield Avenue, London SW15 6HQ; 26B Lynford Road, London W9 3LU Tel: 020 8969 8064 Email: jhmroberts@doctors.org.uk — MB BS 1993 Lond. (St Mary's Hosp. Med. School.) SHO, (Anaesth.), N.wick Pk. Hosp. Lond.

ROBERTS, James John Kennedy HM Prison & Institution, Cornton Vale, Stirling FK9 5NU Tel: 01786 832591 Fax: 01786 834467; 12 Winton Circus, Saltcoats KA21 5DA Tel: 01294 461798 — MB ChB 1976 Ed.; BSc Ed. 1973; MRCGP 1980. (Ed.) Med. Off. HM Prison & Inst. Cornton Vale Stirling. Prev: Clin. Asst. (Med.) W.. Gen. Hosp. Edin.; GP MuirHo.

ROBERTS, James Kennedy Walnut Tree Cottage, Waterley Bottom, North Nibley, Dursley GL11 6EG Tel: 01453 543186 — MB BS 1968 Lond.; MRCS Eng. LRCP Lond. 1968; DObst RCOG 1973. (St. Thos.)

ROBERTS, James Michael Beech House Surgery, Beech House, 69 Vale Street, Denbigh LL16 3AY Tel: 01745 812863 Fax: 01745 816574; Llys Hedydd, Llansannan Road, Henllan, Denbigh LL16 5DE — MB BCh 1985 Wales; DRCOG 1990.

ROBERTS, James Trevor Northern Centre for Cancer Treatment, Newcastle General Hospital, Westgate Road, Newcastle upon Tyne NE4 6BE Tel: 0191 219 4245 Fax: 0191 272 4236; 31 Eskdale Terrace, Jesmond, Newcastle upon Tyne NE2 4DN Tel: 0191 281 1872 — MB BS 1973 Lond.; FRCP Lond. 1993; MRCP (UK) 1976; FRCR 1978. (Westm.) Cons. Clin. Oncol. N. Centre for Cancer Treatm. Socs: Fell. Roy. Soc. Med.; Brit. Inst. Radiol.; Estro Europ. Soc. of Therapeutic Radiol. and Oncol. Prev: Cons. Radiother. & Oncol. Newc. HA; Lect. (Clin. Oncol.) Univ. Camb.; Sen. Regist. (Radiother. & Oncol.) Addenbrooke's Hosp. Camb.

ROBERTS, Jane Elisabeth Camden & Islington Community Health Services NHS Trust, Child & Family Psychiatry, Whittington Hospital, London N19 5NF Tel: 020 7530 2444 Fax: 020 7530 2479 — MB

ChB 1980 Bristol; MSc Brunel 1991; MRCP (UK) 1983; MRCPsych 1986. p/t Cons. Child & Adolesc. Psychiat. Camden & Islington Community Health Servs. NHS Trust Lond. Prev: Sen. Regist. (Child Psychiat.) Tavistock Clin. Lond.; Regist. (Psychiat.) Maudsley Hosp. Lond.; SHO (Paediat.) Qu. Eliz. Hosp. Childr. Lond.

ROBERTS, Jane Elizabeth 14 Kiltongue Cottages, Monklands Hospital, Airdrie ML6 0JS Tel: 01236 713053; 17c Mains Avennue, Giffnock, Glasgow G46 6QY Tel: 0141 638 8258 — MB ChB Aberd. 1969; FRCP Glas. 1994 M 1992; FRCOG 1990, M 1975; DObst 1971; CFM 1995. (Aberd.) Cons. Genitourin. Med. Lanarksh. Prev: Regist. (O & G) Qu. Mother's Hosp. Glas. & W.. Infirm. Glas.; Cons. Genitourin. Med. Gt.er Glas. HB.

ROBERTS, Jane Hazel Alma Street Medical Centre, Alma St., Stockton-on-Tees, Middlesbrough TS1 2AP Tel: 01642 670248; 69 Barker Road, Linthorpe, Middlesbrough TS5 5EW Tel: 01642 607248 — MB ChB 1988 Sheff.; MRCGP 1997; BMedSci Sheff. 1986. (Sheff.) Lect. Primary Health Care, Univ. Of Durh.

ROBERTS, Jane Mary Truan Bach, Cerrigceinwen, Bodorgan LL62 5DH — MB ChB 1994 Sheff.

ROBERTS, Janet Catherine (retired) Marnie, Roseacre Road, Roseacre, Preston PR4 3UE — MB ChB 1971 Liverp.; FFA RCS Eng. 1975; DA Eng. 1973. Prev: Cons. Anaesth. Blackpool Vict. Hosp.

ROBERTS, Janet Eleanor 1 Risca Road, Rogerstone, Newport NP10 9FZ — MB BCh 1973 Wales; BSc Hull 1968.

ROBERTS, Mr Jason Lloyd Barclay 10 Lochard Cottages, Kinlochard, Aberfoyle, Stirling FK8 3TL — MB ChB 1994 Leic.; FRCS Pt. A Ed. 1998; FRCS Pt. B Glas. 1998. (University of Leicester) SHO (Orthop.) W.ern Infirm. Glas.; SHO (Gen./Vasc. Surg.) Gartnavel & W.. Infirm. Glas. Prev: SHO (A & E) Vale of Leven Dist. Gen. Hosp.; SHO (Orthop.) Qu. Med. Centre Nottm.

ROBERTS, Jeffrey Paul Hazel Cottage, 42 Stubbs Wood, Chesham HP5 3RL Tel: 01494 724466 Fax: 01494 724466 Email: jroberts@medrom.u_neb.com — BM BCh Oxf. 1969; MA Oxf. 1975; FRCPsych 1992, M 1973; DPM Eng. 1973. Vis. Cons. Gr.lands Priory Hosp. Lond.; Non-Exec. Dir. Grendon & Springhill Prisons, Grendon Underwood nr. Aylesbury; Mem. Inst. Gp. Anal.; Mem. Managem. Gp. Analytic Pract. Socs: Fell. Roy. Soc. Med.; Gp. Analyt. Soc. Prev: Cons. Psychother. The Roy. Lond. Hosp. & St. Clements Hosp. Lond.; Hon. Cons. Psychother. Guy's Hosp. Lond.; Cons. Psychother. Ingrebourne Centre St. Geo. Hosp. HornCh.

ROBERTS, Jeremy Christopher Radnor Street Surgery, 3 Radnor Street, Glasgow G3 7UA Tel: 0141 334 6111 — MB ChB 1977 Glas.; MRCPsych 1981; DRCOG 1984.

ROBERTS, Jeremy Mark Tel: 01392 403629 (Secretary) Fax: 01392 403620 — MB BS 1983 Lond.; MRCPsych 1990. (Roy. Free) p/t Cons. Psychiat. (Gen. Psychiat.) Wonford Ho. Hosp. Exeter. Prev: Trainee Psychiat. Exeter HA Scheme; Trainee GP Coventry VTS; Sen. Regist. Rotat. (Psychiat.) Bristol.

ROBERTS, Mr Jeremy Openshaw City General Hospital, Newcastle Road, Stoke-on-Trent ST4 6QG Tel: 01782 715444; North Staffordshire Nuffield Hospital, Clayton Road, Newcastle ST5 4DB Tel: 01782 625431 — MB BS 1977 Lond.; MS Lond. 1991; MA Camb. 1978; FRCS Eng. 1983. Cons. Plastic Surg. City Gen. Hosp. Stoke-on-Trent. Prev: Sen. Regist. (Plastic Surg.) Canniesburn Hosp. Glas.; Regist. (Plastic Surg.) Stoke Mandeville Hosp. Aylesbury; Lect. (Surg.) Char. Cross & W.m. Med. Sch.

ROBERTS, Joanne Linda The Surgery, 19 Amwell Street, Hoddesdon EN11 8TU Tel: 01992 464147 Fax: 01992 708698 — MB BS 1987 Lond.

ROBERTS, John (retired) 1 Keyes Avenue, Roath Park, Cardiff CF23 5QQ Tel: 029 2075 1466 — MB BCh 1952 Wales. Prev: GP Cardiff.

ROBERTS, John 89 Northfield Broadway, Edinburgh EH8 7RX Tel: 0131 657 5444 Fax: 0131 669 8116 — MB ChB 1958 Ed. (Ed.) Socs: BMA. Prev: Ho. Phys. Cumbld. Infirm. Carlisle; Ho. Surg. Falkirk Roy. Infirm.; Ho. Off. (Obst.) City Matern. Hosp. Carlisle.

ROBERTS, John Alan Medical Unit, Royal Hampshire County Hospital, Winchester SO22 5DG Tel: 01962 824775 Fax: 01962 825227 Email: alan.roberts.k@weht.swest.nhs.uk; Sainfoin, Winchester Hill, Romsey SO51 7NL Email: alan@roberty@virgin.net — MB ChB 1978 Glas.; BSc (Hons.) (Microbiol.) Glas. 1973, MD 1988; FRCP Lond. 1996; MRCP (UK) 1982. (Glas.) Cons. Gen. & Thoracic Med. Roy. Hants. Co. Hosp. Socs: Brit. Thorac. Soc. Prev: Sen. Regist. (Internal & Respirat. Med.) Soton. Gen. Hosp.; Regist. (Respirat. Med.) W.. Infirm. & Kt.swood Hosp. Glas.; Hon. Research Fell. Strathclyde Univ. Glas.

ROBERTS, Mr John Andrew Diana, Princess of Wales Hospital, Scartho Road, Grimsby DN33 2BA Tel: 01472 74111; Stone House, Stainton le Vale, Market Rasen LN8 6HP Tel: 01472 398605 — MB ChB 1976 Bristol; FRCS Glas. 1981. Cons. Surg. Orthop. & Trauma Grimsby Dist. Gen. Hosp. Socs: BMA; BOA. Prev: Sen. Regist. (Orthop.) W.. Infirm. Glas.

ROBERTS, Mr John Bernard Michael (retired) Dormers, Woodlands Road, Portishead, Bristol BS20 7HE Tel: 01275 843254 — ChM Leeds 1963, MB ChB 1952; FRCS Eng. 1957; FRCGP 1990. Med. Postgrad. Dean Univ. Bristol. Prev: Cons. Urol. Surg. Bristol Roy. Infirm.

ROBERTS, John Brian Priory Medical Group, 19 Albion Road, North Shields NE29 0HT Tel: 0191 257 0223 — MB BS 1978 Newc.

ROBERTS, John Clive (retired) Long Acre, Riverside Road, Dittisham, Dartmouth TQ6 0HS Tel: 01803 722273 — MB BS 1959 Lond.; FFA RCS Eng. 1965; LMSSA Lond. 1959. Cons. Anaesth. St. Mary's Hosp. Lond. Prev: Sen. Regist. (Anaesth.) & Ho. Surg. Surgic. Unit St. Mary's Hosp. Lond.

ROBERTS, John David Victoria Road Health Centre, Victoria Road, Rhymney NP22 5NU Tel: 01685 840627 Fax: 01685 843100 — MB ChB 1977 Liverp.; MRCS Eng. LRCP Lond. 1977.

ROBERTS, John David Arthur c/o Lloyds Bank, 35 Union St., Ryde PO33 2LH — MRCS Eng. LRCP Lond. 1966. (Lond. Hosp.)

ROBERTS, John Gareth BarlowHolsy Srgery, 22 Haniton Terrace, Milfund Daien, Pembroke SA73 35L Tel: 01646 690674 — MB BS 1982 Lond.

ROBERTS, Mr John Gethin Glan-y-Menai, Glyn Garth, Menai Bridge LL59 5NS Email: jrdwrcym@netcomuk.co.uk — BM BCh 1967 Oxf.; MA; FRCS Eng. 1972. (Oxf. & Lond. Hosp.) Cons. Urol. LLa.lli Dynefur Trust LLa.lli. Prev: Sen. Regist. (Urol.) Univ. Hosp. Wales Cardiff; Sen. Regist. (Gen. Surg.) S. Glam. (T) & Clwyd HAs.; Cancer Research Campaign Research Fell. Univ. Hosp. Wales.

ROBERTS, John Guymer The Surgery, Caerffynon, Dolgellau LL40 1LY; Maesyrhedydd, Pencefn Road, Dolgellau LL40 2ET Tel: 01341 422775 — MB BCh 1964 Wales; FRCGP 1990; MRCGP 1969; DObst RCOG 1966. Clin. Asst. (Geriat.) Dolgellau & Barmouth Dist. Hosp.; Police Surg. Dolgellau & Dist.; Chairm. Meirionnydd Med. Soc.; Chairm. N. Wales Fac. RCGP; Sec. Gwynedd LMC. Socs: BMA. Prev: Ho. Phys., Ho. Surg. & SHO (O & G) Maelor Gen. Hosp. Wrexham.

ROBERTS, John Huw (retired) 42 Dunniwood Avenue, Bessacarr, Doncaster DN4 7JT — MB ChB Liverp. 1953; DMRD Eng. 1960; Cons. Radiol. Doncaster Roy. Infirm.

ROBERTS, John Iolo 10 Shawhill Crescent, Newton Mearns, Glasgow G77 5BY — MB ChB 1979 Dundee; FRCR 1986. Cons. (Radiol.) Law Hosp. Carluke. Prev: Sen. Regist. (Radiol.) W.. Infirm. Glas.; Regist. (Radiol.) W.. Infirm. Glas.; SHO (Gen. Med.) Law Hosp. Carluke.

ROBERTS, John Kenneth Cranfield, Gorsey Lane, Ashton-under-Lyne OL6 9BT — MB ChB 1966 Manch.; FRCOG 1984, M 1971. Cons. (O & G) Tameside HA.

ROBERTS, John Kenneth 93 Chapel Street, Billericay CM12 9LR Tel: 22940 — MB BS 1952 Lond.; DObst RCOG 1960. (Middlx. Hosp.) Local Civil Serv. Med. Off.; Med. Off. E.. Elect. Bd. Prev: Ho. Phys. Brighton Gen. Hosp.; Ho. Surg. P. of Wales Gen. Hosp. Lond.; Obst. Sen. Ho. Off. Morriston Hosp.

ROBERTS, John Kenneth (Surgery) Victoria Surgery, Holyhead LL65 1UB Tel: 01407 762713 Fax: 01407 765052; Cae Paradwys, 16 The Rise, Trearddur Bay, Holyhead LL65 2UY Tel: 01407 860529 — MB ChB 1959 Manch. Socs: BMA. Prev: Clin. Asst. (Orthop.) Gwynedd Hosp. Bangor; SHO (Orthop.) Caerns. & Anglesey Gen. Hosp. Bangor; Ho. Surg. Univ. Dept. Orthop. Manch. Roy. Infirm.

ROBERTS, John McKinlay Norcliffe Morris Dean, Henley-by-Fosbury, Marlborough SN8 3RJ Tel: 01264 731250 — MB BS Lond. 1951. (St. Thos.) Prev: Regist. (Med.) St. Mary's Hosp. Portsmouth; Demonst. (Clin. Path.) & Ho. Phys. St. Thos. Hosp.

ROBERTS, John Michael Queen Street House, Queen St., Twyford, Winchester SO21 1QG Tel: 01962 712165 — MRCS Eng. LRCP Lond. 1945; BA Camb. 1941, MB BChir 1949. (Camb. & St. Bart.) Socs: BMA. Prev: Regist. (Surg.) St. Bart. Hosp.; Asst. Lect. (Anat.)

ROBERTS

Char. Cross Hosp. Med. Sch.; Surg. Falkland Is.s Dependency Survey.

ROBERTS, John Milton Digby, OBE Polyphant House, Polyphant, Launceston PL15 7PS Tel: 01566 86518 — MB ChB 1946 Birm.; MRCS Eng. LRCP Lond. 1947; DPH Lond. 1952. Prev: Sen. Specialist (Parasitol.) Min. Health Kenya; Dep. Dir. Med. Serv. Min. Health Kenya; Dir. Div. Vector Borne Dis. Min. Health Kenya.

ROBERTS, John Rees, VRD Iona, St. Margarets Road, Hoylake, Wirral CH47 1HX Tel: 0151 632 4636 — MD 1958 Liverp.; MB ChB 1948; FRCP Lond. 1972, M 1953. (Liverp.) Emerit. Cons. Paediat. Roy. Liverp. Childr. Hosp.; Emerit. Cons. Paediat. Neurol. Liverp. RHB. Socs: Brit. Paediat. Neurol. Assn.; Assn. Brit. Neurols. Prev: Hon. Phys. to HM The Qu.; Surg. Capt. RNR; Fullbright Schol. 1955-56.

ROBERTS, John Richard Lloyd 47 Hugh Street, London SW1V 1QJ Tel: 020 7828 8338 Fax: 020 7233 7616; 17 Perrymead Street, London SW6 3SW Tel: 020 7736 7220 Fax: 020 7731 2732 — MB BChir 1960 Camb.; MA, MB Camb. 1960, BChir 1959; MRCS Eng. LRCP Lond. 1959. (Westm.) GP Lond.; Med. Off. Hellenic Coll.; Sen. Examr. Scott. Widows Fund. Prev: Med. Off. Staff Occupat. Health Unit Chelsea & W.m. Hosp.; Ho. Phys. W.m. Hosp. Lond.; Ho. Surg. Addenbrooke's Hosp. Camb.

ROBERTS, John St Clair Xenova Group plc, 310 Cambridge Science Park, Cambridge CB4 0WG Tel: 01223 423413 Fax: 01223 423458 Email: John-Roberts@Xenova.co.uk — MRCS Eng. LRCP Lond. 1978; FFPM 1999; MFPM 1992. (RCSI) Med. Dir. Xenova Gp. plc. Socs: Fell. Roy. Soc. Med.; Brit. Assn. Pharmaceut. Phys.; Fell. Med. Soc. Lond. Prev: Med. Dir. Merieux UK Maidenhead; Regist. (Path.) Roy. Sussex Co. Hosp. Brighton; Ho. Phys. Roy. Sussex Co. Hosp. Brighton.

ROBERTS, John Taylor 15 Wootton Way, Newnham, Cambridge CB3 9LX Tel: 01223 63539 — MB BS 1956 Lond.; MFCM 1974; DPH Lond. 1960. (St. Mary's)

ROBERTS, John Wyn Anaesthetic Dept, Royal Bolton Hospital, Minerva Road, Farnworth, Bolton BL4 0JR Tel: 01204 390762; 18 Dimple Park, Egerton, Bolton BL7 9QE — MB BCh 1987 Wales; FRCA 1996; DA (UK) 1993; DRCOG 1992. (Univ. Wales Coll. Med.) Cons., (Anaesth.), Bolton Roy. Infirmiry, Bolton, Lancs. Socs: Obst. Anaesth. Assocn. & Difficult Airway Soc. Prev: Trainee GP Mold.

ROBERTS, John Wynne Bousfield Health Centre, Westminster Road, Liverpool L4 4PP Tel: 0151 207 0813 — MRCS Eng. LRCP Lond. 1979; DRCOG 1982. (Liverp.)

ROBERTS, Jon Hilton Windmill Health Centre, Mill Green, Leeds LS14 5JS Tel: 0113 273 3733 Fax: 0113 232 3202; 6 Moor Allerton Drive, Leeds LS17 6RZ — MB ChB 1984 Manch.; DRCOG 1987.

ROBERTS, Jonathan David Vaughan Mayfield Medical Centre, 37 Totnes Road, Paignton TQ4 5LA Tel: 01803 558257 Fax: 01803 663353; Orchard Lodge, Old Road, Harbertonford, Totnes TQ9 7TA Tel: 01803 732879 — MB BS 1985 Lond.; MRCGP 1991; DCH RCP Lond. 1990. GP Princip.; Hon. Lect. Plymouth Postgrad. Med. Sch. Socs: Primary Care Gastroenterol. Soc. Prev: SHO (Paediat.) Plymouth HA; SHO (Geriat.) W. Dorset HA; SHO (A & E) Torbay HA.

ROBERTS, Mr Jonathan Verrier 23 Barnsbury Square, London N1 1JP — MB BCh 1978 Wales; FRCS Eng. 1984. Clin. Research Fell. Dept. Surg. King's Coll. Hosp. Lond. Prev: Regist. (Gen. Surg.) Lond. Hosp. Whitechapel; Regist. (Gen. Surg.) Orsett Hosp. Grays; SHO (Gen. Surg.) Battle Hosp. Reading.

ROBERTS, Judith Alison The Tod Practice, 12 Durham Road, Raynes Park, London SW20 0TW Tel: 020 8946 0069 Fax: 020 8944 2927; 23 Bernard Gardens, Wimbledon, London SW19 7BE — BM BS 1984 Nottm.; BMedSci Nottm. 1982; MRCGP 1989; DRCOG 1989. Clin. Asst. Morris Markowe Unit Springfield Hosp. Lond.

ROBERTS, Judith Mary Flat 2/2, 9 Novar Drive, Glasgow G12 9PX — MB ChB 1989 Glas.

ROBERTS, Judith Mary 122 Fernbrook Road, Wither Green, London SE13 5NH — MB ChB 1994 Birm.; ChB Birm. 1994; DRCOG 1998.

ROBERTS, Julia Elvin Doncaster Royal Infirmary, Armthorpe Road, Doncaster DN2 5LT — MB ChB 1979 Leeds; MRCPsych. 1984; T(Psych) 1991. (Leeds) Cons. Psychiat. Doncaster Healthcare NHS Trust. Prev: Sen. Regist. (Psychiat.) Trent RHA.

ROBERTS, Julian Crown House Surgery, Chapelgate, Retford DN22 6NX Tel: 01777 703672 Fax: 01777 710534 — MB ChB 1982 Liverp.

ROBERTS, Julian Foley Bradford Health, New Mill, Saltaire, Shipley BD18 3LD Tel: 01274 366033 Fax: 01274 366060; 3 Beechwood Grove, Ilkley LS29 9AX Tel: 01943 600480 — MB BS 1980 Lond.; MRCGP 1985; MFPHM 1991; MPH Leeds 1990. Cons. Pub. Health Med. Bradford HA. Prev: Regist. (Community Med.) Leeds Gen. Infirm.

ROBERTS, Julian Mervyn, OBE (retired) Linden Lea, Moor Lane, Menston, Ilkley LS29 6AP Tel: 01943 872574 — MD 1958 Ed. MBChb 1947; MD (Commend.) Ed. 1958, MB ChB 1947; FRCPsych 1971; DPM Leeds 1951. Prev: Cons. Psychiat. St. Jas. Hosp. Leeds.

ROBERTS, Mr Julian Paul 81 Clarendon Road, Fulwood, Sheffield S10 3TQ Tel: 0114 263 0737 — BM 1980 Soton.; MS Soton. 1992; FRCS (Paediat.) 1994; FRCS Eng. 1986; FRCS Ed. 1986. Cons. Paediat. Surg. Sheff. Childr. Hosp. Prev: Regist. (Paediat. Surg.) Roy. Childr. Hosp., Melbourne; Sen. Regist. (Paediat. Surg.) Soton. Gen. Hosp.

ROBERTS, Julie Cheyne Walk Clinic, 3 Cheyne Walk, Northampton NN1 5PT Tel: 01604 231438 Fax: 01604 603823 Email: pam.tates.@nchc-tr.anglox.nhs.uk — MB BCh 1972 Wales; MRCPsych 1984; MBA 1998; FRCPsych 1999. (University of Wales) Cons. Psychother. Cheyne Walk Clinic N.ampton. Socs: Fell.Roy. Soc. of Med.; Mem. Inst. Gp. Anal.; Mem. Gp. Analytic Soc. Prev: Sen. Regist. (Psychother.) Cheyne Walk Clinic N.ampton; Regist. (Psychiat.) St. Crispin Hosp. N.ampton; SHO (Psychiat.) Univ. Hosp. Wales Cardiff.

ROBERTS, Juliet Catherine Udal 8 Michael Close, Maidenhead SL6 4PD — BM 1992 Soton.; BM (Hons.) Soton. 1992; MRCP (UK) 1995. Med. Advisor Cardiovasc. Dept. Boehringer-Ingelheim Ltd. Bracknell. Prev: Regist. (Gen. Med.) John Radcliffe Hosp. Oxf.; SHO (Gen. Med.) Roy. Hants. Co. Hosp. Winchester; SHO (Radiother.) Roy. S. Hants. Hosp.

ROBERTS, Juliet Margaret 51 Lansdowne Road, Tonbridge TN9 1JD — MB ChB 1986 Leeds.

ROBERTS, June Margaret (retired) 2 Manor Close, Bramhope, Leeds LS16 9HQ — MB ChB Leeds 1955; FFA RCS Eng. 1964; DA Eng. 1960.

ROBERTS, Justin 14 Moorside Lane, Parkside, Neston, South Wirral CH64 6QP — MB ChB 1995 Manch.

***ROBERTS, Katherine Ruth** 100 Rhydypenau Road, Cyn Coed, Cardiff CF23 6PW; 34 John Farrant Drive, Gooseberry Hill, Australia — MB ChB 1997 Bristol.

ROBERTS, Kathleen Elizabeth 34 Wheats Avenue, Harborne, Birmingham B17 0RJ — MB ChB 1971 Birm.; MRCGP 1976; DObst RCOG 1973.

ROBERTS, Mr Keith Danford (retired) 75 Reddings Road, Moseley, Birmingham B13 8LP Tel: 0121 449 1959 — MB ChB 1945 (2nd class Hons.)Birmingham; ChM Birm. 1958, MB ChB (2nd Cl. Hons.) 1945; FRCS Eng. 1950; MRCS Eng. LRCP Lond. 1946; MRCS Eng. LRCP Lond. 1946. Hon. Cons. Cardiothoracic Surg. Centr. Birm. HA; Hon. Cons. Thoracic Surg. W. Midl. HA. Prev: Asst. Lect. (Anat.) Univ. Birm.

ROBERTS, Keith Michael 33 George V Avenue, Worthing BN11 5SE — MB BS 1981 Lond.

ROBERTS, Kenneth Jago Rose Hill, Tithe Barn, Alton, Stoke-on-Trent ST10 4AY Tel: 01538 702339 — MA Camb. 1945; MRCS Eng. LRCP Lond. 1948; DObst RCOG 1953; Dip. Audiol. Manch. 1960. (Camb. & St. Mary's)

ROBERTS, Kenneth Norman Rose Cottage, Barracks Lane, Ravensmoor, Nantwich CW5 8PR — MB BS 1973 Newc.; DRCOG 1981.

ROBERTS, Kim Elizabeth St Clements Partnership, Tanner Street, Winchester SO23 8AD Tel: 01962 852211 Fax: 01962 856010; Derwent House, Stoke Charity Road, Kingsworthy, Winchester SO21 2RP — BM Soton. 1983; DRCOG 1986; DCH RCP Lond. 1985; DGM RCP Lond. 1985.

ROBERTS, Laura Gwendoline Ruth Cae Gwyn, Cyffylliog, Ruthin LL15 2DP Tel: 01824 710218; Flat 1, 34 Cleveland Way, Whitechapel Way, London E1 4UF Tel: 020 7790 3585 — MB BS 1996 Lond. (The Royal London Hosp. Med. Coll.) SHO O & G. Kings Coll. Hosp. Cenbewell. Prev: SHO. O & G Greenwich DGH. Greenwich Lond.; Ho. Off. Surg. Roy. Leeds Hosp. Whitechapel.

ROBERTS, Lawrence John Department of Obstetrics & Gynaecology, Scunthorpe & Goole Hospitals Trust, Scunthorpe DN15 7BH Tel: 01742 282282; Leek House, Leek Hill, Winterton, Scunthorpe DN15 9SR Tel: 01724 734384 Fax: 01724 734646 Email: lawrence.roberts@which.net — MB BS 1981 Lond.; MRCGP 1986; MRCOG 1990. Cons. O & G Scunthorpe & Goole Hosps. Trust. Prev: Sen. Cons. O & G BMH Rinteln.

ROBERTS, Lesley Susan Agnes 2 Elfindale Road, London SE24 9NW; Ridge End, The Drive, Wimbledon, London SW20 8TG — MB BS 1993 Lond. (GUYS) Specialist Regist. (O & G).

ROBERTS, Linda Caroline York House Medical Centre, Heathside Road, Woking GU22 7XL Tel: 01483 761100 Fax: 01483 751185; Meadow Croft, 25 Wexfenne Gardens, Woking GU22 8TX — MB BS 1985 Lond.; DRCOG 1988.

ROBERTS, Lindsay Ann Cheltenham Road Surgery, 16 Cheltenham Road, Gloucester GL2 0LS Tel: 01452 522575 Fax: 01452 304321; 9 Red Admiral Drive, Abbeymead, Gloucester GL4 5EA — MB ChB 1980 Leeds; MRCGP 1984; DA (UK) 1987; DRCOG 1983. Prev: SHO (Anaesth.) ScarBoro. Hosp.

ROBERTS, Lisa Helen 6 Dunmoor Grove, Ingleby Barwick, Stockton-on-Tees TS17 0QW — MB ChB 1993 Birm.

ROBERTS, Lisa Maxine Barclays Bank Plc, 83 Wandsworth High Street, London SW18 2PR — MB BS 1991 Lond.; MRCGP 1997; DRCOG 1995. (St Georges) VTS S. Lond. Prev: GP Regist. Bournemouth.

ROBERTS, Llinos Rhianedd Llys y Coed, Meirion La, Bangor LL57 2BU Email: llin3@hotmail.com — MB BCh 1997 Wales.

ROBERTS, Lorna Jane 5 Comfrey Close, Romsey SO51 7RE — BChir 1991 Camb. Specialist Regist. (Anaesth.) Salsbury Dist. Hosp.

ROBERTS, Miss Louise Anne Kent & Sussex Hospital, Mount Ephraim, Tunbridge Wells TN4 8AT Tel: 01892 526111 — MB BS 1983 Lond.; FRCS (A&E) Ed. 1991; FFAEM. Cons., A & E.

ROBERTS, Lucy Lizette 2 Cavendish Dr, Edgware HA8 7NR — MB ChB 1997 Ed.

ROBERTS, Lynn 35 Selby Lane, Keyworth, Nottingham NG12 5AQ Tel: 0115 937 2406 — MB ChB 1978 Dundee; DA Eng. 1983. Prev: Regist. (Anaesth.) Airedale Gen. Hosp.

ROBERTS, Maiben Brian Ronayne Brandlingill Farmhouse, Cockermouth CA13 0RD Tel: 01900 823546 — MB BCh BAO 1961 Dub.; FRCPI 1983, M 1968; DCH RCP Lond. 1966; FRCPCH 1998. (TC Dub.) p/t Locum Cons. Paediat. Socs: HCSA. Prev: Cons. Paediat. W. Cumbria Health Dist.; Sen. Regist. Paediat. Dept. Radcliffe Infirm. Oxf.; Paediat. Specialist Sarawak, Malaysia.

ROBERTS, Margaret Ann Mansionhouse Unit, Victoria Infirmary, South Glasgow University Hospitals NHS Trust, Mansionhouse Road, Glasgow G41 3DX Tel: 0141 201 6129 Fax: 0141 201 6159 — MD 1988 Birm.; FRCP Ed. 1994; FRCP Glas. 1986; MRCP (UK) 1976; FRCP Lond. 1998. (Birmingham University) Cons. Phys. Geriat. Med. Vict. Infirm. Glas. Socs: Brit. Geriat. Soc. Prev: Sen. Regist. (Geriat. Med.) Stobhill Hosp. Glas.; Regist. (Med.) S.. Gen. Hosp. Glas.; Regist. (Geriat. Med.) S.. Gen. Hosp. Glas.

ROBERTS, Margaret Delyth Bradley and Partners, 30 Woodland Avenue, Luton LU3 1RW Tel: 01582 572239 Fax: 01582 494227; 14 The Avenue, Flitwick, Bedford MK45 1BP Tel: 01525 712381 — MB ChB 1972 Liverp.; MRCGP 1978; Cert Contracep. & Family Plann. RCOG & RCGP & Family Plann. Assn. 1975. Bd. Mem. Luton PCG. Prev: SHO (Dermat.) Newsham Gen. Hosp. Liverp.; SHO (Psychiat.) Sefton Gen. Hosp. Liverp.

ROBERTS, Margaret Jane Chirk Surgery, Chirk, Wrexham LL14 5BS — BM BCh 1987 Oxf.; MA Camb. 1988; MRCP (UK) 1991; MRCGP 1994; DRCOG 1992. Gen. Practitioner, Chirk; Clin. Asst., Wrexham Rheum.

ROBERTS, Marguerite Morrell (retired) 2 Birch Cottage, Werneth Low, Hyde SK14 3AD — MB ChB 1963 Manch.; FRCP Lond. 1985; MRCP (UK) 1971. Salford Roy. Hosp.s NHS Trust, N. Manch. Healthcare, W. Pennine Health Auth.

ROBERTS, Marian Elizabeth The Doctors Centre, 41 Broomwood Road, Orpington BR5 2JP Tel: 01689 832454 Fax: 01689 826165; 13 Meadow Way, Farnborough Park, Orpington BR6 8LN Tel: 01689 55730 — MRCS Eng. LRCP Lond. 1967; MB BS (Hnrs. Path., Obst. & Gyn.) Lond. 1967; MRCGP 1981; DObst RCOG 1969. (St. Bart.) Prev: Ho. Surg. P. of Wales Hosp. Tottenham; Ho. Off. (Med.) St. Bart. Hosp. Lond.; SHO (Obst.) Brit. Hosp. Mothers & Babies Woolwich.

***ROBERTS, Marion Jean** 12 Athol Road, Bramhall, Stockport SK7 1BS — MB ChB 1994 Manch.

ROBERTS, Mark The Grove Farm, Aston Pigott, Westbury, Shrewsbury SY5 9HH Tel: 01724 891248 — MB ChB 1986 Liverp.; MRCOG 1991. Research Regist. (O & G) Univ. Newc. u. Tyne. Prev: Research Regist. P.ss Mary Matern. Hosp. Newc.

ROBERTS, Mark Andrew Fax: 01329 834780 — MB ChB 1982 Liverp.; MRCP Ed. 1985; MRCPsych 1991. Cons. Forens. Psychiat.

ROBERTS, Mark Eldon Department of Neurology, Teaching Unit 7, Withington Hospital, Nell Lane, West Didsbury, Manchester M20 2LR Tel: 0161 291 4230 — MB ChB 1989 Liverp.; MD 1999 Liverp.; BSc (Hons.) Physiol. Liverp. 1986; MRCP (UK) 1992. (Liverpool) (Neurol.) Cons. Hope Hosp., Manch. Socs: Assoc. Mem. Assn. Brit. Neurol. Prev: Clin. Research Regist. Inst. Molecular Med. (Dept. Neurosci.) Oxf.; SHO (Neurol.) Nat. Hosp. for Neurol. Lond.; SHO Rotat. (Med.) N. Manch. Gen. Hosp.

ROBERTS, Mark Howard Wakley c/o Disablement Semcel Centre, Cumberland Infirmary, Carlisle CA2 7HY Tel: 01228 523444; The Swifts, Castle Carrock, Carlisle CA8 9NA — MB ChB 1980 Leeds; BA Oxf. 1973; DM Soton. 1991; MRCP (UK) 1983. Cons. (Rehabil. Med.) N. Cumbria.

ROBERTS, Mark Theodore Milward D10 Ward, Box 25, Infectious Diseases Unit, Adenbrooke's Hospital, Cambridge CB2 2QQ Tel: 01223 245151 Fax: 01223 586874; 62 County Road, Gedling, Nottingham NG4 4JC Tel: 0115 953 7580 Email: marktmroberts@compuserve.com — MB BS 1994 Lond.; MRCP 1998 UK; DTM & H 1999 Liverpool; MA 1995 Cantab; MA Camb. 1995; MRCP (UK) 1998. Specialist Regist. Infec. Dis.s and Gen. Int. Med., Addenbrooke Hosp., Camb. Socs: MDU; BMA. Prev: Med. Regist. John Radcliffe Hosp. Oxf.; SHO (Med.) St. Richard's Hosp. Chichester.

ROBERTS, Mr Martin Wood Green, Woods Cross, Narberth SA67 8 — MB BCh 1973 Wales; FRCS Ed. 1979.

ROBERTS, Martin David Victoria Street Surgery, 1 Victoria Street, Norwich NR1 3XQ Tel: 01603 620872 — MB BS 1980 Lond.; MRCGP 1986; DRCOG 1985; DA Eng. 1984.

ROBERTS, Mary Annette Abbey Surgery, 28 Plymouth Road, Tavistock PL19 8BU Tel: 01822 612247 Fax: 01822 618771; 19 Newtake Road, Whitchurch, Tavistock PL19 9BX — MB BCh 1980 Wales; DCH RCPS Glas. 1986.

ROBERTS, Mary Elisabeth The Writtle Surgery, 16A Lordship Road, Writtle, Chelmsford CM1 3EH Tel: 01245 421205 Fax: 01245 422094; 4 Great Godfreys, Writtle, Chelmsford CM1 3PQ — MB ChB 1968 Leeds. (Leeds)

ROBERTS, Mary Louise 3 Elm Road, Prenton, Birkenhead CH42 9NY Tel: 0151 608 1220 Email: teny@marylou4.freeserve.co.uk — MB ChB 1975 Manch.; BSc (Hons.) Med. Biochem. Manch. 1972; VMN 1975; BD BS 1977; BSc 1975. (manch) Socs: BMA; Anthroposop. Med. Assn.; Brit. Soc. Rehab. Med. Prev: Phys. NATO Forces.

ROBERTS, Megan Charlotte Newlands House, Oak Lane, Twickenham TW1 3PA — MB BS 1986 Lond.; MRCPsych 1991. Cons. Gen. Adult Psychiat. Qu. Mary's Univ. Hosp Roehampton. Prev: Regist. (Psychiat.) St. Mary's Hosp. Lond.

ROBERTS, Merryl Wynne 16 Ethelbert Road, Canterbury CT1 3NE Tel: 01227 760294 Fax: 01227 781377 — MB ChB St. And. 1964. SCMO Canterbury & Thanet Health Dist. Socs: Inst. Psychosexual Med. Prev: Asst. Med. Off. Med. Centre Univ. Kent Canterbury; Ho. Surg. Withington Hosp. Manch.; Ho. Phys. St. Alfege's Hosp. Greenwich.

ROBERTS, Michael 67 Tenby Road, Moseley, Birmingham B13 9LY — MB ChB 1987 Birm.; BSc Birm. 1984, MB ChB 1987; MRCGP 1992.

ROBERTS, Michael Andrew Mor A Mon, Meirion Lane, Bangor LL57 2BU — MB ChB 1998 Bristol.

ROBERTS, Michael Bradfield (retired) Westover, Lansdown Road, Bath BA1 5RB — MB ChB 1967 Bristol; FRCR 1975; FFR 1973; DMRD Eng. 1971. Cons. Radiol. Bath Health Dist. Prev: Sen. Regist. (Radiodiag.) United Bristol Hosps.

ROBERTS, Michael George (retired) 13 Linnet Hill, Rochdale OL11 4DA Tel: 01706 49899 — MB ChB 1957 Manch.; BSc (Hons.) Manch. 1954, MB ChB 1957; FFA RCS Eng. 1964. Cons. Anaesth. Rochdale & Dist. Hosp. Gp. Fell. Manch. Med. Soc. Prev: Regist. Anaesth. Manch. Roy. Infirm. & Pk. Hosp. Davyhulme.

ROBERTS

ROBERTS, Mr Michael John 112 Harnham Road, Salisbury SP2 8JW — MB BS 1985 Lond.; FRCS Eng. 1990.

ROBERTS, Michael John Desmond Regional Medical Cardiology Centre, Royal Victoria Hospital, Belfast BT12 6BA; 9 Trossachs Park, Belfast BT10 0AX Tel: 01232 612561 — MB ChB 1984 Ed.; MD Belf. 1992; MRCP (UK) 1987. (Edinburgh University) Cons. Cardiol. Roy. Vict. Hosp. Belf.

ROBERTS, Miranda Jane Lister Medical Centre, Lister House, Staple Tye, Harlow CM18 7LU Tel: 01279 414882 Fax: 01279 439600; 23 Foxley Drive, Bishop's Stortford CM23 2EB Tel: 01279 755732 — MB BS 1985 Lond. GP Lister Med. Centre Harlow. Prev: Trainee GP Harlow.

ROBERTS, Miriam Eluned (retired) Pen Tyle, Meirion Lane, Bangor LL57 2BU — MB BCh 1938 Wales; BSc, MB BCh Wales 1938. Prev: Asst. Med. Off. Caerns. CC.

ROBERTS, Monica Annette Faraway, Hill Top, Beaulieu, Brockenhurst SO42 7YT — MB BCh BAO 1947 Dub. (T.C. Dub.) Prev: Res. Med. Off. Odstock Hosp. Salisbury; ENT Ho. Surg. Kent & Canterbury Hosp.; Ho. Surg. New Sussex Hosp. Brighton.

ROBERTS, Morian 3 Gilfach Road, Rhydding, Neath SA10 8EH — MB BS 1974 Lond.

ROBERTS, Neil Springbank Barn, Gossefoot Lane, Nabs Head, Samlesbury, Preston PR5 0UQ — MB ChB 1996 Dundee.

ROBERTS, Neil Stockwell Lodge Medical Centre, Rosedale Way, Cheshunt, Waltham Cross EN7 6HL Tel: 01992 624408 Fax: 01992 626206.

ROBERTS, Neil Jefferson 17 Tofts Close, Low Worsall, Yarm TS15 9QA — MB BS 1966 Lond.; DObst RCOG 1970. (Char. Cross) Socs: BMA.

ROBERTS, Nest Enerys Morris Chelsea & Westminster Hospital, 369 Fulham Road, London SW10 9NH Tel: 020 8237 5293 Fax: 020 8746 8578 Email: n.roberts@doctors.net.uk; Great Ormond Street Hospital, London WC1 Tel: 020 7405 9200 — MB BS 1983 Lond.; BSc Lond. 1980, MD 1993; MRCP (UK) 1987; FRCP 2000 UK. Cons. Dermat. Chelsea & W.minster Hosp.; Hon. Cons. Paediat. Dermat. Gt. Ormond St. Hosp. for Childr. Lond.; Hon. Lect. (Pharmacol.) Kings Coll. Lond. Socs: Roy. Soc. Med.; Brit. Assn. Dermat.; Brit. Soc. Allergy & Clin. Immunol. Prev: Cons. Dermat. Qu. Mary's Univ. Hosp. Roehampton; Sen. Regist. (Dermat.) Chelsea & W.m. Hosp. Lond.; Regist. (Dermat.) W.m. Hosp. Lond.

ROBERTS, Nesta Gwendolyn (retired) Gorwel, Llanarth SA47 0NN Tel: 01545 580204 — MRCS Eng. LRCP Lond. 1946.

ROBERTS, Nicholas Adrian Department of Medicine for the Elderly, Queens Park Hospital, Blackburn BB2 3HH Tel: 01254 293456 Fax: 01254 293864; The Old Barn, Bowfields Lane, Balderstone, Blackburn BB2 7LW Tel: 01254 814007 — MB ChB 1981 Manch.; FRCP 1996; MRCP (UK) 1985. (Manchester) Cons. Phys. Med. for Elderly Qu.s Pk. Hosp. Blackburn. Socs: Brit. Geriat. Soc.; Brit. Soc. Research on Ageing; Brit. Stroke Research Gp.

ROBERTS, Nicholas David 36 St Catherines Way, Houghton on the Hill, Leicester LE7 9HE — BM BS 1992 Nottm.

ROBERTS, Nicholas Ian 16 Pisgah Street, Kenfig Hill, Bridgend CF33 6BY — MB ChB 1986 Bristol; DA 1988.

ROBERTS, Nicola Jane Forest End Surgery, Forest End, Waterlooville PO7 7AH — MBBS; BSc; DRCOG; MRCP; FP Cert.; MRCGP. (University College Hospital) GP; Course Organiser, Portsmouth Vocational Train. Scheme; GP Trainer.

ROBERTS, Nigel George 2 Little Aston Hall, St.ly, Sutton Coldfield B74 3BH Tel: (0121) 353 0608 Fax: (0121) 352 1929; Bora-Bora, Paynes Bay, St. James, Barbados, West Indies Tel: (001) (246) 432 7345 Fax: (001) (246) 424 8125 — MB BS Lond. 1966; MRCS Eng. LRCP Lond. 1966. Fleet Med. Cons. Cunard Lines Ltd. Prev: PMO RMS Qu. Eliz. 2 Cunard Lines Ltd.

ROBERTS, Norman Glynne The Chalet, Marine Drive, Llandudno LL30 2QZ Tel: 01492 77250 — MB ChB 1956 Liverp.; DObst RCOG 1958.

ROBERTS, Olumuyiwa Adebola 30C Rhyl Street, London NW5 3HA; 14 Damers Court, Damers Road, Dorchester DT1 2JR Tel: 01305 254595 — MB BS 1978 Ibadan; MRCOG 1993. Regist. W. Dorset Gen. Hosp. Socs: BMA & Nigerian Med. Soc.

ROBERTS, Pamela Dorothy (retired) Hilltop, 2 West Road, Prenton, Prenton CH43 9RP Tel: 0151 677 4087 Email: john.pam@tesco.net — MB BS 1956 Lond.; MRCS Eng. LRCP Lond. 1956; DPM Eng. 1966; MRANZCP 1977. Prev: Cons. Child & Adolesc. Psychiat. Merseyside RHA.

ROBERTS, Pamela Fay Caterham Valley Medical Practice, Eothen House, Eothen Close, Caterham CR3 6JU Tel: 01883 347811 Fax: 01883 342929; 76 Tupwood Lane, Caterham CR3 6DP Tel: 01883 347805 — MB BS 1978 Lond.; MRCGP 1982; DRCOG 1981. (Char. Cross)

ROBERTS, Pamela Joan (retired) The Cottage, Woodfield Lane, Woodfield Avenue, London SW16 1LF Tel: 020 8769 7901 — MB BS 1951 Ceylon. Prev: Clin. Med. Off. Merton & Sutton DHA.

ROBERTS, Patrick James 12 Larkhill Lane, Formby, Liverpool L37 1LX — MB BS 1991 Lond.

ROBERTS, Patrick John 1 Walscombe Cottages, Chaffcombe, Chard TA20 4AJ Tel: 01460 62413 Email: katpat@globalnet.co.uk — BM 1993 Soton.; MRCP (UK) 1997. (Southampton) Specialist Regist. (Haemat.) Leicester Roy. Infirm. Leicester.

ROBERTS, Mr Paul Elmwood House, Elm Road, Tutshill, Chepstow NP16 7BX Tel: 01291 629490 Fax: 01291 629490 — MB BS 1981 Lond.; MA Oxf. 1983; MB BS (Hons.) Lond. 1981; FRCS Lond. 1986. (St Mary's) Cons. Orthop. Surg. Roy. Gwent Hosp. Newport. Socs: Brit. Orthop. Research Soc.; Brit. Orthop. Assn.; Brit. Hip Soc.

ROBERTS, Paul Douglas Iona, 13 Green East Road, Jordans, Beaconsfield HP9 2SU — MD 1958 Leeds; MB ChB 1948; DPath. Eng. 1954. Socs: Brit. Soc. Haemat. Prev: Cons. Haematol. W. Middlx. Hosp. Isleworth; Hon. Sen. Lect. Univ. Lond.; Sen. Regist. Lond. Hosp.

ROBERTS, Paul Richard Wessex & Cardiothoracic Centre, Southampton General Hospital, Tremona Road, Southampton SO16 6YD — MB ChB 1990 Leeds; MRCP (UK) 1993.

ROBERTS, Paula Bowling Green Surgery, Bowling Green, Constantine, Falmouth TR11 5AP Tel: 01326 340666 Fax: 01326 340968 — MB ChB 1970 Bristol; MRCGP 1986; Cert. Family Plann. JCC 1975; DRCOG 1973. Trainer (Gen. Pract.) Cornw. VTS. Prev: Family Plann. Off. Gilbert & Ellice Is.

ROBERTS, Paula-Jayne Seven Brooks Medical Centre, Church St., Atherton, Manchester M46 9DE Tel: 01942 873533 Fax: 01942 873859; 2 The Rookery, Newton-le-Willows WA12 9PW Tel: 01925 290181 — MB ChB 1986 Manch.; BSc (Hons.) Physiol. Manch. 1983; MRCGP 1990; DFFP 1995; DCCH RCP Ed. 1992; DCH RCPS Glas. 1989; DRCOG 1988. (Manch.) GP Manch.; Hon. Research Fell. Nat. Primary Care Research & Developm. Centre Manch. Univ. Socs: Brit. Menopause Soc.; Brit. Med. Acupunct. Soc.; Internat. Menopause Soc. Prev: Clin. Med. Off. (Paediat.) Warrington Trust; Clin. Med. Off. (Family Plann.) Wigan Trust.; Clin. Med. Off. Ashton in Makerfield Wigan.

ROBERTS, Pauline 17 Parkanuar Avenue, Thorpe Bay, Southend-on-Sea SS1 3HX — MB BS 1976 Lond.; MRCPsych. 1982.

ROBERTS, Mr Peter, MBE, QHS, Col. F.a.s.c, Army Medical Directorate/CDM, Camberley GU15 4NP Tel: 0127 6412765 Fax: 01276 412737; 10 Osberton Road, Oxford OX2 7NU — MB BS 1965 Lond.; MS Lond. 1982; FRCS Eng. 1972. (Lond. Hosp.) Jt. Prof. Milit. Surg. Roy. Coll. of Surg.s.and Centre for Defence Med., Gosport. Socs: St. Mark's Assn.; ASGBI; Pres., Milit. Surgic. Soc. Prev: Sen. Regist. (Surg.) Lond. Hosp.; Ho. Phys. & Ho. Surg. Lond. Hosp.; Resid. Surg. Off. St. Mark's Hosp. Lond.

ROBERTS, Peter Clifford 45 Kingsmead House, Kingsmead Est., Homerton Road, London E9 5QH — MB BS 1988 Lond.

ROBERTS, Peter John 9 Daws Court, High St., Iver SL0 9NQ — MB BS 1996 Lond.; BSc Lond. 1993. (St Marys Hospital Imperial College) SHO Rotat. (Anaesth.) Hillingdon Hosp./Mt. Vernon Hosp. Prev: Chelsea & W.minster (A & E) St Marys Hosp. Med. & Surgic. Ho. Jobs.

ROBERTS, Mr Peter Neil Oak House, Eastwood Business Village, Coventry CV3 2UB Tel: 02476 561900; 64 Purnells Way, Knowle, Solihull B93 9EE Tel: 01564 772841 — MB ChB Birm. 1969; FRCS Eng. 1975. (Birmingham) Cons. Gen. & Vasc. Surg. Walsgrave Hosp. Coventry.

ROBERTS, Peter Richard Gerald 6 Seaburn Drive, Houghton-le-Spring DH4 5DW; 27 Maindy Road, Cathays, Cardiff CF24 4HL Tel: 01222 232414 — MB ChB 1993 Ed. Specialist Regist. (Anaesth.) Univ. Hosp. of Wales Cardiff.

ROBERTS, Philip Anthony Flat 2, Ronkswood Branch, Worcester Royal Infirmary, Worcester WR5 1HN Tel: 01905 763333; Box BW 100, Borrowdale, Harare, Zimbabwe — MB ChB 1990 Cape Town.

ROBERTS, Philip Franklin Department of Histopathology, Norfolk & Norwich Hospital, Norwich NR1 3SR Tel: 01603 286019 Fax: 01603 286017 Email: philip.roberts.@norfolk-norwich.thenhs.com — MB BS Lond. 1966; MRCP Lond. 1969; MRCS Eng. LRCP Lond. 1966; FRCPath 1984, M 1972; FRCP Lond. 1998. (St. Bart.) Cons. Histopath. Norf. & Norwich Hosp.; Regional. Adviser (Histopath.) Roy. Coll. Paths.; Regional. Adviser (Path.) on Matern. Deaths DHSS Confidential Inquiry; Examr. Histopath. Roy. Coll. Paths.; Mem. Ct. Examrs. RCS Eng.; Mem. (Counc.) Univ. E. Anglia; Mem. Advis. Comm. on Distinc. Awards. Socs: Internat. Acad. Path.; Assn. Clin. Pathologists; BMA. Prev: Dir. (Path.) Norf. & Norwich Hosp.; Regional Represen. Roy. Coll. Paths.; Clin. Tutor Norf. & Norwich Inst. Med. Educat.

ROBERTS, Mr Philip Hugh Martindale, Bridgwater Road, Sidcot, Winscombe BS25 1NN Tel: 01934 844135 Fax: 01934 843075 Email: roberts@martindale75.freeserve.co.uk — MB ChB 1958 Manch.; FRCS Eng. 1964; FRCS Ed. 1964. (Manch.) Hon. Cons. Orthop. Surg. W.on Area Health Trust; Hon. Clin. Teach. Univ. Bristol. Socs: Fell. Bristol M-C Soc.; (Pres.) Bristol Medico-Legal Soc. Prev: Sen. Regist. (Orthop.) Manch. Roy. Infirm.; Regist. (Orthop.) Robt. Jones & Agnes Hunt Orthop. Hosp. OsW.ry; Resid. Surg. Off. Preston Roy. Infirm.

ROBERTS, Philip John 8 Fairview, Erith DA8 2PR — MB BS 1989 Lond.

ROBERTS, Mr Philip John Marsdens, 7 Brook Road, Whitchurch SY13 1QF Tel: 01948 664799 Fax: 01948 664799 — MB BS 1992 Lond.; BSc (Hons.) Lond. 1990; FRCS Eng. 1996. (St. Mary's Med. Sch.) Specialist Regist., Orthop. & Trauma, N. Staffs. Roy. Infirm., Stoke-on-Trent. Socs: BOA; Brit. Orthopaedic Research Soc. Prev: Laming Evans research fell., Roy. Coll. Of Surgs.

ROBERTS, R Elizabeth (retired) 1 Waverley Lodge, The Knowes, Kelso TD5 7BB Tel: 01573 228153 — MB BS 1964 Lond.; MRCS Eng. LRCP Lond. 1964; FFCM 1989, M 1983. Prev: Dir. BrE. Test Wales.

ROBERTS, Rachel Fiona 10 Curlew Lane, Stockton-on-Tees TS20 1NA — MB ChB 1995 Leic.

ROBERTS, Rachel Penelope Ludmilla Station Road Surgery, 11 Station Road, Loughton IG10 4NZ Tel: 020 8276 8708 Fax: 020 8276 8722 — MB BS (Hons.) Lond. 1986; MRCP (UK) 1989; MRCGP 1993; DFFP 1995; DCH RCP Lond. 1990. One session course organiser post Ilford Scheme. Prev: SHO (O & G) Homerton Hosp. Lond.; SHO (Paediat.) St. Mary's Hosp. Lond.; SHO (A & E & Med.) Char. Cross Hosp.

ROBERTS, Raine Emily Ireland, MBE 459 Altrincham Road, Wythenshawe, Manchester M23 1AA Tel: 0161 998 3326 Fax: 0161 998 3326 — MB ChB 1955 Manch.; FRCGP 1982, M 1968; DMJ (Clin.) Soc. Apoth. Lond. 1979; DCH Eng. 1958. (Manch.) Clin. Dir. St. Mary's Centre (Sexual Assault Referral Centre) St. Mary's Hosp. Manch.; Forens. Phys. Gtr. Manch. Police. Socs: Fell. Manch. Med. Soc.; Roy. Soc. Med. (Ex-Pres. Sec. Clin. Forens. Med.). Prev: Regist. (Gen. Med.) Blackburn Roy. Infirm.; Ho. Phys. & Ho. Surg. (Neurosurg.) Manch. Roy. Infirm.; Ho. Phys. (Paediat.) Pendlebury Childr. Hosp.

ROBERTS, Ralph Neville Frank Rothschild House Surgery, Chapel Street, Tring HP23 6PU Tel: 01442 822468 Fax: 01442 825889; Dormers, Buckland Village, Aylesbury HP22 5HY Tel: 01296 630256 Fax: 01296 630256 — MB BS 1974 Lond. (Roy. Free) Socs: Roy. Soc. Med.

ROBERTS, Ralph Nigel Duchess of Gloucester Maternity Unit, Ulster Hospital, Dundonald, Belfast BT16 1RH Tel: 02890 484511 Fax: 02890 561402; Dorn House, Rolly Island, Ringneill Rd, Comber, Newtownards BT23 6EL — MB BCh BAO 1983 Belf.; BSc Belf. 1980; MD Belf. 1996; MRCP (UK) 1986; MFFP 1993; MRCOG 1989; FRCP 2000 Edin. (Queen's University Belfast) Cons. (O & G) Ulster Hosp. Dundonald. Socs: Brit. Med. Assn.; Ulster Obst. & Gyn. Soc.; Brit. Fertil. Soc. Prev: Sen. Regist. (O & G) Qu. Mother's Hosp. Glas.; Lect. (O & G) Univ. Edin.; Research Regist. (O & G) Roy. Matern. Hosp. Belf.

ROBERTS, Rebecca Jane 8 Woodthorn Close, Daresbury, Warrington WA4 6NQ — MB ChB 1995 Manch.

ROBERTS, Rhian Carrington 19 Green Park, Wrexham LL13 7YE — MB BCh 1996 Wales.

ROBERTS, Richard Alun 21 St Georges Road, Formby, Liverpool L37 3HH — MB BCh 1993 Wales.

ROBERTS, Richard Charles Department of Neurology, Ninewells Hospital and Medical School, Dundee DD1 9SY Tel: 01382 660111 Fax: 01382 425739 Email: r.c.roberts@dundee.ac.uk; 67 Camphill Road, Broughty Ferry, Dundee DD5 2LY Tel: 01382 477438 — BM BCh 1976 Oxf.; MA, DPhil Oxf. 1974; FRCP Ed. 1994; MRCP (UK) 1979. (Oxford) Reader in Med., Univ. Dundee; Hons. Cons. Neurol. Tayside Univ. Hosp. NHS trust. Prev: Clin. Lect. Inst. Neurol. Qu. Sq. Lond.

ROBERTS, Richard Clive 7 Woodville Road W., Cinderford GL14 2AT — MB BS 1998 Lond.; MB BS Lond 1998.

ROBERTS, Richard John Bryn Clwyd, Brookhouse, Denbigh LL16 4RF — MB BS 1986 Lond.; BSc Lond. 1983; MPH Wales 1992; MFPHM Lond. 1995; DCH RCP Lond. 1989. Cons. Communicable Dis. Control N. Wales HA. Prev: Sen. Regist. (Pub. Health Med.) Health Prom. Auth. Wales & PHLS CDSC (Welsh Unit).

ROBERTS, Richard John 14 Woodside Road, Portswood, Southampton SO17 2GQ — BM 1977 Soton.; DRCOG 1979.

***ROBERTS, Richard Norman** 22 Meadow Road, Finchfield, Wolverhampton WV3 8EZ — MB ChB 1996 Birm.; ChB Birm. 1996.

ROBERTS, Richard Ralton (retired) 30 Whalley Drive, Bletchley, Milton Keynes MK3 6HS Tel: 01908 373320 — MB BS 1958 Lond.; BSc (Anat.) Lond. 1955; MRCS Eng. LRCP Lond. 1958; DCH Eng. 1961. Prev: Ho. Phys. & Ho. Surg. Cheltenham Gen. Hosp.

ROBERTS, Robert Sion Cynfab Taleithin, Penglais Road, Aberystwyth SY23 2EU — MB BCh 1989 Wales.

ROBERTS, Robin Hugh Ridge End, The Drive, Wimbledon, London SW20 8TG — MB BS 1982 Lond.; MRCP (UK) 1985. (Westm.) Cons. Cardiol. Qu. Marys, Roehampton Kingston Hosp., The Roy. Brompton Hosp.

ROBERTS, Roma Elizabeth Willow Green Surgery, Station Road, East Preston, Littlehampton BN16 3AH Tel: 01903 758152 Fax: 01903 859986; Poundville, Roundstone Lane, Angmering, Littlehampton BN16 4AP — MB BS 1984 Lond.; DRCOG 1989; Cert. Family Plann. JCC 1989. (St. Geo.) Prev: Trainee GP Bordon & Liss; SHO (O & G & Paediat.) Portsmouth.

ROBERTS, Russell George Department of Medicine, The Medical School, Framlington Place, Newcastle upon Tyne NE2 4HH Tel: 0191 222 8128 Fax: 0191 222 8129 Email: russell.roberts@newcastle.ac.uk; 31 Ivy Road, Gosforth, Newcastle upon Tyne NE3 1DB — MB BChir 1990 Camb.; MRCP (UK) 1993. Research Regist. (Nephrol.) Roy. Vict. Infirm. Newc. Prev: SHO (Gen. Med.) Newc. HA.

ROBERTS, Ruth Diane Department of Care of the Elderly, Weston General Hospital, Grange Road, Uphill, Weston Super Mare BS23 4TQ Tel: 01934 636363 Fax: 01934 619275; Long Meadow, 52 Church Lane, Backwell, Bristol BS48 3PQ Tel: 01275 463100 — MB BS 1969 Lond.; DCH Eng. 1971. (St. Geo.) Staff Grade Doctor (c/o the Elderly) W.on Gen. Hosp. W.on-super-Mare. Socs: Brit. Geriat. Soc. Prev: Clin. Asst. (Geriat. Med.) Frenchay Hosp. Bristol; Regist. (Paediat.) Qu. Charlotte's Hosp. Lond.; Regist. (Geriat. Med.) Plymouth Gen. Hosp.

ROBERTS, Ruth Esther Pennant Rosetree Cottage, High St., Elswick, Preston PR4 3ZB — MB ChB 1990 Leeds; MRCP (UK) 1994. SHO (Paediat.) St. Mary's Hosp. Manch. Prev: SHO (Paediat.) Salford Community Health, Booth Hall Childr. Hosp. & Leeds Gen. Infirm.

ROBERTS, Sally Ann 16 Pisgah Street, Kenfig Hill, Bridgend CF33 6BY — MB ChB 1986 Bristol.

ROBERTS, Sally Ann Hawthorne Cottage, Unthank, Dalston, Carlisle CA5 7BA — MB BS 1992 Newc.

ROBERTS, Sally Kathryn 52 Church Lane, Backwell, Bristol BS48 3PQ — MB BS 1998 Lond.; MB BS Lond 1998.

ROBERTS, Sam Craig 30 North Deeside Road, Bieldside, Aberdeen AB15 9AB — MB ChB 1998 Aberd.; MB ChB Aberd 1998.

ROBERTS, Selwyn Pennant Department of Anaesthesia, Withington Hospital, West Didsbury, Manchester M20 2LR Tel: 0161 447 3772 Fax: 0161 447 3774; 69 Kingston Road, Manchester M20 2SB — BM BCh 1982 Oxf.; MA Camb. 1982; FRCA. 1984; DA (UK) 1984. Cons. Anaesth. Univ. Hosp. Manch.; Hon. Lect. (Anaesth.) Univ. Manch.

ROBERTS, Sheila Elizabeth 25 Bartee Gill Drive, Baildon, Shipley BD17 6UE — MB ChB 1977 Sheff. Clin. Med. Off. (Community Child Health & Family Plann.) Yorks.

ROBERTS

ROBERTS, Sheila Mary (retired) Plas Newydd, Glynliifon Park, Caernarfon LL54 5ED — MB BS 1964 Lond. Prev: GP Daventry.

ROBERTS, Sheila Rosemary 74 Windermere Crescent, Looseleigh, Plymouth PL6 5HX Tel: 01752 774774 — MRCS Eng. LRCP Lond. 1976; DLO RCS Eng. 1988. Staff Grade (Ear Nose & Throat) Derriford Hosp. Plymouth. Prev: Clin. Asst. (ENT) Derriford Hosp. Plymouth.

ROBERTS, Sian Catherine Walnut Tree Health Centre, Blackberry Court, Walnut Tree, Milton Keynes MK7 7NR Tel: 01908 691123; 23 Boulters Lock, Giffard Park, Milton Keynes MK14 5QR Tel: 01908 617010 — MB BS 1988 Lond.; DRCOG 1992. (St. Mary's) Prev: Med. Off. Mbale Health Centre, Uganda; Doctor (Family Plann.) Milton Keynes & Trainee GP Milton Keynes VTS; SHO (A & E & Paediat.) & Ho. Off. (Surg. & Med.) Milton Keynes Hosp.

ROBERTS, Sian Eleri 7 Highlands Close, Rhuddlan, Rhyl LL18 2RU — MB BCh 1996 Wales.

ROBERTS, Sian Fiona, Flight Lt. RAF Med. Br. 2 Mount Cottages, Adbaston, Knighton, Stafford ST20 0QQ — MB BS 1992 Lond.; MB BS (Hons.) Lond. 1992; DCH RCP Lond. 1995. Trainee GP RAF Halton Aylesbury. Prev: SHO (Paediat.) St. Geo. Hosp. Lond.; Ho. Off. (Med.) St. Bart. Hosp. Lond.; Ho. Off. (Surg.) N. Middlx. Hosp.

ROBERTS, Mr Simon Nicholas John Robert Jones & Agnes Hunt Hospital, Oswestry SY10 7AG Tel: 01691 404167 — BM BCh 1987 Oxf.; MA Camb. 1988; FRCS Eng. 1992; FRCS (Orth) 1996. (Camb./Oxford) Cons. Orthop. & Sports Injury Surg.; Cons. Othopaedic Surg., Wrexham Maelor Hosp., Croesnewydd Rd., Wrexham CLWTD. Socs: Treas. Brit. Orthopaedic Sports Trauma Assn.; Fell.Brit. Orthopaedic Assoc; BASEM.

ROBERTS, Sophie Amanda 20 Longfield Terrace, York YO30 7DJ — MB BS 1992 Newc. Regist. (Psychiat.) Bootham Pk. Hosp. York.

ROBERTS, Stanley Desmond, OBE 7 Viewfort Park, Upper Malone, Dunmurry, Belfast BT17 9JY Tel: 02896 627006 Fax: 02896627006 — MB BCh BAO 1956 Belf.; MD Belf. 1960; FRCP Ed. 1996; FRCPI 1975, M 1963; FRCP Lond. 1975, M 1963; FRCP 1997. (Qu. Univ. Belf.) Hon. Cons. Phys. & Rheum. Roy. Vict. Hosp. & Musgrave Pk. Hosp. Belf. Socs: Brit. Soc. Rheum.; Assn. Phys. Prev: Pres. Roy. Coll. Phys. Irel.; ARC Research Fell. At MRC Rheum. Research Unit Taplow.

ROBERTS, Stephen Alexander Countess of Chester Hospital, Liverpool Road, Chester CH2 1BQ; 119 Thingwall Road, Liverpool L15 7JX — MB ChB 1992 Liverp.

ROBERTS, Stephen Arthur Paediatric Department, Wythenshawe Hospital, Southmoor Road, Manchester M23 9LT — MB ChB 1970; MD 1982 Edinburgh; FRCP 1990 London; FRCPCH. Cons. Paediat. Univ. Hosp. S. Manch. Socs: Brit. Paediat. Assn.; Brit. Soc. Allergy & Clin. Immunol.

ROBERTS, Stephen John Deben Road Surgery, 2 Deben Road, Ipswich IP1 5EN Tel: 01473 741152 Fax: 01473 743237; 2 Deben Road, Ipswich IP1 5EN — MB ChB 1983 Aberd.; MRCGP 1987.

ROBERTS, Stephen Jones Tel: 01745 342225 Fax: 01745 342773; Llawenydd, Gwaenysgor, Rhyl LL18 6EW Tel: 01745 888588 — MB BCh 1985 Wales. GP.

ROBERTS, Stephen Louis Sunnyside, 19 London Road, Woore, Crewe CW3 9SF — MB BS 1978 Lond.; AFOM RCP Lond. 1990; Dip. Bact. Manch. 1984.

ROBERTS, Stephen Owen Bellamy 14 Fendon Road, Cambridge CB1 7RT — MB BChir 1961 Camb.; MA, MB Camb. 1961, BChir 1960; FRCP Lond. 1979, M 1964; MRCS Eng. LRCP Lond. 1960. (Guy's) Cons. Dermat. E. Anglian RHB & United Camb. Hosps.

ROBERTS, Steven John 1 Prospect Row, Burley-in-Wharfdale, Ilkley LS29 7AT — MB ChB 1992 Leeds.

ROBERTS, Stewart John 49 Seaforth Place, Maryburgh, Dingwall IV7 8DP — MB ChB 1985 Leeds; MB ChB Leeds. 1985; MRCPsych 1990. Regional Forens. Psychiat. Manawatu-Wanganui, NZ.

ROBERTS, Stuart Ashley 5 Gwynfryn Terrace, Llantwit Fardre, Pontypridd CF38 2EL — MB BCh 1988 Wales.

ROBERTS, Stuart Morgan Strawberry Place Surgery, 5 Strawberry Place, Morriston, Swansea SA6 7AQ Tel: 01792 522526 Fax: 01792 411020; Mayfield, 547 Clydach Road, Ynystawe, Swansea SA6 5AA Tel: 01792 845946 — MB ChB 1970 Liverp.; MRCGP 1976; DObst RCOG 1973.

ROBERTS, Susan 21 Gronant .Road, Prestatyn LL19 9DT — MB ChB 1987 Leic.

ROBERTS, Susan Ann Margaret Microbiology Laboratory, Hartlepool General Surgery, Holdforth Rd, Hartlepool TS24 9AH Tel: 01429 266654 Ext: 2420 — MRCS Eng. LRCP Lond. 1976; MRCPath 1983; Dip. Bact. Manch. 1981. (Sheff.) p/t Cons. Med. Microbiol. N. Tees & Hartlepool NHS Trust. Socs: Fell. Roy. Coll. Path.

ROBERTS, Susan Elizabeth Kim East Quay Medical Centre, East Quay, Bridgwater TA6 5YB Tel: 01278 444666 Fax: 01278 445448 — MB ChB 1984 Bristol; MRCGP 1993; DRCOG 1988. Prev: SHO (Gen. Med.) W.on Gen. Hosp. W.on-Super-Mare; SHO (ENT) Bath Roy. United Hosp.; SHO (A & E) Frenchay Hosp. Bristol.

ROBERTS, Susan Holt Northumbria Health Care Trust, Diabetes Resource Centre, North Tyneside District General Hospital, Rake Lane, North Shields NE29 8NH Tel: 0191 293 2708 Fax: 0191 293 2734; 25 Linden Road, Newcastle upon Tyne NE3 4EY Tel: 0191 285 5004 Fax: 0191 285 5004 Email: sue.roberts@cableiner.co.uk — MB BS 1969 Lond.; MSc (Clin. Biochem.) Newc. 1975; BSc (Physiol.) Lond. 1966; FRCP Lond. 1986, M 1972. (Middlx.) Cons. Phys. (Med. & Diabetes) N. Tyneside HA. Socs: Brit. Diabetic Assn.; Educat. Advis. Comm. Prev: Regist. (Gastroenterol.) Roy. Vict. Infirm. Newc.; Lect. (Med.) Memor. Univ. of Newfld. St. John's, Canada; Sen. Regist. (Research) Dept. Med. Newc. Gen. Hosp.

ROBERTS, Suzanne Hannah Kaleidescope Project, 40-46 Cromwell Road, Kingston upon Thames KT2 6RE — MB ChB 1974 Sheff.; DTM & H Liverp. 1991; DRCOG 1976. Ministerial Stud. S. Wales Baptist Coll. Cardiff. Prev: ACRIS Community Health Progr., Mozambique; Clinician i/c BBS Ruhea Clinic Community Health Progr., Bangladesh; Clin. Med. Off. Greenwich HA.

ROBERTS, Sylvia Ann Ashley Centre Surgery, Ashley Square, Epsom KT18 5DD Tel: 01372 723668 Fax: 01372 726796 — MB ChB 1974 Leeds; MRCGP 1978; DCH Eng. 1977; DRCOG 1976.

ROBERTS, Teresa Agnes Leak, Gunn, Fourie, Brennan and Roberts, Witton Medical Centre, 29-31 Preston Old Road, Blackburn BB2 2SU Tel: 01254 262123 Fax: 01254 695759; The Old Barn, Bowfields Lane, Balderstone, Blackburn BB2 7LW — MB ChB 1983 Manch. p/t Princip. in Gen. Pract., Blackburn. Prev: Community Med. Off. Burnley, Pendle & Rossendale HA.

ROBERTS, Teresa Catherine Fax: 01438 361227; 78 Wymondley Road, Hitchin SG4 9PT — BM BS 1984 Nottm.; DRCOG 1989.

ROBERTS, Thomas Gwyn Beechley Medical Centre, 73 Ruabon Road, Wrexham LL13 7PU Tel: 01978 361279 Fax: 01978 350915; T'Yr Gloch Farm, Talwyn, Coedpoeth, Wrexham LL11 3BY — MB ChB 1976 Liverp.; MRCP (UK) 1978; MRCGP 1983; DCH RCP Lond. 1983.

ROBERTS, Timothy Edward The Sycamores, Rectory Rd, Padworth Common, Reading RG7 4JD — MB ChB 1997 Leeds.

ROBERTS, Timothy Lloyd North Devon District Hospital, Raleigh Park, Barnstaple EX31 4JB Tel: 01271 322418 Fax: 01271 322709 Email: tlroberts@beeb.uk; Herders, Kings Heanton, Barnstaple EX31 4ED Tel: 01271 346418 — MB BS 1982 Lond.; BSc Physiol. (Hons.) Lond. 1979, MB BS 1982; MRCP (UK) 1985; MD Lond. 1995; FRCP 2000 London. (Middlx.) Cons. Cardiol. and Phys. N. Devon Dist. Hosp. Socs: Brit. Cardiac Soc. Prev: Regist. (Cardiol.) Soton. Gen. Hosp.; Lect. (Preven. Cardiol.) Univ. Soton.; Clin. Research Phys. Wellcome Foundat.

ROBERTS, Trevor John Hyde Bungeons Farm Cottage, Barking, Ipswich IP6 8HN — MB BS Lond. 1962; MRCS Eng. LRCP Lond. 1965; DObst RCOG 1965. Med. Off. Nat. Blood Serv. Camb.

ROBERTS, Professor Trudie Elizabeth Medical Education Unit, Level 7 Worsley Building, University or Leeds Medical School, Leeds LS2 9NL Tel: 0113 233 1657 Fax: 0113 233 4373 Email: t.e.roberts@leeds.ac.uk — MB ChB 1979 Manch.; PhD Manch. 1987, BSc (Hons.) (Anat.) 1976, MB ChB 1979; MRCP (UK) 1982; FRCP 1999. Prof. of Med. Educat. and Director of the Med. Educat. Unit.

ROBERTS, Vaughan Arthur Bruce 58 Castle Road, Scarborough YO11 1XE Tel: 01723 375050 — MB BS 1981 Lond.; BSc (Hons.) Lond. 1978, MB BS 1981; MRCGP 1986; DRCOG 1984; DCCH RCGP FCM 1985.

ROBERTS, Vivienne Margaret Twyford Health Centre, Loddon Hall Road, Twyford, Reading RG10 9JA Tel: 0118 934 0112 Fax: 0118 934 1048 — MB BS 1979 Newc.; MRCGP 1988; DCH RCP Lond. 1983.

ROBERTSON

ROBERTS, William (retired) 19 West Road, Irvine KA12 8RE — LRCP LRCS Ed. LRFPS Glas. 1945; FRFPS Glas. 1951; FRCP Glas. 1973, M 1962. Prev: Cons. Phys. (with Responsibil. For Infec. Dis.) Ayrsh. Centr. Hosp. Irvine.

ROBERTS, William Glyn 25 Furrocks Lane, Ness, South Wirral CH64 4EH Tel: 0151 336 3325 — MB ChB 1945 Liverp.; DPH Liverp. 1971; Assoc. Fac. Occupat. Med. RCP Lond. 1979. (Liverp.) Prev: Clin. Med. Off. (Community Child Health) Liverp. HA.

ROBERTS, William James Cynfab North Parade Surgery, 26 North Parade, Aberystwyth SY23 2NF Tel: 01970 624545 Fax: 01970 615612; Taleithin, Penglais Road, Aberystwyth SY23 2EU Tel: 01970 623321 — MB BChir 1964 Camb.; MA, BChir 1963; DObst RCOG 1966; FRCGP 1988, M 1977. (Camb. & St. Mary's) Chairm. Heart Beat Wales Charity; Treasury Med. Off.; Med. Off. Nat. Library of Wales; Examr. Welsh Coll. Med.; Internat. reviewer, Health Evidence Bull.s, Wales. Socs: Fell. RCGP (Mem. Welsh Counc. & UK Counc.); BMA; Ct. & Counc. Univ. Wales Aberystwyth. Prev: Provost W. Wales Fac. RCGP; NHS Overseas Fell & Vis. Prof. King Saud Univ. Riahd Saudi Arabia; Non Exec. Mem. Welsh Health Promotion Auth.

ROBERTS, William Owen Bryn Awel, Gyrngoch, Clynnogfawr, Caernarfon LL54 5PG — MB ChB 1966 Liverp.; FFA RCS Eng. 1974; FFA RCSI 1973; DObst RCOG 1970. Cons. Anaesth. Caerns. & Anglesey & St. David's Hosps. Bangor, Eryri; Hosp. Caernarfon & Caernarfon Eye & Cott. Hosp. Prev: Med. Off. Zambian Flying Doctor Serv.

ROBERTS, William Thomas 12 Chater Close, Portico Lane, Whiston, Prescot L35 7LX — MB ChB 1975 Liverp.; Dip. ATLS RCS Eng. 1996; Dip. ALS RCS Eng. 1996; Cert. Family Plann. JCC 1980. F/T Clin. Asst. St Helens & Knowsley Hosp. Trust. Prev: SHO (Cas. & Gen. Surg.) Walton & Fazakerley Hosp. Liverp.; Lect. (Anat.) Univ. Manch.; Ho. Off. St. Helens Hosp.

ROBERTS-HAREWOOD, Marilyn-Rae Diane 64 Cambridge Road, Carshalton SM5 3QS — MB BS 1989 Lond.; MRCP (UK) 1993. (St. Geos.) Clin. Research Fell. (Haemat.).

ROBERTS-HARRY, Nest Gwenllian (retired) 20 Cimla Road, Neath SA11 3PP Tel: 01639 4601 — BSc, MB BCh Wales, 1941; DCH Eng. 1947. Prev: Ho. Phys. Llandough Hosp. Penarth.

ROBERTS-HARRY, Mr Thomas John Department of Ophthalmology, West Wales General Hospital, Glangwili, Carmarthen SA31 2AF — MB BS 1979 Lond.; FRCS Ed. 1986; MRCS Eng. LRCP Lond. 1978; FRCOphth 1994. Cons. Ophth. Surg. Carmarthenshire NHS Trust. Prev: Sen. Regist. Rotat (Ophth.) Univ. Coll., Roy. Free, St. Bart. & Moorfields Eye Hosp. Lond.

ROBERTS-PUW, Elin Hanna Gwynedd Community Health Trust, Women & Children Directorate, Child Health Department, Health Premises, Argyll Road, Llandudno LL30 1DF Tel: 01492 862000; Perthi Mwyar, Tyddyn Mali, Llanddoged, Llanrwst LL26 0DD Tel: 01492 641595 — MB BCh 1982 Wales. SCMO Aberconwy. Socs: BMA; Welsh Med. Soc.; BACCH.

ROBERTS-SHEPHARD, Alison 2 Albury Avenue, Sutton SM2 7JT — MB BS 1977 Lond.; DRCOG 1979; DCH Eng. 1980.

ROBERTS-THOMSON, Mr James Harold 38 Caves Lane, Bedford MK40 3DP — MB BS 1977 Tasmania; BMedSc Tasmania 1980, MB BS 1977; FRCS Glas. 1986.

ROBERTSHAW, Barbara Ann Earls House Hospital, Durham DH1 5RE Tel: 0191 333 6296 Fax: 0191 333 6528 — MB BCh BAO NUI 1967; FRCPsych 1996, M 1974; DPM Dub. 1972. (Galway) Assoc. Med. Dir.Learning Disabil.Co. Durh. & Darlington priority Sev.NHS Trust; Assessor for Advis. Appts. Comms. (Cons. & Hon. Cons.) Roy. Coll. Psychiat. Socs: SSBP. Prev: Regist. St. Patrick's Hosp. Dub. & Earls Ho. Hosp. Durh.; SHO Stewart's Hosp. Palmerstown.

ROBERTSHAW, Carolyn Jane Lee House Surgery, 84 Osborne Road, Windsor SL4 3EW Tel: 01753 861612 Fax: 01753 833695; Willowtree House, 50 Alma Road, Windsor SL4 3HA Tel: 01753 832685 — MB ChB 1985 Manch.; BSc St. And. 1982; MRCGP 1989; DRCOG 1989; DCH RCP Lond. 1987. Socs: Brit. Med. Acupunct. Soc.; BMA. Prev: Trainee GP Milnthorpe & Bracknell; SHO (Paediat.) Roy. Lancaster Infirm.; SHO (Med.) W.moreland Co. Hosp. Cumbria.

ROBERTSHAW, Denise Elizabeth (retired) Flat 2 Springhead Court, 444 Haworth Road, Allerton, Bradford BD15 9LL Tel: 01274 544511 — MB ChB 1958 Ed.; MFCM 1974; DPH Leeds 1965; DCH Eng. 1966. Prev: Cons. Pub. Health Med. Leeds Health Dist.

ROBERTSHAW, Heidi Jane 16 Barmouth Road, London SW18 2DN; Anaesthetic Department, St Mary's Hospital, Praed St., London W2 1NY — MB BS Lond. 1993; FRCA 1998. (St. Bartholomew's Hospital) Anaesth. Regist. St Marys Hosp. Lond.

ROBERTSHAW, John Keith 150 Longmoor Lane, Breaston, Derby DE72 3BE — MB ChB 1981 Bristol.

ROBERTSHAW, Katharine Anna Derbyshire Children's Hopital, Uttoxeter Road, Derby Tel: 01132 340131 — MB ChB 1993 Leeds; MCRP (Edin.) (Paeds) 1996. SpR in Community Paediat., Derbysh. Childr.'s Hosp. Derby. Socs: MRCPCH.

ROBERTSHAW, Mary Freda Ribbleton Medical Surgery, 243 Ribbleton Ave, Ribbleton, Preston PR2 6RD — MB ChB 1974 Manch.

ROBERTSHAW, Nancy Miriam Elsie (retired) Beech Bank, Beetham, Milnthorpe LA7 7AL Tel: 015395 62651 — MB ChB 1945 St. And.; MB ChB (Commend.) St. And. 1945; BSc St. And. 1942; DObst RCOG 1948; DCH Eng. 1953; DPM Eng. 1967. Prev: Assoc. Specialist (Psychiat.) Leighton Hosp. Crewe.

ROBERTSHAW, Richard 5 Park Road, Ketton, Stamford PE9 3SL — MB BS 1962 Lond.; MRCS Eng. LRCP Lond. 1961; FFA RCS Eng. 1966; DA Eng. 1963. (King's Coll. Hosp.) Cons. Anaesth. PeterBoro. Dist. Hosp. Socs: Assn. Anaesths. Prev: Staff Anaesth. Trail-Tadenal Hosp. Canada; Clin. Research Fell. Dept. Anaesth. Hosp. Sick Childr. Toronto; Regist. Dept. Anaesth. Hosp. Sick Childr. Gt. Ormond St.

***ROBERTSHAW, William Edward Guy** West House Farm, Bishop Middleham, Ferryhill DL17 9DY — MB BS 1986 Newc.; MRCPsych. 1991.

ROBERTSON, Adam Alan (retired) 2 Rothsay Place, Edinburgh EH3 7SL Tel: 0131 226 4961 — MB ChB 1951 Ed.; MRCGP 1963. Prev: MuirHo. Med. Gp.

ROBERTSON, Agnes Helen Angela Riverbank Practice, Janet St., Thurso KW14 7AR Tel: 01847 892027; Bruan Lodge, Mid Clyth, Lybster KW3 6BA Tel: 01593 721296 — MB ChB 1974 Ed.; BSc Ed. 1971; DFFP 1997. (Ed.) Princip. (p/t), Riverbank Pract., Thurso, Caithness. Socs: BMA; MDDUS. Prev: Assoc. GP Lybster & Dunbeath Pract.s.

ROBERTSON, Aileen Patricia Eaglestone Health Centre, Milton Keynes MK6 5AZ; 53 Lower Street, Great Doddington, Wellingborough NN29 7TN — MB ChB 1985 Dundee; DRCOG 1989; DCH RCP Lond. 1989.

ROBERTSON, Alan Chalmers Consultant Radiologist, C X-Ray Department, Law Hospital, Carluke ML8 5ER — MB ChB 1980 Glas.; T(R) (CR) 1992.

ROBERTSON, Mr Alan William Mount Florida Medical Centre, 183 Prospecthill Road, Glasgow G42 9LQ Tel: 0141 632 4004 Fax: 0141 636 6036 — MB ChB 1966 Glas.; FRCS Glas. 1973. (Glas.) Hon. Fell. Brit. Soc. Med. & Dent. Hypn.

ROBERTSON, Alasdair Neil 1 Kylepark Crescent, Uddingston, Glasgow G71 7DQ — MB ChB 1995 Glas.

ROBERTSON, Alastair (retired) 11 Woodburn Avenue, Aberdeen AB15 8JQ Tel: 01224 317606 — MB ChB 1940 Ed.; FRCGP 1995, M 1953. Prev: GP Aberd.

ROBERTSON, Alastair Dunn, MBE (retired) 4 Grand Marine Court, Argyll St., Rothesay PA20 0AX Tel: 01700 503398 — MB ChB 1940 Glas. Prev: Med. Off. Polmont Borstal Inst. Brighton Falkirk.

ROBERTSON, Alastair Scott University Hospital Birmingham, Occupational Health Department, Woodlands Nurses Home, Selly Oak Hospital, Birmingham B29 6JF Tel: 0121 627 8286 Fax: 0121 627 8312 Email: alastair.robertson@university-b.wmids.nhs.uk; 9 St Bernards Road, Olton, Solihull B92 7AU Tel: 0121 707 5639 — MB ChB 1978 Aberd.; MRCP (UK) 1981; FFOM 1997; MFOM RCP 1992, AFOM 1989; FRCP 1998. (Aberd.) Cons. Occupat. Health Univ. Hosp. Birm. NHS Trust; Cons. Occupat. Respirat. Dis. Birm. Chest Clinic; Hon. Sen. Lect. Univ. Birm. Socs: Brit. Thorac. Soc. & Soc. Occupat. Med.; Assn. Nat. Health Servs. Occupat. Phys. Prev: Lect. (Occupat. Health) Univ. Birm.; Regist. (Respirat. Dis.) Kings Cross Hosp. Dundee; Ho. Surg. & Ho. Phys. Roy. Infirm. Aberd.

ROBERTSON, Alastair Wilson (retired) Haworth, Lundin Links, Lower Largo, Leven KY8 6AH Tel: 01333 320335 — MB ChB (Commend.) St. And. 1949; MFOM RCP Lond. 1984; DIH Soc.

ROBERTSON

Apoth. Lond. 1976; CIH Dund 1976. Occupat. Phys. St. And. Univ. Fife. Prev: Occupat. Phys. St. And. Univ. Fife.

ROBERTSON, Alexander Delamere, West End Lane, Warton, Preston PR4 1TA — LRCP LRCS 1939 Ed.; LRCP LRCS Ed. LRFPS Glas. 1939.

ROBERTSON, Mr Alexander Alan 22 Dumyat Drive, Falkirk FK1 5PD Tel: 01324 24430 — MB ChB 1949 Glas.; FRCS Ed. 1957. (Glas.) Cons. Orthop. Surg. Stirlingsh. Area, Falkirk & Dist., & Stirling Roy. Infirms. Prev: Cons. Orthop. Surg. Norf. & Norwich & Gt. Yarmouth Hosps.; Sen. Regist. Orthop. Dundee Roy. Infirm. & Bridge of Earn Hosp.; Orthop. Regist. W.. Infirm. Glas.

ROBERTSON, Alexander George 18 Willow Drive, Kirkcaldy KY1 2LF — MB ChB 1992 Dundee. SHO (A & E & Orthop.), Hairmyres Hosp. E. Kilbride. Prev: Ho. Off. Dundee Roy. Infirm. & Hairmyers Hosp.

ROBERTSON, Alick John Cuminestown, 8 Long Hey Road, Caldy, Wirral CH48 1LZ Tel: 0151 625 7248 Fax: 0151 625 0807 Email: drajrcaldy@onetel.net.uk — MB ChB 1942 Liverp.; MD Liverp. 1951; FRCP Lond. 1964, M 1949; MFOM RCP Lond. 1983. (Liverp.) p/t Cons. WHO (Afghanistan); Emerit. Cons. Phys. & Phys. Heart Dept. Roy. Liverp. Hosp.; Mem. Inst. & Emerit. Cons. Phys. King Edwd. VII Hosp. Midhurst; Examr. Milroy Lect. & Fitzpatrick Lect. RCP Lond. Socs: Thoracic Soc.; Assn. Phys.; Internat. Soc. Internal Med. Prev: Edr. Thorax; Samuel Memor. Schol. 1951.

ROBERTSON, Alison Jean Woodside Medical Group B, 80 Western Road, Woodside, Aberdeen AB24 4SU Tel: 01224 492828 Fax: 01224 276173 — MB ChB 1990 Aberd.

ROBERTSON, Alistair Charles 3 Nunburnholme Avenue, North Ferriby HU14 3AW Tel: 01482 634331 — MB ChB 1968 Aberd. (Aberd.) Prev: Ho. Phys. City Hosp. Aberd.; Ho. Surg. Dumfries & Galloway Roy. Infirm.

ROBERTSON, Alistair John Pathology Department, Ninewells Hospital & Medical School, Dundee DD1 9SY Tel: 01382 660111 Fax: 01382 640966; Glendale, Kilspindie, Errol, Perth PH2 7RX — MB ChB 1975 Aberd.; BMedBiol (Hons.) 1972; FRCPath 1993. Clin. Gp. Director, Clin. support Serv.s, Tayside Teachg. Hosp.s NHS Trust.; Cons. & Hon. Sen. Lect. (Path.) Dundee Tech. Hosp. NHS Trust. Socs: Internat. Acad. Path. & Assn. Clin. Pathols. Prev: Lect. & Hon. Sen. Regist. (Path.) Univ. Dundee at Ninewells Hosp.; Cons. in Admin. Charge Lab. Servs. Perth & Kinross Dist.

ROBERTSON, Alistair Stuart House 3, Bridlington District Hospital, Bridlington YO16 5QP; 11 Second Avenue, Bridlington YO15 2LL — MB ChB 1985 Leeds; BSc (Hons.) (Physiol.) Leeds 1982, MB ChB 1985; MRCGP 1989; DRCOG 1989. GP N. Humberside.

ROBERTSON, Amanda May 7 Hatfield Close, Maidenhead SL6 4RJ — MB BS 1990 Lond.

ROBERTSON, Andrea c/o 52 High Ridge, Hythe CT21 5TF — MB ChB 1992 Leic.

ROBERTSON, Andrew The Medical Centre, Station Avenue, Bridlington YO16 4LZ Tel: 01262 670686 Fax: 01262 401685; Westerlands, 95 Martongate, Bridlington YO16 6YE Tel: 01262 672128 — MB ChB 1954 Glas.; DObst RCOG 1956. (Glas.)

ROBERTSON, Andrew George Colin Fyrish, Fordyce Terrace, New Deer, Turriff AB53 6WE Tel: 01771 644675 Fax: 01771 653294 — MB ChB 1974 Aberd.; MRCGP 1978; DObst RCOG 1976.

ROBERTSON, Andrew Gerard 44 Lubnaig Road, Newlands, Glasgow G43 2RX — MB ChB 1975 Glas.; PhD Glas. 1970, BSc (Hons.) 1967, MB ChB 1975; FRCP Glas. 1988, M 1986; FRCR 1980. Cons. Radiol. & Oncol. Beatson Oncol. Centre Glas.; Assoc. Treas. Head & Neck Oncol. Gt. Brit. Prev: Cons. (Radiol. & Oncol.) Glas. Inst. Radiotherap.; Sen. Regist. (Radiother. Oncol.) Christie Hosp. & Holt Inst. Manch.

ROBERTSON, Andrew Graeme Cross Deep Surgery, 4 Cross Deep, Twickenham TW1 4QP Tel: 020 8892 8124 Fax: 020 8744 9801; 86 Fairfax Road, Teddington TW11 9BX Tel: 020 8943 2124 — MB ChB 1979 Aberd.; DRCOG 1981; Dip (Anaesth.)1983; MRCGP 1985; Dip Sports Med.1990; MLCOM 1991. (Aberdeen Univ.) GP; Sports Phys.; Med. Off. Rugby Football Union, Twickenham. Socs: Lond. Coll. Osteop. Med.; Brit. Assoc of Sports Med.; Brit. Inst. of Muscle Skeletal Med. Bimn.

ROBERTSON, Andrew James The Surgery, East Grinstead Road, Lingfield RH7 6ER Tel: 01342 833456 Fax: 01342 836347; Beechlands, Dormans Park, East Grinstead RH19 2NG Tel: 01342 870733 — MB 1966 Camb.; BChir 1965; DA Eng. 1969. (St. Bart.) Prev: Ho. Surg. St. Bart. Hosp. Lond.; Regist. in Anaesth. Qu. Vict. Hosp. E. Grinstead.

ROBERTSON, Andrew Macpherson (retired) 6 Green Tree Gardens, Romiley, Stockport SK6 3JL — MB ChB 1976 Manch.; DRCOG 1978; MRCGP 1982. Prev: Ho. Off. Manch. Roy. Infirm.

ROBERTSON, Andrew Stephen 95 Martongate, Bridlington YO16 6YE — MB BS 1983 Newc.

ROBERTSON, Angela Meadowbank Health Centre, 3 Salmon Inn Road, Polmont, Falkirk FK2 0XF Tel: 01324 715540 Fax: 01324 716723 — MB ChB 1987 Dundee; MRCGP 1992.

ROBERTSON, Anne The Health Centre, 201 Main Street, Barrhead, Glasgow G78 1SA Tel: 0141 880 6161 Fax: 0141 881 7063 — MB BS 1975 Newc.; MRCGP 1980; DRCOG 1979; DCH RCPS Glas. 1977.

ROBERTSON, Anne Elizabeth (retired) 12 Milton Drive, Edinburgh EH15 2JX Tel: 0131 669 5434 — MB ChB 1939 Ed. Prev: Clin. Asst. E. & SE Scotl. Blood Transfus. Serv.

ROBERTSON, Anne Johnston 4 Ruthven Water, Aberuthven, Auchterarder PH3 1JD Tel: 01764 663570 — MB ChB 1952 Ed.; DPH 1959; DObst RCOG 1955.

ROBERTSON, Barbara Catto Lister House Surgery, 35 The Parade, St Helier, Jersey JE2 3QQ Tel: 01534 36336 Fax: 01534 35304; 9 Le Jardin De La Chapelle, St. Aubin, St Brelade, Jersey JE3 8JL — MB ChB 1980 Aberd.; DCCH RCP Ed. 1986; DRCOG 1983.

ROBERTSON, Bodil Ronnfeldt Anaesthetic Department, Kent & Canterbury Hospital, Ethelbert Road, Canterbury CT1 3NG; 36 Long Oaks Court, Sketty, Swansea SA2 0QH — MB ChB 1989 Aberd.

ROBERTSON, Brian, OStJ, TD North Lane Practice, 38 North Lane, Aldershot GU12 4QQ Tel: 01252 344434; 248 A Shawfield Road, Ash, Aldershot GU12 5DJ Tel: 01252 350294 — MRCS Eng. LRCP Lond. 1972. (Roy. Free) Col. L/RAMC (V); Mem. Editr. Bd. Pre-Hosp. Immediate Care. Socs: BMA; BASICS; IEM. Prev: Ho. Surg. New End Hosp. Hampstead; Ho. Phys. St. And. Hosp. Bow.

ROBERTSON, Brian John Dinnington Group Practice, Medical Centre, New Street, Dinnington, Sheffield S25 2EZ — MB ChB 1979 Dundee; MRCGP 1983; DRCOG 1982. Prev: Trainee GP Doncaster VTS.; Ho. Off. (Orthop.) Vict. Hosp. Kirkcaldy; Ho. Off. (Med.) Ninewells Hosp. Dundee.

ROBERTSON, Cameron Giles Beechlands, Dormans Park, East Grinstead RH19 2NG — BM BS 1991 Flinders.

ROBERTSON, Carol Royal Cornhill Hospital, Cornhill Road, Aberdeen AB25 2ZH Tel: 01224 663131; Melrose, Station Road, Ellon AB41 9AR Tel: 01358 720577 — MB ChB 1984 Aberd.; MRCPsych 1991; MRCGP 1988; DRCOG 1987; M Med Sci Aber. Uni, 1995. (Aberdeen) Cons. Grampian HB. Prev: Trainee Psychiat. Aberd.

ROBERTSON, Caroline Lois Hill Farm Barn, Broadwas, Worcester WR6 5NH Tel: 01886 821977 — MB BS 1980 Lond.; MRCGP 1985; DRCOG 1983. (Guy's)

ROBERTSON, Caroline Younger Battersby Moleigh House, Oban PA34 5JD — LRCP LRCS 1946 Ed.; LRCP LRCS Ed. LRFPS Glas. 1946. (Anderson & St. Mungo's Colls. Glas.)

ROBERTSON, Carolyn Margaret McCallum 43 Hope Park Gardens, Bathgate EH48 2QT — MB ChB 1989 Ed.; MRCGP 1994.

ROBERTSON, Catherine Jackson Allan (retired) Montpelier, 32 Barrhead Road, Newton Mearns, Glasgow G77 6BD Tel: 0141 639 1125 — LRCP LRCS Ed. LRFPS Glas. 1948. Prev: Med. Off. Child Health Ayrsh. & Arran HB.

ROBERTSON, Catriona Jane 1/L 103 Queensborough Gardens, Glasgow G12 9RS — MB ChB 1990 Glas.; MRCGP 1994; DRCOG 1993; DCH RCPS Glas. 1992.

ROBERTSON, Catriona Mary 6 Rockford Lodge, Knutsford WA16 8AH — MB ChB 1981 Dundee.

ROBERTSON, Mr Charles Stuart Hill Farm Barn, Broadwas-on-Teme, Worcester WR6 5NH Tel: 01886 821977 Fax: 01886 821977; Worcester Royal Infirmary NHS Trust, Ronkswood Branch, Newtown Road, Worcester WR5 1HN Tel: 01905 760577 Fax: 01905 760786 — MB BS 1980 Lond.; DM Nottm. 1989; FRCS Eng. 1984. (Guy's) Cons. Gen. & Gastrointestinal Surg. Worcester Roy. Infirm. Socs: Assn. Surg.; Assn. Upper G.I. Surg.; Assn.

ROBERTSON

Endoscopic Surgs. Prev: Sen. Regist. Newc.; Lect. Chinese Univ. of Hong Kong; Regist. Nottm.

ROBERTSON, Clare Margaret The Ounsted Clinic, Churchill Hospital, Headington, Oxford OX3 7LJ Tel: 01865 225617 Fax: 01865 225618 — MB ChB 1983 Bristol; MRCP (UK) 1986; FRCPCH. Cons. Paediat. (Community Child Health) Oxf. Prev: Sen. Regist. (Community Paediat.) & Regist. (Paediat.) Oxf.

ROBERTSON, Clifton (retired) Castle Mound, Cressage, Shrewsbury SY5 6AD Tel: 01952 510502 — MB BS 1950 Durh. Prev: Ho. Phys. Childr. Dept. & Regist. (Paediat.) Roy. Vict. Infirm. Newc.

ROBERTSON, Mr Colin (cons. rooms) 3 Broomhall Avenue, Wakefield WF1 2BB Tel: 01924 373373 — MB ChB 1951 Birm.; FRCS Ed. 1962; FRCS Eng. 1963. (Birm.) Orthop. Surg. Pinderfields Hosp. & Wakefield Gp. Hosps. Socs: BMA. Prev: Res. Orthop. Off. Gen. Infirm. Leeds; Orthop. Regist. Robt. Jones & Agnes Hunt Orthop. Hosp. OsW.ry; Sen. Orthop. Regist. Stoke-on-Trent & Robt. Jones & Agnes Hunt.

ROBERTSON, Colin Crawford (retired) 2A Green Hill Road, Leeds LS12 3QA Tel: 0113 263 8782 — MB ChB 1960 Leeds; MRCS Eng. LRCP Lond. 1961. Prev: GP Leeds.

ROBERTSON, David Alasdair (retired) 54 Bay Street, Fairlie, Largs KA29 0AL Email: darmog@cwcom.net — MB ChB 1959 Aberd.; FRCP Canada 1974. Prev: Cons. Psychiat. Ailsa Hosp. Ayr.

ROBERTSON, David Alastair Magdalen Medical Practice, Lawson Road, Norwich NR3 4LF Tel: 01603 475555 Fax: 01603 787210; 12 Hillside Avenue, Norwich NR7 0QW — MB BS Newc. 1987, BMedSci 1986; MRCGP 1991; DRCOG 1991; DCH RCP Lond. 1990.

ROBERTSON, David Alexander Carmondean Medical Group, Carmondean Health Centre, Livingston EH54 8PY Tel: 01506 430031 Fax: 01506 432775 — MB ChB 1982 Ed.

ROBERTSON, Mr David Edward Assisted Conception Unit, Esperance House, Hartington Place, Eastbourne BN21 3BG Tel: 01323 410717 Fax: 01323 410626 Email: acu@dial.pipex.com; 28 Summerdown Road, Eastbourne BN20 8DR Tel: 01323 726151 Email: der@dial.pipex.com — MB ChB 1977 Glas.; MRCOG 1982; FRCOG 1998. (University of Glasgow) Med. Dir. Assisted Conception Unit Esperance Private Hosp.; Hon. Cons. (Obst. & Gyn.) E.bourne DGH. Socs: Brit. Fertil. Soc.; Amer. Fertil. Soc.; ESHRE. Prev: Cons. O & G Awali Hosp.; Regist. (O & G) Leic. Roy. Infirm.; Hall Fell. Midw. Univ. Glas.

ROBERTSON, David Eric The Old Shippon, Bradley Hall, Bradley, Frodsham, Warrington WA6 7EP Tel: 01928 733250 Fax: 0151 424 0299 Email: der@globalnet.co.uk — MB ChB Liverp. 1968; MSc (Community Med.) Manch. 1983; MFFP 1993; FRCGP 1985, M 1973. Cons. Pub. Health Med. Chesh. HA; Hon. Lect. (Gen. Pract.) Liverp. Univ. Socs: Fell. Fac. Community Health.

ROBERTSON, David Iain Stewart 17-19 Raise Street, Saltcoats KA21 5LX Tel: 01294 605141; 4 North Crescent, Ardrossan KA22 0LY Tel: 01294 62517 — MB ChB 1955 Glas.; MRCGP 1968.

ROBERTSON, David James Drumchapel Health Centre, 80-90 Kinfauns Drive, Glasgow G15 7TS Tel: 0141 211 6110 Fax: 0141 211 6140; 11b Winton Drive, Glasgow G12 0PZ — MB ChB 1978 Glas. GP Glas.

ROBERTSON, David Neil Queen Elizabeth Psychiatric Hospial, Mindelsohn Way, Vincent Drive, Edgbaston, Birmingham B15 2QZ — MB ChB 1984 Birm.; MRCPsych 1992. Cons. (Eating Disorders) Qu. Eliz. Psychiat. Hosp. Birm. Prev: Sen. Regist. (Gen. Psychiat.) Qu. Eliz. Psychiat. Hosp. Birm.

ROBERTSON, Dene Michael William 32 Azalea Close, Uxbridge Road, Hanwell, London W7 3QA — MB BS 1987 Lond.; MRCGP 1991; MRCPsych 1994.

ROBERTSON, Denis Wilson (retired) Home Farm House, Hillcrest Avenue, Northampton NN3 2AB Tel: 01604 642012 — MRCS Eng. LRCP Lond. 1950; MRCGP 1967; Cert. Av Med. MoD (Air) & CAA 1973. Hon. JP; Med. Examr. Civil Aviat. Auth.

ROBERTSON, Denise Elexia Herne Hill Group Practice, 74 Herne Hill, London SE24 9QP Tel: 020 7274 3314 Fax: 020 7738 6025 — MB BS 1987 Lond.

ROBERTSON, Derek Dalkeith Medical Centre, 24-26 St. Andrew Street, Dalkeith EH22 1AP Tel: 0131 663 2461 Fax: 0131 561 5555; Ellangowan, 6 Lothian Bank, Dalkeith EH22 3AN Tel: 0131 660 5004 — MB ChB 1977 Ed.; MRCGP 1981; DRCOG 1980.

ROBERTSON, Diana Christine Foote 9 Dickens Wynd, Merryoaks, Durham DH1 3QR Tel: 0191 384 1450 — MB ChB 1980 Ed. Prev: Lothian Health Bd. Retainer Scheme; Trainee GP Bonnyrigg Health Centre; SHO (O & G) Bangour Gen. Hosp.

ROBERTSON, Donald Henry Mouat (retired) Calderstones, 33 Snowdon Place, Stirling FK8 2JP Tel: 01786 475634 — MB ChB 1961 Ed.; FFA RCS Eng. 1966. Prev: Regist. & Sen. Regist. Roy. Infirm. Edin.

ROBERTSON, Donald Macpherson (retired) 7 Chadkirk Road, Romley, Stockport SK6 3JY — MB ChB 1938 Ed. Prev: Apptd. Fact. Doctor.

ROBERTSON, Doreen Colina (retired) Woodend Cottage, Juniper Bank, Walkerburn EH43 6DE Tel: 01896 870523 — MB ChB Ed. 1945.

ROBERTSON, Dorothy Elizabeth (retired) 11 Woodburn Avenue, Aberdeen AB15 8JQ Tel: 01224 317606 — MB ChB 1947 Aberd. Prev: GP Aberd.

ROBERTSON, Dorothy Ruth Caddick Tel: 01225 428331; 10 Chapel Path, Colerne, Chippenham SN14 8DL Tel: 01225 742767 — MB ChB 1976 Glas.; DM Soton. 1994; MRCP (UK) 1979; DCH RCP Lond. 1978; FRCP Lond. 1997. Cons. Geriat. Med. St. Martins Hosp. Bath. Socs: Brit. Geriat. Soc. (Comm. Mem. s/i Gp. Pk.inson's Dis.). Prev: Regist. (Med.) Gen. Hosp. Birm.; Lect. (Geriat. Med.) Soton.; SHO (Med.) Chapel Allerton Hosp. Leeds.

ROBERTSON, Douglas Allan 27 Drummond Crescent, Inverness IV2 4QR — MB ChB 1971 Glas.; MRCPath 1978. Cons. Biochem. Raigmore Hosp. Inverness. Prev: Sen. Regist. Clin. Biochem. Roy. Infirm. Glas.; Jun. Ho. Off. S.. Gen. Hosp. Glas.; Jun. Ho. Off. W.. Infirm. Glas.

ROBERTSON, Douglas Andrew Sandwell General Hospital, Lyndon, West Bromwich B71 4HJ Tel: 0121 553 1831 Fax: 0121 607 3300; Littlefield House, Market Lane, Wall, Lichfield WS14 0AU Tel: 01543 483225 Email: douglas.a.robertson@ntlward.com — BM BCh 1981 Oxf.; MA Camb. 1982, BA 1978; DM Oxf. 1991; MRCP (UK) 1984; FRCP 2000 FRCP (London) 2000. (Oxf.) Cons. Phys. (Diabetes & Endocrinol.) Sandwell Gen. Hosp. W. Bromwich. Socs: Diabetes UK; Soc. Endocrinol. Prev: Sen. Regist. (Diabetes) Newc.; Regist. (Renal) City Hosp. Nottm.; Research Fell. (Diabetes) Gen. Hosp. Birm.

ROBERTSON, Douglas Edward Hocken (retired) 30 Ravensdale Gardens, Walsall WS5 3PX Tel: 01922 29494 — MD 1947 Leeds; MB ChB 1944. Prev: Sen. Clin. Lect. in Dermat. to the Univ. of Birm. 1974 -1980.

ROBERTSON, Mr Douglas James (retired) Roseville, Gatehouse of Fleet, Castle Douglas DG7 2HU Tel: 01557 814250 — MRCS Eng. LRCP Lond. 1942; MB BS Lond. 1942; MS Lond. 1955; FRCS Eng. 1947. Prev: Sen. Surg. Roy. Hosp. Sheff.

ROBERTSON, Douglas Kerr Pennan Place Surgery, 20 Pennan Place, Glasgow G14 0EA Tel: 0141 959 1704 Fax: 0141 958 1100 — MB ChB 1977 Glas.; MRCGP 1987; DRCOG 1983.

ROBERTSON, Duncan Alexander Findlay Royal United Hospital, Combe Park, Bath BA1 3NG Tel: 01225 824547 — MB ChB 1977 Leeds; MD Leeds 1983, BSc (Hons.) Biochem. 1974, MB ChB 1977; FRCP Lond. 1994; MRCP (UK) 1979. Cons. Phys. & Gastroenterol. Roy. United Hosp. Bath; Hon. Sen. Lect. Univ. Bath. Prev: Lect. (Med.) Dept. Med. II Soton Univ.; Regist. (Med.) Selly Oak Hosp. Birm.; Research Fell. (Med.) St. Jas. Univ. Hosp. Leeds.

ROBERTSON, Duncan Alexander Ramsay Southern General Hospital, Glasgow G51 4TF — MB ChB 1958 Ed.; DMRD 1963; FRCR 1975; FFR 1966. Cons. Radiol. S.. Gen. Hosp. Glas. Prev: Sen. Regist. Char. Cross Hosp. Lond.; Regist. Roy. Infirm. Edin.

ROBERTSON, Duncan Alexander Struan (retired) Victoria Mews, 28 Victoria St, St Annes, Alderney GY9 3TA Tel: 01481 823195 — MB ChB 1957 Bristol; DPM Eng. 1962; DObst RCOG 1959.

ROBERTSON, Duncan George, Lt.-Col. RAMC Medical Centre, Infantry Training Centre (3 Bn), Vimy Barracks, Catterick Garrison DL9 3PS; 2 Scotton Park, Catterick Garrison DL9 9PA Tel: 01748 872598 — MB ChB 1985 Ed.; Dip. Sport Med. Bath 2001; MRCGP 1991; DCH RCP Lond. 1989. (Edinburgh University) Prev: Trainee GP/SHO (Paediat.) Catterick; GP ChristCh., NZ.

ROBERTSON, Edwin William Bank Street Surgery, 46-62 Bank Street, Alexandria G83 0LS Tel: 01389 752650 Fax: 01389 752361; 29 Suffolk Street, Helensburgh G84 9QZ — MB ChB Glas. 1982.

ROBERTSON

ROBERTSON, Eileen Old Farm House, Shipley, Alnwick NE66 2LP Tel: 01665 579222 — M.B., B.S. Durh. 1948. (Newc.)

ROBERTSON, Elizabeth Ann 28 Hillview Drive, Cults, Aberdeen AB15 9SA — MB ChB 1975 Birm.; FFA RCS Eng. 1979. Cons. Anaesth. Aberd. Roy. Hosps. NHS Trust. Prev: Cons. Anaesth. Hairmyres Hosp. E. Kilbride.

ROBERTSON, Elizabeth Ann Burdwood Surgery, Station Road, Thatcham RG19 4 Tel: 01635 868006; Heathlands, Upper Woolhampton, Reading RG7 5UA Tel: 01189 714036 — MB ChB 1979 Birm.; DRCOG 1981. (Birm.) GP Non-Princip. Socs: MOSA; NANP. Prev: Clin. Med. Officer (Community Child Health) W. Berks. Clin. Asst. (Haemat.) Roy. Berks. Hosp.

ROBERTSON, Elizabeth Fiona 81 Framingham Road, Sale M33 3RH — MB ChB 1995 Dundee.

ROBERTSON, Elizabeth Hutchings Lee (retired) Barra, Knockfarrie Road, Pitlochry PH16 5DN Tel: 01796 474347 — MB ChB 1952 St. And. Prev: SCMO (Community Health) W. Essex HA.

ROBERTSON, Elizabeth Margaret Tel: 01224 681818 Fax: 01224 840778 Email: emrobertson@arh.grampian.scot.nhs.uk; 95 King's Gate, Aberdeen AB15 4EN — MB ChB 1975 Aberd.; FRCR 1981; DMRD Aberd. 1979. Assoc. Med. Dir., Grampian Univ. Hosp. Trust; Clin. Sen. Lect. (Radiol.) Univ. Aberd.; Cons. (Radiol.) Aberd. Roy. Infirm. Grampian Univ. Hosps. Trust. Prev: Clin. Director of Radiol., Aberd. Roy. Hosp.'s Trust; Sen. Regist. (Diagn. Radiol.) Qu. Mary's Hosp. Roehampton & W.m. Hosp. Lond.; Regist. (Diagn. Radiol.) Aberd. Roy. Infirm.

ROBERTSON, Elspeth Gatelawbridge House, Gatelawbridge, Thornhill DG3 5EA — MB BS 1977 Newc.

ROBERTSON, Euan Thomas Smith Flat 14, Queenscroft, Eccles, Manchester M30 9QQ — MB ChB 1997 Manch.

ROBERTSON, Fergus James Flat 12, 50 Roman Road, London E2 0LT — MB BS 1996 Lond.

ROBERTSON, Fiona Elizabeth Flat 2/Left, 122 Novar Drive, Glasgow G12 9SY — MB ChB 1991 Glas.

ROBERTSON, Fiona Margaret 163 Jay Court, Battersea Park Road, Battersea, London SW11 — MB BS 1979 Lond.; MRCGP 1985; DA (UK) 1986; DCH RCP Lond. 1983; DRCOG 1981. (St. Thos.)

ROBERTSON, Forbes Colquhoun 1 Wostenholm Road, Sheffield S7 1LB Tel: 0114 551124 — MB ChB 1959 Glas. (Glas.) Prev: Cas. Off. W.. Infirm. Glas.; Ho. Off. Gartloch Hosp. Gartcosh.

ROBERTSON, Frank (retired) Crantock, 31 Durham Road, Bishop Auckland DL14 7HU Tel: 01388 602967 — MB BS 1938 Durh.; MD Durh. 1940; FRCP Lond. 1968, M 1946. Hon. Cons. Phys. N. RHA. Prev: Cons. Phys. S.W. Durh. Hosp. Gp.

ROBERTSON, Garth Dundas Shatterwell House, North St., Wincanton BA9 9AZ Tel: 01963 33155 Fax: 01963 34964; London College of Osteopathic Medicine, 10 Boston Place, London NW1 6QH Tel: 020 7262 5250 — MB BCh BAO 1970 Dub.; MRCP (UK) 1975; DMS Med. Soc. Apoth. Lond. 1991; MLCOM 1988; MRO 1988. (Trinity Coll. Dub.)

ROBERTSON, Mr Gavin Scott Miller Department of Surgery, Leicester Royal Infirmary, Leicester LE1 5WW Tel: 0116 258 5997 Email: grobertson@vhl.trent.nhs.uk; 3 Burrows Close, Royal Lodge, Narborough, Leicester LE9 5RG — MB ChB 1984 Leic.; MD Leic. 1993; FRCS Ed. 1988; FRCS (Gen) 1997; FRCS Eng. 1988. (Leic.) Cons., Gen. Surg., Leicester Roy. Infirm., Leicester; Train. Progr. Director in Gen. Surg. (S. Trent). Socs: Brit. Soc. Gastroenterol.; Surg. Research Soc. & Assn. Surg. in Train. Prev: Hon. Sen. Regist. & Clin. Lect. (Surg.) Univ. Leic.; Sen. Regist. (Surg.) Qu. Eliz. Hosp. Adelaide Australia; Clin. Lect. & Hon. Regist. (Surg.) Univ. Leicester.

ROBERTSON, George Duncan (retired) 76 Hillpark Avenue, Edinburgh EH4 7AL Tel: 0131 336 1911 — MB ChB Ed. 1963; AFOM RCP Lond. 1982; DIH 1982; DObst RCOG 1967. Prev: GP Leith Occupat. Health Adviser, Med. Adviser Benefits Agency.

ROBERTSON, George Slessor (retired) Hazlewood, 12 Queen's Den, Woodend, Aberdeen AB15 8BW Tel: 01224 311903 Email: gslessor@12queensden.freeserve.co.uk — MB ChB 1958 Aberd.; MD Aberd. 1973; FRCA 1964. Cons. Anaesth. Aberd. Roy. Infirm.

ROBERTSON, George Stuart (retired) 19 Shepherd Road, St. Annes, Lytham St Annes FY8 3JB — LRCP LRCS 1931 Ed.; MD Toronto 1937, MB 1927; LRCP LRCS Ed. LRFPS Glas. 1931. Prev: Dep. Princip. Sch. Med. Off. Liverp.

ROBERTSON, Gordon Allan Chestertons, Burnt Hill, Yattendon, Thatcham RG18 0XD Tel: 01635 201311 — MB BS 1976 Lond.; MRCS Eng. LRCP Lond. 1976; MRCGP 1981; DCH Eng. 1980; DRCOG 1980. (Roy Free) Hosp. Pract. (Neurol.) Roy. Berks. Hosp. Reading. Prev: SHO (Med.) Nottm. Gen. Hosp.; Ho. Phys. Roy. Free Hosp. Lond.

ROBERTSON, Gordon James (retired) 20 Broadwood Park, Alloway, Ayr KA7 4XE Tel: 01292 441882 — MB ChB St. And. 1958. Prev: Ho. Phys. Heathfield Gen. Hosp. Ayr.

ROBERTSON, Graham Andrew 1 Kylepack Crescent, Uddington, Glasgow G71 7DQ — MB ChB 1995 Glas.

ROBERTSON, Graham Morton (retired) 4 Badgers Close, Ashley Heath, Ringwood BH24 2JH — BM BCh 1949 Oxf.; BM BCh Oxon. 1949; FRCGP 1984, M 1975. Prev: Ho. Surg. Radcliffe Infirm. Oxf.

ROBERTSON, Grant 35 Lutton Place, Edinburgh EH8 9PF — MB ChB 1994 ED.

ROBERTSON, Heidi Joanne Beechlands, St. Margarets Avenue, Dormans Park, East Grinstead RH19 2NG — MB BS 1994 Lond.; MA Camb. 1995.

ROBERTSON, Helen Margaret 30 Kessington Drive, Bearsden, Glasgow G61 2HG — MB ChB 1980 Glas.

ROBERTSON, Henry Keith Ceol - Mara, Tighna Bruaich PA21 2BE Tel: 01700 811172 — MB ChB 1954 Ed.; DTM & H 1961; DObst RCOG 1965. Socs: BMA; RCGP (Assoc.). Prev: Gen. Practitioner (Prinicpal) Hertford, Herts.; Gen. Practitioner (Princip.) Inverness; Med. Off. Keith Falconer Hosp. Aden.

ROBERTSON, Hugh Alexander McNeil (retired) 17A Sussex Heights, St. Margaret's Place, Brighton BN1 2FR — MD 1925 Manch.; BA Manch. 1921; LMCC 1925; MCPS Alta. 1926. Prev: Chest Cons. Dept. Nat. Health & Welf. Canad. Lond.

ROBERTSON, Iain Gregory, TD, OBE, QHP The Uplands, Fulwood Row, Fulwood, Preston PR2 5RU Tel: 01772 700101 Fax: 01772 701240 — MB ChB 1976 Manch.; MD Manch. 1984; BSc (Hons.) Aston 1968; FRCOG 1994, M 1981; MPS 1969. (Manch.) Cons. (O & G) Preston Acute NHS Trust, 1986; BRIG TA AMS, 2000, present. Socs: BMA & N. Eng. Obst. & Gyn. Soc.; BSCCP; TENS Gyn. Soc. Prev: Sen. Regist. (O & G) N.W. RHA; Regist. (O & G) St. Mary's Hosp. Manch.; SHO (O & G) Univ. Hosp. S. Manch.

ROBERTSON, Mr Iain James Alexander Department Neurosurgery, Queens Medical Centre, Nottingham NG7 2UH Tel: 0115 924 9924; The Hollies, Black Lane, Chopwell Butlet, Nottingham NG12 3AD Tel: 0115 933 3672 Email: iain.j.robertson@virgin.net — MB ChB 1981 Ed.; FRCS Ed. 1986. Sen. Regist. (Neurosurg.) Brook Hosp. SE Thames RHA. Cons. Neurosurg., Qu.s Med. Centre. Notts.

ROBERTSON, Iain Kilpatrick 8 Mountbatten Way, Lutterworth LE17 4YD — MB BCh 1979 Wales; BSc Wales 1976, MB BCh 1979; FFA RCS Eng. 1984. Regist. (Community Med.) Oxf. RHA.

ROBERTSON, Iain Robert St James University Hospital, Beckett St., Leeds LS9 7TF — MB ChB 1984 Glas.; MRCP (UK) 1988; FRCR 1991. Cons. Radiol. Dept. Diagn. Imaging St. Jas. Univ. Hosp. Leeds.

ROBERTSON, Iain William, RD Craigallian Avenue Surgery, 11 Craigallian Avenue, Cambuslang, Glasgow G72 8RW Tel: 0141 641 3129; 15 Burnside Road, Burnside, Glasgow G73 4RL Tel: 0141 634 4848 Email: driainrobertson@compuserve.com — MB ChB 1974 Glas. Prev: Regist. (Anaesth.) Vict. Infirm. Glas.

ROBERTSON, Ian Braeside Medical Group, Escomb Road, Bishop Auckland DL14 6AB Tel: 01388 663539 Fax: 01388 601847; 9 Langley Grove, Bishop Auckland DL14 6UJ — MB BS 1978 Newc.; MRCGP 1982.

ROBERTSON, Ian Douglas Cityside Community Mental Health Team, 22 Crawford Square, Londonderry BT48 7HT Tel: 01504 372230 Fax: 01504 267487; 106 Seacoast Road, Limavady BT49 9EG Tel: 015047 63453 Email: ianr@argonauts.demon.co.uk — MB ChB 1977 Aberd.; MRCPsych 1985. Cons. Psychiat. Cityside Community Ment. Health Team Lond.derry. Prev: Sen. Regist. (Psychiat.) Tralee Gen. Hosp.; Sen. Regist. Cork Regional Hosp.; Regist. St. Anne's Hosp. Poole Dorset.

ROBERTSON, Ian Drysdale (retired) 27 Polwarth Terrace, Edinburgh EH11 1NH Tel: 0131 229 1655 — MB ChB 1948 Ed.

ROBERTSON, Ian James Tel: 0117 977 0018 Fax: 0117 972 3428; 36 Archfield Road, Cotham, Bristol BS6 6BE — MB ChB 1979 Birm.; LLB (Hons.) Soton. 1971; MRCGP 1983; DRCOG 1982.

ROBERTSON, Ian Peter Cameron (retired) Greenbraes, 3 Westpark Gate, Saline, Dunfermline KY12 9US Tel: 01383 852000 Fax: 01383 852000 — MB ChB 1950 Glas.; DLO Eng. 1958. Prev: GP Dunfermline.

ROBERTSON, James 19 Mast Lane, North Shields NE30 3DF — MB ChB 1995 Leeds.

ROBERTSON, James Alexander 25 Thornhill Road, Steeton, Keighley BD20 6TN — MB ChB 1976 Leeds; FFA RCS Eng. 1982. Cons. Anaesth. Airedale Gen. Hosp. Prev: Sen. Regist. (Anaesth.) S.W. Region & RN Hosp. Plymouth; Hon. Regist. (Anaesth.) Soton. Gen. Hosp.

ROBERTSON, James Alexander Rose & Crown House, Cleobury Road, Bewdley DY12 2QJ — MB BChir 1966 Camb.; BA Camb. 1963, MB BChir 1966; FRCPsych 1992, M 1973; DPM Eng. 1971. (Middlx.) Cons. Psychiat. Kidderminster Health Dist. Prev: Sen. Regist. (Psychiat.) Maudsley Hosp. Lond.; Sen. Regist. (Psychiat.) Lond. Hosp.; Ho. Surg. Middlx. Hosp. Lond.

ROBERTSON, Mr James Anthony Department of Orthopaedics, Southampton University Hospital, Tremona Road, Southampton SO9 4AY Tel: 02380 796249 Fax: 02380 796249; BUPA Chalybeate Hospital, Chalybeate Close, Tremona Road, Southampton SO16 6UY Tel: 02380 775544 Fax: 017030 701160 — MB BS 1964 Lond.; FRCS Eng. 1969; MRCS Eng. LRCP Lond. 1964. (King's Coll. Hosp.) Cons. Orthop. Surg. Soton. Univ. Hosp.; Hon. Lect. Univ. Soton.; Hon. Clin. Tutor Univ. Soton. Prev: Mem. Bd. Managem. Inst. Sports Med.; Sen. Regist. Roy. Nat. Orthop. Hosp., Univ. Coll. Hosp. & W.m. Hosp. Lond.; Fell. Univ. S. Calif., USA.

ROBERTSON, James Campbell Departments of Rheumatology and Rehabilitation, Salisbury District Hospital, Salisbury SP2 8BJ Tel: 01722 336262 Fax: 01722 337912; New Farm House, 100 Church Road, Laverstock, Salisbury SP1 1RB Tel: 01722 320691 Fax: 01722 415378 — MB BS 1965 Lond.; FRCP Lond. 1986; MRCP (UK) 1971; MRCS Eng. LRCP Lond. 1965; DCH Eng. 1967. (Guy's) Cons. Rheum. & Rehabil. Salisbury & Soton. HAs. Socs: (Ex-Chairm.) Soc. Tissue Viability; Brit. Soc. Rheum.; (Ex-Sen. Sec.) Soc. Research in Rehabil. Prev: Med. Edr. Care, Sci. & Pract.; Dir. Wessex Regional Rehabil. Unit; Sen. Regist. (Gen. Med., Rheum. & Rehabil.) Qu. Mary's Hosp. Roehampton.

ROBERTSON, James Colin (retired) 31 Hayston Park, Balmullo, St Andrews KY16 0DJ Tel: 01334 870576 — MB ChB 1938 Ed.

ROBERTSON, James Douglas Victoria Road Surgery, 129A Victoria Road, Kirkcaldy KY1 1DH Tel: 01592 263332 Fax: 01592 644288 — MB ChB 1974 Ed.; BSc (Med. Sci.) Ed. 1971. (Edinburgh) GP Princip. Prev: SHO (Cardiol.) W.. Gen. Hosp. Edin.; SHO (Renal & Gen. Med.) Ninewells Hosp. Dundee; Ho. Surg. Roy. Infirm. Edin.

ROBERTSON, James Douglas Alexander The Cambridge Medical Group, 10A Cambridge Road, Linthorpe, Middlesbrough TS5 5NN Tel: 01642 851177 Fax: 01642 851176 — MB ChB 1980 Aberd.; BMedBiol Aberd. 1978; MRCGP 1984; DCH RCPS Glas. 1983; DRCOG 1982; MSOM 1999. Clin. Asst. (Rheum.) Middlesbrough. Prev: GP Shenton Med. Gp. Singapore; Trainee GP Highland HB VTS.

ROBERTSON, James Duncan Friary Surgery, Victoria Road, Richmond DL10 4DW Tel: 01748 822306 Fax: 01748 850356 — MRCS Eng. LRCP Lond. 1966; DObst RCOG 1968. (Char. Cross) Prev: SHO (Obst.) Greenbank Matern. Hosp. Darlington; Cas. Off. & Ho. Phys. Mt. Vernon Hosp. N.wood; Ho. Surg. Wembley Hosp.

ROBERTSON, James Gordon Fergus St Nicholas Health Centre, Saunder Bank, Burnley BB11 2EN Tel: 01282 831249 Fax: 01282 425269; Utherstone, 264 Gisbyrn Road, Blacko, Nelson BB9 6LP Tel: 01282 619908 — MB ChB 1982 Dundee.

ROBERTSON, James Hanson McPherson The Surgery, Worsley Road, Immingham, Immingham DN40 1BE Tel: 01469 572058 Fax: 01469 573043; 12 The Avenue, Healing, Grimsby DN37 3NF Tel: 01472 882599 — MB ChB 1955 Manch.; DPH Leeds 1963. Prev: Capt. RAMC; Dept. Med. Off. Lancs. CC; Div. Med. Off. Lancs. CC & Dist. MOH.

ROBERTSON, Professor James Ian Summers Elmbank, Manse Road, Bowling, Glasgow G60 5AA Tel: 0141 873121 Fax: 0141890291 — MB BS 1952 Brussels; MB BS (Hons. Path. & Med.) Lond. 1952; FRS Ed.; BSc Lond. (1st cl. Hons.) 1949; MD (Hons. Causa) Brussels 1986; FRCP Glas. 1984; FRCP Lond. 1970, M 1954. (St. Mary's) Sen. Cons. (Cardiovasc. Med.) Janssen Research Foundat. Worldwide; Sen. Scientif. Adviser Janssen Internat. Research Counc. Prev: Vis. Prof. Med. P. of Wales Hosp. Hong Kong; Pres. Brit. Hypertens. Soc.; Pres. Internat. Soc. Hypertens.

ROBERTSON, James Lake SCBU, Arrowe Park Hospital, Upton, Liverpool — MB ChB 1989 Leeds; MRCP (Paed.) 1996. Staff Grade Paediat. Arrowe Pk. Hosp. Upton, Wirral.

ROBERTSON, James Loudon West Calder Medical Practice, Dickson Street, West Calder EH55 8HB Email: james.robertson@wlt.scot.nhs.uk; Harwood House, 14 Hartwood Road, West Calder EH55 8DG Tel: 01506 873337 — MB ChB 1989 Glas.; BSc (Hons) Glas. 1986; MRCGP 1994; T(GP) 1994; DRCOG 1993. (Glas.) Prev: SHO (Dermat.) Ninewells Hosp. Dundee.

ROBERTSON, James Mowat Department of Oral and MaxilloFacial Surgery, Peterborough District Hospital, Thorpe Road, Peterborough PE3 6DA Tel: 01733 874319 Fax: 01733 875697; 1 Manners Close, Uffington, Stamford PE9 4UB Tel: 01780 766341 Fax: 01780 764380 — MB ChB 1972 Sheff.; BDS 1968; FDS RCS Eng. 1975. Cons. Oral & Maxillofacial Surg. P'boro Hosps. NHS Trust; Hon. Clin. Teach. (Oral & Maxillofacial Surg.) Univ. Sheff. Socs: Fell. BAOMFS; BMA; BDA. Prev: Sen. Regist. (Oral Surg.) Guy's Hosp. Lond. & Qu. Vict. Hosp. E. Grinstead.

ROBERTSON, James Roy Muirhouse Medical Group, 1 Muirhouse Avenue, Edinburgh EH4 4PL Tel: 0131 332 2201; 18 Henderland Road, Murrayfield, Edinburgh EH12 6BB Tel: 0131 337 4707 — MB ChB 1975 Ed.; FRCGP 1988, M 1980. (Edinburgh) Lect. Univ. Edin. Prev: Regist. (Med.) Vict. Hosp. Kirkcaldy; SHO N.. Gen. Hosp. Edin.; Ho. Off. Chalmers Hosp.

ROBERTSON, James Stewart, OBE (retired) Colwell, Brigg Road, Barton-upon-Humber DN18 5DH Tel: 01652 635632 Email: 113031.2524@compuserve.com — MB ChB 1949 Leeds; MRCS Eng. LRCP Lond. 1949; FFPHM 1989; MFCM 1974; DIH Eng. 1957; DPH Lond. 1956. Prev: DMO Scunthorpe HA.

ROBERTSON, James Thomas Weir (retired) 6 Victoria Avenue, Woodhall Spa LN10 6TY Tel: 01526 352363 — MB ChB 1945 Glas.; MD (Distinc.) Mich. 1973; MRCGP 1974; DPhysMed Eng. 1975. Prev: Rockefeller Med. Stud. Univ. Mich. 1942-44.

ROBERTSON, Jane Diana 11 Ashfield Road, Cheadle, Manchester M13 0YP — MB BS 1990 Lond.; BA (Hons.) Oxf. 1987; MRCP (UK) 1993.

ROBERTSON, Jane Kennedy 3 Balmore Court, Kilmacolm PA13 4LX — MB ChB 1972 Glas. Staff Grade Med. Off. Glas. & W. of Scotl. Blood Transfus. Serv.

ROBERTSON, Jane Margaret Chedworth, Goonvrea Road, St Agnes TR5 0AJ; 95a Chiswick High Road, Chiswick, London W4 2EF Tel: 020 8747 9721 — MB BS 1996 Lond.; Dip Child Health, RCPaed & Child Health., 1999. SHO Psychiat. (GPUTS) Hillingdon Hosp., Hillingdon, Middlx.

ROBERTSON, Janette Kelso Street Surgery, 6 Kelso Street, Glasgow G14 0JZ Tel: 0141 211 6999 Fax: 0141 211 6990; 55 Partickhill Road, Glasgow G11 5AB — MB ChB 1993 Glas.; PhD Sheff. 1985; BSc St And. 1976; MPH Glas. 1987. Sen. Partner, Kelso St. Surg.; Hon. Sen. Lect., Glas. Univ.

ROBERTSON, Jean Lesley 15 Barclay Park, Aboyne AB34 5JF Tel: 0133 98 86679 — MB ChB 1968 Aberd. (Aberd.)

ROBERTSON, Jeffrey Hampton (retired) 93 Shandon Park, Belfast BT5 6NY — MB BCh BAO 1954 Belf.; MD Belf. 1958; FRCP Ed. 1981, M 1962; FRCPath 1977, M 1964. Prev: Clin. Path. Belf. City Hosp.

ROBERTSON, Jennie The Chase, Spurgrove, Frieth, Henley-on-Thames RG9 6PA Tel: 01494 881555 — MB BS 1959 Lond.; MRCS Eng. LRCP Lond. 1959. (Roy. Free) Assoc. Specialist (Geriat.) St. Marks Hosp. Maidenhead. Prev: Med. Asst. (Geriat.) St. John's Hosp. Lond.; Regist. (Geriat.) St. John's Hosp. Battersea; SHO Geriat. S. W.. Hosp. Lond.

ROBERTSON, Jennifer Forsyth South Queensferry Group Practice, The Health Centre, Rosebery Avenue, South Queensferry EH30 9HA Tel: 0131 331 1396 Fax: 0131 331 5783; 76 Hillpark Avenue, Edinburgh EH4 7AL Tel: 0131 336 1911 — MB ChB 1963 Ed. Prev: Med. Off. Brook Advis, Centre Edin.; Ho. Phys. & Ho. Surg. P.ss Margt. Hosp. Nassau.

ROBERTSON

ROBERTSON, Joan Arden (retired) Haworth, 33 Leven Road, Lundin Links, Lower Largo, Leven KY8 6AH Tel: 01333 320335 — MB ChB Bristol 1949. Prev: Chairm. Scott. Family Plann. Med. Soc.

ROBERTSON, John Albert (retired) 26 Elsdon Close, Peterlee SR8 1NE Tel: 0191 586 0243 — MB BS 1938 Durh. Prev: Ho. Phys. & Ho. Surg. Tynemouth Jubilee Infirm.

ROBERTSON, John Forsyth Russell 114 Carfin Road, Newarthill, Motherwell ML1 5JX — MB ChB 1980 Glas.

ROBERTSON, John Gareth Jakaranda, Mosstowie, Elgin IV30 8TX — MB ChB 1998 Aberd.; MB ChB Aberd 1998.

ROBERTSON, John Gordon The Health Centre, High Street, Dodworth, Barnsley S75 3RF Tel: 01226 203881 — MB ChB 1959 Aberd. (Aberd.)

ROBERTSON, John Leslie (retired) 99 St Andrews Drive, Glasgow G41 4DH — MB ChB 1946 Glas.

ROBERTSON, John Lindsay (retired) South Acre, Galston KA4 8NB Tel: 01563 820353 — MB ChB 1951 Glas.; DObst RCOG 1953. Prev: Res. Ho. Phys. Glas. Roy. Infirm. & Stobhill Hosp. Glas.

ROBERTSON, Mr John Moore 9 West Werberside, Edinburgh EH4 1SZ — MB ChB 1948 Glas.; FRCS Ed. 1954. (Glas.) Cons. Neurosurg. S. Tees Health Dist. Prev: Sen. Regist. Glas. & W. Scotl. Neurosurg. Unit Killearn Hosp. Glas.; Surg. Regist. Stobhill Hosp. Glas.

ROBERTSON, John Murison Associated Health Specialists, Templeton Business Centre, Templeton St., Glasgow G40 1DA Tel: 0141 554 1566 Fax: 0141 554 1995 — MB BS Lond. 1961; MRCS Eng. LRCP Lond. 1961; AFOM RCP Lond. 1982; CIH Dund 1983. (Guy's) Dir. Assoc. Health Specialists Ltd. Glas. Socs: Soc. Occupat. Med. Prev: Regional Occupat. Phys. Brit. Ship Builders (TES); Med. Off. Standard Telephones & Cables plc.

ROBERTSON, John Richard West London, Healthcare Trust, Uxbridge Road, Southall UB1 3EU Tel: 020 8574 2444 Fax: 020 8354 8671; 74 Clarendon Drive, Putney, London SW15 1AH Tel: 020 8789 2661 Email: rir777@aol.com — MB ChB Ed. 1964; BSc (Hons.) Ed. 1962; FRCPsych. 1989, M 1972; DPM Eng. 1970. (Ed.) Cons. (Psychiat.) W. Lond. Healthcare Trust; Regional Adviser in Psychiat. N. Thames Region (W.). Socs: Roy. Soc. Med. Prev: Surg. Lt. RN & Staff Med. Off. to Second in Command W.. Fleet.

ROBERTSON, John Thomson (retired) Lochanbrae, Strone, Dunoon PA23 8RX Tel: 01369 840366 — MB ChB 1954 Glas.

ROBERTSON, John Watt (retired) East Wing, Kincurdie House, Rosemarkie, Fortrose IV10 8SJ Tel: 01381 621388 Fax: 01381 620325 Email: jwatttrober@aol.com — MB ChB Aberd. 1959; FRCGP 1990, M 1968; DObst RCOG 1962. Prev: Med. Prescribing Adviser W.. Is. HB.

ROBERTSON, Josefina de Unamuno Viewfield Medical Centre, 3 Viewfield Place, Stirling FK8 1NJ Tel: 01786 472028 Fax: 01786 463388 — LMS 1979 Salamanca; LMS 1979 Salamanca; LRCP Edin LRCS Edin LRCPS Glasg 1983. (Salamanca) GP Stirling; Clin. Med. Off., Psychiat.; Regist. Acupunc. & Hypnotherapist. Socs: BMA.

ROBERTSON, Joyce Buchan Peterhead Group Practice, The Health Centre, Peterhead AB42 2XA Tel: 01774 474841 Fax: 01774 474848; Clifton House, Cruden Bay, Peterhead AB42 0HP Tel: 01779 812748 — MB ChB 1982 Aberd.; MRCGP 1986; DRCOG 1985. (Aberdeen) GP Trainer. Socs: (Ex-Chairm.) Educat. Sect. NE Scotl. Fac. RCGP. Prev: Trainee GP Aberd. VTS.

ROBERTSON, Katharine Susan The Forehouse, Main St., Gullane EH31 2AS Tel: 01620 842133; CP 172, Lichinga, Provincia De Niasse, Mozambique — MB ChB 1986 Aberd. Volun. Serv. Overseas. Prev: SHO (Gen. Surg.) Barnsley Dist. Gen. Hosp. S. Yorks.

ROBERTSON, Katherine May, OBE (retired) Bragleenmore, Kilninver, Oban PA34 4UU — MB ChB 1945 Glas. Prev: Med. Tutor Lilongwe Sch. of Health Sci.s Malawi.

ROBERTSON, Katrina Jeanette PO Box 90, Ipswich IP6 9EQ — MB BS 1993 Lond.

ROBERTSON, Kenneth 19 Gardner Road, Aberdeen AB12 5TB — MB ChB 1983 Aberd.; FFA RCS Eng. 1988. SHO (Anaesth.) Vict. Infirm. Glas. Prev: Ho. Phys. S.. Gen. Hosp. Glas.; Ho. Surg. Vict. Infirm. Glas.

ROBERTSON, Mr Kenneth (retired) 1/10 Pentland Drive, Fairmilehead, Edinburgh EH10 6PU Tel: 0131 467 1919 — MB ChB Ed. 1946; FRCS Ed. 1951. Prev: Cons. Gen. Surg. S.. Isles.

ROBERTSON, Kenneth James Royal Hopital for Sick Children, Yorkhill, Glasgow G3 8SJ Tel: 0141 201 0000 Fax: 0141 201 0671 Email: k.j.robertson@clinmed.gla.ac.uk; 16 Craigenlay Avenue, Blanefield, Glasgow G63 9DR Tel: 01360 771022 — MB ChB 1982 Aberd.; FRCP Ed. 1998; FRCPCH 1997. Cons. Paediat. Yorkhill NHS Trust Glas.; Hon. Sen. Clin. Lect. Glas. Socs: Brit. Diabetic Assn.; Advisory Counc. Internat. Soc. Paediatry & Adolesc. Diabetes. Prev: Lecture & Hon. Sen. Regist. (Child Health) Ninewells Hosp. Univ. Dundee; MRC Clin. Research Fell. (Child Health & Biochem.y Med.) Ninewells Hosp. Dundee; Registar (Paediatry) Ninewells Hosp. Dundee.

ROBERTSON, Mr Kevin William Flat 1/L 10 Striven Gardens, North Kelvinside, Glasgow G20 6DZ — MB ChB 1988 Glas.; FRCS Glas. 1992. Research Fell. (Surg.) Glas. Roy. Infirm.; SHERT Schol.sh. Socs: Roy. Coll. Phys. & Surgs. Glas. (Counc. Jun. QUA Surg.).

ROBERTSON, Kirstin Jane 20 Burgess Hill, Linlithgow EH49 6BX — MB ChB 1990 Aberd.; MRCGP 1994; T(GP) 1994.

ROBERTSON, Laura Margaret 212 Osborne Road, Jesmond, Newcastle upon Tyne NE2 3LD — MB BS 1983 Lond.; MRCGP 1987; DRCOG 1985.

ROBERTSON, Lawrence (retired) 1 Sunnyside Close, Freckleton, Preston PR4 1YJ Tel: 01772 632202 — BM BCh 1950 Oxf.; MA Oxf. 1951; Dip. Bact. Lond 1953; FRCPath 1970, M 1964. Prev: Dir., Pub. Health Laborat. Preston.

***ROBERTSON, Lee Margaret** 7 Paradise Road, Dundee DD1 1JB Tel: 01382 201547 — MB ChB 1998 Dund.; MB ChB Dund 1998; BMSc Dund. (1st class Hon) 1995.

ROBERTSON, Lesley Jane Aylesbury Vale Community Healthcare, Tindal Centre, Bierton Road, Aylesbury HP20 1HU — MB ChB 1982 Aberd.; MRCPsych 1988. Cons. Psychiat. Tindal Centre Aylesbury.

ROBERTSON, Linda Marjorie Psychiatric Unit, Hairmyres Hospital, East Kilbride, Glasgow Tel: 0141572532; 11 Arran Gardens, Carluke ML8 4HS Tel: 01555 750582 — MB ChB 1979 Glas.; MRCGP 1985; DCH RCPS Glas. 1982.

ROBERTSON, Lindsey Elizabeth 5 Ava Lodge, Castle Terrace, Berwick-upon-Tweed TD15 1NP — MB BS 1991 Newc.; DRCOG 1995; MRCGP 1996; DFFP 1997. Gen. Pract. Asst. (Centr. Surg.) S. Shields. Socs: MRCGP 1996.

ROBERTSON, Lynne Margaret 55 Osnaburgh Court, Dairsie, Cupar KY15 4SU — MB ChB 1991 Ed.; MRCGP 1997; DCCH 1998. (Edinburgh) Specialist Regist. Pub. Health, Fife Health Bd., Cupar, Fife. Socs: BMA; RCGP. Prev: SHO Rehabil. Med., Astley Ainslie, Edinb.; Community Regist. (Paediat.) Sighthill Health Centre Edin.; GP Regist. W. End Med. Pract. Edin.

ROBERTSON, Margaret House 3, Bridlington General Hospital, Bridlington YO16 5QP; 11 Second Avenue, Bridlington YO15 2LL — MB ChB 1984 Leeds; MRCGP 1988. GP N. Humberside.

ROBERTSON, Margaret Alison East Donnington Street Clinic, East Donnington Street, Darvel KA17 0JR Tel: 01560 320205 Fax: 01560 321643; 31 Milagarholm Avenue, Irvine KA12 0EL Tel: 01294 278341 Fax: 01294 278341 — MB ChB 1988 Glas.; DRCOG 1993. (Univ. Glas.) GP Darvel & Newmilns. Socs: BMA. Prev: GP Castlemilk Health Centre Glas.; SHO (Psychiat.) St. John's Livingston; SHO (O & G) St. John's Livingston.

ROBERTSON, Margaret Elizabeth Castle Street Surgery, 67 Castle Street, Salisbury SP1 3SP Tel: 01722 322726 Fax: 01722 410315 — MB ChB Birm. 1967; DObst RCOG 1969. (Birm.) Police Surg. Salisbury Div. Socs: BMA. Prev: Sch. Med. Off. Wilts. AHA; SHO (Gen. Med.) Good Hope Hosp. Sutton Coldfield; Ho. Surg. Gen. Hosp. Birm.

ROBERTSON, Margaret Foster 139 Hough Green, Chester CH4 8JR — MB ChB 1958 Cape Town; MRCPsych 1972; DPM Eng. 1966. Cons. Psychotherap. N. Wales. Hosp. Denbigh. Socs: Fell. Roy. Coll. Psychiat. Prev: Sen. Regist. (Psychol. Med.) King's Coll. Hosp. Lond.; Regist. (Med.) Groote Schuur Hosp. Cape Town, S. Afr.; SHO (Psychiat.) Middlx. Hosp. Lond.

ROBERTSON, Margaret Jean Stark 19 Wimpole Street, London W1M ADH Tel: 020 7935 8488 Fax: 020 7636 5758; 22 Almeida Street, Islington, London N1 1TB Tel: 020 7226 2730 — MB ChB Glas. 1964; FRCP Glas. 1983; MRCP (UK) 1969; FFA RCS Eng. 1975. (Glas.) Cons. Anaesth. Newham Gen. Hosp. Lond.; Cons. Anaesth. Whittington Hosp. Lond. Prev: Cons. (Anaesth.) Whittington Hosp. Lond.; Sen. Regist. Univ. Coll. Hosp. Lond.

ROBERTSON

ROBERTSON, Margaret Joy Crerar Braids Medical Practice, 6 Camus Avenue, Edinburgh EH10 6QT Tel: 0131 445 5999; Braids Medical Practice, 6 Camus Avenue, Edinburgh EH10 6QT Tel: 0131 445 5999 — MB ChB 1978 Ed.; BSc Ed. 1975, MB ChB 1978; MRCGP 1982. (Ed.)

ROBERTSON, Margaret Mary Dorothy 44 Lubnaig Road, Newlands, Glasgow G43 2RX — MB ChB 1971 Glas.; BSc Glas. 1966, MB ChB 1971; MFCM 1989. Med. Off. Gtr. Glas. Health Bd. Socs: BMA; Soc. of Pub. Health. Prev: Ho. Off. Ayr Co. Hosp. & Heathfield Gen. Hosp. Ayr.

ROBERTSON, Mary Ann Collett 3 Recreation Street, Prestwich, Manchester M25 1HT — MB ChB 1985 Liverp.; FRCS Ed. 1993.

ROBERTSON, Mary Croft (retired) Colwell, 9 Brigg Road, Barton-upon-Humber DN18 5DH Tel: 01652 635632 Email: 113031.2524@compuserve.com — MB ChB 1949 Leeds. Prev: SCMO Scunthorpe Health Dist.

ROBERTSON, Professor Mary May Department of Psychiatry & Behavioural Sciences, UCLMS, Wolfson Building, 48 Riding House St., London W1N 8AA Tel: 020 7679 9471 Fax: 020 7679 9426 Email: rejummr@ucl.ac.uk; Department Neuropsychiatry Box 77, The National Hospital for Neurology & Neurosurgery, Queen Square, London WC1N 3BG Tel: 020 7837 3611 Ext: 3947 Fax: 020 7278 8772 Email: profmmr@a.o.l.com — MB ChB 1971 Cape Town; MD Cape Town 1983; FRCPsych 1991, M 1979; DPM Eng. 1979. (Cape Town) Prof. (Neuropsychiat.) Univ. Coll. Lond. Med. Sch.; Cons. Neuropsychiat. Nat. Hosp. Qu. Sq. Lond.; Hon. Med. Adviser UK & Irish Tourette Syndrome Assns.; Hon. Med. Adviser Tourette Syndrome Foundat. Canada; Hon. Med. Adviser, German Tourette Syndrome Assoc. Socs: Brit. Neuropsychiat. Assn.; Exec. Comm. Internat. Neuropsychiatric Assn. Prev: Reader Univ. Coll. Lond. Med. Sch.; Sen. Lect. Univ. Coll. Lond. Med. Sch.; Sen. Regist. Rotat. Maudsley Hosp. Lond.

ROBERTSON, Matthew Henderson (retired) Barra, Knockfarrie Road, Pitlochry PH16 5DN Tel: 01796 474347 — MB ChB 1951 St. And.; FRCPath 1974, M 1963. Prev: Cons. Microbiol. W. Essex Health Dist.

ROBERTSON, Mhairi Iona 7 Cameron Street, Dunfermline KY12 8DP — MB ChB 1997 Aberd.

ROBERTSON, Mr Michael Alexander Hynd Fiunary, Morvern, Oban PA34 5JQ — MB ChB 1960 Ed.; FRCS Ed. 1993; MRCP (UK) 1965. (Edin.)

ROBERTSON, Moira Royal Alexandra Hospital, Corsebar Road, Paisley PA2 9PN Tel: 0141 887 9111 Ext: 4225 Fax: 0141 580 4112; 31 Newark Drive, Glasgow G41 4QA — MB ChB 1977 Glas.; FRCP 1950; MRCP 1980; FRCP 1980; FRCPath. Cons. Haemat. Roy. Alexandra Hosp. Paisley.

ROBERTSON, Moira Carole 129 Marlborough Road, Swindon SN3 1NJ — Dip Occ Med 1998; FRIPHH; BM BCh Oxf. 1958; MA Oxf. 1959; MFFP 1993; DCH Eng. 1972; DPH Leeds 1963; DObst RCOG 1960. Socs: Fell. Roy. Inst. Pub. Health & Hyg.

ROBERTSON, Morag Wyllie (retired) 26 Heol Tyn y Cae, Rhiwbina, Cardiff CF14 6DJ Tel: 01222 613439 — MB ChB Glas. 1951. Clin. Med. Off. S. Glam. AHA. Prev: Jun. Hosp. Med. Off. Roy. Hosp. Sick Childr. Glas.

ROBERTSON, Nan Agnew 19 Glenwood Road, Kirkintilloch, Glasgow G66 4DY — MB ChB 1973 Glas.

ROBERTSON, Neil James 46 Prospect Road, Bradway, Sheffield S17 4JD — BM BS 1984 Nottm.; BMedSci (Hons) Nottm. 1982, BM BS 1984.

ROBERTSON, Neil Malcolm Woodlands Med. Pract., Blue bell Wood Way, Sutton-in-Ashfield NG17 1JW Tel: 01623 514003 Fax: 01623 554514; 19 The Heyes, Ravenshead, Nottingham NG15 9AU Tel: 01623 795485 — MB BS 1977 Lond.; FRCGP 1996, M 1983; DRCOG 1980. (St. Geo. Hosp. Med. Sch.) Trainer (Gen. Pract.) Mansfield VTS; Coorse Organiser Mansfield Uts. Socs: N. Notts. LMC. Prev: Mem. Centr. Notts. HA; Course Organiser Centr. Notts. VTS; Mem. Vale of Trent Fac. Bd. Rcgp.

ROBERTSON, Neil Patrick Lea, Gate House, Brookwell Lane, Bramley, Guildford GU5 0LQ; The Granary, Black Heath Court, Powderham, Exeter EX6 8SH — MB BS 1986 Lond. Regist. (Neurol.) Bristol Roy. Infirm.

ROBERTSON, Niall Andrew Lochalsh, 1A Forthill Drive, Broughty Ferry, Dundee DD5 3DY — MB ChB 1987 Dundee; BMSc 1984; MRCGP 1991; DRCOG 1991.

ROBERTSON, Nicholas Craig 17 Wetherby Road, York YO26 5BS — MB BCh 1993 Wales.

ROBERTSON, Nicola Jayne Dept of Paediatrics, Imperial College School of Medicine, Hammersmith Hospital Du Cane Road, London W12 0HS Tel: 020 8743 2030 Fax: 020 8740 8281 Email: n.robertson@ic.ac.uk; 10 Silver Crescent, Chiswick, London W4 5SE — MB ChB 1988 Ed.; MRCP (UK) 1995. (Edin) Cons. Neonat.. Hammersmith Hosp. Socs: Brit. Med. Assn.; Brit. Assn. Perinatal Med.; Neonat..Soc. Prev: Regist. (Neonat.) Monash Med. Centre Vict., Austral.; Regist. (Paediat.) Kent & Canterbury Hosp.; SHO (Host Defence) Gt. Ormond St. Hosp.

ROBERTSON, Norman Macnicol Knockanharrie, Isle of Whithorn, Newton Stewart DG8 8JE — MB ChB 1952 Glas. (Glas.) Prev: Ho. Surg. Lennox Castle Matern. Hosp.; Ho. Surg. & Ho. Phys. Hairmyres Hosp. E. Kilbride.

ROBERTSON, Patrick Dugan, OBE (retired) Avila, Rockhill, Wick KW1 5TP Tel: 01955 602728 — MB ChB Aberd. 1954; FRCP Ed. 1978, M 1962. Prev: Cons. Phys. Caithness Hosp. Gp.

ROBERTSON, Patrick Michael Marcham Health Centre, Marcham Road, Abingdon OX14 1BT Tel: 01235 522602; 12 Conduit Road, Abingdon OX14 1DB — MB BS 1983 Newc.; BMedSc Newc. 1980; MRCP (UK) 1986; MRCGP 1996; DRCOG 1989; Cert. Family Plann. JCC 1989. (Newc. u. Tyne)

ROBERTSON, Paul 45 Oakdene Court, Culloden, Inverness IV2 7XL — MB ChB 1998 Ed.; MB ChB Ed 1998.

ROBERTSON, Paula Anne Sisters Home, City Hospital, Dudley Road, Birmingham B18 7QH — MB BS 1995 W. Indies.

ROBERTSON, Paula Jane 12 Swanston Avenue, Edinburgh EH10 7BU — MB ChB 1995 Dundee.

ROBERTSON, Peter Dedridge Health Centre, Nigel Rise, Livingston EH54 6QQ Tel: 01506 414586 Fax: 01506 461806; 77 Kirkfield E., Livingston Village, Livingston EH54 7BB — MB ChB 1984 Ed.; BSc (Hons.) Ed. 1981; MRCGP 1989; DRCOG 1988; Cert. Family Plann. JCC 1989. Prev: Ho. Off. Respirat. Unit City Hosp.; SHO (Cas.) Falkirk Roy. Hosp.; SHO (O & G) Bangour Gen. Hosp.

ROBERTSON, Peter Cowe (retired) Lanercost, Cliftonville Road, Northampton NN1 5BX Tel: 01604 66434 & 34700 Email: pcrob@lanercostpcr.freeserve.co.uk — MD 1969 Dundee; MB ChB (Hnrs.) St. And. 1956; FRCP Lond. 1977, M 1965; FRCP Ed. 1973, M 1961. Prev: Cons. Gen. Phys. N.ampton Gen. Hosp.

ROBERTSON, Peter Gordon Cochrane (retired) The Surgeries, Lombard Street, Newark NG24 1XG Tel: 01636 702363 Fax: 01636 613037 — MB ChB 1958 St. And.

ROBERTSON, Peter Macgregor The Burdwood Surgery, Wheelers Green Way, Thatcham, Newbury RG19 4YF Tel: 01635 68006 Fax: 01635 867484 Email: peter.robertson@gp-k81102.nhs.uk; Heathlands, Upper Woolhampton, Reading RG7 5UA — MB ChB 1978 Birm.; MRCGP 1984; MRCGP 1984.

ROBERTSON, Philip Royal Hospital for Sick Children, 9 Sciennes Road, Edinburgh EH9 1LQ Tel: 0131 667 1991; 15 East Terrace, South Queensferry EH30 9HS — MB ChB 1984 Dundee; BDS 1978; MRCP (UK) 1993. Staff Phys. (Paediat. A & E) Roy. Hosp. for Sick Childr. Edin. Prev: Regist. & SHO (Paediat.) Roy. Hosp. Sick Childr. Edin.; SHO (Paediat.) Ninewells Hosp. Dundee.

ROBERTSON, Philip Warner (retired) 9 Heaton Drive, Edgbaston, Birmingham B15 3LW Tel: 0121 454 3793 — MD 1950 Liverp.; MB ChB 1945; FRCP Lond. 1966, M 1949; DMRD Eng. 1968. Prev: Direct. Radiol. Serv. E. Birm. Hosp.

ROBERTSON, Richard The Health Centre, Whyteman's Brae, Kirkcaldy KY1 2NA Tel: 01592 642178 Fax: 01592 644782; 44 Boglily Road, Kirkcaldy KY2 5NF Tel: 01592 204622 — MB ChB 1967 Ed.; MRCGP 1979; DCH Eng. 1972; DObst RCOG 1971. (Ed.)

ROBERTSON, Richard John Student Health Service, 25 Belgrave Road, Bristol BS8 2AA Tel: 0117 973 7716 Fax: 0117 970 6804 — MB ChB 1970 Ed.; MRCGP 1975; DObst RCOG 1972; DCH RCPS Glas. 1972. Prev: GP Annan Dumfriessh.

ROBERTSON, Rita Mary Prisca 24 Chessington Close, Appleton, Warrington WA4 5HG — MB ChB 1982 Birm.; MFPHM RCP (UK) 1992. Cons. Pub. Health Med. N. Chesh. HA.

ROBERTSON, Robert Chapman Gibson North Glen Medical Practice, 1 Huntsmans Court, Glenrothes KY7 6SX Tel: 01592 620062 Fax: 01592 620465; Wellwood, Kettle Road, Ladybank, Cupar KY15 7PA — MB ChB 1982 Ed.; DRCOG 1986.

ROBERTSON

ROBERTSON, Robert Hennedy Aultbea and Gairloch Medical Practice, The Health Centre, Auchtercairn, Gairloch IV21 2BH Tel: 01445 712229 — MB ChB St. And. 1971. (St. And. & Dundee) Socs: Assoc. Mem. RCGP; BASICS. Prev: GP Dalkeith; Med. Adviser Ethicon Ltd.

ROBERTSON, Robert Hugh 112 Clyde Street, Carluke ML8 5BG — MB ChB 1938 Ed. (Univ. Ed.) Jun. Hosp. Med. Off. Law Hosp. Carluke. Prev: Capt. RAMC 1940-46.

ROBERTSON, Robert John (retired) 1 Fjaere, Brae, Shetland ZE2 9QJ Tel: 01806 522663 — MB ChB Aberd. 1958; CIH Dund 1973.

ROBERTSON, Robert St Clair Department of Diagnostic Radiology, Royal Berkshire Hospital, London Road, Reading RG1 5AN Tel: 0118 987 8035; Peacehaven, The St, Tidmarsh, Reading RG8 8ER Tel: 0118 984 3163 — MB BS 1975 Lond.; BSc Lond. 1972; MRCP (UK) 1981; FRCR 1984; DMRD 1982. (St. Bart.) Cons. Radiol. Roy. Berks. & Battle NHS Trust. Prev: Sen. Regist. (Radiol.) St. Bart. Hosp & Gt. Ormond St. Hosp. for Sick Childr. Lond.

ROBERTSON, Robert Tait 10 Ferguson Road, Walkington, Beverley HU17 8SL — MB ChB 1981 Dundee. Assoc. Specialist (A & E) Hull Roy. Infirm.

ROBERTSON, Robin Andrew The Lindens, 4 Balmuildy Road, Bishopbriggs, Glasgow G64 3BS — MB ChB 1964 Glas.; MRCGP 1966; DObst RCOG 1966; FRCGP 1997. (Glas.) Sen. Tutor Univ. Dept. Gen. Pract. Univ. Glas. Prev: SHO (Matern.) Ayrsh. Centr. Hosp. Irvine.

ROBERTSON, Roderick John Hally 1A Whinbrook Gardens, Moortown, Leeds LS17 6AE — MB ChB 1975 Ed.; MRCP (UK) 1979; FRCR 1986. Cons. Radiol. Killingbeck Cardiothoracic Hosp. & St. Jas. Univ. Hosp. Leeds.

ROBERTSON, Rosemary (retired) 33 Crofton Close, Southampton SO17 1XB Tel: 02380556482 — MB ChB 1955 Ed. Prev: SCMO (Child Health) Soton. Community Health Trust.

ROBERTSON, Sarah Jex Dept. Psychotherapy, Harewood House, Glenburnie Road, London SW17 7RD; Email: sarah@sunray10.freeserve.co.uk — MB BS 1976 Lond.; BSc (Psych.) Lond. 1973; MRCPsych 1983. (St. Bart.) p/t Cons. Psychother. S. W. Lond. & St. Geo.s Ment. Health NHS Trust, Lond.. Socs: ASSOC. Mem. Brit. Psycoanalytic Soc.; Mem. Assn. Psychoanalytic Psychother. in the NHS; Mem. Roy. Coll. Psychiatr. Prev: Sen. Regist. (Psychother.) Maudsley Hosp. Lond.; Research Worker Inst. Psychiat. Lond.; Regist. Maudsley Hosp. Lond.

ROBERTSON, Sheila Anne (retired) Victoria Mews, 28 Victoria St, St Annes, Alderney GY9 3TA Tel: 01481 823195 — MB ChB 1952 Bristol; FRCOG 1973, M 1958. Prev: O & G P.ss Eliz. Hosp. Guernsey.

ROBERTSON, Sheila Jean Barclay Crewkerne, Clovenfords, Galashiels TD1 3ND Tel: 01896 850280 — MB ChB 1955 Ed.; FFA RCS Eng. 1964; DA Eng. 1958. (Ed.) Socs: BMA. Prev: Cons. Anaesth. Borders Gen. Hosp. Melrose; Cons. Anaesth. Peel Hosp. Galashiels; Regist (Anaesth.) Bangour Gen. Hosp. & S. Som. Clin. Area.

ROBERTSON, Simon Bramwell Fyvie Health Group, Health Centre, 27 Parnassus Gardens, Fyvie, Turriff AB53 8QD Tel: 01651 872239 Fax: 01651 872968; Struan, School Road, Fyvie, Turriff AB53 8QE Tel: 01651 891509 — MB ChB 1977 Aberd.; MRCP (UK) 1980; MRCGP 1983; DRCOG 1982; Cert. Family Plann. JCC 1982. (Aberd.) Princip. in Gen. Pract.; Clin. Asst. A & E Dept., Foresthill; Dep. Trainer, Grampian VTS. Socs: (Ex Chairm., Sec. & Treas.) Ythan Med. Soc.; Garioch Med. Assn. Prev: Trainer Grampian VTS; Regist. (Med.) Aberd. Roy. Infirm.; Research Fell. (Med.) Aberd. Univ.

ROBERTSON, Simon James 1 Hollytree Close, Gerrards Cross SL9 0JL Tel: 01753 87474; Flat 3, 4 Cavendish Place, Bath BA1 2UB Tel: 01225 332862 — BM 1994 Soton. (Southampton) SHO (Paediat.) Gloucestershire Roy. Hosp. Gloucester. Prev: SHO (Paediat.) Derriford Hosp. Plymouth.

ROBERTSON, Sonia Margaret Highgate Group Practice, 44 North Hill, London N6 4QA Tel: 020 8340 6628 Fax: 020 8342 8428 — MB ChB 1972 Leeds.

ROBERTSON, Stephen Charles The Cameleon Centre, 34 The Avenue, Watford WD17 4AH Tel: 01923 242565 Fax: 01923 218271; Pendell Cottage, Hungerford Lane, South Hurlock Row, Reading RG10 0NY — MB BChir 1977 Camb.; MA (Hons.) Camb. 1977.

ROBERTSON, Steven Howard, Capt. RAMC Squirrel Preys, Caldy Road, Wirral CH48 1LN — MB ChB 1986 Glas.; MRCPsych 1992; MRCGP 1990.

ROBERTSON, Struan (retired) 5 Kensington Close, Rocks Road, Halifax HX3 0HX — MB ChB 1932 Ed.; DOMS Eng. 1950.

ROBERTSON, Struan John Tannahill (retired) Torranroy, Evelix Road, Dornoch IV25 3HR Tel: 01862 810274 — MB ChB Glas. 1945; MRCGP 1968. Prev: GP Glas. Inaugural Chairm. Woodside Health Centre Glas.

ROBERTSON, Stuart Forrest (retired) 25 Hazlehead Place, Aberdeen AB15 8HD — MB ChB 1964 Aberd. Prev: SCMO (Community Health) Grampian HB.

ROBERTSON, Stuart Hamish Addington Road Surgery, 33 Addington Road, West Wickham BR4 9BW Tel: 020 8462 5771 Fax: 020 8462 8526 Email: stuart.robertson@g84017-nhs.uk; 3 Addington Road, West Wickham BR4 9BW Tel: 020 8462 5297 — MB BS 1976 Lond. (Roy. Free Hosp.) GP & Trainer W. Wickham; Med. Off.; Lect. & Examr. Brit. Red Cross; Chairm. EMDOC Ltd. Prev: Trainee GP Cirencester VTS; Ho. Surg. Edgware Gen. Hosp.; Ho. Phys. Lister Hosp. Stevenage.

ROBERTSON, Stuart Mitchell Queen Elizabeth Hospital, Stadium Road, Woolwich SE18 4QH Tel: 0208 836 5595 — MB BS 1980 Lond.; FFA RCSI 1988. Cons. Anaesth.Qu. Eliz. Hosp., Woolwich, Lond. Prev: Sen. Regist. Rotat. (Anaesth.) NE Thames RHA.

ROBERTSON, Stuart William 25 Hayfield Avenue, Cardiff CF5 1AL — MB ChB 1992 Ed.

ROBERTSON, Susan Elizabeth The Renal Unit, Dumfries Royal Infirmary, Bankend Road, Dumfries DG1 4AP Tel: 01387 241604; Gillfoot Farm, New Abbey, Dumfries DG2 8HD Tel: 01387 850225 Email: sherobertson@hotmail.com — MB ChB 1986 Aberd.; DRCOG 1991. Staff Grade (Renal) Dumfries Roy. Infirm. Prev: Trainee GP/SHO Dumfries & Galloway VTS; Ho. Off. (Med.) Dumfries Roy. Infirm.

ROBERTSON, Tanya Collette 169 Spencefield Lane, Evington, Leicester LE5 6GG Tel: 0116 241 6887; United Leeds Teaching Hospital NHS Trust, Leeds General Infirmary, Leeds LS3 1AB — MB BS 1996 Lond. (St. Georges London) SHO (Paediat.) United Leeds Teachg. Hosp. Leeds.

ROBERTSON, Mr Timothy Damian The Forge, Wichenford, Worcester WR6 6YY — MB ChB 1986 Birm.; FRCS Ed. 1994. (Birm.) Specialist Regist. (Orthop.) Birm. Orthop. Train. Scheme.

ROBERTSON, Professor William Bruce 3 Cambisgate, 109 Church Road, Wimbledon, London SW19 5AL Tel: 020 8947 6731 — MB ChB 1947 St. And.; BSc St. And. 1944, MD 1959; FRCPath 1969, M 1963. (St. And.) Emerit. Prof. Histopath. (Univ. Lond.) St. Geo. Hosp. Med. Sch. Lond.; Hon. Cons. Path. St. Geo. Hosp. Prev: Dir. Studies Roy. Coll. Path.; Vis. Prof. Univ. Leuven, Belgium; Sen. Lect. (Morbid Anat.) Univ. W. Indies, Jamaica.

ROBERTSON, William Graham (retired) 9 Station Road, Biggleswade SG18 8AL Tel: 01767 312124 — MB ChB 1941 Ed.

ROBERTSON, William Shedden Muir The Surgery, 31 Portland Road, Kilmarnock KA1 2DJ Tel: 01563 22118; 29 Glasgow Road, Kilmarnock KA3 1TJ Tel: 01563 24869 — MB ChB 1959 Glas.

ROBERTSON-MACKAY, Fiona Clare Oakdene, Westfields, Whiteleaf, Princes Risborough HP27 0LH; Bayer Plc, Bayer House, Strawberry Hill, Newbury RG14 1JA — MB ChB 1989 Aberd.; MRCP (UK) 1994; AFPM 1998. Med. Adviser Pharmaceut. Div. Bayer plc Newbury.; Clin. Asst. Stoke Mandeville Hosp. Socs: Brit. Thorac. Soc. Prev: Regist. & SHO (Med.) Stoke Mandeville Hosp. Aylesbury.

ROBERTSON-RINTOUL, James (retired) Pictavia, 11 Bonfield Road, Strathkinness, St Andrews KY16 9RR Tel: 01334 850653 — MB ChB 1951 St. And.; MD St. And. 1960; BSc St. And. 1944. Prev: Reader (Clin. Anat.) Univ. St. And.

ROBERTSON-RITCHIE, Hugh The New Surgery, 128 Canterbury Road, Folkestone CT19 5NR Tel: 01303 243516 Fax: 01303 244633 — MB BS 1972 Lond.; Diploma in the Philosophy of Medicine, Society of Apothecaries 2000 Lond.; MPhil Camb. 1996; MRCS Eng. LRCP Lond. 1972; MRCGP 1980; Cert. Family Plann. JCC 1980. (Guy's) GP Trainer. Prev: SHO (Chest Dis.) Univ. Coll. Hosp. Lond.; SHO (Radiother.) St. William's Hosp. Rochester; Ho. Surg. Greenwich Dist. Hosp. Lond.

ROBINSON

ROBERTSON-STEEL, Iain Rhoderick Stewart West Midlands Ambulance Service, Falcon Hse, 6 The Memories, Dudley DY2 8PN Tel: 01384 215555 Fax: 01384 215559; Ivy Lodge, 17 Priorslee Village, Telford TF2 9NW — MB ChB 1979 Birm.; MRCGP 1987; DFFP 1994; Dip. IMC RCS Ed. 1991; DRCOG 1986. (Birm.) Med. Dir., W.Midl.s Ambul. Serv., Med. Dir. NHS Dir. Birm. Black Country & Solihull; Hon. Sen. Clin. Lect. (Primary Care) Univ. Wolverhampton; Hon. Research Fell. Sch. Heath & Social Serv. Univ. of Coventry. Socs: BASICS; Assoc. Fell. Fac. Accid. & Emerg. Med.; Fac. Pre Hosp. Care. Prev: RAF Med. Servs.; GP Leatherhead Surrey; Police Surg. Surrey Police.

ROBIN, Elizabeth Clare Department of Public Health, Redbridge & Waltham Forest HA, West Wing, 713 Eastern Avenue, Ilford IG2 7SJ Tel: 020 8983 2912 — MB BS 1986 Lond.; BA Oxf. 1982; MFPHM RCP (UK) 1994. Cons. Pub. Health Redbridge & Waltham Forest HA.

ROBIN, Mr Ian Gibson (retired) Merchiston, 4 Lodge Gardens, Oakham LE15 6EP — MRCS Eng. LRCP Lond. 1933; MB BChir. Camb. 1933; MA Camb. 1933; FRCS Eng. 1935; FRCS 1936 England. Prev: ENT Surg. St. Mary's Hosp. Lond. & Roy. N.. Hosp. Lond.

ROBIN, John Gilbert The Medical Centre, 12 East King Street, Helensburgh G84 7QL Tel: 01436 672277 Fax: 01436 674526; 5 Queen's Point, Shandon, Helensburgh G84 8QZ Fax: 01436 74526 — MB ChB Glas. 1970; MRCGP 1974; DObst RCOG 1973.

ROBIN, Jonathan Mark Centre for Clinical Pharmacology, The Cruciform Project, Rayne Institute, University College London, London WC1; 25 Oak Tree Close, Virginia Water GU25 4JF — MB BS 1994 Lond.; MB BS (Hons.) Lond. 1994; MRCP (UK) 1997. (UMDS Guy's & St. Thos.) Lect. (Clin. Pharmacol. & Intens. Care Med.) Univ. Coll. Lond. Prev: SHO, Roy. Brompton & Hammersm. Hosp. Lond.; HO. Phys. Guy's Hosp. Lond.

ROBIN, Nicole Marie 14 Alexandra Road, West Kirby, Wirral CH48 0RT Tel: 0151 625 3437 Email: 100573.555@compuserve.com — MB ChB 1990 Birm.; MB ChB (Hons.) Birm. 1990; MRCP (UK) 1993; FRCA 1996; DA (UK) 1994. Regist. (Anaesth.) Mersey RHA.

ROBINS, Alison Margaret 23 Springvale, Waterlooville PO8 9DA — BM 1995 Soton.

ROBINS, Amanda Elizabetta Walnut Yard, Church St., Buckingham MK18 1BY Email: mindyrobins@hotmail.com — BM 1996 Soton. SHO (Med.) Greenwich Hosp. Lond. Socs: Anglo-French Med. Soc. Prev: SHO (A & E) Univ. Coll. Hosp. Lond.

ROBINS, Andrew William Department of Paediatrics, Whittington Hospital, Highgate Hill, London N19 5NF Tel: 020 7288 5188 Fax: 020 72885215 Email: andrew.robins@whittington.nhs.uk; 23 Tavistock Terrace, London N19 4BZ — MB BS 1986 Lond.; MSc (Clin. Paediat.) Lond. 1996; MRCP (UK) 1991; MRCPI 1990; DCH RCP Lond. 1990; FRCPCH 1997. (Roy. Free Hosp. Lond.) Cons. Paediat. Whittington Hosp. Lond. Socs: Fell. Roy. Coll. Paediat. & Child Health; InterNat. Child Health Gp.; BMA. Prev: Sen. Regist. (Paediat.) N. Middlx. Hosp.; Regist. (Paediat.) Whipps Cross Hosp. Lond.; Regist. (Neonat.) Univ. Coll. Hosp. Lond.

ROBINS, David George (retired) 10 Marlyns Drive, Guildford GU4 7LS Tel: 01483 565605 — MB BS 1965 Lond.; FRCP Lond. 1987; MRCS Eng. LRCP Lond. 1965; DCH Eng. 1968; DObst RCOG 1967. Prev: Cons. Paediat. Roy. Surrey Co. Hosp. & St. Luke's Hosp. Guildford.

ROBINS, David Peter Cross Keys House, South Hinkley, Oxford — BM BCh 1969 Oxf.

ROBINS, David Stuart (retired) 26 Bretby Lane, Bretby, Burton-on-Trent DE15 0QN Tel: 01283 548628 Fax: 01238 548628 Email: dave@the-robins.freeserve.co.uk — MB ChB Manch. 1969; DObst RCOG 1971. Prev: Ho. Surg. & Ho. Phys. Manch. Roy. Infirm.

ROBINS, David William Anaesthetic Department, North Hampshire Hospital, Basingstoke RG24 9NA Tel: 01256 313461 Fax: 01256 354224 Email: amaesthetics@bas.swest.nhs.uk — MB BS 1971 Lond.; MRCS Eng. LRCP Lond. 1971; FRCA 1978; DObst RCOG 1973. (Lond. Hosp.) Cons. Anaesth. (Day Surg.) N. Hants. Hosp. Trust Basingstoke. Socs: Eur. Soc. Anaesth.; Brit. Assn. Day Surg. Prev: Dir. ITU; Clin. Dir. (Anaesth.); Sen. Regist. (Anaesth.) Bristol Roy. Infirm., Frenchay Hosp. Bristol & Treliske Hosp. Truro.

ROBINS, Gwyn 2 Elm Grove, Gilwern, Abergavenny NP7 0BE — MRCS Eng. LRCP Lond. 1946.

ROBINS, James Brent Department of Obstetrics & Gynaecology, Inverclyde Royal NHS Trust, Larkfield Road, Greenock PA16 0AN Tel: 01475 633777 Fax: 01475 631700; St. Colms, Duchal Road, Kilmacolm PA13 4AY Tel: 01505 872938 Email: robinsjim@aol.com — MB ChB 1984 Ed.; MRCOG 1990. (Ed.) Cons. O & G Inverclyde Roy. NHS Trust; RCR/RCOG Advanced Train. Obst. Ultrasound 1994. Socs: Brit. Med. Ultrasound Soc.; Brit. Matern. & Fetal Med. Soc. Prev: Sen. Regist. (O & G) Leeds Gen. Infirm.; Regist. (O & G) Glas. Matern. Hosp.; Neonat. Research Fell. Univ. Edin. Simpson Memor. Matern. Pavil. Edin.

ROBINS, Kay 18 Kimberlow Woods Hill, York YO10 5HF — MB BS 1994 Newc.

ROBINS, Nathalie Marie Raunsley Building, Dept. Psychiatry, Manchester Royal Infirmary, Oxford Road, Manchester M13 9WL Tel: 0161 276 5365 Fax: 0161 276 5444; Email: nat@chvc.demon.co.uk — MB ChB 1992 Manch.; MRCPsych 1996; MSc 1999. (Manch.) Sen. Regist. (Psychiat.) Manch. Roy. Infirm.

ROBINS, Mr Robert Henry Cradock (retired) 3 Lemon Villas, Truro TR1 2NX Tel: 01872 273689 Fax: 01872 273689 — MB BChir Camb. 1947; MA Camb. 1949, BA (2nd cl. Nat. Sc. Trip. Pts. I & II) 1944; FRCS Eng. 1950. Prev: Orthop. Surg. Roy. Cornw. Hosp. Truro & Cornw. & I. of Scilly DHA.

ROBINS, Sally Jane The Stubbington Medical Practice, Park Lane, Stubbington, Fareham PO14 2J — MB BS 1992 Lond.; BSc (Biochem.) Lond. 1989; DRCOG 1995; DFFP 1996. (St Thomas) GP. Prev: GP Regist. Portsmouth; SHO c/o Elderly, Qu. Alexandra Hosp. Portsmouth.; SHO Psychiat. St Jane's Portsmouth.

ROBINS, Sandra Betty Woodside Cottage, Rushlake Green, Heathfield TN21 9QR Tel: 01435 830631 — MB BS 1988 Lond.; BSc Lond. 1985; DRCOG 1993; DCH RCP Lond. 1991. GP E. Sussex Retainer Scheme. Prev: Trainee GP Tunbridge Wells VTS.

ROBINSKA, Ewa Maria Eastfields Road Surgery, 1 Eastfields Road, Acton, London W3 0AA Tel: 020 8922 4331 — MB BS 1978 Lond.; MRCGP 1984; DRCOG 1983; DCH RCP Lond. 1982. (Roy. Free) GP Acton. Prev: Ho. Surg. & Ho. Phys. Edgware Gen. Hosp.; Trainee GP Ealing VTS.; GP Greenford.

ROBINSON, Adam Corin James Dept. of Diabetes, Queen Elizabeth Hospital, Sheriff Hill, Gateshead NE9 6SX — MB BS 1987 Lond.; MRCP (UK) 1991. Cons. Diabetes & Endocrinol. Prev: Regist. Rotat. (Gen. Med. & Endocrinol.) Edgware Gen. Hosp., St. Mary's Paddington & N.wick Pk. Hosp.; SHO (Renal Transpl.) Roy. Free Hosp. Lond.; SHO Rotat. (Gen. Med.) Soton. Gen. Hosp.

ROBINSON, Alan Andrew The Briars, Nethergate St., Harpley, King's Lynn PE31 6TN Tel: 01485 520644; 29 Woodcock Road, Norwich NR3 3UA Tel: 01603 425989 Fax: 01603 488315 — MB ChB 1978 Liverp.; MRCP (UK) 1981; MRCGP 1986.

ROBINSON, Alexandra Jane Smallwood House, Church Green W., Redditch B97 4BD; 44 Leslie Road, Edgbaston, Birmingham B16 9DX — MB ChB 1982 Bristol; MRCGP 1985; DRCOG 1986; DCH RCP Lond. 1985. Clin. Asst. (Psychiat. of Old Age & Geriat.) Redditch & Worcs. HA.

ROBINSON, Alexandra Louise Department of Anaesthetics, Birmingham Childrens Hospital, Ladywood Middleway, Birmingham B16 8ET; 5 St. Helier Close, Wokingham RG41 2HA — MB BS 1988 Lond.; FRCA 1993. Sen. Regist. Birm. Sch. Prev: Regist. Rotat. (Anaesth.) Oxf.; Regist. Rotat. (Anaesth.) Milton Keynes Gen. Hosp.; Clin. Fell. Birm. Childr. Hosp.

ROBINSON, Alfred (retired) Oakhurst, 146 Barnham Road, Barnham, Bognor Regis PO22 0EH Tel: 01243 553259 — MB BChir Camb. 1954; MA Camb. 1968, BA 1951; FRCP Lond. 1974, M 1961; DCH Eng. 1961. Prev: Cons. Paediat. Chichester Trust.

ROBINSON, Alfred Alexander Thomas House Surgery, 12 East Bridge Rd, Dymchurch TN29 0PF Tel: 01303 873156 Fax: 01303 874885; Moonfield, Cambers Green, Pluckley, Ashford TN27 0HR Tel: 01233 840254 — MB BS 1965 Lond.; MRCS Eng. LRCP Lond. 1965; DObst RCOG 1970; DCH Eng. 1969. (King's Coll. Hosp.) GP DymCh. Socs: BMA.

ROBINSON, Alison Frances Central Clinic, East Lodge Court, High Street, Colchester CO1 1WR Tel: 01206 744052 Fax: 01206 744001; Priory House, 166 Rushmere Rd, Ipswich IP4 3LP Tel: 01473 723550 Email: afwrobinson@doctors.org.uk — MB BS 1978 Lond.; MA Oxf. 1974; FRCPCH 1994; MRCP (UK) 1981; DCH Eng. 1981. (Charing Cross) Cons. Paediat. Essex Rivers Healthcare Trust; Med. Adviser to Fostering Serv. Essex Co. Counc. Socs: Brit. Assoc.

ROBINSON

of Adoption & Fostering.; Roy. Soc. Med.; Brit. Assoc. of Community Child Health. Prev: Sen. Regist. (Paediat.) Ipswich; SCMO (Child Health) Ipswich.

ROBINSON, Amanda Susan Ann Butt Lane Surgery, 58 Butt Lane, Leeds LS12 5AZ Tel: 0113 263 7635 Fax: 0113 279 1781; 13 Arncliffe Road, Leeds LS16 5AP Tel: 0113 274 6424 Fax: 0113 274 6424 Email: amanda@asr.freeserve.co.uk — MB 1976 Oxf.; ChB Birm. 1979; MA Oxf. 1980; MBA 1989; MRCGP 1983; DRCOG 1981. Dist. Fac. Tutor Roy. Coll. Gen. Pract.; GP Adviser Med. Serv. Commiss.ing Team Leeds HA; Chairm. Leeds W. PCG. Socs: Inst. Psychosexual Med. Prev: GP Gt. Shelford Camb.

ROBINSON, Andrew Garforth Medical Centre, Church Lane, Garforth, Leeds LS25 1HB Tel: 0113 286 5311 Fax: 0113 281 2679 — MB BS 1984 Lond.; DRCOG 1992; DA (UK) 1987. (St. George's Lond.) GP Princip.; Clin. Asst. Anaesth. Prev: Trainee GP Kingston upon Hull.

ROBINSON, Mr Andrew Hugh Neil Box 37, Addenbrooke's Hospital, Hills Road, Cambridge CB3 2QQ Tel: 01223 216426 Fax: 01223 217307 Email: bone2222@hotmail.com; 170 Gwydir Street, Cambridge CB1 2LW — MB BS 1988 Lond.; BSc Lond. 1985; FRCS (Orth.) 1996; FRCS Lond. 1992. Cons. Trauma & Orthop. Socs: BOA; Brit. Ohthopaedic Surg. Soc.; RSM. Prev: SHO (Surg) St. Barts Hosp. Lond.; Higher Surg. Trainee (Orthop.) E. Anglia.

ROBINSON, Andrew John Albany Surgery, Albany Street, Newton Abbot TQ12 2TX Tel: 01626 334411 Fax: 01626 335663; 11 Forde Park, Newton Abbot TQ12 1DB Tel: 01626 365824 — MB ChB 1988 Bristol; BSc (Hons.) Bristol 1985; MRCP (UK) 1991; MRCGP 1993. Prev: Trainee GP/SHO Torbay Hosp. VTS; SHO Rotat. (Gen. Med.) Torbay Hosp. Torquay.

ROBINSON, Angela Joyce Department of Genitourinary Medicine, Mortimer Market Centre, UCLH, off Capper St., London WC1E 6AU Tel: 020 7530 5033 Fax: 020 7530 5044 Email: arobinson@gum.ucl.ac.uk; 36 Palace Road, Crouch End, London N8 8QJ — MB BS 1980 Newc.; MRCP (UK) 1983; FRCP (UK) 1996. Cons. Genitourin. Med. Mortimer Market Centre Lond.; Hon. Sen. Lect. UCL. Socs: MSSVD Pres.; Assn. Genitourin. Med. Mem.; Speciality Chair of Jt. Comm. of Genitourin. Med., RCP. Prev: Sen. Regist. (Genitourin. Med.) Roy. Hallamshire Hosp. Sheff.; Regist. (Haemat.) Univ. Hosp. Wales Cardiff.

ROBINSON, Angus John Radiotherapy Department, Churchill Hospital, Old Road, Headington, Oxford OX3 7LJ Tel: 01865 741841; 68 James Street, Oxford OX4 1EX Tel: 01865 243966 — BM BS 1992 Nottm.; BMedSci Nottm. 1990; MRCP 1996; FRCR Part 1. Regist. Clin. Oncol. Oxf. Radcliffe Hosps. Prev: SHO (Oncol. & Cardiol.) St. Bart. Hosp. Lond.; SHO (Gen. & Respirat. Med.) Ealing.

ROBINSON, Ann Benedict 8 Kimblesworth Grange, Potterhouse Lane, Chester-le-Street DH2 3QS Tel: 0191 371 9141 Email: acjr1@aol.com — MB BS 1991 Lond.; BSc Lond. 1988; MRCP (UK) 1995; DFFP 1996. (King's Coll. Lond.) GP Regist. Lond.

ROBINSON, Ann Chany The Mountfield Surgery, 55 Mountfield Road, Finchley, London N3 3NR Tel: 020 8346 4271 Fax: 020 8371 0187 — MB BS 1984 Lond.; MRCGP 1988; DRCOG 1986; DCH RCP Lond. 1987. (Middlx. Hosp.) Socs: Fell. Roy. Soc. Med.

ROBINSON, Ann Judith 73 Lutterworth Road, Northampton NN1 5JP — MB ChB 1969 Ed.; BSc (Hons., Physiol.) Ed. 1966. (Ed.) Staff Grade Community Psychait. Milton Kynes pt/t. Socs: MRCPsych. Prev: GP Gateshead; Regist. (Psychiat.) Leics. AHA; Med. Research Fell. Dept. Psychiat. Nottm. Univ.

ROBINSON, Ann Louise Windmill Medical Practice, 65 Shoot Up Hill, London NW2 3PS Tel: 020 8452 7646 Fax: 020 8450 2319; 5 Old Dairy Mews, Kentish Town, London NW5 2JW — MB BS 1986 Lond.; MRCGP 1993; DCH RCP Lond. 1992; DRCOG 1990.

ROBINSON, Anne Caroline Radcliff Department of Radiotherapy, Southend Hospital, Prittlewell Chase, Westcliff on Sea SS0 0RY; 1 Fairview Lodge, Underwood Square, Leigh-on-Sea SS9 3QH — MB BCh BAO 1974 Dub.; MA 1992; FRCR 1988; FFR RCSI 1985; MRCPI 1976; DCH NUI 1977; FRCPI 1997. (TC Dub.) Cons. S.end Hosp. W.cliff on Sea. Socs: Fell. Roy. Acad. Med. Irel.; Brit. Oncol. Assn. Prev: Sen. Regist. Christie Hosp. & Holt Radium Inst. Manch.; Radiother. St. Lukes Hosp. Dub.; Hon. Sen. Regist. Cookridge Hosp. Leeds.

ROBINSON, Anne Elizabeth (retired) 18 Hammondswick, Harpenden AL5 2NR Tel: 0158 27 13888 — MB BS Lond. 1954; DObst RCOG 1955. Prev: Clin. Asst. Soho Hosp. for Wom. Lond.

ROBINSON, Anne Elizabeth 76 Birchdale Road, Appleton, Warrington WA4 5AW Tel: 01925 267045 — MB ChB 1983 Liverp.; FRCS Ed. 1988; FRCS Eng. 1988; MRCGP 1990. (Liverp.) Cons. A & E Warrington Hosp. NHS Trust. Prev: Sen. Regist. (A & E) Warrington Hosp. NHS Trust; Regist. (A & E) Whittington Hosp. Lond.; Trainee GP Edgware VTS.

ROBINSON, Anne Penelope Alport Castles Farm, Alport Dale, Bamford, Hope Valley S33 0AB — MB ChB 1975 Birm.; MRCP (UK) 1977.

ROBINSON, Mr Anthony Colin The Clementine Churchill Hospital, Sudbury Hill, Harrow HA1 3RX Tel: 0208 872 3899 Fax: 0208 872 3908; Tel: 020 8723 9001 Fax: 020 8723 9001 — MB BS 1979 Lond.; FRCS Eng. 1985. (Middlx.) Cons. Otolaryngol. W. Middlx. Univ. Hosp. Isleworth. Socs: Fell. Roy. Soc. Med.; Brit. Assn. Otol. And Head & Neck Surg.; Brit. Med. Assoc. Prev: Sen. Regist. (ENT) Roy. Free Hosp. Lond. & Roy. Surrey Co. Hosp. Guildford; Regist. (ENT) Roy, Free Hosp. Lond.; SHO (ENT) Roy. Nat. Throat, Nose & Ear Hosp. Lond.

ROBINSON, Anthony John The Black Country Family Practice, Health Centre, Queens Road, Tipton DY4 8PH Tel: 0121 557 6397; Meadowcroft, Stream Road, Kingswinford DY6 9NX Tel: 01384 401332 Fax: 01384 401332 Email: tony.robinson@tesco.net — MB ChB 1983 Birm.; BSc (Hons.) Nottm. 1978; FRCGP 1997; MFFP 1994; MRCGP 1987; DRCOG 1987. (Birm.) Princip. Gen. Pract.; Trainer (Gen. Pract.) Sandwell; Assoc. Adviser Gen. Pract; Mem. Roy. Coll. GPs Exam. Bd.; Hon. Lect. Univ. Wolverhampton. Socs: Primary Care Assn. for Gastroenterol.; GP Asthma Gp.; Roy. Soc. Med. Prev: Trainee GP Sandwell Dist. Gen. Hosp. W. Bromwich; Ho. Surg. Roy. Shrewsbury Hosp.; Ho. Phys. Sandwell Dist. Gen. Hosp.

ROBINSON, Anthony Michael Tel: 01225 428331 Fax: 01225 824529; Halton Leys, Iford Hill, Westwood, Bradford-on-Avon BA15 2BG Tel: 01225 867644 — MB BCh 1985 Wales; FRCP 2001 (Lond.); BSc Wales 1980; DM Nottm. 1996; MRCP (UK) 1989. (Welsh Nat. Sch. Med.) Cons. Phys. (Diabetes & Endocrinol.) Roy. United Hosp. Bath. Socs: Sec. of Wessex Endocrine and Diabetes Assn. Prev: Sen. Regist. (Diabetes & Endocrinol.) Sheff. Hosps.; Regist. (Med.) Roy. Hallamsh. Hosp. Sheff.; Research Fell. (Diabetic Med.) Qu. Med. Centre Nottm.

ROBINSON, Arthur Thomas Haddef, Tudweiliog, Pwllheli LL53 8NB — MB BS 1954 Lond.; MRCGP 1966. (King's Coll. Hosp.) Prev: Ho. Surg. Orthop. & Urol. Depts. King's Coll. Hosp.; Ho. Phys. Belgrave Hosp. Childr.

ROBINSON, Arthur William (retired) 30 Brueton Avenue, Solihull B91 3EN Tel: 0121 246 0581 — MA Camb. 1953, MD 1956; FRCR 1983. Prev: Cons. Radiol. Coventry Hosps.

ROBINSON, Ashley James Department of Diagnostic Radiology, University of Manchester Medical School, Stopford Building, Oxford Road, Manchester M13 9PT Tel: 0161 275 5114 Fax: 0161 275 5594; 24 St. Lawrence Quay, Salford Quays, Salford M5 2XT Email: dr.ash@dial.pipex.com — MB ChB 1994 Leeds; BSc (Hons.) Leeds 1991; FRCR 1997; Dip. ATLS RCS Eng. 1995. (Leeds) Specialist Regist. (Diagn. Radiol.) Manch. Roy Infirm. Prev: SHO (Gen. Med.) Sescroft Hosp. Leeds; SHO (A & E) Roy. Halifax Infirm.; Ho. Off. (Surg.) St. Jas. Hosp. Leeds.

ROBINSON, Barry John Lyme Practice, Uplyme Road, Lyme Regis DT7 3LS Tel: 01297 445777 Fax: 01297 444917; Valley Farm, Rocombe, Uplyme, Lyme Regis DT7 3RR Tel: 01297 445868 Fax: 01297 445980 Email: drbarryrob@aol.com — BM Soton. 1983; MRCGP 1988; DRCOG 1988. Unit Gen. Manager Lyme Community Care Unit. Socs: Internat. Comm. Wound Managem.; Eur. Wound Managem. Assn.; Wound Care Soc.

ROBINSON, Basil (retired) Hasty Bank, 9 Foxglove Road, Almondbury, Huddersfield HD5 8LW Tel: 01484 532517 — MRCS Eng. LRCP Lond. 1939; MRCGP 1953. Prev: Surg. Lt.-Cdr. RNVR.

ROBINSON, Benjamin Guy 186 Cathays Ter, Cardiff CF24 4HZ — MB BCh 1997 Wales.

ROBINSON, Beverley Louise Department of Radiology, Royal United Hospital, Combe Park, Bath BA1 3NG Tel: 01225 825728 Fax: 01225 825515 Email: louise.robinson@ruh-bath.swest.nhs.uk; Broughton Gifford Manor, Broughton Gifford, Melksham SN12 8PP Tel: 01225 782259 Fax: 01225 783383 Email:

louise.robinson@ruh-bath.swest.nhs.uk — MB BS 1981 Lond.; FRCR 1988; T(R) (CR) 1993. (King's Coll Hosp. Lond.) Cons. Radiol. Roy. United Hosp. Bath. Prev: Cons. Radiol. St. Helier Hosp. Carshalton; Clin. Lect. MRI Dept. Guy's Hosp. Lond.; Sen. Regist. & Regist. (Radiol.) Guy's Hosp. Lond.

ROBINSON, Brian Assessment and Training Unit, 1 Colston Fort, Montague Place, Kingsdown, Bristol BS6 5UB Tel: 0117 944 6388 Fax: 0117 924 8814 — MB BCh 1979 Wales; MRCPsych 1984.

ROBINSON, Brian Fyffe The Manor House, Curry Mallet, Taunton TA3 6SU Tel: 01823 480161 Email: brianrobinson@mcmail.com — MD Lond. 1966, MB BS 1951; FRCP Lond. 1971, M 1953. (St. Geo.) Emerit. Prof. Cardiovasc. Med. Univ. of Lond. Prev: Prof. Cardiovasc. Med. St. Geo. Hosp. Med. Sch. Lond.; Reader in Cardiovasc. Med. St. Geo. Hosp. Med. Sch. Lond.; Nuffield Med. Fell. Cardiol. Br. Nat. Insts. Health Bethesda, MD.

ROBINSON, Brian Hertzel Ashchurch Surgery, 134 Askew Road, Shepherd Bush, London W12 9BP Tel: 020 8743 2920 Fax: 020 8743 1545; 20 Delamere Road, London W5 3JR Tel: 020 8567 6558 — MB BCh BAO 1959 Belf.; DObst RCOG 1962. (Belf.) Socs: BMA. Prev: SHO Waveney Hosp. Ballymena; Ho. Phys. Belf. City Hosp. & Roy. Belf. Hosp. Sick Childr.; Ho. Surg. Musgrave Pk. Hosp. Belf.

ROBINSON, Brian Hugh Bartlett, TD Birmingham Nuffield Hospital, 22 Somerset Road, Edgbaston, Birmingham B15 2QQ Tel: 0121 456 2000 Fax: 0121 454 5293; Five Oaks, 55 Meriden Road, Hampton-in-Arden, Solihull B92 0BS Tel: 01675 442300 Fax: 01675 442300 Email: 101523.1574@compuserve.com — MB BChir Camb. 1954; MA Camb. 1954; FRCP Lond. 1974, M 1959; MRCS Eng. LRCP Lond. 1954. (Camb. & Guy's) Cons. Nephrol. Birm. Nuffield Hosp.; Hon. Cons. Phys. Birm. Heartlands Hosp. NHS Trust (Teachg.). Socs: Renal Assn.; Eur. Renal Assn. Prev: Cons. Phys. & Clin. Dir. (Renal Servs.) Birm. Heartlands Hosp. NHS Trust (Teachg.); Hon. Sen. Clin. Lect. Univ. Birm.; Sen. Regist. Med. Unit Univ. Coll. Hosp.

ROBINSON, Brian Stuart Havant Health Centre Suite A, PO Box 41, Civic Centre Road, Havant PO9 2AJ Tel: 023 9248 2148 Fax: 023 9249 2524 — MB BS 1970 Lond.; MRCS Eng. LRCP Lond. 1970.

ROBINSON, Brian Wilfred 137 Westbrooke Avenue, Hartlepool TS25 5HZ — MB BS 1979 Newc.

ROBINSON, Bronwen Eileen (retired) Padeswood Lodge, Padeswood, Mold CH7 4JF Tel: 01244 546420 Email: johnbron.robinson@btinternet.com — BMed 1952 Otago, NZ 1952; MB ChB New Zealand 1955; FRCP Lond. 1991; FRCPCH 1996; MB ChB 1955 NZ. Prev: Cons. Community Paediat. Countess of Chester NHS Hosp. Trust.

ROBINSON, Bryan Lawrence (retired) 16 Orkney Ct, Taplow, Maidenhead SL6 0JB Tel: 01753 643246 Fax: 01753 643246 — MB BS 1963 Lond.; MRCS Eng. LRCP Lond. 1963; MRCGP 1968; DObst RCOG 1966. Examr. Benefits Agency Med. Serv. Prev: Med. Adviser Benefits Agency Med. Serv. DSS.

ROBINSON, Carmel Jessica Sarah 62 Downhills Road, Liverpool L23 8SP — MB BS 1992 Lond.

ROBINSON, Caroline Anne 52 The Drive, Ickenham, Uxbridge UB10 8AG — MB BS 1996 Lond.

ROBINSON, Catherine Rose Oak Street Medical Practice, 1 Oak Street, Norwich NR3 3DL Tel: 01603 613431 Fax: 01603 767209; 133 Christchurch Road, Norwich NR2 3PG — MB BS 1981 Lond.; BA Oxf. 1978; DTM & H 1989; DCH RCP Lond. 1987; DRCOG 1985. Prev: Trainee GP Norwich VTS; Gen.iste Urgences Amer. Hosp., Paris.

ROBINSON, Cedric Harold (retired) 8 Marton Close, Gargrave, Skipton BD23 3PG Tel: 01756 749534 — MB ChB 1937 Leeds. Prev: Ho. Surg. Leeds Gen. Infirm.

ROBINSON, Charles Adrian 39 Honister Avenue, Newcastle upon Tyne NE2 3PA — MB BS 1988 Newc.

ROBINSON, Charles Graham Francis Department of Diagnostic Imaging, Mobay Hope Medical Centre, P.O.Box 2520, Half Moon P.O., Rose Hall, Montego Bay, Jamaica; Y Bodau O'R Cathod, Llanfallteg, Whitland SA34 0UJ — MRCS Eng. LRCP Lond. 1972; DMRD Eng. 1979. (Lond. Hosp.) Socs: Roy. Coll. Radiol.; Brit. Inst. Radiol.; BMA. Prev: Cons. Radiol. Withybush Gen. Hosp. HaverfordW.

ROBINSON, Charles Patrick c/o X-Ray Department, Cheltenham General Hospital, Sandford Road, Cheltenham GL53 7AN — MB BCh BAO 1971 Dub.; MB BCh Dub. 1971; BA Dub. 1969; FRCR 1978. Cons. Radiol. Cheltenham Gen. Hosp. Prev: Cons. Radiol. Dorset Co. Hosp. Dorchester; State Specialist Radiol. Gen. Hosp. Bandar Seri Begawan Brunei; Sen. Regist. & Regist. (Radiol.) Brist. Roy. Infirm.

ROBINSON, Charles Richard Rockcliffe, Old Chester Road, Helsby, Warrington WA6 9NW Tel: 01928 722277 Email: the.robinsons@hunterlink.net.au — MB BS 1981 Tasmania; BDS Bristol 1974; DObst. Austral. 1986.

ROBINSON, Charlotte Sophia (retired) — MB ChB Glas. 1943. Prev: Clin. Asst. Nottm. Childr. Hosp.

ROBINSON, Christina Jane 18 Ramsey Road, Sheffield S10 1LR — MB ChB 1995 Sheff.

ROBINSON, Christine Anne The Lodge, 4 George St. W., Luton LU1 2BJ Tel: 01582 511003 Fax: 01582 511001; Tel: 020 8299 0015 — MB BChir 1983 Camb.; MA Camb. 1983; MFFP 1994; MRCOG 1990. (Camb./St. Thos.) p/t Cons. Family Plann. & Reproduct. Health Care. Beds. & Luton Community NHS Trust.; Med. Dir., Beds. & Luton Community NHS Trust; Clin. Director Sexual Health Serv.s.

ROBINSON, Christopher High Street Surgery, 1st Floor, 99 High Street, Fort William PH33 6DG Tel: 01397 703773 Fax: 01397 701068; Arkaig Cottage, Achintore Road, Fort William PH33 6RN Tel: 01397 702886 Email: cr@locnater.almac.co.uk — MB BS 1971 Lond.; DObst RCOG 1974; DA Eng. 1973. (Roy. Free) Prev: SHO (Anaesth.) Edgware Gen. Hosp.; SHO (Obst.) Vale of Leven Hosp. Alexandria; SHO (Paediat.) Law Hosp. Carluke.

ROBINSON, Christopher Charles 64 Hall Terr, Macclesfield SK11 0DH — MB ChB 1982 Liverp.; MRCGP 1987; DRCOG 1986; Cert. Family Plann. JCC 1986; Cert. Prescribed Equiv. Exp. JCPTGP 1986.

ROBINSON, Christopher David The Paddock Surgery, Chapel Lane, Thornhill, Dewsbury WF12 0DH Tel: 01924 465343 Fax: 01924 455781 — MB ChB 1982 Sheff. Prev: Trainee GP Mansfield VTS; SHO (A & E) Rotherham Dist. Gen. Hosp.

ROBINSON, Christopher Gurth Goland The Medical Centre, 45 Enderley Road, Harrow Weald, Harrow HA3 5HF Tel: 020 8863 3333; 14 Evelyn Drive, Pinner HA5 4RX Tel: 020 8428 4186 — MB ChB 1977 Dundee; MRCGP 1982; DRCOG 1979. (Dundee University) GP Trainer N.wick Pk. VTS. Prev: Trainee GP Harrow VTS; Ho. Surg. Canad. Red Cross Memor. Hosp. Taplow; Ho. Phys. Wexham Pk. Hosp. Slough.

ROBINSON, Christopher John Canton Health Centre, Wessex Street, Cardiff CF5 1XU Tel: 029 2039 5115 Fax: 029 2039 4846 — MB BCh 1978 Wales; BA Oxf. 1975; MRCGP 1984.

ROBINSON, Christopher Michael TLF, 11 Marchmont Road, Edinburgh EH9 1EL — BM BS 1985 Nottm.

ROBINSON, Claire Richie Foxmills, Bollington Lane, Nether Alderley, Macclesfield SK10 4TB — BM BCh 1998 Oxf.; MB BCh Oxf 1998.

ROBINSON, Clive Flat 10, The Beeches, Simmons Way, Whetstone, London N20 — MB BS 1978 Lond.; BSc. Lond. 1975, MB BS Lond. 1978.

ROBINSON, Colan Denis Belmont Surgery, 12 Belmont Road, St Austell PL25 4UJ Tel: 01726 69444 — MB ChB 1983 Manch.; MRCGP 1993; DObst NZ 1987; DCH S. Afr. 1991; DA (UK) 1985. Prev: Trainee GP Barnstaple; Princip. Med. Off. Kwazulu DoH, S. Afr.; SHO (Anaesth.) S.mead Hosp. Bristol.

ROBINSON, Damian Paul Akenside Unit, Newcastle General Hospital, Newcastle upon Tyne NE4 6BE Tel: 0191 273 6666 Fax: 0191 272 2340; 1 Sutton Close, Milton, Cambridge CB4 6DU — MB BChir 1986 Camb.; MA 1986 Camb.; MFPHM RCP (UK) 1995; MRCPsych 1989. (Cambridge) Cons. Psychiat. Newc. City Health Trust. Prev: Sen. Regist. (Pub. Health Med.) E. Anglian RHA; Sen. Regist. Psychiat. E. Anglia.

***ROBINSON, Daniel Michael** 18 Landor Drive, Loughor, Swansea SA4 6GL — MB BS 1998 Lond.; MB BS Lond 1998.

ROBINSON, Mr David (retired) Ridge House, Blind Lane, Wickham PO17 5HD Tel: 01329 833358 Fax: 01329 834873 Email: drpzround@aol.com — MB BS 1962 Lond.; FRCS Eng. 1969; MRCS Eng. LRCP Lond. 1962. Hon. Cons. ENT Surg. Qu. Alexandra Hosp. Cosham; Cons. Otol. MRC Target Trail.

ROBINSON

ROBINSON, David Alan The Cross Farm, Llansoy, Usk NP15 1DE — MB BCh 1979 Wales; BSc (1st cl. Hons. Chem.) Bristol 1973; MRCP (UK) 1983; FRCR 1985. Cons. Radiol. Nevill Hall Hosp., Abergavenny, Gwent. Socs: (Counc.) Brit. Inst. Radiol. Prev: Sen. Regist. Univ. Hosp. Wales, Cardiff; Post-Grad. Research Fell. RPMS Hammersmith Hosp. Lond.

ROBINSON, David Anthony Department of Anaesthetics, Warwick Hospital, Lakin Road, Warwick CV34 5BW Tel: 01926 495321; Thornwood, New Road, Norton Lindsey, Warwick CV35 8JB Tel: 0192 684 3386 — MB BS 1977 Lond.; FFA RCS Eng. 1985. Cons. Anaesth. Warwick Hosp. Socs: Obst. Anaesth. Assn. Prev: Sen. Regist. Nuffield Dept. Anaesth. Oxf.; Sen. Regist. (Anaesth.) P.ss Margt. Hosp. Swindon; Vis. Asst. Prof. Anesthesiol. Univ. Texas Health Sci. Center Texas, USA.

ROBINSON, David Bird NHS Information Authority (Loughborough), Woodgate, Loughborough LE11 2TG Tel: 01509 211411; 149 Swithland Lane, Rothley, Leicester LE7 7SH Tel: 0116 237 4104 Fax: 0870 056 0319 Email: dbr@rothley.demon.co.uk — MB BS 1979 Lond. Prev: Med. Off. Tristan Da Cunha 1984-85.

ROBINSON, David Charles 8 High View, Ponteland, Newcastle upon Tyne NE20 9ET — MB BS 1998 Newc.; MB BS Newc 1998.

ROBINSON, David Cloberry (retired) Yatton Family Practice, 155 Mendip Road, Yatton, Bristol BS49 4ER Tel: 01934 832277 Fax: 01934 876085 — MB BS 1962 Lond.; DObst RCOG 1964. Prev: Ho. Surg. Orpington Hosp.

ROBINSON, Mr David Derek Worcester Royal Infirmary, Castle St., Worcester WR1 3AS Tel: 01905 763333 Fax: 01905 760166; BUPA South Bank, 139 Bath Road, Worcester WR5 3YB Tel: 01905 350003 Fax: 01905 350856 — MB BS 1983 Lond.; MA Camb. 1984; FRCS (Orth.) 1995; FRCS Ed. 1988. Cons. Trauma & Orthop. Worcester Roy. Infirm. Prev: Sen. Regist. Robt. Jones & Agnes Hunt Hosp. OsW.ry.

ROBINSON, David John Culmer 88 Christchurch Avenue, London NW6 7PE — MB BS 1971 Lond.; MRCS Eng. LRCP Lond. 1971; FFA RCS Eng. 1978; DA Eng. 1975. (St. Bart.) Cons. Anaesth. St. Mary's Hosp. Lond. Prev: Anaesth. RN; Ho. Phys. Hackney Hosp.; Ho. Surg. Hillingdon Hosp.

ROBINSON, David Joseph Old School Surgery, School Street, Pontyclun CF72 9AA Tel: 01443 222567 Fax: 01443 229205 — MB BCh 1974 Wales; BSc Wales, MB BCh 1974; MRCGP 1979; DRCOG 1977. Prev: SHO (Paediat.) & (Gen. Med.) E. Glam. Gen. Hosp.

ROBINSON, David Leonard Department of Paediatrics, King George Hospital, Barley Lane, Goodmayes, Ilford IG3 8YB Tel: 020 8970 8063 Fax: 020 8970 8063 Email: david.robinson@rbhc-tr.nthames.nhs.uk; 2 Christchurch Road, Crouch End, London N8 9QL Tel: 020 341 3300 Fax: 020 341 3300 — MSc (Pol./Admin.) Univ. Lond. 1988; MB BS Lond. 1976; MRCP (UK) 1981; MRCS Eng. LRCP Lond. 1976; DCH RCP Lond. 1978. Cons. Paediat. King Geo. Hosp. Ilford. Prev: Lect. & Hon. Sen. Regist. The Lond. Hosp. Whitechapel; Clin. Fell. Neonatol. Hosp. for Sick Childr. Toronto.

ROBINSON, David Nicoll — MB ChB 1985 Glas.; BSc Open 1996; FRCA 1992. Cons. Paediat. Anaesth., Roy. Hosp. For sick chilkdren Yorkhill NHS Trust Glas. Prev: Regist. (Anaesth.) St. Geo. Hosp. Lond.; Cons. Paediatric Anaesth., Roy. Manch. Childr.s Hosp.

ROBINSON, David Timm Rose Cottage, Witton, North Walsham NR28 9UD — MB ChB 1956 Manch.

ROBINSON, Mr David William 25 Oaklands, Miskin, Pontyclun CF72 8RW — MB BS 1981 Lond.; BSc (Hons) Anat. Univ. Lond. 1978; FRCS Glas. 1989.

ROBINSON, David William 143 Scalby Road, Scarborough YO12 6TB Tel: 01723 372365 — BM BCh 1964 Oxf.; MSc Leeds 1969; BSc, BA Oxf. 1963, MA, BM BCh 1964; FRCOG 1990, M 1970. (Oxf. & St. Mary's) Cons. O & G ScarBoro. Health Dist. Socs: N. Engl. Obst. & Gyn. Soc. Prev: Sen. Regist. (O & G) Yorks. RHA; Regist. (O & G) Radcliffe Infirm. Oxf.; Ho. Surg. & Ho. Surg. Obst. St. Mary's Hosp. Lond.

ROBINSON, David William (retired) 2 Brettles Cottages, Beacon Lane, Shalterford, Bewdley DY12 1TJ — MB ChB 1954 Birm.; BSc (Hons.) Birm. 1951, MB ChB 1954. Prev: Ho. Phys. & Ho. Surg. Gen. Hosp. Birm.

ROBINSON, Denis William (retired) 62 Bricknell Avenue, Hull HU5 4JT Tel: 01482 445122 — MB ChB 1943 Ed.

ROBINSON, Derek Axland-Harwood, 15 Claremont Hill, Shrewsbury SY1 1RD Tel: 01743 243414; 10 Kerris Close, St Michaels Wood, Liverpool L17 5BY Tel: 0151 222 4883 — MD Manch. 1961, MB ChB 1952; FFCM 1980, M 1976; DPH Lond. 1959; DCH Eng. 1959; Dip. Amer. Bd. Preven. Med. 1969. (Manch.) Indep. Internat. Epidemiologist & Med. Edr. Shrewsbury. Socs: Fell. Mass. Med. Soc.; BMA. Prev: Dir. Pub. Health Shrops. HA; Sen. Clin. Lect. Liverp. Sch. Trop. Med.; Instruc. & Research Assoc. Harvard Sch. Pub. Health Boston, USA.

ROBINSON, Mr Derek Edward 2 Alma House, 25 Alma Road, Clifton, Bristol BS8 2BZ Tel: 0117 923 9041 — MB ChB 1990 Manch.; BSc (Hons.) Physiol. Manch. 1990, MB ChB (Hons.) 1993; FRCS (Ed); FRCS (Eng). (Manchester) Specialist Regist. Orthop., Bristol.

ROBINSON, Derek Keith 12 Ty-Mawr Road, Llandaff North, Cardiff CF14 2FN — MB BS 1989 Newc.

ROBINSON, Derek Shillito (retired) Walnut Tree Cottage, Evenlode, Moreton-in-Marsh GL56 0NP — MB BS 1952 Lond.; MRCS Eng. LRCP Lond. 1952. Prev: Ho. Surg., Ho. Phys. & Cas. Off. Cheltenham Gen. Hosp.

***ROBINSON, Diane Elizabeth** 26 Harwood Court, Trimdon Grange, Trimdon Station TS29 6HU — MB BS 1996 Newc.

ROBINSON, Diane Patricia Mourneside Medical Centre, 1A Ballycolman Avenue, Strabane BT82 9AF Tel: 028 7138 3737 Fax: 028 7138 3979; 12 Edgewater, New Buildings, Londonderry BT47 2TE — MB BCh BAO 1983 Belf.; MRCGP 1987; DRCOG 1986.

ROBINSON, Douglas Joseph Denton Park Health Centre, Denton Park Centre, West Denton Way, Newcastle upon Tyne NE5 2QZ Tel: 0191 267 2751 Fax: 0191 264 1588; Tel: 0191 285 8269 — MB BS 1979 Newc.; MRCGP 1984; D.Occ.Med. RCP Lond. 1996; Zeneca Prize Faculty of Occupational Medicine, RCP London 1997. Princip. GP Newc. Prev: GP Hetton Le Hole, Co Durh.; Occupat. Phys. Pipeline Integrity InterNat. & Brit. Gas 1993-2001.

ROBINSON, Douglas Keith (retired) 78 Grafton Way, London W1T 6JF — MB BChir 1954 Camb.; MA, MB Camb. 1954, BChir 1953; DCH Eng. 1957. Prev: Assoc. Specialist Jas. Pringle Ho. Middlx. Hosp. Lond.

ROBINSON, Douglas Stewart Flat 3, 7 Sussex Square, Brighton BN2 1FJ — MB BChir 1984 Camb.

ROBINSON, Elizabeth Angela Eleanor National Blood Authority, Oak House, Reeds Crescent, Watford WD24 4QN Tel: 01923 486820 Fax: 01923 486801; Low Brandon Farm, Brandon Crescent, Shadwell, Leeds LS17 9JH — MB BS Lond. 1967; MRCS Eng. LRCP Lond. 1967; FRCPath 1986, M 1973. (St. Mary's) Med. Dir. Socs: Founder Mem. Brit. Blood Transfus. Soc.; UK Director Europ. Soc. Haemapheresis. - Founder Mem.; Mem. of ISBT. Prev: Chief Exec. Yorks Regional Transfus. Centre Leeds.; Hon. Sen. Clin. Lect. Dept. Med. Leeds Gen. Infirm. & St. Jas. Univ. Hosp.

ROBINSON, Elizabeth Anne (retired) Tanners Pool, Alkerton, Banbury OX15 6NL — LMSSA Lond. 1957. Assoc. Specialist Horton Gen. Hosp. Banbury. Prev: Assoc.Specialist Horton Gen.Hosp.Banbury.

ROBINSON, Elizabeth Mary O'Keefe 14 Queens Park Rise, Brighton BN2 2ZF Tel: 01273 609971 Fax: 01273 609971 Email: shez@mistral.co.uk; 14 Queens Park Rise, Brighton BN2 2ZF Tel: 01273 609971 Fax: 01273 609971 — MB BS 1964 Lond.; DObst RCOG 1966. (St. Mary's) Prev: Sen. GP E. Grinstead.

ROBINSON, Emiko Terasaki Wolfson College, Linton Road, Oxford OX2 6UD — LRCP LRCS Ed. LRCPS Glas. 1995.

ROBINSON, Emma Kate East Sussex Brighton and Hove Health Authority, 36-38 Friars Walk, Lewes BN7 2PB Tel: 01273 485300 Fax: 01273 403600 — MB BS 1991 Lond.; MSc Lond. 1998. (Guy's (United Medical and Dental Schools)) Sen. Resist. (Pub. Health Med.) E. Sussex Brighton & Hove HA. Socs: BMA; Train. Mem. Fac. Pub. Health Med.; Soc. Social Med.

ROBINSON, Ernest Thomson, OBE, TD (retired) 132 Prestonfield, Milngavie, Glasgow G62 7QA Tel: 0141 563 7409 Email: et.robinson@cableol.co.uk — MB ChB 1959 Glas.; FRCGP 1977, M 1963; DObst RCOG 1962. Chairm. (Counc.) St. And. Ambul. Assn. Prev: Maj. RAMC (TA) Regtl. Med. Off. 154 Regt. RCT (TA).

ROBINSON, Finlay McLean The Surgery, 4 Stoke Road, Bishops Cleeve, Cheltenham GL52 8RP Tel: 01242 672007 — MB ChB

ROBINSON

1975 Dundee; BSc (Med. Sci.) St. And. 1972; MRCGP 1982; DCH Eng. 1978; DRCOG 1977.

ROBINSON, Fiona Margaret 64 Eversden Road, Harlton, Cambridge CB3 7ET — MB ChB 1983 Glas.; MRCOG 1990. Regist. (O & G) W. Scotl. Rotat. Scheme.

ROBINSON, Fiona Osborne The Dell, 17 Lawrie Park Crescent, London SE26 6HH Fax: 020 7346 3738 — MB BCh BAO 1986 Belf.; MRCP (UK) 1989; DO RCPSI 1991; FRCOphth 1992. Cons. (Ophth.) Kings Coll. Hosp. Lond. Socs: Counc. Mem. RSM. Prev: Fell. with Dr Serge Morax, Foundat. Rothschild, Paris; Fell. with Dr Alan McNab Melbourne, Australia; Fell. with Mr Richard Collin. Lond.

ROBINSON, Florence Lydia 6 Dillon Heights, Armagh BT61 9HF — MB BCh BAO 1959 Belf.

ROBINSON, Frances Eileen Occupational Health Centre, Purdysborn Hospital, Saintfield Road, Belfast BT8 8BH Tel: 01232 401333; 15 Newforge Lane, Belfast BT9 5NT — MB BCh BAO 1963 Belf.; MRCGP 1972; DObst RCOG 1968; DCH RCPS Glas. 1965. (Qu. Univ. Belf.) Socs: BMA. Prev: Med. Off. Qu. Eliz. Hosp. Bridgetown Barbados, Cheltenham Gen.; esbyt. Mission Hosp. Chogoria, Kenya.

ROBINSON, Frances Lenore Josephine 13 Rosemary Park, Malone Road, Belfast BT9 — MD 1952 Belf.; MB BCh BAO 1947; DCH Eng. 1952; On Staff North. Irel. Fev. Hosp. Belf.

ROBINSON, Frances Patricia 8 Georgian Villas, Omagh BT79 0AT — MD 1987 Belf.; Dip. Pall. Med 1997; MB BCh BAO Belf. 1977; FFA RCSI 1981. Cons. Anaesth. with s/i in Pain Relief and Palliat. Med., Sperrin Lakeland Health & Social Care Trust. Prev: Cons. Anaesth. Tyrone Co. Hosp. Omagh.

ROBINSON, Gareth Mark 7 Buckhurst Road, Frimley Green, Camberley GU16 6LH Tel: 01252 836610 — MB BS 1993 Lond. Trainee GP Frimley Pk. Hosp. VTS.

ROBINSON, Garrett Joseph (retired) 2 Thornfield Grove, Sunderland SR2 7UZ Tel: 0191 567 4144 — MB BCh BAO NUI 1951.

ROBINSON, Geoffrey Brian c/o Lloyds TSB Bank plc, Lloyds Court, 28 Secklow Gate, Milton Keynes MK9 3EH; 5 Shouler Close, Shenley Church End, Milton Keynes MK5 6DZ Tel: 01908 505289 Fax: 0870 056 6397 Email: brian@musicweaver.demon.co.uk — MB BCh BAO 1961 Dub.; MA Dub. 1962; DClinHyp (Distinc.) Univ. Lond. 1994; DPM Eng. 1967. Socs: Brit. Soc. Experim. & Clin. Hypn.

ROBINSON, Geoffrey John Lake Road Health Centre, Nutfield Place, Portsmouth PO1 4JT Tel: 023 9282 1201 Fax: 023 9287 5658; 19 Montgomery Road, Havant PO9 2RH Tel: 023 92 471212 Email: geoff.robinson@btinternet.com — BM 1979 Soton.; BM (Distinc. Clin. Med.) Soton. 1979; MRCGP (Distinc.) 1983; DRCOG 1981; DCH Eng. 1981; DFFP 1996. (Southampton University) GP Trainer Portsmouth; Non-Exec. Dir. Portsmouth HA.

ROBINSON, Geoffrey Lawrence (retired) 5 The Green, Denbury, Newton Abbot TQ12 6DQ Tel: 01803 812996 — MB BChir 1931 Camb.; MA Camb. 1931, MD 1942; MRCS Eng. LRCP Lond. 1929; FRCPath 1964.

ROBINSON, George Anthony (retired) 23 Essa Road, Saltash PL12 4ED Tel: 01752 843722 — MRCS Eng. LRCP Lond. 1942; MRCGP 1966. Prev: Admiralty Surg. & Agent.

ROBINSON, George Clive 22 Lumsden Street, Glasgow G3 8RG — MB ChB 1988 Glas.

ROBINSON, Gillian Ada 27 Frondeg, Llandegfan, Menai Bridge LL59 5TN — BM 1978 Soton.; FRCS Ed. 1985; DO RCS Eng. 1983.

ROBINSON, Gillian Anna Room 1, The Avenue, St Stephens Road, Norwich NR1 3SR — MB BCh 1993 Wales.

ROBINSON, Gillian Elizabeth Flat 7, The Nightingales, 23 Nightingale Lane, London SW12 8TN — MB BS 1980 Lond.

ROBINSON, Gillian Mary 22 The Mall, London N14 6LN — MB BS 1990 Lond.

ROBINSON, Gordon 69 Swanland Road, Hessle HU13 0NN Tel: 01482 648721 — MB ChB 1954 Leeds. Socs: BMA. Prev: Surg. Lt. RNVR; Resid. Obst. Off. Staincliffe Gen. Hosp. Dewsbury; Cas. Off. Roy. Infirm. Bradford.

ROBINSON, Graham Robert Edward Oakhurst, 146 Barnham Road, Barnham, Bognor Regis PO22 0EH Tel: 01243 553259 — MB BS 1996 Lond.; MRCP Part 1 1999. SHO (p/t) (Med.) Worthing Hosp. W. Sussex; Specialist Regist., Radiol., St. Geo. Hosp. Lond.

Socs: Roy. Soc. Med. Prev: Ho. Phys. Worthing Hosp.; Ho. Surg. Roy. Sussex Co. Hosp. Brighton; SHO,(Geriat., St Geo.'s Hosp.).

ROBINSON, Grant Trafford Michael 3 Faraday Road, Wimbledon, London SW19 8PE Tel: 020 8543 1813 — MB BS 1986 Lond.; BSc (Hons.) Lond. 1983, MB BS 1986; MRCP (UK) 1989. Regist. (Haemat.) St. Geo. Hosp. Lond.

ROBINSON, Gwyneth Jean Hillfield, Broadway, Weymouth DT3 4JD Tel: 0130 581 4833 — MB ChB Glas. 1955.

***ROBINSON, Hazel Alice** 29 High Street, Toller Porcorum, Dorchester DT2 0DN Tel: 01300 320961 — MB ChB 1994 Bristol.

ROBINSON, Heather Yvonne Torbay Hospital, Lawes Bridge, Torquay TQ2 7AA Tel: 01803 614567; 22 Bonython Road, Newquay TR7 3AN — MB ChB 1989 Aberd. Regist. (Psychiat.) Torbay Hosp. Socs: BMA & Roy. Coll. Psychiat. Prev: SHO (Psychiat.) Torbay Hosp.; Ho. Off. (Med.) W. Cornw. Hosp.

ROBINSON, Helen Judith Department of Community Paediatrics, St. John's Hospital at Howden, Howden Road W., Livingston EH54 6PP Tel: 01506 419666; 167 Craiglea Drive, Edinburgh EH10 5PT Tel: 0131 447 1884 — MB BS 1974 Lond.; MRCS Eng. LRCP Lond. 1974; MRCGP 1980; DCH RCPS Glas. 1977. (Roy. Free) Staff Grade Paediat. (Community Child Health) St. Johns. Hosp. Howden. Socs: BMA; SACCH; Wom. Med. Federat. Prev: GP Edin. & Livingston; SHO (O & G) Bangour Gen. Hosp. Broxburn.

ROBINSON, Hercules Christopher Douglas TRH 110A Swansea Road, Pontlliw, Swansea SA4 1EJ; 61 Westland Avenue, West Cross, Swansea SA3 5NR Tel: 01792 405723 — MB BS 1974 Lond.; BSc Lond. 1971; MRCS Eng. LRCP Lond. 1974. Med. Adviser. Prev: GP Penclewold Health Centre; GP Cobham Health Centre.

ROBINSON, Hillary Ina (retired) The Old Rectory, Edmundbyers, Consett DH8 9NQ Tel: 01207 255634 — MRCS Eng. LRCP Lond. 1965; FRCS Eng. 1974. Hon. Lect. Univ. Zambia Med. Sch.; Chairm. WOC (UK). Prev: Cons.Orthop. Surg. Shotley Bridge Gen. Hosp. Cons.

ROBINSON, Holly 10 Toberdowney Valley, Ballynure, Ballyclare BT39 9TS — MB BCh BAO 1996 Belf.

ROBINSON, Hugh Malcolm (retired) 14 Meads Road, Seaford BN25 1SY Tel: 01323 893157 — MRCS Eng. LRCP Lond. 1943. Prev: Flight Lt. RAF Med. Br.

ROBINSON, Ian Clive Broom Leys Surgery, Broom Leys Road, Coalville LE67 4DE Tel: 01530 832095; Bay Tree House, 134 The Moor, Coleorton, Coalville LE67 8GF Tel: 01530 835170 Fax: 01530 835170 — MB BS 1978 Lond.; BSc Lond. 1975; DRCOG 1982; Cert. Family Plann. JCC 1982. (Univ. Coll. Hosp.) Clin. Asst. (Clin. Genetics) Leicester Roy. Infirm.; PCG Bd. Mem. NW Leics. PCG (Finance Commiss.ing Lead). Prev: Trainee GP Leics. VTS; Ho. Phys. Roy. United Hosp. Bath; Ho. Surg. Frimley Pk. Hosp. Frimley.

ROBINSON, Ian Frank Gaywood Whitehall Hotel, Tywyn LL36 9DF Tel: 01654 710212 — MRCS Eng. LRCP Lond. 1960. (Lond. Hosp.) Socs: BMA & Med. Soc. Nova Scotia. Prev: Squadron Ldr. RAF Med. Br.

ROBINSON, Ian Hardy, VRD (retired) Sherwood, 26 Fitzroy Road, Fleet, Aldershot GU51 4JJ Tel: 01252 613897 — MB BChir Camb. 1951; FFA RCS Eng. 1971; DA Eng. 1969; DObst RCOG 1956. Prev: Cons. Anaesth. Frimley Pk. Hosp.

ROBINSON, Ian Henry Warnock 59 Ballymena Road, Ballymoney BT53 7EZ — MB ChB 1998 Ed.; MB ChB Ed 1998.

ROBINSON, Ian Stuart Occupational Health Unit, Force Headquarters, Northumbria Police, Ponteland, Newcastle upon Tyne NE20 0BL Tel: 01661 868865 Fax: 01661 868818; The Old Dairy, Rothley Mill, Hartburn, Morpeth NE61 4ED Tel: 01670 774298 Email: occdocrob@msn.com — MB ChB 1972 Sheff.; DObst RCOG 1974; D Occ med 1999; AFOM 1999. Sen. Occupat. Health Phys. N.umbria Police Force Ponteland; Princip. Med. Dir. Police Nat. Diving Sch.; Hon. Cons. S. Tyneside Dist. Gen. Hosp. Socs: Brit. Med. Acupunct. Soc.; Assn. Local Auth. Med. Advisers; Soc. Occupat. Med. Prev: GP Sheff.; Med. Dir. Cavendish Centre.

ROBINSON, Innes (retired) Cappelle, Wereton Road, Audley, Stoke-on-Trent ST7 8EN Tel: 01782 720589 — MB ChB 1949 Birm. Prev: Ho. Phys. N. Staffs. Roy. Infirm. Stoke-on-Trent.

ROBINSON, Ira Ellen 12 Stevenage Road, London SW6 6ES — MB BS 1991 Lond.

ROBINSON, Ivan Alexandre Department of Histopathology, Derbyshire Royal Infirmary, Derby Tel: 01332 347141 Email:

ROBINSON

ivanrobinson@sdah-tr.trent.nhs.uk; 44 St. Bernard's Road, Solihull B92 8NY Tel: 0121 743 7325 Email: dr.robinson@btinternet.com — MB BCh BAO 1985 NUI; MRCPI 1988; LRCPSI 1985; MRCPath 1993. Cons. Histopath. Derbysh. Roy. Infirm. Socs: Path. Soc.; Assn. Clin. Paths.; Brit. Soc. for Oral and Maxillofacial Path. Prev: Sen. Regist. (Histopath. & Cytopath.) St. Geo. Hosp. Lond. & Roy. Surrey Co. Hosp. Guildford.

ROBINSON, Ivor Frantisek St Johns Way Medical Centre, 96 St. Johns Way, London N19 3RN Tel: 020 7272 1585 Fax: 020 7561 1237; 1 The Chine, London N10 3PX Tel: 020 8883 8165 Email: ivorrobinson@hotmail.com — MB ChB 1970 Birm.; DObst RCOG 1972; Cert FPA 1972. (Birm.) Med. Off. Highgate Sch. Lond.; Chairm. CAMIDOC Lond. Socs: Med. Assn. Victims of Torture; BMA. Prev: Hon. Clin. Asst. Whittington Hosp.; Occupat. Health Med. Adviser Performing Righ Soc. Lond. & Whittington Hosp. Lond.; Staff Health Off. St. Mary's Hosp. Lond.

ROBINSON, James (retired) 11 Goose Cote Hill, Egerton, Bolton BL7 9UQ Tel: 01204 307294 — MB ChB Manch. 1950; MRCGP 1958. Prev: GP. Bolton.

ROBINSON, James 7 Squirrel Walk, Acresford Road, Overseal, Swadlincote DE12 6NL — MB ChB 1967 Ed.

ROBINSON, James Andrew 116 Lancaster Road, Salford M6 8AW — BM BCh 1989 Oxf.

ROBINSON, James Edward 7 Dawlish Avenue, Chadderton, Oldham OL9 0RF — MB ChB 1996 Manch.

ROBINSON, Mr James Milner Gloucester Royal Hospital, ENT Department, Great Western Road, Gloucester GL1 3NN Tel: 01452 394207 Fax: 01452 394432; High Meadows, Yartleton Lane, May Hill, Longhope GL17 0RF Tel: 01452 830612 — MB BS 1966 Lond.; FRCS Eng. 1973. (St. Bart.) Cons. ENT Surg. Gloucester Roy. Hosp. Socs: Brit. Assn. Otol.; Roy. Soc. Med. (Ex-Pres. Sect. Otol.). Prev: Sen. Regist. (ENT) United Bristol Hosps.; Sen. Regist. Roy. Nat. Throat, Nose & Ear Hosp. Lond.; Ho. Surg. (ENT) St. Bart. Hosp. Lond.

ROBINSON, Jana Ordsall Health Centre, Regent Park Surgery, Belfort Drive, Salford M5 3PP Tel: 0161 872 2021 Fax: 0161 877 3592; 3A Bowgreen Road, Bowdon, Altrincham WA14 3LX — MRCS Eng. LRCP Lond. 1971. (Lond. Hosp.) Prev: Regist. (Paediat.) Whipps Cross Hosp. Lond.; SHO Qu. Eliz. Hosp. for Childr. Lond.; SHO Lond. Hosp.

ROBINSON, Jane Elizabeth Rebecca 27 Bainbrigge Road, Leeds LS6 3AD Tel: 0113 2740 666 — MB ChB 1995 Leeds. SHO Psychiat. High Royds Hosp. Meston, Nr. Ire. Socs: MPS; MMS; BMA. Prev: SHO (Psychiat.), St. James Hosp, Leeds; SHO (Oncol.) Cookridge Hosp, Leeds; SHO (A&E) Ponte Fralt, Gen. Infirm., Ponte Fralt.

ROBINSON, Jane Emma 30 Wheatley Avenue, Normanton WF6 1HN — MB BS 1993 Lond.

ROBINSON, Jane Freya Dr Dickson & Partners, 7/8 Park St., Ripon HG4 — MB ChB 1982 Leeds; MRCGP 1986; DCH RCP Lond. 1986; DRCOG 1985. Retainee GP, Ripon. Prev: Clin. Med. Off. Hull HA; GP Princip., Montague Med. Centre, Goole.

ROBINSON, Janet Frances Cheslyn Cornergates, Repton, Derby DE65 6GG — MB BChir 1949 Camb.; MA, MB BChir Camb. 1949. (Camb. & Roy. Free)

ROBINSON, Jean Grace Department of Child & Family Psychiatry, Royal Aberdeen Childrens Hospital, Aberdeen AB25 2ZG Tel: 01224 552706 Email: jean.robinson@arh.grampian.scot.nhs.uk; South Leylodge Farmhouse., Leylodge, Kintore, Keith AB55 0XY — MB ChB Aberd. 1977; MRCPsych 1982. Cons. Child & Adolesc. Psychiat. Roy. Aberd. Childr.'s Hosp.

ROBINSON, Miss Jean Margaret Burton House, Withington Hospital, Nell Lane, Manchester M20 2LR Tel: 0161 445 8111 Fax: 0161 291 3425 — MB ChB 1971 Manch.; MD Manch. 1986; FRCP Lond. 1991; MRCP (UK) 1978. Cons. Geriat. Med. Withington Hosp. Manch. Socs: Brit. Geriat. Soc. Prev: Lect., Hon. Cons. & Hon. Sen. Regist. (Geriat. Med.) Withington Hosp. Manch.; Regist. (Gen. Med.) N.. Gen. Hosp. Sheff.

ROBINSON, Jill Alexandra Tryst Medical Centre, 431 King St., Stenhousemuir, Larbert FK5 4HT Tel: 01324 551555; 9 Greenhorn's Well, Well Avenue, Falkirk FK1 5HL Tel: 01324 36092 — MB ChB 1986 Ed.; MRCGP 1990; DRCOG 1988. p/t Long term Locum GP StenHo.muir; Clin. Asst. Roy. Scott. Nat. Hosp. For Ment. Handicap.

Prev: Partner GP Pract. Stirling; Trainee GP Tryst Med. Centre Larbert; Trainee GP/SHO (Psychiat.) Bellsdyke Hosp. Larbert VTS.

ROBINSON, Jo-Anne Patricia 36 Carr Lane, Willerby, Hull HU10 6JW — MB BS 1992 Newc. SHO (Psychiat.) Norwich. Prev: SHO (Paediat.) Norwich.

ROBINSON, Joan Florence Haringey Health Care Trust, St. Ann's Hospital, St Ann's Road, London N15; New River Health Authority, Public Health Department, Alexander Place, Lower Park Road, London N11 — MB BS 1959 Lond.; MFPHM 1972; DPH Eng. 1963; DCH Eng. 1962. Sen. Med. Off. Haringey Health Care Trust & New River HA. Socs: Assoc. Mem. BPA; Harv. Soc. Prev: Sen. Med. Off. Lond. Boro. Haringey.

ROBINSON, Joanna Patricia Jane Barnes Close Surgery, Barnes Close, Sturminster Newton DT10 1BN Tel: 01258 474500 Fax: 01258 471547 — MB BS 1983 Lond.; MRCGP 1987; DFFP 1993; DCH RCP Lond. 1987; DRCOG 1986; Cert. Family Plann. JCC 1986. (Char. Cross) Retained GP Sturminster Newton Barnes Cl. Surg. Prev: Trainee GP E.bourne VTS; SHO (Gen. Med.) St. Mary's Hosp. E.bourne; SHO (O & G, Paediat. & A & E) E.bourne Dist. Gen. Hosp.

ROBINSON, John Charles Newbury Street Practice, Newbury Street, Wantage OX12 7AY Tel: 01235 763451; Fairstead, Old Manor Court, Letcombe Regis, Wantage OX12 9JL Email: jcrobinson@cosi.com — MB ChB 1977 Bristol; MRCGP 1982; DFFP 1993; DRCOG 1980; DA Eng. 1979. GP; Med. Cons. to AAH Meditel. Prev: Trainee GP Avon VTS; SHO (Anaesth.) Roy. United Hosp. Bath.

ROBINSON, John Easton (retired) Padeswood Lodge, Padeswood, Mold CH7 4JF Tel: 01244 546420 — MB BChir 1957; MA Camb. 1958,; FFA RCS Eng. 1964; DA Eng. 1961. Prev: Cons. Anaesth.Chester Dist. Hosp.

ROBINSON, John Francis Lancing Health Centre, Penstone Park, Lancing BN15 9AG Tel: 01903 763144; The Willows, Mill Lane, High Salvington, Worthing BN13 3DJ — MB BS 1977 Lond.; DRCOG 1980. (St. Geo.)

ROBINSON, John Franklin 7 Farrant House, Winstanley Estate, Winstanley Road, London SW11 2ES Tel: 020 8741 0238; 41 Castelnau Mansions, Barnes Castelnau, London SW13 9QU — MB BCh 1943 Witwatersrand. (Witwatersrand) Med. Advis. Hamblin Film & Video (Med. & Scientif.); Script Writer & Edr. Adviser Med. Computer Animation Magic Touch Videographics Lond. Prev: Med. Dir. Med. Ltd. (Med. & Sci. Films) Lincoln; Resid. Surg. Off. Germiston Hosp.; Regist. (Med.) Johannesburg Gen. & Baragwanath Hosps.

ROBINSON, John Frederick 35 Dumgoyne Drive, Bearsden, Glasgow G61 3AW Tel: 0141 942 1861 — MB BS 1954 Lond.; FRCP Lond. 1975, M 1960. Cons. Phys. S.. Gen. Hosp. Glas.

ROBINSON, John Graham Meadowcroft Surgery, Jackson Road, Aylesbury HP19 9EX Tel: 01296 425775 Fax: 01296 330324 — MB BS 1977 Lond.; BSc Lond. 1970; MRCGP 1981; DRCOG 1980. (Royal London Hospital)

ROBINSON, John Richard (retired) 480 Banbury Road, Oxford OX2 8EN Tel: 01865 57128 — MB BS Lond. 1954; FRCPsych. 1982, M 1972; DPM Eng. 1964. Hon. Cons. Psychiat.. Oxf. Ment. Health care NHS Trust. Prev: Nuffield Research Fell. Psychiat. Littlemore Hosp. Oxf.

***ROBINSON, John Robert** Flat 2, 8 Keppel St., Plymouth PL2 1BU — MB ChB 1986 Sheff.

ROBINSON, John Stanley 49 Mavis Drive, Wirral CH49 0UN — MB ChB 1981 Liverp.

ROBINSON, Professor John Stanley 43 Goodby Road, Moseley, Birmingham B13 8RH Tel: 0121 449 8370 Fax: 0121 449 2828 Email: profrob@msn.com — MB ChB 1953 Liverp.; MD Liverp. 1960; FFA RCS Eng. 1958; DA Eng. 1957. (Liverp.) Emerit. Prof. Univ. Birm.; Hon. Cons. Anaesth. W. Midl. RHA; Non.-Exec. Dir. W. Midl. Ambul. Serv. Trust. Socs: Assn. Anaesth. Prev: Prof. Anaesth. Univ. Birm.; Cons. Anaesth. Liverp. RHB; Demonst. (Anaesth.) Univ. Liverp.

ROBINSON, Jonathan Mark 2 Shangarry Park, Belfast BT14 8JD — MB BCh BAO 1988 Belf.; MRCP (UK) 1991.

ROBINSON, Miss Joy 3 Greenhead Park, Bamford, Hope Valley S33 0AS — MB ChB 1992 Sheff.; FRCS Lond. 1997. Surg. Research Assoc. Univ. of Sheff. Socs: BMA; MDU.

ROBINSON, Joyce Mawgan (retired) South Lodge, Great Bardfield, Braintree CM7 4SD Tel: 01371 810511 Fax: 01371

ROBINSON

811428 Email: joyce.antcliffe@btinternet — MB BS Lond. 1961; MRCS Eng. LRCP Lond. 1961. Prev: Ho. Surg. & Ho. Phys. Dulwich Hosp.

ROBINSON, Karen Anne Medical Centre, Easthope Road, Church Stretton SY6 6BL Tel: 01694 722127; Lymehurst, Longhills Road, Church Stretton SY6 6DS — MB ChB 1979 Bristol; MRCGP 1984; DRCOG 1982. (Bristol) GP Trainer.

ROBINSON, Karen Anne 36 South Esk Road, London E7 8EY — MB BS 1996 Lond.

ROBINSON, Karen Elizabeth 176 Main Street, High Blantyre, Blantyre, Glasgow G72 0ER — MB ChB 1991 Glas.

ROBINSON, Katharine Jane 101 Wood Vale, London N10 3DL — MB BS 1996 Lond.

ROBINSON, Katharine Natasha General Hospital, Cliftonville, Northampton NN1 5BD Tel: 01604 634700 Fax: 01604 235670 Email: sprigings.robinson@cableol.co.uk; The Granary, 6 Raynsford Road, Dallington, Northampton NN5 7HP Fax: 01604 478107 Email: sprigings.robmsn@cableol.co.uk — MB BS 1978 Lond.; BA Oxf. 1975; MRCP (UK) 1980; FRCA Eng. 1983. (St. Thos.) Cons. Anaesth. N.ampton Gen. Hosp. Socs: Assn. Anaesth.; Intens. Care Soc.; SCATA. Prev: Cons. Anaesth. Brook Hosp. Lond.; Sen. Regist. (Anaesth.) Brompton Hosp. Nat. Hosp. for Neurol. Lond. & Roy. Free Hosp.; Regist. Nuffield Dept. Anaesth. Oxf.

ROBINSON, Katherine Anne 110 North Parade, Ormeau Road, Belfast BT7 — MB BCh BAO 1990 Belf.

ROBINSON, Kathryn Margaret Liverpool House Surgery, 69 Risedale Road, Barrow-in-Furness LA13 9QY Tel: 01229 832232 Fax: 01229 432156 — MB ChB 1989 Dundee; MRCGP 1994. Socs: Brit. Assn. Med. Acupunct.s.

ROBINSON, Keith, OStJ Rockcliffe, Old Chester Road, Helsby, Warrington WA6 9NW Tel: 01928 722277 — MB ChB Manch. 1948; MFOM RCP Lond. 1981; DIH Eng. 1977. (Manch.) Cleanaway Ltd. Ellesmere Port & Barber Chestergate Cereals Div. Deeside. Socs: Soc. Occupat. Med. Prev: Med. Adviser Optical Fibres Deeside; Med. Off. Schering Agrochem. Ltd. Widnes; Sen. Med. Off. BICC PLC.

ROBINSON, Keith Buxton West Winds, Hampsterley, Bishop Auckland DL13 3QD — MB BS 1966 Durh.; FRCPath 1987, M 1975. Cons. (Histopath.) Dryburn Hosp. Durh.

ROBINSON, Keith Douglas Stoneleigh, 55 Ashwell Road, Heaton, Bradford BD9 4AX Tel: 01274 828994 — MB ChB 1958 Ed.; MRCGP 1969; DObst RCOG 1960. Med. Adviser Allied Colloids plc. Bradford. Socs: Soc. Occupat. Med.; Brit. Assn. Sport & Med.

ROBINSON, Kenneth Francis (retired) Cornergates, The Pastures, Repton, Derby DE65 6GG Tel: 01283 702183 — MRCS Eng. LRCP Lond. 1950; MA, MB BChir Camb. 1950; DObst RCOG 1954. Prev: GP Derbys.

ROBINSON, Kenneth Roger Health Centre, Newgate Street, Worksop S80 1HP Tel: 01909 500266 Fax: 01909 478014; Woodhurst, Sparken Hill, Worksop S80 1AX — MI NUI 1983; DRCOG 1985.

ROBINSON, Kerry Abigail 63 Queens Crescent, Chalk Farm, London NW5 4ES — MB BS 1997 Lond.

ROBINSON, Mr Kingsley Peter 75 Robin Hood Lane, Kingston Vale, London SW15 3QR — MRCS Eng. LRCP Lond. 1955; MS Lond. 1964, MB BS 1955; FRCS Ed. 1959; FRCS Eng. 1959. (Westm.) Cons. Surg. W.m. Hosp. Lond. & Qu. Mary's Hosp. Roehampton; Dir. Limb Surg. Unit Roehampton; Hon. Cons. Surg. New Vict. Hosp. Kingston upon Thames. Socs: Fell. Roy. Soc. Med.; Vasc. Surg. Soc. Gt. Brit. & Irel. Prev: Sen. Lect. Surg. Unit W.m. Hosp. Lond.

ROBINSON, Laura Anne 45 Oak Tree Road, Kendal LA9 6AN — BM BCh 1998 Oxf.; BM BCh Oxf 1998.

ROBINSON, Mr Lee Quenby 88 Barnston Road, Wirral CH60 1UB Tel: 0151 342 2390 — MB ChB 1978 Liverp.; ChM Liverp. 1990; FRCS (Urol) 1992; FRCS Eng. 1984. Cons. Urol. Warrington Hosp. NHS Trust.

ROBINSON, Lena Forest View, Hawthorn Lane, Farnham Common, Slough SL2 3SW Tel: 01753 643246 Fax: 01753 643246 — MB BS Lond. 1962; FRCPath 1996, M 1984. (St. Bart.) Late Sen. Med. Off. DoH Lond. (Food Safety Div.).; Med. Examr. for Benefits Agency. Prev: Sen. Regist. (Med. Microbiol.) Char. Cross Hosp. Lond.

ROBINSON, Lili Ostberg Radiology Department, Leicester Royal Infirmary, Infirmary Square, Leicester LE1 5WW Tel: 0116 254 1414; 8 Outwoods Road, Loughborough LE11 3LY — MB ChB 1975 Leeds; FRCR 1982; DA Eng. 1977. Cons. Radiol. Leicester Roy. Infirm. NHS Trust. Prev: Cons. Radiol. Qu. Mary's Hosp. Sidcup; Sen. Regist. & Regist. (Radiol.) St. Geo. Hosp. Lond.

ROBINSON, Linda Joy 275 Moor Road, Chorley PR7 2NN — MB ChB 1994 Leeds.

ROBINSON, Lisa Giselle Department of Haematology, University Hospital of Wales, Heath Park, Cardiff CF14 4XW Tel: 029 2074 7747; 7 Pontcanna Street, Cardiff CF11 9HQ — MB BS 1990 Lond.; MRCP (UK) 1993; DRCPath 1995. Clin. Lect. & Hon. Sen. Regist. (Haemat.) Univ. Wasles Coll. Med. Cardiff. Prev: Regist. (Haemat.) Roy. Free Hosp. Lond.

ROBINSON, Louise Ann Saville Medical Group, 7 Saville Place, Newcastle upon Tyne NE1 8DQ Tel: 0191 232 4274 Fax: 0191 233 1050; 8 Westfield Avenue, Gosforth, Newcastle upon Tyne NE3 4YH Tel: 0191 285 4793 — MB BS 1985 Newc.; MRCGP 1989; DCH Lond. 1988. Sen. Lect. (Primary Health Care) Univ. Newc. Prev: GP Sunderland.

ROBINSON, Louise Helen Orchard Lodge, Old Road, Harbertonford, Totnes TQ9 7TA Tel: 01803 732879 — MB BS 1985 Lond.; FCAnaesth 1990. Staff Grade Doctor (Anaesth.) Torbay HA. Prev: SHO (A & E) Poole Gen. Hosp.; SHO (Geriat.) Mt. Gould Hosp. Plymouth; Ho. Surg. Roy. Vict. Hosp. Boscombe.

*****ROBINSON, Lucy** 12 The Circle, Birmingham B17 9EE — MB ChB 1995 Birm.; ChB Birm. 1995.

ROBINSON, Madeleine Christina West Timperley Medical Centre, 277 Manchester Road, West Timperley, Altrincham WA14 5PQ Tel: 0161 962 4351 Fax: 0161 962 8410; Rose Cottage, Sunbank Lane, Ringway, Altrincham WA15 0PZ Tel: 0161 980 3087 — MB ChB 1974 Ed.; DRCOG 1981. (Ed.)

ROBINSON, Magda 12 Hayfield Road, Oxford OX2 6TT — BM 1993 Soton.; BM (Hons.) Soton. 1993; DFFP 1994. (Soton.) Sessional Med. Off. (Family Plann.) Brook Advis. Serv. Lond.

ROBINSON, Margaret Osborne Practice Surgery, 25 Osborne Road, Southsea PO5 3ND Tel: 023 9282 1371; 11 Great Southsea Street, Southsea PO5 3BY Fax: 01705 738587 — BM 1982 Soton.; MRCGP 1988. (Southampton) SHO (Med. Rotat.) Qu. Alexandra's Hosp. Portsmouth. Socs: Soc. Med.; Med. & Dent. Hypn. Soc. Metrop. Br.; Med. & Scientif. Network Gp.

ROBINSON, Margaret Denise 210 Whitchurch Road, Cardiff CF14 3NB Tel: 029 2062 1282; 9 Cefn Coed Gardens, Cyncoed, Cardiff CF23 6AX — MB BCh 1979 Wales; BSc (Hons.) (Physiol.) Wales 1974, MB BCh 1979; DRCOG 1982.

ROBINSON, Margaret Mary (retired) Swn-y-Fenai, Bryn Ffynon Road, Port Dinorwic LL56 4SJ Tel: 01248 670389 — BA (Hons.) Wales 1969; MB ChB St. And. 1939. Clin. Med. Off. Gwynedd HA. Prev: Clin. Asst. (Geriat. Med.) Gwynedd AHA.

ROBINSON, Margaret Reynolds (retired) 4 Higham Lane, Tonbridge TN10 4JA — MB BS 1955 Lond.; DA Eng. 1961; DObst RCOG 1956. Prev: Regist. (Anaesth.) & Sen. Ho. Off. (Anaesth. & O & G) St.

ROBINSON, Margaret Valerie Crosby House Surgery, 91 Stoke Poges Lane, Slough SL1 3NY Tel: 01753 520680 Fax: 01753 552780; 8 Ketcher Green, Binfield, Bracknell RG42 5TA — MB ChB 1977 Liverp.; MRCPsych 1982; DRCOG 1979. Prev: Regist. (Psychiat.) Liverp. HA (T); Clin. Med. Off. (Psychiat.) Sefton HA.

*****ROBINSON, Mark Jeremy Charles** 96 Poole Crescent, Birmingham B17 0PB — MB ChB 1996 Birm.; ChB Birm. 1996.

ROBINSON, Marlene Jane (retired) Lime Cottage, Downside Bridge Road, Cobham KT11 3EJ Tel: 01932 862984 Fax: 01932 865328 — MB BS 1957 Lond.; MRCS Eng. LRCP Lond. 1957. Prev: Clin. Asst. Dept. Ultrasound St. Luke's Hosp. Guildford.

ROBINSON, Martin Hurst Clinical Oncology, Weston Park Hospital, Whitham Road, Sheffield S10 2SJ Tel: 0114 226 5000 Fax: 0114 226 5511 Email: m.h.robinson@sheffield.ac.uk; Riplingham, Sheffield Road, Hathersage, Hope Valley S32 1DA — MB BChir 1978 Camb.; MA Camb. 1983; MRCP (UK) 1980; FRCR 1986; MD Camb. 1993; FRCP 1997. Sen. lect. (Clin. Oncol.) W.on Pk. Hosp. Sheff. Socs: BOA (Hon. Sec.). Prev: Sen. Regist. (Radiother.) Roy. Marsden Hosp. Lond.; Regist. (Radiother.) Ch.ill Hosp. Oxf.

ROBINSON, Martyn Gerald Woodland Road Surgery, 20 Woodland Road, St Austell PL25 4QY Tel: 01726 63311; The Oak, Porthpean Road, St Austell PL25 5DG Tel: 01726 65774 — MB BS 1981 Lond.; DRCOG 1981.

ROBINSON

ROBINSON, Maryanne 10 McPherson Drive, Gourock PA19 1LJ — MB ChB 1984 Glas.; DRCOG 1986.

ROBINSON, Mr Maurice Patrick 35 Rope Lane, Wells Green, Crewe CW2 6RB Tel: 01270 67237 — MB BS 1952 Lond.; FRCS Eng. 1958. (Middlx.) Socs: Brit. Orthop. Assn. Prev: Cons. Surg. Orthop. Robt. Jones & Agnes Hunt Orthop. Hosp. & Leighton Hosp. Crewe; Sen. Regist. Middlx. Hosp. Lond.

ROBINSON, Maurice William (retired) 91 Heathermount Drive, Crowthorne RG45 6HJ Tel: 01344 774862 Fax: 01344 774862 Email: mauricewr@bigfoot.com — MB ChB 1960 Sheff.; MRCGP 1971; DObst RCOG 1962. Prev: GP Bracknell.

ROBINSON, Melvyn 6A Twitch Hill, Horbury, Wakefield WF4 6NA — MB ChB 1979 Liverp.

ROBINSON, Mr Melvyn Roland Griffiths The General Infirmary, Friarwood Lane, Pontefract WF8 1PL Tel: 01977 606716; 25 Went Hill Close, Ackworth, Pontefract WF7 7LP Tel: 01977 702196 — MB BS 1957 Lond.; FRCS Eng. 1968; FRCS Ed. 1967; MRCS Eng. LRCP Lond. 1957; DObst RCOG 1959. (Char. Cross) Hon. Cons. Urol., Pontefract NHS Trust. Socs: Fell. Roy. Soc. Med.; Brit. Assn. Urol. Surg.; Eur. Assn. Urol. Prev: Sen. Regist. & Research Fell. Inst. Urol. Lond.; Regist. (Surg.) Mt. Vernon Hosp. N.wood; Med. Off. N.. Nigeria.

ROBINSON, Michael 6 Sycamore Grove, Sandbach CW11 1PJ — MB ChB 1986 Liverp.

ROBINSON, Michael Barney Nuffield Institute University of Leeds, 75-79 Clarendon Road, Leeds LS2 9PL Tel: 0113 245 9034 — MB BS 1982 Lond.; MA Camb. 1979; MSc Lond. 1990; MRCP (UK) 1985; MFPHM RCP (UK) 1991; MRCGP 1986; DRCOG 1989; DCH RCP Lond. 1987. Sen. Lect. (Pub. Health) & Hon. Cons. Pub. Health Med. Leeds HA. Prev: Lect. (Pub. Health Med.) Lond. Sch. Hyg. & Trop. Med.

ROBINSON, Michael David In Practice Systems Ltd., Delta Park, Smugglers Way, London SW18 1EG Tel: 020 7501 7000 Fax: 020 8871 3158 Email: mike.robinson@inps.co.uk; 33 Upfield, Horley RH6 7JY Tel: 01293 783146 — MB BS 1975 Lond.; MRCS Eng. LRCP Lond. 1975. (St. Mary's) Med. Dir. In Pract. Systems Ltd. Prev: Med. Dir. VAMP Health Lond.; GP Surrey.

ROBINSON, Michael Edward Family Practice, 75 Cardiff Road, Dinas Powys CF64 4JT Tel: 029 2051 5455 Fax: 029 2051 5177; 22 Millbrook Heights, Dingwall, Penarth CF64 4JJ Tel: 01222 512535 — MB BCh 1970 Wales. Chairm. Vale LHG. Prev: Research Regist. MRC Pneumoconiosis Unit Dept. Child Health, Llandough Hosp. Penarth.

ROBINSON, Mr Michael Harold Edward University Hospital, Queens Medical Centre, Nottingham NG5 2UH Tel: 0115 924 9924; Crodock Cottage, 74 Brook St, Wynsehold, Loughborough LE12 6TH — BM BCh 1983 Oxf.; MA Camb. 1984; DM Nottm. 1996; FRCS Eng. 1988. (Oxf.) Cons. Gen. Surg. Qu.. Med. Centre Nottm. Socs: Assoc. of ColoProctol.; Brit.Med.Assoc. Prev: Lect. & Regist. Qu. Med. Centre Nottm.; Regist. Roy. Hosp. Gloucester; Cons. Gen. Surg. City Hosp. NHS Trust, Notts.

ROBINSON, Mr Michael John 33c Thornhill Crescent, Islington, London N1; Greenburn Croft, Balfron Station, Glasgow G63 0QY — MB BS 1981 Lond.; BA Camb. 1978; FRCS Ed. 1986. Regist. Inst. Neurol. Sci. S.. Gen. Hosp. Glas.

ROBINSON, Michael Jonathan Hope Hospital, Salford M6 8HD Tel: 0161 787 5273 Fax: 0161 787 5786; 3A Bowgreen Road, Bowdon, Altrincham WA14 3LX — BM BCh 1968 Oxf.; MA, BM BCh Oxf. 1968; MRCP (UK) 1972; FRCP 1998 CH; FRCP 1986. (Univ. Coll. Hosp.) Cons. Paediat. Hope Hosp. Salford & Roy. Manch. Childr. Hosp. Socs: Neonat. Soc.; BAPM. Prev: Sen. Regist. St. Thos. Hosp. Lond.; Vis. Lect. Hadassah Univ. Jerusalem; Regist. Hosp. Sick Childr. Gt. Ormond St. Lond.

ROBINSON, Michael Kefford 17 Herbrand Walk, Bexhill-on-Sea TN39 4TX — MB ChB 1952 Ed. (Ed.)

ROBINSON, Michael Lansdale University Department of Psychiatry, Royal Liverpool Hospital, Prescot St., Liverpool L7 8XP — MD 1984 Belf.; MPsychMed Liverp. 1980; MB BCh BAO Belf. 1970; MRCP (U.K.) 1972; MRCPsych 1976. Sen. Lect. (Psychiat.) Univ. Liverp. Prev: Lect. Psychiat. Univ. Liverp.; Research Worker Inst. Psychiat. Lond.; Regist. (Psychiat.) Maudsley Hosp. Lond.

ROBINSON, Michael Sandwith Tamerton, Plum Orchard, Nether Compton, Sherborne DT9 4QA — MB BS 1985 Lond.; MRCGP 1993.

ROBINSON, Neil Alexander Sinclair c/o Emerg. Dept., Soton. Gen. Hosp., Tremona Road, Southampton SO16 6YD Tel: 02380 794127 Email: poppabear@hotmail.com — MB BS 1991 Lond.; FFAEM 1999; MRCP (UK) 1995; DA (UK) 1996. (Lond. Hosp. Med. Coll.) Cons. in Emerg. Med., Soton. Gen. Hosp. Prev: Specialist Regist. (A & E Med.) Wessex.

ROBINSON, Neville Anthony Ynysangharad Surgery, 70 Ynysangharad Road, Pontypridd CF37 4DA Tel: 01443 480521 Fax: 01443 400260 Email: ynysangharad@nice.walts.nhs.uk; 82 Phillip Street, Graig, Pontypridd CF37 1LZ Tel: 01443 480972 — MB, BS London 1959; DObst RCOG 1961; LMCC Medical Council Canada 1972. (Charing Cross) GP. Socs: BMA. Prev: Chief of Staff, Dartmouth Gen. Hosp., Dartmouth, Nova Scotia, Canada.

ROBINSON, Nicholas David Penrose The Jersey Practice, Heston Health Centre, Cranford Lane, Hounslow TW5 9ER Tel: 020 8321 3434 Fax: 020 8321 3440 — BM BCh 1979 Oxf.; MA Oxf. 1979, BA 1976; MRCGP 1985. (Oxf.) Research Fell. (Primary Care) Char. Cross & W.m. Med. Sch. Socs: Hon. Sec. Brit. Computer Soc. Health Informat. Specialist Gp.; Assoc. Mem. Brit. Computer Soc.

ROBINSON, Nicholas Mark Kuenzlen 129 Fentiman Road, London SW8 1JZ Tel: 020 7735 8641 — MB BChir 1987 Camb.; MA, MB BChir Camb. 1987; MRCP (UK) 1990; MD 1996. (Cambridge University) Sen. Regist. Lond. Chest Hosp. Prev: Regist. (Cardiol.) King's Coll. Hosp. Lond.; Regist. (Cardiol.) Roy. Sussex Co. Hosp. Brighton; SHO (Neurol.) Nat. Hosp. Nerv. Dis. Lond.

ROBINSON, Nicolas Church Highwoods Surgery, Highwoods Square, Colchester CO4 4SR Tel: 01206 752010; Marks Cottage, Lower Layham, Ipswich IP7 5RB — MB BS 1978 Lond.; MRCGP 1982.

ROBINSON, Nigel Norton Medical Centre, Harland House, Norton, Stockton-on-Tees TS20 1AN Tel: 01642 360111 Fax: 01642 558672 — MB ChB 1984 Liverp.; MB ChB Liverp. 1984; MRCGP 1988; Dip. Pract. Dermat. Wales 1992; DRCOG 1988; DGM RCP Lond. 1987. Prev: GP Ayrsh.; Trainee GP E. Cumbria VTS; Med. Off. RAF.

ROBINSON, Oliver Patrick Waring, RD (retired) Lime Cottage, Downside Bridge Road, Cobham KT11 3EJ Tel: 01932 862984 Fax: 01932 865328 — MB BS 1953 Lond.; FFPM RCP (UK) 1989; Dip. Pharm. Med. RCP (UK) 1976; DTM & H Eng. 1962. Surg. Lt.-Cdr. RNR. Prev: Med. Dir. Smithkline Beecham Pharm.

ROBINSON, Paul Danes Dyke Surgery, 463A Scalby Road, Newby, Scarborough YO12 6UB Tel: 01723 375343 Fax: 01723 501582 — MB ChB 1975 Sheff.; DRCOG 1982; Cert. Family Plann. JCC 1982; FFA RCS Eng. 1980. Hosp. Pract. (Anaesth.) ScarBoro. Hosp. Prev: Regist. (Anaesth.) ScarBoro. Hosp.; Regist. (Anaesth.) Wellington Hosp. & Dunedin Hosp., NZ; SHO (Paediat.) Bradford Childr. Hosp.

ROBINSON, Paul David 5 Corringway, London NW11 7ED — MB ChB 1998 Manch.; MB ChB Manch 1998.

ROBINSON, Paul Derek 2 Orchard Gate, Esher KT10 8HY — MB BS 1981 Lond.; PhD Lond. 1992, MB BS 1981; BDS Lond. 1971; FDS RCS Eng. 1976.

ROBINSON, Paul Frank Tinshill Lane Surgery, 8 Tinshill Lane, Leeds LS16 7AP Tel: 0113 267 3462 Fax: 0113 230 0402 — MB ChB 1988 Leeds; MRCGP 1995; DRCOG 1994. Prev: Trainee GP Bradford VTS.

ROBINSON, Paul Hyman Department of Psychiatry, Royal Free Hospital, Pond St., London NW3 2QF Email: paul.robinson@rfh.nthames.nhs.uk; 75 Hillfield Park, London N10 3QU Tel: 020 8444 5228 Fax: 020 8444 5228 Email: paulhrobinson@hotmail.com — MB BS 1974 Lond.; BSc Lond. 1971, MD 1994; MRCP (UK) 1977; FRCPsych 1982, M 1995; MD Lond. 1993. (Univ. Coll. Hosp.) Cons. Psychiat. Roy. Free Hosp.; Hon. Sen. Lect. Roy. Free & Univ. Coll. Med. Sch. Prev: Sen. Lect. (Psychol. Med.) Kings Coll. Hosp. Sch. Med. Lond.; Wellcome Lect. (Ment. Health) Inst. Psychiat. Lond.; Cons. Psychiat. Gordon Hosp. Lond.

ROBINSON, Paul Jeremy Merck, Sharp & Dohme Ltd., Hertford Road, Hoddesdon EN11 9BU Tel: 01992 467272 Fax: 01992 451066 Email: paul_robinson@merck.com — MB BS 1984 Lond.; Dip. Pharm. Med. 1994; MFPM RCP (UK) 1994. (Lond. Hosp.) Dir. Med. Affairs Merck, Sharp & Dohme Ltd. Hoddesdon; Hon. Clin. Asst. (Cardiol.) Chase Farm Hosp. Enfield. Socs: Brit. Cardiac Soc.; Brit. Hypertens. Soc. Prev: Assoc. Dir. (Clin. Research) Chiltern

ROBINSON

Internat. Ltd. Stoke Poges; Research Phys. Romford Cardiovasc. Research; SHO Rotat. (Med.) Newham Gen. Hosp. Lond.

ROBINSON, Paul John The Surgery, Station Road, Snainton, Scarborough YO13 9AP Tel: 01723 859302 Fax: 01723 859036 Email: paul@scarbvts.demon.co.uk; Wayside, Pickering Road, Snainton, Scarborough YO13 9AF — MB BS 1978 Lond.; MMEd Dundee 1998; MA Camb. 1980; MRCGP 1983; DRCOG 1983. (London Hospital) GP ScarBoro.; Course Organiser ScarBoro. VTS. Prev: Trainee GP York VTS; Ho. Off. Lond. Hosp.

ROBINSON, Paula Mary 9 Hawling Road, Market Weighton, York YO43 3JR — MB ChB 1993 Univ. Cape Town.

ROBINSON, Peter Charles Farnham Health Centre, Brightwells, Farnham GU9 7SA Tel: 01252 723122 Fax: 01252 728302; The Limes, 57 The St, Tungham, Farnham GU10 1DD Tel: 01252 651415 Email: pcrcabel@net.ntl.com — MB BS 1981 Lond.; DRCOG 1984. (St. Geo.) Clin. Asst. (Genitourin. Med.) Farnham Rd. Hosp. Guildford.; Clin. Asst. Acorn Community Drug & Alcohol Team Guildford. Prev: SHO (Paediat.) Roy. Surrey Co. Hosp. Guildford; SHO (O & G) Frimley Pk. Hosp.; Ho. Phys. St. Geo. Hosp. Lond.

ROBINSON, Peter Hugh 16 Courthill, Bearsden, Glasgow G61 3SN — MB BCh BAO 1981 Belf.; BSc Belf. 1978, MB BCh BAO 1981; MRCP (UK) 1984.

ROBINSON, Peter John (retired) 2 Riponway, Carlton Miniott, Thirsk YO7 4LR Tel: 01845 522019 — MB ChB 1957 Leeds; MRCGP 1974; DTM & H Eng. 1968.

ROBINSON, Peter John (retired) Cliff House, Chyandour, Penzance TR18 3LQ — MB BCh BAO 1958 Dub.

ROBINSON, Peter Kenneth (retired) 14 St James Villas, Winchester SO23 9SN Email: peterk.robinson@virgin.net — MB BChir 1945 Camb.; MA Camb. 1946, MD 1956; FRCP Lond. 1965, M 1945; MRCS Eng. LRCP Lond. 1944. Prev: Cons. Neurol. Hants. AHA (T).

ROBINSON, Peter William Longton Health Centre, Liverpool Road, Longton, Preston PR4 5HA Tel: 01772 615429 Fax: 01772 611094; The Sandpipers, Marsh Lane, Longton, Preston PR4 5LA — MB ChB 1974 Manch.; MICGP 1987; MRCGP 1986; DRCOG 1977. (Manchester) Trainer (Gen. Pract.) Preston.

ROBINSON, Philip 5 Heywoods Ridge, Audlem, Crewe CW3 0EF Email: philrob66@hotmail.com — MB BCh BAO 1991 Belf.; MB (Hons) BCh BAO Belf. 1991; MRCP (UK) 1994; FRCR (UK) 1998. (Queen's Belfast) Socs: Sen. RCR.

ROBINSON, Mr Philip James ENT Department, Southmead Hospital, Westbury-on-Trym, Bristol BS10 5NB Tel: 0117 959 5161 Fax: 0117 959 5168; Westgate, 17 Old Sneed Park, Bristol BS9 1RG — MB ChB 1981 Bristol; FRCS (Orl.) Eng. 1988; FRCS (Gen. Surg.) Eng. 1986. Cons. ENT Surg. S.mead Hosp. Bristol; Sen. Clin. Lect. Univ. Bristol. Socs: Fell. Roy. Soc. Med. (Hon. Sec. Sect. Otol.). Prev: Sen. Regist. & Regist. (ENT Surg.) Univ. Coll. Hosp. & Middlx. Hosp. Lond.; SHO Rotat. (Surg.) Bristol Roy. Infirm.

ROBINSON, Philip Joseph Andrew 371 Shadwell Lane, Leeds LS17 8AH Tel: 0113 266 0471 — MB BS 1966 Lond.; FRCP Lond. 1989; MRCP Lond. 1969; FRCR 1975; DMRD Eng. 1973. (St. Mary's) Cons. Radiol. Leeds AHA (T).

ROBINSON, Philip Lawrence (retired) 38 Macdona Drive, West Kirby, Wirral CH48 3JD Tel: 0151 625 6843 — MB ChB 1942 Liverp.; MD Liverp. 1949; FRCP Lond. 1972, M 1948. Prev: Cons. Phys. Clatterbridge Gen. Hosp. Bebington.

ROBINSON, Philip Norman Gordon Street Surgery, 72 Gordon Street, Burton-on-Trent DE14 2JB Tel: 01283 563175 Fax: 01283 500638; 133 Field Lane, Burton-on-Trent DE13 0NJ — MB ChB 1981 Birm.; DRCOG 1985.

ROBINSON, Philip William Henry (retired) 203 Haven Road, Haverfordwest SA61 1DQ Tel: 01437 768672 — MB ChB Birm. 1947; MRCS Eng. LRCP Lond. 1947; FFA RCS Eng. 1956; DA Eng. 1952. Prev: Cons. Anaesth. Withybush Gen Hosp. HaverfordW.

ROBINSON, Quentin Lawrence Alleyne Holly Green, Moorfield Road, Ben Rhydding, Ilkley LS29 8BL Tel: 0113 292 3016 — MB ChB 1965 Ed.; FFA RCS Eng. 1970. (Ed.) Cons. Anaesth. Wharfedale Gen. Hosp.; Cons. i/c Wharfedale Br. Yorks. Regional Pain Serv. Socs: Intractable Pain Soc. Prev: Cons. Anaesth. Ahmadu Bello Hosp. Kaduna, Nigeria; Sen. Regist. Leeds Gen. Infirm.; Regist. (Anaesth.) Roy. Infirm. Edin.

ROBINSON, Rachael Marie The Surgery, 21 Stockwell Road, Knaresborough HG5 0JY Tel: 01423 867433, 01423 869633 Email: rachael@coughsandsneezes.com — MB ChB 1990 Leeds; DRCOG 1994; MRCGP 1997. (Leeds) GP Partner; GP Trainer, Dates GPEC. Prev: SHO (Paediat.) LG1; SHO (Palliat. Med.) St Gemmas.

ROBINSON, Mr Ralph Eldon (retired) Thaxted Lodge, 12 Babraham Road, Cambridge CB2 2RA Tel: 01223 248629 Fax: 01223 248629 — MB BS (Hons. Surg., Obst. & Gyn.) Lond. 1960; FRCS Eng. 1964; MRCS Eng. LRCP Lond. (Begley Prize in Surg.) 1960; FRCOG 1980, M 1968. Assoc. Lect. Univ. Camb. Prev: Cons. O & G Addenbrooke's Hosp. Camb. & NW Thames RHA.

ROBINSON, Ralph Henry (retired) The Old Manse, Silver St., Stansted Mountfichet, Stansted CM24 8HD Tel: 01279 815182 — MB BS Lond. 1956; MRCS Eng. LRCP Lond. 1956; FFA RCS Eng. 1963; DTM & H Eng. 1962; DA Eng. 1958. Cons. Anaesth. Prev: Cons. (Anaesth.) E. Herts. NHS Trust.

ROBINSON, Richard Conrad Oliver and Partners, The Guildhall Surgery, Lower Baxter Street, Bury St Edmunds IP33 1ET Tel: 01284 701601 Fax: 01284 702943 — MB ChB 1975 Auckland; MRCGP 1980; DRCOG 1979; DCH Eng. 1978. (Auckland, New Zealand)

ROBINSON, Richard Edward Menaus 14 Queens Park Rise, Brighton BN2 2ZF — MB BCh 1995 Wales.

ROBINSON, Richard John Richard J Robinson, Glenfield Hospital NHS Trust, Groby Road, Leicester LE3 9QP Tel: 0116 287 1471 Fax: 0116 256 3422 Email: richard.robinson@glenfiend.tr.trent.nhs.uk; 35 Station Road, Quorn, Loughborough LE12 8BP Email: rjrob@globalnet.co.uk — MB BS 1989 Lond.; BSc Lond. 1988; MRCP (UK) 1992; MD Leicester 1999. (St Mary's Hospital) Cons. Gastroenterol./ Med., Glenfield Hosp., Leicester. Socs: Brit. Soc. Gastroenterol.; BMA. Prev: Specialist Regist. (Gastroenterol.) Leicester Roy. Infirm.; Research Fell. Leicester Gen. Hosp.; SHO Rotat. (Med.) Bristol Roy. Infirm.

ROBINSON, Richard John Nivana, Pinfold Lane, Fishlake, Doncaster DN7 5LA — MB ChB 1997 Manch.

ROBINSON, Richard Karl 24 Tweskard Park, Belfast BT4 2JZ — MB BCh BAO 1981 Belf.

ROBINSON, Professor Richard Oakley Newcomen Centre, Guys Hospital, London SE1 9RT Tel: 020 7955 4671 Fax: 020 7955 4950; 166 Burbage Road, Dulwich, London SE21 7AG Tel: 020 7733 9127 — MB Camb. 1967, BChir 1966; FRCP Lond. 1983, M 1969. (Camb. & Guy's) Prof. Paediat. Neurol. Guy's Hosp. Lond. Socs: Brit. Paediatric Neurol. Assoc. Past Pres. Prev: Instruc. (Neurol.) Kentucky Univ. Med. Centre; Lect. (Paediat.) Oxf. Univ.; Nuffield Research Fell. Nuffield Inst. Med. Research, Oxf.

ROBINSON, Robert Anthony 7 Wilmer Crescent, Kingston upon Thames KT2 5LU — MB BS 1994 Lond.

ROBINSON, Robert Bruce (retired) 19 St Luke's Court, Hyde Lane, Marlborough SN8 1YU Tel: 01672 515749 — MB BS 1952 Lond.; MSc (Social Med.) Lond. 1971, MB BS 1952; FFPHM RCP (UK) 1989; FFCM RCP (UK) 1982, M 1974. JP. Prev: SCM Hants. AHA (T).

ROBINSON, Robert Timothy Charles Edward 27 Ashdell Road, Broomhill, Sheffield S10 3DA Email: r.t.robinson@sheffield.ac.uk — MB ChB 1992 Liverp.; MRCP (UK) 1996. Specialist Regist., Diabetes & Endocrinol.,Centr. Sheff. Univ. Hosp. Socs: BMA; Diabetics UK; EASD. Prev: Clin. Research Fell. (Diabetes & Endocrinol.) N.. Gen. Hosp. Sheff.

ROBINSON, Professor Roger James (retired) 60 Madeley Road, Ealing, London W5 2LU — BM BCh Oxf. 1959; MA, DPhil. Oxf. 1958; FRCP Lond. 1975, M 1963; DCH Eng. 1964; PhD Aberd. 1998; FRCPCH 1997. Assoc. Edit. Brit. Med. Jl. Prev: Ferdinand James de Rothschild Prof. Paediat. UMDS Guy's & St. Thos. Hosps. Lond.

ROBINSON, Ronald Arthur (retired) 14 Ramsay Garden, Edinburgh EH1 2NA Tel: 0131 225 3125 Email: sam@castledin.freeserve.co.uk — MB BCh BAO Belf. 1949; FRCP Ed. 1979, M 1973; FRCPsych 1973, M 1971; DPM RCPSI 1953. Vice-Chairm. Fac. Psychiat. Of Old Age Roy. Coll. Psychiat. Prev: Sen. Lect. (Psychiat.) Univ. Edin.

ROBINSON, Rosemary Elizabeth Coventry & Warwickshire Hospital, Walsgrave NHS Trust, Stoney Stanton Road, Coventry CV1 4FH Tel: 024 76 224055 — MB BCh BAO 1985 NUI; BSc Dub. 1987; FRCSI 1990; LRCPSI 1985; FRCOphth 1990; DO RCSI 1988. Prev: Sen. Regist. (Ophth.) Birm. & Midl. Eye Hosp.

ROBINSON

ROBINSON, Ruth Christine 4 Alma Farm Road, Toddington, Dunstable LU5 6BG; 60 Wheatfield Road, Luton LU4 0SY — MB BS 1977 Lond.

ROBINSON, Ruth Elizabeth Fairthwaite Park, Cowan Bridge, Carnforth LA6 2HX Tel: 015242 72777 — MB ChB 1951 Leeds. (Leeds) Prev: Clin. Med. Off. (Family Plann.) Airedale Med. Auth.

***ROBINSON, Samuel Myles** Sagamartha, Burrough St., Ash, Martock TA12 6NZ Tel: 01935 822259 — BM BS 1998 Nottm.; BM BS Nottm 1998; BMedSci.

ROBINSON, Sandra Janice Greenwich & Bexley, Cottage Hospice, 185 Bostall Hill, Abbey Wood, London SE2 0QX Fax: 020 8312 2244; 16 Water Meadows, Fordwich, Canterbury CT2 0BF Tel: 01227 711353 Email: kentjan@aol.com — MB BS 1974 Lond.; MSc. Hist. of Sci. and Med. Univ. of Lond. 1996; MRCS Eng. LRCP Lond. 1974. (St. Bart.) Med. Off. (Palliat. Care), Greenwich & Bexley Cottage Hospice Lond. Socs: Assoc. of Palliat. Med, Prev: Clin. Asst. (Palliat. Care) Wisdom Hospice Rochester, Kent; Med. Off. Ellenor Foundat. Dartford Kent; Clin. Asst. (Ophth.) Greenwich Dist. Hosp. Lond.

ROBINSON, Sarah Pantiles, Allendale Road, Hexham NE46 2NH — MB BS 1994 Newc.

ROBINSON, Sarah Julie 6 Sorrel Drive, Whiteley, Fareham PO15 7JL Email: sarah@ripsa.demon.co.uk — BM 1996 Soton. (Southampton) Prev: SHO Orthop.; SHO Acute Gen. Med.; SHO A&E.

ROBINSON, Sasha Clare 27 Queens Road, Wimbledon, London SW19 8NW Tel: 020 8946 1172 — MB BS 1985 Lond.; DRCOG 1989.

ROBINSON, Sheila Mary Park Surgery, Sutherlands Way, Hursley Road, Chandlers Ford, Eastleigh SO50 2ZH Tel: 01703 267355; 19 St Luke's Court, Hyde Lane, Marlborough SN8 1YU Tel: 01672 515749 — MB BChir 1953 Camb.; MA, MB BChir Camb. 1953; DPH Eng. 1956. (Middlx.)

ROBINSON, Simon David Westgate Surgery, Westgate, Otley LS21 3HD Tel: 01943 465406 Fax: 01943 468363; The Old Vicarage, Stripe Lane, Hartwith, Harrogate HG3 3EZ — MB ChB 1982 Leeds; MRCGP 1986; DCH RCP Lond. 1986; DRCOG 1985. (Leeds University) Gen. Practitioner, W.gate Surg., W.gate, Otley, Leeds LS21 3HD.

ROBINSON, Simon David 52 Dromara Road, Dromore BT25 1DR — MB ChB 1998 Ed.; MB ChB Ed 1998.

ROBINSON, Simon Haydn 35 Watery Road, Wrexham LL13 7NP — MB ChB 1992 Liverp.

ROBINSON, Simon Lee 8 Clarks Lane, Newark NG24 2EF — BM BS 1996 Nottm.

ROBINSON, Simon Nicholas Chaddy, Eglwysbach, Colwyn Bay LL28 5UD — MB ChB 1994 Manch.

ROBINSON, Simon Paul 33 Princess Street, Oxford OX4 1DD — MB BS 1992 Lond.

ROBINSON, Simon Timothy Clarendon House, Croft Road, Ipplepen, Newton Abbot TQ12 5SS — MB BS 1997 Lond.

ROBINSON, Sophia Louise Greystones, Church St., Bloxham, Banbury OX15 4ET — MB BS 1989 Lond.; MSc Lond. 1982, BSc (Hons.) 1980, MB BS 1989. Trainee GP Banbury VTS. Prev: SHO (A & E Dermat. & O & G) Banbury VTS.

ROBINSON, Stephen Unit of Metabolic Medicine, Imperial College School of Medicine, St. Mary's Hospital, London W2 1PG Tel: 020 7886 1253 Fax: 020 7886 1790 Email: stephen.robinson@ic.ac.uk — MB BChir 1982 Camb.; MA Camb. 1985, MD 1997; MRCP (UK) 1987; FRCP 1999. (Camb. & Westm.) Cons. Hon. Sen. Lect. (Gen. Med. Diabetes & Endocrinol.) St. Mary's Hosp. Lond. Prev: Sen. Lect., Lect. & MRC train. fell. St. Mary's Hosp. Lond.

ROBINSON, Stephen James 80 Cartington Terrace, Heaton, Newcastle upon Tyne NE6 5SH — MB BS 1998 Newc. With Merit; MB BS Newc 1998; BSc Sackville NB Canada, 1989. (Newcastle) SHO Gen. Paediat., Qu.s Eliz. Hosp. Gateshead. Prev: HO, Med. Wansbeck Gen. Hosp. Ashington; HO, Gen. Surg., N. Tyneside Gen. Hosp. N. Shields.; SHO A&E Sunderland Roy. Hosp., Sunderland.

ROBINSON, Stephen John, Surg. Lt.-Cdr. RN Retd. Ridgeway Practice, Plympton Health Centre, Mudgeway, Plymouth PL7 1AD Tel: 01752 346634 Fax: 01752 341444; Follaton, 5 Bainbridge Avenue, Hartley, Plymouth PL3 5QY Tel: 01752 774187 Email: dr.robinson@bigfoot.com — MB BS 1986 Lond.; DRCOG 1993; MRCGP 1994; DFFP 1994. (St Thomas' Hospital Medical School) GP Princip.; Police Surg. Devon & Cornw. Constab. Prev: SHO (O & G) Freedom Fields Plymouth; SHO (A & E) Derriford Hosp. Plymouth; SHO (Surg., Med. & A & E) Roy. Naval Hosp. Plymouth.

ROBINSON, Stephen Paul 36 Pullens Buildings, Penton Place, London SE17 3SH — MB BS 1992 Lond.; MRCP (UK) 1995. (Roy. Free Hosp.) Clin. Research Fell. & Hon. Regist. (Haemat.) Antigen Presentation Research Gp. Imperial Coll. Sch. Med. N.wick Pk. Lond. Prev: SHO (Med.) N.wick Pk. Hosp. Lond.

ROBINSON, Stephen Philip Rose Cottage, Sunbank Lane, Ringway, Altrincham WA15 0PZ Tel: 0161 980 1498 Fax: 0161 980 1498 Email: steverobinsonfagin@compuserve.com — MB ChB 1971 Manch.; DMJ Soc. Apoth. Lond. 1984; MMJ Soc. Apoth. 1997. Fell. Inst. Med. & Bioethics Univs. Liverpo. & Manch.; Hon. Lect. (Clin. Forens. Med.) Univ. Manch.; Sen. Police Surg. Gtr. Manch. Police; Co-ordinator Forens. Acad. Gp. N.; Mem. Edit. Comm. Jl. Clin. Forens. Med. (Bk. Review Edn.).

ROBINSON, Steven John 12 The Circle, Birmingham B17 9EE — MB ChB 1995 Birm.; ChB Birm. 1995.

ROBINSON, Stuart John 8 Princess Drive, Bollington, Macclesfield SK10 5ER — MB ChB 1992 Manch.

ROBINSON, Susan Institute of Psychiatry, De Crespigny Park, Denmark Hill, London SE5 8AF Tel: 020 7703 5411 — MB ChB 1985 Aberd.; MRCPath 1993. Cons. Neuropath., Dept. of Neuropath. The Inst. of Psychiat. Lond. Prev: Lect. (Neuropath.) St Barth. & The Roy. Lond. Sch. of Med. & Dent.; Lect. (Path.) Univ. Aberd.; SHO (Path.) Centr. Birm. HA.

ROBINSON, Susan Caroline Lavender Hill Group Practice, 19 Pountney Road, Battersea, London SW11 5TU Tel: 020 7228 4042 Fax: 020 7738 9346 — MB BChir 1984 Camb.; MA Camb. 1984.

ROBINSON, Susan Elizabeth Wanstead Place Surgery, 45 Wanstead Place, Wanstead, London E11 2SW Tel: 020 8989 2019 Fax: 020 8532 9124; 28 The Avenue, Wanstead, London E11 2EF — MB BS 1972 Lond.; 1997 Certificate in Health Management (Keele); MRCS Eng. LRCP Lond. 1972; MRCGP 1976; DObst RCOG 1974. (Roy. Free) Sen. Partner in Gen. Pract. Prev: Trainee GP Ilford VTS.

ROBINSON, Susan Jane Regents Park Surgery, Park Street, Shirley, Southampton SO16 4RJ Tel: 023 8078 3618 Fax: 023 8070 3103; 5 Amberley Court, Ashurst Bridge, Southampton SO40 7JX — BM 1982 Soton.; MRCGP 1987; Cert. Family Plann. JCC 1985; DRCOG 1985. (Soton.) Prev: Trainee GP Soton. Gen. Hosp.

ROBINSON, Susan Miriam Emergency Department, Addenbrookes NHS Trust, Hills Road, Cambridge CB2 2QQ Tel: 01223 217031 Fax: 01223 217057 — MB BS 1985 Lond.; FFAEM 1995; FRCS Ed. 1993; MRCP (UK) 1988; FRCP 1999. (Westm. Med. Sch.) Cons. Emerg. Med. Addenbrooke's Hosp. Camb. Prev: Sen. Regist. (Emerg. Med.) E. Anglia; Regist. (Emerg. Med.) St. Mary's Hosp. Lond.

ROBINSON, Terence John The Barn, Combe Cross, Christow, Exeter EX6 7NR — MB ChB 1968 Ed.; MRCPsych 1974. Cons. (Child Psychiat.) Roy. Devon & Exeter Hosp. Exeter.

ROBINSON, Thomas Anthony Sully Surgery, 25 South Road, Sully, Penarth CF64 2TG Tel: 029 2053 0255 Fax: 029 2053 0689; Sunnybank, Swaybridge Road, Sully, Penarth CF64 5UN — MB BCh Wales 1981; MRCP (UK) 1985; MRCGP 1987; DRCOG 1986. GP Sully.; Clin. Asst. Impotence Clinic Llandulch Hosp.

ROBINSON, Thomas John Bracken Hill, 101 Lisnaree Road, Banbridge BT32 4JU — MD 1967 Belf.; MB BCh BAO 1961; FRCP Lond. 1980, M 1968. Cons. Phys. Craigavon Area Hosp. & Banbridge Hosp. Socs: Brit. Soc. Gastroenterol. & Irish Soc. Gastroenterol. Prev: Ho. Off. & Regist. Roy. Vict. Hosp. Belf.

ROBINSON, Timothy Dudley 13 Middle Park, Alston CA9 3AR — MB BS 1991 Lond.

ROBINSON, Timothy William Barton House Surgery, Barton House, Beaminster DT8 3EQ Fax: 01308 863785 — MB BS 1984 Lond.; MFHom 2000; LFHom RCP Lond. 1996; MRCGP 1988; LF Hom 1996; DRCOG 1987; Cert. Family Plann. JCC 1987. Gen. Practitioner; Homeopathic Phys.; Fac. of Homeopathy Lond. Mem. Comm., Represen.; Lect. Homeopathic Med., Briston Homeopathic Hosp.; Convenor Som. / Dorset Homeopathy Forum. Prev: Ho. Surg. Middlx. Hosp. Lond.; ENT SHO Swindon Hosp. ENT; Ho. Phys. Cheltenham Gen. Hosp.

ROBINSON, Miss Toeni 7 Drope Terrace, St Georges, Super-Ely, Cardiff CF5 6EQ — MB BCh 1987 Wales.

ROBINSON, Tony Reynolds (retired) 5 Valley Forge Close, Tonbridge TN10 4EU Tel: 01732 360618 Fax: 01732 360618 — MB BS Lond. 1957; DObst RCOG 1961. Prev: GP Tonbridge.

ROBINSON, Trevor Walter Ernest 99 Harley Street, London W1N 1DF Tel: 020 7637 7325 Fax: 020 7637 5383; 1 Cholmeley Crescent, Highgate, London N6 5EZ Tel: 020 8348 9856 — MB Camb. 1959, BChir 1958; FRCP Lond. 1975, M 1963; MRCS Eng. LRCP Lond. 1959. (St. Bart.) Emerit. Cons. Dermat. Univ. Coll. Lond. Hosps. Socs: Fell. Roy. Soc. Med.; Fell. (Ex-Pres.) St. John's Hosp. Dermat. Soc. Prev: Sen. Regist. & Regist. St. Bart. Hosp. Lond.; SHO St. John's Hosp. Dis. Skin Lond.; Dermatol.Edgware.Con.Hosp.

ROBINSON, Victor Philip Iver House, 78 High St., Iver SL0 9NG Tel: 01753 652020 Fax: 01753 655459 — MB BS 1968 Lond.; MRCOG 1975; FRCOG 1992. (St. Mary's) Cons. O & G Hillingdon, Mt. Vernon, N.wood & Pinner & Dist. Cottage Hosps.; Authorised Med. Examr. for the Civil Aviat. Auth. (AME). Socs: Fell. R.S.M.; B.S.P.O.G.A; Windsor Med. Sailing Soc. Prev: Sen. Regist. (Obst.) St. Geo. Hosp. Lond.; Regist. (Obst.) St. Mary's Hosp. Lond.; Resid. Med. Off. Qu. Charlotte's Matern Hosp. Lond.

ROBINSON, Waring Castlegate Surgery, Castle Street, Hertford SG14 1HH Tel: 01992 589928 — MB BS 1963 Lond. (St. Geo.)

ROBINSON, Wendy Janet Elspeth 5 Bluefield Close, Carrickfergus BT38 7XQ — MB ChB 1991 Ed.; BSc (Hons.) Ed. 1989, MB ChB 1991.

ROBINSON, William Henry The Vesey Practice, James Preston Health Centre, 61 Holland Road, Sutton Coldfield B72 1RL Tel: 0121 355 5150 Fax: 0121 321 2498; 106 Tamworth Road, Sutton Coldfield B75 6DH Tel: 0121 378 0018 Fax: 0121 241 3574 — BM BCh 1972 Oxf.; MA Oxf. 1972; MRCGP 1980; DRCOG 1981. (Westm.) Sen. Partner in the Vesey Pract.; Regional Med. Adviser Simply Health. Socs: BMA. Prev: Maj. RAMC.

ROBINSON, Mr William Liddy (retired) 2 Broomhill Mews, Limavady Road, Londonderry BT47 6WR Tel: 01504 312808 — MB BCh BAO Belf. 1941; FRCS Ed. (Ophth.) 1953; DOMS Eng. 1949. Prev: Cons. Surg. Altnagelvin Hosp. Tyrone Co. Hosp. & Fermanagh Hosp.

ROBINSON, William Michael, Col. late RAMC (retired) 4 Searle Road, Farnham GU9 8LJ — MB BCh BAO Dub. 1958; FRCP Ed. 1976, M 1963; DTM & H Eng. 1960. Asst. Surg. Roy. Hosp. Chelsea. Prev: Asst. Surg. Roy. Hosp. Chelsea.

ROBINSON-WHITE, Catherine Mary 41 Fairview Street, Cheltenham GL52 2JF — MB BS 1989 Lond.

ROBISON, Christine Anaesthestics Department, Royal Infirmary of Edinburgh, Edinburgh Tel: 0131 536 1000; Laverock, 13 Wyvern Park, Edinburgh EH9 2JY Tel: 0131 668 3832 — MB ChB 1978 Ed.; BSc (Med. Sci.) Ed. 1976; FFA RCS Eng. 1984. Assoc. Specialist Lothian Univ. Hosp. Trust. Socs: BMA; Ed. & E. Scot. Soc. Anaesth. Prev: Staff Anaesth. E. Gen. Hosp. Edin.; Staff Anaesth. St. John's Hosp. Livingston; Regist. (Anaesth.) Roy. Infirm. Edin.

ROBISON, Janet Margaret 83 Mountalto Avenue, Motherwell ML1 4AZ — MB ChB 1995 Glas.

ROBLES, Alfonso 1 Westfield Road, London NW7 3BJ — Medico Salvador Argentina 1974.

ROBLESS, Peter Ashley Flat 2/R, 22 Polwarth Street, Hyndland, Glasgow G12 9TY — MB ChB 1992 Aberd.

ROBLIN, David Pfizer Central Research, Sandwich CT13 9NJ Tel: 01304 646210 Fax: 01304 658299 Email: david_roblin.dr@bayer.co.uk — MB BS 1991 Lond.; BSc Lond. 1988; MRCP (UK) 1994. Candidate Team Ldr., Pfizer Centr. Research. Socs: Fell. Roy. Soc. Med.; Roy. Soc. Pharmaceutical Med. Prev: Head of Anti-Infectives, Pharma Europe, Bayer; Clin. Project Manager Pfizer Centr. Research; SHO Rotat. (Med.) St. Geo. Hosp. Lond.

ROBLIN, Mr David Graham 19 Pencisely Avenue, Cardiff CF5 1DZ — MB BCh 1989 Wales; FRCS Ed. 1995.

ROBLIN, (Karen) Jane Manor Surgery, Osler Road, Headington, Oxford OX3 9BP Tel: 01865 762535; 48 Sandfield Road, Headington, Oxford OX3 7RJ Tel: 01865 761216 — MB BS 1981 Lond.; MRCGP 1990; DCH RCP Lond. 1983. GP Oxf.; Clin. Asst. (Infertil.) John Radcliffe Hosp. Oxf.; Assoc. Course Organiser Oxf. VTS. Prev: Trainee GP Oxf.; SHO (Paediat.) Kingston Hosp.; SHO (Cardiol.) Middlx. Hosp.

ROBLIN, Menna Wyn 19 Pencisely Avenue, Cardiff CF5 1DZ — MB BCh 1989 Wales; MRCGP 1993; DCH RCP Lond. 1993; DRCOG 1992. Staff Grade (Community Paediat.) M. Glam.

***ROBLIN, Paul** 3 Coombe Neville,, Warren Road, Kingston upon Thames KT2 7HW Tel: 020 8949 4344 — MB BS 1990 Lond.; FRCS Eng 1995; MSc - Sept 1998, Univ Coll of Lond.

ROBLIN, Paul Howard Summertown Group Practice, 160 Banbury Road, Oxford OX2 7BS Tel: 01865 515552 Fax: 01865 311237; 48 Sandfield Road, Oxford OX3 7RJ Tel: 01865 761216 Fax: 01865 767924 — MB 1978 Camb.; MB Camb., BChir 1978; MRCP (UK) 1980; MRCGP 1983; DCH RCP Lond. 1983. Socs: Sec. Oxon. LMC; Bd. Mem. Oxf. PCG. Prev: SHO Obst. St. Mary's Hosp. Lond.; SHO Paediat. Kingston Hosp. Surrey; SHO Gen. Med. Centr. Middlx. Hosp. Lond.

ROBLIN, Sallyanne The Surgery, 43 London Road, High Wycombe HP12 4DG Tel: 01494 527036 — MB BS 1990 Lond.; MRCGP 1994; DFFP 1994; DRCOG 1993. GP Asst. High Wycombe. Prev: Asst. GP Caterham; Trainee GP E. Surrey Hosp. VTS.

ROBLING, Siri-Ann Local Health Partnerships NHS Trust, West Suffoldk Hospital, Hardwicke Lane, Bury St Edmunds IP33 2QZ Tel: 01242 272374 Fax: 01284 713694 Email: siri.robling@lhp.nhs.uk — MB BChir 1989 Camb.; MRCPsych 1994. Cons. (Gen. Adult) Psychiat. W. Suff. Hosp. Bury, St, Edmunds Suff.. Prev: Sen. Regist. Rotat. (Psychiat.) Addenbrookes, Hosp. Camb.; Regist. (Psychiat.) Fulbourn Hosp. Camb.

ROBLINGS, George Lindsey John (retired) Glynhir, Llanmartin Road, Langstone, Newport NP18 2JX Tel: 01633 412162 — MB BCh 1959 Wales. Prev: GP Newport, Gwent.

ROBSON, Alan Beech Tree Surgery, 68 Doncaster Road, Selby YO8 9AJ Tel: 01757 703933 Fax: 01757 213473; 66 Leeds Road, Selby YO8 4JQ Tel: 01757 702228 — MB ChB 1966 St. And.; DObst RCOG 1968. Prev: Med. Off. Kerugoya Hosp., Kenya; SHO (Paediat.) Seafield Childr. Hosp. Ayr.; SHO (Obst.) Ayrsh. Centr. Hosp. Irvine.

ROBSON, Alastair Malcolm The Surgery, Stowe Drive, Southam, Leamington Spa CV47 1NY — MB BCh BAO 1971 Dub.; MA Dub. 1972; MICGP 1988; DObst RCPI 1983. (TC Dub.)

ROBSON, Lady Alice Eleanor Flat II, The Coach House, 3 Victoria Road, Preston PR2 8ND Tel: 01772 713447 — MB ChB Ed. 1944. (Ed.)

ROBSON, Mr Andrew Kenneth Department of Otolaryngology, Cumberland Infirmary, Carlisle CA2 7HT Tel: 01228 814207 Fax: 01228 814276 Email: andrew.robson@ncumbria.acute.nhs.uk; Holm Hill House, Hawksdale, Dalston, Carlisle CA5 7BX — MB BS 1984 Lond.; FRCS (Orl.) 1993; FRCS Eng. (Otol.) 1990; FRCS Eng. (Gen.) 1988. (Middlx.) Cons. Otolaryngol. Carlisle Hosps. NHS Trust. Prev: Sen. Regist. (Otolaryngol.) Newc. & Sunderland; Tutor Specialist (Otolaryngol.) Dunedin Pub. Hosp., NZ; Regist. (Otolaryngol.) Radcliffe Infirm. Oxf.

ROBSON, Angus Osborn (retired) The Grange, Horsenden, Princes Risborough HP27 9NE Tel: 01844 343015 — MB BS Lond. 1951; MD Lond. 1966; FRCP Lond. 1973, M 1957. Prev: Sen. Regist. Roy. Vict. Infirm. Newc.

ROBSON, Barbara Edith Claire 118 Wimbledon Hill Road, London SW19 7QU Tel: 020 8946 9690 — MB BS Lond. 1952.

ROBSON, Brenda Jean 7 King John's Court, Darras Hall, Ponteland, Newcastle upon Tyne NE20 9AR Tel: 01661 823316 — MB BS 1955 Durh. Asst. Orthop. Surg. Freeman Hosp. Newc. u. Tyne. Prev: Asst. Orthop. Surg. W.J. Sanderson Orthop. Hosp. Gosforth; Ho. Phys. & SHO (Orthop.) Tynemouth Vict. Jubilee Infirm. N. Shields.

ROBSON, Brian John Incle Street Surgery, 8 Incle Street, Paisley PA1 1HR Tel: 0141 889 8809 Fax: 0141 849 1474; 331 Mearns Road, Newton Mearns, Glasgow G77 5LT — MB ChB 1988 Glas.; MRCGP 1992; DRCOG 1991.

ROBSON, Catherine Helen 480 Bristol Road, Selly Oak, Birmingham B29 6BD Tel: 0121 472 0129 — MB ChB 1987 Birm.; MRCGP (UK) 1992.

ROBSON, Christopher Edward Cirencester Memorial centre, Sheep Street, Cirencester GL7 1RQ — MB ChB 1985 Leeds; BSc Psychol. Leeds 1982, MB ChB 1985; MRCPsych 1990. Prev: Sen. Regist. (Rehabil. Psychiat.) Coney Hill Hosp. Gloucester.; Sen. Regist. (Gen. Psychiat.) S.mead Gen. Hosp. Bristol & Barrow Hosp. Bristol.

ROBSON

ROBSON, Christopher James Lochee Health Centre, 1 Marshall Street, Lochee, Dundee DD2 3BR Tel: 01382 611283 Fax: 01382 624480; Briarbank, 7 Albert St, Monifieth, Dundee DD5 4JS Tel: 01382 532808 — MB ChB 1981 Ed.; MRCGP 1985; DRCOG 1986.

ROBSON, Clare Winifred Marine Avenue Medical Centre, 64 Marine Avenue, Whitley Bay NE26 1NQ Tel: 0191 252 5317 — MB BS Lond. 1973; MRCP (UK) 1976; DObst RCOG 1975. (Westm.)

ROBSON, David Allan Haematology Department, Royal Gwent Hospital, Newport Tel: 01633 252244 — MB ChB 1980 Ed.; MRCP (UK) 1985. Staff Grade (Haemat.) Roy. Gwent Hosp. Prev: Regist. (Haemat.) Univ. Hosp. Wales Cardiff; Regist. (Geriat.) Roy. Lancaster Infirm.; Regist. (Gen. Med.) Wythenshawe Hosp. Manch.

ROBSON, David John Queen Elizabeth Hospital, Stadium Road, Woolwich, London SE18 — MB BS 1968 Lond.; FRCP Lond. 1986; MRCP (U.K.) 1972. (Middlx.) Cons. Phys. Qu. Eliz. Hosp., Woolwich. Socs: Brit. Cardiac Soc. Prev: Cons. Phys. Greenwich Dist. Hosp. Lond.

ROBSON, David John Cartington Terrace Medical Group, 1 Cartington Terrace, Heaton, Newcastle upon Tyne NE6 5RS Tel: 0191 265 5755 Fax: 0192 276 2921 — MB BS 1984 Newc.; BMedSc (Hons.) Newc. 1986, MB BS 1984; MRCGP 1989. Prev: Trainee GP N.d. VTS.

ROBSON, Deborah 6 Postcliffe House, Peterculter, Aberdeen AB14 0UY — MB ChB 1996 Liverp. SHO Infec. Dis.s/ Gen. Med., Aberd. Roy. Infirm., Aberd.

ROBSON, Derek Clark, Col. late RAMC (retired) 85 Queens Road, Alton GU34 1JA Tel: 01420 88984 — MB ChB 1957 Leeds; BSc (Hons.) Manch. 1952; MPhil Leeds 1987, MD 1967. Prev: Dir. Army Path.

ROBSON, Derek Keith Department of Pathology, Queens Medical Centre, Clifton Boulevard, Nottingham NG7 2 Tel: 0115 942 1421; 5 Paget Crescent, Ruddington, Nottingham NG11 6FD — MB BS 1980 Lond.; MRCPath 1989. Cons. Neuropath. Qu. Med. Centre Nottm.

ROBSON, Donald John Longford House Surgery, Longford Road, Holyhead LL65 1TR Tel: 01407 762341 Fax: 01407 761554; 7 The Rise, Trearddur Bay, Holyhead LL65 2UY — MB BS 1980 Newc.; MRCGP 1984; DRCOG 1983. Mem. Ment. Health Task Force RCGP. Prev: Trainee GP N.umbria VTS.

ROBSON, Duncan James Silver Lane Surgery, 1 Suffolk Court, Yeadon, Leeds LS19 7JN Tel: 0113 250 4953 Fax: 0113 250 9804; Woodlands, 9 Creskeld Garth, Bramhope, Leeds LS16 9EW — MB ChB 1978 Leeds. Sen. Med. Adviser Yorks. Water Plc Bradford.

ROBSON, Elizabeth St. Andrews Medical Centre, Pinewood Gardens, Southborough, Tunbridge Wells TN4 0LZ Tel: 01892 515455; 22 Yew Tree Road, Tunbridge Wells TN4 0BA Tel: 01892 531655 Fax: 01892 531655 — MB BS 1977 Lond.; MRCGP 1982; DRCOG 1981; AKC. Prev: Trainee GP Brighton VTS; Ho. Surg. Dulwich Hosp. Lond.; Ho. Phys. Gravesend & N. Kent Hosp. Gravesend.

ROBSON, Elizabeth Jane 57 Tabors Avenue, Great Baddow, Chelmsford CM2 7EJ — BM 1983 Soton.

ROBSON, Eva Gwendoline (retired) 7 Waterside, Staindrop Road, Darlington DL3 9AF Tel: 01325 488202 — MB BS 1946 Durh.; DObst RCOG 1948. Prev: GP Hurworth-on-Tees.

ROBSON, Fiona Susan 58 Hollies Way, Bushby, Leicester LE7 9RJ — MB ChB 1977 Leeds.

ROBSON, Georgina Mary Willett East Oxford Health Centre, Manzil Way, Cowley Road, Cowley, Oxford OX4 1XD Tel: 01865 242109; St. Marys Cottage, Church St, Beckley, Oxford OX3 9UT Tel: 01865 351637 — MB BS 1968 Lond.; DCH Eng. 1972; DObst RCOG 1970. (Middlx.) GP Oxf. Prev: Clin. Asst. (Drug Dependency) Char. Cross Hosp. Lond.; SHO (Paediat.) St. Chas. Hosp. Lond.

ROBSON, Guy Ernest William 165 Bury New Road, Prestwich, Manchester M25 9PJ — MB ChB 1970 Leeds; BSc (Hons.) Leeds 1967; FFA RCS Eng. 1976. (Leeds) Cons. N. Manch. Healthcare Trust. Prev: Sen. Regist. Manch. Roy. Infirm.; Regist. Leeds Gen. Infirm.; SHO & Ho. Off. Leeds Gen. Infirm.

ROBSON, Jacqueline (retired) The Old Vicarage, 62 Williams Park, Benton, Newcastle upon Tyne NE12 8BL Tel: 0191 215 9898 — MB BS 1947 Durh. Prev: Anaesth. Regist., Ho. Phys. & Ho. Surg. Roy. Vict. Infirm. Newc. upon.

ROBSON, Professor Sir (James) Gordon, CBE Brendon, Lyndale, London NW2 2NY Tel: 020 7435 3762 Fax: 020 7435 3762 — MB ChB 1944 Glas.; MB ChB (Commend.) Glas. 1944; Hon. FDS RCS 1979; Hon. FFA RACS 1968; DSc McGill 1984; Hon. DSc Glas. 1990; FRCS Eng. 1977; Hon. FRCPS Glas. 1993; Hon. FRCPC 1988; FFA RCS Eng. 1953; DA Eng. 1948; Hon. FFA RCSI 1980. Emerit. Prof. Univ. Lond.; Ex-Chairm. Advis. Comm. Dist. Awards. Socs: Hon. Fell. (Ex-Pres.) Roy. Soc. Med.; Life Vice-Pres. Roy. Nat. Lifeboat Inst.; Hon. Mem. Assn. Anaesth. Prev: Prof. & Hon. Cons. Anaesth. Roy. Postgrad. Med. Sch. Hammersmith Hosp.Lond.; Vice-Pres. RCS Eng.; Wellcome Research Prof. McGill Univ.

ROBSON, James Peter West Gate Health Centre, Charleston Drive, Dundee DD2 4AD Tel: 01382 668189 Fax: 01382 665943; 8 Piperdam Drive, Piperdam DD2 5LY — MB ChB 1988 Dundee; MRCGP 1995; Dip SEM GB & I 2000.

ROBSON, James Scott 1 Grant Avenue, Colinton, Edinburgh EH13 0DS Tel: 0131 441 3508 — MB ChB (Hons.) Ed. 1945; MD Ed. 1946; FRCP Lond. 1978, M 1978; FRCP Ed. 1960, M 1948. (Univs. Ed. & N.Y.) Prof. Med. (Emerit.) Univ. Edin. Socs: Assn. Phys.; Renal Assn. Prev: Hon. Cons. Phys. Roy. Infirm. Edin.; Sen. Regist. Roy. Infirm. Edin.; New York Univ. Postgrad. Fell. Med. Research Rockefeller Fell.

ROBSON, Mrs Jane Mary 96 Chesterton Road, Cambridge CB4 1ER Tel: 01223 365555 Fax: 01223 356848; Herrings House, Wilbraham Road, Fulbourn, Cambridge CB1 5EU Tel: 01223 880277 — MB BChir Camb. 1961; MA Camb. 1961; DObst RCOG 1962. (St. Thos.) GP; Hosp. Pract. (Geriat.). Socs: Accred. Mem. Brit. Med. Acupunc. Soc.

ROBSON, Jannette King Street Surgery, 190 King Street, Cottingham HU16 5QJ Tel: 01482 847250 Fax: 01482 848173 — MB ChB 1987 Leic.; MRCGP 1991; DRCOG 1990. Prev: Trainee GP Walston, Coventry.

ROBSON, Jean, MBE (retired) New Barn Cottage, Alston Lane, Longridge, Preston PR3 3BN Tel: 01772 785395 — MB ChB 1948 Manch.; DCH Eng. 1951. Prev: SCMO (Audiol.) Preston HA.

ROBSON, Jean Elizabeth Charlotte Street Surgery, 1 Charlotte Street, Dumfries DG1 2AG Tel: 01387 267626 Fax: 01387 266824; Farthings, High Road, Hightae, Lockerbie DG11 1JS Tel: 01387 811233 — MB BS 1980 Lond.; MRCGP 1985; Dip. Sports Med. (Lond.) 1988; DRCOG 1987. Socs: Roy. Coll. Gen. Pract. & Brit. Assn. Sports Med.

ROBSON, Jennifer Jane 6 Rosevale, Hoddesdon EN11 8NR — MB BS 1988 Western Australia.

ROBSON, Jo-Anna 23 Broadway, Shifnal TF11 8BB — MB ChB 1996 Glas.

***ROBSON, John David** 25 Florance Road, Wimbledon, London SW19 8TH — MB ChB 1997 Otago.

ROBSON, John Dickson Hilton, New Ridley, Stocksfield NE43 7RQ — MB ChB 1980 Dundee. Prev: Ho. Off. (Gen. Surg.) Arbroath; Ho. Off. (Gen. Med.) N.ampton Gen. Hosp.

ROBSON, John Laidlaw Yew Tree Medical Centre, 100 Yew Tree Lane, Solihull B91 2RA Tel: 0121 705 8787 Fax: 0121 709 0240 — MB BS Newc. 1969; DObst RCOG 1972. Prev: Med.Off.jaguar Cars; med.Off.Land rover; Med.Off.Birm City FC.

ROBSON, John Peter Chrisp Street Health Centre, 100 Chrisp Street, London E14 6PG Tel: 020 7515 4860 Fax: 020 7515 3055 — MB BS 1974 Lond.; MSc Lond. 1984, MB BS 1974; MRCGP 1978; DCH Eng. 1978; DRCOG 1977.

ROBSON, John Ryder (retired) The White Cottage, Newick, Lewes BN8 4SA Tel: 01825 722510 — MB BS 1960 Lond.; MRCS Eng. LRCP Lond. 1960; DObst RCOG 1963.

ROBSON, Julia Claire 115 Sherburn Way, Gateshead NE10 8TZ — MB BCh 1983 Wales; MRCGP 1987; DRCOG 1986. Prev: Trainee GP E. Dist. Glas. VTS.

ROBSON, Keith Henry Bingley Health Centre, Myrtle Place, Bingley BD16 2TL Tel: 01274 362760 Fax: 01274 772345 — MB ChB 1979 Leeds; DA Eng. 1982; Cert. Family Plann. JCC 1984. Prev: Trainee GP/SHO Bradford VTS; SHO (Anaesth.) Bradford Gp. Hosp.; Ho. Off. (Med.) York Dist. Hosp.

ROBSON, Mark Charlton (retired) Maple House, 28 The Green, Hurworth-on-Tees, Darlington DL2 2AA — MB BS 1947 Durh. Prev: GP Hurworth-on-Tees.

ROBSON, Mr Martin John Orthopaedic Department, Rotherham District General Hospital, Moorgate Road, Rotherham S60 2UD Tel: 01709 304554 Fax: 01709 304220; 77 Rundle Road, Sheffield S7 1NW Tel: 0114 258 8660 — MB BS 1966 Lond.; LMCC

ROBSON

Licentiate Medical College of Canada; FRCS Eng. 1971; MRCS Eng. LRCP Lond. 1966. (Char. Cross) Cons. Orthop. Surg. Rotherham Dist. Gen. Hosp. Socs: Fell. BOA; BMA; Soc. Back Pain Research. Prev: Sen. Regist. (Orthop.) Sheff. AHA (T); Sen. Surg. Off. (Orthop.) Oxf. Regional Rheum. Dis. Research Centre Stoke Mandeville; Clin. Fell. St. Michaels Hosp. Toronto, Canada.

ROBSON, Matthew Town End, Far Sawrey, Ambleside LA22 0LH Tel: 015394 47427; 19 Fernbank Road, Redland, Bristol BS6 6QA Tel: 0117 944 6912 — MB ChB 1993 Bristol; MRCP (UK) 1996. Clin. Fell. (Bone Marrow Transpl.) Roy. Hosp. Sick Childr. Bristol. Prev: SHO (Paediat.) S.mead Hosp. & Bristol Roy. Hosp. Sick Childr.; SHO (Neonat. Med.) St. Michael's Hosp. Bristol.

ROBSON, Melanie Jayne Level 4, Women's Centre, John Radcliffe Hospital, Headley Way, Headington, Oxford OX3 9DZ; 64 Margaret Road, Headington, Oxford OX3 8NQ Tel: 01865 760989 Email: melanie.robson@orh.nhs.uk — MB BS 1984 Lond.; MRCOG 1990. Cons. Feto-Matern. Med. Wom. Centre John Radcliffe Hosp. Oxf. Socs: BMUS; Brit. Matern. & Fetal Med. Soc.; Blair Bell Res. Soc. Prev: Research Fell. (Obst.) St. Geo. Hosp. Med. Sch. Lond.; Sen. Regist. Roy. United Hosp. Bath & St. Michael's Hosp. Bristol.

ROBSON, Michael Gregory 117 Sutherland Avenue, London W9 2QJ — MB BS 1992 Lond.

ROBSON, Michael James Allan 25 Avondale Place, Edinburgh EH3 5HX — MB ChB 1988 Ed.

ROBSON, Michael John Pilladilly House, 17 Pilladilly, Slotforth, Lancaster LA1 4PX — MB ChB 1990 Ed.; MRCPsych 1999 Roy. Coll. of Psychiat. Specialists Regist. (Gen. Adult Psychiat.) Roy. Preston Hosp. Socs: Life Mem. Roy. Med. Soc. Edin. Prev: Specialist Regist., Gen Adult Psycian, Ridge Way, Lancaster; Hon. Specialist Regist. & Clincal Research Fell., Roy. Preston Hosp.

ROBSON, Michael Stanley (retired) 4 Cefn Gethinog, Talybont-on-Usk, Brecon LD3 7YN Tel: 01874 676345 Fax: 01874 676292 — MB 1955 Camb.; BChir 1954; DTM & H Lond. 1961.

ROBSON, Mr Michael Stephen Department of Obstetrics & Gynaecology, Wycombe General Hospital, Queen Alexandra Road, High Wycombe HP11 2TT — MB BS 1982 Lond.; FRCS Eng. 1987; MRCOG 1990. Cons. O & G Wycombe Gen. Hosp. Prev: Asst. Master Nat. Matern. Hosp. Dub.

ROBSON, Nicola Kay Poole Hospital, Long Fleet Road, Poole BH15 2JB — MB BChir 1985 Camb.; MA Camb. 1988; BSc Hull 1981; BA Camb. 1983, MB BChir 1985; FRCR 1992; T(R) (CR) 1993; DMRD Lond. 1990. (Cambridge University) Cons. Radiol. Poole Hosp. NHS Trust. Socs: Assoc. Mem. Roy. Soc. Med.; BMA; BNMS. Prev: Sen. Regist. (Radiol.) Soton. Gen. Hosp.; Regist. (Radiol.) Soton. Gen. Hosp.; SHO Rotat. (Med.) Addenbrooke's Hosp. Camb.

ROBSON, Nigel Jonathan 12 Charlotte Road, Edgbaston, Birmingham B15 2NG — MB 1980 Camb.; BChir 1979; FFA RCS Eng. 1983. Cons. Paediat. Anaesth. Childr. Hosp. Birm.

ROBSON, Noel Leslie Kent (retired) 33 Worsley Crescent, Marton, Middlesbrough TS7 8LU Tel: 01642 315384 — MB BS Durh. 1956; DMRT Eng. 1964. Cons. Radiother. & Oncol. Regional Radiother. Serv. Newc. Hosp. & S. Cleveland Dist. Gen. Hosp. Middlesbrough; Assoc. Clin. Lect. (Radiother.) Univ. Newc. Prev: Sen. Regist. (Radiother.) Roy. Infirm. & W.. Gen. Hosp. Edin.

ROBSON, Peter 1 Buttermere Avenue, Whickham, Newcastle upon Tyne NE16 4EX Tel: 0191 488 7519 — MB 1975 Camb.; BA Camb. 1971, MB 1975, BChir 1974; FRCP Lond. 1989; MRCP (UK) 1977. Cons. Phys. Responsibil. c/o Elderly N. Durh. Acute Hosps. NHS Trust.

ROBSON, Peter (retired) 270 Wickham Chase, West Wickham BR4 0BS Tel: 020 8325 7493 Email: e-mail@drrobson.fsnet.co.uk — MB BS 1959 Lond.; FRCP Ed. 1977, M 1968; MRCS Eng. LRCP Lond. 1959; DCH Eng. 1961. Sen. Lect. (Neuro-Developm. Paediat.) KCH Med. Sch. Lond.; Cons. Paediat. King's Coll. Hosp. Lond., Bethlem Roy. & Maudsley Hosps. Prev: Cons. Paediat. Guy's Hosp. Lond.

ROBSON, Peter Anthony (retired) 17 Thornlea, Hepscott, Morpeth NE61 6NY Tel: 01670 516867 Email: peterarobson@thetreeinternot.co.uk — MB BS 1956 Durh. Prev: Ho. Phys. (Child Health) Roy. Vict. Infirm. Newc. u. Tyne.

ROBSON, Peter Grant Ravens Craig, Main St., Kinnesswood, Kinross KY13 9HW — MB ChB 1980 Dundee; MRCGP 1984; DRCOG 1984. GP Kinnesswood.

ROBSON, Mr Peter Napier (retired) The Old Vicarage, 62 Williams Park, Newcastle upon Tyne NE12 8BL — MB BS Durh. 1946; FRCS Eng. 1949; MRCS Eng. LRCP Lond. 1946. Hon. Cons. Orthop. Surg. Newc. HA.

ROBSON, Peter William 38 Keathbank Avenue, Irby, Wirral L62 4XD — MB ChB 1989 Liverp. SHO (A & E) Countess of Chester Hosp.

ROBSON, Philip John Chilton Clinic, The Warneford Hospital, Oxford OX3 7JX Tel: 01865 226288 Fax: 01865 226437 — MB BS 1970 Lond.; MRCP (UK) 1978; MRCPsych 1985. Region Cons. & Cons. Psychiat. Subst. Misuse Oxf.; Sen. Clin. Lect. Univ. Oxf. Prev: Clin. Lect. (Psychiat.) Univ. Oxf.

ROBSON, Piers Cowen (retired) Snuff Mill Cottage, Mitford, Morpeth NE61 3PY — MB ChB 1958 St. And.; MRCPsych 1971; DPM Eng. 1964. Prev: Cons. Psychiat. St. Geo. Hosp. Morpeth & Cherry Knowle Hosp. Ryhope.

ROBSON, Richard Austin Department of Clinical Pharmacology, Roche Products, PO Box 8, Welwyn Garden City AL7 3AV — MB ChB 1977 Otago.

ROBSON, Rita Ann Tel: 01912 596660 Ext: 2968 Fax: 01912 934135 Email: rita.robson@northumbria-healthcare.nhs.uk; Twickenfield, Shotley Bridge, Consett DH8 0NJ — MB ChB 1979 Manch.; BSc 1976 Manch. Univ.; 1985 FRCR. (Manch.) Cons. Radiol. N. Tyneside Gen. Hosp. N.umbria Health Care NHS Trust. Prev: Cons. Radiol. N. Durh. Acute Hosps. NHS Trust; Sen. Regist. & Regist. (Radiol.) Roy. Vict. Infirm. Newc.

ROBSON, Sarah Chainsbridge Medical Partnership, Chainbridge House, The Precinct, Blaydon-on-Tyne NE21 5BT Tel: 0191 414 2856 Fax: 0191 499 0449; Boundary House, Roseworth Terrace, Gosforth, Newcastle upon Tyne NE3 1LU Tel: 0191 213 1132 — MB BS 1985 Lond.; DCH RCP Lond. 1990; DRCOG 1990. (St Bartholomew's Hospital Medical School) Prev: Trainee GP Ashford; Trainee GP W. Middlx. Univ. Hosp. VTS.

ROBSON, Professor Stephen Courtenay Department of Obstetrics & Gynaecology, University Newcastle upon Tyne, Royal Victoria Infirmary, Newcastle upon Tyne NE1 4LP Tel: 0191 232 5131 Fax: 0191 222 5066 Email: s.c.robson@ncl.ac.uk; Email: s.c.robson@ncl.ac.uk — MB BS 1982 Newc.; MD Newc. 1992; MRCOG 1987. Prof. Fetal Med. Univ. Newc. u. Tyne & Roy. Vict. Infirm. Prev: Sen. Lect. (Obst.) & Regist. (O & G) Roy. Vict. Infirm. Newc.; RCOG Train. Fell. (Fetal Med.) Univ. Coll. Hosp. Lond.

ROBSON, Susan Andrée University of Manchester Health and Safety Services, Waterloo Place, 182/184 Oxford Road, Manchester M13 9DG Tel: 0161 275 697011 Fax: 0161 275 6989 Email: susan.a.robson@man.ac.uk; Hollows Farm, Stamford Lane, Christleton, Chester CH3 7QD Tel: 01244 335368 — MB BS Newc. 1968; MFFP 1995; FFOM RCP Lond. 1992, MFOM 1985; FRCP Lond. 1998. (University of Newcastle-upon-Tyne) Dir. Health & Safety Servs., Univ. of Manch.; Hon Lect. Centre for Occup. Health Univ. Manch.; Clin. Med. Off.; family Plann.; primary care trust Chester. Socs: ex Chairm. Assn. of social sulitory Med. Advisers; Curr. Chairm. BMA occup. Health Comm.; Curr. Mem. bma Counc. Prev: Ho. Phys. W. Suff. Gen. Hosp.; Ho. Surg. Chester Roy. Infirm.; Country Med. health and safety, admin Occupat.al health.

ROBSON, Timothy William Cassio Surgery, 62-68 Merton Road, Watford WD18 0WL Tel: 01923 226011 Fax: 01923 817342; 96 Church Road, Watford WD17 4PU Tel: 01923 225798 — MB BS 1975 Lond.; BSc Lond. 1972, MB BS 1975. (Lond. Hosp.) Prev: SHO (Trop. Med.) Hosp. Trop. Dis. Lond.; SHO (Med. Oncol.) Roy. Marsden Hosp. Sutton; SHO (Gen. Med. & Rheum.) N.wick Pk. Hosp.

ROBSON, Victoria-Anne Royal Victoria Infirmary, Queen Victoria Road, Newcastle upon Tyne NE1 4LP — MB BS 1991 Lond.; 2001 EDIC; BSc (Hons.) Lond. 1988; MRCP (UK) 1995; FRCA 1997. (St. George's Hospital, University of London) Cons. Anaesth. ITG Roy. Vict. Infirm. Newc. Socs: Roy. Coll. Of Anaesth.; Assn. of Anaesth.; Intens. Care Soc. Prev: SPR (ITG) Roy. S. Hampton Hosp.; Specialist Regist. (Anaesth.) St. Marys Hosp.; SPR (Anaesth.) Hammersmith Hosp.

ROBSON, William Armstrong Elmsmoor Lodge, Fence Hill Park, Newcastle upon Tyne NE3 2EA — LRCP LRCS 1944 Ed.; LRCP LRCS Ed. LRFPS Glas. 1944.

ROBSON, Winifred Joan Royal Liverpool Children's NHS Trust, AlderHey, Liverpool LI2 2AP Tel: 0151 228 4811; Email:

ROBY JONES

joan@joanmclelland.freeserve.co.uk — MB ChB 1967 Liverp.; FRCS Eng. 1972; FFAEM 1994; FRCPCH 1997. (Liverp.) Cons. Paediat.. Roy. Liverp. Childr. Hosp. Alder Hey.; Liverp. Univ.; Teachg. Asst. Socs: BMA; Brit. Assn. Accid. & Emerg. Med.; Bd. Fac. A&E Med. Prev: Sen. Research Asst. Dept. Child Health Alder Hey Childr. Hosp.; Liverp.; Regist. (Paediat. Surg. & Urol.) Alder Hey Childr. Hosp. Liverp.

ROBY JONES, Christopher (retired) 1 Chichester Close, Instow, Bideford EX39 4JT Tel: 01271 860560 — MB ChB 1958 Liverp.; FRCP Lond. 1980, M 1965. Cons. Phys. in Geriat. N. Devon Hosp. Gp. Prev: Sen. Regist. (Geriat.) Char. Cross Hosp. Gp.

ROBYNS-OWEN, David Treflan Surgery, Treflan, Lower Cardiff Road, Pwllheli LL53 5NF Tel: 01758 701457 Fax: 01758 701209; Treflan, Penlan St, Pwllheli LL53 5D Tel: 01758 612457 — MB ChB 1979 Liverp.; DRCOG 1983.

ROCH-BERRY, Colin Sydney Bertram Fair Acres, Badgeworth Lane, Badgeworth, Cheltenham GL51 4UJ Tel: 01242 862703 Fax: 01242 862703 Email: culinrb@dial.pipex.com — MB BS Lond. 1969; LLM 1991 Cardiff; MRCS Eng. LRCP Lond. 1968; FRCR 1975. (St. Bart.) Cons. Clin. Oncol. Glos.Oncol.Centre Cheltenham; Mem. UK Forum Health Care, Ethics & Law; Caldicott Guardian, EGNHST; Fell. (Governor) Cheltenham & Gloucester Coll. of Higher Educat.; Pres. Cancer Relief Macmillan Fund Gloucester. Socs: Medico-Leg. Soc.; BMA; Roy. Soc. Med. Prev: Sen. Regist. (Radiother.) Christie Hosp. & Holt Radium Inst. Manch.

ROCHA JANEIRO, Maria Magdelena 5 Laurel Bank, The Highlands, Whitehaven CA28 6SW Tel: 01946 694324 — LMS 1984 Barcelona. VTS (GP) Cumbria VTS for Gen. Pract. in W. Cumbria; GP Regist. Whitehaven. Socs: BMA; Med. Protec. Soc. Prev: SHO (O & G) Bishop Auckland Gen. Hosp.

ROCHE, Caroline Jane Heath The Surgery, 2-4 Steerforth Street, Earlsfield, London SW18 4HL; 92 Arthur Road, London SW19 7DT Tel: 020 8947 4916 — MB BS 1955 Lond. (Univ. Coll. Hosp.) Prev: SHO (Path.) Lewisham Hosp.; Ho. Surg. Roy. Hosp. Richmond; Ho. Phys. St. Mary Abbots Hosp. Kensington.

ROCHE, David Belmont Surgery, St. James Square, Wadhurst TN5 6BJ Tel: 01892 782121 Fax: 01892 783989; 3 Eastfield Cottages, Tidebrook, Wadhurst TN5 6PF Tel: 01892 782336 — MB BS 1981 Lond.; BSc Lond. 1977; MRCGP 1986; DRCOG 1982. Prev: Trainee GP Tunbridge Wells VTS.

ROCHE, David Walter (retired) 92 Arthur Road, Wimbledon, London SW19 7DT Tel: 020 8947 4916 — MB BS 1956 Lond. Prev: GP Lond.

ROCHE, Denis Arthur (retired) 44 Corbett Avenue, Droitwich WR9 7BE Tel: 01905 773956 Email: denis.roche@care4free.net — MB BS 1951 Lond.; AFOM RCP Lond. 1982; DIH Dund 1980; DTM & H Liverp. 1976; DTCD Wales 1966; DObst RCOG 1955. Prev: Internat. Med. Adviser Interserve Cyprus.

ROCHE, Donal Francis Ellis The Meadows Surgery, Temple Grove, Gatehouse Lane, Sussex Way, Burgess Hill RH15 9XH Tel: 01444 242860 Fax: 01444 870496 — MB BCh BAO 1979 NUI; MRCGP 1984; MFHom 1989; DRCOG 1986. (University College Dublin)

ROCHE, Duncan Charles James The Central Dales Practice, The Health Centre, Hawes DL8 3QR Tel: 01696 667200 — MB BS 1991 Lond.; BDS Manch. 1983; MRCGP 1995; DRCOG 1994. (St Georges) Socs: BMA; BASICS; Vice-Chairm. N. Yorks. Rd. Accid. Aftercare Scheme. Prev: Trainee GP S. Cumbria VTS; SHO (Oral & Maxillofacial Surg.) Arrowe Pk. Hosp.

ROCHE, John Desmond (retired) Eden Brook, Ivy Mill Lane, Godstone RH9 8NE Tel: 01883 742251 — MRCS Eng. LRCP Lond. 1951. Prev: Gen. Pract.

ROCHE, Justin Southampton General Hospital, Tremona Road, Shirley, Southampton SO16 6YD Tel: 02380 777222; 23 Acorn Grove, Chandlers Ford, Eastleigh SO53 4LA Email: justin.roche@virgin.net — MB ChB 1996 Leeds. (Leeds) SHO Rotat. (Paediat.) Soton. Gen. Hosp. Prev: SHO (Paediat.) St Mary's IOW; PRHO (Paediat. & Gen. Surg.) Leeds Gen. Infirm.; PRHO (Padeiatrics) St Jas. Leeds.

ROCHE, Kenneth Pierce Mary New Lodge, Cardigan Road, Westbury-on-Trym, Bristol BS9 4DY — MB BCh BAO 1949 NUI; Dipl. Obst. 1950; MRCGP 1962. (Cork) Socs: Bristol M-C Soc. & Cossham Med. Soc. Prev: Sen. Ho. Surg. Mercy Hosp. Cork; Sen. Obst. Off. Erinville Hosp. Cork; SHO O & G Roy. Gwent Hosp. Newport.

ROCHE, Mary Teresa West Norwich Hospital, Bowthorpe Road, Norwich NR2 3TU — MB BCh BAO 1980 NUI; MRCP (UK) 1988. Staff Doctor (Med. for Elderly) W. Norwich Hosp. Prev: Regist. (Gen. & Geriat. Med.) Roy. Devon & Exeter Hosp.; Regist. (Gen. Med.) Walsgrave Hosp. Coventry.

ROCHE, Monica Emmet Renal Unit, Manchester Royal Infirmary, Oxford Road, Manchester M13 9WL; 37 The Fairway, Fixby, Huddersfield HD2 2HU Tel: 01484 420918 — MB ChB 1973 Manch. Prev: Clin. Asst. Renal Unit Manch. Roy. Infirm.; Med. Pract.(Family Plann.) Rochdale; SHO (Anaesth.) & SHO (O & G) Wythenshawe Hosp. Manch.

ROCHE, Nicola Anne Frimley Park Hospital, Camberley GU16 7UJ; 16 Esmond Court, Thackeray St, London W8 5HB — MB BCh BAO 1989 Dub.; FRCS Ed. 1993. Specialist Regist. (Gen. Surg.) Frimley Pk. Hosp. Prev: Research Regist. (Gen. Surg.) Roy. Marsden Hosp. Sutton; Regist. Rotat. (Gen. Surg.) St. Helier Hosp. SW Thames.

ROCHE, Ruth Elizabeth The White Rose Surgery, Exchange Street, South Elmsall, Pontefract WF9 2RD Tel: 01977 642412 Fax: 01977 641290; The Copse, Bannister Lane, Skelbrooke, Doncaster DN6 8LU Tel: 01302 723068 Fax: 01302 728330 — MB BS 1987 Lond.; DRCOG 1990; DCH RCP Lond. 1990. (St. Thos. Hosp. Lond.) Clin. Asst. P. of Wales Hospice Pontefract.

ROCHE, Shane William St Marys Hospital, Praed Street W2 1NY Tel: 0207 886 1077; 9 Meadow View, West Street, Harrow on the Hill HA1 3DN Tel: 0208 426 9829 — MB BCh BAO 1980 NUI; LRCPI & LM, LRCSI & LM BAO 1980; MRCP (UK) 1984; FRCP 1997. Cons. Med. for Elderly St. Mary's & St. Chas. Hosp. Lond. Prev: Sen. Regist. (Geriat.) St. Mary's Hosp. Lond.; Regist. (Neurol.) Char. Cross Hosp. Lond.

ROCHE, Professor William Robert Patrick Department of Pathology, University of Southampton, Southampton General Hospital, Southampton SO16 6YD Tel: 02380 796671 Fax: 02380 796603 Email: wrr@soton.ac.uk — MD 1986 NUI; MSc (Path.) NUI 1981, BSc (Path.) 1980, MD 1986, MB BCh BAO 1978; FFPath RCPI 1990; FRCPath 1997, MRCPath 1988. Prof. (Pathol.) Univ. Soton.; Hon. Cons. (Path.) Soton. Univ. Hosps. NHS Trust. Prev: Sen. Lect. Path Univ. Soton; Vis. Investig. Kolling Inst. Med. Research, Roy. N. Shore Hosp. Sydney; Asst. (Path.) Univ. Coll. Dub.

ROCHESTER, Mr John Robert 59 Barholm Road, Sheffield S10 5RR — BM 1986 Soton.; MD Sheff. 1995; FRCS Eng. 1992; FRCS (Gen) 1997.

ROCHETEAU, Marc Steven Department of Anaesthetics, Royal Halifax Infirmary, Free School Lane, Halifax HX1 2YP — MB ChB 1987 Leic.

ROCHFORD, Frances Mary Margaret 12 Newland Park, Cottingham Road, Hull HU5 2DW — MB BS 1974 Lond. (Guy's)

ROCHFORD, John James Templars Way Surgery, Templars Way, Sharnbrook, Bedford MK44 1PZ Tel: 01234 781392 Fax: 01234 781468; Jubilee House, Odell Road, Sharnbrook, Bedford MK44 1JL Tel: 01234 782473 — MB BChir 1980 Camb.; DRCOG 1983; MRCGP 1985; MRCGP 1985; DRCOG 1983. (Barts.) Gen. Practitioner, Beds.

ROCHFORT, Andree Mary Catherine Woodlands Surgery, 1 Greenfarm Road, Ely, Cardiff CF5 4RG Tel: 029 2059 1444 — MB BCh BAO 1987 Dub.; BA, MB BCh BAO Dub. 1987; MRCGP 1991. Prev: Trainee GP S. Glam. VTS; Ho. Off. (Med. Surg.) St. Jas. Hosp. Dub.

ROCHOW, Stuart Blair The Stables, Gillisfauld Farm, Drum Road, Cupar KY15 5DU — MB ChB 1985 Ed.; MRCP (UK) 1990. Cons. Phys. Vict. Hosp. Kirkcaldy. Prev: Sen. Regist. (Gen. & Geriat. Med.) Roy. Cornw. Hosp. Truro; Regist. (Geriat.) City Hosp. Edin.; Regist. (Gen. Med.) Vict. Hosp. Kirkcaldy.

ROCK, Clare Louise Theale Medical Centre, Englefield Road, Theale, Reading RG7 5AS; Englefield Road, Theale, Reading RG7 5AS — MB ChB 1992 Birm.; MRCGP 1997; DFFP 1997. (Birmingham)

ROCK, Iain William 2 Hay Park, Birmingham B5 7LT — MB ChB 1991 Birm.; ChB Birm. 1991.

ROCKALL, Andrea Grace The Middlesex Hospital, Martimer St., London W1T 3AA; 9 Jackson's Lane, Highgate, London N6 5SR Email: timrockall@aol.com — MB BS 1990 Lond.; BSc (1st cl. Hons.) Lond. 1987; MRCP (UK) 1993; FRCR 1997. (King's Coll. Hosp. Med. Sch.) Sen. Regist. (Radiol.) Middlx. Hosp. Lond. Prev: Regist. (Radiol.) St. Mary's Hosp.

ROCKALL, Linda Jane Chestnut House, St. Georges Road, Worthing BN11 2DR Tel: 01903 239861 — MB BS 1971 Lond.; MRCS Eng. LRCP Lond. 1971; FRCR 1977; DMRD Eng. 1975. Cons. Radiol. Worthing & S.lands NHS Trust.

ROCKALL, Mr Timothy Alexander 9 Jackson's Lane, Highgate, London N6 5SR — MB BS 1988 Lond.; FRCS Eng. 1992; FRCS (Gen. Surg.) 1999; MD Lond 1998. (GUYs Hosp.) Higher Surgic. Trainee St. Mary's Hosp. Lond.

ROCKE, Mr Laurence Gilmore Department Accident & Emergency, Royal Victoria Hospital, Belfast BT12 6BA Tel: 01232 240503; 83 Gransha Road, Dundonald, Belfast BT16 1XQ Tel: 01232 481621 — MB BCh BAO 1971 Belf.; FRCS Ed. 1975. Cons. A & E Med. Roy. Vict. Hosp. Belf. Socs: Cas. Brit. Assn. Accid. & Emerg. Med. Prev: Cons. A & E Med. Mater Infirmorum Hosp. Belf.; Sen. Regist. (A & E) Roy. Vict. Hosp. Belf.

ROCKER, Israel (retired) Lawnside, 2 Stow Park Circle, Newport NP20 4HE — MB BS 1950 Lond.; MD Lond. 1963; FRCOG 1968, M 1955; MRCS Eng. LRCP Lond. 1950. Prev: Cons. O & G Roy. Gwent Hosp. & Co. Hosp. Griffithstown.

ROCKER, Michael Daniel 35 Grantham Road, London W4 2RT — MB BS 1994 Lond.; BDS Lond. 1986.

ROCKER, Philip Benjamin County Hospital, North Road, Durham DH1 4ST Tel: 0191 333 3441; 31 Stobbart Terrace, Fishburn, Stockton-on-Tees TS21 4AF — MB BS 1981 Lond.; MRCPsych 1988. Locum Cons. (Psychiat.) Co. Hosp. Durh. Prev: Staff Grade (Psychiat.) Co. Hosp. Durh.; Staff Grade (Psychiat.) Highfield Day Hosp. Chester-le-St.; Regist. (Psychiat.) Winterton Hosp. SW Durh.

ROCKETT, Helena Elizabeth 1 Lister Court, Thorne Road, Doncaster DN2 5AB — MB ChB 1979 Sheff.

ROCKETT, James William Westgate Practice, Greenhill Health Centre, Church Street, Lichfield WS13 6JL Tel: 01543 414311 Fax: 01543 256364 — MB ChB 1991 Birm.

ROCKETT, Mark Peter 33 Sellwood Road, Abingdon OX14 1PE — MB ChB 1993 Bristol.

ROCKLEY, Peter Anderson The Gold Street Surgery, Gold St., Saffron Walden CB10 1EJ Tel: 01799 525325 Fax: 01799 524042 — MB ChB 1966 St. And.

ROCKLEY, Mr Timothy Joseph The Croft House, Station Road, Rolleston-on-Dove, Burton-on-Trent DE13 9AA — MB BCh 1978 Wales; FRCS Eng. 1983; T(S) 1991; MD University of Wales 1999. Cons. ENT Surg. Burton, Lichfield & Tamworth Hosp. Prev: Sen. Regist. W. Midl. Higher Surgic. Train. Progr. in Otolaryngol.; Research Fell. Univ. Toronto, Canada.

ROCKWELL, Susan Rosemary Portslade Health Centre, Church Road, Portslade, Brighton BN41 1LX Tel: 01273 422525/418445 Fax: 01273 413510; 63 Woodland Avenue, Hove BN3 6BJ Tel: 01273 559654 — MB BS 1987 Lond.; DRCOG 1991; DCH RCP Lond. 1991. (Char. Cross & Westm. Med. Sch.) GP; Vice Chairm. of PCG.

ROCKWELL, Valerie Elizabeth Little St John Street Surgery, 7 Little St. John Street, Woodbridge IP12 1EE Tel: 01384 382046 — MB BS 1983 Lond.; DRCOG 1986. (Westm.)

ROCYN-JONES, James Rowland (retired) South Lawn, 18 Hermosa Road, Teignmouth TQ14 9JZ Tel: 01626 772031 — LMSSA 1937 Lond.

ROCYN-JONES, John Melville House, Ruardean, Gloucester GL17 9US — MB BS 1964 Durh.; DObst RCOG 1966. (Newc.) Ho. Phys. Paediat. St. Woolos Hosp. Newport. Prev: Ho. Phys. & Ho. Surg. Cheltenham Gen. Hosp.

RODAN, Konrad S (retired) Squirrels, Kithurst Park, Storrington, Pulborough RH20 4JH Tel: 01798 742971 — MD 1938 Prague; FRCPath 1963. Prev: Dir. Path. Worthing, S.lands & Dist. Hosps.

RODD, Caroline Dawn Highfield, Alexandra Road, Crediton EX17 2DZ — MB BCh 1990 Wales; FRCS Eng. 1996; DCH 1993. (Univ. Wales Coll. Med.) Lect. Vasc. Surg. Char. Cross Hosp. Lond.; Specialist Regist. N. W. Thames Rot. Socs: Affil. Assn. Surgs. GB & Irel.; Affil. Vasc. Surg. Soc.; Assoc. of Surg.s in Train.

RODDA, Louise Claire Mullion Cottage, Church Road, Chrishall, Royston SG8 8QT — MB BS 1997 Newc.

RODDAM, Philip Adrian Kirkside Elton, Stockton-on-Tees TS21 1AG — MB ChB 1987 Ed.

RODDEN, Nigel David 350 Castlereagh Road, Belfast BT5 6AE — MB BCh BAO 1995 Belf.

RODDICK, Isobel Aitchison Garlands Hospital, Carlisle CA1 3SX Tel: 01228 602000 Fax: 01228 602550; 8 Nithsdale Place, Dumfries DG1 3HT Tel: 01387 261610 — MB ChB 1967 Glas.; MRCPsych 1984; DObst RCOG 1970. (Glas.) Clin. Asst. (Adult Psychiat.) Garlands Hosp. Carlisle. Socs: BMA. Prev: Regist. (Child Adolesc. Psychiat.) Crichton Roy. Hosp. Dumfries; Clin. Med. Off. Dumfries & Galloway HB.

RODDICK, Jonathan Neil Woodseats Medical Centre, 4 Cobnar Road, Woodseats, Sheffield S8 8QB Tel: 0114 274 0202 Fax: 0114 274 6835; 19 Hoober Road, Ecclesall, Sheffield S11 9SF Tel: 0114 235 1766 Fax: 0114 235 1766 — MB ChB 1986 Sheff.; MRCGP 1990; Dip Occupat Med 1998. GP Princip. Woodseats Med. Centre; Chairm. S.W. Sheff. PCG. Prev: Occupat. Health Adviser S. Yorks. Police.

RODDIE, Alastair Ewan 81 Harpers Lane, Bolton BL1 6HU — MB ChB 1996 Leeds.

RODDIE, Alison Mary Sherwood Department Medical Genetics, Churchill Hospital, Headington, Oxford OX3 7JL; Alscot Cottage, Alscot Lane, Alscot, Princes Risborough HP27 9RU Tel: 01844 343382 — MB BS 1981 Lond.; MRCP (UK) 1985. (St. Bart.) Socs: Fell. Roy. Soc. Med.; BMA. Prev: Sen. Regist. (Clin. Genetics) Ch.ill Hosp. Oxf.; Clin. Research Phys. Lilly Research Centre Ltd. Windlesham; Regist. (Haemat.) King's Coll. Hosp. Lond.

RODDIE, Katherine Anne Willowfield Surgery, 50 Castlereagh Road, Belfast BT5 5FP Tel: 028 9045 7862 Fax: 028 9045 9785 — MB BCh BAO 1973 Belf.; MRCGP 1978.

RODDIE, Mary Elizabeth Department Diagnostic Radiology, Charing Cross Hospital, Fulham Palace Road, London W6 8RF Tel: 020 8383 0147 Fax: 020 8846 1861 Email: mroddie@hhnt.org; 20 Elm Bank Gardens, London SW13 0NT — BM BS 1983 Nottm.; BMedSci Nottm. 1981; MRCP (UK) 1986; FRCR 1989. (Univ. Nottm.) Cons. Radiol. Char. Cross Hosp. Prev: Cons. Radiol. Kingston Hosp. NHS Trust; Cons., Sen. Regist. & Regist. (Radiol.) Hammersmith Hosp. Lond.

RODDIE, Patrick Huw Department of Haematology, Western General Hospital, Crewe Road, Edinburgh EH4 2XU Tel: 0131 537 1182 Email: huw.roddie@luht.scot.nhs.uk — MB ChB 1989 Ed.; PhD 2001; MRCP (UK) 1992; MRCPath 1997. (Ed.) Cons.(Locum) Haem., Dept. Of Haemat., WGH, Edin. Socs: Brit. Soc. Haemat. Prev: Clin. Research Fell. John Hughes Bennett Laborat. W.ern Gen. Hosp. Edin.; Sen. Regist. (Haematolgy) W.ern Gen. Hosp. Edin.; Regist. Roy. Infirm. Edin.

RODDIE, Mr Robert Kenneth (cons. rooms) St Mary's Private Hospital, Upper Byron Place, Clifton, Bristol BS8 1JU Tel: 0117 987 2727 Fax: 01779 254909; Briar Lodge, 1 Briercliffe Road, Stoke Bishop, Bristol BS9 2DB Tel: 0117 968 1066 — MB BCh BAO 1946 Belf.; FRCS Eng. 1957. Cons. ENT Surg. Avon AHA (T); Head Dept. Otorhinolaryngol. Univ. Bristol; Cons. i/c Hearing & Speech Centre Bristol; Cons. Aurist to Civil Serv. Commrs. Socs: Fell. Roy. Soc. Med. (Mem. Sects. Otol. & Laryng.); Brit. Assn. Otol. Prev: Sen. Regist. (ENT) Belf. Hosp. Gp.; Sen. Regist. Roy. Nat. Throat, Nose & Ear Hosp. & Inst. Laryng. & Otol. Lond.

RODDIE, Thomas Wilson (retired) Lodge Farm, Kirkby Fleetham, Northallerton DL7 0SN Tel: 01609 748673 — MB BCh BAO 1945 Belf.; FRCOG 1963, M 1949, DObst 1946. Prev: Cons. O & G E. Health & Social Servs. Bd. Belf.

RODDIN, Murray John 35 Averill Street, London W6 8ED — MB ChB 1996 Ed.

RODDIS, Michael Joseph Princess Alexandra Hospital NHS Trust, Hamstel Road, Harlow CM20 1QX Tel: 01279 827151 Fax: 01279 429371; 39 Vanbrugh Park, London SE3 7AA Tel: 020 8858 6378 Email: mike@roddidge.dircon.co.uk — MB ChB 1978 Manch.; BSc Manch. 1976, MB ChB 1978; MBA Keele 1990; FRCPath 1995, MRCPath 1984. (Manch.) Med. Dir. & Cons. (Chem. Pathol.) P.ss Alexandra Hosp. NHS Trust, Harlow. Socs: Fell. Roy. Soc. Med. Prev: Dir. (Surg. & Clin. Support) Homerton Hosp.; Dir. Scientif. Servs. & Cons. Chem. Path. WellHo. NHS Trust; Sen. Regist. Centr. Middlx. & Hammersmith Hosps. Lond.

RODDY, Edward 18 Hartlands Road, Eccleshall, Stafford ST21 6DW Tel: 01785 850168 — BM BS 1997 Nottm. SHO (Gen. Med.) Nottm. City Hosp. Prev: Primary Ho. Off. (Gen. Med.) Nottm. City Hosp.

RODDY, Richard James 61 Clewer Park, Windsor SL4 5HD — MB BS 1996 Lond.

RODECK

RODECK, Professor Charles Henry Department of Obstetrics & Gynaecology, University College London Medical School, 86-96 Chenies Mews, London WC1E 6HX Tel: 020 7209 6059 Fax: 020 7383 7429 Email: i.hopton-scott@ucl.ac.uk — MB BS 1969 Lond.; BSc (Anat.) Lond. 1966, DSc (Med.) 1990; FRCPath 1994; FRCOG 1986, M 1975. (Univ. Coll. Lond. & Univ. Coll. Hosp. Med. Sch.) Prof. O & G Univ. Coll. Lond. Med. Sch. Socs: (Ex-Pres.) Internat. Fetal Med. & Surg. Soc.; Hon. Mem. Brit. Assn. Perinatal Med.; Fell. Acad. Med. Soc. Prev: Prof. O & G Qu. Charlotte's & Chelsea Hosp. Lond.; Dir. Harris Birthright Research Centre for Fetal Med. & Sen. Lect. & Cons. O & G King's Coll. Sch. Med. & Dent.; Resid. Off. Chelsea Hosp. for Wom. & Qu. Charlotte's Hosp. Lond.

RODEN, Ann Tyndall 27 Lankers Drive, Harrow HA2 7PA Tel: 020 8866 5944; 31 Downs Avenue, Pinner HA5 5AQ Tel: 020 8866 1148 — MB BS 1959 Lond.; MRCS Eng. LRCP Lond. 1959. (St. Bart.) Craniosrect Therp. & Ayuruedic Lifestyle Adviser & Lect.; Cranio Sacral Therapist 1992; Fell. Fac. Community Health. Socs: Fell. Roy. Soc. Med.; BMA. Prev: SCMO Brent & Harrow HA; SCMO Harrow HA; Clin. Med. Off. Brent & Harrow AHA.

RODEN, Clare Eileen The Clarendon Surgery, 213 Burrage Road, London SE18 7JZ Tel: 020 8854 0356 Fax: 020 8855 5484 — MB BCh 1963 Wales.

RODEN, David 97 Tapton Hill Road, Sheffield S10 5GB — MB ChB 1995 Sheff.

RODEN, Marian SmithKline Beecham, The Frythe, Welwyn AL6 9AR Tel: 01438 782513 Fax: 01438 782992; The Belts, 92 Ermine Way, Arrington, Royston SG8 0AH Tel: 01223 207792 — MB BS 1976 Lond.; MA Oxf. 1974; MRCS Eng. LRCP Lond. 1976; AFOM RCP Lond. 1982. (Roy. Free) Occupat. Med. Dir. SmithKline Beecham Herts. Prev: Med. Off. Nat. W.. Bank plc.; SHO (Anaesth.) Addenbrooke's Hosp. Camb.; Ho. Phys. & Ho. Surg. Roy. Free Hosp. Lond.

RODEN, Rosalind Katrina Woodlands View, Street Lane, Leeds LS8 1DF — BM BCh 1982 Oxf.; FRCS Ed. 1990.

RODEN, Terence George Victor (retired) Fallowfield, Weedon, Aylesbury HP22 4NN Tel: 01296 641434 — MRCS Eng. LRCP Lond. 1951; DPH Lond. 1959. Prev: Ho. Phys. Univ. Coll. Hosp.

RODERIC-EVANS, Jane Elizabeth The Montpelier Surgery, 2 Victoria Road, Brighton BN1 3FS Tel: 01273 328950 Fax: 01273 729767; 29 Florence Road, Brighton BN1 6DL Tel: 01273 270565 Email: jane.roderic-evans@dial.pipex.com — MB BS 1978 Lond.; DCH RCP Lond. 1983; DRCOG 1982. (Lond. Hosp. Med. Coll.)

RODERICK, Anthony Howard (retired) Winter Haven, Bovingdon Green, Marlow SL7 2JQ Tel: 01628 474262 — MB BS 1969 Lond. MRCS Eng. LRCP Lond. 1969; DA Eng. 1976; DObst RCOG 1972. Prev: Marlow GP.

RODERICK, Eleri Mai The Surgery, Caldbeck, Wigton CA7 8DS Tel: 01697 478254 Fax: 01697 478661 Email: eleri.roderick@btinternet.com — MB BCh 1979 Wales; FRCGP 1994, M 1983; DRCOG 1985. Princip. in Gen. Pract.; Chairm. Cumbia Pract. Research Gp.

RODERICK, John Morgan, MC (retired) Ridge Hanger, Rake, Liss GU33 7NN Tel: 01730 893177 — MRCS Eng. LRCP Lond. 1951.

RODERICK, Paul Julian c/o Academic Department of Public Health, B Floor, South Academic Block, Southampton General Hospital, Southampton SO16 6YD — MB BS 1982 Lond.; MSc Lond. 1989; MA Camb. 1979; MRCP (UK) 1985; MFPHM RCP Lond. 1990. Sen. Lect. (Pub. Health Med.) Soton. Univ. Prev: Sen. Regist. & Cons. Pub. Health. Med. NW Thames RHA; Regist. (Haemat.) Roy. Free Hosp.

RODGE, Sally Louise Drayton Medical Practices, The Health Centre, Market Drayton TF9 3BS Tel: 01630 652158 Fax: 01630 652322; Ashfields, Cuddington, Malpas SY14 7EL Tel: 01948 860334 Fax: 01948 860334 — MB BS 1986 Lond. (Middlx. Hosp. Lond. Univ.)

RODGER, Alan Buchanan c/o Accident and Emergency Department, Dr Grays Hospital, Elgin IV30 1SN — MB ChB 1985 Aberd. Staff Surg. (A & E) Dr Gray's Hosp. Elgin. Prev: Med. Adviser Shell Expro (UK) Ltd. Aberd.

RODGER, Alison Jane 4 Park Quadrant, Glasgow G3 6BS — MB ChB 1987 Glas.; MRCP (UK) 1990.

RODGER, Anthony, CStJ Birchwood Surgery, 232-240 Nevells Road, Letchworth SG6 4UB Tel: 01462 683456 — MB BS 1951 Lond.; MRCS Eng. LRCP Lond. 1951. (St. Geo.) Co. Surg. St. John Ambul. Brig.; Med. Off. Letchworth Hosp. Socs: BMA. Prev: Ho. Phys. St. Geo. Hosp.; O & G Ho. Surg. Roy. Vict. Hosp. Folkestone.

RODGER, Christopher James 3 Gardenside Street, Uddingston, Glasgow G71 7BY — MB ChB 1997 Glas.

RODGER, Elaine Margaret Elizabeth 11 Silverburn Drive, Penicuik EH26 9AQ; 34 Regent Road, Gosforth, Newcastle upon Tyne NE3 1ED Tel: 0191 213 0688 — MB ChB 1993 Ed.; FRCA Part 1 1996; FRCA Part 1 1997. Specialist Regist., (Anaesth.), Roy. Vict. Hosp., Newc. Socs: Assn. Anaesth.; Obst. Anaesth. Assn. Prev: Specialist Regist., Freeman Hosp. Newc.; SHO, Sunderland Roy. Hosp.

RODGER, Faye Elizabeth 7 Mill Court, Stow, Galashiels TD1 2SE — MB ChB 1992 Ed.

RODGER, Professor Frederick Carson (retired) The Barn House, Shipton Moyne, Tetbury GL8 8PN Tel: 01666 880208 — MB ChB 1941 Glas.; ChM (Commend.) Glas. 1958, MD (High Commend.) 1952, MB ChB 1941; FRCS Glas. 1961; DOMS Eng. 1947. Sen. Med. Off. Scientif. Exploration Soc. Prev: Sen. Med. Off. Scientif. Exploration Soc.

RODGER, George Neil (retired) Kirkbank, 28 Devon Road, Dollar FK14 7EY Tel: 01259 742868 Email: neil_trodger@compuserve.com — MB ChB 1972 Glas.; DObst RCOG 1974. Prev: GP.

RODGER, Jacqueline Crawford 76 Mansfield Road, London NW3 2HU — MB BS 1998 Lond.; MB BS Lond 1998.

RODGER, James 120 Blythswood Street, Glasgow G2 4EH Tel: 0141 221 5858 Fax: 0141 228 1208; 3 Gardenside Street, Uddingston, Glasgow G71 7BY Tel: 01698 813763 Fax: 01698 811776 Email: jimrodger@btinternet — MB ChB 1972 Glas.; BA Open 1987; BSc (Hons.) Glas. 1970; FRCP (Ed.) 1997; FRCGP 1988, M 1979; DMJ Soc. Apoth. Lond. 1982. Med. Adviser MDDUS; Police Surg. Glas. Socs: Assn. Police Surg.& Brit. Acad. Forens. Sc. Prev: Princip. GP & Assoc. Adviser Hamilton.

RODGER, Jean Christine 12A Kirklee Road, Glasgow G12 0ST — MD 1975 Glas.; MB ChB 1961; FRCP Glas. 1978, M 1965; FRCP Ed. 1982, M 1965; FRCP Lond. 1982, M 1966. Cons. Phys. Monklands Hosp. Airdrie. Socs: Brit. Cardiac Soc.

RODGER, John Douglas (retired) 5 Rose Cottages, East Ogwell, Newton Abbot TQ12 6AR Tel: 01626 52580 — MRCS Eng. LRCP Lond. 1949. Prev: Ho. Surg. (Orthop.) & Cas. Off. St. Geo. Hosp. Lond.

RODGER, Kirsteen Anne 126 Main Street, Symington, Biggar ML12 6LJ — MB ChB 1993 Glas.

RODGER, Mary Wallace Glasgow Royal Infirmary, Castle Street, Glasgow G4 0SF; 4 Dargarvel Avenue, Dumbreck, Glasgow G41 5LD Tel: 0141 419 0446 Email: mary.rodger7@virgin.net — MB ChB 1983 Ed.; MRCOG 1991; DRCOG 1986; MD 2000 Edinburgh. Cons. (O & G) Glas. Roy. Infirm. & Glas. Matern. Hosp. Prev: Regist. (O & G) Rottenrow Hosp. Glas.; Sen.Reg.O & G GRI GRMH.

RODGER, Robert Arthur Ri Cruin, 26 Strathmore Avenue, Dunblane FK15 9HX — MB ChB 1976 Dundee.

RODGER, Robert Stuart Campbell 45 Manse Road, Bearsden, Glasgow G61 3PN — MB ChB 1977 Aberd.; FRCP Ed. 1991; FRCP Glas. 1990; MRCP (UK) 1980. Cons. Nephrol. W.. Infirm. Glas.

RODGER, Sheena Nancy Gordon 44 Leven Road, Lundin Links, Leven KY8 6AH — MB ChB 1977 Dundee.

RODGER, Susan Jane Nicolson Department of Community Child Health, Community Division HQ, Grampian Healthcare NHS Trust, Berryden Road, Aberdeen AB25 3HG Tel: 01224 663131 Fax: 01224 840795; 43 Woodburn Gardens, Aberdeen AB15 8JT — MB ChB 1978 Aberd. Assoc. Specialist (Child Health) Grampian HB.

RODGERS, Alan 11 Keyes Gardens, Jesmond, Newcastle upon Tyne NE2 3RA — MB BS 1980 Newc.; MRCP (UK) 1983. Cons. Phys. i/c Elderly Durh. HA. Socs: Brit. Geriat. Soc. Prev: Sen. Regist. (Gen./Geriat. Med.) Newc. HA; 1st Asst. Clin. Pharmacol. Univ. Newc.

RODGERS, Alan Douglas Department of Histopathology, North Tyneside General Hospital, Rake Lane, North Shields NE29 8NH — MB BChir 1980 Camb.; BSc St. And. 1978; PhD Lond. 1976; BA Oxf. 1971; MRCPath 1988. Cons. Histopath. N. Tyneside Gen. Hosp.

RODGERS, Alison Anne 33 Gortnaskea Road, Stewartstown, Dungannon BT71 5NY Tel: 018687 38751 — MB BCh BAO 1984

NUI; MRCGP 1994; DObst RCPI 1990; DCH 1989. (UCD) Sen. Med. Off. Tansen United Mission Hosp. (Box 126 Kathmandu) Nepal.

RODGERS, Alison Joan Cumming Stockbridge Health Centre, 1 India Place, Edinburgh EH3 6EH — MB ChB 1973 Ed.; MRCGP 1982.

RODGERS, Brandan Niall 9 Queens Park Avenue, Glasgow G42 8BX — MB BCh BAO 1991 Belf.; MB BCh Belf. 1991.

RODGERS, Brian The Barn, Sodom, Bodfari, Denbigh LL16 4DE Tel: 01352 720036 — MRCS Eng. LRCP Lond. 1980; BSc, MB BS Lond. 1979; MRCPath 1988. (Guy's) Cons. Histopath. Glan Clwyd Hosp. Prev: Sen. Regist. (Histopath.) Arrowe Pk. Hosp. Upton.

RODGERS, Catherine Anne Lydia Clinic, Department of Genito-Urinary Medicine, St Thomas's Hospital, Lambeth Palace Road, London SE1 7EH Tel: 020 7928 9292 — MB ChB 1989 Liverp.; BSc (Med. Cell Biol.) Liverp. 1985; MRCP (UK) 1993; Dip. GU Med. Liverp. 1993. Cons. in Genitourin. Med. & HIV Med. St. Thomas' Hosp. Lond. Prev: Sen. Regist. (HIV & Genitourin. Med.) St. Mary's Hosp. NHS Trust Lond.

RODGERS, Colin Principal's Residence, Stranmillis College, Stranmillis Road, Belfast BT9 5DY — MB BCh BAO 1983 Belf.

RODGERS, Colin James 6 Woodlands Mews, Knockmore Road, Lisburn BT28 2XS — MB BCh BAO 1991 Belf.; MRCGP 1996; DRCOG 1995; DCH RCPI 1995; DGM RCPS Glas. 1994.

RODGERS, David Andrew 18 Kalendra Court, Dungannon BT71 6EB — MB BCh BAO 1988 Belf.; MB BCh Belf. 1988; MRCGP 1992.

RODGERS, David Jon Ramsey Road Health Centre, Old Grammar School, Ramsey Road, St. Ives, Huntingdon PE27 5BZ Tel: 01480 466466 — MB ChB 1969 Leeds; MRCP (UK) 1974. (Leeds) Prev: Regist. (Gen. Med.) Sheff. Roy. Infirm.; Ho. Phys. & Ho. Surg. Gen. Infirm. Leeds; Research Asst. Dept. Surg. Guy's Hosp. Lond.

RODGERS, David Marcus Farnham Road Surgery, 301 Farnham Road, Slough SL2 1HD Tel: 01753 520917 Fax: 01753 550680; Arden, One Pin Lane, Farnham Common, Slough SL2 3RD Tel: 01753 644410 — MB BS 1978 Lond.; MRCGP 1989; DRCOG 1982.

RODGERS, Elaine 19 Sandveign, Lerwick ZE1 0RS — MB ChB 1988 Aberd.; MRCGP 1992; DRCOG 1992. Prev: Trainee GP Gt. Yarmouth VTS.

RODGERS, Elaine Margaret Suilven, Bridge End Lane, Prestbury, Macclesfield SK10 4DJ; Suilven, Bridge End Lane, Prestbury, Macclesfield SK10 4DJ — MB ChB 1984 Ed.; BSc (Hons.) Aberd. 1976; FFA RCSI 1989; FCAnaesth 1990. Regist. (Anaesth.) W.m. Hosp. Lond.; Med. Adviser ICI Pharmaceut. Chesh.

RODGERS, Fiona Marie 4 The Drive, Esher KT10 8DQ — MB ChB 1982 Leic.

RODGERS, Frances Russell 40 Valleyview, Clovenfords, Galashiels TD1 3NG Tel: 01896 850643 — MB ChB Glas. 1969. Assoc. Specialist Psych. Lynebank Hosp. Fife; Clin. Asst. Psychiat. Dykebar Hosp. Paisley. Socs: BMA; L.D. Sect. Roy. Coll. Psychiat. Prev: Assoc. Specialist Psych. Borders Network Team Dingleton Hosp. Melrose; Clin. Asst. Psychiat. Dykebar Hosp. Paisley.; Assoc. Specialist Psych. Dykebar Hosp. Paisley.

RODGERS, Helen Department of Medicine (Geriatrics), The Medical School, University of Newcastle upon Tyne, Framlington Place, Newcastle upon Tyne NE2 4HH Tel: 0191 222 8025 Fax: 0191 222 6043 Email: helen.rodgers@newcastle.ac.uk; 5 Camp Terrace, North Shields NE29 0NE — MB ChB 1983 Leeds; MB ChB Leeds. 1983; MRCP (UK) 1986; FRCP 1998. Sen. Lect. (Stroke Med. & Servs.) Univ. Newc. u. Tyne; Hon. Cons. Neurol. Roy. Vict. Infirm. Newc.; Hon. Cons. Phys. N. Tyneside Gen. Hosp.

RODGERS, Helen Clare Respiratory Medicine, Nottingham City Hospital, Clinical Sciences Building, Hucknall R, Nottingham NG5 1PB; 112 Denison Street, Beeston, Nottingham NG9 1DQ Email: helen.rodgers@cwcom.net — MB ChB 1990 Leeds; MRCP (UK) 1994. (Leeds) Specialist Regist. Respirat. Med. Prev: Research Fell. (Cystic Fibrosis) City Hosp. Nottm.; Research Fell. Cystic Fibrosis Respirat. Unit W.. Gen. Hosp. Edin.; SHO (Neurol.) Qu. Med. Centre Nottm.

RODGERS, Henry Jack 12 Corstorphine House Avenue, Edinburgh EH12 7AD — MB ChB 1973 Ed.

RODGERS, Ian David Sefton Park Medical Centre, Smithdown Road, Liverpool L15 2LQ Tel: 0151 734 5666 Fax: 0151 734 1321; 42 Sunny Bank Road, Liverpool L16 7PW Tel: 0151 722 7357 Fax: 0151 734 1321 — MB ChB 1962 Liverp.; DObst RCOG 1964. (Liverp.) Prev: Clin. Asst. (Med.) Mossley Hill Hosp. Liverp.; Clin. Asst. (Surg.) Liverp. Homoeop. Hosp.; Cas. Off. Roy. Liverp. Childr. Hosp.

RODGERS, James Borders General Hospital NHS Trust, Melrose TD6 9BS Tel: 01896 754333 Fax: 01896 823476; 40 Valley View, Clovenfords, Galashiels TD1 3NG Tel: 01896 850643 Email: james.rodgers@btinternet.com — MB ChB Glas. 1969; FRCS Glas. 1974. Cons. Palliat. Med. Borders Gen. Hosp. NHS Trust. Prev: Med. Dir. P. & P.ss of Wales Hospice Glas.

RODGERS, John Somerset (retired) Redhill Farmhouse, Chapel Lane, Barrowden, Oakham LE15 8EB Tel: 01572 747456 — MA Oxf. 1975; MA, MB Camb. 1964, BChir 1963; MB ChB Sheff. 1963; FFCM 1981, M 1974; DPH Bristol 1967; DObst RCOG 1965. Cons. Pub. Health Med. N.ants. HA. Prev: SCM (Social Servs.) Oxon. AHA (T).

RODGERS, Lisbeth Jane The Surgery, Fox Lane, Barnburgh, Doncaster DN5 7ET Tel: 01709 892059 Fax: 01709 888744; 2 The Cottages, Green Lane, Skellow, Doncaster DN6 8JY — MB ChB 1976 Sheff.; DA Eng. 1981; MSc General Practice 1998. (Sheffield)

RODGERS, Lorna Mary 9 Downshire Road, Belfast BT6 9JL — MB BCh BAO 1983 Belf.; BSc (Hons.) Biochem. Belf. 1980; MRCP (UK) 1986; MFOM RCP (UK) 1994, AFOM 1992; MRCGP 1990. Cons. Occupat. Health Belf. City Hosp. Trust. Socs: Assn. NHS Occupat. Phys.; BMA & Soc. Occupat. Med. Prev: Sen. Regist. (Occupat. Health) S.. Health & Soc. Servs. Bd. N. Irel.

RODGERS, Lynne 64 Cambridge Road, Southport PR9 9RH — MB ChB 1979 Manch.

RODGERS, Martin Donative, Queen St., Oadby, Leicester LE2 4NJ — MB ChB 1983 Leic.

RODGERS, Martin Eric The Willows Surgery, Lords Avenue, Salford M5 2JR Tel: 0161 736 2356 Fax: 0161 737 2265; 32 Chatsworth Road, Eccles, Manchester M30 9DY Tel: 0161 789 7661 — MB ChB 1967 Ed.

RODGERS, Mette Ewing 2 Netherford Road, London SW4 6AE — MB BS 1987 Lond.; MRCOG 1993.

RODGERS, Michael Vincent 17 Sunningdale, Omagh BT78 1JX — MB BCh BAO 1993 Belf.

RODGERS, Morfydd Eirian Rosser (Surgery) 555 Chorley Old Road, Bolton BL1 6AF Tel: 01204 848411 Fax: 01204 849968; Suckling Calf Farm, Old Lane, Horwich, Bolton BL6 6QL Tel: 01204 692901 — MB BCh 1967 Wales. Prev: Ho. Surg. (O & G) Crumpsall Hosp. Manch.; SHO (Gen. Paediat. & Cardiol.) Roy. Liverp. Childr. Hosp.; Asst. Div. Med. Off. (Div. 15 Eccles) Lancs. CC.

RODGERS, Pamela Wrightington Wigan & Leigh Trust, Wigan Lane, Wigan WN1 2NN Tel: 01942 244000; 2 Maldon Road, Ashfield Park, Standish, Wigan WN6 0EX Tel: 01257 421288 — MB ChB 1979 Manch.; FRCR 1985. (Manchester) Cons. Radiol. Wigan HA. Socs: Roy. Coll. Radiol.; Manch. Med. Soc.

RODGERS, Peter John Abbey Surgery, 28 Plymouth Road, Tavistock PL19 8BU Tel: 01822 612247 Fax: 01822 618771 — MB BS 1986 Lond.; MRCP (UK) 1991; MRCGP 1996; DRCOG 1992.

RODGERS, Peter Matthew 57 Guilford Road, Leicester LE2 2RD — MB BS 1981 Lond.; MRCP (UK) 1986. Regist. (Radiol.) Univ. Hosp. Nottm. Prev: SHO/Regist. Rotat. Brighton Hosps.; Cas. Off. Guy's Hosp. Lond.; SHO (Med.) Morriston Hosp. Swansea.

RODGERS, Philip Frederic Ewing Church Street Surgery, Church Street, Spalding PE11 2PB Tel: 01775 722189 Fax: 01775 712164; 22 The Terrace, London Road, Spalding PE11 2TA — MB BCh BAO 1974 Dub.; DRCOG 1978. Prev: Trainee Gen. Pract. Banbury Vocational Train. Scheme.

RODGERS, Mr Richard Thomas Boycott 63 Meadow Brook Road, Northfield, Birmingham B31 1ND Tel: 0121 476 0789 Fax: 0121 604 9315 Email: rodgers@charis.co.uk — MB BS 1970 Lond.; MRCS Eng. 1981; MRCS Eng. LRCP Lond. 1970. (St. Bart.) Clin. Asst. Orthop. Birm. Childs. Hosp. Prev: SHO (Gen. Surg.) Derbysh. Roy. Infirm. Derby; Regist. (Orthop.) Gwynedd; Regist. (Orthop.) Roy. Orthop. Hosp. Birm.

RODGERS, Robert Colin Whitegate, Broadwath, Heads Nook, Carlisle CA8 9BA — MB BCh BAO 1979 Belf.; MB BCh Belf. 1979; FFA RCSI 1986. Regist. (Anaesth.) Aberd. Hosps.; Hon. Lect. Clin. Anaesth. Aberd. Univ.

RODGERS

RODGERS, Stephen Arthur Clifton Street Surgery, 15-17 Clifton Street, Belfast BT13 1AD Tel: 028 9032 2330 Fax: 028 9043 9812 — MB BCh BAO 1984 Belf.; MRCGP 1991; DRCOG 1988.

RODGETT, Andrew Francis Mitcheldean Surgery, Brook Street, Mitcheldean GL17 0AU Tel: 01594 542270 Fax: 01594 544897 — MB ChB 1977 Liverp.; DRCOG 1981. Bd. Mem. Forest of Dean PCG.

RODGMAN, Mary Elizabeth UBHT Community Child Health Services, 4th Floor, King Square House, King Square, Bristol BS2 8EF Tel: 0117 900 2350 Fax: 0117 900 2370 Email: mary.rodgman@ubht.swest.nhs.uk; Laurel Farm, Upper Strode, Winford, Bristol BS40 8BG Tel: 01761 462810 — MB BS Lond. 1970; MRCP (UK) 1975; FRCPCH 1997; MFFP 1993; DCH Eng. 1972; DObst RCOG 1972. (Roy. Free) p/t Cons. Paediat. (Community Child Health) United Bristol Healthcare NHS Trust; Hon. Sen. Clin. Lect. (Child Health) Univ. Bristol. Socs: Brit. Assn. Community Child Health; Assn. Research in Infant & Child Developm.; Brit. Assn. Study & Preven. Child Abuse & Neglect. Prev: SCMO (Child Health) United Bristol Healthcare NHS Trust.

RODIE, Vanessa Angela Flat G/L, 5 Cranworth St., Glasgow G12 8BZ — MB ChB 1997 Glas.

RODIN, David Andrew St. Helier Hospital, Wrythe Lane, Carshalton SM5 1AA Tel: 020 8296 2580 Fax: 020 8644 4377 Email: arodin@sthelieir.sghms.ac.uk; Maplehurst, 5 High View, Cheam, Sutton SM2 7DZ — MB BS 1981 Lond.; BSc (Hons.) (Biochem.) Lond. 1978, MD 1991; MRCP (UK) 1986; FRCP 2000. (Univ. Coll. Hosp.) Cons. Phys. & Endocrinol. Epsom & St. Helier NHS Trust, Carshalton, Surrey; Hon. Sen. Lect. (Endocrinol.) St. Geo. Hosp. Med. Sch. Lond.; Sub-Dean (MBBS Cycle 2), St. Geo.'s Hosp. Med. Sch., Lond.; Chairm., Diabetes & Endocrinol. Speciality Train. Comm., S. Thames W.; Regional Speciality Adviser for Diabetes & Endocrinol., S. Thames W. Socs: Soc. for Endocrinol.; Med. & Scientif. Sect. Diabetes UK; Sutton & Dist. Med. Soc. Prev: Clin. Lect. & Hon. Sen. Regist. (Endocrinol.) St. Geo. Hosp. Med. Sch. Lond.; Mem. Clin. Sci. Staff & Hon. Sen. Regist. (Endocrinol.) MRC Clin. Research Centre & N.wick Pk. Hosp. Harrow; Regist. (Gen. Med.) Hillingdon Hosp.

RODIN, Ian Tel: 02392 321115 — BM Soton. 1989; MRCPsych 1994. Cons. Psychiat. Portsmouth Healthcare NHS Trust; Hon. Sen. Lect., Sch. of Postgrad. Med. Univ. of Portsmouth.

RODIN, Marion Josephine Seyan, Saffar and Rodin, The Health Centre, Robin Hood Lane, Sutton SM1 Tel: 020 8642 3848 Fax: 020 8286 2010; Maplehurst, 5 High View, Cheam, Sutton SM2 7DZ Fax: 020 8286 1010 — MB BS 1982 Lond.; MRCGP 1986. (Univ. Coll. Hosp.) p/t Princip. GP Health Centre, Robin Hood La., Sutton, Surrey. Prev: GP Fairbrook Med. Centre Borehamwood.

RODIN, Philip (retired) 115 Blackheath Park, London SE3 0HA Tel: 020 8852 8814 — MB BS 1954 Lond.; FRCP Lond. 1977, M 1965. Prev: Cons. Venereol. Lond. Hosp.

RODITI, Eric 22 Knoll Court, Farquhar Road, London SE19 1SP Tel: 020 8670 1225 — MB ChB 1954 Manch. (Manch.)

RODITI, Giles Hannibal Dept of Radiology, Glasgow Royal Infirmary, 16 Alexandra Parade, Glasgow G31 2ER Tel: 0141 211 4619 Fax: 0141 211 4781 — MB ChB 1985 Aberd.; FRCR 1992; DMRD Aberd. 1991; FRCP 1999 Edin. Cons. Radiologist Glas. Roy. Infirm. Glas.; Hon. Sen. Lect. Uni. Glasg. Socs: BIR; Fell. RCR; Fell. RCRP of Edin. Prev: Sen. Regist. (Radiol.) Aberd. Roy. Infirm.; Lect. (Hon.) Univ. Aberd.

RODMAN, Rebecca 130 Birkworth Court, Offerton, Stockport SK2 5LS — MB ChB 1998 Sheff.; MB ChB Sheff 1998.

RODRICK, Caroline Jane Karis Medical Centre, Waterworks Road, Edgbaston, Birmingham B16 9AL Tel: 0121 454 0661 Fax: 0121 454 9104; 27 Cartland Road, Kings Heath, Birmingham B14 7NS Tel: 0121 444 5595 — MB ChB 1991 Birm.; ChB Birm. 1991; DRCOG 1996; DTM & H Liverp. 1993; DCH 1998. (Birm.) GP Regist. Birm. Prev: SHO (Paediat.) Heartlands Hosp. Birm.; SHO (O & G) Solihull; SHO (Infec. Dis.) E. Birm. HA.

RODRICK, Ian Walker Windrush Surgery, 21 West Bar Street, Banbury OX16 9SA Tel: 01295 251491; Silverdale, Weeping Cross, Bodicote, Banbury OX15 4ED Tel: 01295 253817 — MB ChB 1966 Ed.; DObst RCOG 1972.

RODRICKS, Nigel Patrick 10A Kimberley Drive, Sidcup DA14 4QF Tel: 020 8302 9011 — MB BS 1957 Madras.

RODRIGUES, Anthony James Stonehurst, 46 Garretts Green Lane, Birmingham B26 2HP Tel: 0121 743 3144 — MB BS 1937 Bombay. (Grant Med. Coll. Bombay) Socs: BMA. Prev: Med. Off. Saudi Arabia Mining Syndicate & Lever Bros. (India) Ltd.; Bombay.

RODRIGUES, Camilla 31 St Andrews, Grantham NG31 9PE — MB BS 1971 Nagpur; MRCOG 1987.

RODRIGUES, Christopher Arthur Kingston Hospital, Galsworthy Road, Kingston upon Thames KT2 7QB — MB BS 1978 Poona; PhD Lond. 1991; MD (Med.) Chandigarh 1980; MRCP (UK) 1982; FRCP 1998. (Armed Forces Poona India) Cons. Phys. (s/i in Elderly) Kingston Hosp. Surrey. Socs: Brit. Geriat. Soc.; Brit. Soc. Gastroenterol.; Roy. Soc. Med. Prev: Sen. Regist. (Geriat. & Gen. Med.) Guy's Hosp. Lond.; Research Regist. St. Mark's Hosp. Lond.; Regist. (Med.) St. Mark's Hosp. Lond.

RODRIGUES, Erwin Alexander Aintree Cardiac Centre, University Hospital Aintree, Longmoor Lane, Liverpool L9 7AL Tel: 0151 529 2721 Fax: 0151 529 2724 — MB ChB 1977 Ed.; FRCP Lond. 1994; FRCP Ed. 1992; MRCP (UK) 1979; FACC 1993; FESC 1993; FICA 1988. (Ed.) Cons. Cardiol. & Clin. Dir. Aintree Cardiac Centre & Univ. Hosp. Aintree; Clin. Lect. (Med.) Univ. Liverp.; Cons. Cardiol. BUPA Murrayfield Hosp. Wirral & Abbey Sefton Hosp. Liverp. Socs: Fell. AM Coll. Cardiol.; Fell. Europ. Soc. Cardiol.; Brit. Cardiac. Soc. Prev: Sen. Regist. (Gen. Med. & Cardiol.) BRd.green Hosp. Liverp.; Research Fell. (Cardiol.) N.wick Pk. Hosp. Lond.; Regist. (Cardiol. & Gen. Med.) Roy. Infirm. Edin.

RODRIGUES, Jennifer 15 Sunnygate Road, Grassendales, Liverpool L19 9BS — MB ChB 1992 Liverp.

RODRIGUES, Kevin Francis Abbey Medical Centre, 63 Central Avenue, Beeston, Nottingham NG9 2QP Tel: 0115 925 0862 Fax: 0115 922 0522.

RODRIGUES, Mervyn John Paul 30B Northbrook Road, Ilford IG1 3BS — MB ChB 1987 Manch.

RODRIGUES, Norman Felix Bonifacio London Road Surgery, 501 London Road, Thornton Heath CR7 6AR Tel: 020 8662 8640 Fax: 020 8665 5011 — MB ChB 1987 Dundee; DTM & H Lond. 1993. GP.

RODRIGUES, Rene Joseph Charles The Health Centre, 1 Dunluce Avenue, Belfast BT9 7HR Tel: 01232 204247; 33 Broughton Gardens, Belfast BT6 0BB — MB BCh BAO 1972 Belf.; DCH Dub. 1974.

RODRIGUES, Simon Mathais Duty Housing, Arrow Park Hospital, Arrow Park Road, Upton, Wirral CH49 5PE — MB ChB 1996 Liverp.

RODRIGUEZ, John Martin 41 Bowlingfield, Ingol, Preston PR2 7DE Tel: 01772 734511 Fax: 01572 770538 — MB BS 1979 Lond.; BA (Physiol. Sci.) Oxf. 1976; MRCP (UK) 1982; FRCR 1986; T(R) (CO) 1991. (St. Thos.) Managing Dir. Socs: Collegiate Mem. RCP; Fell. Roy. Soc. Med.; BMA. Prev: Dir. & Chief (Oncol.) Suleiman Fakeeh Hosp. Jeddah, Kingdom of Saudi Arabia; Dir. (Oncol.) Al-Hada Armed Forces Hosp. Al-Taif Kingdom Saudi Arabia; Sen. Regist. SE Lond. Cancer Centre & Roy. Sussex Co. Hosp.

RODRIGUEZ ARNAO, Javier Department of Endocrinology, St. Bartholomews Hospital, West SMmithfield, London EC1A 7BE; 80 East Dulwich Road, London SE22 9AT — LMS 1987 U Complutense Madrid.

RODRIGUEZ CASTELLO, Cesar Sunnyside Roy. Hospital, Hillside, By Montrose, Angus DD10 9JP Tel: 01674 830361 Fax: 01674 830361 Email: cesar.rodriguez@tpct.scot.nhs.uk; 5 Viewmount, Forfar, Forfar DD8 1LJ — LMS 1991 Valencia; MRCPsych 1997. Cons. Old Age Psychiat. Tayside, Primary Care Trust, Sunnyside Roy. Hosp. Montrose.

RODRIGUEZ DE LA SIERRA, Luis 15 Highwood House, 148 New Cavendish St., London W1W 6YH Tel: 020 7580 5460 Fax: 020 7637 0070 — LMS 1969 Barcelona; DNPsych Barcelona 1974. Socs: Brit. Psychoanal. Soc.

RODRIGUEZ GARCIA, Francisco Javier Dryburn Hospital, North Road, Durham DH1 5TW Tel: 0191 333 2333 — LMS 1989 Granada.

RODRIGUEZ SANTOS, Javier Department of Obstetrics & Gynaecology, Crosshouse Hospital, Kilmarnock Road, Kilmarnock KA2 0BE — LMS 1990 Navarre.

RODWAY, Alexander Dominic Flat 4, 101 Finsbury Pavement, London EC2A 1RS — MB BS 1998 Lond.; MB BS Lond 1998.

RODWAY, Anne Elizabeth Pauline Chantry House Surgery, High St., Sevenoaks TN13 1HZ Tel: 01732 453953 — MB BS 1968 Lond.; MRCS Eng. LRCP Lond. 1968; DObst RCOG 1970. (St. Mary's) Socs: Fell. Med. Soc. Lond. Prev: Ho. Off. (Obst.) & Ho. Surg. & Ho. Phys. St. Mary's Hosp. Lond.

RODWELL, Nicola Anne Oakfield, Hither Chantlers, Tunbridge Wells TN3 0BJ — MB ChB 1992 Birm.

ROE, Mr Alan Martin Department of Surgery, Southmead Hospital, Bristol BS10 5NB Tel: 0117 950 5050 Fax: 0117 959 5168; 21 West Dene, Stoke Bishop, Bristol BS9 2BQ — MB ChB 1977 Dundee; ChM Bristol 1988; FRCS Eng. 1982; FRCS Ed. 1982. (Dundee) Cons. Gen. Surg. S.mead Hosp. Bristol. Socs: Surg. Research Soc. & Brit. Soc. Gastroenterol.; Assn. Coloproctol. Prev: Sen. Regist. (Gen. Surg.) St Mark's Hosp. Lond.; Sen. Regist. (Gen. Surg.) S.mead Hosp. Bristol & Derriford Hosp. Plymouth.

ROE, Catherine Margaret Abraham and Partners, 21-23 Morden Hill, Lewisham, London SE13 7NN Tel: 020 8469 2880 Fax: 020 8692 9399; 27 Newstead Road, Lee, London SE12 0SY — MB BS 1985 Lond.; MRCGP 1990; DCH RCP Lond 1988. (The Royal London Hospital) Prev: SHO (O & G) Lond. Hosp. Whitechapel; SHO (Paediat.) Newham Gen. Hosp.; SHO (Med.) Basildon Hosp.

ROE, Mr David Alan 61 Station Road, Gateacre, Liverpool L25 3PY — MB ChB 1990 Liverp.; MB ChB (Hons.) Liverp. 1990; FRCS Ed. 1994; FRCS Eng. 1994. SHO (Gen. Surg.) Wythenshawe Hosp. Manch. Prev: SHO Rotat. (Surg.) S. Manch.

ROE, David Martin 14 Denny Close, Wirral CH49 0XG — MB ChB 1985 Liverp.

ROE, Francis John Caldwell (retired) 11B Raymond Road, Wimbledon, London SW19 4AD Tel: 020 8946 4518 Fax: 020 8947 9171 — BM BCh Oxf. 1948; MA Oxf. 1950, BA 1946, DM 1957; DSc Lond. 1965; FRCPath 1967. Fell. (Vice-Pres.) Marie Curie Cancer Care. Prev: Reader (Experim. Path.) Inst. Cancer Research Roy. Cancer Hosp. Lond.

ROE, Joanna The Health Centre, Creebridge, Newton Stewart DG8 6NR — MB BS 1989 Lond.

ROE, Leslie Morrison (retired) Health Centre, High St., Hoddesdon Tel: 01992 464533 — MB BCh BAO 1944 Dub. Prev: Obst. Regist. St. Albans City Hosp.

ROE, Michael Felix Edward 10 Lodge Drive, Hatfield AL9 5HN — BM BCh 1990 Oxf.; MA Camb. 1991; MRCP (Paediat.) Lond. 1995. SHO (Paediat.) Guy's Hosp. Lond. Prev: SHO (Obst.) Univ. Coll. Hosp. Lond.; SHO (A & E & ITU) Roy. Free Hosp. Lond.; SHO (Neonates) Fazakerley Hosp. Liverp.

ROE, Paul Gerald Department of Anaesthetics, Addenbrooke's Hospital, Hills Road, Cambridge CB2 2QQ Tel: 01223 217434 — MB BS 1982 Lond.; BSc Lond. 1979; FFA RCS Eng. 1988. (Westm.) Cons. Anaesth. Addenbrooke's Hosp. Camb. Socs: Assn. Anaesth. Prev: Vis. Asst. Prof. Dallas (1991-92); Sen. Regist. (Anaesth.) Yorks. RHA; Regist. (Anaesth.) St. Geo. Hosp. Lond.

ROE, Peter Frank (retired) Kirkmead, Staplegrove, Taunton TA2 6AP Tel: 01823 284568 — MB ChB Ed. 1955; MA Camb. 1957; MD Ed. 1969; FRCP Glas. 1981, M 1962. Prev: Cons. Geriat. Som. HA.

ROE, Robert Bradley (retired) 9 Greens Lane, Wroughton, Swindon SN4 0RJ — BM BCh Oxf. 1953; MA Oxf. 1953; LMSSA Lond. 1952; FFA RCS Eng. 1959; DObst RCOG 1955. Prev: Cons. Anaesth. P.ss Margt. Hosp. Swindon.

ROE, Sally Elizabeth The Whitecot, Park Avenue, Farnborough, Orpington BR6 8LL — BM BCh 1978 Oxf.; FRCP Lond. 1994; MRCP (UK) 1980. Cons. Geriat. Qu. Mary's Hosp. Sidcup.

ROE, Simon David Nottngham Renal Unit, Nottingham City Hospital, Hucknall Road, Nottingham NG5 1PB Email: simon.roe@dial.pipex.com; 8 Lapford Close, Mapperley Planis, Nottingham NG3 5SQ Tel: 0115 920 1711 — MB ChB 1991 Manch.; MRCP (UK) 1994. (Univ. Manch.) Specialist Regist. (Nephrol.) Nottm. City Hosp. Prev: Regist. (Gen. Med. & Nephrol.) Derby City Gen. Hosp.; SHO (Gen. Med.) Trafford Dist. Gen. Hosp. & Roy. Preston Hosp.; Ho. Off. (Gen. Med.) Roy. Preston Hosp.

ROE, Yvonneke Olivia Walton The Nunhead Surgery, 58 Nunhead Grove, London SE15 3LY Tel: 020 7639 2715 Fax: 020 7635 6942; 26 Rollscourt Avenue, Herne Hill, London SE24 0EA — MB BChir 1982 Camb.; MA Camb. 1983; MRCGP 1989; DRCOG 1986; DCH RCP Lond. 1985. (St. Thos.) Socs: BMA; BHMA; (Counc.) SMN. Prev: SHO (Gyn.) W. Middlx. Hosp. Lond.; Ho. Phys. St. Thos. Hosp. Lond.; Ho. Surg. Qu. Mary's Hosp. Sidcup.

ROEBUCK, Eric James (retired) Earleydene, 45 Private Road, Sherwood, Nottingham NG5 4DD Tel: 0115 960 9547 — MB BS 1954 Lond.; FRCR 1975; FFR 1963; DMRD Eng. 1960. Cons. Radiol. Nottm. Univ. Hosps.; Regist. Roy. Coll. Radiol.

ROEBUCK, Harold Cornerways, Woolfall Heath Avenue, Huyton, Liverpool L36 — MRCS Eng. LRCP Lond. 1941. (Leeds) Prev: Ho. Surg. Gen. Infirm. Pontefract.

ROEBUCK, Paul David Sheringham Medical Practice, Health Centre, Cromer Road, Sheringham NR26 8RT Tel: 01263 822066 Fax: 01263 823890 — MB ChB 1986 Glas.; MRCGP 1995; DRCOG 1989.

ROEDLING, Ann Sherie 30B Prince of Wales Road, London NW5 3LG — MB BS 1998 Lond.; MB BS Lond 1998.

ROEHR, Stephan Patrick c/o Dr P. Waugh, Coultershaw Farm House, Station Road, Petworth GU28 0JE — State Exam Med 1992 Bochum.

ROEMMELE, Harold Ami 40 Thorn Road, Bearsden, Glasgow G61 4BS — MB ChB 1949 Glas. (Glas.)

ROEMMELE, Mr Peter Michael (retired) Ballinahery, Limavady BT49 0PD Tel: 0150 47 62534 — MB ChB 1943 Ed.; FRCS Ed. 1948. Prev: Cons. Staff Roe Valley Hosp. & NW Gp. Altnagelvin.

ROET, Brian Charles 2 The Mews, 6 Putney Common, London SW15 1HL Tel: 020 8780 2284 Fax: 020 8780 2347 — MB BS 1962 Melbourne. Socs: Brit. Med. & Dent. Hypn. Soc.

ROEVES, Alastair John The Randolph Surgery, 235A Elgin Avenue, London W9 1NH — MB BS 1991 Lond.

ROFAIL, Mr Stephen Dimitri 18 Ticehurst Close, Worth, Crawley RH10 7GN — MRCS Eng. LRCP Lond. 1973; MB BS Khartoum 1972; FRCSI 1991; T(GP) 1991.

ROFFE, Terence Henry Halcyon, Station Lane, Farnsfield, Newark NG22 8LB Tel: 01623 882898 — MB BS (Hons.) Lond. 1950. (Lond. Hosp.) GP Farnsfield. Socs: Fell. Roy. Coll. Gen. Pract. Prev: Demonst. (Anat.) Lond. Hosp. Med. Coll.; SHO (Surgic.) ScarBoro. Hosp.; Ho. Surg. (Orthop.) Lond. Hosp.

ROFFEY, Marc 18 Daisy Bank, Lancaster LA1 3JW — MB ChB 1987 Cape Town.

ROG, David Josef 2 Chester Close, Bletchley, Milton Keynes MK3 5JY — BM BS 1996 Nottm.

ROGAHN, Detlev Queens Medical Centre, Paediatric Department, Nottingham NG7 2UH; 33 Westminster Close, Grappen Hall, Warrington WA4 2QS — State Exam Med. Berlin 1988.

ROGALSKI, Marian (retired) Ymgilio, 9 Garreg Goch, Morfarbychan, Porthmadog LL49 9YD Tel: 01766 512992 — MD 1945 Zurich. Prev: Med. Asst. (Anaesth.) Wrexham, Powys & Mawddach Hosp. Gp.

ROGAN, Anita Marie 3 Lyndhurst, Maghull, Liverpool L31 6DY — MB ChB 1996 Ed.; BSc (Hons.) Lond. 1993. (Edinburgh) SHO (A & E) Roy. Preston Hosp. Prev: SHO (A & E) Warrington Gen. Hosp.; SHO (Gen. Surg.) W.ern Gen. Hosp. Edin.; SHO (Gen. Med.) Galloway Roy. Infirm.

ROGAN, Christian Anne (retired) Northwood House, 18/28 Lauder Road, Edinburgh EH9 2EL Tel: 031 667 1511 — MB ChB 1928 Ed.

ROGAN, Edward (retired) 3 Beechfield Avenue, Blackpool FY3 9JE Tel: 01253 315763 — LRCPI & LM, LRCSI & LM 1952; DPH Bristol 1956.

ROGAN, Jacqueline Therese 6 Sharman Way, Belfast BT9 5FU — MB BCh BAO 1987 Belf.

ROGAN, Patricia Mary (retired) 3 Beechfield Avenue, Blackpool FY3 9JE Tel: 01253 315763 — MB BCh BAO NUI 1952; DPM Eng. 1976.

ROGAN, Sheelagh Mary 118A Earlswood Road, Belfast BT4 3EA; 53 Burrenreagh Road, Castlewellan BT31 9HH — MB ChB 1993 Liverp. SHO. Learnig Difficulties. Muckamore Abbey Hosp. Antrim. Prev: Resistrar in Child Psychiat. Dunedin Hosp New Zealand; SHO. Psychiat. Downshire Hosp Downpatrick.

ROGAWSKI, Mr Karol, Marian Consultant Urologist, Royal Halifax Infirmary, Free School Lane, Halifax HX1 2YP Tel: 01422 357222 Fax: 01422 321087 — Lekarz 1980 Stettin, Poland; FCS (S Afr) Urology 1990; FRCS (Urol) 1995; FRCS Ed 1996. Cons. Urol. Calderdale Healthcare NHS Trust Roy. Halifax Infirm. Socs: Brit.

ROGER

Assn. Urol. Surgs.; Brit. Soc. Endocrinol.; BMA BMA. Prev: Cons. Urol. Dept. Urol. Johannesburg Hosp.

ROGERS, Mark Douglas 65 West End, Redruth TR15 2SQ Tel: 01209 210333 — MB ChB 1996 Manch.; MB ChB (Hons.) Manch. 1996; BSc (Med. Sci.) St And. 1993. SHO (Med.) Blackburn Roy. Infirm. Socs: BMA; Med. Sickness Soc.; MDU.

ROGERS, Adrian John Western Avenue Medical Centre, Gordon Road, Blacon, Chester CH1 5PA Tel: 01244 390755 Fax: 01244 383955 — MB ChB 1985 Manch.

ROGERS, Adrian Rudd Cranmere House, Trews Weir Reach, St Leonards, Exeter EX2 4EG Tel: 01392 258562 Fax: 01392 251827 Email: a@dradrianrogers.co.uk — MB BS 1972 Lond.; MRCS Eng. LRCP Lond. 1972; MRCGP 1978; DObst RCOG 1976. (Guy's) Socs: Acad. of Experts, Exeter Med. Lega Soc.

ROGERS, Alan Llynfi Surgery, Llynfi Road, Maesteg CF34 9DT Tel: 01656 732115 Fax: 01656 864451; 28 Ystad Celyn, Maesteg CF34 9LT Tel: 01656 734610 — MB BCh 1970 Wales; MRCGP 1986; DObst RCOG 1972. Course Organiser Bridgend VTS.

ROGERS, Alan David The Surgery, 1 Forest Hill Road, London SE22 0SQ Tel: 020 8693 2264 Fax: 020 8299 0200 Email: alan.rogers@gp-g85001.nhs.uk — MB BS 1960 Lond.; MRCS Eng. LRCP Lond. 1960; DObst RCOG 1962. (King's Coll. Hosp.) Local Treasury Med. Off.; Chairm. S. S.wark PrimaryCare Gp.

ROGERS, Alexander Mark 2 The Old Pump House, Papcastle, Cockermouth CA13 0JN Tel: 01900 822152; 74 Huntsbury Avenue, Christchurch 8002, New Zealand Tel: 00 64 332 6095 Fax: 00 64 332 6095 Email: mark/rogers@hotmail.com — MB ChB 1991 Leeds; DFFP 1994; DRCOG 1994. GP ChristCh., NZ. Prev: GP/Regist. York; SHO (Paediat. & O & G) Sunderland Dist. Gen. Hosp.; SHO (A & E) York Dist. Hosp.

ROGERS, Alison Mary Carlisle House, 53 Lanegland Street, Poole BH15 1QD Tel: 01202 678484 Fax: 01202 660507; 77 Orchard Avenue, Parkstone, Poole BH14 8AH — MB ChB 1987 Liverp. Prev: GP Wirral Merseyside.

ROGERS, Mr Andrew 46 Nasturtium Way, Pentwyn, Cardiff CF23 8SF — MB BCh 1991 Wales; FRCS (Ed.) 1995. Specialist Regist. (Orthop.) Welsh Rotat.

ROGERS, Andrew John Pendeen Surgery, Kent Avenue, Ross-on-Wye HR9 5AL Tel: 01989 763535 Fax: 01989 768288 — BM BCh 1974 Oxf.; MA Camb. 1974; MRCGP 1978; DRCOG 1977. (Oxf.) Socs: BMA. Prev: Trainee GP Hereford VTS; Ho. Off. Radcliffe Infirm. Oxf.; Ho. Surg. Hereford Co. Hosp.

ROGERS, Anne Katherine Jean The Health Centre, Leypark Walk, Estover, Plymouth PL6 8UE Tel: 01752 776772 Fax: 01752 785108 — MB ChB 1975 Manch.; MRCGP 1979; DRCOG 1978; DCH Eng. 1977.

ROGERS, Mr Anthony Crawford Nugent (retired) 5 Abercromby Place, Stirling FK8 2QP Tel: 01786 473948 Email: trogersstg@aol.com — MB ChB 1963 Glas.; FRCS Eng. 1969; FRCS Glas. 1969. Private Pract.; 2 Session/week, Lead Clinician Cancer Servs. Redesign Unit. Prev: Regist. (Urol.) Gen. Hosp. Newc.

ROGERS, Benedict Aristotle 38 Woodham Waye, Woking GU21 5SJ — MB BS 1997 Lond.; BA Oxf 1994, (Christ Church). (St. Georges) GP Regis. Redhill; BASIC's doc. (Redhill.). Prev: A & E SHO E. Surrey; PRHO St. Geo.s Hosp. Tooting; PRHO Frinley Pk.

ROGERS, Benedict James 4 Lisle Court Cottages, Lymington SO41 5SH — MB BS 1994 Lond.

ROGERS, Bernadette Littledown Surgery, Harewood Crescent, Littledown, Bournemouth BH7 7BU Tel: 01202 309500 — MRCS Eng. LRCP 1988 Lond.; DRCOG 1994; DFFP 1994. p/t GP Princip.; Clin. Asst. Dept. GU Med., Roy. Bournemouth Hosp., Bournemouth.

ROGERS, Brian Maclean (retired) The Swan Surgery, Swan St., Petersfield GU32 3AB — MRCS Eng. LRCP Lond. 1966; BSc (Zool. & Marine Zool., Hons.) Wales 1971; DObst RCOG 1971. Prev: SHO (O & G) Groote Schuur Hosp. Cape Town, S. Afr.

ROGERS, Bryan Keith Harefield Health Centre, Rickmansworth Road, Harefield, Uxbridge UB9 6JY Tel: 01895 822944 Fax: 01895 823755; 36 Westbury Road, Northwood HA6 3BX Tel: 01923 824692 Fax: 01923 824692 — MB BS 1959 Lond.; MRCS Eng. LRCP Lond. 1959; DFFP 1994; DObst RCOG 1961. (St. Mary's) Lead GP Hillingdon Total Purchasing Project. Prev: Course Organiser Hillingdon VTS; Ho. Surg. (Orthop.) St. Mary's Hosp. Lond.; Med. Off. Mengo Hosp. Kampala Uganda.

ROGERS, Caroline Blair 5 Richford St, London W6 7HJ Tel: 020 8749 7883 — MB BS 1993 Lond.; MA Camb.; DFFP 1995; DRCOG 1996; DGM 1997. (St. Bartholomew's) GP Regist. N. End Med. Centre Lond.

ROGERS, Cerilan Breast Test Wales, 18 Cathedral Road, Cardiff CF11 9LH Tel: 029 2078 7802 Fax: 029 2078 7800; Glan Nant, 70 Cemetery Road, Porth CF39 0BL Tel: 01443 681050 — MB BChir 1981 Camb.; MA Camb. 1982, BA 1978; MFPHM RCP (UK) 1995; MRCGP 1989; DRCOG 1984. (Univ. Camb.) Dir. BrE. Test Wales; Dir. Cervical Screening Wales. Prev: Cons. (Pub. Health) N. Wales Health Auth.; GP Ruabon Clwyd; GP Blaenavon Gwent.

ROGERS, Christina 25A Arlington Park Mansions, Sutton Lane N., London W4 4HE — MB BS 1990 Lond.

ROGERS, Christina Margaret Anaesthetics Department, Hope Hospital, Stott Lane, Salford M6 8HD Tel: 0161 787 5107/8 Fax: 0161 787 4677 Email: crogers@hope.srht.nwest.nhs.uk — MB ChB 1980 Otago; FFA RCSI 1989. Cons. Anaesth. (Obst. Anaesth. & Analgesia) Hope Hosp. Salford. Socs: Assn. Anaesth. GB & Irel.; Obst. Anaesth. Assn.; Manch. Med. Soc. Div. Anaesth.

ROGERS, Christopher Evan 35 Carnation Drive, Winkfield Row, Bracknell RG42 7NT — BM BCh 1983 Oxf.; T(R) (CR) 1992.

ROGERS, Clare Elizabeth 35 (IF3) Lutton Place, Edinburgh EH8 9PF — MB ChB 1994 Ed.

ROGERS, Daniel George Charles Burden Centre, Frenchay Hospital, Stapleton, Bristol BS16 1JB Tel: 0117 970 1212 Fax: 0117 965 4141; Cherry House, Frampton End Road, Frampton Cotterell, Bristol BS36 2LA Tel: 01454 773166 — MB BChir 1973 Camb.; MA Camb. 1974; MRCP (UK) 1976; MRCPsych 1982; MD 1998. (Middlx.) Cons. Neuropsychiat. Burden Centre, Frenchay Hosp., Bristol. Socs: Brit. Neuropsychiat. Assn. Prev: Raymond Way Lect. Neuropsychiat. Inst. Neurol. Lond.; Regist. (Psychiat.) Roy. Free & Friern Hosps. Lond.; SHO (Neurol.) Radcliffe Infirm. Oxf. & Maudsley Hosp. Lond.

ROGERS, David Alan 71 Madeley Road, London W5 2LT Tel: 020 8991 9365 — MB BS 1963 Lond.; MRCOG 1972, DObst 1965. (Univ. Coll. Hosp.) Prev: Regist. (O & G) P.ss Margt. Hosp. Nassau, Bahamas.

ROGERS, David Andrew Great Bansons, Bansons Lane, Ongar CM5 9AR Tel: 01277 363028; 66 Glovers Field, Kelvedon Hatch, Brentwood CM15 0BD — MB BS 1987 Lond.; BSc Lond. 1984, MB BS 1987; DCH RCP Lond. 1990. Prev: SHO (Gen. Med. & Geriat.) Thanet Dist. Gen. Hosp.; Trainee GP Thanet VTS.

ROGERS, David Charles The Surgery, 134 Baffins Road, Portsmouth PO3 6BH Tel: 023 9282 7132 Fax: 023 9282 7025; 134 Baffins Road, Portsmouth PO3 6BH — BM BS 1981 Nottm.; BMedSci. Nottm. 1979, BM BS 1981; MRCGP 1985.

ROGERS, David John Flatt Walks Health Centre, 3 Castle Meadows, Catherine Street, Whitehaven CA28 7QE Tel: 01946 692173 Fax: 01946 590406 — MB ChB 1985 Leeds; MRCGP 1990; DA (UK) 1988.

ROGERS, David John Orchard Surgery, Christchurch Medical Centre, Purewell Cross Road, Christchurch BH23 5ET Tel: 01202 481902 Fax: 01202 486887 — MB BCh 1975 Wales; MRCGP 1981; DRCOG 1979.

ROGERS, David John de Sola 147 Beaufort Park, London NW11 6DA Tel: 020 8458 3177 — MB ChB 1970 Birm.; FFA RCS Eng. 1980. Cons. Anaesth. IVF Unit Humana Hosp. Lond. Prev: Sen. Regist. (Anaesth.) St. Mary's Hosp. Lond. & Research Dept.; Anaesth. RCS Lond.; Med. Off. St. Helena, S. Atlantic.

ROGERS, David Joseph Harry (retired) 40 Sherrardspark Road, Welwyn Garden City AL8 7LB Tel: 01707 324494 — MB BS 1947 Lond.; MRCS Eng. LRCP Lond. 1947; AFOM RCP Lond. 1981; MRCGP 1960; DObst RCOG 1952. Prev: Resid. Anaesth. St. Bart. Hosp. Lond.

ROGERS, Deborah Ann Lizbeth Trelawny, 78 Riddlesdown Road, Purley CR8 1DB — MB BS 1993 Lond.

ROGERS, Deborah Jayne The Forensic Medicine Unit, St George's Hospital, Hunter Wing, Cranmer Terrace, London SW17 0RE — MB BS 1983 Lond.

ROGERS, Dorian Wynne Bryncelyn, High St., Pontardawe, Swansea SA8 4JN Tel: 01792 862776 — MB BCh 1981 Wales; FFA RCS Eng. 1987. Cons. Anaesth. Morriston Hosp. NHS Trust Swansea. Prev: Sen. Regist. (Anaesth.) St. Geo. Hosp. Lond. &

ROGERS

Kingston Hosp.; Regist. & Research Regist. Univ. Hosp. of Wales Cardiff; Regist. Guy's, Brighton & E. Grinstead Hosps.

ROGERS, Duncan Paul Evans Tel: 01609 775281 — MB BS 1989 Lond.; MRCGP 1995; DRCOG 1994. (St Mary's)

ROGERS, Euphemia (retired) Funchal, 1 Preston Place, Gourock PA19 1LF Tel: 01475 631240 — MB ChB 1954 Glas.; BSc Glas. 1945, MB ChB 1954; DA Eng. 1959. SHMO Argyll & Clyde Health Bd.; Mem. SHMO Working Party Lond. Prev: Anaesth. Inverclyde Roy. & Dist. Hosps.

ROGERS, Frances Anne Louise Shepperton Health Centre, Shepperton Court Drive, Laleham Road, Shepperton TW17 8EJ — MB BS 1983 Lond.; 1999 (Fac. Of Homeopathy) LFHom; MRCGP 1987; DRCOG 1987.

ROGERS, Gary 10 Oxford Road, Dorchester-on-Thames, Wallingford OX10 7LX — MB BS 1985 Lond.

ROGERS, Mrs Genevieve 70 Wilmot Street, Bethnal Green, London E2 0BT Tel: 020 7729 4883; 62 HathawayCt., rochester ME1 1QY Tel: 01634 846659 — MB BS 1992 Lond.; FRCS (Oto.) Eng. 1998. (Lond. Hosp. Med. Coll.) ENT Specialist Regist. Se hames Reg.

ROGERS, Gregory James Cornwall Gardens Surgery, 77 Cornwall Gardens, Cliftonville, Margate CT9 2JF Tel: 01843 291833 Fax: 01843 293126 — MB ChB 1983 Manch.; MRCGP 1987; DRCOG 1987. Socs: Christian Med. Fell.sh.; BMA.

ROGERS, Helen Jane 37 Grange Avenue, Bangor BT20 3QF — MB ChB 1987 Sheff.

ROGERS, Mr Hugh Stephen West Middlesex University Hospital Trust, Twickenham Road, Isleworth TW7 6AF Tel: 020 8565 5440 Fax: 020 8565 5440 Email: westmid.urol@cableinet.co.uk; 179 Waldegrave Road, Teddington TW11 8LU Tel: 020 8977 6110 Fax: 020 8977 0956 — MB BChir 1975 Camb.; BA Camb. 1971; FRCS Eng. 1978. Cons. Urol. & Gen. Surg. W. Middlx. Hosp. Isleworth; Hon. Cons. Urol. Hammersmith Hosps. Trust; Clin. Dir. (Elective Servs.) W. Middlx. Hosp. Socs: Brit. Assn. Urol. Surgs.; Assn. Surg.; Founder Mem. Brit. Endurol. Assn. Prev: Sen. Regist. (Urol.) Roy. Lond. Hosp.; Sen. Regist. (Gen. Surg.) Roy. Free Hosp. Lond.

ROGERS, Mr Ian South Tynemeade Hospital, Harton Lane, South Shields; 46 Whitburn Road, Cleadon Village, Sunderland SR6 7QS — MB ChB Glas. 1967; FRCP Glas. 1985; FRCS Ed. 1972; MRCP (UK) 1973. (Glas.) Surgic. Dir. Gen. Surg. S. Shields Hosp.; Hon. Lect. (Surg.) Newc. Univ. Socs: Vasc. Soc. GB & Irel. & Brit. Soc. Gastroenterol.; Pres. N Eng. Surg. Soc. Prev: Sen. Regist. Glas. Roy. Infirm.; Regist. W.m. Hosp. Lond.; Resid. Ho. Surg. W.. Infirm. Glas.

ROGERS, James Brian (retired) Porters Hill Farm, Ladywood, Droitwich WR9 0AN Tel: 01905 452397 — MB ChB Liverp. 1951; MRCS Eng. LRCP Lond. 1951. Prev: Clin. Asst. Newtown Hosp. Worcester.

ROGERS, James Edwin Guy Dept of Anaesthetists, Frenchay Hospital, Bristol BS16 1LE; Ayr Cottage, 13 Sutherland Place, Bristol BS8 2TZ — MB BS 1985 Lond.; MRCP (UK) 1988; FRCA 1993. Cons. Amesthetist, N. Bristol NHS Trust.; Sen. Clin. Lect. Uni. Bristol.

ROGERS, Jane Ellaline — BM BCh 1994 Oxf.; DFFP 2001; MRCGP 2001. (Oxford) p/t GP Asst., Carshalton, Surrey.

ROGERS, Janet 3 Drumlar Park, Enniskillen BT74 6NA Tel: 01365 324014 — MB BCh BAO 1990 Belf.; MB BCh Belf. 1990; MRCGP 1995; DCH RCPI 1994; DRCOG 1993.

ROGERS, Jeremy Edward Medical Informatics Group, Computer Science Department, University of Manchester, Oxford Road, Manchester M13 9PL Tel: 0161 275 6145 Fax: 0161 275 6932 Email: jeremy@cs.man.ac.uk; 44 Mill Brow, Marple Bridge, Stockport SK6 5LW — MB ChB 1989 Manch.; MRCGP 1994; DRCOG 1993; DFFP 1993. Clin. Research Fell. (Med. Informatics Gp.) Univ. Manch. Socs: Brit. Med. Informat. Soc. Prev: Trainee GP Sett Valley Med. Centre; SHO (Psychiat.) Stepping Hill Hosp.

ROGERS, Joanne Mary 10 Norwood Avenue, Manchester M20 6EX — MB ChB 1990 Manch.

ROGERS, Mr John 32 Nottingam Place, London W1M 3FD Tel: 020 7486 1515 Fax: 020 7935 4984 Email: jrogers@gordcentre.org; 32 Nottingham Place, London W1U 5NR Tel: 020 7935 4645 Fax: 020 7935 4984 — MB BS 1979 Lond.; MD Lond. 1991; FRCS Eng. 1985. (King's Coll. Hosp.) Cons. Surg. Acad. Surg. Unit Roy. Lond. Hosp.; Arris & Gale Lect. RCS Eng; Hon. Clin. Asst. (Physiol.) St. Mark's Hosp. Lond.; Hon. Clin. Asst.

(Gastroenterol.) Centr. Middlx. Hosp. Lond. Prev: Lect. & Sen. Regist. Acad. Surg. Unit Roy. Lond. Hosp.; Regist. (Gen. Surg.) Centr. Middlx. Hosp. Lond.; MRC Research Fell. (Gastroenterol.) Centr. Middlx. Hosp. Lond.

ROGERS, John Alfred 145 King George V Drive, Heath, Cardiff CF14 4EN; (home) 145 King George V Drive, Heath, Cardiff CF14 4EN Tel: 01222 757532 — MB BCh 1974 Wales; DObst RCOG 1976. Med. Examr. Gresham Life Assur. Co., Med. Sickness Soc. & Hambro Life Assur. & Scott. Mutual Life Assur. Soc.; Authorised Med. Examr. for Civil Aviat. Auth.; Med. Examr. Gen. Foods Ltd.; Exam. Med. Off. DHSS; Med. Screening Off. BUPA; Clin. Asst. (Genito-Urin. Med.) Cardiff Roy. Infirm.; Occupat. Health Med. Off.; GP Cardiff. Socs: Assur. Med. Soc.

ROGERS, John Edward Windsor House, 9 Albert St., Slough SL1 2BH Tel: 01753 20643; 11 Turner Road, Slough SL3 7AL Tel: 01753 22495 — MB BS 1957 Lond.; MRCS Eng. LRCP Lond. 1957; DObst RCOG 1959. (Westm) Mem. Inst. Psychosexual Med. Prev: Res. Obst. Asst. W.m. Hosp. Lond.; Sen. Ho. Off. Chest Unit St. Helier Hosp. Carshalton.

ROGERS, John Howell The Surgery, Victoria Gardens, Neath SA11; 88 Cimla Road, Neath SA11 3UD — MB BS 1964 Lond. (Middlx.) Prev: Squadron Ldr. RAF Med. Br., Sen. Med. Off. RAF Innsworth; Unit Med. Off. RAF Akrotiri, Cyprus; Ho. Surg. Middlx. Hosp. Lond.

ROGERS, Mr John Humphreys 41 Druidsville Road, Liverpool L18 3EL — BM BCh 1965 Oxf.; BA Oxf. 1958, MA, BM BCh 1965; FRCS Eng. 1971; FRCS Ed. 1970; MRCS Eng. LRCP Lond. 1964; DLO Eng. 1969. (Oxf. & St. Thos.) Cons. Surg. (ENT) Liverp. AHA (T); Aurist & Laryng. RNCM. Socs: Liverp. Med. Inst. Prev: Lect. ENT Univ. Liverp.; SHO (ENT) Bristol Roy. Hosp.; Research Fell. in Laryng. Univ. Toronto, Canada.

ROGERS, John Michael 42 Haunch Lane, Birmingham B13 0PX — MB BS 1994 Lond.

ROGERS, John Neville The Central Hospital, Hatton, Warwick CV35 7EE Tel: 01926 491861 — MB ChB 1959 Leeds; MRCPsych 1972; DPM Eng. 1968. Cons. Centr. Hosp. Warwick. Prev: Sen. Regist. Graylingwell Hosp. Chichester; Regist. Shenley Hosp. St. Albans.

ROGERS, John Philip 3 Drumlar Park, Enniskillen BT74 6NA — MB BCh BAO 1997 Belf.

ROGERS, Jonathan Charles Southmead Health Centre, Ullswater Road, Bristol BS10 6DF Tel: 0117 950 7100 Fax: 0117 959 1110; 20 Windsor Road, St Andrews, Bristol BS6 5BP Tel: 0117 924 7380 Fax: 0117 944 5498 — MB ChB 1978 Bristol; MRCGP 1983; DRCOG 1981. (Bristol) GP; Chairm. GP Specialty Working Gp. Clin. Terms; Vice Chairm. Avon Local Med. Comm.; Med. Adviser AAH Meditel. Prev: Sec. Avon Local Med. Comm.

ROGERS, Jonathan David Chawton House, St. Thomas St., Lymington SO41 9ND Tel: 01590 673063 — BChir 1965 Camb.; MB 1966.

ROGERS, Jonathan Huw Price 34 Cherry Tree Road, The Bryn, Pontllanfraith, Blackwood NP12 2PY — MB BS 1993 Lond.

ROGERS, Julian Mark Courtenay Esplanade Surgery, 19 Esplanade, Ryde PO33 2EH Tel: 01983 611444 Fax: 01983 811548; Rowan House, Seaview Lane, Seaview PO34 5DJ Tel: 01983 811468 Fax: 01983 810152 Email: rogers@maranda.demon.co.uk — MB BS 1979 Lond.; MRCGP 1985; DRCOG 1984; DA Eng. 1982. (Lond.)

ROGERS, Kathleen Anne (retired) 21 Broomieknowe Park, Bonnyrigg EH19 2JB Tel: 0131 660 1295 — MB ChB 1975 Glas. Prev: Occupat. Health Phys. Roy. Vict. Hosp. Edin.

ROGERS, Keith Bernard (retired) 12 Church Mount, London N2 0RP Tel: 020 8458 1956 — MD 1948 Lond.; MB BS 1935; MRCS Eng., LRCP Lond. 1934; FRCPath 1963. Prev: Maj. RAMC, Path. Specialist.

ROGERS, Keith Llewellyn (retired) Farthings, The Rise, Tadworth KT20 5QT Tel: 01737 361312 — MB BS 1954 Lond.; MRCPath 1964. Prev: Dir. S. Lond. Blood Transfus. Centre Tooting.

ROGERS, Keith Main Pain Management Clinic, Gartnavel General Hospital, Glasgow G11 0YN Tel: 0141 334 8122; 7 Dargarvel Avenue, Dumbreck, Glasgow G41 5LD Tel: 0141 427 0853 — BSc (1st cl. Hons. Pharmacol.) Glas. 1964, MB ChB 1972; FFA RCS Eng. 1977; DObst RCOG 1975. (Glasgow University) Cons. Anaesth. W.. Infirm. Glas.; Hon. Clin. Sen. Lect. Univ. Glas. Socs: Assn. Anaesth.,

ROGERS

Pain Soc. & Anaesth. Res. Soc. Prev: Sandoz Res. Fell. Dept. Mat. Med. Glas. Univ.; Regist. (Anaesth.) Glas. Roy. Infirm.; Sen. Regist. (Anaesth.) Glas. W.. Infirm.

ROGERS, Professor Kenneth Plymouth Postgraduate Medical School, Derriford Hospital Level 7, Plymouth PL6 8DH Tel: 01752 782711 Fax: 01752 763531 Email: ken.rogers@phnt.swestnhs.uk — MB ChB 1969 Bristol; MD Sheff. 1989; MSc Birm. 1973; FRCS Eng. 1977. Dean & Hon. Cons. Surg. Postgrad. Med. Sch. Derriford Hosp. Plymouth. Socs: Brit. Assn. Surg. Oncol. & Assn. Surg. GB & Irel.; Surg. Research Soc. Prev: Prof. Surg. Univ. Sheff.; Lect. (Surg.) Welsh Nat. Sch. Med.; Regist. (Surg.) Worcester Roy. Infirm.

ROGERS, Lesley Anne Northwick Surgery, 36 Northwick Park Road, Harrow HA1 2NU Tel: 020 8427 1661; 29 Fisher Road, Harrow Weald, Harrow HA3 7JX Tel: 020 8424 0979 — MB ChB 1985 Ed.; MRCGP 1990; DRCOG 1987. (Ed.) Med. Examr. Benefits Agency Med. Servs. Lond.; Asst. GP Harrow Retainer Scheme. Prev: Princip. GP Overdale Med. Pract. Derbysh.

ROGERS, Madeline Jane Asplands Medical Centre, Wood St., Woburn Sands, Milton Keynes MK17 8QP Tel: 01908 582069; 32 Station Road, Woburn Sands, Milton Keynes MK17 8RW Tel: 01908 583670 — MB ChB 1977 Sheff.; DRCOG 1980.

ROGERS, Mark Alan 15 Mereway, Swanland, North Ferriby HU14 3QB — MB ChB 1995 Dundee.

ROGERS, Mr Mark John Pinderfields & Patefruit Hospital NHS Trust, Ainderfields Hospital, Aberfad Road, Wakefield WF1 4DG Tel: 01924 232272 Fax: 01924 213704; 38 Annandale Road, Kirk Ella, Hull HU10 7UU — MB ChB 1985 Leeds; BSc Leeds 1982; FRCS Eng. 1991; FRCS Gen. 1996. (University of Leeds) Cons., Gen. & Colorectal Surg., Pinderfields & Pontrefract Hosp. NHS Trust. Prev: Brit. Med. Assn.; Assoc. of Surgs., GB&Ire; Assoc. of ColoProctol. of GB.

ROGERS, Mark John 34 Edward Avenue, Eastleigh SO50 6EG — MB ChB 1998 Bristol.

ROGERS, Mark Lloyd 31 Chetwynd Drive, Basset, Southampton SO16 3HY — BM BS 1996 Nottm.

ROGERS, Mark Simon Sutherland The Crookes Practice, 203 School Road, Sheffield S10 1GN Tel: 0114 266 0677 Fax: 0114 266 4526 — MB ChB 1993 Leeds.

ROGERS, Mark Thomas Institute of Medical Genetics, University Hospitals of Wales, Heath Park, Cardiff CF14 4XN Tel: 029 2074 4022 Fax: 029 2074 7603 Email: rogersmt@cardiff.ac.uk; 4 Mitre Place, Llandaff, Cardiff CF5 2EQ Tel: 029 2056 1324 — MB BS 1984 Lond.; MRCP (UK) 1995; MRCGP 1990; DRCOG 1989; DCH RCP Lond. 1989. (St. Thos.) Specialist Regist. (Clin. Genetics) Univ. Hosp. of Wales Cardiff. Socs: BMA; Brit. Soc. Human Genetics; Clin. Genetics Soc. Prev: Muscular Dystrophy Gp. Clin. Research Fell. (Research Regist. Med. Genetics) Univ. Wales Coll. Med. Cardiff; GP Oxf.; Trainee GP Aberystwyth VTS.

ROGERS, Martin Christopher 16 Wilderness Gardens, Northam., Rye TN31 6GB — MB BS 1997 Lond.; DRCOG 2000. GP Trainee, Hastings &Rother NHSTrust.

ROGERS, Martyn John Church Street Partnership, 30A Church Street, Bishop's Stortford CM23 2LY Tel: 01279 657636 Fax: 01279 505464; 54 Penningtons, Bishop's Stortford CM23 4LF Tel: 01279 657636 Email: martyn.rogers@bigfoot.com — MB BS 1982 Lond.; MSc Lond. 1985; MRCGP 1988; DRCOG 1987; DFFP 1998; Dip Med Acupunc 1998. (St Bartholomews Hospital London)

ROGERS, Michael (retired) 42 Manor Road, Folksworth, Peterborough PE7 3SU Tel: 01733 241451 — MB ChB 1971 Dundee; DObst RCOG 1974. Prev: Retd. Gen. Practitioner, Yaxley Gp. Pract., Yaxley, PeterBoro..

ROGERS, Michael Anthony Llynfi Surgery, Llynfi Road, Maesteg CF34 9DT Tel: 01656 732115 Fax: 01656 864451; 3 Nicholls Road, Coytrahen, Bridgend CF32 0EP — MB BCh 1979 Wales; MRCGP 1983.

ROGERS, Michael Geoffrey Howden Department of Community Child Health, Alder Hey Children's Hospital, Eaton Road, Liverpool L12 2AP Tel: 0151 228 4811 Fax: 0151 252 5120; 3 Dene Cottages, Great Budworth, Northwich CW9 6HB Tel: 01606 891966 — MB BChir 1964 Camb.; MA, MB Camb. 1964, BChir 1963; DPH Lond. 1967; DCH Eng. 1965. (Westm.) Sen. Lect. (Community Child Health) Univ. Liverp.; Hon. Cons. Community Paediat. Liverp. HA. Socs: Brit. Paediat. Assn. & Brit. Assn. Comm. Child Health.; Fell.

Roy. Coll. of Paediat. and Child Health. Prev: Cons. Community Paediat. Macclesfield HA.

ROGERS, Michael Harvey High House, Ballinger Road, South Heath, Great Missenden HP16 9QJ — MB ChB 1953 Birm.; AFOM RCP Lond. 1979; MFCM 1974; DObst RCOG 1964. (Birm.) Prev: Princip. Med. Off. Jt. H.Q. RAF Germany; CO RAF Hosp. Wegberg; Sen. Ho. Phys. & Obst. Ho. Surg. Manor Hosp. Walsall.

ROGERS, Moira Elizabeth Biel Mill Lodge, Dunbar EH42 1SY — MB ChB 1983 Dundee. Clin. Asst. (Ophth.) St John's Hosp. Livingston W. Lothian.

ROGERS, Neil Kingsley 24 Fulney Road, Sheffield S11 7EW Tel: 0114 230 2093 — BM BCh 1989 Oxf.; DPhil Oxf. 1984, BM BCh 1989; BSc York 1981; FRCOphth 1994. Cons. Ophth., Tashkent Med. Paediat. Inst., Tashkent, Uzbekistan. Prev: Sen. Regist. (Ophth.) Roy. Hallamsh. Hosp. Sheff.

ROGERS, Mr Norman Charles, Maj.-Gen. late RAMC Retd. 110 Mill Street, Kidlington OX5 2EF — MB BS 1939 Lond.; FRCS Eng. 1949; MRCS Eng. LRCP Lond. 1939. (St. Bart.) Socs: Fell. Assn. Surgs. Prev: Hon. Surg. to HM the Qu.; Clin. Supt. & Cons. A & E Guy's Hosp. Lond.; Dir. of Army Surg. MoD.

ROGERS, Pamela Marion 110 Mill Street, Kidlington OX5 2EF — MB ChB 1953 Birm.; AFOM RCP Lond. 1982. (Birm.) Occupat. Health Phys. Guy's & St. Thos. NHS Trust; Gp. Med. Adviser Tate & Lyle plc. Socs: BMA & Soc. Occupat. Med. Prev: Med. Off. Nurses Health Serv. & Occupat. Health Serv. Guy's Hosp. Lond.

ROGERS, Paul Bryan Berkshire Cancer Centre, Royal Berkshire Hospital, London Road, Reading RG1 5AN Tel: 0118 987 5111 Email: rogershme@aol.com; 70 Westwood Drive, Little Chalfont, Amersham HP6 6RW — MB BS 1989 Lond.; MRCP (UK) 1993; FRCR 1996. Cons., Clin. Oncol., Berks. Cancer centre, Roy. Berks. Hosp. Reading; Sen. Specialist Regist., Clin. Oncol., St. Batholomews Hosp.& Mt. Vernon; Vis. Worker: MRC Cell Mutation Unit, Brighton, Sussex. Socs: Amer. Soc. Clin. Oncol.; Eur. Soc. Therap. Radiol. & Oncol.; Brit. Oncol. Assn. Prev: Regist. Rotat. (Radiother. & Oncol.) Roy. Free Hosp., Middlx. Hosp. & Mt. Vernon Hosp.; SHO Rotat. (Med.) Stoke Mandeville Hosp. Aylesbury; SHO Rotat. (Radiother. & Oncol.) Mt. Vernon Hosp. & Char. Cross Hosp. Lond.

ROGERS, Paul Haydon (retired) 3A Watery Lane, Nether Heyford, Northampton NN7 3LN Tel: 01327 340126 — MB BChir 1943 Camb.; FRCP Lond. 1973, M 1948; FRCPsych 1974, M 1971; DPM Eng. 1955. Prev: Cons. Psychiat. & Med. Dir. St. Crispin Hosp. N.ampton.

ROGERS, Paul Nicholas 35 Spenbeck Drive, Allestree, Derby DE22 2UH — MB ChB 1994 Dundee.

ROGERS, Mr Paul Noel Gartnavel General Hospital, Great Western Road, Glasgow G12 0YN — MB ChB 1977 Glas.; MBA Open 1995; MD Glas. 1988; FRCS Glas. 1981. Cons. Gen. Surg. Gartnavel Gen. Hosp. Glas.; Hon. Clin. Sen. Lect. Univ. Glas.

ROGERS, Paul Thomas Lavender Hill Group Practice, 100 Lavender Hill, London SW11 5RE Tel: 020 7228 4042; 16 Eltringham Street, Wandsworth, London SW18 1TE — MB BS 1984 Lond.; BSc Lond. 1981; DRCOG 1988; Cert. Family Plann. JCC 1988. Prev: GP Lond.

ROGERS, Paula Jane 9 Pickersleigh Road, Malvern WR14 2RP — MB ChB 1992 Liverp.

ROGERS, Peter Derek 10 Wilton Place, Southsea, Portsmouth PO5 2BG Email: pter.rogrs@qmailos.porthosp.swest.nhs.uk — MB BS 1974 Lond.; FFA RCS Eng. 1981; DA Eng. 1977. (Westminster) Cons. Anaesth. & Pain Managem., Portsmouth; Clin. Director Dept. of Pain Med.; Chairm. Wessex Pain Gp.; Qu. Alexandra Hosp., Dept. of Anaesthetics, Cosham, Portsmouth PO6 3LY. Socs: Internat. Assn. Study of Pain; BMA; Assn. Anaesth.

ROGERS, Philip Peter 32 The Old Mill, Hillsborough BT26 6RA — MB BCh BAO 1996 Belf.

ROGERS, Richard Department of Anaesthetics, John Radcliffe Hospital, Headley Way, Oxford OX3 9DU Tel: 01865 741166; The Cottage, The Green, Cassington, Witney OX29 4DW Tel: 01865 881322 — MB BS 1987 Lond.; BA Oxf. 1981; FRCA. 1992. Cons. Paediat. Anaesth. John Radcliffe Hosp. Oxf. Prev: Sen. Regist. (Anaesth.) Gt. Ormond St. Hosp. for Childr. & St. Geos. Hosp. & St. Peter's Chertsey, St. Geo. Hosp. Lond. & Hosp. for Childr. Gt. Ormond St. Lond.; Regist. Rotat. (Anaesth.) Guildford, St. Heliers Hosp. Carshalton & St. Geo. Hosp. Lond.; SHO Rotat. (Anaesth.) Lewisham & Guy's Hosps. Lond.

ROGERSON

ROGERS, Richard Thomas Neave Ilkeston Health Centre, South Street, Ilkeston DE7 5PZ Tel: 0115 932 2933 — MB ChB 1983 Leic.

ROGERS, Robert Samuel Boulderson (retired) 1 Royal Crescent, Cheltenham GL50 3DB Tel: 01242 521070 — MB BS 1952 Lond.; DObst RCOG 1955.

ROGERS, Sally Joy Katharine House Hospice, East End, Adderbury, Banbury OX17 3N Tel: 01295 811866; The Retreat, Chapel Lane, Stoke Bruerne, Towcester NN12 7SQ — MB BS 1980 Lond.; MRCGP 1986; DRCOG 1988; Dip. Palliat. Med. 1998. Med. Off. (Palliat. Med.) Katharine Ho. Hospice Banbury.

ROGERS, Simon Neave 33 Woolacombe Lodge Road, Birmingham B29 6PZ Tel: 0121 471 1400 — MB ChB 1990 Birm.; ChB Birm. 1990; BDS Sheff. 1984; FDS RCS Eng. 1988.

ROGERS, Sinead Mary Harlestone Road Surgery, 117 Harlestone Road, Northampton NN5 7AQ Tel: 01604 751832 Fax: 01604 586065; 20 Church Street, Weedon, Northampton NN7 4PL Tel: 01327 340521 — MB BS 1992 Lond.; DFFP 1996; DRCOG 1995; MRCGP 1996. (UMDS (GUYS)) Princip. GP, Dr Gill & Partners, N.hampton.

ROGERS, Stephen 21 The Walk, Hengoed CF82 7AH — MB BCh 1982 Wales.

ROGERS, Stephen Andrew Moordown Medical Centre, 2A Redhill Crescent, Bournemouth BH9 2XF Tel: 01202 516139 Fax: 01202 548525 — MB ChB 1977 Birm.; MRCGP 1984; DRCOG 1981.

ROGERS, Stephen James 29 Kendalls Close, High Wycombe HP13 7NN — MB BS 1987 Tasmania.

ROGERS, Stephen Young Fife Area Laboratory, Hayfield Road, Kirkcaldy KY2 5AG Tel: 01592 643355 Fax: 01592 647037 Email: stephen.rogers@faht.scot.nhs.uk; 2 Telny Place, Aberdour, Burntisland KY3 0TG — MB BS 1983 Newc.; BA Camb. 1980; FRCP Ed. 1996; MRCPath 1992; MRCP (UK) 1986. Cons. Haemat. Vict. Hosp. Kirkcaldy; Hon. Sen. Lect. Edin. Univ.; Hon. Sen. Lect. St Andrews Univ. Prev: Lect. (Haemat.) Univ. Nottm.

ROGERS, Susan Diana 42 Manor Road, Folksworth, Peterborough PE7 3SU Tel: 01733 241451 — MB ChB 1972 Dundee. (Univ. Dundee) Prev: Clin. Asst. Wansford.

ROGERS, Susan Pamela 119 Markwell Road, Parsloe Road, Harlow CM19 5QU — MB BS 1990 Lond.

ROGERS, Suzanne Department of Pathology, Doncaster Royal Infirmary, Armthorpe Road, Doncaster DN2 5LT Tel: 01302 366666 Fax: 01302 553264 — MB ChB 1987 Bristol; BSc Cellular Path. Bristol 1984; MRCPath 1994. Cons. Histopath. Doncaster Roy. Infirm. Prev: Lect. (Path.) Sheff. Univ.

ROGERS, Professor Thomas Richard Frazer Department of Infectious Diseases & Microbiology, Imperial College School of Medicine, Hammersmith Campus, Ducane Road, London W12 0NN Tel: 0208 383 3224 Fax: 0208 383 3394 Email: tomrog@rpms.ac.uk — LRCPI & LM, LRSCI & LM 1972; LRCPI & LM, LRCSI & LM 1972; MSc Lond. 1979; MA (Med. Law & Ethics) 1994; FRCPI 1987, M 1985; FRCPath 1990, M 1978. Prof. Univ. Lond.; Hon. Cons. Hammersmith Hosps. Trust. Socs: Assn. Clin. Path.; Fell. Roy. Soc. Med.; Hosp. Infec. Soc. (Chairm. 97-98). Prev: Sen. Lect. (Med. Microbiol.) Char. Cross & W.m. Med. Sch. Lond.

ROGERS, Timothy Alexander Manor Surgery, Forth Noweth, Chapel Street, Redruth TR15 1BY Tel: 01209 313313 Fax: 01209 313813 — MB BS 1975 Lond.; MRCS Eng. LRCP Lond. 1975; FRCGP 1993, M 1980; DRCOG 1978. (Westm.)

ROGERS, Timothy David Herdmanflat, Aberlady Road, Haddington EH41 3BU Tel: 0131 536 8300 — MB ChB 1983 Aberd.; MPhil Ed. 1990; MRCPsych 1988. Cons. Gen. Psychiat. Herdmanflat Hosp. Haddington & Roy. Infirm. Edin. Prev: Sen. Regist. & Regist. (Psychiat.) Roy. Edin. Hosp.

ROGERS, Trevor Keith Chest Clinic, Doncaster Royal Infirmary, Armthorpe Road, Doncaster DN2 5LT Tel: 01302 366666 Fax: 01302 553192 Email: trevor.rogers@dbh.nhs.uk — MB ChB 1985 Bristol; BSc Bristol 1982; MD Sheff. 1995; FRCP (UK) 1999. (Bristol) Cons. Phys. (Gen. & Chest Med.) Doncaster Roy. Infirm.; Hon. Cons. Sen. Lect., (Div. of Genomic Med., Univ. Sheff.). Socs: Brit. Thorac. Soc.; Amer. Thoracic Soc.; BMA. Prev: Lect. (Med.) Univ. Sheff.; Regist. Rotat. (Med.) Profess. Dept. Med. & Pharmacol. Roy. Hallamsh. Hosp. Sheff.; SHO Rotat. (Med.) Bristol Gen. Hosp.

ROGERS, Valerie Jean Bodymoor Heath Farm, Dog Lane, Bodymoor Heath, Sutton Coldfield B76 9JD — MB BS 1997 Lond.

ROGERS, Vincent Joseph Tel: 01754 766766 Fax: 01754 760632 — MB ChB 1982 Glas. Socs: Roy. Soc. Med.

ROGERS, Walter James Blachford (retired) Achmaha, Rockcliffe, Dalbeattie DG5 — MB BChir 1947 Camb.; MRCP Lond. 1948; MRCS Eng. LRCP Lond. 1941; FRCPsych 1971; DPM Lond. 1952. Prev: Cons. (Child Psychiat.) Dept. Child Psychiat. Crichton Roy. Hosp.

ROGERS, Watson (retired) Little Acre, Priestlands, Sherborne DT9 4HW — MB BChir 1943 Camb.; MRCS Eng. LRCP Lond. 1942; DA Eng. 1957; MRCGP 1953. Prev: Med. Asst. Anaesth. Yeatman Hosp. Sherborne.

ROGERS, William Andrew 27 Alexandra Road, Heaton Moor, Stockport SK4 2QE — MB ChB 1989 Manch. Trainee GP/SHO (Psychiat.) Blackburn Roy. Infirm. VTS. Prev: Ho. Phys. Qu. Pk. Hosp. Blackburn; Ho. Surg. Preston Roy. Hosp.

ROGERS, William Francis (retired) 18 Tavistock Crescent, Westlands, Newcastle Under Lyme, Newcastle ST5 3NW Tel: 01782 615160 — MB BCh BAO 1940 Dub.; MA Dub. 1995, BA 1938, MD 1942; Cert. VD Dr. Stevens' Hosp. Dub. 1948. Vol. Chairm. Vis. Standards/Quality Assur. Comm. Douglas MacMillan Homs Stoke on Trent. Prev: Sen. Cons. Geriat. N. Staffs. Health Dist.

ROGERS, William John Felpham and Middleton Health Centre, 109 Flansham Park, Felpham, Bognor Regis PO22 6DH Tel: 01243 582384 Fax: 01243 584933 — MB BS 1980 Lond.; MRCS Eng., LRCP Lond. 1980; MRCGP 1984; DRCOG 1984. (St. Bart.) Prev: Trainee GP Mid-Sussex VTS; Ho. Surg. Roy. E. Sussex Hosp. Hastings; Ho. Phys. Frimley Pk. Hosp.

ROGERS, Zoe Jane 28 Harrow View Road, Ealing, London W5 1LZ — BM BCh 1992 Oxf.

ROGERSON, Charlotte Ann 19 Fry's Lane, Yateley, Yateley GU46 7TJ — BM BS 1997 Nottm.

ROGERSON, David 7 Church Road, Eggington, Derby DE65 6HP Tel: 01283 734384 Fax: 01283 734384 Email: david.rogerson@virgin.net — MB ChB 1975 Manch.; FFA RCSI 1978; DA Eng. 1978; MMedSci 1997. (Manchester) Cons. Anaesth. Derbysh. Roy. Infirm. Socs: Assn. Anaesth. Gt. Brit. & Irel.; Soc. Med. & Dent. Hypn.; Brit. Med. Acupunc. Soc.

ROGERSON, Grace Gilmour The Health Centre, Kilbowie Road, Clydebank G81 2TQ Tel: 0141 531 6400 Fax: 0141 531 6433; 37 Braehead Avenue, Milngavie, Glasgow G62 6DH — MB ChB 1967 Glas.

ROGERSON, Ian Michael West Chester Hospital, Liverpool Road, Chester CH2 1UL — MB ChB 1991 Liverp. Cons. Psychiat. W. Chesh. Hosp. Chester.

ROGERSON, James William 60 Hawcoat Lane, Barrow-in-Furness LA14 4HQ Tel: 01229 20542 — MRCS Eng. LRCP Lond. 1940. (Liverp.) Socs: Assoc. MRCGP; BMA. Prev: Ho. Surg. David Lewis N.. Hosp. Liverp.; Asst. Phys. N. Lonsdale Hosp. Barrow; RAMC.

ROGERSON, John Grant Broom Cottage, 14 West Lennox Drive, Helensburgh G84 9AE Tel: 01436 78312 — MB ChB 1960 Glas.; DObst RCOG 1962.

ROGERSON, John Patrick Gerard, MBE (retired) Conifers, Alkington Road, Whitchurch SY13 1ST — MB ChB Liverp. 1937; MRCGP 1962. Prev: Venereol. Shrewsbury Gp. Hosps.

ROGERSON, Joseph Thomas Gerard (retired) 11 Northampton Close, Ely CB6 3QT — MB ChB 1962 Liverp.; FFA RCS Eng. 1970; DA Eng. 1964. Prev: Med. Dir. St. John Ambul. Nat. HQ Lond.

ROGERSON, Kirsty Ann Doctors' Residence, Arrowe Park Hospital, Arrowe Park Road, Wirral CH49 5PE — MB ChB 1998 Liverp.; MB ChB Liverp 1998.

ROGERSON, Lynne Joanne 74 Stones Drive, Old Stones Park, Sowerby Bridge HX6 4NY Tel: 01422 824150; 3 The Grove, Boston Spa, Wetherby LS23 6AR Tel: 01937 844029 — MB ChB 1990 Manch.; MRCOG 1996. (Manch.) Specialist Regist. (Obstet. & Gyn.) Leeds Gen. Infirm. Socs: MRCOG; BMA; BSGE.

ROGERSON, Mari Ellen 160 East Dulwich Grove, London SE22 8TB Tel: 020 8299 0499; The White House, Wycombe Road, Studley Green, High Wycombe HP14 3UY — MB BS 1986 Lond.; DRCOG 1990.

ROGERSON, Mark Edward Histopathology Department, Central Pathology Laboratory, North Staffordshire Hospital, Stoke-on-Trent ST4 7PA Tel: 01782 554988; 59 Hodge Lane, Hartford, Northwich

ROGERSON

CW8 3AG Tel: 01606 74669 — MB BS 1975 Lond.; BSc Lond. 1972, MB BS 1975; MRCPath 1994. (Middlx. Hosp.) Cons. Histopath. N. Staff. Hosp.

ROGERSON, Mary Elizabeth Southampton General Hospital, Southampton SO16 0YD Tel: 02380 777222 Email: mary.rogerson@suht.swest.nhs.uk — MB BS 1981 Lond.; BSc Lond. 1978, MB BS 1981; MRCP (UK) 1984; FRCP 1999. Cons. Phys. Renal Med. Soton. Univ. Hosps. Trust. Prev: Sen. Regist. (Nephrol.) Wessex RHA; Clin. Lect. (Nephrol.) Inst. Urol. Lond.; Regist. Rotat. (Med.) Wessex RHA.

ROGERSON, Rowland 52 Beverley Road, Kirkella, Hull HU10 7QB Tel: 01482 653277 — LMSSA 1959 Lond.; MRCGP 1966. (Leeds) Med. Examr. & Adviser Offshore Oil Industries. Socs: Hull Med. Soc.; Soc. Occupat. Health. Prev: SHO (Anaesth. & Med.) Friarage Hosp. N.allerton; Ho. Off. (Obst.) Greenbank Matern. Hosp. Darlington.

ROGERSON, Ruth Elizabeth 14 Gresley Close, Welwyn Garden City AL8 7QB Tel: 01707 339543 — MB ChB 1986 Ed.; MRCGP 1990. Asst. GP Herts. Retainer Scheme. Prev: Trainee GP Qu. Eliz. II Hosp. Welwyn Gdn. City.

ROGERSON, Sheryle Rosemary Keats 17 Oakdale Road, Waterloo, Liverpool L22 9QS Tel: 0151 928 5122 — MB BS 1986 Adelaide.

ROGERSON, Simon Hugh Norwood Medical Centre, 99 Abbey Road, Barrow-in-Furness LA14 5ES Tel: 01229 822024 Fax: 01229 823949; 30 Hawcoat Lane, Barrow-in-Furness LA14 4HF Tel: 01229 825561 — MB ChB 1974 Liverp. Socs: Brit. Med. Acupunct. Soc. & Med. Research Counc.; Gen. Pract. Research Framework.

ROGGER-AMIES, Andrew Melvin Acorns, Orvis Lane, East Bergholt, Colchester CO7 6TT — MB BS 1990 Lond.

ROGOL, Benjamin Wellington Hospital, London NW8 9LE Tel: 020 7586 5959 Fax: 020 7483 0297; 14 Bracknell Gate, Frognal Lane, London NW3 7EA Tel: 020 7435 4168 — MA Dub 1993, BA 1934, MB BCh BAO 1936; LM Rotunda 1938. (T.C. Dub.) Socs: Fell. Roy. Soc. Med. & Med. Soc. Lond.; Brit. Soc. Rheum. Prev: Clin. Asst. (Dermat.) Univ. Coll. Hosp.; SHMO (Rheum.) Hackney & German Hosps.; Resid. Med. Off. P.ss Louise Kens. Hosp. Childr.

ROGOL, Solomon (retired) Flat 5, 99 Hendon Lane, London N3 3SH Tel: 020 8346 2875 — LRCPI & LM, LRCSI & LM 1943. Prev: Ho. Surg. Roy. Berks. Hosp. Reading & Roy. W. Hants. Hosp.

ROGOWSKI, Piotr 185 Hamstead Road, Birmingham B20 2RL Tel: 0121 554 1567 — Med. Dipl. Kovno 1941. (Wilno)

ROGSTAD, Karen Elizabeth Department of Genitourinary Medicine, Royal Hallamshire Hospital, Glossop Road, Sheffield S10 2JF Tel: 0114 270 0928 Fax: 0114 275 9081 — MB BS 1982 (Hons.) Newc.; MRCP (UK) 1985; MRCGP 1987; FRCP. p/t Cons. Genitourin. Med. Roy. Hallamsh. Hosp. Socs: Educat. Sub-Comm. MSSVD; AGUM; Sec. Genitourin. Med. Sub-Comm. RCP. Prev: Sen. Regist. (Genitourin. Med.) City Hosp. Nottm.; Regist. (Gen. Med.) Roy. Vict. Infirm. Newc.

ROHAN, Claire Frances Cedar House, St. Michael's Hospital, Enfield; 280 The Ridgeway, Enfield EN2 8AP — MB BCh BAO 1985 NUI; MRCP (UK) 1990. Cons. Paediat. Chase Farm Hosp. Enfield. Socs: Roy. Coll. Paediat. & Child Health. Prev: SCMO St. Bart. NHS Trust.

ROHAN, Jacques Claude 1180 Palais de la Scala, Avenue Henry Dunant, Monte Carlo 98000, Monaco Tel: 00 33 93 92160436; c/o. 15 Belle Baulk, Towcester NN12 6YE Tel: 01327 352628 — LRCP LRCS Ed. LRFPS Glas. 1945; FRCGP 1983, M 1964.

ROHAN, John Stephen Laurence House, 107 Philip Lane, Tottenham, London N15 4JR Tel: 020 8801 6640; 280 The Ridgeway, Enfield EN2 8AP — MB BCh BAO 1984 NUI; MRCGP 1988; MICGP 1988; DObst RCPI 1987; DCH Dub 1986. GP Trainer Lond.; Clin. Asst. (Ment. Handicap) Chase Farm Hosp. Enfield.; Course Organiser (Gen. Pract.) Enfield & Haringey VTS.

ROHATGI, Krishna Kumar 6 Camstradden Drive W., Bearsden, Glasgow G61 4AJ — MB BS 1961 Bihar; DPM Eng. 1973. (Darbhanga Med. Coll.) Cons. Psychiat. Lanarksh. Health Bd. Socs: Affil. RCPsych; BMA & Mem. Assn. Behavioural Clinicians. Prev: Sen. Regist. (Foren. Psychiat.) Gtr. Glas. Health Bd.; Flight Lt. Indian Air Force; Rotat. Regist. (Psychiat.) Crichton Roy. Hosp. Dumfries.

ROHATGI, Mahindra Kumar Sita Medical Centre, High Street, Goldenhill, Stoke-on-Trent ST6 5QJ Tel: 01782 772242 Fax: 01782 776711; 2 Sandbach Road, Church Lawton, Stoke-on-Trent ST7 3BE Tel: 01270 877910 — MB BS 1967 Jiwaji; DA Eng. 1971. Socs: Med. Protec. Soc.

ROHATGI, Shakuntla Sita Medical Centre, High Street, Goldenhill, Stoke-on-Trent ST6 5QJ Tel: 01782 772242 Fax: 01782 776711; 2 Sandbach Road, Church Lawton, Stoke-on-Trent ST7 3BE Tel: 01270 877910 — MB BS 1965 Delhi; MRCOG 1974. (Lady Harding Med. Coll.)

ROHATGI, Subir 5 Greenhill Road, Whitnash, Leamington Spa CV31 2HG — MB BS 1990 Lond.

ROHATINER, Anna Zofia Stefania 62 South Croxted Road, London SE21 8BD — MRCS Eng. LRCP Lond. 1974; MD Lond. 1984, MB BS 1974; MRCP (UK) 1977. (Guy's) Hon. Sen. Lect. & Cons. Phys. St. Bart. Hosp. Lond.

ROHDE, Simon Peter The Tod Practice, 12 Durham Road, Raynes Park, London SW20 0TW Tel: 020 8946 0069 Fax: 020 8944 2927 — MB BS 1987 Lond.; BSc (Psychol. Med. Sci.) Lond. 1984. SHO (Obst.) W. Lond. Hosp.

ROHLFING, Robert Frederick Eaglestone Health Centre, Standing Way, Eaglestone, Milton Keynes MK6 5AZ Tel: 01908 679111 Fax: 01908 230601 — MB BS 1991 Lond.

ROHMAN, Stephen Owen King's Surgery, Water St., Port Talbot SA12 6LF Tel: 01639 890983 Fax: 01639 870146 Email: srohman@iechy.gpmail; 1 Dynevor Avenue, Neath SA10 7AG Tel: 01639 641341 Email: steve@rohman.freeserve.co.uk — MB BS 1986 Lond.; MRCGP 1991; DRCOG 1989. (St. Bart.) Clin. Asst. (Care Elderly) Cymla Hosp. Neath. Prev: Trainee GP Fairfield Med. Centre Port Talbot; SHO (Gen. Med., Geriat., O & G, Paediat. & A & E) Neath Gen. Hosp.; SHO (A & E) Roy. Gwent Hosp. Newport.

ROITH, Eva 183 Harrow Road, Wollaton Park, Nottingham NG8 1FL — MA Dub. 1958, MB BCh BAO 1949; DPM Eng. 1962; DPH NUI 1953. Prev: Sen. Med. Off. (Ment. Health) Notts. HA; Med. Off. St. Lawrence's Hosp. Caterham; SHO Kettlewell Hosp. Swanley.

ROJO LLANOS, Luis Flat 6, 25-27 Central Road, Manchester M20 4YE — LMS 1990 Saragossa.

ROJO LLANOS, Maria Horton General Hospital NHS Trust, 81A Oxford Road, Banbury OX16 9AL — LMS 1995 Saragossa.

ROKAN AL-MALLAK, Mr Hamid Southend Hospital, Department Accident & Emergency, Prittlewell Chase, Westcliff on Sea SS0 0RY Tel: 01702 221001 Fax: 01702 221009 — MB ChB 1973 Baghdad; FRCSI 1990. Cons. A & E Med. S.end Hosp. W.cliff on Sea. Socs: Fell. Fac. A & E Med.; BMA; BAEM.

ROLAN, Jacinta Maria Frances Helene 24 Moorside, Sheffield S10 4LN — MB BCh BAO 1989 NUI; LRCPSI 1989.

ROLAN, Paul Edward Medeval Ltd., Skelton House, Manchester Science Park, Lloyd Street N., Manchester M15 6SH Tel: 0161 226 6525 Fax: 0161 226 8936 Email: p.rolan@medeval.com — MB BS 1979 Adelaide; MD Adelaide 1995; FFPM RCP (UK) 1997, MF 1996; FRACP 1985; DCPSA 1985. Med. Dir. Medeval Manch.; Hon. Cons. Phys. (Neurol.) Manch. Roy. Infirm.; Dir. Neuraxis Manch. Socs: Assn. Human Pharmacol. Pharmaceut. Industry; Pharmacol. Soc.; Int. Headache Soc. Prev: Head of Clin. Pharmacokinetics Wellcome Research Laborat. UK; Dir. Med. Cairns Base Hosp. Qu.sland, Austral.

ROLAND, Jess 3 The Springs, Park Road, Bowdon, Altrincham WA14 3JH Tel: 0161 927 7554 — MB ChB 1945 Manch. (Manch.) Prev: Asst. Med. Off. Booth Hall Childr. Hosp. Manch.

ROLAND, Jill 12 Huxley Drive, Bramhall, Stockport SK7 2PH Tel: 0161 439 6973 — MRCS Eng. LRCP Lond. 1961; MSc Manch. 1981; FFPHM RCP (UK) 1996; MFCM RCP (UK) 1982.

ROLAND, Jonathan Michael Edith Cavell Hospital, Bretton Gate, Peterborough PE3 9GZ Tel: 01733 874217 Fax: 01733 875159 Email: jonathan.roland@pbh-tr.anglox.nhs.uk; Email: jmrphys@aol.com — MB BS 1972 Lond.; DM Nottm. 1984; BSc Lond. 1969, MB BS 1972; FRCP Lond. 1994; MRCP (UK) 1975. Cons. Phys. PeterBoro. Dist. Hosp. Prev: Sen. Regist. (Med.) Bristol Roy. Infirm.

ROLAND, Mark Arvan 6 Wentworth Avenue, Whitefield, Manchester M45 7GQ — MB ChB 1990 Liverp.; MRCP (UK) 1994.

ROLAND, Professor Martin Oliver National Primary Care Research & Development Centre, Williamson Building, University of Manchester, Oxford Road, Manchester M13 6PL Tel: 0161 275 7659 Fax: 0161 275 7600 Email: m.roland@man.ac.uk; 15 Portland Road, Altrincham WA14 2PA Tel: 0161 928 1748 Fax: 0161 926

ROLLIN

8436 — BM BCh 1975 Oxf.; FRCP, 2001; F.Med sci, 2000; MA Oxf. 1976, DM 1989; MRCP (UK) 1978; FRCGP 1994, M 1979; MFPHM 1988; DRCOG 1977. Prof. Gen. Pract. Univ. Manch.; Director Nat. Primary Care Research & Developm. Centre Univ Manch. Prev: Dir. of Studies Gen. Pract., Camb. Univ. Sch. Clin. Med.; Lect. (Gen. Pract.) St. Thos. Hosp. Med. Sch. Lond.; Trainee GP Camb. VTS.

ROLAND, Mary 14A Essex Road, Enfield EN2 6TZ — MRCS Eng. LRCP Lond. 1936; DPH Eng. 1946. (T.C. Dub.) Prev: Asst. M.O.H. Boro. Scunthorpe; Asst. Med. Off. W. Riding C.C.; Capt. R.A.M.C.

ROLAND, Mr Nicholas John Department of Otorhinolaryngology, Aintree NHS Trust, Liverpool Tel: 0151 529 5259 — MB ChB 1987 Liverp.; MD Liverp, 1997; FRCS Eng. 1992. (Liverp.) Cons. (Otolaryngol & Head & Neck Surg.) Aintree NHS Trust, Liverp.; Hon. Lect. (Otolaryngol. & Head & Neck Surg.) Liverp. Univ. Socs: BMA; Brit. Assn. Otol. & Head & Neck Surg.; Brit. Assn. Cancer Res. Prev: Lect. & Sen. Regist. (Otolaryngol. & Head & Neck Surg.) Roy. Liverp. Univ. Hosp.

ROLAND, Mr Peter Ernest (retired) 34 Regency House, Newbold Terrace, Leamington Spa CV32 4HD Tel: 01926 470980 — MB BS Lond. 1940; FRCS Ed. 1948; MRCS Eng. LRCP Lond. 1939; DLO Eng. 1942. Prev: Cons. Surg. (ENT) Hosp. St. Cross Rugby & Coventry AHA.

ROLANT-THOMAS, Catherine Mabel (retired) Bron Menai, Cadnant Road, Menai Bridge LL59 5NG Tel: 01248 712526 — MRCS Eng. LRCP Lond. 1922; LDS Eng. 1924. Prev: Clin. Asst. Dent. Dept. Gt. Ormond St. Hosp. Sick Childr.

ROLES, Wendy Princess Margaret Hospital, Windsor SL4 3SJ Tel: 01753 743434; 5 The Dell, Bishopsgate Rd, Englefield Green, Egham TW20 0XY Tel: 01784 437645 Fax: 01276 431576 Email: dr.w.roles@tinternet.com — MB BS 1960 Lond.; MRCS Eng. LRCP Lond. 1960; MFFP 1993; RCOG. (Barts) Cons. Psychosexual Med. P.ss Margt. Hosp. Windsor. Socs: Windsor Med. Soc. Prev: Med. Director Slough Family Plann. Clinic; Clin. Asst. Colposcopy Heatherwood Hosp. Ascot.

ROLFE, Alun Bowen The Hall, Merthyr Road, Llanfoist, Abergavenny NP7 9LR Tel: 01783 2148 — MB ChB 1954 Birm.; MRCS Eng. LRCP Lond. 1954; FRCPsych. 1987, M 1972; DPM Eng. 1962. Cons. Psychiat. Llanarth Ct. Hosp. Raglan, Gwent; JP. Prev: Cons. Psychiat. Pen-y-Fal Hosp. Abergavenny; Chairm. Gwent Div. Psychiat.; Mem. Ment. Health Act Commiss.

ROLFE, Diana (retired) 6 Chapman Square, Harrogate HG1 2SL Tel: 01423 567663 — MB BS 1966 Lond.; MRCP Lond. 1969. Prev: SHO (Rheum.) Middlx. Hosp. Lond.

ROLFE, Helena Clare Ilkley Health Centre, Springs Lane, Ilkley LS29 8TQ Tel: 01943 430005; 23 Hillside, Follifoot, Harrogate HG3 1EF Tel: 01423 879932 — MB ChB 1992 Leeds; MRCGP 1996. (Leeds) GP Princip. Prev: SHO (Paediat.) Dewsbury Dist. Hosp.; Trainee GP Leeds.

ROLFE, John Morris (retired) 28 Reayrt Carnane, Tromode Park, Douglas IM2 5LN Tel: 01624 26471 — MB ChB Birm. 1956; DObst RCOG 1962.

ROLFE, Lindsey Margaret Hammersmith Medicines Research, Central Middlesex Hospital, Acton Lane, London NW10 7NS — MB ChB 1992 Ed.; MRCP (UK) 1995.

ROLFE, Michael Garland Carmel, Beech Avenue, Pennsylvania, Exeter EX4 6HE — MB BChir 1947 Camb.; FFA RCS Eng. 1956; DObst RCOG 1950; DA Eng. 1955. (Lond. Hosp.) Socs: Fell. Roy. Soc. Med.; Assn. Anaesths. Prev: Cons. Anaesth. Lond. Hosp. & King Geo. Hosp. Ilford; Regist. Anaesth. Roy. Nat. Throat, Nose & Ear Hosp.; Sen. Regist. Anaesth. Lond. Hosp.

ROLFE, Muriel Elisabeth (retired) The Old House, 24 High St, Bridge, Canterbury CT4 5JY Tel: 01227 832694 — MB BS 1957 Lond.; DO 1961 Eng; MRCS Eng. LRCP 1957 Lond. Prev: Assoc. Specialist Moorfields Eye Hosp. Lond.

ROLFE, Mrs Sally Anne Tel: 01252 835016 Fax: 01252 837908; Portland House, 348 Vale Road, Ash Vale, Aldershot GU12 5LW — MB BS 1961 Lond. (Char. Cross)

ROLFE, Sian Eluned The Hall, Llanfoist, Abergavenny NP7 9LR — MB ChB 1985 Manch.

ROLL, Mrs Helen Camilla de Clery (retired) 'Fairfield', Carr Hall Road, Barrowford, Nelson BB9 6QA Tel: 01282 612766 — MB ChB 1950 Aberd. Prev: Ho. Surg. (Gyn.) Woodend Gen. Hosp. Aberd.

ROLL, Matthew Jeremy Simon 113 Overdale Road, Romiley, Stockport SK6 3EN — MB ChB 1988 Manch.

ROLLAND, Charles Frederick (retired) Knocker House, Caldbeck, Wigton CA7 8EG — MD 1953 Ed.; BA (Nat. Sc. Trip. Pt. I, cl. I) Camb. 1941; MD (High Commend.) Ed. 1953; MB ChB 1944; FRCP Ed. 1956, M 1948. Prev: Phys. Cumbld. Infirm. Carlisle.

ROLLAND, Douglas McIntyre Teviot Medical Practice, Teviot Road, Hawick TD9 9DT Tel: 01450 370999 Fax: 01450 371025; Westwood, Sunnyhill Road, Hawick TD9 7HT Tel: 01450 373633 Email: douglasrolland@msn.com — MB ChB 1989 Aberd.; MRCGP 1993; Cert Prescribed Equiv. Exp. JCPTGP 1993; DCH RCPS Glas. 1991. GP Princip. Hawick. Prev: Trainee GP Borders HB VTS; Ho. Off. (Surg.) Glas. Roy. Infirm.; Ho. Off. (Med.) Woodend Hosp. Aberd.

ROLLAND, Morag Bruce Teviot Medical Practice, Hawick Health Centre, Teviot Road, Hawick TD9 9DT Tel: 01450 372550 Fax: 01450 371025; Westwood, Sunnyhill, Hawick TD9 7HT Tel: 01450 373633 — MB ChB 1988 Aberd.; MRCGP 1993; Cert. Prescribed Equiv. Exp. JCPTGP 1992; DCH RCPS Glas. 1990. (Aberdeen) GP (Retainer). Prev: Trainee GP Highland HB VTS; SHO (Orthop. & Cas.) Borders HB; Resid. Med. Raigmore Hosp. Inverness.

ROLLAND, Philip Andrew 7 Bradgate Drive, Sutton Coldfield B74 4XG — BM BS 1998 Nottm.; BM BS Nottm 1998.

ROLLAND, Philip Stewart Clerklands Surgery, No. 2 Vicarage Lane, Horley RH6 8AP Tel: 01293 783802; 1 Ross Close, Tilgate, Crawley RH10 5DT Tel: 01293 25204 — MB BS 1954 Lond.; DObst RCOG 1958. (Univ. Coll. Hosp.) Hosp. Pract. (Gyn.) Crawley Hosp. Socs: BMA. Prev: Ho. Phys. W. Kent Gen. Hosp. Maidstone; Sen. Ho. Off. Paediat. & Obst. Depts. St. Luke's Hosp. Guildford.

ROLLASON, Stuart Bernard 57 Disraeli Road, London W5 5HS — MB ChB 1985 Birm.

ROLLASON, Terence Paul — MB ChB 1976 Birm.; BSc (Hons.) Birm. 1973; FRCPath 1994, M 1983. Cons. Path.; Clin. Tutor in Path., Univ. of Birm. Prev: Sen. Lect. (Path.) Univ. Birm.; Cons. Histopath. & Cytopath. Maelor Gen. Hosp. Wrexham; Lect. (Path.) Univ. Birm.

ROLLES, Christopher John Bassett Wood House, Bassett Wood Drive, Bassett, Southampton SO16 3PT — MB ChB 1965 Birm.; FRCP Lond. 1984; MRCP (UK) 1970.

ROLLES, Mr Keith University Department of Surgery, The Royal Free Hospital, London NW3 2QG Tel: 020 7830 2198 Fax: 020 7830 2198 — MB BS 1972 Lond.; MA Camb. 1983; BSc Lond. 1969, MS 1985; FRCS Eng. 1976. (Lond. Hosp.) Cons. Surg. Roy. Free Hosp. Lond. Socs: Transpl. Soc. & Europ. Soc. Organ Transpl.; Brit. Trans. Soc.; BMA. Prev: Lect. (Surg.) & Hon. Cons. Surg. Addenbrooke's Hosp. Camb.

ROLLES, Toni Frances Bassett Wood House, Bassett Wood Drive, Bassett, Southampton SO16 3PT — MB ChB 1965 Birm.; MRCGP 1984; DCH Eng. 1969.

ROLLI, Marie-Josee 19 Pot Green, Ramsbottom, Bury BL0 9RG — MB ChB 1985 Manch.

ROLLIN, Anna-Maria Department of Anaesthetics, Epsom General Hospital, Dorking Road, Epsom KT18 7EG Tel: 01372 735270 Fax: 01372 735261 Email: bdawson@sthelier.sghms.ac.uk; 101 College Road, Epsom KT17 4HY Tel: 01372 724772 Fax: 01372 749758 Email: am.rolling@rcanae.org.uk — MB BS 1970 Lond.; MRCS Eng. LRCP Lond. 1970; FFA RCS Eng. 1975; DA Eng. 1972; FRCA Eng. (Guy's) Cons. Anaesth. Epsom Gen. Hosp,Epsom St Helier NHS Trust; Hon. Cons. Anaesth. Tadworth Ct.; Assessor in Anaesthetics, GMC, Lead; Mem. of Counc., Roy. Coll. of Anaesth.s. Socs: Fell. Roy. Soc. Med. (Memb. Counc. Sect. Anaesth.); BMA; (Ex Vice-Pres.) Assn. Anaesth. (GBI). Prev: Sen. Regist. & Regist. Guy's Hosp. Lond.; Regist. Qu. Vict. Hosp. E. Grinstead.

ROLLIN, Henry Rapoport 101 College Road, Epsom KT17 4HY Tel: 01372 724772 — MD Leeds 1947, MB ChB 1935; FRCP Lond. 1993, M 1976; FRCPsych (Hon.) 1989; FRCPsych 1971; DPM Eng. 1939. (Leeds) Emerit. Cons. Psychiat. Horton Hosp. Epsom. Socs: Fell. Roy. Soc. Med. (Pres. Sec. Hist. of Med.). Prev: Hon. Cons. Psychiat. Qu. Eliz. Foundat. for Disabled Leatherhead; Cons. Psychiat. Horton Hosp. Epsom; Wing Cdr. (Neuro-Psychiat. Specialist) RAFVR.

ROLLIN, Sonia 10 Yeomans Drive, Aston, Stevenage SG2 7EJ — MB BS 1947 Lond.; MRCS Eng., LRCP Lond. 1947; DCH Eng. 1954. (Roy. Free) Clin. Med. Off. N. Herts. HA. Prev: Ho. Phys. Chase

ROLLINS

Farm Hosp. Enfield; Sen. Ho. Phys. Roy. Free Hosp. Unit, Hampstead; Asst. Med. Off. Pub. Health Dept. Camb.

ROLLINS, John William, Group Capt. RAF Med. Br. Retd. c/o National Westminster Bank, 68 Palmerston Road, Southsea PO5 3PT — MB BS 1959 Lond.; MRCS Eng. LRCP Lond. 1959; FRCPsych 1985, M 1972; DPM Eng. 1970. (Guy's) Civil. Cons. Psychiat. RN Hosp. Haslar.

ROLLINS, Mark David 8 Gortycavan Road, Coleraine BT51 4LT Tel: 01265 43405 Fax: 01265 50000 — MB BCh BAO 1981 Belf.; MD Qu. Univ. Belf. 1993; MRCPI (Paediat.) 1987; DCH Dub. 1985. Cons. Paediat. Coleraine Hosp. NHSSB. Socs: Brit. Paediat. Assn. & Irish Paediat. Assn. Prev: Sen. Regist. St. Mary's Hosp. Lond.

ROLLO, Alan Geoffrey Townhead Health Centre, 16 Alexandra Parade, Glasgow G31 2ES Tel: 0141 531 8940 Fax: 0141 531 8935; 24 Banavie Road, Dowanhill, Glasgow G11 5AN — MB ChB 1981 Glas.; MRCGP 1986; DRCOG 1984.

ROLLS, Anita Seaton Hospital, Valley View Road, Seaton EX12 2DU Tel: 01297 23901; Lattenbells, Stepps Lane, Axmouth, Seaton EX12 4AR — MB BS 1963 Lond.; MRCS Eng. LRCP Lond. 1963. (Guy's) Clin. Asst. (Psychogeriat.) Seaton Hosp. Prev: GP Seaton; Clin. Asst. (Psychogeriat.) Axminster Day Hosp.

ROLLS, Nigel Paul Acle Medical Centre, Bridewell Lane, Acle, Norwich NR13 3RA Tel: 01493 750888 Fax: 01493 751652; The Old Rectory, North Burlingham, Norwich NR13 4TA Tel: 01603 712221 — MB BCh 1975 Wales; MRCGP 1980. (Wales)

ROLLS, Roger Lewis The Surgery, 35 Great Pulteney Street, Bath BA2 4BY Tel: 01225 464187 Fax: 01225 485305 — MB BChir 1970 Camb.; MB Camb. 1970, BChir 1969; MRCGP 1990; DObst RCOG 1973. (St. Bart.) Socs: Fell. Roy. Soc. Med.; Brit. Inst. Manip. Med. Prev: Resid. (Path.) Radcliffe Infirm. Oxf.; SHO Hosp. Sick Childr. Bristol; Ho. Phys. St. Bart. Hosp. Lond.

ROLPH, Martin James William The St Lawrence Surgery, 79 St. Lanewrence Avenue, Worthing BN14 7JL Tel: 01903 237346; 12 Offington Drive, Worthing BN14 9PN — MB BS 1990 Lond.; MRCGP 1994.

ROLSTON, Eleanor Thomasine Larksfield, 21 Elizabeth Road, Walsall WS5 3PF Tel: 01922 642831 Email: rolston@gpanet.co.uk — MB BS 1952 Lond.; FRCPI 1986, M 1955; MRCPsych 1971; DPM Eng. 1962. (Univ. Coll. Hosp.) Private Cons. Psychiat. and Psychotherapist; Vis. Cons. Psychiat., Woodbourne Hosp. Birm. Socs: Mem. Wolverhampton Med. Inst.; Mem. Of the Inst. of Transactional Anal. Prev: Sen. Regist. (Psychiat.) St. Matthew's Hosp. Burntwood.; Postgrad. Clin. Tutor/Cons. Psychiat., New Cross Hosp., Wolverhampton; Cons. Psychiat., W.on Villa Addic. Unit, St Geo.s Hosp. Stafford.

ROMACHNEY, Peter 6 Herschell Street, Mill Hill, Blackburn BB2 4DQ — MB ChB 1991 Manch.

ROMAN, David Emil Mark 196 Springvale Road, Sheffield S6 3NU — MB ChB 1993 Sheff.; FRCA 1998.

ROMAN, Fiona 196 Springvale Road, Sheffield S6 3NU — MB ChB 1987 Sheff.

ROMAN, Mark Victor 199 Acomb Road, York YO24 4HD Tel: 01904 342999 — MB BS Lond. 1982; MRCGP 1986; DRCOG 1985. (Westm.) GP York.

ROMAN, Mr Raed Mikhail Singleton Hospital, Sketty, Swansea SA2 8QA — MB BCh 1975 Cairo; FRCS Glas. 1983.

ROMAN, Mr Victor (retired) 46 St Helen's Lane, Leeds LS16 8BS Tel: 0113 267 7744 — MD 1946 Innsbruck; FRCS Ed. 1959. Prev: Sen. Med. Off. DHSS.

ROMANES, Professor George John, CBE (retired) Camus na Feannag, Kishorn, Strathcarron IV54 8XA Tel: 01520 733273 — FRS Ed.; Hon. DSc Glas. 1982; BA Camb. 1938, PhD 1941; MB ChB Ed. 1944; FRCS Ed. 1959. Prev: Prof. Anat. & Dean Fac. Med. Univ. Edin.

ROMANES, Mr Giles John, KStJ 20 Dukes Avenue, Dorchester DT1 1EN Tel: 01305 263774; Portesham House, Portesham, Weymouth DT3 4HE Tel: 01305 871300 — MRCS Eng. LRCP Lond. 1945; MA Camb. 1949; FRCS Eng. 1975; FRCOpth 1993; DOMS Eng. 1950. (Camb. & St. Mary's) Socs: Fell. Roy. Soc. Med.; Ophth. Soc. UK. Prev: Cons. Ophth. Surg. W. Dorset; Regist. (Plastic & Jaw) Rooksdown Hse. Basingstoke; 1st Asst. Corneo-plastic Unit & Regional Eye Bank, Qu. Vict. Hosp. E. Grinstead.

ROMANIS, Robert Donald William 22 Lexham House, 45 Lexham Gardens, London W8 5JT — MB BChir 1952 Camb.; MRCS Eng. LRCP Lond. 1953. (St. Thos.) Clin. Asst. Childr. Dept. St. Thos. Hosp. Lond.; Phys. BUPA Med. Centre; Med. Adviser English Tourist Bd., Brit. Tourist Auth. & Courage Ltd.; Staff Med. Off. BUPA. Prev: Chief Med. Off. Phoenix Insur. Co.; Lt. Welsh Guards; Cas. Off. & Ho. Surg. St. Thos. Hosp. Lond.

ROMANIUK, Christopher Stanley MRI Department, Clatterbridge Centre for Oncology, Bebington, Wirral CH63 4JY Tel: 0151 334 4000 Fax: 0151 604 7497 — MB ChB 1983 Manch.; MRCP (UK) 1986; FRCR 1989; T(R)(CR) 1992. Cons. Radiol. (Magnetic Resonance Imaging) Clatterbridge Centre Oncol. The Wirral. Socs: Brit. Inst. Radiol.; Assoc. Mem. Internat. Cancer Imaging Soc. Prev: Sen. Regist. (Diag. Radiol.) St. Jas. Hosp. Leeds & Leeds Gen. Infirm.

ROMANIUK, Deirdre Annamaria New Chester Road Surgery, 525 New Chester Road, Rockferry, Birkenhead CH42 2AG Tel: 0151 645 3464 Fax: 0151 643 1676; Chaddlewood, 7 Oldfield Gardens, Heswall, Wirral CH60 6TG — MB ChB 1983 Manch.; MRCGP 1988; DRCOG 1989. (Manch.) Princip. in Gen. Pract. Prev: Trainee GP Leeds VTS; SHO (Obst.) Leeds Gen. Infirm.; SHO (Geriat. Med.) Manch. Roy. Infirm.

ROMANO, Paolo 56 St Kilda Road, London W13 9DE — State Exam Bologna 1993.

ROMANOS BETRAN, Maria Teresa Flat 2, 55 Shepherds Hill, London N6 5QP — LMS 1995 Saragossa.

ROMANOWSKI, Charles Anthony Jozef Department of Radiology, Royal Hallamshire Hospital, Glossop Road, Sheffield S10 2JF Tel: 0114 271 2957 Fax: 0114 271 2606; Canterbury House, 50 Canterbury Avenue, Fulwood, Sheffield S10 3RU Tel: 0114 230 1230 Email: charles.romanowski@virgin.net — MB ChB 1986 Manch.; BSc (Hons.) Anat. Manch. 1983; MRCP (UK) 1989; FRCR 1992. Cons. Neuroradiol. Roy. Hallamsh. Hosp. Sheff. Socs: Brit. Soc. Neuroradiol.; Eur. Soc. Neuroradiol. Prev: Sen. Regist. (Neuroradiol.) Manch. Roy. Infirm.

ROMAYA, Basil Francis North Lane Practice, 38 North Lane, Aldershot GU12 4QQ Tel: 01252 344434 — LMSSA 1979 London; LMSSA 1979 London.

ROMER, Charles The Tything Surgery, 1 The Tything, Worcester WR1 1HD Tel: 01905 26086; Manor House, Kempsey, Worcester WR5 3JZ Tel: 01905 820206 — MB BS 1947 Lond.; MRCS Eng. LRCP Lond. 1943. (King's Coll. Hosp.) Prev: Surg. Lt. RNVR; Regist. (Med.) Worcester Roy. Infirm.; Phys. i/c Dept. Venereol. Worcester Roy. Infirm.

ROMER, Heike Carolyn Anaesthetic Office, 12th Floor, Royal Liverpool University Hospital, Prescott St, Liverpool L7 8XP Tel: 0151 706 3190 Fax: 0151 706 5646, meddir@heike.co.uk; Highfield, 12 Fairview Road, Oxton Village, Prenton CH43 5SD Tel: 0151 652 8552 Fax: 0151 652 8552 — MB BS 1987 Newc.; FRCA 1993; DA (UK) 1991. (Newcastle upon Tyne) Cons. In Anaesth. and Pain Managem., Roy. Liverp. Uni.Hosp. Liverp.; Cons. Inn Anaesth. and Pain Managem. with admitting rights to the \Lourdes Hosp. Liverp. and Murrayfield Hosp. Wirral.

ROMER, Joseph Max Medical Centre, Church Road, Thornton-Cleveleys FY5 2TZ Tel: 01253 827231 Fax: 01253 863478; Thornwood, 201 Victoria Road W., Thornton-Cleveleys FY5 3QE Tel: 01253 853095 — MB ChB 1958 Liverp.; DObst RCOG 1964. (Liverp.) Clin. Asst. (Psychiat.) Psychiat. Day Hosp. Blackpool. Socs: BMA. Prev: RAMC; Ho. Phys. & Ho. Surg. Walton Hosp. Liverp.; Ho. Off. (Obst.) Glenroyd Matern. Hosp. Blackpool.

ROMERO PORTILLO, Adelaida Ground Floor Left Flat, 5 Park Lane, Stirling FK8 1NN — LMS 1987 Malaga.

ROMILLY, Crystal Sophia Institute of Psychiatry, Crespigny Park, Denmark Hill, London SE5 8AF Tel: 020 7848 0123 Fax: 020 7848 3754 — MB BS Lond. 1987; BSc (Econ.) Lond. 1978; MRCPsych 1993; CCST Forens Psych. 1998 (Roy Coll of Psych.). (Guy's Hosp. Lond.) Clin. Research Worker. Socs: Roy. Coll. Psychiat. Prev: Sen. Regist. Maudsley Hosp. Lond.; Sen. Reg. in Forens. Psych., Bracton RSU; Sen. Reg. in Forens. Psych., BRd.moor.

ROMILLY, Sarah Ann Cassington, Fernleigh Road, Mannamead, Plymouth PL3 5AN — MB BS 1990 Lond.

ROMOTOWSKI, Louise Isobel Drumhar Health Centre, North Methven St., Perth PH1 5PD Tel: 01738 564260 Fax: 01738 564293; 3 James Place, Stanley, Perth PH1 4PD Tel: 01738 827124 — MB ChB 1974 Glas.; Cert. Family Plann. JCC 1979. (Glas.) Staff Grade Paediat. Tayside Univ. Hosp. NHS Trust. Socs: BMA; Scott.

ROOM

Assn. Community Child Health; Brit. Med. Acupunct. Soc. Prev: Clin. Med. Off. (Community Child Health) Perth & Kinross Health Care; Clin. Med. Off. S. Beds. HA.

RON, Maria Antonia 26 Albert Bridge Road, London SW11 4PY — LMS 1966 Madrid; PhD Lond. 1981, MPhil 1974; MRCPsych 1973. (Madrid Med. Sch.) Cons. Psychiat. Nat. Hosp. for Nerv. Dis. Lond.

RONALD, Andrew Lindsay Department of Anaesthesia, Aberdeen Royal Infirmary, Forresterhill, Aberdeen AB25 2ZN Tel: 01224 681818 Fax: 01224 404469 Email: a.l.ronald@abdn.ac.uk; 4 Ashdale Drive, Westhill AB32 6LP Tel: 01224 743526 — MB ChB 1983 Ed.; FRCA 1989. Cons. Anaesth. Aberd. Roy. Hosps. NHS Trust; Clin. Sen. Lect. (Anaesth.) Univ. Aberd. Socs: Assn. Anaesth.; Hist. Anaesth. Soc. & BMA. Prev: Sen. Regist. (Anaesth.) Grampian HB; Regist. (Anaesth.) Lancaster Roy. Infirm. & Assoc. Hosps.; SHO (Anaesth.) Kidderminster Gen. Hosp.

RONALDS, Clare Mary Ladybarn Group Practice, 177 Mauldeth Road, Fallowfield, Manchester M14 6SG Tel: 0161 224 2873 Fax: 0161 225 3276 — BM BS 1976 Nottm.; BMedSci Nottm. 1974; MRCGP 1981. (Nottingham) GP & Trainer Manch.; Tutor (Gen. Pract.) Univ. Manch.

RONALDSON, Philip Noel (retired) 36 Judges Walk, Norwich NR4 7QF Tel: 01603 452097 — MB BCh BAO Belf. 1947. Prev: Med. Off. DHSS Norwich Bd.ing Centre 1980-1993.

RONAY, Susan Amanda Sonning Common Health Centre, Wood Lane, Sonning Common, Reading RG4 9SW Tel: 0118 972 2188 Fax: 0118 972 4633; 28 St. Barnabas Road, Emmer Green, Reading RG4 8RA — MB ChB 1985 Manch.; MRCGP 1989; DRCOG 1988; DCH RCP Lond. 1987. Course Organiser Reading VTS.

RONAYNE, Karen Linda 4 Berber Close, Whiteley, Fareham PO15 7HF Tel: 01489 880913 — BM BS 1994 Nottm.; DRCOG 1997. (Nottm.) Trainee GP Portsmouth. Prev: SHO (ENT & A & E) Qu. Alexandra Hosp. Portsmouth; Ho. Off. (Med.) MusGr. Pk. Hosp. Taunton; Ho. Off. (Surg.) P.ss Margt. Hosp. Swindon.

RONCHETTI, Martin Gerard Pensilva Health Centre, School Road, Pensilva, Liskeard PL14 5RP Tel: 01579 362249 Fax: 01579 363323; Upton Farm House, Upton Cross, Liskeard PL14 5AZ Tel: 01579 362689 Email: martin-ronchetti@msn.com — MB ChB 1984 Bristol; MRCGP 1988; DFFP 1995; DCH RCP Lond. 1987. (Bristol) Prev: SHO (O & G, Paediat. & Cas.) Roy. Cornw. Hosp. Truro.

RONDEL, Professor Richard Kavanagh 2 King George Square, Park Hill, Richmond TW10 6LG Tel: 020 8940 7852 Fax: 020 8940 7852 — MB BS 1956 Lond.; FRCP Lond. 1992; Dip. Pharm. Med. RCP (UK) 1976; DObst RCOG 1963. (St. Geo.) Prof. Clin. Practitioner Univ. Surrey; Med. Dir. Human PsychPharmacol. Research Unit Univ. Surrey. Socs: (Ex-Pres.) Internat. Federat. Pharmaceutical Phys.s; (Ex-Chairm.) & Hon. Life Mem.Brit. Assoc. Pharmaceutical Phys.s. Prev: Regist. Fac. Pharmology Med.; Mem. (Counc.) Roy. Coll. Phys. Lond.; Regist. (Med.), Resid. Med. Off. & Resid. Clin. Path. St. Geo.'s Hosp. Lond.

RONDER, Julia Therese Ticehurst House Hospital, Ticehurst, Wadhurst TN5 7HU Tel: 01580 200391 — MB BS 1986 Lond.; BSc Lond. 1983; MRCPsych 1990. (Univ. Coll. & Middlx.) Cons. Psychiat. Young Person's Unit, Ticehurst Ho. Hosp.; Hon. Lect. Guy's Hosp. Lond. Socs: Roy. Coll. Psychiats.; Assn. Child Psychol. Psychiat. Prev: Sen. Regist. Guys & St. Thos. Hosps. Lond.

RONEY, David Brian 4 Leech Street, Hyde SK14 2PF — MB ChB 1987 Manch.

RONEY, Gerard 145 Wigton Road, Leeds LS17 8SH — MB ChB 1986 Glas. Reegist. (Psychiat.) Leverndale Hosp. Glas.

RONEY, Sheila Margaret 15 Parfrey Street, London W6 9EW — MB BS 1993 Lond.

RONN, Howard Humphrey (retired) Parsonage Farm, Edington, Westbury BA13 4QF — MB BS 1949 Lond.; MB BS (Hnrs.) Lond. 1949; MRCP Lond. 1952. Prev: Surg. Lt.-Cdr. RNR.

RONSON, John Gareth The Lennard Surgery, 1-3 Lewis Road, Bishopsworth, Bristol BS13 7JD Tel: 0117 964 0900 Fax: 0117 987 3227 — MB ChB 1982 Manch.; MRCP (UK) 1985; MRCGP 1989; DRCOG 1987. (Manchester)

RONSON, Julia Anne Manchester Road Surgery, 57 Manchester Road, Southport PR9 9BN Tel: 01704 532314 Fax: 01704 539740 — MB ChB 1992 Sheff.

ROOBAN, R A Carterhatch Lane Surgery, 99 Carterhatch Lane, Enfield EN1 4LA Tel: 020 8804 5312 Fax: 020 8804 5095 — MB BS 1976 Kerala; MB BS 1976 Kerala.

ROOBOTTOM, Carl Ashley Radiology Department, Plymouth PL6 8DH Tel: 01752 777111; Brook House, Sampford Spiney, Yelverton PL20 7QT — MB ChB 1987 Birm.; MB ChB (Hons.) Birm. 1987; BSc (1st cl. Hons.) Birm. 1986; MRCP (UK) 1990; FRCR 1993. Cons. Radiol. Derriford Hosp. Plymouth. Socs: Brit. Soc. Interven. Radiol.; Roy. Coll. Radiol. Prev: Merck Fell. & Lect. (Radiol.) Bristol Roy. Infirm.; Regist. (Diag. Radiol.) Plymouth.; SHO (Med.) Selly Oak Birm.

ROOD, Professor Jan Philip Department of Oral & Maxillofacial Surgery, King's Dental Institute, King's College Hospital, Denmark Hill, London SE5 9RW Tel: 020 7346 3278 Fax: 020 7346 3642 Email: phil.road@kcl.ac.uk — MB BS 1973 Newc.; MSc Manch. 1985; MDS 1976; BDS Durham. 1966; FRCS Ed. 1985; FDS RCS Eng. 1972. Prof. Oral & Maxillofacial Surg. King's Dent. Inst. Lond. Socs: Brit. Assn. Oral Surgs. & Brit. Dent. Assn. & Brit. Assn. Day Surg. Prev: Lect. (Oral Surg.) Univ. Lond.; Sen. Lect. & Hon. Cons. Oral & Maxillofacial Surg. King's Coll. Hosp. Lond.; Prof. Oral & Maxillofacial Surg. Manch.

ROODYN, Leonard, LVO 7 Wimpole Street, London W1G 9SN Tel: 020 7323 1555 — MD 1960 Lond.; MB BS 1946. (Middlx.) Cons. i/c Vaccination Serv. Hosp. Trop. Dis. Lond. Prev: Supernum. Asst. Bland-Sutton Inst. Path. Middlx. Hosp.

ROOHANNA, Rafat 46 Overstone Road, Hammersmith, London W6 0AB Tel: 020 8748 7861 — MD 1966 Pahlavi; MRCPsych 1973; DPM Eng. 1973; DPM Ireland 1973. (Pahlavi Univ.)

ROOHI, Shanila 26 Dawn Close, Ness, South Wirral CH64 4DS — MB ChB 1989 Glas.

ROOK, Christopher Demarquay 16 South Street, Oxford OX2 0BE — MB BS 1996 Lond.

ROOK, Professor Graham Arthur William Department of Bacteriology, Windeyer Building, 46 Cleveland St., London W1T 4JF Fax: 020 7636 8175 Email: g.rook@ucl.ac.uk — MB BChir 1971 Camb.; MD Camb. 1978. Prof. Med. Microbiol. & Hon. Cons. Microbiol. UCL Med. Sch. Lond.

ROOKE, Alfred William Michael (retired) 12 Woodcote Grove Road, Coulsdon CR5 2AB Tel: 020 8660 4221 — MB BS 1930 Lond. Prev: Regional Med. Off. DHSS.

ROOKE, David Kenneth Taunton Road Medical Centre, 12-16 Taunton Road, Bridgwater TA6 3LS Tel: 01278 444400 Fax: 01278 423691 — MB ChB 1977 Manch.; MRCGP 1981.

ROOKE, Henry William Patrick 4 East Court, Cosham, Portsmouth PO6 2NX Tel: 023 92 373244 — BA Dub. 1953, MB BCh BAO 1955; FRCR 1975; FFR 1963; DMRD Eng. 1960. (T.C. Dub.) Prev: Cons. Radiol. Portsmouth Gp. Hosps.; Sen. Regist. (Radiol.) United Birm. Hosps.; Regist. Portsmouth Hosp. Gp.

ROOKE, Kenneth Christopher (retired) 22 Longlands, Worthing BN14 9NN Tel: 01903 236086 — MRCS Eng. LRCP Lond. 1962; DFFP 1993; Cert. Family Plann. JCC 1967. Indep. GP W. Sussex. Prev: GP Worthing.

ROOKER, Mr Guy David Cheltenham General Hospital, Sandford Road, Cheltenham GL53 7AN — MB BS 1971 Lond.; FRCS Ed. (Orth.) 1981; FRCS Eng. 1975; MRCS Eng. LRCP Lond. 1971. Cons. Orthop. Surg. Cheltenham Gen. Hosp. Prev: Sen. Regist. (Orthop.) Radcliffe Infirm. & Nuffield Orthop. Centre; Oxf.; Regist. (Gen. Surg.) Cheltenham Gen. Hosp.

ROOKLEDGE, Marina Margaret Danetre Medical Practice, The Health Centre, London Road, Daventry NN11 4EJ Tel: 01327 703333 — MB BS 1990 Lond.; DFFP 1995; MRCGP 1995; DRCOG 1993. (St. Thomas's Hospital Medical School London)

ROOKLEDGE, Mark Andrew 2 West Avenue, Pinner HA5 5BY — MB BS 1990 Lond.

ROOKWOOD, Karen Jenifer 21 Livingstone Place, Edinburgh EH9 1PD Tel: 0131 667 0566 — BM BS 1978 Nottm.; MRCPsych 1985. Prev: GP Edin.; Regist. (Psychiat.) Edin.

ROOM, Geraldine Rainier Walden Cromwell Hospital, Cromwell Road, London SW5 0TU Tel: 020 7460 2000 Fax: 020 8460 5555; 151 Castelnan, Barnes, London SW13 9EW — MB BS 1973 Sydney; FRACP 1979. (Sydney) Cons. Rheumatologist Private Practitional. Prev: Cons. Rheumatologist, Ealing Hosp; Cons. Phys. (Rheum.) FarnBoro., Bromley & Beckenham Hosps.; Research Scientist Kennedy Inst. Rheum. Lond.

ROOME

ROOME, Jane Katherine Kingswood Surgery, Kingswood Road, Tunbridge Wells TN2 4UH Tel: 01892 511833 Email: janeroome@btinternet.com; 18 Coniston Avenue, Tunbridge Wells TN4 9SP — MB BS 1992 Lond.; MRCGP 1996; DFFP 1996; DRCOG 1994. (St Georges) p/t GP Asst. Socs: Course organiser Tunbridge Wells Non Princip. Gp.; W. Kent LMC Non Princip. Represen. Prev: GP Regist. - Rustham Tunbridge Wells; SHO Paediat. Pembury Hosp.; c/o the Elderly Pembury Hosp.

ROOME, Paul Christian The Surgery, Kingswood Road, Tunbridge Wells TN2 4UJ Tel: 01892 511833 Fax: 01892 517597; 96 Culverden Down, Tunbridge Wells TN4 9TA — MB BS 1993 Lond.; BSc (Hons.) Lond. 1990; MRCGP 1997; DFFP 1996; DRCOG 1995. (St George's Hospital Medical School, Tooting, London) p/t Gen. Practitioner, Kingswood Surg., Tunbridge Wells, Kent; Clin. Asst. Neurol. Dept., Kent & Sussex Hosp., Tunbridge Wells.

ROOMI, Mr Riad 591 Fulham Road, London SW6 5UA Tel: 020 7385 3922 Fax: 020 7381 8180 — MB ChB 1977 Baghdad; FICS 1988; Board Certified (Diploma), Amer Board of Hair Restoration Surg 1998. (Univ. Baghdad Coll. Med.) Cons. Cosmetic Surg. Lond.; Cons. Hair Restoration Surg. Socs: Brit. Assn. Hair Restorat. Surgs.; Amer. Soc. Hair Restorat. Surg.; Amer. Acad. Cosmetic Surg. Prev: Regist. (A & E) St. Stephens Hosp. Lond.

ROOMS, Margaret (retired) 66 Blakes Lane, New Malden KT3 6NX Tel: 020 8942 3542 — MB BS Lond. 1951; MRCS Eng. LRCP Lond. 1951; FFA RCS Eng. 1954; DA Eng. 1953. Prev: Cons. Anaesth. Qu. Mary's Hosp. Carshalton Surrey.

ROOMS, Mark Andrew, Maj. RAMC 2 (Trg) Regt AAC, Middle Wallop, Stockbridge SO20 8DY Tel: 01449 728276; 14 Roman Road, Wattisham, Ipswich IP7 7RW — BM 1988 Soton. Aircrew Train. Prev: GP Wattisham Nr. Ipswich; GP Ballykinler.

ROONEY, Ann 10-12 Lisburn Road, Belfast BT9 6AA — MB BCh BAO 1959 NUI; LAH Dub. 1958. (Univ. Coll. Dub.)

ROONEY, Barbara Ann 1 Appstree Cottages, Ockham Lane, Ockham, Woking GU23 6NR — MB BS 1982 Lond.; MRCPsych 1987. Sen. Regist. (Psychiat.) St. Geo. Hosp. Atkinson Morley Hosps. Lond. Prev: Sen. Regist. (Psychiat.) Qu. Mary's Univ. Hosp. Roehampton; Sen. Regist. (Psychiat.) St. Bernard's Wing Ealing Hosp., Gordon Hosp. & Qu. Mary's Univ. Hosp. Lond.

ROONEY, Brian Patrick Flat 2/L, 9 Grantley Gardens, Shawlands, Glasgow G41 3PY — MB ChB 1993 Glas.

ROONEY, Charles 4 Bowling Street, Coatbridge ML5 1PP Tel: 01236 22621 — MB ChB 1952 Glas.; DObst RCOG 1953.

ROONEY, Christine Mary The Whitfield Practice, Hunslet Health Centre, 24 Church Street, Leeds LS10 2PE Tel: 0113 270 5194 Fax: 0113 270 2795 — MB BS 1982 Lond.

ROONEY, Clair Marie 22 Falkland Rise, Leeds LS17 6JQ Tel: 0113 268 4470 — MB BCh BAO 1989 NUI; MRCGP 1992; DTM & H Liverp. 1993; Cert. Family Plann. JCC 1992; DCH RCP Lond. 1991. (University Coll. Dublin) Prev: Trainee GP Hull; Locum GP Leeds.

ROONEY, Dennis 20 Northumberland Avenue, Gosforth, Newcastle upon Tyne NE3 4XE; The Croft, Galloping Green Road, Wrekenton, Gateshead NE9 6DT — MB BS 1981 Newc.; MRCGP 1985; DRCOG 1985; DCCH RCP Ed. 1984.

ROONEY, Desmond Patrick Diabetes Centre, Victoria Infirmary, Langside Rd, Glasgow G42 9TY; 2/1, 28 Bellwoood ST., Glasgow G41 3ES — MD 1991 Belf.; MB BCh BAO 1984; MRCP (UK) 1987. (Queen's Univ. Belfast) Cons. Phys. Diabetes & Endocrinol. Vict. Infirm. Glas. Prev: Sen. Regist. Belf.; Post Doctoral Assoc. Univ. of Minnesota Minneapolis, USA.

ROONEY, Francis Joseph 22 Falkland Rise, Moortown, Leeds LS17 6JQ Tel: 0113 268 4470 Fax: 0113 268 4470 — MB ChB 1980 Leeds; Cert. Family Plann. JCC 1985; DRCOG 1983. (Univ. Leeds) Prev: BAMS; GP Princip. Leeds; GP Regist. Cornw.

ROONEY, Guy Jonathan Dept. of GU Medicine, Princess Margaret Hospital, Okus Road, Swindon SN1 4JU Tel: 01793 426248 Fax: 01793 426615 — MB BS 1989 Lond.; BSc Lond. 1986; MRCP (UK) 1993; Dip. GU Med. Soc. Apoth. Lond. 1995; DFFP 1997; Dip Sytemative Revius Lond. 1999. Cons., (Genitourin. - Med) P.ss Margt. Hosp. Swindon, Wilts; Cons. (Genitourin. Med), Harrison Dept, Radcliffe Infirm. Socs: MSSVD; BMA; AGUM.

ROONEY, Kevin Donal 53 Camphill Avenue, Glasgow G41 3AX — MB ChB 1994 Glas.

ROONEY, Kevin Joseph (retired) 22 Falkland Rise, Leeds LS17 6JQ Tel: 0113 268 4470 — MB BCh BAO 1952 NUI. Prev: GP Leeds.

ROONEY, Mary Magdalen Elizabeth 174 Ferry Road, Edinburgh EH6 4NS Tel: 0131 554 8166 — MD 1988 Belf.; MB BCh BAO Belf. 1980; MRCP (UK) 1983; DCH Dub. 1985. Lect. Rheum. Univ. Edin. (Rheum. Dis. Unit), N. Gen. Hosp. Edin. Prev: Research Fell. (Rheum.) St. Vincents & St. Jas. Hosps. Dub.; Regist. (Med.) Altnagelvin Hosp. Lond.derry; SHO (Rheum.) Roy. Vict. Hosp. Belf.

ROONEY, Matthew Jonathan Department of Anaesthetics, Birmingham Heartlands Hospital, Bordesley Green E., Birmingham B9 5SS Tel: 0121 424 3488 Fax: 0121 424 1441 — MB BS 1986 Newc.; FRCA 1991. (Newcastle-upon-Tyne) Cons. (Anaesth.) Birm. Heartland & Solihull NHS Trust; Cons. Anaesth. Birm. Heartlands & Solihull NHS Trust Birm. Socs: Assn. Anaesth. & Soc. Computing & Technol. in Anaesth.; Brit. Ophth. Anaesth. Soc. Prev: Sen. Regist. Anaesth. City Hosp. Birm.; Sen. Regist. Qu. Eliz. Hosp. Birm.; Research Fell. Univ. Dept. of Anaesth. Nottm.

ROONEY, Michael Joseph Bramhall Park Medical Centre, 235 Bramhall Lane South, Bramhall, Stockport SK7 3EP Tel: 0161 440 7669 Fax: 0161 440 7671 — MB ChB 1983 Manch.; MRCGP 1987; DGM RCP Lond. 1987. Prev: Trainee GP Hillingdon Hosp.

ROONEY, Nicholas Department of Cellular Pathology, Royal United Hospital, Bath BA1 3NG Tel: 01225 824705 Fax: 01225 461044 — MB ChB 1979 Bristol; MD Sheff. 1986; MRCPath 1986; T(Path) 1991. Cons. Histopath. Roy. United Hosp. Bath. Socs: Brit. Lymphoma Path. Gp.; Sec. Brit. Lymphoma Path GP-Internat. Acad. Path. (Brit. Div.). Prev: Cons. Sen. Lect. Univ. Bristol; Lect. (Path.) Sheff. Univ. Med. Sch.; SHO (Clin. Path.) Roy. Hallamsh. Hosp. Sheff.

ROONEY, Paul Joseph Bacteriology Laboratory, Belfast City Hospital, Belfast BT9 7AB Tel: 02890 263661 Fax: 02890 263991 Email: paul.rooney@bll.nhs.uk — MB BCh BAO 1982 Belf.; MB BCh Belf. 1982; BSc Belf. 1979; MRCPath 1990; DTM & H RCP Lond. 1990. Cons. Med. Microbiol. Belf. City Hosp. Belf.

ROONEY, Mr Paul Stephen Royal Liverpool Hospital, Prescott St., Liverpool L7 8XP Tel: 0161 706 3426 Fax: 0161 706 5828; Loreto, Osbert Road, Blundellsands, Liverpool L23 6UP Tel: 0151 931 1085 — MB ChB 1984 Sheff.; DM Nottm. 1994; FRCS Ed. 1988. Cons. Colorectal Surg. Roy. Liverp. Hosp. Socs: Brit. Assn. Surgic. Oncol.; BSG; Assn. Coloproct. GB & Irel. Prev: Lect. (Gen. Surg.) Nottm.; Lect. (Surg.) 1996-1998.

ROONEY, Richard Geoffrey (retired) 45 Knowsley Road W., Blackburn BB1 9PW Tel: 01254 249008 — MB ChB 1946 Manch.; DCH Eng. 1950.

ROONEY, Stephen James The Fields, Kingsland, Shrewsbury SY3 7AF — BM BS 1986 Nottm.

ROONEY, Veena (retired) Boundary House, Coombe Road, Salisbury SP2 8BT Tel: 01722 334282 Email: rooneybv@aol.com — MB BS Rangoon 1956. SCMO Salisbury HA.

ROOPE, Richard Marcus The Surgery, 51 Locks Road, Locks Heath, Southampton SO31 6ZH Tel: 01489 583777 Fax: 01489 571374; Silverbeck, Lake Road, Curdridge, Southampton SO32 2HH Tel: 01489 795199 — MB BS 1987 Lond.; BA (Psychol.) Camb. 1984, MA 1988; MRCGP 1991; DFFP 1993; DCH RCP Lond. 1990; DGM RCP Lond. 1989; Dip Occ Med RCP Lond. 1998. (Camb. & Roy. Lond. Hosp.) GP Princip. Soton. & Clin. Asst. (Rheum.) Soton. Gen. Hosp. Socs: Christ. Med. Fell.sh. (Wessex Regional Sec.). Prev: Trainee GP Oxf.; Ho. Off. (Med. & Geriat.) Qu. Mary's Hosp. Sidcup, Kent; Ho. Off. (Surg.) Epsom Dist. Hosp. Surrey.

ROOPE, Yvonne Avril 450 Stanley Road, Bootle L20 5AE; 4 Osterley Gardens, Orrell Park, Liverpool L9 8BJ — MB ChB 1958 Liverp. GP Bootle. Prev: Med. Off. Sch. Health Serv. Liverp. AHA (T).

ROOTES, Sarah Jane 160 Heathfield Drive, Mitcham CR4 3RH — MB BS 1996 Lond.

ROOTH, Francis Graham (retired) 6 Church Avenue, Bristol BS9 1LD — MRCS Eng. LRCP Lond. 1964; BA Camb. 1958; MPhil Lond. 1970, MD 1973, MB BS 1964; MRCPsych 1971. Cons. Psychiat. Bristol Health Dist. (T). Prev: Sen. Regist. Bethlem Roy. & Maudsley Hosps.

ROOTH, Jane Alexandra 6 Church Avenue, Stoke Bishop, Bristol BS9 1LD — MB BS 1964 Lond.; MRCS Eng. LRCP Lond. 1964. (Middlx.)

ROOTS, Lila Mabel (retired) 52, Barfield Crescent, Leeds LS7 8RU Tel: 0113 268 1953 — MB ChB 1961; MCPS Ontario 1971; MFCM 1979; DPH Liverp. 1965; LMCC 1971; BA Leeds 1993. Prev: Dep. MOH Metro Windsor, Ont. Canada.

ROOTS, Peter James 6 Linsey Close, Hemel Hempstead HP3 8DA — BM 1996 Soton. SHO (Psychiat.) Qu. Eliz. Psychiat. Hosp. Prev: Ho. Off. (Med.) Redditch Alexandra Hosp.; Ho. Off. (Surg.) Russells Hall Hosp. Dudley.

ROPE, Michael Edwin Todhunters, 97 Uxbridge Road, Rickmansworth WD3 7DJ Tel: 01923 775831 Fax: 01923 774912 — MB BS Lond. 1952; FRCGP 1981, M 1964. (Middlx.) Clin. Complaints.Advis. Med. Defence Union. Socs: Middlx. Hosp. Club.; Watford & SW Herts. Med. Soc. Prev: Sec. Herts. & Beds. LMCs; GP Facilitator Kensington, Chelsea & W.m. FPC; Med. Off. Rank Film Laborats.

ROPE, Tamsin Caroline Maxcroft House, Hilperton Marsh, Trowbridge BA14 7PS — MB ChB 1996 Birm.; ChB Birm. 1996. SHO (A & E) Glos. Roy. NHS Hosp.

ROPEL, Christine Anne 36 High Oaks Road, Welwyn Garden City AL8 7BH Tel: 01707 377414 — MB BS 1979 Lond.; FRCR 1988; DMRD Eng. 1983. Cons. Diag. Radiol. Qu. Eliz. Hosp. Welwyn Gdn. City. Prev: Sen. Regist. (Diag. Radiol.) Char. Cross Hosp. Lond.

ROPER, Alan Frederick (retired) Bulcote Lodge, Bulcote, Nottingham NG14 5GU — MRCS Eng. LRCP Lond. 1951; FFA RCS Eng. 1958. Prev: Anaesth. S. Warw. Hosp. Gp.

ROPER, Barry Windsor Diagnostic X-Ray Department, Neath General Hospital, Neath SA11 2LQ — MB ChB 1957 Birm.; MB ChB (Hons. Obst.) Birm. 1957; MRCP Lond. 1964; FFR 1969; DMRD Eng. 1966. (Birm.) Cons. Radiol. W. Glam. AHA. Socs: Brit. Med. Ultrasound Soc.; S. Wales Ultrasound Gp. Prev: Med. Regist. Dudley Rd. Hosp. Birm.; Clin. Tutor (Radiol.) Univ. Birm.; Sen. Regist. Radiol. United Birm. Hosps.

ROPER, Daniel James Springhead Medical Centre, 376 Willerby Road, Hull HU5 5JT; 376 Willerby Road, Hull HU5 5JT Tel: 01482 52263 — MB ChB 1982 Ed.; MRCGP 1986. GP Hull.

ROPER, David John St Johns Medical Centre, 62 London Road, Grantham NG31 6HR Tel: 01476 590055 Fax: 01476 400042; Ashfield House, Casthorpe Road, Barrowby, Grantham NG32 1DP — MB BS 1974 Lond.; MRCS Eng. LRCP Lond. 1974; MRCGP 1979; DCH Eng. 1978. (Westm.) GP Trainer Grantham. Prev: Trainee GP Cirencester VTS; Ho. Off. (Orhop. Surg.) Qu. Mary's Hosp. Roehampton; Ho. Phys. (Gen. Med.) City Hosp. Nottm.

***ROPER, Emma Cathryn** Kettering General Hospital, Kettering; 215 Avenue Road Extension, Clarendon, Leicester LE2 3ER — MB ChB 1996 Leic.

ROPER, Gordon Paul 6 Wingate Close, Trumpington, Cambridge CB2 2HW Tel: 01223 514752 Fax: 01223 515713 — MB BCh BAO 1984 NUI; LRCPI & LM, LRCSI & LM 1984; BSc New Brunswick 1981. (Roy Coll. Surgs. In Irel.) GP Clin. Asst. Addenbrooke's Hosp. Camb. Prev: GP Regist. Buffisham Surg. Camb.; Med. Resid. Fac. Med. Memor. Univ. Newfld..; Ho. Off. Glas. Roy. Infirm. & Roy. Orthop. Hosp. Birm.

ROPER, Helen Margaret 90 Bourverie Avenue, Salisbury SP2 8DK — MB BS 1967 Lond.; MRCS Eng. LRCP Lond. 1967. (Roy. Free) Clin. Med. Off. Salisbury DHA.

ROPER, Helen Patricia Department Paediatrics, Birmingham Heartlands Hospital, Bordesley Green E., Birmingham B9 5SS Tel: 0121 766 6611 Fax: 0121 773 6458 — MD 1989 Manch.; MB ChB (Hons.) Manch. 1980; FRCP Lond. 1996; MRCP (UK) 1983; DCH RCP Lond. 1982. (Manch.) Cons. Paediat. Birm. Heartlands Hosp. Prev: Tutor (Child Health) Manch. Univ.

ROPER, Ian William Millward King Street Surgery, 22A King Street, Hereford HR4 9DA Tel: 01432 272181 Fax: 01432 344725 — MB ChB 1990 Leic.; DRCOG 1992.

ROPER, Janice Homerton Hospital, Homerton Road, London E9 6SR Tel: 020 8510 7952 Fax: 020 8510 7448; 220 Richmond Road, Hackney, London E8 3QN Tel: 020 7254 4078 Fax: 020 7254 4078 — BM BS 1980 Nottm.; BMedSci Nottm. 1978, BM BS 1980; MRCP (UK) 1984. (Nottingham) Cons. (Neonat. Paediat.) Homerton Hosp. Socs: FRCPCH; BAPM. Prev: Cons. & Sen. Lect. (Neonat. Paediat.) Homerton Hosp. Lond.; Sen. Lect. Med. Coll. St. Bart. Hosp. Lond.; Sen. Regist. (Paediat.) Pk.side HA.

ROPER, John (retired) 2 Levignen Close, Church Crookham, Fleet GU52 0TW Tel: 01252 622234 — MB BS Lond. 1948; MRCS Eng. LRCP Lond. 1948; FRCOG 1968, M 1954. Prev: Cons. O & G W. Surrey & NE Hants. Health Dist.

ROPER, John Patrick 7 Ashburton Avenue, Birkenhead CH43 8TJ — MB BChir 1994 Camb.

ROPER, Mr John Paul The Cottage, Old Road, Thornton in Craven, Skipton BD23 3TB Tel: 01282 843962 — MB BCh BAO 1970 Dub.; FRCSI 1982; FCOphth 1988. Cons. Ophth. Burnley Gen. Hosp. Prev: Sen. Regist. Wolverhampton Eye Infirm.; Regist./SHO Hallamsh. Hosp. Sheff.

ROPER, Joseph Neville (retired) 40 Ranmoor Cliffe Road, Sheffield S10 3HB Tel: 0114 230 7208 — MB ChB 1951 Sheff.; MRCS Eng. LRCP Lond. 1951; DObst RCOG 1955. Prev: GP Derby.

ROPER, Michael (retired) La Corderie, 3 La Vallee, Alderney GY9 3XA — MRCS Eng. LRCP Lond. 1946.

ROPER, Nicholas Alan 47 Douglas Villas, Durham DH1 1JL Email: n.a.roper@ncl.ac.uk — BM BS 1992 Nottm.; BMedSci (Hons.) Nottm. 1990; MRCP (UK) 1995. (Nottm.) Regist. (Diabetes & Endocrinol.) N.ern Deanery.

ROPER, Nigel David King The Surgery, Vicarage Lane, Walton on the Naze CO14 8PA Tel: 01255 674373 Fax: 01255 851005 — BM 1983 Soton.

ROPER, Paul Howard The Surgery, 2 Great Wood Road, Small Heath, Birmingham B10 9QE Tel: 0121 766 8828 Fax: 0121 773 0091; 17 Bellemere Road, Hampton-in-Arden, Solihull B92 0AN Email: paul@roperha.freeserve.co.uk — MB ChB 1980 Manch.; MRCGP 1985; DCH RCP Lond. 1983. (Manch.)

ROPER, Paul Winnard Roper and Partners, Syston Health Centre, Melton Road, Syston, Leicester LE7 2EQ Tel: 0116 260 9111 Fax: 0116 260 9055 — BM BCh 1978 Oxf.; BA Camb. 1975; MRCGP 1986.

ROPER, Phyllis Barbara (retired) Bulcote Lodge, Burton Joyce, Nottingham NG14 5GU Tel: 0115 931 2160 — MB ChB 1951 Sheff. Prev: SCMO (Community Health) Notts. HA.

ROPER, Robin Mark Blackwater Medical Centre, Princes Road, Maldon CM9 7DS Tel: 01621 854204 Fax: 01621 850246; 1 Bergen Court, Maldon CM9 6UH — MB BS 1982 Lond.; MRCGP 1991; DA (UK) 1986.

ROPER, Shena Gillian Bulcote Lodge, Bulcote, Nottingham — MB ChB 1982 Sheff.

ROPER-HALL, Mr Michael John (cons. rooms), 38 Harborne Road, Edgbaston, Birmingham B15 3HE Tel: 0121 454 2721; 51 Church Road, Edgbaston, Birmingham B15 3SJ Tel: 0121 454 2310 Fax: 0121 454 0090 — MRCS Eng. LRCP Lond. 1945; MB ChB Birm. 1945; ChM Birm. 1952; FRCS Eng. 1948; FRCOphth 1988; Hon. FRCOphth 1990; DOMS Eng. 1946. (Birm.) Hon. Cons. Surg. Birm. & Midl. Eye Hosp.; Hon. Cons. Ophth. Qu. Eliz. Hosp. Birm. Socs: Fell. Roy. Soc. Med. (Ex-Pres. Sect. Ophth.). Prev: Ex-Pres. Fac. Ophths. & Ophth. Soc. UK; Mem. Bd. Governors Moorfields Eye Hosp. Special HA; Mem. Counc. & Mem. Ct. Examrs. RCS Eng. (Chairm. Specialist Advis. Comm. (Ophth.) Jt. Comm. on Higher Surg. Train.).

ROPNER, Janet Elizabeth Haematology Department, Gloucestershire Royal NHS Trust, Great Western Road, Gloucester GL1 3NN Tel: 01452 395252; Rossett, Balcarras Road, Charlton Kings, Cheltenham GL53 8QG — MB BS 1971 Lond.; BSc (Special) Lond. 1968; FRCP Lond. 1994; MRCP (UK) 1974; FRCPath 1994, M 1982. (Univ. Coll. Hosp.) Cons. Haemat. Glos. Roy. Hosp. Prev: Sen. Regist. (Haemat.) Oxf. AHA (T); SHO (Med.) Hammersmith Hosp. Lond.; Ho. Phys. Univ. Coll. Hosp. Lond.

ROPNER, Richard John Ronald Rossett, Balcarras Road, Charlton Kings, Cheltenham GL53 8QG — MB ChB 1965 Ed.; MRCPsych 1973; DPM Eng. 1972; DObst RCOG 1970. Cons. (Adult Ment. Illness & Alcoholism) Charlton La. Centre, Cheltnam. Socs: Fell. Roy. Soc. Trop. Med. & Hyg. Prev: Sen. Regist. Warneford Hosp. Oxf.; Rotating Intern Pottsville Hosp., U.S.A.; Med. Off. United Africa Co. (Nigeria) Ltd. Lagos.

ROPNER, Vivien Anne (retired) Tethermill House, 2A Millfield Road, Whickham, Newcastle upon Tyne NE16 4QA Tel: 0161 488 7908 — MB BS 1955 Durh. Prev: Ho. Phys., Ho. Surg. & Res. Med. Off. Roy. Vict. Infirm. Newc.

ROPPER, David Noel (retired) Pennygown House, Campbeltown PA28 6PH Tel: 01586 551050 — MB ChB Glas. 1961; BSc (Hons. Physiol.) Glas. 1958; FRCP Glas. 1981, M 1965; LMCC 1970. Prev: Cons. Geriat. Roy. Alexandra Infirm. Paisley.

ROQUES

ROQUES, Antoine William Wanklyn Dept. Of Haematology, Worthing Hospital, Worthing BN11 2DN Tel: 01903 205111 Fax: 01903 285072 Email: tony.roques@wash-tr.sthames-nhs.uk; 47 Hillside Avenue, Worthing BN14 9QS Tel: 01903 237229 — MB BS 1973 Lond.; FRCP Lond. 1991, M 1976; FRCPath 1991, M 1979. (St. Thos.) Cons. Haemat. Worthing & S.lands Hosps.; Regional Adviser (Path.) S. Thames (W.). Socs: Brit. Soc. Haematol. Prev: Lect. (Haemat.) & Asst. Lect. (Path.) St. Thos. Hosp. Med. Sch. Lond.; Ho. Phys. St. Thos. Hosp. Lond.

ROQUES, Clare Joanna 47 Hillside Avenue, Worthing BN14 9QS — BChir 1996 Camb.

ROQUES, Thomas William 45 Rochester Road, London NW1 9JJ — BM BCh 1994 Oxf.

RORIE, David Archer Terra Nova House Medical Practice, 43 Dura Street, Dundee DD4 6SW Tel: 01382 451100 Fax: 01382 453679 — MB ChB 1973 Aberd.

RORKE, Steuart Flat C, 20A Molyneux Park Road, Tunbridge Wells TN4 8DT — MB ChB 1996 Stellenbosch.

RORRISON, Hugh Webster 342A Perth Road, Dundee DD2 1EQ — MB ChB 1998 Dund.; MB ChB Dund 1998.

ROSALIE, Ralph Marlborough Medical Practice, The Surgery, George Lane, Marlborough SN8 4BY Tel: 01672 512187 Fax: 01672 516809 — MB ChB 1989 Leeds; MB ChB Leeds. 1989; MRCGP 1994. SHO (A & E) Pontefract Gen. Hosp. Prev: Ho. Off. (Surg.) Harrogate Dist. Hosp.

ROSALKI, Jonathan Raymond 78 Loudoun Road, London NW8 0NA — MB BS 1991 Lond.

ROSALKI, Sidney Bertram 10 Wimpole Mews, London W1G 8PE Tel: 020 7486 7517 Fax: 020 7486 7517 — MB BS 1953 Lond.; DSc (Med.) Lond. 1986, MD 1962; FRCP Lond. 1981, M 1958; MRCS Eng. LRCP Lond. 1953; FRCPath 1975, M 1963; MCB Jt. Exam. Bd. (Hon.) 1996. (St. Mary's) Med. Dir. & Cons. Chem. Path. Omnilabs, UK; Hon. Cons. Chem. Path. Roy. Free Hosp. Lond. Socs: Fell. Roy. Soc. Med. (Ex. Pres. Sect. Path.); Internat. Soc. Clin. Enzyme; Amer. Assn. for Clin. Chem. Prev: Cons. Chem. Path. Roy. Free Hosp. Lond.; Cons. Path. St. Mary's Hosp. & Paddington Childr. Hosp. Lond.; Flight Lt. RAF Med. Br.

ROSAM, Michael James William Woodley Centre Surgery, 106 Crockhamwell Road, Woodley, Reading RG5 3JY Tel: 0118 969 5011 Fax: 0118 944 0382; 279 Barkham Road, Wokingham RG41 4BY — MB BS 1981 Lond.; DCH RCP Lond. 1988; DRCOG 1986.

ROSANO, Guiseppe Massimo Claudio National Heart & Lung Institute, Cardiac Medicine, Dovehouse St., London SW3 6LY Tel: 020 7352 8121/3305 Fax: 020 7376 3442; 69 Drury Lane, London WC2B 5SP Tel: 020 7379 5537 — State DMS 1988 Rome. Hon. Regist. Roy. Brompton & Nat. Heart Hosp. Lond.

ROSANWO, Mr Emmanuel Olufemi 17 Stiles Road, Liverpool L33 4EA Tel: 0151 546 8900 Fax: 0151 546 8900 — MB BS 1975 Ibadan; FRCS Ed. 1981.

ROSANWO, Mofolusho Omobola Monisola 17 Stiles Road, Liverpool L33 4EA — MB BS 1974 Ibadan; MB BS Ibadan Nigeria 1974; FFA RCSI 1983. Socs: Liverp. Soc. Anaesth. And Nigerian Med. Forum. Prev: Locum Cons. Anaesth.and Locum Assoc. Anaesth.Aintree Hosps. Fazakerley Liverp.; Regist. (Anaesth.) P. Philip Hosp. Llawelli.

ROSARIO, Amanda Jane Foxhill Medical Centre, 363 Halifax Road, Sheffield S6 1AF Tel: 0114 232 2055 Fax: 0114 285 5963; 21 Ryegate Crescent, Sheffield S10 5FD — MB ChB 1988 Sheff.; MRCGP 1996.

ROSARIO, Derek James Patrick 21 Ryegate Crescent, Sheffield S10 5FD — MB ChB 1988 Sheff.

ROSBOTHAM, Jane Louise 2nd Floor Flat, 11 Mornington Avenue, London W14 8UJ Tel: 020 7371 1998; 2 Spenser Avenue, Weybridge KT13 0ST — MB BS 1988 Lond.; MRCP (UK) 1991. Research Regist. (Dermat.) Guy's Hosp. Lond. Socs: BMA. Prev: SHO St. Mary's Hosp. Lond.; Ho. Phys. Guy's Hosp. Lond.; Ho. Surg. Basingstoke Dist. Hosp.

ROSBOTHAM-WILLIAMS, Gary Martin Holme Green, Lathom Road, Ormskirk L39 0EA — MB ChB 1991 Liverp.

***ROSBOTTOM, Jane Margaret** St Georges Surgery, 46A Preston New Road, Blackburn BB2 6AH Tel: 01254 53791 Fax: 01254 697221 — MB ChB 1986 Manch.; MRCGP 1990; DRCOG 1990.

ROSBOTTOM, Robert Coldside Medical Practice, 129 Strathmartine Road, Dundee DD3 8DB Tel: 01382 826724 Fax: 01382 884129 — MB ChB 1974 Ed.

ROSCOE, Alan Harwood, MBE 80 Fildyke Road, Meppershall, Shefford SG17 5LU Tel: 01462 816153 — MB ChB Manch. 1954; MD Manch. 1983; MFOM RCP Lond. 1981; MRCGP 1965; DAvMed Eng. 1971; DObst RCOG 1955. (Manch.) Cons. Med. Adviser Britannia Airways Luton. Socs: Fell. Roy. Aeronautical Soc.; Fell. Aerospace Med. Assn. Prev: Adjunct. Prof. Embry-Riddle Aeronautical Univ. Florida, USA; Vis. Fell. Cranfield Inst. Technol.; Aviat. Med. Examr. Civil. Aviat. Auth.

ROSCOE, Bruce Luckholds Farm, Alfrick, Worcester WR6 5HW Tel: 01886 32980 — MB ChB 1964 Birm.; FFA RCS Eng. 1969. (Birm.) Cons. (Anaesth.) Hereford & Worcester AHA.

ROSCOE, Elizabeth Joy Haresfield House Surgery, 6-10 Bath Road, Worcester WR5 3EJ Tel: 01905 763161 Fax: 01905 767016; The Tynings, Church Lane, Flyford Flavell, Worcester WR7 4BZ Tel: 0138 682470 — MB ChB Birm. 1964. (Birm.) Prev: Ho. Phys. & Ho. Surg. Ronkswood Hosp. Worcester.

ROSCOE, Janet Dinah (retired) 58 Grantchester Meadows, Cambridge CB3 9JL Tel: 01223 350505 — MB BS 1938 Lond.; MRCS Eng., LRCP Lond. 1938; DCH Eng. 1944. Prev: Res. Asst. Phys. Hosp. Sick Childr. Gt. Ormond St.

ROSCOE, Peter (cons. room), 11 Imperial Square, Cheltenham GL50 1QU Tel: 01242 522646 — MB ChB 1967 Ed.; BSc (Hons.) Ed. 1965; FRCP Ed. 1981; MRCP (UK) 1970. Cons. Phys. Cheltenham Gen. Hosp.; Med. Dir. E. Glos. NHS Trust. Prev: Sen. Regist. (Gen. Med. & Respirat. Dis.) & Regist. (Respirat. Dis.) City Hosp. Edin.; Regist. (Gen. Med. & Clin. Toxicol.) Roy. Infirm. Edin.

ROSCOE, Sally Anne The Tynings, Church Lane, Flyford, Flavell, Worcester WR7 4BZ — MB ChB 1993 Birm.

ROSCOE, Trefor John Beighton Health Centre, Queens Road, Beighton, Sheffield S20 1BJ Tel: 0114 269 5061 — MB ChB 1982 Sheff. Lect. (GP) Univ. Sheff.; GP CME Tutor Informatics N. Trent. Socs: Brit. Healthcare Internet Assn. Research Coordinator; GP Writers Assn.; Soc. Internet in Med. Prev: Trainee GP Worksop VTS.

ROSCROW, Suzanne Elizabeth St. Johns Hosp, Howden, Livingston EH54 6PP Tel: 01506 419666 — MB ChB 1986 Aberd.; MPhil Ed. 1994; MRCPsych 1991. Cons. (Psychiat), St Johns Hosp., Livingstone. Prev: Sen. Regist. (Psychiat.) Roy. Edin. Hosp.

ROSE, Adrian Paul 1 Edwen Close, Childwall, Liverpool L16 5HF — MB ChB 1996 Liverp.; BDS Wales 1983; FDS Glas. 1989. SHO (Gen. Surg., Orthop., A & E, Paediat.) Basic Surgic. Regional Rotat. Whiston Dist. Gen. Hosp. Merseyside; Specialist (Oral Surg.) S. Yorks. Socs: Assoc. Mem. Brit. Assn. Oral & Maxillofacial Surg. Prev: Ho. Off. (Surg. & Med.) Roy. Liverp. Univ. Hosp.; Regist. (Maxillofacial Surg.) Roy. Liverp. Univ. Hosp.

ROSE, Amanda Fiona Flat 8, Albion Terrace, London Road, Reading RG1 5BG — MB BS 1982 Lond.; MRCP Lond. 1986; DCH RCP Lond. 1985. Regist. (Paediat.) Roy. Berks. Hosp., Reading; Regist. (Paediat.) John Radcliffe Hosp Oxf. Prev: SHO (Paediat.) Gt. Ormond St. Hosp.; SHO (Paediat.) Qu. Eliz. Hosp. for Childr. Lond.; SHO (Neonat. Paediat.) Qu. Charlottes Matern. Hosp. Lond.

ROSE, Andrew John The Surgery, 5 Sloane Avenue, London SW3 3JD Tel: 020 7581 3187 Fax: 020 7225 0034; 4 Markham Square, London SW3 4UY — MB ChB 1971 Birm.; BSc (Hons.) (Physiol.) Birm. 1968; MRCGP 1976; MFPM 1989; Dip. Pharm. Med. RCP 1980; DObst RCOG 1975; Cert. Family Plann. JCC 1975. GP Princip.; Med. Off. to Nat. Freight Corpn., Nat.Britannia Ltd.; Wates Gp., Macmillan Cancer Relief; Edit. Bd. Telemed Ltd.; Non-Exec. Chairm. J.H. Lavender & Company Ltd. W. Bromwich. Socs: Chelsea Clin. Soc.; Small Pract.s Assn.; Brit. Assn. Pharmaceut. Phys. Prev: Med. Adviser Beecham Pharmaceuts.; Examr. Dip. Nursing Univ. Lond.; Trainee GP St. Thos. Hosp. VTS & Bristol VTS.

ROSE, Andrew John Baker and Rose, The Surgery, Bowholm, Canonbie DG14 0UX Tel: 01387 371313 Fax: 01387 371244; Chestnut Cottage, Blackford, Carlisle CA6 4EG Tel: 01228 74094 Email: andrew.rose@dial.pipex.com — MB ChB 1987 Manch.; MRCGP 1993; DCOG 1992. (Manch. Med. Sch.) GP Canonbie Med. Pract. Prev: VTS Carlisle.

ROSE, Barry Stuart 626 London Road, Davenham, Northwich CW9 8LG Tel: 01606 42662 Email: bsrose@compuserve.com — MRCS Eng. LRCP Lond. 1959; FFHom 1982, M 1980; DObst RCOG

ROSE

1963. (Manch.) Prev: Dean Fac. of Homoeop.; Pres. Fac. of Homoeop. Roy. Lond. Homoeop. Hosp. Lond.

ROSE, Caroline Jane Theatre Royal Surgery, Theatre St., Dereham NR19 2EN; Lyng House, Rectory Road, Lyng, Norwich NR9 5RA — MB ChB 1982 Bristol; MRCGP 1986; DRCOG 1984.

ROSE, Catherine Elizabeth (Farrage) 19 Redleaf Close, Tunbridge Wells TN2 3UD — MB BS 1993 Newc.; Dip of Family Plann. 2000; Dip Child Health 1996. (Newcastle upon Tyne) p/t GP Princip. Prev: SHO (A & E) Morriston Hosp. Swansea; SHO (Gen. Med.) Shotley Bridge Dist. Gen. Hosp. Consett; SHO (Clin. Geratol. & Rehabil.) Radcliffe Infirm. Oxf.

ROSE, Charles David Lauchlan 42 Bartholomew Villas, London NW5 2LL — MB BS 1986 Lond.

ROSE, Christian 48 Abbotshall Drive, Cults, Aberdeen AB15 9JD — State Exam Med 1992 Berlin.

ROSE, Christopher Francis Linden Medical Group, Linden Medical Centre, Linden Avenue, Kettering NN15 7NX Tel: 01536 512104 Fax: 01536 415930; Werburgh House, 46 Cranford Road, Barton Seagrave, Kettering NN15 5JH Tel: 01536 726051 Email: chris.rose@virgin.net — MB BS 1977 Lond.; BSc (Hons.) Lond. 1974; MRCGP 1984; DRCOG 1982. (King's Coll. Lond. & St. Geo.) LMC Med. Sec. 1998-; Clin. Teach. Univ. Leicester Med. Sch. 1997-. Prev: Trainee GP Bristol VTS; SHO (Med.) Plymouth Health Dist.; Ho. Off. St. Geo. Hosp. Lond.

ROSE, Claire Michelle 2 St Anthonys Close, Ottery St Mary EX11 1EN — BM 1997 Soton.

ROSE, Clement 16 Grand Mansions, Queens Gardens, Broadstairs CT10 1QF Tel: 01843 601660 — MB BS 1947 Lond.; MD Lond. 1951; MRCS Eng. LRCP Lond. 1944; FRCPsych 1975, M 1971; DPM (Ment. Dific.) Lond. 1950; DPM (Psychiat.) Lond. 1949. (Lond. Hosp.) Emerit. Cons. Psychiat. Nottm. Dist. Hosps. Prev: Cons. Psychiat. Mapperley Hosp., Gen. Hosp. & City Hosp. Nottm.; Clin. Teach. Univ. Nottm.

ROSE, Daniel Joseph 2 Nepean Close, Gosport PO12 2BH — MRCS Eng. LRCP Lond. 1972; MRCGP 1984.

ROSE, Daniel Murray Austhorpe View Surgery, 5 Austhorpe View, Leeds LS15 8NN Tel: 0113 260 2262 Fax: 0113 232 8090; 24 Sandhill Oval, Alwoodley, Leeds LS17 8EA Tel: 0113 268 8155 — MB BS 1974 Lond.; MRCGP 1978; Cert FPA. 1980. (King's Coll. Hosp.) Clin. Asst. (A & E) St. Jas. Hosp. Leeds.; Mem. Leeds LMC. Prev: Trainee GP Leeds VTS; SHO (Obst.) St. Mary's Hosp. Leeds; SHO (Paediat.) Roy. Infirm. Huddersfield.

ROSE, David Hill Brow Surgery, Long Croft, Staincross, Barnsley S75 6FH Tel: 01226 383131 Fax: 01226 380100; 339A Darton Lane, Mapplewell, Barnsley S75 6AW Tel: 01226 387756 Email: drosedrose@hotmail.com — MB ChB 1981 Sheff.; MA Camb. 1982; MRCGP 1985; DRCOG 1985. GP; Course Organiser Barnsley VTS; Educat. Lead Barnsley W. PCG.

ROSE, Mr David Harold Mount Pleasent Farm, 105 Moss Lane, Bramhall, Stockport SK7 1EG Tel: 0161 439 7459 Email: d.h.rose@talk21.com — MB ChB 1962 Manch.; FRCS Ed. 1972; DLO Eng. 1970. (Manch.) Coordinator of universal Neonat. hearing screening Progr. Stockport NHS Trust- (Part Time Cons.). Socs: Mem. Brit. Soc. Audiol Full Mem.; Full Mem. Manch. Med. Soc. Prev: Sen. Regist. (ENT) Sheff. AHA (T); Regist. (ENT) United Sheff. Hosps.; Regist. (ENT) Stockport & Buxton Gp. Hosps.

ROSE, David John Anthony Whitecroft, Sandy Lane, Pleasington, Blackburn BB2 6RE — MB ChB 1977 Liverp.; FFA RCS Eng. 1982. p/t Cons. Anaesth. Blackburn Hosps.

ROSE, David Simon Charles Department of Histopathology, Royal United Hospital of Bath, Combe Park, Weston, Bath BA1 3NG Tel: 01225 824716; 40 Combe Park, Bath BA1 3NR Tel: 01225 824963 — MB BS 1987 Lond.; BSc (Hons.) Lond. 1984; MRCPath 1995; DRCPath 1992. Cons. Histopath. Roy. United Hosp. Bath. Prev: Sen. Regist. (Histopath.) Univ. Coll. Ldon. Med. Sch.

ROSE, Donald Hugh Department of Radiology, Nottingham City Hospital, Hucknall Rd, Nottingham NG5 1PB Tel: 0115 969 1169 Ext: 45801 Fax: 0115 962 7776; 1 Pinfold Cl, Woodborough, Nottingham NG14 6DP Tel: 0115 965 2866 Email: danrose@doctors.org.uk — MB BS Lond. 1967; MRCS Eng. LRCP Lond. 1967; FRCR 1975; FFR 1974; DMRD Eng. 1972. (Univ. Coll. Hosp.) Cons. Radiol. City Hosp. Nottm. Prev: Research Fell. Roy. Marsden Hosp. Lond.; Radiol. Sen. Regist. Guy's Hosp. Lond.; Ho. Surg. Univ. Coll. Hosp. Lond.

ROSE, Edward Leslie Halton General Hospital, Hospital Way, Runcorn WA7 2DA Tel: 01928 713714 Fax: 01928 726940; Bank House Farm, 287 Chester Road, Helsby, Warrington WA6 0PT Tel: 01928 722334 — MB BS 1982 Lond.; BA Oxf. 1979, DM 1992; FRCP Ed. 1996; MRCP (UK) 1986; FRCP 1997. (Guy's) Cons. Phys. (Cardiol.) Halton Gen. Hosp. NHS Trust Runcorn. Socs: Brit. Cardiac Soc.; Brit. Soc. Echocardiogr. Prev: Regist. (Gen. Med. & Cardiol.) Aberd. Roy. Infirm.; Research Regist. (Cardiol.) N.wick Pk. Hosp. Harrow; Regist. Rotat. (Med.) Univ. Hosp. Wales Cardiff.

ROSE, Elizabeth, MBE (retired) Ernsheenie, Dalbeattie DG5 4QW — MD 1972 Ed.; MB ChB 1950; FRCGP 1977, M 1965.

ROSE, Elizabeth Margaret (retired) 8 Malta Terrace, Edinburgh EH4 1HR Tel: 0131 332 5823 Fax: 01786 832389 — MB ChB Ed. 1938; FRCOG 1966, M 1947. Prev: Cons. O & G Stirling Roy. Infirm. & Assoc. Hosps.

ROSE, Eric David Vailton Keynes Village Practice, Griffith Gate, Middleton, Milton Keynes MK10 9BQ Tel: 01908 393979 Fax: 01908 393774 Email: 100576.2422@compuserve.com; 3 Sandpiper, Aylesbury HP19 0FP Tel: 01296 486735 Fax: 01296 331104 Email: ericdrose@compuserve — MB BS Lond. 1969; MRCS Eng. LRCP Lond. 1968; MRCGP 1980; Cert. Family Plann. JCC 1984; DObst RCOG 1971. (St. Mary's) GP Princip. Socs: GP Writers Assn. Prev: Sec. Berks. & Bucks. Local Med. Comm.; GP Aylesbury; SHO (Obst.) Roy. Berks. Hosp. Reading.

ROSE, Francis George ICI, 20 Manchester Square, London W10 3AN Tel: 020 7009 5403 Fax: 020 7009 5735 Email: frank_rose@ici.com — MB ChB 1974 Liverp.; DCH 1978 Eng.; FFOM 1990 RCP Lond.; MRCGP 1982. Vice Pres. Gp. SSHE, ICI Lond.; Bd. Mem. Internat. Commiss. Occupat. Health; Hon. Sen. Clin. Lect. Inst. Occupat. Health Univ. Birm. Socs: MEDICHEM; Soc. Occupat. Med.; ACOEM. Prev: Chief Med. Off. ICI plc; Med. Off. HM Forces (Army); Ho. Off. Roy. Infirm. Liverp.

ROSE, Frank Clifford The London Neurological Centre, 110 Harley St., London W1G 7JG Tel: 020 7935 3546 Fax: 020 7935 4172 Email: fcliffordrose@compuserve.com — MB BS 1949 Lond.; FRCP Lond. 1971, M 1954; MRCS Eng. LRCP Lond. 1949; DCH Eng. 1951. (King's Coll. Lond. & Westm.) Cons. Neurol. Lond. Neurol. Centre; Founding Edr. Jl. Hist. Neurosci.; Co-Edr. Headache Quar. Socs: Fell. Roy. Soc. Med. Lond. (Ex-Pres. Neurol. Sect.); Sec. & Treas. Gen. World Federat. of Neurol.; Hon. Life Mem. Internat. Headache Soc. Prev: Neurol. Regional Neurosci. Centre Char. Cross Hosp. Lond.; Dir. Acad. Unit Neurosci. Char. Cross & W.m. Med. Sch. Lond.; Cons. Neurol. Med. Ophth. Unit St. Thos. Hosp.

ROSE, Mr Geoffrey Edward 73 Harley Street, London W1G 8QJ Tel: 020 7935 5385 Fax: 020 7935 5385; Moorfields Eye Hospital, City Road, London EC1V 2PD Tel: 020 7566 2604 Fax: 020 7566 2608 Email: geoff.rose@moorfields.nhs.uk — MB BS 1979 Lond.; BSc (Hons.) Lond. (Pharmacol.) 1976; MS Lond. 1990; FRCS Eng. 1985; MRCP (UK) 1982; FRCOphth 1992; FCOphth 1988. (Kings College Hospital) Cons. Ophth. Surg. Moorfields Eye Hosp. Lond.; Hon. Cons. Ophth. Surg. Hosp. Childr. Gt. Ormond St. Lond. & Roy. Vict. Hosp. Belf. Prev: Lect. Inst. Ophth. Lond.; Sen: Regist. & Regist. (Ophth.) Moorfields Eye Hosp. Lond.

ROSE, George Alan 140 Park Road, Hendon, London NW4 3TL Tel: 020 8202 2900 Fax: 020 8202 2900; 52 Uphill Road, Mill Hill, London NW7 4PU Tel: 020 8959 2015 Fax: 020 8959 2015 Email: 11331.751@compuserve.com — BM BCh 1953 Oxf.; MA Oxf. 1949; BA (Hons. Chem.) Oxf. 1945; DM Oxf. 1956; FRCP Lond. 1975, M 1969; FRCPath 1977, M 1965. (Univ. Coll. Hosp.) Med. Advisor Lond. Gender Clinic; Med. Adviser to Gender Choice Centre, Hong Kong. Prev: Cons. Chem. Path. St. Peter's, St. Philip's, St. Paul's Hosps. Lond. & Roy. Nat. Orthop. Hosp. Stanmore; Lect. (Med.) Univ. Leeds; Asst. Med. Unit & Metab. Ward & Regist. (Med.) Univ. Coll. Hosp. Lond.

ROSE, Gillian Karen 61 Bradford Road, Manchester M40 7EY — MB ChB 1991 Leic.

ROSE, Gillian Linda Queen Charlotte's & Chelsea Hospital, Goldhawk Road, London W6 0XG Tel: 020 8383 1111 Fax: 020 8383 3925; 99 Harley Street, London W1N 1DF Tel: 020 7486 2785 — MRCS Eng. LRCP Lond. 1978; MD Lond. 1990, MB BS 1978; MRCOG 1984. (Royal Free Hospital) Cons. O & G Qu. Charlotte's & Chelsea Hosp. Lond. Socs: Med. Soc. Lond.; Brit. Fertil. Soc.; Brit. Soc. Paediat. & Gynae. Prev: Sen. Lect. & Hon. Cons. Qu. Charlotte's & Chelsea Hosp. Lond.; Sen. Regist. Qu.

ROSE

Charlotte's & Chelsea Hosps. Lond.; Research Regist. Chelsea Hosp. for Wom. Lond.

ROSE, Gillian Sarah 5 Collingham Gardens, London SW5 0HW Tel: 020 8846 6644 — MB BS 1986 Lond.; BSc (Hons.) Lond. 1983; MRCPsych 1990. (University of London) Child Psychiat. InPat. Unit. Eng. Prev: Clin. Lect. & Hon. Sen. Regist. (Child & Adolesc. Psychiat.) St. Mary's Hosp. Med. Sch. Lond.; SHO (Adult Psychiat.) Fulbourn Hosp. Lond. & Barnet Gen. Hosp.; Child & Adolesc. Psychiatr. N.Herts.NHS Trust.

ROSE, Graeme Dick Orchard Medical Centre, 41 Ladywell Road, Motherwell ML1 3JX Tel: 01698 264187 Fax: 01698 267717; 1 Woodlands Street, Motherwell ML1 2PU — MB ChB 1971 Aberd.

ROSE, Harry Kaye (retired) 9 The French Apartments, Purley CR8 2PH Tel: 020 8763 8044 — LRCP LRCS Ed. LRFPS Glas. 1946; FRCPsych 1981, M 1971; DPM Eng. 1955; DPH Glas. 1952. Prev: Cons. Psychiat. HM Prison Maidstone.

ROSE, Heather Mary Croft Medical Centre, 2 Glen Rd, Oadby, Leicester LE2 4PE — MB ChB 1983 Bristol; MRCGP 1987; DCH RCP Lond. 1987; DRCOG 1985. p/t GP Leicester. Prev: GP Reading; Trainee GP Bath VTS; Ho. Phys. & Ho. Surg. Frenchay Hosp. Bristol.

ROSE, Helen Frances (retired) 33 de Freville Avenue, Cambridge CB4 1HW Tel: 01223 312234 — MB 1973 Camb.; BChir 1972. Clin. Med. Off. Camb. HA. Prev: Clin. Med. Off. (Child Psychiat.) Oxf. RHA.

ROSE, Helen Moira Neville Hall Hospital, Abergavenny NP7 7EG Tel: 01873 852091; 5 Park Lane, Abergavenny NP7 5SS — BM 1992 Soton. Trainee GP/SHO Neville Hall Hosp. Gwent VTS.

ROSE, Henry Myer (retired) 40 Spinney Crescent, Blundellsands, Liverpool L23 8TZ Tel: 0151 924 4702 — MRCS Eng. LRCP Lond. 1942; DO Eng. 1961. Prev: Ophth. Sefton & Liverp. HA (T).

ROSE, Howard James Chilcompton Surgery, Wells Road, Chilcompton, Bath BA3 4EU Tel: 01761 232231 — MB BS 1967 Lond.; DPM Eng. 1970; DObst RCOG 1969. (St. Geo.) Med. Off. Downside Sch. Prev: Regist. N. Staffs. Matern. Hosp. Stoke on Trent; Regist. (Psychiat.) St. Geo. Hosp. Med. Sch.; Ho. Off. Cirencester Memor. Hosp.

ROSE, Irving 1 Fulwood Close, Church Road, Hayes UB3 2NF — LRCPI & LM, LRSCI & LM 1949; LRCPI & LM, LRCSI & LM 1949. Med. Off. Hayes Cottage Hosp. Socs: BMA. Prev: Ho. Phys. City Gen. Hosp. Stoke-on-Trent.

ROSE, Jack Harvey (retired) 182 Clarence Gate Gardens, Glentworth St., London NW1 6AR Tel: 020 7262 9482 — MB ChB Glas. 1938.

ROSE, Jacqueline Ann The Surgery, 2 Mark Street, Rochdale OL12 9BE Tel: 01706 43183 Fax: 01706 526640 — MB ChB 1984 Manch.

ROSE, James 69 Muirfield Crescent, Dundee DD3 8QA Tel: 01382 826706 — MB ChB 1949 Aberd.; FRCGP 1977, M 1971. (Aberd.) Med. Ref. Scott. Home & Health Dept. Prev: Ho. Phys. City Hosp. Aberd.; Ho. Surg. Bridge of Earn Hosp.; Ho. Surg. (Cas.) Perth Roy. Infirm.

ROSE, James Denton Worthy, Bantham, Kingsbridge TQ7 3AA — MB BS 1991 Lond.

ROSE, James Dudfield Richardson Burnock Lodge, 13 Racecourse Road, Ayr KA7 2DQ Tel: 01292 263531 — MB BChir 1973 Camb.; MA Camb. 1973, MD 1986; FRCP Glas. 1990; MRCP (UK) 1975. (Camb. & Newc. u. Tyne) Cons. Phys. Ayr Hosp. Socs: Brit. Soc. Gastroenterol.; Assn. Study Liver. Prev: Sen. Regist. (Gen. Med.) Llandough Hosp. & Univ. Hosp. Wales Cardiff; Regist. Addenbrooke's Hosp. Camb.; Ho. Off. Newc. u. Tyne Gen. Hosp.

ROSE, James William Peter St Clements Partnership, Tanner Street, Winchester SO23 8AD Tel: 01962 852211 Fax: 01962 856010 — MB BS 1986 Lond.; BSc Lond. 1981; MRCGP 1994.

ROSE, Jane Deborah Grove Road Surgery, 25 Grove Road, Borehamwood WD6 5DX — MB ChB 1988 Manch.; MRCGP 1993. (Univ. Manch.) p/t Princip. GP Borehamwood Herts. Prev: Trainee GP Borehamwood.

ROSE, Joanna Helen 50 St Laurence Road, Birmingham B31 2AX — MB BS 1988 Lond.; MRCGP 1993; DFFP 1994; DRCOG 1992. Clin. Asst. (Genitourin. Med.) & Doctor (Family Plann.) Birm. Prev: Trainee GP Taunton & Som. Hosp.

ROSE, Jocelyn Margaret (retired) 5 Hilary Close, Wollaton, Nottingham NG8 2SP Tel: 0115 928 4242 — MB ChB 1961 Sheff. Prev: Staff Grade (Anaesth.) Nottm. HA.

ROSE, John David Gardiner Department of Radiology, Freeman Hospital, Freeman Road, High Heaton, Newcastle upon Tyne NE7 7DN Tel: 0191 284 3111; Allendale House, Allendale Road, Hexham NE46 2DE — MB BS 1975 Lond.; FRCP Lond. 1997, M 1978; FRCR 1983; DMRD 1981. (Roy. Free Hosp. Lond.) Cons. Radiol. Freeman Hosp. Newc. Socs: Brit. Soc. Interven. Radiol.; Brit. Inst. Radiol. & Cardiovasc. & Intervent. Radiol. Soc. Europe. Prev: Cons. Radiol. Hillingdon Hosp. Uxbridge; Regist./Sen. Regist. (Radiol.) Newc. Teach. Hosps.

ROSE, John Fraser Harrogate District Hospital, Lancaster Park Road, Harrogate HG2 7SX Tel: 01423 885959 Fax: 01423 555806 Email: johnrose@hhc_tr.northy; Beechfield, The Terrace, Boston Spa, Wetherby LS23 6AH Tel: 01937 843332 — MB BS Lond. 1965; MRCS Eng. LRCP Lond. 1965; FRCR 1973; DMRD Eng. 1971. (Middlx.) Cons. Radiol. & Med. Dir. Harrogate Health Care Trust. Prev: Sen. Regist. (Diag. Radiol.) Univ. (St. Jas.) Hosp. Leeds; Regist. (Diag. Radiol.) Gen. Infirm. Leeds; SHO Profess. Med. Unit United Leeds Hosps.

ROSE, John Stuart Badgerswood Surgery, Mill Lane, Bordon GU35 8LH Tel: 01428 713511 Fax: 01428 713812; Brantfell House, New Road, Whitehill, Bordon GU35 9AX Tel: 01420 487374 — MB BS 1982 Lond.; BSc (1st cl. Hons.) Lond. 1979, MB BS 1982; MRCGP 1986; DCH RCP Lond. 1986; DRCOG 1985. (King's Coll. Hosp.)

ROSE, Justine Ann 5 Badingham Drive, Fetcham, Leatherhead KT22 9ES — BSc Lond. 1989, MB BS 1992; DRCOG Lond. 1996; MRCGP Lond. 1997. (C&WMS) Asst. Gen. Pract. Fairlands Surg. Guildford. Socs: DRCGP; MRCGP.

ROSE, Karen Ingrid 4 Belmont Crescent, Glasgow G12 8EU — MB ChB 1989 Glas.; BSc (Hons.) St. And. 1983; MRCP (UK) 1992. SHO (Gen. Med.) Roy. Alexandra Hosp. Paisley. Socs: Jun. Doctors Comm. Prev: SHO Rotat. (Gen. Med.) Glas. Roy. Infirm.; Research Asst. & Ho. Off. (Med.) W.. Infirm. Glas.; Ho. Off. (Surg.) Roy. Alexandra Hosp. Paisley.

ROSE, Kathleen Fionuala Allendale House, Allendale Road, Hexham NE46 2DE — MB BS 1975 Lond.

ROSE, Mr Keith Graham Surgicare, Parkway House, Palatine Road, Manchester M22 4DB Tel: 0161 945 8688 Fax: 0161 945 8689; The Nook, 1 Essex Avenue, Didsbury, Manchester M20 6AN Tel: 0161 445 5274 — MB BS 1978 Lond.; FRCS Eng. 1984; MRCS Eng. LRCP Lond. 1978. (St. Thos.) Surg. Surgicare Manch. Prev: Surg. to ICRC; Regist. St. Helier Hosp. Carshalton; SHO & Ho. Surg. St Thos. Hosp. Lond.

***ROSE, Kirsten Emma** Polmear, Alexandra Road, Illogan, Redruth TR16 4EN — MB ChB 1998 Birm.

ROSE, Leslie (retired) 41 Burton Road, Burton-on-Trent DE14 3DL Tel: 01283 562358 — MB ChB 1949 Glas.; DObst RCOG 1953. Prev: Obst. Ho. Surg. Glas. Roy. Matern. Hosp.

ROSE, Lionel Clifford (retired) Timbertop, Tye Green Village, Harlow CM18 6QY Tel: 01279 423844 — MB ChB 1958 St. And.; DObst. RCOG 1960.

ROSE, Margaret Anne 2 Westview, Elm Grove, Salisbury SP1 1NE — MB BS 1983 Lond.

ROSE, Mr Martyn John Thatch, Chapel Lane, Old, Northampton NN6 9RD Tel: 01604 781333 — MB ChB 1967 Liverp.; FRCS Eng. 1972. (Liverp.) Cons. Rehabil. Med. St. And. Hosp. N.ampton. Prev: Sen. Regist. (Neurosurg.) Walton Hosp. Liverp.; Regist. (Neurosurg.) Inst. Neurol. Scs. Glas.; Demonst. (Anat.) Univ. Liverp.

ROSE, Mary Royal Hospital for Sick Children, Sciennes Road, Edinburgh EH9 1LF Tel: 0131 536 0000 — MB BS 1985 Lond.; FRCA 1993; DA (UK) 1992. (Royal Free) Cons. (Anaesth.) Roy. Hosp. for Sick Childr. Edin. Socs: Assn. Anaesth.; Pain Soc.; Edin. and E. of Scotl. Soc. of Anaesth.s. Prev: Regist. (Anaesth.) ChristCh. Hosp. NZ; Regist. (Anaesth.) Derriford Hosp. Plymouth.

ROSE, Mary Walker (retired) 45 Stumperlowe Park Road, Sheffield S10 3QP Tel: 0114 230 5671 — MB ChB 1953 Sheff. Prev: Clin. Med. Off. Sheff. AHA.

ROSE, Megan Sandwell Hospital, Lyndon, West Bromwich B71 4HJ — MB ChB 1998 Birm.; ChB Birm. 1998.

ROSE, Mr Michael Barritt Morriston Hospital (Department of Urology), Morriston, Swansea SA6 6NL Tel: 01792 703379; 16 Kilfield Road, Bishopston, Swansea SA3 3DL Tel: 01792 232808 — MB 1966 Camb.; MA; MChir Camb. 1977, MB 1966, BChir 1965; FRCS Eng. 1970; DObst RCOG 1968. (St. Thos.) Cons. Surg. (Urol.)

Swansea Health Dist. Socs: Brit. Assn. Urol. Surgs. Prev: Sen. Regist. (Urol.) Leeds Hosp. Gp.; Regist. (Surg.) St. Thos. Hosp. Lond.; SHO (Surg.) Bath Hosp. Gp.

ROSE, Michael Norman The Limes Surgery, 172 High Street, Lye, Stourbridge DY9 8LL Tel: 01384 422234 — MB ChB 1966 Birm.

ROSE, Mrs Muriel (retired) 36 Seckford Street, Woodbridge IP12 4LY — MRCS Eng. LRCP Lond. 1933; BSc Lond. 1930, MD 1947, MB BS 1935; FRCOG 1962.

ROSE, Naomi Jacqueline 123 Wigton Lane, Alwoodley, Leeds LS17 8SH — MB ChB 1963 Leeds.

ROSE, Nicholas David Bridgeman Littlemore Hospital, Littlemore, Oxford OX4 4XN — MB ChB 1971 Leeds; FRCPsych 1992, M 1977. Cons. Psychiat. Littlemore Hosp. Oxf.; Oxf. Regional Tutor for Vis. Regist.; Oxf. Regional MRCPsych Course Organiser. Prev: Cons. Community Psychiat. & Psychother. High Wycombe; Assoc. Prof. (Psychiat.) Univ. Sains, Malaysia; Lect. (Psychiat.) Univ. Oxf.

ROSE, Nigel Maxwell The Hacketts, Fromes Hill, Hereford — BM BCh 1971 Oxf.; FFA RCS Eng. 1976.

ROSE, Peter Garden House, Old colwall, Malvern WR13 6HF — MB ChB 1969 Sheff.

ROSE, Peter Edgar Hurstwood Park Neurological Centre, Haywards Heath RH16 4EX Tel: 01444 441881 Fax: 01444 417995; 11 Purley Knoll, Purley CR8 3AF — MB BS 1973 Lond.; BSc (Hons.) Lond. 1970, MB BS 1973; FRCPath 1992, M 1980. Cons. Neuropath. Hurstwood Pk. Neurol. Centre Haywards Heath; Hon. Lect. (Morbid Anat.) KCH Med. Sch. Lond. Prev: Clin. Lect. (Neuropath.) Inst. Psychiat. Lond.

ROSE, Peter Edwin Warwick Hospital, Lakin Road, Warwick CV34 5BJ Tel: 01926 482600 Fax: 01926 493567; Ryderdale, Manor Lane, Pinley, Claverdon, Warwick CV35 8NH — MB ChB 1976 Dundee; FRCP Ed. 1994; MRCP (UK) 1979; FRCPath 1995, M 1984. Cons. Haemat. S. Warks. HA.

ROSE, Peter Gerard 33 Lindisfarne Close, Jesmond, Newcastle upon Tyne NE2 2HT — MB ChB 1963 Ed.; FFR 1973; DMRD Eng. 1971. (Ed.) Cons. Radiol. N. RHA & Newc. AHA (T); Hon. Clin. Lect. Univ. Newc. Socs: Brit. Med. Ultrasound Soc.; Brit. Inst. Radiol. Prev: Sen. Regist. (Radiol.) & Regist. (Radiol.) Roy. Vict. Infirm. Newc.; SHO (Med.) & Regist. (Med.) Vict. Hosp. Blackpool.

ROSE, Peter Selborne The Surgery, 59 Mansfield Road, Blidworth, Mansfield NG21 0RB Tel: 01623 795461 Fax: 01623 490514; 118 Main Road, Ravenshead, Nottingham NG15 9GW Tel: 01623 793467 — MB ChB 1966 Ed. (Ed.) Socs: BMA; Nat. Assn. Family Plann. Doctors. Prev: Ho. Off. O & G Bangour Gen. Hosp. Broxburn; Ho. Off. Orthop. Peel Hosp. Galashiels; Ho. Off. Gen. Med. Roy. Infirm. Edin.

ROSE, Peter William Mill Stream Surgery, Mill Stream, Benson, Wallingford OX10 6RL Tel: 01491 838286 — MB BChir 1978 Camb.; MB Camb. 1978, MA, BChir 1977; FRCGP 1994, M 1981; DRCOG 1980; DCH Eng. 1979. Research Fell. ICRF GPRG Dept. Pub. Health & Primary Care Inst. Health Sci.s Oxf. Prev: Trainee GP Banbury VTS.

ROSE, Philip Alfred 30 Winscombe Way, Stanmore HA7 3AU — MB BS 1985 Lond.

ROSE, Philip Francis Doune Health Centre, Castlehill, Doune FK16 6DR Tel: 01786 841213; 9 Elm Court, Doune FK16 6JG — MB ChB 1984 Dundee; MB ChB Dundee. 1984; MRCGP 1988.

ROSE, Ronald 51 Trentham Road, Longton, Stoke-on-Trent ST3 4DU Tel: 01782 310670 — MD 1939 Prague; MRCS Eng., LRCP Lond. 1954; MRCGP 1953.

ROSE, Senga 59 Harefields, Oxford OX2 8HG Tel: 01865 56992 — MB ChB 1961 Glas. (Glas.) Prev: Sen. Med. Off. Coll. Health Serv. Camden & Islington AHA (T).

ROSE, Shamim Akhtar 1 Ewden Close, Abbeyfields, Childwall, Liverpool L16 5HF Tel: 0151 738 0209; Forensic Medical Services, HM Prison Altcourse, Fazakerely, Liverpool L9 7LH Tel: 0151 522 2066 Fax: 0151 522 2153 — MB ChB 1990 Liverp.; DFFP 1997. Prison Med. Off. HM Prison Altcourse Liverp.

ROSE, Mr Sidney Samuel 135 Palatine Road, West Didsbury, Manchester M20 3YA Tel: 0161 445 0128; The Homestead, Whitehall Road, Sale M33 3WJ Tel: 0161 973 4533 — MB ChB 1941 Manch.; MB ChB (2nd cl. Hons.) Manch. 1941; FRCS Eng. 1948. Socs: Fell. Roy. Soc. Med. (Venous Forum); Hon. Fell. Societe Francais De Phlebologie; Manch. Surg. Soc. Prev: Co-Chief Edr. Jl.

Cardiovasc. Surg.; Chief Edr. Phlebol.; Cons. Surg. Withington Hosp. Manch.

ROSE, Silke 48 Abbotshall Drive, Cults, Aberdeen AB15 9JD — State Exam Med 1990 Berlin.

ROSE, Stephen John Department of Paediatrics, Birmingham Heartlands Hospital, Bordsley Green E., Birmingham B9 5SS Tel: 0121 424 1687 Ext: 5069 Fax: 0121 773 6458 Email: roses@heartsol.wminds.nhs.uk; 92 Dovehouse Lane, Solihull B91 2EG Tel: 0121 707 2311 Fax: 0121 682 8397 Email: sbrose98@aol.com — MA Camb. 1976, M BChir 1975; FRCP Lond. 1994; MRCP (UK) 1979; FRCPCH Lond. 1997. Cons. Paediat. & Hon. Sen. Lect. Univ. Birm. Heartlands Hosp. Birm. Socs: Brit. Soc. for Paediatric; Diabetes UK; Brit. Med. Assn. Prev: Lect. in Child Health, Univ. of Aberd.

ROSE, Susan Elizabeth West Green Child Development Centre, Town Barn Road, West Green, Crawley RH11 7EL Tel: 01293 615050 Fax: 01293 535695; Mouse Hall, South Lane, Amberley, Arundel BN18 9LN — MB ChB 1980 Aberd.; MRCGP 1985; DCH RCP Lond. 1986; DRCOG 1983. SCMO Surrey & Sussex Healthcare. Prev: SCMO Mid Sussex NHS Trust; Sen. Clin. Med. Off. Tower Hamlets HA.

ROSE, Susan Louise Holmlea, Church Hill, Wilmington, Dartford DA2 7EH — MB BS 1989 Lond.; MRCP (UK) 1994.

ROSE, Teresa Spa Surgery, 205 High Street, Boston Spa, Wetherby LS23 6PY Tel: 01937 842842 Fax: 01937 841095 — MB BS 1966 Lond.; MMedSc Leeds 1985; MRCS Eng. LRCP Lond. 1966. (Middlx.) Prev: Departm. Med. Off. W. Riding CC Yorks; Ho. Surg. Profess. Surg. Unit Leeds Gen. Infirm.; Ho. Phys. Profess. Med. Unit Middlx. Hosp.

ROSE, William James McQueen 4 Ladycross Cottages, Hollow Lane, Dormansland, Lingfield RH7 6PB — MB BS 1993 Lond.

ROSEBLADE, Christopher Kenneth Wrexham Maelor Hospital, Croesnewydd Road, Wrexham LL13 7TD Tel: 01978 291100 — MB ChB 1984 Manch.; MA Oxf. 1983; BSc St. And. 1981; MRCOG 1990. Cons. O & G Wrexham Maelor Hosp. Socs: Fell. Roy. Soc. Med.; Internat. Continence Soc. Prev: Sen. Regist. (O & G) Withington Hosp. N. W.. RHA; Regist. Rotat. Kings Coll. Hosp. & Brighton; Research Regist. (O & G) Hammersmith Hosp.

ROSEDALE, James Oriel Bernard The Marlborough Surgery, George Lane, Marlborough SN8 4BY Tel: 01672 512187; Thornsend, Kingsbury St, Marlborough SN8 1HZ — MB BS 1964 Lond.; DObst RCOG 1974; DCH Eng. 1966; DTM & H Liverp. 1966. (St. Thos.) Med. Off. Savernake Hosp. MarlBoro. & MarlBoro. Coll. Prev: Med. Off. Brit. Everest Expedit. 1972; Ldr., Brit. Nepal Med. Trust, Nepal; Regist. (Paediat.) Univ. Coll. Hosp. Ibadan, Nigeria.

ROSEDALE, Neville (retired) 46 Hatherley Court, Hatherley Grove, Westbourne Grove, London W2 5RE Tel: 020 7727 9639 Email: nrosedale@hotmail.com — FRCP Ed. 1974, M 1959; MRCS Eng. LRCP Lond. 1945. Prev: Cons. Venereol. W. Middlx. Hosp. Isleworth & Hillingdon Hosp. Uxbridge.

ROSEFIELD, Andrea Ruth 3 Mountview, Barnet Way, Mill Hill, London NW7 3HT Tel: 020 8959 4793 — MB BS 1964 Lond.; MRCS Eng. LRCP Lond. 1965. Clin. Asst. Boosey & Hawkes (Musical Instruments) Ltd. Lond.; Clin. Asst. (Genitourin. Med.) Mortimer Market Centre UCL Hosp.; Clin. Asst. (Genitourin. Med.) Ambrose King Centre Roy. Lond. Hosp. Socs: Soc. Occupat. Med.; Soc. Study VD.

ROSEHILL, Sydney Parkdale, 1 Edward VII Avenue, Newport NP20 4TL Tel: 01633 63467 — MB BCh BAO 1939 NUI; MRCGP 1956. (Cork) Vis. Anaesth. & Med. Asst. Dermat. Dept. Roy. Gwent Hosp. Newport; Vis. Anaesth. St. Woolos Hosp. Newport; Med. Off. Alit-yr-Yn Isolat. Hosp. Socs: BMA & Soc. Anaesths. S. Wales. Prev: Res. Med. Off. St. Luke's Hosp. Huddersfield; Sqaudron Ldr. RAF Med. Br. 1941-45; Ho. Phys. Roy. Gwent Hosp. Newport.

ROSELAAR, Simon Edwin Washington University Medical School, Department of Internal Medicine, 660 South Eucliel Avenue, St Louis 63110, USA Tel: 00 1 314 3623655 Fax: 00 1 314 3623513; 29 Ludlow Way, London N2 0JZ — MB BS 1986 Lond.; BSc (1st cl. Hons.) Physiol. Lond. 1983, MD 1994; MRCP Lond. 1990. Socs: Fell. Div. Atherosclerosis & Lipid Research Washington Univ. Med. Sch.; +St. Louis, USA. Prev: Lect. (Nephrol.) Lond. Hosp.; SHO (Renal Med.) Guys Hosp. Lond.; SHO St. Bart. Hosp., Brompton Hosp. & Hammersmith Hosp. Lond.

ROSELL

ROSELL, Philip Anthony Edward Yew Tree Farmhouse, 152 Botley Road, Swanwick, Southampton SO31 1BU — MB BS 1991 Lond.; BSc Lond. 1988.

ROSELLO, Natalia Susana 10 Doves Yard, Culford Road, London N1 0HQ — MB BS 1996 Lond.

ROSEMEN, Joan Jemima St Giles Surgery, 40 St. Giles Road, London SE5 7RF Tel: 020 7252 5936; 450 Westhorne Avenue, Eltham, London SE9 5LT — MB BS 1978 Newc.; MRCGP 1984; DCH RCP Lond. 1982.

ROSEN, Adam 10 Boyton House, Wellington Road, London NW8 9TH — MB BS 1993 Lond.; BSc Lond. 1990, MB BS 1993.

ROSEN, Bernard Keith 55 Thurleigh Road, London SW12 8TZ — MB ChB 1968 Sheff.; FRCPsych 1988, M 1973; MRCPsych 1973. Sen. Lect. & Hon. Cons. (Psychiat.) Guy's Hosp. Lond. Prev: Lect. & Hon. Cons. (Psychiat.) Guy's Hosp. Lond.; Vis. Lect. (Psychiat.) Memor. Univ. Newfld.

ROSEN, Calmen 26 Wolfreton Garth, Kirk Ella, Hull HU10 7AD — MRCS Eng. LRCP Lond. 1946. Socs: MRCGP.

ROSEN, Edwin David (retired) 47 Canonbury Park N., London N1 2J4 Tel: 020 7226 9823 Fax: 020 7226 9823 Email: edminposen@netscapeoneline.co.uk — MB BS 1957 Lond.; MRCS Eng., LRCP Lond. 1956. Mem. Med Ethic Comm. Moorfields Eye Hosp.Lond. Prev: Obst. Ho. Off. & Med. Off. Radiother. Unit Ch.ill Hosp. Oxf.

ROSEN, Mr Emanuel Saul 10 St John Street, Manchester M3 4DY Tel: 0161 832 8778 Fax: 0161 832 1486 Email: erosen9850@aol.com — MB ChB 1961 Manch.; BSc (Hons.) Manch. 1957, MD 1969; FRCS Ed. 1967; FRCOphth 1988. (Manch.) Cons. (Opthal.) Rosen Eye Surg. Centre, Manch.; Vis. Prof. Vision Sc. Univ. Manch.; Co-Edr. Jl. Cataract & Refractive Surg.; Hon. Cons. Ophth. Manch. Roy. Eye Hosp. Socs: (Ex-Pres.) Europ. Soc. Cataract & Refractive Surg.; (Ex-Pres.) UK Med. Cataract & Refractive Surgic. Soc.; Pres. Internat. Intraocular Implant Club.

ROSEN, Hugh Sir William Dunn School of Pathology, University of Oxford, South Parks Road, Oxford OX1 3RE — MB ChB 1982 Cape Town; DPhil Oxf. 1986. Jun. Research Fell. Jesus Coll. Oxf.

ROSEN, Jan-Paul David 49 Cholmeley Crescent, London N6 5EX — MB BS 1989 Lond.

ROSEN, Maria Rosaline 40 Priory Gardens, Highgate, London N6 5QS Tel: 020 8348 0597 — MB ChB 1965 Glas.; MRCPsych 1973; DPM Ed. & Glas. 1970. (Glas.) Socs: BMA. Prev: Sen. Regist. Tavistock Clinic.

ROSEN, Maurice Howard The Surgery, 21 Commercial Street, London E1 6BD — MRCS Eng. LRCP Lond. 1964; MA Lond. 1997; MSc Lond. 1995; DA Eng. 1966. (St. Mary's)

ROSEN, Professor Michael, CBE 45 Hollybush Road, Cardiff CF23 6TZ Tel: 029 2075 3893 Email: microsen@compuserve.com — MB ChB St. And. 1949; FRCS Eng. 1992; FFA RCSI (Hons.) 1990; FFA RCS Eng. 1957; FRCOG 1989. (St. Andrews) Exec. Off. World Federat. of Socs. of Anaesthesiol. Socs: Roy. Soc. Med.; Amer. Soc. Anaesthesiologists. Prev: Hon. Prof. Anaesth. Univ. Wales Coll. Med.; Pres. Roy. Coll. of Anaesths. 1988-91; Pres. Assn. of Anaesth. Gt. Britain & Irel. 1986-88.

ROSEN, Michael Philip (cons. rooms) 37 Rodney Street, Liverpool L1 9EN Tel: 0151 709 1864 Fax: 0151 428 5399; 121 Church Road, Woolton, Liverpool L25 6HT — LRCPI & LM, LRSCI & LM 1970; LRCPI & LM, LRCSI & LM 1970. (RCSI) Prev: SHO (O & G) St. Mary's Hosp. Manch. & Whiston Hosp. Prescot.

ROSEN, Mr Paul Henry Oxford Eye Hospital, Walton St., Oxford OX2 Tel: 01865 224739 Fax: 01865 224360; Ruperts Bell, 4 Northfield End, Henley-on-Thames RG9 2HN — MB ChB 1980 Manch.; BSc (Hons.) Physiol. Manch. 1977, MB ChB 1980; FRCS Glas. 1985. Cons. Ophth. Surg. Oxf. Eye Hosp. Prev: Lect., Fell. & Sen. Regist. Moorfields Eye Hosp. Inst. Ophth. Lond.

ROSEN, Rebecca Celia The Kings Fund, 11-13 Cavendish Square, London W1G 0AN Tel: 020 7307 2443 Email: rrosen@lehf.org.uk; 32 Coleraine Road, Blackheath, London SE3 7PQ Tel: 020 8305 1694 — MB ChB 1988 Bristol; MSc Lond. 1992; MFPHM RCP (UK) 1995; DCH RCP Lond. 1991; MD Bristol 1998; MFFP (RCOG0 1998. (Bristol) Fell. in Primary Care, The Kings Fund, Lond.; Hon. Lect. (Health Servs. Research) Lond. Sch. Hyg. & Trop. Med.

ROSEN, Stuart David 19 Templars Avenue, London NW11 0PB Fax: 020 8731 6169 Email: stuart@cu.rpms.ac.uk — MB BS 1985 Lond.; MA Camb. 1986, BA 1982; MD Lond. 1996; MRCP (UK) 1990. (Cambridge University & Charing Cross & Westminster Med. Sch.) Sen. Lect. & Hon. Cons. Cardiol., Imperial Coll. Sch. Med. & Hammersmith Hosp. Socs: BMA & Jun. Cardiac Club; Fell. Amer. Coll. Cardiol. & Europ. Soc. Cardiol.; Brit. Cardiac Soc. Prev: Clin. Scientist, MRC Clin. Scis. Centre, Hon. Lect. & Sen. Regist. (Cardiol.) RPMS, Hammersmith & St. Mary's Hosp. Lond.; Regist. (Cardiol. & Med.) & Research SHO (Cardiol.) Char. Cross Hosp. Lond.

ROSENBAUM, Naomi Louise 31 Mount Pleasant, Barnet EN4 9ES — MB BS 1991 Lond.; DFFP 1995; DRCOG 1994. Socs: Assoc. Mem. RCGP. Prev: Trainee GP Edgware VTS.

ROSENBAUM, Mr Tomas Pedro Department of Urology, Ealing Hospital, Uxbridge Road, Southall UB1 3HW Tel: 020 8967 5778 Fax: 020 8813 8607 Email: tom.rosenbaum@eht.org.uk — Medico 1973 Buenos Aires; FRCS (Urol.) 1994; FRCS Ed. 1982; MRCS Eng. LRCP Lond. 1979; FEBU 1996. (Univ. of Buenos Aires) Cons. Urol. Ealing Hosp. S.all Middlx. Socs: Fell. Roy. Soc. Med.; Internat. Continence Soc.; Brit. Assn. Urol. Surg. Prev: Lect. (Urol.) Inst. Urol. Lond.; Sen. Regist. (Urol.) St. Helier Hosp. Carshalton; Sen. Regist. (Urol.) Roy. Marsden Hosp.

ROSENBERG, Aaron (retired) 5 Castle Hill Road, Prestwich, Manchester M25 0FR — LRCPI & LM, LRSCI & LM 1959; LRCPI & LM, LRCSI & LM 1959. Prev: Assoc. Specialist (Psychiat.) Prestwich Hosp. Manch.

ROSENBERG, Mr Bernard Cecil, TD Birkdale Clinic, Parkfield Road, Rotherham S65 2AJ Tel: 01709 828928 Fax: 01709 828372; Montrose, 31 Stumperlowe Crescent Road, Sheffield S10 3PQ Tel: 0114 230 8433 Email: bcr.hallam@demon.co.uk — MB BCh BAO 1962 Dub.; MA Dub. 1992, BA 1960; FRCOG 1983, M 1970; DObst RCOG 1964. Cons. O & G Rotherham Dist. Gen. Hosp. Socs: BMA; Fell. N. Eng. Obst & Gyn. Soc.; Lond. Obst & Gyn. Soc. Prev: Sen. Regist. Hammersmith Hosp. Lond.; Regist. St. Mary's Hosp. W9 & Samarit. Hosp. Lond.; Ho. Surg. & Ho. Phys. Meath Hosp. Dub.

ROSENBERG, Bethel 10 St John Street, Manchester M3 4DY Tel: 0161 819 1111; Email: bethel@waitrose.co, o.e.williams@appleonline.net — MB BCh BAO 1962 Dub.; BA 1961 Dub. (T.C. Dub.) p/t Area Med. Off. Brit. Boxing Bd. of Control.; Occupat.al Health Phys. Manch. Medico Legal Assessm. Prev: SHO (Med.) Bolton Dist. Gen. Hosp.; Ho. Surg. Matern. Hosp. Hull; Ho. Phys. & Cas. Off. Meath Hosp. Dub.

ROSENBERG, David 27 Hillside Gardens, Edgware HA8 8HA — MB ChB 1993 Manch.

ROSENBERG, Mr David Averell 35 Hyndewood, Dacres Road, Forest Hill, London SE23 2NX — MB BS 1970 Lond.; FRCS Ed. 1979; MRCS Eng. LRCP Lond. 1970; MRCOG 1977. (Guy's) Cons. (O & G) St. Albans City Hosp. & W. Herts. Hosp. Hemel. Prev: Sen. Regist. (O & G) St. Geo.'s Hosp. Lond.; Regist. King's Coll. Hosp. Lond.

ROSENBERG, Fraser Guy The Old School House, Main Road, Scalby, Gilberdyke, Brough HU15 2UU — MB ChB 1998 Manch.; MB ChB Manch 1998.

ROSENBERG, Mr Ivor Lawrence 1 Egglescliffe Court, Egglescliffe Village, Stockton-on-Tees TS16 9BU Tel: 01642 781577/ 624595 Fax: 07092 290141 Email: il.rosenberg@ntlworld.com — MB BChir 1966 Camb.; MA Camb. 1966; MChir Camb. 1979,; FRCS Eng. 1971; FRCS Ed. 1971. (Camb. & Leeds) Cons. Surg. N. Tees Gen. Hosp. Stockton on Tees. Socs: Fell. Assn. Surgs.; BASO; Assn. ColoProctol. GB & Irel. Prev: Lect. (Surg.) Leeds Univ. & Hon. Sen. Regist. St. Jas. Hosp. Leeds; Regist. (Surg.) ScarBoro. Hosp.; SHO Hammersmith Hosp. Lond.

ROSENBERG, Jeffrey Nathan The Garden Hospital, 46-50 Sunny Gdns. Road, London NW4 1RP Tel: 020 8457 4500 Fax: 020 8457 4567; 22 Woodland Way, London NW7 2JR Fax: 020 8906 9705 Email: doc jrosenberg@aol.com — MB BS Lond. 1970; FRCP Lond. 1991; MRCP (UK) 1973; MRCS Eng. LRCP Lond. 1970. (Guy's) Hon.Cons Rheum Roy. Nat. Orthopaedic Hosp. Socs: Fell. Hunt. Soc. Hon curator; Fell. Med. Soc. Lond.; Fell Zool. soc of lond. Prev: Sen. Regist. (Rheum.) Lond. Hosp.; Regist. MRC Rheum. Unit Taplow; Regist. (Med.) Guy's Hosp. Lond.

ROSENBERG, Katharine South View, Chapel Road, Nelton, Swaffham PE37 8JA — MB ChB 1993 Leeds.

ROSENBERG, Mr Mervyn Theodore Wrexham Maelor Hospital NHS Trust, Wrexham LL13 7TD Tel: 01978 291100 Fax: 01978 310326; Rackery Hall, Rackery Lane, Caer Estyn, Wrexham LL12 0PB Tel: 01698 760031 — MB BCh 1957 Witwatersrand; MD

W. Virginia 1977; FRCS Eng. 1963. Med. Dir. & Cons. Surg. Wrexham Maelor Hosp. NHS Trust; Freelance Med. Jl.ist. Prev: Cons. Surg. Lawson Memor. Hosp. Golspie; Cons. Surg. Brook Gen. Hosp. Lond.; Sen. Regist. (Surg.) St. Thos. Hosp. Lond.

ROSENBERG, Michael Alexander John South Downs Health NHS Trust, Brighton General Hospital, Elm Grove, Brighton BN2 3EW Tel: 01273 696011 Fax: 01273 242215 — MB BS 1972 Lond.; MRCS Eng. LRCP Lond. 1972; 2001 FRCPsych. (Guy's Hospital) Cons. Psychiat. S. Downs Health NHS Trust Brighton.; Med. Dir. Prev: Sen. Regist. (Psychiat.) St. Geo. Hosp. Lond.; Regist. (Psychiat.) St. Geo. Hosp. Lond.; SHO (Gen. Med.) FarnBoro. Hosp. Kent.

ROSENBERG, Raymond Henry (retired) 59 Shearwater, New Barn, Longfield DA3 7NL Tel: 0147 47 04916 — MB ChB 1953 Cape Town. Prev: Cons. Psychiat. (Ment. Handicap.) Darenth Pk. Hosp. Dartford.

ROSENBERG, Roger Martin 21 Pink Lane, Burnham, Slough SL1 8JP Tel: 01628 603278 Email: roger@rosenberg87.freeserve.co.uk — MB BCh 1966 Witrwatersrand; MB BCh Witwatersrand 1966; BSc (Hons.) Witwatersrand 1983. Head Clin. Strategy Glaxo Wellcome. Socs: FFPM. Prev: Exec. Dir. Clin. Raesearch Marion Merkell Dow Winnersh.; Dir. Strategic Drug Developm. Clintrials Research Ltd.

ROSENBERG, Ronald Basil Collegiate Medical Centre, Brideoak St., Manchester M8 0AT Tel: 0161 205 4364; Flat 2, Radnor House, 25 Upper Park Road, Braughton Pk., Salford M7 4JB Tel: 0161 740 3079 — MB ChB 1953 Manch. (Manch.) Hosp. Pract. Dept. Endocrinol. N. Hosp. Manch. Socs: Fell. Manch. Med. Soc.

ROSENBERG, Susan Elaine 35 Upper Park Road, Salford M7 4JB — MB ChB 1981 Manch. SHO (Neonat. Med.) St. Mary's Hosp. Manch. Prev: SHO (O & G) Univ. Hosp. S. Manch. & Withington Hosp. Manch.; SHO (Paediat.) Booth Hall Childr. Hosp. Manch.; Ho. Off. (Surg.) N. Manch. Gen. Hosp.

ROSENBERG, William Malcolm Charles Nuffield Department Clinical Medicine, John Radcliffe Hospital, Oxford OX3 9DU Tel: 01865 221337; 9 Lakewood Road, Chandlers Ford, Eastleigh SO53 1ER — MB BS 1983 Lond.; DPhil Oxf. 1992, MA 1992; MA Camb. 1984; MRCP (UK) 1987. (Guy's) Clin. Tutor (Med.) Univ. Oxf.; Hon. Sen. Regist. (Gen. Internal Med. & Gastroenterol.) John Radcliffe Hosp. Oxf.

ROSENBLOOM, Lewis Child Development Centre, Alder Hey Hospital, Eaton Road, Liverpool L12 2AP Tel: 0151 252 5328 Fax: 0151 252 5678; 83 Waterloo Ware House, Waterloo Road, Liverpool L3 0BQ Tel: 0151 236 9396 — MB ChB 1961 Liverp.; FRCRCH 1997; FRCP Lond. 1978, M 1965; DCH Eng. 1966. (Liverp.) Cons. Paediat. Neurol. Roy. Liverp. Childr. NHS Trust. Prev: Research Fell. Inst. Child Health Univ. Lond.; Regist. (Paediat.) Guy's Hosp. Lond.

ROSENFELD, Peter Francis Foxcombe Orchard, Boars Hill, Oxford OX1 5JF — MB BS 1993 Lond.

ROSENFELD, Sabine (retired) 360 Brockley Road, Crofton Park, London SE4 2BY — MD 1930 Vienna. Prev: Obst. Regist. Greenbank Matern. Hosp. Darlington.

ROSENFELDER, Alan Frederick Brondesbury Medical Centre, 279 Kilburn High Road, London NW6 7JQ Tel: 020 7624 9853 Fax: 020 7372 3660 — MB BS Lond. 1981; BSc (Hons.) Lond. 1978; MRCGP 1985; DCH RCP Lond. 1984; DRCOG 1983. Socs: Primary Care Genetics Soc.

ROSENFELDER, Eileen 50 Hampstead Way, London NW11 7XX — MB BS 1985 Lond.; BSc Hist. of Med. Lond. 1982; MRCGP 1989; DCH RCP Lond. 1988; DRCOG 1988.

ROSENFIELD, Montague 50 West Drive, Birmingham B20 3SU Tel: 0121 554 4712 — MB BCh BAO 1928 Belf. (Belf.)

ROSENGARD, Leonard Alan Bridgeton Health Centre, 210 Abercromby Street, Glasgow G40 2DA Tel: 0141 531 6630 Fax: 0141 531 6626; 102 Hamilton Road, Rutherglen, Glasgow G73 3DS Tel: 0141 647 2800 Fax: 0141 647 2800 — MB ChB Glas. 1965; MFHOM 1991; MRCOG 1973. Princip. G. P. Prev: Regist. (O & G) E. Dist. Hosp. Glas.; SHO (Gyn.) Glas. Roy. Infirm.; SHO (Obst.) Roy. Matern. Hosp. Glas.

ROSENGREN, Helena 16 Rokeby Avenue, Bristol BS6 6EL — MB ChB 1989 Sheff.

ROSENTHAL, Adam Nicholas 167 Gloucester Avenue, London NW1 8LA — MB BS 1992 Lond.; BSc (Hons.) Physiol. Lond. 1990; DFFP 1997. (St. Mary's Hosp. Med. Sch. Lond.) Gyna. Oncol. Research Fell. St. Barth. Hosp. Lond. Prev: SHO (Genitourin. Med.) St. Mary's Hosp. Lond.; SHO (Obst.) Qu. Charlotte's Hosp. Lond.; SHO (Gyn.) Samarit. Hosp. for Wom. Lond.

ROSENTHAL, Diane The Surgery, 153 Park Road, London N8 8JJ Tel: 020 8340 7940 Fax: 020 8348 1530; 26 Gladwell Road, London N8 9AA — MB ChB 1977 Dundee; MRCGP 1982; DRCOG 1980. Prev: Doctor/Counsellor Lond. Youth Advisory Centre; Whittington Hosp. VTS Lond. 1978-81.

ROSENTHAL, Ferdinand David 17 Knighton Grange Road, Leicester LE2 2LF Tel: 0116 270 7797 Fax: 0116 270 8737 Email: david.rosenthal@virgin.net — MB BS Lond. 1945; MD Lond. 1952; LLB Leic. 1991; FRCP Lond. 1970, M 1948. (King's Coll. Hosp.) Emerit. Cons. Phys. Leicester Roy. Infirm., Leicester Gen. Hosp. & Hinckley Hosp. Socs: Soc. Endocrinol.; Med. Res. Soc.; Brit. Thyroid Assn. Prev: Sen. Regist. (Med.) Leicester Roy. Infirm.; Sen. Regist. (Med.) Roy. Infirm. Sheff.; Ho. Phys. King's Coll. Hosp.

ROSENTHAL, Jane Miranda 52 Holland Park Avenue, London W11 3QY — MB BS 1992 Lond.

ROSENTHAL, Jerrold Malcolm 263 Townsend Lane, Liverpool L13 9DG Tel: 0151 226 1358; 49 Rockburn Avenue, Liverpool L25 4TN — LRCPI & LM, LRSCI & LM 1957; LRCPI & LM, LRCSI & LM 1957.

ROSENTHAL, Jonathan Joseph The The Park Surgery, 153 Park Road, London N8 8JJ Tel: 020 8340 7940 Fax: 020 8348 1530; 57 Barrington Road, Crouch End, London N8 8QT Tel: 020 8342 9893 Fax: 020 8348 5426 — MB BCh 1986 Wales; MSc (Gen. Pract.) Lond. 1994; BSc (Hons.) Psychol. Wales 1981; FRCGP 1997, M 1990; DFFP 1994; DRCOG 1989. (Univ. of Wales Coll. of Med., Cardiff) Sen. Lect. (Gen. Pract.) Roy. Free & Univ. Coll. Med. Sch. Lond. - Princip. in Gen. Pract., Drs Greenbury; Course Organiser Roy. Free Hosp. VTS. Prev: Lect. (Gen. Pract.) Roy. Free Hosp. Sch. Med. Lond.; Trainee GP/SHO Guy's Hosp. Lond. VTS; Ho. Surg. Llandough Hosp. Cardiff.

ROSENTHAL, Keri Louise 2 The Linleys,, Weston, Bath BA1 2XE Tel: 01225484539 — MB BS 1994 Lond.; BSc Kings Coll. Lond. 1993; MRCGP 1998; DFFP 1998. (St Mary's Hospital) Asst. GP -.

ROSENTHAL, Mark Department of Paediatric Respiratory Medicine, Royal Brompton Hospital, Sydney St., London SW3 6NP Tel: 020 7351 8754 Fax: 020 7351 8763 Email: mark.rosenthal@virgin.net; 33 Methuen Park, London N10 2JR Tel: 020 8444 4123 — MB ChB 1981 Manch.; MB ChB (Hons.) (Distinc. Paediat. Surg. Pathol.) Manch. 1981; BSc (1st cl. Hons.) Pharmacol. Manch. 1978, MD 1994; MRCP (UK) 1984; Spec. Accredit. Paediat. JCHMT 1990; FRCPH 1997; FRCP 1999. (Manchester) Cons. Paediat. Respirat. Phys. Roy. Brompton Hosp. Lond. & Qu. Mary's Childr. Hosp. St Helier; Vis. Prof. (Paediat.) Univ. Odessa Ukraine. Socs: Brit. Paediat. Assn.; Brit. Thorac. Soc.; Eur. Respirat. Soc. Prev: Sen. Regist. (Paediat.) Univ. Coll. Hosp.

ROSENVINGE, Gerald Oliver (retired) 1 Slingsby Court, Cavendish Avenue, Harrogate HG2 8HX Tel: 01423 524666 — MB BS Durh. 1940. Prev: Med. Off. KnaresBoro. Hosp.

ROSENVINGE, Henry Paul Thornhill Unit, Moorgreen Hospital, West End, Southampton SO30 3JB Tel: 02380 475242 Fax: 02380 465014 — MB BS 1972 Lond.; FRCPsych 1991,M 1976. (King's Coll. Hosp.) Cons. (Psychogeriat.) Moorgreen Hosp. Soton. Prev: Sen. Regist. (Psychiat.) Newc. Gen. Hosp.; Intern Memor. Univ. Hosps. St. John's, Newfld.; Regist. (Psychiat.) Knowle Hosp. Fareham.

ROSEVEAR, Catherine Linden Hall Surgery, Newport TF10 7HU Tel: 01952 820400 Fax: 01952 825149; South View, The Rank, Gnosall, Stafford ST20 0BU — MB ChB 1981 Birm.; DRCOG 1985.

ROSEVEARE, Christopher David 20 Merrick Way, Valley Park, Eastleigh SO53 4QT; Apple Tree Cottage, 23 Rectory Lane, Woodstock OX20 1UF — BM 1991 Soton.; MRCP (UK) 1994. Consulltant Phys., Soton. Gen. Hosp. Socs: Treas., Soc. for Acute Med. UK. Prev: Specialist Regist. (Gen. Med. & Gastroenterol.) Qu. Alexandra Hosp., Portsmouth; Regist. (Gen. Med. & Gastroenterol.) Roy. Hants. Co. Hosp. Winchester; Regist. (Gastoenterol.) Roy. Bournemouth Hosp.

ROSEVEARE, Helen Margaret (retired) 12 Old Quay Court, Holywood BT18 0HT Tel: 01232 423514 — MB BChir 1951 Camb.; DTM & H Antwerp 1952. Prev: Med. Dir. Nebobongo Hosp., Zaire & Nyankunde Train. Sch. for Med.

ROSEVEARE

ROSEVEARE, Martin Peter Paxton Green Health Centre, 1 Alleyn Park, London SE21 8AU Tel: 020 8670 6878 Fax: 020 8766 7057; 62 Burbage Road, London SE24 9HE — MB 1966 Camb.; BChir 1965; FRCOG 1991; MRCOG 1970, DObst 1967. (Univ. Coll. Hosp.) Prev: Regist. (O & G) King Edwd. Memor. Hosp. Ealing; SHO Centr. Middlx. Hosp. Lond.; Ho. Off. Univ. Coll. Hosp. Lond.

ROSEWALL, Heidede Luise The Medical Centre, Lower Road, Cookham Rise, Maidenhead SL6 9HX Tel: 01628 524646 Fax: 01628 810201; Springfield, Hearns Lane, Gallowstree Common, Reading RG4 9DE Tel: 0118 972 1262 — MD 1966 Vienna; MRCS Eng. LRCP Lond. 1972. Socs: Assoc. Homoep. Soc.

ROSEWARNE, Helen Catherine 6 Beech Avenue, Worcester WR3 8PZ — MB BS 1993 Lond.

ROSEWARNE, Melvyn Douglas 6 Beech Avenue, Worcester WR3 8PZ — MB ChB 1963 Leeds; FRCR 1975; FFR 1972; DMRD Eng. 1970. Cons. Radiol. Worcester Roy. Infirm. NHS Trust. Prev: Sen. Regist. United Sheff. Hosps.; Instr. (Radiol.) Univ. Washington, USA.

ROSHAN, Mohamed 23 Jackson Close, Oadby, Leicester LE2 4SS Tel: 0116 270 7067; 23 Jackson Close, Oadby, Leicester LE2 4US — MB ChB 1984 Leic.; DPM 2000; BSc (Hons.) Leic. 1982; MRCP (UK) 1987; MRCGP 1990; DCH RCP Lond. 1992. Socs: RCGP; Leic. Med. Soc.

ROSIE, Henrietta Anne c/o Drive M. B. O'Neill, 25 Durham Road, Edinburgh EH15 1NY — MB ChB 1975 Sheff.

ROSIER, Nicholas Charles Ian De-Havilland Road, Wisbech PE13 3AN Tel: 01945 583133 Fax: 01945 464465 — MB BS 1978 Lond.; DRCOG 1983. (Middlx.) Prev: Maj. RAMC; Med. Off. Shape Belgium; Regtl. Med. Off. Qu.'s Own Hussars.

ROSIN, Louis Joseph, MBE (retired) The Coach House, Cypress Close, Blackwell, Darlington DL3 8QR Tel: 01325 467393 Fax: 01325 243413 Email: lousierosin@ntlworld.com — MB BS 1940 Durh.; MB BS (Hons.) Durh. 1940; MRCGP 1953. Med. Ref. Darlington Crematorium. Prev: RAMC.

ROSIN, Mr Michael David Department of Cardiothoracic Surgery, 3rd Floor, Walsgrave Hospital, Clifford Bridge Road, Walsgrave, Coventry CV2 2DX Tel: 02476 602020; 4 The Moat, Coventry Road, Berkswell, Coventry CV7 7AZ — MB ChB 1973 Sheff.; FRCS Ed. 1979. Cons. Cardiothoracic Surg. Walsgrave Hosp. Coventry.

ROSIN, Richard Allan c/o 15 Elm Grove, London N8 9AH — BM 1988 Soton. Prev: Regist. (Gen. Pract.) Saffron Walden; Chief Resid. (Psychiat.) Albert Einstein Coll. Med. Bronx, NY, USA.

ROSIN, Mr Richard David 80 Harley Street, London W1G 7HL Tel: 020 7631 3447 Fax: 020 7224 0645 Email: rdrosin@uk-consultants.co.uk; 4 Ledbury Mews, London W11 2AF Tel: 0207 7276331 — MB BS 1966 Lond.; MS Lond. 1977; FRCS Eng. 1972; FRCS Ed. 1971; MRCS Eng. LRCP Lond. 1966. (Westm.) p/t Cons. Surg. St. Mary's Hosp. Lond.; NW Thames RHA Surgic. Adviser to RCS Ed.; Examr. RCS Ed. & FRCS Intercollegiate; Mem.s of Counc. RCS 1994; Pres. BASO 2002-. Socs: Fell. Roy. Soc. Med. (Ex-Pres. Sect. Surg. Clin. Studies); Fell. (Mem. Counc.) Assn.Endoscopic Surgs. GB & Irel.; (Counc.) RCS Eng. Prev: Sen. Regist. (Surg.) W.m. Hosp. Lond.; Regist. (Surg.) St. Helier Hosp. Carshalton; Ho. Phys. Profess. Med. Unit & Ho. Surg. Profess. Surg. Unit W.m. Hosp. Lond.

ROSKELL, Derek Edward John Radcliffe Hospital, Headington, Oxford OX3 9DU — BM BCh 1991 Oxf.; MA Camb. 1992; BA Camb. 1988; BA Oxf. 1988; DRCPath 1996. Cons. John Radcliffe Hosp. Oxf.; Hon. Sen. Regist. Oxf. Radcliffe NHS Trust. Prev: Clin. Tutor (Path.) Nuffield Dept. Path. Univ. Oxf.

***ROSKELL, Helen Grace** 4C Perrin Street, Headington, Oxford OX3 7AS — BM BCh 1998 Oxf.; BM BCh Oxf 1998.

ROSKILLY, John Noel (retired) North View, Hawkins Lane, Rainow, Macclesfield SK10 5TL Tel: 01625 501014 — MB ChB 1958 Manch.; MRCGP 1968; DObst RCOG 1960.

ROSLING, Lesley Elizabeth Annette 95 Queens Road, Richmond TW10 6HF; 8 Gilmour Circle, Constantia, Capetown 7800, South Africa — MB BS 1984 Lond.; DCH RCP Lond. 1989; MRCGP 1996. SACLA health project. Prev: GP reg.Richmond; Reg.med.King Edwd. VII Hosp.

ROSOVSKE, Bernard Merton (retired) 14 Goldfields Avenue, Greetland, Halifax HX4 8LE — LRCPI & LM, LRSCI & LM 1955; LRCPI & LM, LRCSI & LM 1955. Prev: GP Halifax.

ROSS, Adrian Piers 2 St Austell Road, Blackheath, London SE13 7EQ — MB BS 1974 Lond.; MRCP (UK) 1980; DCH Eng. 1977.

ROSS, Mr Alasdair Hugh McLean Dept. of Surgery, Broomfield Hospital, Chelmsford CM1 7ET Tel: 01245 514094 Fax: 01245 514859 Email: hross30849@aol.com; Greenyards, Chelmsford Road, Felsted, Dunmow CM6 3ET — MB ChB 1973 Ed.; ChM Ed. 1985, MB ChB 1973; FRCS Ed. 1978; FRCS 1999. (Edinburgh) Cons. Surg. Chelmsford Hosp. Gp. Socs: Coun., Assn. of Surgs.; Assn. Coloproctol.; Brit. Assn. of Endocrine Surgs. Prev: Sen. Regist. (Surg.) St. Mark's Hosp. Lond.; Ho. Surg. & Regist. Rotat. (Surg.) Roy. Infirm. Edin.; Fell. (Surg.) Univ. Calif. Los Angeles, USA.

ROSS, Alexander 12 The Avenue, Charlton Kings, Cheltenham GL53 9BJ — MB BS 1993 Newc.

ROSS, Alice (retired) 10 West Forth Street, Cellardyke, Anstruther KY10 3HL — MB ChB 1923 Ed. Prev: Asst. MOH Hull & Huddersfield.

ROSS, Alison Wrexham Maelor Hospital, Croes Newydd Road, Wrexham LL13 7TD Tel: 01978 291100; Ochr Farm, Porch Lane, Caergwrle, Wrexham LL12 9HG Tel: 01978 760595 — MRCS Eng. LRCP Lond. 1965; MD Lond. 1972, MB BS (Hons.) 1965; FRCP Lond. 1984, M 1967. (Royal Free Hospital London) Cons. Phys. Wrexham Maelor Hosp.

ROSS, Alison Mary 21 Kintore Place, Rosemount, Aberdeen AB25 2TD — MB ChB 1995 Aberd.; BSc Med. Sci. Aberdeen 1994.

ROSS, Alison Myron Grampain University Hospitals Trust, Department of Anaesthesia, Foresterhill, Aberdeen AB25 2ZN Tel: 01224 681818; South Burnside, Kinella, Aberdeen AB21 0TG Tel: 01224 790255 — MB ChB 1981 Aberd. Prev: Regist. (Anaesth.) Aberd. Roy. Infirm.

ROSS, Mr Alistair Charles The Bath Clinic, Claverton Down Road, Bath BA2 7BR Tel: 01225 835555; Westcombe House, Combe Hay, Bath BA2 7EG Tel: 01225 836058 — MB BS 1976 Lond.; FRCS Eng. 1980; MRCS Eng. LRCP Lond. 1976. (Char. Cross) Cons. Orthop. Surg. Roy. United Hosp. Bath & Roy. Nat. Hosp. Rheum. Dis. Bath; Dir., Bath & Wessex Orthop. Research Unit; Hon. Sen. Lect. Sch. Postgrad. Med. Univ. Bath; John Charnley Tutor in Orthopaedic Surg., Roy. Coll. of Surg.s of Eng. Socs: Fell. Brit. Orthopaedic Assn.; Mem. Educat. Comm. BOA; Mem. Bd. Specialist Socs. Brit. Orthopaedic Assn. Prev: Sen. Regist. (Orthop.) St. Mary's Hosp. Paddington; Regist. (Surg.) Lond. Hosp.; Brit. Orthop. Assn. Europ. Trav. Schol. 1987.

ROSS, Alistair Kenneth, MBE (retired) 30 Leys Drive, Newcastle ST5 3JG Tel: 01782 614945 — MB ChB 1949 Glas.; FRCGP 1974, M 1963. Prev: Med. Ref. Benefits Agency Med. Serv. DSS.

ROSS, Allan (retired) 5 Maywood Close, Beckenham Place Park, Beckenham BR3 5BW Tel: 020 8650 1647 — MRCS Eng. LRCP Lond. 1951; BDS Lond. 1941; LMSSA Lond. 1951; LDS RCS Eng. 1941. Prev: Lt.-Col. RAMC (TA).

ROSS, Allison Mabel Cherryvalley Health Centre, Kings Square, Belfast BT5 7BP Tel: 028 9040 1744 Fax: 028 9040 2069; 27 Fort Road, Ballylesson, Belfast BT8 8LX — MB BCh BAO 1981 Belf.; MRCGP 1986; DCH RCSI 1985; DRCOG 1985. Socs: BMA & Med. Wom. Federat.

ROSS, Amanda Joy The Lennard Surgery, 1-3 Lewis Road, Bishopsworth, Bristol BS13 7JD Tel: 0117 964 0900 Fax: 0117 987 3227 — MB ChB 1992 Bristol; MRCGP 1996; DFFP 1995; DRCOG 1995. (Bristol University) GP Princip. The Lennard Surg. Bristol. Prev: GP/Regist. Frenchay Hosp. Bristol VTS.

ROSS, Andrew Gordon 58 Arkaig Drive, Crossford, Dunfermline KY12 8YW — MB ChB 1992 Ed.

ROSS, Andrew Isdale Daiglen, 8 Mavisbank, Gallowhill Wood, Kinross KY13 8QR Tel: 01577 63803 — MB ChB 1952 Ed. (Ed.) Prev: Ho. Phys. & Ho. Surg. St. Luke's Hosp. Bradford; Ho. Surg. (O & G) St. Luke's Matern. Hosp. Bradford.

ROSS, Andrew Mackenzie (retired) Cherry Tree Cottage, Nether Compton, Sherborne DT9 4QG Tel: 01935 812766 — MD 1937 Ed.; MB ChB 1924; DLO Eng. 1928. Prev: Otorhinolaryngol. Bournemouth & E. Dorset Hosp. Gp.

ROSS, Andrew Munro Northfield Health Centre, 15 St. Heliers Road, Northfield, Birmingham B31 1QT Tel: 0121 478 1850 Fax: 0121 476 0931 — FRCGP 1999; BMedSci. Nottm. 1979, BM BS 1981; MRCGP 1985; DRCOG 1984; DCH RCP Lond. 1983; M Med

ROSS

Sci. 1996. (Nottm.) Partner GP; Research Fell. RCGP. Prev: Trainee GP Rugby VTS.

ROSS, Angus Malcolm Rokeby Villa, The Lendings, Barnard Castle DL12 9AB — MB BS 1994 Newc.

ROSS, Annabel Edith Merton Sutton & Wandsworth Health Authority, Cranmer Road, Mitcham CR4 4TP Tel: 020 8648 3021; 76 Graham Road, Wimbledon, London SW19 3SS Tel: 020 8540 4755 — MB BS 1983 Lond.; MA Camb. 1984; MFPHM RCP (UK) 1996; MRCGP 1989; DRCOG 1987. (Camb. & Roy. Free Hosp.) Cons. (Pub. Health) Merton Sutton & Wandsworth HA; Hon. Sen. Lect. (Publ. Health) St. Geos. Hosp. Med. Sch. Prev: SHO St. Mary's Hospice Birm.; Trainee GP W. Suff. HA; SHO (Med.) Roy. Lancaster Infirm.

ROSS, Anne Elizabeth West Berkshire Occupational Health, 21 Craven Road, Reading RG1 5LE Tel: 01734 877634 Fax: 01734 878778; Balnagowan, Berrick Salome, Wallingford OX10 6JQ Tel: 01865 890047 — MB ChB 1965 Manch.; MSc (Occupat. Med.) Lond. 1985; FRCP Lond. 1996, M 1971; FFOM RCP Lond. 1994, MFOM 1989, AFOM 1985; DObst RCOG 1967. (Manch.) Cons. Occupat. Health Phys. & Specialist (Gen. & Thoracic Med.) Roy. Berks. & Battle NHS Trust. Socs: Soc. Occupat. Med.; Brit. Thorac. Soc. Prev: Sen. Regist. (Gen. & Thoracic Med.) Battle Hosp. Reading; Regist. (Chest Dis. & Cardiol.) Baguley Hosp. Manch.; Regist. (Gen. Med.) Pk. Hosp. Davyhulme.

ROSS, Ardyn Mirande Tufnell Park Road Surgery, 244 Tufnell Park Roa, London N19 5EW Tel: 020 7272 9105 Fax: 020 7272 8996 — MB BS 1992 Lond.; BSc (Hons.) Lond. 1989; DRCOG 1995; DCH RCP Lond. 1994. (Univ. Coll. Lond.) Prev: Trainee GP Univ. Coll. Hosp. Lond. VTS.

ROSS, Arthur 3 Russell House, Eamont St., St John's Wood, London NW8 7DD Tel: 020 7722 6746 Fax: 020 7722 6746 — MB BCh BAO 1950 Dub. (Dub.) Prev: Mem. Lambeth, Lewisham & S.wark LMC; Clin. Asst. (ENT) St. Bart. Hosp. Lond.; Cas. Off. Hampstead Gen. Hosp.

ROSS, Audrey (retired) 4 The Redlands, Laundry Lane, Shrewsbury SY2 6ER Tel: 01743 356651 — MB ChB 1952 Manch.

ROSS, Mr Barry Alan, TD (retired) 8 The Crescent, Chapel Field, Norwich NR2 1SA Tel: 01603 623571 Fax: 01603 767851 Email: bross52593@aol.com — MB BS Lond. 1958; FRCS Eng. 1963; MRCS Eng. LRCP Lond. 1958. Cons. Thoracic Surg. E. Anglian RHA; Lt. Col. Cons. Surg. 257 Gen. Hosp. RAMC (V). Prev: Sen. Regist. (Thoracic Surg.) Guy's Hosp. Lond.

ROSS, Ben The Meadows Surgery, Temple Grove, Gatehouse Lane, Sussex Way, Burgess Hill RH15 9XH — MB BCh 1952 Belfast; MB BCh Belf.1952. (Belfast) GP Burgess Hill, W. Sussex.

ROSS, Mr Brian David Glebe Cottage, Bell Lane, Cassington, Oxford OX29 4DS Tel: 01865 880629; 1291 Meadowbrook Road, Altadena CA 91001, USA Tel: 818 794 2004 — MB BS 1961 Lond.; DPhil Oxf. 1966; FRCS Lond. 1973; FRCPath 1989, M 1976. Dir. Magnetic Resonance Spectroscopy Unit Huntington Med. Research Inst. Pasadena Calif., USA; Vis. Assoc. Calif. Inst. Technol.. Prev: Hon. Cons. Clin. Spectroscopy (N.M.R.) Roy. Postgrad. Med. Sch. Lond.; Cons. Chem. Path. Radcliffe Infirm. Oxf.; Univ. Lect. Metab. Med. Nuffield Dept. Med. Oxf.

ROSS, Bryan Alderley, 24 Canterbury Crescent, Fulwood, Sheffield S10 4JD — MD (Commend.) Sheff. 1964, MB ChB (Hnrs.) 1959; FRCR 1975; FFR 1971; DMRD Eng. 1969. (Sheff.) Cons. in Radiol. Centr. Sheff. Univ. Hosps. (NHS Trust); Hon. Clin. Lect. in Radiol. Univ. Sheff. Socs: BMA; Brit. Inst. Radiol. Prev: MRC Research Asst. Profess. Surg. Unit. Roy. Infirm. Sheff.; Lect. in Physiol. Univ. Sheff.

ROSS, Callum Chalmers Yarra, Ettrickbridge, Selkirk TD7 5JN — MB ChB 1997 Aberd.

ROSS, Calum Neil 44 Colney Lane, Norwich NR4 7RF — MB ChB 1983 Sheff.; PhD 1996; MRCP (UK) 1986.

ROSS, Caroline Paediatric Neurology, Leicester Royal Infirmary, Leicester LE1 5WW Tel: 0116 254 1414 — MB ChB 1988 Manch.; MSc (Paediatrics) University of Birmingham 1998; BSc (Med. Sci.) St. And. 1985; MRCP (UK) 1995. Cons. Paediatric NeUrol., Leicester Univ. Hosps. Trust, Leicester. Socs: Brit. Paediatric Neurol. Assn.; Europ. Paediatric Neurol. Soc.; Roy. Coll. of Paediat. and Child Health. Prev: Trainee GP/SHO & Clin. Med. Off. Tameside Gen. Hosp.; SHO (Paediat.) Roy. Preston Hosp.; Regist. (Paediat.) Walsgrave Hosp. Coventry.

ROSS, Catherine Mary June Balvicar Centre, 46 Balvicar St., Glasgow G42 8QU Tel: 0141 423 8898/9; 5 Queensberry Avenue, Bearsden, Glasgow G61 3LR Tel: 0141 942 2238 Fax: 0141 942 2238 — MB ChB 1962 Glas.; DCH RCPS Glas. 1964. (Glas.) Cons. Paediat. (Community Child Health) Yorkhill Trust Glas. Socs: Brit. Paediat. Assn.; (Ex-Chairm.) Scott. Assn. for Community Child Health; Brit. Assn. Community Drs in Audiol. Prev: SCMO & Clin. Co-ordinator Dumbarton Sect. Argyll Clyde HB.

ROSS, Cathmar MacIver 10 Achany Road, Dingwall IV15 9JB — MB ChB 1986 Aberd. SHO (Anaesth.) Law Hosp. Carluke.

ROSS, Catriona Stirling Kirkwood 26 Barony Street, Edinburgh EH3 6NY Tel: 0131 556 6511 Email: cskross@hotmail.com — MB ChB 1992 Aberd.; BMedBiol Aberd. 1989; MRCP (UK) 1995. Specialist Regist., Palliat. Med., S.E. Socotland Rotat. Prev: Specialist Regist. Palliat. Med. N. Thames Rotat.

ROSS, Charles Duffin Bank House, Salter St., Stafford ST16 2JU Tel: 01785 4348 — MD 1948 Belf.; MB BCh BAO 1939. (Belf.) Socs: BMA. Prev: Squadron Ldr. RAFVR Med. Br.; Res. Med. Off. Belf. City Hosp.; Res. Obstetr. Jubilee Matern. Hosp.

ROSS, Christine Elsie Mancunial Community NHS Trust, Wythershawe Health Care Centre, 1 Stancliffe Road, Shaiston, Manchester M20 2WG; 196 Palatine Road, Didsbury, Manchester M20 8UF — MB ChB 1971 St. And. Staff Grade Paediat., Mancunial Community NHS Trust.

ROSS, Colin Malcolm Douglas (retired) 17 Litchden St, Barnstaple EX32 8ND — MB ChB 1955 Ed.; FRCPath 1978.

ROSS, Colleen Margaret 11 Grantley Gardens, Shawlands, Glasgow G41 3PY — MB ChB 1994 Aberd.

ROSS, Constance Anne Cameron (retired) 67 Munro Road, Glasgow G13 1SL Tel: 0141 959 4919 — MB ChB 1942 Glas.; MD Glas. 1946; FRCPath 1976, M 1964. Prev: Cons. Virol. Regional Virus Laborat. Ruchill Hosp. Glas.

ROSS, David 32 Montacute Road, Lewes BN7 1EN — BM BCh 1990 Oxf.

ROSS, David Andrew, Lt.-Col. RAMC BFG Health Service, Wegberg BFPO 40 Tel: 0049 2161 908 2320 Fax: 0049 2161 908 2420; 37A The Mall, Faversham ME13 8JN Email: doctulse@compuserve.com — MB BS 1985 Lond.; MFPHM 2001; DFFP 2000; MSc (Community Paediat.) Lond 1996; DCCH Ed. 1996; DFPHM 1998. (St Bartholomews Hosp.) Chief Med., UKSC(G). Socs: BMA; Fell. Roy. Soc. Med. Prev: Regist. (Community Paediat.) Brit. Milit. Hosp. Rinteln; SHO (Paediat.) P.ss Margt. Hosp. Swindon; SHO (Gen. Med.) Brit. Milit. Hosp. Munster & Iserlohn.

ROSS, David Anthony Department of Epidemiology & Population Sciences, London School of Hygiene & Tropical Medicine, Keppel St., London WC1E 7HT Tel: 020 7927 2003 Fax: 020 7637 1173 Email: dross@lshtm.ac.uk — BM BCh 1980 Oxf.; MSc Oxf. 1980, MA 1980, BA 1976. Sen. Lect. (Epidemiol.) Lond. Sch. Hyg. & Trop. Med. Socs: Internat. Epidemiol. Assn.; Roy. Soc. Trop. Med. & Hyg. Prev: Lect. (Epidemiol.) Lond. Sch. Hyg. & Trop. Med.; Research Fell. (Epidemiol.) Eval. & Plann. Centre for Health Care Lond. Sch. Hyg. & Trop. Med.; MRC Research Project Grantholder Trop. Med. Oxf. Univ.

ROSS, David George 13A Linden Road, Gosforth, Newcastle upon Tyne NE3 4EY — MB ChB 1997 Manch.

ROSS, Mr David John Consultant Orthopaedic Surgeon, Stirling Royal Infirmary, Stirling FK8 2AU — MB ChB 1973 Glas.; FRCS Ed. 1979. Cons. Orthop. Surg. Stirling Roy. Infirm. Socs: Brit. Orthop. Assn.; Brit. Soc. Surg. Hand.

ROSS, David John St Richards' Hospital, Chichester PO19 4SE Tel: 01243 831728 Fax: 01243 831613 Email: david@boross.fsnet.co.uk — MB BS 1985 Lond.; MSc (Epidemiology) Lond. 1994; MA (Cantab.) 1999; MRCP (UK) 1990. Cons. Phys. Chest Med. St. Richards Hosp., Chichester.

ROSS, David Neilson 21 East Stratton Close, Bracknell RG12 0XY — MD 1948 Glas.; MB ChB 1940; FRFPS Glas. 1947; FRCP Glas. 1970, M 1962. (Univ. Glas.) Prev: Phys. in Admin. Charge Dept. Geriat. Med. W.. Infirm. Glas.; Hon. Lect. Geriat. Med. Univ. Glas.; Cons. Phys. Plymouth Gen. Hosp.

ROSS, David Sloan (retired) Woodlands, 26 Kings Crescent, Elderslie, Johnstone PA5 9AA Tel: 01505 322832 — MB ChB 1956 Glas.; MFPHM RCP (UK) 1989; MFCM RCP (UK) 1979; MFOM RCP Lond. 1978; MFOM RCPI 1977; T(PHM) 1989; T(OM) 1989; DIH

ROSS

Eng. 1961; DPH Manch. 1960. Prev: Cons. Pub. Health Med. Argyll & Clyde HB.

ROSS, David Walter (retired) The Surgery, School Hill House, High Street, Lewes BN7 2LU — MB BS 1956 Lond.; BSc (1st cl. Hons. Physiol.) Lond. 1956; MRCS Eng. LRCP Lond. 1959; DObst RCOG 1961. Staff Vict. Hosp. Lewes. Prev: Resid. Med. Off. & Resid. Obst. Asst. St. Geo. Hosp. Lond.

ROSS, Donald (retired) 5 Riding Close, Hatchelwood Park, Bessacarr, Doncaster DN4 6UZ Tel: 01302 535247 — MB ChB 1951 Glas.

ROSS, Donald (retired) Overcombe, Lewis Lane, Chalfont St Peter, Gerrards Cross SL9 9TS Tel: 0128 13 83091 — LRCP LRCS 1927 Ed.; LRCP LRCS Ed. LRFPS Glas. 1927. Prev: Med. Off. Hoover Ltd. Perivale.

ROSS, Donald Ewen, Wing Cdr. Directorate Health Services, HQ Personnel and Training Command, RAF Innsworth GL3 1EZ Tel: 01452 712612 Ext: 5812 Email: flugharzt@luftschloss.freeserve.co.uk; Flat 4, 28 Larusdown Cresent, Cheltenham GL50 2LF Email: flugarzt@luftschloss.freeserve.co.uk — MB ChB 1986 Aberd.; DCH 1990 RCPS Glas. Command Flight Med. Official Roy. Air Force. Socs: Mem. of Aerospace Med. Assn. Prev: SMO RAF Lossiemouth; SMO RAF Sek Hong; SMO RAF Locking.

ROSS, Donald George North Burnside Croft, Clinterty, Kinellar, Aberdeen AB21 0TG — MB ChB 1967 Aberd.; FFA RCS Eng. 1973. (Aberd.) Cons. Anaesth. Grampian Health Bd.

ROSS, Donald Ian, Col. late RAMC Retd. 28 Pinewood Place, Aberdeen AB15 8LT Tel: 01224 312905 — MB ChB 1955 Aberd. (Aberd.) Prev: Ho. Phys. (Glenburn Wing) & Ho. Surg. (Thoracic Surg.) Woodend Gen. Hosp. Aberd.; SHO (Anaesth.) W.. Infirm. Glas.

ROSS, Mr Donald Nixon 25 Upper Wimpole Street, London W1G 6NF Tel: 020 7935 8805 Fax: 020 7935 9190 Email: dnixonross@msn.com; 35 Cumberland Terrace, Regents Park, London NW1 4HP Tel: 020 7935 0756 — MB ChB 1946 Cape Town; Hon. DSc Cape Town 1982, BSc, MB ChB 1946; FRCS Eng. 1949; Hon. FRCS Thailand 1987; Hon. FRCSI 1984; FACS 1976; FACC 1973; Hon. FACS 1993. (Cape Town) Cons. Emerit. Card. Surg. Middlx. Hosp. Lond.; Cons. Emerit. Thoracic Surg. Guy's Hosp. Lond. Socs: (Ex-Pres.) Soc. Thoracic Surgs. & Soc. & Assocs. Thoracic Surgs.; Hon Mem. RSM. Prev: Sen. Surg. Nat. Heart Hosp. Lond.; Dir. Dept. Surg. Inst. Cardiol. Lond.; Cardiovasc. Research Fell. & Sen. Regist. Thoracic Surg. Guy's Hosp. Lond.

ROSS, Donovan Library House Surgery, Avondale Road, Chorley PR7 2AD Tel: 01257 262081 Fax: 01257 232114; Rose Hill, Leyland Lane, Ulnes Walton, Leyland, Preston PR26 8LB Tel: 01257 450182 Email: donovan@govho.demon.co.uk — MB ChB 1972 Liverp.; MRCGP 1979; DRCOG 1977. Socs: Brit. Med. Acupunct. Soc. Prev: Med. Off. RAF.

ROSS, Mr Edward Raymond Smith Hope Hospital, Eccles Old Road, Salford M6 8HD — MB ChB 1971 St. And.; FRCS Ed. 1976; FRACS 1983. Cons. Orthop. Surg. Hope Hosp. Manch.; Hon. Asst. Lect. Univ. Manch. Prev: Flight Lt. RAF Med. Br.; Sen. Regist. (Orthop.) Robt. Jones & Agnes Hunt Orthop. Hosp. OsW.ry.

ROSS, Elaine Margaret 53 Denoon Terrace, Dundee DD2 2EB — MB ChB 1987 Dundee.

ROSS, Elizabeth Jane Walker 'Eredine', Todlaw Road, Duns TD11 3EW — MB ChB 1970 Glas.

ROSS, Emma Caroline 24 Thornfield Road, London W12 8JG — MB BS 1992 Lond.; BSc (Hons.) Psychol. 1989; MRCP (UK) 1996. (Char. Cross & Westm.) SHO (Neurol. & Neurosurg.) Gt. Ormond St. Hosp. Lond.

ROSS, Eric Buchanan The Pightle, 6 Thornlea, Hepscott, Morpeth NE61 6NY Tel: 01670 57558 — MB ChB 1943 Ed.; MRCGP 1973. (Univ. Ed.) Prev: Ho. Surg. Perth Roy. Infirm.; Ho. Phys. Chalmers' Hosp. Edin.

ROSS, Eric John 47 Campden Street, London W8 7ET Tel: 020 7729 2122 — MB BS Lond. 1951; BSc, PhD Lond., MD 1958; FRCP Lond. 1966, M 1955; MRCS Eng. LRCP Lond. 1951. (Univ. Coll. Hosp.) Prev: Emerit. Prof. Endocrinol. & Hon. Research Fell. Univ. Coll. Med. Sch. Lond.; Cons. Phys. Univ. Coll. Hosp. Lond.; Dir. Metabol. Unit Peter Bent Brigham Hosp. Boston, Mass.

ROSS, Ernest, AE 34 Elmfield Road, Gosforth, Newcastle upon Tyne NE3 4BA Tel: 0191 285 4107 — MB BS 1958 Durh. (Durh.) Med. Mem. Indep. Tribunal Serv. Prev: SHO P.ss Margt. Rose Orthop. Hosp. Edin.; Regist. (Orthop.) Leicester Roy. Infirm.; Ho. Surg. (Orthop.) Roy. Vict. Infirm. Newc.

ROSS, Esther Stuart (retired) 15 Mount Avenue, Bare, Morecambe LA4 6DJ — MB ChB 1963 Glas.; FRCPsych 1993, M 1973; DPM Ed. & Glas. 1967. Prev: Cons. Psychiat. Preston HA.

ROSS, Professor Euan MacDonald Department of Community Paediatrics, King's College London, Mary Sheridan Centre, 405 Kennington Road, London SE11 4QW Tel: 020 7587 0610 Fax: 020 7582 9341 Email: euan.ross@kcl.ac.uk; Linklater House, Mount Pk Road, Harrow HA1 3JZ Tel: 020 8864 4746 Fax: 020 8864 4746 — MB ChB Bristol 1962; MD Bristol 1975; FRCP Lond. 1980; MRCP (UK) 1971; FRCPCH 1997; Hon. FFPHM RCP (UK) 1997; DCH RCPS Glas. 1965. (Bristol) Prof. Community Paediat. & Hon. Cons. Community Paediat. King's Coll. Univ. Lond.; Cons. Comm. Health. S. Lond. NHS; Cons. KCH Lond. Socs: Brit. Paediat. Neurol. Assn.; Brit. Assn. Community Child Health; Brit. Neuro Psych. Assn. Prev: Cons Paediat. & Hon. Sen. Lect. Char. Cross & W.m. Med. Sch. Lond.; Cons. Sen. Lect. St. Mary's Hosp. Med. Sch., Middlx. Hosp. Med. Sch. & Centr. Middlx. Hosp. Lond.; Lect. (Child Health) Univ. Bristol.

ROSS, Ewen Thomas 17 North Square, Aberdeen AB11 5DX — MB ChB 1992 Ed.

ROSS, Felicity Anne Craig End, Kincraig Drive, Sevenoaks TN13 3BB; Flat 3, 1 Salisbury Road, Hove BN3 3AB — MB BS 1992 Lond.; MRCGP 1997; DRCOG 1996.

ROSS, Fiona Kathlyn 14 Upper Stoneborough Lane, Budleigh Salterton EX9 6SX — MB ChB 1985 Birm.; MRCGP 1994; DRCOG 1988.

ROSS, Frances Mary Harrold Medical Practice, Peach's Close, Harrold, Bedford MK43 7DX Tel: 01234 720225 Fax: 01234 720603; 17 Brook Lane, Harrold, Bedford MK43 7BW — MB ChB 1982 Ed.; MRCGP 1988; DRCOG 1985.

ROSS, Frances Mary Hunter 6 Saxe-Coburg Place, Edinburgh EH3 5BR — MRCS Eng. LRCP Lond. 1975.

ROSS, Geoffrey George 58 St Benets Road, Prittlewell, Southend-on-Sea SS2 6LF — BM 1986 Soton.; BA Sheff. 1980; MRCGP 1991. Pharmaceut. Phys. Horsham.

ROSS, Geoffrey McEwen John Brogan and Partners, The O'Connel Street Medical Centre, 6 O'Connell Street, Hawick TD9 9HU Tel: 01450 372276 Fax: 01450 371564; Ravenswood, 3 West Stewart Place, Hawick TD9 8BH — MB ChB 1976 Aberd.; MRCGP 1980; DRCOG 1979. (Aberd.)

ROSS, George (retired) Ingfield House, 57 Northgate, Almondbury, Huddersfield HD5 8RY Tel: 01484 21391 — MB BCh BAO 1940 Belf. Prev: Mem. (Ex-Pres.) W. Riding Irish Med. Soc. Mem. BMA (Chairm. Huddersfield Div.).

ROSS, George Allen Wood Selworthy, 65 Roebuck Lane, Buckhurst Hill IG9 5QX — MB BChir 1968 Camb.; MA, MB BChir Camb. 1968; DObst RCOG 1970.

ROSS, George Innes MacDonald (retired) 25 York Road, Weybridge KT13 9DY Tel: 01932 844428 — MB ChB 1942 Aberd.; FRCPath 1966, M 1963; DCP Lond 1948. Prev: Cons. Path. Ashford Hosp. Middlx.

ROSS, Gillian Margaret 30 Wingrave Road, London W6 9HF — BM 1979 Soton.; MRCP (UK) 1992.

ROSS, Gordon Buchan 4 The Redlands, Laundry Lane, Shrewsbury SY2 6ER Tel: 01743 356651 — MB ChB 1951 Manch. (Manch.)

ROSS, Greta Primary Care Services, South Block, Louth County Hospital, Louth LN11 0EU Tel: 01507 600100; 54 St Mary's Lane, Louth LN11 0DT Tel: 01507 605232 Fax: 01507 602544 Email: gretaross@cs.com — MB BS Sydney 1965; MRCGP Lond. 1977; DCH RCP Glas. 1972. SCMO (Sexual Health & Family Plann. Train.).

ROSS, Harold Stormont (retired) 34 Earlswells Road, Cults, Aberdeen AB15 9NY Tel: 01224 867761 — MB ChB St. And. 1952; FRCPsych 1975, M 1971.

ROSS, Harriet Jeanette Melville (retired) Huntersmoon, 50 Pentland Terrace, Edinburgh EH10 6HE Tel: 0131 447 4559 — MB ChB 1942 Ed. Community Med. Off. Lothian Health Bd. & Family Plann. Assn.

ROSS, Mr Harvey Burton, RD (retired) Springvale, Brewery Common, Mortimer, Reading RG7 3JE Tel: 01189 332374 — MB BS 1952 Lond.; MS Lond. 1966, MB BS 1952; FRCS Eng. 1957. Prev: Surg. Roy. Berks. Hosp. Reading.

ROSS

ROSS, Hector John Taylor (retired) 47 Park Road, West Hagley, Stourbridge DY9 0QQ Tel: 01562 882039 — LRCP LRCS Ed. LRFPS Glas. 1935; FRCP Ed. 1968, M 1947. Hon. Cons. Phys. E. Birm. Hosp. Prev: Med. Supt. Chest Br. E. Birm. Hosp.

ROSS, Helen Grant (retired) 1 Springfields, Hillside, Follifoot, Harrogate HG3 1EF Tel: 01423 870465 — MB ChB 1954 St. And.; FRCPath 1984, M 1972; T(Path) 1991; Dip Bact . Lond. 1969; DTM & H Liverp. 1966. Prev: Cons. Bact. Pub. Health Laborat. Seacroft Hosp. Leeds.

ROSS, Iain Sutherland Clinical Biochemistry Department, Aberdeen Royal Infirmary, Aberdeen AB25 2ZD Tel: 01224 681818 Fax: 01224 694378 — MB ChB 1964 Aberd.; PhD Aberd. 1970, MB ChB 1964. (Aberd.) Cons. i/c Dept. Clin. Biochem. Grampian HB; Clin. Sen. Lect. & Head (Clin. Biochem.) Univ. Aberd.; Dir. of Laborat. Med. Aberd. Roy. Hosps. Trust. Socs: Roy. Soc. Med. (Lond. Br.). Prev: Ho. Off. Woodend Gen. Hosp. Aberd. & Aberd. City Hosp.

ROSS, Ian (retired) 12 Anderson Drive, Aberdeen AB15 4TY Tel: 01224 314716 — MB ChB 1955 Aberd.; MRCGP 1976. Prev: GP Aberd.

ROSS, Ian Hugh Barnard Castle Surgery, Victoria Road, Barnard Castle DL12 8HT Tel: 01833 690707 — MRCS Eng. LRCP Lond. 1968; BDS Durham. 1963; MRCS Eng. LRCP Lond. 1968 FDS RCS Eng. 1968; MRCGP 1994; DObst RCOG 1971. (Roy. Free) Socs: BMA. Prev: Regist. (Oral Surg.) E.man Dent. Hosp. Lond.; SHO (O & G) Darlington Memor. Hosp.; Ho. Phys. Friarage Hosp. N.allerton.

ROSS, Ian Nicholas Willowbrook Cottage, Westborough, Newark NG23 5HQ Tel: 01400 281188 Email: inross@ukgateway.net — MB BS 1972 Lond.; PhD Birm. 1980, MSc 1977; FRCP Lond. 1992; MRCP (UK) 1974; MRCS Eng. LRCP Lond. 1972. (Roy. Free Hosp. Lond.) Cons. Phys. & Gastroenterol. Newark Hosp., Grantham & Dist. Hosp. Socs: Brit. Soc. Gastroenterol.; BMA. Prev: Assoc. Prof. (Med.) Univ. Sains Malaysia, Malaysia; Lect. (Med.) Univ. Manch.; Wellcome Clin. Research Fell. Univ. Birm.

ROSS, Ian Ronald Francis Rose Garden Medical Centre, 4 Mill Lane, Edinburgh EH6 6TL Tel: 0131 554 1274 Fax: 0131 555 2159; 19A Mayfield Terrace, Edinburgh EH9 1RY Tel: 0131 667 8479 — MB ChB 1970 Ed. Med. Off. Gen. Counc. Brit. Shipping, Leith; Med. Adviser Craig & Rose Paint Co.

ROSS, Irene Rayner Portland House Surgery, 75 Mornington Road, Greenford UB6 9HN Tel: 020 8578 1730 — MB ChB 1963 Leeds. (Leeds) Trainer (Gen. Pract.) Greenford Middlx. Socs: BMA. Prev: Med. Off. Lond. Boro. Ealing; SHO Claybury Hosp. Woodford Green; SHO Roy. Childr. Hosp. Melbourne.

ROSS, Jacqueline Axford 11 Petts Wood Road, Orpington BR5 1JT — MB BS 1992 Lond.

ROSS, Mr James Alexander, MBE (retired) 5 Newbattle Terrace, Edinburgh EH10 4RU Tel: 0131 447 2292 — MD 1947 Ed.; MD (Commend. For Thesis) Ed. 1947, MB ChB 1934; FRCS Ed. 1938; FRCS Glas. 1965; Hon. FDS RCS Ed. 1983; Hon. FRCSI 1976; Hon. FRACS 1977. Prev: Pres. RCS Ed.

ROSS, James Douglas The Health Centre, Victoria Road, Leven KY8 4ET Tel: 01333 425656 Fax: 01333 422249; Staneforth, 72 Leven Road, Lundin Links, Leven KY8 6AJ — MB ChB 1977 Aberd.; MRCGP 1982; DRCOG 1980.

ROSS, Sir James Keith, Bt, RD Moonhills Gate, Exbury Road, Hilltop, Beaulieu, Brockenhurst SO42 7YS Tel: 01590 612104; Moonhills Gate, Exbury Road, Hilltop, Beaulieu, Brockenhurst SO42 7YS Tel: 01590 612104 — MB BS Lond. 1950; MS Lond. 1965; FRCS Ed. 1989; FRCS Eng. 1956. (Middlx.) Socs: Fell. Roy. Soc. Med.; (Ex-Pres.) Soc. Cardiothoracic Surgs.; Med. Art Soc. Prev: Emerit. Cons. Surg. Soton. & SW Hants. HA; Cons. Cardiac Surg. Wessex HA, S.ampton; Cons. Cardiac Surg. King. Edwd. VII Hosp. Midhurst & Nat. Heart Hosp.

ROSS, James Roy Young 10 Weston Way, Weston Favell, Northampton NN3 3BL — MB BS 1972 Lond.; BSc Lond. 1969, MB BS 1972; MRCP (U.K.) 1975; MRCPath 1980. (St. Geo.) Cons. Haemat. N.ampton Gen. Hosp. Prev: Sen. Regist. (Haemat.) Childr. Hosp. Birm. SHO (Med.) N. Staffs.; Health Dist.; Ho. Phys. & Ho. Surg. Roy. S. Hants. Hosp. Soton.

ROSS, James William Buchan, Surg. Lt. RN St Budeaux Health Centre, Stirling Road, St. Budeaux, Plymouth PL5 1PL Tel: 01752 361010 Fax: 01752 350675 — MB ChB 1988 Aberd. Trainee GP/SHO Roy. Navy Med. Off.

ROSS, Jean Occupational Health Department, Northwick Park Hospital, Watford Road, Harrow HA1 3UJ Tel: 020 8869 2583 Fax: 020 8869 2599; Linklater House, Mount Pk Road, Harrow on the Hill, Harrow HA1 3JZ Tel: 020 8864 4746 Fax: 020 8864 4746 — MSc Occupat. Med. Lond. 1983; MB ChB St. And. 1963; MFOM RCP 1990; DObst RCOG 1965; FFOM 1997. (St. And.) Cons. in Occupat. Med. N. W. Lond. Hosp. NHS Trust; Cons. In Occupat.. Med. To PHLS Colindale, Lond. Boro. of Harrow, Univ. of W.minster, Harrow and Hillingdon Healthcatre NHS Trust. Socs: Soc. Occupat. Med.; Assn. Local Auth. Med. Advisers; Assn. NHS Occupat. Health Phys. Prev: Occupat. Health Phys. Unilever Lond.; Mem. Scientif. Staff (Perinatal Med.) & Clin. Asst. Clin. Research Centre N.wick Pk. Hosp.; Med. Off. Community Health Depts. Dundee & Bristol.

ROSS, Jean Ruth Williamina (retired) 17 St Joseph's Vale, Blackheath, London SE3 OXF Tel: 020 8463 0725 — BSc Ed. 1946, MB ChB 1947. Prev: Sen. Lect. (Anat.) Char. Cross Hosp. Med. Sch. Lond..

ROSS, Jerard 22 Culloden Road, Balloch, Inverness IV2 7HQ — MB ChB 1994 Aberd.

***ROSS, Jeremy Lionel** 7 Woodsyre, Sydenham Hill, London SE26 6SS Tel: 020 8670 3810 Email: jemross@yahoo.com — MB BS 1997 Lond.

ROSS, Joan Ramsay 31 Birkhill Road, Stirling FK7 9LA — MB ChB 1973 Glas.; Dip. Forens. Med. Glas 1996.

ROSS, John Alexander Strachan Department Environmental & Occupational Medicine, University of Aberdeen, Ashgrove Road W., Aberdeen AB25 2ZD Tel: 01224 681818 Fax: 01224 662990 — MB ChB 1973 Aberd.; PhD Lond. 1986; FFA RCS Eng. 1979. Hon. Cons. Anaesth. Aberd. Roy. Hosp. Trust; Sen. Lect. Environment & Occupat. Med. Univ. Aberd. Socs: Soc. Occupat. Med. & Assn. Anaesth. Prev: Sen. Regist. (Anaesth.) Middlx. Hosp. Lond.; Scientif. Off. MRC Div. Anaesth.; Regist. (Anaesth.) Aberd. Roy. Infirm.

ROSS, John Donald, Surg. Capt. RN Retd. Tawcroft, Belstone, Okehampton EX20 1QZ Tel: 01837 840693 Fax: 01837 840693 — MRCS Eng. LRCP Lond. 1952; DPath Eng. 1965. (St. Mary's) Cons. Med. Adviser (Water Quality & Pub. Health) Thames Water Utilities. Socs: Fell. Roy. Soc. Med. Prev: Med. Adviser Thames Water Auth.; Dir. Health & Research (Naval).

ROSS, John Frederick Gunn Tel: 0131 225 5220 Fax: 0131 226 1910; 6 Saxe-Coburg Place, Edinburgh EH3 5BR Tel: 0131 332 7068 — MB ChB 1972 Aberd.; MRCGP 1984; DObst RCOG 1974.

ROSS, John Houston The Cottage, Ullenhall, Solihull B95 5PB — MB ChB 1989 Birm.

ROSS, John Hugh, MC (retired) Barkstone, 24 Overbury Road, Hereford HR1 1JE Tel: 01432 272717 — MD Camb. 1959, MB BChir 1950; FRCP Lond. 1970, M 1953; DObst RCOG 1952. Prev: Cons. Phys. Heref. Hosp. Gp.

ROSS, Mr John Macaulay Hamilton (retired) C/2 Craufurdland, Braepark Road, Barnton, Edinburgh EH4 6DL Tel: 0131 339 8647 — MB ChB 1937 Ed.; FRCS Ed. 1941. Prev: Cons. Surg. (Urol.) Roy. Infirm. Sunderland.

ROSS, John Macdonald, MBE (retired) Clovelly, 487 Lanark Road, Juniper Green, Edinburgh EH14 5DQ — MB ChB 1937 Ed.; MRCGP 1976. Prev: Ho. Surg. Edin. Roy. Infirm.

ROSS, John Scott Carolside Medical Centre, 1 Carolside Gardens, Clarkston, Glasgow G76 7BS Tel: 0141 644 3511 Fax: 0141 644 5525; 9 Glebe Road, Newton Mearns, Glasgow G77 6DU — MB ChB 1980 Glas.; DRCOG 1983. Clin. Asst. Dermat.

ROSS, Jonathan Denys Crawford Whittall Street Clinic, Whittall St., Birmingham B4 6DH Tel: 0121 237 5721 Fax: 0121 237 5729; Tel: 01527 835416 — MB ChB 1986 Aberd.; FRCP (Edin.) 1998; MRCP (UK) 1989; MD Aberdeen 1995; FRCP (Lond.) 2000. Cons. (GU Med.) Birm. specialist, community NHS Trust.; Sen. Lect. Birm. Univ. 1997- Cons. Phys., Univ. Hosp. trust, Birm..

ROSS, Jonathan James 6 Crossland Road, Hathersage, Hope Valley S32 1AN — MB ChB 1988 Ed.; FRCA 1995. Clin. Research Assoc. (Surgic. & Anaesth. Scis.) Univ. Sheff.

ROSS, Mr Jonathan Knox Occupational Health Department, British Gas plc, 100 Thames Valley Park Drive, Reading RG6 1PT Tel: 0118 929 3146 Fax: 0118 929 3140 Email: ross.jk@bgep.co.uk; 23 Kingsley Avenue, Ealing, London W13 0EQ Tel: 020 8997 6583 — MB BS 1979 Lond.; BSc (Hons.) Lond. 1976; FRCS Eng. 1984; MFOM RCP Lond. 1996, AFOM 1995.

ROSS

(Univ. Coll. Hosp.) Sen. Med. Adviser (Occupat. Health) BG plc. Socs: Roy. Soc. Med.; BMA. Prev: Med. Off. Brit. Antarctic Survey; Regist. (Orthop. Surg.) Hammersmith Hosp. Lond.; Regist. (Gen. Surg.) Mt. Vernon Hosp.

ROSS, Josiah (retired) 32 Montacute Road, Lewes BN7 1EN Tel: 01273 473419 Email: joeross@onetel.net.uk — MB BCh BAO 1958 Belf.; BSc Belf. 1955; MRCPsych 1971; DPM Lond. 1964. Prev: Cons. Child & Adolesc. Psychiat. Mid-Downs & Brighton Health Dist.

ROSS, Joy Ruth 59 Ann Moss Way, London SE16 2TJ — MB BS 1995 Lond.

ROSS, Judith B Banff Health Centre, Clunie St., Banff AB45 1HY Tel: 01261 812027; Blackpots Farm House, Whitehills, Banff AB45 2NS Tel: 01261 861215 — MB ChB 1982 Aberd.; Dip. Sports Med. 1977. GP Banff Health Centre. Prev: SHO (O & G) Cresswell Matern. Hosp. Dumfries; Trainee GP Lockmaben VTS; SHO (Med.) Palmerston Pk. Hosp., NZ.

ROSS, Juliette Wembley Park Medical Centre, 21 Wembley Park Drive, Wembley HA9 8HD Tel: 020 8902 4411 Fax: 020 8795 2987 Email: juliette.ross@e84084.nhs.net; 15 Leavesden Road, Stanmore HA7 3RQ Tel: 020 8954 1851 Fax: 020 8357 0835 Email: juliette.ross@dircon.co.uk — MB BS 1981 Lond.; Dip.Med.ACU 2000 BMAs; MRCGP 1986. (Middlx.) GP Tutor, Roy. Free Hosp. Med. Sch. Prev: GP Trainer (Gen. Pract.) Centr. Middlx. Scheme.

ROSS, Keith Raymond Paediatric Office, New Cross Hospital, Wolverhampton WV10 0QP Tel: 01902 307999; 21 Windsor Gardens, Codsall WV8 2EX Tel: 01902 842432 — MB ChB 1968 Manch.; FRCPCH; FRCP (UK) 1972. p/t Cons. Paediat. Wolverhampton. Prev: Lect. (Child Health) Univ. Aberd.; Regist. (Paediat.) Soton Univ. Hosps.; Jun. Asst. Res. Childr. Hosp. Med. Centre Boston, USA.

ROSS, Kenneth Grant McLagan Adolescent Forensic Service, Prestwich Hospital, Bury New Road, Prestwich, Manchester M25 3BL Tel: 0161 772 3811 Fax: 0161 772 3443; 1 A Arundale Avenue, Whalley Range, Manchester M16 8LS Tel: 0161 881 6566 Email: kenny.ross@tesco.net — MB ChB 1985 Dundee; MRCPsych 1994. (Dundee) Cons. Adolesc. Forens. Psychiat., Adolesc. Forens. Serv., Prestwich Hopsital, Manch.. Prev: Career Regist. Rotat. (Psychiat.) S. Glas.; Sen. Regist. Child Adolesc. Psychiat. Rotat. Manch.

ROSS, Mr Kenneth Raeburn Shepherds Hey, 7 Old Camp Road, Eastbourne BN20 8DH Tel: 01323 641221 — MB BS 1973 Lond.; FRCS Eng. 1979; MRCS Eng. LRCP Lond. 1973. (St. Bart.) Cons. Orthop. Surg. E.bourne Dist. Gen. Hosp. Socs: BMA & Hunt. Soc.; Anglo-Amer. Med. Soc.(Vice-Pres.); Brit. Orthopaedic Assn. Prev: Sen. Regist. Rotat. (Orthop.) St. Bart. Hosp. Lond.; Regist. (Surg.) Mt. Vernon Hosp. N.wood; Ho. Surg. St. Bart. Hosp. Lond.

ROSS, Kevin 60 Crediton Drive, Platt Bridge, Wigan WN2 5HU — BM BS 1997 Nottm.

ROSS, Lesley Anne 15 Belgrave Road, Edinburgh EH12 6NG Tel: 0131 334 3150 Email: lar@srv2.med.ed.ac.uk — MB ChB 1985 Ed.; MRCP Paediat. (UK) 1993; MRCGP 1989; DCH RCP Lond. 1991; DRCOG 1989. (Edinburgh) Specialist Regist. (Paediat.) Roy. Hosp. Sick Childr. Edin. Prev: Clin. Research Fell. (Child Life & Health) Univ. Edin.; Regist. (Paediat.) St. Jas. Univ. Hosp. Leeds. & York. Dist. Hosp.; SHO (Paediat.) St. Jas. Univ. Hosp. Leeds.

ROSS, Mr Leslie David Womens Health, St Helier Hospital, Wryth Lane, Carshalton SM5 1AA Tel: 020 8644 4343 Email: iross@sthelier.sghms.ac.uk; 61 The Ridgeway, Sutton SM2 5JX Tel: 0208 643 3349 — MB BS 1974 Lond.; FRCS Ed. 1980; MRCS Eng. LRCP Lond. 1974; FRCOG 1997, MRCOG 1980, DObst 1975. (Guy's) Cons. O & G St. Helier Hosp. Carshalton; Hon. Sen. Lect. Univ. Lond. Socs: Fell. Roy. Soc. Med.; Soc. for the Study of Fertil. Prev: Sen. Regist. Jessop Hosp. for Wom. Sheff.; Regist. (O & G) Addenbrooke's Hosp. Camb.; Resid. Surg. Off. Hosp. Wom. Lond.

ROSS, Leslie Vernon 74 Station Road, West Wickham BR4 0PU Tel: 020 8777 8245 — LRCPI & LM, LRSCI & LM 1962; LRCPI & LM, LRCSI & LM 1962; DRCOG 1965. Mem. Bromley LMC. Socs: BMA. Prev: Ho. Phys. & Ho. Surg. Meath Hosp. Dub.; Ho. Off. (Obst.) Bromley Hosp.; Ho. Off. (Paediat.) Our Lady's Hosp. Sick Childr. Dub.

ROSS, Linda Margaret 101 Earlbank Av., Scotstoun, Glasgow G14 9DY — MB ChB 1990 Glas.; MRCP (UK) 1994. Specialist Regist. (Med. Paediat.) Yorkhill NHS Trust Glas. Socs: BMA & RCPCH; RCPS Glas.; Scott. Paedia. Soc. Prev: SHO (Geriat. Med.) Lightburn Hosp. Glas.; SHO (A & E Med.) Glas. Roy. Infirm.; Ho. Off. (Gen. Med.) Glas. Roy. Infirm.

ROSS, Lindsey Elizabeth Golspie Medical Practice, Golspie KW10 6TL Tel: 01408 633221/633444 Fax: 01408 633303; An Crasg, West Drummuie, Golspie KW10 6TA Tel: 01408 633978 Fax: 01408 634189 Email: l.e.ross@btinternet.com — MB ChB 1980 Aberd.; BSc (Hons.) Developm. Biol. Aberd. 1980, MB ChB 1985; MRCGP 1990; Cert. Family Plann. JCC 1987. (Aberdeen) Clin. Asst. (Geriat.) Camb. Unit Golspie; JP; Hosp. Pract. GP Unit Lakon Memor. Golspie. Socs: Highland Med. Soc.; BMA; BASICS.

ROSS, Louis (retired) 24 Bentinck Close, Prince Albert Road, London NW8 7RY Tel: 020 7586 2992 — MB BS Lond. 1941; MRCS Eng. LRCP Lond. 1939; MRCGP 1953. Prev: Clin. Asst. (Cardiol.) Middlx. Hosp. Lond.

ROSS, Mairie Annabella Rutland Place Surgery, 21 Rutland Place, Glasgow G51 1TA Tel: 0141 427 3121 Fax: 0141 427 7600 — MB ChB 1978 Ed. Prev: Regist. (Psychiat.) Inverclyde Roy. Hosp. Greenock.

ROSS, Margaret Haigh (retired) (Surgery) 59 Northgate, Almondbury, Huddersfield HD5 8RX Tel: 01484 421391 — MRCS Eng. LRCP Lond. 1964; BSc Lond. 1958. Med. Off. Huddersfield Cervical Cytol. Clinic & Family Plann. Clinics; Med. Off. BrigHo. Family Plann. Comm. Prev: Staff Med. Off. Storthes Hall Ment. Hosp. Kirkburton.

ROSS, Margaret Shirley (retired) 34 Elmfield Road, Gosforth, Newcastle upon Tyne NE3 4BA Tel: 0191 285 4107 — MB BS Durh. 1958; DA Eng. 1984. Prev: Assoc. Specialist (Anaesth.) Sunderland Hosps.

ROSS, Margot Pamela 3 The Coombe, Dartmouth TQ6 9PG — State Exam Med. Berlin 1991.

ROSS, Martin Graham Silloth Group Medical Practice, Lanewn Terrace, Silloth, Carlisle CA7 4AH Tel: 016973 31309 Fax: 016973 32834 — MB ChB 1972 Birm.

ROSS, Mary Joan 10 Melrose Avenue, Seaton Delaval, Whitley Bay NE25 0JR — MB BS 1991 New South Wales.

ROSS, Melvin (retired) 9 Tillingbourne Gardens, Finchley, London N3 3JJ Tel: 020 8346 3556 — MB BS 1950 Lond.; MRCS Eng. LRCP Lond. 1949; FRCGP 1975, M 1960. Prev: Sen. Lect. Dept. Primary Health Care Univ. Coll. & Middlx. Sch. Med. Lond.

ROSS, Mervyn Thomas Anaesthetic Department, Level B, King's Hill Hospital, Mansfield Road, Sutton-in-Ashfield NG17 4JL; 9 Southgreen Hill, Mansfield NG18 4PU — MB ChB 1971 Ed.; FFA RCS Eng. 1977. Cons. Anaesth. Centr. Notts. Health Auth. Prev: Sen. Regist. (Anaesth.) Shackleton Dept. Anaesth. Soton. Gen.; Hosp.

ROSS, Michael Bilton Medical Centre, 120 Lily Road, Bradford BD8 8JT Tel: 01274 490409 Fax: 01274 499112; 2 Yate Lane, Oxenhope, Keighley BD22 9HL Tel: 01535 646763 Fax: 01535 645405 — MB BS 1975 Lond.; MSc Comm. Med. 1980; BSc (Anat.) Lond. 1972; MRCP (UK) 1979; MRCGP 1981; DTM & H Liverp. 1984; DRCOG 1978; Cert JCC Lond. 1978. (Univ. Coll. Hosp.) Instruc. Doctor JCC.

ROSS, Michael Taylor Lincraig, Main St., New Gilston, Leven KY8 5TF — MB ChB 1998 Ed.; MB ChB Ed 1998.

ROSS, Nicholas Elizlea, High St., Errol, Perth PH2 7QJ — MB ChB 1990 Dundee.

ROSS, Oliver Charles Flat 1, Moray House, 4 Morden Road, London SE3 0AA; 44 Lings Coppiu, West Dalwich, London SE21 8SX Email: orossle@compuserve.com — MB ChB 1989 Birm.; FRCA 1994. Specialist Regist., Anaesth. St Geo.'s Hosp. Socs: Assoc. of Anaesth.; Paediat. Intens. Care Soc.

ROSS, Oswald (retired) Flat 6, Fairmead Court, 1441 High Road, Whetstone, London N20 9PF Tel: 020 8343 8575 — MB BCh BAO 1946 Belf.; MRCGP 1960; DObst RCOG 1949.

ROSS, Pamela Mary Dunn 10 Abbey Place, Airdrie ML6 9QT — MB ChB 1998 Glas.; MB ChB Glas 1998.

ROSS, Pamela Susan 16 Ashdale Park, Wokingham RG40 3QS Tel: 01344 775667 — MB BChir 1982 Camb.; MA Camb. 1982; MRCGP 1986. (Middlesex) Asst. in Gen. Pract. at Heathhill Surg., Crowthorne (p/t). Socs: MRCGP. Prev: GP Princip. at Skimped Hill Health Centre Bracknell Berks.

ROSS, Paul Alistair 16 Miles Avenue, Sandford, Wareham BH20 7AT — BM BS 1994 Nottm.

ROSS, Paul Jonathan 99 Rivermead Court, Ranelagh Gardens, London SW6 3SB — MB BS 1990 Lond.; BSc (Hons.) Lond. 1987; MRCP (UK) 1995. Research Fell. & Hon. Regist. (Med. Oncol.) Roy. Marsden NHS Trust Surrey. Prev: Regist. (Gastroenterol. & Gen. Med.) Jersey Gen. Hosp.; SHO (Med. Oncol.) Roy. Marsden NHS Trust Surrey.

ROSS, Peter John 15 Wardie Road, Edinburgh EH5 3QE — MD 1979 Wales; MB ChB 1971; MRCP (UK) 1973. Managing Dir. Private Nursing Homes of Edin. Ltd. Socs: Assoc. Fell. Amer. Coll. Cardiol. Prev: Lect. & Hon. Sen. Regist. (Clin. Cardiol.) Univ. Hosp. Wales Cardiff; Cons. Cardiol. Riyadh Armed Forces Hosp. Saudi Arabia; Exchange; Fell.sh. Cardiovasc. Lab. Loma Linda Univ. Med. Center Calif. USA.

ROSS, Philip Wesley, TD The Old Yard, 38 High Street, Pittenweem, Anstruther KY10 2PL Tel: 0131 661 5415 — MD (Commend.) Aberd. 1970; FRCP Ed. 1989; MRCP Ed. 1985; FRCPath 1988, M 1983; FlBiol 1988; FRCSed 2000. (Aberd.) Reader (Med. Microbiol.) Bact. Univ. Edin.; Hon. Fell., Univ. of Edin.; Vis. Prof., Coll.s of Med. and Med. Sch.s in Africa and India; Hon. Cons. Roy. Infirm. Edin.; FLS; Lt.-Col. RAMC (V) Graded Cons. Path. RARO. Socs: Brit. Soc. Study of Infec.; Pres. Scott. Microbiol. Assn.; U.K Counc. of Inst. of Biol. Prev: Sen. Lect. (Bact.) Univ. Edin.; Ho. Phys. & Ho. Surg. Woodend Hosp. Aberd.; Lect. (Bact.) Univ. Edin. & Univ. Aberd.

ROSS, Rachael Joan Portchester Health Centre, West St., Porchester, Fareham PO16 9TU Tel: 01705 376913; 65 The Keep, Fareham PO16 9PW Email: rachael.ross@virgin.net — MB BS 1987 Newc.; MRCGP 1991; DRCOG 1990; DCH RCP Lond. 1990. (Newc. u. Tyne) Clin. Asst. (Elderly Med.) Gosport War Memor. Hosp. Socs: Soc. Occupat. Med. Prev: Trainee GP Furness Gen. Hosp.

ROSS, Richard Anthony St Andrews Surgery, The Old Central School, Southover Road, Lewes BN7 1US Tel: 01273 476216 Fax: 01273 487587; Kingston Lodge, The St, Kingston, Lewes BN7 3PB Tel: 01273 476216 — MB BS 1974 Lond.; FFA RCS Eng. 1979. (King's Coll. Hosp.) Hosp. Pract. Vict. Hosp. Lewes.

ROSS, Richard John Martin c/o Department of Medicine, Northern General Hospital, Herries Road, Sheffield S5 7AU Tel: 0114 271 4884 Fax: 0114 256 0458 Email: r.j.ross@sheffield.ac.uk — MB BS 1979 Lond.; MD Lond. 1988; FRCP Lond. 1995; MRCP Lond. 1982. Prof. & Hon. Cons. Phys. (Endocrinol.) N.ern Gen. Hosp. Sheff. Prev: Sen. Lect. & Hon. Cons. Phys. (Endocrinol.) & Research Fell. St. Bart. Hosp. Lond.; Sen. Regist. (Med.) King's Coll. Hosp. Lond.

ROSS, Richard Solomon 4 Beechwood Court, Holme Road, Didsbury, Manchester M20 2UA Tel: 0161 445 7903 — MB ChB 1930 Leeds. (Leeds) Prev: Anaesth. St. Ann's Home, Bowdon; Hon. Anaesth. St. John's Ear Hosp. Manch.

ROSS, Mr Robert Alasdair Medical Centre, Commando Trainging Centre Royal Marines, Lympstone EX8 5AX Tel: 01392 414120 Fax: 01392 414155 — MB BS 1985 Lond.; FRCS Eng. 1994; DFFP 1995. (King's Coll. Hosp. Lond.)

ROSS, Robert Armstrong Kirkwood 21 Gilmour Road, Edinburgh EH16 5NS — LRCP LRCS 1946 Ed.; LRCP LRCS Ed. LRFPS Glas. 1946.

ROSS, Robert Bruce Stewart Heathfield, 4 Glenview Drive, Shipley BD18 4AS Tel: 01274 592740 — MB ChB 1951 Glas.; DObst RCOG 1956. Prev: GP Bradford; Med. Adviser William Morrison Supermarkets plc.

ROSS, Robert Jeremy Pudsey Health Centre, 18 Mulberry Street, Pudsey LS28 7XP Tel: 0113 257 6711 Fax: 0113 236 3928 — MB ChB 1974 Dundee.

ROSS, Robert William David 5 Chesham Terrace, Belfast BT6 8GY — MB BCh BAO 1983 NUI.

ROSS, Robin Trevor Andrew (retired) Fir Trees, Lower Oakfield, Pitlochry PH16 5DS Tel: 01796 472419 — MB ChB 1959 Ed.; DObst RCOG 1968. Prev: GP Pitlochry.

ROSS, Roderick Sutherland 5 Buckstone Way, Edinburgh EH10 6PN Tel: 0131 445 3756 Fax: 0131 445 3756 — MB ChB Ed. 1944. (Ed.) Med. Off. (Outpats.) King Faisal Milit. Hosp. Khamis, Saudi Arabia; Mem. Med. Counc. for Alcoholism & Internat. Traffic & Accid. Med. Assn.

ROSS, Mr Ronald MacFarlane (retired) Medical Director, H.C.I. Health Care International,, Beardmore Street, Clydebank G81 4HX Tel: 0141 951 5665 Fax: 0141 951 5006 Email: ronald.ross@hci.co.uk — MB ChB 1959 Glas.; FRCS Glas. 1984; FRCS Ed. 1965. Med. Dir. BrE. Surg. HCI Internat. Med. Centre Glas.. Prev: Cons. Surg. Roy. Alexandra Hosp. Paisley & Hon. Surg. P.ss Louise Scott Hosp. Erskine.

ROSS, Ronald William David The Health Centre, Saintfield, Ballynahinch; 32 Kirkwood Park, Ballynahinch Road, Saintfield, Ballynahinch BT24 7DP — MB BCh BAO 1983 Belf.; MRCGP 1987; DRCOG 1985. Prev: Med. Off. & SHO (Med. & Cardiol.) Ulster Hosp. Dundonald; SHO (Obst.) Ulster Hosp. Dundonald; Ho. Off. Ulster Hosp. Dundonald.

ROSS, Ruth Allyson — MB BS 1986 Lond.; BSc Lond. 1983; MRCPI Irel. 1998. (King's)

ROSS, Sarah 22 Wallfield Place, Aberdeen AB25 2JP — MB ChB 1997 Aberd.

ROSS, Sarah Margaret TF2, 62 Newington Road, Edinburgh EH9 1QN — MB ChB 1994 Ed.

ROSS, Sean David Greencroft Medical Centre (North), Greencroft Wynd, Annan DG12 6BG — MB BCh BAO 1986 Belf. (Qu. Univ. Belf.)

ROSS, Sheena Margaret Ayrfield, 131 Huntingdon Road, Thrapston, Kettering NN14 4NG Tel: 01832 733066 — MB ChB 1972 Ed.; BSc Ed. 1969, MB ChB 1972; FFA RCS Eng. 1979; DRCOG 1976. (Ed.) Cons. Anaesth. Hinchingbrooke Hosp. Huntingdon.

ROSS, Sheila Kerr (retired) 87a Glencairn Drive, Pollokshields, Glasgow G41 4LL Tel: 0141 424 3737 Fax: 0141 424 3747 Email: sheilak.ross@virgin.net — MB ChB 1966 Glas.; FRCP Glas. 1981 M 1969; FRCGP 1993, M 1987. Prev: Med. Prescribing Adviser Ayrsh. & Arran HB.

ROSS, Sheila Maclean 3 Grappenhall Road, Stockton Heath, Warrington WA4 2AJ Tel: 01925 61263 — MB ChB 1946 St. And.; DCH 1949. (St. And.) Socs: BMA. Prev: Obst. Ho. Surg. Roy. Infirm. Perth.; Jun. Med. Regist. Booth Hall Childr. Hosp. Manch.; Ho. Phys. Cumbld. Infirm. Carlisle.

ROSS, Stephen David John Exmouth Health Centre, Claremont Grove, Exmouth EX8 2JF Tel: 01395 273001 Fax: 01395 273771 — MB ChB 1985 Birm.; MRCGP 1991.

ROSS, Wendy Anne 142 Clifton Road, Aberdeen AB24 4RB — MB ChB 1995 Glas.

ROSS, Wendy Elizabeth St Anthony's Medical Group, Thomas Gaughan House, Pottery Bank, Newcastle upon Tyne NE6 3SW Tel: 0191 265 5689 — MB ChB 1986 Ed.; BSc (Hons.) Med. Sci. Ed. 1984; MRCGP 1991; Dip. Ther. Newc. 1994; DRCOG 1989. GP Locality Represen.

ROSS, William Alexander 22A Abban Street, Inverness IV3 8HH Tel: 01463 713939 Fax: 01463 716256 — MB ChB 1980 Aberd.; MRCGP 1985. GP Inverness.

ROSS, William Andrew 1 Bellfield D.r, Eddleston, Peebles EH45 8RG — MB ChB 1949 Aberd.

ROSS, Mr William Mackie, CBE (retired) 62 Archery Rise, Durham DH1 4LA Tel: 0191 386 9256 — MB BS Durh. 1945; MD Durh. 1953; FRCS Ed. 1994; FRCS Eng. 1956; FRCR 1975; FFR 1961; DMRT Eng. 1948. DL. Prev: Lect. (Radiother.) Univ. Newc.

ROSS ERRO, Anne-Louise c/o Erro-Dann, 12 Lillian Road, London SW13 9JG — Lakarexamen Stockholm 1988.

ROSS-MARRS, Roderick Peter Rectory Road Surgery, 7 Rectory Road, Rowhedge, Colchester CO5 7HP Tel: 01206 728585 Fax: 01206 729262; Rowhedge Surgery, 7 Rectory Road, Rowhedge, Colchester CO5 7HP Tel: 01206 728585 — MB BS 1986 Lond.; BSc (Hons.) Lond. 1981, MB BS 1986. (Westminster) Prev: Partner with Drs Sarda, 1991 Patel, Getha Meadow La. Sudbury Suff.

ROSS-MAWER, Jeremy Hugh Ronald 7 South Street, Fowey PL23 1AR — MRCS Eng. LRCP Lond. 1969. (King's Coll. Hosp.) Prev: GP Wilts. & Warlingham Surrey.

ROSS RUSSELL, Fiona Mary Addison House, Milston, Salisbury SP4 8HT — MB BS 1982 Lond.; MRCGP 1997; DRCOG 1986; DCH RCP Lond. 1985.

ROSS RUSSELL, Ian (retired) Lernham, Barrells Down Road, Bishop's Stortford CM23 2SW Tel: 01279 651485 — MB 1955 Camb.; BChir 1954; DObst RCOG 1959. Prev: Area Surg. St. John Ambul. Brig.

ROSS RUSSELL, Ralph William (retired) 23 Regent Terrace, Edinburgh EH7 5BS — DM Oxf. 1962; MA, MD Camb. 1958, MB BChir 1952; FRCP Ed. 1977, M 1966; FRCP Lond. 1967, M 1958.

ROSS RUSSELL

Phys. (Neurol.) Guy's & St. Thos. Trust Lond. Prev: Phys. (Neurol.) Guy's & St. Thos. Trust Lond.

ROSS RUSSELL, Robert Ian Department of Paediatrics, Addenbrooke's Hospital, Hills Road, Cambridge CB2 2QQ Tel: 01223 216878 Fax: 01223 216878 Email: russell@addenbrookes.nhs.uk; Old Tiled House, Red Cross Lane, Cambridge CB2 2QU — MB BChir 1982 Camb.; MD Camb. 1995; FRCPCH 1997; BA Camb. 1979; MRCP (UK) 1986; FRCP (UK) 1997; MA Camb. 1984. Cons. Paediat. Addenbrooke's Hosp. Camb. Prev: Sen. Lect. (Paediat.) King's Coll. Hosp. Lond.; Sen. Regist. (Paediat.) Hosp. Sick Childr. Gt. Ormond St. Lond.

ROSSA, Kanwaljit Kaur Tel: 01522 569033 Fax: 01522 576713 — MB ChB 1981 Glas.; BSc Zambia 1977; DCH RCP Lond. 1985. (Univ. Glas.) Prev: Clin. Med. Off. (Community Paediat.) Sunderland HA.

ROSSALL, Adrian Michael Danebridge Medical Centre, 29 London Road, Northwich CW9 5HR Tel: 01606 45786 Fax: 01606 331977; Southdown, Sutton Field, Whitegate, Northwich CW8 2BD Tel: 01606 882278 Email: rossall@arossall.freeserve.co.uk — MRCS Eng. LRCP Lond. 1978; DRCOG 1985. (Manch.) Prev: Hosp. Pract. (Anaesth.) Leighton Hosp. Crewe.

ROSSALL, Christopher John Deepdale Road Healthcare Centre, Deepdale Road, Preston PR1 5AF Tel: 01772 655533 Fax: 01772 653414; Brookfield Farm, Tabley Lane, Higher Bartle, Preston PR4 0LH Fax: 01772 722221 Email: haighton@aol.com — MB ChB 1974 Liverp. (Liverpool) Prev: Research Regist. Univ. Hosp. S. Manch.; SHO (Obst. & Paediat.) Tameside Gen. Hosp.; Ho. Phys. & Ho. Surg. Roy. Lancaster Infirm.

ROSSDALE, Douglas 37 Montagu Square, London W1H 2LL Tel: 020 7262 8229 Fax: 020 7723 6114; 16 Marston Close, London NW6 4EU Tel: 020 7262 8229 Fax: 020 7674 0378 — MB BS 1948 Lond.; DObst RCOG 1950. (St. Bart.) Adviser (Hyperbaric Med.) Esso Petroleum Co. Ltd. Socs: Affil. Fac. Occupat. Med. RCP Lond; Fell. Hunt. Soc.; Fell. Roy. Soc. Med. Prev: Surg. Regist. Luton & Dunstable Hosp.; Jun. Surg. Regist. & Intern. & Extern. Obst. Dept. St. Bart. Hosp.; Ho. Surg. St. Bart. Hosp. Lond.

ROSSDALE, Martin Roger Department of Anatomy & Developmental Biology, University College, Gower St., London WC1E 6BT; Department of Anatomy & Embryology, University College, Gower St, London WC1E 6BT — BM BCh 1965 Oxf.; DM Oxf. 1978, BM BCh 1965. Sen. Lect. (Haemat.) Univ. Coll. Lond.

ROSSDALE, Michael George Philip The Surgery, 111 Pembroke Road, Clifton, Bristol BS8 3EU Tel: 0117 973 3790; 12 Park Grove, Henleaze, Bristol BS6 7XD — MB BChir 1980 Camb.; MA Camb. 1980; MRCGP 1986; DRCOG 1984; DCH RCP Lond. 1983. (Univ. Coll. Hosp.) Hosp. Pract. (Chest Med.) S.mead Hosp. Bristol. Prev: SHO (Paediat.) S.mead Hosp. Bristol; SHO (Gen. Med.) Cheltenham Gen. Hosp.

ROSSDALE, Richard Albert 10 Phillimore Place, Kensington, London W8 7BX Tel: 020 7937 0712 — LMSSA 1953 Lond.; AFOM RCP Lond. 1979. (St. Geo.) Med. Off. Gulf Oil (GB). Prev: Ho. Surg. (Orthop. & Traum.) & Ho. Phys. Ashford Hosp. Middlx.

ROSSDALE-SMITH, Georgina Jane Poplars, Chinthurst Lane, Shalford, Guildford GU4 8JS — MB BS 1975 Lond.; MRCS Eng. LRCP Lond. 1974.

ROSSER, Anne Elizabeth Cambridge Brain Repair Centre, Cambridge CB1 4YU Tel: 01223 331160 — MB BChir 1988 Camb.; PhD Camb. 1985; MRCP (UK) 1991. MRC Clinician Scientist & Hon. Sen. Regist. (Neurol.) Camb. Centre Brain Repair Addenbrooke's Hosp. Prev: Regist. (Neurol.) Nat. Hosp. Neurol. & Neurosurg. Qu. Sq. Lond.; Regist. (Neurol.) Addenbrooke's Hosp. Camb.; Regist. (Med.) Ealing Hosp. Lond.

ROSSER, Anne Kathryn Dorothy e4 Lentran Farm Cottages, Lentran, Inverness IV3 8RL — MB ChB 1981 Manch.

ROSSER, Betsan 53 Birchgrove Road, Llansamlet, Swansea SA7 9JR — MB BCh BAO 1983 NUI; LRCPI & LM, LRCSI & LM 1983.

ROSSER, Miss Catherine Gwyndy, Upper Garth Road, Bangor LL57 2SS — MB BCh 1988 Wales.

ROSSER, Catherine Anne 15 The Walk, Hengoed CF82 7AH — BM 1994 Soton.

ROSSER, Clive Anthony Khan and Partners, Medical Centre, Church Road, Seven Sisters, Neath SA10 9DT Tel: 01639 700203 Fax: 01639 700010 — MB BS 1981 Lond.

ROSSER, David Michael 2 Huttles Green, Shepreth, Royston SG8 6PR — MB BCh 1987 Wales; FRCA 193; MRCP (UK) 1990.

ROSSER, David William Albert (retired) 2 Priory Avenue, Caversham, Reading RG4 7SE Tel: 01734 472431 Fax: 01734 463340 — MB BCh BAO 1959 Dub.; BA Dub. 1959. Prev: Ho. Off. Lagan Valley Hosp. Lisburn & Roy. Berks. Hosp. Reading.

ROSSER, Edmund Mervyn (retired) 18 Eastlands Crescent, Dulwich Village, London SE21 7EG Tel: 020 8693 4883 — MB BS Lond. 1952; MRCS Eng. LRCP Lond. 1952; MRCGP 1962. Prev: Clin. Tutor (Gen. Pract.) Acad. Dept. Gen. Pract. Primary Med. Care Med. Coll. St. Bart. Hosp. Lond.

ROSSER, Elisabeth Mary Department of Clinical Genetics, Institute of Child Health, 30 Guilford St., London WC1N 1EH Tel: 020 7905 2607 Fax: 020 7813 8141 — MB BS 1986 Lond.; BSc (Genetics) Lond. 1983, MB BS 1986; MRCP (UK) 1993. Cons. (Clin. Genetics) Inst. Child Health & Gt. Ormond St. Hosp. Childr.

ROSSER, Jeffrey Graham Rosser and Partners, Crewkerne Health Centre, Middle Path, Crewkerne TA18 8BX Tel: 01460 72435 Fax: 01460 77957 — MB ChB 1957 Birm.; DO RCS 1989; MCOphth 1990.

ROSSER, Maria Alda 19 Parmin Way, Taunton TA1 2JU — MB ChB 1982 Sheff.

ROSSER, Michael John, Wing Cdr. RAF Med. Br. Retd. Lister House Surgery, 35 The Parade, St Helier, Jersey JE2 3QQ Tel: 01534 36336 Fax: 01534 35304 — MB BS 1974 Lond.; DAvMed 1983. Prev: Sen. Med. Off. HQAFCENT.

ROSSER, Peggy Mildred (retired) Dorset House, Blackfriars Avenue, Droitwich WR9 8DR Tel: 01905 76471 — MB BS Lond. 1939. Prev: Ho. Phys. Postgrad. Med. Sch.

ROSSER, Rosemary Lovann Bulwell Health Centre, Main Street, Bulwell, Nottingham NG6 8QJ Tel: 0115 927 9119 Fax: 0115 977 1236 — MB ChB 1981 Liverp.; MRCS Eng. LRCP Lond. 1981; MRCGP 1988. Prev: GP Sheff.; Trainee GP Romford VTS; SHO (A & E) OldCh. Hosp.

ROSSER, Sally Anne Giffords Surgery, 28 Lowbourne, Melksham SN12 7EA Tel: 01225 703370; Hill Farm House, Seend, Melksham SN12 6RU — MB BS 1982 Lond.; DRCOG 1987; MRCGP 1988; DCH RCP Lond. 1986.

ROSSER, Vaughan Charles Edgar Heavitree Health Centre, South Lawn Terrace, Exeter EX1 2RX Tel: 01392 431355 Fax: 01392 498305; Greenwood House, Ebford Lane, Ebford, Exeter EX3 0QX — MB ChB 1975 Manch.; MRCGP 1980.

ROSSI, Charlotte Anne Melissa The Surgery, Welbeck Street, Creswell, Worksop S80 4HA Tel: 01909 721206; Fuchsia Cottage, 54 Bakestone Moor, Whitwell, Worksop S80 4QD Email: charlotte@sandcrossi.demon.co.uk — MB BS 1991 Newc.; DRCOG 1998; DFFP 1996. GP Princip.; Clin. Asst. Gum. Prev: Trainee GP Bassetlaw VTS; Trainee GP N.d. VTS.

ROSSI, Mr Leo Francis Anthony Spindleberry, Brickworth Down, Whiteparish, Salisbury SP5 2QD — MB BS 1966 Lond.; FRCS Eng. 1971. (Westm.) Cons. Plastic Surg. Odstock Hosp. Salisbury. Prev: Sen. Regist. Burns & Plastic Unit Qu. Mary's Hosp. Roehampton; Sen . Regist. Head & Neck Unit Roy. Marsden Hosp. Lond.; Dir.Wessex Regional Burns Unit.

ROSSI, Maria Kathleen Summerfield House, 2 Eday Rd, Aberdeen AB15 6RE Email: maria.rossi@ghb.grampian.scot.nhs.uk — MSc 2001 (Public Health & Health Services Research) University of Aberdeen; Laurea Medicina & Chirurgia 1989; DTM & H RCP Lond. 1995. (Univ. La Sapienza di Roma) Prev: Field Med. Co-Ord. MSF-B Wajir, Kenya; Field Med. Co-Ordinator MSF-B Dadaab Kenya; SHO (Gen. Med.) Aberd. Roy. Infirm.

ROSSI, Michela 6 Hanbury Street, London E1 6QR — MB BS 1990 Newc.; MRCP (UK) 1994. Research Fell. RPMS Hammersmith Hosp. Lond. Prev: Regist. (Med.) OldCh. Hosp. Essex.

ROSSI, Steven Health Centre, Newgate Street, Worksop S80 1HP Tel: 01909 500266 Fax: 01909 478014; Fuchsia Cottage, 54 Bakestone Moor, Whitwell, Worksop S80 4QD Tel: 01909 720682 — MB BS Newc. 1989; DRCOG 1992; MRCGP 1996. (Newcastle upon Tyne) Princip. GP The Health Centre, Worksop. Socs: RCGP; BMA. Prev: Assoc. GP Lintonville Med. Gp. Ashington; GP Regist. Cestria Health Centre Chester-le-St.; GP Regist. Seaton Hirst Med. Gp. Ashington.

*ROSSI, Susan Isobel 44 Willow Way, Ponteland, Newcastle upon Tyne NE20 9RF; 26 Pinders Green Drive, Methley, Leeds LS26 9BA Tel: 01977 516520 — MB ChB 1998 Leeds.

ROSSINI, Jane North Western RHA, Piccadilly S., Manchester; Rivendell, 56C Manchester Road, Greenfield, Oldham OL3 7HJ Tel: 01457 870470 — MB ChB 1986 Manch. Regist. (Pub. Health Med.) N. W.. RHA.

ROSSITER, Anne Department Occupational Health, Royal Devon & Exeter Hospital (Heavitree), Gladstone Road, Exeter EX1 2EH Tel: 01392 405037; Newcombes, Newton St Cyres, Exeter EX5 5AW Tel: 01392 851235 Fax: 01392 851234 — MB BS 1978 Lond.; AFOM RCP Lond. 1994; MFOM Lond. 1997; DRCOG 1982; DA Eng. 1981. (St. Thos.) Cons. (Occupat. Med.) Exeter.

ROSSITER, Brian Derek Whipps Cross Hospital, London E11 — MB BS 1974 Lond.; FRCP Lond. 1994. Cons. Phys. Med. for Elderly Whipps Cross Hosp. Lond.

ROSSITER, John Michael Alvaston Medical Centre, 14 Boulton Lane, Alvaston, Derby DE24 0GE — MB BCh BAO NUI 1968. (Univ. Coll. Dub.)

ROSSITER, Jonathan David 7 Pear Tree Way, Crowle, Worcester WR7 4SB — BM 1995 Soton. SHO (Ophth.) Birm., & Midl. Eye centre.

ROSSITER, Mary Anne Tel: 020 8887 2945 Fax: 020 8887 4222 Email: mary@rossiter37.fsnet.co.uk; 3 Wentworth Hall, The Ridgeway, Mill Hill, London NW7 1RJ Tel: 020 8906 4433 Fax: 020 8906 8608 — MA Camb. 1963, MB BChir 1962; FRCP Lond. 1985, M 1967; MRCS Eng. LRCP Lond. 1962; FRCPCH 1997; DCH Eng. 1966; DObst RCOG 1964. (Guy's) Cons. Paediat. N. Middlx. Hosp. NHS Trust. Socs: Brit. Soc. Paediat. Gastroenterol.Hepat. & Nutrit.; BASPCAN; Fell. Roy. Soc. Med.Pres. Sect. of Paediat. and Child Health. Prev: Sen. Regist. (Paediat.) United Oxf. Hosps.; Heinz Research Fell. (Hon. Sen. Regist.) Qu. Eliz. Hosp. Childr. Lond.

ROSSITER, Michael Adam The Castle Practice, Health Centre, Central Street, Ludgershall, Andover SP11 9RA Tel: 01264 790356 Fax: 01264 791256; Quercus Cottage, 67 Cadley Road, Collingbourne Ducis, Marlborough SN8 3EB Tel: 01264 850107 Email: mike@quercuscottage.freeserve.co.uk — MB BS 1991 Lond.; MRCGP 1996; DFFP 1995; DRCOG 1994. (Roy. Free Hosp.) GP Princip. Prev: Trainee GP Newquay & Cornw. VTS; Ho. Phys. & Ho. Surg. Roy. Cornw. Hosp. Treliske.

ROSSITER, Mr Nigel Daniel Orthopaedic Dept, Derriford Hospital, Plymouth PL6 8DH Tel: 01752 777111 — MB BS 1988 Lond.; FRCS Ed. 1993; FRCS 1999 Tr & orth. (London Hospital Medical College) Cons. T & O Derriford Hosp., Plymouth. Socs: Brit. Orthopaedic Assn., Fell.; Brit. Trauma Soc.; Combined Serv.s Orthopaedic Soc. Prev: Trauma Fell. Texas, USA (Dallas & San Antonio); Lect. (Milit. Surg.) RAMC; Specialist Regist. (Orthop.) Oxf.

ROSSITER, Stephen Kim Wellwaters, New Street Lane, Eype, Bridport DT6 6AD — MB BCh 1980 Wales; MRCPsych 1990; Dip. Addic. Behaviour (St. Georges Lond.) 1997.

ROSSON, Amanda Kate Fairfield, Wall Hill Lane, Congleton CW12 4TD — MB BS 1990 Lond.; DRCOG 1993.

ROSSON, Mr John William The Royal Surrey County Hospital, Orthopaedic Department, Egerton Road, Guildford GU2 7XX — BM 1979 Soton.; MS 1990; FRCS Eng. 1985; FRCS Ed. 1983.

ROSSOR, Eve Beatrix Mary Sheridan Centre, 5 Dugard Way, off Renfrew Road, London SE11 4TH Tel: 0207 414 1455 Fax: 0207 414 1372 Email: eve.rossor@chsltr.sthames.nhs.uk; 145 Woodwarde Road, London SE22 8UR Tel: 020 8693 0682 — MB BChir 1975 Camb.; FRCPCH 1998; MA Camb. 1974; FRCP Lond. 1995; MRCP (UK) 1978. Dir. Child Health Directorate Community Health S. Lond. NHS Trust; Cons. Paediat. Dir. Learning Assessm. Clinic. Prev: Med. Dir. & Clin. Dir. Community Child Health W. Lambeth Community Care Trust; SCMO W. Lambeth HA; Regist. (Paediat.) Addenbrooke's Hosp. Camb.

ROSSOR, Professor Martin Neil National /Institute Hospital for Neurology & Neurosurgery, Queen Square, London WC1 Tel: 020 7837 3611 Fax: 020 7209 0182; 145 Woodwarde Road, London SE22 8UR Tel: 020 7693 0632 Fax: 020 7725 1422 — MB BChir 1975 Camb.; MA Camb. 1975, MD 1986; FRCP Lond. 1990; MRCP (UK) 1976. Prof. of Clin. Neurol. Inst. of Neurol., Uni. Coll. And Imperial Coll, Lond..; Hon.Cons. Nat. Hosp. for Neurol. and Neurosurg. and St Mary's Hosp., Lond.. Prev: Sen. Regist. Kings Coll. Hosp. & Nat. Hosp. Nerv. Dis. Lond.; Regist. (Neurol.) Nat.

Hosp. Nerv. Dis. Lond.; Clin. Scientist MRC Neurochem. Pharmacol. Unit Camb.

ROSSOUW, Daniel John 72 Margaret Road, Barnet EN4 9NX — MB BCh 1982 Witwatersrand.

ROSSWICK, Mr Robert Paul (cons. rooms), The Wellington Hospital, Wellington Place, London NW8 9LE Tel: 020 7586 3213 Fax: 020 8445 4836; 10 Lorian Close, Holden Road, London N12 7DZ Tel: 020 8445 4792 Fax: 020 8445 4836 Email: rpr@dial.pipex.com — MB BS Lond. 1955; MS Univ. Illinois 1963; FRCS Eng. 1961; DObst RCOG 1957. (Lond. Hosp.) Emerit. Surg. St. Geo. Hosp. Lond. & Hon. Sen. Lect. (Surg.) St. Geo. Hosp. Med. Sch. Lond. Socs: Fell. Roy. Soc. Med.; Fell. (Treas.) Med. Soc. Lond. Formerly Pres. Prev: Surg. Roy. Masonic Hosp. Lond.; Sen. Regist. & 1st Asst. (Surg.) St. Geo. Hosp. Lond.; Robt.son Exchange Fell. (Surg.) Presbyt.-St. Luke's Hosp. Chicago, USA.

ROSTED, Palle Weston Park Hospital, Whitham Road, Sheffield S10 2SJ Tel: 0114 226 5000 Fax: 0114 226 5555; 200 Abbey Lane, Sheffield S8 0BU Tel: 0114 236 0077 Fax: 0114 262 0491 Email: prosted@aol.com — MD Copenhagen 1973. Indep. Med. Acupunc. Sheff.; Cons. Med. Acupunc. W.on Pk. Hosp.; Clin. Lect. Univ. Sheff.; GMC Registered Specialist in Acupunc. Socs: (Ex-Treas.) Brit. Med. Assn. Acupunc.; (Ex Vice-Chairm.) Danish Soc. Acupunc.; Treas. IACMART.

ROSTEN, Bernard Martin Deryke (retired) 160 Twickenham Road, Hanworth, Feltham TW13 6HD — MRCS Eng. LRCP Lond. 1936. Prev: Flight Lt. RAFVR.

ROSTEN, Margaret Helen (retired) 160 Twickenham Road, Hanworth, Feltham TW13 6HD Tel: 020 8979 6222 — MB BS Lond. 1954; DCH Eng. 1957; DObst RCOG 1961.

ROSTRON, Mr Chad Kenneth St George's Hospital, Blackshaw Road, London SW17 0QT Tel: 020 8725 2325 Fax: 020 8725 3026 Email: rostron@sghms.ac.uk; 10 Harley Street, London W1G 9PF Tel: 020 7483 4921 Fax: 020 7467 8312 — MB BS Newc. 1975; FRCS Eng. 1982; FRCOphth 1989; DO Eng. 1979. (Newcastle Upon Tyne) Cons. Ophth. St. Geo. Hosp. Lond.; Hon. Sen. Lect. Univ. Lond.; Mem. Edit. Bd. Eye & Brit. Jl. Optom. & Disp.; Director Keratec Eye Bank, Lond. Socs: Internat. Refractive Surgic. Soc.; Brit. Soc. for Refractive Surg.; United Kingdom Intraocular Implart Soc. Prev: Sen. Regist. (Ophth.) Leicester Roy. Infirm.

ROSTRON, Elizabeth Anne Church Street Practice, 8 Church Street, Southport PR9 0QT Tel: 01704 533666 Fax: 01704 539239 — MB ChB 1971 Manch.

ROSTRON, Mr Kenneth William Briggs (retired) Pentrig, Vicarage Lane, Lelant, St Ives TR26 3EA Tel: 01736 752107 — MB BChir 1937 Camb.; MA, MB BChir Camb. 1937; FRCS Eng. 1950; DOMS Eng. 1947.

ROSTRON, Michael Gordon Rees, Hoe, Rostron and James, Lister House Surgery, Bollams Mead, Wiveliscombe, Taunton TA4 2PH Tel: 01984 623471 Fax: 01984 624357; Church Hill Cottage, Halse, Taunton TA4 3AB Tel: 01823 432815 Fax: 01823 433730 — MB BS 1980 Lond.; MRCGP 1984; DRCOG 1982. (Lond. Hosp.) Trainer GP Taunton.

ROSTRON, Mr Peter Kenneth Makin 88 Rodney Street, Liverpool L1 9AR Tel: 0151 709 2393 Fax: 0151 707 2456; Wensleydale Farm, Gaw Hill Lane, Aughton, Ormskirk L39 7HA Tel: 01695 422848 — MB ChB 1967 Liverp.; MChOrth 1975; FRCS Ed. 1973. (Liverp.) Cons. Orthop. Surg. Whiston & St. Helens Hosps. Prev: Sen. Regist. (Orthop.) Wrightington Hosp. Appley Bridge; Sen. Regist. Alder Hey Childr. Hosp. Liverp.; Demonstr. (Anat.) Univ. Liverp.

ROTBLAT, Frances 50 Muswell Avenue, London N10 2EL — MB BS 1970 Lond.; BSc (Hons.) Lond. 1967, MB BS 1970; FRCPath 1990, M 1978. Sen. Med. Off. Med. Control Agency DoH. Prev: Research Fell. Haemophilia Centre Roy. Free Hosp. Lond.

ROTCHFORD, Alan Paul 2 Barley Way, Rothley, Leicester LE7 7RL — BChir 1990 Camb.

ROTH, Cathy Ellen St. Thomas' Hospital, London SE1 7EH — MB BChir 1989 Camb.

ROTH, Daphne Mary Liddon (retired) 84 North End House, Fitzjames Avenue, London W14 0RX Tel: 020 7603 2384 — MB BS 1948 Lond.; MRCS Eng. LRCP Lond. 1948; DObst RCOG 1952; DCH Eng. 1951. Prev: Clin. Med. Off. (Community Health) Riverside & Wandsworth HA's.

ROTH

ROTH, Dorothy Josephine (retired) Wayside, Botesdale, Diss IP22 1DL — MB BS 1949 Lond.; MRCS Eng. LRCP Lond. 1946; DPhysMed. Eng. 1953. Prev: Asst. Phys. (Physical Med.) Centr. Middlx. Hosp.

ROTH, John Andrew 3 Clevedon Drive, Earley, Reading RG6 5XF Tel: 0118 986 7482 — MB BS Lond. 1962; DO Eng. 1969. (Oxf.) Socs: Oxf. Ophth. Congr.; Coll. Ophth. Prev: Regist. & SHO Oxf. Eye Hosp.; SHO Roy. Berks. Hosp. Reading.

ROTH, Lucy Juliet 68 High Street, Great Broughton, Middlesbrough TS9 7EG — MB BS 1992 Newc.

ROTH, Sir Martin Level 9, Addenbrooke's Hospital, University of Cambridge, Hills Road, Cambridge CB2 2QQ Tel: 01223 242106 Fax: 01223 412193; Trinity College, Cambridge CB2 1TQ Tel: 01223 242106 Fax: 01223 412193 — MB BS 1943 Lond.; DPM RCPSI 1949; MA Camb. 1943; MD Lond. 1946; Hon. ScD Dub. 1972; Hon. DSc Indiana 1993; FRCP Lond. 1958, M 1944; Hon. FRCPS Glas. 1973; MRCS Eng. LRCP Lond. 1941; FRCPsych 1971. (St. Mary's) Emerit. Prof. of Psychiat. Univ. Camb.; Mem. Bd. Governors St. And. Hosp. N.ampton; Fell. Trinity Coll. Camb.; Hon. Fell. Inst. of Advanced Studies Indiana 1991; Hon. Fell. Coll. Med. & Surg. S. Afr.; Founder Pres. & Hon. Fell. Roy. Coll. Psychiat.; Hon. Fell. Austral. & NZ Roy. Coll. Psychiat. Socs: Fell. of the Acad. of Med. Sci. Prev: Scientif. Mem. MRC Counc. & Clin. Research Bd.; Pres. Counc. & Chairm. Ct. of Electors Appeals Comm. RCPsych. & Jt. Comm. Higher Psychiat. Train.; Vice-Pres. & Counc. Med. Defence Union.

ROTH, Michael Gilbert 3 Florence Villas, Milton Road, London SE24 0NN Tel: 020 7737 5576 Email: michelroth@aol.com — BSc Lond. 1965, MB BS 1968. (Westminster Medical School)

ROTH, Simon Christhold Barnet General Hospital, Wellhouse Lane, Barnet EN5 3DJ; 5 Vale Grove, Acton, London W3 7QP — MB BS 1982 Lond.; MRCP (UK) 1986. Cons. Barnet Gen. Hosp. Prev: Clin. Lect. (Paediat.) Univ. Coll. Hosp. Lond.; Research Regist. (Paediat.) Univ. Coll. Hosp. Lond.; Regist. (Paediat.) Whittington Hosp. Lond.

ROTHBURN, Michael Mark University Hospital Aintree, Public Health Laboratory, Longmoor Lane, Liverpool L9 7AL Tel: 0151 529 4900 Fax: 0151 529 4918 — MB ChB 1979 Leeds; BSc (Hons.) (Biochem. Med.) Leeds 1976, MB ChB 1979; FRCPath 1996; Dip. Bact. Manch. 1984. Cons. Med. Microbiol. Liverp. Pub. Health Laborat.; Clin. Lect. Dept. Trop. Med. & Infec. Dis. Univ. Liverp.; Med. Off. (Control of Infect.) Aintree Hosps.; Med. Off. (Control of Infect.) Walton Centre Neurol. & Neurosurg.

ROTHENBERG, Tamar Mirham 107 Hampstead Way, London NW11 7LR — BM BCh 1997 Oxf.

ROTHER, Penelope Bonnyrigg Health Centre, High Street, Bonnyrigg EH19 2DA Tel: 0131 663 7272 Fax: 0131 660 5636; 21 Station Road, Loanhead EH20 9NJ Tel: 0131 440 1019 — MB ChB 1981 Ed.; MRCGP 1985; DRCOG 1983.

ROTHERA, Mr Michael Patrick 20 Harrop Road, Hale, Altrincham WA15 9BZ — MB BS 1977 Lond.; FRCS Eng. 1983.

ROTHERAY, Andrew David Trevaylor Road Health Centre, Trevaylor Road, Falmouth TR11 2LH Tel: 01326 317317; CHY Cara, 37 Penhale Road, Falmouth TR11 5UZ — MB ChB 1973 Liverp.; BSc (Hons. Biochem.) Liverp. 1970, MB ChB 1973.

ROTHERAY, Christine Florence Royal Cornwall Hospital Trust, Treliske, Truro TR1 2XN Tel: 01872 272 4242; Eschol, 6 Mitchell Hill Terrace, Truro TR1 1HY — MB ChB 1973 Liverp.; D.Occ.Med. RCP Lond. 1995; AFOM RCP Lond. 1997. (Liverpool) SHO (Gen. Med.) Roy. Cornw. Hosp. Treliske Truro. Prev: Med. Adviser (Occupat. Health) Cornw. CC; Med. Off. Assessor DSS; Clin. Asst. (Geriat.) Barncoose Hosp. Redruth.

ROTHERHAM, Joann 91 Eastfield Road, Keyingham, Hull HU12 9TP — MB BS 1994 Newc.

ROTHERHAM, Melanie Jane Farndon Green Medical Centre, 1 Farndon Green, Wollaton Park, Nottingham NG8 1DU Tel: 0115 928 8666 Fax: 0115 928 8343 — MB ChB 1988 Leeds; MB ChB Leeds. 1988. GP Nottm. Prev: Trainee GP/SHO Nottm. VTS; Ho. Off. (Med.) Pinderfields Hosp. Wakefield; Ho. Off. (Surg.) Sea Croft Hosp. Leeds.

ROTHERHAM, Neil Eric 2 Waterside Close, Gamston, Nottingham NG2 6QA — MB ChB 1986 Sheff.; MRCP (Pt.I) 1988; Dip. Pharm. Med. 1992; MFPM 1993. Managing Dir. Clinphone Ltd. Prev: Research Phys. Boots Pharmaceutics; SHO (Chest Med./Cardiol.) Wythenshawe Hosp. Manch.

ROTHERY, Anne Moira Tel: 0161 909 8391 Fax: 0161 909 8414 — MB ChB 1979 Manch.; BSc St. And. 1976; MRCGP 1984; DRCOG 1983.

ROTHERY, David James Parkview Clinic, 60 Queens Bridge Road, Moseley, Birmingham B13 8QD Tel: 0121 243 2000; 26 Pine Grove, Lickey, Rednal, Birmingham B45 8HE — MB ChB 1977 Leeds; FRCPsych 1995, M 1982. Cons. Psychiat. Regional Adolesc. Unit. Birm.; Sen. Clin. Lect. Univ. Birm. Prev: Sen. Regist. (Child & Adolesc. Psychiat.) W. Midl. Regional TS.

ROTHERY, Stephen Philip Stonefield Street Surgery, 21 Stonefield Street, Milnrow, Rochdale OL16 4JQ Tel: 01706 46234 Fax: 01706 527946; 24 Ryefields Drive, Uppermill, Oldham OL3 6BX — MB ChB 1979 Manch.; MRCGP 1983; Cert. Family Plann. JCC 1984; DCCH RCGP 1984; DRCOG 1982.

ROTHMAN, Doreen, OBE (retired) 46 Alleyn Road, Dulwich, London SE21 8AL Tel: 020 8670 5297 Fax: 020 8670 5297 Email: drothman@talk21.com — BSc Lond. 1950, MB BS 1955; MRCS Eng. LRCP Lond. 1955; FRCOG 1975, M 1960, DObst 1957. Prev: Sen. Med. Off. Dept. Health & Social Security Lond.

ROTHMAN, Martin Terry Cromwell Hospital, Cromwell Road, London SW5 0TU Tel: 020 7370 6841 — MB ChB 1972 Manch.; FRCP Lond. 1991; MRCP (UK) 1976. Cons. Cardiol. Roy. Lond. Hosp. & Roy. Brompton Nat. Heart & Lung Inst. Hosp. Prev: Sen. Regist. (Cardiac) Kings Coll. Hosp. Lond.; Dir. Cardiac Pacing Stanford Univ. Calif., USA; Fogarty Internat. Post-Doctoral Fell. & MRC Internat. Fell. Stanford Univ. Calif., USA.

ROTHMAN, William Thurlow (retired) Little Wood, Woodlands Rise, Sevenoaks TN15 0HZ Tel: 01732 761445 Fax: 01732 761445 — MB ChB Cape Town 1948; FRCR 1975; FFR 1961; DMRD Eng. 1956. Prev: Cons. Radiol. Tunbridge Wells & Bromley HAs.

ROTHNIE, Douglas William (retired) 38 Hartington Street, Barrow-in-Furness LA14 5SW Tel: 01229 20554 — MB ChB 1957 Aberd.

ROTHNIE, James Robert Glenwood Health Centre, Napier Road, Glenrothes KY6 1HL Tel: 01592 611000 — MB ChB 1960 Glas.; DA Eng. 1962; DObst RCOG 1963. (Glas.) Socs: Brit. Soc. Med. & Dent. Hypn., Brit. Med. Acupunc. Soc. & Internat. Soc. Hypn.. Prev: Res. Med. Off. O & G Robroyston Hosp. Glas.; Sen. Ho. Off. Anaesth. Dept. Glas. Roy. Infirm.; Ho. Surg. Falkirk Roy. Infirm.

ROTHNIE, Mr Neil David Linden Lodge, Church Walk, Rochford SS4 1NL Tel: 01702 540461 — MB BS 1981 Lond.; MS Lond. 1991, MB BS 1981; FRCS Eng. 1986. Cons. Surg. S.end Health Care Trust. Prev: Sen. Regist. (Surg.) St. Bart. Hosp. Lond.

ROTHNIE, Mr Norman George (retired) 1 Ingleside Court, Upper West Terrace, Budleigh Salterton EX9 6NZ Tel: 013954 3986 — MB BS 1950 Lond.; MS Lond. 1960, MB BS 1950; FRCS Eng. 1956. Prev: Sen. Surg. Regist. & Ho. Surg. Surgic. Profess. & Thoracic Units St.

ROTHNIE, Rosalind Jane Diana The Surgery, The High Street, Great Wakering Tel: 01702 577850 — MB BS 1981 Lond.; BSc (Hons. Pharmacol.) Lond. 1978; DFFP 1993; DRCOG 1983; Cert. Family Plann. JCC 1983. (St. Bart.) Gen. Practitioner; Examr. Med. Off. DHSS; Family Plann. Off. S.end HA; Adj. Med. Off. DHSS. Socs: Brit. Med. Assn. Prev: GP Cheshunt; SHO (O & G) St. Bart. Hosp. Lond.; SHO (A & E & Geriat. & Med.) Whipps Cross Hosp. Lond.

ROTHWELL, Anne Catherine Riverside Health Centre, Wellington Street, Canton, Cardiff CF11 9SH Tel: 029 2034 2113 Fax: 029 2034 2686 — MB BCh 1983 Wales.

ROTHWELL, Bryan Peter Oldbury Health Centre, Albert St., Oldbury, Warley B69 4DE Tel: 0121 552 6747; 4 Millbrook Way, Lakeside, Brierley Hill DY5 3YY Tel: 01384 77307 — BM BCh 1984 Oxf.; MA, BM BCh Oxf. 1984; MRCGP 1988; DRCOG 1987. Clin. Asst. (Neonat.) Wordsley Hosp. Stourbridge. Prev: SHO (Paediat./Obst./Med.) Burnley Gen. Hosp.

ROTHWELL, Colin Ian 122 Torvill Drive, Wollaton, Nottingham NG8 2BR Tel: 0115 928 0603 — MB ChB 1981 Leeds; FRCR 1987. Cons. Radiol. Lincoln Co. Hosp. Prev: Research Fell. (Med.) Nottm. Univ.

ROTHWELL, Derek (retired) Penmor, 34 Hunts Lane, Stockton Heath, Warrington WA4 2DT Tel: 01925 264697 — MB ChB Manch. 1951. Prev: Ref. DHSS.

ROUNCEFIELD

ROTHWELL, Jane Elizabeth Chadderton and Hollinwood Medical Group, 370 Manchester Road, Hollinwood, Oldham OL9 7PG Tel: 0161 624 1287 Fax: 0161 620 9466 — MRCS Eng. LRCP Lond. 1982; DRCOG 1986.

ROTHWELL, Kay The Old School Surgery, Hinckley Road, Stoney Stanton, Leicester LE9 4LJ Tel: 01455 271445 Fax: 01445 274526; 82 Underwood Drive, Stoney Stanton, Leicester LE9 4TD Tel: 01455 273181 — BM BS 1985 Nottm.; BMedSci Nottm. 1983; MRCGP 1989; DRCOG 1988. (Nottm.) GP Partner. Prev: Trainee GP/SHO Nottm. VTS; Ho. Off. (Therap.) Qu. Med. Centre Nottm.; Ho. Off. (Surg.) Derby Roy. Infirm.

ROTHWELL, Michael Peter Dept. of Anaesth., Macclesfield Hospital, Victoria Road, Macclesfield SK10 3BL Tel: 01625 661307 — MB BS 1990 Lond.; FRCA 1996. (St. Marys London) Cons. Anaesth.

***ROTHWELL, Nicola Louise** 38 Kinloch Drive, Heaton, Bolton BL1 4LZ Tel: 01204 495936; 38 Kinloch Drive, Heaton, Bolton BL1 4LZ Tel: 01204 495036 — MB ChB 1998 Birm.

ROTHWELL, Mr Peter James Neil Department of Urology, Blackpool Victoria Hospital NHS Trust, Whinney Heys Road, Blackpool FY3 8NR Tel: 01253 306996; 22 The Belfry, Lytham St Annes FY8 4NW Tel: 01253 731633 — MB ChB 1979 Manch.; BSc Manch. 1976, MD 1991; FRCS (Urol.) 1994; FRCS Ed. 1984. Cons. Urol. Blackpool Vict. NHS Trust. Prev: Sen. Regist. Rotat. (Urol.) NW Region.

ROTHWELL, Peter Malcolm Department of Clinical Neurosciences, Western General Hospital, Crewe Road, Edinburgh EH4 2XU Tel: 0131 537 2129; 12 Clackmae Road, Liberton, Edinburgh EH16 6NZ Tel: 0131 658 1591 — MB ChB 1987 Ed.; MD Ed. 1995; MRCP (UK) 1990. Clin. Research Fell. (Neurol.) W.. Gen. Hosp. Edin. Prev: Regist. (Neurol.) W.. Gen. Hosp. Edin.; Regist. (Med.) Falkirk & Dist. Roy. Infirm.; SHO (Med.) Cleveland Hosps.

ROTHWELL, Mr Richard Ian Cookridge Hospital, Leeds LS16 6QB Tel: 0113 267 3411 — MB BS 1966 Lond.; FRCS Eng. 1974; MRCS Eng. LRCP Lond. 1966; FRCR 1983; DObst RCOG 1968. (Middlx.) Cons. Radiother. & Oncol. Cookridge Hosp. Leeds. Socs: BMA; Europ. Soc. Therapeutic Radiol. & Oncol.; Brit. Inst. of Radiol. Prev: Lect. (Radiother. & Oncol.) Cookridge Hosp. Univ. Leeds.; Surg. Govt. of Sabah, Malaysia; Ho. Phys. Middlx. Hosp. Lond.

ROTHWELL, Simon James St. Francis Hospital, Private Bag 11, Katete, Zambia; Thistlegrove, La Grande Route De St Laurent, St Lawrence, Jersey JE3 1FB Tel: 01534 861722 — MB BS 1990 Lond.

ROTHWELL, Susan Elizabeth 3 Chesterford House, Southacre Park, Southacre Drive, Cambridge CB2 2TZ; Barnston Oak House, Parsonage Lane, Barnston, Dunmow CM6 3PA — MB BChir 1993 Camb.; BSc (1st cl. Hons.) Bradford 1983; MSc Neurosensory Physiol. Camb. 1988; FBCO 1988, M 1984; Dip. Opt. Gen. Optical Counc. Worsh Co Spectacle Makers, Freedom City Lond.1984. SHO, (Ophth.) Roy. Bershire Hosp. Reading.; Princip. Optometrist Boots Optical Servs. Camb. Prev: SHO (Ophth.) King Edwd. VII Hosp., P. Chas. Eye Unit, Windsor; Ho. Off. (Gen. Surg. & Transpl.) Addenbrooke's Hosp. Camb.; Ho. Phys. (Gen. Med.) W. Suff. Hosp. Bury st Edmunds.

ROTHWELL HUGHES, Mary Elizabeth Medical Centre, Hay-on-Wye, Hereford HR3 5QX Tel: 01497 820333 — MB ChB 1987 Bristol; MRCGP 1992; DRCOG 1991; DCH RCP Lond. 1989. Prev: SHO (Paediat.) S. Warks. HA.

ROTHWELL-JACKSON, Mr Richard Loxton (retired) The Conifers, Common Road, Kensworth, Dunstable LU6 2PW — MB BChir 1956 Camb.; MChir Camb. 1966, MA 1956; FRCS Eng. 1960. Prev: Cons. Gen. Surg. Luton & Dunstable Hosp.

ROTMAN, Charles Morris Henry 213 Hempstead Road, Watford WD17 3HH Tel: 01923 232010; Bush House, Aldwych, London WC2 — MRCS Eng. LRCP Lond. 1940; MD Lond. 1947, MB BS 1940, DPH 1947; AFOM RCP Lond. 1982; MFCM 1974; MRCGP 1953; DMJ Soc. Apoth. Lond. 1969; DCH Eng. 1949. (King's Coll. & Char. Cross) Mem. Middle Temple. Socs: Nutrit. Soc. & Soc. of Chem. Indust. Prev: Ho. Surg. Char. Cross Hosp.; Phys. Supt. Willesden Fev. Hosp.; Surg. Lt. RNVR 1941-46.

ROTONDETTO, Salvatore 4 Clumber Avenue, Clayton, Newcastle ST5 3AX — State Exam 1991 Naples.

ROTTENBERG, Giles Tobias 11 Bromfield Street, London N1 0QA — MB BS 1988 Lond.; MRCP (UK) 1991; FRCR 1994. Cons. Radiol. Guy's & St. Thom. Trust Lond. Prev: Sen. Regist. Middlx. Hosp. Lond.

ROTTENBERG, Mrs Susi Gerda West Two Health, 33-35 Praed St., London W2 1NR Tel: 020 7402 3013 — MB ChB 1958 Bristol. (Bristol) Prev: Ho. Phys. Roy. Hosp. Sick Childr. Bristol; Ho. Surg. St. Mary's Hosp. Plaistow; Ho. Off. (Anaesth.) W. Middlx. Hosp. Isleworth.

ROTZ, Bernhard 38 Aberdare Close, Chichester PO19 4UG — State Exam Med 1991 Berlin.

ROUALLE, Mr Henri Louis Marcel (retired) 89 Marsh Lane, London NW7 4LE Tel: 020 8959 6042 — MRCS Eng. LRCP Lond. 1937; MD Lond. 1940, MB BS 1937; FRCS Eng. 1940. Prev: Vis. Surg. H.M. Prison Wormwood Scrubs.

ROUD, Philippa Lindsay William Harvey Hospital, Kennington Road, Willesbrough, Ashford TN24 0LZ Tel: 01233 633331; The Laynes, Lickpot Hill, Elham, Canterbury CT4 6TY Tel: 01303 840400 — MB BS 1987 Lond.; BSc (Hons.) Lond. 1984, MB BS 1987. Hosp. Pract. (O & G) William Harvey Hosp. Ashford. Prev: SHO (A & E) Epsom Dist. Hosp.; Ho. Phys. & Ho. Surg. Orsett Hosp.

ROUD MAYNE, Catherine Charlotte Anne 10 Hunts Close, Luton LU1 5JL — MB BChir 1990 Camb.

ROUGH, Donald Percy 3 Grand Court W., Grand Drive, Leigh-on-Sea SS9 1BQ Tel: 01702 479157 Fax: 01702 479157 — MB BS Lond. 1948; MRCS Eng. LRCP Lond. 1948; DObst RCOG 1953. (St. Mary's) Prev: Ho. Phys. New End Hosp. & RAF Med. Br.; Ho. Off. (Obst.) W. Middlx. Hosp. Isleworth.

ROUGH, Sandy Aitken 8 Grey Street, Killin FK21 8SW Tel: 01567 820704 — MB ChB 1993 Glas.; DRCOG 1995; MRCGP 1998.

ROUGHEAD, Peter (retired) 12 Anne Drive, Stenhousemuir, Larbert FK5 4JE Tel: 01324 554246 — MB ChB 1949 Glas.; DPH 1954, DPM Eng. 1957; FRCPsych 1992, M 1971; DPM Durham. 1958. Prev: Cons. Psychiat. Bellsdyke Hosp. Larbert.

ROUGHNEEN, Patrick Thomas Martin The Hospital for Sick Children, Great Ormond St., London WC1N 3JH — MB ChB 1982 Leicester.

ROUGHTON, Helen Clare Oakenhall Medical Practice, Bolsover Street, Hucknall, Nottingham NG15 7UA Tel: 0115 963 3511 Fax: 0115 968 0947 — BM BS 1991 Nottm.

ROUGHTON, Susanna Alice, Maj. RAMC Killead Health Centre, Killead Road, Aldergrove, Crumlin BT29 4EN — MB BS 1989 Lond.; MRCGP Oct 1995; DFFP 1996; DSOM May 1997; Dip Imm C RCS Ed 1999. (GUY's)

ROUHOLAMIN, Mr Ebrahim Worcester Royal Infirmary, Castle Street Branch, Castle St., Worcester WR1 3AS Tel: 01905 763333; Hallow Bank, Hallow Road, Worcester WR2 6DD Tel: 01905 423250 — MD 1969 Tehran; FRCS Glas. 1984. Cons. Orthop. Surg. Worcs. & Dist. HA.

ROULSON, Catherine Jane Anaesthetic Department, University Hospital, Lewisham High St., London SE13 6LH Tel: 020 8333 3000 — MB ChB 1984 Manch.; FRCA. (Manchester University) Cons. Anaesth. Lewisham Hosp.

ROULSON, Jo-An Saville Coach House, Savile Road, Halifax HX1 2BA — MB ChB 1998 Dund.; MB ChB Dund 1998.

ROULSTON, James Russell (retired) The Coach House, 37 Beechwood Avenue, Mirfield WF14 9LG Tel: 01924 493622 — MD 1946 Belf.; MB BCh BAO 1938.

ROULSTON, Miss Lizanne 52 Baycliff Road, West Derby, Liverpool L12 6QU Tel: 0151 228 4702 — MB ChB 1996 Liverp. SHO (Gastroenterol.) Fazakerley Hosp. Liverp. Prev: Ho. Off. (Med. & Surg.) Fazakerley Hosp. Liverp.

ROULSTON, Peter Medical Centre, Connaught Barracks, Dover CT16 1HL; 31 Woodland Close, River, Dover CT17 0NR — MB ChB 1995 Dundee.

ROULSTON, Rose Gwynne (retired) The Coach House, 37 Beechwood Avenue, Mirfield WF14 9LG Tel: 01924 493622 — MB ChB St. And. 1948. Prev: Assoc. Specialist Anaesth. Yorks. RHA.

ROUNCEFIELD, Mrs Angela Mary St. Lawrence Hospital, Boundary Rd, Bodmin PL31 2QT Tel: 01208 251300 Fax: 01208 251512; Broadwater, Restronglet Point, Feock, Truro TR3 7QD Tel: 01872 862751 Fax: 01872 862751 — MB ChB 1962 Liverp.; FRCPsych. 1984, M 1971; DPM Eng. 1965. (Liverp.) Cons. Psychiat. St Lawrence Hosp. Bodmin; Medicla Adviser Cornw. Alcohol and

ROUND

Drug Agency, Truro. Socs: BMA (Chairm.) Cornw. Br.; Cornw. Clin. Soc. (Past Pres.). Prev: Cons. Psychiat. N. Wales Hosp. Denbigh, & Maelor Hosp. Wrexham; Research Fell. & Hon. Sen. Regist. N. Wales Hosp. Denbigh; Regist. (Psychiat.) Sefton Gen. Hosp. Liverp.

ROUND, Alison Pamela North and East Devon HA, Dean Clarke House, Southernhay East, Exeter EX1 1PQ Tel: 01392 406127 Fax: 01392 70910 — MB ChB 1982 Bristol; BSc Med. Microbiol., MB ChB Bristol 1982; MRCP (UK) 1985; MFPHM RCP (UK) 1994; MRCGP 1991. Cons. (Pub. Health Med.) N. & E. Devon HA.

ROUND, Caroline Elizabeth 121 Girton Road, Cambridge CB3 0LS — MB BS 1983 Lond.

ROUND, Jonathan Edward Collier 11 Hansler Road, London SE22 9DJ — MB BS 1990 Lond.

ROUND, Keith William Spring Farm, Coombe, St Austell PL26 7LF — MB ChB 1973 Ed.; MRCGP 1977; DObst RCOG 1976.

ROUND, Leslie Aylesbury Partnership, Aylesbury Medical Centre, Taplow House, Thurlow Street, London SE17 2XE Tel: 020 7703 2205 — MB BS 1974 Lond.; DRCOG 1977.

ROUND, Patrick Michael Glaxo Wellcome R&D, Stockley Park, Uxbridge UB11 1BT Tel: 020 8990 8214 Fax: 020 8990 8245 Email: pr43229@glaxowellcome.co.uk; 37 Brands Hill Avenue, High Wycombe HP13 5PY Tel: 01494 451205 — MB BS 1982 Lond.; FCAnaesth. 1990; AFPM/Dip Pharm Med 1995. (Charin g Cross Hosp. Med. Sch.) Clin. Developm. Director, Pain & Endocrinol.,Glaxowellcome. Prev: Clin. Research Phys., Novo Nordisk Copenhagen.

ROUND, Percy Holcroft (retired) 40 Alfreton Road, South Normanton, Alfreton DE55 2AS Tel: 01773 811421 — MB ChB 1951 Birm. Prev: Ho. Surg. (Obst.) & Ho. Phys. Qu. Eliz. Hosp. Birm.

ROUNDING, Alan (retired) 2 Ashdowne, Crakehall, Bedale DL8 1LF — MB BS 1947 Durh.

ROUNDING, Margaret Sarah (retired) 2 Ashdowne, Crakehall, Bedale DL8 1LF — MB ChB 1951 Leeds; DObst RCOG 1953.

ROURKE, Anne 9 Woodcote Valley Road, Purley CR8 3AL — MB ChB 1973 Dundee; BMSc Dund 1970; MRCPsych 1978. Assoc. Specialist Springfield Hosp. Lond. Prev: Clin. Asst. Springfield Hosp. Lond.; Clin. Asst., Regist. & SHO Barrow Hosp. Barrow Gurney.

ROURKE, Anthony 14 Nether Craigwell, Edinburgh EH8 8DR — MB ChB 1958 Glas. Princip. Med. Off. Scott. Prison Serv. Prev: Sen. Med. Off. H.M. Prison Serv.

***ROURKE, Duncan Matthew Carlton** 38 Darnford Lane, Lichfield WS14 9RN — MB BS 1998 Lond.; MB BS Lond 1998; MA Hons. (Gantab.).

ROUS, Elizabeth Mary 210 Prestbury Road, Macclesfield SK10 3HL — MB ChB 1982 Leic.; MSc 2000 Manch.; MFPHM 1990; MRCGP 1986; DCH RCP Lond. 1985; DRCOG 1985. SHO Psychiat. Socs: Manch. Med. Soc. Prev: Cons. Pub. Health Med. Manch. HA.; Cons. Pub. Health. Med. Stockport H.A.; Cons. Pub. Health Med. N. W.. RHA.

ROUS, Stephen Alexander 62 Upper Bourtree Drive, Burnside, Rutherglen, Glasgow G73 4EU — MB ChB 1986 Stellenbosch.

ROUSE, Alexander John 48 Brookdale, London N11 1BN — MRCS Eng. LRCP Lond. 1934. (St. Bart.) Med. Ref. Co-op. Insur. Co. & Pruden. Assur. Co. Prev: Ho. Surg. Evelina Hosp. Childr.; Res. Med. Off. Willesden Isolat. Hosp.; Capt. RAMC.

ROUSE, Amanda Kate 96 Lonsdale Road, Oxford OX2 7ER — MB BS 1991 Lond.

ROUSE, Andrew Michael Dept of Public Health and Epidemiology, University of Birmingham, Birmingham B15 2TT; Pengarn Fach, Cippin, St Dogmaels, Cardigan SA43 3LT — MB BS 1975 Lond.; MRCS Eng. LRCP Lond. 1975. Sen. Lect. Pub. Health Med., Uni. Birm.

ROUSE, Brian Richard Shephall Way Surgery, 29 Shephall Way, Stevenage SG2 9QN Tel: 01438 312097 — MB BS 1978 Newc.

ROUSE, David Andrew The London Medicolegal Centre, P.O. Box 70, Billingshurst RH14 0YH Tel: 07973 548574 Fax: 01403 753524 Email: d.a.rouse@talk21.com — MB BChir 1985 Camb.; MA Camb. 1985; MRCPath 1991; DMJ(Path) Soc. Apoth. Lond. 1990; FRCPath 2000. Cons. Forens. Med. & Path. Lond. Medico-Legal Centre. Socs: Brit. Acad. Forens. Scs.; Brit. Assn. in Forens. Med.; Forens. Sci. Soc. Prev: Lect. (Forens. Med.) Lond. Hosp. Med. Coll.; SHO (Histopath.) St. Bart. Hosp. Lond.; Ho. Off. Guy's Hosp. Lond.

ROUSE, Eileen Hilda (retired) Oaklee, Pound Lane, Burley, Ringwood BH24 4EE — MB BCh 1953 Witwatersrand.

ROUSE, Eryl Clare Ty'n-y-Cae, Eglwys Bach, Colwyn Bay LL28 5TS — MB BCh Wales 1960; DA Eng. 1963. (Cardiff) Ass. Specialist N. Clwyd Glan Clwyd Hosp. Clwyd. Prev: Regist. (Anaesth.) United Sheff. Hosp.

ROUSE, Gillian Margaret 3 The Cherry Orchard, Staverton, Cheltenham GL51 0TR Tel: 01242 680532 — MB ChB 1969 Birm.; MFFP 1993. (Birm.) SCMO (Family Plann.) E. Glos. NHS Trust & Clin. Asst. (Haemat.) Glos. Roy. Hosp. & Cheltenham Hosp.

ROUSE, Jane Margaret The Princess Royal Hospital, Haywards Heath RH16 4EX Tel: 01444 441881; Little Orchard, Ansty, Haywards Heath RH17 5AG — MB BS 1971 Lond.; FFA RCS Eng. 1976. (St. Mary's) Cons. Anaesth. P.ss Roy. Hosp. Hayward Heath W.Sussex; Cons. Anaesth. Hurstwood Pk. Neurol. Unit Haywards Heath; Clin. Tutor Mid Sussex NHS Trust 1997-. Socs: Roy. Coll. Anaesth.; Assoc of Anaesth. G.B. & Irel.; Neuro anaesth. Soc. Prev: Chairm. Anaesth. Div. Mid Sussex NHS Trust; Coll. Tutor (Anaesth.) RCS; Sen. Regist. (Anaesth.) St. Mary's Hosp. Lond.

ROUSE, Mary Emily 45 Regent Park Square, Glasgow G41 2AF — MB ChB 1996 Glas.; MB ChB (Hons.) Glas. 1996; PhD Glas. 1992; BSc (Hons.) Glas. 1988. (Glasgow) SHO (Med.).

ROUSE, Michael Edward St John's Avenue Surgery, 24 St. John's Avenue, Churchdown, Gloucester GL3 2DB Tel: 01452 713036 Fax: 01452 714726; 3 The Cherry Orchard, Staverton, Cheltenham GL51 0TR Tel: 01452 680532 — MB ChB 1968 Birm. (Birm.) Socs: BMA. Prev: Ho. Surg. Profess. Unit Qu. Eliz. Hosp. Birm.; Ho. Phys. & Ho. Off. (O & G) Dudley Rd. Hosp. Birm.

ROUSE, Robert Turnbull Rysseldene, 98 Conway Road, Colwyn Bay LL29 7LE Tel: 01492 532807 — MB ChB 1961 Ed.

ROUSHDI, Mr Hossam Roushdi Ibrahim Mohamed Ashford and St Peter's Hospital NHS Trust, London Road, Ashford TW15 3AA Tel: 01276 686770 Fax: 01784 886244 Email: roushdi@aol.com; 9 Eliot Close, Camberley GU15 1LW — MB ChB 1975 Alexandria; MS Alexandria 1979; FRCS Glas. 1985. Cons. Orthop. Surg. Ashford & St. Peter's Hosp.

ROUSHDY-GEMIE, May Dyke Road Surgery, 361 Dyke Road, Glasgow G13 4SQ Tel: 0141 959 2118 Fax: 0141 959 9851; 41 Rowallan Gardens, Glasgow G11 7LH Tel: 0141 334 1296 — MB ChB 1984 Glas.; MRCGP 1988; DRCOG 1986. GP Glas. Retainer Scheme.

ROUSSAK, Mr Jeremy Brian 16 Cheverton Road, London N19 3AY Tel: 020 7281 3406 Fax: 020 7281 3406 Email: jeremyr@dcs.qmw.ac.uk — MB BChir 1984 Camb.; MA, MB Camb. 1984, BA 1980, BChir 1983; FRCS Ed. 1988; Dip. Law 1995. (Camb.) Prev: Regist. (Cardiothoracic Surg.) Roy. Brompton Nat. Heart & Lung Hosp. Lond.; Regist. (Cardiothoracic Surg.) Hammersmith Hosp. Lond.; SHO (Cardiothoracic Surg.) Hammersmith Hosp.

ROUSSAK, Neville Jack (retired) 48 Spath Road, Manchester M20 2GT Tel: 0161 445 9292 Email: roussak@aol.com — MB ChB 1945 Manch.; BSc Manch. 1942; FRCP Lond. 1975, M 1948. Prev: Cons. Phys. Withington Hosp. Manch.

ROUSSEAU, Marek Jan 3 Canonbury, Shrewsbury SY3 7AG — MB BS 1988 Lond.; BSc BPharm. (Hons.) Aberd. 1982.

ROUSSEAU, Neil Charles Brocklebank Health Centre, 249 Garratt Lane, London SW18 4UE Tel: 020 8870 1341/871 4448; 249 Garratt Lane, London SW18 4DU Tel: 020 8870 1341 — MB BS 1983 Lond.; BSc (Hons.) Lond. 1980, MB BS 1983. Demonst. (Anat.) & SHO (Cas.) Univ. Coll. Hosp. Lond.; Mem. Edit. Bd. Medonomics Magazine. Prev: SHO (Geriat., Med. & Paediat.) Roy. Free Hosp. Lond.; Ho. Off. (Surg. & A & E) Univ. Coll. Hosp. Lond.; Ho. Off. (Med.) Hillingdon Hosp.

ROUSSEAU, Stephen Anthony PHLSheadquaters, London NW9 5DF Tel: 0208 200 1295 Fax: 01722 414165; 26 Apostle Way, Bishopdown Farm, Salisbury SP1 3GD — MB BS 1967 Lond.; MSc (Med. Microbiol.) Lond. 1979; MRCS Eng. LRCP Lond. 1967; FRCPath 1992, M 1980; DObst RCOG 1974. (St. Bart.) Cons microbiologist; PHLS Med. And Scientif. Postgrad. Dean. Prev: Cons. Microbiol. Pub. Health Laborat. Luton & Dunstable Hosp.; NACT Europ. Trav. Fell. 1989; GP Hants.

ROUSSEL, Osmond Nicholas (retired) La Corbière, Hougue du Moulin, Vale, Guernsey GY3 5NG Tel: 01481 44439 — MRCS Eng. LRCP Lond. 1935; MA Camb. 1937, MD 1941; FFA RCS Eng. 1954. Prev: Cons. Anaesth. Mid Surrey Health Dist.

ROUSSOUNIS, Socrates Hercules 1 Nichols Way, Wetherby LS22 6AD Tel: 01937 584178 — MB BS 1964 Lond.; FRCP Lond. 1989; MRCP (UK) 1972; MRCS Eng. LRCP Lond. 1962; DCH Eng. 1968; DObst RCOG 1966. (St. Geo.) Cons. Paediat. & Dir. Regional Child Developm. Centre St. Jas. Univ. Hosp. Leeds; Hon. Sen. Lect. (Clin. Paediat.) Univ. Leeds. Prev: Sen. Regist. (Paediat.) Char. Cross Hosp. Lond.; Research Fell. & Ho. Phys. (Neurol.) Hosp. Sick Childr. Gt. Ormond St.Lond.

ROUT, David John Willows Medical Centre, Osbourne Drive, Queensbury, Bradford BD13 2GD Tel: 01274 882008 Fax: 01274 818447; Catherine House Farm, Catherine House Lane, Luddenden Dean, Halifax HX2 6XB Tel: 01422 882342 — MB ChB 1981 Leeds; MRCGP 1987.

ROUT, Jonathan Philip Priory Avenue Surgery, 2 Priory Avenue, Caversham, Reading RG4 7SE Tel: 0118 947 2431 Fax: 0118 946 3340; 7 Blenheim Road, Caversham, Reading RG4 7RT Tel: 01734 471738 — MB BS 1977 Lond.; MRCGP 1982; DRCOG 1982. (St. Thos.) Prev: SHO (O & G) Roy. Berks. Hosp. Reading; SHO (Paediat.) & Ho. Phys. Battle Hosp. Reading.

ROUTH, Christina Phoebe Priory Lodge, Ford Road, Upton, Wirral CH49 0TD — MB ChB 1985 Manch.; MRCPsych 1993. Prev: Regist. (Child & Adult Psychiat.) Clatterbridge Hosp. Wirral; Regist. (Child & Adolesc. Psychiat.) Alderhey Childr. Hosp. Liverp.; Regist. (Adult Psychiat.) Clatterbridge Hosp. Wirral.

ROUTH, Curtis Dudley (retired) Tintern Lodge, 86 Lion Road, Bexleyheath DA6 8PQ Tel: 020 8303 3229 — MRCS Eng. LRCP Lond. 1944; MD Lond. 1951; MB BS 1944; FRCP Lond. 1972, M 1951. Prev: Cons. Venereol. Dartford & Gravesham, Medway & Maidstone Health.

ROUTH, Guy Stephen Cheltenham General Hospital, Cheltenham GL53 7AN Tel: 01242 222222 Fax: 01242 273405 — MB BS 1974 Lond.; MRCS Eng. LRCP Lond. 1973; FFA RCS Eng. 1978. (St. Bart.) Cons. Anaesth. Cheltenham Gen. Hosp. & Glos. Roy. Hosp. Gloucester. Prev: Med. Dir. E. Glos. NHS Trust; Sen. Regist. (Anaesth.) Glas. Roy. Infirm.; Research Regist. (Intens. Care) W.. Infirm. Glas.

ROUTH, John Eric (retired) Leyland Park, Tubwell Lane, Crowborough TN6 3RH Tel: 01892 663866 — MRCS Eng. LRCP Lond. 1950; MFCM 1974; DPH Lond. 1961. Prev: Wing Cdr. RAF Med. Br.

ROUTLEDGE, Deborah Jane 21 Coniston Av, West Jesmond, Newcastle upon Tyne NE2 3EY — MB BS 1997 Newc.

ROUTLEDGE, Helen Clare 167 College Road, Collegetown, Sandhurst GU47 0RG; 201 Sherbourne Lofts, Grosvenor Street W., Birmingham B16 8HW Tel: 0121 246 6911 Email: rutters@dial.pipex.com — MB ChB 1996 Birm.; BSc (Hons.) Biochem. Birm. 1994. (Birmingham) SHO (Med.) Birm. Heartlands & Solihull NHS Trust (Teachg.).

ROUTLEDGE, Nicholas Graham High Beech Villa, Beech Road, Newport PO30 2AH — MB BS 1993 Lond.

ROUTLEDGE, Professor Philip Alexander Department of Pharmacology, Therapeutics and Toxicology, University of Wales College of Medeicine, Heath Park, Cardiff CF14 4XN Tel: 029 2074 2051 Fax: 0292074 8316 Email: 106174.22@compuserve.com — MD Newc. 1978, MB BS 1972; FRCP (UK) 1986, M 1975. Prof. Clin. Pharmacol. Univ. Wales Coll. Med. Cardiff; Dir. Therap. & Toxicol. Centre; Dir. CSM Wales; Hon. Cons. Phys. S. Glam. HA; Cons. Toxicol. Welsh Off. Socs: Assn. of Phys.s of GB/NI; Brit. Pharmacol. Soc.; Brit. Toxicological Soc. Prev: Lect. (Clin. Pharmacol.) Univ. Newc.; Asst. Prof. Med. (Med. Research) Duke Univ. Durh., N. Carolina, USA; Merck, Sharpe & Dohme Internat. Fell. (Clin. Pharmacol.) Duke Univ.

ROUTLEDGE, Raymond, OStJ (retired) 9 Gowan Lea, 15 Woodford Road, Snaresbrook, London E18 2ER Tel: 020 8989 7451 — MB BChir 1953 Camb.; MA Camb. 1953; MRCS Eng. LRCP Lond. 1953; MFOM RCP Lond. 1978; DIH Eng. 1959. Prev: Sen. Regional Med. Off. Brit. Telecom. Lond.

ROUTLEDGE, Raymond Crawford Hope Hospital, Eccles Old Road, Salford M6 8HD — MB ChB 1966 Manch.; MRCPath 1975. (Manch.) Cons. Haemat. Salford AHA (T).

ROUTLEDGE, Richard 24 West Bank Lane, Hest Bank, Lancaster LA2 6DB Tel: 01524 824149 — MB ChB 1968 Manch.; MRCGP 1974.

ROUTLEDGE, Thomas Adam The Court, Chapel Lane, Winford, Bristol BS8 3DN — BM BCh 1997 Oxf.

ROUX, Bryant Raphael Flat 2, 65A Chalk Farm Road, London NW1 8AN — MB ChB 1990 Cape Town.

ROUX, Hermanus Johannes 8 Harefield Close, Enfield EN2 8NQ — MB ChB 1988 Stellenbosch.

ROVIRA, Peter Alan Kirkham Medical Practice, St. Albans Road, Babbacombe, Torquay TQ1 3SL Tel: 01803 323541; Red Roofs, Teignmouth Road, Maidencombe, Torquay TQ1 4TP — MB ChB 1970 Liverp.

ROW, Herbert Gordon Tyn yr Allt, Hillside, Prestatyn LL19 9PW — MB ChB 1952 Liverp.; FRCR 1975; DMRD Liverp. 1958; DMRD Eng. 1958. (Liverp.) Cons. Radiol. Clwyd & Deeside Hosp. Gp. Prev: Radiol. Mildura Base Hosp. Australia.

ROW, Kandukar Prabakar 1 Coburg Gardens, Clayhall, Ilford IG5 0PP Tel: 020 8551 3478 — MB BS 1941 Madras; DPH Ed. 1948; DCH Eng. 1950. (Madras)

ROWAN, Christian Andrew Carr c/o M Campbell, 95 Swan Ct, Chelsea Manor St., London SW3 5RY — MB BS 1996 Queensland.

ROWAN, Ian George Ormeau Park Surgery, 281 Ormeau Road, Belfast BT7 3GG Tel: 028 9064 2914 Fax: 028 9064 3993; 281 Ormeau Road, Belfast BT7 3GG — MB BCh BAO 1980 Belf.; MRCGP 1984; DRCOG 1983; DCH RCPSI 1982. GP Belf. Socs: Ulster Med. Soc.; BMA. Prev: SHO Roy. Belf. Hosp. Sick Childr. & Roy. Matern. Hosp. Belf.; Ho. Off. Roy. Vict. Hosp. Belf.

ROWAN, Jeremy Francis 2 Armoured Field Ambulance, Roberts Barracks BFPO 36 — MB BCh BAO 1981 Belf.; MRCGP 1986; DRCOG 1985.

ROWAN, John 27 Surrenden Road, Brighton BN1 6PA — MB ChB 1976 Leeds; MRCGP 1981; DRCOG 1981.

ROWAN, Maurice Glenn Dunluce Avenue Surgery, 1-3 Dunluce Avenue, Belfast BT9 7AW Tel: 028 9024 0884; 17 Magherlave Road, Lisburn BT28 3BW Tel: 01846 675100 Fax: 01846 628168 — MB BCh BAO Belf. 1968; DObst RCOG 1975; DCH RCPSI 1970. (Belf.) Prev: Ho. Off. Roy. Vict. Hosp. Belf.; Regist. & SHO. Roy. Belf. Hosp. Sick Childr.

ROWAN, Peter Arthur The Thatched House, Green Lane, Tivetshall St Margaret, Norwich NR15 2BJ Tel: 01379 674116 Fax: 01379 608014 — MRCS Eng. LRCP Lond. 1974; FRCP 2000; BSc (Hons) Lond. 1971, MB BS 1974; MRCP (UK) 1978; LMSSA Lond. 1974. (Camb. & Lond. Hosp.) Prev: Ships Surg. RRS Discovery.

ROWAN, Peter Rowley The Priory Hospital, Priory Lane, London SW15; 16 Dewhurst Road, London W14 0ET — MB BS 1972 Lond.; MRCPsych 1977.

ROWAN, Robert Anthony (retired) Saracens Cottage, Pluckley, Ashford TN27 0SA Tel: 01233 840253 Email: tonyrowi@compuserve.com — MB BChir 1949 Camb.; MRCGP 1971; DObst RCOG 1954. Prev: Ho. Surg. St. Thos. Hosp. Hydestile & Roy. Portsmouth Hosp.

ROWAN, Robert Martin 13 Buchanan Street, Milngavie, Glasgow G62 8AW Tel: 0141 956 4573 — MB ChB 1959 Ed.; FRCP Glas. 1979, M 1966. (Ed.) Sen. Lect. (Haemat.) Univ. Glas.; Hon. Cons. Gtr. Glas. HB. Prev: Cons. Haemat. Glas. Roy. Infirm; Sen. Regist. (Haemat.) Roy. Infirm. & W.. Gen. Hosp. Edin.

ROWAN, Steven John 3/2, 34 Blantyre St., Glasgow G3 8AR — MB ChB 1996 Glas.

ROWAN-ROBINSON, Martin Neil Macklin Street Surgery, 90 Macklin Street, Derby DE1 2JX Tel: 01332 340381 Fax: 01332 345387; 90 Blagreaves Lane, Littleover, Derby DE23 7FP — MB ChB 1978 Bristol; FRCGP 1996, M 1981; DRCOG 1982. (Bristol) Trainer Derby VTS. Prev: Trainee GP Chesterfield VTS; Ho. Off. (Surg.) Bristol Gen. Hosp. & Vict. Hosp. Blackpool.

ROWBOTHAM, Mr Carl 83 Mansfield Road, Aston, Sheffield S26 4UE Tel: 0114 287 2527 — BM BCh 1993 Oxf.; MA (Hons.) Camb. 1994. (Oxf.)

ROWBOTHAM, Christopher Jeremy Frederick Falconhill, 19 St Bernards Road, Solihull B92 7AU Tel: 0121 707 6427 — MB BS 1962 Durh.; MRCOG 1969. (Durh.) Cons. O & G Solihull & E. Birm. Health Dists. Socs: BMA. Prev: Sen. Regist. O & G Birm. RHB; Regist. O & G United Birm. Hosps.; Regist. (O & G) Newc. Gen. Hosp.

ROWBOTHAM, Professor David John Department of Anaesthesia and Pain Management, Leicester Royal Infirmary, Leicester LE1 5WW Tel: 0116 258 5291 Email: djr8@le.ac.uk —

ROWBOTHAM

MB ChB 1978 Sheff.; MD Sheff. 1991; MRCP (UK) 1983; FRCA 1986; FRCSI 1985. (Sheffield) Prof. Pain Managem. & Anaesth. Leicester Roy. Infirm. Socs: Eur. Soc. Anaesth. (Chairm. Pharmacol. Sub. Comm.); Coun. Mem. Pain Soc.; Anaesth. Res. Soc.

ROWBOTHAM, Hugo Dalyson 147 Harley Street, London W1G 6BL Tel: 020 7935 4444 Fax: 020 7486 3782; 11 Cromwell Crescent, London SW5 9QW Tel: 020 7603 6967 — MB BS 1965 Durh. GP Lond. Socs: BMA & Soc. Occupat. Med.

ROWBOTHAM, Monica Dalyson (retired) Corderoys, Upton, Didcot OX11 9JH Tel: 01235 850261 — MB ChB Manch. 1934; FRCPsych 1974, M 1972; DPM Durham. 1957. Prev: Cons. Child Psychiat. Nuffield Dept. Child Psychiat. & Psychol. Newc.

ROWBURY, Cynthia Anne Temple Fortune Health Centre, 23 Temple Fortune Lane, London NW11 7TE Tel: 020 8458 4431 — MRCS Eng. LRCP Lond. 1972; MRCP (UK) 1978.

ROWBURY, James Lionel Hide Hollow, Brookvale Orchard, Higher Ringmore Road, Shaldon, Teignmouth TQ14 0HH — MB BS 1998 Lond.; MB BS Lond 1998.

ROWDEN, Jennifer Daphne Thornhill Unit, Moorgreen Hospital, West End, Southampton SO30 3JB Tel: 02380 475241/2 — BM 1980 Soton.; MRCGP 1984; DRCOG 1982. Assoc. Specialist, Old Age Psychiat., W. Hants. NHS Trust, Soton.

ROWDEN, Kenneth White Singleton Medical Centre, Singleton, Ashford Tel: 01233 646036; The White House, Sheldwich Lees, Faversham ME13 0NG Fax: 01795 533200 — MB BS 1957 Lond.; MRCS Eng. LRCP Lond. 1957; DCH Eng. 1961; DObst RCOG 1960. (Lond. Hosp.) Prev: Clin. Asst. (Child Psychiat.) Canterbury & Thanet Health Dist.; SHO (Paediat.) OldCh. Hosp. Romford; Ho. Surg. (Obst.) Forest Gate Hosp. Lond.

ROWE, Alan Frank Tel: 028 7034 2650 Fax: 028 7032 1000; 6 Gortgrannagh Drive, Wheatsheaf Heights, Coleraine BT51 3NQ Tel: 01265 54244 — MB BCh BAO 1974 Dub.; BA; MRCGP 1978; DRCOG 1977. (TC Dub.) Prev: SHO (O & G) Route Hosp. Ballymoney; SHO (Psychiat.) & SHO (Med.) Whiteabbey Hosp. Newtownabbey.

ROWE, Alan Inness (retired) Garmoe, Camelford PL32 9TS Tel: 01840 212689 — MB BS Durh. 1947. Prev: Ho. Surg. N. Eng. Thoracic Surg. Centre Shotley Bridge.

ROWE, Alan John, OBE (retired) Haughley Grange, Stowmarket IP14 3QT Tel: 01449 673008 Fax: 01229 774935 Email: arowe@bma.org.uk — LMSSA 1950 Lond.; FRCGP 1982, M 1968. Cons. WHO; Cons. WHO. Prev: Hosp. Pract. (Rheum. & Rehabil.) Addenbrooke's Hosp. Camb.

ROWE, Alexander John Scarth Tan-yr-Allt, Bont Ystrad, Denbigh LL16 3HE — MB BS 1994 Lond.

ROWE, Angela Okehampton Medical Centre, Okehampton EX20 1AY Tel: 01837 52233 — MB BS 1987 Lond.; MRCGP 1994; DRCOG 1995; DFFP 1995; DCH Otago 1991. (St. Thomas' Hospital Medical School) Asst. GP.

ROWE, Anthony Savile Stephen Penmoor, Meaby Lane, Yelverton — BM BCh 1964 Oxf.; MA, BM BCh Oxf. 1964; MRCP Lond. 1968. (Oxf.) Cons. (Geriat. Med.) Plymouth Gen. Hosp. Socs: Brit. Diabetic Assn. & Brit. Soc. Research into Ageing. Prev: SHO Dept. Thoracic Med. Sully Hosp. Cardiff; Sen. Regist. (Research) Bristol Roy. Infirm.; Sen. Regist. (Med.) United Oxf. Hosps.

ROWE, Antonia Jane Trescobeas Surgery, Falmouth TR11 2UN Tel: 01326 434888 — MB ChB 1991 Bristol. Retained Doctor, GP.

ROWE, Bernard, OBE, TD, Brigadier late RAMC Retd. Central Public Health Laboratory, Colindale Avenue, London NW9 5HT Tel: 020 8200 4400 Fax: 020 8905 9992; 14 Barns Dene, Harpenden AL5 2HQ Tel: 01582 715835 — MB BChir Camb. 1961; BA Camb. 1957, MA 1961; FRCPath 1982, M 1978; DTM & H Eng. 1964. (Camb. & Univ. Coll. Hosp. Lond.) Cons. Med. Microbiol. & Dir. Div. Gastro-Intestinal Infects. Centr. Pub. Health Laborat. Colindale; Cons. Path. Defence Med. Servs.; Dir. WHO Internat. Collaborating Centre for Phage Typing & Drug Resistance of Enterobacteria. Prev: Hon. Surg. to HM The Qu.; TA Adviser to Dir. Gen. Army Med. Servs.; Maj. RAMC, Off. i/c Enteric Ref. Laborat. David Bruce Laborats.

ROWE, Brian Ramsey Northgate Medical Centre, 10 Upper Northgate Street, Chester CH1 4EE Tel: 01244 379906 Fax: 01244 379703; 6 Glan Aber Park, Hough Green, Chester CH4 8LF Tel: 01244 674448 — MB BS 1976 Newc.; MRCGP 1980; DRCOG 1979. (Newc. u. Tyne) Gen. Practitioner; Clin. Asst., Chester Drugs Serv. Socs: Bd. of Dirs. Save The Family Charity. Prev: Dist. Med. Off. Nkhata Bay, Malawi.

ROWE, Carla Jane 22 Post House Lane, Great Bookham, Leatherhead KT23 3EA — MB ChB 1993 Birm.; DRCOG 1997. (Birmingham) GP Regist. Portseath Surg. Truro Cornw. Prev: SHO (Ent.) Warwick; SHO (O & G) Banbury; SHO (Paediat.) Warwick.

ROWE, Cecil Eleanor Department of Psychotherapy, Southfield House, 40 Clarendon Road, Leeds LS2 7PJ Tel: 0113 243 9000 — MB BChir 1972 Camb.; MRCP (UK) 1974; FRCPsych 1996, M 1983; Dip. Psychother. Leeds 1983. (Univ. Camb. & St. Thos. Hosp. Lond.) Cons. Psychotherapist Leeds Community & Ment. Health Servs. NHS Teachg. Trust; Hon. Sen. Lect. Univ. Leeds. Prev: Cons. Psychother. St. Jas. Univ. Hosp. Leeds; Sen. Regist. (Psychother.) Leeds E.. HA; Regist. (Psychiat.) Newc. & York HAs.

ROWE, David Jeremy 21 Manorgate Road, Kingston upon Thames KT2 7AW — MB BS 1998 Lond.; MB BS Lond 1998.

ROWE, Eleanor Penwartha, Station Road, Sway, Lymington SO41 6AA — MB BS 1994 Lond.

ROWE, Fiona Jane Howard House Surgery, 62 Leopold Road, Felixstowe IP11 7NR Tel: 01394 282706 Fax: 01394 278955; Tel: 0139 48 838 — MB BS 1986 Lond.; BSc (Hons.) Leeds 1981; MRCGP 1990; DRCOG 1989. (Charing Cross, Univ. Lond.)

ROWE, Gillian Mary X-Ray Department, County Hospital, Hereford HR1 2ER Tel: 01432 355444; Causeway Cottage, Ravens Causeway, Wormsley, Hereford HR4 8LZ Tel: 01432 830363 — MB BS 1974 Lond.; BSc (Biochem.) Lond. 1971; MRCPI 1983; FRCR 1984; DMRD Eng. 1983. Cons. Radiol. Herefordsh. HA.

ROWE, Ian Francis Worcester Centre for Rheumatic Diseases, Highfield Unit, Worcester Royal Infirmary, Newtown Road, Worcester WR5 1JG Tel: 01905 763333 Fax: 01905 760460 — MB BChir 1977 Camb.; MD Camb. 1985, MA 1976; FRCP Lond. 1995; MRCP (UK) 1979 Cons. Rheum. Worcester Acute Hosps. NHS,Trust, Worcester Roy. Infimary. Socs: Mem. Brit. Soc. Rheumatol. Prev: Sen. Regist. (Rheum. & Gen. Med.) Char. Cross & W.m. Hosps. Lond.; MRC Train. Fell. Immunol. Med. Unit & Hon. Sen. Regist. (Med.) Hammersmith Hosp. Lond.; Regist. (Med.) St. Thos. Hosp. Lond.

ROWE, James Benedict Woodtown Cottage, Sampford St., Yelverton PL20 6LJ — BM BCh 1994 Oxf.

ROWE, Jeremy Moseley Hall Hospital, Birmingham B13 8JL Tel: 0121 442 4321; Mayfield, 18 Fiery Hill Road, Barnt Green, Birmingham B45 8LG Tel: 0121 445 1555 — MB ChB 1977 Birm.; FRCP Lond. 1994; MRCP (UK) 1983. Cons. Geriat. Moseley Hall Hosp. Birm.; Clin. Lect. Univ. Birm. Prev: Cons. Geriat. BRd.green Hosp. Liverp.; Lect. (Geriat. Med.) Univ. Birm. & Selly Oak Hosp.

ROWE, Mr Jeremy Geraint Rock Mill, Par PL24 2SS — BM BCh 1988 Oxf.; MA Oxf. 1988, BM BCh 1988; FRCS Eng. 1992. Clin. Fell. MRC Clin. & Biochem. Magnetic Resonance Unit John Radcliffe Hosp. Oxf. Prev: SHO (Gen. Surg. & ENT) Norwich HA; SHO (Orthop. & Neurosurg.) Oxf.

ROWE, Joanne Louise The Grange Clinic, Westfield Avenue, Malpas, Newport NP20 6EY Tel: 01633 855521 Fax: 01633 859490; 2 Wain Close, Pontprennau, Cardiff CF23 8NW Tel: 01222 732729 — MB ChB 1986 Bristol; DFFP 1993; DRCOG 1990. (Univ. Bristol) GP Newport, S. Wales; Community Clin. Med. Off. (Family Plann.) Cardiff & Vale NHS Trust.

ROWE, Julia Lindsay 188 Widney Manor Road, Solihull B91 3JW — MB ChB 1995 Birm.; ChB Birm. 1995.

ROWE, Julie Ann Summerview, Trowes Lane, Swallowfield, Reading RG7 1RQ — MB BS 1982 Lond.

ROWE, Karen Ann Gratton Surgery, Sutton Scotney, Winchester SO21 3LE Tel: 01962 760394 — BM 1990 Soton.; DPhil Oxf. 1986; BSc Lond. 1980; MRCGP 1995. GP Asst. Gratton Surg. Winchester; Retainee Gratton Surg. Winchester. Prev: Trainee GP Hants.; Sen. Health Off. (O & G & Paediat.) Basingstoke Dist. Gen. Hosp.

ROWE, Louise 4 Chapel Avenue, Burnopfield, Newcastle upon Tyne NE16 6NW — MB BS 1990 Newc.; MRCGP 1994; DRCOG 1993.

ROWE, Michael John Hill House, The Mount, Dunton Bassett, Lutterworth LE17 5JL — MB ChB 1981 Leic.

ROWE, Michael Peter Alexandra Villa, 19 Marine Parade, Sheerness ME12 2PQ Tel: 01795 585058 Fax: 01795 585158 — MB BCh 1970 Wales; DAvMed Eng. 1977. (Welsh Nat. Sch. Med.)

ROWE, Mr Paul Harold Capstan House, Western Road, Pevensey bay, Eastbourne BN24 6HG — MB BChir 1977 Camb.; MA, MB Camb. 1977, MChir 1989, B 1976; FRCS Eng. 1981. (Guy's) Cons. Surg. (Gen. Surg.) E.bourne DGH. Socs: Fell. Med. Soc. Lond. & Roy. Soc. Med. Prev: Regist. Rotat (Sen. Surg.) Guy's Hosp. Lond.

ROWE, Paul Robert 27 Rosevalley, Threemilestone, Truro TR3 6BH — MB BCh 1998 Wales.

ROWE, Penelope Claire (retired) Little Court, Matfield, Tonbridge TN12 7JX Tel: 0189 272 2153 — MB BS 1951 Lond.; MRCS Eng. LRCP Lond. 1951; MFFP 1993; DObst RCOG 1953. Prev: Sen. Clin. Off. (Family Plann.) Tunbridge Wells HA.

ROWE, Peter Andrew Department of Renal Medicine, Derriford Hospital, Plymouth PL6 8DH Tel: 01752 792258 Fax: 01752 774651 Email: peter.rowe@phnt.swest.nhs.uk; Tel: 01822 617035 — MB ChB 1979 Bristol; FRCP 2001 Lond; MD Bristol 1990; MRCP (UK) 1983; FRCP Glas. 1998. (Bristol) Cons. Renal Phys. Derriford Hosp. Plymouth; Clin. Director Renal Servs. Plymouth Hosps. NHS Trust. Socs: Renal Assn.; Brit. Transpl. Soc.; Amer. Soc. Nephrol. Prev: Sen. Regist. W.ern Infirm. Glas.; Research Fell. City Hosp. Nottm.; Regist. S.mead Hosp. Bristol.

ROWE, Peter Brian Tudor Cottage, Springhill, Boldre, Lymington SO41 8NG Tel: 01590 674943; Tudor Cottage, Springhill, Boldre, Lymington SO41 8NG Tel: 01590 674943 — MB ChB 1950 Leeds; FRCGP 1982, M 1965.

ROWE, Peter George Oliver Street Surgery, 57 Oliver Street, Ampthill, Bedford MK45 2SB Tel: 01525 402641 Fax: 01525 840764; 87 Station Road, Ampthill, Bedford MK45 2RE — MB BS 1985 Lond.; MRCGP 1994; DRCOG 1989.

ROWE, Peter William c/o Children's Department, Newcastle General Hospital, Westgate Road, Newcastle upon Tyne NE4 6BE — MB BS 1981 Monash.

ROWE, Rachel Elizabeth 230 Kimberley Road, Leicester LE2 1LJ; 22 Swann Lane, Cheadle SK8 7HR — BM BS 1987 Nottm.; DM Nottm. 1995; MRCP UK 1990.

ROWE, Renarta Louise 20 Mallow Way, Rugby CV23 0UE — MB ChB 1995 Leeds.

ROWE, Richard Clive Gentry Heath Road Hospital, Ipswich IP4 5PD Tel: 01473 712233 — MB BS 1967 Lond.; MRCS Eng. LRCP Lond. 1967; FRCPath 1985, M 1973; FDS RCS Eng. 1966. Cons. Histopath. E. Suff. Health Dist.

ROWE, Robert Gerald (retired) Ratley Grange, Awbridge, Romsey SO51 0HN Tel: 01794 340018 — MB BS Lond. 1953; MRCS Eng. LRCP Lond. 1956; FFPHM RCP (UK) 1979, M 1974. Psychother. Med. Counsellor. Prev: Psychother. Med. Counsellor.

ROWE, Sarah Catherine Hawkstone View, Longford, Market Drayton TF9 3PW — MB ChB 1984 Dundee; DA (UK) 1987. GP Retainer Scheme Market Drayton.

ROWE, Siobhan Cringleford Surgery, Cantley Lane, Cringleford, Norwich NR4 6TA Tel: 01603 54678 Fax: 01603 58287; Keswick Cottage, Low Road, Keswick, Norwich NR4 6TZ Tel: 01603 456743 Email: siobhan@keswickcottage.com — MB BS 1988 Lond.; MRCGP 1993; DFFP 1992; DCH RCP Lond. 1991; DRCOG 1990. Prev: Trainee GP/SHO Norf. & Norwich Hosp. VTS; SHO (O & G) St. Thos. Hosp. Lond.

ROWE, Steven David John McKay Clinic, Royal Bolton Hospital Trust, Minerva Road, Bolton BL4 0JR Tel: 01204 390390 — MB ChB 1983 Manch.; BSc Manch. 1980; T(Psychiat.) 1991. Cons. Psychiat. (Ment. Handicap)Roy. Bolton Hosp. NHS Trust. Socs: Manch. Med. Soc.; Brit. Inst. For Learning Disabilities; Europ. Assn. for Ment. Health and Ment. Retardation. Prev: Sen. Regist. (Psychiat. Ment. Handicap.) N. W.. RHA; Regist. (Psychiat.) N. Manch. HA.; Cons. Psychiat. (Ment.Handicap) Olive Mt. Hosp. Liverp..

ROWE, Susan Margaret Eglwysbach Surgery, Pontypridd CF37 2AA Tel: 01443 406813; Plot 8 Tiy-y-Coed, Nant Celwyn, Efail Isaf, Pontypridd CF38 — MB BCh 1977 Wales. GP Pontypridd.

ROWE, Susan Mary 22 Hughes Close, Woodloes Park, Warwick CV34 5FA — MB BS 1993 Lond.

ROWE, Tracey Louise The Vine Medical Centre, 69 Pemberton Road, East Molesey KT8 9LG — MB BS 1987 Lond.; MRCGP 1993; DRCOG Lond. 1991; DCH RCP Lond. 1990.

ROWE, Valerie Bewick 39 South Croxted Road, West Dulwich, London SE21 8AZ — MB BChir 1976 Camb.; MA, MB Camb. 1976, BChir 1975; MRCGP 1981; Dip. Palliat. Med. Wales 1992.

Cons. St. Joseph's Hospice Lond. Prev: SHO St. Joseph's Hospice Lond.; Regist. St. Christopher's Hospice Lond.; Med. Off. Trinity Hospice Lond.

ROWE, Victor Laurie Practice A, Hinckley Health Centre, 27 Hill Street, Hinckley LE10 1DS Tel: 01455 635362 — MB ChB 1977 Ed.; BSc (Med. Sci.) (Hons.) Ed. 1974; MRCGP 1984; DRCOG 1982; DCH Eng. 1980. (Ed.)

ROWE, William Lawrence Department of Anaesthesia, Norfolk & Norwich Hospital, Brunswick Road, Norwich; Keswick Cottage, Low Road, Keswick, Norwich NR4 6TX Tel: 01603 456743 Fax: 01603 287886 Email: lrowe@paston.co.uk — MB ChB 1981 Leeds; FFA RCS Eng. 1987; DRCOG 1984. Cons. Anaesth. Norf. & Norwich Hosp. Prev: Sen. Regist. Rotat. (Anaesth.) E. Anglia RHA; Regist. (Anaesth.) Leic. Roy. Infirm.; Regist. (Anaesth.) Dunedin, NZ.

ROWE-JONES, Mr David Colin Poole General Hospital, Longfleet Road, Poole BH15 2 Tel: 01202 675100; 6 Haig Avenue, Canford Cliffs, Poole BH13 7AJ Tel: 01202 709489 Fax: 01202 709489 — MRCS Eng. LRCP Lond. 1959; MS Lond. 1969, MB BS 1959; FRCS Eng. 1964. (Westm.) Cons. Surg. Poole Gen., & Swanage Hosps.; Hunt. Prof. RCS Eng. Prev: Sen. Regist. (Surg.) W.m. Hosp. Lond.; Regist. (Surg.) Roy. Marsden Hosp. Lond. & Gordon Hosp. Lond.

ROWE-JONES, Mr Julian Mark Royal Surrey County Hospital, Egerton Road, Guildford GU2 7XX Tel: 01483 464112 Fax: 01483 464108 Email: j.rowe-jones@lineone.net — MB BS 1986 Lond.; FRCS (Orl.) 1996; FRCS Eng. 1992. (St. Thos. Hosp.) Cons. (Rhinology & ENT Surg.) Roy. Surrey Co. Hosp. Guildford. Socs: Fell. Europ. Acad. Facial Surg.; Mem. Europ. Rhinolog. Soc.; Mem.Brit. Assn. Otorhinolaryncol. Prev: Sen. Regist. (Otorhinolaryngol.) Char. Cross Hosp. Lond.; Regist. (ENT Surg.) St. Geo. Hosp. Lond. & Roy. Surrey Co. Hosp. Guildford; SHO (ENT) St. Geo. Hosp. & Roy. Nat. Throat, Nose & Ear Hosp.

ROWELL, Andrew Martin The Surgery, 13 Camberwell Green, London SE5 7AF Tel: 020 7703 3788 — MB BS 1978 Lond.; BA Oxf. 1975; MRCGP 1982; DRCOG 1981. (St. Thos.) Forens. Med. Examr. (Metrop. Police). Prev: Ho. Surg. Qu. Mary's Hosp. Sidcup; Ho. Phys. William Harvey Hosp. Ashford; Trainee GP St. Thos. Hosp. Lond. VTS.

ROWELL, Elizabeth Rachel Martin 15 Radlyn Oval, 20 Park Avenue, Harrogate HG2 9BG Tel: 01423 566478 — MB BS Durh. 1952. Prev: Clin. Asst. (Dermat.) Gen. Infirm. Leeds & St. Jas. Hosp. Leeds; Hon. Tutor (Dermat.) Univ. Leeds; Asst. Med. Off. Dept. Stud. Health Univ. Leeds.

ROWELL, Geoffrey Humphery Robin Doctors Surgery, Pembroke Road, Framlingham, Woodbridge IP13 9HA Tel: 01728 723627 Fax: 01728 621064; Oakhill, Earl Soham, Woodbridge IP13 7SL Tel: 01728 685393 — MB 1965 Camb.; BChir 1964; DCH Eng. 1969. (King's Coll. Hosp.) GP Woodbridge.

ROWELL, Professor Neville Robinson Nuffield Hospital, Outwood Lane, Horsforth, Leeds LS18 4HP Tel: 0113 258 8756 Fax: 0113 258 3108; 15 Radlyn Oval, 20 Pk Avenue, Harrogate HG2 9BG Tel: 01423 566478 Fax: 01423 709677 Email: nrowell@onetel.net.uk — MB BS Durh. 1949; MD Newc. 1966; FRCP Lond. 1968, M 1957; DCH Eng. 1952. (Durh.) Emerit. Prof. Dermat. Univ. Leeds. Socs: Med. Appeal Tribunal; (Ex-Pres.) Brit. Assn. Dermat. & N. Eng. Dermat. Soc. Prev: Sen. Cons. Phys. (Dermat.) Gen. Infirm. Leeds & St. Jas. Univ. Hosp. Leeds; Cons. Adviser (Dermat.) DHSS; Tutor (Dermat.) & Sen. Regist. Univ. & Gen. Infirm. Leeds.

ROWELL, Nicholas Phillip Department of Clinical Oncology, Oxford Radcliffe Hospital (Churchill Site), Oxford OX3 7LJ Tel: 01865 225681 Fax: 01865 225660 — MB BChir 1980 Camb.; MA Camb. 1980, MD 1990; FRCP Lond. 1996; MRCP (UK) 1982; FRCR 1987. (King's Coll. Hosp.) Cons. & Hon. Sen. Clin. Lect. (Clin. Oncol.) Ch.ill Hosp. Oxf. Prev: Sen. Regist. (Radiother.) Mt. Vernon Hosp. N.wood; Clin. Research Fell. Roy. Marsden Hosp. Sutton; Regist. (Radiother.) St. Bart's. Hosp. Lond.

ROWELL, Nigel Timothy The Health Centre, PO Box 101(a), The Health Centre, 20 Cleveland Square, Middlesbrough TS1 2NX Tel: 01642 242192 Fax: 01642 231809; 34 Station Road, Stokesley, Middlesbrough TS9 5AJ Tel: 01642 711929 Fax: 01642 711929 — MB ChB 1983 Manch.; BSc (Hons.) St. And. 1980; MRCGP 1987. GP Middlesbrough; Clin. Asst. (Cardiol.) S. Tees HA.; Undergrad Teach. Univ. Newc. upon Tyne. Prev: Trainee GP Cleveland VTS; SHO (Gen. Med.) S. Tees HA.

ROWELL

ROWELL, Patrick John Walter, TD (retired) 3 Poplar Street, Southport PR8 6DT Tel: 01704 543236 — MB ChB 1953 Liverp. Prev: Orthop. Surg. Mersey RHA.

ROWELL, Sidney Stephen (retired) Captain's Piece, Old Bury Road, Stuston, Diss IP21 4AB Tel: 01379 740830 — MB BS 1949 Lond.; MRCS Eng. LRCP Lond. 1949; MRCGP 1956. Prev: Clin. Asst. (Geriat.) Lewisham Health Dist.

***ROWELL, Susan Roberta** 6 Bracken Lane, Retford DN22 7EU — MB ChB 1995 Aberd.

ROWEN, David 5 Taw Drive, Chandlers Ford, Eastleigh SO53 4SL — MB ChB 1983 Leic.

ROWLAND, Alan Charles Medical Centre, RASU BFPO 40 — MB BS 1979 Lond. (St. Bart.) SHO (Med.) W. Suff. Hosp. Bury St. Edmunds. Prev: SHO (Anaesth.) Qu. Mary's Hosp. Sidcup; Ho. Off. (Surg.) Poole Gen. Hosp.; Ho. Phys. Rochford Gen. Hosp.

ROWLAND, Andrew George 6 Banks Cottages, Heathgreen Road, Studland, Swanage BH19 3BX — MB ChB 1988 Sheff.

ROWLAND, Anthony John (retired) Willowmead, Kersbrook, Budleigh Salterton EX9 7AB Tel: 01395 444057 — MB ChB 1952 Bristol; FFCM 1977, M 1974; DPH Bristol 1961; DObst RCOG 1957. Prev: Cons. Communicable Dis. Control Cornw. & I. of Scilly HA.

ROWLAND, Audrey Mary Rose Cottage, Heol-y-Mynydd, Southerndown, Bridgend CF32 0SN — MB ChB 1952 Bristol; MLCOM 1980; Dip. Sports Med. Ed. 1995; DCH Eng. 1966. (Bristol) Osteopath. & Sports Med. P.ss of Wales Hosp. & Recreation Centre Bridgend.

ROWLAND, Barbara Jill, Surg. Lt. RN Retd. c/o 77 Lawsons Road, Thornton-Cleveleys FY5 4DB — MB ChB 1989 Dundee; LMSSA Lond. 1982.

ROWLAND, Christopher Giles Kenton Lodge, Kenton, Exeter EX6 8JE Tel: 01626 890171 Email: crowland@btinternet.com — MB BS 1971 Lond.; BSc (Biochem., Hons.) Wales 1966; MRCS Eng. LRCP Lond. 1971; FRCR 1981; DMRD Eng. 1975; DMRT Eng. 1977. Cons. Radiother. & Oncol. Roy. Devon & Exeter Hosp. Exeter; Sen. Lect. (Radiother & Oncol.) Univ. of Exeter; Dir. FORCE Cancer Research Centre Exeter. Prev: Sen. Regist. (Radiother. & Oncol.) Bristol Health Dist. (T).; Sen. Regist. (Radiother. & Oncol.) Mersey Regional Centre Radiother. & Oncol. Clatterbridge Hosp. Bebington.

ROWLAND, Christopher James, OBE, OStJ (retired) 1 Woodlands Road, Surbiton KT6 6PR Tel: 020 8255 0713 — MB BS Lond. 1959; MRCS Eng. LRCP Lond. 1959; DObst RCOG 1961. Prev: Gen. Practitioner.

ROWLAND, David Harry (retired) 5 Ferndene Court, Moor Road_South, Newcastle upon Tyne NE3 1NN — LRCP LRCS 1945 Ed.; LRCP LRCS Ed. LRFPS Glas. 1945; MRCGP 1962. Prev: Ho. Phys. Qu. Eliz. Hosp. Gateshead.

ROWLAND, Edward Department of Cardiological Sciences, St. George's Hospital Medical School, Cranmer Terrace, London SW17 0RE Tel: 020 8725 2922 Fax: 020 8767 7141 Email: erowland@sghms.ac.uk; 47 Wimpole Street, London W1M 7DG Tel: 020 7573 8899 Fax: 020 7573 8898 — MB BS 1974 Lond.; MD Lond. 1990; MRCS Eng. LRCP Lond. 1974; FACC 1990; FESC 1988; FRCP 1998. (St. Bart. Hosp. Lond.) Cons. & Hon. Sen. Lect. (Cardiol.) St. Geo. Hosp. Med. Sch. Lond.; Cons. Cardiol. Papworth Hosp.; Hon. Cons. Cardiol. Hosp. Childr. Gt. Ormond St. Lond. Socs: Brit. Cardiac Soc., Mem.; Brit. pacing and Electrophysiol. Gp., Counc. Mem. Prev: Lect. Nat. Heart & Lung Inst.; Brit. Heart Foundat. Fell. Roy. Postgrad. Med. Sch.

ROWLAND, Gareth David 11 Moor Grange View, West Park, Leeds LS16 5BN — MB BS 1998 Lond.; MB BS Lond 1998.

ROWLAND, George Frederick Uffdown, St Mary's Road, Bowdon, Altrincham WA14 2PJ — MB ChB 1976 Ed.; BSc (Hons.) Ed. 1974, MB ChB 1976; FRCOG 1997; DCH Eng. 1978. (Ed.) Cons. O & G Univ. Hosp. Aintree Liverp. Prev: Cons. O & G Billinge Hosp. Wigan; Sen. Regist. (O & G) St. Mary's Hosp. Manch.; Specialist Bourn Hall Clinic Cambs.

ROWLAND, Gillian Pamela Child Health Department, East Yorkshire Community Health Care Trust, Temperton House, Beverley Westwood Hospital, Beverley HU17 8BU; 48 Nordham, North Cave, Brough HU15 2LT — MB ChB 1984 Manch.; BSc (Med. Sci.) St. And. 1981.

ROWLAND, Herbert Albert Kenneth Ffosygerwn, Aberbran, Brecon LD3 9LT Tel: 01874 636938 — PhD Lond. 1965; MA, DM Oxf. 1956, BM BCh 1945; FRCP Ed. 1966, M 1957; DTM & H Liverp. 1955. (Oxf.) Prev: Vis. Prof. Med. Coll. of Virginia Richmond, USA; Vis. Prof. Inst. Med. Rangoon, Burma; Mickle Fell. Univ. Lond. 1971.

ROWLAND, John Francis (retired) Rose Cottage, Heol-y-Mynydd, Southerndown, Bridgend CF32 0SN — MB ChB 1951 Bristol; DPH Eng. 1960. Prev: Sen. Med. Off. (Clin.) Bridgend (Ogwr) Health Dist.

ROWLAND, Kenneth Park Road Health Centre, Park Road, Tarporley CW6 0BE Tel: 01829 732401 Fax: 01829 732404 — MB ChB 1967 Liverp. (Liverp.) Course Organiser & Med. Adviser Chesh.

ROWLAND, Lindsey Jane Tors, Fairies Lane, Perth PH1 1NN — BChir 1995 Camb.

ROWLAND, Margaret 2 Camdale View, Ridgeway, Sheffield S12 3XQ — MB ChB 1978 Sheff.

ROWLAND, Michael Garth Murray The Conifers, 16 Hayter Close, West Wratting, Cambridge CB1 5LY Tel: 01223 290788 Fax: 01223 290415 Email: 106002.3265@compuserve.com — MB BS Durh. 1964; FRCP Lond. 1983; MRCP (UK) 1971; FFPHM RCP (UK) 1991; FRCPCH (UK) 1997; MFCM RCP (UK) 1987; DTM & H RCP Lond. 1973; DCH RCP Lond. 1968. Progr. Co-ordinator Europ. Progr. Interven. Epidemiol. Train. Paris. Socs: Life Fell Roy. Soc. Trop. Med. & Hyg.; Soc. Social Med. Prev: Cons. Epidemiol. AORHA & PHLS Communicable Dis. Surveillance Centre; Assoc. Dir. & Head Community Med. Div. Internat. Centre for Diarrh.l Dis. Research Bangladesh; Sen. Sci. MRC Laborat. Fajara, The Gambia.

ROWLAND, Philip Geoffrey 142 Western Road, Lancing BN15 9TY — MB ChB 1992 Birm.

ROWLAND, Raymond Marc Jenner Health Centre, 201 Stanstead Road, London SE23 1HU Tel: 020 8690 2231; 34 Garlies Road, Forest Hill, London SE23 2RT — MB BS 1974 Lond.; MRCS Eng. LRCP Lond. 1974; MRCGP 1979; DRCOG 1976. (Guy's)

ROWLAND, Richard George River Lodge Surgery, Malling St., Lewes BN7 2RD; Arahaza, 29 Montacute Road, Lewes BN7 1EN Tel: 01772 474781 — BM BCh Oxf. 1968; MRCGP 1984; DA Eng. 1971; DObst RCOG 1970; Dip. Trop. Med. Antwerp 1973. Prev: Med. Dir. Hôpital de Gahini, Rwanda.

ROWLAND, Robert George 4 Sunnydown Road, Olivers Battery, Winchester SO22 4LD — MB ChB 1987 Manch. Regist. Rotat. (Anaesth.) NW RHA. Prev: SHO (Obst. & Gyn.) Roy. Preston Hosp.; SHO (Obst. & Gyn.) Chorley & Dist. Hosp.

ROWLAND, Roy MacDonald (retired) 5 Richmond Avenue, Wolverhampton WV3 9JB Tel: 01902 28748 — MB ChB 1954 Aberd. Prev: Surg. Lt. RNR.

ROWLAND, Stephen James Owlthorpe Surgery, 52 Broadlands Avenue, Sheffield S20 6RL Tel: 0114 247 7852 Fax: 0114 248 3691; 2 Camdale View, Ridgeway, Sheffield S12 3XQ Tel: 0114 248 5209 — MB ChB 1978 Sheff.

ROWLAND HILL, Christopher Andrew Centre for Magnetic Resonance Investigations, Hull Royal Infirmary, Anlaby Road, Hull HU3 2JZ Tel: 01482 674083 Fax: 01482 320137; The Nest, 56 George St, Cottingham HU16 5QP Tel: 01482 849173 Fax: 01482 849173 — MB BS 1982 Lond.; BA Oxf. 1979; MRCP (UK) 1985; FRCR 1990. Cons. Neuroradiol. Hull Roy. Infirm. Prev: Sen. Regist. (Radiol.) Nat. Hosp. Neurol. & Neurosurg. Lond.; Regist. (Radiol.) St. Thos. Hosp. Lond.; Regist. (Med.) Whittington Hosp. Lond.

ROWLAND-JONES, Sarah Louise Molecular Immunology Group, Institute of Molecular Medicine, John Radcliffe Hospital, Oxford OX3 9DS Tel: 01865 222316 Fax: 01865 222502 Email: sarah.rowland.jones@ndm.oc.ac.uk; 53 Jack Straw's Lane, Headington, Oxford OX3 7DW Tel: 01865 765608 Fax: 01865 433903 — BM BCh 1983 Oxf.; DM Oxf. 1995; MA Camb. 1984; MRCP (UK) 1986. (Oxf.) MRC Sen. Clin. Fell. Nuffield Dept. Med. Inst. Molecular Med. Oxf.; Hon. Cons. Infec. Dis. John Radcliffe Hosp. Oxf. Prev: Clin. Lect. (Molecular Immunol.) Dept. Med. Inst. Molecular Med. Oxf. & MRC Clincian Scientist Fell.; MRC Train. Fell. (Molecular Immunol.) Inst. Molecular Med. Oxf.; Regist. (Infec. Dis.) Ch.ill Hosp. Oxf.

ROWLAND PAYNE, Christopher Melville Edwin London Clinic, 149 Harley St., London W1G 6DE Tel: 020 7224 1228 Fax: 020 7487 5479 Email: crp@thelondonclinic.co.uk; 19 Cambridge Street, London SW1V 4PR Tel: 020 7821 5929 Fax: 020 7233 7393 Email: crp@thelondonclinic.co.uk — MRCP (UK) 1980. (St. Bart.) Cons. Dermat. The Lond, Clinic, 149 Harley St., Lond. W1; Cons. Dermat. St. Saviour's Hosp Hythe; Vis. Prof. Dermat. Sch. Med. Sci. Kumasi, Ghana; Prof. Clin. Dermat. Ross. Univ. Sch. Med. New York City.

Socs: Brit. Assn. Dermatol.; Mem. Hon. Soc. Francaise de Dermatol. & Syphiligraphie; Sec-Gen. (past Presid.) Europ. Soc. Cosmetic & Aesthetic Dermatol. Prev: Clin. Lect. & Hon. Sen. Regist. (Dermat.) W.m. Hosp. & Char. Cross & W.m. Med. Sch. Lond.; Regist. (Dermat.) St. Thos. Hosp. Lond.; Vis. Prof. Univ. Texas 1986.

ROWLANDS, Alan John 1 Carlin Gate, Blackpool FY2 9QX — MB ChB 1983 Manch.; BSc (Hons.) Med. Biochem. Manch. 1981, MB ChB 1983; DCH RCP Lond. 1987; Cert. Family Plann. JCC 1986; DGM RCP Lond. 1985. Hon. Sec. Tameside LMC.

ROWLANDS, Albert David (retired) Rosemullion, Turkdean, Northleach, Cheltenham GL54 3NT Tel: 01451 860683 — MB BS 1953 Lond.; MRCS Eng. LRCP Lond. 1952; MRCGP 1963; DObst RCOG 1955. Prev: Ho. Surg. (Neurosurg.) Lond. Hosp.

ROWLANDS, Aled Montgomery House Surgery, Piggy Lane, Bicester OX26 6HT Tel: 01869 249222 Fax: 01869 322433; The Plough House, Wendlebury, Bicester OX25 2PS Tel: 01869 321113 Fax: 01869 240694 Email: rowlands@melwood.fsnet.co.uk — MB ChB 1973 Birm.; MRCGP 1978; DObst RCOG 1975. (Birmingham) Gen. Practitioner; Clin. Asst. (ENT) Banbury Hosp. Prev: Regist. (Med.) Whakatane Pub. Hosp. NZ; SHO (Surg.) Birm. Matern. Hosp.; Ho. Surg. Birm. Accid. Hosp.

ROWLANDS, Alison Gail Hope Lodge, 11 Poplar Road, Oxton, Birkenhead CH43 5TB Tel: 0151 652 2834 Email: cons.com@msn — MB BS 1992 Lond.; BSc (Hons.) Lond. 1989; FRCOphth. 1997. (Charing Cross & Westminster London) Specialist Regist. St Paul's Eye Unit Roy. Liverp. Univ. Hosp. Prev: SHO (Ophth.) Birm. & Midl. Eye Centre, Kings Mill Hosp. & Kidderminster NHS Trust Hosp.

ROWLANDS, Andrew Buchan Erleigh, The Street, Rotherwick, Basingstoke RG27 9BG — MB ChB 1990 Ed.; MSc Remot Health Care Robert Gordon University 1997; FRCS (AVE) Ed. 1998. SHO A & E Med.; GP Regist.

ROWLANDS, Angela Mary Stratton Medical Centre, Hospital Road, Stratton, Bude EX23 9BP Tel: 01288 352133; Leemoor, 4 Tamor Terrace, Tavistock Road, Launceston PL15 9EU Tel: 01566 773451 Fax: 01566 777495 Email: arow1@aol.com — MB BS 1980 Lond.; BSc (Hons.) Lond. 1975, MB BS 1980. (Lond. Hosp.) Clin. Asst. in Occupat. Health, Cornw. Healthcare Trust. Prev: GP Swindon.

ROWLANDS, Ann Eleri Church Crescent Surgery, 50 Church Crescent, Finchley, London N3 1BJ Tel: 020 8346 1323 Fax: 020 8343 4026; 8 Etheldene Avenue, Muswell Hill, London N10 3QH Tel: 020 8883 4434 — MB BS 1970 Lond.; MRCS Eng. LRCP Lond. 1970; DObst RCOG 1972. (Roy. Free) Prev: Ho. Surg. (Obst.) Whittington Hosp. Lond.; Ho. Phys. Eliz. G. Anderson Hosp. Lond.; Ho. Surg. Roy. Free Hosp. Lond.

ROWLANDS, Anne Kathleen (retired) 2 Brackenwood Drive, Bruntwood, Cheadle SK8 1JX Tel: 0161 491 3434 — MB ChB Manch. 1960. Prev: Clin. Med. Off. Manch. Centr. Hosp. Community Care Trust.

ROWLANDS, Professor Brian James University of Nottingham, Section of Surgery, Queen's Medical Centre, Nottingham NG7 2UH Tel: 01159 970 9245 Fax: 011599709428 Email: bjr.surgery@nottingham.ac.uk — MB BS Lond. 1968; MD Sheff. 1978; FRCS Ed 1995; FRCSI 1988; FRCS Eng. 1973; FRCPS Glas. 1995; FACS 1983. (Guy's) Prof. Surg. Nottm. Univ. & Cons. Surg. Qu.'s Med. Centre and Div. GI Surg. Sci. Notts Univ Head of Sect. of Surg. Socs: Chairm. RCS (Eng.) c/o the Critically Ill Pat. Working Party 1944-; Chairm. Scientif. Comm., Ass. Surg. GB & Irel. 1997-; Soc Acad. Surgs. Prev: Prof. & Head of Dept. of Surg. Qu.'s Univ. of Belf.; Lect. N.. Gen. Hosp. & Roy. Infirm. Sheff.; Assoc. Prof. Surg. Univ. Texas, Houston, USA.

ROWLANDS, Christopher John Anaesthetic Department, Bradford Royal Infirmary, Duckworth Lane, Bradford BD9 6RJ Tel: 01274 542200 — MB ChB 1987 Leeds; DA (UK) 1993. Staff Grade Anaesth. Bradford Hosps. NHS Trust.

ROWLANDS, Christopher Merlin, MBE Rowallan, 26 Uddingston Road, Bothwell, Glasgow G71 8PN Tel: 07970 309880 — MB BS 1980 Lond.; MRCS Eng. LRCP Lond. 1979; T(GP) 1991; Dip. IMC RCS Ed. 1990; DRCOG 1983. (Guy's) GP Bothewell, Lanarksh.; Mem. BASICS. Socs: MICGP; Fac. Pre Hosp. Care RCSurg. (Edin.). Prev: Emerg. Room Phys., Glagow Roy. Infirm. A & E Dept.; GP Sumburgh Shetland; Resid. Med. Off. Qu. Charlotte's Matern. Hosp. Lond.

ROWLANDS, David Bartlett Peterborough District Hospital, Thorpe Road, Peterborough PE3 6DA Tel: 01733 874000; Ashfield House, Splash Lane, Castor, Peterborough PE5 7BD — MD 1986 Lond.; MB BS 1974; MRCP (UK) 1980; FRCP 1996. (St. Bart.) Cons. Phys. P'Boro. Dist. Hosp.; Vis. Cardiol. Papworth Hosp. Papworth Everard Camb.; Chief Med. Adviser Pearl Assur. Company. Socs: Brit. Cardiac Soc. Prev: Sen. Regist. (Med.) Mersey RHA.; Clin. Research Fell. Univ. Birm.; Hon. Regist. (Cardiol.) E. Birm. Hosp.

ROWLANDS, David Charles Department of Histopathology, The Medical School, University of Birmingham, Vincent Drive, Edgbaston, Birmingham B15 2TT — BM 1982 Soton.; MRCPath 1992. Cons. Path. Univ. Hosp. Birm. NHS Trust. Prev: Lect. (Path.) Med. Sch. Univ. Birm.; Research Regist. (Histopath.) E. Birm. Hosp.; Regist. (Histopath.) Hosp. Wales Cardiff.

ROWLANDS, David Edward (retired) Plas Newydd, Penmaenmawr LL34 6RH Tel: 01492 622306 Fax: 01492 622306 — MRCS Eng. LRCP Lond. 1945; FFA RCS Eng. 1954; DA Eng. 1951. Prev: Anaesth. Llandudno Gen. Hosp.

ROWLANDS, David Francis, CStJ (retired) 19 Barnlake Point, Burton, Milford Haven SA73 1PF — MB BS 1958 Lond.; MFPHM 1989; MFCM 1974; DPH Wales 1966; DObst RCOG 1960. Prev: Cons. Primary Care Phys. Armed Forces Hosp. Riyadh, Saudi Arabia.

ROWLANDS, Mr David John Wirral Hospital, Arrowe Park, Upton, Wirral CH49 5PE Tel: 0151 678 5111 — MB ChB 1985 Birm.; MRCOG 1990. Cons. O & G Wirral Hosp.; Hon. Clin. Lect. (Obst. & Gyn.) Univ. Liverp.

ROWLANDS, Debra 44 Willowmead Drive, Prestbury, Macclesfield SK10 4DD — MB BS 1997 Newc.

ROWLANDS, Derek John The Beeches Consulting Centre, Mill Lane, Cheadle SK8 2PY Tel: 0161 491 2959 Fax: 0161 428 1589 Email: djr@djr12ecg.demon.co.uk — FACC 1985; FESC; FACA; MB ChB (Hons.) Manch. 1961; BSc (1st cl. Hons.) Manch. 1958, MD 1984; FRCP Lond. 1976, M 1964. (Manch.) Hon. Cons. Cardiol. Manch. Roy. Infirm. Socs: Fell. Amer. Coll. Cardiol. 1985; Fell. Europ. Soc. Cardiol.; Brit. Cardiac Soc. Prev: MRC Trav. Fell. Mayo Clinic Rochester, Minn.; SHO (Med.) Hammersmith Hosp.; Cons. Lect. (Cardiol.) Univ. Manch.

ROWLANDS, Dorothy Ann 134 Abbeyfield Road, Sheffield S4 7AY — MB ChB 1985 Sheff.

ROWLANDS, Dorothy Mair Seymour House, Shoreham Lane, St Michael's, Tenterden TN30 6EH Tel: 01580 762967 — MB BCh Wales 1966; DCH Eng. 1968. (Cardiff) SCMO S. Kent Community NHS Trust. Prev: SHO Roy. Liverp. Childr. Hosp.; SHO Mossley Hill Hosp. Liverp.

ROWLANDS, Eirwyn Norman Flat 1, 37 Westbourne Terrace, London W2 3UR Tel: 020 7723 5623 — MD 1938 Manch.; BSc Manch. 1933, MD 1938, MB ChB 1936; FRCP Lond. 1956, M 1945. (Manch.) Prev: Dir. MRC Gastroenterol. Research Unit Centr. Middlx. Hosp. Lond.; Asst. Dir. Dept. of Clin. Investig. & Research Roy. Infirm.; Manch.; Research Fell. Med. Harvard Univ., USA.

ROWLANDS, Elwyn (retired) Flat 1, 57 Water St., Rhyl LL18 1SR — MB ChB 1924 Liverp.

ROWLANDS, Emma Celeste Dept. Medicine, 4th Floor North Block, St Thomas Hospital, Lambeth Palace Road, London SE1 7EH Tel: 020 7928 9292; 3 Lancaster Road, Uxbridge UB8 1AW Email: e.rowlands@virgin.net — MB ChB 1992 Sheff.; FRCOphth 1998. (Sheffield) Research Fell., Oprthalmology, St Thomas, Lond.

ROWLANDS, Frances Mary 37 Redwood, Westhoughton, Bolton BL5 2RU — MB ChB 1987 Leic.

ROWLANDS, Gillian Clare 3 Kippen Drive, Clarkston, Glasgow G76 8JG Tel: 0141 644 2725 — MB ChB 1994 Aberd. GP Asst. Position ChristCh., New Zealand; GP Locum. Socs: MRCGP. Prev: Trainee GP Kemnay Surg. Kemnay; Trainee GP Gt. W.. Rd. Med. Gp., 327 Gt. W.. Rd., Aberd.; SHO (A & E) Aberd. Roy. Infirm.

ROWLANDS, Gillian Patricia Acorn Practice Group, St. Johns Health Centre, Oak Lane, Twickenham TW1 3PH Tel: 020 8891 0073 Fax: 020 8744 0060 — MB BS 1984 Lond.; MRCP (UK) 1987; MRCGP 1990; DRCOG 1989.

ROWLANDS, Gwyn (retired) 1A Boxwell Road, Berkhamsted HP4 3ET Tel: 01442 863666 — MRCS Eng. LRCP Lond. 1951; FFPM 1989; DObst RCOG 1959; DA Eng. 1955. Prev: Med. Adviser Wellcome Foundat. Ltd. Lond.

ROWLANDS

*****ROWLANDS, Helen Elizabeth** Tawny Wings, Roman Road, Meols, Wirral CH47 6AQ Email: hrowlands@doctors.org.uk — MB BS 1997 Lond.

ROWLANDS, Henry Walter David Scranton House, Pantyffynnon, Ammanford SA18 3HN — MB BS 1983 Lond.; MRCGP 1989; MRCOG 1988.

ROWLANDS, Ian Daniel Hope Dunelm Medical Practice, 1-2 Victor Terrace, Bearpark, Durham DH7 7DF Tel: 0191 373 2077 Fax: 0191 373 6216; 7 Dunelm Court, South St, Durham DH1 4QX Tel: 0191 386 5940 — MB BS 1962 Durh. Prev: Ho. Surg. Roy. Vict. Infirm. Newc. & Greenbank Matern. Hosp. Darlington; Ho. Phys. Bishop Auckland Gen. Hosp.

ROWLANDS, Idris Gwynn Lluest, Llangathen, Carmarthen SA32 8QD Tel: 015584 105 — MB BS Lond. 1969; MRCOG 1974; MRCGP 1980. GP Llandeilo, Dyfed. Prev: Regist. (Obst.) Univ. Hosp. Wales Cardiff; SHO (Endocrine), (Gyn.) & (Obst.) Jessop Hosp. Wom. Sheff.

ROWLANDS, Jennifer Louise 531 Blenheim Road, Kingswinford DY6 8SH — MB BS 1997 Lond.

ROWLANDS, John Kendrew Westway Medical Centre, Westway, Maghull, Liverpool L31 0DJ Tel: 0151 526 1121 Fax: 0151 531 2631 — MB BS 1963 Durh.; MRCGP 1971. (Newc.) p/t Hosp. Practitioner. Ashworth Hosp. Maghull. Prev: Demonst. (Path.) & SHO (Dermat.) Univ. Newc.; Lect. (Gen. Pract.) Guy's Hosp. Lond.

ROWLANDS, Mark Pendre Surgery, Coleshill Street, Holywell CH8 7RS Tel: 01352 712029 Fax: 01352 712751; Groes Faen, Babell, Holywell CH8 8QB — MB ChB 1980 Manch.; MRCGP 1984; DRCOG 1982; DCH RCP Lond. 1984. Prev: Trainee GP Clwyd VTS; Clin. Med. Off. (Child Health) Clwyd HA.

ROWLANDS, Martin 6 Broadoak Road, Bramhall, Stockport SK7 3BW — MB BS 1980 Lond.; MRCP (UK) 1984; MRCPath. 1989. Sen. Regist. (Haemat.) N. W.. RHA. Prev: Regist. (Haemat.) Leic. Roy. Infirm.; SHO (Path.) Withington Hosp. Manch.

ROWLANDS, Martin 4 Hunts Lane, Stockton Heath, Warrington WA4 2DT — MB ChB 1998 Sheff.; MB ChB Sheff 1998.

ROWLANDS, Mary Helena 10 Silverdale Close, Huyton, Liverpool L36 5YJ — MB ChB 1977 Dundee; MRCPsych 1984; Cert JCC Lond. 1979. Med. Off. Home Off. Bristol. Socs: Guild Catholic Doctors.

ROWLANDS, Michael Philip William (retired) — MB BCh 1961 Wales. Prev: Dir. of Social Servs. Merthyr Tydfil Co. Boro.

ROWLANDS, Michael William Denton Sturt Priory Hospital, Walton-on-the-Hill, Tadworth KT20 7RQ Tel: 01737 814488 Fax: 01737 813926; 13 White Beam Way, Tadworth KT20 5DL Tel: 01737 812211 Fax: 01737 819747 Email: trudymoon@compuserve.com — MB ChB 1979 Birm.; MRCPsych 1984. Staff Cons. Sturt Priory Hosp. Tadworth. Prev: Cons. Psychiat. E. Surrey; Lect. (Psychol. Med.) St. Bart. Hosp. Lond.; Regist. Rotat. (Psychiat.) St. Geo. Hosp. & Centr. Birm. HA.

ROWLANDS, Molly Patricia (retired) The Gate House, Alderley, Wotton-under-Edge GL12 7QT Tel: 01453 844804 — MB BS Lond. 1968. Prev: GP Sen. Partner Cipping Surg.

ROWLANDS, Nia Catrin 16 Claerwen Drive, Cardiff CF23 6LS — MB BCh 1992 Wales.

ROWLANDS, Patricia Rochdale Healthcare NHS Trust, Rochdale Infirmary, Whitehall St., Rochdale OL12 0NB Tel: 01706 377777 Fax: 01706 755347; Calliard's House, Smithybridge Road, Littleborough OL15 8QF — MB ChB 1982 Leic. Assoc. Specialist (A & E Med.); Dep. Police Surg. Gtr. Manch. Police; Prison Med. Off. HMP Buckley Hall Rochdale. Prev: GP Bolton; SHO (A & E) Rochdale Infirm.; SHO (Psychiat.) Oldham Roy. Infirm.

ROWLANDS, Peter Christopher Radiology Department, Royal Liverpool Hospital, Prescot St., Liverpool L7 8XP Tel: 0151 706 2733 Fax: 0151 706 5799 Email: peter@rluh.u-net.com — BM BS 1981 Nottm.; MRCP (UK) 1985; FRCR 1989. (Nottm.) Cons. Radiol. Roy. Liverp. Hosp. Prev: Sen. Regist. (Radiol.) St. Mary's Hosp. Lond.; Regist. (Med.) Hackney Hosp. Lond.; SHO (Med.) Middlesbrough Hosp. Gp.

ROWLANDS, Peter Julian Cwmbran Village Surgery, Victoria Street, Cwmbran NP44 3JS Tel: 01633 871177 Fax: 01633 860234; Hill View, Michaelston-y-Fedw, Cardiff CF3 6XS — MB BCh 1984 Wales; MRCGP 1989.

ROWLANDS, Philip (retired) Knowsley, Heights Lane, Rochdale OL12 0PZ Tel: 01706 644050 — MB BCh Wales 1954; BSc Wales 1954; MRCP Ed. 1968; DCH Eng. 1965. Prev: GP Rochdale.

ROWLANDS, Philip Kenneth 164 Brougham Court, Peterlee SR8 1PZ Tel: 0191 587 2970 — MB ChB 1990 Dundee; MRCOG 1997. (Dundee) Specialist Regist. (O & G) Dryburn Hosp. Durh.

ROWLANDS, Richard Gareth 1 Coombe Terrace, Wotton-under-Edge GL12 7NA — MB ChB 1995 Manch.

ROWLANDS, Robert Paul 42 St Mary's Gate, Chesterfield S44 1bl — MB BS 1987 Newc.; MRCPsych 1991. (Newcastle University) Cons., Gen.Adult Psychiat., CHCS Chesterfield, Derbysh..

ROWLANDS, Roger John (retired) The Gate House, Alderley, Wotton-under-Edge GL12 7QT Tel: 01453 844804 — MB BS Lond. 1968; LLB (Hons.) Bristol 1995; MRCS Eng. LRCP Lond. 1968; MBAcA 1995; DObst RCOG 1971; DMed Acupunc. 1997. Prev: GP Wotton-under-Edge.

ROWLANDS, Samuel Crosfield EPIC, Regeneration House, York Way, London N1 0BB Tel: 020 7713 1118 Fax: 020 7713 1119 Email: epic1@gpdr.com; 3 Dennis Green, Gamlingay, Sandy SG19 3LQ Tel: 01767 651897 — MB BS 1974 Lond.; MRCGP 1979; MFFP 1993; DCH Eng. 1978; DRCOG 1976. (Lond. Hosp.) Med. Dir., EPIC, Lond.; Family Plann. Instruc. Doctor. Prev: Research Asst. Margt. Pyke Centre Lond.; Trainee GP Redhill VTS; SHO (O & G) Lond. Hosp.

ROWLANDS, Stephen Charles Bradford Road Medical Centre, 60 Bradford Road, Trowbridge BA14 9AR Tel: 01225 754255 Fax: 01225 774391 — MRCS Eng. LRCP Lond. 1977.

ROWLANDS, Stephen Gerent Brynmeddyg Surgery, Llanybydder SA40 9RN Tel: 01570 480244 Fax: 01570 481174; Pantunos, Llanybydder SA40 9RE Tel: 01570 480083 Fax: 01570 480083 — BM BCh 1974 Oxf.; MRCGP 1978; DRCOG 1978. (Oxford) GP Princip. Llanbydder; Clin. Asst. (Dermat.) W. Wales Hosp. Carmarthan.

ROWLANDS, Thomas Kinya 36 Manadon Drive, Plymouth PL5 3DJ — MB ChB 1997 Manch.

ROWLANDS, Timothy Edward 4 Ashfield Park, Grove Road, Headingley, Leeds LS6 2QT Tel: 0113 230 7240 — MB ChB 1993 Leeds; BSc (Hons.) Chem. Path. Leeds 1991; FRCS Eng. 1997. (Leeds) SHO (Surg.) Rotat. Leeds Gen. Infirm. Prev: Demonst. (Anat.) Univ. Leeds; Ho. Phys. Gen. Infirm. Leeds; Ho. Surg. St. Jas. Univ. Hosp. Leeds.

ROWLANDSON, George Forrester, Bowman and Rowlandson, Berry Lane Medical Centre, Berry Lane, Longridge, Preston PR3 3JJ Tel: 01772 783021 Fax: 01772 785809; Lower Cockhill Farm, Hothersll Lane, Longridge, Preston PR3 2XB — BM BS 1984 Nottm.; BMedSci Nottm. 1982; MRCGP 1988; DRCOG 1988; Cert. Family Plann. JCC 1988; DCH RCP Lond. 1987.

ROWLATT, Basil (retired) The Old Vicarage, Healey, Masham, Ripon HG4 — MB BS 1941 Lond.; MRCS Eng. LRCP Lond. 1941. Prev: Ho. Phys. Guy's Hosp.

ROWLATT, Charles (retired) 10 Hampstead Hill Gardens, London NW3 2PL Tel: 020 7435 1285 — PhD Lond. 1971; MA; BM BCh Oxf. 1960. Hon. Research Fell. (Histopath.) Roy. Free Hosp. Med. Sch. Lond. Prev: Staff Scientist Imperial Cancer Research Fund Lond.

ROWLATT, Richard John (retired) 2 Greenbank, Ulverston LA12 7HA Tel: 01229 582536 Email: glowlamps@aol.com — MB BS Lond. 1966; FRCP Lond. 1990; MRCP (UK) 1970; DCH Eng. 1970; FRCPCH 1996. Prev: Cons. Paediat. S. Cumbria HA Barrow in Furness.

ROWLES, Mr John Marshall Derby Royal Infirmary NHS Trust, London Road, Derby DE1 2QY Tel: 01332 347141; East Midlands Nuffield Hospital, Rykneld Road, Littleover, Derby DE23 7SN Tel: 01332 517891 — BM BS 1984 Nottm.; DM Nottm. 1993, BMedSci. 1982; FRCS (Orth.) 1995; FRCS Eng. 1988. Cons. Orthop. & Trauma Surg. Derbysh. Roy. Infirm. NHS Trust. Prev: Clin. Research Fell. Nottm., Leicester, Derby & Belf. Study Gp.

ROWLES, Nicola Horkstow Hall, Horkstow, Barton-upon-Humber DN18 6BE — MB BS 1987 Lond. Socs: BMA.

ROWLES, Susannah Victoria 11 Tivoli Road, Cheltenham GL50 2TD Tel: 0161 225 9689 — MB BS 1991 Lond.; MRCP. (Char. Cross & Westm.) Specialist Regist. Hope Hosp. Manch.

ROWLEY, Christine 16 Tyndall House, Southmead Hospital, Southmead Road, Westbury-on-Trym, Bristol BS10 5NB; 90 Howard Road, Westbury Park, Bristol BS6 7UY — BM 1993 Soton.

ROWLEY, Professor David Ian Department of Orthopaedic & Trauma Surgery, University of Dundee, Ninewells Hospital, Dundee DD1 9SY Tel: 01382 425746 Fax: 01382 496200; Marclann Cottage, Kellie Castle, Arbroath DD11 2PB Tel: 01241 876466 Fax: 01241 431894 — MB ChB 1976 Aberd.; MD Sheff. 1986; BMedBiol Aberd. 1973; FRCS Glas. 1992; FRCS Ed. 1980; FRCS 1998 England. (Aberd.) Prof. Orthop. & Trauma Surg. Univ. Dundee; Clin. Director Taysdide Univ. Hosps. Trust. Socs: Roy. Coll. Surg. Prev: Sen. Lect. (Orthop.) Univ. Manch.; Lect. (Orthop. Surg.) Univ. Sheff.; Sen. Lect. (Orthop. Mech.) Univ. Salford.

ROWLEY, Dorothy Elizabeth Margaret (retired) Greystead, South Road, Ashley Heath, Hale, Altrincham WA14 3HT — MB ChB 1946 Liverp.; DObst RCOG 1948. Prev: SCMO Manch. AHA (T).

ROWLEY, Eric 37 Princess Way, Fleetwood FY7 8AE — MB ChB 1955 Manch. Prev: Regist. (Med.) & SHO (Neurosurg.) Preston Roy. Infirm.; Flight Lt. RAF Med. Br.

ROWLEY, Hungerford Aboyne Thomas The Limes Medical Centre, 65 Leicester Road, Narborough, Leicester LE9 5DU Tel: 0116 284 1347 Fax: 0116 275 2447; 31 Springfield Road, Leicester LE2 3BB Tel: 0116 270 5149 — MB ChB 1986 Leic.; DRCOG 1990; MRCGP 1995.

ROWLEY, Jean (retired) — MB ChB 1956 Manch.; DCH Eng. 1959. Prev: Med. Adviser Benefits Agency DSS.

ROWLEY, John Martin King's Mill Hospital, Mansfield Road, Sutton-in-Ashfield NG17 4JL Tel: 01623 622515; Gamston Wood House, Westfields, Upton, Retford DN22 0RB Tel: 01777 839498 — MB 1976 Camb.; MA Camb. 1979, BA 1972, BChir 1975; MRCP (UK) 1977. Cons. Phys./Cardiol. Kings Mill Centre, Mansfield. Socs: Brit. Cardiac Soc. Prev: Cons. Phys./Cardiol. Mansfield Hosps.; Lect. Dept. Med. Univ. Nottm.

ROWLEY, Kathryn Helen Mary Dept. of Clincial Oncology, Singleton Hospital, Sketty, Swansea SA2 8QA Tel: 01792 285455 Fax: 01792 285455 Email: kath.rowley1@orange.net — MB BCh 1985 Wales; BSc (Med. Biochem.) Wales 1982; MRCP (UK) 1988; FRCR (Clin. Oncol.) 1994. (University of Wales College of Medicine) Cons., Clincal Oncol., Swansea NHS Trust. Socs: Brit. Oncol. Assoc.; BMA-Brit. Med. Assoc.; Roy. Soc. Med. Prev: Research Fell. (Oncol.) Cancer Research Wales; Hon. Sen. Regist. Velindre Hosp. Cardiff; Regist. & SHO (Clin. Oncol.) Velindre Hosp. Cardiff.

ROWLEY, Kenneth Arthur (retired) 9 Croyde Road, Lytham St Annes FY8 1EX Tel: 01253 725595 — MB ChB 1946 Manch.; MB ChB (2nd cl. Hons.) Manch. 1946; FRCR 1975; FFR 1954; DMRD Eng. 1950. Prev: Asst. Radiol. Manch. Roy. Infirm. & St. Mary's Hosps. Manch.

ROWLEY, Lester John Heronswood, The Drive, Wonersh, Guildford GU5 0QW — MB BChir 1944 Camb. (Westminster)

ROWLEY, Megan Ruth Haematology Department, Kingston Hospital, Galsworthy Road, Kingston upon Thames KT2 7QB Tel: 020 8934 2706 Fax: 020 8934 3245 Email: megan.rowley@kn-tr.sthames.nhs.uk — MB BS 1982 Lond.; FRCP 1997; MRCP (UK) 1985; MRCPath 1990; FRCPath 1998. (Guy's Hosp. Med. Sch.) Cons. Haematologist Qu. Mary's Univ. Hosp. Lond. & Kingston Hosp.; Cons. Haemat. Kingston Hosp.; Hon. Cons. Haemat. St Geo. Hosp. Socs: Brit. Soc. Haemat.; Assn. Clin. Path; Brit. Blood Transfus. Soc. Prev: Sen. Regist. (Haemat.) St. Geo. Hosp. Lond.; SHO Roy. Marsden Hosp. Sutton, William Harvey Hosp. Ashford & Guy's Hosp. Lond.

ROWLEY, Norman Clive (retired) The Stone House, College Road, Denstone, Uttoxeter ST14 5HR Tel: 01889 591468 Email: drcliverowley@hotmail.com — MB BChir 1971 Camb.; MB Camb. 1971, Bchir,camb,1970; MA Camb. 1971. Prev: Sen. Partner; Drs Rowley, Elsdon & Rees, Staffs.

ROWLEY, Peter David The Surgery, 18 Thurloe Street, London SW7 2ST Tel: 020 7225 2424 Fax: 020 7225 1874; 148 Felsham Road, London SW15 1DP Email: peterrowley@compuserve.com — MB BS Lond. 1979; Dip. Pract. Dermat. Wales 1990; DRCOG 1988. GP Lond. Prev: SHO (O & G) Louise Margt. Hosp. Aldershot; Ho. Phys. PeterBoro. Dist. Hosp.; Maj. RAMC.

ROWLEY, Steven Alan 90 Howard Park, Westbury Park, Bristol BS6 7UY — BM 1993 Soton.; FRCOphth 1997. Specialist Regist. Ophth., Bristol Eye Hosp. Prev: SHO Ophth. Leicester Roy. Infirm.

ROWLEY JONES, David SmithKline Beecham, SB House, Great West Road, Brentford TW8 9 Tel: 020 8560 5151 — MB BChir 1972 Camb.; MA, MB Camb. 1972, BChir 1971; MRCP (UK) 1977; MFPM 1990. Dir. Worldwide Med. Affairs SmithKline Beecham Brentford. Prev: SHO (Gen. Med.) Univ. Hosp. Wales Cardiff; Ho. Phys. (Gen. Med.) Nevill Hall Hosp. Abergavenny; Ho. Surg. (Orthop. & Traum.) Guy's Hosp. Lond.

ROWLING, Andrew James 102 Silvester Road, Waterlooville PO8 8TS — MB BCh 1995 Wales.

ROWLING, Dorothy Estyn Hillcrest, Blebo Craigs, Cupar KY15 5UQ Tel: 0133 485646 — MB ChB 1938 Leeds; FRCS Ed. 1949.

ROWLING, Mr John Thompson 14 Rutland Park, Sheffield S10 2PB Tel: 0114 266 4982 — MB BChir 1946 Camb.; 1959 MChir MA; BA (Nat. Sc. Trip. Cl. II) Camb. 1942, MD 1961; FRCS Eng. 1952; MRCS Eng. LRCP Lond. 1945. (Camb. & Leeds) Hon. Cons. Surg. Roy. Hallamsh. Hosp. Sheff.

ROWNEY, David Antony 23 Gardners Crescent, Edinburgh EH3 8DE Tel: 0131 622 4621 Email: davidrowney@cableinet.co.uk — MB ChB 1990 Ed.; FRCA 1996. Specialist Regist. (Anaesth.) Edin.

ROWNEY, James Tel: 028 9020 4445, 028 9020 4479 — MB BCh BAO 1988 Belf.; MRCGP 1993; DRCOG 1991. (Belfast)

ROWNEY, William Robert Finaghy Health Centre, 13-25 Finaghy Road South, Belfast BT10 0BX Tel: 028 9062 8211; Dunluce Health Centre, Belfast BT9 7HR Tel: 01232 204245 Fax: 01232 312306 — MB BCh BAO 1961 Belf.; FRCGP 1988, M 1968; Cert. Family Plann. JCC 1976; DObst RCOG 1963. (Qu. Univ. Belf.)

ROWNTREE, Barbara Mary (retired) Riverdale Cottage, West St, Soberton, Southampton SO32 3PL Tel: 01489 877373 — MRCS Eng. LRCP Lond. 1940. Prev: Med. Off. Stud. Health Serv. Univ. Soton.

ROWNTREE, Brenda Maureen (retired) Comp Corner Cottage, Borough Green, Sevenoaks TN15 8QT Tel: 01732 884151 — MB BS Durh. 1947; DFFP 1993; DObst RCOG 1949. Prev: Clin. Med. Off. Family Plann. Serv. Maidstone, Medway & Gravesham HAs.

ROWNTREE, Catherine 75 Lee Road, Blackheath, London SE3 9EN Tel: 020 8852 5622 Fax: 020 8318 2576 — MB 1972 Camb.; BChir 1971; FRCR 1977; DMRD Eng. 1975. Cons. Radiol. Newham Gen. Hosp. Prev: Sen. Regist. Univ. Coll. Hosp. Lond. & Hosp. Sick Childr. Gt. Ormond St. Lond.; Regist. St. Bart. Hosp. Lond.

ROWNTREE, Miss Catherine Anne East Surrey Hospital, Canada Avenue, Redhill RH1 5RH Tel: 01737 768511 Fax: 01737 778535; 23 The Green, Burgh Health, Tadworth KT20 5NP — MB ChB Bristol 1964; FRCOG 1994, M 1979; DObst 1966. (Bristol) Assoc. Specialist (O & G) E. Surrey Hosp. Redhill. Prev: Clin. Asst. (O & G) Redhill Gen. Hosp.; Regist. (O & G) Frimley Pk. Hosp.; SHO (O & G) Addenbrooke's Hosp. Camb.

ROWNTREE, Clare Judith Flat 5, Elmwood Court, Pershore Road, Edgbaston, Birmingham B5 7PB Tel: 0121 440 8926 — MB ChB 1990 Birm.; ChB Birm. 1990.

ROWNTREE, Mr Mark 75 Lee Road, Blackheath, London SE3 9EN — MB BS 1971 Lond.; MB Camb. 1972, BChir 1971; FRCS Eng. 1976; FRCS Ed. 1976. Cons. Orthop. Surg. Qu. Mary's Hosp. Sidcup. Prev: Sen. Regist. St. Bart. Hosp. Lond.; Sen. Regist. Hosp. Sick Childr. Lond.; Sen. Regist. Roy. Nat. Orthop. Hosp. Lond.

ROWNTREE, Penelope Clare 73 Moorside N., Newcastle upon Tyne NE4 9DU — MB BS 1984 Lond.

ROWNTREE, Raymond Staveacre (retired) 91 Princes House, 50 Kensington Park Road, London W11 3BW Tel: 020 7727 8262 — MB BS 1941 Lond.; MRCS Eng. LRCP Lond. 1939. Prev: Resid. Med. Off., The Middlx. Hosp., Lond.

ROWNTREE, Robert Keith (retired) Comp Corner Cottage, Borough Green, Sevenoaks TN15 8QT Tel: 01732 884151 — MB BS Durh. 1944; MRCGP 1953; DObst RCOG 1950. Prev: Sen. Med. Off. Civil Serv. Med. Advisory Serv.

ROWNTREE, Mr Tom (retired) Riverdale Cottage, West St, Soberton, Southampton SO32 3PL Tel: 01489 877373 Fax: 01489 877373 — MB BChir 1941 Camb.; BA (Hons.) Camb. 1937, MChir 1958; MS Lond. 1950, MB BS 1941; FRCS Eng. 1942; MRCS Eng. LRCP Lond. 1940. Prev: Cons. Surg. Soton. & SW Hants. Health Dist. (T).

ROWSE, Mr Alistair David Russells Hall Hospital, Dudley DY1 2HQ Tel: 01384 244201 Fax: 01384 244202; 18 Phoenix Green, Edgbaston, Birmingham B15 3NR Tel: 0121 684 5945 —

ROWSE

MB ChB 1969 Birm.; MSc Birm. 1974, BSc 1966; FRCS Eng. 1976. (Birm.) Cons. Urol. Russells Hall Hosp. W. Midl.

ROWSE, Elizabeth Anne Sunnyhill, Forster Road, Salcombe TQ8 9EB — MB BS 1964 Durh.; MRCP (UK) 1976. (Durh.) Sen. Med. Adviser DVLC Swansea. Prev: Med. Adviser Sec. State for Transport.

ROWSE, Nicholas James 5 Shakesspear Road, Walthamstow, London E17 6AS — MB BS 1979 Lond.; DRCOG 1981.

ROWSELL, Mr Anthony Richard Department of Plastic Surgery, Guy's Hospital, St Thomas St., London SE1 9RT; 41 Leckford Road, Oxford OX2 6HY — MB BS 1968 Lond.; DPhil Oxf. 1988; FRCS Eng. 1975; FRACS (Plast Surg.) 1980. Cons. Plastic Surg. Guy's Hosp. Lond. Prev: Sen. Regist. (Plastic Surg.) Radcliffe Infirm. Oxf.; Cons. Plastic Surg. P. Henry's Hosp. Melbourne, Australia.

ROWSELL, Mary Anne First Floor, 43 Elsinore Road, Manchester M16 0WG — MB ChB 1990 Manch.

ROWSELL, Rachel Margaret Primary Care, Canynge Hall, University of Bristol, Bristol BS8 2PR — MB BCh 1987 Wales; BSc (Hons.) Biochem. Wales 1982; MRCGP 1992; DRCOG 1992. Clin. Lect. (Primary Care) Univ. Bristol.

ROWSELL, Rhiannon Bracher AstraZeneca, Home Park, Kings Langley WD4 8DH Tel: 01923 266191 — MB BCh 1979 Wales; MRCP (UK) 1983; FFPM RCP (UK) 1994, M 1989; Dip Pharm. Med. RCP (UK) 1986. Med. & Regulatory Affairs Dir. AstraZeneca. Socs: FFPM. Prev: Med. Dir. Amersham Internat. plc; Dir. Clin. Investig. SmithKline Beecham Pharmaceut. Harlow, Essex; Regist. (Dermat.) Univ. Hosp. Wales.

ROWSON, Mr John Edmund Department of Oral & Maxillofacial Surgery, Queens Medical Centre, Nottingham NG7 2UH Tel: 0115 924 9924 Ext: 48916 — BM BS 1986 Nottm.; BMedSci Nottm. 1984; BDS Liverp. 1978; FRCS Ed. 1991; FDS RCS Eng. 1990. (Nottm.) Cons. Oral & Maxillofacial Surg. Qu. Med. Centre Univ. Nottm. NHS Trust; Clin. Director, Qu.'s Med. Centre. Socs: Brit. Assn. Oral & Maxillofacial Surg.s; Europ. Assn. of Crniomaxillo Facial Surg.; BMA. Prev: Sen. Regist. (Oral & Maxillofacial Surg.) Trent RHA.

ROWSON, Kenneth Edmund Knight (retired) — PhD Camb. 1977.; MA 1950, MD 1958, MB BChir 1952; MRCS Eng. LRCP Lond. 1950; Dip. Bact. Lond. 1956; MRCPath 1963. Prev: Reader in Virol. Inst. Laryng. & Otol. Lond.

ROWSON, Mr Neil James 33 Edna Street, London SW11 3DP — MB ChB 1982 Leeds; FRCS Glas. 1989; FRCOphth 1993; FCOphth 1989; DO RCS Eng. 1988. Sen. Regist. (Ophth.) Wolverhampton, Birm. & Stoke-on-Trent Hosps. Prev: Resid. Surg. Off. Moorfields Eye Hosp. Lond.

ROWTON-LEE, Martyn Addington St. Anns Hospital, Canford Cuffs, Poole BH13 7LN Tel: 01202 708881; 20 Queens Gardens, Bournemouth BH2 6BH Tel: 01202 769210 — BM BCh 1960 Oxf.; MA, BM BCh Oxf. 1960; FRCPsych 1986, M 1973; DPM Eng. 1970. (Univ. Coll. Hosp.) Cons. Psychiat. St. Ann's Hosp. Canford Cliffs; Vis. Psychother. HM Borstal Portland. Prev: Cas. Surg. Off. Univ. Coll. Hosp. Lond.; Squadron Med. Off. 29th Escort Squadron; Med. Off. RN Sch. Instruc. Diving, H.M.S. Vernon, Portsmouth.

ROXBURGH, Andrew Cathcart Amherst Medical Practice, 21 St. Botolphs Road, Sevenoaks TN13 3AQ Tel: 01732 459255 Fax: 01732 450751; Littlecroft, Woodland Rise, Sevenoaks TN15 0HY Tel: 01732 761159 — MB BS 1984 Lond.; MA Camb. 1985. Clin. Asst. (Neuro-Rehabil.). Prev: Regist. (Med.) St. Chas. Hosp. Lond.; SHO (Renal Med.) St. Thos. Hosp. Lond.; SHO (Clin. Oncol.) Hammersmith Hosp. Lond.

ROXBURGH, Annie May (retired) c/o Barclays Bank, 1 Brompton Road, London SW1 — MB ChB 1920 Ed.; DPH Ed. 1921.

ROXBURGH, Christine Macleod Campbell Mauve Practice, Drumhar Health Centre, North Methven Street, Perth PH1 5PD Tel: 01738 622421 Fax: 01738 444077 — MB ChB 1974 Glas.; DObst RCOG 1976.

ROXBURGH, David Alexander The Snypes, Greenloaning, Dunblane FK15 0LZ Tel: 01786 880378 — MB ChB 1964 Ed.; FRCR 1977; DMRD Eng. 1970. Cons. Radiol. Falkirk & Dist. Roy. Infirm. NHS Trust. Prev: Cons. Radiol. RAF.

ROXBURGH, Hermione Babington (retired) 6 Howard Road, Swanage BH19 2QJ — MB BChir 1948 Camb.; MA Camb. 1948; DCH Eng. 1961. Prev: Leverhulme Schol. RCS Eng.

ROXBURGH, Ian Oliphant (retired) Coverpoint, Goldsithney, Penzance TR20 9LB Tel: 01736 710635 — MB ChB Glas. 1952. Prev: SHO O & G P.ss Beatrice Hosp. Lond.

ROXBURGH, Mr James Cathcart Department of Cardiothoracic Surgery, St Thomas Hospital, Lambeth Palace Road, London SE1 7EH Tel: 020 7928 9292 Fax: 020 7922 8005 Email: james.roxburgh@gstt.sthames.nhs.uk — MB BS Lond. 1981; MS Lond. 1990; FRCS (Cth) 1992; FRCS Eng. 1985. (Middlesex Hospital, University of London) Cons. (Cardiothoracic Surg.) St. Thos. Hosp. Lond.; Hon. Cons. Cardiothoracic Surg., Roy. Surrey Co. Hosp., Guildford. Socs: Fell. Roy. Soc. Med. (Counc. Mem. of Cardiothoracic Sect.); Soc. Cardiothoracic Surg. GB & Irel. (Exec. Mem.); Surgic. Subspeciality Comm. Centr. Cons.s, BMA. Prev: Regist. (Cardiothoracic Surg.) Harefield & St. Thos. Hosp. Lond.; Sen. Regist. (Cardiothoracic Surg.) Guys & St. Thos. Hosp. Lond.; Research Fell. Middlx. Hosp. Lond.

ROXBURGH, Richard Hugh Stephen Richards 25 Birch Polygon, Rusholme, Manchester M14 5HX — MB ChB 1989 Otago.

ROXBURGH, Mr Robert Alexander (retired) 12 South Grove House, South Grove, Highgate, London N6 6LP Tel: 020 8340 8439 — MB BChir 1953 Camb.; MA Camb. 1965; BA (Hons.) Camb. 1950; MChir Camb. 1965; FRCS Ed. 1960; FRCS Eng. 1960. Hon. Cons. Surg. Broomfield Hosp. Chelmsford; Surg. Springfield Med. Centre Chelmsford. Prev: Sen. Regist. (Surg.) Middlx. Hosp. Lond.

ROXBURGH, Ronald Cathcart (retired) Wiggenhall House, Wiggenhall St Mary, King's Lynn PE34 3EH Tel: 01553 617333 — MB BChir 1947 Camb.; MA Camb. 1961, BA (Hons.) 1942, MD 1954; FRCP Lond. 1972, M 1950; MRCS Eng. LRCP Lond. 1944; DCH Eng. 1949; FRCP CH. Prev: Cons. Paediat. King's Lynn Dist. Gen. Hosp. & N. Cambs. Hosp. Wisbech.

ROXBURGH, Mr Stuart Thomas Dalrymple 4 Craigie Knowes Avenue, Perth PH2 0DL Tel: 01738 643347 Email: stuart.roxburgh@virgin.net — MB ChB 1974 Glas.; FRCS Ed. 1979; FRCOphth 1989. (Glasgow) Cons. Ophth. Tayside HB; Hon. Sen. Lect. in Ophth. Dundee Univ.

ROXBY, Christina Mary (retired) The Chestnuts, 21 High St., Walcott, Lincoln LN4 3SN — MB BS 1961 Lond.; MRCS Eng. LRCP Lond. 1961; FRCPath 1991, M 1979. Prev: Cons. Microbiol. Dist. Gen. Hosp. Sunderland.

ROXBY, Elaine Marjory Arran, 40 Admiral Street, Glasgow G41 1HU Tel: 0141 429 2626 Fax: 0141 429 2331 — MB ChB 1971 Glas.

ROXBY, Morven (retired) Bollin Chase, Willowmead Drive, Macclesfield SK10 4BU Tel: 01625 829432 — MB ChB 1965 Ed.; MFCM 1974; FFPHM 1989; FFCM 1988; DPH Glas. 1971. Cons. Pub. Health Med. W. Pennine HA. Prev: Dir. & Cons. Pub. Health Tameside & Glossop HA.

ROY, Alistair Ian Department of Anaesthesia, Sunderland Royal Hospital, Kayll Road, Sunderland SR4 7TP Tel: 0191 565 6256; 15 Elsdon Road, Gosforth, Newcastle upon Tyne NE3 1HY Tel: 0191 213 2877 — MB ChB 1991 Dundee; BSc (Hons.) Med. Microbiol. Dund 1986. Cons. Anaesth. & Intens. Care, Sunderland Roy. Hosp. Prev: SHO (Anaesth.) S. Cleveland Acute Hosps. NHS Trust Middlesbrough.; Specialist Regist. (Anaesth.)Roy. Vict. Infirm., Newc. upon Tyne.

ROY, Professor Arthur Douglas Garden House, Old Feniton Village, Honiton EX14 3BE Tel: 01404 850055 — MB ChB Glas. 1947; FRCSI 1976; FRCS Eng. 1952; FRCS Ed. 1952; FACS 1979; FRCPS Glas. 1963. Emerit. Prof. Qu. Univ. Belf. Socs: Fell. Assn. Surg. E. Afr.; Assn. Surg.; (Pres.) Exeter Med. Soc. Prev: Cons. & Hon. Lect. Univ. Glas. & W.. Infirm.; Foundat. Prof. Surg. Univ. Nairobi, Kenya 1968-72; Prof. Surg. Qaboos Univ. Oman.

ROY, Arun Bewbush Medical Centre, Bewbush Place, Bewbush, Crawley RH11 8XT Tel: 01293 519420 — MB BS 1961 Calcutta. (Calcutta) GP Crawley, W. Sussex.

ROY, Ashok Brian Oliver Centre, Brooklands, Coleshill Road Marston Green, Birmingham B37 7HL Tel: 0121 329 4927 Fax: 0121 779 4695 Email: ashok.roy@nw-tr.wmids.nhs.uk; Tel: 0121 355 2823 — MB BS 1978 Madras; MRCPsych 1985; DPM Madras 1981; FRCPsych 1998. Cons. Psychiat. N. Warks. NHS Trust Birmingham Specialist comm Health NHS Trust; Med. Dir. N. Warks. NHS Trust. Prev: Sen. Regist. (Ment. Handicap) W. Midl. RHA; Regist. (Psychiat.) S. Derbysh. HA.

ROY

ROY, Asoke Haematology Department, Basingstoke District Hospital, Aldermaston Road, Basingstoke RG24 9NA Tel: 01256 473202 — MB BS 1976 Calcutta; MD Chandigarh 1978.

ROY, Barbara Fulton Elm Hayes Surgery, High Street, Paulton, Bristol BS39 7QJ Tel: 01761 413155 Fax: 01761 410573; 1 Sleight View, Bloomfield Road, Timsbury, Bath BA2 0LL — MB ChB 1980 Dundee; MRCGP 1984; DRCOG 1982.

ROY, Bijon Kumar St. Margaret's Hospital, Epping CM16 6TN Tel: 01378 561666; Laurels, Kendal Avenue, Epping CM16 4PL — MB BS 1957 Calcutta; FRCPI 1979, M 1976; DCH Eng. 1965; Fell. Internat. Coll. Angiol. 1978. (Calcutta Nat. Med. Coll.) Cons. Phys. For the Elderly St. Margt. Hosp. Epping. Socs: BMA. Prev: Sen. Regist. S. W.. RHA; Regist. (Med. & Paediat.) I. of Man Health Auth.; Regist. (Med.) Liverp. RHB.

ROY, Birajananda 6 Seathwaite Close, Liverpool L23 6WD; 5 Derwent Drive, Dale View, Littleborough OL15 0BT Tel: 01706 376132 — MB BS 1971 Dibrugarh.

ROY, Chandra Has Abertillery Health Centre, Station Hill, Abertillery NP13 1UJ Tel: 01495 212635 Fax: 01495 320197 — MB BS 1974 Patna; MS Patna 1979.

***ROY, Chandrima** 7 Moorcroft Road, Fulwood, Sheffield S10 4GS Tel: 0114 230 9188 — MB ChB 1998 Leeds; BSc. Hon Pathological Sciences 1995.

ROY, Christopher William Tel: 0141 201 2679 Fax: 0141 201 1294 Email: chris.roy@sgn.scot.nhs.uk; Tel: 0141 644 3713 — MB ChB 1975 Glas.; MRCP (UK) 1980; DRCOG 1977. (Glas.) Cons. Rehabil. Med. S. Glas. Uni. Hosp. NHS Trust; Hon.Clin.Sen.Lect. Uni Glasg. Socs: Brit. Soc. Rehabil. Med.; Soc. Research. Rehabil.; Scott. Seating & Wheelchair Gp.. Prev: Sen. Lect. (Rehabil. Med.) Wellington Sch. Med. Univ. Otago, NZ.; Hon. Sen. Research Fell. Univ.Glasg.

ROY, David Charles Kirkhall Surgery, 4 Alexandra Avenue, Prestwick KA9 1AW Tel: 01292 476626 Fax: 01292 678022; 17 Duart Avenue, Prestwick KA9 1NA — MB ChB 1977 Glas.; MRCGP 1981.

ROY, Diane Helen 6 Sween Avenue, Braehead, Cathcart, Glasgow G44 3PD — MB ChB 1987 Dundee.

ROY, Dilip Kumar Royal Surrey County Hospital, Guildford GU2 7XX Tel: 01483 71122 — MB BS 1967 Calcutta. (Calcutta) Regist. (Orthop.) Roy. Surrey Co. Hosp. Prev: SHO (Gen. Surg.) Hereford Hosp.; SHO (Orthop.) Brook Gen. Hosp. Lond.; Regist. (Orthop.) Worcester Roy. Infirm.

ROY, Dinah Venetia The Surgery, Oxford Road, Spennymoor DL16 6BQ Tel: 01388 815081 Fax: 01388 815100; Midton House, Eamont Road, Ferryhill DL17 8LY Tel: 01740 655766 Fax: 01740 655766 — MB BChir 1984 Camb.; MA Camb. 1986, BA 1981; MRCGP 1989; DRCOG 1989; DA (UK) 1985. (Camb.) GP Spennymoor, Co Durh.; Chairm. Sedgefield PCG. Socs: BMA; Chairm. N. of Eng. Fac. RCGP; Roy. Coll. GPs. Prev: GP Coxhoe, Co. Durh.; Trainee GP Dunstable VTS.

ROY, Dipak — MBBS. (NRS Medical College, Calcutta, India. Calcutta University 1966) Gen. Practitioner.

ROY, Dipak Kumar 4 Woodside Road, Walsall WS5 3LS — MB BS 1992 Lond.

ROY, Elizabeth Helen 363 Jamaica Street, London E1 3HU — MB BS 1998 Lond.; MB BS Lond 1998.

ROY, Gwynneth Aileen 17 Copse Close, Oadby, Leicester LE2 4FD Tel: 0116 271 6429 — MB ChB 1961 Sheff.; MB ChB (Hons.) Sheff. 1961; DPH Bristol 1964; DObst RCOG 1963. Prev: SCMO Leics. HA; Asst. MOH Doncaster & Lond. Boro. Barnet.

ROY, Hiren 912 Walsall Road, Birmingham B42 1TG Tel: 0121 357 1250; 117A Harley Street, London W1 — MRCS Eng. LRCP Lond. 1942; MSc 1935, BSc 1933. (Guy's) Socs: BMA & Brit. Tuberc. Assn. Prev: Sen. Med. Off. & 1st Asst. to Med. Dir., Preston Hall, Maidstone; Ho. Phys. St. John's Hosp. Lewisham; Asst. Med. Off. St. Giles' Hosp. Camberwell.

ROY, Hiresh Lal High Street Surgery, 1st Floor, 97-101 High Street, Fort William PH33 6DG Tel: 01397 703773 Fax: 01397 701068; 20 Zetland Avenue, Upper Achintore, Fort William PH33 6LL Tel: 01397 705188 Email: hr@lochaben.almac.co.uk — MB BS 1967 Dibrugarh; MS (Gen. Surg.) Calcutta 1971; MFHom 1983; Cert. Family Plann. JCC 1982. (Assam Med. Coll.) GP Princip. Socs: Fac. Homoeop. Prev: Regist. (Gen. Surg.) Dunoon Gen. Hosp.

W. Kent Gen. hosp; Hosp. Pract. (Gen. Surg.) Belford Hosp. Fort William; SHO (O & G) Inverclyde Roy. Infirm. Greenock.

ROY, Ian Gordon Briarswood, West Looe Hill, Looe PL13 2HW — MB BS 1985 Lond.

ROY, Ian Leslie (retired) 16 Howard Place, Carlisle CA1 1HR Tel: 01228 526385 — MB ChB Aberd. 1942. Prev: Res. Ho. Surg. Rosedene Matern. Hosp. Inverness.

ROY, Jataveda Greenock Health Centre, 20 Duncan St., Greenock PA15 4LY; 10 Cowal View, Gourock PA19 1EX — MB BS 1974 Calcutta. Clin. Med. Off. (Community & Sch. Health) Greenock Health Centre.

ROY, Julie Paterson 49 Machanhill, Larkhall ML9 2HZ — MB ChB 1995 Glas.

ROY, Koushik Kumar South Street Surgery, 261 South Street, Romford RM1 2BE Tel: 01708 769780 Fax: 01708 722459 — MB BS 1959 Calcutta; MB BS 1959 Calcutta.

ROY, Leena Parklands Hospital, Aldermaston Road, Basingstoke RG24 9RH Tel: 01256 817718 — MB BS 1982 Lond.; MRCPsych 1986. Cons. Psychiat. Pk.lands Hosp. Basingstoke.

ROY, Louise Kathryn Mackay Castlehill Health Centre, Castlehill, Forres IV36 1QF Tel: 01309 672233; Gairland, 8 Hay Place, Elgin IV30 1LZ — MB ChB 1976 Aberd.; DRCOG 1979.

ROY, Lucy Caroline 5 Witham Close, Barley Meadows, Taunton TA1 2RR — MB ChB 1982 Bristol.

ROY, Manatosh Eaglestone Health Centre, Standing Way, Eaglestone, Milton Keynes MK6 5AZ Tel: 01908 679111 Fax: 01908 230601 — Vrach 1980 Minsk Med. Inst. USSR; Vrach Minsk Med Inst USSR 1980.

ROY, Manmatha Kumar Department of Anaesthesia, Hartlepool General Hospital, Holdforth Road, Hartlepool TS24 9AH Tel: 01429 266654, 01429 522192, 01429 522965 Fax: 01429 522194 Email: m.roy@nth.northy.nhs.uk, m.roy@nth.northy.nhsuk; 18 The Spinney, West Park, Hartlepool TS26 0AW Tel: 01429 274180 Fax: 01429 274180 — MB BS 1967 Dacca. (Sir Salimullah Med. Coll.) Cons. Anaesth. (N.tees of Hartlepool. NHS Trust. Cons. Anaesth.-N. Tees and Hartlepool NHS Trust. Socs: N. E. Soc. of Anaesth.; Pain Soc.; Assn. of Anaesth. of G.Band Irel. Prev: Assoc. Specialist (Anaesth.) N. RHA; Med. Asst. (Anaesth.) N.. RHA.

ROY, Mausumi 20 Zetland Avenue, Upper Achintore, Fort William PH33 6LL — MB ChB 1998 Aberd.; MB ChB Aberd 1998.

ROY, Meera Greenfields, Monyhull Hall Rd, Kings Norton, Birmingham B30 3QQ Tel: 0121 255 8014; 85 Monmouth Drive, Sutton Coldfield B73 6JH — MB BS 1980 Madras; MMedSci Birm. 1991; MRCPsych 1986; DPM Madras 1983; FRCPsych 1998. (Christian Medical College Vellore India) Cons. Psychiat. (Learning Disabilities)Birm. Specialist Community Trust. Prev: Sen. Regist. (Ment. Handicap) W. Midl. RHA; Regist. (Psychiat.) Nottm. HA; Regist. (Psychiat.) S. Derbysh. HA.

ROY, Meghnath The Surgery, 35 Maplestead Road, Dagenham RM9 4XH Tel: 020 8595 0017 Fax: 020 8595 7741; 137 Ashburton Avenue, Ilford IG3 9EW Tel: 020 8599 4343 Fax: 020 8595 7741 — MB BS 1967 Banaras Hindu; DA (UK) 1975.

ROY, Munna Sudipto Kumar 40 Cecil Street, Glasgow G12 8RJ — MB ChB 1992 Glas.

ROY, Philippa Jane 8 Autumn Avenue, Knutsford WA16 8LA — MB ChB 1983 Liverp.; DRCOG 1988.

ROY, Prabhat Kumar (cons. rooms), Treetops, Upper Layham, Hadleigh, Ipswich IP7 5JZ Tel: 01473 822253 — MB 1949 Calcutta; DTM 1949; FRCP Ed. 1975, M 1958; FRCPsych 1977, M 1972; DPM Eng. 1954. Prev: Cons. Psychiat. Severalls Hosp. Colchester; Assoc. Prof. Psychiat. NRS Med. Coll., Calcutta.

ROY, Prem Kumar 162 Southcroft Road, London SW17 9TP — MB BS 1988 Lond. SHO (Paediat.) Kent & Canterbury Hosp. Prev: SHO (A & E) Lond. Hosp.; Ho. Phys. Hereford Co. Hosp.; Ho. Surg. Lond. Hosp.

ROY, Premananda 863 Finchley Road, London NW11 8LX — MB BS 1950 Calcutta; DTM & H Eng. 1959.

ROY, Pulin Behari 6 Maesceiro, Bow Street SY24 5BG Tel: 01970 828708 — MB BS 1961 Dacca; DO Eng. 1973. (Dacca) Prev: SHO (Ophth.) W. Wales Gen. Hosp. Carmarthen; Regist. (Ophth.) St. Woolos Hosp. Newport.

ROY, Ramesh (retired) Radford Health Centre, Ilkeston Road, Nottingham NG7 3GW Tel: 0115 979 1313 Fax: 0115 979 1470.

ROY

ROY, Mr Raymond Robert The Oaks, 2 Sarsen Close, Halesworth IP19 8JP — MB ChB 1961 Bristol; FRCS Ed. 1968; FRCS Eng. 1969; Specialist Accredit (Urol.) RCS Eng. 1974. Socs: Brit. Assn. Urol. Surgs. Prev: Sen. Regist. (Urol.) Manch. AHA (T); Regist. Dept. Urol. Hammersmith Hosp. & Tutor in Surg. Roy. Postgrad.; Med. Sch. Lond.

ROY, Mr Ronen 1 Rosemary Avenue, Lower Earley, Reading RG6 5YQ Tel: 01734 868557 — MB BS 1985 Calcutta; FRCS Glas. 1989.

ROY, Ruby 21 Crowden Walk, Barnsley S75 2LU — MB ChB 1998 Manch.; MB ChB Manch 1998.

ROY, Sabita 17 Seldon Close, Westcliff on Sea SS0 0AD Tel: 01702 334139; St Clements Hospital, 2A Bow Road, London E3 — MB BS 1971 Ravishanker; MB BS Ravishankar 1971. Staff Grade (Psychiat.) St Clements Hosp. Lond.

ROY, Sarah Priya 5 Parkwood Crescent, Sherwood Vale, Nottingham NG5 4EA — MB BS 1996 Lond.

ROY, Shambu Nath 1 Barbondale Grove, Knaresborough HG5 0DX Tel: 01423 864103 — MB BS 1966 Ranchi. (Rajendra Med. Coll. Bihar) Staff Grade Phys. (Geriat. Med.) Harrogate Gen. Hosp. Prev: Regist. (Geriat. Med.) Harrogate Gen. Hosp.

ROY, Shib Shekhareswar Barnsley General Hospital, Gawber Road, Barnsley S75 2 Tel: 01226 730000; Suvadra, 21 Crowden Walk, Pogmoor, Barnsley S75 2LU Tel: 01226 244856 — BSc Calcutta 1949, MB BS 1955; FRCP Ed. 1993; FRCP Glas. 1987; MRCP (UK) 1974; DCH RCPS Glas. 1965; DTM & H Calcutta 1961. (Med. Coll. Calcutta) Emerit. Cons. Phys. Barnsley Dist. Gen. Hosp. Socs: Brit. Geriat. Soc. & BMA. Prev: Cons. Phys. & Clin. Head of Servs. c/o Elderly Barnsley Gen. Hosp. & Mt. Vernon Hosps.; Sen. Regist. N.. Gen. Hosp. Sheff.; Regist. (Gen. Med. & Paediat.) Kilton Hosp. Worksop.

ROY, Somnath 99 Pelham Avenue, Grimsby DN33 3NG Tel: 01472 878807 — MB BS Calcutta 1963; FRCP Lond. 1993; MRCP (UK) 1972. (R.G. Kar Med. Coll.) Cons. Phys. (Geriat.) Trent RHA.

ROY, Sonia Lara 17 Copse Close, Oadby, Leicester LE2 4FD — MB ChB 1992 Sheff.

ROY, Sucheta The Surgery, 172 Pitfield Street, London N1 6JP — MB BS 1967 Calcutta.

ROY, Sudhan Rani 3 Elmbourne Drive, Belvedere DA17 6JE — MB BS 1991 Lond.

ROY, Sunil Kanti c/o Drive R. Talukder, 3 Partridge Close, Swanlow Park, Winsford CW7 1PY — MB BS 1970 Dacca; MRCP (UK) 1984; MRCS Eng. LRCP Lond. 1983.

ROY, Supriyo (retired) 17 Copse Close, Oadby, Leicester LE2 4FD — MB ChB 1961 Sheff.; FRCP Lond. 1984, M 1969; DCH Eng. 1963. Prev: Cons. in Rheum. Leicester Area Hosps.

ROY, Syama Prosad 14 Read Head Road, South Shields NE34 6HT Tel: 0191 552498 & profess. 561161 — MB BS 1962 Calcutta; DA Eng. 1971; DA Calcutta 1967. (R.G. Kar Med. Coll.) Assoc. Specialist (Anaesth.) S. Tyneside HA. Prev: Regist. (Anaesth.) Canad. Red Cross Memor. Hosp. Taplow; Regist. (Anaesth.) Ilford & Dist. Gp. Hosps. & Nuneaton Gp. Hosps.

ROY, Tapan Kumar The Surgery, High Street, Talke Pits, Stoke-on-Trent ST7 1QH Tel: 01782 782440 Fax: 01782 763884 — MB BS 1956 Calcutta; MB BS 1956 Calcutta.

ROY, William (retired) 9 Dunchattan Grove, Troon KA10 7AT Tel: 01292 317303 — MB ChB 1946 Glas.; FRCP Glas. 1980, M 1962; FRFPS Glas. 1949; FRCGP 1974, M 1967. Prev: Regist. (Med.) Ballochmyle Hosp.

ROY, William Noel Thompson (retired) Caius House, Wooler NE71 6EE Tel: 01668 281559 — MB BS 1959 Lond.; MRCS Eng. LRCP Lond. 1959; DObst RCOG 1960. Prev: SHO (Paediat.) Preston Hosp.

ROY, William Stuart 124 Kings Road, Cardiff CF11 9DG — MB ChB 1992 Bristol; MPhil Camb. 1994. SHO (Gen. Surg.) Gwynedd.

ROY BURMAN, Bimal Prova 23 Shrubbery Road, London N9 0PA — MB BS 1959 Patna; MRCOG 1977, DObst 1968. (P.W.D. Med. Coll. Patna) Clin. Asst. (Gyn. & Obst.) Redhill Gen. Hosp.

ROY-CHOUDHURY, Debasis (Surgery) 18 Chac Cross Road, Collier Row, Romford RM5 3PR; 187 Brentwood Road, Romford RM2 1JS — MB BS 1975 Lond.; BSc (Hons.) Biochem. Lond. 1971; MB BS 1975; DRCOG 1982.

ROY CHOUDHURY, Manik 14 Hermitage Road, Edgbaston, Birmingham B15 3UR — MB BS 1961 Calcutta; FRCOG 1985, M 1969.

ROY CHOUDHURY, Mr Subhabrata 8 Farmers Close, Sale M33 2LJ — MB BS 1959 Calcutta; PhD Manch. 1971, MSc 1969; FRCS Ed. 1966. Prev: Sen. Lect. (Anat.) Med. Sch. Manch. Univ.; Vis. Assoc. Prof. Anat. Univ. Iowa, USA; Prof. Anat. Kuwait Univ.

ROY CHOWDHURY, Sanjoy Nirala, 90 Links Avenue, Gidea Park, Romford RM2 6NJ — MB BS 1956 Calcutta.

ROYAL, David Mark St John Windsor Road Clinic, Windsor Road, Normanby, Middlesbrough TS6 0RE Tel: 01642 453338 Fax: 01642 468915; The Orchard, 648 Yarn Road, Eaglescliffe, Stockton-on-Tees TS16 0DH — MB BS 1988 Newc.; MRCGP 1994; DFFP 1993; DCH RCP Lond. 1993; T(GP) 1993. Prev: Trainee GP/SHO (O & G) Darlington Memor. Hosp. Cleveland VTS.

ROYAL, Valerie Moira 526 Yarm Road, Eaglescliffe, Stockton-on-Tees TS16 0BH Tel: 01642 790204 — MB ChB 1987 Leeds.

ROYAN, Caroline Nicole BUPA Wellness, 2-6 Austin Friars, London EC2N 2HD Tel: 0207 562 7371; 31 Ordnance Hill, London NW8 6PS Email: nicole@royanryan.fsnet.com — MRCS Eng. LRCP Lond. 1984; MFOM RCP Lond. 1996; MRCGP 1989; T(OM) 1996; T(GP) 1991; DRCOG 1990. (Char. Cross) p/t Cons. (Occupat. Phys.) BUPA Wellness. Socs: Soc. Occup. Med - Counc. Mem. Prev: Med. Adviser Lond. Transport Occupat. Health.

ROYCE, Catherine Margaret 58 Palmerston Street, Romsey SO51 8GG Tel: 01794 514782 — MB BS 1974 Lond.; MS Soton. 1987; FRCS Eng. 1981; DRCOG 1976.

ROYCE, Samuel Lester (retired) 1 Dovehouse Close, Whitefield, Manchester M45 7PE Tel: 0161 766 7002 — MB ChB 1947 Manch. Prev: Ho. Surg. Pk. Hosp. Davyhulme & Roy. Hosp. Salford.

ROYCE, Susan Margaret Top Farm, Barking Tye, Ipswich IP6 8JD Tel: 01473 658583 — MB BS 1967 Lond.; MFFP 1993. (Middlx.) Assoc. Specialist (Reproduc. & Sexual Health) Ipswich Hosp. Trust; Assoc. Specialist (Family Plann. & Reproduc. Health & Psychosexual Med.) Allington NHS Trust.

ROYCROFT, Roger John Roycroft, Madden and Thomas, Chelford Surgery, Elmstead Road, Chelford, Macclesfield SK11 9BS Tel: 01625 861316 Fax: 01625 860075; Roadside House, Chelford, Macclesfield SK11 9AT Tel: 01625 861509 — MB ChB 1958 Manch.; MSc Manch. 1991. (Manch.) Prev: Regist. Duchess of York Hosp. For Babies Manch.; SHO (O & G) Copthorne Hosp. Shrewsbury; Ho. Surg. Manch. Roy. Infirm.

ROYDE, Chaim Alexander (retired) 10 Devonshire Court, New Hall Road, Salford M7 4JT — MD Lond. 1947, MB BS 1940; MRCS Eng. LRCP Lond. 1940; FFCM 1979, M 1974; DPH Eng. 1947. Prev: Area Med. Off. Bury AHA.

ROYDS-JONES, Jonathan Aidan Bridge Medical Centre, Wassand Close, Three Bridges Road, Crawley RH10 1LL Tel: 01293 526025 — MB BS 1973 Lond.

ROYLANCE, John 45 Corvedale Road, Birmingham B29 4LA — MB ChB 1968 Birm.; FFA RCS Eng. 1975.

ROYLANCE, Margaret Helen 79 Tennyson Avenue, Dukinfield SK16 5DR — MB ChB 1992 Leeds.

ROYLANCE, Michael Kingsley Millbrook Gardens Surgery, Millbrook Gardens, Castle Cary BA7 7EE Tel: 01963 350210 Fax: 01963 350366; Joss Cottage, Church Road, Sparkford, Yeovil BA22 7JZ Tel: 01963 440577 — MB ChB Leeds 1969. (Leeds)

ROYLANCE, Pauline Deidre Tattenhall Medical Practice, Mercury House, High St, Tattenhall, Chester CH3 9PX Tel: 01829 770606 Fax: 01829 770144; Yew Tree Farm, Beeston Moss, Beeston, Tarporley CW6 9SU — MB ChB 1973 Manch.; MSc (Primary Med. Care) Keele 1995.

ROYLANCE, Rebecca Ruth 51 Brompton Park Crescent, Fulham, London SW6 1SW — MB BS 1991 Lond.; BSc (Hons.) Lond. 1988; MRCP (UK) 1994.

ROYLE, Mr Clive Alexander Joseph Peel Yeovil District Hospital, Yeovil BA21 4AT Tel: 01935 707472 Email: c_royle@compuserve.com; Langley, Henley Road, Misterton, Crewkerne TA18 8LS Tel: 901460 78580 Email: c-royle@compuserve.com — MB BS 1980 Lond.; MS Soton. 1995; FRCS Eng. 1987. Cons. Gen. & Colorectal Surg. Yeovil Dist. Hosp. Prev: Cons. Gen. Surg. Frimley Pk. Hosp. Milit. Unit; Cons. Camb. Milit. Hosp.; Sen. Regist. Soton. Prof. Unit.

ROYLE, Cyril (retired) Granny Cottage, Chorley House, Clitheroe Tel: 01200 423666 — MB ChB 1935 Manch.; DCH Eng. 1948. Prev: Cas. Off. Centr. Br. & Ho. Surg. Manch. Roy. Infirm.

ROYLE, David Andrew Birchwood Medical Centre, 15 Benson Road, Birchwood, Warrington WA3 7PJ Tel: 01925 823502 Fax: 01925 852422; Summerville House, Summrville Gardens, Grappenhall, Warrington WA4 2EG Tel: 01925 602067 — MB ChB 1983 Liverp.; MRCGP 1988; Cert. Family Plann. JCC 1987; DRCOG 1986. (Liverp.) Socs: N. Chesh. LMC; Bd. Mem. NES PCG. Prev: Trainee GP N. Staffs. VTS; SHO (Cardiothoracic Med.) & Ho. Off. BRd.green Hosp. Liverp.

ROYLE, Deborah Jane 16 Hawthorne Rise, Answorth, Nottingham NG16 2RG — MB ChB 1992 Leeds.

ROYLE, Deborah Tracy Sett Valley Medical Centre, Hyde Bank Road, New Mills, Stockport SK22 4BP Tel: 01663 743483; Herries Cottage, Aspenshaw, Birch Vale, High Peak SK22 1AU Tel: 01663 747593 — MB ChB 1982 Manch.; BSc (Med. Sci.) St. And. 1979; DRCOG 1985. Prev: SHO (O & G) St. Marys Hosp. Manch.; SHO (Cas.) Stockport HA; SHO (Med.) Stepping Hill Hosp. Stockport.

ROYLE, Francis Clifford William (retired) Shearwater, Salterns Lane, Old Bursledon, Southampton SO31 8DH Tel: 023 403575 Fax: 023 8040 3575 — MRCS Eng. LRCP Lond. 1946; MA Camb. 1948. Prev: GP Soton.

ROYLE, Mr Gavin Timothy Wessex Nuffield Hospital, Winchester Road, Chandlers Ford, Eastleigh SO50 2DW Tel: 01280 258434 Fax: 02380 258446; Shawlands House, Shawlands Farm, Bunstead Lane, Hursley, Winchester SO21 2LQ Tel: 01962 775324 Fax: 01962 775324 — MB BS Lond. 1970; MS Lond. 1979; FRCS Eng. 1974; MRCS Eng. LRCP Lond. 1970. (Char. Cross.) Cons. Gen. Surg. Soton. Univ. Hosps.; Cons. Surg. Soton. & Salisbury BrE. Screening Unit; Hon. Sen. Lect. Univ. Soton. Socs: Surgic. Research Soc.; Assn. Surg.; Brit. BrE. Gp. Prev: Sen. Lect. (Surg.) Soton Univ.; Lect. (Surg.) Mass. Gen. Hosp. Boston, USA; Clin. Lect. (Surg.) Nuffield Dept. Surg. Oxf.

ROYLE, Hannah Mary Summerside Medical Centre, 29B Summerside Place, Edinburgh EH6 4NY Tel: 0131 554 3533 Fax: 0131 554 9722; 6 James Street, Edinburgh EH15 2DS — MB ChB 1966 Ed.

ROYLE, Janice Brampton Medical Practice, 4 Market Place, Brampton CA8 1NL Tel: 01697 772551 Fax: 01697 741944 — MB ChB 1984 Manch.; BSc St. And. 1981; MRCGP 1989; DCH RCP Lond. 1988; DRCOG 1988.

ROYLE, John Dinnis Great Harwood Health Centre, Water Street, Great Harwood, Blackburn BB6 7QR; Chorley House, Back Commons, Clitheroe BB7 2DX Tel: 01200 426524, 02476 343337 Fax: 01200 426524 — MRCS Eng. LRCP Lond. 1972; LMSSA Lond. 1971. Princip. Med. Practitioner. Socs: B.M.A.S. Prev: Regist. Psychiat. Lamont Clinic.

ROYLE, Justine Sarah 4 Ennerdale Drive, Sale M33 5NE — MB ChB 1994 Manch.

ROYLE, Martin John 6 Lyndon Drive, Liverpool L18 6HP — MB ChB 1994 Liverp.

ROYLE, Mr Michael Gordon The Hove Nuffield Hospital, 55 New Church Road, Hove BN3 4BG Tel: 01273 720217 Fax: 01273 220919 — MB BS 1960 Lond.; FRCS Eng. 1965; FACS 1972. (St. Mary's) Prev: Cons. Urol. Brighton Health Trust; Resid. (Urol.) Univ. Calif. Los. Angeles, USA; Hon. Sen. Lect. Inst. Urol. Univ. Lond.

ROYLE, Peter, Wing Cdr. RAF Med. Br. Retd. Anaesthetic Department, North Tees Hospital, Hardwick, Stockton-on-Tees TS19 8PE — MB BS 1976 Lond.; FFA RCS Eng. 1983; MBA (Open Univ) 1999. (Guy's) Cons. Anaesth. N. Tees Hosp. Stockton-on-Tees.; MMed. Director, Norht Tees & Hartlrpool NHS Trust. Prev: Cons. Anaesth. RAF Hosp. Wroughton; SHO (Anaesth.) Frimley Pk. Hosp.

ROYLE, Robert Arthur Weaverham Surgery, Northwich Road, Weaverham, Northwich CW8 3EU Tel: 01606 853106 Fax: 01606 854980 — MB ChB 1975 Sheff.; MRCGP 1979.

ROYLE, Mr Stephen Gordon Trafford General Hospital, Moorside Road, Davyhulme, Manchester M41 5SL Tel: 0161 748 4022 (Ext 2947) Fax: 0161 746 2982 Email: stephen.royle@traffdhc-tr.nwest.nhs.uk; Herries Cottage, Aspenshaw, Birch Vale, High Peak SK22 1AU Tel: 01663 747593 Email: steveroyle@ukonline.co.uk — MB ChB Manch. 1982; MD Manch. 1993; FRCS (Orth.) 1994; FRCS Ed. 1986. (Manchester) Cons. Orthop. Surg. Trafford Gen. Hosp.

Manch. Prev: Sen. Regist. Rotat. (Orthop.) N. Manch.; Regist. (Orthop.) Salford & Wythenshawe Hosp. Manch.; Regist. (Surg.) N. Manch. Gen. Hosp.

ROYO MOYA, Javier Salton House, St Mary's Hospital, London W2 1NY — LMS 1989 Saragossa.

ROYSAM, Chandrikha Sashidhar Samsara, 86 Kenton Road, Gosforth, Newcastle upon Tyne NE3 4NP — MB BS 1983 Bangalore; FCAnaesth 1990; FFA RCS Dub. 1989; DA (UK) Lond. 1987; MD (Am. Boards). Cons. Anaesth. Freeman Hosp. Newc. Prev: Resid. Harvard Univ. Boston, USA.

ROYSAM, Mr Gorur Shashidhar South Tyneside Hospital, Harton Lane, South Shields NE34 0PL Tel: 0191 202 4025 — MB BS 1981 Bangalore; MChOrth Liverp. 1991; FRCS (Orth.) 1993; FRCS Glas. 1988; FRCS Ed. 1988; MRCS Eng. LRCP Lond. 1988; FCPS Glas. 1988. Sen. Regist. (Orthop. Surg.) St. Geo. Hosp.; Spine Fell. Robt. Jones Agnes Hunt Orthop. Hosp. OsW.ry. Prev: Regist. & Sen. Regist. St. Geo. Hosp. Lond.

ROYSTON, Ashley Melvyn The Stennack Surgery, The Old Stennack School, St Ives TR26 1RU Tel: 01736 793333 Fax: 01736 793746; Lamerton Manor, Idless, Truro TR4 9QT Tel: 01872 273890 — MB BS 1972 Lond.; MRCP (U.K.) 1976; MRCS Eng. LRCP Lond. 1972. (Guy's) GP St. Ives.

ROYSTON, Mr Christopher Mackie Sheridan 43 Newlands Park, Hull HU5 Tel: 01482 42314 — MB BS 1965 Lond.; FRCS Eng. 1970; MRCS Eng. LRCP Lond. 1965. Cons. (Gen. Surg.) Hull Roy. Infirm. Prev: Sen. Regist. (Surg.) Hammersmith Hosp. Lond.; Sen. Regist. (Surg.) N.ampton Gen. Hosp.; Research Assoc. Middlx. Hosp. Lond.

ROYSTON, Ian McLean Everest House Surgery, Everest Way, Hemel Hempstead HP2 4HY Tel: 01442 240422 Fax: 01442 235045 — MB BS 1974 Lond.; BSc (Hons.) Liverp. 1969; MRCS Eng. LRCP Lond. 1974. GP Hemel Hempstead.

ROYSTON, Nancy Holmwood, 46 Crescent Road, Hemel Hempstead HP2 4AH Tel: 01442 65590 — MB ChB 1969 Ed.; BSc (Hons.) Ed. 1967, MB ChB 1969; FFA RCS Eng. 1974. Cons. Anaesth. St. Vincents' Orthop. Hosp. E.cote; Cons. Anaesth. Chiltern Hosp. Gt. Missenden; Cons. Anaesth. BUPA Hosp. Harpenden. Prev: Cons. Anaesth. Kidderminster Gen. Hosp.; Sen. Regist. (Anaesth.) & SHO (Anaesth.) St. Bart. Hosp. Lond.

ROYSTON, Nigel Joseph Walter (retired) 59 Newland, Sherborne DT9 3JG Tel: 01935 812934 — MRCS Eng. LRCP Lond. 1952; FRCP Ed. 1975, M 1957; DCH Eng. 1954; FRCPCH 1997. Prev: Cons. Paediat. Som. AHA.

ROYSTON, Robin Gray Psychotherapy Department, 2 Cossington Road, Canterbury CT1 3HU; The Red House, Stonewall Pk Road, Langton Green, Tunbridge Wells TN3 0HD Tel: 01892 863858 — MRCS Eng. LRCP Lond. 1974; MRCPsych 1986. Cons. Psychother. Canterbury & Thanet Trust.; Clin. Dir., Acute Psychiatric Unit, Ticehurst Ho. Hosp., E. Sussex; Hon. Research Fell. Univ. Kent.

ROYSTON, Simon Lester 9 Sackville Road, Sheffield S10 1GT — MB ChB 1984 Manch. Regist. Rotat. (Surg.) Hallamsh. Sheff. Prev: SHO (Orthop.) Bolton Roy. Infirm.; SHO (Orthop.) Univ. Hosp. S. Manch.; SHO (A & E) Wythenshawe Hosp. Manch.

ROYSTON, Virginia Helen Central Health Clinic, Tower Hill, Bristol BS1 0AH; 53 Elton Road, Bishopston, Bristol BS7 8DG — MB ChB 1979 Bristol; BSc (Hons.) Bristol 1976; MRCGP 1983; DFFP 1995; Cert. Family Plann. JCC 1984; DRCOG 1982. SCMO Avon Pregn. Advis. Serv. Prev: GP Bristol; Ho. Off. (Med.) Univ. Bristol; Ho. Off. (Surg.) S.mead Hosp. Bristol.

ROYTHORNE, Christopher The British Petroleum Company plc, Britannic House, 1 Finsbury Circus, London EC2M 7BA Tel: 020 7496 4126 Fax: 020 7496 4544 Email: roythorc@bp.com; 1 Pine Close, North Road, Berkhamsted HP4 3BZ Tel: 01442 875496 — MB BS 1969 Newc.; FFOM RCP Lond. 1988, MFOM 1982; DIH Soc. Apoth. Lond. 1977; CIH Dund 1977. Vice Pres. Health B.P. plc. Prev: Sen. Med. Adviser BP Oil UK; Internat. Health Coordinator BHPP Lond.; Med. Dir. Conoco (UK) Ltd. Lond.

ROYTHORNE, Judith Patricia Milton House Surgery, Doctors Commons Road, Berkhamsted HP4 3BY Tel: 01442 874784 Fax: 01442 877694; 1 Pine Close, North Road, Berkhamsted HP4 3BZ Tel: 01442 875496 — MB ChB 1969 Manch.

ROZARIO, Elizabeth Liza 49B Sutton Road, Walsall WS1 2PQ — MB BS 1993 Lond.

ROZARIO

ROZARIO, John Alfred Christopher 25 Enys Quay, Truro TR1 2HH Tel: 01872 222973 — MB BS 1953 Lond.; MRCS Eng. LRCP Lond. 1953. (Guy's) Prev: Med. Supt. Gen. Hosp. Ndola, Zambia; Paediat. Ho. Phys. Freedom Fields Hosp. Plymouth; Obst. Ho. Surg. Roy Bucks. Hosp. Aylesbury.

ROZEWICZ, Deborah Phyllis Simpson House Medical Centre, 255 Eastcote Lane, South Harrow, Harrow HA2 8RS Tel: 020 8864 3466 Fax: 020 8864 1002 — MB BS 1988 Lond.; MRCGP 1994; DRCOG 1991. (St. Geo. Hosp.) Simpons Ho. Med. Centre Harrow. Prev: Trainee GP Mayday Univ. Hosp. VTS; Ho. Off. (Surg.) St. Geo. Hosp. Lond.

ROZEWICZ, Ella Chandos Crescent, 82 Chandos Crescent, Edgware HA8 6HL Tel: 020 8952 7662; 13 Sunningdale Close, Gordon Avenue, Stanmore HA7 3QL Tel: 020 8954 2848 — LMSSA 1978 Lond.; MB Silesia 1963.

ROZEWICZ, Leon Michal Wimbledon CMHT, Nelson Hospital, Kingston Road, London SW20 8DB Tel: 020 8544 9799 Fax: 020 8544 9033 Email: irozewicz@swlstg-tr.nhs.uk — MB BS 1984 Lond.; MRCP (UK) 1989; MRCPsych 1993; MRCGP 1990; T(GP) 1991. Cons. Psychiat. S. W. Lond., St. Geo.'s NHS Ment. Health Trust; Hon. Sen. Lect. in Psychiat., St. Geo.'s Hosp. Med. Sch. Prev: Cons. Psychiat. Centr. Middlx. Hosp. Lond.; Lect. & Hon. Sen. Regist. (Psychiat.) St. Geo. Hosp. Med. Sch. Lond.; Hon. Sen. Regist. & Research Fell. Inst. Neurol. Lond.

ROZKOVEC, Adrian Royal Bournemouth Hospital, Castle Lane E., Bournemouth BH7 7DW Tel: 01202 704596 — MB BS 1974 Lond.; 2001 FESC; BSc Lond. 1971, MD 1987; FRCP Lond. 1995; MRCP (UK) 1977. (Univ. Coll. Lond. & Westm.) Cons. Phys. & Cardiol. Roy. Bournemouth Hosp. Socs: Fell.of the Roy. Soc. Med.; Brit. Cardiac Soc.; Brit. Pacing & Electrophysiol. Gp. Prev: Sen. Regist. (Gen. Med. & Cardiol.) Plymouth & Bristol Roy. Infirm.; Regist. (Cardiol.) Hammersmith Hosp. Lond.; Resid. Med. Off. Nat. Heart Hosp. Lond.

ROZNER, Lorna Margaret (retired) 33 Princess Mary Court, Newcastle upon Tyne NE2 3BG Tel: 0191 281 0770 — MB BS 1947 Durh.; DPH Durh. 1951. Prev: Cons. Psychiat. S. Tyneside AHA.

ROZYCKI, Andrzej Antoni 12 Tewkesbury Drive, Prestwich, Manchester M25 0HG Tel: 0161 798 7890 — Lekarz 1957 Gdansk. Assoc. Specialist Prestwich Hosp. Socs: Ex-Pres. of Warsaw Br. Polish Psychiat. Assn.; Ex-Vice-Pres. Soc. Psychiat. Assn. Poland. Prev: Med. Direct. Drewnica Psychiat. Hosp., Warsaw.

RUAUX, Caroline Denise New Hayesbank Surgery, Cemetery Lane, Kennington, Ashford TN24 9JZ Tel: 01233 624642 Fax: 01233 637304; 7 St. Nicholas Mansions, Trinity Crescent, Tooting, London SW17 7AF — MB BS 1989 Lond.; MRCGP 1994; DRCOG 1991. Prev: SHO (Geriat. Med.) Epsom Gen. Hosp.; SHO (A & E) Kingston Hosp. Lond.; SHO (O & G) St. Helier Hosp. Carshalton.

RUB, Abdul 248 Earls Court Road, London SW5 9AD Tel: 020 7373 9797; (Surgery) 26 Fourth Avenue, London W10 Tel: 020 8960 5252 — MB BS 1954 Calcutta.

RUB, Hasib-ur The Surgery, 42 High Street, Chislehurst BR7 5AX Tel: 020 8467 5551 Fax: 020 8468 7658; 20 Heath Park Drive, Bromley BR1 2WQ — BM 1984 Soton.; BM Soton 1984; MRCGP 1991; DCH RCP Lond. 1988. Mem. LMC. Prev: SHO (O & G) Pembury Hosp.; SHO (Paediat.) Freedon Fields Hosp. Plymouth; SHO (Med.) Lister Hosp. Stevenage.

RUB, Rebecca 208 Church Lane, Kingsbury, London NW9 8SP — MB BS 1994 Lond.; MB BS (Hons Med.) Lond. 1994; BSc (Physiol. with Basic Med. Sci.) Lond. 1991. (St. Geo. Hosp. Lond.) SHO (Paediat.) Roy. Surrey Co. Hosp.

RUBAN, Ernest Peter 1 Freswick Court, Hinckley LE10 0RW — BM BS 1989 Nottm.; BMedSci 1987; MRCPath 1995.

RUBEN, David Henry Lady Hamilton Court, 2 Holders Hill Avenue, London NW4 1EY — MB BS 1989 Lond.; BSc (1st cl. Hons.) Lond. 1986, MB BS 1989; MRCGP 1994.

RUBEN, Lewis Alan (retired) 4 Little Bornes, Dulwich, London SE21 8SE Tel: 020 8670 0430 — MB BCh BAO Dub. 1957; MA Dub. 1960; FRCGP 1979, M 1966; DObst RCOG 1962. Non-Exec. Dir., Community Health S. Lond. NHS Trust. Prev: Dean Postgrad. Gen. Pract. Educat. S. Thomas (E.).

RUBEN, Mr Montague (retired) 20 Seven Stones Drive, Broadstairs CT10 1TW — MRCS Eng. LRCP Lond. 1945; LMS Barcelona 1986; FRCS Eng. 1960; FRCOphth 1989; DOMS Eng. 1949. Hon. Cons. Ophth. Moorfields Eye Hosp. Lond. Prev: Cons. Ophth. & Dir. Dept. Contact Lens & Prosth.s Moorfields Eye Hosp. (City Rd. Br.) Lond.

RUBEN, Pamela Elaine Stockwell Group Practice, 107 Stockwell Road, Brixton, London SW9 9TJ Tel: 020 7274 3225 Fax: 020 7738 5005; 4 Little Bornes, Dulwich, London SE21 8SE Tel: 020 8670 0430 — MB BS 1963 Lond.; MRCS Eng. LRCP Lond. 1963. (St. Geo.)

RUBEN, Mr Simon Timothy Holly House, High Road, Buckhurst Hill IG9 5HZ Tel: 020 8505 3311 Email: streye1@aol.com — MB BS 1985 Lond.; BSc Lond. 1982, MD 1996; FRCS Glas. 1989; FCOphth 1990; DO 1989; MD Lond. 1996. (St. Bart. Hosp. Lond.) Cons. Ophth. Surg. Whipps Cross Hosp. & Harold Wood Hosp. Prev: Sen. Regist. Birm. Eye Hosp.; Regist. W.. Ophth. Hosp.; Fell. (Glaucoma) Moorfields Eye Hosp. Lond.

RUBEN, Susan Mary 5 Pelham Grove, Liverpool L17 8XD Tel: 0151 428 3432 — MB ChB 1978 Ed.; MRCPsych 1983. Cons. Psychiat. Drug Dependency Unit Liverp. HA.

RUBENS, David Harold 25 Homecross House, Fishers Lane, Chiswick, London W4 1YA Tel: 020 8747 4962 — MB BS 1954 Lond.; MRCS Eng. LRCP Lond. 1954. (Lond. Hosp.) Clin. Asst. Centr. Middlx. Hosp. Lond.; Med. Ref. Pruden. & Scott. Life Assur. Cos. Socs: BMA. Prev: Surg. Merchant Navy; Receiv. Room. Off. & Ho. Surg. Lond. Hosp.; Ho. Phys. Brighton Gen. Hosp.

RUBENS, Michael Bernard Flat 6, Harmont House, 20 Harley St., London W1G 9PH Tel: 020 7580 1442 Fax: 020 7580 0494 — MB BS 1971 Lond.; MRCS Eng. LRCP Lond. 1971; FRCR 1976; DMRD Eng. 1975. Cons. Radiol. Roy. Brompton Hosp. Lond.; Hon. Sen. Lect. Heart & Lung Inst. Univ. Lond. Prev: Asst. Prof. (Diagn. Radiol.) Univ. Florida, USA; Fell. (Cardiac Radiol.) Univ. Alabama, USA.; Asst. Prof. Diagn. Radiol. Univ. Miami, USA.

RUBENS, Professor Robert David Guys Hospital, London SE1 9RT Tel: 020 7955 5000 Email: robert.rubens@cancer.org.uk; 5 Currie Hill Close, Arthur Road, Wimbledon, London SW19 7DX Tel: 020 8946 0422 — MB BS Lond. 1967; BSc Lond. 1964, MD 1974; FRCP Lond. 1984; MRCP (UK) 1969; MRCS Eng. LRCP Lond. 1967. (St. Geo.) Prof. Clin. Oncol. Guy's, Kings Coll. & St Thomas's Sch. of Med. & Dent. of King's Coll. Lond.; Chief Med. Off. Swiss Re Life & Health; Chief Med. Off. Legal & Gen. Assur. Soc. Ltd. Socs: BMA; Amer. Soc. of Clin. Oncol.; Assur. Med. sociey (Pres.- elect for 2003-5). Prev: Dir. Imperial Cancer Research Fund Clin. Oncol. Unit Guy's Hosp. Lond.; Regist. St. Geo. Hosp. Lond.; Ho. Phys. Hammersmith Hosp. Lond. & Brompton Hosp.

RUBENSTEIN, David Addenbrooke's Hospital, Cambridge CB2 2QQ Tel: 01223 216243 Fax: 01223 216056 — MB BS LOnd. 1962; MD Lond. 1971; FRCP Lond. 1979, M 1965; MRCS Eng. LRCP Lond. 1962. (Middlx.) Phys. Addenbrooke's Hosp. Camb.

RUBENSTEIN, David Isaac 11 Queens Avenue, Woodford Green IG8 0JE — LRCPI & LM, LRSCI & LM 1964; LRCPI & LM, LRCSI & LM 1964. (RCSI) Prev: Ho. Off. Mercer's Hosp. Dub.

RUBENSTEIN, Ian David Eagle House Surgery, 291 High Street, Ponders End, Enfield EN3 4DN Tel: 020 8351 1000 Fax: 020 8351 1007; 1 Heather Drive, Enfield EN2 8LQ — BM BS 1978 Nottm.; BMedSci (Hons.) Nottm. 1976, BM BS 1978; MRCGP 1983; DRCOG 1982. Clin. Asst. Pain Managem. Course Whittington Hosp. Lond. Socs: Brit. Soc. Med. & Dent. Hypn.. Prev: Stud. Health Off. Lond. Sch. Economics.

RUBENSTEIN, Punam Department of Reproductive Healthcare, Enfield Community Care Trust, Wenlock House, 1 Eaton Road, Enfield EN1 1NJ; 1 Heather Drive, Enfield EN2 8LQ — BM BS 1978 Nottm.; BMedSci (Hons.) Nottm. 1976; MFFP 1993; DRCOG 1980. SCMO (Reproduc. Healthcare) Enfield Community Care Trust. Prev: Doctor (Family Plann. & Child Health) Enfield HA.

RUBERU, Mr Tantirige Ravindra Chintaraj 16 Grovelands, Barracks Road, High Wycombe HP11 1QN Tel: 01494 425405 — MB BS 1982 Colombo; FRCS Eng. 1990.

RUBERY, Eileen Doris, CB, QHP Senior Research Associate, Judge Institute of Management Studies, University of Cambridge, Trumpton St., Cambridge CB2 1AG Tel: 01223 765879 Fax: 01223 766330 Email: e.rubery@jims.cam.ac.uk; Hilltop Farm, 133 High St, Harston, Cambridge CB2 5QD Tel: 01223 870273 — MB ChB 1966 Sheff.; MB ChB (Hons.) Sheff. 1966; PhD (Biochem.) Camb. 1972; FFPHM RCP (UK) 1994; MRCPath 1989; FRCPath 1997; FRCR 1976; DMRT Eng. 1975; FRIPHH. (Sheff.) Sen. Research

Assoc.; Vis. Fell. Girton Coll. Camb.; Course Director, masters in community enterprise; Sen. expert Adviser to food standards agency. Socs: Roy. Inst. Pub. Health & Hyg.; Roy. Soc. Health. Prev: Under-Sec., Dept. of Health; Hon. Cons. Radiother. & Oncol. & Wellcome Sen. Research Fell. Addenbrooke's Hosp. Camb.; Dir. Med. Studies & Sen. Research Fell. Girton Coll. Camb.

RUBIE, Noel George South Manor House, Langdon Hills, Laindon, Basildon SS16 6JB — MB 1947 Calcutta; MRCGP 1969.

RUBIN, Alan Department of Cytology, Watford General Hospital, Vicarage Road, Watford WD18 0HB Tel: 01923 244366 Fax: 01923 217448; 69 Green Lane, Edgware HA8 7PZ Tel: 020 8958 8918 Email: arubin@cix.co.uk — MB BS 1983 Lond.; BSc (Hons.) Lond. 1980, MB BS 1983; MRCPath 1990; FRCPath 1998. (Roy. Free) Cons. Path. Histopath. & Cytol. Mt. Vernon & Watford NHS Trust. Prev: Sen. Regist. (Histopath.) Univ. Coll., Middlx. & Whittington Hosps. Lond.; Regist. (Histopath.) Hammersmith Hosp. Lond.; SHO (Path.) Chase Farm Hosp. Enfield.

RUBIN, Anthony Paul 126 Harley Street, London W1G 7JS Tel: 020 7935 9409 Fax: 0207 224 2520 Email: admin@groupanais.th.tic.services.com — MRCS Eng. LRCP Lond. 1961; MB Camb. 1962, BChir 1961; FFA RCS Eng. 1966; DA Eng. 1963. (Lond. Hosp.) Cons. Anaesth. Nat. Orthop. Hosp. Lond. Socs: Fell. Roy. Soc. Med.; Assn. Anaesths. Prev: Anaesth. Sen. Regist. Char. Cross Hosp. Lond.; Anaesth. Regist. St. Margt.'s Hosp. Epping; Jun. Anaesth. Regist. Lond. Hosp.

RUBIN, Caroline Moira Elizabeth Department of Radiology, Southampton General Hospital, Tremoma Road, Southampton SO16 6YD Tel: 02380 777222 Email: caroline.rubin@suht.swest.nhs.vtc — MB BS 1979 Lond.; MRCP (UK) 1982; FRCR 1986. (Westm.) Cons. Radiol. Soton. Gen. Hosp.

RUBIN, Gary X Ray Department, Royal Sussex County Hospital, Eastern Road, Brighton BN2 5SE; 14 Hove Park Way, Hove BN3 6PT — MB BS 1979 Lond.; BSc (Hons.) Lond. 1976, MB BS 1979; FRCR 1984. (St. Geo.) Cons. (Radiol.) Roy. Sussex Co. Hosp. Brighton. Prev: Sen. Regist. (Radiol.) Roy. Free Hosp. Lond.; Regist. (Radiol.) W.m. Hosp. Lond.; SHO (Med.) Chase Farm Hosp. Enfield.

RUBIN, Gregory Paul The Health Centre, Trenchard Avenue, Thornaby, Stockton-on-Tees TS17 0DD Tel: 01642 762921 Fax: 01642 760608; The Old School House, Worsall Bridge, Low Worsall, Yarm TS15 9PQ — MB ChB 1974 Sheff.; MRCGP 1983; FRCGP 1997. (Sheff.) Sen. Lect. Primary Health Care Univ. Teeside; Hon. Sen. Research Assoc. Dept. Primary Care Newc. Univ. Prev: NoReN research fell. Primary Health Care Newc.Univ.

RUBIN, Ian Duncan Warnell Tyrrellswood, Shere Road, West Horsley, Leatherhead KT24 — MB BS 1980 Lond.; BA Camb. 1975; FFPM 1998. (St. Mary's Hosp) Chief Exec. Matrix Therap. Ltd.

RUBIN, Joseph (retired) 5 Whitehorn Drive, Brighton BN1 5LH Tel: 01273 557117 — LRCP LRCS 1945 Ed.; LRCP LRCS Ed. LRFPS Glas. 1945; DMRD Eng. 1949. Prev: Cons. Radiol. Brighton Health Dist.

RUBIN, Lara Beth Silverstone, Newport Road, Castleton, Cardiff CF3 2UN — MB ChB 1996 Ed.

RUBIN, Professor Peter Charles Dean's Office, Medical School, Queen's Medical Centre, Nottingham NG7 2UH Tel: 0115 970 9380 Fax: 0115 970 9974 Email: peter.rubin@nottingham.ac.uk — BM BCh 1974 Oxf.; BA Camb. 1971; DM Oxf. 1980; FRCP Glas. 1993; FRCP Lond. 1989; MRCP (UK) 1976. (Camb. & Oxf.) Dean of Fac. of Med. & Health Sci. Univ. of Notts. Prev: Wellcome Trust Sen. Fell. (Mat. Med.) Univ. Glas.; Amer. Heart Assn. Research Fell. Stanford Med. Center, USA; SHO (Med.) N. Staffs. Hosp. Centre.

RUBIN, Philip 59 Orchard Drive, Giffnock, Glasgow G46 7AG — MB ChB 1991 Glas.

RUBIN, Susan Penelope-Ann Dept. Of Paediatrics, Queen Elizabeth Hospital, King's Lynn PE30 4ET Tel: 01553 613613; Staines House, Sporle Road, Swaffham PE37 7HL — MB BS 1976 Lond.; FRCPCH 1997; FRCP Lond. 1995; MRCS Eng. LRCP Lond. 1976; DCH Eng. 1979. (Westm.) p/t Cons. Paediat. Qu. Eliz. Hosp. King's Lynn Norf. Prev: Fell. (Perinatol.) Hosp. Sick Childr. Toronto.

RUBINSZTEIN, Judy Sasha Department of Psychiatry, Addenbrooke's Hospital, Box 189, Cambridge CB2 2QQ Tel: 01223 336945 Email: jsr25@cam.ac.uk — MB ChB 1991 Cape Town; MRCPsych. Hon. Specialist Regist.; Research Fell. Prev: Specialist Regist.

RUBIO GOMEZ, Maria Teresa 13 Simpson Street, Crosshouse Hospital, Kilmarnock KA2 0BD — LMS 1989 Cadiz.

RUBIO LAINEZ, Carlos Ricardo Flat 1B, 33 Belsize Park Gardens, London NW3 4JJ — LMS 1988 Cadiz; MD U Autonoma Madrid 1991.

RUBIO RODRIGUEZ, Maria Del Carmen Department of Medicine, Royal Marsden Hospital, Sutton SM2 5PT — LMS 1990 Salamanca.

RUBNER, Janet Vivian Bedford House Medical Centre, Glebe Street, Ashton-under-Lyne OL6 6HD Tel: 0161 330 9880 Fax: 0161 330 9393 — MB ChB 1982 Manch.; DRCOG 1985. (Manchester)

RUBNER, Paul The Surgery, 144-150 Upper Clapton Road, London E5 9JZ; 39 Clifton Gardens, London N15 6AP Tel: 020 8800 0944 — MB BS 1976 Lond.; DRCOG 1979. (St. Bart's)

RUBRA, Timothy David Crouch End Health Centre, 45 Middle Lane, Crouch End, London N8 8PH — MB BS Lond. 1962; MRCS Eng. LRCP Lond. 1962; DObst RCOG 1964. (Westm.)

RUBY, Aisha Ejaz Medical Centre, 276 Dudley Road, Winson Green, Birmingham B18 4HL Tel: 0121 455 6170 — MB BS 1973 Patna.

RUBYTHON, Edith Jill Department of Accident & Emergency, University Hospitals Coventry & Warwickshire NHS Trust., Coventry & Warwickshire Hospital Stoney Station Rd, Coventry CV1 4FH; 15 Lonsdale Road, Harborne, Birmingham B17 9QX Fax: 0121 428 1791 — MB BCh 1990 Wales; MSc Surrey 1984; BSc (Hons.) Aberd. 1978; MRCP (UK) 1994; FFAEM 1999. Cons. Accid. & Emerg. Univ. Hosp.s Coventry & Warks., NHS Trust. Coventry. Prev: Sen. Regist. (A & E) Manor Hosp. Waball; Sen. Regist. (A&E) Birm. Childr.s Hosp.; Sen. Regist. (A & E) City Hosp. Birm.

RUCINSKI, Jacek Medway Hospital, Department of Psychiatry, A Block, Windmill Road, Gillingham ME7 5NY Tel: 01634 830000 Fax: 01634 830082 — DM 1973 Lekarz, Gdansk; MRCPsych 1978; DPM Eng. 1978. (Gdansk Med. Acad.) Cons. Psychiat. Thames Gateway NHS Trust; Lead Clinician, Thames Gateway NHS Trust; Second Opinion Apptd. Doctor - Ment. Health Act Commiss.; Recognised Teach. in Psychiat., Univ. of Lond. Socs: MRC Psych; BMA; PMA. Prev: Sen. Regist. (Psychiat.) St. Thos. Hosp. Lond.; Regist. (Psychiat.) Guy's Hosp. Lond. & Bexley Hosp.

RUCK, Colin Stuart Kenneth, RD (retired) Sheep Plain House, Sheep Plain, Crowborough TN6 3ST Tel: 01892 653896 — BM BCh Oxf. 1955; BA Oxf. 1952, MA 1955; DObst RCOG 1959. Med. Off. BAMS; Med. Off. The Appeals Serv. Prev: GP CrowBoro.

RUCK, Michael John Yarnton Carteknowle and Dore Medical Practice, 1 Carterknowle Road, Sheffield S7 2DW Tel: 0114 255 1218 Fax: 0114 258 4418; 115 Osborne Road, Sheffield S11 9BB Tel: 0114 281 5546 — MB ChB 1967 Bristol; MRCGP 1986. (Bristol) Prev: SHO (Surg. & Urol.) Sheff. Roy. Hosp.; Ho. Phys. & Ho. Surg. Roy. United Hosp. Bath; Demonst. (Anat.) Univ. Sheff.

RUCK, Sarah Elizabeth 115 Osborne Road, Brincliffe, Sheffield S11 9BB — BM BS 1996 Nottm.

RUCKERT, Linden Alexandra Louise City University, Health Centre, 20 Sebastian Street, London EC1V 0JA Tel: 020 7253 4454 Fax: 020 7477 8867 — MB BS 1985 Lond.; DFFP 1995; DRCOG 1988. (Univ. Lond. & Middlx. Hosp. Med. Sch.) p/t Gen. Practitioner. Prev: Trainee GP Taunton VTS; Psychiat. Rotat. Glenside Hosp. Bristol.

RUCKLEY, Professor Charles Vaughan, CBE (retired) 1 Mayfield Terrace, Edinburgh EH9 1RU — MB ChB Ed. 1959; ChM Ed. 1970; FRCP Ed. 1993; FRCS Ed. 1963. Emerit. Prof. Vasc. Surg. Univ. Edin.; Med. Adviser, Clin. Standards Bd. for Scotl. Prev: Cons. Surg. Roy. Infirm. Edin.

RUCKLEY, Mr Robert William Darlington Memorial Hospital, Hollyhurst Road, Darlington DL3 6HX Tel: 01325 380100 Fax: 01325 743798 — MB ChB 1975 Dundee; FRCS Eng. 1980. (Dundee Univ.) Cons. ENT Surg. Darlington Memor. Hosp., Bishop Auckland Gen. Hosp. & Friarage Hosp. N. Yorks.; Lionel Colledge Memor. Fell. Otolaryngol. RCS Eng. 1984-5; Exam. RCS Eng. Prev: Sen. Regist. & Hon. Lect. (ENT. Surg.) Ninewells Hosp. Dundee.; Regist. (Surg.) Ninewells Hosp. Dundee; SHO (Neurosurg. & Orthop. Surg.) & Regist. (Urol.) Dundee Roy. Infirm.

RUCKLEY, Valerie Anne (retired) 1 Mayfield Terrace, Edinburgh EH9 1RU Tel: 0131 667 8678 Fax: 0131 667 8678 — MB ChB Ed. 1962; BSc Ed. 1959; FRCP Ed. 1996. Prev: Sen. Med. Off. Chief Scientist Off. Scott. Home & Health Dept.

RUCKLIDGE

RUCKLIDGE, Matthew William Miles 26B Lydford Road, Maida Vale, London W9 3LU Email: matthew@rucklidge60.freeserve.co.uk — MB BS 1994 Lond.; BSc Lond. 1991. Specialist Regist. Imperial Sch. of Anaesth. Rotat.

RUCKLIDGE, Miles Aspinall (retired) Old Hall Farm, Littledale Road, Brookhouse, Lancaster LA2 9PH Tel: 01524 770450 Fax: 01524 771679 — BM BCh Oxf. 1959; MA Oxf. 1959; FFA RCS Eng. 1966. Prev: Cons. Anaesth. Roy. Lancaster Infirm.

RUDD, Alistair James Flat 4 Fenham Carr, Lancaster Moor Hospital, Quernmore Road, Lancaster LA1 3JR; Red Mays, Lime Walk, Long Sutton, Spalding PE12 9HG — MB ChB 1987 Birm.

RUDD, Ann Gloria 7 Borrowell Terrace, Kenilworth CV8 1ER — MB BCh BAO 1959 Dub.; DObst RCOG 1962. (T.C. Dub.) Med. Asst. (A & E) Warwick Hosp. Socs: BMA.

RUDD, Anthony George 33 Newstead Way, Wimbledon, London SW19 5HR Tel: 020 8946 9713 Fax: 020 8286 1482 Email: anthony.rudd@kol.ac.uk; Guy's & St. Thomas' Hospital Trust, Lambeth Palace Road, London SE1 7EH Tel: 020 7928 9292 Fax: 020 7928 2339 Email: a.rudd@umds.ac.uk — MB BChir 1979 Camb.; FRCP Lond. 1994. Cons. Phys. i/c Elderly Guy's & St Thomas's Hosp. Lond. & Cons. Stroke Phys..; Assoc. Director; Clin. Effectivness and Eval. Unit Roy. Coll. of Phys.s (Lond.). Prev: Lect. (Geriat. Med.) St. Geo. Hosp. Lond.

RUDD, Brigitte Caroline Hatch End Medical Centre, 577 Uxbridge Road, Hatch End, Pinner HA5 4RD Tel: 020 8428 0272 Fax: 020 8421 4109 — MB BS 1977 Lond. (St. Bart.) GP Hatch End. Prev: Ho. Surg. St. Bart. Hosp. Lond.

RUDD, Cyril 43 Coast Road, Redcar TS10 3NN Tel: 01642 484427 — LRCP LRCS 1939 Ed.; LRCP LRCS Ed. LRFPS Glas. 1939.

RUDD, Gillian Nicola Osborne Building, Leicester Royal Infirmary, Leicester LE1 5WW Tel: 0116 258 7512 Fax: 0116 258 7512 Email: nrudd@unl.trent.nhs.uk; High Holme, 43 High St, Hallaton, Market Harborough LE16 8UD Tel: 01858 555714 — MB ChB 1980 Birm.; MRCP (UK) 1984; FRCP 2000. Cons. Phys. (Palliat. Med.) Leics. Roy. Infirm.; Cons. Leics. Hospice.

RUDD, James Harvey Fitzgerald ACCI, Level 6 Box 110, Addenbrookes Hospital, Hills Road, Cambridge CB2 2QQ Tel: 01223 331504; Wolfson College, Cambridge CB3 9BB Tel: 01223 335900 Email: jhfrudd@hotmail.com — MB ChB 1993 Birm.; MB ChB (Hons.) Birm. 1993; MRCP (UK) 1996. BHF Research Fell., Addenbrookes Hosp., Camb. Prev: Assoc Lect (Med) Flinders Univ. Adelaide, Australia.; SHO (Med), Qu. Eliz., Selly Oak Hosp. Birm.

RUDD, Keith Kitson (retired) c/o 28 Greame Road, Bridlington YO16 6TQ — MB ChB 1953 Leeds. Prev: Ho. Surg. Leeds Gen. Infirm.

RUDD, Margaret Elizabeth — MB ChB 1975 Glas. p/t Staff Grade (Dermat.) Roy. Infirm. Edin. & St Johns Livingston; GP Eyre Med. Pract. Edin. Socs: BMA; Scott. Dermatol. Soc. Prev: GP Edin.; Med. Cytol. & Lect. (Cytopath.) Univ. Edin.

RUDD, Margaret Isobel (retired) 5 Northcroft, Winslow, Buckingham MK18 3JR Tel: 01296 713399 — MB ChB 1942 Birm. Prev: Clin. Asst. Dept. Venereol. Stoke Mandeville Hosp. Aylesbury.

RUDD, Peter Goosey — MB BS 1971 Lond.; MRCS Eng. LRCP Lond. 1971; DObst RCOG 1973.

RUDD, Peter Thomas Childrens Centre, Royal United Hospital, Bath BA1 3NG Tel: 01225 824393 Fax: 01225 824212 Email: peter.rudd@ruh-bathswest.nhs.uk; Moregrove, Perrymead, Bath BA2 5AZ Tel: 01222 833292 Fax: 01222 833292 — MB BChir Camb. 1975; MA Camb. 1976, MD 1984; FRCPCh Lond. 1993; MRCP (UK) 1979; DCH Eng. 1978. Cons. Paediat. Roy. United Hosp. Bath. Prev: Wellcome Fell. Univ. Alabama Birm.; Sen. Regist. (Paediat.) Norf. & Norwich Hosp.

RUDD, Robin Michael St Bartholomew's Hospital, West Smithfield, London EC1A 7BE Tel: 020 7601 8888 Fax: 020 7601 7577 Email: r.m.rudd@mds.qmw.ac.uk; 22 Upper Wimpole St, London W1G 6NB Tel: 020 7486 3247 Fax: 020 7486 3248 — MB BChir 1977 Camb.; MA Camb. 1977, MD 1983; FRCP Lond. 1992; MRCP (UK) 1978. (Cambridge & St Georges) Cons. Phys. Lond. Chest Hosp. & St. Bart. Hosp. Socs: Brit. Thoracic Soc.; Amer. Thoracic Soc.; Europ. Respirat. Soc. Prev: Sen. Regist. (Med.) Lond. Chest Hosp. & St. Thos. Hosp. Lond.; Regist. (Med.) St. Geo. Hosp. Lond.

RUDD, Susan Elizabeth 27 Smedley Street, Matlock DE4 3FQ — MB ChB 1987 Leic.

RUDDELL, Kathryn Brenda Louise Winscombe Surgery, Hillyfields Way, Winscombe BS25 1AE Tel: 01934 842211 — MB BS 1983 Lond.; BSc (Anat.) Lond. 1980, MB BS 1983; MRCGP 1987; DRCOG 1985.

RUDDELL, Mark Colin Nottingham Healthcare NHS Trust, Duncan MacMillan House, Porchester Road, Nottingham NG3 6AA Tel: 0115 969 1300 Email: mzyhmer@unix.ccc.nottingham.ac.uk — BM BS 1995 Nottm.; BMedSci (Hons.) Nottm. 1992. (Nottm.) SHO (Psychiat.) Nottm. Healthcare NHS Trust. Socs: BMA; MPS; Roy. Coll. Psychiat. (Inceptor).

RUDDELL, Michael Andrew Lisburn Health Centre, Linenhall Street, Lisburn BT28 1LU Tel: 028 9260 3090 Fax: 028 9250 1310; 101 Osbourne Park, Belfast BT9 6JQ — MB BCh BAO 1985 Belf.; MRCGP 1990; DRCOG 1989; DCH Dub. 1989. (Queen's University, Belfast)

RUDDELL, Nigel John Dromara Surgery, Begney Hill Road, Dromore BT25 2AT Tel: 01238 532217 Fax: 01238 533301 Email: njruddell@dromarasurgery.freeserve.co.uk — MB BCh BAO 1992 Belf.; MRCGP 1996; DRCOG 1996; DCH RCPSI 1995. (Queens Univ. Belf.) Princip., GP. Socs: Fac. Edr., N. Ire., Fac. of Roy. Coll. Of GPs.; Brit. Assn. for Immed. Care.

RUDDELL, William Samuel John 9 Clarendon Place, Stirling FK8 2QW — MD 1979 Birm.; MB ChB 1968; FRCP Ed. 1986; MRCP (UK) 1973. Cons. Phys. & Gastroenterol. Falkirk & Dist. Roy. Infirm.; Hon. Sen. Lect. (Med.) Univ. Edin.

RUDDLE, Adrian Charles St Barnabas' Hospice, Columbia Drive, Worthing BN13 2QF Tel: 01903 264222 Fax: 01903 534031 — MB BS 1971 Lond.; MRCS Eng. LRCP Lond. 1970; MRCGP 1975; DA Eng. 1977; DObst RCOG 1972. (St. Bart.) Med. Dir. St. Barnabas Hospice, Worthing; Hon. Cons. Palliat. Med. Worthing & S.lands Hosps. Trust. Socs: Assn. for Palliat. Med. of Gt. Britain and Irel. Prev: Sen. Regist. St. Gemma's Hospice Leeds; Trainee GP Boston VTS; SHO (Anaesth.) St. Mary's Hosp. Portsmouth.

RUDDLE, Mr Angus Coleridge Flat C11, Foxtorr House, Derriford Hospital, Plymouth PL6 8BQ — BM 1989 Soton.; FRCSI 1993.

RUDDLE, Jane Elizabeth 3 West Avenue, Benton, Newcastle upon Tyne NE12 9PA — MB BS 1977 Lond.; MA Camb. 1978.

RUDDLESDIN, Mr Christopher Barnsley DGH, Gawber Road, Barnsley S75 2EP Tel: 01226 777701 Fax: 01226 283020 Email: chris.ruddlesdin@bdgh-tr.trent.nhs.uk; Grove House, 5 Beech Grove, Barnsley S70 6NG Tel: 01226 283020 Email: ruddlesdin@doctors.org.uk — MB BS 1974 Lond.; FRCS Eng. 1979. (Lond. Hosp.) Med. Dir., Barnsley DGH NHS Trust; Cons. Orthopaed. Surg. Barnsley DGH. Socs: BMA.; Mem. Brit. Assn. Med. Managers. Prev: Sen. Regist. (Orthop.) Roy. Free Hosp. & Windsor Gp. Hosp.; Regist. (Orthop.) Adelaide Childr. Hosp.; Regist. (Surg.) Lond. Hosp.

RUDDOCK, Caroline Jane The Limes Medical Centre, 65 Leicester Road, Narborough, Leicester LE9 5DU Tel: 0116 284 1347 Fax: 0116 275 2447; 23 North Avenue, Leicester LE2 1TL Tel: 0116 270 5393 — MB ChB 1989 Leic.; MRCGP 1993; DRCOG 1992.

RUDDOCK, Fiona Sue Deddington Health Centre, Earls Lane, Deddington, Banbury OX15 0TQ Tel: 01869 338611 Fax: 01869 37009; 1 The Pitts, Sandford St. Martin, Oxford OX7 7AH Tel: 0160 8683 423 — MB ChB 1983 Birm.; BSc (Hons.) Birm. 1980, MB ChB (Hons.) 1983; MRCP (UK) 1986; DRCOG 1989. Prev: GP Moreton-in-Marsh.; Regist. (Gen. Med.) Leicester Roy. Infirm.

RUDDOCK, John Michael Oak Villa, St. Neots Road, Coton, Cambridge CB3 7PH Tel: 01954 210760; 26 Chatworth Avenue, Cambridge CB4 3LT — MB Camb. 1971, BChir 1970; FFA RCS Eng. 1980. Cons. Anaesth. Roy. Nat. Throat Nose & Ear Hosp. Lond. WC1X 8DA.

RUDDY, James Patrick 15 Queens Avenue, Meols, Wirral CH47 0LR — MB ChB 1991 Ed.

RUDDY, Michael Charles Peter 336 Landsee Road, Ipswich IP3 0EL — MB ChB 1990 Sheff.

RUDDY, Rachel Anne Pinewood, Hillside Road, Sidmouth EX10 8JD — MB ChB 1998 Leeds.

RUDENSKI, Aram Soli Clinical Chemistry (NHS), Box 232, Addenbrooke's Hospital, Cambridge CB2 2QQ Tel: 01223 217441 Fax: 01223 216862 Email: ar223@cam.ac.uk — BM BCh 1982 Oxf.; MA Camb. 1983; DPhil Oxf. 1988; MRCPath 1994.

RUDGE, Mr Christopher John Royal London Hospital, Whitechapel, London E1 1BB Tel: 020 7377 7289 Fax: 020 7377 7003; Pennis Farm, Fawkham, Longfield DA3 8LZ Tel: 01474

707522 — MB BS 1972 Lond.; BSc (Hons.) Lond. 1969; FRCS Eng. 1976; MRCS Eng. LRCP Lond. 1972. (Guy's) Cons. Transpl. Surg. Roy. Hosps. Trust Lond. Prev: Cons. Transpl. Surg. Guy's Hosp. Lond. & St. Peter's Hosp. Lond.

RUDGE, James William Bridge House Medical Centre, Scholars Lane, Stratford-upon-Avon CV37 6HE Tel: 01789 292201 Fax: 01789 262087 — BM BS 1988 Nottm.; BM BS (Hons.) Nottm. 1988, BMedSci (Hons.) 1986; MRCGP 1992; DRCOG 1991. Prev: Trainee GP Lincoln VTS.

RUDGE, Peter c/o National Hospital, Queen Square, London WC1N 3BG Tel: 020 7837 3611 — MB BS 1966 Lond.; BSc Lond. 1963; FRCP Lond. 1981, M 1969. (St. Bart.) Cons. Neurol. Nat. Hosp. For Neurol. & Neurosurg. Qu. Sq. Lond.; Cons. Neurol. N.wick Pk. Hosp. Harrow; Hon. Cons. Neurol. MRC Human Movement & balance unit Nat. Hosp. Lond.; Clin. Tutor Nat. Hosp. Lond. Prev: Sub-Dean Inst. Neurol. Univ. Lond.; Sen. Regist. (Clin. Neurol.) Nat. Hosp. Nerv. Dis. Lond.; Ho. Phys. Nat. Hosp. Nerv. Dis. Nerv. Dis. Qu. Sq.

RUDGE, Peter 44 Daniel Street, Cardiff CF24 4NY — MB BCh 1993 Wales.

RUDGE, Peter John Pennine Drive Surgery, 6-8 Pennine Drive, London NW2 1PA Tel: 020 8455 9977; 133 Cricklewood, London NW2 1HS Tel: 020 8452 8840 — MB BS 1972 Lond.; BSc Lond. 1969. (Roy. Free Hosp. Sch. Med.) Gen. Practitioner; Clin. Asst. in Dermat. The Roy. Proc Hosp. Socs: Fell.Roy.soc.Med; Vice-Pres. Hampstead Med. Soc.

RUDGE, Shauna Deirdre Elaine Charing Cross Hospital, Fulham Palace Road, London W6 8RF Tel: 020 8846 1234; 73A Lynton Avenue, London W13 0EA — MB BS 1986 Lond.; MRCPsych 1991. Sen. Regist. (Psychiat.) Char. Cross Hosp. Lond.

RUDGE, Stuart David Castle Gardens Medical Centre, 78 East Hill, Colchester CO1 2QS Tel: 01206 866626; Tel: 01206 272031 — MB BS 1981 Lond.; DGM RCP Lond. 1986; DRCOG 1985. (St. Bart.) Prev: Trainee GP Colchester VTS; Ho. Surg. & Ho. Phys. Essex Co. Hosp. Colchester.

RUDGLEY, Richard John Atherton, Cold Ash Hill, Cold Ash, Newbury RG18 9PH — MB BS 1986 Lond.; MRCGP 1991.

RUDHAM, Samuel James 19 Normanby Road, Nottingham NG8 2TA — BM 1993 Soton.

RUDIN, Clare Susan 235 Derby Road, Long Eaton, Nottingham NG10 4BS — MB BS 1992 Lond.

RUDIN, Claudius Emanuel 25 Stanstead Manor, St James Road, Sutton SM1 2AZ — Diplome Federal 1985 Switzerland; MRCP (UK) 1991.

RUDIN, Joseph Albert Lingholm, 5 Haslemere Road, Long Eaton, Nottingham NG10 4AG Tel: 0115 973 4727 Fax: 0115 946 0197 — MB ChB 1957 Manch. (Manchester) Prev: Ho. Phys. Manch. Roy. Infirm.; Ho. Off. (Obst.) St. Mary's Hosp. Manch.; Ho. Surg. Ancoats Hosp.

RUDLAND, Edward Neville (retired) Green Westerland, Marldon, Paignton TQ3 1RR Tel: 01803 663660 Fax: 01803 663666 — MRCS Eng. LRCP Lond. 1952; MRCGP 1969. Prev: Clin. Asst. Roy. Eye Infirm. Plymouth.

RUDLAND, Simon Victor, Surg. Lt.-Cdr. RN Retd. Stowmarket Health Centre, Violet Hill Road, Stowmarket IP14 1NL Tel: 01449 776000 Fax: 01449 776005; 15 Ipswich Road, Woodbridge IP12 4BS Tel: 01394 388821 Email: ratcliff@reme.co.uk — BM BS 1986 Nottm.; BMedSci Nottm. 1984; MRCGP 1994; DRCOG 1993; DA (UK) 1990. (Nottm.) GP Princip.; GP Professional Developm. Mentor, E. Suff. Prev: Regist. (Emerg. Med.) Fremantle Hosp., W.. Austral.; Med. Off. SST N.. Iraq, Gulf War; Med. Off. HMS Challenger.

RUDLING, Joanne Louise 90 Lascelles Drive, Cardiff CF23 8NQ — MB BCh 1994 Wales. SHO (Gen. Med.) P.ss of Wales Hosp. Bridgend. Prev: SHO (A & E & Psychiat.) P.ss of Wales Hosp. Bridgend; GP/Regist. Porthcawl.

RUDMAN, David John (retired) 167 Percy Road, Whitton, Twickenham TW2 6JE — MB BS 1950 Lond.; MRCS Eng. LRCP Lond. 1945.

RUDMAN, Julie Davina Catherine Street Surgery, 3 Catherine Street, Whitehaven CA28 7PD Tel: 01946 693094 — MB ChB 1978 Leeds; MB ChB 1978 Leeds. (Leeds) GP Whitehaven, Cumbria.

RUDMAN, Robert Jeffrey Doctors Surgery, Hinnings Road, Distington, Workington CA14 5UR Tel: 01946 830207 — MB ChB 1978 Leeds. (Leeds) GP Workington, Cumbria.

RUDMAN, Timothy John The Health Centre, Hermitage Road, St John's, Woking GU21 1TD Tel: 01483 723451 Fax: 01483 751879; Comeragh House, Comeragh Close., Hook Heath, Woking GU22 0LZ Tel: 01483 715621 Fax: 01483 776660 — MB BS Lond. 1967; MRCS Eng. LRCP Lond. 1967; DFFP 1994; DObst RCOG 1970. (Roy. Free) Med. Ref. Home Off. Socs: Woking Med. Soc. Prev: Ho. Off. (Med. & Neurol.) Roy. Free Hosp. Lond.; Ho. Off. (Surg. & Orthop.) N. Middlx. Hosp. Lond.; Ho. Off. (Paediat.) Whipps Cross Hosp. Lond.

RUDNICK, Leanne Rose St Paul's Medical Centre, Dickson Road, Blackpool FY1 2HH Tel: 01253 623896 Fax: 01253 752818 — MB ChB 1990 Manch.

RUDNICK, Steven Phillip St George's Medical Centre, Field Road, New Brighton, Wallasey CH45 5LN Tel: 0151 630 2080 Fax: 0151 637 0370 — MB ChB 1986 Liverp. Prev: SHO/Trainee GP Wirral HA VTS; Ho. Off. (Med. & Surg.) Arrowe Pk. Hosp. Wirral.

RUDOLF, Mary Catherine Joy Department of Community Child Health, Belmont House, Leeds General Infirmary, Leeds LS2 9NP Tel: 0113 292 6352 Fax: 0113 292 6219 Email: mrudolf@smtpgate.ulth.northy.nhs.uk; 1 Crescent Gardens, Leeds LS17 8DR Tel: 0113 268 6442 — MB BS 1975 Lond.; BSc (Human Genetics) Lond. 1972; FRCPCH 1997; DCH RCP Lond. 1985. (Univ. Coll. Hosp.) Cons. Community Child Health Leeds Community & Ment. Health Trust & Hon. Sen. Lect. Univ. Leeds. Prev: Fell. (Pediat. Endocrinol.) Yale Univ, USA; Research Fell. (Ambul. Pediat.) Brown Univ., USA; Paediat. Kupat Holim Child Developm. Centre, Haifa, Israel.

RUDOLF, Michael Ealing Hospital, Uxbridge Road, Southall UB1 3HW Tel: 020 8967 5687 Fax: 020 8967 5660 Email: michael.rudolf@eht.nhs.uk — MB BChir 1970 Camb.; MA Camb. 1970; FRCP Lond. 1989; MRCP (UK) 1973. (Middlx.) Cons. Phys. Ealing Hosp. S.all; Hon. Sen. Lect. (Med.) Imperial Coll. Sch. of Med.; Hon. Cons. Phys. Hammersmith Hosp. Lond. Socs: Fell. Roy. Soc. Med. (Ex-Pres. Sect. Measurem. in Med.); (Pres.) Internat. Asthma Counc.; Brit. Thorac. Soc. (Ex chair, Standards of care Comm.). Prev: Sen. Regist. Hammersmith Hosp. Lond.; Sir Jules Thorn Research Fell. Middlx. Hosp. Med. Sch. Lond.; Regist. Prof. Med. Unit Middlx. Hosp. Lond.

RUDOLF, Noel de Montjoie 22 Devonshire Place, London W1G 6JA Tel: 020 7935 1825 Fax: 020 7224 7220 — BM BCh 1959 Oxf.; MA Oxf. 1958; BA Oxf. 1954. (Oxf. & King's Coll. Hosp.) Cons. (Clin. Neurophysiol.) private Pract. Lond. Socs: Founder Mem. Assn. Brit. Clin. Neurophysiol.; Brit. Soc. Clin. Neurophysiol.; Fell. R.S.M. Prev: Cons. Clin. Neurophysiol. Char. Cross Hosp. & Cheyne Centre Lond.; Hon. Sen. Lect. Char. Cross & W.m. Med. Sch. Lond.; Hon. Cons. Clin. Neurophysiologist Chelsea & W.minster Hosp Lond.

RUDOLPH, Jonathan Kevin Pinn Medical Centre, 8 Eastcote Road, Pinner HA5 1HF Tel: 020 8866 5766 Fax: 020 8429 0251; 15 Brockley Close, Stanmore HA7 4QL Tel: 020 8958 2455 Fax: 020 8954 5966 — MB BCh 1988 Witwatersrand; MRCGP 1994; DRCOG 1994.

***RUDOLPH, Julia** The Red House, 7 High St., Barton, Cambridge CB3 7BG Email: rudolph_julia@hotmail.com — MB BS 1998 Lond.; MB BS Lond 1998.

RUDOLPHIJ, Adelhart Jan Department ENT, St. Helier Hospital, Wrythe Lane, Carshalton SM5 1AA Tel: 020 8644 4343 Fax: 020 8296 3652; 101 Carshalton Park Road, Carshalton SM5 3SJ Tel: 020 8647 7463 — MRCS Eng. LRCP Lond. 1978; St. Mary's. Clin. Asst. (ENT) St. Helier Hosp. Carshalton. Prev: Trainee GP Ashtead; SHO (ENT & O & G) St. Helier Hosp. Carshalton; Resid. Emerg. Med. Bermuda.

RUDOLPHY, Steven Michael c/o Coniston, 5 Wyvern Road, Purley CR8 2NQ — MB BS 1985 Lond.; MRCGP 1990.

RUDRA, Hiren D (retired) 1 Oak Drive, Sawbridgeworth CM21 0AH Tel: 01279 723573 Email: hrudra@compuserve.com — MB BS Calcutta 1956, DGO 1958; MRCOG 1967. Dir. Harlow Occupat. Health Serv. Ltd. Prev: Regist. (O & G) Essex Gen. Hosp. Colchester & Camb. Matern. Hosp.

RUDRA, Thilaka Prakash Colchester General Hospital, Gainsborough Wing, Turner Road, Colchester CO4 5JL Tel: 01206

853535 Fax: 01206 832545 — MB BS 1975 Sri Lanka; FRCP. Cons. Phys. Geriat. Med. Colchester Gen. Hosp.

***RUDRALINGAM, Meenakshi** Musgrave and Clark House, The Royal Groups of Hospitals and, Social Services Trust, Grosvenor Rd, Belfast BT12 6BA — MB BCh BAO 1997 Belf.

RUDRALINGAM, Velauthan 4A Windsor Close, Belfast BT9 6FG — MB ChB BAO 1995 Belf.; MB BCh BAO Belf. 1995.

RUDRAMOORTHY, Thuraiayah 32 Hunter's Oak, Hemel Hempstead HP2 7SW Tel: 01442 232037; 32 Hunter's Oak, Hemel Hempstead HP2 7SW Tel: 01442 232037 — MB BS 1971 Ceylon. p/t Asst. GP. Socs: BMA. Prev: Assessor Benefit Agency.

RUDRAN, Vije Peace Children's Centre, Peace Prospect, Watford WD17 3EW — MB BS 1978 Sri Lanka; FRCPCH 1997 UK; LRCP LRCS Ed. LRCPS Glas. 1984; MRCP (UK) 1987; DCH Eng. 1983.

RUDRAPPA, Chithriki William Way Doctors Surgery, William Way, Wainfleet, Skegness PE24 4DE Tel: 01754 880212 Fax: 01754 880788 — MB BS 1968 Mysore.

RUDRASHETTY, Sarojani Rudrashetty and Partners, Mary Potter Health Centre, Gregory Boulevard, Hyson Green, Nottingham NG7 5HY.

RUDWICK, Ann Louise (retired) Mellstock, 9B Westwood Road, Ryde PO33 3BJ — MB BS Lond. 1956; BSc Durham. 1951; DCH Eng. 1959. Prev: SCMO (Child Health) Richmond, Twickenham & Roehampton HA.

RUDZINSKI, Barbara Mary 16 Broomhill Road, London SW18 4JF — MB BS 1981 Lond.

RUE, (Elsie) Rosemary, DBE (retired) 2 Wheatley Road, Stanton St John, Oxford OX33 1ET Tel: 01865 351546 — MB BS 1951 Lond.; Hon. MA Oxf. 1988; FRCS Eng. 1995; FRCP Lond. 1977, M 1972; FRCGP 1982; FRCPsych 1980, M 1975; FFPHM 1974; DCH Eng. 1962. Prev: Regional Gen. Manager & Med. Off. Oxf. RHA.

RUEL, Ann Hilary (retired) 14 Church Street, Histon, Cambridge CB4 9EP Tel: 01223 563619 — MB BS 1953 Lond.; MRCS Eng. LRCP Lond. 1953; DCH Eng. 1956. Volun. Phys. Med. Foundat. for the c/o the Victims of Torture. Prev: Clin. Asst. (Child & Family Psychiat.) Camb.

RUELL, Jacqueline Ann Holcombe Water, Wiveliscombe, Taunton TA4 2SL — MB ChB 1998 Liverp.; MB ChB Liverp 1998.

RUELL, Sheila Diane Tynyvelin Bungalow, Dolau, Llandrindod Wells — MB ChB 1984 Liverp.; MRCGP 1988; DRCOG 1987.

RUFF, Stephen James 22 Willow Way, Ponteland, Newcastle upon Tyne NE20 9RF — MB ChB 1974 Liverp.; FFA RCSI 1978.

RUFFE, Sarah Helen 19 Moorhead Terrace, Shipley BD18 4LB.

RUFFELL, Elizabeth Anne Eastbourne District General Hospital, Kings Drive, Eastbourne BN21 2UD — MB BS 1973 Lond.; MRCP (UK) 1976; FRCR 1981; FRCP 2000. (St. Georges Hospital Medical School London) Cons. Radiol. E.bourne Dist. Hosps.

RUFFELL, James (retired) 19 Traherne Close, Deer Park, Ledbury HR8 2JF — MB ChB 1952 Glas.

RUFFETT, Douglas Ian Appleton House, Lanchester Road, Durham DH1 5XZ Tel: 0191 333 3232 Fax: 0191 333 3233; 64 Hall Drive, Acklam, Middlesbrough TS5 7EX Tel: 01642 819821 — MB BS 1971 Newc.; MSc (Pub. Health Med.) Newc. 1995; FRCGP 1986, M 1975. Head of Primary Care Support Unit Co. Durh. & Darlington. Prev: GP Middlesbrough; Regional Med. Off. DoH; Primary Care Med. Adviser Tees HA.

RUFFLE, Simon Patrick Twyford Health Centre, Loddon Hall Road, Twyford, Reading RG10 9JA Tel: 0118 934 0112 Fax: 0118 934 1048 — MB BS 1992 Lond.

RUFFORD, Barnaby David High Trees, Lower St., Great Bealings, Woodbridge IP13 6NL — MB BS 1993 Lond.

RUFFORD, Christopher William 28 Brook Street, Woodbridge IP12 1BE — MB BS 1978 Lond.; MRCGP 1986; DCH RCP Lond. 1983; DRCOG 1981. Prev: Trainee GP Wimborne VTS; SHO (O & G) Roy. Sussex Co. Hosp. Brighton.

RUGEN, Joanne 14 Manion Avenue, Liverpool L31 4ED — MB ChB 1997 Bristol.

RUGG, Anthony John Harrogate District Hospital, Lancaster Park Road, Harrogate HG2 7SX Tel: 01423 885959 Fax: 01423 593397; 6 St. John Street, York YO31 7QT Tel: 01904 630507 — MB ChB 1971 Birm.; FRCPsych 1995, M 1976; DPM Leeds 1975; DCH Eng. 1973. Cons. Psychiat. Harrogate HA. Prev: Sen. Regist. (Psychiat.)

Lond. Hosp.; Regist. Naburn & Bootham Pk. Hosps.; SHO (Paediat.) Co. & Fulford Hosps. York.

RUGG, Sarah Ann Matilda The Surgery, 15 Brook Green, London W6 7BL — MB BCh 1995 Wales; DFFP 1998; DCH 1999. (Univ. Wales Coll. Med.) Prev: GP Sen. Regist., Lond.; GP Regist., Fulham, Lond.; SHO Gynaecologist/Obs., Lond.

RUGG-EASEY, Margaret Lilian (retired) 4 Wentworth Drive, Tividale, Oldbury B69 1QD Tel: 01384 850351 — MB BS 1940 Lond.; MRCP Lond. 1947. Prev: Capt. RAMC.

RUGG-GUNN, Fergus James 26 Eastern Way, Ponteland, Newcastle upon Tyne NE20 9PF — MB BS 1994 Lond.

RUGGIER, Romanie Dept of Anaesthesia, St George's Healthcare NHS Trust, London SW17 0QT Tel: 020 8725 3316 Fax: 020 8725 3135 Email: ruggier@sghms.ac.uk; 5 Old Palace Lane, Richmond TW9 1PG Tel: 020 8940 4426 Fax: 020 8940 4426 — MB BS 1987 Lond.; BSc Lond. 1984; Royal College of Anaesthetists 1993. (Royal Free Hospital School of Medicine) Cons. Anaesth. with s/i in Neuroanaesth. & Neurocritical Care.

RUGGINS, Nigel Raymond Derbyshire Children's Hospital, Uttoxeter Road, Derby DE22 3NE Tel: 01332 340131 Fax: 01332 200857; 48 Hazelwood Road, Duffield, Belper DE56 4AA Tel: 01332 842347 Email: niggi@publiconline.co.uk — MB BS 1979 Lond.; BSc (Hons.) (Human Genetics) Lond. 1979; MRCP (UK) 1986; FRCPCH. (Univ. Coll. Hosp.) Cons. Paediat. Derby City Gen. Hosp. & Derbysh. Childr. Hosp.; Paediatric Serv. Director. Prev: Sen. Regist. (Paediat.) Nottm.; Research Fell. Childr. Respirat. Unit Univ. Hosp. Nottm.

RUGGLES, Ruth Marie Brentford Health Centre, Albany Road, Brentford TW8 8DS — BM BCh 1985 Oxf.; MRCGP 1991; DRCOG 1990; DCH RCP Lond. 1989; Cert. Family Plann. JCC 1989.

RUGHANI, Amar Nath Burncross Surgery, 1 Bevan Way, Chapeltown, Sheffield S35 1RN Tel: 0114 246 6052 Fax: 0114 245 0276; 519 Fulwood Road, Sheffield S10 3QB — MB BS 1982 Lond.; BSc 1979 Lond.; FRCGP 1999; MRCGP (Distinc.) 1986; DCH RCP Lond. 1987; DRCOG 1986. (Roy. Lond. Hosp.) Examr. RCGP; Assoc. Course Organiser Sheff. VTS; GP Tutor Continuing Professional Developm., Univ. of Sheff. Socs: Roy. Coll. of Gen. Practitioners, Treas. Sheff. Fac. & Treas.

RUGHANI, Gargi 6 South Park Drive, Ilford IG3 9AG Tel: 020 8599 3654 — MB BS Punjab (India) 1949; Dip. Human Sex. St. Geo. Hosp. 1986; DObst RCOG (Lond.) 1961.

RUGHANI, Vijaykumar Gokaldas 6 South Park Drive, Ilford IG3 9AG Tel: 020 8599 3654 — MB BS Durh. 1957.

RUGMAN, Francis Paul Department of Haematology, Royal Preston Hospital, Sharoe Green Lane, Preston PR2 9HT — MB ChB 1977 Liverp.; MRCP (UK) 1983; FRCPath 1996, M 1988; FRCP Lond. 1998. Cons. Haemat. Roy. Preston Hosp. Prev: Sen. Regist. (Haemat.) Roy. Liverp. Hosp.; Cancer Research Fell. (N. W. Cancer Fund) Univ. Liverp.

RUHI, Shamim Osmani East Ham Memorial Hospital, Shrewsbury Road, Forest Gate, London E7 8QR Tel: 020 8586 5012 — MB BS 1977 Punjab; DHMSA 1983 Punjab; DPMSA 1981 Punjab; DTCD 1979 Punjab; MRCPsych 1985. Cons. Psychiat. Newham HA.; Unit Train. Dir. Prev: Sen. Regist. (Psychiat.) St. Bart. Hosp. Lond.

RUHUL AMIN, Mir Abul Kalam Mohammed 18 Ferme Park Road, London N4 4ED Tel: 020 8340 6050 — MB BS 1956 Dacca; LMSSA Lond. 1968. (Dacca Med. Coll.)

RUIZ, George Antonio 68 Endrick Gardens, Balfron, Glasgow G63 0RD — MB ChB 1996 Glas.

RUIZ, Kenneth 11 Crimicar Drive, Sheffield S10 4EF — MB ChB 1984 Sheff.; BMedSci Sheff. 1982, MB ChB 1984; FRCA 1989.

RUIZ, Maria-Carmen 38 Letterfearn Drive, Glasgow G23 5JL — MB ChB 1998 Glas.; MB ChB Glas 1998.

RUIZ, Ramon Gregory Gary 69 Frankfurt Road, London SE24 9NX — MB BS 1982 Lond.; BSc (Physiol.) Lond. 1979; MRCP (UK) 1986. (King's Coll. Hosp.) Cons. Paediat. King's Coll. Hosp. Lond. Prev: Sen. Regist. (Paediat.) Dudley Rd. Hosp. Birm.; Research Regist. (Paediat.) King's Coll. Sch. Med. & Dent. Univ. Lond.

RUIZ DE ARCAUTE, Javier 21 Rozel Square, Manchester M3 4FQ — LMS 1996 Basque Provinces.

RUIZ FITO, Jose Rafael ENT Department, Barnsley District General Hospital, Gawber Road,, Barnsley S75 2PW; Park View House, Barnsley Road,, Cudworth, Barnsley 572 8SY Tel: 01226 718767 — LMS 1990 Seville. SHO (ENT) (Barnsley Dist. Gen. Hosp.). Prev: SHO

(ENT - Barnsley Dist. Gen. Hosp.); SHO (ENT - Roy. Gwent Hosp., Newport); SHO (ENT - Singleton, Hosp., Swansea).

RUIZ HERRERO, Angel Luis 242 Malone Road, Belfast BT9 5LR Tel: 01232 682916; c/o Estudios No 2, Madrid 28012, Spain Tel: 00 34 1 3669401 — LMS 1989 Madrid; FRCSI 1994. Career Specialist Regist. Belf. City Hosp.; Specialist Regist. (Orthop.) Rotat. Altnagelvin Hosp., Lond.derry, N. Irel. Prev: Career Regist. Rotat. Ulster Hosp., Roy. Vict. Hosp. & Musgrave Pk. Hosp. Belf.; SHO (Surg.) Crawley Hosp. W. Sussex; SHO (Surg. & Orthop.) P.ss Roy. Hosp. Haywards Heath.

RUIZ MARTIN, Marcelino Block 14, Flat 7, Good Hope Hospital, Rectory Road, Sutton Coldfield B75 7RR — LMS 1992 Granada.

RUKMANI, Krishna Sastrigal The Surgery, 145 Portland Road, Hove BN3 5QJ Tel: 01273 734888 Fax: 01273 203232; 97 The Promenade, Peacehaven BN10 8LH — MB BS 1975 Calcutta.

RUKUNAYAKE, Gunasili Nimal Chandrasena 20 Claremont Gardens, Clevedon BS21 5BG — MB BS 1968 Ceylon.

RULE, Mrs Elizabeth Margaret Pensby Road Surgery, 349 Pensby Road, Pensby, Wirral CH61 9NL Tel: 0151 648 1193 Fax: 0151 648 2934; 8 Brancote Road, Oxton, Birkenhead CH43 6TJ — MB ChB 1972 Liverp.; MB ChB Liverp. 1974; BSc (Hons.) (Microbiol.) Liverp. 1972; DCH Eng. 1977; DRCOG 1977.

RULE, Joan Tonna Hospital, Tonna, Neath SA11 3LX Tel: 01639 635404 — MB BCh 1973 Wales; MRCPsych 1977.

RULE, Michael Jeremy Peartree Lane Surgery, 110 Peartree Lane, Welwyn Garden City AL7 3XW Tel: 01707 329292; 62 Peartree Lane, Welwyn Garden City AL7 3UH — MB BS 1981 Lond.; BSc (Hons.) Lond. 1978, MB BS 1981. (St. Bart.)

RULE, Simon Alexander Joseph Department of Haematology, Royal Perth Hospital, Wellington St., Perth, Australia; Stowe Hill House, Netherstowe, Lichfield WS13 6TJ — BM BS 1987 Nottm.; MPhil Nottm. 1986, BMedSci 1984, BM BS 1987. SHO (Med. Rotat.) Taunton & Som. Hosp.

RULEWSKI, Nigel John 37 Saxonwood Road, Cheswick Green, Shirley, Solihull B90 4JR — MB BS 1977 Lond.; DRCOG 1981; DCH RCP Lond. 1982. (St. Bart.) Vice-Pres. Med. Affairs Astra, USA.

RUMBALL, Bernard John Southview Surgery, Guildford Road, Woking GU22 7RR Tel: 01483 763186 Fax: 01483 821526 — MB BCh 1982 Wales.

RUMBALL, Claire Louise Ash House, St Martin's Hospital, Midford Road, Bath BA2 5RP Tel: 01225 840132 — MB BS 1991 Newc.; MRCGP 1996; DFFP 1996. (Newcastle upon Tyne) Clin. Med. Off. (Family Plann.) Bath & Wilts.

RUMBALL, Daphne The Bure Centre, 7 Unthank Road, Norwich NR2 2PA Tel: 01603 671900 Fax: 01603 671920 Email: bure@globalnet.co.uk — MB ChB 1975 Liverp.; MRCPsych 1981; DRCOG 1979; FRCPsych 1997. (Liverpool University) Cons. Psychiat. (Drug Dependency) Norf. Ment. Health Care Trust. Prev: Cons. Psychiat. Gt. Yarmouth & Waveney Health Dist.

RUMBLE, Mr John Anthony 45 Imperial Avenue, Westcliff on Sea SS0 8NQ Tel: 01702 337598; Finches, Church End, Paglesham, Rochford SS4 2DP Tel: 01702 258584 Fax: As Phone — MB ChB Sheff. 1955; FRCS Eng. 1967; FCOphth 1989; DO Eng. 1963; DObst RCOG 1958. (Sheffield University) Cons. Ophth. S.end Health Dist. Prev: Sen. Regist. (Ophth.) United Birm. Hosps.; Res. Surg. Off. Birm. & Midl. Eye Hosp.

RUMBLE, Mark Leonard Ley Surgery, Nathaniel Fish Row, 43 King Street, Great Yarmouth NR30 2PN Tel: 01493 330338 — MB ChB 1971 Dundee; MA UEA 1996.

RUMBLE, Peter Bertram Castle Place Surgery, 9 Park Hill, Tiverton EX16 6RR Tel: 01884 252333 Fax: 01884 252152; Withleigh Goodman, Withleigh, Tiverton EX16 8JG — MB ChB 1978 Bristol; MRCGP 1982; DRCOG 1981; Family Plann. Cert 1981. GP Tiverton Devon. Prev: GP Trainee Backwell.

RUMBOLD, Christopher Alexander Wool Surgery, Folly Lane, Wool, Wareham BH20 6DS Tel: 01929 462376; Kingsmead, Chalkpit Lane, Wool, Wareham BH20 6DW — MB BCh 1974 Wales.

RUMBOLD, John Mark Michael 10 Newland Road, Bordesley Green, Birmingham B9 5PS — MB ChB 1994 Dundee.

RUMFELD, Werner Robert The Cedars Surgery, 26 Swanley Centre, Swanley BR8 7AH Tel: 01322 663111/663237 Fax: 01322 614867 — State Exam Med 1976 Berlin; MD Berlin 1978; MRCGP 1990. (Freie Univ. Berlin) Arzt für Innere Medizin und Rheumatologie, NR W.falen 1985. Socs: Roy. Coll. Gen. Pract.; Med. Defence Union. Prev: Regist. (Rheum.) Univ. Hosp. Wales Cardiff; Regist. (Med.) P.ss Margt. Hosp. Swindon.

RUMIAN, Adam Piotr Crossley House, Sutton Lane, London W4 4HF — MB BS 1998 Lond.; MB BS Lond 1998.

RUMIAN, Ryszard (retired) Crossley House Surgery, Sutton Lane, London W4 4HF Tel: 020 8994 0342 Fax: 020 8994 6927 — LRCPI & LM, LRSCI & LM 1954; LRCPI & LM, LRCSI & LM 1954; DObst RCOG 1959. Clin. Asst. (Orthop.) W. Middlx. Hosp. Isleworth. Prev: Regist. (Orthop., Plastic Surg. & Cas.) W. Middlx. Hosp. Isleworth.

RUMLEY, Joseph James 37 Crofthead Street, Uddingston, Glasgow G71 7JQ — MB ChB 1998 Glas.; MB ChB Glas 1998.

RUMLEY, Sally Jane Abberley cottage, Dowles Road, Bewdley DY12 2EJ — MB ChB 1990 Birm.

RUMLEY, Simon Lawrence Paul York House Medical Centre, Stourport-on-Severn DY13 9EH Tel: 01299 827171 — MB ChB 1989 Leeds; MRCGP 1996; DCH RCP Lond. 1994. GP Princip.

RUMMENS, Ian Frank Cae Glas Doctors Surgery, 34 Church Street, Oswestry SY11 2SP Tel: 01691 652929 Fax: 01691 670175; Cae Cerrig, Sweeney Mountain, Oswestry SY10 9EZ — MB ChB 1978 Birm.; DRCOG 1982. Med. Off., Derwen Coll., OsW.erly SY11 3JA (1985-). Socs: Hon. Sec. Shrops. Local Med. Comm. (1986-).

RUMMENS, Laura Jane Selly Park Surgery, 2 Reaview Drive, Pershore Road, Birmingham B29 7NT Tel: 0121 472 0187 Fax: 0121 472 0187 — MB ChB 1990 Birm.; MRCGP 1996; DCH RCP Lond. 1994; DRCOG 1993. (Birm.)

RUMMENS, Simon David University Medical Practice, Elms Road, Off Pritchatts Road, Edgbaston, Birmingham B15 2SE Tel: 0121 414 5111 Fax: 0121 414 5108; 92 Woolacombe Lodge Road, Selly Oak, Birmingham B29 6PY Tel: 0121 414 5111 — MB ChB 1989 Birm.; MRCGP 1994; DRCOG 1993.

RUMSEY, Jennifer Margaret Anne Greenbank Surgery, 1025 Stratford Road, Hall Green, Birmingham B28 8BG Tel: 0121 777 1490 Fax: 0121 778 6239; 39 Kineton Green Road, Olton, Solihull B92 7DX Tel: 0121 706 0165 — MA, MB Camb. 1972, BChir 1971; DObst RCOG 1975; Cert FPA 1974. (Camb. & St. Geo.) Prev: SHO (Ophth.) Bromley Hosp.; Ho. Off. (O & G) Lambeth Hosp.; Ho. Off. (Ophth. & ENT) St. Geo. Hosp. Lond.

RUMSEY, Sarah 5 Tylers, Sewards End, Saffron Walden CB10 2LN — MB BS 1955 Lond.; MRO 1992; MLCOM 1982; DCH RCP Lond. 1959; DRCOG 1957. Med. Osteop. Essex.

RUNACRES, Anthony Selwyn Robert Blandford House Surgery, 7 London Road, Braintree CM7 2LD Tel: 01376 347100 Fax: 01376 349934 — MB 1972 Camb.; BChir 1971; DObst RCOG 1975. (St. Bart.) p/t Clin. Assist Dermat. Broomfield Hosp. Essex. Prev: Trainee Gen. Pract. Norwich Vocational Train. Scheme.

RUNAGALL, Simon Edward Loughton Mental Health Centre, 8-10 High Beech Road, Loughton IG10 4BL Tel: 0208 2714 000 Fax: 020 8271 4006; 11 Bovingdon Road, Bocking Church St, Braintree CM7 5JR Tel: 01376 553102 Email: simon.runagall@virgin.net — MB ChB 1989 Dundee; DCH RCPS Glas. 1991. Staff Grade Community Ment. Health Centre Loughton. Prev: SHO (Psychiat.) Colchester; SHO (Paediat.) Harlow.

RUNCHMAN, Mr Phillip Charles, Surg. Cdr. RN 5 St Mary Abbots Court, Warwick Gardens, London W14 8RA — BM BCh 1974 Oxf.; FRCS Eng. 1981. Cons. Gen. Surg.

RUNCIE, Colin John Department of Anaesthetics, Western Infirmary, Glasgow G11 6NT Tel: 0141 211 2069; 18 Whittngehame Drive, Glasgow G12 0XX Email: colin@mcgradyoaa.freeserve.co.uk — MB ChB 1982 Glas.; FRCP Glas. 1995; MRCP (UK) 1985; FRCA 1988. Cons. Anaesth. W.. Infirm. Glas.

RUNCIE, Ian James Denmans, 4 The Glebe, Lindfield, Haywards Heath RH16 2JS Tel: 01444 450639 Fax: 01444 414816 Email: denmans@fdn.co.uk — MB BCh 1975 Wales; FRCR 1982; T(R) (CR) 1991. Cons. Radiol. P.ss Roy. Hosp. Haywards Heath.

RUNCIE, James 14 Provost Ferguson Drive, Tain IV19 1RE — MB ChB 1937 Ed.; MF Hom. 1946.

RUNCIMAN, David Martin Inglis 3 Lucerne Road, Oxford OX2 7QB Tel: 01865 516696 Fax: 01865 516696 Email: martin.runciman@virgin.net — MB BS 1988 Lond.; MRCPI 1994; MRCPCH 1996. Specialist Regist. (Paediat. Cardiol.) Oxf.

RUND

RUND, Robin Lindsay Flat 3, Market Place, London N2 8BD — MB ChB 1980 Cape Town.

RUNDELL, Timothy Roy 13 Robin Close, Stanstead Abbotts, Ware SG12 8TX — MB BS 1986 Lond.; DCH RCP Lond. 1990.

RUNDLE, John Alan Little Pastures, 6 Church Road, Brackley NN13 7BU Tel: 01280 705102 Fax: 01280 705102 — MRCS Eng. LRCP Lond. 1951; FRCP Ed. 1995; FRFPS Glas. 1954; MRCP Glas. 1962; MRCP Lond. 1955; MRCP Ed. 1955. (Lond. Hosp.) Cons. Neurol. Essex Nuffield Hosp. Brentwood., Ashcroft Clinic, Deddington, Oxon. & Hartswood Hosp. Brentwood; Vis. Phys. NHS Hosp. Essex; Phys. to Med. Foundat. Lond.; Cons. Neur. Lond. Neurol. Centre. Socs: BMA; Liveryman Soc. Apoth. Lond. Prev: Sen. Regist. Maida Vale Hosp.; Regist. (Med.) Hackney Hosp. & Roy. Lond. Hosp.; Ho. Phys. Nat. Hosp. Nerv. Dis. Lond.

RUNDLE, Mr John Samuel Harris 2 Dover Road, Branksome Park, Poole BH13 6DZ — MB ChB 1973 Ed.; FRCS Ed. 1977. Cons. Urol. Roy. Bournemouth Hosp.

RUNDLE, Paul Anthony Department of Opthalmology, Royal Hallamshire Hospital, Glossop Road, Sheffield S10 2JF — MB BS 1988 Newc. SHO (Orthop.) Cumbld. Infirm. Prev: Anat. Demonst. Univ. Newc. u Tyne; Ho. Surg. Ashington Gen. Hosp. N.d.; Ho. Phys. Roy. Vict. Infirm. Newc.

RUNDLE, Philippa Kate 8 Firs Avenue, East Sheen, London SW14 7NZ — MB Camb. 1969, BChir 1968; DCH Eng. 1971; DObst RCOG 1970. (St. Mary's) Assoc. Specialist (Paediat.) St. Mary's Hosp. Lond.; Sen. Clin. Med. Off. Kingston AHA; Forens. Med. Examr. Metrop. Police. Prev: SCMO Kensington, Chelsea & W.m. AHA.

RUNDLE, Susan Kathleen 39 Sunnybank, Epsom KT18 7DY — BM 1995 Soton.; BSc Soton. 1994; MRCP 1998. (Southampton University Medical School) SHO (Neurol.) Qu. Eliz. Hosp. Socs: BMA. Prev: SHO (Oncol.) Qu. Eliz. Hosp. Birm.; SHO (Endocrinol.) SOH Birm.; SHO (Elderly Care) SOH Birm.

RUNGE, Mrs Anna Marcela 10 St Lucia Close, Sunderland SR2 8AF — Med. Dipl. Warsaw 1935.

RUNNETT, Craig 2 Newland Court, Wakefield WF1 5AG — MB ChB 1993 Leeds.

RUOSS, Mr Christopher Fredrick Combe Hill, 36 The Heights, Worthing BN14 0AJ Tel: 01903 261737 Fax: 01903 261737 — MB BS 1963 Lond.; FRCS Eng. 1967; MRCS Eng. LRCP Lond. 1963; FRCOG 1982, M 1969. (St. Bart.) Cons. O & G Worthing & S.lands Hosps. Socs: Blair Bell Res. Soc. Prev: Cons. Matern. & Child Health WHO Europ. Off. Copehagen, Denmark; Sen. Regist. (O & G) St. Bart. Hosp. Lond.; Resid. Med. Off. Qu. Charlotte's Matern. Hosp. Lond.

RUOTSALAINEN-GARATTONI, Tarja 8 Colwell Gardens, Haywards Heath RH16 4HG — Lic Med 1991 Kuopio.

RUPAL, Anita 26 Downshall Avenue, Ilford IG3 8NB — MB ChB 1988 Aberd.; DRCOG 1993.

RUPAREL, Yashvant Becharlal 27 Commonwealth Avenue, Hayes End, Hayes UB3 2PN Tel: 020 8573 7198 — MB BS 1972 Bombay.

RUPARELIA, Mr Bhanuprasad Anandji Worcester Royal Infirmary, Ronkswood Branch, Worcester WR5 1HN Tel: 01905 763333 Fax: 01905 760584; Holly Lodge, Bosbury Road, Cradley, Malvern WR13 5LT Email: bhanu@baruparelia.freeserve.co.uk — MB BS 1976 Lond.; BSc (Biochem.) Lond. 1973; FRCS Ed. 1982; MRCS Eng. LRCP Lond. 1976; FRCOG 1995, M 1982. (Guy's) Cons. O & G Worcerster Roy. Infirm. NHS Trust; Lead Clinician, Worcester Osteoporosis Unit. Socs: Coun. Mem. - Brit. Menopause Soc.; Mem. Nat. Osteoporosis Soc.; Mem. Brit. Soc. Colposcopy & Cytol. Pathol. Prev: Sen. Regist. Rotat. (O & G) W. Midl. RHA; Clin. Lect. & Regist. (O & G) Guy's Hosp. Lond.; Regist. (Surg.) Beckenham Gen. Hosp.

RUPARELIA, Prina 71 Kingston Av, Stoke-on-Trent ST1 6HG — MB ChB 1997 Bristol.

RUPARELIA, Vibha Kishor Queen Charlotte's Hospital, Goldhawk Road, London W6 Tel: 020 8748 4666; Cintamani Caravan, Wall Hall Cottages, Aldenham, Watford WD25 8AS — MB BS 1992 Lond. Research Fell. (Gyn. Oncol.) St. Thos. Hosp. Lond.; Mem. Trainees Register of RCOG. Prev: SHO (O & G) St. Thos. Hosp. Lond.; SHO (O & G) Whittington Hosp. Lond.

RUPARELIA, Vrajlal Kalyanji — MB BS 1970 Rajasthan. (Bikaner Medical College)

RUPASINGHE, Edmund Priyankara 13 Linden Road, Bedford MK40 2DQ Tel: 01234 273272 — MB BS 1973 Ceylon; MRCS Eng. LRCP Lond. 1985. GP Bedford. Socs: BMA.

***RUSBY, Jennifer Elizabeth** 69 Gloucester Road, Hampton TW12 2UQ Email: rusby@hotmail.com — BM BCh 1998 Oxf.; BM BCh Oxf 1998.

RUSCILLO, Giuseppe Antonio 38 King Street, Lancaster LA1 1RE Tel: 01524 32294; Tel: 01524 841340 — MB ChB 1992 Sheff.; MRCGP 1997. (Sheffield) GP Princip.

RUSCOE, Michael Nicholas John Manor Surgery, Forth Noweth, Chapel Street, Redruth TR15 1BY Tel: 01209 313313 Fax: 01209 313813; 12 Trewirgie Road, Redruth TR15 2SX Tel: 01209 315038 Email: mruscoe@cix.compulink.co.uk — MB ChB 1971 Leeds; MB ChB (Hons.) Leeds 1971; FRCGP 1993, M 1982; MSc 1999. Assoc. Regional Adviser (Gen. Pract.) Bristol Univ. Prev: SHO (Obst.) Leeds Matern. Hosp.; Ho. Phys. St. Jas. Hosp. Leeds; Ho. Surg. Leeds Gen. Infirm.

RUSE, Charlotte Elizabeth 11 Mill Lane, Cropwell Bishop, Nottingham NG12 3BT — MB ChB 1992 Leic.

RUSE, Gareth Antony Cheam Family Practice, The Knoll, Parkside, Cheam, Sutton SM3 8BS Tel: 020 8770 2014 Fax: 020 8770 1864 — MB BS 1985 Lond.

RUSH, Elaine Margaret The Ipswich Hospital, Heath Road, Ipswich IP4 5PD Tel: 01473 712233 Fax: 01472 702643; 18 York Road, Martlesham Heath, Ipswich IP5 3TL Email: elaine.rush@btinternet.com — MB ChB 1976 Liverp.; MRCP (UK) 1983; FFA RCS Eng. 1981. Cons. Anaesth. Ipswich Hosp.

RUSH, Jennifer Mary 26 Crossway, Petts Wood, Orpington BR5 1PE; 65-97 Lowfield Street, Dartford DA1 1HP Tel: 01322 224550 — MB BS 1984 Lond.; BSc Lond. 1981, MB BS 1984; MRCP (UK) 1987; MRCGP 1990; Cert. Family Plann. JCC 1990; DRCOG 1995. (Royal Free Hospital London) GP Tutor Dartford.

RUSH, Mark 2 Sunnyside, Washford, Watchet TA23 0LB — MB BS 1998 Lond.; MB BS Lond 1998.

RUSH, Richard Alan James Hill View, Ashburton Lane, Hook Norton, Banbury OX15 5QE — BM BCh 1988 Oxf.

RUSHAMBUZA, Francis Gratian National Blood Service, Mersey and North Wales Blood Centre, West Derby St., Liverpool L7 8TW Tel: 0151 551 8862 Fax: 0151 551 8895; 2 Beech Lawn, Grassendale, Liverpool L19 0LH Tel: 0151 427 2428 — MB ChB 1968 St. And.; MSc (Clin. Pharmacol.) Manch. 1974; MRCP (U.K.) 1975; FRCP Lond. 1997; DTM & H (Liverp.) 1996; DGUM & Ven (Liverp.) 1998. (St. Andrews) Cons. (Haemat.) Nat. Blood Transfus. Serv. Regional Blood Transfus. Centre Liverp. Socs: Fell. Roy. Soc. Trop. Med. & Hyg.; Brit. Blood Transfus. Soc.; Brit. Soc. Haematol. Prev: Sen. Regist. (Haemat.) Mersey RHA.

***RUSHAMBUZA, Roger Pascal Mugisha** 2 Beech Lawn, Grassendale, Liverpool L19 0LH — MB BS 1998 Newc.; MB BS Newc 1998.

RUSHBROOK, Laurence Alfred William Layer Road Surgery, Layer Road, Colchester CO2 9LA Tel: 01206 546494 Fax: 01206 369912 — MB ChB 1974 Sheff.

RUSHBROOK, Simon Matthew 5 The Ridings, Chelmsford CM2 9RR — MB BS 1997 Lond.

RUSHDY, Amal Abbas Abdel Rahman 282 Overdown Road, Reading RG31 6PP — MB BS 1985 Lond.; MFPHM 1997; MSc 1993 (Pub. Health Med.) Lond.; MSc (Pub. Health Med.) Lond. 1993, MB BS 1985; MRCP (UK) 1989; DTM & H Liverp. 1991. (Guy's Hospital medical school, Univ of London) Clin. Sen. Lect.,Epidemiol. & Pub. Health Univ. of Wales Coll. of Med Cardiff; Sen. Med. Off., Dept. of Health, Lond. Prev: Sen Reg, Pub. health Med., PHLS communicable Dis. surveillance centre Lond.; Detached Nat. Expert, DG Health & Consumer Protec., Europ. Commiss. Luxemberg; Cons epidemiologist PHLS CDSC Lond. Sen. Med. Off., Dept of health, Lond.

RUSHEN, Daniel Jon 6 Links View Avenue, Poole BH14 9QT — BM 1993 Soton.

RUSHEN, Julie Elizabeth Russell Place Farm, Wood St., Guildford GU3 3EZ; 34 Coleshill Road, Teddington TW11 0LJ — MB BS 1988 Lond.; BSc (Hons.) Lond. 1987; MFFP 1993; DRCOG 1992; Cert. Family Plann. JCC 1992; DCH RCP Lond. 1991.

RUSHFORD, Carole Ann Vine Surgery, Hindhayes Lane, Street BA16 0ET Tel: 01458 841122 Fax: 01458 840044; Priors Leigh, Ditcheat, Shepton Mallet BA4 6PS Tel: 01749 860340 — MB ChB

1968 Sheff.; Cert. Family Plann. JCC 1984. (Sheff.) Instruct. Doctor Family Plann. Jt. Comm. Contracept.

RUSHFORTH, Mr Graham Frederick Weaveland, Homington Road, Coombe Bissett, Salisbury SP5 4LY — MB BS 1966 Lond.; FRCS Eng. 1971; MRCS Eng. LRCP Lond. 1966; DObst RCOG 1969. (Guy's) Cons. Orthop. Surg. Salisbury Health Dist. Prev: Sen. Orthop. Regist. St. Geo. Hosp. & S.W. Thames; Orthop. Regist. Roy. Surrey Co. Hosp. Guildford; Surg. Regist. N.ampton Gen. Hosp.

RUSHFORTH, Jean Alison — MB BCh Wales 1985; MRCP (UK) 1989. Cons. Paediat. Glos. Roy. Hosp. Prev: Lect. (Child Health) Univ. Wales Coll. Med. Cardiff; Regist. & SHO (Paediat.) Leeds Gen. Infirm.

RUSHMAN, Geoffrey Boswall (retired) 26 Tyrone Road, Thorpe Bay, Southend-on-Sea SS1 3HF Tel: 01702 586379 Fax: 01702 586379 — MB BS Lond. 1962; MRCS Eng. LRCP Lond. 1962; FFA RCS Eng. 1970. Cons. Anaesth. S.end Hosp., Rochford Hosp. & Runwell Hosp.; FRCA Examr. Roy. Coll. Anaesth. Prev: Sen. Regist. (Anaesth.) St. Bart. Hosp. Lond. & N.ampton Gen. Hosp.

RUSHMAN, Nicholas Richard 47 Hillway, London N6 6AH — MB BS 1992 Lond.

RUSHMAN, Mr Richard William 72 Harley Street, London W1N 1AE Tel: 020 7636 6521 Fax: 020 7436 2642; 47 Hillway, London N6 6AH Tel: 020 8348 2480 — BM BCh 1963 Oxf.; FRCS Ed. 1970; FRCS Eng. 1971. (Oxf. & Univ. Coll. Hosp.) Cons. Orthop. Surg. Roy. Free Hosp. Lond. & Roy. N. Hosp. Lond.; Sec. Brit. Counc. Internat. Coll. Surgs. Prev: Sen. Regist. (Orthop.) W.m. Hosp. Lond. & Univ. Coll. Hosp. Lond.; John Marshall Fell. Univ. Coll. Hosp. Med. Sch. Lond.

RUSHMAN, Sarah Caroline 12 Severn Street, Leicester LE2 0NN — MB ChB 1990 Leic.; BSc Leic. 1987, MB ChB 1990; RFCIA 1998. Specialist Regist. Leicester Roy. Infirm.

RUSHMER, Charles Anthony (retired) Lowside Lodge, Upwell, Wisbech PE14 9BB Tel: 01945 773312 Fax: 01945 773312 — MB BS Lond. 1954; MRCS Eng. LRCP Lond. 1954; DObst RCOG 1956. Prev: SHO (Cas.) Preston Roy. Infirm.

RUSHMER, Robert Jeremy Department Anaesthetics, Royal Infirmary, Lauriston Place, Edinburgh EH3 9HB; 8 Comiston Terrace, Edinburgh EH10 6AH Tel: 0131 447 7716 — MB BS 1987 Lond.; BSc Lond. 1984; MRCP (UK) 1992. SHO (Anaesth.) Roy. Infirm. Edin.

RUSHTON, Andrew Michael Ashley House, 4 Squirrels Corner, Newborough, Burton-on-Trent DE13 8SA — MB ChB 1994 Manch.; BSc St Andrews 1991.

RUSHTON, Andrew Robert Alistair 19 Moorlands, Tiverton EX16 6UF — BM BCh 1987 Oxf.; BA Camb. 1984, MA 1988; FRCA 1993.

RUSHTON, Arthur Four Gables, 14 Overhill Road, Wilmslow Park, Wilmslow SK9 2BE Tel: 01625 523628 Fax: 01625 523916 Email: arthur.rushton@protherics.com — MB ChB 1969 Manch.; MRCP (UK) 1972; FFPM 1989; Dip. Managem. Studies CNAA 1977. (Manch.) Chief. Operat. Off. Protherics plc Chesh. Prev: Med. Dir. Clin. Research Foundat. (UK) Ltd.; Manager (Med. Plann.) ICI Pharmaceuts.; Regist. (Med.) Aberd. Roy. Infirm.

RUSHTON, Arthur Wilsden Medical Practice, Townfield, Wilsden, Bradford BD15 0HT Tel: 01535 273227; Penhallow, Keighley Road, Denholme, Bradford BD13 4LT Tel: 01274 833508 — MB ChB 1955 Manch. (Manch.) Prev: Regist. (Gen. Med.) Bradford Roy. Infirm.; SHO (Med.) & Ho. Off. (O & G) St. Luke's Hosp. Bradford.

RUSHTON, Barbara Elizabeth Anne Newtown Surgery, Station Road, Liphook GU30 7DR Tel: 01428 724768 Fax: 01428 724162; Borreraig, 3 Hollycombe Close, Liphook GU30 7HR Tel: 01428 722173 — BM BCh 1978 Oxf.; BA Oxf. 1975; MRCGP 1982; DRCOG 1980; DFFP 1995. (Oxf.) Prev: Assoc. Specialist (Paediat.) Paddington Green Childr. Hosp. Lond.; GP Hammersmith; Trainee GP Hammersmith Hosp. VTS.

RUSHTON, Charles Alfred 51 Kings Road, Hitchin SG5 1RD — MRCS Eng. LRCP Lond. 1956. (Manch.) Prev: Ho. Phys. Stepping Hill Hosp. Stockport; Obst. Ho. Off. Wakefield Gen. Hosp.

RUSHTON, Claire Ellen Roman Road Health Centre, Fishmoor Drive, Blackburn BB2 3UY Tel: 01254 664832 — BM 1978 Soton.; MRCGP 1982; DRCOG 1980; DCH Eng. 1981. Socs: Chairm. of E. Lancs Small Pract.s Assn.

RUSHTON, David Ian (retired) Department of Pathology, Birmingham Womens Hospital, Edgbaston, Birmingham B15 2TG Tel: 0121 627 2704 Fax: 0121 607 4721 — MB ChB 1960 Manch.; FRCPCH 1997; FRCPath 1980, M 1968. Sen. Lect. (Path.) Univ. Birm. & Birm. Wom.s Hosp.; Hon. Cons. Path. Birm. Wom. Hosp.; Vis. Prof. Path. Univ. Manitoba. Prev: Lect. (Path.) Univ. Birm.

RUSHTON, Professor David Nigel Frank Cooksey Rehab Unit, King's Healthcare, Mapother House de Crespigny Park, Denmark Hill, London SE5 8AZ Tel: 020 7346 5324 Fax: 020 7346 5346; Holly Place, 20 High St, Shoreham, Sevenoaks TN14 7TD Fax: 01959 522985 Email: david@rushtons.demon.co.uk — MB BChir Camb. 1970; MD Camb. 1978; FRCP Lond. 1989; MRCP (UK) 1974. Cons. (Rehabil.) King's Healthcare Trust. Socs: Physiol. Soc.; Assn. Brit. Neurols.; Brit. Soc. Rehabil. Med. Prev: Prof. Rehabil. Lond. Hosp. Med. Coll.; Reader (Neurol. & Physiol.) Inst. Psychiat. Lond.; Hon. Cons. Neurol. King's Coll. Hosp. Lond.

RUSHTON, Donald Gregory (retired) 7 Broomrigg Crescent, Ainstable, Carlisle CA4 9QH — MB BS 1948 Lond.; MRCS Eng. LRCP Lond. 1948; FRCPath 1972, M 1963. Prev: Cons. Foren. Path. & Med. Hamad Gen. Hosp. Qatar.

RUSHTON, George John 43 Hainault Road, Chigwell IG7 5DQ Tel: 020 8500 2641 — MRCS Eng. LRCP Lond. 1963; MA Oxf. 1960, BM BCh 1963. (Oxf. & St. Bart.) Prev: Ho. Phys. & Ho. Surg. Radcliffe Infirm. Oxf.

RUSHTON, Joanne Marie Cedars Surgery, 8 Cookham Road, Maidenhead SL6 8AJ Tel: 01628 620458 Fax: 01628 633270 — MB ChB 1989 Manch.; MRCGP 1994; DRCOG 1993. (Manch.) Prev: Trainee GP Reading VTS; Ho. Off. (Surg.) N. Manch. Gen. Hosp.; Ho. Off. (Orthop. & Cas.) P.ss Margt. Hosp. Swindon.

RUSHTON, Kenneth Lindsay Surrey Hampshire Borders NHS Trust, 49 Farnham Road, Guildford GU1 — MB BCh 1977 Wales. Cons. in Alcohol & Subst. Misuse.

RUSHTON, Michael John West Malling Group Practice, 116 High Street, Milverton, West Malling ME19 6LX Tel: 01732 870212 Fax: 01732 742437; 2 Warden Mill Close, Wateringbury, Maidstone ME18 5DJ Tel: 01622 812878 Email: mike@mrushton.demon.co.uk — MB BS 1975 Lond.; BSc (Physiol.) (Hons.) Lond. 1972, MB BS 1975; DRCOG 1981. (St. Thos.) Prev: SHO (Gen. Med.) Salisbury Gen. Hosp.; SHO (Radiother. & Oncol.) Roy. Marsden Hosp. Lond.; SHO (Neurol.) St. Thos. Hosp. Lond.

RUSHTON, Mr Neil Orthopaedic Research Unit, Box 180, Addenbrooke's Hospital, Hills Road, Cambridge CB2 2QQ Tel: 01223 217551; 37 Bentley Road, Cambridge CB2 2AW — MB BS 1970 Lond.; MA Camb. 1979, MD 1984; FRCS Eng. 1975; MRCS Eng. LRCP Lond. 1970. (Middlx.) Dir. of Orthop. Research Unit Camb.; Hon. Cons. Addenbrooke's Hosp. Camb. Socs: Fell. Magdalene Coll. Camb.; Fell. BOA & Roy. Soc. Med.; Vice-Pres. Europ. Orthop. Research Soc.

RUSHTON, Neil Patrick College Surgery, College Road, Cullompton EX15 1TG Tel: 01884 32373 Fax: 01884 35541; Lower Moorhayes, Cullompton EX15 1QN Tel: 01884 33204 Email: rushton@mail.eurobell.co.uk — MB BS 1976 Lond.; MRCGP 1981. (St. Geo.) Prev: SHO (O & G) St. Geo. Hosp. Lond.; SHO (Cas.) St. Geo. Hosp.; SHO (Paediat.) Mayday Hosp. Thornton Heath.

RUSHTON, Peter David Northampton General Hospital, Cliftonville, Northampton NN1 5BD Tel: 01604 34700; 57 Westwood Road, Heald Green, Cheadle SK8 3JW — MB BS 1989 Newc. SHO (Med.) N.ampton Gen. Hosp.

RUSHTON, Philip John 2 The Orchard, Wolverhampton WV6 9PF — BM 1997 Soton.

RUSHTON, Prudence Felicity Old Rectory Cottage, Burway Road, Church Stretton SY6 6DP — MB BS 1978 Newc.; DCH RCPS Glas. 1987. Sessional Med. Off. Wolverhampton Family Plann.; Sessional Med. Off. Shrops. Family Plann.

RUSHTON, Rebecca Jane Emley Cottage, 8 Wood St., Skelmanthorpe, Huddersfield HD8 9BN — MB ChB 1991 Leeds. Trainee GP Huddersfield VTS. Prev: Ho. Off. (Med. & Surg.) Huddersfield Roy. Infirm.

RUSHTON, Richard James (retired) Redesdale, Papworth-st-Agnes, Cambridge CB3 8QU — MB BChir 1957 Camb.; MA Camb. 1957; MRCS Eng. LRCP Lond. 1956; DA Eng. 1964; DObst RCOG 1963. Prev: GP Huntingdon.

RUSHTON, Sally Catherine Doctors Surgery, Mount Chambers, 92 Coggeshall Road, Braintree CM7 9BY — MB BS 1991 Lond.; BSc

RUSHTON

Lond. 1988; MRCGP 1995; DRCOG 1994. Prev: Job Sharing Princip. GP Braintree; GP Asst. Caterham.

RUSHTON, Sheila Margaret 37 Bentley Road, Cambridge CB2 2AW — MB BS 1970 Lond.; MRCS Eng. LRCP Lond. 1970; DA Eng. 1973. (Middlx.)

RUSHTON, Simon James 53 Andrew Street, Mossley, Ashton-under-Lyne OL5 0DL — MB ChB 1992 Manch.

RUSHTON, Susan Clare 19 Alderley Close, Woodley, Reading RG5 4TG — MB ChB 1977 Liverp.

RUSHTON, Susan Rosemary Louise Woodvale, Clifford St., Chudleigh, Newton Abbot TQ13 0LH — MB BS 1976 Lond.

RUSHWORTH, Elizabeth Ann (retired) Ridings End, Headington, Oxford OX3 8TB Tel: 01865 762302 — MB BS 1948 Lond.; MRCP Lond. 1955; MRCS Eng. LRCP Lond. 1948; DCH Eng. 1953. Prev: Cons. Rehabil. Rivermead Rehabil. Centre Oxf.

RUSHWORTH, Miss Frances Helen Princess of Wales Hospital, Coity Rd, Bridgend CF31 1RQ Tel: 01656 752752; 29 Bowham Ave, Bridgend CF31 3PA Tel: 01656 653808 Email: francesthomas@waitrose.com — MB BS 1989 Lond.; DFFP 1996; MRCOG 1998. (St. Mary's Hosp. Lond.) p/t Specialist Regist. Rotat., S. Wales. Prev: Specialist Regist. (O & G) St Mary's Hosp. Lond.; Specialist Regist. (O & G) W. Middlx. Univ. Hosp.; SHO (O & G) St. Mary's Hosp. & Samarit. Hosp. Lond.

RUSIUS, Christopher William 74 Highfield Avenue, Burnley BB10 2PS — MB ChB 1983 Aberd.; MRCPsych 1989. Cons. Community Health Sheff. Prev: Sen. Regist. & Regist. Middlewood Hosp. Sheff.; SHO Severalls Hosp. Colchester.

RUSIUS, John (retired) 74 Highfield Avenue, Burnley BB10 2PS — LRCP LRCS 1946 Ed.; LRCP LRCS Ed. LRFPS Glas. 1946; FRCPath 1972; DCP Lond 1955. Prev: Cons. Pathol. Path. Laborat. Gen. Hosp. Burnley.

RUSK, Maeve (retired) 18 Morven Road, Inverness IV2 4BU Tel: 01463 232643 — MB ChB 1942 Glas.; DOMS Eng. 1947. Prev: Cons. Ophth. Roy. N.. Infirm. Inverness.

RUSK, Rosemary Anne 15 Harberton Park, Belfast BT9 6TW — MB BCh BAO 1987 Belf.; BSc (Hons.) Belf. 1984; MD 1997; MRCP (UK) 1991. (Queen's University Belfast)

RUSMAN, Michael Victoria Road Health Centre, Washington NE37 2PU — Artsexamen 1988 Utrecht.

RUSNAK, Alexandra Sophie Hannah 85 Teignmouth Road, London NW2 4EA — MB BS 1997 Lond.

RUSS, Sarah Angela Chesterfield Royal Hospital, Medical Directorate, Calow, Chesterfield S44 5BL Tel: 01246 277271; 218 Stannington View Road, Crockes, Sheffield S10 1ST Tel: 0114 266 8032 — MB ChB 1998 Sheff.; MB ChB Sheff 1998. (University of Sheffield) SHO, Med. Rotat., Chesterfield Roy. Hosp. Calow, Chesterfield. Prev: PRHO, Gen Surg. Castle Hill Hosp., Hull; PRHO Gen. Surg, Hull Roy. Infirm., Hull; PRHO, Gen Med. Chesterfield Roy. Hosp.

RUSSELL, Alan John 5 St Marys Place, Bury BL9 0DZ Tel: 0161 764 7484; Dakins, Walker Fold, Bolton BL1 7PU Tel: 01204 842756 — MB ChB 1971 Birm.; FRCOG 1990, M 1977. (Birm.) Cons. O & G Bury Health Care NHS Trust. Prev: Sen. Regist. (O & G) St. Marys Hosp. Manch.; Clin. Tutor (O & G) Univ. Manch. Wythenshawe Hosp. Manch.; Regist. (Obst & Gyn.) Birm. Matern. Hosp. & Birm. & Midl. Hosp. Wom.

RUSSELL, Alan Lawrence 5 Woodborough Road, London SW15 6PX — MB BS 1963 Lond.; MRCP Lond. 1966; MRCS Eng. LRCP Lond. 1963; LMCC 1970. Dir. Brampton Pain Clinic Brampton, Ont.

RUSSELL, Alan Robert 53 Springfield Road, Cumbernauld, Glasgow G67 2RB — MB ChB 1994 Manch.

RUSSELL, Alan S (retired) PO Box 15, Newton-le-Willows WA12 9BF Tel: (01942) 720519 — MB ChB Liverp. 1964.

RUSSELL, Alastair Alexander, Surg. Cdr. RN Cadleigh Lodge, Cadleigh, Ivybridge PL21 9HW Tel: 01752 893536 — MB ChB 1957 Ed.; MCOphth. 1988; DO Eng. 1963. Assoc. Specialist in Ophth. Roy. Eye Infirm. Plymouth. Socs: Ophth. Soc. UK; Fell. Roy. Soc. Med. Prev: Sen. Specialist in Ophth RN; Ho. Surg. & Ho. Phys. Roy. Infirm. Edin.; Asst. Surg. St. John Ophth. Hosp. Jerusalem, Jordan.

RUSSELL, Alec John The Beeches, Walsham-le-Willows, Bury St Edmunds IP31 3AD Tel: 0135 98 259227 — MB BChir 1947 Camb. (St. Thos.)

RUSSELL, Alfred McCarrison 4 Friars Orchard, Salisbury SP1 2SY — MA Dub. 1986, MB BCh BAO 1942; MRCGP 1953. (Dub.) Prev: Ho. Surg. Accid. Serv. Radcliffe Infirm. Oxf.; Squadron Ldr. RAF Med. Br.

RUSSELL, Aline Joan Clayton Department of Clinical Neurophysiology, Institute of Neurological Sciences, Southern General Hospital NHS Trust, 1345 Govan Road, Glasgow G51 4TF Tel: 0141 201 2462; 41 Snowdon Place, Stirling FK8 2JP — MB BS 1975 Lond.; BSc Lond. 1972; MRCP (UK) 1979. (Middlx.) Cons. (Clin. Neurophysiol.) S.. Gen. Hosp. Prev: Sen Regist. (Clin. Neurophysiol.) S.. Gen. Hosp. NHS Trust Glas.; Clin. Asst. (EEG & Epilepsy) Falkirk Dist. Roy. Infirm.; Regist. & SHO (Paediat.) Ninewells Hosp. Dundee.

RUSSELL, Allan Walker Barr (retired) 58 Marchbank Gardens, Paisley PA1 3JD Tel: 0141 810 1709 — MB ChB 1954 Glas.

RUSSELL, Andrew Giles 37 Thirlmere Road, London N10 2DL — MB BS 1989 Lond.

***RUSSELL, Andrew Gordon** Blue Wing Medical Practice, Wallacetown Medical Centre, 3 Lyon Street, Dundee DD4 6RB Tel: 01382 458333 Fax: 01382 461833 — MB ChB 1986 Dundee.

RUSSELL, Andrew Ian 28 All Saints Avenue, Margate CT9 5QW — MB BS 1994 Lond.

RUSSELL, Andrew McNeill 56 Spruce Avenue, Johnstone PA5 9RG — MB ChB 1998 Glas.; MB ChB Glas 1998.

RUSSELL, Andrew Oldrey Sandfield Farm, Hever, Edenbridge TN8 7ES Tel: 01732 863301 — MB BChir Camb. 1955; MA Camb. 1957; MRCGP 1964; DA Eng. 1959; DObst RCOG 1955. (Camb. & St. Thos.) Exam. Med. Pract. Benefit Agency; Mem. Med. Disabil. Hosp.ity Appeal Serv. Socs: BMA; Roy. Soc. Med. Prev: GP Edenbridge; SHO (Anaesth.) Qu. Vict. Hosp. E. Grinstead; Resid. Off. (Obst.) St. Thos. Hosp. Lond.

RUSSELL, Anthony James Barter Headlands Surgery, 20 Headlands, Kettering NN15 7HP Tel: 01536 518886 Fax: 01536 415385; Measures House, Grafton Underwood, Kettering NN14 3AA — MB ChB 1984 Leic.; BA (Open) 1996, BSc Lond. 1978. Prev: Ho. Phys. Kettering Gen. Hosp.; Ho. Surg. Geo. Eliot Hosp. Nuneaton.

RUSSELL, Audrey Serena Melbourne Park Medical Centre, Melbourne Road, Aspley, Nottingham NG8 5HL Tel: 0115 978 6114 Fax: 0115 924 9334 — MB ChB 1983 Dundee; MRCGP 1987. Prev: Trainee GP Doncaster VTS.

RUSSELL, Barry John (retired) Woodlands Family Medical Centre, 106 Yarm Lane, Stockton-on-Tees TS18 1YE Tel: 01642 607398 Fax: 01642 677846 — MB BS 1962 Durh.

RUSSELL, Barry Neil The Surgery, 274 Havant Road, Drayton, Portsmouth PO6 1PA Tel: 023 9237 0422 Fax: 023 9261 8383; The Drayton Surgery, 280 Havant Road, Drayton, Portsmouth PO6 1PA Tel: 023 92 370422 Fax: 01705 618383 — MB BS 1972 Lond.; DObst RCOG 1974.

RUSSELL, Bernard Stephen Hawkley Brook Surgery, Highfield Grange Avenue, Wigan WN3 6SU Tel: 01942 234740 Fax: 01942 820037 — MB ChB 1981 Manch.; MRCGP 1985. Princip. GP Wigan.

RUSSELL, Brian Thomas Feidrfair Health Centre, Feidrfair, Cardigan SA43 1EB Tel: 01239 612021 Fax: 01239 613373; Oakleaves, Mwtshwr, St. Dogmaels, Cardigan SA43 3HZ — MB BCh BAO 1982 Dub.; DCH RCP Lond. 1985. Gen. Practioner, Cardigan Health Centre. Prev: Trainee GP Cardigan Health Centre; SHO (A & E, Med., Paediat. & O & G) Withybush Gen. Hosp. HaverfordW.

RUSSELL, Brigid Ita (retired) 36 Lancaster Road, Wimbledon, London SW19 5DD — MB ChB 1958 St. And.; MA Lond. 1996. Prev: Research Assoc. Yale Univ. Med. Sch., USA.

RUSSELL, Catherine Jane Corner Cottage, Heath Lane, Crondall, Farnham GU10 5AW Tel: 01252 851190 — MB BS 1987 Lond.; MRCGP 1992; DRCOG 1994; DCH RCP Lond. 1991.

RUSSELL, Cecilia Valentine (retired) Newlands, Tranwell Woods, Morpeth NE61 6AG Tel: 01670 515666 — MB ChB 1942 Aberd.; MD Aberd. 1946; DCH Eng. 1943. Prev: Ho. Surg. Roy. Aberd. Childr. Hosp.

RUSSELL, Christina Joan Doctors Surgery, Half Moon Lane, Wigton CA7 9NQ Tel: 016973 42254 Fax: 016973 45464 — MB ChB 1981 Aberd.

RUSSELL

RUSSELL, Christine Marian Lisburn Health Centre, Linenhall Street, Lisburn BT28 1LU Tel: 028 9260 3111 Fax: 028 9266 1335; 4 Harmony Hill, Lisburn BT27 4EP Tel: 028 9267 0706 — MB BCh BAO 1974 Belf.; MRCGP 1980; DRCOG 1977. (Queen's University Belfast) GP Princip. Socs: Brit. Med. Assn.; Roy. Coll. of G.P's; Med. Wom.s' Federat.

RUSSELL, Christopher Ian Fraser Health Centre, Old Street, Clevedon BS21 6DG Tel: 01275 871454; Moorside Farm, Ham Lane, Kingston Seymour, Clevedon BS21 6XQ — MB BS 1976 Lond.; MRCP (UK) 1978; MRCS Eng. LRCP Lond. 1976; MRCGP 1984; DRCOG 1983. Prev: SHO Rotat. (Med.) Whittington Hosp. Lond.; SHO (Infec. Dis.) Coppetts Wood Hosp. Lond.; Med. Off. Swaziland Irrigation Scheme, Swaziland.

RUSSELL, Claire 53 Victoria Road, Netley Abbey, Southampton SO31 5DQ — MB BS 1986 Lond.; Dip. IMC RCS Ed. 1995. Staff Grade (A & E) Soton. Gen. Hosp. Univ. NHS Trust. Prev: Staff Grade (A & E) St. Mary's Hosp. Isle of Wight; Doctor & Crew Mem. 'Maiden', Whitbread Round World Yatch Race 1989/90.

RUSSELL, Claire Holly 35 Bridgend Road, Ballycarry, Carrickfergus BT38 9JZ — MB ChB 1994 Ed.

RUSSELL, Clive John McLean Tyrone County Hospital, Hospital Road, Omagh BT79 0AP Tel: 01662 245211; Lisboy House, 28 Dryarch Road, Omagh BT79 0SQ — MB BCh BAO 1972 Dub.; FRCP Ed. 1988; MRCP (UK) 1976. (Tinity Dub.) Cons. Phys. Tyrone Co. Hosp. Socs: Fell. Ulster Med. Soc.; Ulster Soc. Internat. Med.; Irish Cardiac Soc. Prev: Sen. Tutor (Therap. & Pharmacol.) & Sen. Regist. Qu. Univ. Belf.

RUSSELL, Mr Colin Frederick James, Deputy Lt. Royal Victoria Hospital, Grosvenor Rd, Belfast BT12 6BA Tel: 02890 894904; 8 Deramore Dr, Malone rd, Belfast BT9 5JQ Tel: 02890 660748 Fax: 02090 660748 — MB BCh BAO 1971 Belf.; BDS Belf. 1966; FRCSI 1995; FRCS Ed. 1976. Cons. Gen. & Endocrine Surg. Roy. Vict. Hosp. Belf.; Lect. Surg. Dent. Stud.s Qu.'s Univ. Belf. Socs: Coun. Mem. Assoc. Surg.s Gt. Britain & Irel.; Pres. Brit. Assn. Endocrine Surg.; Exec. Counc. Intnl. Assn. Endocrine Surg.s.

RUSSELL, Colin Robert Union Street Surgery, 75 Union Street, Larkhall ML9 1DZ Tel: 01698 882105 Fax: 01698 886332; 56 Hamilton Street, Larkhall ML9 2AU Tel: 01698 886160 — MB ChB 1982 Dundee; DRCOG 1986.

RUSSELL, David Orchard Court Surgery, Orchard Court, Orchard Road, Darlington DL3 6HS Tel: 01325 465285 Fax: 01325 284034 — MB BS 1980 Newc.; MRCGP 1988. Hon. Med. Off. Hartlepool United F.C.

RUSSELL, David Anthony Gordon House Surgery, 78 Mattock Lane, Ealing, London W13 9NZ Tel: 020 8997 9564 Fax: 020 8840 0533 — MB BS 1969 Lond. (Westm.)

RUSSELL, David Davis Gourock Health Centre, 181 Shore Street, Gourock PA19 1AQ Tel: 01475 634617; Felridge, 3 Divert Road, Gourock PA19 1DR Tel: 01475 632939 — MB ChB 1965 Glas.; DObst RCOG 1967.

RUSSELL, David James Mount Pleasant Health Centre, Mount Pleasant Road, Exeter EX4 7BW Tel: 01392 55722 — MB BCh BAO 1980 Dub.; MRCP (UK) 1985; MRCGP 1986. Course Organiser Exeter.

RUSSELL, David Kenneth Robertson Holmside, 9 South Beach Road, Ardrossan KA22 8AX Tel: 01294 63838 — MB ChB 1961 Glas.

RUSSELL, Derek, Col. late RAMC Retd. (retired) Park House, Hipswell, Catterick Garrison DL9 4AY Tel: 01748 833242 Email: dr.ent@bt.internet.com — MB BS 1950 Durh.; DLO Eng. 1954. Prev: C. O. & Otolaryngol. Duchess of Kent's Milit. Hosp. Catterick Garrison.

RUSSELL, Derrick Ian Department of Oral and Maxillofacial Surgery, Victoria Infirmary, Langside, Glasgow G42 9TY Tel: 0141 201 5415; Cairnmount, Gryffe Road, Kilmacolm PA13 4AZ Tel: 01505 872393 — MB BS 1973 Lond.; BDS Lond. 1968; MRCS Eng. LRCP Lond. 1973; FDS RCPS Glas. 1989; FDS RCS Eng. 1977, L 1967; FFD RCSI 1976. Cons. Oral & Maxillofacial Surg. Glas. Dent. Hosp., W.. Infirm., S.. Gen. Hosp. & Vict. Infirm. Glas.; Cons. Oral Surg. & Hon. Sen. Clin. Lect. Glas. Dent. Hosp. & Sch. Socs: Fell. - Brit. Assn. of Oral and Miaxillo Facial Surg.s; BMA. Prev: Sen. Regist. (Oral Surg.) Roy. Dent. Hosp. Lond. & St. Geo. Hosp. Lond.; Sen. Regist. (Oral Surg.) Guildford & Haslemere Hosps.; Sen. Regist. (Oral Surg.) St. Thos. Hosp. Lond.

RUSSELL, Mrs Diana Winifred West Gate Health Centre, Charleston Drive, Dundee DD2 4AD Tel: 01382 632771 Fax: 01382 633839; 6 Elliot Road, Dundee DD2 1TB — MB ChB 1984 Manch.; BSc St. And. 1981; MFFP 1994; MRCGP 1989; DRCOG 1987. Prev: Trainee GP Dundee VTS; Ho. Off. (Surg.) Stirling Roy. Infirm.; Ho. Off. (Med.) Falkirk Dist. Roy. Infirm.

RUSSELL, Mrs Dorothy Hazel 4 Friars Orchard, St. Ann Place, Salisbury SP1 2SY — MB BCh BAO 1941 Dub.; BA, MB BCh BAO Dub. 1941. (TC Dub.) Prev: Ho. Surg. Adelaide Hosp. Dub.; Ophth. Ho. Surg. Roy. Vict. Hosp. Belf.

RUSSELL, Douglas — MB ChB 1983 Glas.; FRCA 1990; DA (UK) 1989. Cons. Anaesth. S.. Gen. Hosp. Glas. Socs: Hon. Sec, UK Soc. for Intravenous Anaesth. Prev: Research Fell. (Anaesth.) Univ. Glas.

RUSSELL, Douglas Robert Dyfred Powys Health Auth., PO Box 13, Carmarthen SA31 3YH Tel: 01267 325225 Fax: 01267 225024; Brynderw, 16 Wellfield Road, Carmarthen SA31 1DS Tel: 01267 234815 — MB BS 1975 Lond.; BSc Lond. 1972, MB BS 1975; MRCGP 1990; DRCOG 1980. (St. Bart.) Head of GP Develop. Dyfed Powys HA. Prev: GP Carmarthen.

RUSSELL, Eleanor Harriet 37 Dale Street, Leamington Spa CV32 5HL — BM BCh 1998 Oxf.; BM BCh Oxf 1998.

RUSSELL, Elizabeth Caroline The Hildenborough Medical Group, Tonbridge Road, Hildenborough, Tonbridge TN11 9HL Tel: 01732 838777 Fax: 01732 838297 — MB BS 1983 Lond.; MRCGP 1989; MRCPsych 1989. (Guy's)

***RUSSELL, Elizabeth Clare** 55 Woodstock Road, Redland, Bristol BS6 7EW — MB ChB 1995 Birm.

RUSSELL, Professor Elizabeth Mary Department of Public Health, Medical School, Foresterhill, Aberdeen AB25 2ZD Tel: 01224 681818 Fax: 01224 662994 Email: e.m.russell@abdn.ac.uk; Kilburn, Inchgarth Road, Pitfodels, Aberdeen AB15 9NX Tel: 01224 861216 Fax: 01224 861216 — MB ChB 1958 Glas.; MD (Commend.) Glas. 1966; FRCP Ed. 1993; FRCP Glas. 1988; MRCP (UK) 1986; FFCM 1979, M 1974; Dip. Soc. Med. Ed. 1967; DObst RCOG 1960. (Glas.) Prof. & Head Dept. Pub. Health Univ. Aberd. Prev: Sen. Lect. (Community Med.) Univ. Aberd.

RUSSELL, Elspeth Margaret (retired) Downderry, 96 Carrwood, Hale Barns, Altrincham WA15 0ES Tel: 0161 980 3399 Email: russeldom@zen.co.uk — MB ChB Ed. 1956; DCH Eng. 1959. Prev: Gen. Practitioner.

RUSSELL, Emma 71 Hookstone Drive, Harrogate HG2 8PH — MB ChB 1998 Sheff.; MB ChB Sheff 1998.

RUSSELL, Erica Barbara Anne Weir 10 Greenhill Park, Edinburgh EH10 4DW Tel: 0131 447 6379 — MB ChB 1962 Aberd.; MFCM 1974; DSM Ed. 1969; DObst RCOG 1964. Sen. Research Fell. Dept. Community Med. Univ. Edin. Prev: Ho. Phys. Aberd. Roy. Infirm.; Ho. Surg. Roy. Aberd. Hosp. Sick Childr.; Research Lect. Dept. Social Med. Univ. Edin.

RUSSELL, Evelyn Department of Old Age Psychiatry, Withington Hospital, Nell Lane, Manchester M20 2LR — MB ChB 1989 Manch.; PhD Leeds 1975; BSc (1st. cl. Hons.) Leeds 1972; MD 1996 Manch.; MRCPsych 1993. (Manch.) Cons. Old Age Psychiat. Withington Hosp. Manch.

RUSSELL, Fiona Elizabeth 11 Cullen Drive, Glenrothes KY6 2JH Tel: 01592 754908 — MB ChB 1991 Dundee. (Dundee University) Specialist Regist. (anaesth) Glas. Prev: SHO (Anaesth.) Glas.

RUSSELL, Fiona Marion 38 Station Road, Bearsden, Glasgow G61 4AL — MB ChB 1989 Glas.; FRCS Glas. 1993; FRCS Ed. 1993.

RUSSELL, Francis Ellis (retired) 9 St Bride's Road, Glasgow G43 2DU Tel: 0141 632 0081 — MB ChB 1955 Glas.; DPath Eng. 1963; FRCPath 1977, M 1965. Prev: Cons. Bacteriol. Roy. Alexandra Hosp. Paisley.

RUSSELL, Frank Richard 37 Coniscliffe Road, Hartlepool TS26 0BU Tel: 01429 274568 — MRCS Eng. LRCP Lond. 1941; FFA RCS Eng. 1954; DA Eng. 1947. (Guy's) Hon. Cons. Anaesth. Hartlepool Health Dist. Prev: Sen. Cons. Anaesth. Hartlepool Gp. Hosps.; Sen. Regist. Dept. Anaesth. W. Middlx. Hosp. Isleworth; Capt. RAMC.

RUSSELL, Gavin Ian Department of Nephrology, Royal Infirmary, Princes Road, Hartshill, Stoke-on-Trent ST4 7LN Tel: 01782 554167 — MD 1982 Leic.; MB ChB Birm. 1973; FRCP Lond. 1994; MRCP (UK) 1978. Cons. (Renal) Phys. Socs: Internat. Soc. Hypertens. & Renal Assn.; Brit. Hypertens. Soc.

RUSSELL

RUSSELL, George Department of Child Health, University of Aberdeen, Cornhill Road, Aberdeen AB25 22D Tel: 01224 681818 Fax: 01224 840707 Email: g.russell@abdn.ac.uk; 12 Pinewood Avenue, Aberdeen AB15 8NB Tel: 01224 314224 Fax: 01224 314224 Email: libra@ifb.co.uk — MB ChB Aberd. 1959; FRCP Ed. 1993; FRCP Lond. 1977, M 1964; FRCPCH 1996. (Aberd.) Reader Child Health Univ. Aberd.; Hon. Cons. Paediat. Roy. Aberd. Childr. Hosp. Socs: Brit. Thorac. Soc.; Amer. Thoracic Soc.; Eur. Respirat. Soc. Prev: Cons. Paediat. Roy. Aberd. Childr. Hosp.; Fell. (Pediat.) Univ. Colorado Med. Center Denver, USA; Prof. Paediat. Univ. Riyad, Saudi Arabia.

RUSSELL, Professor Gerald Francis Morris Hayes Grove Priory Hospital, Prestons Road, Hayes, Bromley BR2 7AS Tel: 020 8462 7722 Fax: 020 8462 5028; 3 Aberdare Close, West Wickham BR4 9LP — MD 1957 Ed.; MB ChB (Hons.) Ed. 1950; FRCP Lond. 1969, M 1955; FRCP Ed. 1967, M 1954; FRCPsych 1971; DPM Eng. 1958. (Ed.) Dir. Eating Disorders Unit Hayes Gr. Priory Hosp. Hayes, Kent; Emerit. Prof. Psychiat. Univ. Lond.; Emerit. Cons. Phys. Bethlem Roy. & Maudsley Hosp. Lond. Prev: Dean Inst. Psychiat. Univ. Lond.; Prof. Psychiat. Inst. Psychiat. Univ. Lond.; Prof. Psychiat. Roy. Free Hosp. Sch. Med. Lond.

RUSSELL, Glenn Nicholas The Cardiothoracic Centre-Liverpool, Thomas Drive, Liverpool L14 3PE Tel: 0151 228 1616 Fax: 0151 220 8573 — MB ChB 1980 Aberd.; FRCA 1984. Cons. Anaesth. Cardiothoracic Centre Liverp.; Lect. (Anaesth.) Univ. Liverp. Prev: Lect. (Anaesth.) Ottawa Heart Inst., Canada.

RUSSELL, Glynn Alistair Bertrand Department of Child Health, St. Michael's Hospital, Southwell St., Bristol BS2 8EG Tel: 0117 921 5411 Fax: 0117 928 5751 Email: glynn.russell@ubht.swest.nhs.uk — MB ChB 1978 Cape Town; MRCP (UK) 1989; FCP(SA) 1986; DCH (SA) 1983; FRCP 1997; FRCPCH 1997. (Univ. Cape Town) Cons. Neonat. Med. St. Michael's Hosp. Bristol. Socs: Brit. Assn. of Porinatal Med. Mem. Prev: Sen. Regist. (Paediat.) & Research Fell. Liverp. Matern. Hosp.; Regist. (Paediat.) Roy. Liverp. Childr. Hosp.

RUSSELL, Graham Alfred The Health Centre, The Park, Gloucester GL1 1XR Tel: 01452 527217 Fax: 01452 387926; 94B Stroud Road, Gloucester GL1 5AJ — MB ChB 1957 Bristol; DCH Eng. 1960; DObst RCOG 1964. (Bristol)

RUSSELL, Graham Anthony Dept. of Histopathology, Pembury Hospital, Tunbridge Wells TN4 4QJ Tel: 01892 823535 — MB BS 1982 Lond.; BSc (1st cl. Hons.) Lond. 1979; MRCPath 1989. (Guy's) p/t Cons. Histopath.Pembury Hosp. Tunbridge Wells. Prev: Sen. Regist. (Histopath.) Rotat. Bristol HA; Regist. (Path.) Addenbrookes Hosp. Camb.; Ho. Surg. Guy's Hosp. Lond.

RUSSELL, Graham Thomas Bellevue Medical Centre, 26 Huntingdon Place, Edinburgh EH7 4AT Tel: 0131 556 2642 Fax: 0131 557 4430 — MB ChB 1985 Ed.; MRCGP 1990; Dip. IMC RCS Ed. 1995; DCCH RCGP 1990; DRCOG 1989. Clin. Asst. (A & E) Roy. Infirm. Edin.

RUSSELL, Grant Kingsley 7 Glanwern Avenue, Newport NP19 9BU — MB BS 1980 Lond.

RUSSELL, Gregor 16 Hallydown Drive, Glasgow G13 1UF — MB ChB 1996 Glas.

RUSSELL, Guy St John Wychall Lane Surgery, 11 Wychall Lane, Kings Norton, Birmingham B38 8TE Tel: 0121 628 2345 Fax: 0121 628 8282; 27 Middleton Road, Kings Heath, Birmingham B14 7HX Tel: 0121 444 1979 — MB ChB 1988 Birm.

RUSSELL, Harold George Tel: 028 2076 2684 Fax: 028 2076 9891 — MB BCh BAO 1969 Belf.; DObst RCOG 1971. (Belf.) GP Ballycastle; Med. Off. Dalriada Hosp. Ballycastle. Prev: Capt. RAMC, Regt.. Med. Off. 1st Bn. Glos. Regt.

RUSSELL, Harriet Clare Gloucestershire Breast Screening, Linton House, Thirlestaire Road, Cheltenham GL53 7AS Tel: 01242 251081; Fieldgate, Cheltenham Road, Bredon, Tewkesbury GL20 7NA Tel: 01684 77257 — MB BS 1982 Lond. BrE. Phys., Gloucestershire BrE. Screening, Cheltenham, (p/t).

RUSSELL, Hilary Jane Department of Psychotherapy, 4 Shide Road, Newport PO30 1YQ Tel: 01983 521511; 5 Northcourt Close, Shorwell, Newport PO30 3LD — MB BS 1980 Newc. Clin. Asst. (Psychother.) Newport I. of Wight. Prev: Regist. (Child & Adolesc. Psychiat.) I. of Wight; Regist. (Psychiat. Rotat.) Nottm. HA.

RUSSELL, Hugh Bernard Langford (retired) 10 Greenhill Park, Edinburgh EH10 4DW Tel: 0131 447 6379 — MRCS Eng. LRCP Lond. 1941; FFCM 1982, M 1974; DPH Lond. 1951; DTM & H Liverp. 1946. Prev: Sen. Lect. Dept. Community Med. Univ. Edin.

RUSSELL, Iain Cairns Crown Avenue Surgery, 12 Crown Avenue, Inverness IV2 3NF Tel: 01463 710777 Fax: 01463 714511; 1 Bellfield Terrace, Inverness IV2 4ST — MB ChB 1983 Aberd.; MRCGP 1987; DRCOG 1989. Prison Med. Off. HM Prison Inverness. Prev: SHO & Regist. (Gen. Med.) Roy. Infirm. Hosp. Sunderland; Trainee GP N. Edin.; GP N. Edin.

RUSSELL, Iain James Brodie (retired) Highway Farm, Churton, Chester CH3 6LB Tel: 01829 270960 — MB ChB 1948 Ed. Prev: Capt. RAMC.

RUSSELL, Ian Alexander Elms Medical Centre, 31 Hoole Road, Chester CH2 3NH Tel: 01244 351000; Whitethorne, Long Lane, Saughall, Chester CH1 6DN Tel: 01244 880364 — MB ChB 1970 Liverp.; DObst RCOG 1973. (Lond.) Hon. Treas. S. Chesh. LMC; GP Mem. Countess of Chester Hosp. Managem. Bd. Prev: SHO (Paediat. & O & G) Clatterbridge Hosp. Bebington; Asst. Surg. P & O SN Co.

RUSSELL, Ian Archibald (retired) Northfield Road Surgery, Northfield Road, Blaby, Leicester LE8 4GU Tel: 0116 277 1705 — MB BChir 1971 Camb.; MA Camb. 1970; MRCGP 1976; T(GP) 1991; DObst RCOG 1973. Clin. Teach. (Gen. Pract.) Fac. Med. Leicester Univ. Prev: Ho. Surg., Ho. Phys. & Ho. Off. (O & G) Warneford Hosp. Leamington Spa.

RUSSELL, Ian Digby 22 Beechwood Court, Monyhull Hall Road, Birmingham B30 3QL — MB ChB 1991 Birm.; ChB Birm. 1991.

RUSSELL, Mr Ian Dougal 4 Rural Way, Ty Coch, Swansea SA2 9NA Tel: 01792 299739 — MB BCh 1988 Wales. Specialist Regist. (Trauma & Orthop.) Train. Scheme.

RUSSELL, Ian Farquhar Department of Anaesthetics, Hull Royal Infirmary, Anlaby Road, Hull HU3 2JZ Tel: 01482 674542 Fax: 01482 674371; 3 The Paddock, North Ferriby HU14 3JU Tel: 01482 633267 Email: i.f.russel@medschool.hull.ac.uk — MB ChB 1973 Aberd.; BMedBiol. (Hons.) Aberdeen 1970; FFA RCS Eng. 1977. (Aberd.) Cons. Anaesth. Hull Matern. Hosp. Castlehill Hosp. Hull Roy. Infirm. Prev: Sen. Regist. Aberd. Roy. Infirm.; Regist. Aberd. Roy. Infirm.; Sen. Res. Med. Off. Perth Med. Centre, Australia.

RUSSELL, Ian Ronald (retired) Lapley Cottage, Lothians Road, Tettenhall, Wolverhampton WV6 9PN — MB BS 1960 Lond. Prev: Med. Regist. King's Coll. Hosp. Lond. & S.E. Metrop. RHB.

RUSSELL, Ian Speirs Accident & Emergency Department, Hartlepool General Hospital, Hartlepool TS24 9AH — MB ChB 1985 Glas.

RUSSELL, James Conn 27 Ravensdene Park, Belfast BT6 0DA — MB BCh BAO 1995 Belf.

RUSSELL, James Douglas 14 Shiel Hill, Alloway, Ayr KA7 4SY — MB ChB 1957 Glas.; DMRD Eng. 1971.

RUSSELL, James Gordon (retired) Kalmia, Azalea Close, Thakeham Copse, Storrington, Pulborough RH20 3PD Tel: 01903 745030 — MB ChB 1966 Aberd.; MRCGP 1972; FFPM RCP (UK) 1990; Dip. Pharm. Med. RCP (UK) 1977; DObst RCOG 1968. Cons. Pharmaceut. Med. Prev: Head Med. Affairs CIBA Pharmaceut. Horsham.

RUSSELL, Professor James Knox Newlands, Tranwell Woods, Morpeth NE61 6AG Tel: 01670 515666 — MB ChB 1942 Aberd.; MD Aberd. 1954; FRCOG 1958, M 1949. (Aberd.) Emerit. Prof. Univ. Newc.; Hon. Cons. Obst. & Gyn. United Newc. Hosps. Prev: Prof. (O & G) & Dean Postgrad. Med. Univ. Newc.; Cons. O & G United Newc. Hosps.; Cons. Human Reproduc. WHO.

RUSSELL, James Lockhart — MB BCh BAO 1950 Belf.; MS (MSc) (Med. & Physiol.) Minnesota 1960; FRCP Lond. 1976. (Queens University Belfast) Cons. Phys. Belf. City Hosp.

RUSSELL, James Rowland Sheepcote, Harrow Court, Stockbury, Sittingbourne ME9 7UQ Tel: 01795 844005 — MB BChir 1965 Camb.; MA Camb. 1965; DObst RCOG 1968. (Middlx.) Med. Off. Bupa Wellness Alexandra Hosp. Kent.; Med. Off. Screening Unit, Somerield Hosp. Maidstone. Prev: GP Sittingbourne; Ho. Surg. Thoracic Surgic. Unit Middlx. Hosp. Lond.; Sen. Med. Off. Beira Patrol.

RUSSELL, Janet Sandilands 9 South Beach Road, Ardrossan KA22 8AX — MB ChB 1962 Glas.

RUSSELL, Jeremy Johnston 16 Sandringham Road, Dersingham, King's Lynn PE31 6LL Tel: 01485 543118 — MB BS 1985 Lond.; MRCGP 1989; Cert. Family Plann. JCC 1989; DRCOG 1989. GP

RUSSELL

Heacham. Prev: Trainee GP King's Lynn VTS; SHO (Ophth. & ENT) Qu. Eliz. Hosp. King's Lynn.

RUSSELL, Jeremy Paul Anthony 5 Paultons Square, London SW3 5AS Tel: 020 7352 5172, 020 7352 6464 Fax: 020 7352 1617 Email: thepractice@drjeremyrussell.com — MB BChir 1970 Camb.; MA, BChir 1969. (St. Geo.) p/t Clin. Asst. Dept. GU Med. W.m. Hosp. Lond.; Med. Adviser Dupont UK Ltd.; Med. Adviser Abbey Nat. plc. Socs: Liveryman, Worshipful Soc. Of Apoth.; Chelsea Clin. Soc. Prev: Sen. Ho. Phys. Kent & Canterbury Hosp. Canterbury; Paediat. Ho. Phys. St. Geo. Hosp. Lond.; Ho. Surg. Essex Co. Hosp. Colchester.

RUSSELL, Joan 25 Roe Lane, Southport PR9 9EB Tel: 01704 31015 — MB ChB 1950 Liverp. (Liverp.)

RUSSELL, Joanne Rachel 40 Warren Avenue, Cheadle SK8 1ND — MB ChB 1995 Manch.

RUSSELL, Johanna Alice Withymoor Surgery, Turners Lane, Brierley Hill DY5 2PG — MB BS 1989 Lond.; MRCGP 1993; MFFP 1992; DCH RCP Lond. 1992.

RUSSELL, John 2 Kenyon Street, Leigh WN7 5NH — MB ChB 1975 Sheff.

RUSSELL, John Arrowe Park Hospital, Upton, Wirral CH49 5PE Tel: 0151 678 5111 — MB ChB 1975 Liverp.; MA Camb. 1975; MRCP (UK) 1981. Cons. Phys. Geriat. Med. Arrowe Pk. Hosp.

RUSSELL, John Alastair 36 Gorselands, Newbury RG14 6PX — MB ChB 1990 Aberd.

RUSSELL, John Albert Rosehill, 4 Vogrie Road, Gorebridge EH23 4HQ — MB ChB 1967 Ed.; PhD Ed. 1974, BSc (Hons.) 1964, MB ChB 1967. (Ed.) Sen. Lect. Dept. Physiol. Med. Sch. Univ. Edin.

RUSSELL, John Alexander 254 Avenue Road Extension, Leicester LE2 3EL — MB BCh BAO 1990 Belf.; MB BCh Belf. 1990.

RUSSELL, John Anderson Oliver Norah Fry Research Centre, 3 Priory Road, Bristol BS8 1TX Tel: 0117 923 8137 Fax: 0117 946 6553 Email: o.russell@bris.ac.uk; 8 Napier Road, Bristol BS6 6RT Tel: 0117 973 6759 — BM BCh Oxf. 1963; MA Oxf. 1963; FRCPsych 1985, M 1972; DPM Eng. 1968. (Middlx.) Reader (Ment. Health) Univ. Bristol; Hon. Cons. Phoenix NHS Trust United Bristol Health Care Trust; Dir. Norah Fry Research Centre. Univ. Bristol. Socs: BMA; Brit. Inst. Learning Disabil. (Chairm. of Counc.). Prev: Fell. Community Ment. Health Harvard Med. Sch. USA; SHO (Psychiat.) Bristol Roy. Infirm; Ho. Surg. Middlx. Hosp. Lond.

RUSSELL, John Cameron The Health Centre, Holmes Road, Broxburn EH52 5JZ — MB ChB 1980 Glasgow. (Glasgow) GP Broxburn, W. Lothian.

RUSSELL, John David 10 Spencer Close, Cottingham HU16 5NR — MB ChB 1991 Leeds.

RUSSELL, John Gerarde, Squadron Ldr. RAF Med. Br. Retd. Regional Medical Centre, Royal Air Force Lyneham, Chippenham SN15 4PZ Tel: 01249 890381 — MB BS 1982 Lond.; MRCGP 1986; DRCOG 1988. Civil. Med. Pract. RAF Lyneham.; GP Trainer. Prev: GP Princip. Swindon; RAF Med. Off.

RUSSELL, John Graham Buchanan (retired) 96 Carrwood, Hale Barns, Altrincham WA15 0ES Tel: 0161 980 3399 Email: russelldom@zen.co.uk — MB ChB Manch. 1953; FRCR 1975; FFR 1964; DMRD Ed. 1961; DCH Eng. 1956; DObst RCOG 1958. Prev: Mem. Comm. 3 Internat. Commiss. Radiol. Protec.

RUSSELL, Mr John Lambert Department of Oral Surgery, The Leeds Teaching Hospitals NHS Trust, Clarendon Way, Leeds LS2 9LU Tel: 0113 233 6219 — MB ChB 1983 Ed.; BDS Ed. 1976; FRCS (Max. Fac.) Ed. 1989; FDS RCS Ed. 1980. (Edinburgh) Cons. Oral & Maxillofacial Surg. Leeds Teachg. Hosps. NHS Trust; Head of Dept.; Lead Clinician. Prev: Sen. Regist. (Oral Surg.) Leeds Dent. Hosp.

RUSSELL, John Martin Beatson Oncology Centre, Western Infirmary, Dumbarton Road, Glasgow G11 6NT Tel: 0141 211 6356 Fax: 0141 337 6356 Email: martin.russell.wg@northglasgow.scot.nhs.org.uk; 19 Glen Clunie, St. Leonards, East Kilbride, Glasgow G74 2JR Tel: 01355 241401 Fax: 01355 902933 Email: jmartin@russelldyce.freeserve.co.uk — MB ChB 1975 Glas.; BSc (Hons. Path.) Glas. 1973; FRCR 1984; FRCP Glas. 1990; MRCP (UK) 1977. (Glas. Univ.) Cons. Clin. Oncol. Beatson Oncol. Centre Glas.; Hon. Clin. Sen. Lect. (Radiat. Oncol.) Univ. Glas. Socs: Scott. Radiol. Soc.; Brit. Prostate Gp.; Assoc. Mem. BAUS. Prev: Sen. Regist. (Radiother.) Christie Hosp. & Holt Radium Inst. Manch.; Regist. (Radiother. & Oncol.) W.. Infirm. Glas.; Regist. (Med. Oncol.) Gartnaval Gen. Hosp. Glas.

RUSSELL, Joseph George (retired) 141 Argyle Street, Heywood OL10 3SD Tel: 01706 66135 — MB BS 1957 Lond.; MRCGP 1965; DObst RCOG 1960. Prev: Ho. Surg. (O & G) St. Alfege's Hosp. Greenwich.

RUSSELL, Judith Elizabeth Lisboy House, 28 Dryarch Road, Beragh, Omagh BT79 0SQ — MB BCh BAO 1974 Dub.

RUSSELL, Judith Frances Anquetil 57 Falcon Avenue, Edinburgh EH10 4AN — MB BS 1965 Lond.; MRCS Eng. LRCP Lond. 1965; MRCPsych 1977; DPM Eng. 1976. (Univ. Coll. Hosp.) Indep. Cons. Psychother. Edin. Socs: Scot. Assn. Psychoanalytic Psychother.; Scot. Inst. Of Human Relations. Prev: Sen. Regist. (Psychother.) Warneford Hosp. Oxf.; Med. Asst. (Psychiat.) Friern Hosp. Lond.; Regist. (Adolesc. Psychiat.) Warneford Hosp. Oxf.

RUSSELL, Karen 79 London Road, Shrewsbury SY2 6PQ — MB ChB 1984 Manch. Community Med. Off., Sexual Health, (p/t).

RUSSELL, Karen Anna 27 Murrayfield Gardens, Edinburgh EH12 6DG — MB ChB 1997 Bristol.

RUSSELL, Katherine Jane Burleigh Medical Practice, Loch Leven Health Centre, Kinross KY13 8SY Tel: 01577 862112 Fax: 01577 862515; The Steadings, West Netherton, Milnathort, Kinross KY13 0SB Tel: 01577 865674 — MB BS 1989 Lond.; BSc Lond. 1986; MRCGP 1994; Dip. Practical Dermatol. Cardiff 1998. (Lond. Hosp. Med. Coll.) GP Kinross; Clin. Asst. (Dermat.) Perth Roy. Infirm. Prev: Trainee GP Fyvie Health Centre; SHO (Paediat.) Ormskirk Hosp.; SHO (O & G, Psychiat. & Geriat.) W. Cumbld. Hosp.

RUSSELL, Keith John The Health Centre, Loch Road, Tranent EH33 2JX Tel: 01875 610697; Achray, 20 Dovecot Road, Edinburgh EH12 7LE Email: drkjr@compuserve.com — MB ChB 1981 Ed.; MRCGP 1985; DGM RCP Lond. 1986; DRCOG 1984. GP Tranent; GP Audit Facilitor Lothian Health. Prev: Trainee GP N. Lothian VTS; Regist. E. Lothian Geriat. Serv.

RUSSELL, Kenneth A Viewpark Health Centre, Burnhead Street, Uddingston, Glasgow G71 5SU Tel: 01698 813753 Fax: 01698 812062 — MB ChB 1970 St Andrews; MB ChB 1970 St Andrews.

RUSSELL, Lai Fun Mary 20 Dovecot Road, Edinburgh EH12 7LE — MB ChB 1984 Ed.; MRCGP 1988; DTM & H Liverp. 1990. (Edinburgh) GP Edin. Retainer Scheme. Prev: Trainee GP Dunfermline VTS; SHO (Infec. Dis.) Cameron Hosp. Fife; SHO (Cas.) Dunfermline & W. Fife Hosp.

RUSSELL, Leon 55 Park Parade, London NW10 4JB Tel: 020 8965 5093 — MRCS Eng. LRCP Lond. 1948. (Univ. Coll. Hosp.) Prev: RAMC; Ho. Phys. St. Albans City Hosp.; Clin. Asst. Roy. Nat. ENT Hosp.

RUSSELL, Leonie Kay West Suffolk Hospital, Hardwick Lane, Bury St Edmunds IP33 2QZ; c/o Mr & Mrs M. Hardy, 15 Water Lane, Flitwick, Bedford MK45 1LG — MB ChB 1991 Otago.

RUSSELL, Leslie Helen Ferguson Braidcraft Medical Centre, 200 Braidcraft Road, Glasgow G53 5QD Tel: 0141 882 3396 Fax: 0141 883 3224 — MB ChB 1981 Cape Town; MRCGP 1988.

RUSSELL, Lucinda Elizabeth Lingwell Croft Surgery, Ring Road, Middleton, Leeds LS10 3LT Tel: 0113 270 4848 Fax: 0113 272 0030; 26 Rose Croft, East Keswick, Leeds LS17 9HR — MB ChB 1991 Leeds. (Leeds) GP Leeds.

RUSSELL, Malcolm Quentin Waterside House, Keir, Thornhill DG3 4DH — MB ChB 1992 Aberd.

RUSSELL, Manson McCausland (retired) 42 Stanton Lane, Stanton on the Wolds, Nottingham NG12 5BJ — MB BS 1946 Lond. Prev: Ho. Phys. & Cas. Med. Off., & Asst. Pathol. Bland-Sutton Inst.

RUSSELL, Margaret Cleland Tel: 0141 641 1663; 47 Greystone Avenue, Burnside, Rutherglen, Glasgow G73 3SN Tel: 0141 647 1355 — MB ChB 1953 Glas.; MRCGP 1963; DObst RCOG 1955. (Glas.)

RUSSELL, Margaret Winifred (retired) Green Gables, 16 Finlaystown Road, Portglenone, Ballymena BT44 8EA Tel: 01266 821078 — MB BCh BAO. Belf. 1946. Prev: GP Portglenone Health Centre.

RUSSELL, Mark Andrew Goodwin The Flat, Ronksley Hall, Hollow Meadows, Sheffield S6 6GH; Lower Tremenheere Farm, Ludgvan, Penzance TR20 8XG Tel: 01736 331107 — MB BS 1986 Lond.; BA Oxf. 1982.

RUSSELL, Mark Humphreys 43 Princess Marys Road, Crouch Oak Green, Addlestone, Weybridge — MB BS 1972 Lond.; FFA RCS Eng. 1978. (King's Coll. Hosp.) Cons. Anaesth. St. Peters Hosp.

RUSSELL

Chertsey. Prev: Sen. Regist. (Anaesth.) W.m. & Soton. Hosps.; Regist. (Anaesth.) Soton. Gen. Hosp.; SHO (Nephrol.) S.mead Hosp. Bristol.

RUSSELL, Maureen Currie Felridge, 3 Divert Road, Gourock PA19 1DR Tel: 01475 32939 — MB ChB 1964 Glas. (Glas.) Clin. Asst. (O & G Ultrasound) Rankin Matern. Hosp. Greenock. Prev: SHO Paediat. Hawkhead Hosp. Paisley; Ho. Off. O & G Stobhill Hosp. Glas.; Ho. Off. Med. S.. Gen. Hosp. Glas.

RUSSELL, Maurice Frederick Holywood Arches Health Centre, Westminster Avenue, Belfast BT4 1NS Tel: 01232 471188; 60 Hampton Park, Belfast BT7 3JP Tel: 01232 647942 — MD 1968 Belf.; MB BCh BAO 1954; FRCGP 1980, M 1966; DObst RCOG 1957. Staff Med. Off. Ulster Hosp. Dundonald. Prev: SHO Roy. Vict. Hosp. Belf.; Ho. Off. Waveney Hosp. Ballymena & Roy. Matern. Hosp. Belf.

RUSSELL, Maurice Hugh (retired) 64 Colney Lane, Cringleford, Norwich NR4 7RF Tel: 01603 502133 — MB BChir 1948 Camb.; MRCS Eng. LRCP Lond. 1943; DObst RCOG 1950; DCH Eng. 1949. Prev: Ho. Surg. W.m. Hosp.

RUSSELL, Melissa Jane Mechlin April Cottage, Back Lane, Bucks Horn Oak, Farnham GU10 4LW — MB BS 1992 Lond.; BSc Genetics Lond. 1989. Trainee GP N.wick Pk. Hosp. VTS. Prev: Ho. Off. (Med.) Hillingdon Hosp.; Ho. Off. (Surg.) St. Albans City Hosp.

RUSSELL, Professor Michael Anthony Hamilton Maudsley Hospital, Denmark Hill, London SE5 8AF Tel: 020 7703 5411 Fax: 020 7703 6197; 14 Court Lane Gardens, London SE21 7DZ Tel: 020 8693 3606 — BM BCh Oxf. 1957; MA Oxf. 1957; FCP(SA) 1963; FRCP Lond. 1982, M 1964; FRCPsych 1980, M 1971; DPM Lond. 1968. (Oxf. & Guy's) Emerit. Prof. Addic. Inst. Psychiat. Univ. Lond.; Hon. Cons. Psychiat. Maudsley Hosp. Lond.; Hon. Cons. ICRF Health Behaviour Unit, UCL. Prev: Hon. Dir. ICRF Health Behaviour Unit Univ. Coll. Lond.; Mem. Med. Research Counc. Extern. Scientif. Staff.; Ho. Phys. Guy's Hosp. Lond.

RUSSELL, Mohamed Siddock Ahad 37 Thirlmere Road, London N10 2DL — MB BCh BAO 1981 NUI.

RUSSELL, Moira Margaret Alice 213 Woodlands Road, Woodlands, Southampton SO40 7GJ — BM 1986 Soton.

RUSSELL, Neil John Fax: 01782 523085 Email: neil.russell@nshawehmail.nhs.uk; Knypersley Villas, 115 Tunstall Road, Biddulph, Stoke-on-Trent ST8 6LB Tel: 01782 523353 — MB ChB 1982 Liverp.

RUSSELL, Nicholas John West Cumberland Hospital, Whitehaven CA28 8JG; 3 Beech Hill, Oughterside, Carlisle CA7 2QA — MB BChir 1978 Camb.; FRCP Lond. 1996; MRCP (UK) 1980. Cons. Phys. (Geriat. Med.) W. Cumbld. Hosp.

RUSSELL, Nigel Charles Radbrook Green Surgery, Bank Farm Road, Shrewsbury SY3 6DU Tel: 01743 231816 Fax: 01743 344099 — MB ChB 1984 Manch.

RUSSELL, Nigel Hudson 76 Brookside Road, London NW11 9NG Tel: 020 8458 5664 — MD 1980 Liverp.; MB ChB 1973; MRCP (UK) 1976. Leukaemia Research Fund Research Fell. & Hon. Lect. (Haemat.) Roy. Free Hosp. Lond. Prev: SHO (Gen. Med.) Sefton Gen. Hosp. Liverp.; Research Fell. (Haemat.) Liverp. Univ.; Leukaemia Research Fund Trav. Fell.

RUSSELL, Norman Lawn (retired) The Priory, Paternoster Row, Ottery St Mary EX11 Tel: 0140 481 2939 — MRCS Eng. LRCP Lond. 1925; MA Camb. 1922. Prev: Ho. Surg. Hosp. SS. John & Eliz. Lond.

RUSSELL, Patricia Mary Tel: 0161 794 1604 Fax: 0161 727 3615, 0161 794 2371; 5 Quayside Close, Worsley, Manchester M28 1YB Tel: 0161 702 8963 — MB ChB 1981 Manch.; MFHom 2001; MRCGP 1985; DRCOG 1984. GP. Prev: Community Med. Off. N. Manch. HA.

RUSSELL, Patrick Stanley Bruce (retired) 9 Green Lane, Croxley Green, Rickmansworth WD3 3HR Tel: 01923 772016 — MB BS 1951 Lond.; MRCS Eng. LRCP Lond. 1950; DObst RCOG 1954. Prev: Med. Adviser Peace Hosp. Watford.

RUSSELL, Peter Neil 7 Troutbeck Avenue, Maghull, Liverpool L31 9DU — MB ChB 1984 Liverp.

RUSSELL, Richard Edward Kynnersley Department of Thoracic Medicine, Guy's Hospital, London Bridge, London SE1 9RT Tel: 020 7955 5000; 14 Torrington Court, Crystal Palace Pk Road, London SE1 9RT Tel: 020 7955 5000 — MB BS 1992 Lond.; BSc Lond. 1989; MRCP (UK) 1995. (Guy's Hosp. Lond.) Regist. (Chest Med.) Guy's Hosp. Lond. Prev: Regist. Greenwich Dist. Hosp.; SHO Rotat. (Med.) St. Geo. Hosp. Lond.

RUSSELL, Richard Jonathan 27 Jerviston Street, Motherwell ML1 4BL — MB ChB 1997 Manch.

RUSSELL, Richard Kay Top Flat Left, 5/8 Parkside St., Edinburgh EH8 9RL Tel: 0131 668 3794 — MB ChB 1993 Ed. (Ed.) SHO (Paediat.) Edin.

RUSSELL, Robert Gordon (retired) Mill Cottage, Elmley Lovett, Droitwich WR9 0PS Tel: 0129 923412 — MB ChB 1951 Birm. Prev: GP Kidderminster.

RUSSELL, Robert Graham Goodwin Department Human Metabolism & Clinical Biochemistry, Sheffield University Medical School, Beech Hill Road, Sheffield S10 2RX Tel: 0114 276 6222 Fax: 0742 726938; Ronksley Hall Farm, Hollows Meadows, Sheffield S6 6GH Tel: 0114 308437 — MB 1971 Camb.; PhD Leeds 1967; DM Oxf. 1975; BA Camb. 1962, MB 1971, BChir 1970; MRCP FRCP (UK) 1981, M 1974; FRCPath 1986, M 1974. (Camb.) Prof. & Hon. Cons. Dept. Human Metab. & Clin. Biochem. Univ. Sheff. Med. Sch. Socs: Brit. Soc. Rheumat. & Endocrine Soc. Prev: Med. Research Fell. St. Peter's Coll. Oxf.; Asst. Prof. Med. Harvard Med. Sch., U.S.A.; Sen. Lect. Univ. Bern.

RUSSELL, Robert McCulloch Station Road Practice, 66-68 Station Road, Ainsdale, Southport PR8 3HW Tel: 01704 574137 Fax: 01704 573875 — MB ChB 1977 Ed.; MRCGP 1982; DRCOG 1979.

RUSSELL, Professor Robin Irvine Department of Gastroenterology, Royal Infirmary, Glasgow G31 2ER Tel: 0141 942 6613 Fax: 0141 943 2410 Email: rirla@aol.com; 28 Ralston Road, Bearsden, Glasgow G61 3BA Tel: 0141 942 6613 Fax: 0141 943 2410 — MB ChB Glas. 1960; PhD Glas. 1976, MD 1972; FRCP Ed. 1976, M 1965; FRCP Glas. 1972, M 1965. (Glas.) Cons. i/c Gastroenterol. Roy. Infirm. Glas.; Vis. Prof. Univ. Mississippi, USA, Univ. Singapore, Toronto & others. Socs: Assn. Phys.; Brit. Soc. Gastroenterol.; Amer. Gastroenterol. Assn. Prev: Lect. (Med.) Gardiner Inst. W,. Infirm. Glas.; Mem. Med. & Scientif. Staff MRC Gastroenterol. Unit Lond.

RUSSELL, Robin Maxwell 31 Five Mile Drive, Oxford OX2 8HT — MB BS 1985 Lond.; MD Lond. 1997; FRCA. 1990. Cons. Anaesth. Nuffield Dept. Anaesth. John Radcliffe Hosp. Oxf.

RUSSELL, Mr Roland Curtis 7 West Farm Court, 12 Gatcombe Way, Barnet EN4 9TT Tel: 020 8440 0130 — MB BS 1994 Lond.; FRCS Lond. 1999. (Royal Hosp. Of Lond., Whitechapel) SHO (Orthop.) S.end Dist. Hosp.

RUSSELL, Mr Ronald Christopher Gordon 40 Devonshire Place Mews, London W1G 6DD Tel: 020 7486 7602 Fax: 020 7380 9162 Email: rcgrussell@dial.pipex.com; Little Orchards, 6 Layters Way, Gerrards Cross SL9 7QY Tel: 0208 838 5381 Email: sclarke@doctors.org.uk — MB BS Lond. 1963; MS Lond. 1979; FRCS Eng. 1966. (Middlx.) Cons. Surg. Middlx. Hosp. & King Edwd. VII Hosp. for Offs. Lond.; Pres., Assoc. of Surg.s Gt. Britain & Irel.; Chairm., Jt. Comm. On Intercollegiate Exam.s (Surg.); Chairm. Brit. Jl. Surg. Soc.; Mem. of Counc., Roy. Coll. of Surg.s. Socs: (Counc.) Med. Defence Union. Prev: Sen. Regist. (Surg.) Centr. Middlx. Hosp. Lond.; Asst. Dir. Surg. Unit St. Mary's Hosp. Med. Sch. Lond.

RUSSELL, Sally Ann 24 Marine Road, Walmer, Deal CT14 7DN Tel: 01304 373341 Fax: 01304 372864 — MB ChB 1994 Birm. (Birm.) Gen. Practitioner.

RUSSELL, Sarah Ann St. Mary's Hospital, Clinical Radiology, Hathersage Road, Manchester M13 0JH Tel: 0161 276 6136 Fax: 0161 276 6508 — MB ChB 1980 Manch.; FRCR 1986. Cons. Radiol. Centr. Manch. and Manch. Childr.'s Univ. Trust; Hon. Lect. Univ. Manch.; Hon.Lect. Univ. Salford. Prev: Asst. Prof. Ultrasound Univ. Calif., San Francisco, USA.

RUSSELL, Scott Howard Consultant Anaesthetist, Queen Elizabeth Hospital, Edgbaston, Birmingham; 51 Bittel Road, Barnt Green, Birmingham B45 8LX — MB BS 1985 Lond.; FRCA 1990. Cons. Anaesth. Qu. Eliz. Hosp. Birm.

RUSSELL, Sharon Lesley Cadzow Health Centre, 187 Low Waters Road, Hamilton ML3 7QQ Tel: 01698 327028 Fax: 01698 327344 — MB ChB 1989 Glas.; MRCGP 1993; DFFP 1994; DRCOG 1992.

RUSSELL, Sheena Cochrane Department of Dermatology, Queen Margaret Hospital, Whitefield Road, Dunfermline KY12 0SN — MB ChB 1985 Glas.; MRCP (UK) 1989. Cons. Dermatol., Fife Acute Hosps. Trust. Socs: Brit. Assn. of Dermatol.s; Scott. Dermat. Soc.; Brit. Med. Assn.

RUSSELL, Sheenah Jean McKinnon (retired) Machrie, 46 Rotchell Park, Dumfries DG2 7RJ Tel: 01387 254426 — MB ChB 1943 Glas.; MD (Commend.) Glas. 1947; FRCP Ed. 1971, M 1952; DPH Glas. 1953; DCH Eng. 1947. Prev: Cons. Paediat. Dumfries & Galloway Roy. Infirm., Cresswell Matern. & Pk.head Hosps.

RUSSELL, Stanley Samuel 5 Laybrook Lodge, 63 Snaresbrook Road, Wanstead, London E11 1SR Tel: 020 8989 5885 — MB ChB 1954 Liverp.; CPH Eng. 1956.

RUSSELL, Stella Caroline Joanna Ashwell Surgery, Gardiners Lane, Ashwell, Baldock SG7 5PY Tel: 01462 742230 Fax: 01462 742764; Lordship Farm, High St, Melbourn, Royston SG8 6EB Tel: 01763 262479 — MB BS 1975 Lond.; MRCS Eng. LRCP Lond. 1975; MRCGP 1979; DRCOG 1978; DCH Eng. 1978.

RUSSELL, Stephen George The Gables Medical Centre, 45 Waveney Road, Ballymena BT43 5BA Tel: 028 2565 3237 Fax: 028 2564 0754; 151 Old Cullbackey Road, Cullbackey, Ballymena BT43 5PD — MB BCh BAO 1985 Belf.; MRCGP 1989; DMH Belf. 1990; DCH RCPSI 1988; DRCOG 1987. GP Ballymena. Prev: SHO (Psychiat.) Holywell Hosp. Antrim; Trainee GP Broughshane VTS; SHO Waveney Hosp. Ballymena VTS.

RUSSELL, Stephen James Department of Haematology, Addenbrooke's Hospital, Cambridge CB2 2HQ Tel: 01223 402030 Fax: 01223 402140 Email: sjr@mrc-im6.cam.ac.uk; 2701 Salem Road South W., Rochester, Minnesota 55902, USA — MB ChB 1982 Ed.; PhD Lond. 1990; MRCP (UK) 1985; Spec. Accredit. Haemat. JCHMT 1993; MRCPath 1992. (Ed.) MRC Sen. Fell. (Clin.) & Hon. Cons. Haemat. Univ. Camb. Prev: Clin. Research Fell. (Cell. & Molecular Biol.) Chester Beatty Research Inst. Lond.; Regist. (Haemat.) Univ. Coll. Hosp. Lond.; SHO (Gen. Med.) N. Tees Gen. Hosp. Stockton-on-Tees.

RUSSELL, Stephen McCausland High Street, 16 High Street, Great Baddow, Chelmsford CM2 7HQ Tel: 01245 473251 Fax: 01245 478394 — MB BS 1977 Lond.

RUSSELL, Stewart 1B1 Templeton Business Centre, Templeton St., Glasgow G40 1DA Tel: 0141 554 1566 Fax: 0141 554 1995; 185 Nithsdale Road, Pollokshields, Glasgow G41 5QR — MB ChB 1978 Dundee; MRCGP 1982; D.Occ.Med. RCP Lond. 1995. Occupat. Phys. Assoc. Health Servs. Glas. Prev: GP Trainer Glas.; Regional Med. Advisor Manor Hse. Hosp.; Med. Off. Strathclyde Buses Glas.

RUSSELL, Susan Catriona Sandra Dept. of Anaesth., Victoria Hospital, Hayfield Road, Kirkcaldy KY2 5AH — MB ChB 1987 Ed.; FFA RCSI 1993; FRCA 1993. (Ed.) Cons. Anesthetist, Vic. Hosp. Kirkcaldy.

RUSSELL, Susan Gillian Dr McElhone and Partners, Townhead Surgery, 6-8 High St., Irvine KA12 0AY Tel: 01294 273131 Fax: 01294 312832; 22 Broadwood Park, Alloway, Ayr KA7 4UR Tel: 01292 45285 — MB ChB 1979 Glas.; MRCGP 1987; DRCOG 1985.

RUSSELL, Susan Ruth 140 Cranbrook Road, Bristol BS6 7DD — MB ChB 1979 Cape Town; DCH RCP Lond. 19092.

RUSSELL, Susanne Alcorn Maryhill Health Centre, 41 Shawpark Street, Glasgow G20 9DR Tel: 0141 531 8897 Fax: 0141 531 8863; 32 Bailie Drive, Bearsden, Glasgow G61 3AH — MB ChB 1985 Glas.; MRCGP 1989; Dip. Forens. Med. Glas. 1989. (Glasgow)

RUSSELL, Sylvia Ellen (retired) 18 Cherry Hill Road, Barnt Green, Birmingham B45 8LJ Tel: 0121 445 2534 — MB ChB ChB Birm. 1946. JP. Prev: Assoc. Specialist (Geriat. Med.) Selly Oak Hosp. Birm.

RUSSELL, Thea Jayne 60 Old Castle Road, Glasgow G44 5TE Tel: 0141 637 6309 — MB ChB 1953 Glas.; BDS Glas. 1958. (Glas.)

RUSSELL, Mr Thomas Department of Clinical Neurosciences, Lothian University Hospitals NHS Trust, Edinburgh EH4 2XU Tel: 0131 537 2110 Fax: 0131 537 1134 Email: tr@skull.dcn.ed.ac.uk; 15 White Dales, Edinburgh EH10 7JQ Tel: 0131 445 5920 Fax: 0131 445 5920 — MB ChB 1975 Glas.; BSc (Hons.) Glas. 1973; FRCS Ed. 1979; FRCS Glas. 1979; PhD Wales 1998. (Glasgow) Cons. Neurosurg. W.. Gen. Hosp. NHS Trust. Prev: Sen. Regist. (Neurosurg.) Bristol & W.on HA; Lect. & Regist. (Neurosurg.) Univ. Glas.; MRC Regist. (Neurosurg.) Inst. Neurol. Sc. Glas.

RUSSELL, Mr Thomas Simpson (retired) 60 Old Castle Road, Cathcart, Glasgow G44 5TE Tel: 0141 637 6309 — MB ChB 1949 Glas.; FRCS Ed. 1959; DLO Eng. 1957. Prev: Cons. ENT Surg. Vict. Infirm. & S.. Gen. Hosp. Glas.

RUSSELL, Thomas Victor Nivison Willow Lodge, Auchendon Est., Holly Bush, Ayr KA6 7EB — MB ChB 1966 Glas.; MRCOG 1972. Cons. Obst. & Gyn . Ayrsh.

RUSSELL, Tina The New Surgery, Lindo Lodge, Lindo Close, Chesham HP5 2JN; Highfield, Bellingdon, Chesham HP5 2XN — BM BS 1988 Nottm.; MRCGP 1992; DRCOG 1991. SHO (Paediat.) Cheltenham Gen. Hosp.

RUSSELL, William 1 Upper Teddington Road, Hampton Wick, Kingston upon Thames KT1 4DL Tel: 020 8977 2638 Fax: 020 8977 2434; 36 Lancaster Road, Wimbledon, London SW19 5DD Tel: 020 8946 4265 — MB ChB 1957 St. And.; Dip. Amer. Bd. Pediat. 1969; MRCGP 1983. (St. And.) Prev: Sen. Attend. Pediatr. Meriden-Wallingford Hosp., USA.

RUSSELL, William Carnduff Adult Intensive Care Unit, Leicester Royal Infirmary, Leicester LE1 5WW Email: wrussell@lri.org; 24 Main Street, Rotherby, Melton Mowbray LE14 2LP — MB BS 1982 Melbourne; FANZCA 1994. Cons. Anaesth. & Intens. Care Leicester Roy. Infirm.

RUSSELL, William Francis (retired) Offerton Health Centre, 10 Offerton Lane, Offerton, Stockport SK2 5AR Tel: 0161 480 0326 — MB ChB 1977 Birm.; FFA RCS 1983. Prev: Gen.Prac. Offerton Health Centre Stockport SK2 5AR (Retd. March 98).

RUSSELL, William Frederick (retired) Merrilees, Maine Drive, Chaddesden, Derby DE21 6LA Tel: 01332 672121 — MD 1949 Aberd.; MB ChB 1939.

RUSSELL, William Gordon (retired) 34 Norwood Terrace, Newport-on-Tay DD6 8DW Tel: 01382 542280 — MB ChB 1959 Ed.; MRCGP 1978; DObst RCOG 1962. Prev: GP Fife.

RUSSELL, William Ian (retired) 112 Hamilton Avenue, Pollokshields, Glasgow G41 4EX Tel: 0141 427 1383 — MB ChB 1947 Glas.; DObst RCOG 1949. Prev: Ho. Surg. PeterBoro. Memor. Hosp.

RUSSELL, William Smith (retired) The Lawns, 1A Knighton Rise, Oadby, Leicester LE2 2RF Tel: 0116 270 5653 — MB ChB 1931 Aberd.

RUSSELL-EGGITT, Isabelle Mary Department of Ophthalmology, Great Ormond Street Hospital for Children NHS Trust, Great Ormond St., London WC1N 3JH Tel: 020 7813 8524 Fax: 020 7829 8647; Consulting Rooms, 234 Great Portland St, London W1W 5QT — MB BChir 1979 Camb.; MA Camb. 1984; FRCS (Ophth.) Eng. 1984; DO RCS Eng. 1983. Cons. Paediat. Ophth. Hosp. Sick Childr. Gt. Ormond St. Lond.; Hon. Sen. Lect. Inst. Child Health Lond. Socs: FRCOphth. Prev: Lect. (Clin. Ophth.) Jt. Inst. Child Health & Ophth. Univ. Lond.; Resid. Surgic. Off. Moorfields Eye Hosp. Lond.; Regist. Leicester Roy. Infirm.

RUSSELL-JONES, David Lowell Burningfold Court, Dunsford, Godalming GU8 4NZ — MB BS 1985 Lond.; MD Lond. 1994. (St. Thos. Hosp.) Sen. Lect. & Cons. Phys. UMDS Guy's & St. Thos. Hosp. Lond. Prev: Sen. Regist. Portsmouth & UMDS; SHO Hammersmith, Qu. Sq. & Roy. Brompton Hosps.

RUSSELL-JONES, Robin David Skin Tumour Unit, St. John's Institute of Dermatology, St Thomas Hospital, London SE1 7EH Tel: 020 7928 9292 Fax: 020 7922 8138; Atholl House, Church Lane, Stoke Poges, Slough SL2 4NZ — MB BChir 1973 Camb.; MA Camb. 1973; FRCP Lond. 1990, M 1974. Dir. Skin Tumour Unit St. John's Inst. Dermat. St. Thomas' Hosp. Lond.; Hon. Sen. Lect. (Med.) Roy. Postgrad. Med. Sch. Lond.; Cons. Dermat. Ealing Hosp. Lond. Socs: St John's Hosp. Dermatol. Soc. (Ex-Sec.); (Ex-Pres.) Dowling Club; Chair UK Skin Lymphoma Gp. Prev: Sen. Regist. & Tutor (Dermat. & Path.) St. John's Hosp. for Dis. of the Skin Lond.; Sen. Regist. (Dermat.) Char. Cross & Centr. Hosp. Lond.; Regist. (Dermat.) Guy's Hosp. Lond.

RUSSELL-SMITH, Edward Denham Christchurch Hall, Blackridge, Bathgate EH48 3RJ Tel: 01501 51931; Main Point House, 4 High Riggs, Edinburgh EH3 9BX Tel: 0131 228 2015 — MB ChB 1987 Ed.; MRCGP 1992; DRCOG 1990; DCCH RCP Ed. 1990. SHO (Psychiat.) Lothian HB. Prev: Trainee GP Lothian HB; Regist. (Paediat.) Lothian HB.

RUSSELL-SMITH, Roy Barnes Thatch, Romsey Road, Awbridge, Romsey SO51 0HG Tel: 01794 40403 — MRCS Eng. LRCP Lond. 1940; MA Camb. (Camb. & St. Bart.) Prev: Capt. RAMC; Asst. Med. Off. Gr. Pk. Hosp.; Ho. Phys. St. Bart. Hosp.

RUSSELL-TAYLOR, Michelle Ann 213 Beechwood Road, Luton LU4 9RZ; 27 Columba Drive, Leighton Buzzard LU7 3YN Tel: 01525

RUSSELL-WEISZ

756716 — MB BS 1991 Lond.; MRCPI 1996; DCH RCP Lond. 1995. Regist. (Paediat.) Milton Keynes. Prev: Regist. (Paediat.) John Radcliffe Hosp.; Regist. (Paediat.) N.ampton Gen.; Regist. (Paediat.) Wycombe Gen. Hosp.

RUSSELL-WEISZ, David Jonathan 10 Elizabeth Avenue, St Brelade, Jersey JE3 8GR; PO Box 63, Port Hedland WA 6721, Australia — MB ChB 1987 Dundee; MRCGP 1991; DFFP 1992; Dip IMC RCS Ed. 1992; DRCOG 1991. (Dundee) Sen. Med. Off. E. Pilbare Health Serv. W.. Austral.; Chief Med. Off. Roy. Flying Doctor Serv. Broken Hill, NSW, Austral. Prev: Med. Off. Roy. Flying Doctor Serv. Broken Hill, NSW, Austral.; Med. Off. Europassistance Croydon; Trainee GP/SHO (Anaesth.) Mayday Hosp. Croydon.

RUSSELL-WELLS, Sydney John Edward (retired) Riverside, The Shoals, Irstead, Norwich NR12 8XS Tel: 01692 630301 — MB BChir Camb. 1961; MA Camb. 1973; MRCGP 1974; DObst RCOG 1963.

RUSSO, Mario Flat 2, 2 Eccleston Square, London SW1V 1NP — State Exam Med. Padua 1988.

RUSSO, Pamela 37 Lyndon Avenue, Great Harwood, Blackburn BB6 7TP Tel: 01254 884869 — MB ChB 1966 Manch. (Manch.) Clin. Med. Off. Blackburn, Hyndburn & Ribble Valley HA. Prev: SHO (Paediat.) & Ho. Phys. Preston Roy. Infirm.

RUSSON, Lynne Julie Bradford Hospitals trust, Bradford Email: lynne.russon@virgin.net; 17 The Drive, Roundhay, Leeds LS8 1JF — MB ChB 1987 Leeds; MRCP (UK) 1992; MA Keele 1998.

RUSSON, Michael John Primrose Lane Health Centre, Primrose Lane, Wolverhampton WV10 8RN Tel: 01902 731583 Fax: 01902 305789; 32 Newbridge Crescent, Wolverhampton WV6 0LH Tel: 01902 751381 — MB BS 1981 Lond.; BSc Biochem. Lond. 1977, MB BS 1981.

RUST, Jack Harold Laura Mitchell Centre, Halifax Tel: 01422 50011 — MB ChB 1947 Leeds; MRCGP 1954. (Leeds)

RUST, Neil David Horton General Hospital, Oxford Road, Banbury OX16 9AL Tel: 01295 275500; 3 Manchester Terrace, Victoria Road, Bicester OX26 6PT — MB BS 1990 Lond.; BSc Lond. 1987, MB BS 1990.

RUST, Nigel Edward Frimley Green Medical Centre, Beech Road, Frimley Green, Camberley GU16 6QQ — MB BS 1955 Lond.; MRCS Eng. LRCP Lond. 1955; DObst RCOG 1958. (St. Mary's) Prev: Ho. Phys. St. Mary's Hosp.; Ho. Surg. King Edwd. VII Hosp. Windsor & St. Stephen's Hosp. Lond.

RUST, Philippa Ann 7 Salisbury Place, Langton Road, London SW9 6UW — MB BS 1996 Lond. (Guy's & St. Thomas's Hospitals)

RUSTIN, Gordon John Sampson Cancer Treatment Centre, Mount Vernon Hospital, Northwood HA6 2RN Tel: 01923 844389 Fax: 01923 844295 Email: gjrustin@hotmail.com; 15 Wellgarth Road, London NW11 7HP Tel: 020 8455 5943 — MB BS 1971 Lond.; MSc Lond. 1979, MD 1980; FRCP Lond. 1992; MRCP (UK) 1974. (Middlx.) Dir. (Med. Oncol.) Mt. Vernon Hosp. N.wood; Cons. Med. Oncol. Hillingdon Hosp.; Sen. Lect. (Oncol.) UCL. Socs: Counc.Onocolgy Sect.RSM, ACP, ASCO. Prev: Sen. Lect. (Med. Oncol.) & Hon. Cons. Phys. Char. Cross Hosp. Lond.; Sen. Regist. (Med. Oncol.) Char. Cross Hosp. Lond.; Research Fell. Roy. Postgrad. Med. Sch. Lond.

RUSTIN, Joanna Katie 33 Fordington Road, London N6 4TD Tel: 020 8883 4191 Fax: 020 883 4191; The Surgery, 26 Southern Road, London N2 9JG Tel: 020 8444 7478 Fax: 020 8444 7628 — MB BS 1979 Lond.; MRCGP 1983. (Middlx.) GP Asst. Prev: Asst. Phys. City Univ. Stud. Health Serv. Lond.; GP Lond.

RUSTIN, Malcolm Howard Albert 53 Wimpole Street, London W1G 8YH Tel: 020 7935 9266 Fax: 020 7935 3060; 33 Fordington Road, Highgate, London N6 4TD Tel: 020 8883 4191 — MB BS 1976 Lond.; BSc Lond. 1973, MD 1988; FRCP Lond. 1995; MRCP (UK) 1980. (Middlx.) Cons. Dermat. Roy. Free Hosp. Lond.; Cons. Dermat. King Edwd. VII Hosp. Lond. Socs: Fell. Amer. Acad. Dermat.; Fell. Roy. Soc. of Med.; Fell. Brit. Assn. of Dermatols. Prev: Sen. Regist. (Dermat.) Univ. Coll. Hosp. & Middlx. Hosp. Lond.; Muir Hambro Research Fell.ship Roy. Coll. Phys.; Regist. (Dermat.) St. Bart. Hosp. Lond.

RUSTOM, Jane Willow 61 New Street, Salisbury SP1 2PH Tel: 01722 334402; Jasmine Cottage, Church St, Bowerchalke, Salisbury SP5 5BH Tel: 01722 781077 — MB BS 1983 Lond.; DRCOG 1987.

RUSTOM, Rana 37 Roedean Crescent, Brighton BN2 5RG Tel: 01273 602015 — MB ChB 1980 Liverp.; MRCS Eng. LRCP Lond. 1980; MRCPath 1990.

RUSTON, John Joseph Smirke 6 Aldenham Grove, Radlett WD7 7BN — MB BS 1978 Lond.; FFA RCS Eng. 1983. Sen. Regist. (Anaesth.) Harefield Hosp. Middlx. Socs: BMA & Assn. Anaesth. Gt. Brit. & Irel. Prev: Regist. (Anaesth.) Ealing Hosp. S.all, Roy. Nat. Throat, Nose & Ear Hosp. & St. Mary's Hosp. Lond. W2; Sen. Regist. (Anaesth.) Roy. Free Hosp. Lond.; Sen. Regist. (Anaesth.) E.man Dent. Hosp. Lond.

RUSTON, Miranda Ann Bond's Cay, 6 Aldenham Grove, Radlett WD7 7BN Tel: 01923 850484 Fax: 01923 850486 Email: sam@jruston.u-net.com — MB BS 1980 Lond.

RUSTON, Robert The Surgery, 32 Clifton, York YO30 6AE Tel: 01904 653834 Fax: 01904 651442 — MB ChB 1978 Leeds; MA 1999 Leeds; MRCP (UK) 1982; MRCGP 1983. Tutur, Med. Ethics, Univ. of Leeds; Mem. York Local Research Ethics Comm. Socs: York; Leeds. Prev: Regist. (Paediat.) York Dist. Hosp.

RUT, Andrew Richard GlaxoSmithKline, Greenford Road, Greenford CM19 5AW Tel: 020 84223434 Fax: 020 84234401 Email: andrew.r.rut@gsk.com — MB BS 1985 Lond.; BSc (Hons.) Lond. 1982, MB BS 1985; MD Lond. 1995; MRCP (UK) 1989. Vice Pres. Global Clin. Saftey & Pharmacovigilance - Greenford. Prev: Lect. & Sen. Regist. (Med.) Univ. Coll. Lond.

RUTA, Daniel Adolf Department of Epidemiology & Public Health, Ninewells Hospital & Medical School, Dundee DD1 9SY — MB BS 1985 Lond.

RUTENBERG, Sidney Mortimer Felling Health Centre, Stephenson Terrace, Felling, Gateshead NE10 9QG Tel: 0191 469 2311 Fax: 0191 438 4661; 15 Grasmere Street, Gateshead NE8 1TR Tel: 0191 477 1980 — MB BCh 1970 Witwatersrand. (Witwatersrand)

RUTH, Martin Joseph, Squadron Ldr. RAF Med. Br. Department of Anaesthesia, Royal Infirmary of Edinburgh, Edinburgh EH3 Tel: 0131 536 1000 — MB ChB 1990 Glas.; DA (UK) 1995. (Univ. Glas.) Regist. (Anaesth.) Roy. Infirm. of Edin. Prev: Regist. (Anaesth.) Roy. Infirm. Edin.; Regist. (Anaesth.) MDHU PeterBoro. Dist. Hosp.

RUTH, Pauline Mary Maindiff Court Hospital, Abergavenny, Monmouthshire NP18 3XQ Tel: 01633 436844 Fax: 01633 436846; Email: winsor.bowsher@virgin.net — MB BS 1981 Lond.; BSc (1st cl. Hons.) Lond. 1978; MRCPsych 1987. Cons. Old Age Psychiat. Mon.; Head Clin. Director, Ment. Health Serv.s, Gwent Healthcare NHS Trust. Prev: Sen. Regist. Rotat. (Psychiat.) Maudsley Hosp. Lond.; Sen. Regist. Secondm. Roy. Pk. Hosp. Melbourne, Australia; Regist. Rotat. (Psychiat.) Maudsley Hosp. Lond.

RUTHERFORD, Anne Greenock Health Centre, 20 Duncan Street, Greenock PA15 4LY Tel: 01475 724677 Fax: 01475 725380 — MB ChB 1977 Glas.; MRCGP 1981. p/t Gen. Practitioner. Socs: MRCGP; BMA.

RUTHERFORD, Anne Noel New Milton Health Centre, Spencer Road, New Milton BH25 6EN Tel: 01425 621188; Squirrels Hide, The Close, Sway, Lymington SO41 6ED Tel: 01590 682906 — BM 1982 Soton. (Southampton) p/t G.P. Part Time Princip. of New Milton Health Centre. Prev: Trainee GP S.bourne VTS; Trainee GP St. Peters Hosp. Chertsey VTS.

RUTHERFORD, Anthony John Leeds General Infirmary, Clarendon Wing, Belmont Grove, Leeds LS2 9NS Tel: 0113 292 3879 Email: anthonyr@utlh.northy.nhs.uk; Ashfield Lodge, 38 Main St, Thorner, Leeds LS14 3DX Tel: 0113 289 2345 Fax: 0113 289 2345 — MB BS 1980 Lond.; MRCOG 1985; FRCOG 1998. Cons. O & G Leeds Gen. Infirm.; Director, Assisted Conception Unit; Hon. Sen. Lect, O & G.

RUTHERFORD, Arthur Kenneth Desmond, SBStJ (retired) 11 Underwood Close, Dawlish EX7 9RY Tel: 01626 864555 — MB BCh BAO 1943 Dub.; BA Dub. 1943. Prev: Med. Off. Brit. Railways (Engin. Ltd.) Derby.

RUTHERFORD, Daniel Croftwell, Prior Muir, St Andrews KY16 8LP Tel: 01334 474209 Fax: 01334 474209 Email: dan.rutherford@virgin.net; Croftwell, Prior Muir, St Andrews KY16 8LP Email: dan.rutherford@virgin.net — MB ChB 1979 Ed.; FRCP (Edin.) 1999; BSc Ed. 1976, MB ChB 1979; MRCP (UK) 1983; MRCGP 1985. (Edinburgh) p/t Med. Director www.netdoctor.co.uk Ltd.; GP Locum. Prev: Regist. Dundee Teach. Hosps.; Regist.

Gastrointestinal Unit W.. Gen. Hosp. Edin.; Ho. Off. Roy. Infirm. Edin.

RUTHERFORD, Duncan Roy 52 Barnwood Road, Gloucester GL2 0SG — BM 1980 Soton.

RUTHERFORD, Helen Jane 7 Langley Way, Hemingford Grey, Huntingdon PE28 9DB — MB BS 1992 Lond.

RUTHERFORD, Henry Ernest, VRD 12 Hawthorn Hill, Larne BT40 1PW Tel: 01574 2364 — MD 1945 Belf.; MB BCh BAO 1938; DObst RCOG 1946. (Qu. Univ. Belf.) Socs: BMA (Ex-Chairm. Belf. Div.). Prev: Res. Med. Off. Roy. Vict. Hosp. Belf.; Surg. Lt.-Cdr. RNVR.

RUTHERFORD, James Renton Drumart Square Surgery, 1B Drumart Square, Belvoir Estate, Belfast BT8 7EY — MB BCh BAO 1982 Belf.; MB BCh Belf. 1982.

RUTHERFORD, Jane Marion 20 Bradshaw Drive, Holbrook, Belper DE56 0SZ — MB ChB 1989 Ed.; MRCOG 1994. (Ed.) Research Fell. (Obst. Med.) Qu. Med. Centre Nottm. Prev: SHO (O & G) Roy. Infirm. Edin.

RUTHERFORD, Janet Angel Hill Surgery, 1 Angel Hill, Bury St Edmunds IP33 1LU Tel: 01284 753008 Fax: 01284 724744; 88 Queens Road, Bury St Edmunds IP33 3EP Tel: 01284 755700 Fax: 01284 755700 Email: j.k.roberts@tesco.net — MB BS 1985 Lond.; MRCGP 1989; DRCOG 1988. (St. Barth.) GP.

RUTHERFORD, Jean Aitken Steel 38 Gladstone Place, Aberdeen AB10 6XA Tel: 01224 322657 — MB ChB 1948 Glas. (Univ. Glas.)

RUTHERFORD, Joan The Ridgewood Centre, Old Bisley Road, Frimley, Camberley GU16 9QE Tel: 01276 692919 Fax: 01276 605366 — MB BS 1983 Lond.; MPhil Lond. 1992, BSc 1980; MRCPsych. 1987. Cons. Adult Psychiat. Ridgewood Centre Camberley.

RUTHERFORD, John David Ridgefield House, 14 John Dalton St, Manchester M2 6JR Tel: 0161 872 4868 — MB ChB 1972 Sheff.; BSc (Hons.) Sheff. 1969; MRCP (UK) 1981; MRCPath 1987; FRCPath 1997; DMJ(Path) Soc. Apoth. Lond. 1992; FRCP Ed. 1998. Home Off. Path.; Indep. Cons. Forens. Path. Gtr. Manch.; Hon. Lect. (Path.) Manch. Univ. Med. Sch. Socs: Brit. Assn. of Forens. Med.; Brit. Assn. for Forens. Odontology; Manch. & Dist. Medico-Legal Soc.

RUTHERFORD, John Hilton Donaghadee Health Centre, 3 Killaughey Road, Donaghadee BT21 0BU — MB BCh BAO 1977 Belf.; DRCOG 1979; MRCGP 1981.

RUTHERFORD, John Stanley Anaesthetic Department, Dumfries & Galloway Royal Infirmary, Bankend Road, Dumfries DG1 4AP Tel: 01387 246246 Fax: 01387 241639; Greystone, 53 Moffat Road, Dumfries DG1 1NN — MB ChB 1985 Aberd.; FRCA 1990.

RUTHERFORD, Margaret Cooper (retired) 144 South Anderson Drive, Aberdeen AB10 7PU Tel: 01224 315808 — MB ChB 1942 Aberd.

RUTHERFORD, Margaret Elizabeth (retired) 109 Glenburn Road, Belfast BT17 9AR Tel: 01232 629004 — MB BCh BAO 1944 Dub.; BA Dub. 1944. Prev: Med. Asst. (Geriat.) Leics. AHA (T).

RUTHERFORD, Mary Ann Department of Paediatrics, Hammersmith Hospital, Du Cane Road, London W12 0NN — MB ChB 1984 Bristol; MRCP (Paediat.) (UK) 1987. Research Regist. (Paediat.) Hammersmith Hosp. Lond. Prev: SHO Qu. Eliz. Hosp. Lond.

RUTHERFORD, Peter Anthony University of Wales College of Medicine, Wrexham Maelor Hospital, Wrexham LL13 7TD Tel: 01978 727122 Fax: 01978 727124 Email: parutherford@new-tr.wales.nhs.uk — MB BS 1986 Newc.; MB BS (Hons.) Newc. 1986; PhD Newc. 1994; BMedSc (Hons.) Newc. 1983; MRCP (UK) 1989; FRCP Ed 1999. (Newc. u. Tyne) Sen. Lect. (Nephrol.) & Hon. Cons. Phys. Univ. Wales Coll. of Med. Socs: Renal Assn; Am. Soc. Nephrol; Eur. Soc. Clin. Investig. Prev: Lect. (Med. & Nephrol.) Univ. Newc.; MRC Trav. Fell. Yale Univ. Sch. Med., USA; MRC Train. Fell. Univ. Newc. u. Tyne.

RUTHERFORD, Robert Andrew (retired) 6 Transy Place, Dunfermline KY12 7QN Tel: 01383 723907 — MB ChB 1938 Ed. Prev: Res. Ho. Surg. Dunfermline & W. Fife Hosp.

RUTHERFORD, Robert Gordon Fulwell Medical Centre, Ebdon Lane, off Dene Lane, Sunderland SR6 8DZ Tel: 0191 548 3635; 2 Rosedale Avenue, South Bents, Sunderland SR6 8BD — MB BS 1979 Newc.; MRCGP 1983.

RUTHERFORD, Mr Robert James 36 Park Drive, Melton Park, Gosforth, Newcastle upon Tyne NE3 5QB — MB BS 1935 Durh.; MS Durh. 1945, MB BS 1935; FRCS Ed. 1940. (Univ. Durh.) Sen. Surg. S. Shields Gen. Hosp., Ingham Infirm. S. Shields & Ellison; Hall Infirm. Hebburn-on-Tyne. Prev: Vis. Surg. Ashington Hosp. & Thos. Kt. Memor. Hosp. Blyth; Surg. Specialist RAFVR.

RUTHERFORD, Susan Jane Queen Street Surgery, 13A Queen Street, Deal CT14 6ET Tel: 01304 363181 Fax: 01304 381996 — MB BS 1986 Lond.; BA Oxf. 1983; DRCOG 1990. (UMDS Guy's Hosp. Lond.) Socs: Christian Med. Fell.sh. Prev: Ho. Phys. Yeovil Dist. Hosp. Som.

RUTHERFORD, Sylvia 80 Mill Rise, Swanland, North Ferriby HU14 3PW — MB ChB 1980 Dundee; DRCOG 1984.

RUTHERFORD, Mr William Harford, OBE (retired) 113 Glenburn Road, Dunmurry, Belfast BT17 9AR Tel: 0289 062 1622 Email: william.rutherford@ukgateway.net — MB BCh BAO Dub. 1944; FRCS Eng. 1985; FRCS Ed. 1951; FIFEM(Fellow of intntl.Fed.of Emerg.Med.). Prev: Preven. of Injury Adviser DHSS N. Irel.

RUTHERFURD, Harry Napier (retired) Oakley, St Mary St, Kirkcudbright DG6 4AH Tel: 01557 330266 — MB ChB Ed. 1960; DObst RCOG 1964. Estab. Med. Off. Armament Wing RARDE Kirkcudbright. Prev: Surg. Roy. Fleet Auxil. Serv.

RUTHERFURD, Jacqueline Anne Ferguson Oakley, St Mary St., Kirkcudbright DG6 4AH Tel: 01557 330266 — MB ChB 1956 Ed.

RUTHERFURD, Stewart Ferguson Senior and Partners, Morrab Surgery, 2 Morrab Road, Penzance TR18 4EL Tel: 01736 363866 Fax: 01736 367809; Trenow Villa, Trenow, Long Rock, Penzance TR20 8YQ Tel: 01736 710198 — MB ChB 1988 Ed.; MRCGP 1995; DGM RCP Lond. 1991. (Univ. Edin.)

*****RUTHVEN, Elaine** 31 Portree Avenue, Broughty Ferry, Dundee DD5 3EG — MB ChB 1995 Glas.

RUTHVEN, Ian Scott (retired) Westholme, 10 Victoria Drive, Troon KA10 6EN Tel: 01292 313006 — MB ChB 1961 Glas.; FRCP Glas. 1977, M 1968; FRCP Ed. 1983, M 1968; FRCPCH 1997; DObst RCOG 1963. Cons. Paediat. Ayrsh. & Arran HB; Clin. Director (Paediat.) Ayrsh. & Arran Acute Hosp.s NHS Trust. Prev: Postgrad. Tutor S. Ayrsh. Hosps.

RUTHVEN, Jennifer Louise 31 Portree Avenue, Broughty Ferry, Dundee DD5 3EG — MB BS 1998 Manch.; MB BS Manch 1998.

RUTHVEN, Susan Jane 46 Lubnaig Road, Glasgow G43 2RX Tel: 0141 637 8335; 15 Westpark Gardens, Dundee DD2 1NY Tel: 01382 665534 — MB ChB 1997 Dundee.

RUTHVEN-STUART, Ian Alexander (retired) Verney Cottage, East St., Hambledon, Waterlooville PO7 4RX Tel: 02392 632596 Fax: 02392 632596 — MB ChB 1950 Ed.; DObst RCOG 1960. Hosp. Pract. Qu. Alexandra Hosp. Cosham. Prev: Regist. (Orthop.) Roy. Infirm. Edin.

RUTLAND, Andrew Frank Knowles Lilliput Surgery, Elms Avenue, Lindisfarne, Poole BH14 8EE Tel: 01202 741310 Fax: 01202 739122; 17 Brunstead Road, Branksome, Poole BH12 1EJ Tel: 01202 268958 Email: rutdoc@msn.com — MB BS 1988 Lond.; MA Oxf. BA Oxf. 1985; MRCGP Lond. 1993. (Char. Cross & Westm.)

RUTLAND, Eileen (retired) 111 Rotunda Road, Eastbourne BN23 6LQ Tel: 01323 737181 — MRCS Eng. LRCP Lond. 1940.

RUTLAND, Robert Frederick Knowles 31 Beckford, Washington NE38 8TP — MB BS 1987 Lond.

RUTLEDGE, David George Alexander Inverurie Medical Group, Health Centre, 1 Constitution Street, Inverurie AB51 4SU Tel: 01467 621345 Fax: 01467 625374; 17 Wellpark, Daviot, Inverurie AB51 0NF Tel: 01467 671687 — MB BCh BAO 1987 Belf.; MRCGP 1992; DRCOG 1991; DCH RCP Glas. 1991.

RUTLEDGE, Esther Mary The Valley Medical Centre, 20 Cooneen Road, Fivemiletown BT75 0ND Tel: 028 8952 1326; The Glebe, Clogher BT76 0UW Tel: 0166 25 48346 — MB BCh BAO 1960 Belf. (Belf.) GP Clogher. Prev: Sen. Ho. Phys. Belf. City Hosp. & Musgrave Pk. Hosp. Belf.; Sen. Ho. Surg. Tyrone Co. Hosp. Omagh.

RUTLEDGE, Gillian Jane 10 Huby Park, Huby, Leeds LS17 0EE — MB ChB 1987 Ed.; MRCGP 1991; DRCOG Ed. 1989. Prev: SHO (A & E) W.. Gen. Hosp. Edin; SHO (O & G) W.. Gen. Hosp. Edin.

RUTLEDGE, Malcolm Robert 6 Winters Lane, Omagh BT79 0DY — MB BCh BAO 1991 Belf.

RUTLEDGE, Mary Lynda Campbell Department of Anaesthesia, Western General Hospital, Crewe Road, Edinburgh EH4 2XU Tel:

RUTLEDGE

0131 537 1000 Fax: 0131 537 1025 Email: lindarutledge8550@hotmail.uk; Cedar Lodge, 74 Trinity Road, Edinburgh EH5 3JT Tel: 0131 552 4774 — MB ChB 1974 Aberd.; FFA RCS Eng. 1979. Cons. Anaesth. W. Gen. Hosp. Edin. Prev: Sen. Regist. & Regist. (Anaesth.) Lothian HB.

RUTLEDGE, Philip Clinikcal Pharmacology Unit, Western General Hospital, Edinburgh EH4 2XU Tel: 0131 537 1737 Fax: 0131 536 1737; 74 Trinity Road, Edinburgh EH5 3JT Tel: 0131 552 4774 — MB ChB 1974 Aberd.; DRCOG 1978; FRCGP 1999. Director of Med.s Managem.. CPU. WGH. Prev: Med. Prescribing Adviser, Lothian Primary Trust.

RUTT, Graham Alan Proctor and Partners, Doctors Surgery, 42 Heaton Road, Heaton, Newcastle upon Tyne NE6 1SE Tel: 0191 265 5911 Fax: 0191 265 6974; 5 Parkhead Road, High heaton, Newcastle upon Tyne NE7 7DH — MB BS 1978 Newc.; MRCGP 1982; MA Dunelm 1998. (Newcastle upon Tyne) Course Organiser N.umbria VTS.

RUTTER, Dag Allenson 2 Herbert Villas, Pelham Road, London SW19 1NW — MB BS 1991 Lond.

RUTTER, David Allenson Beckling, Britford, Salisbury SP5 4DU — MB BChir 1964 Camb.; MA, MB Camb. 1964, BChir 1963. (Camb. & Univ. Coll. Hosp.) Prev: Med. Off. Centre For Applied Microbiol. & Research Salisbury.

RUTTER, David Vivian Mimosa, 4 Windfield Drive, Winchester Hill, Romsey SO51 7RL — MB ChB 1972 Bristol; FFA RCS Eng. 1977; DObst RCOG 1975. Cons. Anaesth. Soton. Univ. Trust Hosp.; Hon. Clin. Teach. Univ. Fac. Med. Soton. Prev: Sen. Regist. (Anaesth.) Hammersmith Postgrad. Med. Sch. Lond.; Regist. (Anaesth.) Västerås Hosp., Sweden; Regist. (Anaesth.) Bristol Roy. Infirm.

RUTTER, Diana Patricia Leicester Royal Infirmary — MB BS 1972 Lond.; FRCP Lond. 1994; FRCP Canada 1979; MRCP (UK) 1975. Cons. Paediat. Leicester Roy. Infirm., Leicester, LF1 5WW. Prev: Sen. Regist. Roy. Free Hosp. Lond.; Cons. Paediat. Pontefract Gen. Infirm. W.Yorks.

RUTTER, Francis Clarence (retired) 446 Unthank Road, Norwich NR4 7QJ Tel: 01603 451047 — MB BChir Camb. 1951; DObst RCOG 1953.

RUTTER, Mr Francis John (retired) 33 Oakfield Avenue, Wrenbury, Nantwich CW5 8ER — MB ChB 1933 Birm.; FRCS Ed. 1939; DOMS 1938. Prev: Cons. W. of Eng. Eye Infirm. Exeter.

RUTTER, Geoffrey Guy Rolf 15 Lyndale Avenue, London NW2 2QD Tel: 020 8922 7711 Fax: 020 8922 7711 Email: g.rutter@thefree.net — MB BChir Camb. 1979; MRCS Eng. LRCP Lond. 1978; FFA RCS Eng. 1983. Indep. Cons. Anaesth. Lond.

RUTTER, Harold Roderick Oxfordshire Health Authority, Old Road, Headington, Oxford OX3 7LG Tel: 01865 741174 — MB BChir 1992 Camb.; MA Camb. 1992. Specialist Regist. Pub. Health Med. Oxf.shire Health Auth. Oxf.

***RUTTER, Helen Elizabeth** 23 Clifford Road, Boston Spa, Wetherby LS23 6BQ — MB ChB 1998 Birm.

RUTTER, Ian Paul Westcliffe Medical Centre, Westcliffe Road, Shipley BD18 3EE Tel: 01274 580787 Fax: 01274 532210; Green Bank, Otley Road, Eldwick, Bingley BD16 3DA — MB ChB 1976 Leeds; MRCGP 1980. GP Co-ordinator N. Bradford Health Gain Organisation. Prev: GP Course Organiser Bradford VTS.

RUTTER, John Anthony St Thomas Health Centre, Cowick Street, St. Thomas, Exeter EX4 1HJ Tel: 01392 676677 Fax: 01392 676677; Blackdown Cottage, Heath Cross, Whitestone, Exeter EX4 2HL Tel: 01647 61305 — MB BS 1974 Lond.; MRCS Eng. LRCP Lond. 1974; DRCOG 1978. Med. Adviser Hospiscare Exeter.

RUTTER, Josephine (retired) 26 Kerr Crescent, Sedgefield, Stockton-on-Tees TS21 2EG Tel: 01740620472 — MB BS Durh. 1948; FRCPsych 1986, M 1971; DPM Eng. 1954; DPH. Durham 1955. Prev: Cons. Psychiat. Winterton Hosp. Sedgefield & SW Durh. Gp. Hosps.

RUTTER, Judith Mary 12 St Davids Crescent, Aspull, Wigan WN2 1SN — MB ChB 1991 Leeds.

RUTTER, Julie Marguerite 54 Ballards Way, South Croydon CR2 7JL; 18 Heron Grove, Leeds LS17 8XF — MB ChB 1986 Leeds; FRCA. 1992; DA (UK) 1989. (Univ. Leeds) Sen. Regist. (Anaesth.) Yorks. Region. Prev: Sen. Regist. Freemantle Hosp. W.. Austral.; Regist. Rotat. St. Jas. Leeds & Pontefract; SHO (Paediat.) Boston.

RUTTER, Mr Kiko Roderick Peter (retired) 23 Echo Barn Lane, Farnham GU10 4NQ — MB BChir 1967 Camb.; FRCS Eng. 1971. Cons. Surg. Frimley Pk. Hosp. Prev: Lect. (Surg.) Surg. Unit St. Geo. Hosp. Lond.

RUTTER, Lewis Daniel (retired) Lime Tree Cottage, The Hill, Westleton, Saxmundham IP17 3AW Tel: 01728 648506 Email: lewisrutter@aol.com — MB ChB Manch. 1939; MRCGP 1953. Prev: RAFVR 1940-6.

RUTTER, Llewellyn Charles (retired) 14 Queen Mother Court, 151 Sellywood Road, Bournville, Birmingham B30 1TH Tel: 0121 471 2247 — MB ChB Birm. (2nd cl. Hons. Distinc. in Med.) 1930; MRCGP 1953; DObst RCOG 1946. Prev: Regional Med. Off. Dept. Health & Social Security.

RUTTER, Louise Elizabeth 27 French Laurence Way, Chalgrove, Oxford OX44 7YF — BM BCh 1986 Oxf.; MRCGP 1990; DCH RCP Lond. 1988; DRCOG 1988. p/t PMS GP, Bury Knowle Health Centre, Oxf. Prev: Retainer GP Chalfont St Peter; SHO (Palliat. Care) Arthur Rank Hse. Camb.; SHO (Geriat.) Newmarket Gen. Hosp.

RUTTER, Martin Kenneth 52 Percy Gardens, North Shields NE30 4HH — MB ChB 1985 Ed.; MRCP (UK) 1991; MRCPI 1991; DGM RCP Lond. 1991.

RUTTER, Matthew David Wolfson Unit for Endoscopy, St Mark's Hospital, Watford Rd, Harrow HA1 3UJ Tel: 020 8235 4025 Fax: 0208 423 3588 — MB BS 1993 Newc.; MRCP (UK) 1996. (Newc.) Specialist Regist. (Gastroenterol. & Gen. Med.) N. Deanery; Research Fell. Gatroenterol. & Endosc. St Mark's Hosp.

RUTTER, Michael John X-Ray Department, North Devon District Hospital, Raleigh Park, Barnstaple EX31 4JB — MB BS 1962 Lond.; FFR 1969; DMRD Eng. 1966. Cons. Radiol. N. Devon Health Dist.

RUTTER, Professor Sir Michael Llewellyn, CBE Social Genetic & Development Psychiatry Research Centre, Institute of Psychiatry, De Crespigny Park, Denmark Hill, London SE5 8AF Tel: 020 7919 3882 Fax: 020 7919 3866 Email: j.wickham@iop.bpmf.ac.uk; 190 Court Lane, Dulwich, London SE21 7ED — MRCS Eng. LRCP Lond. 1955; FRS 1987; MD (Hons.) Birm. 1963, MB ChB (Distinc. Pharmacol. & Therap.) 1955; FRCP Lond. 1972, M 1958; FRCPsych 1971; DPM (Distinc.) Lond. 1961. Prof. Develop. Psychopathol. Inst. Psychiat. Univ. Lond.; Hon. Cons. Phys. Maudsley Hosp. Lond. Socs: Hon. Fell. Brit. Psychol. Soc.; (Ex-Chairm.) Assn. Child Psychol. & Psychiat.; Hon. Fell. Roy. Soc. Med. Prev: Ho. Phys. & Ho. Surg. Qu. Eliz. Hosp. Birm.; Nuffield Med. Trav. Fell. Dept. Paediat. Albert Einstein Coll. Med. New York.

RUTTER, Professor Nicholas 9 Chestnut Grove, Radcliffe-on-Trent, Nottingham NG12 1AH — MD 1980 Camb.; MB 1971, BChir 1970; FRCP Lond. 1987, M 1972. Prof. Paediat. Med. & Hon. Cons. Paediat. Nottm. Univ. Prev: SHO Qu. Charlottes Matern. Hosp. Lond.; SHO Hosp. Sick Childr. Gt. Ormond St. Lond.; Ho. Phys. St. Thos. Hosp. Lond.

RUTTER, Mr Peter Charles Old Farmhouse, The Pound, Cookham, Maidenhead SL6 9SA — MB BS 1975 Lond.; MS Lond. 1987; MRCS Eng. LRCP Lond. 1975; FRCS Eng. 1980. Cons. Surg. Wexham Pk. Hosp. Slough. Prev: Sen. Regist. (Vasc.) St. Mary's Hosp. Lond.

RUTTER, Philippa 21C Fernhead Road, London W9 3EU — MB BS 1998 Lond.; MB BS Lond 1998.

RUTTER, Rowena Ann Canterbury Road Surgery, 186 Canterbury Road, Davyhulme, Manchester M41 0GR Tel: 0161 748 5559 Fax: 0161 747 1997; 20 Belgrave Avenue, Flixton, Urmston, Manchester M41 8SR Tel: 0161 747 9458 — MB ChB 1971 Manch.; DObst RCOG 1973. GP Partner.

RUTTER, Stephen Michael Queens Medical Centre, Nottingham NG7 2UH; 190 Court Lane, London SE21 7ED — MB ChB 1989 Bristol; BSc (Hons.) Psychol. Bristol 1986; MRCP (UK) 1994. Specialist Regist. Geriats. (TRENT). Socs: Brithish Geriat.s Soc.; Brit. Diabetic Assoc. Prev: SHO (Med.) Kings Mill Hosp. Notts.

RUTTER, Susan Northern General Hospital, Herries Road, Sheffield S5 7AU; 88 Cherry Tree Road, Walton, Wakefield WF2 6LL — MB ChB 1990 Leeds; MRCOG 1997. Specialist Regist. N. Trent Rotat. Prev: SHO (O & G) Jessop Hosp. for Wom. Sheff.; SHO (O & G) Sheff. & Bradford Roy. Infirm.

RUTTER, Mr Timothy Morton 2 Portobello Mews, London W11 3DQ Tel: 020 7727 6686 — MB ChB 1966 Ed.; BSc Ed. 1963, MB ChB 1966; FRCS Ed. 1970; MRCOG 1973. (Ed.)

RUTTER, William (retired) 29 Milford Gardens, Brunton Park, Gosforth, Newcastle upon Tyne NE3 5AT — MB BS 1943 Durh.; MRCGP 1974.

RUTTLEY, Marie-Elisabeth 11 Kirkstall Road, London SW2 4HD — MB BS 1973 Lond.; MRCS Eng. LRCP Lond. 1973. (Char. Cross) Prev: Regist. (Anaesth.) Guy's Hosp. Lond.

RUTTLEY, Michael Samuel Taylor Department of Radiology, University Hospital of Wales, Cardiff CF4 4XW Tel: 029 2074 3955 Fax: 029 2074 3029 Email: michael.ruttley@uhw-tr.wales.nhs.uk; Ty'r Bont, 3 The Paddock, Cowbridge CF71 7EJ Tel: 01446 772598 — MB BS Lond. 1964; FRCP Lond. 1984, M 1967; MRCS Eng. LRCP Lond. 1964; FFR 1970; DMRD Lond. 1969. (St. Geo.) Cons. Radiol. Univ. Hosp. of Wales, Cardiff.; Clin. Dir. Radiol., Univ. Hosp. of Wales, Cardiff. Prev: Ho. Phys. St. Geo. Hosp. Lond.; Clin. Fell. in Radiol. Harvard Med. Sch. Boston, U.S.A.

RUTTY, Professor Guy Nathan Division of Forensic Pathology University of Leicester, Robert Kilpatrick Building Leicester Royal Enfirmary, P.O/ Box 65, Leicester LE3 7ES — MB BS 1987 Lond.; FRCPath 2002; MRCPath 1993; Dip RCPath (Forens.) 1996. (Roy. Free Sch. Med. Lond.) Prof. Forens. Path.) Univ. Leicester; Cons. Path. to Home Office. Socs: Forens. Sci.. Soc.; Counc. Mem. Assn. Clin. Pathol. Prev: Sen. Lect. (Forens. Path.) Univ. Sheff.; Sen. Regist. (Histopath.) Leicester Roy. Infirm.; Regist. (Histopath.) Mt. Vernon Hosp. N.wood.

RUXTON, Andrew McCall (retired) Meadhurst, James St., Armadale, Bathgate EH48 3JG Tel: 01506 30205 — MB ChB 1948 Ed. Prev: Capt. RAMC, TA.

RUZICKA, James Mark Vincent 15 Muir Avenue, Tollerton, Nottingham NG12 4EZ — MB BS 1994 Lond.; BA (Hons.) Camb. 1991. SHO (Anaesth. & IC) St. Geo.'s Hosp., Tooting.

RYALL, Christopher John 3 Cavendish Road, Birkenhead CH41 8AX — MB BS 1980 Newc.; BA Camb. 1974; FRCR 1986. Cons. Radiol. BRd.green NHS Trust Liverp. Prev: Sen. Regist. (Diag. Radiol.) N.. RHA.

RYALL, David Michael 1 Eden Park Road, Hutton Rudby, Yarm TS15 0HS — MB ChB 1983 Aberd. Cons. S. Cleveland Hosp..

RYALL, Mr Robert James (retired) Scrivelsby, Heathbourne Road, Bushey Heath, Watford WD23 1PD Tel: 020 8950 1511 Fax: 020 8950 1511 Email: bob.ryall@btinternet.com — MB BCh BAO 1951 NUI; MCh NUI 1960; FRCS Eng. 1958. Fell. Roy. Soc. Med. Prev: Cons. Surg. Edgware Gen. Hosp.

RYALL, Roger Duncan Hall (retired) Hampton House, Headbourne Worthy, Winchester SO23 7JH Tel: 01962 883270 Fax: 01962 886199 — MB BS Lond. 1962; MRCS Eng. LRCP Lond. 1962; FRCR 1975; FFR 1971; DMRT Eng. 1967. Clin. Tutor Univ. Soton.; Regist. (Clin. Oncol.) & Mem. Counc. Roy. Coll. Radiol. Prev: Clin. Dir. & Cons. Radiother. & Oncol. Wessex Radiother. Centre.

RYALL, Rosemary Elizabeth (retired) Hampton House, Headbourne Worthy, Winchester SO23 7JH Tel: 01962 883270 Fax: 01962 886199 — MB BS Lond. 1963; MRCS Eng. LRCP Lond. 1963. Med. Off. Wom. Screening Clinics Basingstoke, Winchester & Soton.

RYALLS, Michael Robin Royal Surrey County Hospital, Egerton Road, Guildford GU2 7XX Tel: 01483 571122 Fax: 01483 450742; Heath View, 62 Chapel Road, Tadworth KT20 5SE Tel: 01737 213289 Fax: 01737 270521 Email: drmryalls@cwcom.net — MB BCh 1981 Wales; MRCP (UK) 1986. (Welsh National School Medicine) Cons. Paediat. Roy. Surrey Co. Hosp.; Hon. Cons. St. Geo. Hosp. Lond. & Roy. Marsden Hosp. Sutton. Socs: Fell. Roy. Coll. Paediat. & Child Health. Prev: Sen. Regist. (Paediat.) Roy. Lond. Hosp. & Hosp. Sick. Childr. Gt. Ormond St. Lond.; Hon. Regist. (Paediat.) Roy. Childr. Hosp. Melbourne, Austral.; Clin. Research Fell. Roy. Marsden Hosp. Sutton.

RYAN, Alan James The Grange Surgery, 41 York Road, Southport PR8 2AD Tel: 01704 560506 Fax: 01704 563108; 18 Allerton Road, Southport PR9 9NJ — MB ChB 1988 Liverp. Prev: Trainee GP Blackpool Vict. Hosp. VTS.

RYAN, Andrew Royal Hospitals NHS Trust, Whitechapel, London E1 1AD Tel: 020 7377 7000; 43 Liddington Road, Stratford, London E15 3PL Tel: 0958 606667 Email: andrewryan1@msn.com — MB BS 1996 Lond.; BSc (Hons.) 1991. (Lond. Hosp. Med. Coll.) Trainee GP E. Lond. VTS.

RYAN, Anne Marie 6 Grasmere Gardens, Belfast BT15 5EG — MB BCh BAO 1997 Belf.

RYAN, Anthony George Health Centre, Victoria Sq, Portishead, Bristol BS20 6AQ Tel: 01275 847474 Fax: 01275 817516 — MB ChB 1988 Bristol; MRCGP 1994; DGM RCP Lond. 1992.

RYAN, Anthony Gerard Majella Joseph c/o Department of Radiology, University Hospital of Wales & Cardiff, Heath Park, Cardiff CF4 4XW — MB BCh BAO 1990 NUI; FRCSI 1995; MSc, DIC. Imperial Coll. Of Sci., Tech, & Med. Lond. 98. (National Univ. of Ire., Galway) Specialist Regist. in Clin. Radiol.

RYAN, Anthony Philip (retired) 4 Regency Drive, Green Lane, Coventry CV3 6QA Tel: 01203 410409 — LRCPI & LM, LRCSI & LM 1954.

RYAN, Audrey Mary Longthatch, Rodmell, Lewes BN7 3HQ — MB BS 1994 Lond.

RYAN, Bernard Edmund (retired) 10 Henley Close, Rawdon, Leeds LS19 6QB — MB ChB 1968 Liverp.; T(GP) 1991; DTM & H Liverp. 1996. Prev: Med. Off. Univ. Stud. Health Serv. Leeds.

RYAN, Mr Brendan Patrick Trust Headquarters, Wythenshawe Hospital, Southmoor Road, Wythenshawe, Manchester M23 9LT Tel: 0161 291 5422 Fax: 0161 291 2037 Email: brendan.ryan@smuht.nwest.nhs.uk; 10 Granville Road, Timperley, Altrincham WA15 7BE — MB BCh BAO 1981 NUI; FRCSI 1985. (Univ. Coll. Cork) Med. Dir. - S. Manch. Univ. Hosp.s NHS Trust.; Cons. (A&E) Wythenshawe Hosp.. Manch.. Socs: Founding Fell. Fac. A & E Med.; BASICS; Fac. of preHosp. Care (Ed). Prev: Div.al Director of Med.; Clin. Director A/E.

RYAN, Carol Raymonde (retired) Kinross, 8 Well Lane, Heswall, Wirral CH60 8NE — MB ChB Liverp. 1964; FFA RCS Eng. 1970; DObst RCOG 1967. Prev: Cons. Chester Roy. Infirm.

RYAN, Carolyn Mary Spring Gables Surgery, Clint Bank, Birstwith, Harrogate HG3 3DW — MB BCh 1982 Wales; DCH RCP 1987; DRCOG 1988.

RYAN, Catherine Jane 19 Wentworth Avenue, Sheffield S11 9QX — MB ChB 1995 Leeds. GP Regist. Chesterfield.

RYAN, Christopher John Melbourne Park Medical Centre, Melbourne Road, Aspley, Nottingham NG8 5HL Tel: 0115 978 6114 Fax: 0115 924 9334; The Anchorage, Spencer Drive, Nuthall, Nottingham NG16 1DX Tel: 0115 938 4167 — MB ChB Birm. 1969; MRCS Eng. LRCP Lond. 1969; MRCGP 1977; DObst RCOG 1972. (Birm.) Princip. GP; Examg. Med. Practitioner, Nestor Disabil. Anal.; Police Surg. Notts. Constab. Socs: BMA & Assur. Med. Soc.; Fell. Roy. Soc. of Med. Prev: Trainer (Gen. Pract.) Nottm. VTS; Ho. Surg. Surgic. Profess Unit Qu. Eliz. Hosp. Birm.; SHO O & G City Hosp. Nottm.

RYAN, Claire Elizabeth 10 St Andrew's Close, Workstead, North Walsham NR28 9SG — MB ChB 1995 Glas.

RYAN, Damian Jonathan 17 Abbotswood Road, St. Francis Place, East Dulwich, London SE22 8DJ — MB BS 1992 Lond. (UMDS (Guy's)) SHO (Neurosurg.) Atkinson Morley's Hosp. Lond. Prev: SHO (Orthop. & Trauma) Kingston Hosp. Surrey & Soton. Gen. Hosp.; SHO (ENT) Lewisham Hosp.

RYAN, David Alan Department of Anaesthetics, The Ayr Hospital, Dalmellington Road, Ayr KA6 6DX Tel: 01292 610555 Email: david.ryan@aaaht.scot.nhs.uk — MB BS 1976 Lond.; BSc (Hons.) Lond. 1973; FRCA Eng. 1983; DA Eng. 1979. Cons. (Anaesth.) The Ayr Hosp. Prev: Cons. (Anaesth.) Bronglais Hosp. Aberystwyth; Cons. (Anaesth.) Nevill Hall Hosp. Abergavenny; Sen. Regist. S. Glam. HA.

RYAN, David Hugh Community Mental Health Centre, Manor Road, Beverley HU17 7BZ Tel: 01482 887664 Fax: 01482 880026; Park Lodge, York Road, Beverley HU17 8DP — MB ChB 1976 Bristol; MSc Bristol 1988; MRCPsych. 1985; MD Bristol 1995. (Bristol Medical School) Cons. Psychiat.Hull and E. Riding, Community NHS Trust; Project Manager:Investors in Ment. Health. Prev: Sen. Regist. (Psychiat.) Roy. Edin. Hosp.; Regist. (Psychiat.) Exeter.; GP Devon.

RYAN, David Peter Michael Grassendale Medical Practice, 23 Darby Road, Liverpool L19 9BP Tel: 0151 427 1214 Fax: 0151 427 0611; 8 Burrell Road, Prenton, Birkenhead CH42 8NH — MB BCh BAO 1979 NUI; MRCGP 1986.

RYAN, David William Freeman Hospital, High Heaton, Newcastle upon Tyne NE7 7DN Tel: 0191 284 3111 Fax: 0191 223 1401 Email: davidryan@nuth.northy.nhs.uk; 63 The Grove, Gosforth, Newcastle upon Tyne NE3 1NJ Tel: 0191 285 7430 Fax: 0191 223 1180 Email: dwryn@aol.com — MB ChB 1970 Sheff.; FRCA 1974.

RYAN

(Sheff.) Cons. Clin. Physiol. Freeman Hosp. Trust; Meritus, Edr. c/o Critically Ill. Prev: Cons. & Sen. Regist. (Anaesth.) Newc. AHA (T).

RYAN, Declan James (retired) Hillside, 40 Higher Lane, Upholland, Skelmersdale WN8 0NL Tel: 01695 622366 — MB BCh BAO 1949 NUI; FFA RCSI 1962; DA RCPSI 1952. Prev: Cons. Anaesth. Wigan & Leigh & Wrightington Hosp. Gps.

RYAN, Denis 117 High Street, Clay Cross, Chesterfield S45 9DZ — MB ChB 1954 Sheff.; MA (Distinc.) Sheff. 1996.

RYAN, Dermot Patrick Woodbrook Medical Centre, 28 Bridge Street, Loughborough LE11 1NH Tel: 01509 239166 Fax: 01509 238747 — MB BCh BAO 1977 NUI; MRCGP 1981; MICGP 1985; DFFP 1993; DObst RCPI 1980; DCH NUI 1979. (University College Dublin) GP Princip.; Clin. Tutor Leics. Univ. Med. Sch.; Civil Serv. Med. Off. LoughBoro. & Dist.; Clin. Asst. Gastroenterol. LoughBoro. Gen. Hosp. Prev: Lect. (Clin. Med.) Univ. Leicester; Trainee GP Dub. Regional VTS.

RYAN, Elizabeth The Old Stores, Wellshead Lane, Harwell, Didcot OX11 0HD Tel: 01235 832847 — MB ChB 1977 Sheff. (Sheff.) SCMO (Family Plann.) & Sex Therapist Oxf. Socs: Accred. Mem. BASRT; OACGP. Prev: Ho. Off. (Med., Dermat. & Orthop.) Sheff. AHA.

RYAN, Ethne Nanette Moira Barnewall (retired) Cranmore, Buxton Drive, New Malden KT3 3UX — MRCS Eng. LRCP Lond. 1939. Prev: Cas. Med. Off. Out-pat. Dept. Hampstead Gen. Hosp.

RYAN, Eugene Paul Mary The Surgery, 291 Ashby Road, Scunthorpe DN16 2AB Tel: 01724 864426/7/8 Fax: 01724 282570; Glencrest, Ermine St, Scawby, Brigg DN20 9NB Tel: 01652 57768 — MB BCh BAO 1983 Dub.; DCH RCPSI 1986. Trainee GP Barton VTS. Prev: SHO (Geriat.) Castle Hill Hosp. Hull; SHO (Paediat.) Scunthorpe Gen. Hosp.; SHO (Surg.) Craigavon Gen. Hosp.

RYAN, Frances Mary 22 Sussex Way, Barnet EN4 0BJ — MB BS 1991 Lond.

RYAN, Francis Patrick Woodbine Cottage, 2 Vicarage Lane, Dore, Sheffield S17 3GX — MB ChB 1970 Sheff.; MB ChB (Hons.) Sheff. 1970; FRCP Lond. 1987; MRCP (UK) 1973. (Sheff.) Cons. Adviser, Sheff. HA. Prev: Cons., Gastroenterol., N. Gen. Hosp., Sheff..

RYAN, George Low Hill Medical Centre, First Avenue, Low Hill, Wolverhampton WV10 9SX Tel: 01902 728861 — MB ChB 1961 Liverp.; MA Liverp. 1991; DObst RCOG 1964.

RYAN, George Gilbert 30 Winterton House, Deancross St., Commercial Road, Whitechapel, London E1 — MB BCh BAO 1980 NUI.

RYAN, Hubert Sidney Sims The Lime Kiln, Llanvanches, Newport NP26 3AY — MB BS 1953 Lond. (St. Bart.)

RYAN, Hugh Trevor 8 Haden Road, Cradley Heath, Warley B64 6ER Tel: 01384 66479 — MD 1937 Dub.; MA Dub. 1937, MD 1937, MB BCh BAO 1934. (Dub.) Prev: Ho. Surg. Waterloo Hosp. Liverp. & Guest Hosp. Dudley.

RYAN, James David Varley 63 The Grove, Gosforth, Newcastle upon Tyne NE3 1NJ Tel: 0191 285 7430 Fax: 0191 285 7430 — MB ChB 1997 Leic.

RYAN, James Joseph Thadeus 18 Dunamallaght Road, Ballycastle BT54 6PB — MRCS Eng. LRCP Lond. 1948; DA Eng. 1960. (Glas.)

RYAN, Professor James Michael Department of Conflict Recovery, University College London Hospitals, 4 Taviton Street, London WC1H 0BT Tel: 020 7679 4517, 020 7679 4518 Fax: 020 7813 2844 Email: james.ryan@ucl.ac.uk; 111 Alexandra Road, Farnborough GU14 6RR Tel: 01252 673565 — MB BCh BAO NUI 1970; MCh NUI 1990; FRCS Eng. 1978; DMCC Soc. Apoth Lond. 1994; FFAEM (Hon) Fac. Of A&M2000. (Univ. Coll. Dub.) Leonard Chesh. Prof. of Conflict Recovery Univ. Coll. Lond. Hosps.; Sen. Lect. Trauma Care. Socs: Fell. Milit. Surgic. Soc.; Fell. Assn. Surgs.; Assn. Milit. Surg. of the US (AMSUS). Prev: Prof. Milit. Surg. RAMC & Roy. Coll. Surg. Eng.; Cons. Surg. Brit. Milit. Hosps. Hong Kong & Dharan (Nepal); Lect. (Surg.) & Hon. Sen. Regist. Prof. Surg. Unit St. Bart. Hosp. Lond.

RYAN, Jane Alison 26 Ferndale, Waterlooville PO7 7PA — MB BS 1983 Lond.; DCH RCP Lond. 1987.

RYAN, Jeremy Martin Little Holmside Hall, Burnhope, Durham DH7 0DS — MB ChB 1985 Liverp.; BDS Lond. 1978; FDS RCS Eng. 1988; FRCS Ed. 1989. Cons. Oral & Maxillofacial Surg. Sunderland Roy. Hosp. & Shotley Bridge Hosp. Co. Durh.

RYAN, Joan Mary 109 Grove Hill, London E18 2HY — MB BS 1983 Lond.; MRCGP 1991; DCH RCP Lond. 1990; DRCOG Lond. 1990.

RYAN, Joan Spurway 4 Burnham Close, Burnham Green, Welwyn AL6 0PE Tel: 0143 879403 — MB ChB 1938 Liverp. (Liverp.) Socs: BMA. Prev: Med. Off. Roy. Liverp. & Alder Hey Childr. Hosps.

RYAN, Johanna Patricia Anaesthetic Department, Bolton Hospitals NHS Trust, Minerva Road, Farnworth, Bolton BL4 0JR Tel: 01204 390762 Fax: 01204 390763; 111 Moss Lane, Ashton-on-Mersey, Sale M33 5BU — MB BCh BAO 1979 NUI; FFA RCS Eng. 1985; FFA RCSI 1984; DCH RCPSI 1987. Cons. Anaesth. Bolton Hosp.

RYAN, John Brendan Ash Lodge Medical Centre, 73 Old Road, Chesterfield S40 2RA Tel: 01246 203138 Fax: 01246 231824; 22 The Crescent, Holy Moorside, Chesterfield S42 7EE Tel: 01246 569736 — MB ChB 1986 Sheff. (Sheff.) Prev: GP Sheff.

RYAN, John Francis Alverton Surgery, 7 Alverton Terrace, Penzance TR18 4JH Tel: 01736 363741 Fax: 01736 330776 — BM 1982 Soton.; MRCGP 1987; DRCOG 1988. GP Penzance.

RYAN, John Francis Department of Histopathology, Chestnut Villa, Severalls Hospital, Colchester CO4 5HG Tel: 01206 852271 — MB BCh BAO 1980 NUI; MRCPath 1987. Cons. Pathol. Severalls Hosp. Colchester. Prev: Sen. Regist. (Histopath.) The Lond. Hosp.; Regist. (Histopath.) The Roy. Free Hosp.; SHO (Path.) W.m. Hosp. Lond.

RYAN, Mr John Mary 12 Perifield, London SE21 8NG — MB BCh BAO 1982 NUI; LRCPSI 1983; FRCS Ed. 1990.

RYAN, Katherine Elizabeth Rose Haematology Department, Central Middlesex NHS Trust, London NW10 7NS Tel: 020 8453 2112 Fax: 020 8965 1115 Email: kate.ryan@nwlh.nhs.uk; 73 Pennard Road, London W12 8DW Tel: 020 8749 5572 — MB BS 1981 Lond.; MD Lond. 1995; MRCP (UK) 1986; MRCPath 1993; FRC Path 2000. Cons. Haemat. N. W. Lond. Hosps. Prev: Lect. (Haemat.) Univ. Coll. Hosp. Lond.; Regist. (Haemat.) Whittington Hosp. Lond.; Research Fell. (Haemat.) Char. Cross & W.m. Med. Sch. Lond.

RYAN, Kathleen Elizabeth 7 Ambleside Close, Bromborough, Wirral CH62 7JF — MB ChB 1987 Sheff.

RYAN, Margaret Mary (retired) 55 Gleneagles Road, Urmston, Manchester M41 8SB Tel: 0161 748 8389 — MB ChB 1961 Manch.; FFA RCS Eng. 1969. Cons. Anaesth, Manch. Roy. Infirm. Prev: Regist. & Ho. Surg. Pk. Hosp. Davyhulme.

RYAN, Mark Francis 90 Thingwall Road, Wavertree, Liverpool L15 7LA — BM BS 1996 Nottm.

RYAN, Martin Fergus 78 Ashley Terrace, Edinburgh EH11 1RT — MB BCh BAO 1991 Belf.

RYAN, Martin Joseph Roche (retired) Withy House, Bamber Bridge, Preston PR5 6JD Tel: 01772 628357 — MB ChB 1942 Liverp. Prev: Capt. RAMC.

RYAN, Mary Frances Dept of Haematology, Altnagelvin Hospital, Glenshawe Road, Londonderry BT47 6SB Tel: 01504 34517 Email: mryan @alt.n-1nhs.uk — MB BCh BAO 1986 NUI; MRCP (UK) 1990; LRCPI & LM, LRCSI & LM 1986; DCH RCP Lond. 1990; MRCPath 1996. (Royal Coll. Of Surgeons Dublin) Cons., (Haemat.), Altnagelvin Area Hosp., Lond.derry.

RYAN, Mary Joan Louise 37 Gledhow Wood Road, Leeds LS8 4BZ — BM BCh 1980 Oxf.; MRCP (UK) 1984; DRCOG 1987.

RYAN, Mervyn Maurice Benjamin Longton Hall Surgery, 186 Longton Hall Road, Blurton, Stoke-on-Trent ST3 2EJ Tel: 01782 342532 — BM 1981 Soton.; BA (Engin. Sci. & Econ.) Oxf. 1969; DRCOG 1985. (Southampton) GP Stoke on Trent.

RYAN, Michael Francis Department of Biochemical Medicine, Ninewells Hospital, PO Box 120, Dundee DD1 9SY — MB ChB 1987 Ed.

RYAN, Michael Francis Castle Surgery, Kepwell Bank Top, Prudhoe NE42 5PW Tel: 01661 832209 Fax: 01661 836338 — MB ChB 1987 Edinburgh; MB ChB Edin. 1987. GP Prudhoe, N.d.

RYAN, Michael Patrick, MBE Health Systems Division, 2 Redheughs Rigg, South Gyle, Edinburgh EH12 9DQ Tel: 0131 317 7577 Fax: 0131 529 2266; 26 Cluny Gardens, Edinburgh EH10 6BJ Tel: 0131 447 2347 — BM BCh 1968 Oxf.; BSc (1st. cl. Hons.) Lond. 1959; Dip. Community. Med. Ed. 1976; FRCGP 1987, M 1974; MFCM 1980; DObst RCOG 1970. (Oxf. & St. Mary's) Med. Dir. Primary Care System Health Systms Div. Edin. Prev: Ho. Off.

RYANS

Cowley Rd. Hosp.; Ho. Off. Radcliffe Infirm. Oxf.; Ho. Off. Ch.ill Hosp. Oxf.

RYAN, Miranda Jane Residency Block, Greenwich Health Authority, Greenwich District Hospital, Vanbrugh Hill, London SE10 9HE — MB BS 1997 Lond.

***RYAN, Natalie Clare** 9 Town Lane, Sheet, Petersfield GU32 2AF — MB ChB 1996 Birm.

RYAN, Noel Patrick The Health Centre, Madeira Road, West Byfleet, Weybridge Tel: 01932 40411; Glenholme, Wych Hill Lane, Woking GU22 0AH Tel: 014862 63507 — MB BCh BAO 1976 NUI.

RYAN, Noreen Marie Ann 50 Sherrick Green Road, London NW10 1LD — MB BS 1996 Lond.

RYAN, Padraic John Joseph Glaxosmithkline, GSK House, 980 Great West Road, Brentford TW8 9ES Tel: 0208 0475351 Fax: 0208 0476952 Email: padraic.j.ryan@GSK.com — MB BCh BAO 1983 Dub.; FFDM 2000; MA Dub. 1992; MFOM RCP Lond. 1995; MRCGP 1988; T(GP) 1991; T(OM) 1995; DCH RCPSI 1986. (Univ. Dub. Trinity Coll) Director Glaxosmithkline Employee health Managem. Prev: Health & Safety Adviser Kraft Gen. Foods Ltd. Banbury.

RYAN, Patrick Benedict Forest End Surgery, Forest End, Waterlooville PO7 7AH; 26 Ferndale, Waterlooville PO7 7PA — MB BS 1983 Lond.; MRCGP (Distinc.) 1987; DCH RCP Lond. 1987; DRCOG 1987.

RYAN, Paul Francis Glenmill Medical Centre, 1191 Royston Road, Glasgow G33 1EY Tel: 0141 770 4052 Fax: 0141 770 4255 — MB ChB 1979 Glas.; FRCP 1999 Glas.; MRCGP 1983; DRCOG 1981; DCH Glas. 1981. (Glas.) Clin. Asst. (Geriat. Med.) Glas.; Chairm., Dennistown L.H.C.C.

RYAN, Paul John Medway Maritime Hospital Trust, Windmill Road, Gillingham ME7 5NY Tel: 01634 833889 Fax: 01634 846661 — MB BChir 1982 Camb.; MB BChir Camb. 1981; MA Camb. 1982; MSc Lond. Univ. 1991; MRCP (UK) 1986; MD Camb. 1998; FRCP 1999. (Cambridge and Guy's) Cons. Nuclear Med. Medway Hosp. Trust Gillingham.; Hon. Sen. Lect. (Nuclear Med.) Guy's Hosp.; Hon. Cons. (Nuclear Med.) Maidstone Mid. Kent Oncol. Centre. Socs: Amer. Soc. Bone & Mineral Research; Brit. Nuclear Med. Soc.; Eur. Assn. of Nuclear Med. Prev: Sen. Regist. (Nuclear Med.) Guy's Hosp. Lond.; Lect. (Nuclear Med. & Rheum.) Guy's Hosp. Lond.

RYAN, Peter Daniel Derriford Hospital, Derriford Road, Plymouth PL6 8BQ; 10 Grenville Road, Plymouth PL4 9PX — MB BCh 1987 Wales.

RYAN, Peter Donald 2 Upper Wimpole Street, London W1M 7TD Tel: 020 7935 9711 — MB BS 1967 Adelaide; DA Eng. 1976.

RYAN, Mr Peter George 85 Three Acres Lane, off Tythebarn Lane, Dickens Heath, Solihull B90 1NZ Tel: 0121 733 1291 Fax: 0121 733 1291 Email: pgeoryan@aol.com — BM 1978 Soton.; FRCS Ed. 1984; FRCS 1998. Cons. Urol. City Hosp. NHS Trust Birm.; Head of Div. Surg. Anaes. & Critical Care City Hosp. NHS Trust Birm.; Hon. Sen. Lect. (Surg.) Univ. Birm. Socs: Fell. Roy. Soc. Med.; BMA; Brit. Prostate Gp. Prev: Sen. Regist. Rotat. (Urol.) Qu. Eliz. Hosp. Birm.; Clin. Research Regist. (Urol.) St. Woolos Hosp. Newport, Gwent.

RYAN, Petrina Francis Maria O'Tierney, Murphy and Ryan, Health Centre, Summerhill, Warrenpoint, Newry BT34 3JD Tel: 028 4175 4100 Fax: 028 4175 4050; 44 Seaview, Warrenpoint, Newry BT34 3NJ Tel: 016937 74272 — MB BCh BAO 1987 NUI; LRCPSI 1987; MRCGP 1992; DMH Belf. 1992; DRCOG 1991. (Royal College of Surgeons in Ireland) Prev: Trainee GP Warrenpoint; SHO (O & G, Paediat., Med. Cas. & Surg.) Daisy Hill Hosp.; SHO (Psychiat.) Craigavon Area Hosp.

RYAN, Philip John Department of Respiratory Medicine, Hereford County Hospital, Hereford HR1 2ER Tel: 01432 364096 Fax: 01432 364137 Email: philipryan@btinternet.com; Email: philipryan@btinternet.com — MB ChB 1987 Birm.; FRCP 2001; MRCP (UK) 1990; MD 2000. Cons. (Thoracic Med.) Hereford Hosp. Socs: BMA; Brit.Thoracic Soc.; Brit. Soc. Of Allergy & Clin. Immunol. Prev: Regist. (Chest Med.) Birm. Heartlands Hosp.; Regist. (Chest & Gen. Med.) Birm. Gen. Hosp.; SHO (Chest Med.) Warwick Hosp.

RYAN, Philip Michael Barnard Castle Surgery, Victoria Road, Barnard Castle DL12 8HT Tel: 01833 690707 — MB BS 1979 Lond.; AFOM RCP Lond. 1991. Prev: Trainee GP N.allerton VTS; SHO (Infect. Dis.) St. Ann's Hosp. Lond.

RYAN, Robert Alphonsus Highlands, Greenway, Somers Road, Lyme Regis DT7 3EY Tel: 01297 443745 — MB BChir Camb. 1948; MRCS Eng. LRCP Lond. 1947; LMCC 1977; MRCGP 1971; DPH RCPS Eng. 1958. (Camb. & St. Thos.) GP Ripley; Med. Off. Ripley & Dist. Hosp. Socs: Derby Med. Soc. 1960-93; Derby Med. Soc. Prev: Cas. Off. & Ho. Surg. St. Thos. Hosp.

RYAN, Robert Gerard 24 Moorside, Sheffield S10 4LN — MB BCh BAO 1989 NUI; MRCPSI 1989.

RYAN, Robert John 12 Dows Road, Belfast BT8 8LB — MB BCh 1998 Belf.; MB BCh Belf 1998.

RYAN, Robert Patton 18 St Alban Road, Bedford MK40 2NG Tel: 01234 64285 — MB BS 1953 Durh.; FFCM 1980, M 1974; DPH Bristol 1959. (Newc.) DMO N. Bedfordsh. Health Auth.

RYAN, Miss Rowena Marion Northwick Park Hospital, Watford Road, Harrow HA1 3UW Tel: 020 8869 2963 — MB BCh BAO 1982 Dub.; FRCS (Orl.) Eng. 1989; FRCS (Gen. Surg.) Glas. 1986. p/t Cons. in ENT N.wick Pk. Hosp. & Centr. Middlx. Hosp. Prev: Sen. Regist. Roy. Nat. Throat, Nose & Ear Hosp.

RYAN, Sean Michael 27 Cotman Close, Westleigh Avenue, London SW15 6RG — MB BS 1991 Lond.

RYAN, Sean Seosap 3 Lindstrand Gardens, Limavady BT49 0TD — MB BCh BAO 1991 Belf.

RYAN, Sheila Margaret The Roseberry Centre, St. Lukes Hospital, Middlesbrough TS1 3AF Tel: 01642 854958; 33 The Front, Middleton-One-Row, Darlington DL2 1AS Tel: 01325 332456 — MB ChB 1968 Sheff.; MRCPsych 1981. (Newc.) Cons. Child & Adolesc. Psychiat. St. Lukes Hosp. Middlesbrough.

RYAN, Sheila Ruth (retired) 49 Abbot's Grove, Chester CH2 1AV Tel: 01244 381071 — MB ChB 1950 Liverp.; DObst RCOG 1952; DA Eng. 1954; FFA RCS Eng. 1958. Prev: SCMO Barnet HA.

RYAN, Steven William 20 Kirby Park, Wirral CH48 2HA; 19 Woodhall Close, Pudsey LS28 7TX — MD Leeds 1990, MB ChB 1981; MRCP (UK) 1984; DCH RCP Lond. 1985. Sen. Lect. (Child Health) Univ. Liverp. Prev: Tutor & Hon. Sen. Regist. (Paediat. & Child Health) Leeds Gen. Infirm.

RYAN, Terence David Richard Kinross, 8 Well Lane, Heswall, Wirral CH60 8NE — MB ChB 1972 Aberd.; FFA RCS Eng. 1981; FFA RCSI 1980; DCH Eng. 1975; DObst RCOG 1974. Cons. Anaesth. Roy. Liverp. Hosp. & Liverp. Matern. Hosp.

RYAN, Professor Terence John, KStJ Hill House, Abberbury Avenue, Iffley, Oxford OX4 4EU Tel: 01865 777041 — BM BCh 1957 Oxf.; DM Oxf. 1977, MA 1965; FRCP Lond. 1974, M 1965. Emerit. Prof. Oxon DHA (T); Emerit. Prof. Oxf. Brooks Univ. Socs: Chairm. Internat. Foundat. Dermat.; Hon. Pres. Internat. Soc. Dermat. Prev: Clin. Prof. Dermat. Oxf. Univ.; Hons. Cons. Dermat. Roy. Postgrad. Med. Sch. Hammersmith Hosp.; Sen. Lect. Inst. Dermat. Lond.

RYAN, Thomas Declan Salop Road Medical Centre, Salop Road, Welshpool SY21 7ER Tel: 01938 553118 Fax: 01938 553071; Springwater, Shadeoak, Guilsfield, Welshpool SY21 9BT Tel: 01938 2442 — MB BS 1977 Lond.; MRCS Eng. LRCP Lond. 1977; DRCOG 1984; DCH RCP Lond. 1983. Prev: Trainee GP Betws-y-Coed; SHO Birm. Matern. Hosp.; SHO Glos. Roy. Hosp.

RYAN, Thomas George Frazer 29A Cultra Avenue, Holywood BT18 0AZ — MB BCh BAO 1981 Belf.

RYAN, Ursula Saunton, Broseley Avenue, Culcheth, Warrington WA3 Tel: 0192 576213 — MB BCh BAO 1955 NUI.

RYAN, Mr William Gerard Department of Orthopaedic Surgery, F Block, Royal Bolton Hospital, Minerva Road, Farnworth, Bolton BL4 0JR Tel: 01204 390343; 1 Lyme Grove, Altrincham WA14 2AD Tel: 0161 928 6009 — MB ChB 1986 Manch.; FRCS Eng. 1990; FRCS (Orth) 1996. Cons. (Orthop. Surg.) Roy. Bolton Hosp. Prev: Lect. (Orthop. Surg.) Univ. Manch.; Regist. (Orthop. Surg.) Manch.; Sir Harry Platt Fell. Univ. Manch.

RYAN, William James Acre Day Hospital, Homefield Road, Worthing BN11 2HS — LRCPI & LM, LRSCI & LM 1973; LRCPI & LM, LRCSI & LM 1973; MRCPsych 1979.

RYANNA, Kimuli Barbara Wasonga 12 Vanguard Close, London E16 1PN — MB BS 1998 Lond.; MB BS Lond 1998.

RYANS, Robert Ian Castle Practice, Carrickfergus Health Centre, Taylors Avenue, Carrickfergus BT38 7HT Tel: 028 9331 5805 Fax: 028 9331 5947 — MB BCh BAO 1986 Belf.; MSOM 1998; MRCGP 1991; DFFP 1993; DMH Belf. 1990; DCH RCPSI 1990; DRCOG 1988. (Qu. Univ. Belf.) Gen. Pract., Castle Pract., Carrickfergus;

RYATT

Hosp. Pract. Ulster Hosp. Dundonald; Musculoskeletal Prive Pract., Dundonald Physiother. & Sports Injury Clinic, Camber Rd., Dundonald; Med. Mem., Indep. Tribunal Serv., Belf.; Gen. Research Fell., Univ. of Ulster. Prev: Trainee GP W. Lothian VTS; SHO (Gen. Med.) Ulster Hosp. Dundonald; SHO (O & G) Waveney Hosp. Ballymena.

RYATT, Kamaljit Singh 17 Yateley Road, Edgbaston, Birmingham B15 3JP — MD 1984 Manch.; MB ChB 1973; MRCP (UK) 1977. Cons. (Dermat.) Manor Hosp. Walsall & The Skin Hosp. Birm.; Hon. Sen. Lect. Univ. Birm. Prev: Lect. & Hon. Sen. Regist. (Dermat.) Gen. Infirm. Leeds; Sen. Regist. (Gen. & Geriat. Med.) Hope Hosp. Salford, Withington; Hosp. Manch. & N. Manch. Gen. Hosp.

RYATT, Lisel Karen The Broadway Surgery, 3 Broadway Gardens, Monkhams Ave IG8 0HF — MB BS 1994 Lond.; BSc Lond. 1992; DFFP 1997; DGM 1996; DRCOG 1997; MRCGP (Merit) 1998. (London Hospital Medical College) GP Non - Principle.

RYBA, Penelope Catherine Jane Dysart Surgery, 13 Ravensbourne Road, Bromley BR1 1HN Tel: 020 464 4138 — BM BCh 1987 Oxf.; MRCGP 1991; DRCOG 1990. p/t GP Princip. Prev: Trainee GP Oxf. VTS; Ho. Off. (Gen. Med.) Oxf. HA; Ho. Off. (Gen. Surg.) Glos. HA.

RYBINSKI, Eugene Augustyn Burncross Surgery, 1 Bevan Way, Chapeltown, Sheffield S35 1RN Tel: 0114 246 6052 Fax: 0114 245 0276 — MB ChB 1980 Sheff.; MRCS Eng. LRCP Lond. 1980; MRCGP 1986.

RYBINSKI, Paul 1 Carsick Hill Way, Sheffield S10 3LY — MB BS 1998 Lond.; MB BS Lond 1998.

RYCROFT, Henry David Davidsons Mains Medical Centre, 5 Quality Street, Edinburgh EH4 5BP Tel: 0131 336 2291 Fax: 0131 336 1886 — MB BS 1973 Lond.; BSc (Physiol., Hons.) St. And. 1968; MRCS Eng. LRCP Lond. 1973; T(GP) 1991; DObst RCOG 1976. (St. Geo.) p/t Med. Adviser N. Marine Managm. Ltd & Brit. Underwater Engin Leith; Med. Examr.uk.Offshore.Oil.Assn; Med. Examr. Marine Safety Agency (MSA); Med. Examr. Nonwegian Maritime Directorate; Med. Examr. Dutch Min. of Mines (offshore Div.); Offshore & Diving Doctor Norwegian Directorate of Health; Health & Safety Exec. Approved Diving Doctor; HSE Approved Blood Lead Doctor; WHO Approved Yellow Fever Doctor & Immunisation Centre. Prev: Med. Adviser Rigblast Aberd.; Med. Adviser (Cydesdale Bank plc.) Med. Adviser Santa Fe construction Leith.

RYCROFT, John Alfred (retired) Rushes House, Charlton, Malmesbury SN16 9EA Tel: 01666 823607 — MB BS 1951 Lond.; DMRT Eng. 1964. Prev: Asst. Radiotherap. N. Staffs. Regional Radiother. Centre.

RYCROFT, Nicole Elizabeth Child Health Centre, Hospital Road, Bury St Edmunds IP33 3ND Tel: 01284 775075 Fax: 01284 750280 Email: n.rycroft@doctors.net.uk — MB BS 1972 Lond.; MRCS Eng. LRCP Lond. 1972; DCH Eng. 1975. (Westm.) Lead Cons. Paediat. Dept. of Community Paediat.; Forens. Med. Examr. Suff. Constab. Socs: RCPCH; Brit. Assn. Community Child Health. Prev: SCMO (Community Health) Unit W. Suff. HA; Med. Off. Community Child Health Serv. Edin.; Med. Dir. & Cons. Paediat. Community Child Health Mid Anglia Community Trust.

RYCROFT, Richard John Graham St. John's Institute of Dermatology, St. Thomas's Hospital, London SE1 7EH Tel: 020 7922 8076 Fax: 020 7620 0890; 197 Sycamore Road, Farnborough GU14 6RQ Tel: 01252 543695 — MB BChir 1971 Camb.; MA Camb. 1971, MD 1982; FRCP Lond. 1987; FFOM RCP Lond. 1991, MFOM 1982; DIH Eng. 1976. (Guy's) Cons. Dermatol. St. John's Inst. Dermat. St. Thomas Hosp. Lond.; Sen. Med. Adviser (Dermat.) Health & Safety Exec. Lond. Socs: Fell. Roy. Soc. of Med. Lond.; Fell. of St John's Hosp. Dermatological Soc. (Past- Pres); Brit. Assn. Dermatols. Prev: Sen. Regist. (Dermat.) St. John's Hosp. Dis. Skin. Lond.; Regist. (Dermat.) Guy's Hosp. Lond.; SHO (Med.) Hammersmith Hosp. Lond.

RYDER, Christine 16 Graham Park Road, Gosforth, Newcastle upon Tyne NE3 4BH — MB ChB 1958 Ed. Socs: N. Eng. Soc. Anaesth.

RYDER, Clive Alexander John 40 Harrow Road, Selly Oak, Birmingham B29 7DN — MB ChB 1984 Birm. SHO (Med. Rotat.) Russell's Hall Hosp. Dudley.

RYDER, Geoffrey Horace (retired) 3 Jagos Slip, Packet Quays, Falmouth TR11 2UA Tel: 01326 317239 Email: ghr@jagossup.freeserve.co.uk — MB BS 1955 Lond.; FFA RCS Eng. 1965; DA Eng. 1957. Prev: Cons. Anaesth. Walsgrave Hosp. Coventry.

RYDER, Ian George 47 Langfield Road, Knowle, Solihull B93 9PS — MB ChB 1984 Bristol; FRCA 1989. Sen. Regist. (Anaesth.) S. W.. RHA. Prev: Vis. Asst. Prof. Univ. Maryland, USA; Regist. (Anaesth.) Wessex Regional Train. Scheme.

RYDER, Jeffrey Eric Northdown Surgery, St Anthony's Way, Cliftonville, Margate CT9 2TR Tel: 01843 296413 Fax: 01843 231231; 48 Devonshire Gardens, Cliftonville, Margate CT9 3AD Tel: 01843 228339 — MB BS 1971 Lond.; MRCS Eng. LRCP Lond. 1971; DObst RCOG 1973. (Roy. Free) Prev: Ho. Off. (Med.) Coppetts Wood Hosp. Lond.; Med. Off. (Surg.) St. Albans City Gen. Hosp.

RYDER, Jessica Clare Bellegrove Surgery, 174 Bellegrove Road, Welling DA16 3 EW Tel: 020 8856 9648 — MB ChB 1996 Manch.; BSc 1994 St. Andrews University; DRCOG 2000 Lond.; DFFP 2000 Lond. Salaried Gen. Practitioner BelleGr. Surg., Welling. Prev: GP Regist. Ct. Yard Surg., Etham; Obst. & Gyn. SHO, Qu. Mary's Hosp. Sidcup; Paediatric SHO, Qu. Mary's Hosp. Sidcup.

RYDER, John James Dynamic Psychotherapy Service, Humberstone Grange Clinic, Thurmaston Lane, Leicester LE5 0TA Tel: 0116 225 6430 Fax: 0116 225 6432 — MB ChB 1974 Birm.; S. Trent Train. In Dynamic Psychother. 2001; MRCPsych 1979. (Birm.) Specialist Regist. (Psychother.) Dynamic Psychother. Serv. Leic. Prev: Cons. Psychiat. & Psychother. Heronbrook Hse. (Therap. Community for Clergy & Religious) W. Midl.

RYDER, Joseph Bryan (retired) 4 Lansdowne Court, Causey Hill, Hexham NE46 2LP Tel: 01434 3220 — MB BCh BAO 1948 Dub.; MB BCh BAO (Hons.) Dub. 1944; MD Dub. 1948; FRCPI 1969, M 1946; FRCP Lond. 1972, M 1951; Cert. Internat. Med. RCPS Canada 1955. Prev: Chest Phys. Mt.ain Sanat. Hamilton, Ont.

RYDER, Kathryn Olivia PO Box 6779, Dundee DD1 9WN — MB BS 1985 Lond.; DPhil Oxf. 1992; BSc Lond. 1982; MRCP (UK) 1988. (Middlesex London) Civil Servant. Prev: Research Fell. John Radcliffe Hosp. Oxf.; MRC Train. Fell. (Cardiovasc. Med.) John Radcliffe Hosp. Oxf.; SHO (Med.) N.wick Pk. Hosp. Harrow.

RYDER, Michael Herbert (retired) St. David's Home, Castlebar Hill, London W5 1TE Tel: 020 8997 5121 — MRCS Eng. LRCP Lond. 1942; DPH Lond. 1962. Prev: Deptm. Med. Off. Glos. AHA.

RYDER, Patrick Gerard Matthew Ryder Clinic, 20 Dingle Road, Upholland WN8 0EN Tel: 01695 624331 — MB BCh BAO 1982 NUI. SHO (A & E) Warrington Dist. Gen. Hosp., Gen. Practitioner, Upholland, Lancs.; Hosp. Practitioner Gastroenterol., Wrightington, Wigan, Leigh Hosp. Trust. Socs: PCGS Primary Care; Gastroenterol. Dept. Prev: Mem. Professional Fees Comittee, BMA 2001-2002.

RYDER, Robert Charles 16 Llantrisant Road, Llandaff, Cardiff CF5 2PX — MB BCh 1959 Wales; FRCPath 1983, M 1966. Cons. Path. Mid Glam. AHA.

RYDER, Robert Elford John Department of Diabetes, Endocrinology & Lipid Metabolism, City Hospital NHS Trust, Dudley Road, Birmingham B18 7QH Tel: 0121 554 3801 Fax: 0121 507 4988 Email: bob.ryder@cityhospbham.wmids.nhs.uk; 29 Brueton Avenue, Solihull B91 3EN Tel: 0121 705 3067 Fax: 0121 705 3067 — MB BCh 1977 Wales; MD Wales 1988; FRCP Lond. 1996; MRCP (UK) 1981; T(M) 1991. Cons. Phys. Diabetes & Endocrinol. City Hosp. NHS Trust Birm. Prev: Sen. Regist. (Med.) Roy. Hallamshire Hosp. Sheff.; Research Fell. Diabetic Unit Univ. Wales Coll. Med. Cardiff; Regist. (Med.) Univ. Hosp. Wales Cardiff.

RYDER, Sally-Ann 198 Dover Road, Walmer, Deal CT14 7NB — MB BS 1993 Lond.

RYDER, Stephen David Department of Medicine, 4th Floor, South Block, Queens Medical Centre, Nottingham NG7 2UH Tel: 0115 970 9155 Fax: 0115 942 4554; 31A Fernhead Road, London W9 3EX Tel: 020 8960 2975 — BM BS 1985 Nottm.; DM Nottm. 1993; MRCP (UK) 1988. Cons. Hepatol. Qu. Med. Centre Nottm. Prev: Sen. Regist. (Liver Studies) Kings Coll. Hosp. Lond.

RYDER, Timothy Simon The Surgery, 1 Kew Gardens Road, Richmond TW9 3HL Tel: 020 8940 1048 Fax: 020 8332 7644 — MB BS 1989 Lond.; MRCGP 1993; DRCOG 1993.

RYDER, William (retired) Department of Anaesthesia, Royal Victoria Infirmary, Newcastle upon Tyne NE1 4LP Tel: 0191 232 5131 — MB ChB 1958 Ed.; FFA RCS Eng. 1965; DA Eng. 1963. Cons. Anaesth. Roy. Vict. Infirm. Newc.

RYDING, Alisdair Duncan Stuart Flat 5, The Hanover, Hine Hall, Mapperley, Nottingham NG3 5PL — MB ChB 1996 Ed.

RYDING, Frank Noel, OBE Pine Lodge, Dinmore Road, Bodenham, Hereford HR1 3JR — MB BS 1972 Lond. (Univ. Coll. Hosp.) Med. Off. Internat. Comm. Red Cross. Prev: Regist. (Anaesth.) Hereford HA; Med. Off. Brit. Antarctic Survey; Regist. (Anaesth.) RiksHosp.et, Oslo, Norway.

RYDON, Arthur Harold Bruce 3 Roeheath, North Chailey, Lewes BN8 4HR — MRCS Eng. LRCP Lond. 1945; DTM & H Eng. 1956, DPH 1957. (Westm.) Socs: Roy. Soc. Health. Prev: RAMC; Dep. MOH Mombasa, Kenya.

RYE, Adam David 43 Waterloo Gardens, Cardiff CF23 5AB Tel: 029 2074 2373 Email: rye@cf.ac.uk — MB ChB 1992 Bristol; MRCP (UK) 1995; Dip RCPath (Royal Coll. Of Path.) 1999. Specialist Regist., Haemot., Univ. Hosp. Wales, Cardiff.

RYE, Gillian Patricia Osborne Avenue Surgery, 5 Osborne Avenue, Jesmond, Newcastle upon Tyne NE2 1PQ Tel: 0191 281 0041; Tel: 0191 281 8239 — MB BS 1982 Newc.; MRCGP 1986; DCCH Manch. 1987.

RYE, John George 2685 2nd Avenue W., Prince Albert SK S6V 5E3, Canada Tel: 0013067645793 Email: jrye@sk.sympatico.ca; 11 Clarendon Road, Christchurch BH23 2AB — MRCS Eng. LRCP Lond. 1977. (Bristol) Anaesth. & Family Phys. P. Albert S. Hill Med. Centre. Canada. Socs: Fell. Roy. Soc. Med. Prev: Regist. (Anaesth.) Lond. Hosp.; SHO (Anaesth.) St. Geo. Hosp. Lond.; Ho. Off. (ENT) Guy's Hosp. Lond.

RYE, Kara Anne 21 Mill Farm Close, Dunchurch, Rugby CV22 6QL — MB ChB 1996 Leic.

RYE, Stephen St. Chad's Surgery, Midsomer Norton, Bath BA3 2UH Tel: 01761 413334 Fax: 01761 411176; Asquith House, Gurney Slade, Bath BA3 4TD Tel: 01749 840461 — MB BS Lond. 1969; MRCS Eng. LRCP Lond. 1969; Dip. Palliat. Med. Wales 1993; DCH Eng. 1972; DObst RCOG 1971. (Middlx.) Prev: SHO (Accid. & Orthop.) Kettering Hosp. Gp.; Regist. (Paediat.) Kettering Gp. Hosps.

RYECART, Christine Noel Regal Chambers, 50 Bancroft, Hitchin SG5 1LL Tel: 01462 453232; Tel: 01462 431216 — MB BChir 1981 Camb.; MA Camb. 1983; DRCOG 1987. Princip. GP Hitchin. Prev: SHO (O & G & A & E) Lister Hosp. Stevenage; SHO (Geriat.) Hitchin Hosp.

RYLAH, Lindsey Thomas Alan Basildon Hospital, Nether Mayne, Basildon SS16 5NL Tel: 01268 533911 Fax: 01268 592250 Email: lindsey@rylah.fsnet.co.uk; 6 Penwood Close, Billericay CM11 1DY Tel: 01277 631098 — MB BS 1977 Lond.; FFA RCS 1982 Eng.; MRCS Eng. LRCP 1977 Lond.; MSc 2000; MBA 1996; MBA 1996; MRCS Eng. LRCP Lond. 1977; FFA RCS Eng. 1982. (Westm.) Cons. Anaesth. Basildon & Thurrock Trust; Hon. Lect. St. Bart. Med. Sch. Lond.; Hon. Lect. Roy. Lond. Med. Sch. Socs: Expert Panellist Comm. Safety of Med., 1999 -. Prev: Dir. Critical Care Regional Burns Unit St. And. Hosp. Billericay; Sen. Regist. (Anaesth.) Yorks. RHA; Regist. (Anaesth.) W.m. Hosp. Lond.

RYLANCE, George William Children's Hospital, Steelhouse Lane, Birmingham B4 6NH Tel: 0121 454 4851 Fax: 0121 450 6577; 44 St. Agnes Road, Moseley, Birmingham B13 9PN Tel: 0121 449 2623 — MB ChB 1970 Glas.; MRCP (UK) 1974; DObst RCOG 1972. Cons. Paediat. & Paediat. Clin. Pharmacol. The Childr. Hosp. Ladywood Middleway; Vis. Prof. McGill Univ. Montreal. Prev: Lect. (Child Health) Univ. Dundee & Ninewells Hosp. Dundee; Regist. (Paediat.) Univ. Hosp. of Wales, Cardiff; SHO (Paediat.) St. Mary's Hosp. Lond.

RYLANCE, Jonathan Mark 31 Summer La, Halton, Runcorn WA7 2AF — BM BS 1997 Nottm.

RYLANCE, Paul Brian Renal Unit, New Cross Hospital, Wolverhampton WV10 0QP Tel: 01902 307999 Fax: 01902 643192; Roughton Farmhouse, Roughton, Worfield, Bridgnorth WV15 5HE Tel: 01746 716399 Email: pbrylance@aol.com — MB BS 1977 Lond.; BSc (1st cl. Hons.) Lond. 1977; FRCP Lond. 1994; MRCP (UK) 1980. (St. Geo.) Cons. Phys. & Nephrol. New Cross Hosp. Wolverhampton; Sen. Clin. Lect. (Med.) Univ. Keele; Hon. Sen. Lect. (Nephrol.) Inst. Urol. Lond. & Univ. Wolverhampton; Chairm. Midl. Lipid Gp. Socs: Renal Assoc.; Amer. Soc. Of Nephrol.; Euro. Renal Assoc. Prev: Lect. & Hon. Sen. Regist. (Nephrol.) St. Peter's Hosps., Inst. Urol. & Univ. Coll. Hosp. Lond.; Research Fell. (Nephrol.) Kings Coll. Hosp. Med. Sch.; Regist. Rotat. (Med.) St. Geo. Hosp. Lond.

RYLANCE, Wendy Sheila Duncan Street, Wolverhampton WV2 3AN Tel: 01902 459076 Fax: 01902 455309; Roughton Farm House, Roughton, Worfield, Bridgnorth WV15 5HE Tel: 01746 716399 — MB BS 1978 Lond.; MRCGP 1982; DRCOG 1989; DCH Eng. 1980. (St. Geo.) GP. Socs: RCOGP. Prev: Jt. Chair Wolverhampton Commiss.ing Forum; GP Clin. Asst. (Gastroenterol.) New Cross Hosp. Wolverhampton; Clin. Asst. (Diabetes) Roy. Hosp. Wolverhampton.

RYLAND, David Andrew Rose Street, Todmorden OL14 5AT — MB BS 1967 Lond.; MRCP (UK) 1970; MRCS Eng. LRCP Lond. 1967; MRCGP 1977. (Guy's) p/t GP Tutor (Clin. Med. Educat.) Postgrad. Centre Halifax Gen. Hosp. Prev: Lect. (Epidemiol. in Gen. Pract.) Cardiothoracic Inst. Lond.; Dep. Resid. Med. Off. Brompton Hosp. Lond.; Ho. Phys. Guy's Hosp. Lond.

RYLAND, Jonathan Michael 7 Sydenham Terrace, Covington Road, Westbourne, Emsworth PO10 8SZ — MB BS 1986 Lond.; BSc Lond. 1983, MB BS 1986. SHO (O & G) Lond. GP VTS.

RYLAND, Olga Blethyn (retired) St. Govans, Frances Road, Saundersfoot SA69 9AH Tel: 01834 813301 — MB BS Lond. 1942; MRCS Eng. LRCP Lond. 1942.

RYLANDS, Alison Jane 16 Coronation Drive, Crosby, Liverpool L23 3BN Tel: 0151 931 5918 — MB BS Lond. 1986; MA Camb. 1987; BSc (Hons.) Manch. 1978; MPH Liverp. 1991; MFPHM RCP (UK) 1996. (Char. Cross & Westm.) Cons. (Pub. Health Med.) Wirral HA. Prev: Regist. (Pub. Health Med.) Mersey RHA; SHO (Med.) Roy. Liverp. & W.m. Hosps.; Ho. Off. W.m. Hosp.

RYLE, Anthony Munro Centre, Guy's Hospital, London SE1 9RT Tel: 020 7378 3210 Fax: 020 7955 2983 Email: rylecat@cs.com; 3 Goulton Road., London E5 8HA Email: ryleat@cs.com — BM BCh 1949 Oxf.; DM Oxf. 1960; FRCPsych 1980, M 1973; DObst RCOG 1952. (Oxf. & Univ. Coll. Hosp.) p/t Sen. Research Fell. Kings coll & Hon. Cons. Psychother. Div. Psychiat. Guy's Hosp. Lond. Socs: Roy. Soc. of Med.; Pres., Assn. of Cognitive Analytic Ther. Prev: Cons. Psychother. St. Thos. Hosp. Lond.; Ho. Surg. (Obst.) & Ho. Phys. Univ. Coll. Hosp.; Ho. Surg. Colindale Sanat.

RYLE, Cym Anthony Havant Health Centre Suite C, PO Box 44, Civic Centre Road, Havant PO9 2AT Tel: 023 9247 4351 Fax: 023 9249 2524 — BM 1977 Soton.; MRCGP 1981; DCH Eng. 1980; DRCOG 1979. GP Princip.; Bd. Mem. & Clin. Governance Lead E. Hants PCG.

RYLE, Derek Marsden 1 Holmesdale Road, Teddington TW11 9LJ Tel: 020 8977 2220 — MB BS Lond. 1949; AFOM RCP Lond. 1980. (Middlx.) Prev: Ho. Off. Mt. Vernon Hosp. & Radium Inst. N.wood, Char. Cross Hosp.; Unit, N.wood & Kingsbury Matern. Hosp. Lond.

RYLE, Frederick Robert (retired) Whitmoor, Chalk Pit Lane, Monxton, Andover SP11 8AR Tel: 01264 710388 — MB BChir Camb. 1949; MRCGP 1972. Prev: Med. Ref. DHSS S. Region Reading.

RYLEY, Helen Elizabeth The Surgery, Station Road, Clayton, Bradford BD14 6JA Tel: 01274 880650 Fax: 01274 883256; 10 Beechwood Avenue, Wibsey, Bradford BD6 3AF Tel: 01274 677934 — MB BS 1984 Lond.; MA (Hons.) Camb. 1985; MRCGP 1988; DRCOG 1987. Trainee GP Bradford VTS.

RYLEY, Jonathan Paul Ashford Mental Health Centre, 1 Elwick Road, Ashford TN23 1PD Tel: 01233 643407 — BM BCh 1981 Oxf.; MA Camb. 1982; MRCPsych 1987. Cons. Psychiat. (Psychotherapist.) SE Kent HA.

RYLEY, Nicholas Gavin Department of Histopathology, Torbay Hospital, Lawes Bridge, Torquay TQ2 7AA — BM BCh 1984 Oxf.; MA Camb. 1985; MRCPath 1991; FRCPath 1999. Cons. Path. S. Devon Healthcare NHS Trust. Prev: Cons. Path. King Edwd. VII Hosp. Midhurst; Clin. Lect. Nuffield Dept. Path. John Radcliffe Hosp. Oxf.

RYLEY, Simon Philip Berkeley Place Surgery, 11 High Street, Cheltenham GL52 6DA Tel: 01242 513975 — MB ChB 1981 Birm.; MA Camb. 1979; MRCGP 1985; DCH RCP Lond. 1985; DRCOG 1983.

RYMAN, Ann Elizabeth South Tyneside Trust, 10/12 Franligton Place, Newcastle upon Tyne; Thorn Wood, Elm Bank Road, Wylam NE41 8HT — MB ChB 1986 Ed.; BSc (Hons.) Ed. 1984; MRCPsych 1994; MRCGP 1991; DRCOG 1991; Cert. Family Plann. JCC 1990; Mphil. Univ. Of Edinb. 1997. (Ed.) Sen. Regist. (Psychiat.) Newc. &

RYMASZEWSKI

N. Region. Prev: SHO/Regist. (Psychiat.) Lothian HB; Clin. Med. Off. N. Manch. HA; Trainee GP Langley Pk. Co. Durh. VTS.

RYMASZEWSKI, Olgierd (retired) 67 Lyndhurst Avenue, Hazel Grove, Stockport SK7 5LT Tel: 0161 483 5876 — MD Polish Sch. of Med. 1946.

RYMER, Janice Mary Department of Obstetrics & Gynaecology, 6th Floor, N. Wing, St Thomas Hospital, London SE1 7EU Tel: 020 7928 9292 Fax: 020 7620 1227; 56 Scott Sufferance Wharf, 5 Mill St, London SE1 2DE — MB ChB 1981 Auckland; MD Lond. 1994; MRCOG 1987; FRNZCOG 1989. Cons. & Sen. Lect. O & G GUY's, Kings, & St. Thomas Hosp.Lond. Socs: Coun: Mem. RCOG.; Coun. Mem. Brit. Menopause Soc.

RYMER, Michael John Worthing Hospital, Worthing BN11 2DH Tel: 01903 01903 205111; Courtyard House, Greyfriars Lane, Storrington, Pulborough RH20 4HE Tel: 01903 746451 Fax: 01903 746451 — MB BS Lond. 1970; MRCS Eng. LRCP Lond. 1970; MRCOG 1984; FRCOG 1998. (St. Bart.) Cons. O & G Worthing HA. Prev: Sen. Regist. (O & G) Poole Gen. Hosp.; Assoc. Specialist (O & G) W. Dorset Hosp. Dorchester.

RYMES, Nichola Lyndsay — MB ChB 1987 Bristol; MRCP UK; MRCPath UK. Cons. Haemat. Prev: Regist. W. Midls. Haemat. Rotat.; Sen. Regist. (Haemat.) W. Midls.

RYRIE, Gillian Elizabeth Carronbank Medical Practice, Denny Health Centre, Carronbank House, Denny FK6 6GD Tel: 01324 822382 Fax: 01324 826675; 241 Main Street, Larbert FK5 4RA Tel: 01324 553649 — MB ChB 1971 Glas.; DObst RCOG 1974.

RYTINA, Edward Robert Charles Rose Cottage, 36 Glinton Road, Helpston, Peterborough PE6 7DQ — MB BS 1984 Lond.; BSc Lond. 1981, MB BS 1984.

SA'AD, Mr Zahida Ahmad Edinburgh Breast Unit, Western General Hospital, Crewe Road S., Edinburgh EH4 2XU — MB BCh 1973 Al Azhar, Egypt; LRCP LRCS Ed. LRCPS Glas. 1985; FRCS Glas. 1981.

SA'ADU, Alfa Care of Elderly Department, Watford General Hospital, Vicarage Road, Watford WD18 0HB Tel: 01923 217227 Fax: 01923 217577; 2 Kendalmere Close, Muswell Hill, London N10 2DF Tel: 020 8444 4535 Fax: 020 8444 0919 Email: a.saadu@btinternet.com — MB BS 1976 Lond.; PhD (Immunol.) Lond. 1989; BSc (Anat.) Lond. 1973; MSc Clin. Trop. Med. Lond. 1985; MRCP (UK) 1979; DTM & H RCP Lond. 1984. (Univ. Coll. Hosp.) Cons. Phys. Watford Gen. Hosp.; Sen. Lect. UCL Med. Sch. 1995; 2nd Nat. Vice-Pres. Nigerian Med. Assn. Prev: Cons. Phys. Gen. Hosp. Bida, Nigeria 1982-1984; Clin. Lect. & Sen. Regist. (Gen. & Geriat. Med.) Univ. Coll. Lond. Med. Sch. 1992-1994; Sen. Regist. (Clin. Immunol.) Clin. Research Centre Harrow 1988-1992.

SAAB, Mr Michael Bury General Hospital, Bury BL9 6PG — MB BCh BAO 1984 NUI; FRCS Ed. 1994: Sen. Regist. (A & E) Stockport & Manch. Prev: Regist. (A & E) St. Peters Hosp. Chertsey; SHO (Thoracic Surg.) Harefield Hosp.; SHO (surg.) Hammersfield Hosp.

SAAD, Adnan 41 Nathans Road, North Wembley, Wembley HA0 3RZ — MB BS 1996 Lond.

SAAD, Belgami Mohammed c/o Dr S. Ahmed, 58 Buchanan Drive, Bearsden, Glasgow G61 2EP — MB BS 1987 Gulbarga, India.

SAAD, El Sayed Mostafa Flat 28, Moss Manor, The Avenue, Sale M33 4SH — MB BCh 1954 Cairo; LMSSA Lond. 1975; MRCPsych 1972; DIH Eng. 1967; DPM Eng. 1969; DTM & H Liverp. 1967. (Kasr-El Aini) Cons. Psychiat. Bridgwater Hosp. Manch. Prev: Sen. Regist. (Psychiat.) W. Chesh. Hosp. & Moston Hosp. Chester; Regist. & SHO (Psychiat.) Carlton Hayes Hosp. NarBoro.

SAAD, Farahnaz Sherwood Rise Surgery, 31 Nottingham Road, Sherwood, Nottingham NG7 7AD Tel: 0115 962 3080 Fax: 0115 985 6522.

SAAD, Isam El Din Babiker Flat 2, Stratheden Place, Reading RG1 7BH — MB BS 1985 Khartoum, Sudan; MRCP (UK) 1992.

SAAD, Karim Fouad Georgi The Caludon Centre, Clifford Bridge Rd, Walsgrave, Coventry CV2 2TE Tel: 024 76 602020 Email: karimsaad@yahoo.com — MB ChB 1985 Alexandria; MRCPsych 1992. Cons. (Old Age Psych).

SAAD, Mr Khalil Jabbour 6 Anne Arundel Court, Heathhall, Dumfries DG1 3SL — Lekarz 1971 Lodz; FRCSI 1984. (Lodz, Poland) Assoc. Specialist in Orthop. Dumfries & Galloway Roy. Infirm. NH Trust Dumfries.

SAAD, Mr Magdy Naguib The Princess Margaret Hospital, Osborne Road, Windsor SL4 3SJ Tel: 01753 851753 Fax: 01753 851753 Email: mns@buckhurst.demon.co.uk; Old Titness, Buckhurst Lane, Ascot SL5 7QB Tel: 01344 623949 Fax: 01344 291046 — MB BCh Alexandria 1958; FRCS Eng. 1964; FRCS Ed. 1964; MRCS Eng. LRCP Lond. 1964. (Alexandria) Hon. Cons. Plastic Surg. Heatherwood & Wexham Pk. Hosps. Trust. Socs: Fell. Roy. Soc. Med. (Ex-Pres.) Plastic Surg. Sect.; (Ex-Pres.) Brit. Assn. Plastic Surgs.; (Ex-Pres.) Brit. Assn. Aesthetic Plastic Surgs. Prev: Sen. Regist. (Plastic Surg.) Odstock Hosp. Salisbury; Sen. Regist. (Plastic Surg.) Liverp. RHB & United Liverp. Hosps.; Regist. (Plastic Surg.) Mt. Vernon Hosp. N.wood.

***SAAD, Marniza** 22 Huntsmead Close, Thornhill, Cardiff CF14 9HY — MB BCh 1997 Wales.

SAADA, Janak Norfolk and Norwich University Hospital, Colney Lane, Norwich NR4 7UY — MB BS 1987 Lond.; BSc (Hons.) Lond. 1984; MRCP (UK) 1990; FRCR 1994. (University College Hospital Medical School London) Cons. Radiol. Norf. & Norwich Univ. Hosp. Prev: Sen. Regist. (Radiol.) Roy. Free Hosp. Hampstead NHS Trust.

SAADAH, El Sayed Mohamed Sussex Rehabilitation Centre, Brighton General Hospital, Elm Grove, Brighton BN2 3EX Tel: 01273 674391 Fax: 01273 605063; Montrose, 87 Woodland Drive, Hove BN3 6DF Tel: 01273 554333 — MB BCh 1967 Ain Shams; MSc Surrey 1979. (Ain Shams Med. Sch. Cairo) Dir. Rehabil. & Cons. Rehabil. Med. Brighton Gen. Hosp. Prev: Regist. (Orthop.) Hull Roy. Infirm., Ipswich & S.end Gen. Hosps.

SAADAH, Mohga Ali Montrose, 87 Woodland Drive, Hove BN3 6DF Tel: 01273 554333 — MB BCh 1970 Ain Shams; DA Eng. 1978. Clin. Med. Off. (Community Med. & Child Health) Mid Downs HA. Socs: Fac. Comm. Health; Brit. Assn. Community Drs in Audiol. Prev: Regist. (Anaesth.) Roy. Marsden Hosp. Sutton, Guildford Hosp. & Frimley Pk. Hosp. Camberley.

SAADEH, Imad PO Box 14235, Damascus, Syria Tel: 00 963 11 2245118; 10 Wonston Road, Lordwood, Southampton SO16 5JH — MD 1984 Damascus; MRCPI 1993. Cons. Neurol. & Head Neurophysiol. Dept. Teshreen Hosp. Damascus, Syria. Socs: Collegiate Mem. Roy. Soc. Phys. Irel.

SAADIEN-RAAD, Maurice Halifax General Hospital, Free School Lane, Halifax HX1 2YP — MB BCh 1974 Witwatersrand.

SAAFAN, Ahmed Amin Morsi Maindiff Court Hospital, Abergavenny NP7 8NF — MB BCh 1976 Ain Shams.

SAAGANDI, Mr Francis Wee 18 Bryony Road, Harrogate HG3 2UQ; 31 Perseverance Road, Haleland Park, Maraval, Port of Spain, Trinidad, West Indies Tel: 809 629 3224 — MB BCh BAO 1980 NUI; MPhil (Biol. Med. Sci.) Bradford 1993; FRCS Ed. 1986; MRCS Eng. LRCP Lond. 1980; LRCPI & LM, LRCSI & LM 1980; DTM & H Liverp. 1984. (Roy. Coll. Surgs. Irel.) Cons. Gen. Surg. Eric Williams Med. Scs. Comlpex Champs Fleurs, Trinidad, W. Indies; Assoc. Lect. (Surg.) Univ. W. Indies, St. Augustine, Trinidad. Prev: Sen. Regist. (Gen. Surg.) Gen. Hosp., Port of Spain; Regist. (Gen. Surg.) P.ss Roy. Hosp. Hull & Maidstone Gen. Hosp.

SAAKWA-MANTE, Kwaafo (retired) 22B Denbigh Place, London SW1V 2HA — MB ChB 1952 Leeds; MSc Aberd. 1964; MFCM 1974; DPH RCPS Eng. 1956. Prev: Med. Statistician & Community Health Specialist Min. Health Ghana.

SAARY, Mihaly 1 Chester Gardens, London W13 8EP — MB BS Lond. 1964; MRCP (UK) 1971; FRCPath 1987, M 1976. Cons. Haemat. Omnilabs Lond.; Cons. Haemat. Cromwell Hosp. Lond. Socs: Brit. Soc. Haematol.; RSM. Prev: Cons. Haemat. Nat. Guard Hosp. Jeddah, Saudi Arabia & Corniche Hosp. Abu Dhabi; Sen. Regist. (Haemat.) St. Bart. Hosp. Lond.

SAAYMAN, Anton Gerhard King Edward VII Hospital, Midhurst GU29 0BL; 4 Heathfield Close, Midhurst GU29 9PS — MB ChB 1991 Stellenbosch.

SABA, George Yousef Saleh 9 Dee Court, Ribble Road, Liverpool L25 5PW — MB BS 1982 Jordan; FRCA 1994.

SABA, Hisham Peter Tudor House Surgery, 43 Broad Street, Wokingham RG40 1BE Tel: 0118 978 3544 Fax: 0118 977 0420; 4 Stafford Close, Woodley, Reading RG5 4QZ — MB BS 1985 Lond.; BSc Lond. 1982, MB BS 1985; MRCGP 1993; DRCOG 1992.

SABA, Tarek Sami Zahi Wansbeck General Hospital, Woodhorn Lane, Ashington NE63 9JJ Tel: 01670 521212; 23 Abberbury Road, Iffley, Oxford OX4 4ET Tel: 01865 747771 — MB ChB 1992 Ed. Ho. Off. (Cas. & Anaesth.) Wansbeck Gen. Hosp. Ashington.

SABAN, Paul Anthony Pope Woodhead & Associates Ltd., The Old Grammar School, 1 Ramsey Road, St Ives, Huntingdon PE27 5BZ Tel: 01480 465811 Fax: 01480 497970 Email: paul.saban@popewoodhead.co.uk; 47 Rooks Street, Cottenham, Cambridge CB4 8QZ Tel: 01954 250905 — MB BS 1990 Lond. Project Manager Med. Communications Agency Cambs.

SABANATHAN, Kanagasabesan West Norwich Hospital, Bowthorpe Road, Norwich NR2 3TU Tel: 01603 628377 — MB BS 1972 Ceylon; MRCP (UK) 1981; FRCP (UK) 1994. (Colombo) Cons. Phys. (Geriat. Med.) Norwich Hosp. Prev: Sen. Regist. (Geriat. Med.) Leicester Gen. Hosp.; Regist. (Thoracic Med.) St. Thos. Hosp. Lond.

SABAR, Mansoor Ahmad 2 Wilderswood Close, Manchester M20 4XU; 7 rutland Road, Ellesmer parks, Eccles, Manchester M30 9FA Tel: 0161 789 8513 — MB ChB 1985 Manch.; FRCA 1994. (Manch)

SABARATNAM, Subodhini 6 Cobham Avenue, Sittingbourne ME10 4RD — MB BCh 1993 Wales.

SABAT, Atif Lotfy 31 Woodlands Park Road, London N15 3RU — MB BCh 1980 Assiut, Egypt.

SABBAGH, Walid Hull Royal Infirmary, Anlaby Road, Hull HU3 2JZ — MB ChB 1992 Aberd.

SABBAT, Jan Kazimierz Mikolaj 120 Worple Road, Wimbledon, London SW19 4JB — MB BS 1985 Lond.; BSc Lond. 1979; MRCP (UK) 1989.

SABBAT, Jolanta Maria Merck, Sharp & Dohme Idea Inc., Warsaw Branch, Przasnyska Ga, Warszawa 01-756, Poland Tel: 00 48 22 639 7000 Fax: 00 48 22 639 7001 Email: jolanta_sabbat@mercle.com; 38 Parkside, London SW19 5NB — MB BS 1980 Lond.; BSc Lond. 1974; MRCPath 1988; MSc Lond. 1996. (University College Hospital Medical School) Director Healthcare Policy MSD Warsaw, Poland. Prev: WHO Liaison Off. (Pub. Health) Poland; Sen. Regist. (Chem. Path.) Roy. Free Hosp. Lond. & W. Middlx. Hosp.

SABETI, Hamid 53 Rossmore Court, Park Road, London NW1 6XY Tel: 020 7723 1897 — MD 1961 Tehran; DLO RCS Eng. 1983. Clin. Asst. (ENT) Roy. Lond. & Bart. Hosps. Prev: Assoc. Prof. (ENT) Univ. Teheran; Prof. (ENT) Univ. Teheran; Dean Razi Med. Sch. Univ. Teheran.

SABETI, Mona 5 Rowantree Drive, Sale M33 3PA — MB ChB 1996 Manch.

SABETIAN, Mr Manuchehr 27 Welbeck Street, London W1M 7PG Tel: 020 7224 2242 Fax: 020 7224 2493; 7 Boscastle Road, London NW5 1EE Tel: 020 7485 1888 — MB BS 1954 Durh.; ChM Liverp. 1962; FRCS Eng. 1967; FRCS Ed. 1958. (Durh.) Cons. Surg. Lond. Welbeck Hosp. Socs: Mem. World Assn. Hepato-pancreaticobiliary Surg.; BMA; Assoc. Mem. of B.A.U.S. (Brit.Ass of Urological Surg.s). Prev: Sen. Regist. (Surg.) Roy. N.. Hosp. Lond.; Sen. Regist. St. Mark's Hosp. Lond.; Regist. (Surg.) Liverp. Roy. Infirm.

SABHARWAL, Mr Atul Jiwan Raj Yorkhill NHS Trust, Royal Hospital for Sick Children, Glasgow G3 8ST Tel: 0141 201 0000 Fax: 0141 357 3824 Email: asabharw@udcf.gla.ac.uk — MB ChB 1990 Aberd.; FRCS Glas. 1995. (Univ. Aberd.) Specialist Regist. (Paediat. Surg.) Roy. Hosp. For Sick Childr., Glas. Prev: ECMO Clin. & Research Fell. Yorkhill Childr. Hosp. Glas.

SABHARWAL, Mrs Chander Kanta The Surgery, 19 Lancelot Road, Wembley HA0 3AL Tel: 020 8903 0609 — MB BS 1969 Jammu & Kashmir; DObst RCOG 1971. (Srinagar Med. Coll.)

SABHARWAL, Narindar Nath The Surgery, 19 Lancelot Road, Wembley HA0 3AL Tel: 020 8903 0609 — MB BS 1965 Delhi; DTM & H Liverp. 1967. (Maulana Azad Med. Sch.) Prev: Cas. Off. Plymouth Gen. Hosp. & Hertford Co. Hosp.; Ho. Off. (Gen. Med.) Lond. Jewish Hosp.

SABHARWAL, Nikant Kumar 19 Lancelot Road, Wembley HA0 2AL — BM BCh 1996 Oxf.; BSc Lond. 1993. (UMDS Oxf.) SHO (Gen. Med.) N.wick Pk. Hosp. Harrow Middlx.

SABHARWAL, Mrs Sangeeta Department of Obstetrics and Gynaecology, Scunthorpe General Hospital, Cliff Gardens, Scunthorpe DN15 7BH — MB BS 1984 Delhi; MRCOG 1989. Cons. O & G Scunthorpe Gen. Hosp.

SABHARWAL, Mr Tarun Kanwarlal 4 Oakley Close, Isleworth TW7 4HZ Tel: 020 8847 5949 — MB BCh 1990 Wales; FRCSI 1994; FRCR 1997. (Cardiff) Regist. (Radiol.) Char. Cross Hosp. Lond. Prev: SHO (Orthop & Trauma & A & E) Morriston Hosp. Swansea; Demonst. (Anat.) Univ. Birm.

SABHERWAL, Peter 5/7 Ballyoran Hill, Portadown, Craigavon BT62 1DJ — MB BCh BAO 1989 Belf.

SABIH, Irfan 64 Bermuda Road, Nuneaton CV10 7HU — MB BS 1986 Karachi.

SABIH, Mohammad Raouf Kingston Hospital, Galsworthy Road, Kingston upon Thames KT2 7QB Tel: 020 8546 7711 Fax: 020 8974 8388; 12 Ullswater Crescent, London SW15 3RQ Tel: 0208 549 2550 Fax: 0208 459 2550 — MB BCh 1972 Ain Shams; DRCOG 1990. Staff Grade (O & G) Kingston Hosp. Surrey. Prev: Regist. & Clin. Asst. (O & G) Kingston Hosp. Surrey.

SABIN, Mr Howard Ian Royal London Hospital, Department of Neurosurgery, Whitechapel, London E1 1BB Tel: 020 7377 7250 Fax: 020 7377 7024; Chase Cottage, Torrell's Hall, Willingale, Ongar CM5 0SP — MB ChB 1981 Dundee; BMSc (Hons.) Dund 1978; FRCS Eng. 1986; FRCS Ed. 1986. Cons. Neurosurg. St. Bart. Hosp. Lond. & Roy. Lond. Hosp.; NeroSurgic. Tutor, Roy. Coll. of Surg.s of Eng. Lond.. Socs: Brit. Cervical Spine Soc.; Soc. Brit. Neurol. Surgs. Prev: Sen. Regist. (Neurol. Surg.) Qu. Sq. Lond.; Regist. (Clin. Neurosci.) W.. Gen. Hosp. Edin.; Research Fell. Inst. Neurol. Qu. Sq. Lond.

SABIR, Abdul W St Davids Court Surgery, 1 St. Davids Court, 68a Cowbridge Road East, Cardiff CF11 9DU Tel: 029 2030 0266 Fax: 029 2030 0273.

SABIR, Azra Tanweer Waheed 3 Balmoral Close, Lisvane, Cardiff CF14 0EX — MB BS 1972 Bangalor; MB BS Bangalore 1972; MRCPsych 1982. (Bangalore Med. Coll.) Cons. (Child & Family Psychiat.) Brynffynon Mid. Glam. Prev: Sen. Regist. (Child & Family Psychiat.) Cardiff; Regist. (Child Psychiat.) Roy. Hosp. Sick Childr. Glas.

SABIR, Hakimuddin Mohamedali (retired) The Mushrique, 38 Penycae Road, Port Talbot SA13 2EL Tel: 01639 882260 — MB BS 1948 Bombay.

SABIR, Maryam Saba 34 Wheatlands Drive, Bradford BD9 5JJ — MB ChB 1994 Leic.

SABIR, Nadeem Murtaza 9 Berkeley Crescent, Moseley, Birmingham B13 9YD — MB BS 1996 Lond.

SABIR, Omeima Mohy Eldin 57 St Nicholas Street, Carlisle CA1 2EF — MB BS Khartoum Sudan 1986; MRCP (UK) 1992; DCCH RCP Ed. 1993; DCH RCP Lond. 1991.

SABIR, Mr Saleem 56 Holland Street, Hyson Green, Nottingham NG7 5DS — MB BS 1989 Punjab; FRCS Eng. 1994.

SABISTON, Margaret Alison Castlehill Health Centre, Castlehill, Forres IV36 1QF Tel: 01309 672233 Fax: 01309 673445; Redcliffe, Prospect Terrace, Lossiemouth IV31 6JS Tel: 0134 381 3018 Email: nsabiston@aol.com — MB ChB 1975 Aberd.; LFHom 1995. Clinic Spynie Hosp. Elgin.

SABISTON, Neil Laich Medical Practice, Clifton Road, Lossiemouth IV31 6DJ Tel: 01343 812277 Fax: 01343 812396; Redcliffe, Prospect Terrace, Lossiemouth IV31 6JS Tel: 0134 381 3018 — MB ChB 1975 Aberd.; FRCGP 1995, M 1979.

SABONADIERE, Paul Francis 138 Brampton Road, St Albans AL1 4PY — MB ChB 1990 Otago.

SABOURIN, Andrew Cole Hilary Cottage Surgery, Keble Lawns, Fairford GL7 4BQ Tel: 01285 712377 Fax: 01285 713084 — MB BS 1987 Lond.; MRCGP 1991; DCH RCP Lond. 1990.

SABOURN, Paul William 11 Claremont Gardens, Whitley Bay NE26 3SF — MB BS 1983 Newc.; MRCGP 1990.

SABRI, Adel Mohammed El-Sayed Wrexham Maelor Hospital, Croesnewydd Road, Wrexham LL13 7TD Tel: 01978 291100; 24 Harlech Drive, Rhiwderin, Newport NP10 8QS — MB ChB 1980 Alexandria; FFA RCSI 1992.

SABRI, Kourosh Ophthalmology Dept, Leicester Royal Infirmary, Leicester LE2 7LX Tel: 0116 254 1414 — MB ChB 1994 Bristol; FRCOphth 1999. Specialist Regist. (Ophth.) Leicester Roy Infirm. Leicester. Socs: FREphth.

***SABRI, Reehan** 82 Virginia Road, Thornton Heath, Croydon CR7 8EJ Email: shamil@cableinet.co.uk — MB BS 1997 Lond.

SABRINE, Nilofer 4 Lomond Place, Ladybridge, Bolton BL3 4PS Email: n.sabrine5@virgin.net — MB ChB 1989 Sheff.; MRCP (UK) 1994; DCH RCP Lond. 1994. (Univ. Sheff.) Specialist Regist. (Neonat.) S. Cleveland Hosp. Middlesbrough.

SABRINE, Syed Fakhrus Deansgate Health Centre, Deansgate, Bolton BL1 1HQ Tel: 01204 399800 — MB BS 1956 Karachi; DTM & H Liverp. 1960; DCH RCPS Glas. 1965. (Dow Med. Coll.) Prev:

SABROE

Regist. (Med.) Co. Hosp. Louth; Regist. (Med.) W. Bromwich & Dist. Hosps.; Regist. (Paediat.) Rochdale, Bury & Rossendale Hosp. Gp.

SABROE, Ian Leukouyk Biology Section, Biomedical Sciences Division, Imperial College School of Medicine, London SW7 2AZ Email: i.sabroe@ic.ac.uk — MB BS 1989 Lond.; BSc Lond. 1986, MB BS 1989; AKC Lond. 1986; MRCP (UK) 1992; PhD Lond. 1998. (King's Coll.) Research Fell., Imperial Coll. Prev: MRC Clin. Train. Fell. (Appled Pharmacol.) Nat. Heart & Lung Inst.; Regist. & Acting Sen. Regist. (Respirat. Med.) Hammersmith Hosp. Lond.

SABROE, Ruth Allison Dept of Dermatology, Greenwich District Hospital, London SE1 7EH — MB ChB 1988 Sheff.; BMedSci. Sheff. 1986; MRCP (UK) 1991; MD 1999. Cons. (Dermat.) Greenwich Dist Hosp. Lond. Prev: Hon. Sen. Regist. (Dermat.) & Research Fell. St. John's Inst. of Dermat. St. Thos. Hosp. Lond.; Regist. (Dermat.) Bristol Roy. Infirm.; SHO (Dermat.) W.m. Hosp. Lond. .

SABUR, Riyazali Yusufali Lochthorn Medical Centre, Heathhall, Dumfries DG1 1TR Tel: 01387 259944 Fax: 01387 264932; Mill Cottage, Duncow, Dumfries DG1 1TB — MB BCh 1981 Wales; Dip. Travel Med. Glasgow 1998. GP Princip. Dumfries. Prev: Trainee GP Dumfries; Trainee GP/SHO (Cas.) Roy. Aberd. Childr. Hosp.; Regist. Rotat. (Surg.) Aberd. Roy. Infirm.

SACCO, Dominic Francis 11 Primrose Gardens, Hatch Warren, Basingstoke RG22 4UZ — MB BS 1998 Lond.; MB BS Lond 1998.

SACCO, Joseph 85 Hollins Road, Walsden, Todmorden OL14 6PG — MB BCh BAO 1955 NUI; DPH Bristol 1970; TDD Wales 1958.

SACH, Mr Michael Accident and Emergency Department, West Suffolk Hospital, Hardwick Lane, Bury St Edmunds IP33 2QZ Tel: 01284 713024 Fax: 01284 713024; The Chestnuts, Parsonage Green, Cockfield, Bury St Edmunds IP30 0HB Tel: 01284 828122 Fax: 01284 828122 Email: michael.sach@btinternet.com — MB ChB 1974 Birm.; FRCS Eng. 1981; FFAEM 1994. Cons. A & E W. Suff. Hosp. Bury St. Edmunds. Socs: Brit. Assn. of Accid. and Emergencey Med.; Fell.of Fac. of Accid. & Emergencey Med.; Brit. Med. Assn. Prev: Cons. & Head of A & E Dept. Roy. Naval Hosp. Haslar; Higher Professional Trainee A & E Med. RN Hosp. & Affil. NHS Centres; Sen. Regist. (A & E) Soton Gen. Hosp.

SACHA, Mr Bhupinder Singh Hollycroft Medical Centre, Clifton Way, Hollycroft, Hinckley LE10 0XN Tel: 01455 234414 Fax: 01455 632110; 5 Lance Close, Burbage, Hinckley LE10 2NT — MB BS. 1969 Rajasthan; 1975 MS ENT Rajasthan. (Rajasthan) GP Hinckley Leics.; Hosp. Practitioner (ENT). Prev: Assoc. Specialist (ENT) & Sen. Med. Off. (Audiol) N. Manch. Dist.; Regist. (ENT) N. Manch. Dist. (T); Clin. Tutor (ENT) S.M.S. Med. Coll. Hosp. Jaipur.

SACHAR, Amrit 59 Woodfield Road, Hounslow TW4 6LL — MB BS 1993 Lond.

SACHDEV, Arun Pal Singh 26 Albany Avenue, Eccleston Park, Prescot L34 2QW — MB BS 1998 Lond.; MB BS Lond 1998.

SACHDEV, Balwant Singh 2453 Mande Ville Drive, Laguna Hills, California 92653, USA; 67 Hill Side Road, Tonyrefail, Porth Tel: 01443 670591 — MB BS 1933 Punjab; Dipl. Tuberc. Dis. 1953. (K.E. Med. Coll. Lahore) Socs: BMA; Thoracic Soc. Wales. Prev: Med. Off. Mardy Hosp. Merthyr Tydfil; Med. Off. i/c Tuberc. Clinic Gurdaspur, India.

SACHDEV, Bhavesh 36 Addington Road, South Croydon CR2 8RB — MB BS 1994 Lond.

SACHDEV, Nitin Hamish Doctors' Residence, Ninewells Hospital, Dundee DD1 9SY Email: n.sachdev@dundee.ac.uk — MB ChB 1997 Dundee.

SACHDEV, Roopinder Singh 26 Albany Av, Eccleston Park, Prescot L34 2QW — MB ChB 1997 Sheff.

SACHDEVA, Lalta Queens Road Surgery, 7 Queen's Road, Tunbridge Wells TN4 9LL Tel: 01892 520027 Fax: 01892 540833; Mankash, Tree Lane, Plaxtol, Sevenoaks TN15 0QH Tel: 01732 810082 — MB BS 1962 Delhi. Prev: Regist. (Anaesth.) Falkirk & Dist. Roy. Infirm.

SACHDEVA, Rajiv First Floor Flat, 88 Oakley St., London SW3 5NP — MB BS 1988 Newc. PHO Stud. Imperial Coll. Roy. Marsden Hosp. Lond. Prev: SHO (A & E) Sunderland Dist. Gen. Hosp.; Ho. Off. (Surg.) Roy. Vict. Infirm. Newc. u. Tyne; Ho. Off. (Med.) Freeman Hosp. Newc. u. Tyne.

SACHDEVA, S K Queens Road Surgery, 7 Queen's Road, Tunbridge Wells TN4 9LL Tel: 01892 520027 Fax: 01892 540833 — MB BS 1962 Panjab; MB BS 1962 Panjab.

SACHS, John Andre (retired) Department of Immunology, St Bartholomew's and The Royal London School of Medicine, and Dentistry, West Smithfield, London EC1A 7BE Email: j.a.sachs@mds.qmw.ac.uk — PhD Lond. 1970; MB ChB Cape Town 1961; FRCPath 1990, M 1980; Dip. Biochem. Lond 1965. Emerit. Reader in Immunol. St. Bartholomews & Roy. Lond. Sch. of Med. Lond. Prev: Cons. Immunol. Roy. Lond. Trust.

SACHS, Martin Flat 2, 8 Palace Gardens Terr., London W8 4RP Tel: 020 7229 6867 — MB BS 1960 Sydney; MRCOG 1966. Prev: Regist. (O & G) Hillingdon Hosp. Uxbridge; SHO (Gyn.) Hammersmith Hosp. Lond.

SACKETT, Katherine Mary Park House, Park Road, Stroud GL5 2JG Tel: 01453 562100; Email: km@sackett.globalnet.co.uk — MB ChB 1983 Birm.; MRCPsych 1989. (Birm.) Cons in Gen. Psychiat. Stroud. Prev: Sen. Regist. (Psychother.) Bristol.

SACKEY, Adziri Harold Mid Cheshire Hospitals, Leighton Hospital, Crewe CW1 4QJ Tel: 01270 255141 Fax: 01270 612186 — MB ChB 1982 Univ. Ghana; MRCP (UK) 1990; FRCPCH 1997. (Univ. Ghana Med. Sch.) Cons. Paediat. Mid Chesh. Hosps. Socs: BMA; FRCPCh.; Brit. Soc. of Paediatric, Endocrinol. & Diabetes. Prev: Cons. Paediat. W. Cumbria NHS Trust; Sen. Regist. (Paediat.) Hull Roy. Infirm.; Regist. Roy. Liverp. Childr.'s Hosp.

SACKIN, Paul Albert Alconbury and Brampton Surgeries, The Surgery, School Lane, Alconbury, Huntingdon PE28 4EQ Tel: 01480 890281 Fax: 01480 891787; Flat 12 Stukeley Park, Chestnut Grove, Great Stukeley, Huntingdon PE28 4AD Tel: 01480 434198 Fax: 01480 437587 Email: paulsackin@compuserve.com — MB BS Lond. 1970; BSc (Pharmacol.) Lond. 1966; MRCS Eng. LRCP Lond. 1970; FRCGP 1987, M 1974; DObst RCOG 1972. (Univ. Coll. Hosp.) GP Huntingdon; Asst. Edr. Educat. for Gen. Pract.; VTS Course Organiser Camb. VTS. Socs: (Pres.) Balint Soc. (1996-99). Prev: Hon. Sec. Assn. Course Organisers; Tutor (Gen. Pract.) Huntingdon; Course Organiser Huntingdon VTS.

SACKS, Basil Alan 157 Amersham Road, Beaconsfield HP9 2EH Tel: 01494 677702 Fax: 01494 670588 — MB ChB Cape Town 1966; MFGP (Coll. Med. S.Afr.). Socs: Med. Assn. S. Afr.; Amer. Soc. Bariatric Phys.s; Fac. Gen. Pract. Coll. Med. S. Afr.

SACKS, Benjamin Israel 45 Hill Top, London NW11 6EA Tel: 020 8455 9107 — MB ChB 1956 Cape Town; MPhil. Lond. 1970; MRCPsych 1972. Prof. Ment. Handicap Char. Cross & W.m. Med. Sch. Lond.

SACKS, Gavin Paul 79 Meadway, London NW11 6QJ; 294 Woodstock Road, Oxford OX2 7NW — BM BCh 1992 Oxf.; BA (Hons.) Camb. 1989. Clin. Research Asst. Nuffield Dept. O & G John Radcliffe Hosp. Oxf. Prev: SHO (O & G) Rosie Matern. Hosp. Camb. & St. Jas. Hosp. Leeds; Ho. Off. (Surg.) John Radcliffe Hosp. Oxf.

SACKS, Gerald Edmund Manor Surgery, Osler Road, Headington, Oxford OX3 9BP Tel: 01865 762535; Quarry Top Cottage, 69 Quarry High St, Headington, Oxford OX3 8JX Tel: 01865 308363 — MB ChB 1967 Leeds; MB ChB (Distinc.) Leeds 1967; MRCGP 1983. (Leeds) Hon. Vis. Fell Oxf. Brookes Univ.; Club Doctor Oxf. United Football Club; Mem. Green Coll. Oxf.

SACKS, Lisa Jennifer Frenchay Hospital, Beckspool Road, Frenchay, Bristol BS16 1LE Tel: 0117 975 3994 Fax: 0117 975 3846 Email: lisa.sacks@laruelle.freeserve.co.uk — MB BCh 1986 Witwatersrand; FRCS (Lond.) 1998; MMed (Plastic) Witwatersrand 1996; FCSC (Plast) Coll Med S Afr 1994; BSc Witwatersrand 1981. Cons. Plastic Surg. Frenchay Hosp. Bristol. Socs: Brit. Assn. of Plastic Surgs.; Brit. Soc. Surg. Hand.

SACKS, Mark David 20 Belsize Square, London NW3 4HT — MB ChB 1991 Cape Town.

SACKS, Mr Nigel Philip Michael Royal Marsden Hospital, Fulham Road, London SW3 6JJ Fax: 020 7808 2782 Email: nigel.sacks@rmh.nthames.nhs.uk — MB BS 1980 Melbourne; MS Melbourne 1989; FRCS Eng. 1990; FRACS 1989. (Univ. Melbourne) p/t Cons. Surg. The Roy. Marsden & Hon Sen. Lect. Int. of Cancer Research Lond..; Hon. Cons. Surg. Roy. Brompton Hosp. Socs: Brit. BrE. Gp.; BASO (BrE. Gp.); Roy. Soc. Med. Prev: Sen. Lect. & Hons. Cons. Surg. Roy. Marsden Hosp. & Inst. of Cancer Research Lond.; Lect. & Hon. Sen. Regist. John Radcliffe Hosp. Oxf.; Sen. Regist. City Hosp. Nottm.

SACKS, Simon Lawrence The Montpelier Surgery, 2 Victoria Road, Brighton BN1 3FS Tel: 01273 328950 Fax: 01273 729767

— MB BS 1972 Lond.; MRCGP 1980. Med. Off. Brighton & Hove Jewish Home for the Aged.

SACKS, Professor Steven Howard Renal Unit, Guy's Hospital, St Thomas St., London SE1 9RT Tel: 020 7955 4151 Fax: 020 7407 4909 — MB ChB 1975 Bristol; BSc Bristol 1972, MB ChB 1975; PhD Camb. Univ. 1982; FRCP Lond. 1991; MRCP (UK) 1978. Head of Renal Med. Guy's King's & St. Thomas's Sch. Of Med., King's Coll. Lond. Prev: Tutor (Med.) Nuffield Dept. Med. John Radcliffe Hosp. Oxf.; Regist. (Med.) Addenbrooke's Hosp. Camb.; MRC Fell. MRC Laborat. Molecular Biol. Camb.

SACKVILLE WEST, Jane Eleanor Kentish Town Health Centre, London NW5 2AJ Tel: 020 7530 4747 — MB BS 1989 Lond.; DCH RCP Lond. 1992; DRCOG 1992; MRCGP 1994. (Roy.Free.Hosp) GP; Clin.Tutor.UCL.

SACKWOOD, Sidney (retired) 2 Fernhill Lane, Upper Hale, Farnham GU9 0JJ — MB BS 1954 Lond. Prev: Cons. A & E Dept. Frimley Pk. Hosp. Surrey.

SACOOR, Mahomed Hanif Allimahomed Silverstream, Hamm Court, Weybridge KT13 8YB — MB ChB 1963 Sheff.; MRCP Lond. 1967.

SADABA, Mr Justo Rafael Dept. of Cardiothoracic Surgery, Leeds General Infirmary, Great George St., Leeds LS1 3EX Tel: 0113 293 6657; 2 Nunroyd Avenue, Moortown, Leeds LS17 6PN — LMS 1991 Basque Provinces; LMS Basque Provincces 1991; FRCS Ed 1996. Res. Fell. (Cardiothor. Surg.) Leeds Gen Infirm. Leeds. Socs: Eur. Assoc. of Cardiothor. Surg.

SADANA, Mr Arvinder 18 Claremont Park, London N3 1TH — MB BS 1984 Lond.; BSc Pharmacol. Lond. 1981; FRCS Ed. 1989; MRCP (UK) 1987. Cons. A & E Whipps Cross Hosp. Lond. Prev: Sen. Regist. (A & E) Whipps Cross Hosp. Lond.; Regist. (A & E) Whittington Hosp. Lond.

SADDLER, John Mackay Department Anaesthetics, Royal Devon & Exeter Hospital, Barrack Road, Exeter EX2 5DW — MB ChB 1981 Zimbabwe; LRCP LRCS Ed. LRCPS Glas. 1981; FRCA 1986.

SADDLER, Nicola Jill 22 Ennerdale Road, Doncaster DN2 5QR — MB BS 1990 Lond.

SADEK, Mustafa The Surgery, 9 Drakewood Road, London SW16 5DT Tel: 020 8679 6126 — MB BS 1964 Dhaka; MSc Lond. 1968; MRCPI 1976; DTM & H Liverp. 1974. GP Lambeth, S.wark & Lewisham FPC.

SADEK, Rafik Ismail Mohammed 18 Rowan Park, Roundswell, Barnstaple EX31 3QR — MB BChir 1982 Camb.; BA Camb. 1978, MB BChir 1982.

SADEK, Saher Tel: 0121 711 4455 — MB BCh 1980 Ain Shams; MSc (Obst. & Gyn.) Ain Shams 1985; MD Leic. 1996; MRCOG 1988. Cons. O & G Solihull Hosp. Birm. Prev: Sen. Regist. (FetoMatern. Med.) Roy. Matern. Hosp. Belf.; Sen. Regist. Rosie Matern. Hosp. & Addenbrooke's Hosp. Camb.; Clin. Research Assoc. Univ. Leicester.

SADHEURA, Mohinder Kumar 44 St Albans Road, Ilford IG3 8NL — MB BS 1989 Lond.

SADHRA, Kesar Singh 27 Orchard Avenue, Southall UB1 1LF — MB BS 1981 Lond.; MRCP (UK) 1987; MRCGP 1988; DRCOG 1989; DCH RCP Lond. 1987.

SADIDEEN, Mr Munir 175 Express Drive, Goodmayes, Ilford IG3 9RD — MD 1973 Damascus; FRCS Ed. 1981.

SADIEQ, Shamas Ahmed — MB ChB 1993 Dundee; Dip. Family Plann 1998. (Ninewells Hospital Medical School (Dundee)) Vocationally Trained GP. Socs: St. Paul.

SADIK, Sabah Rasoul Rochester Health Centre, Delce Road, Rochester ME1 2EL Tel: 01634 813738 Fax: 01634 831009 — MB ChB 1974 Baghdad; FRCPsych 1996, M 1982; DPM Eng. 1983. (Baghdad Med. Sch.) Cons. Psychiat. (Learning Disabil.) Rochester Health Centre; Hon. Sen. Lect., Kent Uni.; Clin. Dir., Learning Disabilities; Med. Dir., Thames Gateway NHS Trust. Socs: BMA; Fell. Roy. Soc. Med.; World Psychiat. Assn. Prev: Chief Psychiat. Armed Forces Hosp. Khamis, Saudi Arabia; Cons. & Sen. Lect. (Psychiat. Ment. Handicap) Guy's Hosp. Lond.

SADIK, Samir Monir Waterloo Medical Centre, 1 Dunkerley St., Ashton-under-Lyne OL7 9EJ Tel: 0161 330 7087 Fax: 0161 308 2788 — LRCP LRCS 1983 Ed.; MB BS Khartoum 1977; LRCPS Glas. 1983. p/t Clin. Asst. (c/o the Elderly).

SADIK, Wallaa Bashar c/o Haematology Department, Walton Hospital, Rice Lane, Liverpool L9 1AE — MB ChB 1973 Baghdad; MRCP (UK) 1987.

SADIQ, Farakh Jamil Hyde Park Surgery, 3 Woodsley Road, Leeds LS6 1SG Tel: 0113 295 1235 Fax: 0113 295 1220 — MB ChB 1992 Leeds.

SADIQ, Mr Hafiz Asadullah 23 Rannoch Drive, Glasgow G61 2JJ Tel: 0141 943 2495 Fax: 0141 201 0865 — MB BS 1985 Karachi; FRCS Ed. 1992. Assoc. Specialist (Otolaryngol.) Roy. Hosp. Sick Childr. Glas.

SADIQ, Mohamed Najumudeen Mohamed 41 Egerton Gate, Shenley Brook End, Milton Keynes MK5 7HH — MB BS 1965 Ceylon; MRCP (UK) Paediat. 1983; DCH RCP Lond. 1981; DCH Sri Lanka 1976. (Colombo) SCMO (Child Health) Milton Keynes Community NHS Trust. Prev: Paediat. Nawalapitiya Hosp. Sri Lanka; Regist. (Paediat.) Wycombe Gen. Hosp. High Wycombe; SHO (Paediat.) Pilgrim Hosp. Boston.

SADIQ, Mustafa 9 Talbot Road, Fallowfield, Manchester M14 6TA — MB ChB 1987 Dundee.

SADIQ, Mr Pervaiz Iqbal 13 Ferriby Lane, Scartho, Grimsby DN33 3NU — MB BS 1982 Punjab, Pakistan; FRCSI 1990.

SADIQ, Pervez Muhammad Hillside House, Hillside Road, Huyton, Liverpool L36 8BJ Tel: 0151 489 4539 — MB BS 1977 Punjab; MRCP (UK) 1986; DGM RCP Lond. 1986.

SADIQ, Mr Saghir Ahmed Royal Eye Hospital, Oxford Road, Manchester M13 9WH Tel: 0161 276 1234 Fax: 0161 276 6618 — MB BS 1987 Lond.; FRCS Ed. 1992; MRCOphth 1990; DO RCS Eng. 1990. Cons. (Ophth. Surg.) Roy. Eye Hosp. Manch. Prev: Regist. (Ophth.) Univ. Hosp. Nottm. & King's Mill Hosp. Mansfield; SHO (Ophth.) Kingston Hosp. Surrey & St. Geo. Hosp. Lond.

SADIQ, Syed Tariq 2 Long Walk, New Malden KT3 3EJ Email: tsadi@msn.com — BM 1989 Soton.; MSc Lond. 1994; DTM & H 1994; MRCP 1996. Specialist Regist. HIV.

SADIQ, Miss Syeda Shaheena Qamar 70 Brynteg, Cardiff CF14 6TT Tel: 029 2061 8525; Department Radiology, University Hospital of Wales, Heath Park, Cardiff CF14 4XW Tel: 029 2074 7747 Fax: 01222 743838 — MB BS 1993 Lond.; BSc Pharmacology Lond. 1990; FRCS Lond 1998. (Charing Cross & Westminster) Specialist Regist. (Diagnostic Radiol.) Univ. Hosp. Wales, Cardiff. Prev: Sen. SHO (Gen. Surg.) P.ss of Wales Hosp. Bridgend; Sen. SHO Orthop. Cardiff Roy. Infirm.; Sen. SHO Gen. Surg. Llandough Hosp. Cardiff.

SADIQ, Zulfiqar Ali 75 Meltham Avenue, Withington, Manchester M20 1FE — MB ChB 1993 Sheff.

SADIQUE, Mr Tanveer Manor Hospital, Walsall NHS Trust, Moat Road, Walsall WS2 9PS Tel: 01922 721172 Ext: 7287 Fax: 01922 656836; 25 Canning Road, Park Hall, Walsall WS5 3HN Tel: 01922 625466 Fax: 01922 625466 — MB BS 1981 Karachi; FRCS Ed. 1989; FRCS (Orth.) 1995. Cons. Orthop. & Trauma Surg. Manor Hosp. Walsall NHS Trust Walsall; Mem. RCS Fac. for Train. Basic Surgic. Skills; UK Mem. AO Instruc.s Fac. Socs: BOA; AOUK. Prev: Sen. Regist. (Orthop. & Trauma) St James' Univ. Hosp. Leeds.

SADLER, Mr Andrew Geoffrey Department of Oral & Maxillofacial Surgery, County Hospital, Lincoln LN2 5QY — MB BS 1986 Lond.; FRCS Ed. 1991.

SADLER, Anthony Peter Department of Obstetrics & Gynaecology, Torbay Hospital, Torquay TQ2 7AA Tel: 01803 614567; The Moorings, Berry Head Road, Brixham TQ5 9AA Tel: 01803 859965 — MB BS 1980 Lond.; BSc (Hons.) (Biochem.) Lond. 1974; MRCOG 1986. (Middlx.) Cons. O & G Torbay Hosp. Torquay. Socs: Roy. Coll. Obst. & Gyn. Prev: Sen. Cons. Specialist & Hon. Lect. (O & G) Univ. Witwatersrand, S. Afr.; Clin. Research Fell. (O & G) King's Coll. Hosp. Med. Sch. Lond.; Ho. Surg. The Middlx. Hosp. Lond.

SADLER, Carolyn Jane 9 Guildford Drive, Eastleigh SO53 3PR — BM BS 1982 Nottm.; MRCGP 1987; DRCOG 1986; DCH RCP Lond. 1985. Socs: Brit. Menopause Soc.; Fac. Fam. Plann. & Reproduc. Health Care. Prev: GP Chandlers Ford Retainer Scheme.

SADLER, Christopher Leslie 8 Heath Close, Little Heath, Potters Bar EN6 1LT Tel: 01707 665627; The Royal London Hospital, Whitechapel, London E1 1BB Tel: 020 7377 7000 Ext: 7793 — MB BS 1991 Lond.; PhD (Physiol.) Lond. 1987; FRCA 1996. Specialist Regist. (Anaesth.) Roy. Hosps. NHS Trust The Roy. Lond. Hosp. Socs: BMA; Assn. Anaesth.; Fell. Roy. Coll. Anaesth. Prev: SHO (Anaesth.) Univ. Coll. & Middlx. Hosps. Lond.

SADLER

SADLER, David William Department of Forensic Medicine, University of Dundee, Dundee DD1 4HN Tel: 01382 348020 Fax: 01382 348021 Email: d.w.sadler@dundee.ac.uk; 15 Rosewood Terrace, Dundee DD2 1NS — MB ChB 1986 Sheff.; MD Dundee 1996; MRCPath 1994. Sen. Lect. (Forens. Med.) Univ. Dundee Roy. Infirm. Socs: Amer Acad of Forens Sci. Prev: Regist. (Histopath.) N.ampton Gen. Hosp.

SADLER, Derek James (retired) 29 Clos Derwen, Roath Park, Cardiff CF23 5HT — MB BCh 1958 Wales.

SADLER, Ethna 3 Templegrove, Londonderry BT48 0RE; White House, Carrigans, Lifford Co. Donegal, Republic of Ireland Tel: 0174 40233 — MB BCh BAO 1975 NUI; MRCPsych 1982; DPM RCPSI 1979.

SADLER, George Dawson The Surgery, 85 St Quintin Avenue, London W10 6PB Tel: 020 8969 2563 020 8354 3836 Fax: 020 8969 2563; 96 Boileau Road, London W5 3AJ Tel: 020 8997 5755 — MB ChB 1965 Birm.; MRCP (UK) 1970; MRCS Eng. LRCP Lond. 1965. (Birm.)

SADLER, Gillian Mary Kent Cancer Centre, Maidstone Hospital, Hermitage Lane, Maidstone ME16 9QQ Tel: 01622 225041 Fax: 01622 225074 Email: gsadler@mkoc.demon.co.uk; Email: gill.sadler@care4free.net — MB BS 1986 Lond.; MRCP (UK) 1990; FRCR 1994. (Guy's) Cons. (Clin. Oncol.) Mid-Kent. Oncol. Centre Maidstone.

SADLER, James Andrew Stonecrest House, Breach Hill Lane, Chew Stoke, Bristol BS40 8YA — MB ChB 1998 Leic.; MB ChB Leic 1998.

SADLER, Jonathan Calvert The Health Centre, Banks Road, Haddenham, Aylesbury HP17 8EE Tel: 01844 291874 Fax: 01844 292344; Birch House, Rosemary Lane, Haddenham, Aylesbury HP17 8JS Tel: 01844 290210 — MB BS 1968 Lond.; MRCS Eng. LRCP Lond. 1968; MRCGP 1978; LMCC 1971; DCH Eng. 1972; DObst RCOG 1972. (St. Bart.) Prev: Med. Off. St. Barnabas Miss. Hosp. Transkei, S. Africa; SHO (Paediat.) Bristol Roy. Hosp. Sick Childr.; Resid. Paediat. Univ. W.. Ontario, Canada.

SADLER, Kevin Michael Royal Infirmary of Edinburgh, Lauriston Place, Edinburgh Tel: 0131 536 1000, 0131 536 3251; 99 The Murrays Brae, Edinburgh EH17 8UJ Tel: 0131 672 1099 Email: kevin.sadler@virgin.net — MB ChB (Hons.) Ed. 1991; BSc (Hons.) Anat. Ed. 1989; MRCP (UK) 1995; FRCA 1997. Specialist Regist. (Anaesth.) Lothian Univ. Hosps. HNS Trust, Edin. Prev: Specialist Regist. (Anaesth.) Ninewells Hosp. Dundee; Clin. Res. Fell. (Transpl.. Anaesth. & Int. Care).

SADLER, Malcolm Glyn The Surgery, 9-11 Queen St., Whittlesey, Peterborough PE7 1AY Tel: 01733 204611 Fax: 01733 208926; Stanground Surgery, Whittlesey Road, Stanground, Peterborough PE2 8RB Tel: 01733 568569 Fax: 01733 892419 — MB BS 1971 Lond.; MRCS Eng. LRCP Lond. 1971; FRCGP 1989, M 1976; DObst RCOG 1973. (Lond. Hosp.) Bd. Mem. P'boro. S. PCG. Prev: Chairm. LMC.

SADLER, Martin John Morriston Hospital NHS Trust, Morriston, Swansea SA6 6NL Tel: 01792 702222 — MB BS 1991 Lond.; PhD Lond. 1986; BSc Birm. 1982; MRCP (UK) 1994. (Guy's Hospital) Specialist Regist. (Neurol.). Prev: SHO Rotat. (Med.) St. Geo. Hosp. Lond.

SADLER, Mary Aaroon Roseburn Cottage, 40 Purdysburn Hill, Belfast BT8 8JY — MB BCh 1986 Wales; BSc St. And. 1981.

SADLER, Michael Andrew Eastleigh Health Centre, Newtown Road, Eastleigh SO50 9AG; 9 Guildford Drive, Eastleigh SO53 3PR — BMedSci Nottm. 1980, BM BS 1982; MRCGP 1986; DCH RCP Lond. 1985; DRCOG 1985.

SADLER, Michael Robin de Clifford Spindleberries, Chalbury Hill, Wimborne BH21 7EY Tel: 01258 840357 Fax: 01258 840357 Email: robmar.sadler@virgin.net — MB BChir 1967 Camb.; MA Camb. 1967; MRCP (UK) 1970; DObst RCOG 1973. (Camb. & St. Thos.) p/t Hosp. Pract. (Cardiac) Bournemouth Hosp.; GP Specialist in Cardiol., Vict. Hosp. Wimborne. Prev: Regist. (Cardiac) King's Coll. Hosp. Lond.; Regist. (Med.) Poole Gen. Hosp.; GP Princip., Quarter Jack Surg., Wimborne.

SADLER, Paul The Health Centre, Tangmere Drive, Castle Vale, Birmingham B35 7QX Tel: 0121 747 2671 Fax: 0121 749 7863; 146 Lichfield Road, Four Oaks, Sutton Coldfield B74 2TF Tel: 0121 308 2389 — MB ChB 1959 Birm.; MRCS Eng. LRCP Lond. 1959; MRCGP 1980; DFFP 1994; DCH Eng. 1962; DObst RCOG 1961. Diplomatic Family Plann. Birm. Prev: Ho. Surg. Childr. Hosp. Birm.; Ho. Phys. Roy. Hosp. Wolverhampton; Ho. Surg. (Obst.) St. Chad's Hosp. Birm.

SADLER, Paul James, Lt.-Col. RAMC Intensive Care Unit, Queen Alexandras Hospital, Soham, Portsmouth PO14 3UR Tel: 02392 286035 Email: paul@sadler76.freeserve.co.uk; Tel: 01329 664252 Email: paul@sadler76.freeserve.co.uk — MB ChB 1988 Sheff.; FRCA 1994. Cons. (Intens. Care Med.) QAH Portsmouth; Head of Anaestetlc Dept, Roy. Hosp. Haslar. Socs: AAGBI; ICS; RCA. Prev: Sen. Regist. Leicester Rotat.; Sen. Regist. Camb. Milit. Hosp. Aldershot.; Regist. (Anaesth.) Guy's Hosp. Lond.

SADLER, Ralph Leslie, ERD (retired) Apt. 1, Brunswick House, 112 Graham Road, Malvern WR14 2HX — MB ChB 1937 Birm.; BSc Birm. 1932, MB ChB 1937, DPH 1948. Mem. Pneumoconiosis Med. Panel; Hon. Maj. RAMC. Prev: Chest Phys. Doncaster Hosp. Gp.

SADLER, Robert Owen Mildmay Court Surgery, Mildmay Court, Bellevue Road, Ramsgate CT11 8JX Tel: 01843 592576 Fax: 01843 852980; Willow cottage, Bromstone Road, Broadstairs CT10 2HT — MB BS 1979 Lond.; 1999 FRCGP; DRCOG 1982. (Charing Cross) Vice Chairm. E. kent CMC. Prev: Trainee GP Shere Gp. Pract.; SHO (O & G & Paediat.) St. Luke's Hosp. SW Surrey HA.

SADLER, Rory Stephen 79 St Anne's Way, Kirkstall, Leeds LS4 2SQ — MB ChB 1982 Dundee.

SADLER, Stephanie Jane 40 Stallcourt Avenue, Cardiff CF23 5AN — MB BS 1987 Lond.; MRCPsych 1994. Clin. Research Fell. & Hon. Sen. Regist. (Psychiat. Genetics) Univ. Wales Coll. Med. Cardiff.

SADLER, Tonya Rachel 17 Glamis Crescent, Rowlands Gill NE39 1AT Tel: 01207 545931 Fax: 01207 545931 — MB BS 1993 Lond.; BSc (Physiol.) Lond. 1990. (Charing Cross and Westminster Medical School) GP Co. Durh. Prev: SHO (O & G) King's Coll. Hosp. Lond.; Clin. Research Asst. (Genitourin. Med. & Gyn.) King's Coll. Hosp. Lond.; SHO (O & G) St. Thos. & Guy's Hosp. Lond.

SADO, Graham David Jaffe and Partners, Belmont Health Centre, 516 Kenton Lane, Kenton, Harrow HA3 7LT Tel: 020 8427 1213; 18 Royston Park Road, Hatch End, Pinner HA5 4AE — MRCS Eng. LRCP Lond. 1976; BSc Lond. 1973, MB BS 1977; MRCGP 1984. Clin. Asst. (Endoscopy) St Marks Hosp. Harrow.

SADOW, Mr Geoffrey John (retired) 5 Pond Close, Walton-on-Thames KT12 5DR Tel: 01932 269947 Fax: 01932 269942 — MB BS Lond. 1954; FRCS Eng. 1962. Prev: Sen. Cons. Orthop. Surg. Kingston Hosp. Surrey.

SADRANI, Pravin Jagjivandas Tile Hill Health Centre, Jardine Crescent, Coventry CV4 9PN Tel: 024 7647 4744 Fax: 024 7646 9891; 3 Heritage Court, Coventry CV4 7HD — MB BS 1972 Saurashtra.

SADULLAH, Shalal Department of Haematology, Borders General Hospital, Melrose TD6 9BS Email: shalal@netscape.net; Oatlands House, Parsonage Road, Galashiels TD1 3HS Tel: 01896 758451 — MB BS 1982 Karachi; MRCP (UK) 1987; MRCPath 1995. Cons. (Haemat.) Borders Gen. Hosp. Melrose Scotl. Prev: Leukaemia Research Fell. Soton. Univ. & Bournemouth Gen. Hosp.; Regist. (Haemat.) King's Coll. Hosp. Lond.; SHO (Gen. Med.) Roy. Vict. Hosp. Bournemouth.

SAED, Elrasheid Abdel-Hafiz Flat 19, Blcok D, Temple Bank Flats, Duckworth Lane, Bradford BD9 6TB — MB ChB 1983 Alexandria.

SAEDI, Kamran (retired) — MD 1968 Teheran; FRCPsych 2000. Prev: Cons. Child & Adolesc. Psychiat. Hackney Child & Family Consultation Serv.

SAEED, Abdel Moneim Department of Genitourinary Medicine, Victoria Hospital, Whinney Heys Road, Blackpool FY3 8NR Tel: 01253 306925 Fax: 01253 306924; 10 Beach Street, Lytham St Annes FY8 5NS — MRCS Eng. LRCP Lond. 1972; MB BS Khartoum 1964; FRCOG 1989, M 1971; Dip. Ven. Soc. Apoth. Lond. 1978. Cons. Genitourin. Med. Blackpool & Preston Health Dists.

SAEED, Abdul, Maj. RAMC Neelam House, Queens Park Road, Heywood OL10 4UY Tel: 01706 622491; 10 King Street E., Rochdale OL11 3ST Tel: 01706 341303 — MB BS 1965 Punjab; MB BS Punjab (Pakistan) 1965; DA Eng. 1968. (Nishtar Med. Coll. Multan) Princip. GP Rochdale. Prev: Regist. (Anaesth.) Withington Hosp. Manch.; Regist. (Anaesth.) Blackburn Roy. Infirm.; Regist. (Anaesth.) Vict. Hosp. Blackpool.

SAEED, Ibtisam Thannoon Harold Wood Hospital, Gubbins Lane, Harold Wood, Romford RM3 0BE Tel: 01708 345533; 3 Oakwood Chase, Hornchurch RM11 3JT Tel: 01708 457211 Fax: 01708 477211 — MB ChB 1974 Baghdad; FFPath RCPI 1986; FRCPath 1992, M 1982. Cons. Histopath. Harold Wood Hosp. Romford. Socs: Brit. Soc. Gastroenterol.; Brit. Soc. Of Cervical Cytol.; Assn. Of Clin. Path. Prev: Sen. Regist. (Histopath.) St. Geo. Hosp. Lond.; Regist. (Histopath.) King's Coll. Hosp. Lond.

SAEED, Iqbal 8 Queen Victoria Street, Rugby CV21 3SY Tel: 01788 561074 — LRCP LRCS 1986 Ed.; MB BS Pakistan 1977; LRCP LRCS Ed. LRCPS Glas. 1986.

SAEED, Mr Mohammad 140 Elm Road, New Malden KT3 3HS — MB BS 1985 Karachi; FRCS Glas. 1994.

SAEED, Mohammed 17 Crossway, Manchester M20 6TU — MB ChB 1988 Manch.; BSc (Hons.) Anat. Manch. 1986.

SAEED, Nadeem Riaz 48 Leegate Road, Heaton Moor, Stockport SK4 4AX — MB BS 1996 Lond.; BDS Lond. 1988; FDS RCS Eng. 1992.

SAEED, Naveed Riaz 48 Leegate Road, Heaton Moor, Stockport SK4 4AX — MB BS 1992 Lond.

SAEED, Mr Nur Ashton New Road Surgery, 863 Ashton New Road, Clayton, Manchester M11 4PB Tel: 0161 370 7115/6 Fax: 0161 371 1548 — MB BS 1983 Pubjab; FRCSI 1988.

SAEED, Riaz Ashton New Road Surgery, 863 Ashton New Road, Clayton, Manchester M11 4PB Tel: 0161 370 7115/6 Fax: 0161 371 1548; 48 Leegate Road, Heaton Moor, Stockport SK4 4AX Tel: 0161 432 9339 — MB BS 1961 Punjab; MB BS Punjab (Pakistan) 1961.

SAEED, Mr Shakeel Riaz Manchester Royal Infirmary, Oxford Road, Manchester M13 9WL Tel: 0161 276 4426 Fax: 0161 276 5811 Email: shakeek.r.saeed@man.ac.uk; Greyroofs, Cliffside, Wilmslow SK9 4AF — MB BS 1985 Lond.; FRCS (Orl.) Eng. 1990; FRCS Ed. 1989; FRCS 1990 Eng; FRCS 1996 Eng. (Guys Hospital and Kings College Hospital Medical Schools) Cons. Otolaryngologist & Neuro-otological Surg. Manch. Roy. Infirm & Hope Hosp. Salford; Hon. Clin. Lect. Univ. of Manch. Socs: Coun. N Engl. Otorminolaryngological Soc. Prev: Regist. (Otolaryngol.) Orsett Hosp. & Roy. Nat. Throat, Nose & Ear Hosp.; SHO (Otolaryng. & Gen. Surg.) Manch. Roy. Infirm.; Sen. Regist. (otolaryngol) Manch. Roy . Infirm.

SAEED, Tariq 17 Woodville Road, Birmingham B17 9AS — MB BS 1970 Punjab.

SAEED, Mr Waseem Riaz Department of Plastic Surgery, St Jame's University Hospital, Beckett Street, Leeds LS9 7TF Tel: 0113 206 4048 Fax: 0113 206 6423 Email: waseem87@hotmail.com — MB ChB 1987 Manch.; BSc 1984; FRCS Ed. 1992; FRCS Plast.1997; CCST 1999; GMC spec.reg.plast.surg.1999. Cons. Plast. Surg. St James Univ. Hosp. Leeds; Sen. Clin. Lect. Univ. Leeds.

SAEED, Zahedah Pervin 17 Woodville Road, Harborne, Birmingham B17 9AS — MB ChB 1977 Manch.

SAEED-AHMAD, Sheikh Central Medical Centre, 42 St. Pauls Road, Coventry CV6 5DF Tel: 024 7668 1231 Fax: 024 7666 4935; 96 St. Martin Road, Finham, Coventry CV3 6ER — MB BS 1966 Punjab; DTM & H Liverp. 1970.

SAETTA, Mr John Patrick Department of Accident & Emergency, Queen Elizabeth II Hospital, Howlands, Welwyn Garden City AL7 4HQ Tel: 01707 365094 Fax: 01707 391228 Email: jsaetta@aol.com — MRCS Eng. LRCP Lond. 1981; FRCS Eng. 1986; FFAEM 1993. (Middlx. Hosp. Med. Sch.) Clin. Dir. (A & E), OPD. Clin. Servs., Clin Tutor & Cons. Qu. Eliz. II Hosp. Welwyn Garden City; Mem. Specialty Train. Comm. for A & E; Dir. of Educat. (A &E) N. Thames (W.). Prev: Sen. Regist. (A & E) St. Geo. Hosp. Lond.; Regist. (Gen. Surg.) N. Middlx. Hosp. Lond.; Regist. (A & E) Leicester Roy. Infirm.

SAFDAR, Mr Muhammad 326 Old Bedford Road, Luton LU2 7EJ — MB BS 1985 Bahauddin Zakariya Univ. Pakistan; MB BS Bahauddin Zakariya U. Pakistan 1985; FRCS Glas. 1993.

SAFE, Amir Fahim 36 Sunningdale Mount, Ecclesall, Sheffield S11 9HA — MB BCh 1976 Alexandria; MS Alexandria 1981; MD Bristol 1993; MRCP (UK) 1985. Cons. Phys. & Gastroenterol. Barnsley Dist. Gen. Hosp. Trust.

SAFE, George Beverley Lodge, Beverley Gardens, Cullercoats, North Shields NE30 4NS Tel: 0191 252 2065 — MB BS Durh. 1953, BDS 1949. (Durh.)

SAFE, George Antony (retired) 1 Promenade Terrace, Front St., Tynemouth, North Shields NE30 4BU — MB BS 1979 Newc.

SAFFAR, Mr Nabil 30 Pershore Road, Halesowen B63 4QJ Tel: 0121 550 4178 — MB ChB 1971 Mousul; FRCS Glas. 1987.

SAFFER, Clive Mitchell Windmill Health Centre, Mill Green, Leeds LS14 5JS Tel: 0113 273 3733 Fax: 0113 232 3202 — MB ChB 1983 Leeds; Docc Med (Diploma in Occupational Medicine), Faculty of Occupational Medicine,2001; BSc (1st cl. Hons.) Physiol. Leeds 1980; MRCGP 1987; DFFP 1996; T(GP) 1991; DRCOG 1987. Prev: Regist. (Infec. Dis.) Seacroft Hosp. Leeds; Ho. Phys. Profess. Med. Unit & Ho. Surg. Profess. Surg. Unit Leeds Gen. Infirm.

SAFFER, Grant Royal Hampshire County Hospital, Romsey Road, Winchester SO22 5DG — MB BCh 1985 Witwatersrand.

SAFFMAN, Charles Michael Eastfield Group Practice, 1 Eastway, Eastfield, Scarborough YO11 3LS Tel: 01723 582297 Fax: 01723 582528; Blue Bank, 543 Scalby Road, Scarborough YO13 0NW Tel: 01723 353046 Email: c.saffman@btinternet.com — MB ChB 1986 Liverp.; MRCGP 1994; DA (UK) 1990. (Liverpool) GP Princip.; Bd. Mem. ScarBoro., Whitby & Ryedale PCG. Prev: Trainee GP/SHO ScarBoro. VTS; Regist. (ITU) Fremantle, Austral.; SHO (Anaesth.) Whiston Hosp. Prescot.

SAFIR, Jeffrey Gerald The Spitalfields Practice, 20 Old Montague Street, London E1 5PB Tel: 020 7247 7070 Fax: 020 7650 1920; 36 Crystal Palace Park Road, Sydenham, London SE26 6UG — MB ChB 1972 Bristol. Prev: Ho. Surg. Mayday Hosp. Thornton Heath; Ho. Phys. St. Martin's Hosp. Bath.

SAFRANEK, Margaret Mary Schofield Dukes Avenue Surgery, 1 Dukes Avenue, London N10 2PS Tel: 020 8883 9149; 36 Dukes Avenue, London N10 2PU Tel: 020 8883 9556 — MB BS 1980 Lond.; BA 1956 Oxf. (St Thomas's)

SAFRANEK, Mr Peter Michael 15 The Paddock, Longworth, Abingdon OX13 5BX Email: peter.safranek@virgin.net — BM 1993 Soton.; BSc (Hons.) Soton. 1992; FRCS (Eng.) 1997. SpR in Gen. Surg., Oxf. Region. Socs: Affil. Fell. Assn. of Surg. of GB & Irel. Prev: Basic Surgic. Train. Rotat. (Cardiothoracic, Gen. & Orthop. Surg.) Wessex Region; SHO (Orthop. Surg. & A & E) Soton.; Research Fell. (Gen. Surg.) Soton.

SAFWAT, Sherif Moustafa Mohamed Flat 17, James Paget Hospital, Lowestoft Road, Gorleston, Great Yarmouth NR31 6LA Tel: 01493 452524; Fazakerley Hospital, Lower Lane, Liverpool L9 7AL Tel: 0151 529 2392 — MB ChB 1981 Alexandria; MRCP (UK) 1988. Prev: Regist. (Med.) Derriford Hosp. Plymouth.

SAGAR, A Sunlight Surgery, 11 Boundary Road, Port Sunlight, Wirral CH62 5ER Tel: 0151 644 6366.

SAGAR, Mr Chintapalli Vidyasagar 38 Drapers Homes, St Peters Road, Margate CT9 4AJ — MB BS 1974 Andhra; FRCS Ed. 1978. (Andhra Med. Coll. Visakhapatnam) Dir. Kanaka Durga Nursing Home, Governorpet, India. Prev: Regist. (Gen. Surg.) N. Warks. AHA; Rotating SHO (Gen. Surg.) Kent AHA.

SAGAR, Daya (retired) 89 Plumptre Way, Eastwood, Nottingham NG16 3LQ — MB BS 1958 Osmania; DTM & H Ed. 1961.

SAGAR, Derrick Alan Centre for Medical & Dental Education, Pilgrim Hospital, Sibsey Road, Boston PE21 9QS Tel: 01205 364801 Fax: 01205 357494; Keys Toft House, Boston Road, Wainfleet St Mary, Skegness PE24 4EX Tel: 01754 880885 — MB ChB 1976 Leeds; BSc Leeds 1973; FRCA 1981; Dip. ATLS RCS Eng. 1994; ALS (Instruc). (Leeds) Cons. Anaesth. Clin. Tutor Assoc. Director of Clin. Studies Leicester/ Warwick Med. Sch.; Chairm. Lincs. Ambul. Paramedic Steering Comm.; Chairm. LIVES-Basics Immediate Care Scheme; Med. Adviser & Trustee Lincs. & Notts Air Ambul.; S. Trent Represen., Nat. Assn. of Clin. Tutors. Socs: Assn. Anaesth.; Intens. Care Soc.; BMA. Prev: Coll. Tutor Roy. Coll. Anaesth.; Sec. BMA Holland Div.; Chairm. Med. Staff Comm., Pilgrim Hosp.

SAGAR, Giselle Annette Old Brandon Road Surgery, Old Brandon Road, Feltwell, Thetford IP26 4AY Tel: 01842 828481 Fax: 01842 828172; Silver Birches, 2 The Grove, Mundford, Thetford IP26 5HF Tel: 01842 879164 — BM BS 1987 Nottm.; MRCGP 1993; DRCOG 1992; DCH RCP Lond. 1991. Prev: Clin. Asst. (Rheum.) P.ss Margt. Hosp. Swindon; Trainee GP Plymouth HA VTS.

SAGAR, Professor Harvey James Thornbury Hospital, Fulwood Road, Sheffield S10 3BR Tel: 0114 266 1133 Fax: 0114 267 8730; Sycamore House, Cliff Lane, Calver, Hope Valley S32 3XD Tel: 01433 639215 Fax: 01433 639215 Email: harvpip@globalnet.co.uk — BM BCh 1972 Oxf.; BA (Physiol.) Oxf. 1969, MA 1972, DM

SAGAR

1980; FRCP Lond. 1990; MRCP (UK) 1975. Cons. (Neurol.) Thornbury Hosp. Sheff.; Director, Medi-consult Ltd, WWW. Neuroconsult.co.uk. Socs: Movem. Disorder Soc.; Amer. Acad. of Neurol. (Corr. Fell.); Assn. of Brit. NeUrol.s. Prev: Prof. Clin. Neurol. Univ. Sheff.; Cons. Neurol. Roy. Hallamsh. Hosp. Sheff.; Sen. Regist. (Neurol.) Radcliffe Infirm. Oxf.; Clin. & Research.

SAGAR, Jawahar Lal 45 Armroyd Lane, Elsecar, Barnsley S74 8ET Tel: 01226 743012 — MB ChB 1960 Glas. GP Trainer Barnsley VTS. Prev: SHO (Paediat.) & Ho. Off. (Med.) St. Margt. Hosp. Stratton st Margt.; Ho. Off. (Surg.) Poole Gen. Hosp.

SAGAR, Madkuri Vidya Leighton Hospital, Middlewich Road, Crewe CW1 4QJ — MB BS 1969 Osmania.

SAGAR, Peter Jeremy The Surgery, 1 The Ridgway, Woodingdean, Brighton BN2 6PE Tel: 01273 307555 Fax: 01273 304861; 41 Gorham Avenue, Rottingdean, Brighton BN2 7DP Tel: 01273 309799 — MB BS 1980 Lond.; MRCS Eng. LRCP Lond. 1980; MRCGP 1984; DRCOG 1982; DCH RCP Lond. 1983. (Char. Cross)

SAGAR, Prem Park House Surgery, 55 Higher Parr Street, St Helens WA9 1BP Tel: 01744 23705 Fax: 01744 454601 — MB ChB 1984 Liverp.; DRCOG 1988.

SAGAR, Mr Samir Abdulla 31 Hollymead Close, Colchester CO4 5JU Tel: 01206 851913 — MB BCh 1982 Al Fateh; FRCS Ed. 1986.

SAGAR, Mr Shanti Shantiniketan, 18 Stanley Avenue, Higher Bebington, Wirral CH63 5QF — MB BS 1967 Osmania; FRCS Eng. 1975; FRCS Ed. 1971. Cons. Surg. Clatterbridge Hosp. Bebington & Wirral Hosps.; Clin. Lect. (Surg.) Univ. Liverp. Socs: Fell. Assn. Surgs.; Eur. Soc. Surg. Oncol.; Brit. Laser Assn.

SAGAR, Stephen Mark 31 Hillbury Road, Tooting Bec Common, London SW17 8JT Tel: 020 8675 1751 — MB BS 1981 Lond.; BSc (Pharmacol.) Lond. 1978, MB BS 1981. (St. Geo.) Regist. (Med.) Greenwich Dist. Hosp. Prev: SHO (Med.) Roy. Marsden Hosp.; SHO (Med.) St. Jas. Hosp. Balham.

SAGAR, Sushila Daya Parkview Surgery, 89 Plumptre Way, Eastwood, Nottingham NG16 3LQ Tel: 01773 714414 Fax: 01773 533306.

SAGAR, William (retired) Carlton, 156 Barrier Bank, Cowbit, Spalding PE12 6AL Tel: 01406 380382 Fax: 01406380382 — MB ChB Manch. 1963; DObst RCOG 1965. Lincs. Br. Med. Off. Brit. Red Cross Soc.; MEP for DSS (AA's & DLA's); Med. Asst. Abbey. View. Pract. Crowland. Lincs. Prev: GP Boston.

SAGAY, Atiene Solomon 35 Seymour Gardens, London SE4 2DN — MB ChB 1982 Nigeria; MRCOG 1994.

SAGE, Christopher Harrison Student Health Service, 25 Belgrave Road, Bristol BS8 2AA Tel: 0117 973 7716 Fax: 0117 970 6804; 61A Kingsdown Parade, Kingsdown, Bristol BS6 5UG Tel: 0117 942 2819 — MB BS 1973 Lond.; MRCS Eng. LRCP Lond. 1973; MRCPsych 1984; DRCOG 1978. (Middlx.) Med. Off. Stud. Health Serv. Bristol Univ.

SAGE, Fiona Judith Dowstall Cottage, Angarrick, Mylor, Falmouth TR11 5NX — MB BS 1985 Lond.; DCH RCP Lond. 1990; DRCOG 1988.

SAGE, Frederic Jean Anaesthetic Department, East Surrey Hospital, Canada Avenue, Redhill RH1 5RH — MD 1988 Paris; FRCA Lond 1994. Cons. Anesthetist - E. Surrey Hosp. - Redhill RH1 5RH.

SAGE, Hilary The Barn Surgery, Newbury, Gillingham SP8 4XS Tel: 01747 824201 Fax: 01747 825098; Innox Hill Cottage, 35 Innox Hill, Frome BA11 2LN Tel: 01373 467993 — MB BS 1985 Lond.; MRCGP 1995; DRCOG 1987. (Roy. Free Hosp. Sch. Med.) Prev: Trainee GP Welwyn Garden City.

SAGE, Martin 24 Llangorse Road, Cyncoed, Cardiff CF23 6PF Tel: 029 2075 8812 — MB BCh 1964 Wales; FFA RCS Eng. 1969; DObst RCOG 1966. (Cardiff) Cons. Anaesth. Roy. Gwent Hosp. Newport.

SAGE, Naomi Janet (retired) Heath House, Offley Brook, Eccleshall, Stafford ST21 6HA Tel: 01785 280318 — MB BS Lond. 1958; MRCS Eng. LRCP Lond. 1958; DObst RCOG 1960. Prev: Assoc. Specialist (O & G) Dist. Gen. Hosp. Stafford.

SAGE, Roger Edmund Maitland Parkbury House Surgery, St. Peters Street, St Albans AL1 3HD; The Old Post Office, Whipsnade LV6 2LL — MB BS 1978 Lond.; BA Oxf. 1972; MRCS Eng. LRCP Lond. 1978; MRCGP 1990; DRCOG 1980; Cert. Family Plann. JCC 1980. Chair Exec. Comm., St. Albans & Harrendon PCT.

SAGE, Roger James Basildon Hospital, Nether Mayne, Basildon SS16 5NL Tel: 01268 533911 Fax: 01268 593020 — MB BS 1976 Lond.; MRCP (UK) 1980; FRCPath 1996, M 1985. Cons. Med. Microbiol. Basildon Hosp.

SAGER, Jeremy Marshall Shadwell Medical Centre, 137 Shadwell Lane, Leeds LS17 8AE Tel: 0113 293 9999 Fax: 0113 248 5888; 9 Sandhill Grove, Leeds LS17 8ED Tel: 0113 269 2359 — MB ChB 1980 Leeds; MRCGP 1987; DRCOG 1984.

SAGGAR, Anand Kumar St. Georges Hospital Medical School, Cranmer Terrace, London SW17 0RE Tel: 020 8672 1255 Fax: 020 8725 3444 — MB BS 1982 Lond.; MRCP (UK) 1986. (St. Bart. Med. Coll. Hosp. Lond.) Cons. in Clin. Genetics & Gen. Phys. St. Geo. Hosp. Lond.; Hon. Sen. Lect. in Med., St. Geo.'s Hosp. Med. Sch. Socs: Brit. Hypertens. Soc.; Internat. Soc. Nephrol.; Clin. Genetics Soc. (Gen. Sec.). Prev: Williams Fell. Univ. Lond. St. Geo. Med. Sch.; Research Fell. Karolinska Inst. Stockholm, Sweden; Regist. Liver Unit King's Coll. Hosp. Lond.

SAGGAR, Dharam Pal (retired) 115 Thurleigh Road, London SW12 8TY Tel: 020 8673 4746 — MB BS 1952 Calcutta; DCH Eng. 1962. Prev: GP Lond.

SAGGAR, Karam Dev 'Aashiana', 27 Albany Terrace, Dundee DD3 6HS — MB BS Punjab (India) 1954; MRCGP 1968.

SAGGIORATO, Julian James 16 Mallard Court, North Hykeham, Lincoln LN6 9TS — MB BS 1993 Lond.

SAGGU, Rajinder Singh 12 Fairholme Road, Ilford IG1 3QR — MB BS 1988 Newc.; MRCGP 1995.

SAGIAS, Filippos 62 Hilton Drive, Aberdeen AB24 4NP — MB ChB 1998 Aberd.; MB ChB Aberd 1998.

SAGLANI, Sejal 4 Beaconsville Court, Beaconsville Road, London N11 3AF Tel: 020 8361 7807 Email: ssaglani@doctors.org.uk — MB ChB 1994 Leic.; BSc Leic. 1992; MRCP 1997. (Univ. Leic.) Specialist Regist. (Paediat.) Qu. Eliz. II Hosp, Wellyn Garden City. Prev: SHO (Paediat.) Guy's Hosp. Lond.; SHO (Paediat.) St. Mary's Hosp. Lond.; SHO (Paediat.) Roy. Brompton Hosp.

SAGOE, Mr Kofi Bondzie Department of Accident & Emergency, Milton Keynes General Hospital NHS Trust, Eaglestone, Milton Keynes MK6 5LD Tel: 01908 660033; 54 Normandy Way, Bletchley, Milton Keynes MK3 7UW Tel: 01908 643830 — MB ChB 1976 Univ. Ghana; FRCS Glas. 1994. Staff Grade Surg. (Accid & Emerg.) Milton Keynes Gen. Hosp.

SAGOO, Raghbir Singh Newmains Health Centre, 17 Manse Rd, Newmains, Wishaw ML2 9AX Tel: 01325 488075; Downholme, Darlington DL2 2RB Tel: 01325 488075 Email: louise.begg@newmdins.lanpct.scot.nhs.uk, rssdoc1@aol.com — MB ChB 1969 Leeds. (Leeds) Hosp. Practitioner, Rheum., Univ. Hosp. of N. Tees, Stockton on Tees. Socs: Brit. Soc. for Rheumatoly; Pres. Arthritis care, N. Cleveland Div.

SAGOO, Surinder Singh 43 Melrose Gardens, Melrose Avenue, Penylan, Cardiff CF23 9BA — MB BCh 1993 Wales; Dip. Child Health Roy. Coll. Phys. 1996. (University of Wales College of Medicine) Trainee GP Bridgend VTS.

SAGOO, Victor Singh 348 Chester Road N., Sutton Coldfield B73 6RP — MB BCh 1992 Wales.

SAGOR, Mr Geoffrey Roland Department of Surgery, St Albans & Hemel Hempstead NHS Trust, St. Albans City Hospital, Waverley Road, St Albans AL3 5PN Tel: 01727 866122 Ext: 4519 Fax: 01727 897519; 53 Belsize Lane, London NW3 5AU Tel: 020 7431 6448 Fax: 020 7431 6420 — MB ChB Cape Town 1967; ChM Cape Town 1985; FRCS Eng. 1972. p/t Cons. Surg. St. Albans City Hosp. & Hemel Hempstead Gen. Hosp. Socs: Roy. Soc. Med.; Assn. Surg.; Brit. Soc. Gastroenterol. Prev: Sen. Regist. & Regist. (Surg.) Roy. Free Hosp. Lond.; Research Fell. Roy. Postgrad. Med. Sch. Hammersmith Hosp. Lond.

SAGOVSKY, Ruth Lucille van Geest Centre, Peterborough District Hospital, Peterborough PE3 6DA Tel: 01733 318142 — MB ChB 1974 Birm.; MRCPsych 1979. Cons. Psychiat. P'boro. Health Dist. Prev: Research Univ. Camb. Child Care & Developm. Gp.; Sen. Regist. Roy. Edin. Hosp.; Sen. Regist. Fulbourn Hosp. Camb.

***SAH, Anita** 9 Greyfriar Walk, Bradford BD7 4BD — MB ChB 1996 Sheff.; MB ChB Hons Sheff. 1996.

SAHA, Ajoy Kumar 25 Menlove Avenue, Liverpool L18 2EH — MB BS 1957 Calcutta; DObst RCOG 1963; DPH Liverp. 1968. (R.G.

Kar Med. Coll. Calcutta) Med. Off. (Matern. & Child Welf.) Liverp. AHA (T). Prev: Regist. O & G Wakefield, & Pontefract, Castleford & Goole; Hosp. Gps.; Regist. O & G Sefton Gen. Hosp. Liverp.; SHO O & G Roy. Infirm. Stirling.

SAHA, Anirban Romi 40 Highcliffe Gardens, Ilford IG4 5HR Tel: 020 8924 8265 Email: r.saha@iop.bpmf.ac.uk — BM BCh 1994 Oxf.; MA Cantab 1991; MRCP (UK) 1997. (Oxford University and John Radcliffe Hospital) Wellcome Clin. Research Train. Fell. Inst. of Psychiat. Lond.; Hon. Research Regist. (Neurol.) Kings Coll. Univ. Hosp. Lond. Prev: SHO Rotat. (Gen. Med.) King's Coll. Hosp. Lond.

SAHA, Anumita 80 Woodbank Drive, Wollaton, Nottingham NG8 2QU; Child and Adolescent Psychiatry, Thorney Wood Unit, Porchester Road, Nottingham NG3 6LF — MB BS 1987 Calcutta; DPM Bangalove 1989; MRC Psych 1996. (Calcutta) Sen. Regist. (Child & Adolesc. Psychiat.) Thorneywood Unit Nottm.

SAHA, Mr Arabinda Department of Obstetrics & Gynaecology, Northern Lincolnshire and Goole Hospital NHS Trust, Scartho Road, Grimsby DN33 2BA Tel: 01472 874111 Fax: 01472 875452 Email: arabinda.saha@nlg.nhs.uk; Email: arabinda.saha@msn.com — MB BS 1981 Calcutta; FRCOG 2001; MRCOG 1989. (Calcutta) Cons. O & G NE Lincs. NHS Trust. Socs: Charman, Med. Advisery Comm., St Hugh Hosp., Grimsby; Asst. Sec., BMA Grimsby Div.; Mem., Internat. Soc. of Gyn. endoscopist. Prev: Lect. (O & G) St. Mary's Hosp. Manch.; Regist. (O & G) Basildon Hosp.; Research Fell. RCOG Med. Audit Unit.

SAHA, Bijan Kumar Lakeside Medical Centre, Todd Crescent, Church Milton, Sittingbourne ME10 2TZ Tel: 01795 424315; 1 The Crescent, Dollis Hill, London NW2 6HA Tel: 020 8208 1823 — MB BS Dacca 1968; LMSSA Lond. 1981; DFFP 1995; T(GP) 1989; DMRT (Eng.) 1974. (Sir S.M. Med. Coll. Univ. Dacca) Clin. Asst. (A & E) Medway Hosp. Gillingham; Med. Dir. Elvy Ct. Nursing Home Kent. Socs: Fell. Roy. Soc. Med. Prev: Regist. (Radiother. & Oncol.) Roy. Free Hosp. Lond. & Roy. Marsden Hosp. Lond.; Sen. Clin. Research Fell. (Nuclear Med.) Roy. Free Hosp. Lond.

SAHA, Birendra Nath 7 Bramshott Court, South Bank, Surbiton KT6 6DD — MB BS 1967 Calcutta.

SAHA, Mr Jibesh Ranjan 18 Shore Court, Shore Lane, Sheffield S10 3BW — MB BS 1981 Banaras Hindu, India; FRCSI 1994.

SAHA, Minakshi Kennard Street Health Centre, 1 Kennard Street, North Woolwich, London E16 2HR Tel: 020 7473 1971 Fax: 020 7473 2042 — MB BS Calcutta 1971. (Calcutta National Medical College) GP. Socs: BMA; Small Pract.s Assn.; Indian Med. Assn.

SAHA, Monika 46 Ruskin Park House, Champion Hill, London SE5 8TQ — MB BS 1998 Lond.; MB BS Lond 1998.

SAHA, Nani Gopal 8 Forest Way, Fulwood, Preston PR2 8PR — MB BS 1962 Calcutta.

SAHA, Mr Nirmal Kanti Royal Oldham Hospital, Rochdale Road, Oldham OL1 2JH — MB BS 1967 Calcutta; FRCS Eng. 1980; FRCS Ed. 1976; DLO Eng. 1972. (Calcutta Med. Coll.) Cons. ENT Surg. Oldham & Dist. Gen. Hosp. Prev: Sen. Regist. (ENT) Hallamshire Hosp. Sheff.; SHO Roy. Nat. Throat, Nose & Ear Hosp. Lond.; Sen. Regist. (ENT) Leicester Roy. Infirm.

SAHA, Pijush Kumar Tilbury Surgery, 4 Commonwealth House, Montreal Road, Tilbury RM18 7QX Tel: 01375 855755 Fax: 01375 857673; 25 Whitmore Close, Orsett, Grays RM16 3JE Tel: 01375 892724 — MB BS 1965 Dacca; DTM & H Liverp. 1984. (Dhaka Medical College, Bangladesh) Prev: Regist. Rotat. (Gen. Med.) Coronary Care Unit Colchester; SHO Rotat. (Gen. Med. & Chest Dis.) Coronary Care Unit Colchester.

SAHA, Ranjan 12 Erica Grove, Marton Manor Park, Middlesbrough TS7 8RY — MB BS 1995 Lond.

SAHA, Sharmistha 2 Lauriston Close, Darlington DL3 8TU — MB ChB 1997 Manch.

SAHA, Mr Simal Chandra The Whitfield Practice, Hunslet Health Centre, 24 Church Street, Leeds LS10 2PE Tel: 0113 270 5194 Fax: 0113 270 2795 — MB BS 1977 Patna; MS Patna 1981; FRCS Glas. 1991.

SAHA, Sisir Kanti (retired) 5 Pinfold Lane, Norton Canes, Cannock WS11 3PH Email: sisir@sahas.freeserve.co.uk — MB BS Calcutta 1958. Prev: GP Cannock.

SAHA, Mr Sisir Kumar 41 Long Close, Bessacarr, Doncaster DN4 7PN Tel: 01302 537719 — MB BS 1965 Calcutta; FRCS Ed. 1975. (R.G. Kar Med. Coll. Calcutta) Cons. Gen. Surg. Doncaster. Socs: BMA.; FRSM. (Lond.). Prev: Regist. (Surg.) Bronglais Gen.

Hosp. Aberystwyth, Burnley Gp. Hosps. & Rotherham HA; Regist. (Urol.) Ballochmyle Hosp. Mauchline; SHO (Surg.) Hull Roy. Infirm.

SAHA, Mr Tapash Kumar c/o Dr R. K. Dutta, 1 Church Walk, Llwyncelyn, Porth CF39 9TQ — MB BS 1984 Dacca; MRCOG Lond. 1995. (Dhaka Medical College) Specialist Regist. (O & G).

SAHA, Mr Tushar Kanti c/o Mr K. Roy, 421 Ilford Lane, Ilford IG1 2PF — MB BS 1965 Calcutta; MS Calcutta 1967.

SAHADEVAN, Subramaniam Broadstairs Health Centre, The Broadway, Broadstairs CT10 2AJ Tel: 01943 861565 — MBBS; DFFP. (Univ. of Colombu, SriLanka) GP.

SAHAI, Christine Mary (retired) Morris and Partners, 93 Queens Drive, Bedford MK41 9JE Tel: 01234 360482 Fax: 01234 219361 — MB BS Melb. 1966; DObst RCOG 1969; DCH Eng. 1969; DTM & H Eng. 1968. Prev: Gen. Practitioner Putnoe Surg. Bedford.

SAHAI, Indu B Aberaman Surgery, Glamorgan Street, Aberdare CF44 6SR Tel: 01685 872006 Fax: 01685 875380.

SAHAI, Shesh Nandan Aberaman Surgery, Glamorgan Street, Aberdare CF44 6SR Tel: 01685 872006 Fax: 01685 875380; Cartref, Cwmaman Road, Godreaman, Aberdare CF44 6DG — MB BS 1961 Patna; DLO Eng. 1973; Dip Ven Liverp. 1971; DTM & H Liverp. 1968. Prev: SHO (ENT) Frenchay Hosp. Bristol & Roy. Infirm. Sunderland; SHO (Cas.) Ingham Infirm. S. Shields.

SAHAL, Anoop Kumar 46 Sandringham Drive, Stockport SK4 2DE — MB ChB 1985 Manch.

SAHAR, Mohammad Ashraf c/o Dr S. M. Sulaiman, 49 Castle Road, Colne BB8 7AR — MB BS 1957 Pubjab; MB BS Punjab 1957; MRCGP 1975.

SAHARAY, Mr Mrinal Oldchruch Hospital, Waterloo Road, Romford RM7 0BE Tel: 01708 708276 Fax: 01992 571383 Email: saharay@aol.com; 19 Regent Road, Epping CM16 5DL Tel: 01992 571383 Fax: 01992 571383 — MB BS 1985 Calcutta; FRCS Eng. 1992; FRCSI 1990; PhD 1998. (Medical College Calcutta) Cons. Surg., Gastrointestinal and Encocrine, OldCh. Hosp., Romford. Socs: Roy. Soc. Med.; Brit. Med. Assn.; Asslocation of Surg.s in Train.

SAHARIA, Mrs Era Childrens Centre, City Hospitals Trust, Durham Road, Sunderland SR3 9AF Tel: 0191 565 6256 — MB BS 1969 Dibrugarh; MRCP (U.K.) 1974; DCH Dibrugarh 1970. (Assam Med. Coll.) Cons. (Community Child. Health) City Hosps. Sunderland; Hon. Lect. Univ. Newc.

SAHATHEVARAJAN, Navaretnam (retired) The White Rose Surgery, Exchange St., South Elmsall, Pontefract WF9 2RD Tel: 01977 642190 — MB BS 1955 Ceylon.

SAHAY, Prakash Kumar Mirfield Surgery, Scholars Gate, Lea Village, Birmingham B33 0DL Tel: 0121 789 7607 Fax: 0121 686 4542 — MB BS 1975 Ranchi; MB BS 1975 Ranchi.

SAHAY, Pulak Haddlesey Manor, Chapel Haddlesey, Selby YO8 8QQ — MB BS 1978 Ranchi; MRCPI 1986.

SAHAY, Sandhya The Surgery, Wellington Road, Yate, Bristol BS37 5UY Tel: 01454 323366 Fax: 01454 323366 — LRCP LRCS Ed. LRCPS Glas. 1983.

SAHDEV, Anju 2 The Crescent, Gants Hill, Ilford IG2 6JF — MB BS 1991 Lond.; FRCR (Part 1) 1996; MRCP (UK) 1995. (Char. Cross & Westm. Lond.) Specialist Regist. (Radiol.) UCH Hosps. Lond. Prev: SHO (Gen. Med.) N. Middlx. Hosp. Lond.; SHO (A & E) Chase Farm Hosp. Lond.; Ho. Off. (Surg.) Char. Cross Hosp. Lond.

SAHDEV, Ashok Kumar The Surgery, 37 Castle Street, Luton LU1 3AG Tel: 01582 726123 Email: aksahdev@hotmail.com; 185 Old Bedford Road, Luton LU2 7EH Tel: 01582 655353 — MB BS 1979 Lond.; MRCGP 1986; DRCOG 1981. GP Tutor Luton; Trainer Luton & Dunstable Hosp. VTS.

SAHEECHA, Behnam Saeed Harold Hill Health Centre, Gooshays Drive, Romford RM3 9SU Tel: 01708 343991 Fax: 01708 346795 — MB ChB 1968 Mosu; MB ChB 1968 Mosu.

SAHEED, Ahamed Hibishy 59 Carrington Road, Dartford DA1 1XN Tel: 01322 228370 — MB BS 1951 Ceylon; DCH Ceylon 1958. (Ceylon)

SAHGAL, Surender Mohan Friarwood Surgery, Carleton Glen, Pontefract WF8 1SU Tel: 01977 703235 Fax: 01977 600527; 5A Lowther Avenue, Garforth, Leeds LS25 1EP — MB BS 1971 Osmania. (Osmania) GP Pontefract, W. Yorks.

SAHI, Mukesh Kumar 111 Hillcrest Road, Orpington BR6 9AG — MB BS 1979 India; MD A. P. Singh, India 1979, MB BS (Hons.) 1976; MRCP (UK) 1982.

SAHIN

SAHIN, Ayse Newham General Hospital, Glen Road, Plaistow, London E13 8SL Tel: 020 8919 5555 Fax: 020 7476 4000; 25 Strood House, Staple St, London SE1 4LR Tel: 020 7407 5559 — LMSSA 1995 Lond.; LRCS Eng. LRCP Lond. 1995. SHO (O & G) Newham Gen. Hosp. Prev: SHO (O & G) Gravesend Hosp.; Ho. Off. (Gen. & Respirat. Med.) Homerton Hosp. Lond.

SAHLMANN, Lotte, MBE (retired) The Sheiling School, Ashley, Ringwood BH24 2EB Tel: 01425 473444 — MD 1938 Turin. Med. Off. The Sheiling Curative Schs. Ringwood & Thornbury.

SAHNI, Ajit Singh The Surgery, 3 Formby Avenue, Atherton, Manchester M46 0EX Tel: 01942 883044 Fax: 01942 888777; 5 High Bank, Atherton, Manchester M46 9HZ Tel: 01942 877416 — MB BS 1971 Panjab; MB BS Panjab (India) 1971. (Christian Med. Coll. Ludhiana) GP Cons. Med. Defence Union; Mem. Wigan LMC.

SAHNI, Dev Raj 15 High Street, Cheshunt, Waltham Cross EN8 0BX.

SAHNI, Mr Kamal Eye Department, Broglais General Hospital, Aberystwyth SY23 1ER Email: ksahni@mailcity.com — MB BS 1983 Delhi; FRCS Ed. 1992. NHS Cons. Eye Surg.

SAHNI, Parmindar Pontllanfraith Health Centre, Blackwood Road, Pontllanfraith, Blackwood NP12 2YU — MB BS 1969 Panjab.

SAHNI, Vikram Anik Singh 5 High Bank, Atherton, Manchester M46 9HZ — MB BS 1998 Lond.; MB BS Lond 1998.

SAHOTA, Anshoo 4 Church Avenue, Pinner HA5 5JQ Email: a.sahota@hotmail.com — MB BS 1991 Lond.; BSc (Hons.) Lond. 1988; MRCP (UK) 1994. (King's Coll. Lond.) Specialist Regist. (derm.) Roy. Lond. Hosp. Prev: SHO (Dermat.) Middlx. Hosp.; SHO (Cardiol.) St. Geo. Hosp. Lond.; Clin. Lect. Nat. Med. Laser Centre Lond.

SAHOTA, Balbir Singh 16 Old Lindens Close, Streetly, Sutton Coldfield B74 2EJ — MB ChB 1992 Leeds.

SAHOTA, Jesbir Kaur 7 Anthony Way, Coventry CV2 5LJ — MB ChB 1989 Leeds.

SAHOTA, Kirpal Kaur 114 Elgin Avenue, London W9 2HD — MB ChB 1989 Sheff.

SAHOTA, Mandeep 220 City Way, Rochester ME1 2BN; 52 Steele Avenue, Greenhithe DA9 9PH — MB BS 1998 Lond.; MB BS Lond 1998.

SAHOTA, Manpinder 52 Steele Avenue, Greenhithe DA9 9PH — MB BS 1994 Lond.

SAHOTA, Narinder Singh Kingfisher Medical Centre, 66 Fisher St., Willenhall WV12 5RZ Tel: 01902 606303 Fax: 01902 606333; 21 Beacon Road, Walsall WS5 3LF — MB ChB 1983 Manch.; MRCGP 1987; DCH RCP 1986. Prev: Trainee GP Walsall VTS; SHO (A & E) Walsall Gen. Hosp.; SHO (Paediat. & O & G) New Cross Hosp. Wolverhampton.

SAHOTA, Onkar Singh Family Health Practice, 20 Church Road, Hanwell, London W7 1DR Tel: 020 8579 7338 Fax: 020 8840 9928; 19 Thorncliffe Road, Norwood Green, Southall UB2 5RJ Tel: 020 8574 7337 — MB ChB 1983 Sheff.; MRCS Eng. LRCP Lond. 1984; MRCGP 1989; DRCOG 1988. JP. Socs: Fell. Roy. Soc. Med.; BMA. Prev: Trainee GP St. Mary's Hosp. Med. Sch. Lond. VTS; Ho. Phys. Milton Keynes Gen. Hosp.; Ho. Surg. Roy. Hallamsh. Hosp. Sheff.

SAHOTA, Opinder Singh 4 Croxley Gardens, Nuthall, Nottingham NG16 1RR — MB ChB 1992 Dundee; MRCP (UK) 1995. Lect. (Bone Metab.) & Hon. Specialist Regist. & (Gen.: & Geriat. Med.) Nottm. Univ. Prev: Regist. Rotat. (Gen. Med. & Endocrinol.) Nottm.; SHO Nottm. City Hosp.; SHO St. Jas. Univ. Hosp. Leeds.

SAHU, Debendra Nath 42 Worcester Crescent, Woodford Green IG8 0LU Tel: 020 8504 9580 — MB BS 1995 Lond.; BSc (Path.) Lond. 1993; MRCO phth (Part 1) 1999. (Lond. Hosp. Med. Coll.) SHO (Ophth.) Sussex Eye Hosp. - Brighton. Prev: Ho. Off. (Med.) OldCh. Hosp. Romford; Hon. Demonst. (Anat.) Qu. Mary & W.field Coll. Lond.; SHO (Neurosurg.) Kings Coll., Lond., SHO (Ophth.) Qu. Mary's Hosp., Sidcup.

SAHU, Jonathan 17 Denton Road, Wokingham RG40 2DX — MB ChB 1988 Manch.; MRCP (UK) 1991. Fell. (Cardiovasc. Med.) Rush Presbyt.-St. Luke's Med. Center, Chicago, Illinois, USA.

SAHU, Philip 31/1 Lochrin Place, Edinburgh EH3 9RB — MB ChB 1994 Ed.

SAHU, Mr Rama Chandra 126A Burnley Road, Padiham, Burnley BB12 8SJ Tel: 01282 771525 — MB BS 1956 Utkal; FRCS Ed. 1967. Assoc. Specialist (A & E Med.) Blackburn. Prev: Regist. (Gen. Surg.) St. John of God Hosp. Richmond; Regist. (Cas, Traum. & Orthop. Surg.) Batley & Plymouth & Tynemouth; SHO (Orthop.) Sedgefield Gen. Hosp. & SHO (Gen. Surg.) Gen. Hosp. W. Hartlepool.

SAHU, Surendra Prasad Pleck Health Centre, 16 Oxford Street, Pleck, Walsall WS2 9HY Tel: 01922 647660 Fax: 01922 629251 — MB BS 1966 Bihar; DTM & H Liverp. 1973. (Darbhanga Med. Coll.)

SAHU, Upendra Nath 42 Worcester Crescent, Woodford Green IG8 0LU Tel: 020 8504 9580 — MB BS 1965 Utkal; DCH Dub. 1979. (S.C.B. Med. Coll. Cuttack Orissa, India)

SAI SANKAR, Mr Nagamanickam c/o Mr. Sathyamoorthy, 85 Gladstone Avenue, Manor Park, London E12 6NR Tel: 020 8503 5236; 7 Frognal Staff Residences, Queen Mary's Hospital, Sidcup DA14 6LT Tel: 020 8302 2678 — MB BS 1986 Madras; FRCS Glas. 1993. Staff Grade (A & E) Qu. Mary's Hosp. Sidcup. Prev: SHO (Plastic Surg.) Odstock Hosp. Salisbury & Shotley Bridge Gen. Hosp.

SAICH, Andrew Jonathan 10 Hauxton Road, Little Shelford, Cambridge CB2 5HJ — MB BS 1993 Lond.

SAID, Abdul Crosswayws, 72 Upland Road, Sutton SM2 5JB Tel: 020 8661 9041; Health Centre, Robin Hood Lane, Sutton SM1 2RJ — MB BS 1968 Peshawar. (Khyber Med. Coll. Peshawar)

SAID, Mr Ahmed Jamil 6 Alford Court, Bonchurch Close, Sutton SM2 6AY Tel: 020 8643 1017 Fax: 020 8643 1017 — MB ChB 1972 Baghdad; FRCS Ed. 1983. Staff Paediat. Surg. Lewisham Hosp. Prev: Resid. Surg. Off. W.m. Childr. Hosp.

SAID, Joseph Raymond The Surgery, 5 South View, Evenwood, Bishop Aukland, Darlington DL1 9QS — MRCS Eng. LRCP Lond. 1979.

SAID, Wafa Al Din Khairi 8 Sandybed Lane, Scarborough YO12 5LH — MB ChB 1970 Alexandria; MB ChB Alexandria, Egypt 1970.

SAID, Mr Walid Qasim 30 Hall Farm Close, Stocksfield NE43 7NL — MD 1967 Damascus; FRCS Glas. 1978.

SAIDI, Samir Arif 26 Hinde Street, Manchester M40 5LW — MB ChB 1993 Manch.; BSc St And. 1990.

SAIDIN, Dahlia 60 Stoddart House, Meadow Road, London SW8 1ND — MB BS 1986 Malaya.

SAIF, Maha Rosa Water Lane Surgery, 48 Brixton Water Lane, London SW2 1QE Tel: 020 7274 1521 Fax: 020 7738 3258; 89 Balham Park Road, London SW12 8EB — MB BCh BAO 1981 NUI; LRCPI & LM, LRCSI & LM 1981; MRCGP 1985. Store Doctor to Harvey Nichols Lond. Prev: SHO (Gyn.) Eliz. Garrett Anderson Hosp. Lond.; SHO (Obst.) Coventry Matern. Hosp.; SHO (Psychiat.) & Cas. Off. Ealing Hosp. Lond.

SAIFUDDIN, Asif 165 Uxbridge Road, Harrow Weald, Harrow HA3 6DG — MB ChB 1984 Manch.; BSc (Hons.) Path. Manch. 1982; MRCP (UK) 1987; FRCR 1991; T(R) (CR) 1992. Cons. Diagn. Radiol. Roy. Nat. Orthop. Hosp. Stanmore. Prev: Regist. (Diag. Radiol.) Leeds W.. HA.

SAIGAL, Rajkumar Hukumchand Elmfield Health Group, 18 Elmfield Road, Gosforth, Newcastle upon Tyne NE3 4BP Tel: 0191 285 1663 Fax: 0191 284 7015; 68 Beatty Avenue, High West Jesmond, Newcastle upon Tyne NE2 3QS Tel: 0191 285 7543 — MB BS 1975 Saurashtra; FRCS (E) 1984 Ed. (Saurashtra) GP Newc.

SAIGAL, Sudhir Hollies Health Centre, Swan Street, Merthyr Tydfil CF47 8ET Tel: 01685 723363 Fax: 01685 350106 — MB BS 1974 Delhi. (Delhi) GP Merthyr Tydfil.

SAIGOL, Maryam (retired) 75-77 Cotterills Lane, Alum Rock, Birmingham B8 3RZ Tel: 0121 327 5111 — MB BS 1966 Punjab.

SAIGOL, Muhammad Younus The Surgery, 75-77 Cotterills Lane, Alum Rock, Birmingham B8 3RZ Tel: 0121 327 5111 Fax: 0121 327 5111; 6 Metchley Park Road, Edgbaston, Birmingham B15 2PG Tel: 0121 454 6999 — MB BS 1969 Punjab; BSc Punjab (Pakistan) 1965; DPM Eng. 1973. (King Edwd. Med. Coll. Lahore) Affil. RCPsych.

***SAIGOL, Sara Maryam** 4 Fairfax Mews, London E16 1TY — MB ChB 1996 Birm.

SAIHAN, Zubin The Firs, Blidworth Waye, Papplewick, Nottingham NG15 8GB — MB BS 1998 Newc.; MB BS Newc 1998.

SAIKIA, Mr Adhita Nanda Airedale General Hospital, Skipton Road, Steeton, Keighley BD20 6TD Tel: 01535 652511; 6 Woodlands Walk, Skipton BD23 1TZ — MB BS 1978 Gauhati; MChOrth Liverp. 1990; FRCS Ed. 1985; LMSSA 1984. Assoc. Specialist (Orthop.) Airedale Gen. Hosp. Prev: Regist. (Orthop.)

Blackburn Roy. Infirm. & Airedale Gen. Hosp.; Regist. Hip Unit & Upperlimb Serv. Wrightington Hosp.

SAIKIA, Bibhra Allendale, Six Acre Lane, Longton, Preston PR4 4SE Tel: 01772 614158 — MB BS 1966 Gauhati; DObst RCOG 1971. (Assam Med. Coll., India) Med. Off. Preston Acute Trust. Socs: Fac. Family Plann. Prev: GP Drumchapel, Glas.; Regist. & SHO (O & G) Redlands Hosp. Wom. Glas.

SAIKIA, Nripendra Kumar (retired) Preston Med.Ltd, 11 Moor Park Avenue, Preston PR1 6AS Tel: 01772 710232 — MB BS 1960 Gauhati; PhD Glas. 1973; Dip. Ven. Liverp. 1966. Prev: Cons. Dermat. Roy. Preston Hosp.

SAIKIA, Shyamodabhiram The Surgery, 1 Warstone Tower, Bromford Drive, Bromford, Birmingham B36 8TU Tel: 0121 747 9161; 8 Byford Way, The Oaks, Coleshill Road, Birmingham B37 7GH — MB BS 1972 Gauhati.

SAIKIA-VARMAN, Nita Church Lane Medical Centre, 111 Church Lane, Stechford, Birmingham B33 9EJ Tel: 0121 783 2567 — MB BS 1972 Gujarat; MB BS 1972 Gujarat.

SAILER, Samantha 41 Staddon Park Road, Plymstock, Plymouth PL9 9HL Tel: 01752 403725; 1 St John's Court, Kirk Merrington, Spennymoor DL16 7JU Tel: 01388 813130 — MB BS 1994 Newc.; DRCOG 1997. (Newcastle upon Tyne) SHO (A&E) W. Cumbld..Hosp.Whitehaven. Prev: SHO (O & G); SHO (A & E Med.); SHO (Gen. Med.).

SAINI, Asha Rani Royal Marsden Hosptial, Fulham Road, London SW10 — MB BS 1985 Lond.; PhD Lond. 1995; MRCP (UK 1988. Sen. Regist. (Med. Oncol.) Roy. Marsden Hosp. Lond. Prev: Research Fell. (Med. Oncol.) Imperial Cancer Research Fund.; Regist. (Med.) St. Mary's Hosp. Lond.; Hon. Sen. Regist. (Oncol.) Hammersmith Hosp.

SAINI, Avtar Singh Oakeswell Health Centre, Brunswick Park Road, Wednesbury WS10 9HP Tel: 0121 556 2114 Fax: 0121 505 1843; 59 Vernon Road, Edgbaston, Birmingham B16 9SQ Tel: 0121 454 1566 — MB ChB 1990 Glas.; MRCGP 1995. (Glas.) Socs: RCGP; Brit. Med. Accupun. Soc.

SAINI, Mr Gurdev Singh Lynwood Medical Centre, 4 Lynwood Drive, Romford RM5 2RA Tel: 01708 743244 Fax: 01708 736783; Aquatic Lodge, Robinson Road, Horndon-on-the-Hill, Stanford-le-Hope SS17 8PU Tel: 01375 360718 Fax: 01375 645366 — MB BS 1970 Punjab; MS Guru Nanak 1973; MB BS Punjab (India) 1970; FICS 1982. (Med. Coll. Amritsar) GP; Chairm. Romford PCG. Prev: Research Asst. (Surg.) V.J. Hosp. Amritsar, India; SHO (A & E) Lister Hosp. Stevenage; SHO Rotat. (Surg.) Roy. Salop Infirm. Shrewsbury.

SAINI, Mahesh 33 Roseville Avenue, Hounslow TW3 3TE — MB BS 1994 Lond. SHO (Paediat.) Roy. Lond. Hosp.

SAINI, Mandeep Singh 43 Woodend, Handsworth Wood, Birmingham B20 1EW — MB ChB 1998 Liverp.; MB ChB Liverp 1998.

SAINI, Manju Bon Acord, Park Road, Stoke Poges, Slough SL2 4PA — MB BS 1998 Lond.; MB BS Lond 1998.

SAINI, Mohan Singh Soho Health Centre, Louise Road, Handsworth, Birmingham B21 0RY Tel: 0121 523 2343 Fax: 0121 507 1607; 16 The Russells, Moseley, Birmingham B13 8RT Tel: 0121 449 9307 — MB BS 1971 Poona; Univ. of Poona. (Armed Forces Med. Coll.) GP Princip.; Clin. Med. Off. (Ophth.) Sandwell & Dudley HAs. Prev: Trainee GP Sturry Canterbury VTS; SHO (Ophth.) Leeds Gen. Infirm.

SAINI, Sarvesh Ram 45 Ellington Road, Hounslow TW3 4HX — MB BS 1992 Lond.

SAINS, Parvinderpal Singh 241 Beaconsfield Road, Southall UB1 1DD Tel: 020 8574 7176 Email: p.sains@talk21.com — MB ChB 1995 Birm.; ChB Birm. 1995; MRCS.

SAINSBURY, Alan David The Surgery, Hillson Close, Port Isaac PL29 3TR Tel: 01208 880222 Fax: 01208 880633; Springside Barn, Tronetha, Port Isaac PL29 3RU Tel: 01208 880231 Email: sains@springside.demon.co.uk — MB BS 1979 Lond.; DRCOG 1982.

SAINSBURY, Clive Peter Quine Torbay Hospital, Lawes Bridge, Torquay TQ2 7AA Tel: 01803 614567 Fax: 01803 616334; 80 Walnut Road, Torquay TQ2 6HU Tel: 01803 605500 Fax: 01803 617174 — MB ChB 1972 Ed.; FRCP Lond. 1996; MRCP (UK) 1977; FRCPH 1997. (Ed.) Cons. Paediat. Torbay Hosp. Socs: Roy. Coll. Paediat. & Child Health. Prev: Sen. Regist. (Paediat.) Dept. Child Health Univ. Hosp. Wales Cardiff; Research Fell. (Child Life &

Health) Roy. Hosp. Sick Childr. Edin.; Sen. Resid. Hosp. Sick Childr., Toronto.

SAINSBURY, James 107 Ripple Road, Barking IG11 7NY Tel: 020 8594 1311 Fax: 020 8591 4686; 27 Meadow Way, Chigwell IG7 6LR — MB BCh BAO 1959 Dub.; LAH Dub. 1958; DObst RCOG 1963.

SAINSBURY, Jane Anne Hednesford Street Surgery, 60 Hednesford Street, Cannock WS11 1DJ Tel: 01543 503121 Fax: 01543 468024; The Red House, 8 The Green, Milford, Stafford ST17 0UR Tel: 01785 661010 — MB ChB 1973 Birm.

SAINSBURY, Mr John Richard Cochrane Royal Free and University College London Medical School, Dept Surgery, 2nd Floor, Charles Ball House, Riding House Street, London W1V 7EJ Tel: 020 7679 9310 Fax: 020 7636 5176 Email: r.sainsbury@usl.ac.uk; Meltham Hall, Huddersfield HD9 4BQ Tel: 01484 854441 Fax: 01484 854426 — MB BS 1977 Newc.; MD Newc. 1986; FRCS Eng. 1981. Sen. Lect. And Cons. Surg., Univ. Coll. Lond. Prev: Cons. Surg. Huddersfield Roy. Infirm.

SAINSBURY, Matthew Charles Oxford Regional Health Authority, Old Road, Headington, Oxford OX3; 8 The Rookery, Kidlington OX5 1AW — MB BS 1983 Lond.; FCAnaesth 1991; Dip. IMC RCS Ed. 1990. Sen. Regist. (Anaesth.) Oxf. RHA. Prev: Research Regist. (Anaesth.) John Radcliffe Hosp. Oxf.; SHO (Anaesth.) S.mead Hosp. Bristol; SHO (Anaesth.) Roy. Devon & Exeter Hosp.

SAINSBURY, Olga Mary (retired) 50 Rookwood Park, Guildford Road, Horsham RH12 1UB Tel: 01403 255454 — MRCS Eng. LRCP Lond. 1942. Prev: Sen. Resid. Med. Off. Roy. Free Hosp.

SAINSBURY, Paul Antony 34 Beechwood View, Leeds LS4 2LP — MB ChB 1994 Leeds.

SAINSBURY, Peter Pondfield, Cut Mill, Bosham, Chichester PO18 8PT — MD 1950 Camb.; BA Camb. 1938, MD 1950, MB BChir 1942; FRCP Lond. 1976, M 1965; FRCPsych 1971; DPM Eng. 1949. (Camb. & Middlx.) Emerit. Cons. Psychiat. Graylingwell Hosp. Socs: Hon. Fell. RCPsych; Fell. Roy. Soc. Med. (Hon. Mem. & Ex-Pres. Psychiat. Sect.). Prev: Dir. of Research, MRC Clin. Psychiat. Research Unit Graylingwell; Hosp.; Vis. Prof. Univs. Qu.sland, Missouri & Ain Shams (Cairo); Research Asst. Maudsley Hosp.

SAINSBURY, Wendy Alison Rickmansworth Road Surgery, 35 Rickmansworth Road, Watford WD18 7HO Tel: 01923 223232 Fax: 01923 243397 — MB BS 1981 Lond.

SAINT, Thomas Morris Campbell (retired) 1 Reid Park Close, Newcastle upon Tyne NE2 2EZ Tel: 0191 281 3308 — MB BS 1951 Durh.

SAINT-YVES, Ian Fleming Marie (retired) Dunvegan, School Brae, Whiting Bay, Brodick KA27 8PZ — MB ChB Glas. 1960; MD Glas 1976; T(PHM) 1991; DObst RCOG 1962; DTM & H Liverp. 1961. Prev: Head Scott. Clin. Coding Centre Edin.

SAINTEY, Patricia Anne, Maj. RAMC Northay Farmhouse, Northay, Chard TA20 3DN — MB BS 1984 Lond.; MRCGP 1990; Cert. Prescribed Equiv. Exp. 1990. (Westm.) Med. Off. Alanbrooke Barracks, Germany. Socs: BMA. Prev: Cas. Off. Milit. Wing Musgrave Pk. Hosp. Belf.; SHO (Rehabil. & Rheum.) Headley Ct. Defence Servs. Med. Rehabil.; Unit Chessington; Families Med. Off. Roy. Milit. Acad. Sandhurst.

SAINZ MANDIOLA, Antonio South Cleveland Hospital, Loftus House 115-C, Marton Road, Middlesbrough TS4 3TQ — LMS 1991 Basque Provinces.

SAIR, Mark Intensive Care Unit, Derriford Hospital, Plymouth PL6 8DH Tel: 01752 763789 Email: mark.sair@phnt.swest.nhs.uk; Stormcrest, 114 Looseleigh Lane, Plymouth PL6 5HT Email: marksair@hotmail.com — MB ChB 1988 Bristol; MRCP (UK) 1993; FRCA 1994; DA (UK) 1991; PhD Lond. 1998. (Bristol) Cons. In Intens. Care and Anaesth., Derriford Hosp. Plymouth. Socs: Eur.Soc. Intens. Care Med.; Soc. Critical Care Med. USA.; Intens. Care Soc. Prev: Specialist Regist., Hammersmith Hosp. Imperial Coll.; PICU Fell., St. Marys Hosp. Paddington; Clin. Research Fell. (Critical Care) Nat. Heart & Lung Inst. Lond. & Physiol. Flow Studies Gp. Imperial Coll. Sci., Technol. & Med.

SAIT, Christopher Lewis Sketty Surgery, De la Beche Road, Sketty, Swansea SA2 9EA Tel: 01792 206862; De-La-Beche House, 42 De-La-Beche Road, Sketty, Swansea SA2 9AR Tel: 01792 420109 Fax: 01792 291129 — MB BCh 1971 Wales. Socs: BMA.

SAITCH, Christopher David Wadebridge and Camel Estuary Practice, Brooklyn, Wadebridge PL27 7BS Tel: 01208 812222 Fax:

SAIZ

01208 815907 — MB BChir 1982 Camb.; MB Camb. 1983, BChir 1982; MA Camb. 1983. (Cambridge and St Georges) Prev: Trainee GP/SHO Cornw. & I. of Scilly HA VTS; Ho. Phys. St. Jas. Hosp. Lond.; Ho. Surg. Ashford Hosp. Middlx.

SAIZ, Ana Maria Benedicto 35 Crofton Avenue, Bexley DA5 3AS; 2A Foots Cray Lane, Sidcup DA14 4NR — LMS 1982 Basque Provinces.

SAJID, Mr Mahmud Vale of Leven Hospital, North Main St., Alexandria G83 0UA; 42 Woodbank, Gdns., Alexandria G83 0SW — MB BS 1986 Pakistan; FRCS Glas. 1993; FRCS Ed. 1996; FRCS Irel. 1996. (Nishtar) Staff Surg. Prev: SHO (Gastnaval) Gen. Hosp. Glas.

SAJID, Mohammed 3 Careless Green, Stourbridge DY9 8XE — MB ChB 1997 Dundee.

SAJID, Mr Syed Abdul Maryfield Lodge, Bankend Road, Dumfries DG1 4AN — MB BS 1983 Karachi; FRCS Ed. 1991.

SAJJAD, Ali 5 Surrey House, Yardley Green Road, Birmingham B9 5PY — MB BS 1985 Punjab; MRCP (UK) 1990.

SAJJANHAR, Tina 85 Boyne Road, Lewisham, London SE13 5AN — MB BS 1987 Lond.; MRCP (UK) 1993; DCH RCP Lond. 1991; DRCOG 1990. (Guys Hospital) Cons. Paediat. Lewisham Hosp. Prev: Sen. Regist. (Paediat.) St. Thos. Hosp. Lond.; Clin. Research Fell. (Paediat. Intens. Care) Guy's Hosp. Lond.; Regist. Lewisham Hosp.

SAJNANI, Dushant Kumar Sandwell General Hospital, 200/B Hallam Site, West Bromwich B71 4HJ — LMS 1983 La Laguna; MRCOphth 1992. SHO (Ophth.) HM Stanley Hosp. St. Asaph.

SAKEL, Rezina 3 Glyncoli Close, Treorchy, Cardiff CF42 6SU — MB BS 1995 Lond.

SAKHRANI, Lavina Wessex Road Surgery, Wessex Road, Parkstone, Poole BH14 8BQ Tel: 01202 734924; 18 Albert Close, Pearl Street, Saltburn-by-the-Sea TS12 1DU Tel: 01202 701496, 01287 625778 Email: gasgoddess62@hotmail.com — BM 1991 Soton. p/t GP Princip. Poole. Socs: MRCGP.

SAKHUJA, Jagdish Chandar (retired) Flat 5, Chesterton Court, Eaton Rise, London W5 2HJ Tel: 020 8566 7507 — MB BS Panjab (India) 1944; DPM Eng. 1978. Prev: Clin. Asst. (Psychiat.) Severalls Hosp. Colchester.

SAKHUJA, Shashi Bala City Hospital NHS Trust, Birmingham B18 7HQ Tel: 0121 554 3801 — MB BS 1980 Madras; MD Chandigarh 1983; FFA RCSI 1988. Cons. Anaesth. City Hosp. Birm. Prev: Cons. Anaesth. Bolton Hosps. NHS Trust; Sen. Regist. (Anaesth.) Withington Hosp. Manch.; Regist. (Anaesth.) S.. Gen. Hosp. Glas.

SAKKA, Mr Samir Akram Asad Orthopaedic Department, University Hospital, Lewisham, London SE13 6LH Tel: 020 8333 3167 Fax: 020 8333 3159 — MB BS 1985 Lond.; FRCS (Orth) 1997; FRCS Ed. 1990. (St. Geo. Hosp. Med. Sch. Lond.) Cons. (Orthop. & Spinal Surg.) Lond.; Hon. Sen. Lect. UMDS 1998. Prev: Sen. Spinal Fell. Roy. Orthop. Hosp. Birm.; Fell. Scoliosis Unit Roy. Nat. Orthop. Hosp. Stanmore; Career Regist. (Orthop.) NW Thames Region.

SAKKADAS, Ambrose 96 Station Road, London NW4 3SR — Ptychio Iatrikes 1994 Thessalonika.

SAKLATVALA, Jacqueline Haywood Hospital X-ray Department 2, High Lane, Burslem, Stoke-on-Trent ST6 7 Tel: 01782 556239 Fax: 01782 813419; Highwood, Tower Road, Ashley Heath, Market Drayton TF9 4PU — MB ChB 1975 Dundee; FRCR 1982; DMRD Eng. 1981; DA Eng. 1978. Cons. Radiol. (s/i Musculoskeletal Imaging) N. Staffs. Hosp. Trust Stoke-on-Trent. Socs: Roy. Coll. of Radiologists; Brit. Soc. of Skeletal Radiologists; Skeletal Dysplania Gp.

SAKLATVALA, Jeremy 71 Lonsdale Road, London SW13 9DA — MB BS 1968 Lond.; MRCP (UK) 1970; MRCS Eng. LRCP Lond. 1968.

SAKSENA, Joyti 4 Cherry Hills, Little Oxmey Lane, Watford WD19 6DH Tel: 020 8428 6477 Fax: 020 8428 6477 Email: joy@saks.freeserve.co.uk — MB ChB 1995 Dundee; BMSc Dund 1992; MRCS Lond. 1999. (Dundee Univ.) SHO Rotat. (Surg.) Bedford Hosp. Socs: BMA. Prev: SHO (Orthop.) Hillingdon Hosp. Hillingdon; SHO (A&E) Brisbane, Aust.

SAKSENA, M K Heath Road Medical Centre, Heath Road, Runcorn WA7 5JJ Tel: 01928 565881 Fax: 01928 566748 — MB BS 1973 Agra; MB BS 1973 Agra.

SAKSENA, Shiv Chandra 85 Nursery Road, Edgbaston, Birmingham B15 3JU Tel: 0121 454 0116 — MB BS 1950 Lucknow.

SAKTHIBALAN, Maheswaralingam Eastern Avenue Surgery, 167 Eastern Avenue, Redbridge, Ilford IG4 5AW Tel: 020 8550 4532 Fax: 020 8551 2199 — LRCP 1986 Ed.; LRCP, LRCS Ed. LRCPS Glas. 1986.

SAKULA, Alex 7 Grand Avenue, Hove BN3 2LF Tel: 01273 728639 — MB BS 1940 Lond.; MD Lond. 1942; FRCP Lond. 1971, M 1941; MRCS Eng. LRCP Lond. 1940; DHMSA Lond. 1978. (Middlx.) Cons. Phys. (Respirat. Med.); Broderip Schol. 1940; Fitzpatrick Lect. RCP Lond. 1987. Socs: Fell.Roy. Soc. of Med. (Ex. Pres. and Hon. Fell., Sect. of Hist. and Med.; Worshipful Soc. Apoth. (Ex-Pres.) and Hon. Fell. Fac. of Hist. Med.; Osler Club (Ex Pres. & Hon. Fell.). Prev: Cons. Phys. Redhill, Dorking, Crawley & Horsham Hosps.; Maj. RAMC, Med. Specialist; Fitzpatrick Lect. Roy. Coll. Phys. Lond.

SALA, Carmelo Department of Anaesthetics, North Middlesex Hospital, Sterling Way, Edmonton, London N18 1QX; 12 Lancaster Avenue, Hitchin SG5 1PB — State Exam Pisa 1984.

SALA, Mr Matthew John 75A Kensington Gardens Square, Bayswater, London W2 4DJ Tel: 020 7727 3916 Fax: 020 7727 3916 Email: matthew.sala@virgin.net — MB ChB 1983 Liverp.; FRCS (Orth.) 1997; FRCS Eng. 1990; FRCS (Orth.) 1997. (Liverp.) Sen. Regist. Centr. Middlx. Hosp. Lond. Prev: Sen. Regist. Qu. Eliz. II Hosp. Welling Gdn. City, Ealing & Char. Cross Hosp. Lond.

SALA TENNA, Adrianno Michele GFR, 6 South Oxford St., Edinburgh EH8 9QF — MB ChB 1996 Ed.

SALAH, Ibrahim Hussein Ibrahim Ansdell Road Surgery, 2-4 Ansdell Road, Blackpool FY1 5LX Tel: 01253 761293; 208 West Park Drive, Blackpool FY3 9LW — MB BCh 1973 Cairo.

SALAH, Mr Magdy Mohammed Riad Mohammed c/o Mr Coleman, 42 Lavender Road, Holts Village, Oldham OL4 5NY — MB BCh 1977 Ain Shams; FRCS Ed. 1987; FRCSI 1987.

SALAH, Mr Munzer Walid Flat 3, 36 Devonshire Place, London W1G 6JR Tel: 020 7935 4520 — MB BS 1966 Lond.; FRCS Eng. 1972; MRCS Eng. LRCP Lond. 1966. (King's Coll. Hosp.) Socs: BMA; Fell. Roy. Soc. Med.; Fell. Hunt. Soc. Prev: Cons. Surg. Ladbroke Diag. Clinic; Regist. (Surg.) St. Thos. Hosp. Lond.; Sen. Regist. (Surg.) Hillingdon Hosp. Uxbridge.

SALAHUDDIN, Azam 13 Parkwood Road, Wimbledon, London SW19 7AQ Tel: 020 8946 4088 — MB BS 1963 Karachi; DMRD Eng. 1975.

SALAHUDDIN, Mobin The Surgery, 11 Thorpe Road, Staines TW18 3EA Tel: 01784 454965 Fax: 01784 441244 — MB BS 1983 Karachi.

SALAHUDDIN, Mohamed Glan Clwyd Hospital, Bodelwyddan, Rhyl LL18 5UJ — MB BS 1973 Bihar; DA Bihar 1975.

SALAHUDDIN, Mohammad Old Chester Road Surgery, 241 Old Chester Road, Lower Tranmere, Birkenhead CH42 3TD Tel: 0151 645 2306 — MB BS 1971 Punjab; BSc, MB BS Punjab Pakistan 1971; MSc Ed. (Human Genetics) 1981; Dip. Pract. Dermat. Wales 1991. (King Edwd. Med. Coll.)

SALAHUDDIN, Muhammad Junaid 63 Lee Road, Perivale, Greenford UB6 7DA Tel: 020 8991 1787 — MB ChB 1973 Mosul. Assoc. Specialist (Plastic Surg.) City Hosp. Dudley Rd. Birm. Prev: Craniofacial Fell. Qu. Eliz. Hosp. Birm.; Regist. (Plastic Surg.) St. And. Hosp. Billericay.

SALAKO, Abayomi Oluremilekn 171 Charlemont Road, London E6 6AG — MB BS 1985 Ibadan; MRCP (UK) 1993.

SALAM, Imroz Department of Gastroenterology, West Wales General Hospital, Carmarthen NHS Trust, Dolgwili Road, Carmarthen SA31 2AF Tel: 01267 235151 Fax: 01267 227921 — MB BS 1979 Poona; FRCPI 1997, M 1985. (Armed Forces Med. Coll. Pune, India) Cons. Gastroenterol. W. Wales Gen. Hosp. Carmarthen. Socs: FEBG. Prev: Sen. Specialist (Gastroenterol.) Qu. Eliz. Milit. Hosp.; Cons. Gastroenterol. Daharan Med. Center, Saudi Arabia; Regist. (Med.) Ysbyty Gwynedd Bangor.

SALAM, Mr Mahmoud Abdel Mohamed El-Hosseiny The Ipswich Hospital, Heath Road, Ipswich IP4 5PD Tel: 01473 703503 Fax: 014730703111; 145 The St, Rushmene St. Andrew, Ipswich IP5 1DG — MB BCh 1982 Ain Shams; MSc War. 1995; FRCS (ORL.) 1996; FRCS Ed. 1989; MD Ain Shams 1989. Cons. Otolaryngologist (ENT) Ipswich Hosp. Socs: BMA; MDU; BAOL -

HNS. Prev: Sen. Regist. Oxf. & Reading Rotat. (ENT); Regist. W. Midl. Rotat. (ENT) (Birm. Coventry & Warks.).

SALAM, Mohammad Abdus 100 Princes Road, Eastbourne BN23 6HH Tel: 01323 734827 — MB BS 1966 Dacca; MRCOphth 1989; DO RCPSI 1979. Clin. Asst. (Ophth.) Hastings & E.bourne HA's. Prev: SHO (Ophth.) E.bourne HA, Colchester & Whipps Cross Hosps.

SALAM, Samia 17 Brookside Close, Caerphilly CF83 2RR — MB BCh 1992 Wales.

SALAM, Souheir 87 Dudley Gardens, London W13 9LU — MB BS 1998 Lond.; MB BS Lond 1998.

SALAMA, Alan David 41 Ramillies Road, London W4 1JW Tel: 020 8994 8689 — MB BS 1990 Lond.; PhD Lond. 2001; MRCP (UK) 1993. Regist. (Gen. Med. & Nephrol.) Ealing & Hammersmith Hosp.

SALAMA, Amir Adib Kamel 4 Mill Court, City Hospital, Dudley Road, Birmingham B18 7QH — MB ChB 1989 Alexandria.

SALAMA, Mr Fayek Dimitri Thoracic Department, The City Hospital, Hucknall Road, Nottingham NG5 1PB Tel: 0115 691169 — MB BCh 1958 Cairo; FRCS Eng. 1969; FRCS Ed. 1969; LMSSA Lond. 1974. (Ain Shams) Cons. Thoracic Surg. Notts. AHA (T). Socs: Soc. Thoracic & Cardiovasc. Surgs. Gt. Brit. & Irel. & BMA. Prev: Regist. Shotley Bridge Gen. Hosp. Consett; Sen. Regist. W.m. Hosp. & St. Geo. Hosp. Lond.

SALAMA, Nabel Doss The Surgery, 41 Ellers Lane, Auckley, Doncaster DN9 3HT Tel: 01302 770327 Fax: 01302 771302; Orchard Grange, 89 Main St, Auckley, Doncaster DN9 3HJ — MB BCh 1966 Cairo.

SALAMA, Mr Nabil Youssef c/o Postgraduate Medical Centre, Lewisham Hospital, High St., London SE13 6LH Tel: 020 8333 3000; Beaumanor, 23 Manor Way, Beckenham BR3 3LH Tel: 020 8658 3751 Email: nysalama@aol.co.uk — MB BCh 1973 Cairo; FRCS Eng. 1980. (Cairo Univ) Cons. ENT Lewisham NHS Trust; Hon. Sen. Lect. UMDS. Socs: Roy. Soc. Med.

SALAMA, Nadia Salama Ibrahim 52 Cornflower Lane, Shirley Oaks Village, Shirley, Croydon CR0 8XJ — MB BCh 1980 Cairo.

SALAMAN, Professor John Redcliffe (retired) 5 Brooklyn Close, Rhiwbina, Cardiff CF14 6UT Tel: 02920 626539 Fax: 02920 655735 Email: j.salaman@doctors.org.uk — MB BChir Camb. 1963; MChir Camb. 1995, MA 1964; FRCS Eng. 1967; MRCS Eng. LRCP Lond. 1963. Prev: Prof. Transpl. Surg. Univ. Wales Coll. Med. Cardiff.

SALAMAN, Patricia Faith (retired) 5 Brooklyn Close, Rhiwbina, Cardiff CF14 6UT Tel: 02920 626539 — MB BChir 1964 Camb.; MA Camb. 1964; MRCS Eng. LRCP Lond. 1963; FRCR 1979. Prev: Cons. Radiother. Velindre Hosp. Cardiff.

SALAMANI, Mr Murad Mohamed Hassan 29 The Baulk, Worksop S81 0HU — MB BCh 1972 Cairo; FRCS Ed. 1987.

SALAMAT, Ahmed Ali 6 Adria Road, Sparkhill, Birmingham B11 4JN Tel: 0121 449 6074 — MB BCh 1981 Al Fateh Libya; MSc Glas. 1989; MRCP (UK) 1992. Hon. Clin. Research Fell. (Haemat.) Qu. Eliz. Univ. Hosp. Birm. Prev: SHO (Haemat.) Glas. Roy. Infirm. & Whipps Cross Hosp. Lond.; SHO (Med.) Vict. Infirm. Glas.

SALAME, Mahomed Yazeed 81 Carlton Avenue E., Wembley HA9 8LZ Tel: 020 8904 7863 — BSc Basic Med. Scs. & Biochem. (Hons.) Lond. 1985, MB BS 1988; MRCP (UK) 1991. BHF Jun. Research Fell. & Hon. Regist. (Cardiol.) Glenfield Hosp. Leics. Prev: SHO (Med., Cardiol. & Neurol.) Addenbrooke's Hosp. Camb.; Ho. Surg. Char. Cross Hosp. Lond.; Ho. Phys. W.m. Hosp. Lond.

SALAMEH, Yasser Mohammad Mohammad Hassain 17 Atherstone Avenue, Peterborough PE3 9TT — MB BS 1993 Jordan.

SALAMONSKI, John Henry The Surgery, 11 Main Street, Leuchars, St Andrews KY16 0HB Tel: 01334 839210 Fax: 01334 838770 — MB ChB 1989 Dundee; BSc Hons. (Physiol.) St. And. 1984.

SALAR, Taufeeq Ahmad Selly Oak Health Centre, Katie Road, Selly Oak, Birmingham B29 6JG Tel: 0121 472 0016 — MB BS 1973 Punjab; MB BS 1973 Punjab.

SALARIA, Dabeer Ahmad 20 Ensign Close, Staines TW19 7RF — MB BS 1986 Punjab.

SALASA, Mohamed Hassan (retired) 37 Woodhouse Road, Finchley, London N12 9ET — MB ChB 1967 Cape Town; MRCPsych 1972; DPM Eng. 1972. Prev: Cons. Psychiat. Hill End Hosp., St. Albans City Hosp. & St. Crispin Hosp. N.ampton.

SALATHIA, Kulvir Singh 27 Greer Park Heights, Knockbreda, Belfast BT8 7YG — MB BS 1969 Jammu & Kashmir.

SALATIAN, Miral Dunrowan Day Hospital, 37 Maggir Woods Loan, Falkirk FK1 5EH Tel: 01324 639009 Fax: 01324 626238; 62 Kenning Knowes Road, Stirling FK7 9JG Tel: 01786 465943 Fax: 01786 465943 — MD 1971 Vienna; MD Vienna Austria 1971. (Vienna Med. Sch. Austria) Assoc. Specialist (Psychiat.) Forth Valley Primary Care - NHS Trust.

SALCEDO, Aurelio Advincula 175 Clarence Road, London E5 8EE Tel: 020 8985 7096 — LAH Dub. 1966.

SALDANHA, Mr Clyde Bosco Raymond Department of Cardiothoracic Surgery, St. Bartholomews Hospital, Smithfield, London EC1A 7BE; 72 Churston Drive, Morden SM4 4JQ — MB BS 1986 Lond.; FRCS Ed. 1992. Regist. (Cardiothoracic Surg.) St. Bart. Hosp. Lond. Prev: Research Fell. (Cardiovasc. Research) St. Thos. Hosp. Lond.

SALDANHA, Gerald Stephen Department of Histopathology, Level III, Phase III, Leicester Royal Infirmary, Leicester — MB ChB 1989 Leic.; MRCP (UK) 1992. SHO (Histopath.) Leicester Roy. Infirm. Prev: SHO Rotat. (Med.) Leicester Hosps.

SALDANHA, Gerard Joseph Francis 182 Greenvale Road, London SE9 1PQ Email: g.j.saldanha@mds.qmw.ac.uk — MB BS 1989 Lond.; BA (Hons.) Oxf. 1984; MRCP (UK) 1992. (St. Thos. Hosp. Med. Sch.) Research Regist. (Neurol.) Roy. Lond. Hosp. Prev: Regist. (Neurol.) Guy's Hosp. Lond.; Regist. & SHO (Neurol.) Brook Hosp.

SALDANHA, Luis Joseph The Surgery, 131 Thornbridge Avenue, Great Barr, Birmingham B42 2AP Tel: 0121 357 1286 Fax: 0121 505 3705 — MB ChB 1978 Birm.

SALDANHA, Maria Benicia Yvette Watling Medical Centre, 108 Watling Avenue, Burnt Oak, Edgware HA8 0NR Tel: 020 8906 1711 Fax: 020 8201 1283; 31 Mowbray Road, Edgware HA8 8JG — MB BS 1985 Lond.; MRCGP 1995; DCH RCP Lond. 1989. GP Trainer. Prev: Trainee GP Edgware Gen. Hosp. Lond. VTS.

SALE, Andrew Colin Buchanan Stalham Green Surgery, Old Yarmouth Road, Stalham, Norwich NR12 9PS Tel: 01692 580880; Lankaster, Norwich Rd, Ludham, Great Yarmouth NR29 5QD Tel: 01692 678262 — MB BS 1991 Lond.; MA Camb. 1990; MRCGP 1996; DRCOG 1994. (Guy's Lond. Med. Sch.)

SALE, John Philip Stoke Manderville Hospital, Aylesbury HP21 8AL; One Acre, Peters Lane, Whiteleaf, Princes Risborough, Aylesbury HP27 0LG Tel: 01844 345805 — MB BS 1977 Lond.; FFA RCS Eng. 1982.

SALE, Julian Edward M.R.C Laboratory of Molecular Biology, Cambridge CB2 2QH Tel: 01223 252942 Email: jes@mrc-lmb.cam.ac.uk; 3 Coniston Road, Cambridge CB1 7BZ Tel: 01223 572841 — MB BChir 1991 Camb.; MA Camb. 1993, BA 1989; MRCP (UK) 1994; PHD Camb. Uni. 1999. (Cambridge) MRC Clinician Scientist, MRC Laborat. of Molecular Biol., Camb.; Fell. Gonville & Caius Coll. Camb.; Director of Studies in Med., Gonville & Caius Coll. Camb.; Coll. Lecture in Path., Gonville & Caius Coll. Camb. Prev: Regist. (Gen. Med. & Hepatol.) Univ. Hosp. Qu. Med. Centre Nottm.; SHO Rotat. Addenbrooke's Hosp. Camb.

SALE, Steven Michael Department of Anaesthesia, Bristol Royal Infirmary, Marlborough Street, Bristol BS2 8HW — MB ChB 1993 Bristol.

SALEEM, Amtul Karim Najma 15 St Anthonys Way, Haverfordwest SA61 1EL Tel: 01437 764545 — MB BS 1962 Punjab; FRCPath 1981; MRCPath 1979. Cons. Haemat. Withybush Gen. Hosp. HaverfordW.. Prev: Sen. Regist. (Haemat.) W.m. Hosp. Lond.; Sen. Regist. (Haemat.) Co. Laborat. Dorchester; Regist. (Haemat.) Ninewells Hosp. Dundee.

SALEEM, Anneela 39 Cromwell Grove, Manchester M19 3QD — MB ChB 1994 Leeds.

SALEEM, Mrs Asra Liverpool Women's Hospital, Crown St, Liverpool L8 Tel: 0151 708 9988; 24 Burder Road, Heswall, Wirral CH6U 2TY — MB BS 1990 Lond.; FRCS Ed. 1994; MRCOG 1997. (King's Coll. Sch. Med. Lond.) p/t SpR (O&G) Liverp. Wom.'s Hosp. Prev: Regist. (O & G) Addenbrooke's Hosp. Camb.; Specialist Regist. (O & G) Ipswich Hosp.

SALEEM, Haris 2 Fitzwilliam Close, Cross Inn, Pontyclun CF72 8BN — MB BS 1987 Karachi; MRCP (UK) 1993.

SALEEM

SALEEM, Ishrat 55 Ryfold Road, London SW19 8DF — MRCS Eng. LRCP Lond. 1979.

SALEEM, Mubashar Ahmad The Surgery, 158 Alcester Road South, Kings Heath, Birmingham B14 6AA Tel: 0121 444 1186 Fax: 0121 443 3252; 158 Alcester Road S., Kings Heath, Birmingham B14 6AA Tel: 0121 444 1186 Fax: 0121 443 3252 — MB BS 1973 Punjab.

SALEEM, Muhammad 22 Ashmole Close, Lichfield WS14 9RS Tel: 01543 255539 — MB BS 1965 Punjab; MPS ST. Pauls. (Nishtar Med. Coll. Multan) GP S. Staffs. HA.

SALEEM, Mr Muhammad Flat 9, Block D, Queens Hospital, Belvedere Road, Burton-on-Trent DE13 0RB — MB BS 1987 Bahauddin Zakariya U; FRCS Glas. 1995.

SALEEM, Muhammad Fayyaz Department Ophthalmology, Withybush General Hospital, Haverfordwest Tel: 01437 764545; Freshwinds, 15 St. Anthonys Way, Haverfordwest SA61 1EL Tel: 01437 766909 — MB BS 1966 Karachi; MRCOphth 1989; DO RCPSI 1971. Specialist (Ophth.) Pembrokesh. NHS Trust HaverfordW. Prev: Regist. (Ophth.) Ophth. Inst. Glas., Ninewells Hosp. Dundee & Roy.N.. Hosp. Lond.

SALEEM, Muhammed Shiregreen Medical Centre, 492 Bellhouse Road, Sheffield S5 0RG Tel: 0114 245 6123 Fax: 0114 257 0964 — MB BS 1967 Karachi.

SALEEM, Mrs Sabiha The Surgery, 141 Plumstead High Street, Plumstead, London SE18 1SE Tel: 020 8855 0052 Fax: 020 8855 7672; 14 Plumstead High Street, Plumstead, London SE18 1SN Tel: 020 8855 0052 Fax: 020 8855 7672 — MB BS 1954 Osmania.

SALEEM, Shahzadi 44 East Avenue, Oxford OX4 1XP — MB BS 1994 Lond.

SALEEM, Tausif 22 Ashmole Close, Lichfield WS14 9RS — MB BCh 1993 Wales.

SALEEM-UDDIN, Moin Ahson 31 Therapia Road, London SE22 0SF — MB BS 1986 Lond.; MRCP (UK) 1990. Research Fell. (Cell & Molecular Biol.) Gt. Ormond St. Hosp. Lond. Prev: SHO (Paediat. Cardiol.) Alder Hey Hosp. Liverp.; Regist. (Paediat.) Birm. Childr. Hosp.; SHO Rotat. (Paediat.) City Hosp. Nottm.

SALEEMI, Mohammad Hussain Town House Practice, 98 Albert Road, Widnes WA8 6LG Tel: 0151 424 3646 Fax: 0151 424 3646 — MB BS Punjab (Pakistan) 1965; DA Eng. 1970. (King Edwd. Med. Coll. Lahore) GP. Socs: Med. Protec. Soc.; Fell.Roy.Soc.Med.; Assoc. Mem. Roy. Coll. Gen. Pract.

SALEEMI, Mr Mohammed Asad 9A Rydal Road, London SW16 1QF Tel: 020 8696 0371 — MB BS 1990 Lond.; FRCS Eng. 1995. (St. Thos. Hosp. Med. Sch.) Specialist Regist. Rotat. SE Thames. Prev: SHO Rotat. (Surg.) St. Peter's Hosp. Chertsey.

SALEEMI, Sarfraz Ahmed 46 Montana Road, London SW17 8SN Tel: 020 8767 5214 — MB BS 1983 Punjab; MRCP (UK) 1992.

SALEH, Mr Adnan Jamil Bronglais General Hospital, Aberystwyth SY23 1ER — LAH Dub. 1964; FRCS Ed. 1980.

SALEH, Ahmed Hosny Shoukry 31 Northfield, Swanland, North Ferriby HU14 3RG Tel: 01482 631987 Fax: 01482 632631 Email: asleh@compuserve.com — MB BCh 1978 Ain Shams; FFA RCSI 1986; DA (UK) 1984. Cons. Anaesth. Castle Hill Hosp. Hull. Prev: Cons. & Chief Resid. (Anaesth.) King Faisal Specialist Hosp., Riyadh; Assoc. Specialist Castle Hill Hosp. Hull; Sen. Regist. Riyadh Milit. Hosp., Saudi Arabia.

SALEH, Assil 12 Alfriston Avenue, Harrow HA2 7DZ — MB BS 1998 Lond.; MB BS Lond 1998.

SALEH, Badie Tawfiec Scunthorpe General Hospital, Cliff Gardens, Scunthorpe DN15 7BH Tel: 01724 282282 — MB BCh Assiut 1969; MRCPsych 1983; DPM RCPSI 1983. Cons. Psychiat. Community Health Trust Scunthorpe; Clin. Director. Socs: Roy. Coll. Psychiat.; Reg. Psychiat. Assn. Prev: Sen. Regist. (Psychiat.) Glas.; Regist. (Psychiat.) Bridgend S. Wales.

SALEH, Farid Mustafa Mohammed Department of Radiotherapy, St. George's Hospital, Long Leys Road, Lincoln LN1 1EF Tel: 01522 512512; 15 Deep Dale Lane, Nettleham, Lincoln LN2 2LT — MB ChB 1979 Mosul; DMRT Eng. 1990. Staff Doctor (Radiother. & Oncol.) St. Geo. Hosp. Lincoln. Prev: Regist. (Radiother.) Norf. & Norwich Hosp.; Regist. (Radiother.) Ipswich Hosp.; SHO (Radiother.) Coventry Hosp.

SALEH, Mr Farouq Awad Ali 129 Barley Lane, Goodmayes, Ilford IG3 8XH — Vrach 1970 Peoples Friendship U Moscow; Vrach Peoples Friendship U, Moscow 1970; FRCS Glas. 1982.

SALEH, Isam 25 Torquay Drive, Luton LU4 9LL — State Exam Med. Munich 1983.

SALEH, Mehboobali Ismail School Health, Canterbury & Thanet Healthcare Trust, Little Bourne Road, Canterbury CT1 1TD Tel: 01227 459371; 1 Monkton Gardens, Cliftonville, Margate CT9 3HN Tel: 01843 223577 — State Exam Med 1985 Munster; DFFP 1996; DCH RCP Lond. 1993; DRCOG 1993. Staff Grade (Community Paediat.) Canterbury & Thanet Community Healthcare Trust.

SALEH, Professor Michael Department of Orthopaedics, Northern General Hospital, Herries Road, Sheffield S5 7AU Tel: 0114 243 4343 Fax: 0114 256 0472 Email: m.saleh@sheffield.ac.uk — MB ChB 1975 Sheff.; HST RCS England 1986; MSc Biomed. Engineering Sci. Dundee 1982; FRCS Eng. 1980; FRCS Ed. 1980. (Sheffield) Prof. Orthop. Univ. Sheff. & Hon. Cons. N. Gen. Hosp. Sheff.; Prof. Orthop. Sheff.s Childr.s Hosp. Prev: Sen. Regist. (Orthop.) Sheff. HA; Regist. (Orthop.) Tayside HB.

SALEH, Michel Saleh Antoun BMH Rinteln BFPO 29 — MB BCh 1969 Cairo; DA Eng. 1975. Specialist (Anaesth.) RAMC.

SALEH, Mohamed Salah Al Dean Abdul Hamead 101 The Park, Redbourn, St Albans AL3 7LT — MB BCh 1987 Ain Shams; MRCPI 1996; MRCOG 1995.

SALEH, Noorolah Department of Obst. & Gyn., Hope Hospital, Eccles Old Road, Salford M6 8HD Tel: 0161 789 7373; 17 March Bank Drive, Cheadle SK8 1QY — MD 1972 Tehran; MRCOG 1980. Assoc. Specialist (O & G) Hope Hosp. Salford.

SALEH, Roy St Johns Medical Centre, St. Johns Road, Altrincham WA14 2NW Tel: 0161 928 8727 Fax: 0161 929 8550 — MB ChB 1973 Manch. Prev: SHO (Paediat.) Booth Hall Hosp. Manch.; SHO (Obst.) N. Manch. Gen. Hosp.; Ho. Off. (Surg.) Ancoats Hosp. Manch.

SALEH, Sanna St Julians Medical Centre, 13A Stafford Road, Newport NP19 7DQ Tel: 01633 251304 Fax: 01633 221977 — MB ChB 1976 Alexandria; MB ChB 1976 Alexandria; LRCP LRCS Ed. LRCPS Glas. 1980 Edinburgh & Glasgow.

SALEH, Shawqi Suleiman Asi 2 Coulton Drive, East Boldon NE36 0SZ — MB BS 1983 Jordan; MRCOG 1993.

SALEH, Sion 1 Tavistock Square, Off Fernclough Road, Manchester M9 5RD Tel: 0161 205 1638 Fax: 0161 205 1638; Tel: 0161 428 3052 — MD 1974 Teheran; Cert. Family Plann. JCC 1991. GP Manch. Prev: Regist. Gen. Surg.; Reg. Orthop.

SALEK HADDADI, Ali Afraim 88 Truro Road, London N22 8DN Email: afrdim@msn.com — MB BS 1996 Lond. (St. George's London)

SALEM, Mr Fawzi Ahmed Ali Email: drfsalem@doctors.org.uk; Email: drfsalem@doctors.org.uk — MB BCh 1966 Alexandria; FRCS Ed. 1981. Cons. Neurosurg. Lam Wah Ee Hosp. 11600 Penang Malaysia. Prev: Cons. Neurosurg. OldCh. Hosp.; Cons. Neurosurg. Newc. Gen. Hosp.; Assoc. Prof. Neurosurg. Sch. Med. Sc. Univ. Sains Malaysia, Kota Bharu, Malaysia.

SALEM, Jack (retired) 7 Larch Rise, Prestbury, Macclesfield SK10 4UY Tel: 01625 829396 — MRCS Eng. LRCP Lond. 1942; FFCM 1978, M 1972; MRCGP 1957. Prev: Area Med. Off. Trafford AHA.

SALEM, Naglaa 4 Elm Road, Ewell, Epsom KT17 2EU — MB BS 1985 Lond.

SALEM, Mr Richard John The Edinburgh Breast Unit, Western General Hospital, Crewe Road, Edinburgh BL1 4AP Tel: 0131 537 1000 — MB ChB 1967 Manch.; FRCS Eng. 1973; DObst RCOG 1970. Cons. Surg. Fife Acute Hosp.s NHS Trust and Lothian Univ. NHS Trust. Prev: Sen. Regist. (Surg.) Hammersmith Hosp. Lond. & Roy. Berks. Hosp. Reading; Wellcome Surg. Research Fell. Roy. Postgrad. Med. Sch. Lond.; Cons Surge. Bolton Hosp.s NHS Trust.

SALERNO, Javier Oscar Parkway Health Centre, 1 Parkway, New Addington, Croydon CR0 0JA Tel: 01689 841264; 7 Gravel Hill, Addington, Croydon CR0 5BG Tel: 020 8655 4013 Fax: 020 8655 2750 — Medico Cirujano 1977 Univ. Nat. Mayor de San Marcos Peru; LRCP LRCS Ed. LRCPS Glas. 1985. (San Marcos University, Lima, Peru)

SALERNO, Julie Anne Parkway Health Centre, New Addington, Croydon CR0 0JA Tel: 01689 841264 Fax: 020 8655 2750; 7 Gravel Hill, Addington, Croydon CR0 5BG — MB ChB 1984 Liverp.; Cert. Family Plann. JCC 1988. (Liverpool) GP Croydon.

SALES, David Rothwell Northlands Wood Surgery, 7 Walnut Park, Haywards Heath RH16 3TG Tel: 01444 458022 Fax: 01444

415960 — MB BS 1978 Lond.; MRCGP 1985; DRCOG 1982; FRCGP 1997.

SALES, James Douglas Lochinvar, Dalginross, Comrie, Crieff PH6 2ED — MB ChB 1997 Glas.

SALES, Joanna Mary Flat 1 Pilgrims Court, Kidbrooke Grove, Blackheath, London SE3 0PQ — MB BS 1982 Lond.; MRCPsych 1989. Sen. Regist. (Child Psychiat.) Hosp. for Sick Childr. Gt. Ormond St. Lond. Prev: Trainee Psychiat. St. Geo. Hosp. Lond.; Trainee GP Greenwich VTS; SHO (Psychiat.) Univ. Hosp. W. Indies Kingston, Jamaica.

SALES, Mr John Edward Lawson Brackenhurst, Orchehill Avenue, Gerrards Cross SL9 8QL — MB 1962 Camb.; MChir Camb. 1973, MB 1962, BChir 1961; FRCS Eng. 1967. Cons. Surg. Hillingdon Hosp. Uxbridge & Mt. Vernon Hosp. N.wood; Regional Adviser Surg. N. W. Thames; Examr. Surg. Univ. Camb.; Mem. Ct. Examrs. RCS. Socs: Fell. Roy. Soc. Med. & Assn Surgs. Prev: Sen. Surg. Regist. St. Bart. Hosp. Lond.; Research Fell. Univ. Colorado Med. Centre Denver, USA; Lect. in Anat. St. Bart. Hosp. Med. Sch. Lond.

SALES, Norman Ronald (Surgery) 2 Salisbury Road, Farnborough GU14 7AW; The Old Stables, 32 Chobham Road, Frimley, Camberley GU16 8PF Tel: 01276 22130 — MB BS 1953 Lond.; MRCS Eng. LRCP Lond. 1953; MRCGP 1966. (Univ. Coll. Hosp.) Prev: Squadron Ldr. RAF Med. Br.; Med. Regist. Roy. Infirm. Bradford; Ho. Surg. Univ. Coll. Hosp.

SALES, Rebecca Clare 31A Blenheim Grove, London SE15 4QS — MB ChB 1990 Birm.; ChB Birm. 1990.

SALES, Richard Andrew 4 Levylsdene, Guildford GU1 2RS — BM 1990 Soton.

SALES, Stephen Richard Walton Pool, Clent, Stourbridge DY9 — MB ChB 1967 Birm.; MRCP (UK) 1971. Hon. Sen. Lect. Dept. Med. Univ. Birm.

SALES, Timothy Stephen 105 Anderton Park Road, Birmingham B13 9DS — MB ChB 1994 Liverp.

SALFIELD, Derek Julius (retired) c/o 19 Kenwyn Street, Truro TR1 3BU Tel: 01872 263170 — MD 1948 Med. Acad. Dusseldorf; MD Med. Acad. Duesseldorf 1948; BA Studies Lond. 1988; BSc (Psychol.) Lond. 1942; FRCPsych 1971; DPM Lond. 1952; Cert. Psychiat./Psychother. Trier 1974. Indep. Psychother. Truro. Prev: Med. Dir. Alcoholics Unit, Reinerzau, W. Germany.

SALFIELD, Nicolas Julian NHS Executive Trent, Fulwood House, Old Fulwood Road, Sheffield S10 3TH Tel: 0114 263 0300 Fax: 0114 282 0397 Email: nick.salfield@doh.asl.gov.uk; Moorlow Cottage, Moor Road, Great Longstone, Bakewell DE45 1UA Tel: 01629 640091 — MB BS 1978 Newc.; FFPHM 1999; T(GP) 1991; T(PHM) 1991; MFCM RCP Lond. 1988. (Newc.) Cons. Pub. Health Med. NHS Exec. Trent, Sheff. Prev: Dir. Pub. Health N. Derbysh. HA; Cons. Pub. Health Med. Trent RHA; Sen. Regist. (Community Med.) Sheff. HA.

SALFIELD, Stephen Albert William Rotherham District General Hospital, Moorgate Road, Rotherham S60 2UD Tel: 01709 304577 Fax: 01709 304101 Email: stevesalfield@doctors.org.uk — MB BS Newc. 1970; MRCP (UK) 1975; DCH Eng. 1975; DObst RCOG 1972; FRCP (UK); FRCPCH. (Newc.) Cons. (Paediat.) Rotherham Dist. Gen. Hosp. Prev: Lect. (Paediat.) Sheff. Childr. Hosp.; Specialist Med. Off. Papua New Guinea; Ho. Off. Newc. Gen. Hosp.

SALIB, Emad Hollins Park Hospital, Warrington WA2 8WA Tel: 01925 664123 Fax: 01925 664117; 18 Broughton Close, Appleton, Warrington WA4 3DR — MB ChB 1969 Alexandria; MSc Manch. 1994; MRCPsych 1975; FRCPsych 1995; MRCPI 1998. (Alexandria) Cons. Psychiat. Mersey RHA since 1997 Clincal Director of Psychiat., Warrington Community Trust; Chairm. Clin. Audit Quality & Research; Hon. Sen. Lect., Univ. of Liverp..; Roy. Coll. tutor - Psychiat. Hollins Pk. Hosp.

SALIB, Mr Nassif Rizk Plas-y-ffynnon, Maeshafn, Mold CH7 5LR — MB ChB 1951 Cairo; FRCS Ed. 1966; LMSSA Lond. 1962. (Cairo)

SALIB, Sherine Shawky Eskander 9 Burdons Close, Birmingham B34 6ET — MB ChB 1993 Bristol.

SALIB, Zaki Rizk, SBStJ Plas y Ffynnon, Maeshafn, Mold CH7 5LR — MRCS Eng. LRCP Lond. 1951; MRCGP 1965; DObst RCOG 1953. (Liverp.) Div. Surg. St. John Ambul. Brig.

SALIH, Abdalla Ibrahim 11A Endcliffe Crescent, Sheffield S10 3EB — MB BS 1982 Khartoum; MRCOG 1992.

SALIH, Abdel Rahman Mohd Mohd 2 Strafford Road, Twickenham TW1 3AE — MB BS 1972 Khartoum.

SALIH, Abdel Raziq Mustafa Department of Rheumatology, Appleton Wing, Warrington Hospital, Lovely Lane, Warrington WA5 1QG Tel: 01925 662553 Fax: 01925 662284; 7 Farmleigh Gardens, Great Sankey, Warrington WA5 3FA — MB BS 1980 Khartoum; FRCP 1999 Edinburgh; MD Keele Univ. 1996; MRCP (UK) 1988; DGM RCP Lond. 1990; Mmed Khartoum, 1987. (University of Khartoum) Cons. Rheum. Warrington Gen. Hosp. NHS Trust. Socs: Brit. Soc. for Rheum. Prev: SCMO (Rheum.) Haywood Hosp. Stoke-on-Trent; Lect. Sch. Trop. Med. Univ. Liverp.; ARC Fell. Char. Cross & W.m. Med. Sch. Lond.

SALIH, Haluk 20 Cypress Avenue, Enfield EN2 9BZ Tel: 020 8363 4963 Fax: 020 8363 4963 Email: doc@audiotoy.demon.co.uk — MB ChB 1988 Glas.; BSc (Hons) Ed. 1985.

SALIH, Jasmine Elizabeth 21B Rivermount, Walton-on-Thames KT12 2PR — MB ChB 1995 Leeds.

SALIH, Mr Khalid Mohummed 18 Roman Road, Ayr KA7 3SZ Tel: 01292 267900 — MB ChB Mosul 1970; FRCS Glas. 1986.

SALIH, Mohamed Ali St. Mary's Hospital, Newcroft, Newport PO30 5TG Tel: 01983 524081 Fax: 01983 825634; Berridale, Shanklin Road, Sandford, Ventnor PO38 3AJ Tel: 01983 840104 — MRCS Eng. LRCP Lond. 1974; MB BS Khartoum 1962; FRCPsych 1992, M 1972; DPM Eng. 1969. (Khartoum) Locum. Socs: Fell. The Roy. Soc. of Med. Prev: Clin. Asst. Inst. Psychiat. Bethlem Roy. & Maudsley Hosps. Lond.; Jun. Specialist (Psychiat.) Clinic Nerv. Disorders Khartoum, Sudan; Sen. Regist. (Psychiat.) Kensington, Chelsea & W.m. AHA (T).

SALIM, Abdul Salford Medical Centre, 194 Langworthy Road, Salford M6 5PP Tel: 0161 736 2651 Fax: 0161 745 8955.

SALIM, Alena 17 Theobalds Road, Cuffley, Potters Bar EN6 4HQ — BM BS 1993 Nottm. Staff Grade (Dermat.) Walegrave Hosp. Coventry. Prev: SHO (Gen. Med.) Walsgrave Hosp. Coventry; Ho. Off. (Surg.) Yeovil Dist. Hosp.; Ho. Off. (Med.) Qu.'s Med. Centre Nottm.

SALIM, Amer Falcon Road Surgery, 47 Falcon Road, Battersea, London SW11 2PH Tel: 020 7228 1619/3399 Fax: 020 7924 3375 — MB ChB 1988 Manch.; MRCGP 1993; DRCOG 1993. Prev: Trainee GP Croydon VTS.

SALIM, Ferekh 16 Chiltern Rise., Brinsworth, Rotherham S60 5JT Email: fsalim@ukonline.co.uk — MB ChB 1992 Leic.; MRCP Ed. 1996; FRCR 2000. (Leic.) SPR Radiol., Centr. Sheff. Uni. Hosp. Trust.

SALIM, Ghulam Murtaza 50 High Street, Waltham, Grimsby DN37 0PL — MB BS 1962 Punjab; DTM & H Liverp. 1967.

SALIM, Mohammad The Surgery, 157-159 Rotton Park Road, Edgbaston, Birmingham B16 0LJ Tel: 0121 454 0508 — MB BS 1974 Peshawar; MB BS 1974 Peshawar; LRCP LRCS Ed. LRCPS Glas. 1991 Edinburgh & Glasgow.

SALIM, Rahuman 37B Ellesmere Road, Eccles, Manchester M30 9JH — MB ChB 1995 Manch.

SALIM, Rukhsana 16 Heatherbrae, Bishopbriggs, Glasgow G64 2TA — MB ChB 1995 Glas.

SALIM, Saima Namreen 44 Alexander Road, Birmingham B27 6HE — MB BS 1996 Lond.

SALIM, Mr Salaheddin Abdul-Razzak Royal National Throat, Nose and Ear Hospital, Gray's Inn Road, London WC1; 55 Chaseville Park Road, Winchmore Hill, London N21 1PE Tel: 020 8372 8022 — MB ChB 1977 Mosul; FRCS Eng. (Surg.) 1989; FRCS Ed. (ENT) 1987. Cons. Roy. Nat. Throat Nose & Ear Hosp. Lond.

SALIM, Syeda Hamida 2 St John's Hill Grove, London SW11 2RG — MB BS 1993 Lond.

SALIMEE, Sultan Ghani Lambeth, Southwark and Lewisham Health Authority (LSLHA), 1 Lower Marsh, London SE1 7NT Tel: 020 716 7000 Ext: 7615; 83 High Street, Lewes BN7 1XN Tel: 01273 470723 Email: sultan.salimee@shaw.lslha.sthames.nhs.uk — DMFPHA 2001; MD Kabul 1975; MSc London 1997. Specialist Regist. (SpR) Pub. Health Med., Lambeth, S.wark & Lewisham Health Auth., 1 Lower Marsh, Lond. SE1 7NT; Specialist Regist. Pub. Health Med., W. Surrey Health Auth., The Ridgewood Centre, Old Bailey Rd., Camberley, Surrey GU16. Socs: Fell. of theRoy. Inst. of Pub. Health & Hyg. and The Soc. of Pub. Health of the UK (FRIPHH); Fac. of Pub. Health Med. of the Roy. Coll. of Phys.s of UK & Irel. (MFPHM). Prev: Specialist Regist. Pub. Health Med., E.

SALINAS

Sussex, Brighton & Hove Health Auth., Lewes, E. Sussex, UK; Sen. Ho. Off. (SHO) - Pub. Health Auth., Brent & Harrow Health Auth., Lond.

SALINAS, Juan Carmarthen NHS Trust, West Wales General Hospital, Ophthalmology Department, Carmarthen SA31 2AF Tel: 01267 235151 Fax: 01267 227414; 24 Lon-y-Plas, Johnstown, Carmarthen SA31 3NJ Tel: 01267 221906 Fax: 01267 221906 — Medico y Cirujano 1978 Bolivia; MSc (Ophth.) Bristol 1990; MRCOphth 1995. (University Of San Simon, Cochabamba-Boliva) Assoc. Specialist (Ophth.) W. Wales Gen. Hosp. Carmarthen; OMP Carmarthen. Socs: BMA; Amer. Acad. Ophth.; Coll. of Ophthalmol. Prev: Staff Grade (Ophth.) W. Wales Gen. Hosp. Carmarthen; Cons. Ophth. Hosp. Comibol, Catavi & Viedoma Cochabamba, Bolivia; Regist. & SHO (Ophth.) W. Wales Gen. Hosp. Carmarthen.

SALINSKY, John Victor Tansley and Partners, Chalkhill Health Centre, Chalkhill Road, Wembley HA9 9BQ Tel: 020 8904 0911; 32 Wentworth Hill, Wembley HA9 9SG Tel: 020 8904 2844 Fax: 020 8904 2844 Email: jsalinsky@compuserve.co — BM BCh 1965 Oxf.; MA Oxf. 1965; MRCP Lond. 1969; FRCGP 1989, M 1974. Gen. Sec. Internat. Balint Federat.; Course Organiser Whittington Hosp. GP VTS Lond.

SALISBURY, Amanda Jane Department of Radiotherapy & Oncology, Churchill Hospital, Oxford OX3 7LJ Tel: 01865 741841 Fax: 01865 225660; West Wing, Manor House, Piddington, Bicester OX6 0QB Tel: 01844 237049 — BM BCh 1989 Oxf.; BA (Hons.) Physiol. Scis. Oxf. 1986; FRCR 1997; MRCP (UK) 1992. Specialist Regist. (Radiother. & Oncol.) Ch.ill Hosp. Oxf. Prev: Regist. ICRF Clin. Oncol. Unit Oxf.; SHO (Gen. Med.) St. Geo. Hosp. Lond.; SHO (Radiother. & Oncol.) Roy. Free Hosp. Lond.

SALISBURY, Andrew John (retired) 59 Corby Avenue, Swindon SN3 1PR Tel: 01793 527080 — MB BS 1962 Lond.; FRCP Lond. 1983; MRCP (UK) 1970; MRCS Eng. LRCP Lond. 1962; DCH Eng. 1966; DObst RCOG 1965. Prev: Sen. Regist. (Paediat.) N.. Gen. Hosp. Sheff. & Sheff. Childr. Hosp.

SALISBURY, Anthony Kenneth Woodford Surgery, 29-31 Chantry Lane, Grimsby DN31 2LS Tel: 01472 342325 Fax: 01472 251739; White Cottages, Abbey Lane, North Ormsby, Louth LN11 0TJ Tel: 01472 840939 — MB BS 1989 Lond.; BSc (1st cl. Hons.) Lond. 1986; MRCGP 1996; T(GP) 1993. (Roy. Free Hosp. Sch. Med. Lond.)

SALISBURY, Barbara Jean (retired) L'Iraugnie, Candie Road, St Peter Port, Guernsey GY1 1UP Tel: 01481 720232 — MB BS 1950 Lond.; MRCS Eng. LRCP Lond. 1950; MRCPsych 1971; DPM Eng. 1957; DCH Eng. 1953. Prev: Cons. Psychiat. Guernsey Child Guid. Clinic.

SALISBURY, Christopher John Cotham House, Cotham Hill, Bristol BS6 6JL Tel: 0117 9546658 Fax: 0117 9546677 — MB ChB 1979 Bristol; MSc (Distinc.) Univ. Lond. 1989; MD Bristol 1998; FRCGP 1997; MRCGP (Distinc.) 1984; DRCOG 1982. (Bristol) Cons. Sen. Lect. in GP Univ. of Bristol; GP William Budd Health Centre Bristol. Prev: Sen. Lect. Imperial Coll. Lond.; GP Gr.lands Med. Centre Reading.

SALISBURY, David Maxwell, CB Department of Health, Skipton House, 80 London Road, London SE1 6LH Tel: 020 7972 1522 Fax: 020 7972 5758; Pound Cottage, Bell Lane, Brightwell-cum-Sotwell, Wallingford OX10 0QD Tel: 01491 37209 — MB BS 1969 Lond.; FRCP Lond. 1992; MRCP (UK) 1977; MFPHM RCP (UK) 1994; FRCPCH 1997. Princip. Med. Off. DoH Lond.; Hon. Sen. Lect. (Child Health) King's Coll. Lond. Prev: Cons. Paediat. New Cross Hosp. Wolverhampton; Sen. Regist. Hosp. Sick Childr. Gt. Ormond St. & St. Bart Hosp. Lond.; Sir William Coxen Fell. & Regist. (Paediat.) Univ. Oxf. John Radcliffe Hosp. Oxf.

SALISBURY, Helen Rachel 15 Polstead Road, Oxford OX2 6TW — MB BS 1991 Lond.; BA Oxf. 1986; MRCP (UK) 1994.

SALISBURY, Jennifer Ann 41 Crossways, Gidea Park, Romford RM2 6AJ Tel: 01708 726516 — MB BChir 1966 Camb.; BChir 1965; MA; FRCP London. (Camb. & St. Thos.) Cons. Dermat. Prev: Sen. Regist. (Dermat.) Lond. Hosp.

SALISBURY, Jonathan Dept of Anaesthetics, Ninewells Hospital, Dundee DD1 9SY Tel: 01382 660111; Beech House, Foodieash, Cupar FY15 4PW — MB ChB 1997 Dundee; MB ChB Dundee 1997 (Commendation). SHO (Anaesth.).

SALISBURY, Jonathan Bevan 38 Bryn Castell, Abergele LL22 8QA — MB ChB 1991 Liverp.

SALISBURY, Jonathan Richard Department of Histopathology, King's Denmark Hill Campus,, Bessemer Road, London SE5 9PJ Tel: 0207 346 3093 Fax: 0207 346 3670 Email: jonathan.salisbury@kcl.ac.uk; 32 Lillieshall Road, London SW4 0LP Tel: 020 7622 2390 — MB BS 1980 Lond.; BSc (Hons.) Lond. 1977, MD 1993; FRCPath 1997; MRCPath 1986. (Univ. Coll. Hosp.) Reader & Hon. Cons. Histopath. King's, Denmark Hill Campus,. Lond.

SALISBURY, Karen 82 Laing Gardens, Broxburn EH52 6XT — MB ChB 1994 Ed.

SALISBURY, Mark Steven 7 Keld Road, Carlisle CA2 7QX — BM BS 1997 Nottm.

SALISBURY, Mrs Maxine Rina 81 Penrhyn Crescent, Beeston, Nottingham NG9 5PA — MB ChB Birm. 1957; AFOM RCP Lond. 1990. Prev: Clin. Asst. Renal Unit City Hosp. Nottm.; Ho. Surg. Birm. Gen. Hosp.; Ho. Phys. St. Pauls' Hosp. Hemel Hempstead.

SALISBURY, Nigel Swinburne, TD, Maj. RAMC (retired) Church House, Westbury Leigh, Westbury BA13 3SQ — MB BS Lond. 1964; MRCS Eng. LRCP Lond. 1964; DObst RCOG 1966. CMP (Civil. Med. Practitioner). Prev: GP W.bury.

SALISBURY, Richard Sydney Thermoteknix Systems Ltd., Mount Pleasant House, Mount Pleasant, Cambridge CB3 0RN Tel: 01223 500777 Fax: 01223 500888 Email: r.salisbury@thermoteknix.com; Courtings, 301A Hills Road, Cambridge CB2 2QS Tel: 01223 502777 Fax: 01223 503778 Email: r.salisbury@ibm.net — MB BS 1973 Lond.; MRCP (UK) 1978. Managing Dir. Thermoteknix Systems Ltd. Cambs. Prev: Sen. Regist. (Rheum.) Hope Hosp. & Manch. Roy. Infirm.; Research Fell. & Hon. Sen. Regist. Addenbrooke's Hosp. Camb.; Regist. (Med.) Roy. Berks. Hosp. Reading.

SALISBURY, Robert David 72 Cwmfferws Road, Tycroes, Ammanford SA18 3UA — MB BCh 1995 Wales.

SALISBURY, Stephen (retired) The Lodge, 13 Aigburth Hall Road, Liverpool L19 9DG Tel: 0151 427 2503 — MB ChB 1941 Glas.

SALKELD, David Victor, TD (Surgery) 5 Saville Place, Newcastle upon Tyne NE1 8DH Tel: 0191 232 4274; Threeplands, North Brunton, Newcastle upon Tyne NE3 5HD Tel: 0191 236 7691 — MRCS Eng. LRCP Lond. 1946. (Char. Cross) Socs: BMA. Prev: Med. Supt. N.. Cos. Schs. for the Deaf; Maj. RAMC, TA; Ho. Surg. Fract. Clinic, Orthop. Dept. & ENT Dept. Char. Cross Hosp. Lond.

SALKELD, John Walton, TD (retired) 93 Cleadon Lea, Cleadon Village, Sunderland SR6 7TG Tel: 0191 537 4729 — MB BS 1949 Durh. DL Tyne & Wear. Prev: GP Co. Durh.

SALKELD, Judith Victoria Saville Medical Group, 7 Saville Place, Newcastle upon Tyne NE1 8DQ Tel: 0191 232 4274 Fax: 0191 233 1050 — MB BS 1978 Lond.

SALKELD, Susan Anne Portobello Medical Centre, 14 Codrington Mews, London W11 2EH Tel: 020 7727 5800/2326 Fax: 020 7792 9044; 39 Park View Road, London NW10 1AJ — MB BS 1982 Lond.; MA Oxf. 1974; MRCGP 1986; Dip. Primary Care Lond. Therap. 1997. (Lond.)

SALKER, Mr Digamber Mangesh 45 Corringham Road, Wembley Park, Wembley HA9 9PX Tel: 020 8908 3443 — MB BS 1973 Bombay; MS (Gen. Surg.) Bombay 1976, MB BS 1973; FRCS Glas. 1981; FRCS Ed. 1981. Sen. Regist. (Urol.) Armed Forces Hosp. Sultanate of Oman. Prev: Regist. (Urol. & Surg.) Hackney Gen. Hosp. Lond.; Regist. (Gen. Surg.) Stafford Dist. Hosp.; SHO (Gen. Surg.) N. Devon Dist. Hosp.

***SALKIN, Barry David** 40 Quakers Lane, Potters Bar EN6 1RJ — MB BS 1994 Lond.; BSc (Hons.) Manch. 1989.

SALKIN, Cyril 30 Siddall Street, Heywood OL10 2AS Tel: 01706 625098; 10 Elswick Green, Marshside, Southport PR9 9XT Tel: 01704 212451 — MB ChB 1957 Manch.

SALKIN, David Stephen Uppingham Road Medical Centre, 190 Uppingham Road, Leicester LE5 0QG Tel: 0116 276 6605 — MB ChB 1983 Manch.; MRCGP 1992.

SALKIND, Professor Malvin Ronald 8 Heathfielde, Lyttelton Road, London N2 0EE Tel: 020 8455 7971 — MRCS Eng. LRCP Lond. 1950; PhD Lond. 1973; FRCPsych 1980, M 1974; FRCGP 1975. (Univ. Coll. Hosp.) Emerit. Prof. Gen. Pract. Univ. Lond. Prev: Prof. Jt. Acad. Dept. Gen. Pract. & Primary Care St. Bart. Med. Coll. & Lond. Hosp. Med. Coll.; Chairm. Med. Bds. DHSS; Research Fell. Acad. (Psychiat.) St. Bart. Hosp. Lond.

SALKIND, Susan Ruth 43 Cranley Gardens, London N10 3AB — MB ChB 1982 Birm.; ChB Birm. 1982; DRCOG Lond. 1986.

SALLEH, Suhaiza 99 Humprey Road, Old Trafford, Manchester M16 9DE — MB ChB 1996 Manch.

SALLOMI, David Francis X-Ray Department, Eastbourne District General Hospital, Kings Drive, Eastbourne BN21 2UD — MB ChB 1988 Manch.; FRCR 1995. Prev: Sen. Regist. (Radiol.) Guy's & St. Thos. Hosps. Lond.

SALLOUM, Marwan Samir Royal Bournemouth Hospital, Castle Lane E., Hollyhurst Road, Bournemouth BH7 7DW — MB BCh BAO 1987 NUI; LRCPI 1987; LRCSI 1987. Regist. (O & G) Roy. Bournemouth Hosp. Prev: SHO (Anaesth.) Hartlepool.

SALMAN, Mansur Nasrideen 51 Haweswater, Huntingdon PE29 6TW — MB BS 1983 Ahmadu Bello, Nigeria; MRCOG 1994.

SALMAN, Michael Sabah King's College Hospital, Denmark Hill, London SE5 9RS Tel: 020 7737 4000; 13 Knoll House, Carlton Hill, London NW8 9XD — MB BS 1990 Lond.; BSc (Hons.) Lond. 1987; MRCP (UK) 1993; DCH RCP Lond. 1994. Lect. (Paediat. Neurosci.) King's Coll. Hosp. Lond. Prev: Regist. (Paediat. Neurol.) Gt. Ormond St. Hosp. for Childr. Lond.; Regist. (Paediat.) St. Helier Hosp. Jersey; SHO (Paediat.) Lewisham & Guy's Hosps. Lond.

SALMAN, Mr Saad Masud 8 Pear Tree Crescent, Solihull Lodge, Shirley, Solihull B90 1LB — MB BS 1980 Karachi; FRCS Eng. 1993; FRCSI 1990.

SALMAN, Walid Daoud Burnley General Hospital, Casterton Avenue, Burnley BB10 2PQ; Robin Hill, 149 Wheatley Lane Road, Fence, Nelson BB9 6QN — MB ChB 1973 Baghdad; MRCPath 1984; DCPath Baghdad 1979.

SALMASI, Abdul-Majeed Cardiac Department, The Central Middlesex Hospital, Acton Lane, London NW10 7NS Tel: 020 8453 2151 Fax: 020 8453 2157 — MB ChB 1971 Baghdad; PhD Lond. 1979; FACA 1988; FHS 1999; FHRS 1998. Prev: Asst. Dir. Irvine Cardiovasc. Laborat. St. Mary's Hosp. Lond.

SALMON, Andrew Howard John 18 Mymms Drive, Brookmans Park, Hatfield AL9 7AF — MB ChB 1998 Bristol.

SALMON, Anthony James (retired) Past Field, 9 Rotherfield Road, Henley-on-Thames RG9 1NR Tel: 01491 573600 — MB BS 1949 Lond.; DObst RCOG 1955; DCH Eng. 1953. Prev: Med. Off. Townlands Hosp. Henley-on-Thames.

SALMON, Anthony Peter 71 Kingsway, Hiltingbury, Chandlers Ford, Eastleigh SO53 1FH Tel: 01703 270437 — BM BS 1980 Nottm.; FRCP Lond. 1993; MRCP (UK) 1983. Cons. Paediat. Cardiol. Wessex Regional Cardiac Thoracic Centre Gen. Hosp. Soton. Prev: Sen. Regist. (Paediat. Cardiol.) Birm. Childr. Hosp.; Regist. Roy. Childr. Hosp. Melbourne, Austral.; SHO Nottm. Univ. Hosp.

SALMON, Caroline Anne Foxale, 2 Pleasaunce Row, Burnhams Road, Little Bookham, Leatherhead KT23 3AG — MB BChir Camb. 1991; BA Camb. 1988; MRCP (UK) 1995; DRCOG 1992. Flexible Specialist Regist. Paediat. S. Thames. Prev: Specialist Regist. Paediat. St. Peters NHS Trust Chertsey; Regist. Paediat. St Geo.s NHS Trust; SHO (Paediat.) Roy. Brompton NHS Trust Lond.

SALMON, Cecil Roland (retired) Harvest House, Branch Lane, Chilham, Canterbury CT4 8DR — MB BS 1955 Lond.; MRCS Eng. LRCP Lond. 1955. Prev: GP Canterbury.

SALMON, Douglas Neil The Surgery, 190 Aston Lane, Handsworth, Birmingham B20 3HE Tel: 0121 356 4669 — MB ChB 1985 Birm.

SALMON, Geraldine Louise P&O Princess Cruises, Richmond House, Terminus Terrace, Southampton SO14 3PN — MB ChB 1983 Sheff.; DA 1992 UK; DRCOG 1992; BMedSci 1982 Sheff. Ships Doctor P&O P.ss Cruises Soton. Prev: GP Tavistock; Staff Grade (Anaesth.) W.on Gen. Hosp. W.on super Mare; SHO (Anaesth.) Derriford Hosp. Plymouth.

SALMON, Miss Gillian Margaret 26B Frampton End Road, Frampton Cotterell, Bristol BS36 2JZ — MB ChB 1988 Birm.; ChB Birm. 1988.

SALMON, Graham Bentley St Peters Surgery, 49-55 Portsmouth Road, Woolston, Southampton SO19 9RL Tel: 023 8043 4305 Fax: 023 8043 4511; Bay House, 56 Athelston Road, Bitterne, Southampton SO19 4DD Tel: 02380 227902 — MB ChB 1967 Bristol; MRCP (U.K.) 1973; DCH Eng. 1970. (Bristol) Prev: SHO (Med.) Soton. Univ. Gp. Hosps.

SALMON, Haydn (retired) 1 Corwell Lane, Hillingdon, Uxbridge UB8 3DD Tel: 020 8573 0085 — MB BS 1952 Lond. Med. Adviser Brit. Red Cross (Lond. Br.); Cons. Med. Off. Cape Bds. Ltd. Uxbridge Middlx. & Sunk Yong Europe Ltd. Hillingdon; Med. Adviser Hygrade Chilled Foods Lond. Prev: Receiving Ward Off. Whittington Hosp.

SALMON, Mr John Dyster Woodridge, The Ridge, Woldingham, Caterham CR3 7AH Tel: 01883 653250 Fax: 01883 653250 Email: john.salmon@tedn.co.uk — MB BChir 1954 Camb.; MA, MB Camb. 1954, BChir 1953; FRCS Eng. 1967; DObst RCOG 1957; FRCOPath. (St. Bart.) Socs: Ophth. Soc. UK. Mem. Oxf. Ophth. Congr.; Christ. Med. Fell.sh. Prev: Cons. Eye Surg. Kent & Sussex Hosp. Tunbridge Wells; on Staff St. John Ophth. Hosp. Jerusalem; Regist. St. Bart. Hosp. Lond.

SALMON, Mr John Frank Oxford Eye Hospital, Radcliffe Infirmary, Woodstock Road, Oxford OX2 6HE — MB ChB 1976 Pretoria; FRCS Ed. 1984.

SALMON, John Geoffrey David Southmead Surgery, Southmead House, Blackpond Lane, Farnham Common, Slough SL2 3ER Tel: 01753 643195 Fax: 01753 642157; 25 Crispin Way, Farnham Common, Slough SL2 3UD Tel: 01753 645962 Fax: 01753 642157 — MB ChB 1972 Manch.; MRCP (UK) 1975. (Manchester) Partner in Gen. Pract.; Clin. Asst. (Upper Gastrointestinal Endoscopy) Slough. Prev: SHO Booth Hall Childr. Hosp. Manch. & Manch. Roy. Infirm.; Ho. Off. Manch. Roy. Infirm.

SALMON, John Richard Carlton House Surgery, 28 Tenniswold Road, Enfield EN1 3LL Tel: 020 8363 7575 Fax: 020 8366 8228 — MRCS Eng. LRCP Lond. 1964. (Char. Cross) Prev: Ho. Surg. Roy. E. Sussex Hosp. Hastings; Ho. Phys. German Hosp. Lond.

SALMON, Jonathan Bryant, Maj. RAMC The Queen Elizabeth Military Hospital, Woolwich, London SE18 Tel: 020 8856 5533 — MB 1983 Camb.; MA Camb. 1984, MB 1983, BChir 1982; MRCP (UK) 1989. Sen. Specialist (Med.) Qu. Eliz. Milit. Hosp. Lond.

SALMON, Katherine Mary Springlands, Main Road, Little Waltham, Chelmsford CM3 3PA — MB BS 1997 Lond.

SALMON, Mr Leslie Frederic William, MBE Corner Cottage, 46 High St., Wimbledon Common, London SW19 5AX Tel: 020 8946 7503 — MB BS 1938 Lond.; MS Lond. 1949; FRCS Eng. 1948; MRCS Eng. LRCP Lond. 1938. (Guy's) Emerit. Surg. Throat & Ear Dept. Guy's Hosp. Socs: Roy. Soc. of Med.; Hon. Mem.. Sect. of Laryngulogy; Hon. Mem. BMA. Prev: Surg. (ENT) St. Helier Hosp. Carshalton; Mem. Ct. Examrs. RCS Eng.; Lt.-Col. RAMC.

SALMON, Margaret May (retired) 58 Beechwood Road, Newport NP19 8AH Tel: 01633 271631 — MB BCh 1954 Wales; FFCM 1988, M 1974; FFPHM 1989; DPH Wales 1971; DObst RCOG 1956. Cons. Pub. Health Med. Gwent. Prev: Dist. Community Phys. S. Gwent Health Dist.

SALMON, Michael Vaughan (retired) 12 St Mary's Road, Harborne, Birmingham B17 0HA Tel: 0121 427 1708 — LMSSA 1948 Lond.; MD (Path.) Lond. 1953, MB BS 1948; FRCPath 1974. Prev: Cons. Neuropath. Midl. Centre for Neurosurg.

SALMON, Morag Alison Jean 140 Woodsmoor Lane, Stockport SK3 8TJ — MB ChB 1982 Manch. (St Andrews/Manch)

SALMON, Nancy Jane Falcon Square Surgery, 9-10 Falcon Square, Castle Hedingham, Halstead CO9 3BY Tel: 01787 460436 Fax: 01787 462829; Church Farm House, Church Lane, Toppesfield, Colchester CO9 4DR — MB BS 1990 Lond.; MRCP (UK) 1994; DRCOG. (St Mary's Paddington London) GP. Prev: SHO (O & G) Essex.

SALMON, Nigel Paul Department Anaesthetics, Hereford Co. Hospital, Union Walk, Hereford HR1 2ER — BM BS 1977 Nottm.; BMedSci 1975; FFA RCS Eng. 1981. Cons. Anaesth. Hereford. Socs: BMA; Assn. Anaesth.

SALMON, Paul Raymond 80 Harley Street, London W1G 7HL Tel: 07802 873621 Fax: 020 7602 2562 Email: paulsalmon@btinternet.com; Tel: 020 7602 3311 Fax: 020 7602 2562 — MB BS 1961 Lond.; BSc (Anat., 1st cl. Hons.) Lond. 1958; FRCP Lond. 1978, M 1967; FRCP Ed. 1977, M 1966; MRCS Eng. LRCP Lond. 1961. (Middlx.) p/t Cons. Phys. & Gastroenterologist, Independ. Med. Pract. Prev: Cons. Phys. & Sen. Clin. Lect. (Gastroenterol.) Middlx. Hosp. Lond.; Sen. Lect. (Med.) Univ. Bristol & Cons. Phys. Bristol HA (T); Lect. (Med.) Univ. Bristol.

SALMON, Ralph Paul Red House Surgery, 96 Chesterton Road, Cambridge CB4 1ER Tel: 01223 365555 Fax: 01223 356848; 14 Hills Avenue, Cambridge CB1 7XA Tel: 01223 248354 — MB BS 1980 Sydney. (University of Sydney) Clin. Asst. Chesterton Hosp. Cambs.; Police Surg. Camb. Prev: Regist. (Med.) Stoke Mandeville

SALMON

Hosp. Aylesbury; Regist. (Med.) P. of Wales Hosp. Sydney, Austral.; Resid. Med. Off. Roy. N. Shore Hosp. Sydney, Austral.

SALMON, Robert William (retired) Carrington House Surgery, 19 Priory Road, High Wycombe HP13 6SL Tel: 01494 526029 Fax: 01494 538299 — MB BS 1961 Lond.; LMSSA Lond. 1957; DObst RCOG 1962. Company Med. Off. Bucks. Cadet Bn. Roy. Green Jackets; Exam Med. Pract. DoH. Prev: Clin. Asst. (Path.) Wexham Pk. Hosp. Slough.

SALMON, Roland Laurance, SBStJ PHLS Communicable Dis. Surveillance Centre (Wales Unit), Abton House, Wedal Road, Cardiff CF14 3QX Tel: 029 2052 1997 Fax: 029 2052 1987 Email: roland.salmon@phls.wales.nhs.uk — MB BS 1980 Lond.; MA Camb. 1978, BA 1974; FFPHM RCP (UK) 1995, M 1989; MRCGP 1984; DRCOG 1982. (St. Bart.) Cons. Epidemiol. Pub. Health Laborat. Serv. Prev: Sen. Regist. (Community Med.) W. Midl. RHA.

SALMON, Rosemarie Philomena The Grove Medical Centre, Church Road, Egham TW20 9QJ Tel: 01784 433159 Fax: 01784 477208; The Grove Medical Centre, The Grove, Church St., Egham TW20 — MB BS 1980 Lond.; DRCOG 1986. Prev: Ho. Surg. St. Geo. Med. Sch. Hosp. Lond.; SHO (Anaesth. & Gen. Med.) Pboro. Dist. Hosp.; SHO (O & G & Paediat.) St. Peter's Hosp. Chertsey.

SALMON, Zoë Ann, Flight Lt. RAF Med. Br. Retd. 25 Fairways, Sharoe Green Lane, Fulwood, Preston PR2 8FX — MB ChB 1982 Leeds.

SALMOND, Nichola Catriona Napier 8 Victoria Crescent Road, Dowanhill, Glasgow G12 9DB — MB ChB 1986 Glas.

SALMONS, Paula Hilary Altrincham Priory Hospital, Rappax Road, Hale, Altrincham WA15 0NX Tel: 0161 904 0050 Fax: 0161 980 4322; 45 Rodney Street, Liverpool L1 9EW Tel: 0151 708 0842 — MB ChB 1966 Birm.; FRCPsych 1987, M 1976; DCH Eng. 1969. (Birm.) Cons. Psychiat. Altrincham Priory Hosp. Prev: Cons. Psychiat. & Hon. Clin. Lect. Salford HA; Sen. Lect. (Psychiat.) Univ. Birm.

SALOM DE TORD, Ramiro 17 The Millars, Broomfield, Chelmsford CM1 7HJ — LMS 1982 Barcelona.

SALOOJA, Nina Hammersmith Hospital, Du Cane Road, London W12 — MB BS 1986 Lond.; BA Oxf. 1983; MRCP (UK) 1989. Regist. (Haemat.) Hammersmith Hosp. Lond. Prev: SHO (Haemat.) Univ. Coll. Hosp. Lond.; SHO (Med.) Taunton Som.

SALOOJEE, Abdulhay Ahmed 90 East Hill, Wandsworth, London SW18 2HG Tel: 020 8874 1691; 97 Telford Avenue, Streatham Hill, London SW2 4XN Tel: 020 8671 0035 — MB BCh 1950 Witwatersrand. (Witwatersrand)

SALPEKAR, Prabhakar Dattatraya 25 Pear Tree Road, Clayton-Le-Woods, Chorley PR6 7JP Tel: 01772 36679 — MB BS 1956 Agra. (M.G.M. Med. Coll.) Cons. Clin. Physiol. (IC) Roy. Infirm. & Roy. Preston; Asst. (Research) Orthop. & Accid. Surg. Roy. Infirm. Preston Hosp. Socs: Soc. Intens, Care & Liverp. Med. Inst. Prev: Regist. (Orthop.) & SHO (Gen. Surg.) Roy. Infirm. Preston.

SALPEKAR, Shashikar Dattatray The New Surgery, Old Road, Tean, Stoke-on-Trent ST10 4EG Tel: 01538 722323 Fax: 01538 722215 — MB BS 1964 Vikram. (Gandhi Med. Coll. Bhopal) Prev: Ho. Off. (Obst.) Preston Roy. Infirm.

SALT, Alane St Mark's Dee View Surgery, Church Street, Connah's Quay, Deeside CH5 4AD Tel: 01244 812003 Fax: 01244 822609 — MB BS 1984 Lond.; BA Camb. 1981; DRCOG 1988.

SALT, Brigid Deirdre Medical Advisers Office, Foreign & Commonwealth Office, 1 Palace St., London SW1E 5HE Tel: 020 7238 4774 Fax: 020 7238 4777; 13 Grafton Square, London SW4 0DQ Tel: 020 7652 6381 — MB BS 1970 Lond.; MRCS Eng. LRCP Lond. 1970; D.Occ.Med. RCP Lond. 1995. (St. Bart.) Sen. Med. Adviser Foreign & Commonw. Off. Lond. Prev: GP Stockwell; Regist. (Radiol.) & SHO St. Bart. Hosp. Lond.

SALT, Eric Michael (retired) Alyn Lodge, Gun St., Rossett, Wrexham LL12 0HR Tel: 01244 570495 — MB ChB 1950 Birm.; MRCGP 1971; Cert. JCC Lond. 1977; DObst RCOG 1957. Prev: GP Rossett.

SALT, John Campbell 126 Harley Street, London W1N 1AH Tel: 020 7935 9409 Fax: 020 7224 2520; 13 Grafton Square, London SW4 0DQ Tel: 020 7622 6988 Fax: 020 7622 6988 — MB BS 1970 Lond.; MRCS Eng. LRCP Lond. 1970; FFA RCS Eng. 1976. (St. Bart.) Cons. Anaesth. Char. Cross Hosp. & Roy. Masonic Hosp. Lond. Prev: SHO (Anaesth.) Roy. Berks. Hosp. Reading; Regist. (Anaesth.) Sheff. AHA (T); Sen. Regist. (Anaesth.) Brompton Hosp. Lond.

SALT, Melanie Jane Mayfield Surgery, 54 Trentham Road, Longton, Stoke-on-Trent ST3 4DW Tel: 01782 315547; 6 Bergamot Drive, Meir Park, Stoke-on-Trent ST3 7FD — BM 1990 Soton.; DRCOG 1994; MRCGP 1997. (Southampton University) Partner.

SALT, Michael John Glenfield Surgery, 111 Station Road, Glenfield, Leicester LE3 8GS; Spion Lodge, Links Road, Kirby Muxloe, Leicester LE9 2BP Tel: 0116 238 8291 — MB ChB 1978 Liverp.; MRCP (UK) 1986. (Liverp) Princip. GP Leicester. Prev: Trainee GP Measham Med. Unit Burton on Trent; Regist. (Med. & Geriat.) Leicester Gen. Hosp.; Regist. (Med.) St. Albans City Hosp.

SALT, Nicola Jill The Surgery, 77 Thurleigh Road, Balham, London SW12 8TZ Tel: 020 8675 3521 Fax: 020 8675 3800 — MB BS 1987 Lond.; MRCP (UK) 1991.

SALT, Patrick John Department of Anaesthetics, Charing Cross Hospital, Fulham Palace Road, London W6 8RF Tel: 020 8846 1234; 24 Archway Street, Barnes, London SW13 0AR — MB BChir 1975 Camb.; BA Camb. 1968, MA 19970; PhD Camb. 1972; FFA RCS Eng. 1982. (Camb.) Cons. Anaesth. Char. Cross Hosp. Lond. Prev: Cons. Anaesth. St. Jas. Univ. Hosp. Leeds.; Cons. (Anaesth.) St. Vincent's Hosp., Dub.; Sen. Lect. & Hon. Cons. (Anaesth.) Qu. Eliz. Hosp. Birm.

SALT, Paula Jane 126 Viceroy, Close, Edgbaston, Birmingham B5 7UY Tel: 0121 446 5035 Email: psalt.@psalt.demon.co.uk — MB ChB 1993 Birm.; ChB Birm. 1993; MRCP (UK) 1998. Specialist Regist. (Geriat. & Gen. Med.) City Hosp. Birm. Prev: Regist. Barnet Hosp. Lond.; SHO Roy. Masele Hosp. Lond.

SALT, Robert William Richards and Partners, Llanfair Surgery, Llanfair Road, Llandovery SA20 0HY Tel: 01550 720648 Fax: 01550 721428; Ty Rhawg, 74A Broad St, Llandovery SA20 0AY Tel: 01550 721006 — MB BCh 1980 Wales; DRCOG 1982.

SALT, Susan Douglas Calderdale Royal Hospital, Salter Hobble Mill, Halifax HX3 5AR Tel: 01422 357171 — MB BS 1989 Lond.; BSc Lond. 1983; MRCGP 1994; DRCOG 1993. (St. Mary's Hospital Medical School) p/t Specialist Reigst. (Palliat. Med.); Macmillan Cons. in Palliat. Care.

SALTER, Adrian Gerard 55 The Shades, Knights Place, Rochester ME2 2UB — MB ChB 1990 Leic.

SALTER, Angela Lilian The Surgery, Manor Fam Road, Bere Regis, Wareham BH20 7HB — BM 1980 Soton.; MRCGP 1985; DCCH RCGP & FCM 1986; DRCOG 1983. p/t Asst. GP Bere Regis.; Clin. Asst. Community Paediat., Weymouth, Dorset. Prev: Trainee GP Portland.

SALTER, David Graham Welsh Office, Cathays Park, Cardiff CF10 3NQ Tel: 029 2082 5402 Fax: 029 2082 5175; Woodpeckers, St Andrew's Road, St Andrew's Major, Dinas Powys CF64 4HB Tel: 029 2051 5093 — MB BCh Wales 1967. (Cardiff) Sen. Med. Off. Welsh Office Cardiff. Socs: Brit. Assn. Day Surg.; Cardiff Med. Soc.

SALTER, Derek Harold Rex (retired) 265 Chells Way, Stevenage SG2 0HN — MB BS 1957 Lond.; MRCS Eng. LRCP Lond. 1957. Prev: Surg. Lt.-Cdr. RN.

SALTER, Donald McGovern Milton House, Pencaitland, Tranent EH34 5EP — MD 1990 Ed.; BSc (Hons.) Ed. 1978, MD 1990, MB ChB 1981; MRCPath 1989. Sen. Lect. Dept. Path. Med. Sch. Univ. Edin.

SALTER, Edmund John Millbrook, King's Mill, Sutton-in-Ashfield NG17 4JT Tel: 01623 784766 Fax: 01623 636029 — MB BChir 1969 Camb.; MRCP (UK) 1973; MRCPsych 1974; DPM Eng. 1974. (Guy's) Cons. Psychiat. Millbrook King's Mill Notts. Prev: Sen. Regist. (Psychiat.) Mapperley Hosp. Nottm.; Regist. (Psychiat.) St. John's Hosp. Aylesbury; Ho. Surg. & Ho. Phys. Wycombe Gen. Hosp.

SALTER, Hazel Anne Department Child Health, East Lodge Court, High St., Colchester CO1 1UJ; 9 Jefferson Close, Lexden, Colchester CO3 5DR — MB ChB 1980 Leic.; DRCOG 1982.

SALTER, Mrs Helen Rosemary Woodlea, Parklands, Coopersale, Epping CM16 7RF — MB ChB 1988 Leic.; FRCS Ed. 1996. Specialist Regist. A & E Oldenuran Hosp. Romford.

SALTER, John Charles The Health Centre, Beeches Green, Stroud GL5 4BH Tel: 01453 763980; The Orchard, Keble Road, France Lynch, Stroud GL6 8LU — MB ChB 1983 Sheff.; MRCGP 1987; DRCOG 1986.

SALTER, Jonathan Philip Hartley Parkwood, Parklane, Knebworth SG3 6PP — MB BS 1983 Lond.; MRCGP 1989; DRCOG 1988; DA (UK) 1986. Overseas Recruitment Off. (BUPA). Prev: Trainee GP Worcs. VTS.; Dir. Montpellier Health Care Ltd.

SALTER, Mrs Katherine Elizabeth Urmston Kings Road Surgery, Mumbles, Swansea SA3 4AJ Tel: 01792 360933; Southbourne, Groves Avenue, Langland, Swansea SA3 4QF — MB BS 1965 Lond.; MRCS Eng. LRCP Lond. 1965; MFFP 1993; DCH Eng. 1967. (Roy. Free) Prev: Ho. Surg. New End Hosp. Lond.; Ho. Phys. St. And. Hosp. Bow.

SALTER, Mark Steven East Wing, Homerton Hospital, Homerton Row, London E9 6SR — MB BS 1983 Lond.

SALTER, Mark William Arthur Philip Chandos, 30A High St., Rode, Bath BA11 6PA — MB BS 1996 Lond.

SALTER, Mr Michael Charles Patrick 4 Chadwick Road, Westcliff on Sea SS0 8LS Tel: 01702 353181 Fax: 01702 353181 — MB BS 1976 Lond.; FRCS Eng. 1980; MRCS Eng. LRCP Lond. 1976. Cons. Gen. & Vasc. Surg., S.end Gen. Hosp.; Cons. BrE. & Vasc. Surg., S.end Gen. Hosp. Prev: Sen. Regist. (Gen. Surg.) Yorks. RHA.

SALTER, Penelope Ann Balham Health Centre, 120 Bedford Hill, London SW12 9HS Tel: 020 8673 1720 Fax: 020 8673 1549; 28 Lyford Road, Wandsworth Common, London SW18 3LT Tel: 020 8874 9802 — MB BS 1962 Lond.; MRCS Eng. LRCP Lond. 1962. (Roy. Free)

SALTER, Richard James 6 Upper Tyn-y-Parc Terrace, Cardiff CF14 6BY — MB BCh 1995 Wales.

SALTER, Robin Hugh (retired) 13 Newfield Drive, Kingstown, Carlisle CA3 0AG Tel: 01228 515318 — MB BS Lond. 1961; BSc Lond. 1957; FRCP Lond. 1978, M 1964; Dip Med Educat. Dund 1996. Prev: Clin. Tutor Cumbld. Infirm. Carlisle.

SALTER, Sandra Helen Dragons Pool, Peterchurch, Hereford HR2 0TE — BM BS 1989 Nottm.; MRCPsych 1994. Regist. (Psychiat.) W. Midl.

SALTER, Mr Timothy Charles Michael 83 Corfe Road, Stoborough, Wareham BH20 5AY — MB BCh 1980 Wales; FRCS Eng. 1988; FRCS Ed. 1986.

SALTERS, Mark Falls Road Surgery, 186 Falls Road, Belfast BT12 6AG Tel: 028 9032 3062; 57 Old Forge Manor, Belfast BT10 0HY — MB BCh BAO 1983 Belf.; MRCGP 1989; DRCOG 1990; DGM 1987.

SALTISSI, Stephen 5 Queensbridge Park, Isleworth TW7 7LY — MB BS 1973 Lond.; MB BS (Hons. Surg., Obst. & Gyn.) Lond. 1973; MRCP (U.K.) 1976. Sen. Research Fell. (Cardiol. & Nuclear Med.) St. Thos. Hosp. Lond. Prev: Regist. (Cardiol.) St. Thos. Hosp. Lond.; Regist. (Gen. Med.) Poole Gen. Hosp.; SHO (Gen. Med. & Cardiol.) Withington Hosp. Manch.

SALUCCI, Gabriele Umberto North Berwick Health Centre, 54 St. Baldreds Road, North Berwick EH39 4PU Tel: 01620 892169 Fax: 01620 897005 — MB ChB 1987 Ed.; BSc (Hons) Ed. 1984; MRCGP 1993. Trainee GP E. Cumbria VTS. Socs: BMA; Assoc. Mem. RCGP. Prev: Ho. Off. (Med. Surg.); Trainee GP. Edin. VTS.

SALUJA, Balijeet Kaur Tel: 0208 501 5734 — MBBS; DRCPath (Lond.). Primary Care.

SALUJA, Gurpinder Singh Tel: 0208 527 6373 — MBBS; MRCP; DCH; MD. Gen. Pract. Princip.

SALUJA, R S The Saluja Clinic, 36A Northcote Avenue, Southall UB1 2AY Tel: 020 8574 5136 — MB BS 1974 Calcutta; MB BS 1974 Calcutta.

SALUJA, Ranjeet Kaur 9 Cloister Crofts, Leamington Spa CV32 6QG Tel: 01926 428321 — MB BS 1968 Rajasthan. (S.M.S. Med. Coll. Jaipur) Family Plann. Med. Off. Warks. HA.

SALUJA, Surinder Singh (retired) 'Ashton House' Surgery, 15 George St., Leamington Spa CV31 1ET — MB BS 1967 Lucknow. Prev: SHO (ENT) Bridgend Gen. Hosp.

SALUJA, Tilak Raj c/o Mr. S. Madan, 31 Banstead Road S., Sutton SM2 5LG — MB BS 1966 Lucknow.

SALUKHE, Tushar Vilas 24 More Close, London W14 9BN — MB BS 1998 Lond.; MB BS Lond 1998.

SALUSBURY, Ceri Alison Beech House Surgery, Beech House, 69 Vale Street, Denbigh LL16 3AY Tel: 01745 812863 Fax: 01745 816574 — MB ChB 1984 Manch.

SALUSBURY-TRELAWRY, Joanna Mary Leighton Hospital, Middlewich Road, Leighton, Crewe CW1 4Q — MB ChB 1984 Cape Town; MD Cape Town 1996; FRCP Ed. 1997; MRCP (UK) 1988. (Univ. Cape Town) Cons. Phys. (cardiol) Leighton Hopital Crewe. Socs: Manch. Med. Soc. - Fell.; Roy. Coll. of Phys.s of

Educat. - Fell.; Brit. Cardial Soc. - Fell. Prev: Cons. Phys. (Cardiol.) Trafford Gen. Hosp. Manch.

SALVAGE, Mr David Roy Department of Radiology, Hull Royal Infirmary, Anlaby Road, Hull HU3 2JZ Tel: 01482 328541; 36 Manor Road, Swanland, North Ferriby HU14 3PB — MB BS 1985 Lond.; FRCS Glas. 1990; FRCR 1994. (The London Hospital Medical College) Cons. Radiol. Hull Roy. Infirm. Prev: Sen. Regist. & Regist. (Radiol.) Leeds/Bradford Train. Scheme.

SALVAJI, Abhijeetha Pentyla, Pannar Lane, Pentwynmawr, Newbridge, Newport NP11 4GY — MB BCh 1998 Wales.

SALVAJI, Chandra Shaker Newbridge Medical Centre, High Street, Newbridge, Newport NP11 4FW Tel: 01495 243409 Fax: 01495 243746 — MB BS 1967 Osmania.

SALVARY, Ingrid Althea Flat 9A, Staff Residence, James Paget Hospital, Lowestoft Road, Gorleston, Great Yarmouth NR31 6LA — MB BS 1993 West Indies; MB BS West Indies 1987; MRCP (UK) 1993.

SALVESEN, Mr Douglas Ronald Lister Hospital, Stevenage SG1 4AB Tel: 01438 314333; 7 Cranborne Avenue, Hitchin SG5 2BS Tel: 01462 457720 — MD 1994 Lond.; MB BS 1986; MRCOG 1994. (St. Thomas' Hospital London) Cons. (O & G) Lister Hosp. Stevenage. Prev: Sen. Regist. (O & G) Qu. Charlotte's Hosp. Lond.; Regist. St. Thos. Hosp. Lond. & Pembury Hosp. Kent; Research Regist. King's Coll. Hosp. Lond.

SALVESEN, Theodore Michael Noel (retired) Easter Catter, Croftamie, Drymen, Glasgow G63 0EX Tel: 01360 660575 Fax: 01360 660065 — MB ChB 1950 Ed.

SALVI, Anthony Ettore Keith 12 Rothesay Road, Dorchester DT1 2DT Tel: 01305 264908 — MRCS Eng. LRCP Lond. 1935. (Guy's) Socs: BMA.; BMA. Prev: Emerit. Cons. Geriat. W. Dorset Health Dist.; Med. Supt. Douglas Ho. Sanat. W. S.bourne; Asst. Med. Off. Brit. Legion Sanat. Nayland.

SALVI, Vijay Govindrao Elliott Street Surgery, 145 Elliott Street, Tyldesley, Manchester M29 8FL Tel: 01942 892727 Fax: 01942 888847 — MB BS 1956 Bombay. (G.S. Med. Coll. Bombay) GP Police Surg. Gtr. Manch.

SALWEY, Michael Geoffrey 14 Green Road, Weston, Stafford ST18 0JA — LMSSA 1997; LMSSA Lond. 1997.

SALZ, Mr Michael The Nuffield Hospital, Derriford, Plymouth PL6 8BG Tel: 01752 761803; 144 Harley Street, London W1N 1AH Tel: 020 7935 0023 — MRCS Eng. LRCP Lond. 1940; MA Camb. 1943, BA 1937; FRCS Eng. 1948. (Camb. & Middlx.) Socs: Fell. BOA & Roy. Soc. Med. Prev: Regist. Surg.) P.ss Eliz. Orthop. Hosp. Exeter & Mt. Gould Orthop. Hosp. Plymouth; Cons. Orthop. Surg. Mt. Gould Orthop. Hosp. Plymouth & Plymouth Gen. Hosp.

SALZMAN, Nicholas George Woodlands Medical Centre, Woodland Road, Didcot OX11 0BB Tel: 01235 511355 Fax: 01235 512808 — MRCS Eng. LRCP Lond. 1973; DObst RCOG 1975; DCH Eng. 1975. GP Didcot.

SALZMANN, Maurice Brooke Department of Clinical Chemistry, Royal Devon & Exeter Hospital (Wonfrod), Barrack Road, Exeter EX2 5DW Tel: 01392 402933 Fax: 01392 402919 Email: maurice.salzermann@rdehc-tr.swest.nhs.uk; 16 Miller Way, St Martins Gardens, Exminster, Exeter EX6 8TH Tel: 01392 824324 Email: salzmann_millerway@tinyworld.co.uk — MB BS 1982 Lond.; MSc Lond. 1989, BSc 1979; MRCPath 1993; FRCPath 2001. (King's Coll. Hosp.) Cons. Chem. Path. Roy. Devon & Exeter Hosp. Socs: Assn. of Clin. Biochem.s Ordinary Mem. Prev: Sen. Regist. (Chem. Path.) Roy. Devon & Exeter Hosp.; Regist. (Chem. Path.) N.wick Pk. Hosp. Harrow.

SALZMANN, Maurice Michael (retired) 10 Birch Close, Farnham GU10 4TJ Tel: 01252 792174 — LRCP LRCS Ed. LRFPS Glas. 1944; MRCPsych 1972; DPM Lond. 1951. Hon. Cons. Psychiat. Basingstoke & N. Hants Health Dist. Prev: Cons. Psychiat. Pk. Prewett Hosp. Basingstoke.

SAM, George Joseph 3 St Luke's Houses, Armagh BT61 7PJ Tel: 01861 2381 — MB BCh BAO 1965 Belf. (Belf.) Prev: Assoc. Specialist (Psychiat.) St. Luke's Hosp. Armagh; Regist. Psychiat. Downshire Hosp.; Ho. Phys. Moyle Hosp. Larne.

SAM, Rachel Clare 147 Galton Road, Bearwood, Smethwick B67 5JT Email: drsam@compuserve.com — MB ChB 1996 Manch.; MA Camb. 1997. SHO (Surg.) Birm. Heartlands Hosp. Prev: SHO (A & E) City Hosp. NHS Trust Birm.

SAMA

SAMA, Mr Anshul Dept. of Otorhinolaryngology, Queens Medical Centre, University Hospital, Nottingham NG7 2UH Tel: 0115 924 9924 Ext: 35113 — BM BS 1988 Nottm.; FRCS 1997 Otol; BMedSci Nottm.1986; FRCS Eng. 1994; FRCS Ed. 1993. Cons. Otorhinolaryngologist, Univ. Hosp., Nottm. Prev: SHO (ENT) Univ. Hosp. Nottm.; SHO (Gen. Surg.) Leicester, Grantham & Kesteven Gen. Hosps.; SHO (ENT) Leicester Roy. Infirm.

SAMAAN, Anahita Hull Royal Infirmary, Kingston upon Hull, Hull HU3 2JZ Tel: 01482 328451; 9 Cassbrook Drive, Fulstow, Louth LN11 0XR Tel: 01507 363718 — MB BS 1976 Delhi; FFA RCS Eng. 1982; DA Eng. 1980. Cons. Anaesth. Hull Roy. Infirm. Prev: Sen. Regist. (Anaesth.) Leeds Gen. Infirm.

SAMAAN, Mr Nady Mekhaiel 18 Hornton Street, Kensington, London W8 4NR Tel: 020 7937 0040 — MB ChB 1973 Assiut; FRCS Ed. 1993; MRCOG 1992.

SAMAD, Abdul c/o Drive Q. Zaman, 56 Scott Road, Denton, Manchester M34 6FT — MB BS 1979 Peshawar, Pakistan; MRCP (UK) 1990.

SAMAD, Essam Mohamed Abdel-Monem 50 Aylmer Road, Highgate, London N2 0PL Tel: 020 8442 7077 Fax: 020 8442 7078 — MB BCh Ain Shams 1969.

SAMADI, Nasar Roxbourne Medical Centre, 37 Rayners Lane, South Harrow, Harrow HA2 0UE Tel: 020 8422 5602 Fax: 020 8422 3911; 3 Wakehams Hill, Pinner HA5 3AQ Tel: 020 8866 8702 — MB BS 1963 Lucknow; DTCD Wales 1969. (King Geo. Med. Coll.) Prev: Hosp. Pract. (Cardiorespirat.) Watford Gen. Hosp.

SAMAK, Mahrous Aziz Rophael 21 Links Court, Colbert Avenue, Thorpe Bay, Southend-on-Sea SS1 3BW — MB BCh 1956 Ain Shams.

SAMAL, Kamdev Birches Head Medical Centre, Diana Road, Birches Head, Stoke-on-Trent ST1 6RS Tel: 01782 286843 Fax: 01782 535291 — MB BS 1975 Utkal. (Sriram Chandra Bhanj Medical College Cuttack Orissa, India) Princip. (Gen. Pract.) Stoke-on-Trent. Socs: Med. Protec. Soc.

SAMANI, Professor Nilesh Jayantilal Department of Cardiology, Glenfield General Hospital, Groby Road, Leicester LE3 9QP Tel: 0116 256 3236 Fax: 0116 287 5792 Email: njs@le.ac.uk — MD 1994 Leic.; MB ChB 1981 Leics.; FRCP 1994 Lond; MRCP 1984 UK; BSc 1978 (Med Sci) Leics.; FACC 1998. (Leic.) Prof. of Cardiol.. & Hon. Cons. Cardiol. Univ. Leicester & Glenfield Hosp. Socs: Brit. Cardiac Soc.; Assn. of Phys.s; Brit. Hypertens. Soc. Prev: Lect. & Hon. Sen. Regist. (Med.) Univ. Leicester; MRC Train. Fell. Univ. Leic.; SHO (Med.) Hammersmith Hosp. Lond.

SAMANI, Smita The Medical Centre, 144-150 High Road, London NW10 2PT Tel: 020 8459 5550 Fax: 020 8451 7268; 1 Pickwick Place, Harrow on the Hill, Harrow HA1 3BG Tel: 020 8426 8070 — MRCS Eng. LRCP Lond. 1979; MRCGP 1994; MFFP 1993; DRCOG 1992; Cert. Family Plann. JCC 1981. (Manch.) GP Princip. Brent; GP Trainer Brent; Instruc. Dr. (Family Plann.) Harrow; Sessional Clin. Med. Off. (Family Plann.) Lond. Prev: SHO (A & E) Hammersmith Hosp. Lond.; Trainee GP Wembley; SHO & CMO (Paediat.) Centr. Middlx. Hosp.

SAMANIEGO, Nicolas Carlos 91 Carr Road, Walkley, Sheffield S6 2WY Email: ncsamaniego@compuserve.com — MB ChB 1993 Sheff.; MRCP (Lond.) 1997. (Sheff.) Specialist Regist. Barnsley Dist. Gen. Hosp. Prev: SHO (Neurol.) Sheff.; SHO (Gen. & Respirat. Med.) N.. Gen. Hosp. Sheff.; SHO (Cardiol.) N.. Gen. Hosp. Sheff.

SAMANTA, Amal Kumar 15 Merrydale Avenue, Eccles, Manchester M30 9DS — MB BS 1972 Calcutta; MD All India Med. Scs. 1977; T(GP) 1991.

SAMANTA, Ashok Kumar University Hospital of Leicester, Leicester Royal Infirmary, Leicester LE1 5WW Tel: 0116 254 1414; The Mount, Great Glen, Leicester LE8 9FL — MB BS 1977 All India Inst. Scs.; MD Leic. 1988; MD All India Inst Med. Scs. 1980; FRCP Ed. 1994; MRCP (UK) 1981; FRCP (Lond.) 2000. (AU India Inst. Med. Sci. New Delhi) Cons. Phys. Rheum. Leicester Roy. Infirm.; Clin. Tutor (Med.) Univ. Leicester. Prev: Pfizer Clin. Research Fell.; Sen. Regist. (Med.) Leics. HA.

SAMANTA, Asok Kumar 1-3 St John's Road, East Ham, London E6 1NW Tel: 020 8503 5783; 37 Cheyne Avenue, South Woodford, London E18 2DP Tel: 020 8989 6363 Fax: 020 8989 6363 — MB BS Calcutta 1956. (Calcutta Med. Coll.) GP Lond. Socs: BMA. Prev: Regist. (Surg.) Lond. Jewish Hosp.; Regist. (Orthop.) Qu. Mary's

Hosp. & E. Ham Mem. Hosp. Lond.; Regist. (Orthop.) P.ss Margt. Hosp. Swindon.

SAMANTA, Kamal The Health Centre, Commercial Road, Skelmanthorpe, Huddersfield HD8 9DA Tel: 01484 862239; Skelmanthorpe Health Centre, Commercial Road, Skelmanthorpe, Huddersfield HD8 9DA Tel: 01484 862239 — MB BS Calcutta 1967. (R.G. Kar Medical College Calcutta, West Bengal) SHO Med. for the Elderly St. James Hosp. Leeds. Socs: Hudds. Med. Soc.; Ex-Pres. R. G. Kas Med. Coll.

SAMANTA, Nabagopal 4 Wakerfield Close, Nelmes Park, Hornchurch RM11 2TH Tel: 0140 24 42350 — MB BS 1965 Calcutta; DO Eng. 1972. (N.R.S. Med. Coll.)

SAMANTA, Renuka The Health Centre, Commercial Road, Skelmanthorpe, Huddersfield HD8 9DA Tel: 01484 862239; Samanta, Samanta & Welch, Skelmanthorpe Health Centre, Commercial Road, Skelmanthorpe, Huddersfield HD8 9DA Tel: 01464 862239 — MB BS Calcutta 1967. (R.G. Kar Medical College Calcutta) SHO G&O Huddersfield; SHO G&O Dewbury; SHO Psychiat. Huddersfield; Clin. Med. Off. Huddersfield; GP Skelmanthorpe Huddersfield. Socs: Hudds. Med. Soc.; Disp. Pract. Assn.; ODA.

SAMANTA-LAUGHTON, Manjir Flat 2, 3 Blackdown Close, London N2 8JF Email: munchjim@dircon.co.uk — MB BS 1997 Lond.

SAMARAGE, Lalith Hiran Jessop Hospital for Women, Leavygreave Road, Sheffield S3 7RE Tel: 0114 276 6333 — MB BS 1982 Sri Lanka; MRCOG 1991.

SAMARAGE, Mr Shantha Upali Department of Obstetrics & Gynaecology, Friarage Hospital, Northallerton DL6 1JG Tel: 01609 779911 — MB BS 1976 Sri Lanka; MS (Obst. & Gyn.) Sri Lanka 1982, MB BS 1976; MRCOG 1985. (Colombo) Staff Grade (O & G) Friarage Hosp. NHS Trust N.allerton. Prev: Regist. (O & G) St. Mary's Hosp. & Newc. Gen. Hosp.

SAMARAJIWA, Harsha Kamalochana 16 Silver Birch Avenue, Fareham PO14 1SZ — MB BS 1968 Ceylon; FRCP Ed. 1992; MRCP (UK) 1981; MRCS Eng. LRCP Lond. 1981.

SAMARANAYAKE, Bernadette Marina 14 The Hawthorns, Wakefield WF1 3TL — MB BS 1967 Ceylon.

SAMARANAYAKE, Joseph James 14 The Hawthorns, Wakefield WF1 3TL Tel: 01924 871151 — MB BS 1970 Sri Lanka; FFA RCS Eng. 1979.

SAMARASINGHE, Anuji Madara 34 Fontaine Road, London SW16 3PA — MB BS 1997 Lond.

SAMARASINGHE, Chatra Rajiv 34 Fontaine Road, London SW16 3PA — MB BS 1997 Lond.

SAMARASINGHE, Dunisha Gayomi 34 Fontaine Road, London SW16 3PA — MB BChir 1991 Manch.

SAMARASINGHE, Ivan Leslie Perera (retired) 225 Malden Road, New Malden KT3 6AG Tel: 020 8942 3394 — MB BS 1942 Ceylon; DOrth RCS Eng. 1957; FDS RCS Eng. 1956, LDS 1951; LMS Ceylon Med. Coll. 1942.

SAMARASINGHE, Kaluaratchige Percy Bertram 64 Dollis Hill Lane, London NW2 6JE Tel: 020 8452 2611 Fax: 020 8830 5954; 64 Dollis Hill Lane, London NW2 6JG Tel: 020 8452 1853 — MB BS 1959 Ceylon; DPhysMed Eng. 1971. (Ceylon Med. Coll.) Med. Practitioner, Lond., Rheumatologist. Prev: Cons. Rheum. Manor Hse. Hosp. Lond.; Clin. Asst. Roy. Free Hosp. Lond.; Cons. Phys. Physical Med. Gen. Hosp. Ratnapura, Sri Lanka (Ceylon).

SAMARASINGHE, Lionel The Surgery, 391 High Road, Wood Green, London N22 8JB Tel: 020 8889 1115 Fax: 020 8881 4372 — MB BS 1968 Ceylon; MRCOG 1977. Cons. Gyn. Brit. Pregn. Advis. Serv. Socs: Fell. Roy. Soc. Med.

SAMARASINGHE, Louis Alwis Taplow Dixon Day Unit, Yardley Green Unit, East Birmingham Hospital, Yardley Green Road, Birmingham B9 5PX Tel: 0121 766 6611; 67 Pavenham Drive, Birmingham B5 7TN — MB BS 1968 Ceylon; DPM Eng. 1978. (Peradiniya) Assoc. Specialist Asst. (Psychogeriat.) W. Midl. RHA. Prev: Regist. (Psychiat.) Hollymoor Hosp. Birm.

SAMARASINGHE, Nihal 21 High Drive, New Malden KT3 3UJ Tel: 020 8949 3102 — MB BS 1972 Ceylon; MRCP (UK) 1983; DCH Eng. 1980. (Colombo) Assoc. Specialist Merton & Sutton Community NHS Trust. Prev: Regist. (Paediat.) Brook Gen. Hosp. Lond.

SAMARASINGHE, Pulun Chandrika 21 High Drive, New Malden KT3 3UJ Tel: 020 8949 3102 — MB BS 1976 Sri Lanka. (Colombo)

Staff Grade (Anaesth.) Roy. Surrey Co. Hosp. Guildford. Socs: Med. Protec. Soc.; Assn. Anaesth. Prev: Regist. (Anaesth.) P.ss Margt. Hosp. Swindon.

*SAMARASINGHE, Sujith Rohantha 20 Woodbine Lane, Worcester Park KT4 8SZ — MB BS 1998 Lond.; MB BS Lond 1998; BSc (Hons) Lond. 1995.

SAMARASINGHE, Wickramapala 5 The Pastures, Welwyn Garden City AL7 4PX — MB BS Sri Lanka 1966; MRCPsych 1983; DPM Eng. 1979. Med. Fac. (Univ. Colombo); Assoc. Specialist W. Herts. Community NHS Trust. Prev: Regist. (Psychiat.) Qu. Eliz. II Hosp. Welwyn Gdn. City; Regist. (Psychiat.) P.ss Alexandra Hosp. Harlow & Barnet Gen. Hosp.

SAMARASINGHE, Yohan Pradeep 67 The Drive Mansions, Fulham Road, London SW6 5JH Email: yohansamarasinghe@compuserve.com — MB BS 1994 Lond.; BSc (Hons.) Lond. 1992; MRCP Lond. 1999. (Char. Cross & Westm.) SHO (Haemat. & Gen. Med.) Lewisham Hosp. Lond. Prev: SHO (Cardiol. & Med.) Kingston Hosp.; SHO (Genitoryurin. Med. & HIV) Chelsea & W.m. Hosp.; SHO (Respirat. & Gen. Med.) Frimley Pk. Hosp.

SAMARATUNGA, Mr Ranasinhage Dayaratna c/o Oldchurch Hospital, Romford RM7 0BE — MB BS 1957 Ceylon; FRCS Ed. 1973; DLO Eng. 1963. (Ceylon)

SAMARATUNGA, Varuna Sanjaya Taylor Joynson Garrett, Carmelite, 50 Victoria Embankment, Blackfriars, London EC4Y 0DX Tel: 020 7353 1234 Fax: 020 7936 2666; 34 Elmer Cottages, Guildford Road, Fetcham, Leatherhead KT22 9BU — MB BS 1990 Lond.; BSc (Hons.) Immunol. Lond. 1987; Dip (LLB) 1996; MRCGP 1995; Dip. (Legal Practice) 1997; DGM RCP Lond. 1993; DRCOG 1994; DFFP 1993; AKC 1990. (King's Coll.) Lawyer. Prev: Trainee GP Oxf.; SHO (Paediat.) N.ampton Gen. NHS Trust; SHO (Geratol.) Radcliffe Infirm. Oxf.

SAMARAWICKRAMA, Mrs Padma Grace 41 Park Hill Road, Wallington SM6 0SA — MB BS 1968 Ceylon; MRCP (UK) 1974. Clin. Asst. (Geriat.) Hither Green Hosp. Prev: GP Purley; Sen. Lect. (Clin. Pharmacol.) Fac. Med. Peradeniya, Sri Lanka.

SAMARJI, Mr Richard 72 Green Lane, Romiley, Stockport SK6 3JN — MB BCh BAO 1990 NUI; FRCS Ed. 1994; LRCPSI 1990.

SAMAVEDAM, Sam Microbiology, Western Infirmary, Dumbarton Road, Glasgow G11 6NT Tel: 0141 211 2246; 0/1 46 Clarence Drive, Glasgow G12 9TQ Tel: 0141 576 4431 Email: ssamaved@wghut_nhs.org.uk — MB BS 1973 Andhra. Staff Grade Microbiol. W.. Infirm. Glas. Socs: BMA; Hosp. Infec. Soc.; Scott. Microbiol. Assn.

SAMBANDAN, Mr Sidheshwara Bonsai Surgery, Bowthorpe Health Centre, Wendene, Bowthorpe, Norwich NR5 9HA Tel: 01603 748255 Fax: 01603 740741; Sailands, 44 Brettingham Avenue, Cringleford, Norwich NR4 6XQ Tel: 01603 507070 Fax: 01603 506605 — MB BS 1972 Colombo; MRCS Eng. LRCP Lond. 1978; FRCS Eng. 1981; FRCGP 1997; MRCGP 1988; DFFP 1996. (Colombo, Ceylon) GP CME Tutor Norwich Dist.; Clin. Asst. (Adult Psychiat.) Town Cl. Clinic & W. Norwich Hosp.; Hon. Sen. Lect. Univ. E. Anglia, Norwich. Prev: Lect. (Orthop. Surg.) Traumatol. Univ. Malaya; Clin. Specialist Orthop. Surg. Univ. Hosp. Kuala Lumpur.

SAMBASIVA RAO, Mr Gundabolu Shotley Bridge Hospital, Consett DH8 0NB Tel: 01207 583583 Ext: 4317 — MB BS 1977 Andhra; FRCS Ed. 1984; T(S) 1993. (Andhra India) Cons. Plastic & Reconstruct. Surg.

SAMBATAKAKIS, Andreas Orthopaedic Department, Birmingham Heartlands Hospital, Bordesley Green E., Birmingham B9 5SS; 11 Graham Court, Graham Road, Sheffield S10 3DX — State Exam Med 1973 Erlangen.

SAMBHI, Robinder Timothy Singh 29 Clodien Avenue, Cardiff CF14 3NL — MB BCh 1994 Wales.

SAMBROOK, Alison Margaret Sycamore House, Oram Road, Brindle, Chorley PR6 8NT Tel: 01254 852355 — MB ChB 1995 Manch.

SAMBROOK, Andrew James Sycamore House, Oram Road, Brindle, Chorley PR6 8NT — MB ChB 1995 Manch.

SAMBROOK, Mr Denys Knight (retired) 1 Grange Crescent, West Cross, Swansea SA3 5ET — MB BS Lond. 1938; FRCS Eng. 1942; FRCR Eng. 1975. Prev: Cons. Radiother. Swansea & W. Wales Hosps.

SAMBROOK, Janice Helen 4 Garlands Road, Redhill RH1 6NT; 4 Garlands Road, Redhill RH1 6NT — MB ChB 1992 Sheff.

SAMBROOK, Martin Gerard 49 Lenzie Road, Stepps, Glasgow G33 6BZ — MB BS 1992 Lond.

SAMBROOK, Michael Andrew 135 Palatine Road, Manchester M20 34A Tel: 0161 445 0332, 01689 833735 Fax: 01625 584 5347; Southbarn, Whitebarn Road, Alderley Edge SK9 7AN Tel: 01625 590197 — MB ChB 1966 Birm.; MD Birm. 1972; FRCP Lond.1983; MRCP (UK) 1969. (Birm.) Independant Med. Pract., 135, Palantine Rd, Manc. Socs: Assn. Brit Neurol. Prev: Lect. (Neurol.) Univ. Manch.; Regist. (Neurol.) Nat. Hosp. Nerv. Dis. Qu. Sq. Lond.; Sheldon Research Fell. N. Staffs. Hosp. Centre Stoke-on-Trent.

SAMBROOK, Pauline Southbarn, Whitebarn Road, Alderley Edge SK9 7AN Tel: 01625 590197 — MB ChB 1967 Birm.; FRCR 1981; DMRD Eng. 1979. Cons. Radiol. Univ. Hosp. S. Manch.; Lect. (Radiol.) Univ. Manch. Prev: Cons. Radiol. Stepping Hill Hosp. & Stockport Infirm.; Sen. Regist. (Diag. Radiol.) Manch. Roy. Infirm.

SAMEJA, S High Street Surgery, High Street, Pelsall, Walsall WS3 4LX Tel: 01922 694186 Fax: 01922 682644 — MB BS 1977 Karnatak; MB BS 1977 Karnatak.

SAMEL, Vrinda Padmakar Flat 6, Reema Flats, Bedford Hospital (South Wing), Kempston Road, Bedford MK42 9DJ — MB BS 1988 Bombay.

SAMES, Mr Christopher Patrick (retired) Mamre, The High St, Norton St Philip, Bath BA2 7LH Tel: 01373 834547 — MB BS 1937 Lond.; MS Lond. 1943; FRCS Eng. 1939; MRCS Eng. LRCP Lond. 1937. Hon. Cons. Surg. Bath Clin. Area. Prev: Asst. Dir. Surgic. Unit St. Mary's Hosp.

*SAMES, Matthew Peter 45 Fairfield Road, London E3 2QA — MB ChB 1987 Birm.

SAMI, Ammed Sami Abd El Hamid The Bungalow, Llantrisant Road, Pontyclun CF72 8NJ — MB BCh 1972 Cairo.

SAMI, Naweed 25 St Martins Road, Portland DT5 1JY — MB BS 1975 Punjab.

SAMI, Mr Shahid Ahmed 7 Corcullentragh Road, Portadown, Craigavon BT62 4JB — MB BS 1982 Karachi; FRCS Ed. 1989.

SAMI, Syed Z A St David's Street Surgery, St. David's Street, Ton Pentre, Pentre CF41 7NE Tel: 01443 435846 Fax: 01443 431480.

SAMIEI, Haidar Reza 172C George Street, Aberdeen AB25 1HU — MB ChB 1998 Aberd.; MB ChB Aberd 1998.

SAMJI, Faisal 18 Skipton Avenue, Chadderton, Oldham OL9 0QA — MB ChB 1981 Dundee; DRCOG 1986; DCH RCP Lond. 1983.

SAMMES, Heidi Ruth Weston Cottage, 2 Crown Hill, Weston, Bath BA1 4DE — BM 1995 Soton. Socs: MPS; BMA.

SAMMON, Mr Alastair Macnaughton Department of Surgery, Gloucestershire Royal Hospital, Great Western Road, Gloucester GL1 3NN Tel: 01452 395643 Fax: 01452 395643 Email: alistair.sammon@doctors.org.uk — MB ChB 1971 Glas.; MD (Hons.) Glas. 1992; FRCS Glas. 1978. (Glasgow) Cons. BrE. Surg. Gloucester Roy. Hosp. Gloucester; Honarary Sen. Lect. in Surg. Univ. of Bristol. Socs: Christ. Med. Fell.sh.; Brit. Assn. Surg. Oncol; Brit. Soc. Gastroenterol. Prev: Med. Off. i/c Chogoria Hosp., Kenya; Sen. Lect. & Princip. Surgic. Specialist Umtata Transkei, S. Afr.

SAMMON, Mr Douglas John Orthopaedic Department, Royal Hospital for Sick Children, Glasgow G3 8SJ Tel: 0141 201 0276; 10 Kidston Drive, Helensburgh G84 8QA Tel: 01436 675340 — MB ChB 1969 Glas.; FRCS Ed. (Orth) 1980; FRCS Glas. 1974; DObst RCOG 1971. Cons. Orthop. Surg. Roy. Hosp. Sick Childr. Glas. Prev: Cons. Orthop. Surg. CrossHo. Hosp. Kumarnock.

SAMMON, Helen Mary Kirkman Windycot, Cranham, Gloucester GL4 8HS — MB ChB 1982 Bristol; MB ChB (Hons.) Bristol 1982; MA Camb. 1979; MRCGP 1997; DCH RCP Lond. 1984; DRCOG 1998. GP Retainer; Palliat. Care Med. Off. Prev: SHO (Obstetris & Gyn.); GP Regist.; Med. Off. Chogoria, Kenya.

SAMMON, Paul Matthew 5 Chestnut Close, Summerwood Lane, Halsall, Ormskirk L39 8SY — MB ChB 1950 Aberd.; MFCM 1974; DPH Aberd. 1953. Prev: DMO W. Lancs. HA, Lancs. CC & MOH Accrington Dists., Yorks. W. Riding CC & MOH Colne Valley Area.

SAMMUT, Mr Donald Paul The Chesterfield Hospital, 3 Clifton Hill, Clifton, Bristol BS8 1BP Tel: 0117 973 5544 Fax: 0117 973 0323; Tel: 0117 973 0677 Fax: 0117 973 0323 — MRCS Eng. LRCP Lond. 1980; FRCS (Plast) 1994; FRCS Eng. 1984. (Char. Cross) Cons. Plastic Surg. Frenchay Hosp. Bristol; Examr. Europ. Dip.

SAMMUT

Hand Surg. Socs: Of Counc.: Brit. Hand Soc. Prev: Sen. Regist. (Plastic Surg.) Withington Hosp. Manch.; Regist. (Plastic Surg.) St. And. Hosp. Billericay; SHO (Plastic Surg.) Odstock Hosp. Salisbury & Whiston Hosp. Liverp.

SAMMUT, Lino M (retired) 89 Barkby Road, Syston, Leicester LE7 2AH Tel: 01162 606376 — MD 1952 Malta; DObst RCOG 1956. Prev: GP Syston.

SAMMUT, Mario Saviour Freeman Hospital, Freeman Road, High Heaton, Newcastle upon Tyne NE7 7DN Tel: 0191 284 3111 Fax: 0191 223 1180 — MD 1984 Malta; LRCP LRCS Ed. LRCPS Glas. 1988; MRCP (UK) 1989; FFA RCSI 1994; FRCA 1994. cons. Anaesth. Freeman Hosp. New. u. Tyne. Prev: Sen. Regist. (Anaesth.) N.. Region.; Regist. Rotat. (Anaesth.) Newc. u. Tyne; SHO (Anaesth.) Roy. Vict. Infirm. Newc. u. Tyne.

SAMMUT, Robert St. Ann's Hopsital, St. Ann's Road, London N15 Tel: 020 8442 6000; 74 Jessel House, Judd St, London WC1H 9NX Tel: 020 7837 2040 — MB BCh BAO 1983 NUI; MRCPsych 1988. Sen. Regist. Rotat. (Psychiat.) St. Bart. Hosp. Med. Sch. Lond.; Sen. Regist. (Psychiat.) St. Ann's Hosp. Lond. Prev: Research Psychiat. TAPS Friern Hosp. Lond.; Regist. (Psychiat.) Friern Hosp. Lond.; SHO (Psychiat.) Whittington Hosp. Lond.

SAMMUT ALESSI, Carmel William Churchill Medical Centre, Clifton Road, Kingston upon Thames KT2 6PG Tel: 020 8546 1809 Fax: 020 8549 4297; 40 Cranes Park, Surbiton KT5 8AD Tel: 020 8399 5489 Fax: 020 8399 5489 Email: charlesalessi@compuserve.com — MRCS Eng. LRCP Lond. 1980. Vice-Chairm. Kingston & Richmond HA; Chairm. Kingston & Richmond Drug & Therap. Comm.; Non-Exec. Dir. Primary Care Agency. Prev: Non-Exec. Dir. Kingston & Richmond FHSA; Assoc. Med. Dir. Kingston & Dist. Community Trust; Hosp. Pract. Kingston Hosp. Trust.

SAMPAT, Mr Vijay Jamnadas 20 Bounces Road, Edmonton, London N9 8HY — MB BS 1955 Bombay; MS (Gen. Surg.) Bombay 1961, MB BS 1955; FRCS Ed. 1979.

SAMPATH, Mr Raghavan 5 Devonshire House, Devonshire Avenue, Sutton SM2 5JJ — MB BS 1986 Madras; FRCS Ed. 1990; FCOphth 1990.

SAMPATH, Mr Shameem Anthony Carl Blackpool Victoria Hospital, Whinney Heys Road, Blackpool FY3 8NR Tel: 01253 303546 — MB BS 1980 West Indies; MChOrth Liverp. 1991; FRCS Ed. 1987. Cons. Orthop. Surg.

SAMPEYS, Carolyn Susan Old Mill Farmhouse, Lettons Way, Dinas Powys CF64 4BY — BM 1982 Soton.; MRCPCH 1997; DRCOG 1984. Assoc. Specialist (Community Paediat.) Cardiff Community Healthcare Trust. Prev: SCMO (Community Paediat.) S. Glam.

SAMPLE, Sally Obank Emberside House, Warkworth, Morpeth NE65 0XA Tel: 01665 711321 — MB ChB St. And. 1963; DObst RCOG 1965; DA Eng. 1966; DCH RCPS Glas. 1967. (Dundee) SCMO (Wom.s Health) & Clin. Asst. (Anaesth.) N.umberland HA.; CMO Family Plann. N.umbrid Health Care Trust. Prev: SCMO Wom.'s Health & Clin. Asst./Anaesth.

SAMPSON, Andreas The Surgery, 625 Green Lane, Hornsey, London N8 0RE — MB BCh 1974 Wales.

SAMPSON, Christopher Stuart Beacon Surgery, Beacon Road, Crowborough TN6 1AF Tel: 01892 652233 Fax: 01892 668840 — MB BS 1974 Lond.; DCH Eng. 1978; DRCOG 1977. Med. Off. Health Screening Clinic, Nuffield Hosp., Tonbridge Wells, Kent, TN2 4UL. Prev: Vis. Med. Off. Horder Centre for Arthritis CrowBoro.; Ho. Off. (Surg.) King's Coll. Hosp. Lond.

SAMPSON, Elizabeth Lesley 85 Aldborough Road, Upminster RM14 2RS Tel: 01708 449215 — MB ChB 1993 Birm. SHO (Psychiat.) St. Mary's Hosp. Lond. Prev: SHO (Psychiat.) Hill End Hosp. St. Albans; Resid. Med. Off. (Intens. Care & Trauma) Liverp. Hosp. Sydney.

SAMPSON, Gwyneth Ann Department of Psychiatry, Rampton Hospital, Retford DN22 0PD; Hanbury House, Main St, Ulley, Sheffield S26 3YD Tel: 0114 287 2150 — MB ChB 1967 Sheff.; FRCPsych 1991, M 1972; DPM Eng. 1970. (Sheff.) Med. Dir. & Cons. Psychiat. Rampton Hosp. Retford. Prev: Cons. Psychiat. (Community Health) Sheff. NHS Trust.

SAMPSON, Harvey Charles Reginald Burnham Medical Centre, Love Lane, Burnham-on-Sea TA8 1EU Tel: 01278 795445 Fax: 01278 793024; 5 Rattigan Close, Burnham-on-Sea TA8 1QQ Tel: 01278 795504 Email: hcrsampson@aol.com — MB BS 1976 Lond.; MRCS Eng. LRCP Lond. 1976. (St. Mary's) Chairm. - Som. LMC; Clin. Tutor Bristol Univ. Med. Sch.

SAMPSON, Mrs Jane Magretha c/o Kuswin Hospital, Kuswin, Pakistan; Copt. Hall Cottage, Little Wigborough, Colchester CO5 7RD Tel: 0120635 349 — BM BCh 1950 Oxf.; MA; DTM & H 1988. (Oxf. & Middlx) Miss. Doctor Ch. of Pk.istan. Prev: Clin. Med. Off. Sch. Colchester.

SAMPSON, John Stephen Heathgate Surgery, The Street, Poringland, Norwich NR14 7JT Tel: 01508 494343; Woodton Grange, Woodton, Bungay NR35 2LP — BM 1978 Soton.; DCH 1981 Eng.; DCH Eng. 1981. (Soton.) Chairm. S. Norf., Primary Care Gp., S. Norf.

SAMPSON, Professor Julian Roy Institute of Medical Genetics, University of Wales College of Medicine, Cardiff CF14 4XN Tel: 029 2074 3922 Fax: 029 2074 7603 — MB BS 1982 Nottm.; MSc Glas. 1987; DM Nottm. 1990, BMedSci 1980; FRCP 1996; MRCP (UK) 1985. Prof. Med. Genetics Univ. Wales Coll. Med.; Hon. Cons. Clin. Genetics.

SAMPSON, Kathleen (retired) Sandiway, Sir William Hill Road, Grindleford, Hope Valley S32 2HS Tel: 01433 630693 — MB ChB 1949 Sheff. Prev: Asst. Med. Off. (Insp. Nursing Homes) Sheff. HA.

SAMPSON, Keith Gordon and Partners, 1 North Street, Peterborough PE1 2RA Tel: 01733 312731 Fax: 01733 311447; 194 Broadway, Peterborough PE1 4DT — MB ChB 1974 Ed. JP.

SAMPSON, Madeleine Anne Department of Radiology, Southampton General Hospital, Tremona Road, Southampton SO16 6YD Tel: 02380 777222; 18 Olivers Battery Road N., Winchester SO22 4JA — MB ChB 1982 Leic.; MRCP (UK) 1985; FRCR 1988. Cons. Radiol. Soton. Univ. Hosps. Trust; Clin. Teach. Soton. Univ. Prev: Cons. Radiol. Roy. Hants. Co. Hosp. Winchester; Sen. Regist. (Radiol.) N.wick Pk. Hosp. Harrow Middlx.; Regist. (Radiol.) Hallamsh. Hosp. Sheff.

SAMPSON, Marianne Tove 35 Northover Road, Westbury on Trym, Bristol BS9 3LN — BChir 1996 Camb.

SAMPSON, Mark Raymond Crewe Hall, Crewe CW1 1UB; 23 The Nursery, Hartford, Northwich CW8 4UH — MB ChB 1986 Glas.; MRCGP 1991.

SAMPSON, Michael John Norfolk & Norwich University Hospital NHS Trust, Bronswich Road, Norwich NR1 — MD 1992 Lond.; FRCP 1998; BSc Lond. 1980, MD 1992, MB BS 1983; MRCP (UK) 1986. (St Thomas' Hospital) Cons. Phys. Norf. & Norwich Healthcare NHS Trust. Prev: Sen. Regist. (Diabetes & Endocrinol.) Middlx. & Univ. Coll. Hosps. & Whittington Hosp. Lond.; Research Fell. (Diabetes) King's Coll. Hosp. Lond.

SAMPSON, Peter William Sheringham Medical Practice, Health Centre, Cromer Road, Sheringham NR26 8RT Tel: 01263 822066 Fax: 01263 823890 — MB BS 1982 Lond.; BSc (2nd cl. Hons.) Physiol. Lond. 1978; MRCS Eng. LRCP Lond. 1981; DRCOG 1985. (St. Mary's)

SAMPSON, Rena Dora 27 Oakleigh Park S., Whetstone, London N20 9JS — MB BCh 1958 Witwatersrand; BSc Witwatersrand 1954; DCH Eng. 1961. Sen. Med. Off. (Community Med.) Enfield, Haringey & Barnet DHAs; Family Plann. & Psychosexual Counsellor. Socs: MFFP; BSMDH; Inst. Psychosexual Med. Prev: Sen. Res. Med. Off. Belgrave Hosp. Childr. Lond.; Res. Med. Off. Qu. Eliz. Hosp. Childr. Lond.

***SAMPSON, Rod Paul** 3 Woodside Terrace, Raigmore Hospital, Inverness IV2 3UJ — MB ChB 1996 Aberd.

SAMPSON, Sarah Ruth Muluskha Manali Cottage, Gilwern, Abergavenny NP7 0ER — MRCS Eng. LRCP Lond. 1983; DLO RCS Eng. 1986. GP Wimbledon. Prev: SHO (ENT, A & E & O & G) Roehampton Hosp.

SAMPSON, Stephen Andrew 7 Top Park, Beckenham BR3 6RU — MB BS 1986 Lond.

SAMRA, Gurdip Singh 50 Allendale Avenue, Southall UB1 2SW; 145 Oswald Road, Southall UB1 1HJ — MB BS 1986 Lond.; BSc (Biochem.) Lond. 1983, MB BS 1986.

SAMRA, Jagbir Singh The Lodge, Chamberlains Lane, Penn, Wolverhampton WV4 5HT — MD 1992 Birm.; MB ChB 1981; MRCOG 1986. Cons. O & G New Cross Hosp. Wolverhampton. Prev: Sen. Regist. (O & G) Birm. Matern. Hosp. & Birm. & Midl. Hosp.; Regist. (O & G) Dudley Rd. Hosp. Birm.; Clin. Research Fell. Univ. Birm.

SAMRA, Mr Jaswinder Singh 21 Delbush Avenue, Headington, Oxford OX3 8EA — MB ChB 1988 Manch.; FRCS Ed. 1993; FRCS Eng. 1992. Wellcome Research Regist. Univ. Oxf.

SAMRA, Manjeet Kaur Penn Manor Medical Centre, Manor Road, Penn, Wolverhampton WV4 5PY Tel: 01902 331166 Fax: 01902 575078; The Lodge, Chamberlains Lane, Penn, Wolverhampton WV4 5HT — MB ChB Manch. 1982; MRCGP 1986; DRCOG 1986.

SAMRA, Salah Eldin Mohamed Abo Hayling Road Surgery, 171A Hayling Road, South Oxhey, Watford WD19 7QR Tel: 020 8428 0608 — MB ChB Alexandria 1968; LRCP LRCS Ed. LRCPS Glas. 1974. (Alexandria) Clin. Asst. (A & E) Watford Gen. Hosp. Prev: Regist. (Psychiat.) Hartwood Hosp. Shotts; SHO (Orthop., A & E & Cas.) Law Hosp. Carluke; SHO (Dermat. & Gen. Med.) StoneHo. Hosp. Larkhall.

SAMRAI, Paramjit Singh Regional Medico-Legal Service, Pelham House, Peterborough District Hospital, Thorpe Road, Peterborough PE3 9NH Tel: 01733 875283 Fax: 01733 875003; 7 Green Lane, Warwick CV34 5BP Tel: 01926 497153 — MB BS Lond. 1986; LLB (Hons.) Sheff. 1991. (Med. Coll. St. Bart. Hosp. Univ. Lond.) Regional Medico-Legal Adviser. Prev: SHO (Anaesth.) Jas. Paget Hosp. Gt. Yarmouth; SHO (A & E) Colchester Gen. Hosp.; SHO (Med. & Med. for Elderly) Rochford Hosp. Essex.

SAMS, Virginia Ruth Department of Histopathology, Norfolk and Norwich Hospital, Brunswick Road, Norwich NR1 3SR Tel: 01603 289653 Fax: 01603 286017 Email: virginia.sams@norfolk-norwich.menhs.com — MB ChB 1979 Sheff.; BSc (Hons.) Sheff. 1976, MB ChB 1979; FRCS Ed. 1984; FRCPath 2000. Cons. Histopath. Norf. Norwich Hosp. Socs: Brit. Soc. of Gastroenterol.; Brit. Paediatric & Perinatal Path. Assoc.; Internat. Acad. of Path. Prev: Sen. Lect. (Histopath.) Univ. Coll. Lond.

SAMSAMI, Shahla Monireh 17 King's Avenue, Woodford Green IG8 0JD Tel: 020 8505 3211 Fax: 020 8559 1161 — MB BS Lond. 1969; MRCS Eng. LRCP Lond. 1969; DObst RCOG 1971. (St. Mary's)

SAMSON, Geoffrey John 9 Orchard Rise, Richmond TW10 5BX Tel: 020 8876 1684 — MRCS Eng. LRCP Lond. 1961; T(GP) 1991. (St. Mary's) Indep. GP Lond. Socs: Fell. Roy. Soc. Med.; W Lond. M-C Soc.; BMA. Prev: Ho. Surg. & Ho. Phys. Harold Wood Hosp.

SAMSON, Hilarie Christine Stonydelph Health Centre, Ellerbeck, Tamworth B77 4JA; Idle Hollow, 71 South St, Atherstone CV9 1ED — MB ChB 1986 Birm.; DCCH 1994. Staff Grade (Communiy Paediat.) Tamworth.

SAMSON, Jadhav Daniel Health Centre, Great James Street, Londonderry BT48 7DH Tel: 028 7137 8522; 51 Stoneypath, New Buildings, Victoria Road, Londonderry BT47 2AF Tel: 01504 312789 — MB BS Panjab (India) 1966; DCH Punjab (India) 1972. (Christian Med. Coll. Ludhiana) GP Lond.derry. Prev: Regist. (Ment. Health) N. Irel. Hosps. Auth.

SAMSON, Margaret Noel (retired) 5 Millwood Rise, Overton, Wrexham LL13 0EL Tel: 01978 710335 — BM BCh 1955 Oxf.; MA, BM BCh Oxf. 1955. Prev: GP Overton, Wrexham.

SAMSWORTH, Peter Raymond (retired) 26 Western Esplanade, Herne Bay CT6 8RW Tel: 01227 374364 — BM BCh 1954 Oxf.; DObst RCOG 1959. Prev: GP Herne Bay.

SAMTANEY, Narendra Thaverdas Airedale General Hospital, Skipton Road, Steeton, Keighley BD20 6TD Tel: 01535 652511; 3 Oaklands, West Wood Drive, Ilkley LS29 9RE Tel: 01943 817797 — MB BS 1975 Gujarat; MD Gujarat 1978; MFFP 1994; MRCOG 1985. Cons. O & G Airedale Gen. Hosp. Keighley. Prev: Sen. Regist. N.. Region.

SAMTANI, Akash The Surgery, 939 Green Lanes, Winchmore Hill, London N21 2PB Tel: 020 8360 2228 Fax: 020 9360 5702 — BM 1990 Soton.; MRCGP 1994; DFFP 1993. Prev: SHO (Paediat. A & E) Qu. Eliz. Hosp. Hackney.; Trainee GP Soton.; SHO (A & E) Soton. Gen. Hosp.

SAMTANI, Bhagwan Khushaldas, OBE Chatur Nivas, 158 Northampton Road, Kettering NN15 7JY — MB BS 1955 Bombay; FRCP Lond. 1977, M 1962. (G.S. Med. Coll.) Private Med. Socs: BMA; Kettering Med. Soc.; N.ampton Med. Soc. Prev: Cons. Phys. Kettering HA; Sen. Regist. (Med.) N.ampton Gen. & Assoc. Hosps.; Regist. (Med.) High Wycombe & Dist. Hosp. Gp.

SAMUDRI, Meheboob Fhakaruddin The Surgery, 33 Penrose Street, London SE17 3DW Tel: 020 7703 3677 — MB BS 1971 Karnatak; MRCOG 1984, D 1980. (Karnatak Med. Coll. Hubli) GP

Lond.; Clin. Asst. (Obst. & Gyn.) St. Thos. Hosp. Lond. Prev: Regist. (O & G) Roy. Infirm. Huddersfield; SHO (O & G) Cameron Hosp. Hartlepool; GP Trainee Lond.

SAMUEL, Mr Alan Warwick Baybridge Farm, Owslebury, Winchester SO21 1JN Tel: 01962 777757 — MB ChB Manch. 1970; MD 1981; FRCS Eng. 1976; FRCS Ed. 1976. Cons. Orthop. Surg. Roy. Hants. Co. Hosp. Socs: Mem. Brit. Orthopaedic Assn.; Mem. Brit. Orthopaedic Research Soc.; Mem. Brit. Soc. Surg. of the Hand. Prev: Sen. Regist. Manch. Roy. Infirm. & Hip Centre Wrightington Hosp.

SAMUEL, Anne Margaret London Electricity plc, 34-38 Aybrook St., London W1U 4AR Tel: 020 7725 3070 Fax: 020 7725 3199; 50 Clifton Hill, St. John's Wood, London NW8 0QG Tel: 020 7625 5697 — MB BS 1977 Lond.; MSc Lond. 1984; FRCP Lond. 1987; MRCP Lond. 1980; FFOM RCP Lond. 1993, MFOM 1988, AFOM 1984. Occupat. Health Adviser Lond. Electric plc; Assessor for GMC Performance Procedures, 1998. Socs: Fell. Roy. Soc. Med.; Soc. Occupat. Med. Prev: Sen. Employm. Med. Adviser Health & Safety Exec. N. Lond.

SAMUEL, Carolyn 29 Brynfield Road, Langland, Swansea SA3 4SX — MB ChB 1980 Manch.; MRCGP 1984.

SAMUEL, Claire Amanda Laurel Bank Surgery, 216B Kirkstall Lane, Leeds LS6 3DS Tel: 0113 230 7474 Fax: 0113 230 2475; 7 The Cresent, Alwoodley, Leeds LS17 7LU — MB ChB 1981 Bristol; MB ChB (Hon.) Bristol 1981; MRCGP 1985; DRCOG 1985.

SAMUEL, Iain Scott 85/4 East London Street, Edinburgh EH7 4BQ — MB ChB 1998 Aberd.; MB ChB Aberd 1998.

SAMUEL, Janice Louise Grovemead Health Partnership, 67 Elliot Road, Hendon, London NW4 3EB Tel: 020 8203 4466 Fax: 020 8203 1682 — MB BS 1988 Lond.

SAMUEL, Leslie McGillivray Clinical Oncology Department, Aberdeen Royal Infirmary, Foresterhill, Aberdeen Fax: 01224 404495, 01224 553499 — MB ChB 1989 Ed.; BSc (Hons.) Glas. 1982; MSc Surrey 1984; MRCP (UK) 1992; FRCR 1997. MacMillan Cons. Oncologist, Aberd. Roy. Infirm. Prev: Regist. (Med. Oncol.) Auckland Hosp. NZ; SHO (Med.) Roy. Infirm. & E.. Gen. Hosp. Edin.; Sen. Regist. (Oncol.) W.. Gen. Hosp. Edin.

SAMUEL, Mahil Joshua Flat 3, 57 Parsonage Road, Manchester M20 4NG — MB BS 1983 Ibadan; MB BS Ibadan Nigeria 1983; MRCP (UK) 1991; DCH RCP Lond. 1990.

SAMUEL, Malcolm Clifford 14 Fearnley House, Vestry Road, London SE5 8JW — MB BS 1983 West Indies.

SAMUEL, Malcolm Sajjad 4 Stubden Grove, Clifton Moor, York YO30 4UY — MB BS 1982 Punjab, Pakistan.

SAMUEL, Mr Mark John Taff Vale Surgery, Duffryn Road, Rhydyfelin, Pontypridd CF37 5RW Tel: 01443 400940 Fax: 01443 492900 — MB BCh 1978 Wales; FRCS Ed. 1983.

SAMUEL, Mary Baybridge Farm, Owslebury, Winchester SO21 1JN — MB ChB 1970 Manch.; DObst RCOG 1972.

SAMUEL, Mary Harrow Road Surgery, 110 Harrow Road, Leytonstone, London E11 3QE Tel: 020 8519 5627 Fax: 020 8519 9879 — MB BS 1979 Colombo; MB BS 1979 Colombo.

SAMUEL, Memy 9 The Hermitage, Dunmurry, Belfast BT17 9NH — MB BS 1970 Panjab.

SAMUEL, Michael MRC Unit, Hammersmith Hospital, Du Cane Road, London W12 0NN Tel: 020 8383 3162 Fax: 020 8383 2029 Email: mike@wren.rpms.ac.uk — BM BCh 1990 Oxf.; BA Oxf. 19870; MRCP (UK) 1993. (Oxf.) Clin. Scientist MRC Hammersmith Hosp. Lond. Prev: Regist. (Med.) Whittington Hosp. Lond.; SHO (Neurol. & Neurosurg.) Nat. Hosp. Lond.; SHO Rotat. (Med.) Newc. u. Tyne.

SAMUEL, Michel Sadek Hayes Grove Priory Hospital, Prestons Road, Hayes, Bromley BR2 7AS Tel: 020 8462 7722; The Somerfield Hospital, London Road, Maidstone ME16 0DU Tel: 01622 686581 — MB BCh 1956 Ain Shams; BA (Psych.) 1969 Ain Shams; FRCPsych 1974; Dip. Med. 1965 Ain Shams; DPM 1965 Ain Shams. (Ain Shams Univ. Cairo) Hon. Cons. Psychiat. St. Thos. Health Dist. & Maidstone Invicta Community. Socs: Fell. Roy. Soc. Med. Prev: Cons. Psychiat. Maidstone Health Dist.; Sen. Regist. St. Thos. Health Dist.

SAMUEL, Neveen Waheib George 30 Clark Court, Stilton Crescent, London NW10 8DJ — LRCP LRCS LRCPS 1997 Ed., Glas.

SAMUEL, Oliver Wilfred (retired) 24 Lancaster Grove, London NW3 4PB Tel: 020 7419 4624 — MB BCh BAO 1954 Dub.; MB

SAMUEL

BCh BAO Dub, 1954; BA Dub. 1952; FRCGP 1980, M 1965; DObst RCOG 1958. Prev: Clin. Audit Advisor to RCGP 1990-94.

SAMUEL, Mr Peter Roger Ashmore Consulting Rooms, 2 Ashmore Terrace, Sunderland SR2 7DE Tel: 0191 514 0666 Fax: 0191 567 0356; Dalkeith Lodge, Aykley Heads Farm, Durham DH1 5AN Tel: 0191 386 5811 — MB ChB Ed. 1967; FRCS Ed. 1972. Cons. Otolaryngol. Sunderland, Durh. & S. Tyneside AHAs. Socs: Roy. Soc. Med.; N. Eng. Otolaryngological Soc.; BMA. Prev: Sen. Regist. (ENT) Newc. Univ. Hosps.

SAMUEL, Roger de Koning Graham (retired) 39 Alexandra Road, Epsom KT17 4DA Tel: 013727 23478 — MB BS 1957 Lond.; MRCP Lond. 1964; MRCS Eng. LRCP Lond. 1957; FFR 1969; DMRD Eng. 1965.

SAMUEL, Rohit Cherian 32 Westwick Road, Sheffield S8 7BT — MB ChB 1997 Manch.

SAMUEL, Ronald Aneurin (retired) Southway Surgery, Bampfylde Way, Southway, Plymouth PL6 6TA Tel: 01752 776650 Fax: 01752 770249 — MB BCh 1966 Wales.

SAMUEL, Saramma Boyne Avenue Surgery, 57 Boyne Avenue, Hendon, London NW4 2JL Tel: 020 8203 2230 Fax: 020 8202 7900 — MB BS 1972 Madras; MB BS 1972 Madras.

SAMUEL, Thomas Wyn Uplands Surgery, 48 Sketty Road, Uplands, Swansea SA2 0LJ Tel: 01792 298554 / 298555 Fax: 01792 280416 — MB BS 1976 Lond.; MRCGP 1981; DRCOG 1980; DA Eng. 1978.

SAMUEL-GIBBON, Andrew George Askwith Road, Saintbridge, Gloucester GL4 4SH Tel: 01452 500252 Fax: 01452 387844 — BM BCh 1970 Oxf.; BA Oxf. 1967; MRCP (UK) 1973; MRCGP 1983; DTM & H Liverp. 1975; DObst RCOG 1974; DCH Eng. 1974. (Oxf. & Guy's) Socs: Soc. Orthopaedic Med. Prev: Govt. Med. Off. Malawi; Asst. Med. Dir. Lincoln (Insur.).

SAMUELS, Abigail Research Registrar, Rheumatology Unit, Bristol Royal Infirmary, Bristol BS2 8HW Fax: 01179 928 3841 Email: abigail.samuels@bris.ac.uk; 69 Old Park Riding, London N21 2ER — MB BS 1990 Lond.; MRCP Lond. 1993. Clin. Research Fell. Rheum. Unit Bristol Roy. Infirm. Univ. Div. of Med. Bristol.

SAMUELS, Andrew Jonathan Laurie Park Road Health Centre, Park Road, Radyr, Cardiff CF15 8DF Tel: 029 2084 2767 Fax: 029 2084 2507 — MB BS 1987 Lond.

SAMUELS, Bernard Rosarden, 56A Waterloo Road, Hillside, Southport PR8 2LR Tel: 01704 66150 — MB ChB 1944 Manch. (Manch.) Prev: Res. Med. Off. N.. Hosp. Manch. & City Gen. Hosp. Stoke-on-Trent; Res. Surg. Off. Eccles & Patricroft Hosp.

SAMUELS, Bruce Terence Andrew 30 Parrs Wood Avenue, Manchester M20 5ND — MB ChB 1995 Manch.

SAMUELS, Lisa Simone 7 Chaworth Road, West Bridgford, Nottingham NG2 7AE Tel: 0115 982 7239 — MB BS 1991 Lond.; BSc Lond. 1988. Trainee GP Nottm. Train. Scheme.

SAMUELS, Martin Philip Academic Department of Paediatrics, North Staffordshire Hospital, Stoke-on-Trent ST4 6QG Tel: 01782 715444 Fax: 01782 713946 Email: doctorsamuels@hotmail.com — MB BS 1992 Lond.; FRCPCH 1997; BSc Lond. 1978, MD 1992, MB BS 1981; MRCP (UK) 1984; FRCP 1997. (Guy's) Cons. Paediat. N. Staffs. Hosp. Stoke-on-Trent; Sen. Lect. (Paediat.) Univ. Keele. Socs: FRCP; Brit. Paediatric Respirat. Soc.; Neonat. Soc. Prev: Lect. (Paediat.) Nat. Heart & Lung Inst. Roy. Brompton Hosp. Lond.; Research Fell. & Regist. (Paediat.) Roy. Brompton Hosp. Lond.; Regist. (Paediat.) Hillingdon Hosp. Uxbridge.

SAMWAYS, Diana Marjorie PO Box 52, Haslemere GU27 1JA Tel: 01428 643021 Fax: 01428 654850 — MB BS 1964 Lond.; MRCS Eng. LRCP Lond. 1964. (Roy. Free) Indep. Cons. Addic. Disorders, Eating Disorders, Environm. Med. and Food and Inhalant Allergies, Surrey; Hon. Life Mem. (Exec. Comm.) Med. Counc. Alcoholism. Socs: Soc. Occupat. Med.; Expert Witness Inst.; Treas. Brit. Soc. Allergy & Nutrit. Med. Prev: Cons. Addic. Dis. Unit Charter Clin. Chelsea Lond.; Ho. Surg. Roy. Free Hosp. Lond.; Ho. Phys. Hither Green Hosp. Lond.

SAMWORTH, Lucy Jane 27 Thornby Avenue, Solihull B91 2BJ — MB BS 1993 Newc.

SAMY, Mr Ahmed Kamal Eldin Mohamed North East Lincolnshire NHS Trust, Diana, Princess of Wales Hospital, Scartho Road, Grimsby DN33 2BA Tel: 01472 874111 Fax: 01472 875646 Email: aksamy@ntlworld.com — MB BCh 1978 Ain Shams; MSc, Glas. 1991; MD, Aberd. 1997; LRCP Ed. LRCS Ed. LRCPS Glas. 1987; FRCS Glas 1987; FRCS Ed. 1987; FACA 1993. Cons. Gen. & Vasc. Surg. Diana, P.ss of Wales Hosp.; Extern. Examr., Ismailia Univ. Med. Sch.; Examr., Roy. Coll. of Surg.s of Edin. Socs: Vasc. Surg. Soc.; Assn. Surgs.; Brit. Assn. of Endocrine Surg.s. Prev: Cons. Surg. Dumfries & Galloway Acute NHS Trust Scotl.

SAMY, Mahmoud Alaa Eldin 15 Ferriby Lane, Grimsby DN33 3NU Tel: 01472 874111 — MB BCh 1982 Al-Azhar; MSc (Paediat.) Al-Azhar 1989. Staff Grade Paediat. Socs: Assoc. Mem. Roy. Coll. Paediat. & Child Health; Yorks. Paediat. Soc.; Brit. Assn. Perinatal Med. Prev: Paediat. Regist.; Paediat. SSHO; Paediat. SHO.

SAN, Khin Khin 113 Balaam Street, London E13 8AF — MB BS 1976 Med Inst (I) Rangoon; MB BS 1976 Med Inst (I) Rangoon.

SAN, Suman Moira 20 Abingdon Drive, Reading RG4 6SD Tel: 01189 476944; 23 Joseph Conrad House, Tachbrook St, Pimlico, London SW1V 2NF Tel: 020 7821 0702 — MB BS 1990 Lond.; DRCOG; MRCGP. (Royal Free Hospital) Asst. GP. Prev: SHO (O & G) St. Thos. Hosp. Lond.; SHO (A & E) Chase Farm Hosp. Enfield; SHO (ENT) Luton & Dunstable Hosp.

SAN THEIN, Dr 52 Goddard End, Stevenage SG2 7ER — MB BS 1956 Rangoon.

SANAGHAN, Sarah Ann 19 Kirkton Place, E. Kilbride, Glasgow G74 4HS — MB ChB 1991 Glas.

SANAI, Leyla Department of Anaesthetics, Western Infirmary, Dumbarton Road, Glasgow G11 6NT Tel: 0141 211 2069; 2nd Floor Left, 137 Hyndland Road, Glasgow G12 9JA Tel: 0141 339 4885 — MB ChB 1989 Ed.; MRCP (UK) 1992; FRCA 1994. (Edinburgh) Cons. Anaesth., W.ern Infirm., Glas.; News Edr. Brit. Jl. Intens. Care; News Edr. Internat. Jl. Intens. Care; Freelance Contributor to Herald Newspaper. Prev: Specialist Regist. Anaesth., W.ern Infirm. Glas.; Sen. Health Off. (Intens.r Care, Coronary Care & Gen. Med.) W.ern Gen. Hosp. Edin.; Sen. Health Off. (Anaesth.) W.ern Infirm. Glas.

SANATI, Mohammad 33 Templars Avenue, London NW11 0NU — MD 1970 Tehran; MRCPsych 1983.

SANCHEZ, Efren German Churchgate Surgery, 119 Manchester Road, Denton, Manchester M34 3RA Tel: 0161 336 2114 Fax: 0161 320 7045; 33 Reddish Lane, Gorton, Manchester M18 7JH Tel: 0161 223 9438 — Medico Cirujano Peru 1975. GP Tameside FHSA. Prev: Trainee GP Tameside VTS; Regist. (Radiother.) Manch. HA; SHO (Gen. Med.) Bolton HA.

SANCHEZ, Maria-Jose Flat 2, 22 More Lane, Esher Green, Esher KT10 8AD — MB BS 1990 Lond.

SANCHEZ-ANDRADE BOLANOS, Jose Maria Royal United Hospital, Bernard Ireland Hospital, Flat 7-C, Bath BA1 3NG — LMS 1988 Santiago de Compostela.

SANCHEZ BALLESTER, Jordi 2 Oakapple House, Oakapple Lane, Maidstone ME16 9NU — LMS 1993 U Autonoma Barcelona. SHO (Gen. Surg.) Birch Hill Hosp. Rochdale.

SANCHEZ BENITEZ, Almudena 9 Eastbury Court, 37 Lyonsdown Road, New Barnet, Barnet EN5 1LD — LMS 1992 Cordoba.

SANCHEZ DEL AGUILA, Manuel Jesus Flat 2, 267 Walmersley Road, Bury BL9 6NX; 7 Cavendish Gardens, Cavendish Road, Didsbury, Manchester M20 1LA — LMS 1986 Granada. Specialist Regist. Anaesth. N. W.ern Health Auth. Prev: SHO Anaesth. S. Manch. Univ. Hosp. NHS Trust.

SANCHEZ-MOYANO LEA, Jose Manuel The Charlton Lane Medical Centre, Charlton Lane, Cheltenham GL53 — LMS 1994 Cadiz.

SAND, Priscilla Rosemary 5 Selborne Road, Croydon CR0 5JQ — MB BCh BAO 1966 NUI; DCH NUI 1968.

SANDALL, Deborah 3 Deans Walk, Durham DH1 1HA — BM 1993 Soton.; Dip. Anaesth. 1997.

SANDARS, John Edward Cheadle Hulme Health Centre, Smithy Green, Cheadle Hulme, Cheadle SK8 6LU Tel: 0161 485 7233; Wilmslow Road Medical Centre, 166 Wilmslow Road, Handforth, Wilmslow SK9 3LF Tel: 01625 523102 — MB ChB 1975 Sheff.; MB ChB (Hons.) Sheff. 1975; MRCP (UK) 1978; FRCGP 1994, M 1982; Dip. Palliat. Med. Wales 1993; Cert. Family Plann. JCC 1987. (Sheff.) Lect. (Gen. Pract.) Univ. Manch.; Examr. & Exam Course Tutor RCGP; Vice-Chairm. Stockport Med. Audit Advis. Gp. Socs: BMA. Prev: Clin. Tutor (Gen. Pract.) Stepping Hill Hosp. Stockport; SHO (Paediat.) N. Staffs. Hosp. Stoke-on-Trent; SHO (O & G) Hope Hosp. Manch.

SANDBACH, Christopher Shaun 68 Killingworth Drive, Sunderland SR4 8QX — MB BS 1984 Newc.

SANDBERG, Michael Duncan Alexander North Street House Surgery, Cadogan Place Practice, 29 Cadogan Place, London SW1X 9RX Tel: 020 7235 5850 Email: msandberg@cppractice.com; Cadogan Place Practice, 29 Cadogan Place, London SW1X 9RX Tel: 020 7235 5850 Email: msandberg@cppractice.com — MB BS 1983 Lond.; MRCGP 1994. (Char. Cross) GP Princip. In Private Pract.; Echocardiography, Lond. Clinic. Prev: Regist. (Cardiol. & Chest Med.) St. Mary's Hosp. Lond.

SANDBERG, Seija Unelma Tuulikki 131 Court Lane, London SE21 7EE — Lic Med. Turku, Finland 1970.

SANDBY-THOMAS, Mark Glynn 22 Malvern Road, Maida Hill, London NW6 5PP — MB BS 1996 Lond.

SANDE, Winston George Theodore Chanterlands Avenue Surgery, 149-153 Chanterlands Avenue, Hull HU5 3TJ Tel: 01482 343614; 149-153 Chanterlands Avenue, Hull HU5 3TJ Tel: 01482 43614 — MB BS 1969 Bangalore; MRCS Eng. LRCP Lond. 1978.

SANDELL, Julian Mark 12 Gloucester Road, Enfield EN2 0HA Tel: 020 8366 5777 — MB BS 1992 Lond.; MRCPI 1997. (Roy Free Hosp.) Specialist Regist. (Paediat.) Basildon Hosp. N. Thames Deanery; Paediatric Accid. & Emerg. St. Mary's Hosp., Paddington, N. Thames Deanery. Socs: MDU; BMA; Assoc. Mem. RCPCH. Prev: SpR PICU, St. Mary's Hosp.; Specialist Regist. (Paediat.) S.end Hosp. N. Thames Deanery; Community Paediat. Sen. SHO Enfield Community Care Trust Chase Farm Hosp. Middlx.

SANDEMAN, Alison Peters East Riding, The Gardens, Sion Road, Bath BA1 2TJ — MB BS 1985 Lond.; FRCR 1993; DMRD Liverp. 1990. (Univ. Coll. Lond.) Cons. Radiol. Roy. United Hosp. NHS Trust Bath. Prev: Sen. Regist. Rotat. (Radiol.) SW RHA; Regist. Rotat. (Radiol.) Mersey RHA; Regist. & SHO Rotat. (Med.) King's Coll. Hosp. Lond.

SANDEMAN, Mr David Robert Department of Neurosurgery, Frenchay Hospital, Bristol BS16 1LE Tel: 0117 970 1212 Fax: 0117 970 1161 Email: dsandeman@neurosugery.demon.co.uk; East Riding, The Gardens, Sion Road, Bath BA1 2TJ Tel: 01225 428886 Fax: 01225 428886 — MB BS 1979 Lond.; BSc Lond. 1975, MB BS 1979; FRCS Ed. 1983. (Westm.) Cons. Neurosurg. Frenchay Hosp. Bristol. Prev: Regist. (Neurosurg.) Walton Hosp. Liverp.; Sen. Regist. (Neurosurg.) Manch. Roy. Infirm. & Hope Hosp. Salford.

SANDEMAN, Derek David Southampton University Hospital, Tremona Road, Southampton SO16 6 Tel: 02380 794866; Merrie Orchard, Football Green, Minstead, Lyndhurst SO43 7FR — MB BS 1983 Lond.; BSc Lond. 1980, MB BS 1983; MRCP (UK) 1986; FRCP 1999. Cons. (Physican, Diabetes & Endocrin.). Prev: Sen. Regist. (Diabetes & Endocrinol.) Univ. Hosp. Wales Cardiff.

SANDEMAN, James Meldrum Cruden Medical Group, The Surgery, Main St Hatton, Peterhead AB42 0QQ Tel: 01779 841208 Fax: 01779 841239; Gowanlea, Hatton, Peterhead AB42 0RX — MB ChB 1972 Aberd.; MRCGP 1976; DObst RCOG 1974. (Aberdeen)

SANDEMAN, Mr John Charles (retired) Oak Lee, Pound Lane, Burley, Ringwood BH24 4EE — MB BCh 1952 Witwatersrand; MChOrth Liverp. 1964; FCS (S. Afr.) 1963; FRCS Ed. 1963; FRCS Eng. 1963. Indep. Orthop. Pract. Liverp. Prev: Cons. Orthop. Surg. Arrowe Pk. & Clatterbridge Hosps.

SANDEMAN, John Graeme (retired) 153b Burton Road, Woodville, Swadlincote DE11 7JW — MB ChB 1954 Glas.

SANDER, Clare Rachel Top Flat Left, 21 Barony St., Edinburgh EH3 6PD — BM BCh 1997 Oxf.

SANDER, Professor Josemir Wanderley Alves Da Silva National Hospital for Neurology and Neurosurgery, Institute of Neurology, Queen Square, London WC1N 3BG Tel: 020 7837 3611 Fax: 020 7837 3941 Email: lsander@ion.ucl.ac.uk; Tel: 01753 882340 Fax: 01753 891964 — Medico 1981 Federal U Parana Brazil; PhD Lond. 1994. (Faculdade de Medicina, U Parana) Prof. (Neurol.) Univ. Coll. Lond.; Cons. Neurol. Chalfont Centre, Chalfont St. Peter; Hon. Cons. Neurol. Nat. Hosp. for Neurol. & Neurosurg. Lond. Socs: BMA; Fell. RSM. Prev: Sen. Regist. Chalfont Centre; Sen. Lect. (Neurol.), Inst. of Neurol., Lond.

SANDER, Peter Nicholas Orchard House Surgery, St. Marys Road, Ferndown BH22 9HB Tel: 01202 897000 Fax: 01202 897888; Grangewood, Park Homer Road, Wimborne BH21 2SP — MB BS 1973 Lond.; Cert. Av. Med. 1983.

SANDERCOCK, Professor Peter Andrew Gale Department of Clinical Neurosciences, Western General Hospital, Edinburgh EH4 2XU Tel: 0131 537 2928 Fax: 0131 332 5150; Tel: 0131 532 5391 — BM BCh 1976 Oxf.; DM Oxf. 1985; FRCP Ed. 1991; MRCP (UK) 1978. (Oxf.) Prof. (Neurol.) Univ. of Edin.; Hon. Cons. (Neurol.) W.ern Gen. Hosp., Edin. Socs: Assn. Brit. Neurols.; Brit. Atherosclerosis Soc.; Brit. Stroke Research Gp. Prev: Lect. (Neurol.) Walton Hosp. Liverp.; Research Sen. Regist. (Neurol.) Radcliffe Infirm. Oxf.; Regist. (Neurol.) N. Manch. Gen. Hosp. & Manch. Roy. Infirm.

SANDERCOTT, Anne Meryl A&E Department, Royal Berkshire Hospital, London Road, Reading RG1 5AN Tel: 01189 875111; Greenray Cottage, Sunnyside, Theale, Reading RG7 4BE Tel: 01189 302697 — MB ChB 1981 Ed.; DA Eng. 1984. Clin. Asst. (A & E) Roy. Berks. Hosp. Reading.

SANDERS, Alison Jane 131 Penrhyn Road, Sheffield S11 8UP; 9 Westfield Road, Bengeo, Hertford SG14 3DL — MB ChB 1995 Sheff. (Sheff.) SHO A+E. Prev: SHO (Orthop. & A & E) N.ern Gen. Hosp. Sheff.; Ho. Off. Rotherham Dist. Gen.

SANDERS, Anne Deborah Cadbury Heath Health Centre, Parkwall Road, Cadbury Heath, Bristol BS30 8HS Tel: 0117 980 5706 Fax: 0117 960 0164 — MB ChB 1989 Bristol; MRCGP 1996; DRCOG 1995; DCH RCP Lond. 1994.

SANDERS, Awena Ffowcs Royal Dundee Liff Hospital, Dundee DD2 5NF; The Old Bridge House, Douglastown, Forfar DD8 1TL — MB ChB 1992 Manch.; BSc 1989; MRCPsych 1997. (St Andrews and Manchester) Specialist Regist. (Psychiat.) Roy. Dundee Liff Hosp. Socs: BMA; MDU. Prev: SHO (Psychiat.) Roy. Dundee Liff Hosp.; SHO (Psychiat.) Corn Hill Hosp. Aberd.; SHO (Med.) Glan Clwyd Hosp.

SANDERS, Caroline Roberta The Queen Edith Medical Centre, 59 Queen Ediths Way, Cambridge CB1 8PJ Tel: 01223 247288 — MBBS 1984 London; BSc (Hons.) Biochemistry (Univ. Sussex) 1975; Research MPhil (Cambs.) 1977; MRCP (Glas.). (UCH, London) Gen. Practitioner.

SANDERS, David John 18 Sandwon Close, Downend, Bristol BS16 6SJ — BM BCh 1985 Oxf.

SANDERS, David Surendran Gastroenterology & Liver Unit, Royal Hallamshire Hospital, Sheffield S10 2JF — MB ChB 1991 Glas.; MRCP (UK) 1996. Specialist Regist. (Gastroenterol. & Internal Med.) Sheff.; Action Research Train. Fell. 1999-2001.

SANDERS, Donald Scott Anderson 6/2 Rocheid Park, Edinburgh EH4 1RP — MB ChB 1983 Dundee; MRCPath Glas. 1990. Sen. Lect. (Histopath.) Univ. Birm.; Hon. Cons. Path. Birm. Gen. Hosp. Prev: Sen. Regist. (Histopath.) Ninewells Hosp. Dundee.

SANDERS, Eileen Mary The Hadleigh Practice, Hadleigh Lodge, 216A Warhem Road, Corfe Mullen, Wimborne BH21 3LN Tel: 01202 694721; 21 Sorrel Way, Wyke, Gillingham SP8 4TP Tel: 01747 826578 Email: docgil@aol.com — BM 1986 Soton.; DRCOG 1990. (Southampton University) GP; Med. Adviser W. Dorset Youth Advis. Serv.

SANDERS, Eric Universyt Hospital of North Durham, North Road, Durham DH1 5TW Tel: 0191 333 2597 Fax: 0191 333 2747; 101 Thorntons Close, Pelton, Chester-le-Street DH2 1QJ Tel: 0191 370 2133 — MB BCh 1971 Wales; FRCP Lond. 1990; MRCP (UK) 1974. Cons. Phys. Univ. Hosp. of N. Durh., Co. Durh. Prev: Cons. Phys. W. Wales Gen. Hosp. Carmarthen; Lect. (Renal Dis.) Roy. Infirm. Cardiff; Hon. Regist. Research Fell. Inst. Renal Dis. Roy. Infirm. Cardiff.

SANDERS, Fiona Elizabeth Heron Practice, John Scott Health Centre, Green Lanes, London N4 2NU Tel: 020 7690 1172 Fax: 020 8809 6900 — MB BS 1986 Lond.; DFFP 1991; MRCGP 1991. (UCH/Middlesex) GP Principle.

SANDERS, Frances Louise 35 Lansdowne Road, Tonbridge TN9 1JD — MB BS 1998 Lond.; MB BS Lond 1998.

SANDERS, Gillian Linda Tees Health Authority, Poole House, Stokesley Road, Nunthorpe, Middlesbrough TS7 0NJ Tel: 01642 320000; 178 Osborne Road, Jesmond, Newcastle upon Tyne NE2 3LE — MB BS 1973 Newc.; MD Newc. 1989; FRCP Ed. 1995; MRCP (UK) 1976; FFPHM 196; MFPHM 1987. Dir. of Pub. Health. Prev: Cons. Epidemiol. N.. RHA.; Sen. Lect./Cons. Pub. Health Med. Newc. & N. Tyneside HA.

SANDERS

SANDERS, Gillian Margaret 20 Bernard Gardens, London SW19 7BE — MB BS 1980 Lond.; DRCOG 1985; DCH RCP Lond. 1984.

SANDERS, Mr Grant 56 Southway, London NW11 6SA — MB BS 1992 Lond. (St Mary's Hosp.)

SANDERS, Helen Elizabeth Apartment 4, Byron Court, Pittville Circus Road, Cheltenham GL52 2GA — MB ChB 1994 Birm.; ChB Birm. 1994.

SANDERS, John Carl 28 Orchard Road E., Manchester M22 4ER Tel: 0161 613 1965 — MB BS 1986 Lond.; FRCA 1998.

SANDERS, Jonathan Hume Lonsdale 18 Manor Drive, Newcastle upon Tyne NE7 7XN — MB BS 1990 Lond.; MRCPsych 1996. (St. Geo.)

SANDERS, Jonathan James — MB BS 1992 Newc. (Newcastle-upon-Tyne) Cons. Anaesth. Qu. Vict. Hosp., E. Grinstead, W. Sussex RH19 3DZ. Socs: Assoc. of Anaesth.s; Intens. Care Soc.

SANDERS, Judith Ann St Ann's Medical Centre, Effingham Street, Rotherham S65 1BL Tel: 01709 379283/364437; 1 Clifton Crescent N., Rotherham S65 2AS Tel: 01709 837656 — MB ChB 1983 Sheff.; MRCGP 1990; DCH RCP Lond. 1987. (Sheffield University)

SANDERS, Julia 36 Home Park Road, London SW19 7HN — MB ChB 1980 Liverp.; MRCPsych 1987; Dip. Human Sex Univ. Lond. 1991; Dip. Criminol. Lond. 1996.

SANDERS, Kenneth 20 Basing Hill, London NW11 8TH Tel: 020 8458 7809 — MB ChB 1951 Leeds; MD Leeds 1959; MRCGP 1958. (Leeds) Socs: Brit. Psychoanal. Soc. Prev: Ho. Phys. & Ho. Surg. Wakefield Gen. Hosp.; Capt. RAMC.

SANDERS, Mr Kevin John Maxillofacial Unit, Withington Hospital, Nell Lane, Manchester M20 2LR Tel: 0161 291 4095 Fax: 0161 291 4171; The Willows, 1 Hillside, Heaton, Bolton BL1 5DT Tel: 01204 845172 — MB BChir 1989 Camb.; MA Camb. 1989; FRCS Eng. 1992; FDS RCS Ed. 1984; FRACDS 1982. Cons. Maxillofacial Surg. S. Manch. Univ. Hosps. NHS Trust.

SANDERS, Lewis Roger Tilehurst Surgery, Tylers Place, Pottery Road, Tilehurst, Reading RG30 6BW Tel: 0118 942 7528 Fax: 0118 945 2405 — MB BS 1966 Lond.; MRCS Eng. LRCP Lond. 1966. GP Reading.

SANDERS, Mark Kevin 14 Green Lane, Downton, Salisbury SP5 3SY Tel: 01725 573882 Email: mark@mksanders.freeserve.co.uk — MB BS 1992 Lond.; FRCA 1998. Specialist Regist. (Anaesth.) Wessex; Assoc. Prof. (Anaeth.) Univ of Wasington. Seattle. USA.

SANDERS, Mr Mark Nathan 49 Chiltern Crescent, Wallingford OX10 0PG — MB BS 1988 Newc.; FRCS Ed. 1993; FRCS Eng. 1993. Sen. Regist. (Gen. Surg.) Whangarei Area Hosp. Prev: Regist. (Gen. Surg.) Auckland Hosp. New Zealand; Regist. (Orthop Surg.) New Plymouth Hosp. New Zealand; Regist. (Orthop. Surg.) Invercargill Hosp. New Zealand.

SANDERS, Mr Michael David (retired) National Hospital, Queen Square, London WC1 Tel: 020 7837 3611 Ext: 3382 — MB BS 1959 Lond.; FRCS Eng. 1967; FRCP Lond. 1977, M 1964; MRCS Eng. LRCP Lond. 1959; DO Eng. 1962. Cons. Ophth. Nat. Hosp. Qu. Sq. Lond.; Hon. Cons. Neuro-ophth. Sydney Hosp. Univ. Sydney, NSW; Civil Cons. (Ophth.) RAF. Prev: Ho. Off. Guy's Hosp. Lond.

SANDERS, Michael Samuel (retired) 104 Newland Park, Hull HU5 2DU Tel: 01482 342897 — MB ChB 1948 Leeds; FRCGP 1983, M 1961; DObst RCOG 1950. Prev: Provost Humberside Fac. RCGP.

SANDERS, Neil Peter Westgate Surgery, 60 Westgate, Peterborough PE1 1RG Tel: 01733 562420 Fax: 01733 564081; 30 Thorpe Lea Road, Peterborough PE3 6BZ Tel: 01733 60821 — BM BCh 1986 Oxf.; DCH RCP Lond. 1991.

SANDERS, Paul Anthony University Hospital of South Manchester, Withington Hospital, West Didsbury, Manchester M20 2LR Tel: 0161 291 4285 Fax: 0161 291 3785; 21 Dean Road, Handforth, Wilmslow SK9 3AH — MB ChB 1979 Leeds; MD Leeds 1989; MRCP (UK) 1982; FRCP Ed. 1998; FRCP Lond. 1998. Cons. Rheum. Univ. Hosp. S. Manch. & Stepping Hill Hosp., Stockport; Hon. Lect. Univ. of Manch. Socs: Brit. Soc. Rheum. Prev: Research Fell. Hope Hosp. Salford; Manch. Roy. Infirm. Sen. Regist. Rheum.; Tutor in Rheum., Manch. & Salford Hosps. (Hon. Regist.).

SANDERS, Robert Keith Morice (retired) 36 Grayston Close, Tewkesbury GL20 8AY Tel: 01684 293760 — MB ChB 1954 Bristol; MD Bristol 1963; DObst RCOG 1956. Prev: Gen. Sen. Christian Med. Fell.sh. Lond.

SANDERS, Rosemary Susan (retired) Souldern Manor, Bicester OX27 7LF — MB BS 1977 Lond.; MA Oxf. 1978; FFA RCS Eng. 1982. Cons. Anaesth. Horton Gen. Hosp. Banbury.

SANDERS, Roshini 3 Cammo Brae, Edinburgh EH4 8ET Tel: 0131 339 4563; 28 Hillfoot Drive, Bearsden, Glasgow G61 3QF — MB ChB 1984 Glas.; FRCS Ed. 1990; DO RCS Eng. 1988. Cons. Ophth. Qu. Margt. Hosp. Dunfermline. Prev: Sen. Regist. (Ophth.) Ninewells Hosp. Dundee.

SANDERS, Professor Roy Suite 1, 82 Portland Place, London W1N 3DH Tel: 020 7580 3541 Fax: 020 7436 2954 Email: ppc@gateway.co.uk; 77 Harley Street, London W1G 8QN Tel: 020 7935 7417 — MB BS Lond. 1962; BSc (Hons.) Anat. Lond. 1959; FRCS Eng. 1967; MRCS Eng. LRCP Lond. 1962. (Char. Cross) Cons. Plastic Surg. Mt. Vernon Hosp. N.wood, Luton & Dunstable Hosp., Roy. Nat. Orthop. Hosp. Stanmore; Dir. RAFT Inst. Plastic Surg. Socs: (Sec.) Brit. Assn. Plastic Surgs. (Ex-Pres.); Roy. Soc. Med. (Pres. Plastic Surg. Sect.); Internat. Soc. Aesthetic Plastic Surg. Prev: Cons. Plastic Surg. St. Bart. Hosp. Lond. & NE Thames Regional Plastic Surg. Centre St. And. Hosp. Billericay; Hon. Sen. Lect. Univ. Lond.; Vis. Prof. Univ. Genova 1987.

SANDERS, Stuart 22 Harmont House, 20 Harley St., London W1G 9PH Tel: 020 7935 5687 Fax: 020 7436 4387 Email: drsanders@msn.com; 51 Springfield Road, London NW8 0QJ Tel: 020 7586 0175 Fax: 020 7586 0041 — MB ChB 1958 Leeds; MRCS Eng. LRCP Lond. 1959; FRCGP 1996, M 1965; DCH Eng. 1961; DObst RCOG 1960. (Leeds) Indep. Primary Care Phys. & Corporate Doctor Lond.; Med. Adviser Grant Thornton, Lond. Clubs, Swiss Embassy Lond., Swissair Corp., Wickes plc & other Companies; Founder Mem. & Ex-Chairm. Indep. Doctors Forum; Med. Examr. Legal & Gen. & other Insur. Companies. Socs: Fell. Roy. Soc. Med.; (Past Chair.) InDepend. Doctors Forum; (Past Chair.) St Marylebone BMA Div. Prev: Ho. Phys. (Paediat.) Gen. Infirm. Leeds; Hon. Sen. Research Fell. Hosp. Sick Childr. Gt. Ormond St. Lond.; Resid. Path. Roy. Free Hosp. Lond.

SANDERSON, Alan Lindsay 2 Caroline Close, London W2 4RW Tel: 020 7229 8533 Fax: 020 7229 8533 Email: dr.sanderson@lineone.net — MB BS Lond. 1954; MRCP Lond. 1959; MRCPsych 1971; DPM Eng. 1963. (St. Thos.) Cons. Psychiat. in Private Pract. Socs: Scientif. & Med. Network; Fell. Roy. Soc. Med. Prev: Cons. Psychiat. S. Beds. Community Health Care Trust Leighton Buzzard.; Hon. Research Fell. (Psychiat.) Univ. Birm.; Sen. Regist. Maudsley Hosp. Lond.

SANDERSON, Andrea 96 Sunnyside, Underbank Old Road, Holmfirth, Huddersfield HD9 1AS — BM BS 1991 Nottm.; MRCP (UK) 1995. Regist. Rotat. (Radiol.) Leeds & Bradford.

SANDERSON, Andrew Alexander Fleck Sanderson and Partners, Adan House Surgery, St. Andrews Lane, Spennymoor DL16 6QA Tel: 01388 817777 Fax: 01388 811700; Adan House, St. Andrew's Lane, Spennymoor DL16 6QA Tel: 01388 817777 Fax: 01388 811700 Email: andrew.sanderson@which.net — MB BS Newc. 1969; MRCGP 1976; Dip. Pract. Dermat. Wales 1992; Cert. Family Plann. JCC 1980; MA 1998. Mem. Durh. LMC (Vice-Chairm.); Sedgefield PCG. Socs: Durh. Clin. Soc. Prev: Clin. Asst. (Ophth.) Dryburn Hosp. Durh.; SHO (Ophth.) Sunderland Eye Infirm.; SHO (Paediat.) Dryburn Hosp. Durh.

SANDERSON, Anthony John Xray Department, North Devon District Hospital, Raleigh Park, Barnstaple EX31 4JB Tel: 01271 322453; Hillpark House, Whitestone Lane, Knowle, Braunton EX33 2LT Tel: 01271 816033 — MB ChB 1981 Dundee; MRCP (UK) 1986; FRCR 1993. (Dundee Univ.) Cons. Radiol. N. Devon Dist. Hosp. Raleigh Pk., Barnstaple N. Devon. Socs: Fell. Roy. Coll. Radiols. Prev: Sen. Regist. (Diag. Radiol.) Wessex Train Scheme.; Regist. (Diag. Radiol.) Soton.; Reserach Regist. (Med. & Cardiol.) Edin.

***SANDERSON, Ashleigh Victoria** 5 Monkstone Crescent, North Shields NE30 2QG — MB ChB 1997 Sheff.

SANDERSON, Cara Jane 20 Taunton Drive, Aintree, Liverpool L10 8JW — MB ChB 1997 Sheff.

SANDERSON, Charles Hamilton 2/L, 24 Princes Street, Stirling FK8 1HQ — MB ChB 1987 Glas.; Dip. Forens. Med. Glas 1996. Clin. Asst. Geriat. Med. Monklands Dist. Gen. Hosp. Socs: Ordinary Mem. Scott. Medio-Legal Soc. Prev: SHO (Psychiat. & Learning

SANDERSON

Disabil.) Roy. Scott. Nat. Hosp. Larbert; GP/Regist. Alva Med. Pract.; SHO (Anaesth.) Roy. Gwent Hosp. & Stirling Roy. Infirm.

SANDERSON, Charles Joseph (retired) Flat 1, 4 Queen's Park West Drive, Bournemouth BH8 9BX Tel: 01202 304632 — MRCS Eng. LRCP Lond. 1929; DPH Lond. 1935. Prev: Cas. Ho. Phys. St. Bart. Hosp.

SANDERSON, Christine Anne Department of Paediatrics, Childrens Hospital, Western Bank, Sheffield S10 2TH — MB BS 1984 Melbourne.

SANDERSON, Mr Christopher John C/O Whiston Hospital, Warrington Road, Prescot L35 5DR Tel: 0151 426 1600 Fax: 0151 608 1836; Lansdowne, Mountwood Road, Prenton, Birkenhead CH42 8NG Tel: 0151 608 1836 — MB ChB 1971 Liverp.; FRCS Eng. 1977 Gen Surr; FRCS Ed. 1976; MRCS Eng. LRCP Lond. 1971. (Liverpool) Cons. Gen. Surg. St Helens Knawsley H.A. Clin. Dir. Surgic. Serv.s; Hon. Lect. Dept. Surg. Univ. Liverp. Socs: Assn. of Upper GI Surg.s; BMA; Assn. of Surg.s. Prev: Sen. Regist. (Surg.) Mersey RHA; Research Fell. Dept. Surg. Univ. Chicago, USA.

SANDERSON, David Andrew Essex County Hospital, Lexdon Road, Colchester CO3 3NB Tel: 01206 834494 Fax: 01206 834744; Plummers, Plummers Road, Fordham, Colchester CO6 3NP — MB BS 1985 Lond.; MRCOG 1990. Cons. O & G Essex Co. Hosp. Colchester. Prev: Sen. Regist. (O & G) S. Cleveland Hosp. Middlesbrough.; Regist. (O & G) City Hosp. Nottm.

SANDERSON, Eileen Patricia Blackshiels Frm., Blackshiels, Pathhead EH37 5SX Tel: 0187 533288 — MB ChB 1986 Ed.; MRCGP 1992; DRCOG 1990.

SANDERSON, Evelyn — MB BS 1992 Lond.; FRCR 1999; BA (Med. Scis.) Camb. 1983; MRCP (UK) 1995. (St. Bart. Hosp. Med. Sch.) p/t Regist. (Radiol.) Guys' and St. Thomas' NHS Trust. Socs: BMA.

SANDERSON, Frances Nuffield Department Medicine, Level 7, John Radcliffe Hospital, Oxford OX3 9DU Tel: 01865 741166 Email: frances.sanderson@ndm.ox.ac.uk; 2 Caroline Close, London W2 4RW — BM BCh 1987 Oxf.; MA Camb. 1986; MRCP (UK) 1990; PhD London 1996; MSC London 1998. (Camb. & Oxf.) Sen. Fell., Nuffield Dept. Med. John Radcliffe Hosp. Oxf.; SpR (Infec. Dis.s) W. Midl.s. Prev: Sen. Regist. (Nephrol.) Hammersmith Hosp. & RPMS Lond.; Clin. Research Fell. Human Immunogenetics Laborat. Imperial Cancer Research Fund Lond.; Regist. (Med.) John Radcliffe & Ch.ill Hosp. Oxf.

SANDERSON, Gail Yew Tree Cottage Surgery, 15 Leyton Road, Harpenden AL5 2HX Tel: 01582 712126 Fax: 01582 462414; 69 Station Road, Harpenden AL5 4RL — MB BS 1989 Lond.; MRCGP 1993; DRCOG 1992. Prev: Trainee GP St. Albans VTS.

SANDERSON, George (retired) Rockville, School Road, Durness, Lairg IV27 4PP Tel: 01971 511307 Fax: 01971 511307 Email: g.sanderson@zetnet.co.uk — MB ChB 1956 Ed.

SANDERSON, Graham Donald University of Bradford Health Centre, Laneisteridge Lane, Bradford BD5 0NH Tel: 01274 234979 Fax: 01274 235940 — MB ChB 1984 Liverp.; MRCGP 1991; MRCPsych 1990; T(GP) 1991; DTM & H Liverp. 1985.

SANDERSON, Heather (retired) 9 Branksome Crescent, Heaton, Bradford BD9 5LD Tel: 01274 545779 — MB ChB Leeds 1955. Prev: Ho. Surg., Ho. Phys. & Jun. Receiv. Room Off. Leeds Gen. Infirm.

SANDERSON, Helen 10 Thistle Place, Dumfries DG1 3UT — MB ChB 1994 Manch. GP Regist. - Lochmaben Med. Gp. - Lochmaben.

SANDERSON, Hilary (retired) 1 St Chads Grove, Leeds LS6 3PN Tel: 0113 275 5440 — MB ChB 1955 Sheffield; MB ChB Sheff. 1955; BSc (Hons.) Leeds 1945; MD Sheff. 1975; DPM Leeds 1970; DPH Leeds 1963. Prev: Cons. Psychiat. Fieldhead Hosp. Wakefield.

SANDERSON, Hugh Francis Highcroft, Romsey Road, Winchester SO23 9JA Tel: 01962 844588 Fax: 01962 844711 Email: hugh.sanderson@casemix.org.uk; The Pebbles, 5 Stoney Lane, Winchester SO22 6DN Tel: 01962 883320 — MB BS 1972 Lond.; MSc (Social Med.) Lond. 1978, BSc 1969; FFPHM 1987; MFCM 1979. (St. Mary's) Dir. Nat. Casemix Off. IMG G Winchester. Prev: Cons. Pub. Health Med. Wessex RHA; Sen. Lect. (Health Care Plann.) Lond. Sch. Hyg. & Trop. Med.; Sen. Regist. (Community Med.) City & E. Lond. AHA.

SANDERSON, Ian Antony 96 Sunnyside, Underbank Old Road, Holmfirth, Huddersfield HD9 1AS — MB ChB 1990 Manch.; MRCP (UK) 1993; MRCGP 1996. Trainee GP Huddersfield VTS.

SANDERSON, Professor Ian Rutherford St Bartholomew's & the Royal London School of Medicine & Den, tistry, West Smithfield, London EC1A 7BE Tel: 020 7601 8589 Fax: 020 7600 5901 Email: i.r.sanderson@mds.qmw.ac.uk; 6 Markham Street, London SW3 3NP — MB BS 1979 Lond.; BA Oxf. 1975, MSc, MA 1981, MD 1989; MRCP (UK) 1982; FRCPCH 1997. (St. Bart.) Prof. (Paediat. Gastroenterol.). Socs: Fell. Roy. Soc. Med.; Amer. Gastroenterol. Assn.; Brit. Soc. Gastroenterol. Prev: Asst. Prof. Pediatrics Harvard Med. Sch.; Sen. Regist. Hosp. Sick Childr. Gt. Ormond St. Lond.; SHO Qu. Eliz. Hosp. Childr. Lond.

SANDERSON, Isabel Brenda (retired) 5 Winchester Close, Kingston Hill, Kingston upon Thames KT2 7JJ — MB BS 1943 Lond.; MRCS Eng. LRCP Lond. 1941; FFA RCS Eng. 1956; DA Eng. 1955; DCH Eng. 1949. Prev: Cons. Anaesth. Kensington, Chelsea & W.m. AHA (T).

SANDERSON, Isabel Mary 66 Queens Road, Wimbledon, London SW19 8LR Tel: 020 8947 7806 — MB ChB 1968 Glas.; MRCP (U.K.) 1972. (Glas.) Under-Sec. Med. Defence Union. Socs: Med. Legal Soc. Prev: Sen. Regist. (Gen. Med. & Gastroenterol.) St. Geo. Hosp. Tooting; Regist. St. Jas. Hosp. Lond.; Ho. Phys. Profess. Med. Unit Glas. Roy. Infirm.

SANDERSON, Janet Ulgham Grange Nurseries, Ulgham, Morpeth NE61 3AX — MB BS 1967 Durh.

SANDERSON, Jeremy David 93 Black Lion Lane, London W6 9BG — MB BS 1984 Lond.; MD Lond. 1993; FRCP 1998. Cons. Gastroenterol. Guy's & St. Thos. Hosps. Trust Lond. Prev: Sen. Regist. (Gastroenterol.) Guy's Hosp. Lond.; Clin. Research Fell. (Gastroenterol.) St. Geo. Hosp. Med. Sch. Lond.; Sen. Regist. (Gastroenterol.) St. Vincent's Hosp. Melbourne, Austral.

SANDERSON, Joel Harvey 10 Tumblewood Drive, Cheadle SK8 1JZ Tel: 0161 491 3597 & profess. 061 428 1731 — BM BCh 1965 Oxf.; BSc Oxf. 1963, MA, BM BCh 1965; MRCP Lond. 1969; FFPM 1989. Proprietor MediMark Serv. Cheadle. Socs: Brit. Soc. Haemat. Prev: Med. Manager ICI Pharmaceut. (UK) Alderley Pk.; Head Haemat. Sect. ICI plc Centr. Toxicol. Laborat. Alderley Pk.; MRC Clin. Research Fell. Manch. Roy. Infirm.

SANDERSON, John Gilbert (retired) Little Berkeley, Rowhedge, Colchester CO5 7EL Tel: 01206 728060 — MB BS 1954 Lond.; MRCS Eng. LRCP Lond. 1954; DObst RCOG 1956. Prev: Ho. Surg. & Resid. Obst. Asst. St. Geo. Hosp.

SANDERSON, Joseph Brian DDS Medicine Research LTD, Ninewells Hospital & Medical School, Dundee DD1 9SY Tel: 01382 646317 Fax: 01382 645606 Email: bsanderson@delsmr.dundee.ac.uk; 11 Wemyss Gardens, Broughty Ferry, Dundee DD5 3BX Tel: 01382 732604 Email: brian.sanderson@tesco.net — MB ChB 1986 Dundee; MRCGP 1990. Dep. Med. Dir., DDS Med. Research. Prev: Clin. Research Phys. Inveresk Edin.; GP Lochgelly.

SANDERSON, Kenneth Villiers (retired) 15 Aldsworth Avenue, Goring-by-Sea, Worthing BN12 4XQ — MB BS 1943 Adelaide; FRCP Lond. 1969, M 1964; FRACP 1964, M 1951. Hon. Cons. Dermat. St. Geo. Hosp. Lond. Prev: Phys. (Skin Dept.) St. Geo. Hosp. Lond.

SANDERSON, Kirsty Jane Friarwood Surgery, Carleton Glen, Pontefract WF8 1SU Tel: 01977 703235 Fax: 01977 600527 — MB ChB 1994 Leeds; DRCOG 1997. GP Princip. - Full Parity Partner. Socs: BMA.

SANDERSON, Lynne Exmouth Health Centre, Claremont Grove, Exmouth EX8 2JF Tel: 01395 273001 Fax: 01395 273771; 14 Avondale Road, Exmouth EX8 2NQ Tel: 01395 277807 — MB BS 1985 Newc.; BSc Newc. 1980; MRCGP 1989.

SANDERSON, Margaret Lily Trent View Medical Practice, 45 Trent View, Keadby, Scunthorpe DN17 3DR Tel: 01724 782209 Fax: 01724 784472 — MB ChB 1983 Leic.; DRCOG 1987.

SANDERSON, Mark Richard The Spinners, Ramsey Road, St Ives PE27 3TP Tel: 01480 464255 Fax: 01480 356159; 2 Rosenthal Terr, Hemingford Grey, Huntingdon PE28 9BL Tel: 01480 461517 — MB BS 1986 Lond.; BSc Lond. 1983, MB BS 1986; MRCP (UK) 1989; MFPHM 1997; DPH Camb. 1994. Prev: Sen. Regist. (Pub. Health Med.) Camb. & Huntingdon Health Auth.; Regist. (Gen. Med. & Thoracic Med.) Guy's Hosp. Lond.; Regist. (Gen. Med.) Brook Gen. Hosp. Lond.

SANDERSON, Peter Mark Highclere, 11 Glencairn Park Road, Cheltenham GL50 2NA — MB ChB 1988 Ed.; FRCA 1993. (Ed.)

SANDERSON

Cons. (Anaesth.) Glos. Roy. Hosp. Socs: Soc. Anaesth. SW Region; Med. Protec. Soc.; BMA. Prev: Sen. Regist. (Anaesth.) Bristol & SW Region; Clin. Fell. (Paediat. Anaesth.) Brit. Columbia's Childr. Hosp. Vancouver, Canada; Regist. (Anaesth.) Bristol & SW Region.

SANDERSON, Peter William Guidepost Health Centre, North Parade, Guidepost, Choppington NE62 5RA Tel: 01670 822071 Fax: 01670 531068 — MB ChB 1969 Liverp. GP Choppington, N.d.

SANDERSON, Philip James 26 Chalcot Road, London NW1 8LN Tel: 020 7586 4442 — MB BS 1960 Lond.; PhD Lond. 1968; BSc (Anat.) (1st. cl. Hons.) 1957; Dip. Bact. (Distinc.) 1964; FRCPath 1983, M 1971. (Lond. Hosp.) Microbiologist to the N. Lond. Nuffield Hosp., Enfield. Socs: Brit. Antimicrobiol. Chemother. Hosp. Infec. Soc. Prev: Cons. Microbiologist, Edgware & Barnet Hosp.s, Roy. Nat. Orthopaedic Hosp.,Lond.

SANDERSON, Rachelle Wynne Alexandra 70 Milton Road, London W7 1LE — MB BS 1993 Lond.; MA Camb. 1989.

SANDERSON, Richard Anthony The Surgery, 274 Havant Road, Drayton, Portsmouth PO6 1PA Tel: 023 9237 0422 Fax: 023 9261 8383 — MB 1973 Camb.; BChir 1972; MRCGP 1978; DCH Eng. 1977. (St. Mary's)

SANDERSON, Robert Desmond Stuart The Farley Road Practice, 53 Farley Road, Selsdon, South Croydon CR2 7NG Tel: 020 8651 1222 Fax: 020 8657 9297 — MB 1977 Camb.; BChir 1976. Socs: Camb. Med. Grad. Club.

SANDERSON, Mr Robert James 48 Bonaly Road, Edinburgh EH13 0EQ — MB ChB 1984 Manch.; FRCS Eng. 1988; FRCS Ed. 1988.

SANDERSON, Robert Louis, TD (retired) 1 Amberley Close, Harpenden AL5 4TX Tel: 01582 462772 — MB ChB 1937 Ed.; MRCGP 1966. Prev: Tutor (Community Med.) Newc. Univ.

SANDERSON, Rosalind Mary Fleck (retired) Newhouse Farm, Brelston, Goodrich, Ross-on-Wye HR9 6HF — MB BS 1967 Newc.; MRCGP 1976; Cert. Prescribed Equiv. Exp. JCPTGP 1996; DRCOG 1971; DCH RCP Lond. 1970.

SANDERSON, Simon Peter — MB ChB 1989 Bristol; MFPHM 1996; MRCGP 1998; MRCP (UK) 1992; DPH Camb. 1993. Med. Off., Aviat. Med., Qinetd.

SANDERSON, Thomas Allan, OStJ, Col. late RAMC Retd. (retired) Ivy Cottage, 18 Main St., North Queensferry, Inverkeithing KY11 1JG Tel: 01383 419020 — MB ChB Ed. 1952; AFOM RCP Lond. 1981; DTM & H Eng. 1969; DObst RCOG 1956. Prev: Cdr. Med. Army HQ Scotl.

SANDERSON, Tracy Louise The Coachman's Cottage, Carorona, Innerleithen EH44 6PS — MB ChB 1988 Ed.

SANDFORD, Alison Elizabeth 14 Heys Street, Barrmead, Glasgow G78 2EN — MB ChB 1995 Glas.

SANDFORD, Jeremy Mark Hampstead Group Practice, 75 Fleet Road, London NW3 2QU Tel: 020 7435 4000 Fax: 020 7435 9000 — MB BS 1982 Lond.; MRCGP 1988; DRCOG 1986. (Middlesex Hospital Medical School) Clin. Asst. (A & E) Whittington Hosp. Lond.

SANDFORD, John Jennings Psychopharmacology Unit University of Bristol, School of Medical Sciences, University Walk, Bristol BS8 1TD Tel: 0117 925 3066 Fax: 0117 927 7057 — MB ChB 1990 Leic.; MRCPsych 1996; DCH RCP Lond. 1992. (Leicester) Fromside Clinic Blackberry Hill Hosp. Manor Rd. Fishponds Bristol BS16 1TD; Long Fox Unit W.on Gen. Hosp. Upill, W.on Super Mare BS29 4TQ. Socs: Roy. Coll. Psychiat.; Brist. Assn. for Psychopharm.; Brit. Assn For Ment. Health and Law. Prev: Locum Cons. Forens. Psychiat., Fromside; Spr Forens. Psychiat., Butler Clinic; Spr Forens. Psychiat., Francis Clinic.

SANDFORD, Richard Nicholas Dept. of Medical Genetics, Cambridge Institute for Medical Research, Addenbrook's Hospital, Cambridge CB2 2XY Tel: 01223 762616 Fax: 01223 331206; Granby House, 11 Church Street, Haslingfield, Cambridge CB3 7JE Tel: 01223 871190 — MB BS 1985 Lond.; BSc 1982 Lond.; PhD 1995 Cambridge; MRCP (UK) 1988. (St. Thomas' Hospital, London) Wellcome Trust Sen. Fell. in Clin. Research; Hon. Cons. Med. Genetics.

SANDFORD-HILL, Averil Mary Church Street Surgery, 15 Church Street, Calne SN11 0HY; Poona, Fieldside, Coate, Devizes SN10 3LE Tel: 01380 860080 — MB BS 1988 Lond.; BSc (Hons.) Biochem. 1985; DRCOG 1991.

SANDFORD-HILL, Richard Charles Simon Market Lavington Surgery, 15 Church Street, Market Lavington, Devizes SN10 4DT Tel: 01380 812500 — MB BS 1988 Lond.; MRCGP 1992.

SANDFORD-SMITH, Mr John Henry (retired) 14 Morland Avenue, Leicester LE2 2PE — MB 1962 Camb.; BChir 1961; FRCS Ed. 1968; FRCS Eng. 1967; FCOphth 1988; DO Eng. 1967. Cons. Ophth. Leic. Roy. Infirm. Prev: Sen. Regist. Bristol Eye Hosp.

SANDHAM, Patricia Ann Rosamar, Allanfauld Road, Kilsyth, Glasgow G65 9DE — MB ChB 1973 Glas.; MSc (Health Informatics) Glas. 1993. Med. Edr. Statistics & Informat. Unit Gtr. Glas. HB. Prev: Project Doctor Resource Managem. Initiative Yorkhill NHS Trust Glas.

SANDHAR, Babinder Kaur Royal Devon & Exeter Hospital, Barrack Road, Exeter EX2 5DW — BM BS 1980 Nottm.; BMedSci Nottm. 1978, BM BS 1980; FFA RCS Eng. 1985. Cons. Anaesth. Roy. Devon & Exeter Hosp. Prev: Sen. Regist. Leicester Roy. Infirm.; Regist. Nuffield Dept. Anaesth. Oxf.; Lect. Calgary, Canada 1989.

SANDHER, Dilraj Singh 9 Crawford Close, Wollaton, Nottingham NG8 2AZ — MB ChB 1996 Manch.

SANDHU, Mrs Ajaib Kaur 3 Rectory Croft, Stevenage SG1 4BY Tel: 01438 53030 — LMSSA 1967 Lond.; MB BS Mandalay 1963; DObst RCOG 1968. (Med. Coll. Mandalay) Prev: Res. Ho. Off. (O & G) Bedford Gen. Hosp.; Res. Ho. Phys. & Res. Ho. Surg. Gen. Hosp. Mandalay; Res. Med. Off. Ramakrishna Miss. Hosp. Rangoon.

SANDHU, Amandip Singh 18 Sackville Road, Sheffield S10 1GT — MB ChB 1998 Sheff.; MB ChB Sheff 1998.

SANDHU, Mr Bachittar Singh Queen Elizabeth II Hospital, Welwyn Garden City AL7 4HQ Tel: 01707 328111; 3 Rectory Croft, Stevenage SG1 4BY Tel: 01438 353030 — MB BS Punjab (India) 1958; FRCS Eng. 1963; FRCOphth 1989; DO Eng. 1962. (Med. Coll. Amritsar) Cons. Ophth. Surg. Qu. Eliz. II Hosp. Welwyn Gdn. City & Lister Hosp. Stevenage; Mem. Oxf. Ophth. Congr. Socs: BMA. Prev: Sen. Regist. (Ophth.) St. Paul's Eye Hosp. Liverp.; Regist. (Ophth.) Leisham Gp. Hosps. & Derbysh. Roy. Infirm.

SANDHU, Professor Bhupinder Kaur Bristol Royal Hospital For Sick Children, St. Michaels Hill, Bristol BS2 8BJ Tel: 0117 921 5411; 20 West Mall, Clifton, Bristol BS8 4BQ Tel: 01179 973 9278 — MD 1988 Lond.; MB BS 1974; MRCP (UK) 1978; FRCP 1996; FRCPCH 1997. (University College London) Cons. Paediat. (Gastroenterol.) Roy. Hosp. Sick Childr. Bristol. Prof. of paediatric Gastroenterol.; Hon. Sen. Clin. Lect. Univ. Bristol; Vis. Prof. - Univ. of W. of Eng.. Socs: Brit. Soc. Paediat. Gastroenterol.; Eur. Soc. Paediat. Gastroenterol. and Nutrit.; MRCPCH. Prev: Research Fell. Inst. Child Health Lond. & Hon. Sen. Regist. Hosp. Sick Childr. Lond.; Regist. (Paediat.) Middlx. Hosp. Lond.; Lect & Hon. Sen. Regist. Char. Cross & W.minster Med. Sch. & W.minster Childr.'s Hosp. Lond.

SANDHU, Caron 43 William Square, London SE16 5XJ — MB BS 1992 Lond.; BSc (Hons.) Lond. 1989; MRCP (UK) 1995. Specialist Regist. (Radiol.) St. Geo. Hosp. Lond.

SANDHU, Mr Davinder Pal Singh Leicester General Hospital NHS Trust, Gwendolen Road, Leicester LE5 4PW Tel: 0116 249 0490; Winkadale, Uppingham Road, Bushby, Leicester LE7 9RP Tel: 0116 243 3018 — MB BS 1980 Lond.; MD Leic. 1994; FRCS (Urol.) 1991; FRCS Glas. 1986; FRCS Ed. 1986. (Royal Free) Cons. Urol. Surg. Leicester Gen. Hosp. & Hon. Lect. Univ. Leicester; Assoc. Postgrad. Dean for Overseas Doctors. Socs: Brit. Assn. Urol. Surgs.; Roy. Coll. Surgs. Edin.; Amer. Urol. Assn. Prev: Sen. Regist. (Urol.) City Hosp. Nottm. & Derbysh. Roy. Infirm.; Ho. Phys. Roy. Free Hosp. Lond.; Regist. (Urol.) Univ. Hosp. S. Manch.

SANDHU, Gurjinder Singh 42 Quaves Road, Slough SL3 7PA — MB BS 1998 Lond.; MB BS Lond 1998.

SANDHU, Mr Gurpreet Singh ENT Department, Royal Glamorgan General Hospital, Ynys Maerdy, Llantrisant CF72 8XR — MB BS 1990 Lond.; FRCS Eng. 1994; FRCS (Oto) 1996. (Lond. Hosp. Med. Coll.)

SANDHU, Harjinder Singh Tower House Practice, St. Pauls Health Centre, High Street, Runcorn WA7 1AB Tel: 01928 567404; 7 Granby Road, Walton, Warrington WA4 6PH — MB ChB 1989 Liverp.; DRCOG 1994. GP Princip. Prev: GP Trainee, The Knoll, Frodsham; SHO (O & G & Paediat.) Warrington Gen. Hosp.

SANDHU, Harvinder Singh Flat 3, 49 Cavell St., London E1 2BP — MB BChir 1993 Camb.

SANDHU, Inderjit Kaur Horsenden Lane North Surgery, 2A Horsenden Lane North, Greenford UB6 0PA Tel: 020 8869 7910 Fax: 020 8869 7911; 64 High Beeches, Gerrards Cross SL9 7HY Tel: 01753 883640 — MRCS Eng. LRCP Lond. 1978. Socs: MDU; BMA.

SANDHU, Jagjit Singh Arranway Medical Centre, Chelmsley Wood, Solihull Tel: 0121 770 6711 Fax: 0121 779 7067; Sukhmani, Endwood Drive, Little Aston Park, Sutton Coldfield B74 3AJ — MB BS 1964 Delhi; BSc Lucknow 1957. (Maulana Azad Med. Coll. Delhi) GP Solihull; Clin. Asst. (Psychother.) Uffculme Clin. Birm.; Clin. Asst. (Child & Family Ther.) Dudley Rd. Hosp. Birm. Prev: SHO Ophth. Irwin Hosp. New Delhi; Cas. Off. Leicester Roy. Infirm.; Regist. Psychiat. Towers Hosp. Leicester.

SANDHU, Jagteswar Singh 8 Jackers Road, Coventry CV2 1PF — MB BCh 1989 Wales.

SANDHU, Kanwaljit Singh 14 Pirie Close, Bradford BD2 1EP — MB BChir 1991 Camb.; BA Camb. 1987, MA 1991; MRC (UK) 1995. Regist. (Renal & Gen. Med.) Roy. Sussex Co. Hosp. Brighton. Prev: Regist. (Renal & Gen. Med.) St. Thos. Hosp. Lond.; Regist. (Renal) Guy's Hosp. Lond.; Regist. (Gen. Med.) Worthing.

SANDHU, Kirren Flat 5, 6466 Mildmay Park, Islington, London N1 4PR — MB ChB 1993 Birm.

SANDHU, Nirver Singh Alveley Health Centre, Alveley, Bridgnorth WV15 6NG Tel: 01746 780553 Fax: 01746 780976; 11 Beaconsfield, Tasley Park, Bridgnorth WV16 4RX Tel: 01746 761715 — MB ChB 1981 Manch.; MRCGP 1988.

SANDHU, Param Jeet Singh Hammond Road Surgery, 95 Hammond Road, Southall UB2 4EH Tel: 020 8574 5057; 22 Bengeworth Road, Harrow HA1 3SE — MB BS 1972 Punjab; MB BS Punjabi 1972. (Govt. Med. Coll. Patiala) GP S.all. Socs: Primary Care Rheum. Soc. (Mem. Steering Comm.). Prev: SHO (Comm. Dis.) S. Middlx. Hosp. Isleworth; SHO (Rheum.) W. Middlx. Univ. Hosp. Isleworth; SHO (Thoracic. Med.) Colindale Hosp.

SANDHU, Punam Winkadale, Uppington Road, Bushey, Leicester LE7 9RP; Winkadale, Uppington Road, Bushey, Leicester LE7 9RP — MRCS Eng. LRCP Lond. 1987.

***SANDHU, Ravinder Singh** 138 Broadway W., Walsall WS1 4DN — MB ChB 1998 Birm.

SANDHU, Sandeep Singh 41 Kingsleigh Drive, Castle Bromwich, Birmingham B36 9SB — MB ChB 1997 Manch.

SANDHU, Saranjit Singh Flat D, 40 Hermon Hill, London E11 2AP — MB BS 1989 Lond.

SANDHU, Mr Sarbjinder Singh 128 Waye Avenue, Cranford, Hounslow TW5 9SF Tel: 020 8897 8394 — MB BS 1991 Lond.; BSc (Hons.) Biochem. & Med. Sci. Lond. 1988; FRCS Eng. 1993. (Royal Free Hospital London) Specialist Regist. (Urol.) N. Thames Urol. Train. Scheme; Hon. Regist. (Urol.) Roy. Free Hosp. Lond. Prev: Sen. Surg. SHO (Surg.) Swindon; SHO Acad. Dept. Surg. Roy. Marsden Hosp. Lond.; SHO (Urol.) St. Gen. Hosp. Lond.

SANDHU, Sharron Kaur Room 308 Biggart House, Broadway, Belfast BT12 6HG — MB BCh BAO 1994 Belf.

SANDHU, Sukhpal Singh 18 St Bede Avenue, Fishburn, Stockton-on-Tees TS21 4BN — MB ChB 1996 Manch. SHO (A & E) Sunderland Roy. Hosp. Sunderland.

SANDHU, Swairaj 21 Arley Av, Manchester M20 2LQ — MB ChB 1997 Manch.

SANDHU, Virinderjit 2 Mornington Crescent, Hounslow TW5 9SS — BM 1993 Soton.

SANDIFER, Quentin Dudley Department of Public Health Medicine, Iechyd Morgannwg Health, 41 High St., Swansea SA1 1LT Tel: 01792 458066 Fax: 01792 655364; Rhiw Goed, Westra, Dinas Powys CF64 4HA Tel: 01222 515931 Fax: 01222 515898 Email: q_sandifer@compuserve.com — MB BCh 1985 Wales; MFPHM RCP (UK) 1997; MPH Wales 1995; MRCGP 1989; DRCOG 1989. Cons. (Pub. Health Med.) Iechyd Morgannwg Health Swansea. Socs: Chairm. SE Wales Fac. RCGP; Fell. Roy. Soc. Med. (Pres. Sect. Gen. Pract.; Fell. Roy. Soc. Med. (Pres. Sect. Gen. Pract.). Prev: Sen. Regist. (Pub. Health Med.) Bro Taf HA Cardiff; Family Phys. Barrhead Clinic, Alberta, Canada.

SANDIFER, Sydney Charles (retired) 6 Cherwell Court, Broom Park, Teddington TW11 9RT Tel: 020 8943 0190 — MB BS Lond. 1942; MRCS Eng. LRCP Lond. 1942.

SANDIFORD, Richard Hugh (retired) 1 Nodgham Lane, Newport PO30 1NY Tel: 01983 533870 — MRCS Eng. LRCP Lond. 1942; FRCGP 1970.

SANDILAND, Arthur Cleave Ernest (retired) 6 Parkway, Orsett, Grays RM16 3HA Tel: 01375 891847 — MB BS 1948 Lond.; MRCS Eng. LRCP Lond. 1944.

SANDILANDS, Mr David George Douglas 43 Annandale Road, Kirk Ella, Hull HU10 7UT — MB ChB 1970 Manch.; FRCS Eng. 1976.

SANDILANDS, David Willaim Ian MacRae 19 Frederick Road, Edgbaston, Birmingham B15 1JN — MRCS Eng. LRCP Lond. 1955; MB BChir Camb. 2955; MA Camb. 1957; DObst RCOG 1957; DMJ Soc. Apoth. Lond. 1968. (Camb. & St. Thos.) Med. Adviser W. Midl.s Fire Serv. Socs: Assn. Local Auth. Med. Adviser - Life Memer; Assn. Police Surg. - Life Memner. Prev: Ho. Surg. Essex Co. Hosp. Colchester; Ho. Phys. Hereford Co. Hosp.; Ho. Surg. (O & G) St. Thos. Hosp.

SANDILANDS, Gordon Arthur Hamilton (retired) 6 Sheraton Drive, Wollaton, Nottingham NG8 2PR — MB ChB 1944 Glas.; DObst RCOG 1950. Prev: Maj. RAMC.

SANDILANDS, James McKellar 8 Silverbirch Grove, Quarter, Hamilton ML3 7XZ Email: jsandlands@lineone.net — MB ChB 1978 Glas.; MRCGP 1982; DCH RCPS Glas. 1981; DRCOG 1980. (Univ. Glas.) Hosp. Practitioner (Geriat. Med.) Hamilton.

SANDILANDS, Linda Jane 29 Bantaskine Street, Falkirk FK1 5ES — MB ChB 1993 Ed.

SANDISON, Mr Andrew James Paterson Feochan, Hillside, Martley, Worcester WR6 6QN Tel: 01886 888393 — MB BS 1987 Lond.; BA Camb. 1984; FRCS Eng. 1991. Specialist Regist. SE Thames Higher Surg. Train Scheme; Specialist Regist. Kent & Sussex Hosp. Tunbridge Wells. Prev: Research Regist. Guy's Hosp. Lond.; Regist. Guy's Hosp. Lond.; Regist. Conquest Hosp. Hastings.

SANDISON, Anita Louise 145 Itchen Stoke, Alresford SO24 0QZ — BM 1993 Soton.

SANDISON, Ann Department of Histopathology, Charing Cross Hospital, Fulham Palace Road, London SW6 8RF Tel: 020 8846 7139 Fax: 020 8846 1864 Email: asndison@hhnt.org — MB ChB 1989 Ed.; MPhil Ed. 1984, MB ChB 1989; BSc (Hons.) Biol. Sc. E. Anglia 1978; MRCPath 1996. (Edinburgh) Cons Histopath. Hammersmith Hosp.s NHS Trust (Char. Cross Hosp.0. Socs: Path. Soc. of GB & N. Irel.; Internat. Acad. of Pathol.; Roy. Soc. Med. Prev: Clin. Lect. (Histopath.) Univ. Coll. Lond. Med. Sch.; SHO (Histopath.) Med. Sch. Univ. Birm.; Cons. Hisopathologist RNOH Stanmore 1996-1999.

SANDISON, Donald Ross, MC (retired) 63 Learmonth Court, Edinburgh EH4 1PD — LRCP LRCS Ed. LRFPS Glas. 1939; LDS RCS Ed. 1939.

SANDISON, Ronald Arthur Parkview, 28 The Southend, Ledbury HR8 2EY Tel: 01531 631388 Email: sandy@intonet.co.uk — MB BS 1940 Lond.; MRCS Eng. LRCP Lond. 1940; FRCPsych 1971; DPM Eng. 1948. (King's Coll. Hosp.) Socs: Gp. Analyt. Soc.; Fell. Roy. Soc. Med. Prev: Hon. Cons. Margt. Pyke Centre Soho Sq. Lond.; Cons. Psychiat. Shetland HB; Hon. Cons. Psychiat. Grampian HB.

SANDLAND, Richard Mark Maternity & Gynaecology Unit, Whiston Hospital, Prescot L35 5DR Tel: 0151 426 1600; 37 White Hart Gardens, Hartford, Northwich CW8 2FA — MB ChB 1988 Liverp.; MRCOG 1995. Staff Grade (O & G) Whiston Hosp. Prev: Specialist Regist. (O & G) Warrington Gen. Hosp.; Regist. (O & G) Liverp. Wom. Hosp., Countess of Chester Hosp. & Macclesfield Dist. Gen. Hosp.

SANDLE, Professor Geoffrey Ian Molecular Medicine Unit, Clinical Sciences Building, St James's University Hospital, Leeds LS9 7TF Tel: 0113 206 5686 Fax: 0113 244 4475 Email: g.i.sandle@leeds.ac.uk — MB ChB 1971 Leeds; PhD Manch. 1987; BSc (Hons.) Leeds 1968, MD 1980; FRCP Lond. 1993; MRCP (UK) 1974. Prof. of Clin. Sci., Univ. of Leeds; Mem.Ct. of Examrs. RCS of Eng.; Mem Bd. of Examrs. Rep (Lond.). Socs: Amer. Gastroenterol. Assn.; Brit. Soc. Gastroenterol.; Assn. Phys. Prev: MRC Sen. Fell. & Hon. Cons. Phys. Hope Hosp. Salford; Nat. Foundat. for Ileitis & Colitis Sen. Research Fell. (Gastroenterol.) Yale Univ., USA; Sen. Lect. (Med.) Manch. Univ. & Hon. Cons. Phys. Hope Hosp. Salford.

SANDLE, Hugh John (retired) 18 Sharp Road, Bury St Edmunds IP33 2NB — MB BS 1983 Lond.

SANDLE

SANDLE, Lance Nigel Department of Chemical Pathology, Trafford General Hospital, Moorside Rd, Manchester M41 5SL Tel: 0161 746 2473 Fax: 0161 746 8545 Email: lance.sandle@traffdhc-tr.nwest.nhs.uk; Email: lancesandle@yahoo.com — MB ChB 1978 (Distinc. Biochem.) Leeds; BSc (Hons.) Leeds 1975; FRCPath 1996, M 1984. (Leeds) Cons. Chem. Path. Trafford HA; Hon. Clin. Teach. Fac. of Med. Univ. Manch.; Chair. Clin. Audit Comm., Trafford Healthcare NHS Trust. Socs: Assn. Clin. Pathol.; BMA; Assn. Clin. Biochem.s. Prev: Sen. Regist. (Chem. Path.) NW RHA; Resid. Clin. Path. Manch. Roy. Infirm.; Ho. Phys. Profess. Med. Unit St. Jas. Hosp. Leeds.

SANDLE, Linda Henrietta Tel: 0161 205 4364 Fax: 0161 203 5511; 1 Mardale Drive, Cheadle SK8 4AW Tel: 0161 428 4942 — MB ChB 1982 Manch.; MRCGP 1986; DRCOG 1985. (Manchester) Med. Mem. Indep. Trib. Serv. Socs: BMA. Prev: SHO N. Manch. VTS; Ho. Off. (Gen. Surg.) Hope Hosp. Salford; Ho. Off. (Gen. Med.) N. Manch. Gen. Hosp.

SANDLER, Bernard Maurice (retired) Flat No. 2, The Red House, Brick Kiln Lane, Limpsfield, Oxted RH8 0QG — MB BCh 1946 Witwatersrand; FRCOG 1977, M 1954. Prev: Hon. Cons. (O & G) United Bulawayo Hosps. Zimbabwe & Zimbabwe Defence Forces & Zimbabwe Railways.

SANDLER, David Deparment of Geriatric Medicine, Birmingham Heartlands Hospital, Bordesley Green E., Birmingham B5 Tel: 0121 766 6611 Fax: 0121 753 0653 Email: sandled@heartsol.wmids.nhs.uk — MB ChB 1986 Glas.; MSc 1997; MRCP (UK) 1990; FRCP 1999. Cons. Phys. (Geriat. Med.) Birm. Heartlands Hosp. Prev: Sen. Regist. (Med. eriat. & Diabetes); Career Regist. (Geriat.) Glas. Roy. Infirm.; Regist. (Gen. Med. & Diabetes) Glas. Roy. Infirm.

SANDLER, David Anthony Chesterfield & North Derbyshire Royal Hospital, Calow, Chesterfield S44 5BL Tel: 01246 277271 Fax: 01246 552613; 6 Brookfield Avenue, Brookside, Chesterfield S40 3NX — MB ChB 1979 Sheff.; MD Sheff. 1986; FRCP Lond. 1996; MRCP (UK) 1982. Cons. Phys. Cardiol. Chesterfield & N. Derbysh. Roy. Hosp. Socs: Brit. Cardiac Soc. Prev: Lect. (Med.) Univ. Hosp. Nottm.; Hon. Sen. Regist. Nottm. Hosps.; Research Fell. (Med.) Roy. Hallamsh. Hosp. Sheff.

SANDLER, Gerald Sunningdale, 185 Millhouses Lane, Sheffield S7 2HF Tel: 0114 236 6124 — MD 1959 Lond.; MB BS (Hons. & Gold Medal) 1952; FRCP Lond. 1973, M 1956. (Middlx.) Cons. Phys. Barnsley Dist. Gen. Hosp.; Hon. Clin. Lect. in Med. Univ. Sheff. Socs: Brit. Cardiac Soc. & Assn. Phys. Prev: Sen. Med. Regist. United Sheff. Hosps.; Med. Regist. Profess. Therap. Unit Sheff. Roy. Infirm.; Regist. Sheff. Region Cardiovasc. Centre.

SANDLER, Laurence Melvyn Newlands, Bridle Lane, Loudwater, Rickmansworth WD3 4JH; Diabetes Centre, Wycombe General Hospital, High Wycombe HP11 2TI — MB ChB 1974 Cape Town; MRCP (UK) 1977; MD Cape Town 1988; FRCP 1997. Cons. Phys. Wycombe Gen. Hosp. High Wycombe Bucks.; Cons. Phys. Chiltean Hosp. Gt. Missenden Bucks. Socs: Brit. Diabetic Assn.; Brit. Assn. Clin. Diabetologists; Nat. Osteoporosis Soc.

SANDLER, Mark Gerald The Surgery, 19 Amwell Street, Hoddesdon EN11 8TU Tel: 01992 464147 Fax: 01992 708698 — MB ChB 1984 Sheff.; DRCOG 1989. (Sheff.) Socs: BMA. Prev: Trainee GP Lond.; SHO (O & G) Lond. Hosp.; SHO (Anaesth.) St. Mary's Hosp. Lond.

SANDLER, Martin Solihull Hospital, Lode Lane, Solihull B91 2JL Tel: 0121 685 5315 Fax: 0121 685 5057; BUPA Parkway Hospital, Damson Parkway, Solihull B91 2PP Tel: 0121 704 1451 — MB ChB 1983 Glas.; MRCP (UK) 1986; T(M) 1991. Cons. Phys. Solihull Hosp. Socs: Brit. Geriat. Soc. (Mem. Train. Comm.). Prev: Sen. Regist. Rotat. (Gen. & Geriat. Med.) W. Midl.; Regist. (Gen. Med. & Clin. Pharmacol.) Dept. Mat. Med. Stobhill Gen. Hosp. Glas.; Regist. & SHO Rotat. (Med.) Glas. Roy. Infirm.

SANDLER, Professor Merton 33 Park Road, Twickenham TW1 2QD Tel: 020 8383 3099 Fax: 020 8741 1948 Email: adept.lrs@btinternet.com; 33 Park Road, Twickenham TW1 2QD Tel: 020 8892 9085 Fax: 020 8891 5370 — MB ChB Manch. 1949; MD Manch. 1962; FRCP Lond. 1974, M 1955; FRCPsych 1986; FRCPath 1970, M 1963. (Manch.) Emerit. Prof. Chem. Path. Roy. Postgrad. Med. Sch. Univ. Lond.; Hon. Cons. Chem. Path. Qu. Charlotte's & Chelsea Hosp. Lond. Socs: (Pres.) Assn. for Postnatal Illness; (Ex-Pres.) Brit. Assn. Psychopharmacol.; (Ex-Pres.) Harv. Soc. Lond. Prev: Lect. (Chem. Path.) Roy. Free Hosp. Sch. Med.; Jun. Specialist (Path.) RAMC; Ho. Phys. Profess. Unit Roy. Manch. Childr. Hosp.

SANDLER, R M (retired) 2 Breeze Mount, Manchester M25 0AH Tel: 0161 773 1200 — D(oest) RCOG 1965 (Royal College of Obsterics & Gynaecology, London); 1959 MRCGP 1972 Royal College of General Practitioners; MB ChB 1959 Manchester. Princip. in Gen. Pract. (Retd.). Prev: Clin. Asst. in obsterics at St Mary's Hosp., Manch.

SANDLER, Robert 12 Home Close, Upper Wield, Alresford SO24 9RR — MB ChB 1976 Cape Town.

SANDOE, Jonathan Ashley Torlot Craven Ridge House, Giggleswick, Settle BD24 0DY — MB ChB 1992 Manch.

SANDON, Peter Henry Gauvain The Surgery, 263 Goring Road, Goring-by-Sea, Worthing BN12 4PA Tel: 01903 241995 Fax: 01903 241995 — MB BS Lond. 1968. Princip. GP Goring-by-Sea. Prev: Company Med. Off. Singer-Link Miles & Rancing; Flight Lt. RAF Med. Br.

SANDOZ, Maurice Douglas (retired) Neuchatel, Church Walk, Allesley, Coventry CV5 9 Tel: 01203 402711 — M.B., Ch.B. Birm. 1928.

SANDRAMOULI, Mr Soupramanien Wolverhampton & Midland Counties Eye Infirmary, Compton Road, Wolverhampton WV3 9QR Tel: 01902 307999 Fax: 01902 645019; 1 Corfton Drive, Tettenhall, Wolverhampton WV6 8NR — MB BS 1987 Madras; FRCS Ed. 1994. Cons. Ophth. Wolverhampton & Midl. Counties Eye Inirm. Socs: Affil. Mem. Roy. Coll. of Ophth. Prev: Sen. Regist. Birm. Rotat.; SHO Watford & Mt Vernon NHS Trust.

SANDRASAGRA, Anton James Rajadurai Accident & Emergency Dept, Ashford St Peters Hospital, London Rd, Ashford TW15 3AA; 70A Royston Park Road, Hatch End, Pinner HA5 4AF — MB BS 1976 Sri Lanka; MRCS Eng. LRCP Lond. 1990. A & E Ashford St Peters Hosp. Middlx.

SANDRASAGRA, Vasanti The Surgery, 191 Westmount Road, London SE9 1XY Tel: 020 8850 1540 Fax: 020 8859 4737 — MB BS 1973 Sri Lanka; MRCS Eng. LRCP Lond. 1980.

SANDRASEGARAN, Kumar Birmingham Heartlands NHS (Teaching) Trust, Bordesley Green E., Radiology Department, Birmingham B9 5SS Tel: 0121 766 6611 Ext: 4905 Fax: 0121 766 6919 Email: yukshini@easynet.co.uk; 71 Sir Harrys Road, Edgbaston, Birmingham B15 2UX Tel: 0956 941062 Email: k_sandrasegaran@hotmail.com — MB ChB 1985 Zimbabwe; MRCP (UK) 1990; MRCPI 1990; FRCR 1994. Cons. Radiol. Birm. Heartlands Hosp. Socs: BMA; RSNA. Prev: Sen. Regist. Rotat. (Radiol.) Leeds & Bradford.

SANDRESEGARAM, Mr Kasipillai 29 Larkspur Road, Marton Manor, Middlesbrough TS7 8RL Tel: 01642 319538 — MB BS 1973 Sri Lanka; FRCS Eng. 1983; MRCS Eng. LRCP Lond. 1981.

SANDRY, Robert John (retired) Priory Cottage, Church Lane, Flax Bourton, Bristol BS48 3QF — MB ChB Bristol 1944; MD Bristol 1959; FRCPath 1975, M 1963. Prev: Cons. Path. Frenchay Hosp. Bristol.

SANDRY, Sheila Ann Priory Cottage, Church Lane, Flax Bourton, Bristol BS48 3QF — MB ChB Bristol 1957; FRCPath 1978, M 1966. (Bristol) Prev: Sen. Regist. Burden Neuropath. Laborat. Frenchay Hosp. Bristol; Sen. Regist. (Paediat. Path.) Roy. Hosp. Sick Childr. Edin.; Regist. (Path.) S.mead Hosp. Bristol.

SANDS, Amanda Melanie Lewisham Hospital, Paediatric Accident and Emergency, Lewisham High St., London SE13 6LH; 74 Barons Keep, Gliddon Road, London W14 9AU — MB BS 1992 Lond.; DRCOG 1998. (Lond. Hosp. Med. Coll.) SHO (Paediat.) Lewisham Hosp. NHS Trust; GP Regist. Bradford Rd. Surg. Trowbridge Wilts. Prev: SHO (Psychiat.) SHO (Gen. Med. & Cas.); SHO (Paediat.).

SANDS, Andrew John 21 Antrim Road, Lisburn BT28 3ED Tel: 01846 664760 — MB BCh BAO 1992 Belf.; MRCP Ed. 1995. (Qu. Univ. Belf.) Specialist Regist. (Paediat. & Cardiol.) Roy. Belf. Hosp. for Sick Childr.

SANDS, Caroline Jane Northland Surgery, 79 Cunninghams Lane, Dungannon BT71 6BX Tel: 028 8772 752 Fax: 028 8772 7696; 22 Mullaghanagh Road, Dungannon BT71 7AY — MB BCh BAO 1983 Belf.; DCH RCPS Glas. 1986.

SANDS, Fiona Mary Montalto Medical Centre, 2 Dromore Road, Ballynahinch BT24 8AY Tel: 028 9756 2929 — MB BCh BAO 1988

Belf.; MRCGP 1993; DFFP 1995; DRCOG 1992; DCH RCPSI 1992; DMH Belf. 1991. Socs: BMA.

SANDS, Kathleen Anne 2 Edingale Court, Coventry Lane, Bramcote, Nottingham NG9 3LY — MB BS 1983 Lond. Regist. (Dermat.) Derby Roy. Infirm. Prev: SHO/Regist. (Gen. Med. Rotat.) Hull Roy. Infirm.; SHO (Gen. Med./Rheum.) Pilgrim Hosp. Boston.

SANDS, Keith Alexander John Pearl Diabetes Centre, King's Mill Hospital, Mansfield Rd, Sutton-in-Ashfield N617 4JL Tel: 01623 672289 Fax: 01623 672332; Northford House, Langford, Lechade GL7 3LW Tel: 01367 860508, 01623 795926 Email: andrewwilkinson@oxfordmedicolegal.com — MB ChB 1971 Manch.; FRCP 1990; MRCP (UK) 1976. Cons.Endocrinologist & Gen. Phys., Kings M. U. Hosp., Mansfield. Prev: Sen. Regist. (Med.) Roy. Hallamsh. Hosp. Sheff.

SANDS, Mark James 46 Millbank, Headcorn, Ashford TN27 9RD Email: marksands@lycosmail.com — BM 1995 Soton. GP VTS William Harvey Hosp. Ashford. Prev: RMO Rotat. Roy. Darwin Hosp. Darwin, Australia; Ho. Off. (Med.) Roy. S. Hants. Hosp. Soton.; Ho. Off. (Surg.) St. Mary's Hosp., Isle of Wight.

SANDS, Mary Grainne 23 Cleveden Road, Glasgow G12 0PQ — MB ChB 1992 Dundee.

SANDS, Sandra Louise Lisburn Health Centre, Linenhall Street, Lisburn BT28 1LU Tel: 028 9260 3090 Fax: 028 9250 1310; 21 Antrim Road, Lisburn BT28 3ED Tel: 01846 664760 — MB BCh BAO 1992 Belf.; MB BCh BAO (Hons.) Belf. 1992; MRCGP 1996; DFFP 1996; DRCOG 1994; DCH NUI 1994. (Qu. Univ. Belf.) Prev: GP/Regist. HillsBoro. Health Centre Co. Down.

SANDY, Charles John North Hampshire Hospital, Aldermaston Rd, Basingstoke RG24 9NA — MB BS 1986 Lond.; FRCOphth 1993. Cons. Opthalmic Surg. N. Hants. Hosp., Basingstoke. Prev: Research Fell. (Ophth.) St. Mary's Hosp. Lond.; SHO W.. Eye Hosp.; Regist. (Ophth.) Moorfields Eye Hosp. Lond.

SANDY, Nigel Kirkham 15 Station Road, Verwood BH31 7PY Tel: 01202 825353 Fax: 01202 829697; 11 Motcombe Road, Branksome Park, Poole BH13 6DJ — MB BS 1981 Lond.; MRCP (UK) 1984; MRCGP 1986; DRCOG 1984. (St. Geo.) Clin. Asst. (Chest Med.) Roy. Bournemouth. Hosp. Prev: Trainee GP/SHO Scheme E. Dorset HA; SHO (A & E) Salisbury Gen. Hosp.; Ho. Off. (Surg.) Ashford Hosp.

SANDYS, Rebecca Mary 16 Grove Road, Sheffield S7 2GZ — MB BS 1987 Lond.; MRCGP 1993.

SANEHI, Om Parkash Dept. of Anaesth., Trafford General Hospital, Davyhulme, Manchester M41 5SL — MB ChB 1988 Ed. Cons. (Anaesth.) Trafford Gen. Hosp. Manch. Prev: Roy. Nat. Throat, Nose & Ear Hosp.; Nat. Hosp. For Neurol. & Neurosurg.; Gt. Ormond St. Hosp. For Sick Childr.

SANFEY, John Joseph 21 April Street, Hackney, London E8 2EF — MB BCh BAO 1983 NUI.

SANFORD, John Richard Astley Kidderminster General Hospital, Bewdley Road, Kidderminster DY11 6RJ — MB BS 1969 Lond.; FRCP Lond. 1993. Cons. Phys. Geriat. Med. Kidderminster Gen. Hosp. Socs: Brit. Geriat. Soc. & BMA. Prev: Cons. Phys. Hereford Gen. & Co. Hosp.; Sen. Regist. & Ho. Phys. Univ. Coll. Hosp. Lond.

SANFORD, Winifred (retired) 33 The Marlowes, Hastings Road, Bexhill-on-Sea TN40 2NS — MB BS 1956 Lond. Prev: Regist. Springfield Hosp. Lond., Psychiat.

SANGALA, Ann Vanessa Department of Family Planning, Kings College Hospital, 100 Denmark Hill, London SE5 9RS Tel: 020 7346 5000; Email: vsangala@clara.co.uk — MB ChB 1972 Manch.; (Dip. In Genitourin. Med. & Venereol.) Liverpool 1999; MFFP 1993; MA 1996 (Family Plann. Progr. Management) Exeter; MRCOG (Lond.) 1988. (Manch.) Clin. Asst., Dept. of Family Plann. & Reproductive Health Care, Kings Coll. Hosp. Socs: Fell. of Roy. Soc. of Med. Prev: Gen. Practitioner, Newport, Pembrokesh.; Reproductive Health Project Co-ordinator, Overseas Developm. Admin. Progr.; Obst./Gynaecologist, Malawi.

SANGALA, Wesley Onongani Oipa 20 Prince Albert Road, London NW1 7ST — MB ChB 1972 Manch.

SANGAR, Sanjeev Kumar 1 Stewart Avenue, Upminster RM14 2AE — MB BS 1997 Lond.

SANGAR, Mr Vijay Kumar 113 Chiswick Village, London W4 3BZ — MB ChB 1993 Manch.; BSc (Anat.) Manch. 1990; FRCSI 1995. RMO King Edwd. VII Hosp. Off. Lond. Prev: SHO (A & E) Univ. Coll. Lond. Hosp.; Ho. Off. Manch. Roy. Infirm. & Hope Hosp. Salford.

SANGER, Julian Lorimer Field Lane Surgery, 42 Field Lane, Kessingland, Lowestoft NR33 7QA Tel: 01502 740203; The Vale House, Frostenden, Beccles NR34 7JA Tel: 01502 578327 — MB BChir 1976 Camb.

SANGER, Leslie Vincent Towcester Medical Centre, Link Way, Towcester NN12 6HH Tel: 01327 359339 Fax: 01327 358944 — MB BCh Wales 1968.

SANGHA, Marik Singh Flat 7 James Brindley Basin, Piccadilly Village, Great Ancoats St., Manchester M1 2NL — MB ChB 1992 Manch.

SANGHA, Rageni Kaur 3A Benson Avenue, Wolverhampton WV4 5HA — MB BCh 1995 Wales.

***SANGHA, Sukhdev Singh** 5 Sledmore Road, Dudley DY2 8DY — MB ChB 1994 Birm.

SANGHA, Sukhjit — MB BChir 1991 Camb.; BSc Lond. 1987. GP Princip., Rickmansworth. Socs: BMA & Med. Protec. Soc.

SANGHANI, Jagjivan Valji Abercynon Health Centre, Abercynon, Mountain Ash CF45 4SU Tel: 01443 740447 Fax: 01443 740228 — MB BS 1965 Panjab; MB BS Panjab (India) 1965. (Amritsar Med. Coll.)

SANGHANI, Neelam 8 Alexandra Place, Abercynon, Mountain Ash CF45 4YA — MB BCh 1993 Wales.

SANGHANI, Rajesh 8 Alexandra Palace, Abercynon, Mountain Ash CF45 4YA — MB BS 1994 Lond.

SANGHANI, Vinaychandra Valji Avalon House, Rowley Lane, Barnet EN5 3HT — MB BS 1976 Lond.; MRCS Eng. LRCP Lond. 1976.

SANGHERA, Jaswir Singh — MB BCh 1990 (Nul) LRCP & SI; MRCGP; DFFP; DCH. (The Royal College of Surgeons)

SANGHERA, Juggit Singh Severn House Surgery, 96 Albert Road, Stechford, Birmingham B33 8AG Tel: 0121 784 0208 Fax: 0121 789 7351; Grange Farm, Bicken Hill, Solihull B92 0DR — MB ChB 1976 Birm.

SANGHERA, Mubarak Singh 28 Nevil Road, Wellington, Telford TF1 3DE — MB ChB 1993 Manch.

SANGHERA, Paul The Lodge, Edgefields La, Stockton Brook, Stoke-on-Trent ST9 9NS — MB ChB 1997 Leeds.

SANGHERA, Sukhdev Singh Princess Royal Hospital, Apley Castle, Telford TF1 6TF; 40 Cubbington Road, Coventry CV6 7BN — MB ChB 1974 Manch.; FFA RCS Eng. 1981. Cons. Anaesth. P.ss Roy. Hosp. Telford. Prev: Sen. Regist. Rotat. (Anaesth.) W. Midl. RHA.

SANGHERA, Sumayer 1A Douglas Way, London SE8 4AG — MB ChB 1994 Leeds.

SANGHERA, Vichitar 128 Northcote Avenue, Southall UB1 2BA Tel: 0208 574 4381; Tel: 0208 574 4381 — MBBS India; DFFP. (India)

SANGHI, Anita Royal London Hospital, Whitechapel, London E1 1BB Tel: 020 7377 7000; 9 Burnhill Court, Standish, Wigan WN6 0AN Tel: 01257 421161 Fax: 01257 421161 — MB BS 1980 Meerut; MD Manch. 1995; MD Meerut 1983; MRCOG 1987; DObst RCPSI 1986. (L.L.R.M. Medical College Meerut India) Cons. Obst. & Gyanecology Roy. Lond. Hosp., Lond. Socs: BMA; N. Eng. Obst. & Gyn. Soc.; Roy. Coll. Obst. & Gyn. Prev: Sen. Regist. (O & G) St. Mary's Hosp. Manch. (Flexible).; Regist. (O & G) Sharoe Green Hosp. Preston & Marston Green Hosp. Birm.; Sen. Reg (O & G) Roy. Bolton Hosp. (Flexible).

SANGHI, Pradeep Kumar Royal Albert Edward Infirmary, Wigan Lane, Wigan WN1 2NN Tel: 01942 244000 Fax: 01942 822340 — MB BS 1977 Delhi; MD (Med.) Delhi 1981; MRCPI 1986. Assoc. Specialist (Med.) Roy. Albert Edwd. Infirm. Wigan. Socs: Brit. Soc. Gastroenterol.; N. Eng. Gastroenterol. Soc. Prev: Regist. (Med.) Roy. Albert Edwd. Infirm. Wigan; Regist. (Gen. Med.) Bury Gen. Hosp.

SANGHVI, Mukesh Vadilal 86 Elgin Road, Seven Kings, Ilford IG3 8LN — MB BS 1985 Lond.

SANGOWAWA, Olugbenga Oluseun Aylesbury Partnership, Aylesbury Medical Centre, Taplow House, Thurlow Street, London SE17 2XE Tel: 020 7703 2205 — MB BS 1985 Ibadan; T(GP) 1994; DRCOG 1993; DFFP 1993.

SANGRA, Meharpal Singh 26 Marchmont Crescent, Edinburgh EH9 1HG — MB ChB 1996 Ed.

SANGRA, Rai Ahmad Sadiq Gate Medical Centre, 120 Washwood Heath Road, Saltley, Birmingham B8 1RE Tel: 0121 327

SANGSTER

4427; 8 Newmarsh Road, Sutton Coldfield B76 1XW Tel: 0121 351 6148 — MB BS 1965 Punjab; DO RCS Eng. 1968. (Nishtar Med. Coll.)

SANGSTER, Graeme Department Medicine for the Elderly, Arrowe Park Wirral Hospital NHS Trust, Upton, Wirral CH49 5PE Tel: 0151 678 5111; 8 Wicks Gardens, Formby, Liverpool L37 3QS — MB ChB 1975 Ed.; MRCP (UK) 1979; FRCP 1998. Cons. Phys. (Med. for Elderly) Arrowe Pk. Wirral Hosp. Merseyside.

SANGSTER, Ian David The New Bungalow, Salterhill, Covesea Road, Elgin IV30 5PT — MB ChB 1984 Ed. SHO (Gen. Med.) Harrogate Gen. Hosp.

SANGSTER, Pamela Jean (retired) 7A Valley Road, Stone ST15 0DQ Tel: 01785 815266 — MB ChB 1946 Birm. Prev: Clin. Asst. , N. Staffs Roy. Infirmary Stoke on Trent.

SANGTANI, Mr Hargun Jairamdas Ortho Relief Hospital & Research Centre, Opposite Ramkrishna Mission, Dhantoli, Nagpur 440 012, India Fax: 00 91 712 543314 Email: sargtani@nagpur.usnl.net.in; 44 Blackbird Close, Poole BH17 7YA — MB BS 1978 Nagpur; MS (Orthop.) Nagpur 1982; MChOrth. Liverp. 1988; FRCS Glas. 1986. (Govt. Medical College & Hospital, Nagpur, India) Cons. Orthop. Surg. Orth. Relief. Hosp. & Research Centre, Dhantoli, Nagpur, India. Socs: Overseas Fell. BOA; Life Mem. Indian Orthop. Assn. Prev: Sen. Regist. Our Lady's Childr. Hosp. Dub.; Sen. Regist. Pool & ChristCh. Hosp.; Sen. Regist. (Orthop.) Wrightington Hosp. Wigan.

SANIKOP, Shrishail Basavanneppa Royal Gwent Hospital, Newport NP20 2UB Tel: 01633 234234; 12A Llyn Berwyn Close, Rogerstone, Newport NP10 9AU Tel: 01633 897365 — MB BS 1978 Karnatak; MFFP 1995; MRCOG 1989. (Karnatak Med. Coll. Hubli, India) Assoc. Specialist (O & G) Roy. Gwent Hosp. Newport. Prev: Staff Grade Pract. (O & G) Roy. Gwent Hosp. Newport; Regist. (O & G) Falkirk Roy. Infirm.; SHO (O & G) Qu. Pk. Hosp. Blackburn.

SANJEEV, Doraiswamy c/o 114 Cross Street, Nottingham NG5 7BY — MB BS 1979 Bangalor; MB BS Bangalore 1979, DPM 1982; MRCPsych 1988. Sen. Psychiat. Yorkton Ment. Health Centre Saskatchewan, Canada.

SANJEEVA RAO, Veluvolu Earls House Hospital, Durham City, Durham DH1 5RE — MB BS 1972 Andhra.

SANKAR, Deivanayagam 30 Hawthorne Road, Rochdale OL11 5JQ — MB BS 1979 Madras.

SANKAR, Kanthimathinathan Newcastle General Hospital, Westgate Road, Newcastle upon Tyne NE4 6BE Tel: 0191 273 5516 Email: k.n.sankar@ncl.ac.uk; 62 Baronswood, Newcastle upon Tyne NE3 3UB — MB BS 1977 Sri Lanka; MRCP (UK) 1983; FRCP Lond. 1996. Cons. Genitourin. Phys. Newc. Gen. Hosp.; Clin. Lect. Univ. Newc. Socs: Med. Soc. Study VD. Prev: Cons. Genitourin. Phys. E.& W. Cumbria; Sen. Regist. (Genitourin. Med.) Newc. Gen. Hosp.

SANKARAN, Mohanan Department of Neurosurgery, North Staffordshire Royal Infirmary, Princes Road, Hartshill, Stoke-on-Trent ST4 7LN — MB BS 1982 Karnatak, India.

SANKARAYYA, Nanju (retired) 30 Augustus Road, Edgbaston, Birmingham B15 3PQ Tel: 0121 454 3101 — MB BChir 1958 Camb.; MB BChir Camb. 1959; MA Camb. 1960; MRCS Eng. LRCP Lond. 1958; MRCGP 1976. Prev: Capt. RAMC.

SANKEY, Alison Wilhelmina — MB BS 1977 Lond.; MRCPsych 1983. p/t Locum Cons. Child + Adolesc. Psychiat., Ashurst Child + Family Ment. Health Serv., Ashurst Hosp. Ashurst. SO40 7AR.

SANKEY, Arthur Octavius (retired) 34 Stormont Road, London N6 4NP Tel: 020 8340 0133 — MRCS Eng. LRCP Lond. 1945; MRCOG 1956, DObst 1948. Hon. Cons. O & G Newham HA. Prev: Cons. (Obst.) Newham Matern. Hosp. Lond.

SANKEY, Elizabeth Ann Department of Histopathology, The Pilgrim Hospital, Sibsey Road, Boston PE21 9QS Tel: 01205 364801 — MB BS 1985 Lond.; PhD Camb. 1981; BSc (Hons.) Bristol 1977; MRCPath 1993; FRCPath 2001. (Roy. Lond.) Cons. Path. (Histopath. & Cytopath.) Pilgrim Hosp. Boston. Socs: Assn. Clin. Path; Internat. Acad. Path. Prev: Cons. Path. (Histopath. & Cytopath.) Qu. Eliz. Hosp. King's Lynn; Cons. Path. (Histopath. & Cytopath.) Co. Hosp. Hereford.; Lect. & Hon. Sen. Regist. (Histopath.) Roy. Free Hosp.

SANKEY, Karen Lynne 1 Melbourne House, St. Martins Road, Gobowden, Oswestry SY11 3PH — MB BCh 1991 Wales; DRCOG 1994. Prev: Trainee GP/SHO Wrexham VTS.

SANKEY, Rowena Jane Alexandra Hospital, Woodrow Drive, Redditch B98 7UB Tel: 01527 503030 — MB ChB 1977 Liverp.; FRCP Ed 1998; FRCP Lond. 1998; FRCPCH 1998; MRCP (UK) 1981. Cons. Paediat. Alexandra Hosp. Redditch.; Hon. Sen. Clin. Lect. Inst. Child Health Univ. Birm.

SANKEY, Sarah Jane 43 Hayman Avenue, Leigh WN7 3UF — MB ChB 1997 Ed. (Edin.) SHO (Paed.) Forth Pk. Matern. Hosp. Fife.

SANKOH, Mohammed Abioseh (retired) Kirklees, 6 Linwood Grove, Darlington DL3 8DP Tel: 01325 381739 Fax: 01325 484479 — MB BS 1971 Newcastle Upon-Tyne; FRCP 1998 London; MRCP 1976 London; DTM & H 1973 London School of Hygiene & Tropical Medicine; MB BS 1971 Newcastle Upon-Tyne. Locum Cons.-Gen. Med. & chest Med., Medway Martine Hosp., Gillingham, Kent. Prev: Locum Cons. Elderly Med., ystradgynlais/Brewnshire War Memor. Hosp., Brecon, Wales.

SANKSON, Hayley Quarter Jack Surgery, Rodways Corner, Wimborne BH21 1AP Tel: 01202 882112 Fax: 01202 882368 — BM 1991 Soton.

SANMUGANATHAN, Philemon Sabapathy Dept of Medicine and Pharmacology, Level L, Royal Hallamshire Hospital, Sheffield S10 2JF — MRCP 1995 UK; MB BS Peradeniya 1986; MD 1992 Columbo. Hon.Specialist Regist. Socs: BMA; BPS- Brit. Pharmacol. Soc.; BASP- Brit. Assoc. of Stroke Phys.s. Prev: Sennior Lect. in Med. Uiniversity of Peraderivy, Sri Lanka.

SANSBURY, Henrietta Miriam 197 West Princes Street, Woodlands, Glasgow G4 9B2 — BM BCh 1994 Oxf.; BA Oxf. 1991; MRCGP 1998. Clin. Asst. Old Age Psychiat. Orchard Ho. Hosp., Stirling.

SANSBURY, Michael Arthur University Health Centre, Fulton House, Singleton Park, Swansea SA2 8PR Tel: 01792 295321 Fax: 01792 295854; Email: drsansbury@aol.com — MB ChB 1972 Ed.; BSc Ed. 1969. GP Univ. Coll. Swansea. Socs: Hon Pres. Brit. Assn. Health Servs. in Higher Educat.; BMA. Prev: Med. Off. 188th Gen. Disp. US Army Bamberg; Trainee GP Gwynedd VTS.

SANSOM, Alison Elizabeth Anne 12 Monks Mead, Brightwell Cum Sotwell, Wallingford OX10 0RL — MRCS Eng. LRCP Lond. 1956.

SANSOM, Christine Dinah West Wirral Group Practice, 33 Thingwall Road, Irby, Wirral CH61 3UE — MB ChB 1980 Liverp.; DRCOG 1982; DTM & H Liverp. 1997. Socs: Local Med. Comm.

SANSOM, David Thomas Royal Leamington Spa Rehabilitation Hospital, Heathcote Lane, Warwick CV34 6SR; 42 Tenbury Road, Kings Heath, Birmingham B14 6AH — MB BS 1982 Lond.; MRCPsych 1987. Cons. Psychiat. S. Warks. Prev: Sen. Regist. (Ment. Retardation) Monyhull Hosp. Birm.; Regist. (Psychiat.) N.wick Pk. Hosp. Harrow.

SANSOM, Hugh Edward Royal Shrewsbury Hospital, Mytton Oak Road, Shrewsbury SY3 8XQ Tel: 01743 261000 — MB BS 1986 Lond.; MRCP (UK) 1992; FRCR 1995. Cons. (Radiol.) Roy. Shrewsbury Hosp.

SANSOM, Jane Elizabeth Department of Dermatology, Bristol Royal Infirmary, Bristol BS2 8HW Tel: 0117 923 0000 Fax: 0117 928 2845; 2 Codrington Place, Clifton, Bristol BS8 3DE — MB ChB 1984 Bristol; FRCP 2001; MRCP (UK) 1988. Cons. (Dermat.) Bristol Roy. Infirm. Prev: Sen. Regist. (Dermat.) Bristol Roy. Infirm.; SHO (Med. & Neurol.) Frenchay Hosp. Bristol; Ho. Off. (Med.) Frenchay Hosp. Bristol.

SANSOM, Mr Julian Rupert Dale Farm, Thorpe-Next-Haddiscoe, Norwich NR14 6PY — MRCS Eng. LRCP Lond. 1965; FRCS Eng. 1973. (St. Thos.) Cons. (Gen. Surg.) Gt. Yarmouth & Waveney Health Dist. Prev: Surg. Regist. Artific. Kidney Unit Qu. Eliz. Hosp. Birm.; Sen. Regist. Surg. Professional Unit Qu. Eliz. Hosp. Birm.

SANSOME, Alison Donald Community Child Health, Idu Darwin Hospital, Fulburn, Cambridge CB1 5EE Tel: 01223 884162 Fax: 01223 884161; Wimbish Manor, Fowlmere Road, Shepreth, Royston SG8 6QL — BM BCh 1988 Oxf.; MA Camb. 1989, BA 1985. p/t Cons. in Community Paediat. Socs: Wom.s Med. Fed. (Sec.Camb. Distict). Prev: Regist. (Paediat.) Hammersmith Hosp. Lond.; Clin. Research Fell. Hammersmith Hosp. Lond.; Regist (Paediat) Addenbrookes Hosp. Camb.

SANSOME, Andrew Jonathan Thomas Department of Anaesthesia, Southampton General Hospital, Tremona Road, Southampton SO16 6YD Tel: 02380 777222 — MB ChB 1980 Sheff.; FRCA 1984. Cons. Anaesth. Soton. NHS Trust. Socs: Vasc. Anaesth. Soc.; Intens. Care Soc. Prev: Sen. Regist. (Anaesth.) Soton. Gen. Hosp.

SANSOME, David Anthony Woodruff (retired) 11 Meadowcourt Road, Oadby, Leicester LE2 2PD Tel: 0116 271 2994 — MB ChB 1956 Sheff.; MRCS Eng. LRCP Lond. 1956; FRCGP 1984, M 1968; AFOM RCP Lond. 1981; T(GP) 1991; DObst RCOG 1961. Med. Off. & Appt. Doctor EMAS to G.E.C. Power Eng. Whetstone; Med. Off. T. J. Brooks & Premier Screw Leicester. Prev: GP Leicester.

SANSOME, John Frederick (retired) Stonecroft, Post Office Lane, Lighthorne, Warwick CV35 0AP Tel: 01926 651424 Email: jsansome@doctors.org.uk — MB BS 1957 Lond.; DPH Lond. 1968. Prev: SCMO S. Warks. Health Care Trust.

SANSOME, Jonathan David Woodruff Weavers Medical Centre, 50 School Lane, Kettering NN16 0DH Tel: 01536 513494 Fax: 01536 416521 — MB ChB 1992 Leic.; MRCGP. (Leicester)

SANT, Andrew Mark 39 Ash Hayes Drive, Nailsea, Bristol BS48 2LQ; Little Mill, Egremont CA22 2NN Tel: 01946 820056 — BM 1995 Soton. GP Regist. Anne Burrow Thomas Health Centre Workington Cumbria. Socs: Med. Protec. Soc. Prev: SHO (Cardiol. & Neurol.) Poole Hosp. NHS Trust Poole; SHO (Med.) Roy. Bournemouth Hosp. Bournemouth.

SANT, Kathleen Elizabeth Monteagle Surgery, Tesimond Drive, Yateley GU46 6FE Tel: 01252 878992; 21 Crail Close, Wokingham RG41 2PZ — BM BCh 1985 Oxf.; MRCGP 1989; DCH RCP Lond. 1988. (Oxford)

SANT, Keith Godfrey Cross Street Health Centre, Cross Street, Dudley DY1 1RN Tel: 01384 459044 Fax: 01384 232467 — MRCS Eng. LRCP Lond. 1968. (Manch.) Prev: Ho. Off. (Obst.) Stepping Hill Hosp. Stockport.; Ho. Phys. Bury & Rossendale Gen. Hosps.; Ho. Surg. Withington Hosp. Manch.

SANTANA, Isidro Alberto 19 Cranebrook, Manor Road, Twickenham TW2 5DJ Tel: 020 8898 3422 — MD 1976 Autonomus Santa Domingo.

SANTANA GARCIA, Ramon 229 Prince Regent Lane, Plaistow, London E13 8SD — LMS 1983 La Laguna. Regist. (O & G) Harold Wood Hosp. Romford. Prev: SHO (O & G) Dist. Gen. Hosp. E.bourne & Fairfield Gen. Hosp. Bury; SHO (Anaesth.) Roy. Lancaster Infirm.

SANTANA HERNANDEZ, Diego Jose ENT Department, City Hospital, Greenbank Drive, Edinburgh EH10 5SB Tel: 0131 536 6000 — LMS 1988 La Laguna; DLO RCS Eng. 1995. Regist. (ENT) Roy. Infirm. Edin. NHS Trust. Prev: Career SHO (ENT) York Dist. Hosp.; SHO (ENT) Hull Roy. Infirm.

SANTANIELLO-NEWTON, Autilia 17 Lichfield Avenue, Hale, Altrincham WA15 8PG — State Exam Naples 1980.

SANTER, Mr Graham Julian Stoneleigh, Orient Drive, Liverpool L25 5NZ — MB ChB 1957 Liverp.; FRCS Eng. 1963; DObst RCOG 1959. Socs: Liverp. Med. Inst. & BMA.

SANTER, Miriam Clare — MB BChir 1993 Camb.; MRCGP 1996; DFFP 1995; DRCOG 1995. Higher Professional Train. Fell. Edin. Univ. Depart. Gen. Pract.

SANTER, Patricia Maureen Broxburn Health Centre, Holmes Road, Broxburn EH52 5JZ Tel: 01506 852016 Fax: 01506 852466; 9 Ravelrig Park, Balerno EH14 7DL Tel: 0131 449 5278 — MB BS 1970 Lond.; BSc (Physiol.) Lond. 1967; MFFP 1993; MRCGP 1976; Cert. Family Plann. JCC (Instruc. Doctor's Cert.) 1982; Dip. Ven. Soc. Apoth. Lond. 1982; DA Eng. 1974; Cert. FPA 1974; DObst RCOG 1972. (Lond. Hosp.) Locum CMO Family Plann. & Well Wom. Serv. Socs: Scott. Family Plann. Med. Soc. Prev: Co-ordinating Doctor Edin. Brook Advis. Centre; Clin. Asst. (Genitourin. Med.) Ipswich Hosp.; Clin. Asst. (Genitourin. Med.) Roy. Shrewsbury & Wrekin Hosp.

SANTHAN GOPAL, Mr Kakkadasam Srinvasaiyengar Wrexham Maelor Hospital, Croesnewydd Road, Wrexham LL13 7TD — MD 1982 All India Med. Scs.; MB BS Bangalore 1976; FRCS Ed. 1986.

SANTHIAPILLAI, Domingo c/o Mrs Margaret Rajapakse, Red Wood Day Unit, St John's Hospital, Wood St., Chelmsford CM2 9BG — MB BS 1968 Ceylon.

SANTHOUSE, Alastair Marc Maudsley Hospital, London SE5 Tel: 020 7703 6333 — MB BChir 1993 Camb.; MB BChir Camb. 1992; MRCP 1995; MRCPsych 1998. (Camb. Univ.) Specialist Regist. Rotat. (Psychiat.) Maudsley Hosp. Prev: SHO Rotat. (Psychiat.) Maudsley Hosp. Lond.; SHO Rotat. (Med.) Roy. Lond. Hosp.

SANTIAGO, Juan Carlos 12B Valmar Road, London SE5 9NG — LMS 1988 Granada.

SANTINI, Mr Alasdair John Ario Inglis Green House, Inglis Green Road, Edinburgh EH14 2EP — MB ChB 1992 Sheff.; FRCS Glas.

1997; FRCS Eng. 1997. (Sheff.) Mersey Deanery Specialist Regist. Rotat. (Orthop.) 1998. Socs: Assoc. Fell. of Brit. Orthopaedic Assn. (BOA); Brit. Med. Assn. Prev: SHO Rotat. (Gen. Surg.) Roy. Hallamsh. Hosp. Sheff.; SHO & Demonst. (Anat.) Univ. Sheff.; SHO (Orthop. & A & E) Roy. Hallamsh. Hosp. Sheff.

SANTIS, Georghios 19 King's Avenue, London W5 — MB ChB 1983 Leic.; MRCP (UK) 1986. Research Fell. Brompton Hosp. & Nat. Heart & Lung Inst. Lond.

SANTORI, Louise Bernadette Newtown Surgery, 147 Lawn Avenue, Great Yarmouth NR30 1QP Tel: 01493 853191 Fax: 01493 331861 — MB ChB 1991 Birm.; ChB Birm. 1991; MRCGP 1996.

SANTOS, Joseph Pele Dos 33 Wellington Gardens, Victoria Way, London SE7 7PJ — MB BS 1996 Lond.

SANTOS, Sean Rice Anaesthetic Department, Furness General Hospital, Dalton Lane, St Helier, Jersey JE2 3QS Tel: 01224 870870. — MB BS 1987 Lond.; MA Camb. 1987, BA 1983. (St. Geo. Hosp. Lond.) Staff Grade. (Anaesth.) FGH. Socs: BMA; Assn. Anaesth. Prev: Regist. (Anaesth.) Gen. Hosp. St. Helier, Jersey; Regist. Rotat. (Anaesth.) St. Mary's Hosp. Lond.; SHO (Intens. Care) Middlx. Hosp. Lond.

SANTOS RAMON, Angel Cassel Hospital, 1 Ham Common, Richmond TW10 7JF — LMS 1989 Autonoma Madrid; MRCPsych 1995. Sen. Regist. (Psychother.) N. Thames (W.) Regional Psychother. Train. Scheme. Prev: Regist. Rotat. N. Lond. Teachg. Hosp. UCH.

SANTOSH, Celestine Gnanamuthu Department of Neuroradiology, Middlesbrough General Hospital, Middlesbrough TS5 5AZ Tel: 01642 850850; Flat 3, Middlesbrough General Hosptial, Middlesbrough TS5 5AZ Tel: 01642 850850 — MB BS 1983 Poona; FRCR 1990. Cons. Neuroradiol. Middlesbrough Gen. Hosp. Socs: BMA; Med. Protec. Soc.; Roy. Coll. Radiol. Prev: Lect. MRI Univ. Edin.; Asst. Prof. Radiol. (SLTMIST, India).

SANUSI, Mr Fatai Abegboyega Dept. Obstetrics & Gynacology, West Hartfordshire NHS Trust Tel: 01923 244366; 37B Chaplin Road, Willseden, London NW3 5PP — MB BS 1986 Lagos; MRCOG 1992. (Colege of Med. Univ. Lagos) Cons. Obst./ Gynaecologist, W.Herts. NHS Trust, Watford. Socs: Feto-Matern. Med. Soc.; BSCCP. Prev: SpR -St Geo.'s Hosp.; Regist. Barnet & Edgeware Hosps.; SHO Pontefract & Dewsbury Hosps.

SANVILLE, Philip Roland 1 Croft Road, Wilmslow SK9 6JJ — MB BS 1982 Lond.; FRCR Lond. 1991; MRCP (UK) 1988; MRCGP 1986; DCH RCP Lond. 1986; DRCOG 1984. (St. Geo.) Cons. Radiol. Stepping Hill Hosp. Stockport. Prev: Sen. Regist. Rotat. (Radiol.) Manch.; Cook Fell. Interven. Radiol.

SANYAL, Alok 4 White Stone Close, Knowsley, Prescot L34 7HG Tel: 0151 546 0289 — MB BS 1965 Calcutta; DGO 1967; FRCOG 1983, M 1970.

SANYAL, Aparna 15 The Chase, Edgware HA8 5DW — MB ChB 1997 Bristol.

SANYAL, Buddhadeb Kettering General Hospital, Rothwell Road, Kettering NN16 8UZ Tel: 01536 422000; 120 Brambleside, Kettering NN16 9BP Tel: 01536 519811 — MB BS 1968 Sambalpur; DLO RCS Eng. 1980. Regist. (Otolaryngol.) Kettering Gen. Hosp. Socs: Assoc. Mem. Brit. Assn. Otolaryngol. Prev: SHO (ENT) King's Coll. Hosp. Lond.; SHO (ENT) FarnBoro. Hosp.

SANYAL, Debasis Royal Manchester Childrens Hospital, Hospital Road, Pendlebury, Manchester M27 4HA — MD 1992 Manch.; BSc Manch. 1980, MB ChB 1982; MRCPath 1989; Dip. Bact. Manch. 1989. Cons. Microbiol. Roy. Manch. Childr. Hosp. Socs: Hosp. Infec. Soc. & Brit. Soc. Antimicrob. Chemother. Prev: SHO. (Clin. Path.) Manch. Roy. Infirm.; Regist. (Microbiol.) Univ. Hosp. of Wales Cardiff.; Sen. Regist. (Microbiol.) Pub. Health Laborat. N. Gen. Hosp. Sheff.

SANYAL, Karuna Prasad 11 Oak Dene Close, Hornchurch RM11 1HD Tel: 0140 24 51675 — MB BS 1959 Calcutta; DA Eng. 1968. (Calcutta) Assoc. Specialist Anaesth. Dept. OldCh. Hosp. Romford. Socs: BMA. Prev: Cas. Off. Boston Gen. Hosp.; SHO (Anaesth.) Dryburn Hosp. Durh.; Regist. (Anaesth.) Burton-on-Trent Gen. Hosp.

SANZERI, Marcus 24 Rhodes Street, Hightown, Castleford WF10 5LL — MB ChB 1990 Liverp.

SAPARAMADU, P V D D Linden Road Surgery, 13 Linden Road, Bedford MK40 2DQ Tel: 01234 273272 Fax: 01234 340339 — MB BS 1967 Ceylon; MB BS 1967 Ceylon.

SAPER

SAPER, Jerzy (retired) 49 Tyrwhitt Road, London SE4 1QD Tel: 020 8692 5508 — MRCS Eng. LRCP Lond. 1973; MD Warsaw 1958; Med. Dip. Warsaw 1951. Prev: Sen. Regist. (Neurol.) Med. Sch. Warsaw, Poland.

SAPERIA, Joseph (retired) Flat 5, Ambassador Court, Century Close, London NW4 2EE Tel: 020 8202 6263 — MB BCh BAO Belf. 1948; MRCGP 1955. Prev: SHO (ENT) S.end Gen. Hosp.

SAPEY, Elizabeth Homelands, Magdalen Road, Tilney St Lawrence, King's Lynn PE34 4RE — MB BS 1998 Lond.; MB BS Lond 1998.

SAPHERSON, David Andrew 120 High Street, Knaresborough HG5 0HN — MB ChB 1980 Sheff.

SAPHIER, Emanuel (retired) 20 The Vale, Ovingdean, Brighton BN2 7AB Tel: 01273 305240 — MRCS Eng. LRCP Lond. 1940. Prev: Flight Lt. R.A.F.V.R.

SAPHIER, Herta (retired) Trewyn, Llanishen, Chepstow NP16 6QG Tel: 01600 860489 Email: chipstrewyn@aol.com — MB ChB 1948 St. And. Prev: Clin. Research Asst. Bristol Roy. Infirm. & Hosp. Sick Childr.

SAPIER, Nathan Victor (retired) 10 Sandmoor Mews, Leeds LS17 7SA Tel: 0113 268 8877 — MB ChB Leeds 1944. Prev: Ho. Phys. Leeds Gen. Infirm.

SAPPER, Helen 3 Boston Gardens, Chiswick, London W4 2QJ Tel: 020 8742 8313 Fax: 020 8742 8543 Email: helensapper@compuserve.com — MRCS Eng. LRCP Lond. 1959; MSc Lond. 1992, MB BS 1959; FRCGP 1992, M 1973; DHMSA 1997. (Roy. Free) p/t Chairm. Indep. Review Panel for Continuing Care Ealing, Hammersmith & Hounslow HA; Med. Qual. Panel Mem. Appeal Serv. Socs: Fell.Roy. Soc. of Med. Prev: GP Acton Health Centre Lond.; Clin. Asst. Ealing Child Guid. Centre; SHO (Path.) King Edwd. Memor. Hosp. Ealing.

SAPPER, Miriam Esho South Saxon House Surgery, 150A Bexhill Road, St Leonards-on-Sea TN38 8BL Tel: 01424 441361 Fax: 01424 461799 — MB ChB 1966 Baghdad.

SAPRE, S Westway, Maghull, Liverpool L31 0DJ.

SAPSFORD, David John Department of Anaesthesia, Box 93 Level E4, Addenbrooke's Hospital, Cambridge CB2 2QQ Tel: 01223 217889 Fax: 01223 217223 — MB BS 1980 Lond.; FFA RCS Eng. 1987. Sen. Lect. (Anaesth.) Univ. Camb.; Hon. Cons. Anaesth. Addenbrooke's Hosp. Camb. Prev: Lect. (Anaesth.) Leeds Univ.

SAPSFORD, Derrick Willesborough Health Centre, Bentley Road, Willesborough, Ashford TN24 0HZ Tel: 01233 621626 Fax: 01233 622930 — MB ChB 1960 St. And.; DObst RCOG 1963.

SAPSFORD, Ian 27 Trumps Green Avenue, Virginia Water GU25 4EP Tel: 01344 844849; 16A Sandown Avenue, Hornchurch RM12 4JH — BM 1983 Soton.; T(GP) 1991.

SAPSFORD, Mr Ralph Neville 20 Birkdale Road, London W5 1JZ; 66 Harley Street, London W1N 1AE Tel: 020 7631 4820 — MB ChB 1962 Cape Town; ChM Cape Town 1976; FRCS Eng. 1967; FRCS Ed. 1967. (Cape Town) Cons. & Sen. Lect. (Cardiothoracic Surg.) Hammersmith Hosp. & Roy. Postgrad. Med. Sch. Lond.; Hon. Cons. (Cardiothoracic Surg.) St. Mary's Hosp. & Med. Sch. Lond. Prev: Sen. Regist. (Cardiothoracic Surg.) Hammersmith Hosp. Lond.

SAPSFORD, Robert Andrew Rectory Meadow Surgery, School Lane, Amersham HP7 0HG Tel: 01494 727711 Fax: 01494 431790 — MB ChB 1976 Otago; MRCGP 1980; DRCOG 1979; DCH Eng. 1979. (Otago) Clin. Asst. (Gastroenterol.) Amersham Hosp. Socs: Chiltern Med. Soc.

SAPSFORD, Robert John St. James's University Hospital, Leeds LS9 7TF — MB BS 1990 Lond.; BSc 1996 London. Specialist Regist. Cons. Cardiol. St James Univ. Hosp. Leeds.

SAPSFORD, Mr Wayne Flat 2 King's House, 1 Brightlingsea Place, Limehouse, London E14 8DB — 1991 (MB) Camb.; 1992 (BChir) Camb.; MB 1991, BChir 1992; MA Camb. 1992, BA 1988; FRCS Eng. 1997. (Roy. Lond. Hosp. Med. Coll.) Research Fell. Socs: Fell. Roy. Soc. Med.; Freeman Worshipful Soc. Apoths.; Assoc. of Surg. Of GB & I. Prev: Specialist Regist. The Luton & Dunstable Hosp. NHS Trust.

SAPUAY, Biennita Corpuz 65 Roxburgh Road, London SE27 0LE — MB BS 1995 Lond.

SAQIB, Mohammad Najum-Us 31 Maidencastle, Blackthorn, Northampton NN3 8EH Tel: 01604 414520 — MB BS 1987 Punjab; MRCP (UK) 1992.

SAQR, Luna Sami Flat T, 20 Rosedale, Dundee DD1 4LR — MB ChB 1996 Dundee. (University of Dundee) SHO Anaesth. Dept. Kirkcaldy.

SARA RIVERO, Javier Tameside General Hospital, Fountain St., Ashton-under-Lyne OL6 9RW — LMS 1990 Saragossa.

SARAF, Iftikhar Mahmood Lane End Medical Group, 25 Edgwarebury Lane, Edgware HA8 8LJ Tel: 020 8958 4233 Fax: 020 8905 4657 — MB ChB 1976 Liverp.; MRCGP 1982; DRCOG 1979. GP; Clin. Asst.-Clerk Clinic Edgeware Commity Hosp.; GP Trainer.

SARAF, Rajesh Alexandra Group Medical Practice, Glodwick Health Centre, 137 Glodwick Road, Oldham OL4 1YN Tel: 0161 909 8388 Fax: 0161 909 8414 — MB BS 1979 Delhi.

SARAF, Tariq Yusef 26 Ashdown Drive, Wordsley, Stourbridge DY8 5QY; Department of Psychiatry, Bushey Fields Hospital, Bushey Fields Road, Dudley DY1 2LZ — MB BS 1984 Punjab; MRCPsych 1993.

SARAFIAN, Anthony Haig (retired) — MB BS 1961 Lond.; DObst RCOG 1964.

SARAGOUDAS, Sarah 5 Denton Court, 14 Cranes Drive, Surbiton KT5 8AL — MB BS 1996 Lond.

SARAI, Ravinder Kaur 138 Broadway W., Walsall WS1 4DN — MB ChB 1997 Birm.

SARAKI, Olubukola Adebisi Alabuwale 123A Ashley Gardens, Thirleby Road, London SW1P 1HL Tel: 020 7931 0654 Fax: 020 7233 7447 — MB BS 1988 Lond.

SARAN, Sudhir Springfield Farmhouse, Ercall Heath, Newport TF10 8NQ Tel: 01952 550654 Email: saran999@yahoo.com — MB BS 1971 Patna.

SARANG, Amman 150 Runnymede Road, Darras Hall, Ponteland, Newcastle upon Tyne NE20 9HN Tel: 01661 24677 Email: ammansarang@hotmail.com; 11 Barons Keep, Gliddon Road, London W14 9AT Tel: 020 7602 7981 — MB ChB 1991 Dundee; FRCA. Specialist Regist. Roy. Brompton Hosp. Socs: RSM; Intens. Care Soc.; BMA. Prev: Specialist Regist. Centr. Middx, W. Middx, Char. Cross & Roy. Marsden Hosps. Lond. & QEII Welwyn Garden City; Specialist Regist. (Anaesth.) St. Mary's Hosp. Lond.

SARANG, Kavita 150 Runnymede Road, Ponteland, Newcastle upon Tyne NE20 9HN — MB ChB 1992 Manch.

SARANGAPANI, Mr Krishnamoorthi Department of Plastic Surgery, Middlesbrough General Hospital, Ayresome Green Lane, Middlesbrough TS5 5AZ Tel: 01642 854316; Cleveland Nuffield Hospital, Junction Road, Norton, Stockton-on-Tees TS20 1QB Tel: 01642 360100 Fax: 01642 556535 — MB BS 1962 Madras; MS Madras 1967; FRCS Eng. 1970. (Madras Med. Coll.) Cons. Plastic Surg. S. Tees Acute Hosps. NHS Trust Middlesbrough; Hon. Cons. Plastic Surg. Newc. AHA (T). Socs: Brit. Assn. Plastic Surg. & Brit. Assn. Aesthetic Plastic Surgs.; Assoc. Mem. Brit. Soc. Surg. Hand. Prev: Sen. Regist. & Regist. (Plastic Surg.) Newc. AHA (T); SHO (Plastic Surg.) Liverp. Regional Centre Whiston Hosp. Prescot.

SARANGI, Bimal Behari Trafford General Hospital, Moorside Road, Davyhulme, Manchester M41 5SL Tel: 0161 748 4022; 6 Kilworth Avenue, Sale, Manchester M33 4SE Tel: 0161 282 6065 — MB BS 1955 Calcutta; DA (UK) 1971. Assoc. Specialist (Anaesth.) Trafford Gen. Hosp. Manch. Prev: Regist. (Anaesth.) Worthing & Pk. Hosp. Manch.

SARANGI, Kashyap Kumar 6 Kilworth Avenue, Sale M33 4SE — MB ChB 1993 Manch.

SARANGI, Mr Partha Pratim Department of Orthopaedic Surgery, Bristol Royal Infirmary, Marlborough St., Bristol BS2 8HW Tel: 0117 923 0000 — MB ChB 1984 Manch.; MD Bristol 1995; FRCS (Orth.) 1994; FRCS Eng. 1988; FRCS Ed. 1988. Cons. Orthop. Surg. Bristol Roy. Infirm. Prev: Sen. Regist. (Orthop. Surg.) Bristol Roy. Infirm.; Career Regist. (Orthop. Surg.) Bristol Roy. Infirm.; Peri Fell.sh. Regist. (Surg.) Cardiff Roy. Infirm.

SARANTIS, Nicos Glaxo Wellcome Research Development, Greenford Road, Greenford UB6 0HE Tel: 020 8966 3284 Fax: 020 8966 3699; 6 Elham Close, Bromley BR1 2TQ — MB BChir 1983 Camb.; MBA 1992; MA Camb. 1985, MB BChir 1983; MRCP (UK) 1986; Dip. Pharm. Med. RCP (UK) 1992. Europ. Dir. Infec. Dis. & Rheum.

SARAOGI, Mr Krishna Kumar 144 Harley Street, London W1N 1AH Tel: 020 7935 0023 Fax: 01753 571913; Kailash, Church Grove, Wexham, Slough SL3 6LF Tel: 01753 579732 Fax: 01753 571913 — MB BS 1962 Calcutta; MS Patna 1966. (R.G.

Kar Med. Coll. Calcutta) JP. Socs: Windsor. Med. Soc. Prev: Regist. Orthop. Hammersmith Hosp. Lond. & Wexham Pk. Hosp. Slough.

SARASOLA LOPETEGUI, Jose Angel Royal London Homeopathic Hospital, Great Ormond St., London WC1N 3HR — LMS 1993 Basque Provinces.

SARATH MOHAN, Moorkoth 5 Birkdale Close, Mickleover, Derby DE3 5YG Tel: 01332 521571 — MB BS 1979 Calicut; DLO RCS Eng. 1993.

SARATHCHANDRA, Cuda Bandara Consultant Psychiatrist, Clacton and District Hospital, Tower Road, Clacton-on-Sea CO15 1LH Tel: 01255 253527 Fax: 01255 421767 — MB BS 1975 Sri Lanka; MRCPsych 1985; FRCPsych 1999. (Univ. Sri Lanka, Peradeniya) Cons. Psychiat. Clacton Dist. Hosps. Essex. Socs: Brit. Med. Assn.; Med. Protec. Soc.; Brit. Assn. of PsychoPharmacol. Prev: Cons. Psychiat. Yarmouth Regional Hosp. Nova Scotia, Canada.

SARATHCHANDRA, Sunila Felicia Community Mental Health Centre, Holmer Court, Essex St., Colchester CO3 3BT Tel: 01206 287270 Fax: 01206 287272; 12 Woodview Close, Colchester CO4 4QW Tel: 01206 854308 Fax: 01206 854308 — MB BS 1976 Sri Lanka; Dip. Psychol. Med. RCSI 1995. Staff Psychiat. Community Ment. Health Centre Colchester. Socs: Affil. Roy. Coll. Psychiats. Prev: Clin. Asst. (Psychiat.) NE Essex & Mid Essex Ment. Health Trusts; Regist. (Psychiat.) NE Essex Ment. Health Trust Colchester.

SARATHY, Partha Liversedge Health Centre, Valley Road, Liversedge WF15 6DF Tel: 01924 404900; 173 Whitelee Road, Batley WF17 8AS — MB BS 1967 Bangalor; MB BS Bangalore 1967; DTM & H Liverp. 1975; DTCD Wales 1974. (Bangalore Med. Coll.) Socs: BMA.

SARATHY, Shaefali 128 Ashlands Road, Northallerton DL6 1HD Tel: 01609 770471 — MB ChB 1989 Leic.; BSc (Med. Sci.) Genetics Leic. 1986; FRCA (II) 1996; MRCGP 1994; DA (UK) 1995; DRCOG 1994. (Univ. Leic.) Specialist Regist. (Anaesth.) N. Deanery Rotat. Prev: Trainee GP N.allerton VTS; SHO (O & G & Paediat.) Friarage Hosp.; SHO (Anaesth.) S. Tees Hosps. Middlesbrough.

SARAVANAMATTU, Kurunathevy Victoria Road Health Centre, Victoria Road, Washington NE37 2PU Tel: 0191 415 4477; 33 Polwarth Drive, Brunton Park, Gosforth, Newcastle upon Tyne NE3 5NJ — MB BS 1967 Ceylon. GP Washington, Tyne & Wear.

SARAVANAMUTHU, Jamnarathi 4 Imperial Way, Kenton, Harrow HA3 9SW — BM BS 1986 Nottm.

SARAVANAMUTTU, Kasilingham Manohara Ward 34, Newcastle General Hospital, Westgate Road, Newcastle upon Tyne NE4 6BE — MB BS 1965 Ceylon.

SARAVANAN, Ketharanathan 70 Turnpike Link, Croydon CR0 5NY; 21 Minster Court, Liverpool L7 3QB — MB BS 1990 Lond.; MRCP (UK) 1995; DCH RCP Lond. 1993. Regist. (Paediat.) Alder Hey Childr.'s Hosp. Prev: Regist. (Neonates) Liverp. Wom.'s Hosp.; Regist. (Paediat.) Arrowe Pk. Hosp. Wirral.

SARDA, Kailash Little Roseworth Surgery, Little Roseworthy, 22 Meadow Lane, Sudbury CO10 2TD Tel: 01787 310000 Fax: 01787 75245; 54 Friars Street, Sudbury CO10 2AG Tel: 01787 74252 — LM 1969 Rotunda; BA, MB BCh BAO Dub. 1967; DObst RCOG 1973. (TC Dub.) Cons. Med. Off. Dixon-Harris Gp., Shear Chem., Johnson Mathie Gp.; Companies & Dell Gp. Nursing Homes Sudbury. Prev: Clin. Asst. St. Leonard's Hosp. & Walnutree Hosp. Sudbury; Med. Off. Red Cross; SHO (O & G) Rotunda Hosp. Dub.

SARDAR, Jagadish Vijaya Kumar 22 Inverclyde Royal Hospital Complex, Larkfield Road, Greenock PA16 0XN — MB BS 1984 Sri Venkateswara.

SARDAR, Sohail Aabud 12 Sutherland Avenue, Glasgow G41 4JH — MB ChB 1989 Glas.

SARDER, M O G The Surgery, 433 New Cross Road, London SE14 6TD — MBBS; DTCD, DGM, DFFP. (Sir Sallimullah Medical College, Dhaka)

SARDESAI, Bina Suhrud c/o Drive Meena Prabhu, Ajantha, Walpole Gardens, Twickenham TW2 5SL — MB BS 1985 Poona; MRCP (UK) 1987.

SARDESAI, Suhrud Hanmant c/o Dr Meena Prabhu, Ajantha, Walpole Gardens, Twickenham TW2 5SL — MB BS 1982 Poona; MRCP (UK) 1986.

SARDI, Armando Health Care International, Beardmore St., Clydebank G81 4HX — Medico y Cirujano National Univ. 1980.

SAREEN, Sabina Ditlev Regional Medical Centre, RAF St Athan, Barry CF62 4WA Tel: 01446 797471 Fax: 01446 797459; Officers Mess, RAF St. Athan, Barry CF62 4WA — MB BCh 1992 Wales; DRCOG 1996. (UWCM)

SARFRAZ, Azhir Manzur 43 Hillhouse Drive, Billericay CM12 0BA — MB BS 1994 Lond.

SARFRAZ, Mr Hussein Syed 31 Pearson Road, Ipswich IP3 8NL — MB BS 1986 Punjab; FRCS Ed. 1993.

SARFRAZ, Manzur-Ul-Hassan South Green Surgery, 14-18 Grange Road, Billericay CM11 2RE Tel: 01277 651702 Fax: 01277 631894; 43 Hill House Drive, Billericay CM12 0BA Tel: 01277 651702 Fax: 01277 631894 — MB BS 1973 Lond.

SARFRAZ, Muhammad Aamer Portnalls Unit, Farnborough Hospital, Orpington BR6 8ND — MB BS 1987 Punjab.

SARGAISON, Jane Melissa Elm Croft, Elm Grove, Berkhamsted HP4 1AE — MB BChir 1991 Camb.; BA Camb. 1988, MB BChir 1991; MRCP Lond. 1994. Med. Co-ordinator Merlin, Rwanda. Prev: SHO (Endocrinol.) Ealing Hosp. NHS Trust; SHO (Renal) Guy's Hosp. Trust Lond.; SHO (Med.) Hammersmith Hosp. & Postgrad. Med. Sch. Lond.

SARGAISON, Mark Frederick Robert East Donnington Street Clinic, East Donnington Street, Darvel KA17 0JR Tel: 01560 320205 Fax: 01560 321643 — MB BCh BAO 1988 Belf.; MB BCh Belf. 1988.

SARGANT, Emma Frances Rowan Little Horton Lane Surgery, The Horton Park Centre, 99 Horton Park Avenue, Bradford BD7 3EG Tel: 01274 504949 — MB ChB 1988 Sheff. GP Princip.

SARGANT, Nicholas Robert The White House, 97 South Street, Eastbourne BN21 4LR Tel: 01323 720606 Fax: 01323 412331; 61 Park Avenue, Eastbourne BN21 2XH — MRCS Eng. LRCP Lond. 1971; BSc (Biochem.) Lond. 1968, MB BS 1971; DObst RCOG 1974; DCH Eng. 1973.

SARGEANT, Christopher Frederick 52 Beaufort Avenue, Kenton, Harrow HA3 8PF — MB BS 1989 Lond.; DRCOG 1994.

SARGEANT, Mr Ian David 9 Dowding Road, Biggin Hill, Westerham TN16 3BE Tel: 01959 573518 — MB BS 1986 Lond.; FRCS Ed. 1992; DAvMed FOM RCP Lond. 1993; FRCS (Orth.) 1996. Cons. (Trauma & Orthop. Surg.) MDHU PeterBoro. Dist. Hosp. Socs: Assoc. Mem. BOA; Milit. Surg. Soc. Prev: Sen. Regist. (Orthop. & Trauma) Qu.s Med. Centre Nottm.; Regist. (Orthop.) RAF Hosp. Wegburg & RAF Hosp. Halton & Ely; Unit Med. Off. RAF St. Athan.

SARGEANT, Ian Robert Dept of Gastoenterology, Lister Hospital, Correys Mill Lane, Stevenage SG1 4AB Tel: 01438 781245 Fax: 01438 781439; 3 Engel Park, Mill Hill, London NW7 2HE Email: isargent@ntlworld.com — FRCP (UK) 2001; MB BS 1994 Lond.; BSc Lond. 1994, MB BS 1983; MRCP (UK) 1988, MD 1994. (Middlesex Hospital Medical School) Cons. (Gastroenterol. & Gen. Med.) Lister Hosp. Stevenage. Socs: BMA; BSG; RCOP.

SARGEANT, Matthew Paul Wellfield Road Resource Centre, Wellfield Road, Carmarthen SA31 1DS — MB BS 1981 Lond.; MA Camb. 1982; FRCPC 1994; MRCPsych 1987. (Selwyn Coll. Camb. & Lond. Hosp.) Cons. Psychiat. St. David's Hosp. Carmarthen. Prev: Cons. Psych. Millbrook Psychiat. Unit Sutton in Ashfield; Chief of Psychiat. Chatham, New Brunswick; Cons. Psychiat. Merthyr Tydfil.

SARGEANT, Rhona Jean Psychological Therapies Service, Department of Psychiatry, Royal South Hants Hospital, Southampton Tel: 02380 825787 Fax: 02380 825672; 3 Bower Gardens, Salisbury SP1 2RL — MB ChB 1989 Sheff.; BMedSci Sheff. 1989; MRCPsych 1996; MMedSci 1998. (Univ. Sheff.) p/t Flexible Sen. Regist. (Psychother.) S. & W. RHA. Socs: MRCPsych. Prev: Regist (Psych) S&W RHA; Regist. (Psychiat.) W. Midl. RHA; SHO (Psychiat.) N. Birm. HA.

SARGEN, Frances Elizabeth 2 Conifer Close, North Cove, Beccles NR34 7PW — MB ChB 1994 Sheff.

SARGEN, Frances Elizabeth Shelley Road Surgery, Shelley Road, Worthing BN11 4BS Tel: 01903 234844 — MB ChB Sheff.; DCH 1999; DRCOG 1996; MRCGP 2000; DFFP 2000. p/t Gen. Pract. Retainee; Clin. Asst., Family Plann., Centr. Clinic Worthing; Clin. Asst., Dematology, Worthing Gen. Hosp. Prev: GP Regist.; SHO Neonatology, S.ampton; Sho Med., St Richards Hosp., Chichester.

SARGENT, Abigail Margaret Foster The Bedford Park Surgery, 55 South Parade, Chiswick, London W4 5LH; 33 Mount Park Road, London W5 2RS Tel: 020 8997 4695 Email: asargent@waitrose.com — MB ChB 1977 Bristol; MFOM RCP Lond. 1996, AFOM 1991;

SARGENT

DCH RCP Lond. 1981; DRCOG 1980. Socs: BMA; Soc. Occupat. Med. Prev: GP N.olt; Dep. Head of Med. Serv. John Lewis Partnership.

SARGENT, Catherine Sarah 3 Steynings Way, London N12 7LN — BM BCh 1998 Oxf.; BM BCh Oxf 1998.

SARGENT, Claire Blanche (retired) 8 Manse Road, Stoke Newington, London N16 7QD — MB BS 1984 Lond.; MB BS (Hons.) Lond. 1984; BSc Lond. 1981. Prev: Regist. (Histopath.) Univ. Coll. Hosp. Lond.

SARGENT, David Edward (retired) The Tynings, Far Forest, Kidderminster DY14 9TR Tel: 01299 266297 — MRCS Eng. LRCP Lond. 1949; DObst RCOG 1950. Prev: Jun. Obst. Ho. Phys. St. Thos. Hosp.

SARGENT, Helen Margaret Forge House, Marsh Gibbon, Bicester OX27 0ET — MB BCh BAO 1956 NUI; MFFP 1993; DA Eng. 1960. (Univ. Coll. Dub.) SCMO (Family Plann. & Community Child Health) Oxon. Community NHS Trust & Oxf. Radcliffe Hosp. Trust. Socs: Brit. Paediat. Assn.; Nat. Assn. Family Plann. Doctors; Brit. Agencies Adopt. & Fostering. Prev: Regist. (Anaesth.) S.mead Hosp. Bristol; SHO (Paediat.) Roy. Devon & Exeter Hosp.; SHO (O & G) Hereford Co. Hosp.

SARGENT, Jenefer Caroline Tel: 020 7905 2946 Fax: 020 7833 9469; 96 Wanstead Park Avenue, London E12 5EF Tel: 020 8808 1333 Email: jenefer@cisse.freeserve.co.uk — MB BChir 1992 Camb.; MA Camb. 1988; MRCP (UK) 1994. Specialist Regist. Paediatric Neurodisablity. The Wolfson Centre, Gt. Ormond St NHS Trust. Socs: Roy. Coll. Paediat. & Child Health; BMA; Brit. Assn. of Community Child Health. Prev: Sen. Regist. (Community Paediat.) City & Hackney Community Servs. NHS Trust; Regist. (Paediat.) Whipps Cross Hosp. Lond.; SHO Respirat. Unit & CICU Gt. Ormond St. Lond.

SARGENT, John Hector Philip Scott The Old Rectory, Bighton, Alresford SO24 9RB — MRCS Eng. LRCP Lond. 1971; MSc (Rehabil.) Soton. 1997. (Guy's Hosp.) Dir. Sandaire plc; Chairm. Kitnocks Hse. Ltd. & Pentree Hse. Rehabil. Ltd.; Chairm. Med. Screening Servs. Ltd.; Chairm. Nursing Home Servs. Ltd. Prev: GP Ropley.

SARGENT, Mr Nicholas Jon 54 Stanley Avenue, Greenford UB6 8N; 54 Stanley Avenue, Greenford UB6 8NP — MB ChB 1992 Leeds; FRCS FRCS Ed (Ophth) 2000. (Leeds) Specialist Regist., N.ampton Gen. Hosp. Socs: Med. Defence Union; BMA; Med. Contact Lens & Ocular Surface Assn. Prev: SHO (Ophth.) Centr. Middlx. Hosp.; SHO (Ophth.) Roy. Eye Infirm. Dorchester; SHO (Ophth.) Roy. United Hosp. Bath & W. Norwich Hosp.

SARGENT, Norman William, VRD (retired) Forge House, Marsh Gibbon, Bicester OX27 0ET — LMSSA 1954 Lond.; DA Eng. 1962. Prev: Dir. Clin. Studies Ortho Pharmaceut. Ltd. High Wycombe.

SARGENT, Peter Anthony University Department of Psychiatry, Warneford Hospital, Warneford Lane, Headington, Oxford OX3 7JX Tel: 01865 226676 Fax: 01865 793101 Email: peter.sargent@psychiatry.oxford.ac.uk — MB ChB 1986 Birm.; MRCPsych 1994; DCH RCP Lond. 1989. Clin. Tutor (Psychiat.).

SARGENT, Philippa Mary The Old Rectory, Bighton, Alresford SO24 9RB Tel: 01962 732300 — MB BS 1974 Lond.; DO Eng. 1978. (St. Thos.) Clin. Asst. (Ophth.) Soton. Gen. Hosp. Prev: Clin. Asst. Roy. Hants. Co. Hosp. Winchester; Ho. Phys. St. Thos. Hosp. Lond.; Ho. Surg. (Orthop.) Roy. Hants. Co. Hosp. Winchester.

SARGENT, Thomas Stewart Pitt The Richmond Practice, Health Centre, Dean Road, Bo'ness EH51 0DH Tel: 01506 822665 Fax: 01506 825939; 16 Grahamsdyke Road, Bo'ness EH51 9EG Tel: 01506 823302 Fax: 01506 825939 Email: sargents@compuserve.com — MB ChB 1969 Glas.; BSc (Hons.) Physiol. Glas. 1967. GP Trainer Bo'ness. Prev: Regist. (Med.) Gartnavel Gen. Hosp. Glas.; Ho. Phys. & Ho. Surg. W.. Infirm. Glas.

SARGENT, William 38 Polwarth Crescent, Edinburgh EH11 1HN — MB ChB 1997 Ed.

SARGINSON, John, TD 32 Hawthorn Road, Bamford, Rochdale OL11 5JQ Tel: 01706 643256 — MB BS 1954 Durh.; BA Open 1991; FFPHM 1989; FFCM 1980, M 1974; DPH Dur. 1960. Med. Ref. Rochdale MBC. Prev: Dist. Med. Off. Rochdale HA; Dep. Co. Med. Off. N.ants. CC; Sen. Med. Off. Leics. CC.

SARGINSON, Richard Emsley Department of Anaesthesia, Royal Liverpool Childrens Hospital, Eaton Road, Liverpool Tel: 0151 252 5223 Fax: 0151 252 5460 Email: richard.sarginson@rich-tr.nwest.nhs.uk; 31 Hornby Lane, Liverpool L18 3HH — MB ChB 1978 Bristol; BSc Bristol (Physiol.) 1975; MRCGP 1982; DRCOG 1982; FRCA 1986. Cons.(Paediat Anaesth.) Roy Liverp Childr NHS Trust. Prev: Regist. (Anaesth.) Roy. Devon & Exeter Hosp.

SARGISON, Mr Kenneth Duthie (retired) The Rockeries, 16 New Walk, Beverley HU17 7DJ Tel: 01482 868426 — MB ChB 1955 Aberd.; FRCS Ed. 1963. Prev: Cons. Orthop. Surg. Hull Roy. Infirm.

SARHADI, Mr Nanak Singh 28 Ashdown Drive, Wordsley, Stourbridge DY8 5QY — MB BS 1977 Calcutta; MS (Gen. Surg.) Calcutta 1980, MB BS 1977; FRCS Glas. 1986.

SARIN, Mr Ganesh 45 St Leonards Road, Harrogate HG2 8NS — MB BS 1984 Bhagalpur; MB BS Bhagalpur U 1984; FRCS Ed. 1992.

SARIN, Rajiv Academic Unit of Radiotherapy OncolgyRoyal Marsden Hospital, Sutton SM2 5PT — MB BS 1986 Kanpur, India; FRCR 1995.

SARIN, Mr Sanjeev PO Box 187, Northwood HA6 3TR Tel: 01923 217691 Fax: 01923 826554 Email: ssarin@compuserve.com — BM 1984 Soton.; MS Soton. 1993; FRCS (Gen.) 1996; FRCS Eng. 1988. (Univ. Soton.) Cons. Gen. & Vasc. Surg. Mt. Vernon & Watford NHS Trust.

SARIN, Sanjeev 24 Milcote Drive, Sutton Coldfield B73 6QJ Tel: 0121 603 9446; College Road Surgery, 352 College Road, Kingstanding, Birmingham B44 0HH Tel: 0121 373 1244 Fax: 0121 384 6670 — MB ChB 1991 Manch.; DFFP 1995. (Manch. Univ.) GP Regist. Eldington, Birm. Socs: MDU; MSS. Prev: SHO (Paediat., Special Care Baby Unit & O & G) Birm. Heartlands Hosp.; SHO (Geriat.) Sandwell Dist. Gen.

SARIN, Uma c/o Mr C. Sutton, Department Obstetrics & Gynaecology, Royal Surrey County Hospital, Eggerton Road, Guildford GU2 7XX — MB BS 1974 Delhi.

SARJUDEEN, Michael Taijnaraine Melbourne House Surgery, 12 Napier Court, Queensland Crescent, Chelmsford CM1 2ED Tel: 01245 354370 Fax: 01245 344476; 26 Wilshire Avenue, Springfield, Chelmsford CM2 6QW Tel: 01245 494562 — MB BS 1983 Lond.; DRCOG 1993. Prev: Trainee GP Norf.; SHO (O & G) Ipswich Hosp.; SHO (Psychiat.) Hellesdon Hosp.

SARKANY, Imrich (cons. rooms), 132 Harley St., London W1N 1AH Tel: 020 7935 3678 Fax: 020 7935 3678; 2 Romney Close, Hampstead Way, London NW11 7JD — MRCS Eng. LRCP Lond. 1952; FRCP Lond. 1968, M 1956. (St. Thos.) Cons. Dermat. Garden Hosp. Lond. Prev: Cons. Dermat. Roy. Free Hosp. Lond.; Cons. Dermat. Roy. Nat. Throat, Nose & Ear Hosp. Lond.; Sen. Regist. King's Coll. Hosp. Lond.

SARKANY, Robert Paul Edmond Mayday University Hospital, London Rd, Croydon CR7 7YE — MB BS 1986 Lond.; BSc (Hons.) Lond. 1983; MRCP (UK) 1989; M.D Lond 1995. Cons.s (Dermat) Mayday Univ. Hosp., Croyden, Surrey; Hon. Cons. (Dermat) St. John's Inst. of Dermat., Lond. Prev: Regist. (Dermat.) Addenbrooke's Hosp. Camb.; Wellcome Research Fell. & Hon. Regist. (Med.) Addenbrooke's Hosp. Camb.; SHO (Neurol.) Nat. Hosps. Nerv. Dis. Lond.// Sen. Regist (dermat)Addenbrooke's Hosp.Camb.

SARKAR, Ajoy 18 Muchall Road, Penn, Wolverhampton WV4 5SE — MB ChB 1996 Manch.

SARKAR, Bhabendramohan 48 Athol Square, London E14 0NP Tel: 020 7753 1813 — MB BS 1967 Calcutta. (Sir Nilratan Sircar Med. Coll.)

SARKAR, David Anthony Dept. of cardiology, St. Georges Hospital, Blackshaw Road, London SW17 — MB BS 1991 Lond.; BSc (Hons.) Lond. 1988; MRCP (UK) 1994. SpR Cardial St. Geo.s Hosp. Lond.; SpR Cardial Roy. Surrey Co. Hosp. Guildford; Research fell. (BHF) UCL & NHLI; Regist. St. Geo.s Hosp. Lond. Prev: Research Fell. (Brit. Heart Foundat.) UCL & the Nat. Heart & Lung Inst.; Regist. (Cardiol.) St. Geo. Hosp. Tooting; Regist. (Cardiol.) Frimley Pk. Hosp.

SARKAR, Mr Debabrata Fairfield General Hospital, Rochdale Old Road, Bury BL9 7TD Tel: 0161 764 6081 — MB BS 1959 Calcutta; BSc Calcutta 1954, MB BS 1959; FRCS Eng. 1970 FRCS Ed. 1967. (R.G. Kar Med. Coll.) Med. Asst. Orthop. & Accid. Dept. Bury AHA.

SARKAR, Debasish Raby Cottage, 85 Low Etherley, Bishop Auckland DL14 0EX — MB BS 1964 Calcutta.

SARKAR, Dinabandhu 142 Grimsby Road, Cleethorpes DN35 7DL Tel: 01472 699522 Fax: 01472 694652; 52 Humberston Avenue, Humberston, Grimsby DN36 4SS Tel: 01472 567963 Fax: 01472 590629 Email: drdsarkar@ntlworld.com — MB BS 1972 Calcutta;

MSc Calcutta 1972. (Calcutta Med. Coll.) Socs: Fell. Roy. Soc. Med.; BMA; Overseas Doctors Assn.

SARKAR, Jagadis Chandra Crayford Medical Centre, 4-6 Green Walk, Crayford, Dartford DA1 4JL Tel: 01322 520100 Fax: 01322 520101 — MB BS 1961 Calcutta.

SARKAR, Mr Jay Soorya 3 Tudor Close, Stevenage SG1 4DB Tel: 01438 367090 Fax: 01438 367090 Email: jaisarkar@btinternet.com; 3 Tudor Close, Stevenage SG1 4DB Tel: 01438 367090 Fax: 01438 367090 — MB BS 1977 Delhi; FRCS Glas. 1990; FRCS (Orth.) 1998. Specialist Regist. Orthop. Kings Coll. Hosp. Denmark Hill Lond.; Sen. Specialist Regist. (Orthopaed.) Greenwich Dist. Hosp. Lond. Socs: MDU.

SARKAR, Jhumpa 32 Hawk Close, Abbeydale, Gloucester GL4 4WE — MB BS 1993 Lond.

SARKAR, Manjusri 2 Broughton Road, South Shields NE33 2RU — MB BS 1959 Calcutta.

SARKAR, Paresh Nath (retired) 233 Millhouses Lane, Sheffield S11 9HW Tel: 0114 235 2960 — MB BS 1955 Calcutta; MRCPsych 1971; DPM Eng. 1966. Cons. Psychiat. (Ment. Handicap) Maclesfield HA. Prev: Cons. Psychiat. Cranage Hall Hosp.

SARKAR, Paul Pallab 30 Thomson Street, Aberdeen AB25 2QQ — MB ChB 1995 Aberd.

SARKAR, Prabodh Kumar 52 Wood Road, Tettenhall Wood, Wolverhampton WV6 8NF — MB BS 1977 Calcutta; MD (Gen. Med.) Calcutta 1981; MRCPI 1986. Cons. Phys & Head Dept. Med. King Faisal Hosp., Saudi Arabia. Socs: Fell. Internat. Coll. Angiol. USA; Acupunc. Assn. India.; Brit. Geriat. Soc. Prev: Regist. (Med. & Cardiol.) Brighton HA; SHO (Med.) Grantham & Kesteven Gen. Hosp.

SARKAR, Mr Pradip Kumar 6 Torsway Avenue, Blackpool FY3 8JF — MB BS 1969 Calcutta; FRCS Ed. 1981.

SARKAR, Pranab Kumar 45 Springfield Road, Stornoway HS1 2PS — MB BS 1974 Calcutta.

SARKAR, Prosanta Kumar Muchall Lodge, 18 Muchall Road, Wolverhampton WV4 5SE — MB BS 1966 Calcutta.

SARKAR, Saibal Kumar 139 Wilton St., Top Left, Glasgow G20 6DQ Tel: 0141 946 9300 — MB BS 1977 Calcutta; LRCP LRCS Ed. LRCPS Glas. 1982.

SARKAR, Mr Sandip Prasad 6A 36 Buckingham Gate, London SW1E 6PB — MB BS 1989 Lond.; FRCS Eng. 1993; FRCS (Orth) 1999. (St. Thos.) Specialist Regist. Rotat. (Orthop. Surg.) Roy. Nat. Orthop. Hosp. Stanmore. Socs: Fell. Roy. Soc. Med.; BMA. Prev: SHO (Cardiothorcic Surg.) St. Geo. Hosp. Lond.; SHO (A & E) Univ. Coll. Hosp. Lond.; SHO (Surg.) Roy. Marsden Hosp. Lond.

SARKAR, Santosh Kumar (retired) 6 Hammy Close, Shoreham-by-Sea BN43 6BL — MB BS 1951 Patna; MRCP Ed. 1963. Prev: Regist. (Med.) Bridge of Earn Hosp. Perth.

SARKAR, Sharmila Helen 4 Wath Wood Drive, Swinton, Mexborough S64 8UW Tel: 01709 872388 — MB ChB 1998 Leic.; MB ChB Leic 1998. GP Reg. Leics. Prev: Ho. Off. Surg. Kettering Gen. Hosp; HO.med.Leics.Gen.Hosp.

SARKAR, Shyamal Kanti Ramsbottom Health Centre, Carr Street, Ramsbottom, Bury BL0 9DD Tel: 01706 824445 Fax: 01706 821196 — MB BS 1964 Calcutta; DObst. 1967. Prev: Regist. (Psychiat.) Whittington Hosp. Preston; Regist. (Path.) Fazakerley Hosp. Liverp.; SHO (O & G) St. John's Hosp. Keighley.

SARKAR, Subhajit 32 Hawk Close, Abbeydale, Gloucester GL4 4WE — BChir 1995 Camb.

SARKAR, Subhendra Krishna (Surgery), 373 Hainton Avenue, Grimsby DN32 9QW Tel: 01472 357050 — MB BS 1972 Calcutta.

SARKAR, Sucheta 4 Bessy Brook Close, Lostock, Bolton BL6 4EA — MB BS 1972 Calcutta; DA Eng. 1978. (Nilratan Sarkar Med. Coll.)

SARKAR, Usharani (Surgery) 1 East Street, Rochdale Tel: 01706 39002; Darjeeling, 46 Linnet Hill, Bamford, Rochdale OL11 4DA Tel: 01706 59500 — MB BS 1957 Calcutta. (Calcutta) Prev: SHO (Psychiat.) Ashton-Under-Lyne Gen. Hosp.; Ho. Off. (Med.) Macclesfield Hosp.

SARKER, Debashis 2 Kinloch Drive, Bolton BL1 4LZ — MB ChB 1997 Liverp. SHO Gen. Med. Roy. Liverp. Univ. Hosp.

SARKER, Mohammed Abdul Khaleque Ryburn Surgery, 17/21 Ryburn Buildings, Sowerby Bridge HX6 3AH Tel: 01422 831924 — MB BS 1962 Dacca. (Dacca) Socs: BMA. Prev: SHO (Paediat. Surg.)

Nottm. Childr. Hosp.; Ho. Off. (Gen. Med.) Manor Hosp. Nuneaton; SHO City Hosp. Stoke-on-Trent.

SARKER, Prosenjit 5 Algernon Road, London SE13 7AU — MB BS 1992 Lond.

SARKER, Sabyasachi Knotty Ash Medical Centre, 411-413 East Prescot Road, Liverpool L14 2DE Tel: 0151 228 4369 Fax: 0151 252 0030 — MB BS 1969 Calcutta. GP Liverp.

SARKER, Mr Sudip Kumar 89 Cornwall Gardens, London SW7 4AX — MB ChB 1991 Glas. Specialist Regist. in Surg., Roy. Marsden Hosp. Lond. SW3. Socs: BMA; MDDUS; AAAS. Prev: Clin. Research Fell. & SHO (Otolaryngol. & Paediat.) St. Mary's Hosp. Lond.; SHO Rotat (Surg.) St. Mary's Hosp. Lond.

SARKHEL, Rama Prosad Pashimtra, 10 Oaten Hill Place, Canterbury CT1 3HJ Tel: 01227 69246 — MB BS 1962 Calcutta; DGO 1963; MRCOG 1969, DObst 1969; BA 1996 Open University; FRCOG 1984. (Nilratan Sircar Medical College, Calcutta) Cons. (Genito-Urin. Med.) Canterbury & S.E. Kent Gp. Hosps. Socs: FRSH; Med. Soc. Study VD. Prev: Sen. Regist. (Genito-Urin. Med. & Gyn.) Addenbrooke's Hosp. Camb.

SARKHEL, Swantana Tanaya 158 New Dover Road, Canterbury CT1 3EJ — MB BS 1991 Lond.; BSc (Hons.) Lond. 1988. (Char. Cross & Westm.) Regist. (Orthop.) Nambour Gen. Hosp. Qu.sland, Austral. Socs: Med. Defence Union; BMA. Prev: SHO Rotat. (Surg.) Roy. Sussex Co. Hosp. Brighton; SHO (Orthop. & Urol.) St. Richard's Hosp. Chichester.

SARKIES, Mr Nicholas Jonathan Courtenay Ophthalmic Department, Box 41, Addenbrooke's Hospital, Hills Road, Cambridge CB2 2QQ Tel: 01223 245151 Fax: 01223 217968; Wistow, The Green, Hilton, Huntingdon PE28 9NB Tel: 01480 830412 Fax: 01480 831461 — MB BChir 1977 Camb.; MRCP 1979 UK; FRCS 1982 Eng.; FRCOphth; FRCS Eng. 1982; MRCP (UK) 1979; FRCOphth. Cons. Ophth. Addenbrookes Hosp.Camb. Socs: Fell. Roy. Coll. Ophth. Prev: Sen. Regist. (Ophth.) St. Thos. Hosp. & Nat. Hosp. Nerv. Dis. Lond.; Resid. Surgic. Off. Moorfields Eye Hosp. Lond.; Ho. Phys. (Med.) W.m. Hosp. Lond.

SARKOZY, Vanessa Elizabeth 33 Ashton Avenue, Rainhill, Prescot L35 0QQ — MB ChB 1996 Birm.; ChB Birm. 1996. SHO (Paediat.) Roy. Alexandra Hosp. For Sick Childr., Brighton. Prev: SHO (Paediat.) Good Hope Hosp. Sutton Coalfield; Ho. Off. (Surg.) Russells Hall Hosp. Birm.; Ho. Off. (Med.) Heartlands Hosp.

SARMA, Mr Asoke (retired) 8 Wayside Close, Harrogate HG2 8PJ — MB BS 1955 Calcutta; FRCS Ed. 1972. Prev: Asst. (Accid. & Orthop.) Harrogate Dist. Hosp. & Bradford Roy.

SARMA, David Ian Malabar, 19 Woodlands Road, Cleadon Village, Sunderland SR6 7UD; 14 Mill View Close, Ewell Village, Epsom KT17 2DW — MB ChB 1989 Liverp.; FRCR 1995; DMRD Liverp. 1994; MRCP (UK) 1992. Cons. Radiol. Mayday Univ. Hosp. Trust Croydon. Prev: Sen. Regist. (Radiol.) King's Coll. Hosp. Lond.; Regist. (Radiol.) Roy. Liverp. Hosp. & Aintree Trust Hosp.; SHO Rotat. (Med.) Aintree Trust Hosps. Liverp.

SARMA, Jaydeep 8 Wayside Close, Harrogate HG2 8PJ — BChir 1992 Camb.

SARMA, Mr Kishori Mohan Malabar, 19 Woodlands Road, Cleadon Village, Sunderland SR6 7UD — MB BS 1955 Gauhati; FRCS Ed. 1968. (Assam Med. Coll. Dibrugarh) Asst. Orthop. Surg. Orthop. & Accid. Unit, Qu. Eliz. Hosp. Gateshead. Socs: Brit. Orthop. Assn.; BMA. Prev: Orthop. Regist. Orthop. & Accid. Hosp. Sunderland.

SARMA, Mr Kundurty Purnananda 8 Mayfield Park S., Bristol BS16 3NG Tel: 0117 976 1491 — MD 1979 Bristol; MB BS Calcutta 1959; FRCS Eng. 1963.

SARMA, Ramesh Chandra 177 Great North Way, London NW4 1PP Email: rambo1353@hotmail.com — MB BS 1996 Lond. (Kings College Lond.) Prev: SHO, Gen. Med.,James Paget Hosp. Gt. Yarmouth Norf.

SARMA, Tapan Chandra Bentinck Road Medical Centre, 2 Bentinck Road, Arthur's Hill, Newcastle upon Tyne NE4 6UT Tel: 0191 273 3919 Fax: 0191 273 6323 — MB BS 1967 Gauhati. (Gauhati) GP Newc.

SARMA, Umesh Chandra 177 Great Northway, Hendon, London NW4 1PP Tel: 020 8203 4380 Fax: 020 8203 4380 — MB ChB 1989 Ed. (Univ. Edin.) Socs: BMA. Prev: SHO (Cardiothoracic Surg.) Roy. Infirm. Edin.; Ho. Off. Chest Unit City Hosp. Edin.; Ho. Off. (Surg.) W.m. Gen. Hosp. Edin.

SARMAH

SARMAH, Anita 51 Green Pastures, Heaton Mersey, Stockport SK4 3RB; 8 Ashley House, Park Drive, The Park, Nottingham NG7 1DB — MB ChB 1991 Manch.; FRCA 1997. (Manch.) Specialist Regist. Anaesth. Qus. Med. Centre Nottm. Socs: Assn. Anaesth.; BMA.

SARMAH, Mr Bhupendra Dev Department Of Urology, Birmingham Heartlands Hospital NHS Trust (Teaching), Bordesley Green E., Birmingham B9 5SS Tel: 0121 766 6611 Fax: 0121 773 6897; Winchmore Oak, 19 Poundley Close, Castle Bromwich, Birmingham B36 9SZ — MB BS 1971 Gauhati; FRCS Ed. 1980.

SARMAH, N N Chorlton Health Centre, 1 Nicolas Road, Chorlton, Manchester M21 9NJ Tel: 0161 860 4545 Fax: 0161 860 4565 — MB BS 1962 Gauhati; MB BS 1962 Gauhati.

SARMIENTO, Augusto Health Care International, Beardmore St., Clydebank G81 4HX — Medico y Cirujano National Univ. 1952.

SARMOTTA, Jagdish Singh Park View Surgery, 127 Station Road, Rainham, Gillingham ME8 7SP.

SARNA, Nirmal Rai Montague Medical Centre, Fifth Avenue, Goole DN14 6JD Tel: 01405 767600 Fax: 01405 726126 — MB BS 1973 Kanpur; AFOM RCP Lond. 1991; Cert. Prescribed Equiv. Exp. JCPTGP 1981; Cert. Family Plann. JCC 1980; DRCOG 1979. (GSVM Medical College Kanpur) Med. Off. Smith & Nephew; Med. Off. Thorne Poultry, Thorne Goole; Med. Off English Village salads. Socs: Soc. Occupat. Med.; BMA. Prev: Clin. Asst. (Gen. Med.) St. John's Hosp. Goole.

SARNAIK, Bhoopal Sivasiddappa Annapoorna, Helmington Grange, Crook DL15 0SE — MB BS 1963 Karnatak. (Kasturba Med. Coll. Mangalore) Prev: SHO (Orthop., A & E) Bishop Auckland Gen. Hosp.; SHO (Gen. Surg.) W. Cumbld. Hosp. Whitehaven; SHO (Gen. Surg.) Workington Infirm.

SARNAIK, Nirmala Bhoopal Health Centre, Chapel Street, Willington, Crook DL15 0EQ Tel: 01388 746468 — MB BS 1964 Bombay. (Bombay) GP Crook, Co. Durh.

SARNER, Martin (retired) Wellington Hospital, London NW8 9LE Tel: 020 7586 5959 Ext: 2572 Fax: 020 7483 0297 Email: m.sarner@btinternet.com — MB BS 1959 Lond.; FRCP Lond. 1976, M 1962; MRCS Eng. LRCP Lond. 1959. Cons. Pysician, Univ. Coll. Lond. Hosp.s. Prev: Cons. Phys. Portsmouth Gp. Hosps.

SARNICKI, Marek Anthony The Surgery, 321 Shirland Road, London W9 3JJ Tel: 020 8969 2626 Fax: 020 8964 0353; 321 Shirland Road, London W3 Tel: 020 8969 2626 — MB BS 1978 Lond.

SARNOBAT, Meenakshi S Bute Street Health Centre, 34 Bute Street, Treorchy, Cardiff CF42 6BS Tel: 01443 771728 Fax: 01443 772164.

SARNOBAT, Sudheer R Bute Street Health Centre, 34 Bute Street, Treorchy, Cardiff CF42 6BS Tel: 01443 771728 Fax: 01443 772164.

SARODIA, Usman Ahmed 25 Oswald Street, Blackburn BB1 7EF — MB ChB 1994 Leic.

SARRIS, Ioannis Block 5, Flat 1, St. Peter's Hospital, Guildford Road, Chertsey KT16 0PZ — Ptychio Iatrikes 1991 Thessalonika.

SARSAM, Mr Soufian Abdul Ahad 14A Arterberry Road, London SW20 8AJ — MB ChB 1965 Baghdad; FRCS Ed. 1978.

SARSFIELD, Mr David Alan (retired) Vale Cottage, Hawkcombe, Porlock, Minehead TA24 8QW Tel: 01643 862616 — MB ChB Bristol 1943; FRCS Eng. 1948.

SARSFIELD, Patrick Thomas Leo South Laboratory/Pathology Block, Southampton General Hospital, Tremona Road, Southampton SO16 6YD — MB BCh BAO 1981 NUI.

SARSON, Mr David 2 Belle Vue Drive, Holmelands Park, Sunderland SR2 7SF Tel: 0191 283240 — MB BS 1962 Lond.; FRCS Eng. 1966; MRCS Eng. LRCP Lond. 1962. Cons. Surg. Sunderland Roy. Infirm. Prev: Regist. (Surg.) Walton Hosp. Liverp.; Surg. Daboo Hosp., Ivory Coast; Sen. Regist. (Surg.) United Liverp. Hosps.

SARTORI, Josephine Eileen Kings Road Surgery, 2-4 Kings Road, Mumbles, Swansea SA3 4AJ Tel: 01792 360933 Fax: 01792 368930 — MB BCh 1993 Wales.

SARTORI, Naldo Penbryn, 155 Vicarage Road, Morriston, Swansea SA6 6DT Tel: 01792 71115 — MB ChB 1952 Bristol. Police Surg. S. Wales Police, Swansea. Prev: Sen. Cas. Off. Bristol Roy. Infirm.; Ho. Surg. ENT Dept. Bristol Roy. Hosp.; Sen. Ho. Off. Bristol Homoeop. Hosp.

SARTORI, Patricia Carmen Ermina 18 Lynfield Lane, Cambridge CB4 1DR Tel: 01223 312043 — MB BS 1983 Lond.; MD Bristol 1996; MRCP (UK) 1986. (Guy's Hosp. Lond.) Sen. Regist. (Paediat. Oncol.) Addenbrooke's Hosp. Camb.

SARTORI, Rossano Alfredo 54 Over Lane, Almondsbury, Bristol BS32 4BW — MB ChB 1993 Cape Town.

SARTORIS, Anthony Woodland View Surgery, Woodland View, West Rainton, Houghton-le-Spring DH4 6RQ Tel: 0191 584 3809 Fax: 0191 584 9177; School House, Leamside, Houghton-le-Spring DH4 6QR Tel: 0191 512 0533 — MB BS 1974 Newc.; MRCGP 1978. (Newcastle-upon-Tyne) Prev: Trainer, N.umbria VTS Div. Gen. Pract. Univ. Newc., Newc.

SARTORY, Francis Bernard 12 Ferndale Road, Summersdale, Chichester PO19 4QJ Tel: 01243 527984 — MRCS Eng. LRCP Lond. 1950; LDS RCS Eng. 1943. (Guy's)

SARVA ISWERAN, Muttucumaru 49 Orchard Drive, Watford WD17 3DX Tel: 01923 29421 — MB BS 1971 Ceylon; MRCPsych 1980; DPM Eng. 1980; DCH Ceylon 1976. Cons. Psychiat. Leavesden Hosp. Abbots Langley. Prev: Sen. Regist. (Ment. Handicap) Leavesden Hosp. Abbots Langley; Regist. (Psychiat.) Warlingham Pk. Hosp.

SARVANANTHAN, Nagini Leicester Royal Infirmary, Infirmary Road, Leicester LE1 5WW Tel: 0116 254 1414 — MB BS 1992 Newc.; MMedSci Newc. 1993. SHO (Ophth.) Leics.

SARVANANTHAN, Rajini 3 Woodlea Gardens, Meanwood, Leeds LS6 4SE — MB BS 1993 Newc.; MRCP (UK) 1996. Specialist Regist. (Paediatiatrics) p/t. Bradford Roy. Infirm. & St. Luke's Hosp. Bradford. Socs: BMA; Med. Protec. Soc.; MRCPCH. Prev: SHO/Tutor (Paediat.) St. Jas. Univ. Hosp. Leeds; SHO (Paediat., Neonat. & Paediat. Neurol.) Leeds Gen. Infirm.; SHO (Paediat.) York Dist. Hosp.

SARVESVARAN, Joseph Shanker 3 Pierrefonds Avenue, Farnborough GU14 8NB — MB BS 1992 Lond.

SARVESVARAN, Rasaratnam 133 Prospect Road, Farnborough GU14 8JY — MB BS 1956 Ceylon; MRCPath 1994.

SARVOTHAM, Racharla 15 Hill Side, Pen-y-Fai, Bridgend CF31 4BG — MB BS 1967 Osmania; DPM Eng. 1980. (Kakatiya Med. Coll.)

SARWAR, Hamid 6 Snow Hill, Shelton, Stoke-on-Trent ST1 4LT — MB BS 1966 Punjab.

SARWAR, Mohammad Iqbal Mohammad Flat D, 13 Printfield Terrace, Aberdeen AB24 4AL — MB ChB 1998 Aberd.; MB ChB Aberd 1998.

SARWAR, Mohammad Naveed 40 Parkview Road, London W5 2JB — MB BS 1996 Lond.

SARWAR, Nadeem 21 Everton Road, Hunters Bar, Sheffield S11 8RY — MB ChB 1995 Sheff.

SARWAR, Naheed 106 Clayton Street, Nelson BB9 7PR — MB ChB 1992 Manch.

SARWAR, Mr Qamar Westmorland General Hospital, Burton Road, Kendal LA9 7RG — MB BS 1981 Punjab; FRCSI 1992.

SARWAR, Sajjad 45 Treaford La, Birmingham B8 2UF — MB ChB 1997 Birm.

SARWAR, Shakeel 22 Causey Foot, Nelson BB9 0DR — MB ChB 1995 Leeds.

SARWAR-E-ALAM, Abul Kalam Mohammad 26 Matlock Road, Ferndown BH22 8QU Tel: 01202 876703 Fax: 01202 876703; Dorset Health Care NHS Trust, Ringwood BH24 2RR Tel: 01202 895945 — MB BS Dacca 1966; DTM & H 1973; DPH Punjab 1968. Clin. Asst. ElderlyMed.Dorset Health Care NHS Trust. Socs: Med. Protec. Soc.

SASADA, Kay 5 St Paul's Close, Lower Willingdon, Eastbourne BN22 0LT — MB BS 1984 Lond.; MRCGP 1988; DCH RCP Lond.; DRCOG 1987.

SASADA, Martin Paul 4 Holmes Grove, Bristol BS9 4EE — MB BS 1983 Lond.

SASH, Leonard The Surgery, 80 Cambridge Gardens, London W10 6HS Tel: 020 8969 5517 Fax: 020 8964 4766; 71 Lansdowne Road, London W11 2LG Tel: 020 8969 5517 — MB BCh Witwatersrand 1954; DPhysMed. Eng. 1969; DCH Eng. 1961. Cons. Sports Med. St. Mary's Hosp. Lond.; Cons. Phys. (Med.) Arsenal Football Club; Cons. Imperial Coll. in Sports Med. Prev: Assoc. Specialist (Rheum.) St. Chas. & St. Mary's Hosps. Lond.

SASHIDHARAN, Ratnasabapathy Department of Anaesthetics, Royal London Hospital, Whitechapel, London E1 1BB Tel: 020 7377 7793 Fax: 020 7377 7153; 5 Collard Place, Harmood St, London NW1 8DU Tel: 020 7482 1141 — MB BS 1983 Colombo; FRCA 1992; FFA RCSI 1991; DA (UK) 1988. (Faculty of Medicine, University of Colombo, Sri Lanka) Cons. Anaesth. Roy. Hosp. St. Bartholomews, Roy. Lond. Hosp. & Lond. Chest Hosp. NHS Trust; Cons. Anaesth. St Bart. & the Roy. Lond. Hosps. Prev: Hon. Cons. (Anaesth.) Homerton Hosp.; Sen. Regist. (Anaesth.), Roy. Lond. Hosp.

SASHIDHARAN, Professor Sivasankaran Pillay Northern Birmingham Mental Health Trust, Trust Headquarters, 71 Fentham Road, Erdington, Birmingham B23 6AL Tel: 0121 623 5861 Fax: 0121 623 5870 — MB BS 1974 Madras; PhD Ed. 1986, MPhil 1980; MRCPsych 1978. (Jawaharlal Inst. Med. Educat. Pondicherry) Med. Dir., N.ern Birm. Ment. Health Trust, Birm.; Cons. Psychiat., NBMNT; Director, Centre for Community Ment. Health NBMNT and Univ. of Centr. Eng. Prev: Mem. Scientif. Staff MRC Unit Epidemiological Studies in Psychiat. Univ. Dept. Psychiat. Roy. Edin. Hosp.; Sen. Regist. (Psychiat.) Roy. Edin. Hosp.; Prof. of Community Psychiat. Univ. of Birm.

SASITHARAN, Nadrajah 63 Langland, King's Lynn PE30 4TH — MB BS 1983 Sri Lanka; MRCOphth. 1993.

SASITHARAN, Thangaluxmy 35 Colney Heath Lane, St Albans AL4 0TG — MRCS Eng. LRCP Lond. 1979.

SASSE, William Michael Peter (retired) 421 Westleigh Lane, Leigh WN7 5PU Tel: 01942 883793 — MD 1946 Hamburg.

SASSOON, Elaine Moira Dept of Plastic Surgery, West Norwich Hospital, Bowthorpe Road, Norwich NR2 3TU Tel: 01603 286286 Fax: 01603 288378 — MB BS 1983 Lond.; BA (Hons.) Biol. Harvard 1976; FRCS 1989; FRCS Eng 1989; FRCS Plast 1998. (UCL) Cons. Plastic.Surg.W. norwich Hosp and aesthetic Surg.; Fell. Oculoplastic Atlanta Georgia USA. Socs: BAPS; Aesthetic Soc. (USA).

SASSOON, Jeremy Howard 45 High Grove Road, Cheadle SK8 1NW Tel: 0161 428 4765 — MB BS 1988 Lond. Regist. Rotat. (Psychiat.) NW RHA.

SASSOON, Sonia Miriam Helen The Surgery, 404 Honeypot Lane, Stanmore HA7 1JP Tel: 020 8204 1363 Fax: 020 8903 0286; 4 Barn Rise, Wembley Park, Wembley HA9 9NA Tel: 020 8904 5698 — MB BS 1978 Lond.; MRCS Eng. LRCP Lond. 1977; DRCOG 1980. (Roy. Free)

SASTRE CABRER, Juan Antonio 50 Holland Road, London W14 8BB — LMS 1987 Barcelona; LMS Autonoma Barcelona 1987.

SASTRULU, Kanakamedala c/o Newsham General Hospital, Belmont Road, Liverpool L6 4AF Tel: 0151 263 7381; 18 Hornby Lane, Liverpool L18 3HH — MB BS 1971 Andhra; DTM & H Liverp. 1975.

SASTRY, M R Halling Medical Centre, Ferry Road, Halling, Rochester ME2 1NP Tel: 01634 240238 — MB BS 1965 Andhra; MB BS 1965 Andhra.

SASTRY, Sanjay Rajesh Vascular Studies Unit, South Manchester University Hospital, Nell Lane, Withington, Manchester M20 2LR Tel: 0161 291 4527; 102 Parkville Road, Withington, Manchester M20 4TZ Tel: 0161 445 9063 Email: sanjay.rs@virginnet.co.uk — MB ChB 1995 Manch.; BSc St Andrews 1992; MRCP (UK) 1998.

SATARASINGHE, Kathri Achchige Sandya 30 Heol Beili Glas, Swiss Valley, Llanelli SA14 8DS — MB BS 1985 Colombo, Sri Lanka; LRCP LRCPS Ed. LRCPS Glas. 1994.

SATCHELL, Raoul Harold (retired) 3 Grange Hill, Welwyn AL6 9RH Tel: 01438 717508 — MB BS 1947 Lond. Prev: Cas. Off. Watford & Dist. Peace Memor. Hosp.

SATCHELL, Simon Charles 5 Holland Avenue, Knowle, Solihull B93 9DW — MB BS 1992 Lond.

SATCHITANANDA, Muttucumarasamy 55 Gatcome, Great Holm, Milton Keynes MK8 9EA — MB BS 1971 Ceylon; MRCP (UK) 1988.

SATCHITHANANDA, Dunwarakan Kirupanantha Papworth Hospital, Cambridge CB3 8RE; Flat 12, Livemore Court, Grove Park, Liverpool L8 0TL — MB ChB 1991 Liverp. Specialist Regist., Papworth Hosp. Camb.

SATCHITHANANTHAN, N St James Health Centre, 29 Great George Square, Liverpool L1 5DZ Tel: 0151 709 1120.

SATCHITHANANTHAN, Sivakhami Stepaside, Brancote Road, Oxton, Birkenhead CH43 6TL — BChir 1995 Camb.

SATCHWELL, George Malcolm (retired) Trevarrick House, North Curry, Taunton TA3 6LX Tel: 01823 491001 — MB ChB 1965 St. And. Prev: GP Taunton.

SATCHWELL, Victoria Jane 122 New Penkridge Road, Cannock WS11 1HN — MB BS 1991 Lond.

SATHANANDAN, Mr Muttukrishna Harold Wood Hospital, Gubbins Lane, Romford RM3 0BE; 11 Fordyce Close, Hornchurch RM11 3LE — MB BS 1973 Sri Lanka; MPhil Lond. 1989; MRCS Eng. LRCP Lond. 1979; FRCS Ed. 1981; FRCOG (UK) 1994, M 1981; MFFP 1993; T(OG) 1991. Cons. (O & G) Havering Hosp. Trust; Hon. Sen. Lect. UCL & Jt. Med. Sch. of St. Bart. & Roy. Lond. Socs: BMA; Brit. Fertil. Soc.; Brit. Menopause Soc.

SATHANANDAN, Sankarakumaran Blenheim Chase Surgery, 9 Blenheim Chase, Leigh-on-Sea SS9 3BZ Tel: 01702 470336 Fax: 01702 476210; 3 The Spinneys, Leigh-on-Sea SS9 5QZ — MB BS 1979 Sri Lanka; MRCS Eng. LRCP Lond. 1982; MRCGP 1985. GP Princip.

SATHANANTHAN, Dilakshini 24 Lazenby Grove, Darlington DL3 9QD — MB ChB 1992 Sheff.

SATHANANTHAN, Kanagaratnam Dept of Psychiatary, Mayday University Hospital, London Road, Croydon CR7 7YE Tel: 020 8401 3596 Fax: 020 8401 3577 — MB BS 1964 Ceylon; MRCP (U.K.) 1971; MRCPsych 1972; DPM Eng. 1970. (Univ. Ceylon) S. Lond. & Maudsley (NHS) Trust; Med. Dir. Surrey Rest & Nursing Homes Ltd. Prev: Sen. Regist. Bethlem Roy. & Maudsley Hosps. Lond.

SATHANANTHAN, Muttiah (retired) 20 Meadow Close, Farmoor, Oxford OX2 9NZ Tel: 01865 863698 — MB BS 1952 Ceylon; DLO RCS Eng. 1962. Prev: ENT Cons. Sir Lankan Gov. Serv.

SATHANANTHAN, Niranjani 24 Lazenby Grove, Mowden Park, Darlington DL3 9QD — MB ChB 1993 Dundee.

SATHANANTHAN, Roshanthi 30 Castlemaine Avenue, South Croydon CR2 7HQ — MB BS 1991 Lond.; MRCP (UK) 1994.

SATHANANTHAN, Shobana 32 Dulverton Road, South Croydon CR2 8PG — MB BS 1993 Lond.

SATHE, Sharad Bhargav 11 The Brooks, St Helens WA11 7DY — MB BS 1963 Bombay.

SATHI, Navtej 274 Barton Road, Manchester M32 9RD — MB ChB 1995 Manch.

SATHIA, Prabhati Julie 5 Dursley Drive, Cannock WS11 1TN — MB BS 1994 Lond.

SATHIA, Mr Pranab The Surgery, 24 Bideford Way, Cannock WS11 1QD Tel: 01543 571055 Fax: 01543 574930 — MB BS 1955 Utkal; FRCS Glas. 1977. (S.C.B. Med. Coll. Cuttack)

SATHIA, U The Surgery, 24 Bideford Way, Cannock WS11 1QD Tel: 01543 571055 Fax: 01543 574930 — MB BS 1963 Utkal; MB BS 1963 Utkal.

SATHIA, Upali Leena 149A Melrose Avenue, London NW2 4NA — MB BS 1998 Lond.; MB BS Lond 1998.

SATHIYASEELAN, Subbiah Stretton Medical Centre, 5 Hatton Lane, Stretton, Warrington WA4 4NE Tel: 01925 730412 Fax: 01925 730960; 5 Fairways, Appleton, Warrington WA4 5HA Tel: 01925 264650 Fax: 01925 730960 — MB BS 1972 Mysore; Dip. Pract. Dermat. Wales 1993; DIH Eng. 1980. (Kasturba Med. Coll.) Socs: FRSH.

SATHIYASEELAN, Suren Rajesh Kumar 5 Fairways, Appleton, Warrington WA4 5HA — MB ChB 1998 Leeds; BSc (Hons) 1995. SHO. (Gen Med.) St James Univ Hosp. Leeds. Prev: HO. (Gen Med.) St James Univ Hosp. Leeds.; HO. (Surg.) St James Univ Hosp. Leeds.

SATHYA, Hesaraghatta Channappa c/o Meyricks, Coed-eva, Cwmbran NP44 6TU — MB BS 1967 Bangalor; MB BS Bangalore 1967; MRCP (UK) 1974.

SATHYAN, Neena 24 Wheatsheaf Walk, Standish, Wigan WN6 0RH — MB BS 1989 Calicut.

SATHYANARAYANA, Chakralvar Narasimhachar Department of Anaesthesia, Walsgrave Hospital, Clifford Bridge Road, Coventry CV2 2DX — MB BS 1973 Mysore.

SATKUNANAYAGAM, Vaithianathan (retired) 10 Kendor Avenue, Epsom KT19 8RH Tel: 01372 813265 — MB BS 1953 Ceylon; FRCPsych 1980; Acad. DPM Eng. 1963. Prev: Cons. Psychiat. Surrey Heartlands Care St. Ebbas Epsom.

SATKURUNATH, Gayathri 4 Wendover Road, Bromley BR2 9JX — MB BS 1998 Lond.; MB BS Lond 1998.

SATKURUNATHAN

SATKURUNATHAN, Saravanamuttu 48 Eton Avenue, New Malden KT3 5AZ Tel: 020 8942 1901 Fax: 020 8241 2146 Email: satkuru@aol.com — MB BS 1951 Ceylon; FRCP Ed. 1979; MRCP Ed. 1959. Adjudicating Med. Pract. Benefit Agency Med. Servs. Sutton. Socs: Fell. Roy. Coll. Phys.; Brit. Med. & Geriat. Assn.; Ceylon Coll. Phys. Prev: Cons. Phys. (Geriat. Med.) Roy. Vic. Hosp. Dundee; Cons. Phys. (Geriat. Med.) Dorset Co. & Poole Gen. Hosps.; Cons. Phys. Wattala Hosp. & Wattala Hosp. Sri Lanka.

SATSANGI, Jyoti 35 Jack Straw's Lane, Headington, Oxford OX3 1LO — MB BS 1987 Lond.

SATSANGI, Mr Prem Nath Belgrave Avenue Surgery, 113 Belgrave Avenue, Gidea Park, Romford RM2 6PS Tel: 01708 740660 Fax: 01708 722632 — MB BS 1954 Lucknow; MS Lucknow 1958, MB BS 1954; FRCS Eng. 1967; FRCS Ed. 1966. (K.G. Med. Coll.)

SATTAR, Daoud Abdul Englefield Road Surgery, 8 Englefield Road, London N1 4LN Tel: 020 7254 1324 — MB ChB 1962 Baghdad.

SATTAR, Mohammad High Green Surgery, High Green, Brooke, Norwich NR15 1JD Tel: 01508 50204 — MB BS 1964 Dacca; MB BS 1964 Dacca.

SATTAR, Naveed Amjid Glasgow Royal Infirmary, Institute of Biochemistry, Glasgow G4 0SF Tel: 0141 211 4490 Fax: 0141 553 1703 Email: nsattar@clinmed.gla.ac.uk; 88 Mitre Road, Jordanhill, Glasgow G14 9PH Tel: 0141 954 9232 — MB ChB 1990 Glas.; PhD Glas. 1998; Dip RCPath 1998. (Glasgow) Career Regist. (Clin. Biochem.) Glas. Roy. Infirm. Socs: Assn. Clin. Biochem.; Brit. Hyperlipid. Assn.; Scott. Soc. Experim. Med.

SATTAR, Naweed 17 Broomieknowe Gardens, Bonnyrigg EH19 2JE — MB ChB 1992 Manch.

SATTAR, Nedal Bacup Health Centre, Yorkshire St., Bacup OL13 9RA Tel: 01706 875050 — MB ChB 1978 Basrah; PhD Ed. 1989; DCH RCPS Glas. 1991; 1998 MSc Audiological Medicine Manchester. Staff Grade (Paediat.) Burnley Health Care NHS Trust; Assoc. Specialist in Paediatric Audiol., Burnley Health Care NHS Trust. Socs: MRCPCH; Brit. Assn. Community Drs in Audiol.; Brit. Soc. Audiol. Prev: Clin. Med. Off. (Child Health) Argyll & Clyde HB Paisley; Regist. (Paediat.) Roy. Alexandra Hosp.; SHO (Paediat.) Roy. Hosp. Sick Childr. Glas.

SATTAR, Sanjida Ahmed 6 Bradshaw Close, Pogmor, Barnsley S75 2JN — MB ChB 1998 Manch.; MB ChB Manch 1998.

SATTAR, Shaila Ahmed 6 Bradshaw Close, Barnsley S75 2JN — MB ChB 1992 Manch.

SATTARI, Mohsen 24 The Fairway, Westella, Hull HU10 7SB Tel: 01482 658632 — MD 1969 Tehran. (Tehran Univ. Tehran/Iran) A/S Orthop. Surg. Hull Roy. Infirm. Socs: Brit. Orthop. Assn.; BMA.

SATTIANAYAGAM, Aiyadurai The Surgery, 1 Crawley Lane, Pound Hill, Crawley RH10 7DX — MB BS 1970 Ceylon; FRCOG 1997, M 1979.

SATTIARAJAH, Appudurai Immanuel 5 Nodders Way, Biddenham, Bedford MK40 4BJ — MRCS Eng. LRCP Lond. 1977 Lond.; MRCS LRCP Lond. 1977.

SATUR, Mr Christopher Michael Raymond 2 School Croft, Rothwell, Leeds LS26 0UQ Tel: 0113 288 7103 — MB BS 1982 Lond.; MS 1996; FRCS Eng. 1988; DRCOG 1997; DFFG 1999; DCH 1999. (Lond. Hosp.) Specialist Regist. (Cardiothoracic Surg.). Socs: Soc. Cardiothoracic Surg.; CSRC. Prev: Regist. (Cardiothoracic Surg.) Birm Childr Hosp.

SATYA PRASAD, Koneru Westwood Clinic, Wicken Way, Peterborough PE3 7JW Tel: 01733 265535 Fax: 01733 264263; Srinivas, Church St, Alwalton, Peterborough PE7 3UU Tel: 01733 265535 Fax: 01733 264263 — MB BS 1974 Andhra; DFFP 1994; DTM & H Liverp. 1979. GP P'boro. Socs: Fell. Roy. Soc. Health; Accred. Mem. (Chairm.) Brit. Med. Acupunc. Soc.; Fell. Roy. Soc. Med.

SATYANARAYANA, Polubothu 10 Marywell, Kirkcaldy KY1 2RJ — MB BS 1973 Andhra.

SATYAVADANAN, Mr Bangalore Sundaravadanan Darlington Memorial Hospital, Hollyhurst Road, Darlington DL3 6HX Tel: 01325 743110 Fax: 01325 743013; Email: satvad@nilayam.freeserve.co.uk — MB BS Madras 1967; MS (Gen. Surg.) Madras 1971; FRCS Ed. 1976. (Madras Med. Coll.) Cons. Urol. Darlington Mem. Hosp. & S. Cleveland Hosp, Middlesbro'. Socs: BAUS; Eur. Assn. Urol.; Assn. Surgs India. Prev: Urol. Surg. Qu. Eliz. Hosp. Gateshead; Regist.

(Urol.) Kent & Canterbury Hosp., Walsgrave Hosp. Coventry, Leeds Gen. Infirm. & Bradford Roy. Infirm.

SAUJANI, Arvind Vallabhdas Horn Lane Surgery, 156 Horn Lane, Acton, London W3 6PH Tel: 020 8992 4722 — MB BS 1971 Rajasthan.

SAUJANI, Virendra Kumar Tulsidas 39 Huntsmans Way, Rusheymead, Leicester LE4 7ZG — MB BS 1979 Lond.; DRCOG 1982. (Middlx.)

SAUL, Joanna Louise 16 Hunters Place, Spital Tongues, Newcastle upon Tyne NE2 4PB — MB BS 1996 Newc.

SAUL, Peter Anthony Chorley Old Road Surgery, 555 Chorley Old Road, Bolton BL1 6AF Tel: 01204 848411 Fax: 01204 849968 — MB ChB 1968 Manch.; DObst RCOG 1971.

SAUL, Peter Damien Health Centre, Beech Avenue, Rhosllanerchrugog, Wrexham LL14 1AA Tel: 01978 845955 Fax: 01978 846757 — MB ChB 1977 Liverp.; MRCGP 1984; DRCOG 1984; DCH Eng. 1979. Hosp. Pract. (Paediat.) Chester Gp. Hosps.

SAULSBURY, Nicola Kerry Gail Ambrose King Centre, Royal London Hospital, Whitechapel, London E1 1BB; St James' Vicarage, Arlington Square, Islington, London N1 7DS — MB BS 1992 Lond.; BSc (Psychol.) 1989; MRCP (UK) 1995; Dip GUM (Distinction) Soc. Apoth. (St. Mary's Hospital Medical School) Specialist Regist. (Genitourin. & HIV Med.) Roy. Lond. & St. Bart. Hosp. Lond. Socs: BMA; Brit. HIV Assn.

SAUMAREZ, Richard Charles 180 Shelford Road, Trumpington, Cambridge CB2 2NE — MB BS 1975 Lond.

SAUND, Narinder Singh Cross Street Surgery, 5 Cross Street, Hathern, Loughborough LE12 5LB Tel: 01509 646326 Fax: 01509 646098; 19 Linley Avenue, Shepshed, Loughborough LE12 9HJ Tel: 01509 507650 — MB BS 1986 Lond.; DFFP 1994; DRCOG 1992. (Guys Hosp.) Clin. Asst. (Rheum.) Coalville Hosp.; Clin. Asst. (Dermat.) LoughBoro. Hosp.; Clin. Asst. (c/o Elderly) LoughBoro. Hosp.

SAUNDBY, Edith (retired) Persondy, Llangynidr, Crickhowell NP8 1NT Tel: 01874 730932 — MB ChB 1955 Bristol; DObst RCOG 1957.

SAUNDBY, Robert Peter (retired) Persondy, Llangynidr, Crickhowell NP8 1NT Tel: 01874 730932 Email: peter.saundby@virgin.net — MB ChB Bristol 1956; MMedSci Nottm. 1981; FFPHM RCP (UK) 1992, M 1982; T(OM) 1991; T(PHM) 1991; MFOM 1981. Med. Coordinator Europe Air sports; BGA and Med. Coordinator EAS. Prev: Air Commodore, Roy. Air Force.

SAUNDERS, Alan John Everest House Surgery, Everest Way, Hemel Hempstead HP2 4HY Tel: 01442 240422 Fax: 01442 235045 — MB BS 1964 Lond.; DObst RCOG 1966. (Univ. Coll. Hosp.) Prev: Ho. Surg. & Ho. Phys. W. Suff. Gen. Hosp.; Ho. Surg. St. Helier Hosp. Carshalton.

SAUNDERS, Andrew James Selkirk Dept. Of Radiology, Guys Hospital, St Thomas St., London SE1 9RT — MB BS 1964 Lond.; FRCP Lond. 1984; MRCP (U.K.) 1969; FRCR 1975; FFR 1972; DMRD Eng. 1971. Cons. Radiol. Guy's Hosp. Lond.

SAUNDERS, Andrew Paul Gregory 54 Dulwich Road, London SE24 0PA Tel: 020 7733 8360 — MB BChir 1979 Camb.; MA, MB BChir Camb. 1979; MRCP UK 1982.

SAUNDERS, Anna Cleeve Lawn, 117 Hales Road, Cheltenham GL52 6ST Tel: 01242 702104 — MB BS 1979 Lond.; LFHom (Med.) 2001; DFFP 1998 Lond. p/t GP Locum, Cheltenham. Prev: Asst. GP Cheltenham.; Clin. Asst. (Ophth.) Cheltenham.

SAUNDERS, Anne Patricia Sunbury Health Centre Group Practice, Green Street, Sunbury-on-Thames TW16 6RH Tel: 01932 713399 Fax: 01932 713354 — MB BS 1981 Lond.

SAUNDERS, Arthur Courtenay Greenwood Medical Centre, 249 Sneinton Dale, Sneinton, Nottingham NG3 7DQ Tel: 0115 950 1854 Fax: 0115 948 4999; Melton Spinney Farm, Melton Spinney Road, Thorpe Arnold, Melton Mowbray LE14 4SB Tel: 01664 500 5057 Fax: 01664 500 5057 — MB Ch Liverp. 1952; Dip. Clin. Hypn. Sheff. 1991. (Liverp.) Cons. Hypnother. Nottm. Socs: Roy. Soc. Med.; Brit. Soc. Med. & Dent. Hypn.; Brit. Soc. Experim. & Clin. Hypn. Prev: Hon. Med. Sec. Notts. Local Med. Comm.

SAUNDERS, Brian Paul Wolfson Unit For Endoscopy, St. Mark's Hospital, Watford Road, Harrow HA1 3UJ Tel: 020 8235 4225 Fax: 020 8423 3588 Email: saunders@compuserve.com; 50 Nightingale Road, Rickmansworth WD3 7DB Tel: 01923 721269 — MB BS

SAUNDERS

1988 Lond.; MD Lond. 1996; MRCP (UK) 1991. (Univ. Coll. Hosp. Lond.) Cons. Phys. & Sen. Lect. (Endoscopy) St. Mark's Hosp. Lond.; Cons. Gastroenterol. & Endoscopist The Lond. Clinic. Socs: (Treas.) St. Mark's Assn.; Roy. Soc. Med.; Brit. Soc. Gastroenterol. Prev: Sen. Regist. (Gastroenterol.) Guy's Hosp. Lond.; Sen. Regist. (Gen. Med. & Gastroenterol.) Lewisham Hosp. Lond.; Regist. (Med.) Darlington Memor. Hosp.

SAUNDERS, Caroline Scarborough Health Trust, Scarborough YO12 6QL; Key Green Farm House, Egton Grange, Whitby YO22 5AX — MB BS 1985 Lond.; Dip. Occupat Med. (Univ. Coll. Lond.) Occupat. Health Off. ScarBoro. Trust.

SAUNDERS, Charles James Paton Fife Health Board, Springfield House, Cupar KY15 5UP Tel: 01334 656200 Fax: 01334 652210 Email: c.saunders@fhblib.demon.co.uk — MB BS 1982 Lond.; MRCS Eng. LRCP Lond. 1981; MFPHM RCP (UK) 1994; MPH Leeds 1992; DRCOG 1985. (Middlx.) Prev: GP Chatteris; Trainee GP Lenham VTS; Sen. Regist. (Pub. Health Med.) Yorks. RHA.

SAUNDERS, Christobel Mary Dept. Surgery VCL, 67-73 Riding House St., London W1P 7LD Tel: 020 7504 9314 Fax: 020 7636 5176 Email: christobelsaunders@ucl.ac.uk; Seale House, 37 Dartford Road, Sevenoaks TN13 3TD — MB BS 1986 Lond.; FRCS Eng. 1991. Sen. Lect. UCL; Hon. Cons. (Surg.) UCLH.

SAUNDERS, Christopher John The Health Centre, Canterbury Way, Stevenage SG1 1QH Tel: 01438 357411 Fax: 01438 720523; 96 Astwick Road, Stotfold, Hitchin SG5 4BG — MB BS 1989 Lond.; MSc Lond. 1985; BSc Loughborough 1983; MRCGP 1993. (University College Hospital London) Prev: MRC Research Doctor Environm. Epidemiol. Unit Soton. Univ.; Trainee GP Stevenage VTS; SHO (Paediat., O & G & A & E) Lister Hosp. Stevenage.

SAUNDERS, Dame Cicely Mary Strode, OM, DBE (retired) St. Christopher's Hospice, 51-59 Lawrie Park Road, Sydenham, London SE26 6DZ Tel: 020 8778 9252 Fax: 020 8659 8680 — MA Oxf.; Hon. Dr. Med. Qu. Univ. Belf. 1984; Hon. Dr. Law Jewish Theolog. Seminary, New York 1982; Hon. Dr. Law Univ. Camb. 1986; Hon. Dr. Law Univ. Oxf. 1986; Hon. FRCPsych. 1988; MB BS Lond. 1957; FRCS 1986; FRCP Lond. 1974, M 1968; Hon. DSc Yale 1969; Hon. DSc Univ. Lond. 1983; Hon. Dr. Law Columbia Univ. 1979. Hon. Cons. St. Joseph's Hospice Hackney & St. Thos. Hosp. Lond.; Pres. St. Christopher's Hospice, Sydenham.

SAUNDERS, Daniel John Sandwell General Hospital, Lyndon, West Bromwich B71 4HJ — MB ChB 1996 Leic.; BSc (Hons.) Leic. 1994. (Leics.) SHO Med. Rotat. Leicester. Socs: Hon. Sec. - Gay and Lesbian Assoc. of Doctors and Dentists; Hon. Sec. - W. Midl.s Reg. Jun. Doctors Comm.; BMA.

SAUNDERS, Dave Mark 38 Stanley Avenue, Birmingham B32 2HA — BM BS 1989 Nottm.

SAUNDERS, David Arthur, TD Department of Anaesthetics, Southampton General Hospital, Tremona Road, Southampton SO16 6YD; The Gatehouse, 2 Stag Gates, Exbury Road, Blackfield, Southampton SO45 1SR — MB ChB 1968 Leeds; PhD Leeds 1979, BSc 1965, MB ChB 1968; FFA RCS Eng. 1975. Cons. Anaesth. Soton. Univ. Hosps. Trust.

SAUNDERS, David Cameron (retired) Anthony House, 9 Vicarage Road, Penygraig, Tonypandy CF40 1HN — BSc, MB BCh (Commend.) Wales 1949; DCH Eng. 1956; MRCGP 1958. Med. Ref. & Div.al Med. Off. Welsh Office. Prev: RAF.

SAUNDERS, David Clifford H. M. Stanley Hospital, St Asaph LL17 1UL Tel: 01745 589680 Fax: 01745 589770 Email: mr.david.saunders@glanclwyd-tr.wales.nhs.uk — MB ChB 1986 Manch.; FRCOphth Lond. 1991; DO Lond. 1989. Cons. (Ophth. Surg.) HM Stanley Hosp. St. Asaph.

SAUNDERS, David Ian 39 Springbank Road, Sandyford, Newcastle upon Tyne NE2 1PD — MB BS 1994 Newc.; MRCP UK 1997. SHO Anaesth.

SAUNDERS, Dawn Elizabeth Dept. of Radiology, King's College Hospital, Denmark Hill, London SE5 8RS Tel: 020 7346 3331 Fax: 020 7346 3445 Email: dsaunder@sghms.uk; 92 Horne Park Road, Wimbledon, London SW19 7HR Tel: 020 8879 1012 Email: desaund@aol.com — MB BS 1986 Lond.; MD Lond. 1996; MRCP (UK) 1990. (King's Coll. Sch. Med. & Dent.) Sen. Regist. (Radiol.) Kings Coll. Hosp. Lond. Socs: Soc. Magenetic Resonance. Prev: Lect. (Magnetic Resonance) St. Geo. Hosp. Med. Sch. Lond.; Regist. (Thoracic Med.) Bromley Hosp. Kent & King's Coll. Hosp. Lond.; SHO (Cardiol.) Brook Hosp. Lond.

SAUNDERS, Douglas Robert Sinclair (retired) The Stables, 22 White St., West Lavington, Devizes SN10 4LP Tel: 01380 813648 — MB BS Lond. 1944; MRCP Lond. 1951. Prev: Surg. Lt. RNVR.

SAUNDERS, Elizabeth Hesling (retired) Swiss Cottage, Kitty Lane, Marton Moss, Blackpool FY4 5EG — MB ChB 1959 Manch.

SAUNDERS, Elizabeth Jane 149 Kinghsheath Avenue, Liverpool L14 2DQ Tel: 0151 283 4254 — MB BS 1987 Lond.; MSc (Pub. Health) Lond. 1993; DCH RCP Lond. 1991. Paediat. Doctor (A & E)Roy. Liverp. Childrs. Hosp. NHS Trust (Alder Hey).

SAUNDERS, Elizabeth Mary Jane 81 Calder Avenue, Brookmans Park, Hatfield AL9 7AJ — MB ChB 1993 Bristol.

SAUNDERS, Elizabeth Rosemary May (retired) 7 Dan-y-Graig, Machen, Caerphilly CF83 8RF Tel: 02920 884439 — MB BCh Wales 1960; MFCH 1989; DCH Eng. 1964; DObst RCOG 1964. Prev: SCMO Gwent HA.

SAUNDERS, Elizabeth Stewart Coniston Medical Practice, The Parade, Coniston Road, Patchway, Bristol BS34 5TF Tel: 0117 969 5208 Fax: 0117 969 0456; 13 Russet Close, Olveston, Bristol BS35 4EE — MB ChB 1972 Bristol; MRCP (UK) 1980; DCH Eng. 1978; DObst RCOG 1974. Gen. Practitioner.

SAUNDERS, Elizabeth Susanna West Sussex Health Authority, 1 The Causeway, Durrington, Worthing BN12 6BU Tel: 01903 708623 Fax: 01903 502684 Email: lizsaunders@tinyworld.co.uk — MB BS 1981 Lond.; MFPHM RCP (UK) 1992. (Roy. Free) Cons. Pub. Health Med. W. Sussex HA and Crawley PCG. Prev: Sen. Regist. (Pub. Health Med.) Brighton DHA; Regist. (Community Med.) Medway Dist. HA; Research Regist. (Neuropsychiat.) MRC Neuropsychiat. Research Laborat. W. Pk. Hosp. Epsom.

SAUNDERS, Emily Jane 12 Royal Park Mount, Leeds LS6 1HL — MB ChB 1998 Leeds.

SAUNDERS, Emma Jane 9 Welton Mount, Leeds LS6 1ET — MB ChB 1994 Leeds.

SAUNDERS, Emma Jane 8 Farquhar Road E., Birmingham B15 3RD — MB BS 1990 Lond. Trainee GP/SHO Stoke Mandeville Hosp. Aylesbury VTS.

SAUNDERS, Fiona Margaret 15 Bryn Road, Mynydd Isa, Mold CH7 6UR — MB ChB 1989 Manch.; FRCS Ed. 1995; DA (UK) 1994. Regist. (A & E Med.) NW RHA. Socs: Assoc. Mem. Brit. Accid. & Emerg. Med. Soc.

SAUNDERS, Frank Coutts Inglehurst, Deaf Hill, Trimdon Station TS29 6DA — MB BS 1976 Newc.

SAUNDERS, Graham James Witton Street Surgery, 162 Witton Street, Northwich CW9 5QU Tel: 01606 42007 Fax: 01606 350659; 162 Witton Street, Northwich CW9 5QT Tel: 01606 42007 — MB ChB 1978 Manch.; MRCGP 1988; DRCOG 1983.

SAUNDERS, Graham Peter Severus Avenue Surgery, 7 Severus Avenue, Acomb, York YO24 4LX Tel: 01904 791848 Fax: 01904 788210; Garden Cottage, Low Catton Lane End, Kexby, York YO41 5LE Tel: 01759 380695 — MB BS 1974 Lond. (St. Bart.)

SAUNDERS, Hilary Jane Parkgate Surgery, 28 St Helens Road, Ormskirk L39 4QR Tel: 01695 572561 — MB ChB 1994 Liverp.; DRCOG 1996; DFFP 1996. GP Princip. Ormskirk. Prev: Trainee GP/SHO S.port & Formby Dist. Gen. Hosp. VTS.

SAUNDERS, Ian Arthur Tel: 01298 23298 Fax: 01298 73227 — MB BS 1970 Lond.; DFFP; MRCS Eng. LRCP Lond. 1970; AKC. (St. Geo.) Clin. Med. Off. Family Plann. Buxton; Med. Off. Buxton Lime Industs. Socs: N. Derbysh. LMC. Prev: Ho. Phys. Roy. Portsmouth Hosp.; Ho. Surg. Surgic. Unit St. Geo. Hosp. Lond.

SAUNDERS, Ian Michael The Surgery, 25 St Mary's Road, Tickhill, Doncaster DN11 9NA Tel: 01302 742503 — MB ChB 1983 Leeds; BSc (1st cl. Hons. Chem. Path.) Leeds 1980; MRCGP 1988. Prev: Trainee GP Doncaster VTS.; SHO (A & E) Newham Gen. Hosp.; Ho. Off. (Gen. Med.) & (Gen. Surg.) Wharfedale Gen. Hosp. Otley.

SAUNDERS, Irene Gladys Gillian College Grove, 2 College Lane, Ripon HG4 4HE Tel: 01765 688306 — MB BS Lond. 1962; FRCPsych 1996, M 1977. (Char. Cross) Emerit. Cons. Psychiat. The Retreat York; Hon. Cons. Psychiat. St. Lukes Hosp. to the Clergy. Prev: Cons. Psychiat. St. Luke's Hosp. Middlesbrough; Ho. Surg. Bromley Hosp.; Ho. Phys. Brook Hosp. Lond.

SAUNDERS, Jeremy Hugh Bannerman Bedford Hospital, Kempston Road, Bedford MK42 9DJ Tel: 01234 792271 Fax: 01234 792041 Email: jeremy.saunders@beahos.anglox.nhs.uk; The Manor House, Felmersham, Bedford MK43 7JG Tel: 01234 781375 — MD Lond. 1981, MB BS Lond. 1969; FRCP Lond. 1989; MRCP (UK)

SAUNDERS

1973; MRCS Eng. LRCP Lond. 1969. (Roy. Free) Cons. Phys. Bedford Gen. Hosp. Trust; Med.Dir.Bedford Hosp.Trust. Socs: Brit. Soc. Gastroenterol. Prev: Sen. Med. Regist. Dept. Therap. Ninewells Hosp. Dundee; Med. Regist. Qu. Alexandra Hosp. Cosham.; Wellcome Research Fell. Rigs Hosp.et Copenhagen, Denmark.

SAUNDERS, John Nevill Hall Hospital, Abergavenny NP7 7EG Tel: 01873 732432 Fax: 01873 732422 Email: john.saunders@gwent.wales.nhs.uk; 38 Belgrave Road, Abergavenny NP7 7AG Tel: 01873 853950 Email: saundersjohn@doctors.org.uk — MB BS Lond. 1968; MA Wales 1988; MD Lond. 1980; FRCP Lond. 1988; MRCP (UK) 1972; DCH Eng. 1974; Dip. Biochem. (Distinc.) Lond 1965. (St Thomas's) Cons. Phys. Nevill Hall Hosp. Abergavenny; Chairm.,Multi-centre Research Ethnics Comm. for Wales; Hon. Fell. Centre for Philosophy & Health Care, Univ. of Wales, Swansea. Socs: Chairm., Multicentre Research Ethics Comm. for Wales; Sec. Comm. Ethical Affairs Roy. Coll. Phys.s; Clin. Afairs Bd. Roy.Coll.Phys.s. Prev: Lect. (Med.) St. Thos. Hosp. Med. Sch. Lond.; Resid. (Paediat.) Univ. Brit. Columbia & Vancouver Childr. Hosp.; Regist. (Neurol.) Radcliffe Infirm. & Ch.ill Hosp. Oxf.

SAUNDERS, John Pendleside Medical Practice, Clitheroe Health Centre, Railway View Road, Clitheroe BB7 2JG Tel: 01200 422674 Fax: 01200 443652 — MB ChB 1978 Leeds; MRCGP 1982; Dip. Sports Med. Lond 1994; DRCOG 1982; Cert. FPA 1982. GP Clitheroe; Sch. Med. Off. Stoneyhurst Coll. Univ. Wales Swansea. Socs: Brit. Assn. Sport & Med.

SAUNDERS, John Alan (retired) Bede Cottage, Church Lane, Plummers Plain, Horsham RH13 6LU Tel: 01403 891368 — LMSSA 1958 Lond.; MA Oxf. 1961, BA 1954; FRCGP 1978, M 1968. Prev: Hon. Sen. Regist. King's/Brook Family Plann. Dept. King's Coll. Hosp. Lond.

SAUNDERS, Mr John Harris Weston Area NHS Trust, Grange Rd, Uphill, Weston Super Mare BS23 4T Tel: 01934 647090 Fax: 01934647176 Email: john.saunders@what.swest.nhs.uk — MB ChB 1968 Glas.; MBA Ed. 1989; FRCS Glas. 1973. Exec. Med. Dir. W. area NHS Health Trust. Prev: Cons. Surg. Gastrointestinal Unit W.. Gen. Hosp. Edin.; Sen. Regist. (Surg.) Hammersmith Hosp. & Roy. Postgrad. Med. Sch. Lond.; Regist. & SHO Rotat. (Surg.) W.. Infirm. Glas.

SAUNDERS, Joseph Peter, Lt.-Col. RAMC HMP Full Sutton, Moor Lane, Full Sutton, York YO4 1PS Tel: 01759 372447 Fax: 01759 371206 — MB BS 1964 Lond.; MSc (Social Med.) Lond. 1976; MRCS Eng. LRCP Lond. 1964; MFCM 1978; DTM & H Eng. 1974. (Guy's) Med. Off. HM Prison Serv. Socs: Fell. Roy. Soc. Med. & Soc. Pub. Health. Prev: Dir. Clin. Research Reckitt & Colman; Head Clin. Research & Developm. Riker Laborats. LoughBoro.; Chief (Clin. Epidemiol.) US Army Med. Research Unit Kuala Lumpur IMR.

SAUNDERS, Judith Patricia 27 Chesterfield Grove, London SE22 8RP — MB ChB 1993 Leeds.

SAUNDERS, Julia Mary Raleigh Unit, North Devon District Hospital, Barnstaple EX31 4JH Tel: 01271 322557 — MB ChB 1985 Bristol; MRCGP 1989.

SAUNDERS, Kay Butetown Health Centre, Loudoun Square, Cardiff CF10 5UZ Tel: 029 2048 3126 Fax: 029 2034 2122 — MB BCh 1981 Oxf.; BM BCh Oxf. 1981; MA Camb. 1983; MRCGP 1985. Singlehanded GP Butetown Cardiff. Prev: GP Middlesbrough; Asst. GP Middlesbrough Doctors Retainer Scheme; Trainee GP Cleveland VTS.

SAUNDERS, Professor Kenneth Barrett 77 Lee Road, London SE3 9EN — MB BChir 1962 Camb.; MA, MD Camb. 1966; DSc Lond. 1996; FRCP Lond. 1978, M 1963. (Camb. & St. Thos.) Emerit. Prof. Med. St. Geo. Hosp. Med. Sch. Lond. Prev: Prof. Med. St. Geo. Hosp. Med. Sch. Lond.; Sen. Lect. & Reader (Med.) Middlx. Hosp. Med. Sch.; Dean Fac. Med. Univ. Lond.

SAUNDERS, Kenneth Michael (retired) 8 Little Gaddesden House, Little Gaddesden, Berkhamsted HP4 1PL Tel: 01442 842531 — MB BS 1949 Lond. Prev: Capt. RAMC (TA).

SAUNDERS, Lynette Jayne Montgomery House Surgery, Piggy Lane, Bicester; 1 Blacksmith's Close, Church Road, Weston-on-the-Green, Bicester OX25 3FL — MB BS 1993 Lond.; DRCOG 1996. (St. Geo. Hosp. Med. Sch. Lond.) p/t Ass. GP under the Retainer Scheme. Prev: Severn NHS Trust; E. Gloucs NHS Trust; Gloucs Roy. Hosp. NHS Trust.

SAUNDERS, Madeleine Iris Family Planning Clinic, Woking Community Hospital, Heathside Road, Woking GU22 7HS Tel: 01483 714160 — MB BS 1975 Lond.; BSc (Hons. Biochem.) Sussex 1970. (King's Coll. Hosp.) SCMO (Family Plann.) Bournewood Community Trust.; Clin. Asst. - Blanche Hessot - St. Peter's Hosp.. Gyn. Socs: Fac. Fam. Plann. Prev: Research Regist. (O & G) King's Coll. Hosp. Lond.; SHO (O & G) King's Coll. Hosp. Lond.

SAUNDERS, Marcus Lee Lake Road Health Centre, Nutfield Place, Portsmouth PO1 4JT Tel: 023 9282 1201 Fax: 023 9287 5658 — MRCS Eng. LRCP Lond. 1987; BSc Lond. 1983; DRCOG 1991.

SAUNDERS, Margaret Teresa Cherrystones, Cambridge Road, Great Shelford, Cambridge CB2 5JU — MB BS 1978 Lond.; FRCP 2001 UK; MRCP (UK) 1982. (St. Geo.) Cons. (Palliat. Med.) Hinchingbrooke Hosp., Papworth Hospital & Lifespan Trust.

SAUNDERS, Mark Gary Marton Medical Centre, 1 Glastonbury Avenue, Blackpool FY1 6SF Tel: 01253 761321 Fax: 01253 792701; 84 Arundel Drive, Poulton-le-Fylde FY6 7TR — MB ChB 1987 Dundee; MRCGP 1993; T(GP) 1993; DA (UK) 1991. SHO (Psychiat.) Vict. Hosp. Blackpool. Prev: SHO (Gen. Surg., Geriat. & A & E) Auckland Gen. Hosp., NZ; SHO (Anaesth.) Vict. Hosp. Blackpool; Trainee GP Blackpool.

SAUNDERS, Mark Peter Department of Pharmacy, University of Manchester, Oxford Road, Manchester M13 9PL Tel: 0161 275 2428 — MB BS 1986 Lond.; MRCP (UK) 1990; FRCR 1994. MRC Train. Fell. Univ. Manch. Socs: BACR; AACR; ACP. Prev: Clin. Research Fell. ICRF Ch.ill Hosp. Oxf.; Regist. (Clin. Oncol.) Ch.ill Hosp. Oxf.

SAUNDERS, Michael College Grove 2, College Lane, Ripon HG4 4HE Tel: 01765 588396 Fax: 01423 330688 Email: michael.saunders@binternet.com — MB BS (Hons.) Lond. 1962; FRCP Lond. 1978, M 1965; FRCP Ed. 1973, M 1965. (Char. Cross) Emerit. Cons. Neurol. & Neuro-Rehabil. Newc. City Health NHS Trust & Nortallerton NHS Trust. Prev: Clin. Dir. Regional Rehabil. Centre Huntersmoor Hosp. Newc.

SAUNDERS, Michael Charles Little Morton, Tile Barn Lane, Brockenhurst SO42 7UE Tel: 01590 623376 Fax: 01590 623376 — MB BChir 1969 Camb.; DObst RCOG 1971; DA Eng. 1970. (St. Thos.)

SAUNDERS, Michael Graham The Surgery, 9 St. Georges Place, Brighton BN1 4GB Tel: 01273 601112 Fax: 01273 682408; 64 Peacock Lane, Brighton BN1 6WA Tel: 01273 506855 Fax: 01273 682408 — MB ChB 1955 Birm.

SAUNDERS, Mr Michael Peter 51 Summerdown Road, Eastbourne BN20 8DR Tel: 01323 732504 Email: bowel.inspector@virgin.net — MB BS Lond. 1982; BSc Lond. 1979, MS 1995; FRCS Eng. 1988; FRCS Ed. 1987. (Westm. Lond.) Cons. Gen. Surg. E.bourne Dist. Gen. Hosp. Socs: Assn. Surg.; Brit. Soc. Gastroenterol.; Assn. Coloproctol. Prev: Sen. Regist. (Gen. Surg.) Guy's Hosp. Lond.

SAUNDERS, Michael Thomas 3 Devonshire Place, London W1G 6HE Tel: 020 7486 6181 Fax: 020 7935 5503; 317 Andover Road, Newbury RG20 0LN Tel: 01635 48066 — MB BS 1972 Lond.; MRCS Eng. LRCP Lond. 1972; DObst RCOG 1976. (King's Coll. Hosp.) Chief Exec. Med. Defence Union. Socs: Fell. Roy. Soc. Med.; BMA. Prev: GP Berks.; Regist. (Med.), Ho. Phys. & Ho. Surg. Kings Coll. Hosp. Lond.; Med. Off. i/c Govt. Anguilla, Brit. W Indies.

SAUNDERS, Mr Michael William 2 Russell Road, Westbury Park, Bristol BS6 7UB — MB ChB 1988 Bristol; FRCS Eng. 1993.

SAUNDERS, Professor Michele Iris Marie Curie Research Wing, Centre for Cancer Treatment, Mount Vernon Hospital, Northwood HA6 2RN Tel: 01923 844533 Fax: 01923 844167 Email: mcrw@mtvern.co.uk — MD Lond. 1982; MB BS Lond. 1967; MRCS Eng. LRCP Lond. 1967; FRCR 1975; DMRT Eng. 1972; FRCP 1998. (Roy. Free) Cons. Radiother. & Oncol. Centre for Cancer Treatm. Mt. Vernon Hosp. N.wood; Prof. (Oncol.) Univ. Coll. & Middlx. Sch. of Med. Lond.; Director CRC Tumour Biol. & Radiat. Ther. Socs: Europ. Soc. Therapeutic Radiat. Oncol.; Brit. Oncol. Assn. Prev: Regist. Meyerstein Inst. Radiother. Middlx. Hosp. Lond.; Sen. Regist. St. Bart. Hosp. Lond. & Regional Radiother. Centre Mt. Vernon Hosp. N.wood.

SAUNDERS, Nicholas Charles 64 Peacock Lane, Brighton BN1 6WA — MB ChB 1992 Birm.

***SAUNDERS, Nicholas Michael** Olympus, The Avenue, Sherborne DT9 3AJ — MB BS 1998 Lond.; MB BS Lond 1998.

SAUNDERS, Mr Nigel James St George 146 Nottingham Street, Pitsmoor, Sheffield S3 9HL — MB ChB 1977 Manch.; FRCS Ed. 1983; MRCOG 1983.

SAUNDERS, Nigel John 64 Urquhart Road, Aberdeen AB24 5LX — MB ChB 1990 Aberd.

SAUNDERS, Pamela Wollaton Vale Health Centre, Wollaton Vale, Wollaton, Nottingham NG8 2GR Tel: 0115 928 2216 Fax: 0115 928 0590.

SAUNDERS, Paul Anthony 62 Rosemont Road, Aigburth, Liverpool L17 6DA — MB ChB 1982 Liverp.

SAUNDERS, Paul Richard Royal Surrey County Hospital, Egerton Road, Guildford GU2 7XX; Stock Farm House, Tilford Road, Churt, Farnham GU10 2LS — MB BS 1982 Lond.; FFA RCS Eng. 1987. Cons. Anaesth. Roy. Surrey Co. Hosp. Guildford. Prev: Sen. Regist. (Anaesth.) Bristol Roy. Infirm.; Sen. Regist. Rotat. (Anaesth.) Derriford Hosp. Plymouth; Vis. Asst. Prof. Dept. Anaesth. Univ. Texas Med. Sch. Dallas, USA.

SAUNDERS, Peter Courtenay The Surgery, 577 Carlton Road, Nottingham NG3 7AF Tel: 0115 958 0415 Fax: 0115 950 9245; 9 Gordon Rise, Mapperley, Nottingham NG3 5GB Tel: 0115 956 1654 — MB BS 1987 Lond.; DGM RCP Lond. 1990. Prev: GP Ashford; Trainee GP Ashford Kent VTS.

SAUNDERS, Mr Peter George 20 Ailsa Road, St. Margarets, Twickenham TW1 1QW Tel: 020 8891 1919; Flat 1, 14 Queen Anne St, London W1G 9LG Tel: 020 7935 8933 Fax: 020 7580 5985 Email: peter.saunders8@virgin.net — MB BS Lond. 1962; MRCS Eng. LRCP Lond. 1962; FRCOG 1982, M 1969. (St. Thos.) Hon. Cons. & Sen. Lect. (O & G) Univ. Coll. Lond. Hosps.; Dir. of Postgrad. Train. UCL. Socs: Fell. Roy. Soc. Med.; Blair Bell Res. Soc. Prev: Sen. Regist. (O & G) St. Thos. Hosp. Lond.; Res. Med. Off. Qu. Charlotte's Matern. Hosp.; Res. Surg. Off. Chelsea Hosp. Wom. Lond.

SAUNDERS, Mr Peter James Christian Medical Fellowship, 157 Waterloo Road, London SE1 8XN Tel: 020 7928 4694 Fax: 020 7620 2453; 86 Ladies Grove, St Albans AL3 5UB Tel: 01727 839157 Email: 101634.1361@compuseve.com — MB ChB 1982 Auckland; FRACS 1989. (Auckland, New Zealand) Stud. Sec. - Christian Med. Fell.sh. Socs: (Stud. Sec.) Christian Med. Fell.sh.; (Counc.) Med. Miss. Assn.

SAUNDERS, Peter Martin Donnington Health Centre, 1 Henley Avenue, Oxford OX4 4DH Tel: 01865 771313; 36 Argyle Street, Oxford OX4 1SS — MB ChB 1980 Sheff.; MRCGP 1988; DA (UK) 1986. Prev: SHO (Anaesth.) Luton & Dunstable Hosp.; SHO (Trauma & Orthop.) P.ss Margt. Hosp. Swindon; SHO (Anaesth.) Stoke Mandeville Hosp. Aylesbury.

SAUNDERS, Peter Warwick Brooklea Health Centre, Wick Road, Brislington, Bristol BS4 4HU Tel: 0117 971 1211 Fax: 0117 971 6402; The Coach House, Parkhouse Lane, Keynsham, Bristol BS31 2SG Tel: 0117 986 7450 — MB ChB 1981 Manch.; BSc St. And. 1978; MRCGP 1985; DRCOG 1985. GP Facilitator for HIV Avon; Bd. Mem. S. E. Bristol PCG.

SAUNDERS, Peter William Griffiths Newcastle General Hospital, Westgate Road, Newcastle upon Tyne NE4 6BE — MB ChB 1971 Bristol; MRCPath 1977.

SAUNDERS, Philip Bernard Ridgacre House Surgery, 83 Ridgacre Road, Quinton, Birmingham B32 2TJ Tel: 0121 422 3111; 128 Bunbury Road, Northfield, Birmingham B31 2DN Tel: 0121 475 1303 — MB ChB 1991 Birm.; MRCGP 1995. (Birminngham) GP Birm.

SAUNDERS, Philip Oliver Anandgiri, Cuddyshaw Plantations, Thorpe Underwood, York YO26 9ST — MB ChB 1994 Bristol.

SAUNDERS, Raymond Charles Oudot 26 Longdon Wood, Keston, Bromley BR2 6EW — MB BS 1946 Lond.; FFA RCS Eng. 1953; DA Eng. 1950. (Lond. Hosp.) Cons. Anaesth. Orpington & Sevenoaks Hosp. Gp. Prev: Asst. Lect. (Anaesth.) Univ. Glas.; Sen. Regist. Anaesth. Glas. Roy. Infirm.; Regist. Anaesth. Postgrad. Med. Sch. Lond.

SAUNDERS, Mr Richard Nigel The Willows, 461 Otley Road, Adel, Leeds LS16 6AJ Tel: 0113 261 3252; The Willows, 461 Otley Road, Adel, Leeds LS16 6AJ Tel: 0113 261 3252 — BChir 1995 Camb.; MBChir Camb. 1995; MA Camb. 1997; MRCS (Eng) 1998. (Addenbrooke's Hospital Cambridge) Regist Res. (Renal Transpl.ation) Leic. Gen. Hosp. Socs: MPS; BMA. Prev: SHO Surg.

Rotat. Qu.'s Med. Centre Nottm.; SHO (Cardiothor. Surg) City Hosp. Nottm; SHO (Gen. Surg.) QMC Nottm.

SAUNDERS, Sarah Josephine 16 Melbourn Road, Crookes, Sheffield S10 1NS — MB ChB 1989 Sheff.

***SAUNDERS, Simon Andrew** 14 Ambassador Drive, Liverpool L26 6LT Tel: 0151 487 9552; 14 Ambassador Drive, Liverpool L26 6LT Tel: 0151 487 9552 — MB ChB 1998 Liverp.; MB ChB Liverp 1998; BSc (Hons) Liverp 1992.

SAUNDERS, Mr Stephen Michael Francis 9 Cairns Close, Hill End, St Albans AL4 0EA Tel: 01727 863109 Email: s.m.saunders@ic.ac.uk; 6 Eversley Road, Sketty, Swansea SA2 9DA Tel: 01792 208789 Email: msaunders@which.net — MB BS 1993 Lond.; BSc (Hons.) Pharm. 1989 Lond.; FRCS Ed. 1997; MSc 1988. (Univ. Coll. Lond.) Clin. Teachg. Fell. (Gen. Surg.) N.wick Pk. Hosp. Harrow. Prev: Acting Regist. (Gen. Surg.) Roy. Surrey Co. Hosp. Guildford; Sen. SHO (Gen. Surg.) Roy. Surrey Co. Hosp. Guildford; SHO (Gen. Surg.) Lutonhand Dunstable Hosp.

SAUNDERS, Stuart Holly Cottage, Old Brampton, Chesterfield S42 7JH — MB ChB 1985 Glas. Prev: SHO (O & G & Paediat.) Chesterfield Roy. Hosp.; SHO (Psychiat.) Vict. Hosp. Blackpool.

SAUNDERS, Mr Stuart Henry St George's Hospital, London SW17 Tel: 020 8336 0011 Fax: 020 8336 1800; Pinewood Manor, George Road, Kingston upon Thames KT2 7NR Tel: 020 8336 0011 Fax: 020 8336 1800 Email: stuarts@a4u.com — MB ChB Birm. 1964; FRCS Eng. 1971; MRCS Eng. LRCP Lond. 1964. (Birm.) Cons. ENT St. Geo. Hosp. Lond.; Hon. Sen. Lect. Univ. Lond. Socs: Fell. Roy. Soc. Med.; Brit. Assn. Otol. Prev: Sen. Regist. (ENT) Radcliffe Infirm. Oxf.; Regist. (ENT) Char. Cross Hosp. Lond.; SHO (ENT) Lond. Hosp.

SAUNDERS, Timothy Hinton 1 Manorfields, Weston-on-the-Green, Bicester OX6 8FL Email: timsaunders@hotmail.com — MB BS 1994 Lond.; BSc Lond. 1991; MRCP (UK) 1997; FRCR Part1. (St Geos. Hosp.) SHO (Neurol.) Qu. Med. Centre Nottm.; Regist. (Radiol.) John Radcliffe Hosp. Oxf. Prev: SHO Rotat. P.ss Margt. Hosp. Swindon; SHO (Neurol.) Qu.s Med. Centr. Nottm.

SAUNDERS, Timothy Philip Heath Lane Medical Centre, Heath Lane, Chester CH3 5UJ Tel: 01244 348844 Fax: 01244 351057; Hollin Byre, Hollins Hill, Utkinton, Tarporley CW6 0JR Fax: 01829 752652 — MB ChB 1983 Liverp.; BSc Liverp. 1980. GP Health La. Med. Centre; Non Exec. Dir. S. Chesh. HA. Prev: SHO (Opth.) St. Pauls Eye Hosp. Liverp.

SAUNDERS, Westley Peter Penrhys Ty Isaf Farm Cottage, Pontygwaith, Ferndale, Ferndale CF43 3PW — MB BCh 1996 Wales.

SAUNDERS, William Alyn Russells Hall Hospital, Dudley DY1 2HQ Tel: 01384 456111 — MB BCh 1963 Wales; MD Wales 1968; FRCP Lond. 1993; MRCP (UK) 1973. (Cardiff) Cons. Phys. Dudley Gp. of Hosps.; Clin. Dir. (Med.) Dudley Gp. of Hosps.; Assoc. Prof. of Med., St. Geo.'s Univ., Grenada. Socs: Brit. Geriat. Soc. & W. Midl. Phys. Assn. Prev: Sen. Regist. (Geriat. Med.) Centr. Middlx. Hosp.; Regist. (Med.) Roy. Gwent Hosp. Newport; Asst. Lect. & Research Fell. in Pharmacol. Welsh Nat. Sch. Med. Cardiff.

SAUNDERS, William Anthony Meadow Cottage, Otterbourne, Winchester SO21 2EQ — MB BChir Camb. 1966; MA Camb. 1966; FRCPsych 1989, M 1972; DPM Eng. 1970; DCH Eng. 1967. (Middlx.) Cons. Psychiat Soton. Child & Family Guid. Serv.; Hon. Clin. Teach. Univ. Soton. Socs: (Ex-Chairm.) Assn. Profess. in Servs. for Adolesc. Prev: Cons. Psychiat. Leigh Hse. Adolesc. Units Chandlers Ford, Hants.; Sen. Regist. (Child Psychiat.) Bristol Roy. Hosp. Sick Childr.; Regist. Barrow Hosp. Bristol.

SAUNDERS, Yolande 27 Edmonscote, Argyle Road, Ealing, London W13 0HQ Tel: 020 823 8881 — MB BS 1984 Lond.; MRCGP 1989; Cert. Family Plann. JCC 1988. Specialist Regist. in Palliat. Med. N. Thames. Prev: SHO (Palliat. Med.) Isabol Hospice, Ou. Eliz. II Hosp. Welwyn Gdn. City; Princip. GP Hillingdon.

SAUNDERSON, Eric Martin North Street Medical Centre, 274 North Street, Romford RM1 4QJ Tel: 01708 764477 Fax: 01708 757656; 43 Wakerfield Close, Hornchurch RM11 2TH Tel: 01708 472420 — MB ChB 1971 Ed.; MSc Lond. 1997; FRCGP 1992, M 1976; DObst RCOG 1975. (Edinburgh) GP Romford; Dir. Educat. & Train. Barking & Havering HA. Socs: BMA. Prev: Chairm. Barking & Havering Med. Audit Advisory Gp.; Trainee GP Ilford & Dist. VTS.; Examr. RCGP.

SAUNGSOMBOON

SAUNGSOMBOON, Daranee 1 Claremont Court, Henleaze Park, Bristol BS9 4LR — MB BS 1989 Lond.; FRCS Ed. 1994. Specialist Regist. (A & E) Gloucs. Roy. Hosp. Prev: Specialist Regist. (A & E) Frenchay Hosp. Bristol.

SAUTELLE, Alexander Charles 16 Market Place, London NW11 6LB — MB BS 1997 Lond.

SAUVAGE, Mr Alain Daniel Paul West Suffolk Hospital, Bury St Edmunds IP33 2QZ — MB ChB 1984 Aberd.; FFAEM 2001; FRCS Ed. 1992. (Aberdeen) Cons. (A&E), W. Suff. Hosp., Bury St-Edmunds, Suff. Prev: Sen. Regist. (A & E), Luton; Fell. (Retrieval Med.), Sydney, Australia; Sen. Reg. (A&E), Addenbrooke's Hosp, Camb.

SAUVAGE, Josephine Ann Maria City Road Medical Centre, 190 City Rd, London EC1V 2HQ Tel: 0207 530 2750 Fax: 0207 530 2755; 68 St John's Villas, London NI9 3EG Tel: 0207 272 2893 — MB BS 1988 Lond.; BSc (Pharmacol.) Lond. 1985; MRCGP 1997; DCH RCP Lond. 1994. Princip. in Gen. Pract.

SAUVE, Philip Stuart 1A Bassetts Close, Orpington BR6 7AQ — MB BS 1998 Lond.; MB BS Lond 1998.

SAUVEN, Mr Paul David Department of Surgery, Broomfield Hospital, Chelmsford Tel: 01245 514073 Fax: 01245 514024 Email: paul.sauven@meht.nhs.uk; The Guild Hall, Great Waltham, Chelmsford CM3 1DE — MB BS 1975 Lond.; MS Lond. 1984; FRCS Eng. 1980; MRCS Eng. LRCP Lond. 1975. Cons. Surg. Broomfield Hosp. Chelmsford; Clin. Director Chelmsford & Colchester BrE. Screening Serv. Socs: Pres., Sect. Of Oncol. Fell. Roy. Soc. Med. (Mem. Counc. Sects. Surg. & Oncol.); (Hon. Treas.) Brit. Assn. Surgic. Oncol. Prev: Sen. Regist. (Surg.) St. Mary's Hosp. Lond.; Hon. Fell. Memor. Sloan-Kettering Cancer Center NY, USA.

SAVAGE, Adam James Flat 3R, 27 Scott St., Dundee DD2 2AH — MB ChB 1998 Dund.; MB ChB Dund 1998.

SAVAGE, Mr Adrian Paul Department of Surgery, Russells Hall Hospital, Dudley DY1 2HQ Tel: 01384 244093 Fax: 01384 244082 Email: asavage@compuserve.com; Langland House, 62 Salisbury Road, Moseley, Birmingham B13 8JT Tel: 0121 449 2249 — MB BChir 1978 Camb.; MA, MChir Camb. 1988; FRCS Eng. 1982. Cons. Surg. Gen. Surg. Dudley Gp. Hosps. Socs: Assn. Coloproctol.; Assn. Endoscopic Surgs.; Assn. Surg.s GB & I. Prev: Sen. Regist. John Radcliffe Hosp. Oxf.; Clin. Fell. Mass. Gen. Hosp. Boston, USA; Regist. Hammersmith Hosp. Lond.

SAVAGE, Aiden Piers 20 Melton Mews Cottages, Alkington Road, Whitchurch SY13 1SS — BM BS 1995 Nottm.

SAVAGE, Alexandra Clare 22 Brantingham Road, Elloughton, Brough HU15 1HX — MB BS 1992 Lond.

SAVAGE, Andrew William George 55 Huddleston Road, Tufnell Park, London N7 0AD — MB BS 1982 Lond. Med. Regist., Mt. Vernon Hosp.

SAVAGE, Ann (retired) Coddington Vineyard, Ledbury HR8 1JJ Tel: 01531 640668 Fax: 01531 640668 — MB BS 1962 Lond.; MRCPath 1977. Cons. Path. Qu. Eliz. Hosp. Prev: Sen. Regist. (Path.) S.mead Hosp. Bristol.

SAVAGE, Barbara Frances 2 The Brontes, Sun St., Haworth, Keighley BD22 8AF — MB BS 1987 Newc.

SAVAGE, Professor Caroline Olive Sylvia Renal Immunobiology Group, Birmingham Centre for Immune Regulation, University of Birmingham, Birmingham B15 2TT Tel: 0121 414 7042 Fax: 0121 414 6840; Renal Unit, Queen Elizabeth University Hospital, Birmingham B15 2TT Tel: 0121 472 1311 — MB BS 1978 Lond.; PhD Lond. 1987, BSc (Hons.) 1975, MD 1989; FRCS Lond. 1996. (The Royal London Hospital) Progr. Director, The Wellcome Trust, Clin. Research Facility in Birm. Prev: MRC Clin. Scientist & Hon. Cons. Phys. Clin. Research Centre Harrow & Hammersmith Hosp. Lond.; MRC Trav. Fell. Harvard Med. Sch. & Brigham Wom. Hosp. Boston, USA; Sen. Regist. (Nephrol. & Gen. Med.) Hammersmith Hosp. Lond.

SAVAGE, Catherine 16 St Kingsmark Avenue, Chepstow NP16 5LY — MB BCh 1994 Wales.

SAVAGE, Mr Christopher Smallwood (retired) Chimballs, High Easter, Chelmsford CM1 4RE Tel: 01245 231254 — MA Camb. 1943, MB BChir 1952; FRCS Eng. 1948; MRCS Eng., LRCP Lond. 1941. Prev: Cons. ENT Surg. Chelmsford Hosp. & S.end Hosp.

SAVAGE, David Anthony Lawson Road Surgery, 5 Lawson Road, Broomhill, Sheffield S10 5BU Tel: 0114 266 5180; 135 Walkley Bank Road, Walkley, Sheffield S6 5AN Tel: 0114 233 4035 — BM 1984 Soton.; MRCGP (Distinc.) 198; DRCOG 1988.

SAVAGE, Mr David Edmund Consulting Rooms, North London Nuffield Hospital, Cavell Dr., Uplands Park Road, Enfield EN2 7PR Tel: 020 8366 2122; The Wain House, 111 The Chine, Winchmore Hill, London N21 2EG Tel: 020 8360 4010 — MB BS 1946 Lond.; FRCS Eng. 1950; FRCOG 1968, M 1954. (Char. Cross) Socs: Fertil. Soc. Lond. Prev: Cons. Gyn. Highlands Gen. Hosp. Lond.; Cons. Obstetr. Thorpe Coombe Matern. Hosp. Lond.; Cons. Gyn. Finchley Manor Hosp. Lond.

SAVAGE, Deirdre Mary Castlereagh Medical Centre, 220 Knock Road, Belfast BT5 6QF Tel: 028 9079 8308 Fax: 028 9040 3776 — MB BCh BAO 1986 Belf.

SAVAGE, Denis Christopher Lungley (retired) Coddington Vineyard, Ledbury HR8 1JJ Tel: 01531 640668 Fax: 01531 640668 Email: denissavage@aol.com — MD Camb. 1975, MB 1959, BChir 1958; FRCP Lond. 1978, M 1962; MRCS Eng. LRCP Lond. 1958; FRCPCH 1997; DCH RCPS Glas. 1963. Prev: Cons. Paediat. & Endocrinol. Childr. Hosp. Bristol.

SAVAGE, Dereva Mary Fitzroy House, 4 Whiterock Road, Killinchy, Newtownards BT23 6PR — MB BCh BAO 1976 Belf.

SAVAGE, Douglas Saint Vincent Medical Centre, 77 Thorne Road, Doncaster DN1 2ET Tel: 01302 361318; 16 Avenue Road, Wheatley, Doncaster DN2 4AQ Tel: 01302 322541 — MB ChB 1974 Sheff.; MRCGP 1978. GP Doncaster.

SAVAGE, George Crieff Health Centre, King Street, Crieff PH7 3SA Tel: 01764 652456 Fax: 01764 655756; Fernbank, Ferntower Road, Crieff PH7 3DH Tel: 01764 652844 Email: gsavag@msn.com — MB ChB 1982 Glas.; BSc Glas. 1979; MRCP (UK) 1986; MRCCIP 1987. (Glas.) Med. Off. to Crieff Hydro Hotel, Morrison's Acad.; Community Phys. Stratheon; Clin. Asst. Creft Hosp. Socs: Perth and Kinross Immediate Med. Care Soc. Prev: GP Edin.; Regist. & SHO (Med.) S.. Gen. Hosp. Glas.

SAVAGE, Henry (retired) Heathfield, 2 Thorngrove Drive, Wilmslow SK9 1DQ Tel: 01625 524777 — MB ChB 1954 Liverp.; FRCP Lond. 1977, M 1964; DObst RCOG 1957. Prev: Cons. Phys. Macclesfield Dist. Gen. Hosp.

SAVAGE, James Smallwood Staithe Road Surgery, Staithe Road, Ludham, Great Yarmouth NR29 5AB Tel: 01692 678611 Fax: 01692 678295; The Beeches, Horsefen Road, Ludham, Great Yarmouth NR29 5QG Tel: 01692 678615 — MB BS 1975 Lond.; MRCGP 1981; DRCOG 1977. (Lond. Hosp.) Prev: Regist. (Med.) Launceston Gen. Hosp. Tasmania; SHO (O & G) Whipps Cross Hosp. Lond.; Ho. Surg. Lond. Hosp.

SAVAGE, Jane Rosemary Kennedy Way Surgery, Kennedy Way, Yate, Bristol BS37 4AA Tel: 01454 313849 Fax: 01454 329039; Bucklesbury, Engine Common, Yate, Bristol BS37 7PU — MB ChB 1971 Bristol; MB ChB (Hons.) Bristol 1971; MRCGP 1977. (Bristol) Prev: SHO S.mead Hosp. Bristol; SHO Ham Green Hosp. Bristol; SHO Bristol Childr. Hosp.

SAVAGE, John (retired) 2 Christ Church Terrace, Thorne Road, Doncaster DN1 2HU Tel: 01302 323888 — MB ChB 1940 Glas.; MD Glas. 1947. Prev: Cons. Vis. Dermatol. Roy. Infirm. Doncaster.

SAVAGE, John Robert, MBE Rutland, Burgage Lane, Southwell NG25 0ER Tel: 01636 812232 — MB BChir Camb. 1951. (St. Thos.) Prev: Ho. Surg. & Sen. Surg. Cas. Off. St. Thos. Hosp.; Flight Lt. RAF Med. Br.

SAVAGE, Professor Joseph Maurice Department Child. Health, Royal Victoria Hospital, Belfast BT12 Tel: 01232 894743 Fax: 01232 236455 Email: msavage@qub.ac.uk; 10 Kensington Gardens S., Belfast BT5 6NN — MB BCh BAO 1971 Belf.; FRCP Lond. 1989; DCH RCPSI 1973; FRCPCH 1994. Cons. Paediat. & Paediat. Nephrol. Roy. Belf. Hosp. Sick Childr.; Sen. Lect. (Child Health) Qu. Univ. Belf.; Prof. Paediat., Qu.s Univ., Belf.; Asst. Head of Med. Sch. (Educat.) and Director Med. Educat. Unit Qu.s Univ. Belf.. Socs: Eur. Soc. Paediat. Nephrol.; Brit. Paediat. Assn.; Renal Assn. Prev: Lect. (Child Health) Manch. Univ.; MRC Research Fell. Inst. Child Health Lond.

SAVAGE, Julie Elizabeth Evington Lodge, Tewkesbury Road, Coombe Hill, Gloucester GL19 4AS — MB BS 1982 Lond. Family Plann. Off. & Sch. Med. Off. Lond.

SAVAGE, Kathryn Jane Tain and Fearn Area Medical Practice, Health Centre, Scotsburn Road, Tain IV19 1PR Tel: 01862 892759 Fax: 01862 892579 — MB BS 1992 Lond.

SAVAGE, Margaret 5 Savoy Gardens, Ulverston LA12 9LR — MB BChir 1957 Camb.; MB BChir Camb. 1958; BA Camb. 1958; DObst RCOG 1966. (Camb. & St. Mary's)

SAVAGE, Margery Jane Peg House Farm, Slad Road, Stroud GL5 1RG — MB BS 1997 Lond.

SAVAGE, Marie Catherine Ysbyty Gwynedd, Bangor LL57 2PW; Dromana, The Promenade, Llanfairfechan LL33 0BU — MB ChB 1990 Aberd.

SAVAGE, Mark Edmund Regent House Surgery, 21 Regent Road, Chorley PR7 2DH Tel: 01257 264842 Fax: 01257 231387 — MB BS 1981 Lond.; DRCOG 1989.

SAVAGE, Mark William Bury General Hospital, Walmersley Road, Bury BL9 6PG Tel: 0161 705 3315 Fax: 0161 705 3332 Email: m.savage@bury_pgmc.nwest.nhs.uk; 36 Aire Drive, Bradshaw, Bolton BL2 3FX Email: savagemw@aol.com — MB ChB 1986 Manch.; MRCP (UK) 1989; MD Manch. 1987. (Manch.) Cons. Phys. (Diabetes & Endocrinol.) Bury Gen. Hosp. Socs: Endocrine Soc.; Brit. Diabetic Assn. Prev: Sen. Regist. (Gen. Med. Diabetes & Endocrinol.) Liverp.; Research Fell. Univ. Liverp.; Regist. (Med. Endocrinol. & Diabetes) Hope Hosp. Salford.

SAVAGE, Professor Martin Oswald Paediatric Endocrinology Section, Department Endocrinolo, St. Bartholomew's Hospital, West Smithfield, London EC1A 7BE Tel: 020 7601 8468 Fax: 020 7601 8468 Email: m.o.savage@mds.qmw.ac.uk; 55 Doneraile Street, London SW6 6EW Tel: 020 7736 6413 — MB BChir Camb. 1969; MD Camb. 1980, MA 1968; FRCP Lond. 1986; MRCP (UK) 1972; FRCPCH 1997. (St. Bart.) Reader (Paediat Endocrinol.) & Hon. Cons. Paediat. St. Bart. Hosp. Lond. Socs: Roy. Soc. Med. (Mem. Endocrinol. & Paediat. Sects.); Sec. Europ. Soc. Paediat. Endocrinol. Prev: Sen. Regist. (Med.) Hosp. Sick Childr. Gt. Ormond St. Lond.; Clin. Lect. (Growth & Developm.) Inst. Child Health Lond.; Research Fell. (Paediat. Endocrinol.) Hôp. St. Vincent de Paul, Paris.

SAVAGE, Nigel Allen Rivermead Gate Medical Centre, 123 Rectory Lane, Chelmsford CM1 1TR Tel: 01245 348688 Fax: 01245 458800; 92 Broomfield Road, Chelmsford CM1 1SS — MB ChB 1982 Liverp. GP Chelmsford.; Asst. Prison Med. Off.

SAVAGE, Nigel John Twin Oaks Medical Centre, Ringwood Road, Bransgore, Christchurch BH23 8AD Tel: 01425 672741 Fax: 01425 674333 — MB BS 1987 Lond.; MRCGP 1992; T(GP) 1992. (St. Geo. Hosp. Lond.)

SAVAGE, Pamela 38 Runnymede Road, Twickenham TW2 7HF — MB BS 1976 Lond.; DCH Eng. 1980. Complementary Pract. Middlx. Prev: Clin. Asst. NE Lond. Blood Transfus. Serv. Lond.; Regist. (Community Med.) SE Thames RHA; SHO (Path., Paediat. & O & G) Lewisham Hosp. Lond.

SAVAGE, Mr Paul Thwaites (retired) 7 Akenside Road, London NW3 5RA Tel: 020 7435 5305 — MB BS 1939 Lond.; MB BS (Hons.) Lond. 1939; FRCS Eng. 1947; MRCS Eng. LRCP Lond. 1939. Prev: Cons. Surg. Whittington Hosp.

SAVAGE, Mr Peter Edmund Annesley (retired) 2 Lower Shapter Street, Topsham, Exeter EX3 0AT Tel: 01392 874983 Fax: 01392 874983 Email: peasavage@compuserve.com — MB BS Lond. 1960; MS Lond. 1972; FRCS Eng. 1964. Consg. Surg. Qu. Mary's Hosp. Sidcup. Prev: Med. Dir. Qu. Mary's Sidcup NHS Trust.

SAVAGE, Mr Philip Edmund Stoke Mandeville Hospital NHS Trust, Mandeville Road, Aylesbury HP21 8AL Tel: 01296 316914; The White House, Main Street, Gawcott, Buckingham MK18 4HZ Tel: 01280 812264 — MB BS 1976 Lond.; MB BS (Distinc. Surg.) Lond. 1976; MRCS Eng. LRCP Lond. 1976; FRCS Lond. 1981; FRCS Ed. 1981; FRCR 1985. (St. Bart.) Cons. Radiol. Stoke Mandeville Hosp. Aylesbury. Prev: Sen. Regist. & Regist. (Diagn. Radiol.) St. Geo. Hosp. Lond.; Jun. Regist. (Gen. Surg.) St. Bart. Hosp. Lond.

SAVAGE, Mr Philip Edward Warren Lodge, Kington Road, Thornbury, Bristol BS9 4RR — MB BS 1967 Lond.; FRCS Ed. 1976; FRCOG 1988, M 1975; DObst 1969. (St. Bart.) Cons. (O & G) S.mead & Frenchay HA. Bristol.; Clin. Director, Wom.s Health, N. Bristol NHS Trust. Prev: Cons. Sen. Lect. Dept. Obst. Univ. Bristol; Demonst. in Anat. Bristol Univ.; Sen. Ho. Surg. Bristol United Hosps.

SAVAGE, Philip Michael Velindre Hospital, Velindre Rd, Whitchurch, Cardiff CF14 2TS Tel: 029 2061 5888; 7 Melingriffith Drive, Whitchurch, Cardiff CF14 2TS Tel: 029 2052 0748 — MB ChB 1987 Bristol; PhD Lond. 1994; BSc Bristol 1982; MRCP (UK) 1994. Cons. (Med. Oncol) Veliadre Hosp Cardiff & Singleton Hosp Swansea. Prev: Sen. Regist. (Med. Oncol.) Hammersmith & Char. Cross Hosps.

SAVAGE, Rachel Ann 14 Mount Pleasant Avenue N., Radipole, Weymouth DT3 5HW — MB BS 1996 Lond.

SAVAGE, Richard Anthony Stockwell Group Practice, 107 Stockwell Road, London SW9 9TJ Tel: 020 7274 3225 Fax: 020 7738 3005; 53 Dalkeith Road, London SE21 8LT Tel: 020 8670 3334 Fax: 020 8761 5332 Email: richard.savage@kcl.ac.uk — MB BS 1970 Lond.; MSc (Gen. Pract.) Lond. 1989; MRCS Eng. LRCP Lond. 1970; FRCGP 1994, M 1975; DObst RCOG 1972. (St. Thos.) GP Lond.; Chairm. S. Lond. Organisation of VTS; Course Organiser St. Thos. Hosp. VTS. Prev: RCGP Counc. Rep. S. Lond. Fac.; Hon. Clin. Tutor (Gen. Pract.) Guy's Hosp. Lond.; Vis. Med. Off. Home for Aged Jews Lond.

SAVAGE, Richard Henry 2 Richmond Road, Taunton TA1 1EW Tel: 01823 286251 Fax: 01823 327199 Email: mhsavage@doctors.org.uk — MB BS Lond. 1971; BSc Lond. 1968; MRCS Eng. LRCP Lond. 1970; MFHom 1978; DObst RCOG 1972. (Guy's) Indep. Cons. Complementary Med. Taunton. Prev: GP St. Germans, Cornw.; SHO (Geriat.) Taunton & Som. Hosp. (Trinity Br.); SHO (Paediat.) Taunton & Som. Hosp. (MusGr. Pk. Br.).

SAVAGE, Mr Robert Royal Gwent Hospital, Cardiff Road, Newport NP20 2UB — MB BS 1976 Lond.; MS Lond. 1991, MB BS 1976; FRCS Ed. (Orth.) 1989; FRCS Eng. 1981. Cons. Traum. & Orthop. Surg. Roy. Gwent Hosp. Socs: Fell. BOA; BSSH. Prev: Sen. Regist. (Traum. & Orthop. Surg.) Cardiff Roy. Infirm.

SAVAGE, Robert Boundary House, Shields Road, Stobhill, Morpeth NE61 6LA Tel: 01670 516972 Email: rbsavage@msn.com; 70 Church Street, Kilwinning KA13 6BD — MB ChB 1991 Dundee; FRCA 1996. Specialist Regist. (Anaesth.) Newc. u. Tyne. Socs: BMA; Assn. Anaesth.; Intens. Care Soc. Prev: SHO (ImmunoDefic.) King's Cross Hosp. Dundee.

SAVAGE, Ronald Malcolm (retired) 44 Station Road, Cogenhoe, Northampton NN7 1LU — MB ChB Ed. 1956; DObst. RCOG 1962.

SAVAGE, Rosemary Anne Falcon Road Surgery, 47 Falcon Road, Battersea, London SW11 2PH Tel: 020 7228 1619/3399 Fax: 020 7924 3375 — MB BS 1981 Lond.; MRCS Eng. LRCP Lond. 1981; MRCGP 1985; DRCOG 1983. (Char. Cross)

SAVAGE, Sandra Jill Dormer Cottage, 28 Deepdene Wood, Dorking RH5 4BQ Tel: 01306 889374 — MB ChB Bristol 1967; DObst RCOG 1971.

SAVAGE, Stephanie Jane — MB BCh BAO 1995 Belf.; MRCGP 1999; DCH Dub. 1998; DRCOG Lond. 1997. (Queen's Univ. Belf.) GP Locum N.ern Irel.; Doctor of Clin. Serv.s, Action Cancer, MarlBoro. Pk., Belf. Socs: Diplomates Assn. RCOG.

SAVAGE, Suzanne Jane The Surgery, St Andrews Hall, Guildersfield Road, London SW16 5LS Tel: 020 8765 4901; 53 Dalkeith Road, London SE21 8LT Tel: 020 8670 3334 — MB BS 1973 Lond.; FRCGP 1995, M 1979; DObst RCOG 1974. (St. Thos.) Assoc. Dean (PostGrad. Gen. Pract. Educ.) Lond.

SAVAGE, Timothy Richmond Plympton Health Centre, Mudge Way, Plymouth PL7 1AD Tel: 01752 341474 — MB BS 1964 Lond.; MRCS Eng. LRCP Lond. 1964; DObst RCOG 1967; DA Eng. 1967. (Univ. Coll. Hosp.) Socs: Plymouth Med. Soc.

SAVAGE, Victoria Elizabeth 3 Cumberland Avenue, Huddersfield HD2 2JJ — MB ChB 1990 Ed.

SAVAGE, Professor Wendy Diane Academy of Obstetrics & Gynaecology, The Royal School of Medicine & Dentistry, 51-53 Bartholomew Clinic, London EC1 Tel: 020 7601 8260 Fax: 020 7600 1439 Email: w.savage@qmw.ac.uk; 19 Vincent Terrace, London N1 8HN Tel: 020 7837 7635 Fax: 020 7837 7635 — MRCS Eng. LRCP Lond. 1960; MB Camb. 1961, BChir 1960; FRCOG 1985, M 1971; MSc Public Health 1997. (Lond. Hosp.) Sen. Lect. (O & G) Acad. Dept. St.Barts. & Roy. Lond. Sch. Med.& Dent.; Hon. Vis. Prof. Middlx. Univ. Fac. Social Sci. Socs: Fell. Roy. Soc. Med. (Mem. Forum Matern. & Newborn); Med. Soc. Inst. Psychosexual Med.; BMA (Chairm. Local Div. Islington). Prev: Specialist (Obst. Gyn. & Venereol.) Cook Hosp. Gisborne, NZ; Regist. Roy. Free. Hosp. Lond. & Kenyatta Nat. Hosp. Nairobi.

SAVANI, Alena Charlotta Konstancie Colne House Surgery, 99A Uxbridge Road, Rickmansworth WD3 2DJ Tel: 01923 776295 Fax: 01923 777744; 8 Meadow Way, Rickmansworth WD3 7NQ Tel: 01923 896301 — MRCS Eng. LRCP Lond. 1973. (Lond. Hosp.) Prev: SHO (O & G & Paediat.) & Ho. Phys. Lond. Hosp.

SAVANI

SAVANI, Narendra Yashlal Colne House Surgery, 99A Uxbridge Road, Rickmansworth WD3 2DJ Tel: 01923 776295 Fax: 01923 777744; 8 Meadow Way, Rickmansworth WD3 7NQ Tel: 01923 896301 — MB BS 1977 Mysore; MRCS Eng. LRCP Lond. 1977; DRCOG 1977. (Kasturba Med. Coll.) Prev: SHO (Paediat. & Obst. Gyn.) Heatherwood Hosp. Ascot.; Ho. Off. (Surg.) Kent & Canterbury Hosp.; Ho. Phys. Ramsgate Dist. Hosp.

SAVANI, Ramesh Karsandas Manor Top Medical Centre, Ridgeway Road, Sheffield S12 2SS — MB BS 1963 Bombay; MRCOG 1969.

SAVANI, U K Manor Top Medical Centre, Rosehearty, Ridgeway Road, Sheffield S12 2SS Tel: 0114 239 8324.

SAVE, Vicki Elaine Ninewells Hospital and Medical School, Level 6, Department of Molecular and Cellular Pathology, Dundee DD1 9SY Tel: 01382 660111 Email: v.e.save@dundee.ac.uk; 48 Laxton Drive, Lenzie, Glasgow G66 5LR Tel: 0141 776 2178 — MB ChB 1990 Glas.; DRCPath 1996. (Glasgow) Lect. & Hon. Sen. Regist. Tayside Univ. Hosp. Prev: Lect. & Hon Regist., Tayside Univ. Hosp Trust; Regist., Tayside Univ. Hosp Trust; STTO, Tayside Univ. Hosp Trust.

SAVEGE, Peter Beverley Barnet, Enfield & Haringey Health Authority, Holbrook House, Cockfosters Road, Barnet EN4 0DR Tel: 020 8272 5500 Fax: 020 8272 5700; 1 New House Park, St Albans AL1 1UA Tel: 01727 854870 — LMSSA Lond. 1964; MSc (Community Med.) Lond. 1989; DObst RCOG 1966. (St. Bart.) p/t Acting Head of Healthcare Servs. Advice, Barnet, Enfield & Haringey Health Auth. Socs: BMA. Prev: Asst. Director Pub. Health, Herts. Health Agency; Med. Dir. Kent FHSA; GP St. Albans.

SAVEGE, Timothy Michael (retired) — MB BS 1963 Lond.; MRCS Eng. LRCP Lond. 1963; FFA RCS Eng. 1968. Cons. (Anaesth.) Lond. Hosp. Prev: Sen. Lect. & Asst. Dir. Anaesth. Unit Lond. Hosp. Med. Coll.

SAVERIMUTTU, Ritar Kulasegaram Abercromby Health Centre, Grove Street, Edge Hill, Liverpool L7 7HG Tel: 0151 709 2806; Susanella, Chalfont Road, Allerton, Liverpool L18 9UP Tel: 0151 427 4853 Fax: 0151 427 4853 — MRCS Eng. LRCP Lond. 1964; LMSSA Lond. 1961. (Liverp.) Family Pract. Liverp. AHA (T). Socs: Liverp. Med. Inst.; Merseyside Medico-Legal Soc. & BMA. Prev: Hosp. Practitioner, Olive Mt. Childr. Hosp. Liverp. AHA (T); Med. Off. (A & E) Alder Hey Childr. Hosp. Liverp.; Paediat. Regist. Liverp. RHB.

SAVERYMUTTU, Sethna Hugo Broomfield Hospital, Broomfield, Chelmsford CM1 7ET — MB BS 1976 Lond.; BSc (Hons.) Lond. 1973, MD 1989, MB BS (Hons.) 1976; MRCP (UK) 1978. Cons. Phys. Broomfield Hosp. Chelms. Socs: Brit. Assn. Liver Dis. Prev: Lect. (Med.) St. Geo. Hosp. Lond.; Regist. Hammersmith Hosp. Wellcome Research Fell.; Ho. Phys. King's Coll. Hosp.

SAVERYMUTTU, Therese Manel Cookley Surgery, 1 Lea Lane, Cookley, Kidderminster DY10 3TA Tel: 01562 850770 — MB BS 1976 Lond.; MRCGP 1981; DRCOG 1981.

SAVIDGE, Geoffrey Francis Haemophilia Centre, St. Thomas Hospital, London SE1 7EH Tel: 020 7928 9292 Fax: 020 7401 3125 — MB BChir 1965 Camb.; MB BChir Camb. 1966; MD Stockholm 1979; MA Camb. 1979; Med. Lic. Scandinavia 1970; Specialist Accredit. Med. Path. Scandinavia 1977. Dir. Haemophilia Refer. Centre; Sen. Lect. & Hon. Cons. Haemat. St. Thos. Hosp. Med. Sch. Lond.; Prof. Coagulation Med. 1997. Socs: Amer. Soc. Haemat.; NY Acad. Sc.

SAVIDGE, Malcolm John 16 St Cross Court, Kingsgate Road, Winchester SO23 9PZ — MB BS 1989 Lond.; FFA RCSI 1996. (St. Mary's Hosp. Med. Sch. Coll. Surgs. Dub.) Specialist Regist. & Anaesth. Wessex Sch. of Anaesth. S.hampton. Socs: Assn. Anaesth. of GB & Irel.; Pain. Soc and BMA. Prev: Regist. (Anaesth.) Soton. Univ. Hosps. Trust; SHO (A & E) & Ho. Off. (Surg. & Urol.) N.wick Pk. Hosp.; Ho. Off. (Med.) St. Chas. Hosp. Lond.

SAVIDGE, Ronald Stewart (retired) Willows End, Tannington Road, Bedfield, Woodbridge IP13 7JB Tel: 01728 628462 — MD Lond. 1952, MB BS 1939; FRCP Lond. 1969, M 1948; MRCS Eng. LRCP Lond. 1939. Prev: Hon. Cons. Phys. Bury AHA & Rossendale Gen. Hosp.

SAVILE, Christopher Wrey (retired) 133 Wollaton Vale, Nottingham NG8 2PE — MB BChir 1952 Camb.; FRCGP 1985; DTM & H Eng. 1955. Prev: GP E.bourne.

SAVILL, Gary Alen Airedale General Hospital, Skipton Road, Steeton, Keighley BD20 6TD Tel: 01535 652511 Email: gary.savill@group.airedale.northy.nhs.uk; Email: gsavill@doctors.org.uk — MB BCh 1987 Wales; BSc (Biochem.) Cardiff 1984; MRCP (UK) 1992. (University of Wales College of Medicine) Cons. Paediat. Airedale Gen. Hosp. Socs: Roy. Coll. Paediat. & Child Health.

SAVILL, Guy (retired) 50 St Peter Street, Tiverton EX16 6NR Tel: 01884243907 — MRCS Eng. LRCP Lond. 1940; DPhysMed. Eng. 1949. Prev: Cons. Rheum. & Rehabil. Soton. & I. of Wight Gps. Hosps.

SAVILL, Hugh Jonathan Hammett Square Surgery, Hammett Square, Tiverton EX16 6LR Tel: 01884 255353 Fax: 01884 242865; The Old Forge, Stoodleigh, Tiverton EX16 9PH Tel: 013985 202 — MB BS 1977 Lond.; MA Camb.; MRCGP 1983. (Univ. Coll. Hosp.) GP Tiverton; Clin Asst. to Unit for Learning Disabil.. Prev: Trainee GP Univ. Coll. Hosp. Lond.; Trainee GP Kentish Town Health Centre; Winston Ch.ill Memor. Trust Trav. Fell.sh.

SAVILL, Professor John Stewart University of Edinburgh, Department of Medicine, Royal Infirmary of Edinburgh, Edinburgh EH3 9YW Tel: 0131 536 2263 Fax: 0131 536 3255; 133 Wollaton Vale, Wollaton, Nottingham NG8 2PE Tel: 0115 922 3315 Fax: 0115 922 3315 — MB ChB 1981 Sheff.; PhD Lond. 1989; BA Oxf. 1978; MB ChB (Hons.) Sheff. 1981; FRCP Lond. 1994; MRCP (UK) 1984; FRCP Edin 2000; BMedSci 1998. Prof. (Med.) Univ. of Edin.; Head of Centre for Inflammation Research; Director of Univ. of Edin./Med. Socs: (Comm. Phys.) Med. Research Soc.; Internat. Soc. Nephrol.; Founder Fell. Acad. of Med. Prev: Wellcome Trust Sen. research fell., Sen. Lect. & Hon. Cons. Renal Unit. Dept. of Med., Roy. Postgrad. Med. Sch. Lond.; Prof. (Med.) Univ. of Nottm.

SAVILL, Peter John 8 Churchward Gardens, Hedge End, Southampton SO30 2XP Tel: 01489 795552 Email: pjsav@epulse.net — MB BS 1994 Lond.; BSc (1st cl. Hons.) Lond. 1991, MB BS 1994. (Roy. Free Hosp. Sch. of Med. Univ. of Lond.)

SAVILLE, Gillian Mary Trelake Cottage, Trelake Lane, Treknow, Tintagel PL34 0EW — MB ChB 1990 Bristol.

SAVILLE, Mark Anthony Waterlooville Health Centre, Dryden Close, Waterlooville PO7 6AL Tel: 023 9225 7321 — MB BCh 1987 Wales; MRCGP 1993; DRCOG 1991.

SAVILLE, Mark Jonathan 10 Moons Close, Ashingdon, Rochford SS4 3HA — MB BS 1997 Lond.

SAVILLE, Melanie Karen 6 Redbourne House, 24 Redbourne Avenue, London N3 2BT — MB BS 1993 Lond.

SAVILLE, Sheila Dorothy Devonshire Lodge Health Centre, Abbotsbury Gardens, Eastcote, Pinner Tel: 020 8866 0121 — MB BS 1966 Durh. (Newc.) Socs: BMA. Prev: SHO (O & G) Bensham Hosp. Gateshead; SHO (Paediat.) Qu. Eliz. Hosp. Gateshead.

SAVILLE, Stephanie 30 Oakhill Court, Edge Hill, London SW19 4NR Tel: 020 8946 4621 — MB BCh BAO 1949 Dub.; FFA RCS Eng. 1954; DA Eng. 1953. Socs: Assn. Anaesth. Prev: Sen. Regist. (Anaesth.) W.m. Hosp.; Regist. St. Bart. Hosp. Lond. & Albany Hosp. New York; Res. Anaesth. Bristol Roy. Infirm.

SAVIN, Garry Edward 8th Floor, The London Clinic, 149 Harley Street, London W1N 2DH Tel: 020 7935 444 Ext: 3146 — MB BS 1988 Lond.; MRCGP 1993; DRCOG 1991. (Royal Free Hospital) Health Screening Doctor & Gen. Practitioner & Clin. Adviser to Nuffield Hosps. Health Screening.

SAVIN, Helena Mary 11 Bedford Street, Iffley Fields, Oxford OX4 1SU Tel: 01865 245479 — MB BS 1989 Lond.; MRCGP 1995; DCH RCP Lond. 1991. (St. Geo.) Prev: Clin. Asst. (Gen. Pract.).

SAVIN, John Andrew The Royal Infirmary, Lauriston Place, Edinburgh EH3 9YW Tel: 0131 536 1000 Fax: 0131 337 7768; 86 Murrayfield Gardens, Edinburgh EH12 6DQ Tel: 0131 377 7768 Fax: 0131 337 7768 — MB BChir Camb. 1959; MA Camb. 1960, BA (1st cl. Hons.) 1956, MD 1978; FRCP Ed. 1979, M 1973; FRCP Lond. 1978, M 1965; DIH Soc. Apoth. Lond. 1964. (Cambridge and ST Thos.) Socs: (Ex-Pres.) Dowling Club; Roy. Soc. Med. (Ex-Pres. Sect. Dermat.); (Ex-Pres.) Brit. Assn. Dermat. Prev: Sen. Regist. (Dermat.) St. Thos. Hosp. Lond.; Sen. Regist. & Clin. Tutor St. John's Hosp. Dis. of Skin Lond.; Regist. Skin Dept. St. Geo. Hosp. Lond.

SAVIN, Paul Thomas Grove House Practice, St. Pauls Health Centre, High St, Runcorn WA7 1AB Tel: 01928 566561 Fax: 01928 590212; 54 Malpas Road, Runcorn WA7 4AJ — MB ChB 1978 Manch.

SAVINE, Rachel 26 Calton Gardens, Bath BA2 4QG — BM 1998 Soton.; BM Soton 1998.

SAVINE, Richard Laurence Edwin Flat 6, Forest Close, Chislehurst BR7 5QS — MB BS 1992 Lond.

SAVLA, Meenakshi Premchand Highfield Surgery, The Heights, Jupiter Drive, Hemel Hempstead HP2 5NT Tel: 01442 65322 Fax: 01442 256641; 57 Cedar Road, Berkhamsted HP4 2LB Tel: 01442 877682 — MB BS 1979 Newc.; MA Oxf. 1974; MRCGP 1983; DRCOG 1982.

SAVLA, Navin Chandra Woodbury Unit, Department of Psychiatry for the Elderly, James Lane, Leytonstone, London E11 1NR Tel: 020 8535 6843 Fax: 020 8535 6829; 80 Overton Drive, Wanstead, London E11 2NW Tel: 020 8989 0859 — MB BS 1967 Osmania; FRCPsych 1990, M 1972; DPM Eng. 1971. (Gandhi Med. Coll. Hyderabad) Cons. Psych. Woodbury Unit; Clin. Dir. Ment. Health Forest Healthcare Trust; Hon. Sen. Lect. (Psychiat.) UCL. Socs: World Psych. Assn.; Overseas Doctors Assn.; Indian Med. Assn. Prev: Clin. Tutor (Psychiat.) Cherry Knowle Hosp. Ryhope; Sen. Regist. St. Crispin's Hosp. N.ampton; Regist. St. John's Hosp. Lincoln & Cane Hill Hosp. Coulsdon.

SAVORY, Jane Catherine Northbay House, Balnabodach, Castlebay HS9 5UT — MB BS 1997 Lond.

SAVORY, Jonathan Nigel Church Close Surgery, 3 Church Close, Boston PE21 6NB Tel: 01205 311133 Fax: 01205 358986 — MB BS 1968 Lond.; FRCGP 1988, M 1974.

SAVORY, Stephen John The Swineshead Medical Group, Church Lane, Swineshead, Boston PE20 3JA Tel: 01205 820204 Fax: 01205 359050; Jenny Hoolet House, South Road Tetford, Horncastle LN9 6QB, USA — MB BS 1991 Lond.; MRCGP 1995; DFFP 1995; T(GP) 1995. (St. Geo. Hosp. Med. Sch.) GP Princip. Prev: GP Princip., James St. Surg., Boston; GP/Regist. Birchwood Med. Pract. Lincoln; Trainee GP/SHO Lincoln Co. Hosp. VTS.

SAVUNDRA, Joseph Edward Hurst Farm Surgery, Chapel Lane, Milford, Godalming GU8 5HU Tel: 01483 415885 — MB BS 1980 Lond.; BA Oxf. 1976; MRCS Eng. LRCP Lond. 1979; DRCOG 1985.

SAVUNDRA, Peter Aloysius Northwick Park Hospital, Watford Rd, Harrow HA1 3UJ Tel: 020 8869 2030; Burness Farm, Guildford Road, Pirbright, Woking GU24 0LW — BM BCh 1976 Oxf.; MA, BM BCh Oxf. 1976; MSc Lond. 1992; MRCPI 1988; DCH RCP Lond. 1993. (Oxf.) Cons. Phys. (Audiol.) N.wick Pk. Hosp. Lond.; Lect. Inst. Laryngol. & Otol. Univ. Lond. Prev: Sen. Regist. (Neuro-Otol.) Nat. Hosp. for Neurol. & Neurosurg. Lond.; Hon. Sen. Regist. Hosp. Sick Childr. Lond.

SAVVA, Nicholas 48 Grange Road, Netley Abbey, Southampton SO31 5FE — MB BS 1994 Lond.

SAVVAS, Michael Department of Gynaecology, University Hospital Lewisham, Lewisham High St., London SE13 6LH Tel: 020 8333 3000 Fax: 020 8690 1963 — MB BS 1980 Lond.; MRCOG 1986. Cons. O & G & Hon. Sen. Lect. Univ. Hosp. Lewisham. Socs: Roy. Soc. Med. (Counc. Mem. Sect. Obst. & Gyn.). Prev: Sen. Regist. King's Coll. Hosp. Lond.; Regist. (O & G) W.m. Hosp. Lond.; SHO (O & G) Lond. Hosp.

SAVVAS, Savvakis 64 Ashington Road, Eastbourne BN22 9DY — MB BS 1987 Lond.; BSc (2nd cl. Hons.) Physiol. Lond. 1983.

SAVVIDOU, Louiza Kyrou Lister Hospital, Coreys Mill Lane, Stevenage SG1 4AB; 25B Thurlow Road, London NW3 5PP — MB BS 1988 Lond.

SAVY, Lloyd Edward 251 Petersham Road, Richmond TW10 7DA — MB BS 1985 Lond.; BSc Lond. 1981, MB BS 1985; FRCR 1992. Cons. & Hon. Sen. Lect. in (NeuRd.iol.) Roy. Free. Hosp. & Roy. Nat. Throat, Nose & Ear Hosp. Lond. Prev: Sen. Regist. (Diag. Radiol.) Nat. Hosp. Lond.; Sen. Regist. (Diag. Radiol.) Roy. Lond. Hosp.; Regist. (Diag. Radiol.) Centr. Middlx. Hosp.

SAW LWIN AUNG, Dr 11 The Crescent, Lympsham, Weston Super Mare BS24 0BH — MB BS 1968 Med.; MB BS Med. Inst. (II) Mingaladon 1968.

SAW MYINT, Dr 7 The Fletchers, Basildon SS16 5TU — MB BS 1969 Rangoon; MB BS Med Inst (I) Rangoon 1969.

***SAWANT, Nitin Hemant** 1 Eastcroft, Slough SL2 1HT; 1 Eastcroft, Slough SL2 1HT Tel: 01753 643579 Email: sawant@lineone.net — MB BS 1998 Lond.; MB BS Lond 1998; BSc (Hons) Lond. 1995.

SAWAR, Mr Muhammad Omar 18A Le More, Four Oaks Road, Sutton Coldfield B74 2XY — MB BS 1982 Punjab; FRCS Ed. 1987.

SAWCER, David 6 Bretts Cottages, Sandy Lane, Framfield, Uckfield TN22 5PX — MB ChB 1993 Birm.; BSc Liverp. 1985.

SAWCER, Stephen James Addenbrooke's Hospital, Hills Road, Cambridge CB2 2 — MB ChB 1988 Birm.; PhD Camb. 1997; BSc (Physics) Liverp. 1982; MRCP (UK) 1991. Research Regist. (Neurol.) Addenbrooke's Hosp. Camb.; Wellcome Trust Clinician Scientist. Prev: Regist. (Neurol.) N. Manch. HA.

SAWCZENKO, Andrew Bohdan Joseph 64 Mayfield Avenue, Orpington BR6 0AQ Email: a.s@i.am — BM 1987 Soton.; MRCP (UK) 1991; MRCPCH 1997. Specialist Regist. Roy. Hosp. for Sick Childr. Bristol. Prev: Research Fell. Univ. Bristol; SHO (Paediat.) Hosp. for Sick Childr. Gt. Ormond St. Lond., Univ. Hosp. Nottm., Childr. Hosp. Birm. & Roy. Hosp. for Sick Childr. Glas.

SAWCZYN, Paul Gabriel Rosegarth Surgery, Rothwell Mount, Halifax HX1 2XB — MB BS 1982 Lond.; DCH RCP Lond. 1988; MRCGP; DRCOG; Dip. Occ. Med. (St. Bart.) Prev: SHO (Paediat. Nephrol.) Guy's Hosp. Lond.; SHO (Paediat.) Brook Gen., St. Thos. & Guy's Hosps. Lond.

SAWDAYEE-AZAD, Akram 5 Russell Grove, Mill Hill, London NW7 3QU Tel: 020 8959 4521 — MB BS 1973 Lond.; MRCOG 1981. (Middlesex Hospital Medical School London)

***SAWDY, Robert John** 9 Dryden Road, Enfield EN1 2PR Tel: 020 8364 0497 — MB BS 1988 Lond.; BSc (Hons.) Experim. Path. Lond. 1985; MRCOG 1994.

SAWEIRS, Manar Wilson 18 Hillcrest Avenue, Burton-on-Trent DE15 0TZ — MB BS 1998 Newc.; MB BS Newc 1998.

SAWEIRS, Walaa Wilson Matta 16 (2F1) Roseneath Place, Marchmont, Edinburgh EH9 1JB Tel: 0131 229 9085 Email: wsaweirs@aol.com — MB ChB 1994 Ed.; BSc (Hons.) Ed. 1992; MRCP (UK) 1997. (Edin.) SHO (ICU) Qu. Margt. Hosp. Dunfermline. Prev: SHO (Nephrol.) Ch.ill Hosp. Oxf.; SHO (Gen. Med.) Edin. Roy. Infirm.; Ho. Off. (Med. & Surg.) Roy. Infirm. Edin.

SAWEIRS, Wilson Matta Queen's Hospital, Belvedere Road, Burton-on-Trent DE13 0RB Tel: 01283 566333 Fax: 01283 593009; 18 Hillcrest Avenue, Burton-on-Trent DE15 0TZ Tel: 01283 537785 — DM Ain. Shams 1966; MB ChB Cairo 1962; FRCP Lond. 1993; MRCP (UK) 1979; MRCPI 1978; MRCS Eng. LRCP Lond. 1980. (Cairo Univ.) Cons. Phys. Burton Hosp. NHS Trust. Socs: BMA; Brit. Geriat. Soc.; Fell. of The Roy. Coll. of Phys. Prev: Sen. Regist. (Gen. Med.) Selly Oak Hosp. Birm.; Sen. Regist. (Geriat. Med.) Birm. DHA (T); Regist. (Gen. Med.) W. Cumbld. Hosp. Whitehaven.

SAWERS, Alastair David Ian Burton Lodge, 86 Station Parade, Harrogate HG1 1HH — MB ChB 1983 Aberd.

SAWERS, Alistair Henderson Department of Haematology, Worcester Royal Infimary NHS Trust, Ronkswood, Worcester WR5 1HN Tel: 01905 760636 Fax: 01905 760781 — MB ChB 1974 (Commend.) Glas.; BSc (Hons.) Glas. 1972; FRCP Lond. 1995; FRCP Glas. 1989; MRCP (UK) 1977; FRCPath 1994, M 1982. (Glas.) Cons. Haemat. Worcs. Roy. Infirm. Socs: BMA & Brit. Soc. Haemat. Prev: Sen. Regist. (Haemat.) Manch. Roy. Infirm.; Regist. (Haemat.) Stobhill Gen. Hosp. Glas.

SAWERS, Hilary Anne Broughton, 17 Charlton Park Gate, Cheltenham GL53 7DJ — MB ChB 1978 Birm.; MB ChB (Hons.) Birm. 1978; MRCP (UK) 1980.

SAWERS, James Drummond 1 Middlefield Brae, Cupar KY15 4BX Tel: 01334 652993 — MB ChB 1964 Glas.

SAWERS, James Stewart Allison Cheltenham General Hospital, Cheltenham GL53 7AN — MB ChB 1973 Ed.; FRCP Ed. 1990; MRCP (UK) 1975. Cons. Phys. Diabetes & Endocrinol. Prev: Cons. Phys. Angus Unit Tayside Health Bd.

SAWERS, Mr. Robert Stewart 6 Carpenter Road, Birmingham B15 2JT — MB ChB 1969 Ed.; MRCOG 1976; FRCOG 1993; BSc 1966 Ed.; DObst 1972; MB ChB 1969; BSc Ed. 1966; MRCOG 1976, DObst 1972; FRCOG 1993. (Ed.) Cons. Birm. Wom. Hosp.; Med. Dir. Fertil. Centre BMI Priory Hosp. Socs: Blair Bell Res. Soc. & Soc. Study of Fertil.; Brit. Fertil. Soc. Prev: Sen. Lect. (O & G) Univ. Birm.; Hon. Cons. Birm. Matern. Hosp. & Birm. & Midl. Hosp. Wom.; Lect. (O & G) Univ. Sheff.

SAWFORD, Raymond William Northville Family Practice, 521 Filton Avenue, Filton, Bristol BS7 0LS Tel: 0117 969 2164 Fax: 0117 931 5743 — MB ChB 1971 Bristol. Prev: SHO (O & G) Dudley Rd. Hosp. Birm.; Ho. Surg. Qu. Alexandra Hosp. Portsmouth; Ho. Phys. Frenchay Hosp. Bristol.

SAWH, Breehaspaty Falls Road Practice, 181 Falls Road, Belfast BT12 6AF Tel: 028 9032 0547 Fax: 028 9024 9674; Tel: 02890 201321 — MB BCh BAO Belf. 1962; Cert. JCC Lond. 1977. Socs: BMA; Brit. Med. Acupunct. Soc.

SAWHNEY, Bharat Bhushan Neurology Department, Royal Victoria Hospital, Belfast BT12 6BA — MB BS 1961 Panjab; DM (Neurol.) All India Inst. Med. Scs. 1972, MD (Gen. Med.) 1965; MB BS Panjab (India) 1961. (Med. Coll. Amritsar) Cons. (Clin. Neurophysiol.) Roy. Vict. Hosp. Belf. Prev: Asst. Prof. (Neurol.) Postgrad. Inst. Med. Educat. Chandigarh, India.

SAWHNEY, Seema Ranks Hovis McDougall OHSHS, 27/30 King Edward House, King Edward Court, Windsor SL9 1TJ Tel: 01753 621904 Fax: 01753 621907 Email: ssawhney@rhms.co.uk; 40 Tangier Road, Richmond TW10 5DW — MB ChB 1991 Manch.; AFOM Lond. 2000; BSc (Hons) Manch. 1988; MRCGP Lond. 1995. (Manch.) p/t Specialist Regist. (Occupat. Med.) Ranks Hovis McDougall, Windsor.

SAWICKA, Elzbieta Halina Bromley Hospital, Cromwell Avenue, Bromley BR2 9AJ Tel: 020 8289 7000 Fax: 020 8289 7127 — MB BChir 1976 Camb.; MA Camb. 1976, MD 1986; FRCP Lond. 1994; MRCP (UK) 1977. (Camb. & Univ. Coll. Hosp.) Cons. Phys. (Thoracic & Gen. Med.) Bromley Hosp. Lond. Socs: Fell. Roy. Soc. Med.; Brit. Thorac. Soc. Prev: Sen. Regist. (Thoracic & Gen. Med.) Brompton & King's Coll. Hosps.; Doverdale Fell. & Hon. Regist. (Thoracic Med. & I.C.) Brompton Hosp.; Regist. (Gen. Med.) Univ. Coll. Hosp. & Whittington Hosp.

SAWICKI, Veronica Helena Tel: 01367 252264; Laverton House, Fairford GL7 4AB Tel: 01265 711180 — MB BS 1982 Lond. (Roy. Free) GP.

SAWIRES, Mona Ayad Awad The Willows, 54 North Road, Retford DN22 7XG — MB BCh 1978 Ain Shams; DA (UK) 1985. Clin. Asst. (Anaesth.) Bassetlaw Dist. Gen. Hosp. Worksop.

SAWITZKY, Christiane 15 Glen Iris Avenue, Canterbury CT2 8HP — State Exam Med 1993 Berlin.

SAWLE, Guy Victor Division of Clinical Neurology, Queens Medical Centre, Nottingham NG7 2UH Tel: 0115 970 9792 Fax: 0115 970 9738 — BM BS 1981 Nottm.; DM Nottm. 1991, BM BS 1981; MRCP (UK) 1984; FRCP 1998. Reader & Hon. Cons. Neurol. Qu. Med. Centre Nottm. Prev: Lect. & Sen. Regist. (Neurol.) Inst. Neurol. Roy. Postgrad. Med. Sch. Hammersmith Hosp.; Regist. (Neurol. & Med. Ophth.) St. Thos. Hosp. Lond.; Research Regist. Neurol.) Hammersmith Hosp. Lond.

SAWNEY, Philip Edward DSS Office of The Chief Medical Adviser, Room 638, Adelphi, 1-11 John Adam St., London WC2N 6HT Tel: 020 7962 8838 Fax: 020 7712 2330; 36 Manor Drive, Surbiton KT5 8NF — MB BS (Hons.) 1983; BSc (Hons.) Lond. 1978; MBA (Distinc.) Kingston Univ. 1994; MRCGP 1987; DRCOG 1986; DGM RCP Lond. 1986; Cert. Family Plann. JCC 1986. (Univ. Coll.) Med. Policy Manager DSS Lond. Socs: Assur. Med. Soc. Prev: GP Barnes; SCMO Richmond, Twickenham & Roehampton HA; GP Tutor Roehampton.

SAWTELL, Ivor James (retired) 16 Bristol Mews, London W9 2JF — MB BS Lond. 1968; MSc Lond. 1974; MRCS Eng. LRCP Lond. 1968; MFOM RCP Lond. 1980; BA 1998. Med. Adviser Health Care Insur. Lond.

SAWYER, Adam Nicholas 1 Stagbury Avenue, Chipstead, Coulsdon CR5 3PA — MB BS 1981 Lond.

SAWYER, Christopher John 64 Taylor Street, Tunbridge Wells TN4 0DX — MB BS 1996 Lond.

SAWYER, Christopher Nicholas 48 Wimpole Street, London W1M 7DG Tel: 020 7935 4357 Fax: 020 7224 0625 Email: 113535.756@compuserve.com; 46a Belsize Square, London NW3 4HN Tel: 020 7431 6924 — MB BS 1981 Lond.; MRCP (UK) 1985. Med. Cons. to Elf Oil UK Ltd & Bechtel Inc. & The Thomson Corpn. & Second Opinion UK Ltd. Socs: Fell. Roy. Soc. Med.; Internat. Soc. Nephrol. Prev: Lect. (Nephrol.) Lond. Hosp. Med. Coll.

SAWYER, David Hugh 3 Deanston View, South Callander Road, Doune FK16 6AS Tel: 01786 841731 — MB BS 1966 Lond.; MRCS Eng. LRCP Lond. 1966; AFOM RCP Lond. 1982. (Guy's) Med. Adviser Benefits Agency Med. Servs. Socs: BMA; Soc. Occupat. Med. Prev: Sen. Med. Off. Brit. Rail Scotl.; Ho. Surg. Ashford Hosp. Kent; Ho. Phys. WillesBoro. Hosp. Ashford.

SAWYER, Elinor Jane 42 Church Street, Baldock SG7 5AF — MB BS 1991 Lond.; FRCR 1997; MRCP 1994.

SAWYER, James Philip Charles Baytree, Ombersley, Droitwich WR9 0JP — MB ChB 1989 Manch.

SAWYER, Martin Norman Carnau Mawr, Cilcennin, Lampeter SA48 8RG — MB ChB 1984 Manch.

SAWYER, Philip Edward Lawrence 22 Tavistock Avenue, St Albans AL1 2NJ — MB BS 1994 Lond.; BSc Lond. 1991. (Roy. Free Hosp. Sch. Med.)

SAWYER, Richard Anthony 5A Langstone Avenue, Havant PO9 1RU — BM BCh 1967 Oxf.

SAWYER, Richard Hayes X-Ray Department, Wythenshawe Hospital, Southmoor Road, Manchester M23 9LT Tel: 0161 946 2105 Fax: 0161 946 2856 Email: richard.sawyer@man.ac.uk — MB 1983 Camb.; BChir 1982; MRCP (UK) 1986. (St. Thos.) Cons. Radiol. Wythenshawe Hosp. Manch.

SAWYER, Richard John Doctor's Mess, West Suffolk Hospital, Bury St Edmunds IP33 2QZ — MB BCh 1989 Witwatersrand.

SAWYERR, Afolabi Michael Whipps Cross Hospital, Whipps Cross Road, Leytonstone, London E11 1NR Tel: 020 8535 6414 — MB BCh 1982 Wales; BSc Wales 1979; MD Wales 1994; MRCP (UK) 1985; FRCP 1999. Cons. Gastroenterol. Whipps Cross Hosp. Lond. Prev: Lect. Univ. Edin.; Regist. Roy. Free Hosp. Lond.

***SAWYERR, Caroline** 20 Cotham Road S., Bristol BS6 5TZ — MB ChB 1985 Bristol.

SAXBY, John Richard Baber Little Garth, Larkhill Road, Abingdon OX14 1BJ — BM BCh 1952 Oxf.; BM BCh. Oxf. 1952.

SAXBY, Katharine Maria Ordsall Health Centre, Regent Park Surgery, Belfort Drive, Salford M5 3PP Tel: 0161 872 2021 Fax: 0161 877 3592; Tel: 0161 872 2021 — MB ChB 1993 Manch.; MRCGP 1997; DRCOG 1996; DFFP 1996. (Manch. Med. Sch. & Univ. St. And.) GP Princip. Ordsal. Socs: Roy. Coll. Gen. Pract. Prev: GP/Regist. Pendlebury Health Centre Swinton.

SAXBY, Mr Mark Fraser Dept. Of Urology, City of General Hospital, Newcastle Road ST4 6QG Tel: 01782 552167 Fax: 01782 553056 — MB BS 1983 Lond.; BSc Lond. 1980, MD 1996; FRCS (Urol.) 1996; FRCS Eng. 1988. (St. Mary's) Cons. Urol. N. Staffs. Hosp. Socs: Fell. Mem. Brit. Assn. Urol. Surgs.; Eur. Assn. of Urol. Prev: Sen. Regist. Rotat. (Urol.) W. Midl.; Research Regist. Wordsley Hosp.; Regist. Rotat. (Surg.) Dudley HA.

SAXBY, Norman Victor Redfern Health Centre, Shadycombe Road, Salcombe TQ8 8DJ; Redfern Health Centre, Salcombe TQ8 8DJ Tel: 0154 884 2284 — MB ChB 1965 Sheff. (Sheff.) Prev: Ho. Phys. St. Helen's Hosp. Barnsley; Ho. Surg. Roy. Hosp. Sheff; Med. Off. Virol. Research Dept. Sandwich, Kent.

SAXBY, Mr Peter John Department of Plastic Surgery, Royal Devon & Exeter Hospital, Barrack Road, Exeter EX2; Nadder Farm, Nadderwater, Exeter EX4 2JQ Tel: 01392 430709 — MB ChB 1978 Ed.; ChM 1991; FRCS (Plast) 1991; FRCS Eng. 1983. Cons. Plastic Surg. Exeter & N. Devon Hosps. Socs: B. A. Plastic Surg.s; B. A. Aesthetic Plastic Surg.s; Examr. FRCS Plast. Prev: Sen. Regist. (Plastic Surg.) Char. Cross & Mt. Vernon Hosps.

SAXENA, Dolly Doctors Surgery, 7 Felhurst Crescent, Dagenham RM10 7XT Tel: 020 8592 2323 Fax: 020 8984 8732 — MB BS 1958 Agra. (Agra) Socs: BMA. Prev: JHMO St. Luke's Hosp. Rugby.

SAXENA, Indra Rani Richmond Medical Centre, 15 Upper Accommodation Road, Leeds LS9 8RZ Tel: 0113 248 0948 Fax: 0113 240 9898 — MB BS 1971 Lucknow. (Lucknow) GP Leeds.

SAXENA, Manoj Krishnan 54 Hill Road, Mitcham CR4 2HQ Tel: 020 8640 8328 — MB BChir 1994 Camb.; BSc Lond. 1991.

SAXENA, Rajeev 26 Bader Drive, Heywood OL10 2QS; 26 Bader Drive, Heywood OL10 2QS — MB ChB 1994 Sheff.; MB ChB Manch. 1994; MRCP (UK) 1997. Specialist Regist. (Med.) Liverp. Rotat.

SAXENA, Rajiv Narain The Conifers, Coedkernew, Newport NP10 8UD — MB BS 1974 Poona.

SAXENA, Rema 26 Bader Drive, Hopwood, Heywood OL10 2QS — MB ChB 1997 Manch.

SAXENA, Sanjeev c/o Dr A. K. Bisaraya, 83B School Lane, Skelmersdale WN8 8PU — MB BS 1986 Jiwaji, India.

SAXENA, Satish Chandra Sharrow Lane Surgery, 129 Sharrow Lane, Sheffield S11 8AN Tel: 0114 255 6600 — MB BS 1967 Lucknow; DA Eng. 1971. (G.S.V.M. Med. Coll. Kanpur) Clin. Med. Off. Sheff. AHA. Prev: Clin. Asst. (Anaesth.) Roy. Hosp. Chesterfield.

SAYEGH

SAXENA, Savita Sharrow Lane Surgery, 129 Sharrow Lane, Sheffield S11 8AN Tel: 0114 255 6600 — MB BS 1974 Rajasthan. (S.P. Med. Coll. Bikaner) GP Sheff.; Ho. Off. (Chest Med., Infec. Dis. & Gen. Med.) Lodge Moor Hosp. Sheff. Prev: Ho. Off. (Accid. Surg. & Orthop.) N.. Gen. Hosp. Sheff.

SAXENA, Sonia Krishna Dept. of General Practice and Primary Care, 6th Floor, Hunter Wing, St George's Hospital Medical School, Cranmer Terrace, London SW17 0RE Email: s.saxena@sghms.ac.uk — MB BS 1989 Lond.; MRCGP 1995; DGM RCP Lond. 1994; MSC Epidemiology 1999. (St Barts Hosp. Med. School) Clin. Research Fell. S. Thames.

SAXENA, Sunil Anaesthetics Department, St. Mary Hospital, Newport PO30 5TG; 68 Swanmore Road, Ryde PO33 2TG — MB BS 1987 Jiwaji; DA (UK). Staff Grade (Anaesth.) St. Mary Hosp. Newport Isle of Wight. Prev: Staff Grade St. Mary Hosp. Newport; Specialist Regist. St. Geo.'s Hosp. Lond.; Specialist Regist. Wexham Pk. Hosp.

SAXENA, Vinay Raj West Wales General Hospital, Carmarthen SA31 2AF — MB BS 1980 Hyderabad; MRCPI 1989. Cons. (Paediat.) Carmarthenshire NHS Trust, W. Wales.

SAXENA, Vishal 2nd Floor Flat, 11 Palliser Road, London W14 9EB Tel: 020 7385 9859 — MB BS 1990 Lond.; BSc (Hons.) Pharmacol. Lond. 1987; MRCP (UK) 1994. Regist. (Gastroenterol.) P.ss Roy. Hosp. Haywards Heath.

SAXSENA, Surya Prakash The Surgery, Basement Flat, 160 Gloucester Terrace, London W2 6HR Tel: 020 7706 2504 Fax: 020 7706 3870 — MB BS 1964 Vikram; MB BS 1964 Vikram.

SAXTON, Hugh Michael Ash House, Houghton Road, Stockbridge SO20 6LE Tel: 01264 811051 Fax: 01264 811052 Email: hujusaxton@hotmail.com — MB BS 1951 Lond.; FRCP Lond. 1972, M 1956; FRCR 1975; FFR 1960; DMRD Eng. 1957. (St. Mary's) Socs: Brit. Inst. Radiol. Prev: Emerit. Cons. Radiol. Guy's Hosp. Lond.; Cons. Radiol. Cheltenham Gen. Hosp.; Sen. Regist. W.m. Hosp. Lond.

SAXTON, John Christopher Robert East Cleveland Hospital, Alford Road, Brotton, Saltburn-by-the-Sea TS12 2FF Tel: 01287 676215 Fax: 01287 678121 — MB ChB 1987 Leic.

SAXTON, Julie Susan 1 East Terrace, Blennerhasset, Carlisle CA4 3QY — MB ChB 1990 Liverp. Trainee GP Carlisle VTS.

SAXTON, Reginald Somes (retired) Batt's Cottage, 12 Broomfield Road, Henfield BN5 9TY — MA, MB BChir Camb. 1938; MRCS Eng. LRCP Lond. 1935; DTM & H Eng. 1947; DObst RCOG 1949.

SAXTON, Tamsin Nicola 16 Connaught Road, Fleet GU51 3RA — BM 1995 Soton.

SAXTY, Patricia Sexual Health Service, Monkgate Health Centre, 31 Monkgate, York YO31 7WA Tel: 01904 630351 Fax: 01904 642116; 6 Aldwark, York YO1 7BU Tel: 01904 644666 — MB BS Lond. 1964; MFFP 1993; DPM Leeds 1973. (Univ. Coll. Hosp.) Cons. Family Plann. & Sexual Health York Health Servs. NHS Trust; Princip. Investigator/Hon. Research Assoc. Inst. Populat. Studies Univ. Exeter. Socs: York Med. Soc. Prev: Ho. Phys. & Ho. Surg. Cossham Hosp. Bristol; Regist. (Psychiat.) Glenside Hosp. Bristol & Naburn Hosp. York.

SAY, Derek Thomas Kiveton Park Group Practice, The Clinic, Walesmoor Avenue, Kiveton Park, Sheffield S26 5RF Tel: 01909 770213; Peck Mill House, Ladyfield Road, Kiveton Park Station, Sheffield S26 6NR Tel: 01909 773969 Email: dtsay@doctors.org.uk — MB ChB 1980 Manch.; MRCGP 1987; DCH RCP Lond. 1982; DRCOG 1984; DGM RCP Lond. 1985. Primary Care Clin. Champion NSF for Older People Rotherham.

SAYAJI RAO, Mr Kaja Manor Hospital, Walsall WS2 9PS Tel: 01922 721172; 32 Redbourn Road, Bloxwich, Walsall WS3 3XT Tel: 01922 408332 — MB BS 1971 Osmania; FRCS Glas. 1984. Regist. (Orthop. & Train.) Gen. Hosp. Walsall W. Midl.; Asst. Surg. (Orthop.) Manor Hosp. Walsall; Clin. Asst. (Orthop. & Trauma) Gen. Hosp. Walsall. Prev: SHO (Orthop. & A & E) Burton Dist. Hosp.; SHO (Gen. Surg. & Urol.) Pk. Hosp. Manch.

SAYAL, Chandra Dera, 34 Fresco Drive, Littleover, Derby DE23 7EG Tel: 01332 515261 — MB BS 1950 Punjab; MB BS Punjab (India) 1950; MFPHM RCP (UK) 1989; MFCM RCP (UK) 1974; DPH Lond. 1957; DCH Eng. 1952; FRSH 1987. Med. Off. (Environm. Health) & Specialist (Community Med.) S. Derbysh.HA. Prev: Princip. Phys. (Social Servs. & Environm. Health) Camden & Islington AHA; Princip. Phys. (Child Health) Brent & Harrow HA.

SAYAL, Kapil Sen Childrens Department, Maudsley Hospital, Denmark Hill, London SE5 8AF Tel: 020 7703 6333 — BM 1992 Soton.; BSc Soton. 1991; MRCPsych 1996. (Soton.) Specialist Regist. (Child & Adolesc. Psychiat.) Bethlem & Maudsley Hosps. Lond. Prev: Regist. (Psychiat.) Bethlem & Maudsley Hosp.; SHO (Psychiat.) Oxf.

SAYANI, Mr Mohammed Irfan Royal Sussex County Hospital, Eastern Road, Brighton BN2 5BE Tel: 01273 696955; 146 Woodland Avenue, Hove BN3 6BN Tel: 01273 550969 — MB BS 1987 Osmania; FRCS Glas. 1992; FRCS Ed. 1992. Staff Orthop. Surg. Roy. Sussex Co. Hosp. Brighton. Prev: Regist. (Orthop.) King Geo. Hosp. Ilford; Regist. (Orthop.) & Pre Fell.sh. SHO Rotat. N. Middlx. Hosp.

SAYCE, Graham Ewart (retired) Brunswick House, 63 New St., Wem, Shrewsbury SY4 5AE Tel: 01939 232814 — MB BChir 1951 Camb.; MA, MB BChir Camb. 1951. Prev: Ho. Surg. W. Suff. Gen. Hosp.

SAYED, Gyasuddin Mohamed Tel: 01274 544926 — MB BS 1969 Bombay; MRCGP 1977; DTM & H Liverp. 1973; Cert. Family Plann. JCC 1976. (Grant Med. Coll.) Socs: Pakistan Med. Assn. - Exec. Counc. Mem.; Small Pract.s Assn. Bradford Chairm.; Brit. Med. Assn. Bradford Div., Pres.

SAYED, Mr Mohammed Aqeel 2 Taverners Road, Benskins Croft, Leicester LE4 2HZ — BM BS 1992 Nottm.; FRCS Eng. 1996. (Nottm.) Sen. SHO (Trauma) Selly Oak Univ. Hosp. Birm. Prev: SHO (Orthop. Surg.) N.ampton Gen. Hosp.; SHO (Orthop. Surg.) Glenfield Hosp., Leicester.

SAYED, Quaiser Ali Medical Boarding Centre, (Respiratory Diseases), 92/98 Queen St., Sheffield S1 1WU Tel: 0114 272 2181; Bait-ul-Sayed, 67 Moorgate Road, Rotherham S60 2TP Tel: 01709 376005 — MB BS 1962 Karachi; DTCD Wales 1974; DTM & H Liverp. 1965; MFFP RCOG 1966. (Dow Med. Coll. Karachi) Med. Adviser DSS Benefits Agency; Mem. Med. Bd.ing Centre (Respirat. Dis.) Sheff. & Stoke on Trent; Instruc. Family Plann. RCOG & RCGP. Socs: Pakistan Med. Assn.; (Exec. Comm. Rotherham Div.) BMA. Prev: Regist. (Med. & Cardiol.) Civil Hosp. Karachi, Pakistan; Regist. (Med.) New Cross Hosp. Wolverhampton & Gen. Hosp. Warrington.

SAYED, Saiqa 23 Norman Avenue, Nuneaton CV11 5NX — MB ChB 1998 Leic.; MB ChB Leic 1998.

SAYED, Zakia Department of Family Planning & Women's Health, Central Clinic, Doncaster Gate, Rotherham S65 1DW Tel: 01709 824845; Bait-ul-Sayed, 67 Moorgate Road, Rotherham S60 2TP Tel: 01709 376005 — MB BS 1962 Karachi; Spec. Accredit. Community Paediat. JCHMT 1993; DCH RCPS Glas. 1980; Developm. Paediat. Cert. Leeds 1976; MFFP RCOG 1993; Accredit Gen. Paediat. with s/i in Community Child; Health RCP Lond. 1993. (Dow Med. Coll.) Princip. Med. Off. (Child Health) Rotherham Priority Health Trust; Instruc. Family Plann. RCOG & RCGP. Socs: Pakistan Med. Assn. & BMA. Prev: Regist. Childr. Hosp. Karachi, Pakistan; SHO (Gen. Med. & Paediat.) Roy. Hosp. Wolverhampton; Med. Off. Health Dept. Sunderland Co. Boro.

SAYEED-UZ-ZAFAR, Dr 89 Copsewood Way, Northwood HA6 2TX — MB BS 1964 Karachi.

SAYEED, (Abulfatah) Akram, OBE 352 East Park Road, Leicester LE5 5AY; Ramna, 2 Mickleton Drive, Leicester LE5 6GD Tel: 0116 241 6703 Fax: 0116 273 7443 — MB BS 1958 Dacca; FRCGP 1998; FRCP Ed. 1994; MRCGP 1992; FRIPHH 1991; FRSH 1991. (Dacca) Sen. Partner & Princip.; Hon. Adviser. MoH Govt. Bangladesh (UK); Mem. Leics. LMC; Elected Mem., GMC, 1999-2004; Pres., Leiceister Med. Soc., 2001-2002. Socs: Fell. Roy. Soc. Med.; Leics. Med. Audit & Advis. Gp.; Fell. BMA. Prev: SHO (Ophth.) Leicester Roy. Infirm.; Rotat. Intern Monmouth Med. Center Long Br., USA; SHO (Ophth.) Dacca Med. Coll. Hosp.

SAYEED, Iqbal Ahmed 11 Pine Street, Woodley, Stockport SK6 1NN — MB BS 1968 Dacca; MB BS Dacca Bangladesh 1968; FFA RCSI 1981. (Dacca) Regist. (Anaesth.) Salop AHA.

SAYEED, Mr Rana Ahmed Papworth Hospital, Papworth Everard, Cambridge CB3 8RE Tel: 01480 830541 Email: r.a.sayeed@bioc.cam.ac.uk — BM BCh 1991 Oxf.; MA Camb. 1992; FRCS Eng. 1995; MRCP (UK) 1995. (Oxf.) Specialist Regis. In Cardiothoracic Surg.

SAYEGH, Hanna Fouad Lincoln Road Practice, 63 Lincoln Road, Peterborough PE1 2SF Tel: 01733 565511 Fax: 01733 569230; 228 Fulbridge Road, Peterborough PE4 6SN Tel: 01733 575272 — MB BCh 1961 Cairo; MRCP Lond. 1969; MRCS Eng. LRCP Lond. 1970;

SAYER

DTM & H Liverp. 1968. (Cairo) GP P'boro. Prev: Cons. Phys. Ender Clinic Tripoli, Libya; Regist. (Cardiol.) & Sen. Regist. Cardiac Unit Papworth Hosp. Papworth Everard.

SAYER, Antoine 13 Manston Grove, Kingston upon Thames KT2 5GF — MB ChB 1972 Mid Delta U Tanta Egypt; MB ChB Mid Delta U, Tanta Egypt 1972. Med. Off. Roy. Hosp. Neurodisabil. Lond. Socs: Brit. Soc. of Rehabil. Med.; Biol. Engin. Soc.

SAYER, Caroline Susan Adelaide Medical Centre, 111 Adelaide Road, London NW3 3RY Tel: 020 7722 4135 Fax: 020 7586 7558 — MB BS 1983 Lond.; MA Oxf. 1983; DRCOG 1987; DCH RCP Lond. 1986. (Oxf. & Lond. Hosp.)

SAYER, Catherine Ann 28 Fidlas Avenue, Cardiff CF14 0NY — MB ChB 1995 Sheff.

SAYER, Gabriel Leon Flat 5, 21 Pleshey Rd, London N7 0RA — MB BS 1993 Lond.

SAYER, Jeremy William St. Bartholomew's Hospital, West Smithfield, London EC1A 7BE Tel: 020 7601 8888 Fax: 020 7601 8042 Email: jwsains@msn.com; 11 St. Mary's Road, Leyton, London E10 5RB Tel: 020 8556 6532 — MB BS 1987 Lond.; BSc Lond. 1984; MRCP (UK) 1991. Regist. (Cardiol.) Lond. Chest Hosp.; Edr. (Thrombosis Sect.) Curr. Med. Literature. Prev: Regist. (Cardiol.) St. Bart. Hosp. Lond.; Regist. (Gen. Med.) Colchester Gen. Hosp.

SAYER, Joanna Mary Doncaster Royal Infirmary, Armthorpe Road, Doncaster DN2 5LT Tel: 01302 366666; Ivy Cottage, Main St, Epperstone, Nottingham NG14 6AU Tel: 01159 663608 — BM BCh 1986 Oxf.; MA Oxf. 1986; MRCP (UK) 1989; M.D 1998. Cons. (Gen Med & Gastroenterol.). Prev: Sen. Regist. Countess of Chester Hosp. Chester; Sen. Regist. John Radcliffe Hosp. Oxf.

SAYER, John Bernard (retired) Ambleside, Courtlands Way, Goring-by-Sea, Worthing BN12 4BX — BM BCh 1956 Oxf.; BSc Oxf. 1955, MA 1956; DObst RCOG 1958. Prev: GP Worthing.

SAYER, Melissa Maria Ruth 90A Fortress Road, London NW5 2HJ — MB BS 1994 Lond.

SAYER, Nicholas John Furness General Hospital, Dalton Lane, Barrow-in-Furness LA14 4 Tel: 01229 870870; The School House, Scales, Ulverston LA12 0PE — MB ChB 1982 Birm.; MRCGP 1986; Dip. Palliat. Med. Wales 1993; DRCOG 1985; Cert. Family Plann. JCC 1985; MSc Palliative Medicine 1999. (Bristol University) Cons. Palliat. Med. Furness Gen. Hosp. Cumbria; Med. Dir. St. Mary's Hospice Ulverston. Prev: GP Dalton-in-Furness Cumbria & Buxton Derbysh.; Trainee GP SW Cumbria VTS.

SAYER, Mr Richard Earl Department of Cardiothoracic Surgery, St Georges Hospital, Blackshaw Road, London SW17 0QT Tel: 020 8725 3287 Email: richard.sayer@stgeorges.nhs.uk — MB BS 1969 Lond.; FRCS Eng. 1974. Cons. Cardiothoracic Surg. St. Geo. Hosp. Lond. & King Edwd. VII Hosp. Midhurst. Socs: Brit. Thorac. Soc. & Soc. Cardiothoracic Surg. Prev: Sen. Regist. St. Geo. Hosp. Lond. & Wessex Regional Cardiothoracic Unit Soton.; Fell. (Surg.) Washington Univ. St. Louis, USA.

SAYER, Timothy Robert Goudhurst, Maidenthorne Lane, North Waltham, Basingstoke RG25 2DD Tel: 01256 397781 — MD 1992 Aberd.; MB ChB Aberd. 1981; MRCOG 1986. Cons. O & G Basingstoke Dist. Hosp. Prev: Sen. Regist. (O & G) St. Mary's Hosp. Manch.

SAYER, Travers Drewery (retired) Rosedene, Bossington Lane, Linslade, Leighton Buzzard LU7 2TG Tel: 01525 374509 — MB BS Lond. 1957; MRCS Eng. LRCP Lond. 1957; MRCGP 1968; DObst RCOG 1958. Prev: GP Margate.

SAYERS, Brian Edward (retired) 17 Park Avenue, Wolverhampton WV1 4AH Tel: 01902 424748 — MA, Oxf. 1952, BM BCh 1955; MRCGP 1968; DObst. RCOG 1958.

SAYERS, Craig Lee 13 The Cresecent, Worsthorne, Burnley BB10 3LX — MB ChB 1993 Ed.

SAYERS, Donald Eric Gordon (retired) Little Croft, La Rue Du Froid Vent, St Saviour, Jersey JE2 7LJ Tel: 01534 26690 — MB BS 1948 Lond.; MRCS Eng. LRCP Lond. 1948; FRCA 1954. Prev: Cons. Anaesth. Gen. Hosp. Jersey.

SAYERS, Ian Graham Holly House, 17 Murswell Lane, Silverstone, Towcester NN12 8UT — MB BS 1998 Lond.; MB BS Lond 1998.

SAYERS, John Denton Welbeck Surgery, 481-491 Mansfield Road, Nottingham NG5 2JJ Tel: 0115 962 0932 — MB ChB 1974 Birm.; MRCGP 1981; DRCOG 1981; DTM & H Liverp. 1978. (Birm.) Prev: Med. Miss. (Tear Fund) Thailand; Trainee Nottm. VTS; Project Dir. Dacca Camps & Dacope Thana Health Projects, HEED.

SAYERS, Mr Robert David 12 Barrington Road, Stoneygate, Leicester LE2 2RA — MB ChB 1984 Birm.; MB ChB (Hons.) Birm. 1984; MD Leics. 1993; FRCS Eng. 1989; FRCS Ed. 1988. Cons. Vasc. Surg. Leicester Gen. Hosp. Prev: Research Fell. & Lect. (Surg.) Leic. Univ.; Regist. (Gen. Surg.) Leic. Hosp.

SAYERS, Robert David The Surgery, Cornerways, 145 George V Avenue, Worthing BN11 5RZ Tel: 01903 247740/241997 Fax: 01903 242110; 145 George V Avenue, Worthing BN11 5RZ — MB BCh BAO 1987 Belf.; DCH RCP Lond. 1992; MRCGP. (Queen's University of Belfast) Socs: BMA. Prev: Trainee Gp Crawley; SHO (Paediat.) Addenbrookes Hosp. Camb.; Resid. Med. Off. Liverp. Hosp. Sydney, Austral.

SAYERS, Steven James c/o Mr & Mrs I Sayers, 79 Astley Rd, Seaton Delaval, Whitley Bay NE25 0DJ — MB ChB 1997 Ed.

SAYERS, William James Hastings (retired) 15 Bazehill Road, Rottingdean, Brighton BN2 7DB Tel: 01273 305921 — LRCP LRCS 1942 Ed.; LRCP LRCS Ed. LRFPS Glas. 1942; LM Coombe 1947. Hosp. Pract. (Rheum.) Mid Sussex Hosp. Gp. Prev: Clin. Asst. (Physical Med.) Mid-Sussex Hosp. Gp.

SAYES, Rhys Morgan 3 Fron Heulog, Aberdovey LL35 0HF — MB BS 1975 Newc.

SAYNOR, Annette Marie Noelle 3 Sutherland Avenue, Broadstone BH18 9EB — MB BS 1977 Lond.; DRCOG 1980.

SAYNOR, Caroline Elizabeth Harlestone Road Surgery, 117 Harlestone Road, Northampton NN5 7AQ Tel: 01604 751832 Fax: 01604 586065 — MB ChB 1976 Birm. GP N.ampton.

SAYNOR, Gary Charles 4 Tarvin Drive, Bredbury, Stockport SK6 2PW — MB BS 1991 Lond.; MB BS (Hons.) Lond. 1991; BSc (Hons.) Lond. 1988.

SAYOUR, Samir 39 Juxon Street, London SE11 6NH — State Exam Med 1993 Greifswald.

SAYWELL, James Humphrey 24 Fernhill Road, Moorhead, Shipley BD18 4SL — MB ChB 1967 St. And.; DObst RCOG 1969.

SAYWELL, William Richard, Surg. Cdr. RN Department of Radiology, Yeovil District Hospital, Yeovil BA21 4AT Fax: 01935 707572 Email: sayww@gwise.esomerset-tr.swest.nhs.uk — BM BCh 1978 Oxf.; MA Oxf. 1979, BM BCh 1978; FRCR 1987. (Oxford) Cons. Radiol. Yeovil Dist. Hosp. Socs: Brit. Inst. Radiol.; Roy. Soc. Med.; BMA. Prev: Cons. Radiol. RN Hosp. Plymouth; Sen. Lect. NMR Unit. RPMS Hammersmith; Sen. Regist. (Radiol.) Soton. Gen. Hosp.

SAYWOOD, Andrew Mason, Surg. Lt.-Cdr. RN 7 The Pastures, Ranworth, Duffield, Derby DE65 6GG Tel: 01332 840202 Fax: 01332 840101 Email: dol@saywood.f9.co.uk — MRCS Eng. LRCP Lond. 1976; MRCS Eng LRCP Lond. 1976; MRCGP 1982; T(GP) 1991; DFFP 1982; DA (UK) 1976. InDepend. Med. Cons., Med. Ethics in Law, Birm. Univ.; Proprietor & Princip. W.minster Med. Ltd; Examg. Med. Practitioner, Benefits Agency. Socs: BMA; Expert Witness (UK Register) Lond.; Birm. Medico-Legal Soc. Prev: Cons. Forens. Phys. for Med. Advice to Lawyers; Princip. Police Surg.; Princip. GP Derbysh.

SAYYAH-SINA, Kamran The New Surgery, 296 Queens Road, London SE14 5JN Tel: 020 7639 5528 — MB ChB 1986 Birm. GP Princip. Prev: Trainee GP Kent; SHO (Gen. Med., Paediat. & O & G) William Harvey Hosp. Ashford.

SBANO, Hala 35 Dorset Drive, Edgware HA8 7NT Tel: 020 8951 3349 Fax: 020 8952 1136 — MB BS 1996 Lond.; BSc (Biochem. & Med. Sci.) Lond. 1994; MRCP Part 1 1999. (Charing Cross and Westminster) SHO Rotat. Med. Harefield/Hillingdon. Socs: BMA; Med. Protec. Soc.; Med. Sickness Soc. Prev: Ho. Off. (Med.) Chelsea & W.minster Hosp. Lond.; Ho. Off. (Surg.) Bassetlaw Dist. Gen. Hosp. Lond.; SHO Rotat. (Med.) Chelsea & W.minster Hosp.

SCADDEN, John Edward Cartref Care Home, 10 East Back, Pembroke SA71 4HL — MB ChB 1992 Cape Town.

SCADDING, Frank Haddow Coryton, 55 St Mary's Avenue, Northwood HA6 3AY Tel: 01923 821433 — MRCS Eng. LRCP Lond. 1937; MD Lond. 1939, MB BS (Hnrs.) 1937; FRCP Lond. 1955, M 1939. (Middlx.) Hon. Cons. Phys. Middlx Hosp. & Brompton Hosp. Lond.; Emerit. Cons. Phys. King Edwd. VII Hosp. Midhurst. Socs: Brit. Thorac. Assn. & Med. Soc. Lond. Prev: Cons. Phys. Hounslow Hosp.; Hon. Cons. Chest Dis. to the Army; 1st. Asst. Brompton Hosp.

SCADDING, Glenis Kathleen Royal, National Throat, Nose & Ear Hospital Trust, Grays Inn Road, London WC1X 8DA Tel: 020 7915

1674 Fax: 020 7915 1674 Email: g.scadding@ucl.ac.uk; 143 Chevening Road, London NW6 6DZ — MB BChir 1973 Camb.; MRCP 1975 UK; MA 1973 Camb.; MD 1984 Camb; FRCP 1995 Lond. Cons. Phys. (Rhinol., Immunol. & Allergy) Nat. Throat, Nose & Ear Hosp. Lond.; Hon. Sen. Lect. (Immunol.) Univ. Coll. & Middlx. Hosp. Med. Sch. Lond.; Hon. Sen. Lect. (Clin. Immunol.) Roy. Free Hosp. Lond. Socs: Brit. Soc. Allergy & Clin. Immunol. (Chair ENT s/i Gp.); Assoc. Mem. RCPath; Roy. Soc. Med. (Pres. Sect. Immunol.). Prev: Sen. Regist. (Clin. Immunol.) Middlx. Hosp. Lond.; Research Fell. Roy. Free Hosp. Lond.; SHO Med. Unit Brompton Hosp. Lond.

SCADDING, John William The National Hospital for Neurology and Neurosurgery, Queen Square, London WC1N 3BG Tel: 020 7837 3611 — MB BS 1972 Lond.; MD Lond. 1982, BSc (Anat.) 1969; FRCP Lond. 1988, M 1974. Neurol. Nat. Hosp. for Neurol. & Neurosurg. & Whittington Hosp. Lond.; Hon. Sen. Lect. Inst. Neurol. Lond.; Civil. Cons. Adviser Roy. Navy & Roy. Air Force; Hon. Cons. Neurol. Roy. Soc. of Musicians; Hon. Cons. Neurol., St. Luke's Hosp. for the Clergy. Prev: Regist. Nat. Hosps. for Nerv. Dis. Lond.; Research Asst. (Neurol. Scs.) Roy. Free Hosp. & Dept. Anat. Univ. Coll. Lond.

SCADE, Thomas Paterson Riverview Medical Centre, 6/8 George St., Johnstone PA5 8SL Tel: 01505 20151; 38 Hillside, Houston, Johnstone PA6 7NT — MB ChB 1973 Glas.; BSc (Hons. Path.) Glas. 1971; FRCP Glas. 1990; MRCP (UK) 1976.

SCADENG, Miriam X-Ray Department, Addenbrookes Hospital, Cambridge — MB BS 1985 Lond. Regist. (Radiol.) X-Ray Dept. Addenbrookes Hosp. Camb. Prev: SHO Guy's Hosp. Lond.

SCAFFARDI, Roberto Agostino East Bridgford Medical Centre, 2 Butt Lane, East Bridgford, Nottingham NG13 8NY Tel: 01949 20216 Fax: 01949 21283 — BM BS 1984 Nottm.

SCAGLIONI, Francesco Guiseppe Greenland Surgery, Greenland, Millbrook, Torpoint PL10 1BA Tel: 01752 822576 Fax: 01752 823155; (branch Surgery), York Road, Torpoint PL11 2LG Tel: 01752 812152 — MB BS 1985 Lond.

SCAHILL, Shaun James Hawkhill Medical Centre, Hawkhill, Dundee DD1 5LA Tel: 01382 669589 Fax: 01382 645526 — MB ChB 1988 Glas.; PhD Ed. 1981; BSc (Hons) Genetics Leeds 1977.

SCAIFE, Bryan 3 Woodside, Stockton-on-Tees TS17 0ST — MB BS 1956 Lond.; MRCS Eng. LRCP Lond. 1956; DCH RCPS Glas. 1976; DObst RCOG 1958. (King's Coll. Hosp.) Socs: BMA. Prev: Ho. Surg. & Ho. Phys. City Hosp. York; SHO (Paediat.) Co. Hosp. York.

SCALES, Alistair Hugh Westbourne Medical Centre, Milburn Road, Bournemouth BH4 9HJ Tel: 01202 752550 Fax: 01202 769700; 1 Powell Road, Parkstone, Poole BH14 8SG Tel: 01202 743758 — MB BS 1975 Lond.; BSc Lond. 1972; MRCP (UK) 1978.

SCALES, Elizabeth Anna Gorebridge Health Centre, Gorebridge EH23 4TP — MB ChB 1983 Dundee; MRCGP 1987. Prev: Trainee GP Stewarton; Trainee GP Ayrsh. & Arran HB Train. Scheme.

SCALES, Professor John Tracey, OBE, Capt. RAMC Fairbanks, Riverview Road, Pangbourne, Reading RG8 7AU Tel: 0118 984 3568, 01753 663614; 24 Larchmoor, Gerrards Cross Rd, Stoke Poges SL2 4EY Tel: 0118 984 3568, 01753 663614 — MRCS Eng. LRCP Lond. 1944; FRCS Eng. 1969; CI Mech. E. 1966; FIPEM, 1994. (Char. Cross) Emerit. Prof. Univ. Lond. 1985; Hon. Cons. Centre for Plastic Surg. Mt. Vernon Hosp. Trust N.wood Middlx. 198. Socs: BMA; Sen. Fell.Brit. Orthopaedic Assoc.; Hon. Mem. Brit. Assoc. of Plastic Surg.s 1993: Prev: Hon. Dir. RAFT Inst. of Plastic Surg. Mt. Vernon Hosp. NHS Trust N.wood; Emerit. Prof. Biomed. Engin. Inst. Orthop. Univ. Lond.; Cons. Biomed. Engin. Roy. Nat. Orthop. Hosp. Lond. & Mt. Vernon Hosp. N.wood.

SCALES, Michael Frank Wellington House Surgery, Henrietta Street, Batley WF17 5DN Tel: 01924 470333 Fax: 01924 420981; 1 Park Avenue, Rutland Road, Upper Batley, Batley WF17 0LU — MB ChB 1983 Leeds; MB ChB Leeds. 1983.

SCALLAN, Bernard Francis Xavier 46 Harehills, Leeds LS8 5PB Tel: 0113 249 0261 — LM 1948 Dub.; MB BCh BAO NUI 1944, DPH, BSc (Pub Health) 1946; TDD Wales 1949; LM Nat. Matern. Hosp. Dub. 1948. (Galway) Socs: BMA. Prev: Phys. Nat. BCG Comm. St. Ultan's Hosp. Dub.; Asst. Div. MOH Lancs. CC; MOH Kingston Chest Clinic, Jamaica.

SCALLAN, Karen Christina 63 Dennison Road, Dundee DD4 7DT — MB ChB 1987 Dundee.

SCALLAN, Michael John Herbert Royal Brompton Hospital, Sydney St., London SW3 6NP Tel: 020 7352 8121 Fax: 020 7351 8524 — MB ChB Cape Town 1967; FRCA 1983; FFA (SA) 1973. Cons. Anaesth. Roy. Brompton Hosp. Lond.

SCALLY, Bernard Gabriel (retired) 41 Andersonstown Road, Belfast BT11 9AF Tel: 02890 613463 — LRCPI & LM, LRSCI & LM 1948; LRCPI & LM, LRCSI & LM 1948; PhD Dub. 1966; FRCPI 1980, M 1978; FRCPsych 1981, M 1971; DPM RCPSI 1958. Hon. Cons. Muckamore Abbey Hosp. Prev: Mem. Ment. Health Commiss.

SCALLY, Catherine Mary 30 Barmouth Road, Castlerock, Coleraine BT51 4XG — MB BCh BAO 1982 Belf.; MB BCh Belf. 1982; FRCS Ed. 1987.

SCALLY, Gabriel John South West Regional Office, NHS Executive, Westward House, Lime Kiln Close, Stoke Gifford, Bristol BS34 8SR Tel: 0117 984 1810 Fax: 0117 984 1841 Email: gscally@doh.gov.uk; 11 Dowry Square, Hotwells, Bristol BS8 4SH Tel: 0117 926 8510 Fax: 0117 973 3790 — MB BCh BAO 1978 Belf.; MSc (Comm. Med.) Lond. 1982; MFPHM RCPI 1992; FFPHM RCP (UK) 1991, M 1984. Regional Dir. Pub. Health S.W. Regional Office NHS Exec.; Sen. Lect. (Social Med.) Univ. Bristol. Prev: Regional Dir. (Pub. Health) SE Thames RHA; Dir. Pub. Health E.. Health & Social Serv. Bd. Belf.

SCALLY, John Department Medical Imaging, Leighton Hospital, Crewe CW14QJ; 3 The Alreage, Burnbury, Tarporley CW6 9NQ — MB ChB 1980 Liverp.; FRCR 1986; DMRD Liverp. 1985. Cons. Radiol. Leighton Hosp. Crewe. Prev: Sen. Regist. Mersey RHA.

SCALLY, Marie Josephine 9 Brerton Crescent, Belfast BT8 6QD — MB BCh BAO 1973 Belf.

SCAMBLER, Peter James 29 Southfield Park, Harrow HA2 6HF Tel: 020 8248 9098 Fax: 020 7831 0488 Email: pscamble@hgmp.mrc.ac.uk — MB ChB 1982 Manch.; BSc (1st cl. Hons. Med. Biochem.) Manch. 1979, MD 1986; MRCPath 1990. (Manch.) Prof. Molecular Med. Inst. Child Health Lond. Socs: Clin. Genetics Soc.; Amer. Soc. Human Genetics; Brit. Developm. Biol. Soc. Prev: Sen. Lect. (Med. Molecular Genetics) St. Mary's Hosp. Lond.

SCAMBLER, Sarah Miriam Lane End Medical Group, 25 Edgwarebury Lane, Edgware HA8 8LJ Tel: 020 8958 4233 Fax: 020 8905 4657; 29 Southfield Park, Harrow HA2 6HF — MB ChB 1982 Manch.; MB ChB (Hons.) Manch. 1982; MRCGP 1985. Prev: GP Brent & Harrow FPC; Trainee GP N.wick Pk. VTS.

SCAMMELL, Alastair Michael The County Hospital, Greetwell Road, Lincoln LN2 5QY — MB BS 1977 Lond.; MRCP (UK) 1981; FRCPCH. (St. Thomas') Cons. Paediat. Co. Hosp. Lincoln.

SCAMMELL, Brigitte Elfriede Department of Orthopaedics & Accident Surgery, University Hospital, Queen's Medical Centre, Nottingham NG7 2UH Email: b.scammell@nottingham.ac.uk — MB ChB 1982 Birm.; DM Soton. 1995; FRCS (Orth.) 1994; FRCS Eng. 1987; FRCS Ed. 1987. Sen. Lect. & Hon. Cons. Orthop. Qu. Med. Centre & City Hosp. Nottm.

SCANE, Andrew Christopher Department of Medicine, North Tees General Hospital, Hardwick, Stockton-on-Tees TS19 8PE Tel: 01642 617617 Fax: 01642 624922; 15 Ashville Avenue, Eaglescliffe, Stockton-on-Tees TS16 9AU Tel: 01642 659645 — BM BS 1983 Nottm.; BMedSci Nottm. 1981; MRCP (UK) 1988; FRCP Ed 1998. (Univ. Nottm. Med. Sch.) Cons. Phys. (Geriat. Med.) N. Tees Gen. Hosp. Stockton-on-Tees. Prev: Clin. Fell. (Geriat. Med.) W.mead Hosp. Sydney, Austral.; Sen. Regist. (Geriat. Med.) N. & Yorks. RHA; Research Train. Fell. (Geriat.) Univ. Newc. u. Tyne.

SCANLAN, Christopher Mark Eversley, Devons Rd, Torquay TQ1 3PR Tel: 07970 806143 Email: cscanlan@doctors.org.uk — MB ChB 1997 Wales; BSc (Hons) Wales 1994. (Wales) SHO (Anaesth.) Nevue Hall Hosp. Abergavenny.

SCANLAN, Judith 19 Eastfields Grove, Sughall, Chester CH1 6DA — BM 1992 Soton.

SCANLAN, Pascal Henry Taybank Medical Centre, 10 Robertson Street, Dundee DD4 6EL Tel: 01382 461588 Fax: 01382 452121 — MB BCh BAO 1987 NUI.

SCANLON, Francesca Louise Child & Family Psychiatry, The Brow, Burgess Hill, Horsham; 1 Station Road, Horsham RH13 5EZ — MB ChB 1984 Aberd. Clin. Asst. Child & Family Psychiat.). Socs: BMA. Prev: Health Worker RePub. do Pequeno, Vendedor.; Regist. (Psychiat.) SW Thames.

SCANLON, Jacqueline Mary 96 Longmead Av,, Bishopston, Bristol BS7 8EF — MB ChB 1989 Leeds. Specialist Regist. (O & G) S.mead Hosp. Bristol. Prev: Regist. (O & G) Glos. Roy. Hosp.

SCANLON

SCANLON, John Edmond Milnes Worcestershire Acute Hospital NHS Trust, Worcester Royal Infirmary, (WR1 Ronkswood Branch), Newtown Road, Worcester WR5 1HN Tel: 01905 763333 Ext: 34110; 150 Battenhall Road, Worcester WR5 2BT — MB BS 1977 Lond.; FRCPCH 1996; MRCP (UK) 1980; DCH RCP Lond. 1983. Cons. Paediat. Worcs. Ac. Hosp. NHS Trust. Prev: Sen. Regist. (Paediat.) Wessex RHA; Regist. Childr.'s Hosp. Birm.

SCANLON, John Gerard Blackstock Surgery, Lisieux Way, Taunton TA1 2LB Tel: 01823 259444 Fax: 01823 322715; The Cottage, Goosenford, Cheddon Fitzapaine, Taunton TA2 8LH Tel: 01823 412796 — MB BCh BAO 1979 NUI; MRCGP 1987; DCH Eng. 1981. Prev: Regist. (Paediat.) Whitechapel Hosp. Lond.; Regist. (Paediat.) Som. HA; SHO (Paediat.) King's Coll. & Univ. Coll. Hosp. Lond.

SCANLON, John Joseph Oakwood House, St. Mary Hospital, Kettering NN15 7PW Tel: 01536 493131 — MB BCh BAO 1983 NUI; MRCPsych 1990. Cons. Psychiat. & Clin. Dir. (Adult Ment. Illness) N.ants.

SCANLON, Professor Maurice Francis Department of Medicine, University of Wales College of Medicine, Heath Park, Cardiff CF14 4XN Tel: 029 2074 2182 Fax: 029 2074 4671 Email: scanlonmf@cf.ac.uk; 117 Pencisely Road, Llandaff, Cardiff CF5 1DL Tel: 029 2021 2651 Fax: 029 2074 4671 Email: scanlonmf@cf.ac.uk — MB BS 1973 Newc.; BSc Newc. 1970, MD 1981; FRCP Lond. 1986; MRCP (UK) 1975. Prof. Endocrinol. & Cons. Phys. Univ. Wales Cardiff; Dir. of R&D Cardiff & Vale NHS Trust. Socs: Endocrine Soc. & Europ. Neuroendocrine Assn. Prev: Reader (Med.) & Cons. Phys. Univ. Wales Cardiff; Harkness Fell. Commonw. Fund of New York 1979-81.

SCANLON, Peter Henry 4 Haywards Road, Charlton Kings, Cheltenham GL52 6RH — MB BS 1977 Lond.; MRCP (UK) 1980; MCOphth 1988; DO RCS Eng. 1986; DRCOG 1983; DCH 1981.

SCANLON, Thomas John Paul East Sussex, Brighton and Hove Health Authority, 36-38 Friars Walk, Lewes BN7 2PB Email: toms@esbhheath.cix.co.uk; 1 Station Road, Horsham RH13 5EZ — MB ChB 1984 Aberd.; MSc Lond. 1993; MRCGP 1989; DCH RCP Lond. 1988; DRCOG 1988; MFPHM 1996. Cons., Pub. health Med., E. Sussex, Brighton & Hone Health Auth..; Hon. Research Fell. Inst. Of Child Health. Lond.; Non-Princip. GP Horsham. Socs: BMA; Assn. PH. Prev: Regist. (Pub. Health Med.) SW Thames RHA; MSc Stud. Lond. Sch. Hyg. & Trop. Med.; Health Worker Repub. Do Pequeno Vendedor, Brazil.

SCANTLEBURY, Barbara Alexandra Surgery, 2 Wellington Avenue, Aldershot GU11 1SD Tel: 01252 332210 Fax: 01252 312490 — MB ChB 1974 Dundee.

SCARAVILLI, Professor Francesco Department of Neuropathology, Institute of Neurology, Queen Square, London WC1N 3BG Tel: 020 7837 3611 Fax: 020 7916 9546 — MD 1964 Padua; PhD Lond. 1978; FRCPath 1990, M 1985. Prof. Neuropath. & Hon. Cons. Inst. Neurol. Lond. Socs: Brit. & French Neuropath. Soc.; Amer. Neuropath. Soc. Prev: Reader & Sen. Lect. (Neuropath.) Inst. Neurol. Lond.

SCARAVILLI, Nicoletta 4 Carver Road, London SE24 9LT — MB BS 1998 Lond.; MB BS Lond 1998.

SCARBOROUGH, Helen 1 Merle Gardens, Lancaster Park, Morpeth NE61 3RW — MB ChB 1996 Birm. SHO (Med.) N. Staffs. NHS Trust Stoke-on-Trent.

SCARBOROUGH, Mark Andrew Falsgrave Surgery, 33 Falsgrave Road, Scarborough YO12 5EA Tel: 01723 360835 Fax: 01723 503220 — MB ChB 1983 Manch.; MRCGP 1987.

SCARBOROUGH, Matthew Department of Physiology, Queen Mary & Westfield College, Mile End Road, London E1 4NS Tel: 020 7982 6379 — MB BCh BAO 1990 Belf.; MB BCh Belf. 1990; BSc Belf. 1988. Clin. Lect. Qu. Mary & W.field Coll. Lond.

SCARBOROUGH, Nigel Paul Barwell Medical Centre, 39 Jersey Way, Barwell, Leicester LE9 8HR Tel: 01445 842981 Fax: 01445 850065; Brungerley, 122 Leicester Road, Hinckley LE10 1LU Tel: 01455 618739 — MB ChB 1981 Manch.; FRCGP 1996, M 1985; Cert. Family Plann. JCC 1985; DRCOG 1983. (Manch.) GP Princip. Barwell Leics.; Trainer (Gen. Pract.) & Course Organiser Leicester VTS; Clin. Teach. (Gen. Pract.) Univ. Leicester; Clin. Asst., Ophth., Hinckley & Dist. Hosp,. Socs: BMA; Mem. of Fac. Bd., Leicester Fac. RCGP. Prev: Clin. Asst. (Ophth.) Hinckley & Dist. Hosp.; Med. Off.

(Minor Surg.) Hinckley & Dist. Hosp.; Trainee GP Blackburn, Hyndburn & Ribble Valley HA VTS.

SCARBOROUGH, Sarah Ann Barbara 33 Falsgrave Road, Scarborough YO12 5AB — MB ChB 1983 Manch. Gen. Pract. ScarBoro..

SCARFE, David Robert Marston Medical Centre, 24 Cherwell Drive, Headington, Oxford OX3 0LY Tel: 01865 761234 Fax: 01865 74406; 64 Picklers Hill, Abingdon, Oxford OX14 2BB Tel: 01235 201991 Fax: 01865 744066 — MB BS 1984 Lond.; BSc Lond. 1981; MRCGP 1988; DRCOG 1986. Tutor (Pub. Health & Primary Care) Univ. Oxf.

SCARFE, Stephen Andrew Orchard 2000 Medical Centre, 480 Hall Road, Hull HU6 9BS Tel: 01482 854552 Fax: 01482 859900 — MB ChB 1978 Leeds. Socs: Hull Med. Soc.

SCARFFE, Professor John Howard The Wellcome Trust, 183 Euston Road, London NW1 2BE Tel: 020 7611 8888 Fax: 020 7611 8545; Four Winds, Cinder Lane, Thelwall, Warrington WA4 3JL Tel: 01925 263549 Email: hscarffe@compuserve.com — MB BS Lond. 1970; MD Lond. 1980; FRCP Lond. 1986; MRCP (UK) 1973; MRCS Eng. LRCP Lond. 1970. (St. Bart.) Head Program.Career Schemes * Clin. Iniatives. Socs: BMA. Prev: Prof Reader, Sen. Lect. & Lect. (Med. Oncol.) Univ. Manch.

SCARGILL, Margaret Anne Ashville Medical Centre, 430 Doncaster Road, Barnsley S70 3EX Tel: 01226 282280 Fax: 01226 216002 — MB ChB 1992 Leeds; MPhil Sheff. 1989; BSc (Hons.) CNAA 1985; MRCGP 1996. (St. Bart. & Leeds) Socs: Med. Defence Union. Prev: SHO Barnsley VTS.

SCARISBRICK, Christopher David Stanground Health Centre, Stanground, Peterborough PE2 8RB Tel: 01733 568569 Fax: 01733 892419; 9 Queen Street, Whittlesey, Peterborough PE7 1AY Tel: 01733 204611 Fax: 01733 208926 — MB BChir 1974 Camb.; MA, MB Camb. 1974, BChir 1973; FRCGP 1993, M 1977. Vice Chairm. Cambs LMC.

SCARISBRICK, Douglas Arthur Spin Jenny, Main St., Norton Disney, Lincoln LN6 9JU Tel: 01522 788773 Fax: 01522 788773 Email: douglas@dascar.demon.co.uk — MB BS Lond. 1959; FFOM RCP Lond. 1985, MFOM 1978; DIH Soc. Apoth. Lond. 1976. (Char. Cross) Occupat. Phys. Socs: Soc. Occupat. Med.; Fell.Roy.Soc.Med. Prev: Princip. Med. Off. Brit. Coal Corp.; Cons. Occupat. Med. Leics. HA; Sen. Employm. Med. Advis. Health & Safety Exec.

SCARISBRICK, Genevieve Email: k7nog@africaonline.com.gh; 63 Croslands Park, Barrow-in-Furness LA13 9LB Tel: 01229 30142 — MB ChB 1964 Manch.; FRCR 1977; MRCGP 1972; DMRD Eng. 1975; DObst RCOG 1966; DTM & H (Milne Medal Trop. Med.) Liverp. 1965. (Manch.) Prof of Radiol. Sch. of Med. Sci.s UST Private Mailbag Kumasi Ghana. Prev: Cons. Radiologist, Furness Gen. Hosp., Barrow in Furness, Cumbria; Sen. Regist. (Radiol.) Withington Hosp. Manch.; GP Preston.

SCARISBRICK, Julia Jane St John's Hospital, St Thomas's Hospital, Lambeth Palace Road, Westminster, London SE1 7EH Tel: 020 7928 9292; 59 Klea Avenue, Clapham, London SW4 9HY — MB ChB 1994 Birm.; ChB Birm. 1994; MRCP UK 1997. Research Regist. St Johns Inst. Dermat. Prev: SHO Rotat. (Gen. Med.) Roy. Berks. Hosp.

SCARISBRICK, Peter Hugh Princes Park Health Centre, Wartling Road, Eastbourne BN22 7PF Tel: 01323 744644 Fax: 01323 736094 — MB BS 1974 Lond.; DRCOG 1977; MRCGP 1978; DCH Eng. 1978. (Middlx.) Prev: SHO (O & G) St. Helier Hosp. Carshalton; SHO (A & E) St. Helier Hosp. Carshalton; SHO (Paediat.) Qu. Mary's Hosp. Childr. Carshalton.

SCARISBRICK, Sally Ann London Road Surgery, 501 London Road, Thornton Heath CR7 6AR Tel: 020 8684 1172 Fax: 020 8665 5011; Chimneys, 130 Woodcote Valley Road, Purley CR8 3BF Tel: 020 8668 9541 — MB BS 1967 Lond. (Roy. Free)

SCARLAND, Michael Graham 24 Mather Avenue, Mossley Hill, Liverpool L18 5HS — MB ChB 1984 Leeds.

SCARLE, Trevor John Brandon HMP Cardiff, Knox Road, Cardiff CF24 0UG Tel: 029 2049 1212 — MB BS 1972 Lond. Med. Off. Dept. Prison. Med. Servs. Cardiff. Prev: GP Gravesend/.

SCARLETT, Amanda Jane Newton Place Surgery, Newton Road, Faversham ME13; Oak Lodge, 161 The St, Boughton, Faversham ME13 9BH Tel: 01227 751246 — MB ChB 1988 Bristol; MRCGP 1992; DRCOG 1991. Gen. Practioner, Faversham, Kent. Prev:

SCHAMROTH

Trainee GP S.sea VTS; SHO (Paediat. & Obst.) St. Mary's Hosp. Portsmouth.

SCARLETT, Clare Elizabeth 7 Jesmond Vale Terrace, Heaton, Newcastle upon Tyne NE6 5JT — MB BS 1994 Newc.; MA Centab 1979. (Newcastle upon Tyne)

SCARLETT, James Frederick (retired) Stoneycroft, Field Broughton, Grange-over-Sands LA11 6HW — MB ChB 1949 Leeds; MRCGP 1977; DObst RCOG 1954. Prev: GP Leeds.

SCARLETT, Jane Frances East Surrey Health Authority, Horton Lane, Epsom KT19 8PH Tel: 01372 731148 Fax: 01372 729841 — MB ChB 1985 Ed.; MFPHM RCP (UK) 1994; MRCGP 1989. Cons. Pub. Health Med. E. Surrey HA; Hon. Sen. Lect. St. Geo. Hosp. Med. Sch. Lond.

SCARLETT, Nigel John David 16 North Lodge Close, Westleigh Avenue, Putney, London SW15 6QZ Tel: 020 8788 6657 Fax: 020 8788 6657 Email: nigel@scarlnett.demon.co.uk; Oak Tree Cottage, Burney Road, Westhumble, Dorking RH5 6AX Tel: 01306 883139 — MB BS 1988 Lond.; MA Camb. 1976; MRCGP 1996. (Char. Cross & Westm.)

SCARLETT, Sheila Mary (retired) Stoneycroft, Field Broughton, Grange-over-Sands LA11 6HW Tel: 01395 36586 — MRCS Eng. LRCP Lond. 1953. SCMON. Yorks. (Harrogate) HA. Prev: Sen. MO N.Yorks (Harrogate) HA.

SCARPELLO, John Hugh Department of Diabetes and Endocrinology, City General Hospital, Stoke-on-Trent ST4 6QG Tel: 01782 553425 Fax: 01782 553427 — MB BCh 1971 Wales; MD Wales 1978; FRCP Lond. 1989; MRCP (UK) 1974. (Wales) Cons. Phys. City Gen. Hosp. Stoke-on-Trent; Sen. Lect. (Postgrad. Med.) Univ. Keele. Socs: Med. Scientif. Sect. Diabetes UK; Brit. Assn. of Hosp. Managers; Assn. of Brit. Clin. Diabetologists. Prev: Sen. Regist. (Med.) Roy. Hallamsh. Hosp. Sheff.; Postdoctoral Research Fell. Div. Endocrinol. & Metab. Univ. Michigan, Ann Arbor USA; Ho. Phys. Univ. Hosp. Wales. Cardiff.

SCARR, John Dargue (retired) 230 Benfleet Road, Hadleigh, Benfleet SS7 1QQ Tel: 01702 552169 — MB BChir 1970 Camb.; MA Camb. 1970. Prev: Gen. Practitioner Leigh on Sea.

SCARRATT, William Lawrence Herbert (retired) Robins Close, Kingston, Kingsbridge TQ7 4PL Tel: 01548 810786 — MB BS 1962 Lond.; FRCPath 1983, M 1970. Prev: Cons. Histopath. Plymouth Gen. Hosp.

SCARROW, George Davidson (retired) 20 Abbey Road, West Kirby, Wirral CH48 7EW Tel: 0151 625 6799 — MD 1950 Liverp.; MB ChB 1941, MRad(D) 1948; FFR 1974; DMRD Eng. 1948. Prev: Cons. Radiol. Liverp. RHB.

SCARROW, Paul Larwood Surgery, Larwood, Worksop S81 0HH Tel: 01909 500233 Fax: 01909 479722; Lorelei, Old Blyth Road, Ranby, Retford DN22 8HZ — BM BS 1982 Nottm.; BMedSci Nottm. 1980, BM BS 1982.

SCARSBROOK, Andrew Frederick 35a Rossett Avenue, Timperley, Altrincham WA15 6EU — BM BS 1996 Nottm.

SCARTH, Jennifer Clare North Tees General Hospital, Hardwick, Stockton-on-Tees TS19 8PE Tel: 01642 617617; 15 Brundon Avenue, Whitley Bay NE26 1SE Tel: 0191 252 6156 — MB BS 1993 Newc.; MRCP (UK) 1996. Specialist Regist. Rotat. (Paediat.) N.ern Region. Socs: MRCPCH. Prev: SHO Rotat. (Paediat.) Newc. Teachg. Hosps.; SHO (Paediat.) N. Tees Gen. Hosp. Stockton & Roy. Vict. Infirm. Newc.

SCARTH, Leslie George (retired) 4 Beauchamp Road, Edinburgh EH16 6LQ Tel: 0131 658 1283 — MB BS 1964 Durh.; FRCPsych 1987, M 1978; DPM Eng. 1968. Prev: Cons. Child & Family Psychiat. Roy. Hosp. Sick Childr. Edin.

SCASE, Anne Elizabeth Low Lane, Rocklands, Attleborough NR17 1TU — MB ChB 1987 Birm.

SCATCHARD, Katherine Mary Flat A, 106 Keslake Rd, Queen's Park, London NW6 6DG — MB BS 1994 Lond.; BSc Hons 1991; MRCP 1997. (St Marys)

SCATCHARD, Michael Alva The Leeds Road Practice, 49/51 Leeds Road, Harrogate HG2 8AY Tel: 01423 566636 Fax: 01423 569208 — MB ChB 1968 St. And.; MRCGP 1975; Cert. Family Plann. JCC 1974. Tutor (Gen. Pract.) Harrogate Dist. Hosp.; Hosp. Pract. (Dermat.) Harrogate Gen. Hosp. Socs: Brit. Inst. Med. Manipulation. Prev: Regist. (Dermat.) Dundee Teachg. Hosps.; Ch.ill Fell. 1980; Ho. Phys. (Prof.) Dundee Teachg. Hosps.

SCAWN, David Lionel, Maj. RAMC Health Centre, Bridge Street, Rothwell, Kettering NN14 6JW Tel: 01536 418518 Fax: 01536 418373 — LRCPI & LM, LRSCI & LM 1958; LRCPI & LM, LRCSI & LM 1958; Sen. Med. Off. Chatham Dist. Prev: Ho. Surg. & Ho. Phys. N. Staffs. Roy. Infirm. Stoke-on-Trent.

SCAWN, Nigel David Anthony Royal Liverpool University Hospital, Prescot St., Liverpool L7 8XP Tel: 0151 706 2000; 29 Church View Road, Desborough, Kettering NN14 2PS Tel: 01536 760711 — BM 1992 Soton.; BPharm Lond. 1986; DA (UK) 1994; FRCA 1998. Specialist Regist. (Anaesth.) Mersey Deanery NW Region. Socs: Roy. Pharm. Soc.; Fell. Fac. Anaesth. Roy. Coll. Surg. Irel. (FFARCSI) 1997. Prev: SHO (Anaesth.) St. Jas. Univ. Hosp. Leeds & Roy. Liverp. Univ. Hosp.

SCAYSBROOK, Paul Richard The Surgery, Clerk's Field, Headcorn, Ashford TN27 9QJ Tel: 01622 890294 Fax: 01622 891754 — MB 1974 Camb.; BChir 1973; DObst RCOG 1976. (Camb. & King's Coll. Hosp.)

SCEATS, Graham Philip 35 Brighton Road, Aldershot GU12 4HG — MB ChB 1992 Otago.

SCERRI, Mr Godwin, Wing Cdr. RAF Med. Br. Consultant Plastic Surgeon, Department of Plastic & Reconstructive Surgery, Royal Hospital Haslar, Gosport PO12 2AA Tel: 023 9258 4255, 023 9276 2481 Fax: 023 9276 2481 Email: godwscer@dsca.mod.uk; Email: g@scerri.freeserve.co.uk — MRCS Eng. LRCP Lond. 1981; FRCS (Plast) 1995; FRCS Eng. 1988. (Lond. Hosp. Med. Coll.) Cons. Plastic Surg. Roy. Hosp. Haslar Gosport; Cons. Adviser (Plastic Surg.) Defence Med. Servs. Socs: Brit. Assn. Plastic Surg.; Brit. Burns Assn.; Brit. Assn. Aesthetic Plastic Surgs. Prev: Sen. Regist. (Plastic Surg.) Addenbrooke's Hosp. Camb.; Sen. Regist. (Hand Surg.) Nuffield Orthop. Centre Oxf.; Regist. (Plastic Surg.) Canniesburn Hosp. Glas.

SCERRI, Joseph Juliet, Quarries Square, Msida, Malta; 5 Chalgrove Road, Sutton SM2 5JT Tel: 020 8642 7335 — MRCS Eng. LRCP Lond. 1981; DRCOG 1986; DGM 1986. (Westminster Medical School)

SCHACHTER, Joan Parkside Clinic, 63-65 Lancaster Road, London W11 1QT — MB ChB 1971 Birm.; MRCPsych 1976. Cons. Psychiat. (Psychother.) Pk.side Clinic. Socs: Brit. Psychoanal Soc.

SCHACHTER, Michael Dept. Of Clinical Pharmacology, St. Mary's Hospital, London W2 1NY Email: m.schachter@ic.ac.uk; 71 Fortune Green Road, London NW6 1DR — MB BS 1974 Lond.; BSc Lond. 1971; MRCP (UK) 1979. Sen. Lect. (Clin. Pharmacol.) Imperial Coll. Fac. of Med. Socs: Fell. Roy. Soc. Med. Prev: BHF Sen. Research Fell. (Clin. Pharmacol.) St. Mary's Hosp. Med. Sch. Lond.; Research Regist. (Neurol.) King's Coll. Hosp. Lond.; Research Fell. MRC Unit & Univ. Dept. Clin. Pharmacol. Oxf.

SCHADY, Wolfgang Department of Neurology, Manchester Royal Infirmary, Oxford Road, Manchester M13 9WL — MRCS Eng. LRCP Lond. 1975; MRCP (UK) 1978; FRCP Lond. 1989. Sen. Lect. (Neurol.) Univ. Manch.; Hon. Cons. Neurol. Manch. Roy. Infirm.; Hon. Cons. Neurol. Hope Hosp., Salford; Hon.Cons. Neurol. Traffod Gen. Hosp.; Clin. Director, Gtr. Manchetser Neuro Sci. Centre.

SCHAEFER, Andrew Mark 55 Pickering Road, West Ayton, Scarborough YO13 9JE — MB ChB 1994 Leeds; MB ChB Leeds. 1994.

SCHAEFER, Jennifer Ann Nailsea Health Centre, Somerset Square, Nailsea, Bristol BS48 1RR Tel: 01275 856611 Fax: 01275 857074 — MB ChB 1986 Bristol; MRCGP 1990; DRCOG 1991; DCH RCPS Glas. 1988.

SCHAEFER, Wolfgang Cwm-Weeg House, Upper Dolfor, Newtown Tel: 01686 28992 — State Exam Med 1982 Freiburg.

SCHAFLER, Kathrine Freda Queen Mary's University Hospital, Roehampton Lane, London SW15 5PN Tel: 020 8789 6611 Fax: 020 8780 0347 — MB BS 1971 Lond.; MRCPath 1978.

SCHALLAMACH, Sarah 65 Shaftesbury Avenue, Roundhay, Leeds LS8 1DR — MB BS 1989 Newc.; MRCGP 1994; DRCOG 1993.

SCHALLREUTER, Karin Chellow Grange, Malvern Road, Bradford BD9 6AP — State Exam Med 1984 Hamburg; MD Hamburg 1985; Spec.Derm.Ven.1992. Prof. Clin.Experim. Derm. Univ.Bradford; Dir. Inst. Pigmentary Disorders. EM Arndt Univ. Germany. Socs: Brit. Assn. Derm.; Amer. Acad.Derm; Roy. Soc. Med.

SCHAMROTH, Alan Jeffrey Bounds Geen Group Practice, Bounds Green Group Practice, Gordon Road, New Southgate, London N11 2PF Tel: 020 8889 1961 Fax: 020 8889 7844; 19 Manor

SCHAPEL, View, London N3 2ST Tel: 020 8346 1293 — BSc Lond. 1980, MB BS 1983; MRCGP 1987; DCH RCP Lond. 1987; DRCOG 1986. Clin. Lect. (Primary Health Care) Whittington Hosp. UCLMS; Princip. Lect. (Med. Ethics) UCLMS. Prev: Trainee GP N.wick Pk. Hosp. VTS Harrow.

SCHAPEL, Graham John 12 Roxburgh Garden Court, Plymouth Road, Penarth CF64 3DX — MB BS 1964 Sydney.

SCHAPIRA, Andrew Lewis Nightingale Road Surgery, 1 Nightingale Road, London N9 8AJ Tel: 020 8804 3333 Fax: 020 8805 7776 — MB BS 1987 Lond.

SCHAPIRA, Professor Anthony Henry Vernon The National Hospital, Queen Square, London WC1N 3BG Tel: 020 7837 3611; University Department of Clinical Neurosciences, Royal Free Hospital Medical School, London NW3 2PF Tel: 020 7830 2012 Fax: 020 7431 1577 Email: schapira@rfhsm.ac.uk — MB BS 1979 Lond.; BSc (Hons.) Lond. 1976, DSc 1994, MD 1988; FRCP Lond. 1992; MRCP (UK) 1982; DSc Lond. 1994. (Westm.) Chairm. Neurosci. Roy. Free & Univ. Coll. Med. Sch. UCL & Prof. Clin. Neurol. Inst. Neurol. Qu. Sq. Lond.; Vis. Prof. Neurol. Mt. Sinai Med. Sch. NY, USA; Mem. Roy. Inst. Socs: Harveian Soc.; Lond. Med. Soc.; Amer. Neurol. Assn. Prev: Cons. Neurol. Roy. Free Hosp. & Nat. Hosp. Nerv. Dis. Lond.; Regist. & Sen. Regist. Nat. Hosp. Qu. Sq. Lond.

SCHAPIRA, Daniel John 44 Beatrice Avenue, London SW16 4UN Tel: 020 8764 7292 Fax: 020 8764 7292 Email: 101774.2772@compuserve.com — MB BS 1979 Lond.; MSc Lond. 1996; MMedSc Birm. 1995; DCH RCP Lond. 1981; DRCOG 1980. (Middlx.) Lect. (Computer Interface Design) Lond.; Indep. Multi-Media Cons. & Developer Lond. Prev: GP Lond.

SCHAPIRA, Harry 16 Wide Way, Mitcham CR4 1BD Tel: 020 8764 7612; 4 Pollards Hill S., Norbury, London SW16 4LN — MRCS Eng. LRCP Lond. 1952. (Guy's)

SCHAPIRA, Kurt 4 Brookfield, Westfield, Newcastle upon Tyne NE3 4YB Tel: 0191 285 5678 — MB BS 1952 Durh.; MD Durh. 1961; FRCP Lond. 1979, M 1973; FRCPsych 1975, M 1971; DPM Durham. 1963. Emerit. Cons. Psychiat. Newc. HA; Hon. Sen. Research Assoc. (Psychiat.) Univ. Newc. Socs: Fell. Roy. Soc. Med. (Ex.-Pres. Sect. Psychiat.). Prev: Sub Dean Roy. Coll Psychiats.; Sen. Lect. (Psychol. Med.) Univ. Newc.; Pres. N. Eng. Medico-Legal Soc.

SCHAPIRA, Robert Clive 18 Millwell Crescent, Chigwell IG7 5HY — MB BS 1985 Lond.

SCHAPS, Peter (retired) Four Gables, Purton, Swindon SN5 4DE — MB BS 1957 Melbourne.

SCHATZBERGER, Paul Maxim Upwell Street Surgery, 91 Upwell Street, Sheffield S4 8AN Tel: 0114 261 8608; 78 Carr Road, Sheffield S6 2WZ Tel: 0114 233 0523 Email: paul.schatzberges@dial.pipex.com — MB BS 1973 Lond.; MFPHM RCP (UK) 1995; MRCGP (Distinc.) 1977; DObst RCOG 1975. (Univ. Coll. Hosp.) Prev: Sen. Regist. (Pub. Health Med.) Barnsley HA; Regist. (Pub. Health Med.) Sheff. HA; GP Hampstead, Camden & Islington FPC.

SCHEEL, T A Trent Meadows Medical Centre, 87 Wood Street, Burton-on-Trent DE14 3AA Tel: 01283 845555 Fax: 01283 845222 — State Exam Med 1987 Freiburg; State Exam Med 1987 Freiburg.

SCHEELE, Kate Helene 218 Stannington View Road, Sheffield S10 1ST — MB ChB 1998 Sheff.; MB ChB Sheff 1998.

SCHEEPERS, Bruce Duncan Meiring Stalbridge Road Clinic, Stalbridge Road, Crewe CW2 7LP Tel: 01270 654404 Fax: 01270 654437 Email: scheepers@supanet.com — MB ChB 1984 Stellenbosch; MRCPsych 1991. (Stellenbosch (South Africa)) Cons. Neuropsychiat. Mid. Chesh. Hosp. NHS Trust, Crewe; Cons. Neuropsychiat. Chesh. Community Healthcare NHS Trust; Sen. Clin. Lect. Dept. of Psychiat. Univ. Keele; Cons. Neuropsychiat. Transitional Rehabilitation Unit, Haydock. Socs: Brit. Neuropsychiat. Assn.; Internat. League Against Epilepsy; Brit. Epilepsy Assn.

SCHEIMBERG SCHIFF, Irene Beatriz The Royal London Hospital, Whitechapel, London E1 1BB Tel: 020 7377 7347 Fax: 020 7377 7030; 19 Brockwell Park Gardens, London SE24 9BL — LMS 1983 U Complutense Madrid; MRCPath 1994. Sen. Lect. & Hon. Cons. (Paediat. & Perinatal Path.) Roy. Lond. Hosp. Lond. Socs: MRCPath.; Paediatric Pathol. Soc.; Path. Soc. Prev: Lect. Gt. Ormond St. Hosp. for Childr.

SCHELLANDER, Fritz Gerhard 8 Chilston Road, Tunbridge Wells TN4 9LT Tel: 01892 543535 Fax: 01892 545160 — MD 1965 Vienna; LMSSA Lond. 1974. Fell. St. John's Hosp. Dermat. Soc. Prev: Regist. Dept. Dermat. & Venereol. & Regist. Dept. Path. Univ. Vienna; Med. Sch., Austria; Research Fell. & Train. Fell. Inst. Dermat. Lond.

SCHELVAN, Christopher Selvam Keith 119B Dartmouth Road, London NW2 4ES — MB BS 1993 Lond.; FRCR 2000; BSc Lond. 1990; MRCP (UK) 1997. (St. Mary's) Specialist Regist. (Radiol.) UCH Middlx. Hosp. Lond. Prev: SHO (Paediat. & Neonates) N.wick Pk. Hosp. Harrow; SHO (Paediat.) Qu. Eliz. Hosp. Childr. Lond.; SHO (A & E) Univ. Coll. Hosp. Lond.

SCHEMBRI, Joseph Anthony Lindley Village Surgery, Thomas Street, Lindley, Huddersfield HD3 3JD Tel: 01484 651403 Fax: 01484 644198; The Beeches, 30 Occupation Road, Lidley, Huddersfield HD3 3EE — MRCS Eng. LRCP Lond. 1981; D.Occ.Med. RCP Lond. 1995. (Univ. Leics.)

SCHEMBRI WISMAYER, Franz 11 Chertsey Road, Redland, Bristol BS6 6NB — MB BS 1993 Lond.

SCHEMBRI WISMAYER, Joseph Liverpool Road Health Centre, 9 Mersey Place, Luton LU1 1HH Tel: 01582 22525 Fax: 01582 421602; 12 Montrose Avenue, Luton LU3 1HR Tel: 01582 23900 — MD 1958 Malta. Hosp. Pract. (Orthop. & Accid.) Luton & Dunstable Hosp.

SCHENK, Christopher Paul Civil Aviation Authority, Gatwick Airport South RH6 0YR — AFOM 2001; MB BS 1986 Lond.; DAvMED 1992.

SCHENK, Paul Michiel Fore Street Surgery, Fore Street, St Dennis, St Austell PL26 8AG — MB BS 1987 Lond.; BSc Biochem. Lond. 1981. (King's Coll. Lond.)

SCHER, Herschel Ward 5D, Hospital for Sick Children, Great Ormond St., London WC1N 3JH — MB ChB 1983 Cape Town.

SCHER, Leslie Bernard (retired) 41 Albany, Manor Road, Bournemouth BH1 3EJ Tel: 01202 554362 — MB BCh BAO 1942 NUI; BDS 1944; FDS RCS Ed. 1955, HDD 1945; FFD RCSI 1964. Prev: Prof. Dent. Prosth.s, Univ. Coll. Cork.

SCHERF, Caroline Franziska Dept of Medicine, University of Wales College of Medicine, Cardiff CF4 4XX; 23 Chale Road, London SW2 4JD — State Exam Med. Berlin 1988. Res. Fell. (Gyn.) Uni. of Wales, Coll. of Med.

SCHERZINGER, Sabine Hilda Thorpe Health Centre, St. Williams Way, Norwich NR7 0AJ Tel: 01603 701212; 12 Chester Street, Norwich NR2 2AY Tel: 01603 617101 — MB ChB 1992 Cape Town; MSc S. Afr. 1987; BPharm S. Afr. 1985. GP. Socs: MDU 387678F. Prev: SHO (Gen. Med.) Norf. & Norwich Hosp.

SCHETRUMPF, Mr John Robert 17 Harley Street, London W1N 1DA Tel: 020 7637 5005 — MB BS 1964 Sydney; FRCS Ed. 1969. Indep. Cosmetic Surg. Harley St. Lond. Socs: Pres. Brit. Assn. Cosmetic Surg.; Allied Mem. Brit. Assn. Plastic Surgs. Prev: Dir. Regional Burns Unit Mt. Vernon Hosp. N.wood; Sen. Regist. & Burns Research Fell. Qu. Vict. Hosp. E. Grinstead; Sen. Regist. (Plastic Surg.) Hammersmith Hosp. Lond.

SCHEUER, Professor Peter Joseph 47 Northway, London NW11 6PB Tel: 020 8455 5459 Fax: 020 8455 4383 Email: scheuer@scheupj.demon.co.uk — MB BS Lond. 1954; DSc (Med.) Lond. 1986, MD 1962; FRCPath 1976, M 1963. (Roy. Free) Vice Pres., Brit. Liver Trust; Trustee Brit. Liver Trust. Prev: Prof. Histopath. Univ. Lond.; Hon. Cons. Histopath. Roy. Free Hosp. Lond.

SCHEURMIER, Neil Ian Munro The Frome Medical Practice, Park Road, Frome BA11 1EZ Tel: 01737 301300 Email: nemesis@ukonline.co.uk — MB 1981 Camb.; BChir 1980; BSc Hons. (Physiol.) Dundee 1976. (Camb.) GP Assoc., Frome. Prev: GP Hayling Is.; Primary Care Med. Adviser, Wilts. Health Auth.

SCHEY, Stephen Arthur Department of Haematology, Guy's Hospital, St Thomas St., London SE1 9RT Tel: 020 7955 4003 Fax: 020 7955 4002 — MB BS 1974 Lond.; MB BS. Lond. 1974; FRCP Lond. 1993; MRCP (UK) 1978; FRACP 1982; MRCPath. 1985. Hons. Cons. & Sen. Lect. (Haemat.) Guy's Hosp. Lond. Socs: Coun. Mem. Brit. Soc. of Haematol.; Sec. UK Myeloma Forum; Eur. Blood & Marrow Transpl.

SCHIEBAAN, Esther 261 The Sycamores, Milton, Cambridge CB4 6ZD Tel: 01223 863256 — Artsexamen 1994 Rotterdam. Prev: SHO Addenbrookes Hosp. Camb.; SHO (Gen. Paediat.) Addenbrookes Hosp.; SHO (Obst.) Hinchingbrooke Hosp. Huntingdon.

SCHIERENBERG, Tai Seng Francis Department of Surgery, East Surrey Hospital, Canada Avenue, Redhill RH1 5RH Tel: 01958

349386 — MB BS 1992 Lond. (Char. Cross & Westm.) SHO (Gen. Surg.) E. Surrey Hosp. Surrey. Socs: Fell. RCS. Prev: Regist. (Gen. Surg. & Trauma) Baragwanath Hosp. Soweto, Johannesburg, S. Afr.; SHO (Neurosurg.) Frenchay Hosp. Bristol; SHO (Orthop.) Ealing Hosp. Uxbridge.

SCHIESS, Fiona Jane Churchill Medical Centre, Clifton Road, Kingston upon Thames KT2 6PG; Westover 15C, St Albans Road, Kingston upon Thames KT2 5HQ — MB BS 1989 Lond.; T(GP) 1993; DRCOG 1992.

SCHIESS, Mr Frank Alfred Ferneigh Consulting Centre, 27 Alderley Road, Wilmslow SK9 1PQ; Netherfield, Trafford Road, Alderley Edge SK9 7DN — MB BS 1963 Lond.; FRCS Eng. 1969. (Middlx.) Cons. Orthop. Surg. Prev: Lect. in Orthop. Surg. Univ. Manch.; Ho. Surg. Middlx. Hosp.

SCHIFF, Anthony Adam 19 Whistley Close, Bracknell RG12 9LQ — MRCS Eng. LRCP Lond. 1963. Prev: Sen. Med. Adviser E.R. Squibb & Sons Ltd.

SCHIFFER, Gabriele Flat 2, Ridgway Court, London SW19 4SQ — State Exam Pisa 1992.

SCHILL, Eleanor Beatrice, MBE (retired) 18 Jenny Lane, Woodford, Stockport SK7 1PE Tel: 0161 439 4108 — MB ChB 1927 Manch.; DPM Eng. 1937. Prev: Cons. Psychiat. Withington Hosp. Manch.

SCHILLER, Gillian Ida Gateway Consulting Group, 30 Paines Lane, Pinner HA5 3DB Tel: 020 8868 9898 Fax: 020 8898 3973 Email: lmosshrp@dircon.co.uk — MB BS 1979 Lond.; DCH RCP Lond. 1983; MBA 1986.

SCHILLER, Klaus Frederick Richard Acland Nuffield Hospital, Banbury Road, Oxford OX2 6PD Tel: 01865 404142 Fax: 01865 556303; The Mill, Cuddesdon, Oxford OX44 9HQ Tel: 01865 875174 Fax: 01865 872121 — BM BCh Oxf. 1951; MA Oxf. 1953; DM 1966; FRCP Lond. 1977, M 1958. (Oxf. & Lond. Hosp.) Cons. Gastroenterol. Acland Nuffield Hosp. Oxf.; Emerit. Cons. Phys. & Gastroenterol. St. Peter's Hosp. Chertsey. Socs: Brit. Soc. Gastroenterol. (Ex Vice-Pres Endoscopy. Prev: Sen. Regist. (Med.) Radcliffe Infirm. Oxf.; Regist. (Med.), Ho. Phys. & Ho. Surg. Lond. Hosp.

SCHILLING, Christopher John 131 Eaton House, 38 Westferry Circus, London E14 8RN Tel: 020 7719 0444 Fax: 020 7719 0445 Email: schillcj@aol.com; 131 Eaton House, 38 Westferry Circus, London E14 8RN Tel: 020 7719 0444 Fax: 020 7719 0445 Email: schillcj@aol.com — BM BCh Oxf. 1965; MSc Lond. 1982; BA Oxf. 1962; MRCP (UK) 1969; FFOM RCP Lond. 1988, MFOM 1984; T(OM) 1991; DIH Eng. 1981. (St. Thos.) Princip. Med. Adviser Schilling & Schilling (Cons. in Occupat. Health). Socs: Soc. Occupat. Med. Prev: Regional Speciality Adviser Occupat. Med. NE Thames RHA; Area Med. Off. SE CEGB & Div. Med. Off. Research Div. CEGB; Princip. GP Camden & Islington FPC.

SCHILLING, Richard John Cardiology Dept., St. Bartholomews Hospital, Dominion House, West Smithfield, London EC1A 7BE — MB BS 1989 Lond.; MRCP (UK) 1992; MD London 1999. Cons. (Cardiol.) St Bartholomews Hosp. Lond.

SCHINDLER, Jane Louise Chapelthorpe Medical Centre, Standbridge Lane, Wakefield WF2 7GP Tel: 01924 255166 Fax: 01924 257653; 6 Claphouse Fold, Haigh, Barnsley S75 4BY Tel: 01924 830199 — MB ChB 1986 Sheff.; MRCGP 1990. (Sheffield) GP; Eng. Wom. Rugby Team Med. Off.

SCHINDLER, Margrid Brigitte The Intensive Care Unit, Hospital for Sick Children, Great Ormond St., London WC1N 3JH — MB BS 1982 New South Wales; FANZCA 1990. Cons. Paediat. Intens. Care Gt. Ormond St. Hosp. Childr. Lond.

SCHIPPERHEIJN, Johanna Agnes Maria Edgware Community Hospital, Edgware Road, Edgware HA8 0AD — Artsexamen 1984 Amsterdam; MRCPsych 1989. Cons. Psychiat. Prev: Sen. Regist. Rotat. (Psychiat.) St. Mary's Lond.; Regist. (Psychiat.) Middlx. & Univ. Coll. Hosp. Lond.

SCHIRGE, Angelika Sigrid Fairfield House, c/o Accident & Emergency Department, Crawley Hospital, West Green Drive, Crawley RH11 7DH — MB ChB 1996 Stellenbosch.

SCHIRRMACHER, Ulrich Otto Erich Davenal House Surgery, 28 Birmingham Road, Bromsgrove B61 0DD Tel: 01527 872008; 133 New Road, Bromsgrove B61 2LJ Tel: 01527 75954 — MB BS 1965 Lond.; MRCS Eng. LRCP Lond. 1965. (St. Geo.)

SCHIZAS, Mr Constantin Fax: 020 7288 3147; Email: cschizas@compuserve.com — MD 1986 Louvain; MSc (Orthop.) Lond. 1994; FRCS 2000 (ed eundem) Lond.; Qualification en Chirurgie Orthopedique, Paris 1996; Dip. Biomechanics, Strathclyde 1996. (Universite Catholique de Louvain (Belgium)) Cons. Orthop. Surg./Hon. Sen. Lectures, The Whittington Hosp. Lond. Socs: Fell. BOA; Federat. Medicorum Helveticorum.; Fell. Roy. Soc. Med. Prev: Cons. Orthop. Surg. Qu. Mary's Hosp., Sidcup; Oberarzt, Schulthess Hosp., Zurich; Sen. Regist. Roy. Nat. Orthop. Hosp. Stanmore.

SCHLECHT, Bernard Jean Marie Liverpool School of Trop. Medicine, Pembroke Place, Liverpool L3 5QA Tel: 0151 708 9393 Fax: 0151 708 5322; 33A Mauldeth Road, Withington, Manchester M20 4NF Tel: 0161 225 1383 — MD 1974 Paris; MSc Manch. 1990; MRCP (UK) 1979; MFPHM 1990; T(PHM) 1991. (Paris) Lect. (Epidemiol.) Liverp. Sch. Trop. Med. Prev: Sen. Regist. (Community Med.) N. W.. RHA; ARC Med. Off. ARC Epidem. Research Unit Univ. Manch; Regist. (Gen. Med.) St. Martins Hosp. Bath.

SCHLESINGER, Antonia Jane 93 Eastern Way, Ponteland, Newcastle upon Tyne NE20 9RQ — MB ChB 1994 Leeds.

SCHLESINGER, Mr Peter Ernst Department of Gynaecology, Princess Margaret Hospital, Okus Road, Swindon SN1 4JU Tel: 01793 536231; 6 The Beanlands, Wanborough, Swindon SN4 0EJ Tel: 01793 790265 Fax: 01793 790265 — MB BS 1975 Lond.; FRCS Ed. 1981; MRCS Eng. LRCP Lond. 1975; MRCOG 1984; FRCOG 1997. (St. Bart.) Cons. O & G P.ss Margt. Hosp. Swindon; Hon. Sen. Lect. Univ. Soton.; Assoc. Prof. Univ. of W. Indies. Socs: Fell.Roy. Soc. Med.; Brit. Gyn. Cancer Soc.; Internat. Continence Soc. Prev: Sen. Regist. St. Bartholomews Hosp., N. Middlsex Hosp. Lond. & Roy. Marsden Hosp.; Regist. Kings Coll. & Char. Cross Hosp. Lond.; SHO Qu. Charlotte's & Samarit. Hosp. Lond.

SCHLEYPEN, Paulus Franciscus Hubertus Maria Josef Coldstream Health Centre, Kelso Road, Coldstream TD12 4LQ Tel: 01890 882711 Fax: 01890 883547; Hatfield, Duns Road, Coldstream TD12 4DR — Artsexamen 1986 Nijmegen; MRCGP 1991; T(GP) 1991.

SCHLICHT, Justin Orchard Cottage, 23 Far Holme Lane, Sutton-on-Trent, Newark NG23 6PQ Tel: 01636 821081 — MRCS Eng. LRCP Lond. 1966; MSc (Soc. Med.) Lond. 1973, MB BS 1966; MRCPsych 1973. Cons. (Child. Adol. Psychiat.) Bassetlaw Hosp. & Community Servs. NHS Trust. Prev: Cons. (Child & Adolesc. Psychiat.) Göteborg; Cons. Psychother. Bethlem Roy. Hosp. & Maudsley Hosp. Lond.; Cons. Psychiat. Univ. Coll. Hosp. Lond.

SCHLIEN, Maren 19 Ivy Lane, Canterbury CT1 1TU — State Exam Med 1991 Marburg.

SCHMID, Matthias Ludwig Department of Infection & Tropical Medicine, Newcastle General Hospital, Newcastle upon Tyne NE4 6BE Tel: 0114 271 1900 Fax: 0114 275 3061 Email: matthias.schmid@csuh.trent.nhs.uk; 27 Salt Box Grove, Grenoside, Sheffield S35 8SG Fax: 0114 275 3061 Email: matthiasschmid@hotmail.com — State Exam Med 1989 Ulm; MD Ulm 1990; MRCP (UK) 1995; DTM & H Lond. 1996. (Univ. Ulm) Dept. of Infec. & Trop. Med. Newc..; Trav. Fell. Roy. Coll. Physic. & Surgs. Glas. Socs: RCP (Lond.).

SCHMIDT, Annemarie Elizabeth 6 West Hill Court, Millfield Lane, London N6 6JJ — MB ChB 1985 Cape Town.

SCHMIDT, Annette Catherine 55 The Crescent, Haversham, Milton Keynes MK19 7AW — MB ChB 1998 Bristol.

SCHMIDT, Barbara Elisabeth Hunts Cross Group Practice, Hunts Cross Health Centre, 70 Hillfoot Road, Liverpool L25 0ND Tel: 0151 486 1428 Fax: 0151 448 0233 — State Exam Med 1986 Erlangen; MD Erlangen 1990.

SCHMIDT, Jorg Ulverston Health Centre, Victoria Road, Ulverston LA12 0EW Tel: 01229 583732 — State Exam Med 1991 Wurzburg. (Wurzburg) GP Ulverston, Cumbria.

SCHMIDT, Karl Ernst 3 Apple Close, Dowlish Wake, Ilminster TA19 0QG Tel: 01460 55270 — MD 1954 Graz; MRCS Eng. LRCP Lond. 1953; FRCPsych 1987, M 1971; FRANZCP 1983; DPM Manch. 1957. Cons. Psych. NHS Yeovil Dist. Hosp.; Vis. Prof. Neurol. Psychiat. Hans Berger Inst. Friedrich Schiller Univ., Germany; Ment. Health Specialist i/c Ment. Health Serv. Med. Dept. Brunei. Socs: BMA; Assoc. World Federat. Ment. Health; Roy. Soc. Chem. Prev: Cons. Psychol. Med. Yeovil Dist. Hosp. & Tone Vale Hosp. Som.; Chief Adviser (Ment. Health) S. Pacific Commiss. Noumea New Caledonia; Cons. WHO (Geneva & India).

SCHMIDT

SCHMIDT, Paul Erald Flat 1, 7 Macaulay Road, London SW4 0QP Email: paul.schmitt.demon.co.uk — MB ChB 1991 Stellenbosch; B.Med. Sci 1998. (Univ.Stellenbosch,South Africa) Assoc. Special. Med. Assessm. unit Qu. Alex. Hosp. Portsmouth. Prev: Reg.Gen.Med.Roy.Berks. & Battle hosps.Reading; med.Off.ITU Livingstone Hosp.port Eliz. SA; Ho. Off. Livingstone Hosp. Port Eliz. SA.

SCHMITGEN, Catja Foulds House, Briercliffe, Burnley BB10 3QY — State Exam Med 1991 Essen; Medical Doctorate Univ. Essen 1994. (University of Essen, Germany)

SCHMITGEN, Gunther Burnley General Hospital, Casterton Avenue, Burnley BB10 2PQ Tel: 01282 474036 — State Exam Med 1980 Dusseldorf. (University of Düsseldorf) Cons. Orthop. Surg.

SCHMULIAN, Lawrence Richard 36 Monreith Road, Glasgow G43 2NY — MB BS 1966 Newc.; FRCP Glas. 1986; MRCP (UK) 197474. Cons. Phys. (Geriat. Med.) Coathill Hosp. W.er Moffat Hosp. & Monklands Dist. Gen. Hosp. Airdrie. Prev: Med. Asst. Profess. Geriat. Unit Stobhill Hosp. Glas.; Regist. (Geriat.) Lightburn Hosp. Glas.

SCHNEELOCH, Brigitte Fernyhill Medical Practice, Durham Road, Ferryhill DL17 8JJ Tel: 01740 651238 Fax: 01740 656291; 30 South Side, Shadforth, Durham DH6 1LL Tel: 0191 3721 490 — MB BS 1978 Newc.; MRCGP Lond. 1982; DRCOG 1983; DCH RCPS Glas. 1981; Dip. Therap. Newc. 1997. (Newc.)

SCHNEIDAU, Andrea 66 Woodsome Road, London NW5 1RZ — MB BS 1975 Lond.; MRCS Eng. LRCP Lond. 1975; FRCR 1983. (Middlx.) Cons. Radiol. Eliz. Garrett Anderson Hosp. & Soho Hosp. for Wom. Univ. Coll. Lond. Hosp.; Cons. BrE. Radiol. Portland Hosp. for Wom. & Childr. Lond. Prev: Sen. Regist. & Regist. (Radiol.) Middlx. Hosp. Lond.

SCHNEIDER, Mr Harry Joseph Surgical Unit, St. Thomas' Hospital, Lambeth Palace Road, London SE1 7EH; 27 High Street, Otford, Sevenoaks TN14 5PG Tel: 0402 569798 Email: hjscne@ibm.net — MB BS 1988 Lond.; FRCS Eng. 1994. (Char. Cross & Westm.) Higher Surgic. Rotat. Trainee S. Thames (Guy's & St. Thos.). Prev: Research Regist. Roy. Marsden Hosp. Lond.; Resid. (Gen. Surg.) Oregon Health Sci.s Univ. Portland, Oregon, USA; Chief Med. Off. Operat. Raleigh Qu.sland Expedition 1989.

SCHNEIDER, Vanessa 1F3 21 Rossie Place, Edinburgh EH7 5SD — MB ChB 1998 Ed.; MB ChB Ed 1998.

SCHNEPEL, Bernd 24 Jenner House, Restell Close, London SE3 7UW — State Exam Med 1992 Essen.

SCHNETLER, Charlotte 15 Radley Drive, Nuneaton CV10 7HX — MB ChB 1992 Stellenbosch.

SCHNETLER, Mr Jeremy Fredrik Coenraad Department of Oral & Maxillofacial Surgery, Royal United Hospital, Bath BA1 3NG Tel: 01225 824267 Fax: 01225 824275 Email: jeremy.schnetler@ruh-bath.swest.nhs.uk; The Chestnuts, Evercreech, Shepton Mallet BA4 6DU Email: jschnetler@easynet.co.uk — MB BS 1983 Lond.; BDS Lond. 1975; FRCS Ed. 1988; FDS RCS Eng. 1986, L 1976. Cons. Oral Surg. Roy. United Hosp. Bath; Lect. (Oral Surg.) Univ. Bristol. Socs: Fell. Brit. Assn. Oral & Maxillofacial Surg.; BMA. Prev: Sen. Regist. (Oral Surg.) John Radcliffe Hosp. Oxf.; Regist. (Oral Surg.) Guy's Hosp. Lond.; SHO (A & E) King's Coll. Hosp. Lond.

SCHNIEDEN, Vivienne 18 Hillcrest Road, Bramhall, Stockport SK7 3AE — MB BS 1986 Lond.; MA Camb. 1987; MRCPsych 1990; FRANZCP 1996. Cons. Liaison Psychiat. & Dir. Train. P. of Wales Hosp. New S. Wales, Australia; Lect. Univ. NSW. Prev: Anxiety Disorders Unit St. Vincents Hosp. NSW, Austral.

SCHOBER, Paul Carl Department of G. U. Medicine, Leicester Royal Infirmary, Leicester LE1 5WW Tel: 0116 258 6653 — MB BS 1977 Lond.; BSc Lond. 1974; MRCP (UK) 1981. (St. Thos.) Cons. Genitourin. Med. Leicester Roy. Infirm. Prev: Sen. Regist. (Genitourin. Med.) Univ. Coll. Hosp. Lond.

SCHOEMAN, Johan c/o Adrian House, Box 317, Fulbourn Hospital, Cambridge Road, Fulbourn, Cambridge CB1 5EF Tel: 01223 218530 — MB ChB 1985 Orange Free State. SHO (Child & Adolesc. Psychiat.) Brookside Family Consultation Clinic Camb. Prev: SHO (Psychiat.); SHO Psychiat. Servs. for the elderly; SHO Rehabil. Psychiat.

SCHOFIELD, Alison Marjorie 5 Manor Lane, Ettington, Stratford-upon-Avon CV37 7TE — MB BS 1998 Newc.; MB BS Newc 1998.

SCHOFIELD, Mr Andrew Derek Reid 47 Nansen Road, London SW11 5NS — MB BS 1986 Lond.; BSc (Hons.) Lond. 1983; MS Lond. 1995; FRCS Eng. 1991; FRCS Ed. 1990; FRCS Gen. Surg. 1998. (St. Bart. Hosp. Lond.) RSO St. Mark's Hosp. N.wick Pk. & St. Mark's Hosps. NHS Trust; Sen. Regist. (Gen. Surg.) Char. Cross & Barnet Gen. Hosp. Lond.; Sen. Regist. (Gen. Surg.) Chelsea & W.minster Hosp. Lond. Socs: Assn. Surg. Prev: Regist. (Gen. Surg.) W. Middlx. Univ. Hosp. & Char. Cross Hosp. Lond.; SHO (Gen. Surg.) Battle & Roy. Berks. Hosps. Reading; SHO (Cardiothoracic & A & E) St. Bart. Hosp. Lond.

SCHOFIELD, Anne Dollar Gillespie 35 Lubnaig Road, Newlands, Glasgow G43 2RY Tel: 0141 632 8735 — MB ChB 1945 Ed. (Univ. Ed.) Prev: Res. Med. Off. Elsie Inglis Matern. Hosp. Edin.; Ho. Phys. Roy. Edin. Hosp. Sick Childr.; Sen. Ho. Phys. St. James' Hosp. Balham.

SCHOFIELD, Charles Basil Shaw 27 Woodlands, Gosforth, Newcastle upon Tyne NE3 4YN Tel: 0191 285 3659 — MD 1952 Durh.; MB BS 1945; FRCP Glas. 1974, M 1972; FRCP Ed. 1969, M 1959. (Newc. upon Tyne) Socs: Hon. Life Mem. Med. Soc. Study VD & Internat. Union Against VD & Treponematoses. Prev: STD/AIDS Co-ordinator Ministries of Health Zanzibar & Mainland Tanzania; Cons. Sexually Transm. Dis. Gtr. Glas. Health Bd. & Newc. AHA; Adviser in Sexually Transm. Dis. Gt.er Glas. & other Health Bds.

SCHOFIELD, Christine Marie Clinical Oncology Unit, Royal Cornwall Hospital, Truro Tel: 01872 250000 Fax: 01726 66421; Rosemullion, Kerley Downs, Chace Water, Truro TR4 8LA — MB ChB 1977 Leeds; Dip. Therapeut Wales 1997. Clin. Med. Off., Clin. Oncol., Roy. Cornw. Hosp.; Research Fell. (Neurol.) Roy. Cornw. Hosps. (Treliske) Truro. Socs: Inst. Health Educat. Prev: Clin. Asst. (Psychogeriat.) Penrice Hosps. St Austell; Lect. (Health Educat.) Open Univ. & Cornw. Coll. Further Educat.; Clin.Asst. (Palliat.Med.) Mt. Edgcumbe Hospice St Austell.

SCHOFIELD, Mr Christopher Brealey 134 Dora Road, Wimbledon, London SW19 7HJ — MB BS 1979 Lond.; FRCS Eng. 1984. Cons. Orthop. Surg. St. Peter's Hosp. Chertsey Surrey. Socs: Fell. BOA. Prev: Sen. Regist. (Orthop.) St. Geo. Hosp. Lond.; Lect. Orthop. Surg. Char. Cross & W.minster Med. Sch.; Jun. Lect. Dept. Anat. Lond. Hosp. Med. Coll.

SCHOFIELD, Christopher Ian Appleton Village Surgery, 2-6 Appleton Village, Widnes WA8 6DZ Tel: 0151 423 2990 Fax: 0151 424 1032 — MB ChB 1986 Liverp.

SCHOFIELD, Claire Elizabeth Eccleston House, The Old Warren, Broughton, Chester CH4 0EG — MB ChB 1997 Manch.

SCHOFIELD, Claire Elizabeth 58 Park View Road, Lytham St Annes FY8 4JF — MB ChB 1998 Leeds.

SCHOFIELD, Clare Penelope 19 Devonshire Road, Bolton BL1 4PG — MB ChB 1993 Manch.

SCHOFIELD, David John (retired) The Abingdon Surgery, 65 Stert Street, Abingdon OX14 3LB Tel: 01235 523126 Fax: 01235 550625 — MRCS Eng. LRCP Lond. 1966; MRCGP 1972; DObst RCOG 1968. Prev: Clin. Tutor (Gen. Pract.) Dept. Pub. Health & Primary Care Univ. Oxf.

SCHOFIELD, Elisabeth Caroline 41 Armit Road, Greenfield, Oldham OL3 7LN — MB ChB 1986 Ed. Clin. Asst. (A & E) Roy. Oldham Hosp.

SCHOFIELD, Emma Catherine 67 Devonshire Road, Westbury Park, Bristol BS6 7NQ — MB BChir 1990 Camb.; MRCGP 1994; DCH RCP Lond. 1993.

SCHOFIELD, Emma Mary 15 Chaucer Mansions, Queen Club Gardens, London W14 9RF — MB BS 1996 Lond.

SCHOFIELD, Mr Graham Edward (retired) 35 Lubnaig Road, Newlands, Glasgow G43 2RY Tel: 0141 632 8735 — MB BS 1945 Lond.; FRCS Eng. 1952. Cons. Surg. Law. Hosp. Carluke. Prev: Sen. Regist. Vict. Infirm. Glas.

SCHOFIELD, Helen Claire (Western) Tel: 0191 257 8469 — MB BS 1997 Newc. (Newcastle) Gen. Pract., Sunderland.

SCHOFIELD, Hilda Marjorie Vane Cottage, 22 Cleveland Walk, Bath BA2 6JU Tel: 01225 465606 — MB ChB 1942 Liverp. (Liverp.) Socs: Clin. Soc. Bath. Prev: Ho. Surg. (O & G) Roy. Infirm. Liverp.; Capt. RAMC.

SCHOFIELD, Ian James 10 Limes Avenue, Darwen BB3 2SG — MB ChB 1995 Manch.

SCHOFIELD, Ian Richard Alpine House Surgery, 86 Rothley Road, Mountsorrel, Loughborough LE12 7JU Tel: 0116 230 3062 Fax: 0116 237 4218; 30 Waterfield Road, Cropston, Leicester LE7 7HN

Tel: 0116 236 7816 — MB ChB 1982 Leic.; MRCGP 1986; DRCOG 1986.

SCHOFIELD, Ian Stephen 12 Boundary Gardens, High Heaton, Newcastle upon Tyne NE7 7AA — MB BS 1978 Newc.; BMedSc Newc. 1975; FRCP Lond. 1994; MRCP (UK) 1982. Cons. (Neurophysiol.) Newc. Gen. Hosp. Prev: Sen. Regist. (Neurophysiol.) Newc. Gen. Hosp.; SHO (Med.) Roy. Vict. Infirm. Newc.

SCHOFIELD, Jarrod Four Acre Health Centre, Burnage Avenue, Clock Face, St Helens WA9 4QB Tel: 01744 819884 Fax: 01744 850382; 25 Cranshaw Avenue, Clock Face, St Helens WA9 4UR — MB ChB 1992 Liverp.; DFFP. (Liverp.) Prev: Trainee GP Warrington Dist. HA.

SCHOFIELD, John (retired) Wyther Lodge, 185 Victoria Road W., Thornton-Cleveleys FY5 3PZ Tel: 01253 853166 — MB ChB 1933 Manch. Med. Off. Smith's Crisps, Fleetwood. Prev: Cas. Off. Roy. Salop Infirm. Shrewsbury.

SCHOFIELD, John Bellhouse Cellular Pathology Department, Preston Hall Hospital, Maidstone ME20 7NH Tel: 01622 224051 Fax: 01622 224061 Email: johhnschofield2@compuserve.com; 31 New Cross Road, London SE14 5DS — MB BS 1981 Lond.; FRCPath 1999; MRCPath 1990. (St George's Hospital Medical School London) Cons. (Cellular Path.) MidKent Healthcare Trust & Kent Cancer Centre Maidstone. Socs: Brit. Lymphoma Path. Gp.; Assn. ColoProctol. Prev: Sen. Regist. (Histopath.) Roy. Marsden & Hammersmith Hosp. Lond.; Regist. (Histopath.) Hammersmith Hosp. Lond.; Regist. (Histopath. & Cytopath.) St. Stephens Hosp. Lond.

SCHOFIELD, John Gill Elsenham Surgery, Station Road, Elsenham, Bishop's Stortford CM22 6LA Tel: 01279 814730 Fax: 01279 647342; 18 Warwick Road, Bishop's Stortford CM23 5NN Tel: 01279 652783 — MB BS Lond. 1969; MRCS Eng. LRCP Lond. 1969; DObst RCOG 1971. (King's Coll. Hosp.) Assoc. Dean Lond. Deanery.

SCHOFIELD, Mr John Norman McMichael Greystones, Banbury St., Kineton, Warwick CV35 0JS Tel: 01926 640272 Fax: 01926 640272 — MB BS 1950 Lond.; FRCS Eng. 1961; FRCS Ed. 1957; DLO Eng. 1956. (Middlx.) Mem. Appeals Tribunal DHSS; Mem. (Ex-UK Represen.) Europ. Federat. Otol. Surgs. Socs: Pres. Midl. Inst. Otol.; (Ex-Chairm.) Brit. Acad. Otol.; Roy. Soc. Med. (Ex-Pres. Sect. Laryngol.). Prev: Cons. ENT Surg. Warneford, Leamington Spa, Warwick & Stratford-upon-Avon Hosps.; Sen. Regist. Middlx. Hosp. & United Birm. Hosps.; Chairm. 6th Brit. Acad. Conf. Otolaryngol.

SCHOFIELD, Jules 66 St Leonards Road, Leicester LE2 1WR — MB ChB 1998 Leic.; MB ChB Leic 1998.

SCHOFIELD, Julia Kathy Department of Dermatology, St Albans City Hospital, St. Albans & Hemel Hempstead NHS Hospitals Trust, Waverley Road, St Albans AL3 5PN Tel: 01727 897837 Fax: 01727 897837; 18 High Street, Rickmansworth WD3 1ER Tel: 01923 778279 — MB ChB 1979 Manch.; MRCP (UK) 1984; MRCGP 1986; DRCOG 1982; FCRP 1999. Cons. Dermat. St. Albans & Hemel Hempstead NHS Hosps. Trust. Prev: Trainee GP Salford VTS; Sen. Regist. (Dermat.) Watford Gen. & Roy. Lond. Hosp.; Regist. (Dermat.) SW Herts. HA.

SCHOFIELD, Julian Paul 14 Tamar Close, St. Ives, Huntingdon PE27 3JE — MB ChB 1984 Leeds; BSc (Hons.) Leeds 1981, MB ChB 1984; PhD Camb. 1991; MRCP (UK) 1987. Wellcome Advis. Train. Fell. Univ. Dept. Med. Addenbrooke's Hosp. Camb.; Hon. Sen. Regist. (Gen. Med.) Univ. Dept. Med. Addenbrooke's Hosp. Camb. Socs: Med. Res. Soc.

SCHOFIELD, Karen Patricia 4 Willow Way, Didsbury, Manchester M20 6JS — MD 1992 Sheff.; MB ChB 1976; MRCP (UK) 1979; MRCPath 1986; PhD Manch. 1998.

SCHOFIELD, Lewis Paul 1 James Street S., Chadderton, Oldham OL9 9JA — MB BS 1997 Newc.

SCHOFIELD, Linda Elizabeth Gainsborough House, South St., Sherborne DT9 3LT — MB BS 1982 Lond.; MRCPsych 1991; DRCOG 1986.

SCHOFIELD, Louise 12A Hawthorn Road, Alexandra Park, London N8 7NA Tel: 020 8347 5291 — MB BS 1994 Lond.; BSc Lond. 1991; MRCP 1997. (St. Bart. Hosp. Med. Coll.) Specialist Regist. Palliat. Med., N. Thames.

SCHOFIELD, Neil McCallum Nuffield Department of Anaesthetics, John Radcliffe Hospital, Headington, Oxford OX3 9DU Tel: 01865 741166 Fax: 01865 221593; Perrott's Farm, Bicester Road, Long Crendon, Aylesbury HP18 9BP Tel: 01844 201585 — MB BChir 1970 Camb.; BA Camb. 1966, MA 1970; FFA RCS Eng. 1974; (Camb. & St. Thos.) Cons. Anaesth. Nuffield Dept. Anaesth. Oxf. Socs: Assn. Anaesth.; Assn. Paediat. Anaesth.; Brit. Med. Assn.

SCHOFIELD, Olivia Marie Virginia Mine Department of Dermatology, Royal Infirmary Edinburgh, Edinburgh EH3 9YW Tel: 0131 536 2403; 13 Denham Green Place, Edinburgh EH5 3PA Tel: 0131 551 1306 Email: jdwalker@mcmail.com — MB BS 1981 Lond.; MRCP (UK) 1985. Cons. Dermat. Roy. Infirm. Edin. Socs: Brit. Assn. Dermat.; Brit. Soc. Paediat. Dermatol. Prev: Sen. Regist. (Dermat.) Roy. Infirm. Edin. & King's Coll. Hosp. Lond.

SCHOFIELD, Patrick Bernard (retired) 1 Kenmore Close, Kent Road, Kew, Richmond TW9 3JG — MRCS Eng. LRCP Lond. 1949; FRCPath 1967. Mem. Staff Walton Hosp. Prev: GP Walton-on-Thames.

SCHOFIELD, Penelope Jane St Anthony's Medical Group, Thomas Gaughan House, Pottery Bank, Newcastle upon Tyne NE6 3SW Tel: 0191 265 5689; 1 Lesbury Road, Heaton, Newcastle upon Tyne NE6 5LB Tel: 0191 265 8898 — BM BCh 1975 Oxf.; MRCGP 1982; DRCOG 1980.

SCHOFIELD, Peter Charles Hugh 12 Castle Town, Upper Beeding, Steyning BN44 3TR Tel: 01903 813378 — MB ChB 1965 Birm.; MRCS Eng. LRCP Lond. 1965; BDS, LDS Manch. 1956; DA Eng. 1968. Prev: Ho. Phys. Barnet Gen. Hosp.; Ho. Surg. W. Herts. Hosp. Hemel Hempstead.

SCHOFIELD, Professor Philip Furness Longridge, The Dingle, Gee Cross, Hyde SK14 5EP Tel: 0161 368 2811 Fax: 0161 366 7338; (cons. rooms) 15 St John Street, Manchester M3 4DG Tel: 0161 834 7373 — MD 1966 Manch.; FRCS Ed. 1962; FRCS Eng. 1963. Cons. Surg. Christie Hosp. Manch. (Hon); Vis. Prof. Univ. Manch. Socs: Assn. Coloproctol. (Pres.),; Assn. Surg. Prev: Cons. Surg. Ashton, Hyde & Glossop Hosp. Gp.; Cons. Surg. W. Manch. Hosp. Gp.; John M. Wilson Memor Schol. Cleveland Clinic, Ohio.

SCHOFIELD, Philippa Jane New Southgate Surgery, Buxton Place, 91 Leeds Rd, Wakefield WF1; 3 Lakeland Way, Walton, Wakefield WF2 6TG — MB ChB 1990 Leeds; BSc 1985 (Hons) Physiology. (Leeds) p/t G.P. Socs: BMA; Diplomat Fac. Of Family Plann. + Reproductive Health Care.

SCHOFIELD, Roger Paul 35 Dalebrook Road, Sale M33 3LD — MB BS 1985 Lond.; MRCGP 1991; DRCOG 1988.

SCHOFIELD, Ronald (retired) 45 Hustler Road, Bridlington YO16 6RN Tel: 01262 675398 — MB ChB Manch. 1954; MD Manch. 1966; MFCM 1972; DPH Manch. 1962; DCH Eng. 1958. Prev: SCM E. Yorks. HA.

SCHOFIELD, Roy (retired) 29 Church Lane, Lincoln LN2 1QR Tel: 01522 528745 — MB ChB Manch. 1950; DObst RCOG 1954. Prev: Sen. Partner Drs Schofield, Sturton & Mallet Lincoln.

SCHOFIELD, Ruth (retired) 18 Deerswood Lane, Bexhill-on-Sea TN39 4LT — MB BS 1974 Lond.; MRCS Eng. LRCP Lond. 1974.

SCHOFIELD, Sarah Florence The Ramblers, Long St., Wheaton Aston, Stafford ST19 9NF — MB BS 1998 Lond.; MB BS Lond 1998.

SCHOFIELD, Sarah Patricia North Baddesley Health Centre, Norton Welch Close, Fleming Avenue, North Baddesley, Southampton SO52 9EP Tel: 023 8073 4523 Fax: 023 8073 0287; 9 Balmoral Way, Rownhams, Southampton SO16 8LL Tel: 02380 740776 Fax: 01703 740708 — MB ChB 1984 Leic.; MRCGP 1988; DCH RCP Lond. 1987. (Univ. Leic.) Chairm. W. & Test PCG. Prev: Trainee GP Soton. VTS; SHO (A & E) Soton. Gen. Hosp.; Clin. Asst. A & E, Soton. Gen. Hosp.

SCHOFIELD, Sheila Farquharson (retired) 5 Manor Close, Bramhope, Leeds LS16 9HQ Tel: 0113 284 2875 — MB ChB 1944 Leeds; DObst RCOG 1974, London; DPH Glas. 1955; DCH Eng. 1944. Prev: SCMO Bradford HA.

***SCHOFIELD, Shona Jane Alice** 32 Llanishen Street, Heath, Cardiff CF14 3QE; 5 Manor Lane, Ettington, Stratford-upon-Avon CV37 7TE Tel: 01789 740893 — MB BCh 1996 Wales.

SCHOFIELD, Stephanie Ann The Surgery, 225 Milton Road, Portsmouth PO4 8PH — BM 1978 Soton; BM 1978 Soton.

SCHOFIELD, Stephen John Acomb Health Centre, 1 Beech Grove, Acomb, York YO26 5LD Tel: 01904 791094; 2A Knapton Lane, Acomb, York YO26 5PU Tel: 01904 798620 — MB ChB 1980 Manch.; MRCP (UK) 1983; MRCGP 1986; DRCOG 1985.

SCHOFIELD, Terence Scott-Wallace 8 Richmond Gardens, Highfield, Southampton SO17 1RY — BM 1980 Soton.

SCHOFIELD

SCHOFIELD, Mr Theo Legate (retired) Vane Cottage, 22 Cleveland Walk, Bath BA2 6JU Tel: 01225 465606 — MB ChB 1942 Liverp.; MB ChB (Distinc. Surg.) Liverp. 1942; ChM Liverp. 1954; FRCS Eng. 1949; MRCS Eng. LRCP Lond. 1942. Prev: Hon. Med. Cons. Pens. Dept. Roy. Brit. Legion Lond.

SCHOFIELD, Theo Perry Calwell The Medical Centre, Badgers Crescent, Shipston-on-Stour CV36 4BQ Tel: 01608 661845 Fax: 01608 663614; Dolphin Farm, Weatheroak Hill, Alvechurch, Birmingham B48 7EA Tel: 01564 826816 — BM BCh 1968 Oxf.; MA Oxf. 1965; MRCP (UK) 1972; FRCGP 1980, M 1974; DObst RCOG 1970. Lect. (Gen. Pract.) Dept. Pub. Health & Primary Care Oxf. Prev: Ho. Off. (Gen. Med., Surg. & Obst.) & SHO (Gen. Med.) Radcliffe Infirm. Oxf.

SCHOFIELD, Thomas Charles 258 Milton Road E., Edinburgh EH15 2PG Tel: 0131 669 5676 — MB ChB 1979 Ed.; MRCGP 1984; DRCOG 1981.

SCHOFIELD, William Norman The Castle, High St., Presteigne LD8 2BE — MB BCh 1954 Wales; BSc, MB BCh Wales 1954. (Cardiff) Prev: Demonst. Anat. Univ. Manch.; Ho. Surg. & Ho. Phys. Aberystwyth Gen. Hosp.; Capt. RAMC.

SCHOFIELD, Zena June 18 Wilmot Street, London E2 0BS — MB BS 1998 Lond.; MB BS Lond 1998.

SCHOLEFIELD, Charles (retired) — MB BS 1970 Lond.; MRCS Eng. LRCP Lond. 1970; MRCPsych 1976; DA Eng. 1972. Prev: Sen. Regist. Rotat. (Adult Psychiat.) Yorks. VTS.

SCHOLEFIELD, Ida Mary (retired) Savernake, Bagatelle Road, St Saviour, Jersey JE2 7TZ Tel: 01534 35173 — MB ChB 1939 Leeds.

SCHOLEFIELD, Jane Hazel Dinnington Group Practice, Medical Centre, New Street, Dinnington, Sheffield S25 2EZ — MB ChB 1990 Sheff.

SCHOLEFIELD, Professor John Howard Section of Surgery, University Hospital, Nottingham NG7 2UH Tel: 0115 970 9245 Fax: 0115 970 9428 — MB ChB 1983 Liverp.; ChM Liverp. 1991; FRCS Eng. 1988; FRCS Ed. 1987. Prof. of Surg./Hon. Cons.. Univ. Hosp. Nottm. Prev: Lect. (Surg.) Univ. Sheff.; Clin. Research Fell. ICRF Colorectal Unit, St. Mark's Hosp., Lond.; Regist. Rotat. (Surg.) Roy. Hallamsh. Hosp. Sheff.

SCHOLEFIELD, Robert Dean St Katherines Surgery, High Street, Ledbury HR8 1ED Tel: 01531 633271 Fax: 01531 632410 — MB BS 1970 Lond.; MRCS Eng. LRCP Lond. 1969; Cert. Family Plann. JCC 1976; DObst RCOG 1971. (Guy's) Prev: SHO Heref. Hosp. Gp.

SCHOLES, Carol Fiona The Peace Hospice, Peace Drive, Watford WD17 3PH Tel: 01923 330349 Fax: 01923 330331 — MB BS 1988 Newc.; MRCP (UK) 1993. Cons. in Palliat. Med. Dacorum Primary Care Trust; Med. Director Peace Hospice, Watford. Prev: Sen. Regist. (Palliat. Med.) Mt. Vernon & Watford NHS Trust Hosps. Regist. (Palliat. Med.) Mt. Vernon & Watford NHS Trust Hosp. & Camden & Islington NHS Trust.

SCHOLES, George Barrie 61 Wimpole Street, London W1M 7DE Tel: 020 7935 2617 Fax: 020 7224 1680 Email: medcent@dial.pipex.com; 17 Beaumont Street, London W1G 6DG Tel: 020 7935 8081 Fax: 020 7224 1925 Email: gbscholes@avnet.co.uk — MB ChB 1959 Dunedin, NZ; FRCS Eng. 1966; Cert. Av. Med. 1993. (Univ. Otago, Dunedin NZ) Chief Med. Off. Unison Insur.; Med. Examr. (UK) Netherlands Min. Navigation; UK Maritime & Coastguard Agency. Socs: Assur. Med. Soc. Prev: Chief Exec. St. Martins Hosps. Ltd.; MRC Research Asst. & Hon. Sen. Regist. King's Coll. Hosp. Lond.; Dir. Foreign Hosp. Yokohama, Japan.

SCHOLES, Keith Turner Whalebridge Practice, Health Centre, Carfax Street, Swindon SN1 1ED Tel: 01793 692933; Rose Cottage, Queens Road, Hannington, Swindon SN6 7RP Tel: 01793 762515 — MB ChB 1966 Sheff.; DObst RCOG 1968. (Sheff.) Hosp. Pract. (Dermat.) P.ss Margt. Hosp. Swindon.

SCHOLES, Mr Neville Edward, Surg. Cdr. RN (retired) 10 Coxfield Grove, Shevington, Wigan WN6 8DW — MB ChB Ed. 1965; FRCS Ed. 1978; FFAEM. Prev: Cons. (A & E) Wigan & Leigh Health Servs. NHS Trust.

SCHOLES, Pauline Elizabeth Quine Manchester Road Surgery, 63 Manchester Road, Swinton, Manchester M27 5FX Tel: 0161 794 4343 Fax: 0161 736 0669 — MB ChB 1977 Manch. Socs: Fac. Fam. Plann.

SCHOLEY, Gareth Mark 74 Castle Lea, Caldicot, Newport NP26 4PJ — BM BCh 1998 Oxf.; BM BCh Oxf 1998.

SCHOLEY, Julie Anne Brynderwen Surgery, Crickhowell Road, St. Mellons, Cardiff CF3 0EF Tel: 029 2079 9921 Fax: 029 2077 7740 — MB BCh 1984 Wales; MRCGP 1988; DRCOG 1987.

SCHOLFIELD, David Peter Basset House, Hawksdown, Walmer, Deal CT14 7PJ — MB BS 1994 Lond.

SCHOLLER, Ingo Walter 220 Caerleon Road, Newport NP19 7GQ — MB ChB 1990 Cape Town.

***SCHOLTEN, Petrus Albertus** Adden Brooke's Hospital, Long Road, Cambridge CB2 2QQ Tel: 01223 245151; 53 Abington House, Long Road, Cambridge CB2 2QQ Tel: 01223 726007 Email: petefromholland@hotmail.com — BChir 1996 Camb.; MB BChir Camb. 1997.

SCHOLTZ, Marthinus Christoffel The Annex, 67 Cupernham Lane, Romsey SO51 4LE — MB ChB 1995 Orange Free State.

SCHON, Frederick Emanuel Gustav 97 Southwood Lane, London N6 5TB — MB BS 1977 Lond.; PhD Camb. 1974; MRCP (UK) 1979. Cons. Neurol. Mayday Hosp. Croydon & Atkinson Morley Hosp. Wimbledon.

SCHONFIELD, Susan Department of Public Health, South East Regional Office, 40 Eastbourne Terrace, London W2 3QR Tel: 020 7725 2821 Fax: 020 7725 2666 Email: sschonfj@doh.gov.uk; 21 Wallingford Avenue, London W10 6QA Tel: 020 8969 2511 — MB BS 1983 Lond.; MSc Lond. 1987; BA Oxf. 1967; MFPHM RCP (UK) 1995. (St. Mary's Hosp. Med. Sch. Lond.) Cons. (Pub. Health Med.) NHS Exec. S. E. Socs: Med. Wom. Federat. Prev: Sen. Regist. (Pub. Health Med.) N. Thames RHA; Hon. Regist. (Clin. Chem.) Hosp. Sick Childr. Gt. Ormond. St. Lond.; Regist. (Chem. Path.) Centr. Middlx. Hosp. Lond.

SCHOOLMEESTERS, Beatrijs Flat 12, James House, Residential Village, Bovemoors Lane, Exeter EX2 5DS — MD 1992 Louvain.

SCHOPFLIN, Katalin Eva, OBE (retired) 8 Manor Gardens, Diss IP22 4EJ Tel: 01379 643695 Email: kschopflin@aol.com — LRCP LRCS 1954 Ed.; LRCP LRCS Ed. LRFPS Glas. 1954; FRCGP 1977, M 1971; MD 1947. Prev: Dep. Chairm. Attendance Allowance Bd.

SCHOPP, Michael Jurgen 29 Solent Road, Hillhead, Fareham PO14 3LB — State Exam Med 1987 Heidelberg.

SCHOTT, Geoffrey Dennis National Hospital for Neurology & Neurosurgery, Queen Square, London WC1N 3BG Tel: 020 7837 3611 Fax: 020 7419 1714 — MB BChir CAmb. 1969; PhD (RCA) 1998; MD Camb. 1973, MA 1969; FRCP Lond. 1986; MRCP (UK) 1971. (Camb. & Guy's) Cons. Neurol. Nat. Hosp. Neurol. & Neurosurg. Lond., Roy. Nat. Orthop. Hosp. Lond. & Watford Gen. Hosp. Socs: Assn. Brit. Neurol. & Internat. Assn. Study Pain. Prev: Sen. Regist. (Neurol.) King's Coll. Hosp. Lond. & Univ. Dept. Clin. Neurol. Nat. Hosp. Nerv. Dis. Lond.; Regist. (Neurol.) Nat. Hosp. Nerv. Dis. Lond. & Roy. Free Hosp. Lond.

SCHOTT, Jonathan Mark Top Flat, 59 Parliament Hill, London NW3 2TB — MB BS 1996 Lond.; MB BS (Hons.) Lond. 1996; BSc (Hons.) Lond. 1993; MRCP(UK) 1999. (St. Mary's Hosp. Med. Sch.) SHO (Neurol.) Roy. Free Hosp. Lond. Prev: Med. SHO, N.wick Pk. Hosp.

SCHRAIBMAN, Mr Ivor Gerald (retired) 15 Beaufort Avenue, Sale M33 3WL Tel: 0161 973 7523 — MB BCh 1953 Witwatersrand; MCh Witwatersrand 1970; FRCS Eng. 1960; FRCS Ed. 1960. Prev: Cons. Surg. Highfield Private Hosp. Rochdale.

SCHRAM, Catharina Maria Helena Queen's Park Hospital, Haslingden Road, Blackburn BB2 3HH Tel: 01254 687027 — Artsexamen 1984 Rotterdam; FRCOG 2001; MRCOG 1989. (Erasmus Univ. Rotterdam) Cons. O & G Qu.s Pk. Hosp. Blackburn. Prev: Sen. Regist. (O & G) St. Michael's Hosp. Bristol.

SCHRAM, Jennifer Ellen 22 Old Road, Acle, Norwich NR13 3QL Tel: 01493 751562 — MB BS 1985 Lond.; MRCGP 1991; Dip. IMC RCS Ed. 1990; DCH RCP Lond. 1988; DRCOG 1988. (St. Thomas's Hospital, University of London) Asst. GP Fleggburgh Surg. Gt. Yarmouth; Teach. BASICS Educat.; Non-Princip. GP. Socs: Brit. Assn. Immed. Care Schemes. Prev: Princip. GP Acle Norf.

SCHRAMM, Christopher John The Health Centre, Asher Green, Great Selford, Cambridge CB2 5EY — MB BS 1993 Tasmania; DRCOG 1995; MRCGP 1998; DFFP 1999. GP Princip. Prev: GP Regist. - Addenbrookes Hosp. Camb. VTS.

SCHRAMM, Louise Halina 40 Poplar Cresent, West Ewell, Epsom KT19 9ER — MB BS 1996 Lond. (St. Geos. Hosp. Med. Sch.)

SCHRANZ, Mr Peter John Princess Elizabeth Orthopaedic Centre, Barrack Road, Exeter EX2 5DW Tel: 01392 403576 Fax: 01392

403505 Email: pschranz@eurobell.co.uk — MRCS Eng. LRCP Lond. 1981; FRCS Ed. (Orth.) 1991; FRCS Ed. 1985. Cons. Orthop. Surg. Roy. Devon & Exeter Healthcare NHS Trust. Socs: Brit. Orthop. Assn. Prev: Cons. Orthop. RN Hosp. Haslar; Cons. Orthop. RAF; Sen. Regist. (Orthop.) Qu. Med. Centre Nottm.

SCHRECKER, Geoffrey Martin Kenneth Gleadless Medical Centre, 636 Gleadless Road, Sheffield S14 1PQ Tel: 0114 239 6475 Fax: 0114 264 2277 — MB BChir 1985 Camb.; MA Camb. 1986; MRCGP 1991; T(GP) 1981. Prev: Princip. Qu. Edith Med. Pract. Camb.

SCHREIBER, Jennifer Anne 21 Garshake Road, Dumbarton G82 3LQ Tel: 01389 62458 — MB ChB 1983 Glas.; MRCGP l987.

SCHREUDER, Mr Frederik Brett 161 Mayals Road, Mayals, Swansea SA3 5HE; 161 Mayals Road, Mayals, Swansea SA3 5HE — MB ChB 1991 Witwatersrand; FRCS (Eng) 1996. (Med. Sch. Of the Univ. of Witwatersrand) Specialist Regist. Morriston Hosp. Swansea. Prev: Spec. Regist. Whiston Hosp. Liverp.; SHO Plastic Surg., Qu. Mary's Hosp., Roehampton.

SCHRIEBER, Victor Philip Northumberland House Surgery, 437 Stourport Road, Kidderminster DY11 7BL Tel: 01562 745715 Fax: 01562 863010; Apley House, 29 St. John's Avenue, Kidderminster DY11 6AU Tel: 01562 66457 Email: vschrieber@aol.com — MB BS 1972 Lond.; FRCGP 1996, M 1978. (Middlx.) Course Organiser N. Worcs. VTS; Clin. Asst. (Rheum.) Kidderminster Health Care NHS Trust. Socs: BMA; Med. Action Global Security. Prev: Hosp. Pract. (Geriat. Med.) Kidderminster Gen. Hosp.; Regist. (Med.) Leicester Roy. Infirm. & Gen. Hosp.; SHO (Med. & Paediat.) Yeovil Dist. Hosp.

SCHRODER, Ferdinand Henry Hans Joseph Flat 8, Connaught House, Queen Alexandra Hospital, Cosham, Portsmouth PO6 3LY — Artsexamen 1993 Nijmegen.

SCHRODER, Lothar Detlef 48 The Earls of Warwick, St. Nicholas Church St., Warwick CV34 4JD — MB BCh 1992 Witwatersrand.

SCHROEDER, Harry Glynne (retired) Morlan Heights, 399 Redmires Road, Sheffield S10 4LE — MB ChB 1956 Birm.; FFA RCS Eng. 1961; DA Eng. 1959. Cons. Anaesth. Sheff. DHA; Lect. in Clin. Anaesth. & Lect. Intens. Ther. & Resuscitat. Univ. Sheff; Lect. Sheff. Sch. Nursing. Prev: Sen. Regist. Anaesth. United Sheff. Hosps.

SCHROEDER, Kathryn Emma Maria 27 Hindsley Place, London SE23 2NF — MB BS 1989 Lond.

SCHROEDER, Ursula Elisabeth 110 Dudley Road, Manchester M16 8BR — State Exam Med 1986 Berlin; State Exam Med. Berlin 1986.

SCHROVEN, Ivo Orthopaedic Department, Derbyshire Royal Infirmary, London Road, Derby DE1 2QY — MD 1988 Louvain.

SCHRYER, Jeffrey Whittaker Lane Medical Centre, Whittaker lane, Prestwich, Manchester M25 5EX Tel: 0161 773 1580; 18 Castleton Road, Salford M7 4GU Tel: 0161 795 4873 — MB ChB 1986 Manch.; MRCGP 1990; DRCOG 1989.

SCHUFF, Georg Heiner The Marlborough Family Service, 38 Marlborough Place, London NW8 0PJ Tel: 020 7624 8605 Fax: 020 7328 2185 — State Exam Med 1971 Berlin; Dr Med Berlin 1975; MRCPsych 1978. (Free Univ. Berlin) Cons. Psychother. BKGW. Ment. Health NHS Trust. Prev: Sen. Regist. (Psychol. Med.) Hammersmith Hosp.; Regist. (Psychiat.) Maudsley Hosp. Lond.

SCHULENBURG, Mr Wilhelm Edmund 8 Upper Wimpole Street, London W1M 7TD Tel: 020 7486 2257 Fax: 020 7487 3764; 48 Stanhope Road, London N6 5AJ Tel: 020 8348 0026 — MB ChB 1971 Pretoria; FRCS Eng. 1980. Cons. Ophth. Surg. Hammersmith Hosp. & Hon. Sen. Lect. Imperial Coll.; Cons. W.. Ophth. Hosp. Lond. Socs: Roy. Soc. Med. (Counc. Mem. Ophth. Sect.).

SCHULGA, Alison 14 Batterflatts Gardens, Stirling FK7 9JU — MB ChB 1984 Ed.; DCCH RCP Ed. 1989. GP Retainer scheme. Prev: Clin. Med. Off. Lothian HB.

SCHULGA, John 14 Batterflatts Gardens, Stirling FK7 9JU — MB ChB 1984 Ed.; MRCPI 1992; MRCGP 1989; FRCPCH. Cons. Paediat. Stirling Roy. Infirm. Prev: Sen. Regist. (Paediat.) Glas.; Research Fell. (Paediat. Endocrinol.) Glas.

SCHULLER, Ildiko 11 Green Road, Reading RG6 7BS — MB BS 1984 Lond.

SCHULTE, Alison Caroline 9 St Amand Drive, Abingdon OX14 5RQ — BM 1994 Soton.

SCHULTE, Anja Christina 33 Kings Quay, Chelsea Harbour, London SW10 0UX — State Exam Med 1991 Berlin.

SCHULTE, Jane Frances 41 Logan Road, Bishopston, Bristol BS7 8DS Tel: 0117 942 3046 — MB ChB 1981 Bristol; MRCP (UK) 1985; FRCPCH. Cons. Paediat. Community Child Health Frenchay Health N. Bristol NHS Trust Bristol.

SCHULTE-FROHLINDE, Peggy Jeanette Room 16, 23 Norfolk Square, London W2 1NY — State Exam Med. Munich 1990.

SCHULTZ, Sabine Susanne 8 Whiterigg Court, Airdrie ML6 0RG — State Exam Med 1992 Mainz.

SCHULZ, Ulrike Carola Lincluden Surgery, 53 Bellshill Rd, Glasgow G71 7PA Fax: 01698 813873 — State Exam Med 1992 Mainz. Gen. Pract. Princip.

SCHULZE, Karl Robert c/o Department of Surgery, Royal Sussex County Hospital, Eastern Road, Brighton BN2 5BE — MB BS 1986 Monash.

SCHUMAN, Andrew Nicholas New Chapel Surgery, High Street, Long Crendon, Aylesbury HP18 9AF Tel: 01844 208228 Fax: 01844 201906 Email: andrewschuman23@hotmail.com; 131 Magdalen Road, East Oxford, Oxford OX4 1RJ Tel: 01865 246393 Email: andrewschuman23@hotmail.com — MB BS 1993 Lond.; MRCGP 2001; DFFP 1998; BSc Lond. 1989; DRCOG 1996. (St. Thos. Hosp. Med. Sch.) GP Locum, New Chapel Surg. Prev: Trainee GP Angel Hill Surg. Bury St. Edmunds; SHO (Geriat. & O & G) W. Suff. Hosp. Bury St. Edmunds; SHO (Paediat.) Qu. Med. Centre Nottm.

SCHUMANN, Esther Christine Bishop Auckland Hospital, Bishop Auckland DL14 6AD — State Exam Med 1989 Bonn.

SCHUMM, Barbara Alicia Denewell House Surgery, Denewell Avenue, Low Fell, Gateshead NE9 Tel: 0191 487 6123; 57 Reid Park Road, Jesmond, Newcastle upon Tyne NE2 2ER — MB ChB 1972 Manch.; MRCGP 1984.

SCHÜNMANN, Catherine Anne, Surg. Lt. RN Sick Bay, RFA Diligence BFPO Ships; 83 Hilltop Way, Salisbury SP1 3QQ Tel: 01722 331890 — MB ChB 1992 Manch.; BSc (Med. Sci.) St. And. 1989. Gen. Duties Med. Off. RFA Diligence. Prev: Surg. Lt. & Dep. Princip. Med. Off. HMS Collingwood; Surg. Lt. & Med. Off. HMS Manch. & Brazen; SHO (O & G) St. Marys Hosp. Manch.

SCHUPPLER, Philip Ernest Reinhardt Swanswell Medical Centre, 370 Gospel Lane, Acocks Green, Birmingham B27 7AL Tel: 0121 706 5676; 3 Alveley Close, Winyates W., Redditch B98 0JD — MB ChB 1982 Leeds; MRCGP 1989. GP Tutor (CME) Birm. Heartlands Hosp.

SCHUR, Paul Edward Furlong Medical Centre, Furlong Road, Stoke-on-Trent ST6 5UD; Wiggo Cottage, 135 Main Road, Wynbury, Nantwich CW5 7LR — BM BCh 1973 Oxf.; MA 1973 Oxf.; MSc 1999 Notts.; DRCOG 1977; Cert JCC Lond. 1977. Socs: BASM.

SCHUR, Tripta Wiggo Cottage, 135 Main Road, Wybunbury, Nantwich CW5 7LR; Brookland House, 501 Crewe Road, Wistaston, Crewe CW2 6QP Tel: 01270 67250 — MB BS 1973 Rajasthan. (S.M.S. Med. Coll. Jaipur) GP Chesh. Prev: SHO (Gen. Med.) Horton Gen. Hosp. Banbury.

SCHURR, Andrew Jaroslav Vlcek Square Surgery, 23 The Square, Martlesham Heath, Ipswich IP5 3SL Tel: 01473 610028 Fax: 01473 610791; Pear Tree Farm, Clopton, Woodbridge IP13 6QE — MUDr 1982 Prague; MRCS Eng. LRCP Lond. 1985. Trainee GP Hove. Socs: Roy. Soc. Med. Prev: SHO (Gen. Med. & Paediat.) St. Richard's Hosp. Chichester; SHO (Cardiol.) Roy. Sussex Co. Hosp. Brighton.

SCHURR, Mr Peter Howel, CBE Brook House, High St., Ufford, Woodbridge IP13 6EQ Tel: 01394 460350; Brook House, High St., Ufford, Woodbridge IP13 6EQ Tel: 01394 460530 — MB BChir Camb. 1943; MRCP Eng. LRCP Lond. 1943; MA Camb. 1945; FRCS Eng. 1948. (Camb. & Univ. Coll. Hosp.) Socs: Fell. Roy. Soc. Med. (Ex-Vice-Pres. Treas. & Ex-Pres. Sect. Neurol.); Internat. League Against Epilepsy (Ex-Pres. Brit. Br.); (Ex-Pres.) Soc. Brit. Neurol. Surgs. Prev: Emerit. Cons. Neurosurg. Guy's, Bethlem Roy. & Maudsley Hosps. Lond.; Hon. Vis. Neurol. Surg. Johns Hopkins Hosp. Baltimore, USA; Cons. Neurosurg. Qu. Eliz. Hosp. Woolwich.

SCHUSTER, Helmut 66 Meadow Burn, Bishop Briggs, Glasgow G64 3EZ Email: schuster@globalnet.co.uk — State Exam Med. Berlin 1991; MRCP 1998. (Freie, Berlin)

SCHUSTER, Raimund Orthopaedics Department, Southend Hospital, Prittlewell Chase, Westcliff on Sea SS0 0RY — State Exam Med. Munich 1992.

SCHUSTER BRUCE, Martin John Louis 50 Fermantle Road, Bristol BS6 5SU Tel: 0117 923 2404 — MB BS 1991 Lond.; BSc

SCHUSTER BRUCE

(Hons.) Lond. 1988; MRCP (UK) 1994; FRCA 1995. (Lond. Hosp. Med. Coll.) Specialist Regist. Rotat. (Anaesth.) Bristol. Prev: Regist. (Adult Intens. Care) Guy's Hosp. Lond.; SHO (Anaesth.) Roy. Lond. Hosp.; SHO Rotat. (Med.) St. Bart. Hosp. Lond.

SCHUSTER BRUCE, Robert Maurice Charles Tel: 01202 752550 Fax: 01202 769700 — MB BS 1986 Lond.; BSc (Hons.) Biochem. Human Dis. 1983; MRCP (UK) 1990; MRCGP 1991; DRCOG 1991; Dip Occupat. Med. 1996. Prev: SHO Rotat. (Gen. Med.) Poole Gen. Hosp.; Ho. Phys. Char. Cross Hosp. Lond.; Ho. Surg. Roy. Hants. Co. Hosp. Winchester.

SCHUTT, Werner Heinrich 5 Grove Avenue, Coombe Dingle, Bristol BS9 2RN Tel: 0117 968 1181 Fax: 0117 968 1181; 5 Grove Avenue, Coombe Dingle, Bristol BS9 2RN Tel: 0117 968 1181 Fax: 0117 968 1181 — MB BCh Witwatersrand 1953; FRCP Ed. 1969, M 1958; DCH Eng. 1957; FRCPCH 1997. (Witwatersrand) Socs: Paediat. Research Soc. & Genetic Soc. Prev: Cons. Paediat. (Childh. Handicap.) Bristol Health Dist. (T) & Frenchay Health Dist.; Cons. Sen. Lect. Univ. Bristol.; Lect. (Child Health) Univ. Edin.

SCHUTTE, Antje Freeman Hospital, Newcastle upon Tyne NE7 7DN; 4 Sixth Avenue, Heaton, Newcastle upon Tyne NE6 5YN — State Exam Med 1992 Dusseldorf. SHO Rotat. (Anaesth.) Freeman Gp. Hosps. Newc. u. Tyne.

SCHUTTE, Peter Karl 3 Devonshire Place, London W1G 6HE Tel: 020 7486 6181 — MB ChB 1973 Cape Town; MRCGP 1980; DMJ (Clin.) Soc. Apoth. Lond. 1983; DRCOG 1977; DA Eng. 1976. Dep. Head Advis. Servs. Med. Defence Union Ltd. Socs: Fell. Roy. Soc. Med.; Assn. Police Surg. Prev: Princip. GP I. of Wight; Trainee GP Cirencester VTS; SHO (Anaesth.) Roy. Devon & Exeter Hosps.

SCHUURING, Joanne c/o A. Jacques, 38 Lacey Green, Wilmslow SK9 4BA — Artsexamen 1994 Free U Amsterdam; Artsexamen Free Univ Amsterdam 1994.

SCHWARTZ, Ellen Corine Institute of Ophthalmology, 11-43 Bath St., London EC1V 9EL — State Exam Med 1991 Bonn; State Exam Med. Bonn 1991; MSc Lond. 1996.

SCHWARTZ, Jonathan Stephen St Georges Medical Centre, 7 Sunningfields Road, Hendon, London NW4 4QR Tel: 020 8202 6232 Fax: 020 8202 3906 — MB BS 1981 Lond.; MA Camb. 1982, BA 1978; DRCOG 1989. (Lond. Hosp.) GP Lond. Socs: (Sec.) Lond. Jewish Med. Soc. Prev: Trainee GP Borehamwood Herts.; Regist. (Gen. Med.) Newham Gen. Hosp. Lond.; SHO (Obst.) Newham Gen. Hosp. Lond.

SCHWARTZ, Martin Samuel Department of Neurology, Atkinson Morley's Hospital, 31 Copse Hill, London SW20 0NE Tel: 020 8725 4632 Fax: 020 8725 4700 — MD 1965 Maryland; FRCP Lond. 1995; MRCP (UK) 1994. (Univ. Maryland) Cons. Neurophysiol. Atkinson Morley's Hosp. Lond.; Hon. Cons. Neurol. St. Geo. Hosp. Lond. Socs: Amer. Neurol. Assn.

SCHWARTZ, Morris The Surgery, Annie Prendergast Clinic, Ashton Gardens, Chadwell Heath, Romford RM6 6RT Tel: 020 8590 1461 & 081 599 2435 — MB BS 1945 Lond.; MRCGP 1960. (Char. Cross.) Chairm. Barking & Havering LMC. Socs: Assur. Med. Soc. & Jewish Med. Soc. Prev: Maj. RAMC; Res. Obst. Off. & Ho. Surg. Gyn. Unit Char. Cross Hosp.; Res. Surg. Off. Leeds Matern. Hosp.

SCHWARTZ, Ruby Hazel Department of Paediatrics, Central Middlesex NHS Trust Hospital, Acton Lane, London NW10 4NS Tel: 020 8453 2121 Fax: 020 8453 2096 Email: ruby.schwartz@nwth.nhs.uk — MB BS 1972 Lond.; FRCPCH 1997; FRCP Lond. 1995; DObst RCOG 1974. (St. Geo.) Cons. Paediat. Centr. Middlx. Hosp. Lond. Socs: Roy. Soc. Med.; Brit. Paediatric Neurol. Assn.; Roy. Coll. Phys.s. Prev: Sen. Regist. N.wick Pk. Hosp. Harrow & St. Chas. Hosp. Lond.; SHO (Paediat.) Hosp. Sick Childr. Gt. Ormond St.; Ho. Phys. St. Geo. Hosp. Lond.

SCHWARTZ, Anthony Augustine (retired) 56 Monreith Road, Glasgow G43 2NZ — MB ChB 1950 Glas.

SCHWARTZ, Eckart Werner 15A Nassim Road, Singapore 258387, Singapore Tel: 010 65 7358371 Fax: 010 65 7358372; 48 Belmont Road, Bristol BS6 5AT — MB ChB 1988 Bristol. Regional Med. Director (Pharmaceut. Med.) SE Asia & India & SmithKline Beecham Pharmaceuts., Singapore.

SCHWARZ, Professor Kurt 49 Grange Crescent, Chigwell IG7 5JD Tel: 020 8500 4815 — MB BCh 1951 Witwatersrand; MRCP Lond. 1957; FFPHM 1989; FFCM 1974; DPH Witwatersrand 1954; FRIPHH 1981. (Witwatersrand) Princip. Med. Off. Remploy; Adviser & Tutor (Health Care Plann.) Univ. N. Lond. Socs: Fell. Roy. Soc. Med.; Vice-Pres. Internat. Federat. for Hyg. Prev. Med. & Social Med. Prev: Sen. Tutor (Pub. Health, Epidemiol. & Community Med.) Char. Cross & W.m. Med. Schs. Lond.; Prof. & Head. of Dept. of Prev. & Community Med. ChristCh. Clin. Sch. Med. NZ; Hon. Cons. Canterbury Hosp. Bd. NZ.

SCHWARZ, Philip Anthony Rookwood House, Cimla Road, Neath SA11 3TL Tel: 01639 642736 — MB BS 1977 Lond.; BSc Soton. 1968; MRCS Eng. LRCP Lond. 1976; FFA RCS Eng. 1982. (St. Mary's) Cons. Anaesth. Morriston Hosp. Swansea. Prev: Cons. Anaesth. Neath Gen. Hosp.; Sen. Regist. (Anaesth.) Univ. Hosp. Wales Cardiff; Regist. (Anaesth.) Lond. Hosp. Whitechapel.

SCHWARZER, Andreas c/o Drive Chang, Christie Hospital, Wilmslow Road, Manchester M20 4BX — State Exam Med 1986 Leipzig.

SCHWEIGER, Martin Steven 12 Montagu Place, Leeds LS8 2RG Tel: 0113 293 1604 Email: germbuster@schwefam.demon.co.uk — MB ChB 1972 Leeds; MA Leeds 1997; FFPHM 1993; MFCM RCP (UK) 1984; MPH Leeds 1982; DTM & H Liverp. 1981. (Leeds) Cons. Communicable Dis. Control. Leeds HA; Hon. Lect. Univ. Leeds; Mem. Pub. Health Med. Environm. Gp. Socs: Med. Assn. Preven. of War; Soc. Social Med.; Leeds & W. Riding Medico-Legal Soc. Prev: Med. Adviser Rangpur Dinajpur Rehabil. Serv., Bangladesh; SHO (O & G) Airedale Gen. Hosp. Steeton; Med. Off. (Volun. Serv. Overseas) Concern Disp. Saidpur, Bangladesh.

SCHWEITZER, Mr Frank Austen Will The Guildford, Nuffield Hosp, Stirling Road, Guildford GU2 7RF Tel: 01483555860 Fax: 01483555862; Dunrozel, Farnham Lane, Haslemere GU27 1HD Tel: 01428 658301 Fax: 01428 643759 — MB BS Lond. 1962; MS Lond. 1972; FRCS Eng. 1966; MRCS Eng. LRCP Lond. 1962. (Guy's) Cons. Urol. Surg. Guildford Hosps.; Hon. Sen. Lect. Inst. Urol. Lond. Socs: Fell. Roy. Soc. Med.; Brit. Assn. Urol. Surgs. Prev: Regional Specialist Advisor Eng.; Surg. Tutor RCS Eng.; Sen. Regist. (Urol.) & Ho. Off. Guy's Hosp. Lond.

SCHWIGON, Sylvia Sabina Department of Psychiatry, Level 1 East, Crosshouse Hospital, Kilmarnock Road, Kilmarnock KA2 0BE — State Exam Med 1991 Kiel.

SCIVIER, Annette Brookside Health Centre, Brookside Road, Freshwater PO40 9DT Tel: 01983 753433 Fax: 01983 753662 — BM 1987 Soton.; MRCGP 1991; DRCOG 1989.

SCLARE, Goldwyn (retired) 58 Greenbank Crescent, Edinburgh EH10 5SW Tel: 0131 447 3752 — MB ChB 1947 Glasgow; MD (Commend) Glas. 1959; FRCPath 1974, M 1963; MD 1959 Glas. Cons. Path. Bangour Gen. Hosp. Broxburn; Hon. Sen. Lect. (Path.) Univ. Edin. Prev: Lect. (Path.) Univ. Manch.

SCLARE, Helen Ground Floor Flat, 35 Woodford Bridge Road, Ilford IG4 5LL — MB ChB 1969 Glas.; BSc Glas. 1964, MB ChB 1969; MRCP (U.K.) 1974; DCH Eng. 1972; DObst RCOG 1971. (Glas.)

SCLARE, Paul David 17 Rutland Avenue, Manchester M20 1JD — MB ChB 1981 Aberd.

***SCOBBIE, Lisa Joanne** 46 Earls Hall Avenue, Southend-on-Sea SS2 6PD — MB ChB 1994 Sheff.

SCOBIE, Brian Maybole Health Centre and Day Hospital, 6 High Street, Maybole KA19 7BY Tel: 01655 882278 Fax: 01655 889616; 2 Bolestyle Road, Kirkmichael, Maybole KA19 7PN — MB ChB 1976 Glas.; Dip. Pract. Dermat. Wales 1992; DRCOG 1978. Med. Director, Ayr RFC.

SCOBIE, Mr Donald John Plane Tree, 4 Keil Crofts, Benderloch, Oban PA37 1QJ — MB ChB 1973 Glas.; BSc Strathclyde 1968; FRCS Eng. 1980; FRCS Ed. 1979; FRCS Glas. 1978. Cons. Surg. Argyll & Clyde Health Bd.

SCOBIE, Ian Neilson Diabetes Centre, Medway Maritime Hospital, Gillingham ME7 5NY Tel: 01634 830000 Fax: 01634 400484 — MB ChB 1973 Glas.; MD Glas. 1988; FRCP Lond. 1995. Cons. Phys. & Endocrinol. Medway Maritime Hosp. Gillingham. Socs: Brit. Diabetic Assn.; Soc. Endocrinol.; Brit. Thyroid Assn. Prev: Lect. (Med.) St. Thomas's Hosp. Med. Sch. Lond.; Regist. (Gen. Med.) & Ho. Surg. Roy. Infirm. Glas.; Ho. Phys. W. Infirm. Glas...

SCOBIE, James Dinwoodie (retired) Iley Point Cottage, Keyhaven, Lymington SO41 0TR Tel: 01590 644982 Fax: 01590 644549 Email: james.scobie@btinternet.com — MB BChir 1960 Camb.; MA, MB BChir Camb. 1960; FRCGP 1982, M 1975. Prev: GP Barnes Lond.

SCOTCHMAN

SCOBIE, James Quinn Edgwar Community Hospital, Burntoak Broadway, Edgware HA8 0AD — MB BS 1992 Lond.; BSc (Lond) 1986; MRCPsych 1996.

SCOBIE, Mr William Galbraith (retired) 133 Caiyside, Edinburgh EH10 7HR Tel: 0131 445 7404 Fax: 0131 445 7404 — MB ChB 1962 Glas.; FRCS Ed. 1966; FRCS Glas. 1966. Sen. Lect. Dept. Clin. Surg., Univ. Edin. Prev: Regist. (Surg.) Kilmarnock Infirm.

SCOBLE, John Edward 38 South Park Road, London SW19 8SZ — MD 1987 Lond.; MA Camb. 1979; MB BS 1978; MRCP (UK) 1980. Cons. Phys. & Hon. Sen. Lect. Kings Coll. Lond. Prev: Sen. Regist. Roy. Free Hosp. Lond.; Renal Fell. Univ. Washington, St Louis, USA.

SCOBLE, Mr John Edward North Staffordshire Royal Infirmary, Princes Road, Hartshill, Stoke-on-Trent ST4 7LN — MB BS 1972 Lond.; FRCS Eng. 1977; MRCS Eng. LRCP Lond. 1972; FRCR Eng. 1980. Cons. Radiother. N. Staffs. Roy. Infirm. Prev: Sen. Regist. (Radiotherp. & Oncol.) Velindre Hosp. WhitCh. Cardiff.

SCOFFIELD, Miss Julie Louise 6 Bloomfield Manor, 55 Abettea Parade, Belfast BT5 5LA Tel: 02890 225279 — MB BCh BAO 1994 Belf.; FRCSI 1998. (Qu. Univ. Belf.) Specialist Regist. (Surg.)Ulster Hosp., Dundonald. Socs: ASIT. Prev: Specialist Regist (Surg.) Roy. Vict. Hosp.; Specialist Regist.(Surg.) Craigavon Area Hosp.; Specialist Regist. (Surg.) Daisy Hill Hosp. Newry.

SCOFFINGS, Daniel James Flat 2, 324 Lordship Lane, London SE22 8LZ — MB BS 1998 Lond.; MB BS Lond 1998.

SCOLDING, Kim Judith Penylan Surgery, 74 Penylan Road, Cardiff CF23 5SY Tel: 029 2049 8181 Fax: 029 2049 1507 — MB BCh 1988 Wales; MRCGP 1992.

SCOLDING, Neil James 51 North Road, Whittlesford, Cambridge CB2 4NZ — MB BCh 1982 Wales; BSc Wales 1979, MB BCh 1982; MRCP (UK) 1986. Clin. Research Off. Dept. Neurol. Univ. Wales Coll. Med. Prev: Regist. (Gen. Med.) Roy. Gwent Hosp. Newport; SHO (Gen. Med.) P.; Chas. Hosp. Merthyr Tydfil & Llandough Hosp. Penarth Cardiff; SHO (Clin. Haemat.) Univ. Hosp. Wales. Cardiff.

SCOLLAY, Gilbert 32 Brodick Avenue, Kilwinning KA13 6RL — MB ChB 1968 Ed.

SCOLLON, Derek Department of Thoracic Surgery, Hairmyres Hospital, East Kilbride, Glasgow Tel: 0141 220292; 2/5 Dalhousie Court, 42 West Graham St, Glasgow G4 9LH Tel: 0141 353 3656 — MB ChB 1994 Glas. SHO (Thoracic Surg.) Hairmyres Hosp. E. Kilbride.

SCONCE, Fiona Margaret North West Anglia Healthcare Trust, St. James, Extons Road, King's Lynn PE30 5NU Tel: 01553 762911 Fax: 01553 774753; 4 Ravensway, Downham Market PE38 0DB — MB ChB 1972 St. And.; DFFP 1995; T(GP) 1991. (St. Andrews) Staff Grade (Community Paediat.) N. W. Anglia Healthcare Trust Kings Lynn; Family Plann. Med. Off. Prev: GP Princip. N. Brink Pract. Wisbech.

SCONCE, Jonathan Charles Alexander The Howdale Surgery, 48 Howdale Road, Downham Market PE38 9AF Tel: 01366 383405 Fax: 01366 383433 — MB ChB 1972 St. And.

SCOONES, David James 1 Woodlands Walk, Stokesley, Middlesbrough TS9 5QG — MB BChir 1990 Camb.; MA Camb. 1991, BA 1987; MRCPath 1997. Cons. Neuropath. Middlesbrough Gen. Hosp. Prev: Sen. Regist. (Neuropath.) Newc. Gen. Hosp.; Regist. (Histopath.) Mt. Vernon & Harefield Hosps. Middlx. & Hammersmith Hosp. Lond.; SHO (Histopathol.) Qu. Eliz. Med. Centre Birm.

SCOONES, Francis Harold 83 Abbotsbury Road, London W14 8EP Tel: 020 7602 1942 — MRCS Eng. LRCP Lond. 1939; FRCGP 1982, M 1953. (Lond. Hosp.) Clin. Asst. W. Middlx. Hosp. Isleworth; JP. Socs: (Vice-Chairm.) Ealing Dist. Managem. Team; Harv. Soc.; BMA (Ex-Chairm. & Sec. Ealing Div.). Prev: Ho. Surg. Luton & Dunstable Hosp.; Asst. Med. Off. OldCh. Co. Hosp. Romford; Maj. RAMC 1940-46.

SCOOTE, Mark 25 Lilian Gardens, Woodford Green IG8 7DN — MB BS 1997 Lond.

SCOPES, Heather Wynne St Raphael's Hospital, PO Box 35, Korogwe, Tanga Region, Tanzania; 3 Chestnut Avenue, Hampton TW12 2NY Tel: 020 8979 6933 — MB BS 1983 Lond.; MRCGP 1987; DRCOG 1985; DCH RCP Lond. 1985. Med. Dir. U.S.P.G. Mission Hosp. Tanzania. Prev: SHO (Paediat.) Gloucester Roy. Hosp.; SHO (Obst.) Addenbrooke's Hosp. Camb.; Ho. Phys. St. Thos. Hosp. Lond.

SCOPES, Iliana 35 Deerhurst Close, Feltham TW13 7HU; 35 Deerhurst Close, Feltham TW13 7HU — Ptychio latrikes 1983 Thessalonika.

SCORAH, Phillip John Swallownest Health Centre, Hepworth Drive, Aston, Sheffield S26 2BG Tel: 0114 287 2486 Fax: 0114 287 6045; 42 Hallam Road, Rotherham S60 3DA Tel: 01709 374393 — MB ChB 1978 Sheff.

SCORER, Harriet Jane Middleton Whitehall Laboratories, Huntercombe Lane S., Taplow, Maidenhead SL6 0PH Tel: 01628 414846 Fax: 01628 414870 — MB BS 1984 Lond.; MA Camb. 1985; MFPM RCP (UK) 1993; Dip. Pharm. Med. RCP (UK) 1991; DRCOG 1987. Med. Dir. Whitehall Laborat. Maidenhead. Prev: Med. Servs. Manager Abbott Laborat.; Sen. Med. Adviser Abbott Laborat.; Regist. (O & G) St. Luke's Hosp. Guildford.

SCORER, Michael John Stephen (retired) The Little Wing, Loudwater House, Rickmansworth WD3 4HN Tel: 01923 776397 — MB 1958 Camb.; BChir 1957.

SCORER, Rebecca Mowbray The Surgery, 1 Forest Hill Road, London SE22 0SQ Tel: 020 8693 2264 Fax: 020 8299 0200; 121 Bennerley Road, London SW11 6DX — MB BS 1984 Lond.; DRCOG 1988.

SCORER, Richard Charles 163 Lake Road W., Roath Park, Cardiff CF23 5PL — MB BChir 1970 Camb.; MSc (Hons.) Clin. Pyschother. Lond. 1985; MA Camb. 1970; MRCP (UK) 1972; MRCPsych 1976; DPM Eng. 1977. (Lond. Hosp.) Cons. Psychiat. Llandough Hosp. & Community NHS Trust. Prev: Hon. Sen. Regist. & Lect. (Psychol. Med.) Welsh Nat. Sch. Med. Cardiff; Regist. (Med.) Lond. Hosp. (Mile End).

SCOREY, John (retired) Griffin Cottage, Woodrow, Amersham HP7 0QQ Tel: 01494 725851 — MB BS Lond. 1950. Prev: Med. Off. Equity & Law Life Assur. Soc. Ltd.

SCOREY, Phillipa Diana Eagle House Surgery, Eagle House, White Cliff Mill Street, Blandford Forum DT11 7DQ Tel: 01258 453171; Old Down House, Horton, Wimborne BH21 7HL Tel: 01258 840969 Fax: 01258 840969 — MB BS 1984 Lond.; DRCOG 1986. (Guy's) GP Princip. Prev: Med. Off. 'Treads' Youth Advis. Clinic Blandford Forum; Resid. Med. Off. Roy. Newc. Hosp. NSW, Austral.; SHO Poole Gen. Hosp.

SCORGIE, Barbara McDonald The Cottage, 37 Main Road, Castlehead, Paisley PA2 6AN — MB ChB 1970 Glas.; FFA RCSI 1976; DObst RCOG 1972. (Glas.) Cons. Anaesth. Roy. Alexandra Infirm. Paisley. Prev: Sen. Regist. (Anaesth.) Vict. Infirm. Glas.; Regist. (Anaesth.) Wellington Hosp., NZ; SHO (Anaesth.) Roy. Alexandra Infirm. Paisley.

SCORGIE, Iain George Buckingham Terrace Surgery, 31 Buckingham Terrace, Glasgow G12 8ED Tel: 0141 221 6210 Fax: 0141 211 6232 — MB ChB 1975 Glas.; MRCGP 1979; DCH RCPS Glas. 1979; DRCOG 1977.

SCORGIE, Richard Ernest Woodend Hospital, Aberdeen AB15 6XS Tel: 01224 556261 Fax: 01224 556628 Email: dick.scorgie@arh.grampian.scot.nhs.uk — MB ChB 1973 Ed.; FRCP Ed. 1988, M 1976. (Edinburgh) Cons. Phys. (Rehabil. Med.) Grampian Univ. Hosps. NHS Trust; Clin. Sen. Lect. Univ. Aberd.; Assoc. Med. Director (Health Informatics), Grampian Univ. Hops. NHS Trust. Socs: Brit. Geriat. Soc. Prev: Med. Dir. Grampian Healthcare NHS Trust; Med. Off. (Geriat. & Specialist Serv. Unit) Grampian HB; Cons. Phys. (Geriat. Med.) W. Cumbld. Hosp.

SCOTCHER, Clare Veronica Middle Lodge, Westwood Park, Droitwich WR9 0AZ — MB ChB 1987 Bristol; MRCGP 1992; DRCOG 1990. GP. Prev: Trainee GP Exeter VTS; Ho. Surg. W.on Gen. Hosp. W.on Super Mare; Ho. Phys. Ham Green Hosp. Bristol.

SCOTCHER, Lilian Mary (retired) Chestnuts, Beresford Road, Goudhurst, Cranbrook TN17 1DN — MB ChB 1951 Aberd. Prev: GP Tonbridge.

SCOTCHER, Stephen Michael Birmingham & Midland Eye Centre, City Hospital NHS Trust, Dudley Road, Birmingham B18 7QU Tel: 0121 554 3801; Middle Lodge, Westwood Park, Droitwich Spa, Droitwich WR9 0AZ Tel: 01905 772266 — MB ChB 1987 Bristol; BSc (Hons) Bristol 1984; MRCP (UK) 1990; FRCOphth 1993. (Bristol) Specialist Regist. (Ophth.) Birm. Prev: Exchange Regist. Brisbane, Austral.; SHO (Ophth.) Soton. Eye Hosp.; SHO (Med.) Exeter HA.

SCOTCHMAN, Frank George Vivian Garth, Welshmill Road, Frome BA11 2LA — MB BChir 1969 Camb.; MB Camb. 1969; MA,

SCOTHERN

BChir Camb. 1968. (St. Bart. Hosp. Lond.) Socs: Camb. Univ. Med. Soc. Prev: SHO (Radiother.) Norf. & Norwich Hosp.; SHO (Radiother.) Glas. Inst. Radiother. Belvidere Hosp., W.. Infirm. & Roy. Beatson Memor. Hosp.; SHO (Radiother.) N.ampton Gen. Hosp.

SCOTHERN, Gillian Elizabeth 66 Ferres Way, Allestree, Derby DE3 2BB — MB ChB 1976 Leeds; MRCOG 1982.

SCOTHERN, Simon Richard 21 Border Brook Lane, Worsley, Manchester M28 1XJ — MB ChB 1992 Manch.

SCOTHORNE, Audrey Winifred Southerknowe, Friars Brae, Linlithgow Tel: 01506 842463 — MB ChB 1950 Leeds; BSc (1st cl. Hons.) Leeds 1947, MB ChB 1950. (Leeds) Prev: Demonst. Anat. Univ. Glas.

SCOTHORNE, Catherine Louise Cookham Medical Centre, Lower Road, Cookham Rise, Maidenhead SL6 9HX Tel: 01628 524646 — MB 1982 Camb.; MA Camb. 1983, MB 1982, BChir 1981; DRCOG 1985. Clin. Asst., Dept. Rheum., Wexham Pk. Hosp., Slought. Prev: Trainee GP Camb. VTS; SHO (Cas.) Wycombe Gen. Hosp.

SCOTHORNE, Professor Raymond John (retired) Southernknowe, Friars Brae, Linlithgow EH49 6BQ Tel: 01506 842463 — MB ChB (1st cl. Hons.) Leeds 1944; BSc (1st cl. Hons.) (Anat.) Leeds 1941, MD (Distinc.) 1951; MD Chicago 1943; FRCS Glas. 1962; FRSE. Edr. (UK) Clin. Anat. Prev: Regius Prof. Anat. Univ. Glas.

SCOTLAND, Mr Alastair Duncan Chelsea and Westminster Healthcare NHS Trust, Chelsea and Westminster Hospital, 369 Fulham Road, London SW10 9NH Tel: 020 8746 5925 Fax: 020 8746 8248 — MB ChB 1975 Aberd.; FRCP 1999; FFPHM 1993, M 1989; MFCM 1987; FRCS Ed. 1980. (Univ. Aberd.) Dir. Med. Educat. & Research Lond. Socs: Fell. Roy. Soc. Med.; Scott. Soc. Experim. Med.; Brit. Assn. Med. Managers. Prev: Trust Unit Med. Dir. NHS Exec. N. Thames; Regional Med. Off. NE Thames RHA; Cons. Pub. Health Med. NE Thames RHA.

SCOTLAND, Hugh William Fraser Ash Lodge Medical Centre, 73 Old Road, Chesterfield S40 2RA Tel: 01246 203138 Fax: 01246 231824; Wigley House, Wigley, Chesterfield S42 7JJ Tel: 01246 567020 — MB BS 1982 Lond.; BSc (Hons.) Physiol. Lond. 1979; MRCP (UK) 1985; MRCGP 1989. (St. Thos.) Prev: Trainee GP Burton-on-Trent VTS.

SCOTLAND, Jennifer Jane 17 Marchbank Road, Bieldside, Aberdeen AB15 9DJ — MB ChB 1998 Ed.; MB ChB Ed 1998.

SCOTLAND, Mr Thomas Robert 17 Marchbank Road, Bieldside, Aberdeen AB15 9DJ — MB ChB 1971 Ed.; FRCS Ed. 1976. Cons. Orthop. Surg. Grampian Health Bd.

SCOTNEY, Amanda Jane The Granary, Back Lane, South Luffenham, Oakham LE15 9DG — MB ChB 1994 Leeds.

SCOTSON, John Hector (retired) 5 Woodville Road, Altrincham WA14 2AN Tel: 0161 941 2712 — MB ChB 1956 Manch.; MRCS Eng. LRCP Lond. 1957; MRCGP 1974; DObst RCOG 1959. Prev: GP Altrincham.

SCOTT, Mr Adam David Glenfield Hospital, Groby Road, Leicester LE3 9QP Tel: 0116 287 1471 Email: adamscott@uhl-tr.nhs.uk — MB BS 1980 Lond.; BSc (Hons.) 1976; MS Lond. 1990; FRCS Eng. 1986; FRCS Ed. 1985; MRCS Eng. LRCP Lond. 1980. (St. Bart.) Cons. Surg. Glenfield Hosp. Leicester; Clin. Lect. Univ. Leicester, Fac. Med. Socs: Fell. Roy. Soc. Med.; Assn. Coloproctol.; Liveryman Worshipful Soc. Apoth. Prev: Lect. (Surg.) St. Bart. Univ. Lond.; Regist. (Surg.) N.ampton Gen. Hosp.

SCOTT, Adrian Roy 36 George Road, West Bridgford, Nottingham NG2 7QG Tel: 0115 981 6975 — MB BS 1977 Lond.; DM Nottm. 1988; MRCP (UK) 1982; DCH RCP Lond. 1979. (Char. Cross) Cons. Phys. Derby Roy. Infirm. Prev: Regist. Qu. Med. Centre Nottm.; Regist. Battle Hosp. Reading; Med. Off. Makiung Hosp. Tanzania.

SCOTT, Agnes Love Eastfield, Mauchline KA5 5EX Tel: 01290 50205 — MB ChB 1938 Glas.; DPH 1940; FRCP Ed. 1960, M 1950; FRCPath 1963. Prev: Sen. Cons. Pathol. Roy. Infirm. Dumfries; Lect. Path. Univ. Glas.; Pathol. Roy. Infirm. Glas.

SCOTT, Ailsa Rayleigh House, Observatory, Eskdalemuir, Langholm DG13 0QW — MB ChB 1987 Ed.

SCOTT, Alan John The Health Centre, 68 Pipeland Road, St Andrews KY16 8JZ Tel: 01334 473441 Fax: 01334 466508 — MB ChB 1991 Glas.; PhD Glas. 1986, BSc 1982, MB ChB 1991.

SCOTT, Alan Keith Gillygate Surgery, 28 Gillygate, York YO31 7WQ Tel: 01904 624404 Fax: 01904 651813; 15 Rawcliffe Lane, York YO30 6NP Tel: 01904 622349 — MB ChB 1963 St. And.; FRCGP 1988, M 1978. Med. Adviser to York Minster &

Glaziers Trust; Med. Adviser Shepherd Building Gp.; Medico-Legal Examr. for Micrah Servs. Liverp.; for Expedia Servs. Bolton; for Medico-legal Reporting, Reading; for Doctors' Chambers, Windsor; for Export Reports, Redditch; for LAB. Medico Legal Serv.s, Peterlee. Socs: York Med. Soc. Prev: Ho. Phys. (Cardiol.) City & Co. Hosps. York; Ho. Surg. Co. Hosp. York; Ho. Off. (O & G) Matern. & Fulford Hosps. York.

SCOTT, Alan Richard Health and Safety Executive, The Pearson Building, 55 Upper Parliament, Nottingham NG1 6AU Tel: 0115 971 2875 Fax: 0115 971 2802 Email: alanscott@hse.gov.ukatnetmail; 3 Grosvenor Avenue, Mapperley Park, Nottingham NG3 5DX Tel: 0115 960 5645 Fax: 0115 960 5645 — MB BS 1975 Lond.; BSc (Physiol.) Lond. 1972; MRCS Eng. LRCP Lond. 1975; FFOM RCP Lond. 1993, M 1986; Specialist Accredit. Occupat. Med. JCHMT 1986. (St. Mary's) Sen. Med. Insp. Field Operats. Directorate. Health & Safety Exec.; Clin. Asst. (A & E) Univ. Hosp. Nottm. Socs: Soc. Occupat. Med.; Nottm. Med. CH1 Soc. Prev: Lect. (Occupat. Health) Univ. Manch.; Sen. Regist. (Occupat. Med.) Brit. Coal, Boots plc. & Rolls-Royce Ltd.; Regist. (A & E Med.) Univ. Hosp. Nottm.

SCOTT, Alexander (retired) Quatrieme, Platte Saline, Alderney GY9 3XF — MB ChB 1944 Ed.

SCOTT, Alexander Douglas Alnbury, Silverdale Road, Brightons, Falkirk FK2 0TH Tel: 01324 713849 & profess. 0501 30432 — MB ChB 1962 Ed.; LMCC 1964; MFOM RCP Lond. 1978; DIH RCPS Glas. 1975; DPH Glas. 1966; DObst RCOG 1965. Employm. Med. Adviser EMAS. Socs: Soc. Occupat. Med. & Brit. Occupat. Hyg. Soc. Prev: Indust. Med. Off. Stewarts & Lloyds; Med. Off. Brit. Steel Corp. Scotl.; Med. Off. Govt. Train. Centre & Indust. Rehabil. Unit Bellshill.

SCOTT, Alexander Hill (retired) Lauriston, Vicarage Road, E. Budleigh, Budleigh Salterton EX9 7EF Tel: 0139 542483 — MB BCh BAO 1935 Belf.

SCOTT, Alexander William McWilliam, Capt. RAMC Millburn, Sutherland Crescent, Buckie AB56 1DA — MB ChB 1980 Aberd. Med. Specialist Qu. Eliz. Milit. Hosp. Prev: Regtl. Med. Off. 1st Gordons & 1st Roy. Scots.; Ho. Off. Qu. Eliz. Milit. Hosp.; Ho. Off. Camb. Milit. Hosp.

SCOTT, Alexandra Jane Apartment 2, Weir Mill, 101 Mill St., East Malling, West Malling ME19 6DW — MB ChB 1992 Sheff.

SCOTT, Alexandra Kyle 9 Sunnybank Close, Whitchurch, Cardiff CF14 1EQ — MB BCh 1979 Wales.

SCOTT, Alice Laura (retired) Hillside, The Rise, Kingsdown, Deal CT14 8AY Tel: 01304 364624 — MB ChB 1951 Ed.; DObst RCOG 1954.

SCOTT, Alicon Veronica (retired) 1 Highfield Drive, Upton, Macclesfield SK10 3DH Tel: 01625 618062 — MB ChB 1955 Liverp.; FRCOG 1980, M 1961; DObst RCOG 1957. Prev: Cons. O & G Macclesfield Hosp. (W. Pk. & Dist. Gen. Hosp.).

SCOTT, Alison 20 Seton Place, Edinburgh EH9 2JT — MB ChB 1989 Dundee; MRCOG 1994; MFFP 1995. Specialist Regist. (O & G) Roy. Infirm. Edin. Prev: Research Regist. & SHO (O & G) Ninewells Hosp. Dundee; SHO III Aberd. Roy. Infirm.

SCOTT, Alison Margaret St. Albans Medical Group, Felling Health Centre, Stephenson Terrace, Gateshead NE10 9QG Tel: 0191 469 2316; 41 Norwich Road, Newton Hall, Durham DH1 5QA — MB BS 1973 Newc.; MRCGP 1983. Occupat. Health Phys. Gateshead Gp. Hosps. Prev: Ho. Off. (Paediat. & Gen. Med.) Newc. Gen. Hosp.; SHO (Gen. Med.) Dryburn Hosp. Durh.; Regist. (Med.) Gateshead AHA.

SCOTT, Alison Marie-Louise 4 Bracklinn Road, Callender FK17 8EJ Tel: 01877 331001 Fax: 01877 331720; 3 Leighton Place, Callender FK17 8BG Tel: 01877 331725 — MB ChB 1986 Aberd.; DRCOG 1992.

SCOTT, Alison Vivienne Drs Crosby, Steel, Rowe, Scott, The Ann Burrough Thomas Health Centre, South William Street, Workington CA7 8HA Tel: 01900 603985; Rosemount, Fellside, Caldbeck, Wigton CA7 8HA Tel: 016974 78674 Email: alisonscottso@hotmail.com — MB BS 1983 Lond.; MRCGP 1998. GP, The Health Centre, Workington. Prev: SR Pub. Health Med., N. Cumbria Health Auth.; Sen. Regist. (Community Med.) N. W.. RHA.

SCOTT, Alister John 75 Clyde Road, London N22 7AD — MB ChB 1985 Aberd.; MBA 2000 Open Univ.; MRCP (UK) 1988; MFOM

RCP (Lond.) 1996. (University of Aberdeen) Director, Employee Health Managem., GlaxoSmithKline plc.

SCOTT, Allan 53 Kelvin Court, Great Western Road, Glasgow G12 0AG — MB ChB 1947 Glas.; DTM & H Eng. 1955; DObst RCOG 1964. (Univ. Glas.) Prev: PMO Dufflaghur Tea Est., Assam.

SCOTT, Althea Jane Department of Genitourinary Medicine, Clinic 1, Milne Centre, Bristol Royal Infirmary, Bristol BS2 8HW Tel: 0117 928 3010; Quakers Meet, Kingsweston Road, Bristol BS11 0UX Tel: 0117 982 2030 — MB BS Lond. 1962; MRCS Eng. LRCP Lond. 1962. (St. Bart.) Cons. Genitourin. Med. United Bristol Healthcare NHS Trust & W.on Area Health Trust. Socs: BMA & Med. Soc. Study VD. & AGUM. Prev: Sen. Regist. St. Thos. Hosp. Lond.; Ho. Off. St. Bart. Hosp. Lond.

SCOTT, Andrew Carr (retired) 43 Hampton Manor, Belfast BT7 3EL — MB BCh BAO 1953 Belf.; DPH 1964. Prev: Med. Asst. (Geriat.) Braid Valley Hosp. Ballymena.

SCOTT, Andrew Douglas Department of Anaesthetics, Royal Bournemouth Hospital, Castle Lane E., Bournemouth BH7 7DW Tel: 01202 704194 Fax: 01202 704196; Tel: 01725 517054 — MB BS 1983 Lond.; FCAnaesth 1989. (St. Thos.) Cons. Anaesth. Roy. Bournemouth & ChristCh. Hosp. NHS Trust. Socs: Intens. Care Soc.; Assn. Anaesth. Prev: Sen. Regist. Rotat. (Anaesth.) Poole & Soton.; Research Regist. (Anaesth.) Roy. Brompton. Nat. Heart & Lung Hosp. Lond.

SCOTT, Andrew Henry Charles 19 Woodlea Grange, Alderbury, Salisbury SP5 3PA — MB BS 1973 Lond.; FFA RCS 1981; FFA RCSI 1980.

SCOTT, Andrew Kenneth Department of Medicine for the Elderly, Arrowe Park Hospital, Upton, Wirral CH49 5PE; 3 Fieldway, Heswall, Wirral CH60 1UP — MB ChB 1976 Aberd.; BMedBiol Aberd. 1973, MD 1983; FRCP Lond. 1994; MRCP (UK) 1978. Cons. Phys. in Geriat. Med. Socs: Brit. Geriat. Soc.; Brit. Pharm. Soc.; Brit. Hypertens. Soc. Prev: Sen. Lect. (Geriat. Med.) Univ. Manch.; Sen. Lect. (Clin. Pharmacol.) Univ. Liverp.; Lect. (Therap. & Clin. Pharmacol.) Univ. Aberd.

SCOTT, Andrew Peter Blair (Surgery), Holman Way, Topsham, Exeter EX3 0EN Tel: 01392 874646 Fax: 01392 875261; The Coach House, Grove Hill, Topsham, Exeter EX3 0EG Tel: 01392 874296 — MB BS 1966 Lond.; MRCS Eng. LRCP Lond. 1966; MRCGP 1978; DPM Eng. 1976; DObst RCOG 1969; DCH Eng. 1968. (Lond. Hosp.) Socs: Exeter Med. Soc.; (Counc.) Soc. Orthop. Med.

SCOTT, Andrew Raymond Ent Surgery Department, North Staffs Hospital, Hartshill, Stoke-on-Trent ST4 7LN Tel: 01926 851688; 1 Holly Grove, Stone ST15 8PB Email: arscott@rcsed.ac.uk — BM BS 1992 Nottm.; FRCS Ed 1997. (Nottm.) Specialist Regist. (Otolaryngol.) W. Midl. Socs: BMA; MPS; Train. Mem. Assn. of Otolaryngols.

SCOTT, Ann Armistead Child Development Centre, Broughty Ferry Rd, Dundee DD1 9SY Tel: 01382 660111; East Wing, The Steading, Waterybutts, Errol, Perth PH2 7SZ Tel: 01821 642473 — MB ChB 1990 Dundee; BMSc (Hons.) Anat. Dund 1987; MRCP (UK) 1994. (Ninewells Hosp. Med. Sch. Dundee) Staff Grade Paediat. With s/i in child Developm. (PT). Socs: MRCP; MRCPCH.

SCOTT, Anne Ards Hospital, Church St., Newtownards BT23 4AS Tel: 028 9151 0106; 22 Hampton Manor, Belfast BT7 3EL — MB BCh BAO 1980 Belf.; MRCPsych 1984. Cons. Psychiat. Ards Hosp. Co. Down. Prev: Sen. Regist. Purdysburn Hosp. Belf.

SCOTT, Anne Marjory (retired) 9A East Mayfield, Edinburgh EH9 1SD Tel: 0131 667 6729 — MB ChB 1947 Ed.; FRCS Ed. 1953. Prev: Med. Off. DHSS.

SCOTT, Anne Primrose (retired) The Old Rectory, Fornham All Saints, Bury St Edmunds IP28 6JX Tel: 01284 767177 — MB ChB 1959 Bristol. Prev: GP Bury St. Edmunds.

SCOTT, Archibald Cunningham (retired) 22 Rocheid Park, Edinburgh EH4 1RU Tel: 0131 315 2720 — MD 1968 Glas.; MB ChB 1955; FRCPath 1976, M 1964. Prev: Cons. Microbiol. Lothian HB.

SCOTT, Barbara The Surgery, Tennant Street, Stockton-on-Tees TS18 2AT Tel: 01642 613331 Fax: 01642 675612; Corner Ways, Brompton, Northallerton DL6 2RL — MB ChB 1977 Glas.; FRCS Ed. 1981; MRCGP 1988; DRCOG 1988. Asst. Police Surg. Cleveland Constab. Prev: Surg. Arawa Gen. Hosp. N.. Solomon Province, Papua New Guinea.

SCOTT, Barbara Ann 15 Aitken Street, Kirkcaldy KY1 3DR — MB ChB 1979 Ed.; MSc (Audiol. Med.) Lond. 1997; DCCH RCP Ed. 1983. Clin. Med. Off. Child Health Fife Healthcare Trust Kirkcaldy.

SCOTT, Barry Alexander St Martins Surgery, 378 Wells Road, Knowle, Bristol BS4 2QR Tel: 0117 977 5641 Fax: 0117 977 5490 — MB BS 1980 Lond.; MRCGP 1995. (Lond. Hosp. Med. Coll.) GP St. Martins Surg. Bristol.

SCOTT, Betty Diana 18 Arden Road, London N3 3AN Tel: 020 8346 8531 Fax: 020 8346 8531 — MB BCh BAO Dub. 1944. (T.C. Dub.) Prev: Resid. Surg. Off. Kidderminster & Dist. Gen. Hosp.; Ho. Surg. Vict. Hosp. Blackpool; Resid. Med. Off. Finchley Memor. Hosp.

SCOTT, Brian Barry 9 Lee Road, Lincoln LN2 4BJ Tel: 01522 536829 — MRCS Eng. LRCP Lond. 1968; MD Lond. 1976, MB BS 1968; FRCP (Lond.) 1984; MRCP (UK) 1971. (St. Bart.) Cons. Phys. (Gen. Med. & Gastroenterol.) Lincoln Co. Hosp.; Clin. Teach. Nottm. Univ. Med. Sch. Socs: Brit. Soc. Gastroenterol. & BMA. Prev: Sen. Regist. (Gen. Med.) Yorks. RHA; Research Fell. Dept. Med. Univ. Leeds; Regist. (Gen. Med. & Renal Med.) St. Jas. Hosp. Leeds.

SCOTT, Brian John The Greenlaw Practice, Northcroft Medical Centre, North Croft Street, Paisley PA3 4AD Tel: 0141 889 8465 — MB ChB 1991 Glas.; MRCP (UK) 1994; MRCGP 1997. (Glas.) GP Regist. Greenlaw Pract., Paisley; Clin. Asst. Diabetic Centre, Gartnavel Gen. Hosp. Glas.; Clin. Tutor in Gen. Pract. Univ. of Glas.; Clin. Tutor in Communication Skills, Univ. of Glas. Socs: Treas. - Alpha 91 Medics Year Club. Prev: SHO (Psychiat.) Gartnavel Roy. Hosp. Glas.; Med. Intern Amer. Hosp., Paris; SHO (Gen. Med.) W.. Infirm. & Gartnavel Gen. Hosp. Glas.

SCOTT, Mr Brian William Dept. Orthopaedics, St James's University Hospital, Leeds LS9 7TF Tel: 0113 206 6940; Tel: 01200 426015 — MB BS 1982 Newc.; FRCS (Orth.) 1994; FRCS Eng. 1987; FRCS Ed. 1987. Cons. (Paediat. Orthop. Surg.) St James Univ. Hosp. Leeds. Socs: Brit. Orthopaedic Assn.; Brit. Soc. for Childr.s Orthop. Surg.; Fell. Roy. Coll. Surg.s.

SCOTT, Bridget Claire 8 Canon Frome Court, Canon Frome, Ledbury HR8 2TD — BM BCh 1986 Oxf.

SCOTT, Bryan Ogle (retired) 5 Dorchester Crescent, Abingdon OX14 2AH Tel: 01235 559252 — MRCS Eng. LRCP Lond. 1944; MA Oxf. 1967; DPhysMed Eng. 1951. Prev: Dir. & Cons. Phys. Rheum & Rehabil. Radcliffe Infirm. & Oxf. DHA.

SCOTT, Carol Marion 36 Parkstone Road, Poole BH15 2PG Tel: 01202 674344 Fax: 01202 660718; 14 Spur Hill Avenue, Lower Parkstone, Poole BH14 9PH Tel: 01202 731925 — MB ChB 1980 Ed.; DRCOG 1986. (Edin. Univ.) GP.

SCOTT, Caroline Gillianne 6 Slades View Close, Diggle, Oldham OL3 5PE — MB ChB 1995 Leeds.

SCOTT, Carolyn Angwin The Medical Centre, Forest, St Mary Church, Torquay TQ1 4QX Tel: 01803 325128 Email: carolyn.scott@gp-l83063.nhs.uk — MB BChir Camb. 1979; BA Camb. 1975; MRCGP 1982; DRCOG 1980. (Lond. Hosp.)

SCOTT, Catherine Anne Turkey Cottage, Old Vicarage Lane, Sutton, Spalding PE12 9LU — MB BS 1992 Lond.

SCOTT, Catherine Jane Milton Surgery, 132 Mountcastle Drive South, Edinburgh EH15 3LL — MB ChB 1980 Ed.; BA Hons. 1974; MRCGP 1988. GP Edin.

SCOTT, Cedric Mathieson, TD 9 Front Street, West Auckland, Bishop Auckland DL14 9HW Tel: 01388 832352 — MB BS 1949 Durh.; MRCGP 1977. Med. Examr. MoD. Prev: Regional Med. Off. DoH; GP Co. Durh.

SCOTT, Charles Cameron 29 Trafalgar Road, Birkdale, Southport PR8 2HF — MB ChB 1971 Aberd.; FFA RCS Eng. 1979. Cons. (A & E Med.) S.port Gen. Infirm. Prev: Sen. Regist. (A & E) Yorks. RHA; Regist. (Anaesth.) Coventry AHA.

SCOTT, Charlotte Helene Rennie Roundal, Kinsteary, Auldearn, Nairn IV12 5HZ — MB ChB 1997 Aberd.

SCOTT, Christina Sui-Lin (retired) 8 Regents Drive, Keston, Bromley BR2 6BU Tel: 01689 51542 Fax: 01689 855512 Email: suiscott@classicfm.net — MB ChB 1967 Bristol; FFA RCS Eng. 1974. Prev: Cons. (Anaesth.) Croydon Health Dist.

SCOTT, Christine Angela Downside, 48 Harnwood Road, Salisbury SP2 8DB Tel: 01722 336894 — MB BS 1969 Lond.; MRCS Eng. LRCP Lond. 1969; FRCPath 1988, M 1977. (King's Coll. Hosp.) Cons. Dept. Path. Salisbury Dist. Hosp. Prev: Sen. Regist. Dept. Path. Roy. United Hosp. Bath; Regist. Dept. Path. Glas. Roy. Infirm.; Ho. Surg. Kilmarnock Infirm.

SCOTT

SCOTT, Christine Susan 9 Windsor Road, Teddington TW11 0SG — MB BS 1981 Newc.; MRCGP 1985; DRCOG 1985; DCH RCP Lond. 1984; DCCH RCP Ed. 1984.

SCOTT, Christopher Donald Queen Elizabeth Hospital, Sheriff Hill, Gateshead NE9 6SX Tel: 0191 487 8989 — MD 1993 Manch.; MB ChB 1984; MRCP (UK) 1990. Cons. Cardiol. & Gen. Med. Qu. Eliz. Hosp. Gateshead. Prev: Research Regist. (Transpl.) Freeman Hosp. Newc.; 1st Asst. (Cardiol.) Univ. Newc. u. Tyne; Regist. (Cardiol.) N.wick Pk. Hosp.

SCOTT, Christopher John 1 Coverdale Drive, Scarborough YO12 5TP — MB ChB 1991 Leeds.

SCOTT, Christopher John Woodend Hospital, Eday Road, Aberdeen AB15 6XS Tel: 01224 663131 Fax: 01224 404019 Email: cjscott8@hotmail.com; 51 Forest Road, Aberdeen AB15 4BN Tel: 01224 645886 — MB BS 1968 Newc.; MBA Aberd. 1996; FRCP Lond. 1987; FRCP Ed. 1985; MRCP (UK) 1972; MBA 1997. Cons. Phys. (Geriat. Med. & Rehabil.) Woodend Hosp. Aberd. Socs: BMA; Brit. Assn. Med. Managers; Brit. Geriat. Soc. Prev: Sen. Regist. Longmore Hosp. Edin.; Regist. (Gen. Med.) Deaconess Hosp. Edin.; Ho. Phys. Hexham Gen. Hosp.

SCOTT, Christopher Linton Exmouth Health Centre, Claremont Grove, Exmouth EX8 2JF Tel: 01395 273001 Fax: 01395 273771 — MSc Birm. 1975, MB ChB 1980; MRCGP 1985; DA (UK) 1990; DRCOG 1986; DCH RCP Lond. 1984.

SCOTT, Christopher Robin 39 Helix Gardens, London SW2 2JL — MRCS Eng. LRCP Lond. 1961.

SCOTT, Claire Elizabeth 49 Kingsdale Park, Belfast BT5 7BZ — MB BCh BAO 1996 Belf.

SCOTT, Claire Henrietta Margaret Woodgates, Catts Hill, Mark Cross, Crowborough TN6 3NH — MB BS 1993 Lond.

SCOTT, Clifford Graham Jenner Health Centre, Turners Lane, Whittlesey, Peterborough PE7 1EJ Tel: 01733 203601 Fax: 01733 206210 — BM BCh 1975 Oxf.; BA Oxf. 1972.

SCOTT, Colin Andrew The Health Centre, Dunning Street, Stoke-on-Trent ST6 5BE Tel: 01782 425834 Fax: 01782 577599; 4 Burns Close, Rode Heath, Stoke-on-Trent ST7 3UD — MB BS 1986 Lond.; MRCGP 1990; DCCH RCP Ed. 1989.

SCOTT, Colin Russell Medical Centre, 12 High Street, Fochabers IV32 7EP Tel: 01343 820247 Fax: 01343 820132 — MB ChB 1974 Dundee.

SCOTT, Colin William David The Health Centre, Killead Road, Crumlin BT29 4BP — MB ChB 1988 Aberd.; MRCGP 1995; DRCOG 1995. Socs: Assoc. Mem. Brit. Med. Acupunc. Soc.

SCOTT, Colin Wilson St Paul's Medical Centre, Dickson Road, Blackpool FY1 2HH Tel: 01253 623896 Fax: 01253 752818 — MB ChB 1989 Manch.; MRCGP 1993. Prev: Trainee GP Lancs. VTS.

SCOTT, Daniel 59 Morris Lank, Kirkstall, Leeds LS5 3JD — MB ChB 1995 Leeds.

SCOTT, Daphne Margaret Riverside Surgery, George Street, High Wycombe HP11 2RZ Tel: 01494 526500 Fax: 01494 450237; 64 Seeleys Road, Beaconsfield HP9 1TB Tel: 01494 676938 — MB BS 1965 Lond.; MRCS Eng. LRCP Lond. 1965; MRCGP 1980; DObst RCOG 1968. (Roy. Free) Prev: SHO (Obst.) Perivale Matern. Hosp.; SHO (Paediat.) Preston Hosp. N. Shields; Ho. Surg. (Orthop.) Roy. Free Hosp. Lond.

SCOTT, Daphne Mary (retired) Fairbrook, Chichele Road, Oxted RH8 0AG Tel: 01883 714022 — MB ChB 1943 St. And.; MRCP Lond. 1948; FRCS Eng. 1953. Prev: Med. Off. Family Plann. Assn. Clinics Croydon & Oxted.

SCOTT, David Angus Tweedale Medical Practice, High St., Fort William PH33 6EU — MB ChB 1980 Leeds; MRCGP 1989; DRCOG 1983.

SCOTT, David Gilbert 3 Malborough Court, Church Hill, Washingborough, Lincoln LN4 1EN Tel: 01522 791867 — MB BS 1954 Lond.; MRCS Eng. LRCP Lond. 1954; MRCGP 1965. (Westm.)

SCOTT, Professor David Gordon Islay 443 Unthank Road, Norwich NR4 7QN Tel: 01603 259389 Fax: 01603 504101 — MB ChB 1973 Bristol; MD Bristol 1982; FRCP Lond. 1994; MRCP (UK) 1977. Cons. Rheum. Norf. & Norwich Health Care NHS Trust; Hon. Sen. Lect. (Rheum.) Roy. Lond. Hosp. Med. Coll. & Univ. E.Anglia; Hon. Prof. Sch. of Med., Health Policy & Pract., Univ. of E. Anglia. Socs: Pres. elect, Brit. Soc. For Rhuematology. Prev: Lect. (Rheum.) Univ. Birm.; Regist. Roy. Nat. Hosp. Rheum. Dis. Bath; Research Regist. S.mead Hosp. Bristol.

SCOTT, David Henry Thomson Department of Cardiothoracic Surgery, Ward 18, Royal Infirmary of Edinburgh, Edinburgh EH3 9YW Tel: 0131 536 3705 Fax: 0131 229 0659 Email: david.scott@ed.ac.uk; 11 Granby Road, Edinburgh EH16 5NP Tel: 0131 667 4645 — MB ChB 1972 Ed.; BSc Ed. 1969; FRCA 1976. Cons. Anaesth. Roy. Infirm. Edin. Socs: Scott. Soc. Anaesth.; Assn. Cardiothoracic Anaesths.; Founding Mem. Expert Wittness Inst. Prev: Lect. Univ. Edin.; Research Fell. (Anaesth.) Roy. Infirm. Edin.

SCOTT, David John 16 Woodbine Avenue, Gosforth, Newcastle upon Tyne NE3 4EU — MB BS 1965 Durh.; MRCPath 1972. Cons. Path. Newc. Gen. Hosp. & Roy. Vict. Infirm. Newc. Prev: Sen. Regist. (Path.) Newc. Gen. Hosp.

SCOTT, David John 39 The Spinney, Moortown, Leeds LS17 6SP — MB BS 1989 Newc.; MRCP (UK) 1992. Regist. (Chest & Gastroenterol. Med.) Newc. u. Tyne.

SCOTT, David John Conquest Hospital, The Ridge, St Leonards-on-Sea TN37 7RD Tel: 01424 758049 Fax: 01424 757050 Email: scott.david@esht.nhs.uk; Rose Mount, 15 Laton Road, Hastings TN34 2ES Tel: 01424 442455 Fax: 01424 716007 Email: david@rose-mount.co.uk — MB BChir 1974 Camb.; MB Camb. 1975, BChir 1974; FRCP Lond. 1994; MRCP (UK) 1976; FRCPCH 1997, M 1996; DCH Eng. 1980; MBA 2000 Keele. (Guy's) Med. Dir. & Cons. Paediat. E. Sussex Hosps. NHS Trust; Hon. Cons. Paediat. Guy's Hosp. Lond. Socs: Fell. Roy. Soc. Med.; BMA. Prev: Cons. Paediat. RAF Hosp. Wegberg BFPO 40; Hon. Sen. Regist. (Paediat.) Brompton Hosp. & Guy's Hosp. Lond.

SCOTT, Mr David Julian Ashbridge Vascular Laboratory, Lincoln Wing, St James's Hospital, Beckett St., Leeds LS9 7TF Tel: 01132 433144 Fax: 01132 460098 Email: djascott@talk21.com — MD 1991 Leic.; MB ChB 1981; FRCS Eng. 1986; FRCS Ed. 1985. (Leic.) Cons. Vasc. Surg. St. Jas. Univ. Trust Hosp. & Seacroft Hosp. Leeds; Cons. Vasc. Surg. BUPA Hosp. Roundhay Hall Leeds; Mem. Ct. of Examrs. Socs: Comm. Mem. Surg. Research Soc.; Assn. Surg.; RCS Eng. March 1998. Prev: Vasc. Fell. Alfred Hosp. Melbourne Austral.; Research Fell. (Vasc.) & Hon. Tutor (Surg.) Bristol Roy. Infirm. SW RHA; Regist. Rotat. (Gen. Surg.) Leics. HA.

SCOTT, David Lindsay (retired) Ravelstone, Manley, Warrington WA6 9ED Tel: 01928 740376 — MRCS Eng. LRCP Lond. 1942; FFA RCSI 1960; DA RCPSI 1948. Indep. Hypnother. Chesh. Prev: Cons. Anaesth. Whiston & St. Helens Hosps.

SCOTT, Professor David Lloyd Department of Rheumatology, Kings College Hospital, East Dulwich Grove, London SE22 8PT Tel: 020 7346 6195 Fax: 020 7346 6475 Email: d.scott@britjrheum2.demon.co.uk; 8 St. Mary's Way, Chigwell IG7 5BX Tel: 020 8281 9005 — MB ChB 1975 Leeds; MB ChB (Hons.) Leeds 1975; BSc (Hons.) Leeds 1972, MD (Distinc.) 1982; FRCP Lond. 1990; MRCP (UK) 1978. Prof. Clin. Rheum. King's Coll. Hosp. Lond.; Cons. Rheum. St. Bart., Homerton & Kings Coll. Hosps. Lond.; Reader (Rheum.) Kings Coll. Sch. Med. & Dent. Lond. Socs: Brit. Soc. Rheum. Prev: Sen. Lect. (Rheum.) St. Bart. Med. Coll. Lond.; Lect. (Rheum. Research Wing) Birm. Med. Sch.; Regist. (Med.) Leeds Gen. Infirm.

SCOTT, Deborah Margaret Department of Genitourinary Medicine, Royal Berkshire Hospital, London Road, Reading RG1 5AN Tel: 0118 987 5111; 103 Courthouse Road, Maidenhead SL6 6HZ — BM BS 1990 Nottm.; BMedSci Nottm. 1988; MRCGP 1994. (Nottingham) Clin. Asst. (Genitourin. Med.) Roy. Berks. Hosp. Reading.

SCOTT, Debra Ann c/o Medical Centre BFPO 47 — MB BS 1989 Tasmania.

SCOTT, Debra Jayne 11 Beatty Close, Derriford, Plymouth PL6 6LJ — MB ChB Bristol 1987; MRCGP 1991; T(GP) 1991; DCH RCP Lond. 1990; Cert. Family Plann. JCC 1990; DRCOG 1989. (Bristol) GP Retainer Plymouth. Prev: Regist. Emerg. Dept. Concord Hosp. Sydney Austral.

SCOTT, Desiree Catherine Campbell Weston Smithy, Ann Bank, Ayr KA6 5EY — MB ChB 1985 Glas.

SCOTT, Diana Margaret (retired) Cyprus Cottage, Broadway, Harwell, Didcot OX11 0HF Tel: 01235 221031 — MB BS 1950 Lond.; MRCS Eng. LRCP Lond. 1950. Prev: Ho. Surg. Roy. Free Hosp. Lond.

SCOTT, Donald Fletcher 25 Park Gate, Blackheath, London SE3 9XF — MB ChB 1957 Ed.; FRCP Lond. 1977, M 1960; MRCP Ed. 1960; DPM Lond. 1963. (Ed.) Socs: EEG Soc. & Assn. Brit.

Neurol. Prev: Cons. i/c EEG Dept. Lond. Hosp.; Sen. Regist. Maudsley Hosp. Lond.; Research Asst. Mayo Clinic Rochester, USA.

SCOTT, Dorothy Lilian (retired) Cringles, 130 Dynevor Road, Skewen, Neath SA10 6TH Tel: 01792 812106 — MB ChB 1948 Leeds. Div. Med. Off. Brit. Red Cross Soc. Prev: Ho. Phys. St. Jas. Hosp. Leeds.

SCOTT, Douglas Barrie Anstruther Medical Practice, Skeith Health Centre, Crail Rd, Anstruther KT10 3FF Tel: 01333 310352 Fax: 01333 312525; 1 Maree Way, Pitcairn, Glenrothes KY7 6NW — MB ChB 1985 Aberd. Socs: (Co-Chairm.) Banff Med. Soc. Prev: SHO (Paediat.) Perth Roy. Infirm.; GP Anstruther; Clin. Asst Ladybridge Hosp.

SCOTT, Douglas Gavin (retired) 55 Beechfield Avenue, Skelmanthorpe, Huddersfield HD8 9BZ — LRCP LRCS 1945 Ed.; LRCP LRCS Ed. LRFPS Glas. 1945.

SCOTT, Edward Rupert 16 Livingstone Road, Portswood, Southampton SO14 6WN — BM 1998 Soton.; BM Soton 1998.

SCOTT, Elaine Christine Pentland Medical Centre, 44 Pentland View, Currie EH14 5QB Tel: 0131 449 2142 Fax: 0131 451 5855; 517 Lanark Road, Juniper Green EH14 5DQ Tel: 0131 453 3530 — MB ChB 1986 Ed.; MRCGP 1990; DRCOG 1990. Prev: Trainee GP Dunb.a. VTS; SHO (O & G) Falkirk Dist. Roy. Infirm.; SHO (Psychiat.) Livingston.

SCOTT, Miss Elaine Margaret Dept. of Obstetrics & Gynaecology, Royal Free Hospital, Pond St, London NW3 2QG Tel: 020 7794 0500; Flat One, 40 Anson Road, Tufnell Park, London N7 0AB Tel: 020 7700 7811 — MB BS 1984 Lond.; MD Lond. 1991; MRCOG 1993; CCST 1997. (University College London) Cons./Hon. Sen. Lect. In Obst., Roy. Free Hosp. NHS Trust, Lond. Socs: Roy. Soc. Med.; Brit. Matern. & Fetal Med. Soc.; Brit. Soc. Psychosomatic. Prev: Sen. Regist. Qu. Charlotte's Hosp. Goldhawk Rd, Lond.; Sen. Regist. Rotat. (O & G) Luton & Dunstable Hosp. NHS Trust & St. Mary's Hosp. Lond.; Clin. Lect. (O & G) Addenbrooke's Hosp. Camb.

SCOTT, Eleanor Margaret Manny Cussiins Diabetes Centre, Beckett Wing, St James University Hospital, Leeds LS9 7TF; 30 Dam Lane, Saxton, Tadcaster LS24 9QF — BM BS 1992 Nottm.; BMedSci Nottm. 1990; MRCP (UK) 1995. (Nottingham) Specialist Regist. Diabetes/Endocrinol/Gen. Med. St James Univ. Hosp. Leeds; Research Regist., St. James Univ. Hosp., Leeds. Socs: Brit. Diabetic Assn.; Brit. Endocrine Soc.; Roy. Coll. Phys. Prev: SHO (Med.) York Dist. Hosp.

SCOTT, Eleanor Roberta Moorfield, Ferry Road, Dingwall IV15 9QS Tel: 01349 863313; 8 Culcairn Road, Evanton, Dingwall IV16 9YT Tel: 01349 830388 Fax: 01349 830599 Email: eleanorsco@aol.com — MB ChB 1974 Glas.; DCCH RCP Ed. 1986. SCMO Community Child Health Dingwall.

SCOTT, Elisabeth Beatrice Maria Cotlands, Horsham Road, Cowfold, Horsham RH13 8AH — MB ChB 1991 Bristol.

SCOTT, Elizabeth Agnes Joyce 38 Queen's Crescent, Edinburgh EH9 2BA Tel: 0131 667 8417 Fax: 0131 667 8417 — MB ChB 1956 St. And. Mem. Disabil. Appeals Tribunal; Mem. Disabil. Appeals Tribunal; Mem. Social Security Appeals Tribunal. Socs: GP Writers Assn. Prev: Sen. GP Edin.

SCOTT, Elizabeth Aline North Hall Moor, Shipton Lane, Wiggington, York YO32 2RQ — MB BS 1982 Lond.; MSc Lond. 1987, MB BS 1982; FFPHM 1997; MFCM 1988. Dir. of Pub. Health Leeds HA; Hon. Sen. Clin. Lect. Univ. Leeds. Prev: Cons. Pub. Health Med. Yorks. Health.; Cons. Pub. Health Med. SW Herts DHA; Trainee (Community Med.) N.W. Thames RHA.

SCOTT, Elizabeth Amanda 96 East Street, Olney MK46 4DH — MB BS 1998 Lond.; MB BS Lond 1998.

SCOTT, Elizabeth Anne Harvey Health Centre, Bank Street, Cupar KY15 4JN Tel: 01334 653478 Fax: 01334 657305; Ryvoan, 6 Hays Road, Newport-on-Tay DD6 8SJ — MB ChB 1976 Dundee.

SCOTT, Else Jane Beech Tree Surgery, 68 Doncaster Road, Selby YO8 9AJ — MB ChB 1985 Liverp.

SCOTT, Ewan Gilchrist 8 Atholl Place, Edinburgh EH3 8HP Tel: 0131 228 6136 Email: ewanscott@blueyonder.co.uk — BSc Ed. 1973, MB ChB 1976; DMRT Ed. 1982. (Edinburgh) Occupat.al Med. Socs: Soc. Occ. Med.

SCOTT, Fiona Rosemary Department of Histopathology, Mount Vernon Hospital, Rickmansworth Road, Northwood HA6 2RN Tel: 01923 844210 Fax: 01923 844067 — MB ChB 1988 Leic.; BSc (Med. Sci.) Leic. 1985; MRCPath 1997. (Leicester Medical School) p/t Cons. Histopath. Mt. Vernon & Watford NHS Trust Watford. Socs: Assn. Clin. Path.; IAP. Prev: Regist. (Histopath.) Roy. Free Hosp.

SCOTT, Fraser Maclennan Flat 2, Dorchester Court, Marlborough Drive, Darlington DL1 5YD — MB ChB 1995 Dundee.

SCOTT, Freya Elizabeth Hall Floor Flat, 10 Durdham Park, Redland, Bristol BS6 6XA — MB BS 1997 Newc.

SCOTT, Mr Gareth Orthopaedic Department, Royal London Hospital, Whitechapel, London E1 1BB Tel: 020 7377 7000; 54 Priests Lane, Brentwood CM15 8BY Tel: 01277 261841 — MB BS 1979 Lond.; FRCS Eng. 1985; FRCS Ed. 1985. (Middlx.) Cons. Orthop. Roy. Lond. Hosp. Whitechapel; Hon. Sen. Lect. St. Bart & Roy. Lond. Sch. of Med. & Dent. Socs: Fell. BOA; Roy. Soc. Med. Prev: Sen. Regist. (Orthop.) Roy. Lond. Hosp., Roy. Nat. Orthop. Hosp. & Black Notley +Hosp.

SCOTT, Gavin Steuart (retired) St. Just, 169 Worcester Road, Malvern Link, Malvern WR14 1EU Tel: 0168 455808 — MB ChB 1938 Ed. Prev: Ho. Obstetr. W.. Gen. Hosp. Edin.

SCOTT, Geoffrey Burnett Seaview House, 1 Loirston Road, Cove Bay, Aberdeen AB12 3NT — MB ChB 1955 Aberd.; FRCPath 1976, M 1964. Sen. Lect. in Path. Univ. Aberd.; Hon. Cons. in Path. Grampian Health Bd. Socs: Path. Soc. Prev: Ho. Off. Aberd. Matern. Hosp.; Ho. Phys. Woodend Gen. Hosp. Aberd.; SHO (Path.) Leicester Roy. Infirm.

SCOTT, Geoffrey Laurence Department of Haematology, Bristol Royal Infirmary, Bristol BS2 8HW Tel: 0117 928 2655 Fax: 0117 928 2531; Quakers Meet, Kingsweston Road, Bristol BS11 0UX Tel: 0117 982 2030 — MB BChir 1962 Camb.; MD Camb. 1972; FRCP Lond. 1979, M 1964. (St. Bart.) Cons. Clin. Haemat. United Bristol Healthcare Trust & W.on Healthcare Trust; Clin. Lect. Univ. Bristol. Socs: Brit. Soc. Haematol.; BMA. Prev: Sen. Lect. & Hon. Cons. (Haemat.) St. Thos. Hosp. Lond.; Regist. (Med.) & Ho. Phys. St. Bart. Hosp. Lond.

SCOTT, Geoffrey Malcolm Sikes 300 Earlsfield Road, London SW18 3EH Tel: 020 8874 9594 Fax: 020 7388 8514 Email: g.scott@academic.uclh.nthames.nhs.uk — MB BS 1972 Lond.; MD Lond. 1984; FRCP Lond. 1995; MRCP (UK) 1974; MRCS Eng. LRCP Lond. 1972; FRCPath 1996, M 1985; DTM & H Liverp. 1979. (Roy. Free) Cons. Microbiol. Univ. Coll. Hosp. Lond. & Lond. Sch. Hyg. Trop. Med.; Hon. Sen. Lect. UCL. Socs: Fell. Roy. Soc. Med.; Hosp. Infec. Soc.; BSAC. Prev: Scientif. Staff Div. Communicable Dis. MRC Clin. Research Centre & Hon. Sen. Regist. (Med. & Infec. Dis.) N.wick Pk. Hosp. Lond.; Regist. (Med.) W.m. Hosp. Lond.

SCOTT, George Walter Pantiles, Wilderness Road, Chislehurst BR7 5EZ Tel: 020 8467 5344 Email: scottpantiles@aol.com — MRCS Eng. LRCP Lond. 1949; MD Lond. 1952, MB BS 1949; FRCP Lond. 1968, M 1953. (Guy's) Cons. Phys. Emerit. Socs: Fell. Thoracic Soc.; Fell. Assur. Med. Soc. Prev: Clin. Tutor & Med. Regist. Guy's Hosp.

SCOTT, Gillian Cwmfelin Medical Centre, 298 Carmarthen Road, Swansea SA1 1HW Tel: 01792 653941 — MB BS 1961 Lond.; MRCP (U.K.) 1971; DCH Eng. 1965; DObst RCOG 1966. (Middlx.) GP Partner GP Cwmfelin Med. Centre Swansea.

SCOTT, Gillian Kenmore Medical Centre, 60-62 Alderley Road, Wilmslow SK9 1PA Tel: 01625 532244 Fax: 01625 549024 — MB ChB 1988 Leic.; DRCOG 1990.

SCOTT, Gillian Anne Mitchell and Partners, New Chapel Surgery, High Street, Long Crendon, Aylesbury HP18 9AF Tel: 01844 208228 Fax: 01844 201906; 76 Sheerstock, Haddenham, Aylesbury HP17 8EX Tel: 01844 290860 — BM BS 1984 Nottm.; MRCGP 1988.

SCOTT, Gillian Rachel Richmond Medical Centre, 462 Richmond Road, Sheffield S13 8NA — MB ChB 1986 Sheff.; MRCGP 1990; DRCOG 1990; Cert. Family Plann. JCC 1990.

SCOTT, Gordon Wychwood Surgery, 62 High Street, Milton-under-Wychwood, Chipping Norton OX7 6LE Tel: 01993 830260 Fax: 01993 831867; The Doctors House, Shipton-under-Wychwood, Oxford OX7 6BQ Tel: 01993 830144 — MB 1970 Camb.; BChir 1969.

SCOTT, Gordon James Luson Surgery, Fore Street, Wellington, Taunton TA21 8AB Tel: 01823 662836 Fax: 01823 660955 — MB BS 1976 Lond.; DRCOG 1978; Cert. Family Plann. 1981. (Lond. Hosp.)

SCOTT

SCOTT, Gordon James Clelland Sighthill Health Centre, 380 Calder Road, Edinburgh EH11 4AU Tel: 0131 453 5335; 13 Tryst Park, Edinburgh EH10 7HA Tel: 0131 445 2529 — MB ChB 1982 Aberd.; MRCGP 1987; DCCH RCP Ed. 1986. (Aberdeen)

SCOTT, Gordon Robertson Department of Genitourinary Medicine, Lauriston Building, Edinburgh Royal Infirmary, Lauriston Place, Edinburgh EH3 9YW Tel: 0131 536 2103 Fax: 0131 536 2110 Email: gumedia@hotmail.com; 26 Cherry Tree Gardens, Balerno EH14 5SP — MB ChB 1979 Ed.; BSc (Med. Sci.) 1976; FRCP Ed. 1993; MRCP (UK) 1984. Cons. Genitourin. Med. Edin. Roy. Infirm.

SCOTT, Graham Alexander (retired) 5 EILDONBANK, EILDON, Melrose TD6 9HH Tel: 01895 824774 — MB ChB Ed. 1950, DPH 1957; FRCP Ed. 1979, M 1978; FFCM 1978. Prev: Dep. Chief Med. Off. Scott. Home & Health Dept.

SCOTT, Graham Paul 117 Stocks Lane, Penketh, Warrington WA5 2RW — MB BCh BAO 1993 Belf.

SCOTT, Graham Ramsay Herd Prestonpans Health Centre, Preston Road, Prestonpans EH32 9QS Tel: 01875 810736 Fax: 01875 812979; 16 Kings Park, Longniddry EH32 0QL — MB ChB 1976 Dundee.

SCOTT, Mr Gregor Ivan Department of Gynaecology, Leighton Hospital, Crewe Tel: 01270 612175 Fax: 01270 612176; Highlands, Crewe Road, Wistaston, Crewe CW2 6PS Tel: 01293 416604 Email: rswonnacott@lineone.net — MB BS 1978 Lond.; FRCOG 1998; MRCOG 1986. (St. Bart.) Cons. O & G Mid Chesh. Hosps. Trust. Socs: Fell. Roy. Soc. Med.; Fell. N. Gyn. Soc.; Brit. Fertil. Soc. Prev: Sen. Regist. W.m. Hosp. Lond.; Research Regist. (Urodynamics) St. Bart. Hosp. Lond.; RMO Qu. Charlotte's Matern. Hosp. Lond.

SCOTT, Guyon Gavin Gordon 26 Dalkeith Road, Edinburgh EH16 5BS — MB ChB 1997 Ed.

SCOTT, Hazel Ruth (retired) Lismore, 3 Downfield Gardens, Bothwell, Glasgow G71 8UW Tel: 01698 361100 — MB ChB 1988 Glas.; FRCP Glas 1998. Cons. Phys. Law Hosp. Lanarksh..; Postgrad.Tutor.

SCOTT, Helen Mary Bridgegate Surgery, 43 Bridgegate, Retford DN22 7UX Tel: 01777 702381; Forge Cottage, Town St., Askham, Newark NG22 0RS Tel: 01777 838028 — BM BS 1996 Nottm.; MRCGP 2000. (Nottingham) Gen. Practitioner, Retford. Prev: GP Regist., Lincoln.

SCOTT, Helena Clare Fenella Department of Anaestetics, 2nd Floor New Guy's House, Guy's Hospital, London SE1 Tel: 020 7955 4051 Email: hcfscott@hotmail.com — MB BChir 1988 Camb.; FRCA 1993. (St. Mary's) Cons.(Anaesth) Guys Hosp. Londr. Prev: Sen. Regist. (Anaesth.) St. Mary's Hosp. Lond.; Sen. Regist. (Anaesth.) Qu. Eliz. II Hosp. Welwyn Garden City; Regist. (Anaesth.) Edgware, N.wick Pk. & Hammersmith Hosps. Lond.

SCOTT, Hilary Marion Department of Paediatrics, West Suffolk Hospital, Bury St Edmunds IP33 2QZ Tel: 01284 713000 Fax: 01284 701993; The Gables, Rattlesden Road, Drinkstone, Bury St Edmunds IP30 9TL — MB BS 1967 Lond.; FRCP Lond. 1989; FRCPC 1976; MRCP (UK) 1970; MRCS Eng. LRCP Lond. 1967. (Guy's) Cons. Paediat. W. Suff. Hosp. Bury St. Edmunds. Prev: Sen. Regist. (Paediat.) Addenbrooke's Hosp. Camb.; Assoc. Resid. Hosp. Sick Childr. Toronto, Canada.

SCOTT, Howard Alan (retired) Newburn House, Newburn, Newcastle upon Tyne NE15 8LN Tel: 0191 267 1890 — MB BS 1946 Durh. Med. Off. Hexham Racecourse; Mem. Med. Bd. DSS. Prev: GP Newc.

SCOTT, Mr Humphrey James Mutton Farm House, Horsham Road, Abinger Hammer, Dorking RH5 6PW — MB BS 1983 Lond.; MS Lond. 1991; FRCS Eng. 1987. Cons. Surg. (Gen. & Colorectal Surg.) St. Peter's Hosp. Chertsey. Socs: Roy. Soc. Med.; Assn. Coloproctol.; Assn. Endoscopic Surgs. Prev: Sen. Regist. (Gen. Surg.) NW Thames RHA.; RSO St. Mark's Hosp. Lond.

SCOTT, Ian Gerard 17 Hillary Crescent, Liverpool L31 6BL — MB ChB 1992 Liverp.

SCOTT, Ian Graham Southside Road Surgery, 43 Southside Road, Inverness IV2 4XA Tel: 01463 710222 Fax: 01463 714072; Blar-Nan-Craubh, Lentran, Inverness — MB ChB 1979 Aberd.; DRCOG 1981.

SCOTT, Mr Ian Hetherington Kenneth Ipswich Hospital NHS Trust, Heath Road, Ipswich IP4 5PD Tel: 01473 703507 Fax: 01473 702091; Three Corners, Witnesham, Ipswich IP6 9HZ Tel: 01473 785134 — MB BChir 1970 Camb.; MA Camb. 1972, MChir 1984; FRCS Eng. 1975. (Camb. & Guy's) Cons. Coloproctol. Ipswich; Med. Dir. Ipswich Hosp. NHS Trust. Prev: Cons. Surg. Ipswich Hosp.; Sen. Regist. (Gen. Surg.) Addenbrooke's Hosp. Camb.

SCOTT, Ian Victor 92 Belper Road, Derby DE1 3EQ — MB ChB 1966 Ed.; FRCOG 1985, M 1972. Cons. O & G Derbysh. Hosp. Wom. Derby; Hon. Clin. Teach. Univ. Notts. Prev: Sen. Regist. (O & G) Jessop Hosp. Wom. Sheff.; Lect. (O & G) Univ. Manch at Univ. Hosp. of S. Manch.; Withington.

SCOTT, Ian William Henderson (retired) 172 Warbreck Hill Road, Blackpool FY2 0SL Tel: 01253 353312 — MB ChB 1956 Glas.; DObst RCOG 1960. Prev: GP Blackpool.

SCOTT, Jacqueline Louise Walker Medical Group, Church Walk, Walker, Newcastle upon Tyne NE6 3BS Tel: 0191 262 7111; 23 Reid Park Road, Jesmond, Newcastle upon Tyne NE2 2ER — MB BS 1980 Melbourne; DRCOG 1984.

SCOTT, James Gilbert Road Medical Group, 39 Gilbert Road, Bucksburn, Aberdeen AB21 9AN Tel: 01224 712138 Fax: 01224 712239; 45 Glenhome Gardens, Dyce, Aberdeen AB21 7FG Tel: 01224 723495 — MB ChB 1980 Aberd.; MRCGP 1983.

SCOTT, Professor James Department of Medicine, Imperial College of Science, Technology & Medicine, Du Cane Road, London W12 0NN Tel: 020 8383 8822 Fax: 020 8383 2028 Email: jscott@rpms.ac.uk — MB BS 1971 Lond.; MSc Lond. 1978, BSc 1968, MB BS 1971; FRCP Lond. 1986; MRCP (UK) 1974; FRS 1997. Prof. of Med. & Dep. Vice-Dean of Research Head of MRC Molecular Med.; Dir. of Med. Hammersmith Hosps NHS Trust; Prof. & Chairm. Med. Roy. Postgrad. Med. Sch. Lond.; Cons. Phys. Hammersmith Hosp. Lond.; Brit. Heart Foundat. Research Funds Comm. Socs: Advis. Bd. Jl. Lipid Research; Assn. Phys. Biochem. Soc.; Counc. RPMS. Prev: Head of Div. of Molecular Med. MRC Clin. Research Centre Harrow; Postdoct. Fell. Dept. Biochem. & Biophysics Univ. Calif..; Europ. Molecular Biol. Organizat. Fell. 1980-1982.

SCOTT, James Andrew, TD Glebe House Surgery, Church Road, Saxilby, Lincoln LN1 2HJ Tel: 01522 702236 Fax: 01522 703132 — MB BChir 1972 Camb.; MA, MB Camb. 1972, BChir 1971; MRCGP 1978; DObst. RCOG 1974. (Camb. & St. Thos.) Prev: Ho. Surg. (Obst.) Lambeth Hosp. Lond.; Ho. Phys. (Paediat.) St. Thos. Hosp. Lond.; Govt. Med. Off. Kitwe, Zambia.

SCOTT, James Angus Dept of Ophthalmology, Stirling Royal Infirmary, Stirling FK8 2AU Tel: 01786 434000 Fax: 01786 466782 Email: angus.scott@frah.sat.nhs.uk — MB BS 1983 Lond.; BSc (Foetal Endocrinol. & Med. Physics) Lond. 1980; FRCS Glas. 1991; MRCOphth 1990; CCST 1998. (Middlx.) Cons.(Opth.) Forth Valley Hosp. NHS Trust Stirling Roy. Infirm. Stirling FKL8 2AU. Socs: N. Eng. Ophth. Soc.; UK & Irel. Soc. of Cataract & Refractive Surg.; Scott. Ophth. Club. Prev: Corneal Fell. Singapore Nat. Eye Centre; Sen. Regist./ Hon, Lect. Aberd. Roy. Infirm.; Regist. (Ophth.) Merseyside Regional Ophth. Rotat. Roy. Liverp. Univ. Hosp. Liverp.

SCOTT, James Archibald (retired) 62 Leicester Lane, Leamington Spa CV32 7HF Tel: 01926 423620 — MB ChB Glas. 1954; MFOM RCP Lond. 1978; DIH Eng. 1977. Prev: Sen. Med. Off. Minerva Health Managem. Redditch.

SCOTT, James Dudley (retired) 2 Capesthorne, Robins Way, Christchurch BH23 4AT — MB BChir 1948 Camb.

SCOTT, Mr James Empson The Lister Hospital, Chelsea Bridge Road, London SW1W 8RH Tel: 020 7730 9560 Fax: 020 7730 7726; 8 Rectory Grove, London SW4 0EA Tel: 020 7622 0571 — BM BCh 1968 Oxf.; MA Oxf. 1968; FRCS Eng. 1973. (Middlx.) Cons. Orthop. Surg. Chelsea & W.m. Hosp. Lond. Socs: Fell. BOA & Roy. Soc. Med. Prev: Sen. Regist. (Orthop.) Middlx. Hosp. Lond. & Roy. Nat. Orthop. Hosp; Regist. Robt. Jones & Agnes Hunt Orthop. Hosp. OsW.ry.

SCOTT, James Gray (retired) 3 Hook Close, Ampfield, Romsey SO51 9DD Tel: 02080 253860 — MB ChB Glas. 1943. Prev: Ho. Surg. (Cas.) W.. Infirm. Glas.

SCOTT, Mr James Henry Shielswood (retired) 39 Dick Place, Edinburgh EH9 2JA Tel: 0131 667 1637 — MB ChB 1944 Ed.; FRCS Ed. 1950. Cons. Orthop. Surg. Lothian HB. Prev: Sen. Lect. (Orthop. Surg.) Univ. Edin.

SCOTT, James Macdonald Calvert Cottage, Brindle, Chorley PR6 8NH Tel: 0125 485 2509 — MB ChB 1956 Ed.; FRCGP 1986; DObst RCOG 1960. (Ed.) Exam. Med. Off. DHSS. Socs: BMA. Prev:

SCOTT

Course Organiser (Gen. Pract.) Manch. Regional Counc. Postgrad. Med. Educat.; Clin. Asst. (Neurol.) Roy. Infirm. Preston & Clin. Tutor (Gen. Pract.) Preston; Ho. Phys. W.. Gen. Hosp. Edin. & Ho. Surg. Roy. Infirm. Edin.

SCOTT, James Noel, TD Windsor House, City Hospital, Belfast BT9 7AB Tel: 02890 263923 Fax: 02890 263945 Email: jnscot@msn.com — MB BCh BAO 1973 Belf.; FRCP Ed. 1992; MRCP (UK) 1977; MRCPsych 1979. (Queen's Belfast) Cons. Psychiat. Belf. City Hosp. Prev: Sen. Lect. (Psychiat. of Old Age) Qu.'s Univ. Belf.; Research Fell. Roy. Vict. Hosp. Belf.; Sen. Regist. (Psychiat.) Purdysburn Hosp. Belf.

SCOTT, Professor James Steel (retired) Byards Lodge, Knaresborough HG5 0LT Tel: 01423 863353 — MB ChB 1946 Glas.; MD Glas. 1959; FRCS Eng. 1986; FRCS Ed. 1959; FRCOG 1962, M 1953. Prev: Dean Fac. Med. & Prof. O & G Univ. Leeds.

SCOTT, James Thomas (retired) Winter's Lodge, Huish Champflower, Taunton TA4 2BZ Tel: 01984 624632 — MB BS Lond. 1949; MD Lond. 1967; FRCP Lond. 1968, M 1952; MRCS Eng. LRCP Lond. 1949. Hon. Cons. Phys. Char. Cross Hosp. Lond. Prev: Cons. Phys. Hammersmith Hosp. Lond.

SCOTT, Jane Frances Dartford West Health Centre, Tower Road, Dartford DA1 2HA Tel: 01322 223600 Fax: 01322 292282 — MB ChB 1985 Liverp. Prev: SHO (Ophth., Geriat. Med. & O & G) Qu. Mary's Hosp. Sidcup.

SCOTT, Janet McGregor Lodgehill Clinic, Lodgehill Road, Nairn IV12 4RF Fax: 01259 769991; Woodlands, Cowdor Road, Nairn IV12 5EF Tel: 01667 454887 — MB ChB 1971 Ed. Asst. GP Lodgehill Clinic, Nairn.

SCOTT, Janet Nancy (retired) 8 Lasswade Court, 32 School Green, Lasswade EH18 1NB Tel: 0131 663 9344 — MB ChB Manch. 1967; DObst RCOG 1972. Med. Off. Brit. Red Cross (E. Midlothian Br.). Prev: Clin. Asst. Limb Fitting Centre P.ss Margt. Rose Hosp. Edin.

SCOTT, Professor Janine Linda Department of Psychological Medicine, Academic Centre, Gartnavel Royal Hospital, 1055 Great Western Road, Glasgow G12 0XH Tel: 0141 211 3937 Fax: 0141 357 4899 — MB BS 1979 Newc.; MD Newc. 1993; FRCPsych 1995; MRCPsych 1985. (Newcastle) Prof. & Hon. Cons. (Psychiat.) Univ. of Glas. Prev: Sen. Lect. & Cons. (Psychiat.) Univ. Newc.; Vis. Scientist John Hopkins, Baltimore Train. Fell., Centre for Cognitive Ther. Philadelphia.

SCOTT, Jason Albert 38 Gover Road, Southampton SO16 9BR Tel: 02380 862650 — MB BS 1994 Lond. (St. Bart. Hosp. Med. Coll.)

SCOTT, Jean Mary (retired) Spring Court, Dockenfield, Farnham GU10 4EX Tel: 01252 794153 — MB ChB 1940 Birm.; DCH Eng. 1965. Prev: Med. Asst. (Paediat.) St. Peter's Hosp. Chertsey.

SCOTT, Jean Mary, DStJ (retired) Tiriach, Clunie Bridge Road, Pitlochry PH16 5JX Tel: 01796 472403 — MB ChB (Commend.) Glas. 1944; MD (Commend.) Glas. 1948; FRCPath 1975, M 1963. Prev: Cons. Path. Glas. Roy. Matern. & Wom. Hosps. Asst. Pathol. Roy. Infirm., W.. Infirm. & Roy. Matern. Hosp. Glas.

SCOTT, Jeremy Peter Dixon 2 Sarahs Gate, Little Petherick, Wadebridge PL27 7QT — MRCS Eng. LRCP Lond. 1968; MRCPsych 1975; DPM Eng. 1972. (St. Geo.) Assoc. Specialist St. Lawrence's Hosp. Bodmin. Prev: Clin. Asst. St. Laurence's Hosp. Bodmin.

SCOTT, Jo Ann Vinette, Phildraw Road, Ballasalla IM9 3EG Tel: 01624 827220 Fax: 01624 827220 — MB ChB 1987 Sheff.; DRCOG 1991; Cert. Family Plann. JCC 1991. (Sheffield)

SCOTT, Joan Elizabeth 5 Woodthorpe Gardens, Sandal, Wakefield WF2 6RA — MB ChB 1971 Leeds; BA (Hons.) Open 1989; MB ChB Leeds. 1971; DPM Leeds 1975.

SCOTT, Joan Isabel G 0/2 12 Ripon Drive, Glasgow G12 0DX — MB ChB 1995 Glas.

SCOTT, John Adam (retired) 17 Trowlock Island, Teddington TW11 9QZ Tel: 020 8977 5175 — MB ChB 1932 Aberd. Prev: Maj. RAMC.

SCOTT, John Anthony Gerard 13 Turnoak Avenue, Woking GU22 0AJ — BM BCh 1987 Oxf.; BA Camb. 1984; MRCP (UK) 1990. MSc Stud. Lond. Sch. Hyg. & Trop. Med. Prev: Regist. (Infec. Dis.) N.wick Pk. Hosp.; SHO Hosp. for Trop. Dis. Lond.; SHO Rotat. (Gen. Med.) Newc.

SCOTT, Mr John Charles Richard Orthofix Ltd, The Guildway, Old Portsmouth Road, Guildford GU3 1LP Tel: 01483 468800 Fax: 01483 468829 Email: jcrscott@easynet.co.uk; 54 Compton Avenue, Brighton BN1 3PS Tel: 01273 727732 Fax: 01273 738812 Email: j.c.r.s@btinternet.com — MA Camb. 1972, MB 1968, BChir 1967; FRCS Eng. 1974; MRCS Eng. LRCP Lond. 1968. (Univ. Coll. Hosp.) Orthofix Gp. Med. Advisor Internat. Prev: GP Health Centre Univ. Sussex Brighton.

SCOTT, John Clelland (retired) 14 Pitcullen Terrace, Perth PH2 7EQ Tel: 01738 26266 — MB ChB 1954 Ed.; FRCP Ed. 1969, M 1961; FRCPsych. 1981, M 1972; DPM Eng. 1957. Prev: Cons. Psychiat. Perth & Kinross.

SCOTT, Mr John David Eye Department, Box 41, Addenbrooke's Hospital, Hills Road, Cambridge CB2 2QQ Tel: 01223 245151 Fax: 01223 216701 — MB BS Lond. 1960; FRCS Eng. 1964; DO Eng. 1962. (St. Mary's) Cons. Vitreo-Retinal Surg. Socs: Club Jules Gonin. Prev: Sen. Regist. Moorfields Eye Hosp. Lond. (City Rd. Br.); Ho. Phys. (Med), Ho. Surg. & Sen Ho. Surg. Eye Dept. St. Mary's Hosp. Lond.

SCOTT, John Davie East Anglian Ambulance NHS Trust, Hospital Lane, Hellesden, Norwich NR6 5NA Tel: 01603 424265; 23 Coppice Avenue, Great Shelford, Cambridge CB2 5AQ Tel: 01223 843189 — MB ChB 1970 St. And.; Dip. IMC RCS Ed. 1988; DObst RCOG 1973; DA Eng. 1972. Clin. Dir. E. Anglian Ambul. NHS Trust.

SCOTT, Mr John Eric Somerville (retired) 17 Stephenson Court, Wylam NE41 8LA Tel: 01661 853995 Fax: 01661 854140 Email: j.e.s.scott@ncl.ac.uk — MB BChir 1948 CAMB; MB BChir Camb. 1948; MA Camb. 1950, MD 1962; FRCS Eng. 1953. Sen. Lect. (Paediat. Surg.) Univ. Newc.; Hon. Sen. Research Assoc. Univ. Newc. Prev: Cons. Paediat. Surg. Newc. HA.

SCOTT, John Graham (retired) Greystones, 54 Sedbergh Road, Kendal LA9 6BE — MB BS 1937 Durh. Prev: Orthop. Ho. Surg. Roy. Vict. Infirm. Newc.

SCOTT, John Graham (retired) 8 Regent's Drive, Keston BR2 6BU Tel: 01689 55542 Email: johngscott@medix-uk.com — MB BS 1961 Lond.; MRCS Eng. LRCP Lond. 1961; FFA RCS Eng. 1966; DA Eng. 1964. Prev: Cons. Anaesth. Bromley Health Dist.

SCOTT, Mr John James Law Hospital, Carluke ML8 5ER — MB BCh BAO 1983 Dub.; FRCS Ed. 1993; MRCGP 1990; Dip. IMC RCS Ed. 1991; DObst RCPI 1986; FFAEM 1998. Cons. (A&E.) Law Hosp. Lanarksh.; Hon Sen Lect Glas Univ.

SCOTT, John Michael 5 Tany Bonc, Valley Road, Llanfairfechan LL33 0ET — MB ChB 1988 Leic.

SCOTT, John Moffat 22 Brooke Way, Bushey Heath, Watford WD23 4LG — MB ChB 1976 Glas.

SCOTT, John Nicholas c/o Mrs Scott, 9 Emmott Drive, Rawdon, Leeds LS19 6PG — MB BChir 1989 Camb.

SCOTT, Mr John Radford Plastic Surgery Unit, Canniesburn Hospital, Bearsden, Glasgow G61 1QL — MB ChB 1988 Dundee; FRCS 1999 (Plast); FRCS Glas. 1992. Cons. Plastic Surg., Canniesburn Hosp. Glas. Prev: Surg. Train. Rotat. W. Scotl.; Specialist Reg. (Plast. Surg.), Canniesburn Hosp. Gals.

SCOTT, John Richard Brick House, Bury Road, Hitcham, Ipswich IP7 7PX — MB BS 1979 Lond.

SCOTT, John Russell (retired) 17A Goldsmith Lane, London NW9 9AJ Tel: 020 8204 5233 — MB BChir 1955 Camb.; MB Camb. 1955, BChir 1954; MRCS Eng. LRCP Lond. 1954; MRCGP 1967.

SCOTT, John Simon Coleridge Carlisle House, 53 Lanegland Street, Poole BH15 1QD Tel: 01202 678484 Fax: 01202 660507; 22A Lower Golf Links Road, Broadstone BH18 8BH Tel: 01202 699362 — MB BS 1975 Lond.; MRCS Eng. LRCP Lond. 1975. (St. Bart.)

SCOTT, John Walter Netheravon, Seaton Ross, York YO42 4LT — MB ChB 1989 Manch. Prev: Trainee GP Sheff.; SHO (A & E & Community Paediat.) Barnsley.

SCOTT, John Watson (retired) 11A Central Avenue, North Mount Vernon, Glasgow G32 9JP — MB ChB 1948 Glas. Prev: GP. Glas.

SCOTT, Jonathan Crispin Ealing Hammersmith & Fulham Trust, Uxbridge Road, Southall UB1 3EU Tel: 02083548012 Fax: 020 8354 8887 Email: jonathan.scott@eh-tr.nthames.nhs.uk — BM BCh 1986 Oxf.; MA Oxf. 1983; MRCPsych 1992. (Oxford) Cons. (Psychiat.) EHF Trust, Ealing Lond.

SCOTT, Mr Jonathan Woodforde Merton Grange, Wheelers Lane, Bear Wood, Bournemouth BH11 9QJ Tel: 01202 573218 Fax: 01202 573218 — MB BS 1968 Lond.; FRCS Eng. 1974, M 19684;

SCOTT

MRCS Eng. LRCP Lond. 1968; FRCOG 1990, M 1978; DObst RCOG 1970. (Westm.) Cons. O & G Poole Gen. Hosp.; Hon. Sec. Nuffield Vis. Soc. Socs: Fell. Roy. Soc. Med.; BMA. Prev: Sen. Regist. (O & G) Bristol Matern. Hosp.; Regist. (O & G) W.m. Hosp. Lond.; Res. Med. Off. Qu. Charlotte's Matern. Hosp. Lond.

SCOTT, Judy Monica Grimston Medical Centre, Congham Road, Grimston, King's Lynn PE32 1DW Tel: 01485 600341 Fax: 01485 601411 — MB ChB 1989 (Hons.) Leeds; BSc (1st cl. Hons.) Leeds 1986; MRCP (UK) 1993; MRCGP 1997. (Leeds) Gen. Practitioner.

SCOTT, Karen-Anne 22 Stanley Road, Leicester LE2 1RE — MB ChB 1998 Leic.; MB ChB Leic 1998.

SCOTT, Karen Lynn 14 Batt Furlong, Aylesbury HP21 9JJ — BM 1996 Soton.

SCOTT, Katherine Ann Department of Psychiatry, St George's Hospital, Cranmer Terrace, Tooting, London SW17 0RE; Flat 2, 10 Lawrie Park Crescent, London SE26 6HD — MB BS 1988 Lond.; DGM RCP Lond. 1992. Regist. Rotat. (Psychiat.) St. Geo. Hosp. Lond. Prev: Regist. Rotat. (Psychiat.) Univ. Hosp. S. Manch.

SCOTT, Kathleen Edith Annie (retired) The Friars House, 2 Barton Road, Hereford HR4 0AY Tel: 01432 263776 — MB BCh BAO 1938 Dub.; BA (Hons. Nat. Sc.) Dub. 1936, MB BCh BAO 1938; DCH Eng. 1948. Prev: Lady Med. Off. Singapore.

SCOTT, Kathryn Cossart 46 North Road, Belfast BT5 5NH — MB BCh BAO 1990 Belf.; MB BCh Belf. 1990.

SCOTT, Keith Wilson Holywood Arches Health Centre, Westminster Avenue, Belfast BT4 1NS Tel: 028 9056 3354 Fax: 028 9065 3846; 35 Kensington Road, Belfast BT5 6NJ — MB BCh BAO 1980 Belf.; MRCGP 1985; DRCOG 1985; DCH Dub. 1984; Dip. Palliat. Med. 1995. (Univ. of Wales, Cardiff) Clin. Asst. Beaconfield Marie Curie Centre Belf.

SCOTT, Kenneth Garrion, 27 Forest View, Kildrum, Cumbernauld, Glasgow G67 2DB — MB ChB Glas. 1987.

SCOTT, Kenneth, OBE 31 Spencer Close, London N3 3TX Tel: 020 8346 1350 Fax: 020 8346 2399 Email: silverley@talk21.com — MB BS 1953 Lond.; FRCGP 1977, M 1968; DObst RCOG 1955. (Guy's) Socs: Fell. Med. Soc. Lond.; BMA; (Pres.) Nat. Assn. Fundholding Pract.s. Prev: Ho. Surg. (O & G) St. Mary Abbot's Hosp. Kensington; Ho. Surg. & Ho. Phys. Qu. Mary's Hosp. Sidcup.

SCOTT, Kenneth Balfour (retired) Mansewood, Bonhill, Alexandria G83 9AS Tel: 01389 752112 — MB ChB Glas. 1952. Prev: Partner Scott. Pract.

SCOTT, Kenneth William (retired) 6 Dillon Heights, Armagh BT61 9HF Tel: 01861 523136 — MB BCh BAO 1958 Belf.; FRCPI 1974, M 1963. Prev: Cons. Dermat. Craigavon Area Hosp. Portadown.

SCOTT, Kenneth William McKay Histopathology Department, New Cross Hospital, Wolverhampton WV10 0QP Tel: 01902 644810 Fax: 01902 644809 Email: dr.scott@nwh-tr.wmids.nhs.uk; 18 Church Hill Road, Stockwell End, Tettenhall, Wolverhampton WV6 9AT Tel: 01902 753754 — MB ChB 1967 Glas.; MD Glas. 1978; FRCPath 1986, M 1974. (Glas.) Cons. Path. Roy. Hosp. Wolverhampton. Socs: Coun. Roayl Coll. of Pathologists. Prev: Lect. (Path.) Univ. Sheff.; Regist. (Laborat. Med.) S.. Gen. Hosp. Glas.; Home Office Pathologist.

SCOTT, Kim Michelle 9 Braemar Drive, Bridgehall, Bury BL9 7PQ Tel: 0161 797 4243 — MB ChB 1981 Dundee. p/t Med. Asst. DSS Oldham. Prev: Princip. GP Marjory Lees Health Centre Oldham; Trainee GP Collegiate Med. Centre, Cheetham Hill, Oldham VTS; Asst. Pract. Marjory Lees Health Centre Oldham.

SCOTT, Kirsty Nina Lindsey Rosemount, 6 Forthill Road, Broughty Ferry, Dundee DD5 2JU — MB ChB 1996 Glas.

SCOTT, La Vern Anastasia Airedale General Hospital, Skipton Road, Steeton, Keighley BD20 6TD; Flat 3, Chatsworth House, 9 Hyde Terrace, Leeds LS2 9LN — MB BS 1991 West Indies.

SCOTT, Leslie Gordon Trencrom, 17 Southcourt Avenue, Bexhill-on-Sea TN39 3AR Tel: 01424 212583 — MRCS Eng. LRCP Lond. 1939; MD Lond. 1951, MB BS 1940; FRCP Lond. 1969, M 1949; DCH Eng. 1949. (Guy's) Hon. Cons. Paediat. Hastings & E.bourne Gp. Prev: Out-pat. Med. Regist. Hosp. Sick Childr. Gt. Ormond St.; Sen. Regist. Childr. Dept. Guy's Hosp.; Act. Squadron Ldr. RAFVR.

SCOTT, Leslie Thomas (retired) 14 Cove Road, Silverdale, Carnforth LA5 0RR Tel: 01524 701013 — BM BCh 1941 Oxf.; BA, BM BCh Oxf. 1941; FFA RCS Eng. 1957; DA Eng. 1946. Prev: Cons. Anaesth. Lancaster Health Dist.

SCOTT, Liam Richard Tel: 028 9042 6984 Fax: 028 9042 6656; 33 Moira Drive, Bangor BT20 4RW Tel: 01247 454508 — MB BCh BAO 1970 Belf.

SCOTT, Lorna Isobel West Brook, 1 Finlays Road, Newtownards BT23 8SW — MB BCh BAO 1959 Belf.; DCH Eng. 1962.

SCOTT, Louise Group Practice, Health Centre, Springfield, Stornoway HS1 2PS — MB ChB 1989 Dundee; MRCGP 1996; DRCOG 1994. GP.

SCOTT, Louise Ann 139 Dunmow Road, Bishop's Stortford CM23 5HQ — MB BS 1990 Lond.; MRCGP 1994; DRCOG 1993. GP Retainer, Bishops Stortford. Prev: Trainee GP Medway HA; Ho. Off. (Surg.) Joyce Green Hosp. Dartford; Ho. Off. (Med.) Brook Gen. Hosp. Greenwich.

SCOTT, Lucinda Valerie 44 Theberton Street, London N1 0QX — MB BCh BAO 1991 Dub.

SCOTT, Lucy Clare 26 Bawnmore Road, Belfast BT9 6LA — MB BCh BAO 1997 Belf.

SCOTT, Mairi Gray Browning Cairntoul Drive Surgery, 9 Cairntoul Drive, Glasgow G14 0XT Tel: 0141 959 5519 Fax: 0141 950 1028; 10 Marchmont Terrace, Glasgow G12 9LS — MB ChB 1977 Glas.; FRCGP 1992, M 1981; Cert JCC Lond. 1978. GP Glas.

SCOTT, Malcolm Francis 49 Valiant House, Vicarage Crescent, London SW11 3LU Tel: 020 7228 5903 Fax: 020 7228 5903 — MB BS 1974 Lond.; MRCS Eng. LRCP Lond. 1974. (Guy's) Med. Adviser Benefits Agency Lond.; GP Cromwell Hosp. Lond. Prev: GP Lond. (NHS Princip.); Med. Off. Passage Day Centre for the Homeless Lond.; Company Med. Off. Ho. of Fraser plc.

SCOTT, Malcolm Peter Young 34A Church Road, Stoke Bishop, Bristol BS9 1QT — MB BS 1956 Lond.; MRCS Eng. LRCP Lond. 1956; MFOM RCP Lond. 1979; DIH Soc. Apoth. Lond. 1959. (Middlx.) Gp. Med. Adviser Mardon Packaging Internat.; Med. Adviser St. Regis Gp. Bristol. Socs: Soc. Occupat. Med. Prev: Med. Adviser Nat. Cash Register Co. Ltd. Lond.; Asst. Med. Off. Stewarts & Lloyds Corby.

SCOTT, Margaret Christine (retired) 11 The Russets, Wakefield WF2 6JF Tel: 0113 293 4064 — MB ChB 1950 Ed.

SCOTT, Margaret Elizabeth Dourado and Partners, Maybush Medical Centre, Belle Isle Health Park, Portobello Road, Wakefield WF1 5PN Tel: 01924 328132 Fax: 01924 328130; Manor House, 21 School Lane, Walton, Wakefield WF2 6PA Tel: 01924 251452 — MB BS 1975 Newc.; MRCGP 1979; DRCOG 1977. Clin. Assist. G.U.Med., The Chadwick Clinic, Dewsbury + Dist. Hosp., Healds Rd, Dewsbury. Prev: Trainee GP Wakefield VTS; Ho. Off. Cumbld. Infirm. Carlisle & Roy. Halifax Infirm.

***SCOTT, Marianne** Flat 211, 8 Govan Road, Glasgow G51 1HS — MB ChB 1997 Glas.; DRCOG 1999.

SCOTT, Mr Mark John Leonard Department Plastic & Reconstructive Surgery, Stoke Mandeville Hospital, Mandeville Road, Aylesbury HP21 8AL — MB BS 1986 Lond.; FRCS (Plast) 1995; FRCS Eng. 1990. Cons. Plastic Surg. Stoke Mandeville Hosp. Aylesbury. Socs: BMA; Brit. Assn. Plastic Surg.; Brit. Assn. Aesthetic Plastic Surgs. Prev: Sen. Regist. (Plastic Surg.) Qu. Mary's Univ. Hosp. Lond.; Regist. St. Jas. Univ. Hosp. Leeds.

SCOTT, Martha Pasture Lane Farm, Pasture Lane, Hesket Newmarket, Wigton CA7 8JP — MB BS 1998 Lond.; MB BS Lond 1998.

SCOTT, Mary Links Medical Centre, 4 Hermitage Place, Edinburgh EH6 8BW Tel: 0131 554 1036 Fax: 0131 555 3995; 11 Granby Road, Edinburgh EH16 5NP — MB ChB 1973 Ed.; BSc Ed. 1970, MB ChB 1973; Cert JCC Lond. 1976. Gen. Med. Pract.Links Med. Centre Edin. Prev: Med. Off. Brook Advis. Centre Edin.

SCOTT, Mary Reid Nethertown Surgery, Elliot Street, Dunfermline KY11 4TF Tel: 01383 623516 Fax: 01383 624254 — MB ChB 1970 Aberd.; MRCGP 1984; MFFP 1993; Cert. Family Plann. JCC 1976; DObst RCOG 1972. (Aberdeen)

SCOTT, Maureen Easton Portland Street Surgery, 101 Portland Street, Troon KA10 6QN Tel: 01292 313593 Fax: 01292 312020 — MB ChB 1970 Glas.

SCOTT, Maureen Jean Room 405B, Dundonald House, Belfast BT4 3SF Fax: 01232 627423; Laurel Vale House, 121 Ballyskeagh Road, Drumbeg, Belfast BT17 9LL — 1964 MB, B Ch, B.A.D.; MD Belf. 1975, MB BCh BAO 1964; FFPHMI 1993, M 1987; FFPHH (UK) 1990,M 1984. (Belf.) p/t Sen. Lect. (Epidemiol. & Pub. Health Med.) Qu. Univ. Belf.; Cons. Pub. Health Med. EHSSB. Socs: Fell.

Ulster Med. Soc.; Soc. Social Med. Prev: Cons. Pub. Health Med. EHSSB; Friar Research Fell. (Community Med.) Qu. Univ. Belf.

SCOTT, Melanie Jane 217 Shawfield Road, Ash, Aldershot GU12 6SH — MB ChB 1996 Liverp.; BSc (Hons) Liverp. 1993. (Liverpool) SHO (Gen. Surg.) Roy. Liverp. Univ. Hosp. Prev: SHO (A & E) Roy. Liverp. Univ. Hosp. Liverp.; Ho. Off. Roy. Liverp. Univ. Hosp. Liverp.; SHO (Urol.) RLUH, SHO (Gen. Surg.) Warrington Gen. Hosp., SHO (Orthap) Univ. Hosp. Aintree.

***SCOTT, Michael** 17 Beechfield Drive, Annalong, Newry BT34 4TP Tel: 0410 131260 Email: mscott7449@hotmail.com — MB BCh 1998 Belf.; MB BCh Belf 1998.

SCOTT, Michael Andrew Briar Green, Adlington Road, Wilmslow SK9 2BN — BM BS 1995 Nottm.

SCOTT, Michael Edwin Newburn Road Surgery, 4 Newburn Road, Newcastle upon Tyne NE15 8LX Tel: 0191 229 0090 Fax: 0191 267 4830 — MB BS 1976 Newc.; MRCGP 1980.

SCOTT, Michael Ernest (retired) Regional Cardiology Centre, City Hospital, Lisburn Road, Belfast BT9 7AB Tel: 02890 329241 — MB BCh BAO (2nd cl. Hons.(Belf. 1963; BSc (Anat. 1st cl. Hons.) Belf. 1960, MD 1969; FRCP Lond. 1980, M 1966; FRCPI 1975, M 1966; FESC 1988. 25 Derryvolgie Avenue, Belf. BT9 6FN. Prev: Cons. Cardiol. Belf. City Hosp.

SCOTT, Mr Michael Hugh Whiston Hospital, Prescot L35 5DR Tel: 0151 430 1911 Fax: 0151 339 7765 Email: mhscott@dr-mike.co.uk; Springfield House, Margarets Lane, Childer Thornton, South Wirral CH66 5PF Tel: 0151 339 1366 Fax: 0151 339 7765 Email: mhscott@dr-mike.co.uk — MB ChB 1978 Liverp.; ChM Liverp. 1990; FRCS Eng. 1982; MRCS Eng. LRCP Lond. 1978. (Liverpool) Cons. Gen. Surg. Whiston Hosp. Prescot. Prev: Sen. Regist. Rotat. (Gen. Surg.) Merseyside HA; Surgic. Fell. Univ. Calif., San Diego, USA.; Sandoz Transpl. Fell. 1986-88.

SCOTT, Michael Joseph Brookeborough Surgery, Tanyard Lane, Brookeborough, Enniskillen BT94 4AB Tel: 028 8953 1225 Fax: 02889 531857 Email: mscott@brookeborough.com — MB BCh BAO 1984 Belf.; MRCGP 1990; DCH Dub. 1991; DRCOG 1990; DA (UK) 1986.

SCOTT, Mora Joan (retired) St. Michaels, Northfield Terrace, Elgin IV30 1NE Tel: 01343 543832 — MB ChB 1940 Aberd. DL. Prev: Ho. Surg. & Ho. Phys. Roy. Aberd. Hosp. Sick Childr.

SCOTT, Morna Catherine (retired) Grangemount, Alyth, Blairgowrie PH11 8NY Tel: 0182 832600 — MB ChB 1941 Aberd. Prev: Med. Off. City Fev. Hosp. Aberd. & Roy. Hosp. Sick Childr. Aberd.

SCOTT, Mr Nicholas Bruce 19 Bruce Road, Glasgow G41 5EE — MB ChB 1979 Aberd.; FRCS Ed. 1985.

SCOTT, Nicola Christine 52 Warland Way, Corfe Mullen, Wimborne BH21 3NZ — BM 1988 Soton.

SCOTT, Nicola Mary Tel: 01525 402641 Fax: 01245 841107; Sandborne, Clophill Road, Maulden, Bedford MK45 2AA — MB BS 1982 Nottm.; MRCGP 1986; DRCOG 1986. Prev: Trainee GP Doncaster VTS.

SCOTT, Nigel Dept. of Pathology, St James University Hospital, Beckett Street, Leeds LS9 7TF Tel: 0113 206 5590 — MB ChB 1985 Sheff.; MD Sheff. 1995; MRCPath 1993. Cons. Histopath. Leeds.

SCOTT, Mr Nigel Andrew Department of Surgery, Hope Hospital, Stott Lane, Salford M6 8HD Tel: 0161 787 5123 Fax: 0161 787 1276; The Knowle, Dalegarth Avenue, Heaton, Bolton BL1 5DW Tel: 01204 842970 — MB ChB 1979 Manch.; MB ChB (Hons.) Manch. 1979; MD Manch. 1988, BSc (Hons.) 1976; FRCS Eng. 1983. (Manchester) Cons. Gen. Surg. Hope Hosp. Manch.; Hon. Sen. Clin. Lect. Univ. Manch. Socs: Assn. Coloproctol. Prev: Sen. Lect. & Hon. Cons. (Surg.) Univ. Manch.; Lect. (Surg.) Univ. Wales Coll. Med.; Fell. Oncol. Mayo Clinic, USA.

SCOTT, Nigel William The Health Centre, Leypark Walk, Estover, Plymouth PL6 8UE Tel: 01752 784949; 190 Mannamead Road, Hartley, Plymouth PL3 5RE Tel: 01752 783493 Email: nigel_scott@email.msn.com — MB BChir 1989 Camb.; MB BChir Camb. 1988; MA Camb. 1989; MRCGP 1992; DRCOG 1991. (Univ. Camb.)

SCOTT, Olive (retired) Byards Lodge, Boroughbridge Road, Knaresborough HG5 0LT Tel: 01423 863353 — MB ChB 1948 Sheff.; MD Sheff. 1957; FRCP Lond. 1972, M 1955; MRCS Eng. LRCP Lond. 1948; DCH . Lond. 1952. Cons. Paediat. Cardiol. Leeds

Gen. Infirm. & Killingbeck Hosp. Leeds. Prev: Cons. Paediat. Roy. Liverp. Childr. Hosp.

SCOTT, Oliver Christopher Anderson (retired) 31 Kensington Square, London W8 5HH — MD Camb. 1976, MB BChir 1946; MRCS Eng. LRCP Lond. 1946; FRCR (Hon.) 1998. Prev: Consult Inst. Cancer Research Lond.

SCOTT, Oliver John New House, Upper St., Leeds, Maidstone ME17 1RY Tel: 01622 861462 Email: ollyclarescott@yahoo.com — BM BS 1991 Nottm.; Dip. Obst. Auckland 1996; Dip. Paediat. Auckland 1996; MRCGP (RCGP, Lond. 1997). (Nottm.) GP Regist. Maidstone; Locum GP.

SCOTT, Oliver Lester Schreiner South Lodge, South Side, Wimbledon Common, London SW19 4TL Tel: 020 8946 6662 — MB BChir 1943 Camb.; MA Camb. 1943; FRCP Lond. 1964, M 1944; MRCS Eng. LRCP Lond. 1942. (Univ. Camb. St. Thos. Hosp. Lond.) Chev. Nat. du Mérite (Rep. France); Hon. Cons. Dermat. Char. Cross Hosp. Lond., Roy. Surrey Co. Hosp. & St. Luke's Hosp Guildford; Vice-Pres. Roy. Med. Foundat. of Epsom Coll. Socs: Fell. (Ex-Hon. Treas.) Roy. Soc. Med.; Hon. Mem. (Ex-Pres.) Brit. Assn. Dermat.; St John's Hosp. Dermatol. Soc. Prev: Cons. Dermat. King Edwd. VII Hosp. for Offs. Lond.; Cons. Dermat. Dispensaire Francais Lond.; Vice-Dean Char. Cross. Hosp. Med. Sch.

SCOTT, Mr Patrick Damian Rossendale General Hospital, Haslingden Road, Rawtenstall, Rossendale BB4 6NE Tel: 01706 233142; Egerton House, Mather Road, Walmersley, Bury BL9 6RD Tel: 0161 797 4243 — MB ChB 1980 Manch.; MD Manch. 1992; FRCS Ed. 1984; FRCPS 1984. Cons. Gen. Surg. Burnley Healthcare NHS Trust. Prev: Sen. Regist. (Surg.) NW Region.; Tutor (Gen. Surg.) Manch. Roy. Infirm.

SCOTT, Paul Primrose Mill Barn, Waste Lane, Kelsall, Chester CW6 0PE Tel: 01829 751409 Fax: 01829 751416; Primrose Mill Barn, Waste Lane, Kelsall, Chester CW6 0PE Tel: 01829 751409 Fax: 01829 751416 — MB ChB 1989 Leeds; FRCA 1994. Cons. (Anaesth.) Warrington Hosp. NHS Trust. Prev: Regist. (Anaesth.) Univ. Hosp. S. Manch.

SCOTT, Paul Andrew 61 Spottiswoode Street, Marchmont, Edinburgh EH9 1DL — MB ChB 1989 Ed.; LLB Ed. 1993. SHO (Anaesth.) Stirling Roy. Infirm. NHS Trust.

SCOTT, Paul Habershon (retired) Park Cottage, 8, The Green, Royston SG8 7AD Tel: 01763 249974 — MB 1956 Camb.; BChir 1955; DObst RCOG 1958. Prev: Ho. Surg. Middlx. Hosp.

SCOTT, Paul James Bulley and Partners, Hamdon Medical Centre, Matts Lane, Stoke-sub-Hamdon TA14 6QE Tel: 01935 822236 Fax: 01935 826565; D'Evercy, Thorne, Yeovil BA21 3PZ Tel: 01935 33960 Fax: 01935 33960 — MB BChir 1983 Camb.; MRCGP 1987; DRCOG 1987; DCH RCP Lond. 1987. Prev: Trainee GP Kent & Canterbury Hosp. VTS.

SCOTT, Paul Meikle Flat 1, 6 Douglas Crescent, Edinburgh EH12 5BB — MB ChB 1993 Ed.; MRCP (Ed.) 1997. Med. Regist. Borders Gen. Hosp. Melrose, Roxburghsh. Prev: SHO EGH Gen. Med. Edin. (E. Gen. Hosp.); SHO City Hosp. Infec. Dis. United; SHO Haemat. Unit Roy. Infirm. Edin.

SCOTT, Paul Robert David Tel: 01782 612375 Fax: 01782 714036; 3 Heronpool Drive, Baldwins Gate, Newcastle ST5 5LJ — MB BS 1988 Lond.; MRCGP 1995; DFFP 1994; DRCOG 1992. (St. Bart. Med. Coll.) LMC Mem.; Triogl Lead and Counc. Mem., N. Staffs GP CoOperat.; Clin. Adviser, NHS Direct, Midl. Shires. Prev: Trainee GP Stafford VTS.

SCOTT, Mr Peter David Rankin 31 Mearns Road, Clarkston, Glasgow G76 7ES Tel: 0141 638 4396 — MB ChB 1967 Glas.; FRCS Ed. 1971. Cons. Orthop. Surg. Vict. Infirm. Glas.

SCOTT, Mr Peter Douglas Campbell 71G Fitzjohns Avenue, London NW3 6PD Tel: 020 7431 2774 — MB BS 1991 Lond.; BSc Lond. 1988, MB BS 1991; MRCGP 1995; DRCOG 1994; DCH 1993; MRCOG 1999. (St. Barts. HMC) Specialist Regist. (O & G) St. Barts. Hosp. Lond.; Specialist Regist. (Obst. & Gyn.) NE Thames.

SCOTT, Peter Edward 31 Woodchester Road, Dorridge, Solihull B93 8EN Tel: 01564 773647 Fax: 0121 779 7109 — MB ChB 1984 Liverp.; DRCOG 1986; DOH 1999. (Liverpool Univ.)

SCOTT, Peter James Young (retired) Clifton College Santatorium, 83B Pembroke Road, Bristol BS8 3EA Tel: 0117 973 5642 — MRCS Eng. LRCP Lond. 1960. Med. Off. Clifton Coll. Bristol.

SCOTT, Peter John Castle Douglas Medical Group, Castle Douglas Health Centre, Academy Sreett, Castle Douglas DG7 1EE Tel: 01556

SCOTT

503888 Fax: 01556 504302; Chapel Place, Castle Douglas DG7 1EJ — MB ChB 1967 Ed. Clin. Asst. (Genitourin. Med.) Dumfries & Galloway Roy. Infirm.

SCOTT, Peter John Royal Bolton Hospital, Minerva Road, Farnworth, Bolton BL4 0JR Tel: 01204 390390; 1 Hillside, Off Chorley New Road, Bolton BL1 5DT — MB ChB 1984 Leeds; MRCP (UK) 1987. Cons. Phys. (Cardiol.) Roy. Bolton Hosps. Prev: Research Fell. (Cardiol.) Killingbeck Hosp. Leeds.

SCOTT, Mr Peter John (retired) Lady's Grace, Southcott, Westleigh, Bideford EX39 4NH Tel: 01273 475669 Email: pjs.dcs@ladygrace.freeserve.co.uk — MB BS Lond. 1956; FRCS Eng. 1962; T(S) 1991. Prev: Cons. Orthop. & Traum. Surg. N. Devon Dist. Hosp.

SCOTT, Peter John Wellwood 12 Ancaster Drive, Glasgow G13 1ND — MD 1991 Glas.; BSc (Hons.) Glas. 1971, MB ChB 1973; FRCP Glas. 1987. Cons. Phys. Gen. and Geriat. Med., Roy. Alexandra Hosp., Paisley PA2 9PN.

SCOTT, Mr Peter Milton The Old Vicarage, Babraham, Cambridge CB2 4AG — MB BS Lond. 1955; MA Camb. 1974; FRCS Eng. 1960. (Char. Cross) Socs: Fell. BOA; Fell. Roy. Coll. Surgs. Prev: Emerit. Cons. Orthop. Surg. Addenbrooke's NHS Trust Camb.; Sen. Regist. (Orthop.) Addenbrooke's Hosp. Camb. & Aberd. Roy. Infirm.; SHO (Surg.) Roy. Nat. Orthop. Hosp. Stanmore.

SCOTT, Peter Vincent Bromsgrove General Hospital, All Saint's Road, Bromsgrove B61 0BB — MB 1962 Camb.; MA Camb. 1964, MB 1962, BChir 1961; FFA RCS Eng. 1969. (Camb. & Univ. Coll. Hosp.) Cons. Anaesth. BromsGr. Gen. Hosp. Socs: BMA & Assn. Anaesths. Prev: Lect. Dept. Anaesth. Welsh Nat. Sch. Med. Cardiff; Cons. Anaesth. Univ. Hosp. Wales Cardiff; Assoc. Prof. Dept. Anesth. Univ. N. Carolina Sch. Med. Chapel Hill.

SCOTT, Peter William Bowen, OBE (retired) Wellfield, Bwlch, Brecon LD3 7RZ — MB BS Lond. 1962; FRCPath 1989, M 1977, D 1971; DTM & H Eng. 1968; DObst RCOG 1964. Med. Dir.; Cons. Pathol. Nevill Hall Hosp. Abergavenny. Prev: Reader Pathol. Roy. Army Med. Coll. Lond.

SCOTT, Philip Hays (retired) Underhill, 4 Crownpits Lane, Godalming GU7 1NY Tel: 01483 415032 — MB ChB 1940 Ed. Prev: Med. Off. HM Prison Grendon.

SCOTT, Mr Philip Martyn John Poole Hospital NHS Trust, Longfleet Road, Poole BH15 2JB Tel: 01202 442459 Email: philip.se.dial.pipex.com — MB ChB Bristol 1984; FRCS (Orl) 1995; FRCS 1989. Cons. (ENT Surg.) Poole Gen. Hosp.

SCOTT, Philippa Jane 27 Merdon Avenue, Chandlers Ford, Eastleigh SO53 1EH — MB ChB 1978 Birm.

SCOTT, Ralph Easdale (retired) The Old Rectory, Fornham All Saints, Bury St Edmunds IP28 6JX Tel: 01284 767177 — MB BChir 1956 Camb.; MA Camb. 1956; DObst RCOG 1962. Prev: GP Bury St. Edmunds.

SCOTT, Ralph Platt Fisher Department of Anaesthetics, Salisbury District Hospital, Salisbury SP2 8BJ Tel: 01722 336262 Fax: 01722 416515 — MB ChB 1978 Ed.; BSc Ed. 1975, MD 1992; FFA RCS Eng. 1982. Cons. Anaesth. & IC Salisbury Dist. Hosp.; Dir. (Intens. Care) Salisbury Dist. Hosp.; Exam. Roy. Coll. Anaesth. Socs: BMA; Assn. Anaesth.; Internat. Research Soc. Prev: Regist. Nuffield Dept. Anaesth. Radcliffe Infirm. Oxf.; Clin. & Research Fell. Mass. Gen. Hosp. & Instruc. Harvard Med. Sch., USA; Sen. Regist. Soton. Gen. Hosp.

SCOTT, Raymond Deryck The Bridge Street Surgery, 30-32 Bridge Street, Downham Market PE38 9DH Tel: 01366 388888 Fax: 01366 383716; Carburton House, Ryston End, Downham Market Tel: 01366 388859 — MB BCh 1975 Wales; MRCGP 1980; DRCOG 1978; DCH Eng. 1978.

SCOTT, Rhoda Margaret (retired) 39 Dick Place, Edinburgh EH9 2JA Tel: 0131 667 1637 — MB ChB 1944 Ed.; BSc Ed. 1941. SCMO Lothian HB. Prev: Med. Off. Family Plann. Assn.

SCOTT, Mr Richard Alexander 16 Lord Chancellor Walk, Kingston upon Thames KT2 7HG — MB BChir 1983 Camb.; BSc (Hons.) Lond. 1980; FRCS Eng. 1989. Med. Superinten. St. Francis Hosp. Tanzania, E. Africa. Prev: Regist. (Gen. Surg.) Addenbrooke's Hosp. Camb.

SCOTT, Mr Richard John Holly Tree House, New Road, Swanmore, Southampton SO32 2PE — MB BS 1992 Lond.; FRCS Eng. 1998. (United Medical and Dental Schools (Guy's))

SCOTT, Richard McKerchar Werrington Hall, Hall Lane, Werrington, Peterborough PE4 6RA Tel: 01733 326834; 9 Queen St. Surgery, Whittlesey, Peterborough PE7 1AY Tel: 01733 204611 — MB ChB 1977 Leeds; MRCGP 1982. Hosp. Pract. (Endoscopy) PeterBoro. Dist. Hosp.; Trainer Gen. Pract. Socs: Primary Care Soc. Gastroenterol. Prev: GP Trainee P'boro. VTS.

SCOTT, Ritchie Gibson Alexander Whyteman's Brae Hospital, Whyteman's Brae, Kirkcaldy KY1 2ND Tel: 01592 643355; 92 Balcarres Avenue, Glasgow G12 0QN — MB ChB 1996 Ed. SHO (Geriats.) Whyteman's Brae Hosp. Kirkcaldy. Prev: SHO (Psychiat.) Whyteman's Brae Hosp. Kirkcaldy; SHO (A & E) Vict. Hosp. Kirkcaldy.

SCOTT, Mr Robert (retired) Garrion, 27 Forest View, Kildrum, Cumbernauld, Glasgow G67 2DB Tel: 0123 67 22683 — MB ChB 1958 Glas.; MD Glas. 1985; FRCS Ed. 1966; FRCS Glas. 1965. DL; Hon. Lect. Univ. Strathclyde. Prev: Cons. Urol. Roy. Infirm. Glas.

SCOTT, Mr Robert Adam Department of Emergency Medicine, Royal Brisbane Hospital, Herston Road, Brisbane 4061, Australia; 6 Moorside, Knutsford WA16 6EU — MB ChB 1982 Ed.; FRCS Ed. 1992; MRCP (UK) 1987. Regist. (Emerg. Med.) Hope Hosp. Salford. Socs: Brit. Assn. Accid. & Emerg. Med. & Emerg. Med. Research Soc.

SCOTT, Mr Robert Alastair Howie, Wing Cdr. Centre for Defence Medicine, University Hospital Birmingham NHS Trust, Selly Oak Hospital, Birmingham B29 1JD Tel: 0121 627 8535 Fax: 0121 627 8922 Email: rob.scott@lineone.net; Tel: 0121 2422160 Email: rob.scott@lineone.net — MB BS 1988 Lond.; FRCS Ed. 1993; FRCOphth 1993. (St Thomas's Hospital Medical School) Cons. (Ophth.) Centre for Defence Med. Univ. Hosp. Birm.; Roy. Air Force Cons. Adviser in Ophth. Socs: Brit & Eire Assoc. of Vitreoretinal Surgs.; Midl. Ophth. Soc. Prev: Sen. Regist. (Ophth.) Moorfields Eye Hosp. Lond.; Regist. (Ophth.) P.ss Mary's RAF Hosp. Halton, Wendover; Sen. Regist. (Ophth.) Qu. Med. Centre Nottm.

SCOTT, Robert Baliol Lincoln County Hospital, Greetwell Road, Lincoln LN2 5QY — MB ChB 1978 Bristol; FRCA Eng. 1983. Cons. Anaesth. Lincoln Co. Hosp. Socs: BMA & Assn. Anaesth.

SCOTT, Robert John (retired) Seapark, Sheugham St., Stranraer DG9 0ET Tel: 01776 2053 — MB ChB 1953 Glas.; MRCGP 1965; DObst RCOG 1957. Prev: Asst. Radiol. & GP Anaesth. Garrick Hosp. Stranraer.

SCOTT, Robert Mackie The Medical Centre, 4 Bracklinn Road, Callander FK17 8EJ Tel: 01877 331001 Fax: 01877 331720; 3 Leighton Place, Callender FK17 8BG — MB ChB 1987 Aberd.; MRCGP 1991; DRCOG 1990.

SCOTT, Robert William (retired) 8 Mildmay Drive, Queen Camel, Yeovil BA22 7NZ Tel: 01935 850468 — MB ChB Ed. 1951; MRCGP 1968; DObst RCOG 1955. Prev: Chairm. Som. Local Med. Comm.

SCOTT, Robin Douglas Murray 23 Hemwood Road, Windsor SL4 4YX Tel: 01753 854169 — MB ChB 1964 Aberd.; FRCP Lond. 1984, M 1968; FRCP Ed. 1983, M 1968. (Aberd.) Cons. Phys. Heatherwood & Wexham Pk. Hosps. NHS Trust & E. Berks. Community Health NHS Trust. Socs: Brit. Diabetic Assn. (Med. & Scientif. Sect.). Prev: Dist. Clin. Tutor E. Berks.; Lect. (Med.) Univ. Edin.; Research Fell. Washington Univ. Sch. Med. St. Louis, USA.

SCOTT, Robin Ford West Gate Health Centre, Charleston Drive, Dundee DD2 4AD Tel: 01382 668189 Fax: 01382 665943; The Keepers Cottage, Redmyres Farm, Invergowrie, Dundee DD2 5LH — MB ChB 1966 Aberd.; FRCGP 1982, M 1975. (Aberd.) Regional Adviser (Gen. Pract.) Tayside HB. Socs: BMA. Prev: Terminable Lect. (Path.) Univ. Aberd.; Res. Med. Off. Aberd. Roy. Infirm.; Res. Surg. Off. Roy. Aberd. Hosp. Sick Childr.

SCOTT, Robyn Adele Beaumont Practice, Sneinton Health Centre, Beaumont Street, Sneinton, Nottingham NG2 4PJ Tel: 0115 950 1941 (MBBS (pld)) Gen. Practitioner; Hosp. Practitioner, G-U Med., Nottm. Socs: Assn. of Police Surg.s of Gt. Britain.

SCOTT, Roderick John Leith Walk Surgery, 60 Leith Walk, Edinburgh EH6 5HB Tel: 0131 554 6471 Fax: 0131 555 4964; 34 Inverleith Gardens, Edinburgh EH3 5PR — MB ChB 1981 Ed.; MRCGP 1986.

SCOTT, Roger Concorde, The Common, Holcombe, Bath BA3 5DS Tel: 01761 233970 — MB BCh 1968 Wales; LMCC 1976. Prev: SHO (Clin. Path.) Soton. Gen. Hosp.; Ho. Phys. Neath Gen. Hosp.; Ho. Surg. (Accid. Unit & Dermat.) Cardiff Roy. Infirm.

SCOTT

SCOTT, Roger William Station House Surgery, Kendal LA9 6SA Tel: 01539 722660 Fax: 01539 734845; 12 Cliff Terrace, Kendal LA9 4JR — MB ChB 1989 Manch.; DRCOG 1993; MRCGP 1995. (Manchester) GP Kendal.

SCOTT, Ronald Montalto Medical Centre, 2 Dromore Road, Ballynahinch BT24 8AY Tel: 028 9756 2929 — MB BCh BAO 1959 Belf.; DObst RCOG 1962. (Belf.)

SCOTT, Rosemary Jane Department of Histopathology, University College Hospital, Medical School, London WC1E 6JJ — MB BChir 1980 Camb.; MRCP (UK) 1983; MRCPath 1990. Sen. Lect. (Histopath.). Prev: Cons. Lect. Paediat. Path. Univ. Camb.; Sen. Regist. (Histopath.) Roy. Postgrad. Med. Sch. Lond. & Roy. Sussex Co. Hosp. Brighton.

SCOTT, Mr Roy Niblock Ross Hall Hospital, 221 Crookston Road, Glasgow G52 3NQ Tel: 0141 712266 Fax: 0141 760015; 17 Burnside Road, Burnside, Rutherglen, Glasgow G73 4RL Tel: 0141 569 6487 Email: roy.scott1@ntlworld.com — MB ChB 1981 Glas. MD Glas. 1990; FRCS Glas. 1985. Cons. Gen. & Vasc. Surg. Monklands Hosp. Airdrie; Monkland Hosp. Subdean, Univ. of Glas. Socs: Vasc. Surg. Soc.; Assn. of Surg. of Gt. Britain & Irel. Prev: Sen. Regist. Vict. Infirm. Glas. & Glas. Roy. Infirm.

SCOTT, Mr Rupert Alan Prestwich Royal West Sussex Hospital, Chichester — MB BChir 1966 Camb.; MCh Camb. 1980, MA, MB 1966, BChir 1965; FRCS Eng. 1971. (St. Geo.) Cons. Surg. Roy. W. Sussex Hosp. Chichester (St. Richard's). Prev: Sen. Regist. & Lect. Surg. Unit St. Bart. Hosp. Lond.

SCOTT, Sandra Loreen 22A Alexander Street, London W2 5NT — MB BS 1993 Lond.

SCOTT, Sandy Steel (retired) The Bartons, Perlethorpe, Newark NG22 9EH Tel: 01623 823504 — MB ChB 1950 Sheff.; MRCGP 1968. AMP Bds. DSS. Prev: GP Mansfield.

SCOTT, Sara Elizabeth Barnard Medical Practice, 43 Granville Road, Sidcup DA14 4TA Tel: 020 8302 7721 Fax: 020 8309 6579; 145 Southborough Lane, Bromley BR2 8AP — MB BS 1985 Lond.; MRCGP 1989; DFPP 1994; DRCOG 1988. GP Sidcup. Prev: Trainee GP Sidcup; SHO (A & E) Bromley Hosp.; SHO (O & G) FarnBoro. Hosp.

SCOTT, Sarah Theresa X-Ray Department, Dorset County Hospital, Williams Road, Dorchester DT1 2JY Tel: 01305 254131 Fax: 01305 254136 Email: sally.scott@dorch.wdgh-tr.swest.nhs.uk; Merton Grange, Wheelers Lane, Bearwood, Bournemouth BH11 9QJ Tel: 01202 573218 Fax: 01202 573218 Email: sally@mertong.demon.co.uk — MB BS 1972 Lond.; MRCS Eng. LRCP Lond. 1972; FRCR 1985; DMRD 1981. (Westm.) Cons. Radiol. W. Dorset Gen. Hosps. NHS Trust. Socs: BMA; Brit. Med. Ultrasound Soc.; Brit. Soc. Of Paediat. Radiol. Prev: Sen. Regist. (Radiol.) Soton. & Bristol Gen. Hosps.; Resid. Phys. Hosp. San José San Bernardo del Viento, Colombia.

SCOTT, Sharon Anne 21A The Nook, Anstey, Leicester LE7 7AZ Tel: 0191 384 6171 Fax: 0191 386 3743 — MB BS 1987 Newc.; DCH RCP Lond. 1991; DTM & H Liverp. 1989. Prev: Asst. GP Leics.; Trainee GP Tyne & Wear; GP Partner, Durh.

SCOTT, Sheila Stewart (retired) 20 Glamis Terrace, Dundee DD2 1NA — MB ChB 1954 St. And.; DPH St. And. 1963. Prev: Lect. (Med. Microbiol.) Univ. Dundee.

SCOTT, Shelagh Jean Falcon House Surgery, 17/19 Heaton Road, Newcastle upon Tyne NE6 1SA Tel: 0191 265 3361 Fax: 0191 224 3209; 76 Stuart Court, Kenton Bank Foot, Newcastle upon Tyne NE3 2SG — MB BS 1980 Newc.; MRCP (UK) 1984; MRCGP 1989; DRCOG 1988. GP Newc.; Clin. Asst. Nephrol. Prev: Research Regist. (Med.) Roy. Infirm. Sunderland.; Regist. (Med.) Roy. Infirm. Sunderland; SHO (Med.) Roy. Vict. Infirm. Newc.

SCOTT, Simon James Blackhorse Cottage, Lower End, Wavendon, Milton Keynes MK17 8AW; Flat 30, Princes Gardens, Highfield St, Liverpool L3 6LQ Tel: 0151 255 0429 Email: wiksy@aol.com — MB ChB 1992 Liverp.; FRCS Eng. 1997. (Liverpool) Specialist Regist. (Orthop.) Mersey Rotat.

SCOTT, Stephen 4 Marian Way, South Shields NE34 8AL — MB BS 1992 Newc.

SCOTT, Stephen Basil Cuthbert 19 Danecroft Road, London SE24 9PA — MB BChir 1980 Camb.; MRCP (UK) 1988; MRCPsych 1990.

SCOTT, Stephen James 10 Westminser Close, Charlton Kings, Cheltenham GL53 7QP Tel: 01242 522932 Email:

ydw28@dial.pipex.com — BM 1996 Soton. (Southampton) SHO (Med.). Socs: BMA; MDU. Prev: SHO (Med.); SHO (A & E); Ho. Off. (Med.).

SCOTT, Steven Fraser Owen Nunwell Surgery, 10 Pump Street, Bromyard HR7 4BZ Tel: 01885 483412 Fax: 01885 488739; Jenks Cottage, The Downs, Bromyard HR7 4NU — MB ChB 1982 Bristol; DCH RCP Lond. 1986; DA (UK) 1985.

SCOTT, Stewart William Brewery Farm, Longburgh, Burgh by Sands, Carlisle CA5 6AF — MB ChB 1976 Bristol; MRCPsych 1986. Cons. Child & Adolesc. Psychiat. Fairfield Centre Carlisle.

SCOTT, Mr Stuart Dalgleish Norfolk & Norwich Hospital, Norwich NR1 3SR Tel: 01603 286427 — MB ChB 1972 Ed.; BSc Ed. 1969; MS Soton. 1987; FRCS Eng. 1981. Cons. Gen. Surg. Norf. & Norwich Hosp. Socs: Brit. Assn. Surg. Oncol.; Brit. Soc. Antimicrob. Chemother.; BMA. Prev: Lect. (Surg.) Soton. Univ.; Regist. (Surg.) St. Thos. Hosp. Lond.; Lt. Col. RAMC Field Surg. Team Iraq, Kuwait Gulf War.

SCOTT, Stuart Robertson (retired) 87 Broughton Road, Bessacarr, Doncaster DN4 7HN Tel: 01302 535625 — MB ChB 1955 Edinburgh.; MB ChB Ed. 1955; DObst RCOG 1959; BA Open Univ 1999. Prev: GP Partner.

SCOTT, Stuart Thomas Holburn Medical Group, 7 Albyn Place, Aberdeen AB10 1YE Tel: 01224 400800 Fax: 01224 407777 Email: stuart.scott@holburn.grampian.scot.nhs.uk; 289 King's Gate, Aberdeen AB15 6AJ Tel: 01224 208237 Email: stuarttscott@msn.com — MB ChB 1984 Aberd. Med. Dir. Grampian Doctors On-Call Serv. City Hosp. Aberd.; Assoc. Clin. Director, Directorate of Health Informatics, NHS Grampian, Aberd.

SCOTT, Susan Christine Mary Royal Infirmary of Edinburgh, Lauriston Place, Edinburgh EH6 7LN Tel: 0131 536 1000; 2 Crookston Court, Crookston Road, Musselburgh EH21 7TR Tel: 0131 665 3159 — MB ChB 1986 Aberd.; MRCOG 1992. Assoc. Specialist; RCOG/RCR Advanced Obst. Ultrasound 1995. Socs: Ed. Obst. Soc.; BMA. Prev: Staff Grade (O & G) E. Gen. Hosp. Edin.; Regist. (O & G) E.. Gen. Hosp. Edin.; SHO (O & G) E.. Gen. Hosp. Edin.

SCOTT, Susan Joan Barnt Green Surgery, 82 Hewell Road, Barnt Green, Birmingham B45 8NF Tel: 0121 445 1704 Fax: 0121 447 8253; Wheeley House, Wheeley Road, Alvechurch, Birmingham B48 7DD Tel: 0121 445 1569 — MB BChir 1973 Camb.; BA Camb. 1970, MB BChir 1973; MRCP (UK) 1976. GP Birm.

SCOTT, Susan Marie 26 Yarmouth Drive, Westwood Grange, Cramlington NE23 1TS — MB ChB 1984 Manch. Prev: SHO (Psychiat.) Univ. Hosp. Wales.

SCOTT, Sydney Cadzow Campbell (retired) 29 Piercing Hill, Theydon Bois, Epping CM16 7JW Tel: 01992 813164 Fax: 01992 813164 Email: r.s.scott@eggconnect.net — MB BS 1953 Lond.; MD Lond. 1974; LMSSA Lond. 1952; FRCGP 1991, M 1960; DCH Eng. 1966; DObst RCOG 1958. Prev: Ho. Surg. (ENT) Guy's Hosp.

SCOTT, Tara Jane 26 Bawnmore Road, Belfast BT9 6LA — MB BCh BAO 1991 Belf.

SCOTT, Thomas Bell Greystoke Surgery, Kings Avenue, Morpeth NE61 1JA Tel: 01670 511393 Fax: 01670 503282 — MB BS 1966 Durh.; MRCGP 1973; DObst RCOG 1968. (Newc.)

SCOTT, Mr Thomas Douglas 3 Lemon Villas, Truro TR1 2NX Tel: 01872 273689; 31 Knoll Park, Truro TR1 1FF Tel: 01872 223240 — MB ChB 1975 Glas.; BSc (Hons.) Glas. 1973; FRCS Ed. (Orth.) 1988; FRCS Glas. 1980. Cons. Orthop. Roy. Cornw. City Hosp. Truro. Socs: Fell. BOA; Brit. Soc. Surg. Hand; Roy. Soc. Med. Prev: Sen. Regist. (Orthop.) P.ss Eliz. Orthop. Hosp. Exeter.

SCOTT, Thomas McMillan Grange Farmhouse, Grange Road, Dunfermline KY11 3DG — MB ChB Glas. 1970; MRCP (U.K.) 1974; DCH RCPS Glas. 1972.

SCOTT, Professor Thomas Smith 15 Denewood Court, Victoria Road, Wilmslow SK9 5HP Tel: 01625 527001 — MB ChB 1928 Glas.; MSc Manch. 1968; MD (Commend.) Glas. 1959; FRCP Glas. 1966, M 1963; FFOM RCP Lond. 1979; FFOM RCPI 1982; DIH Soc. Apoth. Lond. 1977. (Univ. Glas.) Emerit. Prof. Occupat. Health Univ. Manch.; Hon. Cons. Phys. Manch. Roy. Infirm. Socs: Perm. Internat. Commiss. Occupat. Health; (Ex-Pres.) Manch. Dist. Medico-Legal Soc.; (Ex-Pres.) Soc. Occupat. Med. Prev: Ho. Phys. Roy. Infirm. Bradford; Ho. Surg. Miller Gen. Hosp.; Resid. Med. Off. St. Geo.-In-the-E. Hosp. Lond.

SCOTT

SCOTT, Timothy Edward 25 Cherry Orchard, Highworth, Swindon SN6 7AU — MB BS 1998 Lond.; MB BS Lond 1998.

SCOTT, Timothy Nigel Bradshaw 8 Nursery Gardens, Broadmeadows, South Normanton, Derby — MB ChB 1987 Sheff.

SCOTT, Timothy Peter 27 Merdon Avenue, Chandlers Ford, Eastleigh SO53 1EH — MB ChB 1978 Birm.

SCOTT, Valerie Anne Clackmannan and Kincardine Medical Practice, Health Centre, Main Street, Clackmannan FK10 4JA Tel: 01259 723725 Fax: 01259 724791; Kincardine Health Centre, 19 Kilbagie St, Kincardine, Alloa FK10 4QX — MB ChB 1985 Ed.; MRCGP 1990; DRCOG 1989.

SCOTT, Wendy Elizabeth Directorate of Anaesthesia and Intensive Care, Milton Keynes General Hospital, Milton Keynes MK6 5LD Tel: 01908 243159 Fax: 01908 243159; 9 Sandbrier Close, Walnut Tree, Milton Keynes MK7 7DU Tel: 01908 676213 Fax: 01908 676213 — MB ChB 1974 Aberd.; FFA RCS Eng. 1980; DA Eng. 1977; DRCOG 1976. (Aberdeen) Cons. Anaesth. Milton Keynes Gen. Hosp. Socs: Assn. Anaesth.; Roy. Soc. Med.; Obst. Anaesth. Soc. Prev: Sen. Regist. (Anaesth.) Lister Hosp. Stevenage; Regist. Rotat. (Anaesth.) Lewisham Hosp. & Guy's Hosp. Lond.; Regist. (Anaesth.) St. Helier Hosp. Carshalton.

SCOTT, William c/o Smith, 117 Arkleston Road, Paisley PA1 3TY Tel: 020 8889 2977; 3437 - 111A Street, Edmonton Alb. T6J 3L1, Canada — LRCP LRCS 1952 Ed.; LRCP LRCS Ed. LRFPS Glas. 1952. (Glas.) Prev: SHO Orthop. Unit, Kilmarnock Infirm.; Sen. Ho. Surg. Ingham Infirm. S. Shields; Sen. Ho. Surg. Thoracic Unit, E.. Gen. Hosp. Edin.

SCOTT, Mr William Alexander 152 Harley Street, London W1N 1HH Tel: 020 7935 3834; 2 The Cedars, 3 Westcombe Pk Road, Blackheath, London SE3 7RE Fax: 020 8293 0288 Email: wscott@dircon.co.uk — MB BS 1972 Lond.; FRCS Eng. 1976. (King's Coll. Hosp.) Cons. Orthop. Surg.Qu. Eliz. Hosp. Lond.; Hon. Cons. Blackheath Hosp. Lond. Socs: BMA; W Kent M-C Soc.; Brit. Orthop. Assn. Prev: Sen. Regist. (Orthop.) St. Mary's Hosp., Char. Cross Hosp. Lond. & Roy. Nat. Orthop. Hosp. Stanmore.

SCOTT, William Chisholm (retired) Muston Manor, Winterbourne Muston, Blandford Forum DT11 9BU — MB BS Lond. 1950; FFR 1966; DMRD Eng. 1963. Prev: Cons. Radiol. E. Dorset Health Dist.

SCOTT, William Edward, MBE (retired) 13 Hall Close, Kettering NN15 7LQ — MB ChB Glas. 1940; DIH Lond. 1952. Sen. Med. Off. Brit. Steel Corpn. Prev: Surg. Regist. Glas. Roy. Infirm.

SCOTT, William Gary 10 Swinburne Drive, Crewe CW1 5JE Tel: 01270 587601 — MB BCh BAO 1982 Belf.; MB BCh Belf. 1982; DCH Dub. 1985.

SCOTT, William Jeffrey Cullen, VRD Lochaber, Gartocham, Alexandria G83 8SA Tel: 01389 830211 — MB ChB 1946 Glas.; FFOM RCP Lond. 1995, MFOM 1980; FRCGP 1982; M 1964; Spec. Accredit. Occupat. Med. JCHMT 1981; CIH Dund 1970; DIH Soc. Apoth. Lond. 1971. (Univ. Glas.) Socs: Fell. Roy. Soc. Med.; Fell. BMA. Prev: Surg. Lt.-Cdr. RNR; Ho. Phys. & Cas. Off. W. Infirm. Glas.

SCOTT, William Semion Maryhill Health Centre, 41 Shawpark St., Glasgow G20 9DR Tel: 0141 946 7151; 29 Saint Kilda Drive, Glasgow G14 9LN Tel: 0141 959 4840 — MB ChB 1958 Glas.

SCOTT, William Sinclair Ayr Road Surgery, 69 Ayr Road, Douglas, Lanark ML11 0PX Tel: 01555 851226; Mansefield House, Weaver's Yards, Douglas, Lanark ML11 0QB Tel: 01555 851226 — MB ChB 1968 Glas. (Glas.) Socs: BMA. Prev: SHO (Gyn.) Law Hosp. Carluke; Ho. Off. (Obst.) Glas. Roy. Matern. Hosp. & Qu. Mother's Hosp. Glas.

SCOTT ANDREWS, Margaret Louise Pool Farm House, Mills Lane, Wroxton St Mary, Banbury OX15 6PY Tel: 01295 730486 — MB BS 1970 Lond.; MRCS Eng. LRCP Lond. 1970; MRCGP 1976; DObst RCOG 1972. (Roy. Free) Clin. Med. Off. - family Plann. Prev: Ho. Phys. (Paediat.) Hampstead Gen. Hosp.; Ho. Surg. (Gyn.) Roy. Free Hosp. Lond.; GP.

SCOTT-BARRETT, Sarah Department of Radiology, Norfolk & Norwich Healthcare Trust, Brunswick Road, Norwich NR1 3SR Tel: 01603 286286; South End House, Loddon, Norwich NR14 6DX Tel: 01508 520308 Fax: 01508 520308 — MB BS 1984 Lond.; MRCP (UK) 1990; FRCR 1994. (Guy's Hosp. Med. Sch.) Cons. Radiol. Norf. & Norwich Hosp. Prev: Sen. Regist. (Radiol.) Char. Cross Hosp. Lond.; Regist. (Radiol.) Char. Cross Hosp. Lond.; SHO (Med.) St. Geo. Hosp. & Nat. Heart Hosp. Lond.

SCOTT-BROWN, Andrew William, Surg. Lt. RN Lake Road Health Centre, Nutfield Place, Portsmouth PO1 4JT Tel: 023 92 821201 — MB ChB 1983 Aberd.; MRCGP; DRCOG. (Aberdeen) Hse. Med. Examr. Divers; MSA Med. Examr. Seafarers.

SCOTT-BROWN, Graham The Health Centre, Coxwell Road, Faringdon SN7 7EZ Tel: 01367 242407 — MB BChir 1955 Camb.; FRCP Lond. 1973, M 1956.

SCOTT-BROWN, Mary Muriel Gosport War Memorial Hospital, Bury Road, Gosport PO12 3PW Tel: 01705 524611; Ythan Lodge, 2 Haddon Close, Fareham PO14 1PH Tel: 01392 823675 — MB ChB 1983 Aberd.; MB ChB (Commend.) Aberd. 1983. Staff Grade Psychiat. Gosport War Memor. Hosp. Prev: Regist. (Psychiat.) St. Jas. Hosp. Portsmouth.

SCOTT BROWN, Nigel Myrie (retired) Stuart Lodge, Long St., Sherborne DT9 3DE — MB 1961 Camb.; BChir 1960; DA Eng. 1965; DObst RCOG 1962.

SCOTT-BROWN, Sarah Ruth 20 Market Place, Faringdon SN7 7HU — MB BS 1994 Lond.

SCOTT-COOK, Helen Ruth 78 Addison Road, Kings Heath, Birmingham B14 7EW Tel: 0121 444 6965 — MB ChB 1992 Bristol. SHO (Orthop.) Selly Oak Hosp. Prev: Cas. Off. Birm. Heartlands Hosp.; Lect. (Anat.) Birm. Univ.

SCOTT-COOMBES, Mr David Michael Central Middlesex Hospital, Park Royal, Acton Lane, London NW10; 34 Green Lane, Hanwell, London W7 2PB Tel: 020 8567 9862 — MB BS 1985 Lond.; MS Lond. 1994, MB BS 1985; FRCS Ed. 1990; FRCS Eng. 1990. Sen. Regist. Rotat. (Gen. Surg.) Hammersmith & St. Mary's Hosps. Prev: Regist. Rotat. (Surg.) Hammersmith Hosp.; Hon. Research Regist. (Surg.) Hammersmith Hosp. Lond.; SHO (Surg.) Countess of Chester Hosp.

SCOTT-COOMBES, Emma Lucinda Ealing Hospital, Uxbridge Road, Southall UB1 3EU — MB BS 1989 Lond.; BA Oxf. 1984. Trainee GP/SHO Ealing Hosp. VTS.

SCOTT-FLEMING, Mark Simon 13 Battersea Rise, London SW11 1HG — MB BS 1994 Lond.

SCOTT-JUPP, Claire Elizabeth The Beeches, Nimlet, Cold Ashton, Chippenham SN14 8JX — MB BS 1987 Lond.

SCOTT-JUPP, Robert Henry Salisbury District Hospital, Salisbury SP2 8BJ Tel: 01722 336262 Email: dr.r.scott-jupp@shc-tr.swest.nhs.uk; 7 Church Lane, Lower Bemerton, Salisbury SP2 9NR Email: scottjupp@aol.com — MB BS 1980 Lond.; MRCP (UK) 1986; FRCPCH 1997; DCH RCP Lond. 1983. Cons. Paediat. Salisbury. Dist. Hosp. Prev: Lect. & Hon. Sen. Regist. (Child Health) Univ. Leicester; Regist. (Paediat.) Liverp. Hosps.; SHO (Paediat.) Bristol Hosps.

SCOTT-JUPP, Ruth Martha (retired) 17 Avon Run Road, Friars Cliff, Christchurch BH23 4DX Tel: 01425 275762 — MB BCh BAO 1949 Dub.

SCOTT-JUPP, Wendy Margaret Orchard Surgery, Christchurch Medical Centre, Purewell Cross Road, Christchurch BH23 5ET Tel: 01202 481902 Fax: 01202 486887; 20 Tyrrells Court, Bransgore, Christchurch BH23 8BU Tel: 01425 673625 — BM 1978 Soton.; DRCOG 1982. (Soton.)

SCOTT-KNIGHT, Victoria Catherine Elizabeth Bryn-y-Gwalia Hall, Llangedwyn, Oswestry SY10 9JW — MB BS 1977 Lond.; MRCS Eng. LRCP Lond. 1977; FFA RCSI 1987. (Roy. Free) Cons. Anaesth. Wrexham Maelor Hosp. Prev: Sen. Regist. Midl. Anaesth. Train. Scheme; Regist. (Anaesth.) Edgware Gen. Hosp. Middlx.; Ho. Phys. Roy. Free Hosp. Lond.

SCOTT-KNOX-GORE, Charles Leggett Kings Road Surgery, 67 Kings Road, Harrogate HG1 5HJ Tel: 01423 875875 Fax: 01423 875885 — MB BS 1972 Lond.; DObst RCOG 1975. (Middlx.) Princip. GP N. Yorks. Family Pract. Comm. Prev: Trainee GP Harrogate VTS; Ho. Surg. Mt. Vernon Hosp. N.wood; Ho. Phys. Harrogate Gen. Hosp.

SCOTT-MACKIE, Pauline Lindsay Department of Radiology, Guy's Hospital, St Thomas St., London SE1 9RT Tel: 020 7955 5000 — MB BS 1989 Lond.; MRCP (UK) 1993; FRCR 1996. Specialist Regist. (Radiol.) Guy's & St. Thos. NHS Trust Lond.

SCOTT-MONCRIEFF, Christina Mary Bristol Homoeopathic Hospital, Cotham, Bristol BS6 6JU Tel: 0117 973 1231 Fax: 0117 923 8759; 36 Gipsy Lane, Beckford Green, Warminster BA12 9LR Tel: 01985 846784 Fax: 01985 846784 — MB ChB 1975 Birm.; MFHom 1987. Clin. Fell. Bristol Homoeop. Hosp. Socs: Fell. Roy.

Soc. Med.; BMA. Prev: SHO (Paediat.) Simpson Memor. Matern. Pavil. & Roy. Hosp. Sick Childr. Edin.

SCOTT-MONCRIEFF, Nigel Francis John, Surg. Cdr. RN 9 Devonshire Place, London W1 Tel: 020 7935 8425; 22 Sloane Avenue, London SW3 3JE Tel: 020 7823 9014 — MB BS 1982 Lond.; BSc (Hons.) Lond. 1982; MRCGP 1990. (The Lond. Hosp.) Indep. GP Lond. Socs: Fell. Roy. Soc. Med.; Med. Soc. Lond. Prev: Princip. Med. Off. Her Majesty's Yacht Britannia; Princip. Med. Off. HMS St. Vincent (Lond.); Sen. Med. Off. Roy. Marines Sch. Music Deal.

SCOTT-MUMBY, Keith 3 Ings Hall, Ings, Kendal LA8 9PZ Tel: 07000 781 744, 01539 821625 Email: doc@scott-mumby.com — MB ChB 1971 Manch. Cons. Allergist Food & Environm. Allergy Clin.; Anti Aging Sci. Socs: Roy. Soc. Med.

SCOTT-PERRY, Stephen John 13 Borelli Mews, The Borough, Farnham GU9 7YZ — MB ChB 1985 Dund.

SCOTT-RUSSELL, Ann Margaret 49 Worrin Road, Shenfield, Brentwood CM15 8DH — MB BS 1995 Lond.

SCOTT-SAMUEL, Alex Jeremy Richard Deartment of Public Health, University of Liverpool, Whelan Building, Liverpool L69 3GB Tel: 0151 794 5569 Fax: 0151 794 5588 Email: alexss@liv.ac.uk; 218 Allerton Road, Liverpool L18 6JN — MB ChB 1971 Liverp.; MCommH 1976; FFPHM 1989; FFCM 1988. Sen. Lect. (Pub. Health) Univ. Liverp.; Hon. Cons. Pub. Health Liverp. HA. Prev: Cons. (Pub. Health) Liverp. HA; Sen. Regist. (Community Med.) Mersey RHA; Dept.al Med. Off. Liverp. City Counc..

SCOTT-SMITH, Wesley The Charter Medical Centre, 88 Davigdor Road, Hove BN3 1RF Tel: 01273 738070/770555 Fax: 01273 220 0883; 17 Woodland Avenue, Hove BN3 6BH Email: wesdoc@mcmail.com — MB BS 1979 Lond.; MRCGP 1984; DRCOG 1984. (Guy's) Research Fell. Trafford Centre, Univ. Sussex.

SCOTT WARREN, David Noel Martin, CStJ (retired) Mont du Ouaisng, St Brelade, Jersey JE3 8AW Tel: 01534 742939 Fax: 07797 715417 — MRCS Eng. LRCP Lond. 1948. Prev: Ho. Surg. (ENT & Gen. Surg.) & Ho. Phys. Skin Dept. Lond. Hosp.

SCOTT-WHITE, Lewis Arthur 24 Green Park, Bath BA1 Tel: 01225 24291; Norton Barn, Hinton Charter House, Bath BA2 7SP Tel: 0122 122 2454 — MB BChir 1943 Camb.; MA, MB BChir Camb. 1943. (Camb. & Bristol) Auth. Med. Examr. Civil Aviat. Auth.; Squadron Ldr. Roy. Auxil. Air Force Med. Br.; Apptd. Fact. Doctor; Admiralty Surg. & Agent. Socs: BMA & Bath Clin. Soc. Prev: Div. Police Surg. Avon & Som. Constab.; Hon. Asst. Anaesth. Roy. Nat. Hosp. Rheum. Dis. Bath; Area Police Surg. Som. & Bath Constab.

SCOTT-WILSON, James Hew (retired) 58 Heathfield Road, Keston BR2 6BE Tel: 01689 852473 — BM BCh 1956 Oxf.; MA, BM BCh Oxf. 1956.

SCOTTER, Betty (retired) 38 Gunton Drive, Lowestoft NR32 4QB Tel: 01502 574033 — MB BS 1947 Lond.; MRCS Eng. LRCP Lond. 1946.

SCOTTON, Johanna Elizabeth 5 Filbert St. E., Leicester LE2 7JG — MB ChB 1997 Leic.

SCOTTON, Susan Johnson The Chantry, Dean St., Brewood, Wolverhampton Tel: 01902 850402; Maes y Haf, Porth Tocyn, Abersoch, Pwllheli Tel: 3377 — MB BS 1975 Lond.; MRCS Eng. LRCP Lond. 1975. Store Doctor Marks & Spencer plc.

SCOUGAL, Isabel Jean Falkirk & District Royal Infirmary, Majors Loan, Falkirk FK1 5QE Tel: 01324 624000 Email: isabel.scougal@fuah.scot.nhs.uk; 3 Gardrum Place, Brightons, Falkirk FK2 0EX Tel: 01324 717394 — MB ChB 1985 Ed.; BSc (Hons.) Ed. 1983; MRCP (UK) 1989. (Ed. Univ.) Cons. Phys. in Geriat. Med. Falkirk & Dist. Roy. Infirm. Socs: Brit. Diabetic Assn. (Mem. Scientif. Sect.); Brit. Geriat. Soc. Prev: Sen. Regist. Gen. & Geriat. Med. Manch.; Clin. Lect. (Geriat. Med.) Univ. Manch.; Regist. (Endocrinol., Gen. Med. & Diabetic) Edin. Roy. Infirm.

SCOULAR, Anne Buchanan Department of Genitourinary Medicine, The Sandyford Initiative, Sandyford, Sauchiehall St, Glasgow G3 7NB Tel: 0141 211 8625 Fax: 0141 211 8609 — MB ChB 1978 Glas.; FRCP Glas. 1997; MRCP (UK) 1987; MRCGP 1982; DCH RCPS Glas. 1981; DRCOG 1980; FRCP Glas 1997. (Glas.) Cons. Genitourin. Med. Gt.er Glas. Primary Care Trust. Prev: Sen. Regist. (Genitourin. Med.) Middlx. Hosp. Lond.

SCOULLER, Frances Elizabeth West Pottergate Health Centre, 137 West Pottergate, Norwich NR2 4BX Tel: 01603 628705 Fax: 01603 766789; The Wood Barn, Stoke Lane, Dunston, Norwich NR14 8QD Tel: 01508 471307 — MB BS 1982 Lond.; MRCP (UK) 1985; BSc (Hons) Lond. 1979. (Univ. Coll. Lond.) Princip. GP.

SCOURFIELD, Alan Edward Coalbrook Road Health Centre, 18 Coalbrook Road, Pontyberem, Llanelli SA15 5HU Tel: 01269 870207 Fax: 01269 871314; Bryngwendraeth, Llanddarog, Carmarthen SA32 8PB Tel: 01267 275712 — MB BS 1979 Lond.; MRCS Eng. LRCP Lond. 1979. Clical Asst. Orthopaedic, P. Philip Hosp., Llananelli, Carmarthen; Clin. Asst. Urol., P. Philip Hosp., Lla.lli, Carmarthen.

SCOURFIELD, Alun James Scourfield and Partners, The Surgery, Oakfield Street, Ystrad Mynach, Hengoed CF82 7WX Tel: 01443 813248 Fax: 01443 862283; 3 Pen y Cae, Ystrad Mynach, Hengoed CF82 7FA — MB BS 1972 Lond.; MRCS Eng. LRCP Lond. 1971. Hon. Lect. (Gen. Pract.) Univ. Wales.; CDP Coordinator Caerphilly, Univ. of Wales Coll. of Med. Prev: CME Tutor Rhymach Valley Postgrad. Centre.

SCOURFIELD, Derek Bennett (retired) Maes-y-Llwyn, Llanddarog, Carmarthen SA32 8BJ Tel: 01267 275718 Email: dbscourfield@morsyllwyn75.freeserve.co.uk — MB BCh Wales 1950; BSc Wales 1947. Prev: SHO (Cas.) Cardiff Roy. Infirm.

SCOURFIELD, Dilys (retired) Maes-y-Llwyn, Llanddarog, Carmarthen SA32 8BJ Tel: 01267 275718 — MB BCh Wales 1950; BSc Wales 1947. Prev: SHO (O & G) E. Glam. Hosp. Pontypridd.

SCOURFIELD, Ewan John Coalbrook Road Health Centre, 18 Coalbrook Road, Pontyberem, Llanelli SA15 5HU Tel: 01269 870207 Fax: 01269 871314; Pennant, 29 Heol-y-Felin, Pontyberem, Llanelli SA15 5EH — MB BS 1981 Lond.; MRCS Eng. LRCP Lond. 1981.

SCOURFIELD, Jane Department of Psychological Medicine, University of Wales College of Medicine, Heath Park, Cardiff CF14 4XN — BM BCh 1988 Oxf.; PhD Wales 2000; MSc (Psychiat. Studies) Wales 1994; MA Camb. 1988; MRCPsych 1994. Sen. Clin. Research Fell. (Child and adolescant Psychiat.) Cardiff. Prev: Regist. (Psychiat.) Cardiff; M.R.C Train.Fell. Yale + Cardiff.; SpR child Psychiat.. Cardiff.

SCOVELL, Elizabeth Elaine Roseleat, 22 Middle St., Port Isaac PL29 3RH — MB ChB 1973 Dundee; DMRD Eng. 1978.

SCOWEN, Beverley Manfordway Health Centre, 40 Foremark Close, Hainault, Romford Tel: 020 8500 3088 — MB BS 1992 Lond.

SCOWEN, Mark Kevin Health Centre, Handsworth Avenue, Highams Park, London E4 9PD Tel: 020 8527 0913 Fax: 020 8527 6597 — MB ChB 1980 Leeds.

SCRAGG, Gillian Mary Cedars Medical Centre, 12 Sandbach Road South, Alsager ST7 2AD Tel: 01270 882179 Fax: 01270 216330 — MB ChB 1981 Liverp.; MRCGP 1985. p/t GP. Prev: Partner in Gen. Pract.; Trainee GP Wirral VTS.

SCRAGG, Sheena Elizabeth Fife Palliative Care Service, Victoria Hospice, Victoria Hospital Hayfield Road, Kirkcaldy KY2 5AH Tel: 01592 648072 Fax: 01592 648048; 7 Ettrick Loan, Edinburgh EH10 5EP — MB ChB 1982 Ed.; FRCP Ed. 1995; MRCP (UK) 1986; DRCOG 1984. (Edinburgh) Cons. Palliat. Med. Fife Primary Care Trust Kirkcaldy. Prev: Med. Off. MacMillan Serv. Fife.

SCRASE, Angela Mary Prospect Farm, Llanidloes SY18 Tel: 01978 122789 — MRCS Eng. LRCP Lond. 1965; DPM Eng. 1972. (St. Thos.)

SCRASE, Christopher David Paramor Cottage, 42 New Street, Chiapenham, Ely CB7 5QF — MB BChir 1988 Camb.; MA Camb. 1990; BA (Hons.) Camb. 1986; MRCP (UK) 1992; FRCR 1996. Macmillian Cons., Clin. Oncol., Ipswich Hosp. NHS Trust, Suff. Prev: Sen. Regist. (Clin. Oncol.) Nottm. City Hosp. NHS Trust; Regist. (Clin. Oncol.) Addenbrooke's Hosp. NHS Trust.

SCRASE, Edward Tuppin Prospect Farm, Llanidloes Tel: 01686 412789 — MB BChir 1966 Camb.; MB Camb. 1966, BChir 1965; DTM & H Liverp. 1989; DObst RCOG 1972; FFA RCS Eng. 1970. (St. Mary's)

SCREATON, Gavin Robert Field End, Bayswater Road, Headington, Oxford OX3 9RZ — BM BCh 1987 Oxf.

SCREATON, Nicholas John Field End, Bayswater Road, Oxford OX3 9RZ; 75 Norwich Street, Cambridge CB2 1ND Tel: 01223 354827 — BM BCh 1990 Oxf.; BA Camb. 1987; MRCP (UK) 1993; FRCR 1997.

SCRIMGEOUR

SCRIMGEOUR, John Beocher (retired) Cuilaluinn, Aberfeldy PH15 2JW Tel: 01887 820302 — MB ChB 1962 Ed.; FRCP Ed. 1993; FRCS Ed. 1987; FRCOG 1982, M 1968; DObst 1964. Prev: Med. Dir. W.. Gen. Hosps. Trust Edin.

SCRIMGEOUR, Karen Mathilda Agnes 47 Highcliffe Drive, Sheffield S11 7LT Tel: 0114 230 5757; 19 Shipley Road, Leicester LE5 5BX — MB ChB 1992 Sheff.

SCRIMINGER, Mark William 13 Elmtree Road, Teddington TW11 8SJ — MB BS 1992 Lond.

SCRIMSHIRE, Jacqueline Anne 23 Best Avenue, Kenilworth CV8 2TN — MB ChB 1985 Birm.; DA (UK) 1988.

SCRINE, Marion Department Community Paediatrics, Barham House, Wembley Centre for Health and Care, 116 Chaplin Road, Wembley HA0 4UZ Tel: 020 8795 6340 Fax: 020 8795 6350 — BM BCh 1981 Oxf.; BA Oxf. 1981; MRCPI (Paediat.) 1986; DCH RCP Lond. 1985. Cons. Paediat. & Child Health Pk.side Health NHS Trust Lond.; Cons. Paediat. Centr. Middlx. Hosp. NHS Trust. Prev: Sen. Regist. (Paediat.) W. Lond. Healthcare NHS Trust; Clin. Med. Off. Richmond, Twickenham & Roehampton HA; Lect. (Paediat. & Nephrol.) Roy. Free Hosp. Lond.

SCRIVEN, Anthony James 24 Haldane Road, London SW6 7EU — MB BS 1977 Lond.

SCRIVEN, Barrie Edward Leek Health Centre, Fountain Street, Leek ST13 6JB Tel: 01538 381022 Fax: 01538 398638; Bank House, Sandy Lane, Longsdon, Stoke-on-Trent ST9 9QQ Tel: 01538 399620 — MB ChB 1971 Birm.; MRCGP 1976; DCH Eng. 1974; DObst RCOG 1973. Socs: BMA.

SCRIVEN, Jeanne Mary (retired) Anchorstone, Searle Road, Farnham GU9 8LU Tel: 01252 727378 — MB ChB Manch. 1941. Prev: Orthop. Ho. Surg. & Orthop. Regist. Manch. Roy. Infirm.

SCRIVEN, John Edward 30 Wolverton Gardens, London W6 7DY Tel: 020 8748 7612 — MB BS 1952 Lond.; MA (Med. Ethics & Law) Lond. 1992; MRCGP 1970. (Guy's) Prev: Hosp. Pract. (Geriat.) W. Lond. Hosp.

SCRIVEN, John Kevin Tel: 01535 292185 Fax: 01535 295425 Email: john.scriven@group.airedale.northy.nhs.uk; Littlecroft, 24 Elm Tree Square, Embsay, Skipton BD23 6RA Tel: 01756 797243 Email: jscriven@doctors.net — MB BS 1988 Lond.; FFA RCSI 1995; DA (UK) 1992. (Char. Cross & Westm.) Cons. (Anaesth. & IC Med.) Airedale Gen. Hosp. Socs: Intens. Care Soc.; Yorks. Soc. Anaesth.; Obst. Anaesth. Assn. Prev: SHO (Anaesth.) Bristol Roy. Infirm. & N. Devon Dist. Hosp. Barnstaple; Regist. (Anaesth.) Qu. Eliz. Hosp. Birm.

SCRIVEN, Mr John Mark 41 Sword Close, Glenfield, Leicester LE3 8SY — MB ChB 1989 Leic.; BSc (Hons.) Leic. 1986, MB ChB 1989; FRCS Eng. 1993.

SCRIVEN, Mr Mark William Department of Surgery, Wrexham Maelor Hospital, Croesnewydd Road, Wrexham LL13 7TD Tel: 01978 725430 Fax: 01978 725418 Email: mark.scriven@new-tr.wales.nhs.uk — MB BS 1984 Lond.; BSc (Hons.) Biochem. Lond. 1981, MS 1993, MB BS 1984; FRCS Eng. 1988. (Guy's) Cons. Surg. Wrexham Maelor Hosp. Socs: Vasc. Surg. Soc. Prev: Advanced Surg. Trainee John Hunter Hosp. Newc., NSW, Austral.

SCRIVEN, Nicholas Andrew Calderdale Royal Hospital, Salterhebble, Halifax HY3 0PW Tel: 01422 357171 — MB ChB 1991 Leic.; MRCP (UK) 1994. (Leicester) Cons. Phys., Claderdale Roy. Hosp., Halifax. Socs: Brit. Thorac. Soc.; Yorks. Thoracic Soc. Prev: Sp. Reg. (Reg.) Nottm. City Hosp.

SCRIVEN, Patricia Mary Department of Anaesthesia, Russells Hall Hospital, Dudley Tel: 01384 456111; 87 Fitzroy Avenue, Harborne, Birmingham B17 8RH Tel: 0121 427 2940 — MB ChB Manch. 1970; FFA RCS Eng. 1978. Cons. Anaesth. Russells Hall Hosp. Dudley; Hon. Sen. Lect. Birm. Univ.; Assoc. Postgrad. Dean (W. Midl.s).

SCRIVEN, Sharon Denise 41 Sword Close, Glenfield, Leicester LE3 8SY — MB ChB 1989 Leic.; BSc Leic. 1986, MB ChB 1989; FRCS Glas. 1994.

SCRIVEN, William Ashley Pendyffryn Medical Group, Ffordd Pendyffryn, Prestatyn LL19 9DH Tel: 01745 886444 Fax: 01745 889831 — MB BS 1980 Lond.; BA Oxf. 1977; DRCOG 1985. (St. Mary's)

SCRIVENER, Loraine Elizabeth 44 Franklyn Drive, Alvaston, Derby DE24 0FR — MB BChir 1985 Camb.

SCRIVENER, Sarah Louise Dept. Thoracic Medicine, Royal Bournemouth Hospital, Bournemouth BH7 7DW Email: sarah.scrivener@nottingham.ac.uk; Branksome House, 17 Nelson Road, Westbourne, Bournemouth BH4 9JA — BChir 1994 Camb.; BA (Hons) Cantab 1992; MB Camb. 1995; MA 1996; MRCP (UK) 1998. (Cambridge) Specialist Regist. in Gen. and Respiratory Med., Roy. Bournemouth Hosp. Socs: BMA. Prev: Ho. Off. (Thoracic Surg. & Gen. Surg.) Norf. & Norwich Healthcare NHS Trust; Ho. Phys. W. Suff. Hosp. Bury St. Edmunds; Res. Med. Off. Roy. N.shore & Manly Hosps. Sydney NSW, Australia.

SCRIVENS, James William 44 London Road, Marlborough SN8 2AA — MB ChB 1991 Birm.; ChB Birm. 1991.

SCRIVENS, Stuart Benjamin Flat 11, Tiffany Court, Albert Road, Leicester LE2 2AA — MB ChB 1997 Leic.

SCRIVINGS, Belinda Ann 78 Dale Lane, Heckmondwike WF16 9NU — BM 1985 Soton.; MRCGP 1991; DRCOG 1987. Prev: SHO (Med. for Elderly) S.end HA; Ho. Off. (Med.) & Ho. Surg. St. Mary's Hosp. Portsmouth.

SCROGGIE, Brian McGregor Reith St Pauls Medical Centre, St. Pauls Square, Carlisle CA1 1DG Tel: 01228 524354 Fax: 01228 616660 — MB ChB 1974 Ed.; BSc Ed. 1971; MRCGP 1978. Prev: Trainee GP Highland VTS; Ho. Surg. Roy. N.. Infirm. Inverness; Ho. Phys. Raigmore Hosp. Inverness.

SCRUTTON, Mark James Leslie 6 Pratt Walk, London SE11 6AR Tel: 020 7735 5228 — MB BS 1989 Lond.; FRCA 1993. (St. Thos. Hosp. Lond.)

SCUDAMORE, John Anthony Bassett Road Surgery, 29 Bassett Road, Leighton Buzzard LU7 1AR Tel: 01525 373111 Fax: 01525 853767 — MB 1972 Camb.; MA Camb. 1970, MB 1972, BChir 1971; MRCGP 1994. Clin. Governance Lead & Caldicott Guardian Chiltern Vale PCG; GP Trainer. Prev: SHO (Accid. & Orthop.) Battle Hosp. Reading; Ho. Off. & Resid. Accouch. Lond. Hosp.

SCUDAMORE, Joseph Henry Invermuick, Ballater AB35 5SQ — MB ChB 1951 Bristol; FRCOG 1977, M 1963.

SCUDAMORE, Tom Osbert (retired) 58A Rutland Grove, Sandiacre, Nottingham NG10 5AQ Tel: 0115 939 7293 — MB BChir 1942 Camb.; MA Camb. 1943; MRCS Eng. LRCP Lond. 1942; DObst RCOG 1948. Prev: Cas. Off. & Ho. Surg. Connaught Hosp. Lond.

SCUDDER, Claire Caroline 54 Great King Street, Edinburgh EH3 6QY — BM 1990 Soton.; DRCOG 1995; DFFP 1995.

SCULL, David Alan Kings Park Hospital, Gloucester Road, Boscombe, Bournemouth — MB ChB 1989 Bristol; MRCPsych. Cons. Psychiat. Dorset Healthcare Trust Poole.

SCULL, Judith Jane Land Orchard, Galhampton, Yeovil BA22 7AH Email: docscull@aol.com — MB ChB 1991 Sheff.; DRCOG Oct 1998; DFFP 1999. Prev: Fell.sh. Ophth. Path. McGill Univ. Montreal, Canada.

SCULL, Timothy James 133 Sundridge Park, Yate, Bristol BS37 4DH — MB ChB 1984 Dundee.

SCULLIN, Paula 90 Moneysharvan Road, Maghera BT46 5PT — MB BCh BAO 1997 Belf.

SCULLION, Damian Francis 13 Ballyscullion Lane, Bellaghy, Magherafelt BT45 8NQ — MB BCh BAO 1990 NUI. SHO (Anaesth.) Leicester Roy. Infirm.

SCULLION, Damian Michael The Surgery, 3 Glasgow Road, Paisley PA1 3QS Tel: 0141 889 2604 Fax: 0141 887 9039 — MB ChB 1974 Glasgow; MB ChB Glas. 1974. (Glasgow) GP Paisley, Renfrewsh.

SCULLION, David Anthony Department of Radiology, Harrogate District Hospital, Lancaster Park Road, Harrogate HG1 7SX — MB BS 1985 Lond.; MRCP Lond. 1988.

SCULLION, Helen Clare 26 Glencairn Drive, Glasgow G41 4PW — MB ChB 1980 Glas. Cons. Cytopath. Vale of Leven Dist. Gen. Hosp. Alexandria.

SCULLION, Mr James Edwin Balwherrie, 103 Strathern Road, West Ferry, Dundee DD5 1JU Fax: 01382 730101 Email: edwin.scullion@virgin.net — MB BCh BAO 1969 Belf.; FRCS Ed. 1974. (Queens Univ. Belf.) Cons. (Orthop.) Dundee.

SCULLION, Jane Christine 436 Mosspark Boulevard, Glasgow G52 Tel: 0141 882 5494; 2 Tudor Road, Jordanhill, Glasgow G14 9NJ Tel: 0141 959 2439 — MB ChB 1987 Glas.; MRCGP 1991; DCH RCPS Glas. 1990; DRCOG 1990.

SEAGER-THOMAS

SCULLION, John Francis Easterhouse Health Centre, 9 Auchinlea Road, Glasgow G34 9HQ Tel: 0141 531 8180 Fax: 0141 531 8186 — MB ChB 1985 Glas.; MRCGP 1989; DRCOG 1988.

SCULLION, Lynda Thérèse Balwherrie, 103 Strathern Road, West Ferry, Dundee DD5 1JU — MB ChB 1972 Glas.; DObst RCOG 1974.

SCULLION, Michael Surgery, 75 Bank Street, Alexandria G83 0NB Tel: 01389 752626 Fax: 01389 752169 — MB ChB 1979 Glas.; MRCP (UK) 1983.

SCULLION, Regina 50 Kinross Avenue, Glasgow G52 3JB — MB ChB 1982 Glas.

SCULLION, Ursula Mary Elizabeth 13 Ballyscullion Lane, Bellaghy, Magherafelt BT45 8NQ — MB BCh BAO 1993 Belf.

SCULLION, William 3 Glenwood Avenue, Airdrie ML6 8RY — MB ChB 1981 Glas.

SCULLY, Anne Gabrielle 38 Omagh Road, Drumquin, Omagh BT78 4QY — MB BS 1992 Lond.

SCULLY, Marie Ann 102 Chatsworth Road, Cheam, Sutton SM3 8PN — MB BS 1993 Lond.; BSc (Hons.) 1990. (St Georges London)

SCULLY, Patrick Gerard Main Street Surgery, 6 Main Street, Drumquin, Omagh BT78 Tel: 028 8283 223 — MB BCh BAO 1987 Dub.

SCULLY, Paul Joseph 38 Omagh Road, Drumquin, Omagh BT78 4QY — MB BCh BAO 1987 Dub.; MRCPsych.

SCULLY, Ralph 12 Hinton Avenue, Cambridge CB1 7AS — MB BS 1986 Lond.; BA (Hons.) Camb. 1983; MRCP (UK) 1989. MRC Train. Fell. (Path.) Immunol. Div. Camb. Univ.

SCULLY, Sharon Ann 89 Cardigan Terrace, Newcastle upon Tyne NE6 5NX — MB BS 1989 Newc.

SCULLY, Thomas Leyland (retired) Half Acre, Nursery Lane, North Wooton, King's Lynn PE30 3QB — MB BChir 1952 Camb.; MA, MB BChir Camb. 1952.

SCUPLAK, Stephen Michael Basement Flat, 16A Westwick Gardens, London W14 0BU — MB BS 1987 Lond.

SCURLOCK, Henry Peter (retired) Hillrise, 34 Hanger Hill, Weybridge KT13 9YD — MRCS Eng. LRCP Lond. 1941; DCH Eng. 1948. Prev: Cas. Off. Evelina Hosp. Sick Childr.

SCURLOCK, Hilary Jane Mental Health Unit, Chase Farm Hospital, The Ridgeway, Enfield EN2 8 Tel: 020 8366 6600 — MB BS Lond. 1986; MRCPsych 1991. (Middlx.) Cons. (Gen. Adult Psychiat.) Chase Farm Hosp. Enfield Middx. Prev: Sen. Regist. Char. Cross Hosp. Lond.

SCURR, Andrew James 16 Grange Avenue, Totteridge Common, London N20 8AD Tel: 020 8445 7188 Fax: 020 7792 3236 Email: andrew@scurr.demon.co.uk — MB BS 1985 Lond.; FRCA 1991. (Westm. Med. Sch.) Cons. Anaesth. & Cons. in Intens. Care, Newham Gen. Hosp. Lond. Socs: Fell. Roy. Soc. Med.; Assn. Anaesth.; BMA. Prev: Sen. Regist. (Anaesth.) St Marys Hosp. Lond.; Sen. Regist. & Regist. (Anaesth.) Hammersmith Hosp. Lond.; SHO (Anaesth.) N.wick Pk. Hosp.

SCURR, Cyril Frederick, CBE, LVO 16 Grange Avenue, Totteridge Common, London N20 8AD Tel: 020 8445 7188 — MB BS 1942 Lond.; FRCS Eng. 1974; MRCS Eng. LRCP Lond. 1941; FRCA 1992; FFA RCS Eng. 1953; DA Eng. 1947; Hon. FFA RCSI 1977. (Westm.) Emerit. Anaesth. Hosp. St. John & St. Eliz. Lond. Hon Cons. Anaesth. W.m. Hosp. Socs: Hon. Mem. Assn. Anaesth.; Roy. Soc. Med. (Ex-Pres. & Hon. Mem. Anaesth. Sect.); D'Honneur Société Francaise D'Anaesth. et Reanimation. Prev: Dean Fac. Anaesth. RCS Eng. & Pres. Assn. Anaesth. GB & Irel.; Cons. Anaesth. W.m. Hosp. & Hon. Cons. Anaesth. Hosp. St. John & Eliz. Lond.; Maj. RAMC.

***SCURR, Joanne** 87 Latimer Drive, Bramcote Moor, Beeston, Nottingham NG9 3HT — MB ChB 1995 Birm.

SCURR, Mr John Henry The Lister Hospital, Chelsea Bridge Road, London SW1W 8RH Tel: 020 7730 9563 Fax: 020 7259 9938 Email: jscurr@uk-consultants.co.uk; 5 Balniel Gate, London SW1V 3SD Tel: 020 7834 5578 Fax: 020 7834 6315 — MB BS 1972 Lond.; BSc Lond. 1969; FRCS Eng. 1977. (Middlx.) Sen. Lect. & Hon. Cons. Surg. Middlx. Hosp. & Univ. Coll. Hosp. Lond.; Cons. Surg. Margt. Pyke Family Plann. Centre Lond.; Hon. Cons. Surg. St. Luke's Hosp. for Clergy. Socs: Fell. Roy. Soc. Med.; Surg. Research Soc.; Vasc. Surg. Soc. Prev: Sen. Regist. (Surg.) W.m. Hosp. Lond.; Lect. (Surg. & Physiol.) & Ho. Surg. Middlx. Hosp. Lond.

SCURR, Judith Ann Pathology Department, Princess Margaret Hospital, Okus Road, Swindon SN1 4JU; 57 Newland Mill, Witney OX28 3SZ — MB BS 1971 Lond.; MSc Lond. 1977; FRCPath 1989, M 1977. Cons. Cytol. P.ss Margt. Hosp. Swindon. Prev: Lect. (Chem. Path.) W.m. Med. Sch. Lond.; Sen. Regist. (Chem. Path.) St. Geo. Hosp. Lond.; Regist. (Chem. Path.) W.m. Hosp. Lond.

SCURR, Martin John 121 Ladbroke Grove, London W11 1PN Tel: 020 7792 8060 Fax: 020 7792 3236 Email: martinscurr@nottinghillpractice.com — MB BS 1973 Lond.; MRCP (UK) 1976; MRCS Eng. LRCP Lond. 1973; MRCGP 1977. Phys. W.m. Cathedral. Prev: Clin. Asst. (Otolaryngol.) Brompton Hosp.; Cons. Phys. Terminal Care Hosp. St. John & St. Eliz. Lond.; Ho. Phys. & Ho. Surg. W.m. Hosp. Lond.

SEABORNE, Lisa 12 Manor Park, Newbridge, Newport NP11 4RS — MB ChB 1991 Birm.; MRCGP 1995.

SEABOURNE, Alice Ellen Department of Old Age Psychiatry, Withington Hospital, Nell Lane, West Didsbury, Manchester M20 2LR Tel: 0161 291 4389 — MB ChB 1991 Ed.; BSc (Med. Sci.) Ed. 1989. Sen. Regist. (Old Age Psychiat.) Withington Hosp. Socs: Roy. Coll. Psychiat. Prev: Regist. Rotat. (Psychiat.) NW Region; SHO Rotat. (Psychiat.) S. & Centr. Manch.; Ho. Off. Roy. Infirm. Edin.

SEABRA OLIVEIRA, Armenia Maria Queen Elizabeth Hospital for Children, Hackney Road, London E2 8PS — Lic Med. Oporto 1992.

SEABROOK, Jonathan Derek Wrightington Street Surgery, 1 Wrightington Street, Wigan WN1 2AZ Tel: 01942 231965 Fax: 01942 826427 — MB ChB 1990 Manch.; MRCGP 1996. Prev: Trainee GP Wigan & Leigh NHS Trust; SHO (A & E) Roy. Preston Hosp.

SEABROOK, Ruth Jayne 17 Fairfield Avenue, Cheadle Hulme, Cheadle SK8 6AF — MB ChB 1986 Liverp.

SEABURNE-MAY, Matthew Patrick Old Barn Cottage, Soames Lane, Ropley, Alresford SO24 0ER Email: seaburne@hotmail.com — MB BS 1998 Lond.; MB BS Lond 1998.

SEACOME, Mary Percival Silvester Barnwood Court W., Gloucester GL4 3AD Tel: 01452 66265 — MA, BM BCh Oxf. 1947; FFCM 1980; DPH Bristol 1972. (Oxf.) Prev: SCM (Health Care Plann. & Informat.) Glos. AHA.

SEAGER, Professor Charles Philip (retired) 9 Blacka Moor Road, Dore, Sheffield S17 3GH Tel: 0114 236 1925 Fax: 0114 236 2982 Email: pseager@btinternet.com — MB BCh 1949 Wales; BSc Wales 1949, MD 1960; FRCPsych 1972; DPM Eng. 1954. Cons. to SOVRN Project Sheff. Prev: Prof. Psychiat. Univ. Sheff.

SEAGER, Francis Geoffrey Maundrell (retired) The Old Garage, The Street, Roxwell, Chelmsford CM1 4PB Tel: 01245 248056 — MB BS 1953 Lond.; MRCS Eng. LRCP Lond. 1949; MFOM RCP Lond. 1979; DIH Eng. 1957; DPH Lond. 1956; DObst RCOG 1954; Specialist Accredit (Occupat. Med.) RCP Lond. Prev: Med. Adviser Rank Xerox Ltd.

SEAGER, John Department of Paediatrics, Arrowe Park Hospital, Arrowe Park Road, Upton, Birkenhead CH49 5PE; 2 Waterford Road, Oxton, Prenton CH43 6UT — MD 1976 Liverp.; MB ChB 1966; FRCP Lond. 1987; MRCP (U.K.) 1971; FRCPCH 1997. Cons. (Paediat.) Arrowe Pk. Hosp. Wirral. Clin. Director Wirral Serv.s for Child Health. Prev: Cons. Paediat. Childr. Hosp. Birkenhead & Clatterbridge Hosp. Wirral; Hon. Regist. Hosp. Sick Childr. Gt. Ormond St. Lond.; Research Fell. Inst. Child Health Lond.

SEAGER, Marian Catriona Northgate Hospital, Morpeth NE61 3AS — MB ChB 1990 Ed.; MRCPSych 1996. Specialist Regist. (Psychiat.).

SEAGER, Matthew James Coedmor, Caswell Av, Caswell, Swansea SA3 4RU — MB BCh 1997 Wales.

SEAGER, Sylvia Jeanne c/o Department of Anaesthetics, Glan Clwyd Hospital, Bodelwyddan, Rhyl LL18 5UJ Tel: 01745 583910 Fax: 01745 583143 — MB ChB 1972 Ed.; FFA RCS Eng. 1977. (Edinburgh) Cons. Anaesth. Glan Clwyd Hosp. Bodelwyddan.; Asst. Med. Director; Conwy & Denbighsh. NHS Trust. Socs: BMA; Treas. Soc. Anaesth. Wales; Linkman Assn. Anaesth. Prev: Cons. Anaesth. Grimsby Hosp.; Sen. Regist. (Anaesth.) Yorks. Region; Regist. St. Jas. Univ. Hosp. Leeds.

SEAGER-THOMAS, Robin Griffith (retired) Hafod Onen, 23 Gill Way, E. Beach, Sesley, Chichester PO20 0EX — MRCS Eng. LRCP Lond. 1948; DObst RCOG 1953. Prev: Surg. Lt.-Cdr. RNR.

SEAGGER

SEAGGER, Robin Mark 22 Lansdown Park, Bath BA1 5TG — MB BS 1998 Lond.; MB BS Lond 1998.

SEAGGER, Roger Alan 22 Lansdown Park, Bath BA1 5TG — MB BS 1965 Lond.; MRCS Eng. LRCP Lond. 1965; FFA RCS Eng. 1970. (Westm.) Cons. Anaesth. Bath Health Dist. Socs: Assn. Anaesths.; Brit. Assn. Immed. Care Schemes; Obst. Anaesth. Assn. Prev: SHO (Clin. Measurem.) & SHO (Anaesth.) W.m. Hosp. Lond.; Regist. (Anaesth.) Soton. Gen. Hosp.

SEAKINS, Elizabeth Claire 61 Winnie Road, Birmingham B29 6JU Tel: 0121 472 8922 Fax: 0121 472 8922 — MB ChB Birm. 1986; DRCOG 1994. Med. Off. Forteau, Labrador, Canada. Prev: Trainee GP Kidderminster; SHO Rotat. (Surg.) Dudley Rd. Hosp. Birm.; SHO Qu. Med. Centre Nottm.

SEAL, Anita Nicola 12 Shamrock Way, London N14 5RY — MB BS 1991 Lond.

SEAL, Arnab Kumar 8 Lawns Drive, New Farnley, Leeds LS12 5RJ — MB BS 1988 Calcutta; MRCP (UK) 1993.

SEAL, David Venner 23 Charlton Place, Islington, London N1 8AQ — MRCS Eng. LRCP Lond. 1970; MD Lond. 1984, MB BS 1970; MRCPath 1977; FCOphth 1988; Dip Bact . Lond. 1975; MIBiol 1983. Hon. Sen. Lect. Dept. Path. Inst. Ophth. Lond. Prev: Cons. Microbiol. N.wick Pk. Hosp. & Clin. Research Centre Harrow & Soton. Gen. Hosp.

SEAL, Kenneth Stanley, OBE (retired) 44 Torr Lane, Hartley, Plymouth PL3 5NZ Tel: 01752 772816 — LRCP LRCS Ed. LRFPS Glas. 1939; MFPHM 1974; DPH Lond. 1957; DTM & H Eng. 1947. Prev: Rural Health Adviser MoH, E. Nigeria.

SEAL, Leighton John 12 Shamrock Way, London N14 5RY — MB BS 1992 Lond.; MB BS (Hons.) Lond. 1992; BSc Lond. 1990; MRCP (UK) 1995. (St. Bart. Hosp. Lond.)

SEAL, Louise Ann The Vinery, Wellington, Hereford HR4 8AR — MB ChB 1965 Bristol; DObst RCOG 1968; DA Eng. 1968.

SEAL, Martin Treharne The Old Vicarage, Cilcennin, Lampeter SA48 8RF — MB BCh 1978 Wales; BDS 1972; FDS RCS Eng. 1980; Spec. Accredit. Oral Maxillofacial Surg. RCS Eng. 1992. Cons. Oral & Maxillofacial Surg. HM Armed Forces; Lt.-Col. RADC. Socs: Fell. Dent. Surg. RCS Eng.; BMA; Brit. Assn. Oral & Maxillofacial Surg. Prev: Sen. Specialist (Oral & Maxillofacial Surg.) HM Armed Forces; Hon. Sen. Regist. Char. Cross Hosp. Lond.; GP Dyfed.

SEAL, Patrick James Longfleet Road Surgery, 117 Longfleet Road, Poole BH15 2HX Tel: 01202 676111 Fax: 01202 676111 — MB BS 1985 Lond.; BA Camb. 1982, MA 1986; MRCGP 1990. Gen. Practitioner. Socs: BMA & Med. Protec. Soc.

SEAL, Paul Leonard 45 Wellington Square, Hastings TN34 1PN Tel: 01424 722366 — MB ChB 1992 Sheff.; DRCOG 1997 Lond.; DCH RCP Lond. 1996. (Sheff.)

SEAL, Mr Philip Victor Wye Valley Nuffield Hospital, Venns Lane, Hereford HR1 1DF Tel: 01432 355131 — MB ChB 1964 Manch.; FRCS Eng. 1969. (Manch.) Cons. Orthop. & Traum. Surg. Hereford Gp. Hosps. Socs: Fell. BOA. Prev: Hon. Lect. (Orthop. Surg.) Univ. Hong Kong; Sen. Regist. (Orthop. & Traum. Surg.) Robt. Jones & Agnes Hunt Orthop. Hosp. & Birm. Accid. Hosp.

***SEAL, Philippa Anne** The Vinery, Wellington, Hereford HR4 8AR — MB BS 1996 Lond.

SEAL, Robert Harry (Surgery), Highfield Road, North Thoresby, Grimsby DN36 5RT Tel: 01472 840202; Roberts Farm, Third Lane, Ashby-Cum-Fenby, Grimsby DN37 0QU Tel: 01472 827934 — MB ChB 1973 Sheff. Prev: SHO (Obst.) Jessop Hosp. Wom. Sheff.; SHO (Accid. & Orthop.) Roy. Infirm. Sheff.

SEAL, Robert Leonard Beacon Medical Practice, 40 Algitha Road, Skegness PE25 2AJ Tel: 01754 897000 Fax: 01754 761024; Fairfield House, Chapel Lane, Huttoft, Alford LN13 9RG Tel: 01507 490065 Email: rlseal@aol.com — MB BChir 1980 Camb.; MA Camb. 1981; MRCGP 1987; DRCOG 1987. (Camb. & St. Bart.) GP Princip.; Treas. Lincs. LMC.

SEAL, Roger Martin Ewart (retired) 3 Church Road, Penarth CF64 1AE — MB BCh 1945 Wales; FRCP Lond. 1971, M 1949; FRCPath 1963. Cons. Path. Llandough Hosp. Prev: Ho. Phys. Roy. Infirm. Cardiff.

SEAL, Sarah Helen 5 The Close, Salisbury SP1 2EF — MB BS 1974 Lond. Clin. Med. Off. Community Health Salisbury HA.

SEALE, Anna Nancy Box Cottage, Shirenewton, Chepstow NP16 6LT — BChir 1994 Camb.; MRCP (Paed.). Prev: SHO (Paediat.) Roy. Cornw. Hosp. Truro; SHO (Paediat.) Oxf. Paediat. Rotat.

SEALE, James Richard Cluxton Department of Haematology, Ysbyty Gwynedd, Bangor LL57 2PW Tel: 01248 384370 Fax: 01248 355130 Email: jim.seale@nww-tr.wales.nhs.uk — MB BS 1986 Lond.; MA Camb. 1987; MRCP (UK) 1990; MRCPath 1997; MD Camb 1996. (Cambridge University & Guy's Hospital London) Cons. Haematologist Ysbyty Gwynedd Bangor. Prev: Sen. Regist. (Haemat.) Addenbrookes Hosp. Camb.; Regist. (Haemat.) Hammersmith Hosp. Lond.; SHO (Med.) Brighton Hosps.

SEALE, John Richard (retired) Southcombe House, Widecombe-in-the-Moor, Newton Abbot TQ13 7TU Tel: 01364 621365 — MB BChir 1951 Camb.; MA Camb. 1951, BA (1st cl. Nat. Sc. Trip. Pt. I) 1948, MD 1957, MB BChir 1951; MRCP Lond. 1953; MD 1957. Prev: Cons. Phys. Depts. Genitourin. Med. & Venereol. St. Thos. Hosp. & Middlx. Hosp. Lond.

SEALEY, Annie Robina 63 Rosemary Crescent W., Goldthorn Park, Wolverhampton WV4 5AN Tel: 01902 656015 — MB ChB 1959 Birm.; DFFP 1994; MRCPCH 1997. SCMO (Contracep. & Sexual Health & Child Health) Wolverhampton Healthcare. Prev: Resid. Med. Off. Childr. Hosp. Birm.

SEALEY, Margaret Mary (retired) Queen Elizabeth Hospital, Edgbaston, Birmingham B15 2TH — MB ChB 1968 Birm.; MA (OU) Nov. 2000; MRCS Eng. LRCP Lond. 1969; FFA RCSI 1976; DA Eng. 1971. Prev: Cons. Anaesth. Qu. Eliz. Hosp. Birm.

SEALEY, Sara Louise 5 Eden Road, West ENT, Southampton SO18 3QW Tel: 02380 466083 — BM 1995 Soton.; DRCOG 1997. GP Regist. Portsmouth VTS.

SEAMAN, Alexander George (retired) 8 Oaklands, Lowestoft Road, Reydon, Southwold IP18 6RY Tel: 01502 724380 — MB BS Lond. 1946; MRCS Eng. LRCP Lond. 1941; MRCGP 1953. Prev: Clin. Asst. (Genitourin. Med.) Norf. & Norwich Hosp.

SEAMAN, Andrew Charles 6 Greenway Close, Llandough, Penarth CF64 2LZ — MB ChB 1976 Bristol.

SEAMAN, Fiona Margaret 7 Kent St, Dunfermline KY12 0DJ — MB ChB 1994 Aberd.

SEAMAN, Fiona Margaret 43 Weaver's Way, Tillicoultry FK13 6BD Tel: 01259 752761 — MB ChB 1995 Glas. SHO (Psychiat.) Clackmannan Co. Hosp. Socs: BMA. Prev: SHO (O & G) Stirling Roy. Infirm. Livilands, NHS Trust; SHO (Paediat.) Stirling Ro.; SHO (A & E) Stirling Roy.

SEAMAN, Joan Lillias (retired) Glenuig, Dunshalt, Cupar KY14 7EU Tel: 01334 28647 — MB ChB 1947 Glas. Prev: Med. Off. E. Scotl. Blood Transfus. Serv.

SEAMAN, John Arthur Save The Children Fund (UK), 17 Grove Lane, London SE5 8RD Tel: 020 7703 5400; 2 Coppings Brook Cottages, Leigh, Tonbridge TN11 8PP Tel: 01732 463736 — MB BS 1967 Lond.; MRCS Eng. LRCP Lond. 1967; DCH Eng. 1971. (Lond. Hosp.) Head Policy Developm. Unit Save the Childr. Fund (UK) Lond.; Hon. Sen. Lect. (Human Nutrit.) Lond. Sch. Hyg. & Trop. Med. Lond.

SEAMAN, Muriel Joan (retired) 21 Bailey Mews, Auckland Road, Cambridge CB5 8DR Tel: 01223 323535 — MB BS 1953 Lond.; FRCPath 1976, M 1964. Prev: Cons. Haemat. Addenbrooke's Hosp. Camb.

SEAMAN, Robert Arthur John Larksfield Surgery, Arlesey Road, Stotfold, Hitchin SG5 4HB Tel: 01462 732200 Fax: 01462 730487 Email: rajseaman@aol.com — MB BS 1971 Lond.; MRCS Eng. LRCP Lond. 1971; Dip Obst Auckland 1977. (St. Mary's) Socs: BMA. Prev: Resid. (Psychiat.) St. Brendan's Hosp. Bermuda; Regist. (Paediat.) Palmerston N. Hosp., NZ.

SEAMAN, Terence Frederick Central Surgery, Corporation Street, Rugby CV21 3SP Tel: 01788 574335 Fax: 01788 547693; 22 Beech Drive, Rugby CV22 7LT Tel: 01788 811778 — MB BS 1967 Lond.; MRCS Eng. LRCP Lond. 1966. (St. Thos.) Med. Off. (Occupat. Health) Rugby NHS Trust.

SEAMARK, Clare Jennifer The Surgery, Marlpits Lane, Honiton EX14 2NY Tel: 01404 41141 Fax: 01404 46621; 12 Oak Tree Close, Upottery, Honiton EX14 9QG Tel: 01404 861601 Fax: 01404 861304 — MB ChB 1980 Bristol; MPhil (Med. Sci.) Exeter 1996; MRCGP 1985; MFFP 1993; DRCOG 1982. p/t GP Honiton; Research Fell. Inst. Gen. Pract. Exeter Univ. Prev: Clin. Asst. (Med.) Roy. Devon & Exeter Hosp.; Clin. Med. Off. City & Hackney HA; Trainee GP Lond. Hosp. VTS.

SEAMARK, David Anthony The Surgery, Marlpits Road, Honiton EX14 2DD Tel: 01404 41141 Fax: 01404 46621; 12 Oak Tree Close, Upottery, Honiton EX14 9QG Tel: 01404 861601 Fax: 01404 861304 — MB BS 1985 Lond.; PhD Lond. 1980; MA Oxf. 1977; MRCGP 1989; DCH RCP Lond. 1988. (Lond. Hosp. Med. Sch.) Lect. (Gen. Pract.) Univ. Exeter; Lead Research GP Honiton Research Pract. (NHS funded). Socs: Fell. Roy. Soc. Med.; BMA (Treas. Exeter Div.); (Comm.) Community Hosp. Assn. Prev: Trainee GP Exeter VTS; Ho. Off. (Surg.) Roy. Devon & Exeter Hosp. Wonford Exeter; Ho. Off. (Med.) OldCh. Hosp. Romford.

SEAR, Mr Anthony James (retired) 1 Elms Drive, Colwall Green, Malvern WR13 6JE — MB ChB 1964 Birm.; BDS Birm. 1954; FDS RCS Eng. 1959, L 1953. Cons. Oral & Maxillofacial Surg. S. & Mid. Worcs. Hosp. Gps. Prev: Lect. (Oral Surg.) Univ. Birm.

SEAR, John William Nuffield Department of Anaesthetics, Level 1, John Radcliffe Hospital, Headington, Oxford OX3 9DU Tel: 01865 221590 Fax: 01865 221593; 6 Whites Forge, Appleton, Abingdon OX13 5LG Tel: 01865 863144 Fax: 01865 221593 Email: john.sear@nda.ox.ac.uk — MB BS 1972 Lond.; PhD Bristol 1981; MA Oxf. 1982, BSc (Hons.) Lond. 1969; FANZCA 1995; FFA RCS Eng. 1977; DObst RCOG 1974. (Lond. Hosp.) Clin. Reader (Anaesth.) &previously dir Studies Univ. Oxf.; Hon. Cons. Anaesth. Oxon. HA; Non.-Exec. Dir. Nuffield Orthop. Centre NHS Trust Oxf. Socs: BMA; Assn. Anaesth.of GB & Irel.; Soc. of Intraveous Anaesth.; Pres. 1999-2002. Prev: Lect. & MRC Train. Fell. Univ. Dept. Anaesth. & Biochem. Bristol; dir.Clin.Studies Univ.Oxf.; Examnr part III FRC anaesth.

SEARA ESCUDERO, Mr Javier Orthopaedic Department, North Middlesex Hospital, Sterling Way, London N18 1QX — LMS 1989 Malaga; FRCS Glas. 1993.

SEARBY, Glenda Jean Bridge House, Bolton Road, Bradshaw, Bolton BL2 3EU Tel: 01204 300214 — MB BS 1966 Lond.; MRCS Eng. LRCP Lond. 1966. (Roy. Free) SCMO (Family Plann.) Well Wom. & Young Peoples Serv. Salford Community Health Centre NHS Trust Salford.

SEARGEANT, Janet Muriel St Ann's Hospital, St. Ann's Road, Tottenham, London N15 3TH Tel: 020 8442 6000; 61 Fordington Road, Highgate, London N6 4TH — MB BS Lond. 1967; MRCS Eng. LRCP Lond. 1967; MRCPsych 1983. Cons. Psychiat. Haringey Healthcare Trust St. Ann's Hosp., St Ann's Rd., Lond.

SEARGEANT, Mr Paul William, TD, OStJ (retired) ToL Lyhwood, Tolponds Road, Porthleven, Helston TR13 9LF — MB ChB 1947 Bristol; FRCS Eng. 1953; MRCS Eng. LRCP Lond. 1947. Hon. Cons. Surg. Qu. Eliz. Hosp. King's Lynn; Lt.-Col. RAMC TA. Prev: Sen. Regist. (Surg.) W.m. Hosp.

SEARL, Catherine Patricia 57 Bonaly Crescent, Edinburgh EH13 0EP Tel: 0131 441 5791 — MB ChB 1991 Manch.; MRCP (UK) 1994. Specialist Regist. Anaes. & IC. Prev: SHO (Cardiac Surg. & Cardiol.) Cardiff; SHO Rotat. (Med.) Tayside.

SEARLE, Mr Adam Eric The Royal Marsden Hospital, Fulham Road, London SW3 6JJ Tel: 020 7808 2782 Fax: 020 7808 2235; 30 Mayford Road, London SW12 8SD Tel: 020 8675 4689 Fax: 020 8675 4689 — MB BS 1985 Lond.; BDS 1979; FRCS (Plast) 1994; FRCS Eng. 1989. (Guy's Hosp.) Cons. Plastic & Reconstruc. Surg. Roy. Marsden Hosp. Socs: Brit. Assn. of Plastic Surgs.; Brit. Assn. of Aesthetic Plastic Surg.; Sec. Plastic Surg. Sect. of Roy. Soc. of Med. Prev: Sen. Regist. (Plastic Reconstruc.) Mt. Vernon Hosp. & Roy. Marsden Hosp.; Cons. Surg. Char. Cross Hosp.

SEARLE, Adrian Eric Derbyshire Royal Infirmary, London Road, Derby DE1 2QY Tel: 01332 347141 Email: a_searle@sdah.tr.nhs.uk; The Old Red House, 84 Main St, Etwall, Derby DE65 6LP Email: adrian@searle84.fsnet.co.uk — MB ChB 1979 Birm.; FFA RCS Eng. 1986. Cons. Anaesth. & Pain Managem. Derbysh. Roy. Infirm. Socs: Derby Med. Soc.; The Pain Soc.; Assn. of Anaethetists.

SEARLE, Charles Walter Alban (retired) 17 Lower Common S., London SW15 1BP Tel: 020 8788 0592 — MB BChir Camb. 1935; MA Camb. 1947, BA 1932, MD 1947; MRCS Eng. LRCP Lond. 1935; FRCOphth 1988; DHMSA 1981; DOMS Eng. 1948. Hon. Cons. Ophth. St. Mary's Hosp. Lond. Prev: Col. IMS.

SEARLE, Clare Hilary Rickmansworth Road Surgery, 35 Rickmansworth Road, Watford WD1 7HL Tel: 01923 223232 Fax: 01923 243397 — MB ChB 1989 Leic.; MRCGP 1994.

SEARLE, Rev. Dr John Francis, OBE 8 Thornton HillBelle Isle Lodge, Belle Isle Drive, Exeter EX2 4RY Tel: 01392 432153 Fax: 01392 216132 Email: johnlizex@aol.com — MB BS 1966 Lond.; MRCS Eng. LRCP Lond. 1966; FRCA 1970. (Guy's) Cons. Anaesth. Exeter Health Care. Socs: Vice-Pres. Assn. Anaesths.; Hewitt Lect. RCA 2001. Prev: Pres Hospiscare Exeter; Sen. Regist. (Anaesth.) Guy's Hosp. Lond.; Lect. (Anaesth.) Ghana Med. Sch. Accra Ghana.

SEARLE, Geoffrey Frank 20 Dingle Road, Bournemouth BH5 2DR — MB BS 1982 Lond.; BSc (Pharmacol.) Lond. 1979, MB BS 1982. Research Worker Maudsley Hosp. Lond.

SEARLE, Gwenllian Corner House, 18 Potacre St., Torrington EX38 8BL Tel: 01805 623263 — MRCS Eng. LRCP Lond. 1948; DO Eng. 1952. (Bristol & Cardiff) Ophth. Med. Pract. Supplm.ary Ophth. Serv. Socs: BMA; SW Ophth. Soc. Prev: Assoc. Specialist (Ophth.) N. Devon Dist. Hosp. Barnstaple; Sen. Regist. Swansea Gen. & Eye Hosp.; SHO Roy. Eye Hosp. Lond.

SEARLE, Jane Margaret 15 Walgrove Road, Chesterfield S40 2DW — MB ChB 1988 Sheff.

SEARLE, John Stanley Teague (retired) Corner House, 18 Potacre St., Torrington EX38 8BL Tel: 01805 623263 — MB BS Lond. 1949; MRCS Eng. LRCP Lond. 1945; MRCGP 1965; DObst RCOG 1951. Prev: Sqdn. Ldr. RAFVR.

SEARLE, Julie Michelle 232 Park Lane, Frampton Cotterell, Bristol BS36 2EN — BM 1995 Soton.

SEARLE, Martin Anthony Northlands Surgery, North Street, Calne SN11 0HH Tel: 01249 812091 Fax: 01249 815343; 37 Bremhill, Calne SN11 9LD — MA Camb. 1983, BA 1979, MB 1983, BChir 1982; MRCGP 1988; DRCOG 1988; DCH RCP Lond. 1985. (Camb. & King's Coll.) Prev: Trainee GP Epsom VTS; Ho. Surg. Brighton Gen. Hosp.; Ho. Phys. Dulwich Hosp.

SEARLE, Paul Jonathan Eaton Socon Health Centre, 274 North Road, Eaton Socon, St. Neots, Huntingdon PE19 8BB Tel: 01480 477111 Fax: 01480 403524 — MB ChB 1975 Aberd.; Cert. Family Plann. JCC 1979. (Aberd.) Prev: Trainee GP Aberd. VTS; Ho. Phys. Woodend Gen. Hosp. Aberd.; Ho. Surg. (Thoracic) Roy. Infirm. Aberd.

SEARLE, Stella Margaret Church Farm, 17 Church St., North Cave, Brough HU15 2LJ — MB ChB 1969 Manch. Clin. Med. Off. Hull Health Auth.

SEARLE, Stephen John Occupational Health Service, Birmingham City Council, 137 Newhall St, Birmingham B3 1SF Tel: 0121 303 3300 Fax: 0121 303 4484 Email: stephen_searle@birmingham.gov.uk; 20 Marsett, Wilnecote, Tamworth B77 4QU Tel: 01827 896771 — MB BS 1971 Lond.; MBA Aston Univ. 1996; MSc (Distinc. Occupat. Med.) Lond. 1985; MRCS Eng. LRCP Lond. 1971; FFOM RCP Lond. 1993, MFOM 1985, AFOM 1983; MRCGP 1976; Dip GU Med. Soc. Apoth. Lond. 1988; DIH (Distinc.) Lond. 1983. (Roy. Free) Director Occupat.al Health; Hon. Sen. Lect. (Clin.) Inst. Occupat. Health Univ. Birm. Socs: Fell. Roy. Soc. Med.; Soc. Occupat. Med. Prev: Regional Med. Off. Post Office Occupat. Health Serv. Lond. Postal Region; Ho. Surg. Roy. Free Hosp. Lond.; Ho. Phys. Noble's I. of Man Hosp. Douglas.

SEARLE, Thomas Andrew 7 Clwyd Way, Little Sutton, South Wirral CH66 4GH — MB ChB 1990 Aberd. SHO (O & G) Countess of Chester Hosp.

SEARLE, Wendy Helen Health Centre, Mill Lane TA5 2HB Tel: 01278 652335; Glebe House, Bridgwater TA5 2DF Tel: 01278 662523 — MB ChB 1985 Sheff.; MRCGP 1991; T(GP) 1991; DObst. Auckland 1989. GP Som. Retainer Scheme. Prev: Trainee GP Som.; Regist. (Paediat.) & SHO (O & G) Waikato Hosp., NZ.

SEARLE-BARNES, Peter Gerald The Strand Practice, 2 The Strand, Goring-by-Sea, Worthing BN12 6DN Tel: 01903 243351 Fax: 01903 705804; 19 Third Avenue, Worthing BN14 9NZ Tel: 01903 237689 — MB BS 1980 Lond.; MA Camb. 1981; MRCGP 1984; DCH RCP Lond. 1982; DRCOG 1982. (Guy's)

SEARS, Andrew Fullerton Witley Surgery, Wheeler Lane, Witley, Godalming GU8 5QR Tel: 01428 682218 Fax: 01428 682218; Oaklee, Combe Lane, Wormley, Godalming GU8 5SX — MB BChir 1980 Camb.; FRCP 2001; MA, MB Camb. 1980, BChir 1979; MRCP (UK) 1983; DRCOG 1986. Prev: Regist. (Med.) Roy. United Hosps. Bath; SHO (Med.) Leicester Roy. Infirm.; Ho. Phys. St. Thos. Hosp. Lond.

SEARS, Anna Louise 72 Church Road, Liversedge WF15 7LP — MB ChB 1997 Liverp.

SEARS, Antony Hammond (retired) 21 West Street, Chichester PO19 1QW Tel: 01243 785958 — MB BChir 1956 Camb.; MA, MB

SEARS

Camb. 1956, BChir 1955; LMSSA Lond. 1955; FRCGP 1981, M 1972; DObst RCOG 1960. Prev: Med. Adviser Electrolux & Autoliv.

SEARS, Charles Alistair Newton Grove House Surgery, 18 Wilton Road, Salisbury SP2 7EE Tel: 01722 333034 Fax: 01722 410308; Close House, The Green, Pitton, Salisbury SP5 1DZ Tel: 01722 712745 Email: charles@sears.org.uk — MB BS 1977 Lond.; MRCGP 1987. (Middlx.) Clin. Asst. (Learning Disabil.) Salisbury DHA; Disabil. Partnership, Educat. Comm. Socs: Brit. Inst. Musculo-Skeletal Med.; Roy. Coll. Gen. Pract.; RCP Rehabil. Med. Comm. Prev: SHO Profess. Med. Unit Qu. Eliz. Hosp. Birm.; SHO (Neurosurg.) Whittington Hosp. Lond.; Ho. Off. Middlx. Hosp. Lond.

SEARS, Elizabeth Florence 3 Green's Court, St. Ann St., Salisbury SP1 2SX Tel: 01722 338817 — MB BS 1976 Lond.; MRCP (UK) 1981; MRCGP 1983; Cert. Family Plann. JCC 1982; DCH Eng. 1980. (St. Thos.) GP Soton. Retainer Scheme. Socs: BMA; Salisbury Med. Soc. & Founder Mem. Trustee Pituitary Foundat. Prev: GP Princip. Med. Off. & Phys. Univ. Kent; SHO (Paediat.) Roy. Hosp. Sick Childr. Edin.; Ho. Phys. St. Thos. Hosp. Lond.

SEARS, Mr Richard Tankard Derwent Rise, 136 Edward's Lane, Nottingham NG5 3HU Tel: 0115 926 2168 — MB BChir 1948 Camb.; MA Camb. 1948; FRCS Eng. 1956; FRCOG 1968, M 1955; DObst 1949. (Camb. & Middlx.) Socs: Fell. Roy. Soc. Med.; Fell. N. Eng. & Birm. & Midl. Obst. & Gyn. Soc.; (Ex-Pres.) N. Eng. Obst. & Gyn. Soc. Prev: Sen. Regist. Jessop Hosp. Wom. Sheff.; Regist. City Hosp. Nottm.; Ho. Off. Middlx. Hosp.

SEARSON, James William The Surgery, 1-3 Warrior Square, St Leonards-on-Sea TN37 6BA Tel: 01424 430123/445644 Fax: 01424 433706 — MB BS 1963 Lond.; MRCS Eng. LRCP Lond. 1965; DObst RCOG 1969; DA Eng. 1968. (St. Geo.)

SEARSON, John David Norwood Avenue Practice, 11 Norwood Avenue, Southport PR9 7EG — MB ChB 1971 Liverp.

SEARSON, John Joseph 14 Lowood Place, Revidge, Blackburn BB2 6JD Fax: 01254 667936; Meynell, 14 Lowood Place, Revidge, Blackburn BB2 6JD Tel: 01254 667936 — LAH 1948 Dublin; MB BCh BAO 1949 NUI. (UCD) Socs: BMA.

SEATH, Gillian Louise 56 Banchory Avenue, Inchinnan, Renfrew PA4 9PZ — MB ChB 1992 Glas.

SEATH, Kenneth Ross The Health Centre, 55 High Street, Great Wakering, Southend-on-Sea SS3 0EF Tel: 01702 218678 Fax: 01702 577853 — MB ChB 1972 Ed.

SEATON, Professor Anthony, CBE 8 Avon Grove, Cramond, Edinburgh EH4 6RF Tel: 0131 336 5113 Fax: 0131 336 2710; 71 Urquhart Terrace, Aberdeen AB24 5NJ Tel: 01224 648947 Email: a.seaton@abdn.ac.uk — MB BChir Camb. 1962; BA Camb. 1959, MD 1972; FRCP Ed. 1985, M 1982; FRCP Lond. 1977, M 1964; MRCS Eng. LRCP Lond. 1962; FFOM RCP Lond. 1982, M 1980; Fell. Acad. Med. Sci. 1998. (Camb. & Liverp.) Prof. Environm. & Occupat. Med. Univ. Aberd. 1988; Cons. Phys. Lothian & Grampian HB; Chairm. Dept. Environm. Expert Panel Air Quality Standards. Socs: Brit. Thorac. Soc. (Pres. 1999) & Brit. Soc. Occupat. Med.; Assn. Phys. Prev: Dir. Inst. Occupat. Med. Edin.; Cons. Phys. Respirat. Med. S. Glam. AHA (T); Edr. Thorax 1977-81.

SEATON, Anthony Trevor The Surgery, 27 Burges Road, East Ham, London E6 2BJ Tel: 020 8472 0421 Fax: 020 8552 9912; Seatoller House, Hermitage Walk, London E18 2BN Tel: 020 8989 0532 Fax: 020 8530 5332 — MB 1961 Camb.; MA Camb. 1962, MB 1961, BChir 1960; DObst RCOG 1962. (St. Bart.) Clin. Asst. Roy. Nat. Throat, Nose & Ear Hosp. Lond.; Hosp. Pract. (Cardiol.) Lond. Chest Hosp. Socs: BMA. Prev: Ho. Phys. & Ho. Surg. Metrop. Hosp. Lond.; Ho. Surg. (O & G) Bromley Hosp.

SEATON, David Anderson (retired) 67 Swanston Avenue, Edinburgh EH10 7DA Tel: 0131 445 1899 — MD (Commend.) Glas. 1961, MB ChB 1950; FRFPS Glas. 1957; FRCP Ed. 1967, M 1958; FRCP Glas. 1967; DObst RCOG 1954; MB ChB 1950 Glasgow.

SEATON, David George French Wymondham Medical Partnership, Postmill Close, Wymondham NR18 0RF Tel: 01953 602118 Fax: 01953 605313 — MB BChir 1974 Camb.; MA, MB Camb. 1974, BChir 1973; Dip. Obst Auckland 1976.

SEATON, Derek Norman (retired) Higher Collipriest, Tiverton EX16 4PT Tel: 01884 252018 Fax: 01884 252018 Email: seaton@collip.demon.co.uk — MB BChir 1945 Camb.; MRCP Lond. 1955; MRCS Eng. LRCP Lond. 1945; DObst RCOG 1961. Prev: Med. Regist. Woolwich Hosp. Gp.

SEATON, Douglas King's Field, 23 Park Road, Ipswich IP1 3SX Tel: 01473 216671 — MB ChB 1970 Liverp.; MD Liverp. 1978; FRCP Lond. 1988; MRCP (UK) 1973; MRCS Eng. LRCP Lond. 1970. Cons. Phys. The Ipswich Hosp. Socs: Brit. Thorac. Soc. Prev: Instruc. (Med.) Univ. W. Virginia, USA; Regist. (Cardiothoracic Med.), Ho. Phys. & Ho. Surg. BRd.green Hosp. Liverp.

SEATON, Edward Douglas 23 Park Road, Ipswich IP1 3SX Tel: 01473 216671 Fax: 01473 212011 Email: seatons@compuserve.com — BM BCh 1996 Oxf.; MA (Cambridge) 1997. (Oxf.) SHO (Med.) Leeds Gen. Infirm. Prev: Ho. Off. Med. Oxf. Radcliffe Hosp.; Ho. Off. in Surg. York Dist. Hosp.

SEATON, James Michael Arno 18 Westlands Grove, Stockton Lane, York YO31 1EF — MB ChB 1992 Sheff.

SEATON, John Eric Vernon William Harvey Hospital, Ashford TN24 0LZ Tel: 01233 633331 — MB ChB 1990 Ed.; MRCOG 1997. Cons., William Harvey Hosp., Ashford, Kent. Prev: Specialist Regist. Norf. & Norwich Hosp.; Regist. (O & G) Addenbrooke's Hosp. & Rosie Matern. Hosp. Camb.; SHO (O & G) Roy. Infirm. Edin.

SEATON, John Stuart (retired) Dartford West Health Centre, Tower Road, Dartford DA1 2HA Tel: 01322 23600 — MRCS Eng. LRCP Lond. 1959; DObst RCOG 1961.

SEATON, Judith Ann 47 Downfield Walk, Plymouth PL7 2DS — MB ChB 1994 Sheff.

SEATON, Ronald Andrew King's Cross Hospital, Clepington Road, Dundee DD3 8EA Tel: 01382 660111 Fax: 01382 816178 Email: aseaton66@aol.com; Flat 1, 5 West Road, Newport-on-Tay DD6 8HH Tel: 01382 542351 — MB ChB 1989 Aberd.; MD Aberd. 1996; MRCP (UK) 1992; DTM & H Liverp. 1993. Specialist Regist. (Infect. & Gen. Med.) Dundee Teachg. Hosps. & Med. Sch. Trust. Socs: Fell. Roy. Soc. Trop. Med. & Hyg.; Brit. Soc. Antimicrob. Chemother.; Collegiate Mem. Roy. Coll. Phys. Ed. Prev: Lect. (Med.) Univ. Papua New Guinea; SHO Rotat. (Gen. Med.) Tayside HB; SHO (ImmunoDefic. & Infec. Dis.) Kings Cross Hosp. Dund.

SEAVER, Richard Gordon (retired) St. Johns Copse, 121 Bagley Wood Road, Kennington, Oxford OX1 5NA Tel: 01865 735720 — MB BCh 1944 Belfast; MB BCh BAO Belf. 1944; MA Camb. 1948.

SEAVERS, Janet Elizabeth Rosegrove Surgery, 225-227 Gannow Lane, Burnley BB12 6HY Tel: 01282 423295 Fax: 01282 832609; 6 Higham Road, Padiham, Burnley BB12 9AP Tel: 01282 72351 — MB ChB 1977 Manch.; BSc (Med. Sci.) St. And. 1974.

SEAVERS, Peter Rosegrove Surgery, 225-227 Gannow Lane, Burnley BB12 6HY Tel: 01282 423295 Fax: 01282 832609; 6 Higham Road, Padiham, Burnley BB12 9AP Tel: 01282 72351 — MB ChB 1977 Manch.; MRCGP 1982.

SEBAG-MONTEFIORE, David Joseph Yorkshire Centre for Clinical Oncology, Cookridge Hospital, Hospital Lane, Leeds LS16 6QB Tel: 0113 392 4244 Fax: 0113 392 4186 — MB BS 1983 Lond.; MRCP (UK) 1986; FRCR 1990; FRCP 1999. Cons. Clin. Oncologist, Leeds Cancer Centre, Cookridge Hosp. Prev: Sen. Regist. (Radiother.) St. Bart. Hosp. Lond.; Regist. (Clin. Oncol.) Middlx. & Mt. Vernon Hosp. N.wood.

SEBAG-MONTEFIORE, Stephen Eric (retired) 34 Peninsula Square, Winchester SO23 8GJ Tel: 01962 856121 Fax: 01962 856121 — MB BChir Camb. 1950; MD Camb. 1979; MRCGP 1958. Prev: Clin. Asst. (Psychol. Med.) St. Bart. Hosp. Lond.

SEBAGH, Jean-Louis The French Cosmetic Medical Co Ltd, 25 Wimpole St., London W1M 7AD Tel: 020 7637 0548 Fax: 020 7637 5110 Email: doctor@frenchcosmetic.com — MD 1982 Paris.

SEBARATNAM, Natalie Renuka 33A St Stephens Gardens, Twickenham TW1 2LT — MB BS 1993 Lond.

SEBARATNAM, Noeline Padmini 37 Cunningham Avenue, St Albans AL1 1JJ Tel: 01727 859614; 37 Cunningham Avenue, St Albans AL1 1JJ Tel: 01727 859614 — MB BS 1960 Ceylon; FRCPsych 1989, M 1972; DPM Eng. 1967. Cons. (Psychiat.) W. Herts. Community Health Trust. Prev: Cons. (Psychiat.) Cell Barnes Hosp. St. Albans; Med. Asst. Hill End Hosp. St. Albans; Regist. Cell Barnes Hosp. St. Albans.

SEBASTIAN, Joseph 13 Homer Row, 2nd Floor, London W1H 4AW — MB BS 1960 Karnatak; LAH Dub. 1962.

SEBASTIAN, Mathew 6 Wolverley Grange, Derby DE24 0SS — MB BS 1974 Kerala; MRCP (UK) 1989; DA (UK) 1985.

SEBASTIAN, Thottacherry Chacko 51 Kaye Lane, Huddersfield HD5 8XP — MB BS 1960 Karnatak.

SEBASTIANPILLAI, Chitra 17 Underne Avenue, London N14 7ND — MB BS 1971 Ceylon. (Peradeniya)

SEBASTIANPILLAI, Francis Benedict Yohendiran 17 Underne Avenue, London N14 7ND — MB BS 1971 Ceylon.

SEBASTIANPILLAI, Marina Rita 20 Sanderstead Avenue, London NW2 1SG — MB BS 1965 Ceylon.

SEBASTIANPILLAI, Narishta Joanne 42 Michleham Down, Woodside Park, London N12 7JN Tel: 020 8445 5845 — MB BS 1994 Lond.; DCH RCP Lond. 1996. (Roy. Free Hosp.) GP Regist. Socs: BMA. Prev: SHO (Psychiat.); SHO (ENT); SHO (Paediat.).

SEBEL, Josif (retired) 3 Gaywood, 42 Hawthorne Road, Bromley BR1 2TL — MB BS 1943 Lond.; MRCS Eng. LRCP Lond. 1943. Prev: Ho. Phys. Horton Emerg. Hosp. Epsom.

SEBESTIK, Jan Paul NW Surrey Child and Adolescent Mental Health Service, Ashford & St Peter's NHS Trust, St. Peter's Hospital, Guildford Road, Chertsey KT16 0PZ Tel: 01932 810298 Fax: 01932 692020 Email: jan.sebestik@asph.nhs.uk — MB BS 1984 Lond.; MRCPsych 1989. Cons. Child & Adolesc. Psychiat. St. Peter's Hosp. Chertsey.

SEBIRE, Neil James Great Ormond Street Hospital, Great Ormond Street, London WC1N — MB BS 1992 Lond.; MD 1999 London. (St Mary's, London) Subspeciality Trainee in Paediatric & Private Path. Prev: SPR in Histopath., St Mary's, Lond.; Research Fell., Harris Birtwright Unit, King's Coll. Lond.

SEBUGWAWO, Mr Silas Northamptonshire Health Authority, High Field, Northampton NN1 5DN Tel: 01604 615325 Fax: 01604 615146 Email: silas.segugwano@northants-ha.anglox.nhs.uk; 57 Berry Lane, Wootton, Northampton NN4 6JU — MB ChB 1975 Makerere; MSc (Pharmacol.) Lond. 1979; FRCS Glas. 1984; MFPHM RCP (UK) 1993. (Makerere) Cons. Pub. Health Med. N.ants. HA. Prev: Sen. Regist. (Pub. Health Med.) S. W.. RHA; Regist. (Neurosurg.) Univ. Hosp. Wales Cardiff & Morriston Hosp. Swansea; Regist. (Surg.) W. Fife Hosp. Dunfermline.

SECCOMBE, Martin Peter Jonathan 12 Lynmouth Road, Reading RG1 8DD Tel: 0118 951 1453 Email: mpjs@seccombes.freeserve.co.uk — MB BS 1993 Lond. (UMDS) SHO (Med.) Roy. Berks. Hosp. Reading. Prev: SHO (Paediat.) & Regist. (Med. & Emerg.); Waikato Hosp. Hamilton, NZ.

SECHIARI, Giles Pandely, TD, OStJ 42 Granville Park, Aughton, Ormskirk L39 5DU — MB BCh 1957 Witwatersrand; FRCP Lond. 1977, M 1964. Cons. Phys. & Geriat. Ormskirk & Dist. Hosp. Gp. Prev: Lect. (Endocrinol.) Univ. Liverp.

SECKER, Christopher John 12 Northesk Street, Stone ST15 8EP — BM BS 1988 Nottm.; FRCA 1994. Regist. (Anaesth.) Leicester Roy. Infirm. NHS Trust.

SECKER WALKER, Jonathan University of Wales, College of Medicine, Dept of Clinical Governance, Heaty Park, Cardiff CF14 4XW Tel: 02920745041 Email: j.secker-walker@vhw-tr.wales.nhs.uk; 40 Woodland Gardens, Muswell Hill, London N10 3UA Tel: 020 8444 9426 Fax: 020 8444 9426 Email: jonathansw@classicfm.net — MB BS 1967 Lond.; BSc Lond. 1964; MRCS Eng. LRCP Lond. 1967; FFA RCS Eng. 1972. (Univ. Coll. Hosp.) Sen. Lect. Univ. Wales Coll. Med. Cardiff; Hon. Sen. Lect. (Anaesth.) UCL Med. Sch. Socs: Roy. Soc. Med.; BAAM; Chelsea Clin. Soc. Prev: Gen. Manager UCL Hosps.; Cons. Anaesth. Univ. Coll. Hosp.; Sen. Regist. (Anaesth.) St. Thos. Hosp. Lond.

SECKL, Professor Jonathan Robert University of Edinburgh, Molecular Medicine Centre, Western General Hospital, Edinburgh EH4 2XU Tel: 0131 651 1035 Fax: 0131 651 1085 Email: j.seckl@ed.ac.uk — MB BS 1980 Lond.; PhD Lond. 1989; FRCP Ed. 1993; MRCP (UK) 1983; BSc 1977 London. (Univ. Coll.) Hon. Cons. Phys. (Endocrinol.) Lothian HB Edin.; Moncrieff-Arnott Prof. Molecular Med. Socs: Acad. of Med. Sci.s; Assn. of Phys.s; Soc. Endocrinol. Prev: Wellcome Trust Sen. Research Fell. Clin. Sci. W.. Gen. Hosp. Edin.; Lect. (Med.) Univ. Edin. W.. Gen. Hosp.; Prof. Endocrinol. Univ. Edin.

SECKL, Michael Julian 30 Fairmead Road, London N19 4DF — MB BS 1986 Lond.; PhD Lond. 1995; BSc (Immunol.) Lond. 1983; MRCP (UK) 1990. Sen. Lect. & Hon. Cons. (Med. Oncol.) Char. Cross & Hammersmith Hosps. Lond. Socs: Fell. Roy. Soc. Med.; BMA. Prev: Clin. Research Fell. Imperial Cancer Research Fund Lond.; Hon. Sen. Regist. Roy. Free Hosp. Lond.; Regist. Rotat. (Gen. Med. & Oncol.) Char. Cross Hosp. Lond. & Lister Hosp. Stevenage.

SECRETT, Tracey Joanne 42 Brighton Road, Godalming GU7 1NT — MB BS 1996 Lond.

SEDANO BOCOS, Alberto c/o Dr D Santana-Hernandez, 82 Bootham Park Court, York YO31 8JT — LMS 1992 La Laguna.

SEDAR, Mohammed Iqbal Mawbey Brough Health Centre, 39 Wilcox Close, London SW8 2UD Tel: 020 7622 3827 Fax: 020 7498 1069 — MB BS 1975 Sri Lanka.

SEDDON, Anthony John The Penryn Surgery, Saracen Way, Penryn TR10 8HX Tel: 01326 372502; Killigarth House, Devoran, Truro TR3 6NE — MRCS Eng. LRCP Lond. 1972; MA, BM BCh Oxf. 1972; DA Eng. 1977; DObst RCOG 1974. (Westm.)

SEDDON, Beatrice Mary 114 Chestnut Grove, New Malden KT3 3JT — MB BS 1990 Lond.; BSc Lond. 1987; MRCP (UK) 1994; FRCR 1998. (St. George's) Regist. (Clin. Oncol.) Roy. Marsden Hosp. Prev: Regist. (Clin. Oncol.) Ipswich Hosp.; SHO (HIV) Chelsea & W.m. Hosp. Lond.; SHO (Renal Med.) Guy's Hosp. Lond.

SEDDON, Daniel John South Cheshire Health Authority, 1829 Building, Countess of Chester, Health Park, Liverpool Road, Chester CH2 1UL Tel: 01244 650304 Fax: 01244 650341 — MB ChB Manch. 1981; MFPHM RCP (UK) 1995; MPH Liverp. 1993; MRCGP 1987; DA (UK) 1986. Cons. Pub. Health Med. S. Chesh. HA. Prev: Cons. (Pub. Health Med.) Berks. HA; GP Sandbach, Chesh.

SEDDON, David James Health Care of The Elderly, Queens Medical Centre, University Hospital, Nottingham NG7 2UH Tel: 0115 924 9924 Fax: 0115 970 9496 — MB BChir 1979 Camb.; FRCP(L) 1999; MD Camb. 1993; MRCP (UK) 1982; MA Oxf. 1981, BA 1977. (Oxf. & Camb.) Cons. Geriat. Med. Qu. Med. Centre Univ. Hosp. Nottm. & Nottm. Healthcare NHS Trust; Coll. Tutor, Qu.'s Med. Centre Nottm. Socs: Brit. Geriat. Soc.; BMA. Prev: Sen. Regist. (Gen. & Geriat. Med.) Oxf. & Anglia RHA; Research Fell. & Hon. Regist. (Med. & Nuclear Med.) Char. Cross Hosp. Lond.; Regist. (Med. & Thoracic Med.) Whipps Cross Hosp. Lond.

SEDDON, Geoffrey Boyd (retired) Elmsneath, The Square, Stow-on-the-Wold, Cheltenham GL54 1AF Tel: 01451 830274 — MB ChB 1956 Manch.; DA Eng. 1963.

SEDDON, Ian Department of Histopathology, Essex Rivers NHS Trust, Chestnut Villa, Boxted Rd, Colchester CO4 5HG — FRCPath 1996; MB ChB 1979 Manch.; MRCPath 1986. Cons. Histopath., Essex Rivers NHS Trust; Hon. (Path.) Univ. Manch. Socs: Assn. Clin. Paths.; Internat. Acad. of Path. Prev: Cons. Histopath., Roy. Oldham Hosp.; Lect. (Path.) Univ. Sheff.; Sen. Regist. (Histopath.) Roy. Hallamsh. Hosp. Sheff.

SEDDON, Ian Harold c/o Glyn Mills & Co., Whitehall, London SW1A 2EB — MB ChB 1954 Birm.

SEDDON, James Gideon Winstanley Plas Meddyg Surgery, Station Road, Ruthin LL15 1BP Tel: 01824 702255 Fax: 01824 707221; Bryn Awelon, Llangynhafal, Denbigh LL16 4LN — MB ChB 1981 Liverp.; MRCGP 1986; DRCOG 1984.

SEDDON, James Robert Middleton Manor Hospital Trust, Moat Road, Walsall WS2 9PS Tel: 01922 721172; Durlston Court School, Becton Lane, New Milton BH25 7AQ Tel: 01425 610010 Fax: 01425 622731 — MB BS 1991 Lond.

SEDDON, Joanna Margaret Wick Surgery, 111 High St., Wick, Bristol BS30 5QQ Tel: 0117 937 2214 Fax: 0117 937 4692; The Lawn, 117 High St, Wick, Bristol BS30 5QQ — MB ChB 1978 Birm.; DCH RCP Lond. 1981. Prev: SHO (ENT, Ophth., Derm. & Paediat.) Selly Oak Hosp. Birm.; SHO (Geriat.) & SHO (Supernum. Obst.) Plymouth; Trainee GP Plymouth.

SEDDON, Mr John Anthony 19 Rutland Avenue, Walton, Warrington WA4 6PB Tel: 01925 62859 — MB ChB 1951 Liverp.; ChM Liverp. 1965, MB ChB 1951, DPH 1958; FRCS Eng. 1961; DObst RCOG 1957.

SEDDON, John David Middleton The Coach House, Clevedon Road, Nailsea, Bristol BS48 1HA — MB BS 1992 Lond.

SEDDON, Lesley Maswell Park Health Centre, Hounslow Avenue, Hounslow TW3 2DY Tel: 020 8321 3488 Fax: 020 8893 4368; 13 Murray Avenue, Hounslow TW3 2LQ Tel: 020 8894 5370 — MRCS Eng. LRCP Lond. 1981; BSc Lond. 1978, MB BS 1981.

SEDDON, Norman Ernest (retired) 6 Tarn Close, storth, Milnthorpe LA7 7HZ — MB ChB 1954 Manch.

SEDDON, Paul Christopher Royal Alexandra Hospital for Sick Children, Dyke Road, Brighton BN1 3JN Tel: 01273 328145 Email: paul.seddon@brighton-healthcare.nhs.uk — MB ChB 1981 Manch.; MRCP (UK) 1985; DCH RCP Lond. 1983. Cons. Paediat. Brighton

SEDDON

Health Care. Socs: Brit. Thorac. Soc. Europ. Respirat. Soc. Prev: Research Fell. McGill Univ. Montreal, Canada; Sen. Regist. (Paediat.) S. W.. RHA; Research Fell. Liverp. Univ.

SEDDON, Paul James, Wing Cdr. RAF Med. Br. Station Medical Centre, RAF Leuchars, St Andrews KY16 0JX Tel: 01334 839471 Email: pjseddon@ao1.com; 1 Adam Close, Leuchars, St Andrews KY16 0LR — MB BS 1983 Newc.; BSc Newc. 1978; MRCGP 1992; DCH RCP Lond. 1995; DRCOG 1991. Sen. Med. Off. RAF Leuchars. Socs: BMA. Prev: Unit Med. Off. RAF Linton-on-Ouse; Regist. (Histopath.) Newc. Gen. Hosp.

***SEDDON, Rebecca** 7 Hillhead Terrace, Spital, Aberdeen AB24 3JE — MB ChB 1996 Aberd.

SEDDON, Stephen John Meadowcroft, Sandyfields, Baldwins Gate, Newcastle ST5 5DW — MB ChB 1971 St. And.; FFA RCS Eng. 1975. Cons. Anaesth. N. Staffs. RHA.

SEDDON, Thomas Andrew Aspull Surgery, Haigh Road, Aspull, Wigan WN2 1XH Tel: 01942 831263 Fax: 01942 832065; 23 Avonhead Close, Horwich, Bolton BL6 5QD — MB BS 1987 Lond.; MA Camb. 1987; MRCGP 1991.

SEDDON, Thomas Michael Winster, Hasty Brow Road, Slyne-with-Hest, Lancaster LA2 6AG Tel: 01524 410490 — MB ChB 1962 Aberd. Socs: BMA. Prev: Ho. Phys. & Ho. Surg., & SHO Cas. Vict. Hosp. Blackpool; SHO O & G W.mld. Co. Hosp. Kendal; Terminable Lect. Anat. Aberd. Univ.

SEDDON-SMITH, Robert Ian 54 Limefield Road, Smithills, Bolton BL1 6LA — MB ChB 1994 Birm.; ChB Birm. 1994.

SEDGWICK, Mr David Michael Tigh-A-Chiuil, Badabrie, Fort William PH33 7LX Tel: 01397 772035 — MB ChB 1980 Ed.; BSc (Hons.) (Med. Sci.) St. And. 1977; FRCS Ed. 1984. Cons. Surg. Belford Hosp. Fort William. Prev: Regist. (Gen. Surg.) W.. Gen. Hosp. Edin.; Research Fell. (Gastrointestinal Laborat.) W.. Gen. Hosp. Edin. Univ. & Edin. Med. Fac. Schol.; Regist. (Surg.) Dunfermline & W. Fife Hosp.

SEDGWICK, Professor Edward Michael (retired) Brackendale, 85 Lakewood Road, Chandlers Ford, Eastleigh SO53 5AD Tel: 02380 265073, 02380 266647 Fax: 02380 263793 Email: mike.sedgewick@doctors.org.uk — MB ChB 1962 Bristol; MD Bristol 1967, BSc 1959; FRCP Lond. 1994; MRCP (UK) 1992. Prev: Hon Prof, Clin Neurophysiol. Univ Soton.

SEDGWICK, Emma Child & Adolescent Mental Health Department, Chelsea & Westminster Hospital, Fulham Road, London SW10 9NH — MB BS 1993 Lond.

SEDGWICK, James Edward Charles Woodpeckers, Chilworth Old Village, Southampton SO16 7JP — MB BS 1993 Lond.; BSc Lond. 1990; MRCP (UK) 1996. (Lond. Hosp. Med. Coll.)

SEDGWICK, John Maclaren Wylie (retired) 53 Berry Hill Crescent, Cirencester GL7 2HF — MRCS Eng. LRCP Lond. 1941. Prev: Resid. Surg. Off. Rush Green Hosp. Romford.

SEDGWICK, John Philip The Medical Centre, Brunel University, Kingston Lane, Uxbridge UB8 3PH Tel: 01895 235907 Fax: 01895 270964; Ashley Cottage, 3 Ferry End, Bray, Maidenhead SL6 2AS — MB BS 1965 Lond.; MRCS Eng. LRCP Lond. 1964; DA Eng. 1967. Dir. Med. Serv. Brunel Univ.; Med. Cons. to Coca-Cola Schweppes, Pioneer Hi-Fidelity & Others. Socs: Fell. Roy. Soc. Med.; Soc. Occupat. Med. Prev: Sen. Clin. Med. (Occupat. Health) Hillingdon; SHO (Anaesth.) Roy. Sussex Co. Hosp.; Ho. Phys. Lewisham Hosp.

SEDGWICK, John Rich Hill Brow Road, Liss GU33 7LE; Longhill Cottage, Hillbrow Road, Liss GU33 7LH Tel: 01730 893258 — MB BS 1977 Lond.; MRCS Eng. LRCP Lond. 1977; MRCGP 1981; DRCOG 1979. (St. Thos.) Hosp. Practitioner (ENT) Qu. Alexandra Hosp. Portsmouth.

SEDGWICK, John Vincent King's College Hospital, Denmark Hill, London SE5 9RS; 2 Park Hill, Bickley, Bromley BR1 2JH — BM 1981 Soton.; FFA RCS 1988. Cons. Anaesth. King's Coll. Hosp. Lond. Socs: BMA & Assn. Pain Soc.

SEDGWICK, Mr Mark Accident & Emergency Department, Blackpool Victoria Hospital NHS Trust, Whinney Heys Road, Blackpool FY3 8NR Tel: 01253 303523 Fax: 01253 306668; 7 Forest Close, Meols, Wirral CH47 6BA Tel: 0151 632 1229 Fax: 01253 301984 — MB 1984 Camb.; BChir Camb. 1983; MA Camb. 1988; BA Camb. 1980; MRCP (UK) 1988; FRCS Ed. (A&E Med. & Surg.) 1992; FRCS Ed. 1990; FFAEM, 1994; FRCP 2000. (Camb. & Guy's Hosp.) Cons. A & E Med. Blackpool Vict. Hosp. NHS Trust.

Socs: Brit. Assn. Accid. & Emerg. Med.; Brit. Med. Assn. (Pl. of Work Represen.).

SEDGWICK, Martin Leonard Countess of Chester Hospital, Liverpool Road, Chester CH2 1UL Tel: 01244 365000 Fax: 01244 366455; Tel: 01244 851305 Fax: 01244 851305 — MB ChB 1984 Leeds; BSc (Hons.) Biochem. Leeds 1981; MRCP (UK) 1987; MD Leeds 1994; FRCP 2000. Cons. Phys. & Cardiol. Countess of Chester Hosp. Socs: Brit. Cardiac Soc. Prev: Sen. Regist. (Cardiol.) W.. Infirm. Glas.; Regist. (Cardiol.) Roy. Alexandra Hosp. Paisley & Glas. Roy. Infirm.; SHO (Gen. Med.) Seacroft Hosp. Leeds.

SEDGWICK, Paul Allan 26 Hawkeys Lane, North Shields NE29 0PN — MB ChB 1993 Liverp.

SEDLER, Mark Jonathan 37 Highwood Avenue, Leeds LS17 6EW — MB ChB 1992 Liverp.

SEDLER, Penelope Anne Susan Louise 46 Westwood Road, Sheffield S11 7EY — MB ChB 1979 Sheff.

SEDMAN, Mr Peter Charles Hull Royal Infirmary, Anlaby Road, Hull HU3 2JZ Tel: 01482 328541 Email: psedman@surgery.karoo.co.uk — MB ChB 1985 Leeds; FRCS (Gen.) 1996; FRCS Eng. 1992; FRCS Ed. 1991. Cons. Upper Gastrointestinal & Gen. Surg. Roy. Hull Hosps.

SEE CHYE HENG, Andrew 1 St Crispin's Close, London NW3 2QF — MB BS 1985 Singapore.

SEEAR, Michael 86 Harley Street, London W1G 7HP Tel: 020 7580 3256 — MB BS 1969 Lond.; Diploma of Professional Psychotherapy 1985; MRCGP 1979. (Westm.) Indep Complementary Med. Lond. Socs: Fell. Med. Soc. Lond. (Ex. Mem. Counc.); Fell. Brit. Soc. Med. & Dent. Hypn. - Teach. of Hypnother.; Fell. Roy. Soc. of Med. Prev: RMO King Edwd. VII Hosp. for Off.s (Sister Agnes Founder) Lond.; SHO (Psychiat.) Guy's Hosp. Lond.; Vis. Phys. Bupa Med. Centre Lond.

SEED, Catherine Alison 52 Laverton Road, Fairhaven, Lytham St Annes FY8 1EN — MB ChB 1996 Ed.

SEED, Martin James Department of Clinical Immunology, (Box 109), Adenbrookes Hospital, Cambridge CB2 2QQ — MB ChB 1993 Leeds; BSc Hons. (Chem. Path.) Leeds 1990; MRCP (UK) 1997. Specialist Regist. Clin. Immunol. Addenbrookes Hosp. Camb. Prev: SHO (Gen. Med.) Roy. Hallamsh. Hosp. Sheff.; SHO (Infec. Dis.) Roy. Hallamsh. Hosp. Sheff.; SHO (Renal Med.) St. Jas. Univ. Hosp. Leeds.

SEED, Mary (retired) Lipid Clinic, Private out Patients, 1st Floor Charing Cross Hospital, Fulham Palace Road, London W6 8RF Tel: 0208 846 1148 Fax: 0207 221 4949 Email: drmaryseed@hotmail.com — MRCP 2000; BM BCh Oxf. 1961; MA Oxf. 1961, DM 1992; FRCPath 1996, M 1992. p/t Hon. Consg. Phys. 1st Floor Char. Cross Hosp. Lond.; Cons. King. Edwd. VII Hosp. Midhurst; Cons. Lond. Woms. Clinic Lond. Prev: Sen. Lect. & Hon. Cons. Dept. Chem Path. & Med. Char. Cross Hosp. & W.m. Sch. Lond.

SEED, Peter Robinson (retired) — MB ChB 1956 Birm.; MRCS Eng. LRCP Lond. 1956; DCH Eng. 1973; DObst RCOG 1961. Prev: Obst. Ho. Off. St. Mary's Hosp. Wom. & Childr. Manch.

SEED, Richard Gibson Francis Lloyd E230 Armed Forces Hospital, PO Box 7897, Riyadh 11159, Saudi Arabia Tel: 00 966 14777714 Fax: 00 966 14620625 Email: dicanjo@zajil.net; 18a Granville Road, Waltier, Deal CT14 7LS Tel: 01304 374344 Fax: 01304 374344 — MB BS 1960 Lond.; FRCA 1967; FANZCA 1979; FFA RCSI 1995. (Middx.) Director (Anaesth.) Riyadh Armed Forces Hosp. Riyadh, Saudi Arabia. Socs: Fell. Roy. Soc. Med.; Assn. Anaesth.; Austral. Soc. Anaesth. Prev: Director (Anaesth.) Roy. Perth Hosp., W. Austral.; Director, Sen. Lect. & Hon. Cons. Guy's Hosp. Lond.; Sen. Regist. & Research Asst. Roy. Postgrad. Med. Sch. Lond.

SEED, Professor William Anthony 15 St Olaves Court, St. Petersburgh Place, London W2 4JY; Department of Respiratory Medicine, Imperial College School of Medicine, Charing Cross Hospital, London W6 8RF Tel: 020 8846 7198 Fax: 020 8846 7170 — BM BCh Oxf. 1962; PhD Lond. 1972; BSc Oxf. 1960, MA 1962; FRCP Lond. 1981, M 1965. Prof. (Med.) Imperial Coll. Sch. of Med.; Cons. Phys. Char. Cross Hosp. Lond.

SEEDAT, Najib Ibrahim 60 Erskine Road, London E17 6RZ — MB ChB 1993 Birm.

SEEDHOUSE, Joanna Kate 5 The Beeches, Ebstree Road, Seisdon, Wolverhampton WV5 7EU — MB ChB 1998 Liverp.; MB ChB Liverp 1998.

SEFTON

SEEHRA, Chatranjan Singh 64 Cantwell Road, Shooters Hill, London SE18 3LW; 17 Stanbridge Road, Downend, Bristol BS16 6AW Tel: 0117 957 3242 — MB ChB 1984 Glas.; MRCGP 1989; DCH RCP Lond. 1990; DRCOG 1987; Cert. Family Plann. JCC 1987. Prev: SHO (ENT) Gartnavel Gen. Hosp. Glas.; Trainee GP Bedford VTS; SHO (Psychiat.) Bedford Gen. Hosp.

SEEHRA, Mr Harkiran 3 The Drive, Didsbury Village, Manchester M20 6HZ Tel: 0161 434 8444 Email: 100723.1726@compuserve.com — MB ChB 1986 Manch.; FRCS Ed. 1992. (Manch.) Specialist Regist. (Gen. Surg.) Leighton Hosp. Crewe. Prev: Regist. (Gen. Surg.) Whiston Hosp. Prescot; Regist. (Vasc. Surg.) Roy. Liverp. Univ. Hosp.; Research Fell. (Surg. Gastroenterol.) Univ. Manch.

SEEHRA, Kulwant Kaur 12 Abbey Road, Chertsey KT16 8AL — MB BS 1969 Jammu & Kashmir. (Govt. Med. Coll. Srinagar) SHO Woolwich Memor. Hosp.

SEEHRA, Manjeet Singh The Surgery, High Street, Lowestoft NR32 1JE Tel: 01502 589151 Fax: 01502 566719 Email: manjeetseehra@gp-d83023.nhs.uk — BM BS 1982 Nottm.; BMedSci Nottm. 1980; DRCOG 1987. GP Princ.; Hosp. Practitioner (Renal Unit) James Paget Hosp. Gorleston.

SEEHRA, Mohinderkaur 1 Thistledown Close, Streetly, Sutton Coldfield B74 3EE Tel: 0121 580 9597 — MB BS Vikram 1959. (Mahatma Gandhi Med. Coll. Indore) Deptm. Med. Off. Bexley Health Dist. Socs: BMA. Prev: Ho. Phys. & Ho. Surg. & Regist. (ENT) King Geo. VI Hosp. Nairobi; Kenya; Regist. Radiother. Dept. Roy. N.. Hosp. Lond.

SEEHRA, Surinder Singh 49 Mayfair Avenue, Ilford IG1 3DJ — MB BS 1991 Lond.

SEEHRA, Taljit Kaur 64 Cantwell Road, Shooters Hill, London SE18 3LW — BM 1994 Soton.

SEEL, Edward Hamer Wood Sorrel, Twyncyn, Dinas Powys CF64 4AS — BM 1998 Soton.; BM Soton 1998.

SEEL, James Raymond 1 The Walnuts, Worlingham, Beccles NR34 7EL Tel: 01502 710407 — MB ChB 1954 Ed.; MRCGP 1975. (Ed.) Prev: Med. Off. DHSS; Surg. Lt.-Cdr. R.N.; Med. Off. Roy. Hosp. Sch. Holbrook.

SEELEY, Anthony John Bridgnorth Medical Practices, Northgate House, 7 High Street, Bridgnorth WV16 4BU Tel: 01746 767121 Fax: 01746 765433 — MB ChB 1977 Manch.; DFFP 1995; MRCGP 1981; DRCOG 1982. Princip. in Gen. Pract.; Trainer in Gen. Pract. & Family Plann. Socs: Counc. Mem. Brit. Menopause Soc.

SEELEY, Charles 27 Chesil Street, Winchester SO23 0HU Tel: 01962 860508 — LMSSA 1930 Lond.; MD Lond. 1948, MB BS 1934; FFCM 1974; DPH Eng. 1938. (St. Mary's) Hon. Consg. Phys. St. Geo. Hosp.; Lect. Emerit. Social & Preven. Med. St. Geo. Hosp. Med. Sch.; Lect. St. Geo. Hosp. Sch. Nursing; Vis. Lect. Cornell Med. Coll. & Yale Med. Sch. USA; Examr. Univ. Lond, DPH Eng. & Gen. Nurs. Counc.; Mem. Bd. Studies (Social & Preven. Med.) Lond. Univ. Socs: FRIPHH; FRSH. Prev: Assoc. Phys. Social Med. & Comm. Care Radcliffe Infirm. Oxf. & United; Oxf. Hosps.; Sen. Med. Off. DHSS; Surg. Lt-Cdr. RNVR.

SEELEY, David Dearne Valley Health Centre, Wakefield Road, Scissett, Huddersfield HD8 9JL Tel: 01484 862793 Fax: 01484 866021 Email: david.seeley@gp-b85002.nhs.uk — MB ChB 1984 Sheff.; BA (Physiol. Sci.) Oxf. 1981; MRCGP 1989.

SEELEY, David William 133 Nothfield Road, Sheffield S10 1QP — MB ChB 1993 Sheff.

SEELEY, Hugh Fraser TPMDE, 33 Millman St., London WC1N 3EJ Tel: 020 7692 3178 Fax: 020 7692 3101 Email: hseeley@tpmde.ac.uk; 2 Salisbury House, Somerset Road, London SW19 5HY Tel: 020 8947 0042 Fax: 020 8946 8643 — MB BS Lond. 1969; MSc Stanford Univ. 1964; MA Camb. 1966; FRCA 1973. (St. Thos.) Dean Postgrad. Med. S Thames RO & Univ. Lond. Socs: Roy. Soc. Med.; BMA; Europ.Acad.anaesth. Prev: Cons. Anaesth. & Hon. Sen. Lect. St. Geo. Hosp. Lond.; Lect., Regist. (Anaesth.) & SHO (Clin. Measurem.) W.m. Hosp. Lond.

SEELEY, Stephanie Kate 94 Southdown Crescent, Cheadle SK8 6HA — MB ChB 1993 Manch.; BA (Hons) Birm. 1981; DRCOG 1998. SHO (Paediat.) Stockport.

SEELY, Martin Francis Stirrup Brook Cottage, 5 Stirrup Brook Grove, Worsley, Manchester M28 1SH Tel: 0161 799 2237; 16/18 Victoria Parade, Urmston, Manchester M41 9BP Tel: 0161 746 7086 Fax: 0161 746 7162 Email: m.seeley@btinternet.com — MB ChB 1979 Manch. Med. Examr. RAF Manch.; Forens. Med. Exam. Gtr. Manch. Police; Bd. Mem. Trafford N. PCG.

SEEMUNGAL, Barry Mitra 23 Lancaster Lodge, 83/85 Lancaster Road, London W11 1QH — MB BCh 1993 Wales; BSc (Physiol.) Wales Coll. Cardiff 1989; MRCP Ed. 1996. (Cardiff) Specialist Regist. (Med.) Oxf. Deanery. Socs: Fell. Roy. Soc. Med.

SEENAN, Clare Frances 52 Crompton Avenue, Glasgow G44 5TH — MB ChB 1998 Glas.; MB ChB Glas 1998.

SEENAN, Pamela Julie Wester Ross, Eglinton Ter, Skelmorlie PA17 5ER — MB ChB 1997 Glas.

SEENEY, Barbara Padiham Group Practice, Padiham Medical Centre, Burnley Road, Padiham, Burnley BB12 8BP Tel: 01282 771298 Fax: 01282 777720; 1 Barley Green, Barley, Burnley BB12 9JU — MB ChB 1983 Liverp.; BDS Liverp. 1975, MB ChB 1983; DRCOG 1985.

SEERAJ, Edwin Chandrabhose Lister Health Centre, 1 Camden Square, London SE15 3LW Tel: 020 7708 5413 Fax: 020 7771 3810 — LRCPI & LM, LRSCI & LM 1972; LRCPI & LM, LRCSI & LM 1972.

SEERY, J A Talbot, Ward, Seery and Ahmad, Gardenia Surgery, 2A Gardenia Avenue, Luton LU3 2NS Tel: 01582 572612 Fax: 01582 494553 — MB BCh 1976 Witwatersrand; MB BCh 1976 Witwatersrand.

SEETULSINGH, Prema Saraspathy Department of Microbiology, Hemel Hempstead General Hospital, Hillfield Road, Hemel Hempstead HP2 4AD Tel: 01442 287834 Fax: 01442 287089; 34 Stewart Road, Harpenden AL5 4QB — MB BS 1986 Delhi; FRCPath 2002; MSc Lond. 1989; MRCPath 1994. Cons. Microbiol. Hemel Hempstead Gen. Hosp. Herts. Socs: Hosp. Infec. Soc.; Brit. Soc. Antimicrob. Chemother.; Intern. Soc. of Travel med. Prev: Sen. Regist. (MicroBiol.) Qu. Mary's Univ. Hosp. Lond.; Sen. Regist. (Microbiol.) St. Geo.'s Hosp. Lond.; Fell. (Infec. Dis.) Houston, Texas, USA.

SEEVARATNAM, David Manoharan Department of Mental Handicap, Floor 'E', South Block, University Hospital, Queens Medical Centre, Nottingham NG7 2UH — MB BS 1974 Sri Lanka; MRCPsych 1985. Lect. (Ment. Handicap) Qu. Med. Centre Nottm.

SEEVARATNAM, Mohan Surendra Top Flat, 310 Commercial Way, Peckham, London SE15 1QN; 46 Ventnor Drive, Totteridge, London N20 8BP — MB BS 1988 Lond.; MRCGP 1993; DRCOG 1993. Asst. Gallions Reach Health Centre Lond. Prev: Trainee GP/SHO (O & G) Whitechapel Hosp. Lond. VTS; Ho. Surg. Kent & Sussex Hosp. Tunbridge Wells; Ho. Phys. Hither Green & Lewisham Hosp.

SEEVARATNAM, Nandini Shereen 46 Ventnor Drive, Totteridge, London N20 8BP — MB ChB 1996 Sheff.

SEEWALD, Anke 3 Abbey Road, Stirling FK8 1LH — State Exam Med 1992 Berlin. (Humboldt Universitat Berlin) SHO (O & G) Glas. Rutherglen MH. Prev: SHO (O & G) Lincoln Co. Hosp.

SEEWOONARAIN, Kishore Santa Kumarsingh Runwell Hospital, Wickford SS11 7QE Tel: 01268 366000 Fax: 01268 570946 — MD 1980 Marseilles; FRCPsych 2001; MRCPsych 1985; DTM & H Marseilles 1980. Cons. And Clin. Director Forens. Psychiat. Runwell Hosp. Wickford Essex. Prev: Sen. Regist. (Forens. Psychiat.) Prestwich Hosp. Manch.

SEEX, Derek Michael Brooks Bar Medical Centre, 162-164 Chorlton Road, Old Trafford, Manchester M16 7WW Tel: 0161 226 7777 Fax: 0161 232 9963; 67 Church Road, Urmston, Manchester M41 9EJ Tel: 0161 748 7462 — MB ChB 1976 Leeds; FRCGP 1997; MMedSc (Gen. Pract.) Leeds 1986; DRCOG 1979. Socs: Comm. Mem. Trafford Oncol. Soc. Prev: SHO (O & G & Paediat.) Staincliffe Gen. Hosp. Dewsbury; SHO (Psychiat) St. Lukes Hosp. Huddersfield.

SEFTEL, Avril Louise 50 Roseangle, Dundee DD1 4NB — MB ChB 1994 Dundee.

SEFTON, Armine Margaret Abingdon Lodge, Marloes Road, London W8 5LJ — MB BS 1980 Lond.; MSc Clin. Microbiol. 1987; MRCP (UK) 1984. Lect. (Med. Microbiol.) Lond. Hosp. Whitechapel. Prev: Regist. (Gen. Med. & Infec. Dis.) Rush Green Hosp. Romford; Regist. (Med.) St. Margt. Hosp. Epping & Lond. Hosp. Whitechapel.

SEFTON, Dominic Langham Place Surgery, 11 Langham Place, Northampton NN2 6AA Tel: 01604 38162 Fax: 01604 602457; 3 Holmfield Way, Weston Favell, Northampton NN3 3BJ Tel: 01604 786032 — BM BS 1983 Nottm.; BMedSci Nottm. 1981.

SEFTON

SEFTON, Elizabeth Margaret (retired) Essex Cottage, All Stretton, Church Stretton SY6 6HL Tel: 01694 723226 — MRCS Eng. LRCP Lond. 1945; FFCM 1984, M 1974; DPH Bristol 1955; DCH Eng. 1947; LM Rotunda 1947. Prev: SCM (Child Health) Salop. HA.

SEFTON, Mr Graham Keith 473 Hotham Road, Hull HU5 — MB ChB 1970 Sheff.; FRCS Ed. 1974. Cons. Orthop. Surg. Harrogate Dist. Hosp.

SEFTON, Jennifer Elizabeth 35 Foxglove Avenue, Leeds LS8 2QR — MB BS 1962 Lond.

SEFTON, Sydney Lingwell Croft Surgery, Ring Road, Middleton, Leeds LS10 3LT Tel: 0113 270 4848 Fax: 0113 272 0030; 8 Sandmoor Avenue, Leeds LS17 7DW Tel: 0113 268 6794 — MB BCh BAO 1949 Belf.; MRCGP 1966; MFFP 1994. Prev: SHO Ulster Hosp. Wom. & Childr. Belf.

SEFTON-FIDDIAN, Jill Link End Surgery, 39 Pickersleigh Road, Malvern WR14 2RP Tel: 01684 568466 Fax: 01684 891064 — MB ChB 1977 Birm.

SEFTON-FIDDIAN, Peter 5 Woodcroft Close, Blackwell, Bromsgrove B60 1DA — MB ChB 1978 Manch.

SEGAL, Professor Anthony Walter University College London Medical School, The Rayne Institute, 5 University St., London WC1E 6JF Tel: 020 7679 6175 Fax: 020 7679 6211; 48B Regents Park Road, London NW1 7SX Tel: 020 7586 8745 Fax: 020 679 6175 — MB ChB 1967 Cape Town; PhD Lond. 1979, MSc 1972, DSc (Sci.) 1984; MD Cape Town 1974; FRCP Lond. 1987; MRCP (UK) 1971; F Med Sci 1998; FRS 1998. (Cape Town) Chas. Dent Prof. Med. Univ. Coll. & Middlx. Hosp. Med. Sch. Lond. Socs: Fell.Roy.coll.Phys.

SEGAL, Antony Maurice 98 Vine Lane, Hillingdon, Uxbridge UB10 0BE Tel: 01895 233034 — MB BS 1957 Lond.; MRCS Eng. LRCP Lond. 1956; DAvMed FOM RCP Lond. 1995; DObst RCOG 1960. (St. Geo.) Socs: Roy. Aeronaut. Soc.; Med. Adviser OSTIV Sailpla. Develop. Panel. Prev: Ho. Surg. (Obst.) Soton. Gen. Hosp.; Ho. Phys. (Paediat.) Vict. Hosp. Childr. Chelsea; Ho. Surg. St. Margt. Hosp. Epping.

***SEGAL, Brett Elliott Fabian** 7 Kent House, Stratton Close, Edgware HA8 6PR Email: brettsegal@hotmail.com — MB BS 1998 Lond.; BSc Lond. 1995.

SEGAL, Dennis Selwyn SMA Nutrition, Huntercombe Lane S., Taplow, Maidenhead SL6 0PH Tel: 01628 660633 Fax: 01628 604949 — MB ChB 1962 Cape Town; MPharmMed Pretoria 1977; MFGP S. Afr. Coll. Med. 1974. (Cape Town) Dir. Nutrit. Div. Wyeth Laborat. Taplow Maidenhead. Prev: Sen. Dir. Clin. Affairs Sterling Research Gp. Europe; Med. Dir. Sterling Research Laborat. Guildford; Dir. Med. Servs. Boehringer Ingelheim Ltd. Bracknell.

SEGAL, Hanna Maria 38 Tetherdown, Muswell Hill, London N10 1NG Tel: 020 8883 3225; 44 Queens Avenue, London N10 3NU Tel: 020 8883 3348 — MB ChB 1943 Polish Sch. of Med.; MB ChB Polish Sch. of Med 1943; FRCPsych 1972, M 1971. Socs: (Ex-Pres.) Brit. Psychoanal. Soc. Prev: Vice-Pres. Internat. Psychoanal. Assn.; Pres. Brit. Psychoanal. Soc.; Freud Prof. Univ. Coll. Lond.

SEGAL, Israel Michael (retired) 40 Cameron Road, Seven Kings, Ilford IG3 8LF Tel: 020 8590 1134 — MRCS Eng. LRCP Lond. 1939; MRCGP 1953. Div. Med. Off. Brit. Red Cross Soc.; Lect. 1st Aid Newham Community Coll.

SEGAL, Jonathan Michael Lance The Verwood Surgery, 15 Station Road, Verwood BH31 7PY Tel: 01202 825353 Fax: 01202 829697 — MB BS 1985 Lond.; BA Oxf. 1982; DRCOG 1990. p/t Clin. Asst. (Diabetes Mellitus) Roy. Bournemouth Hosp. Prev: Trainee GP Salisbury VTS; Maua Methodist Mission Hosp., Kenya.

SEGAL, Maximillian Peter Louis Doctor's House, 40 Cameron Road, Seven Kings, Ilford IG3 8LF Tel: 020 8590 1134 Fax: 020 8599 0282; 7 Lincoln Gardens, Ilford IG1 3NF — MB BS 1971 Lond.; DObst RCOG 1973. (Univ. Coll. Hosp.) Lect. Redwood Coll. S. Bank Univ. Socs: Fell. Roy. Soc. Med.; Eur. Soc. Human Reproduc. & Embryol.; Brit. Soc. Colpos. & Cerv. Path. Prev: Hosp. Pract. King Geo. Hosp. Ilford; SHO (O & G) Ilford Matern. Hosp.; SHO (A & E), Ho. Surg. & Ho. Phys. King Geo. Hosp. Ilford.

SEGAL, Norman Harold Oldfield Family Practice, 285 Greenford Road, Greenford UB6 8RA Tel: 020 8578 1914 Fax: 020 8575 6327; 6 Abinger Road, London W4 1EL Tel: 020 8747 1682 — MB ChB 1979 Leeds; BSc (Hons.) Leeds 1976, MB ChB 1979; MRCGP 1983; DRCOG 1983; Cert Family Plann. 1983. L.M.O. Civil Serv. Med. Advis. Serv.; Approved Sect. 12 M.H.A. (1983); Med. Off. H.M. Y.C.C. Feltham Middlx. Prev: Hosp. Pract. Ealing Hosp. Lond.

SEGAL, Susan Melanie Oldfield Family Practice, 285 Greenford Road, Greenford UB6 8RA Tel: 020 8578 1914 Fax: 020 8575 6327; 6 Abinger Road, London W4 1EL Tel: 020 8747 1682 — MB ChB 1976 Leeds; BSc (Hons.) (Pharmacol.) Leeds 1976, MB ChB (Hons.) 1979; DRCOG 1981; Cert. Family Plann. JCC 1981. Assoc. Specialist (Colposcopy) Hammersmith, Qu. Charlotte's & Chelsea Wom. Hosps. Lond. Prev: Trainer (Family Plann.) Qu. Charlotte's Matern. Hosp. Lond.; Clin. Asst. (Dermat.) Char. Cross. Hosp. Lond.

SEGAL, Terry Yvonne Great Ormond Street Hospital, Great Ormond Street, London WC1N 3HZ Email: tysegal@aol.com — MB ChB 1992 Bristol; MRCPCH. p/t Specialist Regist. (Paediat. Endocrin.) Gt. Ormond St. Hosp. & Middx. Hosp. Socs: MRCPCH. Prev: Specialist Regist. Barnet Healthcare; SHO (Paediat.) Guy's & Whittington Hosps. Lond.; SHO (A & E) Edgware Gen. Hosp.

SEGALL, Jacqueline Mandy 1 Manor House Drive, London NW6 7DE — MB BS 1986 Lond.

SEGALL, Jeffrey Joseph (retired) 308 Cricklewood Lane, London NW2 2PX Tel: 020 8455 5005 Fax: 020 8455 5005 — MB BS 1947 Lond.; MRCP (UK) 1972. Prev: Researcher (Clin. Physiol.) N. Middlx. Hosp. Lond.

SEGALL, Malcolm Maurice (retired) 27 Wilbury Avenue, Hove BN3 6HS Tel: 01273 820041 Fax: 01273 820041 Email: ivanamalc@msegall.fsnet.co.uk — MB ChB 1959 Sheff.; MRCP Lond. 1963. Fell. Inst. Developm. Studies Univ. Sussex Brighton. Prev: Adviser to Dir. Gen., Dept. of Health Pretoria S. Africa.

SEGALL, Morris Sidney (retired) 31 Bishopsgate Street, Edgbaston, Birmingham B15 1EJ — MB ChB 1934 Glas.

SEGAR, Eric Philip Ear Nose and Throat Department, Conquest Hospital, The Ridge, St Leonards-on-Sea TN37 7RD; 1 Jubilee Square, Topsham, Exeter EX3 0JG — MB ChB 1988 Cape Town.

SEGAR, Sian Lois Hulme House Medical Centre, 175 Royce Road, Hulme, Manchester M15 5TJ Tel: 0161 226 0606 Fax: 0161 226 5644 Email: sian.segar@gp-p84630.nhs.uk; 66 Brooklawn Drive, Withington, Manchester M20 3GZ — MB ChB 1990 Manch.; MRCGP 1994; DFFP 1993; DRCOG 1993. (Manch.) GP Princip.

SEGARAJASINGHE, John Saverimuttu Rohan 56 Discovery Walk, London E1W 2JG — MB ChB 1995 Manch.

SEGOVIA MARTIN, Antonio Flat H-4 Doctors' Residence, Royal Preston Hospital, Sharoe Green Lane N., Preston PR2 7HT — LMS 1984 Malaga.

SEGUI REAL, Bartolome 10 Oat Close, Aylesbury HP21 9LN — LMS 1986 Bilbao.

SEGWAGWE, Molebedi Medway Hospital, Residence 13, Windmill Road, Gillingham ME7 5NY — MB ChB 1986 Glas.; MRCP (UK) 1991.

SEH YANG LOONG, Dr 3 Ashpark House, Norbiton Road, London E14 7TJ — MB BS 1990 Sydney. SHO Rotat. (Gen. Surg.) St. Bart. Hosp. Lond. Prev: SHO (Orthop.) St. Bart. Hosp. Lond.; SHO (Gen. Surg.) Harold Wood Hosp. & Old Ch. Hosp. Essex; SHO (Gen. Surg. & Orthop.) Gt. Ormond St. Hosp. Lond.

SEHAT, Khosrow Rahbar 61 Ashton Lane, Sale M33 5PE — MB ChB 1996 Bristol.

SEHDEV, Gautam 27 Fenmere Cl, Wolverhampton WV4 5EN — MB BCh 1997 Wales.

SEHDEV, Rajesh Singh 5 Tudor Road, Southall UB1 1NY; 12 Lowndes Cl, Penkull, Stoke-on-Trent ST4 5JG Tel: 01782 410781 — MB ChB 1990 Ed.

SEHGAL, Nav Neet 7 Gideon Close, Belvedere DA17 6DR — MB ChB 1995 Manch.

SEHJPAL, Amarjit 125 Whitehall Road, Walsall WS1 4AT — MB ChB 1998 Birm.; ChB Birm. 1998.

SEHMI, Shashi Kiran The Surgery, 356 Southborough Lane, Bromley BR2 8AA Tel: 020 8468 7081 — LRCPI & LM, LRSCI & LM 1973; LRCPI & LM, LRCSI & LM 1973; DA Eng. 1976.

SEHRA, Ravi Tej Kennard Street Health Centre, 1 Kennard Street, North Woolwich, London E16 2HR Tel: 020 7473 1948 Fax: 020 7511 2040 — MB BS 1973 Panjab.

SEIDELIN, Raymond (retired) Beech Hill, Owler Park Road, Ilkley LS29 0BG Tel: 01943 609042 — MA Oxf. 1949, DM 1953, BM BCh 1947; FRCP Lond. 1974, M 1950; DPM Eng. 1962. Prev: Cons. Phys. Leeds W. Dist.

SEIDEN, Mr Zoheir Ahmed Salim Department of Surgery, Ealing Hospital NHS Trust, Uxbridge Road, Southall UB1 3HW — MB BCh 1975 Ain Shams; FRCS Ed. 1984.

SEIF SAID, Vivian Kathlyn (retired) 48 Parkhurst Road, Torquay TQ1 4EP Tel: 01803 323011 — MB BS Lond. 1953; MRCS Eng. LRCP Lond. 1953; DCH Eng. 1956; DObst RCOG 1955. Prev: SCMO (Family Plann. Coordinator) S. Devon Healthcare Trust.

SEIFERT, Martin Howard The Hospital of St John & St Elizabeth, 60 Grove End Road, London NW8 9NH Tel: 0207 806 4062 Fax: 0207 806 4002; Rheumatology Department, St. Mary's Hospital, Praed St, London W2 1NY Tel: 020 7866 1066 Fax: 020 7886 6083 — MB BS Lond. 1964; FRCP Lond. 1980; MRCP (UK) 1971. (Lond. Hosp.) Cons. Phys. Rheum. St. Mary's Hosp. Lond.; Hon. Sen. Lect. (Clin. Med.) Imperial Coll. Sch. Of Med. Lond. Socs: Fell. Roy. Soc. Med. (Ex.-Pres. Rheum. & Rehabil. Sect.); Med. Soc. Of Lond. (Ex-Sec. & Comm. Mem.); Chairm. SAC on Rheum. Prev: Cons. Rheum. The CharterHo. Rheum. Clinic Lond.; Fell. (Rheum.) Dept. Internal Med. Univ. Colorado Med. Center Denver, USA; Sen. Regist. (Rheum.) St. Thos. Hosp. Lond.

SEIFERT, Ruth 17 Harley Street, London W1N 1DA Tel: 020 7226 1990 Fax: 020 7226 1990 — MRCS Eng. LRCP Lond. 1968; FRCPsych 1988; MRCPsych 1975; DPM Eng. 1972. p/t Hon. Cons. Physcit. St Barts Hosp. Lond.; Cons. Psychiat. Socs: RSM. Fell. Prev: Sen. Regist. Maudsley Hosp. Lond.; SHO (Psychol. Med.) Guy's Hosp. Lond.; Regist. (Psychiat.) Fulbourn Hosp. Camb.

SEIGEL, Jonathan Fred Alrewas Surgery, Exchange Road, Alrewas, Burton-on-Trent DE13 7AS Tel: 01283 790316 Fax: 01283 791863; 170 Main Street, Alrewas, Burton-on-Trent DE13 7ED Tel: 01283 790379 Fax: 01283 792379 Email: 101604.1266@compuserve.com — MB ChB 1975 Cape Town; MRCGP 1983; DA Eng. 1982. Hon. Clin. Lect. Keele Univ.; Course Organiser (Gen. Pract.) Staffs. VTS. Prev: Med. Off. & Med. Supt. Chas. Johnson Mem. Hosp. Kwazulu S. Afr.; SHO (Anaesth.) Horton Gen. Hosp. Banbury.

SEIGER, Christine Paula Newlands House, Clock House Close, Byfleet, Weybridge — BM 1989 Soton.

SEIGER, Darin Guy Northampton Lane North Surgery, 120 Northampton Lane North, Moulton, Northampton NN3 7QP Tel: 01604 790108 Fax: 01604 670827 — MB ChB 1990 Dundee; MRCGP 1994; DFFP 1994; DRCOG 1993. (Dundee) Prev: Trainee GP N.ampton VTS.

SEIGLEMAN, Merton, OBE (retired) 1 Jackdaw Road, Greenmount, Bury BL8 4ER Tel: 01204 885434 Email: sunrayminor@easicom.com — MRCS Eng. LRCP Lond. 1954; DA Eng. 1959; BA Hons. (Open Univ.) 1997. Prev: Cons. Anaesth. Blackburn, Hyndburn, Ribble Valley HA.

SEILER, Edmund Ronald, TD University Health Service, 6 Bristo Square, Edinburgh EH8 9AL Tel: 0131 650 2777 Fax: 0131 662 1813; 30 Spylaw Bank Road, Edinburgh EH13 0JG Tel: 0131 441 1386 Fax: 0131 441 1386 — MB ChB 1959 Ed.; FRCP Ed. 1996; FRCGP 1985, M 1968; DCH Eng. 1965; DObst RCOG 1964. (Ed.) Princip. Univ. Health Serv. Univ. Edin. Socs: BMA; (Treas.) M-C Soc. Edin.; Harv. Soc. Prev: Assoc. Regional Adviser (Gen. Pract.) Postgrad. Bd. Med. Educat. SE Scotl.; Lect. (Community Child Health) Edin.; Ho. Phys. Roy. Infirm. Edin.

SEIMON, Jayawardena Wickramaratna M S C 3 Mandeville Road, Northolt UB5 5HE — MB BS 1991 Lond.

SEIMON, Jayawardena Wickramaratne M D J Methley Cottage, Fulmer Road, Gerrards Cross SL9 7DT — BM 1993 Soton.

SEIMON, Jayawardena Wickramaratne M J B Mandeville Medical Centre, 3 Mandeville Road, Northolt UB5 5HB Tel: 020 8845 3275 Fax: 020 8845 1804 — MB BS Ceylon 1961.

SEIN, Edward Pe 32 Kenton Road, Newcastle upon Tyne NE3 4NA — MB BS 1976 Rangoon.

SEIN WIN, Lim Chung Hwee Red House Surgery, Renfrew Road, Hylton Red House, Sunderland SR5 5PS Tel: 0191 548 1269 Fax: 0191 549 8998 — MB BS 1968 Rangoon; MRCS Eng LRCP Lond 1987. (Rangoon) GP Princip.; EMP (Examg. Med. Practitioner) for Disabil. Assessm., Med. Servs. Newc., Arden Ho., Regent Centre, Newc.-Upon-Tyne; Med. Practitioner, Nat. Slimming Centres, 31 Norf. St., Sunderland. Prev: Dep.sing Doctor, Healthcall Med. Servs., Benton Ho., Newc.-Upon-Tyne.

SEINGRY, David Robert James Royal National Orthopaedic Hospital, Brockley Hill, Stanmore HA7 4LP — MB BS 1971 Lond.; FFA RCS Eng. 1977; DA Eng. 1974.

SEIVEWRIGHT, Helen Elizabeth The Poplars, Hawton, Newark NG24 3RL Tel: 01636 673591 Fax: 01636 673591; Department G.U. Medicine, The Kingsmill Centre for Health Care Services, Mansfield Road, Sutton-in-Ashfield NG17 4JL Tel: 01623 672260 Fax: 01623 672364 — MB ChB 1979 Leeds; MRCGP 1983; Dip. GU Med. Soc. Apoth. Lond. 1992; DRCOG 1983. Clin. Asst. (Genitourin. Med.) Kingsmill Centre for Health Care Servs. Sutton-in-Ashfield Notts.; Clin. Research Fell. Dept. Psychiat. Imperial Coll. Lond.; Clin. Asst. (Dermat.) Kingsmill Centre for Health Care Servs. Prev: GP Leicester; Clin. Asst. (Genitourin. Med.) Leicester Roy. Infirm.; Clin. Asst. (Genitourin. Med.) Roy. Oldham Hosp.

SEIVEWRIGHT, Nicholas Andrew Tel: 0114 271 6802 Fax: 0114 271 6814 Email: nicks@chsheff-tr.trent.nhs.uk — MB ChB 1979 Sheff.; MRCPsych 1986; T(Psych) 1991; DM 1999 Nottingham. Cons. Psychiat. (Subst. Misuse) Community Health Sheff. Socs: Soc. for Study of Addic.; Internat. Soc. Study of Personality Disorders; Fell. Roy. Soc. Med. Prev: Sen. Lect. (Drug Depend.) Dept. Psychiat. Univ. Manch.; Cons. Drug Depend. N. W. Regional Drug Depend. Serv. Prestwich Hosp. Manch.; Sen. Regist. (Psychiat.) Mapperley Hosp. Nottm.

SEJRUP, Otto Roy Wallace (retired) 459 Chester Road, Woodford, Stockport SK7 1PR Tel: 0161 439 3296 — MB ChB 1947 Manch. Prev: SHO (Orthop.) Withington Hosp. Manch.

SEKHAR, Mr Cheemala John Raja Strouden Park Medical Centre, 2A Bradpole Road, Bournemouth BH8 9NX Tel: 01202 532253 Fax: 01202 548524; Maranatha, 10 Woodcocks Crescent, Bournemouth BH7 7JW, India — MB BS 1972 Andhra; MS (Orthop.) Andhra 1976, MB BS 1972; Cert. Family Plann. JCC 1985. (Andhra Med. Coll. Visakhapatnam) Clin. Asst. (Orthop.) Poole Gen. Hosp. Prev: Trainee GP VTS; Regist. Orthop. Dept. Stirling Roy. Infirm.; SHO (Orthop.) Ashington Hosp.

SEKHAR, Mr Killathur Theperumal HM Walton Prison, Walton, Liverpool Tel: 0151 525 5971; 31 Widgeon Road, Altrincham WA14 5NP Tel: 0161 926 8630 — MB BS 1974 Madras; FRCS Ed. 1984. Med. Off. Walton Prison Liverp.

SEKHAR, Palligondi Rudrappa Westbourne Surgery, Shiney Row, Houghton-le-Spring DH4 4QT Tel: 0191 385 2512; 41A Summerhill, East Herrington, Sunderland SR3 3TW Tel: 01783 528 0076 — MB BS 1967 Bangalor; BSc (Nat. Sci.) Mysore 1958; MB BS Bangalore 1967. (Bangalore Med. Coll.) Exam. Med. Off. to DHSS Attendance & Mobility Allowances Units. Prev: Res. SHO Vict. Hosp. Kirkcaldy; Res. SHO St. Michael's Hosp. Aylsham; Med. Regist. Roy. Bath Hosp. Harrogate.

SEKHAR, Ravi Department of Gastroenterology, Wexham Park Hospital, Wexham, Slough Tel: 01753 633000; 406 Rochfords Gardens, Slough SL2 5XN Tel: 01753 692423 Email: sekhars@compuserve.com — MB BS 1986 Madras; MRCP (UK) 1992. Sen. Fell. (Gastroeneterol.) Wexham Pk. Hosp.

SEKHAWAT, Bijendra Singh Medical Centre, Farnham Road Hospital, Farnham Road, Guildford GU2 7LX — MB BS Rajasthan 1969.

SEKHON, Sanjit Singh Health Centre, Rodney Road, Walton-on-Thames KT12 3LB — MB BS 1989 Lond.; DRCOG 1992; Cert. Family Plann. JCC 1992.

SEKWEYAMA, Silvanus Godfrey Galiwango Sekweyama and Pratt, 10 Trafalgar Avenue, London SE15 6NR Tel: 020 7703 9271 Fax: 020 7252 7209; 87 Newport Street, London SE11 6AH — MB BS 1967 Lucknow.

SELBY, Andrew Mark Intensive Care Unit, Alder Hey Childrens Hospital, Eaton Road, Liverpool L12 2AP Tel: 0151 252 5241 Fax: 0151 252 5771; 3 Fletcher's Barn, Menlove Avenue, Liverpool L25 6ET — MB BS 1983 Lond.; MRCP (UK) 1986. Cons. Paediat. (Intens. Care) Alder Hey Childr Hosp. Liverp.

SELBY, Clive Singleton, TD (retired) The Health Centre, Hunter St., Briton Ferry, Neath SA11 2SF Tel: 01639 813272 — MB BCh 1958 Wales.

SELBY, Colin Derek Queen Margaret Hospital, Fife Acute Hospitals NHS Trust, Whitefield Road, Dunfermline KY12 0SU Tel: 01383 623623 Fax: 01383 627042. — BM BS 1982 Nottm.; BMedSci (Hons.) Nottm. 1980, DM 1992; MRCP (UK) 1985; FRCPE 1998. (Nottingham) Cons. (Respirat. & IC) Qu. Margt. Hosp.

SELBY

Dunfermline. Socs: Brit. & Scott. Thoracic Socs.; Scott. Intens. Care Soc. Prev: Lect. (Respirat. Med.) Univ. Edin.; Hon. Sen. Regist. Roy. Infirm. Edin.

SELBY, Edward Michael Borough Road Surgery, 167a Borough Road, Middlesbrough TS4 2EL Tel: 01642 243668 Fax: 01642 222252; Greenlees, 59 Guisborough Road, Nunthorpe, Middlesbrough TS7 0JY Tel: 01642 317740 — MB BS 1979 Newc.; MRCGP 1983; DRCOG 1983; DCCH RCP Ed. RCGP & FCM 1983. Socs: Assn. Brit. Cycling Doctors.

SELBY, Jonathan Neville Christmas Maltings Surgery, Camps Road, Haverhill CB9 8HF Tel: 01440 702010 Fax: 01440 714761; Hall Green Cottage, Great Wratting, Haverhill CB9 7HA Tel: 01440 783384 — MB BChir 1987 Camb.; MA, MB BChir Camb. 1987; DRCOG 1991.

SELBY, Karen Fiona 12 Hallamshire Road, Sheffield S10 4FP — MB ChB 1993 Sheff.

SELBY, Kim 87 High Street, Newington, Sittingbourne ME9 7JJ — MB BS 1983 Lond. Clin. Med. Off. Medway HA.

SELBY, Leonard Milton 31 Queen Anne Street, London W1G 9HX Tel: 020 7636 5250 Fax: 020 7323 0349 — MB ChB 1947 Cape Town. (Cape Town) Socs: Fell. Roy. Soc. Med.; Roy. Coll. Gen. Pract. Prev: Med. Adviser J. Sainsbury Ltd.; Hon. Med. Off. Stellenbosch Hosp., S. Afr.

SELBY, Lesley Anne Benchill Medical Centre, 127 Woodhouse Lane, Benchill, Manchester M22 9WP Tel: 0161 998 4304; 22 Nevill Road, Bramhall, Stockport SK7 3ET Tel: 0115 972 5243, 0161 439 4735 — MB ChB 1985 Leeds; MRCGP 1989. p/t Asst. Gen. Practitioner, Benchill Med. Centre, Manch. Prev: Trainee GP N.umbria VTS.

SELBY, Louise Mary Prideaux Stonefield, St Patricks Lane, Liss GU33 7HQ — MB BS 1994 Lond.

SELBY, Mary Elisabeth Hall Green Cottage, Great Wratting, Haverhill CB9 7HA Tel: 01440 783334 Fax: 01440 783126 Email: selbys@chawa.demon.co.uk — MB BChir 1988 Camb.; MA Camb., MB BChir 1988; DRCOG 1991.

SELBY, Miranda Ruth Brook Lane Surgery, 27 Brook Lane, Bromley BR1 4PX Tel: 020 8461 3333 Fax: 020 8695 5567; 9 Hawthorn Drive, West Wickham BR4 9EY Tel: 020 8462 3884 — BM BS 1983 Nottm.; BMedSci Nottm. 1981, BM BS 1983; MRCGP 1988. (Nottingham) GP Bromley (job-share). Prev: Trainee GP Finchley.

SELBY, Nicholas Michael Londonderry House, Low Pittington, Durham DH6 1BQ — BM BS 1993 Nottm.; BM BS Nottm 1993.

SELBY, Pamela Ann Tel: 01943 466124 Fax: 01943 468373 Email: pam.selby@gp_b86046.nhs.uk; 92 Station Road, Burley-in-Wharfedale, Ilkley LS29 7NS Tel: 01943 862925 — MB ChB 1985 Leeds; DRCOG 1987. (Leeds) Primary Care Head for Cancer NWPCG (Leeds). Prev: Trainee GP Airedale VTS.

SELBY, Professor Peter John St. James's University Hospital, Leeds LS9 7TF Tel: 0113 244 2007 Fax: 0113 242 9886; 17 Park Lane, Roundhay, Leeds LS8 2EX — MB BChir 1975 Camb.; MA 1980, MD Camb. 1980; FRCP Lond. 1990; MRCP (UK) 1976; FRCR 1994. Prof. Cancer Med., Cons. Phys & Dir. ICRF Cancer Med. Research Unit Leeds; Director of the Nat. Cancer Research Network. Socs: Pres. Brit. Oncol. Assn. Prev: Cons. Roy. Marsden Hosp. Lond.; Vis. Fell. (Med.) Ontario Cancer Inst. Toronto, Canada; Regist. (Med.) Univ. Coll. Hosp. Lond.

SELBY, Peter Leslie 22 Nevill Road, Bramhall, Stockport SK7 3ET Tel: 0161 439 4735 — MD 1990 Camb.; MD Camb. 1990 MA, MB 1979, BChir 1978; MRCP (UK) 1980. (Camb. & Birm.) Lect. (Med.) Univ. Manch.; Hon. Cons. Centr. Manch. Healthcare Trust. Prev: Lect. (Med.) Univ. Newc. u Tyne; MRC Clin. Scientif. Staff Mineral Metab. Unit. Gen. Infirm. Leeds.

SELBY, Robin Leslie, Flight Lt. RAF Med. Br. New Chester Road Surgery, 525 New Chester Road, Rockferry, Birkenhead CH42 2AG Tel: 0151 645 3464 Fax: 0151 643 1676 — MB ChB 1984 Liverp.

SELBY, Roger Oldham 11 The Narrows, Harden, Bingley BD16 1HY — MB BChir 1954 Camb.; DA Eng. 1958.

SELBY, Stephen Bryant The Surgery, 1 Norfolk Place, London W2 1RU Tel: 020 7723 7891 Fax: 020 7479 2848 — MB ChB 1981 Birm.; BSC (Anat.) (1st Cl. Hons.) Birm. 1978. SHO Gen. Med. N. Staffs. Hosp. Centre, Stoke-on-Trent.

SELCON, Harold, OStJ (retired) Richmond House, Llandysul SA44 4DF Tel: 01559 363324 — MB ChB 1950 Manch. Prev: Exam. Med. Off. Benefits Agency.

SELF, Ann Elizabeth The Beeches, 67 Lower Olland Street, Bungay NR35 1BZ Tel: 01986 892055 Fax: 01986 895519; 4 Darrow Green Road, Denton, Harleston IP20 0AY Tel: 01986 788128 — MB BChir 1990 Camb.; BA (Hons.) Camb. 1987; MRCGP 1993; DRCOG 1992. (Cambridge)

SELF, Colin Henry Department of Clinical Biochemistry & Metabolic Medicine, The Medical School, Framlington Place, Newcastle upon Tyne NE2 4HH Tel: 0191 222 6931 Fax: 0191 222 6227 — MB BChir 1980 Camb.; PhD Leic. 1970, BSc 1966. Prof. Clin. Biochem. Univ. Newc. u. Tyne; Head Dept. Clin. Biochem. & Metab. Med. Univ. Newc.; Head Clin. Biochem. Diagn. Serv. Roy. Vict. Infirm. Newc. Prev: Sen. Regist. Roy. Postgrad. Med. Sch. Lond.

SELF, Frances Ruth 99 Bamfield, Whitchurch, Bristol BS14 0RB Tel: 0117 983 5005 — MB ChB 1981 Bristol; DRCOG 1987.

SELF, Janet Elizabeth Chrisp Street Health Centre, 100 Chrisp St., London E14 6PG Tel: 020 7515 4860; 162 Albyn Road, St. Johns, London SE8 4JQ — MB BS 1981 Lond.; MRCGP 1986; DRCOG 1985.

SELF, Mr John Bernard Orchard House, Cossington, Leicester LE7 4UX Tel: 01509 812377 — MB BChir 1949 Camb.; MA Camb. 1950; MChir 1962; FRCS Eng. 1952. (Camb. & St. Thos.) Cons. Surg. Emerit. Leicester & LoughBoro. Hosps. Prev: Sen. Regist. (Surg.) Univ. Coll. Hosp. W. Indies; Sen. Regist. (Surg.) & Ho. Surg. &c. St. Thos. Hosp.

SELF, Julian Jeremy 95 Sydney Place, Bath BA2 6NE — MB BChir 1981 Camb.; MA Camb. 1981.

SELF, Mary Catherine 93 Shaftesbury Avenue, Blackpool FY2 9UZ — MB ChB 1988 Liverp.; DA (UK) 1991.

SELF, Richard James 75 Liverpool Road, Chester CH2 1AW — MB ChB 1989 Liverp.

SELFRIDGE, David Ian Health Centre, Kersiebank Avenue, Grangemouth FK3 9EW Tel: 01324 471511; Greencloaks, Linlithgow EH49 7RH Tel: 01506 842926 — MB ChB 1969 Glas. (Glas.)

SELIGMAN, Mr Stanley Albert (retired) 28 Bath Hill Court, Bath Road, Bournemouth BH1 2HP Tel: 01202 290463 — MRCS Eng. LRCP Lond. 1950; MD Lond. 1965, MB BS 1950; FRCOG 1971, M 1959; FRCS Eng. 1955. Prev: Cons. O & G Luton & Dunstable Hosp. Gp.

SELIM, Mr Abobakr Mohamed Hazem 25 Oakwood Avenue, Paisley PA2 9NG — MB BCh 1978 Ain Shams; FRCS Glas. 1988; FRCOphth 1990; DO RCS Eng. 1987. Cons. & Head Eye Unit Almana Gen. Hosp., Saudi Arabia.

SELIM, Samir Alphonse (retired) 14 Pendleton Avenue, Constable Lee Park, Rawtenstall, Rossendale BB4 8UX Tel: 01706 212916 — MB BCh 1956 Ain Shams; DPM Eng. 1981. Prev: Assoc. Specialist (Psychol. Med.) Qu. Pk. Hosp. Blackburn & NW RHA.

SELINGER, Mark Royal Berkshire Hospital, London Road, Reading RG1 5AN Tel: 01734 875111 — BM BS 1976 Nottm.; DM Nottm. 1989, BMedSci 1974, BM BS 1976; MA Oxf. 1987; MRCOG 1985. Cons. Feto-Matern. Med. Roy. Berks. Hosp. Reading. Prev: Lect. (O & G) Nuffield Dept. O & G Univ. Oxf.

SELKON, Joseph Bernard, TD Microbiology Laboratory, John Radcliffe Hospital, Headington, Oxford OX3 9DU Tel: 01865 221226 Fax: 01865 764192; 4 Ethelred Court, Headington, Oxford OX3 9DA Tel: 01865 764098 — MB ChB 1950 Cape Town; FRCPath 1977, M 1965; DCP Lond 1954. (Cape Town) Hon. Cons. Microbiol. Oxf. Radcliffe NHS Trust; Hon. Lect. Dept. Microbiol. Univ. Oxf. Socs: Path. Soc. Gt. Brit. & Irel. & Brit. Soc. Antimicrobial Chemother. Prev: Dir. Oxf. Pub. Health Laborat.; Bacteriol. WHO Tuberc. Chemother. Centre Madras & MRC Unit For Research Into Drug Sensitivity in Tuberc.; Dir. Newc. Pub. Health Laborat.

SELL, Dorothy Mary (retired) 79 Calton Road, Gloucester GL1 5DT — MB BS 1952 Lond. Prev: Sen. Med. Off. (Child Health) Gloucester Health Dist.

SELL, John Norman The Stennack Surgery, The Old Stennack School, St Ives TR26 1RU Tel: 01736 796413 Fax: 01736 796245; Old Orchard Cottage, Church Road, Lelant, St Ives TR26 3LD Tel: 01736 752947 — MB ChB 1969 Bristol; BSc (Hons.) Bristol 1966.

(Bristol) Prev: SHO Off. (Paediat.) Pembury Hosp. Tunbridge Wells; SHO (Psychiat.) Barrow Hosp. Bristol; Ho. Off. Bristol Roy. Infirm.

SELL, Louise Ann Drugs North W., Mental Health Services of Salford, Bury New Road, Manchester M25 3BL Tel: 0161 773 9121 — MB BS 1987 Lond.; MRCP (UK) 1990; MRCPsych 1992. Cons. Psychiat. Drugs NW, Ment. Health Servcs. Salford; Hon. Lect. Univ. Manch. 1998. Prev: Clin. Lect. (Addic.) Inst. Psychiat. Lond.; Sen. Regist. Oxf. RHA; Regist. & SHO Oxon. DHA.

SELL, Mr Philip John Leicester General Hospital, Gwendolen Road, Leicester LE5 4PW — BM 1979 Soton.; MSc Keele 1991; FRCS Eng. 1985. Cons. Spinal Surg., Univ. Hosp. Of Leicester & Qu.s Med. Centre, Nottm. Socs: Sec. Brit. Assoc. Spine Surg.; Brit. Scoliosis Soc. & Brit. Orthop. Assn.

SELLAPPAH, Senathirajan 110 Sandy Hill Road, Plumstead, London SE18 7BA Tel: 020 8854 3736 Fax: 020 8854 3736; 379 Southborough Lane, Bromley BR2 8BQ Fax: 020 8295 0114 — MB BS 1973 Sri Lanka; MRCS Eng. LRCP Lond. 1980; MRCGP 1990; MRCOG 1981; DA (UK) 1989.

SELLAR, Mr Peter William West Cumberland Hospital, Department of Ophthalmology, Whitehaven CA28 8JG Tel: 01946 693181 Fax: 01946 523553 — BM BS 1980 Nottm.; BMedSci Nottm. 1978; FRCS Glas. 1988; FRCOphth 1993. (Nottm.) Cons. Ophth. W. Cumbld. Hosp. Cumbria. Socs: Dutch Ophth. Soc.; N. Eng. Ophth. Soc.; Roy. Coll. Opth. (Fell.). Prev: Cons. Ophth. Maasziekenhuis, Boxmeer, Netherlands; Regist. (Ophth.) Roy. Vict. Hosp. Belf.

SELLAR, Robert John 82 Inverleith Place, Edinburgh EH3 5PA Tel: 0131 552 3393 Fax: 0131 552 8354 Email: rs@skull.ocn.ed.ac.uk — MB BS 1975 Lond.; BSc Lond. 1973; FRCP Lond. 1989; MRCP (UK) 1978; FRCR 1984; DMRD Ed. 1982; FRCS 2000. (St. Thos.) Cons. Neuroradiol. (Surg. Neurol.) Edin.; Sen. Lect. (Med. Radiol.) Univ. Edin. Socs: Brain Interface Gp.; UK Interven.al Neuroradiol. Gp.; Brit. Soc. of NeuroRadiol. Prev: Lect. (Radiol.) & Regist. (Cardiol.) Roy. Infirm. Edin.; SHO Roy. Brompton Hosp. Lond.

SELLAR, William Thomas Kynoch (retired) Murrayfield Medical Practice, 8 Corstorphine Road, Murrayfield, Edinburgh EH12 6HN Tel: 0131 337 6151 — MB ChB 1954 Ed.; DCH RCPS Glas. 1961. GP Edin.; Asst. Chief Med. Off. Standard Life Assur. Co. Edin. Prev: Resid. (Fulbright Award) Pediat. Dept. Univ. Penna. Philadelphia, USA.

SELLARAJAH, Ariaratnam The Surgery, 115 Humberstone Road, Erdington, Birmingham B24 0PY Tel: 0121 351 3321 Fax: 0121 313 0919; Hollyhedge, 432 Jockey Road, Sutton Coldfield B73 5DQ Tel: 0121 355 1927 — MB BS 1970 Ceylon. (Colombo)

SELLARS, Leslie Hull and East Yorkshire Hospitals NHS Trust, Hull Royal Infirmary, Anlaby Road, Hull HU3 2JZ Tel: 01482 674881 Fax: 01482 674998 — MB BS 1974 Newc.; MD Newc. 1981; FRCP Lond. 1993; FRCP Ed. 1988; MRCP (UK) 1976. (Newc. u. Tyne) Cons. Phys. & Nephrol Hull and E. Yorks. Hosp.s NHS Trust. Socs: Renal Assn.; Brit. Hypertens. Soc. Prev: 1st Asst. Med. (Nephrol.) Univ. Newc.

SELLARS, Naomi Anne London Chest Hospital, Bonner Road, London E2 9JX; 2 Winton Road, Farnham GU9 9QW — MB BS 1990 Lond. SHO (Chest.) Lond. Chest Hosp. Lond. Prev: SHO (Neurol.) Roy. Surrey Co. Hosp. Guildford; SHO (Endocrin.) Roy. Free Hosp. Lond.

SELLARS, Neil Robert Kingthorne Group Practice, 83A Thorne Road, Doncaster DN1 2EU Tel: 01302 342832 Fax: 01302 366995; Orchard House, Brockholes Lane, Branton, Doncaster DN3 3NH — MB ChB 1986 Sheff.; MRCGP 1991.

SELLARS, Nigel Henry Leighton Goldsworth Park Health Centre, Denton Way, Woking GU21 3LQ Tel: 01483 767194 Fax: 01483 766042 — MB ChB 1982 Bristol; DRACOG 1988. Clin. Asst. in Diabetes, St Peter's Hosp., Chertsey. Prev: Trainee GP Stroud; Regist. (Med.) Nepean Hosp. Penrith, NSW, Austral.

SELLATURAY, Rajini 55 Russell Road, Northwood HA6 2LP — MB BS 1968 Ceylon. Staff Grade Doctor (Psychiat.) Barnet Health Care Trust Herts.

SELLATURAY, Selvaratnam 55 Russell Road, Northwood HA6 2LP — MB BS 1965 Ceylon; FRCS Ed.; DLO Lond. Staff Grade (ENT) Wycombe Gen. Hosp.

SELLEN, Elizabeth Mary Roper and Partners, Syston Health Centre, Melton Road, Syston, Leicester LE7 2EQ Tel: 0116 260 9111 Fax: 0116 260 9055; 6 Meadowcourt Road, Oadby, Leicester LE2 2PB Tel: 0116 271 2812 — MB ChB 1984 Leic.; DRCOG 1988.

SELLENS, Graham Stuart Manchester Road Health Centre, 7-9 Manchester Road, Haslingden, Rossendale BB4 5SL Tel: 01706 212518; 1 Prospect House, Tanners St, Ramsbottom, Bury BL0 9ES Tel: 01706 821479 — MB ChB 1985 Sheff.; DRCOG 1989.

SELLENS, Kathryn Fiona Bridge Surgery, St. Peters Street, Stapenhill, Burton-on-Trent DE15 9AW Tel: 01283 563451 Fax: 01283 500896; Home Farm Cottage, Chilcote, Swadlincote DE12 8DQ — BM BCh 1990 Oxf.; MRCGP 1994; DRCOG 1992; DCH RCP Lond. 1992. (Oxford) GP Princip. Bridge Surg. Stapenhill.

SELLERS, Mr Jeffrey Irvin (retired) — MB ChB 1954 Birm.; FRCS Eng. (Ophth.) 1964; FRCOphth 1988; DO Eng. 1963. Prev: Sen. Regist. United Sheff. Hosps.

SELLERS, John Wansbeck General Hospital, Woodhorn Lane, Ashington NE63 9JJ Tel: 01670 521212 Fax: 01670 529719; 37 Castle Street, Warkworth, Morpeth NE65 0UN Tel: 01665 711046 — BSc Lond. 1965, MB BS 1968; MRCPath 1975; FRCPath 1998. (Univ. Coll. Hosp.) Cons. Microbiol. Wansbeck Gen. Hosp.; Clin. Lect. (Microbiol.) Univ. Newc. Socs: Assn. Clin. Paths.; Hosp. Infec. Soc. Prev: Cons. Bact. Sundsvall Hosp. Sweden; Sen. Bact. Pub. Health Laborat. Oxf.; Regist. (Clin. Path.) United Bristol Hosps.

SELLERS, Susan Mary Level 4, Women's Centre, Oxford Radcliffe Hospital, Headley Way, Oxford OX3 9DY Tel: 01865 221624 — MB ChB 1972 Manch.; MD Manch. 1983; FRCOG 1994, M 1977. Cons. Obst. John Radcliffe Hosp. Oxf.

SELLERS, William Frederick Shiels Broadgate House, Broadgate, Great Easton, Market Harborough LE16 8SH — MB BS 1970 Lond.; MRCS Eng. LRCP Lond. 1970; FFA RCS Eng. 1978; FFA RCSI 1978; DObst RCOG 1975. Cons. Anaesth. Kettering Gen. Hosp. Prev: Sen. Regist. (Anaesth.) Avon AHA (T); Acting Instruc. Univ. Washington Seattle,USA; Regist. (Anaesth.) Glos. Roy. Hosp. & Cheltenham Gen. Hosp.

SELLEY, Carolyn Anne Psychological Therapies Service, Royal South Hampshire Hospital, Brintons Terrace, off St Mary's Road, Southampton SO14 0YG Tel: 02380 634288 Ext: 2392 — MB ChB 1972 Birm.; MRCGP 1982; MRCPsych 1976. Cons. Psychotherapist Roy. S. Hants. Hosp. Soton. Prev: Sen. Regist. (Psychiat.) Roy. S. Hants. Hosp. Soton.

SELLEY, Peter John Fair Park Surgery, Fair Park, Bow, Crediton EX17 6EY Tel: 01363 82333; Fair Park, Bow, Crediton EX17 6EY — MA 1976; MRCGP 1980; DRCOG 1977. (King's Coll. Hosp.) Prev: Trainee GP Exeter VTS; Ho. Surg. King's Coll. Hosp. Lond.; Med. Off. St. Jude Hosp. Vieux-Fort St. Lucia.

SELLICK, Barry Christopher Apple Tree Cottage, Ridgway, Pyrford, Woking GU22 8PW — MB BS 1975 Lond.; FFA RCS Eng. 1981. Cons. Anaesth. St. Peter's Hosp. Chertsey.

SELLICK, Charles Steven Frome Valley Medical Centre, 2 Court Road, Frampton Cotterell, Bristol BS36 2DE Tel: 01454 772153 Fax: 01454 250078; Penrhys, Chaingate Lane, Iron Acton, Bristol BS37 9XJ Tel: 01454 228431 — MB BS Lond. 1970; MRCS Eng. LRCP Lond. 1970; DObst RCOG 1974. (Middlx.) Princip. GP. Prev: SHO (Surg.) Kettering Hosp.; Ho. Phys. Harefield Hosp.; Ho. Surg. Middlx. Hosp.

SELLICK, Mr Richard James (retired) 10 Wodehouse Road, Hunstanton PE36 6JD Tel: 01485 532082 — MB BChir 1953 Camb.; FRCS Eng. 1961. Prev: Cons. ENT Surg. Norf. & Norwich Hosp.

***SELLORS, Gareth Paul** 2 Shrimpton Road, Knotty Green, Beaconsfield HP9 2AX — MB ChB 1995 Birm.

SELLORS, Jane Elizabeth 22 Lidgett Park Grove, Leeds LS8 1HW — MB ChB 1990 Sheff.

SELLORS, Sir Patrick John Holmes, KCVO (retired) 149 Harley Street, London W1N 2DE Tel: 020 7935 4444 Fax: 020 7486 4616 — BM BCh Oxf. 1958; MA Oxf. 1962, BA 1955; FRCS Eng. 1965; FRCOphth 1988; Hon. FRCOphth 2000. Hon. Cons. Ophth. Croydon Eye Unit & St. Geo. Hosp. Lond. Prev: Cons. Roy. Marsden Hosp. Lond.

SELLS, Elizabeth Lucy Leith Hill Practice, The Green, Ockley, Dorking RH5 5TR Tel: 01306 711182 Fax: 01306 712751; Post Box House, Coldharbour, Dorking RH5 6HD Tel: 01306 712012 — MB BS 1965 Lond. (Univ. Coll. Hosp.) Prev: Regist. & SHO (Radiother.) St. Luke's Hosp. Guildford; Ho. Off. Epsom Dist. Hosp.

SELLS

SELLS, Henry Postbox House, Coldharbour, Dorking RH5 6HD — MB BS 1991 Lond.

SELLS, Martin Frank Lytton Eden Medical Group, Port Road, Carlisle CA2 7AJ Tel: 01228 24477 — MB BChir 1991 Camb.; MA; MRCGP 1996. (Cambridge) GP Princip. Dr Raitt & Partners Carlisle. Socs: Roy. Coll. Gen. Pract.; BMA. Prev: Staff Grade (A & E) Withybush Gen. Hosp. Haverfordshire; SHO (Ophth.) W. Wales Gen. Hosp.

SELLS, Professor Robert Anthony Royal Liverpool University Hospital, Prescot St., Liverpool L7 8XP Tel: 0151 708 0163 Fax: 0151 706 5819 Email: rsells@rlbuh-tr.nwest.nhs.uk; Fax: 0151 706 5819 Email: rsells@rlbuh-tr.nwest.nhs.uk — MA Camb. 1968; MB BS Lond. 1963; FRCS Eng. 1968; FRCS Ed. 1967; MRCS Eng. LRCP Lond. 1962. (Guy's) p/t Cons. Surg. Gen. & Renal Transpl. Roy. Liverp. Hosp.; Hon. Prof. Surg. & Immunol. Univ. Liverp. Socs: (Counc. & Vice-Pres.) Transpl. Soc. (Ex-Vice-Pres. & Ex-Counc.).; Brit. Transpl. Soc. (Ex-Pres.); Moynihan Chirurgical Club (Ex-Pres.). Prev: Cons. Surg. & Dir. Renal Transpl. Roy. Liverp. Hosp.; Lect. (Surg.) & Ho. Off. (Experim. Med.) Guy's Hosp. Lond.; MRC Fell. Harvard Univ. USA.

SELLS, Rupert William Blyth Lyngford Park Surgery, Fletcher Close, Taunton TA2 8SQ Tel: 01823 333355 Fax: 01823 257022; Longview, Buttsway, Milverton, Taunton TA4 1ND Tel: 01823 400349 — MB BS 1991 Lond.; BSc Med. Microbiol. Lond. 1988. (Univ. Coll. Middlx. Sch. Med.) GP Partner.

SELLU, Mr David Patrick Department of Surgery, Hammersmith Hospital & Royal Postgraduate Medical School, Du Cane Road, London W12 0NN Tel: 020 8743 2030; Department of Surgery, Ealing Hospital, Uxbridge Road, Southall UB1 3HW Tel: 020 8967 5530 Fax: 020 8967 5530 Email: dsellu@eht.nhs.uk — MB ChB 1973 Manch.; MSc Lond. 1996; ChM Manch. 1984, MB ChB 1973; FRCS Eng. 1979; FRCS Ed. 1979. (Manch.) Cons. Surg. Ealing Hosp. Lond.; Sen. Lect. & Hon. Cons. Surg. Roy. Postgrad. Med. Sch. & Hammersmith Hosp Lond. Socs: Assn. if Surg.s of Gt. Britain & Irel.; Assn. of Endocrine Surg.s; Assn. of Coloproctologists. Prev: Cons. Surg. Min. of Health, Oman; Ho. Phys. Hope Hosp. Salford; Ho. Surg. Manch. N.. Hosp.

SELLWOOD, Karen 7 Tehidy Terrace, Falmouth TR11 2SZ — BM 1979 Soton.

SELLWOOD, Mark William 7 Evelyn Road, Ham, Richmond TW10 7HU Tel: 020 8948 3874 — MB BS 1990 Lond.

SELLWOOD, Mr Nigel Howard (retired) 7 Tehidy Terrace, Falmouth TR11 2SZ — MB BS 1974 Lond.; FRCS Eng. 1978; MRCS Eng. LRCP Lond. 1974. Prev: Cons. A & E Roy. Cornw. Hosp. Truro.

SELLWOOD, Robert Binford (retired) Greenbanks, Agar Road, Truro TR1 1JU — MB 1961 Camb.; BChir 1960; FFR 1973; DMRD Eng. 1971. Prev: Cons. Radiol. Roy. Cornw. Hosps.

SELLWOOD, William George District General Hospital, Weston Road, Stafford ST16 3SA Tel: 01785 257731; Gobions, Brook Lane, Ranton Green, Stafford ST18 9JY Tel: 01785 823523 — MB ChB 1971 Manch.; FFA RCS Eng. 1977. Cons. Anaesth. Mid Staff. Dist. HA.

SELLY, Eryl William Community Health Centre, Mount Lane, Llanidloes SY18 6EZ — BChir 1975 Camb.; MB 1976; MRCGP 1983.

SELMAN, Joanna Clare 7 Bereweeke Way, Winchester SO22 6BJ — MB ChB 1994 Liverp.

SELMAN, Mark Andrew Mobile: 0771 8017897; 3 Dartside, Totnes TQ9 5HL Mobile: 07718 017897 — BM BS 1991 Nottm.; BMedSci. (Hons.) Nottm. 1989; MRCGP 1996; DCH RCP Lond. 1995; DFFP 1996. (Nottm.) Socs: Chairm. Torbay & S. Devon Non-Princip.s Gp.; Torbay PCG Clin. Governance Steering Comm.; GPC-Non-Princip.s SubComm. Prev: GP Princip. Taunton; GP/Regist. Torbay; SHO (Med.) Roy. Devon & Exeter Hosp. & Derriford Hosp. Plymouth.

SELMAN, Richard Michael 25 Ffordd Argoed, Bryn Awelon, Mold CH7 1LY Tel: 01352 55560 — MB ChB 1988 Liverp. Prev: Trainee GP/SHO (A & E) Warrington Dist. Gen. Hosp. VTS.

***SELMAN, Tara Jayne** 7 Alpine Close, Paulton, Bristol BS39 7SE — MB ChB 1998 Birm.

SELMES, Susan Elizabeth Empingham Medical Centre, 37 Main Street, Empingham, Oakham LE15 8PR Tel: 01780 460202 Fax: 01780 460283; 21 Foxhill, Whissendine, Oakham LE15 7HP Tel:

01664 474715 — MB ChB 1982 Ed.; MRCGP 1986. (Edinburgh) GP Princip.

SELMI, Fahed 2 Palmer Avenue, Willerby, Hull HU10 6LJ — MB BS 1983 Karachi.

SELMON, Mr Guy Philip Ford 6 Medebourne Close, Blackheath, London SE3 9AB Tel: 020 8318 6188 — MB BS 1992 Lond.; FRCS (Tr. & Orth.) 2001; FRCS 1997. (Guy's) Specialist Regist. Rotat. (Trauma & Orthop.) S. E. Thames.

SELSBY, Daniel Sean 43 Leeds Road, Rawdon, Leeds LS19 6NW — MB ChB 1982 Bristol; FRCA 1987. Cons. Anaesth. Leeds Gen. Infirm. Prev: Regist. (Anaesth.) Leeds Gen. Infirm.; SHO (Anaesth.) Univ. Hosp. Nottm.; Cas. Off. Univ. Hosp. Nottm.

SELSON, Michael George (retired) 30 Lymister Avenue, Moorgate, Rotherham S60 3DD Tel: 01709 377332 — MB BS Lond. 1952. Prev: GP Rotherham.

SELTZER, Abigail Ann 6 Erskine Hill, London NW11 6HB — MB ChB 1979 Glas.; MRCPsych 1984.

SELTZER, Basil (retired) 49 Aytoun Road, Glasgow G41 5HW — LRCP LRCS 1948 Ed.; LRCP LRCS Ed. LRFPS Glas. 1948; MRCP Glas. 1952. Prev: Regist. (Med.) St. And. Hosp. Billericay.

SELTZER, Beverley Kim 8 Mansionhouse Gardens, Glasgow G41 3DP — MB ChB 1987 Glas.

SELTZER, Myer Solomon 5 Arran Drive, Giffnock, Glasgow G46 7NL Tel: 0141 638 6677 Fax: 0141 621 0395 Email: myersol1936@lineone.net — MB ChB 1958 Glas.; DObst RCOG 1960; Cert JCC Lond. 1977. (Glas.) Socs: (Ex-Pres.) Brit. Soc. Med. & Dent. Hypn.; Life Mem. Glas. Univ. M-C Soc. Prev: Ho. Off. (Med.) S.. Gen. Hosp. Glas.; Ho. Surg. Vict. Infirm. Glas.; SHO Belvidere Infec. Dis. Hosp. Glas.

SELVACHANDRAN, Mr Prince Selvadurai General Hospital, St Helier, Jersey Tel: 01534 71000 — MB BS 1963 Madras; FRCS Eng. 1971; FRCS Ed. 1970.

SELVACHANDRAN, Mr Sithamparapillai Nadarajah Leighton Hospital, Crewe CW1 4QJ Tel: 01270 255141; 19 Hesketh Croft, Coppenhall, Crewe CW1 4RY Tel: 01270 582575 — MB BS 1975 Sri Lanka; FRCS Glas. 1985; LRCP LRCS Ed. LRCPS Glas. 1982. Assoc. Specialist (Gen. Sug.) Leighton Hosp. Crewe.

SELVADURAI, David Kishan 75 Kempson Avenue, Sutton Coldfield B72 1HF — MB BS 1992 Lond.

SELVADURAI, Mrs Leila Rachel Nevins Department of Radiology, Leighton Hospital, Crewe CW1 4QJ Tel: 01270 255141; 8 Blenheim Court, Alsager, Stoke-on-Trent ST7 2BY Tel: 01270 877500 — MB BS Ceylon 1964; FFR RCSI 1983; DMRD Eng. 1979. (Colombo) Cons. Radiol. Leighton Hosp. Crewe. Socs: BMA; Roy. Coll. Radiol. Prev: Sen. Regist. (Radiodiag.) N. Staffs. Hosp. Centre; Regist. (Radiodiag.) Bristol Roy. Infirm.

SELVADURAI, Mary Ananthavathy Canterbury Way Surgery, 91A Canterbury Way, Stevenage SG1 4LQ Tel: 01438 316646 — MB BS 1966 Ceylon.

SELVADURAI, Vasuki 20 Downsway, Shoreham-by-Sea BN43 5GN — MB BS 1985 Colombo; LMSSA Lond. 1995.

SELVAKUMAR, Mr Sadasivam Consultant Surgeon, Lister Hospital, Stevenage — MB BS 1983 Madras; FRCS Ed. 1988; FRCS (Gen.) 1997. Cons. Vasc. & Gen. Surg., Lister Hosp. Stevenage.

SELVAKUMAR, Shamugam Pillai 19 Bishops Avenue, Worcester WR3 8XA — MB BS 1978 Madurai Kamaraj, India.

SELVAM, Andiappan Chadmoor Medical Practice, 45 Princess St, Cannock WS11 2JT Tel: 01543 571650 Fax: 01543 462304 — MB BS 1973 Madras. (Madras Med. Coll.) Prev: Regist. (Paediat. Surg.) E. Birm. Hosp.; SHO (Gen. & Paediat. Surg.) E. Birm. Hosp.

SELVAN, Subramaniyan Tamil Long Catlis Road Surgery, 119 Long Catlis Road, Parkwood, Rainham, Gillingham ME8 9RR Tel: 01634 360989 — MB BS 1979 Madras; LRCP LRCS Ed. LRCPS Glas. 1981.

SELVANANTHAN, Mr Perampalam Prince Charles Hospital, Merthyr Tydfil CF47 9BT; 53 Ravensbrook, Morganstown, Cardiff CF15 8LT — MB BS 1971 Ceylon; FRCS Glas. (Ophth.) 1985; DO RCS Eng. 1981. (Peradeniya) Regist. (Ophth.) P. Chas. Hosp. Merthyr Tydfil. Prev: SHO (Ophth.) P.ss Margt. Hosp. Swindon, N.E. Essex HA & ScarBoro. Hosp.

SELVANANTHAN, Sivaganga Flat 9, Block 2, Prince Charles Hospital, Merthyr Tydfil CF47 9BT Tel: 01685 721721; 53 Ravensbrook, Morganstown, Cardiff CF15 8LT — MB BS 1973 Ceylon; DPM RCPSI 1986.

SELVANATHAN, Esther Suganthaleela 9 Heath Park Drive, Bromley BR1 2WQ — MB BS 1973 Sri Lanka. Socs: Med. Defence Union.

SELVANATHAN, Mr Gnanapragasam Anton Joseph The Surgery, 27 Clifton Rise, London SE14 6ER Tel: 020 8692 1387; 9 Heath Park Drive, Bromley BR1 2WQ Tel: 020 8295 1696 — MB BS 1973 Sri Lanka; FRCS Ed. 1983; LRCP LRCS Ed. LRCPS Glas. 1985. Socs: Med. Defence Union; BMA.

SELVARAJAH, David Thampoe Merefield, Mere Farm Road, Oxton, Birkenhead CH43 9TS — MB BS 1970 Ceylon; MRCPsych. 1982; DPM Eng. 1979. (Colombo) Cons. Psychiat. Pk. Hosp., Rainhill Hosp. & BRd.green Gen. Hosp. Liverp.; Sen. Regist. (Psychiat.) Univ. Liverp. & Roy. Liverp. Hosp.; Hon. Sen. Regist. (Psychiat.) Pk. La. Hosp. Liverp. Prev: Sen. Regist. (Psychiat.) Winwick Hosp. Warrington; Sen. Regist. (Psychiat.) Rainhill Hosp. Liverp.; Regist. (Psychiat. & EEG) St. Francis Hosp. & Hurstwood Pk. Neurol. Centre Haywards Heath; .

SELVARAJAH, Kanther 43 Brook Road, Newbury Park, Ilford IG2 7EZ — MB BS 1975 Sri Lanka; LRCP LRCS Ed. LRCPS Glas. 1982.

SELVARAJAH, Kumar Nagamuthu 2 Bamford Avenue, Alperton, Wembley HA0 1NB Tel: 020 8810 4638 — MRCS Eng. LRCP Lond. 1992; MB BS Madurai-Kamaraj 1982.

SELVARAJAN, Bright Selvadurai Wandsworth Bridge Road Surgery, 29 Wandsworth Bridge Road, London SW6 2TA Tel: 020 7736 9341 Fax: 020 7384 1493 — MB BS 1968 Madras.

SELVARAJAN, Mahadeva 268 Chadwell Heath Lane, Romford RM6 4YL — LRCP LRCS 1993 Ed.; LRCP LRCS Ed. LRCPS Glas. 1993.

SELVARANGAN, Rengaswami The Surgery, 1 Knoll Rise, Orpington BR6 0EJ Tel: 01689 824563 Fax: 01689 820712 — MB BS 1967 Madras.

SELVARATNAM, Murugesu Aiyampillai Stone House Hospital, Cotton Lane, Dartford DA2 6U Tel: 01322 622222; 27 Hollingbourne Avenue, Bexleyheath DA7 5ET Tel: 01322 440594 Fax: 01322 440881 — MB BS 1972 Ceylon; MRCPsych 1980; DPM Eng. 1979. Cons. Psychiat., Gen. Psychiat., Stone Ho. Hosp., Dartford. Socs: BMA. Prev: Freelance Cons. Psychiat. & GP.

SELVARATNAM, Yamini 25 Listergate, 317 Upper Richmond Road, Putney, London SW15 6ST Tel: 020 8789 9989 Fax: 020 8789 9989 — MB BS 1994 Lond. GP Rotat. UMDS Lond. Prev: SHO (A & E) St. Thos. Hosp. Lond.; SHO (Gen. Med.) Guy's Hosp. Lond.; SHO (O & G) St Thomas' Hosp.

SELVEY, David Morrish 41 Llanvair Drive, Ascot SL5 9LW — MB BCh 1986 Witwatersrand.

SELWAY, Cedric Angus (retired) Coopers Brook, School Lane, Abbess Roding, Ongar CM5 0NY — MB BS 1958 Lond.; DCH Eng. 1961; DObst RCOG 1960. Prev: GP Harlow.

SELWAY, Jennefer Rachel Department of Public Health, Bromley Health, Global House, 10 Station Approach, Hayes, Bromley BR2 7EH; Edensor, Linden Pk Road, Tunbridge Wells TN2 5QL — MB BS 1988 Lond.; MFPHM 2001; MRCGP 1993; DCH RCP Lond. 1993; Dip. Health Economics Aberd 1996. (London) Sen. Regist. (Pub. Health) Bromley Health Lond. Prev: Trainee GP Watford VTS.

SELWOOD, Amber 16 Holme Close, Woodborough, Nottingham NG14 6EX Tel: 0115 965 4298 — MB ChB 1995 Birm.; ChB Birm. 1995.

SELWOOD, David Peter 13 Banckside, Hartley, Longfield DA3 7RD — MB ChB 1996 Leeds.

SELWOOD, Jane Elizabeth 1 Woodberry Avenue, Winchmere Hill, London N21 3LE Tel: 020 8886 2751; Flat 3, 15 Gentlemans Row, Enfield EN2 6PT Tel: 020 8366 5916 — MB BS 1981 Lond.

SELWYN, Alan Willow Tree Family Doctors, 301 Kingsbury Road, London NW9 9PE Tel: 020 8204 6464 Fax: 020 8905 0946 — MB BS 1982 Lond.; MRCGP (Distinc.) 1986; DCH RCP Lond. 1985. (Roy. Free) Lect. Roy. Free Hosp. Sch. Med. Lond. Socs: Yeoman of Worshipful Soc. of Apoth. Prev: Trainee GP Edgware VTS.

SELWYN, David Anthony Leicester Royal Infirmary, Leicester LE1 5WW Tel: 01533 541414 — MB BS 1986 Lond.; FRCA 1993; DA (UK) 1990. Sen. Regist. (Anaesth.) Leic. Roy. Infirm. Prev: Lect. (Anaesth.) Univ. Leicester; SHO (Anaesth.) Qu. Med. Centre Nottm.

SELWYN, Elaine Margaret Harnall Lane Medical Centre, Harnall Lane East, Coventry CV1 5AE Tel: 024 7622 4640 Fax: 024 7622 3859; 43 Rawnsley Drive, Kenilworth CV8 2NX Tel: 01926 850988 — MB BS 1977 Lond.; MFFP 1994; DRCOG 1979. Clin. Med. Off. (Family Plann.) Leamington Spa.

SELWYN, Jane Elizabeth Eborall and Partners, Fountain Medical Centre, Sherwood Avenue, Newark NG24 1QH Tel: 01636 704378/9 Fax: 01636 610875; Old Grange Farm, Sibthorpe, Newark NG23 5PN Tel: 01636 525092 — MB BS 1982 Lond.; MRCP (UK) 1986; MRCGP 1989. (St. Bart.)

SELWYN, Mr Julian Ralph Merriman — MB BS 1981 Lond.; FRCS Eng. 1989; MRCS Eng. LRCP Lond. 1981; MRCGP 1991.

SELWYN, Pamela Tel: 01495 301210 Fax: 01633 350684; Troedy-Foel, Castle Road, Llangyndir, Crickhowell NP8 1NG — MB BCh 1972 Wales. (Cardiff) Prev: Ho. Off. (Gen. Med. & Gen. Surg.) Nevill Hall Hosp. Abergavenny.

SELWYN, Victor Graham Holly Park Clinic, Holly Park Road, London N11 3RA Tel: 0141 560 3577 — MB BS 1969 Lond.; Mem. Brit. Med. Acupuncture Soc.; MRCS Eng. LRCP Lond. 1969; ECFMG Cert 1969; DObst RCOG 1971; Cert Contracep. & Family Plann. RCOG, RCGP &; Cert FPA 1975. (Middlx.) Socs: BMA (Ex-Hon. Sec. Finchley & Barnet Br.). Prev: Clin. Asst. (ENT) Enfield Dist. Hosp.; Clin. Asst. (Obst.) Whittington Hosp. Lond.; SHO Centr. Middlx. Hosp. Lond.

SELZER, Gunther Horst 43 Abington House, Adrian Way, Cambridge CB2 2SA Tel: 01223 726080 — State Exam Med. Kiel 1990; FRCS Ed. 1997. Socs: Brit. Ortho. Train. Assoc.

SEMAO, Melville Alade The Surgery, 6-8 Englefield Road, London N1 4LN — State Exam Med 1968 Freiburg. Socs: Fell. of the Roy. Soc. of Med.

SEMARK, Diane Wendy Ashcroft Road Surgery, 26 Ashcroft Road, Stopsley Green, Luton LU2 9AU Tel: 01582 722555 Fax: 01582 418145 Email: diane.semark@gp-e81006.nhs.uk; The Shambles, 69 Bedford Road, Hitchin SG5 2TU Tel: 01462 432647 — MB BS 1966 Lond.; MFFP; MRCS Eng. LRCP Lond. 1966; DObst RCOG 1969. (Roy. Free) GP; Sen. Clin. Med. Off. (Family Plann.) Bedford. Socs: Brit. Med. Assn.; Brit. Menopause Soc. Prev: GP Sawtry; Phys. (Primary Care) King Faisal Specialist Hosp. Riyadh, Saudi Arabia; Clin. Med. Off. Beds AHA.

SEMBHI, Satvinder Kaur 7 Holmbury Gardens, Hayes UB3 2LU; Mental Health Liaison Team, Waterlow Unit, Whittington Hospital, London N19 5NF Tel: 020 7530 2216 — BM 1990 Soton.; MRCPsych. Specialist Regist. N. Lond./UCLMS Train. Scheme. Prev: Regist. Rotat. (Psychiat.) N. Lond.

SEMENIUK, Petro 221 Priory Road, Hull HU5 5RZ — MB ChB 1981 Manch.; MRCGP 1987. GP Hull. Socs: Hull Med. Soc.; RCGP & BMA.

SEMENOV, Richard Arne Flat 1/3, Jacksons Lane, Highgate, London N6 5SR — MB BS 1990 Adelaide.

SEMERARO, David Histopathology Department, Derbyshire Royal Infirmary, London Road, Derby DE1 2QY Tel: 01332 47141 — MB ChB 1981 Bristol; MRCPath 1990. Cons. Histopath. Derbysh. Roy. Infirm. Socs: Path. Soc.; Assn. Clin. Path. Prev: Sen. Regist. (Histopath.) Univ. Hosp. Wales.

SEMMENS, Jane Marjorie (retired) 32 Aldsworth Court, Goring St., Goring-by-Sea, Worthing BN12 5AG Tel: 01903 244515 Fax: 01903 244515 — MB BS Lond. 1955; MD Lond. 1971; DCH Eng. 1957. Nat. Co-ordinator Med. Wom. Internat. Assn. Prev: Cons. Paediat. Chichester & Worthing Health Dists.

SEMMLER, Jodie Michelle 114 Harvist Road, Ground Floor Flat, Queenspark, London NW6 6HJ — MB BS 1991 Adelaide.

SEMPA, Alexandra Vera 58 Vineyard Road, Northfield, Birmingham B31 1PR — MB ChB 1963 Bristol.

SEMPLE, Alan James 3 Snowdon Place, Stirling FK8 2NH Tel: 01786 61715 — MB ChB 1979 Dundee; FFA RCS Eng. 1983. Cons. Anaesth. Falkirk & Dist. Roy. Infirm. Prev: Sen. Regist. (Anaesth.) Ninewells Hosp. Dundee.

SEMPLE, Andrew Best, CBE, VRD 433 Woolton Road, Liverpool L25 4SY Tel: 0151 428 2081 — MD (Commend.) Glas. 1947, MB ChB (Commend.) 1934; DPH 1936; FFCM 1974. (Univ. Glas.) Surg. Cdr. RNR; Fell. Soc. Community Med. Socs: FRSH (Exec. Vice-Pres. & Treas.). Prev: Hon. Phys. to H.M. The Qu.; Area Med. Off. Liverp. AHA (T); Prof. Community & Environm. Health Univ. Liverp.

SEMPLE, Colin Gordon 53 Tinto Road, Newlands, Glasgow G43 2AH — MB ChB 1977 Glas.; MA, MD Glas. 1990, MB ChB 1977; FRCP (Glas., Ed., Lond.); MRCP (UK) 1980. Cons. Phys. S.ern Gen. Hosp. Glas. Socs: Hon. Sec. RCP & Surg. of Glas.; Chairm.

SEMPLE

Spec. Adv. Comm. on Gen. Internal Med. of Jt. Comm. Higher Med. Train.

SEMPLE, David Alexander — MB BChir 1989 Camb.; MB BChir Camb. 1990; FRCA 1994. (Camb.) Cons. (Anaesth.) Roy. Infirm. Of Edin.

SEMPLE, David Mark 13 Booths Hill Road, Lymm WA13 0DJ — MB ChB 1988 Glas.; MRCOG 1994. Regist. Arrowe Pk. Hosp. Wirral. Prev: Regist. Rotat. (O & G) Liverp. Wom. Hosp.; Regist. Fazakerley Hosp. Liverp.

SEMPLE, Deborah Karon Comber Health Centre, 5 Newtownards Road, Newtownards BT23 5BA — MB BCh BAO 1987 Belf.

SEMPLE, Mr Graham Alan 16 Billendean Terrace, Spittal, Berwick-upon-Tweed TD15 2AX Tel: 01289 307773; 47 Bracklyn Court, Wimbourne St, Hackney, London N1 7EL Tel: 020 7490 1497 Fax: 020 7490 1497 Email: gsemple@compuserve.com — MB BS 1993 Lond.; BSc (Hons.) Lond. 1989; FRCS Eng. 1998. (Univ. Coll. & Middlx. Sch. Med.) SHO (Orthop. Surg.) Barnet Gen. Hosp. Lond. Socs: BMA; Med. Protec. Soc.

SEMPLE, Iain Cameron Ovoca, 460 Didsbury Road, Heaton Mersey, Stockport SK4 3BT Tel: 0161 432 2032 Fax: 0161 947 9689 — MB ChB 1990 Manch.; MRCGP 1994.

SEMPLE, Mr James Campbell 79 Harley Street, London W1G 8PZ Tel: 020 7224 0046 Fax: 020 7224 0082 Email: canpbell@79harleystreet.co.uk; 34 Polwarth St, Glasgow G12 9TX Tel: 0141 339 5455 Fax: 0141 5769656 — MB ChB Glas. 1959; FRCS Glas. 1965; FRCS Ed. 1966. (Glas.) p/t Indep. Pract. (Hand & Surg.) Lond. & Glas. Prev: Cons. Hand Surg. W.. Infirm. Glas.; Lect. Nuffield Dept. Orthop. Surg. Univ. Oxf.; Cons. Hand Surg. Sheff. RHB (Derby Area).

SEMPLE, Judith Mairi The Health Centre, 20 Duncan Street, Greenock PA15 4LY Tel: 01475 724477 Fax: 01475 727140 — MB ChB 1972 St. And.; FRCP Glas. 1994; MRCP (UK) 1977; DCH Eng. 1975.

SEMPLE, Linsey Charlotte Struthers and Partners, 436 Mosspark Boulevard, Glasgow G52 1HX Tel: 0141 882 5494 Fax: 0141 883 1015 — MB ChB 1983 Glas.; MRCGP 1986; DRCOG 1985.

SEMPLE, Margaret Janet Epsom & St Helier NHS TrustDepartment of Haematology, Epsom General Hospital, Dorking Road, Epsom KT18 7EG Tel: 01372 735735 Fax: 01372 748802; 11 Redwoods, Alton Road, Roehampton, London SW15 4NL Tel: 020 8789 6248 — MB BS 1967 Lond.; BSc (Hons. Special Physiol.) Lond. 1967; FRCP Lond. 1996; MRCP (UK) 1974; FRCPath 1989, M 1977. (StThomas) Cons. Haemat. Epsom Gen. Hosp.

SEMPLE, Margaret McIndoe Gowrie House, Royal Dundee Liff Hospital, Liff, Dundee DD2 5NF Tel: 01382 423046 — MB ChB 1979 Glas.; MRCPsych 1988; DObst RCOG 1981. (Univ. Glas.) Cons. Psychiat. Roy. Dundee Liff Hosp. Liff Dundee. Prev: Sen. Regist. & Regist. (Psychiat.) Roy. Dundee Liff Hosp.; Cons. Psychiat. Hairmyres Hosp. E. Kilbride Lanarksh.

SEMPLE, Peter 8 North Park Grove, Roundary, Leeds LS8 1JJ Tel: 0113 240 0044 — BM 1984 Soton.; FCAnaesth 1990; FFA RCSI 1989; DA (UK) 1986. Cons. Anaesth. St. Jas. Hosp. Leeds; Hon. Clin. Lect. Univ. Leeds.

SEMPLE, Peter D'Almaine Inverclyde Royal Hospital, Larkfield Road, Greenock PA16 1JX Tel: 01475 633777 Fax: 01475 656142 Email: peter.semple@irh.nhs.uk; High Lunderston, Inverkip, Greenock PA16 0DU Tel: 01475 522342 — MB ChB Glas. 1970; MD Glas. 1985; FRCP Lond. 1996; FRCP Ed. 1988; FRCP Glas. 1984; MRCP (UK) 1974. Cons. Gen. Med. & Respirat. Dis. Inverclyde Roy. Hosp. Greenock. Prev: Chairm. Med. Audit. Subcomm. CRAG Scott. Home & Health Dept.; Dir. Med Audit RCPS Gls.

SEMPLE, Peter Ferguson University Department of Medicine & Therapeutics, Western Infirmary, Glasgow G11 6NT Tel: 0141 339 8822 Fax: 0141 339 2800; 103 Southbrae Drive, Glasgow G13 1TU Tel: 0141 959 4462 Fax: 0141 959 4462 — MB ChB St. And. 1969; FRCP Glas. 1983; MRCP (UK) 1971. Cons. Phys. Univ. Dept. Med. W.. Infirm. Glas.; Subdean W.ern Infirm. Socs: Assn. Phys. Prev: Regist. (Med.) Glas. Roy. Infirm.; Sen. Lect. Med. W.. Infirm.; Cons. Pysician MRC Blood Pressure Unit W.ern Infirm.

SEMPLE, Stuart Mackenzie Mounthooly, Winchburgh, Broxburn EH52 6PY Tel: 01506 890357 — MB ChB 1962 Ed.; MRCGP 1974; FRCPath 1985, M 1972; MFHom 1979; FFHom 1996; DObst RCOG 1965; LM Rotunda 1965. Chairm. Brit. Homoeop. Research Gp. Prev: Lect. Bact. Univ. Edin.; Regist. Clin. Path. Roy. Infirm. Edin.

SEMPLE, Thomas (retired) Fairhaven, South St., Elie, Leven KY9 1DN Tel: 01333 330540 — MD 1945 Glas.; BSc Glas. 1935, MD 1945, MB ChB 1938; FRFPS Glas. 1941; FRCP Glas. 1964; FRCP Ed. 1951, M 1942; FRCP Lond. 1970, M 1947. Prev: Phys. & Cardiol. Vict. Infirm. Glas.

SEMPLE, Verne Adrienne (retired) Larne House, 31 Buchanan St., Balfron, Glasgow G63 0TS Tel: 01360 440854 — MB ChB Glas. 1948. Prev: Ho. Phys. Vict. Infirm. Glas.

SEMPLE, William Gordon, SBStJ (retired) Larne House, 31 Buchanan St., Balfron, Glasgow G63 0TS Tel: 01360 440854 — MB ChB Glas. 1948. Prev: Squadron Ldr. RAF Med. Br.

SEMPLE, William John 7 Tothill Street, Minster-in-Thanet, Ramsgate CT12 4AG — MB BS 1963 Lond.; MRCS Eng. LRCP Lond. 1962; DA Eng. 1965; DObst. RCOG 1966. (King's Coll. Hosp.)

SEMRAU, Ute 28 Ashley Road, London N19 3AF — State Exam Med 1992 Berlin.

***SEN, Aloke Srinath** 80 Mossley Road, Ashton-under-Lyne OL6 9RQ Tel: 0161 339 3863 Email: alokesen@hotmail.com — MB ChB 1993 Manch.; MB ChB Manch 1993.

SEN, Amitabha 19 The Chesters, West Denton, Newcastle upon Tyne NE5 1AF — MB BS 1967 Calcutta.

SEN, Anup Kumar (retired) 39 Station Road, Hemsworth, Pontefract WF9 4JW — MB BS 1951 Calcutta; DPH Eng. 1953, DIH 1953.

SEN, Arjune Four Oaks, 40 Russell Bank Road, Sutton Coldfield B74 4RQ — BM BCh 1998 Oxf.; BM BCh Oxf 1998.

SEN, Mr Aruni Department of Accident & Emergency, N.E. Wales NHS Trust, Maelor Hospital, Croesnewydd Road, Wrexham LL13 7TD Tel: 01978 291100 Fax: 01978 725168 Email: aruni.sen@new-tr.wales.nhs.uk; 8 Chetwyn Court, Gresford, Wrexham LL12 8EG Tel: 01978 856068 Fax: 01978 856146 Email: thesens@msn.com — MB BS 1982 Calcutta; MS (Surg.) Calcutta 1986; FRCS Eng. 1990; FRCS Ed. 1989; FFAEM 1996. (Med. Coll. Calcutta) Cons. A & E Ysbyty Maelor Wrexham, N. E. Wales NHS Trust. Prev: Sen. Regist. (A & E) W.. Infirm. Glas.; Regist. (A & E) Vict. Infirm. Glas.

SEN, Asha The Surgery, 12 The Slade, Plumstead, London SE18 2NB Tel: 020 8317 3031 Fax: 020 8317 2536 — MB BS 1970 Indore; MB BS 1970 Indore.

SEN, Asim Kumar 6 Fallowfield, Shoeburyness, Southend-on-Sea SS3 8DF — MB BS 1972 Calcutta.

SEN, Balarka (retired) Belmont, Sandheath Road, Beacon Hill, Hindhead GU26 6RU Tel: 01428 609299 — LMSSA 1967 Lond. Med. Asst. (Psychiat.) Geo. Eliot Hosp. Nuneaton. Prev: GP Nuneaton.

SEN, Mr Basav 19 Tankerville Terrace, Jesmond, Newcastle upon Tyne NE2 3AJ Tel: 0191 281 6160 — MB BS 1984 Bhagalpur; FRCS Glas. 1989. Cons. (A & E) Head of Dept. Roy. Vict. Infirm. Newc.

SEN, Mr Binayak 10 Ashville Croft, Halifax HX2 0QJ Tel: 01422 361381 — MB BS 1981 Calcutta; FRCS Glas. 1989.

SEN, Debajit 145 Roll Gardens, Gants Hill, Ilford IG2 6TL — MB BS 1993 Lond.

SEN, Debasish Grove House, Skerton Road, Manchester M16 0RB Tel: 0161 952 8200 Fax: 0161 952 8300 — MB BS 1980 Newc.; MFOM RCP Lond. 1996; MRCGP 1986; DRCOG 1987. (Newcastle upon Tyne) Sen. Med. Insp. Health & Safety Exec.; Examr., Fac. of Occ Med. RCP Lond.; Hon. Lect. Dept. of Pub. Health Med. Univ. of Liverp.; Visit Lect. For Occ & Env Health Univ of Manch. Socs: Soc. Occupat. Med.; MEDICHEM. Prev: Employm. Med. Adviser Health & Safety Exec.; GP Ferryhill.

SEN, Gurmeet 6 Fallowfield, Shoeburyness, Southend-on-Sea SS3 8DF — MB BS 1973 Delhi.

SEN, Indranil Bedlingtonshire Medical Group, Glebe Road, Bedlington NE22 6JX Tel: 01670 822695 Email: l.sen@zen.co.uk; 18 Lime Grove, Littleborough OL15 8RP Tel: 01706 370579 Email: i.sen@zen.co.uk — MB ChB 1996 Manch. GP Regist., Bedlingtonshire Med. grp. Prev: Ho. Off. (Surg.) Birch Hill Hosp. Rochdale; Ho. Off. (Med.) Bury Gen. Hosp. Lancs.; SHO in A&E, Newham Gen. Hosp, Lond.

SENDER

SEN, Jon 5 Swan Road, Starcross, Exeter EX6 8QW Tel: 01626 890621 Email: jonsen@hotmail.com — MB BS 1998 Lond.; MB BS Lond 1998; BSc (Hons). (Univ. Coll. Lond.) SHO (A&E) N.wick Pk. Hosp. Harrow. Socs: BMA; Fell. Roy. Soc. Of Med.; MDU. Prev: PRHO (Oncol. & Radiother.) Mt. Vernon Hosp.; PRHO (Med.) Watford Gen. Hosp.; PRHO (Surg.) Hillingdon Hosp.

SEN, Julia Department of Ophthalmology, Royal Liverpool University Hospital, Prescot St., Liverpool L7 8XP Tel: 0151 706 2000; The Chimes, Glebe Lane, Gnosall, Stafford ST20 0ER Tel: 01785 822311 — MB ChB 1993 Leic. SHO (Ophth.) Roy. Liverp. Univ. Hosp. Socs: Med. Defence Union; BMA. Prev: SHO (Ophth.) P'boro. Dist. Hosp.; SHO (O & G) P'boro. Dist. Hosp.; SHO (Respirat. Med.) Glenfield Hosp. Trust Leicester.

SEN, Purnendu Kumar 18 Lime Grove, Littleborough OL15 8RP Tel: 01706 370579; 1 Bulwer Street, Rochdale OL16 2EU Tel: 01706 356422 — MB BS Calcutta 1959; DA Calcutta 1969; DA Eng. 1975. (Calcutta) GP Rochdale. Prev: Trainee GP Salford; SHO (Psychiat.) St. Mary's Hosp. Hereford; SHO (A & E) Gen. Hosp. Hereford.

SEN, Rabindra Nath (retired) 4 Snipe Close, Holymoorside, Chesterfield S42 7HD Tel: 01246 568292 — MB BS 1958 Calcutta; DO Eng. 1965. Prev: Assoc. Specialist (Ophth.) Chesterfield & N. Derbysh. Roy. Hosp.

SEN, Rachel Angela 54 Malpas Road, Runcorn WA7 4AJ — MB ChB 1978 Manch.

SEN, S K The Surgery, The Chantry, Coxwold, York YO61 4BB Tel: 01347 868426 Fax: 01347 868782 — MB BS 1969 Calcutta; MB BS 1969 Calcutta.

SEN, Salil Ranjan (Surgery), 96 Barnsley Road, Goldthorpe, Rotherham S63 9AB Tel: 01709 890686 Fax: 01709 888347 — MB BS Gauhati 1967; FRIPHH Lond. 1998; BSc Gauhati 1962; DRCOG Lond. 1979; DObst RLPI 1974 Dub; FPA Lond. 1974; Lic. AC Liverp. 1984; DFFP Lond. 1995; FRSM Lond. 1996; FRSH Lond. 1997. Princip. GP; Primary Care Gp. Bd. Mem. Socs: Med. Protec. Soc.

SEN, Sanjay Kumar 12 Hanworth Road, Feltham TW13 5AD Tel: 020 8890 2208; 9 Berwyn Avenue, Hounslow TW3 4ET. GP Feltham. Prev: SHO (Obst. & Psych.) Lister Hosp. Stevenage; SHO (Geriat.) St. Michaels Hosp. Enfield.

SEN, Sanjoy Anilkumar 97 Delaunays Road, Manchester M8 4RE Tel: 0161 795 4567 — MB BS 1980 Poona; MRCOG 1987.

SEN, Sisir Kanti Crawley Road Medical Centre, 479 High Road, Leyton, London E10 5EL Tel: 020 8539 1880 Fax: 020 8556 1318; 66 Broadwalk, South Woodford, London E18 2DW Tel: 020 8989 7988 Fax: 020 8989 7988 Email: docssen@aol.com — MB BS 1959 Calcutta; MRCOG 1970; DGO Calcutta 1961; FRCOG 1997. (NR Sircar Med. Coll.) GP. Socs: MPS; BMA; FMS.

SEN, Subhas Chandra The Surgery, Wood Houses, Little London, Walsall WS1 3EP Tel: 01922 28280 Fax: 01922 23023; 32 Park Road, Walsall WS5 3JU Tel: 0121 357 1979 — MB ChB 1974 Birm.

SEN, Mr Subrata — MB BS 1961 Calcutta; FRCS Eng. 1973. (Calcutta Med. Coll.) p/t Specialist in Orthop. Roy. Bournemouth Hosp. Castle La. Bournemouth.

SEN, Suchit Mohan Dartford East Health Centre, Pilgrims Way, Dartford DA1 1QY Tel: 01322 279881 — MB BS 1964 Calcutta.

SEN, Susmita Tel: 020 8491 3303 Fax: 020 8559 2451; 66 Broadwalk, London E18 2DW Tel: 020 8989 7988 — MB BS 1960 Calcutta; FRCOG 1998; DGO 1962 Calcutta; MRCOG 1968; DA Eng. 1971. (N.R. Sircar Med. Coll. Calcutta)

SEN GUPTA, Pinaki Summervale Medical Centre, Wharf Lane, Ilminster TA19 0DT Tel: 01460 52354 — MB BS 1960 Calcutta.

SEN-GUPTA, Tapan Acocks Green Medical Centre, 999 Warwick Road, Acocks Green, Birmingham B27 6QJ Tel: 0121 706 0501 — MB BS 1989 Lond.

SENANAYAKE, Gamini Memorial Hospital, Darlington DH3 6HX Tel: 01325 380100; 47 Ancroft Garth, High Shincliffe, Durham DH1 2UD — MB BS Ceylon 1970; MRCOphth 1990; DO RCS Eng. 1984. (University of Ceylon, Peradeniya, Sri Lanka) Staff Grade (Ophth.) Memor. Hosp. Darlington.

SENANAYAKE, Hemantha Malinath 8 Winckley Close, Kenton, Harrow HA3 9QW — MB BS 1978 Sri Lanka; MRCOG 1987.

SENANAYAKE, Indrani Pramilla International Planned Parenthood Federation, Regents College, Inner Circle, Regents Park, London NW1 4NS Tel: 020 7487 7852 Fax: 020 7487 7950; 22 Cavendish Avenue, St John's Wood, London NW8 9JE — MB BS 1967 Ceylon; PhD Lond. 1975; DTPH Lond 1971. Asst. Sec. Gen. Internat. Planned Parenthood Federat.; Vice Chairm. Bd. Family Health Internat.; Div. Soc. Advancem. of Contracep. Socs: Fell. Roy. Soc. Health. Prev: Lect. (Pub. Health & Community Med.) Univ. Colombo, Sri Lanka; Epidemiol. WHO (Small Pox Eradication Progr.).

SENANAYAKE, Lakshman Felix Nonis Department of Radiotherapy & Oncology, Royal Free Hospital, Pond St., London NW3 2QG Tel: 020 7794 0500 Fax: 020 7830 2968; The Garden Flat, 24 Parliament Hill, London NW3 2TN — MB BS 1965 Ceylon; MSc (Radiobiol.) Lond. 1974; DMRT Eng. 1973. (Colombo) Cons. & Dir. Radiother. & Oncol. Roy. Free Hosp. Lond. Socs: Chairm. Internat. Adjuvant Ther. Assn.; MRC Brain Tumour Working Party. Prev: Research Regist. Mt. Vernon Hosp. N.wood; Sen. Regist. Middlx. Hosp. Lond.; Regist. Roy. Free Hosp. Lond.

SENAPATI, Asha Queen Alexandra Hospital, Cosham, Portsmouth PO6 3LY Tel: 023 92 286000 Fax: 023 92 286710; Bunchfield, Lynchmere Ridge, Haslemere GU27 3PP Tel: 01428 642176 Fax: 01428 645304 — MB BS 1976 Madras; PhD Lond. 1986; FRCS Eng. 1979; MRCS Eng. LRCP Lond. 1978. Cons. Surg. Qu. Alexandra Hosp. Portsmouth. Socs: Roy. Soc. Med. (Mem. Surg. Sect. Mem. Counc. Sect. & Clin. Sect. & Mem.Coloproctol. Sect.). Prev: Cons. Surg. Mayday Univ. Hosp. Croydon.

SENAPATI, Mr Mihir Kumar (retired) Bunchfield, Lynchmere Ridge, Haslemere GU27 3PP Tel: 01428 652071 Fax: 01428 645304 — MB BS 1948 Patna; FRCS Eng. 1957; FRCS Ed. 1957; FRACS 1984.

SENAPATI, Ranganayaki (retired) Bunchfield, Lynchmere Ridge, Haslemere GU27 3PP Tel: 01428 652071 Fax: 01428 645304 — MB BS 1946 Lucknow.

SENARATH, Violet Lorraine Department of Radiotherapy & Oncology, Norfolk & Norwich Hospital, Norwich NR1 3SR Tel: 01603 286286; 39 Buckland Rise, Eaton, Norwich NR4 6EU Tel: 01603 505565 — MB BS 1971 Ceylon; FRCR 1985. (Colombo) Staff Grade (Radiother.& Oncol.) Norf. & Norwich Hosp. Prev: Regist. (Radiother. & Oncol.) Norf. & Norwich Hosp.; SHO (Radiother.) Norf. & Norwich & Newc. Gen. Hosps.

SENARATH YAPA, Ranjith Sampath Wansbeck General Hospital, Woodhorn Lane, Ashington NE63 9JJ — MB BS 1975 Sri Lanka; MRCP (UK) 1983.

SENARATH YAPA, Sarath Chandra 6 Hasguard Close, Bolton BL1 5FE — MB BS 1976 Sri Lanka.

***SENARATNE, Kollura Mudianselage Jayawickrama** The New Surgery, Adwick Road, Mexborough S64 0DB Tel: 01709 590707 Fax: 01709 571986; 114 Carr Manor View, Moor Town, Leeds LS17 5AT Tel: 0113 269 5474 — LRCP 1987 Ed.; LRCP LRCS Ed. LRCPS Glas. 1987; DGM RCP Lond. 1990.

SENATHIRAJAH, Dharmarajan 45 Oakwood Drive, Fulwood, Preston PR2 3LY — MB BS 1968 Ceylon.

SENATHIRAJAH, Sinnatamby Sanmugam 314 Torbay Road, Harrow HA2 9QW — MB BS 1960 Ceylon; FRCOG 1989, M 1969.

SENDALL, Katherine (retired) 36 Kew Gardens, Whitley Bay NE26 3LY Tel: 0191 252 2672 — MB BS 1963 Durh.

SENDEGEYA, Christina 62 Norseman Close, West Derby, Liverpool L12 5LS Tel: 0151 256 6177 — Ptychio Iatrikes 1989 Athens; MRCP Lond. 1993.

SENDER, Helen 12 Gertrude Street, Chelsea, London SW10 0JN Tel: 020 7352 2411 — MB BCh 1941 Witwatersrand; DPH 1943; DMRD Eng. 1954. (Witwatersrand) Cons. Radiol. Bolingbroke Hosp., St. John's Hosp. & Tooting Bec Hosp. Lond. Socs: Brit. Inst. Radiol. & Fac. Radiols. Prev: Sen. Radiol. Regist. Roy. Marsden Hosp. & St. Helier Hosp.; Radiol. Johannesburg Gen. Hosp.

SENDER, Jerome Merrow Park Surgery, Kingfisher Drive, Guildford GU4 7EP Tel: 01483 503331 Fax: 01483 303457; 4 Coltsfoot Drive, Guildford GU1 1YH Tel: 01483 453138 Email: jsjp@btineternet.com — MB BS 1982 Lond.; MRCGP 1986; DCH RCP Lond. 1986; DRCOG 1986; Dip Occ Med 1998. (St. Mary's) Clin. Asst. Migraine & Headache Clinic Guildford. Prev: Trainee GP Watford VTS.

SENDER, Simon Nathan 12 Gertrude Street, Chelsea, London SW10 0JN Tel: 020 7352 2411 — MB BCh 1953 Witwatersrand; BA Pretoria 1930, LLB 1932; FFR 1967; DMRD Eng. 1957. (Witwatersrand) Emerit. Cons. Radiol. St. Stephen's Hosp. Lond.

SENEVIRATNE

Socs: Fell. Roy. Soc. Med.; FRCR. Prev: Sen. Radiol. Regist. Roy. Marsden Hosp. & St. Helier Hosp.; Radiol. Baragwanath Hosp. Johannesburg.

SENEVIRATNE, Gertrude Nimali 1 Sheerwater Road, London E16 3SU — MB BS 1992 Lond.

SENEVIRATNE, Kirihettige Boniface Clement 1 Sheerwater Road, London E16 3SU — MB BS 1963 Ceylon; DCCH RCGP & FCM 1988. (Ceylon) Staff Grade (Paediat.) Lond. Socs: Fac. Community Health. Prev: Clin. Med. Off. Tower Hamlets Health Dist.

SENEVIRATNE, Saaliya 39C Leyborne Avenue, London W13 9RA — MB ChB 1987 Sheff.

SENGUPTA, Anup 47 Heldhaw Road, Bury St Edmunds IP32 7ES — MBBS Bhopal India 1981; FRCPS Glas. 1992. Staff Grade Surg. E. Surrey Hosp. Prev: Regist. (Surg.) Wycombe Gen. Hosp. High Wycombe.

SENGUPTA, Mr Barun (retired) Sarpda Cottage, 27 Bridlebank Way, Broadway, Weymouth DT3 5RA Tel: 01305 814408 — BSc Calcutta 1955, MB BS 1959; FRCS Eng. 1969. Prev: Regist. (Orthop.) Portland Hosp.

SENGUPTA, Catherine Woodlands, 46 The Causeway, March PE15 9NX — BM BS 1995 Nottm.; BMedSci (Hons.) Nottm 1993 BM BS 1995. SHO Rotat. (Gen. Med.) Kings Coll. Hosp. NHS Trust Lond.

SENGUPTA, Dibyendu 11 Grafton Road, Solihull Lodge, Solihull B90 1NG Tel: 0121 474 4686 Fax: 0121 608 4900 Email: gem@sengupta.demon.co.uk — MB BS Calcutta 1966; DRCOG 1979; DGO Calcutta 1967. (Calcutta Nat. Med. Coll.)

SENGUPTA, Fergus Ranjan The Moorings, Falkirk Rd, Linlithgow EH49 7BQ — MB ChB 1997 Ed.

SENGUPTA, Gautam The Surgery, 49 Essenden Road, St Leonards-on-Sea TN38 0NN Tel: 01424 720866 Fax: 01424 445580 — MB BS 1977 Lond.; DRCOG 1981.

SENGUPTA, Nandita Turners Hill Surgery, 161 Turners Hill, Cheshunt, Waltham Cross EN8 9BH Tel: 01992 624696.

SENGUPTA, Partha Sarathi East Glamorgan Hospital, Church Village, Pontypridd CF38 1AB Tel: 01443 218218 Fax: 01443 217213 — MB BS 1987 Newc.; MRCOG 1993. Regist. (O & G) E. Glam. Gen. Hosp. Pontypridd.

SENGUPTA, Prasun Department of Anaesthetics, Lister Hospital, Coreys Mill Lane, Stevenage SG1 4AB Tel: 01438 781086; The Paddock, High St, Hinxworth, Baldock SG7 5HJ — MB BS Lond. 1976; MRCP (UK) 1980; FFA RCS Eng. 1982. Cons. Anaesth. NW Thames Region. HA.

SENGUPTA, Priyadarshi Geriatric Day Hospital, Royal Alexandra Hospital, Paisley Tel: 0141 887 9111; 44 Balgonie Woods, Paisley PA2 6HW Tel: 0141 884 3839 — MB BS 1975 Calcutta; MD Patna 1980. Staff Grade Phys. (Geriat. Med.) Roy. Alexandra Hops. Paisley.

SENGUPTA, Rita 24A Chedworth Court, Selly Oak Hospital, Raddlebarn Road, Birmingham B29 6JD — MB ChB 1992 Leic.; MB ChB Leic.1992.

SENGUPTA, Sajalbaran Maerdy Surgery, North Terrace, Maerdy, Ferndale CF43 4DD Tel: 01443 733202 Fax: 01443 733730 — MB BS 1963 Calcutta.

SENGUPTA, Shiuli 27 Ailsa Drive, Giffnock, Glasgow G46 6RJ — MB ChB 1998 Glas.; MB ChB Glas 1998.

SENGUPTA, Swapan Kumar Castle Street Medical Centre, Castle Street, Bolsover, Chesterfield S44 6PP Tel: 01246 822983 — MB BS 1969 Ranchi.

SENGUPTA, Tarun Kumar The Moorings, Falkirk Road, Linlithgow EH49 7BQ — MB BS Gauhati 1955. (Assam Med. Coll.) Socs: BMA. Prev: Asst. Surg. Kohima Civil Hosp., India; SHO Stirling Roy. Infirm.; Regist. Falkirk Roy. Infirm.

SENGUPTA, Usha Paediatric Ward, Crosshouse Hospital, Kilmarnock KA2 0BE Tel: 01563 521133; 44 Balgonie Woods, Paisley PA2 6HW Tel: 0141 884 3839 — MB BS 1976 Calcutta; DCH RCP Lond. 1983. Staff Grade (Paediat.) CrossHo. Hosp. Kilmarnock.

SENHENN, Jane Susanne Almond Bourne Hall Health Centre, Spring Street, Ewell, Epsom KT17 1TG; 50 Gerard Road, Barnes, London SW13 9QQ Tel: 020 8748 5431 — MB BS 1982 Lond.; MRCGP 1986; Cert. Family Plann. JCC 1984. (St. Bart.) Prev: SHO (Paediat.) Mayday Hosp. Croydon; SHO (Psychiat.) S. W.. Hosp. Lond.; SHO (O & G) & Cas. Off. St. Thos. Hosp. Lond.

SENIOR, Andrew Park Medical Centre, 164 Park Road, Peterborough, Peterborough PE1 2UF Tel: 01733 552801 — MB BS 1991 Lond.

SENIOR, Mr Andrew John Benbecula Medical Practice, Griminish, Surgery, Griminish, Isle of Benbecula HS7 5QA Tel: 01870 602215 Fax: 01870 602630 — MB ChB 1978 Ed.; FRCS Ed. 1984; MRCGP 1993.

SENIOR, Colin James 6 Rushmoor Grove, Backwell, Bristol BS48 3BW — BM BS 1998 Nottm.; BM BS Nottm 1998.

SENIOR, David 25A Eastgate S., Driffield YO25 6LW; Bridlington & District Hospital, Bessingby Road, Bridlington YO16 4QP Tel: 01262 606666 — MB ChB 1965 Leeds; MRCPsych. 1981; DObst RCOG 1969; DTM & H Liverp. 1970. Cons. Psychiat. Bridlington & Dist. Hosp. N. Humberside. Socs: BMA & World Federat. for Ment. Health. Prev: Sen. Regist. (Psychiat.) St. Bart. Hosp. Gp. Lond.; Sen. Regist. (Psychiat.) Goodmayes Hosp. Ilford; Med. Supt. Catherine Booth Mission Hosp., Zululand.

SENIOR, David Cedric (retired) Dunthwaite, Dark Lane, Barnsley S70 6RE Tel: 01226 205586 — MB ChB 1955 Leeds. Prev: GP Barnsley.

SENIOR, David Frank 22 Parkside, Vanburgh Fields, Blackheath, London SE3 7QQ Tel: 020 8858 7570 — MB BS 1973 Lond.; DA Eng. 1978.

SENIOR, Eileen Mary The Ridge Medical Practice, 3 Paternoster Lane, Great Horton, Bradford BD7 3EE Tel: 01274 502905 Fax: 01274 522060; 11 Lyndhurst Grove, Allerton, Bradford BD15 7AS Tel: 01274 225792 — MB ChB Manch. 1965; FRCOG 1991, M 1972; DObst RCOG 1967. Prev: Resid. Surg. Off. Hosp. Wom. Leeds & Matern. Hosp. Leeds; Ho. Surg. Huddersfield Roy. Infirm.

SENIOR, Emma Louise Littlewood House, 172 Poolbrook Road, Malvern WR14 3JG — BM BCh 1997 Oxf.

SENIOR, Fai Louise Dovedale, Old Woodhouses, Broughall, Whitchurch SY13 4EH — MB ChB 1998 Sheff.; MB ChB Sheff 1998.

SENIOR, Jacqueline 53 School Hill, Newmillerdam, Wakefield WF2 7SP — MB BS 1978 Lond.; MRCS Eng. LRCP Lond. 1978.

SENIOR, Jane Elizabeth Prospect Road Surgery, 22 Prospect Road, Ossett WF5 8AN Tel: 01924 274123 Fax: 01924 263350; 152 Shay Lane, Walton, Wakefield WF2 6LA Tel: 01924 257310 Email: janesenior@aol.com — MB ChB 1983 Manch.; MRCGP 1987; DCH RCP Lond. 1986.

SENIOR, Michael Arthur 26 South Parade, Pudsey LS28 8NZ — MB ChB 1995 Leeds; BChD Leeds 1984.

SENIOR, Nina Margaret The Health Centre, Central St., Countesthorpe, Leicester LE8 5QJ Tel: 0116 277 6336; Pine Garth, 6 Enderby Road, Blaby, Leicester LE8 4GD — MB ChB 1980 Leic.; MRCGP 1986; DRCOG 1983; Cert. Family Plann. JCC 1983.

SENIOR, Mrs Nora Elizabeth (retired) c/o Oliver-Byrne, Gemstone, Bascote Road Ufton, Leamington Spa CV33 9PL Tel: 01926 614294 — MB ChB 1949 Leeds. Prev: SCMO (Developm. Paediat. & Audiol) E. Berks. HA.

SENIOR, Peter Alexander 18 Hillside Terrace, Dundee DD2 1QS — MB BS 1993 Newc.

SENIOR, Robert Elvyn Senior and Partners, Morrab Surgery, 2 Morrab Road, Penzance TR18 4EL Tel: 01736 363866 Fax: 01736 367809 — MB ChB 1961 Sheff.; DObst RCOG 1963.

SENIOR, Robert Simon 19 Navarino Road, London E8 1AD — MB BS 1977 Lond.; BA Camb. 1974.

SENIOR, Roxy Northwick Park Hospital, Watford Road, Harrow HA3 0AX Tel: 020 8869 2547 Fax: 020 8864 0075; 23 Churchill Avenue, Harrow HA3 0AX Tel: 020 8907 9638 — MB BS 1980 Calcutta; 2001 DESC; FRCP(Lond) 1999; MRCP (UK) 1990; MD Cal 1983; DM Cal (Cardiology) 1987. Cons. Cardiol. N.wick Pk. Hosp. Harrow. Socs: Brit. Cardiac Soc.; Brit. Soc. Echocardiogr.; Brit. Nuclear Cardiol. Soc. Prev: Hon. Sen. Regist. N.wick Pk. Hosp. Harrow.

SENIOR, Timothy Patrick Mansell 7 Ox Hey Close, Lostock, Bolton BL6 4BQ — BM BCh 1997 Oxf.

SENNETT, Karen Jane Killick Street Health Centre, 76 Killick Street, London N1 9RH Tel: 020 7833 9939 Fax: 020 7427 2740; 23 Langbourne Avenue, London N6 6AJ Tel: 020 8340 3739 — MB BS 1984 Lond.; MRCGP 1988; Dip. Addic. Behaviour Lond. 1992. (Univ. Coll. Hosp.) GP Partner. Prev: GP Som. Gdns. Health

Centre; GP Facilitator for Homeless People Lond.; GP Hornsey Rise Health Centre Lond.

SENNIK, Avinash Kumar 15 Colombo Road, Ilford IG1 4RH — MB BS 1971 Rajasthan. (S.P. Med. Coll. Bikaner) Off. i/c, US Army Health Clin., Bad Aibling W. Germany.

SENNIK, Surinder Kumar The Surgery, Briset Corner, 591 Westhorne Avenue, Eltham, London SE9 6JX Tel: 020 8850 5022 Fax: 020 8855 4970 — MB BS 1980 Bihar; LRCP LRCS Ed. LRCPS Glas. 1984. (Darbhanga) GP Princip.

SENOR, Concepsion Begona West Side Flat, Cleveland Lodge, Great Ayton, Middlesbrough TS9 6BT — LMS 1989 Cadiz.

SENSIER, Alan Eric Sanderson and Partners, Adan House Surgery, St. Andrews Lane, Spennymoor DL16 6QA Tel: 01388 817777 Fax: 01388 811700; 54 Archery Rise, Nevilles Cross, Durham DH1 4LA Tel: 0191 384 2078 — MB BS 1983 Lond.; MA Camb. 1983; MRCGP 1987; DRCOG 1987. (Cambridge and Middlesex Hospital Medical School) Prev: Trainee GP N.d. VTS.

SENSKY, Penelope Ruth Queens Medical Centre, Nottingham NG7 2 Tel: 0115 942 1421; 105 Julian Road, West Bridgford, Nottingham NG2 5AL — BM BCh 1990 Oxf.; MRCP (UK) 1994; DRCOG 1993.

SENSKY, Thomas Ernest Lakeside Mental Health Unit, West Middlesex University Hospital, Isleworth TW7 6AF Tel: 020 8321 5179 Fax: 020 8321 5474 Email: t.sensky@ic.ac.uk; 33 Great Brownings, College Road, London SE21 7HP Tel: 020 8244 9914 Fax: 020 8244 9917 — MB BS 1979 Lond.; PhD Lond. 1975, BSc 1971; FRCPsych 1993, M 1983. Reader (Psychol. Med.) Imperial Coll. Of Sci., Technol. & Med.; Hon. Cons. Psychia. W. Lond. Ment. Health NHS Trust. Socs: Founding Fell. Acad. Cognitive Ther.; Fell. Intern. Coll. of Psychosomatic Med. Prev: Lect. & Hon. Sen. Regist. (Psychiat.) Char. Cross Hosp. Lond.; Sen. Regist. (Psychiat.) Hellingly Hosp. Hailsham & Bethlem Roy. & Maudsley Hosps. Lond.; Regist. (Psychiat.) Bethlem Roy. & Maudsley Hosps. Lond.

SENTHIL KUMAR, Chitra Department of Gynaecology, Glasgow Royal Infirmary, Glasgow G4 0SF Tel: 0141 211 4000; 61 Moorfoot Way, Bearsden, Glasgow G61 4RL — MB BS 1989 Papua New Guinea; MRCOG 1996. Staff Grade Gyn. Glas. Roy. Infirm.

SENTHILKUMAR, Mr Chinnasamy Department of Orthopaedics, Glasgow Royal Infirmary, Glasgow G4 0SF Tel: 0141 211 5402; 61 Moorfoot Way, Bearsden, Glasgow G61 4RL — MB BS 1986 Madras; FRCS Eng. 1992. Staff Grade Orthop. Surg. Glas. Roy. Infirm.

SENTHILNATHAN, Mr Govindarajan 8 Maude Street, Darlington DL3 7PW — MB BS 1986 Madras; FRCS Glas. 1994.

SENTHIRAMAN, Veeriah 9 Curtis Wood Park Road, Herne Bay CT6 7TY — MB BS 1972 Madras; LMSSA Lond. 1988.

SENTHURAN, Sivagnanavel 282 Coombe Lane, London SW20 0RW — MB BS 1994 Lond.

SEPAI, Tehmton Meherwan The Surgery, 1 Hicks Road, Markyate, St Albans AL3 8LJ — MB ChB 1983 Sheff.

SEPE, Vincenzo 8 Boundary Court, Rathmore Road, Cambridge CB1 7BB — State Exam 1985 Naples; State Exam Naples 1986. (Univ. Federico II Naples, Italy) Univ. Research Assoc. (Immunol.) St. Bart. & Roy. Lond. Sch. Med. & Dent. Prev: Univ. Research Fell. (Med.) Addenbrooke's Hosp. Camb.; Univ. Research Fell. (Nephrol.) Univ. Naples, Italy.

SEPHTON, Beryl Lindsay 18 Hargill Drive, Redmire, Leyburn DL8 4DZ — MB ChB 1955 Manch.; MFPHM RCP (UK) 1990; MFCM 1974; DPH Manch. 1960. Prev: SCMO Blackburn Health Dist.

SEPHTON, Elizabeth Ann Cadbury Heath Health Centre, Parkwall Road, Cadbury Heath, Bristol BS30 8HS Tel: 0117 980 5700 Fax: 0117 980 5701 — MB ChB 1982 Bristol; MB ChB (Hons.) Bristol 1982; MRCP (UK) 1985; MRCGP 1988; DRCOG 1986.

SEPHTON, Jean Edna 38 Old Wells Road, Glastonbury BA6 8EA — MB BS 1953 Lond.; DObst RCOG 1964. (Roy. Free)

SEPHTON, Victoria Claire 12 Albury Close, The County Park, Liverpool L12 0NR Tel: 0151 283 8676 — MB ChB 1995 Leeds; DFFP 1997. SHO (O & G) Liverp. Woms. Hosp. Liverp. Socs: SHO Represent. Mersey Region Train. Comm. Prev: SHO (O & G) Bradford Roy. Infirm.; Ho. Off. Med. Huddersfield Roy.; Ho. Off. Surg. BRI.

SEPPELT, Ian Hugh 10 Cavendish Lodge, Cavendish Road, Bath BA1 2UD Tel: 01225 329273 — MB BChir 1950 Camb.; MA, MB BChir Camb. 1950; MFCM 1974; DPH Eng. 1955. (Camb. & Univ. Coll. Hosp.) Prev: Area Med. Off. Barnet AHA; MOH Lond. Boro. Ealing.

SEPPING, Paul Poole General Hospital, Longfleet Road, Poole BH15 2JB Tel: 01202 665511 Fax: 01202 661671 — MB BS 1971 New South Wales; BSc (Hons.) New South Wales 1968; MRCPsych. 1976; DPM Eng. 1975. (University of New South Wales) Cons. Child & Adolesc. Psychiat. Poole Gen. Hosp.; Mem. Inst. Gp. Anal. Prev: Sen. Regist. Hosp. for Sick Childr. Gt. Ormond St. Gp. Lond.; Lect. St. Bart. Hosp. Med. Sch. Lond.; Research Regist. Guy's Hosp. Gp. Lond.

SEPSAS, Evangelos Harefield Hospital, Harefield, Uxbridge UB9 6JH Tel: 01895 278580 Fax: 01895 822870 — Ptychio Iatrikes 1979 Athens. Thoracic Surg. Harefield Hosp. Middlx.

SEQUEIRA, Jane Mary Ugley Hall, Ugley, Bishop's Stortford CM22 6JB Tel: 01799 543245 Fax: 01799 543339 — MB BS 1979 Lond.; MRCPath 1987; FRCPath 1997. (London) Socs: Brit. Soc. Clin. Cytol.; Internat. Acad. Path. (Brit. Div.). Prev: Cons. Cytopath. Bedford Hosp.; Sen. Regist. & Lect. (Morbid Anat.) Lond. Hosp.

SERAFI, Sohel (Sam) Ingersley Building, Macclesfield District General Hospital, Victoria Road, Macclesfield SK10 3BL Fax: 01625 663107; Clinic, 1 Walker St, Macclesfield SK10 1BH Tel: 01625 421614 — MB BCh 1965 Cairo; MRCPsych 1975; DPM Eng. 1973; Dip. Med. Cairo 1969. (Kasr El Eini, Cairo) Cons. Psychiat. (Alcoholism & Drug Addic.) Macclesfield Dist. Gen. Hosp.

SERAFINI, Franca 53 Tile House Road, London SW18 3EU — State DMS 1984 Padua. Regist. (Anaesth.) Mayday Hosp. Croydon & St. Geo. Hosp. Lond. Socs: Assn. Anaesth. Prev: Regist. (Anaesth.) Joyce Green Hosp. Dartford; SHO (Anaesth.) St. Heliers NHS Trust & St. Geo. Hosp. Lond.; SHO (Anaesth.) W.m. Hosp. Lond.

SERAFY, Alena 55 Queensmill Road, London SW6 6JP — MD 1985 Vienna.

SERAJUDDIN, Mohammed 14 Hearnville Road, Balham, London SW12 8RR Tel: 020 8673 2949 — MB BS 1966 Rajshahi; DA Eng. 1969. (Rajshahi Med. Coll.) Cons. Anaesth. Louth Co. Hosp.

SERCOMBE, Jayne Louise 2A Southbourne Road, Sheffield S10 2QN — MB ChB 1997 Sheff.

***SERCOMBE, Karen Maria** 3 Creek House, Russell Road, London W14 8HZ — MB BS 1996 Lond.

SERENA SANCHEZ, Rafael 6A Oxford Avenue, Wimbledon Chase, London SW20 8LT — LMS 1993 U Autonoma Barcelona.

SERENYI, Anne Gwyneth The Riverside Surgery, Waterside, Evesham WR11 6JP Tel: 01386 40121 Fax: 01386 442615 — MB BS 1976 Lond.; MRCS Eng. LRCP Lond. 1976; DCH Eng. 1980; DRCOG 1978. (Guy's)

SERFATY, Marc Antony 7A Porchfield Square, St John's Gardens, Manchester M3 4FG — MB ChB 1985 Manch.

SERGEANT, Howard Gordon Stanley 152 Harley Street, London W1N 1HH Tel: 020 7935 0023 Fax: 020 7935 5972 Email: howard@hgssergeant.demon.co.uk; 20 Well Walk, Hampstead, London NW3 1LD Tel: 020 7435 2308 Fax: 020 7435 2308 — MB BS 1957 Lond.; FRCP Ed. 1976, M 1965; MRCS Eng. LRCP Lond. 1957; FRCPsych 1978, M 1971; DPM Lond. 1965. (Char. Cross) Hon. Cons. Psychiat. Roy. Free Hosp. Lond. Socs: Fell. Roy. Soc. Med.; BMA. Prev: Cons. Psychiat. Roy. Free Hosp. Lond.; Cons. Psychiat. Roy. N.. & Whittington Hosps. Lond.; Sen. Regist. Bethlem Roy. & Maudsley Hosps. Lond.

SERGEANT, Mr Robert James Nuffield Hospital, Kingswood Road, Tunbridge Wells Tel: 01892 512506; Stone House, Rocks Lane, High Hurstwood, Uckfield TN22 4BN — MB BS 1967 Lond.; MRCS LRCP 1967; FRCS Ed. 1976; FRCS Eng. 1973. (Middlx.) Cons. ENT Surg. Maidstone & Tunbridge Wells NHS Trust. Socs: Fell. Roy. Soc. Med.; Soc. Apoth.; Fell. Zool. Soc. Lond. Prev: Sen. Regist. Roy. Nat. Throat Nose & Ear Hosp. Lond.; Fell. Univ. Iowa, USA; Regist. Mt. Vernon Hosp. N.wood.

SERGIWA, Ahmed Flat M H 78, Leighton Hospital, Middlewich Road, Crewe CW1 4QJ — MB BS 1985 Garyounis, Libya; MRCP (UK) 1995.

SERHAN, Ergin The Royal Hospitals NHS Trust, New Cross Hospital, Wolverhampton WV10 0QP Tel: 01902 307999; Findon, Haughton Lane, Shifnal TF11 8HG Tel: 01952 460795 — MD 1963 Istanbul; LAH Dub. 1969; DCH Eng. 1968. (Istanbul) Specialist (Rheum.) New Cross Hosp. Wolverhampton. Prev: GP Shifnal;

SERHAN

Regist. (Paediat.) & SHO (Orthop. & Paediat.) Wolverhampton Gp. Hosps.

SERHAN, Jonathan Timur Findon, Haughton Lane, Shifnal TF11 8HG — MB ChB 1998 Ed.; MB ChB Ed 1998.

SERIES, Hugh George DPOA, Warneford Lane, Headington OX3 7JX Tel: 01295 229296 — MB BS 1984 Lond.; DM 1996 Oxford; MA Oxf. 1984; MRCPsych 1990. Cons. Psychiat. (Old Age) Oxon. Ment. Healthcare NHS Trust. Prev: Sen. Regist. Rotat. Oxf.; Hon. Sen. Regist. (Psychiat.) Warneford Hosp. Oxf.; Wellcome Train. Fell. Univ. Johns Hopkins Baltimore, USA & Oxf.

SERIES, John Julian Dumbarton District Laboratory, Vale of Leven District General Hospital, Alexandria G83 0UA Tel: 01389 754121 — MB BChir 1981 Camb.

SERIGHT, Mr William (retired) The Oaks, 44 Rotchell Park, Dumfries DG2 7RJ Tel: 01387 252020 — MB ChB Glas. 1946; FRCS Glas. 1972; FRCS Ed. 1952. Prev: Sen. Cons. Surg. Dumfries & Galloway Roy. Infirm.

SERIKI, Dare Mutiyu 518 Claremont Road, Rusholme, Manchester M14 5WA — MB ChB 1995 Leeds.

SERJEANT, Mrs Marion Keith Summerhill Cottage, Denhead, St Andrews KY16 8PA Tel: 01334 850211 — MB ChB 1940 Ed.; DTM & H Eng. 1942. (Ed.) Prev: Welf. Off. Wom. & Childr. Mukalla, E. Aden.

SERLE, Elisabeth Christian Mission Hospital, Sarenea Village & Post Office, Sarenea, Bankura District, West Bengal 722150, India; 3 Oakfern Drive Stewartfield, East Kilbride, Glasgow G74 4UF Tel: 0135 526 5321 — MB ChB 1980 Aberd.; MRCOG 1986; MD Aberd. 1994. (Aberd.) Med. Off. in Obst & Gyn. Rural India. Prev: Research fell. Jessop Hosp. Sheff.; Sen. Reg. Obst & Gyn. St Mary Hosp. Mans.

SERLIN, Matthew Jeremy 32 Westbourne Road, Birkdale, Southport PR8 2JA — MB ChB 1971 Birm.; MD (Hons.) Birm. 1980 (Univ. Birm. MD Prize); FRCP Lond. 1991; MRCP (UK) 1974. Cons. Phys. S.port & Formby Dist. Gen. Hosp. Socs: Brit. Thorac. Soc. Prev: Lect. (Clin. Pharmacol.) Univ. Liverp.; Hon. Sen. Regist. (Med.) Roy. Liverp. Hosp.

SERMIN, Nicola Hilary John Elliott Unit, Birch Hill Hospital, Rochdale Tel: 01706 754305; Eldercot, Chorley New Road, Bolton BL1 5AD — MB ChB 1984 Manch.; MRCPsych 1991. Cons. of Psychiat. (Learning Disabil.) John Elliott Univ. Birch Hill Hosp. Rochdale. Prev: Sen. Regist. & Regist. (Psychiat. Ment. Handicap) NW RHA.

SERPELL, Michael Graham Anaesthetics Department, Western Infirmary, Dumbarton Road, Glasgow G11 6NT Tel: 0141 211 2069 Fax: 0141 211 1806; Dalarne, Pier Road, RHU, Helensburgh G84 8LJ Tel: 01436 820492 — FRCA 1989; MB ChB Dundee 1983. Sen. Lect. Univ. Dept. of Anaesth. Glas.; Lect. Sch. Podiatry Caledonian Univ. Socs: Sec. N. Brit. Pain Assn. (Ex-Sec. & Counc. Mem.); W Scot. Pain Gp. (Ex-Sec. & Counc. Mem.); Roy. Soc. Med. Prev: Sen. Regist. (Anaesth.) Ninewells Hosp. & Med. Sch. Dundee.; Pain Fell. Dartmouth Hitchcock Med. Center Hanover, NH, USA.

SERRA MESTRES, Jordi Wodland Centre, Hillingdon Hospital, Pield Heath Road, Uxbridge UB8 3NN Email: j.serra-mestres@ion.ucl.ac.uk — LMS 1989 U Autonoma Barcelona; MRCPsych 1996. Specialist Regist. (Psychiat.) Char. Cross. Higher Psychiat. Train. Scheme Lond.; Hon. Research Asst. Dept. Neuropsychiat. Inst. Neurol. Lond. Prev: Clin. Research Fell. (Neuropsychiat.) Qu. Mary & W.field Coll. & Inst. Neurol. Lond.; SHO (Psychiat. & Regist.) Fulbourn Hosp. & Addenbrooke's NHS Trust Camb.

SERRANO GARCIA, Jose Antonio Department of Accident & Emergency, Conquest Hospital, The Ridge, St Leonards-on-Sea TN37 7RD — LMS 1995 Saragossa.

SERRANO SANCHEZ, Aurora 1 Somersby Green, Boston PE21 9PH — LMS 1994 Granada.

SERRANO SANCHEZ, Santiago Flat 8, Queen Alewandra Hospital, Southwick Hill Road, Cosham, Portsmouth PO6 3LY — LMS 1987 La Lagona.

SERRELL, Iain Robert Ash Lodge Medical Centre, 73 Old Road, Chesterfield S40 2RA Tel: 01246 203138 Fax: 01246 231824 — MB ChB 1977 Manch.; MRCGP 1982; DRCOG 1981. (Manch.) Clin. Asst. Ment. Handicap. Socs: Roy. Coll. Gen. Pract.

SERVANT, Mr Christopher Terence Jackson 19 Symes Park, Bath BA1 4PA Tel: 01225 336936 Email: chris.servant@virgin.net — MB BS 1990 Lond.; BSc (Hons.) Lond. 1987; FRCS Eng. 1995. (St. Bart. Hosp.) Regist. (Orthop.) Roy. United Hosp. Bath. Socs: Assn. Mem. Brit. Orthop. Assn.; Brit. Trauma Soc.; Brit. Orthop. Sports Trauma Assn. Prev: SHO (Orthop.) Roy. United Hosp. Bath; SHO (Gen. Surg.) Roy. Lond. Hosp.; SHO (Orthop.) Roy. Nat. Orthop. Hosp. Stanmore Middlx.

SERVANT, John Byron Christmas Maltings Surgery, Camps Road, Haverhill CB9 8HF Tel: 01440 702010 Fax: 01440 714761; 60 Lion Meadow, Steeple Bumpstead, Haverhill CB9 7BY — MB ChB 1978 Dundee.

SERVICE, Elaine 8 Bleasdale Road, Bolton BL1 5QS — MB BS 1991 Lond.; MRCPCH 1999. Specialist Regist. Paediat. Roy. Lancs. Infirm.

SERVICE, Margaret Ann Whittle Surgery, 199 Preston Road, Whittle-le-Woods, Chorley PR6 7PS Tel: 01257 262383 Fax: 01257 261019; 2 Juniper Croft, Clayton le Woods, Chorley PR6 7UF — MB ChB 1987 Manch.; MRCGP 1991; DRCOG 1991; DCH RCP Lond. 1990.

SESHAPPA, Vasanth Bag Lane Surgery, 32 Bag Lane, Atherton, Manchester M46 0EE Tel: 01942 896489 Fax: 01942 888793 — MB BS 1971 Osmania; MB BS 1971 Osmania.

SET, Patricia Ai Khoon 6 Beaumont Crescent, Cambridge CB1 8QA — MB BS 1985 Lond.; MRCP 1989 UK; MA 2000; FRCR 1991; MRCP (UK) 1989; FRCR 1991. Cons. (Radiol.) New Addenbrooke's Hosp. Camb.

SETCHELL, Mr Marcus Edward (cons. rooms), 149 Harley St., London W1G 6DE Tel: 020 7935 4444 Fax: 020 7486 3446 Email: marcussetchell@hotmail.com; 64 Wood Vale, London N10 3DN Tel: 020 8444 5266 — MB Camb. 1968, BChir 1967; FRCS Eng. 1974; FRCS Ed. 1973; MRCS Eng. LRCP Lond. 1967; FRCOG 1984, M 1972. (Camb. & St. Bart.) Surg. Gyn. to HM the Qu.; Cons. Obst. & Gyn Whittington Hosp., Lond. & Kiing Edwd. VII Hosp.; Examr. Univ. Lond., Univ. Camb. & RCOG. Socs: Fell. (Past Counc. Mem.) Fell. Roy. Soc. Med.; Brit. Fertil. Soc.; Eur. Endoscopic Surg. Soc. Prev: Sen. Regist. (O & G) Soton. Gen. Hosp.; Regist. (Surg.) Torbay Hosp. Torquay; Ho. Surg. (Gyn.) Ch.ill Hosp. Oxf.

SETH, A K The Surgery, 142 Marshland Road, Moorends, Doncaster DN8 4SU Tel: 01405 740094 Fax: 01405 741063 — MB BS 1967 Calcutta; MB BS 1967 Calcutta.

SETH, Anil Department of Anaesthesia, Royal Preston Hospital, Sharoe Green Lane, Preston PR2 9HT Tel: 01772 716565 Fax: 01772 710162 — MB ChB 1975 Manch.; FFA RCS Eng. 1982. Cons. Anaesth. Roy. Preston Hosp. Socs: MRCAnaesth. & Assn. Anaesth. Prev: Sen. Regist. (Anaesth.) Mersey RHA; Regist. (Anaesth.) W.. Infirm. Glas.

SETH, Ashok University Department of Cardiovascular Medicine, Queen Elizabeth Medical Centre, Edgbaston, Birmingham B15 2TH Tel: 0121 472 1311 — MB BS 1979 Aligarh; MB BS Aligarh Muslim 1979; MRCPI 1986; MRCP (UK) 1984. Clin. Research Fell./Regist. Univ. Dept. Cardiol. Qu. Eliz. Med. Centre Birm. Prev: Regist. (Gen. Med. & Cardiol.) Good Hope Gen. Hosp. Birm.; SHO (Med. Rotat.) Wordsley Hosp. Stourbridge.

SETH, Chhama Handsworth Medical Centre, 1 Fitzalan Road, Sheffield S13 9AW Tel: 0114 269 3044 — MB BS 1969 Lucknow. (G.S.V.M. Med. Coll. Kanpur)

SETH, Harvansh Kishore (retired) 3 Ashton Close, Oadby, Leicester LE2 5WH Tel: 0116 271 4211 Fax: 0116 271 4984 Email: h.k.seth@aol.com — MB BS 1952 Lucknow; DMRE Lucknow 1954. Prev: Phys. (Geriat. Med.) Leicester Gen. Hosp.

SETH, Kesho Nath Baker Street Surgery, Baker Street, Fenton, Stoke-on-Trent ST4 3AG Tel: 01782 45666; 9 Roe Lane, Newcastle ST5 3PL — MB BS 1967 Lucknow.

SETH, Pearlita 69 Baring Road, London SE12 0JS — MB ChB 1983 Leic.; DFFP 1993. Sessional Clin. Med. Off. Optimum Health Serv. NHS Trust Lond.

SETH, Pramod Chandra Handsworth Medical Centre, 1 Fitzalan Road, Sheffield S13 9AW Tel: 0114 269 3044 — MB BS 1967 Lucknow.

SETH, Priya Vallabh 58 Cecil Avenue, Barking IG11 9TF — BM 1976 Soton.

SETH, Ram Vallabh Hithergreen Hospital, Hithergreen Lane, London SE13 6RU Tel: 020 8698 4611 Fax: 020 8698 5655 — BM 1981 Soton.; MRCPsych. 1987. Cons. Gen. Psychiat. Guy's & Lewisham Trust. Socs: Brit. Assn. Psychopharmacol. Prev: Sen.

Regist. Rotat. (Psychiat.) Maudsley Hosp. & St. Mary's Hosp Lond.; Regist. (Psychiat.) Char. Cross Hosp. Lond.

SETH, Ramendra Nath (retired) 592 Derby Road, Adams Hill, Nottingham NG7 2GZ Tel: 0115 978 6956 Email: email@ramiseth.co.uk — MB BS Delhi Univ. 1964; FRCS Edin. 1969. Surg. to the Family Plann. Assn.; Specialist in Erectile DysFunc. Prev: GP in Notts (Retd.).

SETH, Sarah Abigail 18 Hartington Place, Edinburgh EH10 4LE — MB ChB 1996 Ed.

SETH, Vir Royal Surrey County Hospital, Egerton Road, Guildford GU2 7XX Tel: 01483 571122 — MB BS 1972 Delhi; FRCP Lond. 1995; MRCP (UK) 1977. (Maulana Azad Med. Coll.) Cons. Phys. Geriat. Med. SW Surrey Health Dist. Prev: Sen. Regist. (Geriat. Med.) Ipswich & E. Suff. Health Dist.; Regist. (Gen. Med.) Barnsley Dist. Gen. Hosp.

SETH-SMITH, Mr Alan Brian (retired) Les Merriennes, St Martin's, Guernsey GY4 6RN Tel: 01481 36811 — MB BS 1950 Lond.; FRCS Eng. 1956. Prev: Cons. Surg. P.ss Eliz. Hosp. Guernsey.

SETHI, Amarjit Singh St Bartholomews Hospital, West Smithfield, London EC1A 7BE; 301 Brompton Park Crescent, Seagrave Road, Fulham, London SW6 1SP Email: asethi@dial.pipex.com — MB BS 1992 Lond.; BSc Lond. 1989; MRCP (UK) 1995. (UMDS Guy's & St. Thos.) Regist. Rotat. (Cardiol.) St. Bart. Hosp. Lond. Socs: BMA; Roy. Soc. Trop. Med. & Hyg. Prev: Regist. King Geo. Hosp. Ilford; SHO (Med.) Lond. Chest Hosp.; SHO (Med.) Roy. Brompton Nat. Heart & Lung Hosp.

SETHI, Anthony Krishen The Tardis Surgery, 9 Queen Street, Cheadle, Stoke-on-Trent ST10 1BH Tel: 01538 753771 Fax: 01538 752557 — MB ChB 1962 Birm.; DObst RCOG 1964. (Birm.) Asst. Postgrad. Tutor Stoke-on-Trent. Socs: BMA. Prev: SHO (Obst. & Gyn.) City Hosp. Nottm.; Ho. Surg. Stratford-on-Avon Hosp.; Ho. Phys. Walsall Gen. Hosp.

SETHI, Mr Baldev Prakash Cumberland Infirmary, Carlisle CA2 7HY — MB BS 1951 Calcutta; DOMS 1954; FRCS Ed. 1961; FRCS Eng. 1961. (Calcutta) Ophth. Consult. Cumbld. Infirm. Carlisle. Socs: Ophth. Soc. U.K. Mem. N. Eng. Ophth. Soc. Prev: Sen. Ophth. Regist. Roy. Infirms. Sheff. & Edin.; Ophth. Regist. Roy. Eye & Ear Hosp. Bradford.

SETHI, Mr Charanjit Singh 9 Lambourn Way, Chatham ME5 8PU Email: csethi@dial.pipex.com; 91 Brompton Park Crescent, Seagrave Road, Fulham, London SW6 1SP Tel: 020 7610 1488 — MB BS 1994 Lond.; BSc (Hons.) Lond. 1991; FRCOphth. Lond. 1998. (United Med. & Dent. Sch. Guy's & St. Thos. Hosp. Lond.) Vitreo-Retinal Research Regist. Moorfields Eye Hosp. Socs: Fell. Roy. Soc. Med.; BMA. Prev: SHO (Ophth.) Bristol Eye Hosp.

SETHI, Dinesh Health Policy Unit, London School Of Hygiene & Tropical Medicine, Kepple Street, London WC1E 7HT Tel: 020 7927 2122 Fax: 020 7637 5391 Email: dinesh.sethi@lsthm.ac.uk; 43 St Helen's Gardens, London W10 6LN — MB ChB 1990 Liverp.; MSc (Lond. Sch. Hyg. & Trop. Med.) Lond. 1994; MD Liverp. 1990, MB ChB 1980; MRCP (UK) 1984; MFPHM 1996. (Liverpool) Lect. Internat. Pub. Health & P.H. Med. Lon. Sch. Hyg. & Trop. Med. Socs: Fac. Pub. Health Med.; Renal Assn. Prev: Lect. Char. Cross Hosp. Lond.; Sen. Regist. (Pub. Health Med.) Wolfson Inst. Preven. Med. Lond.

SETHI, Gulshan 4 Cotman Drive, Marple Bridge, Stockport SK6 5DL — MB ChB 1997 Leeds.

SETHI, Mr Inder Singh (retired) 30 Marchbank Drive, Cheadle SK8 1QY Tel: 0161 491 1142 Fax: 0161 428 5761 — MB BS 1955 Punjab, India; FRCS Ed. 1966; FRCS Eng. 1966. Prev: Clin. Asst. (A & E) Stockport AHA.

SETHI, Jasbir Kaur Lordswood Health Centre, Sultan Road, Lordswood, Chatham ME5 8TJ Tel: 01634 666996; 9 Lambourn Way, Lordswood, Chatham ME5 8PU — MB BS 1968 Nagpur; DCH Eng. 1976. (Nagpur Med. Coll.) Med. Off. (Child Health & Community Med.) Medway Health Dist. Socs: BMA; Fac. Community Health. Prev: SHO (Anaesth.) Middlesbrough Gen. Hosp.; SHO (Anaesth.) Roy. Halifax Infirm.; SHO (Paediat.) Gravesend & N. Kent Hosp.

SETHI, Jasminder Kaur Tel: 020 8422 5602 Fax: 020 8422 3911; Silver Birches, 53C Gordon Avenue, Stanmore HA7 3QN Tel: 020 8954 6743 Fax: 020 8537 8701 — MB BS 1981 Lond. (St. Thos.) Dep. Chairm. of Independant Ethics Comm. Of N.wick Pk. Hosp.

Prev: Course Organiser Edgware Gen. Hosp. VTS; Mem. Ethics Review Comm. Glaxo-Wellcome.

SETHI, Krishna K 39 College Way, Hayes UB3 3DZ Tel: 0208 573 2365; 25 Arlington Square, London N1 7DP Tel: 020 7226 3456, 0208 421 0454 Fax: 020 7226 3456 Email: gert.siegruhn@which.net — MBBS 1967; FRCOG 1999 Roy. Coll. of Obst. & Gyn., Lond.; MRCOG 1974 Roy. Coll. of Obst. & Gynaecology, Lond.; LF Hom (Med) 1999. (Punjab University Amritsar, India) Socs: Med. Protec. Soc.; Brit. Menopause Soc.; Nat. Osteoporosis Soc.

SETHI, Kulwant Bir Singh, OBE, TD, OStJ, Col. late RAMC Highwood, Endon, Stoke-on-Trent ST9 9AR Tel: 01538 385088 Fax: 01538 385088 — MB BS Punjab, India 1959; BSc Agra 1954; FICS 1965; MRCGP 1977; DLO Eng. 1964; FRCGP 1998. (Med. Coll. Amritsar, Punjab India) Trainer (Gen. Pract.) Stoke-on-Trent; DL Staffs. Socs: Fell. Roy. Soc. Med. & Arts. Prev: Sen. Resid. NW Univ. Med. Sch. Chicago, USA; Co. 224 Field Ambul. RAMC (V); Hon. Col. RAMC.

SETHI, Padam Chand Child Guidance Clinic, 6 Southey Road, Worthing BN11 3HT; White Oaks, 4 Sea Drive, Ferring, Worthing BN12 5HD — MB BS 1968 Rajasthan; MRCPsych 1973; DPM Ed. & Glas. 1972. Cons. Psychiat. Child & Adolesc. Psychiat. Child Guid. Clinic Worthing. Prev: Cons. Psychiat. Stratheden Hosp. Cupar; Sen. Regist. (Child & Adolesc. Psychiat.) Univ. Hosp. Wales Child & Family Centre Cardiff; Sen. Regist. (Psychiat.) Botleys Pk. Hosp. Chertsey.

SETHI, Permindar 62 Grange Park Avenue, London N21 2LL — MB BS 1996 Lond.

SETHI, Pradeep Bury NHS Health Care Trust, Fairfield Hospital, Rochdale Road, Bury M45 7QG Tel: 0161 705 3873 Fax: 0161 705 3707; 29 Fairhaven Avenue, Whitefield, Manchester M45 7QG — MB BS 1977 Panjab; MRCP (UK) 1982; FRCP 1999. Cons. Phys. (Geriat. Med.) Fairfield & Bury Gen. Hosps. Bury. Socs: BGS. Prev: Sen. Regist. (Geriat.) & (Gen. Med. Rotat.) Manch. Gp. Hosps.

SETHI, Mr Rajive Staff Village, Royal Preston Hospital, Sharoe Green Lane N., Preston PR2 9HT — MB BS 1982 Kanpur; FRCSI 1990.

SETHI, Rohit Phoenix Surgery, 9 Chesterton Lane, Cirencester GL7 1XG Tel: 01285 652056 Fax: 01285 641562; Laverton House, Fairford GL7 4AB Tel: 01285 711180 Email: rohit@ciren44.freeserve.co.uk — BM BS 1983 Nottm.; BMedSci Nottm. 1981, BM BS 1983; MRCGP 1988; DA Eng. 1985. Princip. GP; Doctor to Roy. Agricultural Coll.; Hosp. Pract. (Anaesth.) Cirencester Hosp.; Med. Dir. In Touch with Health.

SETHI, Tariq Jabbar 10 Queen's Gate Place, London SW7 5NX — MB BS 1983 Lond.; BSc Lond. 1978; BA Camb. 1980, MA 1984; MRCPI 1989; MRCP (UK) 1989. Clin. Fell. Imperial Cancer Research Fund. Prev: SHO (Gen. Med.) Hammersmith Hosp. Lond.; Lect. (Gen. Med.) Guy's Hosp. Lond.; Regist. (Respirat. Med. & Cardiol.) St. Mary's Hosp. Lond.

SETHIA, Mr Krishna Kumar Hedenham Hall Farm, Hedenham, Bungay NR35 2LG — MB BS 1979 Lond.; DM Oxon. 1990; FRCS Lond. 1984. Cons. Urol. Norf. & Norwich Hosp.

SETHNA, Edulji Rustumji (retired) 32 Little Sutton Lane, Sutton Coldfield B75 6PB Email: eddysethna@virgin.net — MB BS Bombay 1951; FRCP Lond. 1987, M 1956; FRCPsych 1986, M 1971; DPM Eng. 1963; DTM & H Liverp. 1958. Prev: Cons. Psychiat. Hollymoor Hosp. Birm. & Lyndon Clinic Solihull.

SETHU, Parayath Rosewood Medical Centre, 30 Astra Close, Hornchurch RM12 5NJ Tel: 01708 554557 Fax: 01708 554212 — MB BS 1968 Kerala. (Med. Coll. Trivandrum) Prev: Regist. Rush Green Hosp. Romford.

SETHUGAVALAR, Chinnadurai 43 Sylvan Way, Redhill RH1 4DE — MB BS 1978 Mysore; LRCP LRCS Ed. LRCPS Glas. 1981. SHO (O & G) Torbay Hosp. Torquay. Prev: SHO (Gyn.) St. Jas. Hosp. Lond.; SHO (O & G) S.mead Hosp. Bristol; SHO (O & G) Roy. Gwent Hosp. Newport.

SETHURAJAN, Anjana 38 Emlyn Road, Stamford Brook, London W12 9TD Tel: 020 8740 0192 — MB ChB 1991 Glas.; MRCGP 1995; DCH RCP Lond. 1994; DRCOG 1994.

***SETHURAJAN, Shantha** 40 Emlyn Road, London W12 9TD Tel: 020 8743 5294 — MB BS 1994 Lond.; BSc Lond. 1991.

SETIA, Rama (Surgery), 143 Rookwood Avenue, Leeds LS9 0NL Tel: 0113 249 3011; The Manor, Manor House Lane, Leeds

SETIYA

LS17 9JD Tel: 0113 269 7197 — MB BS 1965 Delhi; DMRT Eng. 1971. (Maulana Azad Med. Coll.) Prev: Ho. Surg. (O & G) Irwin Hosp. New Delhi, India; Regist. (Radiother.) Regional Radiother. Centre Cookridge Hosp. Leeds; Clin. Med. Off. Leeds AHA (T).

SETIYA, Megharaj Sukharaj Marfleet Lane Surgery, 358 Marfleet Lane, Hull HU9 5AD Tel: 01482 781032 Fax: 01482 789180 Email: mssetiya@hotmail.com; 7 Northwood Drive, Tranby Park, Jenny Brough Lane, Hessle HU13 0TA — MB BS Bombay 1959; DLO RCS Eng. 1964; DObst.RCOG 1966. (B.J. Med. Coll. Pune, India) Mem. Disabil. Appeals Tribunal; Med. Adviser to Social Security Appeals Tribunals. Socs: Hull Med. Soc.; DRCOG. Prev: Clin. Asst. (Med. for Elderly) Hull; Clin. Asst. Matern. Hosp. Hull; Regist. (ENT) N. Staffs. Roy. Infirm. Stoke-on-Trent.

SETNA, Farokh Jal Department of Radiology, Arrowe Park Hospital, Arrowe Park Road, Upton, Wirral CH49 5PE Tel: 0151 678 5111 Fax: 0151 604 1068; 43 Manvers Road, Childwall, Liverpool L16 3NP Email: 106113.1540@compuserve.com — MB BS 1981 Punjab, Pakistan; BSc Punjab 1975; FFR RCSI (I) Dub. 1991. (King Edwd. Med. Coll. Lahore, Pakistan) Staff Radiol. Arrowe Pk. Hosp. Wirral. Prev: Sen. Regist. (Radiol.) Arrowe Pk. Hosp. Wirral; Sen. Regist. (Radiol.) Whiston Hosp. Prescot, Aintree Hosp. Liverp., Warrington Gen. Hosp. & Roy. Liverp. Univ. Hosp.

SETNA, Mr Piloo Homi (retired) 8 Church Road, Lytham St Annes FY8 5LH Tel: 01253 730474 — MB BS 1953 Lond.; FRCS Eng. 1966; FRCOphth. 1989; DO Eng. 1962. Prev: Cons. Ophth. Blackpool & Fylde Hosp. Gp.

SETON, Alexander (retired) 20 Horsemarket, Kelso TD5 7HA Tel: 01573 2531 — MB ChB 1930 Glas. Prev: Ho. Surg. Hartlepools Hosp.

SETON, Dorothy Lyall (retired) 15 Queen's Road, Aberdeen AB15 4YL Tel: 01224 322624 — MB ChB 1925 St. And.

SETON, Ruth Fiona 3 Bernard Terrace, Newington, Edinburgh EH8 9NU — MB ChB 1996 Ed.

SETT, Mr Pradipkumar Clinical Director, Northwest Regional Spinal Injuries Centre, Southport & Formby District General Hospital, Southport PR8 6NJ Tel: 01704 547471 Fax: 01704 543156; 16 Chesterfield Road, Southport PR8 3JR — MB BS 1972 Calcutta; MS Calcutta 1976; FRCS (SN) 1988; FRCS Ed. 1978. Clin. Dir. NW Regional Spinal Injuries Centre S.port & Formby Dist. Gen. Hosp. Socs: Soc. Brit. Neurosurgs.; Brit. Cervical Spine Soc.; Internat. Med. Soc. Paraplegia.

SETTATREE, Ralph Stewart Princess of Wales Women's Unit, Birmingham Heartlands Hospital, Bordesley Green E., Birmingham B9 5SS Tel: 0121 424 0714 Fax: 0121 424 3130 Email: settatr@hearts.wmids.nhs.uk; 41 Billesley Lane, Moseley, Birmingham B13 9QT Tel: 0121 449 6996 Fax: 0121 449 2038 Email: ralph.settatree@btinternet.com — MB BS Lond. 1969; MRCS Eng. LRCP Lond. 1969; FRCOG 1990, M 1977, DObst 1971. (Guy's) Cons. O & G Birm. Heartlands & Solihull NHS Trust. Socs: BMA; (Ex-Treas.) Birm. & Midl. Obst. & Gyn. Soc.; (Conf. Comm.) Brit. Matern. and Fetal Med. Soc. Prev: Clin. Dir. Confidential Enquiry into Stillbirths & Deaths in Infancy; Sen. Regist. (O & G) Dudley Rd. Hosp. Birm.; MOH Dist. Hosp. Marsabit, Kenya.

SETTERFIELD, Jane Frances St. John's Institute of Dermatology, St. Thomas' Hospital, Lambeth Palace Road, London SE1 7EH Tel: 020 7928 9292 Fax: 020 7922 8232 Email: j.setterfield@umds.ac.uk; 40 Roanalds Road, Highbury, London N5 1XG Tel: 020 7609 3749 — MB BS Lond. 1987; BDS Lond. 1980; MRCP (UK) 1993; MRCGP 1991; LDS RCS Eng. 1981; DRCOG 1991; DCH RCP Lond. 1989. (Univ. Coll. Hosp.) Specialist Regist. (Dermatol.) St John's Inst. Dermatol. St. Thos. & Guy's Hosp. Lond. Socs: Train. Mem. Brit. Assn. Dermat. Prev: Clin. Research Fell. St. John's Inst. Dermat. St. Thos. Hosp. Lond.; SHO (Dermat.) St. John's Inst. Dermat. St. Thos. Hosp. Lond.

SETTLE, Christopher David Jasmine Cottage, Catton, Thirsk YO7 4SH — MB ChB 1990 Ed.

SETTLE, Frances Caroline 1 Meadow Way, Leeds LS17 7QY — MB ChB 1991 Sheff.

SETTLE, Mr John Antony David, OBE Pindersfields Hospital, Aberford Road, Wakefield WF1 4DG Tel: 01924 375217; Iveridge Hall, Wakefield Road, Oulton, Woodlesford, Leeds LS26 8EU Tel: 0113 282 1468 — MRCS Eng. LRCP Lond. 1961; MPhil Leeds 1971; FRCS Ed. 1991; DA Eng. 1964. (Leeds) Med. Dir. Pindersfields Hosp. NHS Trust Wakefield; Hon. Lect. (Surg.) Univ. Leeds. Socs: Hon. Mem. Brit. Assn. Plastic Surg. Prev: Burns Cons. Yorks. Regional Burns Centre, Regist. & Asst. (Plastic Surg.) Pinderfields Hosp. Wakefield.

SETTLE, Paul 11 Old Hall Lane, Westhoughton, Bolton BL5 2HQ — MB ChB 1992 Manch.

SETTLE, Vera (retired) 56 Greenfield Road, Stafford ST17 0PU — MB ChB 1941 Manch.; BSc Manch. 1938; DCH Eng. 1942. Prev: Asst. MOH (Matern. & Child Welf.) Manch.

SETTY, Guduthur Roopa 20 St Michael's Avenue, South Shields NE33 3AN — MB ChB 1995 Dundee.

SETTY, Matta Venkataramanaiah S Stanhope Surgery, 85 Kilndown Close, Stanhope, Ashford TN23 5SU Tel: 01233 636816 Fax: 01233 662188; 2 Summerhill Park, Hythe Road, Willesborough, Ashford TN24 0TG Tel: 01233 636816 Fax: 01233 503606 — MB BS 1971 Bangalor. (Bangalore)

SETTY, Pathiyappa Hallur Raghavendra Countess of Chester Hospital, Liverpool Road, Chester CH2 1UL Tel: 01244 365000 Fax: 01244 365435; 19 Deva Lane, Upton, Chester CH2 1BN Tel: 01244 364766 Fax: 01244 375794 — MB BS 1972 Mysore; DA Eng. 1984. (Govt. Med. Coll. Mysore) Cons. Anaesth. Co. of Chester Hosp. Chesh. Prev: Assoc. Specialist Barnsley; Regist. Doncaster & Barnsley.

SETTY, Shubha 55 Wellington Avenue, Wavetree, Liverpool L15 0EH — MB ChB 1996 Liverp.

SEUKERAN, Daron Carl 4 Low Street, North Ferriby HU14 3DD — MB ChB 1988 Glas.; MRCP (UK) 1993; MRCGP 1992; DCH RCP Lond. 1992; DRCOG 1991.

SEVAR, Raymond 26 Whiteclosegate, Carlisle CA3 0JD Tel: 01228 531691 — BSc St. And. 1976; MB ChB Manch 1979; MFHOM 1994; MRCGP 1983; DCH RCP Lond. 1981. Homoeop. Phys.; 1999 Med. Examr., Fac. of Homoeopathy. Prev: 1994 Lect., Acad. Depts, Glas. Homoeop. Hosp.

SEVENOAKS, Michael Ron Old Cottage Hospital Surgery, Alexandra Road, Epsom KT17 4BL Tel: 01372 724434 Fax: 01372 748171; 11 Chartwell Place, Epsom KT18 5JH — MB BS 1989 Lond.; BSc (Hons.) Lond. 1986; MRCGP 1994; DFFP 1994; DRCOG 1993.

SEVENOAKS, Tamsin Alexandra The Surgery, Tanners Meadow, Brockham, Betchworth RH3 7NJ Tel: 01306 631242 — MB BS 1989 Lond.; DFFP 1994. GP Princip., Dr Kober and Partners.

SEVER, Peter Sedgwick Department of Clinical Pharmacology, NHLI at St Mary's Hospital, Imperial College of Science, Technology & Medicine, London W2 1NY Tel: 020 7886 1117 Fax: 020 7886 6145 — MRCS Eng. LRCP Lond. 1968; PhD Lond. 1975; MB Camb. 1969, BChir 1968; FRCP Lond. 1981; MRCP (UK) 1971. (Camb.) Prof. Clin. Pharmacol. & Therap. & Hon. Cons. Phys. St. Mary's Hosp. Lond. Socs: Fell. Europ. Soc. Cardiol.; (Ex-Pres.) Brit. Hypertens. Soc.; Pres. Elect Europ. Counc. High Blood Pressure & Cardiovasc. Res. Prev: Sen. Lect. (Med.) & Hon. Cons. Phys. St. Mary's Hosp. Lond.; Jun. Research Fell. Med. Research Counc.; Lect. (Med. & Pharmacol.) St. Marys Hosp. Med. Sch. Lond.

SEVERIN, Karin Maria 140 Scartho Road, Grimsby DN33 2AX — State Exam Med. Berlin 1991.

SEVERN, Andrew Moore Lane Head House, 58 Main St., Bolton-le-Sands, Carnforth LA5 8DN — MB BS 1981 Newc.; MA Camb. 1982; FRCA 1987. Cons. Anaesth. Lancaster. Prev: Sen. Regist. (Anaesth.) Manch.; Regist. (Anaesth.) Portsmouth & Bristol.

SEVERN, Michael Department of Microbiology, General Hospital, Northampton NN1 5BD — MB ChB 1961 Birm.; FRCPath. 1982, M 1971. Cons. Microbiol. Gen. Hosp. N.ampton. Prev: Asst. Bact. Pub. Health Laborat. Radcliffe Infirm. Oxf.; Res. Pathol. Roy. Devon & Exeter Hosp.; Ho. Surg. Qu. Eliz. Hosp. Birm.

SEVERS, Professor Martin Peter School of Postgraduate Medicine Gloucester House, c/o School of Health Studies, Queen Alexandra Hospital, Cosham, Portsmouth PO6 3LY Tel: 023 92 286301 Fax: 023 92 286227 Email: spgm@port.ac.uk — MB BS 1980 Lond.; FRCP Lond. 1992; MRCP (UK) 1984; FFPHM 1999. (St Mary's Hospital Medical School) Cons. Geriat. Portsmouth Healthcare NHS Trust; Chairm. Informat. Standards Bd. NHS; Hon. Lect. Univ. Soton. Prev: Chairm. Conf. of Med. Roy. Coll. & their Fac. in UK Informatmat. Advis. Gp. Prof. Univ Portsmouth; Sen. Regist. & Lect. (Geriat. Med.) Portsmouth & Soton.; Med. Dir. Portsmouth Health Care NHS Trust.

SEVERS, Paul Hirst 74 Skipton Road, Keighley BD20 9LL — MB BS 1977 Newc.; MFCH 1989; FRIPHH 1996. (Newcastle) SCMO Airedale HA; Med Ref. to Skipton Cremat. Socs: SPH.(Fell). Prev: Clin. Med. Off. (Child Health) N.d. AHA; Clin. Med. Off. Newc. AHA (T); Trainee GP N.umbria VTS.

SEVILLE, Malcolm Heywood 6 Lansdowne Road, Bare, Morecambe LA4 6AL Tel: 01524 418871 — MB BS 1974 Lond. (St. Thos.) Prev: Clin. Asst. Dermat. Beaumont Hosp. Lancaster.; Clin. Asst. Ophth. Garnett Clinic Lancaster; SHO Path. Roy. Lancaster Infirm.

SEVILLE, Robert Heywood 2 Hayfell Grove, Hest Bank, Lancaster LA2 6DT Tel: 01524 823766 — MB ChB 1944 Leeds; MD Leeds 1948; FRCP Lond. 1973, M 1950. Hon. Cons. Dermat. Roy. Infirm. Lancaster; Hon. Mem. N. Eng. Dermat. Soc. Socs: Fell. Roy. Soc. Med. (Mem. Dermat. Sect.); BMA; The Dowling Club. Prev: Sen. Regist. St. John's Hosp. Dis. Skin Lond.; Regist. Skin & Med. Units Gen. Infirm. & St. Jas. Hosp. Leeds; Maj. RAMC.

SEVITT, Ivor (retired) 30 Ashfield Lane, Chislehurst BR7 6LQ Tel: 020 8467 2483 — MB BCh BAO 1946 Dub.; MRCGP 1966. Prev: SHO Horton Gen. Hosp. Banbury.

SEVITT, Lewis Howard 141 Harley Street, London W1 Tel: 020 7636 3979; 14 Queen Annes Gardens, Bedford Park, London W4 1TU Tel: 020 8994 1493 — MB BCh BAO 1962 Dub.; BA Dub. 1960, MB BCh BAO 1962; FRCP Lond. 1979, M 1965. (T.C. Dub.) Cons. Phys. (Gen. Med. & Renal Dis.) Hillingdon HA; Hon. Sen. Lect. Roy. Postgrad. Med. Sch. Lond.; Hon. Cons. Phys. Hammersmith Hosp. Lond.; Assoc. Teach. St. Mary's Hosp. Med. Sch. Lond. Prev: Clin. Tutor Hillingdon HA; Sen. Regist. Dept. Med. (Renal Unit); Hammersmith Hosp. Lond.; SHO Med. Profess. & Renal Units Roy. Free Hosp. Lond.

SEVITT, Michael Andrew Woodside Adolescent Unit, West Park Hospital, Epsom KT19 8PB Tel: 01372 203404 Fax: 01372 203406 Email: woodside-campus@surreyoaklands.nhs.uk; 7 Upper Park Road, Kingston upon Thames KT2 5LB Tel: 020 8546 4173 — MA; MB Camb. 1969, BChir 1968; MRCP (U.K.) 1971; MRCPsych 1974; MInstGA 1979. (Univ. Coll. Hosp.) Cons. Psychiat. Woodside Adolesc. Unit W. Pk. Hosp. Epsom. Socs: UK Counc. Psychother.; Assn.Child Psychologists and Psychiat.; Chair. Registration Sub committe, Asoc. for Family Ther. Prev: Sen. Regist. (Child & Adolesc. Psychiat.) Wessex Unit for Childr. & Parents Portsmouth; Lect. (Psychiat.) Soton. Gen. Hosp.

SEWARD, Christopher Frederic The Wistaria Practice, 32 St. Thomas' Street, Lymington SO41 9NE Tel: 01590 672212 Fax: 01590 679930; Hillbrow, West Road, Milford-on-Sea, Lymington SO41 0NZ Tel: 01590 645730 Fax: 01590 644950 — BM BCh 1974 Oxf.; MA Oxf. 1974; MRCS Eng. LRCP Lond. 1974; DObst RCOG 1975. (Middlx.) GP. Socs: Roy. Soc. Med.; BMA. Prev: SHO (O & G) W.m. Hosp.; Ho. Surg. Middlx. Hosp.; Ho. Phys. St. Albans City Hosp.

SEWARD, Helen Clare The Croydon Eye Unit, 33 Mayday Road, Thornton Heath, Croydon CR7 7XN Tel: 020 8401 3127 Fax: 020 8401 3489; Shirley Oaks Hospital, Poppy Lane, Shirley Oaks Village, Croydon CR9 8AB Tel: 020 8655 2255 — MB BCh BAO 1976 NUI; FRCS Eng. 1981; FRCOphth 1990; DO RCS Eng. 1980. Cons. Ophth. Surg. Croydon Eye Unit; Mem. (Audit Comm.) Roy. Coll. Ophth.; Mem. Oxf. Ophth. Congr.; Pres., United Kingdom & Irish Soc. of Cataract & Refractive Surg.s. Socs: BMA; (Counc.) UK ISCRS. Prev: Sen. Regist. W.. Eye Hosp. & Moorfields; Regist. (Ophth.) Croydon Eye Unit Surrey; SHO Regional Neurosurg. Servs. Brook Hosp. Lond.

SEWARD, William Percival Castle Road, 2 Castle Road, Chirk, Wrexham LL14 5BS Tel: 01691 772434 Fax: 01691 773840; Grove House, Pontyblew, Chirk, Wrexham LL14 5BH — MB BS 1971 Lond.; DObst RCOG 1973.

SEWART, John Hunter (retired) Hooe Lake Cottage, Hooe Lake, Maker, Torpoint PL10 1JB Tel: 01752 823598 — MB BChir 1952 Camb.; BA Camb. 1952; MFCM 1973; MFOM RCP Lond. 1979; DIH Soc. Apoth. Lond. 1968; DTM & H Liverp. 1961; DPH Lond. 1958. Med. Ref. Marine Safety Agency Dept. Transport. Prev: SCMO (Environm. Health) Cornw. & I. of Scilly HA.

SEWELL, Amanda Claire Cranborne Horsegrove Avenue, Ticehurst, Wadhurst TN5 7DE Tel: 01580 200187 Fax: 01580 201443 Email: amandasewell@hotmail.com — BM 1996 soton.; BM (Hons.) Soton. 1996.

SEWELL, Elizabeth 95 Hunters Way, Uckfield TN22 2BB — MB ChB 1989 Otago; MRCGP 1995; DFFP 1995; Dip. Obst. Auckland 1992. (Otago, NZ) Acad. Asst. (Gen. Pract.) St. Geo. Med. Sch. Prev: Assoc. GP ISL Health Commiss. VTS; Trainee GP Maidstone VTS.

SEWELL, Eric Mansfield (retired) 19 Hinderton Drive, West Kirby, Wirral CH48 8BN Tel: 0151 625 5899 — MB ChB 1940 Glas.; DPH Glas. 1948. Prev: Sen. Asst. Med. Off. Regional Transfus. Serv. Liverp.

SEWELL, Professor Herbert Fitzgerald Department of Immunology, Queens Medical Centre, University Hospital, Nottingham NG7 2UH Tel: 0115 970 9123 Fax: 0115 970 9125; 75 Oakland Avenue, Leicester LE4 7SG — MB ChB 1983 Leic.; PhD Birm. 1978, MSc (Immunol.) 1975, BDS 1973; FRCP Glas. 1989. M 1987; FRCPath (Immunol.) 1992, M 1980. Prof. & Hon. Cons. Immunol. Univ. Hosp. Qu. Med. Centre Nottm. Prev: Sen. Lect. & Hon. Cons. Immunopath. Univ. Aberd. Med. Sch.

SEWELL, Joanne Margaret Abbey House Surgery, Golding Close, Daventry NN11 5RA Tel: 01327 877770 Fax: 01327 310267; 24 Moreton Drive, Buckingham MK18 1JQ — MB BS 1987 Lond.; BSc (Hons.) Lond. 1984; MRCGP 1993; DCH RCP Lond. 1992; DRCOG 1990. Prev: Trainee GP W. Middlx. Hosp. Lond.; GP Princip. N. End Surg. Buckingham.

SEWELL, John Martin Alexander Singleton Hospital, Swansea SA2 8QA Tel: 01792 205666; 7 New Hill Villas, Goodwick SA64 0DS — MB 1977 Camb.; BChir 1976; LMCC 1982; MRCGP 1981; FFA RCS Eng. 1985; DA Eng. 1984; DRCOG 1978. (Lond. Hosp.) Specialist Regist. Rotat. (Anaesth.) Wales; Relate Counsellor Swansea. Socs: Obst. Anaesth. Assn.; Brit. Holistic Med. Assn.; Brit. Med. Acupunct. Soc. Prev: Assoc. Specialist (Anaesth.) Swansea NHS Trust; GP Brecon, Powys; Regist. (Anaesth.) Newc.

SEWELL, John Robin The William Harvey Hospital, Kennington Road, Willesborough, Ashford TN24 0LZ Tel: 01233 633331 Fax: 01233 616118; Fairlight Corner, 138 North Road, Hythe CT21 4AT Tel: 01303 265657 — MB BChir 1971 Camb.; MA Camb. 1970, MB BChir 1971; FRCP (UK) 1990; FRCP Lond. 1989; MRCP (UK) 1972. (Camb. & St. Thos.) Cons. Phys. Rheum. & Rehabil. The William Harvey Hosp & Buckland Hosp. Dover. Socs: Brit. Soc. Rheum. Prev: Hon. Sen. Regist. (Med.) Hammersmith Hosp. Lond.; Lect. Roy. Postgrad. Med. Sch. Lond.; Clin. & Research Asst. St. Thos. Hosp. Lond.

SEWELL, Matthew Stephen North Devon District Hospital, Raleigh Park, Barnstaple EX31 4JB Tel: 01271 22577; Hedna Cottage, Church Town, Parracombe, Barnstaple EX31 4RJ — MB BS 1981 Lond.; MRCPsych 1986. Cons. Psychiat. (Special Responsibil. for Old Age Psychiat.) N. Devon Dist. Hosp.

SEWELL, Maxwell Stanley (retired) 145 Cranley Gardens, London N10 3AG Tel: 020 8883 4409 — MB ChB 1952 Leeds. Prev: Ho. Phys. (Dermat.) Newsham Gen. Hosp. Liverp.

SEWELL, Nigel Bernard 19 Cornaway Lane, Portchester, Fareham PO16 9DA — MB BS 1982 Lond.

SEWELL, Peter Francis John 32 Checkstone Avenue, Bessacarr, Doncaster DN4 7JX Tel: 01302 535766 — MB BS 1957 Lond.; BSc (Zool.) Lond. 1945, PhD 1949; FRCPath 1975, M 1963. (Univ. Coll. Hosp.) Emerit. Cons. Doncaster Roy. Infirm. Socs: Hon. Mem. (Ex-Pres.) Assn. Clin. Biochem.; Emerit. Mem. Amer. Assn. Clin. Chem. Prev: Mem. Assn. Clin. Paths.; Vice-Chairm. Trent RHA; Cons. Clin. Chem. Doncaster HA.

SEWELL, Mr Peter Frederic Toyne Hinchingbrooke Hospital, Huntingdon PE18 8NT Tel: 01480 416416; Tel: 01480 861311 Fax: 01480 861352 — BA (Cantab.) 1966; BChir 1969; MB Camb. 1970; FRCS Ed. 1976. (Cambridge & Middlesex Hospital) Cons. Orthop. Surg. Hinchingbrooke Hosp. Huntingdon. Socs: Brit. Hip Soc. Prev: Lt. Col. RAMC; Cons. Orthop. Surg. P.ss Alexandra Hosp. Wroughton.

SEWELL, Rebecca Caroline Toyne 45 Hawthorn Road, Buckhurst Hill IG9 6JF Tel: 020 8504 4637 — MB BS 1994 Lond.; MA Camb. 1995, BA 1991; MRCP (UK) 1998. (Charing Cross & Westm. Hosps) SHO (Paediat.) P.ss Alexandra Hosp. Haslow. Prev: SHO (Neonat.) Harold Wood Hosp. Romford; SHO (Paediat. Oncol.) St. Barts. Hosp. Lond.

SEWELL, Richard Norman Ash Trees Surgery, Market Street, Carnforth LA5 9JU Tel: 01524 720000 Fax: 01524 720110; Brooklands, 26 Hanging Green Lane, Hest Bank, Lancaster LA2 6JB

SEWELL

Tel: 01524 823220 Fax: 01524 823220 Email: richard@carnforth.demon.co.uk — MB ChB 1982 Dundee; MRCGP 1986; DRCOG 1984.

SEWELL, Mr Robert Henry (retired) 4 Bayards, Warlingham CR6 9BP Tel: 01883 624343 — MB ChB 1943 Manch.; BSc Manch. 1940, ChM 1949; FRCS Eng. 1950; FRCS Ed. 1948; MRCS Eng. LRCP Lond. 1943. Hon. Cons. Orthop. Surg. Greenwich Dist. Hosp. Prev: Sen. Regist. (Orthop.) Roy. Nat. Orthop. Hosp.

SEWELL, Ruth Alexandra Drs Wilson, Keddie & Sewell, 91 Kirkintilloch Road, Bishopbriggs, Glasgow G64 2AA Tel: 0141 772 2242 Fax: 0141 762 3482 Email: administrator@gp43491.glasgow.hb.scot.nhs.uk; 16 Paterson Place, Bearsdon, Glasgow G61 4RU Tel: 0141 943 0729 — MB ChB 1979 Ed.; T(GP) 1991; DCH RCP Lond. 1983. (Ed.) GP Partner. Prev: SHO (Paediat.) Soton. Gen. Hosp.; Trainee GP Aldermoor Soton.; Regist. (Paediat.) Falkirk & Stirling Roy. Infirms.

SEWELL, Stephen Peter Wroughton Health Centre, Barrett Way, Wroughton, Swindon SN4 9LW Tel: 01793 812221; 38 Westlecot Road, Old Town, Swindon SN1 4HB Tel: 01793 497113 — BM 1990 Soton.; MRCGP 1995; DRCOG 1994. (Soton.) Prev: GP/Regist. Wroughton; SHO (Paediat.) P.ss Margt. Hosp. Swindon; SHO (Psychiat.) N. Birm. Hosp. Trust.

SEWELL, William Arthur Carrock MRC Immunodeficiency Research Group, Department of Clinical Immunology, Royal Free Hospital, Rowland Hill St., London NW3 2PF Tel: 020 7794 0500 Fax: 020 7830 2224 Email: carrock@rfhsm.ac.uk — MB BS 1991 Newc.; MRCPath 2001; PhD (UCL) 2000; BMedSc (Hons.) Newc. 1988; MRCP (UK) 1994; DRCPath 1996. Cons. Immunol. Path Links, Gt.er Lincolns. Socs: Fell. Roy. Soc. Med.; Brit. Soc. Allergy & Clin. Immunol.; Assoc. Clin. Pathologists. Prev: Spec. Reg. (Immunol.) King's Coll. Hosp. St Barth. Hosp. Roy. Free Hosp.; Clin. Fell. In Knowledge Architecture, doctors.net.uk Ltd. & NeLH; Regist. (Clin. Immunol.) Oxf. Radcliffe Hosp. NHS Trust.

SEWELL, William Lawson (retired) Spetses, Neilston Walk, Kilsyth, Glasgow G65 9TF Tel: 01236 823298 — MB ChB 1946 Ed.

SEWNAUTH, Dev Kumar 8 Abercrombie Drive, Alderglen, Bearsden, Glasgow G61 4RR Tel: 0141 943 1720 — MB ChB 1972 Glas.; FFA RCS Irel. 1978. Cons. Anaesth. Stobhill Gen. Hosp. Glas. Prev: Cons. Anaesth. Inverclyde Roy. Hosp. Greenock.

SEXTON, Clive Royall 209 Priests Lane, Shenfield, Brentwood CM15 8LE Tel: 01277 223739 Email: clive@crsexton.freeserve.co.uk — MB BS Lond. 1955; DObst RCOG 1960; DCH Eng. 1957. (Lond. Hosp.) Med. Acupunc. Rockleigh Ct. Surg. Shenfield. Socs: Brit. Med. Acupunct. Soc. Prev: GP Shenfield; Phys. MKO Project, Iran; SHO (Paediat.) & Ho. Off. (O & G) Ipswich & E. Suff. Hosp. Heath Rd. Wing.

SEXTON, John Patrick, OBE (retired) 3 Aldermoor Avenue, Storrington, Pulborough RH20 4PT Tel: 01903 742108 — MB ChB 1940 Ed.; MFCM 1973; DMSA Ed. 1960; DPH Ed. 1949; DTM & H Eng. 1942. Prev: Exec. Dean Undergrad. & Postgrad. Studies, Fac. Med. Aberd. Univ.

SEXTON, Nicola Jane 209 Priests Lane, Shenfield, Brentwood CM15 8LE Tel: 01277 223739 — MB BS 1993 Lond.; BSc (Hons.) Hist. Med. Lond. 1989. (Lond. Hosp.) Prev: Clin. Asst. (c/o Elderly) Broomfield Hosp. Chelmsford; SHO (A & E) Broomfield Hosp. Chelmsford.

SEXTON, Rosalind Jane 20 Heathfields, Downend, Bristol BS16 6HS — MB BS 1993 Lond.; BSc Lond. 1990, MB BS 1993.

SEXTON, Shaun Alan The Loaning, Station Road, Sunningdale, Ascot SL5 0QR — MB BS 1998 Lond.; MB BS Lond 1998.

SEYAN, Rabinder Singh Atma Singh Seyan, Saffar and Rodin, The Health Centre, Robin Hood Lane, Sutton SM1 Tel: 020 8642 2010/3848 Fax: 020 8286 1010; 2 Morton, Tadworth Park, Tadworth KT20 5UA Tel: 01737 37321 Email: rari.seyan@onef.co.uk — MB 1980 Camb.; MA (Med. Sci.) Camb. 1976, MB 1980, BChir 1979; MRCGP 1983; DRCOG 1983. (Westm.) GP Tutor St Heliers Postgrad. Centre. Carshalton. Prev: Trainee GP/SHO Herts. & Essex VTS; Ho. Phys. St. Stephens Hosp. Lond.; Ho. Surg. Qu. Mary's Hosp. Roehampton.

SEYAN, Sirjit Singh Atma Singh Simpson House Medical Centre, 255 Eastcote Lane, South Harrow, Harrow HA2 8RS Tel: 020 8864 3466 Fax: 020 8864 1002; Silver Birches, 53C Gordon Avenue, Stanmore HA7 3QN Tel: 020 8954 6743 Fax: 020 8864 1002 — MB BChir 1974 Camb.; MA 1974 Camb.; MRCGP 1979; DCH Eng.

1977; DRCOG 1976. (Westm.) Prev: SHO N.wick Pk. Hosp. Harrow; Ho. Phys. & Ho. Surg. Gordon Hosp. Lond.

SEYED-HARRAF, Farzaneh 367 Street Lane, Leeds LS17 6SE — MB ChB 1998 Leeds.

SEYFOLLAHI, Sonia 10 (IFL) East Norton Place, Edinburgh EH7 5DR — MB ChB 1997 Aberd.

SEYLER, Ina Beata Felicia The Ridgeway Surgery, 6-8 Feckenhame Road, Astwood bank, Redditch B96 6DS Tel: 01527 892418 — Artsexamen 1973 Leiden; Certificate for Equivalent Experience JCTGP 1998; MFFP (Member of the Faculty of Family Planning 1993); Dip. Community Paediat. Warwick 1985; Cert. Family Plann. JCC 1984. (Leiden) Gen. Practitioner Gen. Pract. Redditch Worcs.; Clin. Asst. Old Age Psychiat.; Clin. Med. Off. Family Plann. (Locum Sessions). Socs: Fac. Family Plann. Prev: Clin. Med. Off. (Child Health & Family Plann.) Worcs. HA.

SEYMOUR, Alan Holt Dept of Anaesthetics, Birmingham Heartlands Hospital, Bordesley Green East, Birmingham B95SS Tel: 0121 424 2000 — MB ChB Birm. 1969; FFA RCS Eng. 1975; DA Eng. 1972; DObst RCOG 1971. Cons. Anaesth. Birm. Heartland Hosp. Prev: Sen. Regist. (Anaesth.) Qu. Eliz. Hosp. Birm.; Regist. (Anaesth.) Bristol Roy. Infirm.; SHO (Anaesth.) N. Devon Infirm. Barnstaple.

SEYMOUR, Alexandra Louise Flat 19 Brunswick Place, Amersham Road, High Wycombe HP13 5AQ — MB BS 1998 Lond.; MB BS Lond 1998.

SEYMOUR, Alison Louise 21 Chadacre Road, Epsom KT17 2HD — MB BS 1998 Lond.; MB BS Lond 1998.

SEYMOUR, Andrew Heathville Road Surgery, 5 Heathville Road, Gloucester GL1 3DP Tel: 01452 528299 Fax: 01452 522959 — MB BS 1987 Lond.; MRCGP 1991. Prev: Trainee GP/SHO (Geriat.) W. Norwich Hosp.; SHO (O & G & Paediat.) Norf. & Norwich Hosp.

SEYMOUR, Miss Anne (retired) 35 The Lounen, South Shields NE34 8EQ — MB BS Lond. 1959; FRCS Eng. 1974; MRCS Eng. LRCP Lond. 1959.

SEYMOUR, Anne-Marie Frances Clinical Oncology Department, Guy's Hospital, London SE1 9RT — MB BCh BAO 1984 Dub.; MRCPI 1987. ICRF Clin. Research Fell. Guy's Hosp. Lond.

SEYMOUR, Benjamin John Longmeadow, Burleigh La, Street BA16 0SL — MB ChB 1997 Manch.

SEYMOUR, Professor Carol Anne Office of Parliamentary & Health Service Ombudsman, 13th Floor, 30 Millbank, Millbank Tower, London SW1P Tel: 0207 217 4134 Fax: 0207 217 4035 — BM BCh 1969 Oxf.; MRCPath 1991; BA (Hons) Oxf. 1966; FRCPath 1999; LLDip/CPE 1998; FRCP Lond. 1985; MA Camb. 1977; MSc Lond. 1975; MRCP (UK) 1972; MA Oxf. 1970. Prof. & Cons., Div. of Cardiological Sci. (Metab. Med.) St Geo.'s Hosp. Med. Sch., Lond.; Director for Clin. Advice to Parlimentary & Health Serv., Ombudsman, Lond.; Metab. Phys. Hepatol. Lond.; Prof. (Clin. Biochem. & Metab. Med.); Div. of Cardiological Sci.s (Metab. Med.), St. Geo.'s Hosp. Med. Sch. Lond. Socs: Brit. Hyperlipidaemia Ass.; Brit. Soc. of Gastroenterol.; Assoc. of Phys.s GB & I. Prev: Fell. & Dir. Med. Studies Trintiy Coll. Camb. & Fell. & Sen. Research Fell. Girton Coll. Camb.; Lect. & MRC Research Fell. Roy. Postgrad. Med. Sch. Lond.; Lect. (Med.) & Hon. Cons. Phys. Med. Addenbrooke's Hosp. Camb.

SEYMOUR, Professor David Gwyn Medicine for the Elderly, Foresterhill Health Centre, Westburn Road, Aberdeen AB25 2AY Tel: 01224 663131 Fax: 01224 840683 Email: d.g.seymour@abdn.ac.uk — MB ChB Birm. 1973; BSc Birm. 1970, MD 1988; FRCP Ed. 1995; FRCP Lond. 1994; MRCP (UK) 1975. (Birm.) Prof. c/o Elderly Univ. Aberd. Prev: Sen. Lect. (Geriat. Med.) Univ. Wales Coll. Med. & Rhymney Valley Health Dist. M. Glam.; Sen. Regist. (Geriat.) Roy. Vict. Hosp. Dundee; SHO (Med.) St. Luke's Hosp. Bradford.

SEYMOUR, Ernest John Racton, Breach Avenue, Emsworth PO10 8NB Tel: 01243 373608 — MB ChB 1958 Bristol; DObst RCOG 1964. (Bristol) Psychotherapist. Knowle Hosp. Fareham. Socs: Guildford Centre Psychother. & Brit. Med. Acupunct. Soc. Prev: Capt. RAMC.

SEYMOUR, Gladys Grace (retired) 5 Knockcasle Park, Belfast BT5 6NA Tel: 02890795164 — MB BCh BAO 1945 Belf.; DPH Belf. 1954. Prev: Assoc. Specialist (Geriat. Med.) Ulster & N. Down Gp. Hosps.

SEYMOUR, Hannah Mary White House Farm, Stokesley, Middlesbrough TS9 5LE — MB BS 1996 Lond.

SEYMOUR, Helen Rebecca 180 Balvernie Grove, London SW18 5RW; The Willows, Rectory Road, East Carlton, Norwich NR14 8HT — MB BS 1991 Lond.; BSc Lond. 1989; MRCP (UK) 1995. Regist. (Radiol.) St. Geo. Hosp. Lond.

SEYMOUR, Ian Campbell, TD (retired) 9 Broadgait Green, Gullane EH31 2DW Tel: 01620 842677 — MB ChB 1948 Glas. Prev: Assoc. Specialist Spinal Inj. Clin. Philipshill Hosp. Busby.

SEYMOUR, Jean Elizabeth Ann 33 Hurst Close, Baldock SG7 6TL Tel: 01462 894830 — MB BS 1987 Lond. Retainer Scheme.

SEYMOUR, Jeremy Nether Edge Hospital, Brincliffe Road, Sheffield S11 9BF Tel: 0114 271 6018 Fax: 0114 271 8035 — MB BS 1982 Lond.; MRCPsych 1989; DGM RCP Lond. 1985. Cons. Old Age Psychiat. Community Health Sheff.; Hon. Lect. Sheff. Univ. Prev: Tutor & Hon. Sen. Regist. (Old Age Psychiat.) Univ. Leeds; SHO (Med. for Elderly) Whipps Cross Hosp.; Regist. & SHO (Psychiat.) Sheff.

SEYMOUR, John Hyeyrie, Woodlands, The Narth, Monmouth NP25 4QT — MB ChB 1998 Bristol.

SEYMOUR, Mr Keith c/o Mrs. Seymour, 208 Mowbray Road, South Shields NE33 3BE; Raby House, 15 North View, Hunwick, Crook DL15 0JR Tel: 01388 662559 — BM BS 1991 Nottm.; FRCS Eng. 1996. Specialist Regist. (Surg.) N.ern Region.

SEYMOUR, Lesley Katie 7 Mansion Street S., Accrington BB5 6SH — MB BCh 1978 Witwatersrand.

SEYMOUR, Mary Virginia Wrangham (retired) Hollybank, 11 Seymour Drive, Plymouth PL3 5BG Tel: 01752 660694 — MB ChB 1960 Leeds; DObst RCOG 1962.

SEYMOUR, Matthew Thomas Cookridge Hospital, Yorkshire Regional Centre for Cancer Treatment, Leeds LS16 6QB Tel: 0113 29244270113 3924427 Fax: 0113 292 4361 Email: m.seymour@icrf.icnet.uk — MB BS 1984 Lond.; MA Camb. 1985; MD Lond. 1994; MRCP (UK) 1987; FRCP 1999. (Qu. Coll. Camb. and The Lond. Hosp. M.C.) ICRF Sen. Lect. & Hon. Cons. Med. Oncol. Cookridge Hosp. & Leeds Gen. Infirm. Socs: Brit. Assn. Cancer Research; Assn. Cancer Phys.; Eur. Soc. Med. Oncol. Prev: Sen. Regist. (Med. Oncol.) Roy. Marsden Hosp. Lond. & St. Barts. Hosp. Lond.

SEYMOUR, Matthew Wadham Doctor's Mess, St Georges Hospital, 117 Suttons Lane, Hornchurch RM12 6RS — MB BS 1997 Lond.

SEYMOUR, Mr Michael Thomas James Clare House Practice, Clare House Surgery, Newport Street, Tiverton EX16 6NJ Tel: 01884 252337 Fax: 01884 254401 — MB BChir 1979 Camb.; MA, MB Camb. 1979; FRCS Eng. 1982. (Camb. & Middlx.) Prev: Regist. SW Thames Orthop. Train. Scheme; Demonst. (Anat.) Univ. Camb.; Ho. Surg. Middlx. Hosp. Lond.

SEYMOUR, Mr Neville (retired) 11 Seymour Drive, Mannamead, Plymouth PL3 5BG Tel: 01752 660694 Fax: 01752 660694 Email: neville@nevseymour.freeserve.co.uk — MB ChB Leeds 1957; FRCS Eng. 1962. Prev: Cons. Orthop. & Trauma Surg. Plymouth Health Dist.

SEYMOUR, Noel Richard Empingham Medical Centre, 37 Main Street, Empingham, Oakham LE15 8PR Tel: 01780 460202 Fax: 01780 460283; The Durham Ox, 6 Back Lane, South Luffenham, Oakham LE15 8NQ Tel: 01780 720112 Email: ngjhrm@globalnet.co.uk — MB BS 1972 Lond.; MRCGP 1977; DObst RCOG 1974. (Middlesex) Prev: Dist. Med. Off. Swansea Tasmania; Squadron Ldr. RAF Med. Br.; SHO (Paediat.) Essex Co. Hosp. Colchester.

SEYMOUR, Pamela Jane Consultant Community Paediatrician, WiSCH, Clatterbridge Hospital, Bebington, Birkenhead CH63 4AY Tel: 0151 482 7273; Lansdowne, Mountwood Road, Prenton, Birkenhead CH42 8NG — MB ChB 1970 (Hons.) Liverp.; MSc (Community Paediat.) Nottm. 1994; MRCS Eng. LRCP Lond. 1970; FRCPCH 1997; DCH Eng. 1973; DObst RCOG 1972. (Liverp.) Cons. Community Paediat. Wirral Servs. for Child Health, Wirral Hosp. NHS Trust, Wirral. Prev: SCMO (Child Health) Wirral HA.

SEYMOUR, Richard Department of Radiology, Torbay Hospital, Lawes Bridge, Torquay TQ2 7AA Tel: 01803 655614 Fax: 01803 655638 — MB BChir 1990 Camb.; MA Camb. 1989; MRCP (UK) 1992; FRCR 1995. Cons. (Diagn. Radio.) Torbay Hosp. Torquay. Prev: Sen. Regist. (Diagn. Radiol.) Univ. Hosp. Wales Cardiff; Regist. (Diagn. Radiol.) Univ. Hosp. Wales Cardiff; SHO (Med.) N.wick Pk. Hosp. Harrow.

SEYMOUR, Richard Nicholas New Eagle Medical Practice (Dr Lyons), Oliver Court, Oliver Street, St Anne's, Alderney Tel: 01481 822494; La Tonnelle, Route de Pleinmont, Torteval, Guernsey GY8 0PA Tel: 01481 266327 — MB ChB 1963 Bristol; DObst RCOG 1966. (Bristol) p/t Assoc. Gen. Med. Practitioner Eagel Med. Pract. Alderney. Prev: GP St., Som.; SHO (O & G & Paediat.) Plymouth Gen. Hosp.

SEYMOUR, Ruth Michele Department of Rehabilitation Medicine, Woodend Hospital, Eday Road, Aberdeen AB15 6XS Tel: 01224 663131 Fax: 01224 404019; Blair Lodge, Auchenblae Road, Stonehaven AB39 2NL Tel: 01569 766853 — MB ChB 1983 Dundee; PhD Birm. 1975, BSc 1972; MRCP (UK) 1987; FRCP Ed. 1997. Cons. Rehabil. Med. Woodend Hosp. Aberd. Prev: Sen. Regist. (Geriat. Med.) W. Wing Cardiff Roy. Infirm.; Lect. (Geriat. Med.) Univ. Hosp. Wales; Regist. Rotat. (Chest & Gen. Med.) Llandough Hosp. Cardiff & Cardiff Roy. Infirm.

SEYMOUR, Sarah-Jane 4 St Aubyn's Park, Tiverton EX16 4JG — MB 1983 Camb.; MA Camb. 1983, MB 1983, BChir 1982. (Camb. & Middlx.) Prev: Med. Off. Tidcombe Hall Tiverton.

SEYMOUR, Sharon Christine 4 Collinbridge Court, Newtownabbey BT36 7UZ — MB BCh BAO 1993 Belf.

SEYMOUR, William Martin Vanbrugh Castle, Maze Hill, Greenwich, London SE10 8XQ Tel: 020 8853 2373 — MB BS 1963 Lond.; FRCP Lond. 1981, M 1965; MRCS Eng. LRCP Lond. 1963. (Lond. Hosp.) Cons. Phys. Qu. Mary's Sidcup NHS Trust & Greenwich Health Care NHS Trust. Prev: Sen. Lect. Guy's Hosp. Med. Sch. Lond.; Sen. Regist. Chest & Gen. Med. Guy's Hosp. Lond.; Ho. Phys. Med. Unit. & Regist. (Med.) Lond. Hosp.

SEYMOUR, William Richard Dunham (retired) 15 Blake Avenue, Merrivale Lane, Ross-on-Wye HR9 5JL Tel: 01989 563801 — MB BCh BAO Belf. 1939; MRCGP 1952. Prev: Ho. Surg. Childr. Hosp. Birm. & Coventry & Warw. Hosp.

SEYMOUR-JONES, Mr John Anthony Weald Cottage, 58 Warblington Road, Emsworth PO10 7HH Tel: 01243 372600 — MB BChir 1937 Camb.; FRCS Eng. 1940; MRCS Eng. LRCP Lond. 1935; DLO Eng. 1946. (Camb. & St. Thos.) Cons. ENT. King Ed. VII Hosp. Midhurst; Emerit. Cons. ENT Surg. Portsmouth & SE Hants. Health Dist.; ENT Cons. DHSS. Socs: Fell. Roy. Soc. Med. (Mem. Sects. Laryng. & Otol. & Clin. Med.); BMA (Ex-Chairm. Portsmouth Div.); (Ex-Chairm.) SW Laryngol. Assn. Prev: Cons. ENT Camb. Milit. Hosp. Aldershot; Regist. Portsmouth & S.. Cos. Eye & Ear Hosp.; Ho. Surg. (ENT) St. Thos. Hosp. Lond.

SEYMOUR MEAD, Alison Margaret (retired) Pinley Rudding, Claverdon, Warwick CV35 8LU Tel: 01926 842428 — MB ChB 1972 Birm.; DA (UK) 1974. Prev: SCMO W. Midl. Regional Transfus. Centre Birm.

SEYMOUR MEAD, Richard The Henley in Arden Medical Centre, Prince Harry Road, Henley in Arden, Solihull B95 5DD Tel: 01564 794311 Fax: 01564 793008; Pinley Rudding, Claverdon, Warwick CV35 8LU Tel: 0192 684 2428 — MB ChB 1972 Birm.

SEYMOUR-PRICE, Muriel, Capt. RAMC Retd. (retired) 32 Rheast Mooar Lane, Ramsey IM8 3LW Tel: 01642 2162 — MB BCh BAO Dub. 1948; BA Dub. 1948.

SEYMOUR-SHOVE, Ronald Nonsuch, Hunter's Lodge, 205 North Road, Yate, Bristol BS37 7LG — MB ChB 1954 Bristol; FRCPsych 1985, M 1972; DPM Eng. 1960. (Bristol) Cons. Psychiat. i/c Rehabil. & Drug Addic. Treatm. Centre ScarBoro. Gen. Hosp.; Clin. Tutor Roy. Coll. Psych. Socs: BMA. Prev: Sen. Regist. (Psychiat.) Liverp. United Hosps. & Deva & Moston Hosps. Chester; JHMO Glenside Hosp. Bristol.

SEYMOUR SMITH, Margaret Della 67 Rosemary Hill Road, Little Aston, Sutton Coldfield B74 4HH Tel: 0121 353 5765 — MB ChB Birm. 1947; DCH Eng. 1950. (Birm.)

SEYWRIGHT, Morag Mathews Department of Pathology, Inverclyde Royal NHS Trust, Greenock PA16 0XN Tel: 01475 633777 — MB ChB 1980 Glas.; MRCPath. 1986. (Glasgow University) Cons. Path. Inverclyde Roy. Hosp. Greenock. Prev: Cons. Path. Dermat. W.. Infirm. Glas.

SHA'ABAN, Mahir Abbas Jawad 7 Macneill Drive, East Kilbride, Glasgow G74 4TR — MB ChB 1973 Baghdad; MB ChB Baghdad 1873.

SHAATH, Mr Nebal Mohamed 12 Edinburgh Close, Sale M33 4EZ — MB BCh BAO 1988 NUI; FRCSI 1994; LRCPSI 1988; MSc 1998. Specialist Regist. Lat.

SHABAN

SHABAN, Mohamed Ragai Rashad Woolsthorpe House, Woolsthorpe Belvoir, Grantham NG32 1NZ — MB ChB 1976 Alexandria, Egypt.

SHABBO, Mr Fikrat Putrus Guy's and St Thomas' Hospital Trust, Lambeth Palace Road, London SE1 Tel: 020 7960 5812 Fax: 020 7922 8005; Manor Cottage, Manor Way, Leatherhead KT22 0HS Tel: 01372 844570 — MRCS Eng. LRCP Lond. 1977; FRCS Eng. 1975; MB ChB 1968. (University of Baghdad Medical School) Cons. Cardio-Thoracic Surg. St Thomas' Hosp. Socs: Soc. Cardiovasc. Surg. & Brit. Cardiac Soc. Prev: Sen. Regist. Nat. Heart Hosp. & St. Bart. Hosp. Lond.

SHABDE, Ishita 17 Oaklands, Newcastle upon Tyne NE3 4YQ — MB ChB 1998 Leeds.

SHABDE, Neela Community Child Health Department, Albion Road Clinic, Albion Road, North Shields NE29 0HG Tel: 0191 219 6657 Fax: 0191 219 6650; 17 Oaklands, Gosforth, Newcastle upon Tyne NE3 4YQ Tel: 0191 213 1155 — MB BS 1971 Ravishankar; FRCP Lond. 1996; MRCPI 1987; FRCPCH 1997; DCCH RCP Ed. 1983; DCH Jabalpur 1974. Cons. Paediat. (Community Child Health) N. Tyneside Health Care NHS Trust; Hon. Clin. Lect. (Child Health) Univ. Newc. Prev: Sen. Regist. (Community Child Health) N. Tyneside HA.

SHABESTARY, Mr Shahrokh Moaddab Flat 5, 33 Malmesbury Road, London E18 2NL — MD 1970 Tabriz; FRCS Ed. 1979.

SHABO, Gregory 17 Braziers Quay, Bishop's Stortford CM23 3YN — MD 1992 Louvain. (Louvain, Belgium) SHO. (Gen Med.). Prev: SHO, Gen. Med. Nobles, Isle of Man Hosp.; SHO, Gen. Med. Medway Hosp. Gillingham, Kent; SHO, Gen Med. P.ss Alexandra Hosp. Essex.

SHABROKH, Pedram 12 Twyford Abbey Road, London NW10 7HG Tel: 020 8991 1168 Fax: 020 8991 1168 — MB ChB 1990 Sheff.

SHACKCLOTH, Michael John 2 Sandwell Drive, Sale M33 6JL — MB ChB 1994 Manch.

SHACKEL, Geoffrey George Spinneys, Five Ashes, Mayfield TN20 6HH Tel: 01435 873113 — MB BChir 1964 Camb.; MA Camb. 1964; DObst RCOG 1965. (Camb. & St. Thos.) Prev: Ho. Phys. (Paediat.) Whipps Cross Hosp. Lond.; Ho. Surg. (O & G) St. Thos. Hosp. (Lambeth Hosp.) Lond.; Ho. Phys. St. Helier Hosp. Carshalton.

SHACKELL, Margaret Mary Hillview Surgery, 179 Bilton Road, Greenford UB6 7HQ Tel: 020 8997 4661 Fax: 020 8810 8015 — MB BS 1971 Lond.; MRCP (UK) 1976. (Roy. Free) Lect. (Gen. Pract.) St. Mary's Hosp. Med. Sch. Lond. Prev: Hon. Sen. Regist. (Med.) Whittington Hosp. Lond.; Regist. (Cardiol.) Papworth Hosp. Cambs.; Research Fell. (Cardiol.) Hillingdon Hosp. Uxbridge.

SHACKLES, David Alexander The Taymount Surgery, 1 Taymount Terrace, Perth PH1 1NU Tel: 01738 627117 Fax: 01738 444713 — MB ChB 1987 Ed.; MRCGP 1991; DCCH RCP Ed. 1990. Prev: Ho. Off. (Med.) Roy. Infirm. Edin.

SHACKLETON, Clive David Eskdaill Medical Centre, Eskdaill Street, Kettering NN16 8RA Tel: 01536 513053 Fax: 01536 417572; 12 Queensberry Road, Kettering NN15 7HL Tel: 01536 416680 Email: clive.shackleton@virgin.net — MB BS 1984 Lond.; MRCGP 1988; DLO RCS Eng. 1986. Clin. Asst. (ENT) Kettering Hosp. N.ants. Prev: SHO (ENT & A & E) Worthing Hosp.; Ho. Phys. Ealing Hosp. Lond.

SHACKLETON, David Andrew 1 Nursery View Cottages, Seven Sisters Lane, Ollerton, Knutsford WA16 8RL Tel: 01565 652993 — MB ChB 1990 Manch.

SHACKLETON, David Barry Occupational Health Solutions, Floor 6, Silk House, Park Green, Macclesfield SK11 7QJ Tel: 01625 572054 Email: admin@occhealth.co.uk — MB ChB 1986 Liverp.; MRCP (UK) 1989; MFOM RCP Lond. 1994. Cons. Occupat. Phys. Manch. Socs: Soc. Occupat. Med. Prev: Employm. Med. Adviser Health & Safety Exec. Manch.; Regist. (Med.) Macclesfield HA.

SHACKLETON, Geoffrey Ernest The Ridgeway Surgery, 71 Imperial Drive, North Harrow, Harrow HA2 7DU Tel: 020 8427 2470 — MB BS 1955 Lond.; MRCGP 1975; DGM RCP Lond. 1985. (St. Mary's)

SHACKLETON, Janet Elizabeth The Surgery, 42 High Street, Chislehurst BR7 5AX Tel: 020 8467 5551 Fax: 020 8468 7658 — MB ChB 1987 Manch.

SHACKLETON, John Park (retired) Flat 38 Oak Tree Lodge, Harlow Manor Park, Harrogate HG2 0HH Tel: 01423 561042 — MRCS Eng. LRCP Lond. 1951. Prev: Ho. Surg. Bradford Roy. Infirm.

SHACKLETON, John Robert St Marys Surgery, 37 St. Mary's Street, Ely CB7 4HF Tel: 01353 665511 Fax: 01353 669532 — MB 1973 Camb.; BChir 1972; DObst RCOG 1975. (Lond. Hosp.)

SHACKLETON, Rachel Fell The Croft, Church St., E. Hendred, Wantage OX12 8LA Tel: 01235 833304 — BM BCh 1947 Oxf.; MRCPsych 1972; DPM Eng. 1958. (Oxf.) Cons. Psychiat. Oxon. Family & Child Guid. Clinics. Prev: Med. Dir. Richmond Child Guid. Clinic; Regist. Friern Hosp. Lond.; Rotating Interne Qu. Eliz. Hosp. Childr. Hackney.

SHACKLETON, Sara Elizabeth 24 Cranleigh, Standish, Wigan WN6 0EU — MB ChB 1980 Leeds.

SHACKLETON, Sarah Caroline Newbury Street Practice, Newbury Street, Wantage OX12 7AY Tel: 01235 763451 — MB BS 1984 Lond.; MRCGP 1988.

SHACKLETON BAILEY, John (retired) Westacre Nursing Home, Sleepers Hill, Winchester SO22 4NE — MRCS Eng. LRCP Lond. 1934; MA Camb. 1967, BA 1929. Prev: Regist. (ENT) N. Staffs. Hosp.

SHACKLEY, Mr David Clifford 97 Long Lane, Chadderton, Oldham OL9 8AZ — MB ChB 1992 Manch.; FRCS Ed. 1996.

SHACKLEY, Emma Caroline 74 St Bernards Road, Solihull B92 7BP — BM BS 1988 Nottm.

SHACKLEY, Fiona May 101 Hunter House Road, Hunters Bar, Sheffield S11 8TX — MB ChB 1989 Ed.

SHACKLEY, Timothy Richard 18 Radford Grove Lane, Radford, Nottingham NG7 5QB — BM BS 1987 Nottm.

SHACKMAN, Steven Gerson Northwood Health Centre, Acre Way, Northwood HA6 1TQ Tel: 01923 828488; The Surgery, Mount Vernon Hospital, Rickmansworth Road, Northwood HA6 2RN Tel: 01923 820626 — MB BS 1972 Lond.; MRCS Eng. LRCP Lond. 1972. (Lond. Hosp.) N.wood, Pinner & Dist. Hosp.; Div. Police Surg. Herts. Constab. Prev: SHO Rotat. (Orthop. & Gen. Surg.) Roy. Surrey Co. Hosp. Guildford; SHO Thoracic Surg. Unit Milford Chest Hosp. Godalming; Regist. Regional Radiother. & Oncol. Centre St. Luke's Hosp.

SHAD, Irshad Ahmad Swindon Health Centre, Carfax Street, Swindon SN1 1ED Tel: 01793 619955 Fax: 01793 533920 Email: shad@okeney.fsnet.co.uk; 88 Okebourne Park, Swindon SN3 6AJ Tel: 01793 692064 — MB BS 1968 Punjab, Pakistan. (Nishtar Med. Coll. Multan) Clin. Asst., Accid. & Emerg., P.ss Margt. Hosp., Swindon, Wilts., SN1 4JU.

SHAD, Mr Sujay Kumar 118 Dorchester Way, Coventry CV2 2LX — MB BS 1988 All India Inst. Med. Sciences; MB BS All India Inst. of Med. Sciences 1988; FRCS Glas. 1994. Vis. Regist. Rotat. (Cardiothoracic Surg.) W. Midl. Prev: Regist. (Cardiothoracic Surg.) Harefield Hosp.

SHADBOLT, Clair Louise Department of Diagnostic Radiology, Hammersmith Hospital, Du Cane Road, London W12 0NN — MB ChB 1988 Otago.

SHADBOLT, Clemency Jane Quarry Street Surgery, 24 Quarry Street, Johnstone PA5 8ED Tel: 01505 321733 Fax: 01505 322181 — MB ChB 1986 Bristol; MRCGP 1990; DRCOG 1991; DCH RCP Lond. 1990; T(GP) 1991. (Bristol) Princip. in GP Johnstone. Socs: BMA. Prev: GP Retainer Scheme Glas.; GP Bracknell; SHO (O & G) Perth Roy. Infirm.

SHADDICK, Rowland Allen 107 High Street, Southgate, London N14 6BP Tel: 020 8886 0388 — MRCS Eng. LRCP Lond. 1945; DPhysMed. Eng. 1953. (Lond. Hosp.) Sen. Lect. Rheum. & Orthop. Med. Brit. Sch. Osteopathy Lond. Socs: Brit. Soc. Rheum. Prev: Sen. Cons. Rheum. Enfield Dist. Hosps. & N.E. Regional Rheum. Centre; Regist. Dept. Phys. Med. & Rheum. Middlx. & Lond. Hosps.; Lect. Anat. & Histol. Lond. Hosp. & Univ. Coll. W. Indies.

SHADFORTH, Colin (retired) The Gatehouse, Church Mill, Caistor Road, Market Rasen LN8 3HX — MB BS 1950 Durh. Prev: GP LittleBoro.

SHADFORTH, Michael Fletcher Rheumatology Unit, Haywood Hospital, High Lane, Burslem, Stoke-on-Trent ST6 7AG Tel: 01782 835721; The Beald, Heather Hills, Stockton Brook, Stoke-on-Trent ST9 9PS Tel: 01782 504258 — MB BS 1968 Newc.; MRCP (UK) 1974. (Newc.) Cons. (Rheum.) Staffs. Rheum Centre, Haywood Hosp. Stoke-on-Trent; Hon. Research Fell. Univ. Birm. Socs: Brit.

Soc. Rheum.; Midl. Rheum. Soc. Prev: Rotat. SHO Roy. Vict. Infirm. Newc.; Sen. Regist. Qu. Eliz. Hosp. Birm.; Arthritis & Rheum Counc. Trav.; Fell. Univ. Virginia Charlottesville, U.S.A.

SHADWELL, Richard Neil Highgate Wood Dental Practice, 15 Aylmer Parade, Aylmer Road, London N2 0PE Tel: 020 8340 2455 Fax: 020 8340 2448 — MB BCh 1981 Wales; BDS Lond. 1986; LDS RCS Eng. 1987. Dent. Surg. Lond.

SHADWICK, Peter (retired) 11 Hilton Court, South Promenade, Lytham St Annes FY8 1LZ Tel: 01253 722610 — MB BS 1951 Durh. Prev: Sen. Med. Off. DSS Norcross Blackpool.

SHAEENA, Mr Petrous Roufa 73 Kenilworth Road, Coventry CV4 7AF Tel: 024 76 417515 — MB ChB 1959 Baghdad; FRCS Eng. 1970; FRCS Ed. 1969; LMSSA Lond. 1968; DMJ Soc. Apoth Lond. 1980; ECFMG (USA) 1982. Forens. Med. Examr. W. Midl. Police Coventry. Socs: Assn. Police Surg. & BMA. Prev: Regist. (Orthop.) Coventry & Warks. Hosp. & St. Cross Hosp. Rugby; SHO (Orthop.) Albert Dock Seamen's Hosp. Lond.

SHAFAFY, Masood 23 Cameron House, Comber Grove, London SE5 0UJ Tel: 0207 708 5506 — MB BS 1994 Lond.; FRCS (Eng) 1998. (St. Bartholomew's Hospital Medical College London) SHO (Gen. Surg.) Lond.; SHO (Neurosurg.) The Roy. Lond. Hosp. Whitechapel Lond. Prev: SHO (Orthop. & Trauma) Whipps Cross Hosp. Lond.; SHO (Gen. & Vasc. Surg.) S.end on Sea Essex.

SHAFAR, Jacob (retired) Roebuck House, 58 Carr Hall Road, Barrowford, Nelson BB9 6PY Tel: 01282 613631 — MD 1937 Glas.; MB ChB 1933; FRCP Lond. 1967, M 1940; DPH Wales 1936. Cons. Phys. Burnley & Dist. Hosp. Gp. Prev: Asst. Phys. Out-pats. Roy. Infirm. Glas.

SHAFAR, Susanne (retired) 58 Carr Hall Road, Barrowford, Nelson BB9 6PY Tel: 01282 613631 — MB ChB 1946 Glas.; MB ChB (Commend.) Glas. 1946; FRCPsych 1979, M 1971; DPM Eng. 1950. Cons. Psychiat. N. Manch. Health Dist. Prev: Ho. Surg. Roy. Infirm. Glas.

SHAFFER, Jonathan Lionel Hope Hospital, Salford M6 8HD Tel: 0161 787 5145 Fax: 0161 787 5366 Email: jshaffer@fsi.ho.man.ac.uk — MB BS 1972 Lond.; FRCP Lond. 1995; MRCP (UK) 1978. (Univ. Coll. Hosp.) Cons. Phys. Hope Hosp. Salford; Clin. Dir. (Intestinal Failure Unit); Hosp. Dean for UnderGrad. Stud.s. Prev: Lect. (Gastroenterol. & Clin. Pharmacol.) Univ. Manch.

SHAFFER, Joseph 156 Kennington Park Road, London SE11 4DJ Tel: 020 7735 0661 Fax: 020 7735 1194 Email: drjoe@easynet.com — MB BS 1993 Lond.; BSc (Hons.) Lond. 1991; MRCP (UK) 1996. (United Med. & Dent. Sch. Lond.) SHO (Dermat.) St. John's Inst. Dermat. Lond. Prev: SHO (Respirat. Med.) Roy. Brompton Hosp. Lond.; SHO (HIV & A & E) St. Mary's Hosp. Lond.; SHO (Gastroenterol.) Hammersmith Hosp. Lond.

SHAFFI, Siyana Herne Hill Group Practice, 74 Herne Hill, London SE24 9QP Tel: 020 7274 3314 Fax: 020 7738 6025 — MB BS 1994 Lond.

SHAFFORD, Elizabeth Ann Department Paediatric Oncology, St. Bartholomew's Hospital, West Smithfield, London EC1A 7BE Tel: 020 7601 7850 Fax: 020 7601 7850; 18 Hillclose Close, Billericay CM12 0BB Tel: 01277 659953 — MB BS 1974 Lond.; MRCP (UK) 1979; DCH Eng. 1977. (Middlx.) Clin. Asst. (Paediat. Oncol.) St. Bart. Hosp. Lond. Prev: Research Fell. (Leukaemia) Hosp. Sick Childr. Gt. Ormond St. Lond.

SHAFFU, N G Westcotes Family Practice, 2 Westcotes Drive, Leicester LE3 0QR Tel: 0116 254 7887 — MB ChB 1972 Baghdad; MB ChB 1972 Baghdad; LRCP LRCS Ed. LRCPS Glas.

SHAFI, Abu Imtiaz 21 Streathbourne Road, London SW17 8QZ — MB BS 1994 Lond.

SHAFI, Ghazala 13 Kenerne Drive, Barnet EN5 2NW — MB BS 1987 Lond.; MRCGP 1992; DCH RCP Lond. 1991. GP Princip. Herts. Prev: Trainee GP Ealing.

SHAFI, Mahmood Iqbal Department of Gynaecology, Birmingham Women's Hospital, Edgbaston, Birmingham B15 2TG Tel: 0121 472 1377 Fax: 0121 627 2667 Email: mahmood.shafi@bhamwomens.thenhs.com — MB BCh 1981 Wales; MD Wales 1997; MRCOG 1987; DRCOG 1984; DA Eng. 1984. Cons. (Gyn. Surg. & Oncol.) Birm. Wom.'s Hosp. Prev: Sen. Lect. & Cons. O & G City Hosp. NHS Trust Birm.; Sen. Regist. (Subspecialty Trainee in Gyn. Oncol.) City Hosp. & Birm. Midl. Hosp. for Wom.; Research Fell. & Regist. (O & G) Dudley Rd. Hosp. Birm.

SHAFI, Miheengar Mohamad Lake Street Surgery, 20-22 Lake Street, Leighton Buzzard LU7 1RT Tel: 01525 851995 Fax: 01525 374783; Nishaat, Plantation Road, Leighton Buzzard LU7 3HU — MB BS Gujarat 1966. (M.P.S. Med. Coll. Jamnagar, India) Prev: Dist. Surg. Kashmir, India.

SHAFI, Mohammed Shujauddin PHL Department of Microbiology, Central Middlesex Hospital NHS Trust, Park Royal, London NW10 7NS Tel: 020 8965 1603 Fax: 020 8965 6071 — MB BS 1967 Osmania; FRCPath 1987, M 1975. (Osmania Med. Coll. Hyderabad) Cons. Microbiol. Centr. Middlx. Hosp. Lond. Socs: Assn. Med. Microbiol. Hosp. Infec. Soc. Prev: Cons. Microbiol. Nat. Guard Hosp. Jeddah, Saudi Arabia; Sen. Regist. (Med. Microbiol.) Centr. Middlx. Hosp. Lond.; Lect. & Asst. Lect. Middlx. Hosp. Med. Sch. Lond.

SHAFI, Mohammed Taher 7 Middleton Way, Bridge of Don, Aberdeen AB22 8LU — MB ChB 1992 Aberd.

SHAFI, Mushtaq Ahmed Clovelly, 176 Swallow St., Iver SL0 0HR — MB BS 1980 Ibadan; MRCOG 1991.

SHAFI, Rabina Najma c/o 105 Wilbraham Road, Manchester M14 7DN — MB ChB 1975 Manch.; MRCP (UK) 1980.

SHAFI, Shafiq 51 Buxton Street, Leicester LE2 0FL — MB ChB 1991 Leic.; MRCGP 1995; DRCOG Lond. 1996; DFFP 1995; DCH RCP Lond. 1994. Ship's Doctor (P&O/P.ss Cruises). Socs: Brit. Med. Acupunct. Soc. Prev: GP/Regist. Leicester.

SHAFIGHIAN, Mr Bijan Foscote Private Hospital, Foscote Rise, Banbury OX16 9XP Tel: 01295 229411 Fax: 01295 272877; Stonewalls, Hempton, Banbury OX15 0QS Tel: 01869 338439 — MD 1974 Iran; FRCS Ed. 1986. Cons. Orthop. Surg. Horton Gen. Hosp. Banbury. Socs: Fell. BOA; BMA; Girdlestone Orthop. Soc. Prev: Research Fell., Sen. Regist. (Reconstruc. Surg.) & Regist. (Orthop. & Trauma) Mayday Univ. Hosp. Thornton Heath.

SHAFIK, Amina Mohamed 16 Norbury Way, Bookham, Leatherhead KT23 4RY — MB BCh 1979 Ain Shams.

SHAFIQ, Ayad Ehsan 37 Guffitts Rake, Wirral CH47 7AJ — BM BCh 1991 Oxf.

SHAFIQ, Mohammed 50 Hamstead Road, Birmingham B19 1DB — MB ChB 1996 Liverp. SHO Orthop & Trauma, Sandwell Healthcare, Lyndon, W. Bromwich, B71. Prev: SHO A & E, Walsall Manor Hosp.

SHAFIQ, Mr Muhammad North Manchester General Hospital, Delauney's Road, Crumpsall, Manchester M8 5RB Tel: 0161 795 4567; 6 Kenwood Avenue, Hale, Altrincham WA15 9DE — MB BS 1957 Punjab; FRCS Ed. 1964; LMSSA Lond. 1968. (Nishtar Med. Coll. Multan) Cons. Gen. Surg. N. Manch. Dist.; Assoc. Lect. Univ. Manch. Socs: Soc. Cardiovasc. Surgs. Gt. Brit.; Hosp. Cons. & Specialist Assn.; BMA. Prev: Sen. Regist. (Surg.) Wessex Cardiothoracic Centre Soton.; Sen. Regist. (Surg.) NWR HA. Sen. Surg. Regist. Wessex Cardio-Thoracic Centre, Soton.

SHAFQAT, Mr Syed Owais Department of Orthopaedics, Scunthorpe General Hospital, Cliff Gardens, Scunthorpe DN15 7BH Tel: 01724 290188; The Vicarage, 5 Paul Lane, Appleby, Scunthorpe DN15 0AR Tel: 01724 734905 — MB BS 1977 Karachi; FRCS Glas. 1988. (Dow Medical) Cons. Trauma & Orthop. Surg.: Scunthorpe Gen. Hosp.; Goole & Dist. Hosp.; John Coupland Hosp. GainsBoro.; BUPA Hosp. Hull & E. Riding Anlaby Hull; Pk. Hill Hosp. Doncaster. Socs: BMA; BOA; Brit. Soc. for Revision Surg.

SHAH, Professor Ajay Manmohan Guy's, King's & St Thomas' School of Medicine & Dentistry, Department of Cardiology, Bessemer Road, London SE5 9PJ Tel: 020 7737 4000 — MD 1990 Wales; MB BCh 1982; MRCP (UK) 1985; FRCP 1998; FESC 1997. (Uni. Of Wales College of Medicine) Prof. (Cardiovasc. Med.) King's Coll., Brit. Heart Found. Prev: MRC Sen. Clin. Fell. & Sen. Lect. (Cardiol.) Univ. of Wales Coll. Med. Cardiff.

SHAH, Ajazul Haq 1 Foxhome Close, Chislehurst BR7 5XT — MB BS 1997 Lond.

SHAH, Ajit Hirji The Surgery, 22 Fryent Way, Kingsbury, London NW9 9SA Tel: 020 8204 8228; 115 Elmsleigh Avenue, Kenton, Harrow HA3 8HY Tel: 020 8907 0923 — MB BS 1979 Bombay; MRCS Eng. LRCP Lond. 1988; MRCPI 1990; MRCGP 1996; DGM RCP Lond. 1988; DTM & H RCP Lond. 1984. (Lokmanya Tilak Med. Coll. Bombay) Socs: Fell. Roy. Soc. Trop. Med. & Hyg.; BMA. Prev: Trainee GP Lond.; Regist. (Med. for Elderly) Edgware Gen. Hosp.; SHO (Med. for Elderly) Walton Hosp. Chesterfield.

SHAH

SHAH, Ajit Kumar 49 Erlesmere Gardens, London W13 9TZ Tel: 020 8321 5443 Fax: 020 8321 5961 — MB ChB 1984 Liverp.; MRCPsych 1989. (Liverp.) Sen. Lect. & Hon. Cons. (Psychiat. of Old Age) Char. Cross & W.m. Med. Sch. Lond.

SHAH, Ambrish Kumar Goodmayes Medical Centre, 4 Eastwood Road, Goodmayes, Ilford IG3 8XB Tel: 020 8590 1169 Fax: 020 8590 1170; 45 Manor Road, Chigwell IG7 5PL Tel: 020 8500 7827 — MB BS 1972 India; BSc Aligarh Muslim, India 1965, MB BS 1972; MRCP (UK) 1978. (J.N. Med. Coll.) Clin. Asst. (Med. & Rheum.) King Geo. Hosp. Ilford. Prev: Sen. Regist. (Med.) Walsgrave Hosp. Coventry; Regist. (Med. & Haemat.) Walsgrave Hosp. Coventry; SHO (Med.) Pk. Hosp. Manch.

SHAH, Amrut Chunilal The Surgery, 188/189 Lewes Road, Brighton BN2 3LA Tel: 01273 603616 Fax: 01273 694101 — MB BS 1968 Indore. (Indore) GP Brighton.

SHAH, Arunkumar Revulal Cannock Road Surgery, 66 Cannock Road, Willenhall WV12 5RZ Tel: 01922 475100 Fax: 01922 712934 — MB BS 1972 Bombay.

SHAH, Arvind Rasiklal 86 Bertram Road, Enfield EN1 1LS Tel: 020 8363 7650 — MB BS 1979 Poona; MRCPI 1986.

***SHAH, Ashia** 29 Goldsmith Avenue, Manor Park, London E12 6QB Tel: 020 8470 7992 Fax: 020 8470 7992; 29 Goldsmith Avenue, Manor Park, London E12 6QB Tel: 020 8470 7992 Fax: 020 8470 7992 — MB BS 1998 Lond.; MB BS Lond 1998.

SHAH, Ashwin Mukund Stratford Village Practice, 50C Romford Road, London E15 4BZ Tel: 020 8534 4133 Fax: 020 8534 3860; 45 Gyllyngdune Gardens, Ilford IG3 9HJ — MB BS 1975 Gujarat. GP.

SHAH, Atta Ullah Khyber Surgery, 38 Havelock Road, Saltley, Birmingham B8 1RT Tel: 0121 328 1174 — MB BS 1962 Peshawar; DA Eng. 1965. (Khyber Med. Coll. Peshawar)

SHAH, Atul 51 Galleywood Drive, Leicester LE4 0NH — BM BS 1998 Nottm.; BM BS Nottm 1998.

SHAH, B J Mahavir Medical Centre, 10 Chestnut Way, East Goscote, Leicester LE7 3QQ Tel: 0116 260 1007 Fax: 0116 260 1008 — MB BS 1980 Mysore; MB BS 1980 Mysore; MRCS Eng. LRCP London.

SHAH, Bakhtiar Ahmed c/o Anaesthetic Department, Kent & Canterbury Hospital, Ethelbert Road, Canterbury CT1 3NG — MB BS 1983 Pershawar; FFA RCSI 1988.

SHAH, Miss Bareen Nusarrat 70 Wilson Gardens, Harrow HA1 4EA Tel: 020 8442 9889 Email: bareenshah@compuserve.com; 70 Wilson Gardens, Harrow HA1 4EA Tel: 020 8442 9889 — LMSSA 1986 Lond.; FRCS (Eng) 1992. Specialist Regist. Gen. Surg. Hillingdon Hosp. Socs: RSM; AS &BI.

SHAH, Bella Rupa 7A Temple Road, London W4 5NW — MB BS 1992 Lond.

SHAH, Bhagwandas Damodar 23 Challacombe, Southend-on-Sea SS1 3TY Tel: 01702 582066 — MB BS 1967 Newc.; FRCR 1977; DMRD Eng. 1971. (Newc.) Cons. (Radiol.) S.end Health Dist. Prev: Sen. Regist. (Radiol.) Roy. Vict. Infirm. Newc.; Ho. Off. Qu. Eliz. Hosp. Birm.; Demonst. Anat. Med. Sch. Univ. Newc.

SHAH, Bharati Amritlal The Surgery, 20-22 Bannockburn Road, Plumstead, London SE18 1ES Tel: 020 8855 5540 Fax: 020 8855 4970; 120 Knights Way, Dartford DA1 5SP Tel: 279613 — LMSSA 1978 Lond. (Kasturba Med. Coll. Mangalore) GP. Prev: SHO (Psychiat.) Roy. Cornw. Hosp. (City) Truro; Ho. Surg. Roy. Cornw, Hosp. (Treliske) Truro; Ho. Phys. Joyce Green Hosp. Dartford.

SHAH, Bhupendra Keshavlal Oakview, Thornton Manor Drive, Ryde PO33 1PQ — MB BS 1971 Saurashtra.

SHAH, Bindu Mohanlal 103 Springfield Road, Moseley, Birmingham B13 9NN — MB ChB 1985 Bristol.

SHAH, Bipin Keshavlal (retired) 45 The Avenue, Ystrad Mynach, Hengoed CF82 8BA Tel: 01443 812066 — MB BS Bombay 1958. Prev: Clin. Asst. Ystrad Mynach Hosp.

SHAH, Bipinchandra Balvantlal The Surgery, 27 Clifton Rise, London SE14 6ER Tel: 020 8692 1387; 2 Wellands Close, Bickley, Bromley BR1 2AQ — MB BS 1966 Bombay; MRCOG 1972; DObst RCOG 1969. (Grant Med. Coll. Bombay) Prev: Regist. (Gyn. & Obst.) Lewisham Hosp. Lond.; SHO (O & G) Stepping Hill Hosp. Stockport & Huddersfield Roy. Infirm.

SHAH, Mr Chandrakant Hirachand 27 Filsham Road, St Leonards-on-Sea TN38 0PA Tel: 01424 428433 — MB BS 1953 Bombay; FRCS Ed. 1966; DLO Eng. 1970. (Grant Med. Coll. Bombay) Cons. Surg. ENT Conquest Hosp. Hastings. Socs: Fell. Roy. Soc. Med.; Assn. Otorhinolaryngol. Prev: Cons. Surg. ENT Roy. E. Sussex Hosp. Hastings; Sen. Regist. (ENT) Singleton Hosp. Swansea Cardiff Roy. Infirm.

SHAH, Chandrakant Natverlal Houghton Regis Medical Centre, Peel Street, Houghton Regis, Dunstable LU5 5EZ Tel: 01582 866161 Fax: 01582 865483 — MB BS 1969 Bombay; DRCOG 1977. (Topiwala Nat. Med. Coll.) SHO (O & G) Wordsley Hosp. Stourbridge. Socs: Med. Defence Union.

SHAH, Mr Chandrakant Trambaklal Gulabchand ENT Department, St James's Hospital, James's Street, Dublin, Republic of Ireland Tel: 00353 1416 2677 Fax: 00353 1410 3464 Email: ctshah99@yahoo.com; 23 Beverington Close, Eastbourne BN21 2SB Email: ctshah99@yahoo.com — LMSSA 1986 Lond.; MB BS Gujarat 1976; MS (ENT) Gujarat 1980; FRCS Ed. 1986; FRCS 2001 (ORL-HNS) Glasgow; DLO RCS Eng. 1983. (B. J. Med. Coll. Ahmedabad, India) Cons. ENT Surg., Epsom Gen. Hosp.; Hon. Cons. ENT Surg. Hosp.; ENT Dept., Epsom Gen. Hosp., Dorking Rd, Epsom, KT18 8EG Tel: 01372 735735. Socs: Assn. Otolaryngol. UK; Assn. Otorhinolaryng. India; Brit. Med. Laser Assn. Prev: Cons. ENT Surg. Pinderfield Gen. Hosp. Wakefield; Cons. ENT Surg. Roy. Liverp. Hosp. Liverp.; Cons. ENT Surg. Epsom Gen. Hosp. and St Mary's Hosp. for Childr. Epsom.

SHAH, Chetan Shantilal (retired) 22 Albon House, 3 Neville Gill Close, Wandsworth, London SW18 4BS — MB ChB 1986 Manch. SHO (Gen. Surg.) Epsom Dist. Gen. Hosp. Last Appointment. Prev: SHO (Gen. Surg.) Broomfield Hosp. Chelmsford.

SHAH, Devang Kanubhai Mill Street Surgery, 439 Mill Street, Bradford, Manchester M11 2BL Tel: 0161 223 0637 Fax: 0161 220 7220 — MB ChB 1991 Manch.; MRCGP 1996; DRCOG 1995. GP Princip.

SHAH, Dharmesh Brentfield Medical Centre, 10 Kingfisher Way, London NW10 8TF Tel: 020 8459 8833 Fax: 020 8459 1374 — MB ChB 1992 Leeds.

SHAH, Dhiren Shantilal Canbury Medical Centre, 1 Elm Rd, Kingston upon Thames KT2 6HR Tel: 020 8549 8818 — MB BS 1993 Lond.; BSc Lond 1991; DRCOG 1996; MRCGP 1997. (St. Mary's Hospital Medical School) GP.

SHAH, Dilesh Tel: 01920 830232 — MB ChB 1988 Manch.; MRCGP 1993; DRCOG 1992. GP Watton at Stone Herts. Socs: MRCGP; DRCOG; FMA.

SHAH, Dilip Kumar Bousfield Health Centre, Westminster Road, Liverpool L4 4PP Tel: 0151 207 1468 Fax: 0151 284 6864; Sneheel, Woodlands Park, Liverpool L12 1ND — MB BS 1975 Rajasthan. (R.N.T. Med. Coll. Udaipur)

SHAH, Dilip Kumar Liladhar Raishi Jaina House, 66 Arnos Grove, Southgate, London N14 7AR Tel: 020 8886 4035 Fax: 020 8882 7024 — MB BS 1978 Lond.; MRCGP 1983; DRCOG 1982; DCH RCP Lond. 1981.

SHAH, Dilipkumar Babulal 10 Marguerite Way, Bishop's Stortford CM23 4NB — MB BS 1980 Gujarat; MRCS Eng. LRCP Lond. 1987; MRCP (UK) 1988. Research Fell. & Hon. Regist. (Clin. Cardiol.) Hammersmith Hosp. Lond. Prev: Sen. Regist. (Gen. Med., Cardiol. & I.I.U.) Cromwell Hosp. Lond.

SHAH, Dinesh Karmshi 39 Bourneside, Bedford MK41 7EQ — MB BS 1963 Vikram; MS Vikram 1966. Assoc. Specialist Bedford Hosp. Trust. Prev: Cons. Surg. Raipur, India.

SHAH, Dinesh Panachand 70 St Edmunds Drive, Stanmore HA7 2AU Tel: 020 8424 9974 — MB BS 1973 Saurashtra.

SHAH, Dipak Vidhu Wenlock Street Surgery, 40 Wenlock Street, Luton LU2 0NN Tel: 01582 27094; 9 Cooks Meadow, Edlesborough, Dunstable LU6 2RP Tel: 01525 222349 Email: dipak.shah@btinternet.com — MB ChB 1984 Glas.; DRCOG 1989; Cert. Family Plann. JCC 1988. (Univ. Glas.) Prev: Trainee GP Leighton Buzzard; SHO (Accid. Serv., Orthop, Paediat., O & G, Psychiat. & Paediat.) Luton & Dunstable Hosp.

SHAH, Divyen 51 Park Crescent, Harrow Weald, Harrow HA3 6EU — MB ChB 1990 Manch.

SHAH, Farida 11 Long Leason, Selly Oak, Birmingham B29 4LT — MB ChB 1989 Leeds; MB ChB (Hons.) Leeds 1989; MRCP (UK) 1992. Regist. (Dermat.) Skin Hosp. Birm. Prev: SHO Rotat. (Med.) Qu. Eliz. Hosp. & Gen. Hosp. Birm.; Ho. Off. Leeds Gen. Infirm.

SHAH, Fatima Noorain 142 Trinity Road, London SW17 7HS — MB BS 1996 Lond.

SHAH

SHAH, Fozia Zafar 35 Queen's Road, Blackburn BB1 1QF — MB ChB 1996 Dund.

SHAH, Hasmukh Mohanlal Shah and Thomson, Bute House Medical Centre, Ground Floor, Grove Road, Luton LU1 1QJ Tel: 01582 723357 Fax: 01582 485517 — MB BS 1973 Bombay. GP Luton.

SHAH, Mr Hasmukh Vadilal Thorns Road Surgery, 43 Thorns Road, Quarry Bank, Brierley Hill DY5 2JS Tel: 01384 77524 Fax: 01384 486540; 4 Wigorn Lane, Redlake Drive, Pedmore, Stourbridge DY9 0TB Tel: 01562 886555 — MB BS 1957 Baroda; FRCS Eng. 1967. (Med. Coll. Baroda) Prev: JHMO (Urol.) & Regist. (Urol.) Joyce Green Hosp. Dartford; Regist. (Gen. Surg.) Joyce Green Hosp. & W. Hill Hosp. Dartford.

SHAH, Hasmukhlal Kunvarji 4 Glynde Road, Bexleyheath DA7 4ET — MB BS 1957 Baroda; DLO 1960. (Med. Coll. Baroda)

SHAH, Hasmukhlal Rajpal 93 Empire Avenue, London N18 1AR Tel: 020 8803 9944 — MB BS 1973 Bombay.

SHAH, Mr Hasmukhlal Vadilal 3 Vista Rise, Radyr Cheyne, Llandaff, Cardiff CF5 2SD — MB BS 1972 Baroda; MS (ENT) Baroda 1975, MB BS 1972; DLO Eng. 1978; DLO Baroda 1973. (Med. Coll. Baroda) GP Llwynypia.

SHAH, Hitesh Rasiklal 39 Parson Street, London NW4 1QT — MB ChB 1982 Manch.; MRCGP 1986.

SHAH, Imtiaz Maqbool 38 Annette Street, Glasgow G42 8EQ — MB ChB 1996 Glas.; BSc (Hons) Glasgow 1991; MB ChB Glasgow 1996; MRCP Glasgow 1999. Sen. Health Off. (Med.) W.ern Infirm. Glas.; Research Fell., W.ern Infirm. Glas.

SHAH, Indira Shantilal Sunnybank Health Centre, Bryn Road, Cefn Fforest, Blackwood NP12 1HT Tel: 01495 224321 Fax: 01495 832156 — MB BS 1965 Gujarat. (B.J. Med. Coll. Ahmedabad)

SHAH, Mr Indra Kumar Chimanlal 51 Suffolk Street, Oldham OL9 7DS — MB BS 1959 Calcutta; FRCS Glas. 1969.

SHAH, Irshad Ali Waterloo Medical Centre, 41 Dunkley Street, Wolverhampton WV1 4AN Tel: 01902 23559 — MB BS 1965 Punjab.

SHAH, Jacques 10 Howberry Road, Cannons Park, Edgware HA8 6ST Tel: 020 8952 0874 — MRCS Eng. LRCP Lond. 1941; DTM & H Eng. 1942; MB BS Lond. 1943.

SHAH, Jaffar 67 Church Street, Darlaston, Wednesbury WS10 8 Tel: 0121 526 2924; 21 Parkhall Road, Walsall WS5 3HF Tel: 01922 20608 — MB BS 1962 Peshawar. (Khyber Med. Coll.) Prev: Regist. (Anaesth.) Roy. Albert Edwd. Infirm. Wigan; SHO (Anaesth.) City Gen. Hosp. Stoke-on-Trent.

SHAH, Jayantilal Chhaganlal The Drive Surgery, 90 The Drive, London NW11 9UL Tel: 020 8455 5901 Fax: 020 8731 9517 — MB BS 1965 Baroda.

SHAH, Jayantilal Lakhamshi 15 St Denis Road, Selly Oak, Birmingham B29 4LN Tel: 0121 475 7789 — MB ChB 1961 Birm.; FFA RCS Eng. 1969; DA Eng. 1963. (Birm.) Cons. Anaesth. Birm. AHA (T).

SHAH, Mr Jayendra Kumar Raishi London Lane Clinic, Kinnaird House, 37 London Lane, Bromley BR1 4HB Tel: 020 8460 2661 Fax: 020 8464 5041 — MB BS 1965 Gujarat; FRCS Ed. 1970. (M.P.S. Med. Coll. Jamnagar) Clin. Asst. (Surg.) Bromley Hosp.

SHAH, Jaymin Shantilal 2 The Pastures, Red Hill Grange, Wellingborough NN9 5YR — MB BS 1996 Lond.

SHAH, Joegy Kunjbihari Young and Partners, The Ryan Medical Centre, St. Marys Road, Bamber Bridge, Preston PR5 6JD Tel: 01772 335136 Fax: 01772 626701; 22 Fowler Close, Hoghton, Preston PR5 0DS — MB ChB 1987 Manch.; BSc (Med. Sci) St. And. 1984; MRCGP 1993. Prev: Trainee GP Accrington.

SHAH, Jyotiben 28 Silkfield Road, London NW9 6QU — MB BS 1996 Lond.; BSc Lond. (Hons.) 1993. (Charing Cross of Westminster) SHO Rotat. (Gen. Surg.), St Geo.'s Hosp. Lond. Socs: MDU; BMA.

SHAH, Kaksha Oak Lodge Medical Centre, 234 Burnt Oak Broadway, Edgware MA8 0AP — MB ChB 1995 Leeds; MRCGP 1999; DFFP 1999; DCH 1997; DRCOG 1998. (Leeds) GP Princip. at above professional adress. Socs: BMA; Med. Protec. Soc.

SHAH, Kantilal Devshi Ashcroft Road Medical Centre, 170 Ashcroft Road, Stopsley, Luton LU2 9AY — MB ChB 1964 Glas.

SHAH, Kantilal Rajpal (Surgery), 336 Uxbridge Road, Shepherds Bush, London W12 7LL Tel: 020 8743 5153 Fax: 020 8742 9070 — MB BS 1971 Saurastra; T(GP) 1991. (Univ. Saurastra, India) GP. Socs: Med. Protec. Soc. Prev: GP Kenya; Trainee GP Lond.

SHAH, Ketan Amritlal 43 Stilecroft Gardens, Wembley HA0 3HD — MB BS 1988 Bombay; MRCPath 1994.

SHAH, Khalid The Surgery, 8-10 Coronation Road, Menai Bridge LL59 5BD; 1-2 Felinheli Terrace, Port Dinorwic LL56 4JF — MB BS 1965 Peshawar. GP Menai Bridge.

SHAH, Kinnari 73 Lakeside Gardens, Merthyr Tydfil CF48 1EW — MB ChB 1997 Manch.

SHAH, Kirtikumar Popatlal 71 Streatfield Road, Kenton, Harrow HA3 9BP — MB BS 1970 Bombay.

SHAH, Kishorchandra Jatashanker (retired) — MB ChB 1965 Birm.; FRCPCH 1997; FRCR 1975; FFR 1972; T(R) (CR) 1991; DMRD Eng. 1970. Prev: Ho. Surg. St. Chad's Hosp. Birm.

SHAH, Kuntal Kunjvihari 3 Phillips Court, Whitchurch Lane, Edgware HA8 6QD — MB ChB 1995 Manch.

SHAH, Lalchand Devshi 22 Spencer Close, London N3 3TX — MB BS 1964 Bombay. (Grant Med. Coll.)

SHAH, Madhvi 2 Rosemary Avenue, Finchley N3 2QN — MB BS 1991 Lond.; MRCGP 1995; DRCOG 1995; DCH RCP Lond. 1994; DGM RCP Lond. 1994. (Kings College London) GP Princip. Prev: Trainee GP Bounds Green Gp. Pract. Lond.; Trainee GP/SHO (Paediat.) N. Middlx. Hosp. VTS.

SHAH, Mahendra Popatlal Napsbury Hospital, Shenley Road, London Colney, St Albans AL2 1AA Tel: 01727 823333 Fax: 01727 826245; 50 Elmcroft Crescent, London NW11 9SY Tel: 020 8455 6598 Fax: 020 8455 6598 — MB BS 1965 Baroda. Clin. Asst. (Psychiat.) Napsbury Hosp. St. Albans. Socs: Affil. Roy. Coll. Psychiat.; Diploma - Brit. Med. Acupunct. Soc. Prev: Asst. Gen. Pract.

SHAH, Mahesh Vasantlal Department of Anaesthetics, Leeds General Infirmary, Great George St., Leeds LS1 3EX; Longways, The Firs, Ling Lane, Scarcroft, Leeds LS14 3JH — MB BS 1975 Madras; MRCS Eng. LRCP Lond. 1977; FFA RCS Eng. 1980; Dip. Amer. Bd. Anaesthesiol. 1986. (Christian Med. Coll. & Hosp. Vellore) Cons. Anaesth. Leeds Gen. Infirm.; Clin. Sen. Lect. (Anaesth.) Univ. Leeds. Prev: Sen. Regist. (Anaesth.) S. Glam. HA; Vis. Asst. Prof. Oregon Health Scis. Univ. Portland Oregon, USA; Lect. (Anaesth.) Univ. Wales Sch. Med.

SHAH, Malati Rasikchandra 16 Fisher House, Ward Road, London N19 5EB Tel: 020 7272 0650 — MB BS 1963 Gujarat; DA Eng. 1979; DGO Gujarat 1964. (B.J. Med. Coll. Ahmedabad) Socs: BMA & Assn. Anaesth. Prev: SHO (Anaesth.) Bethnal Green Hosp.; Regist. (Anaesth.) Qu. Eliz. Childr. Hosp. Lond. & Eliz. G.; Anderson Hosp. Lond.

SHAH, Manish Natverlal 16 Wyatts Drive, Southend-on-Sea SS1 3DH — MB BS 1993 Lond.; DFFP 1996; DRCOG 1996; DCH RCP Lond. 1995; MRCGP 1997. (St. Bart. Hosp. Lond.)

SHAH, Mansukhlal Lakhamshi Paston Health Centre, Chadburn, Peterborough PE4 7DH Tel: 01733 572584 Fax: 01733 328131; 81 Baron Court, Werrington, Peterborough PE4 7ZF — MB BS 1980 Gujarat; LMSSA Lond. 1988; MRCS Eng. LRCP Lond. 1988.

SHAH, Mansukhlal Vershi Belsize Priory Health Centre, 208 Belsize Road, London NW6 4DX Tel: 0207 530 2666 Fax: 0207 372 2404 — MB ChB 1974 Sheff.; BDS Sheff. 1969; T (GP); MRCS Eng. LRCP 1974.

SHAH, Manu Department of Dermatology, Dewsbury and District Hospital, Halifax Road, Dewsbury WF13 4HS — MB ChB 1988 Birm.; MD (Birm.) 2000; MRCP (UK) 1993. Cons. Dermatol.; Brit. Assn. of Dermatol.s; Brit. Contact Dermatitis Gp. Prev: Sen. Regist. (Dermat.) Roy. Hallamsh. Hosp. Sheff.; Regist. (Genitourin. Med.) Gen. Infirm. Leeds; SHO (Dermat.) Gen. Infirm. Leeds.

SHAH, Mayank Ramanlal Grove Surgery, 103-105 Grove Road, Walthamstow, London E17 9BU Tel: 020 8521 2221 Fax: 020 8503 7773; 12 Michleham Down, Woodside Park, London N12 7JN Tel: 020 8445 1634 Fax: 020 8446 4614 — MB BS 1984 Lond.; DRCOG 1989. (Lond. Hosp.) Dir. Lotus Healtcare 144 Harley St. Lond. W1N 1AH: health screening, medico-legal reports, primary care Phys. Socs: (Pres.) Walthamstow Med. Soc. Prev: Trainee GP St. Jas. Health Centre Lond. VTS.; SHO (Paediat.) Barking & K. Geo. Hosp. Essex; SHO (A & E) The Lond. Hosp.

SHAH, Mayur Ratilal 59 Ibstone Avenue, Bradwell Common, Milton Keynes MK13 8EB — MB BCh 1983 Wales; MRCGP 1987; DRCOG 1986.

SHAH

SHAH, Minal Navin 12 Templars Crescent, London N3 3QS — MB ChB 1998 Ed.; MB ChB Ed 1998.

SHAH, Minaxi Central Surgery, 22 Cowley Hill Lane, St Helens WA10 2AE Tel: 01744 24849 Fax: 01744 456497 — MB ChB 1988 Leic.

SHAH, Minesh J Bordesley Green Surgery, 143-145 Bordesley Green, Bordesley Green, Birmingham B9 5EG Tel: 0121 773 2170 — MB BS 1969 Gujarat; MD 1973 Gujarat.

SHAH, Minesh Khetshi Glan Clwyd Hospital, Bodelwyddan, Rhyl LL18 5UJ Tel: 01745 583910 Fax: 01745 583143 Email: mshah@sunyford.demon.co.uk — BM BS 1986 Nottm.; BMedSci (Hons.) Nottm. 1984. Staff Cardiol. Glan Clwyd Hosp. Bodelwyddan. Prev: Regist. (Gen. Med.) Glan Clwyd Hosp. Bodelwyddan.

SHAH, Miranda Jane Selma, Winford Road, Chew Magna, Bristol BS40 8QQ — MB ChB 1997 Birm. Ho. Off. (Med.) Birm. Heartlands Hosp. Socs: BMA; MDU. Prev: Ho. Off. (Surg.) Kidderminster Gen. Hosp.

SHAH, Mrudula Vinodchandra 67 Malford Grove, South Woodford, London E18 2DY; 120 Hampton Road, Ilford IG1 2PR Tel: 020 8553 1774 — MB BS 1969 Gujarat; Cert FPA. 1975. (MP Shah Med. Coll. Jamnagar) Trainer FPA Clinic City & E. Lond. AHA.

SHAH, Muhammad Akhtar Ali 42 Sandy Lane, Mitcham CR4 2HD — MB BS 1962 Punjab.

SHAH, Mrs Mukta Prakash Hattersley Group Practice, Hattersley Road East, Hyde SK14 3EH Tel: 0161 368 4161 Fax: 0161 351 1989 — MD 1976 Nagpur; MD (Gyn. & Obst.) Nagpur 1976, MB BS 1972; DGO Nagpur 1974. (Govt. Med. Coll. Nagpur) Ho. Off. (Med.) Dist. Gen. Hosp. Rotherham.

SHAH, Musharaf Motherwell Health Centre, 138-144 Windmill Street, Motherwell ML1 1TB Tel: 01698 265566 — MB BS 1963 Karachi; BSc Peshawar 1957; DO RCPSI 1972. (Dow Med. Coll.) Socs: BMA. Prev: SHO (Paediat.) Roy. Hosp. Sick Childr. Glas.; Regist. (Neonat. Paediat.) Glas. Roy. Matern. Hosp.; Regist. (Ophth.) Glas. Eye Infirm.

SHAH, Nainal 4 Alliance Road, Glenfield, Leicester LE3 8SE — MB BS 1987 Baroda.

SHAH, Najmul Hassan c/o General Office, Corbett Hospital, Stourbridge DY8 4JB — MB BS 1986 Peshawar; MRCP (UK) 1994.

SHAH, Mr Nalin Damodar 3 Ville Franche, Bagatelle, St Saviour, Jersey JE2 Tel: 01534 59095 — MB BS 1971 Indore; MS Gujarat 1974, DLO 1973; FRCS Eng. 1980; DLO RCS Eng. 1975. Cons. Surg. ENT Gen. Hosp. St. Helier Jersey. Prev: Regist. (ENT) Roy. Berks. Hosp. Reading.

SHAH, Nalin Kantilal 40 Acacia Close, Stanmore HA7 3JR — MB BS 1964 Newc.

SHAH, Natvarlal Keshavlal 20 James Close, Woodlands, London NW11 9QX — MB BS 1957 Bombay. (Grant Med. Coll. Bombay) Prev: SHO Anaesth. Roy. Infirm. Huddersfield; Med. Off. Physical Research Laborat. & Experim. Satellite Communic.; Earth Station, Ahmedabad.

SHAH, Natverlal Kantilal North Avenue Surgery, 332 North Avenue, Southend-on-Sea SS2 4EQ Tel: 01702 467215 Fax: 01702 603160 — MB BS 1968 Gujarat; DObst RCOG 1972. (B.J. Med. Coll. Ahmedabad)

SHAH, Mr Navnit Shankerlal (retired) 80 Harley Street, London W1N 1AE Tel: 020 7580 3664 — MB BS Bombay 1958; FRCS Eng. 1964; DLO Eng. 1961; Dip. Otorhinolaryng. 1959. Hon. Cons. Surg. Roy. Nat. Throat, Nose & Ear Hosp. Lond.; Hon. Cons. Otol. Nuffield Hearing & Speech Centre Lond.; Hon. Prof. Portmann Foundat. Bordeaux, France. Prev: Dep. Dir. & Sen. Lect. Profess. Unit. Inst. Laryngol. & Otol. Lond.

SHAH, Nayankumar Chandrakant 8 Sarsfield Road, London SW12 8HN — MB BS 1986 Newc.; MRCGP 1991; DFFP 1993; DRACOG 1990. Princip. GP Kent. Socs: (Counc.) RCGP. Prev: Trainee GP N.d. VTS.

SHAH, Neil Kishore 43 Gillhurst Road, Birmingham B17 8PD Tel: 0121 427 1287 — BM BS 1993 Nottm. SHO (O & G) Nottm. City Hosp.

SHAH, Nicholas 34 Somerville Close, Bromborough, Wirral CH63 0PH — MB ChB 1987 Liverp.

SHAH, Nihar 7 Calthorpe Gardens, Stonegrove, Edgware HA8 7TH — BChir 1996 Camb.

SHAH, Nilofer 1 Foxhome Close, Chislehurst BR7 5XT — MB BS 1965 Punjab; DA Eng. 1979. (Fatima Jinnah Med. Sch.) Assoc. Specialist (Anaesth.) Greenwich Dist. Hosp. Lond. Prev: Regist. (Anaesth.) Greenwich Dist. Hosp. Lond.; SHO (Anaesth.) Brook Gen. Hosp. Lond. & Qu. Mary's Hosp. Sidcup; Med. Off. Univ. Teach. Hosp. Lusaka, Zambia.

SHAH, Nimish Chhaganlal 36 Lodge Avenue, Kenton, Harrow HA3 9LS — MB BS 1992 Lond. SHO (Gen. Surg.) Luton & Dunstable. Prev: SHO (Gen. Surg.& Orthop.) Watford Gen. Hosp.

SHAH, Nimish Shantilal Station Road Surgery, 15-16 Station Road, Penarth CF64 3EP Tel: 029 2070 2301 Fax: 029 2071 2048; Chruchfields, Village Farm, Bonvilston, Cardiff CF5 6TY Tel: 01446 781378 — MB BCh 1987 Wales; MRCGP 1993; DRCOG 1992. (University of Wales) GP Princip. Prev: Trainee GP Bridgend VTS.; SHO (Paediat.) Singleton Hosp. Swansea; Resid. (Med.) K. Edwd. VII Memor. Hosp. Paget, Bermuda.

SHAH, Nirmala Saresh 37 Churnfield, 6 Acres Est., Bigger Staff St., London N4 3LP — MB BS 1975 Saugar Univ. India.

SHAH, Nisha Indu Flat 3, 113 Canfield Gardens, London NW6 3DY — MB BChir 1989 Camb.

SHAH, Nita 35 Central Avenue, Welling DA16 3AZ — MB BS 1992 Lond.

SHAH, Nitin Keshavlal 30 New Heath Close, New Cross Hospital, Wednesfield, Wolverhampton WV11 1XX — MB BS 1970 Baroda.

SHAH, Padma Rashmi 11 Downes Court, Winchmore Hill, London N21 3PT Tel: 020 8886 5540 — MB BS 1965 Bombay; DObst RCOG 1969. (T.N. Med. Coll.) Prev: Clin. Med. Off. Enfield & Haringey AHA; SHO (O & G) W. Middlx. Hosp. Isleworth; Ho. Off. (Psychiat.) P.ss Alexandra Hosp. Harlow.

SHAH, Pallav Lalji Chelsea & Westminster Hospital, 369 Fulham Road, London SW10 9NH Tel: 020 8746 8472 Fax: 020 8746 8547; Tel: 020 7351 8035 Fax: 020 7351 8052 — MB BS 1989 Lond.; MD Lond. 1995; MRCP (UK) 1994. (Guy's) Cons. Phys. (Respirat. Med. & Gen Med.) Chelsea & W.m. Hosp.; Cons. Phys. (Respirat. Med.) Roy. Brompton Hosp. Lond.; Hon. Sen. Lect. (Respirat. Med.) Imperial Coll. Sch. Med. at Nat. Heart & Lung Inst. Lond. Prev: Sen. Regist. Rotat. (Gen. & Respirat. Med.) Roy. Brompton Hosp. & Chelsea & W.m. Hosp.; Regist. Rotat. (Gen. & Respirat. Med.) St. Mary's Hosp. Lond.; Research Fell. Roy. Brompton Hosp. & Nat. Heart & Lung Inst. Lond.

SHAH, Pankaj Ramniklal 227 Barrows Lane, Yardley, Birmingham B26 1RD — MB ChB 1991 Manch.

SHAH, Pankaj S Pantglas Surgery, Aberfan Community Centre, Aberfan, Merthyr Tydfil CF48 4QE Tel: 01443 690382 Fax: 01443 690382.

SHAH, Parag 11 Downes Court, Wichmore Hill, London N21 3PT Tel: 020 8886 5540 Fax: 020 8886 5540 Email: paragshah@compuserve.com — MB BS 1991 Lond.; FRCS Pt. I. (Charing Cross and Westminster) SHO (Neurosurg.).

SHAH, Parag Jitendra Ashmaan, 6 Gatemere Close, Ellenbrook, Worsley, Manchester M28 7UY Tel: 0161 799 6278 — MB ChB 1991 Glas.; MRCPsych 1977. Specialist Regist. (Child & Adolesc. Psychiat.) N. Manch. Health Care NHS Trust. Socs: BMA; Roy. Coll. Psychiat. Prev: Career Regist. (Psychiat.) Glas.

SHAH, Peter Moorfields Eye Hospital, City Road, London EC1V 2PD; 15 St. Denis Road, Selly Oak, Birmingham B29 4LN — MB ChB 1987 Leeds; BSc (Hons.) Leeds 1985, MB ChB 1987; FRCOphth. (Leeds) Sen. Regist./Fell. Moorfields Eye Hosp. Lond. Prev: Regist. Birm. & Midl. Eye Hosp.; SHO (Neurosurg.) Midl. Centre Neurosurg. & Neurol. Birm.

SHAH, Mr Pir Julian Rabani St. Peter's Hospital, Middlesex Hospital, Mortimer St., London W1T 3AA Tel: 020 7504 9303 Fax: 020 7637 7076 Email: j.shah@ucl.ac.uk; King Edward VII Hospital, Emmanuel Kaye House, 37a Devonshire Street, London W1G 6QA Tel: 020 7935 3299 Fax: 020 7487 5927 Email: pjrshah@hotmail.com — MB ChB 1972 Leeds; FRCS Eng. 1976; MRCS Eng. LRCP Lond. 1972. (Leeds Univ.) Sen. Lect. Inst. Urol. Univ. Coll. Lond.; Cons. Spinal Injuries Unit Roy. Nat. Orthop. Hosp. Stanmore; Hon. Cons. Urol. St. Peter's Hosp. & UCL Hosps. Lond. Socs: Brit. Assn. Urol. Surg.; Corr. Mem. Amer. Urol. Assn.; Internat. Continence Soc. Prev: Sen. Regist. (Urol.) St. Peter's Hosp., Guy's & Middlx. Hosp. Lond.; Regist. (Urol.) Norf. & Norwich Hosp. Norwich; Ho. Surg. Profess. Surg. Unit Leeds Gen. Infirm.

SHAH, Piyush Ayrshire & Arran acute Hospitals NHS Trust, Dalmellington Road, Ayr KA6 6DX Tel: 01292 610555 Fax: 01292 614576; 10 Neward Crescent, Prestwick KA9 2JB Tel: 01292 75564

SHAH

— MB BS 1962 Calcutta; MRCOphth 1989; DO Eng. 1970; DOMS Calcutta 1968. (Med. Coll. Calcutta) Assoc. Ophth. Heathfield Hosp. Ayr. Socs: Ophth. Soc. UK; UK Intraocular Implant Soc.; Scott. Ophth. Circle. Prev: Regist. (Ophth.) Heathfield Hosp. Ayr; SHO (Ophth.) P.ss Margt. Hosp. Swindon & Perth Roy. Infirm.

SHAH, Pradipkumar Rasiklal Shotley Bridge General Hospital, Consett DH8 0NB Tel: 01207 583583 Fax: 01207 586000 — MB BS 1972 Gujarat. Staff Grade (Orthop.) Shotley Bridge Gen. Hosp., Co. Durh.

SHAH, Pratik Narendra Mayday University Hospital, London Road, Croydon CR7 7YE Tel: 020 8401 3158 Fax: 020 8401 3681 — MB BS 1985 Lond.; MD Lond. 1996; MRCOG 1990. (St. Geo.) Cons. (O & G), Mayday Hosp.

SHAH, Pravin Hiralal Hanford Clinic, New Inn Lane, Trentham, Stoke-on-Trent ST4 8EX Tel: 01782 642992 Fax: 01782 642992; 3 Fermain Close, Newcastle ST5 3EF — MB BS 1967 Gujarat.

SHAH, Punita 19 Heatherbrook Road, Leicester LE4 1AJ — MB ChB 1994 Leic.

SHAH, Raj 16 Brendon Gardens, Harrow HA2 8NE — MB BS 1992 Lond.; BSc (Hons.) Lond. 1989, MB BS 1992; FRCS. Research Regist. (Cardiothoracic Surg.) Inst. of Molecular Med. Oxf.

SHAH, Rajeev 5 Alma Farm Road, Toddington, Dunstable LU5 6BG — MB BChir 1998 Camb.; MB BChir Camb 1998.

SHAH, Rajnikant Keshavlal Department of Anaesthetics, Burnley General Hospital, Casterton Avenue, Burnley BB10 2PQ Tel: 01282 425071; 33 Pendle Fields, Fence, Burnley BB12 9HN Tel: 01282 694426 — MD (Anaesth.) Bombay 1973, MB BS 1968; FFA RCS Eng. 1977. Cons. Anaesth. Burnley Health Care NHS Trust Burnley Lancs. Socs: Assn. Anaesth.; MRCAnaesth.; Obst. Anaesth. Assn.

SHAH, Ramanlal Bhikhabhai Grove Surgery, 103-105 Grove Road, Walthamstow, London E17 9BU Tel: 020 8521 2221 Fax: 020 8503 7773; Fax: 020 8343 7934 — MB BS Bombay 1957; MRCS Eng. LRCP Lond. 1981. (Grant Med. Coll.) Socs: (Sec.) Walthamstow Med. Soc.; Akshar Health Comm.; Akshar Professional Gp. Prev: SHO (Geriat.) W. Middlx. Hosp.; Ho. Off. (Surg.) G.T. Hosp. Bombay, India; Ho. Off. (Med. & O & G) Methodist Miss. Hosp. Nadiad, India.

SHAH, Ramesh Shankerlal c/o Mr. G. C. Shah, 8 Sunleigh Road, Wembley HA0 4LR — MB BS 1970 Gujarat.

SHAH, Rameshchandra Manilal Thorns Road Surgery, 43 Thorns Road, Quarry Bank, Brierley Hill DY5 2JS Tel: 01384 77524 Fax: 01384 486540 — MB BS 1972 Gujarat; DPM Eng. 1981. (B.J. Med. Coll. Ahmedabad) Socs: St Pauls. Prev: Assoc. Specialist Lea Castle Hosp. Kidderminster; Regist. (Psychiat.) St. Cadoc's Hosp. Newport.

SHAH, Ramnik Bhogilal 2 Glade Close, Coed Eva, Cwmbran NP44 4TF Tel: 0163 332839 — MB BS 1959 Gujarat; MCOphth 1990; DO Eng. 1970; DOMS Gujarat 1966. (B.J. Med. Coll. Ahmedabad) Clin. Med. Off. & SCMO Eye Clinics Gwent Community Health Trust.

SHAH, Rashmi Chunilal 11 Downes Court, Winchmore Hill, London N21 3PT Tel: 020 8886 5540 — MB BS 1962 Bombay; FFA RCS Eng. 1970; DA Eng. 1966; DA Bombay 1965. (T.N. Med. Coll.) Cons. Anaesth. N. Middlx. Hosp. Lond. Socs: Assn. Anaesths.

SHAH, Rashmikant Rasiklal Croide Aaram, 28 Thames Ave, Perivale, Greenford UB6 8JL Tel: 020 8998 3493 — MRCS Eng. LRCP Lond. 1970; MD Lond. 1983, BSc (Hons.) 1967, MB BS 1970; MRCP (U.K.) 1976. (St. Mary's) Chief Internal Med. & Dir. Cardiol. King Fahad Hosp. Saudi Arabia. Prev: Hon. Sen. Regist. (Med.) St. Mary's Hosp. Paddington; Research Regist. (Cardiol.) St. Mary's Hosp. Lond.; Wellcome Research Fell. St. Mary's Hosp. Med. Sch. Lond.

***SHAH, Reena** 2 Warren Heights, Chafford Hundred, Grays RM16 6YH Tel: 01379 480578 Fax: 020 8538 1887 — MB ChB 1998 Leic.; MB ChB Leic 1998.

SHAH, Reena Chhotalal 6 Wildcroft Gardens, Edgware HA8 6TJ — BM 1996 Soton.

SHAH, Rekha The Surgery, 114-116 Carden Avenue, Brighton BN1 8PD Tel: 01273 500155 Fax: 01273 501193; 10 Varndean Holt, Brighton BN1 6QX Tel: 01273 552383 Fax: 01273 552383 — MB ChB 1983 Dundee; DRCOG 1986.

SHAH, Rimi Mansukhlal 32 Edgeworth Crescent, London NW4 4HG — MB BS 1994 Lond.

SHAH, Riyaz Nazeerul Haq Imperial Cancer Research Fund, Molecular Oncology Unit, Hammersmith Hospital, Du Cane Road, London W12 0HS — MB BS 1994 Lond.; BSc (Hons.) Lond. 1991. (UMDS Univ. Lond.) SHO (Renal) Guy's Hosp. Lond. Prev: SHO (Med.) Hammersmith Hosp. Lond.; SHO (Thoracic Med.) Lond. Chest Hosp.; SHO (Med.) Middlx. Hosp. Lond.

SHAH, Sachit 196 East Lane, Wembley HA0 3LF — MB ChB 1985 Manch.; MRCGP 1990. Socs: Canad. Coll. Family Pract.

SHAH, Saima 38 Annette Street, Crosshill, Glasgow G42 8EQ — MB ChB 1996 Aberd.

SHAH, Samina Nuzhat 2 Beaulieu Place, London W4 5SY — MB BS 1998 Lond.; MB BS Lond 1998.

SHAH, Samir 46 Llanvanor Road, London NW2 2AP — MB BS 1986 Lond.

SHAH, Samir Natvarlal 20 James Close, Woodlands, London NW11 9QX — MB ChB 1984 Sheff.; MRCP (UK) 1987; MRCS Eng. LRCP Lond. 1984; Dip. Pharm. Med. RCP (UK) 1990. Sen. Med. Adviser Sandoz Pharmaceut. Camberley; Hon. Lect. (Med.) Dept. Kings. Coll. Hosp. Med. Sch. Lond. Prev: SHO (Ophth.) Soton HA; SHO (Neurol.) Lothian Health Bd.; SHO (Med.) Grampian Health Bd.

SHAH, Sandeep Sobhagchand 26 Valley View, Barnet EN5 2NY Tel: 0410 327691, 07768 552224 — MB BS 1990 Lond.; MBA Imper. Coll. Lond. 1996; DFFP 1994; T(GP) 1994. (Roy. Lond. Hosp. Med. Coll.) GP & Pharmaceut. Phys.; Vis. Lect. W.minster Univ.; Vis. Lect. Imperial Coll.; Counc. Mem. of ABHI (Assn. of Brit. Healthcare Industries). Socs: Fell. RSM; Fell. RSA; Brit. Assn. of Regulatory Affairs.

SHAH, Sangeeta 3 Woodlands Drive, Yarm TS15 9NU — MB ChB 1994 Leic. Trainee GP Leicester VTS. Prev: Ho. Off. Walsgrave Hosp. Coventry; Ho. Off. Glenfield Gen. Hosp. & Leicester Gen. Hosp.

SHAH, Sanjay Hasmukhlal 4 Alliance Road, Glenfield, Leicester LE3 8SE — MB BS 1987 Baroda.

SHAH, Sanjay Kantilal 79 Wychwood Avenue, Canons Park, Edgware HA8 6TQ — MB BS 1987 Calcutta.

SHAH, Sanjiv Suryakant Southend Hospital, Prittlewell Chase, Westcliff on Sea SS0 ORY; 50 Rodney Road, London E11 2DE — MB BS 1988 Lond.

SHAH, Saroj Sudhir Victoria Square, 134 Broad St., Hanley, Stoke-on-Trent ST1 4EQ — MBBS. (M. P. Shah Medical College, India)

SHAH, Shaheen Pravin Khimji 14 Windsor Court, Golders Green Road, London NW11 9PP — MB BS 1997 Lond.

SHAH, Shahnaz New Cross Hospital, Wednesfield, Wolverhampton WV11 1XX Tel: 01902 732255; 24 New Heath Close, Wolverhampton WV11 1XX — MB BS 1971 Punjab; MRCOG 1988; DGO TC Dub. 1980.

SHAH, Shamsul Hudda 62 Craythorne Gardens, North Heaton, Newcastle upon Tyne NE6 5UL — MB BS 1996 Newc.

SHAH, Shantilal Hiralal Sunnybank Health Centre, Bryn Road, Cefn Fforest, Blackwood NP12 1HT Tel: 01495 224321 Fax: 01495 832156 — MB BS 1962 Gujarat. (B.J. Med. Coll. Ahmedabad)

SHAH, Shantilal Mulchand Department of Histopathology, Pilgrim Hospital, Boston PE21 9DW Tel: 01205 364801; 46 Allington Gardens, Boston PE21 9DW Tel: 01205 363439 — MB BS 1967 Gujarat; FRCPath 1992, M 1981. (B.J. Med. Coll. Ahmedabad) Cons. Histopath. Pilgrim Hosp. Boston. Socs: BMA; Assn. Clin. Path.; Internat. Assn. Path. Prev: Sen. Regist. (Histopath.) New Med. Sch. Manch. & Hope Hosp. Salford; Regist. (Path.) Withington Hosp. Manch.

SHAH, Shantilal Ramjibhai 28 Churchill Avenue, Harrow HA3 0AY Tel: 020 8909 2199 — MB BS 1963 Gujarat. Prev: GP Nairobi, Kenya.

SHAH, Shashikant Zaverchand Pinn Medical Centre, 8 Eastcote Road, Pinner HA5 1HF Tel: 020 8866 5766 Fax: 020 8429 0251 — MB ChB 1967 Sheff.; MRCGP 1976.

SHAH, Shobhna 41 Free Trade Wharf, 340 The Highway, London E1W 3ES Tel: 020 7790 2774 — MB BS 1977 Bombay; Cert. Av. Med. 1986; DA (UK) 1978.

SHAH, Snehal Sudhir 48 Meakin Avenue, Westbury Park, Clayton, Newcastle ST5 4EY — BM BS 1998 Nottm.; BM BS Nottm 1998.

SHAH, Sobagchand Mepa 25 Ravenscraig Road, London N11 1AE — MB BS 1965 Gujarat.

SHAH

SHAH, Sobhagchandra Mohanlal Oakington Medical Centre, 41 Oakington Avenue, Wembley HA9 8HX Tel: 020 8904 3021 Fax: 020 8904 0533; 30 Ashworth Mansions, Elgin Avenue, Maida Vale, London W9 1JP Tel: 020 7289 5401 — MB BS 1971 Saurashtra; Cert. Family Plann. JCC 1976. (M.P.S. Med. Coll. Jamnagar) Clin. Asst. (Venereol.) Roy. N. Hosp. Lond. Prev: SHO (Gen. Surg. & A & E) Maidenhead Hosp.; Ho. Phys. (Gen. Med.) Rochford Gen. Hosp.; Ho. Phys. (Paediat.) S.end Gen. Hosp.

SHAH, Sonal Kantilal The Medical Centre, 45 Enderley Road, Harrow Weald, Harrow HA3 5HF Tel: 020 8863 3333 — MB ChB 1992 Manch.

SHAH, Sonia 126 Thornbury Road, Isleworth TW7 4NE — MB BS 1996 Lond.

SHAH, Suerekha Karstensen 19 Carcraig Place, Dalgety Bay, Dunfermline KY11 9ST — MB ChB 1996 Dund.

SHAH, Mr Sunil 20 Farquhar Road, Edgbaston, Birmingham B15 3RB — MB BS 1987 Lond.; FRCS Ed. 1992; FRCOphth 1992. Regist. (Ophth.) Roy. Eye Hosp. Manch.

SHAH, Sunil Mulji — MB BS 1990 Lond.; MSc (Informat. Sci.) City 1992, BSc 1987; MSc (Pub. Health) Lond. 1997; MFPHM, 1999. (St. Geo. Hosp. Med. Sch.) Cons., Pub. Health, E. Surrey HA. Prev: Sen. Regist. (pub.Health), Dept. of pub. Health Sci.s, St Geo.s Hosp. Med. Sch., Lond.; Regist. (Pub. Health) Croydon HA; Sen. Regist. (Pub. Health) E. Surrey HA.

SHAH, Surendra Chimanlal St George's Medical Centre, Field Road, New Brighton, Wallasey CH45 5LN Tel: 0151 630 2080 Fax: 0151 637 0370 — MB BS 1968 Gujarat. (Ahmedabad, India) GP Wallasey; Mem. LMC. Prev: Sec. Wallasey Med. Soc.

SHAH, Susan Broadfield Health Centre, Coachman's Drive, Crawley RH11 9YZ Tel: 01293 531951; 12 Hedingham Close, Horley RH6 9NB — MB ChB 1974 Birm. Assoc. Specialist (Community Child Health) Crawley-Horsham Health Serv. NHS Trust.

SHAH, Syed A High Street Health Centre, High Street, Aberdare CF44 7DD Tel: 01685 874614 Fax: 01685 877485.

SHAH, Syed Azim 103 Henley Road, Ilford IG1 2TU — MB BS 1993 Lond.

SHAH, Syed Ghafoor 62 Craythorne Gardens, Newcastle upon Tyne NE6 5UL — MB ChB 1992 Sheff.

SHAH, Mr Syed Mohammad Ali 854 Great West Road, Isleworth TW7 5NG Tel: 020 8568 2466 Fax: 020 8655 3237; A. O. Clinic, Nazimabad No. 4, Karachi, Pakistan Tel: 009221 668 5564 Fax: 009221 668 5555 — MRCS Eng. LRCP Lond. 1977; MRCS Eng LRCP Lond. 1977; FRCS Ed. 1979; FRCS Glas. 1979; LMSSA Lond. 1980; MBBS Karachi 1970. (Dow Karachi) Cons. Orthop. Surg. A. O. Clinic Karachi. Socs: Fell. Brit. Orthop. Assoc.

SHAH, Syed Mumtaz Ali Cardiology Department, Wythenshawe Hospital, Southmoor Road, Manchester M23 9LT — MB BS 1987 Peshawar.

SHAH, Syed Nadir 17 Mornington Road, Norwich NR2 3NA — MB BS 1987 Peshawar.

SHAH, Mr Syed Tariq Kazim Department of Urology, St. Luke's Hospital, Little Horton Lane, Bradford BD5 0NA Tel: 01274 365865 Fax: 01274 365877 Email: t.shah@dial.pipex.com; Willow House, 107 All Alone Road, Idle, Bradford BD10 8TR Tel: 01274 614229 — MB BS 1975 Karachi; FRCS Glas. 1983; MRCS Eng. LRCP Lond. 1981. (Dow Medical College, University of Karachi) Cons. Urol. Bradford Roy. Infirm. & St. Luke's Hosp. Bradford; Cons. Urol., The Yorks. Clinic, Bradford. Socs: Brit. Assn Urol. Surgs.; Amer. Urol. Assn.; Soc. Internat. Urologie. Prev: Cons. Urol. Lister Hosp. Stevenage; Asst. Prof. & Cons. Urol. Aga Khan Univ. Hosp. Karachi, Pakistan; Lect. Inst. Urol. Lond.

SHAH, Syed Zabier Hussnan 3 Ridgewell Way, Colchester CO2 8NG — BM 1994 Soton.

SHAH, Tahir Hussain Saplings, Weir Road, Hanwood, Shrewsbury SY5 8LA — MB ChB 1995 Wales.

SHAH, Tanja Maria Witley Surgery, Wheeler Lane, Witley, Godalming GU8 5QR Tel: 01428 682218 Fax: 01428 682218 — MB BS 1988 Lond.; MRCGP 1993.

SHAH, Tanuja 5 Ashenden Close, Abingdon OX14 1QE; Flat 6, 35 Henry Road, West Bridgford, Nottingham NG2 7NB — BM BS 1995 Nottm: SHO (Anaesth.) S.ern Derbys. Acute Hosps. Trust. Prev: SHO (Med.) Roy. Perth Hosp.; SHO (A&E) N.ampton; PRHO (Surg.) Bath Roy. United.

SHAH, Tejshri Harivallabh 40 Woodbridge Lawn, Leeds LS6 3LU — MB ChB 1994 Leeds.

SHAH, Tulsidas Haridas Galleries Health Centre, Washington Centre, Washington NE38 7NQ Tel: 0191 416 6130 Fax: 0191 416 6344; 23 Fatfield Park, Washington NE38 8BW Tel: 0191 416 8824 — MB ChB 1964 Glas.; MSc Med. Sc. Glas. 1983. (Glas.) Clin. Asst. (Geriat. Med.) Sunderland AHA; Div.al Surg. St. John Ambul. Assn.; Bd Mem. Sunderland W. PCG. Socs: BMA. Prev: Ho. Phys. Gartloch Hosp. Gartlosh; SHO (Path.) Frenchay Hosp. Bristol; Clin. Asst. (Haemat.) Wolverhampton Gp. Hosps.

SHAH, Upma Willow Tree Family Doctors, 301 Kingsbury Road, London NW9 9PE Tel: 020 8204 6464 Fax: 020 8905 0946; 15 Totternhoe Close, Kenton, Harrow HA3 0HS — MB ChB 1990 Manch.; Dip. Pract Dermat. 1999; MRCGP 1994; DFFP 1994; DRCOG 1992. (Manch.)

SHAH, Usha U The Surgery, 19 Chichele Road, London NW2 3AH Tel: 020 8452 3232 Fax: 020 8452 9812 — MB BS 1969 Gujarat; MB BS 1969 Gujarat.

SHAH, Uttamchand Raishi The Surgery, 19 Chichele Road, London NW2 3AH Tel: 020 8452 3232 Fax: 020 8452 9812; 28 Salehurst Close, Kenton, Harrow HA3 0UG Tel: 020 8204 5377 — MB BS 1969 Gujarat. (B.J. Med. Coll. Ahmedabad)

SHAH, Varsha Minesh Bordesley Green Surgery, 143-145 Bordesley Green, Bordesley Green, Birmingham B9 5EG Tel: 0121 773 2170 — MB BS 1969 Gujarat; MD 1973 Gujarat; MRCPath 1985 U.K.

SHAH, Veena Suhas 35 The Croft, Euxton, Chorley PR7 6LH Tel: 01257 241039 — MB BS 1972 Bombay; DA (UK) 1978.

SHAH, Vibhuti Shantilal 5 Old Mill Avenue, Cannon Park, Coventry CV4 7DY — MB BS 1985 Bombay; MRCP (UK) 1994.

SHAH, Mr Vikram 9 Park Lane, Aberdare CF44 8HN — MB BS 1960 Bombay; FRCS Ed. 1967; DLO Eng. 1965. (Grant Med. Coll.) Dep. Med. Dir. Cons. ENT Surg.; Clin. Dir. Surg./Anaesth. Socs: Chairm. Welsh Assoc. OtorhinoLaryngol. Prev: Sen. Regist. & Hon. Clin. Tutor United Birm. Hosp.

SHAH, Vinaykumar Punja 59 Eversleigh Road, Finchley, London N3 1HY — LMSSA 1978 Lond.

SHAH, Vinit Navinchandra Department of Paediatrics, William Harvey Hospital, Kennington Road, Ashford TN24 0LZ Tel: 01233 633331 Ext: 6211 Fax: 01233 616139 Email: vinitshah@aol.com; 29 Canon Woods Way, Kennington, Ashford TN24 9QY Tel: 01233 629384 Email: clin. asst. (diabetes) bournemouth — MB BS 1984 Bombay; 1999 (FAM) Singapore; MD (Paediat.) Bombay 1988; MRCP (UK) 1992; FRCPCH 1996. Cons. Paediat. William Harvey Hosp. Ashford Kent; Hon. Cons. Paediatric Cardiol. Guy's Hosp. Lond. Socs: Roy. Coll. Paediat. & Child Health; Indian Acad. Paediat.; Fell.Roy. Coll. of Paediat. and Child Health.

SHAH, Vinodchandra Keshavlal (Surgery) 120 Hampton Road, Ilford IG1 1PR Tel: 020 8553 1774 Fax: 020 8514 4622; 67 Malford Grove, South Woodford, London E18 2DY — MB BS 1966 Gujarat; Cert FPA 1972. (M.P. Shah Med. Coll.)

SHAH, Vinodkumar Bhogilal 11 The Hayfield, Beardwood Park, Blackburn BB2 7BP — MB BS 1987 Gujarat.

SHAH, Waqaar Ali 89 Bennerley Road, London SW11 6DT — MB BS 1993 Lond.

SHAH, Yashwant Zaverchand Grahame Park Health Centre, The Concourse, Grahame Park Estate, London NW9 5XT Tel: 020 8205 2301 Fax: 020 8200 9173 — LRCPI & LM, LRSCI & LM 1958; LRCPI & LM, LRCSI & LM 1958.

***SHAH, Yera** 19 Upper Hamilton Road, Brighton BN1 5DF — MB BS 1998 Lond.; MB BS Lond 1998.

SHAH, Yogeshkumar Bhagwatilal Silverdale Drive Health Centre, 6 Silverdale Drive, Thurmaston, Leicester LE4 8NN Tel: 0116 260 0640 Fax: 0116 260 1640 — MB BS 1973 Baroda.

SHAH, Zaheer Hussain 1A Adria Road, Sparkhill, Birmingham B11 4JL — MB ChB 1994 Birm.

SHAH, Zaverchand Padamshi Anaesthetic Department, Queen Elizabeth II Hospital, Welwyn Garden City AL7 4HQ Tel: 01707 328111; 4 Russell Croft Road, Welwyn Garden City AL8 6QT Tel: 01707 321692 — MB BS Bombay 1965; FFA RCS Eng. 1969; DA Eng. 1966. (Topiwalla Nat. Med. Coll.) Cons. Anaesth. Qu. Eliz. II Hosp., Welwyn Garden City. Socs: Assn. Anaesth. Gt. Brit. & Irel.; BMA. Prev: Sen. Regist. (Anaesth.) Gen. Infirm. Leeds; Regist.

(Anaesth.) W. Middlx. Hosp. Isleworth; SHO (Anaesth.) Gen. Hosp. Burton-on-Trent.

*SHAHA, Monica Rose 3 Normanhurst, Ormskirk L39 4UZ Tel: 01695 573370 Fax: 01695 573370 — MB ChB 1997 Manch.

SHAHAB, Khalid Latif 480 Footsway Road, New Eltham, London SE9 3UA; 3 Vogue Court, 107-109 Widmore Road, Bromley BR13AF Tel: 01358 721631 — MB BS Punjab (Pakistan) 1964; DTM & H Eng. 1977; DCH RCPSI 1969. (King Edwd. Med. Coll. Lahore)

SHAHABDEEN, Mr Mohamed Mahir Maidstone Hospital, Hermitage Lane, Barming, Maidstone ME16 9QQ Tel: 01622 729000; 34 Chestnut Close, Kings Hill, West Malling ME19 4FP — MB BS 1981 Sri Lanka; FRCS Eng. 1990. Staff Grade Surg. (Gen. Surg.) Maidstone Hosp.

SHAHABUDDIN, Mr Mohammad Brandon Road Surgery, 108 Brandon Road, Binley, Coventry CV3 2JF Tel: 024 7645 3634 Fax: 024 7663 6886; 37 Asthill Grove, Coventry CV3 6HN Tel: 024 76 501101 — MB BS 1966 Rajshahi; FRCS Ed. 1978. (Rajshahi Med. Coll.) GP Coventry.

SHAHBAZI, Syed Shah Abedul Haque 98 High Street, Golborne, Warrington WA3 3DA — MB BS 1969 Dacca.

SHAHDADPURI, Vivek Dayal 5 St Stephens Close, 20 Avenue Road, London NW8 6DB — MB BS 1996 Lond.

SHAHEEN, Mr Ahmed Aly Mohamed ULH NHS Trust, Family Health Directorate, Dept. Obstetrics & Gynaecology, Pilgrim Hospital, Boston PE21 9QS Tel: 01205 364801 Ext: 2985 Fax: 01205 442139; Brayford Lodge, Fen Lane, East Keal, Spilsby PE23 4AY Tel: 01790 753938 Email: shaheenahmed@ulh.nhstrust.uk — MB BCh 1973 Ain Shams; FRCS Ed. 1992; MRCPI 1994; MFFP 1993; DRCOG 1986, M 1992; DObst RCPI 1985; Cert. Family Plann. JCC 1985. Cons. (O & G) Pilgrim Hosp. Lincs.; Boston Menopause Clinic at The Bostonian Private Wing Pilgrim Hosp. Socs: Brit. Soc. Colpos.; Brit. Menopause Soc.; Brit. Soc. of Obst.s. Prev: Sen. Regist. (O & G) The P.ss Anne Hosp. S.ampton Hants.; Sen Regist. (O & G) Roy Devon & Exeter Hosp. S. Devon; Regist. (O & G) Torbay Hosp. Torquay S. Devon.

SHAHEEN, Jenanne Sameera Omar 24 Eaton Place, Brighton BN2 1EH Tel: 01273 686863 — MB BS 1985 Lond.; DRCOG 1991.

SHAHEEN, Mr Maas Abd El-Kader Ward 11, General Hospital, Holdforth Road, Hartlepool TS24 9AH Tel: 01429 429 266654 — MB BCh 1971 Cairo; MChOrth. Liverp. 1980; FRCS Ed. 1976; FRCS Glas. 1976.

SHAHEEN, Mr Omar Hassan (retired) Flat 3, 4 Shad Thames, London SE1 2YT Tel: 0114 267 0508, 020 7403 3606 Fax: 020 7357 6172 — MB BS 1954 Lond.; MS Lond. 1967; FRCS Ed. 1987; FRCS Eng. 1958. Prev: Cons. Surg. (Head & Neck Oncol. & ENT) Guy's Hosp. Lond.

SHAHEEN, Seif Omar Department of Public Health Sciences, GKT School of medicine (Guy's campus), King's College London, 5th Floor, Capital House, 42 Weston St., London SE1 3QD Tel: 020 848 6635 Fax: 020 848 6605 Email: seif.shaheen@kcl.ac.uk; 32 Cranworth Road, Winchester SO22 6SE — MB BS 1984 Lond.; DFPM 1999; MA Camb. 1985; MSc Epidemiol. Lond. 1993; PhD Epidemiol. Soton. 1996; MRCP (UK) 1987. (Cambridge & Guy's Hospital) Sen. Lect. In Clin. Epidemiol. Dept, Pub. Health Sci.s, GKT Sch. of Med. King's Coll. Lond. Prev: Regist. (Med.) St. Richard's Hosp. Chichester; Wellcome Fell. (Clin. Epidemiol.) MRC Environm. Epidemiol. Unit Soton. Univ.; Lect. (Pub. Health Med) UMDS.

SHAHEIR, Elizabeth Amy The Pines, Deerland Road, Llangwm, Haverfordwest SA62 4NG Tel: 01437 891253 — MB BCh 1995 Wales. (Univ. Wales Coll. Med.) Prev: GP Regist. Newport Pembrookeshire; SHO (Paediat.) Withybush Gen. Hosp. HaverfordW.; SHO (A & E) Fazakerley, Liverp.

SHAHI, Abhishek 2 Rosslyn Avenue, Ackworth, Pontefract WF7 7QF — MB ChB 1992 Sheff.

SHAHI, Manjit 5 Cleeve Mount, Loughborough LE11 4SD — MB BS Lond. 1981; MD Lond. 1991; MRCP (UK) 1984. Cons. Cardiol. Roy. Berks. & Battle Hosp. Reading; Hon. Cons. Cardiol. Middlx. & UCH Lond. Socs: Brit. Cardiac Soc. Prev: Lect. & Sen. Regist. (Cardiol.) St. Mary's Hosp. Med. Sch. Lond.; Regist. (Cardiol.) Manch. Roy. Infirm.

SHAHID, Abdul 95 Bradford Road, Bournemouth BH9 3PL — BM 1988 Soton. Staff Grade- Psychiat. W.ern Hosp., Soton.

*SHAHID, Humma 106 Cairns Road, Bristol BS6 7TG Tel: 0117 942 2383 Email: humma@doctors.org.uk — BM BCh 1998 Oxf.; BM BCh Oxf 1998.

SHAHID, Jamil 18 Cumberland Road, Sale M33 3ER — MB BS 1968 Punjab; MB BS Punjab (Pakistan) 1968; BSc, DDS 1983. (King Edwd. Med. Coll. Lahore) Hon. Clin. Asst. (Dermat.) Univ. Hosp. Wales Cardiff. Prev: SHO (Gen. Med.) N. Cambs. Hosp. Wisbech.

SHAHID, Manjoor 38 Cromwell Street, Burnley BB12 0DB — MB BS 1994 Lond.

SHAHID, Saiyed Zakaullah Deepdale Road Surgery, 228-232 Deepdale Road, Preston PR1 6QB Tel: 01772 555733 Fax: 01772 885406 — MB BS 1969 Bihar; MB BS 1969 Bihar.

SHAHIDI, Mitra Moaven Newham General Hospital, Glen Road, London E13 8SL Tel: 020 7476 4000; 48 Riverine, Grosvenor Drive, Maidenhead SL6 8PF Tel: 01628 623340 Fax: 01628 664333 — MB BS 1993 Lond.; MRCP (UK) 1997. (Char. Cross & Westm. Hosp.) Lect. & Clin. Research Fell. Newham Gen. Hosp. Lond. Socs: Brit. Thorac. Soc. Prev: SHO (Transpl. Med.) Harefield Hosp. Middlx.; SHO (Gen. Med.) Wexham Pk. Hosp. Slough; SHO (Geriat.) Qu. Mary's Hosp. Lond.

SHAHIDULLAH, Begum Sara 170 Upper Road, Greenisland, Carrickfergus BT38 8RW — MB BCh BAO 1988 Belf.; MB BCh Belf. 1988.

SHAHIDULLAH, Hossain 128 Station Road, Broughton Astley, Leicester LE9 6PW — BM BS 1986 Nottm.; BMedSci Nottm. 1984, BM BS 1986; MRCP (UK) 1989. Cons. (Dermat.) Derbsh. Roy. Infirm. Prev: Sen. Regist. (Dermat.) Leicester Roy. Infirm.; Research Fell. (Dermat.) Roy. Infirm. Edin.; Regist. (Dermat.) Roy. Infirm. Edin.

SHAHIDULLAH, Mohammad (retired) 53 Knighton Road, Stoneygate, Leicester LE2 3HL Tel: 0116 270 8970 — PhD (Clin. Dermat.) St. And. 1969; MB BS Dacca 1958; DTM & H Liverp. 1970; Dip. Ven. Liverp. 1971. Locum Cons. in Genitourin. Med. Leicester Roy. Infirm. Prev: Cons. Genitourin Med. Lincoln Co. Hosp.

SHAHIN, Ghodsieh Whitley Bay Health Centre, Whitley Road, Whitley Bay Tel: 0191 253 1113; 47 Oakland Road, West Jesmond, Newcastle upon Tyne NE2 3DR — MB BS 1982 Newc.; DCH RCPS Glas. 1986; MRCP (UK) 1990. Clin. Med. Off. (Child Health) N. Tyneside HA.

SHAHMANESH, Maryam Flat 1, 52 Salisbury Road, Moseley, Birmingham B13 8JT; Flat 1, (Ground Floor), 13 St Charles Square, London W10 6EF Tel: 020 7565 4243 Email: m.shahmanesh@internet.com — BChir 1993 Camb.; MRCP (Lond.) 1997. (Cains College Cambridge)

SHAHMANESH, Mohsen Department of Genitourinary Medicine, Whittall Street Clinic, Whittall St., Birmingham B4 6DH Tel: 0121 237 5720 Fax: 0121 237 5729 — MB BS 1965 Lond.; MD Bristol 1976; FRCP Lond. 1992; MRCP Lond. 1968; MRCS Eng. LRCP Lond. 1965. Cons. Genitourin. Med. Whittall St. Clinic Birm.; Edr. Sex Transm Inf. Med. Prev: Chairm. Specialist Advisory Comm Genitourin. Med.

SHAHNAWAZ, Ghausia 15 The Spinneys, St. Georges Road W., Bickley, Bromley BR1 2NT Tel: 020 8467 9556 — MB BS 1964 Punjab; MRCOG 1969; LicAc, MBAcA 1986. GP/Acupunct. Bromley.

SHAHRABANI, Rashid Majid Jafar 22 Westfields Road, Acton, London W3 0AX — MB ChB 1971 Baghdad; MRCP (UK) 1979. Regist. (Cardiol.) Soton. Gen. Hosp. Prev: Regist. (Cardiol.) Groby Rd. Hosp. Leic.; Regist. (Gen. Med.) Medway Health Dist.

SHAHRAD, Mr Bahram Somerfield Hospital, London Road, Maidstone ME16 0DU Tel: 01622 208000 Fax: 01622 674706; Upton Gray, 119 Ashford Road, Bearsted, Maidstone ME14 4BT Tel: 01622 738896 Email: bshahrad@virginnet.co.uk — MD 1964 Teheran; FRCS Ed. 1977. Cons. Orthop. Surg. Somerfield Hosp. Maidstone. Socs: Fell. BOA. Prev: Cons. Orthop. & Trauma Maidstone Gen. Hosp.

SHAHRAD, P BUPA Hospital, Ambrose Lane, Harpenden AL5 4BP Tel: 01582 763191 Fax: 01582 761358; 22 Harley Street, London W1N 1AP Tel: 020 7637 0491 Fax: 020 7286 6502 — MD 1968 Teheran; Dip. Dermat. Lond. 1973.

SHAHRIARI, Shahrokh 12 Huntly Gardens, Glasgow G12 9AT Tel: 0141 339 3113 — MB ChB 1967 Glas.; MRCPath 1979; DCP Lond 1971. (Glas.) Cons. Haemat. N. Lanarksh. Gp. Hosps. Socs: Assn. Clin. Pathols.; Brit. Soc. Haemat. Prev: Sen. Regist. (Haemat.) W.m. Hosp. Med. Sch. Lond.

SHAHRIZAILA

SHAHRIZAILA, Nortina 3/7 York House, Lincoln County Hospital, Greetwell Road, Lincoln LN2 5QY — BM BS 1997 Nottm.

SHAIDA, Azhar Mohammed 184 Redbridge Lane E., Ilford IG4 5BL Email: ashaida@aol.com — BM BCh 1990 Oxf.; MA (Exp. Psychol.) Camb. 1991; FRCS (Gen. Surg.) Lond. 1994; FRCS (ENT) Lond. 1995. ENT Specialist Regist. E. Anglia Rotat.

SHAIDA, Wahid Asif Roxbourne Medical Centre, 37 Rayners Lane, South Harrow, Harrow HA2 0UE Tel: 020 8422 5602 Fax: 020 8422 3911 — MB BS 1991 Lond.; DCH RCP Lond. 1995; DFFP Lond. 1997. GP Princip. Roxboune Med. Centre, S. Harrow; Primary Care Pract. A & E Whittington Hosp. Lond. Prev: GP/Regist. Caversham Gp. Pract. Kentish Town, Lond.; SHO (Med. & Elderly Care) Edgware Gen. Hosp.; Trainee GP Univ. Hosp. Lond. VTS.

SHAIKH, Abdul Aleem Drummond Street Surgery, 94 Drummond Street, London W1 2HN Tel: 020 7387 4048 — MB BS 1962 Punjab.

SHAIKH, Abdul Mannan Handsworth Grange Medical Centre, 432 Handsworth Road, Sheffield S13 9BZ Tel: 0114 269 7505 Fax: 0114 269 8535 — MB BS 1962 Karachi; MRCGP 1976; DTM & H Eng. 1963. (Dow Med. Coll. Karachi) Socs: Soc. Occupat. Med. Prev: Clin. Asst. (Mass Radiogr.) Sheff.; Regist. (A & E) Doncaster Roy. Infirm.; SHO (Surg.) Doncaster Roy. Infirm.

SHAIKH, Ali Ahmed High Road Surgery, 510 High Road, Leytonstone, London E11 3EE Tel: 020 8539 1513; 26 Tennyson Avenue, Wanstead, London E11 2QN Tel: 020 8989 4336 — MB BS 1950 Karachi; MRCS Eng. LRCP Lond. 1955; DIH Eng. 1971; DCH Eng. 1957. Socs: Brit. Soc. Med. & Dent. Hypn.

SHAIKH, Amanullah Child & Family Consultation Service, 62 Maidstone Road, Grays RM17 6NF Tel: 01375 816900 Fax: 01375 816913; 359 Upper Rainham Road, Hornchurch RM12 4DB Tel: 01708 438997 Fax: 01708 438997 Email: amanullahshaikh@southessex-trust.nhs.uk — MB BS 1969 Dacca; MRCPsych 1980; T(Psych) 1991; DPM Lond. 1977. (Dhaka) Cons. Psychiat. Child & Family Consultation Serv. Grays, Essex. Socs: BMA; Amer. Acad. Child & Adolesc. Psychiat.; Bd. of Managem. - Nat. Child Bureau. Prev: Clin. Dir. & Cons. Psychiat. Child Adolesc. & Family Servs. Lincoln.

SHAIKH, Amer 28 Manor Drive, Wembley HA9 8ED — MB BS 1991 Lond.

SHAIKH, Mr Amjad Gulzar Ahmed c/o Mahmood and South Combe Solicitors, 96 Ilford Lane, Ilford IG1 2LD — MB BS 1982 Karachi; FRCS Ed. 1986.

SHAIKH, Gazala 14 Wellwood Close, Bicton Heath, Shrewsbury SY3 5BP — BM BS 1990 Nottm.

SHAIKH, Ghulam Farid, Squadron Ldr. Retd. Regional Medical Centre, RAF Halton, Aylesbury HP22 5PG Tel: 01296 623535 — MB BS 1977 Karachi; DFFP 1996; DTM & H RCP Lond. 1979. (Dow Med. Coll. Karachi, Pakistan) Civil. Med. Pract. RAF Halton Aylesbury. Prev: Gen. Duty Med. Off. RAF; Regist. (Gen. Med.) Dumfries & Galloway Roy. Infirm. & StoneHo. Gen. Hosp.

SHAIKH, Hizbullah 20 Wordsworth Way, Bothwell, Glasgow G71 8QR Tel: 0141853078 — MB BS 1970 Sind; FRCPath 1990, M 1978.

SHAIKH, Loua 16 Clarence Drive, Hyndland, Glasgow G12 9QX Tel: 0141 339 5096 — MB ChB 1989 Glas.; BSc (Hons.) Dund 1984. Regist. (Anaesth.) Vict. Infirm. Glas.

SHAIKH, M Holderness Road Surgery, 1181 Holderness Road, Hull HU8 9EA Tel: 01482 784966 — MB BS 1968 Karachi; MB BS 1968 Karachi.

SHAIKH, Mohamad Guftar 39 Bright Street, Wolverhampton WV1 4AT — MB ChB 1994 Aberd.

SHAIKH, Muhammad Afzal (retired) 73 Atherstone Avenue, Peterborough PE3 9UG Tel: 01733 263681 — MB BS 1961 Sind; DTM & H Eng. 1963.

SHAIKH, Munawar Saleem The Health Centre, Dunning Street, Stoke-on-Trent ST6 5BE Tel: 01782 425834 Fax: 01782 577599 — MB ChB 1987 Manch.; BSc St. And. 1984; MRCGP 1991. GP Princip.; Clin. Asst. - c/o the Elderly. Socs: BMA. Prev: Trainee GP Blackpool Vict. Hosp. VTS.

SHAIKH, Mr Naeemuddin Ahmed (Nicholas) Department of Urology, Airedale General Hosptial, Skipton Road, Keighley BD20 6TD Tel: 01535 652511 Fax: 01535 652952 — MB BS 1979 Sind; PhD Lond. 1990; FRCS Ed. 1984. Cons. Urol. Airedale Gen. Hosp. Keighley; Edit. Comm. Curr. Opinions in Urol. Socs: Brit. Assn. Urol. Surgs.; Soc. Internat. Urols. Prev: Sen. Regist. (Urol.) Qu. Eliz. Hosp. Birm. & Walsgrave Hosp. Coventry; Regist. (Urol.) Dudley Rd. Hosp. Birm. & Hammersmith Hosp. Lond.

SHAIKH, Najeeba 1 Boardman Fold Close, Middleton, Manchester M24 1PX — MB BS 1994 Newc.

SHAIKH, Mr Nasiruddin 109 Victoria Road, Fallowfield, Manchester M14 6DA — MB BS 1975 Karachi; MB BS Karachi Pakistan 1975; FRCSI 1990; FCOphth 1990; DO RCS Eng. 1982.

SHAIKH, Naveed Ahmed 9 Oaklands Road, London N20 8BA Tel: 020 8446 0925 — MB BS 1998 Lond.; MB BS Lond 1998. (Royal Free Hospital School of Medicine) Newham Gen. Hosp., Lond. Basic Surgic. Train., Rotat. Prev: Surgic. Ho. Off., QE2, WGC, Med. Ho. Office, Watford Gen. & Mt. Vernon Hosps.

SHAIKH, Riaz Ahmed 18 Holcombe Road, Chatham ME4 5RU — MB BS 1982 Karachi; FFA RCSI 1992.

SHAIKH, Shagufta Sophia Parchmore Medical Centre, 97 Parchmore Road, Thornton Heath, Croydon CR7 8LY — MB BS 1990 Lond.; MRCGP 1994; DFFP 1994; DRCOG 1992.

SHAIKH, Shahina Akhtar 88 Turnpike Link, Croydon CR0 5NY — MB BS 1991 Lond.

SHAIKH, Shamsuddin The Surgery, 70 Minehead Road, Harrow HA2 9DS — MB BS 1957 SIND; LMSSA Lond. 1976; DCMT Lond. 1967. Med. Off. Lond. Regional Transport. Socs: Fell. Roy. Soc. Trop. Med.; BMA. Prev: GP Rainham Kent.

SHAIKH, Taiyabur Rahman 23 Pear Tree Lane, Loose, Maidstone ME15 9QY — MB BS 1967 Dacca.

SHAIKH, Zaheer Ahmed (Surgery), Tandon Medical Centre, Kent Street, Upper Gornal, Dudley DY3 1UX Tel: 01902 882243 — MB BS 1965 Karachi.

SHAIKH KONEL, Shaikh Jaffar Flat 8, 155 Hathersage Road, Manchester M13 0HY — MB BS 1984 Malaya.

SHAINE, Bruce Jay Janssen-Cilae Ltd, P.O. Box 79/ Saunderton, High Wycombe HP14 4HJ Tel: 01494 567730 Fax: 01494 567445 Email: bshaine@jacgb.jnj.com; 28 Chaucer Street, Stoneygate, Leicester LE2 1HD Tel: 0116 254 6025 — MB ChB 1990 Leic.; MA Lond. 1993; MA 1999 Sheffield. Med. Adviser, Pharmaceutical Med., Janssen-Cilag Ltd, Bucks. Prev: Regist. (Pub. Health Med.) N. & Yorks. RHA.; SHO (Psychiat.) Nottm. Train. Scheme.

SHAIR, Mr Ahmed Bahaa Eddeen DRTH & Spine Speciality, 6 Burlington House, Peterborough PI1 1ER Tel: 01733 565296; FitzWilliam Hospital, Milton Way, Peterborough PE3 9AQ Tel: 01733 261717 Fax: 01733 330924 — MB BCh 1979 Ain Shams; MS (Orth.) Ain Shams 1983; MCh (Orthop.) Liverp. 1987; FRCS (Orth.) Ed. 1989; FRCS Ed. 1985. Cons. Orthop. Surg. P'boro. NHS Trust; Cons Orthop & Spinal Surg, BUPA Hosp.s; Cons. Orthop. & Spinal Surg, WNPCT (NHS). Socs: Fell. BOA; SICOT; Brit. Assn. of Spinal Surg.s (BASS). Prev: Sen. Regist. (Orthop.) Leicester; Regist. (Orthop.) Liverp.; Lect. Ain Shams Univ. Cairo.

SHAIRP, Brian Edward 3 Carrick Drive, Sevenoaks TN13 3BA Tel: 01732 453289 — MB BChir 1948 Camb.; MRCS Eng. LRCP Lond. 1946. (Camb. & St. Bart.) Prev: Ho. Surg. & Ho. Phys. N.. Hosp. Winchmore Hill; Ho. Surg. High Wycombe War Memor. Hosp.

SHAJAHAN, Polash Mohammed 6 North Avenue, Carluke ML8 5TR — MB ChB 1989 Ed.; MPhil 1997; MRCP (UK) 1993; MRCPsych 1996. (Edinburgh) Regist. Rotat. (Psychiat.) Lothian Train. Scheme; Clin. Scientist & Hon. Specialist Regist. MRC Brain Metab. Unit Roy. Edin. Hosp. Prev: SHO (Med.) Law Hosp. Carluke.

SHAKARCHI, Maher AL Wye Valley Surgery, 2 Desborough Avenue, High Wycombe HP11 2RN Tel: 01494 21044; Eresby House, Rutland Gate, London SW7 1BG Tel: 020 7584 2386 — MB BS 1982 Lond.; MRCGP 1986; DCH RCP Lond. 1987; DRCOG 1987; DA (UK) 1985. Socs: BMA & Chiltern Med. Soc. Prev: SHO (Paediat.) Alder Hey Childr. Hosp. Liverp.; SHO (O & G) St. John's Hosp. Chelmsford; SHO (Anaesth.) St. Mary's Hosp. Lond. W2.

SHAKEEL, Mohamad Hasan Sandwell General Hospital, Lyndon, West Bromwich B71 4HJ Tel: 0121 553 1831 Fax: 0121 607 3133; Foxcroft, 42A Pk Road, Walsall WS5 3JU Tel: 0121 358 3767 — MB BS Karachi 1963; FRCP Lond. 1988; MRCP (UK) 1970. (Dow Med. Coll. Karachi) Cons. Phys. (Elderly Care) Sandwell Healthcare NHS Trust. Socs: BMA; W. Midl. Consulant and Specialist Comm.; Brit. Geriat. Soc. (Chairm. W. Midl. Br.). Prev: Sen. Regist. (Geriat.) Ipswich Gp. Hosps.; Regist. (Med.) Dist. & Gen. Hosp. W. Bromwich; SHO (Med.) N. Cambs. Hosp. Wisbech.

SHAKER, Adel Gamal Assisted Conception Unit, Ross Hall Hospital, 221 Crookston Road, Glasgow G52 3NQ — MB BCh 1978 Ain Shams.

SHAKESPEAR, Shirley 16 Courtlands Mews, Maldon CM9 6YF — MB BS 1984 Lond.

SHAKESPEARE, Carl Frederick Cardiac Department, Queen Elizabeth Hospital, Stadium Road, Woolwich, London SE18 4QH Tel: 0208 836 4349 Fax: 0208 836 4326 — MB BS 1984 Lond.; BSc Lond. 1981, MD 1994; FRCP 2001 UK. (Westminster Medical School) Cons. Cardiol. Qu. Eliz. Hosp. Lond.; Dir. Cardiovasc. Risk Inst. Greenwich. Prev: Sen. Regist. (Cardiol. & Gen. Med.) Roy. Lond. Hosp.; Regist. (Cardiol.) St. Geo. Hosp. Lond.; Clin. Regist. (Cardiol.) St. Thos. Hosp. Lond.

SHAKESPEARE, Mr David Terence Kimberley House, 3 Lillington Avenue, Leamington Spa CV32 5UF — BM BCh 1975 Oxf.; FRCS Eng. 1979. Cons. Orthop. Surg. S. Warwicks. HA.

SHAKESPEARE, Emma Jane 19 Albert hill Street, Didsbury, Manchester M20 6RF Email: rolph@rafe.demon.co.uk — MB ChB 1993 Manch.; MRCP 1997, Glasgow. p/t Specialist Regist. in Paediat., N. W. Rotat.

SHAKESPEARE, John Ash Trees Surgery, Market Street, Carnforth LA5 9JU Tel: 01524 720000 Fax: 01524 720110; The White House, 1 Hatlex Hill, Heast Bank, Lancaster LA2 6ET — MB ChB 1968 Manch.; MRCGP 1974; DObst RCOG 1970. Prev: SHO (O & G) Good Hope Hosp. Sutton Coldfield; Trainee GP Kettering VTS.

SHAKESPEARE, Judith Mary Summertown Group Practice, 160 Banbury Road, Oxford OX2 7BS Tel: 01865 515552 Fax: 01865 311237; 91 Bainton Road, Oxford OX2 7AG Email: judy@shake_speare.demon.co.uk — BM BCh 1975 Oxf.; MRCP (UK) 1977; MRCGP 1980; MFFP 1993.

SHAKESPEARE, Karen Maud Aylesford Medical Centre, Admiral Moore Drive, Royal British Legion Village, Aylesford ME20 7SE; Hognore Farm, Pilgrims Way, Wrotham, Sevenoaks TN15 7NN — MB BS 1980 Lond. (Guys) GP Partner.

SHAKESPEARE, Ruth Marion 9 Barn Road, Broadstone BH18 8NH — BSc Lond. 1975, MB BS 1978; MRCP (UK) 1985; MFPHM 1989; DCH RCP Lond. 1981. (St. Geo.) Cons. Pub. Health Med. Soton. & SW Hants. DHA. Prev: Regist. (Community Med.) Wessex RHA.

SHAKESPEARE, William Martyn Merley Hall Farm, Willett Road, Wimborne BH21 3DH — MB BS 1978 Lond.; MRCGP 1983; DRCOG 1980. (St. Geo.)

SHAKIR, Irfan Calderdale Royal Hospital, Halifax HX3 0PW Tel: 01422 357171 — BM BS 1978 Nottm.; BMedSci Nottm. 1976; FRCP Glas 1995; FRCP Lond 1995; MRCP (UK) 1981. Cons. Phys. Geriat. Med. Calderdale and Huddersfield NHS Trust. Prev: Sen. Regist. (Geriat. Med.) Stobhill Gen. Hosp. Glas.; Regist. (Med.) Leic. Gen. & P.boro. Dist. Hosps.; SHO. (Med.) Nottm. City Hosp.

SHAKIR, Nasaar Ahmad 26 Oswald Road, Southall UB1 1HW — MB ChB 1990 Sheff.

SHAKIR, Naseer Ahmad Bridge Lane Health Centre, 20 Bridge Lane, Battersea, London SW11 3AD Tel: 020 7978 6737 Fax: 020 7924 7385; 26 Oswald Road, Southall UB1 1HW — MB ChB 1984 Sheff. Socs: BMA.

SHAKIR, Raad Abdul Wahab Regional Neurosciences Centre, Charing Cross Hospital, Fulham Palace Road, London W6 8RF Tel: 020 8846 7489 Fax: 020 8846 7487 Email: r.shakir@ic.ac.uk; Central Middlesex Hospital, Acton Lane, Park Royal, London NW10 7NS Tel: 020 8453 2247 Fax: 020 8453 2246 — MB ChB 1971 Baghdad; MSc Glas. 1978; FRCP Lond. 1989; FRCP Ed. 1987; FRCP Glas. 1987; MRCP (UK) 1979. Cons. Neurol. Char. Cross Hosp. & Centr. Middlx. Hosp.; Hon. Sen. Lect. Imperial Coll. Sch. Med.; Sec. Trop. & Geogr. Neurol. Research Gp. World Federat. of Neurol.; Mem. Educat. Comm. ILAE; Mem. (Pub. Relation Comm.) World Federat. of Neurol. Socs: Internat. League Against Epilepsy. Prev: Cons. Neurol. Middlesbrough; Assoc. Prof. & Acad. Vice-Dean Fac. of Med., Kuwait.

SHAKIR, Saad Abdul Wahab 38 Lorne Gardens, Shirley, Croydon CR0 7RY Tel: 020 8966 4641 Fax: 020 8662 1654 Email: shakir@compuserve.com — MB ChB 1976 Baghdad; FRCP Glas. 1994; LRCP LRCS Ed. LRCPS Glas. 1980; MRCP (UK) 1984; FFPM RCP Lond. 1995; MRCGP 1988; FRCP Ed. 1997. Dir. Drug Safety Research Unit Soton.; Vice-Chairm. Soc. Pharmaceut. Med.; Convenor Pharmacovigilance Gp. & Signal Generation & Eval. Gp.

Socs: Soc. Pharmaceut. Med.; Internat. Soc. Pharmacoepidemiol.; Exec. Comm. Europ. Soc. of Pharmacovigilance. Prev: Vice Pres. Worldwide Pharmacovigilance & Pharmacoepidemiol. Rhone Polenc Rover; Head Safety Eval. Gp. Glaxo Wellcome Research & Developm.; Sen. Med. Off. Med. Control Agency.

SHAKIR, Sudad Abdul Wahab 7 Hoppers Way, Ashford TN23 4GP — MB ChB 1973 Baghdad; FFA RCS Eng. 1981.

SHAKOKANI, Adel Abelmajid Flat 5 Addison Court, 2 Brondesbury Road, London NW6 6AS — LMS 1972 Saragossa; MRCOG 1982.

SHAKOOR, Abdul 7 Claremont Road, Luton LU4 8LY — MB ChB 1997 Dundee.

SHAKOOR, Sameena South West Kent Primary Care, The Homoeopathic Hospital, 41 Church Wells, Tunbridge Wells TN1 1JU Tel: 01892 539144 Fax: 01892 532585 Email: sshakoor@invicta-tr.sthames.nhs.uk; 3 Fernside, Bishops Down Road, Tunbridge Wells TN4 8XN Tel: 01892 526029 Email: sameena.shakoor@docors.org.uk — MB BS 1986 Lond.; MA (Hons. Physiol. Sci.) Oxf. 1983; MRCP (UK) 1990; FRCPCH (UK) 1990. (Oxford University & UCH/Middlesex, London) Cons. Paediat. Socs: Brit. Soc. Human Genetics; Brit. Assn. Community Child Health; Roy. Soc. Med. Prev: Sen. Regist. (Paediat.) N.wick Pk. Hosp. Harrow; Regist. Rotat. (Paediat.) Edgware & Middlx. Hosp. Lond.; SHO (O & G) St. Geo. Hosp. Lond.

SHAKOOR, Shaheena 19 North Avenue, Gosforth, Newcastle upon Tyne NE3 4DT — LMSSA 1991 Lond.

SHAKUR, Josephine 9 Monreith Road, Glasgow G43 2NX — MB ChB 1992 Aberd.

SHALDERS, Kerry 30 Newcomen Road, Dartmouth TQ6 9BN — BM BS 1997 Nottm.

SHALDON, Mr Cyril (retired) Robin Hill, Deepdene Park, Wonford Road, Exeter EX2 4PH Tel: 01392 431600 Email: cyril.sheldon@virgin.net — MB BChir 1951 Camb.; MD Bristol 1962; MChir Camb. 1959; FRCS Eng. 1955. Prev: Cons. Urol. Roy. Devon & Exeter Hosp.

SHALES, Carmel Ann Friary House Surgery, Friary House, 2a Beaumont Road, Plymouth PL4 9BH Tel: 01752 663138 Fax: 01752 675805; 32 Burnett Road, Crownhill, Plymouth PL6 5BH Tel: 01752 707127 — MB ChB 1966 Liverp. (Liverp.)

SHALET, Montague 29 The Warren Drive, Wanstead, London E11 2LR — MRCS Eng. LRCP Lond. 1936.

SHALET, Stephen Michael 3 Hulme Hall Avenue, Cheadle Hulme, Cheadle SK8 6LN Tel: 0161 485 1463 Fax: 0161 446 3772; Department of Endocrinology, Christie Hospital, Wilmslow Road, Manchester M20 4BX Tel: 0161 446 3667 Fax: 0161 446 3772 — MB BS Lond. 1969; BSc (Hons.) Lond. 1966, MD 1979; FRCP Lond. 1984; MRCP (UK) 1972; MRCS Eng. LRCP Lond. 1969. (Lond. Hosp.) Cons. Phys. & Endocrinol. Manch. S. Health Dist. (T); Prof. Med. Manch. Univ. Socs: Fell. Roy. Soc. Med. (Pres. Endocrine Sect.); (Counc.) Europ. Soc. Pediatric Endocrinol.; Soc. Endocrinol. Prev: Research Regist. (Endocrinol.) Univ. Manch.; Regist. (Med.) Bristol Roy. Infirm.; Ho. Phys. Med. Unit & Ho. Surg. Lond. Hosp.

SHALHOUB, John Toufic Perywick Farm, Brightling Road, Brightling, Robertsbridge TN32 5HB — MD 1968 Beirut; BSc Amer. Univ. Beirut 1963; MRCOG 1977. (Amer. Univ. Beirut) Med. Dir. Coombe Private Med. Centre. Prev: Regist. King's Coll. Hosp. Lond. & Enfield Dist. Hosp.

SHALL, Larry Department of Dermatology, St. Bartholomew's Hospital, New Road, Rochester ME1 1DS Tel: 01634 403020 — MB BCh 1978 Witwatersrand; MRCP (UK) 1984. Cons. Dermat. St. Bart. Hosp. Rochester.

SHALLAL, Salih Abdul Mahdi Al-Temimi 62 Hollybush Road, Kingston upon Thames KT2 5SE — MB ChB 1960 Baghdad; MRCS Eng. LRCP Lond. 1978; DTCD Wales 1973; DTM & H Liverp. 1970.

SHALLCROSS, Timothy Mark Caithness General Hospital, Wick KW1 5NS Tel: 01955 605050 Fax: 01955 604606; Stirkoke Woods, Wick KW1 5SZ Tel: 01955 604323 Email: tim.shallcross@hotmail.com — MB BS 1982 Lond.; BSc Lond. 1979; MRCP (UK) 1986; FCRP (Edin Glas). (St. Thos.) Cons. Phys. Caithness Gen. Hosp. Wick. Socs: Fell. RCP Edin.& Glas.

SHALLEY, Mr Martin John 9 Kennet Close, Ash, Aldershot GU12 6NN — MB BS 1972 Lond.; FRCS Eng. 1977; MRCS Eng. LRCP Lond. 1972. (Lond. Hosp.)

SHALOM

SHALOM, Mr Albert Saimah (retired) 11 Stonehill Road, East Sheen, London SW14 8RR Tel: 020 8876 9006 Fax: 020 8876 9006 — MB BS Lond. 1954; FRCS (Orl.) Eng. 1961; DLO Eng. 1959. Prev: Sen. Regist. Roy. Nat. Throat, Nose & Ear Hosp. Gray's Inn Rd.

SHALOM, Jane Isabel Kennedy (retired) 11 Stonehill Road, London SW14 8RR Tel: 020 8876 9006 Fax: 020 8876 9006 — BSc Wales 1950, MB BCh 1953; FFA RCS Eng. 1963; DA Eng. 1957; DObst RCOG 1956. Prev: SHO (Anaesth.) Qu. Charlotte's Matern. Hosp. & Chelsea Hosp. Wom.Lond.

SHALOM, Stephen David 19 Cranes Park Avenue, Surbiton KT5 8BS — MB BCh 1980 Wales; MRCP (UK) 1985. Med. Adviser Benefits Agency Med. Servs. Kingston-on-Thames.

SHALTOT, Mohamed Adel Ali 47 Padnell Road, Cowplain, Waterlooville PO8 8EB Tel: 02392 262488 — MB ChB 1964 Alexandria; MRCP (U.K.) 1975; MRCS Eng. LRCP Lond. 1976; FRCR 1979; DMRD Eng. 1979; Dip. Neurol. & Psychiat. Alexandria 1968. (Alexandria) Cons. Radiol. St. Mary's & Qu. Alexandra Hosps. Portsmouth. Prev: Sen. Regist. (Radiol.) King's Coll. Hosp. Lond.; Regist. (Radiol.) King's Coll. Hosp. Lond.; Regist. (Neurol.) Hurstwood Pk. Hosp. Haywards Heath.

SHAM, Julian Ken Wai 433 Valley Road, Nottingham NG5 1HX — MB BS 1994 Lond.

SHAM, Pak Chung Department of Psychological Medicine, Institute of Psychiatry, Denmark Hill, London SE5 8AF — BM BCh 1984 Oxf.; MSc Lond. 1991; MRCPsych 1990. Hon. Lect. & Hon. Sen. Regist. Wellcome Research Fell.

SHAM, Sui-Yuen The Surgery, 108 Banbury Road, Northfield, Birmingham B31 2DN Tel: 0121 475 1050 — MB ChB 1980 Glas.

***SHAM, Tasneem** 21 Stratford Road, West Bridgford, Nottingham NG2 6AZ — MB ChB 1996 Birm.

SHAMAS-UD-DIN, Sakib Flat 10, 38 Ullet Road, Liverpool L17 3BP — MB ChB 1996 Liverp.

SHAMAS-UD-DIN, Sobia 43 Carnwood, Halebarns, Altrincham WA15 0EN — MB ChB 1997 Manch.

SHAMASH, Alan 33 Meadowbank, Primrose Hill, London NW3 3AY Tel: 020 7586 3542 — MRCS Eng. LRCP Lond. 1952; DA Eng. 1958. (Leeds) GP (semi-Retd.). Prev: Regist. (Anaesth.) Edgeware Gen. Hosp.; Ho. Off. (Paediat.) Whipps Cross Hosp. Lond.; Capt. RAMC.

SHAMASH, Jonathan Dept. of Medical Oncology, St Bartholomew's Hospital, London Tel: 020 7601 8522; 14 Elliott Square, London NW3 350 Tel: 01797 225125 Fax: 01797 222812 Email: amckinna@doctors.org.uk — MB ChB 1987 Ed.; MD Ed. 1996; MRCP (UK) 1990. Sen. Lectures in Med. Oncol. St Bart. Hosp Lond. Prev: Clin. Research Fell. (Med. Oncol.) St. Bart. Hosp. Lond.; Regist. (Gen. Med. & Endocrinol.) St. Mary's Hosp. Lond.; Regist. (Gen. Med.) Edgware Gen. Hosp.

SHAMASH, Kim Nevill Hospital, South Downs Health Trust, Laburnum Avenue, Hove BN3 Tel: 01273 821680 Fax: 01273 265553; 74 Peacock Lane, Brighton BN1 6WA — BM 1981 Soton.; MRCPsych 1986. Cons. Psychiat., Ment. Health Serv.s for Old People, S. Downs Health NHS Trust Brighton; Clin. Manager S. Downs NHS Trust.

SHAMBROOK, Anthony St John Anaesthetic Department, Ysbyty Gwynedd, Penrhosgarnedd, Bangor Tel: 01248 384384 — MB ChB 1980 Liverp.; FCAnaesth 1991; DA (UK) 1987. Cons. Anaesth. Ysbyty Gwynedd Bangor. Prev: Sen. Regist. (Anaesth.) Ysbyty Gwynedd Bangor & Univ. Hosp. Wales Cardiff.; Regist. (Anaesth.) Blackburn Roy. Infirm. & Univ. Hosp. Wales Cardiff; Med. Off. (Anaesth.) ChristCh. Hosp., NZ.

SHAMEEM, Maheen 14 Malcolmson Cl, Birmingham B15 3LS — MB BCh 1997 Wales.

SHAMI, Shukri Khalid 14 Napier Road, Wembley HA0 4UA — MB BS 1977 Lond.

SHAMIL, Mr Abdul Shahib Abdul Raheem 54 Cambridge Avenue, Romford RM2 6QU — MB ChB 1970 Baghdad; FRCSI 1990.

SHAMIM, Shamim Uddin 237 Tonbridge Road, Maidstone ME16 8ND Tel: 01622 729000 — MB BS 1968 Karachi; DPM Eng. 1978.

SHAMLAYE, Conrad Francois 60A London Road, Kilmarnock KA3 7DD — MB ChB 1978 Glas.

SHAMOUN, Osman Sid Ahmed Mohamed Jubilee Maternity Ward, Belfast City Hospital, Lisburn Road, Belfast BT9 7AB — MB BCh 1979 Ain Shams; MRCOG 1993.

SHAMPRASADH, Vinod 11 Falcon Close, Dartford DA1 5SA — MB BCh BAO 1990 NUI; MRCGP 1994.

SHAMSAH, Mohammed Ali 85 Goodwood, Newcastle upon Tyne NE12 6LX — MB BS 1993 Newc.

SHAMSEE, Muhammad Yusuf Saleem Elmwood Health Centre, Huddersfield Road, Holmfirth, Huddersfield HD9 3TR Tel: 01484 689111 Fax: 01484 689333 — MB ChB 1992 Leeds.

SHAMSHAD, Sohail 70 Priestfields, Rochester ME1 3AB — MB BS 1975 Karachi.

SHAMSI, Saghir Ahmad Health Clinic, Grindley Lane, Blyth Bridge, Stoke-on-Trent ST11 9JS Tel: 01782 395101 Fax: 01782 398183; Staffordshire Family Health Services Authority, Britania House, 6/7 Eastgate St, Stafford ST16 2NJ Tel: 01785 256341 Fax: 01785 57114 — MB BS Karachi 1962; DPath. Eng. 1972. (Dow Med. Coll. Karachi, Pakistan) Socs: Med. Protec. Soc. Prev: Clin. Asst. Histopath. Lond. Chest Hosp.

SHAMSUDDIN, Mr Altaf Badsha Flat 19, Orchard Court, Stonegrove, Edgware HA8 7SX — MB BS 1972 Madras; BSc Madras 1965; FRCS Glas. 1984. (Madurai Med. Coll.) SHO (Gen. Surg.) Pontefract Gen. Infirm. Prev: SHO (Thoracic Surg.) Colindale Hosp. Lond.

SHAMSUDIN, Norashikin 155a O'Driscoll House, Du Cane Road, London W12 0UB — BM BS 1997 Nottingham.

SHAN, Kesavan 40 Montreal Road, Gants Hill, Ilford IG1 4SH — MB BS 1990 Lond. SHO (A & E) St. Bart. Hosp.

SHANAHAN, Anthony Pius City Walls Medical Centre, St Martin's Way, Chester CH1 2NR Tel: 01244 357800 Fax: 01244 357809 — MB ChB 1978 Manch.; DA Eng. 1981; DRCOG 1981. (Manchester) Gen. Practitioner; Clin. Asst., Dermat. Dept., Countess of Chester Hosp., Chester. Socs: Chester & N. Wales Med. Soc. Prev: G.P. Trainer, Univ. of Liverp.

SHANAHAN, Cyril Valentine 42 Salisbury Road, Cressington, Liverpool L19 0PJ Tel: 0151 427 3501 — MB BCh BAO 1946 NUI. (Univ. Coll. Cork) Emerit. Cons. Geriat. Liverp. HA (T); Med. Adviser Abbeyfield Soc. Liverp.; Med. Assessor. Interact Health Managem., Liverp. Socs: Merseyside & N. Wales Soc. Phys.; Brit. Geriat. Soc.; Liverp. Med. Inst. Prev: Cons. Geriat. Newsham Gen. & BRd. Green Hosps. Liverp.; Lect. (Clin. Geriat. Med.) Univ. Liverp.; Capt. RAMC. (Middle E. Land Forces).

SHANAHAN, Mr Donal 149 Harley Street, London W1N 2DE Tel: 020 7935 4444; Tel: 020 8540 3465 — MB BS 1979 Lond.; MS Lond. 1987; FRCS Eng. 1983. (Westm.) Sen. Lect. (Surg.) St. Bart. Hosp. Lond.; Cons. Surg. Homerton Hosp. Lond. Socs: Roy. Soc. Med.; AESGBI. Prev: Sen. Regist. St. Geo. Hosp. Lond.

SHANAHAN, Mr Michael Denis Ghislain Department of Trauma and Orthopaedics, The Ipswich Hospital, Heath Road, Ipswich IP4 5PD Tel: 01473 702211; Fax: 01394 410089 — MB ChB 1977 Bristol; FRCS Eng. 1981. Cons. Orthop. Surg. Ipswich. Prev: Cons. Orthop. Surg. Gwynedd Health Auth.; Lect. & Hon. Sen. Regist. (Orthop.) Univ. Sheff.; Regist. (Orthop.) Roy. Hallamsh. Hosp. Sheff.

SHANAHAN, Sarah Elizabeth Emma 28 Woodlands Gate, Woodlands Way, London SW15 2SY — MB BCh 1995 Witwatersrand.

SHANAHAN, William John The Chelsea & Westminster Hospital, Lower Ground Floor DTC, 369 Fulham Road, London SW10 Tel: 020 8846 6111 Fax: 020 8846 6112 Email: williamshanahan@dial.pipex.com — MB BCh BAO 1980 Dub.; MRCPsych 1986; DObst. RCPI 1984; DCH Dub. 1983. Cons. Psychiat. Subst. Misuse Serv. Brent kensington & Chelsea and W.minster MHT; Med. Director Florence Nightingale Hosp. 7-11 Lisson Gr. Lond. NW1 5SH and 17 Harley St Lond. W1n 1DA. Prev: Sen. Regist. (Psychiat.) Gordon Hosp., St. Bernards Hosp. & Char. Cross Hosps. Lond.

SHANAZ, Mr Mohamed 18 Laleham Road, London SE6 2HT — MB BS 1982 Colombo; MB BS Colombo Sri Lanka 1982; FRCS Eng. 1991.

SHAND, Alan George Gastrointestinal Unit, Western General Hospital, Edinburgh EH4 2XU Email: ashand@ed.ac.uk — MB ChB 1992 Aberd.; MRCP (UK) 1995. Specialist Regist. Gastrointestinal Unit, W.ern Gen. Hosp. Edin.

SHAND, Claudia Ruth Odiham Health Centre, Deer Park View, Odiham, Hook RG29 1JY Tel: 01256 702371 Fax: 01256 393111 Email: cshand@gp-j82061.nhs.uk; 7 Angel Meadows, Odiham, Hook RG29 1AR Tel: 01256 703178 Email: claudiashand@virgin.net — MB BS 1980 Lond.; LMSSA Lond. 1980; MRCGP 1986; DRCOG 1986. (King's Coll. Hosp.) Prev: RAF Med. Br. 1982-1987.

SHAND, David St. Richards Hospital, Chichester PO19 4SE Tel: 01243 831478; Springwood, Pine Grove, Chichester PO19 3PN Tel: 01243 537249 Fax: 0709 223 5707 Email: davidshand@doctors.org.uk — MB ChB 1984 Manch.; MFOM RCP Lond. 1998; Dip. Travel Med. Lond. 1996; MRCGP 1990; BSc (Med Sci) St. And. 1981. (Manch.) Cons. Occupat. Phys. Chichester & Portsmouth NHS Trust. Socs: Soc. Occ. Med.; Internat. Soc. Travel Med.; Brit. Inst. Musculoskel. Med. Prev: Sen. Med. Off. Brit. Steel plc Teeside; Med. Off. Avesta Sheff. Ltd.; Regist. (Gen. Med.) Stepping Hill Hosp. Stockport.

SHAND, Gill 24 Oatlands Road, Boorley Green, Botley, Southampton SO32 2DE; 116 Heigham Road, London E6 2JQ — MB BS 1996 Lond. SHO Psychiat. (part of GP VTS), Newha, Hralthcare, Lond.

SHAND, Ian Richard Osmaston Road Medical Centre, 212 Osmaston Road, Derby DE23 8JX Tel: 01332 346433 Fax: 01332 345854 — MB ChB 1979 Leeds; MRCGP 1983; DRCOG 1982.

SHAND, Jacqueline Dorothy The Old Manse, Dalriach Road, Oban PA34 5JE — MB ChB 1997 Glas.

SHAND, James Sim Queens Road Medical Group, Aberdeen AB15 4NU Tel: 01224 641560 Fax: 01224 642773 Email: james.shand@qrmg.grampian.scot.nhs.uk; 34 Westholme Avenue, Aberdeen AB15 6AB Tel: 01224 315918 — MB ChB 1964 Aberd. Lect. (Gen. Pract.) Univ. Aberd. Socs: Aberd. M-C Soc.; BMA.

SHAND, Jean Malcolm Bank Street Surgery, 46-62 Bank Street, Alexandria G83 0LS Tel: 01389 752419 Fax: 01389 710521; Tel: 01389 830458 — MB ChB 1980 Aberd.

SHAND, John X-Ray Department, Stobhill Hospital, Balornook Road, Glasgow G21 3UW Tel: 0141 201 3625 Fax: 0141 201 3693 Email: john.shand@no-thglasgow-scot.nhs.uk — MB ChB 1980 Glas.; FRCR 1986. Cons. (Radiol.) Stobhill Gen. Hosp. Glas.

SHAND, Mr John Ewen Greig Street House, Westward, Wigton CA7 8AF — MB ChB 1973 Ed.; FRCS Ed. 1977. Cons. Surg. Carlisle.

SHAND, Lynne Margaret 14 Elrick Gardens, Newmachar, Aberdeen AB21 0PY — MB ChB 1998 Aberd.; MB ChB Aberd 1998.

***SHAND, Rebecca Mia** 23 England Crescent, Langley, Heanor DE75 7BE — MB ChB 1998 Birm.

SHAND, Mr William Stewart (retired) Dan-Y-Castell, Castle Road, Crickhowell NP8 1AP Tel: 01873 810452 — MB BChir 1962 Camb.; MD Camb. 1970; FRCS Ed. 1970; FRCS Eng. 1970; MRCS Eng. LRCP Lond. 1961. Hon. Cons. Surg. St. Bart. & Roy. Lond. Hosps. - Hon. Cons. Surg; Hon. Cons. Surg. St. Mark's Hosp. Lond.; Penrose May Teach. RCS Eng. Prev: Cons. Surg. St. Bart. Hosp. Lond.

SHANDALL, Mr Ahmed Ahmed Abu El Futuh Royal Gwent Hospital, Cardiff Road, Newport NP20 0UB Tel: 01633 234124 Fax: 01633 656064 Email: ahmedshandall@gwent.nhswales.uk; 10 Craig- Yr - Haul, Castleton, Cardiff CF3 2SA — MB BCh 1975 Wales; MCh Wales 1987; FRCS Eng. 1980. Cons. Surg. Roy. Gwent Hosp. Newport; Welsh Surg. Soc. Fell.sh. (USA); Fullbright Fell.sh. (USA) 1985-6. Socs: Internat. Soc. of EndoVasc. Specialists; Vasc. Soc. & Welsh Surg. Soc.; Assoc. Surg.s GB Counc. Prev: Research Fell. Cardiff; Sen. Regist. (Surg.) Univ. Hosp. Wales, Cardiff & Roy. Gwent Hosp.; Vasc. (Clin.) Fell. Albany New York, USA.

SHANKAR, Arun Nathan 11 Bedford Road, Willington, Bedford MK44 3PP — MB BS 1998 Newc.; MB BS Newc 1998.

SHANKAR, Dorairaj Houghton Road Medical Centre, Welfare Road, Thurnscoe, Rotherham S63 0JZ Tel: 01709 894653 — MB BS 1971 Madras.

SHANKAR, Mr Nanjappa Queen Elizabeth Hospital, Sheriff Hill, Gateshead NE9 6SX Tel: 0191 487 8989; 20 Barons Wood, Gosforth, Newcastle upon Tyne NE3 3UB Tel: 0191 285 2995 — MB BS 1979 Bangalore; BSc Bangalore 1972; MChOrth Liverp. 1989; FRCS Glas. 1986; FRCS Ed. 1985. Cons. Orthop. Qu. Eliz. Hosp. Gateshead. Socs: BMA. Prev: Regist. (Orthop.) N. Tyneside Gen. Hosp.; Regist. (Orthop.) Basildon Hosp.; SHO (Orthop.) Warrington Gen. Hosp.

SHANKAR, Rajesh Kumar 2 Exton Gardens, Weavering, Maidstone ME14 5AT — MB BS 1985 Lond.; FRCA 1997. (St. Bart. Hosp. Lond.) Specialist Regist. (Anaesth.) S. Thames (E.).

SHANKAR, Mr Sambasivan Tanglewood, 11 Bedford Road, Willington, Bedford MK44 3PP — MRCS Eng. LRCP Lond. 1976; BDS Madras 1964; FRCS Ed. 1980; LMSSA Lond. 1975; FFD RCSI 1982; FDS RCS Ed. 1970. (Roy. Free) p/t Cons. (A & E Med.) Bedford Gen. Hosp.Clin. Dir. A & E Dept.; CHJ Comission for Health Imporovement - Med. Reviewer; Assesor Performance Preceedures- A&E-GMC; Hon. Sec.-Sect. of A&E Med.- Roy. Soc. of Med. Socs: Fell. Roy. Soc. Med.; Cas. Surgs. Assn. & BMA. Prev: Sen. Regist. (A & E Med.) Oxf. RHA; Regist. (Gen. Surg.) OldCh. Hosp. Romford & Harefield Hosp.; Regist. (Orthop.) Heatherwood Hosp. Ascot.

SHANKAR, Sonal Epsom General Hospital, Epsom KT18 Tel: 01372 735735; 406 Old Bedford Road, Luton LU2 7BP Tel: 01582 491661 — MB BS 1995 Lond. (UMDS Guy's & St. Thos. Hosps. Univ. Lond.) SHO (Gen. Med.) Epsom Gen. Hosp. Prev: SHO (A & E) Hammersmith Hosp. Lond.; Ho. Off. (Gen. Surg.) St. Peter's Hosp. Chertsey; Ho. Off. (Med.) Worthing Hosp.

SHANKAR, Mr Udaya Odstock Centre for Plastic Surgery, Salisbury District Hospital, Salisbury SP2 8BJ — MB BS 1970 Mysore; FRCS Ed. 1977; FRCS Glas. 1977.

SHANKAR, Yelandur Puttaveerappa Health Centre, Trethomas, Newport Tel: 01222 868011; 35 Mountain Road, Caerphilly CF83 1HH Tel: 02920 884241 — MB BS 1956 Mysore. (Mysore) Socs: Med. Defence Union. Prev: Ho. Phys. LLa.lli Hosp.; Regist. Merthyr & Aberdare Gp. Hosps. & St. Joseph's Hosp. Clonmel.

SHANKER, Mr Jyoti 54 Dungannon Chase, Southend-on-Sea SS1 3NJ — MB BS 1960 Rajasthan; FRCS Ed. 1968. Socs: Fell. BOA; BMA.

SHANKER NARAYAN, Padmaja 238 Birmingham Road, Wylde Green, Sutton Coldfield B72 1DH — MB BS 1981 Madras.

SHANKERNARAYAN, Munuswamy Govindarjula Saltley Health Centre, Saltley, Birmingham B8 1RZ Tel: 0121 327 3321 — MB BS 1967 Osmania.

***SHANKLAND, Catherine Ruth** 36 Old Kiln Lane, Bolton BL1 5PD — MB ChB Sheff. 1997.

SHANKLAND, Lorna Jean (retired) 7 The Leas, Wallasey CH45 3HZ Tel: 0151 639 4931 — MB ChB 1950 Manch.; DCH Eng. 1955. Prev: SCMO Liverp. Sch. Health Dept.

SHANKLAND, Pushpa Macfarlane (retired) 13 Bladon Close, London Road, Guildford GU1 9TY Tel: 01483 502814 — MRCS Eng. LRCP Lond. 1932; DCH Eng. 1943; LM Rotunda 1932. Prev: Asst. Co. Med. Off. & Asst. Sch. Med. Off. E. Riding, Yorks.

SHANKS, Adrian Barton Department of Anaesthetics, Cumberland Infirmary, Newtown Road, Carlisle CA2 7HY Tel: 01228 814196; Beck House, Pow Maughan Court, Scotby, Carlisle CA4 8EG — MB BS 1979 Lond.; BSc Lond. 1976; FFARCS Eng. 1984. (St. Thos.) Cons. Anaesth. & Pain Relief Carlisle Hosps. NHS Trust. Socs: Assn. Anaesth. & Pain Soc.; Internat. Assn. Study of Pain. Prev: Sen. Regist. (Anaesth.) Yorks. RHA; Regist. (Anaesth.) N. Staffs. HA; Regist. (Anaesth.) Leic. HA.

SHANKS, Brian Larne Health Centre, Gloucester Avenue, Larne BT40 1PB Tel: 028 2826 1919 Fax: 028 2827 2561 — MB BCh BAO 1970 Belf.; DObst RCOG 1974; DCH RCPS Glas. 1973.

SHANKS, Elizabeth Mary Southlands, Bentinck Crescent, Troon KA10 6JN — MB ChB 1978 Dundee; MB ChB (Hons.) Dundee 1978; FRCS Ed. 1982.

SHANKS, Hazel Anne Campbell Department of Genitourinary Medicine, Falkirk & District Royal Infirmary NHS Trust, Major's Loan, Falkirk FK1; Brackenhirst, Glenmavis, Airdrie ML6 0PP Tel: 01236 763157 — MB ChB Glas. 1968. (Glas.) Staff Grade Doctor Genitourin. Med. Falkirk & Dist Roy. Infirm. NHS Trust .; Clin. Asst. Genito-Urin. Med. & Sexual Health Lanarksh. Prev: Clin. Asst. (Genitourin. Med.) Glas. Roy. Infirm.; Cytopathol. Monklands Dist. Gen. Hosp. Airdrie; SHO (Anaesth.) & Ho. Phys. Law Hosp. Carluke.

SHANKS, Jean Mary 8 South Eaton Place, London SW1W 9JA Tel: 020 7730 3175 Fax: 020 7824 8174; Holywell Hall, Stamford PE9 4DT Tel: 01780 410665 Fax: 01780 410665 — BA, BM BCh Oxf. 1950; Hon. FRCPath 1993. (Middlx.) Dir. Chandos Clin. Research (CCR). Socs: Assn. Clin. Pathols.; (Liveryman) Soc. Apoth.;

SHANKS

Lond. Med. Soc. Prev: Chairm. & Managing Dir. of JS Path. plc; Regist. (Path.) Hosp. Sick Childr. Gt. Ormond St.

SHANKS, John Edward Department of Public Health, Croydon Health Authority, 17 Addiscombe Road, Croydon CR0 6SR Tel: 020 8401 3951 Fax: 020 8401 3769 — MB ChB 1977 Glas.; MB ChB (Commend.) Glas. 1977; BSc (Hons.) Glas. 1973; MRCPsych 1981; MFPHM RCP (UK) 1993. (Univ. Glas.) Dir. Pub. Health Croydon. Prev: Cons. Pub. Health Med. Lambeth S.wark & Lewisham HA; Sen. Regist. St. Geo. Hosp. Lond.; Regist. Maudsley Hosp. Lond.

SHANKS, Jonathan Hugh Department of Histopathology, Christie Hospital, Wilmslow, Manchester M20 4BX Tel: 0161 445 3275 Fax: 0161 446 3300 Email: jonathan.shanks@christie-tr.nwest.nhs.uk; 59 Dalston Drive, Didsbury, Manchester M20 5LQ Tel: 0161 445 3772 — MB ChB 1987 Manch.; BSc (Hons.) Manch. 1984; MD Belf. 1994; MRCPath 1995. Cons. Histopath. Christie Hosp. Manch. Socs: Internat. Acad. Path.; Path. Soc.; Assn. Clin. Path. Prev: Sen. Regist. Rotat. (Histopath.) N. W.. RHA; Regist. & SHO (Histopath.) Roy. Vict. Hosp. Belf.

SHANKS, Michael Fraser Royal Cornhill Hospital, Clerkseat Building, Cornhill Road, Aberdeen AB25 3ZH Tel: 01224 663131; 14 College Bounds, Old Aberdeen, Aberdeen AB24 3DS Tel: 01224 493838 — MB ChB 1971 Aberd.; DPhil Oxf. 1980; BMedBiol (Hons.) Aberd. 1968; FRCPsych 1995, M 1978. Cons. Old Age Psychiat. Grampian Healthcare NHS Trust; Hon. Sen. Lect. Dept. of Psychol. and Ment. Health Univ. of Aberd. Socs: Brit. Assn. Psychopharmacol.; Brit. Neuropsychiatric Assn. Prev: Cons. Psychiat. Highland HB; Sen. Lect. (Psychol. Med.) Univ. Glas.; Lect. Inst. Psychiat. Lond.

SHANKS, Michael Peter Severn Surgery, 159 Uplands Road, Oadby, Leicester LE2 4NW Tel: 0116 271 9042 — MB BChir 1979 Camb.; MB Camb 1979, BChir 1978.

SHANKS, Nicholas Roland c/o Shanks, 7 Hollymount Avenue, Newtownards BT23 7DG — MB ChB 1995 Dundee.

SHANKS, Nigel John Head of Accident & Emergency, Ministry of Health, Abu Dhabi, United Arab Emirates; 2 Church Hill, Ingham, Lincoln LN1 2YE Tel: 01522 730948 — MB ChB 1976 Sheff.; MB ChB Dundee 1976; DIH 1981; DHMSA 1979; DRCOG 1978; PhD Calif. 1989; MSc Manch. 1981; MD Sheff. 1993; MRCGP 1980; DFFP 1993; Dip. Pract. Derm. Wales 1990; DCCH RCP Ed. 1986; DGM RCP Lond. 1985. Head of Accid. & Emerg. MoH Abu Dhabi, UAE; Lect. (Gen. Pract. & A & E) Univ. Sheff. 1986-91; Chairm. Med. Bd. DHSS. Socs: Fell. Soc. Hist. Med.; Fell. Roy. Soc. Med.; Brit. Assn. Sport & Med. Prev: Head of Accid. & Emerg. GHQ Armed Forces Abu Dhabi, UAE; Head (Accid. & Emerg. & Gen. Pract.) King Khalid Nat. Guard Jeddah, Saudi Arabia; Cons. Rehabil. Med. & Cons. Primary Care Riyadh-Al-Kharj Milit. Hosp. Saudi Arabia.

SHANKS, Oliver Edward Pattison (retired) 19 Derryvolgie Avenue, Belfast BT9 6FN — MB BCh BAO 1974 Belf.; MRCP (UK) 1978; FRCPsych 1992, M 1980; DCH NUI 1976. Cons. Psychiat. (Learning Disabil.) Muckamore Abbey Hosp. Antrim. Prev: Sen. Regist. (Child Psychiat.) Roy. Belf. Hosp. Sick Childr.

SHANKS, Robert The Shrubbery, 65A Perry Street, Northfleet, Gravesend DA11 8RD Tel: 01474 356661 Fax: 01474 534542; 16 Orchard Avenue, Gravesend DA11 7NX — MB BCh BAO Belf. 1970. (Belf.) Police Surg.; Childr.'s Serv. Commiss.er for PCG. Socs: BMA & Assn. Police Surgs. Prev: Ho. Off. Waveney Hosp. Ballymena; SHO Belf. City Hosp. & N.. Irel. Radiother. Centre Belf.

SHANKS, Professor Robert Gray Department of Therapeutics & Pharmacology, The Queens' University of Belfast, Whitla Medical Building , 97 Lisburn Road, Belfast BT9 7BL Tel: 01232 335770 Fax: 01232 438346; 19 Magheralave Park N., Lisburn BT27 3NL Tel: 01846 665426 — MB BCh BAO 1958 Belf.; MB BCh BAO (Hons.) Belf. 1958; DSc Belf. 1969, BSc (Physiol.) 1955, MD (Hons.) 1963; FRCP Ed. 1979, M 1975; FRCP Lond. 1987, M 1975; FRCPI 1987. (Belf.) Pro-vice-Chancellor & Whitla Prof. Therap. & Pharm. Qu. Univ. Belf. Socs: Roy. Irish Acad.; Physiol. Soc; Brit. Pharm. Soc. Prev: Dean Fac. Med. Qu. Univ. Belf.

SHANKS, Rosamund Olivia Fyfe (retired) The Cottage, Cockshot Lane, Froxfield, Petersfield GU32 1BB Tel: 0173 084240 — MRCS Eng. LRCP Lond. 1951; DA Eng. 1956. Prev: Clin. Asst. Portsmouth Hosp. Gp.

SHANKS, Sheila Deborah 2 Bellfield Terrace, Inverness IV2 4ST — MB BCh BAO 1985 Belf.; DCH RCPI 1988; MRCP (UK) 1992. (Queens Univ. Belf.) Regist. (Paediat.) Raigmore Hosp. Inverness. Socs: MRCPCH.

SHANKS, Thomas Flat 102, Newheath Close, Elms Block, Wednesfield, Wolverhampton WV11 1XW — MB ChB 1986 Birm.

SHANKS, Walter 21 Park Close, Ilchester Place, London W14 8ND Tel: 020 7602 3438 — MB BCh BAO 1939 Belf.; MSc, MB BCh BAO Belf. 1939; DMR Eng. 1943; FFR 1952. (Belf.) Phys. i/c Radiother. Dept. Lond. Hosp. Socs: Fell. Roy. Soc. Med.

SHANKS, Wilhelmina Ingham, Lincoln LN1 2XT Tel: 01522 730269 — MB BCh BAO 1949 Dub.; BA, MB BCh BAO Dub. 1949. (T.C. Dub.) Prev: Asst. MOH Matern. & Child Welf. Lindsey CC.

SHANLEY, Michael Joseph Winterbottom and Partners, The Health Centre, 97 Derby Road, Stapleford, Nottingham NG9 7AT Tel: 0115 939 2444 Fax: 0115 949 1751 — MB BCh BAO 1986 NUI.

SHANMUGA BHASKAR, Mr Subramanian Glasgow Royal Infirmary, Glasgow G14 Tel: 0141 552 3535; Flat 15A, 25 Broomhill Lane, Glasgow G11 7NL — MB BS 1984 Madras; FRCS Ed. 1988. Vis. Regist. Higher Surg. Train. Gtr. Glas. HB; Vis. Regist. (Surg.) Pancreato-Biliary Unit. Glas. Roy. Infirm. Prev: Regist. (Surg.) Dumfries & Galloway Roy. Infirm.; Regist. (Surg.) Stobhill Hosp. Glas.; Regist. (Surg.) Scunthorpe Gen. Hosp.

SHANMUGALINGAM, Mr Sinnathamboo Kent County Ophthalmic Hospital, Church St., Maidstone ME14 Tel: 01622 673444; 27 Cromford Way, New Malden KT3 3BB Tel: 020 8949 5649 — MB BS 1973 Sri Lanka; FRCS Glas. 1985; FRCOphth 1988; DO RCS Eng. 1981. Assoc. Specialist (Ophth.) Kent Co. Hosp. Maidstone. Prev: Regist. (Ophth.) Roy. Surrey Co. Hosp. Guildford & Huddersfield Roy. Infirm.

SHANMUGALINGAM, Vathany 90 Alpine Rise, Styvechale, Coventry CV3 6NR — BM 1998 Soton.; BM Soton 1998.

SHANMUGANATHAN, Chellappah 146 Ridge Lane, Watford WD17 4WU Tel: 01923 235552; 146 Ridge Lane, Watford WD17 4WH Tel: 01923 235552 Fax: 01923 235552 — MB BS Ceylon 1965; DTM & H Liverp. 1979; DIH Eng. 1978; DPH Eng. 1977; Dip. Ven. Soc. Apoth Lond. 1974; FRIPHH 1976. (Colombo) Indep. GP Watford; Med. Off. H.M. Prison The Mt., Bovington, Herts; Staff Grade - M.O. Learning Disabil. Unit (E. & N. Herts NHS Trust) 305 Ware Rd., Hatley, Herts. Socs: BMA. Prev: Regist. Char. Cross Hosp. Lond.; Med. Off. Gen. Hosp. Bandar Seri Begawan, Brunei; Dist. Med. Off. Kilinochi, Sri Lanka.

SHANMUGANATHAN, Mr Kathirithamby 31 Finmere Crescent, Bedgrove, Aylesbury HP21 9DQ — MB BS Ceylon 1963; FRCS Ed. 1967.

SHANMUGANATHAN, Manohari 31 Finmere Crescent, Bedgrove, Aylesbury HP21 9DQ — MB BS 1967 Ceylon.

SHANMUGANATHAN, Thevarayapillai Long Grove Hospital, Epsom KT19 8PU Tel: 01372 726200 — MB BS 1971 Madras.

***SHANMUGANATHAN, Vijay Anand** 5 Burghfield, Epsom KT17 4ND — MB BS 1996 Lond.

SHANMUGARAJU, Mr Palaniappa Gounder Mayday University Hospital, London Road, Croydon CR7 7YE Tel: 020 8401 3331 Fax: 020 8401 3675; 4 and 6 Abbots Lane, Kenley CR8 5JH Tel: 020 8645 9929 Fax: 020 8240 1044 — MB BS 1978 Madras; FRCS Ed. 1984; LRCP LRCS Ed. LRCPS Glas. 1983; Dip. Urol. Lond 1988. Cons. Urol., Mayday Univ. Hosp., Croydon; Cons. Urol., Shirley Oaks Hosp., Croydon & N. Downs Hosp., Caterham. Socs: BMA; RCS Edin.; BAUS. Prev: Cons. Urol., Law Hosp., Carluke.

SHANMUGARATNAM, Kanagaratnam Bedford Hospital, Kempston Road, Bedford MK42 9DJ Tel: 01234 792146; The Pines, 8 Cryselco Close, Kempston, Bedford MK42 7TJ Tel: 01234 854355 — MB BS 1978 Sri Lanka; FRCP; LRCP LRCS Ed. LRCPS Glas. 1985. (Colombo) Cons. Genitourin. Med. Bedford Hosp. Prev: Sen. Regist. (Genitourin. Med.) Newc. Gen. Hosp.; Regist. (Genitourin. Med.) Roy. N.. Hosp. Lond.; SHO (Gen. Med.) Manch. Roy. Infirm.

SHANMUGASUNDARAM, Govindaraju (retired) 33 Cefn Coed, Bridgend CF31 4PH Tel: 01656 645098 — MB BS 1973 Madras. Regist. (Psychiat.) Parc Hosp. Bridgend. Prev: Trainee GP S. Clwyd VTS.

SHANMUGASUNDARAM, Mr Obli 228 Newton Drive, Blackpool FY3 8NB Tel: 01253 391330 Fax: 01253 391330 — MB BS 1973 Madras; FRCS Ed. 1989; FRCSI 1984; FFAEM 1993. Assoc. Specialist (Orthop.) Vict. Hosp. Blackpool. Socs: Assoc. Mem. BOA;

Brit. Assn. Accid. & Emerg. Med.; (Counc.) Brit. Assn. Sports Med. Prev: Assoc. Specialist (A & E) Vict. Hosp. Blackpool.

SHANN, Debra Jayne 10 Craigmore Dr, Ilkley LS29 8PG — MB ChB 1997 Dundee.

SHANNON, Anne 35 Devonshire Place Mews, London W1G 6DD Tel: 020 7935 4803 — LRCPI & LM, LRSCI & LM 1959; LRCPI & LM, LRCSI & LM 1959. (RCSI) Prev: Med. Off. Marks & Spencer Ltd. Head Office Lond.; Ho. Surg. Roy. Gwent Hosp. Newport; Med. Off. Nat. Blood Transfus. Serv.

SHANNON, Charles John 5 Old Rectory Close, Westbourne, Emsworth PO10 8UB — MB BS 1966 Lond.; MRCS Eng. LRCP Lond. 1966; FFA RCS Eng. 1971. (St. Geo.) Cons. Anaesth. S.E. Hants. Gp. Hosps. Prev: Regist. Nuffield Dept. Anaesth. Radcliffe Infirm. Oxf.; Sen. Regust. (Anaesth.) RiksHosp.er Oslo, Norway.

SHANNON, Claire Nicola 24 Solon Road, London SW2 5UY Tel: 020 7978 9493 — MB BS 1987 Lond.; FRCA 1993. Sen. Regist. (Anaesth.) UCLH Lond. Socs: Assn. Anaesth. Prev: Regist. (Anaesth.) Hosp. for Sick Childr. Gt. Ormond St. Lond.; Regist. Rotat. (Anaesth.) Greenwich Dist., Brook & King's Hosps. Lond.; SHO Rotat. (Anaesth.) Char. Cross & Barnet Gen. Hosps.

SHANNON, Elizabeth Gwendoline Mary Health Centre, John St., Rathfriland, Newry BT34 3JD Tel: 018206 30666; Toorak, 21 Dromore Road, Hillsborough BT26 6HS — MB BCh BAO 1983 Belf.; MRCGP 1987; DRCOG 1986; DCH RCPSI 1985. GP Rathfriland. Socs: Ulster Med. Soc.; Med. Wom. Federat.

SHANNON, Ernest Nathaniel Lodge Health, 20 Lodge Manor, Coleraine BT52 1JX Tel: 028 7034 4494 Fax: 028 7032 1759 Email: e.n.shannon@346.g.p.n.i.nhs.uk — MB BCh BAO 1974 Belf. p/t Med. Off. Dhu Varren Childr. Home Portrush; Med. Off. Ulster Bus Ltd. Coleraine.

SHANNON, Gavin Michael Ground Floor Flat, 24 Solon Road, London SW2 5UY — MB BS 1988 Lond.

SHANNON, Gillian Elizabeth Mary 20 Magheraconluce Road, Dromore BT25 1EE — MB BCh BAO 1991 Belf.; MRCGP 1996; DFFP 1996; DRCOG 1995; DMH Belf. 1994; DGM RCPS Glas. 1994.

SHANNON, Jason Lee 18 Ware Road, Caerphilly CF83 1SX — MB ChB 1996 Birm.; ChB Birm. 1996.

SHANNON, Jeanetta Margaret 17 School Road, Newtownbreda, Belfast BT8 6BT — MB BCh BAO 1961 Belf.; MB BCh Belf. 1961.

SHANNON, John Richard 48 Chestnut Grove, Coleshill, Birmingham B46 1AD — MB BCh BAO 1977 Dub. (TC Dub.) Med. Off. DHSS Birm. Prev: SHO (Gen. Med.) N. Manch. Gen. Hosp.; SHO (Gen. Med./O & G) W. Pk. Hosp. Macclesfield; SHO (Nephrol./Geriat.) Withington Hosp. Manch.

SHANNON, John Wilson 15 Ardaragh Road, Newry BT34 1NY — MB BCh BAO 1986 Belf.

SHANNON, Muriel Susan Department of Haematology, St. George's Hospital, Tooting, London SW17 0QT Tel: 020 8725 5480 Email: m.shannon@eghns.co.uk; Homewood, 4A Drax Avenue, Wimbledon, London SW20 0EH Tel: 020 8946 1893 Fax: 020 8946 3130 Email: eejmiss@supanet.com — MB ChB 1975 Glas.; FRCPath 1994, M 1982. (Glasgow) Clin. Asst. (Haemat.) St. Geo. Hosp. Lond. Socs: Brit. Soc. Haematol. Prev: Clin. Research Fell. Imperial Cancer Research Fund Lond.; Sen. Regist. (Haemat.) Roy. Free Hosp. Lond.; Regist. (Haemat.) W.. Infirm. Glas.

SHANNON, Nora Letitia Clinical Genetics Unit, Birmingham Women's Hospital, Metchley Park Rd, Birmingham B15 2TG — MB BS 1992 Lond.; MRCP (UK) 1995. (St. Geo. Hosp. Med. Sch. Lond.) Cons. Clin. Geneticist, Clin. Genetics Unit, Birm. Wom.'s Hosp. Socs: Brit. Soc. For Human Genetics; The Cancer Genetics Grp.; The Skeletal Dysplasia Grp. Prev: Specialist Regist. (Clin. Genetics) Centre Human Genetics Sheff.

SHANNON, Paul Edington 16 Croft Drive, Tickhill, Doncaster DN11 9UL — MB ChB 1987 Leeds; FRCA 1993. Cons. Anaesth. Doncaster Roy. Infirm. Socs: Assn. Anaesth. & Obst. Anaesth. Assn. Prev: Regist. (Anaesth.) Sheff. HA; SHO (Paediat. & Anaesth.) Bradford Roy. Infirm.; SHO (A & E) Dewsbury Dist. Hosp.

SHANNON, Rita Winifred (retired) 1 Beech Hyde, Hogg End Lane, St Albans AL3 6RF Tel: 01727 850456 — MB BS 1953 Lond.; MRCS Eng. LRCP Lond. 1953; FRCOG 1976, M 1959, DObst 1956; DCH Eng. 1955. Prev: Cons. O & G St. Albans City Hosp.

SHANNON, Robert Ian Reid Health Centre, Rathfriland, Newry BT34 3JD Tel: 0169330666 — LRCPI & LM, LRSCI & LM 1956; LRCPI & LM, LRCSI & LM 1956. (RCSI) Prev: Ho. Surg. Dr. Steevens' Hosp. Dub.; Ho. Off. (Obst.) Daisy Hill Hosp. Newry; Sen. Ho. Off. (Med.) Banbridge Hosp.

SHANNON, Rosemary Susan 3 Llewellyn Court, Off Elmsleigh Avenue, Stoneygate, Leicester LE2 2DH — MB BCh BAO 1966 Dub.; MA, MB BCh BAO Dub. 1966; FRCP Lond. 1973; DCH Eng. 1969. (T.C. Dub.) Cons. (Paediat.) Leicester Roy. Infirm. Prev: Sen. Regist. (Paediat.) Childr. Hosp. Birm.

SHANNON, Sarah White (Surgery) 27 Parkfield Road, Coleshill, Birmingham B46 3LD Tel: 01675 463165; 48 Chestnut Grove, Coleshill, Birmingham B46 1AD Tel: 01675 463255 — MB BCh BAO 1977 Dub.; BSc Loughborough 1972; DCP Warwick 1989; MRCGP 1983; DRCOG 1982; DCH RCPSI 1978. Prev: SHO (Obst. & Neonat. Paediat.) St. Mary's Hosp. Manch.; SHO (Paediat.) Nat. Childr. Hosp. Dub. & Duchess of York Hosp. Manch.

SHANNON, Sian Eirian 5 Hollybush Close, Sevenoaks TN13 3XW — MB BS 1983 Lond.; DRCOG 1986.

SHANNON, Thomas Edward (retired) Oakroyd, Foxholes Road, Horwich, Bolton BL6 6AS Tel: 01204 697883 — MB BCh BAO NUI 1942; DOMS Eng. 1946. Sen. Hosp. Med. Off. Roy. Eye Hosp. Manch. Prev: Cons. Ophth. Bolton Roy. Infirm.

SHANNON, Violet Courtney (retired) Garliebank, Brighton Road, Cupar KY15 5DQ — MB ChB 1964 St. And.; MRCPsych 1972; DPM Ed. & Glas. 1968; DObst RCOG 1966. Prev: Cons. Child Psychiat. Stratheden Hosp. Cupar Fife.

SHANSON, Barnett 1 Ravenscroft Court, 56 Ravenscroft Avenue, London NW11 8BA Tel: 020 8458 9221 — MRCS Eng. LRCP Lond. 1949; MRCS Eng. LRCP Lond. 1932; DPhys. Med. Eng. 1949. (Lond. Hosp.) LCC Certif. of Efficiency in VD; Clin. Asst. Roy. Nat. Throat, Nose & Ear Hosp. Lond. & Brit. Red Cross Clinic For Rheum. Peto Pl; Research Asst. Pulverisation of Renal Calculi by Low Frequency Ultra Sound; Hon. Advis. Edr. Brit. Jl. Physical Med. Socs: Lond. Jewish Med. Soc.; Soc. Rheum.; Founder Mem. Heberden Soc. Prev: Researcher Coley, Fluid in Sarcoma of No Value; Ho. Surg. Roy. Albert Hosp. Plymouth; Hon. Dent. Anaesth. Qu. Mary's Hosp. Stratford.

SHANSON, David Charles 48 Middleway, London NW11 6SG Tel: 020 8455 8238 — MB BS Lond. 1966; MRCS Eng. LRCP Lond. 1966; FRCPath 1986, M 1973. (Westm.) Cons. MicrobiolAPS/Unilabs Clin.Path.27 harley St. Lond; Emerit. Cons. Microbiol. Chelsea & W.minster Hosp. Socs: Fell. Roy. Soc. Med. (Pres. Path. Sect.). Prev: Sen. Lect. & Hon. Cons. Med. Microbiol. Char. Cross, W.m. Med. Sch. & W.m. Hosps. Lond.; Sen. Lect. & Hon. Cons. (Med. Microbiol.) Lond. Hosp.; Sen. Regist. (Microbiol.) Univ. Coll. Hosp. Lond.

SHANSON, Ronald Louis (Surgery) 8 Englefiled Road, Islington, London N1 4LN Tel: 020 7254 1324; 43 Essex Road, Islington, London N1 2SF Tel: 020 7226 8096 — MB BS 1968 Lond.; MRCS Eng. LRCP Lond. 1968. (Univ. Coll. Hosp.) Prev: Regist. (Anaesth.) Hornsby Hosp. Sydney, Austral.; SHO (Anaesth.) Guy's Hosp. Lond.; Cas. Off. Lond. Jewish Hosp.

SHANTHA, A L Lathom Road Clinic, Lathom Road, Huyton, Liverpool L36 5XX Tel: 0151 489 2276.

SHANTHAKUMAR, Ratnasingham Edward Department of Anaesthetics, Wellhouse NHS Trust, Barnet General Hospital, Barnet EN5 3DJ Tel: 020 8216 4000 Fax: 020 8216 5297; 8 Appledore Close, Edgware HA8 6DE Tel: 020 8952 3667 — MB BS 1980 Peradeniya; FRCA 1993; FFA RCSI 1992; DA (UK) 1990; EDICM 1996. (Sri Lanka Peradeniya) Cons. Anaesth. Barnet Gen. Hosp. Socs: BMA; Assn. Anaesth.; Intens. Care Soc. Prev: Fell. (Intens. Care) Univ. Hosp. Groningen, Netherlands; Sen. Regist. Hammersmith Hosp. Lond.

SHANTI RAJU, Kankipati York House Centre, 199 Westminister Bridge Road, London SE1 7UT Tel: 020 7620 0892 — MD 1990 Lond.; MB BS Andhra 1973; FRCOG 1992, M 1979, D 1977; DTCDHE 1986. Cons. & Gyn. Oncol., St. Thos. Hosp. and NHS Trust; Director of Gyn. Oncol. Socs: Internat. Gyn. Cancer Soc.; Past Europ. Gyn. Cancer Soc.; Brit. Soc. of Colposcopy and Cervical Path. Prev: Lect. (Gyn. Oncol.) Inst. Cancer Research & Hon. Regist. Div. Med. Roy. Marsden Hosp. Lond.; Lect. & Sen. Regist. (O & G) St. Thos. Hosp. Med. Sch. Lond.; Regist. (O & G) All St.s Hosp. Chatham.

SHANTIR

SHANTIR, Dauod Yosuf Abdul-Rahman Forest Road Medical Centre, 354-368 Forest Road, Walthamstow, London E17 5JG Tel: 020 8520 7115 Fax: 020 8923 1199 — MB BCh 1971 Ain Shams.

SHAOUL, Doreen Diana Rachel Brook Green Medical Centre, Bute Gardens, London W6 7EG Tel: 020 8237 2800 Fax: 020 8237 2811; Compton Lodge, 140 Upper Richmond Road West, London SW14 8DS Tel: 020 8876 0632 — MB BS Lond. 1962. Prev: Ho. Phys. St. Geo. Hosp. Lond.

SHAOUL, Edward The Brook Green Medical Centre, Bute Gardens, London W6 7BE Tel: 020 8237 2800 Fax: 020 8237 2811; Compton Lodge, 140 Upper Richmond Road W., East Sheen, London SW14 8DS Tel: 020 8876 0632 Email: eshaoul@rpms.ac.uk — MB ChB 1958 Manch.; FRCGP 1981; DObst RCOG 1961. Assoc. Dean (Gen. Pract.) N. Thames W. Region; Hon. Sen. Lect. (Gen. Pract.) Char. Cross & W.m. Med. Sch. Lond.

SHAPER, Professor Andrew Gerald 8 Wentworth Hall, The Ridgeway, Mill Hill, London NW7 1RJ Tel: 020 8959 8742 Fax: 020 8959 8742 Email: agshaper@wentworth.u-net.com; 2 Church Hill, Fremington, Barnstaple EX31 3BH Tel: 01271 373913 — MB ChB Cape Town 1951; FRCP Lond. 1969, M 1955; FFPHM 1972; FRCPath 1976, M 1968; DTM & H Liverp. 1953. (Cape Town) Emerit. Prof. Clin. Epidemiol. Roy. Free & Univ. Coll. Med. Sch. Socs: Internat. Epidemiol. Assn.; Brit. Cardiac Soc.; Brit. Hypertens. Soc. Prev: Mem. Scientif. Staff, MRC Social Med. Research Unit; WHO Research Prof. in Cardiovasc. Dis. Makerere Univ. Med. Sch. Kampala, Uganda; Director, Brit. Regional Heart Study 1975-1992.

SHAPERO, Jonathan Stewart St. Andrew's Hospital, Billing Road, Northampton NN1 5DG Tel: 01604 629696 Fax: 01604 616623 Email: jss9h@aol.com — MB ChB 1978 Birm.; MRCPsych 1982. Cons. Forens. Psychiat. St. Andrews Hosp. N.ampton; Vis. Psychiat. HM Young Offenders' Centre Glen Parva Leicester; Vis. Psychiat. HMP Woodhill Milton Keynes. Socs: BMA. Prev: Cons. Forens. Psychiat. Leicester Ment. Health Trust; Sen. Regist. (Forens. Psychiat.) W. Midl. RHA; Regist. (Psychiat.) Birm. Centr. Health Dist. (T).

SHAPIRO, Mr Andrew Mark James Surgical-Medical Research Institute, 1074 Dentistry-Pharmacy Building, University of Alberta, Edmonton T6G 2N8, Canada Tel: 00 1 403 4928822 Fax: 00 1 403 4310704; 12 Clifton Wood Crescent, Bristol BS8 4TU Tel: 01179 268381 — MB BS 1988 Newc.; BMedSci. 1985; FRCS Eng. 1992. Socs: Fell. (Liver Transpl.) Univ. Edmonton, Alberta, Canada; Fell. Paediat. Islet Research. Prev: Demonst. (Anat.) Univ. of Bristol; Regist. Profess. Surg. Unit Bristol Roy. Infirm.; Ho. Surg. Profess. Surgic. Unit Roy. Vict. Infirm. Newc. u Tyne.

SHAPIRO, Brian William Renfrew Health Centre, 103 Paisley Road, Renfrew PA4 8LL Tel: 0141 886 2455 Fax: 0141 855 0457; 23 Humbie Road, Eaglesham, Glasgow G76 0LX Tel: 013553 2976 — MB ChB 1977 Glas.

SHAPIRO, Emma Bernardine Awbery 34 Henry Gardens, Chichester PO19 3DL — MB BS 1991 Lond.

SHAPIRO, Frank Norman Strahaven Health Centre, The Ward, Strathaven ML10 6AS Tel: 01357 522993 — MB ChB 1976 Glas.; DRCOG 1980; Cert FPA. RCOG 1980. Prison Med. Off. Dungavel Prison Drumclog; GP Strathaven.

SHAPIRO, Harold Joseph Appt. 4, Merelwood, 17 Langham Road, Bowdon, Altrincham WA14 2HT Tel: 0161 928 6497 Fax: 0161 928 6497 — LRCP 1945 Ed.; LRCP, LRCS Ed., LRFPS Glas. 1945. Clin. Research Phys. Obesity Clinic Hope Hosp. Salford Manch. Socs: Roy. Soc. Med.; Fell. Roy. Soc. Med. Assn Study Obesity; Nutrit. Soc. & Obesity Assn. Prev: Clin. Asst. S.. Gen. Hosp. Glas.; Res. Med. Off. Chest Unit, Baguley EMS Hosp. Manch.; Regist. (Med.) Crumpsall Hosp. Manch.

SHAPIRO, Henry 24 Harewood Mews, Harewood, Leeds LS17 9LY Tel: 0113 288 6215 Fax: 0113 288 6183 Email: hshap0922@aol.com — MRCS Eng. LRCP Lond. 1947; MFOM RCP Lond. 1982; MRCGP 1966. (Leeds) Socs: Fell. Roy. Soc. Med.; BMA; Leeds & W. Riding M-C Soc. Prev: Hon. Clin. Asst. Coronary Preven. Clinic St. Jas. Unit Teach. Hosp. Leeds; Cons. Phys. Burton Gp. plc Lond. & Leeds; GP Leeds.

SHAPIRO, Joan Cree 23 Humbie Road, Eaglesham, Glasgow G76 0LX — MB ChB 1977 Glas.

SHAPIRO, Jonathan Abraham Health Services Management Centre, Park House, 40 Edgbaston Park Road, Birmingham B15 2RT Tel: 0121 414 7050 Fax: 0121 414 7051 Email: j.a.shapiro@bham.ac.uk — MB ChB 1977 Birm.; MA Camb. 1978; MRCGP 1981. Sen. Fell. (Health Servs. Managem.) Univ. of Birm. Prev: Indep. Med. Adviser Leics. RHSA; GP Bulkington N. Warks. FHSA; Ho. Phys. Med. Profess. Unit Qu. Eliz. Hosp. Birm.

SHAPIRO, Leonard Melvyn Papworth Hospital, Papworth Everard, Cambridge CB3 8RE Tel: 01480 831284 Fax: 01480 831083 Email: ims@doctors.org.uk — MD 1981 Manch.; BSc Manch. 1973, MD 1981, MB ChB 1976; FRCP Lond. 1994; MRCP (UK) 1978; FACC 1994. Cons. Cardiol. Papworth & Addenbrooke's; Assoc. Lect. Univ. Camb. Socs: Founding Chairm. Brit. Soc. Echocardiography. Prev: Sen. Regist. Nat. Heart & Brompton Hosp.; Regist. Hammersmith Hosp. Lond.

SHAPIRO, Leslie (retired) 4 Windsor House, Regency Crescent, London NW4 1NW Tel: 020 8371 0569 — MB ChB 1952 Leeds. Prev: Regist. (Anaesth.) & Receiv. Room Off. Gen. Infirm. Leeds.

SHAPIRO, Linda Rae River Brook Medical Centre, 3 River Brook Drive, Stirchley, Birmingham B30 2SH Tel: 0121 451 2525 Fax: 0121 433 3214 — MB ChB 1975 Birm.

SHAPIRO, Steven Maurice 48 Kewferry Road, Northwood HA6 2PG — MB BS 1982 Lond.; MRCGP 1988; DRCOG 1986.

SHAPIRO-STERN, Paul Rayd Church End Medical Centre, 66 Mayo Road, Church End Estate, Willesden, London NW10 9HP Tel: 020 8930 6262 Fax: 020 8930 6260; 1 Talbot Walk, Willesden, London NW10 9HU Tel: 020 8451 2401 — MB ChB 1965 Cape Town. (Cape Town)

SHAPLAND, Mr David Eric Penberthy Furness General Hospital, Barrow-in-Furness LA14 4LF Tel: 01229 870870 Fax: 01229 871182; Cilbrydwen, Llanddeusant, Llangadog SA19 9SR — MB BChir Camb. 1967; MA Camb. 1968; FRCS Ed. 1972; FRCOG 1989, M 1973; DObst RCOG 1970. (Camb. & Guy's) RCOG Dist. Tutor; Postgrad. Clin. Tutor S. Cumbria. Socs: Fell. Linnean Soc.; Ospreys Gyn. Soc.; Brit. Fertil. Soc. Prev: Cons. O & G Lond. Fertil. Centre & Humana Hosp. Wellington; O & G P.ss Eliz. Hosp. Guernsey, CI; Regist. (Surg.) Newc. Gen. Hosp.

SHAPLAND, John David (retired) Padilly Cottage, Rock, Wadebridge PL27 6JZ Tel: 01208 862732 — MB BS 1949 Lond.; MRCS Eng. LRCP Lond. 1949. Prev: Hosp. Pract. (Geriat.) Plymouth.

SHAPLAND, Judith Mary Cutlers Hill Surgery, Bungay Road, Halesworth IP19 8HP Tel: 01986 874136 — MB BS 1985 Lond.; MRCGP 1991.

SHAPLAND, Michael Courtenay Donnington Health Centre, 1 Henley Avenue, Oxford OX4 4DH Tel: 01865 774844 — MRCS Eng. LRCP Lond. 1961; MA, BM BCh Oxf. 1962. (Oxf. & Lond. Hosp.) Unit Med. Off. RAF Brize Norton. Prev: Ho. Surg. & Ho. Phys. Morriston Hosp. Swansea; Unit Med. Off. RAF Kai Tak, Hong Kong & RAAF Butterworth, Penang; Malaysia.

SHAPLAND, William David, Wing Cdr. Department of Community Psychiatry, Marham, King's Lynn PE33 9NP — MB BS 1981 Lond.; Cert. Cog. Ther Oxf. (1996); MRCPsych 1990; DRCOG 1985; DA (UK) 1984. (Roy. Lond. Hosp.) Cons. (Gen. Adult) Dept. of Community Psychiat. Marham; Hon. Clin. Fell. (Psychopharmacol) Bristol Roy. Infirm. Socs: BMA; Roy. Coll. of Psychiat.s. Prev: Regist. (Psychiat.) I. of Wight & Moorhaven Hosp. Ivybridge Devon; Hon. Sen. Regist. (Forens.) Fromeside Clinic Bristol; Sen. Reg. P.ss Alexandra Hosp. (Gen./Acute).

SHAPLEY, Mark Wolstanton Medical Centre, Palmerston Street, Newcastle ST5 8BN Tel: 01782 627488 Fax: 01782 662313 — MB BS 1982 Lond.; BA Oxf. 1979; MRCGP 1986; DCH RCP Lond. 1985; DRCOG 1984.

SHAPLEY, Roger West Bar Surgery, 1 West Bar Street, Banbury OX16 9SF Tel: 01295 256261 Fax: 01295 756848; The Old Forge, Main St, North Newington, Banbury OX15 6AF Tel: 01295 730466 — MB BS 1972 Lond.; MRCP (U.K.) 1975; MRCGP 1977; DCH Eng. 1977; DObst RCOG 1976.

SHAR, Mohamed Bahgat Saddleton Road Surgery, 32 Saddleton Road, Whitstable CT5 4JQ Tel: 01227 272809 — MB BCh 1972 Cairo.

SHARAF, Adnan 106 Lawton Road, Alsager, Stoke-on-Trent ST7 2DE — MB BS 1998 Lond.; MB BS Lond 1998.

SHARAF, Loutfy Amin Mosa 5 Cedar Mount, Edgerton, Huddersfield HD1 5QJ Tel: 01484 428582 — MB ChB 1964 Alexandria; FFA RCSI 1975; DA Alexandria 1970. (Alexandria) Cons. Anaesth. Huddersfield Roy. Infirm. Prev: Sen. Regist. Leeds Hosp.

SHARAF, Taher Fathi Ali 4 Shottfield Avenue, London SW14 8EA — MB BS 1998 Lond.; MB BS Lond 1998.

SHARAF, Mr Usama Ibrahim 23 Hoel Ysgawen, Sketty, Swansea SA2 9GS — MB BCh 1979 Ain Shams; FRCS Ed. 1990; FRCS Glas. 1990.

SHARAF-UD-DIN, Syed Kidsgrove Medical Centre, Mount Road, Kidsgrove, Stoke-on-Trent ST7 4AY Tel: 01782 784221 Fax: 01782 781703; The Rowans, 106 Lawton Road, Alsager, Stoke-on-Trent ST7 2DE — MB BS 1962 Karachi; DCH RCPS Glas. 1965. (Dow. Med. Coll.)

SHARAIHA, Mr Yousef Mitri Doctor's Residence, Prince Philip Hospital, Dafen, Llanelli SA14 8QF; Flat C, 30 Kempsford Gardens, London SW5 9LH Tel: 020 7244 6352 — MB BS 1988 Jordan; FRCS Ed. 1994; BA (Psychol.) Univ. India 1983. Regist. (Gen. Surg.) P. Philip Hosp. LLa.lli, Dyfed. Prev: SHO Qu. Eliz. Hosp. King's Lynn; SHO Bradford Roy. Infirm.

SHARAN, Kalpana Springfield Farmhouse, Ercall Heath, Newport TF10 8NQ Tel: 01952 550654 Email: saran999@yahoo.com — MB BS 1971 Patna; MB BS Patna 1976; MRCOG 1983; FRCOG 1998. Assoc. Specialist (O & G).

SHARARA, Abdelmonem Mohammad Office of Jordan Military Naval and Air, 16 Upper Phillimore Gardens, London W8 7HE — MB BS 1980 Jordan; MRCP (UK) 1988.

SHARARA, Mr Fawzi 35 Redclyffe Gardens, Helensburgh G84 9JJ Tel: 01436 678826 Fax: 01436 678826 — MB BCh 1967 Ain Shams; FRCS Eng. 1979. Med. Acupunc./Complementary Med. Practitioner Helensburgh. Socs: Brit. Med. Acupunct. Soc.; Assoc. Mem. Fac. Homeop.

SHARARA, Mr Khaled El-Sayed Hussein The Hall, Northfield Road, Messingham, Scunthorpe DN17 3RZ — MB BCh 1972 Ain-Shams; FRCS Ed. 1982; T(S) 1991.

SHARBAWI, Roslin Binti Brunei Hall, 35-43 Norfolk Square, London W2 1RX — MB BS 1994 Lond.

SHARD, Helen Mary 60 Eagle Brow, Lymm WA13 0LZ — MB BS 1990 Lond.

SHARDA, Arun Dev Stantonbury Health Centre, Purbeck, Stantonbury, Milton Keynes MK14 6BL Tel: 01908 316262 — MB BS 1973 Punjab; MB BS Punjabi 1973. (Govt. Med. Coll. Patiala)

SHARDLOW, Mr David Lloyd 3 Pine Tree Close, Thorpe Willoughby, Selby YO8 9FP — MB BS 1989 Lond.; MSc (Eng) Leeds 1998; FRCS (Eng) 1993. Specialist Regist. (Trauma & Ortho.) St. James Univ. Hosp. Leeds. Socs: BOA; BORS; BOTA.

SHARE, Alison 14 Osbourne Road, Wolverhampton WV4 4AY — MB ChB 1989 Leeds.

SHARE, Aubrey Ingram Sherwood 67 Sandmoor Lane, Leeds LS17 7EA Tel: 0113 268 4401 — MB ChB 1945 Leeds; LDS Leeds 1948. (Leeds) JP. Prev: Ho. Surg. Gen. Infirm. Leeds.

SHAREEF, Syed Hasnain The Health Centre, Canterbury Way, Stevenage SG1 1QH Tel: 01438 357411 Fax: 01438 720523 — MB BS 1958 Dacca. Socs: Med. Defence Union.

SHARER, Nicholas Montague Poole Hospital NHS Trust, Longfleet Road, Poole BH15 2JB Tel: 01202 448315 Fax: 01202 442996 Email: nsharer@poole-tr.swest.nhs.uk — BM 1986 Soton.; BSc (Hons) Wales 1980; MRCP (UK) 1989; FRCP 2000. Cons. Phys. & Gastroenterol. Poole Hosp. NHS Trust. Prev: Regist. & Med. Co-ordinator (Pancreato-Biliary Serv.) Centr. Manch. HA; Regist. (Med.) Newc. u. Tyne Hosps.; SHO (Med.) Portsmouth.

SHARFUDDIN, Imtiaz 215 Sydney Road, London N10 2NL — MB BS 1981 Karachi.

SHARIATMADARI, Mohamad Ebrahim 10 Lee Road, Lincoln LN2 4BH — LMSSA 1973 Lond.; MRCPsych 1974; DPM Eng. 1970. Cons. Emerit. Psychiat. Peter Hodgkinson Centre Lincoln Co. Hosp. Socs: Lincoln Med. Soc.

SHARIEF, Mohammad Kassim Department of Neurology, Medical School Building, Guy's Hospital, London SE1 9RT Tel: 020 7955 4398 Fax: 020 7378 1221 Email: m.sharief@umds.ac.uk; Department of Neurology, St. Thomas's Hospital, London SE1 7EH Tel: 020 7928 9292 Fax: 020 7922 8263 — MB ChB 1980 Baghdad; MRCP (UK) 1993; PhD 1992, MPhil 1989. Sen. Lect. & Cons. Neurol. Lond.

SHARIEF, Nawfal Natheir Younis Paediatric Department, Basildon Hospital, Basildon SS16 5NL Tel: 01268 593979 Fax: 01268 593194; 5 Salcombe Park, Loughton IG10 4QT — MB ChB 1973 Baghdad; PhD Lond. 1980; FRCP Lond. 1996; MRCP (UK) 1983; DCH RCP Lond. 1983; FRCPCH 1997. (Univ. Baghdad) Cons. Paediat. Basildon Hosp. Socs: BMA; Roy. Coll. Paediat. & Child Health; Brit. Assn. of Perinatal Med. Prev: Sen. Regist. (Paediat. Respirat. Dis. & Gastroenterol.) Qu. Eliz. Hosp.; Sen. Regist. (Developm. Paediat. & Neonat.) Qu. Eliz. & Homerton Hosps.

SHARIEFF, Sayeda Fouzia 19 Loughan Road, Coleraine BT52 1UB — MB BS 1973 Osmania.

SHARIF, Ala Towfiq The Albany Clinic, 11 Station Road, Sidcup DA15 7EN Tel: 020 8300 4361 — MB ChB 1973 Baghdad.

SHARIF, Harpreet The New Surgery, 31-35 Linom Road, London SW4 7PB Tel: 020 7274 4220 Fax: 020 7737 0205 — MB ChB 1988 Dundee.

SHARIF, Jalal The Surgery, 62 Windsor Drive, Orpington BR6 6HD Tel: 01689 852204 Fax: 01689 857122 — MD 1976 Isfahan. GP Chelsfield; Clin. Asst. (Cardiol.) FarnBoro. Hosp. Prev: Research Fell. (Cardiol.) Guy's Hosp. Lond.; Regist. (Med.) FarnBoro. Hosp.

SHARIF, Khaldoun Walid Said 22 Aboyne Close, Birmingham B5 7PQ — MB BCh 1985 Ain-Shams; MRCOG 1991.

SHARIF, Mohammad c/o M. A. Nusrat, 9 Carew Road, Thornton Heath, Croydon CR7 7RF — MB BS 1961 Punjab; MRCPSych 1973.

SHARIF, Mr Mohammed 28 Kenver Avenue, Finchley, London N12 0PG Tel: 020 8445 5404 — MB BS 1936 Bombay; DSc (Hon. Causa) Malta 1989; FRCS Eng. 1951; Dip. Genitourin. Surg. Inst. Urol. Lond. 1950; DAvMed. US Air Univ. 1956. (Grant Med. Coll.) Sitara-i-Qaid-i-Azam Pakistan 1961; Life Dep. Governor Amer. Biographical Inst. USA. Socs: FRSH; FICS. Prev: Dir.-Gen. (Health) & Jt. Sec. Min. Health Pakistan; Dir. (Health) & WHO Represen. UNRWA HQ Beirut; Dir. UNRWA Operats. W. Bank Jerusalem.

SHARIF, Mohammed Mahmood Kings Park Surgery, 274 Kings Park Avenue, Glasgow G44 4JE Tel: 0141 632 1824 Fax: 0141 632 0461 — MB ChB 1980 Glas. SHO Orthop. Dept. Glas. Roy. Infirm. Prev: Jun. Ho. Off. (Surg.) Duke St. Hosp. Glas.; Jun. Ho. Off. (Med.) Vict. Infirm. Glas.; Jun. Ho. Off. Gartnavel Gen. Hosp. Glas.

SHARIF, Mr Riadh Ali Mohamed Stoke Mandeville Hospital, Mandeville Rd, Aylesbury HP21 8AL Tel: 01296 315773; 26 North Drive, Stoke Mandeville Hospital, Aylesbury HP21 9AN Tel: 01296 315000 Ext: 3141 Email: ahmed@sharif50.freeserve.co.uk — MB ChB 1976 Baghdad; FRCS 1983 Ed.; FRCS 2000. (Baghdad Iraq) Cons. Surg., Stoke Mandeville (with colorectal interest) substantive job since 01/07/01, Mandeville Rd, Aylesbury, HP21 8AL. Socs: BMA; MDU; BASO. Prev: Sen. Regist. Roy. Lond. and St Bart. NHS Trust, Univ. Hosp. 2000-01; Regist. Mid. Stafford Dist. Hosp.; Regist. Macclesfield Dist. Hosp.

SHARIF, Saba 273 Fullwell Avenue, Clayhall, Ilford IG5 0RE Tel: 020 8550 7793 — MB BS 1996 Lond.; BSc Lond. (UMDS) SHO (Paediat.) UMDS Rotat. Prev: Greenwich Ho. Surg.; Guy's Ho. Med.

SHARIFF, Abdul Ghaffar (retired) 78 The Park Paling, Cheylesmore, Coventry CV3 5LL Tel: 01203 502016 — MB BS 1962 Karachi; BSc Karachi 1955, MB BS 1962; DA Eng. 1965. Clin. Asst. (Anaesth.) Geo. Eliot Hosp. Nuneaton; Clin. Asst. (Endocrinol.) Coventry Warks. Hosp.

SHARIFF, Amina Tazeen 4 hazelbourne Road, London SW12 9NS Tel: 0208 675 0703 — MB BS 1990 Lond.; FRCA 1996. (St. Geo. Hosp.) Specialist Regist. (Anaesth.) King's Coll. Hosp. Lond. Prev: SHO (Ananesth.) St. Richards Hosp. Chichester; SHO (Paediat.) St. Helier Hosp. Lond.; SHO (Anaesth.) Frimley Pk. Hosp. Surrey.

SHARIFF, Sheher Banoo Hammersmith Hospital, Ducane Road, London W12 10H; 47A Cambridge Street, Pimlico, London SW1V 4PS — MB BS 1972 Osmania; MCOphth 1990; DO RCS Eng. 1980. Assoc. Specialist (Diabetic Retinopathy) Hammersmith Hosp. Lond. Socs: BMA.

SHARIFF, Syed Yakub Queens Road Surgery, 17 Queens Road, Broadstairs CT10 1NU Tel: 01843 862648 Fax: 01843 860739 — MB BS 1966 Andhra.

SHARIFF, Uzma Munir 18 Merivale Grove, Chatham ME5 8HP — MB BS 1987 Lond.

SHARIH, Gauhar 276A Uxbridge Road, Rickmansworth WD3 8YL Tel: 01923 710811; 276A Uxbridge Road, Rickmansworth WD3 8YL Tel: 01923 710811 — BM 1995 Soton. SHO (Anaesth.) Roy. Free Hosp. Lond. Socs: MPS. Prev: SHO Anaesth. Roy. Free Hosp. Lond.; SHO Cas. Lister Hosp. Stevenage; SHO Geriat. Soton. Gen. Hosp.

SHARIH, Samina 12 Maxwell Road, Northwood HA6 2YF — MB BS 1991 Lond.

SHARKAWI

SHARKAWI, Eamon 23 Kenerne Drive, Barnet EN5 2NW — MB BS 1996 Lond.

SHARKEY, Amy 405 Victoria Road, Glasgow G42 8RW — MB ChB 1994 Glas.

SHARKEY, Annie Sonia The Surgery, High Street, Moffat DG10 9HL Tel: 01683 220062 Fax: 01683 220453; Pinewood Cottage, Chapelbrae, Moffat DG10 9SB — MB ChB 1989 Aberd.; MRCGP 1994; DRCOG 1993. GP Moffat. Prev: Trainee GP Dumfries & Galloway HB VTS.

SHARKEY, Anthony Gerald Vajraloka, Blaen-Ddol House, Treddol, Corwen LL21 0EN Tel: 01490 81 406; Edendork, Dungannon BT71 6LF Tel: 018687 40448 — MB BCh BAO 1982 Dub. Prev: SHO Cas. Off. Ormskirk Dist. & Gen. Hosp.

SHARKEY, Donald 27 Betony Close, Scunthorpe DN15 8PP — BM BS 1998 Nottm.; BM BS Nottm 1998.

SHARKEY, Dympna Elizabeth Old Corn Store, Hartenoke Lane, Hawkhurst, Cranbrook TN18 — LRCPI & LM, LRSCI & LM 1950; LRCPI & LM, LRCSI & LM 1950. (RCSI) Sch. Med. Off. Hastings Health Dist.

SHARKEY, James (retired) Elm Tree House, Wales Lane, Barton under Needwood, Burton-on-Trent DE13 8JF — MB BS Lond. 1942; BSc. (Physiol.) Lond. 1939; FRCP Lond. 1972, M 1944; MRCS Eng. LRCP Lond. 1942. Prev: Cons. Phys. S.E. Staffs. Health Dist.

SHARKEY, John James Mary Avoca Ward, Knockbracken, Healthcare Park, Saintfield Road, Belfast BT8 8BH Tel: 01232 756 5480; 6 Thompsons Grange, Hillsborough Road, Carryduff, Belfast BT8 8TG — MB BCh BAO 1989 Belf.; MRCPysch 1994; DRCOG 1992; DMH Belf. 1991. Specialist Regist. (Forens. Psychiat.) Knockbracken Healthcare Pk. Belf. Prev: SHO (Psychiat.) Shaftesbury Sq. Hosp. Belf. & Gransha Hosp. Lond.derry; SHO (Psychiat.) Dept. Psychother. Belf., Mater Hosp. Belf. & Muchamore Abbey Antrim.

SHARKEY, Joseph (retired) 89 Chase Side, Enfield EN2 6NL Tel: 020 8363 5765 — MD 1940 NUI; MB BCh BAO 1936. Prev: Cons. (Geriat.) Highlands Gen. Hosp. Lond.

SHARKEY, Patrick Joseph Carryduff Surgery, Hillsborough Road, Carryduff, Belfast BT8 8HR Tel: 028 9081 2211 Fax: 028 9081 4785 — MB BCh BAO 1984 Belf.; MRCP (UK) 1987; MRCGP 1990; DMH 1990; DRCOG 1989; DCH RCPSI 1989.

SHARLAND, Desmond Edward (retired) Cecille Cottage, Church Path, Woodside Lane, London N12 8RH Tel: 020 8445 1214 — MB BS Lond. 1953; BSc (Hons. Anat.) Lond. 1950, MD 1967; FRCP Lond. 1975, M 1960; MRCS Eng. LRCP Lond. 1953; DObst RCOG 1955. Lect. (Anat.) Univ. Coll. Lond. Prev: Cons. Phys. Whittington Hosp. Lond.

SHARLAND, Gurleen Kaur Department Fetal Cardiology, 15th Floor Guy's Tower, St Thomas St., London SE1 9RT Tel: 020 7407 3351 Fax: 020 7955 2637; 48 Palmerston Road, London SW14 7PZ — MD 1993 Lond.; BSc (Physiol.) 1979, MB BS 1982; FRCP 1997. Sen. Lect. & Hon. Cons. Fetal & Paediat. Cardiol. Guy's Hosp. Lond. Prev: Lect. (Perinat. Cardiol.) Guy's Hosp. Lond.

SHARLAND, Michael Roy Paediatric Infectious Diseases Unit, 5th Floor Lanesborough Wing, St Georges Hospital, Cranmer Terrace, London SW17 0RE Tel: 020 872532632 Fax: 020 8725 3262 Email: m.sharland@sghms.ac.uk; 48 Palmerston Road, London SW14 7PZ — MB BS 1982 Lond.; BSc (Physiol.) Lond. 1979, MD 1991; FRCPCH (UK) (Paediat.) 1986; DTM & H RCP Lond. 1994. Cons. Paediat. (Infec. Dis.) St. Geo. Hosp. Lond. Socs: Convenor, Brit. Paediatric Allergy, Immunity and Infec. Gp. Prev: Lect. (Paediat. Infec. Dis.) St. Geo. Hosp. Lond.

SHARLAND, Roy John 19 Deepdene Road, London SE5 8EG Tel: 020 7274 2290 — MB BS Lond. 1953, BDS 1946; FDS RCS Eng. 1951, LDS 1947. (King's Coll. Hosp.) Socs: BDA & Brit. Soc. Study Orthodont. Prev: Ho. Phys. Dulwich Hosp.; Ho. Surg. ENT Dept. King's Coll. Hosp.; Sen. Hosp. Dent. Off. Middlx. Hosp. Lond.

SHARMA, A K Westminster Medical Centre, Aldams Grove, Liverpool L4 3TT Tel: 0151 922 3510 Fax: 0151 902 6071.

SHARMA, Abhishek 2 Manor House, Crawford Village, Upholland, Skelmersdale WN8 9QZ — MB ChB 1998 Manch.; MB ChB Manch 1998.

SHARMA, Alka Central Health Clinic, 1 Mulberry Street, Sheffield S1 2PJ Tel: 0114 271 8153 Email: alkas@echsheff-tr-trent.nhs.uk; 31 Bingham Park Road, Greytones, Sheffield S11 7BD Tel: 0114 268 5639 Email: alka@edincastle-freeserve.ci.uk — MB ChB 1989 Glas.; OFFP 1998; MRCOG 1997. (Glasgow) Cons. Incommunity Gyn. & Reproductive Health Care. Socs: RCOG; FFP; BMS. Prev: Specialist Regist. (O & G) SE of Scott.; Spec. Regist. (O & G) SE of Scott.

SHARMA, Mr Alok, Specialist Registrar High Street Surgery, 77 High Street, Nantyffyllon, Maesteg CF34 0BT Tel: 01656 732217 Fax: 01656 730119 — MB BCh 1994 Wales; FRCS Ed. (Ordocryngology) 1999. Specialist Regist. Otolocryngology, E. Anglia Deanery; Specialist Regist. Otolocryngology Peterbrough Hosp.

SHARMA, Amita 31 Barton Road, London W14 9HB — MB BS 1991 Lond.

SHARMA, Amita 3 Patent House, 48 Morris Road, London E14 6NU — MB BS 1989 Lond.; MRCP (UK) 1992.

SHARMA, Anand 3 Parkwood Road, Liverpool L25 4RJ — MB ChB 1993 Manch.

SHARMA, Anant 10 Inverclyde Gardens, Chadwell Heath, Romford RM6 5SJ — MB 1987 Camb.; MB Camb.1987, BChir 1986.

SHARMA, Angela 49 Green Pastures, Heaton Mersey, Stockport SK4 3RB Tel: 0161 431 6171 — MB ChB 1996 Manch.; BSc (Hons.) 1993. (Manch.)

SHARMA, Mr Anil Soho Health Centre, Louise Road, Birmingham B21 0RY Tel: 0121 554 5151 Fax: 0121 515 2884; Richmond Park House, 1 Belgrove Close, Edgbaston, Birmingham B15 3RQ — MB BS 1980 Lond.; FRCS Ed. 1985; MRCS LRCP Lond. 1981; MRCGP 1986. (Charing Cross Hospital Medical School)

SHARMA, Anil Kumar Fazakerley Hospital, Lower Lane, Liverpool L9 7AL Tel: 0151 529 3695 — MB BS 1968 Punjab; FRCP Lond. 1992; MRCP (UK) 1976. (Amritsar Med. Coll.) Cons. Phys. Walton & Fazakerley Hosps. Liverp.; Hon. Clin. Lect. Univ. Liverp. 1980. Socs: Brit. Geriat. Soc. (Chairm. Mersey Br.). Prev: Sen. Regist. (Med.) Walton & Fazakerley Hosps.; Regist. Rotat. (Med.) Walton, Whiston & Roy. S.. Hosps. Liverp.; SHO (Med.) Whiston Hosp.

SHARMA, Anil Kumar 70 Evelyn Grove, Southall UB1 2BS — MB ChB 1987 Leic.; MRCOG 1996; DGM RCP Lond. 1990; MRNZCOG 1997. (Leicester) Specialist Regist. Roy. Gwent Hosp. Newport. Prev: Regist. (O & G) Waikato Hosp. Hamilton, NZ; Specialist Regist. Univ. Hosp. Wales, Cardiff.

SHARMA, Anjla 103 Friary Road, Birmingham B20 1BA — MB ChB 1990 Birm.; ChB Birm. 1990.

SHARMA, Annpoorna Department of Paediatrics, Central Middlesex Hospital, Acton Lane, London NW10 7NS Tel: 020 8451 8350 Fax: 020 8451 8369 Email: a.sharma@ic.ac.uk; 2 Ashbourne Square, Northwood HA6 3BQ Tel: 01923 820483 — MB BS 1980 Lond.; MSc (Epidemiol.) Lond. 1991; MRCP (UK) 1984; T(M) (Paed.) 1991; DCH RCP Lond. 1983. (Middlesex Hospital Medical School at UCL London) Cons. Paediat. Centr. Middlx. Hosp. Lond. & Pk.side Healthcare NHS Trust; Hon. Cons. Paediat. Roy. Postgrad. Med. Sch.; Hon. Clin. Sen. Lect. (Paediat.) Imperial Coll. Sch. of Med. at St. Mary's; Hon. Clin. Sen. Lect. (Epidemiol.) Imperial Coll. Sch. of Med. at St.Mary's. Socs: Roy. Soc. Med.; Fell. Roy. Coll. Paediat. & Child Health; Roy. Statistical Soc. Prev: SCMO Camden & Islington Community NHS Trust; Sen. Regist. & Hon. Lect. (Child Health) Roy. Free Hosp. & UCL Sch. Med. Lond.

SHARMA, Mr Anup Kumar Department of Surgery, St Georges Hospital, Blackshaw Road, London SW17 0QT Tel: 020 8672 1255 Fax: 020 8725 3466 — MB BS 1985 Lond.; MS Lond. 1994, Bsc (Hons.) 1982, MB BS 1985; FRCS (Gen.) 1997; FRCS Eng. 1990. (Middlesex Hospital Medical School) Cons. (Gen. Surg.) St. Geo.s Hosp. Lond. Socs: BASO and BAES. Prev: Sen. Regist. Cardiff Hosps.; Research Regist. Cardiff.; Regist. (Surg.) Birm. Hosp.

SHARMA, Anuradha 13 The Byway, Sutton SM2 5LE; 13 The Byway, Sutton SM2 5LE — MB BS 1998 Lond.; MB BS Lond 1998; BSc (Hons). (CXWMS) Socs: MDU; BMA.

SHARMA, Arun 24 Shelley Close, Abingdon OX14 1PP — MB ChB 1976 Manch.

SHARMA, Mr Arun Kumar c/o Renal Transplant Unit, The Royal Free Hospital, Pond St., London NW3 2QG — MB BS 1974 Agra; MS Agra 1977, BSc 1969, MB BS 1974; FRCS Ed. 1983; Dip. Urol. Lond 1986. (S.N. Med. Coll.) SHO Renal Transpl. Unit Roy. Free Hosp. Lond. Prev: Regist. (Urol.) All India Inst. Med. Scs. New Delhi; SHO (Surg./Urol.) Oldham Roy. Infirm.; SHO (Paediat. Surg.) Gt. Ormond St. Hosp. Lond.

SHARMA, Arun Kumar 13 Singleton Close, Elm Park, Hornchurch RM12 4LT — BM BCh 1988 Oxf.

SHARMA

SHARMA, Asha 20 Lechmere Avenue, Chigwell IG7 5ET — LRCP LRCS Ed. LRCPS Glas. 1987; MB BS Agra 1975; LRCS Ed. LRCPS Glas. 1987; MRCOG 1988.

SHARMA, Asha The Grove Surgery, Farthing Grove, Netherfield, Milton Keynes MK6 4NG Tel: 01908 668453 Fax: 01908 695064 — MB BS 1978 Delhi; MB BS 1978 Delhi.

SHARMA, Asha Omkar 19 Demontfort Road, Streatham, London SW16 1NF Tel: 020 8769 1017 — MB BS 1968 Bombay. Community Med. Off. Merton, Sutton & Wandsworth AHA.

SHARMA, Ashok Kumar St. Martins Medical Centre, 21 Eastcote Road, Ruislip HA4 8BE Tel: 01895 632410 Fax: 01895 635058; 101 Swakeleys Road, Ickenham, Uxbridge UB10 8DH Tel: 01895 635054 — MB BS 1975 Lond.; DA (UK) 1981. Socs: Med. Protec. Soc.

SHARMA, Ashutosh 123 Robin Hood Lane, Chatham ME5 9NL — MB BS 1992 Lond.; BSc (Hons.) Lond. 1989; MRCP (UK) 1995. (St. Thos. Hosp. Lond.)

SHARMA, Atma Dev (retired) Amatar House, Manor Road, Woodley, Stockport SK6 1RT Tel: 0161 494 6692 Fax: 0161 406 6752 — MB BS 1960 Lucknow; MRCP Glas. 1969; MRCP (UK) 1970; T(M) 1990; DCH RCP Lond. 1964. Indep. Cons. Cardiol. & Specialist Phys. Prev: Cons. Phys. (Gen. Med.) Dennevirke Hosp. NZ.

SHARMA, Awadh Kishore Tennyson Avenue Medical Centre, Saltergate, Chesterfield S40 4SN Tel: 01246 232339; Staddle Stones, Old Brampton, Chesterfield S42 7JG Fax: 01246 209097 — MD Patna 1967, MB BS 1963; MRCPI 1974; MRCP (UK) 1975; DCH RCPS Glas. 1970. Trainer GP Chesterfield. Socs: Roy. Coll. Phys.; Brit. Paediat. Assn. Prev: Sen. Regist. (Paediat. & Developm. Med.) N.ampton & Kettering Health Dists.; SHO (Paediat.) Roy. Liverp. Childr. Hosp.

SHARMA, Bal Krishna 1 Newheath Close, Wolverhampton WV11 1XX — MB BS 1971 Jiwaji.

SHARMA, Bhagat Ram Withybush Hospital, Fishguard Road, Haverfordwest SA61 2PZ — MB BCh 1997 Wales.

SHARMA, Mr Bhu Datt 2 Wisteria Lane, Carluke ML8 5TB Tel: 01555 70601 — MB BS 1960 Lucknow; BSc Agra 1954; MS Allahabad 1968; FRCS Ed. 1964. (King Geo. Med. Coll. Lucknow) Cons. Orthop. Surg. Law Hosp. Carluke.

SHARMA, Bhupinder 149 Firs Drive, Hounslow TW5 9TB — BM 1993 Soton.

SHARMA, Mr Chandra Maulishwar Prasad (retired) 33 Ilston Way, West Cross, Swansea SA3 5LG Tel: 01792 403383 Fax: 01792 403383 Email: csharm@globalnet.co.uk — MB BS 1958 Patna; MS Patna 1962, MB BS 1958; FRCS Eng. 1965. Vist. Cons. Gen. Surg. Indraprastha Apollo Hosps. Prev: Cons. Gen. Surg. Nevill Hall Hosp. Abergavenny.

SHARMA, Davanand Chandranauth Inverclyde Royal Hospital, Larkfield Road, Greenock PA16 0XN Tel: 01475 633777 — MB ChB 1991 Manch.; BSc (Med. Sci.) St. And. 1988; MRCP (UK) 1996. (Manch.) Staff Grade (Resp. Med.), Inverclyde Roy. Hosp., Greenock. Prev: Regist. (Respirat. Med.) Vict. Infirm. NHS Trust, Glasg.; SHO (Med.) HCI Internat. Clydebank 1996; Regist. (Resp. Med.) Vict. Infirm. NHS Trust, Glas. 1997.

SHARMA, Deepak 99 Barclay Road, Bearwood, Smethwick B67 5JY — MB ChB 1998 Leic.; MB ChB Leic 1998.

SHARMA, Devesh 12 Ravenswood Road, Strathaven ML10 6JB — MB ChB 1984 Glas.; BSc (Hons. Biochem.) St. And. 1981. Lect. Anat. Glas. Univ. Prev: Jun. Ho. Off. Glas. Roy. Infirm.

SHARMA, Geeta Tennyson Avenue Medical Centre, 1 Tennyson Avenue, Chesterfield S40 4SN Tel: 01246 232339 Fax: 01246 209097; Staddle Stones, Old Brampton, Chesterfield S42 7JG — MB BS 1964 Agra; MRCOG 1974, DObst 1969; Cert. JCC Lond. 1980. (S.N. Med. Coll.) Prev: Med. Asst. (O & G) Nether Edge Hosp. Sheff.

SHARMA, Gopal Krishan Fosse Medical Centre, 344 Fosse Road North, Leicester LE3 5RR Tel: 0116 253 8988 Fax: 0116 242 5178; Ictara, 21 Warren Lane, LFE, Leicester LE3 3LW Tel: 0116 291 4099 Fax: 0116 291 4099 — MB ChB 1987 Leic.; BMedSci. Leic. 1985; Cert. Family Plann. JCC 1991. (Leicester) GP Princip.; Hosp. Pract. (Rheum.) Leicester; Sess. Med. Off. (Occupat. Health) Leicester Roy. Infirm.; Med. Off. Alliance & Leicester; Med. Off. Nestle UK Ltd.

SHARMA, Harbinder Kumar 2 Glenmore Road, Leicester LE4 9GE — BM BS 1991 Nottm.

SHARMA, Indra Datt Treevale, 60 View Road, Rainhill, Prescot L35 0LS Tel: 0151 493 1741 — MB BS 1967 Agra. (Sarojini Naidu Med. Coll.) Socs: Med. Protec. Soc. Prev: Trainee GP Liverp. VTS; SHO (Med.) Clwyd HA.

SHARMA, Jagdish Chander 87 Barrowby Road, Grantham NG31 8AB Tel: 01476 65646 — MB BS 1973 Punjab; MB BS Punjabi 1973; MRCP (UK) 1981. (Govt. Med. Coll. Patiala) Cons. Phys. Geriat. Med. Hawtonville Hosp. Newark; Sen. Regist. & Hon. Lect. (Geriat. Med.) Roy. Vict. Hosp. Dundee; Regist. (Gen. Med.) Harrogate Gen. & Dist. Hosps. Socs: Brit. Geriat. Soc. Prev: Regist. (Geriat. Med.) Centr. Middlx. Hosp. Lond.

SHARMA, Kailash Chandra 70 The Crescent, Slough SL1 2LG Tel: 01753 29623 — MD 1982 Delhi; MB BS 1978; MRCP (UK) 1985; MRCPI 1985.

SHARMA, Kalpana 1 Crosslands Avenue, Southall UB2 5QY Tel: 020 8574 1906 — MB BS 1982 Lond.; BSc Lond. 1979, MB BS 1982; MRCGP 1987; DCH RCP Lond. 1985; DRCOG 1986. (King's Coll. Hosp.) GP S.all; Course Organiser W. Middlx. Hosp. GPVTS. Prev: Princip. GP N.olt.

SHARMA, Kalpana RHR Medical Centre, Calverton Drive, Strelley, Nottingham NG8 6QN Tel: 0115 975 3666 Fax: 0115 975 3888; Kia-Mena, Bilborough Road, Wollaton, Nottingham NG8 4DR — MB BS 1970 Utkal; MRCOG 1978; DObst RCOG 1976. (S.C.B. Med. Coll. Cuttack) Mem. LMC. Socs: M-C Soc.; (Exec.) Overseas Doctors Assn. Prev: Clin. Asst. (O & G) Univ. Hosp. Nottm.; Clin. Med. Off. (Family Plann.) Nottm. Health Dist. (T); SHO (Anaesth.) Gen. Hosp. Nottm. & Nottm. City Hosp.

SHARMA, Kanika Flat 1, 28 Valentines Road, Ilford IG1 4SA; 1 Vaughan Gargeh, Ilford IG1 3PA — MB ChB 1998 Aberd.; MB ChB Aberd 1998. GP VTS AT Chase Farm Hosp. Enfield Middlx. Socs: MDU; AMS (Aberd. Med. Soc.). Prev: PRHO in Surg. at Wrexham Maelor Gen. Hosp.; PRHO in Med. @ Aberd. Roy. Infirm.

SHARMA, Kiran 73 Standard Road, Bexleyheath DA6 8DR Tel: 020 8306 7063 — MB BS 1993 Lond. (United Med. & Dent. Schs. Guy's & St. Thos. Hosps.)

SHARMA, Kiran Kumari St. Barnabus Hospice, Columbia Drive, Worthing BN13 2QF Tel: 01903 264222 — MB BS 1988 Lond.; BSc Psych. 1985; MRCGP 1994; DRCOG 1993. (The Royal Lond. Hosp.) Cons. (Pall. Med.) St. Barnabas Hospice; Hon. Cons. (Palliat. Med.) Worthing & S.lands Hosp. Trusts. Socs: Assn. of Palliat. Med. Prev: Trainee GP Maidstone Gen. Hosp. Kent VTS; SHO (A & E) S.end Dist. Gen. Hosp.; Spr Palliat. Med.,S. Thames Rotat.

SHARMA, Krishan Kant 26 Coates Hill Road, Bromley BR1 2BJ — MB BS 1951 Panjab; MB BS Panjab (India) 1951.

SHARMA, Kwaman Khydhir Yousif 61 Auckland Avenue, Hull HU6 7SH — MB ChB 1978 Mosul; MRCOG 1991.

SHARMA, Mr Madan Mohan 50 Menzieshill Road, Dundee DD2 1PU Tel: 01382 642612 — MB ChB St. And. 1968; FRCS Ed. 1973. (St. And.) Cons. Dept. Orthop. & Traum. Surg. Ninewells Hosp. Dundee; Hon. Sec. Lect. Dept. of Orthop. & Trauma Surg., Univ. of Dundee.

SHARMA, Madan Mohan Pendlebury Health Centre, Nelson Fold Medical Centre, 659 Bolton Road, Pendlebury, Manchester M27 8HP Tel: 0161 950 4545 Fax: 0161 950 4546; 9 Thornway, Worsley, Manchester M28 1YS Tel: 0161 799 7115 — MB BS 1972 Calcutta; BSc (Hons.) India 1965. (NRS Medical College Calcutta, India) GP; Clin. Asst. (Psychiat.) N. Manch. Gen. Hosp. Prev: SHO (Psychiat. & Gen. & Geriat. Med.) St. Lukes Hosp. Middlesbrough & S. Shields Gen. Hosp.

SHARMA, Malini Anuradha 23 Wedgwood Way, London SE19 3ES Tel: 020 8771 9921 — MB BS 1994 Lond.; BSc (Hons.) Biochem.) 1991; MRCOG 1998. (UMDS London) SHO (O & G) St. Geo.'s Hosp. Lond. Socs: MDU; BMA. Prev: SHO (O & G) St Peter's Chertsey; SHO (Geriat.) St. Geo.'s Hosp. Lond.; SHO (A & E) Guy's Lond.

SHARMA, Manju 1 The Paddock, Blackburn BB2 7QY — MB BS 1973 Indore.

SHARMA, Manjula Occupational Health, 1 Damson Way, Orchard Hill, Fountain Drive, Carshalton SM5 4NR Tel: 020 8770 8308 Fax: 020 8770 8370; 13 The Byway, Sutton SM2 5LE Tel: 020 8661 1689 — MB BS 1968 Lucknow; AFOM RCP Lond. 1993; MFFP 1993. (GSVM Med. Coll. Kanpur, India) SCMO & Regist. (Occupat. Health Serv.) Merton & Sutton Community NHS Trust; Instruc. Doctor Family Plann. Sutton & Merton. Socs: Soc. Occupat. Med.;

SHARMA

Assn. Nat. Health Serv. Occupat. Health Phys.; Assn. Local Auth. Med. Off. Prev: Hon. Cons. Occupat. Med. Roy. Marsden Hosp. Lond. & Surrey; Clin. Med. Off. (Child Health) Merton & Sutton HA; GP CIMAS Ndola, Zambia.

*SHARMA, Manu Shankar 4 Parkland Close, Mansfield NG18 4PR — MB ChB 1998 Birm.

*SHARMA, Meenakshi Walsgrave Hospital, Clifford Bridge, Coventry CV2 2DX Tel: 02476 602020 Email: bhewani1@hotmail.com; 96 Coombe Road, Oadby, Leicester LE2 5TW Tel: 0116 271 8822 Email: bhewani1@hotmail.com — MB ChB 2000 University of Leicester; MB ChB 2000 Leicester.

SHARMA, Mridula 128 Sulgrave Road, London W6 7PU — MB BS 1995 Lond.; BSc Lond. 1989.

SHARMA, Narendra Kumar Compton Acres Medical Centre, West Bridgford, Nottingham NG2 7PA Tel: 0115 984 6767 Fax: 0115 945 5888; 8 Leigh Close, West Bridgford, Nottingham NG2 7TN Tel: 0115 982 2282 Fax: 0115 914 9383 — MB BS 1974 Punjab. (Govt. Medical College, Punjab) p/t GP Clin. Asst. Psychiat. of Old Age.

SHARMA, Mr Naresh Kumar Altnagelvin Hospital, Londonderry BT47 2SB — MB BS 1967 Punjab; PhD Belf. 1984; MB BS Punjabi 1967; FRCS Ed. 1979; DO RCPSI 1976. (Govt. Med. Coll. Patiala) Cons. Ophth. Surg. Alinagelvin Hosp. Lond.derry.

SHARMA, Mr Narinder Kumar Milesgarth, Cawcliffe Road, Brighouse HD6 2HP — MB BS 1974 Punjab; MB BS Punjabi 1974; FRCS Ed. 1981. (Govt. Med. Coll. Patiala) Assoc. Specialist (Gen. Surg.) Halifax Roy. Infirm.

SHARMA, Narinder Kumar 42 Charter Avenue, Newbury Park, Ilford 1G2 7AB — MB BS 1994 Lond.; DRCOG 1997; MRCGP (1998).

*SHARMA, Naveen Kumar 2 Honeybourne Way, Willenhall WV13 1HN — MB ChB 1995 Birm.

SHARMA, Neel-Kumari Fosse Medical Centre, 344 Fosse Road North, Leicester LE3 5RR Tel: 0116 253 8988 Fax: 0116 242 5178 — MB ChB 1991 Leic.

SHARMA, Neha 4 Parkland Close, Berry Hill, Mansfield NG18 4PR — MB ChB 1998 Birm.; ChB Birm. 1998.

SHARMA, Nikuil 220 Minster Court, Liverpool L7 3QH — MB ChB 1998 Liverp.; MB ChB Liverp 1998.

SHARMA, Nirmal Kumar 10 Weld Road, Southport PR8 2AZ Tel: 01704 68029 — MB BS 1967 Delhi; MRCGP 1978; DTM & H 1977; DRCOG 1976.

SHARMA, Nitika 20 Norton Road, Tunbridge Wells TN4 0HE — MB BS 1994 Lond. Ho. Off. (Urol.) Mayday Hosp. Croydon. Prev: Ho. Off. (Gen. Surg.) Mayday Hosp.

SHARMA, Om Prakash Hyson Green Health Centre, Gregory Boulevard, Hyson Green, Nottingham NG7 — MB BS 1969 Vikram; DOrth Kanpur 1971. (Gandhi Med. Coll. Bhopal) GP Nottm.

SHARMA, Omkar Parmanand Medical Centre, 13/15 Barmouth Road, London SW18 Tel: 020 8874 4984; 19 Demontfort Road, Streatham, London SW16 1NF Tel: 020 8769 1017 — MB BS 1969 Bombay.

SHARMA, P Ilford Avenue, 24 Ilford Avenue, Crosby, Liverpool L23 7YF Tel: 0151 931 3181.

SHARMA, Pankaj 38 Tavistock Avenue, Greenford UB6 8AJ Tel: 020 8991 2032 Email: ps100@hgmp.mrc.ac.uk — MB BS 1988 Lond.; PhD Cantab. 1998; MRCP (UK) 1991; DHMSA 1989. (Univ. Lond. & Lond. Hosp.) BHF Clinician Scientist & Fulbright Schol., Harv. Med. Sch. Boston, USA; Clin. Regist. (Pharmacol.) Univ. of Camb. Prev: Regist. Nat. Hosp. for Neurol. & Neurosurg. Qu. Sq. Lond.; SHO Rotat. (Med.) Addenbrooke's Hosp. Camb.; Ho. Surg. Prof. Surg. Unit Lond. Hosp.

SHARMA, Paul 105 Ardleigh Green Road, Hornchurch RM11 2LE — MB BS 1991 Lond.

SHARMA, Peeyush c/o Liver Unit, Transplantation Centre, Freeman Hospital, High Heaton, Newcastle upon Tyne NE7 7DN — MB BS 1981 Jammu.

SHARMA, Poonam Redhill Famils Practice, 11 Redhill, Chislehurst BR7 6DB Tel: 09756827160 — MB ChB 1987 Manch.; BSc (Med. Sci.) St. And. 1984; Cert. Prescribed Equiv. Exp. JCPTGP 1991; Cert. Family Plann. JCC 1990; MFHom 1996. (St. And. & Manch.) Roy. Lond. Homoeop. Hosp. Lond. (Clin. Asst.); Gen. Pract.

SHARMA, Prabani Cliftonville Road Surgery, 61 Cliftonville Road, Belfast BT14 6JN Tel: 028 9074 7361 — MB BS 1971 Gauhati. (Gauhati)

SHARMA, Pradeep 45 Wanstead Place, Wanstead, London E11 2SW Fax: 020 8532 9124 — MB BS 1979 Lond.; BSc (Hons.) (Biochem.) Lond. 1976; MRCS Eng. LRCP Lond. 1979; DRCOG 1985. (Char. Cross)

SHARMA, Praveen TR, 30 Falkland Street, Glasgow G12 9QY — MB ChB 1990 Glas.

SHARMA, Mr Prem Dayal 4 Barlow Fold Road, Romily, Stockport SK6 4LH Tel: 0161 494 1999 — MB BS 1970 Jammu & Kashmir; MS (ENT) Delhi 1975; FRCS Eng. 1979; DLO Eng. 1976. (Govt. Med. Coll. Srinagar) Cons. ENT Surg. Tameside & Glossop HA. Prev: Sen. Regist. (ENT) St. Bart. Hosp. Lond.; Sen. Regist. (ENT) N. Riding Infirm. Middlesbrough.

SHARMA, Priya 14 Bradley Road, Haslington, Crewe CW1 1PN; Flat 2, 2A Dunkraven Road, West Kirby, Wirral L48 4DS — MB ChB 1996 Liverp. VTS Trainee, Wirral NHS Trust.

SHARMA, Mr Raj Kumar 13 Ryecroft Close, Wakefield WF1 2LW — LMSSA 1966 Lond.; MCh Orth Liverp. 1972; FRCS Ed. 1968; MRCS Eng. LRCP Lond. 1975.

SHARMA, Raj Pal Chatham Street Surgery, 121 Chatham Street, Reading RG1 7JE Tel: 0118 950 5121 Fax: 0118 959 0545; 21 Squirrells Way, Earley, Reading RG6 5QT Tel: 0118 987 3650 — MB BS 1974 Rajasthan; DCH RCPSI 1977. (S.P. Med. Coll. Bikaner)

SHARMA, Rajan 3 Winifred Road, Dartford DA1 3BL — MB BS 1993 Lond.

SHARMA, Rajeev 3 Eden Road, Oadby, Leicester LE2 4JP — MB BS 1982 Indore.

SHARMA, Rajendra Chandrakant 87 North Road, Parkstone, Poole BH14 0LT Tel: 01425 461740 Fax: 01428 727875 Email: 16011.2545@compuserve.com — MB BCh BAO 1984 NUI; LRCPI & LM, LRCSI & LM 1984; MFHom 1994. (Royal College of Surgeons Dublin) Med. Dir. 101 Gp. Ltd.; Med. Dir. Hale Clinic, Lond. Socs: Brit. Soc. Nutrit. Med.; Scientif. & Med. Network. Prev: Sen. Lect. Hahnemann Coll. Homeop.

SHARMA, Rajendra Prasad The Surgery, 20 North Sea Lane, Humberston, Grimsby DN36 4UZ Tel: 01472 211116 — MB BS 1965 Patna.

SHARMA, Rajiv Charing Cross Hospital, Fulham Palace Road, London W6 8RF; 49 Ivanhoe Road, Hounslow TW4 7JH Tel: 020 8569 4862 — MB ChB 1984 Aberd.; MRCPsych. 1989. Sen. Regist. (Psychiat.) Char. Cross Hosp. Lond.

SHARMA, Rajiv Sea Road Surgery, 39-41 Sea Road, Bexhill-on-Sea TN40 1JJ Tel: 01424 211616 Fax: 01424 733950; 72 Cowdray Park Road, Bexhill-on-Sea TN39 4EZ Tel: 01424 846059 Fax: 01424 840335 Email: dr-raj-sharma@msn.com — MB BS 1984 Lond.

SHARMA, Rakesh 41 Eyston Drive, Weybridge KT13 0XD — MB ChB 1989 Glas.

SHARMA, Ram Charan, TD 7 Signals Regiment Medical Centre, Javelin Barracks BFPO 35 Tel: 02432 893309 Fax: 02432 893309 Email: lomashram@hotmail.com; 8 Davidson Road, Croydon CR0 6DA Tel: 020 8656 4213 Email: lomashram@hotmail.com — MB BS 1972 Punjab; MB BS Punjabi 1972; DFFP 1993; T(GP) 1991. (Govt. Med. Coll. Patiala, India) Sen. Med. Off. CMP MoD BAOR BFPO 35; Div.al Surg. St. John's Ambul. (Germany Div.). Socs: BMA. Prev: GP Bracknell; SHO (O & G) Fairfield Gen. Hosp. Bury; SHO (A & E) Crawley Hosp.

SHARMA, Ramesh Chandra 23 Pages Hill, Muswell Hill, London N10 1PX Tel: 020 8883 2310 — MB BS 1967 Bangalor; MB BS Bangalore 1967; MRCS Eng. LRCP Lond. 1981. (Bangalore Med. Coll.) Regist. (Orthop.) Manor Ho. Hosp. Lond.

SHARMA, Ranjana Leicester Royal Infirmary NHS Trust, Infirmary Square, Leicester LE1 5WW Tel: 01533 541414; 12 Handley Street, Leicester LE2 8RA Tel: 0116 291 2383 — MB BS 1977 Jiwaji; MFFP 1994; MRCOG 1992. (GP Med. Coll. Gawalior, India) Staff Grade (O & G) Leicester Roy. Infirm. Socs: Med. Defence Union; BMA. Prev: Regist. (O & G) Co. Hosp. Hereford; Acting Cons. & Specialist O & G, Saudi Arabia.

SHARMA, Rashmi 14 Laurel Avenue, Twickenham TW1 4JA — MB ChB 1992 Leeds; MRCP (UK) 1995.

SHARMA, Rewati Raman Department of Neurosurgery, Khoula Hospital, Mina Al Fahal, Muscat, Oman; 25 Clos Crucywel, Park

Gwern Fadog, Cwmrhydyceirw, Morriston, Swansea SA6 6RD — MB BS 1978 Bombay; MS (Neurosurg.) Bombay 1986. Regist. (Neurosurg.) Khoula Hosp. Muscat, Oman & Morriston Hosp. Swansea. Prev: Regist. (Neurosurg.) Roy. Preston Hosp.; Specialist (Neurosurg.) Khoula Hosp. Muscat, Oman; Lect. (Neurosurg.) Kem Hosp. Bombay, India.

SHARMA, Ricky Anupam 25 Etive Drive, Airdrie ML6 9QL; 230 Queens Road, Leicester LE2 3FT — MB BChir 1994 Camb.; MA Camb. 1996; MRCP 1998. (Univ. Camb.) Clin. Res. Fell. Univ. Dept. of Oncol. Leic. Roy. Infirm. Socs: RCP; Fell. Roy. Soc of Med.; Brit. Assn. of Cancer Res. Prev: SHO (Gen. Med.) Leicester Roy. Infirm.; Ho. Off. (Gen. Surg.) Glas. Roy. Infirm.; Ho. Off. (Gen. Med.) Addenbrooke's Hosp. Camb.

SHARMA, Rita 21 Chartfield Road, Reigate RH2 7JZ — MB BS 1993 Lond.

SHARMA, S S Manor Top Medical Centre, Rosehearty, Ridgeway Road, Sheffield S12 2SS Tel: 0114 239 8324.

SHARMA, Sangeeta 74 Castlefields, Bournmoor, Houghton-le-Spring DH4 6HJ — MB ChB 1996 Manch. (Manchester) SHO (Anaesth.) Blackpool Vict. NHS Trust. Socs: Exec. Comm. Mem. Nepalese Doctors Assoc.

SHARMA, Sanjay 44 Minster Walk, London N8 7JS — MB ChB 1989 Leeds.

SHARMA, Sanjay Priory Fields, Nursey Road, Huntingdon PE18 6RJ Tel: 01480 52361 Fax: 01480 434640; 38 West End, Brampton, Huntingdon PE28 4SD — MB BS 1986 Lond. (St. George's Hospital London)

SHARMA, Sanjiv 46 Maswell Park Road, Hounslow TW3 2DW — MB BS 1996 Lond.; BSc Lond. 1993. (King's College London) SHO (Paediat.) Kingston Hosp. Kingston-upon-Thames.

SHARMA, Mr Santosh Kumar c/o Dr R. Sharma, Kemnal Road, Chislehurst BR7 6LT — MB BS 1962 Panjab, India; FRCS (Ophth.) Ed. 1973. Cons. Ophth. Wakefield AHA. Prev: Regist. (Ophth.) St. Paul's Eye Hosp. Liverp.; Regist. Ophth. Inst. Glas.; Sen. Regist. Wolverhampton & Midl. Cos. Eye Infirm.

SHARMA, Sapna Devi 38 Tavistock Avenue, Greenford UB6 8AJ Tel: 020 8991 2032 Email: sapnasharma@email.com — MB ChB 1992 Aberd.; DRCOG 1995; MRCGP 1998; DFFP 1996. Res. Fell. (Genetics) Harv. Med. Sch. Boston, USA. Prev: GP Regist. VTS Worthing Scheme; Ho. Off. (Med./ Renal Prof. Med.) Aberd. Roy. Infirm.

SHARMA, Saroj Bala 22 Lime Crescent, Marriott Grove, Sandal, Wakefield WF2 6RY Tel: 01924 252733 — MB BS 1972 Punjab; MB BS Punjabi 1972. (Govt. Med. Coll. Patiala) SCMO Pontefract HA.

SHARMA, Sarojini Westfield Medical Centre, 2 St Martin's Terrace, Chapeltown Road, Leeds LS7 4JB Tel: 0113 295 4750 Fax: 0113 295 4755 — MB BS 1967 Osmania. (Osmania) GP Leeds.

SHARMA, Satya Kishore 46 Pentwyn, Radyr, Cardiff CF15 8RE — MB BS 1963 Vikram; DOMS Indore 1965; DO Eng. 1970. (M.G.M. Med. Coll. Indore) Clin. Asst. (Ophth.) Univ. Hosp. Wales Cardiff. Prev: Regist. (Ophth.) Gen. Hosp. S.end-on-Sea; Regist. (Ophth.) Singleton Hosp. Swansea.

SHARMA, Satya Vrat Bilston Health Centre, Prouds Lane, Bilston WV14 6PW Tel: 01902 405200 — MB BS 1973 Punjab.

SHARMA, Satyapaul The Surgery, 321 The Drive, Ilford IG1 3PW Tel: 020 8554 3014 Fax: 020 8518 0863 — MB BS 1960 Rajasthan; DIH Eng. 1974. (S.M.S. Med. Coll. Jaipur) Prev: Lect. Dept. Physiol. Maulana Azad Med. Coll. New Delhi, India; Chief Med. Off. Kakira Hosp. Uganda.

SHARMA, Seema The Surgery, 6 Queens Walk, Ealing, London W5 1TP Tel: 020 8997 3041 Fax: 020 8566 9100 — MB BS 1988 Bangalore; MRCP (UK) 1994.

SHARMA, Sheel 35 Windsor House, Whiston Hospital, Prescot L35 5DR — MB BS 1985 Indore.

SHARMA, Shreekant 16 Nicholson Webb Close, Danescourt, Llandaf, Cardiff CF5 2RL Tel: 029 2055 1378 — MB BS 1983 Punjab; MRCPsych 1982.

SHARMA, Sobhna Room 4, Flat 1, Oklea House, Darlington Memorial Hospital, Hollyhurst Road, Darlington DL3 6HX — MB ChB 1992 Liverp.

SHARMA, Soorya Kant 24 Farmway, Leicester LE3 2XA — LRCP LRCS 1983 Ed.; MB BS Panjab 1979; LRCP LRCS Ed. LRCPS Glas. 1983.

SHARMA, Srilakshmi Missula 55 Belsize Road, Harrow HA3 6JL — MB ChB 1998 Bristol.

SHARMA, Subhash Chander c/o Drive Harshad Parikh, 9 Brookwood Close, Westbury Park, Clayton, Newcastle ST5 4HU — M.Phil. Leics. 1978, MB ChB 1982; MRCGP 1987; DCH RCP Lond. 1985; DRCOG 1984. GP Evington.

SHARMA, Sudeep, Maj. RAMC Medical & Dental Centre, Bulford Barracks, Salisbury SP4 9AD — MB BS 1984 Lond.; BSc (Hons. Physiol.) Lond. 1979; MRCGP 1990; DFFP 1993; DRCOG 1992. Sen. Med. Off. Lisburn. Prev: Med. Off. IFRW Hong Kong & Munster.

SHARMA, Sunil 70 Western Road, Crookes, Sheffield S10 1LA — MB ChB 1995 Dundee.

SHARMA, Mr Sunil Dutt Hollybrean, Main St., Tinwell, Stamford PE9 3UD — MB BS 1983 Agra; FRCS Eng. 1990; FRCS Ed. 1990. Regist. Rotat. (Urol.) Norf. & Norwich Hosp.

SHARMA, Sunil Dutt 3 Hemingford Drive, Luton LU2 7BA — MB BS 1998 Lond.; MB BS Lond 1998.

SHARMA, Suraj Prakash Stanley Medical Centre, 60 Stanley Road, Kirkdale, Liverpool L5 2QA Tel: 0151 207 1076 — MB BS 1968 Allahabad.

SHARMA, Surendra Kumar David Medical Centre, 274 Barlow Moor Road, Chorlton, Manchester M21 2HA Tel: 0161 881 1681 Fax: 0161 860 7071; 49 Green Pastures, Heaton Mersey, Stockport SK4 3RB Tel: 0161 431 6171 — MBBS 1969 Rajasthan; BSc Lucknow 1962. Prev: Clin. Asst. (A & E) Altrincham Gen. Hosp. Chesh.; Clin. Asst. (Plastic Surg.) Withington Hosp. Manch.

***SHARMA, Sushma Pramod** 67 Frobisher Road, Coventry CV3 6LZ — LRCP 1987 Lond.; MD (Obst. & Gyn.) Nagpur 1982, MB BS 1978; MRCS Eng.

SHARMA, Sushil Roy Health Centre, Lydney GL15 5NQ Tel: 01594 842167 Fax: 01594 845550; Acre House, Pillowell, Lydney GL15 4QA Email: roysharma@altavista.net — MB BCh 1978 Wales; MA Camb. 1979.

SHARMA, Mrs Sushma 12 Ravenswood Road, Strathaven ML10 6JB — MB BS 1955 Punjab; MB BS Punjab (India) 1955; DA Eng. 1963.

SHARMA, Tina 49 Green Pastures, Stockport SK4 3RB — MB ChB 1997 Manch.

SHARMA, Tonmoy Department Psychological Medicine, Institute of Psychiatry , De Crespigny Park, Denmark Hill, London SE5 8AF Tel: 020 7919 3342 Fax: 020 7701 9044; Flat 90, 340 The Highway, London E1W 3ET Tel: 020 8812 2564 — MB BS 1986 Dibrugarh; MSc Lond. 1994; MRCPsych 1991. Sen. Lect. (Psychol. Med.) Inst. Psychiat. Lond.; Cons. Psychiat. Lond. Socs: BMA; Brit. Assn. Psychopharmacol.; Brit. Neuropsychiat. Assn. Prev: Clin. Lect. (Psychiat.) Inst. Psychiat. Lond.; Sen. Regist. (Research Psychiat.) King's Coll. Sch. Med. & Dent. Lond.; Regist. (Psychiat.) Univ. Coll. Hosp. Lond.

SHARMA, Mr Umesh Chandra 12 Ravenswood Road, Strathaven ML10 6JB Tel: 01355 0827 — MB BS 1955 Nagpur; FRCS Ed. 1967. (Med. Sch. Nagpur) Cons. Orthop. Surg. StoneHo. Hosp.

SHARMA, Ushakumari Farnham Surgery, 279 Farnham Road, Slough SL2 1HA Tel: 01753 520917 Fax: 01753 550680; Squirrel Corner, Village Road, Dorney, Windsor SL4 6QW Tel: 01628 660028 — MB BS 1984 Lond. Prev: Trainee GP Carshalton VTS; Ho. Surg. St. Geo. Hosp. Lond.; Ho. Phys. King's Coll. Hosp. Lond.

SHARMA, Veena Treevale, 60 View Road, Rainhill, Prescot L35 0LS Tel: 0151 493 1741 — MB BS 1969 Agra; DPM RCPSI 1987. (Sarojini Naidu Med. Coll. Agra) Assoc. Specialist Psychiat. Merseyside. Prev: SHO & Regist. (Psychiat.) Rainhill Hosp. Liverp.

SHARMA, Venita Royal Victoria Infirmary, Newcastle upon Tyne NE1 4LP — MB ChB 1988 Glas.; MRCP (UK) 1993; MRCGP 1992. Regist. (Paediat.) Roy. Vict. Infirm.

SHARMA, Vijay Hoylake Road Surgery, 314 Hoylake Road, Wirral CH46 6DE Tel: 0151 677 2425 Fax: 0151 604 0482; 66 Farndon Way, Oxton, Birkenhead — MB BS 1972 Saurashtra; DRCOG 1978. (M.P. Shah Med. Coll. Jamnagar)

SHARMA, Vijay Narain 11 Fernbank, Chorley PR6 7BH Tel: 01257 274220 — BSc Aligarh 1945; MB BS Lucknow 1951; MRCPsych 1972; DPM Eng. 1970; TDD Wales 1957. (G.M. Med. Coll. Lucknow) Cons. Psychiat. Whittingham Hosp. Preston. Prev: Dir. Nat. Tuberc. Servs. Min. of Health Accra, Ghana.

SHARMA

SHARMA, Vijayalaxmi 109 Dormers Wells Lane, Southall UB1 3JA Tel: 020 8574 8614 — MB BS 1977 Bhopal; MRCPsych 1989.

SHARMA, Vikas 89 Little Green Lane, Chertsey KT16 9PS — MB BS 1996 Lond.

SHARMA, Vinod Kumar 373 Wanstead Park Road, Ilford IG1 3TT — MB BS 1971 Delhi.

SHARMA, Vinod Kumar Omparkash 24 Kingcup Close, Leicester Forest Bar, Leicester LE3 3JU — MB BS 1982 Poona; MRCPsych 1995.

SHARMA, Virendra Kilsyth Medical Partnership, Kilsyth Health Centre, Burngreen Park, Kilsyth, Glasgow G65 0HU Tel: 01236 822081 Fax: 01236 826231 — MB BS 1966 Punjab; MB BS Punjabi Univ. 1966. (Govt. Med. Coll. Patiala) Socs: BMA.

SHARMA, Vishwesh Chandra 70 Bank Street, Irvine KA12 0LP — MB BS 1970 Rajasthan.

SHARMA, Mr Yogdutt 14 Ash Street, Bacup OL13 8AJ — MB BS 1981 West Indies; FRCS Glas. 1994.

SHARMA, Yogendra Dutt Dulmer Drive Surgery, Fulmer Drive, Offerton, Stockport SK2 5JL Tel: 0161 483 3363 — MB BS 1972 Delhi.

SHARMA KAVI, Kavindra Nath Alderman Jack Cohen Health Centre, Springwell Road, Sunderland SR3 4HG Tel: 0191 528 2727 Fax: 0191 528 3262; The Stables, Tunstall Lodge Farm, Burdon Lane, Sunderland SR3 2QB — MB BS 1981 Newc.; Dip in Palliative Medicine (Cardiff) 2000; BMedSc (Hons.) Newc. 1980; MRCGP 1985; DCCH RCP Ed. 1985; DRCOG 1985. (Newc.) GP Sunderland; Trainer (Gen. Pract.) Sunderland; Examr. RCGP; Vice Chairm. Sunder LMC; McMillan Facilitator in Cancer for Sunderland. Prev: Co-Chairm. Sunderland Med. Audit Advis. Gp.

SHARMACHARJA, Gopa 20 Sparken Close, Crabtree Park, Worksop S80 1BN — MB BS 1973 Dhaka; MB BS Dhaka, Bangladesh 1973.

SHARMACHARJA, N R Larwood Health Centre, 56 Larwood, Worksop S81 0HH Tel: 01909 500233 Fax: 01909 479722 — MB BS 1967 Dacca; MB BS 1967 Dacca.

SHARMAN, Andrew 21 Herbert Road, Kesgrave, Ipswich IP5 2XX; 21 Herbert Road, Kesgrave, Ipswich IP5 2XX — MB BS 1997 Lond.; BSc (Hons). (Univ. Coll.) Leic. Rotat. In Med. Prev: Med. Norwich; Surg. Roy. Free, Lond.; A&E Leeds.

SHARMAN, Gail 44 Hillcrest Avenue, Edgware HA8 8PA — MB BS 1996 Lond.

SHARMAN, Julie 72 Lawford Road, London N1 5BL Tel: 020 7254 7922 Email: julie.sharman@lineone.net — MB BS 1993 Lond.; MSc Lond. Sch. Economics 1979; DRCOG Oct 1997; DCH 1998. (St. Georges Tooting, Lond.) GP Reg. Prev: SHO (O & G) N. Middlx. Hosp. Lond.; SHO (Med.) OldCh. Hosp. Romford.; SHO (Paediat.) N. Middx. Hosp. Lond.

SHARMAN, Michael Anthony 37 Downs View Road, Seaford BN25 4PU — MB ChB 1996 Manch.

SHARMAN, Michael John Hove Medical Centre, West Way, Hove BN3 8LD Tel: 01273 430088 Fax: 01273 430172 — MB BS 1963 Lond.; MRCS Eng. LRCP Lond. 1963; DObst RCOG 1965. (Guy's)

SHARMAN, Robin Andrew Lockwood Surgery, 3 Meltham Road, Lockwood, Huddersfield HD1 3XH Tel: 01484 421580 Fax: 01484 480100; 24 Primrose Lane, Kirkburton, Huddersfield HD8 0QY — MB ChB 1987 Sheff.

SHARMAN, Sarah Louise 17 Foxcombe Road, Bath BA1 3ED — BM BCh 1993 Oxf.

SHARMAN, Vivian Laurence 11 Park Way, London NW11 0EX Tel: 020 8458 5154 Fax: 020 8458 5154 Email: famsharman@publiconline.co.uk — MB BChir 1971 Camb.; MA, MB Camb. 1971, BChir 1970; FRCP Lond. 1990; MRCP (UK) 1973. (Camb. & Lond. Hosp.) Cons. Phys. King Geo. Hosp. Goodmayes. Prev: Cons. Phys. & Sen. Lect. (Nephrol.) St. Mary's Hosp. Portsmouth; Sen. Regist. (Renal Med.) Lond. Hosp.; Regist. (Med.) Harold Wood Hosp.

SHARMAN, William Angus (retired) The Barn, 25 Crow Lane, Thurley, Bourne PE10 0EZ Tel: 01778 422921 Fax: 01778 422921 — MB ChB 1960 Ed.; FRCOG 1992, M 1973. Hosp. Pract. (O & G) Matern. Unit Kettering Gen. Hosp. Prev: SHO Simpson Memor. Matern. Pavil. Roy. Infirm. Edin.

SHARMAN, William Evans (retired) 9 Rowley Lane, Fenay Bridge, Huddersfield HD8 0JN Tel: 01484 602374 — MB ChB 1953 Sheff. Prev: Ho. Surg. & Ho. Phys. Roy. Hosp. Chesterfield.

SHARNAGIEL, Zbigniew Marian (retired) 249 Felmongers, Harlow CM20 3DR Tel: 01279 424888 — MB ChB 1948 Polish Sch. of Med. Prev: Ho. Phys. City Hosp. Edin.

SHARNAGIEL, Zofia (retired) 249 Felmongers, Harlow CM20 3DR Tel: 01279 424888 — MB ChB 1948 Polish Sch. of Med. Prev: Paediat. Ho. Phys. City Gen. Hosp. Sheff.

SHARP, Mr Andrew John Hughdeburg South Wigston Health Centre, 80 Blaby Road, Wigston LE18 4SE — MB BS 1979 Lond.; FRCS Ed. 1985; MRCGP 1991; DRCOG 1988.

SHARP, Andrew Lance Howard Richmond Surgery, Richmond Close, Fleet GU52 7US Tel: 01252 811466 Fax: 01252 815031; Park Hill, Fitzroy Road, Fleet GU51 4JH Tel: 01252 614126 — MB BS 1976 Lond.; MRCS Eng. LRCP Lond. 1976; MRCGP 1982; DObst. RCOG 1980. (Char. Cross) Prev: SHO (O & G) & (Anaesth.) Frimley Pk. Hosp.; Resid. Med. Off. (Gen. Med.) Roy. Perth Hosp., Australia; Resid. Med.; Off. (Gen. Surg.) Broken Hill & Dist. Hosp. N.S.W. Australia.

SHARP, Andrew Simon 14 The Gardens, Coach Road, Whitehaven CA28 7TG — MB ChB 1998 Ed.; MB ChB Ed. 1998.

SHARP, Benjamin Titus 3 Stapledon Lane, Ashburton, Newton Abbot TQ13 7AE — MB BS 1991 Lond.; BSc Cellular Path. Lond. 1987. Prev: Ho. Off. (Gen. Surg.) Roy. Surrey Co. Hosp. Guildford; Ho. Off. (Cardiol. & Gen. Med.) Roy. United Hosp. Bath.

SHARP, Caroline Denton Turret Medical Centre, 10 Kenley Road, Slatyford, Newcastle upon Tyne NE5 2UY Tel: 0191 274 1840; 4 Elgy Road, Gosforth, Newcastle upon Tyne NE3 4UU Tel: 0191 284 6004 — MB BS 1985 Lond.; BSc Lond. 1982, MB BS 1985; MRCGP 1990; Dip. Pract. Dermat. 1995; DCH RCP Lond. 1988. Socs: BMA.

SHARP, Catherine 1L, 8 Grantley St., Shawlands, Glasgow G41 3PU — MB ChB 1996 Glas. SHO (Orthop.) S.ern Gen. Hosp. Glas. Prev: SHO (A & E) Vict. Infirm. Glas.; SHO (Ear, Nose & Throat) CrossHo. Hosp. Kilmarnock.

SHARP, Christopher AWG plc, Anglian House, Ambury Road, Huntingdon PE29 3NZ Tel: 01480 326979 Fax: 01480 323011 — MB BS 1975 Lond.; DAvMed. RCP Lond. 1982; DCH RCP Lond. 1978; MSc (Occupat. Health) Aberd. 1992; FRCP Lond. 1997; MRCP (UK) 1978; MRCS Eng. LRCP Lond. 1975; MFOM RCP Lond. 1994, AFOM 1992; MRCGP 1980; T(OM) 1994; T(GP) 1991. (Guy's) Gp. Med. Adviser; Cons. Internat. Atomic Energy Agency; Comm. 3, Internat. Comission on Radiological Protec.; Pres.-Elect Sect. of Occupat.al Med., Roy. Soc. of Med. Socs: Fell. Roy. Soc. Med.; Soc. Occupat. Med.; Amer. Coll. Occupat. & Environm. Med. Prev: Head Med. Dept. Nat. Radiol. Protec. Bd.; Hon. Sen. Clin. Lect. Oxf. Univ.; Off. Commanding RAF Aviat. Med. Train. Centre.

SHARP, Clifford William Dingleton Hospital, Chiefswood Road, Melrose TD6 9HN Tel: 01896 822727 Fax: 01896 823807; The Knowe, 24 High Cross Avenue, Melrose TD6 9SU — MB ChB 1985 Ed.; BSc Ed. 1982; MRCPsych 1990. (Ed.) Cons. Psychiat. Dingleton Hosp. Melrose. Prev: Sen. Regist. Roy. Edin. Hosp.; MRC Clin. Sci. 1991-93; Regist. (Psychiat.) Roy. Edin. Hosp.

SHARP, David James 11 Banner Cross Road, Sheffield S11 9HQ — MB BS 1996 Lond.

SHARP, Mr David John Spinal Unit, Orthopaedic Department, Ipswich Hospital, Heath Road, Ipswich IP4 3PD Tel: 01473 702097 Fax: 01473 702094 Email: sharp.sec@ipsh-tr.anglox.nhs.uk; 4 Middlerise Road, Glasgow G68 9DP Tel: 01236 451450, 01473 737266 Fax: 01236 728372 Email: akbodane@doctors.org.uk — MB BS 1972; MD Lond. 1991; FRCS Eng. 1979. (St. Mary's) Cons. Orthop. Surg. Ipswich Hosp. Socs: Roy. Soc. Med.; Brit. Orthopaedic Research Soc.; Brit. Assn. of Spinal Surg.s. Prev: Sen. Regist. Rotat. (Orthop. Surg.) N.ampton & Hammersmith; Regist. Rotat. (Orthop. Surg.) Roy. Orthop. Hosp. Birm. & Coventry.

SHARP, David Stanley Roselands, 4 Middleton Road, Higher Crumpsall, Manchester M8 5DS Tel: 0161 795 9111 Fax: 0161 795 3383; Lyndhurst, 44 Ridgeway Road, Timperley, Altrincham WA15 7EZ Tel: 0161 980 4984 — MB BS 1966 Lond.; MRCS Eng. LRCP Lond. 1966; FRCOG 1989, M 1972. (St. Mary's) Socs: Fell. (Mem. Counc.) Roy. Coll. Obst. & Gyn.; BMA; N. Eng. Soc. Obst. & Gyn. Prev: Clin. Dir. (O & G) N. Manch.; Chairm. Med. Exec. Comm. N. Manch.; Sen. Regist. (O & G) St. Mary's Hosp. Manch.

SHARP, Deborah Janette Taylor and Partners, Shirehampton Health Centre, Pembroke Road, Shirehampton, Bristol BS11 9SB Tel: 0117 916 2233 Fax: 0117 930 8246; 31 Fremantle Road, Cotham, Bristol BS6 5SX Tel: 0117 924 1998 Fax: 0117 924 1998 — BM BCh 1977 Oxf.; PhD Lond. 1993; MA Oxf. 1977; FRCGP 1995; DRCOG 1980. Prof. Primary Health Care Univ. Bristol. Prev: Sen. Lect. & Lect. (Gen. Pract.) UMDS Lond.; Trainee GP Oxf. VTS.; HON. S.L Inst of Psych. Lond.

SHARP, Deborah June Newhaven Health Centre, Chapel St., Newhaven BN9 9PW Tel: 01273 516066 Fax: 01273 611527; 13 Third Avenue, Newhaven BN9 9JA Tel: 01273 513222 — MB BS 1980 Lond.; DRCOG 1983. (Guy's) Prev: Clin. Asst. (Accid & Emerg. Centre) Roy. Sussex Co. Hosp. Brighton; GP Brighton VTS.

SHARP, Miss Elizabeth Jean Queen Elizabeth, The Queen Mother Hospital, St Peter's Rd, Margate CT9 4AN Tel: 01843 225544 Email: alanhakim@aol.com — MB BS 1983 Lond.; MS Lond. 1995; FRCS Eng. 1988; FRCS (Gen) 1998; Specialist Registrar 1999. Cons. Surg. QEQM Hosp., Margate.

SHARP, Estelle 16 Mount Eden Park, Belfast BT9 6RA — MB BCh BAO 1948 Belf.

SHARP, Frank Clinical Sciences Centre, Northern General Hospital NHS Trust, Sheffield S5 7AU Tel: 0114 243 7988 Fax: 0114 244 1728 Email: f.sharp@sheffield.ac.uk; University of Sheffield, School of Medicine, Beech Hill Road, Sheffield S10 2RX Tel: 0114 271 2736 Fax: 0114 271 3960 — MB ChB Glas. 1962; MD Glas. 1975; FRCOG 1979, M 1968; DObst RCOG 1964. (Glas.) Hon. Cons. Obst. & Gyn. Centr. Sheff. Univ. Hosps. NHS Trust. Socs: (Ex-Pres. Ex. Sec.) Brit. Soc. Colposcopy & Cervical Path.; (Foundat. Mem.) Brit. Gyn. Cancer Soc. Prev: Sen. Lect. Midw. Univ. Glas.; Hon. Cons. Obst. Qu. Mother's Hosp. Glas.; Hon. Cons. Gyn. W.. Infirm. Glas.

SHARP, Geoffrey Mark Park Road Medical Practice, Park Road, Shepton Mallet BA4 5BP Tel: 01749 342350 Fax: 01749 346859; Long Barn, Shepton Montague, Wincanton BA9 8JB Tel: 01749 813760 — MB BS 1987 Lond.; MA Camb. 1982; MRCGP 1992; DCH RCP Lond. 1991; DRCOG 1991. GP Princip. Pk. Rd. Med. Pract. Shepton Mallet; Bd. Mem. Mendip PCG. Socs: BMA.

SHARP, The Hon. Gordon Russell Forth Valley Health Board, Occupational Health Service, Central Unit, Stirling Royal Infirmary, Livilands Gate, Stirling FK8 2AU Tel: 01786 73151 — MD 1972 Glas.; PhD Glas. 1970, MD 1972, MB ChB 1958; FRCP Glas. 1987, M 1985; FFOM RCP Lond: 1989. Cons. Occupat. Phys. & Dir. Occupat. Health Servs. Forth Valley HB.; Dir. Occupat. Health Servs. Scott. Health Serv., Common Servs. Agency; Hon. Clin. Lect. Glas. Univ. Prev: I.C.I. Research Fell. & Asst. Lect. Dept. Physiol. Univ. Glas.; Reader Aviat. Physiol. RAF; Cons. Aviat. Med. RAF.

SHARP, Graham Leith Marr Dept of GU Medicine and Sexual Health, The Sandyford Initiative, Sauchiehau Street, Glasgow G3 7NB Tel: 0141 211 8608 Fax: 0141 211 8609; 37 Monreith Road, Newlands, Glasgow G43 2NY Tel: 0141 632 0977 — MB ChB 1972 Aberd.; FRCOG 1994, M 1979. Cons. Genitourin. Med. Gtr. Glas. Primary Care NHS Trust; Hon. Clin. Sen. Lect. (Med.) Univ. Glas. Socs: Med. Soc. Study VD; Brit. Soc. Colposc. & Cervic. Pathol.; Assn. for Genitourin. Med. Prev: Sen. Regist. (Genitourin. Med.) Bristol Roy. Infirm.; Regist. (O & G) Qu. Mother's Hosp. & W.. Infirm. Glas.; Regist. (O & G) Newc., N.d. & N. Tyneside HAs.

SHARP, Guy Thomas Mount Edgcumbe Hospice, Porthpean Road, St Austell PL26 6AB Tel: 01726 65711 Fax: 01726 66421 — MB BS Lond. 1962; MRCS Eng. LRCP Lond. 1963; DObst RCOG 1965. (St. Bart.) Clin. Asst. Mt. Edgcumbe Hospice St. Austell. Prev: GP Truro.

SHARP, Mr Henry Richard Ent Department, Guys Hospital, St Thomas' St., London SE19RT — MB BS 1990 Lond.; FRCS (Oto.) 1996; FRCS Eng. 1995. Specialist Regist. (Otolaryngol.) Guys & St. Thos. Hosps. Lond. Prev: SpR (Otolaryngol.) Gt. Ormand St. Hosp. For Childr.; SHO (Otolaryngol.) Char. Cross Hosp. Lond.; Ho. Surg. & Cas. Off. St. Thos. Hosp. Lond.

SHARP, Hugh Culliford Glastonbury Surgery, Feversham Lane, Glastonbury BA6 9LP; Torside, Coursing Batch, Glastonbury BA6 8BH Tel: 01458 832130 — MB BS Lond. 1969; MRCS Eng. LRCP Lond. 1968; Dip. Sports Med. 1996; DObst RCOG 1970. (Guy's) Sch. Med. Off. Millfield. Socs: Med. Off.s of Sch.s Assn. Prev: SHO ENT & (Surg. & Gyn.) Wycombe Gen. Hosp.; Ho. Off. (Obst.) Radcliffe Infirm. Oxf.

SHARP, Jacqueline Mary Catherine 6 Anne Drive, Stenhousemuir, Larbert FK5 4JE — MB ChB 1988 Glas.; DCH RCPCS Glas. 1994.

SHARP, Jacquelyn The Smethwick Medical Centre, Regent Street, Smethwick, Warley B66 3BQ Tel: 0121 558 0105 Fax: 0121 555 7206; 26 Knightlow Road, Birmingham B17 8QB — MB ChB 1979 Liverp.; MRCGP 1985; DCH RCP Lond. 1986; DRCOG 1985; DTM & H Liverp. 1982. (Liverp.)

SHARP, James Frederick The Wycke, 25 Warwick Road, Walmer, Deal CT14 7JE; Church Lane Surgery, Church Lane, New Romney TN28 8ES — MB BS 1992 Lond.

SHARP, Janet Elizabeth 2A Whin Hill Road, Bessacarr, Doncaster DN4 7AE Tel: 01302 535040 — MRCS Eng. LRCP Lond. 1952. (Leeds.)

SHARP, Jennifer Mary Arran, 40 Admiral Street, Glasgow G41 1HU Tel: 0141 429 2626 Fax: 0141 429 2331 — MB ChB 1988 Glas.; MRCGP 1993; DRCOG 1992.

SHARP, Mr Jeremy Frederick ENT Department, Derbyshire Royal Infirmary NHS Trust, London Road, Derby DE1 2QY Tel: 01332 254657 Fax: 01332 295652; 77 Hazelwood Road, Duffield, Belper DE56 4AA — MB ChB 1984 Birm.; MA Oxf. 1982; FRCS Ed. 1988. (Birm.) Cons. ENT Derbysh. Roy. Infirm. NHS Trust; Lead Head & Neck Cons.; Lead Clinician for Derby/Burton, Head & Neck Cancer, Network Site Special Gp.; Mem. Trent Region Cons. & Specialists Comm. Socs: BMA; Brit. Assn. Otol.; Hon. Treas. Midl.s Inst. Otorhinol. Prev: Sen. Regist. Rotat. (ENT) Qu. Eliz. Hosp. Birm.; Regist. (ENT) City Hosp. Edin.; SHO (ENT) Selly Oak Hosp. Birm.

SHARP, John Tel: 0141 531 8370 Fax: 0141 531 4431; 591 Kilmarnock Road, Newlands, Glasgow G43 2TH — MB ChB 1981 Glas.; MSc (Sports Medicine) 1999; MRCGP 1986.

SHARP, John Clarkson Macgregor (retired) 6 Cammo Hill, Edinburgh EH4 8EY — MB ChB 1955 Ed.; MRCP Glas. 1984; FFCM 1980, M 1972; DPH Ed. 1958. Prev: Cons. Epidemiol. Communicable Dis. (Scotl.) Unit Ruchill Hosp. Glas.

SHARP, John Richard Cowper (retired) Rossie Mills House, Rossie Braes, Montrose DD10 9TJ Tel: 01674 677204 — MB BS 1967 Lond.; MRCS Eng. LRCP Lond. 1966. Prev: GP Kingsteignton.

SHARP, Mrs June Rosemary 22 St Peters Road, Seaford BN25 2HP Tel: 01323 491162 — MB ChB 1954 Sheff. Prev: SCMO Jarvis BrE. Screening Centre Guildford.

SHARP, Madeleine Agnes (retired) 49 Baginton Road, Coventry CV3 6JX Tel: 02476 414512 Fax: 02476) 414512 — MB BS Durh. 1953; DSc (hon causa) Coventry 1995. Prev: Ho. Phys. Workington Infirm.

SHARP, Mr Malcolm (retired) (cons. rooms), St. Anthony's Hospital, Cheam, Sutton Tel: 020 8337 6691 — MB BS 1956 Lond.; FRCS Eng. 1961; MRCS Eng. LRCP Lond. 1956. Cons. ENT Surg. St. Helier Trust Carshalton; Cons. Ent. Surg. St. Geos., NHS Trust; Hon Cons. Surg. Head & Neck Unit Roy. Marsden Hosp. Lond. Prev: Sen. Regist. Roy. Nat. Throat, Nose & Ear Hosp. Lond.

SHARP, Michael Andrew 31 Orchardson House, Orchardson St., London NW8 8NN Tel: 020 7723 4014 — MB BS 1991 Lond.; BSc Clin. Sci. Lond. 1989, MB RS 1991; FRCS Lond. 1995. (St. Mary's Lond.) Specialist Regist. (Gen. Surg.) Oxf.

SHARP, Michael John Aubrey North Lane Medical Centre, 12-14 Gloucester Street, Brighton BN1 4EW Tel: 01273 601112 — MB BChir 1980 Camb.

SHARP, Michael Philip Downlands Medical Centre, 77 High Street, Polegate BN26 6AE Tel: 01323 482323/486449 Fax: 01323 488497 — MB BS 1988 Lond.; MRCGP 1993; DCH RCP Lond. 1992.

SHARP, Michael William (retired) 2A Whin Hill Road, Bessacarr, Doncaster DN4 7AE Tel: 01302 535040 — MB ChB 1950 Leeds; DObst RCOG 1951. Prev: SHO (Obst.) St. Helen's Hosp. Barnsley.

SHARP, Neil Carter, MBE Bellevue House, Mid St., Keith AB55 5AE Tel: 015422 2233 — MB ChB 1940 Aberd.

SHARP, Nigel Stewart 3 Sutherland Avenue, Broadstone BH18 9EB — MB BS 1977 Lond. Garrison Med. Off. Blandford Camp Dorset.

SHARP, Olive Persica (retired) 76 Wessington Park, Calne SN11 0AX — MB BS 1958 Lond.; MRCS Eng. LRCP Lond. 1958; DA Eng. 1961; DObst RCOG 1961. Prev: GP Calne Wilts.

SHARP, Patrick Stephen Department of Diabetes & Endocrinology, Northwick Park Hospital, Watford Road, Harrow

SHARP

HA1 3UJ Tel: 020 8869 2623 Fax: 020 8869 2961; 11 Greenhills Close, Rickmansworth WD3 4BW Tel: 01923 350815 Email: patrick.sharp@virgin.net — MB ChB 1977 Glas.; MD Glas. 1987; MRCP (UK) 1980; FRCP 1996. Cons. Phys. N.wick Pk. Hosp. Harrow.; Hon. Cons. Phys. Moorfields Eye Hosp.

SHARP, Petra 54 Stanhope Road, St Albans AL1 5BL — MB ChB 1992 Bristol.

SHARP, Rachel Jane Inish Fail, Orchard Close, E. Hendred, Wantage OX12 8JJ — MB ChB 1990 Sheff.; MRCGP 1994; DRCOG 1993.

SHARP, Rebecca 6 West Garleton, Haddington EH41 3SL — MB ChB 1997 Aberd.

SHARP, Robert John 121A Hilmanton, Lower Earley, Reading RG6 4HJ; Frogs Meadow, Milton Combe, Yelverton PL20 6HL Tel: 01822 854926 Fax: 01822 854926 — MB BS 1992 Lond. (Lond. Hosp. Med. Coll.)

SHARP, Robert Jonathan c/o The Coach House, 25 North Park Parade, Harrogate — BM BCh 1991 Oxf.

SHARP, Robert Wylie (retired) 53 Hatton Park Road, Wellingborough NN8 5AQ Tel: 01933 222761 — MB ChB 1954 Glas.; MRCOG 1964. Prev: GP WellingBoro. & Port Glas.

SHARP, Ronald Alexander Victoria Infirmary, Langside Road, Glasgow G42 9TY Tel: 0141 201 6000; 52 Castlehill Drive, Newton Mearns, Glasgow G77 5LB Tel: 0141 639 8840 — MB ChB 1974 Dundee; MRCP (UK) 1978; FRCPath 1996, M 1985. Cons. Haemat. Vict. Infirm. Glas.; Hon. Clin. Sen. Lect. Univ. Glas. Socs: Coll. Mem. Roy. Coll. Phys. Edin.; Assn. Clin. Paths. Prev: Sen. Regist. & Hon. Lect. (Haemat.) Ninewells Hosp. & Med. Sch. Univ. Dundee.

SHARP, Valerie Anne Department of G.U. Medicine, City Hospital, Infirmary Hill, Truro TR1 2HZ Tel: 01872 354488; Missenden, 3 Church Road, Mylor, Falmouth TR11 5NL Tel: 01326 374245 Fax: 01326 374245 — MB ChB 1982 Otago; MRNZCGP 1991; Dip GU Med. Soc. Apoth Lond. 1992. (Otago) Staff Grade Doctor Dept. of Genitourin. Med. Socs: MSSVD; BMA; MPS. Prev: Clin. Asst. Genitourin. Med. Serv. Cornw.; GP Wairoa, NZ.

SHARP, William (retired) 49 Emmanuel Road, Southport PR9 9RP Tel: 01704 28664 — MB ChB 1933 Leeds; MRCPsych 1971; DPM Eng. 1938. Prev: Med. Supt. Greaves Hall, Banks.

SHARPE, Andrew Paul Ashley Centre Surgery, Ashley Square, Epsom KT18 5DD Tel: 01372 723668 Fax: 01372 726796; 6 Woodcote Mews, 84 Worple Road, Epsom KT18 7AH — MB BS 1988 Lond.; MRCGP 1995; DRCOG 1992. (St. Geos.) Chairm. New Epsom & Ewell Cottage Hosp.

SHARPE, Bruce David Magill Department of Anaesthesia, Chelsea & Westminster Hospitla, 369 Fullham Road, London SW10 9NH — MB BS 1977 Monash.

SHARPE, Cathleen Margaret Hollywell, Tile Barn, Woolton Hill, Newbury RG20 9XE Tel: 01635 253007 — MB ChB 1967 Leeds; DObst RCOG 1969; DCH Eng. 1970. (Leeds) Community Med. Off. Basingstoke HA; Staff Grade Paediat Lond. NHS Trust N. Hants. Hosp. Basingstoke. Socs: BMA. Prev: GP Ealing; Med. Off. Dept. Health Lond. Boro. Hillingdon; SHO (Paediat.) Warrington Gen. Hosp.

SHARPE, Christopher Erel West Suffolk Hospital, Hardwick Lane, Bury St Edmunds IP33 2QZ Tel: 01284 713000; 21 Collingwood Close, Steepletower, Hethersett, Norwich NR9 3QE — MB BS 1991 West Indies; FRCA 1998. (Univ. of the WI) Specialist Regist. (Anaesth.) W. Suff. Hosp. Bury St. Edmunds. Socs: BMA; Anaesth. Assoc. of GB & Ire. Prev: Specialist Regist. (Anaesth.) Norf. & Norwich Hosp.; SHO (Anaesth.) Mayday Univ. Hosp. Thornton Heath; SHO (Anaesth.) Kingston Pub. Hosp. Jamaica.

SHARPE, Christopher James Viewfield Lane Health Centre, Viewfield Lane, Selkirk TD7 4LJ Tel: 01750 21674 Fax: 01750 23176; Easthill, Anderson Road, Selkirk TD7 4EB Tel: 01750 20546 — MB BS 1968 Lond.; MRCP (U.K.) 1971; MRCGP 1978.

SHARPE, Claire Catherine 37 Birchwood Road, London SW17 9BQ — MB BS 1991 Lond.; BSc Lond. 1988.

SHARPE, Coral Rosemary Woodbridge Road Surgery, 165-167 Woodbridge Road, Ipswich IP4 2PE Tel: 01473 256251 — MB BS 1961 Lond.; MRCS Eng. LRCP Lond. 1961; DObst RCOG 1964.

SHARPE, Damian Patrick 6 Park Road, Exeter EX1 2HP — MB BCh BAO 1984 NUI.

SHARPE, Mr David Antony Charles 14 Stanley Drive, Leeds LS8 2EZ — MB ChB 1984 Liverp.; FRCS Glas. 1986. Regist. Rotat. (Gen. Surg. & Neurosurg.) BRd.green & Walton Hosp. Liverp. Prev: SHO (A & E/Med.) BRd.green Hosp. Liverp.; SHO (Cardiothor. Surg.) BRd.green Hosp. Liverp.

SHARPE, David Robert Kitson 37 Old Holywood Road, Belfast BT4 2HJ Email: dsharpe@nireland.com — MB BCh BAO 1990 Belf.; MRCPI 1993; DPH Camb. 1995; Dip. IMC RCS Ed. 1993; DGM RCP Glas. 1992; MSc (Health Economics & Managem.) Qu. Univ. Belf.; Blegsc (HONS) 1998 QUB; DFFHM 1998. Specialist Regist., Mater Hosp., Belf., A&E. Prev: Sen Reg (Pub. Health Med) SHSS.

SHARPE, David Stephen Bellingham Green Surgery, 24 Bellingham Green, London SE6 3JB Tel: 020 8697 7285 Fax: 020 8695 6094 — MB BS 1990 Lond.

SHARPE, Elizabeth Ann Bryceson (retired) (Surgery) 3 The Square, Buxton SK17 6AZ Tel: 01298 3019 — MB ChB 1961 Sheff. Prev: G.P. The Sq., Buxton.

SHARPE, Elizabeth Louise 25 Merrow Croft, Guildford GU1 2XH — MB BS 1998 Lond.; MB BS Lond 1998.

SHARPE, Evelyn Edith Interhealth, 157 Waterloo Road, London SE1 8US Tel: 020 7902 9000 Fax: 020 7928 0927 Email: psychservices@interhealth.org.uk; 6 Canada Wharf, Flat 6, 255 Rotherhithe St, London SE16 5ES Tel: 020 7237 5118 — MB BCh BAO 1977 Belf.; BA (ICI Internat. Correspondence Inst.) 1990; MRCPsych 1985. (Queen's University Belfast) Cons. Psychiat. Interhealth Lond.; Cons. Psychiat. Greenwich Dist. Hosp. Socs: Ulster Med. Soc.

SHARPE, Fiona Margaret 7A Learmonth Terrace, Edinburgh EH4 1PQ — MB ChB 1993 Ed.

SHARPE, Geoffrey 5 Larch Close, West End, Southampton SO30 3RB — BM 1986 Soton.; MRCP (UK) 1991; FRCR 1996; PhD Soton. 1998. (Soton.) Cons. (Clin. Oncol.) Wessex Cancer Centre, Soton. Prev: Sen. Regist. & Regist. (Radiother. & Oncol.) Roy. Marsden Hosp.; Clin. Research Fell. & Hon. Regist. (Med.) Univ. Soton.; Ho. Phys. & SHO (Med.) Soton. Univ. Hosp.

SHARPE, Geoffrey Frank Appleby Health Centre, Low Wiend, Appleby-in-Westmorland CA16 6QP Tel: 01768 351584 Fax: 01768 353375; Bongate Hall S., Appleby-in-Westmorland CA16 6HW — BM BS 1980 Nottm.; MRCP Ed. 1983; MRCGP 1986.

SHARPE, Georgina Helen Maimie The Corner Surgery, 180 Cambridge Road, Southport PR9 7LW Tel: 01704 506055 Fax: 01704 505818; 12 Hartley Road, Birkdale, Southport PR8 4SA Tel: 01704 567769 — MB BS 1976 Lond.; MA Oxf. 1980; MRCGP 1981. (Guy's) Prev: Trainee GP Coventry VTS.

SHARPE, Gillian Anne 76 North Street, Caistor, Lincoln LN7 6QU — MB BS 1988 Lond.

SHARPE, Gordon Charles William (retired) 3 Shillingford Court, Shillingford, Wallingford OX10 7EP Tel: 01865 858345 — MB BS 1946 Lond.; MRCGP 1978; DObst RCOG 1952. Prev: Receiv. Room Off. Lond. Hosp.

SHARPE, Graeme Douglas Macgregor Dundee Teaching Hospitals NHS Trust, Directorate of Ophthalmology, Ninewells Hospital and Medical School, Dundee DD2 1YY; East Wing, Waterybutts Farm Steading, Grange by Errol, Perth PH2 7SZ — MB ChB 1990 Dundee; BMSc (Hons.) Dund. 1987; MRCOphth 1995. (Dundee) Staff Grade (Ophth.).

SHARPE, Graham Richard Department of Dermatology, Royal Liverpool Hospital, Prescot St., Liverpool L7 8XP Tel: 0151 706 4030 Fax: 0151 706 5842 Email: grs@liverpool.ac.uk — MB ChB 1977 Leeds; PhD Newc. 1994; BA (Hons.) Open 1988; FRCP Lond. 1996; MRCP (UK) 1980; DTM & H Liverp. 1980. Sen. Lect. (Dermat.) Univ. Liverp. Socs: Comm. Mem. Brit. Soc. Paediatric Dermat. Prev: Sen. Regist. (Dermat.) Roy. Newc.; Wellcome Research Fell. (Dermat.) Roy. Vict. Infirm.

SHARPE, Mr Ian Terence 4 Moles Cottages, Exminster, Exeter EX6 8DB — MB BS 1991 Lond.; BSc (Hons.) Lond. 1988; FRCS Eng. 1995. Specialist Regist. Rotat. (Orthop. & Trauma) S. W. (S.).

SHARPE, James Edward 48 Thornwood Terrace, Glasgow G11 7QZ — MB ChB 1992 Glas.

SHARPE, Julia Catherine (retired) Treberfydd, Bagshot Road, Egham TW20 0RS — MB BS 1989 Lond.; BSc Lond. 1986. Regist. (Histopath.) Hammersmith Hosp.

SHARPE, Karen Tacye Appleby Health Centre, Low Wiend, Appleby-in-Westmorland CA16 6QP Tel: 01768 351584 Fax: 01768 353375 — MB BS 1984 Lond.; MRCGP 1990. (St. Bart.) GP N. Cumbria HA.

SHARPE, Keryn Elizabeth 10 Tudor House, Heath Road, Weybridge KT13 8TZ — MB ChB 1993 Leic.

SHARPE, Lawrence David 24 Neville Street, London SW7 3AS Tel: 020 7589 1562 — MB BS 1954 Lond.; DPM 1961; MRCPsych 1980. (Univ. Coll. Hosp.) Asst. Prof. Columbia Univ. New York; Surg. Lt. RNR. Socs: Fell. Roy. Soc. Med. Prev: Instruc. in Paediat. & Psychiat. Johns Hopkins Hosp. Baltimore; Regist. Maudsley Hosp. & Bethlem Roy. Hosp. Lond.; Ho. Phys. & Ho. Surg. Highlands Hosp.

SHARPE, Mandy Sharon Rustlings Road Medical Centre, 105 Rustlings Road, Sheffield S11 7AB Tel: 0114 266 0726 Fax: 0114 267 8394; 2 Slayleigh Drive, Fulwood, Sheffield S10 3RD Tel: 0114 230 6658 Email: msslotus@aol.com — MB BS 1981 Lond.; MRCP (UK) 1984; DRCOG 1987.

SHARPE, Michael Christopher Department of Psychiatry, University of Edinburgh, Kennedy Tower, Royal Edinburgh Hospital, Edinburgh EH10 5HF Tel: 0131 537 6672 Fax: 0131 536 6641 Email: michael.sharpe@ed.ac.uk — MB BChir 1980 Camb.; MA Oxf. 1979; MRCP (UK) 1984; MRCPsych 1987. (Camb.) Sen. Lect. & Hon. Cons. (Psychol. Med.) Univ. Edin. Prev: Clin. Tutor & Hon. Sen. Regist. (Psychiat.) Oxf. RHA.

SHARPE, Nicola Louise — MB ChB 1988 Manch.; BSc St. And. 1985. p/t Specialist Regist. Child & Adolesc. Psychiat. Acad. Unit, Pine Lodge, Chester; Flexible Trainee. Socs: MRCPsych.

SHARPE, Paul Christopher SmithKline Beecham Pharmaceuticals, New Frontiers Science Park, Third Avenue, Harlow CM19 5AW Tel: 01279 644872 Fax: 01279 644440 — MD Lond. 1982, MB BS 1970; MRCS Eng. LRCP Lond. 1970; FFPM RCP Lond. 1989; DObst RCOG 1973. (Guy's) Vice Pres. CNS Project Managem.; Dep. Chairm. of Trustees Internat. Spinal Research Trust; Hon. Prof. Pharmaceut. Med. Imperial Coll. of Sci., Technol. & Med. Lond. Socs: Brit. Pharm. Soc.; Fell. Roy. Soc. Med. Prev: Med. Dir. Roche UK; Sen. Med. Off. Med. Control Agency UK; Research Fell. & Hon. Regist. (Gastroenterol.) W.m. Hosp. Lond.

SHARPE, Peter Carlisle Clinical Biochemistry, Craigavon Area Hospital, 68 Lurgan Road, Portadown, Craigavon BT63 5QQ Tel: 028 3861 2657 Fax: 028 3833 4582 Email: psharpe@cahgt.n-i.nhs.uk; 80 Old Kilmore Road, Moira, Craigavon BT67 0NA Tel: 028 9261 3762 Email: petercsharpe@netscapeonline.co.uk — MB BCh BAO 1988 Belf.; MD Belf. 1997; MRCP (UK) 1992; MRCPath 1997. (Queens University Belfast) Cons., (Chem. Pathol.) Craigavon Area Hosp. Socs: Roy. Coll. Phys. & Surgs. Glas.; MRCPath.; Assn. Clin. Biochem.

SHARPE, Rodney Charles Brookside Group Practice, Brookside Close, Gipsy Lane, Earley, Reading RG6 7HG Tel: 0118 966 9222 Fax: 0118 935 3174; 32 Aldbourne Avenue, Earley, Reading RG6 7DB — MB BS 1977 Lond.; BSc Lond. 1974, MB BS 1977; MRCGP 1989; DCH RCP Lond. 1984; DRCOG 1982. GP Trainer Reading VTS. Prev: Trainee GP York VTS; Med. Off. Ch. of Christ N. Nigeria; SHO (Obst.) Mothers Hosp. Lond.

SHARPE, Roger Malcolm 65 Rossendale Way, London NW1 0XB Email: rsharpe065@aol.com — MB BS 1986 Lond.; BSc Lond. 1983; FRCA 1993. Cons. Anaesth. N.wick Pk. Hosp. Harrow. Socs: Amer. Soc. of Anaesth.; Anaesth. Research Soc. Prev: Lect., Hon. Sen. Regist. & Regist. (Anaesth.) St. Mary's Hosp. Lond.; SHO (Anaesth.) Chelmsford; SHO (Gen. Med.) Colchester.

SHARPE, Ronald Albert Dipple Medical Centre, Wickford Avenue, Pitsea, Basildon SS13 3HQ Tel: 01268 555115; 163 Noak Hill Road, Billericay CM12 9UJ — MB ChB 1958 Bristol; MRCGP 1972; DObst RCOG 1960. (Bristol) Prev: Govt. Med. Off. Bahamas; Ho. Phys. S.mead Hosp. W.bury-on-Trym.

SHARPE, Stephen William Adams and Partners, The Health Centre, Tavanagh Avenue, Portadown, Craigavon BT62 3BU Tel: 028 3835 1393; 19 The Avenue, Portadown, Craigavon BT63 5UJ — MB BCh BAO 1988 Belf.; MRCGP 1992; DFFP 1993; DMH Belf. 1993; DRCOG 1992; T(GP) 1992; DCH RCPSI 1991.

SHARPE, Thomas Daniel Emmett 19B Bridge Road, Helens Bay, Bangor BT19 1TT Tel: 01247 852534 — MB BCh BAO 1978 Belf.; MPhil (Law & Ethics) Belf. 1995; FFA RCSI 1983. Cons. Anaesth. Roy. Vict. Hosp. Belf.; Lect. (Anaesth.) Univ. Calgary 1985.

SHARPLES, Andrew Department of Paediatric Intensive Care, Manchester Children's Hospitals, NHS Trust, Royal Manchester Children's Hospital, Pendlebury, Manchester M27 4HA Tel: 0161 727 2468 Fax: 0161 727 2198 Email: andrew.sharples@man.ac.uk; 22 Arkhome, Ellenbrook, Worsley, Manchester M28 1SJ Tel: 0161 790 1217 — MB BS 1983 Lond.; FRCA 1990; DA (UK) 1985. Cons. Intens. Care & Anaesth. Manch. Childr. Hosp. NHS Trust. Prev: Sen. Regist. (Anaesth.) NW RHA; Regist. (Intens. Care) Roy. Childr. Hosp. Melbourne, Austral.

SHARPLES, Anthony Church View Surgery, 30 Holland Road, Plymstock, Plymouth PL9 9BW Tel: 01752 403206 — MB BS 1979 Lond.; MRCGP 1982.

SHARPLES, Christopher John 1 Mount Close, Bickley, Bromley BR1 2PH — MB BS 1983 Lond.

SHARPLES, Christopher John, QHP, CStJ, Air Vice-Marshal RAF Med. Br. RAF Medical Services, HQ Personnel & Training Command, RAF Innsworth, Gloucester GL3 1EZ Tel: 01452 712612 Ext: 5801 Fax: 01452 510841; Black Swan Spinney, Wansford, Peterborough PE8 6LE — MRCS Eng. LRCP Lond. 1966; MSc Lond. 1981; FFOM RCP Lond. 1990, MFOM 1980; FRAeS 2000 MRAes 1980; DAvMed FOM RCP Lond. 1972. (Kings College) Dir. Gen. Med. Servs. RAF Cons. Occupat. Med.; Examr Fac.Occup.Med Roy.Coll.Phys. Socs: RSM (Vice Pres. Milit. Sect.); SOM; Fell. Roy. Aeronaut. Soc. (Mem. Aviat. Med. Gp. & Comm.). Prev: Asst. Surg. Gen. & Dir. Med. Policy MOD; Dir. Primary Health Servs. RAF; Cons. Adviser Occupat. Med. RAF.

SHARPLES, Claude Alwyn (retired) 3 Dalby Avenue, Bushby, Leicester LE7 9RE — MA Camb. 1957, BA (Hnrs.) 1949, MB BChir 1952; DObst RCOG 1957. Prev: Mem. Leics. Area Local Med. Comm.

SHARPLES, David Lionel (retired) Pippins, Cemetery Road, Yeadon, Leeds LS19 7UR — MB ChB 1947 Liverp.

SHARPLES, Edward John 36 Southlands Avenue, Orpington BR6 9NZ — MB BS 1993 Lond.

SHARPLES, Peta Mary Department of Child Health, The Medical School, Framlington Place, Newcastle upon Tyne NE2 4 Email: peter.sharples@obht.swest.nhs.uk — FRCP 1996; FRCPCH 1997; PhD 1995 Newcastle Upon Tyne; MB BS 1978 Lond.; MRCP (UK) 1983; DCH RCP Lond. 1982. Cons. Paediatric NeUrol. and Sen. Lect., Bristol Roy. Hosp. Socs: Brit. Paediat. Assn. & Brit. Paediat. Neurol. Assn. Prev: Hon. Sen. Regist. & Lect. (Paediat. Neurosci.) Univ. Newc. Upon Tyne; 1st Asst. in Paediatric Neurosci., Univ. of Newc. Upon Tyne; Regist. (Paediat.) John Radcliffe Hosp. Oxf.

SHARPLES, Philip Elwin (Surgery), 229 West Barnes Lane, New Malden KT3 6JD Tel: 020 8336 1773 Fax: 020 8395 4797 — MB BS 1983 Lond.; MRCGP 1987; DRCOG 1989; Dip Occ Med. 1996. (Westm.) GP New Malden. Prev: RMO 1 DERR Hong Kong; BMH Rinteln Germany; RMO Welsh Guards Germany.

SHARPLES, Philip James Duke Street Surgery, 4 Duke Street, Barrow-in-Furness LA14 1LF Tel: 01229 820068 Fax: 01229 813840 — MB ChB 1969 Manch.; MRCGP 1977; Dip. Occ. Med.

SHARPLES, Rachel Harriet 26 Woodkind Hey, Spital, Bebington, Wirral CH63 9JZ — MB BS 1997 Newc.

SHARPLES, Richard Thomas Edward Hillstones, Kemming Road, Knitwell, Ventnor PO38 2RA — MB ChB 1992 Cape Town.

SHARPLEY, John Guy Department of Psychiatry, Royal Hospital Haslar, Gosport PO12 2AA Tel: 023 9276 2205 Fax: 023 9276 2257 — MB BChir 1990 Camb.; MRC Psych 1997. (United Med. & Dental School (Guy's)) Consultants in Gen. Adult Psychiat.

SHARPLEY, Oliver John Sheep Street Surgery, 59 Sheep Street, Burford OX18 4LS Tel: 01993 822176 Fax: 01993 822885; Field House, Westhall Hill, Fulbrook, Burford OX18 4BJ Tel: 01993 822484 — MB BS 1972 Lond.; MRCGP 1983. (St. Thos.) Prev: Med. Off. (O & G) Addington Hosp. Durban, S. Afr.; Ho. Phys. St. Stephen's Hosp. Lond.; Ho. Surg. St. Thos. Hosp. Lond.

SHARPSTONE, Daniel Robert 1 Surrenden Crescent, Brighton BN1 6WE Tel: 01273 552403 — MB BS 1988 Lond.; MRCP (UK) 1991; MD Lond. 1997. (Kings College London) Sen. Regist. (Med.) Chelsea & W.minister Hosp. Lond. Prev: Regist. (HIV) Chelsea & W.m. Hosp. Lond.; Regist. (Med.) Portsmouth HA & Soton. Gen. Hosp.

SHARPSTONE, Paul The Hove Nuffield Hospital, 55 New Church Road, Hove BN3 4BG Tel: 01273 779471 Fax: 01273 220919; 27 Warnham Court, Grand Avenue, Hove BN3 2NJ Tel: 01273 204752 Email: paulsharpstone@excite.co.uk — MB BS 1960 Lond.; FRCP Lond. 1977, M 1964; MRCS Eng. LRCP Lond. 1960. (King's Coll. Hosp.) Cons. Phys. (Gen. & Renal Med.) Brighton Health Care. Socs: Renal Assn.; Eur. Dialysis & Transpl. Assn. Prev: Lect. (Med.) King's

Coll. Hosp. Med. Sch. Lond.; Regist. (Med.) King's Coll. Hosp. & Roy. N.. Hosp. Lond.

SHARR, Mr Michael Maurice 11 Brimstone Close, Chelsfield, Orpington BR6 7ST Tel: 01689 861114 — MB BS 1965 Lond.; FRCS Eng. 1971; MRCP Lond. 1969. (St. Geo.) Cons. Neurosurg. SE Thames Regional Neurosurgic. Unit King's Coll. Hosp. Lond. Prev: Cons. Neurosurg. Walton Hosp. Liverp. & Gwynedd AHA; Sen. Regist. (Neurosurg.) Wessex Neurol. Centre Soton.; Regist. (Neurosurg.) Hosp. Sick Childr. Gt. Ormond St.

SHARRACK, Basil National Hospital for Neurology and Neurosurgery, Queen Square, London WC1N 3BG Tel: 020 7820 8720 Email: b.sharrack@umds.ac.uk; 37 Elizabeth Newcomen House, 38 Newcomen St, London SE1 1YZ — MD 1984 Aleppo, Syria; MRCP (UK) 1989; DHMSA 1994; Dip. Clin. Neurol. Lond 1991. (Aleppo, Syria) Specialist Regist. (Neurol.) Nat. Hosp. for Neurol. & Neurosurg.; Hon. Lect. UMDS Guy's Hosp. Lond. Prev: Regist. (Neurol.) Roy. Hallamsh. Hosp. Sheff.; Research Fell. (Neurol.) Guy's Hosp.

SHARRARD, Gordon Anthony Wells (retired) 1 Cotswold Avenue, Hazel Grove, Stockport SK7 5HJ Tel: 0161 483 1893 Email: gordonsharrad@cwctv.net — BM BCh 1954 Oxf.; DM Oxf. 1973, MA, BM BCh 1954; DLO Eng. 1958. Prev: Clin. Med. Off. (Audiol. Servs.) Tameside (Manch.) AHA.

SHARRARD, Helen Elizabeth Thornbury & Yate CLDT, Unit 5, Thornbury Office Park, Midland Way, Thornbury, Bristol BS35 2BS Tel: 01454 418020 Fax: 01454 418020 Email: helen.sharrard@banes-pct.nhs.uk; Tel: 0117 969 6471 — BM BS 1982 Nottm.; BMedSci Nottm. 1980; MRCPsych 1988. (Nottm.) Cons. Learning Disabil. Bath & W. Comm. Trust, St. Martins Hosp. Prev: Sen. Regist. (Ment. Handicap) Fairleigh Hosp. & Brentry Hosp. Bristol; Regist. & SHO (Psychiat.) Frenchay HA.

SHARRARD, Mark Jonathan 205 Ringinglow Road, Sheffield S11 7PT — MB BS 1988 Lond.; BA (Biochem.) Oxf. 1983. Regist. Rotat. (Paediat.) Sheff. Childr. Hosp. NHS Trust. Prev: SHO (Paediat.) Brompton Hosp.; SHO (Paediat.) Qu. Eliz. Hosp. Lond.; SHO (Paediat.) St. Geo. Hosp. Lond.

SHARRARD, Mr William John Wells (retired) 140 Manchester Road, Sheffield S10 5DL Tel: 0114 266 4918 — MB ChB 1944 Sheff.; MB ChB (Hons.) Sheff. 1944; MD (Distinc.) Sheff. 1954, ChM (Commend.) 1966; FRCS Eng. 1950. Prof. Orthop. Surg. Univ. Sheff. Prev: Cons. Orthop. Surg. Roy. Hallamsh. & Childr. Hosps. Sheff.

SHARRATT, Michael, OBE 28 Stoatley Rise, Haslemere GU27 1AG — MB ChB 1967 Birm.; BSc (Chem.) Lond. 1954; PhD Birm. 1961,; MSc 1958; FRCPath 1983, M 1980; FFOM 1988, M 1980. (Birm.) Prev: Toxicol. Adviser BP Occupat. Health Centre; Sen. Med. Off. (Toxicol.) DHSS; Chief Toxicol. Brit. Indust. Biol. Research Assn. Carshalton.

SHARROCK, John Kieran Clive The Fountains, Park Lane, Blunham, Bedford MK44 3NJ — MB BS 1997 Lond.; BSc (Hons) 1994. (St. Bart's Lond.) GP Train., Chelsea & W.m. Hosp.

SHARVILL, Denis Elliot (retired) New Hayesbank Surgery, By Brook, Kennington, Ashford TN24 9QB — MRCS Eng. LRCP Lond. 1942; FRCP Lond. 1960; MRCP (UK) 1950. Cons. Outreach Clinic Ashford Kent. Prev: Cons. Dermat. SE Kent & Canterbury HAs.

SHARVILL, Nicholas John Balmoral Surgery, 1 Victoria Road, Deal CT14 7AU Tel: 01304 373444; 19 Cowper Road, Deal CT14 9TW Tel: 01304 360516 Email: rogi11111@aol.com — MB BS 1979 Lond.; MRCGP 1983; Dip. Occ. Med. R.C.P. 1997; Dip. IMC RCS Ed.1991; DRCOG 1982; DCH RCP Lond. 1982; Cert. Av. Med. 1992. (King's Coll. Hosp.) Trainer GP; Clin. Asst. (Minor Injuries) Deal Hosp. SE Kent HA; Clin. Asst. (Med.) Folkestone Hosp. SE Kent HA. Socs: BMA; SE Thames Fac. RCGP. Prev: Clin. Asst. (Anaesth.) Deal Hosp.; Trainee GP Kings Lynn VTS; SHO (Anaesth.) Qu. Eliz. Hosp. Kings Lynn.

SHARWOOD-SMITH, Geoffrey Hugh Department of Anaesthetics, Royal Infirmary, Edinburgh EH3 9YW Tel: 0131 536 3651 Email: gssmith@edac.uk — MB ChB 1969 St. And.; FFA RCS Eng. 1974; DA Eng. 1972. Cons. Anaesth. Roy. Infirm. Edin. Socs: BMA; OAA; WAS. Prev: Specialist Anaesth. RAF.

SHASHIDHARAN, Mr Maniamparampil 20C Victoria Drive E., Salisbury District Hospital, Salisbury SP2 8BJ — MB BS 1988 Osmania; FRCS Ed. 1992.

SHASHIKANTH, Subramaniam 43 Ravensdale Mansions, Haringay Park, London N8 9HS — LMSSA 1994 Lond.

SHASTRI, Mr Keshav Devdatta 5 Beechgrove Heights, Magherafelt BT45 5EF Email: kd@shastri21.freeserve.uk; 5 Beechgrove Heights, Magherafelt BT45 5EF Tel: 028 7963 2918 Fax: 028 7963 2918 Email: kd@shastri21.freeserve.uk — MB BS Bombay 1946; BSc Bombay 1941; FRCS Eng. 1953. (Grant Med. Coll.) Hon. Cons. Surg. Mid Ulster Hosp. Magherafelt. Socs: BMA; Mid Ulster Clin. Soc. Prev: Prof. & Head Dept. Surg. Ravindra Nath Tagore Med. Coll. Udaipur, India; Cons. Surg. Mid Ulster Hosp. Magherafelt.

SHASTRI, Mayank Mahendraprasad The Surgery, 22 Shenley Green, Selly Oak, Birmingham B29 4HH Tel: 0121 475 7997 — MB BS 1971 Baroda.

SHATA, Maged Mohamed Hassanin 3 Ackford Drive, Worksop S80 1YQ — MB ChB 1982 Alexandria.

SHATHER, Nabil Aziz Bilston Street Surgery, 25 Bilston Street, Sidgley, Dudley DY3 1JA Tel: 01902 665700 Fax: 01902 688533; Longcroft, Lowe Lane, Kidderminster DY11 5QR — LMSSA 1986 Lond.; MB ChB Baghdad 1972.

SHATTLES, Warren Geoffrey 8 Arthur Road, Horsham RH13 5BQ — MB BS 1982 New South Wales; MRCP (UK) 1987.

SHATTOCK, Gillian Mary (retired) Morningwell Cottage, Piddletrenthide, Dorchester DT2 7QZ — MB BS 1955 Lond.; DCH Eng. 1977. Prev: SCMO (Child Health) S.W. Surrey Health Dist.

SHATWELL, Beryl Lomax (retired) Bunbury House, Warfleet, Dartmouth TQ6 9BZ — MB ChB 1951 Liverp. Prev: GP Devon.

SHATWELL, Mr Michael Antony 32 Baroncroft Road, Woolton, Liverpool L25 6EH — MB ChB 1974 Liverp.; MChOrth Liverp. 1981, MB ChB 1974; FRCS Eng. 1979. Hon. Sen. Regist. (Orthop.) Liverp. HA; Lect. (Orthop. & Accid. Surg.) Univ. Liverp. Socs: Liverp. Med. Inst.; Assoc. Mem. Brit. Orthop. Assn. Prev: Regist. (Orthop.) Alder Hey Childr. Hosp. Liverp. & Roy. Liverp. Hosp.

SHATWELL, William John X-ray Department, Walsgrave Hospital, Clifford Bridge Road, Walsgrave, Coventry CV2 2DX Tel: 02476 602020; 66 Windy Arbour, Coventry CV8 2BB — MB BChir 1979 Camb.; MA Camb. 1974; MRCP (UK) 1986; FRCR 1990. (St. Geo.) Cons. Radiol Univ. Hosp.s Coventry and Warks. NHS Trust. Prev: Sen. Regist. & Regist. (Diagn. Radiol.) John Radcliffe Hosp. Oxf.; SHO (Gen. Med.) Kent & Canterbury Hosp. Canterbury.

SHAUKAT, Mohammed Naeem 16 Hartland Drive, Littleover, Derby DE23 7LU — MB ChB 1985 Manch.

SHAUNAK, Lok Nath 53 A/B Maidstone Road, Rainham, Gillingham ME8 0DP Tel: 01634 231423 Fax: 01634 261665 — MB BS 1973 Jiwaji; BSc Punjab India 1966; MRCS Eng. LRCP Lond. 1982.

SHAUNAK, Rohit Amberley, Waterfall Close, Virginia Water GU25 4QD — MB BS 1987 Lond. SHO (Surg.) Rotat. St. Geo. Hosp. Lond.; Anat. Demonst. St. Geo. Hosp. Med. Sch. Lond.

SHAUNAK, Sunil Imperial College School of Medicine, Hammersmith Hospital, Du Cane Road, London W12 0NN Tel: 020 8383 2301 Email: sshaunak@ic.ac.uk — MB BS 1982 Lond.; PhD Lond. 1993, BSc (Hons.) 1979; FRCP Lond. 1996; MRCP (UK) 1985; FRCP Ed 1999. (St. Geo.) Cons. Phys. (Infec. Dis.) Hammersmith Hosp. Lond.; Hon. Cons. Phys. Chelsea & W.m. Hosp. Lond.; Reader (Infec. Dis.) Imperial Coll. Sch. of Med. at Hammersmith. Prev: MRC Train. Fell. & Hon. Sen. Regist. (Infec. Dis.) Roy. Postgrad. Med. Sch. Hammersmith Hosp. Lond.; Fell. (Infec. Dis.) Duke Univ., USA; SHO (Med.) Nat. Hosp. Lond., Hammersmith Hosp. Lond. & Roy. Infirm. Edin.

SHAUNAK, Vidosava 34 Grain Road, Wigmore, Gillingham ME8 0ND — MB ChB 1975 Leeds; MRCGP 1979; DCH Eng. 1977; DRCOG 1978. Socs: Brit. Assn. Manip. Med.

SHAVE, Norman Rossen Bridge End Surgery, Chester-le-Street DH3 3SL Tel: 0191 388 3236 Fax: 0191 389 0989; 27 Warkworth Drive, Deneside View Estate, Chester-le-Street DH2 3JR Tel: 0191 388 3462 — MB BS 1985 Newc.; MRCGP 1990; DRCOG 1987. Prev: Trainee GP N.umbria VTS.

SHAVE, Peter Adeane (retired) 1 Sadlers Way, Ringmer, Lewes BN8 5HG — MB BS Lond. 1948, DPH 1966; MFCM 1972; DTM & H Eng. 1952. Prev: SCM (Child Health) E. Sussex AHA.

SHAVE, Ruth Mary X-Ray Department, Russell's Hall Hospital, Dudley DY1 2HQ; 9 The Heathlands, Stourbridge DY8 1NR — MB ChB 1981 Sheff.; FRCS Eng. 1987; FRCR 1993. Cons. Radiol. Dudley Gp. Hosps. NHS Trust. Prev: Sen. Regist. (Diagn. Radiol.) W. Midl. RHA.

SHAVREN, Ruth Elaine 9 Manor Road, Salisbury SP1 1JT — MB BS 1990 Lond.

SHAW, Adam Charles Milestone House, High St., Broadway WR12 7AJ — BM 1996 Soton.

SHAW, Alastair Martin Eastmost Cottage, Old Huntly Hill, Stracathro, Brechin DD9 7PU Tel: 01356 622919 Email: amshaw@doctors .org.uk; The Steyne, Forest Road, Colgate, Horsham RH12 4TB — MB ChB 1988 Aberd.; FRACGP 2000; MRCGP 1994; DRCOG 1993; DFFP 1993. Prev: SHO (Med.) Frenchay Hosp. Bristol; SHO (Obst, & Gyn.) Bedford Hosp.; SHO (Med.) Selly Oak Hosp. Birm.

SHAW, Alexander Duncan Tel: 01250 872033 Fax: 01250 874517; Hill House, Upper Allan St, Blairgowrie PH10 6HL Tel: 01250 872078 — MB ChB 1969 Glas.; MRCGP 1973; DObst RCOG 1971; FRCCP 1997. (Glas.) Socs: BMA. Prev: Ho. Off. (Surg. & Med.) Glas. Roy. Infirm.; Trainee Gen. Pract., Glas. Vocational Train. Scheme.

SHAW, Alexander John (retired) The Steyne, Forest Road, Colgate, Horsham RH12 4TB — MB Camb. 1957, BChir 1956. Prev: Ho. Surg. & Ho. Phys. King's Coll. Hosp.

SHAW, Allen Bernard (retired) 2 The Stables, Weeton Lane, Harewood, Leeds LS17 9LP Tel: 0113 288 6907 — MB BS 1961 Lond.; MD Lond. 1972; FRCP Lond. 1979, M 1965; MRCS Eng. LRCP Lond. 1961. Prev: Cons. Phys. Bradford Roy. Infirm. & St. Lukes Hosp. Bradford.

SHAW, Amanda Anaesthetic Department, Trafford General Hospital, Moorside Road, Davyhulme, Manchester M41 5SL Tel: 0161 748 4022; 2A Boothstown Drive, Worsley, Manchester M28 1UF — MB ChB 1984 Birm.; FRCA 1994; Dip. ATLS RCS Eng. 1991; DA (UK) 1988. Staff Grade (Anaesth.) Trafford Gen. Hosp. Manch. Socs: Assn. Anaesth.; Obst. Anaesth. Assn.; Manch. Med. Soc. Prev: Regist. (Anaesth.) City Gen. Hosp. Stoke-on-Trent; Regist. (Anaesth.) P.ss Roy. Hosp. Telford; Ho. Off. (Med.) Ronkswood Hosp. Worcester.

SHAW, Mr Andrew David 18 Dungrass Avenue, Scotstown, Glasgow G14 9DX Tel: 0141 959 7677 — MB ChB 1988 Manch.; FRCS Ed. 1992. Specialist Regist. (Orthop.) W. of Scotl.

SHAW, Andrew David Seagrave 66 Cherry Hills, Watford WD19 6DL — MB BS 1992 Lond.

SHAW, Andrew James Flat 7A, 55 Balmoral Road, Westcliff on Sea SS0 7DB — MB BS 1993 Lond.; BSc Lond. 1986. (Univ. Lond., UMDS) SHO (Genitourin. Med.) St. Thos. Hosp. Lond. Prev: SHO (O & G) King's Coll. Hosp. Lond. & Roy. Sussex Co. Hosp. Brighton.

SHAW, Andrew John 38 Castlepark Drive, Fairlie, Largs KA29 0DG — MB ChB 1993 Manch.

SHAW, Andrew John Department Genitourinary Medicine, Northwick Park Hospital, Harrow HA1 3UJ Tel: 020 869 3143 Fax: 020 8869 3156 — MB BS 1991 Lond.; BSc (Hons.) Lond. 1988, MB BS 1991; MRCP (UK) 1995; Dip. GU Med. 1996. (Kings Coll. Lond.) Cons., (GUM. & HIV) N.wick Pk. Hosp.; Cons., (GUM & HIV) Centr. Middlx. Hosp. Socs: MSSVD; BHIVA (Brit. HIV Assn.). Prev: Sen. Regist., (GUM & HIV) Char. Cross Hosp.

SHAW, Angela Christine Darent Valley Hospital, Darenth Wood Road, Dartford DA2 8DA Tel: 01322 428732 Email: angela.shaw@dag-tr.sthames.nhs.uk; 36 Shearwater, Longfield DA3 7NL — MB BS 1980 Lond.; MSc (Immunol.) Lond. 1990; MA Oxf. 1981; MRCPath 1987. Cons. Microbiol. Darwent Valley Hosp., Dartford; Cons. Microbiologist, Fawkham Manor Hosp., Fawkham, Kent (Private Hosp. Self-employed). Socs: Hosp. Infec. Soc.; Assn. Med. Microbiol. Prev: Sen. Regist. (Microbiol.) Centr. Middlx. Hosp. Lond.; Regist. (Microbiol.) St. Mary's Hosp. Lond.

SHAW, Anne Patricia Leslie 37 Sandy Lodge Road, Rickmansworth WD3 1LP Tel: 01923 827663 Fax: 01923 827663 — MB BS 1963 Lond.; MRCS Eng. LRCP Lond. 1963; DA Eng. 1966. Socs: Inst. Psychosexual Med.; Fac. Fam. Plann. & Reproduc. Health Care. Prev: SCMO (Family Plann.) Harrow HA.

SHAW, Anthony Moorlands Surgery, 139 Willow Road, Darlington DL3 9JP Tel: 01325 469168; Tel: 01325 489690 — MB ChB 1977 Liverp.; MFHom 1996. Bd. Mem. and Ment. Health Lead, Darlington Primary Care Gp. Prev: SHO (Psychiat.) Fazakerley Hosp. Liverp.; SHO (O & G & Paediat.) Clatterbridge Hosp. Bebington.

SHAW, Anthony John, CB, CBE, CStJ, Maj.-Gen. late RAMC Retd. Standing Medical Board, Duchess of Kent Barracks, Aldershot GU11 2DW Tel: 0125 234152 Fax: 0125 284 2654; Plovers Moss, Winchfield, Hook RG27 8SN Tel: 0125 284 2645 Fax: 0125 284 2654 — MB BChir 1955 Camb.; MA Camb. 1955; MRCS Eng. LRCP Lond. 1954; FRCP Lond. 1989; FFCM 1983, M 1972; DTM & H Eng. 1961; DObst RCOG 1957. (Camb. & Westm.) p/t Standing Med. Bd. Aldershot. Socs: Fell. Med. Soc. Lond. Vice Pres. Prev: Dir. Gen. Army Med. Servs.; Cdr. Med. Svc UK Land Forces; Hon. Phys. to HM The Qu..

SHAW, Anthony John Carteknowle and Dore Medical Practice, 1 Carterknowle Road, Sheffield S7 2DW Tel: 0114 255 1218 Fax: 0114 258 4418; 30 Whitworth Road, Sheffield S10 3HD — MB ChB 1984 Sheff.; MRCGP 1990.

SHAW, Antony Leonard 22 Woodhill Grove, Prestwich, Manchester M25 0AE — MB ChB 1996 Liverp.

SHAW, Ashley Scott 26 Lemox Road, West Bromwich B70 0QT — MB ChB 1996 Sheff. SHO (Gen. Med.) Barnet Gen. Hosp. Herts.

SHAW, Aubrey Abraham Arnold 34 Albany Manor Road, Bournemouth BH1 3EN Tel: 01202 291385 — LRCPI & LM, LRSCI & LM 1948; LRCPI & LM, LRCSI & LM 1948. (RCSI) Med. Assessor DHSS Dorset; Med. Off. TA 1st Wessex Infantry. Prev: Ho. Phys. (Orthop.), Ho. Surg. & Asst. to Psychiat. Crumpsall Hosp.

SHAW, Brian Galbraith Queens Crescent Surgery, 10 Queens Cresent, Glasgow G4 9BL Tel: 0141 332 3526 Fax: 0141 332 1150 — MB ChB 1973 Glas.

SHAW, Bronwen Elizabeth 42A Ridley Road, London NW10 5UA — MB ChB 1993 Cape Town.

SHAW, Caroline Department of Accident and Emergency, Norfolk and Norwich Hospital, Brunswick Road, Norwich NR1 3JR Tel: 01603 287324; 157 Mundesley Road, North Walsham NR28 0DD Tel: 01692 406075 — MB BS 1980 Lond. (St Barthelomews Hospital) Staff Grade (A & E) Norf. & Norwich Hosp. Socs: Brit. Assn. Accid. & Emerg. Med. Prev: SHO (A & E) Scunthorpe Gen. Hosp.; Trainee GP S. Humberside; Clin. Med. Off. (Child Health) Wrexham.

SHAW, Caroline Anne (Byrne) Garden City Practice, 11 Guessen Road, Welwyn Garden City AL8 6QW — MB BS 1989 Lond.; DGM RCP Lond. 1991; MRCGP 1997. GP. Prev: GP Asst.Brook Green.Lond; GP Townsville AU; SHO A&E Blue Mt.ains.Au.

SHAW, Catherine Ann 38B Stanhope Road, London N6 5NG — MB BS 1989 Lond.; BSc (Hons.) Anat. Lond. 1986, MB BS 1989; FRCA 1994. Regist. (Anaesth.) Univ. Coll. Hosp. & Middlx. Hosp. Lond.

SHAW, Catherine Louise Elmfield, Moyallen Road, Portadown, Craigavon BT63 5JX — MB ChB 1992 Ed.

SHAW, Catherine Mary Department of Psychiatry, Tameside General Hospital, Fountain St., Ashton-under-Lyne OL6 9RW — MB BChir 1989 Camb.; MSc Lond. 1990; BA Camb. 1985, MB BChir 1989; MRCPsych 1994. Clin. Research Fell. (Psychiat.) Manch. Roy. Infirm. Prev: Regist. (Psychiat.) NW RHA; SHO (Psychiat.) S. & Centr. Manch. HAs.

*****SHAW, Catherine Susan** c/o Kirkstone Unit, Westmorland General Hospital, Burton Road, Kendal LA9 7RG — MB BS 1978 Lond.

SHAW, Charles Drury CASPE Research, 11-13 Cavendish Square, London W1G 0AN Tel: 020 7307 2881 Fax: 020 7307 2422 Email: cshaw@kahf.org.uk; 77 Curzon Street, Calne SN11 0DW Tel: 01249 816100 Fax: 01249 816100 — MB BS 1969 Lond.; PhD Wales 1986; Dip. Health Care Organisat. & Managem. Canad. Hosp. Assn. 1977. (Middlx.) Assoc.Dir. CASPE Research Lond; Chairm. UK Accred. Forum. Lond. Socs: BMA; Scientif. Counc. ANAEs Paris; (Ex-Pres.) Internat. Soc. Quality in Health Care Melbourne, Austral. Prev: Dir. Med. Audit Progr. King's Fund Centre Lond.; Gen. Manager Cheltenham HA; Med. Dir. King Edwd. VII Memor. Hosp. Bermuda.

SHAW, Charles Stuart (retired) Netherbourne, New Farm Road, Alresford SO24 9QH Tel: 01962 732163 — MB BS 1946 Lond.; FRCP Lond. 1975, M 1951; FRCPath 1970; DCH Eng. 1949. Cons. Chem. Pathol. Roy. Hants. Co. Hosp.

SHAW, Christine Jane The Surgery, Long Street, Topcliffe, Thirsk YO7 3RP Tel: 01845 577297 Fax: 01845 577128 — MB ChB 1971 Sheff.; DObst RCOG 1973; Dip. Therap. Newc 1997. Prev: SHO (Obst. & Gen. Med.) Doncaster Roy. Infirm.; SHO (Paediat.) N. Sheff. Univ. Gp. Hosps.

SHAW, Christopher David Strathmore Medical Practice, 26-28 Chester Road, Wrexham LL11 7SA Tel: 01978 352055 Fax: 01978 310689 — MB ChB 1984 Edinburgh; MB ChB 1984 Edinburgh.

SHAW

SHAW, Mr Christopher John Castle Hill Hospital, Castle Road, Cottingham HU16 5JQ Tel: 01482 623021 — BM BCh 1985 Oxf.; MA Camb. 1986; FRCS (Orth.) 1995; FRCS Eng. 1989. Cons.Orthopaedic Surg., Castle Hill Hosp. Cottingham. Socs: Brit. Elbow & Shoulder Soc.

SHAW, Christopher Paul Dane Garth Unit, Furness General Hospital, Barrow-in-Furness LA14 4LF — MB ChB 1982 Birm.; MRCGP 1988.

SHAW, Christopher Quentin 49 Church Road, Altofts, Normanton WF6 2NU Tel: 01924 893989 — MB ChB 1987 Sheff.

***SHAW, Claire Elizabeth** 33 West Busk Lane, Otley LS21 3LY — BM BS 1995 Nottm.

SHAW, Clare Elizabeth, Surg. Lt. RN (retired) 40 Ravenshead Close, Selsdon, South Croydon CR2 8RL Email: ces.kangas.uk@networkmed.com — MB ChB 1992 Sheff.; MRCGP 1998; DRCOG 1998; DFFP 1994. Salaried GP; Clin. Asst. Psych. Red Gables Trowbridge. Prev: SHO (Psychiat.) Glenbourne Unit Plymouth.

SHAW, Clifford Hamer (retired) 7 Celandine Gardens, Sheffield S17 4JJ Tel: 0114 235 2729 — MB BS 1942 Lond.; MD Lond. 1947; MRCS Eng. LRCP Lond. 1942; FFCM 1972; DPA Sheff. 1949; DPH Eng. 1947. Prev: MOH & Princip. Sch. Med. Off. City Sheff.

SHAW, Clive Henry Ringwood Surgery, Cornerways, School Lane, Ringwood BH24 1LG Tel: 01425 472515 Fax: 01425 470030 — MB BS 1984 Lond. GP Ringwood, Hants.

SHAW, Clive Richard Connolly and Partners, 30 Kingsway, Waterloo, Liverpool L22 4RQ Tel: 0151 928 8668 Fax: 0151 949 1117; 37 Elton Avenue, Blundellsands, Liverpool L23 8UW Tel: 0151 931 3365 Email: cliveshaw@aol.com — MB ChB 1981 Dundee; MRCGP 1985. (Dundee) Co-Chair, Crosby & Maghull PCG.

SHAW, Craig 31 Scooniehill Road, St Andrews KY16 8HZ — MB ChB 1998 Aberd.; MB ChB Aberd 1998.

SHAW, David 2 Chapel View, Cadney Lane, Bettisfield, Whitchurch SY13 2LU Tel: 01948 710882 — MB BCh 1964 Wales; MFOM RCP Lond. 1985, A 1981; DIH Eng. 1981. (Cardiff) Occupat. Health Phys. Wrexham. Prev: Sen. Employm. Med. Advisor Health & Safety Exec. Wrexham; Sen. Med. Off. (Occupat. Health) Gwynedd HA.

SHAW, Professor David Aitken, CBE (retired) The Coach House, 82 Moor Road N., Newcastle upon Tyne NE3 1AB Tel: 0191 285 2029 — MB ChB 1951 Ed.; FRCP Lond. 1976, M 1971; FRCP Ed. 1968, M 1955. Hon. Cons. Neurol. Roy. Vict. Infirm. Newc. Prev: Prof. Clin. Neurol. & Dean of Med. Univ. Newc.

SHAW, David Barrington Cardiac Department, Royal Devon & Exeter Hospital, Barrack Road, Exeter EX2 5DW Tel: 01392 403973 Fax: 01392 402067; Bixley Haven, Woodbury, Exeter EX5 1NR Tel: 01395 232531 — MB BS 1952 Lond.; MD Lond. 1959; FRCP Lond. 1973, M 1956; FRCP Ed. 1971, M 1956; MRCS Eng. LRCP Lond. 1952; FESC 1994; T(M) 1991. Hon. Cons. Phys. & Hon. Sen. Lect. Roy. Devon & Exeter Hosp. Exeter. Socs: Brit. Cardiac. Soc. Prev: Sen. Regist. (Med.) Bristol Roy. Hosp. & Tutor (Med.) Bristol Univ.; Regist. (Med.) Postgrad. Med. Sch. Hammersmith; Clin. Asst. Brompton Hosp. Lond.

SHAW, Mr David Lyon The Cottage, Bradford Royal Infirmary, Duckworth Lane, Bradford BD9 6RJ Tel: 01274 364061 Fax: 01274 366592; Email: dlshaw@orthonet.org.uk — MB ChB 1984 Leeds; MSc Salford 1992; FRCS (Orth.) 1995; FRCS Ed. 1988. Cons. Orthop. & Trauma Surg. Bradford Roy. Infirm. Socs: Brit. Orthop. Assn.; Brit. Research Assn.; Amer. Orthopaedic Assn. Prev: Amer. Orthop. Fell., USA.

SHAW, David Murray Ballnalargy, Dalby, Peel IM5 3BP Tel: 01624 844415 Email: dmjeshaw@advsys.co.uk — MB BS Lond. 1953; PhD Lond. 1961; FRCP Lond. 1978, M 1957; FRCPsych 1979, M 1972; DPM Eng. 1967. (St. Bart.) Prev: Hon. Sen. Lect. Univ. Hosp. Wales Coll. Med. Cardiff; Scientif. Off. Med. Research Counc.; Temp. Act. Surg. Lt. RNVR.

SHAW, David Robert New Park Medical Practice, 163 Robertson Road, Dunfermline KY12 0BL Tel: 01383 629200 Fax: 01383 629203; 120 Grieve Street, Dunfermline KY12 8DW Email: davrshaw@aol.com — MB ChB 1976 Ed.; FRCGP; MRCGP 1980. (Ed.) Director of SHO Train. (S.-E. Scotl. Region).

SHAW, Davida Georgina Margaret 543 Yarm Road, Eaglescliffe, Stockton-on-Tees TS16 9BJ — MB BS 1979 Newc.

SHAW, Deborah Aileen Glenbridge Farm, Todley Hall Road, Laycock, Keighley BD22 0PX — MB ChB 1982 Sheff.; FFARCS Eng. 1988. Cons. Anaesth. Airedale Gen. Hosp. Keighley.

SHAW, Deborah Jane 11 Kirklees Close, Farsley, Pudsey LS28 5TF — MB ChB 1996 Leeds.

SHAW, Mr Denis Latimer (retired) Tan Cottage, West Lane, Cononley, Keighley BD20 8NL Tel: 01535 32030 — MB ChB 1940 Leeds; FRCS Eng. 1948. Prev: Cons. Surg. Goole & Pontefract Hosp. Gps.

SHAW, Dominick Edward Warwick Lodge, Piddington Lane, Piddington, High Wycombe HP14 3BD — MB ChB 1998 Liverp.; MB ChB Liverp 1998.

SHAW, Donald George 37 Sandy Lodge Road, Rickmansworth WD3 1LP — BM BCh 1962 Oxf.; MSc Oxf. 1981; BSc 1959; MA 1962; BA (1st cl. Hons.) 1958; FRCP Lond. 1980, M 1965; FRCR 1975; FFR (Rohan Williams Medal) 1970; DMRD Eng. 1968. (Oxf. & Univ. Coll. Hosp.) Radiol. Hosp. Sick Childr. Lond. Prev: Cons. Radiol. Univ. Coll. Hosp.; Med. Regist., & Ho. Off. Med. & Surg. Units Univ. Coll. Hosp. Lond.; Ho. Phys. Lond. Chest Hosp.

SHAW, Mr Donald Grant Forest Health Care, The Health Centre, Dockham Road, Cinderford GL14 2AN Tel: 01594 598030; Armada Lodge, Hope Mansell, Ross-on-Wye HR9 5TL Tel: 01989 750797 Email: dgsebs@globalnet.co.uk — BM 1980 Soton.; FRCS Eng. 1985; MRCGP 1990; Cert. Family Plann. JCC 1990; DRCOG 1987. (Soton.) Socs: Primary Health Care Specialist Computer Gp. & Assn. Gp. Community Hosps. Prev: Regist. Rotat. (Gen. Surg.) N.ampton Gen. Hosp.; SHO (O & G) Bedford Gen. Hosp.; SHO (Gen. Surg.) Mayday Hosp. Croydon.

SHAW, Douglas (retired) Huntly Cottage, Castle Huntly Road, Longforgan, Dundee DD2 5HA Tel: 01382 360600 — MD (Commend) Dundee 1974; MB ChB St. And. 1968; FRCP Ed. 1985; MRCP (UK) 1978; BA (Hons.) Dund 1997. Cons. Phys. (Med. Rehabil.) & Hon. Sen. Lect. Tayside Health Bd. & Univ. Dundee. Prev: Cons. Phys. (Geriat. Med.) & Hon. Sen. Lect. Roy. Vict. Hosp. & Univ.

SHAW, Duncan 3 Elmbank Drive, Kilmarnock KA1 3AT Tel: 01563 25437 — MB ChB 1962 Glas.; DObst RCOG 1964.

SHAW, Duncan Alastair Sinclair Firvale, Heatherlands Road, Chilworth, Southampton SO16 7JB — MB ChB 1994 Sheff.

SHAW, Edward Alan 64 Broom Lane, Salford M7 4RS — MB ChB 1958 Ed.; FFA RCS Eng. 1964; DObst RCOG 1960. Cons. Anaesth. Roy. Manch. Childr. Hosp. & St. Mary's Hosp. Manch.; Hon. Lect. in Paediat. Anaesth. Univ. Manch.

SHAW, Elizabeth Jane (retired) Pine Cottage, East Grimstead, Salisbury SP5 3RT — MB BS 1982 Lond.; MRCS Eng. LRCP Lond. 1982; LMSSA Lond. 1982; MRCGP 1986; DRCOG 1985. Prev: GP Salisbury.

SHAW, Enid Hilary Park End Surgery, 3 Parkend, South Hill Park, Hampstead, London NW3 2SE Tel: 020 7435 7282; 55 Lanchester Road, London N6 4SX — MB BS (Hons.) Lond. 1955; Cert. Family Plann. JCC 1978. (Roy. Free) Socs: Balint Soc.

SHAW, Fabia Melanie Kilburn Park Medical Centre, 12 Cambridge Gardens, London NW6 5AY Tel: 020 7624 2414 Fax: 020 7624 2489 — MB BS Lond. 1980; DRCOG 1981. (Lond. Hosp.) Prev: Out-Pat. Off. Roy. Nat. Throat, Nose & Ear Hosp. Lond.; Teenage Family Plann. Clinic Doctor Haringey.

SHAW, Felicity Ruth Gosport Health Centre, Bury Road, Gosport PO12 3PN Tel: 01705 583344; 12 Garstons Close, Titchfield, Fareham PO14 4EN — BM 1984 Soton.; MRCGP 1989; DRCOG 1987.

SHAW, Frances Eleanor Worlds End Health Centre, 529 Kings Road, London SW10 0UD Tel: 020 7351 0357 Fax: 020 8846 6399; Black Lion Lodge, Kensington Gardens, Bayswater Road, London W2 4RU — MB BCh BAO 1971 Dub.; BA Dub. 1971; MRCP (UK) 1977; DCH RCPSI 1973. (Trinity Coll. Dub.)

SHAW, Fraser Donald 1A Anderton Close, London SE5 8BU — MB BS 1983 Lond.

SHAW, Frederick Antony Bowden House, Market Harborough LE16 9HW Tel: 01858 4242 — MB ChB 1960 Sheff.; DObst RCOG 1964. (Sheff.) Clin. Tutor Dept. Gen. Pract. Leicester Univ. Med. Sch. Socs: BMA. Prev: Rotating Intern St. John's Gen. Hosp. Newfld.; SHO (O & G) Scarsdale Hosp. Chesterfield.

SHAW, Frederick Ernest (retired) Hawkridge, Chantry Crescent, Stanford-le-Hope SS17 — MB BS 1953 Lond.; MRCS Eng. LRCP Lond. 1953; DObst RCOG 1955; LDS RCS Eng. 1944.

SHAW, Frederick Joseph Oak Tree Medical Centre, 273-275 Green Lane, Seven Kings, Ilford IG3 9TJ Tel: 020 8599 3474 Fax:

SHAW

020 8590 8277; 24 Bressey Grove, South Woodford, London E18 2HU Tel: 020 8597 0921 Fax: 020 8590 8277 — MB BCh 1967 Wales; DA Eng. 1969. (Cardiff) Clin. Asst. (Psychiat.) Claybury Hosp. Woodford Bridge.

SHAW, Gavin Brown, CBE (retired) 31 St Germains, Bearsden, Glasgow G61 2RS — MB ChB Glas. 1942, BSc Glas. 1939; Hon. FRCGP 1980; FRCP Lond. 1965, M 1947; FRFPS Glas. 1950; FRCP Glas. 1964, M 1962; FRCP Ed. 1969, M 1964; Hon. FACP 1979; Hon. FRCPI 1980; Hon. FRCPsych 1980. Hon. Cons. Phys. S. Gen. Hosp. Glas. Prev: Cons. Phys. & Cardiol. S.. Gen. Hosp. Glas.

SHAW, Geoffrey Carlton Aspen House, 28 Pilkington St., Rainford, St Helens WA11 8HG — MB ChB 1980 Manch.; MRCOG 1990; DRCOG 1986. Cons. O & G Fazakerley Hosp. Liverp. Prev: Research Regist. (Assisted Conception) Fazakerley Hosp. Liverp.

SHAW, Geoffrey Macfadyen The Wilderness, Ramsdell, Basingstoke RG26 5RB Tel: 01256 850081 — MB BChir 1952 Camb.; MA Camb. 1952; DPH Lond. 1962. (St. Mary's) Socs: Fell. Roy. Soc. Trop. Med. & Hyg. Prev: Med. Off. United Afr. Co.

SHAW, George Frederick (retired) Hillcote W., First Raleigh, Bideford EX39 3NJ Tel: 01237 476189 — MB BCh BAO 1942 Dub. Prev: Capt. RAMC 1943-46 (mentioned in despatches).

SHAW, Gertraud Bullfer Grove, Gunthorpe, Melton Constable NR24 2PD — LMSSA 1972 Lond. Asst. GP Melton Constable.

SHAW, Grainne Marie 18 Station Road, Magherafelt BT45 5PD — MB BCh BAO 1997 Belf.

SHAW, Grant David 12 Garstons Close, Titchfield, Fareham PO14 4EN Tel: 01329 845134 Email: 100573.373@compuserve.com — BM 1984 Soton. (Soton.) Staff Grade (Orthop.) Qu. Alexandra Hosp. Cosham.

SHAW, Granville Lewin 3 Buccleuch Road, Branksome Park, Poole BH13 6LB — LMSSA 1952 Lond. (Guy's) Prev: Ho. Surg. E. Suff. & Ipswich Hosp.

SHAW, Helen Margaret Boots Healthcare International, Queens Road, Nottingham NG2 3AA; 27 London Lane, Wyneswold, Leicester LE12 6UB — MB ChB 1986 Leic. Med. Manager Boots Healthcare Internat. Nottm. Prev: Assoc. Med. Dir. Fisons UK Operats. Coleorton.

SHAW, Mr Henry Jagoe, VRD (retired) Lislee House, Tredenham Road, St Mawes, Truro TR2 5AN Tel: 01326 270223 — BM BCh Oxf. 1945; MD New York State, US 1958; MA Oxf. 1945; FRCS Eng. 1950. Prev: Cons. ENT Surg. St. Mary's Hosp. Lond.

SHAW, Hilary Elizabeth Mill Lodge, Reading Road, Cholsey, Wallingford OX10 9HG — MB BS 1978 Lond.; MRCGP 1983; DRCOG 1980. (St. Mary's)

SHAW, Horace Arthur, Late Major RAMC (retired) Hollies Orchard, Hollies Drive, Mucklow Hill, Halesowen B62 8NX Tel: 0121 422 3769 — MB ChB 1940 Birm.; MRCS Eng. LRCP Lond. 1940; DObst RCOG 1942. Med. Adviser Bronx Engin. Co. Lye, Stourbridge, W. Midl.; Hon. Maj. RAMC (Late Specialist Anaesth.). Prev: Regist. Highcroft Hall Hosp. Birm.

SHAW, Hung Ming Albert 63 Westacre, Bucknall, Stoke-on-Trent ST1 6AF — MB BS 1979 Bangalore.

SHAW, Ian Northgate Hospital, Northgate St., Great Yarmouth NR30 1BU Tel: 01493 337643 Email: ishaw@doctors.org.uk — MB ChB 1981 Birm.; MRCPsych. 1988; DGM RCP Lond. 1992; DRCOG 1983. (Birm.) Cons. Old. Age Psychiat. N.gate Hosp. Gt. Yarmouth. Prev: Sen. Regist. Rotat. (Psychiat.) Devon & Som. Train. Scheme; Regist. (Psychiat.) Walsgrave Hosp. Coventry.

SHAW, Ian Charles Northern General Hospital, Herries Road, Sheffield S5 7AU Tel: 0114 243 4343 Ext: 4818 Email: ian.shaw@sth.nhs.uk — MB ChB 1991 Sheff.; FRCA. Cons. Anaesth., The N.ern Gen. Hosp., Sheff. Socs: BMA; The Assn. of Anaesth.s; The Intens. Care Soc. Prev: SHO Rotat. (Med.) Hull Roy. Infirm.

SHAW, Ian Hewison — MB BChir Camb. 1982; PhD Camb. 1978; BSc (Hons.) Pharmacol. Bradford 1974; FRCA 1987; DA Eng. 1985. (Camb.) Cons. Anaesth. & Intens. Care Newc. Gen. Hosp.; Hon. Clin. Lect. Univ. Newc.; Examr., Final Fell.ship, Roy. Coll. of Annesthetists; Chairm., N.. Region Rita Panel For Anaesth. Socs: Assn. Anaesths.; BMA. Prev: Sen. Regist. (Anaesth. & Intens. Care) Newc. Gen. Hosp.; Regist. (Anaesth.) Nuffield Dept. Anaesth. Radcliffe Infirm. Oxf.; SHO (Gen Med.) Aberd. Roy. Infirm.

SHAW, Ian Jonathan Padgett 8 The Crow's Nest, The Quay, Burnham-on-Crouch CM0 8AT — MB BS 1993 Lond.

SHAW, Ian Stuart 18 Lee Park, West Buckland, Wellington TA21 9PX — MB ChB 1994 Bristol; MRCP (UK) 1997. (University of Bristol) Specialist Regist. (E.roenterology.) Cheltham Gen. Hosp.

SHAW, Imogen Clare Freshwell Health Centre, Wethersfield Road, Finchingfield, Braintree CM7 4BQ Tel: 01371 810328 Fax: 01371 811282 — MB BChir 1985 Camb.; MA Camb., MB 1985, BChir 1984. SHO Heath Rd. Hosp. Ipswich.

SHAW, Isobel Lyall Bay Hotel, Lamlash, Brodick KA27 8JS Tel: 0177 06 224 — MB ChB 1945 Ed. (Ed.) Prev: GP Isle of Arran.; Med. Asst. Wolverhampton & Midl. Cos Eye Infirm.

SHAW, Jacqueline Frances South Wigston Health Centre, 80 Blaby Road, Wigston LE18 4SE; 9 Link Road, Leicester LE2 3RA — BM BS 1984 Nottm.; BMedSci Nottm. 1982.

SHAW, James Alistair MacGregor Diabetes Research Laboratory, Institute of Medical Sciences, Foresterhill, Aberdeen AB25 2ZD Tel: 01224 273130 Fax: 01224 273144 Email: gen231@abdn.ac.uk; 40 New Street, Stonehaven AB39 2LE Tel: 01569 765177 — MB ChB 1990 Manch.; BSc (Hons.) St. And. 1987; MRCP (UK) 1993. (St. And. & Manch.) Specialist Regist. (Diabetes & Endocrinol.) Aberd. Roy. Infirm.; MRC Train. Fell.

SHAW, James Charlton Halliday Waynes Cottage, The Croft, Fairford GL7 4BD — MB BCh BAO Dub. 1944; MA Dub. 1984; BA Dub. 1942; DCH RCPS Dub. 1948. (TC Dub.) Prev: Med. Off. Cirencester Pk. Polo Club (Emerit.); Ho. Phys. Nat. Childr. Hosp. Dub.; Ho. Surg. Roy. I. of Wight Co. Hosp. Ryde.

SHAW, James William, TD The Rest, Albert St., Tayport DD6 9AR — MB BCh BAO 1970 Dub.; BA, MB BCh BAO Dub. 1970; FFR RCSI 1976; DMRD Ed. 1974. (TC Dub.) Cons. Radiol. Ninewells Hosp. Dundee.

SHAW, Janis 31 Broad Lane, Hale, Altrincham WA15 0DQ Tel: 0161 980 3024 — MB ChB 1976 Liverp.; FRCA 1980. Cons. Anaesth. Manch. Roy. Infirm.

SHAW, Jean Margaret Victoria Health Centre, Glasshouse Street, Nottingham NG1 3LW Tel: 0115 948 3030 Fax: 0115 911 1074 — MB BS 1983 Lond.; BA Camb. 1977; MRCGP 1987; DCH RCP Lond. 1987; DRCOG 1986.

SHAW, Jennifer Jayne 7 Moor Park Avenue, Preston PR1 6AS Tel: 01772 886171; Home Farm, Clifton Hill, Forton, Preston PR3 0AR Tel: 01524 791313 — MB ChB 1982 Manch.; MRCPsych 1987.

SHAW, Jeremy Francis 61 Moscow Road, London W2 4JS Tel: 020 7229 6165 — MB ChB 1957 Bristol; MRCPsych 1971; DPM Eng. 1961. (Bristol) Socs: Brit. Psychoanal Soc. & Brit. Assn. Psychother. Prev: Sen. Regist. (Psychol. Med.) Univ. Coll. Hosp. Lond.; Cons. Marie Stopes Memor. Clinic.

SHAW, Jeremy Nicholas The Health Centre, Manor Road, Beverley HU17 7BZ Tel: 01482 862733 Fax: 01482 864958; 15 New Walk, Beverley HU17 7AE — MB ChB 1970 St. And. (St. And. Dundee) Prev: Regist. (Med.) Papworth Hosp. Camb.; SHO (Paediat.) Jenny Lind Hosp. for Childr. Norwich; SHO Rotat. Hull Roy. Infirm.

SHAW, Jessie Marion Anderson Ardblair Medical Practice, Ann Street, Blairgowrie PH10 6EF Tel: 01250 872033 Fax: 01250 874517; Hill House, Upper Allan St, Blairgowrie PH10 6HL Tel: 01250 872078 — MB ChB 1969 Glas.; Cert FPA 1974. (Glas.) GP Blairgowrie. Socs: BMA.

SHAW, Joan Patricia Vivian (retired) 12c Murray Road, Northwood HA6 2YJ Tel: 01923 821811 — MB BS 1953 Lond. Prev: GP N.wood.

*SHAW, Joanna Louise** 17 Broughton Road, Pedmore, Stourbridge DY9 0XP — MB ChB 1995 Birm.

SHAW, John 405 Thornaby Road, Thornaby, Stockton-on-Tees TS17 8QN — MB ChB 1995 Leeds.

SHAW, John David Highfield Surgery, Holtdale Approach, Leeds LS16 7RX Tel: 0113 230 0108 Fax: 0113 230 1309 — MB ChB 1989 Leeds.

SHAW, John Denis Reid 64 Station Road, London E4 7BA — MB BCh BAO 1940 Belf.; MLCO 1968. Socs: Brit. Assn. Manip. Med. Prev: Capt. R.A.M.C.; Ho. Surg. Roy. Vict. Hosp. Belf.

SHAW, Mr John Dennis (retired) The Gables, Sandygate Road, Sheffield S10 5UE Tel: 0114 230 7784 — MB ChB Sheff. 1962; FRCS Eng. 1969; FRCS Ed. 1967. Prev: Cons. ENT Surg. Roy. Hallamsh. Hosp. Sheff.

SHAW, Mr John Francis Longsdon Derriford Hospital, Plymouth PL6 8DH Tel: 01752 777111; Homefield, Grenofen, Tavistock

SHAW

PL19 9EW Tel: 01822 612435 — MB BS 1975 Lond.; ChM Oxf. 1983, BA 1972; FRCS Eng. 1980; MRCS Eng. LRCP Lond. 1975. (Guy's) Cons. Surg. Derriford Hosp. Plymouth. Socs: Surgic. Research Soc.; Brit. Transpl. Soc. Prev: Sen. Regist. (Surg.) Roy. Free Hosp. Lond.; Regist. & Research Fell. (Surg.) Addenbrooke's Hosp. Camb.; Ho. Phys. & Ho. Surg. Guy's Hosp. Lond.

SHAW, Mr John Fraser (retired) 6 Gamekeeper's Park, Edinburgh EH4 6PA Tel: 0131 336 2828 — MB BS 1945 Lond.; FRCP Ed. 1982; FRCS Ed. 1965; FRCS Eng. 1954. Prev: Cons. Surg. Surg. Neurol. Roy. Infirm., W.. Gen. Hosp. & Roy. Hosp. Sick Childr. Edin.

SHAW, John Herbert Thorndike Vine Cottage, Spode Lane, Mark Beech, Edenbridge TN8 7HG Tel: 01342 850592 — MB BS 1955 Durh. Exam. Med. Pract. Benefits Agency Med. Servs. Prev: GP Edenbridge; Ho. Phys. (Paediat.) S.mead Hosp. Bristol; Ho. Surg. Maidenhead Hosp.

SHAW, John Humphrey Wilfred (retired) 10 The Mount Drive, Reigate RH2 0EZ Tel: 01737 226250 Email: johnwshaw@hotmail.com — MB BChir Camb. 1958; MA Camb. 1959; DObst RCOG 1959. Prev: SHO (O & G) & Ho. Phys. Ilford Matern. Hosp. & King. Geo. Hosp. Ilford.

SHAW, Johnstone Eskbridge Medical Centre, 8A Bridge Street, Musselburgh EH21 6AG Tel: 0131 665 6821 Fax: 0131 665 5488 — MB ChB 1979 Ed.; MRCGP 1986; MRCOG 1985. GP Edin.

SHAW, Jonathan Conrad Lister 11 Grand Avenue, Muswell Hill, London N10 3AY Tel: 020 8883 4326 — BM BCh 1962 Oxf.; BA Oxf. 1959, BM BCh 1962; FRCP 1979, M 1967; DCH Eng. 1965. (Univ. Coll. Hosp.) Socs: Neonat. Soc. & Europ. Soc. Paediat. Research. Prev: Cons. Neonat. Paediat. Univ. Coll. Hosp. Lond.

SHAW, Jonathan Greville Havergal (retired) 21 Ventnor Gardens, Barking IG11 9JY Tel: 020 8594 3568 — MB BChir 1948 Camb.; MRCS Eng. LRCP Lond. 1947; DTM & H Liverp. 1970. Prev: Princip. GP Lond.

SHAW, Mr Jonathan Harvey — MB ChB 1991 Ed.; 2000 (MRCSEL) Royal College of Surgeons. Eng.; 1996 (Royal College of Surgeons.Eng.) Dip. IMC RCS Ed.; 1995 (Royal College of Anaesthetists, London) DA. (Edinburgh) Specialist Regist. A & E, N.W. (Manch.) Deanery. Socs: Brit. Assn. Accid. & Emerg. Med.; Fac. Pre-Hosp. Care.

SHAW, Jonathan Patrick Tristram 88 Ethel Street, Benwell, Newcastle upon Tyne NE4 8QA Tel: 0191 273 8666 — MB Camb. 1977, BChir 1976; MRCGP 1983; DCH RCP Lond. 1983.

SHAW, Mr Joseph, RD, CStJ (retired) Monks Meadows, Church Road, Holywood BT18 9BZ — MB BChir Camb. 1956; FRCSI 1983; FRCS Ed. 1965; FFAEM 1993. Civil. Cons. (A & E) RN; Surg. Capt. RNR. Prev: Cons. Surg. Ulster Hosp. Belf.

SHAW, Julia Clare Flat 3/1, 143 Yorkhill St., Yorkhill, Glasgow G3 8NS — MB BS 1996 Lond. (UMDS)

SHAW, Kanika 29 Hayley Bell Gardens, Bishop's Stortford CM23 3HA — BM 1988 Soton.

SHAW, Katharine Lisa Flat 6, 1 Mornington Crescent, London NW1 7RH — MB BS 1991 Lond.

SHAW, Katherine Nicola 37 Sandy Lodge Road, Rickmansworth WD3 1LP Tel: 019238 27663 — BM BS 1994 Nottm.; BMedSci Nottm. 1992.

SHAW, Kathryn Campbell 3 Elmbank Drive, Kilmarnock KA1 3AT — MB ChB 1990 Glas.; MRCGP 1994; T(GP) 1995; DRCOG 1992. Trainee GP Glas.

SHAW, Kathryn Jane 66 Cherry Hills, Watford WD19 6DL — MB BS 1992 Lond.

SHAW, Kenneth Ian Chessel Surgery - Bitterne Branch, 4 Chessel Avenue, Bitterne, Southampton SO19 4AA Tel: 023 8044 7777 Fax: 023 8042 5429 — MB BS 1975 Lond.; DRCOG 1978. (Lond. Hosp.) Prev: Trainee GP Bath VTS.

SHAW, Professor Kenneth Martin Castle Acre, Hospital Lane, Portchester, Fareham PO16 9QP — MB BChir Camb. 1969; MA, MD Camb. 1979; FRCP Lond. 1985; MRCP (UK) 1970. (Univ. Coll. Hosp.) Cons. Phys. & Dir. of Research & Developm. Portsmouth Hosps. NHS Trust; Vis. Prof. Postgrad. Med. Sch. Univ. Portsmouth; Hon. Clin. Teach. Soton. Univ. Med. Sch.; Edr. in Chief Jl. Pract. Diabetes Internat. Socs: Fell. Roy. Soc. Med.; Scientif. Fell. Zool. Soc.; Brit. Diabetic Assn. Prev: Resid. Asst. Phys. Univ. Coll. Hosp. Lond.; MRC Asst. Dept. Clin. Pharmacol. Univ. Coll. Hosp. Med. Sch. Lond.

SHAW, Keren Ann Mayfair, Old Tree Heights, Hoath, Canterbury CT3 4LE — MB BS 1984 Lond. (St. Mary's) GP Herne Bay. Prev: Regist. (Chem. Path.) Qu. Mary's Hosp. Lond.; Ho. Off. Ealing Hosp. Lond.

***SHAW, Kirsty** 67 Urquhart Terrace, Aberdeen AB24 5NJ Tel: 01224 636111 — MB ChB 1998 Aberd.; MB ChB Aberd 1998.

SHAW, Kirsty Jane Torwood, Rowan Park, Carr Bridge PH23 3BE Tel: 01479 841232 Email: torwood@pcscience.net — MB ChB 1993 Dundee; MB ChB (Commend.) Dundee 1993; DRCOG 1995; DFFP 1995; MRCGP (Mevix) 1998. (Dundee)

SHAW, Laurence Marcus Alan St Perters Road, Margate CT9 4AN — MB BS 1978 Lond.; MRCS Eng. LRCP Lond. 1979; FRCOG 1997; MRCOG 1984; DRCOG 1981. (St. Bart.) Cons O&G E. Kent Hosp.s NHS Trust; Hon. Sen. Lect. Univ. of Kent at Canterb. Socs: Fell. Roy. Soc. Med.; Liveryman Worshipful Soc. Apoth. Lond.; (Vice Pres.) SE Gyn. Soc. Prev: Clin. Dir. Woms. & Childrs. Health Qu. Eliz. Qu. Mother Hosp.; Sen. Regist. (O & G) W.m. Hosp. Lond.; Regist. (O & G) Hammersmith Hosp. Lond.

SHAW, Lindsay Jane 141 Sefton Park Road, St. Andrews, Bristol BS7 9AW — MB ChB 1991 Bristol; BSc 1988 Bristol. (Bristol) Dermat. Specialist Regist., Bristol Roy. Infirm. Socs: Brit. Soc. of Paediatric Dermat. Prev: Paediat. Regist. S.mead Bristol; Paediat. Regist. Taunton & Som. Hosp.; Paediat. Regist. Roy. Childr.s Hosp. Melbourne.

SHAW, Lisa Clare 68 Culcheth Hall Drive, Culcheth, Warrington WA3 4PX — BM BCh 1998 Oxf.; BM BCh Oxf 1998.

SHAW, Louise Johanna Royal United Hospital, Combe Park, Bath M13 9WL Tel: 01225 831749; 30 Spencers Orchard, Bradford-on-Avon BA15 1TJ — MB ChB 1992 Sheff.; MRCP (UK) 1995. (Sheff.) Cons. in Geriat. and Stroke Med.

SHAW, Mr Malcolm (retired) 1 Brown Road, Kirkcudbright DG6 4HP Tel: 01557 330900 — MB ChB Glas. 1938; MA Glas. 1938; FRCS Glas. 1962; FFA RCS Eng. 1954; DA Eng. 1946. Prev: Cons. Anaesth. Vict. Infirm. Glas. & Roy. Hosp. Sick Childr. Glas.

SHAW, Mr Malcolm Donald Macalister The Walton Centre for Neurology & Neurosurgery NHS Trust, Lower Lane, Liverpool L9 7LJ Tel: 0151 529 5671/5533 Fax: 0151 529 5509; 33 Budworth Road, Oxton, Prenton CH43 9TQ Tel: 0151 653 5034 — BM BCh 1966 Oxf.; MA Oxf. 1966; FRCS Eng. 1972. (Oxf.) Cons. Neurosurg.; Lect. (Neurosurg.) Liverp. Univ.; Med. Director, Trust Bd., The Walton Centre for Neurol. and Neurosurg. NHS Trust, Liverp. Socs: Oxf. Grads. Med. Club & Soc. Brit. Neurol. Surgs. Prev: Sen. Regist. (Neurosurg.) Inst. Neurol. Sc. S.. Gen. Hosp. Glas.; Regist. (Neurosurg.) Radcliffe Infirm. Oxf.

SHAW, Marcia Susan Torbay Hospital, Lawes Bridge, Torquay TQ2 7AA Tel: 01803 655578; 20 Adelaide St, Plymouth PL1 3JF Tel: 01803 313881 — MB BS 1974 Lond.; MRCP (UK) 1977. Cons. Dermat. Torbay Hosp. Torquay.

SHAW, Margaret (retired) 65 Carter Knowle Road, Sheffield S7 2DW — MRCS Eng. LRCP Lond. 1958. Prev: Ho. Phys. Mansfield Gen. Hosp. Ho. Surg. & SHO Anaesth. Roy. Infirm. Sheff.

SHAW, Maria Emilia Lourdes Cordeira New Ford Health Centre, 2 Baden Road, Smallthorne, Stoke-on-Trent ST6 1SA Tel: 01782 834288; Smallthorne Health Centre, 2 Baden Road, Stoke-on-Trent ST6 1SA Tel: 01782 834288 — LRCPI & LM, LRSCI & LM 1961; LRCPI & LM, LRCSI & LM 1961. GP Stoke on Trent. Socs: BMA.

SHAW, Mark Christopher UMDS Department of Public Health Medicine, 5th Floor Capital House, 42 Weston St., London SE1 3QD Tel: 020 7955 5000 Ext: 6249 Fax: 020 7403 4602 Email: m.shaw@umds.ac.uk; Flat 10, Victoria Court, Victoria Road, Shoreham-by-Sea BN43 5WS Tel: 01273 884522 Email: markcs@mistral.co.uk — MB BS 1988 Lond. Hon. Lect. (Pub. Health Med.) UMDS. Prev: Sen. Regist. (Pub. Health Med.) E. Sussex HA; Regist. (Pub. Health Med.) E. Sussex & Maidstone HA; SHO (Med.) Worthing Hosp.

SHAW, Martin Bellamy Banks Medical Centre, 272 Wimborne Road, Bournemouth BH3 7AT Tel: 01202 512549 Fax: 01202 548534 — MB BS 1976 Lond.; MRCS Eng. LRCP Lond. 1976; D.Occ.Med. RCP Lond. 1995. (Roy. Free) p/t GP Princip. Bournemouth; Occupat. Health Phys.; GP Commr. Socs: Soc. Occupat. Med.; BAMM.

SHAW, Martin Whitney (retired) Manor Farm House, East Dean, Chichester PO18 0JA Tel: 01243 811207 — MB 1966 Camb.; BChir 1965; DA Eng. 1968.

SHAW, Martin Winston 26 Tudor Hollow, Fulford, Stoke-on-Trent ST11 9NP — MB ChB 1998 Liverp.; MB ChB Liverp 1998.

SHAW, Mary Kay (retired) 15 Hatt Close, Moulton, Spalding PE12 6PX — MRCS Eng. LRCP 1951 Lond.; MRCS Eng. LRCP Lond.1951.

SHAW, Matthew Benjamin Keeble 22 Brookfields, Netherton, Wakefield WF4 4NL — BM BCh 1997 Oxf.

SHAW, Matthew Byrom Brookside Group Practice, Brookside Close, Gipsy Lane, Earley, Reading RG6 7HG Tel: 0118 966 9222 Fax: 0118 935 3174 — MB ChB 1987 Bristol.

SHAW, Matthew Jon 19 Glaisedale Grove, Willenhall WV13 1HB — MB BS 1998 Lond.; MB BS Lond 1998.

SHAW, Matthew Philip MRC Laboratory, Fajar, PO Box 273, Banjul, Gambia; 8 Harlesden Gardens, London NW10 4EX Tel: 020 8961 3208 — MB BS 1986 Lond.; MSc Lond. 1995; BSc (Hons.) Sociol. Applied to Med. Lond. 1983; MRCGP 1992; DCH RCP Lond. 1990. Jun. Researcher (Scientif.) HIV Interven. MRC, The Gambia. Prev: GP Fell. (HIV) St Mary's Hosp. Lond.; Trainee GP St Mary's Hosp. Lond.

SHAW, Melanie Sara Brunswick Xray, Norfolk and Norwich Hospital, Norwich NR1 3RR Tel: 01603 286523; The Maltings, South Walsham Road, Panxworth, Norwich NR13 6JG Tel: 01603 270471 Email: mleadbe@aol.com — MB BS 1989 Lond.; BSc Lond. 1986; MRCP (UK) 1994; FRCR (UK) 1997. (St Georges Hospital Medical School) Cons. Pathologist, Norf. and Norwich HNS Health Care Trust. Prev: Regist. (Radiol.) Roy. Lond. Hosp.; SHO (Thoracic Med.) Lond. Chest Hosp.; SHO (Renal Med.) St. Bart. Hosp. Lond.

SHAW, Michael John St Georges Hospital, Morpeth, Birmingham NE61 2NU Tel: 01670 512121 — MB ChB 1990 Leeds. Cons. (Adult Gen. Psychiat), Newc., N. Tyneside and N.d. Ment. Health (NHS) Trust, St Geo.s Hosp. Morpeth. Socs: Roy. Coll. Psychiat.s. Prev: Regist. (Psychiat.) Mersey RHA.; Specialist Regist. (Adult Gen Psychiat.) Mersey RHA.

SHAW, Michael Maurice Bersted Green Surgery, 32 Durlston Drive, Bognor Regis PO22 9TD Tel: 01243 821392 Fax: 01243 842590 — MB BS 1972 Lond.; MRCS Eng. LRCP Lond. 1972; DObst RCOG 1974; DIH Soc. Apoth. Lond. 1976. (Guy's) Socs: BMA. Prev: Med. Off. Brit. Steel Corp. Lackenby; SHO (O & G & Cas.) St. Richard's Hosp. Chichester; Ho. Phys. St. Mary's Hosp. Newport I. of Wight.

SHAW, Muriel Kathleen 19 Upper Crofts, Alloway, Ayr KA7 4QX Tel: 01292 443785 — BM BS 1977 Nottm.; FFA RCS (Eng.) 1981. Cons. Anaesth. CrossHo. Hosp. Kilmarnock. Socs: BMA & Assn. Anaesth. Prev: Sen. Regist. (Anaesth.) Qu. Med. Centre Nottm.; Regist. (Anaesth.) Bristol Roy. Infirm.

SHAW, Neil Howard Po Box 121, Leeds LS16 8XH Tel: 0113 2817741 Fax: 0113 2817741 — MB ChB 1985 Leeds; MRCGP 1991; 2002 Afom RCP Lond; DRCOG 1989; Cert. Prescribed Equiv. Exp. JCPTGP 1989. (Leeds) Occupat.al Phys., Leeds & W.Yorks. Socs: Soc. Occupat. Med. Prev: Trainee GP Bradford VTS; Med. Off. Univ. Leeds Health Serv.; GP Prinncipal, Foundat. Med. Centre, Leeds.

SHAW, Nicholas Alastair Glade House, 27 Harrot Hill, Cockermouth CA13 0BL; 20 Oxford Street, Workington CA14 3AL Tel: 01946 603302 — MB BChir 1978 Camb.; MA Camb. 1979, MB BChir 1978; MRCGP 1982; DRCOG 1981. Prev: Regist. (Med.) Whakatane Hosp. New Zealand; Ho. Surg. Essex Co. Hosp. Colchester; Ho. Phys. Qu. Marys Hosp. Sidcup.

SHAW, Nicholas John 21 Linden Way, Ponteland, Newcastle upon Tyne NE20 9DP — MB ChB 1988 Sheff.

SHAW, Nicholas John — MB ChB 1978 Birm.; FRCPCH 1997; MRCP (UK) 1985; DCH RCP Lond. 1983; DRCOG 1982; DTM & H (Liverp.) 1982. Cons. Paediat. Endocrinol. Birm. Childr. Hosp.; Hon. Sen. Lect. (Paediat.) Univ. Birm. Socs: Roy. Coll. Paediat. & Child Health; Amer. Soc. of Bone & Mineral Research; Eur. Soc. Paediat. Endocrinol. Prev: Sen. Regist. (Paediat. Endocrinol.) Birm. Childr. Hosp.; Lect. (Child Health) Alder Hey Childr. Hosp. Liverp.; Lect. (Paediat.) St. Jas. Univ. Hosp. Leeds.

SHAW, Nigel John 21 Devonshire Road, West Kirby, Wirral CH48 7HR — MB ChB 1980 Birm.

SHAW, Mr Norman Carey Chestnut Byre, Rudham Road, Harpley, King's Lynn PE31 6TH Tel: 01485 520646 Email: carey.shaw@harpley.net — MB BS 1963 Lond.; FRCS Eng. 1970. (Char. Cross) Prev: Cons. (Orthop. Surg. & Trauma) Qu. Eliz. Hosp. Kings Lynn. & N. Cambs. Hosp. Wisbech.; Sen. Regist. Roy. Nat. Orthop. Hosp. Stanmore; Sen. Regist. (Orthop.) Norf. & Norwich Hosp.

SHAW, Mr Norman Merryweather District General Hospital, Scartho Road, Grimsby DN33 2 Tel: 01472 874111 — MB ChB 1956 Manch.; FRCS Ed. 1966. (Manch.) Cons. Orthop. Surg. Grimsby Hosp. Gp. Socs: Fell. BOA. Prev: Sen. Regist. (Orthop.) Leeds RHB; Regist. P.ss Eliz. Orthop. Hosp. Exeter; Ho. Surg. Manch. Roy. Infirm.

SHAW, Professor Pamela Jean Department of Neurology, Ward 11, Royal Victoria Infirmary, Newcastle upon Tyne NE1 4LP Tel: 0191 232 5131 Fax: 0191 227 5267 Email: pamela.shaw@ncl.ac.uk; 20 Parklands, Hamsterley Mill, Rowlands Gill NE39 1HH Tel: 01207 543239 — MD 1988 Newc.; MB BS 1979; FRCP 1994; MRCP (UK) 1981. (University of Newcastle-upon-Tyne) Wellcome Sen. Research Fell. (Clin. Sci.), Prof. Neurol. Med. & Hon. Cons. Neurol. Univ. Newc. u. Tyne.

SHAW, Paul Hamelton 26 Tudor Hollow, Fulford, Stoke-on-Trent ST11 9NP — MB ChB 1993 Liverp.

SHAW, Penelope Jane 45 Hartington Road, Grove Park, Chiswick, London W4 3TS — MB BS 1977 Lond.; MRCP (UK) 1980; FRCR 1983. Cons. Radiol. Univ. Coll. Hosp. Lond.

SHAW, Mr Peter Alan Field House, Sandy Lane, Newcastle ST5 0LZ Tel: 01782 630630 Fax: 01782 630630; Park House, Oakley, Market Drayton TF9 4AG — MB ChB 1965 Leeds; BSc Lond. 1959; FRCS Ed. 1975; DO Eng. 1972. (Leeds) Cons. Ophth. N. Staffs. Roy. Infirm. Stoke on Trent. Socs: FRCOphth. Prev: Sen. Regist. (Ophth.) Leeds Gen. Infirm.; Regist. (Ophth.) Birm. & Midl. Eye Hosp.; Anat. Demonst. Bristol Med. Sch.

SHAW, Mr Peter Cosmo 8 Castlemaine Avenue, South Croydon CR2 7HQ — MB BS 1957 Lond.; FRCS Eng. 1965; FRCS Ed. 1963. (Guy's) Cons. Orthop. Surg. Bromley Gp. Hosps.

SHAW, Peter John The Symons Medical Centre, 25 All Saints Avenue, Maidenhead SL6 6EL Tel: 01628 626131 Fax: 01628 410051; 19A The Cresecnt, Maidenhead SL6 6AA Tel: 01628 541265 Fax: 01628 541266 Email: shorkie@aol.com — MB BS 1985 Lond.; DRCOG 1991. (Char. Cross) GP Tutor E. Berks.; Edit. Bd. Psychiat. in Pract. Prev: SHO (Cardiol. & Transpl. Med.) Harefield Hosp. Middlx.; SHO (Gen. Med.) Heatherwood Hosp. Ascot; SHO (O & G) Luton & Dunstable Hosp.

SHAW, Peter Quentin Stirchley Medical Practice, Stirchley Health Centre, Stirchley, Telford TF3 1FB Tel: 01952 660444 Fax: 01952 415139; Mount Farm, Cruckton, Shrewsbury SY5 8PR — MB BS 1981 Lond.; BSc (1st cl. Hons.) Hist. Med. Lond. 1978; MRCP (UK) 1984; MRCGP (Distinc.) 1989; DRCOG 1989; DCH RCP Lond. 1984. (Univ. Coll. Hosp.)

SHAW, Mr Reginald Ernest (retired) Glebe Cottage, Horn Hill, Barford-St.-Michael, Banbury OX15 0RQ — MB BS 1943 Lond.; FRCSC 1968; FRCS Eng. 1948; DA (UK) 1970; DRCOG 1964.

SHAW, Mr Richard Emmott (retired) 1 Enright Close, Old College Park, Leamington Spa CV32 6SQ Tel: 01926 882985 Email: richard.e.shaw@gatewayuk.net — MRCS Eng. LRCP Lond. 1940; ChM Leeds 1949, MB ChB 1940; FRCS Eng. 1947. Prev: Cons. Urol. Coventry Hosp. Gp.

*****SHAW, Richard John** Flat Top Right, 19 Highburgh Road, Glasgow G12 9YF — MB ChB 1998 Glas.; MB ChB Glas 1998; FDS RCS Eng 1993; BDS (Bristol) 1990.

SHAW, Robert Frederick Holsworthy Health Centre, Western Road, Holsworthy EX22 6DH Tel: 01409 253692 Fax: 01409 254184; Holsworthy Health Centre, Well Park, Holsworthy EX22 6DH Tel: 01409 253692 — MB ChB Leic. 1991.

SHAW, Robert Logan Tel: 01475 633777 — MB ChB 1982 Glas.; BSc 1980 Glas.; FRCS Glas. 1986; FRCR 1990. Cons. Radiologist, Inverclyde Roy. Hosp.,. Prev: Sen. Regist. (Radiol.) N.wick Pk. Hosp. Harrow.

SHAW, Professor Robert Wayne Eastern Deanery, Block 3, 1da Darwin Site, Fulbourn, Cambridge CB1 5EE Tel: 01223 884848 Fax: 01223 884849; Tel: 020 8590 0282 Fax: 020 8599 0282 — MB ChB (Hons.) Birm. 1969; MD (Hons.) Birm. 1975; FRCS Ed. 1978; FRCOG 1993, M 1977. (Birm.) Post Grad. Dean. E.. Deanery, Camb.; Chairm. Matern. & Child Health Research Consortium - Confidential Enquiry into Stillbirth (CESDI). Socs: (Ex-Chairm.) Blair Bell Research Soc. 1986-89; Pres. World Endornetriosis Soc. 2002-05; Pres. Roy. Coll. of Obst.s & Gyn. 1998-. Prev: Prof. Head Acad.

SHAW

Dept. O & G Roy. Free Hosp. Sch. Med.; Prof. Head Acad. Dept. O & G Univ. of Wales Coll. of Med.

SHAW, Robin Richard 3 Pendorlan Road, Penrhyn Bay, Llandudno LL30 3PS — MB ChB 1987 Manch.

SHAW, Roderick John McIntosh, Gourlay and Partners, 1 India Place, Edinburgh EH3 6EH Tel: 0131 225 9191 Fax: 0131 226 6549 — MB ChB 1985 Manch.; MRCGP 1989.

SHAW, Roderick Watson Kingsway Medical Practice, 12Kingsway Court, Glasgow G14 9SS Tel: 0141 959 6000 Fax: 0141 954 6971; 18 Corbie Place, Milngavie, Glasgow G62 7NB Tel: 0141 956 3685 — MB ChB 1980 Glas.; MRCGP 1983; DRCOG 1981. GP Trainer Glas.; Undergrad. Tutor. Glas. Univ. Socs: BMA; Primary Care Rheum. Soc.; Christ. Med. Fell.sh. Prev: Hosp. Pract. S. Gen. Hosp.; SHO (O & G) Stobhill Hosp. Glas.; SHO (Paediat.) Monklands & Dist. Gen. Hosp. Airdrie.

SHAW, Ronald (retired) 48A Warwick Place, Leamington Spa CV32 5DF Tel: 01926 28186 — MRCS Eng. LRCP Lond. 1937; MA Camb. 1937; FFA RCS Eng. 1954; DA Eng. 1938. Prev: Sen. Cons. Anaesth. S. Warw. Hosp. Gp.

SHAW, Professor Rory James Swanton Hammersmith Hospital, Du Cane Road, London W12 0HS Tel: 020 8383 3370 — MB BS 1977 Lond.; BSc (1st cl. Hons.) Lond. 1974, MD 1985; MBA Univ. Lond. 1995; FRCP Lond. 1993; MRCP (UK) 1979; T(M) 1991. (St. Bart.) Prof., Cons. Phys. (Respirat. Med.), Med. Dir. Hammersmith Hosps. Trust Lond.; Chairm. of the Nat. Pat. Safety Agency. Socs: Brit. Thorac. Soc.; Amer. Thorac. Soc. Prev: MRC/Lilly Trav. Fell. & RCP Prophit Sch. Nat. Jewish Centre for Immunol. & Respirat. Med. Denver Co., USA; Cons. Phys. St Mary's Hosp. Lond. & Dir. of Med. Educat. Unit Imperial Coll. Sch. of Med.

SHAW, Rosaleen Amanda Crumlin Road Health Centre, 130-132 Crumlin Road, Belfast BT14 6AR — MB BCh 1988 Dublin.

SHAW, Ruth Elizabeth 11 Magnolia Court, Beeston, Nottingham NG9 3LG — BM BS 1993 Nottm.; BMedSci Nottm. 1991.

SHAW, Sally Anne Old Hall Surgery, 26 Stanney Lane, Ellesmere Port, South Wirral CH65 9AD Tel: 0151 355 1191 Fax: 0151 356 2683; 29 Whitegates Crescent, Willaston, South Wirral CH64 2UX Tel: 0151 327 6706 — MB BS 1980 Lond.; MRCP Ed. 1985; MRCGP 1988. GP Ellesmere Port. Prev: Med. Dir. Hospice of Good Shepherd Chester; Regist. (Radiother.) Clatterbridge Hosp. Wirral; Regist. (Med.) Sheff.

SHAW, Samantha Jane 26 Lewisham Park, London SE13 6QZ — MB ChB 1994 Leic.

SHAW, Samuel MacKay Dufftown Medical Group, Health Centre, Stephen Avenue, Dufftown, Keith AB55 4BH Tel: 01340 820888 Fax: 01340 820593 — MB ChB 1985 Aberd.; MRCGP 1989.

SHAW, Sarah 55 Old Park Avenue, Enfield EN2 6PJ — MB BS 1996 Lond.; BA (Hons.) Oxf. 1992.

***SHAW, Sarah Jane Louise** 146 Welsh House Farm Road, Harborne, Birmingham B32 2JG — MB ChB 1998 Birm.

SHAW, Sheila Joan Drs Angio, Shaw & Owen, Pemberton PCRC, Sherwood Drive, Pemberton, Wigan WB5 9QX — MB ChB 1981 Manch.; T(GP) 1991.

SHAW, Simon Alexander 24 Bressey Grove, London E18 2HU — MB BS 1996 Lond.

SHAW, Simon Andrew Holly House, Smithy Lane, Bardsey, Leeds LS17 9DT — BM BCh 1997 Oxf.; MA (Hons.) Camb. 1994. Res. Med. Off. Roy. Perth Hosp. Perth, Australia. Socs: BMA (Sec. Yorksh. JDS 1997-98). Prev: Ho. Off. (Med. & Surg.) York Dist. Hosp.

SHAW, Simon John Geoffrey Street Health Centre, Geoffrey Street, Preston PR1 5NE Tel: 01772 401760 Fax: 01772 401766 — BM BCh 1986 Oxf.; MA Camb. 1990, BA 1983. (Cambridge 1980-83; Oxford 1983-86) GP Princip. Prev: Trainee GP Sandbach; SHO Rotat. Leighton Hosp. Crewe VTS.

SHAW, Simon Nicholas Leicestershire and Rutland Healthcare NHS Trust, Bradgate Mental Health Centre, Groby Road, Leicester LE3 9EJ Tel: 0116 250 2626; 10 Seaton Road, Uppingham, Oakham LE15 9QX — MB ChB 1988 Ed.; BSc Liverp. 1981; MPhil. Psychiat. Ed. 1997; MRCPsych 1993. (Ed.) Cons. Gen. Psychiat. Leics. & Rutland Healthcare NHS Trust; Clin. Dir.; Clin. Teach. (Fac. of Med.) Univ. Leicester; Hon. Cons. Psychiat. St. Luke's Hosp. for the Clergy Lond. Prev: Sen. Regist. (Psychiat.) Leics.; Regist. (Psychiat.) Fife Train. Scheme; Trainee GP Edin.

SHAW, Stephen Douglas Department of Anaesthesia, Aintree Hospitals NHS Trust, Fazakerley Hospital, Longmoor Lane, Liverpool L9 Tel: 0151 529 2565; 79 Meols Drive, West Kirby, Wirral CH48 5DF — MB ChB 1983 Liverp.; FRCA. 1991. Cons. Anaesth. Aintree Hosps. NHS Trust. Prev: Sen. Regist. Rotat. (Anaesth.) Mersey Regional Train. Scheme.

SHAW, Stephen Hirst The Moorings, 100 Selby Road, West Garforth, Leeds LS25 1LW Tel: 01132 862617 — MB ChB Leeds 1967; FRCPsych 1997; MRCPsych 1972; DMJ (Clin.) Soc. Apoth. Lond. 1972; DPM Leeds 1970; MA 1998. (Leeds) cons. Neuropsychiat.; Hon. Lect. (Psychiat.) Leeds Univ. Socs: World Psychiat. Assn.; Brit. Acad. Forens. Sci. Prev: Sen. Regist. (Forens. Psychiat.) United Leeds Hosps.; SHO (Psychiat.) St. Jas. Hosp. Leeds; Regist. (Psychiat.) Scalebor Pk. Hosp. Burley-in-Wharfedale.

SHAW, Stephen Hywel Dalzell Chippenham Surgery, Monmouth NP25 3EQ Tel: 01600 713811 Fax: 01600 772652 — BM BCh 1974 Oxf.; MRCGP 1985; DRCOG 1980.

SHAW, Stephen Rodney 9 Boston Drive, Marton, Middlesbrough TS7 8LZ — MB ChB 1990 Dundee.

SHAW, Stuart Antony Graham Tonge Moor Health Centre, Thicketford Road, Bolton BL2 2LW Tel: 01204 521094 — MB BS 1980 Lond.; MRCGP 1984; DRCOG 1983. (Westm.) GP Bolton; Clin. Asst. Dept. Genito-Urin. Med. Bolton HA.

SHAW, Mr Stuart John 7 Moor Park Avenue, Deepdale, Preston PR1 6AS Tel: 01772 886171 Fax: 01772 886181 Email: sjshaw@dial.pipex.com — MB ChB; FRCS Ed. FRCS (Orth.). (Manchester) Cons. Trauma & Orthopaedic Surg. Preston & Chorley HHS Trust Roy. Preston Hosp., Preston.

SHAW, Stuart Lawson Woodlands, 2 Autumn Walk, Maidenhead SL6 4ND — MB BS 1996 Lond.; BSc (Hons) Lond. 1991. (UMDS) Med. Off. Roy. Navy.

SHAW, Susan Christine Department of Experimental Psychopathology, Institute of Psychiatry, De Crespigny Park, London SE5 8AF Tel: 020 7919 3363 Fax: 020 7740 5244 Email: spjuscs@iop.bpmf.ac.uk — MB BS 1992 Lond.; BSc Lond. 1989; MRCPsych 1996. (University College Hospital and Middlesex School of Medicine) Specialist Regist. in Old Age Psychiat.; Hon. Specialist Regist. Socs: RCPsych. Prev: Clin. Lect. (Psychother.) Inst. of Psychiat. Lond.; Clin. Research Inst. of Psychiat. Lond.; Regist. Rotat. (Psychiat.) Roy. Free Hosp. Lond.

SHAW, Susan Elizabeth Battersea Fields Practice, 3 Austin Road, Battersea, London SW11 5JP; 52 Burnbury Road, London SW12 0EL — MB ChB 1985 Manch.; MRCGP 1996. Prev: Trainee GP Lond.; SHO (Med. & Rheum.) Trafford Gen. Hosp.; SHO (A & E) Stockport Infirm.

SHAW, Susan Patricia Bootham Park Hospital, Bootham Park, York YO30 7BY Tel: 01904 610777 Fax: 01904 453794 — MB BCh BAO 1977 Dub.; MMedSci Clin. Psychiat. Leeds. 1984; MRCPsych 1981. (TC Dub.) Cons. Psychiat. Bootham Pk. Hosp. York.

SHAW, Therese Bridget St Anne's Hospital, St Anne's Road, London N15 3TH — MB BS 1986 Lond.; MRCPsych 1993.

SHAW, Thomas (retired) Woodlands, May Lodge Drive, Rufford, Newark NG22 9DE Tel: 01623 822379 — MB ChB Birm. 1959.

SHAW, Thomas James Iain 24B Moorbank Road, Sandygate, Sheffield S10 5TR Tel: 0114 230 6723 — MB ChB 1972 Sheff.; FFA RCS Eng. 1976. (Sheff.) Cons. Anaesth. Chesterfield Roy. Hosp. Socs: Assn. Anaesths.; Obst. Anaesth. Assn. Prev: Sen. Regist. & Regist. (Cardiothoracic Anaesth.) Sheff. AHA (T); Staff Anaesth. Univ. Hosp. Groningen, Netherlands.

SHAW, Thomas Raymond Dunlap Department Cardiology, Western General Hospital, Edinburgh EH4 2XU; 29 Merchiston Park, Edinburgh EH10 4PW — MB ChB 1968 Glas.; BSc Glas. 1966, MD 1983; FRCP Glas. 1992; FRCP Ed. 1986; MRCP (UK) 1972; FESC 1993. (Glas.) Socs: Brist. Cardiac Soc.; Brist. Cardiovasc. Interven. Soc. Prev: Sen. Regist. (Cardiol.) Edin. Hosps.; Hon. Regist. (Cardiol. Dept.) St. Bart. Hosp. Lond.; SHO (Gen. Med.) Roy. Infirm. Edin.

SHAW, Timothy Colin 20 Bower Lane, Grenoside, Sheffield S35 8NE — BM BCh 1975 Oxf.; MA Oxf. 1975, BM BCh 1975; FFA RCS Eng. 1979.

SHAW, Timothy John 3 Church Avenue, Norwich NR2 2AQ Email: 100603.726@compuserve.com — BChir 1994 Camb.; MA Camb. 1996; MRCP 1998. (Camb.)

SHAW, Tracy Jane Y Fron, High St., Cemaes Bay LL67 0HU — MB BS 1989 Lond.

SHAW, Valerie Jane Eleanor 13 Dundela Gardens, Belfast BT4 3DH Tel: 01232 654902 — MB BCh BAO 1983 Belf.; MRCGP 1988; DCH RCPI 1987. GP Belf. Retainer Scheme. Socs: Roy. Coll. Gen. Pract. Prev: Trainee GP Belf. VTS.

SHAW, Victoria Marie Diana Nicoresti (retired) 3 Meadsway, 8 Staveley Road, Eastbourne BN20 7LH Tel: 01323 638860 — MB ChB 1943 Leeds; MFCM 1972; DPH Eng. 1949; DObst RCOG 1945. Prev: Specialist Community Med. (Social Servs.) Hillingdon AHA.

SHAW, W A Burncross Surgery, 1 Bevan Way, Chapeltown, Sheffield S35 1RN Tel: 0114 246 6052 Fax: 0114 245 0276.

SHAW, Wendy Alison Newbold Surgery, 3 Windemere Road, Newbold, Chesterfield S41 8DU Tel: 01246 277381; The Old Farm House, 1 Park Farm Mews, The Lane, Spinkhill, Sheffield S21 3XQ Tel: 01246 430120 — MB BS 1991 Lond.; BSc (Hons.) Lond. 1988; MRCGP 1996; DFFP 1995; DCH RCP Lond. 1994; DRCOG 1993. (St. Geo. Hosp. Med. Sch.) Asst. GP Newbold Surg. Chesterfield. Prev: Trainee GP Warwick, SHO (Geriat. Med.) N.ampton Hosp.; SHO (Paediat. & Neonat.) Birm. Heartlands Hosp.

SHAW, William Joseph Samuel Thomas Hillview Medical Centre, 60 Bromsgrove Road, Redditch B97 4RN Tel: 01527 66511; 28 Crumpfields Lane, Webheath, Redditch B97 5PN Tel: 01527 545279 — MB ChB 1963 Birm.; DObst RCOG 1965. (Birm.) Hosp. Pract. Alexandra Hosp. Redditch. Prev: Regist. (Med.) BromsGr. Gen. Hosp.

SHAW, William Lawson Clintrials Research Ltd., Kings Chase, 107/123 King St., Maidenhead SL6 1DP Tel: 01628 508802 Fax: 01628 788337 Email: williamshaw@clintrialsresearch.com; 2 Autumn Walk, Maidenhead SL6 4ND Tel: 01628 674519 Fax: 01628 635045 — MB ChB 1971 Glas.; FFPM RCP (UK) 1989. (Glas.) Pres. Europe Asia/Pacific Clintrials Research Ltd. Maidenhead Berks. Socs: Fell. Roy. Soc. Med.; Soc. Pharmaceut. Med.; Brit. Assn. Pharmaceut. Phys. Prev: Regional Med. Dir. Warner Lambert Pk.e-Davis; Med. Advisor Organon Laborats. Ltd.; Med. Dir. Sandoz Pharmaceut. Ltd.

SHAW, Mr William Mortimer Haigh (retired) Low Birk Howe, Little Langdale, Ambleside LA22 9PA Tel: 015394 37259 — MB ChB 1938 Leeds; MB ChB (Hons.) Leeds 1938; BSc (Hons.) Leeds 1935; FRCS Eng. 1946; MRCS Eng. LRCP Lond. 1938. Prev: Cons. Plastic Surg. Gen. Infirm. Leeds & Plastic Surg. Unit, St. Jas. Hosp. Leeds.

SHAW, Yvonne Pearl Alexandra Gardens Day Hospital, Old See House, 603 Antrim Road, Belfast BT15 4DR — MB BCh BAO 1974 Belf.; MRCPsych. 1981.

SHAW-BINNS, Stephanie 10 McKendrick Villas, North Fenham, Newcastle upon Tyne NE5 3AB — MB BS 1989 Newc.; MRCGP 1994; DRCOG 1994.

SHAW DUNN, Gilbert Leverndale Hospital, Crookston Road, Glasgow G52 Tel: 0141 211 6400 — MB ChB 1973 Glas.; BSc (Path.) Glas. 1971, MB ChB 1973; MRCP (UK) 1978; MRCPsych 1981; FRCP Glasgow 1990. (Glasgow) Cons. Psychiat. Leverndale Hosp. Glas. And S.ern Gen. Hosp. Glas.. (Cons. in Psychiat. of old age). Prev: Sen. Regist. (Psychiat.) Roy. Ed. Hosp.; Regist. (Psychiat.) E.. Glas. Health Dist.; SHO (Med.) Glas. Roy. Infirm.

SHAW-SMITH, Charles James Cliff Farm, Long Lee, Keighley BD21 5RA — BM BCh 1989 Oxf.; MRCP (UK) 1992. Wellcome Research Fell. Gastroenterol. Unit Hammersmith Hosp. Lond. Prev: Regist. (Med.) Hammersmith Hosp. & Ealing Hosp. Lond.; SHO (Med.) Qu. Med. Centre Nottm.

SHAWCROSS, Annette Winifred 73 Cavendish Road, Hazel Grove, Stockport SK7 6HU Tel: 01625 876578; 144A Banstead Road S., Sutton SM2 5LL Tel: 020 8643 8533 — BM BS 1988 Nottm.; BMedSci Nottm. 1986; MRCP (UK) 1997; DCH RCP Lond. 1995. (Nottm.) Specialist Regist. (Paediat.) E. Surrey Hosp. Redhill. Socs: M.R.C.P.Ch (Ordinary). Prev: Specialist Regist. (Paediat.) S. Downs Health Trust; Paediat. Regist. (L.A.T.) Paediat. Gen. & Neonates Lewisham Dist. Gen. Hosp.; Clin. Asst. (Paediat.) Childr. Trust Tadworth.

SHAWCROSS, Carol Joan Totley Rise Medical Centre, 96 Baslow Road, Sheffield S17 4DQ Tel: 0114 236 5450 Fax: 0114 262 0942 — MB ChB 1976 Sheff.; BSc (Hons.) (Physiol.) Sheff. 1971, MB ChB 1976; DRCOG 1978. Prev: SHO (Obst.) N. Gen. Hosp. Sheff.; Ho. Phys. Roy. Hosp. Sheff.; Ho. Surg. N.. Gen. Hosp. Sheff.

SHAWCROSS, Charles Richard Gosport War Memorial Hospital, Bury Road, Gosport PO12 3PW Tel: 02932 524611 Fax: 02932 580360 Email: charles.shawcross@porthc-tr.swest.nhs.uk — MB ChB 1976 (Hons.) Bristol; BSc (Hons.) Bristol 1973; FRCPsych (1997), MRCPsych. 1980. Cons. Psychiat. Gosport War Memor. Hosp. Prev: Sen. Regist. Mapperley Hosp. Nottm.; Regist. & SHO (Psychiat.) Barrow Hosp.; Ho. Phys. & Ho. Surg. Bristol Roy. Infirm.

SHAWCROSS, Colin Stuart Firth Park Road Surgery, 400 Firth Park Road, Sheffield S5 6HH Tel: 0114 242 6406; 6 Riverdale Road, Sheffield S10 3FA Tel: 0114 662073 — MRCS Eng. LRCP Lond. 1974. Med. Adviser to Kvaerner Metals (Sheff.) Ltd., UCAR Carbon Ltd.; Clin. Asst. (Endoscopy) Roy. Hallamshire Hosp. Sheff. Prev: SHO (Anaesth.) Centr. (Sheff.) Health Dist. (T); Ho. Surg. & Ho. Phys. Roy. Hosp. Sheff.

SHAWCROSS, Deborah Lindsay John Radcliffe Hospital, Headley Way, Oxford OX3 9DU Tel: 01865 741166; Tudor Lodge, Franklin Road, North Fambridge, Chelmsford CM3 6NF Tel: 01621 742194 — MB BS 1996 Lond.; BSc (Hons) Lond. 1993; MRCP 1998, Part 1 1998, Part 2, 1999. (St. Mary's Hospital) SHO (Gen. Med.) Rotat. John Radcliffe Oxf. Prev: Mem. BMA; Mem. MPS.

SHAWCROSS, Joanna Hillside Hospice, Hill Gap Road, Eastbourne BN21 2HJ Tel: 01323 644500; Pond Cottage, Friston Place, Eastbourne BN20 0AL Tel: 01323 422422 — MB BS 1976 Lond.; DRCOG 1979; Dip. Palliat. Med. 1996. Cons. in Palliat. Care; Asst. GP Sussex.

SHAWE, Deirdre Jill North Hampshire Hospital, Aldermaston Road, Basingstoke RG24 9NA Tel: 01256 313650 Email: djshawe@aol.com — MB BS 1978 Lond.; MRCP (UK) 1982; MRCGP 1984; DCH 1981. (Char. Cross Hosp. Med. Sch.) Cons. (Rheum.) N. Hants. Hosp. Basingstoke. Prev: Sen. Regist. in Rheum. N.wick Pk. Hosp. Harrow Middlx.

SHAWE, Elizabeth Alison 28 Chestwood Grove, Hillingdon, Uxbridge UB10 0EN — MB BS 1981 Lond.; FFA RCS Eng. 1988; FFA RCS I 1988. (Char. Cross Lond.) Sen. Regist. (Anaesth.) NW Thames. Prev: Regist. (Anaesth.) St. Geo. Hosp. Lond.; Regist. & SHO (Anaesth.) Hillingdon Hosp. Middlx.

SHAWIS, Mr Rang Noory Sadeek Sheffield Children's Hospital, Western Bank, Sheffield S10 2TH Tel: 0114 271 7000 Fax: 0114 276 8419 — MB ChB 1973 Mosul; M Ed 2001 Sheffield; FRCS Ed. 1979. Cons. (Paediat. Surg.) Sheff. Childr.s Hosp.; Hon. Lect. Med. Sch. Sheff. Univ.; Hon. Sen. Lect. Med. Sch. Sheff. Univ.; Examr., Intercollegiate Bd. for Paediatric Surg. Socs: Counc. Mem. BAPS; Brit. Assn. Paed. Gastro. & Nutrit..; BAPES (Brit. Assn. Paed. Endoscopic Surg.). Prev: Cons. (Paediat. Surg.) Tawam Hosp. Alain UAE; Sen. Regist. (Paediat. Surg.) W.m. Childr.s Hosp.; Alder Hey Childr.s Hosp. L'pool.

SHAWIS, Teshk Nouri 10 Westchester House, Seymour St., London W2 2JG — MB ChB 1989 Leeds; MRCP (UK) 1994. Cons (Phys.) Colchester Gen Hosp. Socs: BMA; Brit. Geriat. Soc. Prev: Sen. Regist. (Geriat. Med.) Qu. Alexandra Hosp. Portsmouth; Regist. (Geriat.) Burnley Gen. Hosp.; Regist. (Diabetic & Gen. Med.) Blackburn Roy. Infirm.

SHAWKAT, Mr Said 21 Rutland Crescent, Ormskirk L39 1LP — MB BCh 1967 Cairo; FRCS Ed. 1980.

SHAWKET, Saffana Abdul Jabbar 17 Meadowcourt Road, Leicester LE2 2PD — MB ChB 1974 Baghdad; MSc Camb. 1992; FFA RCSI 1984. Cons. Anaesth. Geo. Eliot Hosp. Nuneaton. Socs: Eur. Soc. Regional Anaesth.; Obst. Anaesth. Assn.; Brit. Soc. of Orthopaedic Anaesth.s. Prev: Sen. Regist. (Anaesth.) Trent RHA; Research Fell. (Clin. Pharmacol.) Camb. Univ. Med. Sch. Addenbrooke's Hosp.

SHAXTED, Edward John Kingswood, 75 The Avenue, Clifftonville, Northampton NN1 5BT Tel: 01604 632309 Fax: 01604 632351 Email: edshax@btinternet.com; 10 Favell Way, Weston Favell, Northampton NN3 3BZ Tel: 01604 403490 — MB BS 1970 Lond.; DM Nottm. 1982; FRCOG 1989, M 1977; DObst 1972. (Lond. Hosp.) Cons. O & G N.ampton Gen. Hosp.; Hon. Sen. Lect. (Obst. & Gyn.) Birm. Univ. Socs: (Counc.) Brit. Soc. Gyn. Endoscopy. Prev: Sen. Regist. (O & G) Nottm. Univ. Hosp.; Regist. (O & G) Addenbrooke's Hosp. Camb.; Sen. Specialist (O & G) RAF Hosp. Halton.

SHAYLOR, Jane Margaret (retired) Bluebell House, Poplar Avenue, Norwich NR4 7LB — MB BS 1967 Lond.; MRCS Eng. LRCP

SHAYLOR

Lond. 1967; MRCP (UK) 1981; FRCP 1999. Prev: Cons. in Repiratory Med. Norf. and Norwich Hosp.

SHAYLOR, Joanne Louise 6 Somerville Drive, Sutton Coldfield B73 6JB — MB ChB 1991 Birm.; BSc Path. (1st cl. Hons.) Birm. 1990, MB ChB 1991. Trainee GP/SHO (Paediat.) Selly Oak Hosp. Birm. VTS.

SHAYLOR, Phillip John 70 Grosvenor Road, Harborne, Birmingham B17 9AN — MB BS 1985 Lond.

SHAYO, Simon Daniel 114 Eden Close, Slough SL3 8TZ — MB BS 1974 Makerere.

SHEA, Mr Frederick William (retired) New Place, 9 Newall Mount, Otley LS21 2DY Tel: 01943 465379 — MB BS 1948 Melbourne; MChOrth Liverp. 1953; FRCS Ed. 1956. Prev: Cons. Orthop. Surg. St. Jas. Univ. Hosp. & Wharfedale Gen. Hosp.

SHEA, Ingeborg 904 Howard House, Dolphin Square, London SW1V 3PQ — MB ChB 1996 Ed.

SHEA, James Neil 9 Cameron Court, Parkhill Drive, Rutherglen, Glasgow G73 2PN Tel: 0141 647 3400 — LRCP LRCS Ed. LRFPS Glas. 1948. Socs: Glas. E. & S. Med. Socs.

SHEA, Mr John Gordon Dewsbury & District Hospital, Halifax Road, Dewsbury WF1 34HS Tel: 01924 512000; Tel: 01900 812653 Email: derek.bell@luht.scot.nhs.uk — MB BS 1966 Lond.; FRCS Eng. 1974; MRCS Eng. LRCP Lond. 1966. (Char. Cross) Cons. Orthop. Surg. Dewsbury Dist. Hosp. Prev: Sen. Regist. (Orthop.) E. Berks. (Windsor) Health Dist.; Sen. Regist. (Orthop.) Roy. Free Hosp. Lond.; Regist. (Gen. Surg.) Mt. Vernon Hosp. N.wood.

SHEAFF, Michael Timothy Morbid Anatomy Department, Royal London Hospital, Whitechapel, London E1 1BB — MB BS 1990 Lond.; BSc Lond. 1988, MB BS 1990; MRCPath 1996. Cons./Hon. Sen. Lect. (Histopath. & Cytopath) Roy. Hosp. Trust Lond. Prev: Regist. & SHO (Histopath.) Roy. Lond. Hosp.

SHEAFF, Peter Charles Neurosciences Department, St. Bartholomews Hospital, 38 Little Britain, London EC1A 7BE Tel: 020 7601 7664; 104 Aldermans Hill, London N13 4PT — MB BS 1962 Lond.; FRCP Lond. 1984, M 1968. (Middlx.) Cons. Neurol. St. Bart. Hosp. & N. Middlx. NHS Trust; Hon. Cons. Clin. Neurophysiol. St. Bart. Hosp. Lond. & The Lond. Hosp. Whitechapel. Socs: EEG Soc.; Assn. Brit. Neurols. Prev: Cons. Clin. Neurophysiol. OldCh. Hosp. Romford; Sen. Regist. (Clin. Neurophysiol.) St. Bart. Hosp. Lond.

SHEALS, David Gordon Royal Albert Edward Infirmary, Wigan Lane, Wigan WN1 2NN; Summerdale House, Cow Brow, Lupton, Carnforth LA6 1PE Tel: 01539 567210 — MB ChB 1977 Liverp.; FRCR 1983; DMRD Liverp. 1981. Cons. Radiol. Wigan HA.

SHEALS, Gail Summerdale House, Cow Brow, Lupton, Carnforth LA6 1PE — MB BCh 1976 Wales; FRCR 1983; DMRD Liverp. 1981. Prev: Cons. Radiol. Ormskirk & Dist. Gen. Hosp.

SHEARD, Alan Varley (retired) 7 Northfield, Swanland, North Ferriby HU14 3RG Tel: 01482 633971 Email: gilalsrid@surflaid.org — MB ChB 1956 Leeds; MFCM 1972; DPH Lond. 1967; DObst RCOG 1962. Prev: Dir. Pub. Health E. Yorks. HA.

SHEARD, Christopher Richard The Health Centre, Springs Lane, Ilkley LS29 8TQ Tel: 01943 602255 Fax: 01943 430005 — MB BChir 1966 Camb.; MB Camb. 1966, BChir 1965; MRCS Eng. 1966 LRCP Lond. 1967; DObst RCOG 1968. (Guy's)

SHEARD, Jonathan Daniel Henry Green Gates, 10 St Georges Road, Formby, Liverpool L37 3HH — MB ChB 1987 Liverp.; MD Liverp. 1997; MRCPath 1993. Cons. Histopath. & Cytopath. Fazakerley Hosp. Liverp. Prev: Sen. Regist. Rotat. (Histopath.) Mersey.

SHEARD, Lucy Doris (retired) 5 West Parklands Drive, North Ferriby HU14 3EX Tel: 01482 634744 — MB ChB 1958 Leeds. Prev: GP S. Cave.

SHEARD, Paul Mackenzie 30 Westbourne Gardens, Glasgow G12 9PF — MB ChB 1979 Ed.; LMCC 1986; FRCPSC 1986; MRCPsych 1984. Cons. Psychiat. Sydney City Hosp. Nova Scotia, Canada.

SHEARD, Peter Hubert Walker (retired) Stroud House, Freshwater PO40 9JA — MB BChir 1957 Camb.; MA Camb. 1957; MRCS Eng. LRCP Lond. 1956. Prev: GP Freshwater, I. of Wight.

SHEARD, Richard Michael 15 Felsham Chase, Burwell, Cambridge CB5 0JP Tel: 01353 741773 — MB BChir 1993 Camb.; BA (Hons.) Camb. 1991.

SHEARD, Simon Charles BMI Health Services, Grey Friars, 10 Queen Victoria Road, Coventry CV1 3PJ Tel: 02476 500705 Fax: 02476 500701 Email: ssheard@bmihs.co.uk; Malt House Farm House, 8 Grange Avenue, Kenilworth CV8 1DD Tel: 01926 864452 Email: saschrel@aol.com — MB ChB 1982 Bristol; FFOM 2000 (RCP) Lond.; MMedSci Birm. 1991; MFOM RCP Lond. 1992; DAvMed FOM RCP Lond. 1988. Director Clin. Developm. Prev: Roy. Navy Med. Off.

SHEARD, Timothy Andrew Boyd Division of Psychiatry, 41 St Michael's Hill, Bristol BS2 8PL Tel: 0117 928 2342 Fax: 0117 928 3865 — BChir 1980 Camb.; MB 1981. CAT Psychotherapist; Clin. Research Fell. Univ. Bristol. Prev: Cancer Research Campaign Train. Fell. Bristol Oncol. Centre.; Phys. Cancer Help Centre Bristol; McMillan Fell. St. Peter's Hospice Bristol.

SHEARD, Timothy Simon Rawdon Surgery, 11 New Road Side, Rawdon, Leeds LS19 6DD Tel: 0113 295 4234 Fax: 0113 295 4228; 66 Broadgate Lane, Horsforth, Leeds LS18 4AG Tel: 0113 258 4401 — MB ChB 1983 Leeds; DRCOG 1987. (Leeds) Mem. Leeds LMC. Socs: Brit. Assn. Sport & Med. Prev: BCG Bd. Mem.; NW Leeds PCG.

SHEARER, Alexander Charles Iain Four Oaks Medical Centre, Carlton House, Mere Green Road, Sutton Coldfield B75 5BS Tel: 0121 308 2080 Fax: 0121 323 4694; Charter House, Church St, Appleby Magna, Swadlincote DE12 7AN Tel: 01570 270257 — MB ChB 1971 Birm.; PhD Birm. (Exp. Path.) 1965; BSc (1st cl. Hons.) St. And. 1960.

SHEARER, Alexander Fleming 5 Fonthill Terrace, Aberdeen AB11 7UR — MB ChB 1971 Aberd.

SHEARER, Alfred James Department of Anaesthesia, Ninewells Hospital, Dundee DD1 9SY Tel: 01382 660111 Fax: 01382 644914; 10 Graystane Road, Invergowrie, Dundee DD2 5JQ Tel: 01382 562444 Email: alfs@dth.tuht.nhs.uk — MB ChB 1971 Aberd.; FFA RCS Eng. 1976. (Aberd.) Cons. Anaesth. & Intens. Care, Tayside Univ. Hosps. Prev: Sen. Regist. & Regist. (Anaesth.) Aberd. Teach. Hosps.; Regist. (Anaesth.) Hosp. Sick Childr. Gt. Ormond St.

SHEARER, Mr Christopher Joseph Flat 1/1, 57 Cresswell St., Glasgow G12 8AD — MB ChB 1995 Glas.; MB ChB Glasgow 1995; MRCS Glasgow 1998. Sen. Health Off. Gen. Surg. CrossHo. Hosp. Kilmarnock.

SHEARER, Donald (retired) Loch Na Moighe, Culloden Moor, Inverness IV2 5EE Tel: 01463 790676 — MB ChB Ed. 1947; MRCGP 1959; FFPHM RCPI 1988, M 1978; DPH Ed. 1956. Prev: Cons. Pub. Health Med. & Community Med. Specialist Highland HB.

SHEARER, Euan Sinclair 22 Lingfield Road, Liverpool L14 3LA — MB ChB 1982 Liverp.; DA Eng. 1985.

SHEARER, Hamish Lawrie 25 Belmont Drive, Griffnock, Glasgow G46 7NZ — MB ChB 1993 Glas.

SHEARER, James Holmes (retired) 4 Dunavon Park, Strathaven ML10 6LP Tel: 01357 521589 — MB ChB 1952 Glas. Prev: Ho. Surg. Vict. Infirm. Glas.

SHEARER, James Malcolm Latham (retired) Grey's Cottage, Maldon Road, Kelvedon, Colchester CO5 9BD Email: malcom.shearer@talk21.com — MB BChir 1948 Camb.; FRCGP 1996, M 1977. Prev: Regist. (Med.) Chelmsford Hosp. Gp.

SHEARER, Mr John Robertson Academic Orthopaedic Unit, RNM CF86, Southampton General Hospital, Tremona Road, Southampton SO16 Tel: 02380 777222; Greystoke, Heatherlands Road, Chilworth, Southampton SO16 7JD Tel: 02380 768815 — MB ChB 1966 Aberd.; PhD Aberd. 1975, MB ChB 1966; FRCS Ed. 1971. (Aberd.) Prof. (Orthop. Surg.) Univ. Soton.

SHEARER, Katrina Helen 63 Clepington Road, Dundee DD4 7BQ — MB ChB 1994 Glas.

SHEARER, Kenneth Bowland Road, 52 Bowland Road, Baguley, Manchester M23 1JX Tel: 0161 998 2014 Fax: 0161 945 6354 — MB ChB 1970 Manch.; MRCGP 1980. Hosp. Pract. (Cardiol.) Wythenshawe Hosp. Manch.

SHEARER, Kieran Springfield Road Surgery, 26 Springfield Road, Belfast BT12 7AG — MB BCh BAO 1982 Belf.; DRCOG 1986.

SHEARER, Lesley Margaret Flat 3, 1 Hamilton Drive, Kelvinbridge, Glasgow G12 8DN Tel: 0141 337 1262 — MB ChB 1996 Glas. SHO (Med. for the Elderly) Mansion Ho. Unit Vict. Infirm. Glas. Prev: SHO (A & E) CrossHo. Ho. Kilmarnock; SHO (Surg.) Hairmyres Hospita Lanarksh.; SHO (Med.) CrossHo. Kilmarnock.

SHEARER, Mr Michael George Dumfries & Galloway Royal Infirmary, Bankend Road, Dumfries DG1 4AP — MB ChB 1977

Glas.; BSc (Hons.) Glas. 1975, MD 1992; FRCS Glas. 1981. Cons. Urol. Dumfries & Galloway Roy. Infirm.

SHEARER, Pauleen Elizabeth Cathcart Practice, 8 Cathcart Street, Ayr KA7 1BJ Tel: 01292 264051 Fax: 01292 293803; 23 Forehill Road, Ayr KA7 3DU — MB ChB 1985 Glas.

SHEARER, Raymund Michael Springfield Road Surgery, 26 Springfield Road, Belfast BT12 7AG — MB BCh BAO 1954 Belf.; MD Belf. 1966.

SHEARER, Mr Robert John (retired) Royal Marsden Hospital, Fulham Road, London SW3 6JJ Tel: 020 7351 2166 Fax: 020 7376 7163 Email: robert.shearer@rmh.nthames.nhs.uk — MB BS Lond. 1962; FRCS Eng. 1967. Prev: Cons. Urol. St. Jas. Hosp. Lond. & St. Geo. Hosp. Lond.

SHEARER, Simon Andrew Devonshire Road Surgery, 467 Devonshire Road, Blackpool FY2 0JP Tel: 01253 352233; 258 Blackpool Road, Poulton-le-Fylde FY6 7QU — MB ChB 1980 Manch.; MRCGP 1984; DRCOG 1983. Socs: BMA.

SHEARES, Caroline Sow Key 20 Melbourne Road, Sheffield S10 1NS — MB ChB 1995 Sheff.

SHEARES, Karen Kwie Kay Clinical Pharmacology Unit, Box 110, Addenbrooke's NHS Trust, Cambridge CB2 2QQ Tel: 01223 245151 — BM BCh 1993 Oxf.; MA oxf. 1995; MRCP (UK) 1996. (Oxf.)

SHEARING, Laura Jane 29 Thyme Way, off Lincoln Way, Beverley HU17 — MB ChB 1988 Leeds.

SHEARMAN, Anthony John Village Surgery, Gillett Road, Poole BH12 5BF Tel: 01202 525252 Fax: 01202 533956; 16 Sandecotes Road, Parkstone, Poole BH14 8NX — BM 1986 Soton.

SHEARMAN, Professor Clifford Paul Department of Vascular Surgery, Southampton General Hospital, Southampton SO16 6YD Tel: 02380 898801 Fax: 02380 825565; Little Thatch, Lower Slackstead, Braishfield, Romsey SO51 0QJ — MB BS 1979 Lond.; BSc Lond. 1976, MS 1989; FRCS Eng. 1983. (Guy's) Prof. of Vasc. Surg./Hon. Cons. Vasc. Surg., S.ampton Univ.; Hon. Sen. Lect. Univ. Soton. Socs: Vasc. Soc. GB & Irel.; Eur. Soc. Vasc. Surg. Prev: Sen. Lect. & Hon. Cons. Surg. Birm. Univ.; Cons. Vasc. Surg. Soton. Univ. Hosps. Trust.

SHEARMAN, Jeremy David Department of Gastroenterology, Warwick Hospital, Lakin Road, Warwick CV34 5BW Tel: 01926 495321 Fax: 01926 482601 Email: jeremy.shearman@swarkhosptr.wmids.nhs.uk — MB ChB 1988 Leeds; DPhil 1996; BSc (Hons.) Path. Leeds 1988; MRCP (UK) 1991. Cons. Gastroenterologist Warwick Hosp. Socs: Brit. Soc. of Gastrenterology; Brit. Assn. for the Study of Liver. Prev: Regist. (Gen. Med.) Oxf. RHA; SHO Rotat. (Oncol., Endocrine & Gen. Med.) Oxf. RHA; SHO (Neurol. & Renal.) Univ. Hosp. Wales Cardiff.

SHEARN, Christopher Anthony Health Centre, Windmill Avenue, Hassocks BN6 8LY Tel: 01273 844242 Fax: 01273 842709; New Close Farm House, London Road, Hassocks BN6 9ND Tel: 01273 846639 — MB BS 1977 Lond.; MRCGP 1981; DRCOG 1980. (Kings College) Sen. Part. Gen. Pract.; Chairm. W. Sussex MAAG. Prev: Clin. Asst. (Clin. Med. for Elderly) Cuckfield Hosp.; GP Tutor Mid. Downs - Base Unit.

SHEARS, Daniel 69D Bushey Grove, Bushey, Watford WD23 2GJ — MB BS 1991 Lond.

SHEARS, Deborah Jane 1 Warren Road, Ickenham, Uxbridge UB10 8AA — MB BS 1990 Lond.; MRCP (UK) 1993; BA Oxon. 1987. (Oxford University/St Bartholomew's) Clin. Research Fell. (Clin. Genetics) Inst. of Child Health Lond.

SHEARS, Mary-Rose Byars Health Centre, University of Sussex, Falmer, Brighton BN1 9RW Tel: 01273 679434; 3A Southdowns Avenue, Lewes BN7 1EL Tel: 01273 472585 — MB BS 1986 Lond.; BA (Hons.) Oxf. 1983; MRCGP 1990; DRCOG 1990. Prev: Ho. Surg. Roy. E. Sussex Hosp. Hastings; Ho. Phys. Roy. Sussex Co. Hosp. Brighton & Brighton Gen. Hosp.

SHEARS, Paul Department of Medical Microbiology, Royal Liverpool Hospital, Prescott St., Liverpool L7 8XP — MD 1991 Liverp.; MB BS Lond. 1980; FRCPath 1996. Sen. Lect. & Cons. Dept. Med. Microbiol. Roy. Liverp. Childr.'s Hosp. and Dept Trop Med Liverp. Sch Trop Med. Prev: Clin. Lect. & Sen. Regist. Dept. Med. Microbiol. Univ. Liverp.; Refugee Health Co-ordinator Oxfam Med. Unit; SHO (Paediat.) John Radcliffe Hosp. Oxf.

SHEARSTONE-WALKER, Christopher George 11 Elgar Drive, Long Eaton, Nottingham NG10 3PY — BM BS 1992 Nottm.

SHEASBY, Marion Judith 66 Broad Street, Bromsgrove B61 8LL — MB ChB 1995 Birm.; ChB Birm. 1995.

SHEAVES, Richard Michael Division Medicine, Jersey Hospital, St Helier, Jersey; Le Havre, La Grande Route Des Sablons, Grouville JE3 9FD — BM BCh 1988 Oxf.; Dphil Oxf.1980; MRCP Lond. 1991; FRCP Lond.1999. (Oxf.) Cons. (Phys.) Jersey. Socs: FRCP; Fell. Amer. Endoc. Soc. Prev: Cons. (Phys.) Singapore; Lect. (Endocrin.) St. Bart's Hosp. Lond.

SHEDDEN, Mr Ronald George 37 Burdon Lane, Cheam, Sutton SM2 7PP Tel: 020 8643 9763 — MD 1976 Manch.; MB ChB Manch. 1963; FRCS Eng. 1970; DCH Eng. 1965. Cons. Orthop. Surg. Croydon AHA.

SHEDDEN, William Ian Hamilton One Port Laing Wynd, North Queensferry, Inverkeithing KY11 1EW Tel: 01383 420778 Fax: 01383 420779 Email: ianshedden@debrett.net — MB ChB Ed. 1959; BSc (1st cl. Hons.) Ed. 1957; MD Birm. 1967; FRCP Lond. 1991, M 1976; FRCP Ed. 1983, M 1980; FFPM RCP (UK) 1990; FACP 1981; FIBiol 1970. (Ed.) Cons. Phys. Institut Henri Beaufour, Paris. Socs: Coroners Soc.; Medico-Legal Soc. Prev: Dir. Speywood Gp. Speywood Pharmaceuts.; Managing Dir. Glaxo Gp. Research Ltd.; Vice-Pres. Eli Lilly & Co. (USA).

SHEE, Charles Damien Queen Mary's Hospital, Sidcup DA14 6LT Tel: 020 8302 2678; Park Farm House, Otford, Sevenoaks TN14 5PQ Tel: 01959 522036 — MD 1987 Lond.; MB BS Lond. 1974; FRCP Lond. 1995; MRCP (UK) 1976. (St. Thos.) Cons. Phys. Qu. Mary's Hosp. Sidcup. Socs: Assn. Palliat. Med.; Brit. Thorac. Soc. Prev: Sen. Regist. (Med.) Lond. Chest Hosp.; Regist. & Lect. (Med.) St. Thos. Hosp. Lond.

SHEEHAN, Anna Loraine Department of Histopathology, Doncaster Royal Infirmary, Armthorpe Road, Doncaster DN2 5LT Tel: 01302 553130 Fax: 01302 553264 Email: lorraine.sheehan@dbh.nhs.uk — MB BS 1983 Lond.; FRCPath 2000; MRCPath 1991. Cons. Histopath. Doncaster Roy. Infirm. Prev: Sen. Regist. (Histopath.) Glos. Roy. Hosp. & Bristol Hosps.; Regist. (Histopath.) Roy. Berks. Hosp. Reading.

SHEEHAN, Mr Anthony John, Wing Cdr. RAF Med. Br. Retd. 9 Ballard Close, Poole BH15 1UH — MB BS 1960 Lond.; FRCS Ed. 1976; DLO Eng. 1965. (St. Mary's) Prev: Cons. in Otorhinolaryng. RAF; Ho. Surg. (ENT & Plastic Surg.) St. Mary's Hosp. Lond.; SHO (Cas. & ENT) Roy. N.. Hosp. Lond. SHO (ENT) Roy. Devon &.

SHEEHAN, Barbara Eimear 17 Cookstown Road, Moneymore, Magherafelt BT45 7QF — MB BCh BAO 1987 Belf.; DRCOG 1992. Clin. Med. Off. (Community Paediat.) Cupar St. Belf. Prev: Trainee GP Ayrsh.

SHEEHAN, Bartholomew David Department of Old Age Psychiatry, Maudsley Hospital, Denmark Hill, London SE5 8AZ — MB BCh BAO 1991 Dub.

SHEEHAN, Brendan David Castle Surgery, 1 Prince of Wales Drive, Neath SA11 3EW Tel: 01639 641444 Fax: 01639 636288 — MB BCh BAO 1973 NUI.

SHEEHAN, Carolyn 9 Fonthill Terrace, Aberdeen AB11 7UR — MB ChB 1993 Glas.

SHEEHAN, Denise Jane Exeter Oncology Centre, Royal Devon & Exeter Hospital, Barrack Road, Exeter EX2 5DW Tel: 01392 402114 Fax: 01392 402112 — MB BCh 1986 Wales; FRCR 1999. Cons. Clin. Oncologist, Exeter Oncol. Centre, Roy. Devon & Exeter Hosp., Exeter. Prev: Regist. (Clin. Oncol.) Roy. Berks. Hosp.; Specialist Regist., Clin. Oncol., Roy. Berks Hosp.; Specialist Regist. Clin. Oncol., Ch.ill Hosp., Oxf.

SHEEHAN, Georgina Eveline Mary Gloucestershire Health Authority, Victoria Warehouse, The Docks, Gloucester GL1 2EL Tel: 01452 300222; 26 Hyde Avenue, Thornbury, Bristol BS35 1JA — MB ChB 1977 Manch.; MFCM 1987; MFPHM. Cons. Pub. Health Med. Glos. HA. Prev: SCM SW RHA.

SHEEHAN, Gerard Patrick Four Seasons, Black Lion Road, Capel Hendre, Ammanford SA18 3SD Tel: 01269 844351 — MB BCh BAO 1948 NUI. (Cork) Prev: Orthop. & Gen. Ho. Surg. Grimsby & Dist. Gen. Hosp.; Capt. RAMC, TA.

SHEEHAN, Jennifer Mary Woodbridge Road Surgery, 165-167 Woodbridge Road, Ipswich IP4 2PE; 11 Mayfield Road, Ipswich IP4 3NE — MB BS 1973 Lond.; BSc (Hons.) Lond. 1970. (Lond. Hosp.)

SHEEHAN

SHEEHAN, John, MC (retired) 18 Dovedale Road, Stoneygate, Leicester LE2 2DJ Tel: 0116 270 1785 — MB BCh BAO 1941 NUI; MRCGP 1953. Prev: Ho. Surg. Shotley Bridge Hosp.

SHEEHAN, John Patrick (retired) 50 Carmarthen Avenue, Cosham, Portsmouth PO6 2AQ Tel: 01705 381607 — MB BCh BAO 1958 NUI.

SHEEHAN, John Patrick Andrew Royal Air Force, Brize Norton, Carterton OX18 3LX — MB BCh 1993 Wales.

SHEEHAN, Leslie James Services for the Elderly, Ipswich Hospital, Ipswich IP4 5PD Tel: 01473 704137 — MB BS 1972 Lond.; FRCP Lond. 1994; MRCP (UK) 1980. (Lond. Hosp.) Cons. Phys. Ipswich Hosp. NHS Trust. Prev: Sen. Regist. (Geriat. Med.) St. Geo. Hosp. Lond.; Regist. (Med.) Lond. Hosp. Whitechapel.

SHEEHAN, Nicholas John Rheumatology Department, The Edith Cavell Hospital, Bretton Gate, Peterborough PE3 9GZ Tel: 01733 875143 Fax: 01733 875633 Email: njsheehan@doctors.org.uk; 52 Casewick Lane, Uffington, Stamford PE9 4SX Tel: 01780 757597 Fax: 01780 480038 Email: njsheehan@doctors.org.uk — MB ChB 1973 Sheff.; MD Sheff. 1990; FRCP Lond. 1994; MRCP (UK) 1977; DPMSA 1982. (Univ. of Sheff.) Cons. Rheum. PeterBoro. NHS Trust. Socs: Brit. Soc. Rheumatol. (Ex-Hon. Treas.); Pres. of Sect. Rheumatol. & Rehab. Roy. Soc. Med.; Treas. of the Brit. League Against Rheumatism. Prev: Sen. Regist. St. Thos. Hosp. Lond.; Regist. Roy. Hosp. Sheff.

SHEEHAN, Pauline Barbara (retired) 63 Wellwood, Llanedeyrn, Cardiff CF23 9JR Tel: 01222 736905 — MB BCh 1966 Wales. Prev: Ho. Off. (Neurol. & ENT) Cardiff Roy. Infirm.

SHEEHAN, Richard Timothy (retired) The Doctor's House, Victoria Road, Marlow SL7 1DN — MB BCh BAO 1941 NUI; DPH 1947. Prev: Ho. Surg. Roy. Infirm. Worcester.

SHEEHAN, Susan Marion Bruntsfield Medical Practice, 11 Forbes Road, Edinburgh EH10 4EY Tel: 0131 228 6081 Fax: 0131 229 4330; 3Fl, 14 Brougham Place, Tollcross, Edinburgh EH3 9JX Tel: 0131 229 9605 — MB ChB 1994 Glas. GP Regist. Bruntsfield Med. Pract. Edin.

SHEEHAN, Thomas Joseph 16 St Andrews Road, Liverpool L23 7UR — MB BCh BAO 1986 NUI.

SHEEHAN, Thomas Michael Department of Radiotherapy & Oncology, St. George's Hospital, Long Leys Road, Lincoln LN1 2EF — BM 1980 Soton.; MRCP (UK) 1990; FRCR 1988.

SHEEHAN-DARE, Robert Alexander Leeds Centre for Dermatology, Leeds General Infirmary, Great George St., Leeds LS1 3EX Tel: 0113 392 2295 Fax: 0113 234 1154 — MB ChB 1982 Leeds; MRCP (UK) 1985; FRCP 1999. Cons. Dermat. Gen. Infirm. Leeds & Hon. Sen. Lect. Univ. Leeds. Socs: FRCP.

SHEEHY SKEFFINGTON, Francis Eugene Denis (retired) 3 Blenheim Road, Wakefield WF1 3JZ Tel: 01924 377358 Email: francis@sheetyskeffs.demon.co.uk — MB BCh BAO 1973 Dub.; MRCP (UK) 1978; DCH NUI 1975 DObst RCOG 1975. Prev: Cons. Community Paediat. Barnsley Community & Priority Servs. NHS Trust.

SHEELA SRIDHAR, Kunjuveetil 594 Howlands, Welwyn Garden City AL7 4ET — MB BS 1984 Bangalor; MB BS Bangalore 1984; FRCS Ed. 1994.

SHEEN, Aali Jan 5 Cotford Road, Thornton Heath, Croydon CR7 8RB — MB ChB 1993 Dundee; FRCS Eng. 1998.

SHEEN, Christopher Letchford Queen Alexandra Hospital, Southwick Hill Road, Cosham, Portsmouth PO6 3LY Tel: 023 92 286000; 4 Malvern Mews, Emsworth PO10 7SR Tel: 07710 923656 Email: clsheen@compuserve.com — MB BS 1991 Lond.; BSc Lond. 1988; MRCP (UK) 1994. (St. Geo. Hosp. Med. Sch. Lond.) Specialist Regist. (Gastro. & Gen. Med.) Qu. Alexandra Hosp. Ports. Socs: Brit. Soc. Gastroenterol. Prev: Specialist Regist. (Gastroenterol.) N. Hants. Hosp. Basingstoke; Specialist Regist. (Gastroenterol. & Hepat.) Soton.; Regist. (Gen. Med. & Gastroenterol.) Whipps Cross Hosp. Lond.

SHEEN, Michael 11 Caldicot Close, Grove Park, Blackwood NP12 1HH Tel: 01495 222551 — MB ChB 1974 Bristol; DRCOG 1977.

SHEEN, Ruth Mary 18 Ambrose Close, Worcester WR2 6JX Tel: 01905 422830 — MB BS 1985 Lond.; MRCPsych 1991. Clin. Asst. (Adult Gen. Psychiat.) Worcester Roy. Infirm. Prev: Regist. (Psychiat.) Worcester Roy. Infirm.

SHEERAN, Ellen Brosna, 180 Liverpool Road, Great Crosby, Liverpool L23 0QW — MB BCh BAO 1951 NUI. (Galw.) Prev: Cas. Off. Maidenhead Gen. Hosp.; Ho. Surg. Mile End Hosp. Lond.; Ho. Surg. & Ho. Phys. Noble's Hosp. Douglas.

SHEERAN, Julia Mary Department of Child & Adolescent Psychiatry, Parkside House, 55 Stockwell Park Road, London SW9 0DA Tel: 020 7738 7101 Fax: 020 7978 9675; 190B Friern Road, London SE22 0BA — MB ChB 1979 Liverp.; MRCPsych. 1992. Sen. Regist. (Child & Adolesc. Psychiat.) Child & Family Consult. Unit Lond.

SHEERAN, Margaret Rachael Mary 5 Marino Villas, Marino Park, Holywood BT18 0AN; 213 Sutton Passey's Crescent, Nottingham NG8 3AE — MB ChB 1992 Leeds; PhD Liverp. 1987. SHO (Histopath.) City Hosp. Nottm. Prev: SHO (Gen. Med.) Pinderfield Hosp. Wakefield.

SHEERAN, Padraig Bernardine Majella Brosna, 180 Liverpool Road, Crosby, Liverpool L23 0QW — MB ChB 1983 Liverp. SHO (Anaesth.) Ealing Hosp. Lond. Prev: SHO (Med. Rotat.) Roy. Liverp. Hosp.; SHO (A & E) Ealing Hosp. Lond.; Ho. Phys. & Surg. Mersey RHA.

SHEERAN, Thomas Patrick Gerard Oakwood, Old Coach Lane, Brocton, Stafford ST17 0TU — MD 1994 Liverp.; MB ChB 1980; MRCP Ed. 1985. Cons. Rheum. Stafford.

SHEERBOOM, Derek John Casa Mia, Halliford Drive, Barnham, Bognor Regis PO22 0AB — MB BS 1948 Lond.; LMSSA Lond. 1948; MFCM 1972; DPH Bristol 1958; DIH Soc. Apoth. Lond. 1975. (Guy's) Prev: Employm. Med. Adviser EMAS; Dir. Health Servs. & MOH Roy. Boro. Kensington & Chelsea.

SHEERIN, Declan Finnian Department of Child & Family Psychiatry, Yorkhill NHS Trust, Glasgow G3 8SJ — MB BCh BAO 1982 NUI; MMedSc (Psychotherap.) NUI 1988; MRCPsych 1987. Cons. Child & Adolesc. Psychiat. Yorkhill NHS Trust Glas. Prev: Sen. Regist. (Child & Adolesc. Psychiat.) Young People's Unit Roy. Edin. Hosp.

SHEERIN, Neil Stephen 41 Holbrook Road, Leicester LE2 3LG — MB BS 1990 Lond.; BSc Lond. 1987, MB BS Lond. 1990. SHO (Thoracic Med.) Roy. Brompton Nat. Heart & Lung Hosp. Lond.

SHEERIN, Sheila Mary Stepaside, 32 Manor Park Avenue, Princes Risborough HP27 9AS Tel: 01844 345353 — MB BCh BAO 1969 Dub.; FRCPath 1993, M 1981. (TC Dub.) Cons. Haemat. Stoke Mandeville Hosp. Aylesbury. Prev: Sen. Regist. (Haemat.) Oxf. RHA; Ho. Surg. W.m. Childr. Hosp. Lond.; Ho. Phys. St. Mary Abbot's Hosp. Lond.

SHEERMAN-CHASE, Gaye Lynn Craven Road Medical Centre, 60 Craven Road, Leeds LS6 2RX Tel: 0113 295 3530 Fax: 0113 295 3542 — MB ChB 1987 Leeds.

SHEERS, Geoffrey (retired) 1 Barton Bridge Close, Raglan NP15 2JW — MB BChir 1938 Camb.; MA, MD Camb. 1951; MRCS Eng. LRCP Lond. 1937. Prev: Cons. Chest Phys. Plymouth Gen. Hosp.

***SHEERS, Helen** Fron Vox, Llandyrnog, Denbigh LL16 4HR — MB ChB 1998 Manch.; MB ChB Manch 1998.

SHEERS, Roger Fron Vox, Llandyrnog, Denbigh LL16 4HR — MB BS 1970 Lond.; MRCP (UK) 1974; FRACP 1978. (St. Thos.) Cons. Phys. & Gastroenterol. Glan Clwyd Hosp. N. Wales. Prev: Sen. Med. Regist. BRd.green Hosp. Liverp.; Regist. (Med.) Burton-on-Trent Gen. Hosp.; Sen. Med. Regist. Roy. Adelaide Hosp. S. Austral.

SHEFFIELD, Dennis Gerard, MC (retired) Apple Cottage, Lt. Mongeham, Deal CT14 0HP Tel: 01304 372697 — MRCS Eng. LRCP Lond. 1938; MD Lond. 1950; MB BS 1939; MRCGP 1953.

SHEFFIELD, Edward Alexander Department of Histopathology, Bristol Royal Infirmary, Marlborough St., Bristol BS2 8HW Tel: 01179 283198 Fax: 01179 292440 Email: e.a.sheffield@bris.ac.uk — BM Soton. 1980; MD Soton. 1990; MRCPath 1986. Cons. Sen. Lect. (Path.) Univ. Bristol; Hon. Cons. (Path.) United Bristol Hosps. Trust. Prev: Sen. Regist. (Path.) Brompton Hosp. Lond. & Roy. Berks. Hosp. Reading.

SHEFFIELD, Jonathan Paul Department of Pathology, East Somerset NHS Trust, Yeovil District Hospital, Yeovil BA21 4AT Tel: 01935 707314 — MB ChB 1981 Dundee; MRCPath 1991. Cons. Histopath. E. Som. NHS Trust. Socs: Brit. Soc. Gastroenterol.; Path. Soc. Prev: Clin. Research Fell. (Path.) Imperial Cancer Research Fund St. Mark's Hosp. Lond.; Regist. (Histopath.) Nottm. Hosps.; SHO (Path.) Leicester Roy. Infirm.

SHEIKH

*SHEFFIELD, Sally Janine 68 High Street, Otford, Sevenoaks TN14 5PH — MB BS 1994 Lond.

SHEFFRIN, Stanley (retired) 7 Alwoodley Chase, Harrogate Road, Leeds LS17 8ER Tel: 0113 266 9846 — MB ChB 1950 Leeds; BSc Leeds 1947; MFOM RCP Lond. 1982, AFOM 1979; MRCGP 1962. Hon. Med. Off. Amateur Swimming Assn.; Local Med. Off. Civil Serv. Occupat. Health Serv. Prev: Cons. Med. Adviser Tibbett & Britten plc.

SHEFLER, Alison Gail Paediatric Intensive Care Unit, Oxford Radcliffe Hospital, Headley Way, Oxford OX3 9DU Tel: 01865 741166 Fax: 01865 222061 Email: alison.shefler@orh.anglox.nhs.uk — MD 1984 Toronto. (Univ. Toronto) Cons. Paediat. Paediat. Intens. & Critical Care Radcliffe Hosp. Oxf. Socs: Fell. Roy. Coll. of Paediat. & Child Health; Fell. Roy. Coll. Phys. & Surg. Canada.

SHEFRAS, Julia c/o David Shefras, 12 Aldenholme, Ellesmere Road, Weybridge KT13 0JF — BChir 1990 Camb.

*SHEHAB, Abdullah Mohammed Abdullah 1 South Tay Street, 3rd Floor Top End, Dundee DD1 1NU — MB ChB 1995 Dundee.

SHEHAB, Mr Zaid Hashim 101A Lichfield Road, Sutton Coldfield B74 2RS — MB BCh BAO 1987 NUI; FRCS Ed. 1994; FRCSI 1994; LRCPSI 1987.

SHEHADE, Suhail James Cook University Hospital, Marton Road, Middlesbrough TS4 3BW Tel: 01642 850850 — MB ChB 1976 Glas.; MRCP (UK) 1983; FRCP (Ed.) 1995. (Glas.) Cons. Dermat. N. Region HA.; Lead Clinician Lasercare (M'bro). Socs: BMA; N. Eng. Dermatol.s Soc.; Brit. Assn. of Dermat. Prev: Sen. Regist. (Dermat.) NW Eng. RHA; Regist. (Dermat.) W. Midl. RHA; Regist. (Med.) E. Cumbria HA.

SHEHADEH, Emil Saleem 253 Albany Road, Roath, Cardiff CF24 3NW Tel: 029 2049 5959 — MB ChB 1988 Glas.; BSc (Hons.) Glas. 1983, MB ChB 1988; MSc Glas. 1984; T(GP) 1993. Prev: Lect. (Psychol.) Cardiff Univ.

SHEHMAR, Manjeet 7 The Coppice, Birmingham B20 2AD — MB BS 1998 Lond.; MB BS Lond 1998.

SHEHU, Abdullahi Department of Neurology, Walsgrave Hospital NHS Trust, Clifford Bridge Road, Coventry CV2 2DX Tel: 024 76 538954 — MB BS 1983 Nigeria; MRCP (UK) 1991; Dip. Clin. Neurol. Lond 1987. Cons. Neurol. Walsgrave Hosp.

SHEHU, Tijjani Halton General Hospital, Hospital Way, Runcorn WA7 2DA Tel: 01928 714567 Email: drtshehu@hotmail.com; Flat A Block 2, Halton General Hospital, Hospital Way, Runcorn WA7 2DA Tel: 01928 714567 Email: drtshehu@hotmail.com — MB BS 1984 Ahmadu Bello Univ. Zaria, Nigeria; DGM 1999 RCP Lond.; LRCPI 1998; MRCPI 1998; MSc 2001 (Cardiology) (Sussex). Staff Phys. in Cardiol., Halton Gen. Hosp. Hosp. Way, Runcorn. Prev: Locum Regist. (Med.), Crawley Hosp.

SHEIK HOSSAIN, Saddeck Mohammed 399 Carlton Hill, Carlton, Nottingham NG4 1HW — BM BS 1994 Nottm.

SHEIKH, Abdul Jawad Department of Psychiatry, Solihull Hospital, Lode Lane, Solihull B91 2JL Tel: 0121 711 7720 Fax: 0121 711 1881 Email: jawad1984@aol.com; 107 Dovehouse Lane, Solihull B91 2EQ Tel: 0121 682 4664 — MB BS 1978 Karachi; MMedSc Birm. 1996; MRCPsych 1987; Dip. Psychiat. Lond. 1986; DGM RCP Lond. 1986. (Dow Med. Coll. Karachi) Cons. Psychiat. Solihull Hosp./Newington Centre; Hon. Sen. Clin. Lect. Univ. of Birm. 1997; Second Opinion Assessm. Doctor (SOAD) for Ment. Health Comm.; Med. Mem. Ment. Health Review Tribunial; Examr. MRCPsych Part II Roy. Coll. of Psychiat.; Parole Bd. Mem. Sept. 1998; Mem. Of Multi-racial Ethics Comm. (MREC); Review for Commisiion for health improvements (CHI) 2001. Socs: BMA; NSF; MDU. Prev: Sen. Regist. (Psychogeriat.) Edwd. St. Hosp. W. Bromwich; Lead Clinician, Burirum team NHS Trust; Sen. Regist. (Adult Psychiat.) All St.s Hosp. Birm. & Midl. Nerv. Hosp. Birm.

SHEIKH, Abdul Qayyum Queens Road Surgery, 48 Queens Road, Walthamstow, London E17 8PX Tel: 020 8520 2625 Fax: 020 8925 4195 — MB BS 1965 Punjab. (Nishtar Med. Coll.) Nat. Chairm. Pakistan Med. Soc. UK.

SHEIKH, Afzal Ahmed 17 Stepney Drive, Scarborough YO12 5DP — MB BS 1971 Punjab; MB BS Punjab, Pakistan 1971.

SHEIKH, Aijaz Ahmed Holbrook Surgery, Bartholomew Way, Horsham RH12 5JB Tel: 01403 755900 Fax: 01403 755909 — MB BS 1970 Pakistan; DPD (Wales) 1997; DCCH Ed 1989; DTM & H (London) 1987; DRCOG (Lond) 1986; MB BS (Pakistan) 1970. GP Horsham, W. Sussex; Sessional Doctor (p/t), Health Screening Clinic, BUPA Gatwick Pk. Hosp. Socs: Primary Care Dermat. Soc.; Brit. Travel Health Assoc.; BMA. Prev: Clin. Asst. Dermat., P.ss Roy. Hosp., W. Sussex 1995-1998.

SHEIKH, Amer 77 Southwood Avenue, Knaphill, Woking GU21 2EZ — MB ChB 1991 Aberd.; MRCGP 1995.

SHEIKH, Asme Kings College Hospital, Denmark Hill, London SE5 9RS — BM 1990 Soton.; DCH (Eng.) 1992; FRCA 1996. (Southampton University) p/t Cons. Anaesth.; With interest in Paediatric Anaesth.

SHEIKH, Azhar Zia Medical Centre, Chesterfield Road, North Wingfield, Chesterfield S42 5ND Tel: 01246 851035 — MB BS 1964 Sind. (Liaquat Med. Coll.) Socs: BMA. Prev: Regist. (Anaesth.) Sunderland Gp. Hosps.; SHO Gen. Surg. Salop Roy. Infirm. Shrewsbury; SHO Psychiat. Barnsley Hall Hosp. BromsGr..

SHEIKH, Aziz Imperial College of Science & Medicine, Dept of General Practice, St. Dunstann's Road, London W6 8RP Tel: 020 7594 3384 Fax: 020 7706 8426 Email: aziz.sheikh@ic.ac.uk — MB BS 1993 Lond.; MSc 2001 Lond.; BSc Lond. 1990; MRCP 1996; MRCGP 1997; DFFP 1997; DCH 1996; DRCOG 1995. (Univ. Coll. & Midddlx. Sch. Med.) NHS Research & Developm. Nat. Primary Care Trainy Fell. Dept. of Gen. Pract., Imperial Coll. of Sci., Technol. & Med. Lond.; GP Asst. Harrow, Middlx.; GP Adviser, BMJ Internat. Edit. Advis. Bd. JRSM. Socs: Roy. Coll. Gen. Pract.; BSACI; GPIAG.

SHEIKH, Haleema Fatima 3 Lord Chancellor Walk, Kingston upon Thames KT2 7HG — MB BS 1998 Lond.; MB BS Lond 1998.

SHEIKH, Idris 9 Winchfield Way, Rickmansworth WD3 4DL — MRCS Eng. LRCP Lond. 1977.

SHEIKH, Ijaz Hussain Winwick Hospital, Winwick, Warrington WA2 8RR — MB BS 1965 Punjab.

SHEIKH, Imran 51 Beech Hall Road, London E4 9NJ — MB BS 1998 Lond.; MB BS Lond 1998.

SHEIKH, Iram Safia 5 Birkbeck Gardens, Woodford Green IG8 0SA — MB BS 1996 Lond.

SHEIKH, Javed Hassan Tel: 020 8646 4282 Fax: 020 8646 2848; Tel: 01737 355556 — MB BCh 1978 Cairo; BSc Karachi 1973; MSc Pain Management 2001 Cardiff; LMSSA Lond. 1988; MRCS Eng. LRCP Lond. 1988. Socs: BMA & Assoc. Mem. RCGP.; Freedom Soc. Apoth. Prev: Civil. Med. Pract. Roy. Engineers 12 RSME Regt. Chattenden Barracks Rochester.

SHEIKH, Javed Younus 20 The Avenue, Sale M33 4PD — MB ChB 1996 Liverp.

SHEIKH, Mohammad Yunus Trafford General Hospital, Davyhulme, Manchester M41 5SL Tel: 0161 748 4022; 20 The Avenue, Sale M33 4PD Tel: 0161 962 1976 — MB BS 1963 Punjab; BSc Punjab 1957, MB BS 1963; DPath Eng. 1970. Cons. (Histopath.) Trafford Gen. Hosp. Manch. Socs: BMA & NW Represen. Nishtarian Med. Soc. (UK). Prev: SHO (Path.) Bury Gen. Hosp.; Regist. (Clin. Path.) United Sheff. Hosps.; Temp. Sen. Lect. Path. Univ. Edin.

SHEIKH, Mohammed Anwar Child & Adolescent Mental Health Service, Gulson Clinic, Gulson Road, Coventry CV1 2SU Tel: 024 76 844060 Fax: 024 76 837074 — MB BS Punjab (Pakistan) 1962; FRCPsych 1991, M 1973; DPM Eng. 1972. (Nishtar Med. Coll. Multan) Cons. Child & Adolesc. Psychiat. Coventry Healthcare NHS Trust; Clin. Co-ordinator CAMHS. Socs: Assn. Child Psychol. & Psychiat. Prev: Chairm. Child & Adolesc. Sub-Sect. Midl. Div. Roy. Coll. Psychiat.; Regist. (Psychiat.) John Conolly Hosp. Birm.; Sen. Regist. (Child Psychiat.) W. Midl. RHA.

SHEIKH, Muhammad Nadeem 118 Glen Road, Oadby, Leicester LE2 4RF — MB BCh 1989 Wales.

SHEIKH, Munir Ahmad Old Orchard, Manor Way, Ratton, Eastbourne BN20 9BL Tel: 01323 508729 — MB BS 1961 Punjab; MB BS Punjab Pakistan 1961; DPM Eng. 1972. (King Edwd. Med. Coll. Lahore) Cons. Psychiat. Ment. Handicap E.bourne & Hastings HA's. Socs: BMA & Overseas Doctors Assn. Prev: Sen. Regist. (Psychiat.) Mersey RHA.

SHEIKH, Mushkoor Ellahie, Squadron Ldr. RAF Bentley Health Centre, Askern Road, Bentley, Doncaster DN5 0JX Tel: 01302 820494 Fax: 01302 820496 Email: drmesheikh.dnsojx.uk@network.med.com; Old School House, Village St, Adwick-le-Street, Doncaster DN6 7AA — MB ChB 1984 Aberd.; Cert. Family Plann. JCC 1986; Cert. Av Med. 1986. Prev: Station Med. Off. RAF Honington; SHO (O & G) P.ss of Wales Hosp. Ely; SHO (A & E) RAF Hosp. Ely.

SHEIKH

SHEIKH, Nargis Fatima 7 Raphael Drive, Watford WD24 4GY — MB BS 1971 Punjab, Pakistan.

SHEIKH, Nassar Seema, Llanvair Drive, Ascot SL5 9LW Tel: 01344 25152; B-2 Belle View Apartments, FL-6 Block 8, Clifton, Karachi, Pakistan Tel: 534762 — MB BS 1986 Karachi; MRCP (UK) 1991. Regist. (Thoracic Med.) Char. Cross Hosp. Lond. Prev: Regist. (Med.) Ashford Hosp. Middlx.; Regist. (Gen. & Thoracic Med.) St. Margt. Hosp. Epping.

SHEIKH, Nissar Ahmad 8 Corone Close, Folkestone CT19 5LJ Tel: 01303 275847 — MB BS 1960 Punjab; MRCP (UK) 1974. Socs: Brit. Med. Assn.; Overseas Doctors Assn. Prev: Free Lance Cons. Phys.

SHEIKH, Raian Rahmat Orchard Medical Practice, Innisdoon, Crow Hill Drive, Mansfield NG19 7AE Tel: 01623 400100 Fax: 01623 400101 — MB BS 1986 Lond.

SHEIKH, Saeed Ahmed Sheikh, 91 St. Peters Road, Leicester LE2 1DJ Tel: 0116 254 3003 Fax: 0116 270 0743; 14 Sycamore Close, Oadby, Leicester LE2 2RN Tel: 0116 270 0743 — MB BS 1967 Karachi; BSc Karachi 1961. (Dow Med. Coll.) p/t Clin. Asst. (Psychogeriat.) Carlton Hayes Hosp. Leicester.

SHEIKH, Mr Saghir Hussain 88 Wordsworth Way, Bothwell, Glasgow G71 8QS — MB BS 1978 Sind; FRCSI 1987.

SHEIKH, Mr Shahid Aziz 252 Bridgwater Road, Wembley HA0 1AS — MB BS 1982 Punjab; FRCS Ed. 1992.

SHEIKH, Shahida Bokhari Sheikh, 91 St. Peters Road, Leicester LE2 1DJ Tel: 0116 254 3003 Fax: 0116 270 0743; 14 Sycamore Close, Oadby, Leicester LE2 2RN Tel: 0116 270 0743 — MB BS 1970 Karachi. (Dow Med. Coll.)

SHEIKH, Turabali Badruddin Noorbhai The Clinic, Charles St., Neyland, Milford Haven SA73 1AS Tel: 01646 600268 Fax: 01646 602080 — MRCS Eng. LRCP Lond. 1973; DRCOG 1978.

SHEIKH, Zahid Inayat York District Hospital, Wigginton Road, York YO31 8HE Tel: 01904 631313; 2 Doe Park, York YO30 4UQ — Vrach 1985 Lvov Med Inst. USSR; Vrach Lvov Med Inst, USSR 1985.

SHEIKH-SAJJAD, Adina Rihab 49 Sharman Close, Penkhull, Stoke-on-Trent ST4 7LS — LMSSA 1996; LMSSA Lond. LRCS Eng LRCP Lond. 1996.

SHEIKH-SOBEH, Mohammed Vascular Unit, Department of Surgery, The Royal London Hospital, London E1 1BB Tel: 020 7377 7695 Fax: 020 7377 7675 — MB ChB 1983 Bristol; MRCS Eng. LRCP Lond. 1982; FRCS (Eng) 1988; FRCS (Gen) 1997. Cons. in Gen. Vasc. & Transpl. Surg.

SHEIL, Louise Jane Mount Florida Medical Centre, 183 Prospecthill Road, Glasgow G42 9LQ Tel: 0141 632 4004 Fax: 0141 636 6036; 61 Braidpark Drive, Giffnock, Glasgow G46 6LY — MB ChB 1984 Manch.; MRCGP 1990; DRCOG 1986. Socs: BMA & Med. Wom. Federat. Prev: SHO (Med.) Manch. Roy. Infirm.

SHEIL, Patrick Alan The Health Centre, 80 Main Street, Kelty KY4 0AE Tel: 01383 831281 Fax: 01383 831825; 24 Ross Avenue, Dalgety Bay, Dunfermline KY11 9YN — MB ChB 1989 Dundee; MRCGP; RCOG.

SHEILL, Michael John Cambridge Court, 37 Cambridge Road, Hastings TN34 1DJ — MB BCh BAO 1985 NUI; LRCPI & LM LRCSI & LM 1985.

SHEILS, Bernard Anthony 40 Upper Galliagh Road, Londonderry BT48 8LW Tel: 01504 265407 — MB BCh BAO 1959 NUI.

SHEIN, Ilana Gabi 4 Downside Crescent, London NW3 2AP — MB BCh 1991 Witwatersrand.

SHEINMAN, Bryan David 5th Floor Consulting Room, Wellington Hospital (South), Wellington Place, London NW8 9LE Tel: 020 7794 0664 Fax: 020 7431 4663; 7 Kidderpore Gardens, London NW3 7SS Tel: 020 7794 0664 Fax: 020 7431 4663 — MB BS 1976 Lond.; MD (Lond.) 1987, BPharm (Hons.) 1971; MRCP (UK) 1980. (St. Bart.) Assoc. Specialist St. Mary's Hosp. Lond. Socs: Brit. Thorac. Soc.; Brit. Soc. Allergy & Clin. Immunol.; Worshipful Soc. Apoth. Prev: Regist. Roy. Free Hosp.; Research Fell. St. Bart. Hosp. Lond.; Lect. Nat. Heart & Lung Inst. Lond.

SHEK, Fanny Wai-Tsing Flat 3, 10 Roxborough Avenue, Harrow HA1 3BU Tel: 020 8423 9735 — BM BS 1993 Nottm.; MRCP UK 1996. Specialist Regist. (Gastroenterol.) P.ss Margt. Hosp. Swindon. Prev: Specialist Regist. (Gastroenterol.) Dorset Co. Hosp. Dorchester.

SHEK, Kwei-Chuen 41 Gloucester Road, Walsall WS5 3PL — MRCS Eng. LRCP Lond. 1982.

SHEK, Rosa Jenny 21 Cuerden Close, Bamber Bridge, Preston PR5 6BX — MB ChB 1994 Ed.

SHEKAR, Chandra Minden Medical Centre, 2 Barlow Street, Bury BL9 0QP Tel: 0161 764 2651 Fax: 0161 761 5967 — MB BS 1972 Mysore. (Mysore Med. Coll.) Clin. Asst. (Chest Med.) Bury Gen. Hosp. Prev: Regist. (Med.) Bury Gen. Hosp.

SHEKAR, Saraswathy c/o Mr Allern Braganza, 345 Strone Road, Manor Park, London E12 6TW — MB BS 1987 Madras; FFA RCSI 1995.

SHEKELTON, Frances Anne 35 Oakwood Lane, Bowdon, Altrincham WA14 3DL — MB ChB 1991 Sheff.

SHEKERDEMIAN, Lara Sevanne Great Ormond Street, Great Ormond St., London WC1N 3JN; Flat C, 22 St Anns Villas, Holland Park, London W11 4RS Email: larashekerdemian@compuserve.com — MB ChB 1990 Birm.; MD Birm. 1997; MRCP (UK) 1993. Paediat. Gt Ormond St Hosp. Lond. Prev: Research Regist. (Paediat. Cardiol.) Roy. Brompton Hosp. Lond.

SHEKHAR, Satish Scunthorpe General Hospital, Scunthorpe DN15 7BH Tel: 01724 282282 Fax: 01724 290151; 11 Chaffinch Close, Scunthorpe DN15 8EL Tel: 01724 343108 Fax: 01724 343109 — MB BS 1980 Magadh; MD (Paediat.) Ranchi 1986; MRCP (UK) 1990; DCH 1983 Patna. Cons. Paediat. Scunthorpe Gen. Hosp.; Hon. Clin. Lect. (Paediat.) Sheff. Univ. Sheff. Socs: Fell. Roy. Coll. Paediat. and Child Health; Roy. Coll. Phys. Prev: Staff Grade (Paediat.) E. Glam. Gen. Hosp. Pontypridd; Regist. (Med.) Roy. Hosp. Sick Childr. Glas.

SHEKHAWAT, Fateh Singh 11 Cheltenham Drive, Kingswinford DY6 9XH — MB BS 1974 Rajasthan.

SHEKHDAR, Mr Homi Hoshang (retired) Shekhdar and Partners, The Surgery, Ancaster Avenue, Chapel St. Leonards, Skegness PE24 5SL Tel: 01754 872541 Fax: 01754 871598 — MB BS Karachi 1957; FRCS Ed. 1967 (Gen. Surg). Prev: Sen. Partner Gen. Pract.

SHELAT, Chandrika Chandramauli c/o Mr P. D. Patel, 30 Audley Road, Hendon, London NW4 3EY Tel: 020 8202 0229 — MD 1973 Gujarat; MD (Obst. & Gyn.) Gujarat 1973, MB BS 1970; DGO Gujarat 1972. (B.J. Med. Coll. Ahmedabad)

SHELBOURN, Kevin Richard 41 Castlegate, Grantham NG31 6SS — BM BS 1997 Nottm.

SHELDON, Ailsa Jane Lindsaye Linkylea House, Haddington EH41 4PE — MB ChB 1997 Aberd.

SHELDON, Charles Samuel 251 Ladbrooke Grove, North Kensington, London W10 6HF — MB BS 1953 Lond.; MRCS Eng. LRCP Lond. 1953.

SHELDON, Christopher David Department of Respiratory Medicine, Royal Devon & Exeter Hospital, Barrack Road, Exeter EX2 5DW Tel: 01392 402132 Fax: 01392 402828 — BM 1981 Soton.; DM Soton. 1993; MRCP (UK) 1984; FRCP 1998; T(M) 1992. Cons. Phys. Respirat. Med. Roy. Devon & Exeter Hosp. (Wonford).; Dir. Adult Cystic Fibrosis Care; Cystic Fibrosis Consortium. Socs: Brit. Thoracic Soc.; Amer. Thoracic Soc. Prev: Sen. Regist. (Gen. & Thoracic Med.) Lond. Hosp. Whitechapel & Lond. Chest Hosp.; Research Fell. Cystic Fibrosis Brompton Hosp. Lond.; Regist. (Med.) Lond. Chest Hosp. & Whittington Hosp. Lond.

SHELDON, David Maxwell The Pease Way Medical Centre, 2 Pease Way, Newton Aycliffe DL5 5NH Tel: 01325 301888; 17 Low Green, Woodham Village, Newton Aycliffe DL5 4TR — MB BS 1978 Newc.; MRCGP 1986. Prev: GP Newton Aycliffe; GP Consett Co. Durh.; Clin. Research Phys. Merck, Sharp & Dohme Ltd.

SHELDON, Debra Elizabeth Barbara — MB BCh BAO 1986 Belf.; Cert. Family Plann. JCC 1991. (Qu. Univ. Belf.) p/t Retainer Gen. Pract. Socs: BMA.

SHELDON, Dennis Westmacott Sirr (retired) Weston House, Tillington, Petworth GU28 0RA Tel: 01798 343593 — MB BChir 1945 Camb.; MA (Nat. Sc. Trip. Pt. I) Camb. 1942; MRCS Eng. LRCP Lond. 1945. Prev: Phys. Harley St. Lond.

SHELDON, Helen Elizabeth Dept. Clinical Psychology, Royal Bolton Hospital, Minerva Road, Farnworth, Bolton BL4 0JR Tel: 01204 390675; 12 Raynham Avenue, Didsbury, Manchester M20 6BW — MB BS 1973 Lond. Adult Psychother. Dept. Clin. Psychol. Roy. Bolton Hosp.

SHELDON, John Victor Eastontown House, Horn Blotton, Shepton Mallet BA4 6SG Tel: 0196324 288 — MRCS Eng. LRCP Lond. 1940; BA Toronto 1961; DOMS Eng. 1948; LMCC 1957. (King's

Coll. Lond. & Westm.) Socs: S.. Ophth. Soc. Prev: Chief of Ophth. Oshawa Gen. Hosp. Canada; Clin. Asst. Moorfields Eye Hosp. Lond.; Ho. Surg. (Eyes) Guy's Hosp.

SHELDON, Jonathan Howard The Keats Group Practice, 1B Downshire Hill, London NW3 1NR Tel: 020 7435 1131 Fax: 020 7431 8501 Email: jsheldon@fonthill.demon.co.uk — MB BChir 1988 Camb.; BA Camb. 1985; MA Camb. 1989; DCH RCP Lond. 1990; DRCOG 1991; MRCGP RCGP 1992. (Camb. Lond.) GP Princip. Lon.; SMO Univ. Coll. Sch. Lon. Prev: CFP USA.; SHO Whittington Hosp. Lond. GP VTS; Ho. Phys. N. Middlx. Hosp.

SHELDON, Jonathan Westmacott Sirr Queens Hospital, Belvedere Road, Burton-on-Trent DE13 0RB Tel: 01283 566333; Crossfield Mews, Cross Lane, Rolleston on Dove, Burton-on-Trent DE13 9EB Tel: 01283 813355 Fax: 01283 812854 — MB BS 1973 Lond.; FRCP Lond. 1991; MRCP (UK) 1976; MRCS Eng. LRCP Lond. 1973. (St. Thos.) Cons. Phys. (Respirat. Med.) Qu. Hosp. Burton on Trent. Socs: Brit. Thorac. Soc. Prev: Cons. Phys. Burton Dist. Hosp. Burton on Trent; Lect. (Med.) St. Thos. Hosp. Med. Sch. Lond.; Sen. Regist. Lond. Chest. Hosp.

SHELDON, Judith Claire Shillingford Lodge, Shillingford Abbot, Exeter EX2 9QQ Tel: 01392 832222 — BM 1981 Soton.; Dip. Occ. Med. 1997; DRCOG 1984. Clin. Asst. Occupat. Med. Roy. Devon & Exeter Hosp. Prev: SHO (Geriat. & O & G) Guy's Hosp. Lond.; SHO (Paediat.) Alder Hey Hosp. Liverp.

SHELDON, Karen Julie Medical Boards, PO Box 1000, Cranwell, Sleaford NG34 8GZ Tel: 01400 61201 Ext: 6786 — MB ChB 1984 Liverp.; MRCGP 1991; Dip. OceMed 1995. (L'pool Univ.) Socs: BMA.

SHELDON, Kenneth Mark Mountain (retired) 10 Borrins Way, Baildon, Shipley BD17 6NP — MA, MB BChir Camb. 1937; MRCS Eng. LRCP Lond. 1937. Prev: Ho. Phys. St. Luke's Hosp. Bradford.

SHELDON, Kenneth Paul Idle Medical Centre, 440 Highfield Road, Idle, Bradford BD10 8RU Tel: 01274 771999 Fax: 01274 772001 — MRCS Eng. LRCP Lond. 1966. Prev: Ho. Surg. Lond. Hosp. Annexe Brentwood; Ho. Phys. Sheppey Gen. Hosp. Minster; Jun. Accouch. All St.s' Hosp. Chatham.

SHELDON, Laurence Alan Priory Hospital North London, The Bourne, Southgate, London N14 6RA Tel: 07947 762995 Fax: 02084 478138 — MB BS 1982 Lond.; BSc (Hist. Med.) 1979; MRCPsych. 1989; DCH RCP Lond. 1992. (Royal Free Hospital School of Medicine, Lond.) Cons. in Child and Adolesc. Psychiat., Priory Hosp.,N. Lond.; Honarary Cons. in Child & Adolesc. Psychiat. St Geo.'s Hosp. Lond. Prev: Sen. Regist. (Child & Adolesc. Psychiat.) Lond; Med. Off. Prof. Dept. Med. Baragwanath Hosp. Soweto, S. Afr.; Regist. (Paediat.) Kenepuru Hosp., NZ.

SHELDON, Michael Graham The Mission Practice, 208 Cambridge Heath Road, London E2 9LS Tel: 020 8983 7303 Fax: 020 8983 6800; 23 Lancaster Drive, Isle of Dogs, London E14 9PT Tel: 020 7538 2375 Fax: 020 7538 1551 Email: mikesheldon@compuserve.com — MB BS 1964 Lond.; BA Open 1994; FRCGP 1982, M 1973. (Middlx.) Hon. Sen. Lect. (Gen. Pract.) St. Bart. & The Roy. Lond. Hosp. Lond. Univ.; Mem. Med. Practs Comm. Socs: Irish Coll. GP's. Prev: Sen. Lect. (Primary Care & Gen. Pract.) Univ. Nottm. Med. Sch.; Lect. (Cardiac Surg.) St. Thos. Hosp. Lond.; Ho. Phys. & Ho. Surg. Middlx. Hosp.

SHELDON, Nicholas Hanson Holmwood Corner Surgery, 179 Malden Road, New Malden KT3 6AA Tel: 020 8942 0066 Fax: 020 8336 1377 Email: Nicholas.Sheldon@gp-H84042.nhs.uk; Osborne Villa, 29 Bellevue Road, Kingston upon Thames KT1 2UD — MB BChir 1976 Camb.; MA Camb., MB BChir 1976; MA Camb. (St. Thoma's Hospital) Vis. Med. Off. Mary Mt. Internat. Sch. Kingston Hill. Prev: Med. Adv. (Occupat. Health) Kingston Hosp. Trust.

***SHELDON, Nina Charlotte** 20 Landells Road, East Dulwich, London SE22 9PG Tel: 020 8693 7459 — MB BS 1997 Lond.; BSc (Hons.) 1994.

SHELDON, Paul Burnett 6 Tieranan Terrace, Murgon 4605, Australia; 33 St. Andrews Drive, Lowfell, Gateshead NE9 6JU — MB ChB 1986 Leeds.

SHELDON, Peter John Herbert Schalscha Department of Microbiology & Immunology, Medical Sciences Building, University Road, Leicester LE1 9HN Tel: 0116 252 2953 Email: pjs@ie.ac.uk; 42 Holmfield Road, Leicester LE2 1SA Tel: 0116 270 6817 — MD 1987 Birm.; MB ChB 1963; FRCP Lond. 1991; MRCP (UK) 1969. Sen. Lect. (Immunol.) Univ. Leicester; Hon. Cons. Rheum. Leicester Roy. Infirm. Socs: Brit. Soc. Immunol. & Brit. Soc. Rheum. Prev: Sen. Regist. (Rheum.) Middlx. Hosp. Lond.; Mem. Scientif. Staff MRC Rheum. Unit Taplow.

SHELDON, Philip Watson Eadon (retired) Rockley Farm House, Cumnor, Oxford OX2 9QH Tel: 01865 862123 — MB ChB 1944 Manch.; MA Oxf. 1964; FRCR 1975; FFR 1953; DMRD Eng. 1949. Cons. Neuroradiol. Radcliffe Infirm. Oxf.; Clin. Lect. Radiol. Univ. Oxf. Prev: Regist. Dept. Radiol. & Ho. Phys. Roy. Infirm. Manch.

SHELDRAKE, Fiona Elizabeth 9A Private Road, Sherwood, Nottingham NG5 4DD; Arden House, 123 Westdale Lane, Carlton, Nottingham NG4 3NW — MB ChB 1961 Ed.; DObst RCOG 1963. (Ed.) GP Nottm.; Hosp. Pract. (Rheum.) Univ. Hosp. & City Hosp. Nottm. Socs: BMA; Assoc. Mem. Brit. Soc. Rheum. Prev: Regist. (Med.) Dept. Rheum. N.. Gen. Hosp. Edin.; Regist. Gen. Med. Aberd. Gen. Hosp. Gp.; Med. Adviser Boots Co. Nottm.

SHELDRAKE, John Hobson Good Hope Hospital NHS Trust, Rectory Road, Sutton Coldfield B75 7RR Tel: 0121 378 2211; Tadorna, 117 Sherifoot Lane, Four Oaks, Sutton Coldfield B75 5DU Tel: 0121 323 3128 — MB ChB 1981 Birm.; BA (Hons.) Oxf. 1976; FRCA 1987. Cons. Anaesth. Good Hope Hosp. Sutton Coldfield. Prev: Sen. Regist. (Anaesth.) W. Midl. RHA.

SHELDRAKE, Lynn Joy Ashfield Surgery, 8 Walmley Road, Sutton Coldfield B76 1QN Tel: 0121 351 3238; Tadorna, 117 Sherifoot Lane, Four Oaks, Sutton Coldfield B75 5DU — MB ChB 1981 Birm.; DRCOG 1984; MRCGP 1986; MRCGP 1986; DRCOG 1984.

SHELDRICK, Caroline Mary 72 Lexden Road, Colchester CO3 3SP — MB BS 1983 Lond.; MCOphth. 1989; DO RCPS Glas. 1988. Clin. Asst. Ophth. Colchester. Prev: SHO (Ophth.) Norwich HA; SHO (Ophth.) Blackpool, Wyre & Fylde HA.; Clin. Asst. Leicester.

SHELDRICK, Mr James Harry 78 Birdwood Road, Cambridge CB1 3TE — MB BS 1984 Lond.; BSc (Physiol.) Lond. 1981, MB BS 1984; FRCS Glas. (Ophth.) 1989; FCOphth. 1989; DO RCS Eng. 1988. Lect. (Ophth.) Leic. Univ.

SHELDRICK, Michael Day (retired) 55 Beauchamp Avenue, Leamington Spa CV32 5TB Tel: 01926 426255 — MB ChB 1952 Bristol. Examg. Med. Off. for the Benefits Agency; Clin. Asst. in Psychiat. S. Warw. Hosp. Gp.; Reserve Mem. Coventry Appeal Tribunal. Prev: O & G Ho. Surg. Warneford Hosp. Leamington.

SHELFORD, Gawain Charles Ommanney 36 Folly Hill, Farnham GU9 0BH — MB BChir 1989 Camb.

SHELLEY, Donald Frederick 7 Vyne Meadow, Sherborne St John, Basingstoke RG24 9PZ Tel: 01256 850573 — MB BS 1969 Lond.; MRCP (UK) 1975; FRCR 1978; DMRD Eng. 1977. (Guy's) Cons. Radiol. N. Hants. Hosp. Prev: Sen. Regist. (Radiol.) Guy's Hosp. Lond.

SHELLEY, Frederick Charles 7-27 Heathside, Avalon, Poole BH14 8HT Tel: 01202 707510 — MB BS 1952 Lond.; MRCS Eng. LRCP Lond. 1952; FRCA Eng. 1961; DA Eng. 1960. (Guy's) Barrister (Gray's Inn). Prev: Secretariat Med. Defence Union.

SHELLEY, James Charles 7 Vyne Meadow, Sherborne St John, Basingstoke RG24 9PZ Tel: 01256 850573 — MB BS 1997 Lond.; BSc (Hons) Lond 1995; DTM & H, Liverp 1999. (Guy's and St Thomas's) SHO in Med., Roy. Hosps. Med. Rotat., Lond. Socs: Fell.of Roy. Soc. Of Trop. Med. and Hygine. Prev: SHO in (A & E), Guy's Hosp.; Ho. Phys. Guy's Hosp.; Ho. Surg., Greenwich Dist. Hosp.

SHELLEY, Joanna Catherine The College Clinic, 4 College Lane, Gibraltar, Gibraltar Tel: 00 350 75769 Fax: 00 350 72791 Email: jshelley@gibnet.gi; Thatch Farm, Glaston, Oakham LE15 9BX Email: jshelley@jet.es — MB BS 1987 Lond.; BA Camb. 1984, MA 1991. (Cambridge, Charing Cross and Westminster) Princip. in Private Gen. Pract. (p/t); Port Health Off., Gibraltar; Police Surg. Roy. Gibraltar Police; BS-AC Med. Ref. Socs: Roy. Soc. Med.; BMA.

SHELLEY, John Richard, Bt South Molton Health Centre, 10 East Street, South Molton EX36 3BZ Tel: 01769 573101 Fax: 01769 574371 — MB BChir Camb. 1967; MA Camb. 1967; MRCGP 1978; DObst RCOG 1969. (St. Mary's) Socs: BMA; Treas. N. & E. Devon. LMC; RCGP. Prev: Ho. Phys. Qu. Eliz. II Hosp. Welwyn Garden City; Ho. Surg. Salisbury Gen. Hosp.; Ho. Surg. (Obst.) P.ss Margt. Hosp. Swindon.

SHELLEY, Katherine Elizabeth 6 Lostock Hall Road, Poynton, Stockport SK12 1DP — MB ChB 1994 Manch.

SHELLEY, Mrs Rosemary Anne Mengage Street Surgery, 100 Mengage Street, Helston TR13 8RF Tel: 01326 435888 Fax: 01326 563310; Tilly Whim, Poldown, Breage, Helston TR13 9NN — MB

SHELLEY

BCh 1976 Wales; MRCGP 1980. (Welsh Nat. Sch. of Med.) GP Helston.

SHELLEY, Simone Avril 59 The Drive, Edgware HA8 8PS — MB BS 1983 Lond.; MRCGP 1988; DRCOG 1987.

SHELLEY-SMITH, Norman John c/o Lloyds Bank, 344 Grays Inn Road, London WC1X 8BX; 30 South Road, Hayling Island PO11 9AE Tel: 01705 467172 — MB BCh BAO 1961 Dub.; BA Dub. 1959, MB ChB Dent.Sc 1955, MB BCh BAO 1961; FFA RCS Eng. 1970; DA Eng. 1966. (T.C. Dub.) Socs: BMA. Prev: Unit Head Aramco Al Hasa Med. Centre, Saudi Arabia.

SHELLIM, Arthur Jonathan 125 Carlton Towers, North St., Carshalton SM5 2EH; (Surgery) 41 Streatham Road, Mitcham CR4 2AD Tel: 020 8648 2611 — MRCS Eng. LRCP Lond. 1971; DObst RCOG 1973. (Guy's) Prev: Ho. Off. (Gen. Surg. & Gen. Med.) Orpington Hosp. Kent; Div. Surg. St. John Ambul. Brig.

SHELLIM, Maurice Arthur 76 Boydell Court, St. John's Wood Park, London NW8 6NG Tel: 020 7722 7598 — MRCS Eng. LRCP Lond. 1939. (Guy's) Socs: BMA. Prev: Regist. (Dermat.) Guy's Hosp. Lond.; Capt. RAMC, Graded Dermatol.

SHELLING, David North Cardiff Medical Centre, Excalibur Drive, Thornhill, Cardiff CF14 9BB Tel: 029 2075 0322 Fax: 029 2075 7705; Bryncoed, 16 Drysgol Road, Radyr, Cardiff CF15 8BT Tel: 02920 842642 — MB BCh 1967 Wales. (Cardiff) Med. Off. Roy. Ordnance Fact. Cardiff; Fact. Med. Off. Amersham Internat. Socs: BMA. Prev: SHO (A & E) Unit Roy Gwent Hosp. Newport; Ho. Surg. (Obst.) St. David's Hosp. Cardiff.

SHELLOCK, Alison Jane 4 Milton View, Hitchin SG4 0QD — BM 1996 Soton.

SHELLY, Maire Patricia Intensive Care Unit, South Manchester University Hospitals NHS Trust, Withington Hospital, Nell Lane, Manchester M20 2LR Tel: 0161 291 3966 Fax: 0161 291 3964 — MB ChB 1979 Birm.; FRCA 1985. (Univ. Birm. Med. Sch.) Cons. Anaesth.& Intens. Care Univ. Hosp. S. Manch.; Hon. Clin. Lect. Univ. Manch.

SHELLY, Martin Anthony 1 Suffolk Court, Yeadon, Leeds LS19 7JN — MB ChB 1980 Leeds; MRCGP 1985; DRCOG 1985.

SHELLY, Mr Richard William 111 Dunvegan Drive, Lordswood, Southampton SO16 8DB — BM 1989 Soton.; BSc (Hons.) Pharmacol. Liverp. 1982; FRCS Ed. 1994.

SHELOCK, Columba Fionnuala McDonagh 99 South Side, Clapham Common, London SW4 9DN — MB BCh BAO 1948 NUI. (Galw.)

SHELSWELL, Anthony Eric (retired) Moorways, Ashover Road, Kelstedge, Chesterfield S45 0DT — MB ChB 1946 Manch. Prev: SHO (Anaesth.) N. & Mid-Chesh. Hosp. Gp.

SHELSWELL, Mr John Hubert (retired) Kiln House, Hall Road, Rochford SS4 1NT Tel: 01702 544185 — MB ChB 1943 Manch.; FRCS Eng. 1950. Cons. Orthop. Surg. S.end-on-Sea Gp. Hosps. Prev: Sen. Regist. Roy. Nat. Orthop. Hosp. Lond.

SHELTON, Diana Mary Chest Clinic, Lewisham Hospital, Lewisham High St., London SE13 6LH Tel: 020 8690 4311; 28 Queensway, Petts Wood, Orpington BR5 1EA Tel: 01689 872953 — MB ChB St. And. 1967; MRCP (UK) 1972. Assoc. Specialist (Respirat. Med.) Lewisham Trust. Socs: Brit. Thorac. Soc. Prev: Sen. Regist. (Respirat. Med.) SE Thames RHA; Regist. (Respirat. & Gen. Med.) New Cross Hosp. Lond.; Hon. Clin. Lect. Cardiothoracic Inst. Lond.

SHELTON, Fiona Carol 112 Teignmouth Road, Selly Oak, Birmingham B29 7AY — MB ChB 1993 Birm.; DRCOG 1995; MRCGP 1997. (Birmingham) Socs: DRCOG; MRCGP.

SHELTON, Matthew Henty 13 St Andrews Lane, Old Headington, Oxford OX3 9DP — MB ChB 1985 Sheff.

SHELTON, Peter John Millwood Surger, Bradwell NR31 8HS Tel: 01493 661549 Fax: 01493 440187 — MB ChB 1984 Sheff.; 1998 FPCert; MRCGP 1989; DRCOG 1988. Prev: Trainee GP Failsworth Health Centre; SHO (Psychiat. & A & E) N. Manch. Gen. Hosp.

SHELTON, Rhidian John Easter Cottage, 25 Low Way, Bramby, Wetherby LS23 6QT — MB ChB 1998 Sheff.; MB ChB Sheff 1998.

SHEMBEKAR, Madhuri Vithal Section of Gene Function, CRC Section of Cell and Molecular Biology, Chester Beatty Laboratories, Fulham Road, London SW3 6JB — MB BChir 1992 Camb.; BA Camb. 1988; DRCPath 1997. (Camb.) Clin. Research Fell. (Gene Func. & Regulat.) Chester Beatty Laboratories Lond. Socs: Assn. Clin. Path.; Internat. Acad. Path. (Brit. Div.); Path. Soc. Prev: Sen.

Regist. St Thomas' Hosp.; Sen. Regist. Lewisham Hosp.; Regist. (Histopath.) W. Middlx., Char. Cross & W.m. Med. Sch. Lond.

SHEMILT, John Christopher 12 Wykeham Road, Glasgow G13 3YT Tel: 0141 954 9885 — MB ChB 1975 Ed.; MPhil. Ed. 1982, BSc (Med. Sc.) Hons. 1972; MRCPsych. 1979. Cons. Child & Adolesc. Psychiat. Dept. Child & Fam. Psych. Yorkhill NHS Trust, Glas.; Hon. Clin. Sen. Lect. Univ. Glas. Socs: Fell. (Ex-Pres.) Roy. Med. Soc. Edin.; Chair. Of Reg. Dev. Comm. Brit. Psychoanalyt. Soc.; Scott. Assn. Psychoanalyt. Psychother.

SHEMILT, Mr Philip (retired) 20 The Close, Salisbury SP1 2EB Tel: 01722 336000 — MB BS Lond. 1938; FRCS Eng. 1947; MRCS Eng. LRCP Lond. 1938. Prev: Cons. Surg. Salisbury Hosp. Gp.

SHEMILT, William Peter, TD (retired) The Old Rectory Farm, Cranford St Andrew, Kettering NN14 4AH Tel: 0153 678287 — MRCS Eng., LRCP Lond. 1936. Med. Off. N.ants. Fire Brig. Prev: Anaesth. Co. Hosp. Ashford.

SHEN, Richard Nanyang 232 Noak Hill Road, Billericay CM12 9UX — MB BS 1984 Punjab; MRCP (UK) 1990.

SHENAI, Mrs Mary Sydney 1 Belsize Park, London NW3 4ET Tel: 020 7435 5952 — MB BS 1952 Lond.; MRCS Eng. LRCP Lond. 1952.

SHENDEREY, Kenneth David 846 York Road, Leeds LS14 6DX Tel: 0113 264 7278; 8 Ring Road, Shadwell, Leeds LS17 8NJ Tel: 0113 265 6550 — MB BS 1969 Lond.; Cert. JCC Lond. 1976; Cert. FPA 1971. (Middlx.) Prev: Ho. Off. Middlx. Hosp.; Ho. Off. Whittington Hosp.; Med. Off. Family Plann. Assn.

SHENFIELD, Francoise 55 Frognal, London NW3 6YA Tel: 020 7380 9435 Fax: 020 7380 9600 Email: mfi@easynet.co.uk — MRCS Eng. LRCP Lond. 1975; MA (Med. Law & Ethics) Lond. 1993; DCH Eng. 1977. (King's Coll. Lond. & St. Mary's) Clin. Lect. (O & G & Infertil.) Middlx. Hosp. Lond. & Univ. Coll. Hosp. Lond.; Fertil. Specialist Lond. Woms. Clinic. Socs: (Comm.) Brit. Fertil. Soc.; Eur. Soc. Human Reproduc. & Embryol.; Scientif. Comm. Condiwater SIG Ethics & Law.

SHENFINE, Claire (retired) 10 Denewell Avenue, Gateshead NE9 5HD Tel: 0191 487 8229 — MB BS 1961 Durh. Prev: Retd. GP.

SHENFINE, Jonathan Flat 1A Eslington Terrace, Jesmond, Newcastle upon Tyne NE2 4RJ Tel: 0191 281 2246 — MB BS 1993 Newc. SHO Rotat. (Surg.) Newc.

SHENFINE, Sharon Diane 1A Esslington Terrace, Jesmond, Newcastle upon Tyne NE2 4RJ — MB BS 1993 Newc.

SHENG, Morgan Hwa-Tze 30 Wykeham Road, London NW4 2SU — MB BS 1982 Lond.

SHENKIN, Professor Alan Department of Clinical Chemistry, Royal Liverpool University Hospital, PO Box 147, Liverpool L69 3GA Tel: 0151 706 4232 Fax: 0151 706 5813; 10 Rockbourne Green, Liverpool L25 4TH — PhD Glas. 1974, BSc (Hons.) 1965, MB ChB 1969; FRCP 1993; FRCP Glas. 1990; FRCPath 1990, M 1987. Prof. Clin. Chem. Univ. Liverp.; Hon. Cons. Chem. Path. Roy. Liverp. Univ. Hosp. Socs: (Ex-Hon. Treas.) Europ. Soc. for Parenteral & Enteral Nutrit.; Assn. Clin. Biochem. (Ex-Chairm. Scientif. Comm.).; Counc. Mem. Nutrit. Soc. Prev: Cons. Dept. Path. Biochem. Glas. Roy. Infirm.; Lect. (Biochem.) Univ. Glas.; Roy. Soc. Europ. Exchange Fell. Karolinska Inst. Stockholm.

SHENKIN, Arthur Manfred 30 Langtree Avenue, Giffnock, Glasgow G46 7LJ Tel: 0141 638 1182; Flat Nine, The Hollows, Ayr Road, Glasgow G46 7JB Tel: 0141 638 1182 — MB ChB Glas. 1942; FRCP Glas. 1971, M 1965; FRCPsych 1971; DPM Eng. 1950. (Univ. Glas.) Emerit. Cons. Psychiat. S.. Gen. Hosp. Glas. Socs: BMA; RCPS (Glas.); RCPsych. Prev: Hon. Lect. Glas. Univ.; Psychiat. Notre Dame Child Guid. Clinic Glas.; Cons. Psychiat. Dykebar Hosp. Paisley.

SHENKIN, Harry Richman (retired) Barosa, La Fredee Lane, Vallée Des Vaux, St Helier, Jersey JE2 3FE Tel: 01534 724719 — MB ChB 1938 Ed. Prev: Cons. Chest Phys. Durh. AHA.

SHENKIN, Ian Richman Cleveland Clinic, 12 Cleveland Road, St Helier, Jersey JE1 4HD Tel: 01534 722381/734121 — MB BS 1967 Durh.

SHENKIN, Susan Deborah The Royal London Hospital, London NW1 Tel: 020 7377 7000; 10 Rockbourne Green, Liverpool L25 4TH Tel: 0151 428 9756 — MB ChB 1994 Ed.; BSc (Med. Sci.) Psychol. (1st cl. Hons.) Ed. 1992; MRCP (UK) 1997. SHO (Neurol.) Roy. Lond. Hosp. Prev: SHO Rotat. (Gen. Med.) Radcliffe NHS Trust

Oxf.; Ho. Off. (Med.) Roy. Infirm. Edin.; Ho. Off. (Surg.) Qu. Margt. Hosp. Dunfermline.

SHENKMAN, John Joseph The Surgery, Stowe Drive, Southam, Leamington Spa CV47 1NY Tel: 01926 812577; Mynyddislwyn, Church Road, Long Itchington, Rugby CV23 Tel: 0192 681 2731 — MRCS Eng. LRCP Lond. 1961; MB Camb. 1962, BChir 1961; DObst RCOG 1963. (St. Mary's) Socs: (Treas.) Gen. Practs. Writers Assn. & BMA. Prev: Ho. Surg. & Ho. Phys. Amersham Gen. Hosp.; Ho. Off. (Paediat.) St. Mary's Hosp. Lond.; Ho. Off. (Obst.) Warneford Hosp. Leamington Spa.

SHENNAN, Andrew Hoseason 33 Julian Avenue, Acton, London W3 9JE Tel: 020 8992 9126 Fax: 020 8740 3507 — MB BS 1985 Lond.; MRCOG 1991. Hon. Sen. Regist. & Lect. Qu. Charlotte's & Chelsea Hosp. Lond. Socs: Roy. Soc. Med. Prev: Regist: (O & G) Qu. Charlottes & Chelsea Hosp. Lond.; Regist. (O & G) Baragwanath Hosp. Johannesburg, S. Afr.

SHENNAN, Douglas Hoseason (retired) 9 Hardwick Green, Ealing, London W13 8DN Tel: 020 8997 4363 — MB ChB 1950 Cape Town; MD Cape Town 1956; DPH Lond. 1954. Prev: Chief Med. Off. (Tuberc.) Transkei DoH.

SHENNAN, Jill Catherine Flat 9, Summertown House, Banbury Road, Oxford OX2 7QZ — MB ChB 1985 Dundee.

SHENNAN, Mr John Millward Tel: 01244 881688 Fax: 01244 881278 Email: john@shennan.co.uk — MB ChB 1963 Liverp.; FRCS Eng. 1968; FRCS Ed. 1967. (Liverp.) Cons. Gen. Surg. Wirral Hosp.NHS Trust; Hon. Lect. In Surg. Univ. Liverp. Socs: Assn. of Surg. GB & Irel.; Soc. Minimal Invasive Surg.; Brit. Assn. Surg. Oncol. Prev: Cons. Gen. Surg. Whiston & St. Helens Hosps.; Cons. Gen. Sur. Wirral NHS Trust Hosp.; Regist. (Surg.) United Liverp. Hosps. & Walton Hosp. Liverp.

SHENNAN, William John Shankland Medical Centre, 3 Edinburgh Road, Perth PH2 8AT — MB ChB 1980 Dundee.

SHENOLIKAR, Mr Aneil 100 Sturthes Hall Lane, Kirkburton, Huddersfield HD8 0PT Tel: 01484 606109 Email: a.shenolikar@virgin.net; Huddersfield Royal Infirmary, Lindley, Huddersfield HD3 3EA Tel: 01484 460582 — MB ChB 1986 Dundee; BMSc Dund 1983, MB ChB 1986; FRCS Glas. 1990; FRCS Orth. 1997. Cons. (Orthop. Surg.) Huddersfield Roy. Infirm. Socs: Brit. Orthopaedic Assn.; Brit. Orthopaedic Foot Surg. Soc. Prev: Sen. Regist. (Trauma & Orthop.) S. Wales; Regist. Rotat. (Orthop.) Morriston Hosp. Swansea, W. Wales Gen. Hosp. Carmarthen & Cardiff Roy. Infirm.; Regist. Rotat. (Surg.) Aberd. Roy. Infirm.

SHENOLIKAR, Mr Balwant Kashinath (retired) Aneil-Sarita, 164 Lower Morden Lane, Morden SM4 4SS — MB 1947 Calcutta; FRCS Eng. 1957; FRCS Ed. 1955; FBIM 1982. Prev: Sen. Med. Off. Dept. Health & Social Security.

SHENOLIKAR, Vindra Y Gilfach Glyd, Plascadwgan Road, Ynystawe, Swansea SA6 5AG; Y Gilfach Clyd, Plas Ladwian Road, Ynystawe, Swansea SA6 5AG Tel: 01792 845705 — MB ChB 1992 Aberd. Ho. Off. (Gen. Surg.) E. Glam. Hosp. Prev: Ho. Off. (Med.) Morriston Hosp. Swansea.

SHENOUDA, Mr Nabil Adib (retired) 31 Whitethorn Gardens, Enfield EN2 6HF Tel: 020 8366 0194 — MB BCh 1965 Cairo; FRCS Ed. 1979; Dip. Orthop. Surg. Cairo 1970; Dip. Gen. Surg. Cairo 1968. Prev: Clin. Asst. (Orthop. Surg.) Harold Wood Hosp.

SHENOY, Ashok Narayan 39 Goodwin Gardens, Waddon Way, Croydon CR0 4HS Tel: 020 8681 5633 — MB BS 1978 Mysore; MD (Anaesth.) Bangalore 1984; FRCA. 1992; DA (UK) 1988. Regist. (Anaesth.) St. Thos. Hosp. Lond.

SHENOY, Kudpi Krishnakantha 16 Abbotsbury Way, Nuneaton CV11 4GB — MB BS 1974 Mysore; Dip. Gen. Psychiat. Keele 1991; DObst RCPI 1984; DRCOG 1984. Staff Psychiat. N. Warks. NHS Trust, Nuneaton.

SHENTON, Antony Frank 39 Aylmer Grove, Newton Aycliffe DL5 4NF — MB BS 1977 Newc.

SHENTON, Frederick George Alan Bybridge, 142 Percy Road, Whitton, Twickenham TW2 6JG Tel: 020 8894 6888 — MRCS Eng. LRCP Lond. 1953; MA Camb. 1952. (Univ. Coll. Hosp.) Socs: MRCGP; BMA. Prev: GP Hounslow; Ho. Surg. & Ho. Phys. City Gen. Hosp. Stoke-on-Trent; Med. Off. RAMC.

SHENTON, Geoffrey Alister 37 Toyne Street, Sheffield S10 1HH — MB ChB 1995 Sheff.

SHENTON, Karyn Clare 15 Keele Road, Newcastle ST5 2JT — MB BS 1990 Lond.; FRCS Eng. 1995. Specialist Regist., SW Thames Rotat., Gen. Surg. Prev: Research Regist. (BrE. Surg.) St. Geo. Hosp. Lond.

SHENTON, Mark Irving Stowmarket Health Centre, Violet Hill Road, Stowmarket IP14 1NL Tel: 01449 776000 Fax: 01449 776005; Stormcrest, 114 Looseleigh Lane, Plymouth PL6 5HT Email: mark-sair@hotmail.com — MB BS 1989 Newc.

SHENTON, Paul Adrian Maswell Park Health Centre, Hounslow Avenue, Hounslow TW3 2DY Tel: 020 8321 3488 Fax: 020 8893 4368; 60 Bridge Way, Whitton, Twickenham TW2 7JJ Tel: 020 8894 2324 Fax: 020 8755 1250 — MB BS 1980 Lond.; MRCGP 1986; DRCOG 1985. (University College Hospital, London) Socs: BMA. Prev: Trainee GP Middlx. VTS.; Ho. Surg. & Ho. Phys. N.ampton Gen. Hosp.

SHEPARD, Clare Louise 19 Limes Way, Shabbington, Aylesbury HP18 9HB — BM 1996 Soton.

SHEPARD, Mr Gordon James Department of Orthopaedics, Manchester Royal Infirmary, Manchester; 10 Wrenswood Drive, Worsley, Manchester M28 7GS Tel: 01204 390390 Email: gshepard@globalnet.co.uk — MB ChB 1990 Leic.; FRCS Ed. 1995. (Leicester) Specialist Regist. NW Region. Socs: BOSTA; BTS; Assoc. Mem. BOA. Prev: Regist. (Orthop.) Roy. Liverp. Hosp., Whiston Hosp. Prescot & Arrowe Pk. Hosp. Wirral.

SHEPHARD, Mr Edmund 10 Harley Street, London W1N 1AA Tel: 020 7467 8300; Grove Lodge, Hunton, Maidstone ME15 0SE Tel: 01622 820318 — MRCS Eng. LRCP Lond. 1940; BM BCh Oxon. 1942; FRCS Eng. 1951. (Oxf. & St. Bart.) Hon. Cons. Orthop. Surg. SE Thames RHA. Socs: Sen. Fell. BOA; Emerit. Fell. Internat. Soc. Orthop. & Accid. Surg; Medico-Legal Soc. Prev: Chief Asst. (Orthop.) St. Bart. Hosp.; Maj. RAMC Surg. Specialist; Ho. Surg. (Orthop.) Hosp. OsW.ry.

SHEPHARD, Edmund Peter 80 Harley Street, London W1G 7HL Tel: 020 7637 4962 Fax: 020 7637 4963 Email: shepardep@bigfoot.com — MB BS Lond. 1970; BA (1st cl Hons. Physics) Oxf. 1964; MD Lond. 1979; MRCP (UK) 1972; T(M) 1991. Hon. Research Fell. Univ. Coll. Lond.; Hon. Cons. Phys. St Luke's Hosp. for the Clergy. Prev: Research Fell. (Nuclear Physics) Ecole Polytechnique Paris & CERN, Geneva; Sen. Regist. & Chief Asst. (Med. Profess. Unit) St. Bart Hosp. Lond.

SHEPHARD, Elizabeth Anne 2 Heron Court, 53 Alexandra Rd, Epsom KT17 4HU Tel: 01372 749130 — MB ChB 1979 Glas.; MRCGP 1984; DCH RCPS Glas. 1983; DRCOG 1982. Asst. GP Crieff. Prev: Asst. Br. Med. Off. Brit. Red Cross Soc. Perth & Kinross.

SHEPHARD, Elizabeth Ruth St. Helier Hospital, Wrythe Lane, Carshalton SM5 1AA Tel: 020 8296 2926 Email: rshephard@sthelier.sghms.ac.uk — MB ChB 1990 Bristol; MRCP (UK) 1994; DRCOG 1995. (Bristol Univ.) Cons. Neonatologist, St. Helier Hosp., Wrythe La., Charshalton, Surrey, SM5 1AA. Prev: SpR Neonat. Medicare, Kings Coll. Hosp.; SpR Neonat. Medicare Mayday Univ. Hosp.; SpR Neonat. Medicare St Geo.'s Hosp.

SHEPHARD, Graham David Hopper (retired) Brook Cottage, Walton Cardiff, Tewkesbury GL20 7BL — MB BChir 1953 Camb.; MA Camb. 1954; DObst RCOG 1954. Prev: on Staff Tewkesbury Hosp.

SHEPHARD, John Andrew 4 The Green, Horrabridge, Yelverton PL20 7QP — MB BS 1991 Lond.

SHEPHARD, John Neville Pinehurst, 12 Bassett Row, Southampton SO16 7FS — MB BS 1985 Lond. Sen. Regist. (Anaesth.) Shackleton Dept. of Anaesth. Soton. Gen. Hosp. Socs: Fell. Roy. Coll. Anaesth.

SHEPHARD, Neville Wilson Peterscroft, Stuckton, Fordingbridge SP6 2HG — MB ChB 1953 Sheff.; FFPM RCP (UK) 1990; DObst RCOG 1958. (Sheff.) Dir. Med. Sci. Research Buckingham. Socs: Fell. Roy. Soc. Med.; Brit. Pharm. Soc. Prev: Med. & Research Dir. Ortho Pharmaceut. Ltd. Saunderton; Head, Clin. Research Roussel Laborats.

SHEPHARD, Mr Reginald Harry The Oaks, 776 Wollaton Road, Wollaton, Nottingham NG8 2AP Tel: 0115 928 5602 Email: tshep5602@aol.com — MB BS 1945 Lond.; MD Yale 1943; FRCS Eng. 1950; MRCS Eng. LRCP Lond. 1944. (Univ. Coll. Hosp. & Yale Univ.) Emerit. Cons. Neurosurg. Derby & Leicester Hosp. Gps. Socs: Soc. Brit. Neurol. Surgs.; Past Pres. Derby. Med. Soc; Leics.Med.Soc. Prev: Sen. Regist. Neurosurg. Lond. Hosp. & Maida Vale Hosp. Nerv. Dis.; Surg. Regist. Univ. Coll. Hosp.

SHEPHEARD

SHEPHEARD, Antony Charles The Health Centre, Madeira Road, West Byfleet KT14 6DH Tel: 01932 336933 Fax: 01932 355681; The Hoyte, Woodham Lane, Woodham, Weybridge KT13 3QA Tel: 01932 34839 — BM BCh 1971 Oxf.

SHEPHEARD, Mr Brian George Frank Parkfield, Park Lane, Greenfield, Oldham OL3 7DX Tel: 0145 773257 — MB BS 1962 Lond.; BSc Lond. 1959, MB BS 1962; FRCS Eng. 1969. (Lond. Hosp.) Cons. Urol. Oldham AHA. Socs: Assoc. Mem. Brit. Assn. Urol. Surgs. Prev: Sen. Regist. Roy. Marsden Hosp. Lond.; Sen. Regist. St. Peters' Hosps. Lond.; Surg. Regist. Lond. Hosp.

SHEPHERD, Alan Neill The Knowe, 43 Queen St., Perth PH2 0EJ — MB ChB 1975 Dundee; BSc (Med. Sci.) St. And. 1972; FRCP Ed. 1989; MRCP (UK) 1978; FRCPS 1990. Cons. Phys. Perth Roy. Infirm.; Hon. Sen. Lect. Univ. Dundee. Prev: Lect. (Hon. Sen. Regist.) Univ. Dept. Med. Ninenwells Hosp. & Med.; Sch. Dundee; Regist. Univ. Dept. Mat. Med. Stobhill Hosp. Glas. & Univ. Dept. Med. W. Infirm. Glas.

SHEPHERD, Alistair John Newbolt National Blood Service Mersey & North Wales Centre, West Derby St., Liverpool L7 8TW Tel: 0151 551 8800 Fax: 0151 551 8895 Email: alistair.shepherd@nbs.nhs.uk; 28 Bath Street, Liverpool L22 5PS Tel: 0151 920 7189 — MB ChB 1967 Liverp.; DOccMed. 1998; FRCPath 1989, M 1977. (Liverp.) Cons. Haemat. Nat. Blood Serv. Liverp. Centre Liverp. Socs: Assn. Clin. Path.; Liverp. Med. Inst.; Soc. Occupat. Med. Prev: Sen. Regist. (Haemat.) Liverp. AHA (T); Regist. (Haemat.) Nottm. City Hosp.; SHO (Haemat.) St. Thos. Hosp. Lond.

SHEPHERD, Mr Allan St. John's Hospital at Howden, Livingston EH54 6PP Tel: 01506 419666; 13 Deanburn Park, Linlithgow EH49 6EZ — MB ChB 1968 Glas.; FRCS Ed. 1973; FRCOG 1985, M 1972. Cons. O & G St. John's Hosp. Livingston; Hon. Sen. Lect. Univ. Edin. Prev: Sen. Regist. Simpson Memor. Matern. Pavil. Edin.

SHEPHERD, Mr Allister Frederick Irwin Ministry of Defence Hospital Unit, Friarage Hospital, Northallerton DL6 1JG Tel: 01609 779911; Elm Cottage, Craggs Lane, Tunstall, Richmond DL10 7RB — MB BCh BAO 1973 Belf.; FRCS Ed. 1978. Cons. Surg. MOD Hosp.Unit.Fiarage Hosp.N.allerton; Cons. Surg. MDHU Friarage Hosp. N. Allerton; Command Off. MOD Hosp.Unit.Friarage Hosp.N.allerton. Socs: Roy. Soc. Med. & Milit. Surg. Soc.; Assn. Surg. Prev: Sen. Regist. (Surg.) Canterbury & Margate Hosps.; Cons. Surg. BMH, Hong Kong; Cons. Surg. Milit. Wing Musgrave Pk.

SHEPHERD, Andrew David Heaton Moor Medical Centre, 32 Heaton Moor Road, Stockport SK4 4NX Tel: 0161 432 0671; 5 Styperson Way, Poynton, Stockport SK12 1UJ Tel: 01625 858840 Fax: 01625 858840 — MB ChB 1971 Manch.; DObst RCOG 1973. (Manch.)

SHEPHERD, Andrew James 40 Wylde Green Road, Sutton Coldfield B72 1HD — MB ChB 1998 Bristol.

SHEPHERD, Angela Mary Urodynamic Unit, Southmead Hospital, Bristol BS10 5NB Tel: 0117 959 5181 Fax: 0117 950 2229; Pine Cottage, Old Down, Tockington, Bristol BS32 4PP Tel: 01454 416466 — MB ChB Bristol 1968; MD Bristol 1980; FRCOG 1988, M 1974. (Bristol) Clin. Dir. Urodynamic Unit S.mead Hosp. Bristol. Socs: Chartered Soc. Physiother.; Bristol M-C Soc.; Internat. Urogyn. Assn. Prev: Research Fell. (Urol.) Ham Green Hosp. Bristol; Regist. (O & G) Roy. Free Hosp. Lond.; SHO (Obst. & Paediat.) Harari Hosp., Zimbabwe.

SHEPHERD, Annie McLeod 8 St Clair Terrace, Edinburgh EH10 5NW Tel: 0131 447 6647 — MB ChB 1950 Ed.; BSc Ed. 1945, MB ChB 1950. Socs: Med. Wom. Federat.

SHEPHERD, Barbara Catherine Green End Surgery, 58 Green End, Comberton, Cambridge CB3 7DY Tel: 01223 262500 Fax: 01223 264401; 4 Eltisley Avenue, Cambridge CB3 9JG Tel: 01223 365571 — MB BChir 1990 Camb.; MA Camb. 1990; MRCGP 1993; DCH RCP Lond. 1993; DRCOG 1991. GP Camb.

SHEPHERD, Beryl Mary 1 Forgan Way, Newport-on-Tay DD6 8JQ — MB ChB 1969 St. And.; MRCPsych 1985. Cons. Psychiat. Roy. Dundee Liff Hosp.

SHEPHERD, Caroline West Grove, 420 Blackness Road, Dundee DD2 1TQ Tel: 01382 68313 — MB ChB 1980 Aberd.; MRCGP 1985; DRCOG 1984; DCCH RCP Ed. 1984.

SHEPHERD, Carolyn Deborah Seaside Medical Centre, 18 Sheen Road, Eastbourne BN22 8DR Tel: 01323 725667 Fax: 01323 417169; Goldrings, PrideAUX Rd, Eastbourne BN21 2ND — MB BS 1983 Lond.

SHEPHERD, Charles Bernard Friars Cottage Surgery, Queens Square, Chalford Hill, Stroud GL6 8EH Tel: 01453 885462 Fax: 01453 885462 — MB BS 1974 Lond. (Middlx.) p/t Private Pract. Seeing Pat.s with ME/CFS; Cons. Med. to UK ME Assn. & Clin. Adviser Media Resource Servs. (CIBA Foundat.). Socs: Med. Adviser to ME Assn. of S. Afr.; BMA & Campaign Against Health Fraud. Prev: Resid. Med. Off. Cirencester Memor. Hosp.; SHO (Sexually Transm. Dis.) Middlx. Hosp. Lond.; SHO (Paediat.) P.ss Margt. Hosp. Swindon.

SHEPHERD, Charles William 44 Mullahead Road, Tandragee, Craigavon BT62 2LA — MB BCh BAO 1979 Belf.; MD Belf. 1995; MRCP (UK) 1984. Cons. Paediat. Craigavon Area Hosp. Prev: Sen. Regist. (Paediat.) Roy. Hosp. for Sick Childr. Glas.; Regist. (Paediat.) Ulster Hosp. Dundonald, Baragwanath Hosp. Johannesburg & Belf. City Hosp.

SHEPHERD, Christopher Michael Filey Surgery, Station Avenue, Filey YO14 9AE — MB BChir 1988 Camb. GP.

SHEPHERD, Daniel Tobias Sherrington Randmoor Cottage, Robins Lane, Coppice Row, Theydon Bois, Epping CM16 7DS — MB BS 1996 Lond.

SHEPHERD, David Brynne 5 Spout Spinney, Stannington, Sheffield S6 6EQ — MB ChB 1985 Leeds; FRCA 1993. Regist. (Anaesth.) Sheff.

SHEPHERD, David Christian (retired) Rosehaven, 490 Pilgrims Way, Wouldham, Rochester ME1 3RB Tel: 01634 861416 Fax: 01634 861416 — MB ChB 1965 Aberd.; DObst RCOG 1968.

SHEPHERD, Mr David Francis Charles Mewstone, 6 Elgin Road, Talbot Woods, Bournemouth BH4 9NL Tel: 01202 761397 — MB 1970 Camb.; BChir 1969; FRCS Eng. 1975; FRCR Eng. 1979. Cons. (Radiol.) E. Dorset Dist. Hosps. Prev: Sen. Regist. (Radiol.) Soton. Gen. Hosp.; Regist. (Gen. Surg.) Peace Memor. Hosp. Watford.

SHEPHERD, David Ian (retired) 12 Stones Drive, Ripponden, Sowerby Bridge HX6 4NY Tel: (01422) 823930 — MB ChB Aberd. 1968; MD (Hons. & Thursfield Award) Aberd. 1976; FRCP Lond. 1985; MRCP (UK) 1973. Cons. Neurol. Hope Hosp., Salford, N. Manch. Gen. Hosp. & Tameside & Rochdale Healthcare Trust; Hon. Assoc. Lect. Med. Univ. Manch. Prev: Sen. Regist. (Neurol.) Wessex Neurol. Centre Soton.

SHEPHERD, David James Saffron Group Practice, 509 Saffron Lane, Leicester LE2 6UL Tel: 0116 244 0888 Fax: 01162 831405 — BM BCh 1985 Oxf.; MRCGP 1989; DRCOG 1989. Socs: BMA. Prev: Med. Off. Berega Hosp., Tanzania.

SHEPHERD, David Richard Thompson Level 8, Belfast City Hospital, 93 Lisburn Road, Belfast BT9 7AB Tel: 01232 329241; 17 Richmond Court, Lisburn BT27 4QU Tel: 01846 665305 — MB BCh BAO 1971 Belf.; FRCP Lond. 1994; MRCP (UK) 1976; MRCGP 1977. Cons. Phys. Belf. City Hosp.

SHEPHERD, Deborah Anne 71 Hornhill Road, Rickmansworth WD3 9TG — MB BS 1990 Lond.

SHEPHERD, Debra Joy 3 Park Terrace, Loftus, Saltburn-by-the-Sea TS13 4HU — MB BS 1996 Lond.

SHEPHERD, Elizabeth Helen 38 Colchester Avenue, Pen-y-Lan, Cardiff CF23 9BP — BM 1996 Soton.

SHEPHERD, Francis George Graham (retired) 308 North Deeside Road, Cults, Aberdeen AB15 9SB Tel: 01224 868721 — MB ChB 1948 Aberd.; FRCGP 1978.

SHEPHERD, Gillian Helen Harrogate District Hospital, Lancaster Park Road, Harrogate HG2 7SX Tel: 01423 885959; Spring Close, 25 Rossett Drive, Harrogate HG2 9NS — MB ChB 1979 Leeds; MB ChB (Hons.) Leeds 1979; FRCS Ed. 1989; FRCOphth. 1989. Assoc. Specialist Ophth. Harrogate. Prev: Regist. (Ophth.) Harrogate Dist. Hosp.

SHEPHERD, Gillian Louise Tel: 020 8966 2067 Fax: 020 8966 2549; 4 Netherton Road, St. Margarets, Twickenham TW1 1LZ — MB BS 1976 Lond.; MD Lond. 1984; MRCP (UK) 1980; MRCGP 1985. (Univ. Coll. Hosp.) Prev: Clin. Director in Cardiovasc. Clin. Developm., Glaxo; Regist. (Med.) Hammersmith Hosp. Lond.; Mem. Clin. Pharmacol. Subcomm. Roy. Coll Phys.

SHEPHERD, Gordon Andrew Allison Ark Occupational Health, 6 BonAccord Cres Lane, Aberdeen AB11 6DF Tel: 01224 584584 Fax: 01224 584567 Email: mail@arkoh.co.uk — MB ChB 1973 Glas.; AFOM RCP Lond. 1991. Occupat. Phys. Socs: Soc. Occupat. Med. Prev: Research Fell. (Clin. Biochem. & Metab. Med.) Roy. Vict.

Infirm. Newc.; Resid. (Endocrinol. & Metab.) Univ. W.. Ontario & Assoc. Hosps., Canada; Regist. (Med.) Raigmore Hosp. Inverness.

SHEPHERD, Henry Robert, DSC (retired) 4 The Glade, Enfield EN2 7QH Tel: 020 8363 3677 — MB ChB 1942 Liverp. Mem. Enfield HA; Mem. Enfield & Haringey FPC. Prev: O & G Ho. Surg. Liverp. Roy. Infirm.

SHEPHERD, Hilary Jean 4 Troon Drive, Bridge of Weir PA11 3HF Tel: 01505 614155 — MB ChB 1965 Glas. (Glas.) Prev: Ho. Phys. Stobhill Hosp. Glas.; Ho. Surg. Roy. Alexandra Infirm. Paisley.

SHEPHERD, Hugh Arkwright Flexford House, Flexford Road, North Baddesley, Southampton SO52 9DF — MB BChir 1976 Camb.; BA (Hons.) Camb. 1972, MA, MB 1976, BChir 1975; MD 1985; MRCP (UK) 1978. Cons. Phys. (Gen. Med. & Gastroenterol.) Roy. Hants. Co. Hosp. Winchester. Socs: Brit. Soc. Gastroenterol. Prev: Research Fell. Gastroenterol. Unit Radcliffe Infirm. Oxf.

SHEPHERD, Professor James Department of Biochemistry, Royal Infirmary, Glasgow G4 0SF Tel: 0141 552 0689 Fax: 0141 553 1703; 17 Barriedale Avenue, Hamilton ML3 9DB Tel: 01698 428259 Fax: 01698 286281 Email: jshepherd@gri-biochem.org.uk — MB ChB 1968 Glas.; PhD Glas. 1972, BSc 1965. (Glas.) Prof. Path. Biochem. Univ. Glas. & Hon. Consult. Path. Biochem. Glas. Roy. Infirm. Socs: Fell. Roy. Coll. Path; Fell. Roy. Coll. Phys. of Glas. Prev: Reader (Path. Biochem.) Univ. Glas.; Asst. Prof. (Med.) Baylor Coll. Med. & Methodist Hosp. Houston, USA; Vis. Prof. (Med.) Cantonal Hosp. Geneva, Switz.; Vis. Specialist Mehlati Hosp & Univ. Helsinki Finland.

SHEPHERD, James Baikie Moir 90 Thorne Road, Doncaster — MB BChir 1963 Camb.; MA, MB BChir Camb. 1963; DTM & H Eng. 1964. (Guy's) Res. Med. Off. Samarit. Hosp. Wom. Lond. Socs: Fell. Roy. Soc. Trop. Med. & Hyg. Prev: Res. Obstetr. & Gyn. Ho. Surg. Guy's Hosp. Lond.; Res. Obstetr. Qu. Charlotte's Hosp. Lond.

SHEPHERD, Jane Caroline 38 Mayfield Road, Sutton SM2 5DT — MB BS 1991 Lond.; MSc (Biochem.) 1988; BA (Chem.) Open 1985.

SHEPHERD, Jane Ellen Elizabeth Foxcote, Harberton Mead, Headington, Oxford OX3 0DB — MB BS 1979 Lond.; FFA RCS Eng. 1983. Cons. Anaesth. St. Mary's Hosp. Lond. Prev: Sen. Regist. St. Mary's Hosp. Lond.; Regist. (Anaesth.) Kings Coll. Hosp. Lond.

SHEPHERD, Jennifer Hazel Legatesden Farm, Pitcaple, Inverurie AB51 5DT — MB ChB 1979 Aberd.; DRCOG 1984. p/t GP Brimmond Med. Gp., Bucksburn, Aberd.; DRS Cardiol., Aberd. Roy. Infirm. Prev: GP Inverurie; SHO (Obst.) Paisley Matern. Hosp.; SHO (Surg.) Bradford Roy. Infirm.

SHEPHERD, Professor John Henry 149 Harley Street, London W1N 2DE Tel: 020 7935 4444 Fax: 020 7935 6224; Pickwick Cottage, 31 College Road, Dulwich, London SE21 7BG Tel: 020 8693 6342 Fax: 020 8299 0453 — MB BS 1971 Lond.; FRCS Eng. 1976; MRCS Eng. LRCP Lond. 1971; FRCOG 1996, M (Gold Medal) 1978; T(OG) 1991; MRCOG (Gold Medal) 1978; FACOG 1981. (St. Bart.) Cons. Gyn. (Surg. & Oncol.) St. Bart. Hosp. & The Lond. NHS Trust, The Roy. Marsden Hosp. NHS Trust Lond..; Prof. Surgic. Gyn. St Bars & Roy. Lond. Clinic of Med. and Dent.; Clin. Director Childr.s Health, Barts and the Lond. NHS Trust. Socs: Fell. Roy. Soc. Med.; Fell. Soc. Pelvic Surgs. (Vice-Pres. 1999); Soc. Gyn. Oncol. Prev: Cons. Surg. Chelsea Hosp. for Wom. Lond.; Vis. Lect. Acad. Med., Singapore 1996; Gyn. Oncol. Cancer Fell. Univ. S. Florida, USA.

SHEPHERD, John Moncrieff Occupational Health Service, Boots Company plc, PO Box 94, Nottingham NG2 3AA Tel: 01159 492484 Fax: 01159 492600 — MB ChB 1977 Manch.; BSc St. And. 1974; AFOM RCP Lond. 1993; MFOM RCP Lond. 1997. Occupat. Phys. The Boots Company. Socs: Soc. Occupat. Med.

SHEPHERD, John Neill (retired) Flat A Park House, Park Road, Cheadle Hulme, Cheadle SK8 7DA Tel: 0161 486 0163 — MB ChB 1935 Manch. Prev: Ho. Phys. Manch. Roy. Infirm.

SHEPHERD, John Steven (retired) 28 Barton Road, Cambridge CB3 9LF Tel: 01223 313058 — MB ChB 1954 Ed.; DCH Eng. 1959. Prev: GP Kirkby Stephen.

SHEPHERD, Mrs Juliet Sarah Upton Road Surgery, 30 Upton Road, Watford WD18 0JS Tel: 01923 226266 Fax: 01923 222324; 37 Mount View, Rickmansworth WD3 7BB — MB BS 1965 Lond.; DA Eng. 1970. (St. Bart.) Prev: SHO (Anaesth.) N. Middlx. Hosp. Lond.; Ho. Surg. Whipps Cross Hosp. Lond.; Ho. Phys. St. Bart. Hosp.

SHEPHERD, Kirsteen Mary 10 Heathfield Drive, Milngavie, Glasgow G62 8AZ — MB BS 1996 Lond.

SHEPHERD, Malcolm Cameron Flat 1 Left, 72 Lauderdale Gardens, Glasgow G12 9QW — MB ChB 1993 Glas.

SHEPHERD, Matthew James 16 Adel Vale, Adel, Leeds LS16 8LF Tel: 0113 245 0340 Email: drshep1@msn.com — MB ChB 1995 Leeds. (Leeds) SHO Rotat. (Med.) Leeds Gen. Infirm. Prev: SHO (A & E) Leeds Gen. Infirm.f; Ho. Off. (Surg.) St. Jas. Univ. Hosp. Leeds; Ho. Off. (Med.) Leeds Gen. Infirm.

SHEPHERD, Michael Anthony Walsham The Surgery, 1-3 Warrior Square, St Leonards-on-Sea TN37 6BA Tel: 01424 430123/445644 Fax: 01424 433706 — MB BS 1972 Lond.; MRCS Eng. LRCP Lond. 1972; FRNZCGP 1998; DFFP 1993; DCH Eng. 1975; DObst RCOG 1974. (Middlx.) GP St Leonards on Sea. Socs: BMA; NZ Med. Assn. Prev: GP Wellington, NZ; Regist. (Med.) Wellington Hosp., NZ; Ho. Phys. Middlx. Hosp.

SHEPHERD, Michael Stanley Mentmore Road Surgery, 30 Mentmore Road, Leighton Buzzard LU7 2NZ Tel: 01525 383202 Fax: 01525 851740; 2 Rannoch Gardens, Linslade, Leighton Buzzard LU7 2XQ — BM BS 1977 Nottm.; BMedSci. 1975; MRCGP 1981; DRCOG 1981. Clin. Asst. (Dermat.) Luton & Dunstable Hosp. Prev: Trainee Gen. Pract. Derby Vocational Train. Scheme.

SHEPHERD, Michelle Caroline Derby City General Hospital Psychiatric Unit, Littoxeter Road, Mickleover, Derby DE22 3NE; 48 Forest Road, Loughborough LE11 3NR — MB ChB 1991 Manch. (Manchester) Cons. Gen. Adult Psychiat., Derby. Prev: SHO (Psychogeriat.) W. Lond. Healthcare Trust Hosp. Lond.; Specialist Regist. Rotat., Leicester; Basic Train. Rotat., Char. Cross, Lond.

SHEPHERD, Nancy Jane The Barn, Grove Place, Nursling, Southampton SO16 9YA — MB BS 1963 Lond.; DA Eng. 1965. (Middlx.)

SHEPHERD, Professor Neil Anthony Department of Histopathology, Gloucestershire Royal Hospital, Great Western Road, Gloucester GL1 3NN Tel: 01452 395263 Fax: 01452 395285; Department of Histopathology, Cheltenham General Hospital, Sandford Road, Cheltenham GL53 7AN Tel: 01242 274073 Fax: 01242 274078 — MB BS 1979 Lond.; FRCPath 1995, M 1985. (St. Bart.) Cons. Histopath. Glos. Roy. Hosp.; Vis. Prof., Univ. of Cranfield. Socs: Hon Sec. Brit. Div. of Int. Acad. of Pathol.; Assn. Clin. Paths.; Brit. Soc. Gastroenterol. Prev: Sen. Lect. & Hon. Cons. (Histopath.) St. Bart. Hosp., St. Mark's Hosp. & ICRF Colorectal Cancer Unit Lond; Lect. (Histopath.) St. Bart. Hosp. & St. Mark's Hosp. Lond.; Regist. (Histopath.) & Ho. Surg. St. Bart. Hosp. Lond.

SHEPHERD, Nicholas Ironside Glover Street Medical Centre, 133 Glover Street, Perth PH2 0JB Tel: 01738 639748 Fax: 01738 635133; Denwood, Strathview Place, Methven, Perth PH1 3PP Tel: 01738 840729 Email: nishep@globalnet.co.uk — MB ChB 1980 Dundee; BMSc (1st cl. Hons.) Pharmacol. Dund 1977; MRCGP 1984; DRCOG 1982. (Univ. Dundee)

SHEPHERD, Patricia Carolyn Anne Department of Haematology, Western General Hospital, Edinburgh EH4 2XU Tel: 0131 537 1633 Fax: 0131 537 2552 Email: p.shepherd@ed.ac.uk; 53A Fountainhill Road, Edinburgh EH9 2LH Tel: 0131 66/ 9530 — MB BCh BAO 1972 Belf.; MRCP (UK) 1979; Amer. Bd. Internal. Med. 1979; FRCPath 1997, MRCPath 1987. Staff Grade Haemat. W.. Gen. Hosp. Edin. & St. Johns Hosp. Howden. Prev: Lect. (Haemat.) W.. Gen. Hosp. Edin.

SHEPHERD, Paul Richard Park Practice, 12 Brodrick Close, Hampden Park, Eastbourne BN22 9NR Tel: 01323 502200/503240 Fax: 01323 500527 — MB BS 1980 Lond.; MRCGP 1984. GP E.bourne.

SHEPHERD, Paul Robert 2 Colepike Hall, Lanchester, Durham DA7 0RW — MB BS 1977 Newcastle; MRCGP 1981. (Newcastle) GP Durh.; Med. Off. in Psychosexual Med. Newc.-Upon-Tyne. Socs: RCGP.

SHEPHERD, Peter Douglas Warwick 49 The Avenues, Norwich NR2 3QR Tel: 01603 250441 Email: petershepherd@btinternet.com — MRCS Eng. LRCP Lond. 1944; MB BS Lond. 1946, DPM 1951; MRCPsych 1971. (Middlx.) Prev: Cons. Psychiat. Rauceby Hosp. Sleaford; SHMO Shenley Hosp.; Ho. Phys. Middlx. Hosp. Lond.

SHEPHERD, Philip George Tel: 028 2826 1611 Fax: 028 2826 1614; 1 Huntersbudy, Larne BT40 2HH — MB BCh BAO 1983 Belf.; MRCP (UK) 1986; MRCGP 1987; DCH Glas. 1986; DRCOG 1986. (Queen's University Belfast) Socs: BMA; RCGP.

SHEPHERD

SHEPHERD, Philip Stephen Department of Immunology, MS3, Guy's Hospital Medical School, UMDS, London Bridge, London SE1 9RT Tel: 020 7955 4656 Fax: 020 7955 2317 Email: p.shepherd@umds.ac.uk; 187 Banstead Road, Carshalton Beeches, Carshalton SM5 4DP Tel: 020 8642 2975 Fax: 020 8642 2975 — MB ChB 1970 Birm.; MSc Birm. 1975, MB ChB 1970; FRCP Lond. 1994; MRCP (UK) 1974. Sen. Lect. & Hon. Cons. Immunol. UMDS Guy's Hosp. Lond.; Head Clin. Immunol. Serv. Guys & St Thos. Trust. Socs: Brit. Soc. Immunol. & Brit. Nuclear Med. Soc. Prev: Clin. Research Fell. Inst. Cancer Resarch Sutton, Surrey.

SHEPHERD, Richard Ian 1 Bronte Old Road, Thornton, Bradford BD13 3HN — MB ChB 1993 Manch.

SHEPHERD, Richard Julian Ash House, Ball La., Caton, Lancaster LA2 9QN Tel: 01524 770476 — MB ChB 1969 Liverp.; MRCOG 1974, DObst 1972. Cons. (O & G) Roy. Lancaster Infirm. Prev: Sen. Regist. (O & G) Hammersmith Hosp. Lond.; Sen. Regist. St. Mary's Hosp. Portsmouth; Regist. (O & G) St. Mary's Hosp. Manch.

SHEPHERD, Richard Thorley The Forensic Medicine Unit, St. George's Hospital Medical School, Cranmer Terrace, London SW17 0RE Tel: 0208 725 0015 Fax: 0208 725 0017 Email: r.shepherd@stgms.ac.uk — MB BS 1977 Lond.; BSc (Hons.) Lond. 1974; MRCPath 1986; DMJ Path.) Soc. Apoth. Lond. 1984; FRCPath 1996. (St. Geo.) Sen. Lect. & Hon. Cons. Forens. Med. St. Geo. Hosp. Med. Sch. Lond. Socs: Fell. Brit. Assn. Forens. Med.; Medico-Legal Soc. Prev: Sen. Lect. & Lect. (Forens. Med.) Guy's Hosp. Lond.; Lect. (Forens. Med.) St. Geo. Hosp. Lond.

SHEPHERD, Robert Barry 70 Shields Road, Sunderland SR6 8JN — MB BS 1997 Newc.

SHEPHERD, Robert Cameron Royal Alexandra Hospital, Corsebar Road, Paisley PA2 9PN Tel: 0141 887 9111 Fax: 0141 580 4207 Email: cameron.sheperd@rah.scot.nhs.uk; 4 Troon Drive, Bridge of Weir PA11 3HF Tel: 01505 614155 — MB ChB Glas. 1965; FRCP Glas. 1980, M 1969; FRCPCH 1996; DCH RCPS Glas. 1967. (Glas.) Cons. Paediat. Roy. Alexandra Hosp. Paisley & Inverclyde Roy. Hosp. Greenock; Hon.Sen. Lect. Univ. Glas. Child Health; Hon.Sen. Lect. Univ. Dundee Child Health. Prev: Sen. Regist. Roy. Hosp. Sick Childr. Glas.; SHO Glas. Roy. Infirm.

SHEPHERD, Robert John Ty Gwyn, 37 Ashfield Road, Stoneygate, Leicester LE2 1LB Tel: 0116 270 7029 Fax: 0116 270 8438 — MB ChB 1968 Liverp.; FRCP Glas. 1997; FRCP Lond. 1995; FRCP Ed. 1992; MRCP (UK) 1975. Cons. Phys. (Med.) Leicester Gen. Hosp., Univ. Hosp. Leicester (UHL) NHS Trust. Socs: BMA; Brit. Geriat.s Soc. (treas.). Prev: Sen. Regist. (Med.) Radcliffe Infirm. Oxf.; Regist. (Med.) Nat. Heart Hosp. Lond. & Roy. S.. Hosp. Liverp.

SHEPHERD, Mr Rolf Carter (retired) Church Villa, Morden, Wareham BH20 7DS Tel: 01929 459265 — MB BChir 1950 Camb.; MChir Camb. 1960; FRCS Eng. 1955. Hon. Surg. Poole Gen. Hosp. Prev: Res. Asst. Surg. St. Thos. Hosp. Lond.

SHEPHERD, Simon Tobias The Clapham Park Surgery, 72 Clarence Avenue, London SW4 8JP Tel: 020 8674 0101 Fax: 020 8674 2941 — MB ChB 1974 Birm.; MRCGP 1981.

SHEPHERD, Stanley George Lawrence Hill Health Centre, Hassell Drive, Lawrence Hill, Bristol BS2 0AN — MB ChB 1979 Bristol; BSc Bristol 1967, MB ChB 1979; DRCOG 1982. Socs: Assoc. MRCGP. Prev: GP Bristol.

SHEPHERD, Stephen Francis Gloucestershire Oncology Centre, General Hospital, Sandford Road, Cheltenham GL53 7AN Tel: 01242 274316 Fax: 01242 273506 Email: stephen.sheperd@egnhst.org.uk — MB ChB (Gold Medallist) Leic. 1987; MRCP (UK) 1990; FRCR 1994. Cons. Clin. Oncol. GloucestershireOncol.Centre Cheltenham Gen. Hosp. Socs: Fell.of Roy. Coll. of Radiologists; UK Assn. Head and Neck Oncol. Prev: Sen. Regist. (Clin. Oncol. & Radiother.) Roy. Marsden NHS Trust Lond. & Sutton; Research Fell. (Stereotactic Radiother.) Roy. Marsden Hosp. Lond.; Regist. Rotat. (Clin. Oncol.) Roy. Marsden Hosp. Lond. & Sutton.

SHEPHERD, Stephen John Dove River Practice, Gibb Lane, Sudbury, Ashbourne DE6 5HY Tel: 01283 812455; 13 Duncan Close, Belper DE56 1FS — MB ChB 1990 Birm.

SHEPHERD, Susan Flat 19, Spice Court, Asher Way, London E1W 2JD — MB ChB 1980 Bristol.

SHEPHERD, Terence Patrick 16 Larch Grove, Sidcup DA15 8WJ — MB BS 1990 Lond.

SHEPHERD, Thomas Huw, Surg. Capt. RN Retd. Constantia, 168 West St., Portchester, Fareham PO16 9XG Tel: 01705 326388 Fax: 01705 326388 Email: doctorhuw@aol.com — MB BS 1971 Lond.; LLM Wales 1994. (Middlx. Hosp.) Medico Legal Adviser to Med. Dir. Gen. (Naval) & MOD (Navy). Prev: Medico Legal Adviser Med. Dir. Gen. (Naval); Med. Off i/c Roy. Naval Hosp., Gibraltar.

SHEPHERD, William Clyne (retired) 8 St Clair Terrace, Edinburgh EH10 5NW Tel: 0131 447 6647 — MB ChB 1950 Ed.; Dip. Community. Med. 1975. Cons. Pub. Health Med. Lothian HB. Prev: Sec. Presbyt. Med. Bd. & Med. Supt. Presbyt. Hosps., Nigeria.

SHEPHERD, William Frederick Ian Deloraine Cottage, Greenend, Longnewton, St Boswells, Melrose TD6 9ES Tel: 01835 23074 — MB BCh BAO 1969 Belf.; FRCS Ed. 1976; DO RCPSI 1974. (Belf.) Cons. Ophth. Borders Gen Hosp. Melrose. Prev: Cons. (Ophth. Surg.) Roy. Vict. Hosp. Belf.; Hayward Fell. & Sub-Warden St. John Ophth. Hosp. Jerusalem, Israel; Fell. (Anterior Segment Surg.) Moorfields Eye Hosp. Lond.

SHEPHERD, William Henry Thompson (retired) 4 Tudor Oaks, Holywood BT18 0PA Tel: 01232 423050 — MD 1950 Belf.; MB BCh BAO 1939; FRCR 1975; FFR RCSI 1962; FFR 1965; DMRD Eng. 1946. Prev: Cons. Radiol. Roy. Vict. Hosp. & Roy. Matern. Hosp. Belf.

SHEPHERDSON, David Hempton House, Hempton Lane, Almondsbury, Bristol BS32 4AR — MRCS Eng. LRCP Lond. 1963; DA Eng. 1968. (Char. Cross) Socs: Canad. Med. Assn. & Coll. Family Pract. Canada. Prev: SHO (Cas. & Anaesth.) W. Lond. Hosp.; Orthop. & Trauma Ho. Surg., Ho. Phys. & Ho. Surg. Ashford Hosp.; Middlx.

SHEPPARD, Adam Peter Lupset Surgery, off Norbury Road, Wakefield WF2 8RE Tel: 01924 376828 Fax: 01924 201649; 19 Ash Grove, Stanley, Wakefield WF3 4JY — MB ChB 1987 Leeds; Cert Family Plann JCC 1992. Prev: SHO (Anaesth.) Pinderfields Gen. Hosp. Wakefield VTS; Ho. Surg. Harrogate Dist. Hosp.; Ho. Phys. Leeds Gen. Infirm.

SHEPPARD, Brigid Sarah 6A Highgate Hill West, London N6 6JR — MB BS 1992 Lond.

SHEPPARD, Carol Ann 18 Rivers Street, Bath BA1 2QA — BM 1990 Soton.

SHEPPARD, Cathryn Jane 3 Lulworth Crescent, Bristol BS16 6SB Tel: 0117 956 1470 — BM 1990 Soton.; MRCGP 1997. GP Non Princip. Prev: GP Regist. Totnes Devon; Regist. (Palliat. Care) Gosford Hosp. NSW, Austral.; SHO (O & G) Torbay Hosp.

SHEPPARD, Clive Thomas The Bridge Street Surgery, 30-32 Bridge Street, Downham Market PE38 9DH Tel: 01366 388888 Fax: 01366 383716 — MB 1983 Camb.; BA Camb. 1980, MB 1983, BChir 1982; MRCGP 1987. Princip. GP Downham Market. Prev: Cas. Off. Heatherwood Hosp. Ascot; Ho. Surg. New Addenbrookes Hosp. Camb.; Ho. Phys. James Paget Hosp. Gt. Yarmouth.

SHEPPARD, David Alan Harley Street Medical Centre, Harley Street, Hanley, Stoke-on-Trent ST1 3RX Tel: 01782 212066 Fax: 01782 201326 Email: daveshep@tinyworld.co.uk; Old Spring House, 51 Dilhorne Road, Forsbrook, Stoke-on-Trent ST11 9DJ Tel: 01782 396919 Fax: 01782 393510 — MB BS 1979 Lond.; BSc (Hons.) Lond. 1976; MRCGP 1986; DMJ(Clin) Soc. Apoth. Lond. 1995; DCH RCP Lond. 1984; DRCOG 1983. (Lond. Hosp.) Police Surg. N. Staffs. Socs: Assn. Police Surg. Prev: Trainee GP N. Staffs. VTS; Ho. Off. & Cas. Off. Lond. Hosp.; Ho. Surg. Epsom Dist. Hosp.

SHEPPARD, Emma Jane Northview House, Farm Road, Goring, Reading RG8 0AA Tel: 01491 872184 — MB BS 1992 Newc.; DRCOG 1994; MRCGP 1997. (Newcastle upon Tyne)

SHEPPARD, Geoffrey Edward The Lodge, 230 Manchester New Road, Alkrington, Middleton, Manchester M24 1NP Tel: 0161 643 4340 — LRCP LRCS 1966 Ed.; LRCP LRCS Ed. LRCPS Glas. 1966. (RCSI) Hosp. Pract. (ENT) Ancoats Hosp. Manch. Prev: GP Manch.; Ho. Off. (Med. & Surg.) N. Manch. Gen. Hosp.; Clin. Asst. (ENT) Ancoats Hosp. Manch.

SHEPPARD, Harvey William Westberts priority Care Trust, 5 Craven Road, Reading RG1 5LE Tel: 01189 862277 Fax: 01189 750297; North View House, Farm Road, Goring-on-Thames, Reading RG8 0AA Tel: 01491 872184 — MRCS Eng. LRCP Lond. 1966; MA Camb. 1966; MRCPsych 1980; DPM Eng. 1980. (Camb. & Lond. Hosp.) Prev: Sen. Regist. (Child Psychiat. & Ment. Handicap) BoroCt. Hosp. Reading; Regist. (Med. & Paediat.) St.

Mary's Hosp. Plaistow; Regist. (Paediat.) Roy. Hosp. Sick Childr. Edin. & Area Serv. Ment.

SHEPPARD, Ian James 24 Hardcastle Gardens, Bradshaw, Bolton BL2 4NZ — MB ChB 1986 Leic.

SHEPPARD, John Midland Road Surgery, Thrapston, Kettering NN14 4JR Tel: 01832 734444 Fax: 01832 734426 — MB BS 1978 Lond.; BSc (Hons.) Lond. 1974. (St. Geo.)

SHEPPARD, Leyland Curtis Fermoy Unit, Queen Elizabeth Hosp, Gayton Royal, King's Lynn PE30 4ET Tel: 01553 613613 Fax: 01223 359062 Email: leyland.sheppard@mrc-cbu.cam.ac.uk; 42 Rathmore Road, Cambridge CB1 7AD Tel: 01223 246275 Email: isheppard@onetel.net.uk — MB ChB 1988 Dundee; BMSc (Hons.) Dund 1985, MD 1994; MRCP (UK) 1991; MRCPsych 1995. (Dundee) Wellcome Research Train. Fell. & Hon. Sen. Regist. (Psychiat.) Addenbrooke's NHS Trust; Sen. Regist. Gen. Adult Psychiat.; Qu. Eliz. Hosp. Kings Lynn. Prev: Sen. Regist. (Psychiat.) Maudsley Hosp.; Regist. (Psychiat.) Camb. HA & Maudsley Hosp.; SHO (Med.) Freeman NHS Trust.

SHEPPARD, Louise (retired) 3 Drummond Close, Pitsford, Northampton NN6 9BA Tel: 01604 880686 — MB BS 1959 Lond.; MRCS Eng. LRCP Lond. 1959; FFR 1971; DMRD Eng. 1969; DObst RCOG 1961; DCH Eng. 1961. Prev: Cons. Radiol. Kettering Gen. Hosp.

SHEPPARD, Mary Noelle Department of Pathology, Royal Brompton Hospital, Sydney St., London SW3 6NP Tel: 020 7351 8424 Fax: 020 7351 4883; Longcourt House, 46 The Drive, South Woodford, London E18 2BL Tel: 020 8530 7758 — MD 1984 NUI; BSc NUI 1979, MD 1984, MB BCh BAO 1977; MRCPath 1986. (Univ. Coll. Cork) Sen. Lect. & Cons. Path. Roy. Brompton Heart & Lung Hosp. Lond. Socs: Fell. Roy. Soc. Med.; Path. Soc. Prev: Sen. Lect. & Cons. Path. Roy. Lond. Hosp.; Sen. Regist. Univ. Coll. & Middlx. Hosps. Lond.; Regist. & Research Fell. Hammersmith Hosp. Lond.

SHEPPARD, Professor Michael Charles Department of Medicine, Queen Elizabeth Hospital, Edgbaston, Birmingham B15 2TH Tel: 0121 627 2380 Fax: 0121 627 2384 Email: m.c.sheppard@bham.ac.uk — MB ChB 1971 Cape Town; PhD Cape Town 1979; FRCP Lond. 1985; MRCP (UK) 1974; F med Sci 1998. (Cape Town) Prof. Med. Univ. Birm. & Hon. Cons. Phys. Qu. Eliz. Hosp. Birm. Socs: Assn. Phys.; RCP (Censor); Soc. Endocrinol. (USA). Prev: Wellcome Trust Sen. Lect. Univ. Birm. & Hon. Cons. Phys. Qu. Eliz. Hosp. Birm.; Sen. Regist. (Gen. Med. & Endocrinol.) Qu. Eliz. Hosp. Birm.

SHEPPARD, Reginald Gilbertson (retired) 18 Bolton Crescent, Windsor SL4 3JQ Tel: 01753 865820 — MB BS Lond. 1943; MRCS Eng. LRCP Lond. 1941; FCA Eng. 1954; DA Eng. 1943. Prev: Cons. (Anaesth.) E. Berks Hosps.

SHEPPARD, Robin Francis (retired) 3 Drummond Close, Pitsford, Northampton NN6 9BA Tel: 01604 880686 — MB BS 1958 Lond.; FRCPath M 1969. Prev: Cons. Haemat. N.ampton Gen. Hosp.

SHEPPARD, Sally Christine Morris, Harker, Bleiker and Partners, Ivybridge Health Centre, Station Road, Ivybridge PL21 0AJ Tel: 01752 690777 Fax: 01752 690252 — BM 1988 Soton.; MRCGP 1994; DRCOG 1993. (Univ. Soton.) p/t GP.

SHEPPARD, Sheila (retired) 8 Kelvin Court, Petitor Road, Torquay TQ1 4QE Tel: 01803 314196 — MB ChB 1950 Leeds. Prev: Sen. Research Fell. Dept. Paediat. & Child Health Leeds Univ.

SHEPPARD, Timothy John Harwood Trevaine, King Charles Road, Newbridge, Newport NP11 4HF — MB BS 1986 Lond.

SHEPPERD, Mr Harold Walter Henry, RD (retired) 68 Osborne Park, Belfast BT9 6JP Tel: 01232 665911 — MB BCh BAO Belf. 1947; FRCSI 1980 (Ad Eundem); FRCS Eng. 1954; DLO Eng. 1952. Prev: Cons. Surg. (Otorhinolaryng.) Roy. Vict. Hosp. Belf.

SHEPPERD, Margaret Joyce (retired) Pennance, Port Navas, Falmouth TR11 5RJ Tel: 01326 340275 — MRCS Eng. LRCP Lond. 1940; DPM Eng. 1965. Prev: Cons. Psychiat. Hersham Child Guid. Clinic S.W. Metrop. RHA.

SHEPPERD, Rosemary Allison Abingdon Child and Family Clinic, Abingdon Community Hospital, Marcham Road, Abingdon OX14 1 Tel: 01235 524551 — MB BS 1984 Lond.; BSc Lond. 1981, MB BS 1984; MRCPsych 1991; MRCGP 1988; DCH RCP Lond. 1987; DRCOG 1986. Cons. (Child & Adolesc. Psychiat.). Prev: Sen. Regist. (Child Psychiat.) Oxf. Region Higher Train. Scheme; Regist. (Child Psychiat.) Tavistock Centre Lond. & Watford Child & Family Clinic.

SHEPPEY, Marie Claire 106 Kingswood Avenue, Bromley BR2 0NP — MB BS 1992 Lond.

SHEPSTONE, Basil John Department of Radiology, University of Oxford, Radcliffe Infirmary, Woodstock Road, Oxford OX2 6HE Tel: 01865 24679 Fax: 01865 816315; Oxfordsh. Health Authority Breast Care Unit, The Churchill Hospital, Headington, Oxford OX3 7LJ Tel: 01865 25319 Fax: 01865 225978 — MD 1977 Cape Town; DSc Orange Free State 1960, MSc 1958; BSc (Hons.) Orange Free State 1957, BSc 1956; MA Oxf. 1978, DPhil 1964, BM BCh 1968; BA (Econ.) Univ. S. Afr. 1982; MRCS Eng. LRCP Lond. 1969; FRCR Eng. 1984; DMRD Eng. 1975. Univ. Lect. (Radiol.) & Head Dept. Univ. Oxf. & Hon. Cons. Nuclear Med. & Radiol. Oxf. HA; Clin. Dir. Oxf. HA BrE. Care Unit. Socs: Fell. & Dean of Degrees Wolfson Coll. Oxf.; Brit. Inst. Radiol.; Brit. Nuclear Med. Soc. Prev: Dir. (Clin. Studies) Oxf. Univ. Clin. Med. Sch.; Clin. Lect. (Radiol.) Univ. Oxf.; Head Dept. Nuclear Med. Groote Schuur Hosp. & Univ Cape Town, S. Africa.

SHER, Carmel 36 Clovelly Road, London N8 7RH — BM BS 1993 Nottm.

SHER, Mr Joel Lester East Molesden House, Molesden, Morpeth NE61 3QF Tel: 0167 075380 — MB BCh 1972 Witwatersrand; BSc Witwatersrand 1968; FRCS Eng. 1980. (Witwatersrand) Cons. Traum. & Orthop. Surg. Ashington Hosp.; Hon. Clin. Lect. Traum. & Orthop. Surg. Univ. Newc. Socs: Brit. Orthop. Assn. & Brit. Soc. Surg. of Hand. Prev: Sen. Orthop. Regist. N.. RHA.

SHER, Karnail Singh Birstall Medical Centre, 4 Whiles Lane, Birstall, Leicester LE4 4EE Tel: 0116 267 5255; 51 Rectory Road, Wanlip, Leicester LE7 4PL Tel: 0116 267 5425 Fax: 0116 267 5425 Email: ksher85768@aol.com — MB BS 1974 Guru Nanak Dev; FRCPI 1995, M 1986. Hosp. Pract. (Gastroenterol.) Leicester Gen. Hosp.; Clin. Tutor (Gen. Pract.) Leicester Univ. Socs: BMA & Med. Defence Union. Prev: Hosp. Pract. (Rheum.) Leicester Roy. Infirm.; Regist. (Med.) Orsett Gen. Hosp. & Leicester Gen. Hosp.

SHER, Mussarat 58 Main Street, Walton-on-Trent, Burton-on-Trent Tel: 01283 712697; Health Centre, Barton-under-Needwood, Burton-on-Trent — MB BS 1970 Punjab; MB BS Punjab (Pakistan) 1970; DRCOG 1974. (King Edwd. Med. Coll. Lahore) Prev: SHO (O & G) St. Catherine Hosp. Birkenhead; SHO (Gyn.) King Edwd. VII Hosp. Windsor; SHO (Gyn. & Obst.) Heatherwood Hosp. Ascot.

SHERAFAT, Hooman 18 Mount View, Mount Avenue, London W5 1PR — MB BS 1992 Lond.; FRCOphth. Lond. 1997. (St. George's Hosp. Med. Sch.) Res. Fell. (Ophth.) Bris. Eye Hosp. Socs: BMA; MDU. Prev: Specialist Regist. Moorfields Eye Hosp. Lond.; Sen. Hse. Off. Rotat. The Roy. Free Hosp. Lond.

SHERATON, Tei Elizabeth 88 Newfoundland Road, Cardiff CF14 3LD — MB BCh 1993 Wales.

SHERBURN, Vincent England (retired) Cogolin, High Meadow, Bawtry, Doncaster DN10 6LT Tel: 01302 710107 — MB ChB 1946 Manch.; MRCS Eng. LRCP Lond. 1946; MFOM RCP Lond. 1986, AFOM 1978. Prev: Sen. Med. Off. Med. Bd.ing Centre (Respirat. Dis.) Sheff.

SHERE, Michael Henry Breast Care Centre, Frenchay Hospital, Bristol BS16 1LE Tel: 0117 956 2036 Fax: 0117 975 3767; Littlebrook Farm, Syston Hill, Bristol BS30 5LU Tel: 0117 956 2036 Email: mshere@globalnet.co.uk — MB BS 1979 Lond.; MRCS Eng. LRCP Lond. 1979. Clin. Asst. BrE. Surg. Fenchey Hosp. Bristol. Socs: Assoc. of BrE. Clinics. Prev: SHO (Surg.) Roy. Devon & Exeter Hosp. Exeter.; SHO (Surg.) Gt. Yarmouth Dist. Gen. Hosp. & Plymouth Hosps.; Regist. Ho. Surg. Watford Gen. Hosp.

SHERE, Stanley Woodley House, Nackington Road, Canterbury CT4 7AX Tel: 01227 458493 — MB BS 1953 Lond.; MRCPsych 1971; DPM Eng. 1964. (St. Bart.) Cons. Psychiat. Godden Green Clinic Sevenoaks; Chairm. Inst. Religion & Med. Socs: BMA. Prev: Cons. Psychiat. SE Kent HA; Sen. Regist. (Psychol. Med.) Guy's Hosp. Lond.; Squadron Ldr. RAF Med. Br.

SHERGILL, Bhavneet Singh 218 Balfour Road, Ilford IG1 4JA — MB BS 1996 Lond.

SHERGILL, Mr Gurd Email: gurdshergill@doctors.org.uk; 79 Kenilworth Road, Coventry CV4 7AF Tel: 02476 418195 — MB BS 1989 Lond.; CRCS 2000 (Orth.); FRCS Eng. 1994. Orthop. Cons., Salisbury Dist. Hosp., Salisbury. Socs: Assoc. BOA; RCS. Prev: Specialist Regist., Roy. Nat. Orthop. Hospial, Starmore.

SHERGILL

SHERGILL, Mr Nilam Singh 79 Kenilworth Road, Coventry CV4 7AF — MB ChB 1982 Leeds; FRCS Eng. 1990; FRCS Ed. 1989.

***SHERGILL, Shubhinder Singh** 32 Chandos Avenue, London N14 7ET Tel: 020 8886 6336 — MB BS 1995 Lond.; BSc (Hons.) Physiol. Lond. 1991.

SHERGILL, Sukhpal SINGH 62 Ward Avenue, Grays RM17 5RW Tel: 07970 259975; Hillview Surgery, 179 Bilton Road, Perivale, Greenford UB6 7HQ Tel: 020 8997 4661 — MB ChB 1994 Leic.; DRCOG 1998; DFFP 1999; DCH 1999. (Leicester) Princip. GP. Prev: SHO (O & G, Paediat. & A & E) Greenwich.

SHERGILL, Sukhwidner Singh 44 Grange Road, Gravesend DA11 0EU — MB BS 1991 Lond.; BSc (Hons.) Lond. 1988, MB BS 1991. Regist. (Psychiat.) Univ. Coll. Hosp. Lond. Prev: Research Regist. Univ. Coll. Lond. Med. Sch.; SHO Univ. Coll. Hosp.

SHERIDAN, Anthony John Glenburn, 5 Elmsway, Hale, Altrincham WA15 0DZ — MB ChB 1977 Liverp.; FFR RCSI 1985; DMRD Liverp. 1982. Cons. Radiol. Warrington Gen. Hosp.

SHERIDAN, Charles Max (retired) Eastwinds, Penylan, Cowbridge CF71 7RY — MB BCh BAO 1942 NUI; MB BCh BAO (Hnrs.) NUI 1942; MRCPI 1950. Prev: Cons. Geriatr. Pontypridd & Rhondda Hosp. Gp.

SHERIDAN, Cyril Henry (retired) 1 Stanhope Road, Highgate, London N6 5NE Tel: 020 8340 3773 — MB BS 1951 Lond.; MRCS Eng. LRCP Lond. 1951. Med. Ref. Crusader, Co-op. & Pearl Insur. Cos. Prev: Clin. Asst. Radiother. Roy. N. Hosp. Lond.

SHERIDAN, Professor Desmond John Academic Cardiology Unit, NHLI Imperial College of Medicine, St Mary's Hospital, London W2 1NY Tel: 020 7886 6129 Fax: 020 7886 6732; 14 Dukeswood Drive, Gerrards Cross SL9 7LR — MD 1974 Dub.; PhD Newc. 1982; MB BCh BAO 1971; FRCP Lond. 1987; MRCP (UK) 1974. Prof. Clin. Cardiol. & Hon. Cons. St. Mary's Hosp. Lond. W2. Prev: Sen. Lect. (Cardiol.) & Hon. Cons. Welsh Nat. Sch. Med. Cardiff; Research Fell. Div. Cardiovasc. Med. Washington Univ. St. Louis, USA; Sen. Regist. (Cardiol.) Newc. Gen. & Freeman Hosp. Newc. u. Tyne.

SHERIDAN, Eamonn Gerard 103 Moss Park Road, Stretford, Manchester M32 9HN — MB ChB 1985 Manch.

SHERIDAN, Edward Ashley Parkstone Health Centre, Mansfield Road, Poole BH14 0DJ Tel: 01202 741370 Fax: 01202 730952 — MB BS 1985 Lond.; MRCGP 1990; DRCOG 1990. Prev: Sen. Ships Phys. P & O Lines.

SHERIDAN, Elizabeth Anne Department of Medical Microbiology, Royal London Hospital, London Tel: 020 7377 7251 — MB BS 1994 Lond.; Dip RCPath 2001; MSc 1998 (Medical Microbiology) QMW London; BA Camb. 1991. (St. Bart. Hosp.) Regist. (Microbiol.) St. Bart. and the Lond. Hosp. Lond.

SHERIDAN, Jacqueline Susan Park Lane Surgery, 8 Park Lane, Broxbourne EN10 7NQ Tel: 01992 465555; 46 Fairley Way, West Cheshunt, Waltham Cross EN7 6LG Tel: 01992 642523 — MB BS 1990 Lond.; DFFP 1994; MRCGP 1994. (University College London) Prev: Trainee GP Harlow; Trainee GP/SHO Whipps Cross Hosp. Lond.

SHERIDAN, Jacqueline Vera 14 Dukes Wood Drive, Gerrards Cross SL9 7LR — MB BCh BAO 1970 Dub.

SHERIDAN, James Anthony Brinsley (retired) 30 Stanbury Close, Barnsley S75 2QX Tel: 01226 252163 — LRCPI & LM, LRSCI & LM 1945; LRCPI & LM, LRCSI & LM 1945.

SHERIDAN, John Hugh Sampford Peverell Surgery, 29 Lower Town, Sampford Peverell, Tiverton EX16 7BJ Tel: 01884 820304 Fax: 01884 821188; 1 Caumont Close, Uffculme, Cullompton EX15 3XY — MB BS 1978 Lond.; BA (Physiol. Sci.) Oxf. 1975; MRCGP 1983. (Oxford and The London Hospital)

SHERIDAN, John Joseph Department of Radiology, The Royal Bournemouth Hospital, Castle Lane E., Bournemouth BH7 7DW — MB BCh BAO 1979 NUI; FRCS Eng. 1985; FRCR 1989. Cons. Radiol. Roy. Bournemouth Hosp.

SHERIDAN, John Simon 98A Drymen Road, Bearsden, Glasgow G61 2SY — MB ChB 1998 Glas.; MB ChB Glas 1998.

SHERIDAN, Linda Mary Lucia 45 Bury Green, Wheathampstead, St Albans AL4 8DB — BA, MB BCh BAO Dub. 1977; DM 1998 (Diploma Health Management) Keele; MSc London Sch. Of Hygiene & Tropical Med.; MRCGP 1983; DRCOG 1981; DCH Dub. 1980; Cert JCC Lond. 1980. (TC Dub.) Specialist Regist. In Pub. Health Med. N.Lond.; Pub. Health Train. Progr., based at Herts. Health Auth. Prev: GP Bedford; SHO Bedford Gen. Hosp. Ho. Phys. & Ho. Surg. St. Jas. Hosp. Dub.; Primary Care Med. Adviser, Beds. Health Auth. ('93-'97).

SHERIDAN, Maria Bernadette 42 West Park Avenue, Leeds LS8 2EB — MB ChB 1984 Manch.

SHERIDAN, Mark Christopher 37 Saul Road, Downpatrick BT30 6PA — MB BCh BAO 1990 Belf.; MB BCh Belf. 1990.

SHERIDAN, Michael Charles 24 Castlehill Drive, Newton Mearns, Glasgow G77 5JZ — MB ChB 1997 Glas.

SHERIDAN, Morris Roger 15 The Brookdales, Bridge Lane, London NW11 9JU Tel: 020 8455 8848 — MRCS Eng. LRCP Lond. 1946. (Univ. Coll. Hosp.) Indep. Anaesth. Lond.; JP; Med. Off. Brit. Boxing Bd. of Control. Socs: Fell Harveian Soc.; Fell. BMA; Fell. Hunt. Soc. Prev: Anaesth. Woodgreen & S.gate Hosp.; Res. Surg. Off. Roy. Lond. Homoeop. Hosp.; Capt. RAMC.

SHERIDAN, Paul John 16 Botanical Road, Botanical Gardens, Sheffield S11 8RP — MB ChB 1996 Sheff.

SHERIDAN, Peter Seacroft Hospital, York Road, Leeds LS14 6UH Tel: 0113 206 3481; Tanglewood House, 16 Grove Lane, Leeds LS6 2AP Tel: 0113 274 0765 Email: pemad@easicam.com — FRCP Lond. 1987; MRCP (U.K.) 1971; MRCS Eng. LRCP Lond. 1965. (Guy's) Cons. Phys. Seacroft Hosp. Leeds and St Jas. Univ. Hosp. Leeds; Sen. Clin. Lect. Univ. of Leeds. Prev: Hon. Cons. Phys. St. Jas. Hosp. Leeds; Sen. Regist. (Research) Roy. Devon & Exeter Hosp.

SHERIDAN, Peter John Enfield & Haringey Health Authority, Holbrook House, Cockfosters Road, Barnet EN4 0DR Tel: 020 8272 5549 Fax: 020 8272 5582 Email: petersheridan@enhar-ha.nthumes.nhs.uk; 45 Bury Green, Wheathampstead, St Albans AL4 8DB Tel: 01582 834804 — MB ChB 1977 Bristol; MSc London 1993; MFPHM RCP (UK) 1995; MRCGP 1983; DRCOG 1980; DCH Dub. 1980; Cert JCC Lond. 1980. Cons. Pub. Health Med. Enfield & Haringey HA. Prev: Sen. Med. Off. DoH; Regist. Pub. Health N. Thames RHA; GP Bedford.

SHERIDAN, Philip Gerard 15 Gleneagles Park, Bothwell, Glasgow G71 8UT — MB ChB 1976 Glas.; MRCGP 1980.

SHERIDAN, Raymond Paul Flat 3 Barons Court, Dedmere Rise, Marlow SL7 1XX — MB ChB 1993 Bristol.

SHERIDAN, Mr Richard Jonathan Watford General Hospital, Vicarage Road, Watford WD18 0HB Tel: 01923 217935 Fax: 01923 217939; Ferndale, Church Lane, Sarratt, Rickmansworth WD3 6HN Tel: 01923 270451 Fax: 01923 260943 — MB BS Lond. 1979; LMSSA Lond. 1979; FRCS Ed. 1985; FRCOG 1998. (Guy's) Cons. O & G Watford Gen. Hosp. Vicarage Rd. Watford WD1 8HB. Socs: Roy. Soc. Med (Sen. Sec. Obst & Gyn BR); Gyn. Res. Soc. Prev: Sen. Regist. (O & G) St. Mary's Hosp. & Samarit. Hosp. for Wom. Lond.; Regist. (O & G) Guy's Hosp. Lond.; SHO Qu. Charlottes Matern. Hosp. Lond.

SHERIDAN, Mr William Gerard John Department of Surgery, West Wales General Hospital, Carmarthen SA31 2NE Tel: 01267 235151 Email: wgsheridan@aol.com; Email: wgsheridan@aol.com — MB BCh BAO 1977 Dub.; MCh Dub 1989, MB BCh BAO 1977; FRCS Eng. 1985; FRCSI 1981; MA Dub 1995. (University of Dublin Trinity College) Cons. Surg. W. Wales Gen. Hosp. Carmarthen; Cons. Surg., Werndale Private Hosp. Banctfelin, Carmarthen. Socs: Assn. Surg.; Assn. Coloproctol.; Welsh Surg. Trav. Club. Prev: Sen. Regist. (Surg.) Univ. Hosp. Wales Cardiff & Singleton Hosp. Swansea; Research Fell. (Surg.) Univ. Hosp. Wales Cardiff.

SHERIF, Mr Ahmed Helmy Mohamed Broadview, North Orbital Road, Chiswell Green, St Albans AL2 2AB Tel: 01727 67331; (surgery) Wrafton House, 24 The Common, Hatfield AL10 0NB — MRCS Eng. LRCP Lond. 1978; MB BCh Ein Shams 1969; FRCS Ed. 1976. (Ein Shams) Prev: Regist. (Orthop.) Broomfield Hosp. Chelmsfield, Black Notley Hosp.; Braintree & Tameside Gen. Hosp. Ashton-under-Lyne.

SHERIF, Ali Sherif Adel Department of Cytology, Royal Gwent Hospital, Cardiff Road, Newport NP20 2UB; c/o Mr. K. Mohamed, 7 Gascony Avenue, West Hampstead, London NW6 4NB — MB BCh 1979 Cairo; MRCPath (UK) 1992.

SHERIF, Tag El Baha'a Ahmed Fathi Brondesbury Medical centre, 279 Kilburn High Road, London NW6 7JQ Tel: 020 7624 9853 Fax: 020 7372 3660; 42 Marlborough Mansions, Cannon Hill, London NW6 1JS Tel: 020 7794 1753 — MRCS Eng. LRCP Lond. 1978; MB BCh Ein Shams 1971; DA Eng. 1975. (Ein Shams) Socs:

Med. Protec. Soc. Prev: GP Hatfield; Clin. Asst. (Cas.) Clacton & Dist. Hosp.; Clin. Asst. (Anaesthetics) Colchester Health Dist.

SHERIF, Tayyaba GP Direct, 5/7 Welback Road, West Harrow, Harrow HA2 0RH Tel: 020 8515 9300 Fax: 020 8515 9300 — MRCS Eng. LRCP Lond. 1980.

SHERIFF, Mr Matin Khalid Mahmood 23 Chester Road, Forest Gate, London E7 8QT — MB BS 1986 Lond.; FRCS Ed. 1993. Ho. Off. (Gen. Surg.) Barnet Gen. Hosp. Prev: Ho. Off. Roy. Nat. Orthop. Hosp.

SHERIFF, Shafiqa 14 Ruxley Lane, Ewell, Epsom KT19 0JA — MB BS 1949 Punjab; MB BS Punjab (Pakistan) 1949; DObst RCOG 1966; DCH RCPS Glas. 1961. (King Edwd. Med. Coll. Lahore) Sessional Med. Off. Merton, Sutton & Wandsworth AHA. Socs: Pakistan Med. Assn. & BMA. Prev: Regist. (O & G) Sobhraj Matern. Hosp. Karachi, Pakistan & United Christian Hosp. Lahore, Pakistan; SHO (O & G) WillesBoro. Hosp. Ashford.

SHERIFI, James (retired) — MB ChB 1975 Dundee; BSc St. And. 1972; DRCOG 1979; Dip. Occ Med 1996. Prev: Regist. (Med. & Paediat.) Yeovil Hosp.

SHERIL, David Brian Surgery, 343 Ripple Road, Barking IG11 7RJ Tel: 020 8594 2770 — MB BS 1979 Lond.; MB BS (Hons.) Lond. 1979; LLB Lond. 1990; AFOM RCP Lond. 1993; DRCOG 1981. (Middlx.) Socs: BMA; Brit. Med. Acupunct. Soc.; Ilford Med. Soc.

SHERLALA, Khaled Hussain X-Ray Department, Walsgrave General Hospital, Clifford Bridge Road, Coventry CV2 2DX — MB BCh 1986 Al-Fateh; MRCP (UK) 1991.

SHERLAW, John Andrew The Surgery, 157-159 Reservoir Road, Erdington, Birmingham B23 6DN — MB BS 1976 Lond.; BSc Lond. 1973; MRCGP 1982; DRCOG 1983; DCH RCP Lond. 1981. (Westm.)

SHERLAW, Shirley Rachel 11 New Church Road, Sutton Coldfield B73 5RT Tel: 0121 354 9132 — MB ChB 1978 Birm.; BSc (Hons.) Birm. 1975; MRCGP 1982; DRCOG 1983; DCH RCP Lond. 1981. (Birm.)

SHERLEY-DALE, Andrew Charles Magnolia House Practice, Magnolia House, Station Road, Ascot SL5 0QJ Tel: 01344 637800 Fax: 01344 637823 — BM BCh 1986 Oxf.; MA Camb. 1987; MRCGP 1990; DRCOG 1990; DCH RCP Lond. 1988. Prev: Trainee GP Ipswich Hosp. E. Suff. VTS.

SHERLOCK, Alexander (retired) 58 Orwell Road, Felixstowe IP11 7PS Tel: 01394 284503 — MB BS 1945 Lond.; MB BS (Hnrs.) Lond. 1945. Mem. Europ. Parliament. Prev: Barrister At Law Grays Inn 1961.

SHERLOCK, Clive Reginald Francis PO Box 4, Chipping Norton OX7 3XP Tel: 01865 308700 Email: crfs@c-sherlock.demon.co.uk — MB BS 1972 Lond.; MRCPsych 1978. (Char. Cross) Counsellor.

SHERLOCK, Mr David James Department of Surgery, North Manchester Healthcare NHS Trust, Delaunays Road, Manchester M8 5RL Tel: 0161 720 2612 Fax: 0161 720 2228; BUPA Hospital Manchester, Russells Road, Whalley Range, Manchester M16 8AJ Tel: 0161 226 0112 Fax: 0161 232 2255 — MB BS 1977 Lond.; MS Lond. 1986; FRCS Eng. 1982; FRCS Ed. 1981. (King's Coll. Hosp.) Cons. Surg. N. Manch. Gen. Hosp.; Cons. Surg. Christie Hosp. Manch. Socs: Assn. Surg.; Brit. Soc. Gastroenterol. Prev: Sen. Lect. (Surg.) Kings Coll. Hosp. Lond.; Sen. Regist. W. Midl. RHA; Chef du Clinique Hosp. Paul Brousse, Villejuif, Paris.

SHERLOCK, Julie Doreen The Peel Medical Practice, Peel Court, 2 Aldergate, Tamworth B79 7DJ Tel: 01827 50575 Fax: 01827 62835 — MB ChB 1979 Bristol; MRCGP 1985; DRCOG 1984.

SHERLOCK, Kevin Edward 49 Moyle Road, Ballycastle BT54 6LG — MB BCh BAO 1968 Belf. (Belf.)

SHERLOCK, William 8 Deans Park, South Molton EX36 3DY — MB ChB 1995 Sheff.

SHERMAN, David Ian Nicholas Department of Gastroenterology & Nutrition, Central Middlesex Hospital, Acton Lane, London NW10 7NS Tel: 020 8453 2202 Fax: 020 8453 2201 Email: dinsherm@centralmid.demon.co.uk; 83 Burlington Lane, Chiswick, London W4 3ET — MB BS 1984 Lond.; MD Lond. 1997; MRCP (UK) 1987. (Char. Cross) Cons. Phys. & Gastroenterol. Centr. Middlx. Hosp. Lond. Socs: Brit. Assn. for the Study of Liver; Brit. Soc. Gastroenterol. Prev: Sen. Regist. (Gastroenterol.) Qu. Eliz. Hosp. Birm. & Inst. Liver Studies King's Coll. Hosp. Lond.; Clin. Research Fell. Liver Unit & (Clin. Biochem.) King's Coll. Hosp. Lond.;

Regist. (Med. & Gastroenterol.) Char. Cross Hosp. Lond. & W. Middlx. Univ. Hosp.

SHERMAN, Mr Ian Walter Wirral Hospital, Arrowe Park, Upton, Wirral CH49 5PE Tel: 0151 678 5111 — BM 1985 Soton.; FRCS (Orl.) 1994; FRCS Eng. 1989. Cons. ENT Surg. Wirral Hosp. Prev: Sen. Regist. Rotat. (Otorhinolaryngol.) W. Midl.; Regist. (Otorhinolaryngol.) Roy. Liverp. Hosp. & Roy. Liverp. Childr. Hosp.

SHERMAN, Jane (retired) 43A Harrow Road, Linthorpe, Middlesbrough TS5 5NT Tel: 01642 828562 — MB BS 1953 Durh. Prev: Hon. Cons. & Cons. Phys. Geriat. Med. N. Manch. AHA (T).

SHERMAN, Janet Mary The Elms, Nunburnholme Avenue, North Ferriby HU14 3AW — BM BCh 1977 Oxf.; MA Camb. 1978; MRCGP 1984; DRCOG 1979. GP Hessle. Prev: Trainee GP Oxf. VTS.

SHERMAN, Mr Jeremy Alan Dept. of Oral & Maxillofacial Surgery, Queen Elizabeth II Hospital, Howlands, Welwyn Garden City Email: jasherman@doctors.org.uk — MB ChB 1990 Manch.; BDS Lond. 1981; FRCS Ed. 1993; FDS RCS Eng. 1992; FRCS (Max Fae) 1998. (Kings College, Manchester) Cons. In O & M Surg., Qu. Eliz. II Hosp., Welwyn Garden City; Cons. In O & M Surg., Lister Hosp., Stevenage. Socs: Brit. Assoc. of Head & Neck Oncologists; Brit. Assn. Oral & Maxillofacial Surg. (Jun. Fell.); BMA. Prev: Career Regist. (Maxillofacial Surg.) Roy. Surrey Co. Hosp. Guildford; Sen. Regist. (Maxillofacial Surg.) Guy's & St Thomas' Hosp.; Sen. Regist. (Maxillofacial Surg.) Ipswich Hosp.

SHERMAN, Mr Kevin Paul 21 Albion Street, Hull HU1 3TG Tel: 01482 20088; The Elms, Nunburnholme Avenue, North Ferriby HU14 3AW Tel: 01482 631552 — BM BCh 1975 Oxf.; MA Camb. 1975; FRCS Eng. 1979. Cons. Orthop. Yorks. RHA. Socs: Brit. Orthop. Assoc. Prev: Sen. Regist. (Orthop.) Oxf..

SHERMAN, Laurence Howard Greyland Medical Centre, 468 Bury Old Road, Prestwich, Manchester M25 1NL — MB ChB 1982 Manch.; MRCGP 1988; DCH RCP Lond. 1988; Cert. Family Plann. JCC 1988. GP Prestwich; Clin. Asst. (Psychiat.) Prestwich Hosp. Manch.; Dep. Police Surg. Rochdale.

SHERMAN, Lionel Maurice Bounds Geen Group Practice, Bounds Green Group Practice, Gordon Road, New Southgate, London N11 2PF Tel: 020 8889 1961 Fax: 020 8889 7844; 36 Arlow Road, London N21 3JU — MB 1983 Camb.; BChir 1982. Socs: Brit. Med. Acupunct. Soc.

SHERMAN, Louise 10 Downs Cote Park, Westbury-on-Trym, Bristol BS9 3JT — MB BS 1994 Lond.; DCH 1997; FRCA 1998. SHO (Anaesth.) Roy. Gwent Hosp. Newport. Prev: SHO (Paediat.) Roy. Gwent Hosp. Newport; SHO (A & E) Frenchay Bristol; SHO (Orthop.) S.mead Hosp. Bristol.

SHERMAN, Mark Andrew Psychiatric Unit, Derby City General Hospital, Uttoxeter Road, Derby DE22 3NE Tel: 01332 624554; 2 Wilson Close, Mickleover, Derby DE3 5DT — MB BS 1981 Lond.; MRCPsych 1987. (St. Bart.) Cons. Psychiat. S. Derbysh. Ment. Health Trust. Prev: Research Regist. (Psychiat.) MRC Units W.Pk. Hosp. Epsom; SHO & Regist. (Psychiat.) Univ. Coll. & Middlx. Hosp. Lond.

SHERMAN, Richard William 16 Acorn bank, West Bridgford, Nottingham NG2 7SH — MB ChB 1991 Sheff.

SHERMAN, Yael Clare House, St. George's Hospital, Blackshaw Road, London SW17 0QT; 13 Talbot Avenue, London N2 0LS — MB BCh 1958 Witwatersrand; DCH Witwatersrand 1973. (Witwatersrand) Sen. Med. Off. Camden & Islington AHA (T); Princip. Phys. (Child Health) Wandsworth HA. Socs: BMA & Soc. Community Med. & Brit. Paediat. Assn. Prev: Med. Off. & Regist. (Paediat.) Transvaal Memor. Hosp.; esburg, S. Africa; Regist. (Paediat.) Baragwanath Hosp. Johannesburg, S. Africa.

SHERON, Nicholas Clive Department of Medicine, Level D, South Path / Lab Block, Southampton General Hospital, Tremona Road, Southampton SO16 6YD — MB ChB 1982 Sheff.

SHERPA, Tsilden Phutarkey St. Mary's Hospital, Newport PO30 5TG Tel: 01983 524081 Fax: 01983 822569; 24 Lark Rise, Carisbrooke, Newport PO30 5YJ Tel: 01983 528613 — MB BS 1977 Shivaji; DA (UK) 1986. Staff Grade Anaesth. I. of. Wight HA. Prev: Regist. (Anaesth.) Plymouth Gen. Hosp.; Regist. (Anaesth.) Dumfries & Galloway Roy. Infirm.

SHERRARD, Elizabeth Sarah May (retired) 5 North Circular Road, Belfast BT15 5HB Tel: 01232 779082 — MB BCh BAO Belf. 1945; DPH Belf. 1952; DObst RCOG 1948. Med. Off. (Community Health) E. Health & Social Servs. BD.

SHERRARD

SHERRARD, Jacqueline Susan Radcliffe Infirmary NHS Trust, Woodstock Road, Oxford OX2 6HE — MB BS 1986 Lond.; MRCP (UK) 1989. Cons. Genitourin. Med. Radcliffe Infirm. Oxf.

SHERRARD, Kieran Edward Dublin Road Surgery, 4 Dublin Road, Castlewellan, Newcastle BT31 9AG; 30 Bryansford Avenue, Newcastle BT33 0LG Tel: 03967 23495 — MB BCh BAO 1973 Belf.; MRCGP 1977. Prev: GP Bedlington; Trainee GP Newc. VTS; Ho. Phys. & Ho. Surg. Altnagelvin Hosp. Lond.derry.

SHERRATT, Janet Flat 9, 19 Raleigh Close, Manchester M20 2BY — MB ChB 1993 Manch.

SHERRATT, Margaret The Surgery, Johnson St., Teams, Gateshead NE8 2PJ Tel: 0191 460 4239; 21 Albert Drive, Low Fell, Gateshead NE9 6EH — MB BS 1978 Newc.; MRCGP 1982; DRCOG 1981.

SHERRATT, Margaret Trafford (retired) 4 Carlton Close, Newcastle upon Tyne NE3 4SA Tel: 0191 285 4115 Email: stan@sherratts.fsnet.co.uk — MB ChB 1951 Birm.; DPH Liverp. 1959; DObst RCOG 1954.

SHERRATT, Reginald Michael Luton & Dunstable Hospital, Lewsey Road, Luton LU4 0DZ Tel: 01582 497069 Fax: 01582 497326; 11 Grange Road, Tring HP23 5JP Email: msherratt@compuserve.com — BM BCh Oxf. 1970; MA Oxf. 1970; FRCP Lond. 1992; MRCP (UK) 1973. Cons. Clin. Neurophysiol. Roy. Free Hosp. Lond. & Luton & Dunstable Hosp.; Emerit. Cons. Chelsea & W.m. Hosp. Lond. Socs: Assn. Brit. Neurol.; Brit. Soc. Clin. Neurophysiol. Prev: Research Fell. Inst. Neurol. Lond.; Sen. Regist. (Clin. Neurophysiol.) Nat. Hosp. for Nerv. Dis. Lond.

SHERRELL, Helen Elizabeth 50 Benson Road, Grays RM17 6DL — MB BS 1992 Lond.

SHERRET, Ian Ritchie Lyndhurst, West Park Road, Cupar KY15 Tel: 01334 52466 — MB ChB 1954 Glas.; FRCPsych 1986; DPM Eng. 1960. Prev: Cons. Psychiat.Stratheden Hosp.; Sen. Regist. (Psychiat.) S.. Gen. Hosp. Glas.; Regist. Hawkhead Ment. Hosp. Glas.

SHERRIFF, David 52A Main Street, Bushby, Leicester LE7 9PP — MB ChB 1998 Dund.; MB ChB Dund 1998.

SHERRIFF, Elizabeth Ann St. Helier Hospital, Wrythe Lane, Carshalton SM5 1AA Tel: 020 8644 4343 Fax: 020 8296 2101 Email: esherrif@sthelier.sghms.ac.uk; 11 Spinney Drive, Great Shelford, Cambridge CB2 5LY Tel: 01223 843914, 020 8788 6682 — MB BS 1981 Lond.; FRCOG 2001; MRCOG 1989. (St. Thos.) p/t Cons. (O & G) St. Helier Hosp. Carshalton. Prev: Clin. Research Fell. & Hon. Sen. Regist. Hammersmith Hosp. Lond.; Regist. (O & G) St. Geo. Hosp. & St. Jas. Hosp. Lond.; Sen. Regist. (O & G) St. Helier Hosp. Carshalton.

SHERRIFF, Mr Howard Munro, OStJ Accident Service Box 87, Addenbrooke's Hospital, Cambridge CB2 2QQ Tel: 01223 217117 Fax: 01223 217057; 11 Lynfield Lane, Cambridge CB4 1DR Tel: 01223 357559 Fax: 01223 357559 — MB ChB St. And. 1966; FRCS Ed. 1974. (St. And.) Cons. Accid. Addenbrooke's Hosp. NHS Trust Camb.; Cons. A & E Camb. & Huntingdon HA. Socs: Brit. Assn. Emerg. Med.; BASICS (Mem. Research Comm. & Chairm. Educat. Managem. Comm.). Prev: Cons. Orthop. Surg. RAF Med. Br.; Wing Cdr. RAF Med. Br.; Sen. Regist. (Orthop.) Addenbrooke's Hosp. Camb. & Newmarket Gen. Hosp.

SHERRIFF, Richard James Kennedy Way, Yate, Bristol BS37 4AA; 35 Canterbury Close, Rectory Meadow, Yate, Bristol BS37 5TL Tel: 01454 311559 — MB ChB 1976 Bristol; BSc (Hatfield) 1971; MRCGP 1981; DRCOG 1981. Prev: Trainee GP Yate; SHO (Obst.) Bristol Matern. Hosp.; SHO (A & E), SHO & Regist. (Path.) Bristol Roy. Infirm.

SHERRIFF, Robert George Greenways, Weydown Road, Haslemere GU27 1DT — MB BS 1987 Lond.

SHERRINGHAM, Paul Edward Charles Well Lane Surgery, Well Lane, Stow on the Wold, Cheltenham GL54 1EQ Tel: 01451 830625 Fax: 01451 830693 — MB ChB 1993 Bristol; BSc (Hons) Bristol 1990; Dip IMC RCS Ed. 1997; DRCOG 1998. SHO (Paediat.) Cheltenham Gen. Hosp. Socs: BMA; MDU; BASICS.

SHERRINGTON, Charles Robert Hope Hospital, Salford M6 8 Tel: 0161 787 1261; 4 The Hollies, Didsbury, Manchester M20 2GD — MB ChB 1988 Liverp.; MRCP (UK) 1991. Cons. Nerologist Hope Hosp., Salford. Socs: BMA (Ethical Comm.). Prev: Specialist Regist. (Neurol.) Manch. Roy. Infirm.; Research Fell. (Neurol.) St. Jas. Hosp.

Leeds & Univ. Leeds; Regist. (Neurol.) St. Jas. Hosp. & Leeds Gen. Infirm.

SHERRINGTON, Jean Maria Sussex West & Downs NHS Trust, The Old Court House, Grange Road, Midhurst GU29 9LT Tel: 01730 811300 Fax: 01730 817512; 12 The Avenue, Chichester PO19 4PU Tel: 01243 530245 — MB ChB 1981 Bristol; MRCPsych 1990. (Bris.) Cons. (Psychiat.). Prev: Sen. Regist. (Psychiat.) Graylingwell Hosp. Chichester.

SHERRINGTON, Joanne Marie Wychall Lane Surgery, 11 Wychall Lane, Kings Norton, Birmingham B38 8TE Tel: 0121 628 2345 Fax: 0121 628 8282 — MB ChB 1989 Liverp.; DCH; MRCGP. GP Princip.

SHERRINGTON, Lesley Jane 53 Cumnor Hill, Oxford OX2 9EY — MB ChB 1995 Leeds.

SHERRINGTON, Peter 15 Sycamore Drive, Frome BA11 2TF — MB ChB 1993 Leeds.

SHERRY, Barclay John (retired) 116 Old Road, Headington, Oxford OX3 8SX — MB ChB 1951 Glas.

SHERRY, Colin Campbell Kennelling Cottage, Kennelling Road, Charing, Ashford TN27 0HF — LMSSA 1951 Lond.; FRCPsych 1990, M 1971; DPM Eng. 1962. (King's Coll. Hosp.) Prev: Vis. Psychiat. HM Prison Holloway Lond.; Cons. Psychiat. Maidstone Hosp.; Psychiat. Ment. Health Servs. Govt., W. Austral.

SHERRY, Eoin Niall Department of Anaesthesia, Guy's Hospital, London SE1 9RT Tel: 020 7976 5151 — MB BCh BAO 1982 NUI; FRCA 1988; DCH RCP Lond. 1984. Cons. Anaesth. Guy's Hosp. Lond.

SHERRY, Kathleen Louise 2 Bishopsgate Road, Glasgow G21 1XD — MB ChB 1986 Glas.; MRCP (UK) 1992. Sen. Regist. (Palliat. Med.) Huntershill Marie Curie Centre Glas.

SHERRY, Kathleen Mary Northern General Hospital NHS Trust, Herries Road, Sheffield S5 7AU Tel: 0114 243 4343; 27 Taptonville Road, Broomhill, Sheffield S10 5BQ Tel: 0114 266 0479 Fax: 0114 266 5552 — MB BS 1975 Lond.; FFA RCS Eng. 1981. Cons. (Anaesth.) N.ern Gen. Hosp. NHS Trust, Sheff.; Anaesth. Coodinator at Nat. Confidential Enquiry into PeriOperat. Deaths (NCEPOD), Lond.

SHERRY, Mark Station Medical Centre, Lumsden Barracks, Fallingbostel BFPO 38, Germany; 4 Piper Street, Headington, Oxford OX3 7AR — MB ChB 1984 Glas.; DCH RCP Lond. 1987; BSc Lond. 1978; MRCGP 1989; Dip. Occ. Med. RCP Lond. 1996; Dip. Sports Med. Scot. 1995; DFFP 1994; DGM RCP Lond. 1990; DRCOG 1988; Cert. Family Plann. JCC 1988. Civil. Med. Pract. MoD & Div. Surg. Fallingbostel, Germany; GP Trainer. Socs: BMA; Soc. Occupat. Med. (Overseas Br.); Brit. Soc. Med. & Dent. Hypn. (Lond. Br.). Prev: GP Oxf.

SHERRY, Mary Kathleen 46 Cumberland Street, London SW1V 4LZ Tel: 020 7834 0767 Fax: 020 7834 0767 — MB BS 1984 Lond.; BSc (1st cl. Hons.) Lond. 1981; MRCP (UK) 1988; MFOM RCP Lond. 1999. (St. Geo.) Indep. Cons. in Occupat.al Med. Socs: Roy. Soc. Med.; Soc. Occupat. Med.; Brit. Occupat. Hyg. Soc. Prev: Regist. (Radiol. Sci.) Guy's Hosp. Lond.; SHO (Med.) St. Geo. Hosp. Lond.; Ho. Surg. St. Geo. Hosp. Lond.

SHERRY, Mr Paul Gordon Warrington Hospital NHS Trust, Lovely Lane, Warrington WA5 4QG Tel: 01925 662383 Fax: 01925 662211; Hunters Moon, Hollins Lane, Antrobus, Northwich CW9 6NL Tel: 01565 777572 — MB BS 1983 Lond.; BSc Lond. 1988; FRCS Ed. 1988; FRCS Eng. 1988. Cons. Orthop. Warrington Hosp. NHS Trust. Socs: Fell. BOA. Prev: Fell. (Orthop.) Sunnybrook Health Sci. Centre Toronto; Sen. Regist. (Orthop.) St. Bart. Hosp. Lond.; Regist. (Orthop.) Poole Gen. Hosp.

SHERRY, Simon Norwood Medical Centre, 360 Herries Road, Sheffield S5 7HD Tel: 0114 242 6208 Fax: 0114 261 9243; 27 Taptonville Road, Sheffield S10 5BQ — MB BS 1975 Lond.

SHERRY, Susan Jane 12 Adria Road, Didsbury Village, Manchester M20 6SG — MB ChB 1987 Manch.

SHERRY, Vincent Francis (retired) 17 Herondale Avenue, London SW18 3JN Tel: 020 8874 8588 — MB BCh BAO NUI 1942; LM Coombe 1942. Prev: Res. Surg. Off. Roy. Masonic Hosp. Lond.

SHERRY-DOTTRIDGE, Florence Gertrude (retired) 15 Westfield Road, Beaconsfield HP9 1EG Tel: 0149 464205 — MB ChB 1920 Manch.; DPH Camb. 1923. Hon. Cons. Dermat. King Edw. VII Hosp. Windsor. Prev: Cons. Dermatol. Lond. Skin Hosp & N.W. Metrop. RHB.

SHERSKI, Leonard Adrian The Groves Medical Centre, 72 Coombe Road, New Malden KT3 4QS Tel: 020 8336 2222 Fax: 020 8336 0297; 3 Coombe House Chase, New Malden KT3 4SL Tel: 020 8336 2233 — MB BCh BAO 1959 Belf.; DCH Eng. 1962; DObst RCOG 1961. (Queens University Belfast) Prev: Regist. Roy. Hosp. Sick Childr. Belf.; Regist. Roy. Vict. Hosp. Belf.

SHERSTON-BAKER, Professor Arthur Joseph Percy (retired) 3 Olden Lane, Purley CR8 2EH Tel: 020 8645 9395 — MB BS 1944 Lond.; MD Lond. 1951; MRCS Eng. LRCP Lond. 1943; DPM Lond. 1949; FRCPsych 1971. Prev: Cons. Psychiat. Guy's Hosp. Gp. Lond.

SHERVEY, Christopher Sydney James Watledge Surgery, Barton Road, Tewkesbury GL20 5QQ Tel: 01684 293278; High Gables, Aston-on-Carrant, Tewkesbury GL20 8HL Tel: 01684 773269 — MB ChB 1972 Bristol; MRCGP 1981; DA Eng. 1974. Socs: BMA. Prev: SHO (Paediat.) Glos. Roy. Hosp.; SHO (Anaesth.) Cheltenham Health Dist.; SHO (A & E) Frenchay Hosp. Bristol.

SHERVINGTON, John Peter 44 Strathdene Road, Sellyoak, Birmingham B29 6QD Tel: 0121 472 6238 — MB BS 1988 Lond.; MRCOG 1994. Regist. (O & G) Good Hope Hosp. Sutton Coldfield. Prev: Regist. (O & G) Dudley Rd. Hosp. Birm.; Regist. (O & G) Walsall Manor Hosp.; SHO (O & G) Birm. Matern. Hosp.

SHERVINGTON, Mr Peter Charles (retired) Vinesend House, Vinesend, Near Cradley, Malvern WR13 5NH Tel: 01886 880775 Fax: 01826 880775 — MRCS Eng. LRCP Lond. 1961; FRCOG 1979, M 1967, DObst 1964. Cons. O & G Worcester Roy. Infirm. Prev: Sen. Regist. (O & G) Hammersmith Hosp. Lond. & St. Helier Hosp. Carshalton.

SHERWELL, David 18 Coombe Gardens, Wimbledon, London SW20 0QU Tel: 020 8879 1152 Email: dsherwell@x-stream.co.uk — BM BCh 1996 Oxf.; BA Oxf. 1993. (Oxf.) GP Regist. Surrey. Prev: SHO (Psychiat.) E. Surrey Hosp.; SHO (A&E) St. Geo.'s Hosp.; Ho. Off. (Gen. Surg.) John Radcliffe Oxf.

SHERWIN, James Robert Alexander 12 Orchard Road, Bardsea, Ulverston LA12 9QN — MB BS 1994 Lond.

SHERWIN, Jeffrey Raphael (retired) — MB ChB 1961 Leeds.

SHERWIN, Julie Deborah 40 Fairefield Crescent, Glenfield, Leicester LE3 8EH — MB BCh 1982 Wales; DA (UK) 1985. Socs: Assn. Anaesth. & BMA.

SHERWIN, Karen Elizabeth 12 Orchard Road, Bardsea, Ulverston LA12 9QN — MB BChir 1992 Camb.; MRCP (UK) 1995. Specialist Regist. (Clin. Oncol.) Addenbrooke's Hosp. Camb.

SHERWIN, Nicholas John Peter Holway Mill, Sandford Orcas, Sherborne DT9 4RZ — MB BS 1998 Lond.; MB BS Lond 1998.

SHERWIN, Simon Roger 30 Bramble Walk, Lymington SO41 9LW — BM 1993 Soton.; MRCGP (Royal College of GP's) 1998; DRCOG (RCObst&Gyn) 1999.

SHERWOOD, Andrew Nicholas St James House Surgery, County Court Road, King's Lynn PE30 5SY Tel: 01553 774221 Fax: 01553 692181 — MB BS 1976 Lond.; MRCGP 1983; DA (UK) 1980; DRCOG 1979.

SHERWOOD, Anthea Joy Department of Histopathology, Derriford Hospital, Derriford Road, Plymouth PL6 8DH Email: anthea.sherwood@phnt.swest.nhs.uk — MB BS 1973 Lond.; BSc Lond. 1970; FRCPath 1992, M 1980. (Univ. Coll. Hosp.) Cons. Histopath. Derriford Hosp. Plymouth. Socs: Assn. Clin. Path. (Mem. Counc. 1988-91); Internat. Acad. Path. (Brit. Div.).; Brit. Soc. of Gastroenterol. Prev: Lect. (Morbid Anat.) Univ. Coll. Hosp. Med. Sch. Lond.; Lect. (Histopath.) Inst. Child Health Gt. Ormond St.; Cons. Histopath., Torbay Hosp.

SHERWOOD, Benedict Thomas Hedgewick, Station Road, Rock, Kidderminster DY14 9UA — BM BS 1998 Nottm.; BM BS Nottm 1998.

SHERWOOD, Graham John Elmete Grange, Main St., Menston, Ilkley LS29 6LA — MB ChB 1978 Leeds; MPhil (Med. Eng.) Leeds 1974, MB ChB (Hons.) 1978; BA (Hons. Chem.) York 1965; MRCGP 1983; DRCOG 1980. GP Princip. Prev: SHO (Infec. Dis.) Seacroft Hosp. Leeds; Ho. Off. Leeds Gen. Hosp, York Dist. Hosp. & Leeds Matern. Hosp.

SHERWOOD, Heather Elizabeth 44 Silverthorn Drive, Longdean Park, Hemel Hempstead HP3 8BX — MB BS 1991 Lond.

SHERWOOD, Helen The Ashgrove Surgery, Morgan Street, Pontypridd CF37 2DR Tel: 01443 404444 Fax: 01443 480917; 75 Colchester Avenue, Penylan, Cardiff CF23 9NY — BM BS 1991 Nottm.; MRCGP 1995; DRCOG 1994. (Nottm.)

SHERWOOD, Julie Isabella 328 Cregagh Road, Belfast BT6 9EX — MB BCh BAO 1991 Belf.; MRCGP 1995; DCH RCPSI 1994; DRCOG 1994. (Qu. Univ. Belf.)

SHERWOOD, Kathryn Elizabeth West Wyke Farm, Wyke Lane, Ash, Aldershot GU12 6EE — BM BS 1998 Nottm.; BM BS Nottm 1998.

SHERWOOD, Mr Mark Brian 4935 North West 51st Place, Gainesville FL 32653, USA; c/o G. J. Sherwood, 4 Key Thorpe, 27 Manor Road, Eastcliffe, Bournemouth BH1 3ER — MB ChB 1976 Manch.; MB ChB (Hons.) Manch. 1976; FRCS Eng. 1982; MRCP (UK) 1979; FRCOphth 1989. Prof. & Chairm. (Ophth.) Univ. Florida Gainesville, USA.

SHERWOOD, Martin Paul 2nd Floor, 2 Devonshire Place, London W1G 6HJ Tel: 020 7580 4691 Fax: 020 7224 2832 Email: dr.paul.sherwood@compuserve.com — MRCS Eng. LRCP Lond. 1942; MA, MB BChir Camb. 1955; FFA RCS Eng. 1955; DA Eng. 1944. (Westm.) Prev: Cons. SW & SE Regional HBs.

SHERWOOD, Naomi Tel: 01223 350325 — MB ChB 1990 Ed.; MRCP 1994; DTM & H Liverp. 1995; DRCOG 1992. (Ed.) p/t Regist. Rotat. (Paediat.) Manch.

SHERWOOD, Nicholas Alexander Department of Anaesthesia, City Hospital NHS Trust, Birmingham B28 0H Tel: 0121 554 3801 — MB ChB 1987 Birm.; FRCA 1993; DA (UK) 1989. Cons.; Clin. Director, Critical Care Serv.s. Socs: RCA; BMA; MPS. Prev: Regist. (Anaesth.) S. Midl. Train Scheme; SHO (Neonat. & Intens. Care) Walsgrave Hosp. Coventry; SHO (Anaesth.) Selly Oak Hosp. Birm.

SHERWOOD, Paul Victor Department of Gastroentebology, Northampton General Hospital, Cufton Ville, Northampton NN1 5BD Tel: 01604 634700; Email: paulsherwood@freenet.co.uk — MB ChB 1991 Leeds; DM 2001 (Nottingham); MRCP (UK) 1994. (Leeds) Cons. Gastro. N.ampton Gen. Hosp. Socs: BMA; BSG.

SHERWOOD, Simon Michael Woodgrange Medical Practice, 40 Woodgrange Road, Forest Gate, London E7 0QH Tel: 020 8250 7585 Fax: 020 8250 7587 — MB ChB 1991 Manch.

SHERWOOD, Thomas (retired) 19 Clarendon Street, Cambridge CB1 1JU — MB BS Lond. 1960; MA Camb. 1978; FRCP Lond. 1979, M 1964; FRCR 1975; FFR 1968; DMRD Eng. 1966; DCH Eng. 1962. Prev: Clin. Dean Univ. Camb.

SHERWOOD, William James 4 The Moorlands, Kidlington OX5 2XX — MB BS 1996 Lond.

SHERWOOD-JONES, David Mark Occupational Health, Babbington Hosp, Derby Rd, Belper DE56 1WH Tel: 01773 828247, 01773 829237; 5 Eastwood Road, Radcliffe-on-Trent, Nottingham NG12 2FZ Tel: 0115 933 2127 — MB BS 1976 Lond.; MRCP (UK) 1980; MRCS Eng. LRCP Lond. 1976; FFOM RCP Lond. 1995, MFOM 1986; DIH Soc. Apoth. Lond. 1983. (St. Thos.) Cons. Occupat.al Med.; Hon. Sec. E. Midl.s Gp. of Soc. of Occupat.al Med. Socs: Soc. Occupat. Med.; Nat. Back Exchange. Prev: Med. Insp. Health & Safety Exec. Midl.s Div.; Med. Regist., Hull Roy. Infirm.; Dep. MO Nat. Coal Bd. S. Yorks. Area.

SHESHGIRI, Mr Jitendra Basavanneppa Accident & Emergency Department, Frenchay Hospital, Frenchay, Bristol BS16 1LE Tel: 0117 970 1212 Fax: 0117 957 2335; 148 Frenchay Park Road, Stapleton, Bristol BS16 1HB Tel: 0117 965 7529 Fax: 0117 965 7529 — MB BS 1980 Karnatak; FRCS Glas. 1988. Assoc. Specialist (A & E) Frenchay Healthcare Trust Bristol. Socs: Assoc. Mem. Brit. Assn. Accid. & Emerg. Med. Prev: Regist. (Cardiothoracic Surg.) Univ. Hosp. Wales Cardiff; Regist. (Surg.) Bishop Auckland Gen. Hosp. Co. Durh.

SHETH, Bipin Chandra Ramniklal Tel: 0191 567 4397 Fax: 0191 514 3740; 31 Briar Dene close, East Herrington, Sunderland SR3 3RU Fax: 0191 528 1506 Email: bipincr@lycos.com — MB BS 1969 Ranchi. (Ranchi) GP Sunderland; Mem. Sunderland LMC. Socs: Fell.Roy. Soc. of Med.; Roy. Soc. of Health.

SHETH, Gyandev Punyadev 63 Ealing Road, Wembley HA0 4BN Tel: 020 8902 7135 — MB BS 1968 Indore; MS (Ophth.) Gujarat 1971, DO 1970. (M.G.M. Med. Coll.)

SHETH, Himanshu 68A West Park Road, Maidstone ME15 7AG — MB BS 1975 Gujarat.

SHETH, Jyotika Gyandev The Surgery, 131 Dartmouth Road, London NW2 4ES Tel: 020 8450 0403 Fax: 020 8450 3355; 63 Ealing Road, Wembley HA0 4BN Tel: 020 8902 7135 Fax: 020 8902 7135 — MB BS 1970 Gujarat; MFFP 1993; Dip. Pract. Dermat. Wales 1992; DCH RCP Lond. 1989; DCH Bombay 1973.

SHETH

(BJ Med. Coll. Ahmedabad) Family Plann. Doctor Ealing HA; Trainer (Family Plann.) Lond.; Examr. Red Cross; Med. Examr. DSS. Socs: BMA; Med. Protec. Soc.; Fac.Fam.Plann.

SHETH, Pradip Kumar Shantilal c/o Mrs Rama G. Sheth, 24 Hood Road, London SW20 0SR — MB BS 1973 Indore.

SHETH, Tanay Rajnikant 114 Albert Road, Epsom KT17 4EL — MB BS 1994 Lond.; MA Camb. 1995.

SHETTAR, Chanabasappa Kuruvatteppa 111A Wood Lane, Isleworth TW7 5EG — MB BS 1956 Bombay. (Grant Med. Coll.) Socs: BMA. Prev: Res. Surg. Off Roy. N.. Hosp. Lond.; Surg. Regist. Gateshead Hosp. Gp.; SHO (Orthop.) Vict. Infirm. Glas.

SHETTY, Ajeya Krishna 192 Lauderdale Tower, Barbican, London EC2Y 8BY — MB ChB 1993 Glas.

SHETTY, Arun 6 Rose Hill Court, Doncaster DN4 5LY — MB ChB 1987 Manch.

SHETTY, Mr Ashokkumar 28 Whitehead Close, Dartford DA2 7PR — MB BS 1975 Karnatak; FRCS Glas. 1986.

SHETTY, Mr Asode Anantharam Medway Hospital, Gillingham ME7 5NY; 6 Barncroft Drive, Hampstead, Gillingham ME7 3TJ — MB BS 1982 Karnatak; FRCS Ed. 1989.

SHETTY, Bola Krishna Kishore Pallion Health Centre, Hylton Road, Sunderland SR4 7XF Tel: 0191 657 1319 — MB BS 1976 Mysore. (Mysore) GP Sunderland.

SHETTY, Jeevan Krishna 1 Bideford Crescent, Glasgow G32 9NQ — MB ChB 1993 Glas.

SHETTY, Manjaya Kaliyur The Surgery, 997 Romford Road, Manor Park, London E12 5JR Tel: 020 8478 2711 Fax: 020 8553 4696 — MB BS 1965 Karnatak. (Kasturba Med. Coll.)

SHETTY, Muniyal Aravinda Shettleston Health Centre, Shettleston Health Centre, 420 Old Shettleston Road, Glasgow G32 7JZ Tel: 0141 531 6250 Fax: 0141 531 6216 — MB BS 1970 Mysore. (Mysore Med. Coll.) GP Glas.

SHETTY, Narendra Vithal Bridge Street Surgery, 48 Bridge Street, Newton-le-Willows WA12 9QS Tel: 01925 225755 — MB BS 1966 Bombay.

SHETTY, Padubidri Ramanand Northowram Hospital, Northowram, Halifax HX3 7SW Tel: 01422 201101; 5 Savile Lea, Halifax HX1 2DD Tel: 01422 252462 — MB BS 1972 Bangalore; DPM RCPSI 1995. (Bangalore Med. Coll.) Assoc. Specialist (Psychiat.) Calderdale HA. Prev: Clin. Asst. (Psychiat.) Calderdale HA; Regist. (Psychiat.) Calderdale HA.

SHETTY, Mr Ramesh (retired) 6 Rose Hill Court, Bessacarr, Doncaster DN4 5LY — MB BS 1960 Bombay; FRCS Ed. 1974; DLO Lond. 1967.

SHETTY, Mr Thimmangoor Thimmappa 50 Larch Drive, Stanwix, Carlisle CA3 9FL — MB BS 1979 Mysore; FRCS Glas. 1987; DO RCPSI 1987. Assoc. Specialist (Ophth.) Cumbld. Infirm. Carlisle.

SHEVILLE, Eli 11 Stone Hall Road, Winchmore Hill, London N21 1LR Tel: 020 8360 6621 — MB ChB Glas. 1951; FRCR Lond. 1975; FFR Lond. 1962; DMRD RCS Eng. 1957. (Glasgow University) Prev: Cons. Radiol. Qu. Eliz. II Hosp. Welwyn Gdn. City; Med. Dir. Herts. Magnetic Imaging Campus Qu. Eliz. II Hosp.; Sen. Regist. (Radiol.) Hosp. Sick Childr. Gt. Ormond St. & Roy. Free Hosp.

SHEVKET, Mehmet 38 Halesowen Road, Halesowen B62 9AB — MB BS 1996 Lond.

SHEVLIN, Bernard Anthony The New Surgery, Old Road, Tean, Stoke-on-Trent ST10 4EG Tel: 01538 722323 Fax: 01538 722215 — MB BCh 1968 Wales; LMCC 1970; MRCGP 1976; DObst RCOG 1972.

SHEVLIN, Peter Vincent Hawthorn Surgery, Wilfrid Terrace, Branch Road, Lower Wortley, Leeds LS12 5NR Tel: 0113 295 4770 Fax: 0113 295 4771 — MB ChB 1983 Leeds.

SHEVLIN (LEECH), Anne Bridget (retired) — MB ChB 1963 Ed.; FRCGP 1993, M 1976; DObst RCOG 1966. Erewash PCT-Mem. of Himp. Prev: Research Regist. (Geriat.) Dryburn Hosp. Durh.

SHEWAN, David Michael 5 St Botolph's Close, Saxilby, Lincoln LN1 2PS Tel: 01522 702097 Fax: 01522 702097 Email: d.shewan@msn.com — MB ChB 1963 Ed.; BA Camb. 1960; FFA RCS Eng. 1968. (Camb. & Ed.) Cons. Anaesth. Lincoln Co. Hosp. Prev: Sen. Regist. (Anaesth.) Edin. Roy. Infirm.; SHO (Anaesth.) Edin. City Hosp.; SHO (Anaesth.) & Ho. Phys. W.. Gen. Hosp. Edin.

SHEWAN, Doreen Baxter (Surgery), Kidlington Health Centre, Kidlington, Oxford OX44 7SS; 19 Stanley Road, Oxford OX4 1QY Tel: 01865 725203 — MB ChB 1970 Aberd.; MRCGP 1976; DObst. RCOG 1975. (Aberd.) Socs: BMA. Prev: SHO (O & G) Raigmore Hosp. Inverness; Ho. Off. (Med.) & Ho. Off. (Surg.) Qu. Eliz. Hosp. Barbados; Resid. (Paediat.) Kingston Gen. Hosp., Canada.

SHEWARD, Jonathan Christopher Tel: 01655 882708 Fax: 01655 882977 — MB ChB 1985 Ed.; MRCGP 1993. (Ed.) Gen. Practitioner Maybole H.C.; Clin. Asst. (Geriat. Med.) Ayrsh.; Chairm. Carrick & Doon LHCC. Socs: MRCGP.

SHEWELL, Mr Peter Charles The White House, Didley, Wormbridge, Hereford HR2 9DA Tel: 01981 570233 Fax: 01981 570233 — MB ChB 1984 Birm.; MSc Birm. 1989; FRCS (Orth.) 1995; FRCS Ed. 1989. Cons. Orthop. Surg. Hereford Gen. Hosp.

SHEWELL, Phyllida Kathleen Royal Devon and Exeter Hospital, Barrack Road, Exeter EX1 2ED; Western Cottage, Church St, Kenton, Exeter EX6 8LU — MB BS 1973 Lond.; BSc Lond. 1971; MRCS Eng. LRCP Lond. 1973; DGM RCP Lond. 1987. Clin. Asst. (Elderly Med.) Roy. Devon & Exeter Hosp.; Clin. Asst. (Elderly Care) Exeter & Dist. Community Health Trust.

SHEWRING, Mr David Joseph Department of Orthopaedics, University Hospital of Wales, Heath Park, Cardiff CF4 4XN Tel: 029 2074 7747; 62 Victoria Road, Penarth CF64 3HZ Tel: 029 2070 8384 — MB BCh 1984 Wales; FRCS (Orth.) 1994; FRCS Ed. 1989; Dip Hand Surg (Europe) 1996. (Welsh National School of Medicine) Cons. (Orthop. & Hand Surg.) Univ. Hosp. Wales NHS Healthcare Trust; Hon. Lect. Univ. of Wales Coll. of Med. Socs: Brit. Soc. Surg. Hand; Brit. Orthop. Assn.

SHEWRING, John Ignatius Llanedeyrn Health Centre, Maelfa, Llanedeyrn, Cardiff CF23 9PN Tel: 029 2073 1671 Fax: 029 2054 0129 — MB BCh 1991 Wales; DRCOG 1995; MRCGP 1998. (Univ. Wales Coll. Med.) Co-Dir. E. Cardiff Co-op. Socs: (Sec.) Welsh Assn. GP Regist.s. Prev: GMSC Regist.s Commiss. (Welsh Represen.).

SHEWRING, Paul Michael Lisson Grove Medical Centre, 3-5 Lisson Grove, Mutley, Plymouth PL4 7DL Tel: 01752 205555 Fax: 01752 205558; 288 Fort Austin Avenue, Crownhill, Plymouth PL6 5SR Tel: 01752 701345 — MB BS 1973 Lond.; MRCS Eng. LRCP Lond. 1973; MRCGP 1980; DCH Eng. 1976; DRCOG 1979.

SHEWRING, Sarah Anne The Emergency Unit, University Hospital of Wales, Heath Park, Cardiff CF14 Tel: 029 2074 7747 — MB BCh 1993 Wales; DFFP 1996; DRCOG 1995; MRCGP 1998. (Univ. Wales Coll. Med.) Middle Grade A & E.

SHEWRY, Sylvia Mary 8 Kings Road, North Luffenham, Oakham LE15 8JH Tel: 01780 720893 Fax: 01780 720893 — MB BS Newc. 1970; DCH Eng. 1975; DA Eng. 1974; DObst RCOG 1972. (Newc.)

SHEYBANY, Shiva Stonewalls, Hempton, Banbury OX15 0QS Tel: 01869 338439 — MD 1974 Tehran; MRCOG 1976. Sen. Regist. (O & G) N.ampton Gen. Hosp. & John Radcliffe Hosp. Oxf. Socs: CCST 1998. Prev: Sen. Regist. & Clin. Lect. John Radcliffe Hosp. Oxf.

SHIA, Gilbert Tsai-Wei 109 Bloxham Road, Banbury OX16 9JT — MB BChir 1988 Camb.; BSc (Hons.) Lond. 1980; MSc Oxf. 1983; DCH 1991; DRCOG 1991. (Cambridge) Socs: BMA.

SHIBIB, Mr Kahtan Jassim Eye Department, Stobhill General Hospital, Glasgow G21 3UW Tel: 0141 558 0111 ext. 359 — MB ChB 1972 Baghdad; FRCS Glas. 1986; DO RCPSI 1979.

SHIBLI, Khalil Ullah 118 Meadowgate Avenue, Sothall, Sheffield S20 2PS Tel: 0114 287 5875 — MB BS 1984 Karachi; FRCA 1994; DA (UK) 1990.

SHIBU, Mr Mohamed Meh 51 Springfield Mount, London NW9 0SH — MB BCh 1981 Al Fateh; FRCS Ed. 1988.

SHICKLE, Darren Arthur Public Health, Scharr, University of Sheffield, Regent Court, 30 Regent St., Sheffield S1 4DA Tel: 0114 222 0818 Fax: 0114 222 0798 Email: d.shickle@sheffield.ac.uk; 262 Abbeydale Road S., Totley Rise, Sheffield S17 3LL — MB BCh 1988 Wales; MPH Wales 1994; MFPHM 1995; MA Wales 1996. Clin. Sen. Lect. (Pub. Health Med.) Univ. Sheff.

SHIEFF, Mr Colin Louis The Royal Free Hospital, London NW3 2QG Tel: 020 7830 2097 Fax: 020 7830 2560 Email: colin.shieff@rfh.nthames.nhs.uk; Tel: 020 7624 9496 Fax: 020 7624 9496 Email: cshieff@btopenworld.com — MB ChB 1973 Liverp.; FRCS Ed. 1979. Cons. Neurosurg. Roy. Free. Hosp. Lond.; Hon. Cons. Neurosurg., Nat. Hosp. for Neurol. + Neurosurg. Lond.; Lt Col RAMC (V). Socs: World Soc. Sterotactid & Funct. Neurosurg.;

Roy. Soc. of Med.; Europ. Soc. Stereotactic & Funct. Neurosug. Prev: Sen. Regist. (Neurosurg.) Midl. Centre for Neurosurg. & Neurol., Birm.; Fell. Duke Univ. Med. Centr. Durh. N. Carolina; Regist. Atkinson Morley's Hosp. Lond.

SHIEFF, Edward (retired) 83 Vernon Road, Edgbaston, Birmingham B16 9SQ Tel: 0121 454 3278 — LRCP LRCS 1937 Ed.; LRCP LRCS Ed. LRFPS Glas. 1937. Prev: Cons. Chest Phys. E. Birm. Hosp. & Birm. Chest Clinic.

SHIEFF, Norman 250 Upper Parliament Street, Liverpool L8 7QG Tel: 0151 709 1263 — MB ChB 1942 Glas.; BSc Glas. 1940, MB ChB 1942, DPH 1947. (Glas.) Admiralty Surg. & Agent. Prev: Maj. RAMC.

SHIEL, Deborah Anne Hillview Medical Centre, 3 Heathside Road, Woking GU22 7QP Tel: 01483 760707 — MB BCh BAO 1986 NUI; MRCGP 1996; DRCOG 1991; DMH Belf. 1990. (Univ. Coll. Galway) Gen. Pract. Trainer. Socs: BMA; RCGP.

SHIEL, Julian Iannis 26 Southway, Lewes BN7 1LY — MB BCh BAO 1990 NUI.

SHIELD, John Edwin Hamilton 93 Kingweston Avenue, Shirehampton, Bristol BS11 0AH Tel: 0117 982 2548 — MB ChB 1959 Bristol.

SHIELD, Julian Paul Hamilton Institute of Child Health, St. Michaels Hill, Bristol BS2 8BJ Email: j.p.h.shield@bristol.ac.uk — MB ChB 1985 Bristol; MD Bristol 1997; MRCP (UK) 1988; FRCPCH (1998). Cons. Sen. Lect. Dept. of Child Health Univ. of Bristol.

SHIELD, Michael James Botts Furlong, Stone, Aylesbury HP17 8PR Tel: 01296 747054 — MB BS 1973 Lond.; MRCPath 1979; FRCPath 1991; MFPM 1990. (Middlesex) Sen. Director, Europ. Med. Operat.s, Searle; Hon. Research Fell. Dept. Med. Physics Univ. of Exeter. Socs: BMA; Fell. Roy. Coll. Pathol.; Fac. Pharmaceut. Med. Prev: Med. Dir. G.D. Searle & Co. High Wycombe; Dir. Clin. Research (Europe) G.D. Searle & Co. High Wycombe; Sen. Lect. & Hon. Cons. (Bacteriol.) St. Mary's Hosp. Med. Sch. Lond.

SHIELD, Nigel Boyd Ringwood Health Centre, The Close, Ringwood BH24 1JY Tel: 01425 478901 Fax: 01425 478239; The Greenaway, 13 Warren Close, Ringwood BH24 2AJ Tel: 01425 477079 — MB BS 1972 Lond.; DObst RCOG 1976; Cert. Family Plann. JCC 1976. (Middlx.) Prev: Trainee GP Salisbury VTS.

SHIELDS, Mr David Alan The County Hospital, Union Walk, Hereford HR1 2ER Tel: 01432 355444; Bank House, Perton, Hereford HR1 4HP — MB ChB 1981 Liverp.; MD Liverp. 1995; FRCS Eng. 1989. Cons. Surg., Hereford Co. Hosp., Union Walk, Hereford, HR1 2ER. Prev: Locum Cons. Surg., Norf. & Norwich Hosp.; Sen. Surgic. Regist., Norf. & Norwich Hosp.; Research Fell. (vasc. Surg.), Middlx. Hosp., Lond.

SHIELDS, Erica Glynis 59 Lyndhurst Parade, Belfast BT13 3PB — MB BCh BAO 1993 Belf.

SHIELDS, Gavin Graham Primrose Hill, Draycote, Rugby CV23 9RB — MB ChB 1989 Birm.

SHIELDS, Gillian Leigh c/o 77 Mullahead Road, Tandragee, Craigavon BT62 2LB — MB BCh BAO 1988 Belf.; MB BCh (Hons.) BAO Belf. 1988; MRGCP 1993; DMH Belf. 1992; DRCOG 1991. Socs: BMA.

SHIELDS, Jean May (retired) de Bathe Cross, North Tawton EX20 2BB Tel: 01837 82218 — MB BS 1953 Lond.; MRCS Eng. LRCP Lond. 1953; DObst RCOG 1955. Prev: G.P. Princip., Okehampton, Devon.

SHIELDS, Jennifer 124 Harrow Road, Wembley HA9 6QQ Tel: 020 8903 4848; 66 The Avenue, London NW6 7NP — MB BS 1976 Lond.; BA (Hons.) Oxf 1973; MRCP (UK) 1980; MRCGP 1983. (Oxford University and Westminster University)

SHIELDS, Martin Oliver 15 Beechmount Park, Newry BT34 1LA — MB BCh BAO 1997 Belf.

SHIELDS, Mary Frances The Health Centre, Park Drive, Stenhousemuir, Falkirk; 40 The Quadrant, Clarkston, Glasgow G76 8AG — MB ChB 1983 Glas.; MRCGP 1987. Prev: SHO (Psychiat.) Woodilee Hosp. Lenzie; Ho. Off. Roy. Alexandra Infirm. Paisley; Ho. Off. Stobhill Hosp. Glas.

SHIELDS, Michael Anthony (retired) Brora, Springfield Court, Gresford, Wrexham LL12 8HY — MB ChB Aberd. 1954; DObst RCOG 1958.

SHIELDS, Mr Michael David Pinderfields Hospital, Aboyon Road, Wakefield WF1 4EE Tel: 01924 201688 Fax: 01924 214147; The Dower House, Heath, Wakefield WF1 5SL Tel: 01924 382361 — BSc (Anat.) Lond. 1965, MB BS 1968; FRCS Eng. 1973; MRCS Eng. LRCP Lond. 1968; FRCOG 1989, M 1975. Cons. (O & G) Wakefield Gp. Hosps. Socs: BMA. Prev: Sen. Regist. Middlx. Hosp. Lond.; Regist. (O & G) W.m. Hosp. Lond.; SHO (O & G) Qu. Charlotte's Metern. & Chelsea Hosps. for Wom.

SHIELDS, Michael David Department of Clinical Health, The Queens University of Belfast, Grosvenor Road, Belfast BT12 6BJ Tel: 01232 240503 Fax: 01232 236455 — MB ChB 1979 Bristol; MD Bristol 1988; FRCP Lond. 1996; MRCP (UK) 1982; FRCPCH 1997. Cons. & Sen. Lect. (Respirat. Paediat.) Nuffield Dept. Child Health Qu.s Univ. Belf. Prev: Sen. Regist. Roy. Belf. Hosp. for Sick Childr.; Research Fell. Sick Childr. Hosp. Toronto.

SHIELDS, Michael Leslie Priory Cottage, 14 Northgate, Cottingham HU16 4HH — MB ChB 1983 Leeds; MRCP (UK) 1989; MRCPath 1994. Cons. Haemat. Hull Hosps. NHS Trust. Prev: Sen. Regist. Rotat. (Haemat.) St. Geo. Hosp. Lond.

SHIELDS, Noel Peter (retired) 21 Mount Street, Taunton TA1 3QF — MA Camb. 1946; MRCS Eng. LRCP Lond. 1938; MRCGP 1956. Prev: Ho. Surg. St. Bart. Hosp.

SHIELDS, Penny Alice Aspley Medical Centre, 511 Aspley Lane, Aspley, Nottingham NG8 5RW Tel: 0115 929 2700 Fax: 0115 929 8276 — MB ChB 1987 Bristol; PhD Lond. 1982; BSc Hons. Leeds 1976. Trainee GP Nottm. VTS. Prev: SHO (A & E) Kingston Hosp. Surrey; SHO (O & G) Mayday Univ. Hosp. Croydon; Ho. (Surg.) Mayday Univ. Hosp. Croydon.

SHIELDS, Philip Lawrence 17 Bilton Close, Harbourne, Birmingham B17 0AL — BM BS 1990 Nottm.; MRCP (UK) 1993.

SHIELDS, Sir Robert 81 Meols Drive, West Kirby, Wirral CH48 5DF Tel: 0151 632 3588 Fax: 0151 632 5613 Email: r.shields@rcsed.ac.uk — MB ChB Glas. 1953; M.B., Ch. B. 1953; Hon. FACS 1991; Hon. FRACS 1997; FRCP Ed 1997; Hon. DSc Wales 1990; MD (Hons.) Glas. 1965; FRCS Eng. 1966; FRCS Ed. 1959; Hon. FRCSI 1996; Hon. FCS HK 1995; Hon. FCS (SA) 1991; FRCPS 1993. (Glas.) Cons. Surg. Emerit. Roy. Liverp Univ. Hosp.. & Prof. Surg. Emerit. Univ. Liverp.; Mem. of cancer Serv.s Accreditation Bd.; NHS Exec., Trent; Mem. Advisery Bd., Control Assur. Sevices Ltd. Socs: Pres., Trav. Surigical Soc.; Regent & Past Pres. RCSEd; (Ex-Pres.) Surgic. Research Soc. & Assoc. of Surgs. Prev: Dean Fac. Med. Univ. Liverp.; Reader (Surg.) & Cons. Surg. Welsh Nat. Sch. Med.; Lect. (Surg.) & Sen. Regist. W.. Infirm. Glas.

SHIELDS, Robert Hay 14 Oxwich House, Burton Pidsea, Hull HU12 9AF — MB BS 1952 Durh. (Newc.) Prev: Ho. Phys. Walkergate Hosp. Newc.; Ho. Surg. P.ss Mary Matern. Hosp. Newc.

SHIELDS, Robert Stuart David 25 Balmoral Road, Andover SP10 3HY — MB ChB 1991 Liverp.; MRCGP 1995.

SHIELDS, Rodger Park (retired) 38 Connaught Way, Tunbridge Wells TN4 9QL Tel: 01892 531577 — MB BS Lond. 1946; MRCS Eng. LRCP Lond. 1945; DTM & H Eng. 1947. Prev: Med. Off. Angolan Refugee Med. Relief (Congo Protestant Relief Agency.

SHIELDS, Sheila Deirdre Allesley Park Medical Centre, Whitaker Road No.2, Coventry CV5 9JE Tel: 024 7667 4123 Fax: 024 7667 2196; Health Centre, University of Warwick, Coventry CV4 7AL Tel: 024 76 523523 — MB BCh BAO 1958 Dub. Prev: Anaesth. Regist. Coventry & Warw. Hosp.

SHIELDS, Simon Alexander National Hopsital for Neurology & Neurosurgery, Queen SQUARE, London WC1N 3BG — BM BCh 1992 Oxf.; MRCP (UK) 1995. (Oxf.) Specialist Regist. Neurol., Nat. Hosp. (Lond.) & Addenbrookes (Camb.). Prev: Regist. (Med. & Cardiol.) Camb.; SHO Lond. & Camb.; MRC Clin. Train. Fell. (Camb. Centre Brain Repair).

SHIELDS, Stephanie Anne 33 Stamperland Av, Clarkston, Glasgow G76 8EX — MB ChB 1997 Glas.

SHIELL, Kate Ann 5 Lomas Close, Stannington, Sheffield S6 6EU — MB ChB 1994 Sheff.

SHIELLS, Gordon McIntyre The Park Medical Group, Fawdon Park Road, Newcastle upon Tyne NE3 2PE Tel: 0191 285 1763 Fax: 0191 284 2374 — MB BS 1983 Newc. SHO (Paediat.) Bishop Auckland Gen. Hosp. W. Durh. HA. Socs: BMA. Prev: Ho. Off. (Gen. Med.) Newc. Gen. Hosp.; Ho. Off. (Gen. Surg.) Ashington Hosp.

SHIELLS, Linda Ann 35 High Street, Brigstock, Kettering NN14 3HA — MB ChB 1995 Dundee.

SHIELLS, William Arnott (retired) Elm Tree Farm, Farnham, Saxmundham IP17 1JZ Tel: 01728 602695 — MB BS Durh. 1951.

SHIELS

SHIELS, Aine Maria Kathryn 28 Dorchester Park, Malone Road, Belfast BT9 6RJ — MB BCh BAO 1991 Belf.; MB BCh Belf. 1991.

SHIELS, Annette Martina 132 Englefield Road, London N1 3LQ Tel: 020 7226 2547 — MB ChB 1989 Birm.; MRCP (UK) 1993.

SHIELS, Rachel Mary 46 Howden Hall Road, Edinburgh EH16 6PJ — MB ChB 1991 Ed.

SHIER, Deborah Lucy John Scott Health Centre, Green Lanes, London N4 2NU; 10 St Pauls Road, Islington, London N1 2QN Tel: 020 7359 4518 — MB BS 1984 Lond.; LMSSA Lond. 1983. (St. Thos.) GP. Prev: Ho. Surg. Qu. Alexandra's Hosp. Portsmouth; Ho. Phys. Medway Hosp. Gillingham.; Ho. Surg. Qu. Alexandra's Hosp. Portsmouth.

SHIER, Dermot levers Beach House, 10 Trevallion Park, Feock, Penryn TR3 6RS Tel: 01872 865385 Fax: 01872 865385 Email: dermot@dishier.freeserve.co.uk — MB BCh BAO Dub. 1968; DObst RCOG 1974; DCH Eng. 1972. (T.C. Dub.) p/t Locum GP. Socs: Med. Defence Union; BMA. Prev: Med. Off. Labrador W. Med. Clinic Labrador City Canada; Resid. (Paediat.) Dr. Chas. A. Janeway Child Health Centre St. John's, Canada.

SHIERS, Caroline Essex Rivers Health Care Trust, Child Health Department, Clacton Hospital, Freeland Road, Clacton-on-Sea CO15 1LH Tel: 01255 201717; 25 Holmbrook Way, Frinton-on-Sea CO13 9LW Tel: 01255 673032 — MB BS Lond. 1968. (St. Mary's) Clin. Med. Off. Essex Rivers Health Care Trust Colchester.

SHIERS, Charles, OStJ (retired) High Meadow, 85 Westwood Park Drive, Leek ST13 8NW — MRCS Eng. LRCP Lond. 1945; MRCGP 1962. Prev: Res. Med. Off. Gen. Hosp. Warrington.

SHIERS, David Edward Leek Health Centre, Fountain Street, Leek ST13 6JB Tel: 01538 381022 Fax: 01538 398638 — MB ChB 1974 Manch.; MRCP (UK) 1977. Prev: Regist. (Gen. Med.) N.. Gen. Hosp. Sheff.; SHO (A & E) & Regist. (Gen. Med.) Pk. Hosp. Manch.

SHIERS, Duncan 25 Holmbrook Way, Frinton-on-Sea CO13 9LW Tel: 01255 673032 — MRCS Eng. LRCP Lond. 1942; BSc, MB BCh Wales 1942; MRCP Lond. 1945. Hon. Cons. (Rheum. & Physical Med.) Chelmsford Hosp. Gp. Prev: Consult. in Rheum. & Physical Med. Chelmsford Hosp. Gp.; Chief Clin. Asst. Arthur Stanley Inst. Middlx. Hosp. & Med. Out-pats.; W. Lond. Hosp.

SHIERS, Mr Leslie Gordon Percival 75 Harley Street, London W1G 8QL Tel: 020 7487 4216 — MRCS Eng. LRCP Lond. 1938; FRCS Ed. 1947. (Cardiff) Socs: Fell. Brit. Orthop. Assn.; Med.-Leg. Soc. Prev: Sen. Orthop. Regist. S.E. Essex Hosp. Gp. & Addenbrooke's Hosp.; Surg. Lt.-Cdr. RNVR 1939-46; Staff Surg. SS Qu. Mary.

SHIEW, Chun Ming Flat 7, Ashdown, 36 Camborne Road, Sutton SM2 6RE Tel: 020 8642 8460 Email: mshiew@aol.com — MB BS 1996 Lond. (St. Geos.)

SHIEW, Marianne May Foon No.7 Ashdown, 36 Cambourne Road, Sutton SM2 6RE — MB BS 1995 Lond.

SHIFFMAN, Ellen Mali (retired) 16 Primrose Road, Calderstones, Liverpool L18 2HE Tel: 0151 280 3051 — LRCP LRCS Ed. LRFPS Glas. 1948; LRCP LRCS Ed., LRFPS Glas. 1948; FRCGP 1980. Prev: Hosp. Pract. (Psychiat.) Sefton Gen. Hosp. Liverp.

SHIFFMAN, Ian Felix Lewisham Medical Centre, 158 Utting Avenue East, Liverpool L11 1DL Tel: 0151 256 9800 Fax: 0151 256 5765; Cliff Cottage, Woolton Hill Road, Liverpool L25 4RF Tel: 0151 428 3548 — MB ChB 1979 Liverp.; MRCS Eng. LRCP Lond. 1979; DRCOG 1983. Prev: Trainee GP Liverp. AHA VTS; SHO (Cardiol.) Sefton Gen. Hosp.; Ho. Surg. BRd.green Hosp. Liverp.

SHIFFMAN, Kenneth 31 Rodney Street, Liverpool L1 9EH Tel: 0151 709 2076 Fax: 0151 707 2922 Email: k.shiffman@virgin.net; 16 Primrose Road, Liverpool L18 2HE Tel: 0151 280 3051 — MRCS Eng. LRCP Lond. 1952; FRCGP 1980. (Liverp.) Socs: Brit. Geriat. Soc.; Med. Assn. Soc.; Liverp. Med. Inst. Prev: Hosp. Pract. (Geriat. Med.) Pk. Hosp. Liverp.; Ho. Phys. BRd.green Hosp. Liverp.

SHIKOTRA, Bharat Keshavji Saffron Lane Health Centre, 612 Saffron Lane, Leicester LE2 6TD Tel: 0116 291 1212 Fax: 0116 291 0300; 12 Kingswood Avenue, Leicester LE3 0UN — MB ChB 1985 Manch.; T(GP) 1992; DRCOG 1990; Cert. Family Plann. JCC 1990; DCH RCP Lond. 1989. GP Leicester. Prev: Trainee GP Leicester VTS; SHO (Geriat.) Leicester Gen. & Groby Rd. Hosp.; SHO (O & G) Chase Farm Hosp. Enfield.

SHIKOTRA, Kishan Keshavji 285 Hinckley Road, Leicester LE3 0TJ — MB BS 1997 Lond.

SHILLAM, Geoffrey Norman Eastfield House Surgery, 6 St. Johns Road, Newbury RG14 7LW Tel: 01635 41495 Fax: 01635 522751 — MB ChB 1975 Bristol; MRCGP 1982; DRCOG 1981; DCH Eng. 1980. Gen. Pract. in Newbury Berks.

SHILLIDAY, Ilona Ruth Renal Unit, Monklands Hospital, Monkscourt Avenue, Airdrie — MB ChB 1984 Ed.; MD Ed. 1998; MRCP Ed. 1987. (Edinburgh) Sen. Cons. Nephrologist and Phys., Monklands Hosp., Airdrie. Prev: Staff Grade (Gen. Med.) Falkirk & Dist. Roy. Infirm.; Research Fell. (Med.) Univ. Glas.; Regist. (Renal) Roy. Infirm. Glas.

SHILLIDAY, Peter Frame 11 Thorpe Avenue, Peterborough PE3 6LA — MB ChB 1990 Manch.

SHILLING, Mr John Stanley St. Thomas' Hospital, Lambeth Palace Road, London SE1 7EH; Blackheath Hospital, 40-42 Lee Terrace, Blackheath, London SE3 9UD Tel: 020 8318 7722 — MB BS 1965 Lond.; FRCS Eng. 1972; DO Eng. 1969. (St. Thos.) Cons. Ophth. Surg. St. Thos. Hosp. Lond. & Greenwich Hosp.

SHILLING, Rosemary Suhasini Solihull Hospital, Department of Anaesthetics, Lode Lane, Solihull B91 2JL Tel: 0121 711 4455 Fax: 0121 685 5476; 168 St. Bernards Road, Solihull B92 7BL — MB BS 1975 Madras; FFA RCS Eng. 1985. (Vellore India) Cons. Anaesth. W. Midl. RHA. Socs: BMA; MDUUS; RCA.

SHILLINGFORD, Michael John Barnhouse Surgery, Barnhouse Close, Lower Street, Pulborough RH20 2HQ Tel: 01798 872815 Fax: 01798 872123; Highfield, Codmore Hill, Pulborough RH20 1BA Tel: 01798 872710 Fax: 01798 875947 Email: mshillpulb@aol.com — MB BS 1972 Lond.; MRCS Eng. LRCP Lond. 1972. (St. Mary's) Socs: Fell. Roy. Soc. Med.; Fell Amer. Coll. of Phys.; Soc. Gen. Internal Med. Prev: SHO (Gen. Med.) Roy. W. Sussex Hosp. Chichester; Ho. Surg. St. Mary's Hosp. Lond.

SHILLINGLAW, Catherine Lily 39 The Glade, Langley, Southampton SO45 1ZP — BM 1993 Soton. Trainee GP Poole Hosp. VTS.

SHILLINGLAW, David 2 Knoll Croft, Styvechale, Coventry CV3 5BZ Tel: 024 76 62318 — MB ChB 1962 Glas.; DObst RCOG 1965. (Glas.) Prev: SHO (Gyn.) & Res. Surg. Roy. Infirm. Glas.; SHO (Obst.) E.. Dist. Hosp. Glas.

SHILLINGTON, Rosemary Kathleen Alexandra 43 Ballykeel Road, Hillsborough BT26 6NN — MB BCh BAO 1971 Belf.; MB BCh Belf. 1971.

SHILLITO, Michael The Manford Way Health Centre, 40 Foremark Close, Hainault, Ilford IG6 3HS; Norlands, 2 Chigwell Park, Chigwell IG7 5BE — MB BS 1956 Lond.; DObst RCOG 1958. (King's Coll. Hosp.) Clin. Asst. (Genitourin. Med.) Herts & Essex Hosp.

SHILLITO, Paul Christopher Royal Hospital for Sick Children, Glasgow G3 8SJ Tel: 0141 339 8888; 28 Viewpark Drive, Burnside, Glasgow G73 3QD Tel: 0141 647 6268 — MB BChir 1985 Camb.; MRCP (UK) 1988. Sen. Regist. (Paediat. Neurol.) Roy. Hosp. for Sick Childr. Glas. Prev: Research Regist. John Radcliffe Hosp. Oxf.; Regist. (Paediat.) Roy. Childr. Hosp. Brisbane; Regist. (Paediat.) Roy. Hosp. for Sick Childr. Edin.

SHILLITO, Robert Nigel 1 Bryn Githw, Moel Fammau, Llanferres, Mold CH7 5ST — MB ChB 1984 Liverp.; BSc Liverp. 1981, MB ChB 1984.

SHILLITO, Tina Jayne Anne 18 The Valley, Alwoodley, Leeds LS17 7NL Tel: 0113 261 1733; University Department of Obstetrics and Gynaecology, Leeds General Infirmary, Leeds LS2 9NS Tel: 0113 243 2799 Fax: 0113 292 6021 — MB ChB 1988 Leeds; MRCOG 1994. Lect. O & G Leeds Univ. Leeds Gen. Infirm. Prev: Research Regist. St. Jas. Hosp. Leeds.; Regist. York Dist. Hosp. & St. Jas. Hosp. Leeds; SHO (O & G) Huddersfield Roy. Infirm.

SHILLITO, Wendy Elizabeth 1 Bryn Eithin, Moel Fammau Road, Llanferres, Mold CH7 5SJ Tel: 01352 85394 — MB ChB 1984 Liverp.; DObst. 1986.

SHIMI, Mr Sami Mahmoud 7 Buckingham Terrace, Glasgow G12 8EB Tel: 0141 339 0248 — MB ChB 1983 Dundee; BSc (Hons.) Dund 1979, MB ChB 1983; FRCS Glas. 1987. Regist. (Surg.) Stobhill Gen. Hosp. Glas. Prev: Regist. (Vasc. Surg.) Stobhill Gen. Hosp. Glas.; Regist. (Plastic Surg.) Canniesburn Hosp. Glas.; Regist. (Urol.) Stobhill Gen. Hosp. Glas.

SHIMMIN, Constance Margaret (retired) 16 Oakley Wharf, Porthmadog LL49 9AS Tel: 01766 513257 — MB ChB 1948 Manch.

SHIMMIN, Hilary Joyce Bransdale, Creskeld Drive, Bramhope, Leeds LS16 9EJ Tel: 0113 267 2623 — MB BChir 1952 Camb.; DObst RCOG 1954. (Camb. & St. Bart.)

SHIMMINGS, Kenneth Ian (retired) 1 Belmont Crescent, Swindon SN1 4EY Tel: 01793 535619 — MB BS 1954 Lond.; FFA RCS Eng. 1962; DA Eng. 1957; DObst RCOG 1960. Cons. Anaesth. P.ss Margt. Hosp. Swindon. Prev: Sen. Regist. Anaesth. United Cardiff Hosps.

SHIMMINS, Charles John 79 Bournmouth Road, Gourock PA19 1HN — MB ChB 1989 Dundee.

SHIN, Christian Young-Myoung Sheet Street Surgery, 21 Sheet Street, Windsor SL4 1BZ Tel: 01753 860334 Fax: 01753 833696 — MB BChir 1989 Camb.

SHINA, Alfred Gourji Plender Street Surgery, 67 Plender Street, London NW1 0LB Tel: 020 7387 1929 Fax: 020 7387 1929 — MB BS 1979 Lond.; MA Oxf. 1979; MRCS Eng. LRCP Lond. 1978; MRCGP 1982; DRCOG 1981. (Oxf. & Westm.)

SHINDE, Samantha Frenchay Hospital, Frenchay, Bristol BS16 1LE Tel: 0117 970 1212 — MB BS 1989 Lond.; BSc (Hons.) Lond. 1986; FRCA 1994. Cons. Anaesth., Frenchay Hosp. Bristol. Socs: AAGBI; RCA; BMA. Prev: Specialist Regist. (Anaesth.) Univ. Coll. Lond. Hosps.

SHINDLER, Elizabeth 13 Corringway, Ealing, London W5 3AB Tel: 020 8998 3660 — MB BS 1960 Lond.; MB BS (Hnrs.) Lond. 1960; MRCS Eng. LRCP Lond. 1960. (Lond. Hosp.) Socs: Soc. Occupat. Med.; BMA. Prev: Staff Med. Off. Lond. Boro. Ealing; Ho. Phys. & Ho. Surg. Wembley Hosp.

SHINDLER, Jeremy Stephen 501 London Road, Thornton Heath, Croydon CR7 6AR Tel: 020 8684 1172 Fax: 020 8665 5011 — MB BS 1982 Lond.; MRCP (UK) 1986; DFFP 1993; MRCGP 1989. (King's Coll. Hosp.) Prev: SHO & Regist. (Med.) King's Coll. & Dulwich Hosps.

SHINE, Alison Mary Esher Green Surgery, Esher Green Drive, Esher KT10 8BX Tel: 01372 462726; 3 Manor Road S., Esher KT10 0PY Tel: 020 8398 3528 — MB BS 1983 Lond.; MRCGP 1988; DRCOG 1987.

SHINE, Brian Sean Francis Department of Biochemistry, Stoke Mandeville Hospital, Aylesbury HP21 8AL Tel: 01296 315353 Fax: 01926 315595 Email: brian.shine@which.net; 14 Midhurst Avenue, London N10 3EN Tel: 020 8365 2200 — MB ChB 1974 Birm.; MSc Lond. 1992; MD Birm. 1985; FRCPath 1994, M 1982. Cons. Chem Path. Stoke Mandeville Hosp. Aylesbury; Hon. Sen. Lect. (Metab. & Molecular Genetics) St. Bart. Hosp. Lond.; Hon. Cons. Endocrinol. Radcliffe Infirm. Oxf.; Hon. Cons. Chem. Path. Horton Gen. Hosp. Banbury. Socs: Fell. Roy. Soc. Med.; Fell. Roy. Statistical Soc. Prev: Hon. Cons. Moorfields Eye Hosp. Lond.; Sen. Lect. (Chem. Path.) Inst. Ophth. Lond.; Lect. (Chem. Path.) St. Bart. Hosp. Lond.

SHINE, David Francis 34 The Firs, Kenilworth Road, Coventry CV5 6QD Tel: 024 76 73078 — MB ChB 1962 Birm.; MRCP (U.K.) 1972.

SHINE, Ian Basil 35 Bryanston Square, London W1H 2DZ — MD 1966 Camb.; MA Camb. 1963, MB 1958, BChir 1957 (Univ. Coll.; Hosp.).

SHINEBOURNE, Elliot Anthony Royal Brompton Hospital, Sydney St., London SW3 6NP Tel: 020 7351 8541 Fax: 020 7351 8544; 45 Larkhall Rise, London SW4 6HT Tel: 020 7498 9878 — MB BS (Hons.) Lond. 1963; MD Lond. 1970; FRCP 1979, M 1965; MRCS Eng. LRCP Lond. 1963; FRCPCH 1997. (St. Bart.) Cons. Paediat. (Cardiol.) Roy. Brompton Hosp.; Sen. Lect. Nat. Heart & Lung Inst. Socs: Brit. Cardiac Soc.; Brit. Paediat. Assn.; Assn. of Europ. Cardiol.s. Prev: MRC Clin. Research Fell. Inst. Cardiol. Nat. Heart Hosp. Lond.; Brit. Heart Foundat./Amer. Heart Assn. Trav. Fell. (Cardiovasc.) Univ. Coll. San Fransisco, USA; Ho. Phys. St. Bart. Hosp. Lond.

SHINER, Robert Joseph Department of Clinical Respiratory Physiology, Chaim Sheba Medical Center, Tel-Hashomer Hospital 52621, Israel Email: r.shiner@ic.ac.uk; Fax: 0207 435 8812 Email: r.shiner@ic.ac.uk — MRCS Eng. LRCP Lond. 1974; FRCPC 1982. (Middlesex) Cons. Phys. (Clin. Respirat. Physiol.) Chaim Sheba Med. Centre Tel-Hashomer, Israel; Lect. (Med.) Tel-Aviv Univ. Med. Sch.; Hon. Sen. Lect./Cons. Imperial Coll. Sch. Of Med. Dept. Of Respir. Med. Hammersmith Campus Du Cane Rd. Lond. W12 0NN. Socs: Eur. Respirat. Soc.; Brit. Thorac. Soc. & Amer. Thorac. Soc. Prev: Staff Specialist (Respirat. Dis.) Tel-Hashomer Hosp. Israel; Resid.

Respirat. Dis. McGill Univ., Montreal, Canada; Vis. Cons. Brompton Hosp. Lond.

SHINGADIA, Delane Vanraj Academic Child Health, Royal London Hospital, Whitechapel, London EC1 1BB Tel: 020 7377 7000 Ext: 3368 Fax: 020 7377 7091 Email: d.v.shingadia@mds.qmw.ac.uk; Tel: 020 7372 5275 — MB ChB 1987 Zimbabwe; MSc 2000 (Public Health) Univ. of Lond.; FRCPCH 2001; MRCP (UK) 1992; DTM & H RCP Lond. 1995. Sen. Lect in Paediat. Infec.s Dis., St Barts & Roy. Lond. Med. & Dent. Sch.; Hon. Cons. At Barts & The Lond. NHS Trust, Gt. Ormond St. Hosp. NHS Trust. Socs: Brit. Paediat. Assn.; RCPCh.; BMA. Prev: Regist. (Paediat.) St. Geo. Hosp. Lond., St. Helier Hosp. Carshalton & St. Peter's Hosp. Chertsey; SHO (Paediat.) Baragwanath Hosp., S. Afr.; Sen. Regist. Gt. Ormond St. Hosp. Lond.

SHINH, Naval 7 Churchfield, Cringleford, Norwich NR4 6UP — LMSSA 1991 Lond.

SHINKFIELD, Mr Mark Noel Forsyth Department of General Surgery, St. Mary's Hospital, Newport PO30 5TG — MB BS 1982 Lond.; BSc (Hons.) Lond. 1979; FRCS Eng. 1986. (Roy. Free) Cons. Gen. Surg. St. Mary's Hosp. Newport. I. of Wight. Socs: Brit. Assn. Surgic. Oncol.; Assn. Surg.; BMA.

SHINKWIN, Mr Charles Antony 19 Balcaskie Close, Edgbaston, Birmingham B15 3UE — MB BCh BAO 1984 NUI; FRCS Eng. 1992; FRCSI 1989.

SHINKWIN, Katherine Rosemary Brandon Mental Health Unit, Leicester General Hospital, Gwendolen Road, Leicester LE5 4PW — MB BCh BAO 1982 NUI; MRCPsych 1989. cons. Psychiat.

SHINKWIN, Mary Patricia 39 Severn Road, Porthcawl CF36 3LN — MB BCh 1979 Wales.

SHINN, Christopher Philip West Yorkshire Police, PO Box 9, Wakefield WF1 3QP Tel: 01924 292727; Lily Green Farm, Greenhow Hill, Harrogate HG3 5JL — MB ChB 1975 Leeds; BSc (Pharmacol.) Leeds 1973. Force Med. Off. W. Yorks. Police.; Hon Sen. Clin. Lect. Leeds Univ. Med. Sch.

SHINNAWI, Ahmed Kamal 45 Montagu Court, Gosforth, Newcastle upon Tyne NE3 4JL — LMSSA 1966 Lond.; MRCP Glas. 1966.

SHINNER, Guy Anaesphetic Dept, Royal Orthopaedic Hospital, Bristol Road South, Northfield, Birmingham B31 2AP — MB BS 1990 Lond.; MB BS (Hons) Lond. 1990; FRCA. Cons. (Anagith) Roy Orthop. Hosp Birm.

SHINTON, Margaret (retired) 22 Winterbourne Road, Solihull B91 1LU Tel: 0121 705 0732 — MB ChB Leeds 1950. Prev: Clin. Asst. (Med.) Coventry & Warwick Hosp.

SHINTON, Professor Neville Keith 22 Winterbourne Road, Solihull B91 1LU Tel: 0121 705 0732 — MB ChB 1947 Birm.; MD Birm. 1961; FRCP Lond. 1972, M 1952; MRCS Eng. LRCP Lond. 1948; FRCPath 1970, M 1963. (Birm.) p/t Convener, Internat. Standards Organisation (ISO) In Vitro Med. devices. Socs: (Ex-Pres.) Brit. Soc. Haematol.; (Ex-Pres.) Assn. Clin. Path. Prev: Dir. & Prof. Sch. Postgrad. Med. Educat. Univ. Warwick; Cons. Path & Haemat. Coventry Hosps.

SHINTON, Roger Anthony Department of Medicine for the Elderly, Birmingham Heartlands Hospital, Birmingham B9 5SS Tel: 0121 424 3768 Fax: 0121 753 0653 Email: r.shinton@bham.ac.uk — MB BChir 1980 Camb.; MSc Lond. 1988; MD Camb. 1992, MA 1980; FRCP 1999. (King's Coll. Hosp.) Cons. Phys. (Med. for the Elderly) Birm. Heartlands Hosp. & Hon. Sen. Lect. Univ. Birm. Socs: Brit. Geriat. Soc. (Sec W. Midl.s Br. 1998-1999); BMA (Sec. Solihull Div. 1994-97); Brit. Assn. of Stroke Phys.s. Prev: Hon. Sen. Regist. (Med.) Dudley Rd. Hosp. Birm.; SHO Rotat. (Med.) E. Birm. Hosp.; Ho. Phys. Kings Coll. Hosp. Lond.

SHINWELL, Eric Stuart c/o L. Shinwell, 63 Edgemont St., Glasgow G41 3EJ — MRCS Eng. LRCP Lond. 1978.

SHIP, Rebecca Harriet Eisner, Goldman and Ship, Shipley Health Centre, Alexandra Road, Shipley BD18 3EG Tel: 01274 589153 Fax: 01274 770882 — BM 1985 Soton.; BA Bristol 1972. Prev: Ho. Off. (Surg.) Dorset Co. Hosp. Dorchester; Ho. Off. (Med.) Newmarket Gen. Hosp.

SHIPLEY, Michael Edward (cons. rooms), University College London Hospitals, 25 Grafton Way, London WC1E 6DD Tel: 020 7380 9851 Fax: 020 7380 9816; 65 Friary Road, London SE15 1QS — MB BChir 1973 Camb.; MA Camb. 1974, MD 1983; FRCP Lond. 1988; MRCP (UK) 1976. (King's Coll. Hosp.) Cons. Rheum. Univ.

SHIPLEY-ROWE

Coll. Lond. Hosps.; Cons. Rheum. King Edwd. VII Hosp. Lond.; Hon. Sen. Clin. Lect. UCL. Socs: Fell. Roy. Soc. Med.; Brit. Soc. Rheum.; Soc. Clin. Française de Lond. Prev: Sen. Regist. (Rheum.) King's Coll. Hosp. Lond.; Regist. (Med.) S.mead Hosp. Bristol; SHO Roy. Nat. Hosp. Rheum. Dis. Bath.

SHIPLEY-ROWE, Ann Patricia Fernville Surgery, Midland Road, Hemel Hempstead HP2 5BL Tel: 01442 213919 Fax: 01442 216433; Avalon, 35 Grange Road, Bushey, Watford WD23 2LQ Tel: 01923 229288 — MB ChB 1984 Manch. (Manch.)

SHIPMAN, Anthony John 16 The Hollies, Shefford SG17 5BX Email: a-johnshipman@compuserve.com — MRCS Eng. LRCP Lond. 1978; MFPM RCP (UK) 1990. Project Ldr. Bone Densitometry Research Gp. Nuffield Orthop. Centre Oxf. Socs: Fac. Pharmaceut. Med. Prev: Med. Dir. Pharmaco UK Ltd. Lond.; Med. & Managing Dir. J. S. Clin. Research; Head Med. Dept. Roche Products Ltd. Welwyn Gdn. City.

SHIPMAN, James Andrew Jonathan 12 Wetmore Road, Burton-on-Trent DE14 1SL Tel: 01283 564848 Fax: 01283 569416 Email: jajs@doctors.org.uk — MB ChB 1989 Leeds; DFFP RCOG Lond. 1994; Dip Occ Med Lond. 1998; MRCGP 1993; DGM RCP Lond. 1993; T(GP) 1993. GP; GP Trainer (2 sessions); Company Doctor (1 session); Pharmaceutical Lead GP for PCG (1/2 Session). Socs: Soc. of Occupat.al Med. Prev: SHO (Paediat.) Leeds Gen. Infirm.; SHO (Cas.) Bradford Roy. Infirm.; Ho. Off. (Gen. Surg.) Chapel Allerton Hosp. Leeds.

SHIPMAN, Paul Adrian Marc Hawkesley Health Centre, 375 Shannon Road, Kings Norton, Birmingham B38 9TJ Tel: 0121 486 4200 Fax: 0121 486 4201 — MB ChB 1977 Birm.; BSc Birm. 1974, MB ChB 1977; MRCGP 1981; DRCOG 1980.

SHIPOLINI, Alex Rudolf 25 Grange Avenue, London SE25 6DW — MB BS 1985 Lond.

SHIPP, Phillida Ann 6 Dale Lane, Delph, Oldham OL3 5HY Tel: 01457 875171; Crickets Lane Clinic, Ashton-under-Lyne OL6 6NG Tel: 0161 339 9400 Fax: 0161 339 8409 — BM BCh Oxf. 1967; MA Oxf. 1967. (Oxf. & Westm.) SCMO (sexual health) Tameside & Glossop Community & Priority Trust; Curr. Asst., gum clinic, Tameside Gen. Prev: Clin. Med. Off. (Child Health) Tameside & Glossop HA; Clin. Asst. (Family Plann.) Roy. Oldham Hosp.; Sen. Clin. Med. Off. (Child Health), Tameside & Glossop Community & Priority Serv.s NHS Trust

SHIPPEY, Benjamin John Mudcroft Farm, Newton in the Isle, Wisbech PE13 5HF — BM BS 1995 Nottm. SHO (Gen. Med.) N.ampton Gen. Hosp. Prev: Ho. Off. (Surg.) Qu. Med. Centre Nottm.; Ho. Off. (Gen. Med.) N.ampton Gen. Hosp.

SHIPSEY, Catherine Mary 4 Parklands Road, Chichester PO19 3DT — MB BS 1981 Lond.; DRCOG 1986.

SHIPSEY, Dean 120 Grosvenor Road, Newcastle upon Tyne NE2 2RQ — MB ChB 1993 Ed. SHO (Orthop.) N. Tyneside Gen. Hosp. N. Shields. Prev: SHO (Cardiothoracic Surg.) Roy. Infirm. Edin.; SHO (A & E) Hull Roy. Infirm.; SHO (Gen. Surg.) E.. Gen. Hosp. Edin.

SHIPSEY, Edward Mervyn (retired) 3 Manor Way, Beckenham BR3 3LH — MB BS 1950 Lond.; FRCGP 1977, M 1960. Hosp. Pract. (Orthop.) Bromley AHA. Prev: Ho. Surg. Radcliffe Infirm. Oxf. & Ch.ill Hosp. Oxf.

SHIPSEY, Margaret Mary (retired) Fairview Cottage, Ham Manor Way, Angmering, Littlehampton BN16 4JQ Tel: 01903 776015 — MB BCh BAO 1953 NUI; DCH Eng. 1955.

SHIPSEY, Mary Josephine 3 Manor Way, Beckenham BR3 3LH — MB BCh BAO 1952 NUI. Prev: Ho. Phys. Mater Miser. Hosp. Dub.; Ho. Off. St. Kevin's Hosp. Dub.; Paediat. Ho. Phys. Whipps Cross Hosp. Lond.

SHIPSEY, Maurice Mary Anthony (retired) Fairview Cottage, Ham Manor Way, Angmering, Littlehampton BN16 4JQ Tel: 01903 776015 — MB BCh BAO 1953 NUI. Prev: Capt. RAMC. Jun. Surg. Specialist.

SHIPSEY, Mr Maurice Richard Lime Tree Surgery, Lime Tree Avenue, Findon Valley, Worthing BN14 0DL Tel: 01903 264101 Fax: 01903 695494 — MB BCh BAO 1981 Dub.; FRCS Ed. 1985; MRCGP 1988; DRCOG 1988. (TC Dub.) Prev: Resid. Med. Off. King Edwd. VII Hosp. for Offs. W.m.

SHIPSEY, Sarah Jane Russell's Hall Hospital, Dudley DY1 2HQ Tel: 01384 456111; 28 Bond Street, Stirchley, Birmingham B30 2LA Tel: 0121 458 4481 — BM BCh 1988 Oxf.; MRCP (UK) 1991. Regist. (Cardiol.) Russell's Hall Hosp. Dudley. Prev: Regist. (Cardiol.) Qu. Eliz. Hosp. Birm.; Regist. (Gen. Med.) Salisbury Infirm.; Ho. Off. (Gen. Med.) John Radcliffe Hosp. Oxf.

SHIPSTON, Alison Mary 28 Wellington Road, Timperley, Altrincham WA15 7RE — MB ChB 1988 Manch.; MRCGP 1992; DRCOG 1991.

SHIPSTON, James Edward 28 Wellington Road, Timperley, Altrincham WA15 7RE — MB ChB 1988 Manch.; MRCGP 1992; DRCOG 1991.

SHIPSTONE, A V Tel: 01925 244655 Fax: 01925 262701 Email: shipstonev@aol.com; 14 Waterbridge Court, Appleton, Warrington WA4 3BJ Tel: 01925 601640 Fax: 01925 262701 Email: shipstonev@yahoo.com — MB BS 1969 Rajasthan. (SMS Medical College, Jaipur, Rajasthan, India) p/t Gen. Pract., Clin. Asst., M.I. Unit, Halton Gen. Hosp., Runcorn WA7 2DA. Socs: D.F.F.P. (Family & Reproductive Diplomate Med.). Prev: Clin. Med. Off.

SHIPSTONE, Mr David Peter Alder Cottage, 19 Myddlewood, Myddle, Shrewsbury — MB ChB 1988 Aberd.; FRCS Eng. 1994. SHO Rotat. (Surg.) N. Staffs. HA.; Specialist Regist. (Urol.) Sheff. Prev: Research Regist. (Urol.) Roy. Shrewsbury Hosp.; SHO (A & E) Leics. Demonst. (Anat.) Univ. Leics.

SHIPTON, Beryl Maude (retired) Virginia House, Shipton Gorge, Bridport DT6 4LL Tel: 01308 897391 — MB ChB 1953 Bristol; DObst RCOG 1956. Prev: Clin. Off. Surrey AHA.

SHIPTON, Peter Francis Croft Medical Centre, Calder Walk, Leamington Spa CV31 1SA Tel: 01926 421153 Fax: 01926 832343 — MB BS 1978 Lond.; MRCGP 1985; DRCOG 1981.

SHIRALKAR, V M Twickenham Drive Surgery, 63 Twickenham Drive, Leasowe, Wirral CH46 2QA Tel: 0151 677 8882 Fax: 0151 604 0122.

SHIRAZ, Mahfel The Surgery, 80 Bickersteth Road, London SW17 9SJ Tel: 020 8682 0521 Fax: 020 8672 6532; 62 Woodcote Avenue, Wallington SM6 0QY Tel: 020 8669 6845 — MB BS 1975 Dacca; MRCP (UK) 1985; DTM & H Liverp. 1984. Socs: Med. Protec. Soc.

SHIRAZI, Hussein Assadallah The Surgery, Riversley Road, Nuneaton CV11 5HN; The Surgery, 123 Pallett Drive, St. Nicolas Park, Nuneaton CV11 6JT — MB ChB 1958 Cairo; LMSSA Lond. 1968.

SHIRAZI, Jane Elizabeth Hillcroft, Buckingham Road, Brackley NN13 7EL Tel: 01280 704340 — MB BS 1986 Lond.; MA Oxf. 1984. (St. Bart.)

SHIRAZI, Tarek Everglades, Shore Road, Wemyss Bay PA18 6AR — MB BS 1989 Lond.

SHIRBHATE, Naresh Champatrao 20 North Lodge, Chester-le-Street DH3 4AZ — MB BS 1974 Nagpur; FFR RCSI 1982.

SHIRE, Catherine Mary Elizabeth The Grange Medical Centre, Dacre Banks, Harrogate HG3 4DX Tel: 01423 780497; Dacre Hall, Dacre, Harrogate HG3 4ET Tel: 01423 780497 — MB BS 1982 Newc.; MRCGP 1986; DRCOG 1986. Socs: BMA. Prev: GP Stocksfield, N.ld.; SHO (Community Paeidat.) N.d.; Trainee GP N.allerton VTS.

SHIRE, Heinz (retired) 22 Fugelmere Close, Birmingham B17 8SE Tel: 0121 429 3310 — MB BCh BAO 1942 Dub.; MRCGP 1953; DCH RCPSI 1945. Prev: Chairm. Dist. Med. Comm. & GP Mem. Dist. Managem. Team W. Birm. HA.

SHIREHAMPTON, Teresa Ann High Street Surgery, High Street, Pewsey SN9 5AQ Tel: 01672 563511 Fax: 01672 563004 — MB BS 1973 Lond. (St. Bart.)

SHIRES, Kirsty Michelle 23 Lynwood Close, Willenhall WV12 5BW — MB ChB 1998 Leeds.

SHIRES, Mr Peter Rodney (retired) Peerie Hame, Guildown, Guildford GU2 4EY Tel: 01483 504378 — MB BChir 1954 Camb.; MA Camb. 1955; FRCS Eng. 1959. Prev: Cons. Orthop. Surg. S.W. Surrey HA.

SHIRES, Susan Elizabeth Elms Farm, Wimbish, Saffron Walden CB10 2PP — MB BS 1986 Lond.; MRCGP 1991; DPH Camb. 1995; DCH RCP Lond. 1989; DRCOG 1988. Prev: Trainee GP OldCh. Hosp. Romford VTS.

SHIRLAW, Herbert Anthony Douglas (retired) 13 Well Cross Road, Up Holland, Skelmersdale WN8 0NU Tel: 01695 622745 — MB ChB Liverp. 1950; DObst RCOG 1954. Prev: Ho. Off. (O & G) Billinge Hosp. Wigan.

SHIRLAW, Norman Alan 12 Crowland House, Springfield Road, London NW8 0QU Tel: 020 7624 3917 — LRCPI & LM, LRSCI & LM 1966; LRCPI & LM, LRCSI & LM 1966; DObst RCOG 1968. (Guy's & RCSI) Prev: SHO (Psychol. Med.) Roy. Free Hosp. Lond.; Ho. Surg. Roy. Sussex Co. Hosp. Brighton; Ho. Phys. S.lands Hosp. Shoreham-by-Sea.

SHIRLEY, Anthony David (retired) c/o Mrs M. S. Thomas, Ardmore, Wellhouse Lane, Headbourne Worthy, Winchester SO23 7JY Tel: 01962 881121 — MB BS Sydney 1941; DCH Eng. 1948.

SHIRLEY, Denise Susanna Lilian 29 Cladymore Road, Mowhan, Armagh BT60 2EW — MB BCh BAO 1995 Belf.

SHIRLEY, Isabel Mary Department of Clinical Radiology, The Hillingdon Hospital, Pield Heath Road, Uxbridge UB8 3NN Tel: 01895 279866 Fax: 01895 279865 Email: diz.shirley@thh.nhs.uk; 6 Waldron Road, Harrow HA2 0HU Tel: 020 8422 6381 Email: diz@farman.com — MB ChB 1969 Glas.; FRCR 1984; DMRD Eng. 1982; DObst RCOG 1971. (Glasgow) Cons. Radiol. Hillingdon Hosp. Middlx.; Clin. Dir. (Radiol.) Hillingdon Hosp.; Div.al Director (Clin. Support), Hillington Hosp.; Caldicot Guardian, Hillingdon Hosp. Socs: Fell. Roy. Soc. Med.; Brit. Med. Ultrasound Soc.; BMA. Prev: Sen. Regist. & Regist. (Radiol.) & Clin. Asst. (Ultrasound) Univ. Coll. Hosp. Lond.

SHIRLEY, Janet Ann The Royal Surrey County Hospital NHS Trust, Egerton Road, Guildford GU2 7XX Tel: 01483 464122 Fax: 01483 464072 Email: jashirley@rsch.nhs.uk; Everley Cottage, Wych Hill Lane, Woking GU22 0AH Tel: 01483 766423 Fax: 01483 766423 Email: shirleyjanet@hotmail.com — MB BS 1971 Lond.; FRCPath 1990, M 1978; Dip. Hlth. Mgt. Keele 1995; DCH Eng. 1974. (Roy. Free) p/t Cons. Haematologist, Roy. Surrey Co. Hosp., Guildford, Assoc. Med. Director, Roy. Surrey Co. Hosp., Guildford. Socs: Brit. Soc. Haematol.; BMA; (Bd.) Brit. Assn. Med. Managers. Prev: Cons. Haematologist & Med. Dir. King dwd. VII Hosp.; Cons. Haemat. & Clin. Dir. (Path.) Frimley Pk. Hosp. NHS Trust; Sen. Regist. (Haemat.) St. Thos. Hosp. Lond.

SHIRLEY, John Craig Nevis Surgery, Belford Road, Fort William PH33 6BU Tel: 01397 702947 Fax: 01397 700655 — MB ChB 1977 Sheff.; MRCGP 1984. GP Fort William.

SHIRLEY, Malcolm (retired) 39 Bells Hill, Mylor Bridge, Falmouth TR11 5SH Tel: 01326 372784 — MA 1947, MB BChir Camb. 1946. Prev: GP Devon.

SHIRLEY, Peter Jeffrey 1 Milton Cottage, Hatton of Fintray, Dyce, Aberdeen AB21 0YL Tel: 01224 790040 — MB ChB 1991 Birm.; FRCA 1996; Dip. IMC RCS Ed. 1997; DA (UK) 1994. (Birm.) Regist. (Anaesth.) Aberd. Roy. Infirm.; Hon. Clin. Lect. Univ. of Aberd. Socs: Assn. Anaesth.; Full Mem. Fac. Pre-Hosp. Care RCSEd.; Fell. Roy. Soc. Med. Prev: SHO (Anaesth.) Aberd. Roy. Infirm.; SHO (A & E) Trauma Centre Stoke-on-Trent; SHO Balfour Hosp. Kirkwall.

SHIRLEY, Robert Alan Bluebell Medical Centre, 356 Bluebell Road, Sheffield S5 6BS Tel: 0114 242 1406 Fax: 0114 261 8074; 23 Stainton Road, Sheffield S11 7AX Tel: 0114 268 7588 — MB ChB 1986 Bristol; MRCGP 1992; DRCOG 1991; DCH RCP Lond. 1989; DGM RCP Lond. 1988.

SHIRLEY-QUIRK, Kathryn Jane The Mill House, Pangbourne, Reading RG8 7BB — MB BS 1985 Lond.; MRCGP 1989; DCH RCP Lond. 1987. GP Reading. Prev: GP Goring.

SHIRODARIA, Champak Vithaldas Longfield Medical Centre, Princes Road, Maldon CM9 5DF Tel: 01621 856811 Fax: 01621 852627 — MB BS 1961 Bombay; DCH Eng. 1965. (Topiwalla Nat. Med. Coll.) Prev: Regist. (Paediat.) Profess. Unit Leeds Gen. Infirm.; Regist. (Paediat. & Med.) P.ss Alexandra Hosp. Harlow.

SHIRODARIA, Cheerag Champak Queens Crawley, Beacon Hill, Wickham Bishops, Witham CM8 3EA — MB BS 1998 Lond.; MB BS Lond 1998.

SHIRREFFS, Eva Cecile Gordon (retired) Little Mount, 2 Wright's Close, Quorn, Loughborough LE12 8TU Tel: 01509 414676 — MB ChB Aberd. 1945. Hosp. Pract. (Dermat.) Leicester Roy. Infirm. Prev: Clin. Asst. (Skin) Leicester Roy. Infirm.

SHIRREFFS, Gordon Chisholm Jubilee Hospital, Huntly AB54 8EX Tel: 01466 792116; 2 Glamourhaugh Avenue, Huntly AB54 8AS Tel: 01466 2357 — MB ChB 1957 Aberd.; DA Eng. 1962. (Aberd.) Prev: Sen. Ho. Off. & Ho. Surg. & Ho. Phys. Aberd. Roy. Infirm.

SHIRREFFS, Murdoch John Gilbert Road Medical Group, 39 Gilbert Road, Bucksburn, Aberdeen AB21 9AN Tel: 01224 712138 Fax: 01224 712239; 72 Gray Street, Aberdeen AB10 6JE Tel: 01224 321998 Fax: 01224 315615 Email: murdock_and_jenny_shirreffs@msn.com — MB ChB 1970 Aberd.; Homeopathic Specialist 2000; MF HoM 1996; FRCGP 1992, M 1974; DObst RCOG 1973. (Aberd.) GP Med. Homoeopath. & Hypnother. Aberd.; Specianst i/c of NHS Grampian Homepathy Serv. Socs: Hon. Sec. Grampian Div.; Brit. Soc. Med. & Dent. Hypn. Prev: Trainee GP Aberd. VTS; Ho. Off. Aberd. Roy. Infirm.

SHIRRIFFS, George Geddes 19 Richmondhill Place, Aberdeen, Aberdeen AB15 5EN Tel: 01224 311044 Fax: 01224 627159 Email: george@shirriffj.fsnet.co.uk; 19 Richmondhill Place, Aberdeen AB15 5EN — MB ChB 1963 Aberd.; MEd Aberd. 1989; FRCGP 1982, M 1974. (Aberd.) Clin. Sen. Lect. (Gen. Pract.) Univ. Aberd.; Nat. Co-ord. Higher Prof. Fell. Prev: Research Fell. (Pharmacol. & Therap.) Univ. Aberd.

SHIRSALKAR, Anand Madusudhan 231 Prince Regent Lane, Plaistow, London E13 8SD — MB BS 1988 Osmania.

SHIRT, Dominic John Walter Sloan Practice, 251 Chesterfield Road, Sheffield S8 0RT Tel: 0114 255 1164 Fax: 0114 258 9006 — MB BS 1992 Newc.

SHIRTCLIFFE, Philippa Margaret 11 Etterby Lea Road, Carlisle CA3 9JW — MB ChB 1991 Otago.

SHIU, Kin Yee 11 Elizabeth Mews, London NW3 4TL — MB BS 1997 Lond.

SHIU, Man Fai Cardiology Department, Walsgrave Hospital, Coventry CV2 2DX Tel: 024 76 538930 Fax: 024 76 538829 Email: shiu@wh.ti.demon.co.uk — MD 1979 Lond.; MB BS 1970; FRCP Lond. 1986; MRCP (UK) 1972. Cons. Cardiol. Walsgrave Hosp. Coventry. Socs: PastChairm. Mem. Brit. Cardiol. Vasc. Interven. Soc.; Brit. Cardiac Soc. (Ex-Counc. Mem.). Prev: Sen. Lect. (Cardiol.) Qu. Eliz. Hosp. Birm.; Sen. Regist. (Paediat. Cardiol.) Birm. Childr. Hosp.; Regist. (Cardiac) St. Thos. Hosp. Lond.

SHIV SHANKER, Mr Vaidyanathan 8 Transom Close, London SE16 7FH — MB BS 1986 Madras; FRCS Ed. 1992.

SHIVA, Fatemeh Golnar 47 Dittisham Road, London SE9 Tel: 020 8851 1303 — MB BS 1968 Lond.; MRCS Eng. LRCP Lond. 1968; DObst RCOG 1970. (Roy. Free)

SHIVANATHAN, Sivasubramaniam 62 South Hill Road, Bromley BR2 0RT Tel: 020 8460 8461 — MB BS 1953 Ceylon; DPM Eng. 1974; DCH Eng. 1966; DPH Lond. 1963; DTM & H Ceylon 1956. Cons. Psychiat. (Ment. Handicap) Lifecare NHS Trust Caterham. Prev: Cons. Psychiat. (Ment. Handicap & Child Developm.) Qu. Marys Hosp. Childr. Carshalton & St. Ebbas Hosp. Epsom; Sen. Regist. (Psychiat.) Qu. Mary's Hosp. Childr. Carshalton; Regist. (Child Psychiat. & Ment. Handicap) Qu. Marys Hosp. Childr. & Child Guid. Clin. Croydon.

SHIVAYOGI, Mahantinamath 51 Wellington Road, Sandhurst, Sandhurst GU47 9AW — MB BS 1972 Mysore; MSc (Neurosci.) Lond. 1993. (Mysore Med. Coll.) Assoc. Specialist BRd.moor Hosp. Berks.

SHLOSBERG, Charles Benjamin Charlotte Keel Health Centre, Seymour Road, Easton, Bristol Tel: 0117 951 2244 — MB BS 1978 Lond.; BA Oxf. 1975; MRCP (UK) 1982; DRCOG 1987; DCH RCP Lond. 1993.

SHLOSBERG, David St Bees Surgery, 34-36 St. Bees Close, Moss Side, Manchester M14 4GG Tel: 0161 226 7615 Fax: 0161 226 0413 — MA Camb.; MRCS Eng. LRCP Lond. 1960; MRCGP 1996. Occupat. Health Phys. Hope Hosp.; Lect. (Gen. Pract.) Univ. Manch.

SHLUGMAN, David Nuffield Department of Anaesthetics, Radcliffe Infirmary, Oxford OX2 6HE Tel: 01865 311188 Email: david.shlugman@nda.ox.ac.uk; 4 Bullsmead, Sunningwell, Abingdon OX13 6RL Tel: 01865 326150 Fax: 01865 736813 — MB ChB 1974 Cape Town; FRCA 1981. Cons. Anaesth. Radcliffe Infirm. Oxf. Socs: BMA; Neuroinaesth. Soc.; Assoc. of Anaesth. GB & Irel.

SHMUELI, Ehoud Integrated Surgical Centre, Northampton General Hospital, Northampton NN1 5BD Tel: 01604 545937; 3 Penfold Drive, Breat Billing, Northampton NN3 9EQ Tel: 01604 469961 Fax: 01604 469960 — MB ChB Bristol 1984; MD Newc. 1993; MRCP (UK) 1987; MD 1993 Newc. Cons. Phys. & Gastroenterol., N.ampton Gen., N.ampton. Prev: Hon. Sen. Regist.; John Radcliffe Hosp., Oxf.; MRC Research Train. Fell.

SHNEERSON, Anne The Burwell Surgery, Newmarket Road, Burwell, Cambridge CB5 0AE Tel: 01638 741234 Fax: 01638 743948; 129 North Street, Burwell, Cambridge CB5 0BB Tel: 01638

SHNEERSON

741393 — MB BS 1971 Lond.; MRCP (UK) 1974; MRCGP 1976. (St. Thomas') Prev: SHO (Neurol.) St. Thos. Hosp. Lond.; SHO Brompton Hosp. Lond. & St. Mary's Hosp. Portsmouth.

SHNEERSON, Gregory (retired) 18A Fairfield Road, Petts Wood, Orpington BR5 1JR Tel: 01689 838854 — MRCS Eng. LRCP Lond. 1937; MD Lond. 1948, MB BS 1938; FRCP Lond. 1973, M 1947. Prev: Cons. Phys. Roy. Free Hosp. Lond.

SHNEERSON, John Michael Papworth Hospital, Papworth Everard, Cambridge CB3 8RE Tel: 01480 830541 Fax: 01480 830620; 129 North Street, Burwell, Cambridge CB5 0BB Fax: 01638 610164 — BM BCh 1971 Oxf.; MA, DM Oxf. 1977; MD Camb. 1987; FRCP Lond. 1986; MRCP (UK) 1973. (Oxf.Univ./St Mary's Lond) Cons. Phys. Papworth, W. Suff & Newmarket Hosps.; Dir. Respirat. Support & Sleep Centre, Papworth Hosp.; Assoc. Lect. Univ. Camb. Socs: Brit. Scoliosis Res. Found.; Fell. Amer. Coll. Chest Phys.; Brit. Sleep Soc. - Comm. Mem. Prev: Sen. Regist. W.m. Hosp. & Brompton Hosp. Lond.; Regist. (Med.) Whipps Cross Hosp. Lond.; SHO (Neurol.) St. Mary's Hosp. Lond.

SHNIER, Darryl Department of Nuclear Medicine, Charing Cross Hospital, Fulham Palace Road, London W6 8RF — MB BS 1985 Melbourne.

SHNYIEN, Naif Kadem 2 Redlodge, Park View Road, Ealing, London W5 2JB Tel: 020 8998 8033 — MB ChB 1965 Mosul.

SHOAIB, Asim 297 Park Road, Oldham OL4 1SF — MB ChB 1995 Manch.

SHOAIB, Taimur 7C Hughenden Gardens, Hyndland, Glasgow G12 9XW Email: taimur@compuserve.com; 7C Hughenden Gardens, Hyndland, Glasgow G12 9XW — MB ChB 1992 Glas.; FRCS Ed. 1997. Research Fell. (Plastic Surg.).

SHOAIBI, Asfia Taskeen 33 Melford Road, London E17 7EN — MB BS 1998 Lond.; MB BS Lond 1998.

SHOBAN, Bandi Krishnarao Lincoln Road Surgery, 435 Lincoln Road, Peterborough PE1 2PE Tel: 01733 551771/551789 Fax: 01733 559123; 28 Magnolia Avenue, Longthorpe, Peterborough PE3 9QT — MB BS 1980 Dibrugarh; LRCP LRCS Ed. LRCPS Glas. 1985.

SHOBOWALE, Folasade Oluyemisi Sherard Road Medical Centre, 71 Sherard Road, Eltham, London SE9 6ER Tel: 020 8850 2120 Fax: 020 8850 1220 — MB ChB 1987 Nigeria; LRCP LRCS Ed. LRCPS Glas. 1994.

SHOEB, Ismail Hani Abdel-Hakim Department of Psychiatry, Royal Surrey County Hospital, Egerton Road, Guildford GU2 7XX Tel: 01483 443660 Fax: 01483 799445 — MB ChB 1974 Ain Shams; MRCPsych 1984. Cons. Psychiat. Roy. Surrey Co. Hosp. Guildford. Prev: Cons. Psychiat. Lister Hosp. Stevenage; Clin. Lect. (Psychiat.) Univ. Coll. & Middlx. Sch. Med. Lond.; Cons. Psychiat. Abha Psychiat. Hosp., Saudi Arabia.

SHOEBRIDGE, Philip John The McGuinness Unit, Prestwich Hospital, Bury New Road, Manchester M25 3BL Tel: 0161 773 9121 — BSc Lond. 1985, MB BS 1988; MRCPsych 1994; DCH RCP Lond. 1991. Sen. Regist. (Child & Adolesc. Psychiat.) Gardner Unit Regional Adolesc. Forens. Ment. Health Serv. Manch. Prev: Regist. (Gen. Psychiat.) Manch. Roy. Infirm.

SHOENBERG, Elisabeth (retired) 22 Stanley Crescent, London W11 2NA Tel: 020 7727 0454 — MRCS Eng. LRCP Lond. 1947; MA Camb.; FRCPsych 1973, M 1971; DPM Eng. 1953. Prev: Cons. Psychiat. Claybury Hosp. Woodford Bridge & Lond. Sch. Hyg. & Trop. Med. MRC Social Med. Unit.

SHOENBERG, Peter Jacques Flat E, 30 Pembridge Villas, London W11 3EL; Flat E, 30 Pembridge Villas, London W11 3EL — MA Camb. 1970; BChir 1969; MRCP (UK) 1972; MRCPsych 1975; FRCPsych 1998. (Univ. Camb. & Middlx. Hosp.) Cons. Psychother. Univ. Coll. Hosp. Trust (for Camden & Islington Ment. Health Servs. NHS Trust); Hon. Sen. Clin. Lect. The Roy. Free and Univ. Coll. Sch. of Med. Socs: Brit. Assn. Psychother.; St. Marks Assn. Prev: Cons. Psychother. Claybury Hosp. Woodford Bridge, Essex.

SHOESMITH, David John The Surgery, Station Road, Clayton, Bradford BD14 6JA Tel: 01274 880650 Fax: 01274 883256; 11 Beechwood Grove, Moorhead, Shipley BD18 4JS Tel: 01274 591984 — MB BS 1976 Lond.; MRCGP 1983. (St. Bart.) GP; Med. Off. Civil Serv.; GP Represen. Bradford Community Trust Corporate Policy Gp.

SHOESMITH, Mr John Harrop 21 Sandhill Lane, Leeds LS17 6AJ Tel: 0113 688186 — MB ChB 1948 Leeds; MB ChB (Hnrs.) Leeds 1948; FRCS Eng. 1952. (Leeds) Gen. Surg. Gen. Infirm. Leeds &

Cons. Surg. Chapel Allerton Hosp. Leeds. Socs: Vasc. Soc. Gt. Brit. & Irel. & Assn. Surgs. Prev: Sen. Surg. Regist. & Thoracic Surg. Regist. Leeds Gen. Infirm.; Res. Surg. Off. St. Jas. Hosp. Leeds.

SHOHET, Naim Ishac Aboudi 1/12 Nitza Boulevard, Netanya, Israel; Red Bank Health Centre, Unsworth St., Radcliffe, Manchester M26 3GH Tel: 0161 723 2624 — MRCS Eng. LRCP Lond. 1945. (St. Bart.) Prev: Res. Surg. Off. Castleford Hosp.; Orthop. Ho. Surg. & Dep. Res. Surg. Off. War Memor. Hosp. Scunthorpe; Ho. Surg. St. Mary Islington Hosp.

SHOHETH, Joseph Raymond (retired) 75 Shortwood Crescent, Plymstock, Plymouth PL9 8TL Tel: 01752 401432 — MB BS 1954 Calcutta; DTM & H Calcutta 1956; DLO Eng. 1961. Prev: Regist. (ENT) Gen. Hosp. Nottm., Dudley Rd. Hosp. Birm. & Plymouth Gen. Hosp.

SHOKAR, Navkiran Kaur 4 Stoneleigh Close, Luton LU3 3XE — BM BCh 1992 Oxf. Trainee GP Horton Gen. Hosp. VTS.

SHOKER, Balvinder Singh 24 Inglewood, Liverpool L12 0NP — MB ChB 1991 Liverp.

SHOKUHI, Sheila 23 Beechfield Road, Liverpool L18 3EG — MB ChB 1993 Liverp.

SHOLAPURKAR, Shashikant Laxman Department of Obstetrics & Gynaecology, Royal United Hospital, Coombe Park, Bath BA1 3NG — MB BS 1984 Poona; MRCOG 1993. Staff Grade Doctor.

SHOLL, Penelope Pat Hawkinge Health Centre, 74 Canterbury Road, Hawkinge, Folkestone CT18 7BP Tel: 01303 892434; 122 Cheriton Road, Folkestone CT19 5HQ Tel: 01303 259596 — MB BS 1977 Lond.; MRCGP 1983; DRCOG Lond. 1980; DCH Eng. 1979; AKC 1977. GP Asst.

SHOME, Chittendra 8 Beadnell Drive, Penketh, Warrington WA5 2EG — MB BS 1969 Gauhati.

SHONE, Mr Geoffrey Richard ENT Department, University Hospital of Wales, Heath Park, Cardiff CF14 4XW Tel: 029 2074 7747; 12 Pen Y Dre, Cardiff CF14 6EP — MB BChir 1979 Camb.; MA, MB Camb. 1979, BChir 1978; FRCS Eng. 1983. Cons. Otolaryngol. Univ. Hosp. Wales Cardiff.

SHOO, Estomih Elikaney Tameside General Hospital, Fountain St., Ashton-under-Lyne OL6 9RW Tel: 0161 331 6000 — MB ChB Makerere 1971; MRCP Dub. 1987; DCH RCP Lond. 1983; DTCH Liverp. 1980. Assoc. Specialist (Paediat.) Tameside Gen. Hosp. Ashton-under-Lyne. Socs: BMA & Brit. Paediat. Assn. Prev: Regist. (Paediat.) Maelor Gen. Hosp. Wrexham & Tameside Gen. Hosp.; SHO (Paediat.) Roy. Liverp. Childr. Hosp. & Roy. Liverp. Childr. Hosp.

SHOOMAN, Hyman Rosana, 4 The Glade, Ling Lane, Scarcroft, Leeds LS14 3JG — M.B., Ch.B. Leeds 1944. (Leeds) Area Cadet Off. St. John Ambul. Brig. Prev: Ho. Phys. & Ho. Surg. Pinderfields Gen. Hosp. Wakefield; Flight Lt. RAF; Med. Regist. Leeds Gen. Infirm.

SHOOTER, Jean (retired) Eastlea, Back Edge Lane, Edge, Stroud GL6 6PE Tel: 01452 812408 — MB ChB Bristol 1942. Prev: Surg. Lt. RNVR.

SHOOTER, Michael Stanhope Ty Bryn Adolescent Unit, St Cadoc's Hospital, Lodge Road, Caerleon, Newport NP18 3XQ Tel: 01633 436831 Fax: 01633 436834; Ty Boda, Upper Llanover, Abergavenny NP7 9EP Tel: 01873 880093 Fax: 01873 880293 — MB 1976 Camb.; MA Camb. 1973, MB 1976, BChir 1975; FRCPsych 1994, M 1980. (Cambridge) Cons. Child & Adolesc. Psychiat.Gwent Healthcare NHS Trust, Clin. Dir., Child & Adolesc. Ment. Health Serv.; Regist. Roy. Coll. Psychiat. Prev: Clin. Dir. S. Glam. Child & Adolesc. Psychiat. Serv.

SHOOTER, Professor Reginald Arthur, CBE (retired) Eastlea, Back Edge Lane, Edge, Stroud GL6 6PE Tel: 01452 812408 — MB BChir Camb. 1940; MA Camb. 1941, MD 1945; FRCS Eng. 1977; FRCP Lond. 1968, M 1961; MRCS Eng. LRCP Lond. 1940; FCPath 1963. Prev: Prof. Med. Microbiol. Univ. Lond.

SHORA, Basharat Saleem Dartford West Health Centre, Tower Road, Dartford DA1 2HA Tel: 01322 280272 Email: basharat.shora@gp82639.nhs.co.uk; Email: basharat_shora"yahoo.co.uk — MBBS; DTM & H. (Kashmir Univ. (Spinagar Medical College)) GP, W. Kent Health Auth.

SHORE, Mr Darryl Francis 148 Woodlands Road, Ashurst, Southampton SO40 7AQ — MB ChB 1971 Sheff.; FRCS Eng. 1976.

SHORE, David James The Surgery, Barr Lane, Brinklow, Rugby CV23 0LU Tel: 01788 832994 Fax: 01788 833021; Fairfield House,

Coventry Road, Brinklow, Rugby CV23 0NE — MB ChB 1984 Birm.; MRCGP 1998. GP Brinklow; Clin. Asst. (A & E) St. Cross Hosp. Rugby. Prev: GP Coventry.

SHORE, Eleanor Mary Custom House Surgery, 16 Freemasons Road, London E16 3NA Tel: 020 7476 2255 Fax: 020 7511 8980 — MB BS 1981 Lond.

SHORE, Elizabeth Catherine, CB (retired) 23 Dryburgh Road, London SW15 1BN — MRCS Eng. LRCP Lond. 1951; FRCP Lond. 1984, M 1973; DObst RCOG 1953; FFCM 1972. Prev: Dep. Chief Med. Off. DHSS.

SHORE, Hannah Ruth The Lodge, 34 Brighton Road, Purley CR8 3AD; 29 Charlotte Road, Stirchley, Birmingham B30 2BT Tel: 0121 433 4097 Email: hshore1006@aol.com — MB ChB 1996 Birm.; ChB Birm. 1996. SHO (Paediat.).

SHORE, Irene The Surgery, King St., Burton-on-Trent DE14 3BX Tel: 01283 568246 — MB ChB 1975 Liverp.; MRCGP 1982; DRCOG 1979.

SHORE, John Hubert (retired) 11 Angmering Lane, East Preston, Littlehampton BN16 2TA Tel: 01903 782356 — MD 1952 Lond.; MB BS 1947; FRCPath 1969, M 1964. Prev: Cons. Pathol. Worthing Hosp. Gp.

SHORE, Kathryn Margaret Demontfort Medical Centre, Burford Road, Bengeworth, Evesham WR11 5AG Tel: 01386 443333 Fax: 01386 422884; The Vicarage, High St., Badsey, Evesham WR11 5EW — MB BS 1989 (Distinc. Clin. Pharmacol. & Therap.) Lond.; MA Oxf. 1987; MRCGP 1993; DFFP 1995; T(GP) 1993; DCH RCP Lond. 1992; DRCOG 1991. (Charing Cross and Westminster) Prev: Trainee GP Worcester; Ho. Off. (Surg.) Wycombe Gen. Hosp.; Ho. Off. (Med.) Stoke Mandeville Hosp.

SHORE, Peter Michael Heathfielde, Lyttlelton Road, London N2 0EE Tel: 020 8458 9262 Fax: 020 8455 0165 — MB BS 1952 Lond. (Char. Cross) Prev: Ho. Surg. Wembley Hosp.

SHORE, Richard John Plot 22 Oswell Road, Severn Meadows, Shrewsbury SY2 5YL — MB ChB 1986 Leeds.

SHORE, Susannah Louise Top Forge Cottage, Wortley, Sheffield S35 7DN — MB ChB 1997 Liverp.

SHORES, John Gresham Clifton House Medical Centre, 263-265 Beverley Road, Hull HU5 2ST Tel: 01482 341423; 43 Low Street, North Ferriby HU14 3DD Tel: 01482 631473 — LMSSA 1960 Lond. (W. Lond.) Clin. Asst. De la Pole Hosp. Willerby; Co. Surg. St. John Ambul. Humberside. Socs: BMA. Prev: SHO Vict. Hosp. Sick Childr. Hull.

SHOREY, Mr Brian Alexander Northwood Consulting Rooms, 7 Greenhill Court, Green Lane, Northwood HA6 2UZ Tel: 01923 826948 Fax: 01923 835794; Broad Oak, 36 Main Avenue, Moor Park, Northwood HA6 2LQ Tel: 01923 821297 — MS Lond. 1978, MB BS 1964; FRCS Eng. 1969. (St. Bart.) Cons. Surg. Hillingdon Hosp. Uxbridge. Socs: Roy. Soc. Med. Assn. Surg.; Brit. Assn. Surg. Oncol. Prev: Hon. Cons. Bristol Childr. Hosp.; Sen. Regist. (Surg.) Bristol Roy. Infirm.; Regist. (Surg.) St. Bart. Hosp. Lond.

SHOREY, Greta Marion A. P. 54, Isla Mujeres, Q.Roo 77400, Mexico Tel: 00 52 98770443 Fax: 00 52 98770443; Arkley, 39 Hathaway Green Lane, Stratford-upon-Avon CV37 9HX — MB ChB 1976 Birm.; MRCGP 1983; FMGEMS 1988; DTM & H Liverp. 1981; DCH Eng. 1980; DRCOG 1979. Med. Dir. (Gen. Pract., Trauma & Disaster Relief) Mexican Red Cross Delegacion ISCA Mujeres. Socs: BMA.

SHORLAND, Jean Eva (retired) 83 Broom Road, Rotherham S60 2SW — MB BS 1965 Lond.; BSc (Physiol.) Lond. 1962; FRCP Lond. 1984, M 1968. Prev: Sen. Regist. Dept. Child Health Univ. Hosp. Cardiff.

SHORNEY, Janet Susan Chiddenbrook Surgery, Threshers, Crediton EX17 3JJ Tel: 01363 772227 Fax: 01363 775528; 2 Westwood Cottages, Westwood Road, Crediton EX17 3PE Tel: 01363 773112 — MB BChir 1978 Camb.; MRCGP 1983; DRCOG 1983.

SHORNEY, Neil Mark 22 Okefield Road, Crediton EX17 2DN — MB BS 1980 Lond.; FFARCS Eng. 1984.

SHORROCK, Christopher John 79 Clarence Road, Kings Heath, Birmingham B13 9UH — MB ChB 1980 Manch.; BSc St. And. 1977; MRCP (UK) 1984. Regist. (Gen. Med./Gastroenterol.) Univ. Dept. Med. Hope Hosp. Manch. Prev: Regist. Univ. Dept. Med. Manch. Roy. Infirm.; Regist. Univ. Dept. Gastroenterol. Manch. Roy.

Infirm.; Regist. Regional Dept. Cardiothoracic Med. Wythenshawe Hosp. Manch.

SHORROCK, Kenneth Medioco Legal Centre, Watery Street, Sheffield S3 7ES Tel: 01142 738721 Fax: 01142798942 Email: k.sharrock@sheffield.ac.uk — MB ChB 1978 Sheff.; MD Sheff. 1989; FRCS Eng. 1982; FRCPath 1991; LLB 1999 Leeds Metropolitan. Sen. Lect. in Forens. Path. Univ. of Sheff. Cons. Pathologist to the Home Office. Socs: Internat. Acad. Path.; Brit. Assn. Forens. Med. Prev: Lect. (Histopath.) Univ. Leicester; Regist. (Histopath.) Nottm. HA; Cons. Pathologist Healthcare NHS Trust.

SHORROCK, Peter (retired) Oak House, Moss Lane, Leyland, Preston PR25 4SE Tel: 01772 422373 — MB ChB 1961 Manch.; Cert Av Med. MoD (Air) & CAA 1975. Approved Examr. Civil Aviat. Auth. Prev: Ho. Off. Manch. Roy. Infirm. & Bolton & Dist. Gen. Hosp.

SHORT, Aidan Dominic 26 Willow Hey, Liverpool L31 3DL — MB ChB 1997 Sheff.

SHORT, Alasdair Ian Kennedy Broomfield Hospital, Chelmsford CM1 7ET Tel: 01245 440761 Fax: 01245 514060 — MB ChB 1975 Ed.; FRCP Lond. 1992; FRCP Ed. 1986; FRCPC 1982; MRCP (UK) 1977. Cons. Phys. Intens. Care Unit Broomfield Hosp. Chelmsford.

SHORT, Alastair Douglas, MBE Anniesland Medical Practice, 778 Crow Road, Glasgow G13 1LU Tel: 0141 954 8860 Fax: 0141 954 0870; 7 Glenburn Road, Bearsden, Glasgow G61 4PT — MB ChB 1977 Glas.; MPH Glas. 1993; FRCGP 1991, M 1981; DRCOG 1980. (Glas.) p/t Dir., Primary Care Div., Gt.er Glas. Primary Care NHS Trust; Asst. Dir., Dept. PGME, Glas. Univ. Socs: FRCGP (Ex-Hon. Sec. W. Scotl. Fac. & Vice-Chairm. Scott. Counc.); (Ex-Pres.) Milngavie & Bearsden Med. Soc. Prev: Audit Faciliator, Chairm. Community & Primary Care Audit Comm. Gtr. Glas. HB; Ex-Med. Off. Remploy.

SHORT, Andrew Worcester Royal Infirmary, Ronkswood Branch, Newton Road, Worcester WR5 1HN Tel: 01905 760736 Fax: 01905 760584 Email: andrew.short@woresacute.auminds.nhs.uk; Stedefield, Church Lane, Flyford Flavelc, Worcester WR7 4BZ Email: shorts@tesco.net — MB ChB 1981 Aberd.; FRCPCH; MRCP (UK) 1987. Cons. Paediat. Worcester Roy. Infirm. Prev: Cons. Paediat. Huddersflield Roy. Infirm.; Sen. Regist. (Paediat.) Leeds & Bradford Hosps.; Regist. (Paediat.) St. Lukes Hosp. Bradford.

SHORT, Andrew Keith Rental Unit, Walsgrave Hospital, Clifford Bridge Road, Coventry CV2 2DX; 40 Dickins Road, Warwick CV34 5NS — MB ChB 1984 Manch.; PhD Camb. 1994; BSc (Hons.) Manch 1981; MRCP (UK) 1987. Cons. Phys. & Nepheologist, Walsgrave Hosp., Coventry. Prev: Research Sen. Regist. Sch. Clin. Med. Addenbrooke's Hosp. Camb.; Regist. (Renal Med.) St. Mary's Hosp. Lond.; SHO Univ. Hosp. S. Manch.

SHORT, Bernard Priory View Medical Centre, 2a Green Lane, Leeds LS12 1HU Tel: 0113 295 4260 Fax: 0113 295 4278 — MRCS 1973 Lond; MRCS Eng LRCP Lond 1973; LMCC (Camb.) 1979. (London) GP Leeds. Socs: BMA; MDU. Prev: GP Comox Brit. Columbia Canada.

SHORT, Carolyn St. Andrews Medical Centre, Pinewood Gardens, Southborough, Tunbridge Wells TN4 0LZ Tel: 01892 515455; 65 Cornwallis Avenue, Tonbridge TN10 4ET Tel: 01732 357413 — MB BS 1986 Lond.; MRCGP 1990; DCH RCP Lond. 1989. Prev: Trainee GP Tunbridge Wells VTS; Ho. Surg. Newham Gen. Hosp. Lond.; Ho. Phys. Lond. Hosp. Whitechapel.

SHORT, Clare Anna Ground Floor, 11 Miles Road, Clifton, Bristol BS8 2JN — MB ChB 1986 Bristol.

SHORT, Colin David Department of Renal Medicine, Manchester Royal Infirmary, Oxford Road, Manchester M13 9WL Tel: 0161 276 4454 Fax: 0161 276 8022; 3 Homelands Road, Sale M33 4BJ — MB ChB 1975 Manch.; BSc Hull 1970; MD Manch. 1990; FRCP Lond. 1995; MRCP (UK) 1979. (Manch.) Cons. Phys. (Renal Med.) Manch. Roy. Infirm.; Hon. Lect. (Med.) Univ. Manch. Socs: Renal Assn.; Med. Res. Soc.; Internat. Soc. Nephrol.

SHORT, David Hugh Dartford West Health Centre, Tower Road, Dartford DA1 2HA Tel: 01322 223600 Fax: 01322 292282; Brambles, Common Lane, Wilmington, Dartford DA2 7BA Email: d.short@virgin.net — MB BS 1984 Lond.; DRCOG 1986. (St Mary's Hospital, London) GP; Sector GP for Bartford Town sector of PCG. Prev: Trainee GP Dartford VTS; Ho. Phys. St. Mary's Hosp. E.bourne; Ho. Surg. Worthing Hosp.

SHORT

SHORT, David James 12 Whitesfield Road, Nailsea, Bristol BS48 2DT Tel: 01275 855294; Western Region, British Rail, Temple Meads, Bristol BS1 6Q Tel: 0117 934 8800 — MRCS Eng. LRCP Lond. 1973; MSc 1977; MFOM RCP Lond. 1987, AFOM 1982; DAvMed RCP Lond. 1990; DIH Eng. 1977. Cons. Occupat. Phys. Frenchay Hosp. Bristol. Prev: Sen. Med. Off. RAF; Sen. Med. Off. Arabian Armed Forces.

SHORT, Professor David Somerset 48 Victoria Street, Aberdeen AB10 1PN Tel: 01224 645853 Email: short@dircon.co.uk — MB BChir 1942 Camb.; PhD Lond. 1957; MA Camb. 1944, MD 1948; FRCP Ed. 1970, M 1964; FRCP Lond. 1964, M 1943. (Bristol) Emerit. Clin. Prof. Med. Univ. Aberd.; Hon. Cons. Phys. Aberd. Roy. Infirm. Socs: Aberd. M-C Soc. (Ex-Pres.). Prev: Phys. to HM the Qu. in Scotl.; Lect. (Med.) Middlx. Hosp. Med. Sch. Lond.; Chief Asst. (Cardiac) Lond. Hosp.

SHORT, Deborah Jill Midlands Centre for Spinal Injuries, Robert Jones & Agnes Hunt Hospital, Oswestry SY10 7AG — MB ChB 1978 Leeds; MRCP (UK) 1981. Cons. in Spinal Injuries Rehabil. Med. Prev: Sen. Regist. Nat. Spinal Injuries Centre Stoke Mandeville.; Cons. Rehabil. Med., Haywood Hosp., Burslem, Stoke on trent.

SHORT, Diane Claire 5 Whitestones, Stocksmoor, Huddersfield HD4 6XQ — MB ChB 1996 Liverp.

SHORT, Donald Harry, RD (retired) Ballacree, West End, Somerton TA11 6RW Tel: 01458 272408 — MB BS 1955 Lond.; FFA RCS Eng. 1964. Prev: Cons. Anaesth. Bristol & W.. HA.

SHORT, Edward Somerset (retired) The Manse, Yatton Keynell Road, Castle Combe, Chippenham SN14 7HD Tel: 01249 782629 — MB ChB 1944 Bristol. Prev: Supt. Bethesda Leprosy Hosp. Narsapur, India.

SHORT, Gerard Peter 101 Dunvegan Drive, Southampton SO16 8DB — MB BS 1992 Lond. SHO (Gen. Med.) Roy. Bournemouth Hosp.

SHORT, Jacqueline Anne Wallingford Clinic, Fairmile Hospital, Wallingford OX10 9HH Tel: 01491 651281 Fax: 01491 652336 — MB ChB 1988 Bristol; MRCPsych 1992. Sen. Regist. (Forens. Psychiat.) Wallingford Clinic. Socs: Roy. Coll. Psychiat. (Forens. Sect.). Prev: Sen. Regist. (Psychiat.) Avon Drug Probl. Team; Regist. (Psychiat.) Coney Hill Hosp.

SHORT, Jane Hyslop (retired) 7 Lochside, Bearsden, Glasgow G61 2SB Tel: 0141 943 1496 — MB ChB 1942 Glas.; BSc 1938, MD (Commend.) Glas. 1949; FRCP Glas, 1980, M 1962; FRFPS Glas. 1945; DMRT Eng. 1975. Prev: Med. Asst. Inst. Radiother. Glas.

SHORT, Jennifer Mary The Brow, Glenhead Road, Liverpool L19 9DA; Department Microbiology, John Radcliffe Hospital, Headington, Oxford Tel: 01865 741166 — MB ChB 1990 Liverp.; MRCP (UK) 1994; DTM & H Liverp. 1995. Specialist Regist. (MicroBiol.) John Radcliffe Hosp. Oxf. Prev: SHO (Infec. Dis.s) City Hosp. Edin.; SHO (Med.) N.ampton Gen. Hosp. & Countess of Chester Hosp.

SHORT, Mrs Joan Anne (retired) 48 Victoria Street, Aberdeen AB10 1PN Tel: 01224 645853 — MB BCh 1948 Wales; BSc Wales 1945. Prev: GP Aberd.

SHORT, John Jack Flat 2, 6E Kelvin Square, 25 Mingarry St, Glasgow G20 8NP — MB ChB 1976 Aberd. Med. Adviser Benefits Agency Glas.

SHORT, Judith Alison 19 Twentywell Road, Bradway, Sheffield S17 4PU — BM BS 1991 Nottm.; BMedSci (Hons.) Nottm. 1989; FRCA 1997. Regist Rotat. (Anaesth.) N. Trent Train. Scheme Sheff. Socs: BMA; Fell. Roy. Coll. Anaesth.; Assn. Anaesth.

SHORT, Laura Clare Penleigh, 2 Melrose Crescent, Bishop Monkton, Harrogate HG3 3SW — BM BS 1998 Nottm.; BM BS Nottm 1998.

SHORT, Lindsay Crawford Airbles Road Centre, 59 Airbles Road, Motherwell ML1 2TP — MB ChB 1992 Sheff.; 1997 JCPTGP- Jt. Comm. Cert. for Post Grad. Traning in Gen. Pract.; DFFP 1996. Airbles Rd. Centre Airbles Rd. Motherwell ML1 2TP, Lanarksh. Prim. Care NHS Trust. Prev: GP Regist. The Surg. 24 Quarry St. Johnstone; SHO (Med. for Elderly) Roy. Alexandra Hosp. NHS Trust Paisley; GP Regist. Avondale Med. Pract. Strathaven Health Centre, The Ward, Strathaven.

SHORT, Lindsay Jane 133 Gardner Road, Formby, Liverpool L37 8DF — MB ChB 1995 Manch.

SHORT, Lindsay Margaret 2/L, 72 Lauderdale Gardens, Glasgow G12 9QW — MB ChB 1988 Glas.; MRCP (UK) 1993. Sen. Regist. (Genitourin. Med.) Sandyford Initiative Glas. Prev: Regist. Rotat. (Genitourin. Med., Gen. Med. & Infec. Dis.) Newc. Gen. Hosp.; SHO Rotat. (Med.) W.. Infirm. & Gartnavel Gen. Hosp. Glas.

SHORT, Mary Bowen 67 Bridge Street, Cambridge CB2 1UR Tel: 01223 355060 Fax: 01223 460812; Madingley Rise, Madingley Hill, Coton, Cambridge CB3 7PQ — MB ChB 1956 Bristol. (Bristol) Prev: SHO (Paediat.) Hereford Co. Hosp.; Ho. Surg. Frenchay Hosp. Bristol; Ho. Phys. Med. Profess. Unit, United Bristol Hosps.

SHORT, Mary Eileen Colette 619 Ormeau Road, Belfast BT7 3JD; 619 Ormeau Road, Belfast BT7 3JD Tel: 01232 640077 — MB BCh BAO 1985 Belf.; MRCGP 1991.

SHORT, Mary Pamela (retired) 4 The Oval, Ashby-de-la-Zouch LN4 3JE Tel: 01526 320420 — MB ChB St. And. 1940; DObst. RCOG 1943. Prev: Med. Off. Family Health New Zealand.

SHORT, Matthew Adam Dr Bell & Partners, The Barn Surgery, Newbury, Gillingham SP8 4XS Tel: 01747 824201 Fax: 01747 825098 Email: gillsurg@clara.tep.co.uk; Elmcroft, Wyke, Gillingham SP8 4NG Tel: 01747 824716 Email: matt+penny@shortdoc.freeserve.co.uk — BM 1978 Soton.; DRCOG 1983. (Southampton) GP Princip. Prev: Trainee GP Netheravon; SHO (O & G, Orthop. & A & E) Salisbury HA.

SHORT, Norton Lynn, MBE Dartford East Health Centre, Pilgrims Way, Dartford DA1 1QY Tel: 01322 274211 Fax: 01322 284329; Keepers, St. Vincents Lane, Addington, Maidstone ME16 5BW — MB BS 1958 Lond.; MA Wales 1989; MRCGP 1969; DPM Eng. 1972; DObst RCOG 1961. (St. Geo.) Prev: Ho. Surg. St. Geo. Hosp. Lond.; Ho. Phys. Ashford Hosp. Kent; Ho. Surg. (Obst.) All St.s' Hosp. Chatham.

SHORT, Penelope Anne Anaesthetic Department, Salisbury District Hospital, Salisbury SP2 8BJ Tel: 01722 425050; Elmcroft, Wyke Road, Gillingham SP8 4NG Tel: 017476 4716 — BM 1977 Soton.; DA (UK) 1984. (Soton.) Staff Grade Anaesth. Salisbury Health Care. Prev: SHO (Anaesth. & Orthop.) Salisbury HA; SHO (A & E) I. of Wight HA.; SHO (Paediat. Surg.) Soton.

SHORT, Peter Lemon Street Surgery, 18 Lemon Street, Truro TR1 2LZ Tel: 01872 73133 Fax: 01872 260900; 3 Tremorvah Crescent, Truro TR1 1NL Tel: 01872 42254 — MB BS 1984 Lond.; MRCGP 1994; DRCOG 1990; DCH RCP Lond. 1989. Prev: Trainee GP Truro.

SHORT, Peter McLay Grove Medical Practice, Shirley Health Centre, Grove Road, Shirley, Southampton SO15 3UA Tel: 023 8078 3611 Fax: 023 8078 3156; 457 Coxford Road, Lordswood, Southampton SO16 5DA Tel: 02380 739513 — MB ChB 1978 Aberd.; MRCGP 1982; DRCOG 1982. GP Shirley.

SHORT, Peter Richard David The Stewart Medical Centre, 15 Hartington Road, Buxton SK17 6JP Tel: 01298 22338 Fax: 01298 72678; The Barn, 91 Green Lane, Buxton SK17 9DJ — MB ChB 1983 Birm.; MRCGP 1988; DRCOG 1986. Prev: SHO (Paediat.) Good Hope Gen. Hosp. Birm.; SHO (O & G) & (Med.) Doncaster Roy. Infirm.; SHO (A & E) Selly Oak Hosp. Birm.

SHORT, Miss Rachel Marian Crosshouse Hospital, Kilmarnock KA2 0BE — BM BS 1986 Nottm.; FRCS (Orth) 1997. Cons. Orthop. Surg., CrossHo. Hosp., Kilmarnock.

SHORT, Stephanie Patricia Minfor Surgery, Park Road, Barmouth LL42 1PL Tel: 01341 280521 Fax: 01341 280912 — MB BS 1980 Lond.; MRCGP 1985; DRCOG 1984; DCH RCP Lond. 1982.

SHORT, Stuart David Cobbs Garden Surgery, West St, Olney MK46 5QG; 22A West End, Stevington, Bedford MK43 7QU — MB BS 1990 Lond.; DFFP 1995. (Roy. Free Med. Sch. Lond.) GP Cobbs Gdn Surg. Olney Bucks; Clin. Asst. Rheum. Bedford Hosp. Bedford. Prev: SHO (Paediat. & O & G) N.ampton Gen. Hosp.

SHORT, Susan Christine 40 Field Way, Rickmansworth WD3 7EJ Tel: 01923 711498 — MB BS 1989 Lond.; BSc Lond. 1986, MB BS 1989; MRCP (UK) 1992; FRCR (UK) 1996. (King's Coll. Lond.)

SHORT, William John South Lodge, Lennox Castle Hospital, Lennoxtown, Glasgow G66 7LB Tel: 0141 329200 — LRCP LRCS Ed. LRCPS Glas. 1964. p/t Acting Cons. Psychiat. Lennox Castle Hosp. Lennoxtown. Prev: SHO Paisley Matern. Hosp.; Ho. Off. (Med.) Hairmyres Hosp. E. Kilbride; Ho. Off. (Surg.) S.. Gen. Hosp. Glas.

SHORT, William Robert, QHP, OStJ, Maj.-Gen. late RAMC PHC Ltd., Talbot House, Green End, Whitchurch SY13 1AJ Tel: 01948

664452 Fax: 01948 666116 Email: robin.short@virgin.net; Beeswing, 26 Orchard Road, Farnborough GU14 7PR Tel: 01252 513328 Fax: 01252 653696 — MB ChB Glas. 1967; FRCP Glas. (Glas.) Operat.s Dir., PHC Ltd. Prev: Dir. Gen. Army Med. Servs.

SHORTALL, Delia Ann 3 Clarendon Road W., Chorlton, Manchester M21 0RN — MB BS 1984 Lond.; MSc Manch. 1995; MRCPsych 1991; DFFP 1995. Cons. Child & Adolesc. Psychiat. Roy. Liverp. Childr. NHS Trust.

SHORTALL, Myles Thomas Meadowlands Surgery, Monaghan Street, Newry BT35 6BW Tel: 028 3026 7534 — MB BCh BAO 1964 Belf.; DObst RCOG 1966. (Qu. Univ. Belf.)

SHORTALL, Therese Nicholette Newton Medical Centre, 14/18 Newton Road, London W2 5LT Tel: 020 7229 4578 Fax: 020 7229 7315; 31 Buckingham Close, Queens Walk, Ealing, London W5 1TS — MB BCh BAO NUI 1970; MPH NUI 1986.

SHORTEN, John Benjamin 13 Tonsley Place, London SW18 1BH — MB BS 1992 Lond.

SHORTEN, Penelope Jane Houghton Health Centre, Church St., Houghton-le-Spring DH4 4DN; 20 Deneside Avenue, Low Fell, Gateshead NE9 6AD — MB BS 1969 Newc. SCMO City Hosps. Wearside.

SHORTEN, Wilson William John Lisburn Health Centre, Linenhall Street, Lisburn BT28 1LU Tel: 028 9260 3090 Fax: 028 9250 1310; 7 Magheralave Road, Lisburn BT28 3BE Tel: 01846 679073 — MB BCh BAO 1983 Belf.; MB BCh BAO Belf. 1980; MRCGP 1984; Cert. Family Plann. JCC 1984; DCH RCPI 1983; DRCOG 1982.

SHORTHOSE, Kathryn Victoria c/o Corme-Ecluse, Main Street, Ravenfield, Rotherham S65 4NA — MB ChB 1996 Bristol.

SHORTHOUSE, Mr Andrew John Royal Hallamshire Hospital, Glossop Road, Sheffield S10 2JF Tel: 0114 271 3143 Fax: 0114 271 3143; 36 Riverdale Road, Sheffield S10 3FB Tel: 0114 266 1781 Fax: 0114 267 9662 Email: shorthouse@doctors.org.uk — MB BS 1971 Lond.; BSc (Hons.) Lond. 1968, MS 1981; FRCS Eng. 1976. (St. Mary's) Cons. Surg. (Colorectal Surg.) Roy. Hallamsh. Hosp. Sheff. Socs: (Hon. Sec.) Assn. Coloproctol.; (Hon. Sec.) Roy Soc Med Coloproctolsect.; Hon. Sec. Europ. Assn. Coloproctol.

SHORTLAND, Betty Elisa (retired) 9 Westergate House, 30 Portsmouth Road, Kingston upon Thames KT1 2NE Tel: 020 8549 9439 — MB BS 1945 Lond.; MRCS Eng. LRCP Lond. 1945; MFCM 1974; DPH 1962; DTM & H Eng. 1950. Prev: Specialist (Community Med.) Lambeth, S.wark, Lewisham & Bromley HA.

SHORTLAND, David Barry Poole General Hospital, Longfleet Road, Poole BH15 2 Tel: 01202 675100; 15 Cogdean Way, Corfe Mullen, Wimborne BH21 3XB Tel: 01202 603303 — MB ChB 1979 Bristol; MD Bristol 1992; MRCP (UK) 1982; DCH RCP Lond. 1982. Cons. Paediat. Poole Gen. Hosp. Socs: Brit. Paediat. Soc.; Neonat. Soc. Prev: Sen. Regist. & Regist. (Paediat.) Univ. Hosp. Nottm.; SHO (Paediat.) Hosps. for Sick Childr. Gt. Ormond St. Lond. & Bristol.

SHORTLAND, Graham John c/o Department of Child Health, University Hospital of Wales, Heath Park, Cardiff CF14 4XW — BM 1983 Soton.; FRCP Lond. 1997; FRCPCH 1997; DCH RCP Lond. 1987. (University of Southampton) Cons. Paediat. Univ. Hosp. Wales Cardiff. Prev: Lect. & Hon. Sen. Regist. Univ. Wales Coll. Med.; Ho. Surg. Roy. S. Hants. Hosp. Soton; Ho. Phys. Roy. Hants. Co. Hosp. Winchester.

SHORTLAND-WEBB, Susan Caroline 40 Tilehouse Green Lane, Knowle, Solihull B93 9EY — MB BCh 1989 Wales.

SHORTLAND-WEBB, William Richard (retired) 40 Tile House, Green Lane, Knowle, Solihull B93 9EY — MB ChB Birm. 1961; FRCPath 1982, M 1971. Cons. Path. City Hosp. NHS Trust.

SHORTRIDGE, Mr Richard Thomas John 8 Summerfield Road, Chapel Ash, Wolverhampton WV1 4PR Tel: 01902 429044 Fax: 01902 773920; Tel: 01902 742747 — MB ChB Sheff. 1970; FRCS Eng. 1976. (Sheff.) Cons. Surg. ENT Wolverhampton & Dudley HA; Cons. Surg. ORL/HNS Roy. Wolverhampton Hosps. NHS Trust & Dudley Gp. of Hosps. NHS Trust. Socs: Treas. Midl. Inst. of Otorhinolaryng.; Fell. RSM; BMA. Prev: Cons. Surg. ENT Kettering & Dist. Gen. Hosp.; Sen. Regist. (ENT) W. Midl. Train. Scheme; Regist. (ENT) Qu. Eliz. Hosp. Birm.

SHORTT, Alan Martin Health Centre, The Health Centre, Level 5, C S Building, University of Huddersfield, Queensgate, Huddersfield HD1 3DH Tel: 01484 430386 Fax: 01484 473085 — MB ChB 1988 Leeds; MRCGP 1994; T(GP) 1993.

SHORTT, Edward Philip Hugh (retired) 41 Lenten Street, Alton GU34 1HE Tel: 01420 83118 — MB BChir Camb. 1947. Prev: Res. Obstetr. Guy's Hosp.

SHORTT, Eleanor (retired) 31 Thaxted Road, Saffron Walden CB11 3AA — LRCPI & LM, LRSCI & LM 1935; LRCPI & LM, LRCSI & LM 1935; MRCVS 1930.

***SHORTT, Michael Whitfield** Dept of Orthopaedics, Charing Cross Hospital NHS Trust, Twickenham Rd, London W6 8RF Tel: 020 88461234 Email: mshortt"doctors.org.uk; Email: mshortt@doctors.org.uk — MB BS 1997 Lond.

SHORTT, Nicholas Lee 3Fl, 147 Dalkeith Road, Edinburgh EH16 5HQ — MB ChB 1996 Ed.

SHORTT, Stephen John The Health Centre, Gotham Lane, East Leake, Loughborough LE12 6SG Tel: 01509 852181 Fax: 01509 852099; 17 Meeting House Close, East Leake, Loughborough LE12 6HY Tel: 01509 853578 — BM BS 1986 Nottm.; BMedSci Nottm. 1984; MRCGP 1991; DRCOG 1992. Clin. Tutor Univ. Nottm.

SHORVON, Philip John Department of Radiology, Central Middlesex Hospital North West London Hospitals NHS Trust, Acton Lane, London NW10 7NS Tel: 020 8453 2270 Fax: 020 8453 2783 Email: philip.shorvon@cmh-tr.nthames.nhs.uk; 27 Stamford Brook Road, London W6 0XJ Tel: 020 8748 0233 Email: phils@intonet.co.uk — MB BS 1976 Lond.; MA Camb. 1975; MRCP (UK) 1979; FRCR 1986. (St. Thos.) Cons. Radiol. Centr. Middlx. Hosp. Lond.; Hon. Lect. (Radiol.) Univ. Lond. Socs: Eur. Soc. of Gastrointestinal and Abdom. Radiol. (Educat. Comm.) (ESGAR); Brit. Soc. Gastroenterol. (BSG); s/i Gp. GI Radiol. (SIGAR) Comm. Prev: Regist. (Med. & Gastroenterol.) & Sen. Regist. (Radiol.) Middlx. Hosp. Lond.; Fell. (Radiol.) McMaster Univ. Med. Centre Canada.

SHORVON, Professor Simon David Institute of Neurology, National Hospital for Neurol. & Neurosurg., Queen Square, London WC1N 3BG Tel: 020 7837 3611 Fax: 020 7837 3941 Email: s.shorvon@ion.ucl.ac.uk; The Brook Studio, 27A Stamford Brook Road, London W6 0XJ Tel: 020 8748 2333 Fax: 020 8563 8583 — MB BChir 1974 Camb.; MA Camb. 1974, MD 1983; FRCP Lond. 1990; MRCP (UK) 1975. (St. Thos.) Prof. Clin Neurol. Inst. Neurol. Qu. Sq. Lond.; Chairm. Clin. Neurol.; Cons. Neurol. Nat. Hosp. Neurol. & Neurosurg. Lond. Socs: (Exec. Comm.) Internat. League Against Epilepsy. Prev: Sen. Regist. & Regist. Nat. Hosp. Nerv. Dis. Qu. Sq. Lond.; SHO (Clin. Neurol.) Univ. Oxf.

SHOTBOLT, John Paul 62 Howards Wood Drive, Gerrards Cross SL9 7HW — MB BS 1996 Lond.

SHOTLIFF, Kevin Peter Tel: 020 8355 2791 Fax: 0208 780 2340; 36 Southwood Gardens, Esher KT10 0DE — MB BS 1987 Lond.; MD 1995 Lond.; DCH RCP 1989 Lond.; MRCP 1991 (UK); MD Lond. 1995; MRCP (UK) 1991; DCH RCP Lond. 1989. (St Geo. Hosp. Med. Sch. Lond.) Cons. (Diabetes & Endocrinol.) Kingston Hosp. & Qu. Mary's Hosp. Prev: Sen. Regist. (Diabetes & Endocrinol.) St. Geo.'s Hosp. Lond.; Research Fell. (Diabetic Retinop.) Roy. Postgrad. Med. Sch. Hammersmith Hosp. Lond.

SHOTT, Claire Helen Flat 3/2, 5 Caird Drive, Glasgow G11 5DZ — MB ChB 1994 Glas.; DRCOG 1998.

SHOTTON, Mr John Carr Kent & Sussex Hospital, Tunbridge Wells TN4 8AT Tel: 01622 226209 Fax: 01622 226191 Email: j.c.shotton@btinternet.com; 7 Holmewood Ridge, Langton Green, Tunbridge Wells TN3 0BN Tel: 01892 862361 Email: j.c.shotton@btinternet.com — MB BCh 1980 Wales; FRCS Eng. (ENT) 1986; FRCS Ed. (ENT) 1986. Cons. Otolaryngol. Maidstone Tunbridge Well NHS Trust; Hon. Cons. Regional Plastic Surg. Unit Qu. Vict. Hosp. E. Grinstead. Prev: Sen. Regist. (Otolaryngol.) SE Thames RHA, Kings Coll. Hosp.; Janet Nash Fell.; Skull Base/ OTO Neurosurg., Zurich 1990.

SHOTTON, Maria Elizabeth 10 Hale End, Woking GU22 0LH — MB BS 1968 Newc.

SHOTTS, Alan (retired) 3 Scotch Common, West Ealing, London W13 8DL Tel: 020 8997 6500 — MRCS Eng. LRCP Lond. 1951; LDS RCS Eng. 1947.

SHOTTS, Nina (retired) 12 Woodville Road, Ealing, London W5 2SF Tel: 020 8997 5671 Fax: 020 8997 5671 Email: nina@padwickshotts.freeserve.co.uk — MRCS Eng. LRCP Lond. 1958; FDS RCS Eng. 1963. Prev: Indep. Specialist Lond.

SHOULER, Mr Philip James, MBE Vale of Leven District General Hospital, Alexandria G83 0UA Tel: 01389 54121 — MB BS 1974 Lond.; FRCPS Glas. 1991; FRCS Eng. 1979; MRCS Eng. LRCP Lond.

SHOULS

1973. Cons. Surg. Vale of Leven Dist. Gen. Hosp. Socs: Brit. Soc. Gastroenterol.; Assn. Surg.; BMA. Prev: Cons. Surg. Roy. Naval Med. Serv.

SHOULS, Jennie Christine 63 The Lynch, Winscombe BS25 1AR — MB ChB 1994 Bristol.

SHOULTS, Clare 4 Graemesdyke Avenue, London SW14 7BJ — MB BS 1998 Lond.; MB BS Lond 1998.

SHOUSHA, Mohamed Sami Mahmoud Department of Histopathology, Charing Cross Hospital, Fulham Palace Road, London W6 8RF Tel: 020 8846 7144 Fax: 020 8846 1364 Email: s.shousha@ic.ac.uk — MB BCh Cairo 1964; MD Cairo 1971; MRCPath 1976. (Faculty of Medicine, Cairo University) Sen. Lect. & Hon. Cons. Char. Cross Hosp. & Imperial Coll. Sch. of Med. Lond. Socs: Fell. Roy. Coll. of Pathologists. Prev: Lect. Roy. Free Hosp. & Sch. of Med.

SHOVE, Mr David Colquhoun 17 Highpoint, North Hill, Highgate, London N6 4BA Tel: 020 8340 9154 — MB ChB 1960 Otago; BA Auckland 1954; FRCS Ed. 1967; FRCPA 1973. Cons. (Path.) Barnet Gen. Hosp.

SHOVE, Roy Frederick (retired) 10 Priory Close, Pevensey BN24 6AD Tel: 01323 769490 — MRCS Eng. LRCP Lond. 1944; FRCGP 1973. Prev: Orthop. Hosp. Pract. Kent & Sussex Hosp. Tunbridge Wells.

SHOVLIN, Claire Louise Senior Lecturer/Hon Consultant Respiratory Med, Imperial College of Medicine, National Heart and Lung Institute, Hammersmith Hospital, Du Cane Rd, London W12 0NN Tel: 020 8383 3269 Fax: 020 8743 9733 Email: c.shovlin@ed.ac.uk; 20 Nelson Street, New Town, Edinburgh EH3 6LJ Tel: 0131 556 6664 Fax: 0131 556 6664 — MB BChir 1987 Camb.; PhD Lond. 1996; MA Camb. 1988, BA (1st cl. Hons.) 1984; MRCP (UK) 1990. (Univ. Camb. & St. Thos. Hosp. Med. Sch.) Sen. Lect./ Hon Cons. Socs: MRS; Brit. Thorac. Soc.; HHT Foundat. Prev: Post Doctoral Fell. (Genetics) Harvard Med. Sch. Boston, Mass., USA; Wellcome Advanced Fell./ Hon Cons., Uni of Edin.; Lect. (Resp.Med) Uni. Edin.

SHOVLIN, William Mathieson (retired) Stourton House, 67 Oakham Road, Dudley DY2 7TH Tel: 01384 253405 — MB ChB Glas. 1952.

SHOWELL, Daniel Gareth Leslie 68 Gaywood Road, King's Lynn PE30 2PT — MB BS 1992 Lond.; DCH RCP Lond. 1995; DTM & H Liverp. 1995. (Royal Free School of Medicine London)

SHOWELL, Nicola Marie 8 Wellside Close, Kingswells, Aberdeen AB15 8EW — MB ChB 1998 Aberd.; MB ChB Aberd 1998.

SHOWGHI, Samina Finsbury Circus Medical Centre, 5 London Wall Buildings, Finsbury Circus, London EC2M 5NS Tel: 020 7638 0909 Fax: 020 7638 9211 — MB BS 1993 Lond.; DCH RCP Lond. 1995; DRCOG Lond. 1996; MRCGP Lond. 1997. (UCMSM) Socs: BMA; RSM.

SHRANK, Alan Bruce (retired) 20 Crescent Place, Town Walls, Shrewsbury SY1 1TQ Tel: 01743 362469 Fax: 01743 362420 Email: alan_shrank@compuserve.com — BM BCh 1956 Oxf.; MA Oxf. 1956; FRCP Lond. 1977, M 1961. Mem. Med. Appeal Tribunals 1988-. Prev: Cons. Dermat. Shropsh. HA.

SHRAVAT, Mr Brijendra Pratap Victoria Hospital, Blackpool FY3 8NR Tel: 01253 34111 — MB BS 1973 Allahabad; MS (Orthop.) Allahabad 1977; FRCS Ed. 1992; DA (UK) 1986. (M.L.N. Med. Coll.) Staff Surg. (A & E) Vict. Hosp. Blackpool.

SHREEVE, David Randal 16 St John Street, Manchester M3 4EA Tel: 0161 834 1100 Fax: 0161 835 1465; Rough Meadow, 4 Gipsy Lane, Rochdale OL11 3HA — MB ChB 1961 Manch.; FRCP Ed. 1980, M 1966; FRCP Lond. 1979, M 1966. Cons. Phys. N. Manch.. HA Retd. From NHS Oct 2000. Socs: Fell. Manch. Med. Soc.; Brit. Soc. Gastroenterol. & Diabetes UK. Prev: Sen. Regist. United Manch. Hosps.; Tutor (Med.) Univ. Dept. Med. & SHO (Med.) Manch. Roy. Infirm.

SHRESTHA, Basant Kumar The Maples Medical Centre, Barnfield Close, Staveley, Chesterfield S43 3UL Tel: 01246 472309 Fax: 01246 470546; 23 Elm Tree Drive, Wingerworth, Chesterfield S42 6QD Tel: 01246 276173 — MB BS 1963 Lucknow; FRCP (Lond.) 1998; MRCP (UK) 1977. (King Geo. Med. Coll. Lucknow) Socs: (Chairm.) Nepalese Doctors Assn. UK. Prev: Regist. (Med.) King's Mill Hosp. Sutton-in-Ashfield; Cons. Phys. Thapathali Kathmandu, Nepal.

SHRESTHA, Mr Bharat Raj 37 Tramway Road, Plymouth PL6 7TQ Tel: 01752 696107 — MB BS 1980 Allanhbad; FRCS Ed. 1992; MRCOphth 1990; DO RCS Eng. 1990. Assoc. Specialist (Ophth.) Taunton & Som. Health Trust. Socs: FRCOphth.

SHRESTHA, Mr Bihari Lal Department of Orthopaedics, Hemel Hempstead General Hospital, Hillfield Road, Hemel Hempstead HP2 4AD Tel: 01442 213141 Fax: 01442 236456; Flat 6, Camden House, Marlowes, Hemel Hempstead HP1 1BE — MB BS 1967 Med. Inst. (I) Rangoon; MSc (Orthop.) Lond. 1987; FRCS Ed. 1975. Staff Grade (Orthop. Surg.) Hemel Hempstead Gen. Hosp. Herts. Prev: Cons. Orthop. Surg. Hargans Nursing Home & TU Teach. Hosp. Nepal; Regist. (Orthop.) Hemel Hempstead Gen. Hosp. Herts.

SHRESTHA, Keshar Lal 74 Castlefields, Houghton-le-Spring DH4 6HJ — MB BS 1968 Calcutta; MRCPsych 1978. (Nilratan Sircar Med. Coll. Calcutta) Cons. Psychiat. Cherry Knowle Hosp. Sunderland.

SHRESTHA, Rekha Department of Obstetrics & Gynaecology, Derriford Hospital, Plymouth PL6 8DH Tel: 01752 777111; 37 Tranmway Road, Plymouth PL6 7TQ — MB BS 1980 Bangalore; MRCOG 1987. Prev: Staff Grade Doctor Plymouth HA.; Regist. (O & G) S.mead Hosp. Bristol, Freedom Fields Hosp. Plymouth & St. Jas. Hosp. Leeds.

SHRESTHA, Subarna Man Oakwood Surgery, Church Street, Mansfield Woodhouse, Mansfield NG19 8BL Tel: 01623 633111 Fax: 01623 423480; 26 North Park, Mansfield NG18 4PB Tel: 01623 21336 — MB BS 1963 Lucknow.

SHRESTHA, Tej Lal Department Medical Microbiology, Pathology Department, District General Hospital, Kayll Road, Sunderland SR4 7TP Tel: 0191 565 6256; 5 Alphine Way, Humbledon Hill, Sunderland SR3 1TN — MB BS Calcutta 1960; MRCPath 1977; Dip. Bact. Manch. 1967; MPH Johns Hopkins 1963. Cons. (Med. Microbiol.) N. RHA. Socs: Assn. Med. Microbiol. & Brit. Soc. Antimicrobiol. & Chemother.; Hosp. Infec. Soc.

SHRIBMAN, Andrew Joseph Lane End Farm, Beat Lane, Rushton Spencer, Macclesfield SK11 0QY Tel: 01260 226304 Email: andrew@laneendfarm.freeserve.co.uk — MB BS 1977 Lond.; FRCA 1981. (Roy. Lond. Hosp. Med. Coll.) Cons. Anaesth. E. Chesh. NHS Trust Macclesfield. Socs: Assn. Anaesth. of GB & Irel.; BMA. Prev: Sen. Regist. (Anaesth.) Leic. HA; Clin. Instruc. (Anaesth.) Med. Coll. Virginia Richmond, USA; Regist. (Anaesth.) Bristol Roy. Infirm.

SHRIBMAN, Jonathan Howard Levitts Surgery, Levitts Road, Bugbrooke, Northampton NN7 3QN Tel: 01604 830348 Fax: 01604 832785; 3 Harrison Court, Bugbrooke, Northampton NN7 3ET Tel: 01604 830380 Fax: 01604 832785 Email: ghs@bugdoc.powernet.co.uk — MB BS 1975 Lond.; MRCP (UK) 1977; MRCGP 1984; DRCOG 1985; DCH RCP Lond. 1983. GP Trainer N.ants. Prev: Trainee GP Moulton N.ampton; Regist. Rotat. (Med.) St. Geo. Hosp. Lond.; SHO (O & G) N.ampton Gen. Hosp.

SHRIBMAN, Sheila Joan Child Development Centre, Northampton General Hospital, Billing Road, Northampton NN1 5BD Tel: 01604 634700; Stonegables, 3 Harrison Court, Bugbrooke, Northampton NN7 3ET Tel: 01604 830380 — MA, MB Camb. 1976, BChir 1975; FRCP Lond. 1993. (Cambridge University Girton College) Med. Director N.ampton Director N.ampton Gen. Hosp. NHS Trust Cliftonville N.ampton NN1 5BD. Socs: Roy. Coll. Paediat. & Child Health; Off. for Workforce Plann. Prev: Sen. Regist. (Paediat.) N.ampton Gen. Hosp.; Sen. Regist. Qu. Mary's Hosp. Carshalton & St. Geo. Hosp.; Clin. Lect. (Paediat. & Pharmacol.) Cardiothoracic Inst. Lond. Rotat.

SHRIDHAR, Sanjiv Wistaston Sugery, Brookland House, 501 Crewe Road, Wistaston, Crewe CW2 6QP; 140 Colleys Lane, Willaston, Nantwich CW5 6NU Tel: 01270 623507 — MB ChB 1988 Dundee; MBA (Masters in Business Administration) 1996; MRCGP 1992. (Dundee) Prev: Trainee GP/SHO Rotat. N. Staffs. Roy. Infirm. VTS; Ho. Off. (Surg.) Leicester Teach. Hosp.; Ho. Off. (Med.) Dundee Teach. Hosps.

SHRIDHAR, Sunita 81 Old Park Avenue, Enfield EN2 6PN; 24 Gelligaer Street, Cathays, Cardiff CF24 4LA — MB BCh 1994 Wales.

SHRIMAN NARAYAN, Mr Ramanthan Harrogate District Hospital, Lancaster Park Road, Harrogate HG2 7SX Tel: 01423 885959; 2 St. Ronans Road, Harrogate HG2 8LE Tel: 01423 886575 — MB BS 1980 Delhi; FRCS Glas. 1990; MS (Orthop.) Delhi 1983. Sen. Staff Orthop. Surg. Harrogate Dist. Hosp. Prev:

Regist. (Orthop.) Grimsby & Newport, Gwent; SHO (Gen. Surg.) Louth.

SHRIMPTON, Grant Russell 6 South Ash, Steyning BN44 3SJ — MB ChB 1991 Otago.

SHRIMPTON, Helen Diane Worvell Cottage, Knole Pit Lane, Knole, Langport TA10 9JD — MB BChir 1992 Camb.

SHRIMPTON, Miranda Kate 31 Alisa Avenue, Twickenham TW1 1NF — MB BS 1995 Lond.

SHRIMPTON, Simon Philip 3 Ashdown House, 17 Rydens Road, Walton-on-Thames KT12 3AB — MB BS 1989 Lond.

SHRIMPTON, Susan Bronwen SmithKline Beecham Parmaceuticals, Welwyn Garden City AL7 1EY Tel: 020 8913 4784 Fax: 020 8913 4492; Clamber Cottage, Northchurch Lane, Ashley Green, Chesham HP5 3PD — MB BChir 1988 Camb.; BA (Path.) Camb. 1984; Dip. Pharm. Med. RCP (UK) 1995; AFPM 1996. (Camb.) Assoc. Dir., Clin. Research & Develop. SmithKline Beecham Pharmaceuts. Welwyn Gdn. City; Head of Product Safety, Smithline Beecham Pharmaceut. UK. Socs: Brit. App.; BrAPP. Prev: Clin. Research Phys. Roche Products Ltd.; Regist. (Clin. Microbiol.) Univ. Coll. Hosp. Lond.; Research Fell. (Path.) N. W.. Memor. Hosp. Chicago, USA.

SHRINATH, Madhukar c/o Drive Sunil Sinha, Gunnergate Lane, Marton, Middlesbrough TS7 8JA — MB BS 1985 Patna; MRCP (UK) 1994.

SHRIVASTAV, Dayanand Prakash 53 High Street, Grimethorpe, Barnsley S72 7BB Tel: 01226 711228 — MB BS 1963 Vikram; BSc, MB BS Vikram 1963.

SHRIVASTAVA, Anupam Departmnt of Paediatrics, Coonsultant Paediatrician, Southend Hospital, Southend-on-Sea SS0 0RY Tel: 01702 221239 Fax: 01702 221252; 140 Barnstaple Road, Thorpe Bay, Southend-on-Sea SS1 3PW Tel: 01702 585122 — MB BS 1983 Calcutta; MRCP (UK) 1991; FRCPCH; M.D(1987). (Calcutta National Medical College, Calcutta) Cons. Paediat. Socs: RCPCH; Fell.; Neonat. Soc.

SHRIVASTAVA, Bhagwan Dayal Jura, Wainfeet Road, Boston PE21 9RW — MB BS 1952 Agra; MRCS Eng. LRCP Lond. 1961; DO Eng. 1957. Socs: Ophth. Soc. UK. Prev: Sen. Ho. Off. Roy. Infirm. Hull; Regist. Ophth. Norf. & Norwich Hosps. & Roy. Hosp. Sheff.

SHRIVASTAVA, Om Prakash The Surgery, Photopia, Limesway, Maltby, Rotherham S66 8JF Tel: 01709 812714 — MB BS 1968 Lucknow.

SHRIVASTAVA, Mr Raj Kumar William Harvey Hospital, Ashford TN24 0LZ Tel: 01233 633331; 67 Primrose Drive, Kingsnorth, Ashford TN23 3NP — MB BS 1979 Indore, India; MCh Liverp. 1988; FRCS (Orth.) 1995; FRCS Glas. 1986; FRCS Ed. 1985. Cons. Orthop. Surg. William Harvey Hosp. Ashford.

SHRIVASTAVA, Rani The Surgery, Photopia, Limesway, Maltby, Rotherham S66 8JF Tel: 01709 812714 — MB BS 1968 Lucknow; DGO Delhi 1973. (G.S.V.M Med. Coll. Kanpur)

SHRIVASTAVA, S K Caerau Lane Surgery, Ely, Cardiff CF5 5HJ Tel: 029 2059 1855 Fax: 029 2059 9739; The Surgery, Caeura Lane, Ely, Cardiff CF5 5 Tel: 01222 591855 — MB BS 1972 Ranchi. (MGM Med. Coll. Jamshedpur) Clin. Asst. (Orthop. & Traum. Surg.) Roy. Gwent Hosp. Newport; Clin. Asst. (Traum. & Orthop. Surg.) Univ. Hosp. of Wales Cardiff. Prev: FICS (Orth.).

SHRIVASTVA, Dwarka Prasad Shrivastva and Partners, 24 Gamble Road, Portsmouth PO2 7BN Tel: 023 9266 0910 Fax: 023 9267 8175 — MB BS 1967 Vikram; MB BS 1967 Vikram.

SHROFF, Behram Jehangir (retired) Holly Bank, Vicarage Road, Halling, Rochester ME2 1BQ Tel: 01634 241896 — MB BS Karachi 1952; LRCP LRCS Ed. LRFPS Glas. 1962.

SHROFF, Katy Jamshed c/o Mrs M. Mountford, 26 Westbourne Park Road, London W2 5PH — MB BS 1976 Punjab; MFFP 1993. Chief Technical Adviser - Romania United Nations Populat. Fund & World Health Organisation (Regional Office for Europe). Prev: Assoc. Dir. Servs. for Wom. Pk.side Health Trust Lond.

SHROFF, Nergish (retired) 5 Bayley Gardens, Naphill, High Wycombe HP14 4QW Tel: 0124024 3099 — MD 1973 Poona; MB BS 1970; MRCOG 1978; FCPS Bombay 1974; DGO Bombay 1972. Prev: Chief Med. Adviser G.D. Searle & Co. Ltd. High Wycombe.

SHROFF, Rekha Whitegates, Maldon Road, Witham CM8 1HU — BM 1997 Soton.

SHROFF, Sandip Brunswick Health Centre, Hartfield Close, Manchester M13 9YA Tel: 0161 273 4901 Fax: 0161 273 5952 — MB ChB 1989 Manch.; BDS Dundee 1981; MRCGP 1993; DRCOG 1992.

SHROFF, Mr Sunil A-81, Annanagar, Madras 600102, India Tel: 00 9 44 6285453 Fax: 00 9 44 6263477 Email: shroff@giasmd01vsnl.net.in; Bridgeford Close, Gorleston, Great Yarmouth NR31 6SS — MB BS 1979 Patna; FRCS Glas. 1986. Assoc. Prof. Urol. & Renal Transpl. Sri Ramachandra Med. Coll. & Research Inst. Madras, India. Socs: Brit. Assn. Urol. Surgs. Prev: Clin. Lect. (Renal Transpl. Surg.) Roy. Lond. Hosp.; Clin. Lect. (Urol.) Univ. Coll. Lond. & St. Peter's Hosp. Lond.; Regist. (Urol.) OldCh. Hosp. Romford.

SHROTRI, Mrs Keyuri Nitin 19 Warden Close, Maidstone ME16 0JL — MB BS 1983 Gujarat; MRCOG 1995. Trust Doctor (O & G) Maidstone Hosp. Maidstone. Prev: Regist. (O & G).

SHROTRI, Mr Nitin Chandrakant 19 Warden Close, Maidstone ME16 0JL — MB BS 1983 Baroda; MB BS Baroda India 1983, MS Gen. Surg. 1986; FRCS Glas. 1993. Specialist Regist. (Urol.) Medway Hosp. Gillingham. Socs: Assoc. Mem. BAUS; Assoc. Mem. BSFE. Prev: Specialist Regist. Lithotristor Unit, St. Thoms. Hosp. Lond.

SHROTRIA, Ms Sunita Tel: 01784 884607 — MB BS 1982; FRCS 1989; MS 1985. Cons. Gen. Surg. with an interest in brE.. Ashford Hosp., Lond. Rd.. Middlx YW15 3AA. Socs: Surg. Research Soc.; Brit. Assoc. of Surgic. Oncologists.

SHROUDER, Raymond David 3 School Lane, Old Somerby, Grantham NG33 4AH — MB ChB 1992 Leic.

SHROUFI, Mr Shamsi St. Mary's, Craig Road, Dumfries DG1 4EU Tel: 01387 2732 — MD 1960 Istanbul; FRCS Glas. 1981. Orthop. Regist. Dumfries & Galloway Health Bd.

SHRUBB, Valerie Ann Ashurst Child & Family Centre, Lyndhurst Road, Ashurst, Southampton SO40 7AR Tel: 02380 743097 Fax: 02380 743033 Email: pat.charman@schs.nhs.uk; 27 Westbroke Gardens, Fishlake Meadows, Romsey SO51 7RQ — MB BS 1975 Lond.; MRCP 1979; FRCP Lond. 1994; MRCS Eng. LRCP Lond. 1975; FRCPCH 1997. (King's Coll. Hosp.) Cons. Paediat. (Community Child Health) Soton. Community Health Servs. Trust; Hon. Sen. Lect. (Community Paediat.) UMDS Guy's & Thos. Hosps. Lond. Socs: Brit. Assn. Community Child Health. Prev: Cons. Paediat. (Community Child Health) Lewisham & S.wark HA.

SHUAIB, M Swanlow Medical Centre, 60 Swanlow Lane, Winsford CW7 1JF Tel: 01606 862868 — MB BS 1965 Punjab; MB BS 1965 Punjab.

SHUBHAKER, Undinti David Cranbrook Road Surgery, 700 Cranbrook Road, Ilford IG6 1HP Tel: 020 8551 2341 Fax: 020 8551 1479 — MB BS 1965 Osmania.

SHUBHAKER, Urmila Cranbrook Road Surgery, 700 Cranbrook Road, Ilford IG6 1HP Tel: 020 8551 2341 Fax: 020 8551 1479 — MB BS 1971 Osmania.

SHUBSACHS, Alexander Philip Woolf Marlborough House Regional Secure Unit, Milton Keynes Community NHS Trust, Hospital Campus, Standing Way, Eaglestone, Milton Keynes MK6 5NG Tel: 01908 243050 — MB BS 1980 Lond.; BSc (Hons.) Psychol. Manch. 1968; MRCPsych 1986. (St. Mary's) Med. Dir. & Cons. Forens. Psychiat. MarlBoro. Hse. Regional Secure Unit Bucks.Ment. Health NHS Trust Milton Keynes Hosp. Campus, Milton Keynes. Socs: BMA; Roy. Coll. Psych. (Forens. Psych. Div.); Fell.Roy. Soc. of Med. Prev: Clin. Dir. & Cons. Forens. Psychiat. Rampton Hosp.; Lect. & Hon. Sen. Regist. (Forens. Psychiat.) Univ. of Edin.; Regist. Roy. Edin. Hosp.

SHUCKSMITH, Mary Richardson (retired) 9 Nichols Way, Wetherby LS22 6AD — MB ChB 1945 Leeds. Prev: SCMO Leeds AHA (T).

SHUFFLEBOTHAM, Jonathan Quinn 4 Berne Avenue, Newcastle ST5 2QJ — MB ChB 1996 Leeds.

SHUI, Elizabeth Margaret Yee-Lai Athena Medical Centre, 21 Atherden Road, Clapton, London E5 0QP Tel: 020 8985 6675 Fax: 020 8533 7775; 21 Rolls Park Road, Chingford, London E4 9BH — MB ChB 1980 Sheff.; MRCGP 1984; DRCOG 1983. GP Hackney; Med. Adviser Hackney Chinese Community Servs. Prev: Ho. Surg. & Ho. Phys. Roy. Hosp. Chesterfield; Trainee GP Chesterfield VTS.

SHUJA, Mr Mushtaq Ahmed East Surrey Hospital, Canada Avenue, Redhill RH1 5RH Tel: 01737 768511; 25 Avondale Close, Horley RH6 8BN Tel: 01293 785615 — MB BS 1978 Punjab; MB BS Punjab, Pakistan 1978; FRCS Glas. 1987; Dip. Urol. Lond 1990.

SHUJAAT

Trust Urol. (Sen. Trust Doctor, Urol.), E. Surrey Hosp., Redhill, Surrey, Eng. Prev: Cons. Urol., Fauti Foundat. Hosp. Rawal pindi-Pakistian; Regist. Surg. & Urol., Mayday Univ. Hosp., Mayday Rd., Thorton Heath, Lond.

***SHUJAAT, Rosina** Yorkhill NHS Trust, Yorkhill, Glasgow G3 8SJ; 1FR 102 Dorcester Avenue, Kelvindale, Glasgow G12 0EB Tel: 0141 339 3414 — MB ChB 1997 Ed.

SHUJJA-UD-DIN, Omar Sadeeq 3 Tadcaster Road, Copmanthorpe, York YO23 3UL — MB ChB 1997 Sheff.

SHUKER, John Philip The Yard House, 20A The Green, Garsington, Oxford OX44 9DF — MB ChB 1997 Birm.

SHUKER, Mr Makki Tawfeeq 32 Clarewood Court, Seymour Place, London W1H 2NL Tel: 020 7724 6410 — MB ChB 1969 Mosul; MSc Manch. 1980; FRCS Ed. 1990.

SHUKLA, Avinash Chandra 3 Patent House, 48 Morris Road, London E14 6NU — MB BS 1989 Lond.

SHUKLA, Chitranjan Jitendrarai 33 Peters Close, Stanmore HA7 4SB — MB BS 1998 Lond.; MB BS Lond 1998.

SHUKLA, Dolarrai Keshavlal (retired) 20 Lawrence Crescent, Edgware Tel: 020 8952 8741 — LAH Dub. 1960.

SHUKLA, Mr Kamal Kant 84 North End Road, West Kensington, London NW11 7SY Tel: 020 7603 7901 Fax: 020 7602 7167 — MB BS 1975 Banaras Hindu; MB BS Banaras Hindu Univ. India 1975; FRCS Glas. 1980. Clin. Asst. (ENT) W. Middlx. Hosp. Isleworth. Prev: Regist. (ENT) N.wick Pk. Hillingdon & Mt. Vernon Hosp. Watford.

SHUKLA, Mr Prabhakar Basantlal c/o Drive Uday Andar, Flat 9 Doctors Residence, Hospital for Sick Children, Great Ormond St., London WC1N 3JH — MB BS 1973 Rajasthan; MS Gujarat 1978; FRCS Ed. 1983. (R.N.T. Med. Coll. Udaipur) Prev: SHO Rotat. (Surg.) N. Staffs. Roy. Infirm. Stoke-on-Trent.

SHUKLA, Mr Rajendra Balkrishna Dukes Medical Centre, 1 Lankers Drive, North Harrow, Harrow HA2 7PA Tel: 020 8868 5268; 140 Streatfield Road, Harrow HA3 9BU Tel: 020 8206 0263 Fax: 020 8206 0263 Email: shukla_dr@yahoo.com — LRCP LRCS 1980 Ed.; MS Gujarat 1976, MB BS 1972; LRCP LRCS Ed. LRCPS Glas. 1980; FRCSI 1979. Surg. Regist. Roy. Free Hosp. Lond.; GP. Socs: Med. Mem. Disabil. Appeal Tribunal; Local Med. Comm. Mem. Prev: Regist. (Gen. Surg.) Guy's & King's Coll. Hosp. Lond.; Regist. (Surg.) St. Vincent's Hosp. & Jas. Connolly Memor. Hosp. Dub.; Lect. (Surg.) Cancer Research Inst. Ahmedabad India.

SHUKLA, Rashmita — BM 1984 Soton.; FFPHM 2001; MRCP (UK) 1988; MFPHM RCP (UK) 1993. Cons. in Pub. Health Med., Leics. Halth. Prev: Cons. Communicable Dis. Control Leics. Health; Sen. Regist. (Pub. Health Med.) Trent RHA; Regist. (Pub. Health Med.) Trent RHA.

SHUKLA, Vinod Kumar 28 Bolton Brow, Sowerby Bridge, Halifax — BM 1983 Soton.

SHUKLA, Yashwant Prataprai H.M.Y.O.I Lancaster Farms, Far Moor Lane, Stone Row Head, Off Quernmore Road, Lancaster LA1 3QZ Tel: 01524 848745 Fax: 01524 849308 — MB BS 1974 Gujarat; DPM RCP Lond. 1981. Med. Off. HM Young Offenders Inst. Lancaster. Prev: Clin. Asst. Psychiat. Roy. Albert Hosp. Lancaster; Regist. (Psychiat.) Pk.side Hosp. Macclesfield & Cranage Hall Hosp.

SHUKRALLA, Zekiya Amin 13 Hookstone Wood Road, Harrogate HG2 8PN — MB ChB Baghdad 1967; MRCOG Lond. 1992; DObst. RCPI Dub. 1976; (DGO)TC Dub. 1976. Cons. (O & G) New Mowasat Hosp. Kuwait Hosp. Kuwait. Socs: Fell. Amer. Med. Soc. (Obst. & Gyn.) Vienna Univ. 1985; Pan Amer. Assn. 1997. Prev: Clin. Asst. (GU Med.) Maelori Hosp.; Clin. Asst. (O & G) Warrington Hosp.

SHULMAN, Caroline Esther London School of Tropical Medicine, Keppel St., London WC1 7HT; 30 Hoodcote Gardens, Winchmore Hill, London N21 2NE Tel: 020 8360 8905 — MB BS 1984 Lond.; MRCGP 1989; DRCOG 1988; DCH RCP Lond. 1986.

SHUM, Chau Ming Walderslade Village Surgery, 62A Robin Hood Lane, Walderslade, Chatham ME5 9LD Tel: 01634 687250; 10 Barncroft Drive, Hempstead, Gillingham ME7 3TJ Email: c.shum@which.net — MB BS 1988 Lond.; MRCGP 1993; T(GP) 1993; DCH RCP Lond. 1992; DRCOG 1991. Partner GP Princip.; Research Assoc. UMDS.

SHUM, Kid Wan Department of Dermatology, Royal Hallamshire, Glossop Rd, Sheffield S10 2JF Tel: 0114 271 1900 Fax: 0114 271 3763 Email: k.w.shum@sheffield.ac.uk — MB BChir 1994 Camb.; MA Camb. 1995, BA 1991; MRCP Lond. 1997. (Camb.) Socs: Roy. Coll. of Phys.s, Lond.; Trainee Mem. Brit. Assn. Dermatol.s; Brit. Soc. of Paediat. Dermat.

SHUM, Poh Lin 17 Burnview Drive, Carryduff, Belfast BT8 8DD Tel: 02890 814546 — MB BCh BAO 1987 Belf. (Queen's University Belfast) Specialist Regist. (Radiother. & Oncol.). Socs: Irish Assn. Cancer Research; Mem. Roy. Coll. Radiol.

SHUM, Wing Kwan Flat 31 The Quadrangle, London W2 2RN — MB BChir 1980 Camb.; BSc Lond. 1972; PhD Camb. 1975, MB BChir 1980. Socs: Brit. Pharmacol. Soc.

SHUMSHERUDDIN, Dean Mohammed 61 Newlands Road, Stirchley, Birmingham B30 2SA — MB ChB 1981 Birm.

SHUN-SHIN, Mr Georges Adrien Wolverhampton & Midland Counties Eye Infirmary, Compton Road, Wolverhampton WV3 9QR Tel: 01902 645006 Fax: 01902 645019; 15 Waterdale, Compton, Wolverhampton WV3 9DY Tel: 01902 710564 Email: g@shun-shin.co.uk — MB BS 1978 Lond.; FRCS (Ophth.) Glas. 1982; DO RCS Eng. 1982; FRCOphth Lond. 1990. (Guy's) Cons. Ophth. Wolverhampton & Midl. Counties Eye Infirm.; Cons Ophth. Manor Hosp. Walsall. Socs: (Treas.) Assn. Eye Research. Prev: Clin. Lect. & Hon. Sen. Regist. Oxf. Eye Hosp.; Research Fell. (Ophth.) Nuffield Laborat. Ophth. Oxf.; Regist. (Ophth.) Roy. Vict. Hosp. Bournemouth.

SHUR, Eric The Priory Hospital, Priory Lane, Roehampton, London SW15 5JJ Tel: 020 8392 4201/ 876 8261 Fax: 020 8876 4015; 10 Harley Street, London W1G 9PF Tel: 020 7467 8300 — MB BCh 1973 Witwatersrand; MPhil (Psych.) Lond. 1981; MRCPsych 1979; FRCPsych 1996. Dep. Med. Dir. Priory Hosp. Roehampton; Clin. Tutor Priory Hosp. Roehampton; Hon. Research Fell. Char. Cross Med. Sch. Lond. Prev: Cons. Psychiat. W.m. Hosp. Lond.; Sen. Lect. (Psychiat.) Char. Cross Med. Sch. Lond.

SHURMER, David Milne The Stannington Health Centre, Uppergate Road, Stannington, Sheffield S6 6BX Tel: 0114 234 8779 Fax: 0114 285 4778 — MB ChB 1986 Sheff.

SHURZ, Alison Mary Lucy 44A Harmer Green Lane, Welwyn AL6 0AT Tel: 0143871 4632 — MB ChB Bristol 1962; FRCP Lond. 1987; DCH Eng. 1965. (Bristol) Cons. Paediatr. & Clin. Dir. Qu. Eliz. II Hosp. Welwyn Garden City. Socs: Fell. Roy. Soc. Med.; Brit. Paediat. Assn. Prev: Sen. Regist. (Paediat.) St. Mary's Hosp. Lond.; Regist. (Paediat. Cardiol.) Roy. Liverp. Childr. Hosp.; Regist. (Med.) S.mead Hosp. Bristol.

SHUSTER, Professor Sam The Medical School, University of Newcastle, Newcastle upon Tyne — MB BS 1951 Lond.; PhD Lond. 1956, MB BS 1951; FRCP Lond. 1969, M 1958. (Univ. Coll. Hosp.) Emerit. Prof. Dermat. Univ. Newc. Prev: Sen. Lect. (Clin. Dermat.) Inst. Dermat. Univ. Lond.; Lect. (Med.) Welsh Nat. Sch. Med. Cardiff; Research Asst. (Physiol.) Univ. Coll. Lond. & Roy. Postgrad. Med.Sch. Lond.

SHUTE, Christine Mary Child Adolescent Family Centre, Ewq House, Surbiton Tel: 020 8390 8151; 5 Orchard Road, Chessington KT9 1AJ — MB ChB 1971 Liverp.; MFCH RCP (UK) 1991. Community Paediat. (SCMO). Kingston & Dist. Community Health Trust. Socs: Soc. Pub. Health. Prev: Clin. Med. Off. Kingston & Richmond DHA.; SHO (Anaesth.) Liverp. Roy. Infirm.; Ho. Off. Sefton Gen. Hosp. Liverp.

SHUTE, Jennifer Catherine Llangybi House, Llangybi, Usk NP15 1NP Tel: 01633 450644 — BM BCh 1974 Oxf.; MA Oxf. 1974. GP Doctors Retainer Scheme Caerleon. Prev: Regist. (Anaesth.) St. Thos. Hosp. Lond.

SHUTE, Justin Telford 5 Ferdinand Street, London NW1 8ES Tel: 020 7916 4307 — MB BS 1993 Lond.; MRCP Lond. 1996. (Roy. Lond. Hosp.) SHO (Psychiat.) Rotat. UCH, Lond.

SHUTE, Mr Kenneth Llangybi House, Llangybi, Usk NP15 1NP Tel: 01633 450644 — MB BS 1968 Lond.; MS 1978 Lond.; FRCS Eng 1972. Cons. Gen. Surg. Roy. Gwent Hosp. Newport. Prev: Sen. Regist. (Gen. Surg.) Nottm. Gen. Hosp.; Wellcome Research Fell. & Lect Surg. St. Thos. Hosp. Lond.; Regist. St. Thos. Hosp. Lond.

SHUTE, Pauline Ericka Child Development Centre, Southlands Hospital, Shoreham-by-Sea BN43 5TQ Tel: 01273 446017 Fax: 01273 446065; Windmill House, 11 Mill Hill, Shoreham-by-Sea BN43 5TG Tel: 01273 463420 — MB BS 1975 Lond.; MSc Univ. Lond. 1991; MRCS Eng. LRCP Lond. 1975; DCH RCP Lond. 1991; DRCOG 1979. (Roy. Free) Cons. Community Child Health Worthing

Priory Care NHS Trust. Socs: Brit. Paediat. Assn.; Brit. Assn. Community Child Health.

SHUTE, Philip Alan Barton Surgery, Lymington House, Barton Hill Way, Torquay TQ2 8JG Tel: 01803 323761 Fax: 01803 316920; Court Barton Farm Cottage, Coffinswell, Newton Abbot TQ12 4SS Tel: 01803 872736 — MB BS 1980 Lond.; MRCGP 1984; DRCOG 1985. (St. Mary's Hospital University of London)

SHUTE, Scott George Andre 14 Emmett Road, Rownhams, Southampton SO16 8JB Tel: 02380 731069 — MRCS Eng. LRCP Lond. 1947. Prev: Ho. Surg. (ENT & Orthop.) Guy's Hosp. Lond.; Cas. Off., Ho. Surg., Ho.Phys., & Resid.Off. Stamford, Rutland & Gen. Infirm.

SHUTES, Jonathan Charles Blackwell Woodcock Road Surgery, 29 Woodcock Road, Norwich NR3 3UA Tel: 01603 425989 Fax: 01603 425989; Gildencroft, 56 Norwich Road, Horsham St. Faith, Norwich NR10 3AE Tel: 01603 891495 — MB BS 1972 Lond.; 2001 Dip Pall Med (UCW); MRCS Eng. LRCP Lond. 1972; DA Eng. 1977; DRCOG 1975. Staff Grade Palliat. Care Norf. & Norwich Univ. Hosp. Prev: Clin. Asst. (Anaesth.) Norf. & Norwich Hosp.

SHUTKEVER, Martin Paul Station Lane Medical Centre, Featherstone, Pontefract WF7 6JL Tel: 01977 600381 Fax: 01977 600776 — MB ChB 1980 Leeds; LLM 1997 Cardiff Univ.; MRCGP 1984; DRCOG 1982. Gen. Practitioner, Featherstone; Professional Exec. CTTE Mem., E.. Wakefield PCT. Socs: Law Soc. Checked Expert Register. Prev: Chief Resid. K. Edwd. VII Memor. Hosp. Bermuda; SHO (A & E) St. Jas. Hosp. Leeds; Ho. Off. (Surg.) ScarBoro. Hosp.

SHUTT, Mr Adrian Michael COU Kisiizi Hospital, PO Box 109, Kabale, Uganda Fax: 00871 761 587166 Email: kisiizi@bushnet.net; 12 Blackbrook Close, Walkhampton, Yelverton PL20 6JF Tel: 01822 854653 — MB BS 1986 Lond.; FRCS Eng. 1991; DTM&H 1999. (St. Mary's Hosp. Lond.) Chief Surg., COU Kissizi Hosp. Kabale, Uganda. Prev: Specialist Regist. (Surg.) Soton. Gen. Hosp.; Specialist Regist. (Surg.) Qu. Alexandra Hosp. Portsmouth; Regist. (Surg.) Wessex PostFell.sh. Train. Scheme.

SHUTT, James David 84 Collingworth Rise, Park Gate, Southampton SO31 1DB — BM 1998 Soton.; BM Soton 1998.

SHUTT, Leslie Ernest Sir Humphry Davy Department of Anaesthesia, Bristol Royal Infirmary, Bristol BS2 8HW Tel: 0117 928 2163 Fax: 0117 928 5209; Dyrham House, 1 Dyrham Close, Henleaze, Bristol BS9 4TF Tel: 0117 942 3332 — MB ChB 1969 Sheff.; FFA RCS Eng. 1973. Cons. Anaesth. (Teach.) United Bristol Health Care NHS Trust. Socs: Assn. Anaesth. GB & Irel. & Soc. Anaesth. S. W.. Region. Prev: Sen. Regist. (Anaesth.) Avon AHA (T); Vis. Asst. Prof. (Anaesth.) Univ. Virginia Med. Center, USA; Regist. (Anaesth.) United Sheff. Hosps.

SHUTTE, Helen Anna Neale Rookwood, Rushmere Lane, Denmead, Waterlooville PO7 6HA — MB BS 1998 Lond.; MB BS Lond 1998.

SHUTTLEWORTH, Barbara Joyce (retired) Linden House, Northbrook Avenue, Winchester SO23 0JW Tel: 01962 861142 — MA Oxf. 1948, BM BCh 1945; DPH Manch. 1954; DObst RCOG 1949. Prev: Clin. Asst. (Psychiat.) Basingstoke Dist. Hosp.

SHUTTLEWORTH, Caroline Angela Rose 57 Riddlesdown Road, Purley CR8 1DJ Tel: 020 8668 3651 — MB BS 1990 Lond.; BA Oxf. 1987; DFFP 1992. Community Med. Off. Croydon Community Health.

SHUTTLEWORTH, David Essex County Hospital, Lexden Road, Colchester CO3 3NB Tel: 01206 744435 Fax: 01206 744756; Cattles Barn, Chappel Road, Fordham, Colchester CO6 3LT Tel: 01206 241428 Email: davidsderm@aol.com — MB BS 1977 Lond.; MRCP (UK) 1980. (Univ. Coll. Hosp.) Cons. Dermat. Essex Rivers Healthcare.

SHUTTLEWORTH, Doris Kathleen (retired) 44 West Street, Scarborough YO11 2QP Tel: 01723 72308 — MRCS Eng. LRCP Lond. 1922.

SHUTTLEWORTH, Garry Neil 12 Crescent Walk, West Parley, Wimborne — MB BS 1991 Lond.

SHUTTLEWORTH, Herbert John (retired) 2 Galloway House, West Burton, Leyburn DL8 4JW Tel: 01969 663460 — MB ChB Liverp. 1939. Prev: Cas. Off. Liverp. Stanley Hosp.

SHWEIKH, Mr Amir Musa Diana Princess of Wales Hospital, Accident & Emergency Department, Scartho Road, Grimsby DN33 2BA Tel: 01472 822211 — MB ChB 1974 Baghdad; FRCS Glas. 1984; FFAEM. Cons. A&E Diana P.ss of Wales.Hosp. Socs: BMA; Brit. Assn. A&E. Med; Fell.Fac.A&E.Med.

SHYAM SUNDAR, Ananthaiah University Hospital of North Tees, North Tees & Hartlepool NHS Trust, Hardwick, Stockton-on-Tees TS19 8PE Tel: 01624 624948, 01642 624194, 01642 642195 Fax: 01642 624948 Email: ananthaiah.shyam-sundar@nth.northy.nhs.uk; 26 Hemingford Gardens, Yarm TS15 9ST Tel: 01642 789435 — MB BS 1981 Bangalore; MRCP (UK) 1992; T(M) 1995; FRCP Ed. 1998; FRCP London 2000. (Bangalore Med. Coll.) Cons. Phys. (Cardiol.) N. Tees Gen. Hosp. & Hon. Cons. Cardiol. S. Cleveland Hosp. S.Tees Acute Hosps. NHS Trust. Socs: Brit. Cardiac Soc.; Brit. Cardiac Interven. Soc.; Eur. Soc. Cardiol. (Mem. Working Gp. Coronary Circ.). Prev: Career Sen. Regist. (Cardiol.) & Sen. Research Fell. Roy. Infirm. Edin.; Regist. (Cardiol.) Univ. Hosp. Wales Cardiff; Regist. (Cardiol.) All India Inst. Med. Sci. New Delhi, India.

SHYAMAPANT, Sanjay 7 Silverbirch Close, Little Stoke, Bristol BS34 6RL — MB BCh 1995 Wales.

SIALA, Maria-Danuta Beeches Surgery, 9 Hill Road, Carshalton Beeches, Carshalton SM5 3RB Tel: 0208 681 7825 Email: maria@danuta-siala.freeserve.co.uk; 33 Manor Way, South Croydon CR2 7BT Tel: 0208 681 7825 — MB ChB 1964 Bristol; DObst RCOG 1966; Cert. Family Plann. JCC 1981; Cert. Prescribed Equiv. Exp. JCPTGP 1981. p/t GP Carshalton Beeches. Socs: Polish Doctors Med. Soc. Prev: Regist. (Paediat.) INAS Hosp. Tripoli.

SIAN, Surinder Singh Spinney Hill Medical Centre, 143 St. Saviours Road, Leicester LE5 3HX Tel: 0116 251 7870 Fax: 0116 262 9816 — MB ChB 1989 Dundee.

SIANI, Nanjit Mavji Argyll Road Surgery, 48 Argyll Road, Westcliff on Sea SS0 7HN Tel: 01702 432040 — MB BS 1976 Sri Venkateswara; JCPTGP 1985; Cert. Family Plann. JCC 1985. p/t Clin. Asst. (Genitourin. Med.) S.end Gen. Hosp. Prev: Regist. & SHO (Gerontol.) Univ. Hosp. Wales & St. Davids Hosp. Cardiff; Clin. Asst. (Geriat. Med.) Llandough Hosp. Cardiff; SHO (Psychiat.) E. Glam. Gen. Hosp. Pontypridd.

SIANN, Tanya Linda Audit Co-ordinator, Audit Resource & Training Centre, Kirklands Hospital, Fallside Road, Bothwell, Glasgow G71 8BU Tel: 0141 854637 Fax: 0141852517; 5 Wheatland Drive, Lanark ML11 7QG Email: tanya_siann@msn.com — MB ChB 1983 Aberd.; MPH Glas. 1990; MRCGP 1988. Clin. Audit. Co-ordinator Lanarksh. HB. Prev: Sen. Regist. (Pub. Health Med.) Lanarksh. HB.

SIAS, Alessandro 31 Downleaze, Sneyd Park, Bristol BS9 1LU — State Exam 1993 Cagliari.

SIBBALD, Alan Ramsay (retired) 7 Glen Chess, Loudwater Lane, Rickmansworth WD3 4HQ Tel: 01923 772989 — MB ChB 1935 Liverp. Prev: Sen. Med. Off. Brit. Overseas Airways.

SIBBALD, Barbara (retired) Ashiestiel, 42 Drumcross Road, Bathgate EH48 1AR Tel: 01506 652745 — MB ChB 1956 Ed. Prev: GP Bathgate.

SIBBALD, David Stewart (retired) Ashiestiel, 42 Drumcross Road, Bathgate EH48 1AR Tel: 01506 652745 — MB ChB 1956 Ed. Prev: GP Bathgate.

SIBBALD, Duncan McQueen 37 Vernon Terrace, Brighton BN1 3JH Tel: 01273 773089 — MB ChB 1942 St. And. (St. And.)

SIBBALD, Robert (retired) 10 Meadow View, Barwick-in-Elmet, Leeds LS15 4NZ — MB ChB Manch. 1961; FRCPath. 1981, M 1969. Prev: Cons. Pathol. Pontefract Gen. Infirm.

SIBBALD, Robert James Inglis (retired) Prospect Lodge, 38 Dean Hill, Plymstock, Plymouth PL9 9AD Tel: 01752 402146 Fax: 01752 480312 — MB BChir 1963 Camb.; MA Camb. 1963; MRCS Eng. LRCP Lond. 1962; FRCGP 1981, M 1970; DCH Eng. 1968; DObst RCOG 1964. Macmillan GP Facilitator in Cancer & Palliat. Med. Plymouth Postgrad. Med. Sch.; Lect. (Primary Health Care & Gen. Pract.) Plymouth Postgrad. Med. Sch. Prev: GP Princip. Plymouth 1965-98.

SIBBEL-LINZ, Anna-Katharina 80 Merton Hall Road, London SW19 3PZ — MB ChB 1997 Birm.

SIBBERING, Mr David Mark Derby City General Hospital, Uttoxeter Road, Derby DE22 3NE Tel: 01332 625537 Fax: 01332 625696; 7 Adelphi Close, Littleover, Derby DE23 7XJ Tel: 01332 523851 — MB BS 1986 Lond.; FRCS Ed. 1991. (St. Thos. Hosp. Med. Sch.) Cons. Surg. (BrE. Dis.) Derby City Gen. Hosp. Prev: Lect. (Surg.) Univ. Nottm.; Hon. Sen. Regist. Mid. Trent Higher Surgic.

SIBELLAS

Train. Scheme; Research Fell. (BrE. Dis.) Profess. Unit. Surg. Nottm. City Hosp.

SIBELLAS, Mary (retired) Banjo Lodge, Common Road, Great Wakering, Southend-on-Sea SS3 0AG Tel: 01702 217458 — MRCS Eng. LRCP Lond. 1957; MD Lond. 1975, MB BS 1957; FFCM 1985, M 1977; T(PHM) 1991; DTM & H Liverp. 1966. Prev: Dir. (Pub. Health) S. Essex HA.

SIBERRY, Hazel Margaret Liffock Surgery, 69 Sea Road, Castlerock, Coleraine BT51 4TW Tel: 028 7084 8206 Fax: 028 7084 9146 — MB BCh BAO 1975 Belf.; MRCGP 1980. (Belf.)

SIBERT, Professor Jonathan Richard Department of Child Health, University of Wales College of Medicine, Academic Centre, Llandough Hospital, Penarth CF64 2XX Tel: 02920 716934 Fax: 02920 350140 Email: sibert@cardiff.ac.uk — MB BChir Camb. 1967; MD Camb. 1977, MA 1967; FRCP Lond. 1986; MRCP (UK) 1971; FRCPCH 1997, MRCPCH 1996; DCH Eng. 1971; DObst RCOG 1969. (Camb. & Univ. Coll. Hosp.) Prof. Community Child Health Univ. Wales Coll. Med.; Head of Dep. Of Child Health Univ. Wales Coll. Med. Socs: (Prev. Chairm.) Brit. Assn. Comm. Child Health; Fell. Roy. Coll. Paediat. & Child Health; Nat. Commiss. Preven. Child Abuse. Prev: Cons. Paediat. (Community CHild Health) S. Glam. HA; Regist. (Paediat.) Newc.

SIBERY, Ashley James 11 Enstone, Skelmersdale WN8 6AW — MB ChB 1997 Manch.

SIBLEY, Anna Clare 2A Helmshore Road, Haslingden, Rossendale BB4 4BG — MB ChB 1990 Manch.

SIBLEY, Eric George, ERD (retired) 10 Canon Drive, Barnack, Stamford PE9 3EG Tel: 01780 740382 — MRCS Eng. LRCP Lond. 1931. Prev: Mem. GP Staff Qu. Vict. Hosp. E. Grinstead.

SIBLEY, Mr Gary Neil Andrew Department of Urology, Bristol Royal Infirmary, Bristol BS2 8HW — BM BCh 1975 Oxf.; BSc (Anat. Hons.) Bristol 1972; MCh Oxf. 1985, DM 1985, BM BCh 1975; FRCS Eng. 1979. Cons. Urol. Surg. Bristol Roy. Infirm. Prev: Clin. Lect. (Urol.) Addenbrooke's Hosp. Camb.; Surgic. Regist. Radcliffe Infirm. Oxf.; Research Fell. Urol. Ch.ill Hosp. Oxf.

SIBLEY, James Anthony Pant-y-Crywn, Letterston, Haverfordwest SA62 5TR Tel: 01348 840897 — MB ChB 1964 Bristol; DObst RCOG 1968.

SIBLEY, Yvonne Diane Leslie (retired) 15 Weylands Grove, Salford M6 7WX — BM BCh 1971 Oxf.; BSc Bristol 1968; FRCS Eng. 1977. Prev: Cons. Paediat. Cardiol. Roy. Manch. Childr. Hosp.

SIBLEY-CALDER, Ian Clifford Eastgate Medical Group, 37 Eastgate, Hornsea HU18 1LP Tel: 01964 532212 Fax: 01964 535007; Westfield, Westwood Avenue, Hornsea HU18 1EE Tel: 01964 534925 Email: sibcald@aol.com — MB BS 1983 Lond.; DRCOG 1986; DCCH RCGP & FCM 1986; Cert. Family Plann. JCC 1985. (St. Bart.) Med. Off. Child Developm. Clinic Hornsea; Mem. (Comm.) UK Sport Diving Med. Comms.; HSE Approved for Commercial Diving Med. Exams.

SIBLY, Mr Thomas Franklin Wye Valley Nuffield Hospital, Venns Lane, Hereford HR1 1DF Tel: 01432 265184 Fax: 01432 265184 Email: frank.silby@talk21.com — MB BS 1982 Lond.; MA Oxf. 1979; FRCS Eng. 1986. (Univ. Coll. Hosp.) Cons. Orthop. Surg. Gen. Hosp. Hereford. Socs: Assoc. Mem. Brit. Soc. Surg. Hand; Brit. Orthop. Assn. Prev: Sen. Regist. (Orthop.) Harlow Wood Orthop. Hosp. & Derbysh. Roy. Infirm.; Regist. (Orthop.) Newc. u. Tyne; N.. Region Research Fell. Durh. Univ. Dept. Bioengin.

SIBSON, Mr Derek Edmund 24 Poplars Farm Road, Barton Seagrave, Kettering NN15 5AF Tel: 01536 512376 — MB 1961 Camb.; BA Camb. 1957, MB 1961; BChir 1960; FRCS Eng. 1966; DObst RCOG 1962. (St. Bart.) Cons. Surg. Kettering Gen. Hosp. Prev: Lect. (Surg.) St. Bart. Hosp. Lond.; Surg. Regist. St. Stephen's Hosp. Lond. & St. Jas. Hosp. Balham.

SIBSON, Keith Richard 24 Poplars Farm Road, Barton Seagrave, Kettering NN15 5AF — MB ChB 1995 Sheff.; MRCP (UK). (Sheffield) Paediat. Reg.W. Middx.Hosp. Prev: SHO paediat.Gt.Ormond.St.Hosp.; SHO Neonat..UCL.Hosp; SHO Community.Paediat.Camden & Islington.

SIBTAIN, Ameenussalam 73 Kynaston Road, London N16 0EB — MB BS 1991 Lond.

SIBTHORPE, Elsie Margaret (retired) Flat 2, Hetton Lodge, 6 Ferndale, Tunbridge Wells TN2 3RU — MD Lond. 1953, MB BS 1945; FRCOG 1966, M 1951. Prev: Cons. Gynaecol. Mildmay Miss. Hosp.

SIBTHORPE, John Oliver Ansteys, New Road, Hemingford Abbots, Huntingdon PE28 9AB — MB BS 1958 Lond.; MRCS Eng. LRCP Lond. 1958; DO Eng. 1963; DObst RCOG 1960. (King's Coll. Hosp.) Clin. Asst. (Ophth.) Addenbrooke's Hosp. Camb. Socs: Midl. Ophth. Soc. Prev: SHO (Ophth.) Qu. Eliz. Hosp. Birm.; Ho. Off. Beckenham Matern. Hosp.; Ho. Phys. Brook Gen. Hosp. Woolwich.

SIBTHORPE, Richard John 58B Ritherdon Road, London SW17 8QG — MB BS 1984 Lond.

SICHA, Marenka Anna Northgate Surgery, Church Street, Uttoxeter ST14 8AG Tel: 01889 562010 Fax: 01889 568948; 3 Milverton Drive, Uttoxeter ST14 7RE Tel: 01889 563739 — MB ChB 1984 Birm.; MRCGP 1988; DRCOG 1987.

SICHEL, Gerald Robert Mackenzie (retired) 1 Groomsland Drive, Billingshurst RH14 9HA Tel: 01403 786905 — MB BS 1943 Lond.; MRCS Eng. LRCP Lond. 1942; MRCGP 1973; FFCM 1978, M 1974. Prev: DMO Tunbridge Wells Health Auth.

SICHEL, John Henry Sylvester Beaumont Street Surgery, 28 Beaumont Street, Oxford OX1 2NT Tel: 01865 311811 Fax: 01865 310327; 13 Park Town, Oxford OX2 6SN Tel: 01865 515636 — MB BS 1975 Lond. (Middlx. Hosp.) Clin. Asst. Young Adult Diabetic Clinic John Radcliffe Hosp. Oxf. Prev: Regist. (Gen. Med. & Nephrol.) St. Helier Hosp. Carshalton; SHO (O & G) Ipswich Hosp.; SHO (Cardiol.) Papworth Hosp. Camb.

SICHEL, Rosemary Joan Stuart (retired) Tregenna, 30 Camden Park Road, Chislehurst BR7 5HG Tel: 020 8467 3468 — MB ChB 1945 Cape Town; FRCPath 1969, M 1964; DCP Lond 1950; DCH Eng. 1947. Prev: Cons. Path. Brook Gen. Hosp. Lond.

SICS, Martin Richard The Cottage, Upper Tankersley, Barnsley S75 3DQ Tel: 01226 744966 — MB ChB 1976 Liverp.; MRCGP 1992. Clin. Governance Head, Barnsley E. PCG. Prev: Clin. Asst. (Respirat. Med.) Barnsley Dist. Hosp.; Audit Facilitator Barnsley MAAG.

SIDA, Elizabeth Clare West Kirby Health Centre, Grange Road, Wirral CH48 4HZ Tel: 0151 625 9171 Fax: 0151 625 9171 — MB ChB 1981 Leeds; MRCGP 1985; DRCOG 1984.

SIDAHMED, Kamil Mohamed Learning Disability Services, 14 Lindum Terrace, Lincoln LN2 5RT Tel: 01522 510888 Fax: 01522 510891; 7 Shaftesbury Avenue, Forest Park, Lincoln LN6 0QN Tel: 01522 683106 — MB BS 1977 Khartoum; MRCPsych 1990. (Univ. Khartoum Fac. Med.) Cons. Psychiat. (Learning Disabil.) Lincoln Dist. Healthcare NHS Trust. Socs: BMA; Nat. Assn. of Clin. Tutors; Nat. Soc. for Epilepsy. Prev: Sen. Regist. (Learning Disabil.) Cheltenham & Glos.; Regist. & SHO (Psychiat.) Lincoln.

SIDANA, Sangat Singh The Surgery, 167 Bridge Road, Grays RM17 6DB Tel: 01375 373322 Fax: 01375 375329; 600 London Road (Branch Surgery), West Thurrock, Grays RM20 Tel: 01708 865444 — MB BS 1961 Rajasthan; DO Eng. 1969. (S.M.S. Med. Coll. Jaipur) Vice Chairm. Small Practs Assn.; Adviser GP Strategic Advis. Comm.; Chairm. GP Locality Forum, Socs: of LMC.

SIDARAS, Dorothea Johanna Gerda 256 Blackmoor Drive, Liverpool L12 3HD Tel: 0151 228 9373 — State Exam Med. Heidelberg 1991.

SIDARAS, Gediminas Albinowitsch 256 Blackmoor Drive, Liverpool L12 3HD — State Exam Med. Heidelberg 1989. Fell. Dept of Anaesth, Univ. Liverpoool.

SIDAT, Imtiaz Ahomed Gulam Mahomed 555 Chorley Old Road, Bolton BL1 6AF Tel: 01204 848411 Fax: 01204 849968 — MB ChB 1985 Zimbabwe; MRCP (UK) 1994; MRCGP 1997. (Godfrey Huggins) p/t GP Bolton. Prev: GP Regist. Halliwell Surg. Bolton; SHO (O & G) Roy. Bolton Hosp.; SHO (O & G) Roy. Bolton Hosp.

SIDAWAY, Muriel Elizabeth 70 Harley Street, London W1 1AE Tel: 020 7580 3383 Fax: 020 7636 6902; 1 Stanhope Road, Highgate, London N6 5NE Tel: 020 8340 3773 — MRCS Eng. LRCP Lond. 1949; MA, MB BChir Camb. 1949; FRCP Ed. 1971, M 1956; MRCP Lond. 1956; FFR 1960; FRCR 1975; DMRD Eng. 1958. (Camb. & Birm.) Cons. Radiol. Harley St. Lond. Socs: Fell. Roy. Coll. Radiol.; Brit. Inst. Radiol. Prev: Sen. Regist. (Radiol.) Univ. Coll. Hosp. Lond. & Hosp. Sick Childr. Gt. Ormond St.; Regist. (Radiol.) St. Bart. Hosp.; Ho. Phys. Gen. Hosp. Birm.

SIDAWAY, Steven Foley Minster Practice, Greenhill Health Centre, Church Street, Lichfield WS13 6JL Tel: 01543 414311 Fax: 01543 418668 — MB ChB 1984 Birm. SHO (Med.) Russells Hall

Hosp. Dudley. Socs: BMA. Prev: Ho. Off. (Med.) E. Birm. Hosp.; Ho. Off. (Surg.) Stafford Dist. Gen. Hosp.

SIDDAL, Miss Jane Nerrol Department Obsterics, Royal Berkshire Hospital, London Road, Reading RG1 5AN Tel: 0118 987 8117 — MB BS 1984 Lond.; MFFP 1993; MRCOG 1989; DHMSA 1992. (Roy. Free, Univ. Lond.) Cons. in Feto-Matern. Med. Roy. Berks Hosp. Reading. Socs: BMA; Reading Path. Soc. Prev: Sen. Regist. (O & G) Wexham Pk. Hosp. Slough; Lect. (O & G) St. Mary's Hosp. Med. Sch. Lond.; Regist. (O & G) Wexham Pk. Slough.

SIDDALL, Barbara Lesley 8 Penmaes, Pentrych, Cardiff CF15 9QS — MB BCh 1977 Wales.

SIDDALL, Howard Scott Charles The Stennings, Brill, Constantine, Falmouth TR11 5UR — MB ChB 1975 Bristol; MRCP (UK) 1978.

SIDDALL, William Jegon Wellard (retired) Moor Tang, Two Mile Oak, Newton Abbot TQ12 6DF Tel: 01803 813434 — MB BS 1958 Lond.; MRCS Eng. LRCP Lond. 1957; FRCA Eng. 1964; DA Eng. 1960. Prev: Cons. Anaesth. Torbay Hosp. Torquay.

SIDDEEQ, Mohamed Usman Abbas and Siddeeq, Clifford Coombs Health Centre, 70 Tangmere Drive, Castle Vale, Birmingham B35 7QX Tel: 0121 747 4633 Fax: 0121 747 1587 — MB BS 1962 Madras. (Madras) Prev: Regist. (Geriat. Med.) Worthing Hosp.; SHO (Med.) Roy. Hosp. W.on-super-Mare; Asst. Phys. Vict. Hosp. Bangalore, India.

SIDDELL, Janet Louise Greenbank Road Surgery, 29 Greenbank Road, Liverpool L18 1HG Tel: 0151 733 3224 Fax: 0151 734 5147; 3 Mersey Road, Aigburth, Liverpool L17 6AG — MB BS 1986 Lond.

SIDDIG, Mohamed Ahmed Nasr Royal Cornwall Hospital (Treliske), Truro TR1 3LJ Tel: 01872 74242; 11 Penair View, Truro TR1 1XR Tel: 01872 223294 — MD 1977 Debrecen, Hungary; MD (Obst. & Gyn.) Budapest 1985; MRCOG 1992. Socs: Arab Bd. Obst. & Gyn. Jordan 1991.

SIDDINS, Mark Threlkeld Baker Flat 1, Emerson Bainbridge House, 47 Cleveland St., London W1T 4JQ — MB BS 1983 Monash.

SIDDIQ, Mirza Azher Luqman Medical Centre, 75 Countess Street, Walsall WS1 4JZ Tel: 01922 621659 Fax: 01922 621702 — MB ChB 1992 Sheff.

SIDDIQI, Afsar Ghouse 'Olive Quill', 52 Nottingham Road, Ravenshead, Nottingham NG15 9HH Tel: 01623 797882 — MB BS 1972 Marathwada.

SIDDIQI, Asma Flat 1, 80 Fitzjohns Avenue, London NW3 5LS — MB BS 1994 Lond.

SIDDIQI, Mashood Ali Ingle House, Margaret Road, Crosby, Liverpool L23 6TR Tel: 0151 931 3108 Fax: 0151 931 3202 — MB BS 1968 Patna; MRCPI 1989; DGM RCP Lond. 1989. Cons. Phys. (c/o Elderly) Fazakerley Hosp. Liverp.

SIDDIQI, Mr Midhat Nafis 2 St Augustines Avenue, Hanger Lane, London W5 1ED — MB ChB 1983 Bristol; FRCS Eng. 1988; FRCS Glas. 1988; FRCS Ed. 1988. Regist. (Paediat. Surg.) St. Thos. Hosp. Lond. Prev: Regist. (Gen. Surg.) Mt. Vernon Hosp. N.wood.

SIDDIQI, Mohd Anwar The Medical Centre, Gun Lane, Strood, Rochester ME2 4UW Tel: 01634 290644; 9 Harlech Close, Strood, Rochester ME2 3QP — MB BS 1965 Dacca; MRCP (UK) 1972; LMSSA Lond. 1974; DTM & H Liverp. 1968. (Chittagong Med. Coll.) Prev: Regist. (Med.) & SHO (Gen. Med.) Medway Hosp. Gillingham; Ho. Off. (Gen. Surg.) N. Cambs. Hosp. Wisbech.

SIDDIQI, Naveed Iqbal 174 Dorset House, Gloucester Place, London NW1 5AH — MB BS 1989 Lond.

SIDDIQI, Mr Nusrat Jamal, Specialist Registrar "Crestar", 6 Pentland Close, Hazel Grove, Stockport SK7 5BS Tel: 0161 456 4556 Fax: 0161 456 4556 — MB BS 1987 Lond.; BDS; FRCS 1997; FDS 1999. (United Guys/St Thomas) Reg.Oral.Surg.; Specialist Regist., Oral and Maxillofacial Surg., Derrifield Hosp., Plymouth. Socs: Roy. Coll. of Surg.s, Eng.; BDA; BMA. Prev: Basic.Surg.Train.Rotat.leeds.Univ.hosp.

SIDDIQI, Sayeeda Fatima 24 Brantwood Road, Luton LU1 1JJ — MB BS 1992 Lond.

SIDDIQI, Shafia Tel: 0161 440 8181 Fax: 0161 456 4556; "Crestar", 6 Pentland Close, Hazel Grove, Stockport SK7 5BS Tel: 0161 456 4556 — MB BS 1963 Dacca; FRCOG 1997; MRCOG 1997; DRCOG 1970. (Dacca Med. Coll., Dacca Univ.) Gen. Practitioner, Stockport; Princip. Gen. Practitioner, Stockport PCT. Socs: Roy. Coll. of Obst.s and Gynaecologists; BMA; MPS.

SIDDIQI, Shahab Ahmad 102 Pirbright Road, London SW18 5NA — MB BS 1993 Lond.; BSc Lond. 1992; FRCS Eng. 1997. (St. Geo. Hosp.) SHO (Gen. Surg.) York Dist. Hosp. Prev: SHO - Guy's & St. Thos. Hosps.; SHO - Cardiothoracic Surg.; SHO (Orthop. Surg.) St. Geos. Hosp.

***SIDDIQI, Shareen Claire** The Coach House, Vicarage Lane, Allithwaite, Grange-over-Sands LA11 7QN; The Coach House, Vicarage Lane, Allithwaite, Grange-over-Sands LA11 7QN — MB ChB 1998 Leic.; MB ChB Leic 1998.

SIDDIQUE, Abdul Quayum Minsmere House, Heath Road Wing, Ipswich Hospital, Ipswich IP4 5PD Tel: 01473 704203; 3 Cecil Road, Ipswich IP1 3NW — MB BS 1966 Dacca; MSc Leic. 1979; MCPS Pakistan (Med.) 1969; MRCPsych 1977; DPM Eng. 1975. (Dacca Med. Coll.) Cons. Psychiat. Old Age St. Clement's Hosp. & Ipswich Hosp. Socs: Brit. Geriat. Soc.; Fell. of the Roy. Soc. of Med. Prev: Cons. Psychiat. Lynfield Mt. Hosp. Bradford; Sen. Regist. Birm. AHA (T).

SIDDIQUE, Abul Basher Mohammad 14 Alleyn Road, London SE21 8AL — MB BS 1968 Dacca.

SIDDIQUE, Dilruba Begum Lewisham Hospital, London SE13 6LH Tel: 020 8690 4311 — MB BS 1968 Dacca; MRCOG 1982.

SIDDIQUE, Farooque Hayder (retired) 18D Orsett Terrace, London W2 6AJ Tel: 020 7262 6064 Fax: 020 7726 6064 — MB BS 1958 Calcutta; DObst RCOG 1964; MFFP 1998 RCOG. Prev: Clin. Asst. (Gyn.) Dulwich Hosp. Lond.

SIDDIQUE, Haroon Aqeel 28 Tyrone Road, Thorpe Bay, Westcliff on Sea SS0 7HB — MB BS 1989 Lond.

SIDDIQUE, Mr Muhammad Farooq 12 Avon Close, Taunton TA1 4SU — MB BS 1975 Pakistan; DLO RCS Eng. 1982; FRCSI 1990.

SIDDIQUE, Neelam 9A North Terrace, Claremont Road, Newcastle upon Tyne NE2 4AD — MB BS 1977 Punjab; MRCP (UK) 1992.

SIDDIQUE, Tariq Ben 3 Waverley Street, York YO31 7QZ — MB ChB 1989 Leeds.

SIDDIQUE, Yaseen 156 Headley Drive, Ilford IG2 6QJ — MB ChB 1991 Manch.; DCH RCP Lond. 1998.

SIDDIQUI, Abdul Majeed Gransha Hospital, Londonderry BT47 6TF Tel: 01504 860261; 10 The Beeches, Drumahoe, Londonderry BT47 3XS Tel: 01504 301653 — BSc Agra 1951, MB BS 1957; DTCD Wales 1972; DMH Belf. 1989. Assoc. Specialist in Psychiat. WHSS Bd. Gransha Hosp. Lond.derry. Socs: Fell. Overseas Doctors Assn. Prev: Med. Off. Karachi Municip. Corp.; Med. Off. Karachi Electric Supply Corp.; Sen. Med. Off. PIDC Karachi, Pakistan.

SIDDIQUI, Abdur Razzaque c/o Mr Amin Haq, 35 Arden Mhor, Pinner HA5 2HR — LAH 1967 Dub.

SIDDIQUI, Adnan Rasheed The Surgery, 6 Galpens Road, Thornton Heath, Croydon CR7 6EA Tel: 020 8684 3450 Fax: 020 8683 0439; 42 Belgrave Court, Sloane Walk, Croydon CR0 7NW Tel: 020 8777 8248 — BM BS 1991 Nottm.; BMedSci Nottm. 1989. (Univ. Nottm.) GP Asst. Thornton Heath; GP Princip. Thornton Heath. Socs: Fell. Roy. Soc. Med. Prev: SHO (c/o Elderly) St. Helier Hosp. Carshalton; SHO (Psychiat. & O & G) E. Surrey Hosp. Redhill; SHO (A & E) Ealing Hosp. S.all.

SIDDIQUI, Ahmad Sayeed The Health Centre, Marmaduke Street, Hessle Road, Hull HU3 3BH Tel: 01482 323449 Fax: 01482 610920 — MB BS 1980 Karachi; LMSSA Lond. 1986. Regist. (Geriat.) Hull Roy. Infirm. & Kingston Gen. Hosp. Prev: Regist. (Geriat.) York: Dist. Hosp. & Ipswich Hosp.

SIDDIQUI, Ahsan Masud Tel: 01942 673578 — MB BS 1968 Punjab; DObst RCOG 1973; DFFP 1997. (NISHTAR Medical College. MULTAN. Pakistan)

SIDDIQUI, Anwar Iqbal Ahmad 54 Preston New Road, Blackburn BB2 6BG Tel: 01254 262121 — MB BS 1963 Karachi; BSc. (Dow Med. Coll. Karachi) Socs: (Pres.) Blackburn & Dist. Med. & Dent. Soc.

SIDDIQUI, Arifa Moin Carisbrooke Road Surgery, 41 Carisbrooke Road, Walthamstow, London E17 7EE Tel: 020 8520 8284 Fax: 020 8520 7077; 15 Broadwalk, London E18 2DL — MB BS 1966 Karachi.

SIDDIQUI, Asim Ali 338 Birkby Road, Huddersfield HD2 2DB — MB ChB 1993 Leeds.

SIDDIQUI, Asra Sabena 86 Swakeley's Drive, Ickenham, Uxbridge UB10 8QG — MB BCh 1993 Wales.

SIDDIQUI

SIDDIQUI, Ayesha Saleem Flat No1, 80 Fitzjohn Avenue, London NW3 5LS — MB BS 1989 London.

SIDDIQUI, Farah 27 Copeland Avenue, Leicester LE3 9BT — MB ChB 1996 Dundee.

SIDDIQUI, Farzana Flat 2, Residence 7, Sunderland District General Hospital, Sunderland SR4 7TP — MB BS 1982 Punjab; MRCOG 1994.

SIDDIQUI, Miss Frah Najeeba 21 Albany Mews, Gosforth, Newcastle upon Tyne NE3 4JW — MB BS 1994 Newc. Prev: SHO (Paediat.) Tyneside Hosp. S. Shields, Tyne & Wear; SHO (Geriat.) Sunderland Dist Gen. Hosp., Sunderland, Tyne & Wear.

SIDDIQUI, Ghazna Khalid 41 Pymmes Green Road, London N11 1DE — MB BS 1996 Lond.

SIDDIQUI, Hameeduddin 112 Conway Drive, Fulwood, Preston PR2 3ER Tel: 01772 787602 — MB BS Sind Pakistan 1959; DPM Eng. 1978; DPH Liverp. 1969; DTM & H Eng. 1965. (Sind) Assoc. Specialist (Psychiat.) Whittingham Hosp. & Roy. Preston Hosp. Socs: Med. Ethical Soc. Prev: Regist. (Psychiat.) Whittingham Hosp.; SHO (Infec. Dis.) Fazakerley Hosp. Liverp.; SHO (Gen. Med.) Newsham Gen. Hosp. Liverp.

SIDDIQUI, Mr Kamran Haider 57 Finchley Court, Ballards Lane, London N3 1NJ Tel: 020 8349 4145 — MB BS 1982 Punjab; FRCS Ed. 1990; FRCS Glas. 1990.

SIDDIQUI, Khalil Ahmed Royal South Hampshire Hospital, Brintons Terrace, Southampton SO14 OYG — MB BS 1964 Karachi.

SIDDIQUI, Mohammad Farooq 12 Balmoral Avenue, Glenmavis, Airdrie ML6 0PY Tel: 01236 761832 — MB ChB 1994 Manch.; BSc (Med. Sci.) St. And. 1991.

SIDDIQUI, Mohammad Fouad 12 Balmoral Avenue, Glenmavis, Airdrie ML6 0PY — MB BS 1996 Lond.

SIDDIQUI, Mohammed Akhtar Jawed 34 Greaves Avenue, Walsall WS5 3QG Tel: 01922 23788 — MB BS 1966 Punjab; MB BS Punjab (Pakistan) 1966; DMRD Eng. 1971.

SIDDIQUI, Mohammed Ghousuddin Gateshead Health Centre, Prince Consort Road, Gateshead NE8 1NB Tel: 0191 477 2243 Fax: 0191 478 6728 — MB BS 1961 Osmania. GP Gateshead, Tyne & Wear.

SIDDIQUI, Mohammed Lutfur Rehman Walnut Way Surgery, 21 Walnut Way, Ruislip HA4 6TB Tel: 020 8845 4400 Fax: 020 8845 4403 — MB BS 1967 Osmania.

SIDDIQUI, Nadeem 69 Fulmer Road, Beckton, London E16 3TE — BChir 1996 Camb.

SIDDIQUI, Mr Nadeem Ahmad Walsgrave Hospital, Clifford Bridge Road, Walsgrave, Coventry CV2 2DX Tel: 024 76 622197; 8 Tarrant Walk, Coventry CV2 2JJ — MB ChB 1985 Aberd.; PhD Newc. 1995; MRCOG 1990. (Aberdeen) Cons. Gyn. Oncol. Prev: Sen. Regist. & Subspecialty Trainee in Gyn. Oncol. Stobhill Hosp. Glas.; Research Fell. (Molecular Biol.) Univ. Newc. u. Tyne.; Regist. (O & G) Newc. u. Tyne.

SIDDIQUI, Naila 15 Lincoln Road, Harrow HA2 7RQ — MB BS 1989 Karachi.

SIDDIQUI, Nasim Ahmed 68 Aberford Road, Wakefield WF1 4AL — MB BS 1966 Karachi.

SIDDIQUI, Mr Raheel 1 Leeses Close, Telford TF5 0NN — MB BS 1985 Karachi; FRCS Ed. 1993.

SIDDIQUI, Sabina 51 Brighton Grove, Manchester M14 5JG — MB ChB 1994 Leic.

SIDDIQUI, Sarwar Jamil c/o A. A. Kadar Esq FRCS, ENT Registrar, Department of Entomology, Wrexham Maelor Hospital, Wrexham LL13 7TD — MB BS 1986 Karachi; MRCPI 1992.

SIDDIQUI, Shahab Kamal Hillingdon Hospital, Pield Heath Road, Uxbridge UB8 3NN; 16 Rancliffe Avenue, Keyworth, Nottingham NG12 5HY — MB ChB 1994 Manch.

SIDDIQUI, Shaukat Ali Mel Valley, 338 Birkby Road, Huddersfield HD2 2DB Tel: 01484 531856 — MB BS 1964 Punjab; MB BS Punjab Pakistan 1964; FFA RCS Eng. 1980 DA Eng. 1978. (Nishtar Med. Coll.) Cons. Anaesth. Calderdale Health Dist. Halifax. Socs: Yorks. Anaesth. Soc.; BMA & Assn. Anaesth. UK & N.Irel. Prev: Sen. Regist. RAF Halton Bucks.; SHO & Regist. (Anaesth.) Huddersfield Roy. Infirm.; Fac. Anaesth. Dallas Texas, USA.

SIDDIQUI, Sughrat 2 Boyce Street, Walkley, Sheffield S6 3JS — MB ChB 1998 Sheff.; MB ChB Sheff 1998.

SIDDIQUI, Syeda Vajiha Akmal Royal Albert Edward Infirmary, Christopher Home Eye Unit, Wigan Lane, Wigan WN1 2NN — MB ChB 1984 Manch.; MRCS Eng. LRCP Lond. 1984; FRCOphth 1989; DO RCS Eng. 1989. (Manchester) Cons. Ophth., Roy. Albert Edwd. Infirm. Prev: Regist. (Ophth.) Manch. Roy. Eye Hosp. & Alder Hey Hosp. Liverp.; SHO. (Ophth.) Kingston Gen. Hosp. & Leeds Gen. Infirm.; Sen. Regist. Roy. Liverp. Univ. Hosp.

SIDDIQUI, Tariq Nadim 19 Briksdal Way, Lostock, Bolton BL6 4PQ — MB ChB 1998 Manch.; MB ChB Manch 1998.

SIDDIQUI, Usma Shaukat 338 Birkby Road, Huddersfield HD2 2DB — MB ChB 1994 Manch. SHO (Anaesth.) N. Manch. Gen. Hosp. Prev: SHO (Geriat. Med.) Withington Hosp. Manch.; Ho. Off. (Surg.) N. Manch. Gen. Hosp.; Ho. Off. (Med.) Roy. Oldham Hosp.

SIDDIQUI, Uzair Ahmad Summerfold House, 152 Leylands Road, Burgess Hill RH15 8JE Tel: 01444 257248 Fax: 01444 257265; Tel: 01444 453748 — MB BS 1960 Sind; MRCPsych 1972; DPM Eng. 1968. Cons. Psychiat. Mid Sussex NHS Trust; Chairm. & Lead Clin. Prev: Cons. Psychiat. Co. Hosp. Durh.

SIDDIQUIE, Shazia 6 Sarazen Court, Motherwell ML1 5TW — MB ChB 1998 Glas.; MB ChB Glas 1998.

SIDDLE, David Ralph (retired) 41 Mount Crescent, Thornes Road, Wakefield WF2 8QG Tel: 01924 374921 — LRCP LRCS Ed. LRFPS Glas. 1957. Prev: Ho. Phys. Co. Gen. Hosp. Wakefield.

SIDDLE, Stephen Geoffrey (retired) 57 Cedar Drive, Chichester PO19 3EH Tel: 01243 782624 — MD 1947 Durh.; MB BS 1944; MRCGP 1954.

SIDDONS, Elizabeth Mary 9 Haywood Close, Evington, Leicester LE5 4JZ Fax: 0116 241 6284 Email: lizsid@aol.com — MB ChB 1993 Sheff.

SIDE, Christopher Douglas The Surgery, Old Forge, High Street, Tring HP23 5AG Tel: 01442 823668 Fax: 01442 891502; 13 Bridgewater Road, Berkhamsted HP4 1HN Tel: 01442 874744 Fax: 01442 879386 Email: chris@c-s-side.demon.co.uk — BM BCh 1975 Oxf.; BSc Lond. 1969. (Oxford) Prev: Clin. Asst. (Diabetes) Hemel Hempstead Hosp.; SHO (O & G), Ho. Phys. & Ho. Surg. N.ampton Gen. Hosp.

SIDE, Lucy Elizabeth Department of Clinical Genetics, Churchill Hospital, Old Road OX3 7LT Email: lucy.side@cellsci.ox.ac.uk — MB ChB 1988 Bristol; MRCP (UK) 1991. Specialist Regist. in Clin. Genetics, Oxf. Radcliffe NHS Trust.

SIDEBOTHAM, Charles Francis The Perranporth Surgery, Perranporth TR6 0PS Tel: 01872 572255; 23 Higher Kings Avenue, Exeter EX4 6JP — MRCS Eng. LRCP Lond. 1979; BSc Lond. 1976, MB BS 1979; MRCGP 1983; DCH RCP Lond. 1986; DRCOG 1984. (Guy's) Syntex Award 1984. Socs: BMA. Prev: Ho. Phys. Torbay Hosp.; Ho. Surg. Kent & Canterbury Hosp.

SIDEBOTHAM, Miss Emma Louise 59 Ribbesford Avenue, Wolverhampton WV10 6DU — MB ChB 1994 Bristol; FRCS Eng. 1998. SHO (Surg.).

SIDEBOTHAM, Peter David Community Child Health, King Square House, King Square, Bristol BS2 8EF Tel: 0117 900 2353 Fax: 0117 900 2370 Email: peter.sidebotham@ubht.swest.nhs.uk — MB ChB 1987 Bristol; MRCP (UK) 1991; MSc 2000 Bath. Cons. Paediat. Community Child Health Bristol. Socs: BMA; Fell. Roy. Coll. Paediat. and Child Health. Prev: Lect. (Community Child Health) Univ. Soton.; Regist. (Paediat.) Roy. Gwent Hosp. Newport; Lect. (Community Child Health) Bath.

SIDEBOTTOM, Mr Andrew James Maxillofacial Unit, Fazakerley Hospital, Longmoor Lane, Liverpool L9 7AL Tel: 0151 529 5280 Fax: 0151 529 5288; 31 Ravenswood Road, Redland, Bristol BS6 6BW Tel: 0117 973 2076 — MB ChB 1993 Birm.; BDS Bristol 1986; FRCS Eng. 1995; FDS RCS Eng. 1992. Regist. (Oral & Maxillofacial Surg.) Regional Maxillofacial Unit Walton Hosp. Liverp. Socs: Assoc. Mem. Brit. Assn. Oral & Maxillofacial Surgs.

SIDEBOTTOM, Desmond Holland (retired) 28 Rockport Park, Londonderry BT47 6JJ Tel: 01504 342665 — MB BCh BAO Dub. 1943.

SIDEBOTTOM, Eric Churchill Hospital, Oxford OX3 7LJ Tel: 01865 226132 Fax: 01865 226978; 27 Hayward Road, Oxford OX2 8LN Tel: 01865 53023 Fax: 01865 53023 — BM BCh 1963 Oxf.; DPhil Oxf. 1969, MA 1963. (Oxf. & St. Bart.) Indep. Cons. Med. Educat. & Research Oxf. Socs: Oxf. Med. Soc.; (Treas.) Oxf. Grad. Med. Club. Prev: Asst. Dir. Research ICR Fund; Univ. Lect. (Experim.

Path.) Univ. Oxf.; Nuffield Research Fell. & Tutor (Med.) Lincoln Coll. Oxf.

SIDEBOTTOM, Paul 27 Hayward Road, Oxford OX2 8LN — MB BS 1994 Lond.; BSc Lond. 1993. SHO (Med.) Sir Geo. Gairdner Hosp. Perth. Prev: SHO (A & E) Frimley Pk. Hosp.; Ho. Off. Qu. Eliz. Hosp. King's Lynn; Ho. Off. Char Cross Hosp. Lond.

SIDERY, John Charles Gurnett Cottage, Blakes Road, Wargrave, Reading RG10 8LA; Redwood House, Canon Lane, Maidenhead SL6 3PH — MB 1977 Camb.; MA Camb. 1976, BA 1973, MB 1977, BChir 1976; DRCOG 1983; DCH RCP Lond. 1981; Dip. Occ. Med. RCP Lond. 1996. GP Berks. HA.

SIDES, Anne Pamela St. Johns House, 12 Station Road, Cullingworth, Bradford BD13 5HN — MB ChB 1978 Leeds.

SIDES, Brian Arthur (retired) Windward Group Practice, 68 Worsley Road, Worsley, Manchester M28 2SN Tel: 0161 794 1603 Fax: 0161 794 2371 — MB ChB 1959 Manchester; FRCGP 1996, M 1972; DObst RCOG 1961.

SIDES, Christopher Andrew St John's House, 12 Station Road, Cullingworth, Bradford BD13 5HN — MB ChB 1978 Leeds; FRCA 1983. Cons. Anaesth. Bradford Roy. Infirm.

SIDES, Jeremy Robert Flat 2, 51 Mill Hill Road, Norwich NR2 3DR Tel: 01603 764344 Fax: 01603 764344 — MB BS 1973 Lond.; BSc (Hons.) (Biochem.), MB BS Lond. 1973; DCH Eng. 1978; DObst RCOG 1976. (The London Hospital) Staff Grade Old Age Psychiat. Julien Hosp. Norwich; Blood Transfus. Session. Off. E. Anglian Blood Centre Cambs; Clin.Med.Off.ADAPT Diana P.ss of Wales Trat.Centre.Mundesley Norf.

SIDES, Kathleen Margaret (retired) Derrygonnelly, Enniskillen BT93 6HW — MB BCh BAO Belf. 1941. Med. Off. Ely Disp.

SIDEY, Sir Ernest, KBE, CB (retired) Callums, Tugwood Common, Cookham Dean, Maidenhead SL6 9TU Tel: 01628 483006 — MD St. And. 1943, MB ChB 1935; FFCM 1976, M 1974; DPH Lond. 1951. Prev: Dir.-Gen. Chest, Heart & Stroke Assn.

SIDEY, Margaret Clare (retired) 2 Ferrings, Dulwich, London SE21 7LU Tel: 020 8693 8106 Fax: 020 8693 8106 — MB ChB 1954 New Zealand; MRCP Lond. 1959. Prev: Clin. Asst. Chelsea & W.m. Hosp. Lond.

SIDFORD, Kenneth Iain, RD St. Stephens Surgery, Adelaide St., Redditch B97 4AL Tel: 01527 65444 Fax: 01527 69218 Email: iainsidford@doctors.org.uk; 44 Salop Road, Redditch B97 4PS Tel: 01527 65444 Fax: 01527 69218 — MB ChB 1977 Birm; BSc Lond. 1963; M.Med.Educat. Dundee 1995. (Birm.) GP Redditch; Lect. Med. Educat. Wolverhampton Univ. Prev: Ho Phys. Dudley Rd. Hosp. Birm.; Ho Surg. Qu. Eliz. Hosp. Birm.; Surg. Lt.-Cdr RNR.

SIDHOM, Atef Tawfik Mikhail Ladywood Surgery, 35 Morville Street, Ladywood, Birmingham B16 8BU Tel: 0121 454 3774 Fax: 0121 456 5713; 93 Augustus Road, Birmingham B15 3LT — MB ChB 1972 Alexandria. GP Edgbaston; Clin. Asst. (Accid. & Trauma) Birm. Gen. Hosp.

SIDHU, Balwinder Singh The Surgery, Chancery Lane, Chapel End, Nuneaton CV10 0PD Tel: 024 7639 4766 Fax: 024 7639 6870; 129 Tresillian Road, Exhall, Coventry CV7 9PP Tel: 02476 315966 — MB BCh 1982 Wales; BSc (Hons.), MB BCh Wales 1982; MRCPI 1984; MRCGP 1986. Prev: Regist. (Med.) Dudley HA; Regist. (Med.) Edgware Lond.

SIDHU, Davinder Singh 64 Metcalf Road, Ashford TW15 1EZ — MB BS 1996 Lond.

SIDHU, Gurpreet Singh North London Nuffield Hospital, Cavell Drive, Enfield EN2 7PR Tel: 020 8366 2122 Email: sidhug@globalnet.co.uk — MB BS 1987 Lond.; MRCGP 1991; DRCOG 1990. (Middlx. Hosp. Med. Sch.) Indep. GP Middlx.; In Flight Doctor (Aviat. Med.) Middlx.

SIDHU, Harmini Kaur 31 Grove Hill Road, Moira, Craigavon BT67 0PP — MB BCh BAO 1985 Belf.; MRCOG 1990. Regist. (O & G) Belf. City Hosp. Socs: BMA & Ulster Med. Soc.

SIDHU, Jagdip Singh 68 Sherington Avenue, Pinner HA5 4DT — MB BS 1994 Lond.; MB BS (Distinc.) Lond. 1994; MRCP (UK) 1997. SHO (Med.) Harefield & Hillingdon Hosps.; Specialist Regist. (Cardiol.) Harefield Hosp. Socs: BMA. Prev: Ho. Off. (Surg.) N.wick Pk. Hosp. Lond.; Ho. Off. (Gen. Med.) Ealing.

SIDHU, Kamlesh Queen Square Surgery, 2 Queen Square, Lancaster LA1 1RP Tel: 01524 843333 Fax: 01524 847550; 7 Peacock Lane, Hest Bank, Lancaster LA2 6EN Tel: 01524 824437 — MB ChB 1983 Manch.; MRCGP 1988. (Manchester)

SIDHU, Paul Singh Department of Diagnostic Radiology, Kings College Hospital, Denmark Hill, London SE5 9RS Tel: 020 7346 3063 Fax: 020 7346 3061 Email: paulsidhu@compuserve.com; 34 Handen Road, Lee, London SE12 8NR Tel: 020 8852 3041 — MB BS 1982 Lond.; BSc Lond. 1979; MRCP (UK) 1987; FRCR 1994; DTM & H RCP Lond. 1988. (St. Mary's) Cons. Diagn. Radiol. King's Coll. Hosp. Lond. Socs: Fell. Roy. Soc. Trop. Med. & Hyg.; Radiol. Soc. N. Amer.; Brit. Med. Ultrasound Soc. Prev: Cons. HCI (Internat.) Hosp. Clydebank; Regist. (Diagn. Radiol.) Hammersmith Hosp Lond.; Lect. Univ. Malaya Kuala Lumpur, Malaysia.

SIDHU, Rajinder Singh 36 Sycamore Road, Birmingham B21 0QL — MB BS 1990 Lond.

SIDHU, Shireen Kaur Flat 1/3, Jackson's Lane, Highgate, London N6 5SR — MB BS 1990 Adelaide.

SIDHU, Sukhdev Singh 3 Lower Calderbrook, Littleborough OL15 9NW — MB BS 1980 Ranchi.

SIDHU, Virinder Singh 14 St Stephens Road, Ealing, London W13 8HD Fax: 020 8997 4582 — MB BCh 1982 Wales; MRCP (UK) 1985; FRCA 1989. Cons. Anaesth. St. Mary's Hosp. Lond. Socs: Intens. Care Soc.; Assn. Anaesth.; Assn. Cardiothoracic Anaesth. Prev: Sen. Regist. Univ. Coll. Lond. Hosps., Gt. Ormond St. Hosp. Sick Childr. & Roy. Brompton Nat. Heart Hosp.

SIDIKI, Sikander Sandro c/o Southern General Hospital NHS Trust, 1345 Govan Road, Glasgow G51 4TF Tel: 0141 201 1583; 10 West Chapelton Drive, Bearsden, Glasgow G61 2DB — MB ChB 1989 Glas.; BSc Miami 1984; FRCOphth 1996. (Univ. Glas.) SHO (Ophth.) S.. Gen. Hosp. Glas. Socs: BMA. Prev: SHO (Ophth.) Gartnavel Gen. Hosp. Glas.; SHO (Geriat.) Vict. Geriat. Unit. Glas.; SHO (Neurosurg.) S.. Gen. Hosp. Glas.

SIDNEY, James Alexander 3 St James Close, Thorpe Thewles, Stockton-on-Tees TS21 3LH — MB ChB 1998 Bristol.

SIDRA, Losil Moris 17 Brackenwood Close, Royton, Oldham OL2 5DE — State Exam Med 1986 Sofia; MRCOG 1994.

SIDRA, Mr Rushdi Shafiq Highfield Health Centre, 2 Proctor Street, off Tong Street, Bradford BD4 9QA Tel: 01274 227700 Fax: 01274 227900 — MB BS 1969 Khartoum, Sudan; FRCS Eng. 1976.

SIDWELL, Ian Philip 63 Redlake Drive, Taunton TA1 2RU — MB BS 1986 Lond.

SIDWELL, Rachel Ursula Charnwood House, Dalby Road, Melton Mowbray LE13 0BJ — MB ChB 1990 Bristol; DFFP 1994; MRCP Lond. 1997; MRCPCH Lond. 1997; DA Lond. 1996. (Bristol) SHO (Paediat.) Guy's Hosp. Lond. Socs: BMA & Med. Protec. Soc. Prev: SHO (Paediat.) Chelsea & W.m. Hosp.; SHO (O & G) Lister Hosp. Stevenage.

SIE, Adrian Hian Ing 80 Lavender Drive, East Kilbride, Glasgow G75 9JJ — MB ChB 1995 Sheff.

SIE, Thwan Hwie Hospital Residences, Block B, Manthorpe Road, Grantham NG31 8DW — Artsexamen 1991 Amsterdam.

SIEBER, Frederick Alexander Furlong Medical Centre, Furlong Road, Tunstall, Stoke-on-Trent ST6 5UD Tel: 01782 577388 Fax: 01782 838610 — MB ChB 1982 Dundee; DA (UK) 1988.

SIEFF, Ivor Flat 8, The White House, Suffolk Road, Altrincham WA14 4QX Tel: 0161 929 0956 — MB ChB Manch. 1949. (Manch.)

SIEGLER, David Ivor Maurice Luton & Dunstable Hospital, Lewsey Road, Luton LU4 0DZ Tel: 01582497236; 8 Barton Road, Luton LU3 2BB Tel: 01582 597544 — MB BS Lond. 1966; MD Lond. 1977; FRCP Lond. 1986, M 1969; MRCS Eng. LRCP Lond. 1966. (Univ. Coll. Hosp.) Cons. Phys. (Gen. & Thoracic Med.) Luton & Dunstable Hosp. Socs: Brit. Thorac. Soc.; Assn. Palliat. Med. Prev: Sen. Regist. (Med.) Roy. Free & Brompton Hosps. Lond.; Regist. (Med.) Univ. Coll. Hosp. Lond.

SIEGLER, Mr Joseph 31 Rodney Street, Liverpool L1 9EH Tel: 0151 709 8522 Fax: 0151 722 7538 Email: j. siegler@talk21.com; 4 Aldbourne Close, Liverpool L25 6JD Tel: 0151 722 1000 Fax: 0151 722 1000 Email: j.siegler@talk21.com — MB BS Lond. 1944; FRCS Eng. 1950; DLO Eng. 1954. (St. Bart.) Emerit. Cons. Otorhinolaryng. United Liverp. Hosps. & Liverp. RHB; Emerit. Clin. Lect. (Otol.) Univ. Liverp. Socs: Fell. Roy. Soc. Med.; Liverp. Med. Inst.; Life Mem. BMA. Prev: Cons. ENT Surg. to the Home Off. at Walton Jail; Sen. Regist. (Otolaryng.) United Liverp. Hosps.; Regist. Roy. Nat. Throat, Nose & Ear Hosp.

SIEGLER

SIEGLER, Sarah Anne Peel Health Centre, Angouleme Way, Bury BL9 0BT Tel: 0161 763 7613 Fax: 0161 763 9625 — MB ChB 1979 Manch.

SIEGRUHN, Gert Cornelius (retired) 25 Arlington Square, London N1 7DP Tel: 020 7226 3456 Fax: 020 7226 3456 — MB ChB 1958 Pretoria; MSc (Community Med.) Lond. 1971; FFPHM RCP (UK) 1990; MFCM RCP (UK) 1988. Prev: DMO Redbridge.

SIEMASZKO, Catherine Olga 6 Worcester Crescent, Bristol BS8 3JA — MB BS 1992 Lond.

SIENKOWSKI, Ian Kazimierz Adelaide Medical Centre, 111 Adelaide Road, London NW3 3RY Tel: 020 7722 4135 Fax: 020 7586 7558 — MB BS 1974 Lond.; MRCS Eng. LRCP Lond. 1974. (Westm.)

SIEPERT, Mirjan South Tyneside District Hospital, Harton Lane, South Shields NE34 0PL — State Exam Med 1992 Dusseldorf.

SIERATZKI, Jechil Harry Flat 39, Parkside, Knightsbridge, London SW1X 7JP — State Exam Med 1979 Giessen.

SIEVERS, Ivan Myer 3A The Close, Heath Lane, Blackheath, London SE3 0UR — LRCPI & LM, LRSCI & LM 1941; LRCPI & LM, LRCSI & LM 1941. (RCSI) Prev: Res. Anaesth. N. Staffs. Roy. Infirm. & Huddersfield Roy. Infirm.; Ho. Surg. Shotley Bridge Emerg. Hosp.

SIEVERS, Paul Frederick St Marys Road Surgery, St. Marys Road, Newbury RG14 1EQ Tel: 01635 31444 Fax: 01635 551316; Crestholme, Well Meadows, Shaw, Newbury RG14 2DS Tel: 01635 42170 — MB BS 1962 Lond.; MRCS Eng. LRCP Lond. 1962; DObst RCOG 1966; DCH Eng. 1966. (Guy's) Hosp. Practitioner & Clin. Asst. (Paediat.) Berks.; Med. Off. Vodaphone Gp., Quantel & Electrolux. Socs: Newbury Med. Soc. Prev: SHO (Paediat.) Pembury Hosp.

SIEVERT, Julia Vale of Leven District General Hospital, Alexandria G83 0UA — State Exam Med 1990 Munich.

SIEW TU, Chooye-Ling 8 Fern Avenue, Flixton, Manchester M41 5RZ Tel: 0161 746 9730 — MB ChB 1984 Manch.

SIFMAN, Morris (retired) 47 The Ridgeway, London NW11 8QP Fax: 020 8731 6276 — MB BCh Witwatersrand 1952. Med. Off. Initiation Soc. GB. Prev: SHO St. Benidicts Hosp. Tooting.

SIGGERS, Benet Richard Charles, Capt. RAMC Portway, Bratton, Westbury BA13 4SZ — MB ChB 1994 Bristol; Dip IMC RCS (Ed). SHO (Anaeth.) Roy Hosp Haslar Gosport. Prev: SHO (A & E) Frimley Pk. Hosp. Surrey; RMO (Primary Care) 29 Commando Regt. RA Plymouth; Ho. Off. (Surg. & Orthop.) CMH Aldershot.

SIGGERS, Diana Joan Eastleigh Surgery, Station Road, Westbury BA13 3JD Tel: 01373 822807 Fax: 01373 828904; Portway, Bratton, Westbury BA13 4SZ Tel: 01380 830894 — MB BS 1966 Lond.; MRCS Eng. LRCP Lond. 1966; DObst RCOG 1976. (Guy's)

SIGGERS, Georgina Rosemary North Star Farm, Beech Road, Mereworth, Maidstone ME18 5QJ Tel: 01622 813794; 6 Mast Court, 1 Boat Lifter Way, London SE16 7WH Tel: 020 7231 8970 Email: gsiggers@aol.com — MB BS 1993 Lond.; BSc (Hons.) Lond. 1990; MRCP (UK) 1997; MRCPCH. (UMDS) Specialist Regist. (Paediat.) Qu. Mary's Hosp. Sidcup. Prev: SHO (Paediat.) Pembury Hosp. Tunbridge Wells.

SIGGERS, Stephen Henton Southbroom Surgery, 15 Estcourt Street, Devizes SN10 1LQ Tel: 01380 720909; Upper Coneygar, Northgate Gardens, Devizes SN10 1JY Tel: 01380 725924 — MRCS Eng. LRCP Lond. 1968. (Guy's)

SIGGINS, Dominic William 26 Grosvenor Road, Harborne, Birmingham B17 9AN — MB BS 1982 Lond.

SIGGINS, Guy Frederick Goodwin (retired) 27 Westbourne Road, Edgbaston, Birmingham B15 3TX Tel: 0121 454 3202 — MRCS Eng. LRCP Lond. 1940; FRCOphth 1991; DOMS Eng. 1949. Surg. Assn. for the Blind Birm. Prev: Cons. Ophth. Surg. Sandwell AHA.

SIGGINS, Paul Charles Chadwick Road Surgery, 33 Chadwick Road, London E11 1NE Tel: 020 8989 2936 Fax: 020 8530 8540 — MB BS 1981 Lond.; MRCGP 1986. (Lond. Hosp. Med. Coll.)

SIGNY, Charles Michael Doctors Surgery, Great Melton Road, Hethersett, Norwich NR9 3AB Tel: 01603 810250 Fax: 01603 812402; Northfield Lodge, Barnham Broom Road, Wymondham NR18 0RN Tel: 01953 602196 — MB BS 1960 Lond.; MRCS Eng. LRCP Lond. 1960; DObst RCOG 1963. (St. Geo.) Prev: Ho. Surg. (O & G) St. Mary Abbot's Hosp. Lond.; Ho. Surg. (Orthop.) & Ho. Phys. St. Geo. Hosp. Lond.

SIGNY, Mark Worthing Hospital, Lyndhurst Road, Worthing BN11 2DH Tel: 01903 205111 Fax: 01903 285011 — MB BS 1978 Lond.; MA Oxf. 1979, BA (Physiol. Sc.) 1975; FRCP Lond. 1994; MRCP (UK) 1980; T(M) 1990. (Oxf. & St. Thos.) Cons. Cardiol. Worthing & S.lands NHS Trust; Hon. Cons. Cardiol. St. Thos. Hosp. Lond.; Hon. Cons. Cardiol. Roy. Sussex Co. Hosp. Brighton. Socs: Brit. Cardiac Soc.; (Ex.-Pres.) Jun. Cardiac Club; Scientif. Fell. Zool. Soc. Prev: Sen. Regist. (Med. & Cardiol.) Medway & St. Thos. Hosp.; Regist. (Cardiac) St. Tho. Hosp. Lond.; SHO (Cardiac) Brompton Hosp. Lond.

SIGSTON, Paul Edmund St. Bartholomews Hospital, West Smithfield, London EC1A 7BE Tel: 020 7601 7518; 8 Priory Gardens, London SW13 0JU — MB ChB 1987 Ed.; MRCP (UK) 1993; FRCA 1994; DA (UK) 1992. Sen. Regist. (Anaesth.) St. Bart. Hosp. Lond. Prev: Regist. (Anaesth.) Gt. Ormond St. Hosp. & St. Bart. Hosp. Lond.; SHO (Med.) Chester; SHO (Anaesth.) Edin.

SIGSWORTH, Elisabeth Rome Crofton Elvington Medical Practice, Church Lane, Elvington, York YO41 4AD Tel: 01904 608224; Sycamore Cottage, Newton Road, Tollerton, York YO61 1QX — MB BS 1980 Lond.; MRCGP 1987; DRCOG 1983. (Roy. Free Hosp. Sch. of Med.) GP Elvington Med. Pract. Prev: GP Retainer Easingwold.

SIGURDSSON, Audun Svavar 11 Kelton Court, Carpenter Road, Edgbaston, Birmingham B15 2JX Tel: 07801 106542; 11 Kelton Court, Carpenter Road, Edgbaston, Birmingham B15 2JX Tel: 07801 106542 — Cand Med et Chir 1983 Reykjavik; FRCS 1991; FRCS (Gen) 1997. (Univ. of Iceland) Socs: Assn. Endoscopic Surgs.; BMA.

SIGURDSSON, Engilbert The Maudsley Hospital, Denmark Hill, London SE5 8AZ Email: e.sigurdsson@iop.bpmf.ac.uk — Cand Med et Chir 1991 Reykjavik.

SIGURDSSON, Mr Helgi Helgason Hammersmith Hospital, Du Cane Road, London W12 0NN Tel: 020 8743 2030; Flat 7, 15 Girdlers Road, London W14 0PS Tel: 020 7602 8066 Fax: 020 7602 8066 — Cand Med et Chir Reykjavik 1988; FRCS Eng. 1992; FRCS Ed. 1992. Career Regist. (Surg.) Hammersmith Hosp. Lond. Prev: Career Regist. (Surg.) Ashford Hosp. Middx.

SIGURDSSON, R G St Albans Road, Hersden, Canterbury CT3 4EX — MD 1990 St Georges U; MD 1990 St Georges U.

SIGWART, Ulrich (retired) — State Exam Med 1967 Freiburg; MD Freiburg 1967; FRCP Lond. 1993; MRCP (UK) 1992. Prof. Med. Univ. Dusseldorf; Hon. Sen. Lec. Nat. Heart & Lung Inst. Univ. Lond. Prev: Cons. Cardiol. Roy. Brompton Nat. Heart & Lung Hosp.

SIHOTA, Jagroop Singh Telfer Road, 190 Telfer Road, Coventry CV6 3DJ Tel: 024 7659 6060 Fax: 024 7660 1607; 31 Whitefield Close, Westwood Heath, Coventry CV4 8GY — MB ChB 1978 Birm. (Birm.) Prev: Trainee GP Coventry AHA VTS; Ho. Phys. St. Chad's Hosp. Birm.; Ho. Surg. Walsgrave Hosp. Coventry.

SIHRA, Bhupinder Singh Colchester General Hospital, Turner Road, Colchester CO4 5JL Tel: 01206 742158 Fax: 01206 742795 Email: bsihra@hotmail.com — BM 1984 Soton.; MRCP (UK) 1989. Cons. (Gen. & Respirat.& Allergy Paediat.) Colchester Gen. Hosp.; Hon. Cons. (Paediatric Allergy) Guy's Hosp., Lond. Socs: MRCP; BSACI. Prev: Regist. (Paediat.) May Day Hosp. Croydon & St. Geo. Hosp. Tooting.; Specialist Regist. (Paediat.) King's Coll. Hosp. Lond.; Clin. Research Fell. (Allergy & Clin. Immunol.) Roy. Brompton Nat. Heart & Lung Inst. Lond.

SIHRA, Perminder Kaur Rampton Hospital, Retford DN22 0PD; 5 The Shetlands, Retford DN22 6YA — MB ChB 1988 Glas. Staff Grade (Forens. Psychiat.) Rampton Hosp. Retford, Notts. Socs: Inceptor Roy. Coll. Psychiats. Prev: Rotat. Psychiat. Hartwood Shotts.; Psychiat. Bellsdyke Hosp. Larbert.

SIKA, Mr Mounir 1 St Ronan's Crescent, Woodford Green IG8 9DQ Tel: 020 8504 8767 — MB BCh 1959 Cairo; FRCS Eng. 1978; DLO Ain Shams 1964. (Cairo) Assoc. Specialist (ENT) Centr. Middlx. Hosp. Lond. Prev: Regist. (ENT) P. of Wales Gen. Hosp. Lond.; Regist. (ENT) Centr. Middlx. Hosp. Lond.

SIKABBUBBA, Joseph Mweetwa BHB Community Healthcare, Warley Hospital, Warley, Hill, Brentwood CM14 5HQ Tel: 01708 464213 Fax: 01277 201713; 341 London Road, Croydon CR0 3PA — MB ChB 1985 Univ. Zimbabawe; MB ChB Univ. Zambia 1985; MRCPsych 1992. (Univ. Zambia, Lusaka) Sen. Regist. (Gen. Psychiat.) Warley Hosp. Brentwood. Prev: Sen. Regist. (Psychiat.) Homerton Hosp. Lond.; Clin. Assoc. (Psychiat.) Gordon Hosp. Lond.; Regist. (Psychiat.) Guy's UMDS & St. Augustine Canterbury.

SIKANDER, Nasreen Jarvis House Surgery, Jarvis Street, Oldham OL4 1DT Tel: 0161 2728 Fax: 0161 628 8876; 95 Fredrick Street, Oldham OL8 1RD — MB BS 1965 Punjab; DA RCPSI 1977. Socs: Med. Defence Soc.

SIKDAR, Atindra Nath Teynham Medical Centre, The Surgery, 72 Station Road, Teynham, Sittingbourne ME9 9SN Tel: 01795 521948 Fax: 01795 520785; Managing Director, Bengal Medical Research, 34/4 Patuatola Lane & 63/2B Surja Sen St, Calcutta 700009, India Tel: 00 91 33 2418210 Fax: 00 91 33 4643072 — MB BS 1962 Calcutta; DGO Calcutta 1972; Cert. JCC Lond. 1974. (R.G. Kar Med. Coll. Calcutta India) Med. Adviser Bengal Med. Research Calcutta & Calcutta Med. Centre. Socs: Med. Protec. Soc. Prev: SHO (Neurosurg.) Morriston Hosp. Swansea; Sen. Health Off. (Anaesth.) Roy. Hosp. Wolverhampton; Ho. Off. (O & G) St. Davids Hosp. Bangor N. Wales.

SIKDAR, N Dartford West Health Centre, Tower Road, Dartford DA1 2HA Tel: 01322 291636/292001 — MB BS 1961 Gauhati; MB BS 1961 Gauhati.

SIKDAR, Mr Tuhinangshu 16 Manor Road, Wendover, Aylesbury HP22 6HQ Tel: 01296 624380 — LMSSA 1989 Lond.; MB BS Bengal 1980; FRCS Eng. 1989.

SIKKA, Chander Kiran 12 St Leonards Way, Hornchurch RM11 1FR — MB BS 1989 Lond. Trainee GP/SHO (O & G) Essex.

SIKKA, Charanpal Singh Oakswell Health Centre, Brunswick Park Road, Wednesday WS10 9HP Tel: 0212 556 2114 Email: sikka@doctors.org.uk — MB BCh 1993 Wales; DCH 1997; DFFP 1997; DRCOG 1997; MRCGP. (UWCM) GP Princip.

SIKKA, Gulshan Manor Hospital, Moat Road, Walsall WS1 3QY Tel: 01922 28911; 13 Athlone Road, Walsall WS5 3QU — MB BS 1964 Vikram; MD (Paediat.) Indore 1968; MFCH 1989; Dip. Community Paediat. Warwick 1985; DCH Indore 1967. (M.G.M. Med. Coll. Indore) Asst. GP Walsall; Clin. Med. Off. (Child Health Community) Walsall HA.

SIKKA, Jangbir Singh Manor Hospital, Moat Road, Walsall WS2 9PS; 13 Athlone Road, Walsall WS5 3QU — MB BS 1962 Panjab; MS Panjab, India 1968. (Med. Coll. Patiala) Clin. Asst. (A & E) Manor Hosp. Walsall.

SIKKA, Mr Om Prakash (retired) 5 Scartho Road, Grimsby DN33 2AB Tel: 01472 878779 — MB BS 1952 Lucknow; FRCS Eng. (Ophth.) 1963; FCOphth 1988; DOMS Lucknow 1954. Prev: Cons. Ophth. Surg. Grimsby Gen. & Assoc. Hosps.

SIKKA, Swadesh 5 Scartho Road, Grimsby DN33 2AB Tel: 01472 78779 — MB BS 1957 Lucknow; DCH Eng. 1961. Clin. Med. Off. Comm. Health Grimsby HA. Socs: Med. Protec. Soc. Prev: Clin. Asst. (Dermat. & Psychiat.) Grimsby HA; Regist. (Infec. Dis.) Leeds Rd. Hosp. Bradford.

SIKLOS, Paul William Leopold West Suffolk Hospital, Hardwick Lane, Bury St Edmunds IP33 2QZ Tel: 01284 713406 Fax: 01284 713406; 58 Hardwick Lane, Bury St Edmunds IP33 2RB Tel: 01284 768043 Email: pasik@anglianet.co.uk — MB BS 1972 Lond.; MB BS (Hons. Surg.) Lond. 1972; MA Camb. 1979; BSc Lond. 1969; FRCP Lond. 1991; MRCP (UK) 1975. (Middlx.) Cons. Phys. (GIM) W. Suff. Hosps. NHS Trust Bury St. Edmunds; Assoc. Clin. Dean Camb. Univ; Director of Camb. Grad. Course in Med. Prev: Clin. Lect. Univ. Camb.; Hon. Sen. Regist. (Med.) Addenbrooke's Hosp. Camb.; Regist. (Med.) Lister Hosp. Stevenage.

SIKORA, Professor Karol Global Clinical Development, Astrazeneca, Mereside SK10 4TG Tel: 01625 513768 Fax: 01625 516904 Email: karol.sikora@astrazeneca.com — MB BChir 1972 Camb.; PhD 1975; FRCP 1980; FRCR 1979. (Middlx.) Global Clin. Expert - Cancer; Prof. of Cancer Med., Hammersmith Hospice, Lond., W12 0NN.

SIKORSKI, Andrew David Alexander Tunbridge Wells Homoeopathic Hospital; Westley, Hackwood, Roberts Bridge TN32 5ER — MB BS 1988 Lond.; MFHom 1999; MRCGP 1997. (Char. Cross & Westm. Hosp. Lond.) p/t Homoeop. Acupunc. Socs: Brit. Holistic Med. Assn.; Fac. Homoeop. -S.E. Eng. Mem. Rep. Prev: GP/Regist. Glastonbury Som.; GP, Robt.s Bridge, E.Sussex; GP Locum, Marylebourne Health Centre, Lond.

SIKORSKI, James Jan Sydenham Green Group Practice, 26 Holmshaw Close, London SE26 4TH Tel: 020 8676 8836 Fax: 020 7771 4710 — MB BS 1978 Newc.; MRCP (UK) 1980; MRCGP 1982; DRCOG 1983. Princip. GP Sydenham Green Health Centre Lond.

SIKORSKI, Mr Jerzy Marian 24 Woodfield Avenue, London W5 1PA — MB BS 1969 Lond.; FRCS Eng. 1974.

SIL, Ajoy Kumar Horden Group Practice, The Surgery, Sunderland Road, Horden, Peterlee SR8 4QP Tel: 0191 586 4210 Fax: 0191 587 0700 — MB BS 1966 Calcutta; DA Eng. 1979.

SIL, Bijoykumar (retired) 67 Ashness Gardens, Greenford UB6 0RW Tel: 020 8902 6533 — MB 1947 Calcutta; DA Eng. 1956. Prev: Cons. Anaesth. Head Dept. Anaesth. & Hon. Lect. UTH Lusaka, Zambia.

SIL, Mr John Robin 28 Wingfield Road, Kingston upon Thames KT2 5LR Tel: 020 8549 0169 — MB BS 1991 Lond.; BSc (Hons.) Lond. 1988; FRCS Eng. 1995; FRCSI 1995. (Char. Cross & Westm. Lond.) Specialist Regist. (Radiol.) Guy's & St. Thos. NHS Trust Lond. Prev: SHO (Gen. Surg.) St. Geo. Hosp. Lond.; SHO (A & E) Char. Cross Hosp. Lond.; Demonst. (Anat.) St. Mary's Hosp. Med. Sch. Lond.

SIL, Mr Samir Kumar Burbage Surgery, Tilton Road, Burbage, Leicester LE7 9F Tel: 01455 634879; Highcliffe, Shilton Road, Barwell, Leicester LE9 8 Tel: 01455 842313 — MB BS 1960 Calcutta; FRCS Ed. 1967. (N.R.S. Med. Coll. Calcutta) Edr. & Sec. Jl. Dispensing Doctors Assn. Socs: BMA. Prev: Med. Asst. (A & E) Manor Hosp. Nuneaton; Regist. Roy. Infirm. Lancaster; Regist. W. Cumbld. Hosp. Whitehaven.

SILAS, Aaron Michael 7 St Mary's Avenue, Wanstead, London E11 2NR Tel: 020 8989 3766 — MB BS 1959 Calcutta; MRCP (UK) 1977; T(M) 1991; DPhysMed. Eng. 1970. (Calcutta Med. Coll.) Socs: Brit. Soc. Rheum. Prev: Cons. Rheum. & Rehabil. OldCh. & Rushgreen Hosps. Romford; Sen. Regist. (Rheum. & Rehabil.) Univ. Coll. Hosp. Lond., Whittington Hosp. Lond. & Med. Rehabil. Centre Lond.; Regist. (Orthop) Brighton Hosp. Gp.

SILAS, Joseph Hyam Cardiovascular Department, Arrowe Park Hospital, Wirral CH49 5PE Tel: 0151 678 5111 Fax: 0151 604 7220 — MB ChB 1970 Sheff.; MD Sheff. 1979; MRCP (UK) 1972; FRCP Lond. 1988. Cons. Phys. (Cardiol.) Arrowe Pk. Hosp. Wirral. Prev: Cons. Phys. (Cardiol.) Clatterbridge Hosp. Bebington, Wirral.

SILBERGH, Alexander Edward, MBE (retired) Ashvale, Midmar St., Buckie AB56 1BJ Tel: 01542 831030 — MA Aberd. 1949, MB ChB 1956. Prev: SHO (O & G) Qu. Vict. Hosp. Morecambe.

SILBIGER, Catherine Anne 12 Kingston Way, Nailsea, Bristol BS48 4RA — MB ChB 1996 Ed.

SILBURN, Janice Nancy Lagmhor Surgery, Little Dunkeld, Dunkeld PH8 0AD Tel: 01350 727269 Fax: 01350 727772 — MB ChB 1968 Ed.; MRCGP 1975; DObst RCOG 1971. (Ed.) GP Dunkeld, Perthsh. Prev: Cas. Off. Whittington Hosp. Lond.

SILBURN, Michael David William Lagmhor Surgery, Dunkeld PH8 0AD Tel: 0135 02 269; Torwood House, St. Mary's Road, Birnam, Dunkeld PH8 0BJ Tel: 0135 02 255 — MB 1971 Camb.; BChir 1970; DObst RCOG 1972.

SILCOCK, John Gerard The Endoscopy Centre, South Cleveland Hospital, Middlesbrough TS4 3BW Tel: 01642 854865 Email: 106223.1046@compuserve.com — MB BS 1986 Newc.; MRCP (UK) 1989. Cons. Gastroenterologist, S. Cleveland Hosp., MiddlesBoro. Prev: Cons. Phys. (Gen. Med. & Gastroenterol.) Sunderland Dist. Gen. Hosp.; Sen. Regist. (Gen. Med. & Gastroenterol.) Roy. Vict. Infirm. Newc. & Middlesbrough Gen. Hosp.; Research Fell. (Virol.) Med. Sch. Newc. u. Tyne.

SILCOCKS, Paul Benet Stevens Trent Institute for Health Services Research, University of Nottingham, Queen's Medical Centre, Nottingham NG7 2UH Tel: 0115 970 9765 Fax: 0115 970 9766 Email: p.b.silcocks@nottingham.ac.uk; Wingates, Shatton Lane, Bamford, Hope Valley S33 0BG — BM BCh 1973 Oxf.; MSc CNAA 1992; MSc Lond. 1982; BSc Bristol 1970; FFPHM RCP (UK) 1996, M 1986; FRCPath 1992, M 1980; MIBiol. 1981; T (Path) 1991; T (PHM) 1991. (Bristol & Oxf.) Sen. Lect. (Cancer Epidemiol.) Univ. Nottm.; Med. Adviser Trent Cancer Registry. Socs: BMA; Assn. Clin. Pathol. Prev: Sen. Lect. (Pub. Health Med.) Univ. Sheff.; Research Fell. ICRF Cancer Epidemiol. Unit Radcliffe Infirm. Oxf.; Lect. (Epidemiol.) St. Geo. Med. Sch. Lond.

SILHI, Ranweer Baldevdutt Canterbury Street Surgery, 511 Canterbury Street, Gillingham ME7 5LG Tel: 01634 573020 Fax: 01634 281287 — MB BS 1969 Nagpur; DTD Nagpur 1972. (Med. Coll. & Hosp. Nagpur, India) GP Hypnother. Gillingham; Mem. Kent LMC; Mem. Rainham and Gillingham PCG. Socs: Med. Defence Union.

SILK

SILK, David Baxter 107 Harley Street, London W1G 6AL Tel: 020 7631 1595 Fax: 020 7224 3019 — MB BS 1968 Lond.; MD Lond. 1974; FRCP Lond.1983; MRCP (UK) 1970; MRCS Eng. LRCP Lond. 1968. (Guy's) Cons. Phys. & Gastroenterol. & NutrtionHosp. Lond. Socs: Brit. Assn. Parenteral & Enteral Nutrit. (Past Pres); Med. Res. Soc.; Brit. Soc. Gastroenterol. Prev: Sen. Lect. & Cons. Phys. (Liver Unit) King's Coll. Hosp. Lond.; Vis. Assoc. Prof. Univ. Calif., USA.

SILK, Mr Frederick Fendley (retired) 9 Broom Road, Kinross KY13 8BU Tel: 01577 864150 — MB ChB 1948 Ed.; FRCS Ed. 1959; MChOrth Liverp. 1960. Prev: Cons. Orthop. Surg. United Leeds Hosps.

SILK, Jane Margaret Department of Anaesthesia, The Royal Hospitals NHS Trust, Whitechapel, London E1 1BB Tel: 020 7377 7793 — MB BS 1980 Lond.; FFA RCS Eng. 1984. Cons. Anaesth. (Paediat. Anaesth.) Barts and The Lond. NHS Trust. Socs: Obst. Anaesth. Assn.; Assn. Anaesth.; Assn. Paediat. Anaesth. Prev: Cons. Anaesth. Univ. Coll. Lond. Hosps.

SILK, Mr John 18 Rowben Close, London N20 8QR — MB ChB 1969 Mosul; FRCSI 1984.

SILK, Nicholas Swan Surgery, Swan Street, Petersfield GU32 3AB Tel: 01730 264011 Fax: 01730 231093; Brownfields, Westmark, Petersfield GU31 5AT Tel: 01730 263822 — MRCS Eng. LRCP Lond. 1968; BSc, MA Oxf., BM BCh 1968; DCH Eng. 1971; DObst RCOG 1970. (Oxf. & St. Thos.)

SILK, Rowena Marvin Foden Community Child Health Department, Oakengrove, Shrubbery Road, High Wycombe HP13 6PP Tel: 01494 426202; 28 Brook End, Weston Turville, Aylesbury HP22 5RF Tel: 01296 614167 — MB BS 1968 Lond.; MRCS Eng. LRCP Lond. 1968; MRCPCH 1996. (Guy's) Staff Grade (Community Paediat.) S. Bucks. NHS Trust. Socs: BMA; Soc. Pub. Health. Prev: Clinic Med. Off. Kent AHA.

SILKE, Carmel Mary Whiston Hospital, Warrington Road, Prescot L35 5DR — MB ChB 1996 Liverp.

SILKOFF, Benjamin Joseph (retired) 24 Grange Park Road, Leyton, London E10 Tel: 020 8539 2962 — MB BS 1948 Lond.; MRCS Eng., LRCP Lond. 1948. Prev: GP Leyton, Lond.

SILL, Peter Richard Ashington Hospital, West View, Ashington NE63 0SA — MB ChB 1978 Liverp.; FRCOG 1996; MRCOG 1983. Cons. O & G N.umbria Healthcare NHS Trust. Prev: Lect. (O & G) Univ. Papua New Guinea.

***SILLARS, Joanne** 103 Briarhill Road, Prestwick KA9 1HZ — MB ChB 1995 Aberd.

SILLENDER, Mark 31 Cottage Road, Leeds LS6 4DD — MB ChB 1993 Ed. SHO (O & G) York Dist. Hosp.

SILLER, Catherine Sandra 15 Peterborough Road, Liverpool L15 9HN — MB ChB 1996 Liverp.

SILLERS, Mr Barrie Royston 111 Harley Street, London W1N 1DG Tel: 020 7935 2573 Fax: 020 758 6024 — MB ChB 1964 Leeds; BChD LDS Leeds 1960; FICOI 1992. Cons. Dent. Surg. Humana Hosp. Lond. Socs: BMA & BDA; Brit. Soc. Occlusal Studies.

SILLETT, Rachel Eileen Wellesley (retired) 12 Town Mill, Marlborough SN8 1NS Tel: 01672 515044 — MB ChB (Hons.) Birm. 1941; MD Birm. 1956; MFCM 1973; DPH Lond. 1954. Prev: Med. Ref. DHSS.

SILLICK, Jennifer Mabel Walton Health Centre, Rodney Road, Walton-on-Thames KT12 3LB Tel: 01932 228999 Fax: 01932 225586 — MB BChir 1983 Camb.; MA Camb. 1984. (Camb. & St. Thos.) p/t Princip. in Gen. Pract. Socs: Assoc. Mem. Roy. Soc. Med. Prev: SHO (A & E) St. Geo. Hosp. Lond.; SHO Rotat. (Med. & Paediat.) St. Peter's Hosp. Chertsey; SHO (O & G) St. Helier Hosp. Carshalton.

SILLIFANT, Kate Louise 72 Buckingham Way, Royston, Barnsley S71 4SL — MB ChB 1988 Leic.

SILLINCE, Claire Cheadle Royal Hospital, 100 Wilmslow Road, Cheadle SK8 3US — MB ChB 1975 Birm.; MRCP (UK) 1977; FRCPsych 1996, M 1980. Cons. Psychiat. Cheadle Roy. Hosp. Prev: Cons. Psychiat. Halton HA; Sen. Regist. (Psychiat.) NW RHA; Regist. (Psychiat.) Manch. HA (T).

SILLINCE, David Norman Holts Health Centre, Watery Lane, Newent GL18 1BA Tel: 01531 820689; Cothers, Moat Lane, Taynton, Gloucester GL19 3AR Tel: 01452 790504 — MB BS 1972 Lond.; MRCGP 1989. (Char. Cross)

SILLITOE, Antony Thomas 2 Hawthorn Road, Roby, Huyton, Liverpool L36 9TT — MB ChB 1996 Liverp.

SILLITOE, Claire 1 Hopgarden Cottages, Filston Lane, Shoreham, Sevenoaks TN14 7SX — MB ChB 1997 Sheff.

SILLITOE, Kate Rose Cottage, Robin Hood Lane, Wrightington, Wigan WN6 9QG — MB ChB 1998 Sheff.; MB ChB Sheff 1998.

SILLITOE, Krystyna Maria Holmwood Corner Surgery, 179 Malden Road, New Malden KT3 6AA Tel: 020 8942 0066 Fax: 020 8336 1377; 6 Fullbrooks Avenue, Worcester Park KT4 7PE — MB ChB 1959 Silesia; LAH Dub. 1964. (Silesia Med. Acad. Poland) Prev: Clin. Asst. (Gyn.) New Vict. Hosp. Kingston u. Thames; SHO St. Geo. Hosp. Tooting; Ho. Phys. Bethnal Green Hosp.

SILLS, David John (retired) 58 The Gardens, Watford WD17 3DW Tel: 01923 243560 — MB BS 1955 Lond.; MRCS Eng. LRCP Lond. 1955; DCH Eng. 1960; DObst RCOG 1959. Prev: GP Watford.

SILLS, David William Queensway Surgery, 75 Queensway, Southend-on-Sea SS1 2AB Tel: 01702 463333 Fax: 01702 603026 — MB BChir 1977 Camb.

SILLS, Jennifer Anne Birmingham Childrens Hospital, Birmingham B16 8ET; 58 The Gardens, Watford WD17 3DW — MB BS 1988 Lond.; MRCP (UK) 1996; DRCOG 1992; DCH RCP Lond. 1990. Regist. (Paediat.) Birm. Childr. Hosp. Prev: SHO (Paediat.) Leicester Roy. Infirm.; SHO (O & G & Paediat.) Roy. Berks. Hosp.; SHO (Paediat. & A & E) Milton Keynes Gen. Hosp.

SILLS, John Anthony 23 Knowsley Park Lane, Prescot L34 3NA; Royal Liverpool Childrens Hospital, Alder Hey, Liverpool L12 2AP Tel: 0151 252 5541 Fax: 0151 252 5928 Email: john.sills@rlch-tr.mwest.nhs.uk — MB Camb. 1969, BChir 1968; MRCP (UK) 1973; FRCP Lond. 1988; DCH Eng. 1972; FRCPCH 1997. (Camb. & St. Bart.) Cons. (Paediat.) Alder Hey Childr. Hosp. Liverp. & Whiston Hosp. Prescot. Prev: Sen. Regist. Roy. Hosp. Sick Childr. Edin.; Regist. Roy. Liverp. Childr. Hosp.

SILLS, Michael Alfred 27 Le Marchant Avenue, Lindley, Huddersfield HD3 3DF — MB Camb. 1974, BChir 1973; MRCP (UK) 1978; DCH RCPS Glas. 1975; DObst RCOG 1975. Cons. (Paediat.) Huddersfield Roy. Infirm. Prev: Regist. (Med.) Roy. Gwent Hosp. Newport; Regist. (Paediat.) Gen. Infirm. Leeds; Sen. Regist. (Paediat.) Yorks. RHA.

SILLS, Michael David Goodinge Health Centre, Goodinge Close, North Road, London N7 9EW Tel: 020 7530 4940 — MB BS 1984 Lond.

SILLS, Oliver Anthony (retired) 128 Cambridge Road, Barton, Cambridge CB3 7AR Tel: 01223 263612 — MRCS Eng. LRCP Lond. 1944; MRCGP 1954. Prev: Hosp. Pract. (Psychiat.) Addenbrooke's Hosp. Camb.

SILLS, Philip Radcliffe The Old Rectory Surgery, 18 Castle Street, Saffron Walden CB10 1BP Tel: 01799 522327 Fax: 01799 525436 — MB ChB 1972 St. And.

SILLS, Richard Oliver c/o 48 Carisbrooke Drive, Mapperley Park, Nottingham NG3 5DS — MB BS 1984 Lond.

SILLS, Susan Catherine Johan Hardwicke House Surgery, Hardwicke House, Stour Street, Sudbury CO10 2AY Tel: 01787 370011 Fax: 01787 376521; Ropers Hall Farm, Assington Road, Bures CO8 5JX Tel: 01787 227500 — MB ChB 1972 Ed.; DPM Eng. 1978. Socs: Sudbury Med. Soc. (Sec.); W Suff. Postgrad. Assn.; Brit. Med. Assn.

SILMAN, Harry 6 Sandmoor Mews, Leeds LS17 7SA Tel: 0113 680880 — MRCS Eng. LRCP Lond. 1935; BSc (Hons. Physiol.) Leeds 1932, MB ChB 1935. (Leeds)

SILMAN, Robert Edward 83 Highgate West Hill, London N6 6LU Tel: 020 7252 2541 Fax: 020 7394 7180 Email: r.e.silman@mds.qmw.ac.uk — MB BS 1971 Lond.; LEsL Paris 1964; PhD Lond. 1980; BSc (1st cl. Hons.) Lond. 1968, MB BS 1971. (Middlx.) Sen. Lect. & Hon. Cons. Dept. O & G/Reproduc. Physiol. Lond. Hosp. Prev: Wellcome Trust Sen. Lect. & Hon. Cons. Dept. Reproduc. Physiol. St. Bart. Hosp. Lond.; Ho. Phys. Med. Profess. Unit & Ho. Surg. (Neurosurg.) Middlx. Hosp. Lond.

SILOVE, Eric Dale Birmingham Childrens Hospital, Ladywood, Middleway, Birmingham B16 8ET Tel: 0121 333 9439 Fax: 0121 333 9441 Email: eric.silove@bhamchildres.wmids.nhs.uk; 19 Hintlesham Avenue, Edgbaston, Birmingham B15 2PH Fax: 0121 243 9941 Email: e.silove@btinternet.com — MB BCh 1958 Witwatersrand; MD Witwatersrand 1976; FRCP Lond. 1979, M 1964; FRCP Ed. 1975, M 1963; FRCPCH. Cons. Paediat. Cardiol. Birm. Childr. Hosp.; Clin. Sen. Lect. Univ. Birm. Socs: (Ex-Pres.) Brit. Paediat. Cardiac Assn.; (Counc.) Brit. Cardiac Soc.; (Pres.) Assn.

Europ. Paediat. Cardiol. (Counc. Scientif. Sect.). Prev: Sen. Research Fell. & Hon. Cons. Hosp. Sick Childr. Gt. Ormond St.; Asst. Prof. Med. Mt. Sinai Hosp. Sch. of Med., NY, USA; Research Fell. (Cardiol.) Univ. Colorado Med. Center Denver, USA.

SILOVE, Yvonne Margaret Flat 5, 25 Avenue Road, London NW8 6BS — MB BChir 1994 Camb.

SILOVSKY, Karol Haven Health Surgery, Grange Farm Avenue, Felixstowe IP11 2FB Tel: 01394 670107 Fax: 01394 282872 — MB ChB 1988 Leic.; T(GP) 1992. (Leics.)

SILSBY, Joseph Francis 138 South Street, Taunton TA1 3AG — MB ChB 1996 Bristol.

SILVA, Ana Queen Elizabeth Hospital for Children, Hackney Road, London E2 8PS — Lic Med 1983 Oporto; Lic Med. Oporto 1983.

SILVA, Audrey Saumya Clair 9 Vernon Court, Stanmore HA7 2BN — MB BS 1992 Lond.

SILVA, Daya The Bayswater Surgery, 46 Craven Road, London W2 3QA Tel: 020 7402 2073 Fax: 020 7723 8579; Flat 1, 4 and 5 Hyde Park Place, London W2 2HL — MB BS Ceylon 1962. (Univ. Ceylon) Socs: RSM.

SILVA, Edward Paul Clarence The Langdale Unit, Guild Park, Whittingham, Preston PR3 2JH — MB ChB 1992 Liverp.

SILVA, Francisco Briones Longmead Surgery, Norman Colyer Court, Hollymoor Lane, Epsom KT19 9JZ Tel: 01372 743432 Fax: 0372 817595; Greenhills, 102 Kingsmead Avenue, Worcester Park KT4 8UT Tel: 020 8395 3728 Fax: 020 8330 6244 Email: alwyn.s@virgin.net — MD Univ. East Philippines 1969.

SILVA, Kottoruge Gilbert Stonleigh Avenue Surgery, 98A Stonleigh Avenue, Longbenton, Newcastle upon Tyne NE12 0UR Tel: 0191 266 2271 — MB BS 1970 Ceylon. (Ceylon) GP Newc.

SILVA, Lakshman Upali Meads End, Forewood Lane, Crowhurst, Battle TN33 9AB Tel: 0142 483388 — MB BS 1962 Ceylon; FFA RCS Eng. 1966.

SILVA, Liyanage Francis Adolphus Fieldhead Hospital, Ouchthorpe Lane, Wakefield WF1 3SP Tel: 01924 375217 — MB BS 1961 Ceylon; MRCPsych 1982; DPH Liverp. 1972; DPM Eng. 1978. (Colombo) Cons. Psychiat. Fieldhead Hosp. Wakefield. Prev: Sen. Regist. Lea Castle Hosp. Kidderminster; SHO (Psychiat.) Hosp. St. Cross Rugby; Regional Med. Off. Leprosy Control S. Ceylon.

SILVA, Mark Timothy 22 Courtenay Avenue, Sutton SM2 5ND — MB BCh 1988 Wales; BSc Wales 1985; MRCP (UK) 1991. Regist. (Neurol.) Roy. Free Hosp. Lond. Socs: Young Fell. Roy. Soc. Med. Prev: Research Regist. (Neurol.) Inst. Neurol. Lond.; Regist. (Neurol.) St. Thos. Hosp. Lond.; SHO Rotat. (Med.) Bristol & W.on HA.

SILVA, Nicholas Charles Community House, Orchard Hill, Fountain Drive, Carshalton SM5 4NR Tel: 020 8770 8000; 4 Molyneux Drive, London SW17 6BA — MB BS 1986 Lond.; Dip. Med. Educat. Dund 1996; DCH RCP Lond. 1988. (St. Geo. Lond.) SCMO Merton & Sutton Community Trust. Socs: Assn. Research Infant & Child Developm.; Brit. Assn. of Community Child Health. Prev: Sen. Regist. (Community Child Health) Qu. Mary's Hosp. Carshalton.; Regist. (Community Paediat.) St. Heliers Hosp. Carshalton; SHO (Paediat.) Guy's Hosp. Lond.

SILVA, Obadage Sarath Gamini 145 Canterbury Road, Harrow HA1 4PA — MB BS 1974 Sri Lanka; MRCS Eng. LRCP Lond. 1979; FFA RCS Eng. 1980.

SILVA, Punsiri Sanjeev 43d Anerley Park, London SE20 8NQ — MB BS 1997 Lond.

SILVER, Mr Alan Jonathan Shieldfield Health Centre, Stoddart Street, Shieldfield, Newcastle upon Tyne NE2 1AL Tel: 0191 232 4872; 25 Richmond Court, Low Fell, Gateshead NE9 5JG — MB BS 1975 Newc.; FRCS Eng. 1979; MRCGP 1983; DRCOG 1983; DFFP 1998. Clin. Asst. (Endoscopy) Freeman Rd. Hosp. Newc.; Vasectomy Surg. Marie Stopes Organisation. Prev: GP Trainee N.ld. VTS; Regist. (Gen. Surg.) Cheltenham Gen. Hosp.; Demonstr. (Anat.) Bristol Med. Sch.

SILVER, Christopher Patrick (retired) 25 Primrose Hill Road, London NW3 3DG — BM BCh 1942 Oxf.; DM Oxf. 1954, MA, BM BCh 1942; FRCP Lond. 1972, M 1948. Prev: Cons. Geriat. Lond. Hosp. & Tower Hamlets HA.

SILVER, David Anthony Trevor Colestocks House, Colestocks EX14 3JR Email: datsrde@hotmail.com — MB BS 1985 Lond.; BSc Lond. 1983; MRCP (UK) 1989; FRCR 1993. (St Barts. Hosp. Med. Coll.) Cons. Radiol. Roy. Devon & Exeter Hosp.; Hon. Sen. Lect. Univ. Bristol. Socs: Brit. Med. Ultrasound Soc.; RCR; Brit. Soc. of Skeletal Radiol. Prev: Fell. (Radiol.) P.ss Alexandra Hosp. Brisbane, Austral.; Regist. (Med.) Soton. Gen. Hosp.; Ho. Surg. St. Bart. Hosp. Lond.

SILVER, Deborah Miriam 28 Windsor Street, Chertsey KT16 8AS — MB ChB 1986 Dundee; MRCP (UK) 1992. Prev: Regist. (Paediat.) Addenbrooke's Hosp. Camb.

SILVER, Gary Alexander Green Lane Cottage, Green Lane, Stanmore HA7 3AB — MB BS 1995 Lond.

SILVER, Hyman (retired) Shearwater, Smithy Lane, Down Holland, Ormskirk L39 7JS Tel: 01704 840106 Fax: As above Email: shearwater.wd@tesco.net — MB ChB 1951 Liverp.; MRCS Eng. LRCP Lond. 1950. Prev: Hosp. Pract. (Paediat.) Fazakerley & Walton Hosps. Liverp.

SILVER, Jack 52 Upper Montagu Street, London W1H 1SJ Tel: 020 722249905 Fax: 020 7224 9907 — MB BCh 1957 Witwatersrand; FFA RCS Eng. 1967; DA (UK) 1961. Prev: Cons. Anaesth. Greenwich Healthcare Trust Lond.; Sen. Regist. Guy's & Lewisham Hosp. Lond.

SILVER, John Russell The Chiltern Hospital, Great Missenden HP16 0EN Tel: 01494 890250; 8 High Street, Wendover, Aylesbury HP22 6EA Tel: 01296 623013 Fax: 01296 623020 — MB BS Lond. 1954; FRCP Lond. 1980; FRCP Ed. 1978, M 1962. (Middlx.) Emerit. Cons. Spinal Injuries Centre Stoke Mandeville Hosp. Aylesbury. Socs: Fell. Inst. Sports Med.; Cervical Spine Soc.; Brit. Assn. Neurol. Prev: Cons. Spinal Injuries Stoke Mandeville Hosp.; Cons. i/c Liverp. Regional Paraplegia Centre (Lect. Surg.); Regist. (Neurol.) Middlx. Hosp. Lond.

SILVER, Lisa Rebecca McWhirter, Barton and Silver, The Surgery, Wanbourne Lane, Nettlebed, Henley-on-Thames RG9 5AJ Tel: 01491 641204 Fax: 01491 641162; 38 St. Andrews Road, Henley-on-Thames RG9 1JB Tel: 01491 571072 Email: drlisasilver@hotmail.com — MB ChB 1988 Manch.; BSc (Hons.) Aberd. 1983; Dip. MedSci. St. And. 1985. (Manch.) GP Oxon.

SILVER, Michael Ellman Fore Street Surgery, 234 Fore Street, Edmonton, London N18 2LY Tel: 020 8803 6705 Fax: 020 8884 2065 — MB BS 1961 Lond.; MRCS Eng. LRCP Lond. 1961; DObst RCOG 1963; AFOM 1978. (St. Geo.) Prev: Employm. Med. Adviser EMAS; Ho. Surg. & Ho. Phys. St. Geo. Hosp. Lond.; Resid. Obst. Off. Cheltenham Matern. Hosp.

SILVER, Nicholas Charles Royal London Hospital, Whitechapel, London E7 1BB Tel: 020 7377 7000; 23 Alexandra Grove, London N12 8HE Tel: 020 8343 8436 Email: n.silvereion.vcl.ac.uk — MB BS 1989 Lond.; PhD Lond. 2001; MRCP (UK) 1992. Specialist Regist. (Neurol.) Roy Lond Hosp. Prev: Research Fell. (Neurol.) Inst. Neurol. Lond.; Regist. Rotat. (Med.) Char. Cross. Lond.; Specialist Regist. (Nevrol) NGH Hosp., Neurol., Lond.

SILVER, Simon Nathan Waldron House, Hoovers Lane, Lea, Ross-on-Wye HR9 5TX — MB BS Newc. 1978; MRCGP 1982. Course Organiser Gloucester & Cheltenham VTS.

SILVER, Trevor 314 Norbury Avenue, London SW16 3RL Tel: 020 8764 2288 Fax: 020 8764 2288 — MB BS 1949 Durh.; FRCGP 1973, M 1960; DA Eng. 1962. (Durh.) Hon. Sen. Lect. (Gen. Pract.) St. Geo. Hosp. Lond. Socs: Hon. Fell. BMA; Fell. Roy. Soc. Med.; Fell. BMA. Prev: Regional Adviser Gen. Pract. SW Thames RHA; Regist. (Anaesth.) & SHO (O & G) Sunderland Hosp. Gp.

SILVERDALE, Montague Adam 15 Larchfield Avenue, Newton Mearns, Glasgow G77 5PW — MB ChB 1995 Glas.

SILVERMAN, Andrew James Niden Manor Estate, Moreton Pinkney, Daventry NN11 3SJ — MB ChB 1991 Dundee; BMSc (Hons.) Dund 1988.

SILVERMAN, Ann Marisa 34 Fawnbrake Avenue, Herne Hill, London SE24 0BY Tel: 020 7274 6222 — BM BCh 1972 Oxf.; BA Oxf. 1969, BM BCh 1972; MRCPsych 1977. Cons. Psychiat. King's Coll. Hosp. Lond. & Cane Hill Hosp. Coulsdon. Prev: Sen. Regist. (Psychiat.) Bethlem Roy. & Maudsley Hosp.; SHO N.wick Pk. Hosp. Harrow; Regist (Psychiat.) Bethlem Roy. & Maudsley Hosps. Lond.

SILVERMAN, Barbara Helen Cloptons, 23 Green Lane, Linton, Cambridge CB1 6JZ Tel: 01223 892107 — BM BCh 1977 Oxf.; BA (Hons.) Oxf. 1974; MRCP (UK) 1980; MRCGP 1980; DRCOG 1980. Clin. Asst. (Rheum.) Addenbrookes Hosp. Cambs. Prev: Trainee GP Newc. VTS; Ho. Phys. Radcliffe Infirm. Oxf.

SILVERMAN, Jonathan David Coles Lane Health Centre, Coles Lane, Linton, Cambridge CB1 6JS Tel: 01223 891456 Fax: 01223 890033; Cloptons, 23 Green Lane, Linton, Cambridge CB1 6JZ Tel:

SILVERMAN

01223 892107 Email: jon@silverpeople.demon.co.uk — BM BCh 1977 Oxf.; BA (Hons.) Oxf. 1974; FRCGP 1995, M 1980; DRCOG 1979. Regional Communication Skills Teachg. Facilitator E. Anglia. Prev: Trainee GP Newc. VTS; Ho. Phys. Radcliffe Infirm. Oxf.; Course Organizer Camb. VTS.

SILVERMAN, Leon Stanley 393 Green Street, Upton Park, London E13 9AU Tel: 020 8552 8784 — MB BS 1971 Lond.; Family Plan Association Cert 1975; Association of Medical Advisers in Pharmaceutical Industry Cert. 1974; Cert. Prescribed Equiv. Exp. JCPTGP 1981; Cert. Family Plann. RCOG & RCGP 1977. (Middlx. Hospital, London) GP Lond. Socs: Fell. Roy. Soc. Med.; BMA. Prev: Clin. Research Med. Adviser Schering Chem.s Ltd., (Pharmaceut.; Div.) Burgess Hill; SHO (Venereol.) & Ho. Phys. (Dermat. & Gen. Med.) & Ho. Surg.

SILVERMAN, Maurice The Fir Trees, 2 Ringley Drive, Whitefield, Manchester M45 7LF Tel: 0161 766 3576 — MB ChB Leeds 1943; MD Leeds 1952; FRCPsych 1971; DPM Eng. 1947. (Leeds) Socs: BMA; Brit. Soc. Med. & Dent. Hypn.; Blackburn Med. Soc. Prev: Mem. Standing Ment. Health Advis. Comm. Centr. Health Servs. Counc.; Sen. Regist. St. Clement's Hosp., Roy. Lond. Hosp. & Psychiat. Unit Bow; Psychiat. RAMC.

SILVERMAN, Professor Michael Department of Child Health, University of Leicester, Clinical Sciences Building, Leicester Royal Infirmary, Leicester LE2 7LX Tel: 0116 252 3262 Fax: 0116 252 3282 Email: ms70@le.ac.uk — MD 1973 Camb.; MB 1968, BChir 1967; MRCP (UK) 1970; DCH Eng. 1972. (Camb. & St. Geo.) Prof. Child Health Univ. Leicester. Socs: Brit. Paediat. Assn. & Brit. Thoracic Soc. Prev: Prof. Paediat. Respirat. Med. Roy. Postgrad. Med. Sch. Lond.; Lect. (Child Health) Univ. Bristol; Lect. (Paediat.) Ahmadu Bello Univ. Zaria, Nigeria.

SILVERMAN, Sharon Ruth 17 Links Road, Wilmslow SK9 6HQ — BM BS 1993 Nottm.

SILVERMAN, Mr Stanley Harry City Hospital NHS Trust, Dudley Road, Birmingham B18 7QH Tel: 0121 554 3801 Fax: 0121 507 4816 Email: stan.silverman@cityhospbham.wmids.nhs.uk; 92 Moorcroft Road, Moseley, Birmingham B13 8LU Tel: 0121 449 1831 Email: sh.silverman@virgin.net — MB ChB 1977 Birm.; MD Birm. 1988; FRCS Eng. 1982; FRCS Ed. 1981. (Univ. Birm. Med. Sch.) Cons. Surg. City Hosp. NHS Trust. Birm. Socs: Vasc. Surg. Soc. GB & Irel.; Assn. Surg.; BMA. Prev: Cons. Surg. Wordsley Hosp. Stourbridge; Lect. (Surg.) Univ. Birm.; Research Regist. Gen. Hosp. Birm.

SILVERSTON, Neville Arnold, MBE (retired) Chapters, 6b Babraham Road, Cambridge CB2 2RA Tel: 01223 249911 Fax: 01223 246862 Email: nevillesilverston@btopenworld.com — MB ChB 1954 Manch.; MRCS Eng. LRCP Lond. 1954; FRCGP 1979, M 1965. Prev: Sen. Med. Resid. Jewish Hosp. Med. Center, Cincinnati, USA.

SILVERSTON, Paul Philip Oakfield Surgery, Vicarage Road, Newmarket CB8 8JF Tel: 01638 662018 Fax: 01638 660294; The Manor House, Little Wilbraham, Cambridge CB1 53Y Tel: 01223 811310 Fax: 01223 811310 — MB ChB 1985 Bristol; BA (Hons.) 1977, MB ChB 1985. Co-ordinator Camb. Pre Hosp. Trauma Life Support Course & Mem. Internat. Fac. Socs: Fac. Pre Hosp. Care. Prev: Trainee GP Addenbrooke's Hosp. VTS.

SILVERSTONE, Mr Anthony Charles The Portland Hospital, 209 Gt Portland St., London W1N 6AH Tel: 020 7383 7884; 77 King Henry's Road, London NW3 3QU — MB ChB 1969 Birm.; FRCS Ed. 1976; FRCS Eng. 1976; FRCOG 1992, M 1978. Cons. Univ. Coll. Lond. Hosps. Prev: Sen. Regist. (O & G) John Radcliffe Hosp. Oxf.; Resid. Surg. Off. Chelsea Hosp. Wom. & Qu. Charlotte's Matern. Hosp. Lond.

SILVERSTONE, Elizabeth Jane Wrexham Maelor Hospital, North East Wales NHS Trust, Wrexham LL13 7TD Tel: 01978 291100 Fax: 01978 725440 — MB BCh 1977 Wales; MRCP (UK) 1981; FRCR 1984. Cons. Wrexham Maelor Hosp. Clwyd.

SILVERT, Barry David Stonehill Medical Centre, Piggott St., Farnworth, Bolton BL4 9QZ Tel: 01204 73445 Fax: 01204 791633 — MB ChB 1966 Manch. Prev: Ho. Surg. Manch. Vict. Memor. Jewish Hosp.; Ho. Phys. Crumpsall Hosp. Manch.

SILVERTON, Kathryn Leigh 20 Bramley Avenue, Coulsdon CR5 2DP — BM 1998 Soton.; BM Soton 1998.

SILVERTON, Nicholas Paul Cardiac Department, Airedale General Hospital, Steeton, Keighley BD20 6TD Tel: 01535 292017 Fax: 01535 292019; The Yorkshire Clinic, Bradford Road, Bingley BD16 1TW Tel: 01274 560311 Fax: 01274 551247 — MB BS 1974 Lond.; MD Lond. 1985; FRCP Lond. 1992; MRCP (UK) 1977. (Middlx.) Cons. Cardiol. Airedale HA; Hon. Cons. Cardiol. N. Gen. Hosp. Sheff. & Leeds Gen. Infirm. Prev: Lect. (Cardiovasc. Studies) & Hon. Sen. Regist. (Cardiol.) Univ. Leeds; Regist. (Cardiol.) Leeds Gen. Infirm.

SILVESTER, Katharine Mary 33 Dorsington Close, Hatton Park, Warwick CV35 7TH — MB BS 1986 Lond.; BSc (Hons.) Lond. 1983, MB BS 1986; FCOphth 1992, M 1991. Prev: SHO (Ophth.) Cheltenham Dist. Gen. Hosp.; SHO (Ophth.) Univ. Hosp. Wales Cardiff.

SILVESTER, Mr Keith Charles Department of Oral & Maxillofacial Surgery, Morriston Hospital, Morriston, Swansea SA6 6NL Tel: 01792 703063; Brynderw, 117 Rhydypandy Road, Rhydypandy, Morriston, Swansea SA6 6PB Tel: 01792 844044 — MB BS 1985 Lond.; BDS Lond. 1976; FRCS Ed. 1989; FDS RCS Eng. 1983. Cons. Oral & Maxillofacial Surg. Morriston Hosp. Swansea. Prev: Sen. Regist. (Oral & Maxillofacial Surg.) Roy. Lond. Hosp.; Regist. (Oral & Maxillofacial Surg.) E.man Dent. Hosp. & Univ. Coll. Hosp. Lond.; SHO Qu. Vict. Hosp. E. Grinstead.

SILVESTER, Neil William Hugh West End Cottage, West End Road, Norton, Doncaster DN6 9EF — MB ChB 1979 Leeds; MRCPsych 1983. Cons. (Psychiat.) Doncaster Roy. Infirm.

SILVESTER, Richard Donald Beaumont Street Surgery, 19 Beaumont Street, Oxford OX1 2NA Tel: 01865 240501 Fax: 01865 240503 — MB BChir 1991 Camb.; MA Camb. 1990; MRCGP 1996; DRCOG 1995. (Lond. Hosp. Med. Coll.)

SILVESTRI, Miss Giuliana Royal Victoria Hospital, Eye and Ear Clinic, Grosvenor Road, Belfast BT12 6BA Tel: 01232 240503 Fax: 01232 330744 Email: g.silvestri@qub.ac.uk; 23 Kilcorig Road, Lisburn BT28 2QZ Tel: 01232 648590 — MD 1994 Belf.; MB BCh BAO 1983; FRCS Ed. 1989; FRCP (1997), MRCP (UK) 1987; ECFMG 1987; FRCOphth 1990. Sen. Lect. & Cons. Ophth. Surg. Roy. Vict. Hosp. Belf.

SILVEY, Hugh Stuart Sea Mills Surgery, 2 Riverleaze, Sea Mills, Bristol BS9 2HL Tel: 0117 968 1182 Fax: 0117 962 6408 — MB ChB 1972 Bristol.

SILVEY, Stuart John (retired) Denewood, 16 Westbury Lane, Bristol BS9 2PE Tel: 0117 968 1577 — MB ChB 1939 Bristol; MRCGP 1952. Prev: Pres. Bristol M-C Soc.

SIM, Alan James The Surgery, 142 Manse Road, Ardersier, Inverness IV2 7SR Tel: 01667 62240; 34 Blackthorn Road, Culloden, Inverness IV2 7LA — MB ChB 1988 Aberd. Trainee GP Inverness. Prev: SHO (Psychiat.) Craig Dunain Hosp. Inverness.

SIM, Alasdair McClure North Waestern Deanery -General Surgery Rotation, Dept. Postgraduate Medicine, Gateway House, Picadilly South, Manchester M60 7LP Tel: 01355 267821 ex directory, 0161 237 2298 — MB ChB 1969 Glas.; FRCPsych 1995, M 1975; DPM Ed. 1975. p/t Cons. Psychiat. Hairmyres Hosp. E. Kilbride. Prev: Cons. Psychiat. Woodilee Hosp. Lenzie.; Med. Dir. Ment. Handicap Serv. Gtr. Glas. HB.

SIM, Mr Andrew John Wyness Department of Surgery, Asean Sheffield Medical College, Suci Teguh Sdn Bhd, 11A Medan Istana 3 Bandar Ipoh Raya, Ipoh Perak 30000, Malaysia; 1 Bridge Street, Portsoy, Banff AB45 2GP Tel: 01261 43000 — MB BS 1971 Lond.; MS Lond. 1988; FRCS Glas. 1975. Prof. Surg. UAE Univ., Al Ain; Chairm. Dept. Surg. Al Ain Med. Dist. Socs: Nutrit. Soc.; Surgic. Research Soc. Prev: Asst. Director Acad. Surg. Unit St. Mary's Hosp. Med. Sch. Lond.; Sen. Regist. Roy. Infirm. Glas.; Research Fell. Harvard Med. Sch.

SIM, Angus James Wyness 14D South Mount Street, Aberdeen AB25 4TB — MB ChB 1996 Aberd.

SIM, Charles Gordon (retired) 22 Coniscliffe Road, Hartlepool TS26 0BT Tel: 01429 274785 — MB ChB Ed. 1946.

SIM, Colville Graeme (retired) Ashcroft, Haltwhistle NE49 0DA Tel: 01434 20079 — MB BS 1943 Durh.; MA 1934, MB BS Durh. 1943.

SIM, David Anthony James Daisy Hill Hospital, Hospital Road, Newry BT35 8DR Tel: 028 303 5000 Fax: 028 3026 8285; Cranmore, 143 Dublin Road, Loughbrickland, Banbridge BT32 3NT Tel: 028 4062 2822 — MB BCh BAO 1980 Belf.; MD Belf. 1991; MRCOG 1986; FRCOG 1999. (Qu. Univ. Belf.) Cons. O & G Daisy Hill Hosp. Newry, Co. Down.

SIM, David Gordon 32 Bath Hill Court, Bath Road, Bournemouth BH1 2HP Tel: 01202 294738 — LRCP, LRCS Ed., LRFPS Glas. 1938. (Ed.)

SIM, David Morrice Longshut Lane West Surgery, 24 Longshut Lane West, Stockport SK2 6SF Tel: 0161 480 2373 Fax: 0161 480 2660; Lothlorian House, Carrwood Road, Bramhall, Stockport SK7 3LR Tel: 0161 486 1213 — MB ChB 1963 Aberd.; MRCGP 1972. (Aberd.) Med. Off. Brit. Boxing Bd. of Control. Prev: Ho. Surg. Roy. Aberd. Hosp. Sick Childr.; Ho. Phys. Newsham Gen. Hosp. Liverp.; SHO Obst. Preston Roy. Infirm.

SIM, David Robert (retired) 13/6 South Oswald Road, Edinburgh EH9 2HQ Tel: 0131 662 0447 — MB ChB Ed. 1951.

SIM, Mr David William Ardmohr, 21 Main Street, East Calder, Livingston EH53 0ES — MB ChB 1982 Glas.; MSc 1985; FRCS (Orl.) 1991; FRCS Ed. 1987; DLO RCS Eng. 1987. Cons. Otolaryngol. Head & Neck Surg. Edin. Prev: Sen. Regist. (Otolaryngol.) Edin.; Lect. (Otolaryngol.) Univ. Edin.

SIM, Douglas William (retired) Tanglewood, Broad Campden Road, Chipping Campden GL55 6DJ Tel: 01386 841509 — MB ChB Manch. 1951. Prev: Gen. Practitioner, Merton.

SIM, Duncan John Fairlight, Playstreet Lane, Ryde PO33 3LJ — MB ChB 1993 Birm.

SIM, Ewen Department of Pathology, Whittington Hospital, Wilmslow Road, Withington, Manchester M20 Tel: 0161 291 3596 Fax: 0161 291 3594; 17 Redland Avenue, South Reddish, Stockport SK5 7JF Tel: 0161 480 5470 Fax: 0161 480 5470 Email: ewen.sim@pobox.com — MB ChB 1990 Ed.; BSc (Hons.) Anat. Ed. 1987. (Edinburgh) Specialist Regist. (Histopath.) Whittington Hosp.; Clin. Asst. (Community Health) Manch. Action on St. Health. Socs: Fell. (Ex-Pres.) Roy. Med. Soc. Edin. Prev: Clin Ass (A & E) St James Hosp. Leeds.

SIM, Fiona Marion Barnet Healthcare NHS Trust, Colindale Hospital, Colindale Avenue, London NW9 5HG Tel: 020 8200 1555 Fax: 020 8200 9499; 111 Newberries Avenue, Radlett WD7 7EN Tel: 01923 852524 — MSc (Community Med.) Lond. 1982, BSc (Hons.) 1975, MB BS 1978; FFPHM RCP (UK) 1992; MFCM RCP (UK) 1984. (Lond.) Med. Dir. Barnet Healthcare NHS Trust. Prev: Dir. Pub. Health Barnet HA.

SIM, Gordon Duns Medical Practice, The Knoll, Station Road, Duns TD11 3EL Tel: 01361 883322 Fax: 01361 882186; Dingleside, Clouds, Duns TD11 3BB Tel: 01361 882578 — MB ChB 1988 Aberd. SHO (Geriat.) Kingston Gen. Hosp. Hull. Prev: SHO (Paediat.) Hull Roy. Infirm.

SIM, Hok Gwan 59 Redlane, Claygate, Esher KT10 0ES — MD 1967 Cologne; LMSSA Lond. 1971; State Exam. Med. Cologne 1965; MRCOG 1978, DObst 1973. Prev: Sen. Regist. (O & G) Caritas Med. Centre Kowloon, Hong Kong; Regist. (O & G) Profess. Unit Welsh Nat. Sch. Med. Cardiff & Vale of Leven Dist. Gen. Hosp. Alexandria.

SIM, Ian Stuart George (retired) 18 Ashfield Road, Compton Road W., Wolverhampton WV3 9DP Tel: 01902 755149 — MB BS 1955 Lond.; MRCS Eng. LRCP Lond. 1954. Prev: GP Wolverhampton.

SIM, Ivor John Ardblair Medical Practice, Ann Street, Blairgowrie PH10 6EF Tel: 01250 872033 Fax: 01250 874517 — MB ChB 1977 Dundee; MRCGP 1983.

SIM, John Wilson The Health Centre, High St., Snaith, Goole DN14 9HJ Tel: 01405 860217 Fax: 01405 862580; 6 Manor Close, Camblesforth, Selby YO8 8HP Tel: 01757 618395 — MB ChB 1964 Aberd. (Aberd.) Socs: BMA. Prev: Ho. Off. Aberd. Roy. Infirm. & Bridge of Earn Hosp. & Ayrsh. Centr. Matern. Hosp.

SIM, Juliet Claire 26B Hunterhill Road, Paisley PA2 6ST — MB ChB 1994 Glas.

SIM, Justein Sarah Noble Royal infirmary of Edinburgh, Laviston place, Edinburgh EH3 9YN; 368 Perth Road, Dundee DD2 1EN — MB ChB 1992 Dundee; BSc (Hons.) Dund 1990; MRCP (UK) 1995. SpR Cardiol. Lothian Univ. Hosps. NHS trust. Prev: Regist: (Cardiol.) Dundee Trust Hosps.; Research Fell. Dept. of Clin. Pharmocology.

SIM, Kuan Tzen 23 Dogfield Street, Cardiff CF24 4QJ — MB BCh 1997 Wales.

SIM, Man Fai Victor 27 Silver Birch Close, Whitchurch, Cardiff CF14 1EL — MB BCh 1985 Wales; MRCP (UK) 1990; MRCGP 1996; DGM RCP Lond. 1994; DRCOG 1991. (Wales) Specialist Regist. (Med. & c/o Elderly) Llandough Hosp. Cardiff; Clin. Asst. (Cardiol.) Roy. Gwent Hosp. Newport. Prev: GP Cardiff.

SIM, Natalie Alexis 175 Machanill, Larkhall — MB ChB 1996 Aberd.

SIM, Pamela Georgina Esplanade Surgery, 19 Esplanade, Ryde PO33 2EH Tel: 01983 611444 Fax: 01983 811548; Fairlight, Playstreet Lane, Ryde PO33 3LJ Tel: 01983 566040 Email: pam@docsim.demon.co.uk — MB ChB 1966 Birm.; DObst RCOG 1968. (Birm.) GP.

***SIM, Richard James** Fairlight, Playstreet Lane, Ryde PO33 3LJ — MB ChB 1994 Birm.; ChB Birm. 1994; MB ChB Birmingham 1994.

SIM, Sheila Margaret Dingleside, Clouds, Duns TD11 3BB Tel: 01361 882578 — MB ChB 1988 Glas. Prev: SHO (O & G) Hull Matern. Hosp.

SIM, Yen Tai Basement Flat, 55A Union St., Greenock PA16 8DR — MB ChB 1994 Dundee.

SIM-DAVIS, Derek, Col. late RAMC Retd. King Edward VII Hospital, Midhurst GU29 0BL Tel: 01730 812341 Fax: 01730 816330; Poynings, 24 Hollycombe Close, Midhurst Road, Liphook GU30 7HR — MRCS Eng. LRCP Lond. 1950; Dip. Dermat. Lond 1971; DTM & H Eng. 1956. (Lond. Hosp.) Cons Dermat. King Edwd. VII Hosp. Midhurst; Fell. St. John's Hosp. Dermat. Socs: Fell. Roy. Soc. Med. Prev: Cons. Dermat. Camb. Hosp. Aldershot.

SIMANOWITZ, Milton David Evergreen, 7 The Avenue, Radlett WD7 7DG Tel: 0192 765007 — MD 1971 Cape Town; MB ChB 1958; FRCOG 1979, M 1965. (Cape Town) Cons. (O & G) Edgware Gen. Hosp. Socs: Infertil. Soc. Prev: Lect. W.m. Med. Sch. Lond.; Sen. Regist. Inst. O & G Hammersmith Hosp. Lond.

SIMCOCK, Antony David 7 Passage Hill, Mylor, Falmouth TR11 5SN Tel: 01326 374026 Fax: 01326 374026 — MB BS 1967 Lond.; MRCS Eng. LRCP Lond. 1967; FFA RCS Eng. 1971. (Lond. Hosp.) Cons. Anaesth. Roy. Cornw. Hosps. Truro; Lect. & Demonst. BASICS. Socs: Intens. Care Soc.; Assn. Anaesths.; BMA. Prev: Sen. Regist. (Anaesth.) United Bristol Hosps.; Regist. & SHO (Anaesth.) Lond. Hosp.

SIMCOCK, David Ewart 7 Passage Hill, Mylor, Falmouth TR11 5SN Tel: 01326 374026; 7 Passage Hill, Mylor, Falmouth TR11 5SN Tel: 01326 374026 — MB BS 1997 Lond. (Guy's & St. Thomas's Hosps.) SHO (Med.) St. Richard's Hosp. Chichester. Prev: Ho. Off. (Med.) Guy's Hosp. Lond.; Ho. Off. (Surg.) E.bourne Dist. Gen. Hosp.; SHO (Med.) Frimley Pk. Hosp.

SIMCOCK, Lolita Anne (Rivas) 29 Park Street, Brighton BN2 2BS Tel: 01273 699767 Email: rich.lol@virgin.net — MB BS 1994 Lond.; MRCGP 2000 Lond.; BSc Lond. 1992; DRCOG 1998. (UMDS) GP Retainer. Prev: Gen. Pract.; SHO (Paediat.); SHO (O & G).

SIMCOCK, Paul David 17 Princess Dr, Sandbach CW11 1BS — MB ChB 1997 Birm.

SIMCOCK, Mr Peter Reginald 4 Manston Terrace, Exeter EX2 4NP Tel: 01392 434141 Fax: 01392 435301 Email: simcock@btconnect.com; Whitley Cottage, 8 Northview Road, Budleigh Salterton EX9 6BZ Email: psimcock@hotmail.com — MB ChB 1983 Leic.; FRCS Eng. 1988; MRCP (UK) 1990; FRCOphth 1990; DO RCS Eng. 1987. (Leicester) Cons. Ophth. Surg. Roy. Devon & Exeter Hosp. Prev: Fell. (Vitreoretinal) Manch. Roy. Eye Hosp.; Sen. Regist. Char. Cross Hosp. & Moorfields Eye Hosp. Lond.; Regist. (Ophth.) Manch. Roy. Eye Hosp.

SIMCOCK, Richard Alexander John Radiotherapy Department, St. Thomas' Hospital, London SE1 7EU; Email: rsimcock@doctors.org.uk — MB BS 1993 Lond.; FRCR 2001 Lond.; MRCP Ireland 1997. (UMDS) Specialist Regist. (Clin. Oncol.) Guys & St. Thomas' NHS Trust Lond.

SIMCOCK, Tracey Anne 20 Fitzwalter Road, Caldicot, Newport NP26 5DA; 81 Kitchener Road, Selly Park, Birmingham B29 7QE — MB ChB 1994 Birm.; ChB Birm. 1994; MRCPI 1998.

SIME, David Patterson (retired) — MB ChB 1965 Glas.; FRCGP 1999; DObst RCOG 1967.

SIME, Joanne Lesley 46 Parkgrove Gardens, Edinburgh EH4 7QS — MB ChB 1997 Ed.

SIME, Linda Anne Alloa Health Centre, Marshill, Alloa FK10 1AQ Tel: 01259 212088 Fax: 01259 724788 — MB ChB 1984 Aberd.; MRCGP 1988; DCH RCPS Glas. 1986; DRCOG 1986.

SIME, Rhona Jean G/L, 181 Kenmure Street, Pollokshields, Glasgow G41 2LE — MB ChB 1986 Glas.

SIMENACZ

SIMENACZ, Mark Anthony 4A Paul Gardens, Croydon CR0 5QL — MB ChB 1990 Leeds.

SIMENOFF, Charles Julius Oak Leigh Medical Centre, 58 Ash Tree Road, Crumpsall, Manchester M8 5SA Tel: 0161 740 1226 Fax: 0161 795 8611 Email: charles.simenoff@zoom.co.uk — MB ChB 1978 Ed.; BSc Ed. 1975; MRCGP 1982; DRCOG 1981. (Edin.) Chairm. Manch. LMC.; Mem. Gen. Pract. Comm. Of BMA. Socs: BMA - GPC; BMA (Mem. Gen. Med. Servs. Comm.). Prev: Trainee GP Unsworth Med. Centre Bury.

SIMEONIDOU, Eftihia 17 Sofokleous Street, Amo Glyfada, Athens 16674, Greece; Department of Academic Cardiology, Freeman Hospital, High Heaton, Newcastle upon Tyne NE7 7DN — Ptychio Iatrikes 1985 Thessalonika. (Aristotle University Thessalonika) Cons. (Cardiol.) Univ. Hosp. of Patras, Greece. Socs: NASPE; Greek Cardiol. Soc.; Greek Gp. of Arrtythmias & Electrophysiol. Prev: Specialist Regist. (Cardiol.) Freeman Hosp. Newc. upon Tyne.

SIMHACHALAM, Dharmana 22 Humberston Avenue, Humberston, Grimsby DN36 4SP — MB BS 1975 Andhra.

SIMHADRI, Nanduri Gloucester Centre, Morpeth Close, Orton Longueville, Peterborough PE2 7JU — MB BS 1968 Andhra.

SIMISON, Mr Alastair John McIvor Arrowe Park Hospital, Upton, Wirral CH49 5PE; 7 Belmont Road, West Kirby, Wirral CH48 5EY — MB ChB 1973 Ed.; BSc (Hons.) Ed. 1970; MChOrthop Liverp. 1984; FRCS Ed. (Orth.) 1984; FRCS Ed. 1978. Cons. Orthop. Surg. Arrowe Pk. & Clatterbridge Hosps.

SIMISTER, John Michael (retired) 80 King Street, Seahouses NE68 7XS — MB BChir 1952 Camb.; MA Camb. 1959, MB BChir 1952. Prev: Med. Dir. Lundbeck Ltd. Luton.

SIMKIN, Mr Eric Philip Beechwood, 84 Beech Lane, Calderstones, Liverpool L18 3ER; 35 Rodney Street, Liverpool L1 9AB Tel: 0151 708 6252 — MB BChir 1952 Camb.; MChir Camb. 1967, MA, MB BChir 1952; FRCS Eng. 1960. (Camb. & Middlx.) Cons. (Gen. Surg.) Roy. Liverp. Hosp. Socs: Fell. Assn. Surgs., & Roy. Soc. Med. Prev: Sen. Surg. Regist. Liverp. RHB & United Hosps.; Surg. Regist. Liverp. Roy. Infirm.; Accid. Off. Middlx. Hosp. Lond.

SIMKISS, Douglas Eric Birmingham Specialist Community NHS TrustTrust, BCCC, 61 Bacchus Road, Winson Green, Birmingham B18 4QY Tel: 0121 507 9508 Fax: 0121 507 9533 Email: douglas.sinkiss@bscht.wmds.nhs.uk; 41 Sandhills Lane, Bernt, Worcester B45 8NY Tel: 0121 445 6425 — MB ChB 1988 Sheff.; MSc Warwick 1997; BMedSci Sheff. 1987; MRCP (UK) 1991; DTM & H Liverp. 1992; DCH RCP Lond. 1991. (Sheff.) Cons. (Paediat.) Birm. Specialist Community NHS Trust; Vis. Sen. Lect., Warwick Univ.; Hon. Sen. Lect., Birm. Univ. Socs: MRCPCH. Prev: Sen. Regist. (Community Child Health) N. Birm. Community NHS Trust; Regist. Rotat. Birm. Childr. Hosp.; SHO (Paediat.) Birm. Childr. Hosp., Walsgrave Hosp. & Gt. Ormond St. Hosp. Lond.

SIMLER, Dennis Joseph 12 Brentfield Gardens, Hendon Way, London NW2 — MB BS 1963 Lond.; MRCS Eng. LRCP Lond. 1963. (Guy's) SHO Med. New Cross Hosp. Lond. Socs: BMA. Prev: Paediat. Ho. Off. Evelina Childr. Hosp. of Guy's Hosp. Lond.; Res. Obstetr. Guy's Hosp.

SIMLER, Nicola Ruth North West Lung Research Centre, Wythenshawe Hospital, Southmoor Road, Manchester M23 9LT Tel: 0161 291 5054 Fax: 0161 291 5054 Email: nsimler@aol.com — MB ChB 1993 Manch.; MRCP Royal College of Physicians London 1996 July. (Manchester) Research Regist. Respirat. Med. N. W. Lung Centre Wythenshawe Hosp. Prev: Mem. Brit. Thoracic Soc.; Mem. IC Soc.

SIMM, Andrew South Tyneside District General Hospital, Harton Lane, South Shields NE34 0PL Tel: 0191 454 8888; 4 The Firs, Gosforth, Newcastle upon Tyne NE3 4PH Tel: 0191 284 4803 — MB ChB 1991 Manch. Specialist Regist. (O & G) S. Tyneside Dist. Gen. Hosp. S. Shields. Prev: Regist. (O & G) Dryburn Hosp. Durh.; Regist. (O & G) Qu. Eliz. Hosp. Gateshead; SHO & Acting Regist. (O & G) Roy. Vict. Infirm. Newc. u. Tyne.

SIMM, Francis 3 Mount Avenue, Bare, Morecambe LA4 6DJ — MRCS Eng. LRCP Lond. 1951. (King's Coll. Lond. & St. Geo.) Asst. Div. Med. Off. Lancs. CC. Socs: Fell. Soc. MOH. Prev: Asst. MOH & Sch. Med. Off. Co. Boro. Warrington.

SIMM, Janet Margaret Allerton Medical Centre, 6 Montreal Avenue, Leeds LS7 4LF Tel: 0113 295 3460; 6 Montreal Avenue, Leeds LS7 4LF Tel: 0113 295 3460 Fax: 0113 295 3469 — MB ChB 1973 Leeds. (Leeds)

SIMMONDS, Anthony James Wood Farmhouse, Hasketon, Woodbridge IP13 8JJ Tel: 0147 335521 — MRCS Eng. LRCP Lond. 1960; DObst RCOG 1962. (Lond. Hosp.) Socs: BMA.

SIMMONDS, Anthony John Preston Grove Medical Centre, Preston Grove, Yeovil BA20 2BQ Tel: 01935 474353 Fax: 01935 425171; Michaelmas Cottage, North Lane, Hardington Mandeville, Yeovil BA22 9PF Tel: 01935 862078 — MB ChB 1969 Liverp.; DObst RCOG 1973. S. Som. PCG Bd. Mem. and Hi MP Lead. Socs: Brit. Assn. Sport & Med. Prev: Clin. Asst. (A & E) Yeovil Hosp. Som.; Ho. Phys. & Ho. Surg. David Lewis N.. Hosp. Liverp; Flight Lt. RAF Med. Br.

SIMMONDS, Edward John Walsgrave Hospitals NHS Trust, 121 Beechwood Avenue, Earlsdon, Coventry CV5 6FQ; University Hospitals, Coventry and Warwickshire NHS Trust, Clifford Bridge Road, Walsgrave, Coventry CV2 2DX Tel: 01203 602020 — B. Med. Sci. 1985 Shef.; MB ChB Sheff. 1982; MD Sheff. 1994; MRCP (UK) 1987. (Sheff.) Cons. Paediat. Walsgrave Hosps. NHS Trust. Prev: Clin. Research Fell. (Cystic Fibrosis) St. Jas. Univ. Hosp. Leeds.

SIMMONDS, Jeffrey Philip 65 Trafalgar Road, Birkdale, Southport PR8 2NJ — MB BS 1971 Lond.; FRCP Lond. 1991; MRCP (UK) 1974; MRCS Eng. LRCP Lond. 1971. (Char. Cross) Cons. Phys. S.port Dist. Gen. Hosp. Prev: Sen. Regist. (Med.) Leicester Roy. Infirm.; Med. Regist. W.m. Hosp. Lond. & King Edwd. VII Hosp. Windsor.

SIMMONDS, Katherine Anne Ivy House Surgery, 27 The Parade, St Helier JE2 3QQ — MB BS 1993 Lond.; MRCGP 1999; BSc (Hons.) Anat. Lond. 1990; DRCOG 1997; DFFP 1998. (Char. Cross & Westm.) GP Non-Princip., Jersey; Clin. Asst. Dermat. Prev: GP/Regist. Torbay Hosp. Torquay VTS.

SIMMONDS, Mark Kenneth — MB ChB 1984 Bristol; CCST (Anaesth.) 2000; MRCGP 1990; FRCA 1996; DA (UK) 1990; Cert. Family Plann. JCC 1987. Clin. Research Fell., Dept. Anaesthesiology & Pain Med., 3B2.32 Walter Mackenzie Health Sci. Centre, Univ. of Alberta, Edmonton, Canada T6G 2B7. Tel: 001 780 407 3552. Prev: GP Springdale Newfld. Canada; Doctors/Ldr. Rambler Holidays (UK) Nepalese Himalaya; Trainee GP N. Devon Dist. Hosp. Barnstaple VTS.

SIMMONDS, Martin John, TD 54 St. Augustines Road, Bedford MK40 2NA — MB BS 1964 Lond.; MRCS Eng. LRCP Lond. 1964; DObst RCOG 1969; AKC Lond. 1964. (Westm.) Prev: GP Luton; SHO Obst. Orsett Hosp. Grays; Ho. Surg. Qu. Mary's Hosp. Roehampton.

SIMMONDS, Martin Richard 2 Cairn Close, Nailsea, Bristol BS48 2UT; 29 St marys Close, Nailsea, Bristol BS48 4NQ — MB BS 1989 Lond. Neonat. Research Fell. St Michaels Hosp. Bristol.

SIMMONDS, Michael 1 Viner Close, Walton-on-Thames KT12 2YE — MB BS 1991 Lond.; MRCP (UK) 1994.

SIMMONDS, Michael Norman (retired) 1 Emily Place, Camp Road, Clifton, Bristol BS8 3ND Tel: 0117 973 1087 Fax: 0117 973 6953 — MB ChB Bristol 1951; DObst RCOG 1959.

SIMMONDS, Nicola Jane The Luton & Dunstable Hospital, Lewsey Road, Luton LU4 0DZ Tel: 01582 497519 — BM BCh 1984 Oxf.; MRCP 1987 (UK); MA 1985 Camb.; DM 1993 Oxf.; FROP 2000; DM Oxf. 1993; MA Camb. 1985; MRCP (UK) 1987. (Oxford University) Cons. Phys. (Gen. Med. & Gastroenterol.) Luton & Dunstable Hosp. NHS Trust. Prev: Sen. Regist. (Med. & Gastroenterol.) Roy. Hants. Co. Hosp. & Soton. Gen. Hosp.; Lect. (Gastroenterol.) Lond. Hosp. Med. Coll.; Regist. (Med.) Whittington Hosp. Lond. & Univ. Coll. Hosp. Lond.

SIMMONDS, Nicola Sally Joondalup Community Mental Health, Regents Park Rd, Joondalup WA 6027, Australia Tel: 08 9400 9499; 12 The Chase, Chervil Way, Reading RG7 3YX Tel: 08 9400 9499 — MB BS 1990 Lond.; FRANZCP 2001; MRCPsych 1995. (St Bartholomew's HMC) p/t Cons. Psychiat., Joondalup, WA, Australia. Prev: Regist. (Psychiat.) St. Bart. Hosp. Lond.

SIMMONDS, Peter Norman 1 Glengyle Terrace, Edinburgh EH3 9LL — BM 1982 Soton.; PhD Ed. 1988.

SIMMONDS, Robert Canterbury Health Centre, 26 Old Dover Road, Canterbury CT1 3JH Tel: 01227 780437 Fax: 01227 784979 — MB ChB 1980 Leeds; MRCGP 1984; DRCOG 1983. Clin. Asst. (Endoscopy) Kent & Canterbury Hosp.; Trustee of Candoc Chestfield. Socs: BMA; RCGP; BSG.

SIMMONDS, Sally-Jane The Tower, Victoria Road, Aldeburgh IP15 5EG — BM 1987 Soton.

SIMMONDS, Walter Bernard Guy (retired) 1 Liskeard Close, Chislehurst BR7 6RT Tel: 020 8467 6432 — MRCS Eng. LRCP Lond. 1942; DMJ (Clin.) Soc. Apoth. Lond. 1963.

SIMMONS, A Louise E Hunter Health Centre, Andrew Street, East Kilbride, Glasgow G74 1AD Tel: 01355 906643 — MB ChB 1972 Glas.

SIMMONS, Adrian Victor 47 Whinfield, Adel, Leeds LS16 7AE Tel: 0113 267 4033 Fax: 0113 267 4033 Email: arsimmons@doctors.org.uk — MB ChB 1962 Manch.; BSc (Hons. Physiol.) Manch. 1960, MB ChB 1962; FRCP Lond. 1980, M 1967; DObst RCOG 1964. (Manch.) Socs: Brit. Soc. Of Gastroenterol. Prev: Cons. Phys. St. Jas. Univ. Hosp. Leeds; Sen. Med. Regist. United Leeds Hosps.; Med. Regist. Univ. Coll. Hosp. Lond.

***SIMMONS, Alison Jane** 2 Church Road, London N6 4QT — MB BS 1991 Lond.

SIMMONS, Andrea Jacqueline 64 Ladbrooke Drive, Potters Bar EN6 1QW — MB ChB 1994 Manch.

SIMMONS, Catherine Mary Howdenhall Surgery, 57 Howden Hall Road, Edinburgh EH16 6PL Tel: 0131 664 3766 Fax: 0131 672 2114 — MB ChB 1968 Aberdeen. (Aberdeen) GP Edin.

SIMMONS, Cecilia Mary (retired) Meadow Court, 6 Northland Road, Bolton BL1 7JN Tel: 51158 — MB BCh BAO 1940 NUI; DOMS Eng. 1948. Prev: Cas. Off. Coventry & Warw. Hosp.

SIMMONS, Mr Clifford Alan (retired) 21 Heath Rise, Kersfield Road, Putney, London SW15 3HF Tel: 020 8789 2166 — BM BCh 1942 Oxf.; MA Oxf. 1944; BA Oxf.1939; FRCS Eng. 1950; FRCOG 1964, M 1952. Hon. Cons. Gyn. Roy. Marsden Hosp. Lond., Mt. Vernon Hosp. & Radium Inst. Prev: Cons. Gyn. Post Office & Civil Servants Sanitorium Soc.

SIMMONS, Damon John 42 Coroners Lane, Widnes WA8 9JB — MB ChB 1994 Liverp. (Liverp.) SHO (Orthop.) S. Manch. Univ. Hosps. NHS Trust.

SIMMONS, David Alastair Ross (retired) 21 Dougalston Avenue, Milngavie, Glasgow G62 6AP Tel: 0141 956 3900 — MB ChB 1951 St. And.; DSc Glas. 1972; MD (Hons.) St. And. 1957; FRCPath 1976, M 1963. Prev: Sen. Lect. Bact. & Immunol. Univ. Glas.

SIMMONS, Gillian Sandra (retired) 17 Tenterden Grove, London NW4 1SX Tel: 020 8203 6242 Email: gilsimmons@aol.com — MB ChB 1964 Liverp.; MRCS Eng. LRCP Lond. 1964; MFPHM 1973; DObst RCOG 1966. Course Organiser GP VTS Centr. Middlx. Hosp. Prev: GP Wembly (Brent & Harrow HA).

SIMMONS, Heather Olive Addiction Services, 4 Manor Road, Chatham ME4 6AG Tel: 01634 830114 — MB BS 1986 Lond. (St. George's Hospital Medical School London) Staff Grade (Psychiat.) Addic. Servs. Thames Gateway Trust.

SIMMONS, Helen 130 St William's Way, Thorpe, Norwich NR7 0AR Tel: 01603 433428 — BM BCh 1992 Oxf.; MA Oxf. 1997, BA 1992; MRC Psych 1999. (Oxf.) Regist. Maudsley Hosp. Lond. Socs: Med. Defence Union; BMA. Prev: SHO Roy. Free Hosp. NHS Trust Lond. VTS; SHO (A & E) St. Geo. Healthcare NHS Trust.

SIMMONS, Ian Geoffrey c/o 102 Kenwood Drive, Beckenham BR3 6RA — MB ChB 1990 Manch.

SIMMONS, Jeremy Paul Spa Surgery, 6 Spa Road, Melksham SN12 7NS Tel: 01225 703236 Fax: 01225 706075 Email: spasurgery@aol.com — MB BS 1979 Lond.; MRCP (UK) 1983; DRCOG 1986. GP Melksham & Lacock.

SIMMONS, Joanna Top Flat, 31 Rye Hill Park, London SE15 3JN Tel: 020 7358 1940 — MB BS 1993 Lond. SHO (Psychiat.) Goodmayes Hosp. Ilford. Socs: BMA.

SIMMONS, John Alexander School House, Muddles Green, Chiddingly, Lewes BN8 6HN — MB BS 1996 Lond.

SIMMONS, Jonathan David Gastroenterology Unit, Gibson Laboratories, Radcliffe Infirmary, Woodstock Road, Oxford OX2 6HE Tel: 01865 224829 Fax: 01865 790792 Email: jon.simmons@ndm.dx.ac.uk; 14 Woodman Court, Cross St, Oxford OX4 1DH — BM BCh 1990 Oxf.; MA Oxf. 1993; MRCP (UK) 1993. Wellcome Trust Research Train. Fell. Gastroenterol. Unit Radcliffe Infirm. Oxf. Socs: Med. Res. Soc. Prev: Regist. (Gastroenterol.) John Radcliffe Hosp. Oxf.; Regist. (Gen. Med.) Wycombe Gen. Hosp.; SHO (Neurol. Radcliffe Infirm. Oxf.

SIMMONS, Katherine Leah 1A Grove Cottages, Falconer Road, Bushey, Watford WD23 3AE — MB ChB 1992 Liverp.

SIMMONS, Margaret Elizabeth Shelcote Brow, Montford Bridge, Shrewsbury SY4 1EG Tel: 01743 850430 — MB ChB 1962 Sheff.; FRCP Lond. 1980, M 1966. Cons. Phys. Roy. Shrewsbury Hosp. Socs: Brit. Cardiac Soc.; Brit. Pacing & Electrophysiol. Gp. Prev: Sen. Regist. (Med.) Univ. Coll. Hosp. Lond.; Sen. Regist. (Research) Bristol Gen. Hosp.; Regist. (Med.) Bristol Roy. Infirm.

SIMMONS, Margaret Rose (retired) Vales Court, Vales Road, Budleigh Salterton EX9 6HS — MB ChB Ed. 1967.

SIMMONS, Mark Andrew 47 Whinfield, Adel, Leeds LS16 7AE — BM BCh 1993 Oxf.

SIMMONS, Maureen Helen 5 Fishpond Lane, Egginton, Derby DE65 6HJ — BM 1985 Soton.

SIMMONS, Michael David Public Health Laboratory, West Wales General Hospital, Carmarthen SA31 2AF Tel: 01267 237271 Email: mike.simmons@phls.wales.nhs.uk — MB ChB 1976 Liverp.; MSc Lond. 1983; FRCPath 1996; MRCPath 1986. Dir. Pub. Health Laborat. Carmarthen.

SIMMONS, Michael George (retired) Hatt Farm, Hatt Common, Newbury RG20 0NJ Tel: 01635 253408 — BM BCh 1940 Oxf.; MA, BM BCh Oxf. 1940. Prev: Flight Lt. RAFVR.

SIMMONS, Michael John (retired) 22 Reading Road, Wallingford OX10 9DS — MB BS 1968 Lond.; MRCS Eng. LRCP Lond. 1968; FRCR 1975; DMRD Eng. 1973. Cons. Radiol. Roy. Berks. Hosp. & W. Berks. Health Dist. Prev: Sen. Regist. (Diag. Radiol.) St. Bart. Hosp. & Hosp. Sick Childr. Gt.

SIMMONS, Michael Richard Lewis The Surgery, 34 Raymond Road, Upper Shirley, Southampton SO15 5AL Tel: 02380 227559; 32 Hickory Gardens, West End, Southampton SO30 3RN Tel: 02380 473183 — MB ChB 1962 Bristol; DObst RCOG 1965. Prev: Med. Off. i/c Govt. Hosp. Leribe, Lesotho; Ho. Off. S.mead Hosp. Bristol & Soton. Gen. Hosp.

SIMMONS, Moira 21 Dougalston Avenue, Mmilngavie, Glasgow G62 6AP — MB ChB 1983 Glas.; FFA RCS Eng. 1987. Sen. Regist. (Anaesth.) Ninewells Hosp. Dundee.

SIMMONS, Norman Alan, CBE (retired) 7-9 William Road, London NW1 3ER Tel: 020 7388 0890 Fax: 020 7388 1890 Email: nasimmons@doctors.org.uk — MB BS Lond. 1958; MRCS Eng. LRCP Lond. 1958; FRCPath 1977, M 1965. p/t Emerit. Cons. Microbiol. Guy's & St. Thos. Hosp. Trust; Hon. Sen. Lect. (Microbiol.) Lond. Hosp. Med. Coll. Prev: Cons. Clin. Microbiol. Guy's Hosp. Lond.

SIMMONS, Paul Douglas (retired) 98 Thomas More House, Barbican, London EC2Y 8BU Tel: 020 7588 5583 — MB ChB Leeds 1971; FRCP Lond. 1992, M 1976; DFFP 1993. Prev: Cons. Genitourin. Phys. St. Bart. Hosp. Lond.

SIMMONS, Peter Anthony Mark Mental Health Unit, Enfield Community Care NHS Trust, Chase Farm Hospitals, The Ridgeway, Enfield EN2 8JL — MB BS 1985 Lond.; MRCGP 1990; T(GP) 1991.

SIMMONS, Peter Hamilton (retired) 1 Queens Road, Barnet EN5 4DH Tel: 020 8449 4130 — MB BS Lond. 1950; FFA RCS Eng. 1954; DA Eng. 1952. Hon. Cons. Anaesth. Roy. Free Hosp., N. Middlx. Hosp. Edmonton & Roy. N. Hosp. Lond. Prev: Hon. Cons. Anaesth. Lond. Chest Hosp.

SIMMONS, Peter Michael High Street Surgery, 87 High Street, Abbots Langley WD5 0AJ Tel: 01923 262363 Fax: 01923 267374; 125 Mobcroft Cottages, Bragmans Lane, Flaunden, Hemel Hempstead HP3 0PL Tel: 01442 832632 — MB BS 1973 Lond.; DRCOG 1976. (St. Thos.) Prev: Trainee GP Watford VTS; Ho. Surg. Lambeth Hosp. Lond.; Ho. Phys. Shrodells Hosp. Watford.

SIMMONS, Philip Arthur Circuit Lane Surgery, 53 Circuit Lane, Reading RG30 3AN Tel: 0118 958 2537 Fax: 0118 957 6115 Email: phil.simmons@gp-k81067.nhs.uk; 33 Honey End Lane, Reading RG30 4EL Tel: 0118 957 5157 Email: philsimmons33@yahoo.co.uk — MB ChB 1973 Bristol; BSc (Hons.) (Anat.) Bristol 1970; MRCGP 1980; DObst RCOG 1975. (Bristol)

SIMMONS, Philip James 8 Bluebell Bank, Bingham, Nottingham NG13 8UL Tel: 01949 838656 — MB BS 1996 Lond.; BSc Lond. 1993. (Lond. Hosp.) SHO (Paediat.) Mid-Trent Rotat. Prev: SHO (A & E) Roy. Lond. Hosp.

SIMMONS, Philip Talbot 14 Cherry Orchard Road, Tetbury GL8 8HX — MB BS 1991 Newc.

SIMMONS, Richard Lewis Laurence 40 Parkhill Road, Bexley Village, Bexley DA5 1HU Tel: 01322 522056 — MRCS Eng. LRCP Lond. 1966; MRCOG 1974; MRCGP 1975. (St. Mary's) Clin. Asst. (Gyn.) Lond. Hosp. Socs: Fell. Roy. Soc. Med.; Brit. Soc. Med. &

SIMMONS

Dent. Hypn. Prev: Regist. (O & G) Lond. Hosp.; Resid. (O & G) Foothills Prov. Gen. Hosp. Calgary, Canada.

SIMMONS, Roger Eric The Surgery, Kinloch Rannoch, Pitlochry PH16 5PR Tel: 01882 632216 — MB ChB 1974 Ed.; BSc (Hons.) Ed. 1971; FRCP Ed. 1993; MRCP (UK) 1978; MRCGP 1980; DCH RCPS Glas. 1977. (Edinburgh) GP Princip. Socs: M.O.s of Schs. Assn. Prev: Sen. Med. Off. (Primary Care) Scott. Off. Edin.; GP & Trainer N. Berwick.

SIMMONS, Sheila (retired) 11 Roecliffe Grove, Stockton-on-Tees TS19 8JU Tel: 01642 618880 — MB BS 1949 Durh. Prev: Clin. Med. Off. SW Durh.

SIMMONS, Sir Stanley Clifford, KBE (retired) 23 Chapel Square, Virginia Park, Virginia Water GU25 4SZ Tel: 01344 844029 Fax: 01344 844067 — MB BS Lond. 1951; FRCS Eng. 1957; Hon. FRCS Ed. 1994; FRCOG 1971, M 1960; Hon. FACOG 1992; Hon. FRCOG 1991; DObst 1953; Hon. F.Inst.Obst.RCP Irel. Prev: Cons. O & G Heatherwood Hosp. Ascot & King Edwd. VII Hosp. Windsor.

SIMMONS, Stephen 77 Bedford Road, Southport PR8 4HU — MB ChB 1983 Glas.; MRCPsych 1989.

SIMMONS, Valerie Elizabeth Eli Lilly & Company Ltd., Lilly Research Centre, Erl Wood Manor, Sunninghill Road, Windlesham GU20 6PH Tel: 01276 853320 Fax: 01276 853325 Email: simmons_valerie@lilly.com; 28 Clarendon Road, Ealing, London W5 1AB — MB BS 1979 Lond. Dir. Global Pharmacovigilance, Eli Lilly & Company (Erl Wood). Socs: Fac. Pharmaceut. Med. Prev: Dir. Internat. Product Safety & Pharmacovigilance Glaxowellcome Research & Developm. Greenford; Sen. Research Phys. Glaxo Gp. Research Ltd. Greenford; Med. Adviser Janssen Pharmaceut. Ltd. Wantage.

SIMMONS, Vivienne (retired) Flat 7, St Leonards Road, Thames. Ditton KT7 0RW Tel: 020 8398 9510 — MRCS Eng. LRCP Lond. 1947; MFCM 1972; DCH Eng. 1950. Prev: Sen. Med. Off. DHSS.

SIMMONS, William Busby Road Surgery, 75 Busby Road, Clarkston, Glasgow G76 7BW Tel: 0141 644 2669 Fax: 0141 644 5171; Brucefield, 11 Otterburn Drive, Giffnock, Glasgow G46 6PZ Tel: 0141 638 4070 — MB ChB 1973 Glas.; MPhil. Glas. 1992; MRCGP 1979; DFM Glas. 1989; DRCOG 1980.

SIMMONS, William Henry (retired) 6 Northland Road, Sharples, Bolton BL1 7JN — MB BCh BAO 1925 NUI. Prev: Anaesth. Bolton Hosp. Gp.

SIMMONTE, Muriel Gwyneth Prestonpans Health Centre, Preston Road, Prestonpans EH32 9QS Tel: 01875 810736 Fax: 01875 812979; 16 Cotlands Avenue, Longniddry EH32 0QU — MB ChB 1979 Ed.; MRCGP 1983; DRCOG 1982; DCH RCP Lond. 1981.

SIMMS, Anne Beatrice The Old House, 107 Hall Lane, Maghull, Liverpool L31 3ED Tel: 0151 526 8181 — MB BS 1965 Lond.; MRCS Eng. LRCP Lond. 1965; DObst RCOG 1967. (St. Mary's) Prev: SHO (Gyn.) Samarit. Hosp. Lond.; SHO (Obst.) St. Mary's Hosp. Lond.; SHO (Paediat.) City Gen. Hosp. Stoke on Trent.

SIMMS, Caryn Margaret 7 Lennox Avenue, Glasgow G14 9HF — MB ChB 1994 Glas.; DRCOG 1996; DFFP 1996. GP Regist. S.. Gen. Hosp. Glas. Socs: BMA. Prev: SHO (O & G & Med.) S.. Gen. Hosp. Glas.; Ho. Off. (Surg.) Inverclyde Roy. Hosp.

SIMMS, Mr John Michael Chesterfield & North Derbyshire Royal Hospital, Chesterfield S44 5BL; 4 Slayleigh Drive, Sheffield S10 3RD — MD 1985 Sheff.; MB ChB Glas. 1974; FRCS Eng. 1979. Cons. (Gen. Surg.) N. Derbysh. HA. Prev: Lect. (Surg.) Roy. Hallamsh. Hosp. Sheff.; Regist. Roy. Infirm. Sheff.; Ho. Surg. Roy. Infirm. Glas.

SIMMS, Mr Malcolm Harold Quarry Cottage, 80 Quarry Lane, Northfield, Birmingham B31 2PY — MB BS 1969 Lond.; FRCS Eng. 1974. (St. Geo.) Cons. Surg. (Vasc. Interest) Selly Oak Hosp. Birm. Prev: Lect. (Surg.) Univ. Birm. Med. Sch; Regist. (Renal Transpl.) & Research Fell. (Renal Transpl.) Qu. Eliz.; Hosp. Birm.

SIMMS, Matthew Stewart 80 Quarry Lane, Birmingham B31 2PY — MB ChB 1993 Sheff.

SIMMS, Mr Philip The Old House, 107 Hall Lane, Maghull, Liverpool L31 3ED Tel: 0151 526 8181 — MB BS 1965 Lond.; FRCS Eng. 1970; MRCS Eng. LRCP Lond. 1965; DTPH Lond 1975. (St. Mary's) Cons. A & E Med. Fazakerley Hosp. Prev: Sen. Regist. (A & E Med.) Walton Hosp. Liverp.; Surg. Regist. Wythenshawe Hosp. Manch.; Dir. Rural Health Care Project Kunri, Pakistan.

SIMMS, Rosemary Jane 4 Slayleigh Drive, Sheffield S10 3RD — MB ChB 1980 Sheff. Prev: Regist. (Psychiat.) N.. Gen. Hosp. Sheff.; Ho. Off. Roy. Hallamshire Hosp. Sheff.

SIMMS, Stirling Andrew Richard 24 Willow Road, Banbury OX16 9EX — BM BCh 1974 Oxf.

SIMON, Adam Stuart 10 Holmfield Avenue, Prestwich, Manchester M25 0BH — MB BS 1993 Lond.

SIMON, Chantal Anne Else 7 The Rampart, Lymington SO41 9FR — BM BCh 1990 Oxf.; MA Camb. 1992; MRCGP 1994; DRCOG 1992; Cert. Fam. Plann. JCC 1992.

SIMON, Dominic William Neil 88 Dalling Road, London W6 0JA — MB BS 1996 Lond.

SIMON, Edward Emanuel 274 Norbury Avenue, London SW16 3RL — MD 1970 Bonn; State Exam Med Bonn 1967 DPath. Eng. 1974; DCP Lond 1974; Cert FPA. 1980. SCMO W. Lambeth Health Auth. Socs: Brit. Soc. Clin. Cytol.

SIMON, Ellis Julian Department of Anaesthetics, Critical Care and Pain Medicine, Royal Infirmary, Lauriston Place, Edinburgh EH3 9YW Tel: 0131 536 3651; 100 Findhorn Place, Edinburgh EH9 2NZ Tel: 0131 662 4321 Fax: 0131 662 9506 Email: e.simon@ed.ac.uk — MB ChB 1984 Ed.; FRCA 1991; FFA RCSI 1990. (Ed.) Cons. (Anaesth.) Roy. Infirm. Edin. Prev: Clin. Fell. Transport of The Critically Ill W.. Infirm. Glas.

SIMON, Emily Lucy (retired) Connaught Court, St Oswalds Road, Fulford, York YO10 4FA Tel: 01904 634977 — MB BS Lond. 1933; MD Lond. 1940; MFCM 1972; DPH Eng. 1936, DCH 1938. Prev: Sen. Med. Off. Matern. & Child Health City York.

SIMON, Francesca Louise RMO, Kings Royal Hussars BFPO 17 — MB BS 1992 Lond.

SIMON, Gowry Raji 23 Woodcote Road, Tettenhall, Wolverhampton WV6 8LP — MB BS 1980 Bombay; FFA RSCI 1992.

SIMON, Jacob (retired) 143 Hammerson House, The Bishop's Avenue, London N2 0BE Tel: 020 8455 3648 — MRCS Eng. LRCP Lond. 1935; MRCS Eng., LRCP Lond. 1935. Hon. Maj. RAMC. Prev: Sen. Ho. Surg. LoW.oft & N. Suff. Hosp.

SIMON, John Wingate 21 Hinstock Close, Farnborough GU14 0BE Tel: 01295 516425 — MRCS Eng. LRCP Lond. 1974; MA, BM BCh Oxf. 1974; MRCP (UK) 1982.

SIMON, Patrick Dorairaj The Surgery, 119 Sheldon Heath Road, Sheldon, Birmingham B26 2DP Tel: 0121 784 5465 Fax: 0121 789 6707 — MB BS 1973 Bangalor; MB BS Bangalore 1973.

SIMON, Raji Idicula 23 Woodcote Road, Tettenhall, Wolverhampton WV6 8LP — MB BS 1980 Bombay; MRCOG 1994.

SIMON, Ron David Ben 9 Mary Street, London N1 7DL — MB BS 1991 Lond.; BSc (Hons) Chem. Lond. 1984.

SIMON, Sacha Dominic 84 Ivy Lane, Headington, Oxford OX3 9DY — MB BS 1996 Lond.; BSc (Biochem.) Lond. 1994. (Char. Cross & Westm.) Ho. Off. (Surg.) King Edwd. VII Hosp. Midhurst; SHO (A & E) Ealing Hosp.; SHO (Paediat. Surg.) John Radcliffe Hosp. Prev: Ho. Off. (Med.) Char. Cross Hosp. Lond.

SIMON, Sybil 57 Stanley Road, Broughton Park, Salford M7 4FR — MB ChB 1965 Manch.; DCH RCP Lond. 1968. Dir. Manch. Tay-Sachs Screening Progr. Roy. Manch. Childr. Hosp. Socs: Fell. Manch. Med. Soc. Prev: Cas. Off. Booth Hall Hosp. Childr. Manch.; MRC Schol. in Med. Genetics; Ho. Off. (Paediat. Med.) Duchess of York Hosp. Babies Manch.

SIMONDS, Anita Kay Royal Brompton & Harefield NHS Trust, Sydney St., London SW3 6NP Tel: 020 7351 8911 Fax: 020 7351 8911 — MB BS 1979 Lond.; MD Lond. 1988; FRCP Lond. 1994; MRCP (UK) 1983. Cons. Respirat. Med. Roy. Brompton Hosp. Prev: Sen. Regist. N. Tees & Newc. Hosps. Gp.; Doverdale Fell. Brompton Hosp. Lond.

SIMONDS, Mr Geoffrey Walter (retired) Pear Tree Farm, Loversall, Doncaster DN11 9DD Tel: 01302 852554 — MB BS 1960 Lond.; MChOrth Liverp. 1968; FRCS Eng. 1966; MRCS Eng. LRCP Lond. 1960. Prev: Cons. Orthop. Surg. Doncaster Roy. Infirm.

SIMONE, John Joseph Lawrence 15 Milnthorpe Road, Grove Park, Chiswick, London W4 3DX Tel: 020 8995 2780 — MB BS 1974 Sydney; DMS Med. Soc. Apoth. Lond. 1993; MLCOM 1990. Sen. Clin. Tutor Lond. Coll. Osteop. Med. Socs: Counc. Mem. Brit. Osteop. Assn.; Counc. Mem. Osteopath. Assn. Trusts.; Inst. Musculo-Skeletal Med.

SIMONIS, Mr Robert Brand Norfolk Lodge, 7 Farmhouse Close, Pyrford, Woking GU22 8LR Tel: 01932 351427 Email: simonis7@hotmail.com — MB BS 1967 Lond.; FRCS Ed. 1974; MRCS Eng. LRCP Lond. 1967. (Univ. Coll. Hosp.) Cons. Orthop. St.

SIMPSON

Peter's Hosp. Chertsey; Hon. Cons. St. Thos. Hosp. Lond. Socs: Fell. BOA & Soc. Surg. of Hand. Prev: Sen. Regist. (Orthop.) St. Thos. Hosp. Lond.; Vis. Assoc. Prof. Orthop. Albert Einstein Coll. Med. New York, USA; Sen. Regist. (Orthop.) Soton. Gen. Hosp.

SIMONOFF, Emily Ann Department of Child and Adolescent Psychiatry, Institute of Psychiatry, De Crespigny Park, London SE5 8AZ Tel: 020 7703 5411 — MD 1983 Harvard; MRCPsych 1986.

SIMONS, Mr Adrian William Lawn Cottage, Shrewsbury St., Hodnet, Market Drayton TF9 3NS Email: a-simons@hotmail.com — MB BS 1990 Lond.; BSc (Hons.) Lond. 1987, MB BS 1990; FRCS (Eng) 1994. Specialist Regist. Orthop. & Trauma- stroke- OsW.ry Rotat.

SIMONS, Dawn Margaret 216 The Avenue, Acocks Green, Birmingham B27 6NR — MB ChB 1987 Sheff.

SIMONS, Edward Laurence (retired) Carabela, Brigsteer, Kendal LA8 8AL — MB BChir 1943 Camb.; FRCPath 1969. Prev: Cons. Pathol. Pontefract Castleford Hosp. Gp.

SIMONS, Eric Gregory Cromwell Hospital, Cromwell Road, London SW5 OTU Tel: 020 7460 5713 Fax: 020 7460 5726; 12 Saracens Wharf, Ferry Stratford, Milton Keynes MK2 2AL Tel: 01908 630579 Fax: 01908 630579 — MB ChB 1961 Pretoria; FRCOG 1983, M 1970. Cons. Gyn. (IVF); Hon Cons. Singleton Hosp. Swansea. Socs: Fell. Roy. Soc. Med. & Roy. Soc. Obst. & Gyn.; BMA. Prev: Cons. O & G Harare, Zimbabwe; Cons. Obst. IVF Unit Humana Hosp. Lond.; Cons. O & G Internat. Hosp. Bahrain.

SIMONS, Gregory Donald North End Surgery, High St., Buckingham MK18 1NW Tel: 01280 813239 Fax: 01280 823449; 5 Huntingdon Crescent, Bletchley, Milton Keynes MK3 5NT Tel: 01908 379539 — MB BCh BAO 1988 NUI; MRCGP 1995; DFFP 1993; LRCPSI 1988. GP Princip. Prev: Med. Off. 4th Field Ambul., 22 Field Hosp. RAMC & 212 Field Hosp. (v).

SIMONS, Henry Roy (retired) 14 Moorend Lane, Thame OX9 3BQ Tel: 01844 261005 — MB BS 1955 Lond.; FRCPsych. 1982, M 1972; DPM Eng. 1970. Prev: Cons. Psychiat. (Ment. Health of Elderly) Aylesbury & High Wycombe Clin. Area.

SIMONS, Joan Edwina (retired) Carabela, Brigsteer, Kendal LA8 8AL — MB ChB 1946 Birm.; MRCS Eng. LRCP Lond. 1946; FRCR 1975; FFR 1974; DMRD Eng. 1971; DCH Eng. 1969. Prev: Cons. (Radiol.) Pinderfields Dist. Gen. Hosp. & Clayton Hosp.

SIMONS, Mary Ann Prudence 4 Greensleeves, Hartopp Road, Sutton Coldfield B74 2QE; City Hospital NHS Trust, Dudley Road, Birmingham B18 7QH Tel: 0121 507 4906 — MB BS 1974 Newc.; MRCP (UK) 1979; FRCP 1998. Cons. Phys. (Geriat. Med.) W. Birm. HA; Hon. Sen. Lect. (Geriat. Med.) Univ. Birm. Prev: Lect. & Hon. Sen. Regist. (Geriat. Med.) Univ. Birm.; Regist. Newc. Gen. Hosp.

SIMONS, Mr Philip Neville (retired) Appleby, Restronguet Point, Feock, Truro TR3 6RB Tel: 01872 862538 — MB BS 1936 Sydney; FRCS Ed. 1949; FRCOG 1964, M 1940. Prev: Sen. Cons. (O & G) Cornw. & Isles of Scilly HA.

SIMONS, Phillip Stuart Willow Surgery, Coronation Road, Downend, Bristol BS16 5DH Tel: 0117 970 9500 Fax: 0117 970 9501 — MB ChB 1992 Manch.; BSc (Hons) Manch. 1990; MRCGP 1997; DRCOG 1997; DCH 1995; DFFP 1998. (Manch.) GP Princip. Bristol.

SIMONS, Mr Richard Michael (retired) 42 Somerville Road, Sutton Coldfield B73 6HH Tel: 0121 354 6537 — MB BChir 1959 Camb.; MA Camb. 1959; FRCS Eng. 1967; MRCS Eng. LRCP Lond. 1958. Prev: Cons. ENT. Surg. E. Birm. Hosp. Gp.

SIMONS, Robert Stuart, QHP c/o Department Anaesthesia, Royal Free Hospital, Pond St., London NW3 2QG Tel: 020 7794 0500 Fax: 020 7830 2245 — MB ChB 1967 Otago; FRCA 1980; FANZCA 1972. (Otago) Cons. Anaesth. Roy. Free Hosp. Lond.; Hon. Sen. Lect. (Anaesth.) Roy. Free Hosp. Sch. Med. Lond. Socs: (Exec.) Resucit. Counc.; Intens. Care Soc. Prev: Sen. Regist. (Anaesth.) Hammersmith Hosp. Lond.; Regist. (Anaesth.) W.m. Hosp. Lond.; Regist. (Anaesth.) Auckland Hosp., N.Z.

SIMONS, Steven Edward Danbolt Square Medical Practice, High Street, Godalming GU7 1AZ Tel: 01483 415141 Fax: 01483 414881 — MB BS 1989 Lond.; MRCGP 1996; DFFP 1996; DA (UK) 1992. (Middlx. Hosp. Lond.) Med. Off. Meath Home Godalming. Socs: Roy. Coll. Gen. Pract.; Fac. of family plann. and reproduct. Health c/o RCOG.

SIMONSEN, Helen Flat 2B, 42 West Port, Dundee DD1 5ER — MB ChB 1997 Dundee.

SIMONTON, Hilary Frances Diamond Medical Centre, Magherfelt Tel: 028 7936 1001 Fax: 028 7936 1010 — MB ChB 1985 Manch.; BSc (Hons.) St. And. 1982; DRCOG 1990. Socs: Roy. Coll. Gen. Pract.

SIMOYI, Tirivanhu 89 Northdown Road, Solihull B91 3ND Tel: 0121 704 9202 — MRCPath 1989.

SIMPKIN, Nicola Diane 94 Foley Road, Stoke-on-Trent ST3 2LH — MB ChB 1991 Manch.

SIMPKIN, Paul 2 Upper Wimpole Street, London W1M 7TD Tel: 020 7935 5614 — MB BS 1970 Lond.; MRCP (U.K.) 1974; AFOM RCP Lond. 1982. (St. Thos.) Cons. Occupat. Health Phys.; Occupat. Health Adviser to Various Pub. Bodies & Cos. Prev: Med. Adviser Lond. Residuary Body; Cons. Phys. Gtr. Lond. Counc.; Regist. (Med.) & Hon. Clin. Asst. Chest Dept. St. Thos. Hosp. Lond.

SIMPKINS, Howell Grant 78 Pastoral Way, Sketty, Swansea SA2 9LY — MB BCh 1998 Wales.

SIMPKINS, Keith Charles (retired) The Mount, Main St., Kirk Deighton, Wetherby LS22 4EB Tel: 01937 582661 Email: keithsimpkint@aol.co.uk — MB BS 1956 Lond.; FRCP Lond. 1982, M 1964; FRCP Ed. 1982, M 1964; FRCR 1975; FFR (Rohan Williams Medal) 1968; FRACR (Hon.) 1985; DMRD Eng. 1966; DTM & H Liverp. 1961. Hon. Sen. Lect. (Radiol.) Univ. Leeds. Prev: Cons. Radiol. Leeds Gen. Infirm.

SIMPKISS, Michael John (retired) 41 Western Road, Branksome Park, Poole BH13 6EP — MB ChB Birm. 1947; FRCP Lond. 1972, M 1951. Hon. Sen. Lect. Inst. Child Health Lond.; Hon. Cons. (Paediat.) Hosp. Sick Childr. Lond.; Hon. Clin. Teach. Child Health Soton. Univ. Med. Sch. Prev: Cons. (Paediat.) E. Dorset Health Dist.

SIMPSON, Alan Geraint 59 Harley Street, London W1G 8QT Tel: 020 7631 3732; 27 Weymouth Street, London W1G 7BL Tel: 020 7637 3131 — MB BS 1967 Lond.; MRCS Eng. LRCP Lond. 1967; DPM Eng. 1979. (Roy. Free) Dir. Indep. Personnel Servs. & Remedy Med. Lond. Socs: Fell. Roy. Soc. Med.; BMA. Prev: 1st Asst. Dept. Psychiat. Roy. Free Hosp. Lond.; Surg. Lt. Cdr. RNR; Lect. Physiol. St. Bart. Hosp. Lond.

SIMPSON, Mr Alasdair Hamish Robert Wallace NDOS, Nuffield Orthopaedic Centre, Headington, Oxford OX3 7LD — BM BCh 1981 Oxf.; MA Camb. 1981; DM Oxf. 1993; FRCS Eng. 1985; FRCS Ed. 1985. Clin. Reader & Hon. Cons. Orthop. Surg. Oxf. Univ. Socs: Fell. BOA; Brit. Orthop. Research Soc.; (Educat. Sec.) Brit. Limb Reconstruction Soc. Prev: Sen. Regist. (Orthop.) John Radcliffe Hosp. Oxf.; Research Fell. Brit. Orthop. Assn.

SIMPSON, Mr Alexander Eli Lilly and Company Limited, Dextra Court, Chapel Hiill, Basingstoke RG21 5SY Tel: 01256 315252 Fax: 01256 315108 — MB ChB 1979 Ed.; BSc (Med. Sci.) Ed. 1976, MB ChB 1979; FRCS Ed. 1983; MFPM 1990; Dip. Pharm Med. RCP(UK) 1989; FRCP Ed. 1997. Med. Dir. UK & Irel. Socs: Fell. Roy. Med. Soc. Edin.; Fell. Roy. Soc. Med. Prev: Med. Dir. Eli Lilly & Co Ltd. Nordic Area.

SIMPSON, Mr Alexander Ian 17 Smith Drive, Elgin IV30 4NE — MB BS 1960 Durh.; FRCS Ed. 1966; DMRD Eng. 1969.

SIMPSON, Alexander John 14 Mertoun Place, Edinburgh EH11 1JZ — MB ChB 1990 Aberd.; BMedBiol. (Hons.) Aberd. 1989; MRCP (UK) 1993. Wellcome Train. Fell. & Specialist Regist. (Respirat. Med.) Rayne Laborat. Univ. Edin. Prev: SHO Aberd. Teachg. Hosps.

SIMPSON, Alison Mary 9B Queen Square, Glasgow G41 2BG — MB ChB 1987 Ed.

SIMPSON, Amanda Maxine Church Street Surgery, 4 Church Street, Wingate TS28 5AQ Tel: 01429 838217; 5 Church Close, Peterlee SR8 5QT Tel: 0191 586 8996 — MB ChB 1981 Leic.

SIMPSON, Mr Andrew Donald James Paget Hospital NHS Trust, Lowestoft Road, Gorgleston on Sea, Great Yarmouth NR31 6LA Tel: 01493 453180; 3 Ferrier Court, Barleycroft, Hemsby, Great Yarmouth NR29 4NS Tel: 01493 730272 Email: bearsden@talle21.com — MB BS 1987 Lond.; MB BS London 1987; MA Cambridge 1987; FRCS Eng 1992; FRCS (Urol) 1998. (St Bartholomew) Cons. (Urol.) James Paget Hosp. NHS Trust. Prev: Regist. (Urol.) Camb. & Addenbrooke's NHS Trust; Regist. (Urol.) Ipswich Hosp.

SIMPSON, Andrew Hugh Portglenone Road Surgery, 23 Portglenone Road, Ahoghill, Ballymena BT42 1LE; Casaloma, 3

SIMPSON

Carnearney Road, Ahoghill, Ballymena BT42 2QR Tel: 01266 871303 — MB BCh BAO 1957 Dub.

SIMPSON, Mr Andrew Neil Hartlepool General Hospital, Holdforth Road, Hartlepool TS24 9AH Tel: 01429 266654 Fax: 01429 522755; 15 Hillston Close, Naiseberry Park, Hartlepool TS26 0PE — MB BS 1988 Lond.; FRCS Ed. 1993; DCH RCP Lond. 1994; FFAEM 1998. (Royal Free Hospital School Of Medicine) Cons.(A&E.) Hartlepool Gen Hosp. Socs: Fac. of A&E Med. (Fell); BAAE; BPAE. Prev: Regist. (A & E) Sheff. Childr. Hosp.

SIMPSON, Andrew Paul Forsythe Marlow and Partners, The Surgery, Bell Lane, Minchinhampton, Stroud GL6 9JF Tel: 01453 883793 Fax: 01453 731670 — MB ChB 1991 Bristol; MRCP (UK) 1995; MRCGP 1997; DCH RCP Lond. 1996; Dip. IMC RCS Ed. 1994; DRCOG 1994. (Bristol) GP Partner Minchinhampton Surg. Socs: Co-ordinator Stroud PostGrad. Centre. Prev: GP Regist. Minchinhampton; SHO (Paediat.) Glos. Roy. Hosp.; SHO Rotat. (Med.) Frenchay Hosp. Bristol.

SIMPSON, Andrew Rutherford Hawick Health Centre, Teviot Road, Hawick TD9 9DT Tel: 01450 371025; Netherfield, Buccleich Road, Hawick TD9 0EL Tel: 01450 72459 — MB ChB 1962 Ed.; DObst RCOG 1964. Socs: BMA (Mem. Scott. Counc.). Prev: Ho. Phys. Roy. Infirm. Edin.; Ho. Surg. Peel Hosp. Galashiels & Cresswell Matern. Hosp. Dumfries.

SIMPSON, Angela Trafford General Hospital, Trafford, Manchester M41 5SL; 14 Fletcher Drive, Bowdon, Altrincham WA14 3FZ — MB ChB 1991 Manch.; MD 2000 Manchester; BA Oxf. 1988; MRCP (UK) 1994. Specialist Regist. (Respirat. & Gen. Med.) NW Region. Socs: Brit. Thorac Soc.; Manch. Med. Soc.; Roy. Coll. of Phys.s. Prev: Research Fell., N. Wing Key Centre, Wythslave Hosp. Manch.

SIMPSON, Ann Isabella 2 Addison Road, Broughty Ferry, Dundee DD5 2NB Tel: 01382 75546 — MB ChB 1959 Ed.; CIH Dund 1983.

***SIMPSON, Anna Christine** 34 High Street, Bassingbourn, Royston SG8 5LD Tel: 01763 243350 — MB ChB 1998 Sheff.; MB ChB Sheff 1998.

SIMPSON, Anna Louise 2 St Hilary Close, Bristol BS9 1DA — BM BS 1997 Nottm.

SIMPSON, Anne Brigid 7 The Common, Ealing, London W5 3TR Tel: 020 8567 7140 — MB ChB 1980 Otago; MRCGP 1993.

SIMPSON, Anne Jennifer Grahame Walnut Tree House, 15 The Pingle, Woodhouse Road, Quorn, Loughborough LE12 8AJ — MB BS 1977 Lond.; MRCS Eng. LRCP Lond. 1977.

SIMPSON, Anthony Noel Brace Spring Gardens Health Centre, Providence Street, Worcester WR1 2BS Tel: 01905 681781 Fax: 01905 681766; The Sycamores, Old Rectory Gardens, Leigh, Worcester WR6 5LD — MB ChB 1969 Birm.; DCH Eng. 1972; DObst RCOG 1971.

SIMPSON, Archibald Craig Cathcart Practice, 8 Cathcart Street, Ayr KA7 1BJ Tel: 01292 264051 Fax: 01292 293803; 47 Midton Road, Ayr KA7 2SQ Tel: 01292 263738 — MB ChB 1972 Glas.; FRCP Glas. 1994; MRCP (UK) 1978; MRCGP 1979. (Glasgow) GP Trainer.

SIMPSON, Barbara Jean (retired) The Oaks, 1 Penfold Way, Dodleston, Chester CH4 9NL Tel: 01244 661041 — MRCS Eng. LRCP Lond. 1962; FRCOG 1991, M 1968, DObst 1964. Prev: MO & Instruc. Doctor Family Plann., Ante Natal & Well Wom. Servs. Clwyd HA.

SIMPSON, Beulah Llandudno General Hospital, Llandudno LL30 1LB; 16 Hafod Road E., Penrhyn Bay, Llandudno LL30 3NH — PhD Birm. 1955, BSc (Hons.) 1952, MB ChB 1970; FRCP Lond. 1987; MRCP (UK) 1975; DCH Eng. 1972; DTM & H Liverp. 1972. (Birm.) Emerit. Cons. Geriat. Med. Gwynedd HA. Socs: Brit. Geriat. Soc. Prev: Cons. Phys. (Geriat. Med.) Llandudno Gen. Hosp.; Sen. Regist. (Geriat. Med.) Ipswich Hosp.; Regist. (Gen. Med.) Caerns. & Anglesey Gen. Hosp. Bangor.

SIMPSON, Brian (retired) 20 Greenfield Crescent, Wesham, Preston PR4 3EH — MB ChB 1965 Birm.; AFOM RCP Lond. 1986. Prev: Sen. Med. Off. Benefits Agency Med. Serv.s, Blackpool.

SIMPSON, Mr Brian Arthur Department of Neurosurgery, University Hospital of Wales, Heath Park, Cardiff CF14 4XW Tel: 029 2074 2708 Fax: 029 2074 2560 — MB 1974 Camb.; MA 1974 Camb.; BChir 1973 Camb.; MD 1984 Camb.; FRCS Eng. 1978. (Lond. Hosp.) Cons. Neurosurg. Univ. Hosp. of Wales Cardiff. Socs: Internat. Neuromodulation Soc. Pres. Prev: Sen. Regist. Neurosurg. Lond. Hosp.

SIMPSON, Bruce, Col. late RAMC Retd. (retired) Tall Trees, Rhinefield Road, Brockenhurst SO42 7SQ Tel: 01590 623655 — MB ChB 1956 Ed.; MA Ed. 1950; FRCP Ed. 1975, M 1961. Prev: Cons. Phys. Army Med. Servs. & Al Qassimi Hosp. Sharjah, United Arab Emirates.

SIMPSON, Carol 16 Esk Drive, Craigshill, Livingston EH54 5LD — MB ChB 1993 Ed.

SIMPSON, Carolyne Alexandra 11 Dreghorn Loan, Edinburgh EH13 0DF — MB ChB 1998 Aberd.; MB ChB Aberd 1998.

SIMPSON, Catherine Nuala (retired) Department of Haematology, Ipswich Hospital, Ipswich IP4 5PD Tel: 01473 703718 Fax: 01473 703730 — MB BS Lond. 1964; FRCP Lond. 1995; MRCP (UK) 1978; MRCS Eng. LRCP Lond. 1964; FRCPath 1996, M 1985; DCH Eng. 1966. Cons. Haemat. Ipswich Hosp.

SIMPSON, Charles Ednam, Air Vice-Marshal RAF Med. Br. Retd. Am Bruach, Fore Road, Kippen, Stirling FK8 3DT Tel: 01786 870281 — MB ChB 1954 Glas.; MSc Lond. 1970; FFOM RCP Lond. 1986, MFOM 1980; MFCM 1974. (Glas.) Socs: Fell. Roy. Soc. Med.; Soc. Occupat. Med. Prev: Princip. Med. Off. HQ RAF Strike Command; Asst. Surg. Gen. (Environm. Health & Research) MOD; CO P.ss Alexandra Hosp. RAF Wroughton.

SIMPSON, Christine Helen Burscough Health Centre, Stanley Court, Lord Street, Burscough, Ormskirk L40 4LA Tel: 01704 892254 Fax: 01704 897182 — MB ChB 1983 Aberd.; DA (UK) 1987.

SIMPSON, Christopher Guy Borril Email: chris@trewylan.freeserve.co.uk; Bronglais Hospital, Aberystwyth SY23 1ER Tel: 01970 623131 Email: christopher.simpson@cevedigion-tr.wales.nhs.uk — MRCS Eng. LRCP Lond. 1973; BSc Lond. 1970, MB BS 1973; FRCPath. 1994, M 1981. (Char. Cross) Cons. Histopath. Bronglais Gen. Hosp. Aberystwyth. Socs: Assn. Clin. Path.; Internat. Acad. Path. Prev: Lect. (Path.) Newc. Gen. Hosp. & Char. Cross Med. Sch.

SIMPSON, Christopher Jack Friarage Hospital, Northallerton DL6 1JG Tel: 01609 779911 — MB BS 1980 Lond.; MPhil Lond. 1986; MRCPsych 1984; Dip. Health Serv. Management 1997; FRCPsych 1997. Cons. Psychiat. Friarage Hosp. N.allerton. Prev: Sen. Regist. (Psychiat.) N. W.. HA; Regist. (Psychiat.) St. Geo. Hosp. Lond.

SIMPSON, Claire Kathryn Fazakerley Hospital, Longmoor Lane, Liverpool L9 7AL — MB ChB 1998 Liverp.; MB ChB Liverp 1998.

SIMPSON, Claire Linda 2 Clarendon Road, Alderbury, Salisbury SP5 3AS — MB BS 1980 Lond.

SIMPSON, Constance Cowan 20 Whittingehame Drive, Glasgow G12 0XX Tel: 0141 339 0504 — MB ChB 1967 Glas. (Glas.)

SIMPSON, David 25 Dunkirk Avenue, Fulwood, Preston PR2 3RY — MB ChB 1993 Sheff.

SIMPSON, David Alexander Anaesthetic Department, Medway Hospital, Windmill Road, Gillingham ME7 5NY Tel: 01634 830000 Email: dasimpson@doctors.org.uk — MB BS 1977 Lond.; FFA RCS (Eng.) 1982. (St. Bart.) Cons. Anaesth. Medway HA. Prev: Sen. Regist. (Anaesth.) Kings Coll. Hosp. Lond.; Regist. (Anaesth.) Char. Cross Hosp. Lond.; SHO (Anaesth.) Roy. Sussex Co. Hosp.

SIMPSON, Mr David Andrew 37 Mill Croft Close, New Costessey, Norwich NR5 0ST — MB BS 1977 Lond.; FRCS Eng. 1980; MRCS Eng. LRCP Lond. 1977. (King's Coll. Hosp.) Sen. Regist. (A & E) Addenbrooke's Hosp. Camb. Socs: Assoc. Mem. of Brit. Orthop. Assn.; of Cas. Surgs. Assn. Prev: Regist. (Orthop.) Rotat. W.m. Hosp. Lond.; Surg. Regist. W.m. Hosp. Lond.

SIMPSON, Mr David Charles ENT Department, Stobhill Hospital, Balornock Road, Glasgow G21 3UW; 20 Treemain Road, Lower Whitecraigs, Glasgow G46 7LB Tel: 0141 638 9518 — MB ChB 1979 Bristol; FRCS Ed. 1984; MRCS Eng. LRCP Lond. 1979. Cons. ENT Stobhill Hosp. Glas.

SIMPSON, David Creffield The Surgery, New Street, Stockbridge SO20 6HG Tel: 01264 810524 Fax: 01264 810591; Greenways, School Lane, Broughton, Stockbridge SO20 8BZ — MB BCh 1980 Wales; MRCGP 1986; DCH RCP Lond. 1984; DRCOG 1982. Prev: Trainee GP/SHO Neath Gen. Hosp. VTS.

SIMPSON, Professor David Ian Hewitt Department of Microbiol. & Immunol., Queens University Belfast, Grosvenor Road, Belfast BT12 6BN Tel: 01232 240503 Fax: 01232 247895; 129 Ballylesson Road, Belfast BT8 8JU Fax: 01232 439181 — MD 1971 Belf.; MB BCh BAO 1959; FRCPath 1983, MRCPath 1971. (Qu. Univ. Belf.)

SIMPSON

Prof. Microbiol. & Immunobiol. Qu.s Univ. Belf. Socs: Fell. Roy. Soc. Trop. Med. & Hyg. Prev: Cons. Dir. Special Pathogens Ref. Laborat., PHLS Centre for Applied Microbio. & Research Porton Down; Sen. Lect. (Med. Microbiol.) Lond. Sch. Hyg. & Trop. Med.; Research Off. E. Afr. Virus Research.

SIMPSON, David Laurence 22 Summerside Street, Edinburgh EH6 4NU — MB ChB 1976 Ed.; FFA RCS Eng. 1982.

SIMPSON, David Stewart 9 Windsor Place, Stirling FK8 2HY — MB ChB 1971 Glas.; FFA RCS Eng. 1975.

SIMPSON, Deborah Susan Blackdown Hospital, 34 Buxton Road, Weymouth DT4 9PJ Tel: 01305 786905 — MB ChB 1986 Aberd.; MSc Manch. 1993; MRCPsych 1990. Cons. (Gen. Adult & Rehabil. Psychiat.) Wet Dorset Community Health Trust Weymouth. Socs: BMA. Prev: Sen. Regist. Rotat. (Psychiat.) Manch.; Regist. Rotat. (Psychiat.) Prestwich Hosp.; SHO & Regist. Rotat. (Psychiat.) N. Manch. Gen. Hosp.

SIMPSON, Derek (retired) Holly Garth, Spaunton, Appleton-le-Moors, York YO62 6TR Tel: 01751 417615 — MB ChB Ed. 1945. Prev: Clin. Asst. Anaesth. Huntingdon Co. Hosp.

SIMPSON, Douglas Bowie Clydebank Health Centre, Clydebank G81 Tel: 0141 952 2080 — MB ChB 1978 Glas. GP Glas.

SIMPSON, Douglas Donald George 18 Battlefield Avenue, Glasgow G42 9HP — MB ChB 1951 Glas.; DA Eng. 1957. Prev: Res. Ho. Surg. Vict. Infirm. Glas.

SIMPSON, Mr Edmond (retired) 24 Perries Mead, Folkestone CT19 5UD Tel: 01303 259094 — MB BS 1961 Durh.; FRCS Eng. 1972; FRCOphth 1989; DO RCS Eng. 1969. Cons. Ophth. S. Kent NHS Trust. Prev: Sen. Regist. (Ophth.) Roy. Free Hosp. & Maida Vale Hosp. Lond.

SIMPSON, Elizabeth Davis Liken (retired) 9 Boyne Terrace Mews, Holland Park, Kensington, London W11 3LR — MB BCh BAO 1941 Dub.; BA 1939, MB BCh BAO Dub. 1941; FRCS Eng. 1952; DOMS Eng. 1944. Hon. Ophth. Surg. St. Jas. Hosp. Balham, St. Geo. Hosp. Tooting & S. Lond. Hosp. Wom. Prev: Ophth. Surg. Qu. Mary's Hosp. Childr. Carshalton.

SIMPSON, Professor Elizabeth Margaret Murray (retired) 42 St Aidans Road, Carlisle CA1 1LS Tel: 0191 285 2029 — MB ChB 1937 Aberd.

SIMPSON, Elizabeth Marguerite Hood (retired) 87 Glencairn Drive, Glasgow G41 4LL Tel: 0141 423 2863 — MB ChB 1948 Ed. Prev: Med. Off. Glas. Family Plann. Centre.

SIMPSON, Emily 45 Great Nelmes Chase, Hornchurch RM11 2PS — MB ChB 1991 Pretoria; DA (UK) 1995. SHO (Anaesth.) Kent & Sussex Hosp. Tunbridge Wells. Prev: SHO (Anaesth.) Broomfield Hosp. Chelmsford.

SIMPSON, Emma Katherine 46 Bridge Street, Godalming GU7 1HL Tel: 01483 414147 Fax: 01483 414109 — MB BS 1994 Lond.

SIMPSON, Eric Walter The Village Surgery, 24-28 Laughton Road, Thurcroft, Rotherham S66 9LP Tel: 01709 542216 Fax: 01709 702356; 23 High Street, Laughton-en-le-Morthen, Sheffield S25 1YF Tel: 01909 567018 Fax: 01909 565263 Email: ews@rocdoc.demon.co.uk — MB ChB 1974 Sheff.; DA Eng. 1981. (Sheff.) GP Rotherham Family Pract. Comm. Mem. RCS; Mem. Rotherham LMC. Prev: Trainee GP Barnsley; Regist. (Anaesth.) Rotherham & Sheff. AHA (T).

SIMPSON, Fiona Mary Fontana and Partners, Silsden Health Centre, Elliott Street, Silsden, Keighley BD20 0DG Tel: 01535 652447 Fax: 01535 657296; Old Quarry, Borgue Road, Kirkcudbright DG6 4SA — MB ChB 1981 Aberd.; MRCGP 1987; DRCOG 1986.

SIMPSON, Francis Vivian (retired) Nutgrove, 498 Scalby Road, Scalby, Scarborough YO13 0RA Tel: 01723 360726 Fax: 01723 360726 Email: viviansimpson@virgin.net — MB BChir 1952 Camb.; MA Camb. 1952; MRCGP 1974; BA (Music) Leeds 1999. Prev: Capt. RAMC.

SIMPSON, Frank Anthony (retired) Stabekk, Hough Lane, Norley, Frodsham, Warrington WA6 8JZ Tel: 01928 788577 — MB ChB 1957 Liverp.

SIMPSON, Gary Taylor 13 Holborn Drive, Ormskirk L39 3QL; 138 Liverpool Road N., Maghull, Liverpool L31 2HW Tel: 0151 526 2161 — MB ChB 1980 Aberd.; MRCGP 1987.

SIMPSON, Gavin David 9 Windsor Pl, Stirling FK8 2HY — MB ChB 1997 Ed.

SIMPSON, Gavin John Stuart (retired) Oulder Hill House, Oulder Hill Drive, Rochdale OL11 5LB Tel: 01706 630301 — MB ChB 1956 Ed.; MRCPsych 1973; DPM Eng. 1967. Prev: Cons. Child Psychiat. Rochdale DHA.

SIMPSON, Graeme Cameron The Basement Flat, 15 Crown Terrace, Glasgow G12 9ES — MB ChB 1998 Aberd.; MB ChB Aberd 1998.

SIMPSON, Graeme Kenneth Department of Medicine for Elderly, Royal Alexandra Hospital, Paisley PA2 9PN Tel: 0141 887 9111; Weybridge, 18 Stanley Drive, Paisley PA2 6HE Tel: 0141 884 2760 — MB ChB 1980 Ed.; BSc Med. Sc. Ed. 1978; FRCP Ed. 1995; MRCP (UK) 1983. Cons. Phys. Geriat. Med. Roy. Alexandra Hosp. Paisley. Socs: Life Mem. Roy. Med. Soc. Prev: Sen. Regist. (Gen. & Geriat. Med.) N.. RHA.

SIMPSON, Professor Hamish 24/2 Rothesay Terrace, Edinburgh EH3 7RY Tel: 0131 226 2370 — MD 1973 Ed.; MB ChB 1957; FRCP Lond. 1986; FRCP Ed. 1971, M 1964; DObst RCOG 1962; DCH Eng. 1962. (Ed.) Emerit. Prof. Child Health Univ. Leicester. Prev: Cons. & Sen. Lect. (Child Life & Health) Univ. Edin.

SIMPSON, Hazel 16 Jesmond Vale Terrace, Newcastle upon Tyne NE6 5JT — MB BS 1994 Newc. Vocational Train. (N.umbria VTS). Prev: Ho. Off. (Surg.) N. Tees Gen. Hosp. Stockton; Ho. Off. (Med.) Dryburn Hosp. Durh.

SIMPSON, Helen Anne 34 Banknowe Drive, Tayport DD6 9LN — MB ChB 1991 Ed.

***SIMPSON, Helen Jane** 1 Victoria Grove, Brimington Common, Chesterfield S43 1QR — MB ChB 1995 Birm.

SIMPSON, Helen Louise Flat 2, Wilton Court, Cavell St., London E1 2BN — MB BS 1993 Lond.

SIMPSON, Henry Keith Lindsay Renal Unit, Royal Infirmary, Castle St., Glasgow G4 0SF Tel: 0141 211 4000 Fax: 0141 211 4843 Email: keith_simpson@compuserve.com — MB ChB 1979 Glas.; BSc (Hons.) Aberd. 1974; FRCP Glas. 1992. (Glasgow University) Cons. Phys. Renal Unit Roy. Infirm. Glas. Socs: Scott. Intens. Care Soc.; Eur. Renal Assn. Registry Comm.; Chair Scottiscch Renal Registry.

SIMPSON, Howard Keith 50 Bracken Road, North Baddesley, Southampton SO52 9DN Email: hksimpsn@globalnet.co.net — BM 1990 Soton.; FRCS Ed. Specialist Regist. (A&E.) Wessex Rotat.

SIMPSON, Hugh Cameron Tel: 01366 500331 Fax: 01366 501375 — MB ChB 1982 Glas.; BSc Glas. 1982; MRCGP 1986. (Univ. Glas.) Unit Med. Off. RAF Markham Norf. Prev: Sen. Med. Off. (RAF) Sek Kong Med. Recep. Station, Hong Kong; Sen. Med. Off. RAF Gatow Berlin, Germany.

SIMPSON, Hugh Charles Rowell Tel: 0118 987 7969 Fax: 0118 987 8930 Email: hugh.simpson@rhbh-tr.anglox.nhs.uk; Laurel Cottage, Rotten Row, Bradfield, Reading RG7 6LL Tel: 0118 974 4418 — MB BS 1973 Lond.; MD Lond. 1984; FRCP Lond. 1993; MRCP (UK) 1977; MRCS Eng. LRCP Lond. 1973. (St. Bart.) Cons. Phys. Roy. Berks. Hosp. Reading. Socs: Brit. Hyperlipid. Assn.; Roy. Soc. Med.; Diabetes UK (Med. & Scientif. Sect.). Prev: Lect. (Diabetes & Endocrinol.) Univ. Soton.; Regist. (Endocrinol. & Gen. Med.) St. Geo. Hosp. Lond.; Research Regist. (Diabetes) Radcliffe Infirm. Oxf.

SIMPSON, Professor Hugh Walter University Department of Surgery, Royal Infirmary, Glasgow G4 0SF; 7 Cleveland Crescent, Glasgow G12 0PD Tel: 0141 357 1091 Fax: 0141 5779 4224 — PhD Glas. 1965; MD Ed. 1959, MB ChB 1954; FRCP Glas. 1987, M 1986; FRCPath 1981, M 1967. (Ed.) Hon. Sen. Research Fell. Dept. of Surg. Glas. Roy. Infirm.; Prof. Path. Roy. Infirm .Glas.; Exec. Edr. Internat. Jl. Chronobiol.; Vis. Prof. Path. & Laborat. Med. Univ. Minn. U.S.A. Socs: Path. Soc. Prev: Cons. & Head Univ. Div. & NHS Dept. Path. Roy. Infirm. Glas.; Vis. Prof. Path. Minnesota Univ., U.S.A.; Vis. Scientist Hypertens.-Endocrine Br. Nat. Inst. Health Bethesda, USA.

SIMPSON, Iain Alastair Wessex Cardiothoracic Centre, Southampton General Hospital, Tremona Road, Southampton SO16 6YD Tel: 02380 796648 Fax: 02380 796352 Email: ias@cardiology.co.uk — MB ChB 1980 Glas.; MD Glas. 1987; FRCP Lond. 1996; FRCP Glas. 1993; MRCP (UK) 1983; FACC 1994. Cons. Cardiol. Wessex Regional Cardiac Centre. Prev: Sen. Regist. (Cardiol.) Roy. Brompton Nat. Heart & Lung Hosp. St. Geo. Hosp. Lond.; Brit. Heart Foundat. Research Fell. Univ. Calif. San Diego, USA.

SIMPSON

SIMPSON, Ian Grahame Mackintosh House, 120 Blythswood St., Glasgow G2 4EA Tel: 0141 221 5858 Fax: 0141 228 1208 Email: igs@mddus.mhs.compuserve.com; Ellengower, Garelochhead, Helensburgh G84 0EJ Tel: 01436 810337 Email: i.g.simpson@btinternet.com — MRCGP 1998; MB ChB Aberd. 1966; Dip. Soc. Med. Ed. 1970. (Aberd.) Chief Exec. & Sec. Med. & Dent. Defence Union Scotl. Socs: Fell. Roy. Soc. Med.; BMA; Fell. Roll. Soc. Arts. Prev: Under Sec. MDU Lond.; Dist. Med. Off. S. Grampian Health Dist.; Specialist (Community Med.) Grampian HB.

SIMPSON, Ian John Phoenix Surgery, 9 Chesterton Lane, Cirencester GL7 1XG Tel: 01285 652056 Fax: 01285 641562; The Coach House, Cranhams Lane, Cirencester GL7 1TZ Tel: 01285 651264 — MB ChB 1975 Bristol; MRCGP 1982. Hosp. Pract. (Orthop.) Cirencester Hosp.

SIMPSON, Ian Macdonald (retired) 13 Dundee Road W., Stannergate, Dundee DD4 7NY — MB ChB 1949 Ed. Prev: Gen. Practitioner.

SIMPSON, Ian Robert (retired) 1 Kingston Way, Whitley Bay NE26 1JL Tel: 0191 252 4955 — MB ChB Glas. 1943. Prev: Ho. Surg. Clackmannan Co. Hosp. Alloa.

SIMPSON, Ian Taylor Ellon Group Practice, Health Centre, Schoolhill, Ellon AB41 9AH Tel: 01358 720333 Fax: 01358 721578; 32 Craigpark Circle, Ellon AB41 9FH — MB ChB 1977 Aberd.; MRCGP 1981.

SIMPSON, James (retired) 17 Woodlands Road, Motherwell ML1 2PX Tel: 01698 263454 — MB ChB 1944 Glas. Prev: Ho. Surg. Greenock Roy. Infirm. & Bellshill Matern. Hosp.

SIMPSON, James Dalziel (retired) Craignair, 25 Rotchell Park, Dumfries DG2 7RH Tel: 01387 255588 — MB ChB 1958 Glas.; DObst RCOG 1959. Prev: Ho. Phys. & Ho. Surg. Glas. Roy. Infirm.

SIMPSON, James Donald 2A St. Wilfrids Square, Calverton, Nottingham NG14 6FP Tel: 0115 965 2294 — MB BS; MRCS Eng. LRCP Lond. 1966; MRCGP 1972. (Westm.) Prev: Squadron Ldr. RAF Med. Br.

SIMPSON, James Martin 45 Weymouth Crescent, Gourock PA19 1HR — MB ChB 1995 Glas.

SIMPSON, James Oliver 9 York Road, Strensall, York YO32 5XT — BM BS 1998 Nottm.; BM BS Nottm 1998.

SIMPSON, Janice 19 Beechwood Drive, Mossley, Ashton-under-Lyne OL5 0QJ — MB ChB 1977 Ed.

SIMPSON, Janice Clare 82 Potternewton Lane, Leeds LS7 3LW — MB BS 1987 Lond.; MRCP (UK) 1993.

SIMPSON, Jason Trevor 3 Claragh Crescent, Strathfoyle, Londonderry BT47 6XQ — MB ChB 1998 Glas.; MB ChB Glas 1998.

SIMPSON, Jennifer Ann 8 Aubery Crescent, Largs KA30 8PR — MB ChB 1993 Aberd.

SIMPSON, Jennifer Linda 1 Hungry Lane, Bradwell, Hope Valley S33 9JD — MB ChB 1976 Manch.; DCH Eng. 1979. Regional Head of Resource Managem. Mersey RHA Liverp. Socs: Amer. BMA Coll. Phys. Exec. Prev: Resource Managem. Project Manager Sheff. Childr. Hosp.

SIMPSON, Joanna Elizabeth 29 Vyner Street, York YO31 8HR — MB ChB 1993 Sheff.

SIMPSON, Joanna Kate Middlesex Hospital, Mortimer St., London W1T 3AA Tel: 020 7636 8333; 53 Priory Road, Chiswick, London W4 5JA Tel: 020 8742 7577 — MB BS 1987 Lond.; MRCP (UK) 1991. Regist. (Clin. Oncol.) Mt. Vernon & Middlx. Hosps.

SIMPSON, John (retired) 88A Drymen Road, Bearsden, Glasgow G61 2SY Tel: 0141 942 3726 — MB ChB 1945 Glas.; MD Glas. 1952; FRCP Glas. 1972, M 1968; DPH Belf. 1951. Prev: Cons. Rheum. & Dir. Med. Rehabil. Units Uddingston & Hamilton.

SIMPSON, John 25 Dunkirk Avenue, Fulwood, Preston PR2 3RY — MB ChB 1994 Leeds.

SIMPSON, John Alexander Psychiatric Unit, Craigavon Area Hospital, Craigavon — MB BCh BAO 1981 Belf.; MRCPsych 1986. Cons. Psychiat. Craigavon Hosp. Co. Armagh. Prev: Regist. (Psychiat.) Ards Hosp. Co. Down.

SIMPSON, John Alexander 87 Glencairn Drive, Glasgow G41 4LL Tel: 0141 423 2863; 87 Glencairn Drive, Glasgow G41 4LL Tel: 0141 423 2863 — MB ChB 1944 Glas.; MB ChB (Commend.) Glas. 1944; FRSE; MD (Hons. Bellahouston Medal) Glas. 1964; DSc Glas. 1993; DSc Ed. 1992; FRCP Lond. 1964, M 1949; FRCP Glas. 1964, M 1962; FRCP Ed. 1961, M 1958; FRFPS Glas. 1950. (Univ. Glas.) Emerit. Prof. Neurol. Univ. Glas. Socs: Assn. Phys.; (Ex-Pres.) Assn. Brit. Neurol.; Amer. Acad. Neurol. Prev: Phys. (Neurol.) Inst. Neurol. Sc., S.. Gen. Hosp. & W.. Infirm. Glas; Reader (Neurol.) Univ. Edin.; Hon. Cons. Neurol. Brit. Army, Scott. Command.

SIMPSON, John Cameron 32 Oakley Avenue, Ealing, London W5 3SD Tel: 020 8992 6171 Fax: 020 8992 6944 — MB BS Lond. 1962; MRCS Eng. LRCP Lond. 1962; FFA RCS Eng. 1966; DA Eng. 1965. (Guy's) Hon. Cons. Anaesth. Roy. Brompton And Harefield NHS Trust; Hon. Sen. Lect. Imperial Coll. Sch. of Med. Socs: Intens. Care Soc. & Assn. Cardiothorac. Anaesth.; Anaesthetic Research Soc. Prev: Cons. Anaesth. Roy. Brompton & Warefield Hosps. NHS Trust; Regist. (Anaesth.) & Ho. Phys. (Neurol.) Guy's Hosp. Lond.; Sen. Regist. (Anaesth.) St. Thos. Hosp. Lond. & Hosp. Sick Childr. Gt. Ormond St. Lond.

SIMPSON, John Derek Smithfield Medical Centre, 7 Smithfield Place, Ballymena BT43 5HB Tel: 028 2565 2301 Fax: 028 2563 0869; Carnearney House, Ahoghill, Ballymena Tel: 01266 871526 — MB BCh BAO 1965 Belf.; FRCGP 1987, M 1971.

SIMPSON, Mr John Ernest Peter London Implementation Group, 40 Eastbourne Terrace, Paddington, London W2 3QR Tel: 020 7725 2500; 31 Hillbrow, Richmond Hill, Richmond on Thames, Richmond TW10 6BH Tel: 020 8940 0935 — BM BCh 1967 Oxf.; MA, BM BCh Oxf. 1967; FRCS Eng. 1972; MFPHM 1990. (St. Thos.) Med. Adviser Lond. Implementation Gp. Socs: Fell. Roy. Soc. Med.; BMA; (Counc.) Brit. Assn. Day Surg. Prev: Regional Med. Off. Mersey RHA; Tutor King's Fund Coll. Lond.; Ho. Surg. & Lect. (Community Med.) St. Thos. Hosp. Lond.

SIMPSON, Professor John Gruer Department of Pathology, University of Aberdeen, Foresterhill, Aberdeen AB25 2ZD Tel: 01224 552848 Fax: 01224 663002 Email: j.g.simpson@abdn.ac.uk; Fae-Me-Well, Cothal, Fintray, Aberdeen AB21 0HU Tel: 01224 722500 Fax: 01224 722066 Email: j.g.simpson@abdn.ac.uk — MB ChB 1965 Aberd.; ILTM 2000; MB ChB (Hons.) Aberd. 1965; PhD Aberd. 1975; FRCP Ed. 1995; FRCPath 1986, M 1973. Head of Dept. (Path) Univ Aberd., Ass. Dean (Med. Educat.) Univ Aberd; Hon. Cons. Aberd. Grampian Univ. Hosp. NHS Trust. Prev: Vis. Prof. Univ. Michigan, USA; MRC Jun. Research Fell. (Med.) Univ. Aberd.; Ho. Off. Aberd. Roy. Infirm.

SIMPSON, John Harold (retired) 2 Salutary Mount, Heavitree, Exeter EX1 2QE Tel: 01392 273815 — MB BChir Camb. 1943; MD Camb. 1952, MA 1943; FRCP Lond. 1969, M 1949; MRCS Eng. LRCP Lond. 1942. Prev: Cons. Phys. Exeter Clin. Area.

SIMPSON, John Lawson 1 Clarendon Road, Alderbury, Salisbury SP5 3AS — MB BS 1984 Lond.; DRCOG 1984; DCH RCP Lond. 1983.

SIMPSON, John Mark Wallace M.I.S. House, 23 St Leonards Road, Eastbourne BN21 3PX Tel: 01323 724889 Fax: 01323 721161; 13 De Roos Road, Eastbourne BN21 2QA Tel: 01323 643824 — MB BChir 1982 Camb.; BSc (Hons.) St. And. 1979; AFOM 1997; MRCGP 1987; DRCOG 1985; MFOM 1998; MIOSH 1998. Med. Dir. Health Support Div. PPP Healthcare. Socs: Soc. Occupat. Med.; Assur. Med. Soc.; Fac. Of Occupat. Med.

SIMPSON, John Munro Department of Paediatric Cardiology, Guy's Hospital, London Bridge, London SE1 9RT Tel: 020 74073351 Fax: 020 7955 2637 Email: john.simpson@gstt.sthames.nhs.uk — MB ChB 1987 Ed.; MD 2000, Univ. Lond; BSc (Hons.) Ed. 1985; MRCP (UK) 1990. (Edin.) Cons. (Fetal & Paediat. Cardiol.) Guy's Hosp. Lond. Socs: Brit. Paediat. Cardiac Assn.; Brit. Cardiac Soc.; Internat. Soc. of Ultrasound in Obst. & Gynaecol. Prev: Fell. (Fetal & Paediat. Cardiol.) Guy's Hosp. Lond.; Fell. (Paediat. Cardiol.) Univ. of Calif., San Francisco, USA.

SIMPSON, John Roger (retired) Stacks, Priest Hill, Hailey, Witney OX29 9TT Tel: 01993 704549 — BM BCh Oxf. 1964; MA Oxf. 1964. Prev: GP Long HanBoro. & Eynsham.

SIMPSON, Jonathan Christian Gerard Dept. Respiratory Medicine, Manchester Royal Infirmary, Oxford Road, Manchester Tel: 0161 276 1234; 14 Fletcher Drive, Bowdon, Altrincham WA14 3FZ — MB ChB 1989 Manch.; MD 1996; BSc (Med. Sci.) St. And. 1986; MRCP (UK) 1992; AFOM RCP Lond. 1995. (St Andrews & Manchester) Cons. (Respirat. & Gen Med.) Manch. Roy. Infirm., Manch. Socs: Brit. Thorac. Soc.; Assoc. Fac. Occupat. Med; Manch. Med. Soc. Prev: Cons. (Respirat. & Gen. Med.) Stepping Hill Hosp. Stockport; Sen. Regist. (Respirat. Med.) Wythenshawe Hosp. Manch.; Clin. Lect. (Respirat. Med.) Manch. Roy. Infirm.

SIMPSON

SIMPSON, Judith Christina 88 Stewarton Drive, Cambuslang, Glasgow G72 8DJ — MB BS 1972 Newc.; DCCH RCP Ed. 1989. Clin. Med. Off. (Community Child Health) Bellshill. Socs: Fac. Comm. Health; MRCPCH.

SIMPSON, Judith Helen 37a Aytoun Road, Glasgow G41 5HW Tel: 0141 424 0173 — MB ChB 1989 Ed.; MRCGP 1994; MRCP (UK) 1996; DRCOG 1992; DCH 1993. (Edinburgh) Specialist Regist. in Paediat.

SIMPSON, Judy Hope Gibson Court Medical Centre, Gibson Court, Boldon Colliery NE35 9AN Tel: 0191 519 0077 Fax: 0191 537 3559 — MB BS 1982 Newc.; MRCGP 1986; DRCOG 1985.

SIMPSON, Julie Ann 15 Wrights Lane, Sutton Bridge, Spalding PE12 9RH — BM BS 1996 Nottm. (Univ. Nottm.)

SIMPSON, June Margaret (retired) Marliam, Guards Road, Lindal, Ulverston LA12 0TN — MB BS 1962 Durh. Prev: SCMO S. Cumbria Health Auth.

SIMPSON, Karen 23 Riverpark, Nairn IV12 5SP — MB ChB 1996 Ed.

SIMPSON, Karen Hilary Pain Management Service, St. James's University Hospital, Beckett St., Leeds LS9 7TF Tel: 0113 206 4001 Fax: 0113 206 4001 Email: k.simpson@btinternet.com; Glebe House, Scholes Lane, Scholes, Leeds LS15 4NE — MB ChB 1979 Leeds; FRCA Eng. 1983. Cons. Pain Managem. & Anaesth. St. Jas. Univ. Hosp. Leeds.

SIMPSON, Karen Louise 53 Fairfield Road, Newcastle upon Tyne NE2 3BY Tel: 0191 281 6229 — MB BS Newc. 1991; FRCA 1998. SHO Anaesth. Freeman Newc. Prev: Ho. Off. (Gen. Med.) S. Cleveland Hosp.; Ho. Off. (Gen. Surg.) S. Tyneside Dist. Hosp.

SIMPSON, Kathryn Lisa 46 Wentworth Road, Dronfield Woodhouse, Sheffield S18 8ZU — MB ChB 1991 Leeds; MRCGP 1996; DRCOG 1995. Prev: GP/Regist Windsor.

SIMPSON, Kathryn Rose 71 Lochmaben Road, Glasgow G52 3NG — MB ChB 1998 Glas.; MB ChB Glas 1998.

SIMPSON, Kenneth 6 Springfield Road, Leicester LE2 3BA Tel: 0116 270 7968 — MD 1951 Lond.; MB BS 1948; FRCP Lond. 1974, M 1951. (Guy's) Emerit. Cons. Paediat. Leicester Area. Socs: Brit. Paediat. Assn. Prev: Sen. Regist. Bristol Roy. Hosp. Sick Childr.; Regist. St. Thos. Hosp.; Ho. Phys. Hosp. Sick Childr. Gt. Ormond St.

SIMPSON, Kenneth James Scottish Liver Transplantation Unit, Royal Infirmary, Edinburgh EH3 9YW — MB ChB 1983 Dundee; MD Dundee 1990; PhD Edin. 1997; MSc Lond. 1988; MB ChB (Hons.) Dundee 1983, BMSc (Hons.) 1980; MRCP (UK) 1986. Sen. Lect., Div. of Clin. and Surgic. Servs., Univ. of Edin.; Hon. Cons. Phys., Scott. Liver Transpl.ation Unit, Roy. Infirm., Edin. Socs: Brit. Assn. of Study of the Liver; Europ. Assn. of Study of the Liver; Amer. Assn. of Study of the Liver. Prev: Regist. (Med.) Kings Coll. Hosp. Lond.; Sen. Regist. and Lect. in Med., Roy. Infirm., Edin.; MRC Trav. Fell. Univ. of Michigan, Michigan, USA.

SIMPSON, Kenneth Malcolm 62 Hillfield Court, Belsize Avenue, London NW3 4BG — MB BS 1958 Lond.; MRCS Eng. LRCP Lond. 1958.

SIMPSON, Kirsty Elizabeth 14 Kingsmeadows Gardens, Peebles EH45 9LB — MB ChB 1998 Glas.; MB ChB Glas 1998.

SIMPSON, Laura Sandra 24 Thorndene, Elderslie, Johnstone PA5 9DB — MB ChB 1991 Glas.; DRCOG 1996; MRCGP 1997; DFFP 1997. GP Princip. Newmains Health Centre Wishaw. Socs: MDDUS; BMA. Prev: Trainee GP Dorema Pract. Kilmalcom, Renfrewsh.

SIMPSON, Linda Keld Head House, Stainton, Penrith CA11 0EQ — MB BS 1991 Newc.; MSc 1999 Univ. Glasgow; MRCGP 1995; DFFP 1995; DRCOG 1994. (Univ. of Newc. Upon Tyne) p/t Retained Gen. Practitioner, 18 Lemon St, Truro.

SIMPSON, Lynsey Nicola Flat 2 Right, 75 Queen Margaret Drive, Glasgow G20 8PA — MB ChB 1991 Glas.

SIMPSON, Mari Rebecca (retired) 53 Elms Road, Stoneygate, Leicester LE2 3JD Tel: 0116 270 5661 — MRCS Eng. LRCP Lond. 1947; MA Camb. 1945, MB BChir 1947. Assoc. Specialist Neurol. Leicester Roy. Infirm. & Derby Roy. Infirm. Prev: Sen. Med. Off. Family Plann. Assn. (Leicester Br.).

SIMPSON, Marie Patricia Alexandria Medical Centre, Bank St., Alexandria G83 0LS Tel: 01382 756029; 99 Drymen Road, Bearsden, Glasgow G61 3RP Tel: 0141 942 6243 — MB ChB Glas. 1968; MFFP 1993; DObst RCOG 1970. (University of Glasgow) Prev: SCMO Domiciliary Family Plann. Glas.

SIMPSON, Marion Lordswood House, 54 Lordswood Road, Harborne, Birmingham B17 9DB Tel: 0121 426 2030 Fax: 0121 428 2658; 55 Wentworth Road, Harborne, Birmingham B17 9SS Tel: 0121 427 2945 — MB ChB 1971 Birm. (Birm.)

SIMPSON, Mark David Charles 6 Cambridge Road, Middlesbrough TS5 5NQ — MB ChB 1990 Dundee. SHO (Gen. Surg.) Darlington Memor. Hosp. Prev: SHO (A & E) Leicester Roy. Infirm.; SHO (Orthop. & Trauma) N.ampton; Ho. Off. (Gen. Med.) Cleveland.

SIMPSON, Mark James The Surgery, Lorne Street, Lochgilphead PA31 8LU Tel: 01546 602921 Fax: 01546 606735; (resid.) Drimlussa, Kilduskland Road, Ardrishaig, Lochgilphead PA30 8EQ Tel: 01546 3297 — BSc Ed. 1976, MB ChB 1979; MRCGP 1986; DRCOG 1983; DCH Glas. 1982. (Ed.) Prev: GP Trainee Pembs. VTS; Ho. Phys. & Ho. Surg. at Roy. Infirm Edin.

SIMPSON, Mary Bradford Hopefield, Wannock Road, Polegate BN26 5EA Tel: 01323 483851 — MB ChB 1956 Glas.; MFCM 1979; DHMSA 1993; DPH Eng. 1967; DA Eng. 1962.

SIMPSON, Maureen June c/o Family Care, Medical Services, PO BOX 528, Springhill Qld 4004, Australia; St. Monans, 3 Hayshead Road, Arbroath DD11 5AZ Tel: 01241 879184 — MB ChB 1986 Aberd.; MRCGP 1993; DRCOG 1990. Locum GP Qu.sland Australia. Prev: Long-term Locum GP Dargaville, New Zealand; CMP Herford BFPO 15; Assoc. GP I. of Mull.

SIMPSON, Michael Menzies (retired) Birch Hill, Backies, Golspie KW10 6SE Tel: 01408 633414 — MB ChB 1959 Ed.; FRCGP 1993, M 1980; DObst RCOG 1962. Prev: Clin. Asst. (Geriat.) Cambusavie Unit Golspie.

SIMPSON, Mr Michael Thomas Lonach, 8A Bushmead Avenue, Bedford MK40 3QL Tel: 01234 214995 Fax: 01234 214998 — MB BS 1981 Lond.; BDS 1973; MRCS Eng. LRCP Lond. 1981; FFD 1984. Cons. Oral & Maxillofacial Surg. Milton Keynes Hosp., Bedford Gen. Hosp. & Lister Hosp. Stevenage; Cons. to various private Hosp.s. Socs: BMA; BDA; Brit. Assn. Hand and Neck Oncologists. Prev: Sen. Regist. St. Geo. Hosp.; Sen. Regist. Chichester Hosp. St Richards; Sen. Regist. (Oral & Maxillofacial Surg.) St. Thos. Hosp. Lond.

SIMPSON, Milda Eileen 111 Kiln Road, Thundersley, South Benfleet, Benfleet SS7 1TG — MB ChB 1970 Bristol; BSc (Hons.) (Biochem.) Bristol 1967, MB ChB 1970; DObst RCOG 1972; FFA RCS Eng. 1976.

SIMPSON, Neil 64 Moorside S., Fenham, Newcastle upon Tyne NE4 9BB — MB ChB 1987 Leeds.

SIMPSON, Neil Royal Infirmary, 1 Lauriston Place, Edinburgh EH3 9YW Tel: 0131 536 1000; 60 Meadowbank Road, Kirknewton EH27 8BS — MB ChB 1993 Ed. SHO (Med.) Roy. Infirm. Edin. Prev: SHO (Cas.) Roy. Infirm. Edin.; SHO (Surg.) St. Johns Hosp. Livingston; SHO (Med.) W.. Gen. Hosp. Edin.

SIMPSON, Neill John Borders Primary Care NHS Trust, 1 Dingleton Cottages, Dingleton Road, Melrose TD6 9HR Tel: 01896 823682 — MB ChB 1977 Ed.; MSC Psych. Manch. 1984; MRCPsych 1982; PhD 1999. Cons. Psychiat. (Learning Disabil.) Borders Primary Care NHS Trust. Socs: Roy. Soc. Med. Prev: Cons. Psychiat. (Learning Disabil.) Centre Manch. Healthcare Trust; Hon. Clin. Lect. (Psychiat.) & Hon. Research Fell. Univ. of Manch.

SIMPSON, Nicholas Barry Department of Dermatology, Royal Victoria Infirmary, Newcastle upon Tyne NE1 4LP Tel: 0191 282 4597 Fax: 0191 227 5058 Email: nick.simpson@ncl.ac.uk — MB BCh 1971 Wales; MD Wales 1981; FRCP Lond. 1992; FRCP Glas. 1990. Cons. Dermat. Roy. Vict. Infirm. Newc. u. Tyne. Prev: Sen. Lect. & Cons. Dermat. Roy. Vict. Infirm. Newc. u Tyne; Cons. Dermat. Glas. Roy. Infirm.; Sen. Regist. (Dermat.) Leeds Gen. Infirm.

SIMPSON, Mr Nicholas Harold Randell Barrow Health Centre, 27 High Street, Barrow on Soar, Loughborough LE12 8PY Tel: 01509 413525 Fax: 01509 620664; Walnut Tree House, 15 The Pingle, Woodhouse Road, Quorn, Loughborough LE12 8AJ Tel: 01509 621078 — MB BS 1976 Lond.; MA Oxf. 1977; FRCS Eng. 1981; DRCOG 1982. (St. Mary's Hosp. Med. Sch.)

SIMPSON, Mr Nigel Alastair Buist Academic Division of Obstetrics & Gynaecology, D Floor, Clarendon Wing, Leeds General Infirmary, Belmont Grove, Leeds LS2 9NS Tel: 0113 392 3891 Fax: 0113 392 6021 Email: n.a.b.simpson@leeds.ac.uk — MB BS 1986 Lond.; MRCOG 1993. (St Thomas's Hosp. Med. Sch.) Sen. Lect. & Hon. Cons. in Obst. & Gyn., Leeds Gen. Infirm. Prev: Lect. & Hon.

SIMPSON

Sen. Regist., St. James Univ. Hosp., Leeds 1996-99; Reseach Fell. Div. of Perinatology, Ottawa Gen. Hosp., Ottawa 1993-96; 3) Regist., St Bart. Hosp., Lond., 1991-93.

SIMPSON, Mr Nigel Shaun 6 Greenstone Place, Dundee DD2 4XB — MB BCh BAO 1984 Belf.; FRCS Ed. 1988.

SIMPSON, Noel Robert Wyndham (retired) 53 Elms Road, Stoneygate, Leicester LE2 3JD — MB BS 1946 Lond.; MRCS Eng. LRCP Lond. 1942; DPhysMed. Eng. 1948. Prev: Cons. (Rheum. & Rehabil.) Leics. AHA (T).

SIMPSON, Patricia Wigan & Leigh NHS Trust, Jack Ashley Centre, Park Road, Hindley, Wigan WN2 3RY Tel: 01942 526311 Fax: 01942 208007; Hill Crest, Wigan Road, Leyland, Preston PR25 2UD Tel: 01772 424571 Fax: 01772 424571 Email: alpat@btinternet.com — MB ChB Manch. 1966; MSc (Audiol. Med.) Manch. 1992; DA Eng. 1968. Cons. Paediat. (Community Audiol.) Wigan & Leigh Health Servs. NHS Trust. Socs: FRCPCH. Prev: SCMO Wigan HA.

SIMPSON, Paul David Station House Surgery, Station Road, Kendal LA9 6SA Tel: 01539 722660 Fax: 01539 734845; Oak Bank Mill, Skelsmergh, Kendal LA8 9AQ Tel: 01539 720764 — MB BS 1986 Newc.; MRCGP 1990; Cert. Family Plann. JCC 1990. Prev: GP Windermere.

SIMPSON, Peter Butler (retired) 8 High Drive, New Malden KT3 3UG Tel: 020 8942 7472 — MB ChB 1954 Leeds. Med. Off. Health Control Unit Heathrow Airport Lond. Prev: GP Morden Surrey.

SIMPSON, Peter Jeffery 2 St Hilary Close, Stoke Bishop, Bristol BS9 1DA Tel: 0117 968 1537 Fax: 0117 904 8725 Email: psimpson@tcp.co.uk; Department of Anaesthetics, Frenchay Hospital, Bristol BS16 1LE Tel: 0117 970 2020 Fax: 0117 957 4414 — MD Lond. 1978, MB BS 1970; MRCS Eng. LRCP Lond. 1970; FFA RCS Eng. 1975. (St. Bart. Hosp.) Cons. Anaesth. Frenchay Hosp. Bristol; Sen. Clin. Lect. (Anaesth.) Univ. Bristol.; Med. Dir. Frenchay Healthcare Trust.

SIMPSON, Peter Michael (retired) 28 Elwyn Road, Sutton Coldfield B73 6LB Tel: 0121 321 3284 — MB ChB 1961 Birm.; FRCA Eng. 1975; DObst RCOG 1966. Prev: Sen. Regist. (Anaesth.) W. Midl. RHA.

SIMPSON, Peter Michael Andrew Bodmin Road Health Centre, Bodmin Road, Ashton on Mersey, Sale M33 5JH Tel: 0161 962 4625 Fax: 0161 905 3317 — MB ChB 1980 Manch.; MRCGP 1984; DRCOG 1983.

SIMPSON, Philip Millbrook, Guelles Road, St Peter Port, Guernsey GY1 2DB — MB ChB 1978 Manch.; MRCP (UK) 1982.

SIMPSON, Philip John Mayfield Medical Centre, Park Road, Jarrow NE32 5SE Tel: 0191 489 7183; 65 Langdale Way, East Boldon NE36 0UF — MB BS 1983 Newc.; MRCGP 1990; DRCOG 1990; DA (UK) 1986. Prev: Trainee GP ScarBoro..

SIMPSON, Rachael Joanne 80 Wroxham Road, Norwich NR7 8EX Tel: 01603 410523 — MB ChB 1994 Leeds. SHO (Orthop.) Sheff. Childr. Hosp. & N. Gen. Hsop. Sheff. Prev: Demonst. (Anat.) Leeds; SHO (Transpl. Surg.) St. Jas. Hosp. Leeds.

SIMPSON, Mr Ralph Nelson Robert Springbank Surgery, York Road, Green Hammerton, York YO26 8BN Tel: 01423 330030 Fax: 01423 331433; 6 Springfield Rise, Great Ouseburn, York YO26 9SE Tel: 01423 331410 Email: ralph.simpson@virgin.net — MB BS 1980 Newc.; FRCS Ed. 1985; MRCGP 1987; DRCOG 1987; Cert Family Plann 1987. (Newcastle u Tyne)

SIMPSON, Rhian Margaret Clinical Gerontology, University of Cambridge, School of Clinical Medicine, Addenbrooke's Hospital, Cambridge CB2 2QQ; 45 Rathmore Road, Cambridge CB1 7AB — MB BS 1990 Lond.; MPhil Camb. 1995; MRCP (UK) 1993. Clin. Research Assoc. (Gerontol.) Addenbrooke's Hosp. Camb. Prev: Regist. (Geriat. & Gen. Med.) P'boro. Hosp.

SIMPSON, Richard Alistair Peter House Surgery, Captain Lees Road, Westhoughton, Bolton BL5 3UB Tel: 01942 812525 Fax: 01942 813431 Email: richard.simpson@gp-p82015.nhs.uk; 305 Wigan Lane, Wigan WN1 2QY Tel: 01942 496635 — MB ChB 1985 Manch.; Dip. Occ. Health 2000; MRCGP 1989; DRCOG 1988. (Manchester) Socs: Bolton Med. Soc. Prev: Trainee GP Salford VTS.

SIMPSON, Professor Richard John Dr. Richard Simpson M.S.P., The Scottish Parliament, Edinburgh Tel: 0131 348 5000; Coniston, 18 Kenilworth Road, Bridge of Allan, Stirling FK9 4DU Tel: 01786 833179 — MB ChB 1966 Ed.; FRCPsych 1994, M 1976; DPM Ed. & Glas. 1972; MRCGP 1997. (Edinb.) MSP Octtl. ('Finance' and 'Health and Community Care Comm.'); Prof. Univ. Stirling; Adviser on Adoption & Fostering Falkirk, Stirling & Clackmanan Auth; Director Forth Valley Primary Care Research Gp. Socs: Assoc. Mem. BAUS. Prev: Lect. (Sociol.) Univ. Stirling; Hosp. Pract. (Psychiat.) Bellsdyke Hosp. Larbert; Princip. in Gen. Pract.

SIMPSON, Richard Sinclair 51 Queens Road, Cheadle Hulme, Cheadle SK8 5HQ — BM BCh 1972 Oxf.

SIMPSON, Robert Anthony (retired) 23 Larkhill, Rushden NN10 6BG Tel: 01933 314952 Email: robert.simpson.@talk21.com — MB BS Durh. 1951. Prev: Clin. Asst. Electromyog. N. Staffs. Roy. Infirm. Stoke-on-Trent.

SIMPSON, Robert Arthur Hyem (retired) 37 Tartane Lane, Dymchurch, Romney Marsh TN29 0LJ Tel: 01303 872052 — MRCS Eng. LRCP Lond. 1940. Prev: Temp. Surg. Lt. R.N.V.R. 1940-46.

SIMPSON, Robert Burgoyne Royal Alexandra Hospital, Corsebar Road, Paisley PA2 9PN Tel: 0141 887 9111 — MB ChB 1991 Glas.; BSc (Hons.) Glas. 1988; FRCA Lond. 1995. Cons. Anaestetist, RAM, Paisley. Socs: Glas. W. of Scot. Soc. of Anaesth.; BMA; MDDUS. Prev: SHO (Anaesth.) Roy. Alexandra Hosp. Paisley; Specialist Regist. (Anaesth.) Vict. Infirm. Glas.

SIMPSON, Robert Cyril North Street Surgery, 22 North Street, Ilminster TA19 0DG Tel: 01460 52284 Fax: 01460 57233 — MB BCh BAO 1960 Dub.; MRCGP 1972.

SIMPSON, Robert David 5 Church Farm Lane, Sidlesham, Chichester PO20 7RE Tel: 01243 641321 Fax: 01243 641321 — MB BChir 1965 Camb.; MA Camb. 1970, BA 1962; FRCP Lond. 1990; MRCP (UK) 1970. (St. Mary's) Cons. Phys. St. Richards Hosp. Chichester.; Clin. Teach. St. Mary's Hosp. Paddington. Socs: Brit. Diabetic Assn.; Brit. Endocrine Soc.; Eur. Assn. Study Diabetes. Prev: Lect. Metab. Unit St. Mary's Hosp. Paddington; Sen. Regist. (Med.) Radcliffe Infirm. Oxf.; Regist. (Med.) St. Mary's Hosp. Paddington.

SIMPSON, Mr Robert Gavin 20 Whittingehame Drive, Glasgow G12 0XX Tel: 0141 339 0504 — MB ChB 1967 Glas.; FRCS Ed. 1972.

SIMPSON, Robert Ian Dyer (retired) Dean Wood House, Woodcote, Reading RG8 0PL Tel: 01491 681593 — MB BS Lond. 1958; MRCS Eng. LRCP Lond. 1958; MRCGP 1968; Cert. Contracep. & Family Plann. RCOG, RCGP &; Cert FPA 1975; DObst RCOG 1960. Prev: Ho. Phys., Ho. Surg. & Sen. Obst. Intern. St. Bart. Hosp. Lond.

SIMPSON, Robert Loudon, TD (retired) 105 Brierton Lane, Owton Manor, Hartlepool TS25 5DW Tel: 01429 274724 — MB ChB 1949 Ed. Prev: Ho. Phys. Roy. Infirm. Edin.

SIMPSON, Robert McDonald Paediatric Department, Dumfries and Galloway Royal Infirmary, Bankend Road, Dumfries DG1 4AP Email: r.simpson@dgri.scot.nhs.uk — MB ChB 1973 Ed.; BSc (Med. Sci.) 1970; FRCP Ed. 1990; MRCP (UK) 1976; MRCGP 1978; DCH Eng. 1976; DObst RCOG 1975; FRCPCH 1998. (Edinburgh) Cons. (Paediat.) Dumfries & Galloway HB; Hon. Sen. Lect. (Child Life & Health) Univ. Edin.; Post Grad. tutor, Dumfries and Galloway Roy. Inf. Prev: Sen. Regist. (Paediat.) Grampian HB; Leukaemia Research Fund Fell. Roy. Hosp. Sick Childr. Edin.; Fell. (Neonat..) Hosp. Sick Childr. Toronto, Canada.

SIMPSON, (Robert)Neil Child Health Department, Newbridge Hill, Bath BA1 3QE Tel: 01225 731500 Email: neil.simpson@banes-pct.nhs.uk; 19 Fairfield Park Road, Bath BA1 6JW Tel: 01225 334915 Email: neilsimpson@btinternet.com — MB BS 1988 Lond.; MRCP (UK) 1992; DRCOG 1993; DCH RCP Lond. 1991; MSC-Health Policy, Plannings, Financing and Financing, Lond.1998; FPHM Part 1, U.K 1998. (St. Bartholomews) Cons. Paediat. Community Child Health, Bath. Socs: MRCPCH.

SIMPSON, Robert Wallace (retired) 2 Milford Manor Gardens, Shady Bower, Salisbury SP1 2RN Tel: 01722 334643 — MD 1955 Glas.; MB ChB 1942; FRCPsych 1971; DPM Lond. 1951. JP. Prev: Sen. Cons. Psychiat. & Phys. i/c Old Manor Hosp. Salisbury.

SIMPSON, Robin Gordon, Lt.-Col. RAMC SO 1 Med, Primary Care, Army Medical Directorate, The Former Staff College, Slim Road, Camberley GU15 4NP — MB ChB 1983 Aberd.; 2001 D Occ Med; 2000 FRCCP; MFFP 1995; MRCGP 1987; DRCOG 1990. SOI Med Primary Care Army Med. Directorate; MRCGP Examr. Prev: Regional Clin. Director MRS Fennelgan; Sen. Med. Off. EPIS KOPI BFPU 53; Sen. Med. Off. Garrison Med. Centre Dortmund BFPO 20.

SIMS

SIMPSON, Roderick Howard Wallace Area Department of Pathology, Church Lane, Heavitree, Exeter EX2 5DY Tel: 01392 402941 Fax: 01392 402964 Email: roderick.simpson@virgin.net — MB ChB 1974 Dundee; BSc St. And. 1972; MMed (Anat. Path.) Stellenbosch 1981; FRCPath 1996, M 1983. Cons. & Sen. Lect. Histopath. Roy. Devon & Exeter Hosp. & Univ. Exeter. Socs: Counc. Mem. Europ. Soc. Pathol. Prev: Cons. & Sen. Lect. (Histopath. & Neuropath.) Univ. Witwatersrand Johannesburg, S. Africa; Regist. (Anat. Path.) Tygerberg Hosp. Cape Town, S. Africa; Regist. (Clin. Path.) Guy's Hosp. Lond.

SIMPSON, Roger James South Cheshire Health Authority, 1829 Building, Countess of Chester, Health Park, Liverpool Road, Chester CH2 1UL Tel: 01244 650342 Fax: 01244 650341 — MB ChB 1981 Manch.; MPhil Bath 1990; FFPHM 1997, MFPHM 1989; MFCM 1987. (Manch.) Dir. Pub. Health S. Chesh. HA; Hon. Lect. Liverp. Univ. Socs: Treas. Assn. Directors of Pub. Health; Chester & N. Wales Med. Soc. Prev: Dir. Pub. Health Chester & Wirral HAs; Cons. Pub. Health Med. W. Berks. HA; Sen. Regist. (Community Med.) Wessex RHA.

SIMPSON, Roland Lee Brook House Surgery, 98 Oakley Road, Shirley, Southampton SO16 4NZ Tel: 023 8077 4851 Fax: 023 8032 2357 — BM Soton. 1981; MRCGP 1988; DRCOG 1987; DCH RCP Lond. 1985. Prev: SHO (O & G) King's Mill Hosp. Mansfield; SHO (Geriat. & Paediat.) Nottm. Univ. Hosp.; Clin. Med. Off. (Community Paediat.) Nottm.

SIMPSON, Ronald Duncairn Gardens Surgery, 36 Duncairn Gardens, Belfast BT15 2GH — MB BCh BAO 1980 Belf.

SIMPSON, Rosalind Margaret Brook House Surgery, 98 Oakley Road, Shirley, Southampton SO16 4NZ Tel: 023 8077 4851 Fax: 023 8032 2357; 59 Brookvale Road, Highfield, Southampton SO17 1QS Tel: 02380 900640 Fax: 01703 900650 — BM 1981 Soton.; MRCGP 1987; DRCOG 1985; Cert. Family Plann. JCC 1985. Clin. Asst. (Rheum.) Soton.; Med. Attendants Alcohol Unit & Homeless Unit Soton. Prev: Trainee GP Nottm. VTS.

SIMPSON, Ruth 22 Norrishill Drive, Heaton Norris, Stockport SK4 2NN — MB ChB 1986 Aberd.; FRCS Eng. 1990. Regist. Rotat. (Gen. Surg.) S. Manch. HA. Prev: SHO Rotat. (Gen. Surg.) S. Manch. HA.

SIMPSON, Seonaid Anne Kirkhall Surgery, Prestwick KA9 1AW Tel: 01292 476626; 4 Grey Gables, Southwood Road, Troon KA9 1UR — MB ChB 1982 Aberd.; MRCGP 1986; DRCOG 1984.

SIMPSON, Sheelagh Margaret (retired) Kingsbridge, 32 Silverdale Road, Gatley, Cheadle SK8 4QS — MB ChB 1954 Manch.; MFFP 1993; DObst RCOG 1956. Prev: Med. Off. Manch. & Dist. & Wilmslow & Dist. Family Plann. Clinics.

SIMPSON, Sheila Anne Medical Genetics, Medical School, Aberdeen Royal Hospitals NHS Trust, Foresterhill, Aberdeen AB25 2ZD Tel: 01244 681818 Fax: 01244 662839 Email: s.a.simpson@abdn.ac.uk; SunnyVale, Kemnay, Inverurie, Aberdeen AB51 5PE — MB ChB 1974 Aberd.; BSc (Hons.) Aberd. 1987; MD Aberd. 1992; DCH RCPS Glas. 1977; DObst RCOG 1976. (Aberdeen) Assoc. Specialist in Clin. Genetics, Grampian Univ. Hosp. Aberd.; Lect. Univ. of Aberd.; Hon. Lect. (Med.) Aberd. Roy. Hosp. Socs: Brit. Soc. Human Genetics; World Federat. Neurol. HD Research Gp.; UK Coordinating Gp. for Predictive Testing in HD. Prev: Research Fell. (Med. Genetics) Grampian HB.

SIMPSON, Stephen Richard Chevron Oil, 43 - 45 Portman Suare, London W1H 0AG Tel: 020 7487 8844 Fax: 020 7487 8947 Email: stsi@chevron.com — MB ChB 1978 Birm.; MBA Brunel 1995; MFOM RCP Lond. 1989; T(OM) 1991. (Birm.) Regional Med. Director Africa. Socs: Fell. Roy. Soc. Med.; Soc. Back Pain Research; Soc. of Occupat. Med. Prev: Sen. Med. Dir. Chevron Nigeria Ltd.; Gp. Med. Dir. Trafalgar Hse. Lond.

SIMPSON, Stephen William Department of Old Age Psychiatry, Forston Clinic, Dorchester DT2 9TB — MB ChB 1987 Aberd.; MRCPsych 1992. Sen. Regist. (Psychiat.) Manch. Roy. Infirm. Prev: Lect. (Psychiat.) & Hon. Sen. Regist. Withington Hosp.; Sen. Regist. (Neuropsychiat.) MRI Manch.; Regist. (Forens. Med.) St. Brendan's Hosp. Bermuda.

SIMPSON, Thomas David Tavistock Clinic, 120 Belsize Lane, London NW3 5BA Tel: 020 7435 7111 — MB ChB 1977 Bristol; BSc (Hons.) Bristol 1974; FRCP Ed. 1997, M (UK) 1981; MRCPsych 1983; T(Psych) 1991; FRCPsych 1999. (Bristol) Cons. (Child & Adolesc. Psych) Tavistock Clinic Lond.; Private Prac. (Psycho-Anal.); Hon. Sen. Lect. (Child & Adolesc. Psychiat.) Roy. Free Hosp. Lond. Socs: Collegiate Mem. & Fell. Roy. Coll. of Phys.; Fell. Roy. Coll. Psychiat.; Assoc. Mem. Brit. Psychoanalyt. Soc. Prev: Cons. (Child & Adolesc. Psychiat.) Watford Child & Family Clinic; Cons. (Child & Adolesc. Psychiat.) Barnet Healthcare Trust; Sen. Regist. Maudsley Hosp. Lond.

SIMPSON, Thomas James Peter Department of Anaesthesis, Royal United Hospital, Coombe Park, Bath BA1 3NG Tel: 01225 825057 Email: tom.simpson@rah.swest.nhs — MB BS 1991 Lond.; BSc Lond. 1988; FRCA 1996. (St. Mary's Hosp. Lond.) Cons. Anaesth., Roy. United Hosp., Bath. Prev: Specialist Regist. (Anaesth.) SW Region, Bristol.

SIMPSON, Thomas William Old Machar Medical Practice, 526 King Street, Aberdeen AB24 5RS Tel: 01224 480324 Fax: 01224 276121; 147 Blenheim Place, Aberdeen AB25 2DL Tel: 01224 641623 — MB ChB 1964 Aberd.; DA Eng. 1968. Prev: Regist. (Anaesth.) NE RHB (Scotl.); Ho. Phys. Dumfries Roy. Infirm.; Ho. Surg. (Thoracic Surg.) Woodend Hosp. Aberd.

SIMPSON, Victoria Margaret Anne Fernlea, West End Lane, Henfield BN5 9RA — MB BS 1997 Lond.

SIMPSON, William (retired) Glen Cottage, Glen Road, Dunblane FK15 0DJ Tel: 01786 823248 — MB ChB 1958 Glas. Prev: Ho. Surg. & Ho. Phys. Roy. Infirm. Glas.

SIMPSON, William 64 Moorside S., Newcastle upon Tyne NE4 9BB — MB ChB 1958 Ed.; FRCR 1975; FFR 1966; DMRD Eng. 1964. p/t Cons. Radiol. Newc. Gen. Hosp. Prev: Sen. Regist. Roy. Vict. Infirm. Newc.; Ho. Phys. Edin. Roy. Infirm.; Capt. RAMC.

SIMPSON, Mr William Alasdair Cumming (retired) Stirling Royal Infirmary, Livilands, Stirling FK8 2AU Tel: 01786 73151 — MB BS 1974 Lond.; BSc Toronto 1969; MRCS Eng. LRCP Lond. 1974; FRCS (Ophth.) Ed. 1981; FRCOphth. Cons. Ophth. Stirling Roy. Infirm., Falkirk & Dist. Roy. Infirm.; Cons. Ophth. King's Pk. Hosp. Stirling. Prev: Hon. Sen. Regist. & Fell. Moorfields Eye Hosp. Lond.

SIMPSON, William Allan (retired) Flat 15, Craiglockhart Court, 75 Lockharton Avenue, Edinburgh EH14 1BD Tel: 0131 443 1326 — MB ChB Ed. 1951; MFCM 1972; DPH Ed. 1955. Prev: MOH Co. W. Lothian.

SIMPSON, William George Tel: 028 2589 1420 Fax: 028 2589 1557; Salisbury House, Queen St, Ballymena BT42 2BD — MB BCh BAO 1962 Belf. Apptd. Fact. Doctor.

SIMPSON, William Gordon Department of Clinical Biochemistry, Aberdeen Royal Infirmary, Aberdeen AB25 2ZD Tel: 01224 681818 Ext: 54620 Fax: 01224 694378 Email: w.g.simpson@arh.grampian.scot.nhs.uk — MB ChB 1984 Glas.; MRCPath 1994. Cons. (Clin. Biochem.ry) Grampian Univ. Hosps. Trust. Prev: Sen. Regist. (Clin. Biochem.ry) Grampian HB.

SIMPSON, William Scott Health Centre, The Glebe, Kirkliston EH29 9AS Tel: 0131 333 3215 — MB ChB 1978 Edinburgh. (Edinburgh) GP Kirkliston, W. Lothian.

SIMPSON-WHITE, Robert (retired) The Old Rectory, English Bicknor, Coleford GL16 7PQ Tel: 01594 861113 — MB ChB 1947 Bristol; FRCGP 1979, M 1955. Hosp. Pract. (Psychogeriat.) Moorhaven Hosp. Ivybridge. Prev: Ho. Phys. & Ho. Surg. Bristol Roy. Infirm.

***SIMPSON-WHITE, Robert William Carroll** 2 Boyce Street, Sheffield S6 3JS Tel: 0114 233 9645; 2 Boyce Street, Sheffield S6 3JS Tel: 0114 233 9645 — MB ChB 1998 Sheff.; MB ChB Sheff 1998; MA (CANTAB) 1997.

SIMS, Adrian John 951 Manchester Road, Bury BL9 8DN Tel: 0161 766 3255 — MB BS 1951 Lond.; MRCS Eng. LRCP Lond. 1951; FFA RCS Eng. 1956; DA Eng. 1953. (St. Bart.) Cons. Anaesth. Bury & Rossendale Hosp. Gp. & Sch. Dent. Serv. Lancs. CC. Prev: Capt. RAMC, Jun. Specialist Anaesth.; Anaesth. Regist. Chelmsford Hosp. Gp.; Sen. Ho. Off. (Anaesth.) S.E. Essex Hosp. Gp.

SIMS, Professor Andrew Charles Petter Division of Psychiatry, St. James's University Hospital, Leeds LS9 7TF Tel: 0113 206 5646 Fax: 0113 243 5053 — MB BChir Camb. 1963; MA Camb. 1964, MD 1974; FRCP Ed. 1993, Lond. 1997; MRCS Eng. LRCP Lond. 1963; FRCPsych 1979, M 1971; DPM Eng. 1969; DObst RCOG 1965; MD Lambeth 1995. (Westm.) Prof. Psychiat. Univ. Leeds; Cons. Psychiat. St. Jas. Univ. Hosp. Leeds. Socs: Fell. Roy. Soc. Med.; Christ. Med. Fell.sh.; Assn Europ. Psychiat. Prev: Pres. & Deans Dir., Continuing Professional Developm. Roy. Coll. Psychiat.;

SIMS

Cons. Psychiat. & Sen. Lect. Qu. Eliz. Hosp. Birm. & Univ. Birm.; Cons. Psychiat. All St.s' Hosp. Birm.

SIMS, Brian Alexander (retired) 2 Orchard Hill, Gracehill, Ballymena BT42 1JP Tel: 028 2564 3463 — MB BCh BAO 1964 Belf.; MD Belf. 1968; FRCP 1987; MRCP (UK) 1970. Prev: Cons. Phys. Antrim Area Hosp. & Waveney Hosp. Ballymena.

SIMS, Charles David Petter Child and family unit, Hillbrook, Mayfield Road, Keighley BD20 6LD Tel: 01535 661531 — MB BChir 1990 Camb.; MA Camb. 1991. Socs: Roy. Coll. Psychiat.

SIMS, Mr Colin David 82 Harley Street, London W1G 7HN Tel: 020 7636 2766 Fax: 020 7631 5371; Huntley Cottage, 29 The Downs, Wimbledon, London SW20 8HG Tel: 020 8946 1978 — MB Camb. 1963, BChir 1962; FRCS Ed. 1969; FRCOG 1987, M 1973. (Westm.) Cons. Gyn. Char. Cross & Chelsea & W.m. Hosp. Lond.; Cons. O & G Qu. Charlotte's & Chelsea Hosp. for Wom. Lond. Retd.

SIMS, Diana Elizabeth Barton Surgery, Barton, Horn Lane, Plymouth PL9 9BR Tel: 01752 407129 Fax: 01752 482620; 43 Furzehatt Road, Plymstock, Plymouth PL9 8QX Tel: 01752 406512 — MB ChB 1969 Liverp.; DA Eng. 1973. Prev: Regist. (Anaesth.) Plymouth Gen. Hosp.; Ho. Phys. & Surg. St. Bernards Hosp. Gibraltar; Ho. Phys. & Surg. Winston Hosp. Prescot.

***SIMS, Don Graham** 45 Glenmore Drive, Kings Norton, Birmingham B38 8YR — MB ChB 1996 Birm.

SIMS, Douglas Gordon St Mary's Hospital, Hathersage Rd, Manchester M13 0JH Tel: 0161 276 6543 Fax: 0161 276 6536 — MB ChB Bristol 1966; FRCP Lond. 1987; MRCP (UK) 1972; FRCPCH 1997; DObst RCOG 1968. Cons. Neonatologist. St. Mary's Hosp. Manch. Socs: BMA Brit. Assn. of Perinatal Med. Prev: Sen. Regist. (Paediat.) St. Mary's Hosp. Manch.; Sen. Research Assoc. & Hon. Sen. Regist. Dept. Child Health & Virol.; Univ. Newc.

SIMS, Eliot Craig 36 Elm Walk, Radlett WD7 8DP; 32 Rowlands Avenue, Pinner HA5 4BH — MB BChir 1993 Camb.; MA Camb. 1994, MB BChir 1993. SHO Rotat. (Med.) Whipps Cross Hosp. Leyton; SHO (Radiother.) St. Bart. Hosp. Lond.

SIMS, Enoch Harrington, Surg. Cdr. RN Retd. (retired) The Mill, Swinbrook, Burford OX18 4DY Tel: 01993 823108 — MB ChB Sheff. 1954; FRCP Ed. 1982, M 1968. Prev: Surg. Cdr. RN.

SIMS, Gwyneth Maclean (retired) 19 Milton Road, Ickenham, Uxbridge UB10 8NH Tel: 01895 633007 — MB BCh 1942 Wales; BSc Wales 1939, MD 1954; FRCPath 1970, M 1963. Prev: Cons. Path. Harefield & N.wood Gp. Hosps.

SIMS, Hemalini North End Medical Centre, 211 North End Road, London W14 9NP; 21 Cherrywood Drive, London SW15 6DS Tel: 020 8789 4989 — MB BS 1992 Lond.; MRCGP 1997; DRCOG 1996; DFFP 1996. Prev: Clin. Asst. (Genitourin. Med.) Chelsea & W.m. Hosp.

SIMS, Justine Shirley Portchester Health Centre, West Street, Portchester, Fareham PO16 9TU — MB BCh 1992 Wales; MRCGP 1995; DRCOG 1994; DFFP 1994. GP Princip. -Portsmouth and SE Hants.

SIMS, Michael Andrew Dipple Medical Centre, Wickford Avenue, Pitsea, Basildon SS13 3HQ Tel: 01268 555115 Fax: 01268 559935; 8 Burns Avenue, Basildon SS13 3AG — MB BS Lond. 1991.

SIMS, Miss Pamela Frances Hexham General Hospital, Hexham NE46 1QJ Tel: 01434 655655 Fax: 01434 655347; Ivy Cottage, Lowgate, Hexham NE46 2NN Tel: 01434 606700 Fax: 01434 606700 Email: sims@nobbs38.freserve.co.uk — MB BCh Wales 1969; FRCS Eng. 1979; FRCOG 1994, M 1981. (Cardiff) Vis. Cons. Roy. Vict. Infirm. Socs: Brit. Soc. Colpos. & Cerv. Path. Prev: Sen. Regist. Rotat. (Obst & Gyn.) Newc. HA; Regist. (O & G) Hammersmith Hosp. Lond. & Luton & Dunstable Hosp.

SIMS, Professor Peter Anthony The School of Medicine and Health Sciences, POBox 5623, Boroko, Papua New Guinea Tel: 675 3243859 Fax: 675 3243859 Email: petersims@upung.ac.pg; Maynes Orchard, Silver St, Braunton EX33 2EN Tel: 01271 814933 Email: p.sims@sosi.net — MB BS 1969 Lond.; BDS Lond. 1965; MSc (Social Med.) Lond. 1975; BSc (Hons.) Physiol. 1962; LDS RCS Eng. 1965; MRCS Eng. LRCP Lond. 1969; MFCM 1976; MRCGP 1982; FFPHM RCP (UK) 1991. (Guys) Prof. of Pub. Health Med., Div. of Pub. Health, The Sch. of Med., Papua New Guinea. Socs: Fac. Comm. Health (Fell.). Prev: Prof. Community Med. Univ. Zambia, Lusaka; Director Pub. Health N. Devon.; Med. Director NHS Direct S.W. Exeter.

SIMS, Peter Justin 46 Pemdevon Road, Croydon CR0 3QN — MB BS 1992 Lond.

SIMS, Rebecca Jane Alexandra Catesby Lodge Farm, Catesby, Daventry NN11 6LB — BM BS 1998 Nottm.; BM BS Nottm 1998; BMedSci Nottm 1996. (Nottingham) SHO (A&E) Addenbrookes - Camb.

SIMS, Roy Thomas (retired) 7 Chestnut Close, Grayshott, Hindhead GU26 6LN — MA Camb. 1957; BSc Lond. 1952, MD 1967, MB BS 1955; MFCMI 1978.

SIMS, Ruth Marie The Grange, 92 Whitcliffe Rd, Cleckheaton, Wakefield WF1 2DQ Tel: 01132 814541 Fax: 01132 814531; Gledholt, Oakwood Drive, Leeds LS8 2PA Tel: 01532 650479 Fax: 01532 650479 — LMSSA 1983; M.Psychotherapy 1992; MA Camb. 1967, MB BChir 1983; MRCPsych 1988. (Cambridge) Cons. Child & Adolesc. Psychiat. In Private Pract. Socs: BMA; MDU; Assoc. of Family Therapists. Prev: Cons. Child and Adolesc. Psychiat., Wakefield, and Pontefract Community NHS Trust.

SIMS, Stanley Robert (retired) 5 St Peter's Close, Horton, Ilminster TA19 9RW — MB BS Lond. 1946. Prev: Asst. Chest Phys. P'boro. & Huntingdon Chest Clinic Areas.

SIMS WILLIAMS, Heather Gillian The Family Practice, Western College, Cotham Road, Bristol BS6 6DF Tel: 0117 946 6455 Fax: 0117 946 6410 — MB ChB 1970 Bristol.

SIMSON, Mr Jay Nicholas Litton Department of Surgery, St. Richard's Hospital, Spitalfield Lane, Chichester PO19 4SE Tel: 01243 788122; 24 West Street, Chichester PO19 1QP Tel: 01243 789630 — MB BChir 1974 Camb.; MA Camb. 1971; MChir Camb. 1982; FRCS Eng. 1979; MRCP (UK) 1976; FCS(SA) 1977. Cons. Surg. St. Richard's Hosp. Chichester. Socs: Roy. Soc. Med.; Assn. Coloproctol.; Assn. Surg. Prev: Research Fell. Harvard Univ.; Sen. Regist. St. Mark's Hosp. Lond. & Guy's Hosp. Lond.

SIN, Julie Pui Yee 34 Waverney Drive, Altrincham WA14 4UQ — MB ChB 1990 Manch.

SINANAN, Rabindra Druva Kenneth 137 Strensall Road, Earswick, York YO32 9SJ — MB BCh BAO 1976 Belf.

SINASON, Michael David Adrian Forest House Psychotherapy Clinic, Thorpe Coombe Hospital, 714 Forest Road, London E17 3HP Tel: 020 8535 6899 Fax: 020 8535 6849; Email: michael.simpson@virgin.net — MB BS 1974 Lond.; BSc (Hons. Psychol.) Lond. 1971; MRCPsych 1979; T(Psych.) 1991. (Univ. Coll. Hosp.) Private psychoanalytic pract. Lond.; Locum Cons. (Psychother.) Forest Hse. Psychother. Clinic Thorpe Coombe Hosp. Lond. Prev: Cons. Psychother. Willesden Centre for Psychol. Treatm. Willesden Hosp. Lond.; Cons. Psychother. Shenley Hosp.; Sen. Regist. Psychother, Maudsley Hosp., Lond.

SINCLAIR, Aisla Mary Robertha 9 Clarendon Place, Stirling FK8 2QW — MB BCh BAO 1970 Dub. Clin. Med. Off. Forth Valley Health Bd.; Med. Off. (Occupat.) Health Serv. Forth Valley HB. Prev: Regist. (Gen. Med.) Stoke Mandeville Hosp. Aylesbury; Ho. Off. Dr. Steevens' Hosp. Dub.; SHO (Gastroenterol.) Sir P. Dun's Hosp. Dub.

SINCLAIR, Alan George Huntly Health Centre, Jubilee Hospital, Bleachfield Street, Huntly AB54 8EX Tel: 01466 792116 Fax: 01466 794699; The Beeches, Deveron Road, Huntly AB54 8DU Tel: 01466 793625 — MB ChB 1972 Aberd.; MRCGP 1977; DObst RCOG 1975; DA Eng. 1974; Cert. Family Plann. JCC 1981; ATLS 1995. (Aberd.) Hosp. Practitioner Jubilee Community Hosp. Huntly.

SINCLAIR, Alan James University Department of Geriatric Medicine, Cardiff Royal Infirmary, Cardiff CF24 0SZ Tel: 029 2049 2233; Glenholm, Bradford Place, Penarth CF64 1AF — MB BS 1979 Lond.; BSc (1st cl. Hons.) Lond. 1976, MD 1993, MB BS 1979; MRCP (UK) 1985; MRCS Eng. LRCP Lond. 1979; T(M) 1992. (St. Bart.) Sen. Lect. (Geriat. Med.) Univ. Wales Coll. of Med. Socs: Brit. Geriat. Soc.; Brit. Diabetic Assoc. Prev: Research Fell. & Regist. (Med.) St. Barts Hosp. Lond.; Lect. (Geriat. Med.) Univ. Birm.; Med. Regist. (Geriat.) Hammersmith Hosp. Lond.

SINCLAIR, Alison Alexandra McKenzie Medical Centre, 20 West Richmond Street, Edinburgh EH8 9DX Tel: 0131 667 2955; 27 Ormidale Terrace, Edinburgh EH12 6DY Tel: 0131 337 7693 — MB ChB 1982 Ed.; MRCGP 1987; DCCH RCP Ed. 1986; DCH RCP Lond. 1986; DRCOG 1984. (Ed.) Clin. Lect. (Gen. Pract.) Univ. Edin.

SINCLAIR, Alistair (retired) 9 Ash Grove, Messingham, Scunthorpe DN17 3QY — MB ChB 1955 Aberd.; FFOM RCP Lond. 1985, M 1980; DIH Soc. Apoth. Lond. 1962. Prev: Chief Med. Off. Brit. Steel.

SINCLAIR

SINCLAIR, Allan (retired) Glendale, 13 Glasgow Road, Uddingston, Glasgow G71 7AU Tel: 01698 813578 — MB ChB 1952 Glas.; FRCP Glas. 1976, M 1962; FRCPsych 1987, M 1971; FRFPS Glas. 1960; DPM Eng. 1958. Prev: Cons. Psychiat. Hartwood Hosp. Shotts & Monklands Dist. Gen. Hosp. Airdrie.

SINCLAIR, Allan Alexander Darwen Health Centre, Union Street, Darwen BB3 0DA Tel: 01254 778366 Fax: 01254 778367 — MB ChB 1988 Manch.; BSc St. And. 1985; MRCGP 1993; Cert. Prescribed Equiv. Exp. JCPTGP 1993; DGM RCP Lond. 1990.

SINCLAIR, Amanda Susan The Surgery, 22 Shenley Green, Selly Oak, Birmingham B29 4HH Tel: 0121 475 7997 Fax: 0121 475 9239; 70 Ashmead Rise, Cofton Hackett, Birmingham B45 8AD Tel: 0121 447 7206 Fax: 0121 447 7206 — MB ChB 1987 Birm.; MRCGP 1991. Prev: Trainee GP BromsGr. & Redditch VTS.

SINCLAIR, Andrew Michael 199 Farley Road, Croydon CR2 7NP — MB BS 1998 Lond.; MB BS Lond 1998.

SINCLAIR, Ann Begg (retired) Kenland House Surgery, 37 Station Road, Milngavie, Glasgow G62 8BT Tel: 0141 956 1005 Fax: 0141 955 0342 — MB BS 1963 Durh.; DA Eng. 1967. Prev: Regist. (Anaesth.) S.. Gen. Hosp. Glas.

SINCLAIR, Anne Department of Ophthalmology, Queen Margaret's Hospital NHS Trust, Whitefield Road, Dunfermline KY12 0SU Tel: 01383 623623 Fax: 01383 624156; 10 Raith Crescent, Kirkcaldy KY2 5NN Tel: 01592 206571 — MB ChB 1979 Ed.; FRCS Ed. 1992; DO Eng. 1981. Assoc. Specialist (Ophth.) Qu. Margt. Hosp. NHS Trust. Prev: Staff Grade (Ophth.) Fife HB.

SINCLAIR, Anne-Marie 25 Garrygall, Castlebay HS9 5UH — MB ChB 1987 Glas.

SINCLAIR, Barbara Jane Higher Hewish, Muddiford, Barnstaple EX31 4HH — MB ChB 1986 Sheff.; MRCGP 1990; DRCOG 1990. GP Retainer Scheme Braunton & Ilfracombe. Prev: GP Clin. Asst. (Genitourin. Med.) Roy. Gwent Hosp. Newport; Trainee GP Doncaster VTS.

SINCLAIR, Barbara Louise 30 Lochinver Crescent, Dundee DD2 4UA — MB ChB 1981 Aberd.

SINCLAIR, Beatrice Margaret Kilkerry, 105 Beach Road, Hartford, Northwich CW8 3AB Tel: 01606 74335 — LRCP LRCS 1950 Ed.; LRCP LRCS Ed. LRFPS Glas. 1950. (Ed.)

SINCLAIR, Beryl Euman (retired) 5 The Grove, Harrogate HG1 5NN — MB ChB 1948 Ed.

SINCLAIR, Catherine Margaret 66 Southlands Avenue, Standish, Wigan WN6 0TT — BM BS 1998 Nottm.; BM BS Nottm 1998.

SINCLAIR, Catriona Jane 33 Runnymede, Nunthorpe, Middlesbrough TS7 0QL — MB ChB 1991 Dundee.

SINCLAIR, Christopher Chalmer Ross Laundry Cottage, Habyn, Rogate, Petersfield GU31 5HS — MB BS 1982 Lond.

SINCLAIR, Colin David Calsayseat Medical Group, 2 Calsayseat Road, Aberdeen AB25 3UY Tel: 01224 634345 Fax: 01224 620210; Newhills House, Newhills, Aberdeen AB21 9SQ Tel: 01224 714439 — MB ChB 1971 Aberd. Prev: Jun. Ho. Off. Stracathro Hosp. Brechin; SHO Aberd. Roy. Infirm.

SINCLAIR, Colin John 'Mazoe', 2 Grange Road, Ballymena BT42 2DS Tel: 028256 42743 — MB BCh BAO 1966 Belf.; FRCR 1972; DMRD Eng. 1970. (Relf) Cons. Radiol. Waveney Hosp. & Mid Ulster Hosp.

SINCLAIR, Colin John Department of Anaesthetics, The Royal Infirmary of Edinburgh, Layriston Place, Edinburgh EH3 9YW Tel: 0131 536 3706 Fax: 0131 229 0659 Email: colin.sinclair@ed.ac.uk; Viewforth, Broomieknowe, Lasswade EH18 1LN Tel: 0131 663 8868 — BSc 1973; MBChB 1976; FRCA 1980. (Edinburgh) Cons. Anaesth., Cardiothoracic Unit, Roy. Infirm. of Edin.

SINCLAIR, Professor David Cecil Apartment 3, Netherby, 1 Netherby Road, Cults, Aberdeen AB15 9HL Tel: 01224 867151 — MB ChB 1937 St. And.; MD St. And. 1947; DSc (Univ. West. Austral.) 1965; FRCS Ed. 1966. Emerit. Prof. Univ. W. Austral.; Life Governor Austral. Postgrad. Federat. Med. Socs: Anat. Soc. of GB & Irel.; Formerly Edr., Jl. of Anat. Prev: Foundat. Prof. Anat. Univ. W. Austral.; Dir. Postgrad. Med. Educat. Qu. Eliz. II Med. Centre, Perth, W.. Austral.; Regius Prof. Anat. Univ. Aberd.

SINCLAIR, David Graeme Torbay Hospital, Torquay TQ2 7AA Tel: 01803 655116 Email: dgsinc@globalnet.co.uk; Monks Thatch, Abbots Kerswell, Newton Abbot TQ12 5NW Tel: 01626 69605 — MB ChB 1981 Birm.; MD Birm. 1996; MRCP (UK) 1987; FRCP (Lond.) 1998. Cons. Phys. (Respirat. & Intens. Care Med.) Torbay Hosp.; Hon. Sen. Lect. (Critical Care) Nat. Heart & Lung Inst. Lond. Socs: Brit. Thorac. Soc.; Intens. Care Soc.

SINCLAIR, David James Jubilee Surgery, Barrys Meadow, High St Titchfield, Fareham PO14 4EH Tel: 01329 844220 Fax: 01329 841484 — MB BCh BAO 1975 Dub.; MRCPI 1983; MRCGP 1984; DCH Dub. 1977. (Trinity College, Dublin) Hosp. Pract. (Cardiol.) St. Mary's Hosp. Portsmouth.

SINCLAIR, David John MacGregor South Cleveland Hospital, Marton Road, Middlesbrough TS4 3BW Tel: 01642 850850; Highfield West End, Hutton Rudby, Yarm TS15 0DJ — MB ChB 1971 Aberd.; FRCP Ed. 1989; FRCP Lond. 1988; MRCP (UK) 1974. Cons. Phys. Gen. & Respirat. Med. S. Cleveland Hosp. Middlesbrough.

SINCLAIR, David Maxwell The Health Centre, Victoria Road, Leven KY8 4ET Tel: 01333 425656 Fax: 01333 422249 — MB ChB 1976 Ed.; BSc (Med. Sci.) Ed. 1973, MB ChB 1976; MRCGP 1980; DRCOG 1978. Trainer (Gen. Pract.) Leven; Clin. Asst. Colposcopy Clinic N. Pk. Hosp. Kirkcaldy; Civil. Med. Pract. Army Careers Office Leven. Socs: BMA & Anglo-French Med. Soc. Prev: Regist. (Gen. Med.) Vict. Hosp. Kirkcaldy; SHO (O & G) W.. Gen. Hosp. Edin.; Ho. Phys. Leith Hosp. Edin.

SINCLAIR, Mr David William Division Biomedical Sciences (School of Biology), University of St Andrews, Bute Medical Buildings, St Andrews KY16 9TS Tel: 01334 463169 Fax: 01334 462144 Email: dwsl@st-and.ac.uk; 26 Drumcarrow Road, St Andrews KY16 8SE Tel: 01334 474349 — MB ChB 1972 St. And.; FRCS Ed. 1982; Dip. Med. Educat. Dund 1993. (Univ. of St. Andrews) Sen. Lect. (Anat.) Div. of Med. Sci. Sch. Of Biol. Univ. St Andrews; Pro-Dean (Med. Sci.) Univ. St Andrews; Examr. (Anat.) RCS Edin. Socs: Fell. Brit. Assn. Clin. Anat.; Anat. Soc. Prev: Regist. (Surg.) Lothian Health Bd.; Ho. Surg. Profess. (Surg. Unit) Dundee Roy. Infirm.; Demonst. (Human Morphol.) Univ. Nottm.

SINCLAIR, Derek Urquhart (retired) Royal Scottish National Hospital, Larbert FK5 4SD — MB ChB 1964 Glas.; MA (Hons.) Glas. 1970; MRCGP 1975; DPM Ed. & Glas. 1973. Prev: Med. Dir. Centr. Scotl. Healthcare NHS Trust.

SINCLAIR, Donald Henderson 19 Welbeck Avenue, Kirk Hallam, Ilkeston DE7 4NL — LRCP LRCS 1945 Ed.; LRCP LRCS Ed. LRFPS Glas. 1945.

SINCLAIR, Donald Ian 17 Millwood Vale, Long Hanborough, Witney OX29 8DF — MB ChB 1986 Bristol; MRCP (UK) 1990.

SINCLAIR, Mr Donald Malcolm (retired) Achnacree, Tighnabruaich PA21 2EB Tel: 01700 811382 — MB ChB 1944 Glas.; BSc Glas. 1941, MB ChB 1944; FRFPS Glas. 1948; FRCS Ed. 1956; FRCS Glas. 1962. Prev: Cons. Surg. Glas. Roy. Infirm.

SINCLAIR, Dorothy Buckley 8 Seafield Crescent, Elgin IV30 1RE Tel: 01343 2154 — MB ChB 1963 Glas.; DObst RCOG 1965. (Glas.) Family Plann. Instruc. Doctor Elgin. Prev: Clin. Asst. (Psychiat.) Bilbohall Hosp. Elgin; Resid. Vict. Infirm., S.. Gen. Hosp. & E.. Dist. Hosp. Glas.

SINCLAIR, Douglas Neil (retired) Tablehurst, Lindfield Road, Ardingly, Haywards Heath RH17 6TS Tel: 01444 892693 — MRCS Eng. LRCP Lond. 1952; DObst RCOG 1954; MRCGP 1956. Prev: Surg. Lt. RNVR.

SINCLAIR, Elizabeth Anne The Surgery, 409 Kings Road, Chelsea, London SW10 0LR Tel: 020 7351 1766 Fax: 020 7352 2240 — MB BS 1990 Lond. (Char. Cross & Westm.)

SINCLAIR, Elizabeth Morton 26 Drumcarrow Road, St Andrews KY16 8SE Tel: 01334 474349 Email: emsi@st_and.ac.uk — MB ChB 1975 Dundee; BSc (Med. Sci.) St. And. 1972. Clin. Asst. Meds. Research DDS LTD, Dundee; Blood Transfus. Serv. E Scotl. Socs: Assn. Anaesth. Gt. Brit. Prev: Regist. (Anaesth.) Tayside Health Bd.; Regist. (Med.) Tayside Health Bd.; Demonst. (Physiol.) Univ. St. And.

SINCLAIR, Elizabeth Romana Tunnel Road Surgery, 24 Tunnel Road, Beaminster DT8 3AB Tel: 01308 862225; Greenway Cottage, Ryall, Bridport DT6 6EN Tel: 01297 489519 Fax: 01297 489139 — MB ChB 1973 Bristol.

SINCLAIR, Emma Louise 15 Aberdare Gardens, London NW7 1DS — MB ChB 1995 Manch.

SINCLAIR, Fiona Margaret — MB ChB 1986 Sheff.; DFFP 1996; DRCOG 1991; MRCGP 1990; T(G)) 1991. GP Non-Princip.; Clin. Asst., BrE. Clinic, Hertford Co. Hosp., Hertford. Prev: GP Princip., Birchwood Surg., Letchworth.

SINCLAIR

SINCLAIR, Flora Margaret 59A Lockharton Avenue, Edinburgh EH14 1BB — MB ChB 1985 Glas. Prev: Ho. Off. (Med.) S.. Gen. Hosp. Glas.; Ho. Off. (Surg.) Vale of Leven Hosp. Alexandria.

SINCLAIR, Gillian Winifred 17 Millwood Vale, Long Hanborough, Witney OX29 8DF — BM 1987 Soton.; DA (UK) 1990.

SINCLAIR, Gordon Burton Croft Surgery, 5 Burton Crescent, Leeds LS6 4DN Tel: 0113 274 4777 Fax: 0113 230 4219 — MB ChB 1986 Leeds; MRCGP 1993; DCH RCP Lond. 1991.

SINCLAIR, Hilary Deborah North Middleton Hospital, Sterling Way, London N18 1QX Tel: 020 8887 2698 — MB BS 1980 Lond.; BSc Lond. 1977, MD 1995; MRCP (UK) 1983; FRCP 1998. (St. Geo.) Cons. Rheum. N. Middlx. Hosp. Socs: BMA; Brit. Soc. Rheum. Prev: Sen. Regist. Roy. Free Hosp. Lond.; Research Fell. Univ. Coll. & Middlx. Sch. Med. Lond.; Research Assoc. Duke Univ. Med. Centre Durh., N. Carolina, USA.

SINCLAIR, Mr Ian Scott Robertson (retired) 15 Belgrave Crescent, Edinburgh EH4 3AJ Tel: 0131 332 3502 — MB ChB 1945 Ed.; MB ChB (Hns.) Ed. 1945; FRCS Ed. 1949. Prev: Cons. Surg. Roy. Infirm. Edin.

SINCLAIR, Jack Michael (retired) 2 Meadow Close, Bardsey, Leeds LS17 9BJ Tel: 01937 72592 — MRCS Eng. LRCP Lond. 1940.

SINCLAIR, Janet Carolyn Flat 3 Forge Lodge, Gumley Gardens, Isleworth TW7 6PP — MB BS 1982 Lond.; MRCPsych 1987. Sen. Regist. Rotat. (Psychiat.) Wessex VTS.

SINCLAIR, Janet Isobel The Taymount Surgery, 1 Taymount Terrace, Perth PH1 1NU Tel: 01738 627117 Fax: 01738 444713 — MB ChB 1950 Glasgow; DCH, DRCOG 1977. (Aberdeen) GP Perth.

SINCLAIR, Mr John 7 Bridgegait, Milngavie, Glasgow G62 6NT Tel: 0141 956 3247 — MB ChB 1965 Ed.; FRCS Ed. 1969. Cons. (Urol.) S.. Gen. Hosp. Glas. Prev: Sen. Regist. (Urol.) Glas. Roy. Infirm.; Surg. Regist. Lewis Hosp. Stornoway & S.. Gen. Hosp. Glas.

SINCLAIR, John Alan Appletree Cottage, Elstead, Godalming GU8 6DG — MRCS Eng. LRCP Lond. 1934.

SINCLAIR, John Alfred George 17 Flodden Way, Billingham TS23 3LF — MB BS 1992 Newc.

SINCLAIR, John Anthony (retired) The Manor House, Houghton-le-Spring DH5 8AF Tel: 0191 584 2839 — LRCP LRCS 1942 Ed.; LRCP LRCS Ed. LRFPS Glas. 1942. Prev: Cas. Off. & Ho. Surg. (ENT) Roy. Infirm. Sunderland.

SINCLAIR, John Fraser Yorkhill NHS Trust, Glasgow G3 8SJ Tel: 0141 201 0000 — MB ChB 1980 Aberd.

SINCLAIR, John Maxwell (retired) 4 Manderlea Court, Links Road, Lundin Links, Leven KY8 6AT Tel: 01333 320438 — MB ChB 1944 Glas. Prev: Ho. Surg. W.. Infirm. Glas.

SINCLAIR, John Meehan (retired) Fairhurst, The Avenue, Fairlight, Hastings TN35 4DE — MB ChB 1957 Leeds; MFHom 1972. Prev: Asst. Dir. of Health Care HM Prison Serv.

SINCLAIR, John Raymond Royal Cornwall Hospital Trust (Treliske), Truro TR1 2XN Tel: 01872 74242 — MB ChB 1979 Wales; FFA RCS Eng. 1984. Cons. Anaesth. & Intens. Care. SW RHA. Prev: Sen. Regist. (Anaesth.) S. W.. RHA; Lect. (Anaesth.) Univ. Zambia, Lusaka; Regist. (Anaesth.) King's Coll. Hosp. Lond.

SINCLAIR, Mr John Stephen 55 Knockairn Road, Dundrod, Crumlin BT29 4UE Tel: 01232 825278 — MB BCh BAO 1987 Belf.; FRCSI 1991.

SINCLAIR, Julia Margaret Anne 1 East Cliffe, Winchester SO23 0JB — MB BS 1994 Lond.

SINCLAIR, Keith Gareth Alexander Buen, Crowborough Hill, Crowborough TN6 2HJ Tel: 01892 663911; 126 Volunteer Drive, Somerset KY 42501-1926, USA Tel: 00 1 606 678 5602 Fax: 00 1 606 679 9308 Email: keithsinclair@yahoo.com — MB BS 1982 Lond.; BSc Psychol. & Pharmacol. Manch. 1975. (Middlx.) Attend. Surg. Lake Cumbld. Regional Hosp. Som. KY, USA. Socs: BMA; Fell. Amer. Coll. Surgs. Prev: Resid. Gen. Surg. Univ. of Florida; SHO (Cardiothoracic Surg.) Oxf. HA; Demonstr. (Human Anat.) Oxf. Univ.

SINCLAIR, Kenneth (retired) 2 Kirk Cottages, High St., Aberdour, Burntisland KY3 0SR Tel: 01383 860073 — MB ChB 1946 Ed.; FRCP Ed. 1965, M 1951; MRCP Lond. 1956. Prev: Cons. Phys. Head Of Med. & Clinics, Abdulla Fouad Hosp. Dammam, Saudi Arabia.

SINCLAIR, Leonard 152 Harley Street, London W1G 7LH Tel: 020 7935 3834 Fax: 020 7224 2574; 34 Armitage Road, London NW11 8RD Tel: 020 8458 6464 Fax: 020 8905 5433 — MB BS 1954 Lond.; FRCPCH 1998; BSc Physiol. (Hons.) Lond. 1952; FRCP Lond. 1974, M 1960; DCH Eng. 1957. (Middlx.) Emerit. Cons. Paediat., Chelsea & W.m. Hosp., Lond. SW10. Socs: Fell. Roy. Soc. Med. (Mem. Counc. & Ex-Sec. Sect. Paediat. & Mem.; Soc. Study of Inborn Errors of Metab.; Mem. of BHA. Prev: Sen. Regist. (Paediat.) W.m. Hosp. & W.m. Childr. Hosp.; Regist. (Med.) Qu. Eliz. Hosp. Childr. Lond.; New Health Trust Clin. Research Fell. Qu. Eliz. Hosp. Childr. Lond.

SINCLAIR, Margaret (retired) 4 Manderlea Court, Links Road, Lundin Links, Leven KY8 6AT Tel: 01333 320438 — MB ChB 1944 Glas. Prev: Ho. Surg. (Gyn.) Roy. Infirm. Glas.

SINCLAIR, Margaret Ann 9 Newmill Gardens, St Andrews KY16 8RY — MB ChB 1993 Aberd.

SINCLAIR, Michael Edward 104 Southmoor Road, Oxford OX2 6RB Tel: 01865 559496 — MB ChB 1976 Bristol; FFARCS Eng. 1981. Cons. Cardiothoracic Anaesth., Nuffield Dept. Anaesth., Oxf. Prev: Sen. Regist. & Lect. Nuffield Dept. Anaesth., Oxf.; Sen. Lect. Univ. Hosp. Geneva; SHO Rotat. (Anaesth.) Bristol Roy. Infirm.

SINCLAIR, Michael Jeffrey 24 Dawson Place, London W2 4TJ; Sinclair Montrose Trust Limited, 5th Floor, Cheapside House, 138 Cheapside, London EC2V 6LH Tel: 020 7776 1500 Fax: 020 7776 1592 — BSc Lond. 1965, MB BS 1967. (Middlx.)

SINCLAIR, Michelle 6 Swan Drive, Aldermaston, Reading RG7 4UZ Tel: 01189 713351 — MB BS 1992 Lond.; MRCGP July 1997; DRCOG Nov 1995; DFFP 1995.

SINCLAIR, Neil Edward 1A Baptist Gardens, London NW5 4ET — MB BS 1998 Lond.; MB BS Lond 1998.

SINCLAIR, Niall Mackay The Surgery, High Street, Epworth, Doncaster DN9 1EP Tel: 01427 872232 Fax: 01427 874944; 1 Mill Lane, Westwoodside, Doncaster DN9 2AF Tel: 01427 752193 — MB ChB 1971 Ed.; BSc (Med. Sci.) Ed. 1968; FRCGP 1995, M 1975; DObst RCOG 1974. Course Organiser Doncaster VTS. Socs: Anglo-French Med. Soc. Prev: Trainee GP Doncaster VTS.

SINCLAIR, Paul 126 Blenheim Place, Aberdeen AB25 2DN; Waratah Apartments, 24/71 Victoria St, Potts Point, Sydney 2011, Australia Tel: 00 61 2 3573870 — MB ChB 1989 Dundee.

SINCLAIR, Paul Millfield Medical Centre, 63-83 Hylton Road, Sunderland SR4 7AF Tel: 0191 567 9179 Fax: 0191 514 7452 Email: dr.sinclair@gp-a89017.northy.nhs.uk — MB BS 1976 Newc. (Newcastle)

SINCLAIR, Penelope Mace Bradford University Health Centre, Bradford BD7 1DP; 16 Oakburn Road, Ilkley LS29 9NN — BM 1984 Soton.; MRCGP 1988; DRCOG 1988.

SINCLAIR, Mr Peter Kemp East Cheshire NHS Trust, Macclesfield. District General Hospital, Victoria Road, Macclesfield SK10 3BC Tel: 01625 421000 Fax: 01625 661644; Bon Vista, 89 High St, Bollington, Macclesfield SK10 5PF Tel: 01625 573379 Fax: 01625 573379 — MB ChB 1969 Glas.; FRCS Eng. 1976; FRCS Glas. 1974; FRCR Eng. 1983. Cons. Radiol. Macclesfield Dist. Gen. Hosp.

SINCLAIR, Powell Derek Lingwell Croft Surgery, Ring Road, Middleton, Leeds LS10 3LT Tel: 0113 2704848/705372 Fax: 0113 272 0030; 7 Gateland Drive, Leeds LS17 8HU Tel: 0113 273 7361 — M.B., Ch.B. Leeds 1950. Prev: Ho. Phys. Profess. Med. Unit St. Jas. Hosp. Leeds; Res. Med. Off. Ida & Robt. Arthington Hosp. Leeds.

SINCLAIR, Robert Gillies (retired) Inchmahome, Arbuthnot Est., Dorrator Road, Camelon, Falkirk FK1 4BN Tel: 01324 623202 — MB ChB 1949 Glas.; FRCGP 1974, M 1958; DObst RCOG 1954. Prev: Hospice Med. Cons. Strathcarrow Hospice Denny.

SINCLAIR, Robin Douglas 141 Whyteleaf Road, Caterham CR3 — MRCS Eng. LRCP Lond. 1964; MB Camb. 1965, BChir 1964. (Camb. & Guy's) Prev: Ho. Surg. Obst., Cas. Off. & Ho. Phys. W. Middlx. Hosp. Isleworth.

SINCLAIR, Ronald Kilpatrick (retired) Westgarth, Garelochhead, Helensburgh G84 0AT Tel: 01436 810542 Fax: 01436 810542 — MB ChB 1965 Glas.; DObst RCOG 1967. Prev: SHO (Obst.) Rankin Memor. Hosp. Greenock.

SINCLAIR, Ruth Margaret Flat 2, Rosemont, 80/81 Mount Ephram, Tunbridge Wells TN4 8BU — MB ChB 1985 Glas.; FFA RCSI 1994. Staff Grade (Anaesth.) Monklands & Bellshill Hosps. Lanarksh. Prev: Career Regist. (Anaesth.) Glas. Roy. Infirm.

SINCLAIR, Shona 56 Pentland Avenue, Dundee DD2 2BS Tel: 01382 642052; 22 Duchess Street, Stanley, Perth PH1 4NG — MB

ChB 1984 Dundee; DRCOG 1988. Clin. Asst. Murray Roy. Hosp. Perth.

SINCLAIR, Simon Chester-le-StreetCMHT, Chester-le-Street — MB BS 1977 Lond.; MA Oxf. 1977; PhD Lond. 1996, MSc 1992, MB BS 1977; MRCPsych 1987; DTM & H RCP Lond. 1983. p/t Cons. Psychiat.s, Co. Durh. and Darlington Priority Servs. NHS Trust, Chester-li-St.; Hon. Fell., Dept. of Anthropol. Prev: Field Doctor Brit. Nepal Med. Trust, Bhojpur, E. Nepal.; Sen. Regist. Oxf. Ment. Healthcare NHS Trust.

SINCLAIR, Siobhan Alexandra University Hospital of North Durham, North Rd, Durham DH1 2UD — MB ChB 1988 Ed.; MRCP (UK) 1994. p/t Cons. Dermatol., Univ. Hosp. of N. Durh.; Cons. Dermatol., Univ. Hosp. of N. Durh. Socs: BAD; BAD; BSDP. Prev: SHO (Med. & Dermat.) S. Cleveland. Hosp.; SHO (A & E) Middlesbrough Gen. Hosp.

SINCLAIR, Stuart Alexander, OStJ (retired) Pentlands, 35 Windrush Crescent, Malvern WR14 2XG — MB ChB 1939 Ed. Prev: Sen. Med. Off. Lovedale Hosps. S. Afr.

SINCLAIR, Susan Isabelle Grace 39 Eburne Road, Finsbury Park, London N7 6AU — MB BS 1985 Lond.

SINCLAIR, Tessa Annemarie Lewis 6 Haverfield Gardens, Kew, Richmond TW9 3DD — MB BS 1989 Lond.

SINCLAIR, Thomas (retired) 67 Chew Valley Road, Greenfield, Oldham OL3 7JG Tel: 01457 873100 Fax: 01457 873100 Email: tomsinclair@doctors.org.uk — MB BS 1961 Durh.; DObst RCOG 1966; Cert Av Med MoD (Air) & CAA; Aviat. Auth. 1977. p/t Authorised Med. Examr. Uk Civil.Aviat.Auth.Jt. Aviat.Auth. Prev: Teach. (Gen. Pract.) Univ. Manch.

SINCLAIR, Thomas Stewart 15 Richmond Hills Place, Aberdeen AB15 5EN — MB ChB 1975 Aberd.; MRCP (UK) 1977. Cons. Phys. (Gastroenterol.) Aberd. Hosp.; Hon. Clin. Sen. Lect. (Med.) Aberd. Univ. Prev: Res. Fell. (Gastroentrol.) St. Bart. Hosp. Lond.

SINCLAIR, Torquil Macleod (retired) West Lodge, Longridge Towers, Berwick-upon-Tweed TD15 2XQ Tel: 01289 307499 — MB ChB Ed. 1954.

SINCLAIR, William Wells (retired) 5 Cammo Parkway, Cammo, Barnton, Edinburgh EH4 8EP — MB ChB 1932 Glas.; MRCPsych 1971; DPH Eng. 1936, DPM 1960. Prev: Cons. Psychiat. & Supt. Phys. Lynebank & Glenlomond Hosps. Fife.

SINCLAIR, William Yuille (retired) The Shieling, 10 Aspen Place, Strathaven ML10 6PY Tel: 01357 23033 — MB BS 1959 Durh.; FRCOG 1977, M 1963: Clin. Lect. (Obst. & Gyn.) Univ. Newc. Prev: Cons. O & G Gateshead AHA.

SINDALL, Fiona Mary Putneymead Medical Centre, 350 Upper Richmond Road, Putney, London SW15 6TL — BM 1986 Soton.; DA 1988. GP Retainer Putneymead Med. Centre Lond. Prev: GP Trainee; SHO (O & G) P.ss Anne Hosp. Soton.; SHO (Anaesth.) Soton Gen. Hosp.

SINDELL, James Armstrong Deolali, Ganges Close, Mylor Harbour, Falmouth TR11 5UG Tel: 01326 72760 — MB BS 1944 Lond. (St. Mary's) Prev: Ho. Phys. Harefield EMS Hosp.; Asst. Med. Off. City Gen. Hosp. Stoke-on-Trent & Netherne Hosp. Coulsdon.

SINDEN, Mark Peter Maidstone & Tunbridge NHS Trust, c/o Anaesthetics Department, Kent & Sussex Hospital, Mount Ephraim, Tunbridge Wells Tel: 01982 526111 Ext. 2529; Yew Tree Cottage, 4 Station Road, Hurst Green, Etchingham TN19 7PL Tel: 01580 861331 Email: mpsinden@btinternet.com — MB BS 1985 Lond.; DFFP 1993; FRCA 1996; DA (UK) 1993; T(GP) 1990; DCH RCP Lond. 1989. (Guy's Hospital, London University) Cons. Anaesth. Socs: Obst. Anaesth. Assn.; Difficult Airway Soc.; Assn. of Anaesth. GB & Irel. Prev: Sp REG (Anaesth.) Guy's Hosp., Lond.; Regist. (Anaesth.) E.bourne DGH Sussex; Regist. (Anaesth.) E. Grinstead Qu. Vict. Hosp.

SINFIELD, Caroline Jane 6 Marcus Terrace, London SW18 2JW — MB ChB 1996 Liverp.

SINFIELD, Karen Elizabeth The Laurels Medical Practice, 28 Clarendon Road, St Helier, Jersey JE2 3YS Tel: 01534 733866 Fax: 01534 769597 — MB BS 1979 Lond.

SINGAL, Ajay Greenbank Surgery, 1025 Stratford Road, Hall Green, Birmingham B28 8BG Tel: 0121 777 1490 Fax: 0121 778 6239; 6 Brampton Crescent, Solihull B90 3SY — MB BS Newc. 1986; MRCGP 1990; DRCOG 1988.

SINGAL, Arun Kumar Northgate Medical Centre, Anchor Meadow Health Centre, Aldridge, Walsall WS9 8AJ Tel: 01922 450900 Fax: 01922 450910; 26 Newick Avenue, Little Aston, Sutton Coldfield B74 3DA — MB BS 1984 Newc.; MRCGP 1988; DRCOG 1987.

SINGAL, Ashish Kumar 70 Launceston Road, Walsall WS5 3EE — MB BS 1992 Newc.

SINGANAYAGAM, Jeyakumar Queens Hospital, Department of Radiology, Burton Hospital NHS Trust, Belvedere Road, Burton-on-Trent DE13 0RB Tel: 01283 566333 Fax: 01283 593013 — MB BS 1981 Peradeniya; FRCS Ed. 1987; FRCR 1993. (university of Peradeniya, Sri Lanka) Cons. Radiol. Qu.s Hosp. Burton Hosp. NHS Trust Burton-upon-Trent. Prev: Sen. Regist. (Radiol.) N. Staffs. Hosp. Centre Stoke on Trent; Regist. (Radiol.) N. Staffs. Hosp. Centre Stoke-on-Trent; Regist. (Surg.) Dumfries & Galloway Roy. Infirm.

SINGARAJAH, Clement Uthayakumar 70 Beeches Avenue, Carshalton Beeches, Carshalton SM5 3LW Tel: 020 8647 8493 — MB BS 1990 Lond.; BSc Biochem. Lond. 1987, MB BS 1990. SHO (Anaesth.) Worthing Hosp. Sussex. Socs: BMA & Med. Defence Union. Prev: Ho. Off. (Surg.) St. Richard's Hosp. Chichester; Ho. Off. (Med.) W. Middlx. Univ. Hosp. Lond.

SINGARAYER, Chandrakumar 24 St Andrews Avenue, Sudbury, Wembley HA0 2QD — MB BS 1994 Lond.; Board Certified by the American Board of Internal Medicine 1999; BSc Lond. 1991. (Royal Free Hosp. Sch. Of Med.) Cons., Internal Med., Memor. Hosp., N. Conway, New Hants., USA; Clin. Fell. (Med.) Harvard Med. Sch. Socs: Mass. Med. Soc.; Amer. Med. Assn. Prev: SHO (A & E) Qu. Eliz. II Hosp. Welwyn Bdn. City; Ho. Off. (Med.) Roy. Free Hosp. Lond.; Ho. Off. (Gen. Surg. & Orthop.) Lister Hosp. Stevenage.

SINGARAYER, Karen Naomi Montcalm, 11 Lankaster Gardens, London N2 9AZ — MB BS 1993 Lond.

SINGER, Mr Adolf 16 Manor Court, Aylmer Rd, Finchley, London N2 0PJ Tel: 001 631 287 2561, 020 8348 8448 Fax: 001 631 287 2561; 191 Herrick Road, Southampton, New York 11968, USA Tel: 001 631 283 9531 Fax: 001 631 287 2561 — MB BS 1951 (Hons) London; FRCS 1956; FACS 1964; MD New York 1979. (Univ. Coll. Hosp., London) p/t Assoc. Clin. Prof (Surg.), Albert Einstein Coll. Of Med., New York; 16 Manor Ct., Aylmer Rd, Fingale, Lond, N20 0PJ, Tel: 0208 348 8448. Socs: Sen. Mem. NY Surg. Soc.; Fell. Emerit. Amer. Coll. Angiol.; Sen. Mem. Internat. Cardiovasc. Soc. Prev: Emerit. Attend., N.Y. Hosp. Med. Centre Qu.; Hon. Attend. Long Is. Jewish. Hosp.; Hon. Attend. N. Shore Univ. Hosp.

SINGER, Professor Albert Department of Gynaecology, Whittington Hospital, London N19 5NF Tel: 020 7288 5408 Fax: 020 7288 5066 Email: alber.singer@whittington.thnhs.com; (cons. rooms), 212-214 Great Portland St, London W1N 5HG Tel: 020 7390 8442 Fax: 020 8458 0168 Email: albert.singer@virgin.net — MB BS 1962 Sydney; DPhil Oxf. 1973; PhD Sydney 1972; FRCOG 1980, M 1967; DGO Sydney 1967. (Sydney) Cons. O & G Whittington Hosp. Lond.; Prof. Gyn. Research Univ. Lond.; Vis. Prof. Dept. Molecular Pathol. UCL. Socs: Brit. Soc. for Colposcopy and Cervical Path. (BSCCP) - Trustee.; Europ. Research Organisation on Genital Infec.s and Neoplasia (EROGEN) - Exec. Comm..; Brit. Gynaecological Endoscopy Soc. Prev: Reader (O & G) Univ. Sheff.; Cons. O & G Jessop Hosp. Sheff.; Research Fell. & Clin. Lect. Nuffield Dept. O & G Univ. Oxf.

SINGER, Mr Brian Robert Perth Royal Infirmary, Perth PH1 1NX Tel: 01738 474480 Fax: 01738 473990 Email: brian.singer@tuht.scot.nhs.uk — MB ChB 1983 Aberd.; FRCS 2001 Ed.; FRCS (Orth.) 1994; FRCS Eng. 1988. Cons. Orthop. Surg. Perth Roy. Infirm. Prev: Sen. Regist. (Orthop.) Qu. Eliz. Milit. Hosp. Lond.; Cons. Orthop. Surg. Roy. Hosp. Haslar P.ss Margt. Rose Orthop. Hosp.

SINGER, Charles Robert John Department of Haematology, Royal United Hospital, Bath BA1 3NG Tel: 01225 824760 Fax: 01225 461044 Email: charles.singer@ruh-bath.swest.nhs.uk; 40 Garstons, Bathford, Bath BA1 7TE Tel: 01225 859396 Email: crjsinger@crjsbath.demon.co.uk — MB ChB 1977 Glas.; MB ChB (Commend.) Glas. 1977; BSc (Hons.) Glas. 1975; FRCP Lond. 1996; FRCP Glas. 1990; MRCP (UK) 1980; MRCPath 1987; FRCPath 1997. (Glas.) Cons. Haemat. Roy. United Hosp. Bath; Postgrad. Clin. Tutor Bath. Socs: Brit. Soc. for Haemat., (Comm. Mem. 1998-2000), Treas. 2000; Amer. Soc. Hematology, 1998. Prev: Lect. (Haemat.) Univ. Coll. & Middlx. Sch. of Med. Lond.; Regist. (Haemat. & Gen. Med.) Glas. Roy. Infirm.

SINGER, Delius Michael Frederick Fir Tree Cottage, Duncryne Road, Gartocharn, Alexandria G83 8RY — MB ChB 1994 Glas.

SINGER

SINGER, Donald Robert James Department of Pharmacology & Clinical Pharmacology, St. George's Hospital Medical School, Cranmer Terrace, London SW17 0RE Tel: 020 8725 5607 Fax: 020 8682 0487 — MB ChB 1978 Aberd.; MD Aberd. 1995, BMedBiol. 1975; MRCP (UK) 1981. (aberdeen) Reader (Clin. Pharmacol.) & Hon. Cons. Phys. St. Geo. Hosp. Med. Sch. Lond.; Hon Cons. in Cardiovasc. Med.; Hon. Sen. Lect. Imperial Coll. Nat. Heart & Lung Inst. Heart Sci. Centre, Harefield. Socs: Brit. Cardiac Soc. & Hypertens. Soc.; Amer. Heart Assn. Prev: Brit. Heart Foundat. Intermediate & Jun. Research Fell. Research Fell (Med.) St. Geo. Hosp.; Sch. Lond. & Char. Cross & W.m. Med. Sch. Lond; Regist. (Med.) Renal Unit Hammersmith Hosp. Lond.

SINGER, Helen Grant Bramhall Health Centre, 66 Bramhall Lane South, Bramhall, Stockport SK7 2DY Tel: 0161 439 8213 Fax: 0161 439 6398 — MB ChB 1971 Glas.; DObst RCOG 1973.

SINGER, Iain Ogilvie Flat 2/3, 170 Elmbank St., Glasgow G2 4NY Tel: 0141 332 5195 Email: iain@ioscm.demon.co.uk — MB ChB 1987 Glas.; BSc (Hons.) Immunol. Glas. 1984, MB ChB 1987; MRCP (UK) 1991; MRCPath 1997. (Glas.) Career Regist. (Haemat.) Stobhill Gen. Hosp. Glas.; Specialist Regist. Stobhill NHS Trust Glas. Prev: SHO (Med.) Monklands Dist. Gen. Hosp. Airdrie; Ho. Off. (Med.) Glas. Roy. Infirm.; Ho. Off. (Surg.) S.. Gen. Hosp. Glas.

SINGER, Jack Donald Academic Department of Child Health, Chelsea & Westminster Hospital, 369 Fulham Road, London SW10 9NH Tel: 020 8746 8627; 73 Harley Street, London W1N 1DE Tel: 020 7935 2023 Fax: 020 7935 3857 — MD 1962 Washington Univ.; Lic. Newfld. Med. Bd. 1975; FRCPCH 1997; T(M) (Paediat.) 1991. Hon. Sec. Lect. (Child Health) Chelsea & W.m. Hosp. Lond. Socs: Brit. Paediat. Assn. & Clin. Genetics Soc. Prev: Sen. Lect. & Hon. Cons. Human Genetics King's Coll. Hosp. & Med. Sch. Lond.; Med. Off. P. Philip Research Laborat. Paediat. Research Unit Guy's Hosp. Med. Sch.; Sen. Regist. (Paediat.) Guy's Hosp. Lond.

SINGER, Jonathan 11 Newcombe Park, London NW7 3QN — MB BCh 1974 Witwatersrand.

SINGER, Julian Mark Department of Oncology, The Hammersmith Hospital, Du Cane Road, London W12 0NN Tel: 020 8743 2030 Fax: 020 8740 3169; 16 Canonbury Park N., London N1 2JT Tel: 020 7226 8933 Email: julian@jmsinger.sonnet.co.uk — MB BS 1984 Lond.; MRCP (UK) 1988; FRCR 1993. (Roy. Lond. Hosp. Med. Coll.) Sen. Regist. (Clin. Oncol.) Hammersmith Hosp. Lond. Prev: Research Regist. (Oncol.) Middlx. Hosp. Lond.

SINGER, Juliet Amanda 23 Cocksheadhey Road, Bollington, Macclesfield SK10 5QZ; Flat 3 16 Marlborough Road, London N19 4NB Tel: 020 7272 7266 — MB BCh 1993 Wales. SHO Rotat. (Psychiat.) Roy. Free Hosp. Lond.

SINGER, Jutta (retired) 17 Schonfield Square, Lordship Road, London N16 0QQ Tel: 020 8800 0406 — MRCS Eng. LRCP Lond. 1946; BA (Hons.) Psychol. Lond. 1952; DTM & H RCP Lond. 1955; Cert. Family Plann. JCC 1955. Prev: Regist. (Path.) St. Peter's Hosp., Eliz. Garret. Anderson Hosp. & Roy. N.. Hosp.

SINGER, Laura Jane 26 St Bridget Crescent, Stonehaven AB39 2GL — MB ChB 1997 Manch.

SINGER, Lawrence Lydia House Surgery, 8 Sutherland Boulevard, Leigh-on-Sea SS9 3PS Tel: 01702 552900 Fax: 01702 553474; 1809 London Road, Leigh-on-Sea SS9 2ST — MB ChB 1967 Manch.; DObst RCOG 1969. GP Leigh-on-Sea. Socs: BMA & N. Lond. Gp. Anaesths. Prev: Regist. (Anaesth.) P. of Wales Hosp. Tottenham; SHO (O & G) St. Mary's Hosp. Manch.

SINGER, Malcolm Harold (retired) 10 Eltham Hill, London SE9 5JX Tel: 020 8859 2072 Fax: 020 8859 2072 — MB ChB 1949 Leeds. Prev: Capt. RAMC.

SINGER, Mervyn University College London Medical School, Rayne Institute, University St., London WC1E 6JJ Tel: 020 7209 6208 Fax: 020 7209 6211; 19 Hornsey Lane Gardens, Highgate, London N6 5NX Tel: 020 8348 8762 — MB BS 1981 Lond. Sen. Lect. (Intens. Care Med.) UCL Med. Sch.

SINGER, Nicola Elaine Flat B, 8 Highbury Crescent, London N5 1RN Tel: 020 7700 4412 — MB BS 1989 Lond.

SINGER, Paul Ashley Liverpool Road Health Centre, 9 Mersey Place, Liverpool Road, Luton LU1 1HH Tel: 01582 31321 — MB ChB 1984 Liverp. GP Computing Facilitator Beds. FHSA. Prev: Trainee GP Milton Keynes VTS.

SINGER, Ralph 1 Latimer House, Morning Lane, London E9 6HE Tel: 020 8985 2249; 3 Thornton Way, London NW11 6RY Tel: 020 8458 7929 — MRCS Eng. LRCP Lond. 1944; DCH Eng. 1949. (St. Bart.) Prev: Ho. Off. (Obst.) St. And. Hosp. Bow; Regist. Pk. Hosp. Hither Green; Ho. Phys. (Paediat.) Whipps Cross Hosp.

SINGER, Ronald Victor Julius The Health Centre, 2A Forest Road, Edmonton, London N9 8RZ Tel: 020 8804 0121 — MB BChir 1973 Camb.; MRCGP 1987.

SINGER, Ruth Snaefell Avenue Surgery, 14 Snaefell Avenue, Liverpool L13 7HA Tel: 0151 228 2377; Parkview, Allerton Road, Liverpool L18 3JU Tel: 0151 724 5160 — MRCS Eng. LRCP Lond. 1963; BSc (Physiol) Lond. 1960. (Univ. Coll. Lond. & Liverp.) Prev: Med. Off. St. Helens Co. Boro. & Liverp. Educat. Comm.

SINGFIELD, Catherine Jane 182 Grace Way, Stevenage SG1 5AG Tel: 01438 359249 — MB BS 1991 Lond.

SINGH, Ajai Pratap 21 Moorcroft Road, Fulwood, Sheffield S10 4GS — MB BS 1972 Lucknow; DA Agra 1974. (King Geo. Med. Coll. Lucknow) Assoc. Specialist Regional Transfus. Centre Sheff.

SINGH, Ajit Glan Yr Afon Surgery, Shop Row, Tredegar NP22 4LB Tel: 01495 722460 Fax: 01495 724410 — MB BS 1962 Panjab; DPM Eng. 1973. (Govt. Med. Coll. Patiala) Sen. Regist. Cheadle Roy. Hosp. Prev: Regist. Hellesdon Hosp. Norwich, S.H.M.S. Hosp. Srinagar, India & Claybury Hosp. Woodford Bridge.

SINGH, Aman Deep Bangour Village Hospital, Broxburn EH52 6LR; 14A Station Road, Haddington EH41 3NZ — MB ChB 1987 Ed.

SINGH, Amarendra Kumar 5 Netherfield Road, London N12 8DP — MB BS 1958 Patna; PhD Lond. 1968; FFPath (RCPI - Dub.) 1997. (Patna) Sen. Lect. & Cons. Dept. Haemat. St. Thos. Hosp. & Med. Sch. Lond.; Assoc. Prof. (Haemat.) Med. Sch. Hazall Zimbabwe March 1997.

SINGH, Amarjeet 6 Forest Close, Pinders Heath, Wakefield WF1 4TL — MB BS 1976 Ranchi; MRCPI 1984.

SINGH, Amarjit (retired) 21 Broadway, Atherton, Manchester M46 9HW — MB BS 1961 Punjab; MB BS Punjab (India) 1961; DO Eng. 1969. Hosp. Pract. (Ophth.) Leigh Infirm. Prev: Hosp. Pract. (Ophth.) Hope Hosp. Salford.

SINGH, Amrik Marine Surgery, 29 Belle Vue Road, Southbourne, Bournemouth BH6 3DB Tel: 01202 423377 Fax: 01202 424277; 37 Keswick Road, Boscombe Manor, Bournemouth BH5 1LR — MB ChB 1976 Manch. (Manch.) GP Bournemouth. Socs: Assoc. Mem. Brit. Med. Acupunc. Soc.; Assoc. Mem. Fac. Homeop. Lond.

SINGH, Amrit Bir Royal Shrewsbury Hospital, Shelton, Bicton Heath, Shrewsbury SY3 8DN Tel: 01743 261296; 12 Highridge Way, Radbrooke Green, Shrewsbury SY3 6DJ Tel: 01743 369123 — MB BS 1977 Punjab; BSc Punjab 1969, MB BS 1977; MRCPsych 1982; DPM Eng. 1980.

SINGH, Anirudh Prasad St Peters Hospital, Guildford Road, Chertsey KT16 0PZ — MB BS 1973 Patna.

SINGH, Mr Anoop Kumar 30 Nursey Road, Rainham, Gillingham ME8 0DS; 320 Applewood Drive, Slidell 70461, USA Tel: 001 985 7817903 Fax: 001 985 7817904 Email: anoopks@bellsouth.net — MB BS 1978 Poona; MPhil (Bioengineering) Strathclyde 1993; FRCS Ed. 1983; MRCS Eng. LRCP Lond. 1985; Dip. Biomechanics Strathclyde 1990. Asst. Prof. in Emerg. Med., Louisiana State Univ. Baton Rouge, LA, USA. Socs: Assoc. Mem. BOA; Internat. Soc. Biomech. Prev: Regist. (A & E) St. Peters' Hosp. Chertsey; Research Fell. Univ. Calif., Los Angeles; Regist. (Orthop.) Medway Hosp. Gillingham & Odstock Hosp. Salisbury.

SINGH, Arun Kumar Wynyard Road Surgery, 35-37 Wynyard Road, Hartlepool TS25 3LB Tel: 01429 223195 Fax: 01429 296007; 14 Endeavour Close, Hartlepool TS25 1EY Tel: 01429 236682 — MB BS 1974 Panta; MS (ENT) Panta 1979; DLO RCS Eng. 1981.

SINGH, Arvind Kumar Diabetes & Endocrinology, Paula Carr Diabetes Centre, William Harvey Hospital, Ashford Tel: 01233 616047 Fax: 01233 616049; Musafir House, 31 Foley Close, Willesborough, Ashford TN24 0XA — MB BS 1982 Patna; MB BS Patna 1979; MD (Med.) Patna 1982; MRCP (UK) 1989. Staff Phys. (Diabetes & Endocrine) Paula Carr Diabetes Centre William Harvey Hosp. Ashford, Kent. Socs: Med. Defence Union; BMA; BDA. Prev: Regist. (Gen. Med.) Burnley Gen. Hosp. Lancs.; Specialist Phys. Centr. Hosp. Coal India Ltd. Dhanbad, India.

SINGH

SINGH, Ashok Nandan Beaconfield Mental Health Resource Centre, Beacon Lane, Grantham NG31 9DF Tel: 01476 591233 Fax: 01476 591739 — MB BS 1978 Mithila; MD Patna 1985. Cons. Psychiat. Rauceby Hosp. Sleaford. Prev: Staff Psychiat. W.m. Hosp. Lond.; Regist. St. Brigid's Hosp. Ardee; Regist. St. John's Hosp. Aylesbury.

SINGH, Avtar St Pauls Surgery, 36-38 East Street, Preston PR1 1UU Tel: 01772 252409 Fax: 01772 885509.

SINGH, Baldev Malkit Wolverhampton Diabetes Centre, New Cross Hospital, Wolverhampton WV10 0QP Tel: 01902 643035 Fax: 01902 642864 — MB BS 1979 Lond.; MD Lond. 1988; MRCP (UK) 1982; FRCP 1998. Cons. Phys. (Diabetes Endocrinol.) Wolverhampton; Reader in Diabetic Med. Univ. of Wolverhampton. Prev: Sen. Regist. (Endocrinol.) Char. Cross Hosp. Lond.

SINGH, Baljit 9 Pennant Road, Burbage, Hinckley LE10 2LA — BM BCh 1992 Oxf.; BA (Physiol. Sci.) Oxf. 1989; FRCS (Irel.) 1997; FRCS (Eng.) 1997; Royal College of Surgeons of England Research Felolowship 1998. (Oxf. Univ.) SHO Rotat. (Gen. Surg.) Leics.

SINGH, Bhawna Holton Grange, Station Road, Holton-le-Clay, Grimsby DN36 5HT — MB ChB 1998 Leic.; MB ChB Leic 1998.

SINGH, Bijendra Narayan Garden Street Surgery, 28A Garden Street, Brompton, Gillingham ME7 5AS Tel: 01634 845898 Fax: 01634 817823; 29 Barleymow Close, Walderslade, Chatham ME5 8JZ Tel: 01634 316841 — MB BS 1971 Bihar; MD (Mlthila) 1978.

SINGH, Bikram Jit Flat 2, 79 Lancefield Quay, Glasgow G3 8HA — LRCP LRCS 1984 Ed.; LRCP LRCS Ed. LRCPS Glas. 1984.

SINGH, Binoy Kumar Institute Road Surgery, 14 Institute Road, Eccleshill, Bradford BD2 2HX Tel: 01274 637417 Fax: 01274 776511 — MB BS 1967 Ranchi; BSc Bihar 1961; MB BS Ranchi India 1967. (Rajendra Med. Coll.)

SINGH, Bir Bahadur Hillside Health Centre, Tanhouse Road, Tanhouse, Skelmersdale WN8 6DS Tel: 01695 726888 Fax: 01695 556330 — MB BS 1973 Patna; MB BS 1973 Patna.

SINGH, Bishnu Deo Narayan 164 Melwood Drive, Liverpool L12 4XH — MB BS 1974 Patna.

SINGH, Boota Deepdale Road Surgery, 98 Deepdale Road, Preston PR1 5AR; Fairwinds, Highrigg Drive, Broughton, Preston PR3 5LJ Tel: 01772 862054 — MB BS 1968 Lucknow. GP. Prev: Med. Off., Rainfall Agency.

SINGH, Brijindera Balbir Ridgecrest, 9 Foxlands Avenue, Penn, Wolverhampton WV4 5LX Tel: 01902 336861 — MB BS 1980 Lond.; MRCGP 1985; DCH RCP Lond. 1984; DRCOG 1984.

SINGH, Bulu Deepdale Road Surgery, 98 Deepdale Road, Preston PR1 5AR Tel: 01772 821069; Fairwinds, High Rigg Drive, Broughton, Preston PR3 5LJ Tel: 01772 862054 Fax: 01772 862054 — MB BS 1968 Lucknow; MB BS Lucknow 1968 (King Geo. Med. Coll.); DFFP. GP; Clin. Asst. in Obstetrics & Gyn.; Clin. Asst. in Genifo Urin. Med.

SINGH, Bupinder Ashingdon Medical Centre, 57 Lascelles Gardens, Ashingdon, Rochford SS4 3BW Tel: 01702 544959 Fax: 01702 530160 — MB BS 1972 Jammu & Kashmir.

SINGH, Mr Chandra Bhan Springfield Hospital, Chelmsford CM1 7QH Tel: 01245 234000; Carlton House, Beehive Lane, Chelmsford CM2 8RJ Tel: 01245 359038 Fax: 012445 280616 — MB BS 1961 Vikram; FRCS Eng. 1970; DLO Eng. 1970. (Gajra Raja Med. Coll. Gwalior) Cons. ENT Surg. Mid Essex HA. Prev: Sen. Regist. (Otorhinolaryng.) Notts HA.

SINGH, Chandra Deo Prasad 4 Overton Place, West Bromwich B71 1RL — MB BS 1961 Bihar.

SINGH, Clare Antonia 57 Cork Road, Bowerham, Lancaster LA1 4AY — MB ChB 1993 Leeds.

SINGH, Dave Gobin 1 Hayes Barton, Thorpe Bay, Southend-on-Sea SS1 3TS Tel: 01702 585455 — MD 1969 Odessa Med. Inst. USSR.

SINGH, Davendra Park Grove Surgery, 124-126 Park Grove, Barnsley S70 1QE Tel: 01226 282140 Fax: 01226 213279 (Call before faxing) — MB BS Calcutta 1966; DTM & H Liverp. 1968; Dip. Ven. Liverp. 1968. (Nat. Med. Inst. Calcutta) Socs: Fell. Roy. Soc. Trop. Med. & Hyg.; BMA. Prev: Ho. Off. (Gen. Surg.) & Resid. Ho. Off. (Med.) Safder Jung Hosp. New Delhi, India; Resid. SHO (ENT) St. Hilda's Hosp. Hartlepool; Resid. SHO (Obst.) Stirling, Falkirk & Alloa Gp. Hosps.

SINGH, Dev Raj 10 Garrett Close, Maiden Bower, Crawley RH10 7UP Tel: 01293 885516 — MB BS 1972 Panjab; MD Delhi 1975; MRCOG 1982.

SINGH, Devendra Rockview Health Centre, Rockview Place, Helmsdale KW8 6LF Tel: 01431 821225 Fax: 01431 821567 — MB BS 1970 Rajasthan; DFFP 1994; Cert. Family Plann. JCC 1983. GP Highland HB. Socs: Assoc. Mem. RCGP. Prev: Civil Asst. Surg. Govt. Rajasthan; Med. Off. Govt. Hosp. Weir, Rajasthan.

SINGH, Dhinesh PRN Medical Agency, c/o Martyn Fenwick, 42 Theobalds Road, London WC1X 8NW — MB BCh 1993 Witwatersrand.

SINGH, Dhruva Narayan Prasad Peartree Medical Centre, 159 Pear Tree Road, Derby DE23 8NQ Tel: 01332 360692 Fax: 01332 368181 — MB BS 1973 Bihar.

SINGH, Dinesh Pratap 417 Chorley Avenue, Swinton, Manchester M27 9UQ Tel: 0161 794 4239 — MB BS 1970 Kanpur; BSc Lucknow 1965. (G.S.V.M. Med. Coll.) GP Swinton Manch.

SINGH, Mr Dishan Royal National Orthopaedic Hospital, Stanmore HA7 4LP Tel: 020 8909 9314 Fax: 020 8909 9314 — MB ChB 1983 Manch.; FRCS (Orth.) 1995; FRCS Eng. 1988. (Manch.) Cons. Roy. Nat. Orthop. Hosp. Stanmore & Barnet Gen. Hosp.; Hon. Sen. Lect. Univ. of Lond. Socs: Fell. BOA; Brit. Orthop. Foot Surg. Soc.; Amer. Orthop. Foot & Ankle Soc. Prev: Sen. Regist. (Orthop.) Roy. Nat. Orthop. Hosp. Lond.; Regist. (Orthop.) Roy. Lond. Hosp.

SINGH, Gajendra The Windmills, Broomfield, Chelmsford CM1 7HL — MB BS 1988 Lucknow.

SINGH, Gautam Kumar Department of Paediatric Cardiology, Southampton General Hospital, Tremona Road, Southampton SO16 6YD Tel: 02380 777222 — MB BS 1978 Ranchi; MD (Paediat.) 1982; MRCP (UK) 1988; DCH RCP Lond. 1987. SHO (Paediat. Cardiol.) Soton. & S. W. Hants. HA. Socs: Med. Protect. Soc. Prev: SHO (Paediat. Cardiol.) Hosp. Sick Childr. Gt. Ormond St.; Regist. (Paediat) St. Peter's Hosp. Chertsey; SHO (Paediat. Nephrol.) E. Birm. Hosp.

SINGH, Gian Beechdale Centre, Edison Road, Walsall WS2 7HS Tel: 01922 775200 Fax: 01922 775203; 15 Sydney Close, West Bromwich B70 0SR — LMSSA 1992 Lond.; MB BS Panjab 1987.

SINGH, Gurbachan (Surgery), 26 Rough Road, Kingstanding, Birmingham B44 0UY Tel: 0121 354 8213 — MB ChB 1953 Birm.; MRCS Eng. LRCP Lond. 1953. (Birm.) Prev: Ho. Surg. Solihull Hosp.; Ho. Off. Obst. Burton-on-Trent Gen. Hosp.

SINGH, Gurcharan Collington Surgery, 23 Terminus Road, Bexhill-on-Sea TN39 3LR Tel: 01424 217465/216675 Fax: 01424 216675; 121 Cooden Drive, Bexhill-on-Sea TN39 3AJ — MB BS 1986 Lond.; BSc (Hons.) Path. Lond. 1985. Clin. Asst. (Rheum.) E. Sussex. Prev: Trainee GP Lond.

SINGH, Gurdial (retired) 14 Birchdale Close, Greasby, Wirral CH49 2SE Tel: 0151 605 0508 — MB 1951 Calcutta; DTM & H Liverp. 1955. Prev: Med. Off. Tanganyika Civil Serv.

SINGH, Gurminder Pal Oakwood Surgery, Glenhow Rise, Leeds LS8 4AA Tel: 0113 295 1515 Fax: 0113 295 1500; 56 Alwoodley Lane, Leeds LS17 7PT Tel: 0113 230 1079 Fax: 0113 295 1510 — MB BS 1975 Delhi; LRCP LRCS Ed. LRCPS Glas. 1981; MRCGP 1985; DRCOG 1982. (Maulana Azad Med. Coll. New Delhi) GP Leeds; Mem. Disabil. Appeal Tribunal. Socs: BMA. Prev: Med. Off. (Homeless & Rootless in Leeds) Leeds W.. HA.; SHO (Psychiat.) Pontefract AHA; SHO (O & G) Dewsbury AHA.

SINGH, Gurmit 15 Regency House, Newbold Terrace, Leamington Spa CV32 4HD Tel: 01926 33774 — MB ChB 1987 Manch.

SINGH, Mr Gurpreet Consultant Urologist, Southport & Ormskirk Hospital, Southport PR8 6PN Tel: 01704 704025 Fax: 01704 704518 Email: gsurol@hotmail.com; 18 Westbourne Road, Southport PR8 2JA — MB BS 1981 Delhi; FRCS 1997 (Urology); FRCS Ed. 1985; FRCS Glas. 1985. Cons. Urol., S.port. Socs: Brit. Assn. of Urol. Surg.s; Int. Continence Soc.; S.port Med. Soc. Prev: Sen. Regist. (Urol.), Sheff.; Lect. (Urol.), Sheff.; Regist. (Urol.), Canterbury.

SINGH, Gyan Prakash 1 Holly Court, Hyde SK14 3DF — MB BS 1973 Patna.

SINGH, H K Halifax Crescent Surgery, 4 Halifax Crescent, Thornton, Liverpool L23 1TH Tel: 0151 924 3532 Fax: 0151 924 3171.

SINGH, Hardeep 11 Glenesk Road, London SE9 1AG — MB BS 1993 Lond.

SINGH

SINGH, Hardev Fishergate Hill Surgery, 50 Fishergate Hill, Preston PR1 8DN Tel: 01772 254484 Fax: 01772 881835; 50 Fishergate Hill, Preston PR1 8DN Tel: 01772 54484 — MB ChB 1977 Manch.; MRCGP 1981. Socs: Brit. Med. Acupunct. Soc.

SINGH, Hardev Calfaria Surgery, Regent Street, Treorchy, Cardiff CF42 6PR Tel: 01443 773595 Fax: 01443 775067 — MB BS 1971 Panjab; MB BS Panjab (India) 1971. (Govt. Med. Coll. Amritsar) SHO (Orthop. & Trauma) Singleton Hosp. Swansea. Prev: SHO (Orthop. & Trauma) Neath Gen. Hosp.

SINGH, Hardial Department of Cardiology, Walsgrave Hospital, UHCW NHS Trust, Clifford Bridge Road CV2 2DX Tel: 02476 538932; Priors Close, 24a Birchges Lane, Kenilworth CV8 2AD — MB ChB 1973 Ed.; MD Ed. 1986; FRCP Lond. 1993; MRCP (UK) 1976; T(M) 1991. Cons. Cardiol. Walsgrave Hosp. Coventry. Socs: Brit. Cardiac Soc.; Brit. Cardiac Interven. Soc.; BMA. Prev: Lect. (Cardiol.) Univ. Wales Coll. Med.; Regist. (Cardiol.) Hammersmith Hosp. & Gt. Ormond St. Lond.

SINGH, Hari B Clare Road Medical Centre, 150 Clare Road, Grangetown, Cardiff CF11 6RW Tel: 029 2023 1109 Fax: 029 2034 2122.

SINGH, Harikrishna 28 Hospital Close, Evington, Leicester LE5 4WP — MB BS 1990 W. Indies.

SINGH, Harinandan Prasad 12 Leander Close, Littleover, Derby DE23 7TN — MB BS 1973 Patna.

SINGH, Harjit 53 Mighell Avenue, Redbridge, Ilford IG4 5JP — MB BS 1964 Lucknow; BSc Allahabad 1959. (King Geo. Med. Coll.) Socs: BMA. Prev: Ho. Phys. Walton Hosp. Liverp.; SHO Barrowmore Hosp. Gt. Barrow; Med. Regist. Colindale Hosp. Lond.

SINGH, Harjit Eccles Health Centre, Corporation Road, Eccles, Manchester M30 0EL Tel: 0161 788 7337 Fax: 0161 707 0504 — MB BS 1971 Panjab. GP Princip.

SINGH, Harjit Manor Court Surgery, 5 Manor Court Avenue, Nuneaton CV11 5HX Tel: 024 7638 1999 Fax: 024 7632 0515 — MB BS 1964 Lucknow.

SINGH, Hem Chandra Springwell House Surgery, Durham Road, North Moor, Sunderland SR3 1RN Tel: 0191 528 3251 Fax: 0191 528 3100 — MB BS 1969 Bihar. (Bihar)

SINGH, Himani 53 Hope Park, Bromley BR1 3RG Tel: 020 8464 8633 Email: suveer.singh@ic.ac.uk — LMSSA Lond. 1995. (UMDS Lond.)

SINGH, Hiralal Bendasari 23A Four Oaks Road, Sutton Coldfield B74 2XT Tel: 0121 308 1855 — LRCP LRCS 1951 Ed.; LRCP LRCS Ed. LRFPS Glas. 1951. Prev: GP W. Midl.

SINGH, Inder Pal 98 Seamons Road, Altrincham WA14 4LB — MB BS 1980 Ranchi.

SINGH, Inder Pal Health Centre, Great James Street, Londonderry BT48 7DH Tel: 028 7137 8500 — MB BS 1971 Allahabad. (Allahabad) GP Lond.derry.

SINGH, Inderjit 3 The Bantocks, West Bromwich B70 0PA — MB BS 1994 Lond.

SINGH, Mr Inderjit 7 Wykeham Hill, Wembley Park, Wembley HA9 9RY Tel: 020 8904 6119 — MB BS 1973 Lucknow; FRCS (Ophth.) Eng. 1980; MRCS Eng. LRCP Lond. 1978; DO Eng. 1978. (King Geo. Med. Coll. Lucknow) Res. Surg. Off. Moorfields Eye Hosp. Lond. Prev: Regist. Dept. Ophth. W.m. Hosp. Lond.

SINGH, Mr Inderjit Drumchapel Health Centre, 80 Kinfains Drove, Drumchapel, Glasgow G15 6EG Tel: 0141 211 6090 — MBBS 1971 Medical College, Amritsar; 1979 FRCS Glas. Gen. Pract., Drumchapel Health Centre, Glas.; Hosp. Practitioner Grade, ENT, Hairmyers Hosp., E. Kilbridge, G76. Socs: Gen. Med. Counc.; Overseas Doctor's Assoc.; SIKH Doctor's Assoc. OPU.K.

SINGH, Iqbal Hillingdon Hospital, Field Heath Road, Uxbridge UB8 3NN; 7 Grovewood Close, Chorleywood, Rickmansworth WD3 5PU Tel: 01923 282663 — MB BS 1974 Punjab; FRCPsych 1995, M 1983. Cons. Psychiat. Hillingdon Hosp. Middlx. & Horizon NHS Trust Herts.; Vis. Cons. Psychiat. HM Prison Psychiat. Servs. Prev: Cons. Psychiat. Leavesden Hosp. Abbots Langley & Hillingdon Hosp. Middlx.; Sen. Regist. Rotat. (Psychiat.) Leavesden & Char. Cross Hosp. Lond.; Regist. Rotat. P.ss Alexandra Hosp. Harlow & St. Bart. Hosp. Lond.

SINGH, Irengbam Mohendra Kensington Street Health Centre, Whitefield Place, Girlington, Bradford BD8 9LB Tel: 01274 499209 — MB BS 1962 Agra; BSc Agra 1957, MB BS 1962; MRCGP 1977. (S.N. Med. Coll. Agra)

SINGH, Mr Jagmohan 23 Sharman Close, Stoke-on-Trent ST4 7LS — MB BS 1975 Poona; FRCS Glas. 1987.

SINGH, Jasbir 11 Stanley Close, Ravenshead, Nottingham NG15 9GE — MB BS Panjab 1967; MRCPsych 1980.

SINGH, Jasminder Kaur 52 Eamont Court, Shannon Place, London NW8 7DN — MB BS 1997 Lond.

SINGH, Jaswant HM Prison, Greenwell Road, Lincoln LN2 4BD; 1 Elm Drive, Sudbrooke, Lincoln LN2 2SG Tel: 01522 595155 — MB BS 1973 Bangalor; MB BS Bangalore 1973; MRCPsych. 1986. Prison Med. Off. Lincoln.

SINGH, Mr Jaswinder 68 Comiston Drive, Edinburgh EH10 5QS — MB ChB 1986 Glas.; MSc St. And. 1983; FRCS Ed. 1992; BSc Hons. (St. And.) 1982. (Glasgow) Cons. (Ophth.) P.ss Alexandra Eye Pavilion Edin.; Hon. Sen. Lect., Univ. of Edin.; Examr. for Roy. Coll. of Surg.s of Edin.

SINGH, Jillian Kaur St Pauls Surgery, 36-38 East Street, Preston PR1 1UU Tel: 01772 252409 Fax: 01772 885509 — MB BS 1969 Delhi; MB BS 1969 Delhi.

SINGH, Joginder Paul 12 Bellevue Terrace, Southampton SO14 0LB — MB ChB 1974 Glas.

SINGH, John Lawrence Shaftesbury Medical Centre, 480 Harehills Lane, Leeds LS9 6DE Tel: 0113 248 0392 Fax: 0113 235 1585 — MB BS 1963 Vikram. (Vikram) GP Leeds.

SINGH, John Pratap (retired) Pondfield House, Bellingdon, Chesham HP5 2XL — MRCS Eng. LRCP Lond. 1962; BSc Nagpur 1947, MB BS 1952; LMSSA Lond. 1960; FFA RCS Eng. 1965; DA Eng. 1960. Indep. Cons. Anaesth. Herts. Prev: Cons. Anaesth. Centr. Middlx. Hosp. Lond.

SINGH, Joy Carmelina Indira 38 Newport Road, London E10 6PJ — MB BS 1994 Lond.

SINGH, Mr Juswant c/o Orthopaedic Department, Princess Royal Hospital, Telford TF1 6TF — MB BS 1979 Lond.; FRCS Ed. 1986. Staff Orthop. Surg. P.ss Roy. Hosp. Telford. Prev: Regist. (Orthop.) N. Middlx. Hosp. Lond.; SHO Rotat. (Surg.) Worcester Roy. Infirm.; SHO P.ss Eliz. Orthop. Hosp. Exeter.

SINGH, Jyoti Prakash Barkerend Health Centre, Bradford BD3 8QH Tel: 01274 661341 Fax: 01274 775880 — MB BS 1973 Patna. (Patna) GP Bradford, W. Yorks.

SINGH, K The Surgery, 14a Northeads Lane, Bigginhill, Westerham TN16 3XS Tel: 01959 574488.

SINGH, Kamala Pati 32 Waldorf Road, Cleethorpes DN35 0QD Tel: 01472 812002 — MB BS 1967 Bihar; DCH RCPI 1981.

SINGH, Kamaljit 6 Downing Drive, Leicester LE5 6PB Tel: 0116 241 8252 Email: kamaljit.singh@virgin.net — MB ChB 1990 Leeds; BSc (Hons.) Physiol. Leeds 1987; MRCGP 1995. GP Leicester Med. CoOperat. Prev: Regist. Leics. VTS; SHO (Haemat.) Leicester Roy. Infirm.; Ho. Off. (Med. & Surg.) Leeds Gen. Infirm.

SINGH, Kanimbakam Rameshwari Lynwood, 33 Danygraig Drive, Talbot Green, Pontyclun CF72 8AQ — MB BS 1965 Osmania; DPM Eng. 1973. (Osmania Med. Coll. Hyderabad) Clin. Asst. Ely Hosp. Cardiff.

SINGH, Karan Vir Windward Group Practice, 68 Worsley Road, Worsley, Manchester M28 2SN Tel: 0161 794 1603 Fax: 0161 794 2371 — MB ChB 1975 Manch.

SINGH, Karen Jit 93 Whitehall Road, Gateshead NE8 4ER — MB BS 1994 Lond.; BSc Lond. 1991. SHO (A & E) N. Tyneside. Prev: Ho. Off. (Med.) Croydon.

SINGH, Karnail 21 Ferry Road, Eastham, Wirral CH62 0AJ — MB ChB 1974 Liverp.

SINGH, Mr Kaushlendra Narayan Department of Orthopaedics, Hillingdon Hospital, Pield Heath Road, Uxbridge UB8 3NN Tel: 01895 238282 Fax: 01895 811687; 80 Harlington Road, Uxbridge UB8 3EY Tel: 01895 462720 Fax: 01895 462720 Email: kaushal@postmaster.co.uk — MB BS 1981 Bhagalar; MB BS Bhagalar, India 1981; MS (Orthop.) Patna 1985; Dip. Orthop. Patna 1983. (Bhagalpur & Patna) Staff Orthop. Surg. Hillingdon Hosp. Uxbridge. Socs: BMA. Prev: Regist. Rotat. Roy. Orthop. Hosp. Birm.

SINGH, Mr Kewal 10 Abingdon Close, Uxbridge UB10 0BU — MB BS 1978 Delhi; FRCS Eng. 1990.

SINGH, Kirpal 184 Lady Margaret Road, Southall UB1 2RW — MB BS 1967 Jammu & Kashmir.

SINGH, Krishna Ballabh Prasad Coatbridge Health Centre, 1 Centre Park Court, Coatbridge ML5 3AP Tel: 01236 421434 — MB BS 1974 Patna.

SINGH, Mr Krishna Kumar 43 Barnton Park Avenue, Edinburgh EH4 6HD — MB BS 1986 Poona; FRCS Glas. 1989.

SINGH, Krishna Mohan 201 Rochford Gardens, Slough SL2 5XD — MB BS 1973 Patna.

SINGH, Kuljinder Tel: 01355 236331 Fax: 01355 234977 — MB ChB 1989 Glas.; MRCGP 1994. GP.

SINGH, Kulvinder The Medical Centre, 10A Northumberland Court, Shepway, Maidstone ME15 7LN Tel: 01622 753920 Fax: 01622 692747; Saran-Nivas, Queens Avenue, Maidstone ME16 0EN Tel: 01622 670495 Fax: 01622 675475 — MB BS 1978 Delhi; LRCP LRCS Ed. LRCPS Glas. 1983.

SINGH, Mr Kulwant (retired) 21 Lushington Road, Eastbourne BN21 4LG Tel: 01323 410441 Fax: 01323 410978 — MB BS 1959 Calcutta; BSc Punjab 1953; FRCS Ed. 1969; DLO RCS Eng. 1964. Cons. (Private Pract.); Cons. Otol Link-Brit. Centre for Deafened People E.bourne. Prev: Cons. ENT Surg. E.bourne Hosps. NHS Trust.

SINGH, Kumar Himanshu Prasad Elizabeth Ash Road, Hartley, Longfield DA3 8HA — MB BS 1966 Bihar.

SINGH, Kumar Sitaram Prasad Narain The Medical Centre, Keldholme Lane, Alvaston, Derby DE24 0RY Tel: 01332 571677 — MB BS 1973 Patna. (P. of Wales Med. Coll.) GP Derby; Capt. RAMC (V). Prev: SHO (Accid., Emerg. & Orthop.) Ashington Hosp.; Trainee GP Lincoln VTS; GP Co. Durh.

SINGH, Kumari Kavita 38 Longdon Wood, Keston BR2 6EW Tel: 01689 853303 — LMSSA 1975 Lond.; MD (Paediat.) Jabalpur 1970, MB BS 1967; MRCP (U.K.) 1974; DCH Jabalpur 1969. SCMO Oxleas NHS Trust. Socs: Brit. Paediat. Assn. Prev: Regist. (Paediat.) Whipps Cross Hosp. Lond.; SHO Roy. Belf. Hosp. Sick Childr.; Clin. Med. Off. Ealing HA.

SINGH, Lehmbar Millfield Medical Centre, 63-83 Hylton Road, Sunderland SR4 7AF Tel: 0191 567 9179 Fax: 0191 514 7452; October House, 18 Silksworth Hall Drive, Sunderland SR3 2PG — MB ChB 1986 Manch.; MRCGP 1990; DRCOG 1990; DCH RCP Lond. 1989.

SINGH, Linda Nalini Department of Histopathology, St. Helier Hospital, Wrythe Lane, Carshalton SM5 1AA Tel: 020 8644 4343 — MB BS 1975 Madras; MRCPath 1984.

SINGH, Madan Mohan Department of Obstetrics & Gynaecology, Leazes Wing, Royal Victoria Infirmary, Queen Victoria Road, Newcastle upon Tyne NE1 4LP — MB ChB 1965 Aberd.

SINGH, Mahendra Pratap 9 Coniston Gardens, Ashby-de-la-Zouch LE65 1FB — MB BS 1970 Kanpur.

SINGH, Mala Basudeo 2 Moatlands House, Cramer St., London WC1H 8DF — MB ChB 1982 Baghdad.

SINGH, Malvinder Pal Broadmoor Hospital, Crowthorne RG45 7EG Tel: 01344 773111 — MD 1970 Banaras Hindu; MD (Preven. & Social Med.) Banaras Hindu 1970, MB BS 1966; DPM Eng. 1978. (Inst. Med. Scs. Varanasi)

SINGH, Maneesha 2 The Sidings, Worsley, Manchester M28 2QD — MB BS 1995 Lond.

SINGH, Mr Manmeet (retired) Holly House Hospital, High Road, Buckhurst Hill IG9 5HX Tel: 020 8559 2339 Fax: 020 8559 2339 — MB BS 1960 Lond.; FRCS Eng. 1966. Cons. Urol. Surg. Whipps Cross Hosp.; Hon. Sen. Lect. Inst. Urol. Univ. Lond. Prev: Sen. Lect. (Urol.) Lond. Hosp. Med. Coll.

SINGH, Mehar M. O. Wallis and Partners, 5 Stanmore Road, Stevenage SG1 3QA; 204 Ynysdy, Pontyclun, Pontyclun CF72 9UD Tel: 01443 229571 Email: mehar@singh60.freeserve.co.uk — MB BS 1985 Guru Nanak Dev India; DOrtho 1997. G.P. M.O. Wallis & Partners Stevenage. Prev: Trust Specialist (Trauma & Orthop.) P. Chas. Hosp. Merthyr Tydfil.

SINGH, Mira 17 Bank Street, Horbury, Wakefield WF4 6LN — MB BS 1975 Mithila, India.

SINGH, Mohan Bhadoor Arrow Lodge Medical Centre, Kinwarton Road, Alcester B49 6PX Tel: 01789 763293; Arrow Lodge, Alcester B49 5QY Tel: 01789 763293 — MB BS 1967 Patna. Hosp. Pract. Alcester Hosp. Prev: Sen. Med. Off. McCord Zulu Miss. Hosp. Durban S. Africa; Regist. Surg. R.K. Khan Hosp. Durban; Med. Asst. Accid. Dept. Watford Gen. Hosp. (Peace Memor. Wing.).

SINGH, Monica Fairwinds, Highrigg Drive, Durton Lane, Broughton, Preston PR3 5LJ — MB BS 1996 Lond.

SINGH, Mreenal Nandan 15 Riplingham Road, Kirkella, Hull HU10 7TS — MB BCh 1993 Wales.

SINGH, Mukhtar 5 Park Avenue, Goldthorn Park, Wolverhampton WV4 5AL — MB ChB 1986 Glasg.

SINGH, Nandita Woodcroft, Barnet Wood Road, Bromley BR2 8HJ — MB BS 1994 Lond.

SINGH, Narayani Prasad Dinas Lane Medical Centre, 149 Dinas Lane, Huyton, Liverpool L36 2NW Tel: 0151 489 2298 — MB BS 1968 Allahabad; MB BS Allahabad. 1968.

SINGH, Narendra 38 Colne Road, Burnley BB10 1LG Tel: 01282 448244 Fax: 01282 448282; Edge End Hall, Edge End Lane, Nelson BB9 0PR Tel: 01282 611008 Fax: 01282 690808 — MB BS 1963 Rajasthan. (Sawai Man Singh Med. Coll. Jaipur) Prev: SHO Dept. Dermat. Roy. Vict. Infirm. Newc.; Ho. Off. Glos. Roy. Hosp. Gloucester; Ho. Off. (Med.) Roy. Vict. Hosp. Boscombe.

SINGH, Narendra Pal 44 Grimsby Road, Cleethorpes DN35 7AB Tel: 01472 342763 Fax: 01472 344490 — BSc 1965 Agra Univ. India; MBBS 1970 Kanpur Medical Coll. India. (Agra Univ. India & Kanpur Medical College, India) GP, NHS, Grimsby; Clin. Asst., Family Plann. & Sexual Health. Prev: Regist. Orthapaedic Surg., Scunthorpe Gen. Hosp. Scunthorpe.

SINGH, Nitish Kumar 76 Emm Lane, Heaton, Bradford BD9 4JH — MB BS 1998 Lond.; MB BS Lond 1998.

SINGH, Nivedita 51 Thurlestone Road, London SE27 0PE — MB BS 1992 Lond.

SINGH, Padm Deo Narayan c/o Barclays Bank, Haverfordwest SA61 2DA Tel: 01793 30045 — MD 1957 Bihar; MB BS 1954; MRCP (U.K.) 1971. (Darbhanga Med. Coll.) Cons. Phys. P.ss Margt. & St. Margt. Hosps. Swindon. Prev: Cons. Phys. St. Jas. Hosp. Leeds; Sen. Regist. (Med.) Singleton Hosp. Swansea; Cons. Geriat. Phys. Hartlepool Gen. Hosp.

SINGH, Padma Nand North Street Surgery, 87 North Street, Milton Regis, Sittingbourne ME10 2HJ Tel: 01795 475882; 18 Woodcourt Close, Sittingbourne ME10 1QT — MB BS 1961 Bihar; DTM & H Ed. 1970. (Darbhanga Med. Coll.)

SINGH, Param Jit Daybrook Health Centre, Salop Street, Daybrook, Nottingham NG5 6HP.

SINGH, Parminder Jit 43 Barnes Heath Road, Rowlatts Hill, Leicester LE5 4LB — MB BS 1996 Lond.

SINGH, Parvinder 27 Alexander Road, Hounslow TW3 4HW Email: drpsnarang@yahoo.com — MB BS Delhi 1980, DCH 1982; MRCP (UK) 1986; DCH Eng. 1984. (Maulana Azad Medical College Delhi) Regist. (Community Paediat.) Centr. Middlx. Hosp. Lond. Prev: SHO (Paediat. Gastroenterol.,Metos. Dis.) Gt. Ormond St. Lond.; Regist. (Paediat.) Maidstone Gen. Hosp.

SINGH, Pawanjit 12 Skelton Court, Newcastle upon Tyne NE3 2TD — MB BS 1998 Newc.; MB BS Newc 1998.

SINGH, Phulwantjit c/o Barclays Bank Ltd, Clapham Common Branch, PO Box 4038, London SW12 9YB — LRCP LRCS Ed. LRCPS Glas. 1983.

SINGH, Pradeep Kumar Fryerns Medical Centre, Craylands, Basildon SS14 3SS Tel: 01268 532344 Fax: 01268 287641 — MB BS 1974 Calcutta.

SINGH, Pradip Flat 17, York House, Queen Alexandra Hospital, Cosham, Portsmouth PO6 3LY Tel: 023 92 379451; c/o Drive O. S. Singh, 8 Cobblestones, Duke's Meadow Drive, Gillingham ME7 3NT Tel: 01634 378345 — MB BS 1980 Banaras Hindu; MD Med. Banaras Hindu 1983, MB BS 1980; MD 1993 Med. Banaras Hindu; MRCP (UK) 1986. Research Fell. (Gastroenterol.) Qu. Alexandra Hosp. Portsmouth & Roy. Naval Hosp. Haslar.

SINGH, Prashant Kishore 125 Hatherton Road, Cannock WS11 1HH — BM BS 1997 Nottm.

SINGH, Prem 2 Weaver Avenue, Birmingham B26 3AA — MB BCh 1990 Wales.

SINGH, Priya Darshani Arrow Lodge, Alcester B49 5QY — MB ChB 1990 Leic.

SINGH, Raj Pal The Health Centre, High Street, Dodworth, Barnsley S75 3RF Tel: 01226 203881 — MB BS 1972 Kanpur; DCH RCPSI 1979. (G.S.V.M. Med. Coll.)

SINGH, Raj Vir 14 Harden Close, Pogmoor, Barnsley S75 2JJ Tel: 01226 242452 — MB BS 1975 Aligarh; MB BS Aligarh Muslim 1975; MRCP (UK) 1987. Staff Haemat. Roy. Hosp. Chesterfield.

SINGH

Prev: Regist. (Clin. Heamat.) Barnsley Dist. Gen. Hosp. S. Yorks.; Regist. (Med.) & SHO (Rheum/Cardiac Care Unit) Barnsley.

SINGH, Rajendra Kumar Maypole Road Surgery, Maypole Road, Tiptree, Colchester CO5 0EN Tel: 01621 816119 — MB BS 1959 Patna; MD Patna 1965; DCH Patna 1966. Socs: Med. Protec. Soc.

SINGH, Rajinder 43 Barnes Heath Road, Leicester LE5 4LB — MB BS 1995 Lond.

SINGH, Rajinder 8A Beech Road, London N11 2DA Tel: 020 8888 5157 — MB BS 1977 Poona; MRCS Eng. LRCP Lond. 1989; DMedRehab. RCP Lond. 1986. SHO (O & G) N. Middlx. Hosp. Lond. Prev: SHO (Geriat., A & E) Middlx. Hosp. Lond.

SINGH, Rakesh Kumar 2 Rosslyn Ave, Ackworth, Pontefract WF7 7QF — MB BS 1986 Patna.

SINGH, Ram Chandra Prasad Robins Hill, Bent Lane, Colne BB8 7AA — MB BS 1962 Patna; MRCP (UK) 1971.

SINGH, Rameet Whipps Cross Hospital, Leytonstone, London E11 1NR Tel: 020 8539 5522 Fax: 020 8558 8115; 19 Lansdowne Road, South Woodford, London E18 2AZ Tel: 020 8530 4370 Email: rosandrameet@compuserve.com — MB BS 1972 Lond.; DA Lond. 1980. (Lond. Hosp.) Assoc. Specialist (Anaesth.) Whipps Cross Hosp. Lond. Socs: Fell. Roy. Soc. Med.; Assn. Anaesth.; BMA. Prev: GP Lond.

SINGH, Miss Rashmi Department of Surgery, St. Georges Hospital, Blackshaw Road, Tooting, London SW17 0QT Tel: 020 8672 1255; Flat 8, Clockhouse Place, Lytton Grove, Putney, London SW15 2EL Tel: 020 8789 6533 Email: rashmi@kv.ac.uk — MB BS 1994 Lond.; BSc (Hons.) Genetics Lond. 1991; FRCS (Eng) 1998. (UMDS Guy's & St. Thos.) Clin. Res. Fell. (Urol.) Roy. Marsden Hosp. Lond. Socs: Wom. Surgic. Train.; Med. Protec. Soc. Prev: SHO (Urol.) Roy. Marsden; SHO Rotat. (Surg.) St. Geo. Hosp. Lond.; SHO (A & E) St. Thos. Hosp. Lond.

SINGH, Ravi Kumar 1 Deepdale Drive, Burnley BB10 2SD — MB BCh 1994 Wales; MRCP (UK) 1998. SHO (Clin. Cardiol.) Glenfield Hosp. Leicester. Prev: SHO (Gen. Med.) Doncaster Roy. Infirm.

SINGH, Ravinder 76 Townley Road, Bexleyheath DA6 7HN — MB BS 1996 Lond. (Lond.) SHO (Trauma & Orthop.) Kent & Canterbury Hosp. Prev: SHO (Accid.) Emerg.) Kent & Canterbury Hosp.; Ho. Off. (Surg.) Wartling Hosp.; Ho. Off. (Med.) Qu. Mary's Hosp. Sidcup.

SINGH, Rema 28 Charlbert Court, Charlbert St., London NW8 7BX — MB BS 1993 Lond.; MA Camb. 1994. SHO (Respirat. Med.) Roy. Brompton Hosp. Lond.

SINGH, Roger Rambaran 42 Epping Close, Mawyneys, Romford RM7 8BH; 205 Henley Road, Ilford IG1 2TP Tel: 020 7924 5271 — MB BS Lond. 1996. (Royal London Hospital, Whitechapel) SHO in Psychiat. Prev: Ho. Off. Surg. Roy. Lond. Hosp.; Ho. Off. Surg. King Geo. Hosp.; SHO Psychiat. Goodmayes Hosp.

SINGH, Roma Kumari 18 Plantation Road, Blackburn BB2 4OA — MB BS 1971 Patna.

SINGH, Rudolph Bickram (retired) 10 Princes Avenue, Petts Wood, Orpington BR5 1QS — MB ChB (Commend.) Glas. 1969; MSc Ed. 1982; BSc (Hons.) Glas. 1965. Prev: Sen. Med. Off. DoH.

SINGH, S The Surgery, 14a Northeads Lane, Bigginhill, Westerham TN16 3XS Tel: 01959 574488.

SINGH, S Townsend Lane Surgery, 263 Townsend Lane, Clubmoor, Liverpool L13 9DG Tel: 0151 226 1358.

SINGH, S 104 Tarbock Road, Huyton, Liverpool L36 5TH.

SINGH, S B P 4 Halifax Crescent, Thornton, Liverpool L23 1TH.

SINGH, Mr Sadmeet 97 Hainault Road, Chigwell IG7 5DL Tel: 020 8500 6137 Email: sadmeet@yahoo.com — BM BS 1993 Nottm.; BMedSci Nottm. 1991; FRCS (Eng) 1998.

SINGH, Mr Sakaldip 1 The Chenies, Orpington BR6 0ED — MB BS 1959 Patna; MS Patna 1966; FRCS Ed. 1977. Cons. A & E Med. Greenwich Dist. Hosp. Lond. Socs: BMA; W Kent M-C Soc.; Brit. Assn. Accid. & Emerg. Med. Prev: Cons. A & E Brook Gen. Hosp. Lond.

SINGH, Salil 42 Druids Park, Liverpool L18 3LJ — MB ChB 1997 Ed.

SINGH, Sandip 10 Girdlers Close, Coventry CV3 6LS Email: singhs@globalnet.co.uk — MB ChB 1987 Liverp.; Dip. Amer. Bd Anesthesiol 1997. Prev: Fell. (Critical Care Med.) Univ. of Texas at Houston USA; Resid. (Anesthesiology) Univ. of Texas at Houston USA; Resid. (Internal Med.) Univ. of Connecticut USA.

SINGH, Mr Sanjay Kumar James Paget Hospital, Lowestoft Rd,, Gorleston, Great Yarmouth NR31 6LA Tel: 01493 452452 Fax: 01493 452666; Peddars Croft, Main Road, Rollesby, Great Yarmouth NR29 5EQ Tel: 01493 748739 Fax: 01493 748068 — MB BS 1985 Delhi; MS (Gen. Surg.) Delhi 1990; FRCSI 1994. Assoc. Specialist (Gen. Surg.) Jas. Paget Hosp. Gt. Yarmouth. Prev: Regist. (Gen. Surg.) Jas. Paget Hosp. Gt. Yarmouth.

SINGH, Sanjay Kumar Geeta, Primrose Lane, Bredgar, Sittingbourne ME9 8EH — MB BS 1990 L.N. Mithila, India; MRCP (UK) 1994.

SINGH, Sanjeev Kumar 11 Hillsea Street, London E5 0SG — MB BS 1996 Lond.

SINGH, Mr Sant Parkash 16 Kirkby Lane, Kirkby Fleetham, Northallerton DL7 0TT — MB BS 1957 Agra; FRCS Ed. 1964.

SINGH, Santokh 13 Mellor Street, Rochdale OL12 6XD — MB ChB 1985 Manch.

SINGH, Sarban 155 The Ryde, Hatfield AL9 5DP — LRCP LRCS 1984 Ed.; LRCP LRCS Ed. LRCPS Glas. 1984.

SINGH, Mrs Sarla St. Peters Hospital, Chertsey KT16 0PZ; Dorin Lodge, 6 Dorin Court, Woking GU22 8PS Tel: 01932 347950 Fax: 01932 347950 Email: satishsingh@compuserv.com — MB BS 1971 Jiwaji; MRCOG 1981; FRCOG 1997; MS (Obs & Gynae) Jiwaji 1973. Staff O & G St. Peter's Hosp. Guildford Rd. Chertsey. Prev: Specialist (O & G) Dammam Matern. Hosp. Dammam, Saudi Arabia.

SINGH, Satish Shankar Medicine Control Agency, Market Towers, 1 Nine Elms Lane, London SW8 5NQ Tel: 020 7273 0420; Dorin Lodge, 6 Dorin Court, Pyrford, Woking GU22 8PS — MB BS 1969 Banaras Hindu; MD (Gen. Med.) Banaras Hindu 1974, MB BS 1971; FRCP Ed. 1992; MRCP (UK) 1978. (Inst. Med. Scs. Varanasi) Sen. Med. Off. Med. Control Agency Lond. Prev: Cons. Cardiol. Dammam Centr. Hosp. Saudi Arabia; Regist. (Cardiol.) Regional Adult Cardiac Centre BRd.green Gen. Hosp. Liverp.; Regist. (Gen. Med.) Middlesbrough Gen. Hosp.

SINGH, Satpal Harvey House Surgery, 13-15 Russell Avenue, St Albans AL3 5ES Tel: 01727 831888 Fax: 01727 845520 — MB BS 1968 Delhi.

SINGH, Satwant Ahluwalia 4 Gledhow Wood, The Chase, Kingswood, Tadworth KT20 6JQ Tel: 01737 833783 — LRCP LRCS 1952 Ed.; MB BS Panjab 1949; FRCP Ed. 1982, M 1952; LRCP LRCS Ed. LRCPS Glas. 1952.

SINGH, Mr Sewa Surgical Directorate, Doncaster Royal Infirmary, Armthorpe Road, Doncaster DN2 5LT Tel: 01302 553225 Fax: 01302 553266; 56A Sunderland Street, Tickhill, Doncaster DN11 9QJ — MB ChB 1983 Sheff.; MD Sheff. 1992; FRCS Ed. 1988. Cons. Surg. Doncaster Roy. Infirm.; Roy. Coll. of Surg.s Tutor.

SINGH, Shambhu Nath Queens Drive Surgery, 73 Queens Drive, Mossley Hill, Liverpool L18 2DU Tel: 0151 733 2812 — MB BS 1973 Patna.

SINGH, Shareen Royal Hospitals Trusts, Royal Victoria Hospital, Department Of Anaesthetics, Grosvenor Rd, Belfast BT12 6BA — MB ChB 1992 Univ. of Natal Med. Sch.; 1995 Diploma in Anaesth. (DA, SA) Coll. of Med. of SA, Fac. of Anaesthetists; 1998 Primary FFARCSI, Fac. of Anaesthetists, Roy. Coll. of Surgeons of Irel. (Univ. of Natal Med. Sch., Durban, S. Africa) Staff Grade, Anaesthetics, Roy. Vict. Hosp., Belf. Socs: N.. Irel. Soc. of Anaesth.s; Assn. of Anaesth.s of GB & Irel.; Roy. Coll. of Anaesth.s. Prev: Sen. Ho. Off. Anaesthetics, Belf. City Hosp.; Sen. Ho. Off. Anaesthetics, Ulster Hosp., Belf.; Sen. Ho. Off. Anaesthetics, Craigavon Hosp., Craigavon, N.. Irel.

SINGH, Shatrughna Prasad Singh, Craven Park Health Centre, Shakespeare Crescent, London NW10 8XW Tel: 020 8965 0151 Fax: 020 8965 4921 — MB BS 1960 Patna.

SINGH, Mr Shiva Dayal 206 Emblem House, London Bridge Hospital, 27 Tooley St., London SE1 2PR Tel: 020 7935 3763 Fax: 020 7403 2523 Email: shivasingh@aol.com — MB BS Kanpur 1970; FRCS Eng. 1975; FRCS Ed. 1975. Cons. Surg. Lond. Bridge Hosp. & Highgate Private Hosp. Lond.; Vis. Cons. Surg. N. Downs Hosp. Caterham; Cons. Surg. Devonsh. Hosp. Lond. & Suttons Manor Clinic Stapleford Tawney; Vis. Cons. Surg. Hosp. of St. John & St. Eliz. Nuffield Hse. Guy's Hosp. & Med. Sch. Lond. Socs: Fell. Assn. Surgs.; Fell. Med. Soc. Lond.; BMA. Prev: Chief Surg. Nat. Iranian Oil Company Hosp. Aghajari & Oil Fields; Regist. (Cardiothoracic) Freeman Hosp. Newc. u. Tyne; Regist. (Surg.) Stepping Hill Hosp. Stockport.

SINGH

SINGH, Shree Krishna Department of Medicine (General Medicine), Burnley General Hospital, Casterton Avenue, Burnley BB10 2PQ Tel: 01282 425071 Fax: 01282 474607 — MB BS 1971 Patna; Dip. Cardiol. Lond 1985; DTM & H Liverp. 1983. Assoc. Specialist (Med.) Burnley Gen. Hosp. Burnley. Prev: Assoc. Specialist (Med. Elderly) Burnley Gen. Hosp.; Regist. (Gen. & Geriat Med.) Burnley Gen. Hosp.

SINGH, Shyam Pratap 101 Westfield Road, Edgbaston, Birmingham B15 3JE Tel: 0121 454 5943 — MB BS Lucknow 1954; FRCP Ed. 1971, M 1959. (King Geo. Med. Coll. Lucknow) p/t Cons. Cardiol. City Hosp. Univ. Dept. of Med. Birm.; Sen. Fell. Univ. Birm.; Examr. MRCP (UK). Socs: Brit. Cardiac. Soc. & Assn. Europ. Paediat. Cardiols.; Working Gp. Grown Up Congen. Heart Dis.; Eur. Soc. Cardiol. Prev: Director Cardiac Thoracic Unit, Birm. Childr.s Hosp. 1990-1983; Sen. Clin. & Research Fell. (Med.) Mass. Gen. Hosp. Harvard Univ., USA; Vis. Sci. Mayo Clinic USA.

SINGH, Sudarshan Springhill Medical Centre, Arley, Coventry CV7 8FD; 34 Bulkington Lane, Nuneaton CV11 4SA — MB BS 1956 Punjab; MB BS Punjab (India) 1956; MRCP Ed. 1967; DTM & H Liverp. 1965. Hosp. Pract. Gulson Hosp. Coventry; Hosp. Pract. Med. OPD Geo. Eliot Hosp. Nuneaton. Socs: Overseas Doctors Assn. & BMA. Prev: Clin. Asst. High View Hosp. Exhall; Med. Regist. Geo. Eliot Hosp. Nuneaton; Jun. Ho. Phys., Sen. Ho. Phys. & Cas. Med. Off. Rajendra Hosp.

SINGH, Sujaan Flat 1, Victoria Hospital, Thursby Road, Burnley BB10 3HP — MB BS 1975 Delhi.

SINGH, Sukh Dave 4 Oaks Drive, Colchester CO3 3PR — MB BChir 1992 Camb.

SINGH, Sukhbinder University Hospital NHS Trust, Queen Elizabeth Hospital, Edgbaston, Birmingham B15 2TH Tel: 0121 472 1311; 132A Rosemary Hill Road, Sutton Coldfield B74 4HN Email: sukhbinder.singh@virgin.net — BM 1991 Soton.; DA Roy. Coll. Anaesth. 1997; MRCP Roy. Coll. Psychiat. 1995; FRCA 1999. (Soton) Specialist Regist. Anaesth & Intens. Care Med. Uni. Hosp. NHS Trust. Birm. FT. Socs: RCA; Brit. Intens. Care Soc.; Brit. Pain Soc. Prev: SHO Anaesth & Inten. Care Med.; SHO Med.

SINGH, Sukhdev Department Gastroenterology, Good Hope Hospital, Rectory Road, Sutton Coldfield B75 7RR — MB ChB 1986 Leeds; MB ChB (Hons.) Leeds 1986; BSc (1st cl. Hons. Physiol.) Leeds 1983; MD Leeds 1995; MRCP (UK) 1989. Hon. Cons. & Sen. Lect. Univ. of Birm. Socs: Brit. Soc. Gastroenterol. Prev: MRC Train. Fell. Univ. Birm.; SHO Rotat. (Med.) Leicester Gen. Hosp.

SINGH, Sukhdev Bellevue Medical Group Practice, 6 Bellevue, Edgbaston, Birmingham B5 7LX Tel: 0121 446 2000 Fax: 0121 446 2015 — MB ChB 1984 Dundee; MRCGP 1988; Cert. Family Plann. JCC 1988. Med. Off. Woodbourne Clinic Edgbaston.

SINGH, Sukhdev Sanghera 5 Rectory Close, Exhall, Coventry CV7 9PA — MB ChB 1975 Manch.

SINGH, Mr Sukhpal Frimley Park Hospital NHS Trust, Portsmouth Road, Frimley, Camberley GU16 7UJ Tel: 01276 604604; 79 Sheepfold Road, Guildford GU2 9TU Tel: 01483 566378 Fax: 01483 566378 Email: slems@msn.com — MB BS 1983 Lond.; MS Lond. 1993; FRCS (Gen.) 1995; FRCS Eng. 1988; FRCS Ed. 1987. (Guys Hosp. Med. Sch.) Cons. Surg. Prev: Sen. Regist. Qu. Alexandra Hosp. Portsmouth, Roy. Surrey Co. Hosp., St. Geos. Hosp. & St. Thos. Hosp.; Regist. (Surg.) Roy. Surrey Co. Hosp. Guildford & Qu. Mary's Hosp. Roehampton.

SINGH, Surendra Pratap The Surgery, 69 Stockingate, South Kirkby, Pontefract WF9 3PE — MB BS 1974 Patna. (Patna) GP Pontefract, W. Yorks.

SINGH, Sureshwar Prasad 146A Griffin Road, London SE18 7QA — MB BS 1954 Bihar.

SINGH, Surinder 60 Vicar's Hill, Lewisham, London SE13 7JL Tel: 020 8690 6524 — BM 1982 Soton.; MRCGP 1986; DGM RCP Lond. 1985; DRCOG 1985. Community Med. AIDS Fell. St. Stephens Hosp. Lond.; Lect. (Pub. Health & Populat. Sci.) Roy. Free Hosp. Lond.; Community Med. Off. W. Lambeth HA. Socs: BMA. Prev: Princip. Med. Off. Lond.; Community AIDS Fell. St. Stephens Hosp. Lond.; Princip. Med. Off. Lond.

SINGH, Surinder 44/46 Wyresdale Road, Bolton BL1 4DN Tel: 01204 494133 Fax: 01204 848919; 77 Timberbottom, Bradshaw, Bolton BL2 3DQ — MB ChB 1984 Glas.; MRCGP 1989; DRCOG 1988; LF Hom. 1995. (Glas.) GP. Prev: SHO (Paediat.) Seafield

Hosp. Ayr; SHO (A & E) Hairmyres Hosp. E. Kilbride; SHO (Obst.) Bellshill Matern. Hosp.

SINGH, Mr Surjait Malhi Queen Elizabeth Hospital, Gayton Road, King's Lynn PE30 4ET Tel: 01553 613697; Mansfield House, 14 Sandringham Hill, Dersingham, King's Lynn PE31 6LL Tel: 01485 544577 — MB ChB 1980 Leeds; ChM 1991 (Commend.) Leeds; FRCS Eng. 1986; FRCS Glas. 1985. Cons. Surg. King's Lynn & Wisbech NHS Trust. Socs: Assn. Surg.; BMA; Vasc. Surg. Soc. Prev: Sen. Regist. Yorks. RHA; Regist. E. Anglia RHA.

SINGH, Suveer Unit of Critical Care, Royal Brompton Hospital, Sydney St., London SW3 6NP Tel: 020 7351 8528 Fax: 020 7351 8524; 53 Hope Park, Bromley BR1 3RG Email: suveer.singh@ic.ac.uk — MB BS 1992 Lond.; BSc (Hons.) Lond. 1989; MRCP (UK) 1995.

SINGH, Swaran Preet Department of Psychiatry, B Floor, South Block, Queens Medical Centre, Nottingham NG7 2UH Tel: 01159 249924 Fax: 01159 709706 Email: swaran.singh@nottingham.ac.uk — MB BS 1985 Jammu India; MD 1990; MRCPsych 1993. Cons. Psychiat. (Gen. Adult Psychiat.) Nott. Healthcare NHS Trust; Clin. Teach. Univ. of Nottm. Socs: BMA; Indian Psychiat. Soc.; MRCPsych. Prev: Lect. & Hon. Sen. Regist. (Psychiat.) Univ. Nottm.

SINGH, Tara 35 Warren Road, London E11 2LX — MB BS 1994 Lond.

SINGH, Tej Narayan Johnstone Health Centre, 60 Quarry Street, Johnstone PA5 8EY Tel: 01505 324348 Fax: 01505 323710 — MB BS 1961 Bihar. (Bihar) GP Johnstone, Renfrew.

SINGH, Tejinder Gurmit Stanley Corner Medical Centre, 1-3 Stanley Avenue, Wembley HA0 4JF Tel: 020 8902 3887 — MB BS 1969 Panjab. p/t Princip., G.P.; Clin. Assist. Dermatol., Hillingdon Hosp., Hillingdon, Middx. Socs: BMA; Brit. Med. Accupuncture Soc.; Soc. Of Famm. Plann. & Reproductive Med.

SINGH, Tejwant 10 Girdlers Close, Stivichall Grange, Coventry CV3 6LS Tel: 024 76 411742; 190 Telfer Road, Coventry CV6 3DR Tel: 024 76 596060 — MB BS 1960 Vikram. (G.M. Med. Coll. Bhopal)

SINGH, Thakur Hari Hensol Hospital, Pontyclun CF7 8YS Tel: 01443 237373 Fax: 01443 238284; Lynwood, 33 Danygraig Drive, Talbot Green, Pontyclun CF72 8AQ — MB BS 1965 Osmania; FRCPsych 1989, M 1973; DPM Eng. 1971. (Gandhi Med. Coll. Hyderabad) Cons. (Psychiat.) Hensol Hosp. Pontyclun. Prev: SHO & Regist. (Psychiat.) Penyval & Maindiff Ct. Hosps. Abergavenny; Rotat. Regist. (Psychiat.) Barrow Hosp. Bristol & SW Hosp. Bd.; Sen. Regist. (Psychiat.) St. Clement's Hosp. Ipswich.

SINGH, Thakur Sukdeo Harold Street Surgery, 2 Harold Street, Sheffield S6 3QW Tel: 0114 233 5930 — MB BS 1964 Agra; DObst RCOG 1968; DA Eng. 1970. (S.N. Med. Coll. Agra) p/t Gen. Practitioner. Socs: Med. Practitioner Soc. Prev: Cas. Off. Birm. Gen. Hosp.; ENT Regist. Burnley Gen. Hosp.

SINGH, Thangjam Man Ridvan, Etterby, Carlisle CA3 9QS — MB BS 1963 Gauhati; MRCP (UK) 1972; MRCPsych 1973; DPM Eng. 1973. (Assam Med. Coll. Dibrugarh) Cons. Psychiat. (Ment. Illness) Monklands Dist. Gen. Hosp. Airdrie. Prev: Cons. Psychiat. (Ment. Illness) E. Cumbria Health Dist.; Sen. Regist. (Psychiat.) St. John's Hosp. Stone; Hon. Sen. Regist. (Psychiat.) Oxf. Univ.

SINGH, Upendra Birleywood Health Centre, Birleywood, Skelmersdale WN8 9BW Tel: 01695 728073 Fax: 01695 556172 — MB BS 1969 Bihar; MB BS 1969 Bihar.

SINGH, Vakil Main Street Surgery, 86 Main Street, Gortin, Omagh BT79 8NN Tel: 028 8164 8216 — MB BS 1972 JAMMU & KASHMIR.

SINGH, Valishti Malini Mahani C43 Musgrave House, Royal Bolton Hospital, Minerva Road, Farnham, Bolton DL4 0JR — MB BS 1996 W. Indies.

SINGH, Vatsala Institute Road Surgery, 14 Institute Road, Eccleshill, Bradford BD2 2HX Tel: 01274 637417 Fax: 01274 776511 — MB BS 1967 Ranchi; DObst RCOG 1973; DA Eng. 1971. (Rajendra Med. Coll.) SCMO Bradford AHA.

SINGH, Mr Vijay Tel: 01443 443443 — MB BS 1981 Himachal Pradesh; FRCS 1999 (ORL-HNS); FRCS Ed. 1991; DLO RCS Eng. 1990.

SINGH, Vijoy Kumar Severn Street Health Centre, 25 Severn Street, Leicester LE2 0NN Tel: 0116 254 3253 — MB BS 1971 Patna.

SINGH

SINGH, Vivian 2 Southgate Road, Warsop, Mansfield NG20 0QZ Tel: 01623 842864; 18 Ampthill Road, Aigbirth, Liverpool L17 9QW Tel: 0151 728 9625 — MB ChB 1992 Liverp.; MB ChB (Hons.) Liverp. 1992. Demonst. (Anat.) Univ. Liverp. Prev: Ho. Off. Walton Hosps.

SINGH, Warbhajan Shah G Pendlebury Health Centre, The Lowry Medical Centre, 659 Bolton Road, Pendlebury, Manchester M27 8HP Tel: 0161 793 8686 Fax: 0161 727 8011.

SINGH, Yadavindra Shah 3 Glenart, Ellesmere Park, Eccles, Manchester M30 9HT — MB BS 1997 Lond.

SINGH, Yashwant Westminster Medical Centre, Aldams Grove, Liverpool L4 3TT Tel: 0151 922 3510 Fax: 0151 902 6071 — MB BS 1971 Patna.

SINGH JOSSON, Kashmir Monsoon, Minffordd, Bangor LL57 4DR — MB BS 1976 Punjab; MRCOG 1985.

SINGH KHANNA, Harmohan Dayal 3 Pinewood Avenue, Edwinstowe, Mansfield NG21 9JS — MB BS 1966 Punjab; MRCGP 1971.

SINGH-NIJJER, Bhajan 1A Field Street, Willenhall WV13 2NY — MB ChB 1990 Manch.

SINGH-RANGER, Deepak 28 Circle Gardens, London SW19 3JU — MB BS 1994 Lond.

SINGH-RANGER, Gurpreet 28 Circle Gardens, London SW19 3JU — MB BS 1997 Lond.; BSc (Hons) 1994. (UMDS)

SINGH RANGER, Ravinderpal Department of General Surgery, Royal United Hospital, Bath BA1 3NG Tel: 01225 428331; 28 Circle Gardens, London SW19 3JU — MB BS 1991 Lond.; BSc (Hons.) Lond. 1988; FRCS Eng. 1995. (Middlx. & Univ. Coll. Med. Sch.) Research Fell. (Vasc.) Univ. Coll. Lond. Prev: Specialist Regist. (Surg.) Wessex Region; SHO (Surg.) Broomfield Hosp. Chelmsford; Prosector (Anat.) & SHO (A & E) Univ. Coll. Hosp. Lond.

SINGHA, Mr Hiran Sirikantha Kirthi Department of Genito-Urin. Medicine, Royal South Hampshire Hospital, Brinton's Terrace, off St Mary's Road, Southampton SO14 0AJ — MB BChir 1951 Camb.; MChir Camb. 1963, MB BChir 1951; FRCS Eng. 1955; FRCS Ed. 1955. Sen. Lect. (Genitourin. Med.) Univ. Soton.; Cons. Genitourin. Med. Soton. & S.W. Hants. HA. Prev: Prof. Surg. Univ. Ceylon.

SINGHAI, Satyen 28 Prior Avenue, Sutton SM2 5HY — MB ChB 1995 Manch.

SINGHAI, Soumit 13 Ranelagh Gardens Mansions, Ranelagh Gardens, London SW6 3UG — MB BS 1995 Lond.

SINGHAL, Arun Kumar Hillside Road Surgery, 30 Hillside Road, Huyton, Liverpool L36 8BJ Tel: 0151 480 4205 Fax: 0151 489 2204 — MB BS 1973 Allahabad; MS (Orthop.) Allahabad 1977; Dip. Orthop. Surg. Allahabad 1975. (M.L.N. Med. Coll.) Prev: Police Surg. Liverp.

SINGHAL, Atul 13 Bure Close, North Brickhill, Bedford MK41 7TX — MB BS 1986 Lond.; MRCP (UK) 1989; DCH RCP Lond. 1988.

SINGHAL, Mr Hemant 15 Furrowfelde, Basildon SS16 5HB Tel: 01268 521035 — MB BS 1984 Delhi; MS New Delhi 1989, MB BS 1984; FRCS Ed. 1989.

SINGHAL, Mr Keshav 30 Beechwood Grove, Pencoed, Bridgend CF35 6SU — MB BS 1985 Jiwaji; MS (Orthop.) Jiwaji 1987, MB BS 1985; MCh Liverp. 1990. Regist. (Orthop.) Roy. Orthop. Hosp. Birm. Train. Scheme. Prev: Regist. (Orthop.) Chester Roy. Infirm.; SHO (Orthop.) BRd.green Hosp. Liverp.

SINGHAL, Saket 7 Gilchrist Drive, Edgbaston, Birmingham B15 3NG Tel: 0121 684 1236 — BM BCh 1991 Oxf.; BA (Hons.) Oxf. 1988; MRCP (UK) 1994. (Univ. Oxf.) Specialist Regist. Birm. Heartland Hosp.

SINGHAL, Shradha Nand The Alexandra Hospital, Woodrow Drive, Redditch B98 7UB Tel: 01527 503030; 3 Finlarigg Drive, Edgbaston, Birmingham B15 3RH — MB BS 1964 Lucknow; FRCP Lond. 1989; MRCP (UK) 1972. Cons. Phys. Geriat. & Gen. Med. The Alexandra Hosp. Redditch.

SINGHAL, Sumeet 3 Finlarigg Drive, Edgbaston, Birmingham B15 3RH — MB ChB 1996 Manch.

SINGHAL, Mr Virender Kumar 36 Chichester Road, Street BA16 0QX Tel: 01458 45867; 15 Davenport Avenue, New York 10805, USA Tel: 914 654 1249 — MB BS 1978 Delhi; FRCS Ed. 1985; MRCS Eng. LRCP Lond. 1986.

SINGHANIA, Rati c/o Drive (Mrs.) P. S. Prasad, Henderland Road, Bearsden, Glasgow G61 1AH — MB BS 1985 Magadh.

SINGLETON, Carol Dorothy North Derbys. Health, Scarsdale, Newbold Road, Chesterfield S41 7PF Tel: 01246 231255 Fax: 01246 277919; Highfields, 41 Eversleigh Rise, South Darley, Matlock DE4 2JW Tel: 01629 733642 — BM BS 1981 Nottm.; MFPHM RCP (UK) 1993; MRCGP 1985; DRCOG 1983; Cert. Family Plann. JCC 1983. Dir. of Pub. Health & Health Policy N.ern Derbysh. Health. Prev: Cons. in Pub. Health N. Derbysh. Health Chesterfield; Dep. Dir. Of Pub. Health S.ern Derbys. Health.

SINGLETON, Christine Dora Attenborough Surgery, Bushey Health Centre, London Road, Bushey, Watford WD23 2NN Tel: 01923 231633 Fax: 01923 818594 — MB ChB 1975 Manch.

SINGLETON, Geoffrey John Room 30, Mowden Hall, Staindrop Road, Darlington DL3 9EE Tel: 01325 392889 Email: geoff.singleton@dfee.gov.uk; Ancroft, Elvaston Pk Road, Hexham NE46 2HT Tel: 01434 605361 Email: geoff.singleton@onyxnet.co.uk — MB BS 1972 Lond.; MRCGP 1977; DRCOG 1976; DCH Eng. 1975. (St. Mary's) Med. Adviser Dept. Educat. & Employm. Darlington. Med.Dir. GS Med. Adviser. Prev: GP N.d.; Med. Adviser Benefits Agency Med. Servs.

SINGLETON, Nicholas Andrew Talbot Court Medical Practice, 1 Talbot Court, Stretford, Manchester M32 0ZL Tel: 0161 865 1197 Fax: 0161 864 1966; 18 Elgol Close, Davenport, Stockport SK3 8UP Tel: 0161 456 7357 — MB ChB 1982 Manch. Prev: SHO (Cas.) War Memor. Hosp. Wrexham; SHO (O & G & Geriat.) Leighton Hosp. Crewe.

SINGLETON, Nicola Jane 72 Milton Street, Fleetwood FY7 6QS — MB ChB 1998 Liverp.; MB ChB Liverp 1998.

SINGLETON, Stephen James Bolam House, Rothbury, Morpeth NE65 7UA — MB ChB 1979 Leeds; MSc Newc. 1992; MFPHM RCP (UK) 1993; MRCGP 1985; FFPHM 1998. Dir. (Pub. Health) N.d. HA; Lect. (Epidemiol. & Pub. Health) Univ. of Newc.

SINGTON, James Daniel The John Radcliffe Hospital, Headly Way, Oxford OX3 9DU Tel: 01865 741166 — MB ChB 1998 Sheff.; MB ChB Sheff 1998.

SINHA, Abhijit 10 The Circuit, Manchester M20 3RA — MB ChB 1992 Sheff.; DA (UK) 1995. SHO (Anaesth.) Manch. Roy. Infirm. Prev: SHO (Paediat.) Qu. Mary's Hosp. Childr. Carshalton; SHO (Anaesth.) Epsom Hosp. Surrey; SHO (Emerg. Med.) Gosford Hosp., Austral.

SINHA, Ajay Consultant Ophthalmologist, Broomfield Hospital, Court Road, Chelmsford CM1 7ET Tel: 01245 514899 Fax: 01245 514898; Fairwood, Coppins Close, Chelmsford CM2 6AY Tel: 01245 264731 — MB BS 1976 Delhi; MD Delhi 1978; FRCOphth 1990. Cons. Ophth. Socs: MRCOphth.; BMA; All India. Ophth.

SINHA, Mr Alokmoy 8 Belgrave Close, Abergavenny NP7 7AP — MB BS 1967 Calcutta; FRCS Eng. 1973 (Nat. Med. Inst. Calcutta). GP Abergavenny & Hon. Clin. Asst. (Gen. Surg.) Neville Hall Hosp. Abergavenny. Socs: Med. Protec. Soc. Prev: Resid. Surgic. Off. Staffs. Gp. Hosps.; Regist. (Neurosurg.) N. Staffs. Gp. Hosps.; Regist. (Gen. Surg.) Nevill Hall Hosp. Abergavenny.

SINHA, Amar Krishna (retired) 45 Parkers Road, Sheffield S10 1BN Tel: 0114 266 8394 — MB BS 1958 Bihar; MRCPsych 1974; DPM Eng. 1972; DTM & H Eng. 1968. Hon. Clin. Lect. Sheff. Univ. Prev: Cons. Psychiat. (Learning Disabil.) Community Health Sheff. NHS Trust.

SINHA, Anant Kumar Cheriton Medical Centre, Cheriton Crescent, Portmead, Swansea SA5 5LB Tel: 01792 561122 — MB BS 1969 Ranchi. (Ranandra Med. Coll. Hosp. Ranchi)

***SINHA, Aparna** 8 Belgrave Close, Abergavenny NP7 7AP — MB ChB 1998 Birm.

SINHA, Arun Kumar Greenmount Surgery, 25 Church Road, Caerau, Cardiff CF5 5LQ Tel: 029 2059 3003 Fax: 029 2059 1771; 8 Knightswell Close, Culverhouse Cross, Cardiff CF5 4NA Tel: 029 2059 3284 Fax: 01222 593284 Email: renuarun@aol.com — MB BS 1980 Patna; LRCP LRCS Ed. LRCPS Glas. 1984. (Patna Med. Coll. Patna (India)) GP Princip. Caerau La. Surg. Cardiff. Socs: Assoc. Mem. RCGP. Prev: SHO (Geriat.) Arrowe Pk. Hosp. Upton; SHO (Ophth.) Gloucester Roy. Hosp.; SHO (A & E) P. Chas. Hosp. Merthyr Tydfil.

SINHA, Ashok Kumar (Surgery), 16 Rosslyn Road, Longton, Stoke-on-Trent ST3 4JD Tel: 01782 599822 — MB BS 1974 Patna.

SINHA, Mr Ashok Kumar Associate Specialist Orthopaedics and Trauma, City Hospital NHS Trust, Dudley Rd, Birmingham B18 7QH Tel: 0121 554 3801 Fax: 0121 507 5483; 8 Meadow Rise,

Bournville, Birmingham B30 1UZ Tel: 0121 605 6167 — MB BS 1986 Patna; FRCS Glas. 1992. Assoc. Specialist Trauma & Orthop., City Hosp. NHS Trust, Dudley RD, Birm., B18 7QH. Socs: BMA; BOA.

SINHA, Aswinee Kumar (Surgery), 258 Westborough Road, Westcliff on Sea SS0 9PT Tel: 01702 348800; 33 Kilworth Avenue, Southend-on-Sea SS1 2DS — MB BS 1957 Calcutta; BSc Calcutta 1951; DCH Eng. 1966; DTM & H Liverp. 1966. (N.R.S. Med. Coll. Calcutta) GP S.end-on-Sea. Socs: Fell. Roy. Soc. Trop. Med. & Hyg.; Assoc. of Internat. Fed. of Sports Med.; BMA. Prev: Med. Off. Sierra Leone Developm. Co. Ltd. Freetown & Nat. Diamond Mining Company Ltd. Yengema, Sierra Leone; Regist. W. Hendon Hosp. Lond.

SINHA, Avinash Kumar 36 Mortain Road, Rotherham S60 3BX — MB ChB 1993 Manch.

SINHA, B K Bigdale Drive, Kirkby, Liverpool L33 6XJ.

SINHA, Baij Nath West Cheshire District General Hospital, Liverpool Road, Chester CH1 3SS — MB BS 1957 Bihar; DCH Calcutta 1960. (Darbhanga Med. Coll.) Prev: SHO (Geriat.) & SHO (Infec. Dis.) W. Norwich Hosp.; SHO (Psychol. Med.) Hellesdon Hosp. Norwich.

SINHA, Bharat Prasad Sinha, 56 Western Avenue, Acton, London W3 7TY Tel: 020 8743 4133; 6 Highway Avenue, Maidenhead SL6 5AF Tel: 01628 771515 Fax: 01628 771515 — MD 1978 Patna; MB BS 1969; DTM & H Liverp. 1976. (P. of Wales Med. Coll.) Socs: BMA. Prev: GP Maidenhead.; visit.med.Off.Subst. misuse .E. Berks.

SINHA, Bhupendra Kumar Birchdale Road Medical Centre, 2 Birchdale Road, London E7 8AR Tel: 020 8472 1600 Fax: 020 8471 7712 — MB BS 1964 Patna. (Patna Med. Coll.) Prev: SHO (Cas. & Orthop.) Hackney Hosp. Lond.; SHO (Orthop.) OldCh. Hosp. Romford; SHO (Gen. Surg.) German Hosp. Lond.

SINHA, Birendra Kumar Edge Hill Health Centre, Crosfield Road, Liverpool L7 5QL Tel: 0151 260 2777 — MB BS 1973 Patna; MRCP (UK) 1980; MRCPI 1980; DTCD Wales 1976.

SINHA, Chitra 26 The Crayke, Bridlington YO16 6YP; Bridlington Hospital, Bridlington YO16 4QP Tel: 01262 607187 — MB BS Jodhpur, India 1981; LRCP LRCS Ed. LRCPS Glas. 1984; MRCOG 1995; DRCOG 1990; DObst RCPI 1989. Specialist Regist. (O & G) York Dist. Hosp. Socs: Obst. & Gyn. Soc. Prev: Regist. (O & G) W. Wales Gen. Hosp. Carmarthen; SHO (O & G) Warnford Hosp. Roy. Lamington Spa, Hosp. St. Cross Rugby & Dudley Rd. Hosp. Birm.

SINHA, Gauri Hatfield Road Surgery, 61 Hatfield Road, St Albans AL1 4JE Tel: 01727 853079.

SINHA, Gopal Chandra 63 Mayford Road, Lordswood, Chatham ME5 8QZ Tel: 01634 201877 Email: gsinha3531@aol.com; Grove Park Surgery, 116 Sutton Road, Maidstone ME15 9AP Tel: 01622 753211 — LRCP LRCS Ed. LRCPS Glas. 1983; MFFP 1994; T (GP) 1991. GP Sessional Family Plann. M.O. Socs: FRSH; Soc. Occupat. Med.; Fac. Fam. Plann. Prev: Med. Off. HM Prison Serv.

SINHA, Guria 27 Nursery Avenue, Ormskirk L39 2DY — MB ChB 1998 Manch.; MB ChB Manch 1998.

SINHA, Gyanranjan Prasad Department of Paediatrics, Manor Hospital, Moat Road, Walsall WS2 9PS — MB BS 1973 Patna; MRCP (UK) 1990; DCH (RCPS of Irel.); MD (Patna Univ.); FRCP 1999 Glasgow; FRCPCH. Cons. Paediat. & Hon. Sen. Lect. Univ. Birm. Socs: BMA; Med. Protec. Soc.; W Midl. Paediat. Soc.

SINHA, Jaisi 52 Corporation Road, Newport NP19 0AW — MB BS 1996 Lond.

SINHA, Jayanta Kumar 54 Codicote Drive, Garston, Watford WD25 9QY Tel: 01923 673974 — MB BS 1967 Calcutta; DIH Lond. 1984; DPH Lond. 1983. Regional Med. Off. BT Lond. Centr. Socs: Soc. Occupat. Med.; Internat. Soc. Travel Med. Prev: Sen. Regist. (Occupat. Med.) Clwyud HA; SHO (Gen. Med.) Tynemouth Infirm. Clwyd HA; Regist. (Infec. Dis.) Benghazi Univ. Hosp.

SINHA, Mr Joydeep Department of Orthopaedics, King's College Hospital, Denmark Hill, London SE5 9RS Tel: 020 7346 3463 Fax: 020 7346 3497 Email: joydeep.sinha@btinternet.com; Email: joydeep.sinha@btinternet.com — MB ChB Manch. 1985; BSc (Hons.) (Pharmacol.) Manch. 1982; FRCS (Orth.) 1995; FRCS Eng. 1990; FRCS Ed. 1989. (University of Manchester) Cons. (Orthop. Surg.) King's Coll. Hosp. Lond. Socs: Fell. BOA; Fell. Brit. Elbow and Shoulder Soc.; Fell. Brit. Soc. Surg. Hand. Prev: Sen. Regist. (Orthop.

& Trauma) King's Coll. Hosp. Lond.; Fell.sh. Train. USA (Seattle & NY).

SINHA, Mr Kunja Madhab 26 Lighcliffe Road, London N13 5HD Tel: 020 8882 4271 — MB BS 1961 Calcutta; BSc Calcutta 1955, MB BS 1961; FRCS Ed. 1973; FRCS Glas. 1973. (R.G. Kar Med. Coll.) Prev: Regist. Dept. Gen. Surg. R. G. Kar Med. Coll. Hosps. Calcutta, India; Resid. Div. Gen. Surg. Wesley Med. Center Wichita, U.S.A. & St.; Joseph's Hosp. Phoenix, U.S.A.

SINHA, Leena 30 Springdale Court, Mickleover, Derby DE3 5SW — MB BCh 1993 Wales.

SINHA, Manas Kumar Coronary Artery Disease Research Unit, Cardiological Sciences, St Georges Hospital Medical School, Cronmer Terrace, London SW17 0RE Tel: 020 8725 3327 Fax: 020 8725 3328 Email: msinha@sghms.ac.uk; 20 Brudenell Road, Tooting, London SW17 8DA Tel: 020 8767 3933 Email: manas@msinha.freeserve.co.uk — MB BS 1994 Lond.; BSc (Hons.) Med. Sci. & Clin. Pharmacol. Lond. 1991; MRCP (UK) 1997. (St. Geo. Hosp.) Clin. Research Fell. In Cardiol. St. Geo.s Hosp. Med. Sch. Cronmer Terr. Lond. SW17 0RE. Prev: SHO SW Thames Renal Unit St. Helier Hosp. Carshalton; SHO Rotat. (Med.) St. Geo. Hosp. Lond.; SHO (Endocrinol.) St. Helier Hosp. Surrey.

SINHA, Mr Mukesh The Surgery, 28 Church Road, Aston, Birmingham B6 5UP Tel: 0121 327 2348; 17 Hainfield Drive, Solihull B91 2PL Tel: 0121 705 2802 — MB BS 1980 Bihar; FRCS Ed. 1984; MRCGP 1990; Cert. Family Plann. JCC 1989. Hosp. Pract. (Surg.) Solihull Hosp.; Provision of Minor Surg. (including Vasectomy) mainly for Fundholding GPs. Socs: MDU. Prev: Regist. (Gen. Surg.) E. Birm. Hosp.; Regist. (Paediat. Surg.) E. Birm. Hosp.; SHO Rotat. (Gen. Surg./Urol./Thoracic Surg./Trauma) E. Birm. Hosp.

SINHA, Murli Pleck Health Centre, 16 Oxford Street, Pleck, Walsall WS2 9HY Tel: 01922 647660 Fax: 01922 629251 — MB BS 1971 Patna; MS (Gen. Surg.) Patna 1975. (Patna India) GP Walsall Clin. Asst. (Psychiat.). Socs: BMA; ODA.

SINHA, N K Aintree Road Practice, 2 Aintree Road, Bootle L20 9DW Tel: 0151 922 1768.

SINHA, Narveshwar Researcher in Health Management, Judge Institute of Management Studies, University of Cambridge, Cambridge CB2 1AG Tel: 07711 278957 Email: ns223@cam.ac.uk; 2 Shrewsbury Road, Sale M33 3TP Tel: 0161 610 1182 Fax: 0161 610 1182 Email: ns223@hotmail.com — MB BS 1980 Aligarh Muslim; MS (ENl) India 1989; DLD (RCS) 1989; PhD. (JN Med. Coll. Aligarh) Sen. Cons. Indraprastha Appollo Hosp. Delhi, India; Res. Schol.; Locum Appts. in ENT Surg. Socs: Assn. Otolaryn. Of India; Treas. Indian Soc. Of Otol.; Brit. Cochlear Implant Gp.

SINHA, Prithwiraj Wingate Surgery, Medical Centre, Front West Street, Wingate TS28 5PZ Tel: 01429 838203 Fax: 01429 836928 — MB BS 1968 Calcutta.

SINHA, Rabindra Nath c/o Drive R. P. Yadava, 40 Caverstral Road, Blyth Bridge, Stoke-on-Trent ST11 9BG — MB BS 1968 Patna.

SINHA, Raghavendra Prasad 41 Reedfield, Reedley, Burnley BB10 2NJ Tel: 01282 696006; 90 Worsley Road N., Walkden, Worsley, Manchester M28 3QW Tel: 01204 791409 — MD 1979 Patna; MB BS Patna 1974. (Patna Med. Coll.) GP Worsley. Prev: SHO (Psychiat.) Oldham & Dist. Gen. Hosp.; SHO (Geriat. Med.) Grantham & Kesteven Gen. Hosp.; SHO (Gen. Med.) Stracathro Hosp. & Arbroath Infirm. Brechin.

SINHA, Raj Kumar 35 Staveley Way, Rugby CV21 1TP — MB BS 1980 Ranchi, India.

SINHA, Rajeshwar Prasad Rainbow Medical Centre, 265 Dunstable Road, Luton LU4 8BS — MB BS 1972 Bihar.

SINHA, Rama Shankar Kumar Bridlington District Hospital, Bridlington YO16 4QP Tel: 01262 607034; The Crayke, Bridlington YO16 6YP — MB BS 1973 Ranchi; DTM & H Liverp. 1986. Staff Grade (A & E) Bridlington Hosp. E. Yorks. Socs: Fell. Roy. Soc. Trop. Med.

SINHA, Ranjan Kumar 16 Lime Close, Crawley RH11 7NN — MB BS 1984 Calcutta; MRCOG 1990. Clin. Research Fell. (O & G) Roy. Lond. Hosp. & Newham Gen. Hosp. Lond. Prev: Regist. (O & G) Luton & Dunstable Hosp. & Roy. Lond. Hosp.

SINHA, Ravi Nandan 4 Poplar Drive, Milton of Campsie, Glasgow G66 8DZ — MB ChB 1987 Manch.

SINHA, Ritendra Nath The Health Centre, Lawson Street, Stockton-on-Tees TS18 1HX Tel: 01642 676520 Fax: 01642

SINHA

614720; The Gables, 607 Yarm Road, Eagescliffe, Stockton-on-Tees TS16 9BN — MB BS 1969 Patna.

SINHA, S K Aintree Road Practice, 2 Aintree Road, Bootle L20 9DW Tel: 0151 922 1768.

SINHA, Sanjay Alexandra Park Health Centre, 2 Whitswood Close, Manchester M16 7AW Tel: 0161 226 3620 — MB BChir 1988 Camb.; BA (Hons.) Physiol. Camb. 1985; MRCP (UK) 1992. (Camb.) MRC Clin. Train. Fell. Univ. Manch. Prev: Regist. (Cardiol. & Gen. Med.) Castlehill Hosp. Cottingham; SHO (Gen. Med.) Wythenshawe Hosp. Manch. & Hope Hosp. Salford.

SINHA, Sanjay Kumar 8 Gordonsfield, Ackworth, Pontefract WF7 7QN — MB BS 1984 Bihar, India.

SINHA, Sankarprasad George Eliot Hospital, College Street, Nuneaton CV10 7DJ Tel: 01203 865392 Fax: 01203 865095 Email: drsps@yahoo.com; 20 Falstaff Close, Whitestone, Nuneaton CV11 6FB Tel: 01203 375142 Fax: 01203 375142 — MB BS 1987 Calcutta; FRCR 1996; DMRD Calcutta 1991; DNB (Radiodiagnosis) New Delhi 1992. (R. G. Kar Med. Coll. Calcutta, India) Cons. Radiol. Geo. Eliot Hosp. Nuneaton. Socs: BMA; MDU; Brit. Healthcare Internet Assn. Prev: Specialist Regist. (Radiol.) Roy. Liverp. Univ. Hosp. Eng.; Specialist Regist. (Radiol.) Alder Hey Childr. Hosp. Liverp.; Specialist Regist. (Radiol.) Whiston Hosp. Prescot, Merseyside.

SINHA, Santosh Vidya Medical Centre, 12 Charnwood Street, Derby DE1 2GT Tel: 01332 345406 Fax: 01332 345863 — MB BS 1964 Bihar. (Darbhanga Med. Coll. Laheriasarai) Prev: SHO (Obst.) Lincoln Co. Hosp.; SHO (Geriat.) Castle Hill Hosp. Cottingham; SHO (Gen. Surg.) Hull Roy. Infirm.

SINHA, Sarla 2 Gilescroft Avenue, Northwood, Kirkby, Liverpool L33 9TW Tel: 0151 546 3396 — MB BS 1961 Delhi. (Lady Hardinge Med. Coll.)

SINHA, Saurabh 47 Pentland Terrace, Edinburgh EH10 6HD — BM BCh 1994 Oxf.; BA (Hons.) Oxf. 1991.

SINHA, Seema 4 St Margarets Road, Whitchurch, Cardiff CF14 7AA — MB BS 1989 Newc.; BSc Chem. (Hons.) 1984; MRCGP 1994; DRCOG 1993.

SINHA, Shashi Kiran Balfour Road Surgery, 92 Balfour Road, Ilford IG1 4JE Tel: 020 8478 0209 Fax: 020 8220 8777 — MB BS 1966 Patna.

SINHA, Shirley 10 Knoll Avenue, Uplands, Swansea SA2 0JN — BM 1986 Soton.

SINHA, Shobha Brookfield Park Surgery, 2 Brookfield Road, London NW5 1ER Tel: 020 7485 7363 — MB BS 1971 Patna.

SINHA, Shubhada 37 Hills Avenue, Cambridge CB1 7UY — BChir 1992 Camb.

SINHA, Shyama Withybush Hospital, Fishguard Road, Haverfordwest SA61 2PZ; 9 Heritage Park, Haverfordwest SA61 2QF Tel: 01437 768722 — MB BS 1982 Patna; MRCOG 1992, D 1992. Staff Grade (O & G) Withybush Hosp. HaverfordW.

SINHA, Subrata Glan Yr Afon Surgery, Shop Row, Tredegar NP22 4LB Tel: 01495 722630 Fax: 01495 726173 — MB BS 1965 Calcutta. Clin. Asst. (Elderly Care) Nevill Hall & Dist. NHS Trust.

SINHA, Sudhir Kumar Brookfield Park Surgery, 2 Brookfield Road, London NW5 1ER Tel: 020 7485 7363 — MB BS 1971 Patna.

SINHA, Suman Kumar 2 Clare Close, Bury BL8 1XN — MB BS 1973 Bihar.

SINHA, Sunil Kumar Alderney Hospital, Ringwood Road, Poole BH12 4NB Tel: 01202 735537 Fax: 01202 730657; 16 Fontmell Road, Broadstone BH18 8NW — MB BS 1988 Ranchi; MB BS Ranchi. 1988. Assoc. Specialist. Prev: Trainee GP BRd.stone.

SINHA, Supriya Kumar 4 Havisham Place, London SE19 3HN — MB BS 1995 Lond.

SINHA, Vineeta 62 Green Lane, Stockport SK4 3LH — MB ChB 1993 Manch.; BSc St And. 1990. Demonst. (Anat.) Univ. Dundee. Prev: Ho. Off. (Surg. & Med.) Manch. Roy. Infirm.

SINHA, Vishwambhar Nath Prasad Crane Park Medical Centre, 748 Hanworth, Hounslow TW4 5NT Tel: 020 8893 4567 Fax: 020 8893 8026 — MB BS 1974 Patna.

SINHA ROY, Amarendra Nath Lakeside Surgery, Church St., Langold, Worksop S81 9NW Tel: 01909 540488 Fax: 01909 540477; 'Moonrakers', 77 Thievesdale Lane, Worksop S81 0PG Tel: 01909 472616 — MB BS Calcutta 1960. Prev: Med. Protec. Soc.

SINHA ROY, Salil Kumar 1 Clos Rhymni, Parc Gwernfadog, Morriston, Swansea SA6 6RB — MB BS 1956 Calcutta; DGO 1958; DA Eng. 1970. (Calcutta Med. Coll.) Prev: Regist. (Anaesth.) Morriston Hosp., Singleton Hosp. Swansea & W.; Wales Gen. Hosp. Carmarthen.

SINNAMON, Derek George Avondale, 108 Mountsandel Road, Coleraine BT52 1TA — MB BCh BAO 1969 Belf.; FRCP Ed. 1991; MRCP (UK) 1976; LMCC Ottawa 1971; DRACOG Otago 1973. Cons. Phys. Coleraine Hosp. N. Irel.

SINNATAMBY, Mr Chummy Sundararaja Royal College of Surgeons of England, 35-43 Lincoln's Inn Fields, London WC2A 3PE Tel: 020 7405 3474 Fax: 020 7973 2118 Email: csinnatamby@rcseng.ac.uk; 11 Meadowcroft, St Albans AL1 1UD Tel: 01727 850027 — MB BS Ceylon 1960; FRCS Eng. 1965. Head Teach. Dept. Educat. RCS Eng. Socs: Fell. Brit. Assn. Clin. Anat. Prev: Prof. Surg. Univ. Colombo, Sri Lanka & King Faisal Univ. Dammam, Saudi Arabia.

SINNATAMBY, Ruchira Department of Radiology, Addenbrooke's Hospital, Cambridge CB2 2QQ Email: ruchi.sinnatamby@addenbrookes.nhs.uk; Granta Cottage, 11 Meadow Lane, Linton, Cambridge CB1 6HX — MB BChir 1988 Camb.; BA (Hons.) Camb. 1986; MRCP (UK) 1991; FRCR 1994. (Univ. Camb.) p/t Cons. Radiologist Addenbrooke's Hosp. Camb.; Fell. & Coll. Lect. (Anat.) & Dir. Studies of Clin. Med. New Hall Univ. Camb.

SINNATAMBY, Mrs Selvadevi Northwick Park Hospital, Watford Road, Harrow HA1 3UJ Tel: 020 8869 2309; 11 Meadowcroft, St Albans AL1 1UD Tel: 01727 850027 — MB BS 1961 Ceylon; PhD Lond. 1973; MRCPsych 1987; DA Eng. 1964. Cons. Psychiat. N.wick Pk. Hosp. Harrow. Prev: Clin. Asst. Shenley Hosp. Radlett; Sen. Lect. (Pharmacol.) Univ. Colombo, Sri Lanka.

SINNATHAMBY, Subothini Wendy 13 Stradbrooke Grove, Ilford IG5 0DN — MB BS 1994 Lond.

SINNATHURAY, Kanaga Raj Flat CF2, Rosemount Halls, Farmers Hall Lane, Aberdeen AB25 4XF — MB ChB 1996 Aberd.

SINNERTON, Mr Richard Jacob Ashford & St Peter's Hospital, London Road, Ashford TW15 3AA Tel: 01784 884329 Fax: 01784 884244; 22 Windle Close, Windlesham GU20 6DY Tel: 01276 470164 Email: sinnertonr@aol.com — MB BS 1988 Lond.; FRCS (Orth.) 1997; FRCS Eng. 1992. (St. Thos.) Cons. (Orthop. Surg.) Ashford & St. Peters Hosp. Prev: Regist. Rotat. (Orthop.) St. Mary's Hosp. Lond.

SINNERTON, Timothy John L'Aumone and St. Sampsons Practice, L'Aumone Surgery, Castel, Guernsey GY5 7RU Tel: 01481 256517 Fax: 01481 255190; Thomery, Les Grand Jardins, St. Martins, Guernsey Tel: 01481 39454 — MB BS 1988 Lond.; MRCGP 1995; DRCOG 1993. (St. Thos. Hosp. Med. Sch. (Lond.))

SINNETT, Mr Hugh Dudley Department Surgery, Charing Cross Hospital, Fulham Palace Road, London W6 8RF Tel: 020 8846 7303 Fax: 020 8846 1617; 6 Wilbury Avenue, Cheam, Sutton SM2 7DU Tel: 020 8770 3806 Fax: 020 8770 3806 — MB BS 1972 Lond.; MS Lond. 1984, MB BS 1972; FRCS Eng. 1976. (Char. Cross) Cons. Surg. Char. Cross Hosp. Lond.; Mem. Ct. Examrs. RCS Eng. Prev: Sen. Lect. & Hon. Cons. Surg. Roy. Marsden Hosp. Lond.; Sen. Regist. (Surg.) St. Bart. Hosp. Lond.

SINNETT, Kate Joanne 90 Squires Gate, Rogerstone, Newport NP10 0BQ — MB BCh 1998 Wales.

SINNIAH, Anton Ravindra Department of Chest Medicine, Fairfield General Hospital, Rocudale Old Road, Bury BL9 7TD Tel: 0161 778 2652 — MB BS 1989 Lond.; MRCP (UK) 1992; Dip. Trop. Med. RCSI 1995. (St. Geo. Hosp. Med. Sch.) Cons. (Thoracic & Gen Med.) Bury Gen Hosp. Manc. Prev: Regist. (Thoracic & Gen. Med.) Char. Cross Hosp. Lond.; Regist. (Thoracic, ICU, Neurol. & Gen. Med.) Centr. Middlx. Hosp. Lond.; Regist. (Thoracic & Transpl. Med.) Harefield Hosp. Uxbridge.

SINNIAH, Arulrajah Thiruchelvam North London Nuffield Hospital, Cavell Drive, Enfield EN2 7PR Tel: 020 8366 2122; Shalimar, 9 Greenway, Totteridge, London N20 8EE Tel: 020 8445 4472 Fax: 020 8446 5491 — MB BS 1960 Punjab; MB BS Punjab. (India) 1960; FRCP Ed. 1994; MRCP Ed. 1967. (Manch. & Ludhiana) Cons. Phys. N. Lond. Nuffield Hosp. Socs: BMA. Prev: Cons. Phys. Highlands Hosp. Lond.; Cons. Phys. Dept. Geriat. Med. High Wycombe & Dist. Hosp. Gp. Bucks. CC.

SINNOTT, Anthony David Imperial Road Surgery, 8 Imperial Road, Matlock DE4 3NL Tel: 01629 583249 — MB ChB 1983 Sheff.; DRCOG 1987.

SINNOTT, Brendon Simon Broomhill House, 1 Broomhill Park, Belfast BT9 5JB; Broomhill House, 1 Broomhill Park, Belfast BT9 5JB Tel: 01232 209962 — MB BCh BAO 1985 NUI; LRCPI & LM, LRCSI & LM 1985; BSc 1987; FRCSI 1991; FFAEM 1996. Cons. (A & E) Down Lisburn Trust Lagan Valley Hosp. Lisburn Co. Antrim. Socs: BMA; BAEM.

SINNOTT, Claire Rose 7 Sutherland Grove, Teddington TW11 8RP — MB BChir 1985 Camb.; MRCP (UK) 1989.

SINSON, John Denis (retired) 10 Avondale Court, Shadwell Lane, Leeds LS17 6DT Tel: 0113 268 7862 — MB BS 1948 Durh.; FRCGP 1977, M 1969. Prev: Med. Dir. St. Gemma's Hospice Leeds.

SINTLER, Mr Martin Peter 131 Beaumont Road, Bournville, Birmingham B30 1NT — MB ChB 1993 Birm.; FRCS (Eng) 1998. (Birm.)

SINTON, Janet Elizabeth Ophthalmology, Altnagelvin Hospital, Glenshane Road, Londonderry BT47 6SB Tel: 01504 345171 Fax: 01504 611218; 91 Glenmore Park, Altnagelvin, Londonderry BT47 2JY Tel: 01504 313086 Email: janetsinton@msn.com — MB BCh BAO 1988 Belf.; FRCOphth 1992. Cons. (Ophth.) Altnagelvin Hosp. Lond.derry N. Irel. Prev: Sen. Regist. (Ophth.) Roy. Vict. Hosp. Belf.; Regist. (Ophth.) Roy. Vict. Hosp. Belf.

SINTON, John Roger Wardlaw (retired) Meadowfield Cottage, 32 Ramsey's Lane, Wooler NE71 6NY Tel: 01668 281944 — MB BS 1947 Durh.

SINTON, Richard Ian Rae 174 Blagdon Road, New Malden KT3 4AL Tel: 020 8286 1941; Hungerdown Barn, Brittens Lane, Fontwell, Arundel BN18 0ST Tel: 01243 544094 Fax: 01243 544094 — MB BChir 1960 Camb.; FRCA 1967. (Westm. Hosp. Lond.) Cons. Anaesth. Kingston. Hosp.Kingston on Thames. Prev: Attend. Anaesth. Highline Hosp. Seattle, USA; Asst. Prof. Anesthesiol. Univ. Washington Seattle, USA.

SINTON, William Srigley (retired) Flat 2, Westfield House, Cote Lane, Westbury on Trym, Bristol BS9 3UL Tel: 0117 949 4802 — MB BS 1953 Lond.; DObst RCOG 1955. Prev: Ho. Surg. Lond. Hosp.

SINUFF, Syama Hamid Flat 3, 275A Fulwood Road, Broomhill, Sheffield S10 3BD — MB ChB 1997 Sheff.

SIODLAK, Mr Martyn Zbyszek ENT Department, The General Hospital, St Helier, Jersey Tel: 0151 529 4691 — MB BS 1979 Lond.; FRCS Lond. 1984; MRCS Eng. LRCP Lond. 1979; T(S) 1991. (Char. Cross) Cons. Otolaryngol. Head & Neck Surg. Gen. Hosp. St. Helier. Prev: Cons. Otolaryngol. Head & Neck Surg. Walton Hosp. & Ormskirk Dist. Gen. Hosp.; Sen. Regist. (ENT Surg.) Mersey Regional Rotat. Scheme; Clin. Research Fell. (Otorhinolaryngol.) Univ. Liverp.

***SIOW, Wenchee** 45 Broadley Terrace, London NW1 6LG — MB BS 1998 Lond.; MB BS Lond 1998.

SIPPERT, Alan Flat 3, Lesley Court, 23/33 Strutton Ground, London SW1P 2HZ Tel: 020 7222 7264 — MB ChB 1950 Manch.; FRCPsych 1984, M 1974; FFPHM 1979, M 1972; DPH Manch. 1960. Socs: BMA.

SIPPLE, Mr Mushtaq Ahmad 135 Glebe Farm Road, Birmingham B33 9NE Tel: 0121 784 4228 — MB BS 1956 Punjab; MS (Neurosurg.) Punjab Pakistan 1964, MB BS 1956; MRCPsych 1979; DPM Eng. 1975. (Nishtar Med. Coll.) Cons. Psychiat. St. Matthew's Hosp. Walsall. Socs: World Psychiat. Assn. Prev: Neurosurg. Specialist Pakistan Army Med. Corp.; Cons. Neurosurg. Centr. Hosp. Riyadh, Saudi Arabia; Sen. Regist. (Adult Psychiat.) St. Jas. Univ. Hosp. Leeds.

SIRCAR, Manisha Lynwood Medical Centre, 4 Lynwood Drive, Romford RM5 2RA Tel: 01708 743244 Fax: 01708 736783 — MB BS 1964 Calcutta; MRCOG 1972; DA Eng. 1968. (N.R. Sircar Med. Coll.) Prev: Regist. Dept. O & G Romford Gp. Hosps.

SIRCUS, Wilfred (retired) Easter Flisk, Blebo craigs, Cupar KY15 5UQ Tel: 01334 850064 — MD 1949 Liverp.; PhD Sheff. 1956; MB ChB (Silver Medal Pub. Health) 1943; FRCP Lond. 1965, M 1948; FRCP Ed. 1961, M 1958. Cons. Phys. W.. Gen. Hosp. Edin.; Reader (Med.) Univ. Edin. Prev: Sen. Research Regist. Sheff. Roy. Infirm.

SIRELING, Lester Ian Barnet Psychiatric Unit, Department of Psychiatry, Barnet Hospital, Wellhouse Lane, Barnet EN5 3DJ Tel: 020 8216 4616 Fax: 020 8216 4595 Email: lester.sireling@bhc-tr.nthames.nhs.uk — MB BS 1974 Lond.; MRCS Eng. LRCP Lond. 1974; MRCPsych 1979; FRCPsych 2000. (Guy's) Cons. Psychiat. Barnet and Edwd. Hosps. Socs: Mem., Brit. Assn. for PsychoPharmacol..; Hon. Off. in Psychosis, Primary Care Psychiat. Prev: Sen. Regist. & Lect. (Psychiat.) St. Geo. Hosp. Lond.; Clin. Research Fell. (Adult Psychiat.) St. Geo. Hosp. Med. Sch. Lond.

SIRIMANNA, Mr Kusum Sekera Consultant Audiological Physician, Great Ormond Street Hospital for Children, Great Ormond St., London WC1N 3JH; 10 Vincent Close, New Barnet, Barnet EN5 5NR Tel: 020 8441 3171 — MB BS 1977 Sri Lanka; MSc (Audiological Med.); MS Sri Lanka 1987; FRCS Ed. 1985; DLO RCS Eng. 1983. Cons. Audiol. Phys. Gt. Ormond St. Hosp. for Childr. Lond.; Hon. Sen. Lect. (Clin. Sci.) Inst. Child Health Univ. Lond. Socs: Brit. Assn. of Audiol. Phys.; Internat. Assn. Phys. in Audiol.; Internat. Soc. Audiol. Prev: Cons. Audiol. Phys. N.wick Pk. Hosp. Harrow; Sen. Regist. (Audiol. Med.) Univ. Hosp. Wales Cardiff; Cons. ENT Surg. Base Hosp. Matara, Sri Lanka.

SIRIPURAPU, Mr Ankaiah (retired) 4 Dunhugh Park, Londonderry BT47 2NL Tel: 028 7134 8994 — MB BS 1966 Andhra; BSc Andhra 1960; MS Banaras 1975; DLO 1973; FRCS Ed. 1979. Prev: Cons. Otolaryngol. Altnagelvin Area Hosp. Lond.derry.

SIRISENA, Liyana Arachchige Premachandra Crosshouse Hospital, Kilmarnock KA2 0BE Tel: 01563 521133 Fax: 01563 577774; 46 Bathurst Drive, Alloway, Ayr KA7 4QY Tel: 01292 443253 Email: 106270.3676@compuserve.com — MB BS 1968 Ceylon; MRCPsych 1983; DPM Eng. 1979. Cons. Psychiat. CrossHo. Hosp. Kilmarnock. Prev: Assoc. Specialist (Psychiat.) Alisa Hosp. Ayr; Cons. Psychiat. Bendigo Vict., Austral.

SIRISENA, Udawattage Nihal Harischandra 3 Sefton Avenue, Mill Hill, London NW7 3QB; 36 Christchurch Avenue, Harrow HA3 8NJ — MB BS 1976 Ceylon; DFFP 1993; DRCOG 1992; DA (UK) 1986.

SIRISENA, Walpita Gamage 27 St George's Avenue, Grays RM17 5XB Tel: 01375 78840 — MB BS Bombay 1953; DTM & H Ceylon 1962. (Topiwala Nat. Med. Coll.) Med. Off. Health Dept. Basildon & Thurrock Health Dist. Prev: SHO (Geriat.) & SHO (Accid. & Orthop.) W. Suff. Gen. Hosp. Bury St.; Edmunds.

SIRIWARDANA, Nimmilee Chandanee Piyadasni Earls House Hospital, Lanchester Road, Durham DH1 5RE; 9 St Oswalds Drive, Durham DH1 3TE — MB BS 1979 Peradeniya; MB BS Peradeniya Sri Lanka 1979; MRCPsych 1992.

SIRIWARDENA, Mr Ajith Kumar Department of Surgery, Manchester Royal Infirmary, Oxford Road, Manchester M13 9WL Fax: 0161 276 4530 Email: ajith@mri3.cmht.nwest.nhs.uk — MB ChB 1982 Manch.; MD (Gold Medal) Manch. 1991; FRCS Ed. 1986; FRCS Eng. 1988; FRCS (Gen) 1995. (University of Manchester) Cons. Surg. & Hon. Sen. Lect. In Surg., Manchster Roy. Infirm. Prev: Sen. Regist. (Gen. Surg.) N. W.. RHA; Sen. Lect. & Cons. Surg. Edin. Roy. Infirm.

SIRIWARDENA, Aloysius Niroshan The Minster Practice, Cabourne Court, Cabourne Avenue, Lincoln LN2 2JP Tel: 01522 568838 Fax: 01522 546740; North Dene, Langworth Road, Scothern, Lincoln LN2 2UP Tel: 01522 568838 — MB BS 1984 Lond.; MMedSci Nottm. 1995; MRCGP 1989; DCH RCP Lond. 1989; DRCOG 1988. (St. Bart. Hosp. Lond.)

SIRIWARDENA, Miss Dilani Krishni 42 Limehouse Court, 46 Morris Road, Poplar, London E14 6NQ — MB BS 1992 Lond.; FRCOphth 1997. MRC Research Fell. Moorfields Eye Hosp. Lond.

SIRIWARDENA, Mr Goigodagamage Jewendra Ariyathilaka DHSS Artificial Limb & Appliance Centre, Oak Tree Lane, Moseley, Birmingham B29 6JA Tel: 0121 472 5343; 57 Moorcroft Road, Moseley, Birmingham B13 8LT — MB BS 1957 Ceylon; FRCS Ed. 1967. Hon. Cons. (Prosth.s & Orthotics) W. Midl. RHA; Hon. Sen. Lect. Univ. Birm.; Med. Off. DHSS Artific. Limb & Appliance Centre Birm.; Fell. Scientif. Counc. Internat. Coll. Angiol. Socs: Internat. Soc. Prosthetists & Orthotists. Prev: Regist. (Surg.) Crewe & Dist. Memor. Hosp.; Surg. Accid. Serv. Colombo, Ceylon; Surg. Gen. Hosp. Chilaw, Sri Lanka.

SIRIWARDENE, Seetha Kaushalyani (retired) 9 Hartland Close, Winchmore Hill, London N21 2BG — MB BS 1957 Ceylon; MFCM 1974; DCH Eng. 1965. GP Dudley FPC. Prev: SCMO Dudley AHA.

SIRIWARDHANA, Shyrana Abeysinghe 191 Anson Road, London NW2 4AU — MRCS Eng. LRCP Lond. 1979. Prev: Ho. Surg. St. Andrews Hosp. (T) Lond.; Ho. Phys. Fazakerley Gen. Hosp. (T) Liverp.; SHO (A & E) St. Helier Hosp. (T) Carshalton.

*SIRKER, Alexander Avijit 37 Fontmell Close, St Albans, St Albans AL3 5HU — BChir 1996 Camb.

SIROTAKOVA, Maria 51 Lampern Crescent, Billericay CM12 0FE; Timravinaz, Bratislava 81106, Slovak Republic Tel: 00 427 5312077 — MUDr 1973 Komensky Univ. Czech.; MUDr Komensky U Czechoslovakia 1973. Clin. Asst. (Plastic Surg.) S. And. Hosp. Billericay.

SIRR, Hubert Clement Ritchie 7 Shannon Road, Stubbington, Fareham PO14 3RL Tel: 01329 667150 — MB BCh BAO 1973 Dub.; MRCGP 1980. (TC Dub.) Prev: Maj. RAMC; SHO SHAPE BFPO 26.

SIRRI, Teoman Necati Courtlands, 26 Eversley Crescent, London N21 1EJ — MRCS Eng. LRCP Lond. 1981; MSc. (Dist.) Pharmacol. Lond. 1976; BSc (Hons.) Phys. & Biochem. 1974. (St. Mary's) Clin. Asst. (Dermat.) Enfield & Haringey HA; Vis. Prof. Bursa Med. Fac. Turkey. Prev: Regist. (Psychiat.) St. Ann's Hosp. Lond.; SHO (Psychiat., O & G, Geriat. & A & E) N. Middlx. Lond.

SISODIA, Neelam Psychiatric Unit, Derbycity General Hospital, Uttoxeter Rd, Derby DE22 3NE Tel: 01332 623874 — MB BS 1983 Newc.; MRCPsych 1994; MA Uni.Lond. 1997. Cons. (gen. Adult Psychiat.). Prev: Sen. Regist. (Gen. Adult Psychiat.) Univ. Hosp. Nottm.

SISODIYA, Sanjay Mull Institute of Neurology, Queen Square, London WC1N 3BG — MB BChir 1989 Camb.; MRCP (UK) 1991; PhD London 1996.

SISSON, Jennifer 7 St Saviours Place, Leas Road, Guildford GU1 4QN — MB BS 1991 Western Australia.

SISSON, Jonathan Reed 11 Emberson Court, Chalmer Village, Chelmsford CM2 6TP — MB BS 1992 Lond.

SISSONS, Amanda Jane Elizabeth Lane Ends House, Clay Lane, Endon, Stoke-on-Trent ST9 9DP — MB ChB 1985 Birm.; ChB Birm. 1985; MRCGP 1990; DRCOG 1990.

SISSONS, Angela Mary Tel: 023 9282 8281 Fax: 023 9282 2275; Tel: 02392 632544 — MB BS 1967 Durh.

SISSONS, Claire Louise 5 Newland Avenue, Driffield YO25 6TX — BM BS 1998 Nottm.; BM BS Nottm 1998.

SISSONS, Clifford Ernest Grosvenor Nuffield Hospital, Wrexham Road, Chester CH4 7QP Tel: 01244 680444; Cintra, Hillock Lane, Gresford, Wrexham LL12 8YL Tel: 01978 855565 Fax: 01978 854014 — MB ChB Liverp. 1958; FRCP Lond. 1977; MRCP (UK) 1966. (Liverp.) Cons. PhysBUPA Yale Hosp.Wrexham; Cons.Phys.Grosvenor Nuffield Hosp.Chester. Socs: BMA; Brit. Soc. Echocardiogr.; Brit. Hyperlipid. Assn. Prev: Cons. Phys. Wrexham Mealor Hosp. NHS Trust; Sen. Regist. (Med.) Sefton Gen. Hosp. Liverp.; Regist. Profess. Med. Unit. Liverp. Roy. Infirm.

SISSONS, David Ashley The Pines, Kinnerton Lane, Chester CH4 9BG — MB ChB 1973 Liverp.; MRCS Eng. LRCP Lond. 1973.

SISSONS, Guy Richard James Radiology Department, Countess of Chester Hospital, Liverpool Road, Chester CH2 1BQ Tel: 01244 366712 Fax: 01244 366728; 2 The Paddock, Little Heath Road, Christleton, Chester CH3 7AJ Tel: 01244 332159 Fax: 01244 332159 Email: sissons.chester@btinternet.com — MB ChB 1982 Birm.; MRCP (UK) 1985; FRCR 1989; T(R) (CR) 1991. Cons. Diagn. Radiol. Countess of Chester Hosp. Socs: Brit. Inst. Radiol.; Brit. Soc. Interven. Radiol. Prev: Sen. Regist. (Radiol.) Univ. Hosp. Wales & Flinders Med. Centre Adelaide, S, Austral.

SISSONS, Helen Margaret Rysseldene Surgery, 98 Conway Road, Colwyn Bay LL29 7LE Tel: 01492 532807 Fax: 01492 534846; 1 Llys Dedwydd, Ebberston Road W., Rhos-on-Sea, Colwyn Bay LL28 4AP Tel: Colwyn Bay 47375 — BSc (Pharmacol.) Lond. 1976, MB BS 1979; MRCGP 1983; DRCOG 1984; DCH RCP Lond. 1982. (Univ. Coll. Hosp.) Prev: SHO Bronglais Hosp. Aberystwyth; Ho. Surg. Univ. Coll. Hosp. Lond.; Ho. Phys. Treliske Hosp. Truro.

SISSONS, Professor John Gerald Patrick Department of Medicine, University of Cambridge Clinical School, Addenbrooke's Hospital, Hills Road, Cambridge CB2 2QQ Tel: 01223 336849 — MB BS Lond. 1968; MD Lond. 1977; FRCP Lond. 1983; MRCP (UK) 1970; FRCPath 1996. Prof. Med. Univ. Camb. Prev: Prof. Infec. Dis. Roy. Postgrad. Med. Sch. Lond.; Wellcome Sen. Lect. (Med.) Roy. Postgrad. Med. Sch. Lond.; Asst. Mem. Research Inst. Scripps Clinic La Jolla, Calif., USA.

SISSONS, John Peter The Orchard House, 61 Links Lane, Rowlands Castle PO9 6AF — MB BS 1997 Lond.

SISSONS, Mark Christopher John The Grange, Grange Road, Hambleton, Poulton-le-Fylde FY6 9DB — MD 1988 Birm.; MB ChB 1980; MRCPath 1987. Cons. Histopath. Blackpool Vict. Hosp. Prev: Lect. (Path.) Univ. Liverp.

SISSONS, Michael Paul The Orchard House, 61 Links Lane, Rowlands Castle PO9 6AF — MB ChB 1995 Leeds.

SISSONS, Paula Jane The Grange, Grange Road, Hambleton, Poulton-le-Fylde FY6 9DB — MB ChB 1980 Birm.; MRCP (UK) 1983. Med. Off. DSS Blackpool.

SISSOU, Panikos 9 Belgrave Gardens, Oakwood, London N14 4TS Tel: 020 8360 7193 — MB BS 1990 Lond.; BSc (Hons.) Lond. 1989, MB BS 1990.

SITARAS, Dimitrios 44 Vulcan Way, London N7 8XP — Ptychio latrikes 1968 Thessalonika.

SITHAMPARANATHAN, Shamini 56 Compton Road, London SW19 7QD — MB BS 1998 Lond.; MB BS Lond 1998.

SITHAMPARANATHAN, Thuraiappah The Surgery, 191 Westmount Road, London SE9 1XY Tel: 020 8850 1540 Fax: 020 8859 4737 — MB BS 1974 Sri Lanka; MRCS Eng. LRCP Lond. 1986.

SITHAMPARAPILLAI, Sivaja 67 Hayes Chase, West Wickham BR4 0HX — MB BS 1997 Lond.

SITHIRAPATHY, Sivakumary Taara, Avenue Road, Bray, Maidenhead SL6 1UG Tel: 01628 76675 Fax: 01628 76675 — MRCS Eng. LRCP Lond. 1987; MRCOG 1996; DRCOG 1995. (Univ. Colombo, Sri Lanka) GP Regist. Bracknell. Prev: GP/Regist. Cookham, Berks.; Regist. (O & G) Hemel Hempstead Herts.; SHO (O & G) Centr. Middlx. Hosp. Lond.

SITJES LLADO, Narciso 134 Woodway Lane, Coventry CV2 2EJ — LMS 1994 Barcelona; LMS Autonoma Barcelona 1994.

SITLANI, Pushpa Kishin Cherry Trees, 17 Pownall Avenue, Bramhall, Stockport SK7 2HE Tel: 0161 439 6050 — MB BS 1961 Osmania; FRCPath 1981, M 1969. Cons. Haemat. Gp. Laborat. Stepping Hill Hosp. Stockport & N. Derbysh. Health Dist. Socs: Assn. Clin. Pathol. Prev: Sen. Regist. (Haemat.) St. Geo. Hosp. Lond. & S. Lond. Transfus. Sutton;Centre; Regist. (Path.) S. Lond. Hosp. Wom.

SITTAMPALAM, Ganeshwaran 18 Wycherley Crescent, New Barnet, Barnet EN5 1AR — MB BS 1998 Lond.; MB BS Lond 1998.

SITTHER, Mr Balasingh Hillary 94 Old Penkridge Road, Cannock WS11 1HY Tel: 01543 505171 — MB BS 1982 Madras; FRCS Ed. 1989.

SITWELL, Isla Ashley Hurt Sitwell and Partners, Little Common Surgery, 82 Cooden Sea Road, Bexhill-on-Sea TN39 4SP Tel: 01424 845477 Fax: 01424 848225 — MB BChir Camb. 1969. (Camb. & St. Bart.)

SIU, Simon Kai Leung 34A Seafield Road, Dundee DD1 4NP — MB ChB 1998 Dund.; MB ChB Dund 1998.

SIUDA, Zbigniew Edmund 20A West End, Swanland, North Ferriby HU14 3PE — Med. Dipl. Poznan 1936. (Poznan) Prev: Res. O & G Asst. Gen. Hosp. Chorzow.

SIVA, Anjana 259 Lauderdale Mansions, Lauderdale Road, London W9 1LZ Tel: 020 7286 4387 Fax: 020 7286 4387 — MB BChir 1992 Camb. Regist. (Cardiol.) Kent & Canterbury Hosp.

*SIVA, Roshan 2 Bourne Drive, Ravenshead, Nottingham NG15 9FN — MB BS 1996 Lond.

SIVA PRAKASH, Pappali Gopalan G C P Systems Ltd., Director, 222 Metro Central, 119 Newington Causeway, London SE1 6BW Tel: 020 79678 760 — MB BS 1975 Kerala; MB BS Kerala, India 1975; MSc Computer Studies S. Glam.; DMRT Eng.; DRM Delhi; DTCD Delhi. (Kottam Med. Coll., Kerala) Company Dir. G.C.P. Systems Lond. Prev: IT Cons. Centr. Health Outcodes Unit, Dept. of Health, Lond.

SIVABALAN, Ponnudurai Edge Hill Health Centre, Crosfield Road, Liverpool L7 5QL Tel: 0151 260 2777 — MB BS 1979 Sri Lanka; DGM RCP Lond. 1987.

SIVABALAN, Thambimuthu 57B Days Lane, Biddenham, Bedford MK40 4AE — MB BS 1971 Ceylon; MRCOG 1983.

SIVABALASINGHAM, Suganya 5 Wyresdale Crescent, Perivale, Greenford UB6 8TQ — MB BS 1997 Lond.; BSc Lond. 1994. (St Bart's Lond.) SHO Rotat. (Med.).

SIVAGAMASUNDARI, Umapathy 5 Cooper Close, Langstone, Newport NP18 2LD Tel: 01633 413962 — MB BS 1976 Madras;

MRCPsych 1989. Cons. Psychiat. Gwent Community NHS Trust. Prev: Sen. Regist. Phoenix Trust Bristol.

SIVAGNANAM, Chelliah (Surgery), 137 Greenwich South St., Greenwich, London SE10 8PP Tel: 020 8691 8999; 3 Papillons Walk, London SE3 9SF — MB BS 1955 Ceylon.

SIVAGNANAM, Thamotharampillai Royal Infirmary, Blackburn Tel: 01254 687235; 20 Bosburn Drive, Mellor Brook, Blackburn BB2 7PA Tel: 01254 813281 — MB BS 1972 Sri Lanka; FFA RCS Eng. 1982. Cons. Anaesth. & Pain Relief Roy. Infirm. Blackburn. Socs: Assn. Anaesth.; Pain Soc.; NW Pain Soc. & Palliat. Med.

SIVAGNANASUNDARAM, Sivasundaram Winlaton Surgery, 139 Winlaton Road, Bromley BR1 5QA Tel: 020 8698 1810 — MB BS 1978 Sri Lanka; LMSSA Lond. 1989. (Colombo, Sri Lanka) Socs: Med. Protec. Soc.

SIVAGNANAVEL, Sarathadevi 34 Leamington Avenue, Morden SM4 4DW Tel: 020 8542 7608 — MB BS 1966 Ceylon.

SIVAGURU, Arulmaran 5 Maclean Avenue, Loughborough LE11 5XX — MB ChB 1991 Leeds.

SIVAJI, Mr Chellappan 55 Nelson Road, Leigh-on-Sea SS9 3HX — MB BS 1986 Madurai Kamaraj Univ. India; FRCS Eng. 1992.

SIVAKUMAR, Branavan 7 Gossington Close, Chislehurst BR7 6TG — MB BS 1998 Lond.; MB BS Lond 1998.

SIVAKUMAR, Kanagaratnam Department Genitourinary Medicine, Queen Elizabeth Hospital, Gayton Road, King's Lynn PE30 4ET Fax: 01553 613833; 3 Old Kiln, West Winch, King's Lynn PE33 0EG Tel: 01553 841975 — MB BS 1980 Colombo; FRCP 1998, MRCP 1986; LRCP LRCS Ed. LRCPS Glas. 1985. Cons. Phys. (Genitourin. Med.) Qu. Eliz. Hosp., King's Lynn & Dist. Hosp. PeterBoro. Prev: Sen. Regist. (Genitourin. Med.) Bournemouth & Soton. Gp. Hosps.

SIVAKUMAR, Kandiah Invicta Community Care NHS Trust, Priority House, Hermitage Lane, Maidstone ME16 9PH Tel: 01622 725000 Fax: 01622 725290; 7 Gossington Close, Chislehurst BR7 6TG Tel: 020 8468 7181 — MB BS Ceylon 1970; DPM Eng. 1979; MRCPsych 1979; FRCPsych 1996. (University of Ceylon, Colombo) Cons. (Psychiat.) Invicta Community Care NHS Trust; Hon. Cons. (Psychiat.) KCH; Hon. Sen. Lect. Div. of Psychiat. Guys Hosp. Lond.

SIVAKUMAR, Mr Muthuthamby Queen Elizabeth, Queen Mother Hospital, Margate CT9 4AN Tel: 01803 225549 Email: msivakumar@resed.ac.uk — MB BS 1983 Colombo; FRCS Ed. 1992. Staff Surg. Prev: Sur. Regist. Jersey Gen. Hosp. Cl.; SHO, Surg. Thanet Dist. Gen. Hosp.

SIVAKUMAR, Paramasivam Luton & Dunstable Hospital, Lewsey Road, Luton LU4 0DZ Tel: 01582 491122 Fax: 01582 497280; 273 Luton Road, Harpenden AL5 3LN Tel: 01582 461695 Email: p.siva@connect-2.co.uk — MB BS 1979 Sri Lanka; MRCP (UK) 1989; MRCS Eng. LRCP Lond.1986; DCH RCP Lond. 1987. Cons. Paediat. Luton & Dunstable Hosp.

SIVAKUMAR, Ranjesthanayakey 55 Elm Drive, St Albans AL4 0EH — MB BS 1977 Colombo.

SIVAKUMAR, Sinnathamby 29 Birch Hill Crescent, Rochdale OL12 9QF; 13 Petrel Close, Bamford, Rochdale OL11 5QT — MB BS 1978 Sri Lanka; LMSSA Lond. 1990. Staff Grade(Ophth.) Birch Hill Hosp. Rochdale.

SIVAKUMAR, Thaiman Queens Avenue Surgery, 46 Queens Avenue, Muswell Hill, London N10 3BJ Tel: 020 8883 1846 Fax: 020 8365 2265; 2 Larkfield Avenue, Harrow HA3 8NF Tel: 020 8907 5616 Email: thaimans@aol.com — MB BS 1975 Sri Lanka; MRCOG 1987. GP.

SIVAKUMARAN, Muttuswamy 2A Thorpe Avenue, Peterborough PE3 6LA — MB BS 1979 Peradeniya, Sri Lanka; LRCP LRCS Ed. LRCPS Glas. 1983; MRCP (UK) 1986.

SIVAKUMARAN, Shantha Ruweena 182 Holmes Chapel Road, Congleton CW12 4QB — BChir 1996 Camb.

SIVAKUMARAN, Sivagnanam 3 Sackville Close, New Malden KT3 5QG — MB BS 1963 Ceylon; MRCPath 1980.

SIVAKUMARAN, Vijayasegaram 72 Rhydydefaid Drive, Skeety, Swansea SA2 8AN — MB BS 1975 Sri Lanka; MRCS Eng. LRCP Lond. 1982.

SIVALOGANATHAN, Malathy 15 Verulam Avenue, Purley CR8 3NR — MB BS 1994 Lond.

SIVALOGANATHAN, Sampanthanathan 15 Verulam Avenue, Purley CR8 3NR — MB BS 1967 Ceylon.

SIVALOGANATHAN, Saraswathy 15 Verulam Avenue, Purley CR8 3NR — MB BS 1967 Ceylon; MRCPsych 1980; T(Psych) 1991.

SIVANANDAN, Manoranjini 4 Tollgate Drive, London SE21 7LS — MB BS 1978 Sri Lanka; FFA RCSI 1987.

SIVANANTHAN, Anushtayini Elderly Mental Health Directorate, West Cheshire Hospital, Liverpool Road, Chester CH2 1UL Tel: 01244 364158 — MB ChB 1991 Liverp.; MRCPsych 1995; DGM 1997. (L'pool) Cons. (Elderly Ment. Health).

SIVANANTHAN, Nadarajah Quedgeley Medical Centre, Olympus Park, Quedgeley, Gloucester GL2 4NF Tel: 01452 728882 — MB BS 1975 Sri Lanka; MRCP (UK) 1982; LRCP LRCS Ed. LRCPS Glas. 1982. (Univ. Ceylon, Colombo-Sri Lanka) Socs: Collegiate Mem. RCP Lond. Prev: Regist. Rotat. (Med.) Dudley HA; Regist. (Med.) Leighton Hosp. Crewe.

SIVANANTHAN, Nalliah Alexandra Surgery, 125 Alexandra Park Road, London N22 7UN Tel: 020 8888 2518; 279 Stradbroke Grove, Clayhall, Ilford IG5 0DH Tel: 020 8924 9512 Email: siva@stradbroke.u_net.com — MB BS 1972 Ceylon; MRCOG (UK) 1982. Socs: Med. Inst. of Tamil.

SIVANANTHAN, Sureshan Siddhartha Russell Ct, Claremont St., Belfast BT9 6JX — MB BCh BAO 1997 Belf.

SIVANANTHAN, Uduvil Mohanaraj 9 Portland Grove, Westbury Park, Clayton, Newcastle ST5 4JH Tel: 01782 660374 — MB BS 1979 Colombo; MRCP (UK) 1984; DMRD Lond. 1987.

SIVANESAN, Ratnam (Surgery), 6 Townsend Road, Southall UB1 1EX Tel: 020 8574 2794 — MB BS 1978 Ceylon; MRCP (UK) 1978; DCH Lond. 1978; DRCOG Lond. 1980. (Ceylon)

SIVANESAN, Vaithilingam Nagalingam Brereton Surgery, 88 Main Street, Brereton, Rugeley WS15 1DU Tel: 01889 575560 Fax: 01889 575560 — MB BS 1971 Ceylon.

SIVAPALAN, Sivagnanam Department of Genitourinary Medicine, North Staffs Hospital NHS Trust, Hartshill Road, Stoke-on-Trent ST4 7PA Tel: 01782 554135 Fax: 01782 846660 — MB BS 1974 Sri Lanka; MRCOG 1986. (Colombo Med. Sch. Univ. Ceylon) Cons. Genitourin. Med. N. Staffs. HA. Prev: Sen. Regist. (Genitourin. Med.) E. Dorset HA; Regist. (O & G) Clwyd HA.

SIVAPATHASUNDARAM, Loshana 64 Cruise Road, Nether Green, Sheffield S11 7EF — MB ChB 1994 Sheff.

SIVAPATHASUNDARAM, Paraneetharan 1 Percival Road, Hornchurch RM11 2AH — MB ChB 1997 Sheff.

SIVAPATHASUNDARAM, Mr Vythilingam Royal London Hospital, Whitechapel Road, London E1 1BB Tel: 020 7377 7240; 18 Highcliffe Gardens, Redbridge, Ilford IG4 5HR Tel: 020 8924 7950 — MB BS 1967 Ceylon; MRCOG 1981; FRCOG 1995. Cons. O & G Roy. Lond. Hosp. Socs: Fell. Roy. Soc. Med.

SIVAPATHASUNTHARAM, Logeswary 317 Dunchurch Road, Rugby CV22 6HT Tel: 01788 522548 — MB BS 1972 Ceylon.

SIVAPRAGASAM, Mr Sinnathamby Worcestershire Acute Hospitals NHS Trust, Alexandra Hospital, Woodrow Drive, Redditch B98 7UB — MB BS 1974 Sri Lanka; FRCS Eng. 1989; FRCS Ed. 1986; MRCS Eng. LRCP Lond. 1986. (Colombo, Sri Lanka) Cons. Surg. (Gastroenterol.) Alexandra Hosp. Redditch. Socs: BMA; Hosp. Cons. & Spec. Comm. (HCSC); Fell. ASGBI.

SIVARAJAH, Tharmalingam Flat 2, Donne Court, Orpington Hospital, Sevenoaks Road, Orpington BR6 9JU; 2 Harefield Close, Enfield EN2 8NQ — MRCS Eng. LRCP 1988 Lond.; MRCS Eng LRCP Lond. 1988.

SIVARAJAN, Kandiah 89 Broadwater Road, Tooting, London SW17 0DY Tel: 020 8767 1134 — MB BS 1972 Sri Lanka.

SIVARAJAN, Sweeta Carrfield Medical Centre, Carrfield Street, Sheffield S8 9SG; 24 Selby Close, Walton, Chesterfield S40 3HA — MB BS 1972 Kerala. (Kottayam Med. Coll.)

SIVARAJAN, Vivek 24 Selby Close, Walton, Chesterfield S40 3HA — MB ChB 1997 Ed.

SIVARAMALINGAM, Thillaiampalam Ravishanker 75 Oaklands Road, London W7 2DT Tel: 020 8579 3319 — MB BS 1988 Lond.; MRCGP 1997; DFFP 1997; DCH 1996; DRCOG 1996. (Char. Cross & Westm.)

SIVARDEEN, Gani Mathul Fawzia Cromartie Street Surgery, 39 Cromartie Street, Longton, Stoke-on-Trent ST3 4LG Tel: 01782 329488 — MB BS 1963 Ceylon; MCOphth 1989; DO Eng. 1977. (Colombo) GP Stoke-on-Trent; Med. Pract. (Ophth.) Stoke-on-Trent & Stafford.

SIVARDEEN

SIVARDEEN, Mr Khawaja Ashraff Ziali 11 Meliden Way, Stoke-on-Trent ST4 5DZ — BM BS 1994 Nottm.

SIVASAMBU, Kuhan Room 192, D Block, Arrowe Park Hospital, Upton, Wirral CH49 5PE — MB BCh 1997 Wales.

SIVASANKER, Kemraj 5 Oakleigh Avenue, Edgware HA8 5DT Tel: 020 8952 0058 — MB BS 1969 Patna; MD (Paediat.) Patna 1974. (P. of Wales Med. Coll.) Community Paediat. (Audiol. & Adopt.) Middlx. Socs: Fell. Roy. Inst. Pub. Health & Hyg.; Fac. Comm. Health. Prev: Regist. (Paediat.) Chester City Hosp. & W. Chesh. Hosp. Matern. Wing Chester; SHO (Paediat.) Hemel Hempstead Gen. Hosp.

SIVASINMYANANTHAN, Kathiravellupillai The Surgery, 326 Philip Lane, Tottenham, London N15 4AB Tel: 020 8808 0322 — MB BS 1974 Sri Lanka; LRCP LRCS Ed. LRCPS Glas. 1984; DPD 1998. Socs: BMA. Prev: Clin. Asst. (Rheum.) Chase Farm Hosp. Enfield; SHO (Rheum.) Devonsh. Roy. Hosp. Derby; SHO (Geriat.) P'boro Hosp. Lond.

SIVASUBRAMANIAM, Chandrika 18 Cumberlands, Kenley CR8 5DX — MB BS 1983 Lond.

SIVATHASAN, Sivadevi 303 Hempstead Road, Hempstead, Gillingham ME7 3QJ — MB BS 1970 Ceylon; FFA RCS Eng. 1980. (Ceylon)

SIVATHASAN, Sivalingam 60 Central Hill, Upper Norwood, London SE19 1DT Tel: 020 8670 7117 Fax: 020 8670 1671; 2A Oakfield Gardens, Beckenham BR3 3AZ Tel: 020 8663 6668 — MB BS 1978 Sri Lanka; MRCS Eng. LRCP Lond. 1987; MRCOG 1991; DRCOG 1991. (Faculty of Medicine University of Colombo, Sri Lanka) GP. Socs: Med. Protec. Soc.; Roy. Coll. Obst. & Gyns. Prev: Regist. (O & G).

SIVAYOHAM, Indira S East Lancashire Federated Ophthalmic Services, The Royal Infirmary, Blackburn BB2 3LR Tel: 01254 263555 Fax: 01254 662043; Shakthi Vihar, 23 Ryburn Avenue, Blackburn BB2 7AU Tel: 01254 662887 — MB BS 1958 Ceylon; FRCS Eng. 1963; FRCOphth 1988. Cons. Ophth. Surg. Roy. Infirm. Blackburn & Burnley Gen. Hosp. Socs: Eur. Soc. Cataract & Refractive Surgs.; UK Intra Ocular Implant Soc.; BMA. Prev: Cons. Ophth. Surg. Lancaster Moor Hosp.; Cons. Ophth. Surg. W. of Eng. Eye Infirm. Exeter; Cons. Ophth. Surg. Teachg. Hosp. Colombo, Sri Lanka.

SIVAYOHAM, Narani 5 Copperfield Court, 146 Worple Road, Wimbledon, London SW20 8QA — MB ChB 1992 Liverp.; BSc (Hons.) Liverp. 1989; MRCP (UK) 1996. (Liverp.) Specialist Regist. Rotat. (A & E Med.) St. Geo. Hosp. Lond. Prev: SHO Rotat. (Med.) S. Cleveland Hosp. Middlesbrough.

SIVAYOHAM, Sabapathy 23 Ryburn Avenue, Blackburn BB2 7AU Tel: 01254 662887 — MB BS Ceylon 1961; MD Colombo 1981; MFPHM RCP (UK) 1990; MFCM 1974; DIH Eng. 1973; DTPH 1972. Cons. Communicable Dis. Control & Pub. Health Med. S. Lancs. HA Eccleston, Chorley. Socs: Manch. Med. Soc. (Pres. Pub. Health Sect.). Prev: Dir. of Pub. Health Chorley & S. Ribble HA; Specialist (Community Med.) S. Cumbria HA.

SIVAYOKAN, Ponniah Department of Anaesthetics, General Hospital, Bishop Auckland DL14 6AD — MB BS 1970 Ceylon; FFA RCS Eng. 1983; DA Eng. 1980. Cons. Anaesth. Gen. Hosp. Bishop Auckland. Prev: Regist. (Anaesth.) PeterBoro. Dist. Hosp.; Sen. Regist. (Anaesth.) Addenbrooks Hosp. Camb.; Sen. Regist. (Anaesth.) City Gen. Stoke on Trent.

SIVES, Deirdra Ann 41 Glendevon Park, Winchburgh, Broxburn EH52 6UF — MB ChB 1990 Ed.

SIVITER, Gretchen 59 Acres Road, Chorlton, Manchester M21 9EB Tel: 0161 881 2809 — MB ChB 1992 Manch.

SIVORI, Robert Emmanuel 14 Hollybank Road, Mossley Hill, Liverpool L18 1HP — MB ChB 1997 Liverp.

SIVRIDIS, Anestis Rampton Hospital, Retford DN22 0PD — Ptychio Iatrikes 1977 Thessalonika.

SIVYER, Janet Elizabeth Regent Street Surgery, 73 Regent Street, Stonehouse GL10 2AA Tel: 01453 822145 Fax: 01453 821663; Woodfield Cottage, 157 Slad Road, Stroud GL5 1RD — MB ChB 1981 Sheff.; DRCOG 1984.

SIX, Serge Pembroke Surgery, 9 Eldon Square, Reading RG1 4DP; 11 Allcroft Road, Reading RG1 5HJ Tel: 01734 872550 — MD 1977 Brussels. Hon. Sec. BMA W. Berks. Div. Socs: BMA (Chairm. Oxf. Regional Counc.).

SIXSMITH, Andrew Milton 15 South Row, Horsforth, Leeds LS18 4AA — MB ChB 1994 Leeds.

***SIXSMITH, Clare** 6 Cliff Castle, Castle Hill, Seaton EX12 2QW Email: clairesixsmith@hotmail.com — BM BCh 1998 Oxf.; BM BCh Oxf 1998.

SIXSMITH, Dona Jeromi Inoka 15 Melyd Avenue, Prestatyn LL19 8RN — MB ChB 1995 Leeds.

SIXSMITH, Mark 39 Antonine Way, Houghton, Carlisle CA3 0LG — MB ChB 1994 Manch.

***SIZER, Andrew Richard** 99 Rhymney Street, Cardiff CF24 4DH — MB BCh 1994 Wales; PhD Wales 1991, BSc (Hons.) 1988, MB BCh 1994.

SIZER, Angela Jane 1 Quayside Walk, Marchwood, Southampton SO40 4AH — MB BS 1996 Lond.

SIZER, Bruce Francis 23 Guithavon Street, Witham CM8 1BJ — MB ChB 1983 Birm.; ChB Birm. 1983.

SIZER, Elizabeth 119 Dunvegan Road, London SE9 1SD — MB BS 1993 Lond.

SIZER, Jeremy Mark 1 Riverside View, Milton Ernest, Bedford MK44 1SG Email: jsizer007@aol.com — MB BS 1985 Lond.; FCAnaesth 1990; DCH RCP Lond. 1988. (Kings) Cons. (Anaesth.) Bedford Hosp. NHS Trust.

SIZER, Karen Ann 28 Hillmead Gardens, Bedhampton, Havant PO9 3NL — BM 1978 Soton.

SIZMUR, Fiona Margaret Meadow Cottage, Forest Road, Burley, Ringwood BH24 4DQ; 21 Chaworth Road, Ottershaw, Chertsey KT16 0PF — MB ChB 1989 Liverp. Regist. (O & G) Bournemouth Hosp. Prev: Regist. (O & G) Leicester Gen. Hosp.; SHO (O & G) Leicester Roy. Infirm.

SJOLIN, Mr Soren Upton West Suffolk Hospital, Hardwick Lane, Bury St Edmunds IP33 2QZ Tel: 01284 712552 Fax: 01284 712551 — MD 1981 Odense; FRCS (Orth.) 1996. (Odense, Denmark, 1981) Cons. Orthop. Surg. W. Suff. Hosp. Bury St Edmunds. Prev: Sen. Regist. Roy. Infirm. Edin.

SKAIFE, Paul Gerard Patrick 21 Towers Road, Liverpool L16 8NT — MB ChB 1990 Leeds.

SKAILES, Geraldine Elizabeth Phyllis Cancer Services Directorate, Royal Preston Hospital, Sharoe Green Lane N., Fulwood, Preston PR2 9HT Tel: 01772 710984 Fax: 01772 710963; Whinfell, Woodhouse Lane, Heversham, Milnthorpe LA7 7EW Tel: 015395 63941 — MB BS 1988 Lond.; MRCP (UK) 1991; FRCR 1995. Cons. (Clin. Oncol.) Roy. Preston Hosp.

SKALICKA, Anna Elizabeth Ave Group Practice, 2 Elizabeth Avenue, London N1 3BS Tel: 020 7226 6363 — MB ChB 1973 Leeds; MRCP (U.K.) 1975; MRCGP 1977; DCH Eng. 1977.

SKAN, Delia Ida Mary 7 Notting Hill, Belfast BT9 5NS — MB BCh BAO 1975 Belf.; MB BCh BAO (Hons.) Belf. 1975; MRCP (UK) 1980; MFOM RCPI 1992, AFOM 1987; MRCGP 1982; DCH RCPSI 1977. Occupat. Physic., Employ. Med. Advis. Serv. DHSS.

SKAN, John Phillip 20 Penrhyn Road, Hunters Bar, Sheffield S11 8UL Tel: 0114 266 0793 Email: jskan@aol.com — MB ChB 1981 Sheff.

SKANDEROWICZ, Mr Andrew George 2 Wentworth Drive, Lichfield WS14 9HN Tel: 01543 257454 — MB BS 1974 Lond.; FRCS Eng. 1979; MRCS Eng. LRCP Lond. 1974. (St. Bart.) Socs: BACS.

SKARBEK, Count Andrew Charles 26 Belsize Square, London NW3 4HU Tel: 020 7794 6857 — MRCS Eng. LRCP Lond. 1954; PhD Lond. 1969, MB BS 1954; FRCPsych 1983, M 1971. (St. Mary's) Cons. Psychotherap. to Basildon, Runwell & Rochford Hosps.; Dir. Clinic of Psychotherap. Lond. Socs: Brit. Psycho-Anal. Soc. Prev: Assoc. Prof. Psychiat. Univ. Ottawa.

SKARIA, Joseph Hillcrest Medical Centre, Pryce Street, Mountain Ash CF45 3NT Tel: 01443 473783 Fax: 01443 477420; Pukkunnel, 1 Ynys y Coed, Llandaff, Cardiff CF5 2LU — MD 1975 Banaras Hindu; MB BS 1971. Socs: Soc. Occupat. Med., Assur. Med. Soc. & Christian Med. Fell.sh.

SKARROTT, Pauline Helen Ling House Surgeries, 130 Skipton Road, Keighley BD21 3AN Tel: 01535 605747 Fax: 01535 602901 — MB ChB 1979 Birm.

SKARSTEN, Anders Roy Hargrave Bracton Clinic, Bexley Hospital, Old Bexley Lane, Bexley DA5 2BW Tel: 01322 294300 Fax: 01322 293595; 43 Codicote Road, Welwyn AL6 9TT Tel: 0374

892164 Fax: 020 7787 0739 Email: skarsten@dircon.co.uk — MB BS 1990 Lond.; BSc (Pharmacol.) Lond. 1987. Forens. Research Fell. Bracton Clinic UMDS Dept. Psychiat. Guy's Hosp. Lond.

SKEA, George Keillor 15 The Shires, Gilwern, Abergavenny NP7 0EX — MB ChB 1984 Glas. SHO (Anaesth.) Leicester Roy. Infirm.

SKEATES, Stuart John North Baddesley Health Centre, Norton Welch Close, Fleming Avenue, North Baddesley, Southampton SO52 9EP Tel: 023 8073 4523 Fax: 023 8073 0287; 55 Cherville Street, Romsey SO51 8FB Tel: 01794 522192 — MB BS 1974 Lond.; MA (Mathematics) Camb. 1972; MRCGP 1980; DRCOG 1978. Course Organiser Soton.

SKEATH, Thalia Helen Old Home Farm, Compton St., Compton Dundon, Somerton TA11 6PS — MB ChB 1986 Leeds; MRCPsych 1996. (Leeds) Clin. Med. Off. (Psychiat.) Avalon Trust Som. Prev: Regist. (Psychiat.) Avalon Trust Som.; Regist. (Psychiat.) Norwich HA.

SKEATS, Christina Jane 42 Morris Road, South Nutfield, Redhill RH1 5SA — MB ChB 1987 Sheff.

SKEAVINGTON, John Reginald Crown House Surgery, Chapelgate, Retford DN22 6NX Tel: 01777 703672; Birnam House, Stone Lane, North Wheatley, Retford DN22 9DF Tel: 01427 880759 — MB ChB 1960 Sheff.; MRCP Lond. 1968. (Sheff.) p/t Gen. Practitioner Princip. (half time). Socs: BMA.(1960-2000); Med. Charitable Soc. of the W. Riding of the Co. of York. Prev: Med. Regist. Derbysh. Roy. Infirm. Ho. Surg. Dept. Neurol. Surg. Roy.; Infirm. Sheff.; Ho. Phys. City Gen. Hosp. Sheff.

SKEEN, Elizabeth Susan Garden Flat, Llanharan House, Llanharan, Pontyclun CF72 9NR — MB BS 1989 Melbourne.

SKEENS, Erwine Mary (retired) 8 North Street, Fowey PL23 1DD — MRCS Eng. LRCP Lond. 1954.

SKEENS, Esmond Courtenay (retired) Amity House, 8 North St., Fowey PL23 1DD — MB ChB 1955 Bristol.

***SKEET, Lynsey Jane** Copita, Colchester Rd, Wivenhoe, Colchester CO7 9EU — MB ChB 1997 Leeds.

SKEET, William Anthony George 2A Sydervelt Road, Canvey Island SS8 9EG — MB ChB 1962 St. And.; Dip. Pract. Dermat. Wales 1992; DObst RCOG 1966. (St. And.) Clin. Asst. (Dermat.) Basildon Hosp.

SKEETE, Harry Jerome c/o Drive John Glees, 5 Leopold Ct., Leopold Avenue, Wimbledon, London SW19 7EU Tel: 020 8946 2204 — MB BS 1969 W. Indies; FRCR 1976; DMRT Liverp. 1973.

SKEGGS, David Bartholomew Lyndon Radiotherapy Department, Cromwell Hospital, London SW5 0TU Tel: 020 7460 2000 Fax: 020 7460 5622; The Coach House, Barnes Common, London SW13 0HS Tel: 020 8876 7929 Fax: 020 8876 7929 — BM BCh 1952 Oxf.; MA Oxf. 1952; FRCR; FFR 1964; DMRT Eng. 1961. (Oxf. & St. Bart.) Hon. Cons. Radiother. Roy. Free Hosp. Lond.; Dir. (Radiother. & Oncol.) Cromwell Hosp.; Hon. Cons. Radiother. Roy. N. Hosp. Lond. Prev: Dir. (Radiother.) Roy. Free Hosp. Lond.; Sen. Regist. (Radiother.) St. Bart. Hosp. Lond.; Chairm. Bd. Examrs. Part 1 FRCR.

SKEGGS, Peter Lyndon (retired) Valley House, Preston Candover, Basingstoke RG25 2DN — MA, BM BCh Oxf. 1945; FRCPath (Hon.) 1994. Prev: Local Treasury Med. Off.

SKEHAN, John Douglas Glenfield NHS Trust, Groby Road, Leicester LE3 9QP Tel: 0116 256 3888 Fax: 0116 231 4751; 87 Chaveney Road, Quorn, Loughborough LE12 8AB Tel: 01509 620325 — MB BS 1977 Lond.; BSc (Hons.) Lond. 1974, MB BS 1977; FRCP (UK) 1996; MRCP (UK) 1980. (Lond. Hosp.) Cons. Cardiol. Glenfield NHS Trust Leics.; Clin. Director, CardioRespirat. Directorate, Univ. Hosp.s Leicester Trust. Socs: Brit. Cardiac Soc.; (Counc. Mem.) Brit. Pacing & Electrophysiol. Gp.; BMA. Prev: Jun. Research Fell. Brit. Heart Foundat. Lond. Hosp.; Sen. Regist. Cardiac Dept. Lond. Hosp. Whitechapel; Regist. (Med.) OldCh. Hosp. Romford & Lond. Hosp.

SKEHAN, Paul Francis John 5 Orchard Gate, Larkhall ML9 1HA — MB BCh BAO 1982 NUI.

SKELDON, Ian 4 Staveley Road, Ashford TW15 1TF — MB ChB 1977 Bristol.

SKELKER, Miriam Hilary Windmill Medical Practice, 65 Shoot Up Hill, London NW2 3PS Tel: 020 8452 7646 Fax: 020 8450 2319 — MB BS 1985 Lond.

SKELLERN, Elizabeth PM (retired) Snailscroft Farm, Waytown, Bridport DT6 5LF — MB BS 1975 Lond. Clin. Asst. (Rheum.) Bridport. Prev: GP Whitehaven & Egremont.

SKELLERN, Mr George Skellern and Partners, Bridport Medical Centre, North Allington, Bridport DT6 5DU Tel: 01308 421109 Fax: 01308 420869; Snailscroft Farm, Waytown, Bridport DT6 5LF Tel: 01308 488498 — MB BS 1974 Lond.; FRCS Eng. 1979; MRCS Eng. LRCP Lond. 1974. (Roy. Free) Clin. Asst. (Gen. Surg. & Orthop.) Dorset.

SKELLETT, Sophie Clare Christina Little Heath House, Kent Hatch Road, Limpsfield Chart, Oxted RH8 0SZ — MB BChir 1990 Camb.; MA Camb. 1990; MRCP (UK) 1995. (Camb. Univ. & Guy's Hosp.) Paediat. Regist. Guy's Hosp. Prev: Regist. (Paediat.) FarnBoro. Hosp.; SHO (Paediat.) Hammersmith & Qu. Charlottes Hosps.; SHO Rotat. (Paediat.) Guy's & Lewisham Hosps.

SKELLY, Cecil Michael Prebend Street Surgery, 15 Prebend Street, London N1 8PG Tel: 020 7226 9090 Fax: 020 7354 3330 — MB BCh BAO 1970 NUI.

SKELLY, Florence Joan (retired) 2 Thorny Road, Douglas IM2 5ED — MB ChB 1947 Leeds. Prev: Assoc. Specialist Hortham Hosp. Almonsbury & Brentry Hosp. Bristol.

SKELLY, Robert Henry Flat 1, 7 Clumber CrescentS., Nottingham NG7 1EH — MB BS 1989 Lond.; MRCP (UK) 1993.

SKELLY, Roderick Thomas Dept of Surgery, Royal Victoria Hospital, Belfast BT12 6BJ; 46 Lyttlesdale, Garvagh, Coleraine BT51 5EA — MB BCh BAO 1995 Belf.

SKELLY, William John 18 Sussex Place, Slough SL1 1NS Tel: 01753 26478 — MB BCh BAO 1951 Belf. (Qu. Univ. Belf.) Socs: Brit. Med. Acupunc. Soc.

SKELSEY, Eleanor Lois (retired) Room 16, Astell, Overton Park Road, Cheltenham GL50 3BT Tel: 01242 573480 — MRCS Eng. LRCP Lond. 1942.

SKELTON, Carol Elizabeth 7 Corstorphine Hill Avenue, Edinburgh EH12 6LF — MB BCh BAO 1985 Belf.; MRCGP 1990; DRCOG 1989. Regist. (Rehabil. Med.) Astley Ainslie Hosp. Edin.

SKELTON, David Andrew Wingfield South Road Medical Centre, 40 South Road, Kingswood, Bristol Tel: 0117 967 5135; High Croft, Bury Hill, Winterbourne Down, Bristol BS36 1AD — MRCS Eng. LRCP Lond. 1964; DObst RCOG 1967.

SKELTON, Janina Beth Chestnut Lodge, Chestnut Grove, Nottingham NG3 5AD — MB ChB 1991 Birm.; ChB Birm. 1991.

SKELTON, Marie Lilian 178 Charlton Road, London SE7 7DW — MB ChB 1941 Bristol.

SKELTON, Martin Oliver (retired) 178 Charlton Road, London SE7 7DW Tel: 020 8856 1170 — MB ChB 1941 Bristol; FRCPath 1963. Prev: Pathol. Gp. Laborat. Lewisham.

SKELTON, Norman John (retired) 27 Bradda Avenue, Burnside, Rutherglen, Glasgow G73 5BZ — MB ChB 1954 Glas.; DPH Glas. 1966.

SKELTON, Philip Edmund The Maltings Family Practice, 10 Victoria Street, St Albans AL1 3JB Tel: 01727 853296 Fax: 01727 862498; 139 Beechwood Avenue, St Albans AL1 4XX — MB BS 1976 Lond. (St. Geo.) Prev: Trainee GP Luton & Dunstable VTS; Ho. Phys. St. Albans City Hosp.; Ho. Surg. Luton & Dunstable Hosp.

SKELTON, Ruth Elizabeth Hull Maternity Hospital, Hedon Road, Hull HU9 5LX Tel: 01482 376215 Email: r.e.skelton@leeds.ac.uk; 18 Willow Grove, Beverley HU17 8DS — BM BS 1985 Nottm.; MRCP (UK) 1989; DRCOG 1987; RCPCH. Cons. Paediat. Hull. Matern. Hosp. Socs: Roy. Coll. Paediat. & Child Health. Prev: Lect. (Paediat.) Leeds Univ. & Leeds Gen. Infirm.; Fell. (Neonat..) King Geo. V Hosp. Sydney.

SKELTON, Vanessa Ann Tel: 0207 737 4000 — MB BS 1991 Lond.; FRCA 1996. (Guy's Hospital) Cons. Anaesthetics, King's Coll. Hosp. Lond.

SKENE, Mr Anthony Iain Royal Bournemouth Hospital, Castle Lane East, Burley, Bournemouth BH7 7DW Tel: 01202 704070 Fax: 01202 704069; The Old Rectory, Madresfield, Malvern WR13 5AB Tel: 01425 403413, 01684 572495 Fax: 01425 402032 — BM 1981 Soton.; MS Soton. 1990; FRCS Ed. 1986. (Univ. Soton. Med. Sch.) Cons. Surg. Roy. Bournemouth Hosp. Socs: Brit. Assn. Surgs. Oncol.; Brit. Assn. Endocrine Surgs.; Assn. Surg. Prev: Sen. Regist. & Regist. (Surg.) Chelsea W.m. Hosp. Lond.; Regist. (Surg.) Roy. Marsden Hosp. Lond.; SHO Rotat. (Surg.) Basingstoke Dist. Hosp.

SKENE

SKENE, Christopher Graham (2F2) 6 Roseneath Terrace, Edinburgh EH9 1JN — MB ChB 1997 Ed.

SKENE-SMITH, Hilary Susan 10 The Glebe, Belbroughton, Stourbridge DY9 9TH — MB ChB 1963 Birm.

SKENNERTON, Deborah Elaine 5 Tichborne, Thame OX9 3XJ — MB ChB 1991 Leic. SHO Rotat. (Surg.) Wycombe Gen. Hosp.

SKENSVED, Henrik 61 Chalcot Road, London NW1 8LY — MD 1983 Aarhus; T(OG) 1994.

SKEOCH, Aidan Robert Forest House Surgery, 25 Leicester Road, Shepshed, Loughborough LE12 9DF Tel: 01509 508412; 7 Mill Close, Shepshed, Loughborough LE12 9UA Tel: 01509 650697 — MB BS 1986 Lond. (St. Bart.)

SKEOCH, Charles Hugh 21 Burnside Road, Rutherglen, Glasgow G73 4RW — MB ChB 1978 Manch.

SKEOCH, Helen Mary Craigallian Avenue Surgery, 11 Craigallian Avenue, Cambuslang, Glasgow G72 8RW Tel: 0141 641 3129 — MB ChB 1978 Manch.

SKEOCH, Jill Elizabeth Cill Chuimein Medical Practice, Fort Augustus PH32 4BN Tel: 01320 366216 Fax: 01320 366649; Shorelands, Fort Augustus PH32 4BN Tel: 01320 366216 Fax: 01320 366649 — BM 1982 Soton.; MRCGP 1987; DRCOG 1987.

SKERRETT, Francis David (retired) The Surgery, Rawlings Lane, Fowey PL23 1DT Tel: 01726 832464 — MB ChB 1958 Bristol; DObst RCOG 1960. Prev: Ho. Off. (Paediat.) S.mead Hosp. Bristol.

SKERRITT, Mrs Ethel (retired) 24 Clarendon Court, Carr Bank Lane, Sheffield S11 7FN — MRCS Eng. LRCP Lond. 1918; MD Sheff. 1933; MB ChB 1918; DPH Manch. 1924. Prev: Cas. Off. & Ho. Surg. Sheff. Roy. Hosp.

SKERROW, Beverley Anne The Health Centre, Coronation Road, Peterculter AB14 0RQ Tel: 01224 733535; 17 The Meadows, Milltimber AB13 0JT — MB BS 1980 Lond.; MB BS (Hons. Path.) Lond. 1980; MRCGP 1986; DRCOG 1984; DCH RCP Lond. 1983. (St. Geo.) Prev: Princip & Trainer (Gen. Pract.) Epsom.

SKERRY, Caroline Anne Leedham Ward, Pembury Hospital, Pembury, Tunbridge Wells TN2 4QJ Tel: 01892 823535 — MB BS 1982 Lond.; Cert. Family Plann. JCC 1986; DRCOG 1985. Staff Grade (Psychiat.) Pembury Hosp. Tunbridge Wells. Prev: Trainee GP Tunbridge Wells HA VTS; SHO (Psychiat.) Hellingly Hosp. E.bourne; SHO (A & E) Qu. Eliz. Hosp. King's Lynn.

SKEW, Barbara Lesley Fertility Clinic, Southmead Hospital, Monks Park Avenue, Westbury on Trym, Bristol BS10 5NB Tel: 0117 959 5102; 22A Somerset Street, Kingsdown, Bristol BS2 8LZ Tel: 0117 924 7152 — MB BS Lond. 1970; MRCS Eng. LRCP Lond. 1970; DObst RCOG 1974. (Westm.) Staff Grade (Gyn.) S.mead Hosp. Bristol; Med. Dir. Tower Ho. Clinic Bristol; HFEA Licensed Fertil. Clinic. Socs: BMA; Brit. Fertil. Soc.; Brit. Soc. Colpos. & Cerv. Path. Prev: Clin. Asst. (Gyn.) Roy. United Hosp. Bath & S.mead Hosp. Bristol; SHO (O & G) St. Martins Hosp. Bath; SHO (Radiother.) W.m. Hosp. Lond.

SKEW, Peter Graeme 66 Saxmundham Road, 1 Adeburgh IP15 5DA Tel: 01728 454 976 Fax: 01728 454 976 Email: peterskew@bimm.org.uk — MB BS 1976 Lond.; MRCS Eng. LRCP 1976 Lond.; Dip MS Med Soc. Apoth. Lond. (Westm.) Sen. Clin. Servs. Developm. Off., Previa UK Ltd.; Doctor to Eng. Nat. Ballet. Socs: Brit. Soc. Med. & Dent. Hypn.; (Pres.) Brit. Inst. Musculoskeletal Med.; (Exec. Off.) BackCare. Prev: Indep. GP N.wood Specialist (Muscoskeletal Med.); Sch. Dr. RNIB Sunshine Ho. Sch. N.wood; Indep. GP N.wood & Specialist (Musculoskeletal Med.).

SKEWES, David Garland Royal Marsden Hospital, Fulham Road, London SW3 6JJ Tel: 020 7352 8171 Email: david.skewes@rmh.nthames.nhs.uk; 90 Grange Road, Ealing, London W5 3PJ Tel: 020 8579 7477 Fax: 020 8840 9560 — MB BS 1971 Melbourne; FFA RCS Eng. 1977. (Melb.) Cons. Anaesth. Roy. Marsden Hosp. Lond. Socs: Assn. Anaesth. & Intens. Care Soc. Prev: Sen. Regist. Roy. Marsden Hosp. Lond. & Hammersmith Hosp. Lond.; Lect. Lond. Hosp.

SKIA, Barbara 42 Cissbury Ring N., London N12 7AH Tel: 020 8445 4827 Email: marios@the.forthnet.gr — Ptychio Iatrikes 1988 Thesslonika; FRCS 1994; MSc Lond. 1996.

SKIDMORE, David James 53 Slayleigh Lane, Sheffield S10 3RG — MB ChB 1969 Sheff.; FRCR 1977; DMRD Eng. 1974; DObst RCOG 1971.

SKIDMORE, Mr Frederic David, OBE London Bridge Hospital, 27 Tooley St., London SE1 2PR Tel: 020 8318 6923 Fax: 020 8852 6919 Email: dskidmore@doctors.or.uk; Tel: 020 8318 6923 Fax: 020 8852 6919 Email: dskidmore@doctors.org.uk — MB BChir 1964 Camb.; MD Camb. 1974, MA 1965; FRCS Eng. 1971; FRCS Ed. 1968. (Camb. & Birm.) Hon Sen.Lect (Surg) Univ.Coll.Lond.Med. Sch. Socs: Fell. Roy. Soc. Med.; Brit. Assn. Surg. Oncol.; Assn. of Surg.s of Gt. Britain & Irel. Prev: Lect. (Surg.) Univ. Manch., Withington Hosp. Manch. & Christie Hosp. &Holt. Radium Inst. Manch.; Brit. Heart Foundat. Research Fell. Camb. UK and Baltimore USA; Registar Cariothoracic Surgey Harefield Hosp.

SKIDMORE, James Richard The Surgery, Limes Avenue, Alfreton, Derby DE55 7DW Tel: 01773 832525; Hollybush Farm, Moorwood Moor, South Wingfield, Derby DE55 7NW Tel: 01629 534842 — MB BS 1977 Newc.; MRCGP 1981; DRCOG 1981.

SKIDMORE, Jennifer Ruth Human Morphology, University of Southampton, Biomedical Sciences Building, Bassett CrescentE., Southampton SO16 7PX — MB ChB 1980 Leic.; PhD Soton. 1996. Lect. (Human Morphol.) & Admissions Tutor Soton. Univ.

SKIDMORE, Marion Jane 80 Hazelwood Road, Hyson Green, Nottingham NG7 5LB Tel: 0115 970 4220 — MB BChir 1990 Camb. Prev: SHO (A & E) Falkirk & Dist. Roy. Infirm.

SKIDMORE, Richard Bryan Duncan Health Centre, Hunter St., Briton Ferry, Neath SA11 2SF Tel: 01639 812270 — MB BS 1959 Lond.; MRCS Eng. LRCP Lond. 1959. (St. Mary's) Prev: Ho. Phys. & Ho. Surg. Morriston Hosp. Swansea; Ho. Off. (O & G) Neath Hosp.

SKILBECK, Anthony Bernard Kingswinford Medical Practice, Standhills Road, Kingswinford DY6 8DN Tel: 01384 271241 Fax: 01384 297530 — MB ChB 1974 Birm.; Dip. Occ. Med. RCP Lond. 1997. Sen. Partner in a Gen. Pract. in Kingswinford W. Midl.; Occupat. Health Cons. to Stuart & Sons Ltd. RedHo. Glassworks Wordsley, Stourbridge.

SKILBECK, Bethel 4A Pippins Close, Deeside CH5 1PE Tel: 01244 831079 — MB ChB 1992 Liverp.; T(GP) 1996; DRCOG 1995. (Liverp.) Socs: Assoc. Mem. RCGP; BMA. Prev: Trainee GP Sutton Med. Centre S. Wirral; Trainee GP/SHO N. Staffs. Hosp. Centre VTS; Ho. Off. (Med.) Wirral Hosp. NHS Trust.

SKILLERN, Laurence Howard Department Obstetrics & Gynaecology, St. George's Hospital Medical School, London SW17 0RE Tel: 020 8672 1255; 20B Ravenswood Road, Balham, London SW12 9PS Tel: 020 8675 4509 — MB BS 1986 Lond.; BSc Lond. 1983, MB BS 1986; DRCOG 1989. Research Fell. (O & G) St. Geo. Hosp. Med. Sch. Lond.

SKILLMAN, Joanna Margaret 21 St Stephen's Road, Cheltenham GL51 3AB Email: joskillman@hotmail.com; 20A Bridge Street, Pinner HA5 3EH Tel: 020 8426 1175 — BM BCh 1996 Oxf.; BA (Hons) Cantab. (Cambridge and Oxford) SHO (Plastic Surg.). Prev: Regist. (Surg.) St. Vincent's Hosp. Sydney; SHO Dryburn Hosp. Durh.; SHO John Radcliffe Hosp. Oxf.

SKILTON, Guy Henry Stewart The Surgery, Hazeldene House, Great Haywood, Stafford ST18 0SU Tel: 01889 881206 Fax: 01889 883083 — MB BS 1988 Lond.; T(GP) 1992.

SKILTON, Mr John Stewart Redcliffe, Stone ST15 — MB BS 1963 Lond.; MSc Birm. 1967, ChM 1973; FRCS Eng. 1969; MRCS Eng. LRCP Lond. 1963.

SKILTON, Juliet Ann The Surgery, Hazeldene House, Great Haywood, Stafford ST18 0SU Tel: 01889 881206 Fax: 01889 883083 — MB BS 1963 Lond. GP Gt. Haywood Surg. Mid Staffs HA.

SKILTON, Roger William Howard 28 Hewitt Street, Hoole, Chester CH2 3JD — MB BS 1983 Lond.; MRCP (UK) 1987; FRCA 1994; Cert. Family Plann. JCC 1990. Sen. Regist. (Anaesth.) Frenchay Hosp. Bristol; Vis. Instruct. Univ. Michigan Med. Centre.

***SKIMING, Judith Anne** 219 Long Lane, Aughton, Ormskirk L39 5BU — BM BCh 1998 Oxf.; BM BCh Oxon 1998; MA (CANTAB) 1999.

SKINGLE, Ian Stewart The Surgery, Kingsmount, 444 Kingstanding Road, Kingstanding, Birmingham B44 9SA Tel: 0121 373 1734 — MB ChB 1981 Birm.; DCH RCP Lond. 1986.

SKINNER, Adam John Winterton Surgery, Russell House, Westerham TN16 1RB Tel: 01959 564949 — MB BS 1980 Lond.; DRCOG 1983.

SKINNER, Adam Victor 2nd Floor Flat, 17 Caledonia Place, Clifton, Bristol BS8 4DJ Tel: 01179 730967 — MB ChB 1994

SKINNER

Bristol; BSc (Hons.) Bristol 1991; MRCP (UK) 1998. SHO (anaesth.) Cheltenham Gen. Hosp. Prev: SHO Phys. (Med.) MusGr. Pk. Hosp. Taunton; SHO (A & E) Bristol Roy. Infirm.; Ho. Phys. (Med.) Roy. United Hosp. Bath.

SKINNER, Alyson Margaret Mary Department of Paediatrics, City Hospital NHS Trust, Winson Green, Birmingham B18 8QH — MB BCh BAO 1981 NUI; M.D. (NUI) 1994; MRCP (UK) 1985; DCH RCP Lond. 1987. (Univ. Coll. Dub.) Cons. Paediat. City Hosp. NHS Trust Birm. Socs: Fell. Roy. Coll. Paediat. & Child. Health; Brit. Soc. Prenatal Med. Prev: Clin. Fell. B.C. Childs. Hosp. Vancouver, Canada; Sen. Regist. (Paediat.) Univ. Hosp. Wales Cardiff.

SKINNER, Andrew Charles Summerfield, Windmill Lane, Preston on the Hill, Warrington WA4 4AZ Tel: 0151 430 1267 Fax: 0151 430 1155 Email: skinner_doc@compuserve.com — BM BS 1978 Nottm.; BMedSci (Hons.) Nottm. 1976; FFA RCS Eng. 1983. (Nottingham) Cons. Anaesth. St. Helens & Knowsley Hosps. Trust; Dir. of Educat. & Train., St Helens & Knowsley Hosps. Trust. Prev: Sen. Regist. (Anaesth.) Mersey RHA; Regist. (Anaesth.) Nottm. Hosps.; SHO (Anaesth.) Gen. Hosp. Nottm.

SKINNER, Benjamin Charles 36 Brunstane Road, Edinburgh EH15 2QR — MB ChB 1998 Dund.; MB ChB Dund 1998.

SKINNER, Catherine Kelly (retired) Inchgarth Cottage, Inchgarth Road, Cults, Aberdeen AB15 9NT Tel: 01224 868689 — MB ChB Aberd. 1958. Prev: Clin. Med. Off. S. Grampian Health Dist.

SKINNER, Celia Jean Ambrose King Centre, Royal London Hospital, Whitechapel Road, London E1 1BB Tel: 020 7377 7309 Fax: 020 7377 7648 — MB ChB 1987 Birm.; MRCP (UK) 1991. Cons. Phys. Genitourin. Med. & HIV Roy. Lond. Hosp. Prev: Sen. Regist. (GUM/HIV) Roy. Lond.

SKINNER, Charles Peter Robin Rock Cottage, Mill Lane, Furners Green, Uckfield TN22 3RN — MB ChB 1998 Bristol.

SKINNER, Clare Maria Park View Cottage, Wash Hill, Woodburn, High Wycombe HP10 0JA — MB BS 1993 Lond.; FRCA Part I 1996; FRCA Part II 1998. (St. Bart's Lond.) Specialist Regist. (Anaesth.) Oxf.

SKINNER, Craig Fax: 0121 772 0292 Email: ingridandcraigskinner@btinternet.com; 305 Blossomfield Road, Solihull B91 1TE Tel: 0121 704 2968 — MB ChB 1965 Aberd.; MB ChB (Hons.) Aberd. 1965; FRCP Lond. 1983; MRCP (UK) 1970. Cons. Phys.& Med. Dir. Birm. Heartlands & Solihull NHS Trust; Sen. Clin. Lect. Med. Univ. Birm.; Respirat. Specialist, Healthcare Ltd. Socs: Brit. Thorac. Soc. (Chairm. Jt. TB Comm.); Pres. Midl. Thoracic Soc.

SKINNER, Mr David Victor Northcott, Chiltern Road, Chesham Bois, Amersham HP6 5PH Tel: 01494 431652 — MB BS 1975 Lond.; MRCS Eng. LRCP Lond. 1974; FRCS Glas. 1993; FRCS Eng. 1990; FRCS Ed. 1981. (Roy. Free) Clin. Dir. (A & E) John Radcliffe Hosp. Oxf. Socs: Brit. Assn. Accid. & Emerg. Med. Prev: Cons. A & E St. Bart. & Homerton Hosps. Lond.; Lect. (Anat.) Kings Coll. Hosp. Lond.; Regist. (A & E) N.wick Pk. Hosp. Harrow.

SKINNER, Mr Derek William Department of Otolaryngology, Royal Shrewsbury Hospital NHS Trust, Mytton Oak Road, Shrewsbury SY3 8XQ Tel: 01743 261000; Albany House, Butler Road, Shrewsbury SY3 7AJ Tel: 01743 243501 Fax: 01743 356212 Email: skinnerdw@compuserve.com — MB ChB 1978 Dundee; FRCS (Orl.) Eng. 1985; FRCS (Gen. Surg.) Ed. 1983; Hon. FCSHK 1995. Cons. Otolaryngol. Eye, Ear & Throat Hosp. Shrewsbury.; Post Grad. Clin. Tutor, Roayl Shrewsbury Hosp. Shrewsbury; Progr. Director, W. Midl.s HST OtorhinoLaryngol. W. Midl.s. Prev: Regist. (ENT) Univ. Hosp. Wales Cardiff; Sen. Regist. (ENT) Nottm. & Leicester Hosps.; Vis. Lect. Chinese Univ., Hong Kong.

SKINNER, Evelyn George (retired) 2A Coniston Road, Basingstoke RG22 5HS Tel: 01256 323199 — MB BS 1962 Lond.; MA Camb. 1952; MRCS Eng. LRCP Lond. 1962. Prev: SHO Soton. Childr. Hosp.

SKINNER, Fiona Margaret Leith Mount, 46 Ferry Road, Edinburgh EH6 4AE Tel: 0131 554 0558 Fax: 0131 555 6911 — MB ChB 1971 Ed.; MRCGP 1975; DCH RCPS Glas. 1975. (Edinburgh University) Managem. Gp. Mem. N-E Edin. LHCC. Prev: Clin. Med. Off. (Community Paediat.) Lothian HB; Trainee GP (N..) VTS.

SKINNER, Geoffrey Besley (retired) 57 Portland Avenue, New Malden KT3 6BB Tel: 020 8942 0157 — MB BS 1952 Lond.; MRCS Eng. LRCP Lond. 1952; FRCPath 1975, M 1964; DPath Eng. 1960. Prev: Cons. Path. St. Helier Gp. Laborat.

SKINNER, Gordon Robert Bruce Harborough Banks, Old Warwick Road, Lapworth, Solihull B94 6LD — MB ChB 1965 Glas.; DSc Birm. 1989, MD (1st cl. Hons.) 1975; FRCPath 1989, M 1988; FRCOG 1984, M 1972. (Glas.) Private Pract. Vaccine Research Scientist Birm.Vaccine Research Inst.; Chairm. Vaccine Research Trust 1983; Private Practitioner, Specialist interests in Endocrinol. and Sexually Transm. Dis. Socs: Soc. Gen. Microbiol.; Birm. and Midl.; Obst.al Soc. Prev: Dir. Vaccine Research Foundat. Ltd.; Med. Research Internat. Ltd.; HIV-Vac Inc.

SKINNER, Helen Louise 113 High Steet S., Stewkley, Leighton Buzzard LU7 0HU — MB ChB 1996 Manch. SHO (Med) St. James Univ., Leeds. Prev: SHO (c/o the Elderly) Blackpool Vict. Hosp.; Ho. Off. (Med.) Hope Hosp.; Ho. Off. (Surg.) Roy. Oldham Hosp.

SKINNER, Howard David 18 Wentworth Drive, Stretton, Burton-on-Trent DE13 0YJ Tel: 01282 544523 — MB BS 1991 Lond.; BSc (Psych.) Lond. 1988; MRCGP 1996; DFFP 1996; DRCOG 1995. (Univ. Coll. Lond.) Trainee GP/SHO (Paediat.) Burton Dist. Hosp. VTS; GP. Prev: SHO P'boro. Dist. Hosp.

SKINNER, James Allan Tain and Fearn Area Medical Practice, Health Centre, Scotsburn Road, Tain IV19 1PR Tel: 01862 892759 Fax: 01862 892579 — MB ChB 1969 Aberd.

SKINNER, Jane Garforth Medical Centre, Church Lane, Garforth, Leeds LS25 1ER — MB BS 1959 Lond.; MRCS Eng. LRCP Lond. 1959. (King's Coll. Hosp.) Prev: Ho. Phys. King's Coll. Hosp.

SKINNER, Jane Sarah Ward 49 Office, Royal Victoria Infirmary, Queen Victoria Road, Newcastle upon Tyne NE1 4LP Tel: 0191 232 5131 Fax: 0191 261 8505; 27 Queensway, Gosforth, Newcastle upon Tyne NE3 5NS Tel: 0191 236 6279 — MB BS 1985 Newc.; MB BS (Hons.) Newc. 1985; MD 1997; BSc (Hons.) Lancaster 1980; MRCP (UK) 1990; DRCOG 1988. (Newcastle upon Tyne) Cons. Community Cardiol. Roy. Vict. Infirm. Newc. Socs: BMA; Brit. Cardial Soc. Prev: Cons. Phys. (Cardiol.) Bishop Auckland Gen. Hosp.; Research Regist. (Cardiol.) Roy. Vict. Infirm. Newc. u. Tyne.; Regist. (Cardiol.) Newc. Gen. Hosp.

SKINNER, Janet 8 Dalgety Avenue, Edinburgh EH7 5UE — MB ChB 1994 Ed.

SKINNER, Jennifer Mary Murdishaw Health Centre, Gorsewood Road, Murdishaw, Runcorn WA7 6ES Tel: 01928712061; Summerfield, Windmill Lane, Preston on the Hill, Warrington WA4 4AZ Tel: 01928 716883 — BM BS 1978 Nottm.; BMedSci (Hons.) Nottm. 1976, BM BS 1978; MRCGP 1982. Prev: Clin. Med. Off. Penketh Warrington; Clin. Med. Off. Selby N. Yorks. & Heanor Derbysh.

SKINNER, Mr John Andrew McInnes Thrombosis Research Instutute & Department of Orthopaedic Su, King's College Hospital, Denmark, London SE5 9PJ Tel: 020 7326 3015; Waterloo Lane, Trowell, Nottingham NG9 3QQ — MB BS 1988 Lond.; FRCS Eng. 1992. Research Fell. & Hon. Regist. (Orthop.) King's Coll. Hosp. Lond.

SKINNER, John Bernard Department of Anaesthetics, The Ipswich Hospital NHS Trust, Heath Road, Ipswich IP4 5PD Tel: 01473 703435 — MB BS 1971 Lond.; FRCA 1977. (St. Marys) p/t Cons. Anaesth. & Pain Managem. Ipswich Hosp. NHS Trust.

SKINNER, John Malcolm Campingland Surgery, Campingland, Swaffham PE37 7RD Tel: 01760 721786 Fax: 01760 723703; Orwell House, 22 Station St., Swaffham PE37 7LH Tel: 01760 723978 Fax: 01760 723703 Email: mskin55@aol.com — MB BS Lond. 1969. (St. Bart.) Hosp. Pract. (Orthop. Surg.) N. Cambs. Hosp. Wisbech & Qu. Eliz. Hosp. Kings Lynn; Hon. Med. Adviser Swaffham & Watton Br. Far E. Prisoner of War Assn; Asst. Police Surg. Norf. Constab; Mem. WNPCG Bd. (Shadow). Prev: Mem. Area Med. Advis. Comm. Norf. AHA & Norf. LMC; Research Fell. (Surg.) Scs. RCS Eng.

SKINNER, Joyce Isobel (retired) 18G John Spencer Square, London N1 2LZ — MRCS Eng. LRCP Lond. 1959; MA Ed. 1945; MRCPath 1970.

***SKINNER, Laura Jane** 3 Allenstyle Drive, Yelland, Barnstaple EX31 3DY — MB ChB 1996 Bristol.

SKINNER, Lesley Phyllis Howden Health Centre, Howden West, Livingston EH54 6TP Tel: 01506 423800 Fax: 01506 460757; 6 Murrayfield Drive, Edinburgh EH12 6EB Tel: 0131 337 5185 — MB ChB 1985 Ed.; FRCGP 1999; MRCGP 1990; DCCH RCP Ed. 1991;

SKINNER

DRCOG 1989. Assoc. Adviser, SCPMDE, SE Scotl. Socs: Fell. RCGP. Prev: Trainee GP W. Lothian VTS; Ho. Off. (Gen. Med.) Bangour Gen. Hosp. W. Lothian; Ho. Off. (Gen. Surg.) Freeman Hosp. Newc.

SKINNER, Michael David 41A Sneyd Avenue, Newcastle ST5 2PZ — MB ChB 1969 Sheff.; FRCR 1977; DMRD Eng. 1976. Cons. Radiol. N. Staffs. Roy. Infirm.

SKINNER, Michael Patrick 7 Edward Road, Clarendon Park, Leicester LE2 1TF — MB BS 1994 Lond.

SKINNER, Mr Paul Patrick 695 Manchester Road, Sheffield S10 5PS — MB ChB 1988 Sheff.; FRCS Eng. 1992. Career Regist. Rotat. (Surg.) N. Trent.

SKINNER, Mr Paul William Orthopaedic Department, Kent & Sussex Hospital, Mount Ephraim, Tunbridge Wells TN4 8AT Tel: 01892 526111; 1 Hurstwood Lodge, Hurstwood Lane, Tunbridge Wells TN4 8YA Tel: 01892 532451 — MB BS 1977 Lond.; FRCS Eng. 1981. (Middlx.) Cons. Orthop. Surg. Kent & Sussex Hosp. Tunbridge Wells. Socs: Fell. BOA; Fell. Roy. Soc. Med. Prev: Sen. Regist. (Orthop.) King's Coll. Hosp. Lond.; Sen. Regist. (Orthop.) Sir Chas. Gairdner Hosp. Perth, W. Austral.; Regist. (Gen. Surg.) Poole Gen. Hosp.

SKINNER, Peter John Newport Pagnell Medical Centre, Queens Avenue, Newport Pagnell MK16 8QT Tel: 01908 611767 Fax: 01908 615099 — MB BS 1972 Lond.; MRCS Eng. LRCP Lond. 1972. (Guy's)

SKINNER, Peter Victor (retired) Ramhurst Oast, Powder Mill Lane, Leigh, Tonbridge TN11 9AS Tel: 01732 832244 — MA Oxf. 1953, BM BCh 1951; DObst RCOG 1955. Prev: Resid. Obst. Roy. Hants. Co. Hosp. Winchester.

SKINNER, Phillip James St James Medical Centre, Coal Orchard, Taunton TA1 1JP Tel: 01823 285400 Fax: 01823 285405 — MB 1977 Camb.; MSc 2001 Univ. of Lond.; BChir 1976; MRCGP 1983. GP Princip.

SKINNER, Richard Osmond, Capt. RAMC (retired) Minton House, Staplehurst, Tonbridge TN12 0AS Tel: 01580 893358 — MB BS Lond. 1958; DObst RCOG 1960; Da RCP LmdeRCSEng 1971; MA Open University 2000. Prev: Ho. Phys. Roy. Vict. Hosp. Folkestone.

SKINNER, Roderick Institute of Child Health, Royal Victoria Infirmary, Queen Victoria Road, Newcastle upon Tyne NE1 4LP Tel: 0191 202 3025 Fax: 0191 202 3060 Email: roderick.skinner@ncl.ac.uk — MB ChB 1983 Birm.; MB ChB (Hons.) Birm. 1983; PhD Newc. 1995; BSc (Hons.) Birm. 1980; MRCP (UK) 1986; FRCPCH 1997; DCH RCP Lond. 1987. (Birm.) Cons. Paediat. (Child Health) & Sen. Lect. (Paediat. Oncol.) Roy. Vict. Infirm.and Newc. Gen. Hosp. Newc. u. Tyne. Socs: UK Childr. Cancer Study Gp.; Eur. Gp. Blood & Marrow Transpl.; Brit. Assn. Cancer Research. Prev: Lect. & Hon. Sen. Regist. (Paediat. Oncol.) Newc. Med. Sch.; MRC Train. Fell. (Child Health) Newc. u. Tyne Med. Sch.; Ho. Phys. Qu. Eliz. Hosp. Birm.

SKINNER, Roger Keith Alwyn Morgan Food Standards Agency, 125 Kingsway, London WC2B 6NH Tel: 020 7276 8984 Fax: 020 7276 8910 Email: roger.skinner@foodstandards.gsi.gov.uk; 66 Dartmouth Park Road, London NW5 1SN Tel: 020 7267 4791 — MB BS 1969 Lond.; MSc (Epidemiol.) Lond. 1988, MSc Biochem, Lond. 1973, MD 1980; MRCS Eng. LRCP Lond. 1969; FRCPath 1991, M 1980. Head of MicroBiol. Safety Div. (Princip. Med. Off.) Food Standards Agency Lond. Socs: Fell. Roy. Soc. Med. Prev: Sen. Med. Off. DHSS Richmond Hse. Lond.; Lect. (Chem. Path.) Roy. Free Hosp. Sch. Med. Lond.; Sen. Regist. (Chem. Path.) St. Geo. Hosp. Lond.

SKINNER, Rory Robert 69 Ifield Road, London SW10 9AU — MB BS 1987 Lond.

SKINNER, Rosalind Scottish OfficeExecutive Health Service, St. Andrews House, Regent Road, Edinburgh EH1 3DE Tel: 0131 244 2296 Fax: 0131 244 2683 Email: rosalindskinner@scotland.gov.uk; 19 Comely Bank, Edinburgh EH4 1AL Tel: 0131 332 8435 — MB BS 1969 Lond.; MSc Ed. 1986; MD Lond. 1975; FRCPE 1995; Cert. Family Plann. JCC 1976; MFCM 1988. (Lond. Hosp.) Princip. Med. Off. Scot. Exec.Health Dept. Socs: Clin. Genetics Soc.; Fac. Pub. Health Med.; Fell.Roy.Coll.Phys.Ed. Prev: Lect. (Human Genetics) Univ. Edin.; Sen. Regist. (Community Med.) Lothian HB; Resid. Clin. Pathol. St. Mary's Hosp. Lond.

SKINNER, Sarah Melissa 26 Collington Street, Beeston, Nottingham NG9 1FJ — MB ChB 1990 Bristol.

SKINNER, Terence Alan, Wing Cdr. RAF Med. Br. Department Anaesthetics, Royal Hospital Haslar, Gosport PO12 2AA Tel: 01705 584255 Fax: 01705 762555 Email: anaesthetics@haslib.demon.co.uk; 35 Barton Drive, Bradley Barton, Newton Abbot TQ12 1PD — MB BS 1982 Lond.; FRCA 1990; DA (UK) 1986. Cons. Anaesth. RAF; Dir. Pain Servs. Prev: Sen. Regist. Frenchay Hosp. Bristol.

SKINNER, Terence Gordon (retired) 124 Thurlow Park Road, West Dulwich, London SE21 8HP Tel: 020 8670 3538 — MB BS 1954 Lond.; DObst RCOG 1957. GP (Private Pract.). Prev: SHO (Surg.) WillesBoro. Hosp. Kent.

SKIOLDEBRAND, Jessie Louise Primrose House, 48A Primrose Hill Road, London NW3 3AA Tel: 020 7483 2459 — BSc (Hons.) Lond. 1985, MB BS 1988; MRCGP 1993; DRCOG 1992; DCH RCP Lond. 1991. SHO (Psychiat.) Gordon Hosp. Lond. Socs: BMA & Med. Protec. Soc. Prev: SHO (A & E) Univ. Coll. Hosp. Lond.; SHO (Paediat. & O & G) St. Mary's Hosp. Lond.; Trainee GP Soton.

SKIPP, David Gordon Park Surgery, Albion Way, Horsham RH12 1BG Tel: 01403 01403 217100 Fax: 01403 214639 Email: parksurg@pucl.co.uk — MB BS 1974 Lond.; MRCS Eng. LRCP Lond. 1974; MRCGP 1979; Cert. JCC Lond. 1977; DRCOG 1976. (Char. Cross) Dep. Coroner W. Sussex. Prev: Trainee GP Mid-Sussex VTS; Ho. Phys. & Ho. Surg. Char. Cross Hosp. Lond.; Trainer SW Thames Region.

SKIPP, Helen Joyce Beech Community Clinic, Horsham Hospital, Hurst Road, Horsham RH12 2DR Tel: 01403 227012; 48 Grebe Crescent, Horsham RH13 6ED Tel: 01403 253306 — MB BS 1974 Lond.; MRCS Eng. LRCP Lond. 1974; Cert JCC Lond. 1977; MFFP 1996. (Char. Cross) SCMO Horsham & Crawley Family Plann.; CMO Haywards Heath Family Plann. Prev: Ho. Phys. & Ho. Surg. Char. Cross Hosp. Lond.

SKIPPER, Colin Doctor's Corner, Aldborough, Norwich NR11 7NR Tel: 01263 761512 — MB ChB 1957 Leeds. (Leeds) Prev: Clin. Asst. S.lands Hosp. Shoreham by Sea & Littlehampton Hosp.; Ho. Phys. (Paediat.) St. Jas. Hosp. Leeds; Ho. Surg. (Obst.) Manygates Matern. Hosp. Wakefield.

SKIPPER, Mr David Bedford Hospital Trust, Kempston Road, Bedford MK42 9DJ Tel: 01234 792319 Fax: 01234 792302 — MB BS 1978 Lond.; MS Soton. 1989; MA Camb. 1979; FRCS Eng. 1984. Cons. Surg. Bedford Hosp. Trust.

SKIPPER, Mr John Joseph, Wing Cdr. RAF Med. Br. ENT Department, The Royal Hospital, Haslar, Gosport PO12 2AA Tel: 02392 584255 Ext: 2629, 02392 762506 Email: johnskip@dsca.gov.uk — MB BCh 1979 Wales; FRCS Ed. 1985; T(S) 1991. Cons. Adviser OtoLaryngol. Defence Med. Servs.; Cons. Otolaryngologist Roy. Hosp. Haslar Gosport.; Cons. Otalaryngologist, Portsmouth NHS Trust. Socs: Fell. Roy. Soc. Med.; BMA; Brit. Assn. Otol. Prev: Cons. Otolaryngologist RAF Halton; Cons. Otolaryngologist RAF Akrotiri; Hon. Sen. Regist. (Ear, Nose & Throat) Leicester Roy. Infirm.

SKIPSEY, Ian Gerald Department Anaesthetics, Raigmore Hospital, Inverness Tel: 01463 704000 Fax: 01463 711322; 69 Drumsmittal Road, North Kessock, Inverness IV1 3JU Tel: 01463 731734 — MB ChB 1984 Manch.; FRCA 1989. Cons. Anaesth. Raigmore Hosp. Inverness.

SKIRROW, Martin Bingham Western Lodge, Hanley Swan, Worcester WR8 0DL Tel: 01684 310343 Email: martin.skirrow@camdenmusic.com — MB ChB 1952 Birm.; PhD Liverp. 1963; FRCPath 1979, M 1967; DTM & H Liverp. 1962. Hon. Emerit. Cons. Microbiol. Pub. Health Laborat. Serv. Glos. Roy. Hosp. Socs: Brit. Infec. Soc; Assn. Clin. Pathols. Prev: Cons. Med. Microbiol. Worcester Roy. Infirm.; Sen. Regist. (Path.) Childr. Hosp. Birm.; Lect. (Trop. Med.) Univ. Ibadan, Nigeria.

SKITT, Beryl 5 Muston Road, Filey YO14 0BT Tel: 01723 513210 — MB ChB 1963 Manch. (Manch.) Counsellor Camb. Centre ScarBoro.. Prev: Dist. AIDS Co-ordinator ScarBoro. Dist.; Clin. Asst. Coleshill Hall Hosp.; GP Tile Cross & Marston Green.

SKITT, Robin Charles Greenmeadow Surgery, Greenmeadow Way, Cwmbran NP44 3XQ Tel: 01633 864110 Fax: 01633 483761; Grasmoor, 6 Brechfa Close, Ponthir, Caerleon, Newport NP18 1GY — MB ChB 1977 Bristol; DRCOG 1979. GP Cwmbran.

SKIVINGTON, Jane Elizabeth 13 Nine Acres, Midhurst GU29 9EP — MB ChB 1993 Aberd.

SKIVINGTON, Michael Anthony (retired) 34 Ravine Road, Boscombe, Bournemouth BH5 2DU Tel: 01202 432936 Email: mikeskiv@yahoo.co.uk — MB BS Lond. 1961; FFA RCS Eng. 1966. Prev: Cons. Anaesth. Roy. Bournemouth & ChristCh. NHS Trust.

SKLAR, Eric Maurice, MBE Medical Centre, 144-150 High Road, London NW10 2PT Tel: 020 8459 5550 Fax: 020 8451 7268; 32 Sidmouth Road, London NW2 5HJ Tel: 020 8459 5550 Fax: 020 8451 7268 — MRCS Eng. LRCP Lond. 1949; FRCGP 1985, M 1953. (St. Geo.) Chairm. N. Thames (W.) GP Postgrad. Comm. Socs: Balint Soc. & BMA. Prev: Sen. Lect. (Gen. Pract.) Middlx. Hosp. Med. Sch. & Univ. Coll. Lond Sch. Med.; Capt. RAMC; Paediat. Hadassah Childr. Hosp. Israel.

SKLAR, Ian David The Surgery, 38 Cockington Road, Bilborough, Nottingham NG8 4BZ Tel: 0115 928 2231 Fax: 0115 928 4917 — MB BS 1981 Lond.

SKLAR, Jonathan Basement flat, 21 Church row, Hampstead, London NW3 6UP Tel: 020 7794 1085 Fax: 020 7433 1056 Email: jsklar@connectfree.co.uk — MB BS 1974 Lond.; MRCS Eng. LRCP Lond. 1973; MRCPsych 1977; TQAP Tavistock 1983. (Roy. Free) Train., Lond. Socs: Brit. Psychoanal. Soc.; Train. Analyst. Mem. Brit. Psychoanal. Soc. Prev: Cons. Psychother. Addenbrooke's & Fulbourn Hosps. Camb.; Vis. Prof. Arhus Univ. Psychiat. Hosp. Riskov, Denmark; Sen. Regist. (Psychother.) Adult Dept. Tavistock Clinic Lond.

SKOBLO, Max The Medical Centre, 17-19 Clarence Road, London NW6 7TG Tel: 020 7624 1345 Fax: 020 7624 7292; 45 Northumberland Road, Barnet EN5 1EB Tel: 020 8449 2868 — MB BS 1947 Lond. (St. Bart.) Prev: Cas. Off. Willesden Gen. Hosp.; Ho. Surg. St. Chas. (LCC) Hosp.; Capt. RAMC 1948-50.

SKOGSTAD, Helga 52 Glasslyn Road, London N8 8RH — State Exam Med. Wurzburg 1979.

SKOGSTAD, Wilhelm Herbert The Cassel Hospital, 1 Ham Common, Richmond TW10 7JF Tel: 020 8237 2965 Fax: 020 8237 2996 Email: wilhelm.skogstad@lineone.net; Tel: 020 8341 1198 Email: wskogstad@lineone.net — State Exam Med 1978 Munich; MRCPsych 2001; 2001 Psychoanalyst; State Exam Psych. 1991; State Exam Psychother. & Psychoanal. 1986. (Munich) Cons. Psychother. Cassel Hosp. Richmond; Private Pract. as Psychoanalyst 75 Cromwell Av. Lond. N6 5BS. Socs: Roy. Coll. of Psychiat.s; Brit. Psycho-Analyt. Soc. (Assn. Mem.). Prev: Psychiat. Ment. Hosp. Haar, Munich.

SKOLAR, Alfred (retired) 36 Grosvenor Gardens, London NW11 0HG Tel: 020 8458 4787 — MRCS Eng. LRCP Lond. 1936.

SKOLAR, Peter Justin Brunswick Medical Centre, 53 Brunswick Centre, London WC1N 1BP Tel: 020 7837 3811 Fax: 020 7833 8408; 7 Greenhalgh Walk, Hampstead Garden Suburb, London N2 0DJ Tel: 020 8455 1652 — MB 1969 Camb.; BChir 1968. (Camb. & Middlx.) Chairm. Camden & Islington LMC. Socs: GMSC (NE Thames Region). Prev: Ho. Surg. Forest Gate Matern. Hosp.; Ho. Surg. St. Mary's Hosp. Plaistow; Ho. Phys. Middlx. Hosp.

SKONE, John Francis Gowanbank, 60 Ely Road, Llandaff, Cardiff CF5 2JG Tel: 029 2056 5618 Fax: 029 2056 5618 — MB BS 1948 Lond.; MD Lond. 1952; BSc (Hons.) Open 1996; MRCS Eng. LRCP Lond. 1948; I LM Wales 1990; FFPHM 1989; FFCM 1974; DCH Eng. 1950, DPH (Distinc.) 1952, DIH 1952; BA Open 1998. (Lond. Hosp.) Med. Ref., Thornhill Crematorium. Cardiff. Socs: Fell. BMA; Fell. Roy. Inst. Pub. Health & Hyg.; Cardiff Med. Soc. Prev: MOH, Princip. Sch. Med. Off. & Chief Welf. Off. W. Bromwich Co. Boro.; MOH, Princip. Sch. Med. Off. & Welf. Off. I. of Wight CC; Chief Admin. Med. Off. & Dir. Pub. Health Med. S. Glam. DHA (T).

SKOYLES, Julian Robert 5 Ennerdale Close, Leicester LE2 4TN Tel: 0116 271 2193 — MB BS 1984 Lond.; BSc (Hons.) Lond. 1981, MB BS 1984; FCAnaesth. 1990; DA (UK) 1986. Sen. Regist. Leicester Roy. Infirm.; Research Fell. (Anaesth.) N.. Gen. Hosp. Sheff. Prev: Regist. (Anaesth.) Roy. Hallamsh. Hosp. Sheff.; SHO Intens. Care Unit Char. Cross Hosp. Lond.

SKRINE, Ruth Lister Castanea House, Sham Castle Lane, Bath BA2 6JN Tel: 01225 465440 Fax: 01225 461414 — MB ChB Bristol 1953; MRCGP 1979. Socs: Fell. Fac. Family Plann.; Inst. Psychosexual Med. Prev: Sen. Lect. (Family Plann. & Psychosexual Med.) Univ. Bristol; Ho. Phys., Ho. Surg. & Cas. Off. Pontefract Gen. Infirm.; Ho. Off. (Geriat.) Headlands Hosp. Pontefract.

SKRZYPIEC-ALLEN, Alan Irvin 53 Mersey Road, Sale M33 6LF Tel: 0161 973 8528 — MB ChB 1978 Manch.; DRCOG 1986.

SKUCE, Angela Margaret South Lambeth Road Practice, 1 Selway House, 272 South Lambeth Road, London SW8 1UL Tel: 020 7622 1923 Fax: 020 7498 5530 — MB BCh BAO 1988 Dub.; MRCGP 1992; MICGP 1992; DFFP 1994; DCH RCPSI 1991.

SKUDDER, Jonathan Memorial Medical Centre, Bell Road, Sittingbourne ME10 4XX Tel: 01795 477764 — MB BS 1975 Lond.

SKUES, Mark Alastair Threefield House, Mannings Lane, Hoole Bank, Chester CH2 4ET — MB BS 1980 Nottm.; BMedSci (Hons.) Nottm. 1978, BM BS 1980; FFA RCS Eng. 1986. Rotat. Regist. (Anaesth.) Bristol Gp. Hosps. Prev: Tutor/Specialist (Anaesth.) Waikato Hosp. Hamilton, New Zealand.

SKULL, Angela Jane 39 Albermarle, Parkside, London SW19 5NP Tel: 020 8785 9261 — MB BS 1991 Lond.; FRCS 1996. Regist. (Gen. Surg.) SW Thames Rotat. Prev: SHO (Ost. & Gyn.) St. Geo. Hosp. Lond.

SKULL, Jonathan Douglas Centre for Reproductive Medicine and Fertility, The Jessop Wing,Sheffield Teaching Hospitals NHS Trust, Tree Root Walk, Sheffield S10 2SF Tel: 0114 226 8050 Fax: 0114 226 8052 Email: jonathan.skull@sth.nhs.uk; 102 Greystones Road, Sheffield S11 7BQ Tel: 0114 266 2913 Email: jonathan.skull@lineone.net — MB ChB 1988 Bristol; MRCOG 1994. (Bristol) Cons. in Reprod. Med. Sheff. Teach. Hosp. NHS Trust. Prev: Specialist Regist. (O & G) Bassetlan Hosp. Worksop; Hon. Sen. Regist. & Research Regist. IVF Unit Hammersmith Hosp. Lond.; Regist. (O & G) Doncaster Roy. Infirm.

SKUSE, Professor David Henry Behavioural & Brain Sciences Unit, Institute of Child Health, University of London, 30 Guilford St., London WC1N 1EH Tel: 020 7831 0975 Fax: 020 7831 7050 Email: dskuse@ich.ucl.ac.uk; 53 The Avenue, Kew, Richmond TW9 2AL — MB ChB 1973 Manch.; MD 1995; FRCP Lond. 1993; MRCP (UK) 1976; FRCPCH 1997; FRCPsych 1991, M 1978. Prof. Behavioural & Brain Scis. Inst. Child Health Lond.; Hon. Cons. Hosp. for Sick Childr. Gt. Ormond St. Lond. Socs: Brit. NeuroPsychiat. Assn., (Treas.); Assn. for Child Psyihology & Psychiat., (former Treas.). Prev: Sen. Lect. (Child Psychiat.) Inst. Child Health; Lect. (Child Psychiat.) Inst. Psychiat. Lond.; SHO Rotat. (Med.) United Oxf. Hosps.

SKYERS, Paul Andrew 21 Larkspur Gardens, Luton LU4 8SA — MD 1990 Yale, USA.

SKYRME, Andrew David 116 Kidbrooke Park Road, Blackheath, London SE3 0DX — MB BS 1993 Lond.

SKYRME, Manon Llwyd 21 Tewkesbury Street, Cathays, Cardiff CF24 4QQ — MB BCh 1993 Wales; DCH 1996; DObst 1997; MRCGP 1997.

SKYRME, Robert John 21 Tewkesbury Street, Cardiff CF24 4QQ — MB BCh 1993 Wales.

SKYRME-JONES, Rex Andrew Paul Guy's and St. Thomas NHS Trust, Lambeth Palace Rd, London Tel: 020 8928 9292 Fax: 020 8852 3709 Email: andrew@skgrmej.fsnet.co.uk; 101 Quentin Road, London SE13 5DG Email: andrew@skyrmej.fsnet.co.uk — MB ChB 1989 Bristol; BSc Bristol 1986; MRCP (UK) 1993. Specialist Regist., Cardiol. Prev: Interven.al Fell., Monash Med. Centre Melbourne, Australia; Research Fell., Monash Med. Centre, Melbourne, Australia; Regist., John Radcliffe Hosp., Oxf.

SLACK, Andrew John Ham Meadow, Northway, Halse, Taunton TA4 3JL — MB BS 1998 Lond.; MB BS Lond 1998.

SLACK, Carole Bernadette Therese 366 Rochdale Road, Middleton, Manchester M24 2GJ — MB ChB 1986 Manch.; BSc (Hons.) Manch. 1983, MB ChB 1986; MSc Open 1992; MRCGP 1995. Socs: Brit. Holistic Med. Assn.; Manch. Med. Soc.; Brit. Med. Acupunc. Soc. Prev: Lect. (Gen. Pract.) Univ. Manch.; Regist. (Pub. Health Med.) N. Manch.

SLACK, Mr Christopher John 588 Bury Road, Bamford, Rochdale OL11 4AU Tel: 01706 32828 — MB ChB 1969 Manch.; FRCS Eng. 1977. (Manch.)

SLACK, Mr Cyril Charles (retired) Priory Mead, 27 Parsonage Downs, Great Dunmow, Dunmow CM6 2AT Tel: 01371 874203 — MRCS Eng. LRCP Lond. 1940; MChOrth Liverp. 1948, MB ChB 1940; FRCS Ed. 1943. Prev: Cons. Orthop. Surg. N. Tyneside, Newc. (T) & N.Id. AHAs.

SLACK, Graeme Barrie Friarwood Surgery, Carleton Glen, Pontefract WF8 1SU Tel: 01977 703235 Fax: 01977 600527 — MB ChB 1979 Leeds. (Leeds) GP Pontefract, W. Yorks.

SLACK

SLACK, Janet Elizabeth Lovemead Group Practice, Roundstone Surgery, Polebarn Circus, Trowbridge BA14 7EH Tel: 01225 752752 Fax: 01225 776388; The Old Farm House, Ashley Road, Bradford-on-Avon BA15 1RT Tel: 01225 867658 — MRCS Eng. LRCP Lond. 1984; BA (Hons.) Lond. 1973; MRCGP 1995; DRCOG 1991. (Middlx.) Socs: BMA. Prev: SHO John Radcliffe Hosp. Oxf.; SHO Stoke Mandeville Hosp. Aylesbury.; GP Princip. Edwd.s Partners Aylesbury.

SLACK, Lady Joan (retired) Hillside Cottage, Tower Hill, Stawell, Bridgwater TA7 9AJ Tel: 01278 722719 Fax: 01278 722719 — BM BCh 1949 Oxf.; DM Oxf. 1972, BA, BM BCh 1949; FRCP Lond. 1979; MFCM 1974; DCH Eng. 1952. Prev: Hon. Cons. Clin. Genetics St. Mark's Hosp. Lond.

SLACK, Malcolm Charles 35 Station Road, Felsted, Dunmow CM6 3HD — MB BS 1974 Lond.

SLACK, Margaret Mary (retired) Oaklynn, Keighley Road, Laneshaw Bridge, Colne BB8 7HL — MB ChB 1963 Aberd.; FRCPsych 1988, M 1972; DPM Leeds 1971. Prev: Cons. Child & Adolesc. Psychiat. Burnley Health Dist.

SLACK, Mark Clifford Ermine House, Post St., Godmanchestr, Huntingdon PE29 2BA — MB BCh 1980 Witwatersrand; MRCOG 1992.

SLACK, Martin Harry 4 Grosvenor Drive, Winchester SO23 7HF Tel: 01962 852597 Email: msslack@hotmail.com — MB BChir 1994 Camb.; MRCP (UK) 1996. (Camb.) Specialist Regist. (Paeds.) - St Mary's Hosp. - Portsmouth. Prev: SHO Rotat. (Paediat.) Soton. Hosps.; SHO (Paediat.) St. Mary's Hosp. Portsmouth; SHO (A & E) Roy. Hants. Co. Hosp. Winchester, Specialist Regist. (Paediat.) Roy. Hants Co. Hosp. Winchester.

SLACK, Mary Paulina Elizabeth Bacteriology Department, Level 6/7, John Radcliffe Hospital, Oxford OX3 9DU Tel: 01865 220859 Fax: 01865 220890 Email: mary.slack@ndp.ox.ac.uk; Hampden House, Clifton Hampden, Abingdon OX14 3EG — MB BChir 1973 Camb.; MB BChir Camb. (Distinc. Path.) 1973; MA Oxf. 1976, BM BCh 1977; MA (1st cl. Hons.) Camb. 1974; FRCPath 1991, M 1979. (King's Coll. Hosp.) Univ. Lect. (Bacteriol.) Oxf. Univ.; Dir. PHLS Haemophilus Refer. Unit John Radcliffe Hosp. Oxf.; Hon. Cons. (Bact.) John Radcliffe Hosp. Oxf.; Hon. Cons. Pub. Health Laborat. Serv.; Supernum. Fell. Green Coll. Oxf.; PHLS Refer. Expert on Haemophilus Influenzae. Prev: Demonst. (Path.) King's Coll. Hosp. Lond.; Ho. Surg. King's Coll. Hosp.; Ho. Phys. Brook Gen. Hosp. Lond.

SLACK, Nicola Frances 23 Redland Grove, Redland, Bristol BS6 6PT — MB ChB 1976 Birm.; FRCR 1982. Cons. Radiol. Frenchay Hosp. Bristol. Prev: Sen. Regist. (Ultrasound & Nuclear Med.) Roy. Marsden Hosp. Lond.; Sen. Regist. (Radiol.) Bristol HA.

SLACK, Patricia Mary 5 Magdala Road, Mapperley Park, Nottingham NG3 5DE Tel: 0115 960 5940 Email: tishslack@hotmail.com — MB BS Lond. 1969; MRCS Eng. LRCP Lond. 1969; MRCPsych 1984; DCH Eng. 1972. (St. Mary's) Prev: Ho. Phys. (Paediat.) Unit St. Mary's Hosp. Lond.; Scientif. Off. Div. Communicable Dis. Clin. Research Centre, Harrow.; Cons. Psychotherapist Nottm. Psychother. Unit.

***SLACK, Rachel Olivia** 106 Long Road, Cambridge CB2 2HF — BM BS 1996 Nottm.

SLACK, Richard Charles Bewick Nottingham Health Authority, Standard Court, Park Row, Nottingham NG1 6GN Tel: 0115 912 3344 Fax: 0115 912 3351 Email: richard.slack@nott.ac.uk — MB BChir Camb. 1969; MRCPath 1977; DObst RCOG 1970; FFPHM 1999. (Camb. & St. Mary's) Cons. Communicable Dis. Control Nottm. HA; Sen. Lect. (Microbiol.) Univ. Nottm.; Hon. Cons. Pub. Health Laborat. Serv. Socs: Pres. Assn. Med. Microbiol.; Hosp. Infec. Soc.; Chair Fed. Inf. Soc. Prev: Lect. (Path.) Univ. Nairobi, Kenya; Temp. Lect. (Path.) Middlx. Hosp. Med. Sch. Lond.; Ho. Surg. St. Mary's Hosp. Lond.

SLACK, Richard Francis Yeardsley Pump Cottage, 3 New Way Lane, Threshers Bush, Harlow CM17 0NT Tel: 01279 641122; Pump Cottage, 3 New Way Lane, Threshers Bush, Harlow CM17 0NT Tel: 01279 641122 — MB BS 1992 Lond. Princip. Med. Off. (A. & E.) Cairns Base Hosp. Cairns Qu.sland Australia. Prev: Clin. Asst. (A & E) Roy. Free Hosp. Lond.; SHO (A & E) Roy. Free Hosp. Lond.; Sen. Ho. Off. (Med.) King Geo. Hosp. Ilford Essex.

SLACK, Richard Stuart Maythorn House, Thorpe Waterville, Kettering NN14 3ED — MB ChB 1994 Manch.

SLACK, Robert Alexnder Mendip, Hawks Hill, Bourne End SL8 5JQ — MB BS 1994 Lond.

SLACK, Mr Robert William Talbot The Bath Clinic, Claverton Down, Bath BA2 7BR Tel: 01225 835555 Fax: 01225 825466 Email: robert.slack@rub-bath.swest.nhs.uk — MB ChB 1977 Bristol; BSc Lond. 1974; FRCS Eng. 1984; FRCS Ed. 1981. Cons. ENT Surg. Roy. United Hosp. Bath.; Elected Mem. of Gen. Med. Counc. Socs: Counc. Mem. Sect. of Laryngol. Roy. Soc. Med. Prev: Sen. Regist. (ENT Surg.) Bristol & Bath HA; Regist. Roy. Nat. Throat Nose & Ear Hosp. Lond.; SHO (ENT & Gen. Surg) Bristol United Hosp.

SLACK, Roger Dutton (retired) Sycamore Cottage, Hellesvean, St Ives TR26 2HG Tel: 01736 795067 — BA Camb. 1940, MB BChir 1942; MRCS Eng. LRCP Lond. 1942.

SLACK, Stephen James Highbury New Park Surgery, 49 Highbury New Park, London N5 2ET Tel: 020 7354 1972 — MB BS 1987 Lond.; MRCGP 1995. (Lond. Hosp. Med. Sch.) Socs: BMA.

SLACK, Mrs Susanna Elizabeth 4 Grosvenor Drive, Abbotts Barton, Winchester SO23 7HF Tel: 01962 852597 Email: msslack@hotmail.com — BM BCh 1992 Oxf.; MA Camb. 1993; FRCS Eng. 1997. (Oxf.) Specialist Regist. (A & E) Qu. Alexandra Hosp. Portsmouth. Prev: SHO (A & E) Qu. Alex. Hosp. Portsmouth; SHO (Gen. Surg.) Roy. Hants. Co. Hosp. Winchester; SHO (Orthop.) Roy. Hants. Co. Hosp. Winchester.

SLACK, Walter Kenneth (retired) Pump Cottage, 3 New Way Lane, Threshers Bush, Harlow CM17 0NT Tel: 01279 641122 Fax: 01279 441496 — MRCS Eng. LRCP Lond. 1949; FRCA. 1992; FFA RCS Eng. 1986; DA Eng. 1954; Cert. Av. Med. 1979. Hon. Cons. Anaesth. Whipps Cross Hosp. Lond. Prev: Cons. Anaesth. Whipps Cross & Wanstead Hosps. Lond. & Cons. i/c Regional Hyperbaric Oxygen Unit Whipps Cross Hosp. Lond.

SLACK, Sir William Willatt, KCVO Hillside Cottage, Tower Hill, Stawell, Bridgwater TA7 9AJ Tel: 01278 722719 Fax: 01278 722719 — BM BCh 1950 Oxf.; MA Oxf. 1950, MCh 1961, BM BCh 1950; FRCS Eng. 1955. Emerit. Surg. Middlx. Hosp.; Hon. Fell. UCL. Socs: Fell. Roy. Soc. Med. Prev: Sgt. Surg. to HM the Qu.; Dean Univ. Coll. & Middlx. Sch. Med. Lond.; Ex-Pres. Sect. Proctol. Roy. Soc. Med.

SLADDEN, Christopher Simon 43 Hurst Road, Hinckley LE10 1AB — MB ChB 1992 Wales; BSc Wales 1985, MB ChB 1992.

SLADDEN, David Kerrison Lawrence (retired) Old Rectory, Felthorpe, Norwich NR10 4EB Tel: 01603 754634 Email: dlksladden@hotmail.com — MRCS Eng. LRCP Lond. 1948; DObst RCOG 1948; MMSA Lond. 1959. Med. Off. Rehabil. Centre Norf. Prev: Med. Asst. (Anaesth.) Norf. & Norwich Hosp.

SLADDEN, Jonathan Michael Crosby, Skene and Partners, College Way Surgery, Comeytrowe Centre, Taunton TA1 4TY Tel: 01823 259333 Fax: 01823 259336; 6 Stone Close, Comeytrowe, Taunton TA1 4YG — MB ChB 1978 Sheff.; MRCGP 1983. GP Taunton.

SLADDEN, Michael Joseph Department of Dermatology, Leicester Royal Infirmary, Leicester LE1 5WW Tel: 0116 258 5162 Fax: 0116 258 6792 Email: m.sladden@utas.edu.au — MB ChB 1985 Leic.; MRCP 2001 UK; FRACGP 1992; MRCGP 1989; DRCOG 1989; Master Appl. Epidemiol. Austral. Nat. Univ. 1996. (Univ. of Leicester) Specialist Regist., Dermat., Leicester Roy. Infirm. Socs: Brit. Med. Assn.; Brit. Assn. of Dermatol. Prev: Sen. Lect., Gen. Pract., Univ. of Tasmania, Mobart; GP, Mobart, Tasmania; Trainee GP Leic. VTS.

SLADDEN, Robert Arthur (retired) 7 Peninsula Square, Winchester SO23 8GJ Tel: 01962 850297 — BSc Oxf. 1954, DM 1953, BM BCh 1944; FRCPath 1968, M 1964; DTM Liverp. 1946. Prev: Cons. Histopath. N.ampton Gen. Hosp.

SLADE, Alistair Kenneth Bannerman Department of Cardiology, Royal Cornwall Hospitals Trust, Treliske Hospital, Truro TR1 3LJ Tel: 01872 252517 Fax: 01872 252877; Trevean, 11 St Johns Terrace, Devoran, Truro TR3 6NE Tel: 01872 864568 Fax: 01872 252877 Email: alistair.slade@rcht.west.nhs.uk — MB BS 1984 Lond.; BA Camb. 1981; MRCP (UK) 1988. (Middlx.) Cons. Cardiol. Roy. Cornw. Hosp. Trust Treliske Hosp. Truro Cornw. Socs: BMA; Brit. Pacing & Electrophysiol. Gp.; Brit. Cardiac Soc. Prev: Lect. & Hon. Sen. Regist. (Cardiol. Sci.s) St. Geo. Hosp. Med. Sch. Lond.; Brit. Heart Foundat. Research Fell. (Cardiol. Sci.s) St. Geo. Hosp. Med.

Sch. Lond.; Regist. (Cardiol.) Bournemouth & Roy. Brompton & Nat. Heart Hosp.

SLADE, Andrew Mark c/o 170 Burden Road, Beverley HU17 9LN — MB ChB 1993 Liverp.

SLADE, Dawn Elizabeth 28 Llanberis Cl, Tonteg, Pontypridd CF38 1HR — MB ChB 1997 Leic.

SLADE, Diana Elizabeth Marianne 22 Ashmeads Way, Wimborne BH21 2NZ — MB BS 1993 Lond.; BSc 1990; FRCS Eng 1997. (Charing Cross/Westminster) SHO Plastic Surg. Socs: BMA; Roy. Soc. Med.; RCS (Eng.). Prev: SHO surg.Rotat.; SHO plast.surg.

SLADE, Mr Dominic Alexander James Vascular Studies Unit, Withington Hospital, Nell Lane, Manchester M20 2LR Fax: 0161 291 3844 Email: d-slade@fsi.with.man.ac.uk; 15 Seamons Road, Altrincham WA14 4ND Tel: 0161 941 5462 Email: dom.slade@breathemail.net — MB ChB 1992 Birm.; FRCS (Eng.) 1997. Research Regist. (Dept. Surg. Univ. Manch.).

SLADE, Guy Malcolm (retired) 46 Roslin Road S., Bournemouth BH3 7EG Tel: 01202 510243 Fax: 01202 510243 — MRCS Eng. LRCP Lond. 1960; DObst RCOG 1962.

SLADE, Joanna Margaret 69 Home Farm Lane, Bury St Edmunds IP33 2QL — MB BCh 1985 Oxf.; MRCP (UK) 1994. Regist. (Paediat.) Oxf. & E. Anglia RHA. Socs: Brit. Paediat. Assn. Prev: Clin. Med. Off. (Community Paediat.) Soton. Area HA; Resid. Med. Off. (Cas.) Childr. Hosp. Adelaide, S. Austral.; SHO (Paediat.) Soton. Gen. Hosp.

SLADE, John Michael Department of Anaesthetics, West Suffolk Hospital, Bury St Edmunds IP33 2QZ Tel: 01284 713330 — BM BCh 1984 Oxf.; FCAnaesth. 1989. Cons. Anaesth. W. Suff. Hosp. Bury St. Edmunds. Socs: Pain Soc.; Soc. Computing & Technol. in Anaesth. Prev: Sen. Regist. (Anaesth.) Soton. Gen. Hosp.; Sen. Regist. (Anaesth.) Roy. Adelaide Hosp., Austral.; Research Off. Univ. Hosp. Wales Cardiff.

SLADE, Jonathan Andrew Nicholas, Maj. RAMC 654 Squadron, 4 Regt. Army Air Corps BFPO 41; Lanx House, Princes St, Corbridge NE45 5DB Tel: 01434 632025 — MB ChB 1987 Birm.; ChB Birm. 1987. Specialist Aviat. Med. Germany. Prev: Ho. Off. Gen. Hosp. & Qu. Eliz. Hosp. Birm.

SLADE, Karen 20 Penygraig, Aberystwyth SY23 2JA — BM 1997 Soton.

SLADE, Mark Gaisford High Beech, Turnips Lane, Kirby Cross, Frinton-on-Sea CO13 0PB — MB BS 1991 Lond.

SLADE, Paul Jonathan Baker Irnham Lodge Surgery, Townsend Road, Minehead TA24 5RG Tel: 01643 703289 Fax: 01643 707921 — MRCS Eng. LRCP Lond. 1974; MRCGP 1980; DRCOG 1977. Clin. Asst. (Ophth.); Clin. Asst. Som. Drug Serv. Prev: SHO Kent & Canterbury Hosp.; Med. Off. RAF Med. Br.

SLADE, Paul Martin Bristol-Myers Squire, 141-9 Staines Road, Hounslow TW3 3JA Tel: 020 8754 3600 Fax: 020 8572 7345 Email: p.slade@.bms.com; 24 Kings Road, St Margaret's, Twickenham TW1 2QS Tel: 020 8892 9014 Email: paul.slade@ukgateway.net — MB BChir 1991 Camb.; MA Camb. 1991; MRCP (UK) 1996. (Univ. Camb. & St. Mary's Hosp. Lond.) Med. Advisor (Anti-infectives) Bristol-Myers Squibb; Hon. Clin. Asst. St. Mary's Hosp. Lond. Prev: Acad. Regist. (Communicable Dis.) St. Mary's Hosp. Lond.

SLADE, Philip Herbert Eastoft, 249 Normanby Road, South Bank, Middlesbrough TS6 6TB Tel: 01642 453457 — LRCP LRCS 1948 Ed.; LRCP LRCS Ed. LRFPS Glas. 1948. (Newc.) Prev: Ho. Phys. & Res. Obst. Off. Bensham Gen. Hosp. Gateshead-on-Tyne.

SLADE, Mr Philip Ridd Helyar (retired) 6 Rockleaze, Bristol BS9 1NE — ChM Bristol 1955, MB ChB 1939; FRCS Eng. 1947. Prev: Cons. Thoracic Surg. Groby Rd. Hosp. Leicester.

SLADE, Richard 28 Glenbarry Close, Chorlton-Cum-Medlock, Manchester M13 9XR Tel: 0161 273 8481 — MB ChB Aberd. 1980; MRCPsych 1989; MRCGP 1986; T(GP) 1991; DRCOG 1985. (Univ. Aberd.)

SLADE, Mr Richard John Hope Hospital, Stott Lane, Salford M6 8HD Tel: 0161 789 7373; Fieldgarth, 6 The Mount, Altrincham WA14 4DX — MB ChB 1984 Leic.; FRCS RCPS Glas. 1989; MRCOG 1991. (Leicester) Cons. O & G Hope Hosp. Salford; Cons. Gyn. Surg. Christie Hosp. Manch. Socs: Brit. Gyn. Cancer Soc. Prev: Sen. Regist. (O & G) Univ. Hosp. Wales Cardiff & St. Davids Hosp. Bangor; Regist. (O & G) John Radcliffe Hosp. Oxf.; SHO (O & G) Bristol Gen. Hosp. & Leicester Roy. Infirm.

SLADE, Robert Rodney (retired) Trust Headquarters, Southmead Hospital, Westbury-on-Trym, Bristol BS10 5NB Tel: 0117 959 5206 Fax: 0117 959 1102 Email: slade.r@southmead.swest.nhs.uk — MB BS 1973 Lond.; BSc (Biochem.) Lond. 1968; FRCP Lond. 1993; MRCP (UK) 1976; FRCPath (Haemat.) 1993, M 1980. Dir. Path. S.mead Hosp. Univ. Bristol; Med. Dir. WTE, N. Bristol NHS Trust. Prev: Clin. Dean & Cons. Haemat. S.mead Hosp. Univ. Bristol.

SLADE, Valerie Jane Copse Cottage, Church Lane, Brook, Godalming GU8 5UQ Tel: 01428 683866 — MB ChB 1988 Bristol; FRCA 1994. (Bristol University) Cons. Anaesth., Frimley Pk. Hosp. Camberley. Socs: Intens. Care Soc.; BMA; Assn. Anaesth.

SLADEN, Gordon Edward George (retired) Anchor Oast, Rochester Road, Aylesford ME20 7EA Tel: 01622 882395 — BM BCh 1960 Oxf.; MA Oxf. 1961, DM 1970; FRCP Lond. 1975, M 1963. Prev: Cons. Phys. (Gastroenterol.) Guy's Hosp. Lond. 1976-1994.

SLADER, Christopher John Llangennech Surgery, Llangennech, Llanelli SA14 8YR — MB ChB 1969 Sheff.; BSc Lond. 1964; MRCP (U.K.) 1973; MRCGP 1981. LLa.lli VTS Course Organiser.

SLADER, Marian Isabel Llangennech, Llanelli SA14 8YB — MB ChB 1972 Sheff. Prev: Clin. Asst. (Psychiat.) Dyke Bar Hosp. Paisley.

SLAFFER, Simon Neil Les Saisons Surgery, 20 David Place, St Helier, Jersey JE2 4TD Tel: 01534 720314 Fax: 01534 733205 — MB BS 1972 Lond.; MRCS Eng. LRCP Lond. 1973; ATLS RCS Eng. 1991; MRCGP 1979; DRCOG 1980. (St. Bart.) Specialist (Musculoskeletal Med.) Jersey; Lect. (Orthop. Med.) Internat. 1990; Hon. Lect. Jersey Wildlife Preservation Trust 1994; Maj. Incident Med. Off. Jersey; Certified Mem. Cyriax Foundat. (Exam. 1985). Socs: (Pres.) Jersey Med. Soc.; BMA (Chairm. Jersey Br.); Brit. Inst. Musculoskeletal Med. Prev: SHO Worcester Roy. Infirm.; Ho. Surg. St. Bart. Hosp. Lond.; Maj. RAMC.

SLANE, Frank 43A Roman Road, Bearsden, Glasgow G61 2QP Tel: 0141 943 0597 — LRCP LRCS Ed. LRFPS Glas. 1951; DPH Glas. 1958.

SLANE, Peter Wright Blue Wing Medical Practice, Wallacetown Medical Centre, 3 Lyon Street, Dundee DD4 6RB Tel: 01382 458333 Fax: 01382 461833; 8 Arbuthnott Loan, Balgillo Park, Broughty Ferry, Dundee DD5 3TN — MB ChB 1983 Dundee; MRCP (UK) 1986; MRCGP 1990; DRCOG 1990.

SLANEY, Charlotte Julia 455 Chester Road, Hartford, Northwich CW8 2AG — BM BCh 1998 Oxf.; BM BCh Oxf 1998.

SLANEY, Sir Geoffrey, KBE 23 Aston Bury, Edgbaston, Birmingham B15 3QB Tel: 0121 454 0261 — MB ChB 1946 Birm.; MB ChB Birm. 1947; MSc (Surg.) Illinois 1956; ChM Birm. 1961; FRCS Eng. 1953; Hon. FRCSI 1984; Hon. FRCSC 1986; Hon. FRACS 1984; Hon. FACS 1985 Birm.; Hon. FRCA 1986. (Birm.) Emerit. Prof. Surg. Univ. Birm.; Hon. Cons. Surg. Qu. Eliz. Hosp. Birm. Socs: Fell. Assn. Surgs.; Fell. Amer. Surg. Assn. Prev: Pres. Roy. Coll. Surg. Eng.; Barling Prof. Dept. Surg. Univ. Birm.; Cons. Surg. Qu. Eliz. Hosp. Birm.

SLANEY, Mark West Hampshire NHS Trust, Cannon House, 6 Cannon Street, Shirley SO15 5PQ; 18 Plantation Road, Tadley RG26 4QU — MB BS 1983 Lond.; MA Oxf. 1984; MRCPsych 1989; T(GP) 1991; Cert. Prescribed Equiv. Exp. JCPTGP 1989; DRCOG 1987; T (Psychiat.) 1993. Locum Cons. Gen. Adult Psychiat., W. Hants. NHS Trust, Soton. Socs: BMA. Prev: Locum Cons. Psychiat., Frankston Hosp. Melbourne, Vict.; Locum Cons. Gen. Adult Psychiat. Portsmouth Healthcare NHS Trust; Locum Cons. Psychiat. Loddon NHS Trust, Basingstoke.

SLANEY, Penelope Louise Radiology Department, Ronkswood Hospital, Worcester Royal Infirmary NHS Trust,, Newtown Road, Worcester WR1 5HN Tel: 01905 763333 Fax: 01905 760774 — MB ChB 1983 Birm.; FRCS Ed. 1989; FRCR 1994. Cons. Radiol. Worcester Roy. Infirm. NHS Trust. Socs: BMA; BSIR; CIRSE. Prev: Sen. Regist. (Diagn. Radiol.) Russells Hall Hosp. Dudley; Regist. (Radiol.) Bristol Roy. Infirm.; SHO (Urol. & Gen. Surg.) Roy. Shrewsbury Hosp.

SLANN, Hilary Elizabeth Rose 27 Glasgow Road, Denny FK6 5DW — MB ChB 1990 Glas.; MRCGP 1994.

SLAPAK, Gabrielle Isabelle Abbey House, Itchen Abbas, Winchester SO21 1BN — MB BS 1988 Lond.

SLAPAK, Mr Maurice, CBE, Maj. RAMC World Transplant Games Federation, Highcroft, Winchester Tel: 01962 840767 Ext: 3 Email: wtgf@wtgf.demon.co.uk; Abbey House, Itchen Abbas, Winchester

SLASKI

SO21 1BN Tel: 01962 779233 Fax: 01962 779673 Email: mslapak@compuserve.co — MB BChir 1957 Camb.; MChir Camb. 1967; FRCS Eng. 1963; FRCS Canada 1966; FACS 1970. (Westm.) Cons. Surg. Cromwell Hosp. Lond.; Cons. Gen. Surg. Qu. Alexandra's Hosp. Cosham; Sen. Lect. Soton. Univ. Socs: Transpl. Soc.; Eur. Soc. Organ Transpl. (Ex-Vice-Pres.); Roy. Soc. Med. (Ex.Pres. Transpl. Sect.). Prev: Sen. Surg. Wessex Regional Transpl. Unit St. Mary's Hosp. Portsmouth; Asst. Prof. Surg. Harvard Med. Sch. Boston, USA; Sen. Assr. Surg. Camb. Univ.

SLASKI, Mark Christopher Acorn Cottage, Ingestre St., Stafford ST18 0RE; 24 Brookhouse Road, Caton, Lancaster LA2 9QT — MB ChB 1985 Manch.; MRCGP 1989.

SLATER, Alan Brooklands, Durton Lane, Broughton, Preston PR3 5LD — MB BCh 1961 Liverp.; DObst RCOG 1963. Socs: BMA.

SLATER, Alan John Clatterbridge Centre for Oncology NHS Trust, Bebington, Wirral CH63 4JY Tel: 0151 334 1155 Fax: 0151 482 7675 Email: alans@ccotrust.co.uk; 5 Burlingham Avenue, West Kirby, Wirral CH48 8AJ Tel: 0151 625 9868 — MB ChB 1972 Birm; BA Open 1988; FRCR 1980. Cons. Clin. Clatterbridge Centre for Oncol NHS Trust Wirral. Socs: BMA. Prev: Clin. Sci. MRC Clin. Oncol. & Radiother. Unit Addenbrooke's Hosp. Camb.; Resid. (Radiat. Oncol.) P.ss Margt. Hosp. Toronto; MRC Clin. Assoc. Leukaemia) & Hon. Lect. (Haemat.) Univ. Hosp. Wales Cardiff.

SLATER, Alan Martin 2 Lovelace Close, Hurley, Maidenhead SL6 5NF — MB BS 1997 Lond.

SLATER, Alison Margaret 19 Station Road, Whyteleafe CR3 0GP Tel: 01883 624181; 65 Hartley Hill, Purley CR8 4EQ Tel: 020 8645 0275 — MB BS 1983 Lond.; MRCGP 1987; DRCOG 1986. p/t GP Princip. Prev: Trainee GP Croydon VTS; SHO (O & G & Geriat.) Mayday Hosp. Croydon; SHO (ENT/Paediat.) Bangour Gen. Hosp.

***SLATER, Andrew** 1 Shepley Close, Hazel Grove, Stockport SK7 6JJ — MB ChB 1976 Birm.

SLATER, Andrew James 6 South Terrace, High St., Farningham, Dartford DA4 0DF — MB BS 1990 Lond.; BSc (Clin. Sci.) Lond. 1989. Regist. Rotat. (Anaesth.) Guy's Hosp. Lond.

SLATER, Andrew James 4 Ely Cl, Amersham HP7 9HS — MB ChB 1997 Manch.

SLATER, Anne Christine Southbank Road Surgery, 17-19 Southbank Road, Kirkintilloch, Glasgow G66 1NH Tel: 0141 776 2183 Fax: 0141 777 8321 — MB ChB 1967 Ed. (Ed.) GP Kirkintilloch. Prev: Ho. Off. (Paediat.) Falkirk Dist. Roy. Infirm.; Ho. Phys. Vict. Hosp. Kirkcaldy; Ho. Surg. Falkirk & Dist. Roy. Infirm.

SLATER, Anne Jennifer Rivington, Little Plucketts Way, Buckhurst Hill IG9 5QU — MB BS 1974 Lond.; MRCS Eng. LRCP Lond. 1974. (Char. Cross Hosp. Med. Sch.)

SLATER, Mr Barry Joseph North Tyneside General Hospital, Rake Lane, North Shields NE29 8NH Tel: 0191 293 2527 Email: barry.slater@northumbria-healthcare.nhs.uk — MB ChB 1987 Manch.; FRCS Ed. 1992; FRCS Eng. 1992; FRCS Gen Surg. 1999. Cons. Surg. N. Tyneside Gen. Hosp., Tyne and Wear.

SLATER, Basil Crandles Smith, OBE (retired) 2/2 East Suffolk Road, Edinburgh EH16 5PH Tel: 0131 667 5964 — MD Ed. 1964, MB ChB 1952; FRCP Ed. 1988, M 1984; FFCM 1989, M 1980; FRCGP 1970, M 1960. Prev: Cons. Pub. Health Med. Edin. Roy. Infirm.

SLATER, Camilla Jane Silver Stream, Hackney Road, Melton, Woodbridge IP12 1NN — MB BS 1996 Lond.

SLATER, Catherine Brooklands, D'Urton Lane, Broughton, Preston PR3 5LD — BChir 1990 Camb.

SLATER, Catriona Susan 4 Tatton View, Withington, Manchester M20 4BU — MB ChB 1995 Manch.; BSc Med Sci 1993. SHO (Gen. Med.) Manch. Roy. Infirm.; Flexible Trainee. Prev: Clin. Fell. Wythenshawe Hosp. Manch.

SLATER, Charles Bell Long Barn Lane Surgery, 22 Long Barn Lane, Reading RG2 7SZ Tel: 0118 987 1377 Fax: 0118 975 0375 — MRCS Eng. LRCP Lond. 1981.

SLATER, Charles Stewart 3 Bradda Court, Bradda Road, Port Erin IM9 6PQ — MB ChB 1965 Ed.

SLATER, Clare 36 Great Barrington, Burford OX18 4UR — MB BS 1983 Lond.; MA (Chem.) Oxf. 1981; MSc (Epidemiol.) Lond. 1992; MRCP (UK) 1990; DFFP 1995; MRCGP 1998. (Char. Cross)

SLATER, Colin Anthony Ann Burrow Thames Health Centre, South William St., Workington CA14 2ED Tel: 01900 602244 Fax: 01900 871131 — MB BS 1975 Lond.; BSc (Physiol.) Lond. 1972,

MB BS 1975; DCH RCP Lond 1983. (St. Thos.) SCMO W. Cumbria Healthcare NHS Trust & Audiol. Childr. Serv. Prev: Clin. Med. Off. Cornw. & Is. Scilly HA.

SLATER, David Neil Tel: 0114 271 3378 Fax: 01142712200 Email: david.slater@sth.nhs.uk; 23 Redmires Road, Sheffield S10 4LA — MB ChB 1971 Sheff.; BMedSci Sheff. 1968; FRCPath 1990, M 1978. Cons. Dermatopathologist, Histopath. Dept., Roy. Hallamshire Hosp., Sheff.; QA Dir. for Trent NHSCSP; Dir. N. Eng. Dermatopath. Serv.; Hon. Clin. Sen. Lect (Path) Sheff. Univ. Socs: Internat. Acad. Path. & Assn. Clin. Paths.; (Counc.) Brit. Soc. for Clin. Cytol. Prev: CCons. Path. Rotherham NHS Hosps. Trust; Sen. Lect. (Path.) Sheff. Univ.; SHO Nottm. Gp. Hosps.

SLATER, David Richard Royal Crescent and Preston Road Practice, 25 Crescent Street, Weymouth DT4 7BY Tel: 01305 774466 Fax: 01305 760538 — MB ChB 1974 Leeds; DRCOG 1977.

SLATER, Edna Valerie (retired) Taney, Green Lane, West Clandon, Guildford GU4 7UR — MB BCh BAO Dub. 1960; MA Dub. 1964. Prev: Clin. Asst. (Geriat. Med.) Beechcroft Hosp. Woking.

SLATER, Edwin Antony Work (retired) Suleskerry, Ryanview Crescent, Stranraer DG9 0JL Tel: 01776 703903 — MB ChB 1961 Ed.; FRCGP 1994, M 1972; DObst RCOG 1963. Prev: GP Stranraer.

SLATER, Elinor Margaret 58 Paisley Crescent, Edinburgh EH8 7JQ Tel: 0131 661 5137 Email: elcapitarn@geocities.com — MB ChB 1990 Aberd.; LLB Ed. 1994; Primex Examination 1998. Gen. Pract. Locum.

SLATER, Elizabeth 3F1 18 Montaigne Street, Edinburgh EH8 9QX — MB ChB 1998 Ed.; MB ChB Ed 1998.

SLATER, Mr Eric George Winston BUPA Roding Hospital, Rodding Lane, Redbridge, Ilford IG4 5PZ Tel: 020 8551 1100; 'Rivington', Little Plucketts Way, Buckhurst Hill IG9 5QU Fax: 020 8559 0151 Email: eric.slater_frcs@virgin.net — MB BS Lond. 1966; FRCS Eng. 1975. (The London Hospital) Cons. Surg. in Private Pract. Prev: NHS Cons. in Gen. Vasc. and BrE. Surg.

SLATER, Ethel Valerie 65 Garstrang Road, Preston PR1 1LB Tel: 01772 53554 Fax: 01772 880105; Brooklands, Durton Lane, Broughton, Preston PR3 5LD Tel: 01772 862240 — MB ChB 1961 Liverp.; MRCGP 1996. (Liverp.) Trainer (Gen. Pract.) N. W.. RHA. Socs: Assoc. MRCGP; BMA. Prev: SHO (Path.), Ho. Surg. & Ho. Off. (O & G) Preston Roy. Infirm.

SLATER, Eva Marie Cleveland Clinic, 12 Cleveland Road, St Helier, Jersey JE1 4HD Tel: 01534 722381/734121 — MB ChB 1983 Glas.

SLATER, Geoffrey Dowell New Southgate Surgery, Buxton Place, off Leeds Road, Wakefield WF1 3JQ Tel: 01924 334400 Fax: 01924 334439; Oakland House, 16 Oxford Road, St Johns., Wakefield WF1 3LB Tel: 01924 201034 — MB ChB 1968 Leeds; DPM Leeds 1972. Prev: Regist. High Royds Hosp. Menston; Ho. Off. (Gen. Surg.) Chapel Allerton Hosp. Leeds; Ho. Off. (Gen. Med.) St. Jas. Hosp. Leeds.

SLATER, George Ian (retired) Ty'n Rhedyn, Marianglas LL73 8PW Tel: 01248 851093 — MB ChB Ed. 1954. Prev: Med. Off. Roan Consolidated Mines, Luanshya, Zambia.

SLATER, Mr Guy Haining Minimal Access Therapy Training Unit, Royal Surrey County Hospital, Guildford GU2 7XX — MB BS 1990 Lond.; FRCS Eng. 1994. Regist. (Gen. Surg.) Roy. Surrey Co. Hosp. Guildford. Prev: Regist. St Thos. Hosp. Lond.; Regist. Frimley Pk. Hosp.; Regist. Mayday Univ. Hosp.

SLATER, Henry Bertram (retired) 63 Meltham Avenue, Withington, Manchester M20 1FE Tel: 0161 445 1294 — MB ChB 1936 Manch.; MRCS Eng. LRCP Lond. 1936. Prev: Cons. Phys. (Chest) Tameside & Manch. AHAs.

SLATER, Ian (retired) Taney, Green Lane, West Clandon, Guildford GU4 7UR Tel: 01483 222775 — MB BCh BAO 1960 Dub.; MA Dub. 1964. Prev: Regist. (Psychiat.) St. Patrick's Hosp. Dub.

SLATER, Jane Bodriggy Health Centre, 60 Queens Way, Bodriggy, Hayle TR27 4PB Tel: 01736 753136 Fax: 01736 753467 — MB BS 1984 Lond.; MRCGP 1993; DRCOG 1988. Trainer (Gen. Pract.) Cornw. Prev: SHO DHCE City Hosp. Nottm.; SHO (O & G) Roy. Cornw. Truro; SHO (Orthop. & A & E) N.wick Pk. Hosp. Middlx.

SLATER, John David Eliot 40 Poplar Road, Botley, Oxford OX2 9LB — MB ChB 1989 Bristol; MPH 1999 Birmingham University; MA Camb. 1979, BA 1976; MRCGP 1993; MRCPsych 1999; Postgrad. Cert. Leeds 1977. Specialist Regist. Rehabil. Med.;

Locum GP. Prev: Trainee in Psychiat. Oxf. Rotat.; Res. Fell. Birm. Univ.; GP RAF Cramwell.

SLATER, John Edward St Lawrence Medical Centre, 4 Bocking End, Braintree CM7 9AA Tel: 01376 552474 Fax: 01376 552417 — MB ChB 1982 Manch.; MRCGP 1986; DRCOG 1985. (Manch.) Prev: Trainee GP Stockport VTS.

SLATER, John Norman Botley Medical Centre, Elms Road, Botley, Oxford OX2 9JS Tel: 01865 248719 Fax: 01865 728116; 43 Yarnells Hill, Botley, Oxford OX2 9BE Tel: 01865 248134 — MB ChB 1971 Aberd.; DCH Eng. 1976.

SLATER, Jonathan Charles 1 Broadacres, Fleet GU51 4EU — MB BS 1997 Lond.

SLATER, Mr Keith David 83 Craiglea Drive, Edinburgh EH10 5PQ — MB ChB 1983 Aberd.; FRCS Ed. 1988; MRCGP 1993. Regist. (Basic. Surg.) Edin. Train. Scheme.

SLATER, Kerry Elizabeth 153 Hanover Road, Willesden Green, London NW10 3DN — MB BS 1972 Queensland. (Queensld.)

SLATER, Laurence Billingsley 15 Brook Green, London W6 7BL Tel: 020 7603 7563; 2 Hartswood Gardens, Stamford Brook, London W12 9NR Email: drl@slater.org.uk — MB BS 1982 Lond.; MRCGP 1991; DCH RCP Lond. 1990. Computer Fell. (EHH Health Agency). Socs: BMA. Prev: Hammersmith PCG Bd. Mem.; Regist. (Paediat.) Greenwich Dist. Hosp. Lond.; Regist. (Med.) Dulwich Hosp. Lond.

SLATER, Lindsay Kay Townsend House Medical Centre, 49 Harepath Road, Seaton EX12 2RY Tel: 01297 20616 Fax: 01297 20810; Higher Bolshayne Barn, Whitwell Lane, Colyton EX24 6HS Tel: 01297 552102 — MB BS 1982 Lond.; BSc Hons. Lond. 1976; MRCGP 1985; DRCOG 1985; DCH RCP Lond. 1984. Prev: Trainee GP Ealing VTS.

SLATER, Lorna Kay 41 Hatfield Road, Ainsdale, Southport PR8 2PE — MB ChB 1996 Sheff.

SLATER, Margaret (retired) 18 Trefonwys, Belmont Road, Bangor LL57 — MB ChB Liverp. 1944; MFCM 1973; CPH Eng. 1947; DCH Eng. 1947. Prev: Princip. Sen. Med. Off. Child Health Serv. Gwynedd AHA.

SLATER, Mark Stephen Shrodells Unit, Watford General Hospital, Vicarage Road, Watford WD18 0HB Tel: 01923 217441 Fax: 01923 217931 Email: markslater@doctors.org.uk — MB ChB 1983 Otago; MRCPsych 1989. Cons. Psychiat. W. Herts. Community NHS Trust. Socs: BMA; W Herts. & Watford Med. Soc. Prev: Sen. Regist. (Psychiat.) Roy. Lond. Hosp.; Regist. (Psychiat.) Bethlem Roy. & Maudsley Hosps. Lond.; SHO (Psychiat.) Middlx. Hosp. Lond.

SLATER, Michele Anne Brixton Hill Group Practice, 22 Raleigh Gardens, Brixton Hill, London SW2 1AE — MB ChB 1987 Glas.; MRCGP 1992.

SLATER, Mr Nicholas Desmond 1 Wilton Villas, London N1 3DN Tel: 020 7354 3507 — MB BS 1977 Lond.; MS Lond. 1990; MRCS Eng. LRCP Lond. 1977; FRCS Eng. 1982. (Guy's Hosp. Lond.) Cons. Surg. Lewisham Hosp. Lond. Prev: Sen. Regist. St. Bart. Hosp. Lond.

SLATER, Nicolas Gilbert Pasternak (retired) 85 Balfour Road, London N5 2HE Tel: 020 7359 2287 Fax: 020 7503 6827 Email: nicolasslater@email.com — MA Oxf. 1965; Dip. Biochem. Lond 1967; MB BS Lond. 1970; FRCP Lond. 1993, M 1973; FRCPath 1990, M 1978. Prev: Sen. Lect. & Hon. Cons. (Haemat.) United Med. & Dent. Sch. St. Thos. Hosp. Lond.

SLATER, Noel Arthur John 100 Poplar Avenue, Edgbaston, Birmingham B17 8ES Tel: 0121 429 4237 — MB ChB 1961 Birm.; FFA RCS Eng. 1978; DA Eng. 1964; DObst RCOG 1964.

SLATER, Patricia Carol-Ann St. Helier Hospital, Wrythe Lane, Carshalton SM5 1AA Tel: 020 8644 4343; 10 Victoria Court, Victoria Road, Shoreham-by-Sea BN43 5WS — MB BS 1988 Lond. Regist. (Anaesth.) St Helier Hosp. Carshalton. Prev: SHO (Paediat. & Neonat.) Roy. Alexandra Hosp. for Sick Childr. Brighton; SHO (Anaesth. & ITU) Qu. Alexandra Hosp. Portsmouth.

SLATER, Mr Peter Anderson (retired) 28 St Andrew Street, Brechin DD9 6JJ Tel: 01356 622554 Email: peisoslater@themail.co.uk — MB ChB 1966 Aberd.; FRCS Ed. 1972; T(S) 1991. Prev: Hon. Clin. Sen. Lect. Univ. Aberd.

SLATER, Peter Forrester (retired) 5 Bede Court, College Grove Road, Wakefield WF1 3RW Tel: 01924 373077 — MB ChB 1954 St. And.

SLATER, Peter John (retired) 14 Rowan Crescent, Lenzie, Kirkintilloch, Glasgow G66 4RE — MB ChB 1965 Glas.; FFA RCS Eng. 1975; MRCOG 1970, DObst 1967. Cons. Anaesth. Stobhill Hosp. Glas.

SLATER, Philip Denis Trevaylor Road Health Centre, Trevaylor Road, Falmouth TR11 2LH Tel: 01326 317317; Timminoggy, 20 Boscawen Road, Falmouth TR11 4EN — MB BS 1970 Lond.; MRCS Eng. LRCP Lond. 1970. (St. Mary's)

SLATER, Mr Richard University Department of Surgical & Anaesthetic Sciences, 1st Floor, Royal Hallamshire Hospital, Glossop Road, Sheffield S10 2JF Tel: 0114 271 3861; Tel: 0114 269 1012 — BM BS 1993 Nottm.; BMedSci (Hons.) Nottm. 1991; FRCS (Eng) 1998. (Nottingham) Surgic. Research Assoc., Gen. Surg. Univ. of Sheff., Sheff. Socs: Fell. Of Roy. Coll. of Surg. Of Eng. Prev: Specialist Regist. (Gen. Surg.) Barnsley Dist. Gen. Hosp.; SHO (Gen. Surg.) Chesterfield Roy. Hosp.

SLATER, Mr Robert Neil Summers Department of Orthopaedic Surgery, The Maidstone Hospital, Hermitage Lane, Maidstone ME16 9NN Tel: 01622 729000; 1 Clare Wood Drive, West Malling, West Malling ME19 6PA Tel: 01732 875292 — MB BChir 1984 Camb.; MB 1984 Camb.; FRCS (Orth.) 1992; FRCS Ed. 1987. Cons. Orthop. Surg. Maidstone Hosp. Socs: Fell. Roy. Soc. Med. (Orthop. Sect.); Brit. Orthop. Assn. Prev: Sen. Regist. (Orthop.) Guy's & St. Thos. Hosp. Lond.

SLATER, Roger Martin Department of Anaesthesia, Manchester Royal Infirmary, Oxford Road, Manchester M13 9WL Tel: 0161 276 4551; 41 Eyebrook Road, Bowdon, Altrincham WA14 3LQ Email: rmslate@ibm.net — MB BCh 1979 Manch.; BSc (Med. Sci.) 1976; MB ChB Manch. 1979; MRCP (UK) 1982; FFA RCS Eng. 1984. (St Andrews and Manchester Medical School) Cons. Anaesth. Manch. Roy. Infirm. Socs: BMA; Assn. Anaesth.; Intens. Care Soc. Prev: Cons. Anaesth. Univ. Hosp. Nottm.; Sen. Regist. (Anaesth.) N. W.. RHA.

SLATER, Mr Ronald MacCallum Westward, 39 Sheridan Drive, Helens Bay, Bangor BT19 1LB Tel: 01247 852373 — MB BCh BAO 1955 Belf.; FRCS Ed. 1964; DObst RCOG 1957. Cons. Plastic Surg. Ulster Hosp. Dundonald. Roy. Vict. Hosp. & Belf. Hosp. Sick Childr.

SLATER, Sarah Elizabeth Tel: 0207 601 7045 Fax: 0207 601 7577; Tel: 0208 670 5909 — MB BS 1989 Lond.; CSST Medical Oncology 2001; MD 2000; MRCP 1993. (St. Barts.) Specialist Regist. (Med. Oncol.) & Hon. Lect. St. Barts. Hosp. Lond. Prev: Clin. Res. Fell. ICRF.

SLATER, Stefan Daniel (retired) — MB ChB 1963 Glas.; MD (Hons.) Glas. 1975; FRCP Lond. 1990; FRCP Glas. 1978; MRCP (UK) 1969; FRCP Ed 1998. Locum Cons. Phys. Work; Examr., Roy. Col. Prev: Hon. Sec. RCPS Glas. 1995-8.

SLATER, Susan Denise 10 Woodside Road, Beaconsfield HP9 1JG — MB BS 1987 Lond.; MSc Lond. 1989, MB BS 1987; MRCPath 1996. Cons. & Hon. Sen. Lect. Univ. Coll. Hosp. Lond. Prev: Clin. Lect. (Histopath.) Univ. Coll. Hosp. Lond.; Hon. Regist. & Regist. (Histopath.) Hammersmith Hosp. Lond.; Regist. (Histopath.) Roy. Marsden Hosp. Lond.

SLATER, Victoria Margaret Anne 14 Rowan Crescent, Lenzie, Glasgow G66 4RE; 283 Crow Road, 3rd Floor Left, Glasgow G33 7BQ Tel: 0141 357 1279 — MB ChB 1993 Glas. GP Regist. Prev: SHO (Neonat. Med.) Irvine Centr. Hosp.; SHO (Gen. Paediat.) CrossHo. Hosp. Kilmarnock; SHO (O & G) Monklands & Beushin NHS Trust.

SLATER, Wendy Jane Ardroy, Westpark Road, Blairgowrie PH10 6EL — MB ChB 1994 Glas.

SLATFORD, Kenneth Royal Edinburgh Hospital, Morningside Park, Edinburgh EH10 5HF Tel: 0131 537 6000; 27 Rutland Street, Edinburgh EH1 2AE — MB ChB 1978 Glas.; BSc (Hons.) Glas. 1976; MPhil Ed. 1992; FRCP 1998; MRCPsych 1987. (Glasgow) Cons. Gen. Psychiat. Roy. Edin. Hosp.; Hon. Sen. Lect. Univ. Edin. Socs: Fell. Roy. Coll. Phys. Edin. Prev: Cons. Psychiat. Rosslynlee Hosp.; Sen. Regist. (Psychiat.) Roy. Edin. Hosp.; Sen. Regist. (Genitourin. Med.) Univ. Edin. Roy. Infirm. Edin.

SLATOR, David Anthony 37 St Peters Road, Broadstairs CT10 2AP; The Limes, Hawley St, Margate CT9 1 Tel: 01843 227567 — BM BCh 1977 Oxf.; MA, BM BCh Oxf. 1977; MRCGP 1982.

SLATOR, James (retired) 20 Cromer Road, Holt NR25 6DX Tel: 01263 2129 — BM BCh 1947 Oxf.; BM BCh Oxon. 1947; FRCP Ed. 1979.

SLATOR

SLATOR, Rona Caroline The Children's Hospital, Steelhouse Lane, Birmingham B4 6NH Tel: 0121 333 8132 Fax: 0121 333 8131 Email: rona.slator@bhamchildrens.wmids.nhs.uk — MB BS 1984 Lond.; DPhil Oxf. 1982; FRCS (Plast) 1995; FRCS 1989. Cons. Plastic Surg. Childr. Hosp. Birm.

***SLATTER, Deborah Jeanne** 6 Barbel Road, Colchester CO4 3EJ — MB ChB 1998 Birm.

SLATTER, Elaine St. Fillans, 8 Woodham Road, Woking GU21 4DL — MB BS Lond. 1965; MRCS Eng. LRCP Lond. 1965. (Roy. Free) Clin. Asst. (Genitourin. Med.) St. Thos. Hosp. Lond. Prev: Med. Off. Surrey AHA; Ho. Phys. Nat. Temperance Hosp. Lond.; Ho. Surg. S. Lond. Hosp. Wom. & Childr.

SLATTER, Kenneth Hubert Hinderton Hall Farm, Chester High Road, Neston, South Wirral CH64 7TU Tel: 0151 336 1781 — MB ChB Liverp. 1943; MD Liverp. 1957; FRCP Lond. 1971, M 1951. (Liverp.) Emerit. Cons. Neurol. (Med. & Surg. Neurol.) Walton Hosp. Liverp. Socs: Assn. Brit. Neurols.; Liverp. Med. Inst. Prev: Lect. (Med.) Univ. Liverp.; Clin. Lect. (Neurol. Sci.) Univ. Liverp.; Resid. Med. Off. Liverp. Roy. Infirm.

SLATTER, Mary Anne Newcastle General Hospital, Westgate Road, Newcastle upon Tyne NE4 6BE Tel: 0191 273 8811 Fax: 0191 273 0183; 15 Harley Terrace, Newcastle upon Tyne NE3 1UL — MB ChB 1987 Bristol; MRCP (UK) 1993. Staff grade Paediat. Childr.s Bone Marrow Transpl.ation; Paediat.,Nyankunde, democratic rePub. of Cango. Prev: SHO (Paediat.) S.mead Hosp. Bristol; Regist. Community Paediat., Leeds.

SLATTERY, David Antony Douglas, MBE (retired) 99 South Quay, Wapping Dock, Liverpool L3 4BW Email: david@slatt30.freeserve.co.uk — MB BS 1953 Lond.; FRCP Lond. 1986; FFOM RCP Lond. 1981; FFOM RCPI 1977; DIH Soc. Apoth. Lond. 1961. Hon. Civil Cons. (Occupat. Med.) RAF. Prev: Adviser Occupat. Health Policy Mersey RHA 1992-94.

SLATTERY, Maria Anna Preston Park Surgery, 2A Florence Rd, Brighton BN1 6DJ Tel: 01273 559601 Fax: 01273 507746 — MB BS 1994 Lond.; MRCGP 1999; DFFP 2000; DRCOG 1997. p/t GP Princip. Preston Pk. Surg. Brighton. Prev: Clin. Asst. in Psychiat. Priory Clinic, Hove.

SLATTERY, Michael Anthony Orford Lodge Surgery, 100 Bancroft, Hitchin SG5 1ND Tel: 01462 432042 Fax: 01462 436505 — MB BCh BAO 1976 NUI; 2000 Dip. In Primary Care Therap., Imperial Coll. Of Sci. Techn. & Med.; MRCGP 1980; DCH Dub. 1981; DRCOG 1978. GP Hitchin.

SLATTERY, Simon Antony Downs House, Baydon, Marlborough SN8 2JS Tel: 01672 40755; 4 Suzi Turn Plaza, Providenciales, Turks & Caicos Islands Tel: 00 1 809 9465252 — MB BS 1984 Lond.

SLATTERY, Zoë Taschereau (retired) The Limes, The Street, Walsham Le Willows, Bury St Edmunds IP31 3AZ Tel: 01359 259422 — MB BS 1948 Lond.; FRCPsych 1985, M 1974; DCH Eng. 1951. Cons. Psychiat. W. Suff. Gen. Hosp. Bury St. Edmunds. Prev: Cons. Psych. W. Suff. Hosp.

SLAVEN, Andrew Edward West Middlesex University Hospital, Isleworth TW7 6AF Tel: 020 8560 2121 — MB BCh 1984 Witwatersrand.

SLAVEN, Catherine Frances Greenlaw Medical Centre, 27 Glasgow Road, Paisley PA1 3PA Tel: 0141 889 8465 Fax: 0141 889 8073 — MB ChB 1984 Glas.; MRCP (UK); MRCGP 1990.

SLAVIK, Zdenek Paediatric Surgical Unit, Harefield Hospital, Harefield, Uxbridge UB9 6JH Tel: 01895 823737 Fax: 01895 828554 — MD 1982 Prague; MD Charles U Prague 1982; DM Soton. 1998. Cons. Paediat. Cardiol./Intens. Care Hosp. Harefield Harefield.

SLAVIN, Brenda Mary (retired) 8 Normanhurst Park, Darley Dale, Matlock DE4 3BQ Tel: 01629 375644 — MB ChB 1957 Ed.; BSc Witwatersrand 1953; FRCPath 1984, M 1972; MCB Roy. Inst. Chem. 1972. Prev: Prof. Path. Al Quds Univ. Jerusalem.

SLAVIN, Brendan Michael 1 Yeats Close, Newport Pagnell MK16 8RD Tel: 01908 617371 Email: bms@hamish.bytenet.co.uk — MB BS Lond. 1985; BSc Lond. 1982; FRCA 1992. Cons. Anaesth. Milton Keynes Gen. Hosp. Socs: Assn. Anaesth. GB & Irel.; Obst. Anaesth. Assn. Prev: Sen. Regist. W. Midl. Anaesth. Train. Scheme; SHO (Anaesth.) Oxon. HA; Ho. Phys. Roy. Free Hosp. Lond.

SLAVIN, Professor Gerard (retired) 8 Normanhurst Park, Darley Dale, Matlock DE4 3BQ Tel: 01629 735644 Email: gsbms@darleyd.fsnet.co.uk — MB ChB 1957 Ed.; BSc 2001 Lond.; 2000 FGS; FRCP Glas. 1979, M 1963; FRCPath 1979, M 1967; DPath Eng. 1964. Emerit. Prof. Histopath. St. Bart. Med. Coll. Lond. Prev: Prof. Histopath. St. Bart. Hosp. Med. Coll. Lond.

SLAVIN, James Andrew Hunter Health Centre, Andrew Street, East Kilbride, Glasgow G74 1AD Tel: 01355 906655 — MB ChB 1988 Glas.; MRCGP 1994. Gen. Med. Practitioner Princip. Hunter Health Centre E. Kilbridge.

SLAVIN, Mr John Patrick 2 Straud Road, Hoylake, Wirral CH47 2DA — MB BS 1981 Lond.; MB BS (Distinc.) Lond. 1984; BSc (1st cl. Hons.) Lond. 1981, MS 1995; FRCS Eng. 1984. Sen. Regist. (Surg.) Roy. Liverp. Univ. Hosp. Prev: Research Fell. (Surg.) Univ. Calif., San Francisco, USA.; Regist. (Surg.) W.m. Hosp. & Mersey RHA.

SLAVOTINEK, Anne Michele c/o Department of Clinical Genetics, Churchill Hospital, Old Road, Oxford OX3 7LJ; 8 Barrett Street, Osney, Oxford OX2 0AT Tel: 01865 248002 — MB BS 1987 Adelaide.

SLAWINSKA, Mrs Krystyna Maria (retired) Silver Birches, 425 London Road, Holtwood, Ditton, Maidstone ME16 Tel: 01622 717205 — MB ChB 1949 Ed. Prev: SCMO Maidstone Dist. Health Auth.

SLAWSON, Jane Ann Medical Centre, Church Road, Tiptree, Colchester CO5 0HB Tel: 01621 816475 Fax: 01621 819902 — MB ChB 1985 Leic.; MRCGP 1991; DRCOG 1989; DGM RCP Lond. 1987.

SLAWSON, Keith Brian (retired) 27 Craigmount View, Edinburgh EH12 8BS Tel: 0131 339 4786 Email: brianlawson@cableinet.co.uk — MB ChB 1958 Ed.; BSc Ed. 1955; FRCA 1962; Dip. Sports Med. 1997. Cons. Anaesth. E. Gen. Hosp. Edin. Prev: Lect. (Anaesth.) Univ. Edin.

SLAYMAKER, Ann Elizabeth Leeds General Infirmary, Great George St., Leeds LS1 3EX; The Gables, 8 Old Vicarage Lane, Monk Fryston, Leeds LS25 5EA Email: ann@thegables.demon.co.uk — MB ChB 1990 Leeds; FRCA 1996. (Leeds) Specialist Regist. (Anaesth.) Leeds. Gen. Infirm. Prev: Regist. & SHO (Anaesth.) Leeds Gen. Infirm.

SLEAP, Angela Gillian The Health Centre, 9 Carrington Way, Wincanton BA9 9JY; Oak cottage, Kingsdon, Somerton TA11 7JU — BM 1978 Soton. GP Asst.,.

SLEAP, Peter Guy Frederick Oak Cottage, Kingsdon, Somerton TA11 7JU — MB ChB 1971 Ed. Staff Grade (Anaesth.) Yeovil Dist. Hosp. Som. Prev: GP Anaesth. Shell Petroleum Port HarCt., Nigeria.

SLEATH, Jonathan Duncan The Surgery, Kingstone, Church Road Lyde, Hereford HR2 9EY Tel: 01981 250215 Fax: 01981 251171; The Villa, Kingstone, Hereford HR2 9ET — BM BCh 1985 Oxf.; MA Camb. 1986; MRCGP 1990; DRCOG 1988. Socs: BMA. Prev: Med. Asst. St. Michael's Hospice Hereford; SHO Dr. MacKinnon Memor. Hosp. Isle-of-Skye; Ho. Surg. John Radcliffe Hosp. Oxf.

SLEATOR, Alexandra Moira Gay Fynescourt, Boundary Road, Grayshott, Hindhead GU26 6TX — MB BCh BAO 1972 Dub.

SLEATOR, David John Douglas West Surrey Health Authority, The Ridgewood Centre, Old Bisley Road, Camberley GU16 9QE Tel: 01276 671718 Fax: 01276 605491 — MB BCh BAO 1972 Dub.; BA Dub. 1970; MSc 1998. Head of Clin. Developm. W. Surrey Health Auth. Camberley. Prev: Med. Adviser Surrey FHSA Surbiton; GP Hindhead Surrey; Ho. Phys. & Ho. Surg. Sir P. Dun's Hosp. Dub.

SLEE, Mr Gerald Charles Lindley House, Hinton Road, Hereford HR2 6BN Tel: 01432 272827 Fax: 01432 272827 Email: geredslee @aol.com — MB ChB Liverp. 1947, MCh Orth. 1955; FRCS Eng. 1953. (Liverp.) Medico-Legal Pract. (Orth. & Traum.). Socs: Girdlestone Orthopaedic Gp.; Fell. Brit. Orthop. Assn.; S. W. Orthopead.Club. Prev: Sen. Regist. Roy. Infirm. Edin. & P.ss Margt. Rose Orthop.; Hosp. Edin.; Regist. Accid. Serv. Radcliffe Infirm. Oxf.

SLEE, Ivor Patterson 9 Salamander Quay, Lower Teddington Road, Hampton Wick, Kingston upon Thames KT1 4JB Tel: 020 8977 5616 Fax: 020 8977 5616 Email: steamboat@ondigital.com — MB BS 1960 Lond.; FFA RCS Eng. 1966. (St. Thos.) Cons. Anaesth. Char. Cross Hosp. Lond. Socs: Roy. Soc. Med.; Med. Sect. of Roy. Photographic Soc. Prev: Sen. Regist. St. Geo. Hosp. Lond.; Regist. (Anaesth.) & Ho. Off. (Orthop. & Plastic Surg.) St. Thos. Hosp. Lond.

SLEEMAN, Martin Lamont Derwent Practice, Norton Road, Malton YO17 9RF Tel: 01653 600069 Fax: 01653 698014;

Paddock House, Swinton Grange, Malton YO17 6QP Tel: 01653 694168 — MB ChB 1973 Liverp.; DObst RCOG 1976.

SLEEP, Tamsin Joanna Stoke, West Pentire, Crantock, Newquay TR8 5SE Email: tsleep@compuserve.com — BM BCh 1993 Oxf.; BA (Hons.) Oxf. 1990; FRCOphth Lond. 1997. (Oxf.) Specialist Regist. (Ophth.) Wessex Rotat. Prev: SHO (Ophth.) Qu. Med. Centre Nottm.

SLEET, Rodger Arthur (retired) Green Shutters, The Spinney, Bassett, Southampton SO16 7FW Tel: 01703 767310 — MB ChB 1959 Ed.; FRCP Ed. 1987; FFAEM 1993; FRCGP 1981, M 1968. Prev: Cons. (A & E) Soton Univ. Hosps.

SLEGGS, John Hedworth Victoria Cross Surgery, 168/9 Victoria Road, Swindon SN1 3BU Tel: 01793 535584 Fax: 01793 497526; 11 Stratton Heights, Cirencester GL7 2RH Tel: 01285 651919 Email: johnsleggs@hotmail.com — MB ChB 1971 Manch.; MRCP (UK) 1974; MRCGP 1988; DTM & H Liverp. 1981. (Manch.) Socs: Christ. Med. Fell.sh. Prev: Chief of Med., Patan Hosp., Kathmandu, Nepal; Specialist (Med.) Thimphu Gen. Hosp. Bhutan, 1981-1984; Hosp. Pract. (Med.) Cirencester Hosp.

SLEIGH, Gillian Cheyne Child Development Service, Chelsea & Westminster Hospital, 369 Fulham Road, London SW10 9NH Tel: 020 8846 1286 Fax: 020 8846 1284; 1 Walton Crescent, Oxford OX1 2JG Tel: 01865 510206 Fax: 01865 510206 — MB BS Lond. 1963; MRCP (UK) 1985; DCH Eng. 1966. (Roy. Free) Cons. Paediat. (Community Child Health) Chelsea & W.m. Hosp. Lond. Socs: Brit. Paediat. Neurol. Assn.; Brit. Paediat. Assn.; Brit. Assn. for Community Child Health. Prev: Cons. Paediat. (Community Child Health) Univ. Hosp. Wales; SCMO Hugh Ellis Paediat. Assem. Centre Oxf.; Med. Dir. P.ss Eliz. Centre Physically Handicap. Childr. Trinidad, W. Indies.

SLEIGH, Professor James Douglas (retired) 63 Newton Grove, Newton Mearns, Glasgow G77 5QJ Tel: 0141 616 2409 — MB ChB 1953 Glas.; MB ChB (Hons.) Glas. 1953; FRCP Glas. 1982, M 1979; FRCPath 1976, M 1964. Prev: Prof. Bact. Univ. Glas.

SLEIGH, John (retired) Bodran, St. Mary's Road, Monmouth NP25 3JE Tel: 01600 712899 — MB ChB Aberd. 1940; BA Open 1984; DPH Ed. 1946. Prev: Asst. MOH & Sch. Med. Off. Bristol.

***SLEIGHT, Claire Leila** Wrangling Green, Castle Hill, Brenchley, Tonbridge TN12 7BX; Flat 5 Berrylands Lodge, 2 The Avenue, Surbiton KT5 8JQ Tel: 020 8287 5754 Email: ssleight@usa.net — MB BS 1996 Lond.

SLEIGHT, Elizabeth (retired) Flat 4, 41 Sunderland Road, London SE23 2PS — MB ChB 1987 Sheff.; MRCP (UK) 1992; DCH RCP Lond. 1991.

SLEIGHT, Mrs Gillian (retired) Wayside, 32 Crown Road, Wheatley, Oxford OX33 1UL Tel: 01865 872491 Fax: 01865 874169 — MB BS 1953 Lond.; MRCS Eng. LRCP Lond. 1953. Prev: SCMO Community Health Oxon. HA.

SLEIGHT, Professor Peter John Radcliffe Hospital, Room 5617, Level 5, Oxford OX3 9DU Tel: 01865 760564 Fax: 01865 768844; Wayside, 32 Crown Road, Wheatley, Oxford OX33 1UL Tel: 01865 872491 Fax: 01865 874169 — MB BChir 1953 Camb.; DM Oxf. 1965; MD Camb. 1965; Hon. MD Univ. Pernambuco; FRCP Lond. 1969, M 1957; MD 2000 Hon University of Gdansk. (Camb. & St. Bart.) Hon. Cons. John Radcliffe Hosp. Oxf.; Field Marshal Alexander Emerit. Prof. Cardiovasc. Med. Univ. Oxf. John Radcliffe Hosp Oxf; Chairm. Isis Trials Gp; Emerit. Fell. Exeter Coll. Oxf. Socs: (Ex-Pres.) Brit. Hypertens. Soc.; (Vice-Pres.) Action on Smoking & Health; (Ex-Counc.lor) Europ. Soc. Cardiol. Prev: Civil Cons. Med: RAF; Warren McDonald Fell. & Vis. Prof. Hallstrom Inst. Cardiol. Univ. Sydney; Cons. Phys. Cardiol. Radcliffe Infirm. Oxf.

SLEIGHT, Peter James Torbay Hospital, Lawes Bridge, Torquay TQ2 7AA Tel: 01803 614567 x 5516 Fax: 01803 616334; Old Vicarage, Orley Road, Ipplepen, Newton Abbot TQ12 5SA — MBBS Lond. 1973, MSc 1980; MRCP UK 1977. (St. Bart.)

SLEIGHT, Simon Paul Bridleway, 9 Woodrough Copse, Bramley, Guildford GU5 0HH — MB BS 1996 Lond.

SLEIGHT, Vivien Pamela (retired) Derrydown, Pouchen End Lane, Hemel Hempstead HP1 2SA Tel: 01442 876152 Fax: 01442 876151 Email: vsleight@doctors.org.uk — MB BS 1977 Lond.; MRCS Eng. LRCP Lond. 1977; LLM 1998.

SLEIGHTHOLM, Marcus Alexander Seacroft Hospital, York Road, Leeds LS14 6UH Tel: 0113 264 8164 — MD 1988 Liverp.; FRCP 2001; MB ChB Liverp. 1979; MRCP (UK) 1983. Cons. Phys. Interest in Elderly Seacroft Hosp. Leeds; Sen. Lec. (Med.) Leeds Univ.

SLEMP, Margaret Christine Boundary House Surgery, Boundary House, Mount Lane, Bracknell RG12 9PG Tel: 01344 483900 Fax: 01344 862203; 5 Lawrence Grove, Bracknell RG42 4BL — MB BCh 1975 Wales.

SLESENGER, Joseph Phillip Baronsmere Road Surgery, 39 Baronsmere Road, East Finchley, London N2 9QD Tel: 020 8883 1458 Fax: 020 883 8854 — MB ChB 1986 Manch.; MRCGP 1990; DRCOG 1990; DGM RCP Lond. 1989; DCH RCP Lond. 1989. Prev: Trainee GP VTS.

SLESS, Herzl, MBE (retired) Flat 25, 15 Grand Avenue, Hove BN3 2NG Tel: 01273 735632 Fax: 01273 735632 — MB BCh BAO 1946 NUI; LM Rotunda 1947; DObst RCOG 1963. Prev: Med. Off. Rotunda Hosp. Dub.

SLESSER, Miss Betty Vivian (retired) Yew Trees, 56 Anstey Lane, Thurcaston, Leicester LE7 7JA Tel: 0116 235 9970 — MB ChB Ed. 1941; FRCS Eng. 1974; FRCS Ed. 1945. Prev: Cons. Surg. Regional-Cardiothor. Unit Groby Rd. Hosp. Leicester.

SLESSOR, Donald Munro 39 Westholme Avenue, Aberdeen AB15 6AB Tel: 01224 319196 — MB ChB 1950 Aberd. (Aberd.)

SLESSOR, Ian Munro (retired) 2 Birch Tree Walk, Nascot Wood, Watford WD17 4SH Tel: 01923 236430 — MB ChB 1956 Aberd.; MSc CNAA 1978; MRCGP 1968; FFPM RCP Lond. 1991. Prev: Med. Dir. Informat. Glaxo Gp. Research Ltd. Greenford.

SLEVIN, Maurice Louis 149 Harley Street, London W1G 6BN Tel: 020 7224 0685 Fax: 020 7224 1722; Tel: 020 7243 0704 — MB ChB 1973 Cape Town; MD Cape Town 1984; FRCP Lond. 1989; MRCP (UK) 1978. (Cape Town) Cons. Phys. (Med. Oncol.) St. Bart. Hosp. Lond. Prev: Lect. & Hon. Sen. Regist. (Med. Oncol.) St. Bart. Hosp. Lond.; Regist. (Med.) Groote Schuur Hosp. Cape Town; Regist. (Med. Oncol.) St. Bart. Hosp. Lond.

SLEVIN, Nicholas John Dept. Clinical Oncology, Christie Hospital, Manchester M20 4BX; 4 Clayton Avenue, Didsbury, Manchester M20 6BN — MB ChB 1978 Birm.; MRCP (UK) 1981; FRCR 1987; FRCP 1998. (Birmingham) Cons. Radiother. & Oncol. Christie Hosp. Manch. Prev: Sen. Regist. (Radioth. & Oncol.) Christie Hosp. Manch.; Regist. (Med.) ChristCh. Hosp., NZ.

SLEVIN, Paul Gerard Latham House Medical Practice, Sage Cross Street, Melton Mowbray LE13 1NX Tel: 01664 854949 Fax: 01664 501825; Fax: 02476 849199 — MB BCh BAO 1987 NUI; MRCOG 1995; DFFP 1995. (Univ. Coll. Dub.)

SLIBI, Mr Mahmoud 132 Woodway Lane, Coventry CV2 2EJ — MD 1986 Damascus; FRCS Glas. 1994.

SLIGHT, Robert David 11 Boreland Park, Inverkeithing KY11 1ES — MB ChB 1996 Aberd.

SLIM, Jacqueline Margaret The Health Centre, Beeches, Green, Stroud GL5 4BH Tel: 01453 764471; Woodlands, South Woodchester, Stroud GL5 5EQ Tel: 01453 872158 — MB ChB 1987 Bristol; DA (UK) 1991. GP Stroud Retainer Scheme.

SLIMMINGS, Peter George The Surgery, 4 Stoke Road, Bishops Cleeve, Cheltenham GL52 8RP Tel: 01242 672007; Ivybank, Lye Lane, Cleeve Hill, Cheltenham GL52 3QD — MB ChB 1972 Birm.; DObst RCOG 1975. Trainer GP Cheltenham VTS; Hosp. Pract. (Dermat.) Cheltenham Gen. Hosp. Prev: Ho. Surg. Qu. Eliz. Hosp. Birm.; Ho. Phys. & SHO (Gen. Med. & Infec. Dis.) E. Birm. Hosp.

SLINGER, Barry Christopher 14 The Grove, Shipley BD18 4LD — MB ChB 1971 St. And.; DObst RCOG 1974.

SLINGER, Keith Michael Aldren Newton Lea, West Newton, Carlisle Tel: 01228 20018 — MB ChB 1966 St. And.; DA Eng. 1969.

SLINGSBY, Andrew John 49 Elmwood Close, Retford DN22 6SL — MB BS 1994 Lond.; DRCOG 1997. (Roy. Free Hosp.) Prev: SHO (O & G) St. Richards Hosp. Chichester; SHO (ENT) Qu. Alexandra Hosp. Cosham; SHO Orthop. Epsom Gen. Hosp.

SLINN, Rebecca Mary Hill View Lodge, Bath Royal United Hospital, Weston, Bath Tel: 01225 428331; Cotswold House, Manor Road, Abbots Leigh, Bristol BS8 3RP — MB BS 1991 Lond.; MRCPsych 1996. (Barts.) Specialist Regist.; Oldage Psychiat. Cossham Hosp. Bristol.

SLIWINSKI, Sonja 54A Sothall Green, Beighton, Sheffield S20 1FH — MD 1993 Louvain.

SLOAN, Barbara Elizabeth Horton Bank Practice, 1220 Great Harlow Road, Bradford BD7 4PL Tel: 01274 410666 Fax: 01274 521605; 11 Paternoster Lane, Bradford BD7 3DS Tel: 01274 410666 Fax: 01274 521608 — MB ChB 1977 Leeds; MRCGP

SLOAN

1981; Cert. Family Plann. JCC 1981; DCH RCP Eng. 1981; DRCOG 1979. (Leeds) Clin. Asst. (Obst.) St. Luke's Hosp. Bradford.

SLOAN, Catherine Emma Linda 23 Brier Mill Road, Halesowen B63 3HA — MB ChB 1996 Birm. (Birmingham) SHO (Neurosurg.) Birm.; SHO ENT N. Staffs Hosp. Prev: ENT; A&E; Orthop.

SLOAN, David John Barking & Havering FHSA, St. Georges Hospital, Suttons Lane, Hornchurch RM12 6SD Tel: 014024 72011; 5 Elrington Road, Hackney, London E8 3BJ Tel: 020 7249 2471 — MB BChir 1972 Camb.; MA, MB Camb. 1972, BChir 1971; MRCP (UK) 1975; MRCGP 1978; DRCOG 1977. (Camb. & St. Bart.) Med. Adviser Barking & Havering FHSA. Prev: SHO (Paediat.) Qu. Eliz. Hosp. Childr. Lond.; Princip GP. Hackney; Ho. Off. Poole Gen. Hosp.

SLOAN, David John 48 Main Street, Ballycarry, Carrickfergus BT38 9HH — MB BAO 1954 Belf.; FFCM RCPI 1985, M 1978; MFCM 1985; DPH Eng. 1967. (Qu. Univ. Belf.) Prev: Dep. Chief Med. Off. DHSS N. Irel.; Sen. Med. Off. Scott. Home & Health Dept.

SLOAN, David Robert (retired) Flat 4, Marlborough House, Marlborough Hill, Kingsdown, Bristol BS2 8EZ Tel: 0117 929 1781 — MB ChB 1938 Glas. Prev: Ho. Surg. Dorset Co. Hosp.

SLOAN, Felicity Jane Family Planning Clinic, St. Paul's Wing, Cheltenham General Hospital, Sandford Road, Cheltenham GL53 7AN Tel: 01242 272375; Mulberry House, Cleeve Hill, Cheltenham GL52 3QE Tel: 01242 241290 Fax: 01242 571292 Email: sanderling@demon.co.uk — MB BS 1972 Lond.; MFFP 1995 Fac. of Fam. Planning RCOG; Dobst RCOG 1974. (St. Mary's) Head of Family Plann. Reproductive Health E. Glos. NHS Trust; Clin. Asst. Pregn. Advis. Clinic Cheltenham Gen. Hosp. Prev: Clin. Med. Off. (Child Health) Glos. HA.; GP Princip.

SLOAN, Geoffrey Drew 7 Montrose Avenue, West Didsbury, Manchester M20 2LA Tel: 0161 434 0256 — MB ChB 1996 Ed.; BSc (Hons) 1993. (Edinburgh) SHO (A & E) Manch.

SLOAN, Herbert Hill, TD (retired) Glenwherry, Blackburn Old Road, Great Harwood, Blackburn BB6 7UW Tel: 01254 885070 Fax: 01254 885070 Email: sloan.h@talk21.com — MB BCh BAO Belf. 1947. Prev: Ho. Phys. & Ho. Surg. Ulster Hosp. Childr. & Wom. Belf. & City Hosp.

SLOAN, James Martin Queen's University Belfast, Institute of Pathology, Grosvenor Road, Belfast BT12 6BL — MB BCh BAO 1964 Belf.; MD Belf. 1969; FRCPath 1984, M 1972; DObst RCOG 1966. Reader (Path.) Qu. Univ. Belf. & Cons. Path. Roy. Vict. Hosp. Belf. Prev: Lect. (Path.) Univ. Sheff.; Path. ICI Pharmaceut. Div. Macclesfield.

SLOAN, John Bankier Hunter Health Centre, Andrew Street, East Kilbride, Glasgow G74 1AD Tel: 01355 906639 Email: john.sloan@hunter.lanpct.scot.nhs.uk — MB ChB 1987 Glas.; MBA 2001 Open Univ.; LFHom RCP Lond. 1995; MRCGP 1991; DRCOG 1994; DGM RCP Glas. 1992. (Glasgow)

SLOAN, Mr John Peter 357 Street Lane, Moortown, Leeds LS17 6RU Tel: 0113 293 5628 Fax: 0113 266 5924 Email: jsloan@btinternet.com — BM BS 1978 Nottm.; BMedSci Nottm. 1976; FRCS Ed. 1985; FRCS Glas. 1982; FFAEM 1994. Cons. A & E Gen. Infirm. Leeds; Sen. Clin. Lect. (Surg.) Univ. Leeds. Socs: Brit. Assn. Accid. & Emerg. Med.; Emerg. Med. Research Soc. Prev: Sen. Regist. (A & E) Univ. Hosp. Nottm. & Roy. Infirm. Derby.

SLOAN, Kathleen 1 Sandyknowe Crescent, Kelloholm, Sanquhar DG4 6SX Tel: 01659 67526 — MB ChB 1993 Aberd. SHO (O & G) Glas. Roy. Matern. Hosp. Prev: SHO (A & E) Vale of Leven Dist. Gen. Hosp.; SHO (Oncol.) Beatson Oncol. Centre; SHO (O & G) Llandough Hosp. NHS Trust.

SLOAN, Linda Margaret Sloan Practice, 251 Chesterfield Road, Sheffield S8 0RT Tel: 0114 255 1164 Fax: 0114 258 9006 — MB ChB 1977 Leeds; DRCOG 1980.

SLOAN, Lorna Doris Elspeth Tel: 01642 607398 Fax: 01642 604603 — MB BCh BAO 1979 Belf.; MRCGP 1985; Dip. Occ. Med. 1996; DRCOG 1984; DTM & H Liverp. 1983; DA (S. Afr.) 1982. (Queens University of Belfast)

SLOAN, Lucy Malcolm Drs Gillies, Gillies & Crosby, 6 Church Place, Moffat DG10; Glendale, Lochmaben, Lockerbie DG11 1RF — MB ChB 1984 Ed.; DRCOG 1986. (Ed.) Retainer GP Moffat. Prev: Trainee GP Dumfries VTS; Retainer GP Lockerbie.

SLOAN, Marian Kathleen Department of Anaesthetics, Belfast City Hospital, Belfast; 29 Malone Meadows, Belfast BT9 5BG — MB BCh BAO 1978 Belf. Staff Grade (Anaesth.) Belf. City Hosp.

SLOAN, Marion Edith Sloan Practice, 251 Chesterfield Road, Sheffield S8 0RT Tel: 0114 255 1164 Fax: 0114 258 9006 — MB ChB 1975 Leeds; MB ChB (Hons.) Leeds 1975; MRCP (UK) 1978; MRCGP 1982. Teach. Gen. Pract. Dept. Community Med. Univ. Sheff. Med. Sch.; Clin. Asst. Dept. Gastroenterol. Roy. Hallamsh. Hosp. Sheff.

SLOAN, Mark Anthony Regent House Surgery, 21 Regent Road, Chorley PR7 2DH Tel: 01257 264842 Fax: 01257 231387 — MB BS 1984 Lond.; MRCGP 1990.

SLOAN, Melanie Gail Rose Isle, Aldie Crescent, Darnick, Melrose TD6 9AY — MB ChB 1997 Glas.

SLOAN, Morag Elizabeth Holland House, 31 Church Road, Lytham, Lytham St Annes FY8 5LL Tel: 01253 794999 Fax: 01253 795744; 6 Greenfields Crescent, Wesham, Preston PR4 3EH — MB ChB 1986 Aberd.; MRCGP 1992. Police Surg. Preston. Prev: Trainee GP Gt. Eccleston; SHO (Geriat.) Lancaster HA; SHO (Med., Haemat. & A & E) Blackpool & Wyre HA.

SLOAN, Myra Caroline Chapeltown Health Centre, Spencer Place, Leeds LS7 4BB Tel: 0113 240 9090 Fax: 0113 249 8480; 357 Street Lane, Moortown, Leeds LS17 6RU Tel: 0113 266 5924 — BM BS 1978 Nottm.; BMedSci Nottm. 1976. GP Princip. Leeds. Prev: Trainee GP Nottm. VTS.

SLOAN, Peter John McLean Haslucks Green Road Surgery, 287 Haslucks Green Road, Shirley, Solihull B90 2LW Tel: 0121 744 6663 Fax: 0121 733 6895 — MB ChB 1977 Sheff.; MRCP (UK) 1980. Princip. GP Solihull.

SLOAN, Richard Davidson Craigshill Health Centre, Craigshill Road, Livingston EH54 5DY Tel: 01506 432621 Fax: 01506 430431; South Lodge, Kirknewton EH27 8DA Tel: 01506 880286 Email: richard_kelsey@compuserve.com — BM BS 1984 Nottm.; BMedSci (Hons.) Nottm. 1982, BM BS 1984; MRCGP 1990; DPD 1997; DFFP 1996; DRCOG 1989. Clin. Asst. in Diabetes St. John's Hosp. Livingston BUPA Health Screening Edin.

SLOAN, Richard Ernest George Tieve Tara, Rear of Park Dale, Airedale, Castleford WF10 2QT Tel: 01977 552360 Fax: 01977 603470 — MB BS 1969 Lond.; PhD (Med.) Lond. 1976, BSc (Anat.) 1966, MB BS 1969; MRCGP 1984. Prev: Lect. (Physiol.) Lond. Hosp. Med. Coll.; Ho. Phys. Mile End Hosp. (Lond. Hosp.); Ho. Surg. Lond. Hosp.

SLOAN, Richard Herbert 4 Southwalks Road, Dorchester DT1 1ED — MB BS 1976 Lond.; MRCS Eng. LRCP Lond. 1976; MRCGP 1983; DRCOG 1980; DA Eng. 1978. (St. Mary's) Med. Dir. Joseph Weld Hse. Hospice-Respite Centre Dorchester; Hon. Cons. Palliat. Med. W. Dorset Gen. Hosps. NHS Trust. Prev: Regist. (Palliat. Med.) St. Christopher's Hospice Lond.; GP W.way Med. Centre Merseyside; Sen. Lect. (Gen. Pract.) Univ. Liverp.

SLOAN, Robert Lance Fife Rehabilitation Service, Sir George Sharp Unit, Cameron Hospital, Cameron Bridge, Windygates, Leven KY8 5RR Tel: 01592 712472 Fax: 01592 715851; Berwyn, James Place, Cupar KY15 5JT Tel: 01334 652564 — MB ChB 1981 Aberd.; MRCP (UK) 1986; FRCP Ed 1998. (University of Aberdeen) Cons. Rehabil. Med. Fife Primary Care NHS Trust. Socs: Soc. Research Rehabil. & Brit. Soc. Rehabil. Med. Prev: Sen. Regist. (Rehabil. Med.) Astley Ainslie Hosp. Edin.; Regist. Profess. Rheum. Dis. Unit N.. Gen. Hosp. Edin.; Regist. Rotat. (Med.) The Lond. Hosp.

SLOAN, Rosemary 1 Shanlieve Court, Hilltown, Newry BT34 5YP — MB BCh BAO 1994 Belf.

SLOAN, Samantha Anne 18 Sandyknowes Drive, Newtownabbey BT36 5DF — MB BCh BAO 1994 Belf.

SLOAN, Samuel, SBStJ 25 Dunmurry Lane, Dunmurry, Belfast BT17 9RP Tel: 01232 301934 — MB BCh BAO 1945 Belf. (Belf.) Apptd. Fact. Med. Off. Falls Flax Spinning Co. Ltd. Belf. & Irish Linen Mills Ltd. Belf.; Co. Surg. St. John Ambul. Brig. (Cadets). Socs: Roy. Coll. Gen. Pract.; BMA & Belf. Postgrad. Soc. Prev: Teach. Domicilary Midw. Roy. Matern. Hosp. Belf.

SLOAN, Sara Barbara Sloan Practice, 251 Chesterfield Road, Sheffield S8 0RT Tel: 0114 255 1164 Fax: 0114 258 9006; 73 Ranmoor Road, Sheffield S10 3HJ — MB ChB 1980 Leeds; MRCGP 1984; DTM & H Liverp. 1987; DCCH RCP Ed. 1985; DRCOG 1983.

SLOAN, Stanley Buchanan (retired) 63 Cricketers Lane, Herongate, Brentwood CM13 3QB — MB BCh BAO Dub. 1949; MA Dub. 1949; MRCGP 1970; Cert. Family Plann. JCC 1974. Prev: Med. Pract. 1950-85.

SLOAN, Stephanie Caroline 22 Balmoral Av, Belfast BT9 6NW — MB BCh BAO 1997 Belf.

SLOCOMBE, Gareth Wynne 39 Sutton Road, Shrewsbury SY2 6DL — MB BS 1977 Lond.; BSc Lond. 1974, MB BS 1977; MRCP (UK) 1980; MRCPath 1983. Cons. Haemat. P.ss Roy. Hosp. Telford. Prev: Sen. Regist. (Haemat.) Lond. Hosp.

SLOCOMBE, Geoffrey 23 Marroway, Weston Turnville, Aylesbury HP22 5TQ — MRCS Eng. LRCP Lond. 1953; MB BS Lond. 1953, DPH 1959.

SLOCOMBE, Robert Leslie Bacons Road Medical Centre, 16 Bacon Road, Norwich NR2 3QX Tel: 01603 503917; 22 Cotterall Court, Norwich NR5 9AZ Tel: 01603 741953 — MB BChir 1985 Camb.; MRCGP 1990. Prev: Trainee GP W. Suff. HA.

SLOCZYNSKA, Christine Wanda Comely Bank Clinic, Ravenswood Road, Walthamstow, London E17 9LY Tel: 020 8521 8742; 3 Ashbourne Avenue, South Woodford, London E18 1PQ Tel: 020 8989 7212 — MB ChB 1976 Ed.; MRCPCH 1996; DCH RCP Eng. 1979. (Univ. Ed.) SCMO (Child Health) Forest Healthcare Trust. Socs: RCPCH; BACCH.

SLOKA, Richard Anthony 30 Broadmead, Heswall, Wirral CH60 1XD — MB ChB 1974 Liverp.; FRCR 1981; DMRD Liverp. 1978. Cons. Radiol. Countess of Chester Hosp. Chester.

SLOLEY, Lorna Jane The Old Vicarage, Bramshaw, Lyndhurst SO43 7JF — MB BS 1997 Lond.

SLOME, John Joseph The Surgery, 146 Walm Lane, London NW2 4QE Tel: 020 8452 3003 — MRCS Eng. LRCP Lond. 1952; MB BS Lond. 1954; DPH Lond. 1958; DIH Eng. 1959, DCH 1957; DObst RCOG 1956. (St. Geo.)

SLOMINSKI, Henryk Bronislaw Mere Green Clinic, Mere Green Road, Sutton Coldfield B75 5BL Tel: 0121 308 2137; (home), 63 Braemar Road, Sutton Coldfield B73 6LZ — MB ChB 1975 Birm.

SLOMKA, Henryk Withycombe Lodge Surgery, 123 Torquay Road, Paignton TQ3 2SG Tel: 01803 525525 Fax: 01803 550314 — BM BS 1975 Nottm.; BMedSci Nottm. 1973, BM BS 1975. Princip. GP Devon.

SLOPER, Constance Myra Louise 46 New Park Road, Newgate Street Village, Hertford SG13 8RF — BM BCh 1973 Oxf.; MRCP (UK) 1983; DO RCPSI 1991; FRCOphth 1992. Sen. Regist. (Med. Ophth.) Univ. Hosp. Nottm. Prev: Research Fell. Univ. Hosp. Nottm.; Blackmore Fell. Ophth. Roy. Vict. Hosp. Belf.; SHO Oxf. Eye Hosp.

SLOPER, Irene Mary Susan (retired) 43 Sandy Lodge Road, Rickmansworth WD3 1LN Tel: 01923 823100 — MB BChir 1945 Camb.; MRCS Eng. LRCP Lond. 1945; DObst RCOG 1947. Prev: Assoc. Specialist Matern. Unit Watford Gen. Hosp.

SLOPER, Mr John Jenvey Tel: 020 7566 2013 Email: john.sloper@dial.pipex.com — BM BCh 1975 Oxf.; DPhil Oxf. 1978; FRCS Ed. 1990; FRCOphth 1991; DO RCS Eng. 1989. Cons. Strabismus & Paediat. Servs. Moorfields Eye Hosp. Prev: Sen. Regist. (Ophth.) Univ. Hosp. Nottm.; Regist. (Ophth.) Roy. Vict. Hosp. Belf.; Roy. Soc. Research Fell. Univ. Oxf.

SLOPER, Katherine Susan Department of Paediatrics, Ealing Hospital NHS Trust, Southall UB1 3HX Tel: 020 8574 2444 Fax: 020 8967 5445 — BM BCh 1973 Oxf.; FRCPH 1998; FRCP Lond. 1995; MA, DM Oxf. 1989; MRCP (UK) 1976. Cons. Paediat. Ealing Hosp. NHS Trust Lond.; Hon. Sen. Lect. Roy. Postgrad. Med. Sch. Lond. Prev: Sen. Regist. (Paediat.) Centr. Middlx. Hosp. & Brompton Hosp. Lond.; Regist. (Paediat.) Middlx. Hosp. Lond.; SHO (Neonat. Paediat.) John Radcliffe Hosp. Oxf.

SLOPER, Philip 46 New Park Road, Newgate St Village, Hertford SG13 8RF — MB BS 1998 Lond.; MB BS Lond 1998.

SLOPER-AITCHISON, Marguerite Lucy (retired) Bod Awen, 19 Bridge St., Llandeilo SA19 6BN Tel: 01558 822874 Email: margaret8@lineone.net — MB BS 1953 Lond.; MRCS Eng. LRCP Lond. 1953.

SLORACH, Charles Cameron Stuart Hunter Health Centre, Andrew St., East Kilbride, Glasgow G74 1AD; (surgery) 126 Westwood Square, East Kilbride, Glasgow G75 8JQ — MB ChB 1953 Glas.; DObst RCOG 1957. Prev: Sen. Ho. Phys. W.. Dist. Hosp. Glas.; Flight Lt. RAF Med. Br.

SLORACH, Colum Alasdair 38 Old Coach Road, East Kilbride, Glasgow G74 4DT — MB ChB 1996 Glas.

SLORACH, John 58 Leicester Road, Narborough, Leicester LE9 5DG Tel: 0116 286 3169 — MB ChB 1937 Aberd.; BSc Aberd. 1929, MB ChB 1937; DPM Eng. 1942. (Aberd.) Cons. Emerit.

Carlton Hayes Hosp. NarBoro.. Prev: Mem. Sheff. Region Ment. Health Rev. Tribunal; Dep. Phys. Supt. Pk. Prewett Hosp. Basingstoke; Assoc. Chief Asst. Skin (Psychosomatic) Dept. St. Bart. Hosp.

SLORACH, Marc 3 Stratford Close, Killingworth, Newcastle upon Tyne NE12 6GU — MB ChB 1990 Aberd.; MRCGP 1996; DRCOG 1995; DA (UK) 1995.

SLOSS, Gordon Alexander Sannox Farm, Sannox, Brodick KA27 Tel: 01770 81230 — MB BCh 1989 Wales; BSc (Hons.) St. And. 1985; MRCPsych 1996. Specialist Regist. St. Mary's Hisher Psychiat. Train. Scheme Lond. Prev: Regist. Rotat. (Psychiat.) St. Mary's Hosp. Lond.; SHO Rotat. (Psychiat.) Roy. United Hosp. Bath; Ho. Off. (Med. & Gen. Surg.) Univ. Wales Hosp. Cardiff.

SLOSS, John Dario Gregorio Grant Storrsthwaite, Storrspark, Bowness-on-Windermere, Windermere LA23 3LF — MB BS 1990 Lond.

SLOSS, John Murray Dept of Microbiology, Pathology Laboratory, Darlington Memorial Hospital, Darlington DL3 6HX Tel: 01325 743241 Fax: 01325 743622; 33 Wells Green, Burham DL10 6NH Tel: 01325 339061 Fax: 01325 339061 — MB BS 1977 Lond.; MSc Lond. 1989, BSc (Hons.) 1974; FRCS Ed. 1986; FRCPath 2000. (St. Bart.) Cons Med. Microbiol S. Durh. NHS Trust. Socs: Assn. Clin. Path.; Hosp. Infec. Soc.; Dales Microbiol. Audit Gp. Prev: Cons. Path. (Med. Microbiol.) BMH Rinteln BFPO 29; Cons. Path. (Med Microbiol.) Duchess of Kent Hosp. Catterick Garrison; Cons Path (Med Microbiol) MDHU N.allerton.

SLOT, Michael Joseph William Blackmore Health Centre, Blackmore Drive, Sidmouth EX10 8ET Tel: 01395 512601 Fax: 01395 578408 — MB ChB 1980 Bristol; MB ChB 1980 Bristol.

SLOTOVER, Mr Max Leonard (retired) 28 Arlington House, Arlington St., London SW1A 1RL Tel: (20) 7495 1870 Fax: (20) 7495 6132 — LRCP & LM, LRSCl & LM 1934; LRCPI & LM, LRCSI & LM 1934; FRCS Ed. 1939; LM Rotunda. Prev: Resid. Obst. Off. Withington Hosp. Manch.

SLOVAK, Andrej Jan Michal British Nuclear Fuels plc, Hinton House, Risley, Warrington WA6 3AS Tel: 01925 832890 Fax: 01925 835864; 102 Market Street, Ashby-de-la-Zouch LE65 1AP — MB BS 1970 Lond.; MD Lond. 1996; FRCP Lond. 1996; MRCS Eng. LRCP Lond. 1970; FFOM RCP Lond. 1991; DIH Soc. Apoth. Lond. 1976. Chief Med. Off. Brit. Nuclear Fuels plc; Sen. Lect. Centre Occupat. Health Manch. Univ. Med. Sch.

SLOVICK, David Ian Department of Medicine for the Elderly, Southend Hospital, Prittlewell Chase, Westcliff on Sea SS0 0RY Tel: 01702 221203 Fax: 01702 221377; 6 The Ridgeway, Westcliff on Sea SS0 8NT Tel: 01702 711115 — MB BS 1979 Lond.; PhD Lond. 1977; MA Oxf. 1977; MRCP (UK) 1983. (Middlx.) Cons. Phys. S.end Health Care NHS Trust. Socs: Fell. Roy. Soc. Med.; Brit. Geriat. Soc. Prev: Sen. Regist. (Gen. & Geriat. Med.) Hammersmith Hosp. Lond.; Sen. Med. Off. DoH Lond.; Ho. Phys. (Med.) Middlx. Hosp. Lond.

SLOVICK, Sidney 143 Sydenham Hill, London SE23 3PH Tel: 020 8693 3169 — MRCS Eng. LRCP Lond. 1947; MRCGP 1959. (Univ. Coll. Hosp.) Med. Examr. Pruden. Assur. Co. & United Friendly Insur. Co.; Mem. S.wark, Lambeth & Lewisham Family Pract. Comm. & Local Med. Comms. Socs: Brit. Assn. Manipulat. Med.; BMA (Ex-Chairm. Camberwell Div.). Prev: Flight Lt. RAF; Ho. Surg. Co. Hosp. FarnBoro. (Kent); Orthop. Ho. Surg. & Cas. Off. Roy. N.. Hosp.

SLOWE, John Jeremy, VRD Park Farm House, Shincliffe, Durham DH1 2PA Tel: 0191 386 4777 — MRCS Eng. LRCP Lond. 1942; FFA RCS Eng. 1954; DA Eng. 1946. (St. Bart.) Hon. Cons. Anaesth. Durh. Health Dist. Socs: Fell. Roy. Soc. Med.; BMA. Prev: Cons. Anaesth. Durh. Gp. Hosps.; Surg. Cdr. RNR.

SLOWE, Michael Robert Ian Rookery Medical Centre, Rookery House, Newmarket CB8 8NW Tel: 01638 665711 Fax: 01638 561280; Wilwyn Cottage, 4 Hamilton Road, Newmarket CB8 0NQ — MB BS 1980 Lond.; MRCGP 1989; DRCOG 1982. (Char. Cross) Clin. Asst. (Gastrointest. Endoscopy) W. Suff. Hosp. Prev: GP Hadlow, Kent; GP Trainee Tunbridge Wells VTS.

SLOWEY, Heather Frances Department of Anaesthetics, Singleton Hospital, Swansea SA2 8QA — MB BS 1976 Lond.; MRCS Eng. LRCP Lond. 1976; FFA RCS Eng. 1981. (St. Mary's) Cons. Anaesth. (p/t), Singleton Hosp. Swansea. Prev: Lect. (Anaesth.) Univ. Hosp. Wales Cardiff; Regist. (Anaesth.) Univ. Hosp. Wales Cardiff; SHO (Anaesth.) Nottm. Gen. Hosp.

SLOWIE

SLOWIE, Dominic Francis 42 Warwick Street, Heaton, Newcastle upon Tyne NE6 5AQ — MB BS 1991 Newc. SHO (O & G) S. Cleveland Hosp. Middlesbrough. Prev: SHO (Med. Oncol.) Regional Radiother. Unit Newc. Gen. Hosp.

SLOWTHER, Christine Mary 1 Pembroke Close, Warwick CV34 5JA — MB ChB 1986 Manch.

SLUGLETT, Max (retired) 3 Dinard Drive, Glasgow G46 6AH Tel: 0141 633 1206 — MB ChB 1942 Glas.

SLY, Ian Leslie Colin The Meads Surgery, Grange Road, Uckfield TN22 1QU Tel: 01825 765777 Fax: 01825 766220; Lilac Cottage, Chillies Lane, High Hurstwood, Uckfield TN22 4AA — MB BS 1971 Lond.; MRCP (UK) 1977; MRCS Eng. LRCP Lond. 1971; MRCGP 1979; DCH Eng. 1974. (Char. Cross) Prev: Regist. (Med.) Wycombe Gen. Hosp. High Wycombe; Regist. (Med.) High Wycombe AHA; SHO (Obst.) Derby City Hosp.

SLY, Janet Mary James Fisher Medical Centre, 4 Tolpuddle Gardens, Bournemouth BH9 3LQ Tel: 01202 522622 Fax: 01202 548480 — MB BS 1977 Newc.; MRCGP 1982; DRCOG 1981. GP Bournemouth.

SLYNE, Denis Joseph 36 Ernest Street, Merthyr Tydfil CF47 0YP — MB BCh BAO 1979 NUI; DRCOG 1983.

SMAHLIOUK, Petros c/o Ophthalmic Secretaries, Mayday University Hospital, London Road, Croydon CR7 7YE — Ptychio Iatrikes 1988 Thessalonika.

SMAIL, Mr David Hayden 7 Bowbrook Grange, Shrewsbury SY3 8XT Tel: 01743 340744; 41 Jubilee Road, Newbury RG14 7NN Tel: 01635 821656 — MB BS 1991 Lond.; FRCOphth 1997. Prev: SHO (Ophth.) Univ. Hosp. Wales Cardiff; SHO (Ophth.) Shrops. HA; Ho. Off. St. Bart. Hosp. Lond.

***SMAIL, Joanna Kathryn** Frimley Park Hospital, Portsmouth Rd, Flimley, Camberley GU16 7UJ Tel: 01276 604604; 46 Dan-y-Bryn Avenue, Radyr, Cardiff CF15 8DD Tel: 01276 843230 — BM BCh 1997 Oxf.; DCH 1999.

SMAIL, Margaret Valmai 7 Bowbrook Grange, Shrewsbury SY3 8XT Tel: 01743 340744; 13 Layton Place, Kew, Richmond TW9 3PP Tel: 020 8948 4356 — MB ChB (Medal in Clin. Med. & Surg.) Sheff. 1966. Prev: Ho. Surg. & Ho. Phys. Coventry & Warks. Hosp.; Lect. (Sch. Orthop.) Coventry.

SMAIL, Peter James Royal Aberdeen Childrens Hospital, Aberdeen AB25 2ZG Tel: 01224 681818 Fax: 01224 550704 Email: p.smail@arh.grampian.scot.nhs.uk; 36 Ashley Gardens, Aberdeen AB10 6RQ Tel: 01224 325597 — BM BCh Oxf. 1968; MA Oxf. 1968; FRCP Ed. 1995; FRCP Lond. 1987; FRCPCH 1997; DCH RCPS Glas. 1974; DObst RCOG 1971. (Oxf.) Clin. Gp. Coordinator Combined Child Health Serv. Grampain Universities Hosps. Socs: Eur. Soc. Paediat. Endocrinol. Prev: Lect. (Child Health) Dundee Univ.; Fell. Health Sci. Centre Winnipeg; Regist. (Med.) Roy. Cornw. Hosp. (Treliske) Truro.

SMAIL, Simon Andrew School of Postgraduate Studies, University of Wales College of Medicine, Heath Park, Cardiff CF14 4XN Tel: 029 2074 3927 Fax: 029 2075 4966 Email: postgrad@cardiff.ac.uk; 46 Dan-y-Bryn Avenue, Radyr, Cardiff CF15 8DD — BM BCh 1970 Oxf.; ILTM 2001; MA Oxf. 1970; FRCGP 1984 M (Distinc.) 1975; Cert. Family Plann. JCC 1975; DCH Eng. 1974; DRCOG 1973. (Oxf.) Dean & Dir. Sch. of Postgrad. Med. and Dent. Educat. Socs: Chairm. UK Conf. Postgrad. GP Adviser. Prev: Sen. Lect. (Gen. Pract.) Univ. Wales Coll. Med. Cardiff; Chairm. Health Promotion Auth. for Wales; Mem. Health Educat. Counc.

SMAILES, Alison Martha 45 Bargate, Richmond DL10 4QY — MB ChB 1989 Bristol; MRCGP 1993; DRCOG 1992. Prev: Trainee GP Lewisham VTS.; Ho. Off. (Med.) W.on Super Mare Hosp.; Ho. Off. (Surg.) Bristol Roy. Infirm.

SMAILES, Catherine Mary 2 Ballard Close, Milton, Cambridge CB4 6DW — MB BS 1996 Lond.

SMAILES, Charlotte Louise 2 Kiels Cottages, Back Lane, Hampstead, London NW3 1HN — MB BS 1994 Lond.

SMAILES, June The Hollies Medical Centre, 20 St. Andrews Road, Sheffield S11 9AL Tel: 0114 255 0094 Fax: 0114 258 2863 — MB ChB 1981 Sheff.; DRCOG 1986; DCH RCP Lond. 1985. (Sheff.)

SMAILES, Robert Andrew 10 Cobthorne Drive, Allestree, Derby DE22 2SY — MB ChB 1979 Leeds; DA Eng. 1984.

SMAJE, Laurence Hetherington Medicine, Society & History Division, The Wellcome Trust, 183 Euston Road, London NW1 2BE Tel: 020 7611 8425 Fax: 020 7611 8526 Email: l.smaje@wellcome.ac.uk — MB BS Lond. 1961; PhD Lond. 1967, BSc 1958. (Univ. Coll. Hosp.) Dir. Med., Soc. & Hist. Div., The Wellcome Trust. Socs: Physiol. Soc.; Roy. Soc. Med.; Brit. Microcirculat. Soc. Prev: Prof. & Head Phys. Dept. Char. Cross & W.m. Med. Sch.; Sen. Lect. (Physiol.) Univ. Coll. Lond.; Ho. Phys. & Ho. Surg. Univ. Coll. Hosp. Lond.

SMALDON, David Leslie 15 Chepstow Rise, Croydon CR0 5LX — MB BCh 1970 Wales.

SMALE, Elisabeth Mary (retired) 7 Maclarens, Wickham Bishops, Witham CM8 3XE — MB ChB 1963 Manch.; DObst RCOG 1965. Non Exec. Director of Mid Essex Hosp. trust,Broomfielt Ct., Pudding Wood La., Chelmsford, Essex, CM1 7WE. Prev: Sch. Med. Off. & Asst. MOH S.end-on-Sea.

SMALE, Simon Jonathan 68 Whitelake Road, Tonbridge TN10 3TJ — BM BS 1992 Nottm.

SMALES, Charles Hall Farm, Tunstall, Roos, Hull — MB ChB 1968 Leeds; FFA RCS Eng. 1973. SHO Anaesth. Leeds Gen. Infirm. & Leeds 'A' Hosp. Gp. Prev: Ho. Phys. & Ho. Surg. Harrogate Gen. Hosp.

SMALES, Elizabeth Department of Health, Skipton House, 80 London Road, London SE1 6LH — MB BS 1972 Lond.; BSc Lond. 1969, MB BS 1972; FRCR 1978. Princip. Med. Off. (Toxicol. & Environm. Health) DoH Lond. Prev: Sen. Regist. (Radiother.) Roy. Marsden Hosp. Lond. & Surrey.

SMALES, Jeanne Rachael Breast Screening Unit, York District Hospital, York YO31 8HE — MB ChB 1976 Leeds; DRCOG 1980.

SMALES, Keith Anthony Lovemead Group Practice, Roundstone Surgery, Polebarn Circus, Trowbridge BA14 7EH Tel: 01225 752752 Fax: 01225 776388 — MB BS 1970 Lond.; MRCP (UK) 1975; MRCS Eng. LRCP Lond. 1970; DObst RCOG 1976.

SMALING, Alan Peter (retired) Stag Medical Centre, 162 Wickersley Road, Rotherham S60 4JW — MB ChB Manch. 1968; DObst RCOG 1970.

SMALL, Barry John 11 Elmoor Avenue, Welwyn AL6 9PG — MB BS 1992 Lond.

SMALL, Christina Mary 55 Holyrood Crescent, St Albans AL1 2LY Tel: 01727 30097 — MB BS 1940 Lond.; DPH Eng. 1947.

SMALL, Colin McGregor (retired) 11 Greenbank Crescent, Edinburgh EH10 5TE Tel: 0131 447 8277 — MB ChB Ed. 1960; FFA RCS Eng. 1969; DObst RCOG 1965. Prev: Cons. Anaesth. St Johns Hosp. 1989-1998.

SMALL, Cormac 8 Kensington Gardens, Belfast BT5 6NP — MB BCh BAO 1996 Belf.

SMALL, David Gordon 1 North Place, Oxford OX3 9HX — BM BCh 1965 Oxf.; MRCP (UK) 1971. Hon. Cons. (Clin. Neurophys.) Nat. Hosp. Nerv. Dis. Qu. Sq.; Hon. Cons. Dept. Clin. Neurol. Radcliffe Infirm. Oxf. Prev: Cons. (Clin. Neurophys.) & Sen. Lect. Dept. Neurol. Nat. Hosp. Nerv.; Dis. Qu. Sq.; Regist. & Hon. Sen. Regist. Dept. Clin. Neurol. Ch.ill Hosp. Oxf.

SMALL, David James Accident and Emergency Department, Bedford Hospital, South Wing, Kempston Road, Bedford MK42 9DJ — MB ChB 1983 Bristol.

SMALL, Feline Majella 26 Ravensdene Park, Ravenhill Road, Belfast BT6 Tel: 01232 641439; 25 Drummiller Lane, Gilford, Craigavon BT63 6BS Tel: 01762 831466 — MB BCh BAO 1989 Belf.

SMALL, Frances Teresa Herrison House, Herrison Hospital, Dorchester DT2 9RL Tel: 01305 251851; 4 Maiden Castle Road, Dorchester DT1 2ER — MB ChB 1976 Leeds; MPH Leeds 1987. Cons. Pub. Health Med. W. Dorset HA.

SMALL, Gary Robert 8 Castle Street, Raglan NP15 2DS — MB BCh 1996 Wales.

SMALL, Gillian 26 Hatchet Lane, Stonely, Huntingdon PE19 5EG — MB BS 1988 Lond.; DCH 1992; DRCOG 1992; MRCP 1995.

SMALL, Mr Gordon Ian, Colonel L/RAMC Retd. (retired) 48 Dartford Road, Bexley DA5 2AT Tel: 01322 528758 — MB BS 1952 Lond.; FRCS Eng. 1962. Prev: Cons. Orthop. Surg. Dartford & Gravesham HA.

SMALL, Helen Jane St Woolos Hospital, Stow Hill, Newport NP20 4SZ Tel: 01633 238237; The Cross, School Road, Hanbury, Bromsgrove B60 4BS — MB BCh 1987 Wales; DGM RCP Lond. 1996; DRCOG 1991. (Univ. Wales Coll. Med.) Staff Grade Pract. (Geriat. Med.) St. Woolos Hosp. Newport. Prev: Clin. Asst. (Rheum. & Geriat. Med.) & Trainee GP/SHO (Anaesth.) Roy. Gwent Hosp.

SMALLMAN

SMALL, Hellen Mary Muir Ravenscraig Hospital, Greenock PA16 9HA Tel: 01475 633777; Craiglyn Kim, Dunoon PA23 8HH — MB ChB Glas. 1968. Assoc. Specialist (Psychiat.) Ravenscraig Hosp. Greenock.

SMALL, Iain Robert Peterhead Group Practice, The Health Centre, Peterhead AB42 2XA Tel: 01774 474841 Fax: 01774 474848; Landfall, 1 Arran Avenue, Peterhead AB42 1PZ — MB ChB 1983 Dundee; MRCGP 1987.

SMALL, Mr James Oliver The Ulster Independent Clinic Ltd, Stranmillis Road, Belfast BT9 5JH Tel: 01232 661212 — MB BCh BAO 1976 NUI; FRCSI 1980. Cons. (Plastic Surg.) Temple St. & St Master Hosps. Dub. Socs: Full Mem. Brit. Assn. of Plastic Surgs.; Full Mem. Brit. Assn. of Aesthetic Plastic Surgs.; Full Mem. Brit. Soc. for Surg. of the Hand. Prev: Sen. Regist. (Plastic Surg.) E. Health & Social Serv. BD. N. Irel.; Regist. (Plastic Surg.) Qu. Mary's Hosp. Roehampton.; Cons. (Plastic Surg.) E. Health & Social Serv. Bd. N. Irel.

SMALL, Jeremy Hugh Department of Radiology, Royal Bournemouth Hospital, Castle Lane E., Bournemouth BH7 7DW Tel: 01202 704894; 6 Middle Lane, Ringwood BH24 1LE — MB BS 1983 Lond.; MRCP (UK) 1988; FRCR 1993. (Middlx. Hosp. Med. Sch.) Cons. Radiol. Roy. Bournemouth Hosp. Prev: Sen. Regist. (Radiol.) Addenbrooke's Hosp. Camb.

SMALL, Laura Louise Whiteabbey Health Centre, Doagh Road, Newtownabbey BT37 9QN; Tel: 028 9086 4341 Fax: 028 9086 0443 — MB BCh BAO 1980 Belf.; MRCGP 1984; DRCOG 1983. GP Newtownabbey.

SMALL, Mandy Jayne 39 Caiystane Terrace, Edinburgh EH10 6ST — MB ChB 1988 Aberd.

SMALL, Margaret Lilian Forrester, Bowman and Rowlandson, Berry Lane Medical Centre, Berry Lane, Longridge, Preston PR3 3JJ Tel: 01772 783021 Fax: 01772 785809 — MB ChB 1975 Glas.; DRCOG 1977; MRCGP 1979.

SMALL, Mrs Margaret Smith Stuart (retired) 26 Bell Place, Edinburgh EH3 5HT Tel: 0131 332 6591 — MB ChB 1945 Glas.; MRCPsych 1972; DPM Eng. 1948. Prev: Cons. (Child & Adolesc. Psychiat.) Gartnavel Roy. Hosp. & Roy. Hosp.

SMALL, Michael (retired) 5 The Oriels, 146 Kingston Road, Wimbledon, London SW19 3NB Tel: 020 8287 3180 — MB BS 1951 Lond.; FRCP Lond. 1971, M 1959. Prev: Cons. NeUrol.

SMALL, Mr Michael Higher Alston, Preston Road, Ribchester, Preston PR3 3XL Tel: 01254 878130 — MB ChB 1977 Glas.; FRCS Glas. 1981. Cons. ENT Surg. Roy. Preston Hosp. Prev: Sen. Regist. (Otolaryngol.) Edin. Roy. Infirm. & City Hosp. Edin.

SMALL, Michael Gartnavel General Hospital, 1053 Great Western Road, Glasgow G12 0YN; 6 Coltmuir Gardens, Bishopbriggs, Glasgow G64 2SX — MD 1986 Glas.; MB ChB 1978; FRCP Ed. 1991; FRCP Glas. 1988; MRCP (UK) 1980. (Glasgow) Cons. Phys. Gartnavel Gen. Hosp. Glas.

SMALL, Nicolas Mark Warren 102 Mollison Way, Edgware HA8 5QT — MB BS 1987 Lond.; BSc Lond. 1983, MB BS 1987. Ho. Off. (Urol. & Gen. Surg.) N.wick Pk. Hosp. Harrow. Prev: Ho. Off. (Med.) Bedford Gen. Hosp.

SMALL, Mr Peter Kenneth Dept of General Surgery, Sunderland Royal Hospital, Kayll Road, Sunderland SR4 7TP Tel: 0191 565 6256; 3 Eastfields, Whitburn, Sunderland SR6 7DA Tel: 0191 529 2275 — BMedSci 1979 ED; MB ChB Ed. 1982; MD Ed. 1996; BSc (Med. Sci.) Ed. 1979; FRCS Ed. (Gen.) 1997; FRCS Ed. 1989. (University of Edinburgh) Cons. Gen. Surg. Sunderland Roy. Hosp. Kayll Rd. Sunderland.

SMALL, Philip George XRay Department, University Hospital Trust, Queens Medical Centre, Nottingham NG7 2UH Tel: 0115 942 1421 — MB ChB 1962 Sheff.; FRCR 1975; FFR 1969; DMRD Eng. 1967; DObst RCOG 1965. (Sheff.) Cons. Radiol. (Paediat.) Univ. Hosp. Trust Nottm.; Managing Edr. Paediat. Radiol.; Hon. Clin. Tutor Univ. Nottm. Socs: Eur. Soc. Paediat. Radiol.; Centr. Manpower Comm.; BMA (POWAR).

SMALL, Ramsay George (retired) 46 Monifieth Road, Broughty Ferry, Dundee DD5 2RX Tel: 01382 778408 — MB ChB 1954 St. And.; FRCP Ed. 1987; MRCP (Ed.) 1984; FFCM RCP (UK) 1978, M 1972; DPH St. And. 1958. Prev: Chief Admin. Med. Off. Tayside HB.

SMALL, Robert George Dennis (retired) High Walls, North Lane, South Harting, Petersfield GU31 5NW Email: t.small@which.net — MB BChir 1954 Camb.; DObst RCOG 1955. Prev: Ho. Surg. & Ho. Off. (O & G) Middlx. Hosp.

SMALL, Rosemary Byers Holywood Arches Health Centre, Westminster Avenue, Belfast BT4 1NS Tel: 02890 563350; 41 Castlehill Road, Belfast BT4 3GN — MB BCh BAO 1977 Belf.; DRCOG Lond. 1980; MRCGP 1982. Gen. Practitioner; Mem. of DLA Tribunal Panel.

SMALL, Una Roisin 54 Dunlambert Park, Belfast BT15 3NL — MB BCh BAO 1991 NUI; MRCGP 1995; DRCOG 1994. Trainee GP Downpatrick Co. Down.

SMALL, Mr William Porteous, VRD (retired) 71 Trinity Road, Edinburgh EH5 3HS Tel: 0131 552 3684 Email: bill.small@which.net — MB ChB 1942 Ed.; ChM Ed. 1964, MB ChB 1942; FRCS Ed. 1947; FRCP Ed. 1966, M 1950. Prev: Surg. W.. Gen. Hosp. Edin.

SMALL, Yvette Jean 33 Fairmile Lane, Cobham KT11 2DL Tel: 01932 862557 — MB BS 1977 Lond.; MRCS Eng. LRCP Lond. 1977. SCMO (Occupat. Health) Wandsworth HA & Lond. Boro. Richmond u. Thames. Prev: SCMO (Occupat. Health) Richmond, Twickenham & Roehampton HA.

SMALLBONE, David Frank Foxlow Grange, Harpur Hill, Buxton SK17 9LU Tel: 01298 24507 Fax: 01298 73011 Email: davidsmallbone28@netscapeonline.co.uk — MB ChB 1961 Birm.; MRCS Eng. LRCP Lond. 1962. Socs: Fell.Roy.Soc.Med; Fac. Homoeop.

SMALLCOMBE, Gerald William (retired) 35 Wychwood Crescent, Earley, Reading RG6 5RA Tel: 01734 871739 — MB BChir 1952 Camb.; BSc Camb. 1952, MA 1952. Prev: SHO Peppard Chest Hosp.

SMALLDRIDGE, Ann Oswald Medical Practice, 4 Oswald Road, Chorlton, Manchester M21 9LH Tel: 0161 881 4744 Fax: 0161 861 7027; 22 Langham Road, Bowdon, Altrincham WA14 3NN Tel: 0161 928 1752 — BM BS 1981 Nottm.; MRCGP 1991; DCH RCP Lond. 1984; DRCOG 1982. Prev: GP Lond.

SMALLDRIDGE, Jacqueline 618 Wells Road, Knowle, Bristol BS14 9BD; 18 Anglesea Street, Posonby, Auckland, New Zealand — MB BS 1986 Lond.; MRCOG 1991; DObst Auckland 1989. Regist. (O & G) Nat. Wom. Hosp. & Wellington Hosp. NZ. Prev: SHO (Gyn.) Bloomsbury HA; SHO (Obst.) Nat. Wom. Hosp. Auckland NZ; Regist. (Paediat.) P.ss Mary Hosp. Auckland NZ.

SMALLDRIDGE, Norman James Frank 33 Hillfield Avenue, Fishpools, Bristol BS16 4JP — BM BCh 1975 Oxf.

SMALLEY, Andrew Dennis Dean Street Surgery, 8 Dean Street, Liskeard PL14 4AQ Tel: 01579 343133 Fax: 01579 344933 — MB BS 1987; BSc (1st cl. Hons.) Lond. 1984, MB BS 1987; MRCGP 1991; DCH RCP Lond. 1990; DGM RCP Lond. 1990. (Guys) GP Trainer.

SMALLEY, Carolyn Church Langley Medical Practice, Church Langley, Harlow CM17 9TG — MB BS 1982 Lond.; MRCGP 1986.

SMALLEY, Christine Angela Central Health Clinic, East Park Terrace, Southampton SO14 0YL Tel: 02380 902562 Fax: 02380 902602 — MB ChB 1969 Sheff.; FRCP Lond. 1988; MRCP (UK) 1973; FRCPCH 1997; DCH Eng. 1971. Cons. Paediat. Community Child Health Soton. City PC. Trust. Prev: Cons. Paediat. S. Birm. HA.; Sen. Regist. (Paediat.) Birm. AHA (T); Research Fell. (Clin.) Inst. Child Health Birm. Univ.

SMALLEY, David Simon Nuffield House Surgery, The Stow, Harlow CM20 3AX Tel: 01279 425661 Fax: 01279 427116 — FRCGP 2001; BSc Lond. 1979, MB BS 1982; MRCGP (Distinc.) 1985; DCH RCP Lond. 1985; DRCOG 1985. Examr. RCGP.; Hon. Sec. Essex RCGP.

SMALLEY, Dorothy Mary Wilson Street Surgery, 11 Wilson Street, Derby DE1 1PG Tel: 01332 344366 Fax: 01332 348813; 11 Oak Road, Thulston, Derby DE72 3EW Tel: 01332 574259 Fax: 01332 574259 — MB ChB Sheff. 1969; MRCGP 1976. (Sheff.) Prev: Med. Off. Stud. Health Serv. Sheff. Univ.; SHO (Gen. Med.) Doncaster Roy. Infirm.; Ho. Phys. & Ho. Surg. United Sheff. Hosps.

SMALLMAN, Jayne Mary Bernadette 52 Ranelagh Road, London W5 5RP — MB BS 1980 Lond.; FFA RCS 1987. Cons. Anaesth. Wexham Pk. Hosp. Slough. Prev: Cons. Anaesth. St. Bart. Hosp. Lond.

SMALLMAN, Lesley Ann Alexandra Hospital, Worcestershire Acute Hospitals NHS Trustq, Woodrow Drive, Redditch B98 7UB Tel: 01527 512008 Ext: 35156 Fax: 01527 512007; Pint Bar Cottage, Foredraught Lane, Tibberton, Droitwich WR9 7NH Tel: 01905

SMALLMAN

345259 Fax: 01905 345601 Email: grimar@pintbar.w_net.com — MB ChB 1978 Birm.; MB ChB (Hons.) Birm. 1978; FRCPath 1996, M 1985. Cons. Pathologist Alexandra Hosp., Worcs. Acute Hosp.s NHS Trust; Adviser (Path.) J. Laryngol. & Otol; Mem. Ct. Examrs MRCS RCS Eng.; Hon. Sen. Lect. Med. Sch. Univ. Birm.; Extern. Examr. Cardiff Dent. Sch. Socs: Assn. Clin. Pathol.; Brit. Soc. Clin. Cytol.; Internat. Acad. Path. Prev: Sen. Lect. & Hon. Cons. Path. Med. Sch. Univ. Birm. & Gen. Hosp. Birm.; Lect. Path. Med. Sch. Univ. Birm.

SMALLMAN, Robert Ian Bulling Lane Surgery, Bulling Lane, Crich, Matlock DE4 5DX Tel: 01773 852966 Fax: 01773 853919; Hollins Grove, Little London, Holloway, Matlock DE4 5AZ — MB ChB 1982 Birm.; MRCGP 1986; DRCOG 1986. Prev: Trainee GP S. Warks. VTS.

SMALLPEICE, Mr Christopher John North Staffordshire Royal Infirmary, Princes Road, Hartshill, Stoke-on-Trent ST4 7LN Tel: 01782 554249 Fax: 01782 554830 — MB BS 1972 Lond.; FRCS Eng. 1978; MRCS Eng. LRCP Lond. 1972. (King's Coll. Hosp.) Cons. Cardiothoracic Surg. N. Staffs. Health Dist. Stoke-on-Trent. Prev: Sen. Regist. (Cardiothoracic Surg.) W. Midls. RHA; Regist. (Cardiothoracic Surg.) King's Coll., Brook & Guy's Hosp.; Lond.

SMALLSHAW, John Kendall (retired) 2 Stagbury Close, Chipstead, Coulsdon, Croydon CR5 3PH Tel: 01737 552512 — MRCS Eng. LRCP Lond. 1960. Prev: Med. Off. Roy. Alfred Seamen's Soc. & Banstead Pl. Qu. Eliz. Foundat.

SMALLWOOD, Bernard Henry Turning Cottage, Garway, Hereford HR2 8RJ Tel: 01600 750411 — MB ChB 1973 Birm.; DObst RCOG 1976. Prev: GP Kingstone Herefordsh.

SMALLWOOD, Diana Margaret 9 Ribblesdale Drive, Ridgeway, Sheffield S12 3XB — MRCS Eng. LRCP Lond. 1972; DObst RCOG 1975.

SMALLWOOD, Elizabeth Helen 69 Orchard Grove, Gerrards Cross SL9 9ET — MB BS 1990 Lond.; DRCOG 1994; DCH RCP Lond 1994. (Char. Cross & Westm.) Retainer scheme.

SMALLWOOD, Humphrey Marten (retired) 6 Barnsley Road, Edgbaston, Birmingham B17 8ED Tel: 0121 420 1700 — MB ChB 1940 Birm.

SMALLWOOD, Mr James Anthony Department of Surgery, E-Level, West Wing, Southampton General Hospital, Tremona Road, Southampton SO16 6YD; Whispers, Hadrian Way, Chilworth, Southampton SO16 7HX Tel: 01703 768543 — MB BS 1976 Lond.; MS Soton. 1986; FRCS Eng. 1980; MRCS Eng. LRCP Lond. 1975. (St. Bart.) Cons. Gen. Surg. (Surg. Oncol.) Soton. Gen. Hosp. Socs: (Vice-Pres.) Europ. Surgic. Research Soc. Prev: Research Fell. BrE. Cancer Soton.; Regist. (Surg.) Crawley Hosp.; SHO (Surg.) Char. Cross Hosp. Lond.

SMALLWOOD, Neil Nicholas Barnfield Hill Surgery, 12 Barnfield Hill, Exeter EX1 1SR Tel: 01392 432761 Fax: 01392 422406; 4 Lower Summerlands, Exeter EX1 2LJ Tel: 01392 496955 — MB ChB 1985 Bristol; MRCGP 1991; DCH RCP Lond. 1989.

SMALLWOOD, Robert Ingamar Larsen Parkside Hospital, 53 Parkside, London SW19 5NE Tel: 020 8946 4202; 86 Marryat Road, London SW19 5BN — MRCS Eng. LRCP Lond. 1947; DObst RCOG 1951. (St. Bart.) Med. Ref. Various Insur. Cos.; Authorised Examr. Bd. Civil Aviat. Auth. Br. Socs: Med.-Leg. Soc. Prev: RAF; Intern. Gyn. Dept. St. Bart. Hosp.; Sen. Res. Obst. Off. Luton & Dunstable Hosp.

SMALLWOOD, Stephen Hugh Wickham Surgery, Station Road, Wickham, Fareham PO17 5JL Tel: 01329 833121 Fax: 01329 832443; Westwood, Droxford Road, Swanmore, Southampton SO32 2PY — MB BS 1973 Lond.; BSc (Biochem. Hons.) Lond. 1970, MB BS 1973; MRCP (UK) 1979; Dip. IMC RCS Ed. 1991; DCH Eng. 1975. (St. Thos.) Prev: Regist. (Paediat.) St. Peter's Hosp. Chertsey; Regist. (Gen. Med.) Mayday Hosp. Thornton Heath; SHO (Neonat.) Hammersmith Hosp. Lond.

SMARASON, Alexander Kristinn Nuffield Department of Obstetrics and Gynaecology, University of Oxford, John Radcliffe Hospital, Oxford OX3 9DU Tel: 01865 221021; 27 Walkers Close, Freeland, Witney OX29 8AY Tel: 01993 883686 Email: alexander.smarason@obs-gyn.ox.ac.uk — Cand Med et Chir Reykjavik 1987; DPhil. Oxf. 1994; MRCOG 1997. Clin. Lect. (Obstretrics & Gyn.) Univ. of Oxf. Socs: BMA; MDU.

SMART, Alexander Charles (retired) The Surgery, 1 Streatfield Road, Harrow HA3 9BP Tel: 020 8907 0381 Fax: 020 8909 2134 — MB BS 1966 Lond.; MRCS Eng. LRCP Lond. 1966.

SMART, Amanda Lucy Whitby Group Practice, Spring Vale Medical Centre, Whitby YO21 1SD Tel: 01947 820888 Fax: 01947 603194 — MB ChB 1985 Leeds.

SMART, Andrew Galloway Weir The Health Centre, 80 Main Street, Kelty KY4 0AE Tel: 01383 831281 Fax: 01383 831825; Keston, 78 Muirs, Kinross KY13 8AY — MB ChB 1979 Ed.

SMART, Anna Rachel Theresa Isadora 4 Cairnaquheen Gardens, Aberdeen AB15 5HJ — MB ChB 1998 Aberd.

SMART, Mr Christopher James Department of Urology, Southampton General Hospital, Southampton SO16 6YD Tel: 02380 777222; The Old Vicarage, Emery Down, Lyndhurst SO43 7EA Tel: 01421 282000 Fax: 01421 282000 — MB BS 1965 Lond.; FRCS Eng. 1971. (St. Bart.) Cons. Urol. & Gen. Surg. Soton. & SW Hants. Health Dist. (T).

SMART, Christopher Jeremy Northwood Medical Centre, 10/12 Middleton Hall Road, Kings Norton, Birmingham B30 1BY Tel: 0121 458 5507 — MB ChB 1967 Birm.; MRCGP 1972; DObst RCOG 1970; DMJ Soc. Apoth. Lond. 1983; DA Eng. 1970. Hosp. Pract. (Geriat. Med.) W. Heath Hosp. Birm.; Div. Police Surg. W. Midl. Police. Socs: Counc. Mem. Assn Police Surgs. Gt. Brit.; Fell. Roy. Soc. Med.; Clin. Forens. Med. (Counc.).

SMART, Mr Colin Campbell Queen Mary's Sidcup NHS Trust, Frognal Avenue, Sidcup DA14 6LT Tel: 020 8302 2678 Fax: 020 8302 3155 — MB ChB 1985 Glas.; FRCS (Tr. & Orth. 1999); Dip Biomech. 1996; FRCS Glas. 1991. Cons. Orthopaedic Surg., Qu. Mary's Sidcup NHS Trust, Sidcup.

SMART, David James Garfield Hanway Road Surgery, 2 Hanway Road, Buckland, Portsmouth PO1 4ND Tel: 023 9281 5317 Fax: 023 9289 9926 — MB 1981 Camb.; MA Camb. 1981, MB 1981, BChir 1980; MRCGP 1984; DRCOG 1983. Clin. Asst. (Ophth.) Qu. Alexandra Hosp. Portsmouth. Prev: Trainee GP Portsmouth VTS.

SMART, David John Leicester Terrace Health Care Centre, 8 Leicester Terrace, Northampton NN2 6AL Tel: 01604 33682 Fax: 01604 233408; 79 Holly Road, Northampton NN1 4QN — MB ChB 1985 Leic.; MRCGP 1990. (Leicester) Trainee GP Kettering VTS.

***SMART, David Keith Archibald** 117 Dane Road, Sale M33 2BY — MB ChB 1996 Manch.

SMART, David Wilson Dunelm Medical Practice, 1-2 Victor Terrace, Bearpark, Durham DH7 7DF Tel: 0191 373 2077 Fax: 0191 373 6216; Kelvin House, 1/2 Victor Terrace, Bearpark, Durham DH7 7DR — MB ChB 1981 Glas.; MRCGP 1985; DRCOG 1983.

SMART, Donald McGregor (retired) 14 Framers Court, Lane End, High Wycombe HP14 3LL — MRCS Eng. LRCP Lond. 1944. Prev: GP Hayes.

SMART, Felicity Anne Llanilar Health Centre, Llanilar, Aberystwyth SY23 4PA Tel: 01974 241556 Fax: 01974 241579; Fairview, Penyfron, Llanbadarn Fawr, Aberystwyth SY23 3QU — MB ChB 1976 Birm.; MRCGP (Distinc.) 1982; DCH RCP Lond. 1982.

SMART, Sir George Algernon Taffrail, Crede Lane, Bosham, Chichester PO18 8NX Tel: 01243 572608 Email: smartgeo@aol.com — BSc, MD Durham. 1939, MB BS 1937, FRCP Lond. 1952, M 1940. (Univ. Durh.) Emerit. Prof. Univ. Lond.; Hon. Cons. Phys. Nat. Hosp. Nerv. Dis.; Hon. Cons. Phys. Roy. Vict. Infirm. Newc. Socs: Med. Roy. Soc. Med.; Fell. Roy. Soc. Med.; Life Vice-Pres. Roy. Nat. Lifeboat Inst. Prev: Dir. Brit. Postgrad. Med. Federat.; Dean & Prof. Med. Univ. Newc.; Vice-Pres. & Sen. Censor RCP.

SMART, Mr George Edward Beechcroft, 24 Cramond Road N., Cramond, Edinburgh EH4 6JE Tel: 0131 312 8499 Email: gesmart@ed.ac.uk; Royal Infirmary of Edinburgh, Lauriston Place, Edinburgh EH3 9YW Tel: 0131 536 1000 Fax: 0131 536 4254 — MB ChB Ed. 1960; FRCS Ed. 1968; FRCOG 1979, M 1967. Cons. O & G Simpson Memor. Matern. Pavil. & Roy. Infirm. Edin.; Hon. Sen. Lect. Univ. Edin. Prev: Cons. Sen. Lect. O & G Univ. Bristol & Hon. Cons. S.mead Hosp. & United Bristol Hosps.; Sen. Fell. Gyn. Oncol. State Univ. New York Downstate Med. Center Brooklyn, USA.

SMART, Hazel Elizabeth Linlithgow Health Centre, 288 High Street, Linlithgow EH49 7ER Tel: 01506 670027; 20 Kettilstoun Grove, Linlithgow EH49 6PP — MB ChB 1988 Ed.; MRCGP 1994; DRCOG 1992.

SMART, Howard Leighton Royal Liverpool Broadgreen University Hospitals NHS Trust, Prescot St., Liverpool L7 8XP Tel: 0151 706

3557 Fax: 0151 706 5832 Email: howard@docusmart.freeserve.co.uk — MB BS 1979 Lond.; DM Nottm. 1988; FRCP Lond. 1996; MRCP (UK) 1982. (St. Bart.) Cons. Phys. (Gastroenterol.) Roy. Liverp. & BRd.green Univ. Hosps. NHS Trust; Clin. Lect. (Med.) Univ. Liverp. Socs: Brit. Soc. Gastroenterol.; Brit. Assn. for the Study of the Liver. Prev: Lect. (Med.) Univ. Sheff.; Research Fell. (Med.) Univ. Hosp. Nottm.; Regist. (Med.) City Hosp. Nottm.

SMART, Iain Seymour Mackintosh Bonnyrigg Health Centre, High Street, Bonnyrigg EH19 2DA Tel: 0131 663 7272 — MB ChB 1967 St. And.; MRCGP 1976; DObst RCOG 1967. (St. And.) Socs: BMA. Prev: SHO (O & G) Dundee Roy. Infirm.; SHO (Gen. Surg.) & (Gen. Med.) Falkirk Roy. Infirm.

SMART, Isobel Alice (retired) Holmwood, Holt, Wimborne BH21 7DQ Tel: 01202 841943 — MB BS Durh. 1961.

SMART, James Ambler, MBE (retired) Marwood Hill, Barnstaple EX31 4EB Tel: 01271 342528 — MB BS Lond. 1937; MRCS Eng. LRCP Lond. 1937; DA Eng. 1946. Prev: Cons. Anaesth. N. Devon Infirm. Barnstaple.

SMART, James Anderson Crossways, 39 Windson Rd, Radyr, Cardiff CF15 8BQ — MB ChB 1994 Leic.

SMART, James Finlayson Union Street Surgery, 75 Union Street, Larkhall ML9 1DZ Tel: 01698 882105 Fax: 01698 886332 — MB ChB 1969 Glas.

SMART, James Matthew The Old Vicarage, Emery Down, Lyndhurst SO43 7EA — MB ChB 1992 Leic.

SMART, John Charles Woodbury Cottage, Chatley, Ombersley, Droitwich WR9 0AP Tel: 01905 621088; Woodbury Cottage, Chatley, Ombersley, Droitwich WR9 0AP Tel: 01258 837251, 01905 621088 — MB ChB 1948 Birm.; DObst RCOG 1950. (Birm.) JP. Socs: Fell. Roy. Soc. Med.; Nat. Chairm. Brit. Soc. Med. & Dent. Hypn. Prev: Ho. Surg. & Ho. Phys. Gen. Hosp. Birm.; Ho. Surg. (Obst.) Birm. Matern. Hosp.

SMART, Mr John Gordon (cons. rooms), The Nuffield Hospital, Scraptoft Lane, Leicester LE5 1HY Tel: 0116 246 1646; Alford House, Wymeswold, Loughborough LE12 6UE Tel: 01509 880868 — MB BS 1949 Lond.; MS Lond. 1965; FRCS Eng. 1957. (Middlx.) Cons. Urol. Nuffield Hosp. Leicester; Emerit. Cons. Surg. & Urol. Leicester Roy. Infirm., Leicester Gen. Hosp. & LoughBoro. Gen. Hosp.; Tutor (Surg.) RCS Eng. & Leicester Med. Sch.; Examr. Surg. Roy. Coll. Nurs. Socs: Fell. Roy. Soc. Med. (Ex-Counc. Sect. Urol.); Brit. Assn. Urol. Surgs. (Ex-Counc. Mem.). Prev: Sen. Regist. (Surg.) St. Thos. Hosp. Lond. & St. Peter's Hosp. Chertsey; Regist. (Surg.) Fulham Hosp. Squadron Ldr. RAF Med. Br.

SMART, John Howard (retired) The Penthouse, Flat E, 1 Madeira Grove, Woodford Green IG8 7QH Tel: 020 8504 9530 — MB BS 1938 Lond.; MRCS Eng. LRCP Lond. 1938. Prev: RAFVR 1941-46.

SMART, Kieran 45 Laurel Drive, Penperlleni, Pontypool NP4 0BQ Tel: 0966 508220 Email: kieran.smart3@vgn.net — MB ChB 1992 Bristol; BA Open Univ. 1987; MRCGP 1987. Socs: Aerospace Med. Assn.

SMART, Lesley Newbattle Medical Practice, Mayfield, Dalkeith E22 4AA Tel: 0131 663 1051; 6 Ancrum Bank, Dalkeith EH22 3AY — MB ChB 1979 Glas.; MRCGP 1983; DRCOG 1981. Clin. Med. Off., Family Plann. and Reproductive Health, Edin.

SMART, Lesley Margaret St. John's Hospital at Howden, Livingston — MB ChB 1982 Ed.; BSc (Hons.) (Med. Sc.) Ed. 1979, MB ChB 1982; MRCP (UK) 1985; FRCR 1989. Cons. Radiol. St. John's Hosp. at Howden. Livingston. Prev: Sen. Regist. & Regist. (Radiol.) Lothian HB.

SMART, Louise Mary Pathology Department, Medical School Building, Foresterhill, Aberdeen AB25 2ZD Tel: 01224 552836 Fax: 01224 663002 Email: louise.smart@arh.gramplan.scot.nhs.uk; The Glen, 1 Station Road E., Peterculter AB14 0PT — MB ChB 1984 Aberdeen; MD Aberd. 1991, MB ChB 1984; MRCPath 1992. Cons. Cytopath. Aberd. Roy. Hosp. Prev: Sen. Regist. (Path.) Aberd. Roy. Hosp.

SMART, Lynda Kay 41 Melville Avenue, South Croydon CR2 7HZ — MB BS 1984 Lond.; DRCOG 1987. GP Lond.

SMART, Michael Alan Brent House Surgery, 14 King Street, Bridgwater TA6 3ND Tel: 01278 458551 Fax: 01278 431116 — BM 1985 Soton.; MRCGP 1989.

SMART, Neil Gow 96 Beechwood Drive, Glasgow G11 7HH — MB ChB 1984 Glas.; BSc (Hons.) Glas. 1981, MB ChB 1984; FFA RCSI 1989; DA (UK) 1986. Regist. (Anaesth.) Glas. Roy. Infirm. Prev: SHO Dept. of Anaesth. Glas. Roy. Infirm.; Jun. Ho. Phys. Stobhill Gen. Hosp. & W.. Infirm. Glas.

***SMART, Olivia Catherine** The Laithe Barn, Old Mount Farm, Woolley, Wakefield WF4 2LD — MB BS 1998 Lond.; MB BS Lond 1998.

SMART, Mr Paul James Gregory (retired) Hockhams House, Martley, Worcester WR6 6QR — MS Lond. 1968, MB BS 1955; FRCS Eng. 1962; DObst RCOG 1957. Prev: Cons. Surg. Worcester Roy. Infirm.

SMART, Peter Charles 5 The Oaks, Vicarage Road, Blackwater, Camberley GU17 9BE Tel: 01276 33844 Fax: 01276 33844 — MB BS 1953 Lond.; MRCS Eng. LRCP Lond. 1953; DA Eng. 1955. (St. Geo.) Police Surg. Winchester Div. Hants. Constab. Socs: BMA. Prev: Clin. Tutor (GP) St. Geo. Hosp. Lond.; SHO (Anaesth.) St. Geo. Hosp. Lond.

SMART, Peter Donald (retired) 26 Lilburn Gardens, South Gosforth, Newcastle upon Tyne NE3 1SU Tel: 0191 285 4754 — MB BS 1954 Durh. Prev: Res. Med. Off. Preston Hosp. N. Shields.

SMART, Peter Howard La Route Du Fort Surgery, 2 La Route Du Fort, St Helier, Jersey JE2 4PA Tel: 01534 31421 Fax: 01534 280776; Felsted, La Rue de Guilleaume et D'Anneville, St Martin, Jersey JE3 6DP — MB BCh 1973 Wales; MRCS Eng. LRCP Lond. 1973; MRCGP 1978; DRCOG 1979; Cert. Av Med. MoD (Air) & Civil Av Auth. 1977. (Univeristy College Cardiff & Welsh National School Medicine)

SMART, Philip John Edward 10 Langstrath Drive, West Bridgford, Nottingham NG2 6SD — MB BS 1994 Lond.; MA Camb. 1987.

SMART, Rosemary Ann The Surgery, Worcester Road, Great Witley, Worcester WR6 6HR Tel: 01299 896370 Fax: 01299 896873; Hockham's House, Martley, Worcester WR6 6QR Tel: 01886 812276 — MB ChB 1967 Ed. (Ed.) Prev: Hosp. Pract. (A & E) Worcester Roy. Infirm.

SMART, Russell George 37 Eton Wick Road, Eton Wick, Windsor SL4 6LU — MB BS 1984 Lond.

SMART, Sara Carol 69 Hall Lane, Aspull, Wigan WN2 2SF — MB ChB 1991 Leic.

SMART, Sharon Rachel Sara 20 Telford Close, High Shincliffe, Durham DH1 2YJ — MB BS 1983 Lond.

SMART, Simon Jeremy The Chase, Watery Lane, Weatheroak, Birmingham B48 7JN — MB BS 1996 Lond.

SMART, Victoria Mary Eve Hill Medical Practice, 29-53 Himley Road, Dudley DY1 2QD Tel: 01384 254423 Fax: 01384 254424 — MB ChB 1984 Birm.; DCH RCP Lond. 1988. Prev: Ho Surg. Gen. Hosp. Birm.; Ho. Phys. Dudley Rd. Hosp.; Trainee GP Dudley VTS.

SMEATON, Nicola Clare Wallacetown Health Centre, Lyon Street, Dundee DD4 6RB Tel: 01382 457629 Fax: 01382 450365 — MB ChB 1986 Dundee.

SMEDH, Rolf Kennet Colorectal Research Unit, North Hampshire Hospital, Aldermaston Road, Basingstoke RG24 9NA — Lakarexamen 1978 Stockholm.

SMEDLEY, Mr Frank Herbert Wildwood, Cudham Lane S., Cudham, Sevenoaks TN14 7QA — MB BS 1978 Lond.; MS Lond. 1987; FRCS Eng. 1983.

SMEDLEY, Mr Geoffrey Thomas (retired) Chalklands, Rockbourne, Fordingbridge SP6 3NA Tel: 01725 518543 — MB BS Lond. 1949; FRCS Eng. 1953; FRCOG 1972, M 1957. Prev: Cons. O & G Salisbury Hosp. Gp.

SMEDLEY, Howard Martin c/o Department of Radiotherapy, Kent & Canterbury Hospital, Ethelbert Road, Canterbury CT1 3NG — MB BS 1977 Lond.; FRCR 1982. (Univ. Coll. Hosp.) Cons. Radiother. & Oncol. Kent & Canterbury Hosp.; Clin. Tutor Kent Postgrad. Med. Centre. Prev: Clin. Scientist & Hon. Sen. Regist. Ludwig Inst. Cancer Research Camb.; Sen. Regist. (Radiother. & Oncol.) Addenbrooke's Hosp. Camb.

SMEDLEY, Julia Carol Occupational Health Department, Southampton General Hospital, Tremona Road, Southampton SO16 6YD Tel: 02380 794156 Fax: 02380 794324 Email: jcs@mrc.soton.ac.uk — BM BS 1985 Nottm.; BMedSci Nottm 1983; MRCP (UK) 1988; MFOM 1997; DM Southampton 1999. Cons. Occupat. Phys. Soton. Univ. Hosps. NHS Trust Soton. Socs: Soc. Occupat. Med.; Assoc. of NHS Occupat. Phys. (ANHOPS). Prev: Sen.

SMEED, Regist. (Occupat. Med.) Soton.; Regist. (Haemat.) King Coll. Hosp.; SHO (Gen. Med.) Soton. Gen. Hosp.

SMEED, Richard Charles Kenneth Church Cottage, Claypit Lane, Ledsham, South Milford, Leeds LS25 5LP Tel: 01977 684566 — MB ChB 1975 Leeds; AFOM RCP Lond. 1995. Company Med. Advisor Elida Fabergé (Unilever) Leeds & Kalon Gp. plc Batley; Clin. Asst. Elderly Sick Day Hosp. Castleford. Socs: Soc. Occupat. Med. Prev: GP Kippax & Garforth Leeds.

SMEETH, Liam Keats Group Practice, 1B Downshire Hill, London NW3 1NR — MB ChB 1990 Sheff.; MSc Lond. Sch. of Hyg. & Trop. Med. 1998; DRCOG 1996; MRCGP 1995; DCH 1994. (Sheffield) GP; Clin. Lect. Dept. of Primary Care & Populat. Sci. Roy. Free & UCL Med. Sch.

SMEETON, Anthony Keith Gloucester Road Medical Centre, Tramway House, 1A Church Road, Horfield, Bristol BS7 8SA Tel: 0117 949 7774 Fax: 0117 949 7730; Hereford House, Clifton Park, Clifton, Bristol BS8 3BP Tel: 0117 974 5232 — MB ChB 1961 Bristol. Police Surg. Avon & Som. Constab. Socs: BMA; Assn. Police Surg. Prev: Ho. Phys. Ham Green Hosp. Bristol; Ho. Surg. (Cas. & Orthop.) Bristol Roy. Infirm.; Ho. Surg. (Obst.) Roy. United Hosp. Bath.

SMEETON, Fiona Janet 6 Long Acre E., Bingham, Nottingham NG13 8BY — MB BS 1996 Lond.; BSc Lond 1993; MRCP June 1999. (Charing Cross & West Minster) SHO Med., Sthelier Hosp., Carshalton.

SMEETON, Richard James Chilham House, 5 The Spinney, Thurnby, Leicester LE7 9QS — MRCGP 1975; DObst RCOG 1970. (Univ. Coll. Hosp.) Indep. Occupat. Health Phys.; Med. Off. & Police Surg. Leics. Constab. Socs: BMA. Prev: GP Leicester.

SMEKAL, Walter 4 Chestnut Way, Newton Poppleford, Sidmouth EX10 0DL — MD 1938 Brno. (Brno)

SMELLIE, Alexander James (retired) Roselea, Victoria Road, Brookfield, Johnstone PA5 8TZ Tel: 01505 320266 — MB ChB 1955 Glas.; DObst RCOG 1959. Med. Assessor Indep. Tribunal Serv. Prev: Ho. Phys. Glas. Roy. Infirm.

SMELLIE, Anne Stephen 62 Gough Way, Cambridge CB3 9LN Tel: 01223 352035 — MB BS 1957 Lond. (St. Thos.)

SMELLIE, Florence Mary Devlin McCalman 39 Falkland Street, Glasgow G12 9QZ Tel: 0141 334 4255 — MB ChB 1954 Glas. (Glas.) Med. Asst. Dept. Path. W.. Infirm. Glas.; Med. Off. Family Plann. Assn. Socs: Scott. Assn. Clin. Cytol. & Nat. Assn. Family Plann. Doctors. Prev: Asst. Lect. Dept. Anat. Univ. Glas.; Cas. Off. Roy. Hosp. Sick Childr. Glas.; Ho. Phys. (Paediat.) Stobhill Hosp. Glas.

SMELLIE, Janet Helen (retired) Glenelg, Seafield Court, Grantown-on-Spey PH26 3LE — MB ChB (Hons.) Liverp. 1947; DCH Eng. 1949; MB ChB 1947. Prev: Ho. Phys. Liverp. Roy. Infirm. & Roy. Childr. Hosp. Liverp.

SMELLIE, Jean McIldowie 23 St Thomas' Street, Winchester SO23 9HJ Tel: 01962 852550 Fax: 01962 852550 — BM BCh Oxf. 1950; MA Oxf. 1951, BA 1947, DM 1981; FRCP Lond. 1975, M 1954; Hon. FRCPCH 1996; DCH Eng. 1953. (Oxf. & Univ. Coll. Hosp.) Emerit. Cons. Paediat. Univ. Coll. Lond. Hosps.; Hon. Cons. (Paediat.) Guy's Hosp. & Hosp. Sick Childr. Lond; Scientif. Adviser, InterNat. Reflux Study in childr. 1982-present. Socs: Hon Mem. Brit. Assn. for Paed. Nephrol.; Europ. Soc. for Paediatric Nephrol.; Hon Mem. Amer. Urological Assn. Prev: Sen. Lect. (Paediat.) Univ. Coll. Lond. Med. Sch.; Hon. Sen. Clin. Lect. (Community Child Health) Univ. of Soton.; Fell. (Path.) Johns Hopkins Hosp. Baltimore, USA.

SMELLIE, Maida Kelly Reid 25 Earls Way, Doonfoot, Ayr KA7 4HF — MB ChB 1975 Ed.; BSc Ed. 1972,; MFCM 1985; MPH Glas. 1982.

SMELLIE, Vivien Rachel 4 Stoke road, Bishops Cleeve, Cheltenham GL52 8RP Tel: 01242 672007 — MB BS 1992 Lond.; BSc (Hons.) KQC 1989 (Lond.); DRCOG 1996; DCH 1995; DRCOG 1996. (Univ. Coll. and Middlx. Hosp. Med. Sch.)

SMELLIE, Mr William Alastair Buchanan (retired) 62 Gough Way, Cambridge CB3 9LN Tel: 01223 352035 — MB 1958 Camb.; BA Camb. 1954, MChir 1966, MB 1958, BChir 1957; FRCS Eng. 1962. Cons. Surg. Addenbrooke's Hosp. Camb.; Assoc. Lect. Univ. Camb; Examr. (Surg.) Univs. Oxf., Camb. & Lond.; RCS Regional Adviser in Surg. E. Anglia; Hon Col. RAMC. Prev: Res. Asst. Surg. St. Thos. Hosp. Lond.

SMELLIE, William Buchanan (retired) Glenelg, Seafield Court, Grantown-on-Spey PH26 3LE — MB ChB 1947 Liverp.; MRCGP 1960. Prev: Univ. Med. Off. Univ. Liverp.

SMELLIE, Mr William James Buchanan 7 Brunel Lodge, 34 Vicarage Crescent, London SW11 3LD Tel: 020 7223 2988 — MB BChir 1988 Camb.; BA Camb. 1985; FRCS 1992. Sen. Regist. (Endocrine Surg.) Hammersmith Hosp. Lond. Prev: Regist. (Gen. Surg.) St. Thos. Hosp. Lond.; Regist. (Gen. Surg.) St. Geo. Hosp. Lond.; Clin. Research Fell. Roy. Marsden Hosp. Lond.

SMELLIE, William Stuart Adams Bishop Auckland Hospital, Cockton Hill Road, Bishop Auckland DL14 6AP Tel: 01388 454064; Morely Farm, Morley Lane, Brancepeth, Durham DH7 8DS Tel: 0191 373 9416 Fax: 0191 373 9417 Email: info@smelli.com — BM BCh 1985 Oxf.; MA Camb. 1986; DM Oxf. 1996; MRCP (UK) 1989; MRCPath 1994. Cons. Bishop Auckland NHS Trust. Prev: Sen. Regist. Glas. Roy. Infirm.

SMELT, Mr Graham Jonathan Casterton ENT Department, The Royal Infirmary, Lindley, Huddersfield HD3 3EA Tel: 01484 342693 Fax: 01484 342147 — MB BS 1976 Lond.; BSc Lond. 1973; FRCS Ed. 1982; LMCC 1985. (St. Thos.) p/t Cons. ENT Surg. Calderdale & Huddersfield NHS Trusts. Socs: N. Eng. Otol. Soc. Prev: Sen. Regist. Nottm. & Leics. HAs; Regist. St. Bart. Hosp. Lond.

SMERDON, Albert Charles (retired) Allerdale, Vicarage Lane, Wilpshire, Blackburn BB1 9HX Tel: 01254 49565 — MB ChB 1937 Liverp. Prev: Ho. Surg. Roy. S.. Hosp. Liverp.

SMERDON, Anthony William Stockbridge Village Health Centre, Leachcroft, Waterpark Drive, Stockbridge Village, Liverpool L28 1ST Tel: 0151 489 9924; 16 Brooke Road W., Liverpool L22 7RW Tel: 0151 920 9246 — MB ChB 1967 Liverp.; MSc Liverp. 1990, MB ChB 1967; MRCGP 1975.

SMERDON, Mr David Laurence North Riding Infirmary, Newport Rd, Middlesbrough TS1 5JE Tel: 01642 854069; Hazel Grove, Whorl Hill, Faceby, Middlesbrough TS9 7BZ Tel: 01642 700013 — MB ChB 1978 Dundee; FRCS Ed. 1983; FRCOphth 1989. Cons. Ophth. Surg. N. Riding Infirm. Middlesbrough; Chairm. of Ocular Tissue Advisory Gp. of U.K. Transpl. Socs: Treas. Oxf. Ophth. Congr.; Sec. UKISCRS; Hon Treas Enter. Prev: Sen. Regist. (Ophth.) Birm. & Midl. Eye Hosp.; Regist. (Ophth.) St. Pauls Eye. Hosp. Liverp.; SHO (Ophth.) Ninewells Hosp. & Med. Sch. Dundee.

SMERDON, Geoffrey Hugh, MBE (retired) Maleme Roseland, Liskeard PL14 3PQ Tel: 01579 343460 — MB BS Lond. 1949; MRCS Eng. LRCP Lond. 1949; FRCGP 1980, M 1953; DCH Eng. 1959; DObst RCOG 1955.

SMERDON, Geoffrey Thomas (retired) The White Cottage, 190 Wivenhoe Road, Alresford, Colchester CO7 8AH Tel: 01206 822055 — BM BCh 1950 Oxf.; MA Oxf. 1950; MFOM RCP Lond. 1978. Prev: Civil. Med. Pract. Med. Reception Centre, Sennelager 1979-81.

SMERDON, George Robert The Spinney Surgery, The Spinney, Ramsey Road, St. Ives, Huntingdon PE27 37P Tel: 01480 492501 Fax: 01480 356159 — MB BS 1969 Lond.; FRCGP 1989; MRCGP 1975; DObst RCOG 1973. (St. Thos.)

SMEREKA, Adam Kazimierz Church Street Medical Centre, 11B Church Street, Eastwood, Nottingham NG16 3BP Tel: 01773 712065 Fax: 01773 534295 — MB BCh BAO 1964 NUI.

SMETHURST, Dominic Paul Dermatology Unit, University of Nottingham, Queen's Medical Centre NG7 2UH — BChir 1996 Camb. (Cambridge) Research Fell. Univ. of Nottm. Prev: SHO (Gen. Med.) Qu.'s Med. Nottm.; Pre-Regist. Ho. Off. (Gen. Surg.) Milton Keynes; Pre-Regist. Ho. Off. (Gen. Med.) Addenbrookes.

SMETHURST, Fraser Andrew 22 Kingsmead Road N., Oxton, Birkenhead CH43 6TB Tel: 0151 652 3470 — BM BCh 1987 Oxf.; BA (Hons.) Oxf. 1984; FRCR 1984; DMRD Liverp. 1982. Cons. Radiol. Aintree Hosp. Trust. Prev: Sen. Regist. (Radiol.) Fazakerley Hosp. Liverp.

SMETHURST, John Roderic (retired) 4 Warren Drive, Dorridge, Solihull B93 8JY Tel: 01564 776387 Fax: 01564 776387 Email: 106043.3424@compuserve.com — MB ChB Birm. 1959; FFA RCS Eng. 1966; FRCA 1992. Sen. Clin. Lect. Univ. Birm. Prev: Cons. Anaesth. Birm. Centr. Health Dist. (T).

SMETHURST, Marianne 62 Leamington Street, Crookes, Sheffield S10 1LW — MB ChB 1995 Sheff.

SMETHURST, Marion Elizabeth West Kirby Health Centre, Grange Road, Wirral CH48 4HZ Tel: 0151 625 9171 Fax: 0151 625

SMITH

9171 — BM BCh 1987 Oxf.; BA (Hons.) Oxf. 1984; DRCOG 1990. (Oxf.) GP. Prev: Trainee GP/SHO (O & G) Horton Gen. Hosp. Banbury.

SMETHURST, Meera Elizabeth The Surgery, St. Peters Close, Cowfold, Horsham RH13 8DN Tel: 01403 864204 Fax: 01403 864408 — BM BCh 1985 Oxf.; MA Camb. 1986; DRCOG 1988. GP Cowfold, Horsham.

***SMEULDERS, Naima** 3 The Nursery, Sutton Courtenay, Abingdon OX14 4UA — BChir 1994 Camb.

SMEYATSKY, Norman Raphael St. Michael's Hospital, St. Michael's Road, Warwick CV34 5QW Tel: 01926 406789; 15 Willes Terrace, Leamington Spa CV31 1DL Tel: 01926 831702 — MB BCh 1979 Witwatersrand; BSc Witwatersrand 1975; MRCPsych 1985. Cons. Old Age Psychiat. St. Michael's Hosp. Warwick.

SMIBERT, George McMillan 44 Mount Road, Penn, Wolverhampton WV4 5SW Tel: 01902 341574 — MB ChB 1946 Ed. (Univ. Ed.)

SMIBERT, Mr John Graham Yeovil District General Hospital, Yeovil — MB BS 1976 Lond.; FRCS Lond. 1980; FRCS Ed. 1980. Cons. Orthop. Yeovil Dist. Gen. Hosp. Prev: Sen. Regist. Rotat. (Orthop.) Kings Coll. Hosp. Lond.

SMIDDY, Mr Francis Geoffrey (retired) Flat 2, 95 The Drive, Leeds LS17 7QG Tel: 01532 757129 — MD 1963 Leeds; ChM Leeds 1960, MD 1963, MB ChB 1944; FRCS Eng. 1950. Mem. Ct. Examrs. RCS Eng. Prev: Cons. Surg. Leeds Gen. Infirm. & Seacroft & Clayton Hosps.

SMILEY, Clare Colette 152 Loughinisland Road, Downpatrick BT30 8QZ — MB BCh BAO 1993 Belf.; BSc (Hons.) Belf. 1988, MB BCh BAO 1993.

SMILEY, Elita Gartnavel Royal Hospital, 1055 Great Western Road, Glasgow G12 OXH Tel: 0141 211 3600; 7 Brierie Hills Court, Crosslee, Houston, Johnstone PA6 7DU — MB ChB 1993 Glas. SHO (Psychiat.) Gartnavel Roy. Hosp. Glas.

SMILLIE, Dorothy Clair River Place Health Centre, Essex Road, London N1 2TS Tel: 020 7226 1473 — MB ChB 1974 Dundee. Socs: BMA. Prev: SHO (Gen. Med.) Stracathro Hosp. Brechin; Med. Edr. Med. News; SHO (Paediat.) Edgware Gen. Hosp.

SMILLIE, Mr Gavin Douglas (retired) 44 Terregles Avenue, Glasgow G41 4LX — MB ChB 1949 Glas.; FRCS Ed. 1962; FRCS Eng. 1962; FRFPS Glas. 1961; DObst RCOG 1954. Prev: Cons. Surg. Vict. Infirm. Glas.

SMILLIE, Jane Fiona Riversdale Surgery, Riversdale House, Merthyrmawr Road, Bridgend CF31 3NL Tel: 01656 766866 Fax: 01656 668659 — MB ChB 1981 Bristol; MRCPsych 1988; MRCGP 1985; Dip. Palliat. Med. Wales 1991. GP Bridgend.

SMILLIE, Martin Watt (retired) The Surgery, Union Road, Camelon, Falkirk FK1 Tel: 01324 22854 — MB ChB 1956 Glas.; DObst RCOG 1961. Prev: Resid. Stobhill Gen. Hosp. & Glas. Roy. Infirm.

SMIRK, Thomas Winfield Haslington Surgery, Crewe Road, Haslington, Crewe CW1 5QY Tel: 01270 581259 Fax: 01270 257958; 336 Crewe Road, Winterley, Sandbach CW11 4RP — MB BS 1974 Newc.

SMIRL, Jeanine Elizabeth Highbury New Park Surgery, 49 Highbury New Park, London N5 2ET Tel: 020 7354 1972; 160 Culford Road, London N1 4HU Tel: 020 7254 6922 — MB BS 1987 Lond.; DRCOG 1991; DCH RCP Lond. 1990. GP Trainer. Prev: SHO (O & G) Lond. Hosp.; SHO (Paediat.) King Geo. Hosp. Ilford.; SHO (A & E) Broomfield Hosp. Chelmsford.

SMIT, Ian David 6 Gatton Close, Sutton SM2 5QL — MB ChB 1968 Pretoria.

SMITH, Rt. Hon. Lord, KBE 135 Harley Street, London W1N 1DJ Tel: 020 7935 1714 — MRCS Eng. LRCP Lond. 1937; MS Lond. 1941, MB BS 1937; Hon. FRCS S. Afr.; Hon. FDS RCS Eng.; Hon. MD Zurich 1979; FRCS Eng. 1939; Hon. DSc Exeter & Leeds; Hon. FRACS; Hon. FRCS Glas.; Hon. FRCS Ed. Hon. FACS; Hon. FRCS Canada; Hon. FRCSI. Emerit. Cons. in Surg. to Army; Hon. Consg. Surg. St. Geo. Hosp. Lond.; Hon. Cons. Surg. Roy. P. Alfred Hosp. Sydney, Austral. Socs: Biennial Prize Internat. Soc. Surg. 1975; Fell. (Ex-Pres.) Roy. Soc. Med.; Hon. Mem. Assn. Anaesth. Prev: Pres. Roy. Soc. Med. 1978-80; Pres. RCS Eng.; Surg. RAMC 1941-45.

SMITH, Mr Adam Neil (retired) 2 Ravelston House Park, Edinburgh EH4 3LU Tel: 0131 332 4077 — MB ChB 1948 Glas.; MB ChB (Commend.) Glas. 1948; FRSE 1982; DSc Ed. 1995; MD

(Hons.) Glas. 1959; FRCP Ed. 1988; FRCS Ed. 1956. Prev: Wade Prof. Surg. Studies Roy. Coll. Surg. Edin.

SMITH, Adrian Curtis 58 Hargreaves Road, Oswaldthistle, Accrington BB5 4RN — MB ChB 1983 Manch.

SMITH, Adrian David 20 Whitworth Street, London SE10 9EN — MB BS 1991 Lond.

SMITH, Adrian Grenville 301 Court Lane, Erdington, Birmingham B23 5JS — MB ChB 1984 Birm.; MB ChB (Hons.) Birm. 1984; MRCP (UK) 1988. Regist. (Haemat.) Selly Oak Hosp. Birm.

SMITH, Adrian Henry Lampard Nethergreen Road Surgery, 34-36 Nethergreen Road, Sheffield S11 7EJ Tel: 0114 230 2952; 133B Tom Lane, Sheffield S10 3PE Tel: 0114 230 9625 — MB ChB 1985 Sheff.; MRCGP 1990; DFFP 1994; DRCOG 1989. Prev: Trainee GP Sheff. VTS.

SMITH, Alan Douglas Forensic Psychiatry Service, (Box 175) S3, Addenbrooke's Hospital, Cambridge CB2 2QQ Tel: 01223 216442 Fax: 01223 217941 — MB ChB 1990 Glas.; BSc (Hons.) Glas. 1987; MPhil Ed. 1996; MRCPsych 1994. (Glas.) Cons. (Forens. Psychiat.) Addenbrooke's Hosp. Cambs. Prev: Lect. (Forens. Psychiat.) Inst. Of Psychiat. & Maudsley Hosp. Lond.; Lect. & Sen. Regist. (Forens. Psychiat.) Univ. Camb. & Norvic Clinic Norwich; Regist. & SHO (Psychiat.) Roy. Edin. Hosp.

SMITH, Alan George Edward (retired) 28 Barrow Street, Much Wenlock TF13 6EN Tel: 01952 728247 — MB ChB 1959 Birm.

SMITH, Alan Inglis Murrayfield Medical Practice, 8 Corstorphine Road, Edinburgh EH12 6HN Tel: 0131 337 6151 Fax: 0131 313 3450 — MB ChB 1983 Ed.

SMITH, Mr Alan Malcolm (retired) 29 Sunningdale Close, Birmingham B20 1LH — BM BCh 1954 Oxf.; MA Oxf. 1954; FRCP Ed. 1979, M 1968; FRCS Ed. 1963; FRCOG 1973, M 1960, DObst 1956. Prev: Cons. O & G Wolverhampton Gp. Hosps. & W. Bromwich Hosp. Gp.

SMITH, Alan Mark 125 Cholmley Gardens, London NW6 1AA — MB ChB 1993 Leeds.

SMITH, Alan McGregor Kenilworth Med. Centre, 1 Kennilworth Court, Glasgow G67 1BP Tel: 01236 727816 Fax: 01236 726306 Email: kenilworthmc@hotmail.com; Hollybank, 2A Mill Road, Riggend By Airdrie ML6 7ST Tel: 01236 830031 — MB ChB 1961 Ed.; MRCGP 1980; DObst RCOG 1963. (Edin. Univ.)

SMITH, Alan Peter Watson Health Centre, Balmellie Road, Turriff AB53 4DQ Tel: 01888 562323 Fax: 01888 568682 — MB ChB 1978 Aberd.

SMITH, Alan Robert 5 Crimond Court, Fraserburgh AB43 9QW — MB ChB 1997 Aberd.

SMITH, Mr Alan Robert Clifton Wrythe Green Surgery, Wrythe Lane, Carshalton SM5 2RE Tel: 020 8669 3232/1717 Fax: 020 8773 2524 — MB BS 1983 Lond.; FRCS Eng. 1989. Prev: Trainee GP Crawley VTS; Regist. Rotat. SW Thames; Cas. Off. & SHO St. Geo. Hosp. Lond.

SMITH, Alan William McIntosh (retired) 29 Links Road, Lundin Links, Leven KY8 6AT Tel: 01333 320221 — MB ChB 1950 Ed.; MB ChB (Hons.) Ed. 1950; FRCP Ed. 1962, M 1952. Hon. Sen. Lect. (Med.) Univ. Edin. Prev: Cons. Phys. Vict. Hosp. Kirkcaldy & E. Fife Gp. Hosps.

SMITH, Alastair Gordon Haematology Department, Southampton General Hospital, Southampton SO16 6YD Tel: 02380 798807, 02380 825335 Fax: 02380 825338 Email: alistair.smith@suht.swest.nhs.uk; 24 Oakenbrow, Sway, Lymington SO41 6DY Tel: 01590 683484 Email: agsmith@tcp.co.uk — MB ChB 1974 Glas.; BSc (Hons.) Glas. 1972; FRCP Lond. 1994; FRCP Glas. 1988; MRCP (UK) 1976; MRCPath 1981. Cons. Haemat, Clin. Director, Clin. Soton. Univ. Hosps.; Hon. Clin. Sen. Lect. Soton. Univ. Socs: Brit. Soc. Haematol.; Amer. Soc. Haemat. Prev: Sen. Regist. (Haemat.) W.. Infirm. Glas.; Regist. (Haemat.) Stobhill Hosp. Glas.; SHO (Med.) Stobhill Hosp. Glas.

SMITH, Alastair William, MBE, OStJ (retired) Wayside, Birkett Hill, Bowness-on-Windermere, Windermere LA23 3EZ Tel: 015394 43658 — LRCP LRCS Ed. LRFPS Glas. 1942. Prev: Clin. Asst. Glas. Roy. Infirm.

SMITH, Albert Edward Centre for Occupational Health & Environmental, University of Manchester, C Block, Humanities Building, Manchester M13 9PL, Switzerland Tel: 0161 275 5202 Fax: 0161 275 5625 Email: ted.smith@man.ac.uk; North Wing, Harewood Lodge, Broadbottom, Hyde SK14 6BB Tel: 01457 762665

SMITH

Email: ted.smith@clara.net — MB BS 1966 Lond.; BSc Lond. 1963; MRCGP 1974; FFOM RCP 1992, MFOM 1983, AFOM 1981; DIH Eng. 1979; DObst RCOG 1968. (Univ. Coll. Hosp.) p/t Sen. Clin. Fell. Centre Occupat.al Health Univ. Manch.; Cons. Occupat. Phys. Roy. Oldham Hosp. Socs: BMA; Soc. Occup. Med.; Brit. Occup. Hyg. Soc. Prev: Corporate Occupat.al Phys. Novartis Internat.; Gp. Occupat.al Phys. Ciba-Geigy UK; Head Med. Serv. UK Atomic Energy Auth. Dounreay Nuclear Power Developm. Estabm.

SMITH, Alexander Charles Allison (retired) 246 Argyll Street, Dunoon PA23 7HW Tel: 01369 703252 Fax: 01369 706680 — MB ChB 1967 Ed.; BSc Ed. 1962; DObst RCOG 1971. Prev: Regist. (Surg.) Belford Hosp. Fort William.

SMITH, Alexander David Stuart 18 Craigleith View, Edinburgh EH4 3JZ — MB ChB 1976 Manch.; BSc (Hons.) St. And. 1969. Med. Adviser Benefits Agency. Prev: Sen. Regist. (Clin. Biochem.) Glas. Roy. Infirm.

SMITH, Alexander Gordon Lochhead (retired) 6 Bishops Close, Old Coulsdon, Coulsdon CR5 1HH Tel: 01737 554576 — MB ChB 1958 Ed.; DFFP 1993; DObst RCOG 1961. Prev: SHO (O & G) Buchanan Hosp. St. Leonards-on-Sea.

SMITH, Alexander James (retired) Foxstones, 29 Friar Crescent, Brighton BN1 6NL Tel: 01273 506566 — MB ChB Aberd. 1953. Prev: Med. Off. RAF Med. Br.

SMITH, Alexander John (retired) The Manor House, Stretton-on-Dunsmore, Rugby CV23 9NA Tel: 01203 542718 — MB BS Lond. 1952; MRCS Eng. LRCP Lond. 1952; FRCPath 1972, M 1963; DPath Eng. 1960. Prev: Cons. Path. Hosp. St. Cross Rugby, Warwick Hosp.Coventry.

SMITH, Mr Alexander McEwen, VRD (retired) 46 Lichfield Lane, Mansfield NG18 4RZ Tel: 01263 25281 — MB ChB Ed. 1939; FRCS Ed. 1948. Prev: Cons. Surg. Mansfield Gen. Hosp. & King's Mill Hosp. Sutton in.

SMITH, Alexander Peter Holmview, Penyturnpike, Derby CF64 4HG Tel: 01222 513231 — MD 1976 Sheff.; MB ChB 1965; FRCP Lond. 1984, M 1968. (Sheff.) Cons. Phys. S. Glam. AHA (T). Socs: Brit. Thoracic Soc. & Brit. Soc. for Allergy & Clin. Immunol. Prev: Lect. (Med.) & Sen. Regist. King's Coll. Hosp. Lond.; MRC Trav. Schol. Marseille France.

SMITH, Alfred Leonard Gordon (retired) 125 Caldercliffe Road, Taylor Hill, Huddersfield HD4 7RH Tel: 01484 532332 — MB ChB Glas. 1947; FRCPsych 1971; DPM RCPSI 1950. Prev: Med. Supt. Storthes Hall Hosp. & Cons. Psychiat. St. Luke's Hosp. Huddersfield.

SMITH, Alison Church View Surgery, School La, Collingham, Wetherby LS22 5BQ Tel: 01937 573848 Fax: 01937 574754; Shrewton House, Harewood Road, Collingham, Wetherby LS22 5BY Tel: 01937 572280 — MB ChB 1967 Ed.; DObst 1973 (NZ); MRCP (UK) 1970; DCH RCP Lond. 1974.

SMITH, Alison Doreen Northbourne Medical Centre, Eastern Avenue, Shoreham-by-Sea BN43 6PE; Magnolia House, 49 Southwick St, Southwick, Brighton BN42 4TH Tel: 01273 593963 Fax: 01273 593963 — MB ChB 1978 Birm.; MRCGP 1984; DFFP 1993; DRCOG 1980. (Birm.) Chair Adur PCG. Prev: Non-Exec. Dir. W. Sussex HA.

SMITH, Alison Duff Craig Nevis Surgery, Belford Road, Fort William PH33 6BU Tel: 01397 702947 Fax: 01397 700655 — MB ChB 1985 Dundee.

SMITH, Alison Elisabeth Exwick Health Centre, New Valley Road, Exwick, Exeter EX4 2AD Tel: 01392 270063 Fax: 01392 431884 — MB ChB 1985 Sheff.; MRCGP 1990. GP Princip.

SMITH, Alison Elizabeth Castle Douglas Medical Group, Castle Douglas Health Centre, Academy Sreett, Castle Douglas DG7 1EE Tel: 01556 503888 Fax: 01556 504302 — MB ChB 1985 Ed.

SMITH, Alison Jane Westerhope Medical Group, 377 Stamfordham Road, Westerhope, Newcastle upon Tyne NE5 2LH Tel: 0191 243 7000 Fax: 0191 243 7006; 29 First Avenue, Newcastle upon Tyne NE6 5YE — MB BS 1987 Newc.; MRCGP 1991; DRCOG 1991. Prev: Trainee GP/SHO (Psychiat.) St. Geo. Hosp. N.d.; Trainee GP/SHO (A & E) Qu. Eliz. Hosp. Gateshead.

SMITH, Alison Jane Dept Anaesthesia, Weston General Hospital, Grange Road, Weston Super Mare BS23 4TQ Tel: 01934 647162 — MB BS 1988 Lond.; BSc Lond. 1985; DA (UK) 1990; FRCA 1993. Cons. (Anaesth.) W.on Gen Hosp.

SMITH, Alison Jane 8 Huddersfield Road, New Mill, Huddersfield HD9 7JU — MB ChB 1997 Glas.

SMITH, Alison Kay A & E Department, Barnsley District General Hospital, Gawber Road, Barnsley S75 2EP Tel: 01226 730000 — MB ChB 1990; FFAEM 1999; MB ChB Sheff. 1990; MRCP (UK) 1995. Cons. Emergengy Med., Barnsley Dist. Gen. Hosp.

SMITH, Alison Lindsay Church View Surgery, 14 Church View, Dundrum, Newcastle BT33 0NA; 50 Sunningdale Drive, Newcastle BT33 0QJ Tel: 013967 23983 — MB ChB 1982 Ed.; BSc (Hons.) Ed. 1979, MB ChB 1982. Trainee GP Newc. VTS. Prev: SHO (Psychiat., Geriat & Cas.) Roy. Vict. Hosp. Edin.

SMITH, Alistair Fairley Department of Clinical Biochemistry, Royal Infirmary, Edinburgh EH3 9YW Tel: 0131 536 2758 Fax: 0131 229 3543 Email: a.f.smith@ed.ac.uk; 38 Cammo Road, Edinburgh EH4 8AP Tel: 0131 339 4931 Fax: 0131 339 9113 — MB BChir 1961 Camb.; MA Camb. 1957, MD 1971; FRCP Ed. 1973, M 1965; FRCPath 1979, M 1967. (Lond. Hosp.) Sen. Lect. (Clin. Biochem.) Roy. Infirm. Edin. Prev: Ho. Phys. Lond. Hosp. & Addenbrooke's Hosp. Camb.; Jun. Asst. Path. Univ. Camb.

SMITH, Allison Lucy Blair Schopwick Surgery, Everett Court, Romeland, Elstree, Borehamwood WD6 3BJ Tel: 020 8953 1008 Fax: 020 8905 2196; 77 Upper Paddock Road, Oxhey Village WD19 4DY Email: alisonsmith77@aol.com — MRCGP 1993; BSc 1982; MB BS 1987 London; MB BS 1987 London. (Royal Free Hospital School of Medicine)

SMITH, Amanda 79 Farquhar Road, Edgbaston, Birmingham B15 2QP — MB ChB 1983 Leic.; MBA 1993; DA (UK) 1985.

SMITH, Amanda Elizabeth Rachel 18 Westfield Garden, Chesterfield S40 3SN — MB BS 1987 Lond.; MFFP (1) 1997; MRCGP 1993; DFFP 1993; DRCOG 1992. (Guy's Hosp. Lond.) Clin. Med. Off. (Family Plann. & Wom.'s Health) Chesterfield & Mansfield. Socs: Soc. Advancem. of Sexual Health; N. InterBr. Doctors GP (Affil.d to FFPRHC). Prev: Med. Coding Author NHS Centre for Coding & cl.ification LoughBoro.; Asst. GP Chesterfield; Clin. Asst. (Genitourin. Med.) Redford.

SMITH, Amanda Jean The Garth Surgery, Westgate, Guisborough TS14 6AT Tel: 01287 632206 Fax: 01287 635112; 10 Sandwood Park, Hutton Gate, Guisborough TS14 8EH — MB BS 1982 Lond.; MRCGP 1986; DRCOG 1985. (Royal Free) Socs: Primary Care Rheum. Soc.; Local Med. Comm. Prev: Clin. Asst. Carter Bequest Hosp. Middlesboro.; Trainee GP/SHO (Med.) Middlesbrough Gen. Hosp.; Trainee GP/SHO (O & G) N. Tees Hosp.

SMITH, Amy 135/C Newby House, South Cleveland Hospital, Marton Road, Middlesbrough TS4 3TJ — MB ChB 1994 Manch.

SMITH, Andrew Medway Hospital, Windmill Road, Gillingham ME7 5NY Tel: 01634 830000 — MB BS 1990 Lond.; BSc (Hons.) 1987; MRCP (UK) 1994. Regist. (Diabetes, Endocrinol. & Gen. Med.) Medway Hosp. Gillingham.

SMITH, Andrew Combe Down Surgery, Combe Down House, The Avenue, Combe Down, Bath BA2 5EG Tel: 01225 832226 Fax: 01225 840757 Email: andrew.smith@GP_l81065.nhs.uk — MB BS 1989 Lond.; BSc Lond. 1986; MRCGP 1995; DRCOG 1995; DCH RCP Lond. 1993. (Univesity College London) GP. Prev: Non Princip. GP Bath; Sen. Med. Off. Aboriginal Med. Serv. Carnarvon, W.ern Australia; GP Regist. Bath VTS.

SMITH, Andrew Douglas 8 Bishopsmill Ct, 212 Old Dumbarton Rd, Glasgow G3 8QB — MB ChB 1997 Glas.

SMITH, Andrew Edward Rodney The Old Rectory Surgery, 18 Castle Street, Saffron Walden CB10 1BP Tel: 01799 522327 Fax: 01799 525436 — MB BS 1972 Lond.; BSc (Anat.) Lond. 1969; MRCS Eng. LRCP Lond. 1972; DObst RCOG 1976. (Westm.) Prev: Trainee GP Camb. VTS; SHO Auckland Pub. Hosp. Auckland, NZ; Ho. Off. (Med.) W. Middlx. Hosp. Isleworth.

SMITH, Andrew Fairley Department of Anaesthesia, Royal Lancaster Infirmary, Ashton Road, Lancaster LA1 4RP Tel: 01524 583517 Fax: 01524 583519 Email: andrew.smith@i.bay-tr.nwest.nhs.uk — MB BS 1988 Newc.; MRCP (UK) 1991; FRCA 1994. Cons. Anaesth. Morecambe Bay Hosps. NHS Trust; Hon. Research Fell. in Anaesth. Univ. of Manch.; Hon. Research Fell., Inst. for Health Research, Lancaster Univ. Socs: Fell. Manch. Med. Soc.; Assn. Anaesth.; Assn. for Study of Med. Educat. Prev: Sen. Regist. (Anaesth.) NW RHA; SHO (Gen. Med.) Stepping Hill Hosp. Stockport; Ho. Phys. Freeman Hosp. Newc. u Tyne.

SMITH, Andrew George Ellesmere, 2 Sutherland Drive, Newcastle ST5 3NB Tel: 01782 614512 — MB BChir Camb. 1970; MD Camb. 1982; FRCP Lond. 1989; MRCP (UK) 1972; MRCS Eng. LRCP Lond.

1969. (Camb. & St. Mary's) Cons. Dermat. N. Staffs. Hosp. Centre Stoke on Trent & Staffs. Dist. Gen. Hosp. Prev: Sen. Regist. & Wellcome Research Fell. (Dermat.) Newc. Univ.; Ho. Phys. (Med.) St. Mary's Hosp. Lond.

SMITH, Andrew Gourdie Path House Medical Practice, Path House, Nether Street, Kirkcaldy KY1 2PG Tel: 01592 644533 Fax: 01592 644550; 20 Townsend Crescent, Kirkcaldy KY1 1DN — MB ChB 1977 Ed. Prev: Trainee GP W. Lothian VTS; Ho. Phys. Bangour Gen. Hosp. Broxburn; Ho. Surg. Peel Hosp. Galashiels.

SMITH, Andrew Gregory College Surgery Partnership, College Rd, Cullompton EX15 1TG Tel: 01884 831300 Fax: 01884 831313 Email: andy.smith@gp-l83092.nhs.uk — MB ChB 1991 Bristol; BSc (Microbiol.) 1988; MRCGP 1997; DCH 1996; DRCOG 1995. (Bristol) GP Cullompton, Devon.

SMITH, Andrew James Barrow Hospital, Barrow Gurney, Bristol BS48 3SG — MB BS 1987 Lond. SHO (Geriat. Med.) St. Stephens Hosp. Lond.

SMITH, Mr Andrew Malvern — MB BS 1991 Lond.; BSc (Hons.) Lond. 1989; FRCS Eng. 1995; DM Nottm. 1999. (St. Mary's Hospital) Lect. (Surg.) Univ. of Hull; Hon. Specialist Regist. (Gen. Surg.) Mid-Trent Rotat.; Specialist Regist. (Gen. Surg.). Socs: Surg. Research Soc.; Assn. Surg. Train.; Assn. of Upper Gastrointestinal Surg.s. Prev: Research Fell. & Hon. Regist. (Surg.) Univ. Nottm.; SHO Rotat. (Surg.) Leicester; Lect. (Surg.) Univ. of Nottm.

SMITH, Andrew Michael Flat 9, 1-2 Percival Terrace, Brighton BN2 1FA — MB BS 1993 Lond.

SMITH, Andrew Neil Leigh View Medical Centre, Bradford Road, Tingley, Wakefield WF3 1RQ Tel: 0113 253 7629 Fax: 0113 238 1286 — MB ChB 1984 Leeds; MRCGP 1991. Prev: Trainee GP/SHO (A & E) Dewsbury Dist. HA VTS.

SMITH, Mr Angus 42 Kenilworth Road, Bridge of Allan, Stirling FK9 4RP Tel: 01786 833455 — MB ChB 1976 Glas.; BSc (Hons.) Glas. 1974, MB ChB 1976; FRCS Ed. 1993; FRCS Glas. 1981. Cons. Surg. Stirling Roy. Infirm.

SMITH, Mr Angus Cameron (retired) 1103 Aikenhead Road, Cathcart, Glasgow G44 5SL — MB ChB 1950 Glas.; FRCS Glas. 1962; FRFPS Glas. 1961; DLO Eng. 1954. Prev: Cons. ENT Surg. Vict. Infirm. Glas. & S. Gen. Hosp. Glas.

SMITH, Anina Mary Brindley 34 Rugby Road, Bulkington, Nuneaton — MB ChB 1975 Manch.

SMITH, Anna Elizabeth Clark Kirkhall Surgery, 4 Alexandra Avenue, Prestwick KA9 1AW Tel: 01292 476626 Fax: 01292 678022 — MB ChB 1973 Aberd.; DRCOG 1977.

SMITH, Anna Isabella (retired) 19 St Clare Road, Colchester CO3 3SZ Tel: 01206 574592 — MB BCh BAO 1950 Dub. Prev: Clin. Asst. (Dermat.) Essex Co. Hosp. Colchester.

SMITH, Anna Mary Louise Merchiston Surgery, Highworth Road, Swindon SN3 4BF Tel: 01793 823307 Fax: 01793 820923 — MB BS 1990 Lond.; MRCGP 1994; DRCOG 1994; DFFP 1994. p/t GP Partner Swindon.

SMITH, Annabelle Toni Maria 185 Barnfield Avenue, Kingston upon Thames KT2 5RQ Tel: 020 8549 9003 — MB BS 1993 Lond. Prev: SHO (paed) St Geo.'s Hosp.; SHO (Paediat.) Chelsea & W.minster Hosp.

SMITH, Anne Helen Walmsley 19 Hazel Drive, Dundee DD2 1QQ — MB ChB 1969 St. And.; MRCPsych 1974. (St. And.) Cons. Psychiat. Roy. Dundee Liff Hosp. Prev: Lect. in Psychiat. Univ. Dundee.

SMITH, Anne Louise 45 Conduit Road, Stamford PE9 1QL Tel: 01780 762940 Email: phil.zeidler@virgin.net — MB ChB 1992 Leic.; MRCP (UK) 1996. (Leicester) Regist. (Paediat.) P'boro. Dist. Hosp. Socs: Roy. Soc. Med. Prev: SHO (Paediat. Cardiol.) Glenfield Hosp. Leicester; SHO (Paediat.) P'boro. & Leicester Roy. Infirm.

SMITH, Anne Margaret Smith (retired) 34 Lsulworth Lodge, 5 Palatine Road, Southport PR8 2BS Tel: 01704 566141 — MB ChB 1939 Aberd.

SMITH, Anne Patricia Mary 15 Station Road E., Peterculter, Aberdeen — MB ChB 1977 Aberd.; MD Aberd. 1994; DRCOG 1984. Assoc. Specialist (Ultrasonics & Colposcopy) & Hon. Lect. (O & G) Aberd. Matern. Hosp. Socs: Brit. Med. Ultrasound Soc. (Counc. & Scientif. Educat. Advis. Comm.).

SMITH, Anne Vera Shieldfield Health Centre, Stoddart Street, Shieldfield, Newcastle upon Tyne NE2 1AL Tel: 0191 232 4872; 6 The Crescent, Longbenton, Newcastle upon Tyne NE7 7ST Tel: 0191 215 0268 Fax: 0191 270 2151 Email: anne.smith@btinternet.com — MB BS 1966 Newc. (Newc.) Specialist (Psychosexual Med.) Newc. HA. Socs: Inst. Psychosexual Med. (Director of Train.); Inst. Psychosexual Med.

SMITH, Anthony Bernard Upton Group Practice, 32 Ford Road, Wirral CH49 0TF Tel: 0151 677 0486 Fax: 0151 604 0635; Roseneath, Arno Road, Oxton, Prenton CH43 5UX Tel: 0151 652 1108 Email: drabsmith@aol.com — MB ChB 1984 Leeds; BSc (Hons.) Leeds 1981; MRCGP 1989; DFFP 1993; DRCOG 1987. (Leeds) Prev: Trainee GP Burnley Gen. Hosp. VTS; SHO (Clin. Path.) Roy. Hallamsh. Hosp. Sheff.

SMITH, Anthony Clive Mill House, Higher Wych, Malpas SY14 7JR — MB ChB 1998 Manch.; MB ChB Manch 1998.

SMITH, Anthony David Addison Derby Psychotherapy Unit, Temple House, Mill Hill Lane, Derby DE23 6SB Tel: 01332 364512; 59 South Avenue, Darley Abbey, Derby DE22 1FB — MB BS 1976 Newc.; MRCPsych 1981; Dip. Psychother. Leeds 1985. Cons. Psychother. (Community Psychiat. Servs.) S.. Derbysh. HA. Prev: Sen. Regist. (Psychother.) St. Jas. Hosp. Leeds.

SMITH, Anthony Derek Kinmylies Medical Practice, Charleston Court, Assynt Road, Inverness IV3 6PB Tel: 01463 239865 Fax: 01463 711218 — MB ChB 1971 Ed.; MRCPCH 1998; FRCP Ed. 1997; MRCP (UK) 1980; DCH RCPS Glas. 1974. (Ed.) Assoc. Adviser in Gen. Pract. N. Scotl.; Hosp. Pract. GUM.; Med. Adviser Highland Counc.; Police Surg. Socs: Div.al Hon. Sec. BMA; SACCH; Vice-Pres. Highland Med. Soc.

SMITH, Mr Anthony Mighell Pilgrim's Hospice, 56 London Road, Canterbury CT2 8JA Tel: 01227 459700 Fax: 01227 812606 Email: jc.pilgrims@dial.pipex.com; Gillrock House, Main Road, Sellindge, Ashford TN25 6AQ — MB BChir Camb. 1963; MA Camb. 1963; FRCS Ed. 1972; T(M) 1990; DObst RCOG 1964; Cert. Med. Educat. Univ. of Dundee 1998. (Camb. & St. Geo.) Med. Dir. Pilgrims' Hospices of E. Kent, Canterbury & Margate and Ashford. Socs: Assn. Palliat. Med.; Christ. Med. Fell.sh. Prev: Dir. of Studies St. Christopher's Hospice Sydenham; Med. Dir. St. Francis Hospice Romford; Assoc. Specialist (Orthop. & A & E) E. Reach Hosp. Taunton.

SMITH, Anthony Richard The Surgery, Chilton Place, Ash, Canterbury CT3 2HD Tel: 01304 812227 Fax: 01304 813788 — MB BS 1981 Lond.; DRCOG 1987.

SMITH, Anthony Ross Broadhurst 23 Anson Road, Victoria Park, Manchester M14 5BZ Tel: 0161 225 1616 Fax: 0161 225 6488 Email: asmith@ugynae.cmht.nwest.nhs.uk; Foden Bank Farm, Byrons Lane, Macclesfield SK11 0HA Tel: 01625 614102 — MB ChB 1977 Manch.; BSc St. And. 1974; MD Manch. 1985; FRCOG 1995, M 1982. Cons. Gyn. St Mary's Hosp. Manch. Socs: Pres. Brit. Soc. Gyn. Endoscopy. Prev: Lect. Jessop Hosp. Sheff.; Research Regist. (O & G) St. Mary's Hosp. Manch.; Regist. (O & G) St. Mary's Hosp. Manch.

SMITH, Mr Antony Langley The Lea, South Cresent Road, Queens Park, Chester CH4 7AU Email: tonys@dial.pipex.com — MB ChB 1989 Ed.; FRCS Ed. 1995; FRCS Eng. 1995. (Edin.) Specialist Regist. (Orthop.) Robt. Jones & Agnes Hunt Orthop. Hosp. OsW.ry. Socs: Assoc. Mem. BOA. Prev: Maj RAMC.

SMITH, Archibald Brian (retired) Cove Villa, 83 Hecklegirth, Annan DG12 6HL Tel: 01461 203250 Fax: 01461 203250 Email: archie@covevilla.freeserve.co.uk — MB ChB St. And. 1969.

SMITH, Arthur Gourdin (retired) 2A Cliff Avenue, Cromer NR27 0AN Tel: 01263 512678 — MB ChB 1937 Ed.; MA Ed. 1937. Prev: Resid. Med. Off. City. Gen. Hosp. Carlisle.

SMITH, Arthur Hopper Low Reins Gill, Middleton-in-Teesdale, Barnard Castle DL12 0RY Tel: 01833 640502 — MB BS 1955 Durh. Locum Gen. Practitioner.

SMITH, Arthur Thomas Stockton Heath Medical Centre, The Forge, London Road, Stockton Heath, Warrington WA4 6HJ Tel: 01925 604427; 36 Kildonan Road, Grappenhall, Warrington WA4 2LJ — MB BCh 1971 Wales; MRCGP 1978. Prev: Ho. Phys. & Ho. Surg. Roy. Alexandra Hosp. Rhyl.

SMITH, Ashley Lee Nicola Flat 5, 4 Wandle Road, Morden SM4 6AH — MB BS 1996 Lond.

SMITH, Audrey Christine 116 Ainsworth Road, Bury BL8 2RX — MB ChB 1997 Liverp.

SMITH, Augustine Martin James 37 Church Road, Hayes UB3 2LB — MB BCh BAO 1993 NUI; LRCPSI 1993.

SMITH

SMITH, Mr Austen Thornton 94 Monthermer Road, Cardiff CF24 4QY — MB BCh 1988 Wales; FRCS Ed. 1991.

SMITH, Averil Joy Epping, 15 Windermere Road, Wrexham LL12 8AG Tel: 01978 364256 — MB ChB 1949 St. And. (St. And.) Socs: BMA. Prev: Asst. MOH Co. Denbighsh.; Ho. Surg. (Obst.) Elsie Inglis Matern. Hosp. Edin.; Ho. Surg. Qu. Mary's Hosp. For E. End.

SMITH, Barbara Anne New Cumnock Surgery, 67 Afton Bridgend, New Cumnock, Cumnock KA18 4BA Tel: 01290 338242 Fax: 01290 332010 — MB ChB 1982 Glas.; BSc Glas. 1979, MB ChB 1982. SHO (Gyn.) CrossHo. Hosp. Kilmarnock. Socs: BMA; Inceptor of Roy. Coll. Psychiat. Prev: Jun. Ho. Off. (Med. & Surg.) Glas. Roy. Infirm.; SHO (Psychiat.) Woodilee Hosp. Gtr. Glas. Health Bd.; Regist. (Psychiat.) Woodilee Hosp. Gtr. Glas. Health Bd.

SMITH, Barrie Stanley 104 Kingsbury Road, Erdington, Birmingham B24 8QU Tel: 0121 373 6740 — MB ChB 1956 Birm.; FRCP Lond. 1978, M 1964; MRCS Eng. LRCP Lond. 1956. Med. Off., Aston Villa FC. Prev: Cons. Phys. Sandwell Dist. Gen. Hosp. (Retd.); Ho. Phys. Qu. Eliz. Hosp. Birm.; Cons. Phys. W. Bromwich Hosp. Gp.

SMITH, Barry Sabden & Whalley Medical Group, 42 King St., Whalley, Clitheroe BB7 9SL Tel: 01254 823273 Fax: 01254 824891; The Old Vicarage, Mitton, Whalley, Blackburn BB6 9PH Tel: 01254 826473 — MB ChB 1962 Manch.; DObst RCOG 1964; FRCGP 1990, M 1970; Cert Contracep. & Family Plann. RCOG & RCGP 1974.

SMITH, Barry Arthur Charles, TD Whitehouse Farm, Miles Green, Stoke-on-Trent ST7 8LQ — MB ChB 1975 Birm.; FRCA 1980. Cons. Anaesth. N. Staffs. Hosp. NHS Trust. Socs: Midl. Anaesth. Soc.; Anaesth. Soc. Prev: Asst. Prof. Univ. Texas Med. Sch. Houston, USA; Sen. Regist. (Anaesth.) Midl. Train. Scheme.

SMITH, Basil John 13A Rawlinson Road, Oxford OX2 6UE — MB BS 1978 Lond.; DPhil Oxf. 1964; BSc Lond. 1961; MRCP (UK) 1981; FRCR 1986. (St. Bart.) Cons. Clin. Oncol. New Cross Hosp. Wolverhampton. Prev: Sen. Regist. (Radiother. & Oncol.) Univ. Coll. Hosp. Lond.; Regist. (Radiother. & Oncol.) W.m. Hosp.; SHO Nuffield Dept. Med. John Radcliffe Hosp. Oxf.

SMITH, Benjamin John 15 (2Fl) Gladstone Terrace, Edinburgh EH9 1LS — MB ChB 1994 Ed.

SMITH, Blair Hamilton Dept. of General Practice & Primary Care, University of Aberdeen, Foresterhill Health Centre, Westburn Road, Aberdeen AB25 2AY Tel: 01224 553972 Email: blairsmith@abdn.ac.uk; North Arnybogs, Methlick, Ellon AB41 7BT — MB ChB 1987 Glas.; MRCGP 1993; DFFP 1993; MD 2000 Aberdeen; MEd. 1998 Aberdeen. (1). Sen. Lect. in Gen. Pract., Univ. of Aberd., (2). GP Deveron Med. Pract., Banff; Surg. Lt. Cdr., Roy. Naval Reserve HMS Scotia, Rosyth. Socs: Assn. of Univ. Dept.s of Gen. Pract.; Internat. Epidemicological Assn. Prev: SHO (Endocrinol. & Infertil.) Jessop Hosp. for Wom. Sheff.; SHO (O & G) N.. Gen. Hosp., Aberd. Roy. Infirm. & Jessop Hosp. Sheff.; GP Trainee, Aberd.

SMITH, Brendan Edward The Berrow Hill Medical Centre, Berrow Hill, Feckenham, Redditch B96 6QS — MB ChB 1977 Sheff.; FFA RCS Eng. 1984.

SMITH, Brendon Glenn Timperley Health Centre, 169 Grove Lane, Timperley, Altrincham WA15 6PH — MB ChB 1980 Manch.; MRCGP 1984; DCH RCP Lond. 1983; DRCOG 1982; Cert. Family Plann. JCC 1982. Princip. GP Timperley.

SMITH, Brent Charles Howden Well Close Square Surgery, Well Close Square, Berwick-upon-Tweed TD15 1LL Tel: 01289 356920 Fax: 01289 356939 — MB ChB 1970 St. And.; LMCC 1972; DA Eng. 1977; DObst RCOG 1974. Hosp. Pract. (Anaesth.) Berwick Infirm. Socs: Coll. Phys. & Surg. Brit.; Columbia & Fac. Anaesth. RCS Eng.

SMITH, Mr Brian David (retired) 38 Fiskerton Road, Cherry Willingham, Lincoln LN3 4AP Tel: 01522 751603 Fax: 01522 751603 — MB ChB 1957 St. And.; FRCS Eng. 1967. Cons. Mem. Med. Appeals Tribunal Nottm. Prev: Sen. Cons. Orthop. Surg. Lincoln N. DHA.

SMITH, Brian Hall (retired) 26 Metchley Park Road, Edgbaston, Birmingham B15 2PG Tel: 0121 454 6538 — MB ChB Birm. 1948; MRCS Eng. LRCP Lond. 1948; FRCA 1954. Prev: Cons. Anaesth. Qu. Eliz. Hosp. Birm.

SMITH, Brian James 43 West Bank, Abbotts Park, Chester CH1 4BD — MB ChB 1987 Birm.

SMITH, Brian Leslie Wexham Park Hospital, Slough SL2 4HL Tel: 01753 633000 Fax: 01753 634460; Fairview, River Road, Taplow, Maidenhead SL6 0BG Tel: 01628 674321 Fax: 01628 621845 — MB BS Lond. 1962; MRCS Eng. LRCP Lond. 1962; DObst RCOG 1963; FRCA. 1970. (St. Mary's) Clin. Dir. Anaesth. Heatherwood & Wexham Pk. Hosp. Trust. Socs: Assn. Anaesths., B.M.A., H.C.S.A. Prev: Sen. Regist. (Anaesth.) Middlx. Hosp. Lond.; Asst. Anaesth. S.well Hosp. (Kuwait Oil Co.) Ahmadi, Kuwait; Asst. Prof. Anaesth. Univ. Calif. San Francisco, USA.

SMITH, Brian Spencer (retired) LongFriday Fieldhouse, Canon Pyon Road, Hereford HR4 7SL Tel: 01432 263498 — MB BS Lond. 1955; MRCS Eng. LRCP Lond. 1955. Prev: Gen. Pract. Ross-on-Wye.

SMITH, Brian Thomas Rickleton, Washington NE38 9HR — MB BS 1989 Newc.

SMITH, Brigid Teresa Mary Health Centre, Great James Street, Londonderry BT48 7DH Tel: 028 7136 4016 — MB BCh BAO 1981 Belf.; FRCGP 1997; MRCGP 1986; DRCOG 1984.

SMITH, Bruce Alexander Murison (retired) 197 Millhouses Lane, Sheffield S7 2HF Tel: 0114 361870 — MB ChB 1956 Leeds; FRCP Ed. 1978, M 1962; DCH Eng. 1959; DObst RCOG 1960. Prev: Cons. Paediat. N.. Gen. Hosp. Sheff.

SMITH, Cameron Cairns 198 Rullion Road, Penicuik EH26 9JF — MB ChB 1991 Aberd.

SMITH, Carlyle Wilhelm Ernst 213 Northdown Park Road, Margate CT9 3UJ — MB BS Ceylon 1958; FRCP Lond. 1981, M 1968. (Colombo) JP; Cons. Phys. (Geriat.) I. of Thanet & Canterbury Hosp. Gp. Socs: Brit. Geriat. Soc.; BMA. Prev: Regist. (Med.) Croydon Gen. Hosp.; Cons. Chest Phys. Canterbury Hosp. Gp.

SMITH, Carol Ann Woodeside Health Centre, Barr Street, Glasgow G20 7LR Tel: 0141 531 9570 Fax: 0141 531 9572 — MB ChB 1970 Glas.

SMITH, Carol Jane 31 Crosslet Vale, Greenwich, London SE10 8DH Tel: 020 8691 9642 — MB BS 1992 Lond. (Kings College, London University) Staff Grade (Community Paediat.) Community Health S. Lond. NHS Trust. Prev: Clin. Med. Off. (Community Paediat.) W. Lambeth.

SMITH, Caroline Anne 9 Argyle House, Ham St., Richmond TW10 7HD — MB BS 1993 Lond.

SMITH, Caroline Anne 84 Reservoir Road, Solihull B92 8AR — BM BS 1997 Nottm.

SMITH, Caroline Donna 3 Chaldon Close, Redhill RH1 6SX — MB BS 1994 Newc. SHO (Oncol.) Derbysh. Roy. Infirm. Derby.

SMITH, Caroline Eunice Department of Anaesthetics, Warrington District Hospital, Lovely Lane, Warrington WA5 1QG Tel: 01925 635911 — MB ChB 1988 Manch.; FRCA 1993; FFA RCSI 1992. Cons. Anaesth. Warrington Hosp.

SMITH, Caroline Frances 28 Okefield Road, Crediton EX17 2DL — MB BS 1990 Newc. SHO (Psychiat.) Barrow Hosp., Flexible Trainee, Psychiat. Wonford Ho. Hosp.,Exeter. Prev: Trainee GP Backwell, Avon.; Flexible Traniee; Psychiat. Bristol.

SMITH, Caroline Margaret Stone Hill House, West Hoathly Road, East Grinstead RH19 4HW — MB BS 1984 Lond.; MRCGP 1991. (Univ. Lond. & Char. Cross) Socs: BMA. Prev: Trainee GP Lightwater, Surrey; Asst. GP E. Grinstead.

SMITH, Carolyn Margaret Braehead, St. Margaret's Drive, Dunblane FK15 0DP — MB ChB 1983 Glas.; MRCP (UK) 1989; FFA RCS Eng. 1994; DRCOG 1986. Staff Grade (Anaesth.) Falkirk NHS Trust.

SMITH, Carolyn Sarah Northville Family Practice, 521 Filton Avenue, Horfield, Bristol BS7 0LS Tel: 0117 969 2164 Fax: 0117 931 5743 — MB BCh 1983 Wales.

SMITH, Carolyne Dawn Meadowside Family Health Centre, 30 Winchcombe Road, Solihull B92 8PJ Tel: 0121 743 2560 — MB ChB 1990 Birm.; MRCGP 1996; DRCOG 1993. (Birm.) p/t GP Meadowside Surg. Solihull; Clin. Asst. Dermatol. Solihull Hosp. Socs: BSMDH. Prev: Trainee GP/SHO E. Birm. Hosp. VTS; Ho. Off. Dudley Rd. & Goodhope Hosps.

SMITH, Mrs Catharine Elizabeth (retired) 19 Moira Road, Ashby-de-la-Zouch LE65 2GB Tel: 01530 415287 — MB BS 1945 Lond.; MRCS Eng. LRCP Lond. 1944. Prev: SCMO Leics. HA.

SMITH, Catherine 7 Holford Way, Newton-le-Willows WA12 0BZ — MB ChB 1998 Manch.; MB ChB Manch 1998.

SMITH, Catherine Anne 109 Queens Den, Aberdeen AB15 8BN — MB ChB 1993 Aberd.

SMITH, Catherine Anne Dunlule, 1 Ben Rhydding Drive, Ilkley LS29 8AY — MB ChB 1998 Dund.; MB ChB Dund 1998.

SMITH, Catherine Claire The Facts Centre, 23/25 Weston Park, London N8 9SY Tel: 020 8348 9195 Fax: 020 8340 5864; 7 Devonshire Place, London W1G 6HW — MB BChir 1985 Camb.; PhD Camb. 1987; BSc (Hons.) Lond. 1978. Med. Dir. Facts Centre Lond. Socs: BMA & Anglo-French Med. Soc. Prev: Regist. (Genitourin. Med.) Roy. Lond. Hosp.; Ho. Phys. Addenbrooke's Hosp. Camb.

SMITH, Catherine Gaynor St. Luke's (Cheshire) Hospice, Grosvenor House, Queensway, Winsford CW7 4AW Tel: 01606 551246 Fax: 01606 861129; 33 Rushton Drive, Middlewich CW10 0NJ Tel: 01606 737108 — MB ChB 1982 Manch.; MRCGP 1990; Dip. Palliat. Med. Wales 1991; DRCOG 1986. (Manch.) Med. Dir. St. Luke's Hospice Chesh.; Hon. Cons. (Palliat. Med.) Mid Chesh. Hosps. Trust.

SMITH, Catherine Howard Department of Dermatology, University Hospital Lewisham, Lewisham High St., London SE13 6LH Tel: 020 8333 3000 Fax: 020 8333 3096 — MB BS 1986 Lond.; FRCP 2001; MD Lond. 1994; MRCP (UK) 1989. Cons. & Sen. Lect. (Dermat.) Univ. Hosp. Lewisham. & St. John's Inst. Dermat. St. Thos. Hosp. Lond. Prev: Sen. Regist. St. John's Inst. Dermat. St. Thos. Hosp. Lond.; Regist. Guy's Hosp. Lond.

SMITH, Catherine Louise 62 Fentiman Road, London SW8 1LF — MB BS 1993 Lond.

SMITH, Catriona Margaret Argyll and Clyde Health Board, Ross House, Hawkhead Road, Paisley PA2 7BN Tel: 0141 842 7208 Fax: 0141 848 0165 Email: catriona.smith@achb.scot.nhs.uk; Email: csmith@ntlworld.com — MB ChB 1984 Glas.; BSc Glas. 1981; MPH Glas. 1995; MRCOG 1989; MRCGP 1988; MFPHM 1998. (Glasgow University) Cons. (Pub. Health Med.) Argyll & Clyde HB.

SMITH, Cecil Conway (retired) 4 Orchard Court, Tenbury Wells WR15 8EZ — MB BS 1941 Durh.; DMRD Eng. 1949. Prev: Cons. Radiol. Ashington, Alnwick & Berwick Hosps.

SMITH, Cecilia Catherine Mary 143 Rochdale Road, Abbey Wood, London SE2 0UR — MB BS 1976 Lond.; MRCS Eng. LRCP Lond. 1976; DCH Eng. 1979.

SMITH, Charles Christopher Wards 25/26 and the Infection Unit, Aberdeen Royal Hospitals NHS Trust, Aberdeen Royal Infirmary, Foresterhill, Aberdeen AB25 2ZN Tel: 01224 681818; Lynston Park, Maryculter, Aberdeen AB12 5GJ Tel: 01224 732878 Fax: 01224 840919 — MB ChB Ed. 1963; FRCP Lond. 1994; FRCP Ed. 1977; MRCP (UK) 1967. Cons. Phys. & Head of Serv. Infec. & Trop. Med. Infec. Unit Aberd. Roy. Infirm.; Clin. Sen. Lect. (Med). Univ. Aberd.; Examr. MB Finals, MRCP (UK), PLABS, LRCP & S (UK); Extern. Examr. MB Univ. Dundee, M.Med Malaysia & MRCP Hong Kong & Malaysia; Mem. UEB. Socs: Assn. Phys.; Brit. Soc. Infec. & Antimicrob. Chemother. Prev: Sen. Regist. (Infec. Dis.) City Hosp. Edin. & (Med. & Therap.) Roy. Infirm. Edin.; Regist. Univ. Dept. Med. & Thoracic Med. Edin.; Invited Lect. Hong Kong, Singapore, Malaysia, Zimbabwe, Kenya, Saudi Arabia, Irel. & S. Afr.

SMITH, Mr Charles William (retired) 21 Shipton Road, York YO30 5RE Tel: 01904 653500 — MB BS 1948 Lond.; FRCS Eng. 1954; MRCS Eng. LRCP Lond. 1947; DLO Eng. 1950. Mem. Ct. Examrs. RCS Eng. Prev: Hon. Cons. Surg. (ENT) York Hosps.

SMITH, Charles William Lauder (retired) 74 Twyford Avenue, London N2 9NN Tel: 020 8883 6868 — MB BS 1963 Lond.; MRCS Eng. LRCP Lond. 1962; MRCGP 1973; DObst RCOG 1964.

SMITH, Cheryl Christine 4 Swisspine Gardens, St Helens WA9 5UE — MB ChB 1990 Liverp.

SMITH, Christine Anne (retired) 23/7 Clarence Street, Edinburgh EH3 5AE Tel: 0131 556 5515 Email: c.a.smith@ukgateway.net — MB ChB 1959 St. And.; DA Eng. 1963. Prev: GP Stranraer Health Centre.

SMITH, Christine Mary Lee Department of Neuropathology, Royal Hallamshire Hospital, Glossop Road, Sheffield S10 2JF Tel: 0114 271 2949 Fax: 0114 271 2200; 10 Moorbank Close, Sheffield S10 5TP — MB ChB Sheff. 1969; BA Oxf. 1966; FRCPath 1986. Cons. Neuropath. Roy. Hallamsh. Hosp. Sheff.

SMITH, Christine Pamela (retired) Rolleston, Oaksway, Heswall, Wirral CH60 3SP Tel: 0151 342 2094 — MB ChB 1967 Birm. Prev: Regist. (Anaesth.) United Sheff. Hosps.

SMITH, Christine Rosemary Aylmer Lodge Surgery, Broomfield Road, Kidderminster DY11 5PA Tel: 01562 822015 Fax: 01562 827137 — MB ChB 1971 Birm.

SMITH, Christopher Department of Anaesthetics, St. Richards Hospital, Chichester PO19 4SE Tel: 01243 788122 Email: chris1smith@compuserve.com; The Old School House, School Lane, North Mundham, Chichester PO20 6LA Tel: 01243 530874 — MB BS 1983 Lond.; FRCA 1989. (Lond. Hosp. Med. Coll.) Cons. Anaesth. St. Richard's Hosp. Chichester. Socs: BMA; Assn. Anaesth.; MRCAnaesth. Prev: Sen. Regist. (Anaesth.) Midl. Train. Scheme; Regist. Rotat. (Anaesth.) Whipps Cross & Lond. Hosps.; Vis. Assoc. (Anaesth.) Duke Univ. Med. Centre N. Carolina, USA.

SMITH, Christopher David 47 Murrayfield Drive, Willaston, Nantwich CW5 6QF — MB BCh 1998 Wales.

SMITH, Christopher Eric Timothy District Laboratory, Frimley Park Hospital, Portsmouth Road, Frimley, Camberley GU16 7UJ — MB BS 1980 Lond.; MA Camb. 1981; MRCPath 1988. (St. Geo.) Cons. Histopath. & Cytopath. Frimley Pk. Hosp. Surrey. Prev: Sen. Regist. (Histopath.) N.. Gen. Hosp. Sheff.

SMITH, Christopher John The Surgery, 66 Crown Road, Twickenham TW1 3ER Tel: 020 8892 2543 Fax: 020 8744 3055 — MB BChir 1982 Camb.; MRCGP 1986.

SMITH, Christopher John 20 Gatley Gate, Sale M33 2RQ — MB BS 1988 Newc. SHO (Psychiat.) St. Luke's Hosp. Middlesbrough.

SMITH, Christopher John Peel House, 18 Peel Road, Mansfield NG19 6HB — MB ChB 1998 Leeds.

SMITH, Christopher Michael Meadowcroft Surgery, Jackson Road, Aylesbury HP19 9EX Tel: 01296 25775 Fax: 01296 330324 — MB ChB 1984 Bristol; FRCGP 2000; MRCGP 1989. GP Trainer.

SMITH, Christopher Michael Dodds Aylmer Lodge Surgery, Broomfield Road, Kidderminster DY11 5PA Tel: 01562 822015 Fax: 01562 827137 — MB ChB 1971 Birm.; BSc (Hons.) Birm. 1968, MB ChB 1971.

SMITH, Claire Blomfield House Health Centre, Looms Lane, Bury St Edmunds IP33 1HE Tel: 01284 775271 — MB ChB 1972 Birm.; MFFP 1993; DObst RCOG 1974. Cons. in Family Plann. & Reproductive Healthcare, Local Health Partnership NHS Trust Suff.

SMITH, Claire Percival Blackburn, Hyndburn and Ribble Valley Health Care NHS Trust, Queens Park Hospital, Haslingden Road, Blackburn BB2 3HH Tel: 01254 293750; Weaver's Cottage, 43 Cross Lane, Holcombe, Ramsbottom, Bury BL8 4LY Tel: 01706 828291 — MD 1990 Lond.; MB BS 1977 Lond.; FRCP 1997; MRCP (UK) 1980; FRCPCH 1997. (The London Hosp.) Cons. Paediat. Qu.s Pk. Hosp. Blackburn. Socs: Brit. Diabetic Assn.; Brit. Soc. Paediat. Endocrinol. Prev: Cons. (Paediat.) Booth Hall Childr.s Hosp. Manch.; Sen. Regist. Roy. Manch. Childr. Hosp.; Research Fell. (Childh. Diabetes) Qu. Eliz. Hosp. for Childr. & St. Bart. Hosp. Lond.

SMITH, Clare Elizabeth 6 South Croft, Elsfield Road, Old Marston, Oxford OX3 0PF — BM BCh 1987 Oxf.; BA Camb. 1984; MRCPsych 1991. Socs: BMA; Roy. Coll. Psychiats. Prev: Clin. Lect. & Hon. Sen. Regist. (Psychiat.) John Radcliffe Hosp. Oxf.

SMITH, Clare Elizabeth 86 Bates Street, Crrokcs, Sheffield S10 1NQ Email: clare.adrian@ic24.net — MB ChB 1995 Sheff. SHO (Anaesth.).

SMITH, Clare Hilda Greengates, Scots Lane, Astley Burf, Stourport-on-Severn DY13 0SD — MB ChB 1986 Sheff.; DFFP 1993.

SMITH, Clare Joanne Marion 24 Millsmead Way, Loughton IG10 1LR — BM BS 1994 Nottm.

SMITH, Clare Margaret Magnolia Cottage, 1 Risborough Road, Stoke Mandeville, Aylesbury HP22 5UP Tel: 01296 612839; Brickwall Farm, Susans Hill, Woodchurch, Ashford TN26 3RG — MB BS 1986 Lond.; MRCGP 1991; T(GP) 1991.

SMITH, Clare Nicola 54 Spring Lane, Fordham Heath, Colchester CO3 5TG — MB ChB 1998 Leeds.

SMITH, Clifford Corbett, OStJ The Health Centre, Bath Road, Thatcham, Newbury RG18 3HD Tel: 01635 867171 Fax: 01635 876395 Email: clifford.smith@gp-k81073.anglox.nhs.uk; 36 Fylingdales, Thatcham RG19 3LB Tel: 01635 864903 — MB BS 1971 Lond.; MRCS Eng. LRCP Lond. 1971; MRCGP 1975; DObst RCOG 1974; DCH Eng. 1973; Cert. FPA 1975. (Char. Cross) Co. Commiss.er St. John Ambul. Roy. Berks. Socs: Assn. BRd.casting Doctors. Prev: SHO (Obst.) N.wick Pk. Hosp. Harrow; SHO (Paediat.)

SMITH

Char. Cross Hosp. Fulham; SHO Profess. Dept. Paediat. Hammersmith Hosp. Lond.

SMITH, Colin (retired) Farthing Piece, Oddingley, Droitwich WR9 7NE Tel: 01905 773548 — MB BS 1963 Durh.; MRCGP 1977.

SMITH, Colin 60 Kinloch Road, Newton Mearns, Glasgow G77 6LX — MB ChB 1992 Glas.

SMITH, Colin Haigh (retired) 6 Shorts Lane, Beaminster DT8 3BD Tel: 01308 862440 — BM BCh Oxf. 1958; MSc Lond. 1988; MA Oxf. 1963; FRCGP 1988, M 1976; DCH Eng. 1967. Prev: Asst. Regional Adviser Audit.

SMITH, Colin Lunn Southampton General Hospital, Southampton SO16 6YD Tel: 02380 796737 — MD 1978 Leeds; BSc Leeds 1960, MD 1978, MB ChB 1962; FRCP Lond. 1980, M 1965; Fmed.Sci.1998. (Leeds) Sen. Lect. Med. & Gastroenterol. & Cons. Phys. Univ. Soton. & Soton. Gen. Hosp. Socs: Brit. Soc. Gastroenterol. Prev: Lect. Med. Gen. Infirm. Leeds; Asst. Prof. Med. (Gastroenterol.) Univ. Cincinnati, U.S.A.

SMITH, Colin Stanley 94 Saughall Massie Lane, Upton, Wirral CH49 6ND Tel: 0151 677 6674 — MB ChB 1964 Liverp.; FRCP Lond. 1981, M 1969. (Liverp.) Sen. Lect. Child Health Univ. Liverp. Prev: Sen. Regist. & Regist. (Paediat.) Alder Hey Childr. Hosp.; Clin. Fell. Endocrin. Div. Hosp. Sick Childr. Toronto, Canada.

SMITH, Constance Frances Isis Cottage, 4 Ray Park Road, Maidenhead SL6 8QR Tel: 01628 782819 — MB BS 1990 Lond.; BSc Biochem. Lond. 1985; MRCGP 1994; DRCOG 1996; DFFP 1993; DCH RCP Lond. 1993. (St. Mary's Hosp. Med. Sch.) Socs: BMA; Windsor Med. Soc.

SMITH, Craig Anthony 2 Ashford Avenue, Lancaster LA1 5BA — MB ChB 1987 Sheff.

SMITH, Craig John 123 Blairbeth Road, Rutherglen, Glasgow G73 5BT — MB ChB 1994 Glas.

SMITH, Craig Manderson The Chilterns, The Old Road, Leavenheath, Colchester CO6 4QB — MB ChB 1990 Dundee.

SMITH, Damian Michael 1 Elliot Drive, Giffnock, Glasgow G46 7NT — MB ChB 1996 Glas.

SMITH, Daniel Joseph 71 Orchardville Gardens, Finaghy, Belfast BT10 0JU — MB ChB 1996 Ed.

SMITH, Daniel Kenneth Sunnybank, Cutmere, Tideford, Saltash PL12 5JU Tel: 01752 851850 — MB ChB 1982 Bristol; DCH RCPS Glas. 1987; DA (UK) 1985; MRCGP 1989.

SMITH, Daniela Gerda Anna-Elisabeth 6 Glenavon Court, Glenavon Park, Bristol BS9 1RH — MB BCh 1978 Witwatersrand; FFA RCSI 1987.

SMITH, Danielle Joanne 10 Cousley Close, Gloucester GL3 3RN — MB BS 1992 Lond.; DRCOG Lond 1995; MRCGP (LOND) July 1997; DFFP (Lond) 1998. (Guy's Hosp Med School) GP Locum.

SMITH, Darren Jeffrey 115 Rivington Drive, Burscough, Ormskirk L40 7RW — MB ChB 1998 Liverp.; MB ChB Liverp 1998.

SMITH, Darron Eufryn Brynteg Surgery, Brynmawr Avenue, Ammanford SA18 2DA Tel: 01269 592058 — MB BCh 1991 Wales.

SMITH, David (retired) Headway, 8 Church Hill, Hensingham, Whitehaven CA28 8NE Tel: 01946 693018 — MB ChB Manch. 1956; FRCPath 1977, M 1965; DPath Eng. 1962. Prev: Cons. Pathol. W. Cumbld. Hosp. Whitehaven.

SMITH, David Great Harwood Health Centre, Water Street, Great Harwood, Blackburn BB6 7QR Tel: 01254 885764 Fax: 01254 877360; 2 Meins Croft, Blackburn BB2 6QH — MB ChB 1981 Manch.; DRCOG 1983.

SMITH, David Alistair Locking Hill Surgery, Stroud GL5 1UY Tel: 01242 820056; Chapel Cottage, Gloucester Rd, Andoverford, Cheltenham GL54 4HR Tel: 01242 820056 Email: alistair@taskas.demon.co.uk — BM BCh 1994 Oxf.; MA Oxf. 1996; DRCOG 1996; DFFP 1997; MRCGP 1998. (Oxf.) GP Princip.; Med. Off. Cheltenham Town F.C. Prev: GP Regist. Brockworth Glos.; SHO (Psychiat.) Cirencester Memor. Centre Glos.; SHO (O & G) Gloucester Roy. Hosp.

SMITH, David Andrew Grove Surgery, Charlotte Street, Wakefield WF1 1UJ Tel: 01924 372596 Fax: 01924 200913; 45 Sheridan Street, Wakefield WF1 3TP Tel: 01924 820949 — MB ChB 1985 Birm.; MRCGP 1989; DRCOG 1988.

SMITH, David Andrew 16 Port Lane, Hursley, Winchester SO21 2JS Tel: 01962 775447; Cardiological Sciences, St George's Hospital Medical School, Cranmer Terrace, London SW17 0RE Tel: 020 8672 9944 Fax: 020 8725 3328 Email: dasmith@sghms.ac.uk — BM 1993 Soton.; MRCP UK 1997. Regist. (Cardiol.) Roy. Bournemouth Hosp.; Research Fell. & Hon. Lect. in Cardiol. St. Geo. Hosp. Med. Sch. Socs: BMA. Prev: SHO Rotat. (Gen. Med.) Roy. Bournemouth Hosp.; Ho. Off. (Med.) Qu. Alexandra Hosp. Cosham, Portsmouth.

SMITH, David Anthony Wansbeck General Hospital, Woodhorn Lane, Ashington NE63 9JJ Tel: 01670 521212; Blackfords, Jesmond Park E., Newcastle upon Tyne NE7 7BT Tel: 0191 281 6128 — MB BChir 1975 Camb.; MA, MB Camb. 1975, BChir 1974; MRCP (UK) 1979; MRCPath 1985. (Camb.) Cons. Histopath. Wansbeck Gen. Hosp. Ashington. Prev: Sen. Regist. (Histopath.) King's Coll. Hosp. Lond.; SHO (Gen. Med.) N.wick Pk. Hosp.; Ho. Off. Univ. Coll. Hosp. Lond.

SMITH, David Balfour 284 Telegraph Road, Heswall, Wirral CH60 7SG — MD 1988 Ed.; MB ChB 1978; MRCP (UK) 1981. Cons. Med. Oncol. Clatterbridge Centre for Oncol. Wirral. Prev: Sen. Regist. (Med. Oncol.) Char. Cross Hosp. Lond.; Regist. (Med.) Roy. Lancaster Infirm.; Research Fell. (Med. Oncol.) Christie Hosp. Manch.

SMITH, David Charles Department of Anaesthesia, Southampton General Hospital, Southampton SO16 6YD Tel: 02380 796135 Fax: 02380 794348; Little Herons, Heron Lane, Timsbury, Southampton SO51 0ND Tel: 01794 367134 — BM BS 1980 Nottm.; FFA RCS Eng. 1985; DM Nottm. 1996; BMedSci 1978 Nottm. (Nottm.) Cons. & Sen. Lect. (Anaesth.) Soton. Gen. Hosp. Socs: Assn. of Cardiothoracic Anaestetists, Comm. Mem.; Soc. of Cardiovasc. Anaesthesiologists; Europ. Assn. of Cardiothoracic Anaesthesiologists. Prev: Cons. Anaesth. W.. Infirm. Glas.

SMITH, Mr David Cunningham 333 Albert Drive, Glasgow G41 5HJ Tel: 0141 423 2801 Fax: 0141 423 5117 — MB ChB 1966 Glas.; FRCS Eng. 1971; FRCS Glas. 1970. (Glas.) Cons. Surg. Vict. Infirm. Glas.; Hon. Clin. Sen. Lect. (Surg.) Univ. Glas. Socs: Glas. S.ern Med. Soc., Pres. (1999-2000); Roy. Coll. of Phys.s & Surg.s of Glas., Vice Pres. (Surgic. 2000). Prev: Regist. (Orthop. & Gen. Surg.), Ho. Surg. & Ho. Phys. W.. Infirm. Glas.

SMITH, David Dow Oxford Terrace Medical Group, 1 Oxford Terrace, Gateshead NE8 1RQ Tel: 0191 477 2169; 9 Swinburne Place, Newcastle upon Tyne NE4 6EA — MB BS 1979 Newc.; MRCGP 1984.

SMITH, David Fairclough (retired) Blackthorn, 5 Front St., Whickham, Newcastle upon Tyne NE16 4HF — MB BS 1951 Durh.

SMITH, Mr David Flett (retired) 52 Moor Crescent, Gosforth, Newcastle upon Tyne NE3 4AQ Tel: 01632 851694 — MB ChB 1935 Aberd.; FRCS Ed. 1938; FRCOG 1961, M 1949. Prev: Sen. Obst. Gyn. Gateshead AHA.

SMITH, David Frank Department of Neurosciences, Walton Hospital, Rice Lane, Liverpool L9 1AE — MB ChB 1983 Aberd.; MD Aberd. 1993; MRCP (UK) 1987. Lect. & Hon. Sen. Regist. (Neurosci.) Univ. Liverp. Socs: Assoc. Mem. Assn. Brit. Neurol. Prev: Research Regist. (Neurosci.) Walton Hosp. Liverp.

SMITH, David Geoffrey Malagay Barn, Church Road, West Tilbury, Grays RM18 8UB — MB ChB 1969 Ed.

SMITH, David Gordon Brookland House, 501 Crewe Road, Wistaston, Crewe CW2 6QP Tel: 01270 567250 Fax: 01270 665829; 4 Mill Race Drive, Wistaston, Crewe CW2 6XG Tel: 01270 668195 — MB ChB 1988 Dundee; MRCGP 1994. (Dundee)

SMITH, David Ian Andrew 27 Fiskerton Road, Cherry Willingham, Lincoln LN3 4LA — MB BS 1983 Lond.

SMITH, David Ian Hamilton Rosegarth Surgery, Rothwell Mount, Halifax HX1 2XB; Upper Greystones, Manor Heath Road, Halifax HX3 0EE — MB BS 1978 Lond.; MRCGP 1982; DCH RCP Lond. 1982. Clin. Asst. (A & E.) Roy. Halifax Infirm.; Hon. Hosp. Pract. (Gastroenterol.) Roy. Halifax Infirm. Prev: Trainee GP Calderdale AHA VTS; Ho. Phys. Epsom Dist. Hosp.; Ho. Surg. Roy. Cornw. Hosp. Truro.

SMITH, David Keith Flat 3, 45 Cavendish Road, London NW6 7XS — MB BS 1997 Lond.

SMITH, David Lindsey Department of Medicine, Frenchay Hospital, Frenchay Park Road, Bristol BS16 1LE Tel: 0117 970 1212 Fax: 0117 957 3075 — BM 1982 Soton.; DM Soton. 1995; MRCP

SMITH

(UK) 1986; MRCPI 1986; FRCP 2000. (Univ. Soton.) Cons. Phys. (Respirat. & Gen. Med.) Frenchay Hosp. Bristol. Socs: Brit. Thorac. Soc.; Amer. Thoracic Soc.; Europ. Respirat. Soc. Prev: Sen. Regist. Glenfield Hosp. Leicester; Sen. Regist. Chelsea & W.m. Hosp. Lond.; Clin. Tutor Brompton Hosp. Lond.

SMITH, David Mark Haresfield House Surgery, 6-10 Bath Road, Worcester WR5 3EJ Tel: 01905 763161 Fax: 01905 767016; The Mount, Red Hill Lane, Worcester WR5 2JL — MB ChB 1976 Manch.; MRCGP 1980; DRCOG 1979. (Manch.)

SMITH, David Michael Midland Medical Osteopathic Practice, 162 Jockey Road, Boldmere, Sutton Coldfield B73 5PP Tel: 0121 355 2155 Fax: 0709 223 0859 Email: david@myspine.org.uk; Birmingham Nuffield Hospital, 22 Somerset Road, Edgbaston, Birmingham B15 2QQ Tel: 0121 355 2155 — MB ChB 1967 St. And.; MLCOM 1983; MFHom 1983; MRCGP 1974. (Dundee) Med. Osteopath. W. Midl.; Nuffield Health Screening Doctor, Birm. Socs: Brit. Inst. Musculoskeletal Med. Prev: Trainee GP S. Birm. VTS; Tutor Lond. Coll. Osteop. Med.

SMITH, Mr David Monro The Friarage, 4 Little Causeway, Forfar DD8 2AD — MB ChB 1983 Ed.; MD Ed. 1993; FRCS Ed. 1987. Cons. Surg. Ninewells Hosp. Dundee. Prev: Sen. Regist. (Surg.) Ninewells Hosp. Dundee.

SMITH, David Morton Wylie 10 Hopeward Court, The Stables, Dalgety Bay, Dunfermline KY11 9TF — MB ChB 1948 Ed.

SMITH, Mr David Neal Wirral Hospital NHS Trust, Arrowe Park Hospital, Arrowe Park Road, Wirral CH49 5PE Tel: 0151 678 5111; 12 Oaksway, Heswall, Wirral CH60 3SP Tel: 0151 342 2094 — MB ChB 1967 Birm.; FRCS Ed. 1973. (Birm.) Cons. (Orthop. Surg.) Wirral Hosp. NHS Trust. Socs: Fell. BOA; BMA. Prev: Sen. Regist. (Orthop.) Birm. AHA; Regist. (Neurosurg.) Roy. Infirm. Sheff.; Regist. (Surg.) United Birm. Hosps.

SMITH, David Phillip c/o Barnsoul Farm, Irongray, Dumfries DG2 9SQ — MB ChB 1966 Leeds; PhD Leeds 1973; BSc (Hons. Pharmacol.) 1968; MRCPath 1977. (Leeds)

SMITH, David Ross Sutherland 20 Herefordshire Drive, Durham DH1 2DQ — MB BS 1967 Newc.; FRCPCH 1997; FRCP Lond. 1990; MRCP (UK) 1974; DCH Eng. 1973; DObst RCOG 1971. (Newc.) Cons. Paediat. Univ. Hosp. of N. Durh. Socs: BMA & Brit. Paediat. Assn. Prev: Sen. Regist. (Paediat.) Middlx. Hosp. Lond.; Research Fell. Hosp. Sick Childr. Toronto, Canada; Regist. (Paediat.) Brompton Hosp. Lond.

SMITH, David Trevor Mitchell Barcroft Medical Practice, Barcroft Medical Centre, Amesbury, Salisbury SP4 7DL Tel: 01980 623983 Fax: 01980 625530; 4 South Mill Close, Amesbury, Salisbury SP4 7HS Tel: 01980 623207 Fax: 01980 623207 — MB BS 1961 Lond.; MRCS Eng. LRCP Lond. 1961. (Guy's) Med. Off. Pains Wessex Schermuly Ltd. Salisbury. Prev: Dep. MOH & Port Med. Off. Grimsby RD.

SMITH, David Walter (retired) The White House, Higher Boskerris, Carbis Bay, St Ives TR26 2TL Tel: 01736 798675 — MB BS 1949 Lond.; PhD Lond. 1955, BSc 1943, MB BS 1949; MRCPsych 1971. Prev: Cons. Psychiat. Cornw. & I. of Scilly AHAs.

SMITH, David Ward (retired) The Knowltons, Podington, Wellingborough NN29 7HX Tel: 01933 353306 — MB BChir 1951 Camb.; MRCGP 1971; DObst RCOG 1956. Prev: Ho. Surg. Middlx. Hosp.

SMITH, David Ward Lawson (retired) Warlaby House, Warlaby, Northallerton DL7 9JS Tel: 01609 774812 Fax: 01609 783720 Email: smithd@wanlaby.freeserve.co.uk — MB ChB St. And. 1965. Sec. BMA Yorks. Regional Counc. Prev: Ex-Vice-Chairm. N.allerton HA.

SMITH, David William, Brigadier late RAMC BFG Health Commission, HQ UKSC (G) BFPO 140 Tel: 00 49 2161 472866 Fax: 00 49 2161 472360; Clifton Lodge, Banff Road, Keith AB55 5ET Tel: 01542 882617 Email: dave.lil@virgin.net — MB ChB 1971 Aberd.; FRCGP 1987; DObst RCOG 1976. (Aberd.) Dir. Army Gen. Pract. Prev: Com.MedGP Brit. Army, Germany; Command. Med. Adviser Brit. Forces, Cyprus; Course Organiser SW Dist. HM Armed Forces.

SMITH, Dawn Ann Crownhall Medical Group, Felling Health Centre, Stephenson Tce, Gateshead NE10 9QJ Tel: 0191 469 2311 Fax: 0191 438 4661 — MB BS 1987 Newc.; MRCGP 1991; DRCOG 1990.

SMITH, Deborah Anne Leeds Student Medical Practice, 4 Blenheim Court Walk, Leeds LS2 9AE Tel: 0113 295 4488 — MB BS 1980 Lond.; DFFP 1998; MRCGP 1986; DRCOG 1985; DCH RCP Lond. 1985. (Guy's Hosp. Lond.) GP Leeds Stud. Med. Pract. Prev: CMO (Family Plann.) Leeds Community & Ment. Health Trust; GP W.field Med. Centre Leeds.

SMITH, Deborah Jane 16 Brompton Avenue, Sefton Park, Liverpool L17 3BU — MB ChB 1993 Liverp.

SMITH, Deborah Jane 31 Crofters Fold, Galgate, Lancaster LA2 0RB — MB ChB 1995 Leic.

SMITH, Debra Ellen Harrogate District Hospital, Lancaster Park Road, Harrogate HG2 7SX Tel: 01423 885959; 28 Scriven Road, Knaresborough HG5 9EJ — MD 1992 Camb.; MA Camb. 1981, MD 1992, MB BChir 1979; MRCP (UK) 1985. Cons. Paediat. Harrogate HA.

SMITH, Dena Alexandra 76 Cunningham Drive, Bromborough, Wirral CH63 0JZ — MB ChB 1990 Manch.; DRCOG 1995; MRCGP 1995.

SMITH, Dennis Gutteridge Carrington House Surgery, 19 Priory Road, High Wycombe HP13 6SL Tel: 01494 526029; Mountjoys Retreat, Plomer Green Lane, Downley, High Wycombe HP13 5XN — MB BS 1974 Lond.; DCH Eng. 1979; DRCOG 1977. (St. Geo.) GP High Wycombe. Prev: SHO (Paediat.) Worcester Roy. Infirm. (Ronkswood Br.); SHO (Med.) Battle Hosp. Reading; SHO (O & G) Heatherwood Hosp. Ascot.

SMITH, Desmond Allen (retired) Blenheim Cottage, Nether Wallop, Stockbridge SO20 8EN Tel: 01264 781205 — MB ChB Ed. 1947; DMRD Eng. 1961; FRCP Ed. 1986, M 1955; FRCR 1964. Prev: Radiol. Salisbury Gen. Hosp.

SMITH, Desmond James Lawrence Berkley Laboratories, Building 74-174, 1 Cyclotron Road, University of California, Berkeley CA 94720, USA Tel: 00 1 510 4865090 Fax: 00 1 510 4866746; 72 Ormesby Way, Kenton, Harrow HA3 9SF Tel: 020 8204 0081 — MA Oxf. 1987; BA Oxf. Physics (1st cl. Hons.) & Prize Distinc. 1981, BM BCh; PhD Camb. 1986. Prev: Ho. Off. (Surg.) John Radcliffe Hosp. Oxf. Univ.; Ho. Off. (Med.) Wycombe Gen. Hosp. High Wycombe.

SMITH, Desmond Murray Brenkley Avenue Health Centre, Brenkley Avenue, Shiremoor, Newcastle upon Tyne NE27 0PR Tel: 0191 251 6151; 34 King Edward Road, Tynemouth, North Shields NE30 2RP — MB BS 1977 Newc.

SMITH, Diane Elizabeth Croft Cottage, 29 Langton Road, Tunbridge Wells TN4 8XA — MB ChB 1989 Birm.

SMITH, Dianne Elizabeth Glodwick Health Centre, 137 Glodwick Road, Oldham OL4 1YN Tel: 0161 909 8370; Goldturf Pits, Moorside, Oldham OL4 2NA — MB ChB 1987 Manch.; MRCGP 1991; DRCOG 1990. (Manchester)

SMITH, Dominic Paul 1 Goodwin Walk, Peterborough PE4 6GQ — BM BS 1993 Nottm.

SMITH, Donald (retired) 9 Monastery Avenue, Dover CT16 1AB Tel: 01304 206366 Fax: 01304 306366 — MB BS Durh. 1948. Prev: Asst. Dir.-Gen. AMD 3.

SMITH, Donald 25 Firth Road, Troon KA10 6TF Tel: 01292 314187 — MB ChB 1958 Glas.; FRCOG 1978, M 1964. (Glas.) Cons. Obstetr. & Gynaecol. Ayrsh. Centr. Hosp. Irvine & Assoc. Hosps. Socs: Glas. Obst. & Gyn. Soc. & BMA. Prev: Sen. Lect. (O & G) Qu. Univ. Belf.; Consult. Belf. Teach. Hosps; Ho. Phys. & Ho. Surg. Glas. Roy. Infirm.

SMITH, Donald Angus (retired) 12 Sutcliffe Court, Anniesland, Glasgow G13 1AP Tel: 0141 954 3971 — MB ChB 1948 Glas.

SMITH, Donald Robert Crossways, Roundhay Park Lane, Leeds LS17 8AR Tel: 01132 663139 — MB BS (Hons.) Durh. 1955; MD Malaya 1961; FRCP Lond. 1972, M 1958. (Durh.) p/t Med. Chairm. Pens. Appeal Tribunals Eng. & Wales. Socs: Brit. Cardiac Soc. Prev: Med. Dir. United Leeds Teach. Hosps. NHS Trust; Cons. Cardiol. United Leeds Teachg. Hosp. NHS Trust; Sen. Lect. Unit. Leeds.

SMITH, Donalda Matheson (retired) 6 Field Lane, Willersey, Broadway WR12 7QB Tel: 01386 852628 — MB ChB Ed. 1950; FFOM RCP Lond. 1986, MFOM 1979; DIH Soc. Apoth. Lond. 1972; DObst RCOG 1954. Prev: Sen. Employm. Med. Adviser EMAS, Marches Area.

SMITH, Dorothy Lindsay 15 Mansionhouse Road, Edinburgh EH9 1TZ Tel: 0131 667 4665 — MD Ed. 1980, MB ChB 1954.

SMITH

SMITH, Dorothy Mary Agnes (retired) 17 Knapp Close, Ledbury HR8 1AW Tel: 01531 634620 — MB ChB 1942 Aberd.; DObst RCOG 1953.

SMITH, Douglas Harrison Kerr 14 Lakeside Road, Raith Lake, Kirkcaldy KY2 5QJ Tel: 01592 266503 — MB ChB 1963 Ed.; FRCP Ed. 1994; MRCP Ed. 1987; FRCR 1975; FFR 1973; DMRD Ed. 1970. (Ed.) Cons. Radiol. Vict. Hosp. Kirkcaldy; Hon. Sen. Lect. St. And. Univ. Socs: Fell. Roy. Med. Soc. Prev: Sen. Regist. (X-Ray) Roy. Infirm. Edin.; Regist. (Med.) Vict. Hosp. Kirkcaldy.

SMITH, Douglas Peter Quance (retired) Ryecroft, 54 Cross Road, Tadworth KT20 5ST Tel: 01737 812037 — MB BS 1951 Lond.; MRCS Eng. LRCP Lond. 1951; DObst RCOG 1953. Prev: Resid. Med. Off. St. And. Hosp. Dollis Hill.

SMITH, Douglas Robert Walter 15 Hugh Mill, Shepherds Loan, Dundee DD2 1UN — MB ChB 1996 Dundee.

SMITH, Drew Dept. of Anaesth., Walton Building, Glasgow Royal Infirmary, Castle St., Glasgow G4 0SF Tel: 0141 211 4620 Fax: 0141 211 4622 Email: drew.smith@northglasgow.scot.nhs.uk — MB ChB 1989 Glas.; FRCA 1995. (Glas. Univ.) Cons. (Anaesth.) Glas. Roy. Infirm. Glas. Socs: Mem. of Roy. Coll. Anaesth. Scott. Bd. Prev: Specialist Regist. (Anaesth.) Glas. Roy. Infirm.; SHO (Anaesth.) Glas. Roy. Infirm. & Law Hosp. Carluke.

SMITH, Edmund Mervyn 36 Glen Road, Craigavad, Holywood BT18 0HB — MB BCh BAO 1976 Belf.

SMITH, Edna Kydd (retired) Birmingham Heartlands Hospital, Bordesley Green E., Birmingham B9 5SS Tel: 0121 766 6611 — MB ChB 1962 St. And.; FRCOG 1981, M 1968, DObst. 1964; T(OG) 1991. Cons. (O & G) Marston Green Hosp. Birm.

SMITH, Edward Baxter Owen, VRD The Manor House, Ewelme, Wallingford OX10 Tel: 01491 36036 — MB BS Lond. 1953, DPM 1962; FRCP Ed. 1972, M 1964; FRCPsych 1975, M 1971. (St. Thos.) Emerit. Cons. Psychiat. John Radcliffe Hosp. Oxf. Prev: Emerit. Civil. Advisor RN; Cons. Psychiat. John Radcliffe Hosp. Oxf.; Clin. Lect. (Psychiat.) Univ. Oxf.

SMITH, Mr Edward Ernest John Cardiothoracic Unit, St George's Hospital, Blackshaw Road, London SW17 0QT Tel: 020 8725 3551 Fax: 020 8946 3130 Email: eejmss@supanet.com; Homewood, 4A Drax Avenue, Wimbledon, London SW20 0EH Tel: 020 8946 1893 Fax: 020 8946 3130 Email: eejmss@supanet.com — MD 1991 Camb.; MB BChir 1974; FRCS Eng. 1978. Cons. Cardiothoracic Surg. St. Geo. Hosp. Lond. & Roy. Surrey Co. Hosp. Guildford. Prev: Regist. (Surg.) Hammersmith Hosp. Lond.; Cas. Off. & Ho. Surg. St. Thos. Hosp. Lond.

SMITH, Edward Maxim Moor Park Surgery, 49 Garstang Road, Preston PR1 1LB Tel: 01772 252077 Fax: 01772 885451 — MB ChB 1970 Ed.

SMITH, Eileen Dorothy (retired) 36 Westminster Road, Ellesmere Park, Eccles, Manchester M30 9EA — MB BS 1970 Lond.; MRCS Eng. LRCP Lond. 1961; FRCPsych. 1988, M 1973; DPM Eng. 1973. Med. Mem. Ment. Health Review Tribunal. Prev: Cons. Psychiat. Salford AHA (T).

SMITH, Eileen Philomena (retired) The Willows, 10 Weld Road, Birkdale, Southport PR8 2AZ — MB ChB Liverp. 1950.

SMITH, Elaine Caroline Consultant Rheumatologist, North West London Hospitals NHS Trust, Northwick Park & Central Middlesex, London Tel: 020 8864 3232 Fax: 020 8864 2009 Email: ecsmith@marylebone.u-net.com — MB BS 1985 Lond.; MD 1997; MRCP (UK) 1989. (St. Bart. Hosp. Lond.) Cons. Rheum. N.wick Pk. and Centr. Middlx. Hosp.s, Lond.; Edr.ial Bd. of the Druga nd Therap. Bull. since 1998. Socs: Brit. Soc. Rheum.; Mem. for Sect. Rheumatol. and Rehabil. Roy. Soc. Med.; Edr.ial Bd. Drugs and Therap. Bull. 1998-2001. Prev: Staff Phys., Dubbo Base Hosp., NW Australia; Locum Cons. (Rheum.) Guy's Hosp. Lond.; Sen. Regist. (Rheum.) King's Coll. Hosp. Lond.

SMITH, Elaine Nicola Keepers Cottage, Raycombe Lane, Coddington, Ledbury HR8 1JH Tel: 01531 2409 — MB BS 1975 Lond.; MRCS Eng. LRCP Lond. 1975; DRCOG 1978.

SMITH, Elaine Paula 1 Grange Drive, Manchester M9 7AJ Tel: 0161 740 9434 — MB ChB 1994 Manch.; BSc (Med. Sci.) St. And. 1991. SHO (Cardiothoracic Med.) Wythenshawe Hosp. Manch. Prev: Ho. Off. (Gen. Med. & Renal Med.) Hope Hosp. Salford; Ho. Off. (Gen. & Vasc. Surg. & Urol.) Univ. Hosp. S. Manch.

SMITH, Eleanor Grace Birmingham Public Health Lobaratory, Heartlands Hospital, Birmingham B9 5SS — MB BS 1979 Lond.; BSc (Hons.) Lond. 1976; MRCP (UK) 1982; FRCPath 1998; FRCP 2000. (St. Thomas) Cons. Microbiologist Birm. Pub. Health Laborat. Birmingham Heartlands Hosp.

SMITH, Elizabeth Margaret Musters Medical Practice, 214 Musters Road, West Bridgford, Nottingham NG2 7DR Tel: 0115 981 4124 Fax: 0115 981 3117; 40 St Helens Road, West Bridgford, Nottingham NG2 6EX Tel: 0115 923 1144 — BM BS Nottm. 1986, BMedSci 1984; MRCGP 1990; DRCOG 1991; DCH RCP Lond. 1990.

SMITH, Elizabeth Mary 12 Droke Lane, East Dean, Chichester PO18 0JH — MB BS 1987 Lond.; MRCGP 1996; DRCOG 1990.

SMITH, Elizabeth Mary Stuart Dunrowan, 19 Middlepenny Road, Langbank, Port Glasgow PA14 6XB — MB ChB 1989 Glas.

SMITH, Elizabeth Robin 46 Fitzroy Road, London NW1 8TY — MB BS 1996 Lond.

SMITH, Elizabeth Sheila Highfield Surgery, Holtdale Approach, Leeds LS16 7RX Tel: 0113 230 0108 Fax: 0113 230 1309; 63 Otley Old Road, Lawnswood, Leeds LS16 6HG Tel: 0113 261 4118 — MB ChB 1974 Ed.; MRCGP 1978; DCH RCPS Glas. 1977. Prev: Trainee GP Lothian HB VTS; Ho. Phys. (Infec. Dis. Unit) City Hosp. Edin.; Ho. Surg. (Profess. Surg. Unit) Roy. Infirm. Edin.

SMITH, Ellen (retired) 704 Kings Court, Ramsey IM8 1LW Tel: 01624 814554 — MB BChir Camb. 1949; MRCS Eng. LRCP Lond. 1949; DObst RCOG 1950. Prev: Clin. Asst. (Dermat.) Birm. Gen. & Birm. Skin Hosps.

SMITH, Elliot Jonathan 133 High Lane, Whitefield, Manchester M45 7WH — MB BS 1994 Lond.

SMITH, Elvet Edward Highfield Private Hospital, Manchester Road, Rochdale OL11 4LZ Tel: 01706 655121 Fax: 01706 718250; 76 Bamford Way, Bamford, Rochdale OL11 5JL Tel: 01706 644534 — MB ChB 1971 Bristol; FRCP Lond. 1991; MRCP (UK) 1974; BA (Open) 1996. Cons. Rheum. & Rehabil. Rochdale HA. Socs: Brit. Soc. Rheum.; Brit. Soc. Rehab. Med.; Fell. Roy. Soc. Med. Prev: Sen. Regist. (Rheum. & Rehabil.) Manch. Roy. Infirm. & Withington Hosp.; Research Regist. ARC Field Unit Epidemiol. Dept. Community Med. Univ. Manch.; Ho. Phys. Prof. Med. Unit Bristol Roy. Infirm.

SMITH, Emmanuel Ademola (retired) 33 Radley House, Gloucester Place, London NW1 6DP Tel: 020 7724 6481 — MRCS Eng. LRCP Lond. 1961; DPH Lond. 1966; MS (Hyg.) Talune 1971. Assoc. Lect. Univ. Lagos, Nigeria; Med. Dir. Ademola Smith Holdings Nigeria Ltd. Charity Clinic Maryland Ikeja, Nigeria. Prev: Director Pub. Health Servs. Nigeria.

SMITH, Enid Joan Cheddar Medical Centre, Roynon Way, Cheddar BS27 3NZ Tel: 01934 742061 Fax: 01934 744374 — MB ChB 1968 Bristol; DObst RCOG 1970.

SMITH, Eric Ernest (retired) The Garth, Windmill End, Epsom KT17 3AQ — MB BS 1956 Lond.; MRCS Eng. LRCP Lond. 1956.

SMITH, Eric Harry (retired) Ty'n Llechwedd, Dinbren, Llangollen LL20 8EB Tel: 01987 869364, 0131 667 9087 — MB ChB 1963 Ed.; LLM (Cardiff) 1999; FRCPCH 1977; FRCP Lond. 1988; MRCP (UK) 1971; DCH Eng. 1968. Prev: Cons. (Paediat.) Kettering Gen. Hosp.

SMITH, Eric John Queens Road Medical Practice, The Grange, St. Peter Port, Guernsey GY1 1RH Tel: 01481 724184 Fax: 01481 716431; Les Lohiers, La Grande Lande, St. Saviours, Guernsey GY7 9 — MB BS 1970 Lond.

SMITH, Eric Leslie King Khaled Hospital, Jeddah 21423, Saudi Arabia Tel: 00 966 2 6653400; Dunkery Lodge, Townsend Road, Minehead TA24 5RQ Tel: 01643 6170 — MB ChB 1959 Aberd.; FRCP Ed. 1978, M 1964. Head of Dept. Dermat./Venereol./ Med. Educat. Dept. King Khaled Hosp. Jeddah. Prev: Cons. Derm. MusGr. Pk. Hosp. Taunton.; Govt. Hosp. UAE; Sen. Regist./Tutor Dermat. St. John's Hosp. Dis. of Skin Lond.

SMITH, Professor Ernest Alwyn, CBE Plum Tree Cottage, Silverdale Road, Arnside, Carnforth LA5 0AH Tel: 01524 761976 — MB ChB 1952 Birm.; MSc Manch. 1971; PhD Birm. 1955; FRCP Lond. 1983; FRCP Ed. 1981; FRCP Glas. 1971, M 1967; FRCGP 1973; FFCM 1972; DPH (Distinc.) Lond. 1956. (Birm.) Emerit. Prof. Epidemiol. & Social Oncol. Univ. Manch. Socs: (Ex-Pres.) Fac. Pub. Health Med.; Soc. Social Med. Prev: Prof. Community Med. Univ. Manch.; Sen. Lect. i/c Social Paediat. Research Gp. Univ. Glas.; Med. Statistician Scott. Home & Health Dept.

SMITH, Esther Grace 3 Orchard Close, Freckleton, Preston PR4 1UP — MB ChB 1996 Ed.

SMITH, Everhardus Johannes c/o Drive D. Kolditz, Department of Anaesthetics, Royal Berkshire Hospital, Reading; Flat 6 Glenavon Court, Glenavon Park, Bristol BS9 1RH — MB BCh 1979 Witwatersrand; BSc Cape Town 1974.

SMITH, Rev. Felicity Ann 14 Oakwood Grove, Warwick CV34 5TD Tel: 01926 492452 Fax: 01926 407083; 14 Oakwood Grove, Warwick CV34 5TD Tel: 01925 492452 Fax: 01926 407083 — MB ChB 1963 Bristol; MFFP 1993; DObst RCOG 1965. (Bristol) SCMO (Family Plann.) Warks. & Solihull HA.

SMITH, Fiona Catherine 40 Highwoods Drive, Marlow Bottom, Marlow SL7 3PY — MB ChB 1990 Leeds; DRCOG 1994; DFFP 1994. Prev: GP Bradford VTS.

SMITH, Fiona Eugenie Winifred Dumfries & Galloway Royal Infirmary, Bankend Road, Dumfries DG1 4AP Tel: 01387 246246; West Gallaberry, Kirkmahoe, Dumfries DG1 1SY Tel: 01387 710210 — MB ChB Aberd. 1964; DA Eng. 1970; DObst RCOG 1966. (Aberd.) Clin. Asst. Dumfries & Galloway Acute Servs. Trust; Anaesth. Prev: Regist. (Anaesth.) Dumfries & Galloway Roy. Infirm.; Regist. (Anaesth.) Wellington Hosp. NZ; SHO (Obst.) Nat. Wom. Hosp. Auckland, NZ.

SMITH, Fiona Gail 4 Arthur Street, Cambridge CB4 3BX — BChir 1994 Camb.

SMITH, Frances Homemead, 17 Lower Acreman St., Sherborne DT9 3EX — MB BCh 1996 Wales.

SMITH, Francesca Clare 42 Cambrian Avenue, Redcar TS10 4HF — MB BS 1997 Lond.

SMITH, Francis Herbert Nixon (retired) Turnstones, Perrancoombe, Perranporth TR6 0HX Tel: 01872 573324 — MB ChB Birm. 1947; MRCS Eng. LRCP Lond. 1948; DObst RCOG 1951. Prev: Sch. Med. Off. Newquay Area.

SMITH, Francis Robert Highcroft, Wessex Deanery, Romsey Road, Winchester SO22 5DH Tel: 01962 863511 Fax: 01962 877211 Email: fsmith@doh.gsi.gov.uk — MB ChB 1974 Birm.; MB ChB (Hons.) Birm. 1974; MRCP (UK) 1977; FRCGP 1996, M 1984; MSC 1998. Dir. of Postgrad. GP Educat. Prev: Sen. Lect. (Gen. Pract. & Primary Care) St. Geo. Hosp. Med. Sch. Lond.; Ment. Health Fell. TPMDE S. Thames (W..); GP Caterham, Surrey.

SMITH, Francis William Woodend Hospital, Eday Road, Aberdeen AB15 6XS Tel: 01224 556040 Fax: 01224 556232; 7 Primrosehill Road, Cults, Aberdeen AB15 9ND Tel: 01224 868745 — MD 1987 Aberd.; MB ChB 1970; FRCP Ed. 1992; FFR RCSI 1978; Dip. Sports Med. Scotl. 1992; DMRD Aberd. 1975; FRCR 1997. (Aberdeen) Cons. Radiol. Grampian Univ. Hosp. NHS Trust; Prof. of Health Sci.s, The Robt. Gordon Univ. Aberd.. Socs: Scott. Inst. Sports Med. & Sports Sci.; Internat. Soc. Magnetic Resonance in Med.; Brit. Inst. Radiol. Prev: Cons. Nuclear Med. Aberd. Roy. Hosp. NHS Trust.

SMITH, Mr Frank Charles Theodore University Department of Surgery, Level 7, Bristol Royal Infirmary, Bristol BS2 8HW Tel: 0117 9272 696; The Old Halt, Downleaze, Sneed Park, Bristol BS9 1NA — MB ChB 1984 Birmingham; BSc (Hons.) Pharmacol. Birm. 1981; FRCS 1990 England; FRCS 1989 Edinburgh; FRCS 1989 Glasgow; MD 2000 Birmingham. Cons. Sen. Lect. (Gen. & Vasc. Surg.) Univ. Bristol Bristol Roy. Infirm.; Vis. Cons. (Vasc. Surg.) W.on Gen. Hosp. Socs: Surgic. Research Soc.; Eur. Soc. Vasc. Surg.; Vasc. Surgic. Soc. Prev: Sen. Regist. Rotat. (Gen. & Vasc. Surg.) SW RHA; Career Regist. Rotat. (Surg.) W. Midl. RHA; Research Fell. (Vasc. Surg.) Qu. Eliz. Hosp. Birm.

SMITH, Frank Reginald (retired) Elm Bank, Oak Hill, East Budleigh, Budleigh Salterton EX9 7DW Tel: 0139 543537 — MB ChB 1929 Birm.; MRCS Eng. LRCP Lond. 1935.

SMITH, Frederic M S (retired) Fairview, 176 Stony Lane, Burton, Christchurch BH23 7LD Tel: 0135 48 485375 — MRCS Eng. LRCP Lond. 1939. Prev: GP Dorset.

SMITH, Mr Frederick 37 Broadsway, Morecambe LA4 5BQ Tel: 01524 410096 — MD Manch. 1968, MB ChB 1951, DPH 1962; FRCS Ed. 1978; MRCP (UK) 1984; FRCGP 1985; DCH Eng. 1959, DIH 1964; DObst RCOG 1960. Socs: Fell. Manch. Med. Soc.; Manch. Med. Soc. Prev: Asst. Div. Med. Off. Lancs. CC; Rotating Intern N.ampton Gen. Hosp; Nuffield Research Fell. Manch. Univ.

SMITH, Frederick Duncan X-Ray Department, Derbyshire Royal Infirmary, London Road, Derby DE1 2QY — MB ChB 1976 Sheff.; MRCP (UK) 1979; FRCR 1985. Cons. Radiol. S.. Derbysh. HA.

SMITH, Frederick George Mammatt 10 Park Crescent, Merthyr Tydfil CF47 0EU — MB ChB 1943 Glas.; DObst RCOG 1949. (Univ. Glas.) Prev: Regist. Luton Matern. Hosp.; Ho. Surg. Co. Lanark Matern. Hosp. Bellshill; Ho. Phys. Stobhill Hosp. Glas.

SMITH, Freya Marion Pollokshaws Doctors Centre, 26 Wellgreen, Glasgow G43 1RR Tel: 0141 649 2836 Fax: 0141 649 5238; 28 Sherbrooke Drive, Glasgow G41 5AA Tel: 0141 427 9524 — MB ChB 1978 Ed.; MPhil Glas. 1994; MRCGP 1982; DRCOG 1981.

SMITH, Gareth David Phelps Neurology Department, Taunton and Somerset NHS Trust, Musgrove Park, Taunton TA1 5DA Tel: 01823 342137 Fax: 01823 324209 — MB BCh 1984 Wales; MRCP UK. 1988; MD 1996. Cons. NeUrol. Taunton and Som. NHS Trus; Cons. NeUrol. Yeovil NHS Trust. Socs: Assn. Brit. NeUrol.s. Prev: Sen. Regist. (Neurol Bristol); Regist. (Med.) Plymouth.; Research Fell. Autonomic Unit Inst. Neurol. Qu. Sq. Lond.

SMITH, Gareth Lindsay 31 Regent Park Square, Glasgow G41 2AF — MB ChB 1992 Aberd.

SMITH, Garry Michael 100 St Richards Road, Deal CT14 9LD — BM 1998 Soton.; BM Soton 1998.

SMITH, Gary Brian c/o Department of Intensive Care Medicine, Queen Alexandra Hospital, Portsmouth PO6 3LY Tel: 023 92 286844 Fax: 023 92 286967 Email: gary.smith@porthosp.nhs.uk — BM 1977 Soton.; FRCA 1981; FCRP 2000. (Soton.) Cons. in Intens. Care Med., Portsmouth Hosp. NHS Trust; Honarary Sen. Lect. in Critical Care, Sch. of PostGrad. Med., Univ. of Portsmouth. Socs: Assn. Anaesth.; Coun. Mem. of Intens. Care Soc.; Roy. Soc. Med. Prev: Sen. Regist. (Anaesth.) Soton. Gen. & Portsmouth Hosps.; Instruc. (Anaesth.) Yale Univ., USA; Regist. (Anaesth.) Bristol Roy. Infirm.

SMITH, Geoffrey 3 Hall Court, Ravenfield Lane, Rotherham S65 4QZ — MB ChB 1983 Ed.; MSc Lond. 1987; MRCPath 1995.

SMITH, Geoffrey Barry, OStJ, TD (retired) Lutterworth, The Square, South Harting, Petersfield GU31 5PZ Tel: 01730 825336 — MB BS 1957 Lond.; MRCS Eng. LRCP Lond. 1957; FFA RCS Eng. 1963; DA Eng. 1959. Prev: Cons. Anaesth. Moorfields Eye Hosp. Lond.

SMITH, Geoffrey Charlton (retired) 16 Kelsey Close, Hunstanton PE36 6HL Tel: 01485 532955 Fax: 01485 532955 Email: jgsmith@btinternet.com — MRCS Eng. LRCP Lond. 1957; DObst RCOG 1961. Prev: Pres. Med. Commiss. Internat. Water Ski Federat.

SMITH, Geoffrey Francis 118 Redland Road, Redland, Bristol BS6 6QT Tel: 0117 947502 — MB ChB 1951 Manch.; FFOM RCP Lond. 1985; DIH Soc. Apoth. Lond. 1958; DObst RCOG 1953. (Manch.) Regional Med. Off. S.W. Brit. Telecom. Socs: Soc. Occupat. Med.

SMITH, Professor Geoffrey Harry Stable House, Main St., Great Longstone, Bakewell DE45 1TZ Tel: 01629 640143 Fax: 01629 640852 Email: geoffrey@smithderby.freeserve.co.uk — MB BS 1961 Lond.; MB BS (Hons.) Lond. 1961 Distinction in Surgery; FRCS Eng. 1965; MRCS Eng. LRCP Lond. 1961. (St. Mary's) Med. Advisor Brit. Counc. Socs: Soc. Cardiothoracic Surgs. GB & Irel.; Eur. Assn. Cardiothoracic Surg. Prev: Vis. Prof. Cardiac Surg. Norrlands Univ. Sweden; Prof. Cardiac Surg. Univ. Sheff.; Sen. Regist. (Surg.) Hosps. For Dis. of Chest.

SMITH, Geoffrey John Medical Centre, The Grove, Rowlands Gill NE39 1PW Tel: 01207 542136 Fax: 01207 543340; 6 Greenhead Terrace, Chopwell, Newcastle upon Tyne NE17 7AH Tel: 01207 562227 — MB ChB 1983 Aberd.; MRCGP 1988. Prev: Regist. (Gen. Med.) Rockhampton Base Hosp. Qu.sland., Austral.

SMITH, Geoffrey Keay 70 New Wokingham Road, Crowthorne RG45 6JJ — MB ChB 1993 Birm.

SMITH, Geoffrey Leighton 15 Attlee Terrace, Maesteg CF34 0YF; 50 Parc Tynywaun, Llangynwyd, Maesteg CF34 9RG — MB BS 1993 Lond. (St. George's Hosp. Med. Sch.) GP. Prev: Trainee GP Bridgend VTS.

SMITH, Geoffrey Paul 4 Bowes Lyon Place, Lytham St Annes FY8 3UE — MB BS 1994 Lond.

SMITH, Geoffrey Taylor Worcester Royal Infirmary, Castle St., Worcester WR1 3AS Tel: 01905 25238; Tutnall House, Claines Lane, Claines, Worcester WR3 7RN — MB ChB 1975 Sheff.; MRC Path. 1981. Cons. Histopath. Worcester Roy. Infirm.

SMITH, Geoffrey Vincent Digestive Diseases Research Centre, 2 Newark St, Whitechapel, London E1 Tel: 020 7295 7203 Email: g.v.smith@mds.qmw.ac.uk; 26 Aberavon Road, Bow, London E3 5AR Tel: 020 8880 6839 — MB BS 1993 Lond.; MRCP (UK) 1997. (Lond. Hosp. Med. Coll.) Specialist Regist. (Gastroenterol. &

SMITH

Gen. Internal Med.) NE Thames. Prev: SHO (High Dependency Med.) St. Thos. Hosp. Lond.; SHO (Haemat. & Oncol.) St. Bart. Hosp. Lond.; SHO Rotat. (Med.) Roy. Lond. Hosp.

SMITH, George (retired) 18 South Brommage Avenue, Larbert FK5 3LF Tel: 01324 562482 — LRCP LRCS Ed., LRCS LRFPS Glas. 1939; LRCP LRCS Ed., LRFPS Glas. 1939. JP. Prev: Ho. Surg. W.. Dist. Hosp. Glas.

SMITH, George Intensive Therapy Unit, Aberdeen Royal Infirmary, Foresterhill, Aberdeen AB25 Tel: 01224 552970 Fax: 01224 840724; Tel: 01224 861744 — MB ChB 1970 Aberd.; FFA RCS Eng. 1977; DObst RCOG 1973; DA Eng. 1973. (Aberd.) Cons Anaesth. & Intens. Care Med.Aberd Roy. Infirm. Socs: BMA; Intens. Care Soc.; Scott. Intens. Care Soc. Prev: Sen. Regist. (Anaesth.) Nottm. City Hosp. Derbysh. Roy. Infirm. & The Groby Rd. Hosp. Leicester; Squadron Ldr. (Rtd.) RAF Med. Br.

SMITH, George Dobbie Department of Pathology, Ninewells Hospital and Medical School, Dundee DD1 9SY Tel: 01382 660111 32548 Email: george.d.smith@tuht.scot.nhs.uk; East Lynwood, 2 Douglas Avenue, Lenzie, Glasgow G66 4NU — MB ChB 1977 Glas.; BSc (Hons.) Glas. 1973; MRCPath 1983; Dip. Forens. Med. Glas. 1990; FRCPath 1995. Cons. Path. Ninewells Hosp. & Med. Sch. Dundee (Tayside Univ. Hosp. NHS Trust). Socs: Path. Soc.; Assn. Clin. Path.; Internat. Acad. of Path. Prev: Cons. Path. Admin. Charge Stobhill Gen. Hosp. Glas.; Lect. (Path.) Univ. Edin.; Hon. Sen. Regist. (Path.) Lothian HB.

SMITH, George Lindsay (retired) Creag Ruadh, 13 Balfour Crescent, Milnathort, Kinross KY13 9TA Tel: 01577 864911 — MB ChB Glas. 1950; DObst RCOG 1954. Prev: Clin. Asst. (Community Med.) Fife HB.

SMITH, George William (retired) 6 Hop Gardens, Henley-on-Thames RG9 2EH — MRCS Eng. LRCP Lond. 1950. Prev: Clin. Asst. (Dermat.) Heatherwood Hosp., King Edwd. VII Hosp., Windsor.

SMITH, Georgina Ann 42 Hyde Terrace, Newcastle upon Tyne NE3 1AT — MB BS 1997 Newc.

SMITH, Gerald Martin 26 Abercorn Place, St. John's Wood, London NW8 9XP Tel: 01895 232102 Fax: 01895 235969 Email: geraldmsmith@msn.com — MB BS 1983 Lond.

SMITH, Gerald Norman Haematology Department, Guys Hospital, St Thomas St., London SE1 9RT Tel: 020 7955 4609 Fax: 020 7955 4002; 23 Burlington Road, Chiswick, London W4 4BQ Tel: 020 8995 9008 — MB BS Lond. 1964; PhD Lond. 1976, BSc 1961; FRCPath 1986, M 1975. (St. Mary's) Cons. Haemat. Guy's & St. Thos. Trust. Prev: Cons. Haemat. N.wick Pk. Hosp. Harrow; Sen. Regist. (Haemat.) St. Thos. Hosp. Lond.; on Scientif. Staff MRC Haemat. Unit St. Mary's Hosp. Med. Sch.

SMITH, Gideon Paul 91 Harpers Lane, Bolton BL1 6HU — MB ChB 1982 Manch. Cons. Pub. Health Med. & Communicable Dis. Control Wigan & Bolton HA.

SMITH, Gilbert Reginald The Birmingham Medical Clinic, 69-71 Whitehead Road, Aston, Birmingham B6 5EL Tel: 0121 327 2255 Fax: 0121 327 2255; 79 Farquhar Road, Edgbaston, Birmingham B15 2QP Tel: 0121 454 6969 — MB ChB 1954 Birm. Indep. GP Birm. Socs: Sands Cox Soc. Birm. Grad.s.

SMITH, Giles Rowan Grove Surgery, Grove Lane, Thetford IP24 2HY Tel: 01842 752285 Fax: 01842 751316 — MB ChB 1971 Birm.; MRCP (UK) 1975.

SMITH, Gillian Brindle 35 Milbourne Lane, Esher KT10 9EB — MB ChB 1972 Liverp.; FFA RCS Eng. 1977. Cons. Anaesth. Kingston Hosp. Kingston upon Thames. Socs: Intractable Pain Soc. Prev: Sen. Regist. Dept. Anaesth. W.m. Hosp. Lond.

SMITH, Gillian Dawn 69 Prince George Avenue, Southgate, London N14 4TL — MB BCh 1989 Wales; FRCS Ed. 1994. Specialist Regist. (Plastic Surg.) Selly Oak Hosp. Birm.; Clin. Hand Fell., Gt. Ormond St. Hosp., Lond. Prev: SPR (Plastic Surg.) City Gen. Hosp., Stoke-on-Trent; SPR (Plastic Surg.) Birm. Childr.'s Hosp.; SPR (Plastic Surg.) Selly Oak Hosp., Birm.

SMITH, Gillian Deborah Longfleet House Surgery, 56 Longfleet Road, Poole BH15 2JD Tel: 01202 666677 Fax: 01202 660319; 7 Greenwood Avenue, Lilliput, Poole BH14 8QD — BM 1983 Soton.; BM (Hons.) Soton. 1983. (Southampton)

SMITH, Gillian Lesley Ferguson Department of Oral Medicine, Glasgow Dental Hospital & School, 378 Sauchiehall St., Glasgow G2 3JZ Tel: 0141 211 9600 — MB ChB 1996 Ed.; Intercollegiate Diploma Oral Med. 1999; PhD Ed. 1985; BDS Ed. 1982; FDS RCS Ed. 1990. Cons./Hon. Sen. Lect. Oral Med., Glas. Dent. Hosp. & Sch. Socs: BMA; Brit. Soc. Oral Med.; Internat. Assn. Dent. Research. Prev: Regist. (Oral Med.) Glas. Dent. Hosp. & Sch.; Preregistration Ho. Off. (Med.) (W.. Gen. Edin.) & Surg. (E. Gen. Edin.); Lect. Oral Med. Dent. Sch. Edin.

SMITH, Miss Gillian Louise Flat 2, 98 Greencroft Gardens, London NW6 3PH — MB BS 1990 Lond.; MA Oxf. 1993, BA 1987; FRCS Eng. 1995; FRCS Ed. 1994.

SMITH, Gillian Margaret Flat 3, 6 Albany Road, Bexhill-on-Sea TN40 1BZ — MB BCh BAO 1977 Belf.; MRCPsych 1982. SCMO (Adult Psychiat.) Bexhill-on-Sea.

SMITH, Gillian Wilson Rotherham District General Hospital, Moorgate Road, Oakwood, Rotherham S60 2UD Tel: 01709 304169 Fax: 01709 304276 Email: smith.sec@rgh-tr.trent.nhs.uk — MB ChB 1982 Ed.; FRCP Lond. 2001; BSc (Hons.) Glas. 1979; MD Ed. 1993; MRCP (UK) 1988. Cons. Rheumat. Rotherham Dist. Gen. Hosp. Rotherham. Socs: Collegiate Mem. RCP Edin.; Brit. Soc. Rheum.; BMA. Prev: Sen. Regist. (Rheum. & Gen. Med.) Rheumatic Dis. Unit W.ern Gen. Hosp. Edin.; Research Fell. & Regist. (Rheum.) Rheum. Dis. Unit W.ern Gen. Hosp. Edin.; Regist. Rotat. (Gen. Med.) Liverp. Hosps.

SMITH, Gladys Honeyman 325A Albert Drive, Glasgow G41 5EA — MB ChB 1962 Glas. (Glas.)

SMITH, Godfrey William Thomas 106 Warwick Road, Bounds Green, London N11 2ST Tel: 020 8361 2127 — MB BChir 1976 Camb.; MB Camb. 1976, MA, BChir 1975; MRCP (UK) 1979. (Middlx.) Lect. (Med. Microbiol.) Roy. Free Hosp. Lond. Socs: Fell. Roy. Soc. Med. Prev: Resid. Med. Off. Nat. Heart Hosp. SHO (Neurol.) Radcliffe Infirm.; Oxf.; SHO (Thoracic Med.) Brompton Hosp. Lond.

SMITH, Mr Gordon Western General Hospital, Crewe Road, Edinburgh EH4 2XU; 137 Mayfield Road, Edinburgh EH9 3AN Tel: 0131 668 3683 Fax: 0131 668 3683 Email: smith_gordon_edin_uro@msn.com — MB ChB 1976 Ed.; FRCS Glas. 1981. Cons. Urol. W.. Gen. Hosp. Trust Edin.

SMITH, Professor Gordon Campbell Sinclair Department of Obstetrics & Gynaecology, Rosie Hospital, Robinson Way, Cambridge CB2 2SW — MB ChB 1987 Glas.; MD 1995; MRCOG 1995; PhD 2001; BSc (1st cl. Hons.) Physiol. Glas. 1987. Prof., Obst. & Gyn., Camb. Univ, Cambr. Socs: Mem. of the Roy. Coll. of Obst.s & Gynaecologists. Prev: Sub-Specialist Trainee Matern. Fetal Med., Glas.; Clin. Research Fell. Cornell Univ. USA.

SMITH, Gordon Francis Nelson Department of Anaesthetics, Victoria Hospital, Hayfield Road, Kirkcaldy KY2 5AH Tel: 01592 643355; 1 Silverbank, Leslie Road, Scotlandwell, Kinross KY13 9JE Tel: 01592 840484 Email: gasicv@aol.com — MB ChB 1971 Glas.; FFA RCS Eng. 1976. Cons. Anaesth. Vict. Hosp. Kirkcaldy, Fife Acute Hosps. NHS Trust.; Clin. Director, Theatre & Anaesthetics, Fife Acute Hosps. NHS Trust. Socs: BMA; Assn. of Anaesth.; Scott. Soc. Anaesth.

SMITH, Mr Gordon Graham (retired) Mullagrach, Polbain, Achiltibuie, Ullapool IV26 2YW — MB ChB 1966 Glas.; FRCS Glas. 1978; CIH Dund 1974. Cons. ENT Surg. Vict. Hosp. Kirkcaldy. Prev: Ho. Off. (Surg. & Med.) Glas. Roy. Infirm.

SMITH, Gordon Stirling 9 St Mary's Court, Porthcawl CF36 5SD — MB ChB 1970 Sheff.

SMITH, Graeme Angus 7 Wykeham Road, Glasgow G13 3YP — MB ChB 1993 Aberd. SHO Rotat. (Surg.) W.. Infirm. Glas.

SMITH, Graeme Murray Dept. of Haematology, Leeds General Infirmary, Great George St., Leeds LS1 3EX Email: graemes@pathology.leeds.ac.uk — MD Lond. 1992, MB BS 1980; FRCP (UK) 1997; FRCPath 1998. (Guy's) Cons. Haemat. Leeds Gen. Infirm. & Wharfedale Gen. Hosp. Otley. Socs: Brit. Soc. Haematol. Prev: Sen. Regist. (Haemat.) Yorks. RHA; Hon. Regist. (Haemat.) E. Birm. Hosp.; Regist. (Chest & Gen. Med.) Walsgrave Hosp. Coventry.

SMITH, Graham (retired) Inbhir-Vig, Borve, Isle of Lewis HS2 0RU Tel: 01851 850327 — MB BS 1954 Durh. Prev: Ho. Surg. & Ho. Phys. Newc. Gen. Hosp.

SMITH, Professor Graham University Department of Anaesthesia, Leicester Royal Infirmary, Leicester LE1 5WW Tel: 0116 258 5291 Fax: 0116 285 4487; 12 Sycamore Close, Oadby, Leicester LE2 2RN — MRCS Eng. LRCP Lond. 1966; BSc Lond. 1963, MD 1972, MB BS 1966; FRCA. 1969. (Guy's) Prof. Anaesth. Univ. Leicester; Hon.

Cons. (Anaesth.) Leicester DHA; Edr. Brit. Jl. Anaesth.; Acad. Europ. Acad. Anaesth. Socs: (Counc.) Roy. Coll. anaesth.; Hon. Mem. Amer. Assn. Univ. Anaesthesiol. Prev: Sen. Lect. (Anaesth.) Univ. Glas.; Cons. Anaesth. W.. Infirm. Glas.; MRC Trav. Fell. (Anaesthesiol.) Univ. Washington, USA.

SMITH, Graham Colin Department of Child Health, University Hospital of Wales, Heath Park, Cardiff CF4 4XN Tel: 029 2074 3310 Fax: 029 20944822 Email: smithgc@cardiff.ac.uk; 5 Ffordd Bodlyn, Sovereign Chase, Cynloed, Cardiff CF23 5NG Tel: 029 2074 4822 — MB BS 1986 Lond.; MA Camb. 1984; MRCP (UK) 1989. Cons. Paediat. Nephrol. Univ. Hosp. of Wales. Socs: Brit. Assn. Paediat. Nephrol.; Fell. Roy. Coll. Paediat. and Child Health; Eur. Soc. Paediat. Nephrol. Prev: Sen. Regist. (Paediat.) Roy. Hosp. Sick Childr. Glas.; Fell. (Paediat. Nephrol.) Hosp. Sick Childr. Toronto, Canada; Research Fell. (Paediat. Nephrol.) Birm. CHildr. Hosp.

SMITH, Graham David North Manchester General Hospital, Crumpsall, Manchester M8 5RL Tel: 0161 795 4567 Email: graham.d.smith@dial.pipex.com; 1 Gloucester Place, Cheltenham GL52 2RJ Tel: 01242 250099 — MB ChB 1996 Bristol. (Bristol) SHO (Surg.) N. Manc Gen Hosp. Socs: BMA (Jun. Doctor). Prev: SHO(A & E) Gloucestershire Roy Hosp; SHO (A&E/Trauma) Gloucestershire Roy Hosp.

SMITH, Graham Douglas Guardian Street Medical Centre, Guardian Street, Warrington WA5 1UD Tel: 01925 650226 Fax: 01925 240633 — MB ChB 1970 Liverp.

SMITH, Graham ian Itchen Down Farm, Itchen Abbas, Winchester SO21 1BS Tel: 01962 779963 — MB ChB 1996 Bristol; BDS (Hons.) 1991; FDS RCS Eng. 1996. Sen. SHO (Oral & Maxillofacial Surg.) Soton. Socs: BMA; BAOMS; RCS (Eng.). Prev: SHO (Orthop.) RHCH Winchester; SHO (Gen. Surg.) Soton.

SMITH, Graham Lawrence Rainbow Medical Centre, 333 Robins Lane, St Helens WA9 3PN Tel: 01744 811211; 35 Ashton Avenue, Rainhill, Prescot L35 0QQ — MB ChB 1978 Liverp.; DRCOG 1982.

SMITH, Graham Michael 46 Quarry Street, Leeds LS6 2JU — MB ChB 1994 Leeds.

SMITH, Mr Graham Munro (retired) 1 Sycamore Close, Knighton Rise, Oadby, Leicester LE2 2RN Tel: 0116 270 8304 — MB ChB 1960 Glas.; FRCOG 1980, M 1967; DObst RCOG 1961. Cons. O & G Gen. Hosp. Leicester. Prev: Sen. Regist. Nottm. Hosp. Wom. & Jessop Hosp. Wom. Sheff.

SMITH, Graham Nicholas Community Mental Health Unit, St. Charles Hospital, Exmoor St., London W10 6DZ — MB BS 1986 Lond. Clin. Asst. (Psychiat.) St. Chas. Hosp. Lond. Prev: SHO (Psychiat.) P.ss Alexandra Hosp. Harlow; Ho. Off. (Med.) S. Cleveland Hosp. Middlesbrough; Ho. Off. (Surg.) St. Helier Hosp. Carshalton.

SMITH, Graham Thomas Hexworthy House, Lawhitton, Launceston PL15 9PE Tel: 01566 777024 — BM BCh Oxf. 1962; MA Oxf. 1962. (St. Geo.)

SMITH, Graham Yates Govanhill Health Centre, 233 Calder St., Glasgow G42 7DR Tel: 0141 424 3003; 19 Rozelle Avenue, Newton Mearns, Glasgow G77 6YS — MB ChB 1983 Glas.; MRCGP 1987; DRCOG 1986.

SMITH, Grahame Bower 12 Almondbury Close, Almondbury, Huddersfield HD5 8XX — MB ChB 1966 Manch.; MRCP (U.K.) 1971. Cons. Phys. (Geriat. Med.) Bradford AHA. Prev: Cons. Phys. (Geriat. Med.) Doncaster AHA. Late Sen. Regist . N..; Gen. Hosp. Sheff.

SMITH, Grahame David Northgate Surgery, Northgate, Pontefract WF8 1NF Tel: 01977 703635 Fax: 01977 702562; 54 Carleton Road, Pontefract WF8 3NF Tel: 01977 600880 Email: grahamesmith1@compuserve.com — MB BS 1968 Lond.; Dip. Clin. Hypn. Sheff. 1991; DA Eng. 1973; DObst RCOG 1970. (Univ. Coll. Hosp.) Local Med. Off. Civil Serv. Med. Advis. Serv. Socs: Accredit. Mem. Brit. Soc. Med. & Dent. Hypn. Prev: Hosp. Pract. (Anaesth.) Pontefract & Wakefield; Med. Off. i/c Governm. Hosp. Mankayane, Swaziland; SHO (Paediat.) Worcester Roy. Infirm.

SMITH, Guy Courteney 15 Trenchasrd Meadow, Lytchett Matravers, Poole BH16 6NA — LMSSA 1953 Lond.; MB BS Lond. 1956.

SMITH, Mr Guy St John Tristram 27 Murray Road, Ealing, London W5 4XR — MB BS 1994 Lond.; BSc (Hons.) 1991; FRCOphth 1998. (St Thomas' Hospital, UMDS, London University)

SHO (Ophth.) Sussex Eye Hosp. Brighton. Socs: Undersea & Hyperbaric Med. Soc.

SMITH, Gwendoline (retired) St. Monance, Coggins Mill, Mayfield TN20 6UL Tel: 01435 2301 — MRCS Eng. LRCP Lond. 1926; MD Lond. 1930, MB BS 1926; FRCS Eng. 1929. Prev: Surg. S. Lond. Hosp. Wom. & Childr.

SMITH, Harold Rubislaw Terrace Surgery, 23 Rubislaw Terrace, Aberdeen AB10 1XE Tel: 01224 643665 Fax: 01224 625197 — MB ChB 1973 Aberdeen; MB ChB 1973 Aberdeen.

SMITH, Harry Charles Thomson 12 Avondale Road, Ponteland, Newcastle upon Tyne NE20 9NA Tel: 01661 823636 Fax: 01661 823636 — MB ChB St. And. 1951; DPA Glas. 1960; DPH Glas. 1956. Prev: SCM (EnviroMent. Health) Gateshead HA.

SMITH, Harry Napier Far Lane Medical Centre, 1 Far Lane, Sheffield S6 4FA Tel: 0114 234 3229; 10 Moorbank Close, Sheffield S10 5TP — MB ChB 1969 Sheff.; MRCGP 1977; DObst RCOG 1971.

SMITH, Harvey Ronald 19 Arlington Place, Gordon Road, Winchester SO23 7TR — MB BS 1990 Lond.

SMITH, Heather Jane 2 Norfolk Hill Croft, Greoside, Sheffield S35 8SE — MB BS 1991 Lond.; MRCGP 1995.

SMITH, Heather Joy Macklin Street Surgery, 90 Macklin Street, Derby DE1 2JX Tel: 01332 340381 Fax: 01332 345387; 36 South Avenue, Littleover, Derby DE23 6BA Tel: 01332 765020 — BM BS 1988 Nottm.; BMedSci Nottm. 1986; MRCGP 1993. (Nottm.) Clin. Asst. (Palliat. Med.) Nightingale Continuing Care Macmillan Unit, Derby. Prev: Trainee GP Derby VTS; SHO/Macmillan Fell. Hayward Hse. Nottm. City Hosp.

SMITH, Heather Lesley Department of Paediatrics, The General Hospital, Bishop Auckland DL14 6AD Tel: 01388 454000 Fax: 01388 454107; Tel: 01388 663996 — MB BS 1979 Lond.; Cert Med Educat 2001 Univ. Newc. upon Tyne; MRCS Eng. LRCP Lond. 1979; FRCP (UK) 1997, MRCP 1982; FRCPCH 1997; DCH RCP Lond. 1982. Cons. Paediat. Bishop Auckland Gen. Hosp. Socs: Brit. Soc. Paediat. Gastroenterol. & Nutrit.; Fell. Roy. Coll. Paediat. & Child Health; Fell. Roy. Coll. of Phys. Prev: Sen. Regist. (Paediat.) S. Cleveland Hosp. Middlesbrough; Clin. Research Fell. Inst. Child Health Univ. Birm.; Regist. (Paediat.) Leicester Roy. Infirm.

SMITH, Helen Elizabeth Primary Medical Care, Aldermoor Health Centre, Aldermoor Close, Southampton SO16 5ST Tel: 02380 797740 Fax: 02380 701125 Email: hes@soton.ac.uk; 72 Westwood Road, Southampton SO17 1DP — BM BS 1981 Nottm.; MSc (Comm. Med.) Lond. 1988; DM Nottm. 1996, BMedSci 1979; MFPHM RCP Lond. 1989; DCH RCP Lond. 1983. (Nottingham) Dir. Wessex Research Network; Sen. Lect. (Primary Care) Univ. Soton. Socs: Soc. Social Med.; AUDGP; WONCA. Prev: Vis. Sc. Univ. Brit. Columbia Health Care & Epidemiol. Vancouver; Sen. Regist. (Pub. Health Med.) W. Midl. RHA; Regist. (Community Med.) SW Thames RHA.

***SMITH, Helen Jane** 79 Bower Mount Road, Maidstone ME16 8AS Email: drhjsmith@hotmail.com — MB ChB 1996 Birm.; DRCOG 1998.

SMITH, Helen Leisa 27 King Edgar Close, Ely CB6 1DP Tel: 01353 669018 Fax: 01353 669175 — MB BS 1989 Lond.; FRCA 1993; DA (UK) 1991. (University Colege London) Specialist. Regist. (Anaesth.) Addenbrookes's Hosp. Camb. Socs: Train. Mem. Assn. AnE.h. Prev: Regist. (Anaesth.) Addenbrooke's Hosp. Camb.; SHO (Anaesth.) Hammersmith Hosp. & Edgware Gen. Hosp. Lond.

SMITH, Helen Lesley Ninewells Hospital & Medical School, Dundee DD1 9SY — MB ChB 1997 Dundee.

SMITH, Helen Mary Ash-View, Tamworth Rd, Corley, Coventry CV7 8BQ — MB ChB 1990 Birm.; ChB Birm. 1990.

SMITH, Helen Muriel (retired) Kilmory, Burbo Bank Road, Blundellsands, Liverpool L23 6TH Tel: 0151 924 3063 — MB ChB Liverp. 1940. Prev: Clin. Med. Off. Liverp. AHA.

SMITH, Helen Patricia 590 King Street, Aberdeen AB24 5SQ — MB ChB 1997 Aberd.

SMITH, Helena Rebecca 133 Higher Lane, Whitefield, Manchester M45 7WH — MB ChB 1991 Liverp.

SMITH, Hilary Maltings Surgery, 8 Victoria Street, St Albans AL1 3JB Tel: 01727 855500 Fax: 01727 845537; 4 Faircross Way, St Albans AL1 4SD — MB BS 1976 Lond.; MRCGP Lond. 1981. (Univ. Coll. Hosp.) GP Trainer W. Herts. HA.

SMITH

SMITH, Hilary Louise 97 Mountbatten Avenue, Wakefield WF2 6HH — MB ChB 1993 Birm.; DRCOG 1996.

SMITH, Miss Hilary Margaret 7 Highfield Crescent, Taunton TA1 5JH Tel: 01823 283323 — MB BS 1967 Lond.; DA Eng. 1970; FRCOG 1986, M 1974, DObst 1970. (Lond. Hosp.) Cons. (O & G) MusGr. Pk. Hosp. Prev: Regist. & Sen. Regist. Lond. Hosp.; Regist. MusGr. Pk. Hosp. Taunton.

SMITH, Hilary Royle 1 Railway Path, Ormskirk L39 4TR — MB ChB 1987 Dundee.

SMITH, Hillas George 24 Oakleigh Avenue, Whetstone, London N20 9JH Tel: 020 8445 1876 — MB BCh BAO 1951 Dub.; BA Dub. 1948, MA, MD 1961, MB BCh BAO 1951; FRCP Lond. 1975, M 1964. (T.C. Dub.) Cons. Phys. Roy. Free Hosp., Dept. Infec. Dis. Coppetts Wood Hosp.; Lister Unit N.wick Pk. Hosp. Harrow; Emerit. Edr. Jl. Infec. Prev: Leverhulme Research Schol. Middlx. Hosp.; Ho. Off. Char. Cross Med. Unit, Mt. Vernon Hosp. N.wood & Adelaide; Hosp. Dub.

SMITH, Hillas Rodney Freiern Watch Avenue Surgery, 1 Friern Watch Avenue, London N12 9NX Tel: 020 8445 2352 Fax: 020 8445 2352; 49 Crescent W., Hadley Wood, Barnet EN4 0EQ Tel: 020 8440 4774 — MB BS 1981 Lond.; BSc (Hons.) Lond. 1978, MB BS 1981; MRCGP 1986; DRCOG 1984. Clin. Asst. (Dermat.) Barnet Gen. Hosp. Prev: Whipps Cross Hosp. VTS; Trainee Highgate Gp. Pract. Lond.

SMITH, Mr Howard Duncan (retired) 42 Hayes Road, Bromley BR2 9AA — MB BS Lond. 1961; FRCS Eng. 1967. Prev: Sen. Regist. (Orthop.) St. Bart. Hosp. Lond.

SMITH, Howard George 61 Stafford Place, Weston-super-Mare BS23 2QZ Fax: 01934 627300 — MB ChB 1966 Bristol; MRCPsych 1975; DPM Eng. 1972.

SMITH, Howard Stephen anaesthetics Dept, Peterborough District Hospital, Thorpe Road, Peterborough PE3 6DA Tel: 01733874000 Email: howard.s.smith@tesco.net — MB BS 1972 Lond.; MRCS Eng. LRCP Lond. 1972; FFA RCS Eng. 1980. (Lond. Hosp.) Cons. (Anaesth. & IC) PeterBoro. Dist. Hosps. PeterBoro., Camb. Prev: Sen. Regist. Cambs. AHA (T); Sen. Specialist (Anaesth.) RAF.

SMITH, Hugh Norman, MC (retired) 9 Harvey Orchard, Beaconsfield HP9 1TH Tel: 01494 673830 — MRCS Eng. LRCP Lond. 1942; MA Camb. 1946. JP.; Maj. RAMC TARO. Prev: GP Beaconsfield.

SMITH, Iain David Gartnavel Royal Hospital, 1055 Great Western Road, Glasgow G12 0XH — MB ChB 1983 Glas.; BSc (Hons.) Glas. 1980, MB ChB 1983; MRCPsych 1987. Cons. & Hon. Sen. Clin. Lect. Gartnavel Roy. Hosp. Prev: Lect. (Psychol. Med.) Univ. Glas.; Regist. (Psychiat.) Argyll & Bute Hosp. Lochgilphead; Regist. (Psychiat.) Dykebar Hosp. Paisley.

SMITH, Iain James 19 Fortis Way, Huddersfield HD3 3WW — MB ChB 1974 Ed.; MBA Leeds 1994; FRCP Ed. 1996; FRCPCH 1996; MPH Leeds 1990. Sen. Lect. (Health Servs. Research) & Hon. Cons. Child Health N. Yorks. HA & N. & Yorks. Regional Exec. Prev: Project Manager Yorks. Health; Lect. (Paediat.) Univ. Leeds.

SMITH, Iain James MacArthur Flat 1FL, 43 Falcon Drive, Edinburgh EH10 4AL — BChir 1990 Camb.

SMITH, Mr Ian 29 Temple Row Close, Colton, Leeds LS15 9HR — MB ChB 1989 Sheff.; FRCS Ed. 1994.

SMITH, Ian 19 Beauclair Drive, Liverpool L15 6XG — MB ChB 1937 Leeds; MRCS Eng. LRCP Lond. 1937. Mem. Liverp. Med. Inst. Prev: Ho. Phys. & Ho. Surg. Oldham Roy. Infirm.

SMITH, Ian Afton Shiel, 8 North Deeside Road, Bieldside, Aberdeen AB15 9AJ Tel: 01224 867799 — MB ChB 1961 Aberd.; FFA RCS Eng. 1969; DObst RCOG 1963. Cons. Anaesth. Aberd. Roy. Infirm. Prev: Obst. Ho. Surg. Dundee Roy. Infirm.; Paediat. Ho. Phys. Inverness Hosp. Gp.; Staff Anaesth. Toronto Gen. Hosp.

SMITH, Ian Directorate of Anaesthesia, North Staffordshire Hospital, Newcastle Road, Stoke-on-Trent ST4 6QG Tel: 01782 553054 Fax: 01782 719754 Email: damsmith@btinternet.com — MB BS 1984 Lond.; BSc Lond. 1981; FRCA Eng. 1988. (Westm.) Cons. & Sen. Lect. N. Staffs. Hosps. Stoke-on-Trent; Vis. Asst. Prof. Univ. Texas S.W.. Med. Center Dallas, Texas. Socs: Coun. Mem. Brit. Assn. of Day Surg.; Chairm. Ambulatory Anaesthetics Subcomm.of the Europ. Soc. of Anaesthosiolists; Coun. Mem. Midl. Soc. of Anaesth.s. Prev: Sen. Regist. (Anaesth.) Midl. Anaesth. Train. Scheme Birm.; Research Fell. Washington Univ. St. Louis, USA; Regist. (Anaesth.) E. Birm. Hosp.

SMITH, Ian Charles Sheringham Medical Practice, Health Centre, Cromer Road, Sheringham NR26 8RT Tel: 01263 822066 Fax: 01263 823890 — BM BS 1985 Nottm.; DRCOG 1992; DCH 1992.

SMITH, Ian Charles 18 Beechgrove Place, Aberdeen AB15 5HF — MB ChB 1992 Aberd.

SMITH, Mr Ian Christopher Evanson Abergele Hospital, Llanfair Road, Abergele LL22 8DP Tel: 01745 832295 Ext: 3483 Email: ian.smith@cd-tr.wales.nhs.uk — MB BS 1987 Lond.; FRCS 2000; FRCS Eng. 1992. (St Georges London) Cons. Orthopaedic Surg., Abergele Hosp. Prev: SHO (Orthop. & Trauma) Rowley Bristow Orthop. Unit St. Peter's Hosp. Chertsey; SHO (Paediat. & Gen. Surg.) St. Geo. Hosp. Lond.; Spec.regist, (trauma & Orthop) Welsch Train. scheme.

SMITH, Ian Douglas Department of Anaesthesia, Princess Margaret Hospital, Okus Road, Swindon SN1 4JU Tel: 01793 536231 — MB BS 1981 Lond.; FRCA 1990; DRCOG 1985. Cons. Anaesth. P.ss Margt. Hosp. Swindon. Prev: Sen. Regist. Trent RHA; Lect. (Anaesth.) Univ. Hong Kong; Regist. NW Thames RHA.

SMITH, Ian Duncan 12 Woodmansterne Road, Carshalton Beeches, Sutton SM5 4JL Tel: 020 8643 4122 Fax: 020 8643 4122; 12 Woodmasterne Road, Carshalton Beeches, Carshalton SM5 4JL Tel: 020 8643 4122 Fax: 020 8643 4122 — MB BS 1955 Lond.; MRCS Eng. LRCP Lond. 1955; MRCGP 1968. (King's Coll. Hosp.) Indep. GP Carshalton; Examr. Scott. Widows & Legal & Gen. Assur. Soc.; Hon. Sec. Sutton & Distance Med. Soc.; Expert Witness. Socs: BMA; Indep. Doctors Forum; Sutton Med. Soc. Prev: Ho. Off. Paediat. & Ho, Off. Surg. (O & G) King's Coll. Hosp. Gp.; HOPhysican St JamesHosp. Lond.

SMITH, Ian Edward The Respiratory Support & Sleep Centre, Papworth Hospital, Papworth Everard, Cambridge CB3 8RE Tel: 01480 830541 Fax: 01480 830620; 31 Leys Avenue, Cambridge CB4 2AN Tel: 01223 368976 — MB BS 1987 Lond.; MD Camb. 1997; MRCP (UK) 1990; MA Camb. 1988, BA 1984; FRCP 2001 (UK). (Caius College Cambridge (Pre-Clinical); Royal London Hospital Medical College) Cons. (Chest Med.) Respirat. Support & Sleep Centre Papworth Hosp. Camb., Addenbrookes Hosp. Camb. & Bedford Hosp.; Assoc. Lect., Univ. of Camb. Socs: Brit. Thorac. Soc.; Brit. Sleep Soc. Prev: Sen. Clin. Fell. (Chest Med.) Respirat. Support & Sleep Centre Papworth Hosp. Camb.; Regist. (Chest Med.) Papworth & Addenbrooke's Hosps. Camb.; SHO (Cardiol.) Brook Hosp. Lond.

SMITH, Professor Ian Edward Royal Marsden Hospital, Downs Road, Sutton SM2 5PT Tel: 020 8661 3280 Fax: 020 8643 0373 Email: ian.smith@rmh.nthames.nhs.uk; Tel: 020 7352 5441 — MB ChB 1971; BSc (Hons.) Ed. 1968, MD 1978.; FRCP Ed. 1984; FRCP Lond. 1988; MRCP (UK) 1973. (Ed.) Cons. Med. Oncol. Roy. Marsden Hosp. Lond. & Sutton Med. Director; Prof. of Cancer Med. Inst. of cancer research. Socs: Amer. Soc. Clin. Oncol. & Brit. Assn. Cancer Phys.; Past Chairm. Assn. Cancer Phys.; Chairm.NCRI Lung Cancer Clin. Studies Gp. Prev: Hon. Sen. Lect. Inst. Cancer Research Lond.; Lect. (Med.) Roy. Marsden Hosp. Sutton; Research Fell. Inst. Cancer Research Sutton.

SMITH, Ian Fairley (retired) 13 The Drive, Kilner Park, Ulverston LA12 0DT Tel: 01229 582144 — MB BChir 1952 Camb.; MA Camb. 1952; MRCS Eng. LRCP Lond. 1952; DCH Eng. 1956; DObst RCOG 1955. Prev: Ho. Off. (O & G) Wom. Hosp. Wolverhampton.

SMITH, Ian Geoffrey Synexus Ltd, Sandringham House, Achurst Park, Chorley PR7 1NY Tel: 01257 230723 Fax: 01257 231981 Email: ian.smith@synexus.co.uk; The Cottage, Grundys Lane, Duxbury, Chorley PR7 4DZ Tel: 012571 266130 — MB ChB 1974 Manch.; BMedSc (Hons.) Dundee 1971. Med. Director, Synexus Ltd.; Hon. Research Fell. (Clin. Chem.) Univ. Liverp.; Hon. Research Fell. (Nuclear Med.) Guy's Hosp. Lond. Prev: Partner in Gen. Pract.

SMITH, Ian Inglis (retired) 15 Mansionhouse Road, Edinburgh EH9 1TZ Tel: 0131 667 4665 — PhD Ed. 1974, MB ChB 1954. Cons. Pathol. Roy. Hosp. Sick Childr. Edin.

SMITH, Ian Lennox Taylor Merstow Green Medical Practice, Merstow Green, Evesham WR11 4BS Tel: 01386 765600 Fax: 01386 446807; 16 Andrews Drive, Evesham WR11 6JN — MB ChB 1982 Birm.; BSc Chem. Glas. 1974. Socs: BMA. Prev: Regist. (O & G) Qu. Eliz. Hosp. Barbados; SHO (Paediat.) Worcester Infirm.; Ho. Off. (Surg.) Worcester Infirm.

SMITH

SMITH, Ian Mark 34 Newport View, Leeds LS6 3BX Tel: 0113 275 9230 Fax: 0113 225 7116 — MB ChB 1997 Leeds; MSc Leeds 1996; BDS Birm. 1988; FDS RCS Eng. 1992.

SMITH, Ian Mark Andrew The New Surgery, Hillyfields Way, Winscombe BS25 1AF Tel: 01934 842211; Hunters Lodge, Cooks Lane, Banwell, Weston Super Mare BS24 0AD Tel: 01934 824135 — MB BS 1987 Lond.; MRCP (UK) 1992; DFFP 1994; T(GP) 1994. GP Princip. Winscombe, Som. Prev: Med. Off. Bethesda Hosp. Kwazulu, RSA.; CMO (Obst. & Paediat.) Maitland Hosp. NSW, Austral.; Trainee GP Cinderford, Glos.

SMITH, Ian Michael 22 Hazel Grove, Stotfold, Hitchin SG5 4JZ — MB ChB 1986 Leeds.

SMITH, Mr Ian Michael ENT Department, Royal Cornwall Hospital (Treliske), Truro TR1 3LJ Tel: 01872 253401/ 2 Fax: 01872 253406; Treveth, Kea, Truro TR3 6AJ Tel: 01872 862805 — MB ChB 1981 Dundee; BDS Dundee 1975; MD Dundee 1993; FRCS Ed. 1983. Cons. ENT Surg. Roy. Cornw. Hosp. (Treliske) Truro. Prev: Sen. Regist. St. Michael's Hosp. Bristol.

SMITH, Ian Robertson Culduthel Road Health Centre, Ardlarich, 15 Culduthel Road, Inverness IV2 4AG Tel: 01463 712233 Fax: 01463 715479; Dromard, 43 Midmills Road, Inverness IV2 3NZ Tel: 01463 236741 — MB ChB 1968 Glas.; FRCGP 1991, M 1975; DObst RCOG 1970. (Glas.) Ness Doc.; Highland Hospice Dir. Socs: Past Pres. Highland Med. Soc.; Past Chairm. N. Scotl. Fac. RCGP. Prev: Ho. Phys. Roy. Alexandra Infirm. Paisley; Ho. Surg. Roy. N.. Infirm. Inverness; Ho. Off. (Obst.) Raigmore Hosp. Inverness.

SMITH, Mr Ian Stanley 16 Albert Drive, Bearsden, Glasgow G61 2PF Tel: 0141 942 7452 — MB ChB 1962 Glas; Dobst RCOG 1964; FRCS 1981 Glas.; FRCS 1967 Ed.; FRCS Glas. 1981; FRCS Ed. 1967; DObst RCOG 1964. Cons. Surg. Vict. Infirm. Glas.

SMITH, Ian Stewart The Department of Clinical Neurophysiology, The General Infirmary at Leeds, Gt George St, Leeds LS1 3EX Tel: 0113 392 3530 Fax: 0113 392 6337 — MB 1974 Camb.; BChir 1973; FRCP Lond. 1995; MRCP (UK) 1975. (Univ. Coll. Hosp.) Cons. Clin. Neurophysiol. Leeds Gen. Infirm. Prev: Sen. Regist. (Clin. Neurophysiol.) Qu. Eliz. Hosp. Birm.; Research Asst. (EEG) Nat. Hosp. Qu. Sq. Lond.; Regist. (Neurol.) Roy. Free Hosp. Lond.

SMITH, Ian William The Surgery, 14 Queenstown Road, Battersea, London SW8 3RX Tel: 020 7622 9295 Fax: 020 7498 5206; Flat 3, 3 Leinster Square, London W2 4PL — MB BS 1984 Lond.; BSc Lond. 1981; MRCGP 1988; DRCOG 1988.

SMITH, Ini Akpan 27 Tranmere Road, London N9 9EJ Tel: 020 8364 2879 — BM BCh 1977 Nigeria.

SMITH, Irene Graham Dumfries & Galloway Royal Infirmary, Bankend Road, Dumfries DG1 4AP — MB ChB 1985 Aberd.; MRCGP 1990; DRCOG 1987. Staff Grade (Geriat. Med.) Dumfries & Galloway Roy. Infirm.

SMITH, Mr Irvine Battinson 3 Holland Park, Barton under Needwood, Burton-on-Trent DE13 8DU Tel: 01283 712734 Fax: 01283 712734 — MB BChir 1947 Camb.; MA Camb., MD 1959, MB BChir 1947; FRCS Eng. 1949; MRCS Eng. LRCP Lond. 1944. (Camb. & Univ. Coll. Hosp.) Prev: Cons. Urol. SE Staffs. Health Dist.; Research Fell. Mayo Foundat. USA; Mem. Counc. Brit. Assn. Urol. Surg.

SMITH, Isabel 23 Burlington Road, Chiswick, London W4 4BQ Tel: 020 8995 9008 — MB BS Lond. 1965; BSc Lond. 1962; FRCP Lond. 1984; FRCPCH 1997; MRCP (UK) 1969; DCH Eng. 1968. (St. Mary's) Cons. Hosp. Sick Childr. Gt. Ormond St. Lond.; Hon. Sen. Lect. Inst. Child Health Lond. Socs: MRCPCH; FRCP.

SMITH, Isabel Frances Anaesthetics, Bromley Hospital, Bromley BR2 9AJ — MB BS 1994 Lond.

SMITH, Isabella Marshall c/o Drive Peter Illingworth, Department of Obstetrics & Gynaecology, Westmead Hospital, Westmead NSW 2145, Australia; 11 Belgrave Place, Edinburgh EH4 3AW — MB ChB 1980 Glas.; MFPHM RCP (UK) 1993; MPH Dundee 1990; MRCGP 1988. Med. Dir. & Cons. Pub. Health Med. Nat. Servs. Div. Edin. Prev: Regist. (Pub. Health Med.) Tayside HB.

SMITH, Mr Ivo (retired) 229 Princes Gardens, London W3 0LU Tel: 020 8992 0939 — MA Camb. 1960, BA 1954, MChir 1965, MB, BChir 1957; FRCS Eng. 1960. Indep. Surg. Lond.; Mem. Med. Appeals Tribunals; Med. Chairm. Pens. Appeal Tribunals. Prev: Cons. Surg. Guy's & Lewisham Trust.

SMITH, Jaclyn Ann 57 Longford Road W., Stockport SK5 6EU — MB ChB 1992 Manch.

SMITH, Jacqueline Cos Lane Medical Practice, Woodside Road, Glenrothes KY7 4AQ Tel: 01592 752100 Fax: 01592 612692; 5 The Row, Letham, Cupar KY15 7RS Tel: 01337 810404 — MB ChB 1988 Dundee; MRCGP 1992; DRCOG 1991.

SMITH, Jacqueline Sarah 148 Campbell Drive, Cardiff CF11 7TQ — MB BCh 1995 Wales.

SMITH, James 6D Golf Court, Strathview Park, Netherlee, Glasgow G44 3LD Tel: 0141 637 1239 — MB ChB Glas. 1938, DPH 1948. (Univ. Glas.)

SMITH, James Core Sorbie (retired) 4 Fullarton Drive, Troon KA10 6LE Tel: 01292 314256 Email: jcss@globalnet.co.uk — MB ChB 1957 Glas.; FRCR 1975; FFR 1970; DMRD Eng. 1968; DObst RCOG 1961. Cons. Radiol. CrossHo. Hosp. Kilmarnock. Prev: Ho. Off. (Obst.) Stobhill Hosp. Glas.

SMITH, Mr James Edward Morgan 21 Swarthmore Road, Selly Oak, Birmingham B29 4NQ Tel: 0121 475 3976 — MB 1947 Calcutta; FRCS Eng. 1951. (Calcutta) Cons. Surg. (Orthop.) Priory Hosp. Birm.; Sen. Clin. Lect. Univ. Birm. Prev: Cons. Surg. Birm. Accid. Hosp.; Sen. Regist. Orthop. Surg. N. Staffs. Roy. Infirm.; Chief Asst. to Clin. Dir. Birm. Accid. Hosp.

SMITH, James George Elder, CStJ Tristans, Grandfield Crescent, Radcliffe-on-Trent, Nottingham NG12 1AN Tel: 0115 933 3920 — LRCP LRCS Ed. LRFPS Glas. 1950; FFOM RCP Lond. 1988, M 1978; DIH Soc. Apoth. Lond. 1971. (Ed.) Indep. Cons. Nottm. Socs: Fell. Roy. Med. Soc. Edin.; (Ex-Chairm.) Soc. Occupat. Med.; Brit. Occupat. Hyg. Soc. Prev: Princip. Med. Off. (York.) Brit. Coal Doncaster; Area Med. Off. Boots Co. Ltd. Nottm.; Ho. Surg. & Ho. Off. (O & G) Dist. Gen. Hosp. Bolton.

SMITH, James Hogg (retired) 3 Mains of Dun Cottages, Montrose DD10 9LQ Tel: 01674 810274 — MB ChB 1956 Glas.; MRCGP 1965. Prev: Relief Med. Off. U.K.A.E.A. Chapelcross.

SMITH, James Mark Perry 175 Victoria Road, Lockwood, Huddersfield HD1 3TT — BM BCh 1980 Oxf. Regist. Community Med. Norwich Health Auth.

SMITH, Mr James Michael Court View Surgery, Rosemary Street, Mansfield NG19 6AB Tel: 01623 623600 Fax: 01623 635460 — MB ChB 1969 Sheff.; FRCS Ed. 1975; FRCS Eng. 1975; MRCGP 1988. GP Mansfield. Prev: Rotating Orthop. Regist. Battle Hosp. Reading & Nuffield Orthop.; Centre Oxf.

SMITH, James Michael Beth-Shalom, Laxton, Newark NG22 0PA — MB ChB 1993 Leeds.

SMITH, James Murray The Surgery, 2 Heathcote Street, Newcastle ST5 7EB Tel: 01782 561057 Fax: 01782 563907 — MB ChB 1961 Glas.; BA Open Univ. 1979. Prev: Ho. Surg. & Ho. Phys. Ballochmyle Hosp.

SMITH, James Neil (retired) c/o 9 Wellington Drive, Grantham NG31 7HU — MB ChB 1957 Leeds; DObst RCOG 1961. Prev: GP Grantham.

SMITH, Mr James Richard Lister Hospital, Chelsea Bridge Road, London SW1W 8RH Tel: 020 7730 0431 Fax: 020 7730 6861; The Garrochty, Kingarth, Rothesay PA20 — MB ChB 1982 Glas.; MD 1992; MRCOG 1988; FRCOG 2000. (Glasgow) Cons. Gyn Chelsea & W.m. Hosp. Lond.; Hon. Sen. Lect. Imperial Coll. Sch. of Med.; Vis. Assoc. Prof. New York Univ. Med. Center New York USA; Hon. Cons. Gynecologist RMH; Honary Cons. Obst. and Gynaecologist RBH. Socs: Fell. Roy. Soc. Med.; Brit. Gyn. Cancer Soc.; Med. Soc. Study VD. Prev: Sen. Lect. & Cons. O & G Char. Cross & W.m. Med. Sch., Chelsea & W.m. Hosp. Lond.; Research Fell. (O & G & Genitourin. Med.) St. Mary's Hosp. Lond.; Lect. (O & G) Char. Cross & W.m. Med. Sch. Lond.

SMITH, Jamie Christian A7 Office, University Hospital of Wales, Heath Park, Cardiff CF14 4XW Email: jamie.smith@virgin.net; 18 Elizabeth Close, Thornbury, Bristol BS35 2YN Tel: 01454 415414 — MB BCh 1993 Wales; MRCP (UK) 1996. (University of Wales)

SMITH, Jan Meldrum Heathbank, Scotstown Road, Newmachar, Aberdeen AB21 7PP — MB ChB 1986 Aberd.

SMITH, Jane Katharine Wolverhampton Eye Infirmary, Compton Road, Wolverhampton WV3 9QR Tel: 01902 307999 Fax: 01902 564019; 15 Waterdale, Compton, Wolverhampton WV3 9DY Tel: 01902 710564 Email: jane@shamshin.swinternet.co.uk — MB BCh 1977 Wales; BSc (Physiol. & Biochem.) Soton 1972; MCOphth 1990; DO RCS Eng. 1982. Clin. Asst. Wolverhampton & Cos. Eye Infirm.

SMITH

SMITH, Jane Louise Mansfield Medical Centre, 56 Binley Road, Coventry CV3 1JB Tel: 024 7645 7551 Fax: 024 7644 2250; 6 Montpellier Close, Styvechale, Coventry CV3 5PL — BM BS 1986 Nottm.; MRCGP 1991; DRCOG 1990. (Nottm.) Prev: Trainee GP Walsgrave Hosp. Coventry VTS.

SMITH, Janet Elizabeth Wykeham, Score Lane, Blagdon, Bristol BS40 7RX — MB BS 1998 Lond.; MB BS Lond 1998.

SMITH, Janet Linda The Surgery, Station Road, Bridge of Weir PA11 3LH Tel: 01505 612555 Fax: 01505 615032; Rosslyn, Bonar Crescent, Bridge of Weir PA11 3EH — MB ChB 1981 Aberd.; DRCOG 1983. GP Bridge of Weir.

SMITH, Janet Marie Bristol Royal Hospital for Sick Children, St. Michaels Hill, Bristol BS2 8BJ Tel: 0117 929 4530; Lower Flat, 8 Cowper Road, Redland, Bristol BS6 6NY — MB ChB 1983 Bristol; MRCPsych 1991. (Bristol) Cons. Child Psychiat. Childr.s Hosp., Bristol (P/T). Prev: Sen. Regist. (Child Adolesc. Psychiat.) SW RHA.

SMITH, Janet Urquhart Abernethy 39 Colwyn Road, Bramhall, Stockport SK7 2JG — LRCP LRCS 1951 Ed.; LRCP LRCS Ed. LRFPS Glas. 1951; DObst RCOG 1954.

SMITH, Jason Edward The Park Medical Group, Shopping Centre, Fawdon Park Road, Newcastle upon Tyne NE3 2PE Tel: 0191 285 1763 Fax: 0191 284 2374 — MB BS 1992 Newc.; MRCP Lond. 1998. (Newcastle upon Tyne) GP Newc.

SMITH, Jason James, Surg. Lt. RN RNSQ, HMS Drake, Devonport, Plymouth PL2 2BG; 33 Dartford Road, Aylestone, Leicester LE2 7PQ Tel: 0378 707892 — MB ChB 1995 Leic. Med. Off. Second Submarine Squadron.

SMITH, Mr Jason John Charing Cross Hospital, Dept. of Vasculas Surgery, Fulham Palace Road, London W6 8RP Tel: 020 8846 7320 Fax: 020 8846 7330 Email: jj.smith@ic.ac.uk; Greenways, Nags Head Lane, Great Missenden HP16 0HD Email: jason@smithfrcs.freeserve.co.uk — MB BS 1992 Lond.; FRCS Eng. 1996. (Roy. Free Hosp. Lond.) Specialist Regist. (Gen. Surg.). Socs: Fell. Roy. Soc. Med.; Affil. Mem. Vasc. Surg. Soc. of GB & Irel.; Jun. Mem. Europ. Soc. Vasc. Surg. Prev: Research Fell. & Regist. (Vasc. Surg.) Char. Cross Hosp. Lond.

SMITH, Jayne Mary 9 Hayhouse Road, Earls Colne, Colchester CO6 2PD — MB ChB 1976 Leeds.

SMITH, Jean Mendip Country Practice, Coleford, Bath BA3 5PG Tel: 01373 812244 — BM BS 1975 Nottm.; MRCGP 1979; DRCOG 1978.

SMITH, Jean Hamilton Lang Hollybank, 2A Mill Road, Riggend, Airdrie ML6 7ST Tel: 01236 830640 Fax: 01236 830640 — MB ChB 1961 Glas.; DObst RCOG 1963. (Glas. Univ.)

SMITH, Jeannette Alexandra (retired) 50 Endcliffe Hall Avenue, Sheffield S10 3EL Tel: 0114 266 1722 — MB ChB 1959 Liverp.

SMITH, Jeffrey Terence Leroy 41 Smithies Avenue, Sully, Penarth CF64 5SS — MB BS 1983 Lond.; BSc Lond. 1980; MB BS 1983. Research Fell. Acad. Dept. Med. Roy. Free Hosp. Lond.

SMITH, Jenifer Ann Evelyn South West Cancer IntelligenceService, Highcroft, Romsey Road, Winchester SO22 5DH Tel: 01962 863511 Fax: 01962 878360; 8 Portersbridge Street, Romsey SO51 8DJ — MB BS 1980 Lond.; MSc Lond. 1987; MRCP (UK) 1985; FFPHM 1997, M 1990. (Charing Cross Hospital) Dir. S. W. Region Cancer Intelligence Serv., Winchester. Prev: Cons. Pub. Health Med. Soton. & SW Hants. DHA; Sen. Regist. (Community Med.) Oxf. RHA; Regist. (Gen. Med. & Rheum.) Univ. Hosp. Wales Cardiff.

SMITH, Jennette Mary-Theresa 47 Colgrove Road, Loughborough LE11 3NL — MB ChB 1997 Leic.; BSc Hons 1992.

SMITH, Jennifer Catherine 16 Priory Farm Close, Liverpool L19 3RS Tel: 0151 494 9647 — MB ChB 1989 Leeds; BSc (Hons. Path.) Leeds 1985; MRCP (Edin.) 1997. (Leeds) Specialist Regist. In Palliat. Med., Mersey Region. Socs: RCP(Ed.); Assn. Palliat. Med.; Roy. Soc. Med. Prev: SHO (Palliat. Med.), Liverp., Marie Curie Centre; SHO (Neurol.) St. Jas. Hosp. Leeds; SHO (Oncol.) St James' Hosp. Leeds.

SMITH, Jennifer Jane Mary Directorate of Obstetrics & Gynaecology, Cygnet Wing, South Wing Hospital, Bedford MK42 9DJ Tel: 01234 355122; Standalone Farm, Sutton Road, Potton, Sandy SG19 2DT Tel: 01767 260248 Fax: 01767 262440 Email: dpsmith4@aol.com — MB ChB 1966 Birm.; MFFP 1994; DRCOG 1979. (Lond.) Clin. Asst. (O & G) Bedford Hosp. NHS Trust; Clin. Med. Off. & Instruc. Doctor Family Plann. Beds. & Luton NHS Comm. Trust. Prev: Ho. Surg. (O & G) & Ho. Phys. (Med.) Bedford Gen. Hosp.

SMITH, Jennifer Margaret 18 Newland Mews, Culcheth, Warrington WA3 4EN — MB ChB 1991 Glas.

SMITH, Jennifer Marie (retired) 61 Melbreck Road, Allerton, Liverpool L18 9SF Tel: 0151 494 9656 & profess. 051 706 2000 — MB ChB 1959 Sheff.; FFA RCS Eng. 1970; DCH Eng. 1962, DA 1965; DObst RCOG 1964. Cons. (Anaesth.) Mersey RHA & Liverp. AHA (T). Prev: Ho. Phys. Gen. Hosp. & Baragwanath Hosp. Johannesburg, S. Africa.

SMITH, Jennifer Susan 14 Bielby Drive, Holmechurch Lane, Beverley HU17 0RX — MB ChB 1987 Sheff.

SMITH, Jenny 22 Horn Lane, Woodford Green IG8 9AA — MB ChB 1994 Manch.

***SMITH, Jeremy Edward** 4 Barne Close, Nuneaton CV11 4TP — MB ChB 1998 Birm.

SMITH, Jeremy Vaughan 17 The Lea, Kidderminster DY11 6JY — MB ChB 1993 Leic.

SMITH, Jill Elaine The Park Medical Group, Fawdon Park Road, Newcastle upon Tyne NE3 2PE Tel: 0191 285 1763 Fax: 0191 284 2374 — MB BS 1989 Lond.

SMITH, Jillian Beverley Flat 18, Lexham House, Lexham Gardens, London W8 5JT — MB BCh 1967 Wales; FFA RCS Eng. 1972. (Cardiff) Cons. Anaesth. St. Mary's Hosp. Lond. Prev: Regist. (Anaesth.) Hosp. Sick Childr. Gt. Ormond St. Lond. & St.; Thos. Lond.; Rotating Sen. Regist. (Anaesth.) Hosp. Sick Childr. Gt. Ormond St. &.

SMITH, Joanna Claudia Somerton House Surgery, 79A North Road, Midsomer Norton, Bath BA3 2QE Tel: 01761 412141 Fax: 01761 410944 — BSc Lond. 1986, MB BS 1989; MRCGP 1995. (Univ. Coll. Lond.)

SMITH, Joanna Kathreen Royal Edinburgh Hospital, Morningside Terrace, Edinburgh EH10 5HF Tel: 0131 537 6000; 72 Falcon Avenue, Edinburgh EH10 4AW Tel: 0131 447 6326 — MB ChB 1996 Aberd. SHO (Psychiat.) Edin. Lothian & Fife Rotat. Socs: BMA.

SMITH, Joanne Deborah 25 Ashley Drive, Belfast BT9 7BE Tel: 01232 683153 — MB BCh BAO 1994 Belf.

SMITH, Joanne Louise 25 Glengarry Gardens, Wolverhampton WV3 9HX — MB ChB 1998 Bristol.

SMITH, Joanne Marie 19 Chynance, Portreath, Redruth TR16 4NJ — MB ChB 1991 Manch.

SMITH, John The Surgery, Carloway, Stornoway Tel: 01851 73333; 9 Holm Village, Stornoway HS1 OAE — MB ChB 1968 Aberd.; FRCGP 1994, M 1975.

SMITH, John, OBE, TD (retired) 5/10 Oswald Road, Edinburgh EH9 2HE Tel: 0131 667 5617 — MB BChir Camb. 1938; MB ChB Glas. 1938; MA Camb. 1943; FRCP Glas. 1967, M 1965; FRCP Ed. 1969; FFPHM 1989 (FFCM 1972). Prev: Dep. Chief Med. Off. Scott. Home & Health Dept.

SMITH, John St. Mary's Hospital, I.O.W. Healthcare Trust, Newport PO30 5TG Tel: 01983 524081 Ext: 4808/4859 Fax: 01983 825437; Ashlake House, Ashlake Copse Road, Fishbourne, Ryde PO33 4EY Tel: 01983 882497 — BM BCh 1965 Oxf.; BSc (Hons. Anat.) Leeds 1962; FRCPath 1988, M 1976; DCP Lond 1972. (Leeds & Oxf.) Cons. Chem. Path. & Metab. Med. St. Mary's Hosp. Newport I. of Wight; Hon. Clin. Teach. Univ. Soton. Med. Sch. Socs: Assn. Clin. Biochems.; BMA; Nat. Osteoporosis Soc. Prev: Cons. Chem. Path. Inst. Path. & Trop. Med. RAF Halton Aylesbury; Cons. Clin. Path. RAF Hosp. Wegberg W. Germany; Wing Cdr. RAF Med. Br.

SMITH, Mr John Allan Raymond Northern General NHS Trust, Herries Road, Sheffield S5 7AU Tel: 0114 243 4343 Fax: 0114 256 0472; 4 Endcliffe Grove Avenue, Sheffield S10 3EJ Tel: 0114 268 3094 Fax: 0114 267 0295 — MB ChB 1966 Ed.; FCRS ED 1972; FRCS Eng. 1972; PhD Aberd. 1979. (Ed.) Cons. Surg. N. Gen. Hosp. Sheff.; Chairm. Jt. Comm. Higher Surgic. Train. Socs: Brit. Soc. Gastroenterol. & Assn. Surgs. Prev: Sen. Lect. (Surg.) Univ. Sheff. & Hon. Cons. Surg. Roy. Hallamsh. Hosp. Sheff.; Sen. Regist. (Surg.) S. Grampian (Aberd.) Health Dist.; Ho. Phys. & Ho. Surg. Roy. Infirm. Edin.

SMITH, John Anthony (retired) The Old Rectory, Great Massingham, King's Lynn PE32 2EY Tel: 01485 520806 Fax: 01485 520806 Email: john.smith35@whichnet — MB BS 1956 Durh.; DTM & H Liverp. 1960. Med. Examr. Benefts Agy. Prev: Hon. Surg. Newc. Gen. Hosp.

SMITH, John Anthony James 81 Thurlow Park Road, London SE21 8JL Tel: 020 8670 6610 — MB BChir 1952 Camb.; MRCS Eng. LRCP Lond. 1951. (Camb. & Guy's)

SMITH, John Dawson Lochmaben Medical Group, The Surgery, 42-44 High Street, Lochmaben, Lockerbie DG11 1NH Tel: 01387 810252 Fax: 01387 811595 — MB ChB 1977 Aberd.; MRCGP 1981; DRCOG 1981. GP Stonehaven. Prev: Trainee GP Dumfries & Galloway Roy. Infirm. VTS.

SMITH, John Eric 9 Dunedin Drive, Barnt Green, Birmingham B45 8HZ Tel: 0121 445 1431 — MB ChB 1969 Liverp.; FFA RCS Eng. 1979. Cons. Anaesth. Univ. Hosp. Birm.

SMITH, John Francis Boucher Little Broich, Kippen, Stirling FK8 3DT — MB ChB 1962 St. And.; FRCP Glas. 1986; MRCP Lond. 1967. Cons. Phys. Stirling Roy. Infirm.

SMITH, John Francis Ferguson, VRD 42 Kelvin Court, Glasgow G12 0AE — MB ChB 1944 Glas. (Univ. Glas.) Cons. Dermatol. Vict. Infirm. Glas., & Dumfries & Galloway Hosps. & Corp. of Glas. & Co. of Renfrew Sch. Health Servs.; Hon. Phys. to HM the Qu.; Surg. Capt. RNR. Prev: Sen. Regist. Dept. Dermat. & Ho. Surg. W.. Infirm. Glas.; Asst. Regist. Dept. Dermat. Univ. Coll. Hosp. Lond.

SMITH, John Glyn (retired) 48 Lime Tree Avenue, Retford DN22 7BA Tel: 01777 703837 — MB ChB 1966 Sheff.; MRCGP 1978; DCH Eng. 1969; DObst RCOG 1968. Prev: SHO (Paediat. Med.) Childr. Hosp. Sheff.

SMITH, Professor John Graham Department of Haematology, Royal United Hospital, Combe Park, Bath BA1 3NG Tel: 01225 824731 Fax: 01225 461044; Crinan, Miller Walk, Bathampton, Bath BA2 6TJ Tel: 01225 460358 Fax: 01225 461044 — MB ChB 1977 Glas.; BSc (Hons.) Immunol. Glas. 1975, MD 1985; FRCP Lond. 1994; MRCP (Glas.) 1980; FRCPath 1996, M 1984. Cons. Haematologist Roy. United Hosp. Bath; Prof. Haemat. Univ. W. Eng. Bristol 1997; Designated AIDS Phys. Bath; Med. Dir. Roy. United Hosp. Socs: Fell. Internat. Soc. Haematol.; Brit. Soc. Haematol. & Assn. Clin. Path.; (Chairm.) BCSH Clin. Haematol. Task Force. Prev: Sen. Regist. (Haemat.) W. Infirm. Glas.; Clin. Dir. (Path.) Roy. Univ. Hosp.; Clin. Dir. (Med.) Roy. United Hosp.

SMITH, John Harry 96 Harley Street, London W1G 7HY Tel: 020 7935 9904 Fax: 020 7486 5770 — MB BChir 1978 Camb.; MD Camb. 1990, MA 1978; MRCOG 1983. (St. Thos. & Camb.) Cons. O & G St. Mary's Hosp. Lond. Prev: Sen. Regist. St. Mary's Hosp. Lond.; Research Fell. John Radcliffe Hosp. Oxf.; Regist. (O & G) Pembury Hosp. & SE Thames.

SMITH, John Henry Wilfred (retired) c/o Coutts & Co., Adelaide Branch, 440 The Strand, London WC2R 0QS — MB ChB 1947 Leeds; FFA RCS Eng. 1954; DA Eng. 1949. Prev: Cons. Anaesth. Leic. Roy. Infirm. & Rutland Memor. Hosp.

SMITH, John Herbert Frederick Department of Histopathology, Royal Hallamshire Hospital, Sheffield S10 2JF Tel: 0114 2713728 Fax: 0114 2712200 Email: john.smith@sth.nhs.uk — MB BS 1977 Lond.; MB BS (Hons.) Lond. 1977; BSc (Hons.) Lond. 1974; FRCPath 1996, M 1985. (Middlx.) Cons. Histopath.Roy. Hallamshire Hosp; Hon.Sen. Clin. Lect. Univ. Sheff.; Dir. Sheff. Cytol. Train centre. Socs: Brit. Div. Internat. Acad. Path. & Assn. Clin. Path.; Brit. Soc. Clin. Cytol.(Hon. Asst. secetary 1992-95); Internat. Acad. of Cytol. Prev: Sen. Regist. (Histopath.) S.mead & Frenchay Hosps. Bristol & Bristol Roy. Infirm.; Lect. (Toxicol.) St. Bart. Hosp. & DHSS Toxicol. Unit.

SMITH, John Joseph 6 West Lawn, Ashbrooke, Sunderland SR2 7HW Tel: 0191 282562 — MB BCh BAO 1941 Belf. (Belf.) Prev: Res. Surg. Off. Birm. Accid. Hosp. & Doncaster Roy. Infirm.

SMITH, John Joseph 1-3 Church Street, Ballymena BT43 6DD Tel: 01266 630588 Fax: 01266 630696 Email: eyespec@hotmail.com — MB BCh BAO 1990 Belf.; BSc Biochem. (Hons.) Belf. 1987, MB BCh BAO 1990; MRCOphth 1994; FRCS (Ophth) 1996. Staff Grade Ophth. Dept. of Ophth. Roy. Vict. Hosp. Belf.; Lect. (Ophth.) Univ. of Ulster Coleraine N. Irel.; Dir. of Waveney Eye Care Ltd. Socs: Irish Coll. Ophth.; Brit. Contact Lens Assn.

SMITH, John Lister (retired) Ravelston Cottage, 16 Ravelston Dykes Road, Edinburgh EH4 3PB Tel: 0131 332 9541 — MB ChB 1954 Ed. Prev: Ho. Surg. P.ss Margt. Rose Hosp. Edin.

SMITH, Mr John Robert (retired) The Anchorage, Alves, Elgin IV30 8UY Tel: 01343 850274 — MB ChB Glas. 1945; FRCS Ed. 1952. Prev: Cons. Surg. Dr. Gray's Hosp. Elgin.

SMITH, John Robertson (retired) Greenways, Drum Farm Road, Fankerton, Denny FK6 5HJ Tel: 01324 822469 — MB ChB 1940 Ed.; MRCGP 1960. Prev: GP Denny, Stirlingsh.

SMITH, John Simon Kettering & District General Hospital, Rothwell Road, Kettering NN16 8UZ Tel: 01536 492000 Fax: 01536 492567; 34 Poplars Farm Road, Barton Seagrave, Kettering NN15 5AG Tel: 01536 513786 — MB BS 1970 Lond.; FRCGP 1991, M 1977; DObst RCOG 1972. Cons. Palliat. Med. N.amptonshire Healthcare NHS Trust, Cransley Hospice, Kettering & Dist. Gen. Hosp. & Cynthia Spencer Hospice N.ampton. Prev: Ho. Surg. Middlx. Hosp. Lond.

SMITH, Mr John Strathdee 14 Woodland Crescent, Eaglesham, Glasgow — MB ChB 1974 Glas.; FRCS Glas. 1979.

SMITH, John Taylor (retired) 252 Elwick Road, Hartlepool TS26 0EL Tel: 01429 274570 — MB ChB Glas. 1947. Prev: Clin. Asst. Dept. Psychiat. Gen. Hosp. Hartlepool.

SMITH, John Warner (retired) Crow End, Graveley, Hitchin SG4 7LX Tel: 01438 353248 — BM BCh 1940 Oxf.; BA 1937, BM BCh Oxf. 1940. Prev: Med. Regist. Metrop. Hosp.

SMITH, John Weston The Secret House, 101 Main Road, Wiggington, Tamworth B79 9DU Tel: 01827 69283 — MB ChB 1944 Birm.; MRCGP 1968; DA Eng. 1954; DObst. RCOG 1946. (Birm.) Anaesth. & Med. Off. Tamworth Hosps.; Clin. Asst. Psychother. Uffculme Clinic Birm. Socs: Fac. Anaesths. Prev: Gyn. Regist. Dudley Rd. Hosp. Birm; Regist. Roy. Hosp. Wolverhampton; Obst. Ho. Surg. Birm. United Hosps.

SMITH, Jonathan Harvey — MB BS 1993 Lond.; FRCA 1999. Specialist Regist. - UCL Hosps. - Lond.

SMITH, Jonathan Hayden Department of Cardiothoracic Anaesthesia, Freeman Hospital, High Heaton, Newcastle upon Tyne NE7 7DN Tel: 0191 284 3111 Fax: 0191 223 1175; Chapel Cottage, Halton Shields, Corbridge NE45 5PZ — MB ChB 1982 Leeds; MRCP (UK) 1986; FRCA 1989. Cons. Paediat. (Cardiothoracic Anaesth. & Intens. Care) Freeman Hosp. Newc. u. Tyne; Cons. Anaesth. (Paediat. Cardiothoracic & Intens. Care). Prev: Instruc. (Paediat. Anaesth.) CS Mott Childr. Hosp. Ann Arbor Michigan, USA; Regist. (Anaesth.) Our Lady's Hosp. for Sick Childr. Dub.; Anaesthesiol. Project Orbis.

SMITH, Jonathan Kenneth Laing Fernbank Surgery, 18 Church Road, Lytham, Lytham St Annes FY8 5LL Tel: 01253 736453; Stanley House, 89 Preston Old Road, Freckleton, Preston PR4 1HD — MB ChB 1979 Ed.; MRCGP 1983; DRCOG 1983.

SMITH, Jonathan Mark 31 Forest Hills Drive, Talbot Green, Pontyclun CF7 8JB — MB BCh 1986 Wales; MRCPsych 1992. Cons., Old Age Psychiat., E. Glam. Hosp. Prev: Regist. (Psychiat.) S. Glam. HA.

SMITH, Jonathan Neil 30 Downs Side, Sutton SM2 7EQ — BM 1992 Soton.; BM Soton 1992; DRCOG 1996; DCH 1997; MRCP 1999. Specialist Regist. (A&E) Qu.'s Med. Centre, Nottm.

SMITH, Jonathan Paul 5 Meadow Court, Ponteland, Newcastle upon Tyne NE20 9RA — BChir 1992 Camb.

SMITH, Jonathan Robert 7 Silk Mills Close, Sevenoaks TN14 5AZ Email: jonathan.smith@breathmail.net — MB ChB 1991 Sheff.; FRCA Eng. 1997. Specialist Regist. (Anaesth.) Guy's Hosp. Lond.

SMITH, Jonathan Timothy 69 Leicester Road, Fleckney, Leicester LE8 8BG — MB ChB 1995 Manch.

SMITH, Mr Joseph Colin, OBE (retired) 23 Banbury Road, Oxford OX2 6NX — MB BS Lond. 1954; MS Lond. 1966; FRCS Eng. 1958; MRCS Eng. LRCP Lond. 1954. Prev: Cons. Urol. Surg. Oxf.

SMITH, Joseph Donald Robert (retired) 106 Kenton Lane, Newcastle upon Tyne NE3 3QD — MB BS 1948 Durh.

SMITH, Joseph Gerard 34 Hazel Bank, Milton of Campsie, Glasgow G66 8JG — MB ChB 1993 Leic.; BDS Liverp. 1986.

SMITH, Sir Joseph William Grenville (retired) 95 Lofting Road, London N1 1JF — MB BCh 1953 Wales; MD Wales 1966; FRCP Lond. 1987; FFPHM 1976, M 1972; FRCPath 1975, M 1963; Dip. Bact. Lond 1960. Co-Chairm. WHO Global Poliomyelitis Commiss.; Chairm. WHO Europ. Region Poliomyelitis Commiss. Prev: Dir. Pub. Health Laborat. Serv.

SMITH, Julia Clare — MB ChB 1992 Manch.; BSc (Hons.) Physiol. Manch. 1989; MRCP (UK) 1996; DRCOG 1997; MRCGP 1998. (Manch.) Gen. Practitioner; Clin. Asst. Dermat.,W.morland Gen. Hosp.

SMITH

SMITH, Julia Rosemary Gladstone Imaging Department, Queen Elizabeth Hospital, Stadium Rd, Woolwich, London SE18 4QH Tel: 020 8836 6000 Fax: 020 8228 6109 — MB BS 1977 Lond.; MRCP (UK) 1981; FRCR 1984. Cons. Radiol. Qu. Eliz. Hosp., Woolwich. Prev: Greenwich Dist. Hosp.; Cons. Radiol. Brook Gen. Hosp. Lond.

SMITH, Julian Abel 4 Aston Road, Chipping Campden GL55 6HR — MB BS 1996 Lond.

SMITH, Julian Harold Joshua 10 York Street, Altrincham WA15 9QH — MB ChB 1984 Dundee. Med. Off. HM Prison Lewes. Prev: Ho. Off. (Gen. Med.) Law Hosp. Carluke; Regtl. Med. Off. 5 Reg. RA RAMC; SHO (A & E) William Harvey Hosp. Ashford Kent.

SMITH, Julie Carol 5 Imperial Avenue, Beeston, Nottingham NG9 1EZ Email: j.pollock@btinternet.com — BM BCh 1993 Oxf.; MA Camb. 1990; MRCP (UK) 1996. (Oxf.) Specialist Regist. (Paediat.) Univ. Hosp. Nottm.

SMITH, Julie Elizabeth The Bull Ring Surgery, 5 The Bull Ring, St. John's, Worcester WR2 5AA Tel: 01905 422883 Fax: 01905 423639; The Mount, Red Hill Lane, Worcester WR5 2JL — MB ChB 1978 Birm.; DRCOG 1980.

SMITH, Juliet Ann 51 Kennedy Road, Kingsland, Shrewsbury SY3 7AA — MB BS 1991 Lond.

SMITH, June Mary (retired) Ava Cottage, 46 The Butts, Chippenham SN15 3JS Tel: 01249 652675 — MB ChB 1949 Bristol; MB ChB (Hnrs.) Bristol 1949; MRCS Eng. LRCP Lond. 1949; DObst. RCOG 1951; DCH Eng. 1953.

SMITH, Justin Barham Rose Croft, North Lane, South Harting, Petersfield GU31 5NN — MB BS 1988 Lond.

SMITH, Justin Deval 50 Langdale Grove, Bingham, Nottingham NG13 8SS Tel: 01949 875899 Email: justinsmith@unotts.co.uk — MB BCh 1993 Wales; DCH 12/97 RCP.; DCH RCP Lond. 1997. SHO (O & G) (GP Regist). Prev: SHO (Psychiat.); SHO (Acc. & Emerg.); SHO (Med.).

SMITH, Justin Michael Alaric Royal Eye Unit, Kingston General Hospital, Galsworthy Road, Kingston upon Thames KT2 7QB; 20 Glebeland Gardens, Shepperton TW17 9DH — MB ChB 1988 Bristol; MRCP (UK) 1992; FRCOphth 1995. Med. Retina Clin. Research Fell. (Ophth.) Moorfields Eye Hosp. Prev: Specialist Regist. Rotat. (Ophth.) SW Thames; SHO (Ophth.) Chelsea & W.m. Hosp. Lond., Frimley Pk. Hosp. & Cheltenham Gen. Hosp.; SHO Rotat. (Gen. Med.) Bristol & W.on HA.

SMITH, Justine Lydia 101 Hailgate, Howden, Goole DN14 7SX Tel: 01430 431449 — MB ChB 1994 Manch.; BA (Hons.) Oxf. 1990. SHO Med. Rotat. - Hull Roy. Infirm.

SMITH, Karen 56 Grampian Way, Bearsden, Glasgow G61 4RW — MB ChB 1993 Glas.

SMITH, Karen Patricia Brunswick House Medical Group, 1 Brunswick St., Carlisle CA1 1ED Tel: 01228 515808; Fellend, Heads Nook, Carlisle CA8 9DA — MB BS 1986 Newc.; MRCGP 1990; DRCOG 1990.

SMITH, Katharine Alison Fulbrook Centre, Warneford Hospital, Churchill Hospital, Oxford OX3 7JU — BM BCh 1990 Oxf.; DM 2000 Oxford. Specialist Regist. in Psychiat. of oold age, fulbrook centre, Ch.ill Hosp., Oxf.. Prev: Clin. Lect., Univ. Dept of Psychiat. Oxf. welcome Train. Fell., Iniv. Dept of Psychiatr. Oxf..

SMITH, Katherene Sheila Baxter Crossbrook Surgery, 126 Crossbrook Street, Cheshunt, Waltham Cross EN8 8JY Tel: 01992 622908 Fax: 01992 624756 — MB BS 1984 Lond.; DPD 1996; DRCOG 1989. Prev: GP Berkhamstead; SHO (O & G & Paediat.) Wexham Pk. Hosp. Slough.

SMITH, Katherine Sarah Howard Brookside Group Practice, Brookside Close, Gipsy Lane, Earley, Reading RG6 7HG Tel: 0118 966 9222 Fax: 0118 935 3174 — MB ChB 1981 Bristol; MRCGP 1986; DRCOG 1985; Cert. Family Plann. JCC 1985. (Bristol) Socs: BMA. Prev: Clin. Asst. (Psychiat.) I. of Wight HA; Trainee GP/SHO I. of Wight VTS.

SMITH, Kathleen Thornthwaite Cottage, Copsale Road, Maplehurst, Horsham RH13 6QY — BM BS 1992 Nottm.; BMedSci Nottm. 1990, BM BS 1992. SHO (Med.) Derbysh. Roy. Infirm.

SMITH, Kathleen Lilley 19 Wheatley Lane, Winshill, Burton-on-Trent DE15 0DX Tel: 01283 42745 — MB BS Lond. 1945. (Univ. Coll. Hosp.)

SMITH, Kathleen Mary The Ragged School, 51 Roxburgh St., Kelso TD5 7DS Tel: 01573 226009 Fax: 01573 225134 — MB ChB Ed. 1952.

SMITH, Kathryn Jane 17 Newton Road, Torquay TQ2 5DB — MB ChB 1984 Bristol.

SMITH, Kathryn Shauna Minsmere House, Heath Road, Ipswich IP4 5PD Tel: 01473 704203 — BM 1988 Soton.; DA (UK) 1992. Staff Grade (Psychiat. of Old Age) E. Suff. Local Health Servs. Trust, Ipswich. Prev: Clin. Med. Off. in Psychiat. of Old Age E. Suff. Local Health Servs. Trust Ipswich; SHO (Psychiat.) St. Clements Hosp. Ipswich; Trainee GP Ipswich.

SMITH, Katrina 24 Windmill Way, Kegworth, Derby DE74 2FA — MB ChB 1996 Ed.

SMITH, Katrina Louise 14 Chaddesley Road, Kidderminster DY10 3AD — BM BCh 1996 Oxf.

SMITH, Kay 40 South Road, Taunton TA1 3DY — MB BS 1970 Lond.; MRCS Eng. LRCP Lond. 1970; Dip. Clin. Bact. Lond 1983; DObst RCOG 1973. (Lond. Hosp.) Staff Grade (c/o Elderly) Taunton & Som. NHS Trust; Clin. Asst. St. Margt. Hospice Som.

SMITH, Kay Louise Northern Centre for Cancer Treatment, Newcastle general Hospital, Westgate Road, Newcastle upon Tyne NE4 6BE Tel: 0191 285 2025; 123A Craig Walk, Bo'ness LA23 3AX Tel: 01539 446813 Email: 113200.3552@compuserve.com — MB ChB 1991 Manch. Specialist Regist. (Clin. Oncol.) N.ern Centre for Cancer Treatm.; Attachment at S. Cleveland. Prev: SHO (Med.) King Edwd. VII Hosp. Midhurst & Shotley Bridge Gen. Hosp.; SHO (A & E) Wythenshawe & Withington Hosps. Manch.; Ho. Off. (Med.) Qu. Eliz. Hosp. Gateshead.

SMITH, Kaye Lorraine The Health Centre, Aylesbury Road, Wendover, Aylesbury HP22 6LD Tel: 01296 623452; Canal Cottage, Halton Village, Aylesbury HP22 5NS Tel: 01296 622601 — MB BS 1978 Monash; MRCGP 1984; DCH RCP Lond. 1982. (Monash Univ. Melbourne) Trainer (Gen. Pract.) Aylesbury.

SMITH, Keay Gordon 20 Wiltshire Drive, Wokingham RG40 1TQ — MB BCh Witwatersrand 1965; MFOM RCP Lond. 1987; DIH Lond. 1982. (Witwatersrand) Princip. Occupat. Health Off. Lond. Boro. Ealing; Cons. Occupat. Phys. Wycombe Gen. Hosp. High Wycombe Bucks. Socs: Soc. Occupat. Med.; Assn. Local Auth. Med. Advisers.; BMA. Prev: Occupat. Phys. Hants. Fire & Rescue Serv.; Med. Adviser Hants. CC; Sen. Med. Off. Brit. Airways Health Servs. Heathrow.

SMITH, Kenneth Carl Pfeiffer 13 Wallcroft, Durham Park, Bristol BS6 6XJ Tel: 0117 734830 — MRCS Eng. LRCP Lond. 1937; MRCPsych 1972; DPM Eng. 1946. (Bristol) Med. Adviser Sutcliffe Sch. for Maladjusted Boys. Prev: Cons. Child Psychiat. Wilts. & Som. Cos; Squadron Ldr. RAF Med. Br.; Psychiat. Nat. Nautical Sch. Portishead.

SMITH, Mr Kenneth Halstead — MB ChB 1943 Manch.; FRCS Eng. 1952; MRCS Eng. LRCP Lond. 1943. (Manch.) Prev: Emerit. Cons. Surg. Gwynedd HA.; Cons. Accid. Surg. Gen. Hosp. N.ampton; Res. Surg. Off. Ancoats Hosp. Manch.

SMITH, Kerry Marie 165 High Street, Quarry Bank, Brierley Hill DY5 2AE; 42 Sandyacre Way, Stourbridge DY8 1JD — MB ChB 1988 Birm.

SMITH, Mr Kevin David 18 Enstone Court, Westbury Park, Clayton, Newcastle ST5 4JE — MB BS 1987 Lond.; FRCS Ed. 1992.

SMITH, Kevin John 4 Rufford Close, Birmingham B23 5YZ — MB BS 1994 Lond.

SMITH, Kevin Joseph General Medicine, Northern General Hospital NHS Trust, Herries Road, Sheffield S5 7AU — MB ChB 1995 Sheff.

SMITH, Kevin Meynell Lower Farm, Headington, Oxford OX3 9SD — MB BS 1986 Lond.; BSc Lond. 1983; MRCOG 1996; DGM RCP Lond. 1991. (St. Bart. Hosp. Lond.) Specialist Regist. (O & G) John Radcliffe Hosp. Oxf. Prev: Regist. (O & G) Wexham Pk.; SHO (O & G) City Hosp. Nottm. & John Radcliffe Oxf.

SMITH, Mr Kevin Robert Hodson All Nations Christian College, Ware SG12 8LX Tel: 01920 461243 Fax: 01920 462997; 47 Church Hill, Northfield, Birmingham B31 2JA — MB ChB 1988 Birm.; BSc (Hons.) Anat. Birm. 1985; FRCS Eng. 1993; DTM & H Liverp. 1995. Socs: Fell. Roy. Soc. Trop. Med. & Hyg.; Med. Protec. Soc. Prev: SHO (O & G) Walsall Manor Hosp.; SHO Rotat. (Surg.) Dudley Rd. Hosp. Birm.

SMITH, Kirsten Teresa Elizabeth 1 Appleton Court, Thornton, Bradford BD13 3TD — BM 1998 Soton.; BM Soton 1998.

SMITH, Laura Jane Anderson 10 Hindon Square, Vicarage Road, Edgbaston, Birmingham B15 3HA — MB ChB 1991 Leeds.

SMITH, Lesley-Ann 71 Harriet Street, Cardiff CF24 4BW — MB BCh 1998 Wales.

SMITH, Lesley Anne Abbey Medical Centre, Lonend, Paisley PA1 1SU Tel: 0141 889 4088; 1 Victoria Gardens, Kilmacolm PA13 4HL Tel: 01505 874884 — MB ChB 1985 Glas.; DRCOG 1988. (Univ. Glas.) Gen. Asst., Merchiston Hosp., Brookfield by Johnstone.

SMITH, Leslie David Rosslyn Cardiac Department, Royal Devon & Exeter Hospital, Wonford, Exeter EX2 5DW Tel: 01392 402276 Fax: 01392 402276; 26 Salutary Mount, Exeter EX1 2QE — MB BS 1977 Lond.; BSc Lond. 1974, MB BS 1977; MRCP (UK) 1980; FRCP 1996. Cons. Cardiol. Roy. Devon & Exeter Hosp. Socs: Sec. of the Brit. CardoVasc. Interven. Soc. Prev: Sen. Regist. (Cardiol.) St. Thos. Hosp. Lond.; Regist. (Cardiol.) Brompton Hosp. Lond.

SMITH, Leslie Ernest (retired) 4 Conifer Close, Botley, Oxford OX2 9HP Tel: 01865 724316 — MRCS Eng. LRCP Lond. 1939. Prev: Asst. Med. Off. Lambeth Hosp.

SMITH, Leslie Ronald Nimmo North Avenue Surgery, 18 North Avenue, Cambuslang, Glasgow G72 8AT Tel: 0141 641 3037 Fax: 0141 646 1905; 82 Stewarton Drive, Glasgow G72 8DJ — MB ChB 1977 Glas.; MRCGP 1981; DRCOG 1979.

SMITH, Leslie Stuart Meikle Dumfin, Helensburgh G84 9EE — MB ChB 1975 Manch.; MRCGP 1982. Socs: Assoc. Fac. Occupat. Med.

SMITH, Mrs Lindsay 18 Telford Street, Gateshead NE8 4TT — MB BS 1951 Durh.; DObst RCOG 1953.

SMITH, Lindsay Anne Flat 2F1, 73 Dundas Street, Edinburgh EH3 5DQ — MB ChB 1997 Ed.

SMITH, Lindsay Frederick Paul Ilchester Surgery, 17 Church St., Ilchester, Yeovil BA22 8LN Tel: 01935 840207 Fax: 01935 840002 — MB ChB 1982 Bristol; BSc Bristol 1979, MD 1996; MRCP (UK) 1985; FRCGP 1996, M 1987; DRCOG 1988; Cert. Family Plann. JCC 1987. (Bristol) Hon. Cons. Sen. Lect. Qu. Mary & W.field Coll. Univ. Lond. Socs: Chairm. Clin. Network RCGP; Edit. Bd. Brit. Jl. Gen. Pract.; Assn. for Community Based Matern. Care. Prev: RCGP Train. Fell.

SMITH, Lindsey Fiona Fraser Moorfields Eye Hospital, 162 City Rd, London EC1V 2PD Tel: 020 7829 8651 — MB ChB 1987 Sheff.; BMedSci (Hons.) Sheff. 1985; FRCOphth 1993. (Univ. Sheff. Med. Sch.) Specialist Regist. Ophth. Moorfields eye Hosp. Prev: Regist. (Ophth.) Univ. Hosp. Nottm.; Demonst. (Anat.) Univ. Coll. Lond.; SHO (A & E) Univ. Coll. Hosp. Lond.

SMITH, Lorna Katherine Ritchie Fox and Partners, South Park Surgery, 250 Park Lane, Macclesfield SK11 8AA Tel: 01625 422249 Fax: 01625 502169; 114 Prestbury Road, Macclesfield SK10 3BN — MB ChB 1975 Liverp.; MRCGP 1980; DRCOG 1977.

***SMITH, Louise Jane** Lammas Cottage, 30 Meadrow, Godalming GU7 3HT — MB BS 1994 Lond.; BA Camb. 1991.

SMITH, Lucy Clare Itchen Down Farm, Itchen Abbas, Winchester SO21 1BS — MB BS 1993 Lond.; BA Oxf. 1990. (Lond. Hosp. Med. Coll.) SHO (Anaesth.) Soton. Univ. Hosps. NHS Trust. Socs: Train. Mem. Assn. Anaesth.; Christ. Med. Fell. Prev: SHO (Neonatology) Roy. Devon & Exeter Hosp. SHO (Anaesth.) Roy. Lond. Hosp.

SMITH, Malcolm Davies Hunsbury Surgery, Overslade Close, East Hunsbury, Northampton NN4 0RZ Tel: 01604 700042 Fax: 01604 700040 — BMedSci (1st cl. Hons. Anaesth.) Sheff. 1979, MB ChB 1980; MRCGP 1984; DRCOG 1984. Clin. Tutor Dept. Gen. Pract. Univ. Leicester.

SMITH, Malcolm Dunlop 155 West Princess Street, Helensburgh G84 8EZ — MB ChB 1991 Glas.; FRCA 1996; DA (UK) 1995. Specialist Regist. (Anaesth.) W.. Infirm. Glas. Socs: BMA; Glas. & W. Scot. Soc. Anaesth.

SMITH, Malcolm Gavin 18 Beechgrove Place, Aberdeen AB15 5HF — MB ChB 1997 Aberd.

SMITH, Malcolm John Whickham Health Centre, Rectory Lane, Whickham, Newcastle upon Tyne NE16 4PD Tel: 0191 488 5555 Fax: 0191 496 0424 — MB BS 1976 Newc.; MRCGP 1980; DRCOG 1978.

SMITH, Malcolm Joseph The Gainsborough Practice, Warfield Green Medical Centre, Whitegrove, Bracknell RG42 3JP Tel: 01344 428742 Fax: 01344 428743; 58 Sturges Road, Wokingham RG40 2HE — MB BChir 1977 Camb.; MA Camb. 1977; MRCGP 1981; Dip. Sports Med. RCS Ed. 1994; DFFP 1993; DRCOG 1979. Clin. Asst. (Sports Med.) Heatherwood & Wexham Pk. Hosps. Trust. Socs: Brit. Assn. Sport & Med.

SMITH, Malvin Edward 4 Adel Garth, Adel, Leeds LS16 8JU — MB ChB 1995 Leeds.

SMITH, Marcus Cooke 8 Greystoke Drive, Bolton BL1 7DW — MB ChB 1988 Liverp. SHO (Anaesth.) S. Manch. HA.

SMITH, Margaret 7 Elm Walk, Bearsden, Glasgow G61 3BQ Tel: 0141 942 3134 — MB ChB 1976 Glas.; MRCPsych 1981. Cons. Geriat. Psychiat. Dykebar & Roy. Alexandra Hosps. Paisley. Prev: Cons. Geriat. Psychiat. Stobhill & Woodilee Hosps. Glas.

SMITH, Margaret Albertha Elder 25 Turnberry Road, Glasgow G11 5AH Tel: 0141 339 7400 — MB ChB 1946 Glas.; FRCPsych 1979, M 1973. Indep. Cons. Forens. Psychiat. Glas. Prev: Cons. Psychiat. Douglas Inch Centre for Forens. Psychiat. Glas.; Hon. Clin. Lect. (Postgrad. Med. Educat.) Glas. Univ.; Regist. (Psychol. Med.) E. Dist. Hosp. Glas.

SMITH, Margaret Anne Norton Brook Medical Centre, Cookworthy Road, Kingsbridge TQ7 1AE Tel: 01548 853551 Fax: 01548 857741 — MB ChB 1986 Glas.; MRCGP 1994; DRCOG 1990; DCH RCPS Glas. 1988. Prev: Trainee GP Salcombe.

SMITH, Margaret Baillie 38 Ralston Road, Bearsden, Glasgow G61 3BA Tel: 0141 942 0670 — MB ChB Glas. 1953; DObst RCOG 1955. (Glas.) Socs: Fac. Comm. Health. Prev: Clin. Asst. Canniesburn Hosp. Glas.; SCMO Community Health Glas.

SMITH, Margaret Campbell 2 Easter Ferrygate Park, Abbotsford Road, North Berwick EH39 5DB — MB ChB 1948 Ed.; DObst RCOG 1953. Prev: Ho. Phys. Stracathro Hosp. Brechin; Ho. Surg. N. Staffs. Roy. Infirm. Stoke-on-Trent; Obst. Ho. Surg. Elsie Inglis Memor. Matern. Hosp. Edin.

SMITH, Margaret Catherine Govan Health Centre, 5 Drumoyne Road, Glasgow G51 4BJ Tel: 0141 531 8400 Fax: 0141 531 8404 — MB ChB 1974 Glas.; MRCGP 1978. GP Glas..

SMITH, Margaret Fisher 2/4 Littlefield Lane, Grimsby DN31 2LG Tel: 01472 342250 Fax: 01472 251742; Lichfields, 63A Bargate, Grimsby DN34 5AA Tel: 01472 70794 — MB ChB 1959 Manch. (Manch.) Prev: SHMO (Cas.) Grimsby Gen. Hosp.; Ho. Phys. Lincoln Co. Hosp.; Ho. Surg. Salisbury Gen. Infirm.

SMITH, Margaret Irene (retired) Glandore, Armscote Road, Tredington, Shipston-on-Stour CV36 4NP Tel: 01608 663778 — MB ChB Birm. 1954. Prev: SCMO S. Warks. HA.

SMITH, Margaret Isabella Abernethy (retired) Summerfield, Bronygarth, Weston Rhyn, Oswestry SY10 7LY — LRCP LRCS 1950 Ed.; LRCP LRCS Ed. LRFPS Glas. 1950; DObst RCOG 1953. Prev: Clin. Med. Off. Shrops. HA.

SMITH, Margaret Josephine Feddinch House, Feddinch, St Andrews KY16 8NR — MRCS Eng. LRCP Lond. 1974. (Middlx.) Community Health Off. Ealing & Hammersmith HAs. Socs: BMA. Prev: Ho. Off. (Med. & Surg.) St. Martins Hosp. Bath.

SMITH, Margaret Lothian (retired) 2 Willow Road, Grange Est., Kilmarnock KA1 2HL Tel: 01563 525251 — MB ChB St. And. 1944; MRCOG 1958; DObst 1949. Prev: Assoc. Specialist (O & G) Ayrsh. & Arran HB.

SMITH, Margaret Mary (retired) Park Lodge, Ripley, Harrogate HG3 3DN — MB BS 1957 Lond.

SMITH, Margaret Nancy (retired) 6 Westbrook Park, Weston, Bath BA1 4DP Tel: 01225 424795 — MB ChB Leeds 1942, DPH. (Distinc.) 1947. Prev: Ho. Surg. Leeds Matern. Hosp.

SMITH, Margaret Rebecca 22 Cull's Road, Normandy, Guildford GU3 2EP — MB BS 1980 Lond.; FFA RCS Eng. 1987.

SMITH, Margaret Ruth The Surgery, 1 Church St., Newtownards BT23 Tel: 028 9181 6333 — MB BS 1991 Lond.; DCH Dub. 1995; DRCOG 1995; DGM RCPS Glas. 1994; MRCGP Lond. 1997 RCGP; DFFP 1997. (Roy. Lond. Hosp.) GP Retainee. Prev: GP Regist. Bangor Co. Down; Trainee GP Ulster, N. Downs & Ards Hosp. Trust Belf.; SHO (Med., A & E & O & G & Paediat.) Ulster Hosp. Belf.

SMITH, Margaret Whyte Little Broich, Kippen, Stirling FK8 3DT — MB ChB 1963 St. And.; MRCPsych 1985; DPM Ed. 1967.

SMITH, Marguerita Reid 51 Coulard Hill, Lossiemouth IV31 6LA — MB ChB 1993 Glas.

SMITH, Marguerite Elizabeth (retired) 36 Eton Court, Eton Avenue, London NW3 3HJ Tel: 020 7722 6316 — MB BS Lond. 1956; FRCP Lond. 1991, M 1964; DCH Eng. 1961; FRCPCH 1997. Prev: Sen. Med. Off. DoH Lond.

SMITH

SMITH, Marie Clare Lee Cottage, Slade Lane, Mubberley, Knutsford WA16 7QP — BM BCh 1989 Oxf.

SMITH, Marie Linda Department of Nuclear Medicine, Royal Liverpool & Broadgreen University Hospital Trust, Prescot St., Liverpool L7 8XP — MB ChB 1978 Glas.; BSc (Hons.) Glas. 1975; FRCP Lond. 1996; FRCP Glas. 1992; MRCP (UK) 1980.

SMITH, Marilyn Jane c/o 24 Victoria Road, Hartlepool TS26 8DD Tel: 01429 234324 — MB BS 1963 Lond.; MRCS Eng. LRCP Lond. 1963; FRCPsych 1996; MRCPsych 1981; MD 1998. (Roy. Free) Prev: Cons. Psychiat. N. Tees Gen. Hosp. Stockton-on-Tees.

SMITH, Marion Jane Tel: 020 8340 7736 — MB BS 1992 Lond.; DCH 1997; DFFP 1999. (Kings College London) Prev: SHO Obstetics & Gyn. Whittington Horp 1998; SHO Neonates Qu. Charlottes Hosp. 1997; SHO Paediatrics, Greenwich Hosp. 1996.

SMITH, Mark Alistair 4 Old School Court, Appuldurcombe Road, Wroxall, Ventnor PO38 3DL Tel: 01983 853793; 4 Old School Court, Appuldurcombe Road, Wroxall, Ventnor PO38 3DL — BM 1986 Soton. Prev: Trainee GP I. of Wight VTS; GP Rotat. Frankston Hosp. Vict., Austral.; Ho. Phys. Qu. Alexandra Hosp. Portsmouth.

SMITH, Mark Anthony 32 Larden Road, Acton, London W3 7SU — MB BS 1988 Lond.; DA (UK) 1990; FRCA 1994. Cons. Hillingdon Hosp. Prev: SHO (Anaesth.) Hillingdon Hosp., Univ. Coll. Hosp. & Middlx. Hosp. Lond.

SMITH, Mark Antony Lane End Surgery, 2 Manor Walk, Benton, Newcastle upon Tyne NE7 7XX Tel: 0191 266 5246 Fax: 0191 266 6241 — MB ChB 1986 Leeds. GP Newc.

SMITH, Mark Boraston Ellel Bank, Bay Horse, Lancaster LA2 0JD — MB BS 1980 Lond.; FFA RCS Eng. 1985. Cons. Anaesth. Lancaster HA. Prev: Sen. Regist. Rotat. (Anaesth.) Addenbrooke's Hosp. Camb. & P'boro.; Vis. Asst. Prof. Anaesthiol. Oklahoma Univ., USA.

SMITH, Mark Charles 36B Surrey Road, Bournemouth BH4 9BX — MB BS 1996 Lond.

SMITH, Mark Christopher Sullivan Way Surgery, Sullivan Way, Scholes, Wigan WN1 3TB Tel: 01942 243649 Fax: 01942 826476 — MB ChB 1981 Manch.

SMITH, Mark Edward Jaunty Springs Health Centre, 53 Jaunty Way, Gleadless, Sheffield S12 3DZ; 48A Boundary Road, West Bridgford, Nottingham NG2 7BZ — BM BS 1983 Nottm.

SMITH, Mr Mark Eric Ballacurn, Ballaugh, Kirk Michael Tel: 01624 7577 — MB BS 1959 Lond.; BA Oxf. 1954; FRCS Eng. 1968; MRCS Eng. LRCP Lond. 1959; DO Eng. 1964. (St. Thos.) Socs: Fell. Roy. Soc. Med. Prev: Cons. Ophth. Surg. Chelmsford Hosp. Gp.; Sen. Regist. St. Bart. Hosp. Lond.; Regist. St. Thos. Hosp. Lond.

SMITH, Mark Ernest Fitzgerald Department Histopathology, Plymouth Hospitals NHS Trust, Derriford Hospital, Derriford Road, Plymouth PL6 8DH — MB ChB 1981 Leeds; PhD Lond. 1990; MRCP (UK) 1984; MRCPath 1991. Cons. Histopath. Derriford Hosp. Plymouth. Prev: Sen. Lect. (Histopath.) Univ. Coll. Med. Sch. Lond.

SMITH, Mark Patrick 25 Adam and Eve Mews, Kensington, London W8 6UG — MB ChB 1985 Otago

SMITH, Mark Paul Blackbrook Surgery, Lisieux Way, Taunton TA1 2CB Tel: 01823 259444 Fax: 01823 250200 — MB ChB 1986 Bristol; MRCGP 1993; DRCOG 1992. (Bristol) GP; Police Surg. Prev: SHO (O & G) Brit. Milit. Hosp. Iserlohn FRG; SHO (Psychiat.) Brit. Milit. Hosp. Hannover.

SMITH, Mark Peart Astrazeneca, Alderley House, Alderley Park, Macclesfield SK10 4TF Tel: 01625 517986 Fax: 01625 590913 Email: mark.smith@alderley.zeneca.com; 103 Bollington Road, Turner Heath, Bollington, Macclesfield SK10 5EL Tel: 01625 572274 — MB ChB 1982 Birm.; MRCP (UK) 1987. Head of Oncol. & Immunol. Research Sandoz Pharmaceut. Ltd. Surrey.; Global Product Dir. (Oncol.) at Astrazeneca, Alderley Pk., Macclesfield. Prev: Pharmaceut. Phys. Farmitalia Carlo Erba Ltd. St Albans; Regist. (Med.) Walsgrave Hosp. Coventry; Lect. & Regist. (Haemat.) Univ. Coll. Hosp. Lond.

SMITH, Mark Stephen Haley Department of Gastroenterology, Royal Shrewsbury Hospital, Mytton Oak Road, Shrewsbury SY3 8XQ Tel: 01743 261065 Fax: 01743 261066 — MB BS 1985 Lond.; MD Lond. 1995; 2001 FRCP (UK). (Univ. Lond.) Cons. (Phys. & Gastro.) Roy. Shrewsbury Hosp. Socs: Brit. Soc. Gastroenterol.; Midl. Gastroentoological Soc., W.Midl.s Phys.s Assn. Prev: Sen. Regist.

(Gastroenterol. & Gen. Med.) N. Staffs. Hosp. Stoke-on-Trent; Regist. (Med.) Roy. Free Hosp. Hampstead.

SMITH, Martin Tavistock Surgical ITU, National Hospital for Neurology & Neurosurgery, Queen Square, London WC1N 3BG Tel: 020 7837 3611 Fax: 020 7829 8734 — MB BS 1980 Lond.; FFA RCS Eng. 1985. (Roy. Free) Cons. Anaesth. Nat. Hosp. for Neurol. & Neurosurg. Lond.; Hon. Sen. Lect. (Anaesth.) Univ. Coll. Lond. Socs: Fell. Roy. Soc. Med.; Assn. Anaesth.; Intens. Care Soc. Prev: Sen. Regist. (Anaesth.) St. Thos. Hosp. Lond.; Jules Thorn Research Fell. (Med.) The Middlx. Hosp. Lond.; Lect. (Human Anat.) Stanford Univ. Sch. Med. Calif., USA.

SMITH, Martin Clive 40 New Road, Little Kingshill, Great Missenden HP16 0EZ — MB ChB 1979 Birm.; DCH RCP Lond. 1983.

SMITH, Martin Daniel Swallowfield Medical Practice, The Street, Swallowfield, Reading RG7 1QY Tel: 0118 988 3134 Fax: 0118 988 5759; Wayside, Brunces Shaw Rd, Farley Hill, Reading RG7 1UU — MB 1971 Camb.; BChir 1970.

SMITH, Martin David Arrandene, 60 Bank Crescent, Ledbury HR8 1AE — MB ChB 1984 Birm.; DA (UK) 1987. Clin. Anaesth. Dudley Gp. Hosps. NHS Trust. Prev: Regist. Rotat. (Anaesth.) W. Midl. RHA.

SMITH, Martin Graham Milner 12 Clandon Road, Guildford GU1 2DR Tel: 01483 531825 Fax: 01483 829184 Email: martingsmith@btinternet.com; 12 Clandon Road, Guildford GU1 2DR Tel: 01483 531825 Fax: 01483 829184 Email: martingsmith@btinternet.com — MB 1967 Camb.; BChir 1966; FRCP Lond. 1982, M 1969. (St. Thos.) Cons. Phys. Roy. Surrey Co. Hosp.; MRCP Examr. RCP. Socs: (Ex-brit. Represen) Internat. Soc. Internal Med.; Brit. Soc. Gastroenterol.; (Ex Sec.) Harv. Soc. Prev: Sen. Regist. (Med.) King's Coll. Hosp. Lond.; Regional Adviser (Med.) RCP Lond.; Med. Off., Roy. Surrey Co. Hosp.

SMITH, Martin Nicholas 5 Espland Close, Newton Reigny, Penrith CA11 0AR — MB ChB 1989 Ed.

SMITH, Martin Ralph William 68 Balfour Road, Bromley BR2 9SL — MB ChB 1974 Liverp.

SMITH, Martin Richard 6 Eastfield Road, Benton, Newcastle upon Tyne NE12 8BD — MB BS 1992 Newc.; MRCP 1996. SHO (Med.). Newc. Gen. Hosp.; Regist. Paediat. Roy. Vict. Infirm. Newc.

SMITH, Martin Robert Dept. Metabo;ic Medicine, St. Mary's Hospital, London W2 1NY Tel: 020 7886 6666; 185 Barnfield Avenue, Ham, Kingston upon Thames KT2 5RQ Tel: 020 8549 9003 — MB BS 1992 Lond.; BSc Lond. 1989; MRCP (UK) 1995. (Char. Cross & Westm. Med. Sch.) Specialist Regist. (Diabetes & Endocrinol.), St. Mary's Hosp., Lond., W2. Socs: Soc. for Endocrinol.; Brit. Diabetic Assn.; Brit. Thyroid Assn. Prev: Regist. (Diabetes & Endocrinol.) Hemel Hempstead Hosp.; Regist. Watford Gen. Hosp.; Regist. Chelsea & W.minster Hosp.

SMITH, Martyn Vernon Kiddrow Lane Health Centre, Kiddrow Lane, Burnley BB12 6LH Tel: 01282 426840 Fax: 01282 433252 — MB BChir 1972 Camb.; MA Camb. 1972; DObst RCOG 1973. (King's Coll. Hosp.) Prev: SHO (A & E) St. Jas. Hosp. Leeds; SHO (Paediat.) St. Luke's Hosp. Bradford; Ho. Off. (Gen. Surg., Gen. Med. & O & G) King's Coll. Hosp.

SMITH, Mary Burnside Cottage, Edlingham, Alnwick NE66 2BL Tel: 01665 74280 — MB BS 1945 Durh. (Durh.)

SMITH, Mary Jane Carvers, Litte St., Norton-sub-Hamdon, Stoke-sub-Hamdon TA14 6SR — MB ChB 1972 Manch.; MRCP (UK) 1976; DCH Eng. 1974.

SMITH, Mary Josephine 236 Nottingham Road, Mansfield NG18 4SH — BM BS 1979 Nottm.

SMITH, Mary Neville (retired) 39 Wimbledon Close, The Downs, Wimbledon, London SW20 8HL — MB BS 1953 Lond.; DCH Eng. 1957; Hon. FRCPCH 1998. Prev: Hon. Assoc. Specialist (Paediat.) Kingston Hosp.

SMITH, Matthew Benjamin 17 Kelly Gardens, Abbeymeads, Swindon SN25 4YH — MB BS 1993 Newc.

SMITH, Matthew Guy 14 Cowesby Street, Manchester M14 4UG — MB ChB 1997 Manch.

SMITH, Matthew John 21 Monterey Gardens, Exeter EX4 5EN — MB BS 1992 Lond.

SMITH, Matthew Leonard 11 Highroyd Lane, Huddersfield HD5 9DN — MB ChB 1989 Leeds.

SMITH, Matthew Liam Walker 12 Julien Road, Coulsdon CR5 2DN — MB BS 1994 Lond.; MRCP Lond. 1997. (Kings Coll. Med. Sch.) Specialist Regist./Lect. (Haemat.) Roy. Lond. Hosp. & St. Bart. Hosp., Lond.

SMITH, Maureen Hanretty The Health Centre, Port Glasgow; 1 Lennox Avenue, Bishopton PA7 5BP — MB ChB 1978 Glas.; DRCOG 1982.

SMITH, Maurice Anthony Department Medicine of The Elderly, Harold Wood Hospital, Gubbins Lane, Romford RM3 0BE Tel: 01708 708257 Fax: 01708 708283 Email: mauricas@aol.com — MB ChB 1979 Liverp.; FRCP Lond. 1998. Cons Phys Geriat.s, Highwood Hosp. Brentwood; PostGrad. Acad. Organiser, Harold Wood Hosp. Romford Essex; Cons Geriat.ian Nuffield Hosp. Brentwood Essex.; Cons Geriat.ian, Wellington Hosp. Lond. NW8. Socs: BMA & Brit. Geriat. Soc. Prev: Sen. Regist. Middlx. Hosp. & Univ. Coll. Hosp. Lond.; Sen. Regist. N.wick Pk. Hosp. Harrow; Regist. (Med.) Roy. Liverp. Hosp.

SMITH, Maurice Raymond Mather Avenue Practice, 584 Mather Avenue, Liverpool L19 4UG Tel: 0151 427 6239 Fax: 0151 427 8876 — MB ChB 1986 Manch.; MRCGP 1990; Dip. Occ. Med. 1997; DRCOG 1988. GP Princip.; Occupat. Phys.; Occupat. Phys. for Type Talk Liverp. Socs: Soc. Occupat. Med.

SMITH, Megan Kirkmoors, Main St., Huby, York YO61 1HS; 3F2/ 4 Merton Place, Edinburgh EH11 1JZ Tel: 0131 229 3002 — MB ChB 1998 Ed.; MB ChB Ed 1998; BSc (Hons) 1995. (Edinburgh) JHO.Qu Margt. Hosp. Dunfermline.

SMITH, Megan Rachel Birmingham Children's Hospital, Steelhouse Lane, Birmingham B4 6NH Tel: 0121 333 9652; 20 Hursthead Walk, Brunswick, Manchester M13 9UT Tel: 0161 274 4807 — MB ChB 1994 Manch.; MRCP (UK) 1997; MRCPCH. (Univ. Manch.) Specialist Regist. (Paediatric Intens. Care) Birm. Childr.'s Hosp. Prev: SpR Paediat. - N.W.; SHO (Neonat. Med.) St. Mary's Hosp. Manch.; Ho. Off. Manch. Roy. Infirm.

SMITH, Melanie Jane 26 Marmion Road, Liverpool L17 8TX — MB BS 1980 Adelaide.

***SMITH, Melissa Ann** 15 Vine Avenue, Sevenoaks TN13 3AH — MB ChB 1998 Bristol; BSc (Hons) 1995.

SMITH, Michael Flat 3/2, 21 Thornwood Avenue, Glasgow G11 7PH — MB ChB 1998 Glas.; MB ChB Glas 1998.

SMITH, Michael Arthur (retired) 19 St Clare Road, Colchester CO3 3SZ Tel: 01206 574592 — BM BCh 1952 Oxf.; DM Oxf. 1958; FRCP Lond. 1976, M 1958; DObst RCOG 1954. Prev: Dermatol. Colchester & Dist. Gp. Hosps.

SMITH, Mr Michael Clive Franklyn ENT Department, County Hospital, Union Walk, Hereford HR1 2ER Tel: 01432 364074 Fax: 01432 364149; Urdimarsh Farm, Marden, Hereford HR1 3HB Fax: 01432 359893 Email: mikesmith@urdimarsh.freeserve.co.uk — MB BS 1977 Lond.; FRCS (Otol.) Eng. 1985; MRCS Eng. LRCP Lond. 1976; T(S) 1991; DLO Eng. 1980. (St. Mary's) Cons. ENT. Co. Hosp. Hereford, & Roy. Infirm., Worcester. Socs: Indian Assn. Otolaryngols.; Indian Soc. Otol.; Nepal Med. Assn. Prev: Cons. ENT W.. Regional Hosp. Pokhara, Nepal; Sen. Regist. (ENT) Freeman Hosp. Newc. u. Tyne; Regist. (ENT) Warwick Gen. Hosp.

SMITH, Michael Colin George 19 Counting House Road, Disley, Stockport SK12 2DB Email: smithm@icrf.ic.net.uk — MB ChB 1988 Birm.

SMITH, Michael David Public Health Laboratory, Musgrove Park Hospital, Taunton TA1 5DB — BM 1979 Soton.; MRCP (UK) 1984; MRCPath 1990. Cons. Microbiol. Prev: Sen. Clin. Lect. Wellcome · Mahidol Univ. Oxf. Trop. Med. Research Progm. Mahidol Univ. Bangkok, Thailand.

SMITH, Mr Michael Fleming, TD Stirling Royal Infirmary, Livilands, Stirling FK8 2AU Tel: 01786 434000 Fax: 01786 450588 Email: michael.smith@fuah.scot.nhs.uk; Dunardoch, St. Margaret's Drive, Dunblane FK15 0DP Tel: 01786 824261 Fax: 01786 824261 Email: smith.dun@btopenworld.com — MB ChB Ed. 1970; MA Camb. 1971; ChM Ed. 1980; FRCS Ed. 1975; MRCOG 1975; T(S) 1991. (Univ. Camb. & Univ. Ed.) Cons. Urol. Stirling Roy. Infirm. & Falkirk & Dist. Roy. Infirm. Prev: Cons. Urol. Law Hosp. Carluke; Sen. Regist. (Urol. Surg.) Roy. Infirm. Edin.; Fell. (Surg.) Harvard Med. Sch. Boston, USA.

SMITH, Michael Francis The Ryegate Childrens Centre, The Childrens Hospital, Tapton Crescent Road, Sheffield S10 5DD Tel: 0114 267 0237 — MB BS 1972 Lond.; FRCP Lond. 1991; MRCP (UK) 1978; FRCPCH 1998. (Lond. Hosp.) Cons. Paediat. Ryegate Childr. Centre; Cons. Paediat. Jessop Hosp. for Wom.; Clin. Tutor (Paediat.) Univ. Sheff. Socs: Brit. Paediat. Neurol. Assn.; Neonat. Soc.; Brit. Assn. for Perinatal Med. Prev: Sen. Regist. Sheff. Childr. Hosp.; Regist. & Research Regist. St. Thos. Hosp. Lond.

SMITH, Michael Graham 94 Hayclose Road, Kendal LA9 7ND — MB BS 1991 Lond.; BSc (Microbiol. & Immunol.) Lond. 1988; MRCP (UK) 1994. (St. Mary's Hosp. Med. Sch.) GP/Regist. Poplars Surg. Birm. Prev: SHO (O & G) Good Hope Hosp. Sutton Coldfield; SHO Rotat. (Med.) Dudley Rd. Hosp. Birm.

SMITH, Mr Michael Hanby 38 Billy Bunns Lane, Wombourne, Wolverhampton WV5 9BP Tel: 01902 893140 — MB BS 1971 Lond.; FRCS Ed. 1977.

SMITH, Michael Inglis Bank House Surgery, The Health Centre, Victoria Road, Hartlepool TS26 8DB Tel: 01429 274386 Fax: 01429 860811 — MB ChB 1985 Ed.; BSc (Hons.) Ed. 1983, MB ChB 1985; MRCGP 1991; DRCOG 1990.

SMITH, Michael John 22 Southwell Road, Benfleet SS7 1JB Tel: 01268 751728 — MRCS Eng. LRCP Lond. 1960.

SMITH, Michael John Department of Medicine, Heatherwood Hospital, Ascot SL5 8AA Tel: 01344 877186 Fax: 01344 877620; Moorlands, Coronation Road, South Ascot, Ascot SL5 9HF — MD 1986 Manch.; MB ChB 1973; FRCP Lond. 1994; MRCP (UK) 1977. (Manchester) Cons. Phys. Gen. & Thoracic Med. Heatherwood Hosp. Ascot.; Assoc. Med. Dir. Heatherwood & Wexham Pk. Hosp. Trust; Lead Cancer Clinician H/WPH Trust. Socs: Brit. Thoracic Soc. Prev: Sen. Regist. (Thoracic & Gen. Med.) Brompton Hosp. Lond.; Clin. Lect. & Hon. Regist. Cardiothoracic Inst. Brompton Hosp. Lond.; Regist. (Med.) Qu. Mary's Hosp. Roehampton.

SMITH, Michael John The Royal Surrey County Hospital, Egerton Road, Guildford GU2 7XX Tel: 01483 571122; 13 Fairway, Merrow, Guildford GU1 2XQ Tel: 01483 38053 Fax: 01483 574508 — MB BS 1957 Durh.; FRCP Lond. 1977, M 1962. (Newc.) Cons. Phys. Guildford & Godalming Gp. Hosps.; Sen. Lect. (Biochem.) Univ. Surrey. Socs: Fell. Roy. Soc. Med.; BMA; Brit. Diabetic Assn. Prev: Regist. Postgrad, Med. Sch. Hammersmith; Research Fell. NIH, Univ. S.. Calif. USA; 1st Asst. Univ. Dept. Med. Roy. Vict. Infirm. Newc.

SMITH, Michael John Moon 1-5 Newington Causeway, London SE1 6ED Tel: 020 7407 4248 Fax: 020 7234 0849; 41 Manor Road N., Hinchley Wood, Esher KT10 0AA — MB BChir Camb. 1950. (Univ. Coll. Hosp.)

SMITH, Michael Joseph Department of Psychological Medicine, Gartavel Royal Hospital, 1055 Great Western Road, Glasgow G12 0XH Tel: 0141 211 3908 Fax: 0141 357 4899 — MB ChB 1990 Liverp.; BSc (Hons.) Liverp. 1987; MRCPsych 1996; MRCGP 1994. (Liverp.) Cons. Psychiat., Dykebar Hosp., Paisley; Sen. Research Fell.. (Psychol. Med.) Univ. Glas. Prev: Specialist Regist. (Psychiat.) Gartnavel Roy. Hosp. Glas.

SMITH, Michael Lawson The Surgery, Station Road, Clayton, Bradford BD14 6JA Tel: 01274 880650 Fax: 01274 883256 — MB ChB 1971 St. And.; FRCP Ed. 1990; MRCP (UK) 1976; DRCOG 1973; FRCPCH 1996. Med. Dir. Bradford NHS Trust; Hon. Sen. Lect. (Paediat.) Leeds Univ. Prev: Cons. Paediat. Bradford DHA; Sen. Regist. (Paediat.) Derbysh. & Notts. (T) AHAs; Regist. (Paediat.) Ninewells Teach. Hosp. Dundee.

SMITH, Michael McDonald The Health Centre, Clitheroe Tel: 01200 25201 — MB ChB 1960 St. And.; FRCGP 1984, M 1969; DObst RCOG 1962; Assoc. Fac. Occupat. Med. RCP Lond. 1980. (St. And.) Socs: Soc. Occupat. Med.

SMITH, Michael Ralph Dolly Barn, Ash Lane, Etwall, Derby DE65 6HT — MB BCh 1962 Wales; FRCOG 1980, M 1967; DObst RCOG 1964. (Cardiff) Cons. O & G Burton Hosps. NHS Trust. Socs: BMA. Prev: Cons. O & G E. Anglia RHA; Sen. Regist. Plymouth Gen. Hosp.; Surg. Cdr. RN.

SMITH, Michael Robert Paddock House, 7 Orchard View, Skelton, York YO30 1YQ — MB ChB 1995 Leeds.

SMITH, Michael Robert 23 Blenheim Avenue, Liverpool L21 8LN — MB ChB 1998 Sheff.; MB ChB Sheff 1998.

SMITH, Michael Stuart Checkley Lodge, Checkley, Nantwich CW5 7QA — MB ChB 1974 Liverp.

SMITH, Michael Thomas 21 St Andrews Way, Bromsgrove B61 7NR — MB ChB Birm. 1993; BSc Birm. 1990; FRCA (Lond.) 1998. (Birmingham) Specialist Regist. Anaesth. & ITU Birm. Sch. Qu. Eliz. Hosp. Birm.

SMITH

SMITH, Michael Victor 38 East Sheen Avenue, London SW14 8AS Tel: 020 8876 1570 — MB BS 1963 Lond.; MRCS Eng. LRCP Lond. 1963; MFPHM 1989, MFCM 1972; DPH Lond. 1967; DObst RCOG 1964. (Guy's) Indep. Med. Author & BRd.caster; Hon. Med. Adviser Pet Health Counc.; Med. Edr. Woms. Own. Socs: Hon. Fell. Nat. Assn. Family Plann. Doctors; Med. Jl.ists Assn. Prev: Chief Med. Off. Family Pann. Assn.; Research Assoc. GP Research Unit Guy's Hosp. Lond.; Dir. (Pub. Health) Kingston & Esher HA.

SMITH, Michael William 4 Burlingham Avenue, West Kirby, Wirral CH48 8AP — MB ChB 1975 Liverp.; FCAnaesth. 1989. Regist. Rotat. (Anaesth.) Mersey RHA.

SMITH, Myles Gerard 22A Ipswich Road, Woodbridge IP12 4BU Tel: 01394 385600 — MB BS 1974 Lond.; FFA RCS Eng. 1979. Cons. Anaesth. Ipswich Hosp. Ipswich.

SMITH, Nancy Heron (retired) 1 Edge Point Close, Knights Hill, London SE27 0QS Tel: 020 8670 6475 — MB ChB (Hons.) Leeds 1945; MRCGP 1960; DObst RCOG 1948. Prev: Ho. Surg.Birm.Accid..Hosp.

SMITH, Naomi The Farmhouse, Hillhead, Portlethen, Aberdeen AB12 4QP Tel: 01224 783778 — MB ChB 1996 Dundee; BMSc (Hons.) 1993; DRCOG RCOG. 1998; DFFP RCOG. 1998. (Dundee) SHO GP VTS Aber. Roy. Infirm.; Paediat. Roy. Aberd. Child. Hosp. Prev: SHO A & E Abdn. Roy. Infirm; SHO (O & G) Aber. Roy. Infirm.; Jun. Ho. Off. (Surg.) Roy. Infirm. Shirley.

SMITH, Neil Andrew Montague Health Centre, Oakenhurst Road, Blackburn BB2 1PP Tel: 01254 268436 Fax: 01254 268440 — MB ChB 1990 Manch.; MB ChB (Hons.) Manch. 1990; MRCP (UK) 1992; MRCP Ed. 1992; DRCOG 1993; DFFP 1993. Trainee GP Chesh. Prev: Trainee GP/SHO Trafford Gen. Hosp.

SMITH, Neil Andrew Leighton Fontana and Partners, Silsden Health Centre, Elliott Street, Silsden, Keighley BD20 0DG Tel: 01535 652447 Fax: 01535 657296 — MB BS 1982 Lond.; MRCGP 1986; DRCOG 1985; Dip Occ Med RCP Lond. 1995. (St. Tos.) NHS Occupat. Health Phys. Socs: BMA; Soc. of Occupat. Med.; ANHOPS.

SMITH, Neil Anthony National Blood Service Birmingham Centre, Edgbaston, Birmingham B15 2SQ Tel: 0121 253 4016 Fax: 0121 253 4003 — MB ChB 1979 Birm.; MRCP (UK) 1984; MRCPath 1994. Cons. Haemat. Nat. Blood Serv., Birm. Centre; Cons. Haemolologist Roy. Wolverhampton Hosp.s NHS Trust.

SMITH, Neil Franklin Flat 3, Belle Vue Court, Bellevue Gardens, Brighton BN2 2AN — MB ChB 1995 Cape Town.

SMITH, Neil Jonathan Flat 5, 4 Wandle Road, Morden SM4 6AH — MB BS 1996 Lond.

SMITH, Neil Mitchell 14 Castle Gate, Bothwell Castle Estate, Bothwell, Glasgow G71 7HU Tel: 0141814631 — MB ChB 1953 Glas. Socs: Affil. Mem. Roy. Coll. Psychiat.; Assur. Med. Soc. Prev: Sen. Med. Off. (Prisons Div.); Sen. Med. Off. HM Prison Barlinnie.; Cons. Psychiat. Hartwood Hosp. 1992-1995.

SMITH, Neil Robert Ling House Medical Centre, 49 Scott Street, Keighley BD21 2JH Email: nsmith@bradford-ha.nhs.uk — MB BS 1983 Lond.; MRCP (UK) 1986. Partner in Gen. Pract.

SMITH, Neville Vincent (retired) Department of Medicine, University Hospital, Queens Medical Centre, Nottingham NG7 2UH — MB ChB 1963 Sheff.; MRCP (UK) 1994; MRCS Eng. LRCP Lond. 1966. Hon. Clin. Asst. Gen. Med. Dept. Med. Univ. Hosp. Nottm.

SMITH, Niall Cameron 33F Herbert Street, Glasgow G20 6NB — MB ChB 1993 Glas.; DRCOG 1996; MRCGP 1997.

SMITH, Nicholas 17 Colliery Green Drive, Little Neston, South Wirral CH64 0UA Tel: 0151 336 7452 — MB ChB 1979 Liverp.; FRCS Ed. 1986; DMRT 1997. Staff Grade Oncol. Clatterbridge Centre for Oncol. Clatterbridge Hosp. Bebington Wirral.

SMITH, Nicholas Anthony Gould Danks, Smith, Sykes and Farrell, 134 Beeston Road, Beeston Hill, Leeds LS11 8BS Tel: 0113 276 0717 Fax: 0113 270 3727 — MB ChB 1976 Leeds; DRCOG Lond. 1981. GP Leeds. Prev: Trainee GP Aylesbury VTS.

SMITH, Mr Nicholas Charles 19 Old Brickfields, Broadmayne, Dorchester DT2 8UX — BM 1978 Soton.; FRCS Ed. 1983; FRCR 1987. Cons. Radiol. W. Dorset Gen. Hops. NHS Trust. Prev: Sen. Regist. (Diag. Radiol.) W. Midl. Region. HA.

SMITH, Nicholas James 62 New Hall Lane, Bolton BL1 5LG — MB ChB 1981 Manch.; FRCA.

SMITH, Nicholas Peter 49 Preston Down Road, Paignton TQ3 2RR Tel: 01803 557038; Flat 2, 31 Corfton Rd, Ealing, London W5 2HP Tel: 020 8998 0682 — MB BS 1991 Lond. Regist. (HIV & Genitourin. Med.) St. Stephens Clinic Chelsea & W.m. Healthcare Lond.

SMITH, Nicholas Stephen Burton Road Surgery, 32 Burton Road, Withington, Manchester M20 3EB Tel: 0161 445 5907 Fax: 0161 448 0466; 14 Salisbury Road, Chorlton-Cum-Hardy, Manchester M21 0SL — MB ChB 1990 Manch.; MRCGP 1994; DFFP 1994. GP Manch.

SMITH, Nicholas William Patrick 175 Whitham Road, Broomhill, Sheffield S10 2SN — MB ChB 1995 Sheff.

SMITH, Nicola Aileen Directorate of GUM/HIV Chelsea and Westminster NHS Trust Trust, Charing Cross Hospital, Fulham Palace Road, London W6 8RF Tel: 020 8846 1578 Fax: 020 8846 7582 Email: nicola@chelwest.org — MB BS 1989 Lond.; BSc Lond. 1986; MRCP (UK) 1992; DFFP 1994; Cert of Completion of Specialist Training 1997 (Genitourinary Medicine). (St. George's London) Cons. (HIV/GUM) Directorate Chelsea & W.minster NHS Trust Char. Cross Hosp. Lond. Socs: Med. Soc. Study VD; Brit. Soc. Colpos. & Cerv. Path.; Brit. HIV Assn. Prev: Sen. Regist. (Genitourin. Med.) St. Thomas Hosp. Lond.; Regist. (Genitourin. Med.) Chelsea & W.minster Hosp.; SHO (Oncol.) Hammersmith Hosp. Lond.

SMITH, Nicola Lisbeth Whaddon Way Surgery, 293 Whaddon Way, Bletchley, Milton Keynes MK3 7LW Tel: 01908 375341 Fax: 01908 374975 — MB ChB 1989 Leic.

SMITH, Nigel Ian Bromley House, Ormes Lane, Tettenhall Wood, Wolverhampton WV7 3QG — MB ChB 1976 Liverp.

SMITH, Nigel Jollyon Clinical Neurophysiology (EEG) Department, University Hospital, Nottingham NG7 2UH; The Grange, Bunny, Nottingham NG11 6QX — MB BChir 1972 Camb.; MA Camb. 1972; MRCP (UK) 1975; LMSSA Lond. 1971; FRCP Lond. 1996. (St. Thos.) Cons. Clin. Neurophysiol. Univ. Hosp. Nottm. & Derbysh. Roy. Infirm.; Clin. Teach. Univ. Nottm. Socs: Fell. Roy. Soc. Med.; (Ex-Pres.) Electrophysiol. Tech. Assn.; (Ex-Mem. Counc.) Brit. Soc. Clin. Neurophysiol. Prev: Sen. Regist. (Clin. Neurophysiol.) Wessex Neurol. Centre; Regist. (Neurol.) Derbysh. Roy. Infirm.; Regist. (Neurosurg.) Nat. Hosp. Qu. Sq. Lond.

SMITH, Nigel Kenneth Gladstone 33 Lambley Lane, Burton Joyce, Nottingham NG14 5BG — MB BS 1976 Newc.; DM Nottm. 1994; FRCP Lond. 1995; MRCP (UK) 1979. Cons. Phys. (Med. for Elderly) Nottm. City Hosp. Prev: Cons. Phys. (Med. for Elderly) Leicester Gen. Hosp.; Cons. Phys. (Health c/o Elderly) Univ. Hosp. Nottm.

SMITH, Nigel Peter David 16 Menelik Road, London NW2 3RP — MB BS 1994 Lond.

SMITH, Noel Howard Waldron Health Centre, Stanley Street, London SE8 4BG Tel: 020 8692 2314; 41 Manor Way, Blackheath, London SE3 9XG Tel: 020 8852 5823 — MB BCh BAO 1956 NUI; DCH 1960; DObst RCOG 1961. Med. Off. Tunnel Refineries Greenwich.

SMITH, Norman Charles Aberdeen Maternity Hospital, Cornhill Road, Peterculter AB14 0PT Tel: 01224 681818 — MD 1983 Aberd.; MB ChB 1974; FRCOG 1991, M 1979. Cons. Obst & Gyn. i/c Fetal Med. Aberd. Matern. Hosp. Prev: Lect. (O & G) Dept. Midw. Qu. Mother's Hosp. Glas.

SMITH, Oladimeji Omabegho 16 Hallamshire Drive, Sheffield S10 4FL — MB BS 1990 Benin, Nigeria; MRCP (UK) 1995; DCH RCP Lond. 1996. Specialist Regist. Rotat. (Paediat.) Sheff. Childr. Hosp. NHS Trust. Socs: Brit. Paediat. Assn.; BMA. Prev: Specialist Regist. (Paediat.) N.. Gen. Hosp. Sheff. & Pembury Hosp. Tunbridge Wells, Kent; SHO (Neonatol.) Hammersmith Hosp. Lond.

SMITH, Pamela Jane 3 Siskin Green, Liverpool L25 4RY — MB ChB 1990 Liverp. SHO (Med.) S.port & Formby NHS Trust.

SMITH, Patricia Ann Park Road Group Practice, The Elms Medical Centre, 3 The Elms, Dingle, Liverpool L8 3SS Tel: 0151 727 5555 Fax: 0151 288 5016; 23 Court Hey Drive, Bowring Park, Liverpool L16 2NB Tel: 0151 489 4742 — MB ChB 1978 Liverp.; MRCS Eng. LRCP Lond. 1978; MRCGP 1992; DA Eng. 1984. GP Liverp.

SMITH, Patricia Anne Howden Health Centre, Livingston EH54 6TP Tel: 01506 418518 Fax: 01506 460757 — MB ChB 1981 Glas.; MRCGP 1986.

SMITH, Patricia Anne Fields Farm, Alt Hill Lane, Ashton-under-Lyne OL6 8AP Tel: 0161 330 5413 Fax: 0161 339 0763 Email: trish.smith@dial.pipex.com — BM BS 1981 Nottm.; BMedSci Nottm. 1979; MRCP (UK) 1984; Dip. Pharm. Med. RCP (UK) 1989. Indep. Pharmaceut./Healthcare Cons. Ashton-under-Lyme.

SMITH

SMITH, Patricia Elizabeth (retired) The Rea House, Neenton, Bridgnorth WV16 6RL Tel: 017462 254 — MB ChB 1946 Birm.; MRCS Eng. LRCP Lond. 1946. Prev: Paediat. Regist. Jessop Hosp. Sheff.

SMITH, Patricia Jane City General Hospital, Stoke-on-Trent ST4 6QG Tel: 01782 715444; 2 Hawthorn Cottages, Main Road, Betley, Crewe CW3 9AB Tel: 01270 820398 — MB BCh BAO 1976 Dub.; BA 1976; MRCP (UK) (Paediat.) 1982; FRCPCH 1997; FRCP 1997. (T.C. Dub.) Cons. Paediat. (Endocrinol. & Diabetes) City Hosp. Stoke on Trent. Socs: Brit. Paediat. Assn.; Brit. Soc. Paediat. Endocrinol.; Eur. Soc. Paediat. Endocrinol. Prev: Cons. Paediat. (Endrocrinol. & Diabetes) Roy. Vict. Infirm. Newc.; Research Regist. (Paediat. Endocrinol.) Middlx. Hosp. Lond.; Sen. Regist. Yorkhill Childr. Hosp. Glas.

SMITH, Patricia Joyce 3 Oakfield Road, Didsbury, Manchester M20 6XA Email: 101603.2115@compuserve.com — MB ChB 1969 Manch.; FRCP Lond. 1989; MRCP (UK) 1971. Cons. Rheum. Blackburn Health Dist. Socs: Fell. Manch. Med. Soc. Prev: Sen. Regist. (Rheum.) Manch. RHB; Regist. (Cardiol.) Baguley Hosp. Manch.; SHO (Med.) Withington Hosp. Manch.

SMITH, Patrick (retired) Heathfields, Forest Hill, Mansfield NG18 5BQ Tel: 01623 465821 — MB BS Lond. 1960.

SMITH, Mr Patrick Joseph Bradshaw Litfield House, Clifton, Bristol BS8 3LS Tel: 01179 731323 Fax: 01179 733303 — ChM Bristol 1970, MB ChB 1962; FRCS Eng. 1967. (Bristol) Cons. Urol. Surg. Bristol Roy. Infirm. Prev: Cons. Urol. Surg. United Bath Hosps. SHO Gen. Surg. Bristol Roy.; Infirm.; SHO (Urol.) United Bristol Hosps.

SMITH, Paul Ainsdale Village Surgery, 2 Leamington Road, Southport PR8 3LB Tel: 01704 577866 Fax: 01704 576644; 11 Clinning Road, Birkdale, Southport PR8 4NU Tel: 01704 565355 — MB ChB 1983 Liverp.

SMITH, Paul Andrew 5 Banklands Avenue, Silsden, Keighley BD20 0JL — MB ChB 1996 Leeds.

SMITH, Paul Dominic Elmhirst, Ninelands Road, Hathersage, Hope Valley S32 1BJ — MB ChB 1985 Bristol; FRCA 1992. Lect. (Anaesth.) Univ. Leeds. Prev: Regist. Rotat. (Anaesth.) Univ. Hosp. S. Manch.; SHO (Anaesth.) Univ. Hosp. S. Manch.

SMITH, Mr Paul John Bishopswood Hospital, Rickmansworth Road, Northwood HA6 2JW Tel: 01923 828100 Fax: 01923 844849; Kimble Farm, Fawley, Henley-on-Thames RG9 6JP — MB BS 1968 Newc.; FRCS Glas. 1974. (Newc.) Cons. Plastic Surg. Hosp. for Childr. Gt. Ormond St., Mt. Vernon Hosp. N.wood, St. Albans City Hosp. Socs: (Counc. Mem.) Brit. Soc. Surg. Hand.; Brit. Assn. Aesth. Plastic Surg.; Brit. Assn. Plastic Surg. Prev: Vis. Prof. Dept. Plastic Surg. Salt Lake City; Christine Kleinert Fell. Hand Surg. Louisville, USA; Resid. & Clin. Instruc. (Plastic Surg.) Duke Univ. USA.

SMITH, Paul Jonathan 240 Fulbridge Road, Peterborough PE4 6SN — MB ChB 1992 Leeds.

SMITH, Paul Kirkel Woodwiss Westfield Surgery, Radstock, Bath BA3 3UJ Tel: 01761 436333 Fax: 01761 433126 Email: westfield@compuserve.com; Silverstones, Kilmersdon, Bath BA3 5SU — BM BS 1975 Nottm.; BMedSci (Hons.) Nottm. 1973; MRCGP 1979; DRCOG 1978. (Nottm.) GP Bath; Trainer Bath VTS. Prev: Trainer & Tutor GP Bath VTS; Trainee GP Exeter VTS; GP Mem. Avon PCAG.

SMITH, Paul Mapleston Woodside, Park Road, Dinas Powys CF64 4HJ Tel: 02920 514127 — MB BS 1959 Lond.; MD Lond. 1969; FRCP Lond. 1978, M 1964. (St. Thos.) p/t Cons. Phys. BUPA Hosp., Cardiff. Socs: (Ex-Pres.) Cardiff Med. Soc.; (Ex-Pres.) Brit. Soc. Gastroenterol.; (Ex-Pres.) Soc. Phys in Wales. Prev: Hon. Lect. (Med.) King's Coll. Hosp. Lond.; Research Fell. Boston Univ. Sch. Med., USA; Cons. Phys., Llandough Hosp., Penarth.

SMITH, Paul Robert Diabetes Centre, Ward 24, Birmingham Heartlands Hospital, Bordeley Green E., Birmingham B9 5SS; 132 Rectory Road, Sutton Coldfield B75 7RS Tel: 0121 311 1694 Email: p.r.smith@bham.ac.uk — MB ChB 1988 Leeds; BSc (Hons.) Psychol. in relation to Med. Leeds 1985; MRCP (UK) 1992. Lect./Hon. Specialist Regist. (Gen. Med., Diabetes & Endocrinol.)Birm. Heartlands Hosp. Prev: Lect./Hon. Specialist Regist. (Gen. Med., Diabetes & Endocrinol.) Qu. Eliz. Hosp. Birm.; Research Fell. Dept. Med. Univ. Birm.; Regist. (Gen. Med., Diabetes & Endocrinol.) Birm. Heartlands Hosp.

SMITH, Paul Stevenson (retired) Easdon Hill Cottage, Manaton Road, North Bovey, Newton Abbot TQ13 8QX Tel: 01647 221318 — MB BS 1960 Lond.; MB BS (Hons.) Lond. 1960; BSc (Hons.) Lond. 1957; MRCGP 1985. Prev: GP Sandhurst.

SMITH, Paula Jane Rudgwick Medical Centre, Station Road, Rudgwick, Horsham RH12 3HB Tel: 01403 822103; 15 Grange Park, Cranleigh GU6 7HY Tel: 01483 271042 — MB BS 1986 Lond.; MA Camb. 1983; MRCGP 1993. Princip. GP Rudgwick, W. Sussex. Prev: GP Windsor; Trainee GP Tadworth Surrey VTS; Regist. (Gen. Med.) King Edwd. VII Hosp. Windsor.

SMITH, Penelope Ann Dept. Of Anaesthesia, Dewsbury & District Hospital, Halifax Rd, Dewsbury WF13 4HS Tel: 0115 969 1169, 01924 816038 Email: dbeggs@ncht.org.uk; Cherry Garth, 43 Birkdale Road, Dewsbury WF13 4HH — MB ChB 1974 Leeds; FFA RCS Eng. 1979. Cons. Anaesth. Dewsbury Dist. Hosp..

SMITH, Penelope Frances Litchdon Medical Centre, Landkey Road, Barnstaple EX32 9LL Tel: 01271 23443 Fax: 01271 25979; Hannaford House, Landkey, Barnstaple EX32 0NY Tel: 01271 830271 — MB BS 1976 Lond.; MRCP (UK) 1979; MRCS Eng. LRCP Lond. 1976; MRCGP 1985.

SMITH, Penelope Susan 14 Montagu Drive, Leeds LS8 2PD Tel: 0113 240 2987 — MB BS 1984 Lond.; MA (Cantab) 1981; DA (UK) 1987. SpR Anaesthetics N. & W. Yorks. Deanery. Prev: Clin. Asst. (Anaesth.) Leeds Gen. Infirm.

SMITH, Mr Peter 17 Fortwilliam Drive, Belfast BT15 4EB — MB BCh BAO 1960 Belf.; FRCS Ed. 1966; FRCOG 1979, M 1966.

SMITH, Peter 12 Shepherds Avenue, Worksop S81 0JA — MB ChB 1977 Bristol.

SMITH, Peter Andrew University Department of Pathology, Duncan Building, Daulby St., Liverpool L69 3GA Tel: 0151 706 4495 Fax: 0151 706 5859 Email: peter.smith@rlbuh-tr.nwest.nhs.uk — MB BS 1976 Lond.; BSc (Anat.) Lond. 1974; MRCS Eng. LRCP Lond. 1976; FRCPath 1996, MRCPath 1984. (Char. Cross) Cons. Cytopath. Roy. Liverp. Univ. Hosp.; Hon. Lect. Univ. Liverp. Socs: (Pres.) Brit. Soc. Clin. Cytol.; Internat. Acad. of Cytol. Prev: Cons. Histopath. Roy. Liverp. Hosp. & Wom. Hosp. Liverp.; Lect. (Histopath.) Char. Cross & W.m. Med. Sch. Lond.; Regist. (Histopath.) Sir Chas. Gairdner Hosp. Perth, W. Austral.

SMITH, Peter Anthony 4 Swisspine Gardens, St Helens WA9 5UE — MB ChB 1990 Liverp.

SMITH, Peter Arthur John (retired) Pond Farm House, Southwater, Horsham RH13 7BS Tel: 01403 730323 — MB BS 1946 Lond.; FRCP Lond. 1969, M 1949; MRCS Eng. LRCP Lond. 1941. Prev: Regist. (Dermat.) Guy's Hosp. Lond.

SMITH, Peter Campbell 33 Tithebarn Street, Poulton-le-Fylde FY6 7BY — MB ChB 1987 Manch.

SMITH, Peter Charles Wymondham Medical Partnership, Postmill Close, Wymondham NR18 0RF Tel: 01953 602118 Fax: 01953 605313 — MB BS 1977 Lond.; MRCGP 1981. Prev: VTS. Canterbury.

SMITH, Peter David Frederick Wolverhampton Road Surgery, 13 Wolverhampton Road, Stafford ST17 4BP Tel: 01785 258161 Fax: 01785 224140; March Cottage, Whitgreave Lane, Great Bridgeford, Stafford ST18 4SJ — MB BS 1982 Lond.

SMITH, Peter Donald 34 Goldsmith Lane, Kingsbury, London NW9 9AH Tel: 020 8204 2029; Garden Flat, 49 Avonmore Road, West Kensington, London W14 8RT Tel: 020 7602 7652 — MB BS 1980 Lond.; MRCS Eng. LRCP Lond. 1980; DRCOG 1985. (Char. Cross) Family Plann. Doctor Brook Advis. Center Lond. Socs: BMA. Prev: Natural Growth Project Co-Worker Med. Foundat. c/o Victims of Torture; SHO (Neonat. Paediat.) Whittington Hosp. Lond.; Regist. (O & G) St. Bart. Hosp. Lond.

SMITH, Peter Gareth David Yelverton Surgery, Westella Road, Yelverton PL20 6AS Tel: 01822 852202 Fax: 01822 852260 — MB BS 1983 Lond.; MA Camb. 1983; MRCGP 1987; DCH RCP Lond. 1986; DRCOG 1985. Prev: Med. Off. P.ss Alice Hospice Esher; Trainee GP Camb. VTS; Ho. Phys. (Gen. Med.) Guy's Hosp. Lond.

SMITH, Peter George (retired) Landyke, Ton Lane, Lowdham, Nottingham NG14 7AR — MB BS 1956 Lond.; FRCPath 1977, M 1965. Prev: Cons. Histopath. Univ. Hosp. Nottm.

SMITH, Peter Henry 11 St John Street, Manchester M3 4DW Tel: 0161 832 9999; Harwood Lodge, Harwood, Bolton BL2 4JA Tel: 01204 387085 Fax: 01204 382637 — MB ChB Manch. 1963;

SMITH

FRCP Lond. 1982, M 1967. Hon. Clin. Lect. Rheumatol. Manch. Univ. Prev: Cons. Rheum. N. Manch. Gen. & Ancoats Hosps.

SMITH, Peter Hubert (retired) 1A Woodlands Way, Middleton, Manchester M24 1WL Tel: 0161 643 4604 — MRCS Eng. LRCP Lond. 1944. Treasury Med. Off. Prev: Dep. Med. Off. Jericho EMS Hosp. & Inst. Bury.

SMITH, Peter James 28 Elmdale Close, Warsash, Southampton SO31 9RX — BM 1992 Soton. (Soton.) GP Fareham. Socs: Fareham Med. Soc. Prev: GP Regist. Lyndhurst; SHO (Psychogenat.) Moorgreen; SHO (Paediat.) Soton. Gen. Hosp.

SMITH, Peter John Roland Hillview Medical Centre, 3 Heathside Road, Woking GU22 7QP Tel: 01483 760707; Goldsworth Park Health Centre, Denton Way, Woking Tel: 01483 768858 — MB BS 1977 Lond.; MRCGP 1984; DRCOG 1981. Clin. Asst. (Cardiol.) St. Peters Hosp. Chertsey. Prev: GP Trainee Frimley Pk. Hosp. VTS.

SMITH, Peter John Wells The Health Centre, Shelf Moor Road, Shelf, Halifax HX3 7PQ Tel: 01274 602088 — MB BChir 1969 Camb.; MA, MB Camb. 1969, BChir 1968. Prev: Lect. (Anat.) Lond. Hosp. Med. Coll.; Ho. Phys. & Ho. Surg. The Lond. Hosp.

SMITH, Peter Karl Edward Kent House Surgery, 36 Station Road, Longfield DA3 7QD Tel: 01474 703550; 65 Redhill Wood, New Ash Green, Longfield DA3 8QP Tel: 01474 874292 — BM BCh 1975 Oxf.; MA.

SMITH, Mr Peter Lincoln Chivers The Cardiothoracic Unit, Hammersmith Hospital, Du Cane Road, London W12 0HS Tel: 020 8383 3125 Fax: 020 8383 2034 Email: s.rhind-tutt@ic.ac.uk; plsmith@hhnt.org — MB BS 1975 Lond.; FRCS Eng. 1980; FRCP 1997, M 1978. (St Bartholemews Hosp Med School) Cons. Cardiothoracic Surg. Hammersmith Hosps. Trust Lond. Socs: Soc. Thoracic & Cardiovasc. Surg. GB & Irel.; Eur. Assn. Cardiothoracic Surg.; Eur. Soc. Cardiol. Prev: Sen. Regist. (Cardiothoracic Surg.) Hammersmith, Harefield & Middlx. Hosps. Lond.; Regist. (Cardiothoracic Surg.) Harefield Hosp. Lond.; Resid. Surg. Off. (Cardiothoracic Surg.) Brompton Hosp. Lond.

SMITH, Peter Robin 232 Milton Road, Weston Super Mare BS23 8AG Tel: 01934 625022 Fax: 01934 612470 Email: docsmith@freenet.co.uk; Elmhurst, Eastertown, Lympsham, Weston Super Mare BS24 0HY Tel: 01934 750041 Email: elmhurst@cwcom.net — MB BS 1976 Lond.; DRCOG 1980; Dip. Occ. Me. 1997. (Middlx.) Occupat. Med. Adviser (Occupat. Med. Serv.) W.on super Mare; Lead Clinician (Clin. Governance); Caldicott Guardian (Data Protec.).

SMITH, Peter Saeward (retired) Churchtown Medical Centre, 137 Cambridge Road, Southport PR9 7LT Tel: 01704 24416 Fax: 01704 507168 — MB ChB 1964 St. And.; PhD Glas. 1970; MRCGP 1976.

SMITH, Peter Samuel Churchill Medical Centre, Clifton Road, Kingston upon Thames KT2 6PG Tel: 020 8546 1809 Fax: 020 8549 4297 — MB ChB 1983 Sheff.; Cert. Family Plann. JCC 1987. Socs: Assoc. Mem. Fac. Homoeopath; Brit. Med. Accupunc. Soc.

SMITH, Peter Stewart Haxby Health Centre, The Village, Wiggington, York — MB ChB 1975 Liverp.; MRCGP 1981; DRCOG 1980; DCH Eng. 1979. Prev: SHO (Med.) Walton Hosp. Liverp.; SHO (Paediat.) York Dist. Hosp.

SMITH, Peter Stuart (retired) Keepers Lodge, Hadley Heath, Droitwich WR9 0AR Tel: 01905 620897 — MB BChir Camb. 1943; MRCS Eng. LRCP Lond. 1943. Prev: Princip. Gen. Pract.

SMITH, Peter Thomas Lanes Farm, Marlborough Road, Wootton Bassett, Swindon SN4 7SA — MB BS 1997 Lond.

SMITH, Philip Charles Harris Tudor 19 The Moorings, Willow Way, Christchurch BH23 1JJ — MB BCh 1984 Wales; MRCGP 1995; Dip. Pract. Dermat. Wales 1991; DRCOG 1990; DLO RCS Eng. 1987. Clin. Asst. (Dermat.) ChristCh.

SMITH, Philip Eric Main Department of Neurology, University Hospital of Wales, Heath Park, Cardiff CF14 4XW Tel: 029 2074 2834 Fax: 029 2074 4166 Email: smithpe@cardiff.ac.uk; 3 Fordwell, Liandaff CF5 2EU — MB ChB 1979 Liverp.; MD Liverp. 1988; MRCP (UK) 1982. (Univ. Liverp.) Cons.Neurol. Cardiff. Prev: Cons. Neurol. Roy. Cornw. Hosp.; Sen. Regist. (Neurol.) Cardiff HA; Regist. (Neurol.) Newc. HA.

SMITH, Philip George 7 High Street, Tibshelf, Alfreton DE55 5NY — MB BS 1990 Lond.; BSc (Hons.) Lond. 1987, MB BS 1990; MRCGP 1994. (Lond. Hosp.) GP Notts. HA. Socs: Roy. Soc. Med.; BMA. Prev: Trainee GP/SHO Kings Mill Hosp. Sutton-in-Ashfield.

SMITH, Philip George Lock The Ridgeway, 46A Main St., Repton, Derby DE65 6FB — MB ChB 1979 Manch.

SMITH, Philip Harold Thie Plaish, Gelen Road, Colby, Castletown IM9 4NX Tel: 01624 832226 — MB ChB 1973 Manch.

SMITH, Mr Philip Henry BUPA Hospital, Jackson Avenue, Leeds LS8 1NT Tel: 0113 269 3939 Fax: 0113 268 1340; 2 Creskeld Lane, Leeds LS16 9AW Tel: 0113 267 3616 Fax: 0113 285 7247 — MB ChB Leeds 1957; FRCS Eng. 1960. Socs: Brit. Assn. Urol. Surgs.; Internat. Soc. Urol. Prev: Med. Dir. St. Jas. Hosp. Leeds; Cons. i/c Dept. Urol. St. Jas. Hosp. Leeds.

SMITH, Philip Malcolm The Surgery, 18 Fouracre Road, Bristol BS16 6PG Tel: 0117 970 2033 — MB ChB 1975 Bristol; MRCGP 1986.

SMITH, Philip Russell Beccles Medical Centre, 7-9 St. Marys Road, St. Marys Road, Beccles NR34 9NQ Tel: 01502 712662 Fax: 01502 712906; Castanea, Staithe Court, Beccles NR34 9EA Tel: 01502 714923 — MB BS 1972 Lond.; MRCP (U.K.) 1975; DA Eng. 1978; DRCOG 1977. Hosp. Pract. (Anaesth.) Gt. Yarmouth & Waveney HA; Med. Adviser Sanyo (UK) LoW.oft. Prev: Regist. (Gen. Med.) Newmarket Gen. Hosp.; SHO (Obst.) Mill Rd. Matern. Hosp. Camb.

SMITH, Phillip Alexander Litfield House, Clifton Down, Bristol BS8 3LS Tel: 0117 973 1323 Fax: 0117 973 3303 Email: litfieldhuse@dial.pipex.com; Druids Mead, Shirehampton Road, Stoke Bishop, Bristol BS9 1BL Tel: 0117 968 1894 Email: pasmithgyn.aol.com — MB BS 1976 Lond.; FRCOG 1994, M 1981. (Lond. Hosp.) Cons. O & G S.mead Hosp. Bristol. Socs: Fothergill Club; Gyn. Res. Soc.; Treas. Brit. Pelvic Floor Soc. Prev: Sen. Regist. The Lond. Hosp.; Resid. Fell. King's Coll. Hosp. Lond.; Resid. Qu. Charlotte's & Chelsea Hosp. Lond.

SMITH, Phillip Hywel St Isan Road Surgery, 46 St. Isan Road, Heath, Cardiff CF14 4LX Tel: 029 2062 7518 Fax: 029 2052 2886 — MB BCh 1981 Wales; MRCGP 1984.

SMITH, Priscilla Claire Conamore Raymede Clinic, St Charles Hospital, Exmoor St., London W10 6DZ Tel: 020 8962 4450 Fax: 020 8962 4451 — MB BS 1976 Lond.; MFFP 1994. Dir. Servs. for Wom. Pk.side Health NHS Trust; Cons. Family Plann. & Reproductive Health Care. Socs: Chairm. (Clin. Advisory Comm.) Family Plann. Assn. Prev: Cons. to Clin. Effectiveness Comm. Fac. of Family Plann. & Reproductive Health.

SMITH, Rachel 48 Llwyn Castan, Cardiff CF23 7DA — MB BCh 1997 Wales.

SMITH, Rachel Bland 3 Lodge Cottage, Main St., Staveley, Knaresborough HG5 9NJ; 3 Lodge Cottage, Main St., Staveley, Knaresborough HG5 9NJ — MB BS 1994 Newc.; MRCGP 2000. (Newc.) Clin. Asst. Palliative Care, St. Leonards Hospice, York. Socs: Med. Protec. Soc.; BMA; RGCP.

SMITH, Rachel Hurndall 26 Davenfield Grove, Didsbury, Manchester M20 6UA — MB ChB 1992 Manch.; BSc (Med. Sci.) St. And. 1989; FRCAI 1997. (Manch.) Specialist Regist. (Anaesth.) N.W. Rotat. Socs: BMA; MRCAnaesth.; Assn. Anaesth.

SMITH, Rachelle Victoria 53 Augusta Road, Birmingham B13 8AE — MB ChB 1998 Aberd.; MB ChB Aberd 1998.

SMITH, Raymond Ernest (retired) 6 Owlswick Close, Littleover, Derby DE23 7SS Tel: 01332 517621 — MB ChB 1953 Sheff. Prev: Obst. Ho. Surg. Derby City Hosp.

SMITH, Mr Raymond Malcolm Department of Orthopaedic Surgery, Chancellors Wing, St James' University Hospital, Beckett St., Leeds LS9 7TF Tel: 0113 243 3144 Fax: 0113 206 5156 — MB ChB 1979 Leeds; MD Leeds 1988; FRCS Eng. 1984; FRCS Glas. 1983. (Leeds) Cons. Trauma & Orthop. St. Jas. Univ. Hosp. Leeds; Sen. Clin. Lect. Univ. Leeds. Socs: Brit. Trauma Soc. (Ex-Comm. 94-97) Pres. 200-2002; Orthopaedic Trauma Assoc.; Edr.ial Bd. Jl. of Bone Jt. Surg. Prev: Fell. (Orthop. Surg.) Univ. Harvard Boston Mass.; Clin. Lect. (Orthop. Surg.) Univ. Oxf.; Sen. Lect. (Orthop. & Trauma) Univ. Leeds.

SMITH, Raymond Stephen Wordsley Hospital, Stourbridge DY8 5QX; Russell's Hall Hospital, Dudley DY1 2HQ Tel: 01384 456111 — MB ChB 1973 Birm.; MD Birm. 1985; FRCP Lond. 1995; MRCP (UK) 1977. Cons. Phys. & Nephrol. Wordsley Hosp. Stourbridge, Russell's Hall Hosp. & Corbett Hosp. Stourbridge. Socs: Renal Assn. Prev: Lect. (Renal Med.) N. Staffs. Roy. Infirm.

SMITH, Raymond Thomas Department of Anaesthesia, St. James University Hospital, Beckett St., Leeds LS9 7; 2 Ash View, Whinney

Lane, Harrogate HG2 9LY Tel: 01423 508994 — MB ChB 1988 Leeds; MRCP (UK) 1992; FRCA 1994. Sen. Regist. (Anaesth.) St. Jas. Hosp. Leeds. Prev: Regist. (Anaesth.) Leeds Gen. Infirm.; SHO (Anaesth. & Renal Med.) St. Jas. Hosp. Leeds.

SMITH, Rebecca Louise Sheffield Childrens Hospital, Western Bank, Sheffield GL5 3RT; Lynthorpe, Rodborough Hill, Stroud GL5 3RT — MB ChB 1997 Sheff. SHO. (A&E.) Sheff. Childr. Hosp. Prev: SHO.(Gen Paediat.) Rotherham Dist Hosp.; PRHO. (Orthop Surg.) Barnsley Dist Hosp.

SMITH, Rebekah Alison 4 Kentsford Drive, Radcliffe, Manchester M26 3XX — MB ChB 1996 Manch.

SMITH, Mr Redmond John Hamilton (retired) 9 Birkdale Road, London W5 1JZ Tel: 020 8998 1883 — MS Lond. 1956, MB BS 1946; FRCS Eng. 1952; DO Eng. 1950. Hon. Cons. Ophth. Surg. St. Mary's Hosp. & W.. Eye Hosp. Lond.; Hon. Cons. Moorfields Eye Hosp. Lond. Prev: Edr. Brit. Jl. Ophth.

SMITH, Rhona Gail c/o Victoria Geriatric Unit, Victoria Infirmary, Mansions House Road, Glasgow G42 9TY; 56 Kierhill Road, Cumbernauld, Glasgow G68 9BH — MB ChB 1993 Glas.

SMITH, Richard, Squadron Ldr. RAF Med. Br. Retd. Park Surgery, 2 Oak Road N., Middlesbrough TS1 3LF Tel: 01642 247008 Fax: 01642 245748; Ashton House Farm, Kirry Sigston, Northallerton DL6 3TE Tel: 01609 883727 Fax: 01609 883105 — MB ChB 1984 Sheff.; DCH RCP Lond. 1989. (Shiff. Univ. Med. Coll.) GP Princip.; Police Surg. N. Yorks. Police. Socs: Assn. of Police Surg. Prev: Med. Off. RAF Leeming N. Yorks.

SMITH, Richard Anthony 4 Westway, Chellow Dene, Bradford BD9 6AZ — MB ChB 1977 Leeds.

SMITH, Richard Barry Valorum Ltd, Alexander House, Gatehampton Road, Goring-on-Thames, Reading RG8 0EN Tel: 01491 874255 Fax: 01491 875326 — MB ChB Manch. 1965; BSc (Hons. Anat.) Manch. 1962, MD 1969; FFPM RCP (UK) 1989; Dip. Pharm. Med. RCP (UK) 1976. (Manch.) Pres. Directeur Gen.e Valorum SA. Socs: Fell. Roy. Soc. Med. & Manch. Med. Soc. Prev: Med. Adviser ICI Ltd. Pharmaceut. Div. Macclesfield; Research & Developm. Dir. Reckitt & Colman Pharmaceut. Div. Hull; Lect. (Anat.) Univ. Manch.

SMITH, Mr Richard Daron Nut-Tree Cottage, Littlefield Green, White Waltham, Maidenhead SL6 3JN Email: daron@discon.co.uk — BM BCh 1994 Oxf.; MA Camb. 1994; FRCS (Eng) 1998. (Camb. & Oxf. Univ.) Research Fell. (Urol.), N.wick Pk. Inst. of Med. Research. Prev: SHO Rotat. (Surg.) N.wick Pk. & St. Mark's NHS Trust; Demonst. (Anat.) Camb. Univ.; Resid. Med. Off. St. Edmunds Hosp. Bury St. Edmunds.

SMITH, Richard Dennis (retired) Furahi, 64 Horsham Road, Crawley RH11 8PA Tel: 01293 521644 — MB BS 1957 Lond.; DObst RCOG 1959. Prev: Ho. Surg., Ho. Phys. & Resid. (Obst.) Guy's Hosp. Lond.

SMITH, Richard Edward Wallice Huddersfield Royal Infirmary, Lindley, Huddersfield HD3 3EA Tel: 01484 422191 Fax: 01484 422191; Rest Harrow, Cleeve Road, Goring-on-Thames, Reading RG8 9BH Tel: 01491 875283 — MB ChB 1995 Leeds; BSc Leeds 1992. (Leeds) SHO Rotat. (Gen. Med.) Huddersfield Roy. Infirm. Huddersfield. Prev: Ho. Off. (Gen. Med.) St. Jas. Univ. Hosp. Leeds; SHO Rotat. (Gen. Med.) P.ss Alexandra Hosp. Brisbane, Austral.

SMITH, Mr Richard Geoffrey Department of Ophthalmology, Stoke Mandeville Hospital, Mandeville Road, Aylesbury HP21 8AL Tel: 01296 315033 Fax: 01296 314893 — MB ChB 1982 Birm.; FRCS Eng. 1986; FRCOphth 1988; DO RCS Eng. 1985. Cons. Ophth. Stoke Mandeville Hosp. Aylesbury & Hemel Hempstead Gen. Hosp. Socs: Internat. Soc. Clin. Electrophysiol. of Vision. Prev: Sen. Regist. Roy. Berks. Hosp. Reading & Moorfields Eye Hosp. Lond.; Regist. Qu. Med. Centre Nottm.; SHO Birm. & Midl. Eye Hosp.

SMITH, Richard Graham Morant Wem and Prees Medical Practice, New Street, Wem, Shrewsbury SY4 5AU — MB ChB 1978 Birm.; DRCOG Lond. 1981.

SMITH, Richard Ian Eller Yew, Sweden Bridge Lane, Ambleside LA22 9EX Tel: 015394 32560 — MB ChB Liverp. 1953; MRCGP 1963; DObst RCOG 1955. Socs: BMA.

SMITH, Richard James Wellside Surgery, 45 High Street, Sawtry, Huntingdon PE28 5SU Tel: 01487 830340 Fax: 01487 832753; 53 Townsend Way, Folksworth, Peterborough PE7 3TU Tel: 01733 240669 — BM BS 1990 Nottm.; MRCGP 1996. Princip. in GP. Prev: Trainee GP P'boro. VTS.

SMITH, Richard Luther (retired) Bellamy House, Heath, Wakefield WF1 5SL Tel: 01924 372457 — MB BChir 1952 Camb. Prev: Ho. Off. (Surg.) St. Pancras Hosp. & (Obst.) Univ. Coll. Hosp.

SMITH, Richard Mark 13 Rockleaze Road, Sneyd Park, Bristol BS9 1NF; Academic Renal Unit, Southmead Hospital, Bristol BS10 5NB Tel: 0117 959 5438 Email: richard.smith@bris.ac.uk — BM BCh 1986 Oxf.; MRCP (UK) 1990; PhD (Cambridge) 1995. Lect. Renal Med. Univ. Bristol.

SMITH, Richard Naylor Parkstone Health Centre, Mansfield Road, Poole BH14 0DJ Tel: 01202 741370 Fax: 01202 730952 — MB BS 1983 Lond.

SMITH, Richard Nicholas Evans Birchwood Medical Practice, Jasmin Road, Lincoln LN6 0QQ Tel: 01522 501111 Fax: 01522 682793 — MB ChB 1988 Leeds; BSc Leeds 1985; MRCGP 1992; DRCOG 1991; MSc 1996. LMC Mem. Prev: Clin. Research Fell. Centre for Research Primary Care Univ. Leeds.

SMITH, Mr Richard Paul Powell Dept. Obstetrics & Gynaecology, Norfolk & Norwich Hospital, Brunswick Road, Norwich NR1 3SR Tel: 01603 286286; Email: richardsmith@ukgateway.net — MD ChB 1992 Birm.; MRCOG 1998 (Prize Medal). Specialist Regist. Rotat. (O & G) E. Anglian. Socs: Brit. Med. Ultrasound Soc.; Brit. Matern. & Fetal Med. Soc.; fetal & Neonat. Physiol. Soc. Prev: Research Fell. (Obs & Gynae) Qu. Charlotte's Hosp. Lond.

SMITH, Richard Spalding Portsonachan, Meadle, Aylesbury HP17 9UD Tel: 0184 444096 — MRCS Eng. LRCP Lond. 1942; DMRD Eng. 1949. (Middlx.) Cons. Radiol. Roy. Bucks. Co. Hosp. Aylesbury, High Wycombe Memor. Hosp. & Stoke Mandeville Hosp. Aylesbury. Prev: Cas. Off. Roy. Sussex Co. Hosp. Brighton; Ho. Surg. Kingston Co. Hosp.; Regist. Radiodiag. Dept. Middlx. Hosp.

SMITH, Richard William Milton Keynes General NHS Trust, Standing Way, Eaglestone, Milton Keynes MK6 5LD Tel: 01908 660033; Copper Beeches, Heath Lane, Aspley Heath, Woburn Sands, Milton Keynes MK17 8TN Tel: 01908 584449 — MB ChB 1980 Dundee; MRCP (UK) 1985; FRCP 1999. Cons. Phys. & Rheum. Milton Keynes Hosp. Prev: Cons. Phys. & Rheum. Derriford Hosp. Plymouth.

SMITH, Robert (retired) Department of Obstetrics & Gynaecology, Ninewells Hospital, Dundee DD1 9SY — MB ChB 1969 St. And.; MRCOG 1975. Cons. O & G Ninewells Hosp. Dundee. Prev: MRC Fell. Univ. Aberd.

SMITH, Mr Robert 47 Ravenstone Drive, Sale M33 2WD — MB ChB 1994 Manch.; FRCS 1998. SHO (Ortho.)Stepping Hill Hosp. Prev: SHO (A & E) The Roy. Oldham Hosp.; Ho. Off. (Med.) N. Manch. Gen. Hosp.; Ho. Off. (Neurosurg.) Hope Hosp. Salford.

SMITH, Robert Aidan Rodney University Health Centre, 9 Northcourt Avenue, Reading RG2 7HE Tel: 0118 987 4551 — MB 1980 Camb.; MA Camb. 1979, MB 1980, BChir 1979; MRCGP 1983; DRCOG 1982. (Westm.) Asst. Phys. Reading Univ. Health Serv.

SMITH, Robert Andrew Lisanelly Lodge, 9 Gortin Road, Omagh BT79 7DH — MB BCh BAO 1990 Belf.; DGM RCPS Glas. 1994; DRCOG 1993.

SMITH, Robert Andrew 67 Hayling Rise, Worthing BN13 3AG — MB BS 1993 Lond.

SMITH, Robert Antony 128 Tadcaster Road, Dringhouses, York YO24 1LU — MD 1990 Wales; MB BCh 1982; MRCP (UK) 1985. Cons. Paediat. York Dist. Hosp. Socs: Brit. Paediat. Assn. Prev: Sen. Regist. (Paediat.) Newc.; Research Fell. Inst. Med. Genetics Cardiff; Regist. (Paediat.) Newc.

SMITH, Robert Benjamin Department of Obstetrics & Gynaecology, Hereford County Hospital, Union Walk, Hereford HR1 2ER Tel: 01432 364125 Fax: 01432 364169 Email: rob.smith@hh-tr.wmids.nhs.uk — MB BCh 1981 Wales; MRCOG 1991. Cons. (Obstet. & Gyn.) Hereford Co. Hosp. Socs: Brit. Menopause Soc.; Welsh Obst. & Gynaecologists Soc. Prev: Sen. Regist. (O & G) Llandough Hosp., Cardiff; Sen. Regist. (O & G) Wrexham Maelor Hosp.; Clin. Research Fell. (O & G) Univ. Wales Coll. Med. Cardiff.

SMITH, Mr Robert Cameron Department of Surgery, Falkirk & District Royal Infirmary, Major's Loan, Falkirk FK1 5QE Tel: 01324 624000 Fax: 01324 616073; 18 Keir Street, Bridge of Allan, Stirling FK9 4AY Tel: 01786 832940 Email: robsmith@sol.co.uk — MB ChB Ed. 1970; ChM Ed. 1983; FRCS Ed. 1974. Cons. Surg. Falkirk &

SMITH

Dist. Roy. Infirm.; Hon. Clin. Teach. Univ. Edin. Socs: Vasc. Surg. Soc.; Scott. Thoracic Soc.; BMA.

SMITH, Robert Chad Smith, Feltbower and Venn, 41 Westminster Road, Coventry CV1 3GB Tel: 024 7622 3565 Fax: 024 7623 0053; Ash View, Tamworth Road, Corley, Coventry CV7 8BQ Tel: 01676 540555 — MB ChB 1964 Birm.; MRCS Eng. LRCP Lond. 1964; DA Eng. 1966. (Birm.) Socs: BMA. Prev: SHO (Anaesth.) Dudley Rd. Hosp. Birm.; Ho. Phys. Aberystwyth Gen. Hosp.; Ho. Surg. (O & G) St. Chad's Hosp. Birm.

SMITH, Robert Charles (retired) 8 Belmont, Shrewsbury SY1 1TE Tel: 01743 232360 — MB ChB 1957 Birm.; DObst RCOG 1960. Prev: GP Shrewsbury.

SMITH, Robert Gladstone The Thatched Cottage, 53 Woodcote Avenue, Wallington SM6 0QU Tel: 020 8647 4636 — MB BS Lond. 1951; MRCS Eng. LRCP Lond. 1951; MRCGP 1967; DA Eng. 1961; DObst RCOG 1957. (King's Coll. Hosp.) Socs: BMA & Assur. Med. Soc.; RCGP. Prev: Med. Off. & Clin. Asst. (Anaesth.) Carshalton, Beddington & Wallington Dist. War Memor. Hosp.; Ho. Surg., Jun. Anaesh. & Cas. Off. (ENT Dept.) King's Coll. Hosp. Lond.; Ho. Surg. (Obst.) St. Jas. Hosp. Lond.

SMITH, Robert Houghton 21 Lancaster Place, Great South West Road, Hounslow TW4 7NE — MB BS 1954 Lond. (Middlx.)

SMITH, Robert John 17 Orlingbury Road, Pytchley, Kettering NN14 1ET Tel: 01536 790602 — MB BS 1964 Lond.; MRCS Eng. LRCP Lond. 1964; FRCOG 1984, M 1971. (King's Coll. Hosp.) Cons. (O & G) Kettering & Dist. Gen. Hosp. Prev: Sen. Regist. (O & G) Kings Coll. Hosp. Lond.

SMITH, Robert Malcolm Christie Castle Road, 2 Castle Road, Chirk, Wrexham LL14 5BS Tel: 01691 772434 Fax: 01691 773840; Hillside, Pont-y-Blew, Chirk, Wrexham LL14 5BH Tel: 01691 773487 — BM BCh 1979 Oxf.; BA Camb. 1976; MRCGP 1985; DCH RCP Lond. 1982; DRCOG 1982.

SMITH, Robert Newton New England Cottage, London Road, St Ippolyts, Hitchin SG4 7NG Tel: 01462 437362 Fax: 01462 437364 Email: robert.n.smith@btinternet.com — MB ChB 1958 Birm.; BSc (1st cl. Hons.) Birm. 1955, MD 1969, MB ChB 1958; FRCP Lond. 1991; FRCP Ed. 1983, M 1967; FFPM 1989; DObst RCOG 1960. (Birm.) Cons. Pharmaceut. Med. Robt. Smith Assoc. Hitchin; Edr. Int. J. Pharm. Med. Socs: Fell. Roy. Soc. Med. & Fac. Pharm. Med.; BMA & Med. Res. Soc. Prev: Med. Dir. Glaxo Gp. Research Ltd. Greenford; Dir., Clin. Research & Drug Developm. Hoffmann-La Roche Basel; Sen. Lect. (Clin. Pharm. & Therap.) & Cons. Phys. Sheff. Univ. & Roy. Infirm.

SMITH, Robert Norman Frankley Health Centre, 125 New St., Frankley, Rubery, Rednal, Birmingham B45 0EU Tel: 0121 453 8211 Fax: 0121 457 9690 — MB ChB 1964 Manch. (Manch.)

SMITH, Robert Reekie Currie Road Health Centre, Currie Road, Galashiels TD1 2UA Tel: 01896 752476; Hiltons Hill, St Boswells, Melrose TD6 0DL Tel: 01835 823281 — MB ChB 1980 Ed.; BSc (Med. Sci.) Ed. 1977; MRCGP 1984. (Edinburgh) Gen. Practitioner, Galashiels. Socs: Mem. of the Soc. of Orthopaedic Med.; Mem. of the Brit. Inst. of Musculoskeletal Med.; Mem. of the Primary Care Rheum. Soc.

SMITH, Robert Russell The Health Centre, 2 Kirkland Road, Kilbirnie KA25 6HP Tel: 01505 683333 Fax: 01505 684098; Carrick, 96 Milton Road, Kilbirnie KA25 7HY Tel: 01505 683223 — MB ChB 1959 Glas.; MRCGP 1971; DObst RCOG 1961. (Glas.) Local Treasury Med. Off. Socs: BMA. Prev: Ho. Surg. & Ho. Phys. Kilmarnock Infirm.; Ho. Off. Braeholm Matern. Hosp. Helensburgh & Overtoun Matern. Hosp. Dumbarton.

SMITH, Robin Frederick Arthur 55 Palmer Road, Plaistow, London E13 8NU Tel: 020 7474 2455 — MB BS 1985 W. Indies.

SMITH, Robin Pierre Department of Chest Medicine, Victoria Hospital, Kirkcaldy KY2 5AH Tel: 01592 643355 Fax: 01592 647090 Email: robin@glenavd1.demon.co.uk; 33 High Street, Auchtermuchty, Cupar KY14 7AP — MB ChB 1988 Ed.; MRCP (UK) 1992. (Ed.) Cons. Phys. Vict. Hosp. Kirkcaldy. Prev: Sen. Regist. (Respirat. Med.) Frenchacy Hosp. & Bristol Roy. Infirm.; Research Fell. (Respirat. Med.) Grenoble, France; Regist. (Respirat. Med.) King's Cross Hosp. Dundee.

SMITH, Robin Wellesley Ancrum Road Surgery, 12-14 Ancrum Road, Dundee DD2 2HZ Tel: 01382 669316 Fax: 01382 660787 — MB ChB 1981 Dundee.

SMITH, Roderick Andrew Balmore Park Surgery, 59A Hemdean Road, Caversham, Reading RG4 7SS Tel: 0118 947 1455 Fax: 0118 946 1766; 7 Jefferson Close, Emmer Green, Reading RG4 8US Tel: 01734 473587 — MB BChir 1973 Camb.; MA Camb. 1973; FRCGP 2000; DObst RCOG 1976. (Camb. and Middlx. Hosp.)

SMITH, Rodney Stewart J D Lansdowne and Partners, Helston Medical Centre, Trelawney Road, Helston TR13 8AU Tel: 01326 572637 Fax: 01326 565525 — MRCS Eng. LRCP Lond. 1968.

SMITH, Roger Nuffield Orthopaedic Centre, Headington, Oxford OX3 7LD Tel: 01865 741155; 6 Southcroft, Elsfield Road, Old Marston, Oxford OX3 0PF Tel: 01865 790800 — MB BChir Camb. 1956; PhD Lond. 1971; MD Camb. 1960; FRCP Lond. 1974, M 1963. (Univ. Coll. Hosp.) Cons. Phys. & Cons. Metab. Med. Nuffield Orthop. Centre Oxf.; Emerit. Fell. Green Coll. Oxf. Socs: Assn. Phys.; Med. Res. Soc. Prev: Fell. Nuffield Coll. Oxf.; Clin. Reader & Cons. Phys. Nuffield Depts. Med. & Orthop. Surg. Oxf.; Sen. Wellcome Research Fell. Med. Unit & Hon. Sen. Lect. & Cons. Univ. Coll. Hosp.

SMITH, Roger The Health Centre, Coatham Road, Redcar TS10 1SX Tel: 01642 475157 Fax: 01642 470885 — MB ChB 1986 Leeds; DFFP 1990. (Leeds) Hon. Med. Asst., Roy. Nat. Lifeboat Inst., Redcar & Teesmouth Stations. Socs: Brit. Assn. of Immidiate Care.

SMITH, Mr Roger Abbey The Old Hall, Somerton TA11 7NG — MB ChB 1940 Liverp.; MCh Liverp. 1948; FRCS Eng. 1971; FRCS Ed. 1943.

SMITH, Mr Roger Battersby 11 Moor Park Avenue, Preston PR1 6AS Tel: 01772 251507 Fax: 01772 881975 Email: rbsmith@uk-consultants.co.uk — BSc (Anat.) Lond. 1967, MB BS 1970; FRCS Eng. 1975; MRCS Eng. LRCP Lond. 1970. (St. Geo.) Cons. Orthop. Surg. Roy. Preston Hosp. Socs: Fell. BOA; Edit. Sec. BASK. Prev: Sen. Regist. (Orthop.) Gen. Infirm. & St. Jas. Hosp. Leeds; Regist. (Surg.) Roy. Infirm. Edin.; Regist. (Orthop.) Bristol Roy. Infirm.

SMITH, Roger Charles The Surgery, Grove St., Petworth GU28 0LP Tel: 01798 342248 Fax: 01798 343987 — MB BS 1966 Lond.; MRCS Eng. LRCP Lond. 1966. (Univ. Coll. Hosp.) Med. Off. Seaford Coll. Petworth.

SMITH, Roger Galbraith 56 Alnwickhill Road, Edinburgh EH16 6LW Tel: 0131 664 1745 — MB ChB 1966 Ed.; FRCPS Glas. 1991; FCRP Lond. 1989; FRCP Ed. 1980; MRCP (UK) 1971; DObst RCOG 1973. (Ed.) Cons. Phys. Geriat. Med. Roy. Vict. Hosp. Edin. Socs: Brit. Geriat. Soc. & M-C Soc. Edin. Prev: Sen. Lect. (Geriat. Med.) Univ. Edin.; Sen. Regist. (Geriat.) Roy. Vict. Hosp. Edin.; Surg. Lt. RN.

SMITH, Roger Hugh Norfolk House, 4 Norfolk St., Sheffield S1 2JB Tel: 0114 271 8866 Fax: 0114 271 6814; 38 Edgehill Road, Sheffield S7 1SP Tel: 0114 258 8489 — MB BS 1967 Lond. (Westm.) Primary Care Special.Drug.Depend. Community Health Sheff.

SMITH, Roger Huntington North Tees General Hospital, Hardwick, Stockton-on-Tees TS19 8PE Tel: 01642 617617; The Sheiling, High St, Wolviston, Billingham TS22 5JS — MB ChB 1969 Ed.; BSc (Physiol.) (Hons.) Ed. 1966; FRCP Lond. 1987; FRCP Ed. 1984; MRCP (UK) 1972. (Ed.) Cons. Phys. (Gen. Med. & Cardiol.) & Clin. Dir. (Med.) N. Tees NHS Trust. Socs: Fell. (Ex-Sen. Pres.) Roy. Med. Soc. Edin. Prev: Research Fell. (Cardiol.) Freeman Hosp. Newc.; Sen. Regist. (Med.) Newc. HA; Regist. (Cardiol.) W.. Gen. Hosp. Edin.

SMITH, Roger Macleod Laing Mount Farm Surgery, Lawson Place, Bury St Edmunds IP32 7EW — MB ChB 1977 Ed.

SMITH, Roger Nigel John Department of Obstetrics & Gynaecology, Queen Marys Hospital, Sidcup DA15 6LT Tel: 020 8308 3085; 43 Camden Road, Sevenoaks TN13 3LU Tel: 01732 453098 Email: rnjs@mcmail.com — MB ChB 1983 Manch.; MRCP (UK) 1987; MRCOG 1990. Cons. (O & G) Qu. Marys Hosp., Sidcup, Kent. Prev: Sen. Regist. Kings Coll. Hosp. Lond.; Research Fell. King's Coll. Hosp. Lond.; Regist. Rotat. Qu. Charlotte's, Chelsea & Hillingdon Hosps. Lond.

SMITH, Roger Philip Roy 4 Manor Close, Lincoln LN2 1RL; 4 Manor Close, Lincoln LN2 1RL — MB ChB 1987 Sheff.; FRCA 1997; Dip. Obst. Auckland 1990. Specialist Regist. Anaesth. Socs: Manch. Med. Soc.

SMITH, Mr Roger Philip Sutherland Eye Department, Cumberland Infirmary, Carlisle CA2 7HY; Holcombe House, Irthington, Carlisle CA6 4NJ — MB BS 1975 Newc.; MA Camb. 1974; FRCS Ed. 1979; FCOphth. 1989; DO Eng. 1978. Cons. Ophth. N. RHA; Mem. Oxf. Ophth. Congr. Socs: Life Mem. Camb. Univ. Med. Soc. Prev: Sen. Regist. (Ophth.) Gen. Infirm. Leeds.

SMITH, Mr Roger William Queen Victoria Hospital, Holtye Road, East Grinstead RH19 3DZ Tel: 01342 410210 Fax: 01342 317959 Email: rwsmith@uk-consultants.co.uk — MB BChir 1978 Camb.; BA Camb. 1974, MChir Camb. 1987; FRCS Eng. 1982; T(S) 1991. Cons. Plastic & Reconstrvc. Surg. Qu. Vict. Hosp. E. Grinstead; Vis. Cons. Plastic & Reconstruc. Surg. to Maidstone & The Dartford Hosp. Gp. Socs: BAPS; BAAPS; RSM. Prev: Sen. Regist. (Plastic & Reconstruc. Surg.) Frenchay Hosp. Bristol.

SMITH, Ronald Bertram 8 Fletchers, Basildon SS16 5TU Tel: 01268 45228 — MB BS 1963 Lond.; MRCS Eng. LRCP Lond. 1962; MRCGP 1975; DObst RCOG 1964. (Univ. Coll. Hosp.) Socs: BMA. Prev: Ho. Off. (Med.) & Ho. Off. (Surg.) S.end Gen. Hosp.; Ho. Off. (Obst.) Rochford Gen. Hosp.

SMITH, Ronald Campbell Department of Child Health, Postgraduate Medical School, University of Exeter, Church Lane, Exeter EX2 5SQ Tel: 01392 403144 Fax: 01392 403158 Email: r.c.smith@ex.ac.uk; 35 Rosebarn Avenue, Exeter EX4 6DY Tel: 01392 254034 — MB BS 1975 Lond.; MRCP (UK) 1981; DRCOG 1982; FRCPCH 1996. (L.H.M.C.) Cons. Paediat. Roy. Devon & Exeter NHS Trust; Lect. Univ. Exeter. Socs: Brit. Paediat. Assn.; Brit. Assn. Community Child Health. Prev: Cons. Paediat. (Community Child Health) Banbury & Oxon. HA; Sen. Regist. Newc. HA; Research Fell. Univ. Exeter Paediat. Research Unit.

SMITH, Ronald Clifford (retired) 28 Thorney Green Road, Stowupland, Stowmarket IP14 4AB — MB BS 1952 Lond.; DObst RCOG 1953.

SMITH, Ronald Mitchell (retired) 140 Kinghorn Road, Burntisland KY3 9JU Tel: 01592 873304 — MB ChB 1961 Ed. Prev: Med. Adviser Benefits Agency Edin.

SMITH, Rose Kemp (retired) 32 Riverside Park, Linn Park Avenue, Glasgow G44 3PG — MB ChB 1945 Glas. Prev: Clin. Med. Off. Glas. Corp. Pub. Health Dept.

SMITH, Rosemary Helen 136A Southbrae Drive, Glasgow G13 1TZ — MB ChB 1971 Glas. Regist. (Bacteriol.) Roy. Infirm. Glas. Prev: Lect. Anat. Univ. Manch.; Ho. Phys. W.. Infirm. Glas.; Ho. Surg. S.. Gen. Hosp. Glas.

SMITH, Rosemary Rose Yew Tree Medical Centre, 100 Yew Tree Lane, Solihull B91 2RA Tel: 0121 705 8787 — MB ChB 1983 Birm.; MRCGP 1988; DCH RCP Lond. 1987; DRCOG 1986. (Birmingham) p/t GP; Clin. Asst. Dermat., Solihull Hosp. Socs: MDU.

SMITH, Rowena Elizabeth 27 Hillside Road, Cheam, Sutton SM2 6ET — MB ChB 1984 Manch.; BSc St. And. 1980. Sen. Regist. (Histopath.) Char. Cross Hosp. Lond.

SMITH, Rowland Michael Hamilton Spring Gardens Health Centre, Providence Street, Worcester WR1 2BS Tel: 01905 681681 Fax: 01905 681699; 52 Beech Avenue, Worcester WR3 8PY — MB BS 1975 Lond.; BSc Lond. 1970, MB BS 1975; MRCGP 1980; DRCOG 1979; DCH Eng. 1979; ARCS 1970. GP Worcester.

SMITH, Roy Norman Compton (retired) 5 Ferry Road, Barnes, London SW13 9RX — MB BS 1932 Lond.; MRCS Eng. LRCP Lond. 1931; FRCGP 1970. Prev: Ho. Phys. & Cas. Off. St. John's Hosp. Lewisham.

SMITH, Rupert Alexander Department of Oncology, ICI Pharmaceuticals, Macclesfield; 1 Broomfield Road, Broomfield Villas, Heaton Moor, Stockport SK4 4NB — MB ChB 1976 Liverp.; MRCP (UK) 1980; DCH Eng. 1979. Research Fell. & Hon. Sen. Regist. Univ. Oxf. Childr. Cancer Research Gp.; Med. Adviser ICI Pharm. Chesh.

SMITH, Rupert Alistair Four Elms Medical Centre, 103 Newport Rd, Roath, Cardiff CF24 0AF — MB BCh 1997 Wales. (UWCM) GP Princip. Four Elms Med. Centre, Cardiff. Socs: BMA; MDU. Prev: GP Reg., Portway PCE, Porthcawl; GP Registra Woodlands Surg. Masteg.; SHO (A & E) P.ss of Wales Hosp., Bridgend.

SMITH, Rupert Noel Flat 1-1, 170 Lochee Road, Dundee DD2 2NH — MB ChB 1998 Dund.; MB ChB Dund 1998.

SMITH, Russell Edward Ashleigh Good Hope Hospital, Rectory Road, Sutton Coldfield B75 7RR Tel: 0121 378 6188 Ext: 2370 Fax: 0121 378 6095; 8 Foxes Meadow, Walmley, Sutton Coldfield B76 1AW — MB BS 1984 Lond.; FRCP; BSc (1st cl. Hons.) Lond. 1981, MD 1992; MRCP (UK) 1988. Cons. Phys. (Cardiol.) Good Hope Hosp. Sutton Coldfield; Hon. Cons. Univ. Hosp. Birm. Socs: Fell. Roy. Soc. Med.; BMA; Brit. Cardiac Soc. Prev: Lect. & Hon. Sen. Regist. (Med. & Cardiol.) King's Coll. Sch. Med. & Dent. Lond.; Research Regist. (Cardiol.) Kings Coll. Hosp. Lond.; Regist. & SHO Rotat. (Med.) The Lond. Hosp.

SMITH, Ruth Alice Griffin House, Appledore Heath, Ashford TN26 2BA Tel: 01233 83 564 — MB ChB 1976 Manch. Clin. Med. Off. (Community Child Health) SE Kent HA. Prev: Med. Off. Transkei Health Serv., SE Africa.; Community Med. Off. (Child Health) Camberwell HA.

SMITH, Sally Agnes Culver The Surgery, Highwood Road, Brockenhurst, Lymington SO41 7RY Tel: 01590 622272 Fax: 01590 624009; The Surgery, Station Road, Sway, Lymington SO41 6BA Tel: 01590 682617 Fax: 01590 682226 — MB ChB 1973 Glas.; MRCGP 1977; DObst RCOG 1975. (Glas.) Hon. Clin. Lect. Soton. Univ. Med. Sch. Prev: Trainee GP Glas. (S. Gen. Hosp.) VTS; Clin. Asst. (Geriat. Med.) Lymington Hosp.; Ho. Off. (Med.) & Ho. Off. (Surg.) S.. Gen. Hosp. Glas.

SMITH, Sally Jane Manford Way Health Centre, 40 Foremark Close, Hainault, Ilford IG6 3HS Tel: 020 8500 3088 Fax: 020 8559 9355 — BSc Lond. 1986, MB BS 1989; MRCGP 1994. (Royal London Hospital Medical College) Hon. GP Tutor.

SMITH, Sally Megan 6 Cragg Terrace, Rawdon, Leeds LS19 6LF — MB ChB 1992 Leeds; MRCGP 1996; MRCP (Paed.) 1998. (Leeds) Specialist Regist. St James Univ. Hosp. Leeds.

SMITH, Samantha Joanne The Coach House, Clevedon Road, Nailsea, Bristol BS48 1HA — BM 1995 Soton.

SMITH, Samuel David Coulter 10 Highgate Spinney, Crescent Road, London N8 8AR — MB BCh BAO 1986 NUI; LRCPSI 1986.

SMITH, Samuel McCall (retired) Cornerstones, Oulston Road, Easingwold, York YO61 3PR Tel: 01347 823319 Fax: 01347 823319 — MB ChB 1950 Ed.; DMRD 1958. Prev: Cons. Radiol. Peel Hosp. Galashiels.

SMITH, Samuel Peter Helsby Health Centre, Lower Robin Hood Lane, Helsby, Warrington WA6 0BW Tel: 01928 723676 Fax: 01928 725677 — MB 1978 Camb.; BChir 1977.

SMITH, Samuel Pullar (retired) Graziers, 137 The Hill, Burford OX18 4RE Tel: 01993 823196 — MB ChB 1950 Glas.; MD (Commend.) Glas. 1959; DMRD Eng. 1961. Prev: Cons. Radiol. Roy. Infirm. Kingston upon Hull.

SMITH, Sandra Ann, Flight Lt. RAF Med. Br. 17 Penylan Road, Pontypridd CF37 1EG — MB BCh 1993 Wales.

SMITH, Sandra Margaret Mill Bank Nethermill, Hatton, Peterhead AB42 0SN — MB ChB 1987 Aberd.

SMITH, Sara Brooklands, Brooklands Parade, Wolverhampton WV4 4XE — MB ChB 1994 Liverp.; MRCPsych 2000; BClinSci (Hons.) Liverp. 1993. Specialist Regist. (Psychiat.), W. Midl.s Rotat.

SMITH, Sara Joanna 63 Park Street, Swinton, Manchester M27 4UN — MB ChB 1989 Leic.

SMITH, Sara Melody Linda Buchanan Llys Meddyg, Manthrig Lane, Caersws SY17 5EX Tel: 01686 688225 Fax: 01686 688344; CEFN, Trefeglwys, Caersws SY17 5QT Tel: 01686 430508 Email: saramlsm1@aol.com — BM 1980 Soton.; MRCGP 1984; Dip. Pract. Dermat. Wales 1996; DFFP 1994; DRCOG 1983; DPD 1996. (Soton.) Clin. Asst. (Ment. Handicap.) Powys. Prev: Trainee GP E. Lond. VTS; Ho. Surg. Basingstoke Dist. Hosp.; Ho. Phys. Brook Gen. Hosp. Lond.

SMITH, Sarah Alexandra (retired) 2 River Row, Blowing House, Redruth TR15 3AT Tel: 01209 218555 — MB BS 1986 Lond.

SMITH, Sarah Alexandra 10 Blakebrook, Kidderminster DY11 6AP — MB BS 1998 Lond.; MB BS Lond 1998.

SMITH, Sarah Ann Rhianfa, The Highway, Croesyceiliog, Cwmbran NP44 2HE — MB ChB 1998 Bristol.

SMITH, Sarah Carolyn The Surgery, 10 Compayne Gardens, London NW6 3DH Tel: 020 7624 5883 Fax: 020 7328 8670; Flat 2, 17 Adamson Road, London NW3 3HU — MB BS 1986 Lond.; MRCOG 1990; DRCOG 1988; T(GP) 1991.

SMITH, Sarah Catherine Dept. of Clinical Geratology, Radcliffe Infirmary, Woodstock Road, Oxford OX2 6HE; Flat 1, 21 Chilswell Road, Oxford OX1 4PQ Tel: 01865 452403 — MB BS 1994 Lond.; MRCP Lond. 1997; BSc Lond. 1990. (St. Mary's Hosp. Med. Sch.

SMITH

Lond.) Specialist Regist. (Geratology & Gen. Med.) Oxf. Region. Prev: SHO Intens. Care Sussex Co. Hosp. Brighton.

SMITH, Sarah Jane Parsonage House, 17 Orlingbury Road, Pytchley, Kettering NN14 1ET — MB ChB 1994 Leic.; DCH 1996; DRCOG 1998; MRCGP 1998. (Leicester) GP non-Princip.

SMITH, Sarah Jane 50 Langdale Grove, Bingham, Nottingham NG13 8SS Email: sarahsmith@innotts.co.uk — MB BCh 1993 Wales; MRCP (UK) 1997. Locum Grade (Paediat.) Grantham & Dist. Hosp. Prev: SHO (Paediat.) Community Paediat.; SHO (Paediat.) Qu. Med. Centre Nottm.

SMITH, Sarah Jane Louise 6A Glenfield Road, London SW12 0HG — MB ChB 1997 Ed.

SMITH, Sarah Napier 10 Moorbank Close, Sheffield S10 5TP — MB ChB 1994 Bristol; MRCP (Lond.) 1998. (Bristol) Med. SHO Roy. Devon & Exeter Healthcare Trust. Socs: BMA.

SMITH, Sarah Nicola (Neal) Taverham Surgry, Sandy Lane, Taverham, Norwich NR8 6JR — MB ChB 1992 Birm.; DFFP 1995; DRCOG 1995; MRCGP 1998. GP Asst. Norwich. Prev: GP Asst. Middlx.; GP Locum N.ampton; Clin. Asst. Palliat. Care N.ampton.

SMITH, Mrs Saraswati 32 Long Buftlers, Harpenden AL5 1JE Tel: 01582 761313 — MB BS 1958 Bihar; MS Bihar 1963, MB BS 1958; MRCOG 1969. Sen. Med. Off. S. (Beds.) Health Dist.

SMITH, Scott Mackenzie 45 Colinhill Road, Strathaven ML10 6HF — MB ChB 1996 Aberd.

SMITH, Selwyn Trevor 23 Albion Avenue, Blackpool FY3 8NA Tel: 01253 38473 — MB ChB 1963 Manch.

SMITH, Sharon Elizabeth 35 Castle Terrace, Edinburgh EH1 2EL — MB ChB 1989 Ed.

SMITH, Sharon Janet Taverham Surgery, Sandy Lane, Taverham, Norwich NR8 6JR Tel: 01603 867481 Fax: 01603 740670 — MB BS 1980 Lond.; DCH RCP Lond. 1986. Gen. Practitioner Clin. Med Off (Family Plann.).

SMITH, Sheila Gordon (retired) David Place Medical Practice, 56 David Place, St Helier, Jersey JE1 4HY Tel: 01534 33322 — MB ChB 1977 Aberd. Prev: GP Jersey.

SMITH, Sheila Margaret 23 Dundonald Road, Kilmarnock KA1 1RU — MB ChB 1972 Glas. Paediat. (Child Protec.) Ayrsh. Prev: Clin. Med. Off. Community Child Health Ayrsh. Centr. Hosp. Irvine; Regist. (Med.) Kilmarnock Infirm.; SHO (Anaesth.) Glas. Roy. Infirm.

SMITH, Shelagh Jean MacSorley Department of Clinical Neurophysiology, The National Hospital for Neurology, Queen Square, London WC1N 3BG Tel: 020 7837 3611 Ext: 3350 Fax: 020 7713 7743 — MB ChB 1981 Birm.; BSc Birm. 1978; FRCP Lond. 1995; MRCP (UK) 1984. Cons. Clin. Neurophysiol. Nat. Hosp. Lond., Nat. Soc. for Epilepsy & Chalfont Centre for Epilepsy Bucks. Socs: (Counc.) Brit. Soc. Clin. Neurophysiol.; & Hon. Sec. Assn. Brit. Clin. Neurophysiol.; Assn. Brit. NeUrol.s. Prev: Sen. Regist. (Clin. Neurophysiol.) Nat. Hosp. Lond.

SMITH, Shubulade Mary Eniola 2E Abbeville Road, London SW4 9NJ Tel: 020 8673 7125; Institute of Psychiatry, 103 Denmark Hill, Camberwell, London SE5 8AZ Email: s.smith@iop.bpmf.ac.uk — MB BS 1991 Lond.; MRCPsych 1995. (Guy's Hospital) Research Fell. (Psychol. Med.) Inst. of Psychiat.) Lond.; Hon. Sen. Regist. Maudsley Hosp. Lond. Prev: S. Thames Research Train. Fell. Inst. of Psychiat.; Hon. Sen. Regist.; Regist. Rotat. Maudsley Hosp.

SMITH, Simon Fordingbridge Surgery, Bartons Road, Fordingbridge SP6 1RS Tel: 01425 652123 Fax: 01425 654393 — MB BS 1987 Lond.; MRCGP 1993; DCH RCP Lond. 1994; DRCOG 1994. Socs: Wessex Educat.al Trust; BMA. Prev: Trainee GP Guildford VTS; Clin. Med. Off. Bournemouth Health Trust; Ho. Off. (Orthop. & Gen. Surg.) St. Stephens Hosp.

SMITH, Simon Anthony 65 Kidmore Road, Caversham Heights, Reading RG4 7LZ — MB ChB 1996 Leic.

SMITH, Simon David Longton Hall Surgery, 186 Longton Hall Road, Blurton, Stoke-on-Trent ST3 2EJ Tel: 01782 342532; 2 Post Office Terrace, Fulford, Stoke-on-Trent ST11 9QS Email: simonsmith@talk21.com — MB BS 1990 Lond.; BSc (1st cl. Hons.) Biochem. Lond. 1987; MRCGP 1994; DFFP 1996; DRCOG 1992. (Lond. Hosp. Med. Coll.) GP Stoke-on-Trent; Med. Off. Macmillan Hospice Stoke-on-Trent. Prev: Lect. (Primary Care) Univ. Soton.; Trainee GP/SHO Soton. VTS; Ho. Surg. P.ss Margt. Hosp. Swindon.

SMITH, Simon Donald Shropshire's Community and Mental Health Services NHS Trust, Shelton Hospital, Bilton Health, Shrewsbury SY3 8DN Email: oe69@dial.pipex.com — MB ChB 1987 Birm.; MB ChB (Hons.) Birm. 1987; MMedSci Birm. 1993; MRCPsych 1991. (Birm.) Cons. Psychiat. Shrops.'s Community & Ment. Health Servs. NHS Trust.

SMITH, Mr Simon Duncan 56 Buckingham Road, London E18 2NJ — MB ChB 1985 Aberd.; FRCS (Orth.) 1997; FRCS Glas. 1989. Sen. Regist. (Orthop.) Norf. & Norwich Hosp. Prev: Sen. Regist. (Orthop.) Lond. Hosp.; Regist. Holly Hse. Hosp. Essex; Regist. (Orthop.) Bury St. Edmonds.

SMITH, Simon George Twyman 26 Ruthein Road, Blackheath, London SE3 7SH Tel: 020 8853 0308 Email: s.g.t.smith@ic.ac.uk — MB BS 1993 Lond.; BSc (Hons.) Neurosci. Lond. 1990, MB BS 1993; FRCS Eng. 1997. (St Marys) Surg. Clin./Research Fell. (St Marys Minimal Access Surgic. Unit) Imperial Coll. Sch. of Med. St Marys Hosp. Lond.; Specialist Regist. (Gen. Surg.) NW Thames. Socs: Roy. Soc. Med.; Assn. Surg. Train. Prev: SHO Rotat. (Surg.) St Mary's Hosp. Lond.; Ho. Phys. Wexham Pk. Hosp. Slough; Ho. Surg. St Mary's Hosp. Lond.

SMITH, Simon Guy Weston Department of Pathology, Conquest Hospital, The Ridge, St Leonards-on-Sea TN37 7RD Tel: 01424 755255 — MB BChir 1983 Camb.; MA Camb. 1983; MRCP (UK) 1985; MRCPath 1990. Cons. Haemat. Conquest Hosp. Hastings; Hon. Sen. Lect. (Med.) UMDS Lond. Prev: Lect. (Haemat.) UMDS St. Thos. Hosp. Lond.

SMITH, Simon Leslie Dept. of Imaging, The Ipswich Hospital NHS Trust, Heath Road, Ipswich IP4 Email: simon.smith@psh_tr.anglox.nhs.uk; Wanda Cottage, Ipswich Road, Pettaugh, Ipswich IP4 6DN Tel: 01332 517016, 01473 890844 Email: simonsmith@ukonline.co.uk — BM BS 1991 Nottm.; BMedSci (Hons.) Nottm. 1989; MRCP (UK) 1995; FRCR 1998. Regist. (Radiol.) Nottm. Univ. Hosps.; Cons. Radiologist. Prev: SHO Rotat. (Med.) Ipswich Hosp.; Regist. (Radiol.) Nottm. Univ. Hosps.

SMITH, Simon Michael 1 Brockley Gardens, Brockley, London SE4 1SZ — MB BS 1993 Lond.

SMITH, Simon Paul Lanner Vean Barns, Porthleven, Helston TR13 0RQ — MB BS 1992 Lond.

SMITH, Mr Simon Robert Gray University Hospital Birmingham NHS Trust, Raddlebarn Road, Birmingham B29 6JD Tel: 0121 627 1627 Email: simon.smith@university-gwmids.nhs.uk; 14 Barlows Road, Edgbaston, Birmingham B15 2PL — MB BS 1971 Lond.; MS Lond. 1988; FRCS Eng. 1977; MRCS Eng. LRCP Lond. 1971. (St. Bart.) Cons. Surg. (Gen. & Vasc.) Univ. Hosp. Birm. NHS Trust. Socs: Vasc. Soc. GB & Irel.; Assn. Surg. Prev: Sen. Regist. St. Mary's Hosp. Lond.; Regist. Char. Cross Hosp. Lond.; Regist. St. Albans City Hosp.

SMITH, Simon Timothy Christmas Maltings Surgery, Camps Road, Haverhill CB9 8HF Tel: 01440 702203 Fax: 01440 712198 — MB BS 1980 Lond.; BSc Lond. (Pharmacol.) 1977; MRCGP 1988; FFA RCS Eng. 1985; DRCOG 1987; DA (UK) 1985. (St. Thos.)

SMITH, Stanley (retired) 15 Waxwell Lane, Pinner HA5 3EJ Tel: 020 8429 4316 — MB ChB 1942 Leeds; MD Leeds 1947; FRCP Lond. 1968, M 1949; FRCPsych 1971; DPM Lond. 1951. Mem. (Ex-Chairm.) Lancs. HA. Prev: Med. Supt. Lancaster Moor Hosp.

SMITH, Stephanie Anne Department of Paediatric Accident & Emergency, University Hospital, Clifton Boulevard, Nottingham NG7 2UH Tel: 0115 924 9924; Ashwick, 13 Shop Lane, Nether Heage, Belper DE56 2AR Tel: 01773 852482 Email: docsmithharvey@aol.com — BM BS 1983 Nottm.; MRCP (UK) 1989. Cons. Emerg. Paediat. Univ. Hosp. Nottm. Socs: FRCPCH. Prev: Sen. Regist. & Regist. (Paediat.) Trent RHA.

SMITH, Stephanie Jane Evans Abington Park Surgery, Christchurch Medical Centre, Ardington Road, Northampton NN1 5LT Tel: 01604 630291 Fax: 01604 603524 — BM BCh 1987 Oxf.; MA Camb. 1984; MRCGP 1991; DRCOG 1989.

SMITH, Stephen 7 Knowles Street, Widnes WA8 6QX — MB ChB 1996 Ed.

SMITH, Stephen Andrew Birmingham Heartlands and Solihull Hospital Trust, Bordesley Green E., Birmingham B9 5ST Tel: 0121 424 2156 Email: smiths@heartsol.wmids.nhs.uk; Mayfield House, 45 Wake Green Road, Moseley, Birmingham B13 9HU Tel: 0121 449 4982 — MB ChB 1978 Bristol; MD Bristol 1989; FRCP 1997; MRCP (UK) 1981. Clin. Dir. Renal Servs. & Cons. Gen. Med. & Nephrol. Birm. Heartlands Hosp. Socs: BMA; Brit. Renal Assn.; Eur. Dialysis & Transpl. Assn. Prev: Sen. Regist. (Nephrol.) St. Helier

SMITH

Hosp. Carshalton; Regist. (Nephrol.) Qu. Eliz. Med. Centre Birm.; Trav. Fell. Brit. Heart Found, Adelaide.

SMITH, Stephen Charles Department of Histopathology, Taunton and Somerset NHS Trust, Musgrove Park Hospital, Taunton TA1 5DA Tel: 01823 333444 — MB BS 1973 Lond.; FRCPath 1994; BSc Lond. 1970, MB BS 1973. (London Hospital Medical College) Cons. Histopath. MusGr. Pk. Hosp. Taunton. Prev: Lect. (Path.) Med. Sch. Univ. Nottm.; Lect. (Human Morphol.) Med. Sch. Univ. Nottm.; Lect. (Anat.) Lond. Hosp. Med. Coll. Univ. Lond.

SMITH, Stephen Clifford 167 Radcliffe Road, Bolton BL2 1NZ — MB ChB 1988 Liverp.

SMITH, Stephen Cullum e78 Bibby Road, Southport PR9 7PS — MB BS 1990 Lond.

SMITH, Stephen Edward 38 Oakfield Gardens, Dulwich Wood Avenue, London SE19 1HQ — BM BCh 1953 Oxf.; PhD Lond. 1960; MA Oxf. 1954, DM 1974; DA Eng. 1955. Socs: Brit. Pharm. Soc.; Roy. Soc. Med. Prev: Emerit. Prof. Applied Pharmacol. & Therap. Univ. Lond.; Resid. Anaesth., Ho. Phys. & Cas. Off. St. Thos. Hosp. Lond.

SMITH, Professor Stephen Kevin University of Cambridge Clinical School, Department of Obstetrics & Gynaecology, The Rosie Maternity Hospital, Robinson Way, Cambridge CB2 2SW Tel: 01223 336871 Fax: 01223 248811 Email: sks1000@cam.ac.uk; 14 Hertford Street, Cambridge CB4 3AG Tel: 01223 357736 — MB BS 1974 Lond.; MA Camb. 1993; MD Lond. 1983; MRCS Eng. LRCP Lond. 1974; MRCOG 1979; FRCOG 1997; F.I.Biol. (Westm.) Prof. Dept. O & G Univ. Camb. Clin. Sch.; Hon. Cons. Obst. & Gyn. Addenbrooke's Hosp. Camb. Socs: Eur. Assn. Obst. & Gyn. (Scientif. Comm.); FIGO; Euop. Soc. Human Reproduc. & Embryol. Prev: Cons. MRC Reproduc. Biol. Unit Centre for Reproduc. Biol. Edin.; Hon. Cons. Simpson Memor. Matern. Pavil. & Roy. Infirm. Edin.; Lect. (O & G) Univ. Sheff. & Jessop Hosp. Wom.

SMITH, Stephen Mark 58 Avenue Road, London N6 5DR — MB BS 1990 Newc.; PhD Newc. 1987; BMedSc. Newc. 1984. SHO (Neurol.) Nat. Hosp. Neurol. Lond.

SMITH, Stephen Michael Vincent Windrush Health Centre, Welch Way, Witney OX28 6JS Tel: 01993 702911 Fax: 01993 700931 — MB BS 1990 Lond.; MRCGP 1995; DRCOG 1994; DFFP 1995. (St. Barts) GP Partner.

SMITH, Stephen Patrick 88 Station Road, Greenisland, Carrickfergus BT38 8UP — MB BCh BAO 1990 Belf.; MB BCh Belf. 1990.

SMITH, Stephen Richard Department of Haematology, Torbay Hospital, Lawes Bridge, Torquay TQ2 7AA Tel: 01803 655236 Fax: 01803 655244 Email: smits@vmsmail.sdevon-tr.swest.nhs.uk — MB ChB 1982 Liverp.; MD Liverp. 1990; MRCP (UK) 1985; MRCPath 1993; FRCP 2000. Cons. Haemat. Torbay Hosp. S. Devon Healthcare. Prev: Sen. Regist. (Haemat.) Centr. Newc. Hosps.; Research Fell. MRRC Univ. Liverp.; Regist. (Haemat.) Roy. Liverp. Hosp.

SMITH, Stephen Rolf Horton General Hospital, Oxford Radcliffe NHS Hospitals Trust, Oxford Road, Banbury OX16 9AL Tel: 01295 275500; 4 Old Glebe, Tadmarton, Banbury OX15 5TH — MB ChB 1975 Birm.; BSc (Hons.) Birm. 1972, MD 1982; FRCP Lond. 1994; MRCP (UK) 1978. (Birmingham) Cons. Phys. (Gen. & Respirat. Med.) Horton Gen. Hosp Oxf. Radcliffe NHS Hosp.s Trust. Prev: Sen. Regist. (Med.) Qu. Eliz. Hosp. Birm.

SMITH, Stephen Roy 5 Birch Avenue, Burscough, Ormskirk L40 5SA — MB BCh 1976 Wales.

SMITH, Steven Evans (retired) Moorlands Friar's Gate, Crowborough TN6 1XF — BLitt, MA Oxf. 1946, BM BCh 1954.

SMITH, Steven Jonathan Croft Hall Medical Practice, 19 Croft Road, Torquay TQ2 5UA Tel: 01803 298441 Fax: 01803 296104 — MB ChB 1977 Manch.

SMITH, Steven Mark 2 Hepburn Gardens, Bromley BR2 7HL — MB BS 1984 Lond.

SMITH, Steven Michael 87 Springside Road, Bury BL9 5JG Tel: 0161 705 1670 Email: sup@globalnet.co.uk — MB ChB 1977 Liverp.; MRCGP 1985; T(GP) 1991. GP Princip. Socs: BMA. Prev: Trainee GP Bury HA; Med. Off: Brit. Antarctic Survey Camb.

SMITH, Stuart Leslie Balintore Farmhouse, Kirkhill, Inverness IV5 7PX Tel: 01463 831337 Fax: 01463 831337 Email: stuartsmith@doctors.org.uk — MB ChB 1991 Aberd.; MRCGP 2000; MRCP (UK) Ed. 1995; DRCOG 1997; DFFP 1997. GP non Princip.

SMITH, Mr Stuart Lindley 19 Chantrey's Drive, Elloughton, Brough HU15 1LH Tel: 01482 665660 Fax: 01482 665660 — BM BCh 1975 Oxf.; MA Oxf. 1975; FRCS Eng. 1981. (University of Oxford) Cons. Dept. Otolaryngol. Roy. Hull. Hosps. Trust. Prev: 1st Asst. Dept. Surg. Newc.; Regist. (ENT) Radcliffe Infirm. Oxf.; SHO (Neurosurg. & Accid.) Radcliffe Infirm. Oxf.

SMITH, Stuart Nicholas 161 Horbury Road, Wakefield WF2 8BG — MB BS 1985 Lond.

SMITH, Susan 52 Shaftesbury Road, Bournemouth BH8 8ST — BM 1985 Soton.

SMITH, Susan Elizabeth Nelson Health Centre, Cecil St., North Shields NE29 0DZ Tel: 0191 257 1191 — MB BS 1984 Newc.; MRCGP 1988. GP N. Shields, Tyne & Wear Trainee GP N.umbria VTS.

SMITH, Susan Hilary 34 Wintersdale Road, Leicester LE5 2GJ — MB ChB 1987 Leic.; MRCPsych 1992.

SMITH, Susan Jane Second Flat Left, 54 Polwarth St., Glasgow G12 9TL — MB ChB 1990 Glas. SHO (Anaesth.) Vict. Infirm. Glas. Prev: SHO (Spinal Injuries) Nat. Spinal Injury Unit S.. Gen. Hosp. Glas.

SMITH, Susan Jane Norwich Road Surgery, 199 Norwich Road, Ipswich IP1 4BX Tel: 01473 289777 Fax: 01473 289545; 61 Gainsborough Road, Ipswich IP4 2XE Tel: 01473 258968 — BM BCh 1986 Oxf.; MA Camb. 1986; MRCGP 1990. (Oxford) GP Trainer Ipswich.

SMITH, Susan Jane Amy Evans Centre, 190 Holton Road, Barry CF63 4HN Tel: 01446 420953 Email: sue.smith@vhw-tr.nhs.uk; 3 Bryn Calch, Morganstown, Cardiff CF15 8FD Tel: 02920 844466 Email: suespaul@tinyworld.co.uk — MB BCh 1988 Wales; MRCPsych 1993. (Univ. of Wales) Cons. Psychiat. (Gen. Adult & Perinatal Psychiat.) Cardiff & Vale NHS Trust.

SMITH, Miss Susan Joy 1 St Thomas St, London Bridge, London SE1 9RY Tel: 020 7403 3363 Fax: 020 7403 8552; 59 Maltings Place, London SW6 2BX Tel: 020 7371 8314 — MB BS 1977 Lond.; MRCOG 1983. (St Marys Hoapital) Dep. Med. Dir. Bridge Fertil. Centre Lond.

SMITH, Susan Maree c/o 45 Ailesbury Road, Dublin 4, Republic of Ireland; 9 Grenfell Road, Didsbury, Manchester M20 6TG — MB BCh BAO 1987 Dub.; MSc (Econ.) Wales 1994; MRCPI 1989; MRCGP 1992; DCH RCPI 1990. (Trinity Coll. Dub.) SHO (Palliat. Med.) St. Ann's Hospice Manch.

SMITH, Susan Margaret 39 Egerton Road, Bishopston, Bristol BS7 8HN — MB ChB 1991 Liverp. Staff Grade Adult Psychiat. Coleford Resorce Centre Coleford Forest of Dean.

SMITH, Susan Margaret Occupational Health Service, Camden & Islington Community Health Services NHS Trust, St.Pancras Hospital,, London NW1 0PE Tel: 0207 530 3450 Fax: 0207 530 3451; 63 Connaught Gardens, London N10 3LG Tel: 0208 444 9491 — MB BS 1976 Lond.; BSc Lond. 1973; AFOM RCP Lond. 1992; DCH Eng. 1978. (St. Bart.) SCMO (Occupat. Health) Camden & Islington Community Health Servs. NHS Trust. Socs: BMA; Soc. Occupat. Med.; Fac. Occupat. Med. Prev: Clin. Asst. (Occupat. Health) Islington HA; Clin. Med. Off. (Family Plann.) Haringey HA; SHO (Paediat.) St. Stephen's Hosp. Lond.

SMITH, Susan Mary Durrington Health Centre, Durrington Lane, Worthing BN13 2RX Tel: 01903 264151 — MB BCh 1975 Wales. Cons. Family Plann. & Reproduc. Health Care Worthing. Socs: Fac. Fam. Plann. & Reproduc. Health Care; Inst. Psychosexual Med.

SMITH, Susan Penelope Anaesthetic Department, Cheltenham General Hospital, Sandford Road, Cheltenham GL53 7AN; Ash House, 9 Sydenham Road, Cheltenham GL52 6ED — MB BS 1980 Lond.; BSc Lond. 1977; MRCP (UK) 1985; FFA RCS Eng. 1985; FRCP 1999. Cons. Anaesth. & Dir. Intens. Care Cheltenham Gen. Hosp. Prev: Gen. Profess. Train. (Anaesth.) Guys & Lewisham Hosps. Lond.; Sen. Regist. (Anaesth. & Intens. Care) Reading & Oxf.

SMITH, Sydney 1 Bowgreen Mews, Bowgreen Road, Bowdon, Altrincham WA14 3LX Tel: 0161 941 1632 — MB BCh BAO 1943 Belf.; MRCGP 1952. (Belf.) Exam. Med. Off. Min. of Pens. & Nat. Insur. Prev: Hosp. Pract. (Surg.) Withington Hosp. Manch.; Res. Surg. Off. Eccles & Patricroft Hosp.; Ho. Phys. & Cas. Off. Vict. Memor. Jewish Hosp. Manch.

SMITH

SMITH, Sydney Ainsworth Hampson House, Wood Lane, Bardsey, Leeds LS17 9AN — MB ChB 1939 Leeds.

SMITH, Sydney James (retired) 1 Keble Close, Bishopthorpe, York YO23 2TE Tel: 01904 704787 — MRCS Eng. LRCP Lond. 1943. Prev: Ho. Surg. Char. Cross Hosp.

SMITH, Tanya Lillipot Surgery, Elmj Avenue, Poole BH14 8EE Tel: 01202 739122; Elysian, Wimborne Road, Lytchett Matravers, Poole BH16 6DH Tel: 01202 624352 — BM 1986 Soton.; MRCGP 1994; Dip. Of Pall. Med. 1998. (Southampton) p/t GP Lillipot Poole Dorset. Prev: Med. Off. Joseph Weld Hospice Dorchester; GP BRd.stone. Poole.

SMITH, Tasha Judine 38 Granada Close, Waterlooville PO8 9AU — BM 1997 Soton.

SMITH, Teresa Mary Parliament Hill Surgery, 113-117 Highgate Road, London NW5 1TR Tel: 020 7485 1095; 5 Summerlee Avenue, East Finchley, London N2 9QP — MB BS 1980 Lond.; MFHom Faculty of Homeopathy London 1999; DRCOG 1982. Med. Examr. Friends Provident, Commercial Union, Sun. Alliance & Other Insur. Co's. Prev: Clin. Asst. (Family Plann.) Dulwich & Kings Coll. Hosps Lond.; Trainee GP Barnet Gen. Hosp. VTS; Community Health Child Health & Family Plann. Camberwell HA.

SMITH, Thomas Connal Gemmell The Croft, Poundland, Pinwherry, Girvan KA26 0RU Tel: 01465 841643 Fax: 01465 841643 Email: tom.smith@virgin.net — MB ChB Birm. 1962; Dip. Pharm. Med. RCP (UK) 1976. (Birm.) Med. Jl.ist Columnist Sunday Mail, Bradford Telegraph, Argus & The News Portsmouth; Adviser Jl. Dist. Nursing. Socs: BMA; Med. Jl.ists Assn. Prev: Ho. Surg. & Ho. Phys. Dudley Rd. Hosp. Birm.; Ho. Phys. Childr. Hosp. Birm.

SMITH, Thomas John Tyndall Top Floor Flat, 18 Bellevue, Bristol BS8 1DB — MB ChB 1995 Bristol.

SMITH, Thomas Keith 23 Meadway, Liverpool L15 7LY — MB ChB 1986 Liverp.

SMITH, Thomas Scott 2 Little Hame, Milton Keynes Village, Milton Keynes MK10 9AN — MB BS 1998 Lond.; MB BS Lond. 1998.

SMITH, Mr Thomas William David Cleveland House, 3 Whitworth Road, Sheffield S10 3HD Tel: 0114 230 8398 Fax: 0114 230 9091 Email: t.w.smith@sheffield.ac.uk — MB 1964 Camb.; MA MB (Distinc. Pharm. & Therap.) Camb. 1964; BChir 1963; FRCS Ed. 1967; FRCS Eng. 1968. (Camb. & St. Mary's) Cons. Orthop. Surg. N. Gen. Hosp. & Sheff. Childs. Hosp. NHS Trusts; Clin. Dir. Sports Med. N. Gen. & Roy. Hallamshire Hosp. NHS Trust; Exec. Edr. The Foot; Edr. Foot & Ankle Surg.; Hon. Sen. Lect. Univ. of Sheff. Socs: Fell. BOA; S. Yorks. Medico-Legal Soc. (Ex-Pres.). Prev: Sen. Regist. (Orthop. Surg.) United Sheff. Hosps. & Sheff. RHB; Regist. (Orthop.) Nuffield Orthop. Centre Oxf.; Ho. Surg. & Cas. Surg. St. Mary's Hosp. Lond.

SMITH, Timothy Charles Department of Anaesthesia, Alexandria Hospital, Woodrow Drive, Redditch B98 7UB — MB ChB 1984 Birm.; MD Birm. 1994; FRCA 1989. Cons. Anaesth. Alexandra Hosp. Redditch.

SMITH, Timothy David Department of Anaesthetics, Royal Gwent Hospital, Newport NP20 2UB — MB BCh 1994 Wales.

SMITH, Timothy Donald Weston Latham House Medical Practice, Sage Cross Street, Melton Mowbray LE13 1NX Tel: 01664 854949 Fax: 01664 501825 — MB ChB 1975 Birm.; MRCGP 1980; DRCOG 1977. GP Melton Mowbray; Lect. (Community Med.) Univ. Leicester.

SMITH, Timothy Gervase Cloudesley 5 Parkside Road, Reading RG30 2DA — MB BS 1968 Lond.; MRCS Eng. LRCP Lond. 1968; FFA RCS Eng. 1974; DA Eng. 1972; DObst RCOG 1970. (St. Bart.) Cons. (Anaesth.) Roy. Berks. Hosp. Reading.

SMITH, Timothy James Scott Top Floor Flat, 1 Albyn Place, Edinburgh EH2 4NG — MB ChB 1996 Ed.

SMITH, Mr Tom (retired) Highfields, Bage Hill, Walton, Chesterfield S42 7LN — MB ChB 1940 Glas.; FRCS Glas. 1962; FRCS Ed. 1947; FRFPS 1946; FRCOG 1962, M 1948. Prev: Cons. Surg. Jessop Hosp. Sheff.

SMITH, Toni Jacqueline 39 DeHavilland Way, Abbots Langley WD5 0XF — BChir 1994 Camb.

SMITH, Tracey Glen Dr H. J. Dobson & Partners, Wells Green Surgery, 501 Crewe Road, Wistaston, Crewe CW2 6QP; 4 Millacre Drive, Wistaston, Crewe CW2 6XG Tel: 01270 668195 — MB ChB 1988 Dundee. (Univ. Dundee) Prev: GP Regist. Chesh.; Trainee GP/SHO (Geriat.) Leighton Hosp. Crewe VTS.

SMITH, Tracy Amanda Smith, Niemczuk, Woolrych and Marcus, 279-281 Mill Road, Cambridge CB1 3DG Tel: 01223 247812 Fax: 01223 214191; Hope Cottage, 10 Brook Lane, Coton, Cambridge CB3 7PY Tel: 01223 211183 — MB BS 1983 Lond. (St. Mary's Hosp.)

SMITH, Trevor 14 Longlands Glade, Worthing BN14 9NR — BChir 1958 Camb.; MA Camb. 1960, BChir 1958, MB 1959; MFHom 1975; DPM Eng. 1960. Cons. Phys. Winchester Clinic Winchester. Socs: Fac. Homoeop.; Brit. Homoeop. Assn. Prev: Sen. Regist. Tavistock Clinic.

SMITH, Trevor Allan Ranks Hovis McDougall Ltd., 27/30 King Edward Court, Windsor SL4 1TJ Tel: 01753 621904 Fax: 01753 621907; 11 Tithe Meadows, Virginia Water GU25 4EU — MB ChB 1978 Manch.; BSc St. And. 1975; MRCP (UK) 1981; MFOM RCP Lond. 1986, A 1984. Prev: Div. Med. Off. Fisons Pharmaceut. Div. LoughBoro.; Sen. Med. Off. Brit. Steel Corpn. Tubes Div. Corby.

SMITH, Trevor Richard 101 Atherstone Avenue, Netherton, Peterborough PE3 9UJ — BM 1995 Soton. SHO Rotat. (Gen. Med.) Bath Roy. United Hosp. Prev: Med. Off. (IC) Sir Chas. Gairdner Hosp. Perth, W.ern Australia; SHO (Gastroenterol.) Soton. Gen. Hosp.

SMITH, Ursula Magdalena (retired) 26 Metchley Park Road, Edgbaston, Birmingham B15 2PG Tel: 0121 454 6538 — MD Bonn. 1952; LAH Dub. 1958; DA Eng. 1957.

SMITH, Valerie Mary Mandeville Surgery, Hannon Rd, Aylesbury HP21 8TR Tel: 01296 431515 Fax: 01296 399597 — MB BS 1973 Lond.; DCH Eng. 1976; DObst RCOG 1975.

SMITH, Vaughan Pearson Lyngford Park Surgery, Fletcher Close, Taunton TA2 8SQ Tel: 01823 333355 Fax: 01823 257022; 41 Peile Drive, Taunton TA2 7SZ Tel: 01823 353061 Email: vsmith1951@aol.com — BM BCh 1975 Oxf.; MA Oxf. 1977, BA (1st cl. Hons.) 1972; MRO 1994; MLCOM 1994; FRCGP 1993, M 1978; DMS Med. Soc. Apoth. Lond. 1994; DCH Eng. 1978. (Oxf.) Registered Osteop. Som.; Tutor Lond. Coll. Osteop. Med. Socs: Soc. Orthop. Med.; Brit. Med. Acupunct. Soc.; Brit. Inst. Musculoskel. Med. Prev: Trainee GP Gt. Yarmouth VTS.

SMITH, Vaughn Leslie The Priory Hospital, Rappax Rd, Hale WA15 0NX Tel: 0616 904 0050; 15 Yoxall Avenue, Hartshill, Stoke-on-Trent ST4 7JJ Tel: 01782 44692 — MB ChB 1971 Birm. Clin. Asst. Altringham Priory Hosp.

SMITH, Vernon (retired) 34 Springkell Avenue, Glasgow G41 4AB Tel: 0141 423 1968 Email: v.smith@btinternet.com — MB ChB Leeds 1941. Prev: GP Glas.

SMITH, Mr Vernon Hope (retired) 24 Broadway, Morecambe LA4 5BJ Tel: 01524 427494 — MB BChir 1950 Camb.; MA Camb. 1950; FRCS Ed. 1961; FRCS Eng. 1955; FRCOphth 1989; DO Eng. 1961. Cons. Surg. Birm. & Midl. Eye Hosp. & E. Birm. Hosp. Gp.; Sen. Clin. Tutor Birm. Univ.; Mem. Oxf. Ophth. Congr. Prev: Resid. Surg. Off. Manch. Roy. Eye Hosp.

SMITH, Victoria Clair Flat 48, Queens Court, Queens Road, Richmond TW10 6LB — MB BS 1992 Lond.

***SMITH, Victoria Helen** Hillcrest, Booth Road, Waterfoot, Rossendale BB4 9BP — MB ChB 1998 Birm.

SMITH, Victoria Jane Hawthorn Cottage, Seven Sisters Lane, Ollerton, Knutsford WA16 8RL — MB ChB 1983 Liverp.

SMITH, Victoria Jane Department of Psychiatry, Rannsle Building, Mancester Royal Infirmary, Hathersage Road, Manchester M13 9WL; 43 Austin Drive, Manchester M20 6FA — MB BCh 1992 Wales.

SMITH, Walter Dermot PO Box 26, Queensway House, Essex St., Southend-on-Sea SS2 5TD — MB BCh BAO 1940 NUI.

***SMITH, Warren Emerson David** 196 Cambridge Road, Great Shelford, Cambridge CB2 5JU Tel: 01223 841529 — BChir 1991 Camb.

SMITH, Wayne Richard (retired) 9 Harding Road, Abingdon OX14 1SF Tel: 01235 521994 — MB BS Lond. 1970; BSc (Hons) Lond. 1967; MRCS Eng. LRCP Lond. 1970; MRCGP 1975; Cert. Family Plann. JCC 1973; DObst RCOG 1973. Prev: SHO (Psychol. Med.) Guy's Hosp. Lond.

SMITH, Wilfred Donald Fitzroy, RD Adult & Elderly Medicine, Countess of Chester Hospital, Liverpool Road, Chester CH2 1BQ Tel: 01244 366294 Fax: 01244 366110; Trenance, 57 Mill Lane, Upton-by-Chester, Chester CH2 1BS Tel: 01244 380422 Fax: 01244

SMITHELLS

380422 — MB ChB 1974 Liverp.; MD Liverp. 1995; MRCP (UK) 1979. (Liverpool) Cons. Phys. (c/o Elderly) Countess of Chester Hosp. Socs: Liverp. Med. Inst.; Brit. Geriat. Soc. Prev: Sen. Regist. (Gen. & Geriat. Med.) Frenchay Hosp. Bristol & Derriford Hosp. Plymouth; Research Fell. Univ. W.. Ontario, Lond., Canada.

SMITH, William Alexander Malcolm, TD (retired) 2 Arnwood Drive, Glasgow G12 0XY Tel: 0141 334 3678 — MB ChB 1944 Glas.; BA (Hons.) Open 1978; FRCOphth 1993; FCOphth 1988; DOMS Eng. 1949. Lt.-Col. RAMC, TA. Prev: Cons. Ophth. Glas. Eye Infirm. & Gartnavel Gen. Hosp. Glas.

SMITH, Professor William Cairns Stewart Department of Public Health Medical School, Foresterhill, Aberdeen AB25 2ZD Tel: 01224 681818 Fax: 01224 662994 Email: w.c.s.smith@abdn.ac.uk; 3 Broom Park, Cults, Aberdeen AB15 9NF Tel: 01224 869405 — MB ChB 1974 Aberd.; PhD Dundee 1990; MD Aberd. 1986; FRCP Ed. 1992; MPH Dundee 1982; FFPHM RCP (UK) 1989; MFCM 1982. Prof. (Pub. Health) Aberd.; Hon. Cons. Pub. Health Med. Grampian HB. Prev: Assoc. Prof. Nat. Univ. Singapore; Epidemiol. (Cardiovasc. Epidemiol. Unit) Dundee Univ.; Sen. Regist. (Community Med.) Tayside HB.

SMITH, William Cletus Bridge Medical Centre, Wassand Close, Three Bridges Road, Crawley RH10 1LL Tel: 01293 526025 — MB BS 1963 Lond.; DObst RCOG 1965.

SMITH, William David 1 Vaudrey Drive, Cheadle Hulme, Cheadle SK8 5LR Tel: 0161 485 6557 — MB ChB 1968 Liverp.; FFA RCS Eng. 1972. Cons. Anaesth. Manch. Roy. Infirm.; Hon. Assoc. Lect. Anaesth. Univ. Manch. Socs: Fell. Manch. Med. Soc. (Mem. Sect. Anaesth.); Assn. Anaesth. Prev: Sen. Regist. (Anaesth.) United Manch. Hosps. & Manch. Rhb; Regist. (Anaesth.) Wythenshawe & N. Chesh. Gp. Hosps. & Univ. Hosp.; S. Manch.

SMITH, William Denis Ashley, OBE (retired) 11 Moorland Drive, Leeds LS17 6JP Tel: 0113 268 4220 — MB BS 1952 Lond.; MD Lond. 1969; FFA RCS Eng. 1961; DA Eng. 1956. Prev: Reader (Anaesth.) Leeds Univ.

SMITH, William Duncan (retired) 7 Adelaide Terrace, Dundee DD3 6HW Tel: 01382 225880 — MB ChB 1956 St. And.; DObst RCOG 1958; MRCGP 1965. Prev: GP Dundee.

SMITH, Rev. William Ernest 3 Inglenook, East Keswick, Leeds LS17 9EU — MRCS Eng. LRCP Lond. 1944; MA (Hnrs. Philos.) Leeds 1934. (Leeds) Med. Off. Barnbow Ordnance Fact. Leeds. Socs: Leeds Regional Psychiat . Assn. Prev: Res. Med. Off. Pontefract Gen. Infirm.

SMITH, William Gerard Kate Marsden Unit, St. Ann's Hospital, St Ann's Road, London N15 3TH Tel: 020 8442 6000 Fax: 020 8442 6354 — MB ChB 1969 Cape Town; FRCPsych 2001; MRCPsych 1976; DPM Eng. 1976. Cons. Psychiat. St. Anns Hosp. Lond.; Hon. Sen. Lect. Roy. Free Med. Sch.; Dir. Med. Educat. St. Geo. Grenada W. I. Prev: Sen. Regist. (Psychiat.) Roy. Free Hosp. Lond.; Regist. (Psychiat.) Maudsley Hosp. Lond.; Regist. (Psychiat.) Lond. Hosp. (St. Clement's).

SMITH, William Homer Bedruthran House, The Royal Cornwall Hospital, Truro TR1 3LJ — MB BS 1970 Lond.; MRCS Eng. LRCP Lond. 1970; FRCR 1977; DMRD Eng. 1974. (Guy's) Cons. Radiol. Roy. Cornw. Hosp.; Med. Dir. Roy. Cornw. Hosp., Truro. Prev: Cons. Radiol. RAF Hosp. Ely; Cons. Advisor Radiol. to RAF; Cons. Radiol. RAF Hosp. Nocton Hall Lincoln.

SMITH, William Homer (retired) Tanglin, Meavy Lane, Yelverton PL20 6AP Tel: 01822 852851 — MB BS 1943 Lond.; MRCS Eng. LRCP Lond. 1943; DMRD Eng. 1950. Prev: Cons. Radiol. Plymouth HA.

SMITH, William Howard Thornton 373 Ring Road, Moortown, Leeds LS17 8NP Email: medws@leeds.ac.uk — MB BChir 1994 Camb.; MA Camb. 1995, BA 1991, MB BChir 1994; MRCP 1996. (Addenbrooke's Cambridge) Research Fell. Inst. for Cardiovasc. Research Univ. of Leeds.

SMITH, William Marcus Victor Pepper Arden Hall, Pepper Arden, Northallerton DL7 0JF Tel: 01325 378548; Pepper Arden Hall, Pepper Arden, Northallerton DL7 0JF Tel: 01325 378548 — MB BS 1969 Lond.; MRCGP 1974. (Lond. Hosp.)

SMITH, William Merson 11 Bankside Close, Upper Poppleton, York YO26 6LH Tel: 01904 790307 — MB ChB Aberd. 1969; MRCGP 1977. (Aberd.) Sen. Medico-Legal Adviser Med. Protec. Soc., Leeds.

SMITH, Mr William Philip Maxillofacial Unit, Northampton General Hospital, Northampton NN1 5BD Tel: 01604 544579; Maxillofacial Unit, Kettering General Hospital, Kettering NN16 8UZ Tel: 01536 492597 — MB BS 1987 Lond.; BDS (Hons.) Bristol 1980; FRCS Eng. 1997, Ed. 1990; FDS RCS Eng. 1985. (The London Hospital) Cons. Maxillofacial Surg. N.ampton & Kettering Gen. Hosp. NHS Trust. Socs: Fell. Brit. Assn. Oral & Maxillofacial Surg. Prev: Sen. Regist. (Oral & Maxillofacial Surg.) Roy. Surrey Co. Hosp. Guildford; Regist. (Oral & Maxillofacial Surg.) Poole Gen. Hosp.; SHO (A & E, Med & Orthop.) St. Richards Hosp. Chichester.

SMITH, William Russell The Medical Centre, 7 Hill Place, Arbroath DD11 1AE Tel: 01241 431144 Fax: 01241 430764 — MB ChB 1973 Glas.; MRCGP 1977; DObst RCOG 1976.

SMITH, William Thomas Malcolm Lour Road Group Practice, 3 Lour Road, Forfar DD8 2AS Tel: 01307 463122 Fax: 01307 465278; Kisimul, Welton Corner, Kingsmuir Road, Forfar DD8 2RQ — MB ChB 1978 Ed.; BSc Ed. 1975, MB ChB 1978; MRCGP 1983; DRCOG 1982.

SMITH, Yuriko 26 Strath, Gairloch IV21 2DA — MB ChB 1996 Liverp.

SMITH, Yvette Louisa Osmond Grove Medical Practice, 49 Richford Gate, Richford Street, London W6 7HY Tel: 020 8846 7555 Fax: 020 8846 7538; 48 Fairlawn Grove, London W4 5EH — MB BS 1987 Lond.; MRCGP 1991; DGM RCP Lond. 1989. Prev: Trainee GP/SHO Edgware VTS.

SMITH-HOWELL, Michael Arnold 5A Norton Road, Loddon, Norwich NR14 6JN — MB ChB 1995 Leic.

SMITH-LAING, Gray Farthing Green Farm, New Barn Road, Hawkenbury, Staplehurst, Tonbridge TN12 0EE — MB BS 1973 Lond.; MD Lond. 1983; FRCP Lond. 1993; MRCP (UK) 1975. Cons. Phys. & Gastroenterol. Medway Hosp. Gillingham. Prev: Sen. Regist. (Gastroenterol.) St. Mary's Hosp. Lond.; Research Fell. Med. Unit Roy. Free Hosp. Lond.

SMITH-MOORHOUSE, Grahame Peter Holme House, Luddenden, Halifax HX2 6TG Tel: 01422 842333 — MB ChB 1969 Leeds.

SMITH-PETERSEN, Vibeke 22 Sparkford Close, Winchester SO22 4NH — MB BCh 1983 Wales.

SMITH-STANLEIGH, Pamela Field House, Field House Drive, Meole Brace, Shrewsbury SY3 9HL — BM BCh 1973 Oxf.

SMITH-WALKER, Malcolm Thomas South Meadow Surgery, 3 Church Close, Eton, Windsor SL4 6AP Tel: 01753 833777 Fax: 01753 833689; Bucks, 25 York Road, Windsor SL4 3NX Tel: 01753 833372 Fax: 01753 833372 — MB BS 1966 Lond.; MRCS Eng. LRCP Lond. 1965; DObst RCOG 1969. (St. Bart.) Socs: Windsor Dist. Med. Soc.; Assoc. Mem. Brit. Med. Acupunc. Soc.; Fell.The Roy. Soc. Med.

SMITHARD, David Graeme Health Care of Older People,, William Harvey Hospital, Kennington Road, Ashford TN24 0LZ Tel: 01233 632331 Fax: 01233 616222 Email: david.smithard@mtcch-tr.sthames.nhs.uk — MB BS 1986 Lond.; BSc (Biochem.) Lond. 1983; MRCP (UK) 1989; MD Lond. 1997; FRCP 1998. (Roy. Lond. Hosp. Med. Coll.) Cons. Phys. (Elderly & Stroke Med.) E. Kent Hosp.; Vis. Lect. Roehampton Inst.; Dir. Of Research & Dev., E. Kent Hosp. Socs: Brit. Geriat. Soc.; BMA; Brit. Assoc. Stroke Phys. Prev: Cons. Phys. (Elderly & Stroke Med.) Qu. Mary's Sidcup; Sen. Regist. (Geriat. & Gen. Med.) St. Thos, Hosp. Lond.; Regist. (Geriat. Med.) Univ. Hosp. S. Manch.

SMITHARD, David John Rochdale Infirmary, Whitehall Street, Rochdale OL12 0WB Tel: 01706 517101; Greenway, Bagslate Moor Road, Rochdale OL11 5XT Tel: 01706 641914, 01707 872270 — MB ChB 1970; FRCP Lond. 1991; MRCP (UK) 1974. (Manchester) Cons. Phys. Rochdale NHS Trust; Cons. Renal Phys., Bury NHS Trust, Bury. Socs: Internat. Soc. Peritoneal Dialysis; Europ. Renal Assn. Prev: Sen. Regist. (Med.) Manch. AHA; Research Fell. (Med.) Dept. Therap. Univ. Nottm.; Regist. (Med.) Glas. Roy. Infirm.

SMITHELLS, Professor Richard Worthington 5 North Grange Mews, North Grange Road, Leeds LS6 2EW Tel: 0113 275 7280 Fax: 0113 275 7280; 4 Duddon Court, Duddon Hall, Broughton-in-Furness LA20 6EU Tel: 01229 716876 — MB BS 1949 Lond.; MD Lond. 1985; FRCP Lond. 1969, M 1956; FRCP Ed. 1969, M 1955; MRCS Eng. LRCP Lond. 1948; FRCPCH 1996; FRCOG 1994; DCH Eng. 1950. (St. Thos.) Emerit. Prof. Paediat. Univ. Leeds. Socs: Hon. Mem. Developm. Path. Soc.; Hon. Mem. Brit. Assn. Perinatal Med. Prev: Prof. Paediat. & Child Health Univ. Leeds.

SMITHERS

SMITHERS, Andrew John Bennetts Road North Surgery, 2 Bennetts Road North, Keresley End, Coventry CV7 8LA Tel: 024 7633 2636 Fax: 024 7633 7353; Fradley, Tamworth Road, Corley, Coventry CV7 8BX Email: asmithers@profiad.com — MB BS 1984 Lond.; Cert. Family Plann. JCC 1989. (St. Bart.) Network Co-ordinator Profiad Ltd. Socs: Brit. Menopause Soc.; ACRPI. Prev: SHO (Psychiat.) Centr. Hosp.; SHO (O & G) Warnford Hosp.; Trainee GP Bertie Rd. Surg. Kenilworth VTS.

SMITHERS, Deborah Anne 'The Back of November', Donkey Lane, Burton, Bradstock DT6 4QB — MB ChB 1990 Liverp.; MRCP CH 1999. Specialist Regist. (Paediat.) W. Sussex Rotat. Prev: PICU Fell. Bristol Childr.s Hosp.

SMITHIES, Alison, OBE 1 De Vaux Place, Salisbury SP1 2SJ Tel: 01722 239505 — MB BS 1954 Lond.; MD Lond. 1977; MRCPath 1988; DObst RCOG 1956. (Univ. Coll. Hosp.) Socs: Fell. Roy. Soc. Med. Prev: Regional Cons. Primary Med. Care Wessex RHA; Princip. Med. Off. DoH; Med. Asst. (Cytol.) N.wick Pk. Hosp. Harrow.

SMITHIES, Joan Mary Agnes 3 Silverdale Road, Southampton SO15 2NG — MB BS 1977 Lond.; MRCS Eng. LRCP Lond. 1977; DGM RCP Lond. 1985; MRCPsych 1984. Sen. Regist. (Psychogeriat.) Moorgreen Hosp. Soton. Prev: Regist. (Psychiat.) Roy. S. Hants. Hosp.

SMITHIES, Mark Nicholas University Hospital of Wales, Heath Park, Cardiff CF14 4XW Tel: 029 2074 3084 Fax: 029 2074 3799 Email: mark.smihies@uhw-tr.wales.nhs.uk; 34 Lake Road E., Roath Park, Cardiff CF23 5NN — MB BS 1981 Lond.; MRCP (UK) 1984. Dir. Intens. Care Univ. Hosp. Wales Cardiff; Clin. Director, Critical Care, Cardiff NHS Trust. Prev: Cons. Intens. Care Guy's Hosp. Lond.

SMITHSON, Carolyn Jane 25 Seagers, Hall Road, Great Totham, Maldon CM9 8PB — MB ChB 1998 Sheff.; MB ChB Sheff 1998.

SMITHSON, Donald Laurence Carisbrooke, 625 Dawsheath Road, Hadleigh, Benfleet SS7 2NH Tel: 01702 559056 — MB BS 1954 Lond.; MRCS Eng. LRCP Lond. 1954. (Guy's) Prev: Orthop. Ho. Surg. Guy's Hosp.; Paediat. Ho. Phys. & O & G Ho. Surg. FarnBoro. Hosp.

SMITHSON, Edel Frances 8 St Patricks Av, Weymouth DT4 9EQ — MB BCh 1997 Wales.

SMITHSON, Jacquelyn Anne Jane Department of Gastroenterology, Hull Royal Infirmary, Anlaby Road, Hull HU3 2JZ Tel: 01482 674862 Fax: 01482 675033 — MB BS 1987 Lond.; MRCP (UK) 1992; FRCP 2000. Cons. and Sen. Lectuurer, Hull Roy. Infirm. Prev: Sen. Regist. (Gastroenterol. & Gen. Med.) Hull Roy. Infirm.; Research Fell. (Gastroenterol. & HIV) Chelsea & W.m. Hosp. Lond.; Regist. (Gen. & AIDS Med.) W.m. Hosp. Lond.

SMITHSON, John Edmund Gastroenterology Dept, Southmead Hospital, Westbury-on-Trym, Bristol BS10 5NB Tel: 0117 950 5050; Tel: 0117 317 9447 — MB ChB 1986 Bristol; BSc (Hons. 1st cl. Anat.) Bristol 1983, MB ChB 1986; MRCP (UK) 1989; MD 1995 Bristol. Cons. Gastroenterologist N. Bristol NHS Trust. Prev: Regist. (Gen. Med.) S.mead Hosp. Bristol; SHO Nat. Heart & Chest Hosps.; Ho. Off. Profess. Units of Med. & Surg. Bristol Roy. Infirm.

SMITHSON, Jonathan Michael The Old Vicarage, Hallgarth, Pittington, Durham DH6 1AB Tel: 0191 372 0253 Fax: 0191 372 2326 — MB ChB 1996 Liverp.; Dip. Trop. Med. & Hyg 1997. (L'pool)

SMITHSON, Nicola 40 Clopton Gardens, Hadleigh, Ipswich IP7 5JG — MB ChB 1993 Birm.; MB ChB (Hons.) Birm. 1993; BSc (Hons.) Birm. 1992. Prev: Ho. Off. (Med.) Selly Oak Hosp. Birm.; Ho. Off. (Surg.) Heartlands Hosp. Birm.

SMITHSON, Nicola Jane 3 West Preston Street (Flat 2F1), Newington, Edinburgh EH8 9PX — MB ChB 1996 Ed.

SMITHSON, Philippa District Health Centre, Palmalmal Pomio District, East New Britain, Papua New Guinea; 1 Beech Avenue, Northenden, Manchester M22 4JE — MB ChB 1994 Liverp.; Dip of Tropical Medicine and Hygiene (DTM&H), University of Liverpool, DEC, 1998; MRCEP, 1998. (Univ. Liverp.) Prev: GP Regist., Lancaster.

SMITHSON, Richard David Western Health & Social Services Board, 15 Gransha Park, Clooney Road, Londonderry BT47 1TG — MB ChB 1981 Birm.; MFPHM 1989. Cons. Communicable Dis. Control & Pub. Health Med. WHSSB.

SMITHSON, Sarah Elizabeth North West Regional Health Authority, Department of Primary Care, Hamilton House, 24 Pall Mall, Liverpool L3 6AL Tel: 0151 236 4620 — MB BChir 1989 Camb.; MRCP (UK) 1993; MRCGP 1995. Assoc. GP (Primary Care Initiative) NW RHA.

SMITHSON, Sarah Francesca Department of Genetics, Bristol St Michaels' Hospital, Bristol BS2 8EG Tel: 0117 928 5653 Email: sarah.smithson@ubht.swest.nhs.uk; 5 York Gardens, Clifton, Bristol BS8 4LL Tel: 0117 317 9447 — MB ChB Bristol 1986, BSc 1983; MRCP (UK) 1989; DCH RCP Lond. 1988; MD Univ. of Bris. (Bris.) Cons. (Clin. Genetics) & Hon. Sen. Lect. In Clin. Genetics. Prev: Sen. Regist. (Clin.. Genetics) Gt. Ormond St. Hosp.

SMITHSON, Simon Richard Pallion Health Centre, Hylton Road, Sunderland SR4 7XF Tel: 0191 567 4673; 24 Underhill Road, Cleadon, Sunderland SR6 7RS — MB BS 1980 Newc.; MRCGP 1984; DRCOG 1983. Prev: Trainee GP N.Id. VTS.

SMITHSON, William Henry The Surgery, Escrick, York YO4 19LE Tel: 01904 728243 Fax: 01904 728826 Email: henrysmithson@compuserve.com — MB ChB 1976 Dundee; FRCGP 1997, M 1985; DRCOG 1980. (Univ. of Dundee) Princip. GP; RCGP/NSE P. of Wales Educat. Fell. in Epilepsy 1996-98; Course Organiser, York GP VTS.

SMITHURST, Helen Jane 5 Buck Lane, Ashton on Mersey, Sale M33 5WF — MB ChB 1989 Birm.; MRCP (UK) 1993. Regist. Rotat. (Diabetes & Endocrinol.) Trafford Pk. Manch. Prev: Regist. (Med., Diabetes & Endocrinol.) Wythenshawe Hosp. Manch.; Regist. (Endocrinol.) Hope Hosp. Salford.

SMITS, Margaretha Maria Englefield House, 23 Highgale High Street, London N6 3ST — MD 1983 Copenhagen. GP Lond.

SMOLLETT, Margaret Amelia Newton Craig, 99 Ayr Road, Prestwick KA9 1TF Tel: 01292 78166 — MB ChB 1977 Glas.

SMOUT, Arthur John Russell (retired) Little Baileys, 57 Henwood Green Road, Pembury, Tunbridge Wells TN2 4LH Tel: 01892 822031 — MB ChB 1958 Birm.; DA Eng. 1968. Prev: Clin. Asst. (Psychogeriat.) Hastings HA & (Ment. Health for Elderly) St. Helens Hosp. Hastings.

SMOUT, Shirley Margery Ticehurst House Hospital, Ticehurst, Wadhurst TN5 7HU Tel: 01580 200391 Fax: 01580 201006; Little Baileys, 57 Henwood Green Road, Pembury, Tunbridge Wells TN2 4LH Tel: 0189 282 2031 — MB ChB 1958 Birm.; MRCPsych 1973; DPM Eng. 1972. (Birm.) Cons. (Psychiat.) Ticehurst Hse. Hosp. Socs: BMA. Prev: Cons. (Psychogeriat.) Pembury Hosp.; Cons. Psychiat. Hellingly Hosp. Hailsham; Sen. Regist. (Psychiat.) Qu. Eliz. Hosp. Birm.

SMOUT, Susan Mary Stonelands, 2 South Road, Newton Abbot TQ12 1HL — MB BS 1987 Lond.

SMULDERS, Thomas Cornelis MEDACS Professional Recruitment plc, High Street House, New Market St., Skipton BD23 2HU — Artsexamen 1993 Amsterdam.

SMULLEN, Simon (retired) 6 Ravenscourt, Thorntonhall, Glasgow G74 5AZ Tel: 0141 644 5110 — MB BCh BAO 1941 Dub.; MA Dub. 1952, MD 1952.

SMURTHWAITE, Denise 9 Churton Avenue, Birkenhead CH43 2NG — MB ChB 1993 Manch.

SMURTHWAITE, Glyn Jonathon Folly Bank Farm, Goodshaw Lane, Rossendale BB4 8DW — MB ChB 1985 Leeds; BSc (Hons.) Leeds 1982; FRCA 1992; FFA RCSI 1991; DA (UK) 1988. Cons. Anaesth. Hope Hosp. Univ. Manch. Prev: Sen. Regist. (Anaesth.) NW RHA.

SMURTHWAITE, William Aston, MC (retired) 6 Normandy Court, West Parade, Worthing BN11 3QY Tel: 01903 230304 — MB BS Lond. 1964; MRCS Eng. LRCP Lond. 1942; FRACR 1987, M 1968; FRCR 1975; FFR 1968; MRACR 1968; DMRD Eng. 1963. Prev: Regist. (Radiol.) W.m. Hosp. Lond.

SMYE, Richard Anthony Somerville Medical Practice, 4 Somerville, Poulton Road, Wallasey CH44 9ED Tel: 0151 638 9333 Fax: 0151 637 0291; 41 Gayton Road, Lower Heswall, Wirral CH60 8QE — MB ChB 1981 Liverp.

SMYK, Darren The Family Practice, Western College, Cotham Road, Bristol BS6 6DF Tel: 0117 946 6455 Fax: 0117 946 6410 — MB ChB 1990 Bristol.

SMYLIE, Ann Hillsborough Health Centre, Ballynahinch Street, Hillsborough BT26 6AW Tel: 028 9268 2216 Fax: 028 9268 9721 — MB BCh BAO 1969 Belf.; FRCGP 1991, M 1974; DCH RCPSI 1972; DObst RCOG 1971. Socs: Ulster Med. Soc.; Soc. Occupat. Med.

SMYLIE, Carol Anne The Dower House, Chestnut Lea, Mont A L'Abbe, St Helier, Jersey JE2 3HA — MB BS 1982 Lond.

SMYLLIE, Hugh Curle (retired) 30 Whin Hill Road, Bessacarr, Doncaster DN4 7AF — MB BS 1950 Lond.; MD Lond. 1959; FRCP Lond 1972, M 1953. Prev: Cons. Phys. with Special Duties in Chest Dis. Doncaster Roy. Infirm.

SMYLLIE, John Hugh Dewsbury District Hospital, Healds Road, Dewsbury WF13 4HS Tel: 01924 816179 — MB BS 1980 Lond.; MD Lond. 1994; MRCP (UK) 1985. Cons. Cardiol. Dewsbury Dist. Hosp.; Hon. Cons. Cardiol. Yorks. Heart Centre Leeds Gen. Infirm. Leeds. Socs: Brit. Cardiac Soc.; Brit. Cardiac. Interven. Soc. Prev: Sen. Regist. (Cardiol.) Leeds; Research Fell. Thoraxcentre Erasmus Univ. Rotterdam; Regist. (Cardiol.) Soton.

SMYLY, Eileen May Bell (retired) 71 Brickhill Drive, Bedford MK41 7QE — MD 1919 Belf.; MD Belf. (Gold Medal) 1919, MB BCh BAO 1916.

SMYLY, Philip Adrian Jocelyn 40 Hill Road, Watlington OX49 5AD Tel: 01491 612455; Woosehill Surgery, Emmview Close, Wokingham RG41 3DA Tel: 0118 978 8266 Fax: 0118 979 3661 — MB ChB 1978 Birm.; MRCGP 1983; DRCOG 1980. (Birm. Univ.) GP Woosehill Surg. Wokingham, Berks. Socs: BMA; Med. Protec. Soc. Prev: GP Watlington, Oxon.; Govt. Med. Off. Elim Hosp., Zimbabwe Seconded by Oxfam (UK).

SMYRNIOU, Nedi Nicou Benchill Medical Practice, 127 Woodhouse Lane, Benchill, Wythenshawe, Manchester M22 9WP Tel: 0161 998 4304 Fax: 0161 945 4028; 23 Pine Road, Didsbury, Manchester M20 6UY — MB ChB 1982 Manch.; MRCP (UK) 1985. Prev: Trainee GP Wythenshawe; SHO (Gen. Med.) Oldham & Dist. Gen. Hosp.; SHO (Cardiothoracic Med.) Wythenshaw Hosp. Manch.

SMYTH, Alan Robert Department of Paediatrics, Nottingham City Hospital, Hucknall Road, Nottingham NG5 1PB Tel: 0115 969 1169 Fax: 0115 9620564 Email: dralansmyth@compuserve.com — MB BS 1987 Lond.; MA Camb. 1988; MD Liverp. 1995; MRCP (UK) 1990; FRCPCH 1996. Cons. Paediat. Respirat. Med. Nottm. City Hosp. Nottm.; Special Sen. Lect. in Child Health, Univ. Nottg. Socs: Brit. Thorac. Soc.; FRCPCh. Prev: Regist. (Paediat.) Roy. Liverp. Childr. Hosp. Alder Hey; SHO (Paediat.) Bristol Roy. Hosp. Sick Childr.; SHO (Paediat.) Leicester Roy. Infirm.

SMYTH, Alan Theodore (retired) 72 Fentham Road, Hampton-in-Arden, Solihull B92 0AY Tel: 01675 443506 — MB ChB Birm. 1951. Prev: GP Solihull.

SMYTH, Mr Alistair Graham 18 Percy Gardens, North Shields NE30 4HQ — MB BS 1988 Newc.; BDS 1981; FRCS Ed. 1991; FDS RCS Eng. 1986. Regist. (Oral. & Maxillofacial Surg.) Sunderland Dist. Gen. Hosp.

SMYTH, Anita Elizabeth 18 Tullyhirm Road, Derrynoose, Armagh BT60 3DU — MB BCh BAO 1991 Belf.; MB BCh Belf. 1991.

SMYTH, Anthony Shanroe House, Mullabawn, Newry BT35 9RD Tel: 01693 888042 Fax: 01693 888977 — MB BCh BAO 1952 Belf.; FRCGP 1984; DCH RCPSI 1962. Hosp. Pract. (Paediat.) Daisy Hill Hosp. Newry; Mem. S.. Health & Social Serv. Bd. Socs: Irish Racecourse Med. Off. Assn.; BMA; Ulster Med. Soc. Prev: Clin. Asst. (Paediat.) Daisy Hill Hosp. Newry; Ho. Surg. & Cas. Off. Mater. Infirm. Hosp. Belf.

SMYTH, Mr Brian Turbett (retired) Tree Tops, Vicarage Close, Stoke Gabriel, Totnes TQ9 6QT Tel: 01803 782806 — MB BCh BAO 1945 Belf.; FRCS Eng. 1952. Prev: Cons. Paediat. Surg. Roy. Belf. Hosp. Sick Childr. & Ulster Hosp. Dundonald.

SMYTH, Caroline Carmel Anne 5 Ryder Crescent, Aughton, Ormskirk L39 5EY Tel: 01695 423867 — MB ChB 1996 Liverp. SHO (Anaesth.)roy.Liverp.Univ.Hosp.

SMYTH, Caroline Lucy Flat 2, 32 Princes Square, London W2 4NJ — MB BS 1993 Lond.

SMYTH, Colin Michael 5 Ryder Crescent, Ormskirk L39 5EY — MB ChB 1991 Dundee.

SMYTH, Denis Gerard 12 Webb Close, Oundle, Peterborough PE8 4HS — MB BCh BAO 1979 Dub.; MA Dub. 1989; FFA RCSI 1994; DA (UK) 1987.

SMYTH, Desmond Alcorn (retired) Bedmond, New Barn Road, Longfield DA3 7JF Tel: 01474 702560 — MB BS 1942 Durh.; MFCM 1972; DPH Durh. 1948. Prev: Dist. Community Phys. Dartford & Gravesham Health Dist.

SMYTH, Diane Patricia Lesley Child Development and Neurology Service, St. Mary's Hospital, London W2 1NY Tel: 020 7886 1545 Fax: 020 7886 6952; Austins, Warners Hill, Cookham Dean, Maidenhead SL6 9NU Tel: 01628 482533 Fax: 01628 481439 — MB BS 1966 Lond.; MD Lond. 1980; FRCP Lond. 1990; MRCP (UK) 1971; MRCS Eng. LRCP Lond. 1967; FRCPCH 1997; DCH RCPS Glas. 1968. (St. Bart.) Cons. Paediat. (Child Developm. & Neurol.) St. Mary's Hosp. Lond. Socs: Brit. Paediat. Neurol. Assn.; Standing Comm. on Disabil. (Chair) Roy. Coll. Paediat and Child Health; Child Developm. & Disabil. Gp. Roy. Coll. Paediat. & Child Health. Prev: SCMO Wycombe HA; Lect. (Child Health) Qu. Eliz. Hosp. Childr. Lond.; Sen. Regist. (Neurol.) Nat. Hosp. Nerv. Dis. & Hosp. Sick Childr. Gt. Ormond St. Lond.

SMYTH, Edward Francis 134 Monlough Road, Saintfield, Ballynahinch BT24 7EU — MB BCh BAO 1997 Belf.

SMYTH, Mr Edward Hugh Jackson (retired) Sun Cottage, Churt, Farnham GU10 2LH Tel: 01428 604882 — MB BS 1936 Lond.; FRCS Ed. 1953; MRCS Eng. LRCP Lond. 1936; FACS 1951. Hon. Orthop. Cons. IOW AHA & Wessex Regional Orthop. Centre Treloar Hosp. Alton. Prev: Cons. Orthop. Surg. (Civil) Camb. Milit. Hosp. Aldershot.

SMYTH, Edward Thomas Martin Department of Bacteriology, The Royal Hospitals, Belfast BT12 6BA Tel: 01232 230503 Fax: 01232 311416 Email: edward.smythe@bll.n-i.nhs.uk; 13 Glenshane Park, Jordanstown, Newtownabbey BT37 0QN — MD 1993 Belf.; MB BCh BAO 1976; FRCPath. 1995, M 1983; Hon. FFP RCPI 1985. Cons. Bact. Roy. Hosps. Belf. Socs: Hosp. Infec. Soc.; Soc. for Healthcare Epidemiol. of Amer.; Brit. Infec. Soc. Prev: Cons. Bact. Roy. Vict. Hosp. Belf.

SMYTH, Edward Timothy 57 Naseby Way, Norwich NR7 0TP — MB BCh BAO 1983 Belf.; MRCP (UK) 1988.

SMYTH, Elizabeth Helen Aberdeen Royal Infirmary, Foresterhill, Aberdeen AB25 2ZN; 7 Royston Terrace, Edinburgh EH3 5QU — MB ChB 1988 Ed.; FRCS (Gen.) 2000; FRCS Eng. 1993. (Edinburgh) Cons. Surg., Aberd. Roy. Infirm. Socs: ASIT; WIST; BASO - Brit. Assn. Surgic. Oncol. Prev: Clin. Scientist MRC Human Genetics Unit Edin.; Specialist Regist. SE Scotl. Higher Surgic. Train. Scheme.

SMYTH, Fiona 28 Massey Court, Belfast BT4 3GJ — MB BCh BAO 1981 Belf.; DRCOG 1983.

SMYTH, Frederick Brian CDSC (NI), McBrien Building, Belfast City Hospital, Belfast BT9 7AB Tel: 02890 263765 Fax: 02890 263511 Email: bsmyth@phls.org.uk; The Old Manse, 25 Dreen Road, Cullybackey, Ballymena BT42 1EB — MB BCh BAO 1978 Belf.; MSc Community Med. Ed. 1985; FRCP Ed. 1994; MRCP (UK) 1982; FFPHM RCP (UK) 1997, M 1989; MFCM 1988; FRCP(L) 1998. (Belf.) Reg. Epidemiolog. Communicable Dis. Surveillance Centre, Belf. Hosp. Socs: Fell. Ulster Med. Soc. Prev: Cons. Pub. Health Med. & Communicable Dis. Control, N. Health Bd.

SMYTH, Mr George Thomas Chase Malago Surgery, 40 St. Johns Road, Bedminster, Bristol BS3 4JE Tel: 0117 966 3587 Fax: 0117 963 1422; 25 Montague Hill, Kingsdown, Bristol BS2 8ND Tel: 0117 942 1238 — MB BS 1975 Lond.; FRCS Eng. 1980; MRCGP 1983; DRCOG 1982. GP Princip.; GP Clin. Tutor. Prev: Resid. Surg.Off. Manch. Roy. Infirm.; Surgic. Regist. Groote Schuur Hosp., Cape Town.

SMYTH, Gerald Vincent 'Craggets Lodge', Craggets Lane, Church St., Henfield BN5 9NS — LRCPI & LM, LRSCI & LM 1937; LRCPI & LM, LRCSI & LM 1937. (RCSI) Prev: Chairm. Bd. Dept. of Health & Social Security (S.E. Region) & War; Pens. S.E. Region; Mem. Brighton & Sussex M-C Soc.

SMYTH, Gerard Paul 2 Brownhills Gardens, St Andrews KY16 8PY — MB ChB 1991 Aberd.

SMYTH, Heather Jane 3 Kilburn Crescent, Woodburn Park, Waterside, Londonderry BT47 5PZ — MB BCh 1998 Belf.; MB BCh Belf 1998.

SMYTH, James Harold Smyth Care Homes, 108-100 Cambridge Road, Churchtown, Southport PR9 9RZ Tel: 01704 25717 — LRCPI & LM, LRSCI & LM 1956; LRCPI & LM, LRCSI & LM 1956. Prev: Ho. Surg. Jervis St. Hosp. Dub.; Ho. Phys. S.port Infirm.

SMYTH, Professor John Fletcher University Department of Clinical Oncology, Western General Hospital, Crewe Road, Edinburgh EH4 2XU Tel: 0131 467 8449 Fax: 0131 332 8494 Email: smyth@icrf.co.uk; 18 Inverleith Avenue S., Edinburgh EH3 5QA — MB BChir 1970 Camb.; FRSE 1996; MSc Lond. 1975; MA Camb. 1971, MD 1976; FRCS Ed. 1993; FRCP Lond. 1983; FRCP Ed. 1981; MRCP (UK) 1973; FRCR 1996. (St. Bart.) Prof.

SMYTH

Med. Oncol. Univ. Edin.; Head Dept. Clin. Oncol. W. Gen. Hosp. Edin.; Hon. Dir. ICRF Med. Oncol. Unit Edin.; Head Dir. Molecular & Clin. Med. W. Gen. Hosp. Edin. Socs: (Ex-Pres.) Europ. Soc. Med. Oncol.; (Treas.) Federat. Europ. Cancer Socs. Prev: Sen. Lect. Div. Med. Inst. Cancer Research; Hon. Cons. Phys. Roy. Marsden Hosp. Sutton; Vis. Fell. Nat. Cancer Inst., USA.

SMYTH, John Seymour 21 Lucerne Parade, Strawmills, Belfast BT9 5FT — MB BCh BAO 1993 Belf.

SMYTH, John Walter 1 The Grange, Off Dobb Brow Road, Westhoughton, Bolton BL5 2AZ — MB ChB 1990 Manch.

SMYTH, Joseph Ernest Cookstown Health Centre, 52 Orritor Road, Cookstown BT80 8BM Tel: 028 7976 2995 Fax: 028 7976 1383 — MB BCh BAO 1973 Belf.

SMYTH, Mr Julian Michael 27 Kennington Palace Court, Sancroft St., London SE11 5UL Tel: 020 7735 4866 — MB 1964 Camb.; MA Camb. 1957, MB 1964, BChir 1963, VetMB 1958; FRCS Eng. 1972. (St. Mary's) Prev: Cons. Palliat. Med. St. Josephs Hospice Lond.; Ho. Phys. Med. Unit St. Mary's Hosp. Lond.; Med. Off. St. Raphaels Hospice N. Cheam.

SMYTH, Katherine Lorna 8 Bursar Close, Newton-le-Willows WA12 9JS Tel: 01925 227716 — MB ChB 1989 Liverp.; MB ChB (Hons.) Liverp. 1989.

SMYTH, Marcellino Gerard Mooney 200 Lordswood Road, Birmingham B17 8QH — MB BCh BAO 1981 NUI.

SMYTH, Margaret Gavina Stewart (retired) Halycon House, Cable St., Formby, Liverpool L37 7DH Tel: 0170 48 74078 — MRCS Eng. LRCP Lond. 1937. Prev: Med. Off. Family Plann. Assn. Liverp.

SMYTH, Mark Gordon 3 Eden Park, Bothwell, Glasgow G71 8SL — MB ChB 1991 Glas.; DRCOG 1993. Prev: Trainee GP S.. Gen. Hosp. Glas. Train. Scheme.

SMYTH, Martin 27 Coleville Road, Farnborough GU14 8PY — MB BS 1988 Lond.

SMYTH, Maurice Samuel 17 Moat Avenue, Donaghadee BT21 0DJ — MB BCh BAO 1951 Belf.; DObst RCOG 1954. (Belf.) Prev: Ho. Off. Roy. Vict. Hosp. & Roy. Belf. Hosp. Sick Childr. Belf.

SMYTH, Mr Michael David Laurence Castlefields Health Centre, Chester Close, Castlefields, Runcorn WA7 2HY Tel: 01928 566671 Fax: 01928 581631; Stane Brae, Hall Park, Scotforth, Lancaster LA1 4SH Tel: 01524 37252 Email: thesmyths@compuserve.com — MB ChB 1986 Liverp.; FRCS Ed. 1991; MRCGP 1993. Med. Adviser Morecombe Bay HA. Prev: Assoc. Phys. NW Primary Care Initiative.

SMYTH, Michael Gerard Maguires Bridge Surgery, The Surgery, Maguiresbridge, Enniskillen BT94 4PB Tel: 028 6772 1273 Fax: 028 6772 3303; Dr M. Smyth, Drumgoon, Maguiresbridge, Enniskillen BT94 4PB Tel: 01365 722528 Fax: 01365 723303 — MB BCh BAO 1981 Belf.; MRCGP 1986; DRCOG 1984. (Belf.) GP Maguiresbridge Co. Fermanagh; Med. Assessor, Indep. Tribunal Serv. Socs: BMA; Ulster Med. Soc. Prev: SHO (Med. & Cas.) Erne Hosp. Enniskillen; SHO (Obst.) Altnagelvin Hosp. Derry; SHO (Psychiat.) Tyrone & Fermanagh Hosp. Omagh.

SMYTH, Michael James Wards Medical Practice, 25 Dundonald Road, Kilmarnock KA1 1RU Tel: 01563 526514 Fax: 01563 573558 — MB ChB 1974 Glas.; FFA RCS Eng. 1980; DCH RCPS Glas. 1978; DRCOG 1977.

SMYTH, Nigel Wesley 6 Innishowen Park, Ballymena BT43 5NE — MB ChB 1998 Glas.; MB ChB Glas 1998.

SMYTH, Patrick Joseph Evanson St Johns Road Surgery, 10 St. Johns Road, Newbury RG14 7LX Tel: 01635 40160; Orchard Cottage, Adbury Park, Newbury RG20 4HB — MB BS 1971 Lond.; MRCS Eng. LRCP Lond. 1971; DA Eng. 1974. (Guy's) Prev: Regist. (Anaesth.) Guy's Hosp.

SMYTH, Patrick Robert Francis Long Lane Farmhouse, Long Lane, Wimborne BH21 7AQ — MB BS 1972 Lond.; FFA RCS Eng. 1979; DA Eng. 1974. (St. Bart.) Cons. (Anaesth.) Poole Gen. Hosp. Prev: Sen. Regist. (Anaesth.) W.m. Hosp. Lond.; Regist. (Anaesth.) Roy. Devon & Exeter Hosps.; Med. Off. Britain Nepal Med. Trust.

SMYTH, Paul William John (retired) Stone Cottage, Mill Lane, Chideock, Bridport DT6 6JS — MB BS 1959 Lond. Apptd. Fact. Doctor.

SMYTH, Robert Andrew Colhoun Broadway Medical Centre, 65-67 Broadway, Fleetwood FY7 7DG Tel: 01253 874222 Fax: 01253 874448 — MB ChB 1988 Manch.; MRCGP 1992; DRCOG 1991.

(Manchester University) Prev: SHO (Med. & O & G) N. Manch. Gen. Hosp.; SHO (Paediat.) Booth Hall Hosp.

SMYTH, Rosalind Jane 41 Crafordsburn Road, Newtownards BT23 4EA — MB BCh BAO 1996 Belf.

SMYTH, Professor Rosalind Louise Royal Liverpool Children's Hospital, Alder Hey, Liverpool L12 2AP Tel: 0151 252 5693 Fax: 0151 252 5929 Email: r.l.smyth@liv.ac.uk; Wexford Lodge, Noctorum Lane, Oxton, Birkenhead CH43 9UE — MB BS 1983 Lond.; MA Camb. 1984, MD 1993; MRCP (UK) 1986. Brough Prof. of Paediatric Med., Univ. of Liverp. Prev: Cons. Paediat. (Respirat. & Infec. Dis.) Roy. Liverp. Childr. Hosp.; Sen. Regist. (Paediat.) Mersey Region; Reasearch Regist. Papworth Hosp. Cambs.

SMYTH, Rosemary Ballysillan Group Practice, 321 Ballysillan Road, Belfast BT14 6RD Tel: 028 9071 3689/7843 Fax: 028 9071 0626 — MB BCh BAO 1983 Belf.; DRCOG 1990.

SMYTH, Sheila Catherine Douglas Street Surgery, 1 Douglas Street, Hamilton ML3 0DR Tel: 01698 286262; 3 Eden Park, Bothwell, Glasgow G71 8SL Tel: 01698 854546 — MB ChB 1991 Glas.; MRCGP 1995; DRCOG 1994.

SMYTH, Ursula Rachel (retired) 72 Fentham Road, Hampton in Arden, Solihull B92 0AY Tel: 01675 443506 — MB ChB Birm. 1952. Prev: Ho. Phys. & Ho. Surg. Qu. Eliz. Hosp. Birm.

SMYTH, William Randall 1 Church Road, Ballynure, Newtownabbey BT36 9UF — MB BCh BAO 1980 Belf.; DRCOG 1992.

SMYTHE, Raymond 1 Antrim Road, North Shore, Blackpool FY2 9UR Tel: 01253 52161.— MB ChB 1968 Manch. (Manch.) Prev: Ho. Phys. & Ho. Surg. Ancoats Hosp.; Ho. Off. Fulford Matern. Hosp. York.

SMYTHE, Robert Hastings Brookfield, Goosenford, Cheddon Fitzpaine, Taunton TA2 8LJ Tel: 01823 412532 — LRCPI & LM, LRSCI & LM 1938; LRCPI & LM, LRCSI & LM 1938. (Univ. Dub. & RCSI) Prev: Maj. RAMC.

SMYTHIES, John Raymond 8 East Mount Road, York YO24 1BD — MD 1955 Camb.; MB BChir 1945; DPM Eng. 1952. Emerit. Irel. Prof. Univ. Alabama, USA.; Vis. Schol. Dept. Philosophy Univ. Stanford, USA. Prev: Reader Psychiat. Univ. Edin.; Sen. Regist. Maudsley Hosp. Lond.

SNADDEN, David Tayside Centre for General Practice, Kirsty Semple Way, Charleston Drive, Dundee DD2 4AD Tel: 01382 632771 Fax: 01382 425627 Email: dsnadden@dundee.ac.uk; Rowanholme, Lundie, Dundee DD2 5NW Tel: 01382 580744 — MB ChB 1977 Dundee; MCISc Univ. West. Ontario 1991; FRCGP 1995, M 1981; DCH RCPS Glas. 1979; DRCOG 1979; MD, Dundee, 1998. (Univ. Dundee) Dir. of Postgrad. Gen. Pract. Educat. E. Scotl.; Sen. Lect. Dundee Univ. Socs: BMA. Prev: Sen. Lect. (Gen. Pract.) & Assoc. Adviser Dundee Univ.; Grad. Fell. Univ. W.. Ontario; GP Beauly.

SNAITH, Alan Harrison (retired) Haddeo House, Upton, Taunton TA4 2HU Tel: 01398 371297 — MD Durh. 1961, MB BS 1947; DPH Eng. 1961; FFCM 1973; FRCPath 1963.

SNAITH, Michael Linton Molecular & Genetic Medicine, The Medical School, Beech Hill Road, Sheffield S10 2RX Tel: 0114 271 3780 Fax: 0114 271 3781 Email: m.snaith@sheffield.ac.uk; Oakdale House, 25 Millhouses Lane, Sheffield S7 2HA Tel: 0114 235 1141 Fax: 0114 235 1668 — MB BS 1965 Newc.; MD Newc. 1973; FRCP Lond. 1980, M 1968. (Newc.) Sen. Lect. (Rheum.) Molecular & Genetic Med. Fac. Med. Sheff. Univ.; Hon. Cons. Rheum. Sheff. Socs: Brit. Soc. Rheum.; BMA; Amer. Coll. Rheum. Prev: Cons. Rheum. Univ. Coll. & Middlx. Hosp. Lond.; Cons. Rheum. St. Stephens & W.m. Hosps. Lond.; Sen. Regist. (Rheum.) Nuffield Orthop. Centre Oxf.

SNAITH, Richard Philip The Harrogate Clinic, Ripon Road, Harrogate HG1 2JL; 30 Gledhow Wood Road, Leeds LS8 4BZ Tel: 0113 240 2446 Email: r.p.snaith@leeds.ac.uk — MD Lond. 1966, MB BS 1957; FRCPsych 1976, M 1971; DCH Eng. 1960, DPM 1962. (Guy's) Hon. Cons. & Sen. Lect. Leeds Univ. Dept. Psychiat.

SNAITH, Rosemary Jane 9 Kersland Drive, Milngavie, Glasgow G62 8DG — MB ChB 1998 Glas.; MB ChB Glas 1998.

SNAPE, Catherine Jane The Gillygate Surgery, 28 Gillygate, York YO 31 7WQ Tel: 01904 624404 Email: cjsnape@yahoo.com — MB BS 1982 Newc.; MMSc 1982 Leeds; MRCGP 1986; DRCOG 1987.

SNAPE, Elizabeth Elaine Bridge Lane Health Centre, 20 Bridge Lane, Battersea, London SW11 3AD Tel: 020 7585 1499 Fax: 020 7978 4707 — MB ChB 1981 Ed.; MRCGP 1987; DRCOG 1984.

SNAPE, Jeremy Cross House, Main Road, Higham, Derby DE55 6EH — MB ChB 1974 Birm.; DTM & H 1977 Liverp.; FRCP Lond. 1993; MRCP (UK) 1982. Cons. Geriat. Mansfield Notts. Socs: Brit. Geriat. Soc.; Internat. Continence Soc. Prev: Sen. Regist. (Geriat. Med.) Leicester Gen. Hosp.

SNAPE, John William Frank 14 Haylands Lane, Putnoe, Bedford MK41 9BT — MB BS 1980 Lond.

SNAPE, Olivia Jayne 35 Oathall Avenue, Haywards Heath RH16 3ES — MB BS 1989 Lond.; MRCGP 1995. (St. Thos. Hosp. Lond.)

SNAPE, Peter Evans 6 Rubislaw Terrace, Aberdeen AB10 1XE Tel: 01224 622440 Fax: 01224 646612 Email: psnape@btconect.com; 206 King's Gate, Aberdeen AB15 6DQ Tel: 01224 311209 Fax: 01224 322810 — MB ChB 1975 Aberd.; BMedBiol 1972; AFOM RCP Lond. 1991. Indep. Occupat. Health Phys. Socs: Soc. Occupat. Med. Prev: GP Aberd.

SNAPE, Sarah Louise Dept Anaesthetics, Bedford Hospital, Kemptston Road, Bedford MK42 9DJ; Honeystone, 22a West End, Stevington, Bedford MK43 7QU — MB BS 1988 Lond.; BSc 1985 Lond.; FRCA 1993; BSc Lond. 1985; FRCA 1993. (Roy. Free Hosp.) Cons. Anaestetist Bedford Hosp. Prev: Regist. John Radcliffe Hosp. Oxf.; SHO (Anaesth.) N.ampton Gen. Hosp. Cliftonville; SR John Radcliffe Oxf.

SNAPE, Simon Richard Orleton Surgery, Millbrook Way, Orleton, Ludlow SY8 4HW Tel: 01584 831300 — MB BS 1962 Lond.; MRCS Eng. LRCP Lond. 1962. (St. Thos.) GP Herefordsh. Prev: Cas. Off. St. Thos. Hosp. Lond.; Med. Regist. Hereford Hosp. Gp.

***SNAPE, Sonya Louise** Pinehurst, Patshill Road, Pattingham, Wolverhampton WV6 7BG — MB ChB 1996 Birm.

SNASHALL, David Charles 2 Charity Cottages, Petsoe End, Emberton, Olney MK46 5JL Tel: 01234 711072 — MB ChB Ed. 1968; MSc Lond. 1979; LLM Cardiff 1996; FRCP Lond. 1993; MRCP (UK) 1972; FFOM RCP Lond. 1987, MFOM 1983; DTM & H RCP Lond. 1980; DIH Lond. 1979. (Ed.) Clin. Dir. & Hon. Cons. (Occupat. Health) Guy's & St. Thos. NHS Trust; Chief Med. Adviser Health & Safety Exec. Socs: Internat. Commiss. Occupat. Health; Soc. Occupat. Med. Prev: Med. Adviser Hse. of Commons Lond.; Chief Med. Adviser Foreign & Commonw. Office.

SNASHALL, Phillip Douglas 4 Copeland Court, Archery Rise, Durham DH1 4LF — MB BS (Hons.) Lond. 1967; BSc (Hons.) Lond. 1964, MD 1974; FRCP Ed. 1995; FRCP Lond. 1986; MRCP (UK) 1970; MRCS Eng. LRCP Lond. 1967. (Char. Cross) Harold Macmillan Prof. Med. Univ. Newc. u. Tyne; Hon. Cons. Phys. N. Tees Gen. Hosp. Stockton-on-Tees; Sub-Dean (Teeside Div.) Fac. Med. Univ. Newc. Socs: Brit. Thorac. Soc.; Amer. Thoracic Soc.; Assn. for Med. Educat. Prev: Asst. Dean (Med. Educat.) Char. Cross & W.m. Med. Sch.; Sen. Lect. (Med.) Char. Cross Hosp. Lond.; Sen. Research Fell. Wellcome Trust.

SNASHALL, Susan Elizabeth St. George's Hospital, Blackshaw, Tooting, London SW17 0QT Tel: 020 8725 1886 Fax: 020 8275 1874 Email: susans@enta.net; 18A Beech Lane, Guildford GU2 4ES Tel: 01483 571615 — MB BS 1966 Lond.; MD Lond. 1995; MRCS Eng. LRCP Lond. 1966. (Char. Cross. Hosp. Lond.) Cons. Audiological Phys. St. Geo. Hosp. Lond. & St. Helier's Hosp. Carshalton; Mem. (Chairm.) Pan Thames Speciality Train. Comm. Audiol. Med. Socs: Brit. Assn. Audiol. Phys. Prev: Cons. Audiological Phys. Roy. Surrey Co. Hosp. Guildford.

SNEAD, Alan Roger (retired) Ty'n Llain, Mynedd Mechell, Amlwch LL68 0TN Tel: 01407 711302 — MB ChB Birm. 1957; DObst RCOG 1961. Prev: GP Newport, Shrops.

SNEAD, David Robert John Department of Histopathology, Walsgrave Hospital, Clifford Bridge Road, Walsgrave, Coventry CV2 2DX Tel: 024 76 538855 Email: david.snead@uh-tr.wmids.nhs.uk; Wellington Cottage, Bourton-on-Dunsmore, Rugby CV23 9QS Tel: 01926 633754 — MB BS 1989 Lond.; MRCPath 1995. (St Thomas's Hospital) Cons. Histopath. Walsgrave Hosp. Coventry. Prev: Sen. Regist. Nottm.; Regist. (Histopath.) Bristol Roy. Infirm. & Frenchay Hosp.; SHO (Histopath.) Nottm.

SNEAD, Mr Martin Paul Addenbrooke's Hospital, Box 41, Hills Road, Cambridge CB2 2QQ Tel: 01223 216701 Fax: 01223 217968 — MB BS 1984 Lond.; MD Lond. 1996; FRCS Eng. 1989; FRCOphth 1989; DO Lond. 1988. (St. Thos. Hosp. Med. Sch) Cons. Ophth. Surg. Addenbrooke's NHS Trust Camb. Socs: FRSM. Prev: Vitreo-Retinal Fell. Addenbrooke's NHS Trust; Oxf. Ophth. Research Sholarsh. Molecular Genetics Laborat. Camb.

SNEAD, Mrs Shirley Margaret (retired) Tyn Llain, Mynydd Mechell, Amlwch LL68 0TN Tel: 01407 711302 Fax: 01407 711302 Email: alansnead@ukonline.co.uk — MB BCh BAO 1957 Dub.; BA Dub. 1957; MRCS Eng. LRCP Lond. 1957; DObst RCOG 1958. Clin. Asst. (Psychosexual) Shrops. HA. Prev: Med. Off. (Psychosexual Med.) Wolverhampton & Mid. Staffs. Has.

SNEARY, Michael Alfred Brinson (Surgery), 141 Brigstock Road, Thornton Heath, Croydon CR7 7JN Tel: 020 8684 1128 Fax: 020 8689 3647; Silwood, 129 Pollards Hill S., Norbury, London SW16 Tel: 020 8679 6966 — MB BS 1960 Lond.; MRCS Eng. LRCP Lond. 1960; MRCGP 1977; DObst RCOG 1962. (Guy's)

SNEATH, Paula Epsom General Hospital, Dorking Road, Epsom KT19 7EG Tel: 01372 726100 Fax: 01372 735261; Berrow End, Downs Avenue, Epsom KT18 5HG Tel: 01372 722286 Fax: 01372 726933 Email: 10457.3633@compuserve.com — MB BS Lond. 1968; MRCP (U.K.) 1972; MRCS Eng. LRCP Lond. 1968; DCH Eng. 1970; FRCP (UK) 1996; FRCPCH 1998. (St. Mary's) Cons. Community Paediat. Epsom Health Care Trust. Prev: SCMO (Child Health) Tower Hamlets Health Dist. (T); Lect. (Child Health) Acad. Unit Qu. Eliz. Hosp. Childr. Lond., St.; Bart. & Lond. Hosps. Med. Schs.; Resid. MO W.m. Childr. Hosp. Lond.

SNEATH, Peter Henry Andrews c/o Midland Bank, 3 North St., Bourne PE10 9AE — MRCS Eng. LRCP Lond. 1947; MD Camb. 1959, MB BChir 1948; Dip. Bact. Lond 1953. (Camb. & King's Coll. Hosp.) Emerit. Prof. Microbiol. Univ. Leicester. Prev: Prof. Microbiol. Univ. Leicester; Dir. MRC Microbiol. Systematics Unit, Univ. Leicester; Demonst. (Path.) King's Coll. Hosp. Med. Sch.

SNEATH, Mr Robert James Saville 55 Monument Lane, Rednal, Birmingham B45 9QQ Email: rsneath@hotmail.com — MB BS 1991 Lond.; FRCS (Eng) 1995. (The London Hospital Medical College) Orthop. on the N. W. thames Rotat. (Specialist Regist.).

SNEATH, Mr Rodney Saville (retired) The Priory Hospital, Priory Road, Birmingham B5 7UG Tel: 0121 440 2323 — MB ChB 1957 Sheff.; FRCS Eng. 1958; MRCS Eng. LRCP Lond. 1948. Cons. Orthop. Surg. Roy. Orthop. Hosp. Birm.; Dir. Birm. Bone Tumour Treatm. Serv. Prev: Sen. Regist. Roy. Nat. Orthop. Hosp.

SNEDDEN, Ann Elizabeth Department of Child & Family Psychiatry, Possilpark Health Centre, 85 Denmark St., Glasgow G22 5EG Tel: 0141 531 6106 Fax: 0141 531 6106; 4A Prince Albert Road, Dowanhill, Glasgow G12 9JX — MB ChB 1983 Glas.; MRCGP 1987; DRCOG 1985; Cert. Family Plann. JCC 1985; MRCPsych 1990. (University of Glasgow) Cons. Child & Adolesc. Psychiat.; Hon. Sen. Lect. Socs: Roy. Coll. Psychiat.

SNEDDON, Alasdair James Cameron Muiredge Surgery, Merlin Crescent, Buckhaven, Leven KY8 1HJ Tel: 01592 713299 Fax: 01592 715728 — MB ChB 1981 Manchester; MB ChB Manch. 1981. (Manchester) GP Leven, Fife.

SNEDDON, Alison Mavis 9 Lothian Drive, Clarkston, Glasgow G76 7NA — MB ChB 1986 Dundee.

SNEDDON, David Thomas Castlehill Health Centre, Castlehill, Forres IV36 1QF Tel: 01309 672233 Fax: 01309 673445 — MB ChB 1976 Aberd.; MRCGP 1980; DRCOG 1978.

SNEDDON, Derek John Crawford The Pentlands Medical Centre, 44 Pentland View Court, Currie, Edinburgh EH14 5QB Tel: 0131 449 2142 Fax: 0131 451 5855; Lane Edge, Nisbet Road, Gullane EH31 2BQ Tel: 01620 842815 — MB ChB 1959 Ed.; FRCGP 1980, M 1974. (Ed.) Socs: Roy. Coll. Gen. Pract. (SE Scotl. Fac.); BMA; Ed. Clin. Club. Prev: Ho. Surg. Roy. Infirm. Edin.; Ho. Phys. Chalmers Hosp. Edin.

SNEDDON, Frances Elizabeth Horsham Hospital, Hurst Road, Horsham RH12 2DR — MB BS 1987 Lond.; BSc Lond. 1984; MRCP (UK) 1992; MRCGP 1995. GP Surrey. Prev: Regist. (Med.) Greenwich Dist. Hosp.; SHO (Med.) St. Geo. Hosp. Lond.

SNEDDON, James Findlay Crawley Hospital, West Green Drive, Crawley RH11 7DH Tel: 01293 527866 — MB BS 1983 Lond.; MRCP (UK) 1986. Cons. Phys. Cardiol. Crawley Health Serv. Trust. Prev: Research Fell. St. Geo. Hosp. Lond.

SNEDDON, James John St Peters Hill Surgery, 15 St. Peters Hill, Grantham NG31 6QA Tel: 01476 590009 Fax: 01476 570898; 110 Barrowby Road, Grantham NG31 8AF Tel: 01476 62221 — MB

SNEDDON

ChB 1965 St. And.; DA Eng. 1969. (St. And.) Prev: Regist. (Anaesth.) Dundee Roy. Infirm.; Demonst. (Physiol.) Univ. Dundee.; SHO (Obst.) Maryfield Hosp. Dundee.

SNEDDON, Lorna Margaret 28 Starlaw Avenue, Bathgate EH48 1LJ — MB ChB 1993 Aberd.

SNEE, Kevin North Derbyshire DHA, Scarsdale Hospital, Newbold Road, Chesterfield S41 7PF Tel: 01246 231255; 332 Bolton Road W., Ramsbottom, Bury BL0 9QY — MB ChB 1982 Liverp.; MSc Manch. 1991; MRCGP 1986; MFPHM RCP (UK) 1992. Cons. Pub. Health Med. Scarsdale Hosp. Chesterfield. Prev: Lect. (Pub. Health) Univ. Liverp.; Regist. (Pub. Health Med.) Mersey Region.

SNEEDEN, Arthur Elvin Townsend (retired) Ladywood, 2 Wester Boghead, Lenzie, Glasgow G66 4SR Tel: 0141 775 2091 — MB ChB 1944 Glas.; MRCGP 1968.

SNELL, Anthony David East Kent Health Authority, Protea House, New Bridge, Marine Parade, Dover CT17 9HQ Tel: 01304 222230 Fax: 01304 222229 Email: tony.snell@ekentha.nhs.uk; Monchique, Bower Road, Mersham, Ashford TN25 6NW Tel: 01233 503070 Fax: 01233 503070 — MB ChB 1977 Liverp.; MRCGP 1983; DRCOG 1985. (Liverpool) Med. Adviser & Dep. Dir. Performance Managem. (Developm.); Gen. Princip. Prev: Dir. of Primary Care Barnet Health Agency; GP Colchester; Med. Off. RN.

SNELL, Barbara Jean THe Old Schoolhouse, Pishill, Henley-on-Thames RG9 6HJ — MRCS Eng. LRCP Lond. 1972; BSc (Hons.) (Physiol.) Lond. 1969, MB BS 1972; MRCOphth. 1993; DO Eng. 1976. (St. Bart.) Med. Off. Eye Unit Roy. Berks. Hosp. Reading. Socs: Med. Contact Lens Assn. Prev: Ho. Phys. Edgware Gen. Hosp.; Ho. Surg. Wycombe Gen. Hosp.; SHO (Ophth.) Roy. Berks. Hosp. Reading.

SNELL, Caroline The New House, 2A Kilham Lane, Winchester SO22 5PS — MB BS 1976 Lond.; DRCOG 1980.

***SNELL, Caroline Jane Holmes** 46 Coniston Av, West Jesmond, Newcastle upon Tyne NE2 3HA — MB BS 1997 Newc.

SNELL, Eric Saxon (retired) 4 Flintcombe Square, Poundbury Village, Dorchester, Dorchester DT1 3GG Tel: 01305 261942 Email: dr.e.snell@tesco.net — MB BS Lond. 1948; MA Oxf. 1961; MD Lond. 1967; FRCP Lond. 1973, M 1952. Prev: Dir. Med. & Scientif. Affairs Assn. Brit. Pharmaceut. Indust.

SNELL, Jeffrey Kennard (retired) Highbury, Compton, Chichester PO18 9EX — MRCS Eng. LRCP Lond. 1954; MA Camb. 1955, BA 1950, MB BChir 1953; DObst RCOG 1960. Prev: Ho. Surg. ENT Dept. King's Coll. Hosp.

SNELL, Jennifer Anne Fieldhead Surgery, 65 New Road Side, Horsforth, Leeds LS18 4JY Tel: 0113 295 3410 Fax: 0113 295 3417; 4 Redbeck Cottages, Woodbottom, Horsforth, Leeds LS18 4GQ Tel: 01132 503402 — MB ChB 1978 Leeds; DRCOG 1981. Gen. Practitioner.

SNELL, Louise Rebecca 1 Temple Row Close, Leeds LS15 9HR — MB ChB 1996 Leeds.

SNELL, Margaret Jane The Lodge, Lower End, Layer-de-la-Haye, Colchester CO2 0LE Tel: 01206 734698 — MB BS 1959 Lond.; MRCS Eng. LRCP Lond. 1959; DCH Eng. 1962. (St. Mary's) Community Med. Off. N. Essex HA. Socs: Colchester Med. Soc. Prev: Regist. (Paediat.) Essex Co. Hosp. Colchester; SHO (Paediat.) Pembury Hosp.; Sen. Ho. Phys. St. Richard's Hosp. Chichester.

SNELL, Mr Michael Edward Lindo Wing, St Mary's Hospital, Praed St., London W2 1NY Tel: 020 7636 9934 — MB BChir 1960 Camb.; MA, MChir Camb. 1972, MB BChir 1960; FRCS Eng. 1963; MRCS Eng. LRCP Lond. 1960. (St. Mary's) Moynihan Fell. 1969; Cons. Urol. St. Mary's Hosp. & King Edwd. VII Hosp. for Offs. Lond. Socs: Brit. Assn. Urol. Surgs. & Internat. Soc. Urol. Prev: Sen. Surg. Regist. St. Mary's Hosp. Lond.; Sen. Regist. (Urol.) St. Peter's Hosp. Lond.; Research Assoc. Div. of Urol. Stanford Univ., U.S.A.

SNELL, Noel James Creagh The Old School House, Pishill, Henley-on-Thames RG9 6HJ Tel: 01491 638842 Fax: 01491 638842 — MB BS 1972 Lond.; FRCP Lond. 1997, M 1977; MRCS Eng. LRCP Lond. 1971; FFPM RCP Lond. 1995, M 1989; Dip. Pharm. Med. RCP (UK) 1985; DA Eng. 1977; DObst RCOG 1973; FIBiol. 1995, M 1985. (St. Bart.) Europ. Head of Anti-Infect. & Respirat. Therap. Areas, Bayer plc; Hon. Sen. Fell. Nat. Heart & Lung Inst.; Hon. Clin. Asst. Roy. Brompton Hosp.; Co-Ed. Int. Jl. Pharmaceut. Med. Socs: Brit. Thorac. Soc. & Brit. Pharmacol. Soc.; Brit. Assn. for Lung Research (Ex-Chairm.). Prev: Assoc. Med. Dir. Glaxo UK; Dir.

Clin. Research Boehringer Ingelheim Ltd.; Clin. Scientist MRC Tuberc. & Chest Dis. Unit.

SNELL, Paul Heath, OBE (retired) Hope House, Saltergate Lane, Bamford, Hope Valley S33 0BE Tel: 01433 651533 Fax: 01433 651533 Email: paul@phsnell.swinternet.co.uk — BM BCh 1962 Oxf.; MA Oxf. 1962; FRCP Lond. 1982, M 1966; FFPHM RCP (UK) 1990, M 1985; DTM & H RCP Lond. 1971. Adviser to Health Projects in Frencophone W. Africa. Prev: Dir. Policy & Pub. Health Sheff. Health & Hon. Clin. Lect. Univ. Sheff.

SNELL, Peter (retired) The Lodge, Lower End, Layer-De-La-Haye, Colchester CO2 0LE Tel: 01206 734698 — MB BChir 1960 Camb.; MA, MB Camb. 1960, BChir 1959; DCH Eng. 1962; DObst RCOG 1962. Med. Off. Colchester United Football Club; Dep. Police Surg. Colchester Area. Prev: Ho. Surg. St. Mary's Hosp. Paddington.

SNELL, Robert Olufemi Lionel Hilltop, Bicknoller, Taunton TA4 4ES — MB ChB 1990 Birm.; ChB Birm. 1990.

SNELL, Theodore Peter (retired) Manali Cottage, Maesgwartha, Gilwern, Abergavenny NP7 0ET Tel: 01873 831033 — BM BCh 1956 Oxf. Prev: Sen. Lect. Christian Med. Coll. Ludhiana, India.

SNELL, Wendy Margaret 22 Abbey Gardens, London NW8 9AT; City Healthcare, 36 Moorgate, London EC2 Tel: 020 7638 4988 — MB BS 1983 Lond.; DRCOG 1990; DGM RCP Lond. 1988; DCH RCPS Glas. 1987.

SNELLING, John Philip Betws, 38 Edgeley Road, Whitchurch SY13 1EU Tel: 01948 2128 — MB BS 1985 Lond.; MRCGP 1990; DRCOG 1989. Prev: GP Basingstoke VTS.

***SNELLING, Tristram Henry** 9 West Hill, South Croydon CR2 0SB — MB BS 1994 Lond.

SNELSON, Edward John 66 Slinn Street, Crookes, Sheffield S10 1NX — MB ChB 1996 Sheff. SHO (Med.). Socs: BMA; Catholic Doctors Guild.

SNELSON, Michael Geoffrey Glenbourne, Morlax Drive, Derriford, Plymouth PL6 5AF Tel: 01752 763131 Fax: 01752 763133 — MB ChB 1971 Liverp.; MRCPsych 1976; DPM Eng. 1975. Cons. Psychiat. Plymouth Community Servs. NHS Trust.

SNEYD, Fiona Mary Catherine South Coldrenick, Menheniot, Liskeard PL14 3RQ Tel: 01503 240316 Fax: 01503 240885 — MB ChB 1980 Birm.; T(GP) 1991; DRCOG 1983. (Birm.) Prev: Clin. Med. Off. Wandsworth HA; Community Med. Off. (Child Health) Macclesfield HA.

SNEYD, John Robert Department of Anaesthesia, Derriford Hospital, Derriford, Plymouth PL6 8DH Tel: 01752 763790 Fax: 01752 763287 Email: robert.sneyd@phnt.swest.nhs.uk; South Coldrenick, Menheniot, Liskeard PL14 3RQ Tel: 01503 240316 Fax: 01503 240885 — MB BChir 1981 Camb.; MA Camb. 1979, BA 1978, MD 1989; FRCA 1985; T(Anaesth.) 1992. (Camb.) Reader in Anaesth., Univ. of Plymouth. Socs: Assn. Anaesth.; Physiol. Soc. Prev: Instruc. (Anaesth.) Univ. Michigan Med. Sch. Ann Arbor, USA; Sen. Regist. (Anaesth.) Univ. Hosp. S. Manch.; Med. Adv. ICI Pharmaceuts.

SNOBL, Jindrich James Paget Hospital NHS Trust, Lowestoft Road, Gorleston, Great Yarmouth NR31 6LA; Lavendelhof 75, 4907 AS Oosterhout, Netherlands, Netherlands — Artsexamen 1991 Rotterdam.

SNODGRASS, Christine Averil (retired) 15 Moor Lane, Darras Hall, Ponteland, Newcastle upon Tyne NE20 9AD — MB ChB Ed. 1958; MA (Hons.) Ed. 1997; MD (Commend.) Ed. 1968; FRCOG 1976, M 1963; DObst RCOG 1960. Prev: Cons. O & G Roy. Vict. Infirm. Newc.

SNODGRASS, Graeme John Anthony Inglis Department of Child Health, Royal London Trust, Whitechapel, London E1 1BB Tel: 020 7377 7428 Fax: 020 7377 7759 Email: g.j.a.snodgrass@mds.qmw.ac.uk; 42 Newark Street, London E1 2AA Tel: 020 7375 2417 — MB ChB Ed. 1958; FRCP Ed. 1976, M 1964; DCH Eng. 1960; FRCPCH 1997. (Ed.) Cons. Paediat. & Sen. Lect. Paediat. Lond. Hosp. Prev: Sen. Lect. Child Health Guy's Hosp. Med. Sch. Lond.; Sen. Regist. (Paediat.) Char. Cross Hosp. Lond.; Paediat. Regist. Qu. Eliz. Hosp. Childr. Lond.

SNODGRASS, Marjory Black (retired) 26 Garngaber Avenue, Lenzie, Glasgow G66 4LL Tel: 0141 776 1600 — MB ChB 1946 Glas.; FRCP Glas. 1980; DOMS Eng. 1949. Sen. Hosp. Med. Off. Stirling Roy. Infirm. Prev: Asst. Ophth. Surg. Stirling Roy. Infirm.

***SNOOK, Helen Mary** 42 Langley Way, Watford WD17 3EG — MB BS 1996 Lond.

SNOOK, Jonathon Anthony Poole Hospital NHS Trust, Longfleet Road, Poole BH15 2JB Tel: 01202 442357 — BM BCh 1982 Oxf.; DPhil. Oxf. 1990, MA 1987, BM BCh 1982; FRCP 1997; MRCP (UK) 1985. (Oxf.) Cons. Phys. Poole Gen. Hosp. Prev: Sen. Regist. (Med. Gastroenterol.) Roy. Hants. Co. Hosp. Winchester & Soton. Gen. Hosp.; Research Fell. (Gastroenterol.) Radcliffe Infirm. Oxf.; Regist./SHO (Med.) Soton. Gen. Hosp.

SNOOK, Nicola Jane Little Bretons, Swan St., Chappel, Colchester CO6 2EE; Hillside Cottage, 1 Sandy Lobby, Old Pool Bank, Pool in Wharfedale, Otley LS21 1EL — MB ChB 1988 Leeds; FRCA 1994. Regist. (Anaesth.) St. Jas. Univ. Hosp. Leeds.

SNOOK, Roger Norman Neston Medical Centre, 14-20 Liverpool Road, Neston, South Wirral CH64 3RA Tel: 0151 336 4121 Fax: 0151 353 0151; 16 Kirby Park, West Kirby, Wirral CH48 2HA Tel: 0151 625 5390 — MB ChB 1970 Liverp. Prev: SHO (O & G & Paediat.) Clatterbridge Hosp. Bebington.

***SNOOK, Simon** 9 Ellerslie Close, Charminster, Dorchester DT2 9QQ — MB ChB 1996 Birm.

SNOOKS, Mr Steven James King George Hospital, Barley Lane, Goodmayes, Ilford IG3 8YB Tel: 020 8983 8000 Fax: 020 8970 8001; 27 Lindsey Street, Epping CM16 6RB Tel: 01992 572185 — MB BS Lond. 1978; MD Lond. 1985; FRCS Eng. 1982. (Middlx.) Cons. Gen. Surg. King Geo. Hosp. Ilford. Socs: Assn. Coloproctol.; Assn. Surg.; BASO. Prev: Sen. Regist. (Gen. Surg.) St. Bart., N. Middlx. & Whipps Cross Hosps. Lond.; Sir Alan Pk.'s Research Fell. St. Mark's Hosp. Lond.

***SNOW, Adele Louise** 7 St Stephens Manor, St. Stephens Road, Cheltenham GL51 3AF — MB ChB 1995 Manch.

SNOW, Alice Frances Culloden Medical Practice, Keppoch Road, Culloden, Inverness IV2 7LL Tel: 01463 793777 Fax: 01463 792143; The Old Mill House, Culcairn, Evanton, Dingwall IV16 9XN — MB ChB 1990 Aberd.; BMed Biol. Aberd. 1987; MRCGP 1995. Prev: Trainee GP Raigmore Hosp. Inverness VTS.

SNOW, Andrew Richard Station Approach Health Centre, Station Approach, Bradford-on-Avon BA15 1DQ Tel: 01225 866611 — MB BS 1969 Lond.; MRCS Eng. LRCP Lond. 1969; DCH Eng. 1973; DObst RCOG 1971.

SNOW, Angele Mabel Peggy (retired) Apple Acre, Sampford Brett, Taunton TA4 4LB Tel: 01984 632545 — MB BS 1944 Lond.; MRCS Eng. LRCP Lond. 1942; FFPHM 1979, M 1973; DPH Eng. 1967; DCH Eng. 1947. Prev: SCM. (Child Health) Brent & Harrow AHA.

SNOW, David James Hampton Lodge, Hampton Avenue, St Marychurch, Torquay TQ1 3LA — MB ChB 1985 Leic.; FRCA 1992.

***SNOW, David Martyn** 30A Cadoxton Terrace, Neath SA10 8BR — MB ChB 1997 Ed.

***SNOW, Howard David John** 7 St Stephens Manor, St. Stephens Road, Cheltenham GL51 3AF — MB BS 1994 Lond.

SNOW, Janet Ann Wrington Vale Medical Group, Station Road, Wrington, Bristol BS40 5NG Tel: 01934 862532 Fax: 01934 863568 — MB BCh 1990 Witwatersrand.

SNOW, Mr John Thornton Greenlands, Greenhills, Barham, Canterbury CT4 6LE Tel: 01227 831756 — MB BS 1955 Lond.; FRCS Ed. 1967; DO Eng. 1961. (St. Bart.) Cons. BMI Chaucer Hosp. Canterbury & BUPA St. Saviours Hosp. Hythe. Socs: Fell. Roy. Coll. Ophth.; UK Introcular Implant Soc. Prev: Hon. Cons. Ophth. SE Kent, Canterbury & Thanet Health Dists.; Sen. Regist. Kent Co. Ophth. & Aural Hosp. Maidstone; Asst. Lect. (Ophth.) Manch. Univ.

SNOW, Lynn Ruth Holbrook 10 Ashley Rise, Ashley, Tiverton EX16 5PW — MB ChB 1991 Sheff.; MRCP 1997; DTM & M Liverp. 1997. Primary Child Health Off. Guinea W. Africa. Socs: Overseas Mem. RCPCH. Prev: SHO (Paediat. Neurol.) Sheff. Childr.'s Hosp.; Sen. SHO (Gen. Paediat.) Doncaster Roy. Infirm.

SNOW, Michael Harry Dept of Infection and Tropical Medicine, Newcastle General Hospital, Newcastle upon Tyne NE4 6BE Tel: 0191 273 8811 Fax: 0191 273 0900 Email: michael.snow@nuth.northy.nhs.uk — MB BS 1969 Newc.; FRCP Lond. 1985; MRCP (UK) 1973. Cons. Phys. (Gen. Med. & Infec. Dis.) Newc. Gen. Hosp. And Roy. Vict. Infirm., Newc.; Sen. Lect. (Med.) Univ. Newc. u. Tyne. Socs: Brit. Soc. Antimicrob. Chemother.; Brit. Soc. Study of Infec.; Brit. HIV Assn.

SNOW, Percy John Deryk, OBE (retired) 4 Fairlea Avenue, Didsbury, Manchester M20 6GN — MB ChB 1948 Manch.; MD (Commend.) Manch. 1955; FRCP Lond. 1970, M 1950; MRCS Eng. LRCP Lond. 1948. Prev: Cons. Phys. Bolton Roy. Infirm. & Bolton Gen. Hosp.

SNOW, Philip John Ruperra House, St. Mary St., Brecon LD3 7AA Tel: 01874 2121 — MB BS 1962 Lond.; MRCS Eng. LRCP Lond. 1962; MRCGP 1979; FFA RCS Eng. 1969; DObst RCOG 1964; DA Eng. 1965. Socs: BMA. Prev: Ho. Off. Roy. Hants. Co. Hosp. Winchester; Gen. Med. Off. Lesotho Govt.; Regist. (Anaesth.) S.mead Hosp. Bristol.

SNOW, Robert Geoffrey (retired) The Manor House, Town Ditch, Rossett, Wrexham LL12 0AN — MB ChB Birm. 1950; FFA RCS Eng. 1958. Prev: Cons. Anaesth. Chester & Centr. Wirral Hosp. Gps.

SNOW, Ronald Edward, CB, LVO, OBE, Surg. Rear-Admiral c/o Naval Secretary, Victory Building, HM Naval Base, Portsmouth PO1 3LS — MB BCh BAO 1960 Dub.; MA Dub. 1960; MFOM RCPI 1980; DA RCPSI 1965; LMCC 1963. Prev: Phys. to HM the Qu.; Surg. Rear-Admiral (Operat. Med. Servs.) & (Support Med. Servs.); Fleet Med. Off. Cdr.-in-Chief Fleet & Med. Adv. Cdr.-in-Chief Channel & E.. Atlantic.

SNOW, Stella Ray (Twyford) Abergwdi, Ffrwdgrech, Brecon LD3 8NA Tel: 01874 624045 Email: ray@abergwdi.force9.co.uk — MB BCh 1962 Wales; Dip. Palliat. Med. Wales 1993. (Cardiff) p/t Co-ordinator of Macmillan GP, facilitators in Powys. Prev: Assoc.Special. c/o the elderly Bronllys. Hosp.; Trainee GP Worcester; Clin.Asst. High Wycombe.

SNOWDEN, Ann Elizabeth Alice Kings Lane Medical Practice, 100 Kings Lane, Bebington, Wirral CH63 5LY; 52 Covertside, West Kirby, Wirral CH48 9UL — MB ChB 1973 Manch.; BSc (Hons.) (Med. Biochem.) Manch. 1973.

SNOWDEN, Christopher Paul Freeman Hospital, Freeman Road, High Heaton, Newcastle upon Tyne NE7 7DN Email: c.p.snowden@ncl.ac.uk; The Coach House, 26 Adderstone Crescent, Jesmond, Newcastle upon Tyne NE2 2HH — MB BS 1989 Newc.; B.Med.Sci. (Hons.) Newc. 1987; FRCA. (Newcastle upon Tyne) Cons. (Anaesth.) Freeman Hosp. Newc.; Sen. Lect. (Newc. upon Tyne).

SNOWDEN, Geoffrey 78 Tranby Lane, Anlaby, Hull HU10 7DU — MB ChB 1940 Leeds; DLO Eng. 1944. (Leeds) Assoc. Specialist ENT Dept. Roy. Infirm. Hull.

SNOWDEN, Howard Neil North Manchester General Hospital, Manchester M8 5RL Tel: 0161 720 2602; 8 Springdale Gardens, Didsbury, Manchester M20 2GX Email: neil@snowdenshome.freeserve.co.uk — MB 1984 Camb.; FRCP 2001; BChir 1983; MRCPath 1996; MRCP (UK) 1986. Cons. (Rheum.) N. Manch. Gen. Hosp.

SNOWDEN, John (retired) Barnes Close Surgery, Barnes Close, Sturminster Newton DT10 1BN Tel: 01258 474500 Fax: 01258 471547 — BM BCh 1972 Oxf.; MA.

***SNOWDEN, Karen Alison Vaines** 24 Stainsby Street, Thornaby, Stockton-on-Tees TS17 6HP — MB BS 1997 Newc.

***SNOWDEN, Katharine Louise** 33 Arcadia Av, Sale M33 3RT — MB ChB 1997 Dundee.

SNOWDEN, Michael Brian Samuel 10 Smugglers Way, Rhu, Helensburgh G84 8HX — MB ChB 1993 Aberd.

SNOWDEN, Peter Richard Department of Forensic Psychiatry, Edenfield Centre, Salford Mental Health Trust, Bury New Road, Manchester M25 3BL Tel: 0161 772 3681 Fax: 0161 772 3446 — MB ChB 1976 Liverp.; BSc (Hons.) (Biochem.) Liverp. 1973; FRCPsych 1995, M 1980. Cons. Forens. Psychiat. N. W.. HA & Home Office; Hon. Clin. Lect. (Forens Psychiat.) Univ. Manch.; Mem. Home Secretaries Advis. Bd. on Restricted Pat.s. Prev: Sen. Regist. (Forens. Psychiat.) Pk. La. Hosp. Liverp.; Hon. Lect. & Regist. (Psychiat.) Liverp. Univ.

SNOWDEN, Susan Ann 77 Sydenham Hill, London SE26 6TQ — MB ChB 1968 Liverp. (Liverp.) Clin. Asst. Renal Unit King's Coll. Hosp. Lond.

SNOWDON, Brian Armstrong Society of Analytical Psychology, 1 Daleham Gardens, London NW3 5BY Tel: 020 7435 7696 — MB ChB Manch. 1957; FRCPsych 1988, M 1972; DPM Lond. 1965. Socs: Profess. Mem. Soc. Analyt. Psychol. Prev: Dir. C.G. Jung Clinic Lond.; Cons. Psychiat. Middlx. Hosp. Lond. & Social Serv. Dept. City W.m.; Sen. Regist. Tavistock Clinic Lond.

SNOWDON, Colin Maxwell Harbury Surgery, Mill Street, Harbury, Leamington Spa CV33 9HR Tel: 01926 612232 Fax: 01926 612991 — MB ChB 1986 Birm.

SNOWDON

SNOWDON, Derek Vernon 173 Woodford Road, Woodford, Stockport SK7 1QE — MB ChB 1966 Manch. (Manch.) Socs: BMA. Prev: Clin. Asst. (Gastroenterol.) Stockport AHA; Clin. Asst. (Anaesth.) Stockport AHA; Asst. Lect. (Physiol.) Univ. Manch.

SNOWDON, Jennifer Claire 131 Binley Road, Coventry CV3 1HX — MB BS 1984 Lond.

SNOWDON, Richard Lewis 112 Greenloons Drive, Formby, Liverpool L37 2LR — MB ChB 1996 Liverp.; MRCP 1999. SHO (Cardiol.) L'pool. Prev: SHO Rotat. Roy. L'pool & BRd.green Univ. Hosps. NHS Trust.

SNOWISE, Neil Gabriel Glaxosmithkline, Stockley Park West, Uxbridge UB11 1BT; Narom, Sham Castle Lane, Bath BA2 6JL Tel: 01225 447 150 — BM BCh 1980 Oxf.; DRCOG 1985; Cert Family Planning 1984 (JCC); MA 1980 Oxf.; DA 1984 Eng.; BA 1977 Oxf; MRCGP 1985. (Oxford) Pharmaceutical Phys. Socs: BMA & Clin. Soc. Bath. Prev: SHO (Anaesth.) Roy. United Hosp. Bath; SHO (Med.) Roy. Cornw. Hosp. (Treliske) Truro; Primary Care Research Phys. Roy. Nat. Hosp., Rheumatic Dis.

SNYDER, Melvyn Lewisham Medical Centre, 158 Utting Avenue East, Liverpool L11 1DL Tel: 0151 256 9800 Fax: 0151 256 5765 — MB ChB 1964 Liverp.; MRCGP 1977. (Liverp.)

SO, Elizabeth (retired) 5 Stafford House, Maida Vale, London W2 1TE — MB BS 1993 Lond.; DRCOG 1998.

***SOAR, Beverley Anne** 11 Banks Av, Pontefract WF8 4DL — MB ChB 1997 Leeds.

SOAR, Jasmeet 6 Walcote Drive, Wilford Hill, Nottingham NG2 7GR — BChir 1990 Camb.

SOAR, Noreen Mary The Surgery, Low Moor Road, Kirkby in Ashfield, Nottingham NG17 7BG Tel: 01623 759447 Fax: 01623 750906; 14 Parkside, Nottingham NG8 2NN — MB BCh BAO 1979 NUI.

SOARES, Ann-Marie Rose Mount Chambers Surgery, 92 Coggeshall Road, Braintree CM7 9BY Tel: 01376 553415 Fax: 01376 552451 — MB BS 1991 Lond.

SOARES, Philip Orlando Bosco Longwood Gardens Surgery, 150 Longwood Gardens, Clayhall, Ilford IG5 0BE Tel: 020 8550 6362 — MB ChB 1987 Birm.

SOBAHI, Elamin Mohamed 13 Shelton Crescent, Bicton Heath, Shrewsbury SY3 5AB — MB BS 1982 Sudan; MRCP (UK) 1991.

SOBALA, George Michael John 2 Occupational Road, Lindley, Huddersfield HD3 3AZ — BM BCh 1983 Oxf.; MA (Camb.) 1984; MRCP (UK) 1986. Cons. Gen. Med. & Gastroenterol. Huddersfield NHS Trust. Socs: Brit. Soc. Gastroenterol. Prev: Sen. Regist. (Gen. Med. & Gastroenterol.) Yorksh. Region; Tutor (Med.) Univ. Leeds.

SOBEIH, Mr Salah El-Din Raghip Goole & District Hospital, Woodland Avenue, Goole DN14 6RX Tel: 01405 720720; 184 Boothferry Road, Goole DN14 6AH Tel: 01405 720128 — MB BCh 1974 Ain Shams; FRCS Ed. 1984. Clin. Asst. (Orthop.) Goole & Dist. Hosp. N. Humberside. Prev: Clin. Asst. (Urol., A & E) Goole & Dist. Hosp. N. Humberside.; Regist. (Trauma & Orthop.) Huddersfield Roy. Infirm.

***SOBHANI, Sarfaraz** 74 Duncan Road, Longsight, Manchester M13 0GU — MB ChB 1998 Manch.; MB ChB Manch 1998.

SOBHI, Nabil Hanna Tyr Meddyg, 67a Crymlyn Road, Skewen, Neath SA10 6EG; The Poplars Surgery, 28 Vivian Park Drive, Port Talbot SA12 6RT Tel: 01639 890730 Fax: 01639 882082 Email: poplars.surg@usa.net — MB BCh 1968 Cairo. GP Princip., The Poplars Surg. Port Talbot. Prev: GP Neath, W. Glam.

SOBHY, Yacout Mohammed 2 Western Avenue, London W3 7UD — LMSSA 1967 Lond.

SOBO, Abayomi Olusola 39 Beech Court, Ponteland, Newcastle upon Tyne NE20 9NE — MD 1970 Newc.; MB BS Durh. 1960; DMRT Ed. 1965; MFCM 1985. S.C.M. (Environm. Health) Gateshead HA; WHO Represen. Freetown Sierra Leone. Prev: S.C.M. (Capital Plann.) N.ern RHA Newc.-u-Tyne.

SOBOLEWSKI, Olek Andrew Hilly Fields Medical Centre, 172 Adelaide Avenue, London SE4 1JN Tel: 020 8314 5552 Fax: 020 8314 5557 — MB BS 1993 Lond.; BSc (Hons.) Sociol. Applied to Med. Lond. 1990. Trainee GP/SHO Chelsea & W.m. Hosp. VTS.

SOBOLEWSKI, Stanislaw 32 Linden Way, Boston PE21 9DS Tel: 01205 51655 — MRCS Eng. LRCP Lond. 1977; PhD Bradford 1987; MB BS Bialystok 1967; MRCPath 1979. (Med. Acad. Bialystok) Cons. Haemat. Trent RHA & Pilgrim's Hosp. Boston. Socs: Assn. Clin. Pathols. & Brit. Soc. Haemat. Prev: Sen. Regist. (Haemat.) Leeds & Bradford HAs; SHO (Rheum.) Roy. Bath Hosp. Harrogate; Regist. (Clin. Haemat.) Centr. Sheff. HA(T).

SOBONIEWSKA, Krystyna Maria Teresa The Portland Road Practice, 16 Portland Road, London W11 4LA Tel: 020 7727 7711 Fax: 020 7226 6755 — MB BCh BAO NUI 1965; DObst RCOG 1968. Socs: BMA. Prev: Ho. Phys. & Ho. Surg. Dreadnought Seamen's Hosp. Lond.; Ho. Surg. O & G St. Mary Abbot's Hosp. Lond.

SOBOWALE, Adetokunbo Oluyomi 7 Garswood Close, Maghull, Liverpool L31 9PF Tel: 0151 531 0196 — MB BS 1981 Ibadan; MRCOG 1993.

SOBTE, Usha 233 St Margaret's Road, Twickenham TW1 1ND — MB BS 1966 Agra.

SOBTI, Anil Kumar Post Office Occupational Health Services, 9th Floor, Commerial Union House., 24 Martineau Square, Birmingham B2 4UU Tel: 0121 233 7206; Mockley Manor Nursing Home, Forde Hall Lane, Ullenhall, Solihull B95 5PS Tel: 01564 741841 — MB BS 1972 Delhi.

SOBTI, Upender K The Surgery, 5 Brampton Road, Kingsbury, London NW9 9BY Tel: 020 8204 6919 Fax: 020 8206 0883 — MB BS 1975 Meerut; MB BS 1975 Meerut. (Meerut U.P., India)

SOCKALINGAM, Mahendra Clent Grange, Clent, Stourbridge DY9 9RL — MB ChB 1974 Bristol; MRCGP 1981; DRCOG 1976; DCH Eng. 1978.

SOCKALINGAM, Roger Rajendra Kenilworth Medical Centre, 1 Kenilworth Court, Greenfields, Cumbernauld, Glasgow G67 1BP Tel: 01236 727816 Fax: 01236 726306 — MB BS 1972 Lond. (The London Hospital Medical college)

SOCKALINGHAM, Inthuvathany North Herts NHS Trust, Lister Hospital, Correys Mill Lane, Stevenage SG1 4AB Tel: 01438 314333 — MB BS 1983 Sri Lanka; FFA RCSI 1992; FRCA 1992; DA (UK) 1988.

SOCKETT, Gareth John Peter Oral and Maxillofacial Department, Royal Surrey County Hospital, Egerton Road, Guildford GU2 7XX Tel: 01483 571122; Broomsquares, Thursley Road, Eutfad, Godalming GU8 6ED Tel: 01252 703917 — MB ChB 1982 Dundee; BDS Liverp. 1974; FDS RCS Ed. 1978. Cons. Oral & Maxillofacial Surg. Roy. Surrey Co. Hosp. Guildford & Frimley Pk. Hosp. Prev: Sen. Regist. Yorks. RHA.

SOCOLOVSKY, Merav Physiological Laboratory, Downing St., Cambridge CB2 3EG Tel: 01223 333899; 12 Hinton Avenue, Cambridge CB1 7AS — MB BS 1986 Lond.; MRCP (UK) 1989.

SOCRATES, Mr Antony North Devon District Hospital, Barnstaple EX31 4JB Tel: 01271 322577 Fax: 01271 311696; 42 West Yelland, Barnstaple EX31 3HF Tel: 01271 860819 Email: socrates@bigwig.net — MB BChir 1982 Camb.; MA Camb. 1983, BA 1979, MB BChir 1982; FRCS Eng. 1990; FCOphth. Lond. 1990, M 1989; DO RCS Eng. 1985. (Camb.) Staff Grade (Ophth.) N. Devon Dist. Hosp. Barnstaple, Socs: Fell. Roy. Coll. Of Ophth.; Fell. Roy. Coll. Of Surgs. Prev: Lect. (Ophth.) Univ. Hosp. Kuala Lumpar; Regist. (Ophth.) Roy. Vict. Eye Hosp. Bournemouth.; SHO (Neurol. & Neurosurg.) Midl. Centre for Neurosurg. & Neurol.

***SODEN, Frank Benjamin** Wyatts Close, Sibford Gower, Banbury OX15 5RT — MB ChB 1998 Liverp.; MB ChB Liverp 1998.

SODEN, Katie Ann 80 Newton Wood Road, Ashtead KT21 1NW — MB BS 1991 Lond.; MRCGP 1996. (St. Mary's, Paddington)

SODERA, Mr Vija Kumar White Lodge Surgical Clinic, 37 Gossamer Lane, Aldwick, Bognor Regis PO21 3BX Tel: 01243 266248 — MB ChB 1975 Sheff.; FRCS Ed. 1980. Cas. Surg. Bognor Regist. War Memor. Hosp. W. Sussex; Indep. Surg. White Lodge Surgic. Clinic. Prev: Regist. (Neurosurg., Gen. & Vasc. Surg. & Orthop. Surg.) Sheff.

SODHI, Hardeep Kaur (retired) 67 Sunnymede Drive, Barkingside, Ilford IG6 1LD Tel: 020 8550 1186 — MB BS 1958 Bombay. Prev: Intern P. Geo. Co. Hosp. Cheverly, MD.

SODHI, Mr Mahinder Singh The Clementine Churchill Hosp. (cons. rooms), Sudbury Hill, Harrow HA1 3RX Tel: 020 8872 3872; 119 Woodcock Hill, Kenton, Harrow HA3 0JW Tel: 020 8907 3356 — MB BS 1957 Calcutta; FRCS Eng. 1967. (Calcutta) Cons. Surg. Clementine Ch.ill Hosp. Harrow. Socs: Assoc. Mem. BAUS; Assn. Coloproctol. Prev: Sen. Regist. (Surg.) Luton & Dunstable Hosp.; Urol. Resid. New York Univ. Med. Centre, USA; Regist. (Surg.) St. Nicholas' Hosp. Lond.

SODHI, Rajveen Kaur Rajsheel, Onslow Road, Sunningdale, Ascot SL5 0HW — MB BS 1993 Lond.

SODHI, Satnam Mahinder 2 Windover, London Road, Harrow on the Hill, Harrow HA1 3JQ — MB BS 1992 Lond.

SODHI, Sukhdev Singh Bridge Street Health Centre, Bridge Street, Ebbw Vale NP23 6EY Tel: 01495 302268 Fax: 01495 305169 — MB BS Punjab (India) 1962; DCH Eng. 1972. Prev: Asst. Clin. Dermat. Nevill Hall Hosp. Abergavenny.; Ho. Off. (Med.) St. Woolos Hosp. Newport; SHO Med. Nevill Hall Hosp. Abergavenny.

*****SODHI, Sundeep Paul Singh** 5 Pantyfforest, Ebbw Vale NP23 5FR — MB BCh 1995 Wales.

SODIPO, Joseph Oladeinde c/o Royal Overseas House, Park Place, St James's, London SW1A 1LR — LRCPI & LM, LRSCI & LM 1957; LRCPI & LM, LRCSI & LM 1957; FFA RCS Eng. 1964.

SODIPO, Julius Adebiyi Junior Park Hospital, Moorside Road, Davyhulme, Manchester M41 5SL; 54 Arundel Avenue, Flixton, Urmston, Manchester M41 6NG — MB BCh BAO 1979 Dub.; MRCS Eng. LRCP Lond. 1979.

SOE AUNG, Dr 10 Chenotrie Gardens, Birkenhead CH43 9WU Tel: 0151 652 0097 — MB BS 1974 Mingaladon; MRCP (UK) 1994.

SOE THAN MYINT, Dr Chorley General Hospital, Preston Road, Chorley PR7 1PP Tel: 01257 261222; 16 Orchard Drive, Whittle-le-Woods, Chorley PR6 7JZ Tel: 01257 249968 — MB BS 1976 Rangoon; MB BS Med Inst. Rangoon 1976; DA (UK) 1995. Staff Grade (Anaesth.) Chorley Hosp.

SOEKARJO, Damayanti Dorothea Humares Ltd., 55-57 Tower St., Winchester SO23 8TA — Artsexamen 1994 Utrecht.

SOFAER, David 94A Northend House, Fitzjames Avenue, London W14 0RY Tel: 020 7603 9172 — MB BS 1944 Lond.; MRCP Lond. 1946; MRCS Eng. LRCP Lond. 1944. (Lond. Hosp.) Hotel Doctor Cunard Internat. Hotel Ltd. & other Hotels; Med. Dir. Spodefell Ltd.; Flight Personnel Med. Off. Singapore Airlines; Chairm. Med. Bd. Dept. Health & Social Security; Med. Adviser Brit. Vending Industries.

SOFAT, Mr Ajit 44 Greenacres, Leverstock Green, Hemel Hempstead HP2 4NA Tel: 01442 257579; 22 Waterslea Drive, Heaton, Bolton BL1 5FJ — MB ChB 1982 Manch.; FRCS Ed. 1988; FRCS (SN) 1996. Cons. (Neurosurg.) Hope Hosp. Salford. Prev: Sen. Regist. (Neurosurg.) King's Coll. Hosp.; Research Fell. Inst. Neurol. Lond.; Regist. (Neurosurg.) Roy. Preston Hosp.

SOFAT, Nidhi 10 Paines Lane, Pinner HA5 3DQ — MB BS 1996 Lond.; BSc (Immunol. with Basic Med. Scis.) 1993. (Univ. Coll. Lond. Med. Sch.) SHO (Gen. Med.) Char. Cross & Hammersmith Hosps.

SOFFE, Nicola Sarah Kerswell Cross, Chudleigh TQ13 0DW Tel: 0207 346 3629 — MB ChB 1980 Liverp.; MRCS Eng. LRCP Lond. 1980; DRCOG 1985; LFHOM 1997.

SOFI, Mr Mohamad Abdullah Flat 5, 80 Fitzjohns Avenue, London NW3 5LS — MD 1973 Patna; FRCP Ed. 1991; FRCP Lond. 1991; FRCS Ed. 1990; MRCP (UK) 1981; MRCPI 1980.

SOFOLUWE, George Oluwole (retired) 35 Danta Way, Baswich, Stafford ST17 0BA Tel: 01785 49487 — MB ChB 1957 St. And.; DPH 1961, DIH 1965. Prof. & Head Dept Community Health & Prof. Occupat. Health Univ. Benin, Nigeria; Dir. Gen. Inst. Occupat. Health Ibadan, Nigeria. Prev: Region. Med. Advis. World Health Organisations.

SOFOLUWE, Grahame Oluwole Billericay Health Centre, Stock Road, Billericay CM12 0BJ Tel: 01277 658071 Fax: 01277 631892 — MB BS 1984 Ibadan; AFOM 2001; MRCS Eng. LRCP Lond. 1992; MRCGP 1993; DRCOG 1994; DCH RCP Lond. 1993. Socs: Soc. of Occupat.al Med.

SOGLIANI, Franco The Middlesex Hospital, Mortimer St., London W1T 3AA Tel: 020 7636 8333; 18 Walsingham Gardens, Stoneleigh, Epsom KT19 0LU Tel: 020 8393 3791 Fax: 020 8393 3791 Email: franco@agics.demon.co.uk — State Exam 1987 Turin; FRCSI Dub 1998; Dip. Card Surg 1992. Specialist Regist. Middx Hosp. Lond. Socs: EACTS; Soc. of CT Surg. UK & Irel.; ASIT. Prev: Specialist Regist. (Cardiothoracic Surg.) St Geo.'s Hosp. Lond.; Sen. Regist. (Cardiothoracic Surg.) St. Mary's Hosp. Lond.; Regist. St. Mary's Hosp. Lond.

SOH, Joo Kim 20 Abbey Court, Abbey Road, St John's Wood, London NW8 0AU Tel: 020 7625 5303 — MB BS 1987 Singapore.

SOH, Vicky Ai Leen 25 Thorpe Way, Cambridge CB5 8UJ — MB BS 1994 Lond.

SOHAIB, Syed Azfer Aslam Radiology Dept, Roayl Marsden Hospital, Downs Road, Sutton SM2 5PT — MB BS 1990 Lond.; BSc Lond. 1987; MRCP (UK) 1993; FRCR 1996. (Guy's Hospital Medical School) Cons. Radiologist Radiol. Dept Roy. Marsden Hosp. Sutton Surrey.

SOHAIL, Rashid 100 Birkby Hall Road, Huddersfield HD2 2TN — MB ChB 1989 Aberd.

SOHAIL SAHIBZADA, Mr Ahmed Department of Orthopaedics, Dundee Royal Infirmary, Barrack Road, Dundee DD1 9ND — MB BS 1978 Peshawar; FRCS Ed. 1987; FRCSI 1987.

SOHAL, Aneel Singh 21 Roger Drive, Wakefield WF2 7NE Tel: 01924 250436 — MB BS 1976 Rajasthan; MSc Med. Microbiol. Surrey 1986; MRCPath 1985. Cons. Microbiol. Pinderfields Gen. Hosp. Wakefield. Prev: Sen. Regist. Dept. Clin. Bacteriol. & Virol. Guy's Hosp. Lond.

***SOHAL, Hardip** 17 Petworth Way, Elm Park, Hornchurch RM12 4LR — MB ChB 1996 Leeds.

SOHAL, Mamta 267 Rochford Gardens, Slough SL2 5XH — BM BS 1993 Nottm.

***SOHI, Dalbir Kalir** 1018 Great Western Road, Glasgow G12 0NP — MB ChB 1998 Glas.; MB ChB Glas 1998.

SOHI, Malvinder Singh The Surgery, 57 Gladstone Avenue, Manor Park, London E12 7NR Tel: 020 8471 4764 Fax: 020 8472 3378; Cedar Medical Centre, 4 Granville Road, Ilford IG1 4JY Tel: 020 8270 0040 Fax: 020 8270 0042 — MBBS; MB BS Punjab 1969; DOMS Punjab 1970. (Govt. Med. Coll. Patiala) Socs: Newham Med. Soc.

SOHN, Leslie Flat 1, 17 Prince Albert Road, London NW1 7ST — MB ChB 1944 Cape Town; FRCPsych. 1977, M 1972; DPM Eng. 1949. (Cape Town) Sen. Tutor & Hon. Cons. Psychother. Dept. Maudsley Hosp. Lond. Socs: Brit. Psycho-Anal. Soc. Prev: Cons. Psychother. Shenley Hosp. St. Albans; Regist. Maudsley Hosp.

SOILE, David Olayiwola 7 Haredon Close, London SE23 3TG — MB BS 1985 Ibadan, Nigeria.

SOILLEUX, Elizabeth Jane Department of Histopathology, (Box 235), Addenbrookes Hospital, Hills Rd, Cambridge CB2 2QQ Tel: 01223 217 163 Fax: 01223 216 980 Email: ejs17@cam.ac.uk; 22 Fromont Close, Fulbourn, Cambridge CB1 5HS Tel: 01223 473954 Email: ejs17@cam.ac.uk — BChir 1996 Camb.; PhD 2002 Cantab.; BA Cantab. 1994; MA Cantab. 1998. (Cambridge) Specialist Regist. (Histopath.) Camb.; Teachg. Fell. in Path. Ch.hill Coll. Camb. Univ. Socs: BMA - (Past Sec.BMA, E. Anglian Regional Jun. Doctors' Comm. 1997-1998); MDU. Prev: Research Regist. (Histopath.) Camb. + MRC Clin. Train. Fell., Univ of Camb.; SHO (Histopath.) Camb.; PRHO (Gen. Surg.) Milton Keynes.

***SOILLEUX, Sally Ann** Longhill House, Coddington, Ledbury HR8 1JH — BM 1998 Soton.; BM Soton 1998.

SOIN, Bob 198 Queens Road, London SW19 8LY — MB BChir 1992 Camb.

***SOIN, Gunninder Bir Singh** Flat 109, Waterloo Warehouse, Waterloo Rd, Liverpool L3 0BQ — MB ChB 1997 Liverp.

SOIN-STANLEY, Simon Anthony John Tower Medical Centre, 129 Cannon Street Road, London E1 2LX Tel: 020 7488 4240 Fax: 020 7702 2443 — MB BS 1982 Lond.; DCH RCP Lond. 1989.

SOINNE, Nicolle 24 Victoria Gardens, Kilmacolm PA13 4HL — MB ChB 1988 Glas.

***SOJITRA, Nilesh Mavji** 53 Hailes Gardens, Edinburgh EH13 0JH — MB ChB 1997 Ed.

SOJKA, Yves Jan Franciszek 24 Park Way, Ruislip HA4 8NY Tel: 018956 32858 — MB ChB 1950 Sheff. (Sheff.) Prev: Orthop. Ho. Surg. Roy. Hosp. Sheff.; Ho. Phys. Wharncliffe Hosp. Sheff.

SOKAL, Michael Peter Jacob Wieselberg 27 Oundle Drive, Wollaton Park, Nottingham NG8 1BN — MB ChB 1970 Sheff.; FRCP Lond. 1991; MRCP (UK) 1974; FRCR 1978. Cons. (Radiother. & Oncol.) City Hosp. Nottm. Prev: Sen. Regist. (Radiother. & Oncol.) Roy. S. Hants. Hosp. Soton.; Regist. (Radiother. & Oncol.) Roy. Marsden Hosp. Lond.

SOKHI, Mr Gurmit Singh (retired) BUPA Parkway Hospital, Damson Parkway, Solihull B91 2PP Tel: 0121 704 1451 — MB ChB 1962 Glas.; FRCS Ed. 1967. Prev: Sen. Regist. (Surg.) Roy. Infirm. Glas. & Profess. Dept. Surg. Univ.

SOKHI, Jasminder Singh O'Colmain and Partners, Fearnhead Cross Medical Centre, 25 Fearnhead Cross, Fearnhead, Warrington WA2 0HD Tel: 01925 847000 Fax: 01925 818650; 17 Edward

SOKOL

Gardens, Martinscroft, Warrington WA1 4QS Tel: 01925 485641 — MB ChB 1978 Liverp. Socs: BMA (Treas. Warrington Br.). Prev: SHO (Orthop.) Warrington HA.

SOKOL, Robert Josef (retired) 14 Harley Road, Ecclesall, Sheffield S11 9SD — MB ChB 1968 Shef.; PhD Sheff. 1984, DSc 1992, MD 1979,; FRCP Ed 1997; FRCPath 1986, M 1974.

SOLAN, Chantal Leigh 73 Kippington Road, Sevenoaks TN13 2LN — MB ChB 1992 Cape Town.

SOLAN, Katharine Jane 55 Marine Drive, West Wittering, Chichester PO20 8HQ — MB BS 1994 Lond. (St. Barts. Hosp. Med. Sch.) Roy. Hosps. Trust Anaesth. SHO.

SOLAN, Mr Matthew Charles Welcomes, 7 Monks Walk, Reigate RH2 0SS — MB BS Lond. 1992; FRCS (Eng). (St Thomas' Hospital) Specialist Regist. Opthopaedics S. Thames (W.).

SOLAN, Nerith Lindsay 29A Astonville Street, London SW18 5AN Tel: 020 8870 2619 — MB ChB 1990 Cape Town; MRCGP Lond. 1997; DFFP Lond. 1997; DRCOG Lond. 1996; DCH Lond. 1993. Socs: Med. Protec. Soc.

SOLANGI, Mr Bashir Ahmed Northern Area Armed Forces Hospital, PO Box 10018, Hafar Al Batin 31991, Saudi Arabia Tel: 00 966 3 7871777; 7 Torquay Gardens, Redbridge, Ilford IG4 5PU Tel: 0208 550 6774 Fax: 0208 550 6774 — MB BS 1970 Sind; FRCS Ed. 1984. (Liaquat Med. Coll.) Cons. Urol. N.. Area Armed Forces Hosp., Saudi Arbia. Prev: Regist. & SHO (Gen. Surg. & Urol.) OldCh. Hosp. Romford; SHO (Orthop.) Harold Wood Hosp.; Assoc. Prof. Surg. Dow Med. Coll. & Hosp. Karachi, Pakistan.

***SOLANKI, Dharmendra Amarshi** 160 Manor Dr N., Worcester Park KT4 7RU — MB BS 1997 Lond.

SOLANKI, Mr Guirish Arquissandas Department of Surgical Neurology, The National Hospital for Neurology & Neurosurgery, Queen Square, London WC1N 3BG Tel: 020 7837 3611 Fax: 020 7813 1138 Email: g.solanki@aix.150.ion.bpmf.ac.uk; 42 Finland Street, The Lakes, Rotherhithe, London SE16 7TP Tel: 020 7237 3048 Fax: 020 7237 3048 Email: 106055.361@compuserve.com — MB BS 1988 Bombay; FRCSI 1991. (Goa Med. Coll.) Spinal Research Fell. (Surgic. Neurol.) & Sen. Regist. (Neurosurg.) Nat. Hosp. for Neurol. & Neurosurg. Lond. Socs: Brit. Cervical Spine Research Soc.; Soc. Brit. Neurol. Surgs. Prev: Career Regist. Rotat. (Neurosurg.) Roy. Lond. Hosp. & OldCh. Hosp.; Sen. Regist. (Neurosurg.) Humana Hosp. St. Johns Wood, Lond.; Regist. (Neurosurg.) Roy. Free Hosp.

SOLANKI, Jitendra Uttam Email: j.solanki@btinternet.com — MB ChB 1993 Birm.; MRCGP 2000; DRCOG May 1997 (RCOG); DCH 1998 June; DFFP 1998. (Birm.) Med. Advisor.- Pharmacia, Milton Keynes.

SOLANKI, Pragna 4 Oakland Avenue, Leicester LE4 7SF — BM 1993 Soton.

SOLANKI, Tarunkumar Gordhandas Musgrove Park Hospital, Taunton TA1 5DA Tel: 01823 333444 Fax: 01823 344747 Email: tarun.solanki@tst.nhs.uk — MB BCh 1984 Wales; MSc Lond. 1994; BSc (Hons.) Wales 1981; FRCP. Cons. Phys. special responsibil. Elderly MusGr. Pk. Hosp. Taunton; Clincial Director Community & Primary Care Directorate; Taunton & Som. NHS Trust. Socs: Brit. Geriat. Soc.; BMA. Prev: Sen. Regist. (Gen. & Geriat. Med.) W. Midl. Regional Train. Scheme; Regist. (Gen. Med. & Nephrol.) St. Mary's Hosp. Portsmouth.

SOLARI, John Ruddock Alvechurch Medical Centre, 5-6 The Square, Alvechurch, Birmingham B48 7LB Tel: 0121 445 1084; 52 Grassmoor Road, King's Norton, Birmingham B38 8BU Tel: 0121 458 4480 — MB ChB 1958 Birm.; BSc Physiol. (1st cl. Hons.) Birm. 1958, MB ChB 1961; MRCGP 1969; DObst RCOG 1964. (Birm.) Hosp. Pract. Sheldon Geriat. Hosp. Rednal; Med. Dir. GP Deputising Serv.; Treas. Birm. Local Med. Comm.; Mem. St. John Ambul. Aeromed. Serv. Socs: BMA. Prev: Clin. Asst. (Geriat.) Sheldon Geriat. Hosp. Rednal; Ho. Surg. (O & G) Dudley Rd. Hosp. Birm.; Ho. Phys. & Ho. Surg. Qu. Eliz. Hosp. Birm.

SOLARI, Louise Ann 58 Fore Street, Kingsteignton, Newton Abbot TQ12 3AU — MB BS 1988 Lond.; MRCGP 1993. Prev: Trainee GP/SHO Paignton, Devon & Torbay VTS; SHO (c/o Elderly) N. Devon & Dist. Hosp. Barnstaple; SHO (A & E) Torbay Hosp. Torquay.

SOLARI, Timothy John Robinson, Ashton, Leung, Solari and Thompson, James Preston Health Centre, 61 Holland Road, Sutton Coldfield B72 1RL Tel: 0121 355 5150 — MB ChB 1986 Birm.

SOLDI, Donatella Francesca Dept of Child & Adolescent Health, St. Leonards Primary Care Centre, Nuttall St., London NW1 — MB ChB 1990 Manch.; BA (Econ.) Hons. Manch. 1978; SRN UKCC 1982; DCH RCP Lond. 1994. (Manchester) Clin. Med. Off. (Community Child Health) City & Hackney Community NHS Trust. Prev: SHO (Paediat. & Neonat.) Whittington Hosp. Lond.; SHO (Infec. Dis.) Monsall Hosp. Manch.; SHO (Med.) Monsall Hosp. Manch & N. Manch. Gen. Hosp.

SOLDINI, Marcus John Francesco Gordon House Surgery, 78 Mattock Lane, Ealing, London W13 9NZ Tel: 020 8997 9564 Fax: 020 8840 0533 — BM 1986 Soton.; MRCGP 1996; DGM RCP Lond. 1987.

SOLE, Mr Graham Martin Southbourne, Dinmore, Hereford HR1 3JR Tel: 01432 355444 — MB BS 1976 Lond.; BSc Lond. 1973, MS 1986; FRCS Eng. 1980. (Univ. Coll. Hosp.) Cons. Urol. Hereford Co. Hosp. Prev: Sen. Regist. Rotat. (Urol.) Leeds & Bradford; Regist. (Urol.) Qu. Eliz. Hosp. Birm.; Regist. (Surg. & Urol.) Dudley Rd. Hosp. Birm.

SOLE, Peter Wallis (retired) 17 Craigweil Lane, Aldwick, Bognor Regis PO21 4AN Tel: 01243 821809 — MB BChir 1950 Camb.; MA Camb. 1950.

SOLE, Suzanne Linda 37 Hamilton Crescent, London N13 5LN — MB BS 1985 Lond.; MRCPsych 1990.

SOLEBO, Junaid Oluseyi Kings George Hospital, Barley Lane, Ilford IG3 8 Tel: 020 8983 8000; 318 White Hart Lane, London N17 8LA Tel: 020 8808 3115 — MB BS 1977 Lagos; DCH RCPS Glas. 1984. (College of medicine - University of Hagos - Nigeria) Staff Grade (Paediat.) King Geo. Hosp. Ilford Essex. Prev: Regist. (Paediat.) Lewisham Hosp. Lond.; SHO (Paediat.) Watford Gen. Hosp.; SHO (Paediat.) Roy. Hosp. Chesterfield, SHO (Paed) Kettering Hosp.

SOLEIMANI, Mr Behzad Cardiothoracic Unit, The A Block, Hammersmith Hospital, Ducane Road, London W12 0HS Tel: 020 8383 3944 Fax: 020 8383 2725 Email: bsoleimani@excite.com — MB BChir 1994 Camb.; MA 1995, BA (Hons.) Camb. 1991; FRCS Eng. 1997. (Camb.) Specialist Regist. (Cardiothor. Surg.) Hammersmith Hosp. Lond. Socs: BMA. Prev: SHO (Gen. Surg.) Ealing Hosp. Lond.; SHO (Orthop.) Ealing Hosp. Lond.; SHO (Cardiothorac. Surg.) Hammersmith Hosp. Lond.

SOLER Y LOPEZ, Maria del Mar 7 Princes Terrace, Glasgow G12 9JP — LMS 1980 U Complutense Madrid; MSc Glas. 1993; MPH Glas. 1989. Research Fell. (Pub. Health) Univ. Glas. Prev: Research Co-ordinator Pub. Health Gr. Glas. HB; Regist. (Pub. Health Med.) Gtr. Glas. HB.; Phys. (Pub. Health) Teach. & Research Unit INSALUD, Spain.

SOLESBURY, Kathryn Anne Spring Gardens Health Centre, Providence Street, Worcester WR1 2BS Tel: 01905 681781 Fax: 01905 681766; Brock Hall, Suckley WR2 6QR Tel: 01886 884192 Email: kathy@bellamybfsnet.co.uk — MB ChB 1983 Birm.; MFFP 1995; MRCGP (Distinc.) 1987; DRCOG 1987; DCH RCP Lond. 1986; MFFP. Gen. Practitioner Worcester. Prev: Trainee GP Worcester VTS.

SOLICH, Ferdynand (retired) 2 Spicer's Close, Claverley, Wolverhampton WV5 7BY Tel: 01746 710611 — MB ChB 1941 Polish Sch. of Med.; MRCGP 1953.

SOLIMAN, El Sayed Queen's Park Hospital, Blackburn BB2 3HH — MB ChB 1965 Alexandria; MRCP (UK) 1978; LRCP LRCS Ed. LRCPS Glas. 1980. (Alexandria) Cons. Phys. (Geriat. Med.) N. W.. RHA. Socs: BMA; Brit. Geriat. Soc. Prev: Rotat. Sen. Regist. (Geriat. Med.) & Hon. Clin. Tutor Sheff. Med.; Sch.; Regist. (Geriat. Med.) Gwent AHA; SHO (Psychiat.) St. Nicholas Hosp. Gt. Yarmouth.

SOLIMAN, Mohamed Ossama Amin Mohamed Hanley Health Centre, Upper Huntbach Street, Hanley, Stoke-on-Trent ST1 2BN Tel: 01782 202422 — MB BCh 1964 Cairo.

SOLIMAN, Soliman Mikhail Mohsen (cons. rooms), 29 Devonshire Place, London W1 Tel: 020 7935 9973 Fax: 020 8653 9628; (Surgery), 86 Woodland Road, London SE19 1PA Tel: 020 8670 3689 Fax: 020 8653 9628 — MB BCh 1956 Cairo; LMSSA Lond. 1968; Cert. Family Plann. JCC 1976. Socs: Fell. Roy. Soc. Med. Prev: Hosp. Pract. Beckenham Hosp.; Community Health Pract. (Child Health) Bromley Schs.

SOLIMAN, Yehia Michael 29 Devonshire Place, London W1N 1PE Tel: 020 7935 9973 — LMSSA 1968 Lond.; MB BCh Cairo 1957, Dipl. Med. 1963. (Cairo) Socs: Fell. Roy. Soc. Trop. Med. & Hyg. &

Roy. Soc. Med. Prev: Regist. Nat. Heart Hosp., Harefield Hosp. & Watford Gen. Hosp.

SOLIS REYES, Carlos Flat 1, Glebedale Court, Clebedale Road, Stoke-on-Trent ST4 3LT — LMS 1987 La Laguna.

SOLJAK, Michael Anthony Ealing, Hammersmith & Hounslow Health Authority, 1 Armstrong Way, Southall UB2 4SA — MB ChB 1976 Auckland; 1988 FAFPHM; MFPHM RCP (UK) 1993; FRACP 1984. Dir. of Strategy & Health Gain Ealing, Hammersmith & Hounslow HA. Socs: FAFPHM 1988.

SOLLEY, Mr Rupert Tarn, Oxhey Drive, Northwood HA6 3ET Tel: 0192 74 28373; 144 Harley Street, London W1 — MRCS Eng. LRCP Lond. 1936; MB Camb. 1937, BChir 1936; FRCS Eng. 1948. (Camb. & Lond. Hosp.) (Nat. Sci. Trip. Pts. I & II); Cons. Surg. Acton Hosp.; Clin. Asst. St. Peter's Hosp. Socs: Fell. Roy. Soc. Med.; Assoc. Mem. BAUS. Prev: Sen. Regist. (Surg.) St. Peter's & St. Paul's Hosp. Lond. & Nat. Hosp. Lond.; Temp. Supernum. Surg. 1st Asst. & Regist. Lond. Hosp.

SOLLIS, Maria Emma 1 Maes Glas, Ynysawdre, Tondu, Bridgend CF32 9JZ — MB BS 1992 Lond.

SOLMAN, Nicola Seymour House Surgery, 154 Sheen Road, Richmond TW9 1UU Tel: 020 8940 2802 Fax: 020 8332 7877; 37 Larkfield Road, Richmond TW9 2PG — MB BS 1986 Lond.; DRCOG 1990.

SOLOFF, Neville 16 Chartwell Avenue, Northampton NN3 6NT Tel: 01604 644378 — MB ChB 1959 Leeds; AFOM RCP Lond. 1982; DPH Leeds 1970. (Leeds) Sen. Med. Off. N.ants. HA. Socs: Fac. Community Health; Soc. Occupat. Med.; Soc. Pub. Health. Prev: Med. Off. Repat. Dept., S. Austral.; Squadron Ldr. RAF Med. Br.

SOLOMKA, Bohdan Theodore 13 Stalham Road, Hoveton, Norwich NR12 8DG — BM BS 1988 Nottm.

***SOLOMON, Andrew Martin** 12 Chestnut Av, Edgware HA8 7RA — BM BCh 1997 Oxf.

SOLOMON, Anthony Leopold Salop Road Medical Centre, Salop Road, Welshpool SY21 7ER Email: wmc@doctors.org.uk; Elmhurst, Severn Road, Welshpool SY21 7AR Tel: 01938 552744 Email: anthony.solomon@lineone.net — MB ChB 1969 Birm.; DObst RCOG 1971. Prev: Med. Off. Brit. Solomon Isles Protectorate; Ho. Surg. Childr. Hosp. Birm.; Ho. Phys. Med. Profess. Unit Qu. Eliz. Hosp. Birm.

***SOLOMON, Belinda** 6 Aintree Drive, Rochdale OL11 5SH — MB BS 1998 Lond.; MB BS Lond 1998.

SOLOMON, Cedric Matthew Queens Walk Surgery, 69 Queens Walk, Ruislip HA4 0NT Tel: 020 8842 2991 Fax: 020 8842 2245; 54 Oakleigh Park N., London N20 9AS — MB BS 1981 Lond.; MRCGP 1985; DCH RCP Lond. 1985; DGM RCP Lond. 1985.

SOLOMON, Christine Lorraine Medical Research Council,Environmental Epidemiology Unit, University of Southampton, Southampton General Hospital, Southampton SO16 6YD Tel: 02380 725537 Fax: 02380 725509 Email: cls@mrc.saton.ac.uk; Beulah, 71 Station Road, Netley Abbey, Southampton SO31 5AE Tel: 02380 561217 — BM BCh 1985 Oxf.; MA Camb. 1986; MRCGP 1989; DGM RCP Lond. 1988; Cert. Family Plann. JCC 1988; DRCOG 1988; DCH RCP Lond. 1987; MFPHM Lond. 1998. (Camb. & Oxf.) Consultant (Pub. Health Med.) MRC S.ampton. Prev: Regist. (Pub. Health Med.) SE Thames RHA and S&W RHA; Clin. Fell. (Continuing c/o Elderly) Riverside HA; Trainee GP Davenport Hse. Harpenden VTS.

SOLOMON, Frank Stuart Blossoms Inn Medical Centre, 21 Garlick Hill, London EC4V 2AU Tel: 020 7606 6159 Fax: 020 7489 1134; 8 Millfield Lane, Highgate, London N6 6JD Tel: 020 8340 2376 Email: 101707.2436@compuserve.com — MB ChB 1971 Cape Town; MB ChB (Hons.) Cape Town 1971; MRCP (UK) 1977. Neurol. N.wick Pk. Hosp. & City of Lond. Migraine Clinic; Chief Med. Off. ERC Francona Re, Barclays Life, Legal & Gen., Roy. Bank Scot., Chase Bank & Bankers Trust. Socs: Brit. Assoc. for Study of Headache; Assur. Med. Soc. Prev: Sen. Regist. (Neurol.) Groote Schur Hosp. S. Afr.; Clin. Fell. Nat. Hosp. Qu. Sq.

SOLOMON, George The Black Country Family Practice, Health Centre, Queens Road, Tipton DY4 8PH Tel: 0121 557 6397; 25 Wenlock Close, Sedgley, Dudley DY3 3NJ — MB ChB 1978 Glas.; DRCOG 1984. Prev: SHO/Trainee GP Som. VTS; SHO (Surg.) Taunton & Som. Hosps. Taunton; SHO (Surg. Specialties) W.. Infirm. Glas.

SOLOMON, Jacob Israel Queens Walk Surgery, 69 Queens Walk, Ruislip HA4 0NT Tel: 020 8842 2991 Fax: 020 8842 2245; 26 The

Squirrels, Wakenham Hill, Pinner HA5 3BD — MB BS 1980 Lond.; 1999 D Occ. Med. RCP Lond.; BSc (Immunol.) Lond. 1977; MRCGP 1984; Cert. Family Plann. JCC 1985; DCH RCP Lond. 1983. (Univ. Coll. Hosp.) Chairm. NW Thames Region GP Trainee Represen. Comm.; Med. Edr. Pulse Young Practitioner; Vice-Chairm. Hillingdon MAAG; Edit. Bd. Mem. Prescriber Magazine & Brit. Jl. Med. Economics; Bd. Mem. N. Hillingdon PCG; Med. Adviser Barnet Enfield & Haringay HA. Prev: Trainee GP N.wick Pk. Hosp. Harrow; Ho. Surg. (Thoracic, Gen. & Orthop. Surg.) Univ. Coll. Hosp. Lond.; Ho. Phys. (Cardiol.) Hillingdon Hosp. Uxbridge.

SOLOMON, Laurence Richard Royal Preston Hospital, PO Box 66, Sharoe Green Lane, Preston PR2 4HT Tel: 01772 716565; 2 Oakwood Drive, Fulwood, Preston PR2 3LX — MB BChir 1973 Camb.; MA Camb. 1973, MD 1988; FRCP Lond. 1994; MRCP (UK) 1974. Cons. Gen. Phys. (Renal Med.) Preston HA. Socs: Renal Assn.; Internat. Soc. Nephrol. Prev: Lect. (Geriat. Med.) Univ. Liverp.; Tutor (Renal Med.) Manch. Roy. Infirm.; Lect. (Med.) Univ. Manch. & Withington Hosp. Manch.

SOLOMON, Lemke Solent Department of Urology, St Mary's Hospital, Milton Road, Portsmouth PO3 6AD Tel: 023 9228 6000 — MB BCh BAO 1989 NUI; LRCPSI 1989.

SOLOMON, Leslie Ashley 101 Sevington Road, London NW4 3RU — MB BS 1993 Lond.

SOLOMON, Louis (retired) Pleasant, 32 Barcombe Heights, Paignton TQ3 1PT Tel: 01803 550156 — BA (Hons.) Dub. 1938, MA 1941, MB BCh BAO 1940; MFCM 1974; DCH Eng. 1949; DPH Lond. 1947; LM Rotunda 1946. Founder Med. Offs. Audiol. Gp. Prev: Dep. Controller Community Servs. Torbay Co. Boro.

SOLOMON, Professor Louis Department of Orthopaedic Surgery, Bristol Royal Infirmary, Bristol BS2 8HW Tel: 0117 973 3953 Fax: 0117 973 3953 Email: louis.solomn@virgin.net; 7 Cotham Road, Cotham, Bristol BS6 6DG Tel: 0117 973 3953 Fax: 0117 973 3953 — MB ChB 1951 Cape Town; MD Cape Town 1963; FRCS Eng. 1959; FRCS Ed. 1958. Emerit. Prof. Orthop. Surg. Univ. Bristol; Hon. Cons. Bristol Roy. Infirm. Socs: Fell. BOA; Internat. Hip Soc. Prev: Prof. Orthop. Surg. Univ. Witwatersrand, Johannesburg.

SOLOMON, Patricia 6 Aintree Drive, Bamford, Rochdale OL11 5SH — MB ChB 1974 Ghana; FRCR 1984. Cons. (Radiol.) Roy. Oldham Hosp. Socs: BMA; Brit. Inst. Radiol.; Roy. Coll. Radiol. Prev: Cons. (Radiol.) Barnsley Dist. Hosp.

***SOLOMON, Rebecca** PO Box 3858, London NW4 4JY — MB BS 1995 Lond.

SOLOMON, Ruth Anne Willow House, Littlemore Hospital#Littlemore, Oxford OX4 4XN Tel: 01865 223148146 — MB ChB 1981 Dundee; MRCPsych 1985. Cons. Psychiatrist. Prev: Regist. (Psychiat.) (Rotat.) Oxon. HA.

SOLOMON, Samuel Appiah Department of Adult Medicine, Royal Oldham Hospital, Rochdale Road, Oldham OL1 2JH Tel: 0161 627 8479 Fax: 0161 627 8694 Email: samuel.solomon@oldham-tr.nwest.nhs.uk; 6 Aintree Drive, Bamford, Rochdale OL11 5SH — MB ChB 1974 Ghana; MRCP 1981 (UK); FRCP 1999 (Lond); MRCP (UK) 1981; FRCP (Lond) 1999. (Univ. Ghana Med. Sch.) Cons. Phys. Roy. Oldham Hosp. Socs: BMA; Brit. Geriat. Soc. Prev: Sen. Regist. Rotat. (Med. & Geriat.) Manch.; Research Fell. Roy. Hallamsh. Hosp. Sheff.; Regist. Rotat. (Med.) Liverp.

SOLOMON, Stephen Maxwell Ernest 79 Grays Inn Road, London WC1X 8TP Tel: 020 7405 9360 Fax: 020 7831 1964 — MB BS 1979 Lond.; Cert. Family Plann. JCC 1984; DRCOG 1983. (University College Hospital London) GP Partner; Occupat. Phys. Brit. Gas plc; Forens. Med. Examr.; Occupat. Phys. Transco Plc. Socs: (Counc.) Assn. Police Surgs.; Roy. Soc. Med. (Clin. Forens. Med. Sect.); Brit. Acad. Forens. Sci.

SOLOMON, Sylvia Nunes 4 Briardene Crescent, Kenton Park, Newcastle upon Tyne NE3 4RY — MB ChB 1945 Manch.; BA (Hons.) Open Univ. 1991; BA Open Univ. 1988; MRCP Lond. 1949; DCH Eng. 1950; MRCGP 1968. (Manch.) Clin. Asst. Newc. BTS. Prev: M. O. Tshilidzini Hosp. Vendaland; Princip. GP Paediat. Regist. Leeds.

SOLOMON, Terence A The Farmhouse, 1 Gatehill Road, Northwood HA6 3QB Tel: 01923 825067 — MB BS 1945 Calcutta; DObst RCOG 1948. Socs: Fell. Roy. Soc. Med. (Mem. Obst. Sect.); Fell. Amer. Coll. Sexol.; Life Mem. New York Acad. Sc. Prev: Ho. Surg. (Gyn.) Derbysh. Roy. Infirm.; Resid. Obst. Off. Bearsted Memor. Hosp.; Capt. RAMC 1945-48.

SOLOMON

SOLOMON, Thomas Wellcome Trust Clinical Research Unit, Centre for Tropical Diseases, CHO Quan Hospital, 190 Ben Hamtu, Quan 5, Ho Chi Minh City, Vietnam Tel: 00 848 353954 Fax: 00 848 353904; Centre for Tropical Medicine & Infectious Disease, Nuffield Department of Clinical Medicine, John Radcliffe Hospital, Oxford OX3 9DU Tel: 01865 220970 Fax: 01865 220984 — BA (Hons.) Phys. Scis. Oxf. 1987, BM BCh 1990; MRCP (UK) 1993; DCH RCP Lond. 1994. Clin. Research Fell. & Hon. Regist. Wellcome Trust, Vietnam. Socs: Osler Club Lond.; Hist. Med. Soc. Prev: Regist. (Med.) City Hosp. Nottm.; SHO (Paediat.) Derbysh. Childr. Hosp.; SHO (Med.) Qu. Med. Centre Nottm.

SOLOMON, Winston Christadoss Asir St Clement's Surgery, 38 Bathurst Road, Ilford IG1 4LA Tel: 020 8554 1371 Fax: 020 8491 3345 — MB BS 1975 Madras; FRCS Ed. 1985; FRCS Glas. 1985; DRCOG 1991; DCH RCP Lond. 1990.

SOLOMONS, Bethel Eric Robert 7 Wimpole Street, London W1M 7AB Tel: 020 7584 1580 — MB BCh BAO 1940 Dub.; MA Dub. 1955, MD 1944; FRCPI 1951, M 1947. (Dub. & Middlx.) Hon. Cons. Dermat. Chelmsford & Essex Gen. Hosp. Socs: Fell. (Mem. Dermat. Sect.) Roy. Soc. Med.; Brit. Assn. Dermat.

SOLOMONS, Carole Ann Tel: 020 8441 9440 Fax: 020 8440 5176 Email: carole.solomons@gp-e83017.nhs.uk — MB BS 1981 Lond.; BSc (Hons.) Lond. 1976; MRCGP 1985; Dip. Psychosexual Med. 1994; Cert. Family Plann. JCC 1985; DRCOG 1984. (Univ. Coll. Hosp.) Tutor (Gen. Pract.) Roy. Free Hosp. Med. Sch. Socs: Inst. Psychosexual Med.; RCGP. Prev: Trainee GP Chesham; SHO (Paediat.) Amersham Gen. Hosp.; SHO (Obst. & Psychiat.) Wycombe Gen. Hosp.

***SOLOMONS, Gary Elliott** White Thorns, South Hill Avenue, Harrow on the Hill, Harrow HA1 3NZ — MB BS 1996 Lond.

SOLOMONS, Neil 39 Woodland Gardens, London N10 3UE — MB BS 1991 Lond.

SOLOMONS, Mr Neil Barry Mount Alvernia Hospital, Harvey Road, Guildford GU1 3LX Tel: 01483 451473 Fax: 01483 454286 Email: lasersol@msn.com; Beech house, The Street, Shalfford, Guildford GU4 8BU Tel: 01483 570513 Fax: 01483 566017 Email: neilsolomons@hotmail.com — MB ChB 1979 Cape Town; FRCS Eng. 1984; FRCS Ed. 1987. Cons. Otolaryngol. Head & Neck Surg. St. Peter's Hosp. Chertsey & Roy. Surrey Co. Hosp. Guildford. Prev: Sen. Regist. (Otolaryngol.) Roy. Free Hosp. Lond. & Roy. Surrey Co. Hosp. Guildford; Regist. (Otolaryngol.) Glos. Roy. Hosp.; Regist. (Otolaryngol.) Groote Schuur Hosp., Cape Town.

SOLOMONS, Richard Edgar Bethel Ling House Surgeries, 130 Skipton Road, Keighley BD21 3AN Tel: 01535 605747 Fax: 01535 602901; Fell Edge Farm, Straight Lane, Addingham, Ilkley LS29 9JY Tel: 01943 830841 Fax: 01943 830841 Email: solomons@mcmail.com — MB BS 1977 Lond.; MSc (Community Health in Developing Countries) Lond. 1982; BSc Lond. 1974; MRCGP 1984; DRCOG 1983. (Middlesex)

SOLOMONS, Stanley (retired) 18 Harvist Road, London NW6 6SE Tel: 020 8969 7711 — BM BCh 1953 Oxf.; MA Oxf. 1953; MRCGP 1971. Prev: Med. Off. Coll. of NW Lond.

SOLOMONSZ, Mr Francis Allistair Queens Medical Centre NHS Trust, University Hospital, Nottingham NG7 2UH Tel: 0115 924 9924; Sheriwill, 131A Melton Road, West Bridgford, Nottingham NG2 6FG Tel: 0115 945 2668 — MB BS 1975 Sri Lanka; MRCOG 1983. Socs: Brit. Med Assoc.; Brit. Fert. Soc.; Brit. Soc. For Colposcopy & Cervical Path.

***SOLTANI, Hassan** 80 Chime Bank, Smedley Road, Crumpsall, Manchester M8 0QL — MB ChB 1997 Sheff.

SOLTANPOUR, Mr Abbas (retired) 58 Rosecroft Gardens, Twickenham TW2 7PZ Tel: 020 8 898 2870 — MD 1959 Teheran, Iran; FRCS Ed. 1972. Prev: Asst. Prof. Orthop. Tehran Univ.

SOLTAU, Mr David Henry Kenneth (retired) Cotswold House, Winchcombe, Cheltenham GL54 5LX Tel: 01242 602559 — MB BChir 1944 Camb.; MA Camb. 1945; FRCS Eng. 1951; MRCS Eng. LRCP Lond. 1948; FRCOG 1968, M 1955. Prev: Cons. O & G Cheltenham Health Dist.

SOMAIYA, Rupin Suresh Fiveways Stores, Sturt Road, Charlbury, Chipping Norton OX7 3SX — MB BCh 1993 Wales.

SOMALINGAM, Ramalingam 26 Orleans Road, Upper Norwood, London SE19 3TA — MB BS 1963 Ceylon.

SOMAN, Ashish 1354 London Road, Leigh-on-Sea SS9 2UH — MB BS 1991 Lond.

SOMAN, Vijay Bhaskarrao Church Lane Surgery, 77 Church Lane, Harpurhey, Manchester M9 1BA Tel: 0161 205 2714 Fax: 0161 205 2716 — MB BS 1966 Poona; DOMS CPS Bombay 1968. (B.J. Med. Coll.) GP Manch. Prev: SHO (Ophth.) Roy. Eye Hosp. Manch.; SHO (Ophth.) Singleton Hosp. Swansea & Newc. Gen. Hosp.

SOMANATHAN, Lakshman Hill Croft, Green Lane, Chessington KT9 2DS; 43 Alwyne Road, Wimbledon, London SW19 7AE Tel: 020 8879 3900 Fax: 020 8879 3900 — MB BS 1994 Lond.; FRCS Eng. 1996. (Charing Cross & Westm.) SHO (Surg.) Char. Cross Hosp. Lond. Prev: SHO (Surg.) W. Middlx.

SOMANI, Mr Nandkishor Radhakishan West Dorset Hospital, Damers Road, Dorchester DT1 2JY Tel: 01305 251150 — MB BS 1965 Marathwada; MS (ENT) Bombay 1969; FCPS (ENT) Bombay 1969. Assoc. Specialist ENT, W. Dorset Hosp. Dorchester.

SOMANI, Neeta 32 Maiden Castle Road, Dorchester DT1 2ES; 32 Maiden Castle Road, Dorchester DT1 2ES — MB BS Lond. 1994. (St George's Hospital Medical School) GP Non Princip. Prev: SHO Paediat. Penbury Hosp. Tunbridge Wells Kent; SHO c/o the Elderly Penbury Hosp. Tunbridge Wells Kent; SHO O & G Penbury Hosp. Tunbridge Wells Kent.

***SOMANI, Riyaz** 44 Ellesmere Road, Leicester LE3 1BF — MB ChB 1998 Leeds.

SOMANI, Rizwan 2 Lyndhurst Avenue, Twickenham TW2 6BY — MB ChB 1988 Leeds. Trainee GP Hastings HA VTS.

SOMARATNE, Mr Dammearachchi Anuja 3 Kynance Gardens, Stanmore HA7 2QJ Fax: 020 8357 6630 Email: ratne@dircon.co.uk — MB BS 1976 Sri Lanka; FRCS Ed. 1984. (University of Colombo Colombo Medical College) Cons. Surg. New Nawaloka Hosp. Colombo, Sri Lanka & Asiri Hosps. Colombo, Sri Lanka. Socs: Coll. Surg. Sri Lanka; Roy. Coll. Surg. of Ed.

***SOMASEGARAM, Priya Dharshini** 69 Wansunt Road, Bexley DA5 2DJ — MB BS 1998 Lond.; MB BS Lond 1998.

SOMASUNDARA-RAJAH, Jegatheswary Moseley Medical Centre, 21 Salisbury Road, Moseley, Birmingham B13 8JS Tel: 0121 449 0122 Fax: 0121 449 6262 — MB BS 1967 Ceylon.

SOMASUNDARA-RAJAH, Kandiah Moseley Medical Centre, 21 Salisbury Road, Moseley, Birmingham B13 8JS Tel: 0121 449 0122 Fax: 0121 449 6262 — FRCS (Edin.) 1970; FRCS (Glas.) 1970; MB BS 1966 Calcutta; MB BS 1966 Calcutta.

***SOMASUNDARAM, Anna Anbu** 48 Claverdale Road, London SW2 2DP — MB ChB 1997 Dundee.

SOMASUNDARAM, Aravinthan c/o Harryville, 140 Scrabo Road, Newtownards BT23 4NN — MB BCh BAO 1992 Belf.

SOMASUNDARAM, Veerappapillai Cleland House, Rm. 301, Page St., London SW1P 4LN Tel: 020 7217 6678 Fax: 020 7217 6345; 25 The Ridings, Epsom KT18 5JQ Tel: 01372 721488 Email: somas@mc.mailcom — MB BS 1968 Madras; MRCPsych 1986; DPM Eng. 1982. (Tanjore Med. Coll.) Health Care Adviser. Prev: Sen. Med. Off. HMP Brixton; Med. Off. HM Prison Wandsworth; Regist. W. Pk. Hosp. Epsom.

SOMASUNDERAM, Balakrishnan The Manor, 6 Manor Court Avenue, Nuneaton CV11 5HX Tel: 02476 321537 Fax: 02476 349793; 32 Copperfield Road, Cheadle Hulme SK8 7PN Tel: 0161 440 9533 — MB BS 1968 Ceylon; MRCPsych 1986; DPM Eng. 1982. (Colombo) Cons. Old Age Psych. N. Warks. NHS Trust, The Manor, 6 Manor Ct. Av, Nuneaton CV11 5HX. Socs: BMA; Pres. Sri-Lankan Psychiat.s Assn. (UK); Internal PsychoGeriat. Assn. Prev: Cons. in Old Age Psychiat., St Michaels Hosp. Lichfield, Staffs; Cons. in Old Age Psychiat., Thameside Gen. Hosp., Ashton Under Lyne; Cons. in Old Age Psychiat., Fairfield Gen. Hosp., Bury Lancs.

SOMAUROO, John Deelun The Cardiothoracic Centre, Thomas Drive, Liverpool L14 3PE Tel: 0151 228 1616 Fax: 0151 228 5539; 7 Ludlow Drive, West Kirby, Wirral CH48 3JG Tel: 0151 529 2724 — BM BS 1989 Nottm.; MB BS.(Nottm) 1989; MRCP (UK) 1994. (Univ. Nottm.) Research Fell. (Cardiol.) Liverp Cardiol Centre & Univ Hosp Aintree.; Assoc. Coll. Tutor Roy. Coll. Phys. Socs: BMA; Brit. Cardiovasc. Interven. Soc. Prev: Specialist Regist. (Cardiol.) Fazakerley Hosp. Liverp.; SHO (Intens. Care., Neurol. & Rehabil. & Psychiat.) Derriford Hosp. Plymouth.

SOMER, Kenneth Gordon Ross (retired) The Old Oast House, 72 The Hill, Littlebourne, Canterbury CT3 1TD Tel: 01227 728347 — MB BS 1956 Lond.; MRCS Eng. LRCP Lond. 1956; DHMSA 1994; DCH Eng. 1960; DObst RCOG 1958; Cert. Family Plann. JCC 1976. Prev: GP Canterbury.

SOMERFIELD, David James South Devon Healthcare, Chadwell Bay Hospital, Torquay Road, Paignton TQ3 2DW Tel: 01803 559163 Fax: 01803 559163 — MB ChB 1989 Sheff.; MRCPsych 1995. Cons. (Psychiat.) Torbay Hosp. Prev: Sen. Regist. (Psychiat.) Barrow Hosp. Bristol.

SOMERS, Henry Benedict Anton 2 Walnut Garth, Reepham, Lincoln LN3 4FF — LRCPI & LM, LRCSI & LM 1960; MB Lond. 1956; MRCPsych 1971; DPM Eng. 1966. Hon. Cons. Psychiat. Scunthorpe Community Health NHS Trust. Socs: Hon. Mem. Lincoln Med. Soc. Prev: Cons. Psychiat. Co. Hosp. Lincoln; Cons. Forens. Psychiat. Rampton Hosp. Retford; Asst. Psychiat. Herrison Hosp. Dorchester.

SOMERS, John Michael 3 Sheraton Drive, Nottingham NG8 2PR — MB ChB 1981 Liverp.; MRCP (UK) 1984; FRCR 1989. Cons. Paediat. Radiol. Nottm. City Hosp. NHS Trust & Univ. Hosp. NHS Trust.

SOMERS, Lisa Jane 57 Berrylands Road, Surbiton KT5 8PB Tel: 020 8399 0264 Fax: 020 8399 7733 Email: lisa@lsomers.freeserve.co.uk — MB BS 1993 Lond.; MRCP UK 1997. (Char. Cross & Westm. Lond.) Specialist Regist. (A&E) S. E. Thmaes.

SOMERS, Mr Shaw Stefano Department of Surgery, Queen Alexandra Hospital, Cosham, Portsmouth PO6 3LY — MB ChB 1986 Leeds; BSc (Hons.) Leeds 1983, MD 1993; FRCS Eng. 1992. Cons. Surg. (Gen. Surg.) Qu. Alexandra Hosp. Portsmouth. Socs: Assoc. of Surg.s of Gt. Britain & Irel.; Brit. Soc. of Gastroenterol. Prev: Sen. Lect. St James Univ. Hosp. Leeds; Assoc. Prof. Surg. P. of Wales Hosp. Shatin, Hong Kong; Hunt. Prof. RCS Eng. 1994-5.

SOMERS, Stanley Abram (retired) 10 Wedgewood Court, North Park Avenue, Leeds LS8 1DD Tel: 0113 266 6649 — MB ChB 1944 Leeds. Prev: Anaesth. Seacroft Hosp. Leeds.

SOMERS HESLAM, Judith 64A Glebe Road, Cambridge CB1 7SZ — Artsexamen 1993 Amsterdam; DRCOG 1996. GP Regist. E. Barnwell Health Centre Camb. Socs: Med. Protec. Soc. Prev: SHO (Gen. Med.) Huntingdon; SHO (Paediat.) Ipswich Hosp.; SHO (O & G) Ipswich Hosp.

SOMERSET, Alison Mary Annandale Surgery, Mutton Lane, Potters Bar EN6 2AS Tel: 01707 64451; 30 Potters Road, New Barnet, Barnet EN5 5HW Tel: 020 8441 7154 — MB BS 1991 Lond.; MRCGP 1997; DRCOG 1998. (Royal Free) p/t GP Retainer Potters Bar Herts. Prev: SHO (O & G) UCH Lond.; GP Regist. Potters Bar Herts.

SOMERSET, David Alan Dept. of Foetal Medicine, 3rd Floor, Birmingham Women's Hospital, Birmingham B15 2TG — BM 1992 Soton.; DM 2001 Birmingham. (Southampton) Lect. in Obst. & Gyn., Birmingha Wom.'s Hosp.; Specialist Regist. (O & G) W. Midl. Deanery. Socs: Roy. Coll. of Obst. & Gynaecologists.

SOMERSET, Robert Birley (profess.) 26 Oakwood Road, Birmingham B11 4HA Tel: 0121 777 3082; 33 Grove Avenue, Birmingham B13 9RX Tel: 0121 449 1530 — MB ChB 1957 Birm.; DObst RCOG 1961. GP Birm. Prev: SHO Wom. Hosp. Wolverhampton; Capt. RAMC; Ho. Surg. Gen. Hosp. Birm.

SOMERVAILLE, Tim Charles Plomer 12 Old Coppice, Lyth Hill, Shrewsbury SY3 0BP Email: tim@dummerclump.demon.co.uk — MB BS 1993 Lond.; BSc (Lond. 1990; MRCP (UK) 1996. (St. Mary's Hosp. Med. Sch.) Regist. (Haemat.) Univ. Coll. Hosp. Lond. Prev: Regist. (Haemat.) Mt. Vernon & Watford Hosps. NHS Trust; SHO (Respirat. Med.) Roy. Brompton Hosp. Lond.; SHO (Nephrol.) Middlx. Hosp. Lond.

SOMERVELL, David Howard (retired) Hap Cottage, Lynch Road, France Lynch, Stroud GL6 8LT Tel: 01453 886224 — MRCS Eng. LRCP Lond. 1955; DObst RCOG 1966. Prev: GP Glos.

SOMERVELL, Mr James Lionel (retired) 3 Orchard Close, Cressage, Shrewsbury SY5 6BZ Tel: 01952 510755 — MB BChir Camb. 1951; FRCS Eng. 1960; MRCS Eng. LRCP Lond. 1951. Prev: Cons. Surg. Walsall Hosp. Gp.

SOMERVILLE, Deborah Ruth Thatched Cottage, Eridge Rd, Eridge Green, Tunbridge Wells TN3 9JU — MB ChB 1997 Birm. GP VTS, Maidstone Kent.

SOMERVILLE, Douglas Mark 6 Woods Lea, Hillside, Chorley New Road, Bolton BL1 5DU — MB ChB 1951 Manch.; DO Eng. 1961. (Manch.) Cons. Ophth. Blackburn Roy. Infirm.

SOMERVILLE, Mr Douglas William 28 Island Bank Road, Inverness IV2 4QS — MB ChB 1976 Glas.; FRCS Ed. 1983. Cons. Orthop. Surg. Raigmore Hosp. Inverness. Prev: Cons. Orthop. Surg. Roy. Naval Hosp. Haslar Gosport.

SOMERVILLE, Elizabeth Mary 15/2 Braehead Avenue, Barnton, Edinburgh EH4 6AU — MB ChB 1948 Aberd. (Aberd.)

SOMERVILLE, Eric Townshend, SBStJ North Brink Practice, 7 North Brink, Wisbech PE13 1JR Tel: 01945 585121 Fax: 01945 476423; River Bend, 64 North Brink, Wisbech PE13 1LN Tel: 01945 585756 Fax: 01945 476423 — MB BS 1966 Lond.; MRCS Eng. LRCP Lond. 1966; DObst RCOG 1969. (St. Mary's) Prev: SHO (Obst.) Zachary Merton Matern. Hosp. Rustington; Ho. Phys. St. Mary's Hosp. Lond.; Ho. Surg. Bolingbroke Hosp. Lond.

SOMERVILLE, Froma 31 Wilmington Square, London WC1X 0EG — MB BS 1954 Lond.; MRCS Eng. LRCP Lond. 1954; DO Eng. 1958. (Westm.) Med. Asst. Moorfields Eye Hosp. Lond.

SOMERVILLE, Gordon, Col. late RAMC Retd. 25 Camden Road, Brecon LD3 7RS — MB ChB 1959 Glas.; DTM & H Eng. 1975. Socs: BMA. Prev: Comd. Med. HQ Wales; Sen. Med. Off. HQ Brit. Forces Belize; Regtl. Med. Off. 6th Qu. Eliz. Own Gurkha Rifles.

SOMERVILLE, Graham Waterson (retired) 2 Chapel Mews, Elloughton, Brough HU15 1HQ Tel: 01482 668463 — MB ChB 1960 Ed. Prev: GP Hull.

SOMERVILLE, Irene Dione The Calderdale Royal Hospital, Salter Habble, Halifax HX3 0PW Tel: 01422 357171; White Chimneys, Rawson Avenue, Halifax HX3 0LR Tel: 01422 341997 — MB BCh BAO 1970 Dub.; FFA SA 1980; DA RCSI 1972. (Trinity College Dublin) Cons. Anaesth. The Canderdale Roy. Hosp. Prev: Sen. Regist. (Anaesth.) Leeds Gen. Hosp.; Sen. Regist. (Anaesth.) King. Edwd. VIII & King Geo. V Hosp. Durban, SA.

SOMERVILLE, Professor Jane 81.83 Harley St, London Tel: 0207 637 3442 Fax: 0207 580 3225; 30 York House, Upper Montagu St, London W1H 1FR Tel: 020 7262 2144 Fax: 020 7724 2238 — MRCS Eng. LRCP Lond. 1955; MD Lond. 1966, MB BS 1955; FRCP Lond. 1973, M 1957; FACC 1973; FESC 1988. (Guy's) p/t Cons. Phys. Congen. Heart Dis. Middlx. Hosp./ Univ. Coll. Lond. Socs: Brit. Cardiac Soc.; Hon. Mem. Assn. Paediat. Cardiol.; Harv. Soc. Prev: Chairm. Med. Comm. Nat. Heart Hosp.; Cons. Phys. Hosp. Sick. Childr. Lond.; Sen. Lect. Cardiothoracic Inst. Lond.

SOMERVILLE, Jennifer Elizabeth Histopathology & Cytopathology Department, Craigavon Area Hospital, 68 Lurgan Road, Portadown, Craigavon BT63 5QQ Tel: 02838 612693 Fax: 02838 612690 — MB BCh BAO 1986 Belf.; BSc Belf. 1983; MRCPath 1992. Cons. Path. Craigavon Area Hosp. Co. Armagh.

SOMERVILLE, Jonathan Mark 4 Irwell Close, Chandlers Ford, Southampton — MB BS 1989 Lond.; FRCA 1997. (Charing Cross and Westminster)

SOMERVILLE, Mr Julian John FitzGerald Department of Urology, Calderdale Royal Hospital, Salterhebble, Halifax HX3 0PW Tel: 01422 357171; White Chimneys, Rawson Avenue, Halifax HX3 0LR Tel: 01422 341997 — MB BCh BAO 1970 Dub.; MA Dub. 1974, MD 1974; FRCS Ed. 1976. (Trinity Coll. Dub.) Cons. Urol. Calderdale & Huddersfield NHS Trust, Halifax. Socs: BMA; Brit. Assn. Urol. Surgs.; Internat. Soc. Urol. Prev: Sen. Regist. & Regist. (Urol.) Leeds HA; Sen. Regist. & Regist. (Urol.) King Edwd. VIII Hosp. Durban, S. Afr.

SOMERVILLE, Kevin William 33 Oxhey Road, Oxhey, Watford WD19 4QG Fax: 020 7204 3544 Email: kevin.somerville@swissre.com, kevin_somerville@swissre.com — MB ChB 1976 Auckland; BSc Auckland 1973; DM Nottm. 1990; FRCP 1995; FRACP 1981. (Auckland, New Zealand) Div. Cons. Phys. to Swiss Re Life & Health Lond.; Clin. Asst. Neuro-Ophth. Moorfields Eye Hosp. Lond. Socs: Amer. Geriat. Soc.; Brit. Geriat. Soc.; Assur. Med. Soc. Prev: Sen. Lect. & Hon. Cons. Phys. (Geriat. Med.) St. Bart. Hosp. Lond.; Cons. Phys. Middlemore Hosp. Auckland, NZ; Sen. Regist. Oxf. RHA.

SOMERVILLE, Margaret South & West Devon Health Authority, The Lescaze Offices, Shinner's Bridge, Dartington, Totnes TQ9 6JE Tel: 01803 866665 Fax: 01803 861853 Email: margaret.somerville@sw-devon-ha.swest.nhs.uk; Willow Barn, Pitt Hill, Ivybridge PL21 0JJ — MB BS 1978 Newc.; MD Newc. 1990; MPH Liverp. 1992; MRCP (UK) 1981; MFPHM RCP (UK) 1994. (Newcastle-upon-Tyne) Cons. Pub. Health Med. S. & W. Devon HA. Prev: Sen. Regist. (Pub. Health Med.) S. & W. RHA.

SOMERVILLE, Melanie Jane Flat 2/R, 17 Dalnair Street, Yorkhill, Glasgow G3 8SD — MB ChB 1994 Glas.

SOMERVILLE

SOMERVILLE, Neil Alexander McCrie (retired) Sydenham House Boulevard, Hull HU3 2TA Tel: 01482 326818 Fax: 01482 218267 — MB ChB Ed. 1956; FRCGP 1980, M 1965; Cert. Family Plann. JCC 1974; DCH RFPS Glas. 1960. Med. Adviser P & O N. Sea Ferries; Med. Examr MCA UKOOA Indep. Med. SMES. Prev: Ho. Surg. (O & G) W.wood Hosp. Beverley.

SOMERVILLE, Nicola Suzanne 27 Box Lane, Hemel Hempstead HP3 0DH — MB BS 1993 Lond.; DA (Lond.) 1995; DCH RCP Lond. 1998; FRCA Lond 1999. (St Georges Hosp Medical School) Specialist Regist. Anaesth., Finley Pk. Hosp., Camberley, St Geo.s' Specialist Regist. Rotat. Prev: SHO (Anaesth.) QA Portsmouth; SHO (Anaesth.) Frimley Pk. Hosp. Camberley; SHO (Paeds & Neonates), Brighton.

SOMERVILLE, Mr Philip Graham (retired) Chandos Lodge, 50 Paddockhall Road, Haywards Heath RH16 1HW Tel: 01444 413495 — MB BChir 1943 Camb.; MChir Camb. 1953, MA, MB BChir 1943; FRCS Eng. 1945; MRCS Eng. LRCP Lond. 1944; FACS 1983. Ct. Examrs. RCS Eng.; Exmar. Primary FRCS Eng. Prev: Cons. Surg. Roy. Sussex Co. Hosp. Brighton & Cuckfield Hosp. Mem.

SOMERVILLE, Simon James The John Kelso Practice, Park Medical Centre, Ball Haye Road, Leek ST13 6QR Tel: 01538 399007 Fax: 01538 370014 — MB BS 1987 Lond.; MRCGP 1991; T(GP) 1991; DFFP 1991; DCH RCP Lond. 1990. Research Fell. N. Staffs. GP Research Network Keele Univ. Prev: Trainee GP P'boro. Dist. Hosp. VTS.

SOMERVILLE, Walter, CBE (retired) Flat 30, York House, Upper Montagu St., London W1H 1FR Tel: 020 7262 2144 Fax: 020 7724 2238 — MD 1940 NUI; MB BCh BAO 1937; FRCP Lond. 1957, M 1940; FACC 1972. Hon. Phys. (Cardiac) Middlx. Hosp. Lond.; Hon. Lect. (Cardiol.) Middlx. Hosp. Med. Sch.; Hon. Cons. (Cardiol.) to The Army & RAF; Assn. RN Offs. & King Edwd. VII Convalesc. Hosp. Offs. Osborne; Edr. Brit. Heart Jl.; Trustee Brit. Assn. Performing Arts Med. Prev: Cons. Cardiol. Thoracic Surgic. Unit Harefield Hosp.

SOMERVILLE, Wendy Watford General Hospital, Vicarage Road, Watford WD18 0HB Tel: 01923 244366/217614 Fax: 01923 217715 — MB ChB 1976 Auckland; MSc (Hons.) Auckland 1973; FRCP 1996; FRACP 1981. Cons. Phys. (Geriat. Med.) W. Herts Hosp.s Trust E.ern Region. Socs: Brit. Geriat. Soc.; Amer. Geriat. Soc.; Alzheimers Dis. Soc. Prev: Cons. Geriat. Med. Nottm. & Newark, Trent RHA; Cons. Geriat. Med. Auckland HB, NZ.

SOMJEE, Miss Shehnaz 8 Martine Close, Melling, Liverpool L31 1DJ Tel: 07850 574761 Email: s.somjee@cablenet.co.uk — MB BS 1979 Karachi; FRCS Eng. 1989; DLO RCS Eng. 1986; LLB (Hons.) Liverp. John Moores 1998. Socs: Liverp. Med. Inst. & BMA (Hon. Treas. Liverp. Div. 1989-92). MWF; Brit. Assn. of Ocorhino-Laryngol./Head & Neck Surg.s; Founder & Chairm. Locum Doctors' Assn. (June 1997 to date).

***SOMMERFIELD, Andrew John** 178 Park Road, Timperley, Altrincham WA15 6QW — MB ChB 1996 Ed.

SOMMERFIELD, Joanne Flat 12, Bloomfield Court, Bourdon St., London W1K 3PU — MB BS 1976 New South Wales.

SOMMERLAD, Mr Brian Clive The Old Vicarage, 17 Lodge Road, Writtle, Chelmsford CM1 3HY Tel: 01245 422477 Fax: 01245 421901 Email: brian@sommerlad.co.uk — MB BS 1966 Sydney; FRCS Eng. 1971; FRCS (Hon) 2000. Cons. Plastic Surg.Broomfield Hosp. Chelmsford, Hosp. for Childr. Gt. Ormond St. & Roy. Lond. Hosp. Socs: Fell. Roy. Soc. Med. (Ex-Pres. Plastic Surg. Sect.); Brit. Assn. Plastic Surgs. (Pres. 1998); Craniofacial Soc. GB (Pres.1996-7. Prev: Sen. Regist. (Plastic Surg.) NE Thames RHA; Regist. (Surg.) Univ. Coll. Hosp. Lond.; Resid. Med. Off. Sydney Hosp., Austral.

SOMMERLAD, Marian Gwyneth The Old Vicarage, 17 Lodge Road, Writtle, Chelmsford CM1 3HY Tel: 01245 422477 — MB BS 1972 Lond.; MRCS Eng. LRCP Lond. 1972. (Univ. Coll. Hosp.) Clin. Asst. Broomfield Hosp. Chelmsford. Prev: Clin. Asst., Ho. Phys. & Ho. Surg. Barnet Gen. Hosp.

***SOMMERS, Andrew James** 28 Church Street, Bramcote, Beeston, Nottingham NG9 3HD — MB ChB 1994 Leic.

SOMMERS, Stephanie Marguerite 28 Church Street, Bramcote, Beeston, Nottingham NG9 3HD — MB ChB 1993 Leic.

SOMERVILLE, David Frank Head of Drug Surveillance, Bayer PLC, Bayer House, Strawberry Hill, Newbury RG14 1JA Tel: 01635 563369 Fax: 01635 563703; Butts Close House, Weeke Hill, Winchester SO22 5JA Tel: 01962 867411 Fax: 01962 867411 — MB BS 1974 Lond.; DRCOG 1979. Head Drug Surveillance Bayer plc; Med. Adviser Bayer UK. Socs: Fac. Pharmaceut. Med.

SOMMERVILLE, Garth Paul 4 Kensington Gardens, Portsmouth Road, Kingston upon Thames KT1 2JU — MB BCh 1990 Witwatersrand.

SOMMERVILLE, Gordon Peter Westlands Medical Centre, 20B Westlands Grove, Portchester, Fareham PO16 9AE Tel: 023 92 377514 Fax: 023 92 214236 — MB BS 1979 Lond.; BSc (Hons.) Lond. 1976; MRCGP 1984; DRCOG 1981. (St. Thos.)

SOMMERVILLE, James Gardner (retired) 2 Lentune Way, Lymington SO41 3PF Tel: 01590 673351 — MB ChB Ed. 1943; MD (Commend.) Ed. 1958; FRCP Lond. 1978, M 1969. Cons. Adviser Med. Rehabil. Centre, Univ. Coll. Hosp., St. Geo. Hosp. Lond. & Qu. Eliz. Foundat. for Disabled People Leatherhead, Surrey; Cons. Adviser Roy. Brit. Legion, Ch.ill Rehabil Centre Kent; Hon. Sen. Clin. Lect. Dept. Med. Univ. Lond.; Governor Qu. Eliz. Foundat. Disabled Leatherhead; Mem. Advis. Panel Disabled Living Foundat. Prev: Med. Dir. Med. Rehabil. Centre Lond.

SOMMERVILLE, John MacLeod Portland Road Surgery, 31 Portland Road, Kilmarnock KA1 2DJ Tel: 01563 522118 Fax: 01563 573562; 18 Howard Street, Kilmarnock KA1 2BP Tel: 01563 537915 — MB ChB 1975 Glas.; MRCP (UK) 1979; MRCGP 1984. GP Princip. Prev: Regist. (Med.) Stobhill Gen. Hosp. Glas.; Regist. (Med.) Roy. Alexandra Infirm. Paisley.

SOMMERVILLE, Julia Anne 2 Brownhills Gardens, St Andrews KY16 8PY — MB ChB 1991 Aberd.

SOMMERVILLE, Mary Josephine Blantyre Health Centre, Victoria Street, Blantyre, Glasgow G72 0BS Tel: 01698 828868 Fax: 01698 823678 — MB ChB 1984 Glas.; MRCGP 1991; DRCOG 1987. GP Glas. Socs: Brit. Soc. Med. & Dent. Hypn.; Brit. Med. Acupunc. Soc. Prev: Research Fell. Dept. Community Med. Glas. Roy. Matern. Hosp.

SOMMERVILLE, Peter (retired) 3 Burley Road, Summerley Est., Bognor Regis PO22 7NF Tel: 0124 358 3587 — MB ChB 1939 Glas.; MRCGP 1953. Prev: Resid. Med. Off. Oakwood Hall Sanat. Rotherham.

SOMMERVILLE, Robert Gardner (retired) 3 Shore Road, Carradale, Kintyre, Campbeltown PA28 6SH — MD 1960 Glas.; MB ChB 1950; FRCP Glas. 1974; FRCPath 1972. Prev: Prof. (Med. Microbiol.) Sultan Qaboos Univ. Muscat.

SOMMERVILLE, William Taylor 35 Whitemoss Road, E. Kilbride, Glasgow G74 4JB Tel: 01355 220717 — MB ChB Glas. 1953; DObst RCOG 1957. Insur. Panel Doctor; Fact. Med. Off. Socs: (Ex-Pres. & Ex-Hon. Sec.) E. Kilbride Med. Soc. Prev: Jun. Hosp. Med. Off. (Obst.) Lennox Castle Matern. Hosp. Glas.; Ho. Surg. W.. Infirm. Glas.; Ho. Phys. Stobhill Gen. Hosp. Glas.

SOMNER, Alan Robert (retired) 88 The Rise, Ponteland, Newcastle upon Tyne NE20 9LQ Tel: 01661 23769 — MD 1951 Ed.; MB ChB 1946; FRCP Ed. 1961, M 1952. Cons. Phys. Preston Hosp. N. Shields. Prev: Ho. Phys. Roy. Infirm. Edin.

SOMNER, Joan 88 The Rise, Ponteland, Newcastle upon Tyne NE20 9LQ Tel: 01661 23769 — MB ChB 1950 Ed. (Ed.) Asst. Med. Off. Community Med. N. Tyneside Health Auth. Prev: Asst. Dept. Med. Univ. Edin.; Ho. Surg. Roy. Infirm. Edin.; Ho. Phys. Roy. Hosp. Sick Childr. Edin.

SOMORIN, Adolphus Owolabi 57 Osborne Road, London E7 0PJ — MRCS Eng. LRCP Lond. 1965.

SOMPER, John Dennis 18 Wimpole Street, London W1M 7AD Tel: 020 7637 1113; 160 Fishpool Street, St Albans AL3 4RZ Tel: 01727 856440 — MB BS Lond. 1952; MFHom 1969. (St Mary's Hospital Paddington London W2)

SONANIS, Sanjay Valmikrao Orthopaedic Department, Airedale General Hospital, Skipton Road, Steeton, Keighley BD20 6TD Tel: 01535 655129 Email: svsdnanis@aol.com; 22 Styveton Way, Steeton, Keighley BD20 6TP Tel: 01535 654149 Email: svsonanis@aol.com — MB BS 1985 Bombay; MSOrth (Bombay) 1989; MChOrth. 1997. Staff Surg. (Orthop.).

SONDHEIMER, Josef 16A Westbourne Grove, London W2 5RH — MB BS 1939 Lond.; MRCP Lond. 1945. (Lond. Hosp.) Itinerant Cons. Phys. UK. Prev: Clin. Asst. & Ho. Phys. Lond. Hosp.; Regist. (Med.) Univ. Coll. Hosp.; Sen. Regist. (Med.) Roy. Gwent Hosp. Newport.

SONDHI, Ravindra Portland Medical Centre, 184 Portland Rd, London SE25 4QB Tel: 0208 662 1233 Fax: 0208 662 1223 — MB

SONODA

BS 1984 Lond.; MBA City University 2000; BSc (Hons.) Lond. 1981. (St George's Medical School) Clin. Asst. in Gastroenterol. and Endoscopy, Mayday Hosp. Lond. Rd, Thornton Heath; Clin. Asst. in Urol.; Med. Director, Croydon, Doctors on call; Primary Care Practitioner in Accid. & Emerg., Kings/ Lewisham/ St Thomas's. Prev: Clin. Asst. Rheum.; Lect. Kings Coll. for UnderGrad.s.

SONEYE-VAUGHAN, Felicia Temitayo 264 Barley Lane, Chadwell Heath, Romford RM6 4XU — LRCPI & LM, LRSCI & LM 1969; LRCPI & LM, LRCSI & LM 1969; FFR RCSI 1976.

SONG, Fiona Mary 56 Dedworth Road, Windsor SL4 5AY Tel: 01753 860136 Fax: 01753 860136 — MB ChB 1988 Sheff.

SONG, Soon Hoo Diabetes Research, University Dept of Medicine, Western General Hospital, Crewe Road, Edinburgh EH4 2XU Tel: 0131 537 3074 Fax: 0131 537 1709 Email: shsong@ed.ac.uk; 43 Barclay Place, Edinburgh EH10 4HW Tel: 0131 228 4615 — MB ChB 1992 Ed.; MRCP (UK) 1996. (Ed.) Clin. Research Fell. (Diabetes) Diabetes Research Univ. Dept. Med. W.. Gen. Hosp. Edin. Socs: BMA; Brit. Diabetic Assn. Prev: Med. SHO - Vict. Hosp., Kirkcaldy; Med. SHO - Sunderland City Hosp.; Ho. Off. (Med. & Surg.) Roy. Infirm. Edin.

SONGHURST, Lorice Zaki The Laurels, Lynch Close, London SE3 0RN — MB BCh 1968 Cairo; FFA RCS Eng. 1977.

SONGO-WILLIAMS, Rosie AF c/o 10 Algernon Road, Lewisham, London SE13 7AT Tel: 020 8692 7832 — MD 1974 Berne; MRCP(I) 1984; DObst RCPSI 1978; DTM & H Liverp. 1978; DCH RCPSI 1976; Dip. Arzt 1973. (University of Berne Switzerland) Socs: MRCPCH; Fell. of the Roy. Soc. Of Med.

SONGRA, Ashok Kumar 1 Dorset Drive, Edgware HA8 7NT — MB BS 1994 Newc.; BSc (Hons.) 1983; BDS Wales 1986; FFDRCSI Irel. 1996. (Univ. Newc.) Specialist Regist (Oral & Maxillofacial Surg.) Roy. Lond. Trust. Hosp. Socs: BMA; Brit. Oral and Maxillofacial Surg. Assn. Prev: SHO (ENT) Qu. Eliz. Hosp. Birm.; SHO (Gen. Surg.) Sunderland DG Hosp.; SHO (A&E) Sunderland DG Hosp.

SONI, Mr Bakulesh Madhusudan Spinal Injuries Centre, Southport & Formby District General Hospital, Town Lane, Southport PR8 6PN Tel: 01704 547471 Fax: 01704 543156; 10 Rutland Road, Southport PR8 6PB Tel: 01704 546276 — MB BS 1974 Gujarat; Ms Neurosurg. 1977. (Ahmedabad India) Cons. (Spin. Injury) Dist. Gen. Hosp. S.port Town La. S.port PR8 6PN UK. Socs: BMA; Internat. Med. Soc. Paraplegia. Prev: Assoc. Specialist (Spinal Injury) DGH S.port; Sen. Regist. (Neurosurg.) Walton Hosp. Liverp.; Regist. (Neurosurg.) Walton Hosp. Liverp.

SONI, Inder Rekha 26 Bromham Road, Bedford MK40 2QD; 29 Donnelly Drive, Bedford MK41 9TT — MB BS 1974 Delhi; DTM & H Liverp. 1978. (Lady Harding Med. Coll.) Clin. Asst. (Psychiat.) Bedford & Shires Trust. Socs: MBA (Brit. Indian Med. Assn.). Prev: Clin. Asst. (Psychiat.) N.ampton HA; Regist. (Psychiat.) Stanley Royd Hosp. Wakefield; SHO (Psychiat.) Stanley Royd Hosp.

SONI, Neil Cranson 164 Court Lane, Dulwich, London SE21 7ED — MD 1993 Lond.; MB ChB Bristol 1976; FRCA 1991; FANZCA 1982; FFICANZCA 1983. Sen. Lect. Anaesth. W.m. Char. Cross Med. Sch.; Hon. Cons. Chelsea & W.m. Hosp. 1985.

SONI, Raj 19 Lombard Road, Merton, London SW19 3RH — MB BS 1960 Delhi; MRCOG 1978; DA Eng. 1977. (Lady Hardinge Med. Coll. New Delhi)

SONI, Ram Kripal c/o Drive V.K. Salsena, 9 Forest Grove, Eccleston Park, Prescot L34 2RY — LRCP LRCS 1982 Ed.; Mch (Orthop.) Liverp. 1984; LRCP LRCS Ed. LRCPS Glas. 1982. Regist. (Orthop.) Merseyside HA.

***SONI, Sarita** 79 Carrwood, Halebarns, Altrincham WA15 0ER — MB ChB 1997 Manch.

SONI, Saroj Meadowbrook, Department of Psychological Medicine, Stott Lane, Salford M6 8HG Tel: 0161 787 5700 Fax: 0161 787 5707; 79 Carrwood, Hale Barns, Altrincham WA15 0ER Tel: 0161 980 4341 Fax: 0161 980 4341 — MB BS 1964 Bombay; FRCPsych 1989, M 1978; MRCOG 1969; DPM Eng. 1976. (Grant Med. Coll. Bombay) Cons. Psychiat. (Ment. Handicap) Salford Community Healthcare NHS Trust; Hon. Assoc. Lect. Univ. Manch.

SONI, Somdatta Gurudatta Cromwell House, Community Mental Health Centre, Cromwell Road, Eccles, Manchester M30 0QT Tel: 0161 787 8496 Fax: 0161 787 8560; 79 Carrwood, Hale Barns, Altrincham WA15 0ER Tel: 0161 980 4341 — MD 1966 Poona; PhD Belf. 1970; FRCP Ed. 1983, M 1968; MRCS Eng. LRCP Lond. 1973; FRCPsych 1981, M 1972; DPM Ed. & Glas. 1970. Cons.

Psychiat. (Ment. Health Servs.) Salford; Hon. Assoc. Lect. Univ. Manch. Prev: Research Fell. Qu. Univ. Belf.

SONI, Virendra Kumar Bedford General Hospital, South Wing, Kempston Road, Bedford MK42 9DJ; 29 Donnelly Drive, Bedford MK41 9TT — MB BS 1968 Punjab; MB BS Punjabi 1968; MS (Ophth.) Agra 1969; MCOphth 1991; DTM & H Liverp. 1978; DO RCS Eng. 1975; MRC Ophth 1991. (Govt. Med. Coll. Patiala) Sen. Med. Off. (Ophth.) N. Beds. HA. Socs: BMA; MRCPCH; MRCPCH. Prev: Regist. Dept. Ophth. Pinderfields Gen. Hosp. Wakefield.

SONIGRA, Hasmukh Karsan 4 Trent Gardens, London N14 4PY Tel: 020 8 441 6175 Email: hsonigra@hotmail.com; 2 Cale Street, Cale Green, Stockport SK2 6SW — MB ChB 1997 Manch.; BSc (Hons). (Manch.) SHO (Cardiorespirat. Med.) Wythenshawe Hosp. Manch. Prev: Ho. Off. (Surg.) Hope Hosp. Manch.; Ho. Off. (Med.) Hope Hosp. Manch.

SONKSEN, Camilla Jane X-Ray Department, Royal Sussex County Hospital, Eastern Road, Brighton BN2 5BE Tel: 01273 696955; 3 Park Road, Lewes BN7 1BN — MB BS 1985 Lond.; MRCP (UK) 1989; FRCR 1993. Cons. Radiol. Roy. Sussex Co. Hosp. Prev: Sen. Regist. (Radiol.) King's Coll. Hosp. Lond.; SHO (Med.) Roy. Sussex Co. Hosp.; SHO (Paediat.) S.lands Hosp. Shoreham by Sea.

SONKSEN, Julian Richard Anaesthetic Dept, Russells hall Hospital, Dudley DT1 2HQ — MB ChB 1988 Birm.; ChB Birm. 1988; FRCA 1994. (Birmingham) Cons. Anaesth. Russells Hall Hosp. Dudley.

SONKSEN, Patricia Mary (retired) The Wolfson Centre, Institute of Child Health, Mecklenburgh Square, London WC1N 2AP Tel: 020 7837 7618 Fax: 020 7837 9469 Email: p.sonksen@ich.ucl.ac.uk — MB BS 1960 Lond.; MD Lond. 1979; MRCP (UK) 1992; DObst RCOG 1961; FRCPCH 1997; FRCP 1995. Prev: Hon. Cons. Paediat. Gt. Ormond St. Hosp. for Childr. NHS Trust Lond.

SONKSEN, Professor Peter Henri Department of Medicine, St. Thomas' Hospital, London SE1 7EH Tel: 020 7928 9292 Fax: 020 7928 4458 Email: p.sonksen@umds.ac.uk; East Wing, Preshaw House, Preshaw, Upham, Southampton SO32 1HP Tel: 01962 771029 Fax: 01962 771029 — MB BS Lond. 1960; MD Lond. 1968; FRCP Lond. 1976, M 1963. (Middlx.) Hon. Cons. Phys. Guy's & St. Thos. Hosp. Trust; Prof. Endocrinol. Guy's, King's Coll. & St Thomas' Hosps. Med. & Dent. Sch. Lond.; Mem. Med. Commiss. & Sub. Commiss. of 10C Doping & Biochem. in Sport (Internat. Olympic Comm.); Edr. in Chief Growth Hormone & IGF Research; Chairm. EASD Study Gp. Do It. Socs: EASD; Brit. Diabetic Assn.; Brit. Endocrine Soc. Prev: Edr. Clin. Endocrinol.; Harkness Fell. Harvard Med. Sch., USA; Chairm. Div. of Med. UMDS.

SONNABEND, Joseph Adolph 30 Hamilton Terrace, London NW8 9UG Tel: 020 7289 0932 — MB BCh 1956 Witwatersrand; MRCP Ed. 1961.

SONNENBERG, Miss Sabine — State Exam Med 1991 Cologne; FRCS 1997; MD 1992. p/t Specialist Regist. Crawley & Horsham Hosp. Prev: Specialist Regist. (Gen. Surg.) St. Thomas's Hosp. Lond.; SpR Frimley Pk. Hosp.; SpR E. Surrey Hosp.

SONNEX, Christopher Addenbrooke's Hospital, Hills Rd, Cambridge CB2 2QQ Tel: 01223 217141; The Rookery, 15 Scotby Village, Scotby, Carlisle CA4 8BS Tel: 01228 513554 — MB BS 1978 Lond.; FRCP Lond. 1995; MRCP (UK) 1984. Cons. Phys. (Genitourin. Med.) Addenbrooke's Hosp. Camb. Socs: Assn. Genitourin. Med.; Brit. Soc. Study of Vulval Dis.; Med. Soc. for the Study of Venereal Dis. Prev: Clin. Lect. Acad. Dept. Genitourin. Med. Middlx. Hosp. Lond.

SONNEX, Timothy Stephen Purdis Hall, Foxhall, Ipswich IP10 0AD — MRCS Eng. LRCP Lond. 1975; BSc (Hons.) Lond. 1972, MD 1988, MB BS 1975; MRCP (UK) 1979. (Middlx.) Sen. Regist. St. John's Hosp. Dis. Skin Lond.

SONODA, Ienari Luke 11 Barrie House, 29 St Edmund's Terrace, St John's Wood, London NW8 7QH Tel: 020 7586 7410 Fax: 020 7586 7410 Email: luke.i.sonoda@btinternet.com; Christ's College, University of Cambridge, Cambridge CB2 3BU Tel: 01223 334900 — MB BChir 1994 Camb.; MA Camb. 1993; BA Camb. 1990. (Camb.) Researcher in Radiol. Sci. at Guy's, King's & St. Thos. Hosp. Lond. Socs: Fell. Roy. Soc. Med.; Assn. Endoscopic Surgs.; Assn. of Surgs. Prev: Lect. (Anat.) UMDS Guy's & St. Thos. Hosps. Univ. Lond.; SHO (Orthop. Surg.) Addenbrooke's Health NHS Trust Camb.; Ho. Off. (Surg.) Addenbrooke's Health NHS Trust Camb.

SONTHALIA

SONTHALIA, Vijay Bihari Hunter Health Centre, Andrew St., East Kilbride, Glasgow G74 1AD Tel: 01355 906633 Fax: 01355 906639 Email: vijay.sonthalia@hunter.lonpet.scot.nhs.uk — MBBS. GP. Socs: Out of hours Co-op Assoc.; Local Med. Comm.; Aeromed. Comm.

SONTHEIMER, Hemantee Devi Talangerstrasse 5, 82152 Krailling, Germany; 76 Yew Tree Avenue, Lichfield WS14 9UA — MB ChB 1986 Leeds.

***SOO, Julia Kay** 45 Sandown Avenue, Swindon SN3 1QQ — MB BS 1998 Lond.; MB BS Lond 1998.

SOO, Kooi Guat 3 Elms Avenue, Great Shelford, Cambridge CB2 5LN Tel: 01223 2265 — LMS 1949 King Edwd. VII Coll.; LMS King Edwd. VII Coll. Med. Singapore 1949.

SOO, Shelly 53 Taylor's Lane, Dundee DD2 1AP — MB ChB 1986 Dundee. Med. Rotat. Tayside HB.

SOO, Shiu-Ching Luton & Dunstable Hospital, Lewsey Road, Luton LU4 0DZ — MB BChir 1988 Camb.; MA Camb. 1989; MRCP (UK) 1990. (Univ. of Camb.) Cons. Diabetes & Endocrinol. & Gen. Med., Luton & Dunstable Hosp.

SOO, Shiu-Shing Department Microbiology, Nottingham City Hospital, Hucknall Road, Nottingham NG5 1PB Tel: 0115 969 1169 Ext: 45572 — MB BChir 1987 Camb.; PhD 1999; MRC Path 1994; MA Camb. 1987. (The Clinical School, Addenbrooke's Hospital, Cambridge) Cons. Microbiologist, Dept. of Microbiol., Nottm. City Hosp., Nottm. Socs: Roy. Coll. of Pathologists. Prev: Regist. (Microbiol.) Addenbrookes Hosp. Camb.

SOO, Sze Shun The Princess Street Group Practice, 2 Princess St., Elephant and Castle, London SE1 6JP Tel: 020 7928 0253 Fax: 020 7261 9804; 11 Alfreton Close, London SW19 5NS — MB BCh BAO 1990 NUI; LRCPSI 1990.

SOOD, Anil Kumar Dovercourt Health Centre, 407 Main Road, Dovercourt, Harwich CO12 4ET Tel: 01255 506451 — MB ChB 1987 Birm.; MRCGP 1991; DRCOG 1991.

SOOD, Archana 1(b) The Green, Twickenham TW2 5TU Tel: 020 8893 8579 Email: archana.sood@gp-h84044.nhs.uk — MB ChB 1990 Glas.; MRCGP 1994; T(GP) 1994; DFFP 1993. (Glasgow) GP Twickenham. Prev: Trainee GP StoneHo. Hosp. VTS; GP asst. W. Lond.

SOOD, Arvind Flat 2, 2 Victoria Crescent Road, Glasgow G12 9DB — MB ChB 1994 Glas.

SOOD, Chander Kanta James Paget Hospital, Lowestoft Road, Gorleston, Great Yarmouth NR31 6LA — MB ChB 1972 Makerere.

SOOD, Harish Chandra 19 The Cloverlands, The Hawthorns, Nottingham NG2 7TF — MB BCh 1986 Wales; MRCGP 1990.

SOOD, Kamal Kumar Abington Park Surgery, Christchurch Medical Centre, Ardington Road, Northampton NN1 5LT Tel: 01604 630291 Fax: 01604 603524; 45 Thorburn Road, Weston Favell, Northampton NN3 3DA Tel: 01604 401426 — MB BS 1981 Lond.; BSc Lond. 1978, MB BS 1981; MRCP (UK) 1984; MRCGP 1989; DRCOG 1988.

SOOD, Loopinder 20 Duncryne Place, Bishopbriggs, Glasgow G64 2DP — MB ChB 1986 Glas.; BSc (Hons) Glas. 1983. (Glas. Univ.) Trainee Psychiat.

SOOD, Mr Manoj Kumar 8 Brabourne Heights, Marsh Lane, Blackheath, London NW7 4NU Email: manojsood@yahoo.com — MB BS 1992 Lond.; BSc (Hons.) Lond. 1989; FRCS Eng. 1996. Specialist Regist. (Orthop. & Trauma) RNOH Rotat. Socs: BOTA; Assoc. BOA; Roy. Soc. of Med. (Fell.). Prev: Sen. SHO (Orthop. & Trauma) Whipps Cross Hosp. Lond.; SHO (Plastic & Hand Surg.) Wexham Pk. Hosp. Slough; Surgic. SHO Rotat. King's Healthcare Lond.

SOOD, Manu Raj 103 Friary Road, Handsworth Wood, Birmingham B20 1BA — MB BS 1987 Himachal Pradesh, India; MRCP (UK) 1994.

SOOD, Meena Garners Cottage, Nottingham Road, Lount, Ashby-de-la-Zouch LE65 1SD — MB ChB 1991 Leic.

SOOD, Naresh Chander Family Medical Centre, 171 Carlton Road, Nottingham NG3 2FW Tel: 0115 504068 Fax: 0115 950 9844.

SOOD, Mr Rajinder Kumar Shanti-Nivas, 9 Longhill Avenue, Alloway, Ayr KA7 4DY — MB BS 1962 Bombay; FRCS Ed. 1971; MRCS Eng. LRCP Lond. 1978. Cons. ENT Surg. Ayr Co. Hosp.

SOOD, Ram Parkash Glodwick Health Centre, Glodwick Road, Oldham OL4 1YN Tel: 0161 652 5311 — MB BS 1960 Bombay; DTM & H Liverp. 1962; DPH Eng. 1962. (Nat. Med. Coll. Bombay) Prev: Regist. (Med.) Ransom Hosp. Rainworth & Peppard Hosp.; Henley-on-Thames.

SOOD, Ravinder Nath New Road Side Surgery, 127 New Road Side, Horsforth, Leeds LS18 4QD Tel: 0113 295 3322 Fax: 0113 295 3323 — MB BS Lucknow 1965; BSc Lucknow 1958; DObst RCOG 1971; DLO Lucknow 1966. (King Geo. Med. Coll. Lucknow) GP Horsforth. Prev: GP Horsforth.

SOOD, Mr Sanjai 127 New Road Side, Horsforth, Leeds LS18 4QD Fax: 01132 953323 Email: sanjsood@aol.com; 17 Lakeland Road, Alwoodley, Leeds LS17 7PJ — MB ChB 1991 Leic.; FRCS (Surg.) Ed; FRCS (Otol) Ed. Specialist Regist. (Otol, Head & Neck Surg.) Leeds Gen. Infirm. Socs: Fell. Roy. Coll. Of Surgs. Of Edin.; Assoc. Brit. Assoc. Otol. Head & Neck Surgs; BMA. Prev: SHO Rotat. (Surg.) Qu.'s Med. Centre, Nottm.; Anat. Prosector, Oxf. Univ.

SOOD, Mr Satish Chandra 130 Harley Street, London W1N 1AH Tel: 020 7935 4000 — LRCPI & LM, LRCSI & LM 1962; FRCS Ed. 1972; DTM & H Liverp. 1965. Cons. Plastic Surg. Whittaker Life Sci. Corpn.; Clin. Director, Twenty 1st Century Helthcare Ltd. Socs: Fell. Roy. Soc. Med. & Internat. Coll. Surgs. (Plastic Surg.); Counc. & Cons. Plastic Surg. Ramana Health Foundat. Prev: JIC Davis Research Fell. Univ. Liverp.; Sen. Regist. Hosp. Sick Childr. Gt. Ormond St. & Guy's Hosp. Lond.

SOOD, Sunil Heston Health Centre, Cranford Lane, Heston, Hounslow TW5 9ER Tel: 020 8321 3410 Fax: 020 8321 3409 — MB ChB 1984 Glas. (Glas.) GP Princip. Hounslow. Socs: BMA; Med. Protec. Soc. Prev: SHO (O & G) Chase Farm Hosp. Enfield; SHO (Orthop. & Accid & Emerg.) Law Hosp. Carluke; SHO (Geriat. Med.) St. Michael's Hosp. Aylsham.

SOOD, Tara Suman 5 Tocil Croft, Coventry CV4 7DZ Tel: 024 76 415885 — MB ChB 1997 Bristol; BSc 1994. (Bristol) SHO A&E John Radcliffe Hosp.Oxf. Socs: BMA.

SOOD, Ved Brat Springcliffe Surgery, 42 St. Catherines, Lincoln LN5 8LZ Tel: 01522 520443 Fax: 01522 543430; Isben House, 13 Lincoln Road, North Hykeham, Lincoln LN6 8DL Tel: 01522 681885 — MB BS 1965 Delhi; DO Aligarh 1967; Cert JCC Lond. 1976. (M.A. Med. Coll. Delhi) Socs: Mem. Overseas Doctor Assn. Prev: Regist. (Clin. Path.) Lond. Chest Hosp.; Regist. (Haemat. & Bact.) Nat. Hosp. Nerv. Dis. Qu. Sq. Lond.; Regist. (Haemat.) Lond. Hosp. (Whitechapel).

SOODEEN, David Elliott Charlotte Keel Health Centre, Seymour Rd, Easton, Bristol BS2 — MB BCh 1993 Wales.

SOODEEN, Patricia Inez (retired) 19 Downs Hill, Beckenham BR3 5HA — MB BS 1956 Bombay; DObst RCOG 1967. Prev: GP Lond.

SOODEEN, Sally Jane Hartcliffe Health Centre, Hareclive Road, Hartcliffe, Bristol BS13 0JP — MB BCh 1993 Wales.

***SOOKLALL, Conrad Richard Suresh** 37 Wadbrough Road, Sheffield S11 8RF — MB ChB 1995 Sheff.

***SOOKUR, Dharmendra** 47 Lawnswood Drive, Swinton, Manchester M27 5NH — MB ChB 1994 Manch.

SOOLE, Martin John High Street Surgery, 26 High Street, Wanstead, London F11 2AQ Tel: 020 8989 0407 Fax: 020 8518 8435; 46 Preston Road, London E11 1NN — MB BS 1986 Lond.; MRCGP 1994; DRCOG 1988.

SOOLTAN, Abdool Rajack The Surgery, 179 York Road, Leeds LS9 7RD Tel: 0113 248 0268 Fax: 0113 248 8490 — MB ChB 1972 Leeds; ECFMG Cert 1975; MRCGP 1976; DObst RCOG 1975; DCH Eng. 1977.

SOOLTAN, Mohammed Ali 49 Ridgeway, Leeds LS8 4DD Tel: 0113 265 9190 — MRCS Eng. LRCP Lond. 1964; MRCP (U.K.) 1973; DTM & H Liverp. 1968. (Leeds) Regist. (Med.) Pontefract Gen. Hosp.

SOOLTAN, Yasmin 67 Shortridge Terrace, Jesmond, Newcastle upon Tyne NE2 2JE Tel: 0191 281 3907 — MB BS 1991 Newc. Trainee GP Newc. u. Tyne.

SOOMAL, Rabinder Singh Academic Unit of Radiotherapy,Orchard House, Royal Marsden Hospital NHS Trust, Downs Rd, Sutton SM2 5PT Tel: 020 8642 6011 Fax: 020 8661 3127 Email: rubin.soomal@rmh.nthames.nhs.uk — MB BS 1992 Lond.; FRCR Lond. 1999; BSc Hons. Physiol. Lond. 1989; MRCP Lond. 1995. (Char. Cross. & Westm.) Specialist Regist. (Clin. Oncol.) Roy. Marsden Hosp. NHS Trust Lond. Socs: BMA; Roy. Coll. Radiol.;

Roy. Coll. Phys.s. Prev: Specialist Regist. (Clin. Oncol.) Guys & St. Thos. NHS Trust Lond.; SHO (Med.) Brighton.

SOOMRO, Ghulam Mustafa Springfield Hospital, London SW17; 4 Twickenham Close, Beddington, Croydon CR0 4SZ Tel: 020 8680 1346 — MB BS 1979 Sind; 2000 Dip. E Divence Based Med. Oxford; 1999 Dip. Systematic Reviews, Lond.; MSc 2001 Social Research Surrey; MRCPsych 1993; Dip. Psychiat. Lond. 1986.

SOOMRO, Mr Jamil Ahmed 196 Crofton Lane, Orpington BR6 0BW — MB BS 1973 Sind; FRCS Eng. 1990.

SOOMRO, Mansoor Broad Street Surgery, 129 Broad Street, Coventry CV6 5BD Tel: 024 7666 3111 — LRCP LRCS 1961 Ed.; LRCP LRCS Ed. LRFPS Glas. 1961.

***SOON, Christine Cheng Young** 2 Kingston Av, Sutton SM3 9TZ — BM 1997 Soton.

***SOON, Sing Yang** 15/8 East Parkside, Edinburgh EH16 5XL — MB ChB 1997 Ed.

SOON, Su Yang Flat 2, 44 Limehill Road, Tunbridge Wells TN1 1LL; PO Box 151, Sibu 96007, Sarawak, Malaysia — BM BS 1992 Nottm.; MRCP (UK). Specialist Regist. (Gastroenterol.) Kent & Sussex Hosp.

SOON, Ying 25 Priory Road, Newbury RG14 7QS — MB BS 1985 Lond.

SOON, Yuen 79 Grosvenor Road, Harborne, Birmingham B17 9AL — MB BS 1991 Lond.

SOONG, Chee Voon 6 Woodlands Close, Lisburn BT28 2XR — MB BCh BAO 1985 Belf.; MB BCh Belf. 1985.

SOOPRAMANIEN, Anbananden Duke of Cornwall Spinal Treatment Centre, Salisbury District Hospital, Salisbury SP2 8BJ Tel: 01722 336262 Ext: 2433 Fax: 01722 336550 Email: asoopraman@aol.com; 5 Thompson Close, Salisbury SP2 8QU Tel: 01722 339691 Fax: 01722 341422 — MD 1985 Amiens; MD (Amiens) 1985; PhD (Toulouse) 1977; MB BCh (Bordeaux) 1982. Cons. (Spinal Injuries & Rehabil. Med.). Socs: Internat. Med. Soc. of Paraplegia; BMA; Roy. Soc. Med. Prev: Cons. (Rehabil. Med.) Lincoln.

SOOR, Sajjan Singh (retired) 44 Newlands Lane, Heath Hayes, Cannock WS12 5HH Tel: 01543 279975 — MB BS 1960 Lond. Prev: Ho. Phys. Huddersfield Roy. Infirm.

SOORAE, Mr Ajaib Singh The Cardiothoracic Centre NHS Trust, Thomas Drive, Liverpool L14 3PE Tel: 0151 228 1616 Fax: 0151 228 5539 Email: ajaib.soorae@ccl-tr.nwest.nhs.uk; Tel: 0170 48 77799 — MB BS 1966 Punjab; FRCS Ed. 1971; FRCS Eng. 1975; LRCP (UK) 1975; T(S) 1991; Glancy Med. Coll. Amritsar). (Glancy Medical College, Amritsar) Cons. Cardio-Thoracic Surg. The Cardiothoracic Centre NHS Trust Liverp.; Hon. Lect. Univ. Liverp. Socs: Defence Union.; Soc. Thoracic & Cardiovasc. Surgs. Gt. Brit. & Irel. & Med.; Europ. Assn. for Cardiothoracic Surg. Prev: Sen. Regist. (Cardiothoracic Surg.) Roy. Vict. Hosp. Belf.; Regist. (Cardiothoracic Surg.) Walsgrave Hosp. Coventry; SHO (Gen. Surg.) St. Annes Hosp. Lond.

SOORAE, Sarabjit Singh Ashfield Surgery, 8 Walmley Road, Sutton Coldfield B76 1QN Tel: 0121 351 7955 Fax: 0121 313 2509 — MB ChB 1994 Birm.; ChB Birm. 1994.

SOORIAKUMARAN, Mr Sellaiah Queen Mary's University Hospital, Roehampton Lane, London SW15 5PR Tel: 020 8355 2725 Fax: 020 8355 2952 Email: soori.qmrh@virgin.net; 50 High Drive, New Malden KT3 3UB Tel: 020 8949 4234 Email: soori.qmrh@virgin.net — MB BS 1974 Sri Lanka; FRCS Glas. 1983; FRCS Ed. 1983; FRCS Eng. 1982; MRCS Eng. LRCP Lond. 1981; FRCP 2000. (Sri Lanka) Cons. Rehabil. Qu. Mary's Univ. Hosp. Lond. Socs: RCS; BMA; Roy. Soc. Med. Prev: Med. Off. & Sen. Regist. DSC Qu. Mary's Univ. Hosp. Lond.; Regist. (Gen. Surg.) Dewsbury & Staincliffe Gen. Hosps.

SOORIAKUMARAN, Velaiuthar 260 Prittlewell Chase, Westcliff on Sea SS0 0PR — MB BS 1973 Sri Lanka; LMSSA 1983; MRCGP 1986. GP Leigh-on-Sea.

SOORMA, Mr Akbar Maidstone Hospital, Hermitage Lane, Maidstone ME16 9QQ Tel: 01622 729000 Ext: 4216 Fax: 01622 224600 — MB BS 1982 Karachi, Pakistan; FRCS Glas. 1994; FFAEM 1996. Cons. A & E Med. Maidstone Hosp. Kent. Socs: Brit. Assn. Accid. & Emerg. Med.; Med. Protec. Soc.; BMA. Prev: Sen. Regist. Rotat. (A & E Med.) S. Thames (W.); Cons. A & E Med. Newham Gen. Hosp. Lond.

SOOSAY, Geraldine Nirmala Department of Histopathology, King George Hospital, Barley Lane, Goodmayes, Ilford IG3 8YB Tel: 020 8970 8419 — MB BS 1982 Lond.; MSc Lond. 1986, MB BS 1982; MRCPath 1990. Cons. Histopath. King Geo. Hosp. Goodmayes.

SOOTHILL, James Stephen Department of Medical Microbiology, 2nd Floor, Clinical Sciences Building, Manchester Royal Infirmary, Oxford Road, Manchester M13 9WL Tel: 0161 276 8830 Fax: 0161 276 8826 Email: james.soothill@man.ac.uk — MB BS 1985 Lond.; MD Lond. 1993; MRCPath 1997. (Guy's Hospital Medical School London) Lect. Med. MicroBiol.

SOOTHILL, Professor John Farrar Pensylvania, Lodge Lane, Axminster EX13 5RT Tel: 01297 33800 — MB BChir 1949 Camb.; MA Camb. 1951; FRCP Lond. 1971, M 1954; FRCPath 1974, M 1965; FRCPaed 1997. (Guy's) Emerit. Prof. Inst. Child Health Lond. Socs: Brit. Soc. Immunol. Ex. Comm. Chairm.; Brit. Soc. Of Allergy & Clin. Immunol.; Brit. Gp. for Paediat. Immunol. and Infec. Dis.s. Prev: Hon. Cons. Immunol. Hosp. Sick Childr. Gt. Ormond. St. Lond.; Hugh Greenwood Prof. Immunol. Inst. Child Health Lond.; Sen. Lect. (Experim. Path.) Univ. Birm. Med. Sch.

SOOTHILL, Professor Peter William Department of Obstetrics & Gynaecology, University of Bristol, St Michaels Hospital, Southwells St., Bristol BS2 8EG Tel: 0117 928 5277 Fax: 0117 928 5683 Email: peter.soothill @bristol.ac.uk — MB BS 1982 Lond.; BSc Lond. 1979, MD 1987; MRCOG 1989. (Guy's) Cons. (Matern. & Fetal Med.) St Michael's Hosp. Bristol. Prev: Prof. Matern. & Fetal Med. & O & G Univ. Bristol; Sen. Lect. & Cons. O & G Univ. Coll. Lond.; Lect. & Sen. Regist. (O & G) King's Coll. Hosp. Lond.

SOPER, Frederick Robert Charles 1 Mackie Place, Aberdeen AB10 1PF — MB ChB 1957 Aberd.; MFCM 1986; MCFPC 1981; LMCC 1980; Cert. Family Plann. JCC 1978. Comm. Med. Specialist Grampian Health Bd. Prev: Sen. Med. Off. Bonavista Hosp.; Ho. Phys. St. Woolos Hosp. Newport; Ho. Surg. Aberd. Roy. Infirm.

SOPER, James William (retired) White Horses, Sycamore Close, Milford-on-Sea SO41 0RY Tel: 01590 673564 — MB BChir 1959 Camb.; MA, MB Camb. 1959, BChir 1958; DA Eng. 1961; DObst RCOG 1959. Prev: GP Lymington.

SOPER, Richard Henry Victoria Surgery, Victoria Street, Bury St Edmunds IP33 3BD Tel: 01284 725550 Fax: 01284 725551; Cobbs Hall, Great Saxham, Bury St Edmunds IP29 5JN Tel: 01284 755123 — MB BS Lond. 1968; MRCS Eng. LRCP Lond. 1968; DA Eng. 1971; DObst RCOG 1971. (St. Bart.)

SOPHER, Brian Joseph Unsworth Medical Centre, Parr Lane, Unsworth, Bury BL9 8JR Tel: 0161 766 4448 Fax: 0161 767 9811; 35 Upper Park Road, Salford M7 4JB Tel: 0161 795 7834 — MB ChB 1977 Manch.; BSc St. And. 1974; MRCGP 1981. Occupat. Health Phys. Bolton Metrop. Local Auth. Socs: Soc. Occupat. Med.; Assn. Police Surg. Prev: Clin. Asst. (Obst.) St. Mary's Hosp. Manch.; SHO (O & G & Paediat.) St. Mary's Hosp. Manch.; Ho. Surg. N. Manch. Gen. Hosp.

SOPHER, Solomon Mark 22 Lower Belgrave Street, London SW1W 0LN — MB BS 1990 Lond.; MB BS (Distinc.) Lond. 1990; BSc Basic Med. Sci. & Physiol. 1st cl. Hons. Lond. 1987; MRCP (UK) 1993. Research Fell. (Cardiol. Sci.s) St. Geo. Hosp. Med. Sch. Lond. Prev: SHO Nat. Hosp. Qu. Sq. Lond.; SHO Hammersmith Hosp. Lond.; SHO (ITU) St. Thos. Hosp. Lond.

SOPPET, Pamela Elizabeth Rose 1 Great Wheatleys Road, Rayleigh SS6 7AL — MB 1975 Camb.; BChir 1974; DCH Eng. 1977.

SOPPITT, Andrew James Poole General Hospital, Longfleet Road, Poole BH15 2 — MB ChB 1988 Birm.; BSc Birm. 1985, ChB 1988; MRCP (UK) 1991. Regist. (Anaesth.) Poole & Bournemouth Gen. Hosps. Prev: SHO (Anaesth.) Roy. United Hosp. Bath & Soton. Gen. Hosp.; SHO Rotat. (Med.) Kidderminster Gen. Hosp. & Dudley Rd. Birm.

SOPPITT, Helen Suzanne 5 Millflat, Auchtermuchty, Cupar KY14 7BQ; 31 Pitwllen Terrace, Perth PH2 7EQ — MB ChB 1992 Ed. (Edinburgh) GP Princip.

SOPPITT, Richard William Child and Family Unit, Northbrook Health Centre, 93 Northbrook Road, Solihull B90 3LX — MB ChB 1989 Birm.; MRCPsych 1995; MMedSci 1997. (Birm.) Cons. Solihull Health Care Trust; Hon. Sen. Lect. Birm. Univ. Prev: Sen. Regist. (Child Psychiat.) Pk.view Clinic Birm.

SOPWITH, Arthur Marcus 27 Woodcote, Maidenhead SL6 4DU Tel: 01628 638633 — MB BChir 1976 Camb.; MD Camb. 1983;

SORAGHAN

MRCP (UK) 1978; MFPM RCP (UK) 1996. Prev: Pfizer Centr. Research; Celltech R&D.

SORAGHAN, Pauline Gertrude 9 Stirling Drive, Bearsden, Glasgow G61 4NX — MB BCh BAO 1980 NUI.

SORAPURE, John Boileau 14 Caledon Road, Parkstone, Poole BH14 9NN Tel: 01202 722947 — MB BS 1958 Lond.; MRCS Eng. LRCP Lond. 1958; DObst RCOG 1960. (Lond. Hosp.) Socs: BMA & Bournem. Med. Soc. Prev: Clin. Asst. (Paediat.) Roy. Vict. Hosp. Boscombe; Ho. Surg. St. And. Hosp. Dollis Hill; Ho. Phys. & Ho. Surg. (Obst.) Lond. Hosp.

SORBY, Nicholas Geoffrey Dare Parklands Hospital, Basingstoke RG24 9RH Tel: 01256 376355 Fax: 01256 376452 — MB BS 1979 Lond.; FRCPsych 2001. (Middlx.) Cons. Psychiat. Surrey Hants. borders NHS Trust.

SOREFAN, Oomar Mia Ayoob 27 St Stephens Court, Canterbury CT2 7JP Tel: 01227 66253 — MB ChB 1981 Sheff.; MRCPI 1984; MRCGP 1988; DGM RCP Lond. 1989. SHO (O & G) OldCh. Hosp. Romford. Prev: SHO Rotat. Kent & Canterbury Hosp.; Trainee GP Canterbury Health Centre.

SOREN, Dhuni Boarijore, 33 Longmeadow Road, Knowsley, Prescot L34 0HN — MB BS 1963 Patna.

SORENSEN, Michael Harry Berwyn House Surgery, 13 Shrubbery Avenue, Worcester WR1 1QW Tel: 01905 22888 Fax: 01905 617352; 2 Nash Close, Worcester WR3 7YD — MB ChB 1975 Bristol.

SORENSEN, Sorrel Adair Allport Flat 2/1, 10 Kersland St., Hillhead, Glasgow G12 8BL — MB ChB 1998 Glas.; MB ChB Glas 1998.

SORENSEN-POUND, David John Plowright Surgery, Market Place, Swaffham PE37 7LQ Tel: 01760 722797 Fax: 01760 720025; Pear Tree Farm, Southburgh, Thetford IP25 7TE Tel: 01362 821403 Email: peartree11@yahoo.com — MB BS 1983 Lond.; MRCGP 1988; DRCOG 1987; DA (UK) 1985. Prev: Med. Off. Oman; GP Shipdham Norf.; Med. Off. Tristan Da Cunha.

SORIA, Andres 4 The Woodlands, Puddingwood Lane, Broomfield, Chelmsford CM1 7ES — LMS 1992 U Complutense Madrid.

SORKIN, Stanley Lingwell Croft Surgery, Ring Road, Middleton, Leeds LS10 3LT Tel: 0113 270 4848 Fax: 0113 272 0030 — MB ChB 1958 Leeds; DObst RCOG 1960.

SORNALINGAM, Chelliah Parkway Health Centre, Parkway, New Addington, Croydon CR0 0JA Tel: 01689 848939; 54 Kendall Avenue S., South Croydon CR2 0QQ Tel: 020 8660 3604 — MB BS 1958 Ceylon; MRCOG 1975, DObst 1973. (Ceylon) GP S. Croydon.

SORNALINGAM, Narendra Alexandra Surgery, 39 Alexandra Road, London SW19 7JZ Tel: 020 8946 7578 Fax: 020 8944 5650; 19 Fir Grove, New Malden KT3 6RH — MSBS Lond. 1991; DRCOG RCOG 1995; DFFP 1996 (RCOG). (Univ. Coll. & Middl. Hosp.) GP Princip. Wimbledon, Lond.

SOROOSHIAN, Khodayar Central Health Centre, North Carbrain Road, Cumbernauld, Glasgow G67 1BJ Tel: 0141 731738; Tower House, Luggiebank, Cumbernauld, Glasgow G67 4AB — MB ChB 1958 Glas. (Glas.) Prev: Regist. Orthop. & Accid. Lister Hosp. Hitchin; Regist. in Orthop. Lord Mayor Treloar Hosp. Alton; SHO Path. Roy. Hants. Co. Hosp. Winchester.

SOROUR, Gillian Ann 34C Edbrooke Road, London W9 2DG — MB BCh 1993 Witwatersrand.

***SORRELL, Deborah Natalie** 3 Tudor House, 6 Pinner Hill Road, Pinner HA5 3RY — BM BS 1997 Nottm.

SORRELL, Jennifer Anne Portfields, Port Lane, Rugeley WS15 3DX — MB BS 1969 Lond.; MSc Manch. 1976. Chief Exec. S. Staffs. HA. Prev: Dir. (Pub. Health) SE Staffs.; Specialist Community Med. (Health Care Plann.) Derbysh. AHA; Specialist Community Med. (Plann. & Informat.) Trafford AHA.

SORRELL, John Eric, OStJ Milton Keynes Occupational Health Service Ltd., 9 Darin Court, Crownhill, Milton Keynes MK8 0AD Tel: 01908 262464 Email: john.e.sorrell@btinternet.com; Border Green, 81 Hartwell Road, Hanslope, Milton Keynes MK19 7BY Tel: 01908 510953 — MRCS Eng. LRCP Lond. 1971; BSc (Hons.) Lond. 1968, MB BS 1971; MRCGP 1976; mFOM Lond. 2000; DCH Eng. 1975; DObst RCOG 1973. (St. Bart.) Med. Dir. MKOHS Ltd. Socs: Fell.Roy.Soc.Med. Prev: GP Trainer Oxf. Region, Milton Keynes Scheme; G.P. Bucks.

SORRIE, George Strath, CB (retired) 30 Irvine Crescent, St Andrews KY16 8LG Tel: 01334 474510 Email: gsorrie@excite.co.uk — MB ChB 1957 Aberd.; FFOM RCP Lond. 1982; DIH Dund 1976; DPH (Distinc.) Lond. 1963; DObst RCOG 1962. Prev: Med. Adviser to Civil Serv. & Dir. Civil Serv. Occupat. Health Serv.

SORSBIE, Leigh Firth Park Road Surgery, 400 Firth Park Road, Sheffield S5 6HH Tel: 0114 242 6406 — MB ChB 1990 Sheff.

SORTSIS, Andreas 17 Leopold Road, Crawley RH11 7BN — Ptychio latrikes 1988 Patras.

SORUNGBE, Akanni Olufemi Olakunle 10 Gratton Terrace, London NW2 6QE Tel: 020 8450 6015 Fax: 020 8450 6015 — MB BS 1960 Lond.; MCRS Eng. LRCP Lond. 1960; DPH Eng 1974; FRIPHH 1985. Socs: BMA; Roy. Soc. Trop. Med. & Hyg.; Fell. Roy. Inst. Pub. Health & Hyg.

***SOSIN, Michael David** Sandwell General Hospital, Lyndon, West Bromwich; 48 Savoy Close, Harborne, Birmingham B32 2JA — MB ChB 1998 Birm.

SOSKIN, Michelle Anne Anaesthetic Department, 1 Watford General Hospital, Vicarage Road, Watford WD18 0HB Tel: 01923 244366 Email: michellemike@hotmail.co.uk — MB ChB (Hons) Manch. 1987; FRCA 1993. Cons. (Anaesth. & Intens. Care) Watford Gen. W. Herts Trust. Socs: Intens. Care Soc.; Assn. Anaesth. Prev: Sen. Regist. Rotat. (Anaesth. & Intens. Care) Roy. Free Hosp.; Regist. Middlx. & Univ. Coll. Hosps.

SOSNOWSKI, Marcin Andrzej 54 Dumbleton Avenue, Leicester LE3 2EG — MB ChB 1992 Leeds.

SOTHERAN, Wendy Justine 14 West Street, Titchfield, Fareham PO14 4DH — MB BS 1990 Lond.; BSc Lond. 1987; FRCS Eng. 1995. (St. Mary's Hosp. Lond.) Guernsey Research Fell. Univ. Soton.

SOTHI, Sharmila 1C Earlham Grove, London N22 5HJ — MB BS 1990 Lond.; MRCP (UK) 1993. Regist. (Clin. Oncol.) Birm. Oncol. Centre. Prev: SHO Rotat. (Med.) Brighton.

SOTIRIOU, Sotirios 22 Lyveden Road, London SE3 8TP — Ptychio latrikes 1994 Athens.

SOTO MALET, Victor Flat 2, 12 Canadian Avenue, London SE6 3AS — LMS 1994 U Autonoma Barcelona.

SOTT, Miss Andrea Helene 5 Cavendish Court, Cavendish Road, Weybridge KT13 0JN Email: cbusch9965@aol — State Exam Med 1991 Bochum; FRCS (Eng.) 1995. (Germany) Specialist Regist. Rotat. (Orthop.) SW Thames Kingston Hosp.

SOUBERBIELLE, Bernard Eric 88 Egmont Road, Sutton SM2 5JS — MD 1984 Paris. Wellcome Research Fell. Univ. St. And.; Lect. Kings Coll. Lond. Prev: SHO (Path.) Selly Oak Hosp. Birm.

SOUCEK, Sava ENT Department/Audiology, St. Mary's Hospital, London W2 1NY Tel: 020 7725 1015 Fax: 020 7725 6200; Fax: 020 7388 6360 — MUDr 1959 Prague; PhD Lond. 1987. (Charles University) Cons. Audiol. Phys. St. Mary's Hosp. Lond. Socs: Internat. Soc. Audiol.; BMA; Brit. Assn. Audiol. Phys. (Social Sec.). Prev: Sen. Regist. (Audiol. Med.) Roy. Nat. Throat, Nose & Ear Hosp. Lond.; Sen. Regist. (ENT) Chas. Univ. Prague.

SOUHAMI, Professor Robert Leon Faculty of Clinical Sciences, University College London Administration, Gower St., London WC1E 6BT Tel: 020 7209 6303 Fax: 020 7383 2462; 135 Rosebery Road, Muswell Hill, London N10 2LD Tel: 020 8444 6660 Fax: 020 8444 6660 — MB BS Lond. 1962; BSc Lond. 1959, MD 1975; FRCP Lond. 1979, M 1966; FRCR 1992. (Univ. Coll. Hosp.) Dean Gower St. Campus Roy. Free & Univ. Coll. Med. Sch.; Cons. Phys. Univ. Coll. & Middlx. Hosps. Lond.; Hon. Cons. Phys. (Med. Oncol.) Whittington Hosp. & Roy. Nat. Orthop. Hosp. Lond.; Fell. UCL. Socs: (Pres.) Europ. Musculo-Skeletal Oncol. Soc.; Assn. Phys. Prev: Prof. Clin. Oncol. Univ. Coll. Lond. Med. Sch.; Cons. Phys. Poole Gen. Hosp.

SOUKIAS, Nikolaos 2 Roundwood Close, Cyncoed, Cardiff CF23 9HH — Ptychio latrikes 1985 Thessalonika.

SOUKOP, Michel 2nd Floor Administration, St Mungo Institute, Link Corridor, Glasgow Royal Infirmary, Glasgow G4 OSF Tel: 0141 211 1160 Fax: 0141 211 0515 Email: michael.soukop@northglasgow.scotnhs.uk; 15 Cleveden Gardens, Glasgow G12 0PU Tel: 0141 357 1455 — MB ChB 1971 St. And.; FRCP Lond. 1994; FRCP Ed. 1991; FRCP Glas. 1986; MRCP (UK) 1974. Cons. Phys. & Med. Oncol. Glas. Roy. Infirm.; Hon. Sen. Lect. Glas. Univ.; Represen. Jt. Counc. RCP & RCR in Oncol.; Sec. to the SAC in Med. Oncol. Socs: Assn. Cancer Phys.; BMA (Chairm. GCHMS & Represen. to SCHMS & CCSC). Prev: Vis. Lect. (Human Oncol.) Univ. Wisconsin, Madison, USA; Sen. Regist. & Research Fell. (Med. Oncol.) Glas. Univ. & Gartnavel Gen. Hosp. Glas.

SOUL, Mrs Anne Rosemary Knowle House Surgery, 4 Meavy Way, Crownhill, Plymouth PL5 3JB Tel: 01752 771895 Fax: 01752 766510 — MB BS 1972 Lond.; MRCS Eng. LRCP Lond. 1969; DRCOG 1986. (Guy's)

SOUL, Mr John Oliver, Surg. Capt. RN Retd. Trevenevow, Crapstone Road, Yelverton PL20 6BT Tel: 01822 854923 — MB BS Lond. 1971; FRCS Eng. 1976; MRCS Eng. LRCP Lond. 1970; LMSSA Lond 1970. (Guy's) Freeman Worshipful Soc. Apoth. Lond. Prev: Cons. Surg. RN Hosp. Plymouth; Hon. Sen. Regist. (Thoracic Surg.) E. Birm. Hosp.

SOUL, Jonathan David Marfleet Group Practice, 350 Preston Road, Hull HU9 5HH Tel: 01482 701834; Swallownest, 15 Bond St, Hedon, Hull HU12 8NY Tel: 01482 890308 — MB ChB 1990 Sheff. (Sheff.) Prev: Trainee GP Bassetlaw VTS.

SOULBY, Georgina Carol 35 Harrison Road, Crofton, Wakefield WF4 1NE; Keighley Health Centre, Oakworth Road, Keighley BD21 1SA Tel: 01535 606111 — MB ChB 1975 Dundee; FRCP (UK) 1978; DCH RCP Lond. 1982; FRCPCH. Cons. Community Paediat. Airedale NHS Trust. Prev: SCMO Leeds Community & Ment. Health Servs. Trust; SCMO Wakefield HA; Clin. Med. Off. Wakefield HA.

SOULIOTI, Alexia Maria Angeliki 49 Shrewsbury House, Cheyne Walk, London SW3 5LW — MRCS Eng. LRCP Lond. 1975; BSc Lond. 1971; MRCP (UK) 1982; FFA RCS Eng. 1979; DCH Eng. 1978.

SOULSBY, Niel Warren 3 Hunters Lodge, The Green, Wallsend NE28 7ES — MB BS 1992 Newc.

***SOULSBY, Rachel Emma** Holy Trinity Rectory, The Village, Orton Longueville, Peterborough PE2 7DN — MB BS 1998 Lond.; MB BS Lond 1998.

SOULSBY, Ruth Helen Rosemary — MB ChB 1989 Sheff.; FRCS Ed. 1995.

SOULSBY, Thomas Peter 22 High Street, Liverpool L25 7TE — MB ChB 1986 Liverp.; MRCP (UK) 1990; DA (UK) 1994.

SOUNDARARAJAN, Portonovo Chockalingam North Gate Hospital, Morpeth NE61 3BP Tel: 01670 394000 Fax: 01670 394004 — MB BS 1966 Madras; MRCPsych 1981; DPM Eng. 1978. (Thanjavur Med. Coll.) Cons. N.gate Hosp. Morpeth; Lect. (Psych. Med.) Univ. Newc. u. Tyne.

SOUNDY, Victoria Clare Department of Histopathology, Gloucestershire Royal Hospital, Great Western Road, Gloucester GL1 3NN Tel: 01452 395262; 5 Wallbank House, Denmark Road, Gloucester GL1 3HZ — MB BS 1993 Lond.; BSc (Hons. Path.) Lond. 1990. (Char. Cross & Westm.) Specialist Regist. (Histopath.) Gloucester/Bristol. Socs: Med. Defence Union; Train. Mem. Assn. Clin. Path. Prev: Specialist Regist. (Histopath.) Univ. Coll. Hosp. Lond.; SHO (Histopath.) John Radcliffe Hosp. Oxf.; SHO (A & E) Chelsea & W.m. Hosp. Lond.

SOUPER, Dorothy Kilner (retired) 154 Christchurch Road, Norwich NR2 3PQ Tel: 01603 54126 — MB BChir 1939 Camb.; MA, MB Camb. 1939, BChir 1933; DOMS Eng. 1940. Mem. Oxf. Ophth. Congr. Prev: Ho. Surg. Cheltenham Eye Hosp.

SOUPER, Katharine 18 Fulmer Road, Sheffield S11 8UF; Yule Cottage, Upham St, Upham, Southampton SO32 1JA Tel: 0148 96 225 — MB BS 1990 Lond.; BSc Lond. 1987; MRCP (UK) 1993.

SOURIAL, Amoun Sity Aziz Flat 57, 6/9 Charterhouse Square, London EC1M 6EU Tel: 020 7251 1106 — MB BCh 1978 Cairo. Med. Adviser to Callenders Ltd. Basildon, Vulcanite Ltd., Wakefield, Flat Bed J. V. Chester & Laybond Products Chester, P.U.R. Systems Glossop. Socs: Soc. Occupat. Med. Prev: Occupat. Med. Adviser Med. & Indust. Servs. Ltd. E.bourne.

SOURINDHRIN, Ittiacandy Dykebar Hospital, Paisley PA2 7DJ — MB BS 1968 Madras; MRCPsych 1980. (Jawaharlal Inst. Postgrad. Med. Pondicherry) Cons. Psychiat. Dykebar Hosp. Paisley. Prev: Sen. Regist. (Psychiat.) Gtr. Glas. Health Bd.; Regist. (Psychiat.) Duke St. Hosp. Glas. & Gartloch Hosp. Gartcosh; SHO Midl. Centre Neurosurg. & Neurol. Smethwick.

SOUSSI, Mr Ahmad Chafic 8 Rowallan Gardens, Glasgow G11 7LJ — MB ChB 1972 Cairo; FRCS Glas. 1987.

SOUSTER, Howard (retired) Norwood, 14 Park Road, Ipswich IP1 3ST Tel: 01473 720170 — MRCS Eng. LRCP Lond. 1941. Prev: Med. Ref. Methodist Homes For The Aged.

SOUSTER, John Leonard 2 Cooper's Barns, Camel St., Marston Magna, Yeovil BA22 8DB — MB BS 1946 Lond.; MRCS Eng. LRCP Lond. 1943. (Lond. Hosp.) Prev: Ho. Surg. Lond. Hosp.; Surg. Lt. RNVR.

SOUTAR, Alastair James (retired) Firdene, Redlynch, Salisbury SP5 2PR Tel: 01725 510210 — MB ChB 1944 Aberd.

SOUTAR, Alice Lindsay Duncan 80 Western Road, Woodside, Aberdeen AB24 4SU Tel: 01224 492828; 8 Braeside Place, Aberdeen AB15 7TU Tel: 01224 322053 — MB ChB 1986 Dundee; MRCGP 1991; DCH RCPS Glas. 1990; DRCOG 1988. Prev: Trainee GP/SHO (Community Paediat.) Highland & Glas. VTS.

SOUTAR, Sir Charles John Williamson, KBE, Air Marshal RAF Med. Br. (retired) Oak Cottage, 57 High St., Aldeburgh IP15 5AU Tel: 01728 452201 — MB BS Lond. 1945; LMSSA Lond. 1945; FFCM 1979, M 1974; DIH Eng. 1960; DPH Lond. 1959. Prev: Dir.-Gen. Med. Servs. RAF.

SOUTAR, Colin Andrew Institute of Occupational Medicine, 8 Roxburgh Place, Edinburgh EH8 9SU Tel: 0131 667 5131; 8 Ravelston Rise, Edinburgh EH4 3LH Tel: 0131 337 2104 — MB BS 1966 Lond.; MD Lond. 1977; FRCP Ed. 1989; MRCP (UK) 1969; MRCS Eng. LRCP Lond. 1966; FFOM RCP Lond. 1994. (Guy's) Chief Exec. Inst. Occupat. Med. Edin.; Hon. Sen. Lect. Univ. Edin. Prev: Head Med. Br. Inst. Occupat. Med. Edin.; Asst. Prof. of Med. (Pulm.) Univ. Illinois Med. Centre Chicago, USA; Hon. Cons. Phys. City Hosp. Edin.

SOUTAR, Mr David Strang The Glasgow Nuffield Hospital, Beaconsfield Road, Glasgow G12 0PJ Tel: 0141 334 9441 Fax: 0141 339 1352; Raheen, 7 Chesters Road, Bearsden, Glasgow G61 4AQ Tel: 0141 942 4175 — MB ChB 1972 Aberd.; ChM Aberd. 1987; FRCS Glas. 1983; FRCS Ed. 1977. Cons. Plastic Surg. W. Scotl. Regional Plastic & Oral Surg. Unit Canniesburn Hosp. Glas.; Hon. Clin. Sen. Lect. Univ. Glas.; Chariman- Div. of Trauma and Related Serv.s N. Glas. Univ NHS Trust. Socs: Brit. Assn. Plastic Surg.; Brit. Assn. Aesthetic Plastic Surgs.; Brit Assn. Head and Neck Oncologists. Prev: Sen. Regist. W. Scotl. Regional Plastic & Oral Surg. Unit Canniesburn Hosp. Glas.; Regist. (Gen. Surg.) Grampian HB.

SOUTAR, Ian 79 Slateford Road, Edinburgh EH11 1QW Tel: 0131 313 2796; 15 Douglas Crescent, Edinburgh EH12 5BA Tel: 0131 225 4593 — MB ChB 1956 Glas.; DObst. RCOG 1961.

SOUTAR, Richard Lewis Department of Haematology, Monklands District General Hospital, Airdrie ML6 0JS Tel: 01236 748748 Email: richard@mdghhaem.demon.co.uk; 5 Claremont Avenue, Kirkintilloch, Glasgow G66 1BB Tel: 0141 776 5363 — MB ChB 1986 Dundee; MD Dundee 1996; BMSc (Hons.) Dund 1983; MRCP (UK) 1989; MRCPath 1994, D 1993. Cons. Haemat. Monklands Dist. Gen. Hosp. Airdrie; Sen. Lect. Dept. Haemat. W.. Infirm. Glas. Socs: Brit. Soc. Haematol.; Scott. Soc. of Experim. Med.; Roy. Coll. Phys. Edin. Prev: Sen. Regist. (Haemat.) Aberd. Roy. Infirm.; Resid. (Haemat.) McMaster Univ. Hamilton, Ontario; Regist. (Haemat.) Glas. Roy. Infirm.

SOUTER, Andrew John Department of Anaesthesia, Royal United Hospital, Combe Park, Bath BA1 3NG Tel: 01225 825056 Fax: 01225 825061; 2 Cedric Close, Weston, Bath BA1 3PQ Tel: 01225 424393 Email: ajsouter@aol.com — MB ChB 1986 Ed.; FRCA 1992. (Ed.) Cons. Anaesth. Roy. United Hosp. Bath. Socs: Obst. Anaesth. Assn.; Pain Soc.; Assn. Anaesth. Prev: Sen. Regist. & Regist. (Anaesth.) Nuffield Dept. Anaesth. Oxf.; Vis. Asst. Prof. Univ. Texas, Dallas, USA.

SOUTER, Keith Moray New Southgate Surgery, Buxton Place, off Leeds Road, Wakefield WF1 3JQ Tel: 01924 334400 Fax: 01924 334439; 106 Manygates Lane, Sandal, Wakefield WF1 7DP Tel: 01924 256201 Fax: 01924 256201 — MB ChB 1976 Dundee; DSc Colombo 1993; MRCGP 1981. Hon Tutor (Gen. Pract.) Univ. Leeds. Socs: Brit. Soc. Med. & Dent. Hypn. & Brit. Med. Acupunc. Soc.

SOUTER, Michael James Institute of Neurological Sciences, Southern General Hospital, 1345 Govan Road, Glasgow G51 4TF Tel: 0141 201 1100; 7 Gloucester Place, Edinburgh EH3 6EE Tel: 0131 225 2974 Email: m.j.souter@ed.ac.uk — MB ChB 1984 Ed.; FRCA. 1992; DA (UK) 1990. (Edinburgh) Cons. (Neuroanaesth. & Neuro-IC) Inst. of Neurol. Sci.s S.ern Gen. Hosp. Glas.; Sen. Lect. (Anaesth.) Univ. Glas. Prev: Lect. (Anaesth.) Edin.; Sen. Regist. (Anaesth.); MRC Clin. Res. Fell. (Clin. Neurosci.) Univ. of Edin.

SOUTER, Mr Robin Graham Milton Keynes Hospital NHS Trust, Standing Way, Eaglestone, Milton Keynes MK6 5LD Tel: 01908 660033 Fax: 01908 669348 Email: robinsouter@al.com; 10

SOUTER

Cottisford Crescent, Great Linford, Milton Keynes MK14 5HH Tel: 01908 666196 Fax: 01908 665947 — MD 1981 Glas.; FRCS Edinb. (Hons.) 2001; MB ChB Glas. 1971; FRCS Eng. 1977; FRCS Glas. 1976. Cons. Gen. Surg. Milton Keynes Hosp.; Lead Clinician Cancer Servs.; Chair Oxf. Regional Surg. Professional Developm. Comm.; Examr. Roy. Coll. of Surg.s of Glas. Socs: Assn. of Surg.s of Gt. Britain & Irel.; Vasc. Surgic. Soc.; Brit. Assn. of Surgic. Oncol. Prev: Lect. Nuffield Dept. Surg. John Radcliffe Hosp. Oxf.

SOUTER, Mr William Alexander Princess Margaret Rose Hospital, Frogston Road, Edinburgh EH10 7ED Tel: 0131 536 4600 Fax: 0131 536 4601; Old Mauricewood Mains, Penicuik EH26 0NJ Tel: 01968 672609 Email: 106727.1762.compuserve.com — MB ChB (Hons.) Ed. 1957; FRCS Ed. 1960. (Ed.) Hon. Research Cons. Orthop. Surg. P.ss Margt. Rose Orthop. Hosp. Edin. Socs: Fell. (Counc.) BOA; (Pres.) Brit. Soc. Surg. Hand.; (Pres.) Europ. Rheum. Arthritus Surgic. Soc. Prev: Sen. Regist. (Orthop.) Edin. Roy. Infirm. & P.ss Margt. Rose Hosp.; Regist. (Hand Surg.) Derbysh. Roy. Infirm.; Instruc. (Orthop.) Univ. Washington, Seattle, USA.

SOUTER, William Angus (retired) Ardlui, 7 Iain Road, Bearsden, Glasgow G61 4LX Tel: 0141 942 3787 — MB ChB 1940 Glas.; MRCOG 1950; FRCOG 1998.

***SOUTH, Alison Louise** 3 Central Av, Greenfield, Oldham OL3 7DH — MB ChB 1997 Leeds.

SOUTH, David The Mede, Cotheridge, Worcester WR6 5LZ — MB ChB 1964 Birm.; FRCR 1980; DMRD Eng. 1974; FFA RCS Eng. 1972. Cons. Radiol. Worcester HA. Prev: Sen. Regist. (Radiol.) Birm. AHA (T); SHO (Med.) King Edwd. VII Memor. Chest Hosp.; Ho. Off. (Med.) Roy. Hosp. Wolverhampton.

SOUTH, Mrs Elizabeth Ann (retired) Neville Cottage, Warren Rise, New Malden KT3 4SJ Email: south@warrenrise.freeserve.co.uk — MB ChB 1962 Manch. Prev: SCMO Merton & Sutton HA.

SOUTH, Joanna Pirians Tilt, Aviary Road, Pyrford, Woking GU22 8TH Tel: 0148 62 46876 — MB BS 1960 Lond.; MRCS Eng. LRCP Lond. 1960; MRCOG 1967, DObst 1961; DA Eng. 1962.

SOUTH, Mr John Roger Neville Cottage, Warren Rise, New Malden KT3 4SJ — MB ChB 1961 Manch.; FRCS Eng. 1967. Prev: Sen. Lect. & Cons. Neurosurg. Chinese Univ. Hong Kong; Sen. Regist. Nat. Hosp. & Atkinson Morley's Hosp. Lond.

SOUTH, Leah Marie Pullen Barn, Staplehurst Road, Frittenden, Cranbrook TN17 2EE Tel: 0158 080332 — MB BS 1968 Lond.; MS Lond. 1979; FRCS Eng. 1973. (St. Bart.) Cons. Gen. Surg. Maidstone Hosp. Socs: Fell. Roy. Soc. Med.; Vasc. Soc. GB & Irel. Prev: Sen. Regist. (Gen. Surg. & Urol.) St. Geo. Hosp. Lond.; Sen. Regist. (Surg.) St. Jas. Hosp. Balham; Bernard Sunley Research Fell. RCS Eng.

SOUTH, Peter John Pullen Barn, Staplehurst Road, Frittenden, Cranbrook TN17 2EE Tel: 01580 852332 — MB BS 1968 Lond.; MRCP (UK) 1971; MRCGP 1977. (St. Bart.) Prev: Regist. (Med.) Hastings Gp. Hosps.; Regist. (Gen. Med. & Cardiol.) St. Stephen's Hosp. Lond.; Ho. Phys. (Chest Dis.) Lond. Chest Hosp.

SOUTH, Philippa Winifred 30 South Park Road, London SW19 8SX — MB ChB 1993 Manch.; BSc (Hons.) Path. Manch. 1991. SHO (Paediat.) Manch.

SOUTH, Richard Paul 43 Lateward Road, Brentford TW8 0PL — MB ChB 1987 Liverp. (Liverp.) Director (Malaria Progr.s & Treatm. Access) Global Community Partnerships. Prev: Scientif. Manager, Hoechst Marion Roussel.

SOUTHALL, Edward Mayfield Medical Centre, 37 Totnes Road, Paignton TQ4 5LA Tel: 01803 558257 Fax: 01803 663353 Email: edward.southall@gp-l83014.nhs.uk — MB BS 1975 Lond.; MRCP (UK) 1979; Cert. Family Plann. JCC 1983. (St. Geo.) Hosp. Pract. (Cardiol.) Torbay Hosp. Torquay. Socs: Brit. Soc. Echocardiogr. Prev: Regist. (Med. Cardiol. & Med. Gastroenterol.) Roy. United Hosp. Bath; Regist. (Med.) Torbay Hosp. Torquay.

SOUTHALL, Graham John Westgate Practice, Greenhill Health Centre, Church Street, Lichfield WS13 6JL Tel: 01543 414311 Fax: 01543 256364; 4 Park Road, Alrewas, Burton-on-Trent DE13 7AG — MB BS 1972 Lond.; DA Eng. 1978; DCH Eng. 1976; DObst RCOG 1975; MRCGP 1978. (Roy. Free) Prev: GP Trainee Coleshill Warks.; Med. Off. Shining Hosp. Pokhara, Nepal.

SOUTHALL, Joseph Gerard Anthony St Peters Hill Surgery, 15 St. Peters Hill, Grantham NG31 6QA Tel: 01476 590009 Fax: 01476 570898 — MB ChB 1988 Leeds; MRCGP 1995.

SOUTHALL, Peter James Pathology Laboratory, The General Hospital, Gloucester St., St Helier, Jersey JE2 3QS Tel: 01534 59000 Fax: 01534 59805 — MB BS 1977 Lond.; MRCPath 1988. (St. Bart.) Cons. Histopath. & Cytopath. Jersey Gen. Hosp. Prev: Cons. Histopath. & Cytopath. Aintree Hosps. Liverp.; Research Fell. & Hon. Sen. Regist. (Path.) Char. Cross & W.m. Med. Sch. Lond.; Regist. & Hon. Lect. (Path.) Bristol Roy. Infirm.

SOUTHALL, Philippa Helen Porking Barn, Clifford, Hereford HR3 5HE — M.B., Ch.B. Birm. 1947.

SOUTHALL, Tonya Ruth 21a Gloucester Avenue, London NW1 7AU Tel: 020 7267 0292 Email: tonya.southall@virgin.net; 316 Knightsfield, Welwyn Garden City AL8 7NQ — BM BS 1994 Nottm.; BMedSci Nottm. 1992. GP Reg. Lond. Prev: Ho. Off. (Surg.) Salisbury; Ho. Off. (Med.) Qu. Med. Centre Nottm.; SHO (O & G) Univ. Coll. Lond.

SOUTHAM, Mr John Armitage (retired) South Lodge, 49 Paul's Place, Ashtead KT21 1HN Tel: 01372 274452 — MB ChB Manch. 1953; FRCS Ed. 1961; FRCS Eng. 1961. Hon. Cons. Surg. Epsom Health Care NHS Trust; Mem. Med. Appeal Tribunals SE Eng. Prev: Sen. Regist. (Surg.) United Birm. Hosps.

SOUTHAM, Professor John Chambers (retired) 13 Corstorphine House Avenue, Edinburgh EH12 7AD Tel: 0131 334 3013 — MB BChir 1958 Camb.; BChD, LDS Leeds 1962; MD Camb. 1981; FDS RCS Ed. 1981; FRCPath 1983, M 1971. Prev: Vice-Dean & Sec. Fac. Dent. Surg. RCS Ed.

SOUTHAM, Richard John Capal Medical Practice, 95 Goodrest Avenue, Halesowen B62 0HP; 9 Oakdene Drive, Barnt Green, Birmingham B45 8LQ — MB ChB 1983 Birm.; D.OCC.Med. 2001; MRCGP 1988; DRCOG 1985. GP W. Midl.; Occupat.al Medicare.

SOUTHAN, Adam Warwick 14 Derwen Deg, Bryncoch, Neath SA10 7FP — MB BCh 1994 Wales; DRCOG 1997. (Cardiff) GP Regist.

SOUTHCOTT, Anne Marie Interstitial Lung Disease Unit, NHLI, Emmanuel Kaye Building, Manresa Road, London SW3 6LR — MB BS 1984 Adelaide; FRACP 1991.

SOUTHCOTT, Barbara Maud Creswick Department of Radiotherapy & Oncology, Charing Cross Hospital, Fulham Palace Road, London W6 8RF Tel: 020 8846 1731 Fax: 0208 746 8429 Email: bsouthcott@hhnt.org; 29 Melville Avenue, South Croydon CR2 7HZ Tel: 020 8688 2393 — MB BS 1967 Lond.; MRCS Eng. LRCP Lond. 1966; FRCR 1975; FFR 1974; DMRT Eng. 1971. Sen. Lect. & Hon. Cons. Radiother. & Oncol. Char. Cross Hosp. Lond.; Hon. Cons. Oncologist, W. Middlx. Hosp. And Roy. Marsden Hosp.; Hon. Cons. Radiother. & Oncol. Mayday Hosp. Thornton Heath & Ealing Hosp. Chelsea & W.m. Hosp. Lond. Socs: Brit. Inst. Radiol. & Brit. Oncol. Assn.; Brit. Radiol. Soc.; Rad. Soc. Prev: Sen. Regist. (Radiother. & Oncol.) Char. Cross Hosp. Lond.; SHO (Path.) Lewisham Hosp. Lond.

SOUTHCOTT, Michael Robert Pytchley Court Health Centre, 5 Northampton Road, Brixworth, Northampton NN6 9DX Tel: 01604 880228 Fax: 01604 880467 — MB BS 1975 Lond.; MRCS Eng. LRCP Lond. 1975; MRCGP 1981; DCH 1980; DRCOG 1977.

SOUTHCOTT, Mr Roy David Creswick 29 Melville Avenue, South Croydon CR2 7HZ Tel: 020 8688 2393 — MB BS 1956 Lond.; MB BS (Hons.) Lond. 1956; FRCS Eng. 1964; MRCS Eng. LRCP Lond. 1956; DTM & H Eng. 1961. (Guy's) Hon. Cons. Urol. E. Surrey Hosp.; Lt.-Col. RAMC (V). Socs: Assoc. Mem. BAUS; Brit. Prostate Gp. Prev: Cons. Surg. Mayday Hosp. Croydon; Sen. Regist. Roy. Free Hosp. Lond.; Ho. Off. Guy's Hosp. Lond.

SOUTHERN, David Andrew 1 Bracken Rise, Ellesmere SY12 9ET Tel: 01691 622725 — MB ChB 1988 Glas.; BSc (Hons.) Glas. 1985; FRCA 1993; DA (UK) 1991. Cons. (Anaesth.) Wrexham Maeler Hosp. Socs: BMA & Assn. Anaesth. Prev: Sen. Regist. (Anaesth.) Soton. Gen. Hosp.; Sen. Regist. & Regist. (Anaesth.) Townsville Gen. Hosp. Qu.sland, Austral.; Regist. (Anaesth.) Glan Clwyd Hosp. Wales & Univ. Hosp. Wales Cardiff.

SOUTHERN, Keith John Harold Health Centre, Fareham PO16 7ER Tel: 01329 823456; Ash House, Lee Ground, Fareham PO15 6RP Tel: 01329 844618 — MB ChB 1963 Liverp.; DObst RCOG 1968.

SOUTHERN, Kevin William Dept of Paediatrics, University of Leeds Infirmary, Leeds LS2 9NS Tel: 0113 283 6999 Fax: 0113 283 6999 Email: k.w.southern@leeds.ac.uk; 21 Rochester Terrace, Headingley, Leeds LS6 3DF Tel: 0113 275 5054 — MB ChB 1987

Leeds; PHD Leeds 1998. (Leeds) Lect. Univ of Leeds.; MRC Clin. Research Fell. St. Jas. Hosp. Leeds. Socs: Roy. Coll. Paediat. & Child Health; Yorks. Regional Paediat. Soc. Prev: SHO (Paediat.) Leeds W.. HA; Ho. Off. (Med.) Seacroft Leeds; Ho. Off. (Paediat.) Clarendon Wing Leeds.

SOUTHERN, Lee Patricia Tarleton Group Practice, The Health Centre, Tarleton, Preston PR4 6UJ — MB ChB 1990 Birm.; 2000 LFHom; DFFP 1995. (Univ. Birmingham) GP Princip. Prev: Trainee GP Wroughton; SHO Centr. Birm. VTS; Princip., Jubilee Field Surg.

***SOUTHERN, Paul Brian** St. James's University Hospital, Beckett St., Leeds LS9 7TF Tel: 0113 243 3144; 15 Sandringham Way, Moortown, Leeds LS17 8BX Tel: 0113 269 1244 — MB ChB 1996 Leeds.

SOUTHERN, Peter John Dicconson Terrace Surgery, Dicconson Terrace, Wigan WN1 2AF Tel: 01942 239525 Fax: 01942 826552 — MB BS 1983 Lond.; DRCOG 1987.

SOUTHERN, Robert John Cunliffe (retired) Cardunneth, Corby Hill, Carlisle CA4 8PJ Tel: 01228 560596 — MB ChB 1943 Ed.; FRCP Ed. 1993; MRCP (UK) 1950. Prev: Cons. Chest Phys. Carlisle & E. Cumbria.

SOUTHERN, Mr Stephen James 40 Birkenpale, Sheffield S6 3NJ Tel: 0114 234 8848 Email: 40birkendale@cw.com.net — MB BS 1987 Lond.; FRCS (Plast); FRCS Ed. 1992. Cons. Plastic, Reconstruc. and Hand Surg.

SOUTHERTON, Joanne Warden Lodge Surgery, Albury Ride, Cheshunt, Waltham Cross EN8 8XE Tel: 01992 622324 Fax: 01992 636900 — MB ChB 1985 Leic.; DRCOG 1990. (Leicester)

SOUTHEY, Trevor James The William Fisher Medical Centre, High Street, Southminster CM0 7AY Tel: 01621 772360 Fax: 01621 773880 — MB BS 1974 Lond.; MRCGP 1978; DGM RCP Lond. 1997; DRCOG 1977. GP Princip.; Clin. Asst. (Geriat.) Chelmsford.

SOUTHGATE, Brian Andrew (retired) Watersmeet, Churchill Way, Appledore, Bideford EX39 1PA Tel: 01237 477062 — MB BS 1953 Lond.; FFPHM 1980, M 1974; DAP & E Lond. 1965. Prev: Sen. Lect. (Trop. Hyg.) Lond. Sch. Hyg. & Trop. Med.

SOUTHGATE, Clive Jonathan The Riverside Health Centre, Station Road, Manningtree CO11 1AA — MB BS 1984 Lond.; Cert. Family Plann. JCC 1985. (Guy's) Prev: Clin. Asst. (ENT) Essex Co. Counc. Colchester.; Trainee GP Colchester VTS.; SHO (O & G) Beverley N. Humberside.

***SOUTHGATE, Crispin Robert William** The Coach House, Woodlands Close, Cople, Bedford MK44 3UE — MB BCh 1996 Wales.

SOUTHGATE, Mr George William Town Farmhouse, Old Weston, Huntingdon PE28 5LL — MB ChB 1973 Liverp.; FRCS Eng. 1979. Cons. Orthop. Surg. Hinchingbrooke Hosp. Huntingdon. Prev: Sen. Regist. (Orthop.) Leeds Gen. Infirm.; Regist. (Orthop. & Gen. Surg.) Liverp. Postgrad. Train. Prog.; Regist. Orthop. Train. Prog. Soton. Gen. Hosp.

SOUTHGATE, Herbert John Old Stile, 179 Middleton Road, Middleton-on-Sea, Bognor Regis PO22 6DF — MRCS Eng. LRCP Lond. 1976; BSc (Hons.) Lond. 1973, MB BS Lond. 1976; MRCP (UK) 1983; MRCPath 1984.

SOUTHGATE, Mr Jeremy James Royal Bournemouth Hospital, Castle Lane, Bournemouth BH7 7DW Tel: 01202 303626; Manor Farmhouse, Old Ham Lane, Little Canford, Wimborne BU21 7LP — MB BS 1986 Lond.; FRCS Eng. 1991; FRCS 1997 (orth). (The London Hosp. Med. College) Socs: BOA; Brit. Assn. for Surg. of the Hand. Prev: Regist. (Orthop.) Winchester & Portsmouth Hosps. Wessex Train. Progr.; Sen. Regist. S.ampton Wessex Rotat.; Hand Fell. Sydney & St Luke's Hosp. Australia.

SOUTHGATE, Joanne Louise Room 1, Flat 9, Chartwell House, Churchill Hospital, Oxford OX3 7ZJ Tel: 01865 741841; 13 Lisbon Road, Shirley, Southampton SO15 3DF — BM 1992 Soton.; BSc (Molecular Cell Biol.) Soton. 1991. SHO Rotat. (Med.) John Radcliffe & Ch.ill Hosps. Oxf.

SOUTHGATE, Professor Lesley Jill, DBE Centre for Health Informatics & Multiprofessional Education, University College London Medical School, 4th Fl. Archway Wi, Holborn Union Bld Archway Campus Highgate Hill, London N19 3UA Tel: 020 7288 5209 Fax: 020 7288 3322 Email: l.southgate@chime.ucl.ac.uk — MB ChB 1967 Liverp.; MClinSci. Univ. West. Ontario 1980; FRCP 1997; FRCGP 1985, M 1974. Prof. Univ. Coll. Lond. Med. Sch. Whittington Hosp. Socs: BMA. Prev: Prof. Gen. Pract. & Primary

Care St. Bart. Hosp. Med. Coll. Lond.; GP Hoddesdon; W.K. Kellog Fell. (Family Med.) W.. Univ. Ontario, Canada.

SOUTHGATE, Matthew John Lower Road Medical Health Centre, Lower Road, Cookham Rise, Maidenhead SL6 9HX Tel: 01628 524646 Fax: 01628 810201; Tanglewood, Dean Lane, Cookham Dean, Maidenhead SL6 9BG Tel: 01628 890290 — BM BCh 1975 Oxf.; BA Oxf. 1970, BM BCh 1975. (Oxford) Clin. Asst. (Obst.) St. Mark's Hosp. Maidenhead. Socs: Windsor & Dist. Med. Soc. & Soc. Med. & Dent. Hypn.; Roy. Soc. Med. Prev: Ho. Off. (Med.) Wycombe Gen. Hosp.; Ho. Off. (Surg., Obst. & Paediat.) Canad. Redr. Hosp. Taplow.

SOUTHWARD, Catherine Gwendolyn Braye Cottage, Sandwith, Whitehaven CA28 9UP Tel: 01946 693740 — MB ChB 1955 Ed.; DObst RCOG 1958. Hosp. Pract. W. Cumbld. Hosp. Whitehaven.

SOUTHWARD, Nigel Ralph, CVO 9 Devonshire Place, London W1N 1PB Tel: 020 7935 8452 Fax: 020 7224 0533; 10 Bristol Mews, London W9 2JF Tel: 020 7266 3414 Fax: 020 7266 1039 — MB BChir Camb. 1965; MA Camb. 1966; MRCP Lond. 1969. (Middlx.) Apoth. to HM the Qu. & HM Ho.hold & Ho.holds of P.ss Margt. Countess of Snowdon, P.ss Alice & Duke & Duchess of Gloucester; Surg. Apoth. King Edwd. VII Hosp. for Offs. Lond. Socs: Fell. Med. Soc. Lond. Prev: Ho. Surg. & Cas. Med. Off. Middlx. Hosp.; Ho. Phys. Centr. Middlx. Hosp.

SOUTHWARD, Mr Robert Dougal Accident & Emergency Dept., University Hospital of Hartlepool, Holdforth Road, Hartlepool — MB BS 1990 Newc.; FFAEM 2000 RCS, London; FRCS Eng. 1996. (Univ. Newc. u. Tyne) Cons., Accid. & Emerg. Dept., Univ. Hosp. of Hartlepool. Prev: SHO (Anaesth.) Qu. Eliz. Hosp. Gateshead; Demonst. (Anat.) Univ. Newc. u. Tyne; Specialist Regist. (A & E) N.ern Deanery Rotat.

SOUTHWARD, Stephen Paul Sea Road Surgery, 39-41 Sea Road, Bexhill-on-Sea TN40 1JJ Tel: 01424 211616 Fax: 01424 733950; 7 Collington Grove, Bexhill-on-Sea TN39 3UB Tel: 01424 842454 Email: steve@southward35.freeserve.co.uk — MB BS 1986 Lond. (St Bartholomews)

SOUTHWELL, Arthur Gerrard William Street Surgery, 87 William Street, Lurgan, Craigavon BT66 6JB Tel: 028 3832 2509 Fax: 028 3834 7673 — MB BCh BAO 1979 NUI; BSc (Hons.) Belf. 1971; MSc (Clin. Psychol.) 1973; MRCGP 1984; DRCOG 1981.

SOUTHWELL, Katherine Fiona Forest House Surgery, 25 Leicester Road, Shepshed, Loughborough LE12 9DF Tel: 01509 508412 — MB BS 1990 Lond.; BSc Basic Med. Scs. & Physiol. Lond. 1987; MRCGP 1995. (St. Bart.) Prev: Trainee GP Leics. VTS.

SOUTHWOOD, Margaret Carleton (retired) 1 Aldwick Avenue, Bognor Regis PO21 3AQ Tel: 01243 823073 — MB ChB Ed. 1954; FFA RCS Eng. 1959; DA Eng. 1957. Prev: Cons. Anaesth. Roy. United Hosp. Bath & United Bristol Hosps.

SOUTHWOOD, Professor Taunton Ray Department of Rheumatology, University of Birmingham, Birmingham B15 2TT Tel: 0121 414 6784 Fax: 0121 414 6794 Email: t.r.southwood@bham.ac.uk; Hazelhurst, 34 Russell Road, Moseley, Birmingham B13 8RE Tel: 0121 449 2882 — BM BS 1980 Flinders; FRCP Lond. 1994; FRCPA 1989; FRACP 1987; FRCPCH 1997. (Flinders University South Africa) Prof. (Paediat. Rheum.) Univesity Birm.; Cons. & Clin. Dir. (Paediat. & Rheum.) Birm. Childr. Hosp. NHS Trust. Socs: Brit. Soc. (Vice-Chairm. Hebeden Comm.); Fell. Roy. Coll. Paediat. & Child Health; Convenor Brit. Paediat. Rheum. Gp. Prev: Clin. Research Fell. Brit. Columbia's Childr.s Hosp. Vancouver, BC, Canada.

SOUTHWOOD, Timothy Michael Tower House Medical Centre, Stockway South, Nailsea BS48 2XX Tel: 01275 866700 — MB BS 1981 Lond.; BDS 1975; MRCGP 1988; DFFP 1993; DGM RCP Lond. 1987; DRCOG 1986. (St Georges) Socs: Christian Med. Fell.sh.; BMA; Bristol M-C Soc. Prev: Regist. (Maxillofacial Surg.) Roy. Lond. Hosp.

SOUTHWOOD, Mr William Frederick Walter (retired) 1 Aldwick Avenue, Bognor Regis PO21 3AQ Tel: 01243 823073 — MB BChir Camb. 1948; MA Camb. 1951, BA 1946, MD 1964, MChir 1956; FRCS Eng. 1954; MRCS Eng. LRCP Lond. 1948. Cons. Surg. Bath Health Dist. Prev: Sen. Regist. (Surg.) Roy. Infirm. Bristol & Roy. Hosp. Sick Childr. Bristol.

SOUTHWORTH, Stephen Andrew 38 Willow Tree Road, Altrincham WA14 2EG — MB ChB 1980 Aberd.

SOUTTER

SOUTTER, Andrew Peter Lena Peat Resource Centre, 33-34 Sydenham Road, Croydon CR2 2EF Tel: 020 8700 8700; 3 Crossway, Bush Hill Park, Enfield EN1 2LA — MB BS 1984 Lond.; MRCPsych 1989. Cons. Psychother. Croydon. Prev: Sen. Regist. (Adult Psychother.) NE Thames RHA; Regist. Rotat. (Psychiat.) N. Lond. Train. Scheme; Clin. Lect. (Psychiat.) Univ. Coll. Hosp. Lond.

SOUTTER, Catherine Isabel (retired) 5 Old Kirk Place, Dunfermline KY12 7ST Tel: 01383 726231 — MB BS 1955 Lond.; DPM Eng. 1972; DObst RCOG 1958; DCH Eng. 1959.

SOUTTER, Douglas Alistair Fraser Street Surgery, 10/14 Fraser Street, Largs KA30 9HP Tel: 01475 673380 Fax: 01475 674149 — MB ChB 1984 Glas.

SOUTTER, Frances Anne St. Romans Health Centre, Innerleithen EH44 6QU; 9 Leithen Cresent, Innerleithen EH44 6JL — MB ChB 1980 Dundee; DRCOG 1986; DCH RCP Glas. 1983. GP Princip.

SOUTTER, Linda Patricia All Saints Hospital, Magpie Hall Road, Chatham ME4 5NG Tel: 01634 407311; 48 Goodrich Road, London SE22 9EQ Tel: 020 8693 8604 — MB BS 1981 Lond.; MRCP (UK) 1985; DCH RCP Lond. 1985. Cons. Paediat. (Community Child Health) Medway NHS Trust.

SOUTTER, Percy Adams Matthews (retired) Trent Lodge, 6 Essex Road, Enfield EN2 6TZ Tel: 020 8363 4350 — MB BS 1929 Lond.; MRCS Eng. LRCP Lond. 1927.

SOUTTER, Peter George 3-5 Bounds Green Road, Wood Green, London N22 8HE; 9 Queen Annes Grove, Bush Hill Park, Enfield EN1 2JP Tel: 020 8360 5261 — MB BS 1959 Lond.; MRCS Eng. LRCP Lond. 1961; DObst RCOG 1961. (Westm.) Socs: BMA. Prev: Ho. Surg. W.m. Hosp.; Ho. Phys. St. Stephen's Hosp. Fulham.

SOUTTER, Robert Ian Currie Road Health Centre, Currie Road, Galashiels TD1 2UA Tel: 01896 754833 Fax: 01896 751389 — MB ChB 1981 Glas.; MRCGP 1985; DRCOG 1983. (Glasgow) GP Galashiels.

SOUTTER, William (retired) 56 Cranford Road, Aberdeen AB10 7NL — MB ChB 1951 Aberd. Prev: Civil Med. Pract. MoD Arborfield Garrison.

SOUTTER, William Patrick Institute of Obstetrics & Gynaecology, Hammersmith Hospital, Du Cane Road, London W12 0HS Tel: 020 8383 3267 Fax: 020 8383 8065 Email: p.soutter@ic.ac.uk — MB ChB 1967 Glas.; MSc Glas. 1972, MD 1979; FRCOG 1988, M 1975; DObst RCOG 1969. Reader Inst. O & G Univ. Lond. Prev: Sen. Lect. (O & G) Univ. Sheff.; Lect. (Midw.) Qu. Mother's Hosp. Glas.; Med. Off. (Gyn.) King Edwd. VIII Hosp. Durban.

SOUTZOS, Theodore 27 Chatsworth Road, London W5 3DD — MB BS 1990 Lond.

SOUYAVE, Janet 31 Southfield Road, Burley-in-Wharfedale, Ilkley LS29 7PB — MB ChB 1977 Leeds; MRCGP 1981; DRCOG 1979.

SOUZA FARIA, Frederick Philip 25 Peacock Road, Kings Heath, Birmingham B13 0NZ Tel: 0121 444 5171 — MB BS 1984 Bombay; MRCPSych 1992. Cons. Psychiat. Brookhaven P.ss of Wales Community Hosp. Worcs. Prev: Regist. Rotat. Birm.

SOWA, Peter Karl 62 Vauxhall Road, Hemel Hempstead HP2 4HR — State Exam Med 1993 Bochum.

SOWAH, Adjei 4 Lister Close, Lister Hospital, Coreys Mill Lane, Stevenage SG1 4AB Tel: 01438 781184 — MB ChB 1984 Ghana; MB ChB U Ghana 1984; MRCOG 1992.

SOWARD, Katherine Margaret 24 Wandsworth Road, Heaton, Newcastle upon Tyne NE6 5AD Tel: 0191 265 2542 — BM BS 1994 Nottm.

***SOWDAGER, Ahsan** 128 Southgate Road, London N1 3HX — LMSSA 1996 Lond.

SOWDEN, David Stewart Measham Medical Unit, High Street, Measham, Swadlincote DE12 7HR Tel: 01530 270667 Fax: 01530 271433; 18 Tower Gardens, Ashby-de-la-Zouch LE65 2GZ — MB ChB 1979 Leeds; FRCGP 1991, M 1983; DRCOG 1981; DCH RCPS Glas. 1982. Dir. Postgrad. Gen. Pract. Ed. S. Trent.

SOWDEN, Gareth Richard North Devon District Hospital, Barnstaple EX31 4JB — MB BS 1973 Lond.; MRCS Eng. LRCP Lond. 1973; DABA 1981; FFA RCS Eng. 1978. Cons. Anaesth. N. Devon Dist. Hosp. Barnstaple. Socs: Eur. Resusc. Counc.; Assn. Anaesth. Prev: Sen. Regist. (Anaesth.) Bristol Roy. Infirm.; Ho. Phys. Med. Unit King's Coll. Hosp. Lond.; Instruc. Anaesth. Harvard Univ., USA.

SOWDEN, Helen 1 Woodslee Cottages, Spital Road, Bromborough, Wirral CH62 2BJ — MB BS 1991 Lond.; Dip CT, Salford, 2001; MRCPsych 1998.

SOWDEN, Jonathan Mark Dermatology Dept, Wrexham Hospital, Wrexham LL13 7TD Tel: 01978 725 5688 — BM BS 1983 Nottm.; BMedSci Nottm. 1981; FRCP (UK) 1988. (Nottm.) Cons. Dermat. Wrexham Maelar Hosp. Prev: Sen. Regist. (Dermat.) Univ. Hosp. Nottm.; Regist. (Dermat.) N. Staffs. Hosp. Centre Stoke-on-Trent; Regist. & SHO (Med.) Glan Clwyd Hosp.

SOWDEN, Lesley Margaret, Surg. Lt. RN 69 Frensham Road, Southsea PO4 8AE Tel: 01705 864092 — MB ChB 1994 Manch. (Manchester) Gen. Duties Med. Off. Roy. Navy. Prev: Surg. Roy. Navy.

SOWDEN, Matthew Charles 34 Lancaster Avenue, Kirk Sandall, Doncaster DN3 1NG — MB ChB 1993 Manch.

SOWDEN, Penelope Anne Crown Road Surgery, 66 Crown Road, Twickenham TW1 3ER Tel: 020 8892 2543 Fax: 020 8744 3055 — BM BS 1987 Nottm.; BMedSci 1985 Nottm.; MRCGP 1991; DRCOG 1991. Prev: SHO Nottm. VTS.

SOWEMIMO, George Morounfolu 1 Warwick Terrace, Lea Bridge Road, London E17 9DP — MB BS 1979 Ibadan; MB BS 1979 Ibadan.

SOWERBUTTS, John George (retired) Upton Forge, Upton Magna, Shrewsbury SY4 4UD Tel: 01743 709330 — MB BS 1949 Lond.; FRCP Ed. 1971, M 1958; MRCS Eng. LRCP Lond. 1949; FRCR 1957; DMRD Eng. 1954. Prev: Cons. Radiodiag. E. Surrey. Hosp. Redhill.

***SOWERBY, Emma Louise** 12 Fortescue Chase, Thorpe Bay, Southend-on-Sea SS1 3SS Tel: 01702 586982 — MB ChB 1996 Manch.

SOWERBY, Howard Anthony Staffa Health Centre, 3 Waverley Street, Tibshelf, Alfreton DE55 5NU Tel: 01773 872252 Fax: 01773 591712; Ellenborough House, 95 High St., Stonebroom, Alfreton DE55 6JY Tel: 01773 874315 Fax: 01773 591703 Email: ros@hsowersy.fsnet.co.uk — MB BChir 1973 Camb.; MA Camb. 1973. Prev: Regist. (Med.) W. Suff. Hosp. Bury St. Edmunds; Ho. Phys. & Ho. Off. (Paediat.) Guy's Hosp. Lond.

SOWERBY, Mary Kathleen Jane The Surgery, 29 High Stile, Leven, Beverley HU17 5NL Tel: 01964 542155 Fax: 01964 543954; Four Views, Grange Road, North Frodingham, Driffield YO25 8LN — MB BS 1991 Newc.; MRCGP 1995; DFFP 1994; DCH RCP Lond. 1994. (Univ. Newc. u. Tyne)

SOWERBY, Peter Redmore Bladeley House, Buckland Newton, Dorchester DT2 7BS — MB BS 1950 Lond.; MRCS Eng. LRCP Lond. 1950; FRCGP 1976, M 1963. (Guy's) Socs: 1987, Founder:Egton Med. Informat. Systems Ltd.

SOWERBY, Rachel The Woodland Medical Practice, Jasmin Road, Birchwood, Lincoln LN6 0QQ Tel: 01522 683590 Fax: 01522 695666; 19B Drury Lane, Lincoln LN1 3BN — MB ChB 1987 Dundee; MRCGP 1991; DRCOG 1991; DCH RCPS Glas. 1990.

SOWERBY, Roger Fielding 2 Troon Close, Bedford MK41 8AY Tel: 01234 214045 Fax: 01234 214045; 2 Troon Close, Bedford MK41 8AY Tel: 01234 214045 Fax: 01234 214045 — MB ChB 1957 Liverp.; MRCGP 1966; MFOM RCP Lond. 1980; T(OM) 1991; DAvMed Eng. 1970. (Liverp.) p/t Med. Examr. Civil Aviat. Auth.& Europ. Jt. Aviat. Auth.; Cons. Occupat. Med. Bedford. Prev: Gp. Capt. RAF Med. Br.; Ho. Off. (Orthop.) & Med. Profess. Unit Liverp. Roy. Infirm.

SOWERBY, Roy George Rowton Grange E., Whitchurch Road, Rowton, Chester CH3 6AF — MB ChB 1969 Manch.; DCH Eng. 1971.

SOWINSKA, Elzbieta 11 Hill Cliffe Road, Walton, Warrington WA4 6NX — MB ChB 1979 Manch.

SOWLER, Elisabeth Mary Kay Scottish executive Health Department, St. Andrews House, Edinburgh EH1 3DG Tel: 0131 244 2827 Fax: 0131 244 2069; 19 Avondale Place, Edinburgh EH3 5HX Tel: 0131 332 6526 — MB ChB Ed. 1969, BSc (Med. Sci.) 1966; MRCPsych 1983; DA Eng. 1975; DObst RCOG 1975. (Ed.) Princip. Med. Off. Scott. Exec.Health.Dept.

SOWOOD, Peter John Covance Clinical And Periapproval Services, 7 Roxborough Way, Maidenhead SL6 3UD Tel: 01628 548150 Fax: 01628 824508 — BM BCh 1978 Oxf.; PhD Lond. 1988; MBA Open 1993; MA Camb. 1978; DAvMed. FOM RCP Lond. 1983. (Oxford University Medical School) Dir. Resources Europe. Socs:

Aerospace Med. Assn.; Roy. Aeronaut. Soc.; Soc. Occupat. Med. Prev: Head Physiol. Centre for Human Sci.s Defence Eval. & Research Agency FarnBoro.; RAF Cons. Aviat. Med.

SOWRAY, Professor John Herbert (retired) 44B Sutton Court Road, Chiswick, London W4 4NJ Tel: 020 8995 5999 Email: jhsowray@aol.com — MRCS Eng. LRCP Lond. 1959; BDS Lond. 1953; FDS RCS Eng. 1963, LDS 1953; FRCS Ed. 1986. Prev: Prof. Oral & Maxillofacial Surg. (Univ. Lond.) King's Coll. Hosp. Med. Sch.

SOWTER, Emma Mai 5 Holmes Close, Wokingham RG41 2SG Tel: 01734 782691 Fax: 01734 782691 — BM 1986 Soton. Prev: SHO (Psychiat.) Heatherwood & Wexham Pk. Hosp. Trust Slough.; Ho. Phys. Medway HA; Ho. Surg. Wycombe HA.

SOWTER, Martin Christopher Department of Obstetrics and Gynaecology, National Womens Hospital, Claude Road, Epsom, Auckland, New Zealand Tel: 00 64 9 638 9919 Fax: 00 64 9 630 9858 Email: mcsowter@ihug.co.nz; First Floor Flat, 46 Arley Hill, Cotham, Bristol BS6 5PP — MB ChB 1988 Birm.; ChB Birm. 1988; BSc Path 1987; MRCOG 1994; MRNZCOG 1996. (Birmingham) Research Fell. Univ. of Auckland. Socs: Brit. Fertil. Soc.; Austral. Fertil. Soc.; Internat. Gyn. Endoscopy Soc.

SOWTON, John Victor (retired) Charman Cottage, Nutfield Marsh Road, Nutfield, Redhill RH1 4EU Tel: 01737 643488 Fax: 01737 644195 — MB BS 1956 Lond.; MRCS Eng. LRCP Lond. 1956; FRCGP 1990; DObst RCOG 1963. Chief Med. Off. Friends Provident Life Off. Dorking. Prev: GP Redhill.

SOWTON, Timothy James Charman Cottage, Nutfield Marsh Road, Nutfield, Redhill RH1 4EU Tel: 01737 643488 — MB BS 1990 Camb.; MA Camb. 1985; MRCGP 1994; DTM & H RCP Liverp. 1995; DCH RCP Lond. 1994; DGM RCP Lond. 1993. (Char. Cross & Westm.) Clin. Asst. (Palliat. Med.) W. Cumbld. Hosp. Whitehaven; GP Whitehaven. Prev: Médecins sans Frontières, Holland; Trainee GP/SHO Redhill VTS.

***SOYE, Jonathan Albert** 10 Lester Avenue, Lisburn BT28 3QD — MB BCh 1998 Belf.; MB BCh Belf 1998.

SOYEMI, Adeoya Olakumle 92 Ashridge Way, Morden SM4 4ED — MB BS 1972 Lond.; MRCOG 1979.

SOYER, Jacques Anthony Kailash, Centre of Oriental Medicine, 7 Newcourt St., St Johns Wood, London NW8 7AA Tel: 020 7722 3939 Fax: 020 7722 7878; 19 Chepstow Crescent, London W11 3EA — MB BS 1981 Sydney.

SOYSA, Priyantha Naomal Chiswick Health Centre, Fishers Lane, London W4 1RX Tel: 020 8994 4482 Fax: 020 8742 7816 — MB BS 1970 Ceylon; MRCP (UK) 1981; FRCOG 1991, M 1978.

SOYSA, Mr Shanti Mahendra Royal Berkshire Hospital, London Road, Reading RG1 5AN Tel: 01189 877012 Fax: 01189 878662 Email: shantsoysa@aol.com; 2 Lincoln Close, Winnersh, Wokingham RG41 5SZ Tel: 0118 977 4820 Fax: 0118 978 8209 — MB BS 1970 Ceylon; FRCS Ed. 1979; FRCS Eng. 1979; FFAEM. (Colombo) Cons. Surg. (A & E) Roy. Berks. Hosp. Reading; Cons. i/c, Minor injuries unit, Newbury Dist. Hosp.; Cons. i/c, minor injuries unit, Townlands Hosp., Henley on Thames. Socs: BMA; BAAEM; FAEM. Prev: Sen. Regist. (A & E) Soton. Gen. Hosp.; Regist. (Surg.) Soton. Gen. Hosp. & Roy. Liverp. & Alder Hey Hosps.

SPACKMAN, David Derek Sibford Surgery, Sibford Gower, Banbury OX15 5RQ Tel: 01295 780213; The Stone House, Backside Lane, Sibford Gower, Banbury OX15 5RS Tel: 01295 780734 — MB BS 1981 Lond.; MRCGP 1986; DRCOG 1984; Dip. Occupat. Med. 1996. (Char. Cross Hosp.)

SPACKMAN, David Robert 160 Culford Road, London N1 4HU Tel: 020 7254 6922 Email: gasbag@globalnet.co.uk — MB BS 1988 Lond.; FRCA 1994. Cons. Anaesth. St. Thomas' Hosp. Lond. Socs: Assn. Anaesths.; Assn. Cardiothoracic Anaesths.

SPAFFORD, Peter John Douglas Child Health Nithbank, Dumfries DG1 2SD Tel: 01387 244000 Fax: 01387 244564; Banks O'Troqueer, Troqueer Road, Dumfries DG2 7DF Tel: 01387 247229 — MB ChB 1984 Cape Town. Staff Grade (Community Paediat.) Nithbank.

SPAGNOLI, Erio Aldo Pawaroo and Partners, The Old Forge Surgery, Pallion Pk, Pallion, Sunderland SR4 6QE Tel: 0191 510 9393 Fax: 0191 510 9595; 4 Grassholm Meadows, Tunstall, Sunderland SR3 1PZ — MB ChB 1981 Dundee; MRCGP 1987; DRCOG 1986. (Dundee) GP Sunderland; Duty Crowd Dr. Sunderland FC.

SPAIGHT, Patrick Quin Maunsell (retired) Castle Farm House, Castle Rising, King's Lynn PE31 6AH Tel: 01553 631345 — MRCS Eng. LRCP Lond. 1931; MRCGP 1953. Prev: Ho. Surg. Gen. Hosp. Birm.

SPAIN, John Robert Grange Medical Centre, Dacre Banks, Harrogate HG3 4DX Tel: 01423 780436 Fax: 01423 781416; 4 Holly Villas, Dacre Banks, Harrogate HG3 4EG Tel: 01423 780313 Email: bobspain@dacre.banks.freeserve.co.uk — MB BS 1982 Newc.; MRCGP 1986. (Newcastle) Prev: Trainee GP Newc. VTS; SHO (Cardiol.) Freeman Hosp. Newc.; SHO (Gen. Med. & Paediat.) Dryburn Hosp. Durh.

SPAINE, Mr Lloyd Ayodeji 30 The Gardens, Heath Road, Halifax HX1 2PL Tel: 01422 340543 — MB BCh BAO 1984 NUI; FRCS Ed. 1988.

SPALDING, Anne Elizabeth Roxton Practice, Worsley Road, Immingham DN4U 1BT; Westwood, 4 The Avenue, Healing, Grimsby DN41 7NG — MB ChB 1985 Sheff.; MRCGP 1989; DRCOG 1989; DGM RCP Lond. 1988.

SPALDING, Duncan Richard Castell 19 Newfound Drive, Norwich NR4 7RY — MB ChB 1989 Birm.

SPALDING, Elizabeth De Carteret (retired) 4 The Old Stables, St Andrews Lane, Old Headington, Oxford OX3 9DP Tel: 01865 761509 — MB BS 1944 Lond.; MRCP Lond. 1947; DCH Eng. 1945. Prev: Instruc. Doctor Family Plann. Serv. Oxon AHA (T).

SPALDING, Elizabeth Margaret 309 Cressex Road, High Wycombe HP12 4QF Tel: 01494 426925 Fax: 01494 426852 — MB BS 1971 Lond.; MRCPsych 1984; DObst RCOG 1974; DTM & H Eng. 1974; DCH Eng. 1973. (Middlx.) Cons. Learning Disabil. & Child Psychiat. S. Bucks. NHS Trust. Socs: BMA; MWF; NHSCA. Prev: Sen. Regist. (Ment. Handicap.) Kidderminster HA.

SPALDING, John Anthony Boyer (retired) 5 Curzon Road, Weybridge KT13 8UW Tel: 01932 843422 — MB BS Lond. 1954; MRCGP 1966; DCH Eng. 1958. Prev: Princip. GP Lond.

SPALDING, John Michael Kenneth 4 The Old Stables, St. Andrews Lane, Old Headington, Oxford OX3 9DP Tel: 01865 761509 — BM BCh 1946 Oxf.; MA Oxf. 1944; DM Oxf. 1952; FRCP Lond. 1964, M 1951. (Oxf.) Cons. & Research Neurol. United Oxf. Hosps. Socs: Assn. Brit. Neurols. & Physiol. Soc. Prev: Sen. Regist. (Med.) Maida Vale Hosp. Nerv. Dis.; Ho. Phys. (Paediat.) Radcliffe Infirm. Oxf.

SPALDING, John Philip The Surgery, Hemming Way, Chaddesley Corbett, Kidderminster DY10 4SF Tel: 01562 777239 Fax: 01562 777196; 30 Hill Grove Crescent, Kidderminster DY10 4RY — MB ChB 1982 Birm.; MRCGP 1986.

SPALDING, Robert Neil Spencer — MB ChB 1995 Dundee; MRCPsych 1999. Specialist Regist. Oxf. Psychiatric Rotat. Prev: SHO Rotat. (Psychiat.) Oxf.

SPALDING, Mr Timothy John Wallis, Surg. Cdr. RN Retd. Orthopaedic Department, Coventry and Warwickshire Hospital, Stoney Stanton Rd, Coventry CV1 4FH — MB BS 1982 Lond.; FRCS (Orth.) 1994; FRCS Ed. 1988. (Charing Cross Hospital London) Cons. Orthop. Surg.Coventry & Warks. Hosp., Coventry. Prev: Fell. (Orthop. & Arthritics) Toronto, Canada; Sen. Regist. RN Hosp. Gosport Hants.; Regist. (Helicopter Emerg. Med. Serv.) Lond. Hosp. Whitechapel.

SPALTON, Mr David John King Edward VII Hospital, Devonshire Street, London W1G 6AA Tel: 020 7935 6174 Fax: 020 7467 4376 Email: spalton@eyepractice.fsnet.co.uk — MB BS Lond. 1970; FRCP Lond. 1990; FRCS Eng. 1975; MRCP (UK) 1973; MRCS Eng. LRCP Lond. 1970; FRCOphth 1989; DO Eng. 1975. (Westm.) Cons. Ophth. Surg.St. Thos. Hosp. Lond.; Hon. Cons. Ophth. Surg. Roy. Hosp. Chelsea Lond.; Ophth. Surg. King Edwd. VII Hosp. for Offs. Lond.; Hon. Sen. Lect. (Ophth.) UMDS Lond.; Ophth. Adviser to Metrop. Police. Prev: Cons. Ophth. Surg. Char. Cross Hosp. Lond.; Sen. Regist. (Ophth.) St. Thos. Hosp. Lond.; Resid. Surg. Off. Moorfields Eye Hosp. Lond.

SPANKIE, Alison Claire 8 Highgate West Hill, London N6 6JR — MB BS 1982 Lond.

SPANN, Richard George 14 Fane Way, Maidenhead SL6 2TL — MB BS 1989 W. Indies.

SPANNER, Rebekah Mair Family Planning Department, Heathfield Family Centre, 131-133 Heathfield Road, Handsworth, Birmingham B19 1HL Tel: 0121 255 7587; 96 Woodlands Farm Road, Erdington, Birmingham B24 0PQ Tel: 0121 240 0555 — MB BS

SPANNUTH

1980 Lond.; DRCOG 1984. (Royal Free Hospital School of Medicine) SCMO (Family Plann. & Wom. Health) N. Birm. Community Trust. Prev: GP Birm.; Staff Med. Off. Across, Juba, S. Sudan; Trainee GP Enfield & Haringey FPC.

SPANNUTH, Frank Kingsfield Medical Centre, 146 Alcester Road South, Kings Heath, Birmingham B14 6AA Tel: 0121 444 2054 Fax: 0121 443 5856 — State Exam Med 1986 Tubingen; State Exam Med 1986 Tubingen.

SPANOS, Vassilios c/o Doctors Mess, Tameside General Hospital, Ashton-under-Lyne OL6 9RW; Flat 7, 48 Palatine Road, Didsbury, Manchester M20 3YB Tel: 0161 448 0574 — Ptychio Iatrikes 1989 Athens. SHO (Med.) Tameside Gen. Hosp. Ashton-under-Lyne.

SPANSWICK, Christopher Charles Manchester & Salford Pain Centre, Hope Hospital, Stott Lane, Salford M6 8HD Tel: 0161 789 7373; 33 Cartier Close, Bridle Chase, Old Hall, Warrington WA5 8TD — MB ChB 1973 Manch.; FFA RCS Eng. 1978. Cons. Pain Managem. & Anesth.; Hon. Clin. Lect. (Anaesth.) Hope Hosp. Salford. Socs: Internat. Assn. Study of Pain; Assn. Anaesths.; (Hon. Asst. Treas.) Pain Soc. Prev: Cons. Anaesth. Trafford AHA.

SPANSWICK, Robert 36 Chaucer Road, Crowthorne RG45 7QN — MB BS 1988 Lond.

SPANTON, Denis Burke (retired) 74 Pickersleigh Road, Malvern WR14 2RS Tel: 01684 575177 — MB BS 1948 Lond.; MRCS Eng. LRCP Lond. 1945; FRCOG 1974, M 1961, DObst 1948. Hon. Cons. O & G W. Cumbria HA. Prev: Specialist O & G Govt. of W. Nigeria.

***SPANTON, Ian Dale Alexander** 3 Burdett Avenue, London SW20 0ST — MB BS 1996 Lond.

SPARE, John Turner (retired) 2 Gordon's Close, Shoreditch Road, Taunton TA1 3DA Tel: 01823 284822 — MB BS Lond. 1941; MRCS Eng. LRCP Lond. 1942. Prev: Obst. Ho. Surg. Roy. United Hosp. Bath.

SPARE, Timothy John West Walk Surgery, 21 West Walk, Yate, Bristol BS37 4AX Tel: 01454 272200; The Old Farm House, Holly Hill, Iron Acton, Bristol BS37 9XZ Tel: 01454 228257 — MB BS 1972 Lond.; MRCS Eng. LRCP Lond. 1972; DObst RCOG 1975. (Middlx. Hosp.) GP Princip. Bristol. Prev: Sen. Med. Off. Solomon Is. Govt.

SPAREY, Colette 15 Lyndhurst Avenue, West Jesmond, Newcastle upon Tyne NE2 3LJ — MB ChB 1987 Manch.; MRCOG 1993. Sen. Regist. (O & G) Roy. Vict. Infirm. Newc. u. Tyne. Prev: Research Fell (O & G) Countess of Chester Hosp.; Regist. Rotat. (O & G) Mersey RHA.

SPARGO, Anne Elizabeth Whitminster Lane, Frampton on Severn, Gloucester GL2 7HU; Ashleigh House, The St, Frampton-on-Severn, Gloucester GL2 7ED Tel: 01452 741147 — MB BChir 1977 Camb.; DRCOG 1979. p/t Gen. Practitioner; Clin. Asst. G.U.M. Dept, Gloucester Roy. Hosp.

SPARGO, James Robert 4 Shannon Close, Willaston, Nantwich CW5 6QG — MB ChB 1992 Sheff.

SPARGO, John Barnes (retired) 22 Southview Gardens, Worthing BN11 5JA — MB BChir 1950 Camb.; MA, MB BChir Camb. 1950. Prev: Resid. Med. Off., Ho. Phys. & Ho. Surg. Nat. Temperance Hosp.

SPARGO, Paul Michael — MB BS 1977 Lond.; MRCP (UK) 1982; FFA RCS Eng. 1984. (St. Mary's) Cons. Anaesth. Shackleton Dept. Anaesth. Soton. Gen. Hosp. Prev: Sen. Regist. (Anaesth.) Soton HA; Instruc. Dept. Anesthesiol. Univ. Michigan Ann Arbor, USA; Regist. (Med.) Roy. Berks. Hosp. Reading.

SPARGO, Mr Peter John Ralph Whitminster Lane, Frampton on Severn, Gloucester GL2 7HU Tel: 01452 740213 Fax: 01452 740989; Ashleigh House, The St, Frampton-on-Severn, Gloucester GL2 7ED Tel: 01452 741147 Fax: 01452 740989 — MB BChir 1977 Camb.; MA Camb. 1976; FRCS Ed. 1982; FRCS Eng. 1982; MRCGP 1989. Prev: Med. Supt. Bonda Mission Hosp., Zimbabwe.

SPARK, Evelyn Diana 36 Ashley Park, Ashley Heath, Ringwood BH24 2HB Tel: 0142 545193 — MB BS 1966 Lond.; FFA RCS (Eng.) 1981; DA Eng. 1969; DObst RCOG 1968. (Middlx.)

SPARK, Mr James Ian 88 Elton Road, Darlington DL3 8NA Tel: 01325 480964 — MB ChB 1988 Leeds; MD 2000 Leeds; FRCS 2001 FRCS (Gen.Surg.); FRCS Eng. 1992. (Leeds University) Specialist Regist. (Surg.) Leeds Gen. Infirm. Prev: Research Regist. (Vasc. Surg.) St. Jas. Univ. Hosp. Leeds.

SPARK, Michael Gallwey (retired) West House, 19 Meadow Lane, Beadnell, Chathill NE67 5AJ Tel: 01665 720255 — MB BS 1956 Durh.; DObst RCOG 1958. Prev: GP Gateshead.

SPARKE, Paul Berthon (retired) St Giles Mount, Stratton Road, Winchester SO23 0JQ — MB BS Lond. 1950; MRCS Eng. LRCP Lond. 1950; DObst RCOG 1954. Prev: GP W. Kingdown, Kent.

SPARKES, David John 31 Nettlecombe Avenue, Southsea PO4 0QW — MB BS 1993 Lond.

SPARKES, Julian Malcolm Shilpa Medical Centre, 1C Ashfield Avenue, Kings Heath, Birmingham B14 7AT — MB ChB 1979 Birm.; DRCOG 1988.

SPARKES, Robert Sedlescombe House, 8 Sedlescombe Road South, St Leonards-on-Sea TN38 0TA Tel: 01424 720574/435004 Fax: 01424 440199 — MB BS 1986 Lond.; MA Camb. 1984; MRCGP 1990; DFFP 1994; DRCOG 1990. Prev: Trainee GP Gt. Yarmouth VTS.

SPARKS, Mary, Group Capt. RAF Med. Br. Retd. 42 Broughton Avenue, Richmond TW10 7UQ Tel: 020 8940 727 — LRCP LRCS 1939 Ed.; LRCP LRCS Ed. LRFPS Glas. 1939. (Roy. Colls. Ed.) Socs: BMA. Prev: Sen. Med. Off. Lond. Detachm. RAF; Dep. PMO HQ Train. Command RAF; on Staff RAF Personnel Managem. Centre Min. of Defence.

SPARKS, Mr Michael John Whitaker 38 Oak Avenue, South Wootton, King's Lynn PE30 3JQ Tel: 01553 672372 — MB BS 1979 Lond.; FRCS Ed. 1989; FRCR 1994. Cons. Radiol. Qu. Eliz. Hosp. King's Lynn.

SPARKS, Richard Alfred Cardiff Royal Infirmary, Newport Road, Cardiff CF24 0SZ Tel: 029 2033 5205 Fax: 029 2048 7096 Email: richard.sparks@uhw-tr.wales.nhs.uk — MB BCh 1967 Wales; MFFP 1993; FRCOG 1989, M 1973; Dip. GU Med. Soc. Apoth. Lond. 1979; Cert. Family Plann. FPA 1972; DObst RCOG 1970. (Cardiff) Cons. Genitourin. Med. Cardiff Roy. Infirm. & Clin. Teach. (Genitourin.) Univ. Wales Coll. Med. Socs: Med. Soc. Study VD & Assn. Genitourin. Med. Prev: Sen. Lect. (Genitourin. Med.) Univ. Birm.; Cons. Genitourin. Med. Manch. Roy. Infirm.; Research Fell. (Human Reproduc.) Univ. Soton.

SPARKS, William Benjamin (retired) Corner House, Perrin Close, Temple Cloud, Bristol BS39 5LR Tel: 01761 452636 — MB BS Lond. 1951. Prev: Hosp. Pract. (ENT) Char. Cross Hosp. Lond.

SPARROW, Alice Ivy (retired) 11 Lodge Drive, Hatfield AL9 5HL Tel: 01707 264268 — MB BCh BAO 1934 Belf. Prev: Ho. Off. Lady Chichester Hosp. Hove, Roy. Vict. Hosp. Belf.

SPARROW, Geoffrey Edward Alan Station Road Surgery, Station Road, Stalbridge, Sturminster Newton DT10 2RG Tel: 01963 362363 Fax: 01963 362866 Email: geoff@stalbridgesurgery.co.uk; Stayners Farm, Lydlinch, Sturminster Newton DT10 2JA Tel: 01258 473136 Email: geoff@stalbridgesurgery.co.uk — MB BS 1975 Lond.; FRCP 2001; MRCP (UK) 1978; MRCS Eng. LRCP Lond. 1975. (Guy's) Gen. Practitioner, Stalbridge; Assoc. Specialist Yeovil Dist. Hosp.; Trainer (Gen. Pract.) Dorset. Prev: Lect. (Med. Oncol.) Guy's Hosp. Lond.; Regist. (Gen. Med.) & SHO (Med. & Paediat.) Yeovil Dist. Hosp.

SPARROW, Ian Michael McNulty and Partners, Torkard Hill Medical Centre, Farleys Lane, Shieldfield, Nottingham NG15 6DY Tel: 0115 963 3676 Fax: 0115 968 1957.

SPARROW, Ian Robert Christopher Balmoral Surgery, 1 Victoria Road, Deal CT14 7AU Tel: 01304 373444 — MB BS 1985 Lond.; MRCGP 1992; DRCOG 1990; DCH RCP Lond. 1989. (St. Thos. Hosp. Med. Sch.) Prev: Trainee GP/SHO William Harvey Hosp. Ashford VTS; Ho. Surg. St. Thos. Hosp. Lond.; Ho. Phys. William Harvey Hosp. Ashford.

SPARROW, Michael Anthony Lifton Surgery, North Road, Lifton PL16 0EH Tel: 01566 784788 — MB BS 1981 Lond.

SPARROW, Michael John The Health Centre, Bingham, Nottingham NG13 8BG — MRCS Eng. LRCP Lond. 1956.

SPARROW, Nigel James Newthorpe Medical Practice, Eastwood Clinic, Nottingham Road, Eastwood, Nottingham NG16 3GL Tel: 01773 760202 Fax: 01773 710951; 1 Rectory Gardens, Wollaton Village, Nottingham NG8 2AR — MB ChB 1979 Bristol; BSc (Hons.) Bristol 1976; MRCGP 1984; DRCOG 1983. Hosp. Pract. (Colposc.) Qu. Med. Centre Nottm.; Lect. (Gen. Pract.) Univ. Nottm.; Mem. Notts. MAAG. Socs: RCGP (Vale of Trent Fac. Bd.). Prev: SHO (Med.) Univ. Hosp. Nottm.; Ho. Phys. S.mead Hosp. Bristol; Ho. Surg. Leicester Roy. Infirm.

SPARROW, Mr Owen Charles Southampton General Hospital, Tremona Road, Southampton SO16 6YD — MB BCh 1974 Witwatersrand; MMed (Neurosurg.) 1986; FRCS Ed. 1980.

SPARROW, Pamela Marian (retired) Miranda Lodge, Broadlands Road, Brockenhurst SO42 7SX — MB BS 1954 Lond.; MRCS Eng. LRCP Lond. 1953. Prev: Ho. Surg. & Ho. Phys. St. Chas. Hosp.

SPARROW, Robert Andrew 5 Long Row, The Sreen, Kingston-on-Soar, Nottingham NG11 0DA — BM BS 1980 Nottm.

SPARROW, Roger William Claremont Surgery, 2 Cookham Road, Maidenhead SL6 8AN Tel: 01628 673033 Fax: 01628 673432; Merion House, White Waltham, Maidenhead SL6 3RU — MB BS 1959 Lond. (Middlx.) Socs: Med. Soc. Study VD. Prev: Ho. Phys. Middlx. Hosp. Lond.

SPARROW, Sally Angela La Route Du Fort Surgery, 2 La Route Du Fort, St Helier, Jersey JE2 4PA Tel: 01534 31421 Fax: 01534 280776 — MB ChB 1974 Sheff.; BSc. (Hons) Sheff. 1969.

SPARROW, Susan Thistle Cottage, 2 Soonhope Holdings, Peebles EH45 8BH Tel: 01721 720410 Email: xoa36@dial.pipex.com — MB ChB 1972 Birm.; DObst RCOG 1974. Locum GP Peebles. Prev: GP Princip. Shrewsbury; SHO (Anaesth.) Roy. Shrewsbury Hosp. Shrewsbury; Trainee GP Ch. Stretton Health Centre.

SPATHIS, Anna Olga 7 Kildare Gardens, London W2 5JS — MB BChir 1992 Camb.; MRCP 1996.

SPATHIS, Gerassimos Spyros 7 Kildare Gardens, London W2 5JS Email: gspathis@orangenet.co.uk — DM Oxf. 1971, MA, BM BCh 1960; FRCP Lond. 1977, M 1963; D Med y Cir. (Guy's) Prof. & Chairm., Fac. of Med., Kigezi Internat. Sch. of Med.; Hon. Sen. Lect. St. Geo. Hosp. Med. Sch.; Hon. Phys. Roy. Marsden Hosp. Sutton; Hon. Phys. St. Helier Hosp. Carshalton. Socs: Med. Soc. Lond. & Brit. Diabetic Assn. Prev: Regist. (Med.) Middlx. Hosp. Lond., Addenbrooke's Hosp. Camb. & St. Thos. Hosp. Lond.; Sub Dean St Geo. Hosp. Med. Sch. Lond.; Mem. & Vice Chairm. SW Thames RHA.

SPAUL, Kerrie Alice Juniper 61 Downing Drive, Leicester LE5 6LL Tel: 0116 241 4083 — MB ChB 1991 Sheff.; MRCGP 1995. (Sheff.) Assoc. GP Highfield Surg. Leicester. Socs: BMA. Prev: SHO (O & G) URI NHS Trust; SHO (Psychiat) Bassetlaw NHS Trust; GP/Regist. Dunnington Gp. Pract.

SPEAK, Nigel James Manor Practice, James Preston Health Centre, 61 Holland Road, Sutton Coldfield B72 1RL Tel: 0121 354 2032 Fax: 0121 321 1779; 59 Somerville Road, Sutton Coldfield B73 6HJ — MB ChB 1982 Birm.; MRCGP 1986; DRCOG 1986; DCH RCP Lond. 1985.

SPEAKE, John Graham The Medical Centre, The Medical Centre, Fore Street, St Marychurch, Torquay TQ1 4QX Tel: 01803 325123 Fax: 01803 322136 — MB BS 1976 Newc.; FFA RCSI 1984. Prev: Regist. (Anaesth.) Univ. Hosp. Wales Cardiff & Torbay Hosp.; SHO (Anaesth.) Qu. Eliz. Med. Centre Birm.

SPEAKE, Malcolm Douglas (retired) Dockyard, Kettlebaston, Ipswich IP7 7QA Tel: 01449 740254 Fax: 01449 740903 — MB ChB 1965 Leeds. Prev: Research Asst. Univ. Leeds.

SPEAKMAN, Alice Rosie 130 Dicconson Street, Wigan WN1 2BA — MB ChB 1979 Manch.

SPEAKMAN, Mr Christopher Thomas More Norfolk and Norwich University Hospital, Colney Lane, Norwich NR4 7UY Tel: 01603 287947 Fax: 01603 287947 Email: chris.spearman@norfolk-norwich.thenhs.com — MB BS 1983 Lond.; MD Lond. 1993; FRCS Ed. 1988. Cons. Gen. Surg. Norf. & Norwich Hosp.; Hon. Sen. Lect. Univ. E. Anglia. Socs: St. Mark's Assn.; Assn. Coloproctol.; Assn. Surg. Prev: RSO St. Marks Hosp. Lond.; Sen. Regist. (Surg.) Char. Cross Hosp. Lond.; Sir Alan Pk.s Research Fell. St. Marks Hosp. Lond.

SPEAKMAN, David William c/o Northern and Yorkshire Regional Health Authority, Medical Staffing Sec, Postgraduate Institute for Medicine, 10-12 Framlington Place, Newcastle upon Tyne NE2 4AB — MB BS 1988 Monash.

SPEAKMAN, Helen Mary Anne 10 High Street, Edlesborough, Dunstable LU6 2HS — MB BS 1989 Lond.

SPEAKMAN, John Kenneth Wordsley Green Health Centre, Wordsley Green, Wordsley, Stourbridge DY8 5PD Tel: 01384 277591 Fax: 01384 401156; Broom Barn, Redhall Lane, Broome, Stourbridge DY9 0EZ — MB ChB 1990 Birm.; DRCOG 1994. Socs: BMA. Prev: SHO (Med.) Russells Hall Hosp. Dudley.

SPEAKMAN, Mr Mark Joseph Taunton & Somerset NHS Trust, Musgrove Park, Taunton TA1 5DA Tel: 01823 343571; Greenfield, Wild Oak Lane, Trull, Taunton TA3 7JS Tel: 01823 257891 Fax: 01823 257891 Email: speakmanmj@aol.com — MB BS 1978 Lond.; MS Lond. 1988; MRCS Eng. LRCP Lond. 1978; FRCS Eng. 1983. (Char. Cross) Cons. Urol. & Director of Research & Developm. Taunton & Somserset NHS Trust; Mem. Counc. Brit. Assn. Urol. Surgs. Socs: BMA; Brit. Assn. Urol. Surgs.; Roy. Soc. of Med. (Fell.). Prev: Research Regist. (Urol.) (MRC) Ch.ill Hosp. Oxf.; Regist. (Surg.) John Radcliffe Hosp. Oxf.; Sen. Regist. (Urol.) W.. Infirm. Glas.

SPEAKMAN, Melanie Jane 12 Allerton Avenue, Leeds LS17 6RF — MB ChB 1993 Leic.

SPEAKMAN, Philip Frank Buckley Health Centre, Padeswood Road, Buckley CH7 2JL Tel: 01224 550555 Fax: 01224 545712; Grassmere, Tram Road, Buckley CH7 3NH Tel: 01244 545889 — MB ChB 1973 Liverp.; MRCGP 1978; DCH Eng. 1976; DObst RCOG 1975. Co. Staff Off. St. John Ambul. Brig.; Phys. Clwyd Mt.ain Rescue Team. Prev: SHO Pk. Psychiat. Day Hosp. Liverp., Mill Rd. Matern. Hosp. & Alder; Hey Childr. Hosp. Liverp.

SPEAR, Brian Scott Edenbridge Medical Practice, West View, Station Road, Edenbridge TN8 5ND Tel: 01732 864442 Fax: 01732 862376 — MB BS 1973 Lond.; MRCGP 1984; DCH Eng. 1978; DRCOG 1976. (Lond. Hosp.) Fraser Rose Medal RCGP 1984; GP Edenbridge; Jt. Sec. Edenbridge Hosp. Clin. Soc.; Hosp. Pract. (Gastroenterol.) Kent & Sussex Hosp. Socs: Primary Care Soc. Gastroenterol. Prev: Ho. Phys. & Ho. Surg. Lond. Hosp.; SHO Sydenham Childr. Hosp.

SPEAR, David William Shiphay Manor, 37 Shiphay Lane, Torquay TQ2 7DU Tel: 01803 615059 Fax: 01803 614545; Laurel Place, The Woods, Higher Lincombe Road, Torquay TQ1 2HS Tel: 01803 290673 Fax: 01803 290673 Email: woof@mail.eclipse.ac.uk — MB BS 1989 Lond.; BSc Physiol. Lond. 1986; MRCGP 1994; DRCOG 1993; DFFP 1993. (Middlesex Hospital & University College London) Prev: Trainee GP/SHO (Paediat.) Torbay Hosp. Torquay.

SPEAR, Frank Graham 326 Ecclesall Road S., Sheffield S11 9PU Tel: 0114 236 6766 Fax: 0114 236 6766 — MB ChB Bristol 1954; MD Bristol 1964; FRCPsych 1974, M 1971; DPM Eng. 1958. (Bristol) Prev: Cons. Psychiat. Sheff. Ment. Illness Serv.; Lect.(Psychiat.) Univ. Sheff.; Vis. Psychother. HM Prison Wakefield.

SPEAR, George Edwin (retired) 39 The Empire, Grand Parade, Bath BA2 4DF Tel: 01225 313409 — MB BChir 1940 Camb.; MB BChir Camb.1940; BA Camb. (Nat. Sc. Trip. Pt. I, cl. 1) 1937; MRCP Lond. 1949; MRCS Eng. LRCP Lond. 1940. Prev: GP Relvedon Colchester.

SPEARS, Frances Dorothy Dept of Anaestetics, Luton and Dunstable Hospital NHS Trust, Lewsey Road, Luton LU4 0DZ — MB ChB 1985 Dundee; FRCA 1992. Cons. Anaesth. Luton & Dunstable Hosp. NHS Trust Luton.

SPEARS, John Robert (retired) 32 Roxwell Road, Chelmsford CM1 2NB Tel: 01245 354173 — MRCS Eng. LRCP Lond. 1948; FRCA 1992; FFA RCS Eng. 1954; DA Eng. 1953. Hon. Cons. Anaesth. Mid-Essex HA. Prev: Cons. Anaesth. Broomfield Hosp., St. John's Hosp. Chelmsford & OldCh. Hosp. Romford.

SPEARS, Joseph (retired) 8 Guards Road, Lindal-in-Furness, Ulverston LA12 0TN — MB ChB 1937 Glas.; MD Glas. 1946; FRCGP 1971, M 1964; DCH Eng. 1951. Prev: Late. Act. Squadron Ldr. RAFVR.

SPECK, Mr Edward Holmes Rannoch, 50 Woodgates Lane, North Ferriby HU14 3JY Tel: 01482 634201 — MB BS 1968 Lond.; FRCS Ed. 1976; FRCOG 1988, M 1975. (Middlx.) Cons. (O & G) Hull Health Dist. Prev: Sen. Regist. (O & G) Leeds & Bradford AHAs; Regist. (Gen. Surg.) Orsett Hosp. Grays Thurrock; Regist. (O & G) Jessop. Hosp. Wom. Sheff.

SPECK, Eirlys (retired) Dolphin House, Glyn Garth, Menai Bridge LL59 5PF Tel: 01348 713515 — LRCP LRCS Ed. LRFPS Glas. 1948.

SPECTOR, Professor Roy Geoffrey Guys Drug Research, United Medical Schools, 6 Newcomen St., London SE1 1YR Tel: 020 7910 7700 Fax: 020 7910 7800 Email: 100601.734@compuserve.com; 3 St. Kilda Road, Orpington BR6 0ES Tel: 01689 810069 — MB ChB Leeds 1956; PhD Lond. 1964; MD Leeds 1962; FRCP Glas. 1972, M 1962; FRCP Ed. 1971, M 1959; FRCPath 1976, M 1965; Dip. Biochem. (Distinc.) Lond. 1966. (Leeds) Hon. Cons. Guy's Hosp. Lond.; Emerit. Prof. Applied Pharmacol. Univ. Lond. Socs: Brit. Pharm. Soc.; Med. Res. Soc. Prev: rof. Applied Pharmacol. Univ.

SPECTOR

Lond.; Vis. Prof. Clin. Pharmacol. W. China Med. Univ., Chengdu; Lect. (Experim. Path.) & Sen. Lect. (Experim. Biol.) Paediat. Research Unit. Guy's Hosp. Med. Sch. Lond.

SPECTOR, Timothy David Twin Research Genetic Epidemiology Unit, St. Thomas' Hospital, London SE1 7EH Tel: 020 7960 5557 Fax: 020 7922 8234; 22 Aberdeen Road, London N5 2UH — MD 1989 Lond.; MSc Lond. 1986, MD 1989, MB BS 1982; FRCP 1997, MRCP 1985. (St. Bartholomews) Cons. Rheum. St. Thos. Hosp. Lond.; Hon. Sen. Lect. MDS; Dir. Twin Research & Genetic Epidemiol. Unit. Prev: Lect. (Epidemiol.) & Sen. Regist. (Rheum.) St. Bart. Hosp. Lond.; Wellcome Research Fell. Dept. Clin. Epidemiol. Lond. Hosp.; Hon. Regist. (Rheum.) & SHO (Gen. Med.) St. Bart. Hosp. Lond.

SPEDDING, Anne Valerie Department of Histopathology, Queen Alexandra Hospital, Southwick Hill Road, Cosham, Portsmouth PO6 3LY Tel: 023 92 286458 — MB ChB 1985 Manch.; FRCPath 2001. Cons. Histopath. Qu. Alexandra Hosp. Portsmouth.

SPEDDING, Ruth Lynn Accident and Emergency, Warrington Hospital, Lovely Lane, Warrington WA5 1QG Tel: 01925 635911 Fax: 01925 662184 — MB BCh BAO 1988 Belf.; FRCS Ed: 1993; MRCP (UK) 1992; FFAEM 1997. Cons. (A & E) Warrington Hosp. Warrington Chesh. Prev: Altnagelvin Hosp. Derry Co. Lond.derry; Belf. Regist. Rotat. (A & E).

SPEDDING, Sheila Margaret (retired) The Great Barn, Moot Lane, Downton, Salisbury SP5 3JP Tel: 01725 510319 — MRCS Eng. LRCP Lond. 1974; BSc Manch. 1953; MRCPsych 1979; T(Psych) 1991. Prev: Cons. Child Psychiat. Marchwood Priory Hosp.

SPEDEN, Deborah Jane Wrightington Hospital, Hull Lane, Appley Bridge, nr Wigan WN6 9EP Tel: 01257 252211; 18 Dobson Close, Appley Bridge, nr Wigan WN6 9ES Tel: 01225 427282 — MB BS 1990 Tasmania; FRACP 1998. Specialist Regist. (Rheum.), Wrightington Hosp., nr Wigan. Socs: Brit. Soc. Rheum.; Fell.of RACP. Prev: Clin. Research Fell. (Rheum.) Roy. Nat. Hosp. Rheum. Dis. Bath.

SPEECHLY-DICK, Marie Elsya The Middlesex Hospital, Mortimer St., London W1N 3AA — MB BChir 1987 Camb.; BSc (Hons.) St. And. 1984; MD Camb. 1996; MRCP (UK) 1989. (Univ. St. And & Univ. Camb.) p/t Sen. Lect. & Hon. Cons. (Cardiol.) Univ. Coll. Lond. Hosps. NHS Trust. Prev: Clin. Regist. (Cardiol.) Univ. Coll. Hosp. NHS Trust; Research Fell. (Cardiol.) Middlx. & Univ. Coll. Hosp. Lond.; SHO Nat. Heart & Chest Hosp. Lond.

SPEED, Catherine Anne The Staddles, Prinsted Lane, Emsworth PO10 8HS — BM BS 1989 Nottm.; BMedSci (Hons.) 1987. SHO (Med.) Newc. HA.

SPEED, Dorothy Elizabeth Maud 19 Bathwick Hill, Bath BA2 6EW — MB ChB Liverp. 1956; DFFP 1960. (Univ. Liverp.) Mem. Parole Bd. Socs: Affil. Mem. Roy. Coll. Psychiat.; Fell. Counc. Europ.; Fell. Roy. Soc. Med. & Galton Inst. Prev: Princip. Med. Off. Directorate Prison Med. Servs. Home Office; Hon. Cons. Phys. Roy. Marsden Hosp. & Sen. Lect. Inst. Cancer Research Lond. Hosp.; Dir. Populat. Control (Mauritius: Min. Overseas Developm.).

SPEED, Henry Peter (retired) 30 Ballalough, Andreas, Ramsey IM7 4HS Tel: 01624 880428 — MRCS Eng. LRCP Lond. 1944. Prev: Clin. Asst. St. Lawrence's Hosp. Bodmin.

***SPEED, Katharine Mary** 3 Brookhouse Road, Walsall WS5 3AE — MB BCh 1997 Wales.

SPEED, Kevin Ralph 6 Northumberland Close, Grimsby DN34 4TE — MB BS 1974 Lond.; MSc Lond. 1979, MB BS 1974; MRCPath 1982. (St. Geo.) Cons. (Haemat.) Grimsby Dist. Gen. Hosp. Prev: Lect. (Haemat.) St. Geo. Hosp. Med. Sch. Lond.

SPEED, Mary Allison Widcombe Surgery, 3-4 Widcombe Parade, Bath BA2 4JT Tel: 01225 310883 Fax: 01225 421600 — MRCS Eng. LRCP Lond. 1980.

SPEED, Penelope Jane c/o Whistlers, Inmans Lane, Sheet, Petersfield GU32 2AN Tel: 01730 62729 — MB BS 1987 Monash. SHO (Psychogeriat.) York Dist. Hosp.

SPEED-ANDREWS, Shonagh Carol 6 Glen Road, Ings Lane, Rochdale OL12 7DY — MB ChB 1985 Glas.; MRCGP 2001; DFFP 2000. p/t Clin. Asst. (Genitourin. Med.). Prev: Clin. Asst. (Dermat.) Cumbria; Trainee GP Cumbria VTS; Clin.. Asst. A & E Med.

SPEEDIE, Catherine Alison Chadmoor Medical Practice, 45 Princess St, Cannock WS11 2JT Tel: 01543 571650 Fax: 01543 462304 — MB BCh BAO 1984 Belf.; MB BCh Belf. 1984.

SPEER, Peter George Barnham Medical Centre, 134 Barnham Road, Barnham, Bognor Regis PO22 0EH — MB BS 1985 Lond.; DRCOG 1988. Clin. Asst. (Rheum.) St Richards Hosp. Chichester.

***SPEERS, Alan Gordon** Heatherdene, 1 Bramblewood Place, Fleet GU51 4EF — MB BS 1997 Lond.

SPEIDEL, Brian David (retired) 224 Cranbrook Road, Redland, Bristol BS6 7QX Tel: 0117 949 5789 — BM BCh Oxf. 1965; BA Oxf. 1962; MD Bristol 1976; FRCP Lond. 1982, M 1969; FRCPCH 1997; DCH Eng. 1971. Prev: Cons. Paediat. (Neonat. Med.) S.mead Hosp. Bristol & St. Michael's Hosp. Bristol.

SPEIGHT, Arthur Nigel Podmore Department of Paediatrics, University Hospitals of North Durham, Durham DH1 5TW Tel: 0191 333 2333 Fax: 0191 333 2327; Southlands, Gilesgate, Durham DH1 1QN Tel: 0191 384 7727 Fax: 0191 384 7727 Email: speightuk@yahoo.co.uk — MB BChir 1967 Camb.; MA, 1967; FRCP Lond. 1986; FRCPCH 1997; DCH Eng. 1976. (Univ. Coll. Hosp.) Cons. Paediat. N. Durh. Acute NHS Trust; Hon. Sen. Lect. Univ. of Newc. Upon Tyne. Socs: BMA & Roy. Coll. Paediat. & Child Health & NHS Cons. Assn. Prev: 1st Asst. (Child Health) Roy. Vict. Infirm. Newc.; Lect. Med. Univ. Dar es Salaam, Tanzania; Sen. Regist. (Paediat.) Newc. Gen. Hosp.

SPEIGHT, Colin Graham 6 Union Street, Oxford OX4 1JP — MB ChB 1998 Ed.; MB ChB Ed 1998.

SPEIGHT, Emma Lucy Department of Dermatology, Royal Victoria Infirmary, Newcastle upon Tyne NE1 4LP Tel: 0191 232 5131 — MB BS 1984 (Hons. Path.); MA Camb. 1985; MD Lond. 1994; MRCP (UK) 1988. Cons. Dermatol. Roy. Vict. Infirm. Newc.-upon-Tyne. Prev: Sen. Regist. (Dermat.) Univ. Hosp. Nottm.; Research Fell & Regist. (Dermat.) Roy. Vict. Infirm. Newc.

SPEIGHT, Helen Margaret West End Cottage, Blyth Road, Ranskill, Retford DN22 8LR; Offa's Holt, Claypits, Yazor, Hereford HR4 7BB — BM BS 1989 Nottm.

SPEIGHT, Julian Michael Combe House, Throop Road, Templecombe — MB BS 1993 Lond.; BSc (Hons.) Lond. 1990. Phys. Prosector & SHO (A & E) Som.

SPEIGHT, Lenka 34 Ritchie Street, London N1 0DG Tel: 020 7837 1663 Fax: 020 7837 3656; 105 Gloucester Avenue, London NW1 8LB — MRCS Eng. LRCP Lond. 1971.

SPEIGHT, Martyn Bryan Grovegarth Cottage, Whitehouses Lane, Fellbeck, Pateley Bridge, Harrogate HG3 5EN Tel: 01423 712490 Fax: 01423 712490 Email: cyclemedic@aol.com — MB ChB 1993 Sheff.

SPEIGHT, Michael David Tel: 01642 452727 — MB ChB 1989 Ed.; MA Camb. 1988. (Ed.)

SPEIGHT, Peter 16 Clifton Street, Beeston, Nottingham NG9 2LS — BM BS 1993 Nottm. SHO (Psychiat.) Nottm. Healthcare NHS Trust. Socs: Inceptor Roy. Coll. Psychiat. Prev: SHO (Psychiat.) W. Chesh. NHS Trust.

SPEIGHT, Robert Glynn The Park End Surgery, 3 Park End, Hampstead, London NW3 2SE Tel: 020 7435 7282; 105 Gloucester Avenue, London NW1 8LB — MB BS 1972 Lond.; BA (Fine Arts) Lond. 1978; MRCS Eng. LRCP 1971.

SPEIGHT, Timothy John West End Cottage, Blyth Road, Ranskill, Retford DN22 8LR — BM BS 1990 Nottm.

SPEIRS, Alastair Thomas Orr (retired) 21 Glengarry Way, Friars Cliff, Christchurch BH23 4EH Tel: 01425 279528 — MRCS Eng. LRCP Lond. 1939; DOMS Eng. 1948. Prev: Clin. Asst. Roy. Eye Hosp. & King's Coll. Hosp. Lond.

SPEIRS, Alexander Logan, OBE (retired) 8 John Murray Drive, Bridge of Allan, Stirling FK9 4QH — MB ChB 1943 Aberd.; MD Aberd. 1954; FRCP Lond. 1971, M 1949; FRCP Glas. 1971, M 1967; DCH Eng. 1952; FRCPCH. Prev: Cons. Paediat. Roy. Hosp. Sick Childr. Glas., Stirling Roy. Infirm. & Falkirk & Dist. Roy. Infirm.

SPEIRS, Christopher James 82 Lower Road, Fetcham, Leatherhead KT22 9NG — MB ChB 1970 Liverp.; MSc (Epidemiol.) Lond. 1990; MRCP (UK) 1973; FFPM RCP (UK) 1993, M 1991. (Liverp.) Socs: Roy. Soc. Med.

SPEIRS, Colin Fairholme Medicines Control Agency, Market Towers, 1 Nine Elms Lane, London SW8 5NQ Tel: 020 7273 0460 Fax: 020 7273 0170; 3 Heathpark Drive, Windlesham GU20 6JA Tel: 01276 473744 — MB ChB Ed. 1961; FRCP Lond. 1994; FRCP Ed. 1974, M 1965; FFPM RCP (UK) 1989. Sen. Med. Off. Med. Control Agency Lond. Socs: Liveryman Worshipful Soc. Apoth. Lond.; Fell. Roy. Soc. Med. Prev: Head Europ. Med. Servs. Lilly Research

Centre Ltd. Windlesham; Sen. Regist. (Infec. Dis.) City Hosp. Edin.; Regist. (Med.) Gardiner Inst. W.. Infirm. Glas.

SPEIRS, Gail Elisabeth Department of Pathology, Level 1, North Devon District Hospital, Barnstaple EX31 4JB Tel: 01271 322355 Fax: 01271 322328 Email: gail.speirs@ndevon.swest.nhs.uk; Prixford House, Prixford, Barnstaple EX31 4DX Tel: 01271 329979 Fax: 01271 329979 — MB ChB 1982 Birm.; MRCPath 1989; FRCPath 1997. (Birmingham University) Cons. Clin. Microbiol. N. Devon Dist. Hosp. Barnstaple. Socs: Hosp. Infec. Soc.; Brit. Soc. Animicrobial Chemother. Prev: Sen. Regist. (Clin. Microbiol.) N. Devon Dist. Hosp. Barnstaple & S.mead Hosp. Bristol; Sen. Regist. (Clin. Microbiol.) Addenbrooke's Hosp. Camb.; Regist. (Clin. MicroBiol.) Addenbrooke's Hosp. Camb.

SPEIRS, Jean Marion The Priory Hospital, Priory Lane, London SW15 5JJ Tel: 020 8876 8261 Fax: 020 8392 2632 — MB BS 1973 Lond.; MRCS Eng. LRCP Lond. 1972; MRCPsych 1977. (Guy's) Cons. Psychiat. Priory Hosp. Lond. Socs: Marce.Soc. Prev: Regist. (Psychiat) W.m. Hosp. Lond.

SPEIRS, Mhairi Wilson 6 Minster Road, Oxford OX4 1LX — MB ChB 1990 Glas. Specialist Regist. (anaesth.) John Radcliffe Hosp. Oxf. Socs: Intens. Care Soc. Prev: SHO (Anaesth.) Wycombe Gen. Hosp.

SPEIRS, Norma Isabelle Battenburg Avenue, Portsmouth PO2 0TA Tel: 023 92 670346 Fax: 023 92 672258; The Cedars, Maori Road, Guildford GU1 2EL Tel: 01483 567242 — MB ChB 1977 Ed. Staff Grade Doctor Portsmouth. Prev: SCMO Havant Hants.; GP Bristol.

SPEIRS, Norman Thomas (retired) 24 Liberton Place, Edinburgh EH16 6NA Tel: 0131 672 2662 — MB ChB Ed. 1947; BSc Ed. 1946; DMRD Ed. 1953. Prev: Cons. Radiol. Roy. Vict. Disp. Chest Clinic Edin., Roy. Edin. Ment. Hosp. & Roodlands Hosp. Haddington.

SPEIRS, Richard Bradley Abbey Health Centre, East Abbey Street, Arbroath DD11 1EN Tel: 01241 870307 Fax: 01241 431414; 1 Fraserfield, Arbroath DD11 2LW Tel: 01241 890384 Fax: 01241 431414 — MB ChB 1968 St. And. Socs: Dundee Med.Soc.

SPEIRS, Robert Craig (retired) 99 South Street, Greenock PA16 8QN Tel: 01475 722577 Email: docspiers99south@cs.com — MB ChB Glas. 1962; DObst RCOG 1964. Prev: SHO Rankin Memor. Hosp. & Gateside Hosp. Greenock.

SPEIRS, William McArthur (retired) Ard Mara, 7 Laxdale, Lane, Stornoway HS2 0DR Tel: 01851 702019 — MB ChB 1953 Glas.; DA Eng. 1958; DObst RCOG 1957. Prev: Cons. Anaesth. Lewis & Co. Hosps. Stornoway.

SPELDEWINDE, Deirdre Catherine Mary 10 Plymouth Wharf, Saunderness Road, London E14 3EL — MB BCh BAO 1991 NUI. (Galway) Regist. (Paediat.) P.ss Mgt. Hosp. Perth, WA, Australia.

SPELLER, Christopher John Learning Disability Service, Beaver House, Victoria Road, Swindon SN1 3BU Tel: 01793 644900 — MB ChB 1982 Bristol; MRCPsych 1991. (Bristol) p/t Cons. (Psychiat. in Learning Disabil.) Wilts. & Swindon Trust. Prev: Sen. Regist. (Psychiat. Ment. Handicap) Hanham Hall Hosp. Bristol.; Regist. (Psychiat.) Glenside Hosp. Bristol; SHO (Psychiat.) Bristol & W.on HA.

SPELLER, David Charles Endersby 9 Dowry Road, Bristol BS8 4PR Tel: 0117 929 8425 Fax: 0117 925 2893 — BM BCh Oxf. 1961; MA Oxf. 1961; FRCP Lond. 1981, M 1965; FRCPath. 1982, M 1970. (Oxf.) Emerit. Prof. (Clin. Bact.) Univ. Bristol. Socs: (Ex-Pres.) Hosp. Infec. Soc.; Hon. Mem. (Ex-Pres.) Brit. Soc. for Antimicrobial. Chemother.; Hon. Mem. Brit. Soc. Med. Mycology. Prev: Head of Antibiotic Ref. Unit. Centr. Pub. Health Laborat. Lond.

SPELLER, Jeremy Clive Tavistock Clinic, 70 Plymouth Road, Tavistock PL19 8BX — MB ChB 1981 Manch.; MRCPsych 1986. Cons. Gen. Adult Psychiat.. Plymouth Primary Care Trust. Prev: Cons. Gen. Psychiat. Avalon Som. NHS Trust; Cons. Gen. Psychiat. Plymouth HA.; Clin. Research Fell. (Psychiat.) Char. Cross Hosp. Med. Sch. Lond.

SPELLER, Peter Joslin (retired) Limebank, Quantock Rise, Kingston St Mary, Taunton TA2 8HH — MB ChB Bristol 1949; MFCM 1973; DPH Bristol 1955. Prev: SCM (Dist. Support) Bristol & W.on HA.

SPELMAN, John Francis St James Surgery, 8-9 Northampton Buildings, Bath BA1 2SR Tel: 01225 422911 Fax: 01225 428398; 9 Sunny Bank, Lyncombe Vale, Bath BA2 4NA — MB ChB 1981 Birm.; MRCGP 1986; DRCOG 1984.

SPENCE, Alan Kerr, QHP (retired) Brook Cottage, The Sallies, Kinnersley, Hereford HR3 6QE Tel: 0154 46 721 — MB BCh BAO 1961 Dub.; MA Dub. 1968, MB BCh BAO 1961; FFCM 1981, M 1972; DPH Liverp. 1966; DCH NUI 1967. Prev: Chief Admin. Med. Off. & Dir. Pub. Health Med. Powys HA.

SPENCE, Professor Alastair Andrew, CBE University Department Anaesthetics, Royal Infirmary, Edinburgh EH3 9YW Tel: 0131 536 3652 Fax: 0131 536 3672; 3/9 Dunard Garden, Oswald Road, Edinburgh EH9 Tel: 0131 667 0231 — MB ChB 1960 Glas.; MD Glas. 1976; FRCP Ed. 1993; FRCS Eng. 1994; FRCS Ed. 1991; FRCP Glas. 1980; FDS RCS Eng. (Hons.) 1994; FCAnaesth 1984. Prof. Anaesth. Univ. Edin. Socs: Pres. RCAnaesth. Prev: Hunt. Prof. RCS Eng.; Prof. & Head Univ. Dept. Anaesth. W.. Infirm. Glas.; Edr. Brit. Jl. Anaesth.

SPENCE, Mr Alexander James (retired) The Gables, Shore Road, Aberdour, Burntisland KY3 0TU Tel: 01383 860120 Fax: 01383 860120 Email: aspence1@uk.packardbell.org — MB ChB 1943 Aberd.; FRCS Eng. 1950; FRCS Ed. 1968. Cons. Surg. E. & W. Fife Health Dists. & P.ss Margt. Rose Orthop. Hosp. Edin. Prev: Sen. Regist. & Res. Surg. Off. Roy. Nat. Orthop. Hosp. Stanmore.

SPENCE, Alexander Stewart (retired) Woodlea, Forres IV36 0DN Tel: 01309 672692 — MB ChB 1938 Aberd.

SPENCE, Anthony James 154 Little Breach, Chichester PO19 4UA — MB BS 1986 West Indies.

SPENCE, Colin Stanley Tramways Medical Centre, Farmley Road, Newtownabbey BT36 7XX Tel: 028 9034 2131 Fax: 028 9083 9111; 124 Circular Road, Jordanstown, Newtownabbey BT37 0RH — MB BCh BAO 1982 Belf.; MRCGP 1987; DRCOG 1988; Cert. Family Plann. JCC 1987; DCH Dub. 1986. Socs: Brit. Assn. Sport & Med.; BMA. Prev: Ho. Off. (A & E) Belf. City Hosp. & Ulster Hosp.; Ho. Off. (Med.) Tyrone Co. Hosp.; Ho. Off. (Paediat.) Belf. City Hosp.

SPENCE, David George HCI International Medical Centre, Beardmore St., Clydebank G81 4HX Tel: 0141 951 5908 Fax: 0141 951 5869 Email: david.spence@hci.co.uk; 28 Hughenden Gardens, Glasgow G12 9YH Tel: 0141 357 4119 — MB ChB 1973 Glas.; BSc (Hons.) (Path.) Glas. 1971; FRCP Ed. 1991; MRCP (UK) 1976; FRCPath 1992, M 1980. Chief of Haemat. Dir. BMT Program. HCI Internat. Med. Centre, Clydebank. Socs: Assn. Clin. Path. & Brit. Soc. Haemat. Prev: Sen. Cons. Haemat. King Fahd Nat. Guard Hosp. Riyadh, Saudi Arabia; Staff Haemat. (Oncol.) King Faisal Specialist Hosp. & Research Centre Riyadh, Saudi Arabia; Cons. Haemat. Tayside HB & Sen. Lect. Univ. Dundee.

SPENCE, David Peter Saunders Maynooth Hall, Knayton, Thirsk YO7 4AU — MB ChB 1983 Leic.; MD Leic. 1993; MRCP (UK) 1987. Cons. Respirat. & Gen. Phys. Friarage Hosp. N.allerton.

SPENCE, David Stephen Bristol Homoeopathic Hospital, Cotham Hill, Bristol BS6 6JU Tel: 0117 973 1231 Fax: 0117 923 8759 Email: david.spence@ubht.swest.nhs.uk — MB BS 1969 Lond.; MRCS Eng. LRCP Lond. 1969; FFHom 1987, MFHom 1978; DObst RCOG 1971. (St. Geo.) Cons. Homoep. Phys. United Bristol Healthcare (NHS) Trust; Clin. Dir. Directorate of Homoeop. Med. Socs: Fell. Roy. Soc. Med.; Fell. (Ex-Pres.) Fac. Homoeop. Prev: Regist. (Med.) Mt. Vernon Hosp. N.wood; Ho. Phys. St. Geo. Hosp. Lond.

SPENCE, Deborah Jane The Vyne, 35 Ellis Avenue, Worthing BN13 3DY — BM 1979 Soton. Prev: SHO (Psychiat., O & G & A & E) & Trainee GP Felpham & Middleton Health Centre.; Ho. Surg. (Gen. Surg.) & Ho. Phys. (Gen. Med.) P.ss Margt. Hosp. Swindon.

SPENCE, Derek Wilson 33 Dore Road, Sheffield S17 3NA Tel: 0114 235 2508 — MB BCh BAO 1972 Belf.; FRACGP 1978; DA (UK) 1976; DObst RCOG 1975; DCH RCP Lond. 1974; FRACMA 1982. (Queen's Belfast) Managem. Cons. Prev: Chair Regional Specialities Trent RHA; Supra Regional Contracts Gp. Mem.; Chief Exec. & Med. Dir. P.ss Margt. Hosp. Childr. Perth, W.. Austral.

SPENCE, Desmond Frederick Maryhill Health Centre, 41 Shawpark Street, Glasgow G20 9DR Tel: 0141 531 8811 Fax: 0141 531 8808 — MB ChB 1990 Glas. Prev: Trainee GP/SHO (Geriat.) Vict. Infirm. Glas.; SHO (A & E) Stobhill Hosp. Glas.

SPENCE, Eileen Margaret (retired) 14 Cairnlee Road, Bieldside, Aberdeen AB15 9BN Tel: 01224 861891 — MB ChB 1949 Aberd.; MRCP Lond. 1955.

SPENCE, Elizabeth 5 Links View, Larkhall ML9 2JT — MB ChB 1998 Glas.

SPENCE

SPENCE, Fiona Mary University Medical Practice, University of Aberdeen, Block E, Taylor Buildings, Old Aberdeen, Aberdeen AB24 3UB Tel: 01224 272410 Fax: 01224 272394 Email: fiona.spence@university.grampian.scot.nhs.uk; 111 Brighton Place, Aberdeen AB10 6RT Tel: 01224 312078 — MB ChB 1980 Aberd.; MRCGP 1994; DGM RCPS Glas. 1991. Gen. Practitioner, Univ. Med. Pract., Grampian Primary Care Trust, Aberd.

***SPENCE, Gary Mervyn** 25 Mount Royal, Lisburn BT27 5BF — MB BCh BAO 1994 Belf.

***SPENCE, Gavin Malcolm** 2 Wingfield House, Gascoigne Place, London E2 7LZ — MB BS 1994 Lond.

SPENCE, Gerald George Shettleston Health Centre, 420 Old Shettleston Road, Glasgow G32 7JZ Tel: 0141 531 6220 Fax: 0141 531 6206 — MB ChB 1978 Aberd.

SPENCE, Imogen Pamela Westwater 2 Bramway, Bramhall, Stockport SK7 2AP — MB ChB 1989 Manch.

SPENCE, Joanna Rosalie The Shrubbery, 26 High St., Eynsham, Witney OX29 4HB Tel: 01865 881385 Fax: 01865 881342 — MB BS 1973 Lond. (Roy. Free) Asst. GP Windrush Health Centre Witney. Prev: Ho. Phys. Roy. Free Hosp. Lond.; Ho. Surg. Lister Hosp. Stevenage; Ho. Surg. (O & G) Roy. Sussex Co. Hosp. Brighton.

SPENCE, John Cameron 67 Gilbertfield Street, Glasgow G33 3TU; Stable End, 1A Middlemuir Road, Lenzie, Kirkintilloch, Glasgow G66 4NA Tel: 0141 774 5987 — MB ChB 1977 Glas.; MRCGP 1989.

SPENCE, John Couper (retired) 116 Elizabeth Road, New Oscott, Sutton Coldfield B73 5AS Tel: 0121 355 6717 Email: ioannes@globalnet.co.uk — MB ChB 1958 Glas.; MRCGP 1980; DObst RCOG 1965. Prev: SHO (Med. & Cardiol.), Ho. Phys. & Ho. Surg. Vict. Infirm. Glas.

SPENCE, John Edward Waterside Health Centre, Glendermott Road, Londonderry BT47 6AU Tel: 028 7132 0100 Fax: 028 7132 0117; 3 West Lake, Londonderry BT47 6WE Tel: 028 7186 1650 — MB BCh BAO 1983 NUI.

SPENCE, John Mountfort (retired) The Well House, Spa Close, Brill, Aylesbury HP18 9RZ Tel: 01844 237639 Fax: 01844 238568 — MB BS 1956 Lond.; MRCS Eng. LRCP Lond. 1956; DObst RCOG 1958. Prev: GP Aylesbury.

SPENCE, Joyce Sylvia Angulus Iste, Cotmaton Road, Sidmouth EX10 8ST — MRCS Eng. LRCP Lond. 1939. (Bristol) Prev: Ho. Surg. Bristol Roy. Infirm. & Nottm. Childr. Hosp.; Ho. Phys. Salisbury Gen. Infirm.

SPENCE, Kenneth Archibald Edmund, TD, SBStJ 36 Limmer Lane, Felpham, Bognor Regis PO22 7EU Tel: 01243 823464 — MRCS Eng. LRCP Lond. 1951. (Guy's) Maj. RAMC, RARO. Socs: BMA. Prev: Ho. Phys. (Paediat.) Worthing Gen. Hosp.

SPENCE, Magnus Peter (retired) 13 College Road, London SE21 7BG Tel: 020 8693 2412 — MB BChir Camb. 1947; FRCP Lond. 1975, M 1948. Prev: Cons. Phys. St. Albans City Hosp. & Qu. Eliz. II Hosp. Welwyn Gdn.

SPENCE, Margaret Ruth Coppins, Elm Green Lane, Danbury, Chelmsford CM3 4DR — MB BS 1984 Lond.; MRCGP 1989; DRCOG 1989. (Guy's) GP Retainer Chelmsford. Socs: (Region. Rep.) Christian Med. Fell.ship. Prev: GP Retainer Maldon; Trainee GP Chelmsford VTS.

***SPENCE, Mark Sinclair** 25 The Spires, Dromore BT25 1QE Email: spencebest@clara.net — MB BCh BAO 1995 Belf.

SPENCE, Martin Terence Wigan & Bolton Health Authority, Bryan House, 61 Standishgate, Wigan WN1 1AH Tel: 01942 772825 Fax: 01942 772769; 24 Tennyson Close, Briarsmount, Heaton Mersey, Stockport SK4 2ED — MB BCh BAO 1981 Belf.; MFPHM RCP (UK) 1995. Cons. Pub. Health Med. Wigan & Bolton HA. Socs: Manch. Med. Soc.; Ulster Med. Soc.

***SPENCE, Peter Johnson** 6 Lisburn Road, Moira, Craigavon BT67 0JP — MB BCh 1998 Belf.; MB BCh Belf 1998.

SPENCE, Richard William Spence Group Practice, Westcliffe House, 48-50 Logan Road, Bishopston, Bristol BS7 8DR Tel: 0117 944 0701; Birchwood, Eastfield, Westbury-on-Trym, Bristol BS9 4BE Tel: 01179 628848 — MB BChir Camb. 1970; MRCS Eng. LRCP Lond. 1970. (St. Bart.) Hosp. Pract. (Gastroenterol.) Frenchay Hosp. Bristol. Socs: (Mem. Steering Comm.) Primary Care Soc. Gastroenterol. Prev: SHO (Respirat. & Infec. Dis.) Unit Ham Green Hosp. Bristol; Research Regist. (Gastroenterol.) & SHO (Gen. Med.) Frenchay Hosp. Bristol.

SPENCE, Robert Nicholas Francis The Strand Practice, 2 The Strand, Goring-by-Sea, Worthing BN12 6DN Tel: 01903 243351 Fax: 01903 705804; 35 Ellis Avenue, Worthing BN13 3DY — MB BChir 1975 Camb.; MA Camb. 1975; DRCOG 1983. (Guy's Hosp. Lond.)

SPENCE, Professor Roy Archibald Joseph Belfast City Hospital, Lisburn Road, Belfast BT9 7AB Tel: 01232 329241 Fax: 01232 326614 Email: roy.spence@beh.n-i.nhs.uk; 7 Downshire Crescent, Hillsborough BT26 6DD Tel: 01846 682362 Fax: 01846 682418 — MB BCh BAO 1977 Belf.; MB BCh BAO (Hons.) Belf. 1977; MA Belf. 1997; MD Belf. (Hons.) 1984; FRCS Ed. 1981; FRCSI 1981. (Queens University Belfast) Cons. (Surgey) Belf. City Hosp.; Hon. Lect. (Surg.) Qu.s Univ. Belf.; Arris & Gale Lect. RCS Eng.; Hon. Lect. (Anat.); Hon. Lect. (Oncol.); Hon. Prof. Univ. of Ulster. Socs: Fell. Assn. Surgs.; Brit. Soc. Gastroenterol.; Moynihan Club. Prev: Cons. (Surgey) Groote Schuur Hosp., Cape Town; Exec. Dir. Belf. City Hosp. Trust Bd. (1993-1997); Vis. Prof. Cleveland Clinic Ohio, USA 1993.

SPENCE, Sinclair Dick Ballykennedy House, Nutt's Corner, Belfast — MB BCh BAO 1967 Belf.

SPENCE, Thomas Alfred (retired) Pine Lodge, Armagh Tel: 02837 523893 — LRCPI & LM, LRSCI & LM 1940; LRCPI & LM LRCSI & LM 1940; DPH Belf. 1942; MRCGP 1967. Police Surg. Prev: Ho. Surg. Armagh Co. Infirm.

SPENCE-JONES, Mr Clive 149 Harley Street, London W1N 2DE Tel: 020 7935 4444 Fax: 020 7486 2580 — MB BS 1981 Lond.; FRCS Ed. 1986; MRCOG 1988. Cons. O & G Whittington Hosp. Lond.

SPENCE-SALES, Dorothy (retired) 41 Christchurch Road, London SW14 7AQ — MA New Zealand 1932, BSc 1933; MB ChB New Zealand 1938; DA Eng 1953; FFA RCS Eng. 1953. Prev: Cons. & Sen. Lect. Roy. Postgrad. Med. Sch. Lond.

SPENCELEY, James Howard Gairnshiel, 22 Beaufort Road, Inverness IV2 3NP — MB ChB 1967 Ed.; FFA RCS Eng. 1972. (Ed.) Cons. Anaesth. Raigmore Hosp. Inverness.

SPENCELEY, Jane Elizabeth Occupational Health, Nestlé Rowntree, York YO91 1XY Tel: 01904 602343 — BM BCh 1990 Oxf.; AFOM 2001; DFFP 1996; MRCGP 1996; DRCOG 1997. (Oxf.) Specialist Regist. in Occupat. Health, Nestle Rowntree York. Socs: Oxf. Med. Soc.; Roy. Coll. Gen. Pract.; Soc. of Occupat.al Med.

SPENCELEY, Judith Anne Gairnshiel, 22 Beaufort Road, Inverness IV2 3NP — MB ChB 1967 Ed.; DObst RCOG 1970. (Ed.)

SPENCELEY, Kenneth Reid Merton Lodge Surgery, West Street, Alford LN13 9DH Tel: 01507 463262 Fax: 01507 466447 — MB ChB 1973 Glas.; MRCGP 1977; DRCOG 1978.

SPENCELEY, Neil Campbell c/o Spenceley, 22 Beaufort Road, Inverness IV2 3NP — MB ChB 1993 Ed.

SPENCELEY, Simon Richard The Surgery, 162 Long St., Dordon, Tamworth B78 1QA — MB ChB 1986 Birm.

SPENCELY, Mary Windyridge, Adlington Road, Wilmslow SK9 2BS — MB ChB 1966 Ed.; FFCM 1984, M 1978; Dip. Soc. Med. Ed. 1970. (Ed.) Dir. Pub. Health S. Lancs. HA.

SPENCER, Alfred George, GM (retired) High Gate, Rock, Wadebridge PL27 6JZ — MRCS Eng. LRCP Lond. 1939, MD Lond. 1947, MB BS (Hnrs.) 1940; FRCP Lond. 1962, M 1947. Prev: Cons. Phys. St. Bart. & Univ. Coll. Hosps.

SPENCER, Alison Catherine 10 Blandford Drive, Macclesfield SK11 8WB — MB ChB 1991 Manch.

SPENCER, Amanda Jane Bellowswood House, Ballinger, Great Missenden HP16 9LF — MB ChB 1993 Liverp.

SPENCER, Anne Elizabeth The Surgery, Earby Colne, Colne BB18 6QT Tel: 01282 843407; 35 York Fields, Barnoldswick, Colne BB18 5DA — MB ChB 1981 Leeds.

SPENCER, Anne Fiona University Hospital, Queens Medical Centre, Nottingham NG7 2UH; Flat 1, 11 Cavendish Crescent S., The Park, Nottingham NG7 1EN Tel: 0115 947 3415 — MB ChB 1985 Bristol; BSc (Med. Microbiol.) Bristol 1982; DM Nottm. 1995; FRCS Glas. 1990; FRCOphth 1990. Sen. Regist. (Ophth.) Univ. Hosp. Nottm. Prev: Lect. (Ophth.) Univ. Hosp. Nottm.; Regist. (Ophth.) Glas. W.. Infirm.

SPENCER, Arthur 10 Highfield Road, Ringwood BH24 1RQ — MB BS 1952 Lond.

SPENCER, Branwell Barry 109 Milner Road, Wirral CH60 5RX — MB ChB 1992 Liverp.

SPENCER

SPENCER, Brian Trevor Holmside Medical Group, 142 Armstrong Road, Benwell, Newcastle upon Tyne NE4 8QB Tel: 0191 273 4009 Fax: 0191 273 2745; 20 Willow Way, Darras Hall, Ponteland, Newcastle upon Tyne NE20 9RJ — BSc (Special, Pharmacol.) Lond. 1967, MB BS 1970; MRCP (UK) 1975; MRCGP 1976. (St. Geo.)

SPENCER, Bryan John ThE Elizabeth Courtauld Surgery, Factory Lane West, Halstead CO9 1EX Tel: 01787 475944 Fax: 01787 474506; 30 Chapel Street, Halstead CO9 2LS Tel: 01787 473535 — MB BS 1974 Lond.; BSc (Physiol.) Lond. 1971; MRCS Eng. LRCP Lond. 1974; MRCGP 1978.

SPENCER, Caroline Melanie Cherrygarth, 1 Weston Lane, Weston, Bath BA1 4AA Tel: 01225 317057; Department of Cardiology, Royal United Hospital, Combe Park, Bath BA1 3NG Tel: 01225 428331 — MB BS 1985 Lond.; MRCGP 1994; DRCOG 1987; Cert. Family Plann. JCC 1987. (Roy. Free) Clin. Asst. (Cardiol.) Roy. United Hosp. Bath. Socs: Assoc. Mem. BMA; Assoc. Mem. RCGP. Prev: Asst. GP Bath & Oxf.; SHO (Palliat. Med.) Sir Michael Sobell Hse. Oxf.

SPENCER, Charles Guy Chapman High Gate, Rock, Wadebridge PL27 6JZ — MB BS 1990 Lond.; MRCP (UK) 1994. Research Fell. (Cardiol.) Univ. Dept. of Med., City Hosp. Birm. Prev: Specialist Regist. (Cardiol.) Sandwell Healthcare NHS Trust, W. Bromwich; Regist. (Cardiol.) Univ. Hosp. Birm.; Regist. (Cardiol.) Birm. Heartlands Hosp.

SPENCER, Clifford Michael The Ruddington Medical Centre, Church Street, Ruddington, Nottingham NG11 6HD Tel: 0115 921 1144 Fax: 0115 940 5139; Bradmere Barn, Loughborough Road, Bradmore, Nottingham NG11 6PA Tel: 0115 984 6333 — MB ChB 1977 Sheff.; MRCGP 1993; DRCOG 1981. Trainer Nottm. VTS Scheme; Clin. Asst. (ENT) Nottm. Univ Hosp.; Clin. Tutor (Community Med.) Univ. Nottm.

SPENCER, Colin Wigmore The Marches Medical Practice, Mill Lane Surgery, 46 Mill Lane, Buckley CH7 3HB Tel: 01224 550939 Fax: 01224 549592 — MB ChB 1967 Liverp.; BDS 1961; MRCGP 1977.

SPENCER, David Anthony Regional Cardiothoracic Centre, Freeman Hospital, Newcastle upon Tyne NE7 7DN Tel: 0191 284 3111 Fax: 0191 213 2167; Low House, Berwick Hill, Newcastle upon Tyne NE20 0BJ Tel: 01661 821354 — MB BS 1981 Lond.; MD Lond. 1992; MRCP (UK) 1985; FRCPCH 1997. (Royal Free London) Cons. Respirat. Paediat. Freeman Hosp. Newc. u. Tyne. Socs: Brit. Thorac. Soc.; Amer. Thoracic Soc.; Eur. Respirat. Soc. Prev: Cons. Respirat. Paediat. Birm. Childr. Hosp.; Sen. Regist. (Paediat.) W. Midl. RHA; Research Fell. (Thoracic Med.) King's Coll. Hosp. Lond.

SPENCER, David John Department of Psychiatry, Royal Hospital, Calow, Chesterfield Tel: 01246 277271 Fax: 01246 552612; Croft Lodge, Church Lane, Great Longstone, Bakewell DE45 1TB — MB ChB 1960 Sheff.; FRCPsych 1986, M 1972; FRANZCP 1975; DPM Eng. 1966. Cons. Psychiat. Chesterfield & N. Derbysh. HA; Asst. Prof. Psychiat. Univ. W. Austral; Ment. Health Review Tribunal Serv. (Trent). Socs: Roy. Soc. Med. Prev: Cons. Psychiat. Sir Chas. Gairder Hosp. Shenton Pk. Perth, Austral.; Dir. Clin. Servs. W.. Austral. Alcohol & Drug Auth.; Psychiat. Supt. Heathcote Hosp. Perth, W. Austral.

SPENCER, David John Oakhaven Hospice, Lower Pennington Lane, Lymington SO41 8ZZ Tel: 01590 670346 Fax: 01590 679624; 280 Burley Road, Bransgrove, Christchurch BH23 8DQ Tel: 01425 672927 — MB BS 1970 Lond.; MSc (Social Med.) Lond. 1978; MRCGP 1974; DObst RCOG 1973; DCH Eng. 1973. (St. Geo.) p/t Cons. Palliat. Med. Oakhaven Hospice Lymington. Socs: Assn. Palliat. Med.; (Founder) Mind and Mortality. Prev: Cons. Palliat. Med. & Clin. Dir. Prospect Hospice Swindon; Cons. Phys. St. Barnabas' Hospice Worthing.

SPENCER, Douglas Anthony (retired) 25 Standing Stones, Great Billing, Northampton NN3 9HA Tel: 01604 414825 — MB ChB 1956 Ed.; FRCPsych 1982, M 1971; DPM Leeds 1962. Prev: Phys. Supt. & Cons. Psychiat. Meanwood Pk. Hosp. Leeds, Wharfe Grange Hosp. Wetherby & Crooked Acre Hosp. Leeds.

SPENCER, Elizabeth Mary Department of Anaesthetics, Gloucester Royal Hospital, Great Western Road, Gloucester GL1 3NL Tel: 01452 394442 — BM 1981 Soton.; DM Soton. 1992; FFA RCS Eng. 1988. Cons. Anaesth. & Intens. Care Gloucester Roy. Hosp. Socs: Assn. Anaesth.; Intens. Care Soc. Prev: Sen. Regist. (Anaesth.) Plymouth & Bristol; Research Fell. Intens. Ther. Unit Bristol Roy. Infirm.; Regist. (Anaesth.) Derby & Nottm.

SPENCER, Emma Freda Anne (retired) 6 The Plateau, Piney Hills, Belfast BT9 5QP — MB BCh BAO Belf. 1961. Prev: Clin. Asst. Gastroenterol. Belf.

SPENCER, Geoffrey Stuart Bideford Medical Centre, Abbotsham Road, Bideford EX39 3AF Tel: 01237 476363 Fax: 01237 423351 — MB BS 1986 Lond.; MRCGP 1992; T(GP) 1992.

SPENCER, Geoffrey Tallent, OBE 40 Cleaver Square, London SE11 4EA Tel: 020 7735 9357 — MB BS 1954 Lond.; FFA RCS Eng. 1960. (St. Thos.) Cons. Anaesth. & Consult. i/c Respirat. Unit St. Thos. Hosp. Lond.; Hon. Cons. Brompton Hosp. Lond.; Hons Cons. REFRESH. Prev: Vis. Prof., Childr.s Med Hosp. Chicago USA; Cons. W.H.O.

SPENCER, Mr George Robert The Health Centre, Langholm DG13 0JY — MB ChB 1973 Ed.; BSc (Med. Sci.) Ed. 1970; LMCC 1985; FRCS Ed. 1978. Chief of Staff St. Therese Hosp. St. Paul Alberta, Canada.

SPENCER, Gillian Mary North & Mid Hampshire Health Authority, Harness House, Aldermaston Road, Basingstoke RG24 9NB Tel: 01256 312250 — MB BS 1981 Lond.; MFPHM RCP (UK) 1991; MRCPsych 1986. Cons. Pub. Health Med. N. & Mid Hants. Health Auth. Prev: Sen. Regist. (Community Med.) Sheff. HA; Regist. (Community Med.) Trent RHA.

SPENCER, Glenn MacDonald Front Drive Offices, Oldchurch Hospital, Waterloo Road, Romford RM7 0BE Tel: 01708 708285 Fax: 01708 708285 — MB BS 1988 Lond.; BSc Basic Med. Scs. & Physiol. (Hons.) Lond. 1985; MRCP (UK) 1991. (St. Geo.) Cons. Phys. & Gastroenterol., Barking, Havering & Redbridgeps. NSH Trust, Old Ch. Hosp., Romford. Socs: BMA. Prev: Lect. (Gastroenterol.) Middlx. Hosp. Lond.; Regist. Rotat. (Med.) Ipswich Hosp.; SHO Rotat. (Med.) Derby Roy. Infirm.

SPENCER, Graeme Thomas Russell Tel: 01282 698036 — MB ChB 1989 Liverp.; MRCGP 1993; T(GP) 1993; DFFP 1993; DRCOG 1991. (Liverp.) Gen. Practitioner, Nelson. Prev: SHO (A & E Paediat. & O & G) Leighton Dist. Gen. Hosp. Crewe; SHO (c/o the Elderly) Leighton Dist. Gen. Hosp. Crewe.

SPENCER, Greg Bushey Fields Hospital, Bushey Fields Road, Dudley DY1 2LE Tel: 01384 244957 — MB ChB 1991 Aberd.; MRCPsych 1995. Cons. in Old Age Psychiat. Bushey Fields Hosp., Dudley W. Midl.s. Socs: Roy. Coll. Psychiat. (Fac. Old Age Psychiat.); BMA; W Midl. Assn. Old Age Psychiatr. Prev: Sen. Regist. Rotat. (Old Age Psychiat.) W. Midl.; Regist. (Child Psychiat.) Selly Oak Hosp. Birm.; Regist. (Old Age Psychiat.) Highcroft Hosp. Birm.

SPENCER, Hal Lloyd Cruck Barn, Stocksbridge, Sheffield S36 4GH — MB BS 1993 Lond.; MRCP (UK) 1997; MA Camb. 1993. (Lond. Hosp./Camb. Univ.) Regist. (Gastroenterol.), Sheff. Teachg. Hosp.s. Prev: SHO (Gen. Med.) City Hosp. Nottm.; Ho. Off. (Gen. Surg.) S. Warwicks Hosp.; Ho. Off. (Med.) Roy. Lond. Hosp.

SPENCER, Heather Dawn 11 Upper High Royds, Mapplewell, Barnsley S75 5FB — MB ChB 1992 Leeds.

SPENCER, Helen 446 Pinhoe Road, Exeter EX4 8EW — MB ChB 1993 Manch.; DCH RCP Lond. 1995. SHO (Paediat.) S. Manch. Trust Hosps. Prev: SHO (A & E) Blackpool; Ho. Off. (Med.) Chester; Ho. Off. (Surg.) Blackpool.

SPENCER, Helen Amanda 9 Southlands, Town Close, Horsforth, Leeds LS18 5BR — MB BS 1980 Lond.; FFARCS Eng. 1988; DCH RCP Lond. 1984; DRCOG 1984. (Roy. Free) Cons. Anaesth. St. Jas. Univ. Hosp. Leeds. Socs: Assn. Anaesth.; Eur. Soc. Regional Anaesth. Prev: Sen. Regist. Rotat. (Anaesth.) Leeds; Post-Fell.sh. Regist. (Anaesth.) Middlx. Hosp. Lond.; Regist. (Anaesth.) Roy. Free Hosp. Lond.

SPENCER, Helen Frances The Spinney, Chapel Lane, Bruera, Chester CH3 6EW — BM BCh 1977 Oxf.; MA Oxf. 1982. Socs: Chester & N. Wales Med. Soc. Prev: Trainee GP Brighton; Ho. Surg. Radcliffe Infirm. Oxf.

SPENCER, Helen Janet Greenview Surgery, 129 Hazeldene Road, Northampton NN2 7PB Tel: 01604 791002 Fax: 01604 721822; 70 Glenfield Drive, Great Doddington, Wellingborough NN29 7TE — BM BS 1987 Nottm.; BMedSci Nottm. 1985; MRCGP 1991; DRCOG 1990. Prev: Trainee GP/SHO (Psychiat.) Lincoln VTS.

SPENCER, Helen Margaret Radula Scott The Lindley Village Surgery, Thomas Street, Lindley, Huddersfield HD3 3JD Tel: 01484 651403 Fax: 01484 644198; Radula, 21A Hopton Hall Lane, Upper

SPENCER

Hopton, Mirfield WF14 8EA Tel: 01924 494301 — MB ChB 1975 Leeds. Sen. Partner, Gen. Pract. Socs: (Sec.) Huddersfield Med. Soc. Prev: Clin. Asst. (A & E) Huddersfield Roy. Infirm.

SPENCER, Hilary Susan South Tyneside District Hospital, Harton Lane, South Shields NE34 0PL Tel: 0191 454 8888 Email: hilary.spencer@eem.sthct.northy.nhs.uk; 5 Park Head Road, Newcastle upon Tyne NE7 7DH — MB BS 1979 Newc.; MRCP (UK) 1982; FRCR 1986. Cons. Radiologist S. Tyneside Healthcare NHS Trust.

SPENCER, Ian Newcastle & North Tyneside Health Authority, Benfield Road, Newcastle upon Tyne NE6 4PF Tel: 0191 219 6000 Fax: 0191 219 6084 Email: ian.spencer@nant-ha.northy.nhs.uk — MB BS 1974 Newc.; MSc (Pub. Health Med.) Newc. 1992. Head of Primary Care Developm. Newc. & N. Tyneside HA. Socs: DURG. Prev: Trainee (Pub. Health Med.) N. RHA; GP Ferryhill Co. Durh.; Demonst. (Path.) Univ. Newc.

SPENCER, Ian, Group Capt. RAF Med. Br. Retd. 3 Leazes Court, Durham DH1 1XF Tel: 0191 386 0799 Email: spencer@isathome.demon.co.uk — MRCS Eng. LRCP Lond. 1971; FRCA 1980; DObst RCOG 1974. Cons. Anaesth. Dryburn Hosp. Durh. Socs: NESA; Assn. Anaesth.; BMA. Prev: RAF Cons. Adviser in Anaesth.; Hon. Sen. Regist. Frenchay Hosp. Bristol; SHO (Anaesth., O & G) N. Manch. Hosp.

SPENCER, Jason Richard Flat 26d, South Residence, King George Hospital, Barley Lane, Ilford IG3 8YB — MB BS 1992 Lond.

SPENCER, Jean Elizabeth Dept. of Psychiatry, Royal South Hants Hospital, Southampton SO14 0YG; Oakwood, Park Lane, Carhampton, Minehead TA24 6NL — MB BS 1979 Lond.; MRCPsych 1984; DIP Clin. HYP. 1998. (St. Bart.) Specialist Regist. (Psychiat.) Roy. S. Hants Hosp., Soton. Socs: Fell. RSM; Brit. Soc. Med. Dent. Hypn. Prev: Clin. Asst. (Psychiat.) S.mead Hosp. Bristol.; Regist. (Psychiat.) Mapperley Hosp. Nottm.

SPENCER, John 19 Station Road, South Cave, Brough HU15 2AA — MB BS 1962 Durh.

SPENCER, Mr John Hammersmith Hospital, Du Cane Road, London W12 0HS Tel: 020 8743 2030 Fax: 020 8740 3179 — MB BS 1957 Lond.; MS Lond. 1975, MB BS 1957; FRCS Eng. 1963. (Char. Cross) Reader in Surg. Imperial coll. Sch. of Med.; Cons. Surg. Hammersmith Hosp. Socs: Fell. Assn. Surgs.; Surg. Research Soc. Prev: Ho. Phys. Char. Cross Hosp.; Med. Off. Uganda Med. Serv.; Surg. Regist. Bath Gp. Hosps.

SPENCER, John Andrew Adelaide Medical Centre, Adelaide Terrace, Benwell, Newcastle upon Tyne NE4 8BE Tel: 0191 219 5599 Fax: 0191 219 5596; 38 Moorside S., Fenham, Newcastle upon Tyne NE4 9BB Tel: 0191 226 0585 Email: john@moorside38@demon.co.uk — MB ChB 1973 Ed.; FRCGP 1991, M 1979; DA Eng. 1976. (Edinburgh) Sen. Lect. (Primary Health Care) Sch. of Health Sci. Univ. Newc. u. Tyne; Princip. in Gen. Pract.; Sen. Tutor for Professional Developm., Fac. of Med. Univ. of Newc. Prev: Princip. GP Gateshead.

SPENCER, John Anthony — MB BChir 1983 Camb.; MB (Hons. Distinc. Med.) Camb. 1983, BChir 1982; MA Camb. 1983, MD 1996; MRCP (UK) 1985; FRCR 1988. (Camb. & Westm.) Cons. Radiol. St. Jas. Univ. Hosp. Leeds. Socs: Fell. Roy. Soc. Med.; Radiol. Soc. N. Amer.; Internat. Cancer Imaging Soc. Prev: Vis. Asst. Prof. Radiol. Thos. Jefferson Univ. Hosp. Philadelphia, USA; Regist. (Radiol.) John Radcliffe Hosp. Oxf.; SHO Hammersmith Hosp. Lond.

SPENCER, Mr John Anthony David Department Obstetrics & Gynaecology, Northwick Park & St Mark's NHS Trust, Watford Road, Harrow HA1 3UJ Tel: 020 8869 2861 Fax: 020 8869 2864 Email: john.spencer@nwth.nhs.uk; 33 Eastbury Road, Northwood HA6 3AJ Tel: 01923 822991 Fax: 01923 822168 Email: jadspencer@msn.com — MB BS 1976 Lond.; BSc (Hons.) Lond. 1973; FRCOG 1993, M 1981. (St..Geo.) Cons. O & G N.wick Pk. & St. Mark's NHS Trust, Harrow; Hon. Sen. Clin. Lect. UCL Med. Sch. Lond. Univ.; Hon.Sen. Clin. Lect. Imperial Coll. Med. Sch., Lond. Socs: (Ex-Hon. Sec. 1991-1994) Blair Bell Research Soc.; Neonat. Soc.; (ex.Exec. Comm.) Brit. Assn. Perinatal Med. Prev: Sen. Clin. Lect. UCL Med. Sch. Lond. Univ.; Sen. Lect. Inst. O & G Univ. Lond.; Clin. Lect. John Radcliffe Hosp. Oxf.

SPENCER, John Dalby (retired) The Elms, 4 West End, Beeston, Nottingham NG9 1GL — MB BS 1958 Lond. Prev: Ho. Surg. N. Middlx. Hosp. Lond.

SPENCER, Mr John Derek Orthopaedic Department, Guy's Hospital, London SE1 9RT Tel: 020 7955 5000 Fax: 020 7955 2759; 18 King George Street, Greenwich, London SE10 8QJ Tel: 020 8694 1931 — MB BS Lond. 1967; MS Lond. 1988; FRCS Eng. 1974; MRCP Lond. 1971; MRCS Eng. LRCP Lond. 1967. (Guy's) Cons. Orthopaedic & Trauma Surg. Guys & St Thomas' Hosp. Lond. Socs: Fell. BOA; Brit. Soc. Surg. Hand; Fell. Roy. Soc. Med. Prev: Reader Trainer Guy's & St Thomas' Hosps. Lond.; Exchange Prof. Guy's Hosp. & John Hopkins Baltimore, USA 1992; Sen. Regist. (Orthop.) Roy. E. Sussex Hosp. & Guy's Hosp. Lond.

SPENCER, John Gordon Spring Hall Group Practice, Spring Hall Medical Centre, Spring Hall Lane, Halifax HX1 4JG Tel: 01422 349501 Fax: 01422 323091 — MB ChB 1967 St. And. (St. And.) Socs: BMA.

SPENCER, Jonathan OHSAS, 1 Edward St., Dundee DD1 5NS Tel: 01382 346030 Fax: 01382 346040; Landalla House, Kirkton of Glenisla, Blairgowrie PH11 8PH Tel: 01575 582213 — MB ChB 1977 Ed.; MSc Occupat. Med. Lond. 1983; BSc (Hons.) Ed. 1974; FFOM RCP Lond. 1995, MFOM 1984; DIH Eng. 1982. (Edinburgh) Cons. Occupat.al Phys. OHSAS, Dundee. Socs: Soc. Occupat. Med. Prev: Manager Occupat. Med. BP Gp. Occupat. Health Centre; Med. Off. MoD Roy. Aircraft Estab. FarnBoro.; Med. Off. MoD Army Personnel Research Estab. FarnBoro.

***SPENCER, Jonathan Matthew Frank** 22 Spencer Walk, Rickmansworth WD3 4EE — MB BS 1994 Lond.

SPENCER, Jonathan Patrick Greer BAA Occupational Health Service, Ashdown House, Gatwick Airport, Gatwick RH6 0NP Tel: 01293 503662 Fax: 01293 504404; 11 Woodland Way, Caterham CR3 6ER Tel: 01883 340867 — MB ChB 1978 Ed.; MSc Lond. 1986; AFOM RCP Lond. 1990; MRCGP 1982; DAvMed Lond. 1988; DRCOG 1980. (Ed.) Occupat. Phys. BAA Gatwick & Stansted Airports. Prev: Med. Off. Civil Aviat. Auth. Gatwick; Occupat. Phys. St. Bart. Hosp. Lond.; Sen. Staff Phys. Sirte Oil Company, Libya.

SPENCER, Judith Vivien Calabar, Pica, Workington CA14 4PZ — MB BCh 1979 Wales.

SPENCER, Keith Paul Dawley Medical Practice, Doseley Road, Dawley, Telford TF4 3; 9 Lees Farm Drive, Madeley, Telford TF7 5SU — MB BS 1976 Lond.; DRCOG 1981; DA Eng. 1979. (St. Bart.) Socs: BMA (Sec. Salop. Div.). Prev: Chairm. W. Midl. Regional Hosp. Jun. Staff Comm.

SPENCER, Li Lian Lonsdale Medical Centre, 24 Lonsdale Road, London NW6 6RR Tel: 020 7328 8331 Fax: 020 7328 8630; 180 Goldhurst Terrace, London NW6 3HN — MB ChB 1968 Birm. (Birm.) Prev: Med. Off. City of Birm. Pub. Health Dept.; SHO (Anaesth.) Dudley Rd. Hosp. Birm.

SPENCER, Lisa Graham 54 Coronation Street, Salford M5 3SA — MB ChB 1995 Leeds; MB ChB (Hons.) Leeds 1995; BSc (Hons.) Physiol. Manch. 1990. (Leeds)

SPENCER, Maria Jadwiga Melford Lodge, 16 Beech Drive, London N2 9NY Tel: 020 8883 8888 Fax: 020 8883 8888 — Lekarz 1965 Warsaw, Poland; MD Poland 1975; ECFMG 1969. (Med. Acad. Warsaw) Clin. Asst. (Cardiol.) Roy. Free Hosp.; Hosp. Pract. (Cardiol.) Ealing Hosp. Lond.; Patent Holder for Frozen Display & Cardiac Arrest Timer. Socs: BMA; Polish Med. Assn.; Brit. Cardiac Soc. Prev: Dir. Polish Clinic Lond.; Managing Dir. Cardiac Recorders Ltd. Lond.; Research Regist. (Cardiol.) St. Mary's Hosp.

SPENCER, Mark Mount View Practice, London Street Medical Centre, London Street, Fleetwood FY7 6HD Tel: 01253 873312 Fax: 01253 873130; 114 Breck Road, Poulton-le-Fylde FY6 7HT — MB BS 1986 Lond.; MRCGP 1990; DRCOG 1987. GP Fleetwood.

SPENCER, Mary Elizabeth Market Street Clinic, 20 Market St., Woolwich, London SE18 6QR Tel: 020 8317 9415; 56 Brooklands Park, London SE3 9AJ Tel: 020 8852 0394 — MB BS 1968 Lond.; MRCS Eng. LRCP Lond. 1968; MFFP 1993; DCH Eng. 1970; DObst RCOG 1969. (Guy's) SCMO (Child Health & Family Plann.) Greenwich Health Care Trust. Socs: Inst. Psychosexual Med.; MRCPCH; Coun. Mem. W. Kent Med-Chi. Soc.

SPENCER, Michael Anthony Saxonbury House, Croft Road, Crowborough TN6 1DL Tel: 01892 652266 Fax: 01892 668607 — MB BS 1978 Lond.; MA Camb. 1969; MRCGP 1982; DFFP 1997; DRCOG 1980. (King's Coll. Hosp.) GP CrowBoro.; Tutor E.bourne Annual GP Refresher Course. Prev: Trainee GP Frome; Trainee GP Bath VTS; Ho. Phys. (Profess. Med. Unit) King's Coll. Hosp. Lond.

SPENCER

SPENCER, Michael Anthony Patrick North End Surgery, High St., Buckingham MK18 1NU Tel: 01280 813239 Fax: 01280 823449 — MB BS 1968 Lond.; MRCS Eng. LRCP Lond. 1968; DObst RCOG 1973. (St. Bart.) Hosp. Pract. Dept. ENT Surg. Stoke Mandeville Hosp. Aylesbury. Socs: BMA. Prev: SHO (Cas.) Char. Cross Hosp. Lond.; SHO (ENT) Essex Co. Hosp. Colchester; Ho. Surg. (Neurosurg.) St. Bart. Hosp. Lond.

SPENCER, Michael Charles Charity House, Church St., Finedon, Wellingborough NN9 5NA — MB BS 1968 Lond.; MRCS Eng. LRCP Lond. 1968; DObst RCOG 1971. (Middlx.)

SPENCER, Michael Charles (retired) 8 Dolphin Close, Chichester PO19 3QP Tel: 01243 789938 — BM BCh 1949 Oxf.; MA, BM BCh Oxf. 1949; MRCGP 1974; DTM & H Antwerp 1952. Prev: GP Leiston.

SPENCER, Mr Michael Grant Department of Otolaryngology, Countess of Chester Hospital, Liverpool Road, Chester CH2 1UL Tel: 01244 366322; The Spinney, Chapel Lane, Bruera, Chester CH3 6EW — BM BCh 1975 Oxf.; MA Oxf. 1975; FRCS Eng. 1982. (University of Oxford) Cons. Otolaryngol. Countess of Chester Hosp. Socs: Fell. Roy. Soc. Med.; Europ. Acad. Facial Surg. Prev: Sen. Regist. St. Thos. Hosp. Lond.; Ho. Surg. Nuffield Dept. Surg. Radcliffe Infirm. Oxf.; Demonst. (Human Anat.) Univ. Oxf.

SPENCER, Michael Richard Welbeck Road Surgery, 1A Welbeck Road, Bolsover, Chesterfield S44 6DF Tel: 01246 823742; 18 The Pinfold, Glapwell, Chesterfield S44 5PU Tel: 01632 810136 — MB ChB 1978 Aberd.; MRCGP 1982. (Aberdeen) VTS Tutor Sheff. Univ.

SPENCER, Murdoch Harris 11 Torrington Avenue, Giffnock, Glasgow G46 7LH Tel: 0141 638 8484 — LRCP LRCS 1951 Ed.; LRCP LRCS Ed. LRFPS Glas. 1951.

SPENCER, Naomi Marydell Stapenhill Surgery, Fyfield Road, Stapenhill, Burton-on-Trent DE15 9QD Tel: 01283 565200 Fax: 01283 500617; Ridgeway, 64 Burton Road, Repton, Derby DE65 6FN — BM BS 1984 Nottm.

SPENCER, Professor Nicholas James School of Postgrad. Medical Education, University of Warwick, Coventry CV4 7AL Tel: 024 76 523167 Fax: 024 76 524415 Email: n.j.spencer@warwick.ac.uk; 5 Castle Road, Kenilworth CV8 1NG Tel: 01926 512436 — MRCS Eng. LRCP Lond. 1969; MPhil. Nottm. 1980; MRCP (UK) 1975; DCH Eng. 1973; FRCP Ed 1990; FRCPCH. (Sheffield) Prof. of Child Health Univ. of Warwick; Hon. Cons. Paediat. Coventry Healthcare NHS Trust. Socs: MRCPCH.

SPENCER, Nicholas James Blakey Pinderfields General Hospital, Aberford Road, Wakefield WF1 4EE — MB ChB 1987 Leeds; MRCP (UK) 1991; FRCR 1994. Cons. Radiol. Pinderfields Hosp. Wakefield. Prev: Regist. (Radiol.) Nottm. HA.

SPENCER, Nigel George Church Close Surgery, 3 Church Close, Boston PE21 6NB Tel: 01205 311133 Fax: 01205 358986; Lynton House, 35 Sibsey Road, Boston PE21 9QY — MB ChB 1966 Birm. (Birm.) GP Boston.

SPENCER, Pamela Mary (retired) High Gate, Rock, Wadebridge PL27 6JZ — MB BS 1950 Lond.; FRCS Eng. 1957; MRCS Eng. LRCP Lond. 1950; FRCOG 1973, M 1960, DObst 1952. Prev: Cons. O & G Eliz. G. Anderson Hosp. & Whittington Hosp. Lond.

SPENCER, Paul Andrew Stephen Department Medical Imaging, Rotherham Hospital Trust, Moorgate Road, Rotherham S60 2UD Tel: 01709 304413; Email: paul@fian.globalnet.co.uk — MB BS 1978 Lond.; BSc (Hons.) Lond. 1975; MRCS Eng. LRCP Lond. 1978; FRCR 1988; MRCP (UK) 1982. (St. Mary's) Cons. Radiol. Rotherham Gen. Hosp. Trust; Hon. Lect. Univ. Sheff. Prev: Cons. Radiol. Rotherham Dist. Hosp. & Hon. Lect. Sheff. Univ.

SPENCER, Pauline Westgate Surgery, Westgate, Otley LS21 3HD Tel: 01943 465406 Fax: 01943 468363; Glenthorne, Burras Lane, Otley LS21 3EW Tel: 01943 465906 — MB ChB 1977 Leeds; BSc (Hons.) Leeds 1974. Clin. Asst. Minor Injuries Unit Wharfedale Gen. Hosp. Otley. Socs: Whafedale Med. Soc. Prev: SHO (A & E) Leeds Gen. Infirm.; Ho. Off. Wharfedale Gen. Hosp. Otley.

SPENCER, Peter David (Surgery) 7 Bedford Row, Barnstaple EX32 8NR Tel: 01271 373346 Fax: 01271 327808 — MB BS 1976 Lond.; PhD Physiol. Lond. 1985, BSc Physiol. 1973, MB BS 1976; DO RCS Eng. 1989. (UCH Lond.) Indep Med. Osteopath. Barnstaple; Princip. Lond. Sch. Osteop. Prev: Regist. (Community Med.) Riverside HA; Lect. (Physiol.) Char. Cross Med. Sch.; SHO (Cardiol.) W. Middlx. Hosp.

SPENCER, Mr Peter John West Suffolk Hospitals NHS Trust, Hardwick Lane, Bury St Edmunds IP33 2QZ Tel: 01284 713405; 111 Westley Road, Bury St Edmunds IP33 3SA Tel: 01284 706133 — MB BChir 1970 Camb.; MA Camb. 1970; FRCS Eng. 1976; FRCS Ed. 1976; FRCOG 1990; MRCOG 1978, DObst 1972. (Camb. & St. Thos.) Cons. O & G, W. Suff. Hosp., Bury St. Edmunds. Socs: Sec. E. Anglian Obst. & Gyn. Soc.; Brit. Soc. Colposcopy & Cervical Path. Prev: Clin. Lect. Dept. O & G Univ. Cam. Clin. Sch. Addenbrooke's Hosp.; Sen. Regist. (O & G) Norf. & Norwich Hosp; Regist. (O & G) Birm. & Midl. Hosp. Wom. & Birm. Matern. Hosp.

SPENCER, Philip Mark Doctors Surgery, Friar Row, Caldbeck, Wigton CA7 8DS Tel: 01697 478254 Fax: 01697 478661 — MB ChB 1990 Bristol; PhD Soton. 1986, BSc 1983; MRCGP 1994; Dip. Ther. Newc. 1995; DRCOG 1994; Dip. IMC RCS Ed. 1994. (Bristol)

*SPENCER, Rachael Elizabeth** 89 Cowley Lane, Chapeltown, Sheffield S35 1SX — MB BS 1998 Newc.; MB BS Newc. 1998.

SPENCER, Rachel May Harrogate General Hospital, Harrogate HG2 7ND Tel: 01423 885959; High Green, Burton Leonard, Harrogate HG3 3RW — MB ChB 1989 Leeds. Staff Paediat. Harrogate Gen. Hosp.

SPENCER, Richard Wellesley (retired) 2 Elliscombe Park, Higher Holton, Wincanton BA9 8EA Tel: 01963 824427 — MB ChB Birm. 1944; FRCP Lond. 1975, M 1951; FRCPath 1972, M 1964. Prev: Cons. Chem Path. Cornw. & I. of Scilly DHA.

SPENCER, Robert Christopher Public Health Laboratory, Level 8, Bristol Royal Infirmary, Marlborough St., Bristol BS2 8HW Tel: 0117 928 2879 Fax: 0117 929 9162 Email: robertspencer@bristolphl.freeserve.co.uk; 18 Lavender Close, Thornbury, Bristol BS35 1UL Tel: 01454 416454 Fax: 01454 850486 — MB BS 1970 Lond.; MSc Lond. 1977; FRCPath 1989, M 1977; Hon.DipHIC 1999; FRCPG 1999. (St. Mary's) Cons. Med. Microbiol. Bristol PHL; Sen. Clin. Lect. Bristol Univ.; Asst. Edr. Jl. Hosp. Infec.; Edr. Jl. Antimicrob. Chemother. Socs: Brit. Soc. Antimicrobiol. Chemother.; Hosp. Infec. Soc.; Assn. Clin. Path. Prev: Cons. Bacteriol. Roy. Hallamsh. Hosp. Sheff.; Reader (Experim. & Clin. Microbiol.) Sheff. Univ.

SPENCER, Roy Ernest Baughan The Surgery, Estate House, Pembroke Road, Sevenoaks TN13 1XR Tel: 01732 54545 — MB BChir 1945 Camb.; BA Camb. 1943, MA 1947, MB BChir 1945; MRCGP 1976. (Camb. & St. Thos.) Med. Off. Sevenoaks & Sundridge Hosps.

SPENCER, Ruth Elizabeth 41 Old Park Avenue, Enfield EN2 6PJ Tel: 020 8366 6825; Top Floor Flat, 3 Redland Park, Bristol BS6 6SA Tel: 0117 973 7800 — MB ChB 1988 Bristol; MRCP (UK) 1992; DTM & H Liverp. 1995. Clin. Research Fell. (IC) Bristol Roy. Infirm. Prev: SHO (Anaesth.) S.mead Hosp. Bristol; Regist. (Cardiol.) Hereford Co. Hosp.; Regist. (Nephrol.) Qu. Eliz. Hosp. Birm.

SPENCER, Ruth Mary 14 Burnbrae Avenue, Bearsden, Glasgow G61 3ER — MB ChB 1988 Ed. p/t Med. Off. Homeless Addic. Team, Galsgow; GP Pk.head Health Centre, Galsgow. Prev: GP Galston, Ayrsh.

SPENCER, Sabina Anna 6 Queens Walk, Stamford PE9 2QE — BChir 1990 Camb.

SPENCER, Miss Sarah Elizabeth 39 Gloucester Road, Maidenhead SL6 7SN Email: sarah@webtribe.net — MB BS 1994 Lond.; FRCS (Eng) 1999.

SPENCER, Seymour Jamie Gerald (retired) 13 Victoria Court, 5 London Road, Headington, Oxford OX3 7SP Tel: 01865 434471 Fax: 01865 434715 Email: sjgspencer@aol.com — BM BCh Oxf. 1943; DM Oxf. 1958; FRCPsych 1975, M 1971; DPM Lond. 1951. Hon. Cons. Psychiat. Oxf. HA; Sub-Edr. & Contributor Catholic Med. Quarterly. Prev: Clin. Lect. (Psychiat.) Univ. Oxf.

***SPENCER, Simon Paul** 16 William Peck Road, Spixworth, Norwich NR10 3QB — MB BS 1998 Lond.; MB BS Lond 1998.

SPENCER, Stephen Andrew Neonatal Unit, Maternity Block, North Staffordshire Hospital (NHS Trust), Newcastle Road, Stoke-on-Trent ST4 6QG Tel: 01782 552450 Fax: 01782 552481 Email: andy.spencer@nstoffs.wmids.nhs.uk — BM BS 1976 Nottm.; DM Nottm. 1983, BMedSci 1974; FRCP Lond. 1993; MRCP (UK) 1979; FRCPCH 1997. Cons. Paediat. N. Staffs. Matern. Hosp. Stoke-on-Trent; Sen. Lect. (Paediat. Med.) Univ. Keele. Socs: Neonat. Soc. Prev: Lect. (Child Health) Nottm. Univ.; Sen. Regist. W. Birm. RHA.

SPENCER, Stephen John Wellesley Worcester Royal Infirmary, Castle St., Worcester WR1 3AS — MB BS 1983 Lond.; BSc Lond.

SPENCER

1980, MD 1993; MRCP (UK) 1986 Fell. 2000. Cons. Phys. & Nephrol. Worcester Roy. Infirm. Prev: Sen. Regist. (Med. & Nephrol.) Soton. Univ. Hosp. Trust.

SPENCER, Stephen Mark Uxbridge Road Surgery, 337 Uxbridge Road, Acton, London W3 9RA Tel: 020 8993 0912; 136 Meadvale Road, Ealing, London W5 1LS Tel: 020 8933 4849 Email: markspencer@compuserve.com — MB BS 1984 Lond.; MRCGP 1995; DRCOG 1987. (Char. Cross & Westm.) GP Trainer; Vice Chairm. PCG. Prev: Trainee GP/SHO Hammersmith Hosp. VTS.

SPENCER, Mr Stephen Ralph Royal Halifax Infirmary, Free School Lane, Halifax HX1 2YP; Whinney Bank House, Whinney Bank, Holmfirth, Huddersfield HD9 1US — MB BS 1979 Newc.; FRCS Eng. 1984; FRCOphth 1989; DO RCS Eng. 1983. Cons. Ophth. Calderdale HA. Prev: Sen. Regist. (Ophth.) Yorksh. RHA; Regist. (Ophth.) St. Thos. Hosp. Lond. & Newc. Gen. Hosp.; Research Regist. (Ophth.) Roy. Vict. Infirm. Newc.

SPENCER, Susan Frances Overgate Hospice, 30 Hullenedge Rd, Elland HX5 0QY Tel: 01422 379151; Upper Greystones, Manor Heath Road, Halifax HX3 0EE Tel: 01422 367643 — MB BS 1978 Lond.; MRCS Eng. LRCP Lond. 1978. (St Bartholomew's Hospital) p/t Med. Off. (Palliat. Med.) Overgate Hospice Elland. Prev: Med. Dir. Overgate Hospice, Elland; Trainee GP VTS Calderdale AHA; Clin. Asst. N.owram Hosp. Halifax.

SPENCER, Susan Mary Almondbury Surgery, Longcroft, Almondbury, Huddersfield HD5 8XW Tel: 01484 421391 Fax: 01484 532405 — MB BS 1979 Newc.; MRCGP 1983; DRCOG 1983. (Newcastle-upon-Tyne)

SPENCER, Teresa Marian 13 Oakhill Court, Edge Hill, London SW19 4NR — MB ChB 1955 Manch. Prev: Ho. Phys. Roy. Lancaster Infirm.

SPENCER, Mr Timothy Smedley c/o Woking Nuffield Hospital, Shores Road, Woking GU21 4BY Tel: 01483 762897 Fax: 01483 763687; Overmead, 26 Mayfield Road, Weybridge KT13 8XB Tel: 01932 829647 — MB BS Lond. 1963; MB BS Lond. 1963; FRCS Ed. 1969; FRCS Ed. 1969; MRCS Eng. LRCP Lond. 1962; MRCS Eng. LRCP Lond. 1962; FRCOG 1981, M 1968, DObst 1964; FRCOG 1981, M 1968, DObst 1964. (Guy's) Cons. O & G St. Peter's Hosp. Chertsey; Hon. Sen. Lect. St Geo. Hosp. Med. Sch. Socs: Nat. Comm. Anglo French Med. Soc.; Brit. Assn. Med. Managers; Brit. Assn. Med. Managers. Prev: Sen. Regist. Middlx. Hosp., Hosp. Wom. Soho Sq. & Centr. Middlx. Hosp. Lond.; Regist. Middlx. Hosp., Hosp. Wom. Soho Sq. & St Luke's Hosp. Guildford.

SPENCER, Wilfred Harrison Merlie Court, 35 Liverpool Road, Ashton-in-Makerfield, Wigan WN4 9LX; Merlie Court, Garswood Park, Ashton-in-Makerfield, Wigan WN4 9LX — MRCS Eng. LRCP Lond. 1940. (Guy's)

SPENCER-GREGSON, Richard Nicholas (retired) Pinfold House, 11 Main Road, Long Bennington, Newark NG23 5EH Tel: 01400 281356 — MB BS 1955 Durh.; MSc Bradford 1969; FRCOG 1979, M 1964, DObst 1959. Hon. Cons. Gyn. Grantham & Kesteven Gen. Hosp. Trust; Hon. Clin. Tutor Univ. Leeds; Approved Lect. Roy. Coll. Midw. Prev: Cons. Gyn. Grantham & Kesteren Gen. Hosp. Trust.

***SPENCER HAMMON, Catherine Anne** 4F1, 139 Buccleuch Street, Edinburgh EH8 9NE — MB ChB 1997 Ed.

SPENCER JONES, Christopher John Wiltshire Health Authority, Southgate House, Pans Lane, Devizes SN10 5EQ Tel: 01380 733764 Fax: 01380 722443; 1 Cranhill Road, Bath BA1 2YF — MB ChB 1986 Bristol; MSc Pub. Health Med. Lond. 1992; MFPHM RCP Lond. 1995; MRCGP 1990. (Bristol) Cons. Pub. Health Med. Wilts. HA. Prev: Primary Care Med. Adviser Soton. & SW Hants HA; Sen. Regist. (Pub. Health Med.) NW Thames RHA; Trainee GP Exeter VTS.

SPENCER-JONES, Julia Mary Tutbury Health Centre, Monk Street, Tutbury, Burton-on-Trent DE13 9NA Tel: 01283 812210 Fax: 01283 815810; Sandalwood, 34 Church Road, Rolleston-on-Dove, Burton-on-Trent DE13 9BE Tel: 01283 813433 Email: spencer_jones@compuserve.com — MB BChir 1973 Camb.; MA Camb. 1974, MB BChir 1973; MRCGP 1977; DCH Eng. 1976; DObst RCOG 1975. (Cambridge & St. Bartholomew's London) Princip. in Gen. Pract. Prev: Trainee Gen. Pract. N.ampton Vocational Train. Scheme.

SPENCER-JONES, Roland Godfrey Tutbury Health Centre, Monk Street, Tutbury, Burton-on-Trent DE13 9NA Tel: 01283 812210 Fax: 01283 815810; 1 Callow End Cottages, Mappleton, Ashbourne DE6 2AB Tel: 01335 350455 Email: spencer_jones@compuserve.com — MB BChir 1974 Camb.; MA Camb. 1974; MRCP (UK) 1976; MRCGP 1977; DObst RCOG 1975. (Camb. & St. Thos.) Med. Educat.; Co-Founder 'Scaling the Heights'. Prev: Trainee GP N.ampton VTS.

SPENCER-PALMER, Caroline Mary Colne Health Centre, Market Street, Colne BB8 0LJ Tel: 01282 862451 Fax: 01282 871698; 5 Woolpack, off Lenches Road, Colne BB8 8HQ Tel: 01282 870718 — MB BS 1979 Lond.; MRCGP 1984; DRCOG 1982. (Lond. Hosp.) Gen.ist - Specialist to Community Drug Team, Burnley. Socs: Balint Soc. Prev: SHO (Psychiat.) Burnley Gen. Hosp.; Paediat. Save The Childr. Fund; SHO (Hospice Home Care Team) St. Josephs Hospice Lond.

SPENCER-SILVER, Professor Peter Hele Barclays Bank, Jewry St., Winchester SO23 8RG — PhD (Anat.) Lond. 1952, MB BS 1945; MRCS Eng. LRCP Lond. 1945. (Middlx.) Emerit. Prof. Anat. Univ. Lond. Socs: Anat. Soc. & Physiol. Soc. Prev: S.A. Ct.auld Prof. Anat. Univ. Lond.; Prof. Embryol. Univ. Lond.; Sub-Dean Middlx. Hosp. Med. Sch.

SPENCER-SMITH, Elizabeth Margery (retired) — MB ChB 1949 Bristol; FRCGP 1978, M 1951. Prev: Mem. S.mead Dist. HA Dist. Managem. Team.

SPENCER-SMITH, John (retired) 71 Bell Barn Road, Stoke Bishop, Bristol BS9 2DF Tel: 0117 968 3148 — MRCS Eng. LRCP Lond. 1944; FRCGP 1975, M 1951. Prev: Anaesth. Winford Orthop. Hosp. Bristol.

SPENCER-SMITH, Maxwell General Council of British Shipping, 19/23 Canute Road, Southampton SO14 3FJ Tel: 023 8022 3546 Fax: 02380 228446 — MB BS 1967 Lond.; MRCS Eng. LRCP Lond. 1967; AFOM RCP Lond. 1992; MRCGP 1980; T(GP) 1991; DRCOG 1970. (Middlx. Hosp. Med. Sch.) Cons. Occupat. Phys. Ocean Med. Serv. Socs: Soc. Occupat. Med.; Fac. Occupat.al Helpline; Internat. Maritine Health Assn. Prev: Regional Med. Off. Gen. Counc. of Brit. Shipping; Sen. Phys. King Faisal Specialist Hosp. & Research Centre, Riyadh, Saudi Arabia.

SPENDER, Quentin Wynn Child and Family Service for Mental Health, Orchard House, 9 College Lane, Chichester PO19 6PQ Tel: 01234 815514 Fax: 01234 815499 Email: spender@sghms.ac.uk; 16 Hemingford Road, Sutton SM3 8HG Tel: 020 8644 8245 Fax: 020 8644 9009 Email: quentin.spender@btinternet.com — MB BS 1979 Lond.; MRCP (UK) 1983; MRCPsych 1990; DCH RCP Lond. 1981; Dip Family Ther (IFT) 1996. (Roy. Free) Cons. & Sen. Lect. W.Sussex Health & Social Care NHS Trust W. Sussex; Hon. Cons. Pathfinder NHS Trust; Sen. Lect. St. Geo. Hosp. Med. Sch. Lond. 1995. Socs: Child Psychiat. Research Soc. Scientif. & Med. Network. Prev: Regist. Rotat. (Psychiat.) Oxf. Train. Scheme; Exchange Regist. Childr. Hosp. Philadelphia Pennsylvania, USA; Regist. (Paediat.) Hosp. Sick Childr. Gt. Ormond St. Lond.

SPENS, Fiona Jane Whitethorn House, 2 Perth Road, Milnathort, Kinross KY13 9XU — MB BS 1983 Newc.; MRCGP 1987; DRCOG 1987. GP E. Yorks. Retainer Scheme. Prev: Clin. Med. Off. (Child Health) Angus.

SPENS, Heather Julie Department of Anaesthetics, Royal Infirmary of Edinburgh, Lauriston Place, Edinburgh EH3 9YW Tel: 0131 536 3652; 4 Cluny Garden, Edinburgh EH10 6BQ Tel: 0131 447 4544 — MB ChB 1986 Ed.; FCAnaesth. 1991; DA (UK) 1989. Cons. Anaesth. Roy. Infirm. Edin. Edin. Prev: Sen. Regist. (Anaesth.) Lothian Area Train. Scheme.

SPENSLEY, Charis Anne 84 Hill Crescent, Bexley DA5 2DB — MB ChB 1989 Leeds; MRCP (UK) 1995. Prev: Specialist Regist. (Paediat.) S. E. Thames Region.

***SPENSLEY, Paul James** 6 Conisbord Way, Caversham Heights, Reading RG4 7HT — BM BS 1997 Nottm.

***SPERBER, Galia** 8 Freston Park, London N3 1UP — MB ChB 1998 Liverp.; MB ChB Liverp 1998.

SPERBER, Steven Flat 5 159 Marine Parade, Brighton BN2 1EJ — MB ChB 1997 Liverp.

SPERRING, Steven Jeffrey 2221 Old Hickory Boulevard, Nashville TN 37215, USA; Norley House, 1 Furness Road, Eastbourne BN21 4EX Tel: 01323 647392 — MB BS 1978 Lond.; FFA RCS Eng. 1982. (Guy's) Fell.sh. Prize Fac. Anaesth. RCS 1982; Staff Anaesthesiol. Hermann Hosp. Houston, USA; Asst. Prof. Univ. Texas Med. Sch. Houston. Socs: Obst. Anaesth. Assn. Prev: Staff Anesthesiol. Beth Israel Hosp. Boston, USA; Instruct. Anesthesiol.

Harvard Med. Sch. Camb., USA; Regist. (Anaesth.) Guy's Hosp. Lond.

SPERRY, David Arthur 50 Willow Tree Road, Altrincham WA14 2EG — MB BS 1990 Lond.; BA Oxf. 1987; MRCP (UK) 1993. Regist. Rotat. (Anaesth.) Withington Hosp. Manch.

SPERRY, Helen Jean 41 Norman Avenue, Abingdon OX14 2HJ — MB BS 1988 Lond.

SPERRY, Lynn Margaret 41 Norman Avenue, Abingdon OX14 2HJ — MB BS 1987 Lond.; BSc Lond. 1984, MB BS 1987.

SPERRY, Tanya Lesley Helen Uppingham Road Medical Centre, 190 Uppingham Road, Leicester LE5 0QG Tel: 0116 276 6605 — MB ChB 1981 Leic.; MRCGP 1985; DRCOG 1985. GP Leicester.

SPERRYN, Professor Peter Neville 49 Blakes Lane, New Malden KT3 6NS Tel: 020 8949 0607 — MB BS Lond. 1961; FRCP Glas. 1982, M 1968; DPhysMed Eng. 1970. (St. Mary's) Prof., Assoc. in Sports Med. Dept. of Sport Sci.s Brunel Univ. Socs: Fell. Amer. Coll. Sports Med.; (Vice Pres.) Brit. Assn. Sport & Med. (Ex. Hon Sec). Prev: Cons. Physical & Sports Med. Hillingdon Hosp. Trust; Hon. Med. Off. Brit. Amateur Athletic Bd.; Winston Ch.ill Trav. Fell.

SPIBY, Jacqueline Global House, Hayes, Bromley BR2 7EH Tel: 020 8462 2211; Heathside, 15 The Meadow, Chislehurst BR7 6AA — MB BS 1978 Lond.; FFPHM RCP (UK) 1994. Dir. Pub. Health Bromley HA.

SPICE, Claire Louise Royal Hampshire County Hospital, Winchester SO22 5DG — BM 1993 Soton.

SPICE, William Matthew 7 Gardiner House, Master Gunner Place, Baker Road, Woolwich, London SE18 4NT — MB BS 1998 Lond.; MB BS Lond 1998.

SPICER, Alan John, Col. late RAMC Occupational Health Unit, Kent Police Headquaters, Maidstone ME15 9BZ Tel: 01622 690690 — MB BS 1959 Lond.; MD Lond. 1979; FRCP Lond. 1983, M 1968; MRCS Eng. LRCP Lond. 1959; DTM & H Eng. 1973; DCH Eng. 1970. (King's Coll. Hosp.) Sen. Occupat. Phys. Kent Police Force. Socs: Fell. Roy. Soc. Health.; Soc. Occupat. Med. Prev: Cons. Phys. Camb. Milit. Hosp. Aldershot; Cons. Phys. Brit. Milit. Hosp. Rinteln; Cons. Phys. Qu. Eliz. Milit. Hosp. Lond.

SPICER, Clive Colquhoun Churchtown, Michaelstow, St Tudy, Bodmin PL30 3PD — MRCS Eng. LRCP Lond. 1941; MRCP Lond. 1974; Dip. Bact. Lond 1951; Dip. FSS 1949. (Guy's) Prev: Hon. Research Fell. Dept. Mathematical Statistics Exeter Univ.; Head Div. Med. Computing Clin. Research Centre N.wick Pk. Hosp. Harrow; Chief Med. Statistician Gen. Regist. Office Som. Hse.

SPICER, Dominic David Mark c/o Holt's, The Royal Bank of Scotland, Lawrie House, Victoria Road, Farnborough GU14 7NR — MB BS 1989 Lond.

SPICER, John Edmund Andrew Woodside Health Centre, 3 Enmore Road, London SE25 5NS Tel: 020 8656 5790 Fax: 020 8656 7984 — MB BS 1977 Lond.; MRCGP 1984; DFFP 1982. (Middlesex) GP; Course Organiser Mayday Hosp. Croydon VTS. S. Thames Region. Socs: Assn. Course Organisers. Prev: Med. Off. (Psychiat.) Sunnyside Hosp. ChristCh., NZ.

SPICER, Nicholas Adrian Albert Nunwell Surgery, 10 Pump Street, Bromyard HR7 4BZ Tel: 01885 483412 Fax: 01885 488739; The Old Rectory, Malvern Road, Stanford Bishop, Worcester WR6 5TT Tel: 01886 884058 Fax: 01886 884734 — MB ChB 1977 Birm.

SPICER, Nicola Ann Joy Kingsley Mayfield Medical Centre, 37 Totnes Road, Jubilee Road, Paignton TQ4 5LA Tel: 01803 558257; Darracott, Jubilee Rd, Totnes TQ9 5BW Tel: 01803 864124 — MB BS 1985 Lond.; MRCGP 1989; DRCOG 1987. (Kings Coll. Sch. of Med. and Dent., Lond.) Gen. Practitioner Princip.

SPICER, Mrs Rachel Faith Elizabeth Haughton, OBE (retired) 31 Aberdeen Park, London N5 2AR Tel: 020 7226 4366 — MB BS Lond. 1944. Prev: Dir. Lond. Youth Advis. & Med. Dir. Brook Advis. Centres.

SPICER, Ranald John Stranraer Health Centre, Edinburgh Road, Stranraer DG9 7HG — MB ChB 1976 Aberd.; FFA RCSI 1986; MRCGP 1980; DA Eng. 1985. Cons. Anaesth. Garrick Hosp. Stranraer; Regist. (Anaesth.) W. Infirm. & S. Gen. Hosp. Glas. Prev: SHO (Anaesth.) Dumfries & Galloway Infirm.; Ho. Phys. (Gen. Med.) & Ho. Surg. (Gen. Surg.) Raigmore Hosp.; Inverness.

SPICER, Mr Richard Dudley Department of Paediatric Surgery, Bristol Children's Hospital, St Michael's Hill, Bristol BS2 8BJ Tel: 0117 928 5708 Fax: 0117 928 5701 Email: richardspicer@ubht.swest.uk — MB BS 1968 Lond.; FRCS Eng. 1974; MRCS Eng. LRCP Lond. 1968; FRCPCH 1997; DCH Eng. 1973. (Guy's) Cons. Paediat. Surg. Bristol Childr. Hosp.; Sen. Clin. Lect. (Paediat. Surg.) Univ. Bristol. Socs: (Sec. & Hon. Treas.) Soc. Paediat. Surgic. Oncol.; (Exec.) Brit. Assn. Paediat. Surgs.; Société Internat. D'Oncol. Paediat. Prev: Cons. Paediat. Surg. Leeds; Cons. Paediat. Surg. Muscat, Oman.

***SPICK, Emma Lucy** c/o 55 Bromley Heath Road, Bristol BS16 6HY — BM BS 1998 Nottm.; BM BS Nottm 1998.

SPICKETT, Gavin Patrick Regional Department of Immunology, Royal Victoria Infirmary, Queen Victoria Road, Newcastle upon Tyne NE1 4LP Tel: 0191 232 5131 Fax: 0191 227 5071 — BM BCh 1980 Oxf.; DPhil. Oxf. 1983, MA 1981; FRCP Lond. 1995; MRCP (UK) 1985; MRCPath 1990; T(Path) 1991; T(M) 1991; FRCPath 1999. (Oxford) Cons. & Sen. Lect. Immunol. Roy. Vict. Infirm. Socs: Brit. Soc. Allergy & Clin. Immunol.; Brit. Soc. Immunol. Prev: Clin. Scientist & Hon. Sen. Regist. Clin. Research Centre Harrow; Regist. (Med.) The Ipswich Hosp.; Mary Goodger Research Schol. MRC Cellular Immunol. Research Unit Oxf.

SPIEGLER, William John North Street Health Centre, North Street, Ashby-de-la-Zouch LE65 1HU Tel: 01530 414131 — MB ChB 1978 Birm.; MRCGP 1983; DRCOG 1982. Clin. Teach. (Gen. Pract.) Fac. Med. Univ. Leic.; GP Ashby.

SPIER, Adolph 24 Merryfield Gardens, Marsh Lane, Stanmore HA7 4TG Tel: 020 8954 6612 — MD 1940 Lyon. (Dijon)

SPIER, Gareth Walter City Medical Services Ltd., 17 St.Helen's Place, London EC3A 6DG Tel: 020 7638 7090 Fax: 020 7256 5295 Email: gspier@citymedical.co.uk; 106 Kenilworth Court, Lower Richmond Road, London SW15 1HA Tel: 020 8785 2452 Fax: 020 8788 7265 — MB ChB 1965 Liverp. (Liverp.) Med. Dir. City Med. Servs. Lond.; Non-Exec. Dir. Lond. Ambul. Serv. NHS Trut. Socs: Soc. Occupat. Med.; Fell.Roy.Coll.Med; Amer. Occupat. Med. Assn. Prev: Ho. Phys. & Ho. Surg. Clatterbridge Hosp. Bebington; Sen. Ho. Surg. (Orthop.) & Cas. Off. Liverp. Roy. Infirm.

SPIER, Sarah Joanne Redwood House Practice, Redwood House, Cannon Lane, Maidenhead SL6 3PH Tel: 01628 826227 Fax: 01628 829426; Ellums, Cockpole Green, Wargrave, Reading RG10 8NT Tel: 0118 940 3849 — MB ChB 1991 Manch. Socs: Windsor Med. Soc.; Roy. Soc. Med.

SPIERS, Professor Alexander EW Donaldson, TD, Lt.-Col. (retired) Quarry Wood End, Gibraltar Lane, Cookham, Maidenhead SL6 9TR Tel: 01628 475635 Fax: 01628 475655 Email: spierssuch@globalnet.co.uk, spiersuk@globalnet.co.uk — MB BS 1960 Melb.; MB BS Melb.1960; FRACP 1972; MD melb.1975; FRCPE 1982; PhD 1967; FRCPath 1982; FACP 1977. Prev: Prof.med.Univ.S.Florida.

SPIERS, David Ronald Raleigh Surgery, 33 Pines Road, Exmouth EX8 5NH Tel: 01395 222499 Fax: 01395 225493; 39 Regents Gate, Exmouth EX8 1TR Tel: 01395 275562 Fax: 01395 266882 Email: drs@davidspiers.free-online.co.uk — MB ChB 1983 Leic.; MRCGP 1988. (Leicester) GP; Cons. Pharmaceut. Med. DRS Servs. Exmouth. Socs: BMA. Prev: Head of UK CVS Research E. Merck Pharmaceut.; Med. Adviser SmithKline & French; SHO (Chest Med.) Warwick Hosp.

SPIERS, Diana Patricia Jockey Road Surgery, 519 Jockey Road, Sutton Coldfield B73 5DF Tel: 0121 354 3050 Fax: 0121 355 1840; 33 Beech Hill Road, Sutton Coldfield B72 1BY — MB ChB 1978 Birm.

SPIERS, Elizabeth May Lubnaig, 442 Blackness Road, Dundee DD2 1TQ Tel: 01382 667547 — MB BS 1966 Lond.; MRCP (UK) 1971. (Middlx.) Assoc. Specialist (Pathol.) Ninewells Hosp. Dundee. Prev: Regist. (Haemat.) Univ. Hosp. Wales Cardiff & Ninewells Hosp. Dundee.

SPIERS, James Martin Mill Bank Surgery, Water Street, Stafford ST16 2AG Tel: 01785 258348 Fax: 01785 227144 — BM BS 1984 Nottm.; MRCGP 1989. Prev: Trainee GP Pembrokesh. VTS.

SPIERS, Martin Richard Harrogate Road Surgery, 23 Harrogate Road, Bradford BD2 3DY Tel: 01274 639857 Fax: 01274 627006 — MB ChB 1973 Leeds; DObst RCOG 1975. Prev: SHO (O & G) St. Jas. Hosp. Leeds; SHO (Infec. Dis.) Seacroft Hosp. Leeds.

SPIERS, Richard John Stepping Stones Medical Practice, Stafford Street, Dudley DY1 1RT Tel: 01384 459966 Fax: 01384 459885 — MB ChB 1977 Leeds; DRCOG 1981.

SPIERS

SPIERS, Richard Jonathan 3M Health Care, 3M House, Morley St., Loughborough LE11 1EP Tel: 01509 613003 Fax: 01509 613843 Email: rspiers1@mmm.com; Windmill Cottage, 8 Tinwell Road, Stamford PE9 2QQ Tel: 01780 756590 Fax: 01780 480804 Email: richard@windmill3.demon.co.uk — MB BS 1975 Lond.; MRCS Eng. LRCP Lond. 1975; MRCGP 1982; Dip. Pharm. Med. RCP (UK) 1992; DAvMed FOM RCP Lond. 1985. (St. Mary's) Med. Dir. 3M Health Care UK & Irel.. Prev: Wing Cdr. RAF Med. Br.; Med. Adviser Europ. Div. 3M Health Care LoughBoro..

SPIERS, Stanley Paule (retired) 15 Welland Road, Barrow upon Soar, Loughborough LE12 8NA Tel: 01509 412966 — MB BS 1952 Lond.; BA (Law) CNAA 1982; DObst RCOG 1958.

SPIES, John Anthony Priory Medical Practice, 48 Bromham Road, Bedford MK40 2QD Tel: 01234 262040 Fax: 01234 219288; Mistletoe Cottage, Grange Road, Felmersham, Bedford MK43 7HJ Tel: 01234 782088 — MB BS Lond. 1963; MSc (Social Med.) Lond. 1972; MRCP Lond. 1969; DCH Eng. 1966. (St. Geo.) GP Bedford. Prev: Lect. (Community Paediat.) St. Mary's Hosp. Med. Sch. Lond.; Research Fell. Wolfson Centre Inst. Child Health Lond.; Research Fell. (Social & Occupat. Med.) Welsh Nat. Sch. Med.

SPIKKER, Angela Claire Wilhelmina 44 Wellmeadow Lane, Uppermill, Oldham OL3 6DX — LRCPI & LM, LRSCI & LM 1971; LRCPI & LM, LRCSI & LM 1971; DObst RCPI 1974; DCH NUI 1973.

SPILG, Edward George Dept. Of Medicine for The Elderly, Gartnavel General Hospital, 1053 Great Western Rd, Glasgow G12 0YN Tel: 0141 211 3166, 0141 211 3465 Email: ed.spilg@northglasgow.scot.nhs.uk — MB ChB 1990 (Hons.) Glas.; FRCP 2001 Glas.; MRCP (UK) 1993. Cons (Ger. Med.) Garnavel Gen. Hosp. Glas.; hon. Clin. Sen. Lect Univ Glas. Prev: Career Regist. (Geriat. Med.) Roy. Infirm. Glas.; Sen. Regist. (Geriat. Med.) Gartnavel Gen. Hosp. Glas.; Sen. Regist (Gen Med) Vict. Inf. Glas.

SPILG, Sandra Jane Dr MacBrayne and Partners, 19 Dinmont Road, Shawlands, Glasgow G41 3UJ Tel: 0141 632 8883 Fax: 0141 636 0654 — MB ChB 1988 Glas.; MRCGP 1992; DRCOG 1991. Socs: S.. Med. Soc. & BMA. Prev: Trainee GP Glas.

SPILG, Walter Gerson Spence (retired) 4B Newton Court, Newton Grove, Newton Mearns, Glasgow G77 5QL Tel: 0141 639 3130 Fax: 0141 616 2190 Email: walter.spilg@talk21.com — MB ChB (Hons.) Glas. 1964; FRCP Glas. 1988; MRCP (Glas.) 1986; FRCPath 1982, M 1970. Prev: Cons. Path. i/c Glas. Vict. Infirm. & Assoc. Hosps. (1972-99).

SPILL, Werner Fritz Ysbyty Gwynedd Hospital, Penrhosgarnedd, Bangor LL57 2PW; 1 Frondeg, Tregarth, Bangor LL57 4PA — State Exam Med 1986 Essen.

SPILLANE, Kathleen Tel: 01382 632357 Fax: 01382 425739 — MB BCh 1988 Wales; PhD Leeds 1982, BSc (Hons.) 1979; MRCPI 1996. Cons. Clin. Neurophysiol. Ninewells Hosp., Dundee; Hon. Sen. Lect. Univ. Dundee. Prev: Cons. (Neurophysiol.) St James' Univ. Hosp. Leeds; Sen. Regist. (Neurophysiol.) St. Bart. Hosp. Lond.; SHO (Gen. Med.) Qu. Eliz. Hosp. & Gen. Hosp. Birm.

***SPILLER, Jayne Elizabeth** Greenmeadow Farm, Llangynwyd, Maesteg CF34 9RU — MB BCh 1994 Wales.

SPILLER, Juliet Anne 25/5 Spylaw Road, Edinburgh EH10 5BN Email: drjas@compuseve.com — MB ChB 1993 Aberd.; MRCP (UK) 1998. Specialist Regist., Palliat. med. Prev: SHO (Infec. Dis.s, Palliat. Med. & Psychol. Med.).

SPILLER, Penelope Anne St. Mary's Hospice, 176 Raddlebarn Road, Birmingham B29 7DA Tel: 0121 472 1191; 12 Meadow Rise, Bourneville, Birmingham B30 1UZ Tel: 0121 472 4247 — MB BS 1972 Lond.; MRCS Eng. LRCP Lond. 1972; DRCOG 1978; DCH Eng. 1977; Dip. Palliat. Med. Wales 1996. (Royal Free Hospital School of Medicine) Clin. Asst. (Palliat. Med.) St. Mary's Hospice Birm. Prev: GP Warks..

SPILLER, Richard Wallace The Health Centre, 10 Gresham Road, Oxted RH8 0BQ Tel: 01883 714361 Fax: 01883 722679 — MB BS 1973 Lond.; MRCP (UK) 1976.

SPILLER, Robin Charles 3 St George's Road, Kingston, Kingston upon Thames KT2 6DL — MD 1985 Camb.; MSc Lond. 1972; MB BChir 1975; MRCP (UK) 1977. (Univ. Coll. Hosp.) Sen. Regist. (Gastroenterol.) Centr. Middlx. & St. Mary's Hosps.; MRC Trav. Fell.sh. Mayo Clin. Rochester, Minnesota, USA.

SPILLER, Violet (retired) 63 Water Lane, Seven Kings, Ilford IG3 9HW Tel: 020 8590 6787 — MD Geneva 1929; MRCS Eng. LRCP Lond. 1931; DPH Lond. 1937. Prev: Sen. Asst. Med. Off. Barking.

SPILLING, Roy Alfred Eadie 160 Banbury Road, Oxford OX2 7BS Tel: 01865 515552 — BM BCh 1968 Oxf.; MA Oxf. 1969, BM BCh 1968; MRCGP 1976; DCH Eng. 1971; DObst RCOG 1970. (Oxf. & Lond. Hosp.) Prev: Dep. Res. Med. Off. Qu. Eliz Hosp. Childr. Lond.; Sen. Res. Accouch. & Ho. Surg. Orthop. Unit Lond. Hosp.

SPILLMAN, Ian David Macclesfield District General Hospital, Victoria Road, Macclesfield SK10 3BL Tel: 01625 661302 Fax: 01625 663055 Email: ian.spillman@echeshire-tr.nwest.nhs.uk; 138 Prestbury Road, Macclesfield SK10 3BN — MB BS 1978 Lond.; FRCPCH 1994; MRCP (UK) 1985; DTM & H RCP Lond. 1984; DCH RCP Lond. 1982; DA Eng. 1981. (Roy. Free) Cons. Paediat. Macclesfield Dist. Gen. Hosp.; Clin. Lect. Liverp. Univ. Socs: Christ. Med. Fell.sh.; FRCPCH; Brit. Paediatric Respirat. Soc. Prev: Sen. Regist. (Paediat.) Luton & Dunstable Hosp.; Med. Supt. Kisilizi Hosp. SW Uganda; Tutor (Child Health) Qu. Eliz. Hosp. for Childr. Lond.

SPILSBURY, Bernard Gwilym (retired) The Gables, Church Lane, Thrumpton, Nottingham NG11 0AW Tel: 0115 983 1020 — MB ChB 1951 Birm. Prev: Med. Off. RAF.

SPILSBURY, Richard Adrian (retired) Steeplechase, Horse & Groom Lane, Galleywood, Chelmsford CM2 8PJ — MB BS 1962 Lond.; MRCS Eng. LRCP Lond. 1962; FFA RCS Eng. 1967; DA Eng. 1965. Cons. Anaesth. Chelmsford Hosp. Gp. Prev: Sen. Regist. (Anaesth.) Lond. Hosp.

SPINCER, John Lister House Surgery, Lister House, 53 Harrington Street, Pear Tree, Derby DE23 8PF Tel: 01332 271212 Fax: 01332 271939; Post Office Farm, 18 Rectory Lane, Breadsall Village, Derby DE21 5LL — MB ChB 1976 Leeds; PhD Leeds 1969, BSc 1966; MRCGP 1981; DRCOG 1981. GP Derby; Tutor GP Derby; Sen. Phys. (Occupat. Health) S. Derby Community Trust; Clin. Asst. Nightingale McMillan Unit Derby; Princip. Police Surg. Derbysh. Constab. Socs: Derbysh. Med. Soc. Prev: Capt. RAMC; Med. Off. 3rd Bn. Light Infantry Catterick Garrison.

SPINDLER, Mr John J (Surgery), 12 Sternhall Lane, London SE15 4NT Tel: 020 7635 5628 Fax: 020 7639 0835; 114 Burbage Road, London SE24 9HD Tel: 020 7733 9457 — MB BS 1964 Lond.; MB BS (Hons.) Lond. 1964; FRCS Eng. 1969; MRCS Eng. LRCP Lond. 1964; AMQ 1966. (King's Coll. Hosp.) Prev: Sen. Regist. (Gen. Surg.) King's Coll. Hosp. Lond. & Guy's Hosp. Lond.

***SPINDLER, Kim Danielle** Rosendale, Rucklers Lane, Kings Langley WD4 9NB — MB ChB 1997 Manch.

SPINK, Carina Elizabeth Ann Rose, Spink, Smith and Walker, Spring Terrace Health Centre, Spring Terrace, North Shields NE29 0HQ Tel: 0191 296 1588 Fax: 0191 296 2901 — MB ChB 1981 Manch.; DCCH RCGP & FCM 1989; DRCOG 1986; MFHom 1997. (Manchester) GP Princip. Prev: SHO (Community Paediat.) NW Durh.; Clin. Med. Off. SW Surrey HA; SHO (Paediat.) Bolton HA.

SPINK, Farley Richard 17 Nottingham Road, Croydon CR6 2AR Tel: 020 8688 0534; Mead House, Wheelers Lane, Brockham, Betchworth RH3 7HJ Tel: 01737 843238 — MB BChir 1954 Camb.; MFHom 1959. Prev: Regist. (Med.) Roy. Lond. Homoeop. Hosp.

SPINK, John Douglas (retired) Timmins, Henley Road, Marlow SL7 2BZ Tel: 01628 483678 — MB BS Lond. 1955; MRCS Eng. LRCP Lond. 1955. Prev: Med. Off. HM Young Offender Inst. Finnamore Wood Marlow.

SPINK, Malini Farnham Health Centre, Brightwells, Farnham GU9 7SA Tel: 01252 723122 Fax: 01252 728302 — MB ChB 1981 Bristol; MRCGP 1985; DA (UK) 1987; DRCOG 1985. Prev: Trainee GP/SHO Chase Farm Hosp. Enfield VTS; SHO (A & E & Anaesth.) W.on-super-Mare Gen. Hosp.

SPINK, Margaret 3 Castle Drive, Berwick-upon-Tweed TD15 1NS — MB BS 1955 Durh.

SPINK, Martin Samuel Southmead, Wycollar Drive, Blackburn BB2 7AG Tel: 01254 57445 — MD 1936 Camb.; MRCS Eng. LRCP Lond. 1933. (Camb. & Guy's) Prev: Pathol. Blackburn & Dist. Hosps.; Lect. Bact. Univ. Sheff.

SPINK, Mrs Prudence (retired) The Finches, Brancaster Staithe, King's Lynn PE31 8BW — MRCS Eng. LRCP Lond. 1940.

SPINK, Spencer Charles Euan The Mount, Spring St, Easingwold, York YO61 3BJ Tel: 01347 821562 Fax: 01347 821562 Email: doceuan@clara.net — MB ChB 1956 Ed.; DA Eng. 1962. (Ed.)

Prev: GP York; SHO (Anaesth.) Leicester Roy. Infirm.; Med. Examr. Civil Aviat. Auth.

SPINKS, Brian Christopher Department of Radiology, Chorley & South Ribble District General Hospital, Preston Road, Chorley PR7 1PP Tel: 01257 245868 Fax: 01257 247130; Whinfell, 767 Belmont Road, Bolton BL1 7BY Tel: 01204 309109 Fax: 01204 596718 Email: chris.spinks@lineone.net — MB ChB 1980 Dundee; FRCR 1988. (Univ. Dundee) Cons. Radiol. Chorley & S. Ribble Dist. Gen. Hosp. Socs: BMA. Prev: Ho. Off. & SHO Hull Roy. Infirm. & W.wood Hosp. Beverley; Regist. (Radiol.) N.wick Pk. Hosp. & Clin. Research Centre Harrow; Sen. Regist. Rotat. (Radiol.) N. Manch. Gen. Hosp. & Hope Hosp. Salford.

***SPINKS, Joanne** 32 Heathermount Dr, Crowthorne RG45 6HN — BM 1997 Soton.

SPINKS, Julian Thomas William Court View Surgery, 2A Darnley Road, Strood, Rochester ME2 2HA Tel: 01634 290333 Fax: 01634 295131; 7 Keefe Close, Bluebell Hill, Chatham ME5 9AG — MB BS 1984 Lond.; BSc (Hons.) Lond. 1981; DGM RCP Lond. 1986. (St. Geo.) Bd. Mem. Rochester & Strood PCG. Socs: (Sec.) Medway Fundholders Assn.; GP Writers Assoc. Prev: Trainee GP Rochester VTS; Ho. Surg. St. Bart. Hosp. Rochester; Ho. Phys. St. Helier Hosp. Carshalton Surrey.

SPINKS, Margaret Jane Woodhouse Medical Centre, 5 Skelton Lane, Woodhouse, Sheffield S13 7LY Tel: 0114 269 2049 Fax: 0114 269 6539 — MB ChB 1982 Manch.; MRCGP 1986; DRCOG 1985.

***SPINOZA, Marc Howard** 18 Cuffley Hill, Goff's Oak, Cheshunt, Waltham Cross EN7 5EU — MB BS 1994 Lond.

SPINTY, Stefan 57 Carr Manor Drive, Leeds LS17 5AP — State Exam Med 1991 Hamburg.

SPIRA, Michael Ashcroft Road Surgery, 26 Ashcroft Road, Stopsley Green, Luton LU2 9AU Tel: 01582 722555 Fax: 01582 418145; North Limbersey Farm, Maulden, Bedford MK45 2EA Tel: 01525 841381 Fax: 01525 841387 Email: michael@spira.demon.co.uk — MB BS Lond. 1968; MRCS Eng. LRCP Lond. 1967. (St. Bart.) Med. Cons. Weight Managem. UK Ltd. Socs: Brit. Soc. Med. & Dent. Hypn.; Assn. Study Obesity; NLP Certified Practitioner. Prev: Phys. Inst. of Dir.s & BUPA Med. Centre, Lond.; SHO (O & G) St. Margt.'s Hosp. Epping; Ho. Surg. Eye Dept. St. Bart. Hosp. Lond.

SPIRES, Robert Christopher Stewart Davenal House Surgery, 28 Birmingham Road, Bromsgrove B61 0DD Tel: 01527 872008; Tel: 01527 31110 — MB ChB 1965 Birm.; DObst RCOG 1967. (Birm.) Prev: SHO O & G Nottm. City Hosp.; SHO Clin. Path. Birm. Gen. Hosp.; Ho. Surg. City Gen. Hosp. Stoke-on-Trent.

SPIRMAN, Mina 9 Exeter Road, London NW2 4SJ — MD 1939 Prague.

SPIRO, David Michael Maida Vale Medical Centre, 40 Biddulph Mansions, Elgin Avenue, London W9 1HT Tel: 020 7286 6464 Fax: 020 7266 1017 — MB BChir 1982 Camb.; MA Camb. 1982; MRCGP 1995; Cert. Family Plann. JCC 1986; DRCOG 1984. (Cambridge) GP. Socs: Fell. Roy. Soc. Med.

SPIRO, Jonathan Gabriel RGIT Ltd., B364, Harwell Business Centre, Didcot OX11 0RA Tel: 01235 434374 Fax: 01235 435752 Email: jgs@rgit.co.uk; The Granary, E. Challow, Wantage OX12 9SS Tel: 01235 763180 — MB BS 1979 Lond.; MA Camb. 1979; MRCP (UK) 1982; MFOM Lond. 1997. (Westm.) Sen. Occupat. Phys. Occupat. Health RGIT Ltd. Socs: Soc. Occupat. Med.; BMA. Prev: Regist. Roy. Vict. Infirm. Newc., Sunderland Roy. Infirm. & Luton & Dunstable Hosp.

SPIRO, Mr Martin (retired) The Red House, Epping Road, Toothill, Ongar CM5 9SQ Tel: 01992 522402 Email: spirocoochill@calk21.com — MB BChir 1955 Camb.; MA Camb. 1955, MChir 1967, MB BChir 1955; FRCS Eng. 1964; FRCS Ed. 1964. Prev: Cons. Gen. & Periph. Vasc. Surg. Barking HA.

SPIRO, Martin (retired) 18A Hendon Avenue, London N3 1UE Tel: 020 8346 1559 — MB BS Durh. 1945; DMRD Eng. 1948. Prev: Cons. Radiol. Manor Hse. Hosp. Lond.

SPIRO, Professor Stephen George The Middlesex Hospital, Dept of Respitary Medicine, Mortimer Street, London W1M 8HA Tel: 020 7380 9004; 66 Grange Gardens, Pinner HA5 5QF Tel: 020 8868 1815 — BSc (Hons. Anat.) Manch. 1964, MD 1975, MB ChB 1967; FRCP (UK) 1981, M 1969. (Manch.) Cons. Phys. Gen. & Thoracic Med. Univ. Coll. Lond. Hosps. Trust; Hon. Sen. Lect. Univ. Lond.; Prof. Respirat. Med.; Chairm. RCP Sub Comm. Respirat. Med.; Clin. Director, Med. Serv.s UCLH. Socs: Past Pres. Europ. Respirat. Soc.; Counci. Mem. Brit. Thoracic Soc.; Prog. Comm. Amer.Thoracic Soc. Prev: Cons. Phys. Roy. Brompton Hosp. Lond.; Exec. Edr. Thorax; Pres. Europ. Respirat. Soc.

SPITERI, Hector Paul Cameron Road Surgery, 40 Cameron Road, Seven Kings, Ilford IG3 8LF Fax: 020 8599 0282 — MRCS Eng. LRCP Lond. 1982; FRCGP 2001 DFFP; MRCGP 1987; T(GP) 1991. (Lond. Hosp.) GP Ilford; Clin. Asst. (Neurol.) King Geo. Hosp. Ilford; Clin. Governance Lead Redbridge PCG; Chairm. Redbridge GP on Call (Out of Hours CoOperat.); Bd./Exec. Comm. Mem., Redbridge. Socs: BMA (Former Chairm. Redbridge & Stratford Div.); Redbridge & Waltham Forest Local Med. Comm.(former Chairm.); Ilford Med. Soc. (Vice Pres.).

SPITTAL, Murray James Anaesthetic Department, Pilgrim Hospital, Sibsey Road, Boston PE21 9QS — MB ChB 1983 Leeds; FRCA 1989; DA (UK) 1987. Cons. Anaesth. Lead Clinician for IC. Socs: MDU & Assn. Anaesth.; UHMS; ICS. Prev: Cons. Anaesth.TPMH, RAF Alcrotiri; Cons. Anaesth. P.ss Alexandra Hosp. RAF Wroughton; Hon. Sen. Regist. (Anaesth.) Bristol Roy. Infirm.

SPITTLE, Margaret Flora The Middlesex Hospital, Mortimer St., London W1T 3AA Tel: 020 7380 9090 Fax: 020 7436 0160 Email: liz.pratt@uclh.org; The Manor House, Beaconsfield Road, Claygate, Esher KT10 0PW Tel: 01372 465540 Fax: 01372 470470 — MB BS Lond. 1963; MSc (Radiobiol.) Lond. 1969; FRCP Lond. 1995; MRCS Eng. LRCP Lond. 1963; FRCR 1968; DMRT Eng. 1966; AKC 1963. (Westm.) p/t Cons. Clin. Oncol. Meyerstein Inst. Oncol. Middlx. Hosp. Lond.; Cons. Radiother. St. John's Centre Dis. Skin St. Thos. Hosp. Lond.; Hon. Cons. Radiother. Roy. Nat. Throat, Nose and Ear Hosp.. Lond.; Chairm. UK AIDS Oncol. Gp. Socs: (Pres..Open Sect.) Roy. Soc. Med.; (Library Comm.) Brit. Inst. Radiol.; Chair UK AIDS Onc. Gp. Prev: Sen. Regist. (Radiother.) W.m. Hosp. Lond.; Instruc. Stanford Univ. Med. Center, USA; Dean Roy. Coll. Radiol.

SPITTLE, Martin Charles Homecroft Surgery, Voguebeloth, Illogan, Redruth TR16 4ET Fax: 01209 843707; Mill Cottage, Menadarva, Kehelland, Camborne TR14 0JH Tel: 01209 716465 — MB ChB 1983 Birm. Prev: Trainee GP Pool Cornw.; SHO (Med., Surg. & Paediat.) Cornw. & I. of Scilly HA.

SPITTLEHOUSE, Kenneth Ernest (retired) 36 Waldron Road, Broadstairs CT10 1TB Tel: 01843 862127 — MD Sheff. 1956, MB ChB 1949; FRCPath 1970, M 1964. Hon. Cons. (Chem. Path.) Canterbury & Thanet HA.

SPITTLER, Irmgard c/o Smith, 289 Bansley St., Wigan WN6 7HY — State Exam Med. Heidelberg 1990.

SPITZ, Professor Lewis Institute of Child Health, 30 Guilford St., London WC1N 1EH Tel: 020 7242 9789/829 8691 Fax: 020 7404 6181 Email: l.spitz@ich.ucl.ac.uk — MB ChB 1963 Pretoria; 1986 FAAP, (hons) amer. Acad of Ped; MD 2002 (Hons) Sheffield; PhD (Med.) Witwatersrand 1980; FRCS Eng. 1981; FRCS Ed. 1969; FRCPCH 1997. (Pretoria) Nuffield Prof. Paediat. Surg. Inst. Child Health Lond.; Cons. Paediat. Surg. Gt. Ormond St. Hosp. for Childr. Lond.; Neonat. Surg. Univ. Coll. Hosp. Lond. Socs: (Pres.) Brit. Assn. Paediat. Surg. (Specialist Advis. Comm. & Train. & Teach. Comm.); (Acad. Bd.) Brit. Paediat. Assn.; Past Pres. BAPS. Prev: Sen. Paediat. Surg. Baragwanath & Transvaal Memor. Hosps. Johannesburg & Childr. Hosp. Sheff.

SPITZER, Joseph The Surgery, 62 Cranwich Road, London N16 5JF Tel: 020 8802 2002 Fax: 020 8880 2112; 66 Rostrevor Avenue, London N15 6LP Tel: 020 8802 4104 — MB BS 1981 Lond.; MRCGP 1985; Cert. FPA 1984; DRCOG 1984; DCCH RCGP & FCM 1984. (King's Coll. Hosp.) Hon. Sen. Lect. (Gen.) Med. Coll. St. Bart. & Roy. Lond. Hosps. Socs: Fell. Roy. Soc. Med.; BMA. Prev: CMO (Child Health) Islington HA; Trainee GP N.d. VTS; Ho. Off. Sunderland Roy. Infirm.

SPITZER, Robert John Southend Hospital, Prittlewell Chase, Westcliff on Sea SS0 ORY Tel: 01702 221238 Fax: 01702 221234; 59 Fairleigh Drive, Leigh-on-Sea SS9 2HZ Tel: 01702 710395 — MB BS 1959 Lond. (St. Mary's) Cons, Genitourin. Phys. S.end Health Care NHS Trust. Socs: BMA & Med. Soc. Study VD. Prev: Ho. Surg. Childr. Hosp. Paddington; Cas. Off. Lambeth Hosp.; JHMO Dept. Venereol St. Thos. Hosp. Lond.

SPIVEY, Mr Christopher John (retired) Kings Road Private Consulting Rooms, 151A Kings Road, Westcliff on Sea SS0 8PP Tel: 01702 476650 Fax: 01702 711787 — MB BS Lond. 1960; FRCS

SPIVEY

Eng. 1966; MRCS Eng. LRCP Lond. 1960. Hon. Cons. Orthop. Surg. S.end Health Dist.; Cons. Orthop. Surg. BUPA Wellesley Hosp. S.end-on-Sea. Prev: Sen. Orthop. Regist. Lond. Hosp.

*SPIVEY, Michael Hugh Hollybank, 126 London Road, Westerham TN16 1GR — BM BS 1997 Nottm.

SPIVEY, Rosemary Sarah The Brow, 96 Cumnor Hill, Oxford OX2 9HY Tel: 01865 862132 — MB BS Lond. 1963; MRCS Eng. LRCP Lond. 1963; MFFP. (St. Bart.) Research Asst. Diabetic Research Laborat. Radcliffe Infirm. Oxf.; Sen. Clin. Med. Off. (Family Plann.) Oxon. HA; Clin. Asst. (Obst. & Gyn.) John Radcliffe Hosp. Oxf. Socs: Fac. Fam. Plan.; Brit. Menopause Soc.; Wom.s Med. Fed. Prev: Med. Off. John Radcliffe Hosp. Oxf.; Ho. Phys. N. Staffs. Roy. Infirm. Stoke-on-Trent; Ho. Surg. N. Middlx. Hosp. Lond.

SPOFFORTH, Peter Ash Surgery, 1 Ashfield Road, Liverpool L17 0BY Tel: 0151 727 1155 Fax: 0151 726 0018 — MB ChB 1988 Liverp.

*SPOKES, Elizabeth Ann 40 Baginton Road, Coventry CV3 6JW — MB ChB 1996 Manch.

SPOKES, Ernest George Sutherland Leeds General Infirmary, Great George St., Leeds LS1 3EX Tel: 0113 292 3296 Fax: 0113 292 6337 — MB ChB Leeds 1972; BSc Leeds 1969, MD 1979; FRCP Lond. 1989; MRCP (UK) 1975. Cons. Neurol. Leeds Gen. Infirm. Prev: Cons. Neurol. York Dist. Hosp.; Dir. Neuropsychiat. Unit Bootham Pk. Hosp. York.

SPOKES, Gillian Ann 40 Baginton Road, Coventry CV3 6JW — MB ChB 1969 Birm.; DObst RCOG 1971. (Birm.)

SPOKES, Jonathan Mark Market Hill House, Market Hill, Medon HY12 8JD Tel: 01482 899111; Tel: 01482 890578 — MRCS Eng. LRCP Lond. 1982; MRCGP 1986; DRCOG 1988.

SPOKES, Robert Michael Spokes and Partners, Phoenix Family Care, 35 Park Road, Coventry CV1 2LE Tel: 024 7622 7234 Fax: 024 7663 4816 — MB ChB 1966 Birm.; MRCGP 1974; DObst RCOG 1969. (Birm.)

SPOLTON, Elizabeth Mary Somers Town Health Centre, Blackfriars Close, Southsea PO5 4NJ Tel: 023 9285 1202 Fax: 023 9229 6380; 52 Southleigh Road, Havant PO9 2QH Tel: 01705 484904 — MB BCh Wales 1972; MRCGP 1976; DObst RCOG 1975.

SPONG, Ambrose Henry Rowan (retired) Sunny Bank, Staveley, Kendal LA8 9PH Tel: 01539 822027 — MB BS Lond. 1957; FFA RCS Eng. 1963. Prev: Cons. Anaesth. Lincoln Hosp. Gp.

SPOONER, Andrew Lawrence Grosvenor Medical Centre, Grosvenor Street, Crewe CW1 3HB Tel: 01270 256340 Fax: 01270 250786; Gresty Brook Medical Centre, Brookhouse Drive, Crewe CW2 6NA Tel: 01270 650012 — MB BS 1983 Newc.; FRCGP, 1998; MRCGP 1987. (Newc. u. Tyne) Hon. Fell. Nat. Primary Care Research And Developm. Centre. Prev: Chairm. Mersey Regional Assn. Fundholding Pract.; Assoc. Med. Dir. Chesh. Community Health Care Trust; Trainee GP E. Cumbria VTS.

SPOONER, Catherine Ann The White House, 14 Park Avenue, Dronfield, Dronfield S18 2LQ — MB ChB 1990 Liverp.; MRCGP 1995.

SPOONER, David 9 St Bernards Road, Sutton Coldfield B72 1LE — MB ChB 1973 Birm.; BSc Birm. 1970; FRCP Lond. 1993; MRCP (UK) 1975; FRCR 1979. Cons. Clin. Oncol. Qu. Eliz., Dudley Rd., Sandwell & Childr. Hosps. Birm. Socs: Fell. RCP. Prev: Sen. Regist. (Radiother.) Roy. Marsden Hosp. Sutton & Lond.; Lect. (Radiother.) Inst. of Cancer Research Lond.; Regist. (Med.) Selly Oak Hosp. Birm.

SPOONER, John Bradley 8 Beaconsfield Road, Claygate, Esher KT10 0PW — MB 1963 Camb.; BChir 1962. (Middlx.)

SPOONER, Kay Joanna Chaseways, Feathers Hill, Hatfield Broad Oak, Bishop's Stortford CM22 7HB Tel: 01279 718705 Fax: 01279 718333 Email: kay.spooner@virgin.net — MB BS 1996 Lond.; B.Med.Sci 1995 Lond. (St Barthlolmew's Hospital, Chelmsford, Essex) SHO Anaesth., Broomfield Hosp., Chelmsford, Essex. Prev: SHO A & E Broomfield Hosp., Chelmford, Essex; RMO A&E/Rehabil./Gastro- Australia.

SPOONER, Laurel Loveday Rosemary North Station Road Surgery, 78 North Station Road, Colchester CO1 1SE Tel: 01206 574483 Fax: 01206 767558; 5 Ireton Road, Colchester CO3 3AT Tel: 01206 573860 — MB BChir 1979 Camb.; MA Camb. 1979; MRCP (UK) 1983; MRCGP 1983; DCH RCP Lond. 1983; DRCOG 1982; Cert. Family Plann. JCC 1982. GP Colchester; Chairm. Colchester PCG.

SPOONER, Louise 17 Armthorpe Road, Sheffield S11 7FA — MB BS 1987 Lond.

SPOONER, Monica Anne (Tyack) (retired) 30 South Oswald Road, Edinburgh EH9 2HG Tel: 0131 667 2555 Fax: 0131 668 2121 Email: monica@jasper.co.uk — MB BS 1964 Lond.; MRCS Eng. LRCP 1964 Lond.; DCCH RCP Ed. RCGP & FCM 1986; DObst RCOG 1967. Prev: Clin. Med. Off. Lothian HB.

SPOONER, Shirley Mildred 406 Uppingham Road, Leicester LE5 2DP Tel: 0116 243 2951 Fax: 01162 418740 Email: ashwoodo@demon.co.uk — MB BS 1960 Lond.; MRCS Eng. LRCP Lond. 1960. (Roy. Free)

SPOONER, Simon Jonathan 33 Cheltenham Road, Manchester M21 9GL — MB BCh 1995 Wales.

SPOONER, Stephen Francis Department of Obstetrics & Gynaecology, Rotherham District General Hospital, Moorgate Road, Rotherham S60 2UD; 27 Moor Oaks Road, Sheffield S10 1BX — MB BChir 1977 Camb.; FRCOG 1998. (Cambridge/St Thomas London) Cons. O & G Rotherham Hosp.

SPOONER, Timothy Casswell 15 Florian Road, Putney, London SW15 2NL — MB BS 1969 Lond. (St. Bart.) Prev: Ho. Surg. Lincoln Co. Hosp.; Ho. Phys. St. Paul's Hemel Hempstead; SHO (Orthop.) Roy. United Hosp. Bath.

SPOONER, Veronica Josephine Lensfield Medical Practice, 48 Lensfield Road, Cambridge CB2 1EH Tel: 01223 352779 Fax: 01223 566930; 11 Barton Close, Cambridge CB3 9LQ — MB BS 1978 Lond.; MRCGP 1983; DRCOG 1982. (St. Mary's Hospital London)

SPOOR, Kathleen Mary 15 Burnhouse Road, Wooler NE71 6BJ Tel: 01668 281575 Fax: 01688 282442; East Longstone House, Church Hill, Chatton, Alnwick NE66 5PY — MB BS Newc. 1982; MRCGP 1987; DCCH RCP Ed. 1986. GP Wooler, N.d.

SPORIK, Richard Bernard 196 Battersea Park Road, London SW11 4ND — BM 1980 Soton.; DM Soton. 1994, BM 1980; MRCP (UK) 1986; DRCOG 1984; DCH RCP Lond. 1983.

SPORTON, Simon Charles Edwin Department of Cardiology, Middlesex Hospital, Mortimer St., London W1T 3AA Tel: 020 7636 8333; 1 Pike End, Stevenage SG1 3XA Tel: 01438 358326 Email: scesporton@aol.com — MB BS 1991 Lond.; BSc Lond. 1988; MRCP (UK) 1994. Specialist Regist. (Cardiol.) NE Thames. Prev: Clin. Research Fell. (Cardiol.) Univ. Coll. Lond.; Regist. Rotat. (Med.) SW Thames; SHO Rotat. (Med.) Seacroft & Killingbeck Hosps. Leeds.

SPOTO, Giuseppe Department of Psychiatry, Crawley Hospital, West Green Drive, Crawley RH11 7DH Tel: 01293 600300 Fax: 01293 600411 Email: gspoto@cwcom.net; 101 Camberwell Grove, London SE5 8JH Tel: 020 7703 3228 Fax: 020 7703 3228 Email: gspoto@cwcom.net — MD 1972 Pisa; MRCPsych 1982. (Italy) Cons. (Psychiat. Psychother.) Crawley & Horsham NHS Trust; Med. Mem. Ment. Health Review Tribunal. Socs: Soc. Psychother. Research; Soc. Psychosomatic Research; Roy. Soc. Med. Prev: Sen. Regist. (Psychiat.) & Hon. Clin. Lect. Univ. Coll. Hosp.; Regist. (Child Psychiat.) Child Guid. Train. Centre Lond.; Regist. Roy. Free Hosp. Lond.

SPOTSWOOD, Valerie Janet Villiers House, Tolworth Hospital, Red Lion Road, Surbiton KT6 7QU Tel: 020 8990 0102 — MB BS Lond. 1963; MRCS Eng. LRCP Lond. 1963; MRCPsych 1973; DPM Eng. 1972. (King's Coll. Hosp.) Cons. Gen. Psychiat. Tolworth Hosp. Prev: Cons. Psychiat. (Elderly) Long Gr. Hosp. Epsom; Sen. Regist. (Psychiat.) Lond. Hosp.; Regist. (Psychiat.) St. Mary's Hosp. Lond.

SPOUDEAS, Helen Alexandra Dept. of Adolescent Med., U.C.L.H., 3rd Floor Dorville House, Middlesex Hospital, Mortimer St., London W1T 3AA Tel: 020 7380 9459, 020 7380 9950 Fax: 020 7636 2144 Email: h.spoudeas@ucl.ac.uk; "Kladas", 33 Methuen Park, London N10 2JR Tel: 020 8444 4123 Email: helen.spoudeas@virgin.net — MB BS 1981 Lond.; MD Lond. 1995; MRCP (UK) 1985; FRCP 2000 Lond; DRCOG 1963 Lond; FRCPCH 1999. (St. Bart. Hosp. Lond.) p/t Cons. Paediatric Endocrinol., Neuroendoc. & Late Effects of Childh. Malignancy, Lond. Centre of Paediat. Endocrin. at Univ. Coll. & Gt. Ormond St. Hosp. Lond.; Hon. Cons. (Paediat. Endocrin.) Barnet and Chase Farm Hosp.; Hon. Sen. Lect. (Paediat. Endocrin.) UCL & Inst. Of Child Health; Volun. Mem. Of Fundraising Comm. RMBF.; Volun. RMBF rep on Nat. Counc. Servs. for sick. Socs: Eur. & Brit. Socs. Paediat. Endocrinol.; Fell., Roy. Coll. Of Phys.; UK Childr.'s Cancer Study Gp. Prev: Sen. Regist. (Paediat. Endocrinol.) Middlx. Hosp. Lond.; Research Fell.

(Paediat. Endocrinol.) Middlx. Hosp. Lond.; Regist. Rotat. (Paediat.) Char. Cross Hosp. Lond.

SPOULOU, Vassiliki Institute of Child Health, Department Of Immunology, 30 Guildford St., London WC1N 1EH Tel: 020 7405 9200 — Ptychio Iatrikes 1985 Athens.

SPOWAGE, Paul Martin The Surgery, Queens Road, Earls Colne, Colchester CO6 2RR Tel: 01787 222022 — MB BS 1986 Lond.; DRCOG 1990; DCH RCP Lond. 1989. GP Earls Colne.

SPOWART, Keith John Morrison Lanarkshire Acute Hospitals Trust, Hairmyres Hospital, East Kilbride, Glasgow G&5 8RG Tel: 0141 220292 Fax: 0141 234064; 56 Corrour Road, Newlands, Glasgow G43 2ED Tel: 0141 649 8260 — MB ChB 1983 Glas.; BSc (Hons.) (Pharmacol.) Ed. 1978; MRCOG 1989. (Glas.) Cons. Gyn. Hairmyres Hosp. E. Kilbride; Cons. (Obst.), Wishaw Gen. Hosp., 50 Netherton St., Wishaw, Lanarksh. Socs: Glas. Obst. & Gyn. Soc.; Brit. Menopause Soc. Prev: Sen. Regist. Rotat. (O & G) Glas.; Regist. - Stobhill Hosp. Galsgow (Obs. + Gyn.); Research Regist. - Stobhill Hosp. Galsgow (Menopause Clinic).

SPRACKLING, Margaret Ellen 6 Hillbrow, Richmond Hill, Richmond TW10 6BH Tel: 020 8948 3517 — MB BS 1958 Lond.; FRCP Lond. 1987; MRCP (UK) 1970; MRCS Eng. LRCP Lond. 1958. (Middlx.) Emerit. Cons. Phys. (Geriat. Med.) City Hosp. Nottm. Socs: (Ex-Pres. & Ex-Treas.) Trustee Nottm. M-C Soc.; (Ex-Pres.) Med. Wom. Federat.; BMA (Ex-Sec. and Ex-Chairm. Nottm. Div.). Prev: Cas. Off. King Edwd. Memor. Hosp. Ealing; Ho. Surg. Mt. Vernon Hosp. N.wood; Ho. Phys. Middlx. Hosp. Lond.

SPRACKLING, Peter Dennis Derby Road Health Centre, 292 Derby Road, Nottingham NG7 1QG Tel: 0115 947 4002; Flat 2, 25 Park Valley, The Park, Nottingham NG7 1BS — MB BS 1958 Lond.; FRCGP 1978, M 1972; DObst RCOG 1960. (Middlx.) Prev: Regional Adviser (Gen. Pract.) Trent RHA. Lect. Dept. Community Health Med. Sch. Nottm. Univ.; Ho. Off. (Obst.) Hammersmith Hosp. Lond.; Ho. Surg. & Ho. Phys. Roy. Berks. Hosp. Reading.

SPRAGGETT, David Thomas The Castle Medical Centre, 22 Bertie Road, Kenilworth CV8 1JP Tel: 01926 857331 Fax: 01926 851070; 12 Elizabeth Way, Kenilworth CV8 1QP — MB ChB 1981 Birm.; MRCGP 1985; DCH RCP Lond. 1986; DRCOG 1984. Prev: Ho. Surg. Walsall Manor Hosp.; Ho. Phys. Good Hope Hosp. Sutton Coldfield.

SPRAGGINS, Debra The Health Centre, Laindon, Basildon SS15 5TR Tel: 01268 546411 Fax: 01268 491248 — MB ChB 1991 Manch.; DFFP.

SPRAGGS, Mr Paul David Robert The Hampshire Clinic, Basing Road, Old Basing, Basingstoke RG24 7AL; The Bothy, College Lane, Basingstoke RG25 2QE — FRCS 1996; MB BS 1987 Lond.; FRCS Eng. 1991. Cons. OtoLaryngol., N. Hants. Hosp. Prev: Sen. Regist. (Otolaryngol.) Char. Cross Hosp. Lond.

SPRAGUE, Daphne Sharpe (retired) 14 Stephenson Terrace, Wylam NE41 8DZ Tel: 01661 852719 — MB BS 1948 Durh. Prev: SCMO (Family Plann.) S. Shields.

SPRAGUE, Nigel Bond 14 Stephenson Terrace, Wylam NE41 8DZ Tel: 01661 852719 — MB BS 1945 Durh.; DA Eng. 1971. Assoc. Specialist (Anaesth.) Newc. HA. Prev: Ex-Pres. Newc. on Tyne & N.. Counties Med. Soc.; Ho. Phys. Dryburn Hosp. Durh.; Ho. Surg. Newc. Gen. Hosp.

SPRAGUE, Valerie Ruth 24 Horsecastle Farm Road, Yatton, Bristol BS49 4QQ Email: coombe01@globalnet.co.uk — MB ChB 1997 Bristol; BSc 1996. (Bris.) VTS for Gen. Pract. Socs: Med. Protect. Soc.; Med. Wom.s Fed. Prev: A&E; O & G.

SPRAKE, Caroline Mary Lane End Surgery, 2 Manor Walk, Benton, Newcastle upon Tyne NE7 7XX Tel: 0191 266 5246 Fax: 0191 266 6241 — MB BS 1986 Newc.; MB BS (Hons.) Newc. 1986, BMedSci (Hons.) 1983; MRCP (UK) 1989; MRCGP 1991.

SPRANGEMEYER, Dawn The Cottage, 67 Island Road, Sturry, Canterbury CT2 0EF — MRCS Eng. LRCP Lond. 1971; BSc Lond. 1967, MB BS 1971; DCCH Adelaide 1985. SCMO Community Health & Ment. Handicap Servs. Canterbury & Thanet HA. Prev: Resid. Med. Off. Child Health Servs. Townsville, Qu.sland.

SPRATLEY, Terence Arthur (retired) Mount Zeehan Unit, St. Martin's Hospital, Littlebourne Road, Canterbury CT1 1TD Tel: 01227 761310 — MRCS Eng. LRCP Lond. 1961; MPhil Lond. 1969, MB BS 1961; MRCP Lond. 1966; MRCPsych 1973. Cons. Psychiat. St. Martins Hosp. Canterbury.

SPRATT, Henry Clifford General Hospital, St Helier, Jersey JE1 3QS Tel: 01534 622000 Fax: 01534 622895; La Falaise, Le Hocq, St. Clement, Jersey JE2 6FQ Tel: 01534 855256 Fax: 01534 851169 — MD Dub. 1974, MB BCh BAO 1969; FRCP Lond. 1986; MRCP (UK) 1973; FRCPCH 1997. (TC Dub.) Cons. Paediat. Gen. Hosp. St. Helier Jersey. Socs: RCPCH. Prev: Lect. (Paediat.) McGill Univ. Montreal, Canada.

SPRATT, James Samuel 59 Ballyquin Road, Limavady BT49 9EY; Flat 3F1, 29 Falcon Gardens, Morningside, Edinburgh EH10 4AR Email: j.spratt@ed.ac.uk — MB ChB 1993 Manch.; BSc MedSci Edin. 1998; MRCP (UK) 1996. Specialist Regist. (Cardiol.) W.ern Gen. Hosp. Edin. Prev: Res. Fell. (Clin. Pharma.) Univ. of Edin.

SPRATT, Jonathan Daunton 6 Hownam Close, Newcastle upon Tyne NE3 4YS — MB BChir 1992 Camb.; MA Camb 1992; FRCS Glas. 1997; FRCS Eng. 1996. (Specialist Regist. Diag. Radiol. North. Train. Scheme)

SPRAY, Christine Helen The Gastroentgrology Department, The Children's Hospital, Steelhouse Lane, Birmingham B4 6NH; Flat 2, 31 Wentworth Road, Harborne, Birmingham B17 9SN Tel: 0121 427 2600 — MB ChB 1987 Liverp. Clin. Lect. (Paediat., Gastroenterol. & Hepat.) Childr. Hosp. Liverp. Prev: Clin. Research Fell. (Paediat. Hepat.) & Regist. Newc.

SPRAY, Rowland John (retired) 2 Sandringham Road, Swindon SN3 1HP Tel: 01793 537502 — MB BChir 1952 Camb.; MA Camb. 1953, BA 1949; MRCGP 1968; DObst RCOG 1970; DCH Eng. 1969. Prev: GP Swindon.

SPREADBURY, Kate Victoria Hansford 6 Woodford Road, Bournemouth BH1 3PQ — BM 1994 Soton.; BM (Hons. Distinc. Clin. Med.) Soton. 1994; DRCOG 1998. Trainee GP Taunton VTS; SHO (A & E). Prev: SHO (Psychiat.).

SPREADBURY, Peter Lawrence Little Oaks, 218 Stakes Hill Road, Waterlooville PO7 5UJ Tel: 0170 143336 — MB BS 1966 Lond.; FFA RCS Eng. 1973; DA Eng. 1969. (Lond. Hosp.) Cons. Anaesth. Portsmouth & S.E. Hants. Health Dist. Prev: Anaesth Sen. Regist. Soton. Univ. Hosp.

SPREADBURY, Thomas Hugh (retired) 52 Bridge End, Warwick CV34 6PB — MB 1961 Camb.; BChir 1960; FFA RCS Eng. 1968; DA Eng. 1966. Prev: Cons. Anaesth. Warwick.

SPRECKLEY, Debra Elizabeth 12 Waterside Avenue, Marple, Stockport SK6 7LZ — MB ChB 1996 Birm.; MB ChB (Hons.) Birm. 1996.

SPRIGG, Alan Department of Radiology, Sheffield Childrens Hospital, Western Bank, Sheffield S10 2TH Tel: 0114 271 7201 Fax: 0114 271 7514 — MB ChB 1978 Manch.; FRCPCH 1997; FRCR 1985; DMRD Eng. 1983; DRCOG 1981; DCH Eng. 1980. Cons. Paediat. Radiol. Sheff. Childs. Hosp. NHS Trust; Cons. Radiol. Jessop Wing of Hallamshire Hosp., Sheff. Prev: Cons. Paediat. (Radiol.) Mersey RHA; Fell. (Radiol.) Hosp. Sick Childr., Toronto.

SPRIGG, Nikola 12 Sackville Road, Sheffield S10 1GT — MB ChB 1995 Sheff.

SPRIGG, Sandra Jane 105 Rustlings Road, Sheffield S11 7AB Tel: 0114 266 0726 — MB ChB 1978 Manch.; MRCGP 1985; DCH RCP Lond. 1983; DRCOG 1981. GP Retainer Scheme Sheff. Prev: Regist. & Clin. Med. Off. Sheff. Childr. Hosp.; SHO (Cas.) Sheff. Childr. Hosp.

SPRIGGE, John Squire Department Anaesthesia, Arrowe Park Hospital, Wirral CH49 5PE Tel: 0151 678 5111 — MRCS Eng. LRCP Lond. 1972; BA Camb. 1969, MB BChir 1973; FFA RCS Eng. 1976. (Westm.) Cons. (Anaesth.) Arrowe Pk. Hosp. Wirral.; Clin. Tutor Arrowe Pk. Hosp. Prev: Clin. Tutor Wirral Hosp.; Sen. Regist. (Anaesth.) Hammersmith Hosp.; Regist. (Anaesth.) Liverp. AHA (T).

SPRIGGS, Arthur Ivens (retired) 1 Gozzards Ford, Abingdon OX13 6JH Tel: 01865 390618 — BM BCh 1943 Oxf.; BA Oxf. 1941, DM 1952; FRCP Lond. 1968, M 1944; FRCPath 1973, M 1964. Prev: Cons. Cytol. Oxon HA.

SPRIGINGS, David Campbell Northampton General Hospital, Cliftonville, Northampton NN1 5BD Tel: 01604 545901 Fax: 01604 545436 Email: david.sprigings@ngh-tr.anglox.nhs.uk; 6 Raynsford Road, Northampton NN5 7HP — BM BCh Oxf. 1980; BA Oxf. 1977; FRCP 1997, MRCP (UK) 1983. (Oxf. Univ.) Cons. Cardiol. N.ampton Gen. Hosp. Socs: Brit. Cardiac Soc. & Brit. Soc. Echocardiogr. Prev: Clin. Lect. John Radcliffe Hosp. Oxf.

SPRING, Colin Department Anaesthesia, Worthing Hospital, Lyndhurst Road, Worthing BN11 2DH Tel: 01903 205111 Fax: 01903 285045; Pine Lodge, Fir Tree Lane, West Chiltington RH20 2RA Tel: 01903 815514 — MB BS 1987 Lond.; MRCGP

SPRING

1991; FRCA 1995. (St George's Hospital Medical School) Clin. Director,Cons. Anaesth Cons. Intens. Care. Worthing & S.lands Hosp. W. Sussex. Prev: Regist. Rotat. (Anaesth.) Bristol & S. W.; Regist. (Anaesth.) Roy. Hobart Hosp. Tasmania, Austral.; Regist. (Anaesth.) MusGr. Pk. Hosp. Taunton.

SPRING, Jane Elizabeth Department of Obstetrics, Heatherwood Hospital, Lond. Road, Ascot SL5 8AA — MB BS 1978 Lond.; MRCP (UK) 1985; MRCOG 1984; DCH RCP Lond. 1983. Cons. O & G Heatherwood Hosp. Ascot. Prev: Sen. Regist. (O & G) Guy's Hosp. Lond.

SPRING, Jennifer Thea Manor Way Surgery, 27 Manor Way, Borehamwood WD6 1QR Tel: 020 8953 3095 — MB BS 1967 Lond.; BSc Nottm. 1962; MRCS Eng. LRCP Lond. 1967; DObst RCOG 1969. (St. Bart.) Prev: Ho. Off. City of Lond. Matern. Hosp.; Ho. Surg. St. Albans City Hosp.; Ho. Phys. St. Paul's Hosp. Hemel Hempstead.

SPRING, Linford Craig Medical Services, Sutherland House, 29-37 Brighton Road, Sutton SM2 5AN Tel: 020 8652 6450 Fax: 020 8652 6022; 3 Horley Row, Horley RH6 8DN — MB BS 1979 Adelaide. Med. Adviser Med. Servs. Sutton (Lond. S.). Socs: BMA. Prev: GP Crawley & Horley; SHO (O & G) Guy's Hosp. Lond.; SHO (Paediat.) New Ealing Hosp. S.all & Perivale Hosp. Greenford.

SPRING, Mark William Department of Metabolic Medicine, Kingston Hospital, Galsworthy Road, Kingston upon Thames KT2 7QB Tel: 020 8546 7711; 235 London Road, Morden SM4 5PU — MB BS 1990 Lond.; BSc (Hons.) Lond. 1987; MRCP (UK) 1993. (UMDS Guy's) Cons. (Diabetes Endocrinolory & Gen Med) Kingston & Qu. Mary's Hosps. Prev: Cons. Gen.Med Guy's Hosp. Lon; Sen. Regist. (Metab. & Gen Med) Guy's Hosp; Regist & Sho (MED) St. Geo Hosp, Lon.

SPRING, Robert David Leslie Harpers Lane Surgery, Harpers Lanes, Presteigne LD8 2AN Tel: 01544 267985 Fax: 01544 267682 — MB BS 1982 Lond.; BA Oxf. 1979; MRCP (UK) 1985.

***SPRING-BARRETT, Victoria Jane Mary** Heroncot, Rushmere Lane, Orchard Leigh, Chesham HP5 3QY — MB ChB 1996 Leeds.

SPRINGALL, Christopher James 20 Woodgreen Road, Oldbury, Oldbury B68 0DF — MB ChB 1978 Liverp.

SPRINGALL, Mr Roger Graham 149 Harley Street, London W1G 6BN Tel: 020 7486 7927 Fax: 020 7486 7927 Email: rgspringal@aol.com; Oak End Mill, Amersham Road, Gerrards Cross SL9 0PU Tel: 01753 882880 — MB ChB 1973 Liverp.; ChM 1984; FRCS Eng. 1977. Cons. Surg. (Gastrointestinal & Oncol. Surg.) Char. Cross Hosp. Lond.; Cons. Surg. King Edwd. VII Hosp. for Offs. Lond.; Hon. Cons. Surg. St. Luke's Hosp. for the Clergy Lond. Socs: Fell. Roy. Soc. Med.; Assn. Coloproctol.; Fell. Assn. Surg. Prev: Resid. Surgic. Off. St. Mark's Hosp. Lond.; Sen. Regist. (Surg.) St. Bart. Hosp. Lond.; Demonst. (Anat.) Univ. Camb.

SPRINGER, Adele Leona Cynthia 1 Scoonie Court, Leven KY8 5TH — MB ChB 1988 Aberd.

SPRINGER, Heath Weston 4 Pembroke Road, Ilford IG3 8PH; 106 Cambridge Road, Ilford IG3 8LY — MB BS 1992 Lond.

SPRINGER, Jana Department of Ophthalmology, King's College Hospital, Denmark Hill, London SE5 9RS; 12 Deepdene Road, London SE5 8EG Tel: 020 7733 1024 — Promovany Lekar Chas. Univ. Prague 1959. Asst. Specialist (Ophth.) King's Coll. Hosp. Lond. Socs: BMA & Soc. Ophth. Surgs. Prev: Asst. Specialist (Ophth.) St. Thos. Hosp. Lond. & Kingston Hosp. Surrey.

SPRINGER, Miss Simona Ava Vlasta Eva Kings College Hospital, Camberwell, London SE5 — MB BS 1987 Lond.; FRCS Ed. 1994.

SPRINGER, Susan Elizabeth 32a Chalsey Road, London SE4 1YW — MB ChB 1992 Manch.

SPRINGETT, Victor Henry (retired) 33 Royal Marine Appartments, Marine Road, Nairn IV12 4EN Tel: 01667 452902 — MB BS 1943 Lond.; MD Lond. 1950; MRCS Eng. LRCP Lond. 1942; FRCP Lond. 1964, M 1955; FFCM 1974. Prev: Med. Dir. Birm. Chest Clinic.

SPROAT, Lois Mary Elizabeth The Health Centre, Academy St., Castle Douglas DG7 1NQ; Strathmore, Abercromby Road, Castle Douglas DG7 1BA — MB ChB 1976 Dundee; DRCOG 1980.

SPROSON, Janet Christine Ros-an-Dinas, Lamorna, Penzance TR19 6NY — MB ChB 1974 Manch.

SPROSTON, Antony Raymond Mark Flat 4 Rosewood Gardens, Hart Avenue, Sale, Manchester M33 2JS Tel: 0161 976 1609 — MB ChB 1985 Manch.; MRCOG 1991. Clin. Research Fell. (Experim. Radiat. Oncol.) Paterson Inst. Cancer Research Christie Hosp. Manch. Prev: SHO (O & G) Wythenshawe Hosp. Manch.; Regist. (O & G) Arrow Pk. Hosp. & Wom. Hosp. Liverp.

SPROTT, Margaret Mary 21 Dart Road, North Brickhill, Bedford MK41 7BT — MB BS 1983 Lond.

SPROTT, Veronica Mary Alexandra 24 Andover Road, Southsea PO4 9QG Email: vmasprott@aol.com — MB BS 1983 Lond.; BSc 1980 Lond.; MRCP (UK) 1986; MRCGP 1989. (Charing Cross Hospital London) GP Asst. Prev: GP Soton; Regist. (Med.) Gen. Hosp. Soton. HA; Regist. (Med.) Qu. Alexandra's Hosp. Portsmouth.

SPROULE, Brian James (retired) Ladiesfield, 3 Kelso Road, Coldstream TD12 4LG Tel: 01890 882271 — MB ChB 1947 Ed.; FRCGP 1979, M 1965. Prev: Ho. Phys. Roy. Infirm. Edin.

SPROULE, Michael William Flat 1/R, 28 Gray Street, Kelvingrove, Glasgow G3 7TY Tel: 0141 334 5770 — MB ChB 1988 Ed.; MRCP (UK) 1992; FRCR 1996. (Ed.) Sen. Regist. (Radiol.) Glas. Roy. Infirm. Socs: RCP Edin.; BMA; Roy. Coll. Radiol. Prev: Career Regist. (Radiol.) Glas. Roy. Infirm.; SHO (Gen. Med.) Roy. Shrewsbury Hosp.

SPROULE, William Bradley (retired) 23 Antrim Road, Lisburn BT28 3ED Tel: 028 9266 2080 Fax: 028 9266 2080 — BA Dub. 1964, MD 1975, MB BCh BAO 1964; FRCOG 1982, M 1969. Prev: Ho. Off. Dr. Steevens' Hosp. Dub.

SPRUCE, Barbara Ann Department of Anatomy & Physiology, The University, Dundee DD1 4HN — MB BS 1979 Newc.; PhD Lond. 1990; MRCP (UK) 1981. Wellcome Sen. Research Fell. (Clin. Sci.) Univ. Dundee.

SPRUELL, David Andrew Forest End Surgery, Forest End, Waterlooville PO7 7AH; 10 The Fairway, Rowlands Castle PO9 6AQ Tel: 01705 413279 — MB ChB 1977 Dundee; MRCGP 1981; DRCOG 1979.

SPRUELL, Richard Iain Binscombe Medical Centre, 106 Binscombe Lane, Godalming GU7 3PR Tel: 01483 415115 Fax: 01483 414925 — MB ChB 1975 Dundee.

SPRUNT, Deirdre Catriona Caoirtiona 17 Claremont Drive, Bridge of Allan, Stirling FK9 4EE Tel: 01786 833607 — MB ChB 1957 Aberd. (Aberd.) Assoc. Specialist Histopath. Forth Valley Health Bd. Prev: SHO Aberd. Roy. Infirm.; Med. Off. Glas. Blood Transfus. Serv.; Ho. Off. (Med. & Orthop.) Bridge of Earn Hosp. Perth.

SPRUNT, Elizabeth Mary 100 Randolph Road, Glasgow G11 7EE — MB ChB 1955 Aberd. (Aberd.) Assoc. Specialist E. Scott. Blood Transfus. Serv. Prev: Trainee Gen. Pract. Dundee & Perth Vocational Train. Scheme; Med. Off. Health Dept. City Dundee; SHO (Anaesth.) Dundee Gen. Hosp.

SPRUNT, John William Ellis Otaki Medical Centre, 2 Aotaki St., Otaki, New Zealand Tel: 00 64 6364 8555; c/o 418 Crow Road, Glasgow G11 7EA Tel: 0141 357 1637 — MB ChB 1983 Dundee; MRCGP 1989; Dip. Sports Med. Lond 1996. Socs: Brit. Assn. Sport & Med.; NZ Federat. of Sports Med. Prev: Clin. Asst. (Accid. & Emerg.) S. Tyneside Dist. Gen. Hosp.; Asst. GP. St. Anthony's Med. Centre Newc. u. Tyne.

SPRUNT, Mr Thomas Glassford (retired) 17 Claremont Drive, Bridge of Allan, Stirling FK9 4EE — MB ChB 1951 St. And.; FRCS Ed. 1959. Cons. Orthop. Surg. Stirling & Falkirk Roy. Infirm. Prev: Sen. Regist. (Orthop. Surg.) Aberd. Roy. Infirm.

SPRUYT, Odette Wilhelmina 5 Bishopswood's Almshouse, Lower Clapton Road, London E5 6QH — MB ChB 1981 Otago.

SPRY, Professor Christopher John Farley (retired) Department of Cellular & Molecular Sciences, St. George's Hospital Medical School, Cranmer Terrace, London SW17 0RE Tel: 020 8725 5819 Fax: 020 8725 5821 Email: cspry@cspry.co.uk — MB BChir Camb. 1965; DPhil Oxf. 1971; MA Camb. 1965; FRCP Lond. 1984, M 1967; FRCPath. 1985, M 1980. Prof. Cardiovasc. Immunol. Univ. Lond.; Hon. Cons. (Med.) St. Geo. Hosp. Med. Sch. Lond. Prev: Sen. Lect. (Immunol.) & Hon. Cons. Med. Roy. Postgrad. Med. Sch. Lond.

SPURGIN, Hilary Margaret Kirkhouse Rozel, Round St., Cobham, Gravesend DA13 9BA — MB BS 1949 Lond.; MRCS Eng. LRCP Lond. 1949. (Univ. Coll. Hosp.)

SPURLING, Basil Martin Elm Hayes Surgery, High Street, Paulton, Bristol BS39 7QJ Tel: 01761 413155 Fax: 01761 410573; Meadgate House, Camerton, Bath BA2 0NL Tel: 01761 470496 — MRCS Eng. LRCP Lond. 1971.

SPURLING, Susan Gisela Meadgate House, Meadgate West, Camerton, Bath BA3 1NL Tel: 01761 70496 — MB BS 1971 Lond.

SPURLOCK, Christina Jane Banks Street Surgery, 7 Banks Street, Willenhall WV13 1SP Tel: 01902 8624 Fax: 01902 602280 — MRCS Eng. LRCP Lond. 1969.

SPURR, David Westgarth, 56 Albert Road W., Heaton, Bolton BL1 5HG — BM BCh 1969 Oxf.; FRCP Lond. 1990; MRCP (UK) 1973. Cons. Phys. Bolton Gen. Hosp.

SPURR, James Irving Stanhope Health Centre, Dale St., Stanhope, Bishop Auckland DL13 2XD Tel: 01388 528555 Fax: 01388 526122 — MB BS 1964 Newc.

SPURR, Jennifer June (retired) 1 Mayfield Road, Bickley, Bromley BR1 2HB Tel: 020 8467 9358 — MB BS Lond. 1957; MRCS Eng. LRCP Lond. 1957. Assoc. Specialist in Rheum. Tunbridge Wells NHS Trust. Prev: Med. Asst. (Physical Med. & Rheum.) Sevenoaks & Orpington Hosps.

SPURR, Michael Jeremy Towson and Partners, Juniper Road, Boreham, Chelmsford CM3 3DX Tel: 01245 467364 Fax: 01245 465584; Boreham Manor, Church Road, Boreham, Chelmsford CM3 3EJ Tel: 01245 464195 Email: spurr.family@lineone.net — MB BS 1981 Lond.; LMSSA Lond. 1980; DRCOG 1984; Dip. Occ. Med. 1998. (St. Thos. Hosp. Med. Sch. Lond.) GP; Occupat. Health Phys. Chelmsford. Prev: Princip. Dist. Med. Off. Mulanje Dist. Hosp. Malawi, Afr.

SPURRELL, John Richard Roworth 334 Dyke Road, Brighton BN1 5BB Tel: 01273 507049 — BM BCh 1959 Oxf.; MA, BM BCh Oxf. 1959; FRCP Lond. 1979, M 1963. (Guy's) Cons. Phys. Brighton & Lewes & Mid Sussex Hosp. Gps.

SPURRELL, Mark Thomas 46 Westwood Avenue, Timperley, Altrincham WA15 6QF — MB ChB 1983 Manch.

SPURRELL, Philip Anthony Roworth 334 Dyke Road, Brighton BN1 5BB — MB BS 1993 Lond.

SPURRELL, Roworth Adrian John Suite 501, 50 Wimpole St., London W1M 7DG Tel: 020 7935 3922 Fax: 020 7935 1637 — MRCS Eng. LRCP Lond. 1960; BSc (Physiol.) Lond. 1962, MD 1974, MB BS 1966; FRCP Lond. 1979, M 1969; FACC 1975. Sen. Cons. Cardiac Dept. St. Bart. Hosp. Lond. Socs: Brit. Cardiac Soc. Prev: Sen. Regist. (Cardiol.) Guy's Hosp. Lond.; Regist. (Cardiol.) St. Geo. Hosp. & Nat. Heart Hosp. Lond.

SPURRIER, Peter David Maywood Surgery, 180 Hawthorn Road, Bognor Regis PO21 2UY Tel: 01243 829141 Fax: 01243 842115; 6 A'Beckets Avenue, Aldwick Bay, Bognor Regis PO21 4UL Tel: 01243 265292 Fax: 01243 842115 Email: docspur@aol.com — BM 1980 Soton.; MRCGP 1986; DRCOG 1984.

SPURRING, Richard Drew Lyndon (retired) Garth, Beech Way, Selsdon, South Croydon CR2 8QR Tel: 020 8657 2273 — MB BS 1957 Lond.

SPYCHAL, Mr Robert Thomas 249 Spies Lane, Halesowen B62 9SN — MB BS 1982 Newc.; MD Newc. 1991; FRCS Ed. 1986. Cons. Gen. Surg. City Hosp. Birm.

SPYER, Ghislaine Department of Diabetes & Vascular Health, Royal Devon & Exeter Hospital, Barrack Road, Exeter EX2 5DW Tel: 01392 402281; 59 Long Fallow, Chiswell Green, St Albans AL2 3ED Tel: 01727 867150 — MB BS 1993 Lond.; BSc (Med. Biochem.) Birm. 1988; MRCP (UK) 1997. (Char. Cross. & Westm.) Specialist Regist. Diabetes & Endocrin. Roy. Devon & Exeter Hosp.

SPYRANTIS, Niki 1 Podsmead Road, Manchester M22 1UZ — State Exam Med 1992 Berlin.

SPYRIOUNIS, Petros Northern General Hospital, Plastic Surgery Department, Herries Road, Sheffield S5 7AU — Ptychio Iatrikes 1988 Thessalonika.

SPYROU, Mr George 169D Stourbridge Road, Lye, Stourbridge DY9 7BD Tel: 01384 894034 — Ptychio Iatrikes 1988 Thessalonika; FRCS Ed. 1996. (Aristotelian Univ. Thessaloniki) SHO (Plastic Surg.) Wordsley Hosp. W. Midl. Prev: SHO Rotat. (Gen. Surg.) Roy. Devon & Exeter Hosp.

SPYROU, Nicolaos Department of Clinical Cardiology, Waller Cardiothoracic Centre, St Mary's Hospital, Praed Street, Paddington, London W2 1NY Tel: 020 7886 1250 Fax: 020 7886 1736; 44 Burntwood Grange Road, London SW18 3JX — MB BS 1986 Lond.; BSc Lond. 1983, MB BS 1986; MRCP (UK) 1990. Sen. Regist. (Cardiol.) St Mary's Hosp. Socs: BCS; BICS. Prev: Regist. (Cardiol. & Gen. Med.) St. Mary's Hosp. Lond. & Hemel HempstedHostp.; Regist. (Gen. Med. & Gastroenterol.) Luton & Dunstable Gen. Hosp.

SQUIER, Marian Valerie Department of Neuropathology, Radcliffe Infirmary, Oxford OX2 6HE Tel: 01865 224932 Fax: 01865 224508 Email: waney.squier@clneuro.ox.ac.uk — MB ChB 1972 Leeds; BSc Leeds 1969; MRCP (UK) 1974; FRCPath 1993, M 1981. Cons. & Clin. Lect. (Neuropath.) Radcliffe Infirm. Oxf. Socs: Brit. Neuropath. Soc.; French Neuropath. Soc.; Brit. Paediat. Neurol. Assn. Prev: Sen. Regist. (Neuropath.) Inst. Psychiat. Lond.; Lect. (Histopath.) Inst. Child Health Lond.

SQUIRE, Alison Mary 16 Grosvenor Gardens, London SW14 8BY — BSc (Psych.) ChB Bristol 1973, MB ChB 1983; MRCGP 1990; DRCOG 1990; DCH RCP Lond. 1988. Prev: SHO (Paediat.) Freedom Fields Hosp. Plymouth.

SQUIRE, Andrea Jane 5 Middle Road, Berkhamsted HP4 3EQ — MB ChB 1992 Sheff.

SQUIRE, Mr Benjamin Roly Department of Paediatric Surgery, St. James University Hospital, Leeds LS9 7TF Tel: 0113 243 3144 Fax: 0113 283 7059; Scott Hill House, 72 Main St, Thorner, Leeds LS14 3BU Tel: 0113 289 2537 — MB BS 1977 Lond.; FRCS (Paediat.) 1992; FRCS Eng. 1982; MRCS Eng. LRCP Lond. 1977; DCH Eng. 1981. (St. Mary's) Cons. Paediat. Surg. St. Jas. Univ. Hosp. Leeds & Leeds Gen. Infirm.; Hon. Sen. Lect. Univ. Leeds. Prev: Sen. Regist. (Paediat Surg.) Hosp. for Sick Childr. Gt. Ormond St. Lond.; Regist. (Surg.) Roy. Manch. Childr. Hosp.; Research Fell. (Paediat Surg.) Childr. Hosp. Buffalo, USA.

SQUIRE, Christopher Michael Squire and Partners, Market Place, Hadleigh, Ipswich IP7 5DN Tel: 01473 822961 Fax: 01473 824895; Langdale, The St, Aldham, Ipswich IP7 6NH Tel: 01473 823026 — MRCS Eng. LRCP Lond. 1968; LMSSA Lond. 1967; DCH Eng. 1972. (St. Mary's) Prev: Clin. Asst. (Paediat.) St. Geo. Hosp. Lond.; Squadron Ldr. RAF Med. Br.; SHO (O & G) Ipswich Hosp.

SQUIRE, Iain Department of Medicine & Therapeutics, Clinical Sciences Building, Leicester Royal Infimary, Leicester LE2 7LX Tel: 0116 252 3125 Fax: 0116 252 3108 Email: is11@le.ac.uk — MB ChB 1987 Glas.; BSc Strathclyde 1982; MRCP (UK) 1990; MD Glasgow 1997. Sen. Lect. in Med. & Therap., Univ. of Leicester; Hon. Cons. Phys., Leicester Roy. Infirm. Socs: Brit. Pharmacological Soc.; Brit. Soc. for Heart Failure. Prev: Lect. in Clin. Pharmacol., Univ. of Leicester; Lect. in Med. & Therap., Univ. of Glas.; Clin. Research Fell. Univ. of Glas.

SQUIRE, Janet Katherine Sue Ryder Care Centre, Thorpe Hall, 6 Longthorpe, Peterborough PE3 6LW Tel: 01733 330060 Fax: 01733 269078; Rushton Manor, Rushton, Kettering NN14 1RH Tel: 01536 711451 — MB BS 1971 Lond.; Dip. Palliat. Med. Wales 1995; DObst RCOG 1973. (Middlx.) Med. Dir., Sue Ryder Care Centre, Thorpe Hall, PeterBoro.; Hon. Cons. Palliat. Med. P'boro Hosps. Trust. Prev: Clin. Asst. (Palliat. Med.) Cynthia Spencer Hse. Manfield Hosp. N.ants.

SQUIRE, John Walter (retired) Squirrels, Cagefoot Lane, Henfield BN5 9HD Tel: 01273 492254 Email: johnsquire@doctorsorg.uk — MRCS Eng. LRCP Lond. 1942; FRCGP 1969; DObst RCOG 1949. Prev: Hon. Antenatal Off. Sussex Matern. Hosp. Brighton.

SQUIRE, June Mary (retired) Rose Cottage, Church Oakley, Basingstoke RG23 7LJ Tel: 01256 780225 — MB BS 1959 Lond.; MRCS Eng. LRCP Lond. 1959; FFA RCS Eng. 1966. Cons. Anaesth. Basingstoke & Dist. Hosp. & Lord Mayor Treloar's Hosp. Alton. Prev: Sen. Regist. (Anaesth.) St. Geo. Hosp. Lond.

SQUIRE, Philip Legh Brinsmead St James Medical Centre, St. James Street, Taunton TA20 1DB Tel: 01823 285400 Fax: 01823 285404; Oakdene, 3 Mountfields Park, Taunton TA1 3BH — MB BS 1977 Lond.; MRCGP 1982. (The Royal London) GP Taunton; Clin. Governance Lead & Bd. Mem., Taunton & Area PCG. Prev: Med. Off King's Coll & King's Hall, Taunton & Som. CCC.

SQUIRE, Stephen Bertel Liverpool School of Tropical Medicine, Pembroke Place, Liverpool L3 5QA Tel: 0151 708 9393 Fax: 0151 708 8733; Salisbury House, 18 Nicholas Road, Blundellsands, Liverpool L23 6TU Tel: 0151 932 0819 Fax: 0151 932 0936 — MB BChir 1984 Camb.; BSc Lond. 1982; MD Camb. 1995; MRCP (UK) 1988. Wellcome Trust Fell. (Virol.) Roy. Free Hosp. Lond. Prev: Clin. Research Fell. (HIV/AIDS) Dept. Thoracic Med. & Virol. Roy. FreeHosp. Lond.; Regist. (Gen. Med.) OldCh. Hosp. Romford.

SQUIRES, Mr Benjamin 15 Fremantle Road, Cotham, Bristol BS6 5SY Tel: 0117 946 6188 — MB BS 1990 Lond.; FRCS 2000 (Tr. & Orth.); FRCS Eng. 1995. Bristol Specialist Regist. Orthop. Rotat. Prev: SHO Rotat. (Surg.) Bristol Roy. Infirm.; Ho. Phys. Kent & Canterbury Hosp.; Demonst. (Anat.) Sheff. Univ.

SQUIRES

SQUIRES, Hildegard Gertrud Eugenie 95 Middle Drive, Darras Hall, Newcastle upon Tyne NE20 9DW Tel: 01661 24554 — MD 1952 Berlin; State Exam Med 1950.

SQUIRES, Julian Patrick Teign Estuary Medical Group, Glendevon Medical Centre, Carlton Place, Teignmouth TQ14 8AB Tel: 01626 770955 Fax: 01626 772107; Riverside Surgery, Albion St, Shaldon, Teignmouth TQ14 0D Tel: 01626 873331 — MB BCh 1986 Wales; LLM 2000 Wales; MRCGP 1990; DRCOG 1990. (Univ. Wales Coll. Med.) Clin. Asst. (Med.) S. Devon Healthcare; Mem. S. & W. Devon LMC. Prev: Trainee GP Torbay VTS; SHO (O & G & Paediat.) Torbay HA; SHO (Clin. Oncol.) Exeter HA.

SQUIRES, Michael Jackson 30 Grove Road, Eastbourne BN21 4TR Tel: 01323 720140 — MB BS 1946 Lond.; MRCS Eng. LRCP Lond. 1946; DOMS Eng. 1949. (King's Coll. Lond. & St. Geo.) Assoc. Specialist (Ophth.) E. Sussex. Socs: BMA; Medico-Legal Soc. Prev: Sen. Med. Off. W.. Ophth. Hosp.; Designated Aviat. Med. Examr. Govt. Austral.; Ophth. Adviser Unilever.

SQUIRES, Neil Frederick Department for International Development, 1 Palace Street, London SW1E 5HE Tel: 0207 0230405 Email: n-squires@dfid.gov.uk; 62 Stanford Avenue, Brighton BN1 6FD — MB ChB 1986 Sheff.; MFPHM Lond. 1995; MPH Liverp. 1993. Sen. Health & Popul. Advisor, Dept. for Int. Devel. Prev: Specialist (Pub. Health) Dept. for Internat. Developm. Lond.; Cons. (Pub. Health) Liverp. Health Auth.

SQUIRES, Richard Charles (retired) Old Church House, Priory Road, Wantage Tel: 012357 2785 — MRCS Eng. LRCP Lond. 1962. Prev: Ho. Surg. S.lands Hosp. Shoreham-by-Sea.

SQUIRES, Stephen John, Surg. Cdr. RN Retd. Queen Victoria Hospital, East Grinstead RH19 3DZ Tel: 01342 410210 Fax: 01342 323420; Woodlands, Cansiron Lane, Ashurst Wood, East Grinstead RH19 3SE Tel: 01342 822901 — MB BS 1979 Lond.; FFA RCS Eng. 1984. (St. Geo.) Med. Dir. Qu. Vict. Hosp. E. Grinstead. Socs: Assn. Anaesth.; Brit. Burns Assn.; Soc. Naval Anaesth. Prev: Cons. Anaesth. Burns Unit Qu. Vict. Hosp. E. Grinstead; Cons. Anaesth. RN Hosps. Haslar, Plymouth & Gibraltar; Sen. Regist. (Anaesth.) Bristol Roy. Infirm.

SQUIRRELL, Christopher Andrew 11 Revenscourt Road, Mackworth, Derby DE22 4DL — MB BS 1996 Lond.

SQUIRRELL, David Michael 6 Ryegate Road, Sheffield S10 5FA — MB ChB 1995 Sheff.

SRAM, Iqbail Singh 128 Boundary Lane, Manchester M15 6FW — MB ChB 1981 Manch.

SREEDARAN, Elayathamby 5 Denvale Walk, Goldsworth Park, Woking GU21 3PF — MB BS 1985 Peradeniya, Sri Lanka.

SREEDHARAN, Kamprath Brunswick Health Centre, Hartfield Close, Manchester M13 9YA Tel: 0161 273 4901 Fax: 0161 273 5952; 6 Green Pastures, Stockport SK4 3RA — MB BS 1971 Kerala.

SREEHARAN, Nadarajah New Frontiers Science Park, Third Avenue, Harlow CM19 5AW Tel: 01279 644048 Fax: 01279 646446 — MB BS 1970 Ceylon; PhD Leeds 1979; MD Colombo 1974; FRCP Lond. 1986; FRCP Ed. 1986; FRCP Glas. 1985; MRCP (UK) 1976; FACP 1994. Dir. & Vice Pres. Clin. Research & Developm. & Med. Affairs. SmithKline Beecham Research & Developm. Prev: Prof. & Head of Dept. Med. Univ. Jaffna Sri Lanka; Cons. Phys. Univ. Hosp. Jaffna; Vis. Prof. Cardiol. Univ. Alberta, Canada.

SREEHARI RAO, Singu Amington Surgery, 130 Tamowrth Road, Amington, Tamworth B77 3BZ Tel: 01827 54777 Fax: 01827 59539; Wigginton Grange, 163 Gillway Lane, Tamworth B79 8PN — MB BS 1971 Andhra; FFA RCSI 1981; DA RCSI 1974; DObst RCPI 1979.

SREEKANTA, Gopalarao Edward Street Day Hospital, Edward St., West Bromwich B70 8NJ Tel: 0121 553 7676 Fax: 0121 607 3576; 11 Holly Wood, off White Crest, Great Barr, Birmingham B43 6EH Tel: 0121 357 2703 — MB BS 1971 Bangalor; Dip. Clin. Psychiat. RCP&S of Ire. 1997; MB BS Bangalore 1971. (Govt. Med. Coll. Bangalore, Karnataka, India) Clin. Asst. (Pychogeriats.) Edwd. St. Day Hosp. W. Bromwich. Socs: Med. Protec. Soc. Prev: Regist. (Psychiat.) Pastures Hosp. Mickleover, Derby & St. Geo. Hosp. Stafford; SHO Carlton Hayes Hosp. Leicester.

SREENIVASA RAO, Lt. Col. Pavar Madhavarao, Lt.-Col. RAMC Consultant Advisor HIV & GU Medicine, Defence Medical Service, Frimley Park Hospital, Camberley GU16 5UJ Tel: 01276 604069 Fax: 01276 604297 Email: sreenivasarao@talk121.com; 2 Silverdale Drive, London SE9 4DH Tel: 020 8851 2259 Fax: 020 8697 2920 Email: spavar@yahoo.com — MB BS 1971 Madras; MD Madras 1980; MRCOG 1979; Dip. Ven. Liverp. 1983. (Jipmer, India) Cons. Adviser (HIV & Genitourin. Med.) Defence Med. Serv. Frimley Pk. Hosp. Surrey. Socs: BMA, Soc. Study of VD., AGUM, BHIVA. Prev: Sen. Regist. (Genitourin. Med.) Roy. Liverp. Hosp.; Regist. (Genitourin. Med.) Chester & Arrowe Pk. Hosps.; Regist. (O & G) Walton & Fazakerley Hosp. Liverp. & Lister Hosp. Stevenage.

SREERAM, Narayanswami 98 Park Hill, Moseley, Birmingham B13 8DS — MB BS 1982 Madras; MRCP (UK) 1986.

SREETHARAN, Maharojani St Ebba's Hospital, Hook Road, Epsom KT19 8QJ Tel: 01372 22212; 1 Balmoral Gardens, South Croydon CR2 0HN — MB BS 1971 Ceylon; DPM Eng. 1980. (Colombo) Clin. Asst. Epsom.

SREETHARAN, Mathiaparanam Parkway Health Centre, Parkway, New Addington, Croydon CR0 0JA; Mathura, 1 Lupin Close, Shirley Oaks Village, Croydon CR0 8XZ — MB BS 1971 Ceylon. (Colombo)

SREEVALSAN, samtha K Oakwood Surgery, 380 Bishops Drive, Oakwood, Derby DE21 2DF Tel: 01332 281220 Fax: 01332 677150; 19 Gleneagles Close, Mickleover, Derby DE3 5YB Tel: 01332 513273 — MB BS 1966 Kerala. Socs: Med. Protec. Soc.

SREEVALSAN, Mrs Santha Kumari Oakwood Surgery, 380 Bishops Drive, Oakwood, Derby DE21 2DF Tel: 01332 281220 Fax: 01332 677150 Email: santhasreevalsan@hotmail.com — MB BS 1966 Kerala; MRCOG 1978 London. Socs: Med. Protec.-Full; Gen. Med. Counc.; Roy. Coll. of Obst. & Gynaecologists.

SRI GANESHAN, Moothathamby 107B Grand Drive, London SW20 9EB Tel: 020 8542 1369; 26 Marlings Park Avenue, Chislehurst BR7 6QW Tel: 01689 824780 Fax: 01689 813748 — MB BS 1973 Ceylon; MRCOG 1987. GP Shewsbury Rd., Health Centre Lond. Socs: Roy. Coll. Obst. & Gyns. Prev: Regist. (Obst. & Gyna.) Barking Hosp.

SRI KRISHNA, Mudumbi The Surgery, 76 Herbert Road, London SE18 3PP Tel: 020 8854 3964 Fax: 020 8317 8512 — MB BS 1961 Osmania.

SRI KRISHNA, Rama The Surgery, 76 Herbert Road, London SE18 3PP Tel: 020 8854 3964 Fax: 020 8317 8512 — MB BS 1961 Osmania; MB BS 1961 Osmania.

SRIDHAR, Janga Department of Anaesthesia, Tameside General Hospital, Fountain St., Ashton-under-Lyne OL6 9RW — MB BS 1977 Sri Venkateswara; FFA RCSI 1986.

SRIDHAR, Mangalam Kumaraswasmy Tel: 020 8846 7174, 020 8846 7182 Fax: 020 8846 7170 Email: Msridhar@hhnt.nhs.uk; Email: mangalam.sridhar@btinternet.com — MB BS 1986 Madras; FRCP (USA) 1999; FRCP 2000 Lond.; FCCP 1999 USA; FRCP Ed 1999; PhD Glas. 1996; MRCP (UK) 1989. Cons. Phys. Hammersmith Hosps. NHS Trust, Lond.; Hon. Sen. Lect., NHLI Div., Fac. of Med. Imperial Coll. of Sci., Technol. of Med. Socs: Brit. Thorac. Soc. Prev: Research Fell. (Med. & Human Nutrit.) Univ. Glas.; Regist. (Respirat. Med.) Glas. Roy. Infirm.; Cons. Phys., Mid-Staffs. NHS Trust.

SRIDHAR, Subbaramiah 9 Stirling Drive, Gourock PA19 1AH — MB BS 1979 Mysore; MRCP (UK) 1987.

SRIDHARAN, Mr Damodaraswamy Ramakrishnan 24 Brockspark Wood, Brentwood CM13 2TH — MB BS 1977 Madras; FRCS Glas. 1991; FCOphth 1991.

SRIDHARAN, Ganapathyagraharam Venkatanarayana 4 Peaslake Close, Romiley, Stockport SK6 4JX — MB BS 1975 Madras; MRCPI 1983.

SRIKANTHARAJAH, Indradevi 52 Regal Way, Harrow HA3 0RY — LRCP LRCS 1982 Ed.; LRCP LRCS Ed. LRCPS Glas. 1982.

SRINIVAS, Kandadai Gopalaswamy (Surgery), 32 Sunbury St., Woolwich, London SE18 5LY Tel: 020 8854 0157 — MB BS 1964 Osmania.

SRINIVAS, Ranjit Kandadai 6 Warwick Close, Bexley DA5 3NL — MB ChB 1986 Manch.

SRINIVAS, Mr Subrahmanyam Accident & Emergency Department, Kent & Canterbury Hospital, Ethelbert Road, Canterbury CT1 2NG — MB BS 1986 Madras; FRCS Glas. 1993.

SRINIVASA, Kanabur Flat 5, Beech Holme Court, 143 Lichfield Road, Sutton Coldfield B74 2RY — MB BS 1971 Bangalor; MB BS Bangalore 1971.

SRINIVASA MURTHY, Mr Lakkur Nagappa 184 Osborne Road, Newcastle upon Tyne NE2 3LE — MB BS 1965 Mysore; FRCR

SRIVASTAVA

1983; FRCS Eng. 1970; DMRD Eng. 1982. (Bangalore Med. Coll.) Cons. Radiol. Freeman Hosp. Newc. u. Tyne. Prev: Surg. Hosp. Dr. Baski Gonbad-e-Qabus Iran; Surg. Shanthi Surg. Nurs. Home Bangalore, India; Regist. & Sen. Regist. Univ. Dept. Radiol. Newc. u. Tyne.

SRINIVASAN, Arul Malar Broomfield Hospital, Coourt Road, Chelmsford CM1 7ET Tel: 01245 515231 Fax: 01245 515207 — MB BS 1977 Madras; LMSSA Lond. 1986; MRCP (UK) 1990; DGM RCP Lond. 1989. Cons. (Rheum.), Broomfield Hosp., Chelmsford. Socs: Memb. Of The Brit. Soc. For Rheum.; Memb. Of The Brit. Med. Assn. Prev: Regist. (Gen. Med.) Stoke Mandeville Hosp. Aylesbury; Regist.Rheumatogy stoke Mandeville Hosp., Aylesbury; SHO (Geriat.) Wythenshawe Hosp. Manch.// Sen.Reg. RNOHT of HOMERTON.

SRINIVASAN, Janaki Siambar Wen, Llanfair Road, Abergele LL22 8DL — MB BS 1986 Madras.

SRINIVASAN, Mr Kuntrapaka 15 Dingle Road, Abergavenny NP7 7AR — MB BS 1981 Sri Venkateswara; FRCS Glas. 1994.

SRINIVASAN, Malini Newham General Hospital, Glen Road, Plaistow, London E13 8SL — MB BS 1968 Ceylon; DCH RCP Lond. 1982. (Colombo) Regist. (Paediat.) Newham Gen. Hosp. Lond. Prev: SHO (Paediat.) Harold Wood Hosp. Romford.

SRINIVASAN, Ramaiah Salisbury House, Lake St., Leighton Buzzard LU7 1RS Tel: 01525 373139; 12 Cooks Meadow, Cow Lane, Edlesborough, Dunstable LU6 2RP Tel: 01525 222284 Fax: 01525 853006 — MB BS 1972 Bangalor; MB BS Bangalore 1972; DCH Dub. 1977.

SRINIVASAN, Singanayagam c/o Mrs V. Sivoyothy, 156 Balfour Road, Ilford IG1 4JB — MB BS 1964 Ceylon. (Colombo) Socs: BMA.

SRINIVASAN, Sujatha The Surgery, 20 Southwick St., Southwick, Brighton BN42 4TE Tel: 01273 596077 — MB BS 1992 Lond.; DFFP 1996; DRCOG 1995; MRCGP 1997. GP Princip.

SRINIVASAN, Thottuvai Ramaiyer 2 Hall Drive, Burley in Wharfedale, Ilkley LS29 7LL — MB ChB 1971 Leeds; BSc (Hons.) (Biochem.) Leeds 1971, MB ChB Leeds 1974; FRCP Lond. 1992; MRCP (UK) 1978. Cons. Phys. Dept. Geriat. St. Jas. Univ. Hosp. Leeds.; Hon. Sen. Lect. (Med.) Since 1991.

SRINIVASAN, Mr Vaikuntam Glan Clwyd Hospital, Bodelwyddan, Rhyl LL18 5UJ Tel: 01745 583910 Fax: 01745 583143; Siamber Wen, Llanfair Road, Abergele LL22 8DL Tel: 01745 832071 Fax: 01745 832071 Email: mrvsrini@aol.com — MB BS 1979 Madurai; MS (Gen. Surg.) Madurai 1982; FRCS Ed. 1986; Dip. Urol. Lond 1988. Cons. Urol. Glan Clwyd Hosp. Bodelwyddan Rhyl. Socs: Brit. Assn. Urol. Surgs.; Welsh Urol. Soc.; Corres. Mem. Amer. Urol. Assn. Prev: Regist. (Urol.) Edith Cavell Hosp. P'boro.

SRINIVASAN, Mr Venkataramanan 205 Brasenose Avenue, Gorleston, Great Yarmouth NR31 7DX — MB BS 1986 Madras; FRCS Ed. 1994.

SRIPURAM, Sudhakara Gupta Broadway Surgery, 9 The Broadway, Whitehawk Road, Brighton BN2 5NF Tel: 01273 600888 Fax: 01273 605664; 16 Martyns Close, Ovingdean, Brighton BN2 7BU — MB BS 1975 Andhra; DO Bangalore 1978. GP.

SRIRAM, Sujata 2 Flemington Street, Glasgow G21 4TG Tel: 0141 558 9806 Fax: 0141 558 9806 — MB BS 1986 Bombay; MD Bombay 1989; MRCP (UK) 1995. (Grant Med. Coll., Bombay) Staff Grade Phys. Gartnavel Gen. Hosp. Glas. Socs: Roy. Coll. Phys. & Surgs. Glas.; Brit. Thorac. Soc.; BMA.

SRIRAMULU, Venkataramanappa Grimethorpe Surgery, Dorbren House, Cemetery Road, Grimethorpe, Barnsley S72 7JB Tel: 01226 716809 — MB BS 1974 Bangalore. (Bangalore) GP Grimethorne, Barnsley.

SRIRANGALINGAM, Sivaneshwary Medical Centre, Grosvenor Terrace, Trimdon Colliery, Trimdon Station TS29 6DH Tel: 01429 880284 Fax: 01429 881405; Medical Eye Centre, Willowfield House, Trimdon Station TS29 6DH Tel: 01429 880284 Fax: 01429 881405 — MB BS 1967 Ceylon; Dip. Ven. Liverp. 1982; DO Lond. 1973. (Colombo) Ophth. Med. Pract. Trimdon Station.

SRIRANGALINGAM, Thambiya Sivagurunathan Sellam (Surgery), Willowfield House, Trimdon Station TS29 6DU — MB BS 1966 Ceylon; MRCOG 1980; Dip. Venereol. Liverp. 1981. (Colombo)

***SRIRANGAM, Shalom Justus** Blackburn Royal Infirmary, Infirmary Rd, Blackburn BB2 3LR; 93 Cromwell Road, Stretford, Manchester M32 8QL — MB ChB 1997 Manch.

SRISKANDAN, Kumar Rookery Medical Centre, Rookery House, Newmarket CB8 8NW Tel: 01638 665711 Fax: 01638 561280; Durleigh, Falmouth Avenue, Newmarket CB8 0NB — MB BChir 1983 Camb.; MA, MB Camb. 1983, BChir 1982; MRCGP (Distinc.) 1989; DRCOG 1987; DCH RCP Lond. 1989. (Cambridge) Prev: Trainee GP Greenwich & Brook VTS.

SRISKANDAN, Shiranee Department of Infectious Diseases, Faculty of Medicine, Imperial College of Science, Technology and Medicine, Hammersmith Hospital, Du cane Road, London W12 0NN Tel: 020 8383 2065 Fax: 020 8383 3394 Email: s.sriskandan@ic.ac.uk — MB BChir 1988 Camb.; 2001 FRCP; MA Camb. 1985, MB BChir 1988; PhD (Lond.) 1997; MRCP (UK) 1991. Sen. Lect./Hon. Cons.Infec.dis.Fac. of Med., Imperial Coll., Hammersmith Hosp.. Lond. Prev: MRC Clinican Scientist (infect. Dis), ICSM.

SRITHARAN, Sathasivam Department of Anaesthetics, Maidstone Hospital, Hermitage Lane, Maidstone ME16 9NN Tel: 01622 729000 Fax: 01622 723061; Shree-Rangham, 203 Willington St, Maidstone ME15 8EE Tel: 0850 666543 — MB BS 1972 Sri Lanka; LMSSA Lond. 1985; FFA RCS Eng. 1985; DA Eng. 1980. Cons. Anaesth. Maidstone Hosp.

SRIVASTAVA, Anand Swarup 33 Keynell Covert, Kings Norton, Birmingham B30 3QT Tel: 0121 458 2619; Anand Villa, 99 Bells Lane, Kings Heath, Birmingham B14 5QJ Tel: 0121 458 5432 — MB BS 1958 Lucknow; DCP Baroda 1966. (King Geo. Med. Coll.) Socs: Med. Protec. Soc. Prev: Clin. Asst. (A & E) Selly Oak Hosp. Birm. & Corbett Hosp. Stourbridge; Regist. (Path.) Accid. Hosp. Birm.

SRIVASTAVA, Anil Kumar Brookside Surgery, Bridge Street, Troedyrhiw, Merthyr Tydfil CF48 4DT Tel: 01443 692647 Fax: 01443 693255; Madhushala, 11 Hill Top Crescent, The Common, Pontypridd CF37 4AD Tel: 01443 406232 Fax: 01443 693255 — MB BS 1966 Ranchi; BSc Ranchi 1966; Dip. Palliat. Med. Wales 1993; Dip. Therapeut. Wales 1997; Cert. Med. Law Glas. 1996; Mse (Paed) Glamorgan 1998. (Rajendra Med. Coll.) Clin. Asst. (Renal Med.) Merthyr Tydfil; GP CME Tutor Merthyr Tydfil; Clin. Asst. (Acc. & Emerg.) Llwnypia Hosp. Socs: MRSH; Fell. Roy. Soc. Trop. Med. & Hyg.; Fell. Internat. Coll. Angiol. Prev: Resid. St. John's Hosp. St. John Canada; SHO (Orthop.) St. David's Hosp. Cardiff; Regist. Velindre Hosp. WhitCh.

SRIVASTAVA, Anjuli Arnold Medical Centre, 204 St. Annes Road, Blackpool FY4 2EF Tel: 01253 346351 Fax: 01253 400244 — MB BS 1970 Allahabad; MRCOG 1978; FRCOG 1994. (Hoti Lal Nehru Med. Coll. Allahabad U.P India) GP Princip.

SRIVASTAVA, Arun Kumar The New Surgery, Health Centre, Adwick Road, Mexborough S64 0BY Tel: 01709 590707 Fax: 01709 571986; Melton Mill House, High Melton, Doncaster DN5 7TD Tel: 0170 988 3891 — MB BS Madras 1955. (Madras Medical College) Clin. Asst. Oak Cl. Disabled Childr. Hosp. Socs: BMA; ODA (Pres. Doncaster Div.); Fell. Roy. Soc. Med. Prev: Hosp. Pract. Fract. Clinic Doncaster Roy. Infirm.; Med. Asst. (A & E Dept.) Rotherham Hosp.; Regist. (Orthop. Surg.) Salisbury Hosp. Gp.

SRIVASTAVA, Emmanuel Devaprasad Dept. Medicine, Royal Gwent Hospital, Newport NP20 2UB — MD 1992 Lond.; MB BS 1984; MRCP (UK) 1987. Cons. Phys. Gen. Med. & Gastroenterol. Roy. Gwent Hosp. Newport. Prev: Sen. Regist. (Gen. Med. & Gastroenterol.) N.. RHA Newc. u. Tyne; Regist. (Gastroenterol.) Univ. Hosp. Wales Cardiff; Research Fell. Univ. Hosp. Rotterdam, Netherlands.

SRIVASTAVA, Geeta South Norwood Hill Surgery, 21B South Norwood Hill, London SE25 6AA Tel: 020 8653 0635 Fax: 020 8771 8013 — MB BS 1974 Lucknow.

SRIVASTAVA, Krishna Kumar The Smethwick Medical Centre, Regent Street, Smethwick, Warley B66 3BQ Tel: 0121 558 0105 Fax: 0121 555 7206 — MB BS 1967 Lucknow.

SRIVASTAVA, Madhu Shivam, 5 Dorcas Close, Thornhill, Nuneaton CV11 6XL Tel: 01203 372809 — MB BS 1976 Kanpur; FRCA 1997. Specialist Regist. (Anaesth.) Cov. Sch. Of Anaesth.

SRIVASTAVA, Prabodh Kumar North Park Health Centre, 290 Knowsley Road, Bootle L20 5DQ Tel: 0151 922 3841 Fax: 0151 933 7335; Ganano Que, Burbo Bank Road, Blundellsands, Liverpool L23 6TQ Tel: 0151 931 1980 Fax: 0151 933 7335 — MB BS 1971 Osmania. (Osmania Med. Coll. Hyderabad) Prev: SHO Birkenhead

SRIVASTAVA

Gen. Hosp., W. Suff. Hosp. Bury St. Edmunds & Norf. & Norwich Gen. Hosp.

SRIVASTAVA, Prakash Chandra Consultant Haematologist, Burton Hospitals, Burton-on-Trent DE14 3QH Tel: 01283 66333; 105 Field Lane, Burton-on-Trent DE13 0NJ — PhD Sheff. 1971; MD 1964; MB BS 1960; BSc Lucknow 1954. (King Geo. Med. Coll.) Cons. Haemat. W. Midl. RHA. Socs: Assn. Clin. Pathols. & Brit. Soc. Haemat.; Roy. Soc. Med.; BMA. Prev: Asst. Haemat. & Regist. N. Gen. Hosp. Sheff.

SRIVASTAVA, Mr Pramod Kumar c/o Drive R.C. Prasad, 8 Hilderthorpe, Nunthorpe, Middlesbrough TS7 0PT Tel: 01642 317825 — MB BS 1978 Banares Hindu India; FRCS 1990.

SRIVASTAVA, Prasima 63H Richmond Street, Aberdeen AB25 2TS Tel: 01224 643226; 178 Culduthel Road, Inverness IV2 4BH — MB ChB 1993 Aberd.; BSc (Med. Sci.) (Hons.) Aberd. 1991; MRCP (UK) 1997. SHO (Med.) Aberd. Roy. Infirm.; Research Fell. (Respirat. Med.) Dept. of Childhealth Med. Sch. Aberd. Roy. Trust Hosp. Prev: Ho. Off. (Surg.) Raigmore Hosp. Inverness; Ho. Off. (Med.) Aberd. Roy. Infirm.

SRIVASTAVA, Ravindra Nath (Surgery) 89 Fulham Palace Road, London W6 8JA Tel: 020 8748 3197; 116 Corringway, Hanger Hill, Ealing, London W5 3HA Tel: 020 8997 6438 — MB BS 1964 Lucknow; Cert. Family Plann. JCC 1976; DTCD Lucknow 1966. (G.S.V.M. Med. Coll. Kanpur) GP Hammersmith. Prev: SHO (Geriat. Med.) Bridgend Gen. Hosp.; SHO (Chest Dis.) Plaistow Hosp. Lond.; GP Trainee.

SRIVASTAVA, Satya Prakash 28 Earnshaw Way, Beaumont Park, Whitley Bay NE25 9UN Tel: 0191 253 3886 Fax: 0191 253 3886 — MB BS 1966 Lucknow; MSc Allahabad 1960; DMRD Eng. 1972; DMRE Lucknow 1967. (G.S.V.M. Med. Coll. Kanpur) Cons. Radiol. N.umbria Health Care NHS Trust, N. Shield. Socs: BMA & Roy. Coll. Radiols. Prev: Sen. Regist. Midl. Centre for Neurol. & Neurosurg. Smethwick; Sen. Regist. (Radiol.) & Regist. (Radiol.) Selly Oak Hosp. Birm.; Trainee Regist. (Radiol.) United Birm. Hosps.

SRIVASTAVA, Mr Shekhar Consultant Plastic Surgeon, George Eliot Hospital, College St., Nuneaton CV11 6XL Tel: 01203 865428 — MB BS 1973 Kanpur; MS Kanpur 1976; FRCS (Plast) 1996; FRCS Eng. 1981; FRCS Ed. 1981. Cons. Plastic Surg. Geo. Eliot Hosp. Nuneaton Warks. Socs: Assoc. Mem. Brit. Assn. Plastic Surgs.; Assoc. Mem. BSSH. Prev: Regist. (Plastic Surg.) Wordsley Hosp. Stourbridge.

SRIVASTAVA, Shobha (retired) South Tyneside District Hospital, Harton Lane, South Shields NE34 0PL Tel: 0191 454 8888 — MB BS Lucknow 1955; MS (Anaesth.) Bihar 1964; MD (Physiol.) Lucknow 1961; FFA RCS Eng. 1978; FFA RCSI 1977. Examr. Fac. Anaesth. RCS Irel. Prev: Cons. Anaesth. S. Tyneside Dist. Hosp. S. Shields.

SRIVASTAVA, Sunil Kumar Richmond Medical Centre, 15 Upper Accommodation Road, Leeds LS9 8RZ Tel: 0113 248 0948 Fax: 0113 240 9898; 6 Sandmoor Avenue, Leeds LS17 7DW — MB BS Kanpur 1970; DTM & H Liverp. 1976; DTCD Kanpur 1974. (GSVM Med. Coll. Kanpur) Socs: Assoc. Inst. Psychosexual Med. Lond; Soc. Occupat. Med.

SRIVASTAVA, Mr Suresh Prasad Arnold Medical Centre, 204 St. Annes Road, Blackpool FY4 2EF Tel: 01253 346351 Fax: 01253 400244; 18 Cotswold Road, Blackpool FY2 0UH Tel: 01253 55974 — MB BS 1963 Agra; MS Lucknow 1967; FRCS Ed. 1974. (S.N. Med. Coll. Agra)

SRIVATSA, Geeta 1 Mardale Road, Swinton, Manchester M27 0YJ — MB BS 1992 Lond.

SRIVATSA, Surath Sanjay 23 Oaklands Avenue, Romford RM1 4DB — MB BChir 1988 Camb.

SRIWARDHANA, Kamala Bandumathie ENT Department, Gwynedd District General Hospital, Penrhos Garnedd, Bangor Tel: 01248 370007; 11 Coed-y-Castell, Bangor LL57 1PH — MB BS 1967 Ceylon; FRCS Glas. 1983; DLO Eng. 1978. (Colombo) Assoc. Specialist (ENT Surg.) Gwynedd Dist. Gen. Hosp. Prev: Regist. (ENT) Gwynedd Gen. Hosp.; Regist. (ENT) Monkland Dist. Gen. Hosp.; SHO (ENT) Leicester Roy. Infirm.

SRODON, Mr Paul Damian 28 Tamworth Road, Coventry CV6 2EL Tel: 024 76 333253 — MB ChB 1988 Birm.; FRCS Eng. 1992; MD Birm. 1997. Specialist Regist. Roy. Lond. Hosp. and St. Bart. Hosp. Lond. Prev: Specialist Regist. UCL Hosps. Lond.; Lect. (Surg.) Med. Coll. of St. Bart. Hosp. Lond.

***SROUJI, Ibrahim Albert** Southampton General Hospital, Tremona Road, Southampton SO16 6YD — BM 1998 Soton.; BM Soton 1998.

ST. BLAIZE-MOLONY, Ronald Thomas (retired) The Oak House, Westham, Pevensey BN24 5LP Tel: 01323 769784 — MB BCh BAO 1952 NUI; LAH Dub. 1952; MRCPsych 1971; DPM Eng. 1959. Prev: Cons. Psychiat. St. Thos. Hosp. Lond.

ST. CLAIR, Mr David Malcolm Clinical Research Centre, Royal Cornhill Hospital, Aberdeen AB25 2ZH — BM BCh 1975 Oxf.; DM Oxf. 1994; FRCS Eng. 1978; MRCPsych 1984. Sen. Lect. (Med.) Univ. Aberd.

ST. GEORGE, David Philip Southampton University Hospitals NHS Trust, Southampton General Hospital, Tremona Road, Southampton SO16 6YD Tel: 023 8077 7222 — MB ChB 1974 Auckland; BSc (Human Biol.) Auckland 1971; MFPHM 1989; Dip. Epidemiol. & Health McGill 1977. (Auckland Sch. Med.) Director of Research and Clin. Effectiveness, Soton. Univ. Hosps. NHS Trust, Soton.; Sen. Lect. (Clin. Epidemiol.) Roy. Free & Univ. Coll. Med. Sch. Lond.; Cons. in Clin. Epidemiol., Roy. Free Hosp., Lond.; Cons., Pub. Health Med.; Director of Plann. and Developm. Prev: Cons. Pub. Health Med. Bloomsbury HA; Dir. Plann. & Developm. Camden & Islington FHSA; Sen. Regist. (Community Med.) NE Thames RHA.

ST. HILL, Charles Arthur (retired) 102 Druids Cross Road, Liverpool L18 3HN Tel: 0151 722 0640 — MB ChB 1939 Bristol; FRCPath 1963. Prev: Home Office Path. Liverp. Area.

ST. JOHN, Hanny Elizabeth Ward 36, Royal Infirmary of Edinburgh, 1 Lauriston Place, Edinburgh EH3 9YW; 11/2 Torpichen Street, Edinburgh EH3 8HX — MB ChB 1992 Ed.; BSc Ed. 1987; MRCOG 1997. (Edinburgh) Specialist Regist. (O & G) Roy. Infirm. Edin. Socs: BMA; MPS. Prev: SHO (O & G & Gen. Surg.) Roy. Infirm. Edin.; SHO (O & G & Gynae. Surg.) Roy. Infirm. Edin.

ST. JOHN, Janet Isabella (retired) 31 Upper Oldfield Park, Bath BA2 3JX Tel: 01225 334331 — MB ChB Ed. 1949.

ST. JOHN, Joan Mary 65 Wyverne Road, Chorlton-cum-Hardy, Manchester M21 0ZW — MB ChB 1982 Birm.; MRCGP 1987; DCH RCP Lond. 1989; DRCOG 1986.

ST. JOHN JONES, Lima Siljan Harpscot, Slaugham Lane, Warninglid, Haywards Heath RH17 5TH — MB BCh BAO 1969 Dub.; FFA RCS Eng. 1978. Cons. Anaesth. Crawley Horsham NHS Trust.

ST. JOHN SMITH, Paul Barnet Psychiatric Unit, Barnet General Hospital, Wellhouse Lane, Barnet EN5 3DJ Tel: 020 8216 4400 — BM BCh 1979 Oxf.; MA Oxf. 1980; MRCPsych 1990. Cons. (Psychiat.) Barnet Gen. Hosp. Lond. Socs: Roy. Coll. Psychiat. Prev: Clin. Research Phys. (Psychopharmacol.) Roche Products Ltd., Welwyn Gdn. City.

ST. JOHNSTON, Charles Fisher Pinhoe Surgery, Pinn Lane, Exeter EX1 3SY Tel: 01392 469666 Fax: 01392 464178 — MB BS 1965 Lond.; DA Eng. 1973. (Lond. Hosp.) Prev: Ho. Off. Lond. Hosp.

ST. JOSEPH, Anne Vivien Creffield Road Surgery, 19 Creffield Road, Colchester CO3 3HZ Tel: 01206 570371 Fax: 01206 369908; Mell Farm, Tollesbury, Maldon CM9 8SS — BM BCh 1983 Oxf.; MRCGP 1987; DRCOG 1986. GP Colchester.

ST. LEGER, Sarah Ann Brunswick House, 299 Glossop Road, Sheffield S10 2HL Tel: 0114 271 6890 — MB ChB 1989 Sheff. p/t Saff grade in Psychiat.

ST JOHN, Andrew Frank Robert Tel: 0116 277 1705; Fairlawn, Lutterworth Road, Dunton Bassett, Lutterworth LE17 5LF Tel: 0116 277 1705 — MB BS 1969 Lond.; MRCS Eng. LRCP Lond. 1969; DObst RCOG 1971. (St. Bart.) Prev: SHO (Anaesth. & O & G) Harold Wood Hosp. Essex.

ST JOHN, Hazel Margaret Ruth 52 Lodge Road, Walsall WS5 3LA — MB BS 1975 Lond.; MRCS Eng. LRCP Lond. 1975.

ST JOHN, Martyn David Farnham 5 Athelstane Grove, London E3 5JG — MB BS 1985 Lond.

ST JOHN, Michael Arthur Farnham 45-47 Ben Jonson Road, London E1 4SA Tel: 020 7790 1059; 79 Lyal Road, Bow, London E3 5QQ — MB BS 1976 Lond. (St. Bartholomews Hospital) Partner. Socs: MDU.

ST JOHN OF BLETSO, Lady Helen Jane 31 Hurlingham Gardens, London SW6 3PH Tel: 020 7610 9612 Fax: 020 7610 9613 Email: asj@enterprise.net — MB ChB 1988 Bristol. (University of Bristol) SHO (O & G) St Albans Herts.; SHO (A & E) St Bartholomews; SHO (Obst. & Gyn.) Hammersmith Lond. Socs: MRCOG; Dip Family Plann.

Prev: SHO (Genitourin. Med.) Kings Lond.; Research Regist. (Gyn.) Kings Coll.; GP Regist. Pimlico Lond.

ST ROSE, Alison Jean 106 Crown Lane, Horwich, Bolton BL6 7QN — MB ChB 1988 Dundee.

STABER, Manfred Anton 13 Clarence Drive, Glasgow G12 9QL — State Exam Med 1991 Munich.

STABILE, Mrs Isabel 3086 Waterford Drive, Tallahassee FL 32308, USA Tel: 00 1 904 8933601 Fax: 00 1 904 5746704; Flat 7, Rowan, 48-50 Muswell Road, London N10 2BY Tel: 020 8883 5087 — MRCS Eng. LRCP Lond. 1981; PhD Lond. 1988; MRCOG 1989. Research Scientist Center for Biomed. Research Florida State Univ., USA; Prof. & Dir. Program Environm. Health Educat. & Train. Univ. Florida Gainsville, Florida USA. Prev: Regist. & Research Fell. Acad. Unit Obst. & Gyn. Lond. Hosp.

STABLEFORD, John Samuel George Peter (retired) Millview, 5 Tickow Lane, Shepshed, Loughborough LE12 9LY Tel: 01509 503202 — MB BS 1954 Lond.; LMSSA Lond. 1949. Prev: Local Treasury Med. Off.

STABLEFORTH, Carol Frances 6 Arlington Park Mansions, Sutton Lane N., Chiswick, London W4 4HE; 17 Springfield Road, Wimbledon, London SW19 7AL Tel: 020 8879 3448 — MB ChB 1988 Bristol; FRCA 1995. Cons. Anaesth., Dept. Anaesthetics, Kingston Hosp., Galsworthy Rd. Kingston Upon Thames Surrey KT2 7QB.

STABLEFORTH, David Edward Birmingham Heartlands Hospital, Bordsley Green E., Birmingham B9 5ST Tel: 0121 424 2000 Fax: 0121 772 0292 Email: stabled@heartsol.wmids.nhs.uk; Tower House, Spencers Lane, Berkswell, Coventry CV7 7BZ Tel: 01676 533279 — MB BChir 1968 Camb.; MA Camb. 1968; FRCP (UK) 1983, M 1970. (St. Mary's & Camb.) Cons. Phys. (Gen. & Thoracic Med.) Heartlands Hosp. Birm.; Hon. Sen. Lect. Univ. Birm. Socs: Brit. Thorac. Soc. & Europ. Respirat. Soc.; Midl. Thoracic Soc. Prev: Sen. Regist. (Med.) Brompton Hosp. Lond.; Sen. Regist. (Med.) St. Jas. Hosp. Balham; Regist. (Med.) Univ. Coll. Hosp. Lond.

STABLEFORTH, Mr Paul Godwin The Paddocks, Pilgrims La, Chew stoke, Bristol BS40 8TZ — MB BS 1957 Lond.; FRCS Eng. 1965. (Middlx.) Cons. Traum. Orthop. Surg. United Bristol Hosps. Prev: Sen. Regist. Orthop. Serv. Edin.

STABLEFORTH, Penelope Jane Tower House, Spencers Lane, Berkswell, Coventry CV7 7BZ — MB BS 1968 Lond.; MB BS (Hnrs.) Lond. 1968; MRCPath 1977. (St. Mary's) Cons. Haemat. Sandwell Dist. Gen. Hosp. Prev: Sen. Regist. (Haemat.) E. Birm. Hosp.; Sen. Regist. (Haemat.) Roy. Free Hosp. Lond.

***STABLEFORTH, William David** The Tower House, Spencers Lane, Berkswell, Coventry CV7 7BZ — MB BCh 1997 Wales.

STABLER, Jacqueline Marcelle Hollies Medical Practice, Tamworth Health Centre, Upper Gungate, Tamworth B79 7EA Tel: 01827 68511 Fax: 01827 51163; Dryden House, 5 Comberford Road, Tamworth B79 8PB Tel: 01827 68382 — MB BS 1968 Newc.; DObst RCOG 1971. (Newc.) Med. Asst. Sir Robt. Peel Hosp. Tamworth. Prev: Ho. Phys. & Ho. Surg. Roy. Vict. Infirm. Newc.; SHO (Paediat.) Sunderland Childr. Hosp.; SHO (O & G) Dryburn Hosp. Durh.

STABLER, Robert John Department of Radiology, The Queen Elizabeth Hospital, Gayton Road, King's Lynn PE30 4ET Tel: 01533 613613 Fax: 01533 613838 Email: john.slater@klshosp.anlok.nhs.uk; The Red House, Church St, North Creake, Fakenham NR21 9AD — BM BCh 1963 Oxf.; BA Oxf. 1960; FRCR 1968; DMRD Eng. 1966. (Oxf.) Cons. Radiol. King's Lynn & Wisbech Hosps NHS Trust. Prev: Cons. Radiol. Gateshead HA; Cons. Radiol. & Sen. Regist. (Radiol.) Roy. Vict. Infirm. Newc.

STABLES, Alison Barbara Jane Lime Tree Surgery, 38 Cann Hall Road, Leytonstone, London E11 3HZ Tel: 020 8519 9914 Fax: 020 855 7109; 189 Twickenham Road, Leytonstone, London E11 4BQ Tel: 020 8556 7872 — MB BS 1980 Lond.; DRCOG 1984. (Lond. Hosp.) Prev: Princip GP Sixpenny Handley; Trainee GP W. Essex VTS.

***STABLES, Gareth** Ael y Mor, Llanfawr Road, Holyhead LL65 2PP — MB ChB 1998 Liverp.; MB ChB Liverp 1998.

STABLES, Philippa Rosemary Joan 40A St George's Drive, London SW1V 4BP — MB ChB 1988 Bristol.

STABLES, Rodney Hilton, TD Cardiothorac Centre, Thomas Drive, Liverpool L14 3PE Tel: 0151 293 2468 Email: r.stables@heart.org.uk — BM BCh 1985 Oxf.; MA Camb. 1985; MRCP (UK) 1989; DM Oxf. 2000. Cons. Cardiol., Roy. Liverp. Uni. Hosp. & Cardiothorac Centre, Liverp. Socs: Brit. Cardiac Soc. Prev: Regist. (Cardiol.) Roy. Brompton & John Radcliffe Oxf.; Sen. Regist. (Cardiol.) Roy. Brompton & Harefield NHS Trust.

STACEY, Andrew Robert Microbiology Department, Royal Berkshire Hospital, London Road, Reading RG1 5AN Tel: 0118 987 5111 — MB BS 1978 Lond.; MRCS Eng. LRCP Lond. 1978; FRCPath 1996, M 1984. (Char. Cross) Cons. (Microbiol.) Roy. Berks. Hosp. Reading. Prev: Sen. Regist. Microbiol. Dept. St. Mary's Hosp. Lond.; Regist. (Microbiol.) Char. Cross Hosp. Lond.

STACEY, Anne Geraldine Lower Addiscombe Road Surgery, 188 Lower Addiscombe Road, Croydon CR0 6AH — MB BS 1970 Lond.; DObst RCOG 1972. (Univ. Coll. Hosp.)

STACEY, Anthony Cedric Elvin General Medical Clinics, Tower Hill Medical Centre, 10 Lloyds Avenue, London EC3N 3AX Tel: 020 7709 7171 Fax: 020 7709 7799 — MB BS 1975 Lond.; MRCS Eng. LRCP Lond. 1975; MRCGP 1980; Dip. Occ. Med. 1997; DFFP 1996; DRCOG 1981; DAvMed. 1982; DCH Eng. 1979. (Roy. Free Hosp. Sch. Med.) Private GP. Socs: Roy. Aeronautical Soc. (Med. Gp.); Soc. Occup. Med. Prev: Regional Med. Off. Foreign & Commonw. Office, Warsaw, Poland; Regional Med. Off. New Delhi, India; Company Med. Off. Anglo-Amer. Corpn. Zambia.

STACEY, Anthony Nicholas Email: astacey@compuserve.com — MRCS Eng. LRCP Lond. 1981; MDCH 1998; DFFP 1995; DRCOG 1984. (Sheff.) Gen. Practitioner. Prev: Resid. Med. Off. St. Brendan's Hosp., Bermuda; Dist. Med. Off. Grenfell Regional Health Servs. Newfld., Canada; Trainee GP Torbay VTS.

STACEY, Bernard Stephan Frank 13 Sunset View, Barnet EN5 4LB Tel: 020 8449 7155 Fax: 020 8449 7155 Email: bsfstacey@msn.com — MB ChB 1990 Bristol; MRCP (UK) 1995. (Bristol) Specialist Regist. (Gastroenterol.) Roy. United Hosp. Bath. Socs: Brit. Soc. Gastroenterol. Prev: Regist. (Gastroenterol.) P.ss Mgt. Hosp. Swindon; Regist. (Gastroenterol.) Roy. Hosp. Haslar Gosport; Regist. (Gen. Med.) Frimley Pk. Hosp. & Camb. Milit. Hosp.

STACEY, Carolyn Mary Women and Young Peoples Services, St Leonards Primary Care Centre, Nuttall St, London N1 5LE — MB BS 1980 Lond.; MRCOG 1989. Cons. Community Gyn. - St Leonards Primary Care Centre and Homerton Hosp.

***STACEY, Cheika Sian** 71 St Cenydd Road, Caerphilly CF83 2TA — BM BS 1994 Nottm.

STACEY, David John Longlands, Westbourne Drive, Lancaster LA1 5EE Tel: 01524 34331 Fax: 01524 842556 — MB ChB 1981 Manch.; BSc (Hons.) St. And. 1977; MRCGP 1985; DCCH RCGP & FCM 1989; Cert. Family Plann. JCC 1987; DRCOG 1983. (St And. & Manch.) Cons. Community Paediat. Lancaster. Socs: Fell. Roy. Coll. Paediat. & Child Health; Roy. Coll. Gen. Pract. Prev: SCMO (Child Health) Lancaster.

STACEY, Rev. Helen Norman Greystones House, Avebury, Marlborough SN8 1RE Tel: 01672 539289 — MB ChB 1945 Ed.; PhD Ed. 1949. (Univ. Ed.) Socs: Physiol. Soc.; Brit. Pharmacol. Soc.; Fell.Roy. Soc. Med. Prev: Med. Off. HQ Med. Research Counc.; Reader (Physiol.) Middlx. Hosp. Med. Sch. Lond.; Lect. (Physiol.) Roy. Free Hosp. Sch. Med. Lond.

***STACEY, Jonathan Carey** 13 Holland Close, The Links, Rogerstone, Newport NP10 0AU — MB BCh 1996 Wales.

STACEY, Louise Tanworth Lane Surgery, 2 Tanworth Lane, Shirley, Solihull B90 4DR Tel: 0121 744 2025 Fax: 0121 733 6890 — BM BS 1989 Nottm.; MRCGP 1993; DRCOG 1992.

STACEY, Mark Reginald William Department Anaesthetics, Llandough Hospital, Cardiff Tel: 029 2071 6860 Fax: 029 2070 2435; 67 Heol Don, Whitchurch, Cardiff CF14 2AS Tel: 029 2061 8100 — MB BChir 1987 Camb.; MA Camb. 1988; FCAnaesth 1992. Cons. Anaesth. Llandough Hosp. Cardiff. Prev: Sen. Regist. & MSc Lect. (Anaesth.) Univ. Hosp. Wales; Regist. (Anaesth.) Univ. Hosp. Wales; SHO (Anaesth.) Bristol Roy. Infirm. & Withy Bush Hosp. HaverfordW.

STACEY, Richard Grant Willson Kingston Hospital, Galsworthy Road, Kingston upon Thames KT2 7QB Tel: 020 8546 7711 — MB BS 1983 Lond.; FFA RCS Eng. 1988; DA (UK) 1987. (Char. Cross Hosp. Med. Sch.) Cons. Anaesth. Kingston Hosp. Socs: Assn. Obst. Anaesth. Prev: Cons. Anaesth. W. Middlx. Univ. Hosp.; Sen. Regist. St. Geo. Hosp. & Brompton Hosp. Lond.; Regist. (Anaesth.) Hammersmith & Roy. Marsden Hosps. Lond.

STACEY

STACEY, Robert Kevin High Melton, Oakwood Road W., Rotherham S60 3AB — MB BS 1972 Lond.; MRCS Eng. LRCP Lond. 1972; FFA RCS Eng. 1977; DObst RCOG 1974.

STACEY, Sheila Margaret Cornwall House, Cornwall Avenue, London N3 1LD Tel: 020 8346 1976 Fax: 020 8343 3809; 23 Clifton Avenue, London N3 1BN — MB BChir 1969 Camb.; MA Camb. 1970, MB BChir 1969; MRCGP 1983; DObst RCOG 1971. (Camb. & Westm.)

*STACEY, Simon 63 Nelthorpe Street, Lincoln LN5 7SJ — MB ChB 1994 Manch.

STACEY, Simon Gareth 16 Beacon Road, London SE13 6EH — MB BS 1990 Lond.; FRCA 1995. (St. Mary's Hosp. Lond.) Regist. (Anaesth.) Char. Cross Hosp. Lond. (Calman Rotat.).

*STACEY, Simon John 44 Corporation Street, London E15 3HD — MB BS 1994 Lond.

STACEY, Susan Ese — MB BS 1990 Lond.; LFHom (Med) 1999; MSc (Sports Med.) Lond. 1996; MRCGP 1995; DRCOG 1994; DCH RCP Lond. 1994. (St Mary's) GP Retainer. Lond. Socs: BMA; RCGP; Brit. Assn. Sports Med. Prev: Fell. (Sports Med.) Childr.'s Hosp. Inst. Sports Med. (CHSM) Roy. Alexander Hosp. Childr. Sydney, Australia.

STACEY, Professor Terence Edward 5 Purley Knoll, Purley CR8 3AF Tel: 020 8668 2627 — MB BChir 1971 Camb.; MA, MB Camb. 1971, BChir 1970; FRCP Lond. 1985; MRCP (UK) 1973. (Camb. & Univ. Coll. Hosp.) Dir. Research & Developm. S. Thames; Vis. Prof. Child Health St. Geo. Hosp. Med. Sch. Prev: Prof. Child Health St. Geo. Hosp. Med. Sch.; Head Sect. Perinatal & Child Health Clin Research Centre Harrow; Hon. Cons. (Paediat.) N.wick Pk. Hosp. Harrow.

STACEY-CLEAR, Mr Adam East Surrey Hospital, Canada Avenue, Redhill RH1 5RH Tel: 01737 768511; Rookery Farm, Rookery Hill, Outwood, Redhill RH1 5QZ — MB BS 1978 Lond.; BSc (Anat.) Lond. 1974, MS 1989; FRCS Eng. 1983. Cons. Surg. (BrE. & Endocrinol.) E. Surrey Hosp. Redhill. Socs: Brit. Assn. Surgic. Oncol.; Brit. Assn. Endrocrin. Surg. Prev: Sen. Regist. (Surg.) St. Thos. Hosp. Lond.; Fell. (Surg.) Harvard Med. Sch. Mass. Gen. Hosp., USA.

STACK, Bryan Hilleary Rowan Respiratory Medicine Unit, Level 6, Gartnaval General Hospital, Great Western Road, Glasgow G12 0YN Tel: 0141 211 3247 Fax: 0141 211 3464; 8 West Chapelton Crescent, Bearsden, Glasgow G61 2DE Tel: 0141 942 3921 Fax: 0141 211 3464 Email: wosacfc@hotmail.com — MB ChB 1960 Ed.; MD Ed. 1982; FRCP Glas. 1982, M 1979; FRCP Lond. 1980, M 1963; FRCP Ed. 1975, M 1963; FRCPI 1999. (Ed.) Cons. Phys. Respirat. Dis. W.. Infirm. & Gartnavel Gen. Hosp.; Dir. W. Scotl. Adult Cystic Fibrosis Centre; Hon. Sen. Lect. (Med.) Glas. Univ. Socs: Brit. Thorac. Soc. & Scott. Thoracic Soc.; Scott. Soc. Phys. Prev: Sen. Regist. City Hosp. Edin.; Sen. Regist. Univ. Coll. Hosp. Lond.; Regist. Respirat. Dis. Unit N.. Gen. Hosp. Edin.

STACK, Charles Graham Sheffield Children's Hospital, Western Bank, Sheffield S10 2TH Tel: 0114 271 7000 Fax: 0114 271 7195; 6 Clumber Road, Ranmoor, Sheffield S10 3LE Tel: 0114 230 8696 — MB BS 1980 Lond.; BSc Lond. 1977; FFA RCS Eng. 1985. (Middlx.) Cons. Anaesth. & Dir. Paediat. Intens. Care Sheff. Childr. Hosp. Socs: Hon. Sec. Paediat. Intens. Care Soc. Prev: Cons. Anaesth. Birm. Childr. Hosp.; Sen. Regist. (Anaesth.) Nottm. & E. Midl. Higher Prof. Train. Scheme; Regist. (Anaesth.) Hosp. for Sick Childr. Gt. Ormond St. Lond.

STACK, Mary Monica Jenner House Surgery, 159 Cove Road, Farnborough GU14 0HH Tel: 01252 373738 Fax: 01252 373799; 49 Nethervell Mead, Church Crookham, Aldershot, Fleet GU52 0YQ Tel: 01252 816163 — MB BCh BAO 1983 NUI; DObst RCPI 1988; DCH RCPSI 1987.

STACK, Mr Michael Maurice Milltop House, Leicester Road, Swadlincote DE12 7HF — MB BCh BAO 1979 NUI; LRCPI & LM, LRCSI & LM 1979; FRCSI 1983.

STACK, William Alphonsus 29 Alford Road, West Bridgford, Nottingham NG2 6GJ — MB BCh BAO 1987 NUI.

STACK, Winifred Clemence Oxford Terrace Medical group, 1 Oxford Terrace, Bensham, Gateshead NE8 1RQ — MB BS 1985 Newc.; MA (Human Resource Managem.) Newc. 1992; MRCP (UK) 1988; MRCGP 1994. Gen. Practitioner (PMS). Prev: Sen. Regist. (Genitourin. Med.) Newc. Gen. Hosp.(1991-1992).

STACKHOUSE, John Richard Cricketfield Surgery, Cricketfield Road, Newton Abbot TQ12 2AS Tel: 01626 208020 Fax: 01626 333356 — MRCS Eng. LRCP Lond. 1972; MRCGP 1980; DA Eng. 1976; DObst RCOG 1974.

STACKWOOD, Deborah Anne 24 Whielden Street, Amersham HP7 0HT — MB ChB 1987 Liverp.

STACPOOLE, Harold Adam Westover Surgery, Western Terrace, Falmouth TR11 4QJ Tel: 01326 212120 — MB BCh 1986 Wales. Socs: BMA.

STACPOOLE-RYDING, Frank (retired) 21 Percy Road, Broadstairs CT10 2BJ — MRCS Eng. LRCP Lond. 1952; BA Open 1990.

STAFF, Anthony, Flight Lt. RAF Med. Br. Retd. Island Cottage, Fore St., Looe PL13 2EZ Tel: 01503 4765 — MRCS Eng. LRCP Lond. 1983; BA Open 1975; Cert. Family Plann. JCC 1986. Indep. Med. Pract. Caradon Clinic Cornw. Prev: GP RAF Chivenor Devon; GP RAF St. Mawgan Cornw.; Trainee GP Afcent, Netherlands.

STAFF, Catherine Jayne 6 Newton Street, Barry CF63 1EY — MB BS 1991 Lond.

STAFF, David Malcolm 24 Isham Road, Orlingbury, Kettering NN14 1JD — MB ChB 1971 Leeds; MB ChB (Hons.) Leeds 1971; MRCGP 1975; DObst RCOG 1973. Prev: Trainee Gen. Pract., Wakefield Vocational Train. Scheme; SHO (O & G), Ho. Phys. & Ho. Surg. Huddersfield Roy. Infirm.

STAFF, Mr William Glenville 1 Queens Square, Lancaster LA1 1RN Tel: 01524 63080; The Birks, Silverdale Road, Arnside, Carnforth LA5 0EH Tel: 01524 761381 — MD 1970 Manch.; MB ChB 1960; FRCS Eng. 1965. (Manch.) Cons. Urol. Surg. Lancaster DHA & S. Cumbria DHA. Prev: Sen. Regist. (Urol.) United Manch. Hosps. & Manch. RHB; Sen. Regist. United Cardiff Hosps.; Regist. (Surg.) United Sheff. Hosps.

STAFFORD, Anthony James Mansion House Surgery, Abbey Street, Stone ST15 8YE Tel: 01785 815555 Fax: 01785 815541 — MB ChB 1986 Sheff.; BMedSci Sheff. 1985; MRCGP 1992; DRCOG 1991. (Sheff. Univ.) Socs: RCGP.

STAFFORD, Caroline Jane 179 Hemingford Road, London N1 1DA — MB BChir 1993 Camb.

STAFFORD, Deborah Mary The Whitehouse, 6 St John's Avenue, Oulton, Stone ST15 8UD — MB ChB 1987 Birm.; DCH 1991; DRCOG 1990. (Birm.) p/t Retainor Scheme - Gen. Pract. Prev: Trainee GP City Gen. Hosp. Stoke-on-Trent VTS.

STAFFORD, Doreen Muriel (retired) Four Winds, Court Road, Newton Ferrers, Plymouth PL8 1DD Tel: 01752 872483 — MB ChB Birm. 1945. Prev: Clin. Asst. (Orthop. Med.) Mt. Gould Hosp. Plymouth.

STAFFORD, Elizabeth Anne 4 Edwards Close, Swanton Morley, Dereham NR20 4JZ — MB BS 1987 Lond.; MRCGP 1998.

STAFFORD, Eric John Highfield, 14 Stamford Road, Colsterworth, Grantham NG33 5JD Tel: 01476 860712 — MB BS 1949 Lond.; LMSSA Lond. 1948. (Guy's) Prev: RAMC; Ho. Phys. & Ho. Surg. Croydon Gen. Hosp.

STAFFORD, Mr Francis William The Washington Hospital, Picktree Lane, Rickleton, Washington NE38 9JZ Tel: 0191 415 1272 Fax: 0191 415 5541; 22 Granville Road, Jesmond, Newcastle upon Tyne NE2 1TP Tel: 01912095186 Fax: 01912095186 — MB BS 1978 Newc.; FRCS Eng. 1984; FRCS Ed. 1982. Cons. Otolaryngol Cons. Otolaryngolist Freeman Hosp. Newc. Upon Tyne. Prev: Cons Otolary, Sunderland Roy. Hosp.; Cons Otolary, Aberd. Roy. Inf.

STAFFORD, Heather Gay The Surgery, 25 Greenwood Avenue, Beverley HU17 0HB Tel: 01482 881517 Fax: 01482 887022 — MB ChB 1978 Leeds; BSc Leeds 1976. Prev: GP Muswell Hill, Lond.; Trainee GP Whittington Hosp. VTS.

*STAFFORD, Helena Mary c/o Mrs Stafford, Southfields House, St Pauls St., Stamford PE9 2BQ — BM 1998 Soton.; BM Soton 1998.

STAFFORD, Ilva Cruddas Park Surgery, 178 Westmorland Road, Cruddas Park, Newcastle upon Tyne NE4 7JT — MB BS 1967 Newc.; MRCP (U.K.) 1970. (Newc.)

STAFFORD, James West Cumberland Hospital, Whitehaven CA28 8JG Tel: 01946 693181 — MB BS 1969 Lond.; MRCS Eng. LRCP Lond. 1969; FRCOG 1990,M 1978. (Univ. Coll. Hosp.) Cons. O & G W. Cumbld. Hosp. Whitehaven.

STAFFORD, John (retired) Uplands, 9 Mill Hill, Shoreham-by-Sea BN43 5TG Tel: 01273 452545 — MRCS Eng. LRCP Lond. 1945; MRCGP 1966. Prev: Clin. Asst. (Dermat.) S.lands Hosp. Shoreham-by-Sea.

STAFFORD, John Bryce, Maj. RAMC (retired) 5 Glebelands, Sunrising, Looe PL13 1NP Tel: 01503 265715 — LRCP LRCS Ed.

LRFPS Glas. 1940; DPH Eng. 1958. Sen. Asst. Psychiat. Brookhall Hosp. Lancs. Prev: Sen. Pub. Health Off. & Advisor to Pres. Ghana Govt.

*STAFFORD, Kevin Paul 19 Crathie, Birtley, Chester-le-Street DH3 1QJ — MB ChB 1997 Leeds.

STAFFORD, Mary Teresa 37 Bristol Gardens, London W9 2JQ — MB BCh BAO 1983 NUI; LRCPI & LM, LRCSI & LM 1983; MRCGP 1991; MRCOG 1989.

STAFFORD, Michael Alfred 3 Cricklewood Park, Londonderry BT47 5QU — MB BCh BAO 1993 Belf.

STAFFORD, Michael Anthony Department of Anaesthesia, Royal Victoria Infirmary, Queen Victoria Road, Newcastle upon Tyne NE1 4LP Tel: 0191 232 5131 — MB BChir 1974 Camb.; MSc (Computing Sc.) Lond. 1977; MA, MB Camb. 1974, BChir 1973; FFA RCS Eng. 1980. Cons. Anaesth. Roy. Vict. Infirm. Newc. u. Tyne. Prev: 1st Asst. & Sen. Lect. (Anaesth.) Univ. Newc.; Regist. (Anaesth.) Avon HA.

STAFFORD, Michael Keith Dept of Gynaecology, Chelsea & Westminster Hospital, 369 Fulham Road, London SW10 9NH Tel: 020 8746 8218 Fax: 020 8846 7998; 70 Thames St, Sunbury-on-Thames TW16 6AF — MB BS 1987 Lond.; MRCOG 1993; MD 1998. Cons. Chelsea &W.minster.Hosp. Socs: BMA; MRCOG; RSM. Prev: Research Fell. St. Mary's Hosp. Med. Sch. Lond.; Regist. (O & G) Chelsea & W.m. Hosp. Riverside HA & N.wick Pk. Hosp. Harrow; Sen. Regist. & Lect. (O & G) Char. Cross & W.m. Hosp. Lond.

STAFFORD, Moyra Patricia Claridge (retired) Uplands, 9 Mill Hill, Shoreham-by-Sea BN43 5TG Tel: 01273 452545 — MRCS Eng. LRCP Lond. 1945.

STAFFORD, Mr Nicholas David 10 New Walk, Beverley HU17 7AD — MB ChB 1977 Leeds; FRCS (Orl.) Eng. 1983. Cons. ENT & Head & Neck Surg. Hull Roy. Infirm.; Prof. ENT Head & Neck Surg. Univ. Hull; Head of Sch. Of Med. Univ. Of Hall. Prev: Cons. ENT Surg. St. Mary's Hosp. & Char. Cross Hosp. Lond.; Sen. Regist. (ENT) St. Mary's & Roy. Marsden Hosps. Lond.; Resid. Etranger Inst. Gustave Roussy, Paris.

STAFFORD, Nicholas James 39 de Havilland Way, Abbots Langley WD5 0XF — MB BS 1992 Lond.; BSc (Hons.) 1991; DRCOG 1996. (St. Mary's Lond.) SHO Psychiat. Hillingdon Hosp. Pield Herth Rd. Uxbridge Middlx. Socs: Roy. Coll. Psychiat.

STAFFORD, Peter James 27 Burton Street, Loughborough LE11 2DT — MB BS 1984 Lond.; BSc (1st cl. Hons.) Lond. 1981; MD Lond. 1995; MRCP (UK) 1987. (Lond Hosp. Med. Coll.) Lect. & Locum Hon. Cons. Cardiol. Glenfield Hosp. Leicester. Socs: Brit. Cardiac Soc. Prev: Hon. Sen. Regist. (Cardiol.) Glenfield Gen. Hosp. Leicester; Research Fell. (Cardiol.) Groby Rd. Hosp. Leicester; Regist. (Cardiol.) Roy. Sussex Co. Hosp. Brighton & King's Coll. Hosp. Lond.

*STAFFORD, Sarah Jill 22 Ballykennedy Road, Gracehill, Ballymena BT42 2NP — MB BCh BAO 1996 Belf.

*STAFFORD, Selma 14 Shirlock Road, London NW3 2HS — MB ChB 1996 Manch.

STAFFURTH, Jean Forbes (retired) Rosedene, 30 Mays Hill Road, Bromley BR2 0HT Tel: 020 8460 3538 — MB BS 1953 Lond.; DMRT Eng. 1960. Prev: Hon. Cons. Radiother. Chelsea Hosp. for Wom. Lond.

STAFFURTH, John Nicholas Oncology Department, St. Thomas' Hospital, Lambeth Park Road, London SE1 7EH; 1E Westgrove Lane, Greenwich, London SE10 8QP Tel: 020 7928 9292 Fax: 020 7928 9968 Email: lidstonev@staffurthj.freeserve.co.uk — MB BS 1992 Lond.; MRCP (UK) 1995. (United Medical and Dental Schools) Regist. Clin.Oncol.St. Thomas' Hosp. Lond.

STAFFURTH, John Samuel 30 Mays Hill Road, Bromley BR2 0HT Tel: 020 8460 3538 — MRCS Eng. LRCP Lond. 1942; MD (Distinc.) Lond. 1948, MB BS 1942; FRCP Lond. 1967, M 1947. (St. Thos.) Hon. Cons. Phys. Guy's & Lewisham Hosps. Socs: Assn. Phys. Gt. Brit. & Irel.; Fell. Roy. Soc. Med. Prev: Censor R.C.P. Lond.; Res. Asst. Phys. St. Thos. Hosp.; Med. Regist. P. of Wales' Hosp. Plymouth.

STAGG, Caroline Elizabeth The Surgery, 35 Great Pulteney Street, Bath BA2 4BY Tel: 01225 464187 Fax: 01225 485305 — MB BS 1979 Lond.; MRCGP 1983; DRCOG 1981. (Char. Cross) Prev: Trainee GP Weymouth VTS.

STAGG, Martin James Richmond Group Medical Centre, 1 Albion Street, Ashton-under-Lyne OL6 6HF Tel: 0161 339 9161 Fax: 0161 343 5131; 41 Moorlands Drive, Mossley, Ashton-under-Lyne OL5 9DB — MB ChB 1985 Manch.; MRCGP 1989. Prev: Trainee GP Oldham HA VTS.

STAGKOU, Argyri Institute of Liver Studies, Kings College Hospital, Denmark Hill, London SE5 9RS — Ptychio latrikes 1988 Thessalonika.

STAGLES, Mr Martin John 89 Tyntyla Road, Llwynypia, Tonypandy CF40 2SR — MB BS 1974 Newc.; FRCS Ed. 1994.

STAHL, Mr Timothy James 217 Carmel Road N., Darlington DL3 9TF Tel: 01325 483268 — MB ChB 1967 Manch.; FRCS Eng. 1974. Cons. (Orthop. Surg.) Darlington Memor. Hosp. & Friarage Hosp. N.allerton. Prev: Leverhulme Research Fell. (Orthop. & BioMech.) Leeds Univ.; Sen. Regist. Robt. Jones & Agnes Hunt Orthop. Hosp. OsW.ry; Regist. (Accid. & Orthop. Surg.) N. Staffs. Roy. Infirm. Stoke-on-Trent.

STAHLSCHMIDT, Jens Dept. of Histopathology, St James University Hospital, Leeds LS9 7TF Tel: 0113 206 5432 — State Exam Med 1993 Hamburg; MD Hamburg 1994. (Univ. Hamburg) Specialist Regist. (Histopath.) Leeds Gen. Infirm. Socs: Internat. Acad. of Path. (Brit. Div.). Prev: SHO (Histopath.) Manch. Roy. Infirm.

STAHLSCHMIDT, Jens Ulrich Hableton House, South Otterington, Northallerton DL7 9HE — State Exam Med 1993 Hamburg.

*STAIANO, Jonathan James Anna-Capri, Gyllyngvase Road, Falmouth TR11 4DJ — MB BS 1994 Lond.

STAIG, David (retired) St. Kilda, Fairfield Road, Goring-on-Thames, Reading RG8 0EX — MRCS Eng. LRCP Lond. 1955; MA, BM BCh Oxf. 1955; DO Eng. 1959. Prev: Med. Off. Contact Lens Dept. Moorfields Eye Hosp. Lond.

STAIGHT, Guy Barrington 2 Pelham Street, London SW7 2NG Tel: 020 7581 4222 Fax: 020 7581 4676 — MB BS 1980 Lond.; MRCS Eng. LRCP Lond. 1980; MRCP (UK) 1984. (Char. Cross Hosp.) Indep. GP Lond.; Dep. Chief Med. Off. Jockey Club. Prev: SHO (Gen. Med.) & Ho. Phys. N.ampton Gen. Hosp; Ho. Surg. Char. Cross Hosp. Lond.

STAINER, Gordon Cowes Health Centre, 8 Consort Road, Cowes PO31 7SH Tel: 01983 295251 Fax: 01983 280461; Hillis House, Hillis Gate Road, Northwood, Cowes PO31 8NA Tel: 01983 295088 Email: drgstainer@cs.com — MB ChB 1980 Birm.; BSc (Psychol.) Birm. 1974; MRCGP 1984; DRCOG 1982. (Birm.) Socs: BMA. Prev: Trainee GP Hereford VTS.

STAINER, Mary Ruth Cowes Health Centre, 8 Consort Road, Cowes PO31 7SH Tel: 01983 295251 Fax: 01983 280461; Hillis House, Hillis Gate Road, Northwood, Cowes PO31 8NA Tel: 01983 295088 — MB BCh 1980 Wales; MRCGP (Distinc.) 1984; DRCOG 1983. Prev: Trainee GP Hereford VTS; SHO (A & E) Kingston Hosp.

STAINER-SMITH, Andrew Martin East Street Medical Centre, East Street, Okehampton EX20 1AY Tel: 01837 52233; Waterside, Sticklepath, Okehampton EX20 2NH Email: andrew@stainersmith.demon.co.uk — MB 1976 Camb.; MA; BChir 1975; MRCP (UK) 1978; MRCGP 1980. Socs: Inst. Psychosexual Med.

STAINES, Frederick Howard (retired) Woolston, Guildford Road, Cranleigh GU6 8PR — MRCS Eng. LRCP Lond. 1942. Prev: Ho. Surg. S.. Hosp. Dartford.

STAINES, James Edward Health Centre, Bishops Close, Spennymoor DL16 6ED Tel: 01388 811455 Fax: 01388 812034; Hull's Close, 1 Foxes Row, Brancepeth, Durham DH7 8DH Tel: 0191 378 0858 Fax: 01388 812034 Email: edward.staines@btinternet.com — MB BS 1974 Newc.; MRCGP 1978. Company Med. Off. Electrolux Home Products. Socs: BMA. Prev: Trainee GP Newc. VTS.

STAINES, Jillian Anne Nottingham Psychotherapy Unit, St. Ann's House, 114 Thorneywood Mount, Nottingham NG3 2PZ Tel: 0115 962 7891; 50 St. Albans Road, Leicester LE2 1GE — MB ChB 1981 Leeds; MRCPsych 1987. Sen. Regist. (Psychother.) Nottm. & Trent Region. Prev: Sen. Regist. Rotat. (Psychiat.) Leicester & S. Lincs HA.

STAINES, Jonathan David Crosshouse Hospital, Kilmarnock KA2 0BE Tel: 01563 521133; St. Judes, 3 Ladeside Lane, Kilmaurs, Kilmarnock KA3 2TJ Tel: 01563 538221 — MB BS 1983 Lond.; MRCP (UK) 1991. Cons. Paediat. Ayrsh. Centr. Hosp. Irvine & Ayr Hosp. Prev: Sen. Regist. & Career Regist. (Paediat.) Roy. Hosp. Sick Childr. Glas.; Regist. (Paediat.) Kettering Gen. Hosp.

STAINFORTH

STAINFORTH, John Nicholas Croft Hall Medical Practice, 19 Croft Road, Torquay TQ2 5UA Tel: 01803 298441 Fax: 01803 296104 — BM 1976 Soton.; BM (Hons.) Soton. 1976; MRCP (UK) 1979; MRCGP 1985; DRCOG 1985. Prev: Research Fell. (Med.) Univ. Soton.; Regist. Rotat. (Med.) N. Staffs. Hosp. Med. Centre Stoke on Trent.

STAINFORTH, Julia Margaret Department of Dermatology, York District Hospital, Wiggington Road, York YO31 8HE Tel: 01904 631313; Tel: YO32 9SF — MB ChB 1986 Leeds; MRCP (UK) 1989. (Leeds) p/t Cons. Dermat. York Dist. Hosp. Socs: Brit. Assn. Dermat.; BMA; Brit. Soc. Dermatological Surg. Prev: Sen. Regist. (Dermat.) Qu. Med. Centre Nottm.; Regist. (Dermat.) Leeds Gen. Infirm.; SHO (Gen. Med.) Leeds E.. HA.

STAINSBY, Dorothy National Blood Service, Newcastle Centre, Holland Dr., Barrack Road, Newcastle upon Tyne NE2 4NQ Tel: 0191 219 4436 Fax: 0191 219 4505 Email: dorothy.stainsby@nbs.nhs.uk; 9 Meadow Court, Ponteland, Newcastle upon Tyne NE20 9RB Tel: 01661 824389 — MB BS Newc. 1970; FRCP Lond. 1993; MRCP (UK) 1973; FRCPath 1996, M 1984. Cons. Transfus. Med. Nat. Blood Serv. Newc. u. Tyne.; Hon. Lect. (Med.) Univ. Newc. Socs: Assn. Clin. Path.; Brit. Soc. Haematol.; Brit. Blood Transfus. Soc. Prev: Cons. Haemat. Shotley Bridge Hosp.; Sen. Regist. (Haemat.) Newc. Hosps.

STAINSBY, Mr George David (retired) 9 Meadow Court, Darras Hall, Ponteland, Newcastle upon Tyne NE20 9RB Tel: 01661 824389 — MB 1958 Camb.; BChir 1957; FRCS Eng. 1962. Prev: Cons. Orthop. Surg. Newc. Univ. Hosps.

STAINTHORP, David Henry 96 Kennersdene, Tynemouth, North Shields NE30 2NW — BM 1983 Soton.

STAINTON, Richard Timothy The Surgery, Decima St., Bermondsey, London SE1; Broom Cottage, 19 Gilpin Road, Ware SG12 9LZ — MB BS 1993 Lond.; DRCOG 1996; DGM RCP Lond. 1995. (Lond. Hosp. Med. Coll.) GP Regist. Lond.

STAINTON-ELLIS, David Michael (retired) Roke House, 15 Clarefield Drive, Pinkneys Green, Maidenhead SL6 5DW — MB BS 1956 Lond.; DIH Eng. 1963; MFOM RCP Lond. 1978; DObst RCOG 1961. Prev: Sen. Med. Off. Roy. Fleet Auxil. Serv.

STAINTON-ELLIS, John Anthony (retired) 22 Bellair Road, Havant PO9 2RG — MB BS 1955 Lond.; DA Eng. 1957; DObst RCOG 1960. Prev: GP Havant.

STAIRMAND, Rosemary Agnes 54 Park Road, Great Meols, Hoylake, Wirral CH47 7BQ — MB ChB 1985 Leic.; DCH RCP Lond. 1992.

***STAITE, Deborah Lynn** 40 Relley Garth, Langley Moor, Durham DH7 8XU — MB BS 1994 Newc.

STAITE, Michael Edward 41 Station Road, Codsall, Wolverhampton WV8 1BY Tel: 01902 843764 — MB ChB 1990 Birm.; ChB Birm. 1990. Trainee GP Wolverhampton VTS. Prev: Ho. Off. (Surg.) Dudley Rd. Hosp.; Ho. Off. (Med.) New Cross Hosp. Wolverhampton.

***STAITE, Patrick Edward** The Grange, Llanon SY23 5LR — MB ChB 1996 Birm.

STAKER, Paul 35 Lower Elmstone Drive, Tilehurst, Reading RG31 5EB — MB BS 1987 Lond.

STAKES, Annette Frances Department of Anaesthesia, St James's University Hospital, Beckett St., Leeds LS9 7TF Tel: 0113 206 5580 Email: annette.stakes@leedsth.nhs.uk — MB BS 1972 Lond.; MRCS Eng. LRCP Lond. 1972; FFA RCS Eng. 1979; DA Eng. 1975. (St. Bart.) Cons. Anaesth. St. Jas. Univ. Hosp. Leeds. Prev: Cons. Anaesth. Calderdale HA; Sen. Regist. (Anaesth.) Yorks. RHA; Regist. (Anaesth.) St. Jas. Hosp. Leeds.

STALDER, Catriona Mary Aberdeen Mathernity Hospital, Cornhill Road, Aberdeen, Aberdeen AB25 2XG Tel: 01224 681818; 250 Rosemount Place, Aberdeen AB25 2XT Tel: 01224 634552 — MB ChB 1987 Aberd.; MRCOG 1993. Specialist Regist. Obst. & Gyn., Aberd. Prev: Regist. (O & G) Grampian HB.

STALDER, Gillian Patricia Mary Glencairn, Austenwood Common, Gerrards Cross SL9 8NL Tel: 01753 882390 — MB BS 1960 Lond.; DA Eng. 1969. (St. Bart.) Assoc. Specialist Anaesth. Oxf. Regional Hosp. Bd. Prev: Ho. Phys. St. And. Hosp. Bow; Ho. Phys. Paediat. Windsor Hosp.; Ho. Surg. Canad. Red Cross Memor. Hosp. Taplow.

STALEY, Christopher John St. Andrews Hospital, Billing Road, Northampton NN1 5DG Tel: 01604 616000 Fax: 01604 232325 — BM BS 1977 Nottm.; BMedSci (Hons.) Nottm. 1975, BM BS 1977; MRCPsych 1983. Cons. Psychiat. St Andrews Hosp.

STALEY, Frances Marilyn 39 Sunnyside, Newhall, Burton-on-Trent DE13 8 — MB ChB 1965 Sheff.; DObst. RCOG 1967.

STALEY, Margaret Glebelands Avenue Surgery, 2 Glebelands Avenue, London E18 2AB Tel: 020 8989 6272 Fax: 020 8518 8783; 17 Glebe Avenue, Woodford Green IG8 9HB Tel: 020 8504 7906 — MB BS 1976 Lond.; MRCP (UK) 1979; MRCGP 1983; DRCOG 1982; DCH Eng. 1978. (Univ. Coll. Hosp.)

STALEY, Petra Katherina The Hollow, Penn Lane, Melbourne, Derby DE73 1EP Tel: 01283 865252; The Dove River Practice, Gibb Lane, Sudbury, Ashbourne, Derby DE6 5HY Tel: 01283 585215 — MB BS 1988 Lond. GP on Retainer Scheme.

STALKER, Alexander Mitchell, TD 65 Dalkeith Road, Dundee DD4 7JH Tel: 01382 451470 — MB ChB 1944 St. And.; MB ChB St.And. 1944. Socs: BMA. Prev: Med. Regist. Roy. Infirm. Dundee; Sen. Staff Phys. Rochester State Hosp. Rochester Minn, USA; Hon. Lect. Dept. Pharmacol. Therap. Univ. Dundee.

STALKER, Deborah Jane Post Office Cottage, Compton Road, Hilmarton, Calne SN11 8SG Tel: 01249 760201 Email: drdeb@pocottage.prestel.co.uk — MB ChB 1984 Manch.; BSc (Hons.) Manch. 1981; MRCP (UK) 1993; MRCPCH 1996; DCCH RCP Ed. 1991; DCH RCP Lond. 1989. (Manch.) Regist. (Paediat.) St. Michael's Hosp. Bristol.

STALKER, Harry (retired) Viewlands House, Viewlands Road, Perth PH1 1BL Tel: 01758 624092 — MB ChB 1935 Ed.; MD (Commend.) Ed. 1939; FRCP Ed. 1943, M 1939; FRCPsych 1972; Dip. Psych 1938. Prev: Commonw. Fund Fell. NY Hosp. & Presbyt. Hosp. NY 1947-8.

STALKER, Malcolm John The Surgery, 24 Eaton Place, Brighton BN2 1EH Tel: 01273 686863 Fax: 01273 623402; 45 Crescent Drive N., Woodingdean, Brighton BN2 6SL — MB BS 1979 Lond.; MRCGP 1985; DRCOG 1982. (Middlx.)

STALKER, Randal (retired) Shenstone, 15 Clitheroe Road, Whalley, Clitheroe BB7 9AA Tel: 01254 823262 — MB ChB Ed. 1939; MD Ed. 1957. Prev: Cons. In Respirat. Med., Blackburn Roy. Infirm.

STALKER, Robert (retired) 27A Ingham Road, Bawtry, Doncaster DN10 6NN Tel: 01302 710772 — MB ChB 1951 Aberd.; FFPHM RCP (UK) 1991; DPH Leeds 1961. Prev: Dir. Pub. Health Doncaster HA.

STALLABRASS, Mr Peter (retired) The Manor House, Peppard Common, Henley-on-Thames RG9 5JE — MB BS 1955 Lond.; BSc (Hons.) Lond. 1951, MB BS 1955; FRCS Eng. 1959; FRCOG 1975, M 1962, DObst 1957. Cons. Obstetr. & Gynaecol. Roy. Berks. Hosp. Reading; Assoc. Teach. in Obst. St. Mary's Hosp. Med. Sch. Prev: Sen. Regist. Dept. O & G St. Thos. Hosp. & Lambeth Hosp. Lond.

STALLARD, James Matthew 232 Westbourne Park Road, London W11 1EP — MB BS 1993 Lond.

STALLARD, Mr Matthew Charles Tewin Lodge, Tewin Water, Welwyn AL6 0AB Tel: 0143 871 7500 — MB 1968 Camb.; BChir. 1967; FRCS Eng. 1973. (Camb. & St. Bart.) Cons. Orthop. Surg. Qu. Eliz. Hosp. Welwyn Garden City & Hertford Co. Socs: Fell. Brit. Orthop. Assn. Mem. Roy. Soc. Med. Prev: Sen. Regist. (Orthop.) Char. Cross Hosp., St. Mary's Hosp. & Roy.; Nat. Orthop. Hosp. Lond.; Regist. Windsor Gp. Hosps.

STALLARD, Nicholas James 1 Colton Road, Shrivenham, Swindon SN6 8AZ — MB BCh 1989 Wales.

STALLARD, Noelle Christine Tewin Lodge, Tewin Water, Tewin, Welwyn AL6 0AB Tel: 01438 717500 — MB BS 1972 Lond.; FFA RCS Eng. 1976. (St. Mary's) Prev: Sen. Regist. (Anaesth.) Char. Cross Hosp. Lond.; Regist. (Anaesth.) Char. Cross Hosp. Lond.; SHO (Cardiothoracic Surg.) Harefield Hosp.

STALLARD, Mrs Priscilla Mary Cedars Surgery, Maidenhead SL6 8AJ; 8 Station Rise, Marlow SL7 1EH — MB BS 1967 Lond.; MRCS Eng. LRCP Lond. 1967. (St. Bart.) Prev: Med. Off. Berks. AHA; Ho. Surg. St. Jas. Hosp. Balham; Ho. Phys. Eliz. G. Anderson Hosp. Lond.

STALLARD, Sheila 84 Springkell Avenue, Glasgow G41 4EH — MB ChB 1981 Aberd.; FRCS Glas. 1986. Staff Surg. W.. Infirm. Glas.

STALLEY, Linda Fay Springfield House, New Lane, Eccles, Manchester M30 7JE Tel: 0161 789 5858 — BM BS 1983 Nottm.; BMedSci (Hons.) 1981; MRCP (UK) 1986; DRCOG 1989.

STALLEY, Nicholas James Royal Crescent and Preston Road Practice, 25 Crescent Street, Weymouth DT4 7BY Tel: 01305 774466 Fax: 01305 760538 — MB BS 1974 Lond.

STALLWOOD, Mark Ian 12 Barnaby Rudge, Chelmsford CM1 4YG — MB ChB 1993 Liverp.; Prim. FRCA Lond. 1998. (Liverp.) SHO (Anaesth.) Fazukerley Hosp. Liverp. Prev: SHO (Med.) Wrexham Maelor Hosp.; SHO (Anaesth.) Wrexham Maelor Hosp.

STALLWORTHY, Elizabeth Gay The Surgery, 9 Ebdon Road, Worle, Weston Super Mare BS22 6UB Tel: 01934 514145; Email: lizsta@lineone.net — MB BS 1984 Lond.; MRCGP 1988; DRCOG 1988. (Middlesex Hospital Medical School) Gen. Practitioner.

STALLYBRASS, Frank Clifford Tregarthen, Shrubberies Hill, Porthleven, Helston TR13 9BH Tel: 01326 564291 — MB BChir 1947 Camb.; MA Camb. 1948, MD 1963. (Camb. & St. Bart.) Socs: Path. Soc.

STAMATAKIS, Mr Jeffrey Demetre Princess of Wales Hospital, Bridgend CF31 1RQ — MB BS 1969 Lond.; BSc (Pharm.) 1966 Lond.; MS 1979; FRCS 1974 Eng. (King's Coll. Hosp.) Cons. Surg. P.ss of Wales Hosp. Bridgend. Socs: Fell. Roy. Soc. Med. (Pres.); Assn. Coloproctol. Prev: Sen. Regist. (Surg.) King's Coll. Hosp. Lond.; Ho. Off. Hosp. Sick Childr. Gt. Ormond St. Lond.; Ho. Off. St. Jas. Hosp. Lond.

STAMBACH, Thomas Aubrey 30 Ickwell Green, Biggleswade SG18 9EG — MB BS 1989 Lond.

STAMBOULTZIS, Naoum Flat 8, 37 Croxteth Road, Liverpool L8 3SF — Ptychio Iatrikes 1988 Thessalonika.

STAMBULI, Mr Pius Moshi Mangotsfield Surgery, 26 Stockwell Drive, Mangotsfield, Bristol BS16 9DN — MB ChB 1967 University of East Africa. (University of East Africa)

STAMENKOVIC, Steven Aleksandar 14 Frederick Sq, London SE16 5XR — MB ChB 1992 Manch.

STAMER, Jurgen 1 Orchard Dere, Cuddington, Northwich CW8 2UZ Tel: 01606 889044 — State Exam Med 1989 Hamburg. Specialist Regist. (Orthop. Surg.) Mersey Region.

STAMFORD, John Anthony (retired) 32 Rook Wood Park, Horsham RH12 1UB — MB BChir 1954 Camb.

STAMM, Reinhard Gustav Wolfgang 416 Russell Court Complex, Lisburn Road, Belfast BT9 6AA — State Exam Med 1992 Marburg.

STAMMERS, Trevor Gordon The Surgery, 2 Church Lane, Merton Park, London SW19 3NY Tel: 020 8542 1174 Fax: 020 8544 1583 — MB BS 1980 Lond.; BSc Lond. 1977; MRCGP 1985; DRCOG 1982. Tutor (Gen. Pract.) St. Geo. Hosp. Med. Sch. Lond. Prev: Hon. Regist. St. Geo. Hosp. Lond.; Research Fell. (Gen. Pract.) St. Geo. Hosp. Lond.

STAMP, Elizabeth Jane 22 Spiers Close, Knowle, Solihull B93 9ES — BM BS 1985 Nottm.; MRCGP 1989; DRCOG 1988.

***STAMP, Michael Paul** 1 The Meadows, Wilberfoss, York YO41 5PY — MB ChB 1995 Manch.

STAMP, Philip Jonathan 65 Malcolm Street, Newcastle upon Tyne NE6 5PL — MB BS 1991 Newc.

STAMP, Robert Albert (retired) Darwin House, Darwing Lane, Fulwood, Sheffield S10 5RG Tel: 0113 230 1414 — MB ChB 1940 Leeds; DPM Eng. 1957. Prev: Cons. Psychiat. High Royds Hosp. Ilkley & St. Jas. Hosp. Leeds.

STAMP, Stephen Andrew Wellington House Practice, New Surgery, Station Road, Chinnor OX9 4PL Tel: 01844 351230 — BM BCh 1990 Oxf.

STAMP, Lord Trevor Charles Bosworth (Private rooms), Royal National Orthop. Hospital Trust, 45-51 Bolsover St., London W1P 8AQ Tel: 020 7387 5070; 15 Ceylon Road, London W14 0PY Tel: 020 7603 0487 Fax: 020 7603 5874 — BChir 1961 Camb.; MD Camb. 1972; FRCP Lond. 1978, M 1967; MRCP Ed. 1967; MRCS Eng. LRCP Lond. 1960. Emerit. Cons.UCL Hosp, lond. Hon.Cons.Roy.Nat.Orthop.Hosp.Lond; Cons. Phys. Roy. Nat. Orthopaedic Hosp. Socs: Bone & Tooth Soc. (Hon. Life Mem.); Internat. Skeleton Soc. (Hon. Life Mem.); Nat. Orteopowesis (Mem., Scientif. and Advis. Comm.). Prev: Hon. Sen. Lect. (Hum. Metab.) Univ. Coll. Hosp. & Med. Sch. Lond.; Regist. (Med.) St. Mary's Hosp. Lond.

STAMPER, Peter Ellesmere Park, Crundale, Haverfordwest SA62 4EN — MB BCh 1969 Wales; FRCR 1975. Cons. Radiol. Pembrokesh. HA Withybush Gen. Hosp. HaverfordW.. Prev: Cons. Radiol. Nuffield Orthop. Centre & John Radcliffe Hosp. Ox.

STAMPFLI, Sarah Louise Tel: 01271 863840 — MB BS 1990 Lond.; BSc Lond. 1986; DRCOG 1995. (St. Mary's) GP Princip. Prev: SHO (Ophth.) N. Devon Dist. Hosp.

STAMPS, Victoria Rebekah John Howard Centre, 2 Crozier Terrace, London E9 6AT — MB BS 1993 Lond.

STANAWAY, Stephen Eric 16 Brompton Avenue, Sefton Park, Liverpool L17 3BU — MB ChB 1993 Liverp.

***STANBRIDGE, Andrea Joy** 1 Bryn Ucha, Rhosrobin Road, Rhosrobin, Wrexham LL11 4PL — MB BS 1998 Lond.; MB BS Lond 1998.

STANBRIDGE, Judith Elizabeth 51 Redmoss Road, Aberdeen AB12 3JJ Email: jstanbridge@hotmail.com — MB ChB 1997 Glas.

STANBRIDGE, Mr Rex De Lisle St. Mary's Hospital, Praed St., Paddington, London W2 1NY Tel: 020 7886 6038 Fax: 020 7706 7302; Campions, Loudwater Lane, Croxley Green, Rickmansworth WD3 3JD Tel: 01923 774499 Fax: 01923 777567 Email: rex.stanbridge@btinternet.com — MB BS 1971 Lond.; BSc (Hons.) Lond. 1968; FRCP Lond. 1994; FRCS Eng. 1976; MRCP (UK) 1977; MRCS Eng. LRCP Lond. 1971. (St. Mary's) Cons. Cardiothoracic Surg. St. Mary's Hosp. Lond.; Cons. Thoracic Surg. Centr. Middlx. Hosp. Lond. Socs: Fell. Roy. Soc. Med.; Soc. Thoracic & Cardiovasc. Surg. GB & Irel.; Brit. Thorac. Soc. Prev: Cons. Cardiothoracic Surg. Hammersmith Hosp. Lond.; Sen. Regist. (Cardiothoracic Surg.) Hosp. Sick Childr. Gt. Ormond St., Harefield, Hammersmith & Middlx. Hosps. Lond.; Specialist Research Fell. Cardiac. Surg. Univ. Alabama Birm.

STANBRIDGE, Thomas Nigel Department of Microbiology, Wythenshawe Hospital, Southmoor Road, Manchester M23 9LT Tel: 0161 291 2884/85 Fax: 0161 291 2125 — MRCS Eng. LRCP Lond. 1961; MD Lond. 1973, MB BS 1961; FRCPath 1980, M 1968; Dip. Bact. (Distinc.) Manch. 1967. (Guy's) Cons. Microbiol. Wythenshawe Hosp.; Hon. Lect. in Bact. Univ. Manch. Socs: Assn. Clin. Pathols.; BMA. Prev: Sen. Bact. Pub. Health Laborat. Serv.; Lect. in Bact. Univ. Manch.; Sen. Lect. in Med. Microbiol. Welsh Nat. Sch. Med.

STANBURY, Peter Norman 51 Buxton Avenue, Caversham, Reading RG4 7BT — MRCS Eng. LRCP Lond. 1939; MA Camb. 1940. (Camb. & St. Bart.)

STANBURY, Rosalyn May Toad Hall, 21 Sandown Road, Esher KT10 9TT — MB ChB 1980 Bristol; FRCS Eng. 1986; MRCP (UK) 1984; DO RCS Eng. 1986. Socs: FRCOphth; Sen. Regist. (Med. Ophth.) St. Thos. Hosp. Lond.

STANCLIFFE, James Bennett West Farm Cottages, Seaton, Seaham SR7 0NA Tel: 0191 581 0107 — MB BS 1964 Durh.

STANDAGE, Kevin Francis Bennett Centre, Richmond Terrace, Shelton, Stoke-on-Trent ST1 4ND Tel: 01782 425182 Fax: 01782 425174; 16 Nantwich Road, Woore, Crewe CW3 9SB Tel: 01630 647810 Email: standage.kevinf@nsch-tr.wmids.nhs.uk — MB BS Lond. 1964; PhD Canada 1977; MRCS Eng. LRCP Lond. 1964; MRCPsych 1972. (Guys) Cons. Psychiat. Combined Healthcare NHS Trust Stoke-on-Trent; Sen. Clin. Lect. Keele Univ. Socs: Fell. Roy. Soc. Med.; Fell. Roy. Coll. Psychiat.; Fell. RCP Canada. Prev: Head Dept. Psychiat. Vict. Gen. Hosp. Halifax, Nova Scotia, Canada.

STANDART, Sally Collingwood Clinic, St. Nicholas Hospital, Gosforth, Newcastle upon Tyne NE3 3XT Tel: 0191 223 2206 Fax: 0191 223 2206; 2A Holly Avenue, Jesmond, Newcastle upon Tyne NE2 2PY Tel: 0191 281 9497 Fax: 0191 281 9497 Email: s.h.standart@btinternet.com — MB ChB 1982 Manch.; MRCGP 1988; DRCOG 1987; UKCP 1994. (Manchester) SHO (Psychiat.). Prev: Lect. Primary Health Care Univ. Newc.

STANDEN, A S Kingsbury Court Surgery, Church Street, Dunstable LU5 4RS Tel: 01582 663218 Fax: 01582 476488 — MB BS 1961 N U Ireland; MB BS 1961 N U Ireland.

STANDEVEN, Patricia Anne Howard 6 Brassey Avenue, Broadstairs CT10 2DS Tel: 01843 861999 — MB BS 1975 Lond.

STANDFIELD, Mr Nigel John 80 The Avenue, West Wickham BR4 0DZ — MB BS 1975 Lond.; FRCS Eng. 1979; FRCS Ed. 1978; MRCS Eng. LRCP Lond. 1975. (King's Coll. Hosp.) Moynihan Medal Assn. Surgs. Gt. Brit. & Irel. 1983; Sen. Regist. (Gen. Surg.) KCH Lond. Prev: Pfizer Research Fell. Thrombosis Unit King's Coll. Hosp. Lond.; Regist. (Gen. Surg.) King's Coll. Hosp. Lond.; SHO (Gen. Surg.) St. Jas. Hosp. Lond.

STANDING, Beth Louise The Surgery, 35 Great Pulteney Street, Bath BA2 4BY Tel: 01225 464187 Fax: 01225 485305 — BM BCh 1988 Oxf.; MRCGP 1992; DRCOG 1992; DCH RCP Lond. 1990.

STANDING

STANDING, P A Minden Medical Centre, 2 Barlow Street, Bury BL9 0QP Tel: 0161 764 2652 Fax: 0161 761 5967 — MB ChB 1970 Bristol; MB ChB 1970 Bristol.

STANDLEY, Carole Derwendeg Medical Centre, Heol Llanelli, Trimsaran, Kidwelly SA17 4AG Tel: 01554 810223; Bronyn Farm, Ferryside SA17 5TW Tel: 01267 267591 — MB ChB 1968 Liverp. Clin. Med. Off. Community/Family Plann. Dyfed HA; Clin. Asst. (Geriat.) Brythic Hosp. Dyfed HA.

STANDLEY, David Martin 109 Hawthorn Chase, Lincoln LN2 4RF — MB BS 1990 Lond.

STANDLEY, Helen Suzanne (retired) Pastures, Bilsington, Ashford TN25 7JX Tel: 0123 720300 — MRCS Eng. LRCP Lond. 1942; DCH Eng. 1944. Clin. Med. Off. Kent AHA. Prev: Ho. Surg. Hosp. Sick Childr. Newc.

STANDLEY, Thomas David Auger Woodton House, Leiston Road, Aldeburgh IP15 5QD Tel: 01728 454738 — MB ChB 1996 Birm.; ChB Birm. 1996. (Birm.) SHO Anaesth.Ipswich hosp.

STANDRING, Alexandra Fisher St. Davids, The Sands, Farnham GU10 1JW Tel: 01258 782112 — MB ChB 1990 Bristol; MRCGP 1996; DFFP 1997; DRCOG 1995. GP Locum. Socs: MDU.

STANDRING, John Nixon Kingston, 8 Far Dene, Kirkburton, Huddersfield HD8 0QZ Tel: 01484 602450 — MB ChB 1953 Manch.; DCH Eng. 1958. Prev: Ho. Phys. Paediat. Bolton Dist. Gen. Hosp.; Ho. Surg. Manch. Roy. Infirm.; RAF Med. Br.

STANDRING, Peter Dr P Standring, Alexandra House, Le Freteanux, St Martin, Jersey JE2 7WG Tel: 01481 725241 Email: p.standring@doctors.org.uk — MB ChB 1987 Cape Town; MRCP (UK) 1991; DCH RCP Lond. 1991; PHD,Southampton University 1998. (University of Cape Town) Cons. Paediat., Med. Specialist Gp., Guernsey. Prev: Regist. (Paediat.) Leeds Gen. Infirm.; Clin. Res. Fell. (Soton. Gen. Hosp.); Regist. Paediat. Respirat. Med. (Adelaide), Australia.

STANEK, Mr Jan Jiri 101 Harley Street, London W1N 1DF Tel: 020 7487 4457 Fax: 020 7487 4090 Email: janstanek@aol.com — BM BCh 1975 Oxf.; MA Oxf. 1976, BM BCh 1975; FRCS Eng. 1981. (Oxford) Indep. Pract. Lond.; Vis. Prof Plastic Surg Brno Univ. Czech RePub. Socs: Amer. Acad. Cosmetic Surg.; Roy. Soc. of Med.; Ctech Soc. of Aesthetic plastic Surg.s. Prev: Sen. Regist. & Regist. (Gen. Surg.) W.m. Hosp. Lond.; Regist. (Gen. Surg.) Qu. Mary's Hosp. Lond.

STANFIELD, Alan Campbell Lodgehill Road Clinic, Lodgehill Road, Nairn IV12 4RF Tel: 01667 452096 Fax: 01667 456785; Fax: 01667 456785 — MB ChB 1977 Glas.; MRCGP 1983; DRCOG 1982; Cert FPA. 1982. (University of Glasgow) Gen. Practitioner Lodeghill Clinic, Nairn; Med. Off. Nairn Town & Couny Hosp.; Dep. Police Surg. Nairn; Med. Off. Brit. Red Cross Soc.; Sen. Lect. (Clin.) Gen. Pract. Univ. of Aberd.; Med. Off. Nairn Town & Co. Hosp. Socs: Highland Med. Soc. Prev: Ho. Off. (Surg.) Stirling Roy. Infirm.; Ho. Off. (Med.) Glas. Roy. Infirm.

STANFIELD, Susan Margaret Lisburn Health Centre, Linenhall St., Lisburn BT28 1LU Tel: 01846 665181; 282A Ballynahinch Road, Hillsborough BT26 6BP Tel: 01846 638847 — MB BCh BAO 1973 Belf.; DCH Dub. 1982. SCMO Lisburn.

STANFORD, Andrew James Posterngate Surgery, Portholme Road, Selby YO8 4QH Tel: 01757 700561 Fax: 01757 213295; 10 Silver Street, Riccall, York YO19 6PB Tel: 01757 248442 — MB BS 1967 Lond.; MRCS Eng. LRCP Lond. 1967; DA Eng. 1970. (King's Coll. Hosp. Lond.) Prev: Ho. Phys. & Ho. Surg. King's Coll. Hosp. Lond.; Med. Off. i/c Magila Hosp., Tanzania.

STANFORD, Claire Nicola — MB ChB 1984 Leic.; BA Oxf. 1981; DRCOG 1988. Asst. Gp Shrewsbury.

STANFORD, Colin Andrew Callow Fold, Middlehope, Craven Arms SY7 9JT — MB ChB 1981 Birm.; MRCGP 1987; DRCOG 1984. Prev: Trainee GP Walsall VTS & BridgN.; SHO (Psychiat.) W. Midl. RHA; Resid. Anaesth. Kingston, Jamaica.

STANFORD, Hermione Mary 11 Gertrude Street, London SW10 0JN — MB BS 1981 Lond.

STANFORD, John Lawson Department of Medical Microbiology, University College London Med. School, 67-73 Riding House St., London W1P 7LD Tel: 020 7380 9488 Fax: 020 7636 8175; Mill House, Claygate, Marden, Tonbridge TN12 9PE Tel: 01892 730298 — MD 1970 Lond.; MB BS Lond. 1962; MRCS Eng. LRCP Lond. 1962. Reader (Microbiol.) Univ. Coll. Lond. Med. Sch. Lond. Socs: Internat. Union Against Tuberc. & Lung Dis.; Internat. Leprosy Assn.

STANFORD, Margaret Elspeth Anaesthetic Department, Ealing Trust Hospital, Uxbridge Road, Southall UB1 3HW Tel: 020 8574 2444 Fax: 020 8967 5797 Email: sally@ealingas.demon.co.uk; 92 Peregrine Road, Sunbury-on-Thames TW16 6JP Tel: 01932 783473 — MB ChB 1973 Cape Town; FFA RCS Eng. 1979; DA Eng. 1977. (Cape Town) Assoc. Specialist (Anaesth.) Ealing Trust Hosp. Middlx. Prev: Sen. Regist. & Regist. (Anaesth.) Hammersmith Hosp. Lond.; Regist. (Anaesth.) Hillingdon Hosp. Uxbridge.

STANFORD, Michael Francis Ashby Turn Primary Care Centre, Ashby Link, Scunthorpe DN16 2UT Tel: 01724 842051 Fax: 01724 280346 — MB BCh BAO 1973 NUI.

STANFORD, Mr Miles Richard 11 Gertrude Street, London SW10 0JN — MB BChir 1979 Camb.; MB Camb. 1979, BChir 1978; MSc Med. Immunol. Lond. 1986; MA Camb. 1979, MD 1994; FRCS (Ophth.) Eng. 1985; FCOphth. 1989; DO RCS Eng. 1984. Sen. Lect. (Ophth.) UMDS St. Thos. Hosp. Lond.

STANG, Fanny (retired) 1 Falmer House, 35 Belsize Park, London NW3 4DY Tel: 020 7431 1554 — MD 1938 Vienna; LRCP LRCS Ed. LRFPS Glas. 1944; MFCM 1971; DPH Manch. 1954. Prev: SCM. Bromley AHA.

STANGER, Elizabeth The Three Swans Surgery, Rollestone Street, Salisbury SP1 1DX Tel: 01722 333548 Fax: 01722 503626; Brindle Lodge, Nunton, Salisbury SP5 4HZ Tel: 01722 324380 — MB BChir 1981 Camb.; BA Camb. 1978; Cert. Family Plann. JCC 1985; DRCOG 1985; Dip. Occ. Med. 1998. GP Princip. (Wom.'s Health Occupat. Med.). Prev: Trainee GP Salisbury VTS.

STANGER, Miles Justin Bay Tree Cottage, Church End, Standlake, Witney OX29 7SG — MB BS 1988 Lond.; MSc Manch. 1992; MRCGP 1993. GP Med. Off. Socs: MDDUs; BMA; Soc. of Occupat.al Med. S.O.M. Prev: CMP - UK; Sen. Med. Off. - Lond.

STANGER, Nicholas Robert Yorke St Ann Street Surgery, 82 St. Ann Street, Salisbury SP1 2PT Tel: 01722 322624 Fax: 01722 410624; Brindle Lodge, Nunton Drove, Nunton, Salisbury SP5 4HZ — MB BS 1982 Lond.; MRCGP 1987; Cert. Family Plann. JCC 1987; DCH RCP Lond. 1987. (St. Thos.) Prev: Trainee GP Salisbury VTS.

STANGER, Robert Arthur (retired) 71 Peters Road, Locks Heath, Southampton SO31 6EL Tel: 01489 581452 — BA, MB BChir Camb. 1948; MRCS Eng. LRCP Lond. 1948. Prev: Ho. Phys. (Obst.) St. Thos. Hosp.

STANGER, Robin John Roe Charles Hicks Centre, 75 Ermine Street, Huntingdon PE29 3EZ Tel: 01480 453038 Fax: 01480 434104 Email: john.stanger@gp-j81050.nhs.uk — MB BS 1977 Lond.; MRCGP 1986. (St. Thos.) Socs: GP Asthma Gp. Prev: Trainee GP Ramsbury Wilts.; SHO Balclotha Hosp., NZ.

STANGROOM, Craig Dennis c/o 134 Barkham Ride, Wokingham RG40 4EL; UMN, PO Box 126, Kathmandu, Nepal — BM BS 1989 Nottm.; MRCGP 1994; DFFP 1993; DRCOG 1992.

STANHILL, Vivian 88 Dukes Avenue, Theydon Bois, Epping CM16 7HF — MB BS 1950 Lond.; FFA RCS Eng. 1959; DA Eng. 1955. (Middlx.) Cons. Anaesth. Redbridge HA. Prev: Sen. Regist. Anaesth. United Sheff. Hosps.; Jun. Res. Anaesth. Middlx. Hosp. Lond.; Capt. RAMC.

STANHOPE, Paul Bernard 29 Cyrano Way, Aylesby Park, Grimsby DN37 9SQ — MB BS 1982 Lond.

STANHOPE, Richard Graham Department of Endocrinology, Great Ormond Street Hospital for Children, Great Ormond St., London WC1N 3JH Tel: 020 7405 9200, 020 7905 2139 Fax: 020 7813 8496 Email: r.stanhope@ich.ucl.ac.uk; Department of Paediatric Endocrinology, The Middlesex Hospital, Mortimer St, London W1T 3AA Tel: 020 7380 9221 Fax: 020 7636 2144 — MB BS 1974 Lond.; BSc Lond. 1971, MD 1989; FRCP Lond. 1994; MRCP (UK) 1977; FRCPCH, 1996; DRCOG 1980; DCH RCP Lond. 1981. (St. Bartholomews) Cons. (Paediat. Endocrinol.) Gt. Ormond St. Hosp. for Sick Childr. & Middlx. Hosp. Lond.; Med. Adviser to the Child Growth Assn. UK; Med. Adviser to Congeital Adrenal Hyperplasia Gp. UK; Med. Adviser to Contact A Family UK. Socs: Fell. Roy. Soc. Med. (Mem. Sect. Endocrinol. & Progr. Sect.); Eur. Soc Paediat. Endocrinol.; Soc. Endocrinol. (Jt. Progr. Sect.). Prev: Research Fell. (Paediat.) Middlx. Hosp. Lond.; Regist. (Paediat.) Middlx. & Centr. Middlx. Hosps.; SHO St. Bart., Guy's, Brompton, Gt. Ormond St. & Kings Coll. Hosps. Lond.

STANIFORTH, Andrew Denis 4 Cadogan Gardens, South Woodford, London E18 1LU — MB ChB 1991 Birm.; BSc Birm.

STANLEY

1988, MB ChB 1991; MRCP (UK) 1994. (Birm.) Specialist Regist. (Cardiol.) Roy. Lond. Hosp. NHS Trust. Prev: Research Regist. (Cardiovasc. Med.) Qu. Med. Centre Nottm.; SHO (Med.) Sheff. HA.; SHO (Med.) Leics. HA.

STANIFORTH, Arabella Sophie Caroline 99G Albemarle Road, Beckenham BR3 5HP Tel: 020 8402 2877 — MB BS 1994 Lond.; BSc (Hons.) Lond. 1991. (St. Mary's Hosp. Lond.) SHO (Anaesth.) E.bourne Dist. Gen. Hosp. Prev: SHO (Cas.) Kingston Hosp. Surrey; Ho. Off. (Surg.) N.wick Pk. Hosp.

STANIFORTH, Christopher The Health Centre, Beeches Green, Stroud GL5 4BH Tel: 01453 764696 Fax: 01453 756548 Email: chris.staniforth@gp-l84077.nhs.uk; Woodlands, Culver Hill, Amberley, Stroud GL5 5BB — MB BS 1985 Lond.; MA Oxf. 1986; MRCGP 1989; DCH RCP Lond. 1990; Cert. Family Plann. JCC 1990. (King's Coll. Hosp. Lond.) Gen. Pract. Trainer; Clin. Asst., Phys. Weavers Croft, PsychoGeriat. Hosp., Stroud, Glos. Socs: BMA; RCGP. Prev: Trainee GP Tunbridge Wells VTS.

STANIFORTH, Joanne Louise 69 Cromwell Rise, Kippax, Leeds LS25 7QQ — MB ChB 1998 Sheff.; MB ChB Sheff 1998.

STANIFORTH, John 127 Glyn Eiddew, Cardiff CF23 7BR — MB BCh 1993 Wales.

STANIFORTH, Mr Paul Royal Sussex Co. Hospital, Eastern Road, Brighton BN2 5BE — MB ChB 1970 Birm.; FRCS 1975 Eng.; BSc (Anat.) 1967 Birm.; FRCS 1981 Ed. (Orth.); BSc (Anat.) Birm. 1967; FRCS Ed. (Orth.) 1981; FRCS Eng. 1975. Cons. Orthop. Surg. Roy. Sussex Co. Hosp. Brighton; Dep. Edr. & Exec. Bd. Mem. Injury. Socs: Fell. BOA; Brit. Soc. Surg. Hand. Prev: Sen. Regist. (Orthop.) Bristol Roy. Infirm.; Orthop. Fell. Roy. Childr. Hosp. Melbourne; Regist. (Orthop.) Robt. Jones & Agnes Hunt Hosp. OsW.ry.

STANILAND, John Robert Department of Health Care for the Elderly, Ladywell Building, Hope Hospital, Salford M6 8HD Tel: 0161 787 4042 Fax: 0161 787 4031; 29 Cavendish Road, Ellesmere Park, Eccles, Manchester M30 9JE Tel: 0161 788 0545 Email: jstaniland@hope.srnt.nwest.nhs.uk — MB BChir 1978 Camb.; MB Camb. 1978, BChir 1977; MA Camb. 1978; MRCP (UK) 1985; FRCP 1998. Cons. Phys. Med. for the Elderly Salford Roy. Hosps. Trust. Socs: BMA & Brit. Geriat. Soc. Prev: Cons. Phys. Med. for the Elderly Wigan & Leigh NHS Trust; Sen. Regist. Rotat. (Med. for the Elderly) N. W.. RHA; Regist. (Gen. Med. & Nephrol.) Leeds Gen. Infirm.

STANISLAS, Mr Joseph Mathias Chandran 3 Manor Cottages, Culworth Road, Chipping Warden, Banbury OX17 1LB — MB BS 1988 Bangalore; FRCS Ed. 1993.

STANLEY, Adrian George Cardiovascular Research Institute, Department of Medicine & Therapeutics, Leicester Royal Infirmary, PO Box 65, Leicester LE2 7LX — BM 1992 Soton.; BSc Soton. 1991; MRCP (UK) 1996. Clin. Lect. in Med. univ. Leci.; Hon. specialist Regist. in Med. univ. hosp. Leci. NHS Trust.

STANLEY, Adrian John Dept. of Gastroenterology, Glasgow Royal Infirmary, 84 Castle St., Glasgow G4 0SF Tel: 0141 211 4073 — MB ChB 1988 Ed.; MRCP (UK) 1991; MD Edin. 1998. Cons. (Gastro.) Glas. Roy. Infirm. Socs: BMA; Brit. Soc. Of Gastroenterol.; Brit. Assoc. for the study of liver Dis.s. Prev: Lect. (Med.) Univ. Edin. Roy. Infirm.; Regist. Rotat. (Med.) Edin. Roy. Infirm.; SHO (Med.) William Harvey Hosp. Ashford.

STANLEY, Adrian Michael Charles Street Surgery, Charles Street, Otley LS21 1BJ Tel: 01943 466124; Avalon, 30 Farnley Lane, Otley LS21 2BH Tel: 01943 466868 Fax: 01943 468373 — MB ChB 1979 Leeds.

STANLEY, Ann Katharine The Norvic Clinic, St Andrew's Business Park, Thorpe St Andrews, Norwich NR7 0HT Tel: 01603 439614 Fax: 01603 701954 — MB BS 1986 Lond.; BSc 1983 Lond.; MMedSc (Psychiat.) Birm. 1993; MRCPsych 1992. Cons. (Forens. Psychiat.) Norwich. Prev: Sen. Regist. (Psychiat.) W. Midl. RHA.; Regist. Rotat. (Psychiat.) Birm. HA.; SHO (Med.) United Norwich Hosp.

STANLEY, Anthony Joseph 27 Sanderson Road, Jesmond, Newcastle upon Tyne NE2 2DR — MB BCh BAO 1991 NUI; LRCPSI 1991.

STANLEY, Barry 7 Camsey Ash, Widnes WA8 9GP — MB BChir 1987 Camb.; BA Oxf. 1984; T(GP) 1993. Trainee GP York VTS. Prev: SHO (ENT & O & G) York Dist,. Gen. Hosp.; SHO (Geriat.) Halton Gen. Hosp. Runcorn.

STANLEY, Belinda Susan Cumberland Infirmary, Newtown Road, Carlisle CA2 7HY Tel: 01228 814814; The Old Vicarage, Dacre, Penrith CA11 0HH — BM 1982 Soton.; MRCP (UK) 1987; FRCP (UK) 1998. Cons. Genitourin. Med. Carlisle Hosps. Trust. Prev: Lect. & Hon. Sen. Regist. (Genitourin. Med.) Middlx. Hosp. Lond.; Regist. (Genitourin. Med.) St. Mary's Hosp. Lond.; SHO Rotat. (Med.) Soton. HA.

***STANLEY, Catherine Anne Mary** Rose Heath, The Mount, Heswall, Wirral CH60 4RE — MB BS 1997 Lond.

STANLEY, Charles Kincaid Cross House, 1 Ranmoor Crescent, Ranmoor, Sheffield S10 3GU — MB BS 1982 Lond.

STANLEY, Christopher Paul Larwood Health Centre, 56 Larwood, Worksop S81 0HH Tel: 01909 500233 Fax: 01909 479722 — MB BS 1982 Newc.; MRCGP 1989. Prev: Regist. (Respirat. & Gen. Med.) St. Jas. Univ. Hosp. Leeds.

STANLEY, Clare Alexandra 2 Wildwood Terrace, London NW3 7HT Tel: 020 8455 5109 — MB ChB 1992 Cape Town.

STANLEY, Clare Hazel Priorslegh GP Practice, Civic Centre, Park Lane, Poynton, Stockport SK12 1GP — MB ChB 1983 Manch.; MRCGP 1988; DRCOG 1986; MRCGP 1988; DRCOG 1986.

STANLEY, Mr David The Orthopaedic Department, Northen General Hospital, Sheffield S5 7AU Tel: 0114 243 4343 Fax: 0114 226 6796 Email: claire.faulkner@northngh-tr.trent.nhs.uk; Ranworth, 1 Chorley Road, Fulwood, Sheffield S10 3RJ Tel: 0114 230 4808 — MB BS 1977 Lond.; BSc (Physiol., 1st cl: Hons.) Lond. 1974; FRCS Eng. 1985. (St George's London) Cons. Orthop. & Trauma Surg. N. Gen. Hosp. Sheff. Socs: Brit. Elbow & Shoulder Soc. (Sec.); Eur. Rheum. Arthrit. Surg. Soc.; Eur. Soc. Surg. of Shoulder & Elbow. Prev: Sen. Regist. (Orthop.) Sheff. Teach. Hosps.

***STANLEY, David Peter** Meadow House, Brimley Cross, Bovey Tracey, Newton Abbot TQ13 9DL — MB ChB 1996 Birm.

STANLEY, Derek John Peter The Stokes Medical Centre, Braydon Avenue, Little Stoke, Bristol BS34 6BQ Tel: 01454 616767; 26 Russell Grove, Westbury Park, Bristol BS6 7UE Tel: 0117 924 8685 — MB BCh BAO 1971 Dub.; BA Dub. 1969; MRCGP 1980; DObst RCOG 1973. (TC Dub.) Prev: SHO (Obst.) St. Mary's Matern. Hosp. Portsmouth; SHO (Gen. Med. & Paediat.) Glos. Roy. Hosp.

STANLEY, Diane Elizabeth Riverside Surgery, Barnard Avenue, Brigg DN20 8AS Tel: 01652 650131; The Old Post Office, Askerswell, Dorchester DT2 9EL — MB ChB 1985 Leeds.

STANLEY, Elizabeth Margaret Gordon (retired) Staples Farm, Datchworth, Knebworth SG3 6RN Tel: 01438 813001 Fax: 01438 814388 Email: stanley@ashwell.com — MRCS Eng. LRCP Lond. 1962. Hon. Sen. Lect. (Human Sexuality) St. Geo. Hosp. Med. Sch. Prev: Dir. Human Sexuality Unit St. Geo. Hosp. Med. Sch. Lond.

STANLEY, George Edward Flat 2, 18 Nairn Road, Poole BH13 7NQ — BM 1988 Soton.

STANLEY, Harold Wheldale Plantation House, Salcombe TQ8 8JJ Tel: 01548 842538 — MB BS 1951 Lond.; MRCS Eng. LRCP Lond. 1949; DA Eng. 1954. (St. Bart.) Socs: Founder Assoc. MRCGP; Plymouth Med. Soc. & Brit. Med. Acupunc. Soc. Prev: Anaesth. S. Hams Hosp. Kingsbridge; GP Salcombe, Devon; Ho. Surg. & Ho. Surg. Thoracic Unit St. Bart. Hosp. Lond.

STANLEY, Ian Roger 6 Ash Close, Barrow, Clitheroe BB7 9FF — MB BChir 1992 Camb.

***STANLEY, James Charles** Rydal Mount, Ruff Lane, Ormskirk L39 4QZ — MB BS 1998 Lond.; MB BS Lond 1998.

STANLEY, James Clive 18 Plantation Road, Lisburn BT27 5BP Tel: 01846 676386 — MB BCh BAO 1978 Belf.; FFA RCSI 1983. Cons. Anaesth. Roy. Gp. Hosps. Belf. Socs: BMA; Assn Anaesth. GB & Irel.; Affil. Mem. Amer. Soc. Anesthesiol.

STANLEY, James Derek 46 Brook Lane, Chester CH2 2ED Tel: 01244 40532; 46 Brook Lane, Chester CH2 2ED Tel: 01244 40532 — MB BCh BAO 1969 Dub.; BA Dub. 1967, MB BCh BAO 1969. Mem. Med. Bd. DHSS. Prev: Cas. Off. Roy. City of Dub. Hosp.; Ho. Off. Roy. City of Dub. Hosp.

STANLEY, Joanna Ruth 1 Steps End Cottages, Rydal, Ambleside LA22 9LP — MB ChB 1990 Manch. SHO (Cas.) Roy. Lancaster Infirm. Prev: SHO (O & G) Lancaster Infirm.; SHO (Med.) W.morland Gen. Hosp.; SHO (Paediat.) Roy. Lancaster Infirm.

STANLEY, Joanne Kay The Medical Centre, Pinkham, Cleobury Mortimer, Kidderminster DY14 8QE Tel: 01299 270209 Fax: 01299 270482; 15 Grove Meadow, Cleobury Mortimer, Kidderminster DY14 8AG — MB ChB 1989 Birm.; MRCGP 1992. (Birm.) Prev:

STANLEY

Trainee GP/SHO Kidderminster Gen. Hosp. VTS; Ho. Off. (Med.) Goodhope Hosp. Sutton Coldfield; Ho. Off. (Surg.) Kidderminster Gen. Hosp.

STANLEY, Professor John Knowles 20 Derby St. West, Ormskirk L39 3NH Tel: 01695 575210 Fax: 01695 575210; Rydal Mount, Ruff Lane, Ormskirk L39 4QZ Tel: 01695 575210 Fax: 01695 575210 Email: profstanley@btinternet.com — MB ChB Liverp. 1968; MChOrth Liverp. 1975; FRCS Eng. 1974; FRCS Ed. 1973. (Liverp.) Cons. Hand Surg., Wrightington, Wigan and Leigh NHS Trust; Prof. Hand Surg. Dept. Orthop. Univ. Manch. (p/t); Hon. Cons., Hope Hosp., Glan Clwyd Hosp., Alexandra Hosp., Fairfield Hosp., Manch. Childr.'s Hosp., Roy. Glam. Hosp. Socs: Founder Mem. Brit. Shoulder & Elbow Soc.; (Ex-Pres.) Brit. Assn. Hand Therapists; (Ex-Pres.) NW Physiother. Soc. Prev: Sen. Regist. Roy. Liverp. Hosp., Roy. S.. Hosp. Liverp. & Wrightington Hosp. Centre Hip Surg.; Cons. Oruskirk & Dist. Gen. Hosp. 1979-1984.

STANLEY, John Steven Dr J. Stanley, Department of Anaesthesia, Newcastle General Hospital, West Road, Newcastle upon Tyne NE4 6BE Tel: 0191 256 3198 Fax: 0191 256 3154 Email: john@stanley.freeserve.co.uk; 13 Moresby Road, Cramlington NE23 3XP Tel: 01670 739499 Email: john@stanleyne.freeserve.co.uk — MB BS 1987 Newc.; FRCA 1996. Cons. Anaesth., Newc. Hosp. NHS Trust. Socs: Assn. Anaesth.; N. E. Soc. of Anaesth.

STANLEY, Katharine Paula Norfolk and Northwich University Hospital NHS Trust, Brunswick Road, Norwich NR1 3RS Tel: 01603 740747 — MB ChB 1982 Liverp.; MRCOG 1987. Cons. Obst. & Gyn. Norf. & Norwich Univ. Hosp. NHS Trust.

STANLEY, Mairi Christine 43 Marchmont Road, Edinburgh EH9 1HU Tel: 0131 229 8118 — MB ChB 1992 Ed.; DRCOG 1995; MRCGP 1997.

STANLEY, Nigel Noel 82 Harley Street, London W1N 1AE; Staples Farm, Datchworth, Knebworth SG3 6RN Tel: 01438 813001 Fax: 01438 814388 Email: stanley@ashwell.com — MD 1976 Camb.; MB 1964, BChir 1963; FRCP Lond. 1981, M 1967. (Camb. & St. Thos.) Cons. Phys. Lister Hosp. Stevenage. Socs: Med. Res. Soc. & Brit. Thoracic Soc. Prev: Regist. (Med.) Roy. Free Hosp. Lond.; Lect. (Med.) Middlx. Hosp. Lond.; Asst. Prof. Med. Univ. Penna. Sch. Med. Philadelphia, USA.

STANLEY, Oliver Hugh Southmead Hospital, Bristol BS10 5NB — MB BChir 1979 Camb.; BA Camb. 1973, MD 1988; FRCP Lond. 1994; MRCP (UK) 1981; DCH Eng. 1980. Cons. Paediat. (Community) S.mead Hosp. Bristol; Sen. Lect. (Child Disabil.) Univ. Bristol.

STANLEY, Paula Bernadette 131 Rendlesham Road, London E5 8PA — MB BCh BAO 1990 NUI.

STANLEY, Peter Hugh Riverside Surgery, Le Molay Littry Way, Bovey Tacey, Newton Abbot TQ13 9QP Tel: 01626 832666 — MB ChB 1969 Manch.; BSc (Hons. Physiol.) Manch. 1966; MRCGP 1976.

STANLEY, Philip John Seacroft Hospital, York Road, Leeds LS14 6UH Tel: 0113 264 8164 Fax: 0113 206 2132 Email: p.j.stanley@leeds.ac.uk; 3 Avondale Villas, Thorner, Leeds LS14 3DQ Tel: 0113 289 2846 — MB BS 1976 Lond.; MD Lond. 1988; FRCP Lond. 1994; MRCP (UK) 1978; MRCS Eng. LRCP Lond. 1976; DTM & H RCP Lond. 1987. (Westm.) Cons. Phys. (Infec. Dis.) Seacroft Hosp. Leeds; Clin. Sen. Lect. Univ. Leeds. Prev: Sen. Regist. (Communicable & Trop. Dis.) E. Birm. Hosp.; Regist. (Med.) St. Stephen's Hosp. Chelsea; Clin. Lect. Cardiothoracic Inst. Lond.

STANLEY, Mr Richard Adrian, Wing Cdr. Retd. Caithness General Hospital, Wick KW1 5NS Tel: 01955 605050; Lealands, Bilbster, Wick KW1 5TA Tel: 01955 621237 Email: stanley.richard@haht.scot.nhs.uk — MB BS Lond. 1970; FRCS Eng. 1977; MRCS Eng. LRCP Lond. 1970. (Roy. Free) Cons. Surg. Caithness Gen. Hosp. Wick. Socs: Brit. Med. Assn.; Sec. Local Negotiating Comm. Prev: Wing. Cdr. RAF Med. Br.

STANLEY, Richard Sheridan Clerklands, Vicarage Lane, Horley RH6 8AR — MB BS 1971 Lond.; MRCS Eng. LRCP Lond. 1971; DObst RCOG 1976.

STANLEY, Richard Stephen Grant The Surgery, Astonia House, High Street, Baldock SG7 6BP Tel: 01462 892458 Fax: 01462 490821 — MB BS 1989 Lond.; BSc (Hons.) Lond. 1986; MRCGP 1995; DCH RCP Lond. 1994; DFFP 1994; DRCOG 1993. (Roy. Free Hosp. Sch. Med.) GP Princip., Drs Thomas, Cockburn, Georgiou, Stanley, Golding & Haeward. Socs: Brit. Med. Acupunct. Soc. Prev: Clin. Med. Off. (Comunity Paediat.) SW Herts. HA; Resid. Med. Off. (Psychiat.) P. Henry Hosp. Sydney, Austral.

STANLEY, Sally Elizabeth Ann Charles Street Surgery, Charles Street, Otley LS21 1BJ Tel: 01943 466124; Avalon, 30 Farnley Lane, Otley LS21 2BH Tel: 01943 466868 Fax: 01943 468373 — MB ChB 1980 Manch.; MRCGP 1984.

STANLEY, Stephen Department of Child Health, Dorset Children's Centre, Damers Road, Dorchester DT1 2LB Tel: 01305 251150; Dairy Cottage, 10 Shitterton, Bere Regis, Wareham BH20 7HU Tel: 01929 471588 — MB ChB 1973 Dundee; BSc St. And. 1970; MRCPsych 1982; MCPCH 1996; FRCPCH 1997. (St Andrews and Dundee) Cons. Child & Adolesc. Psychiat. W. Dorset Gen. Hosp. & Dorset Health Care NHS Trust.; Vis. Cons. Purbeck View Sch. for Autism Disorders & Milton Abbey Sch. Socs: Assn Family Ther.; Assn. Psychiat. Study Adolesc. Prev: Vis. Cons. Child & Adolesc. Psychiat. Ment. Health Serv. States of Jersey; Cons. Child & Adolesc. Psychiat. W. & E Dorset Health Dists.; Sen. Regist. (Child Psychiat.) S. W.. HA.

STANLEY, Susan Patricia The Surgery, 223 London Road, Waterlooville PO8 8DA Tel: 02392 263491 Fax: 02392 340504; 110B The Causeway, Petersfield GU31 4LL — BM BS 1986 Nottm.; MRCGP 1990.

STANLEY, Trevor Mark New Hayesbank Surgery, Cemetery Lane, Kennington, Ashford TN24 9JZ Tel: 01233 624642 Fax: 01233 637304 — MB BS 1990 Lond.; Dip. Geriat. Med. 1993; DCH 1994; MRCGP 1994; DRCOG 1995; DFFP 1997. (St. George's Hosp. Med. Sch. Lond.)

STANLEY, Wayne Edgar 73 Manor Road, Scarborough YO12 7RT — MB ChB 1991 Pretoria.

STANLEY, William John (retired) 8 Crossfield Grove, Marple Bridge, Stockport SK6 5EQ — MB ChB 1951 Liverp.; MD Liverp. 1961; MRCS Eng. LRCP Lond. 1951; FRCPsych. 1981, M 1972; DPM Eng. 1959. Prev: Cons. Psychiat. N. W.. RHA.

STANLEY-JONES, Mr Douglas Full Circle, Townshend, Hayle TR27 Tel: 0173 685223 — MRCS Eng. LRCP Lond. 1929; BSc (Hons. Physiol.) Lond. 1925, MB BS (Distinc; Physics, Pt. I, Pharmacol. Pt. II) 1930; FRCS Eng. 1933. (St. Bart.) Dir. Full Circle Foundat. for Educat. & Research; Vis. Lect. NY State Univ., Brain Research Inst. Los Angeles & Loyola Univ. Chicago, USA. Prev: Teach. Clin. Surg. Bristol Univ.; Demonst. Physiol. St. Bart. Hosp.; Surg. Regist. Bristol Gen. Hosp.

STANLEY-JONES, Geoffrey Harvey Martin The Beeches, Perranwell, Truro TR3 7LZ — MB BS 1968 Lond.; MRCS Eng. LRCP Lond. 1968; FFA RCS Eng. 1973; DA Eng. 1971; DObst RCOG 1970. (St. Mary's) Cons. Anaesth. Cornw. & I. of Scilly AHA. Prev: Sen. Regist. (Anaesth.) Avon AHA (T) & S. W.. RHA; Regist. & Sen. Regist. (Anaesth.) Guy's Hosp. Lond. & Roy. Sussex Co.; Hosp. Brighton.

STANLEY-JONES, Jillian Katherine Vivien Foxbury, Westhumble, Dorking RH5 6BQ Tel: 01306 884955 Fax: 01306 884955 — BM BCh 1970 Oxf.; MA Oxf. 1970; DCH Eng. 1973; DObst RCOG 1972.

STANLEY-SMITH, Stephen Peter Osmaston Road Medical Centre, 212 Osmaston Road, Derby DE23 8JX Tel: 01332 346433 Fax: 01332 345854; 42 Broadway, Duffield, Belper DE56 4BU Tel: 01332 841424 — MB BS 1984 Lond.; BSc Lond. 1981; MRCGP 1989; DRCOG 1988. GP Derby. Socs: Derby Med. Soc.

STANLEY-WHYTE, Elinor Mary (retired) 10 Clatto Place, St Andrews KY16 8SD Tel: 01334 475294 — MB ChB St. And. 1957. Prev: SCMO Lothian HB.

STANNARD, Catherine Faith Jubbs Court, Failand Lane, Failand, Bristol BS8 3SS — MB ChB 1984 Liverp.; FCAnaesth. 1989. Sen. Regist. (Anaesth.) E. Anglian RHA. Prev: Regist. (Anaesth.) Arrowe Pk. Hosp. Wirral; Regist. (Anaesth.) Nuffield Dept. Anaesth. Oxf.

***STANNARD, Clare Louise** 19 Sendall Court, Winstanley Estate, London SW11 2HE — MB BS 1996 Lond.

STANNARD, Edward John Queens Road Surgery, Earls Colne, Colchester CO6 2RR Tel: 01787 222022 Fax: 01787 224634 — MB BS 1977 Lond.

STANNARD, Mr Kevin Peter Dept of Ophthalmology, Royal Victoria Infirmary, Queen Victoria Road, Newcastle upon Tyne NE1 4LP Tel: 0191 232 5131 — MB BS 1978 Lond.; FRCS Eng. 1984; FRCOphth 1988; DO Eng. 1982. (Kins College Hospital

Medical School) Cons. Ophth. Surg. Roy. Vict. Infirm. Newc. Prev: Sen. Regist. Kings Coll. Hosp., Moorfields Eye Hosp. & Nat. Hosp. for Nerv. Dis.

STANNARD, Laura 12 Viola Street, Bootle, Liverpool L20 7DP — MB ChB 1992 Manch.

STANNARD, Paul John Torbay Hospital, Lawes Bridge, Torquay TQ2 7AA Tel: 01803 654608 Fax: 01803 615472 Email: stan@vmsmail.sdevonhk.tr.swest.nhs.uk — MB BS Lond. 1972; FRCOG 1991, M 1978. Cons. (O & G) Torbay Hosp. Torquay. Prev: Lect. (Hon. Sen. Regist.) Char. Cross & W. Lond. Hosps.

STANNARD, Philip Anthony Doncaster Royal Infirmary, Armthorpe Road, Doncaster DN2 5LT; 8 Grange Close, Doncaster DN4 6SE Tel: 01302 532391 — MB BS 1985 Lond.; BA Camb. 1981; FRCR 1992. Cons. Radiol. Doncaster Roy. Infirm. & Montagu Hosp. NHS Trust. Prev: Sen. Regist. (Radiol.) Leeds Gen. Infirm.

STANNARD, Timothy John Friarsgate Practice, Friarsgate Medical Centre, Friarsgate, Winchester SO23 8EF Tel: 01962 853599 Fax: 01962 849982 — BM BS 1983 Nottm.

STANNARD, Wendy Anne 10 Queens Avenue, Heathfield Road, Kings Heath, Birmingham B14 7BU — MB ChB 1996 Birm.; ChB Birm. 1996.

STANNERS, Andrew John Pinderfields Hospital, Aberford Road, Wakefield WF1 4DG Tel: 01924 201688 — BM 1983 Soton.; MRCP (UK) 1988. Cons. Phys. (c/o Elderly) Pinderfields Hosp. Wakefield.

STANNING, Alison Margaret — MB BS 1985 Lond.; MRCGP 1989; DRCOG 1988.

STANOWSKI, Maria 10 Campden Hill Square, London W8 7LB Tel: 020 7727 6877 Fax: 020 7727 6877 Email: mstanowski@aol.com — State Exam 1994 Rome; State Exam. Rome 1994. (Univ. Rome La Sapienza, Italy) SHO (Psychiat. St Thos. Hosp. Lond. of Old Age); Guys Hosp. Learn. Disabil. Socs: BMA Med. Defence Union & Roy. Coll. Psychiat (Inceptor). Prev: Pre-reg Ho. Off. (Med.) N. Tees Hosp. Stockton on Tees; Pre-reg HO (ENT/Surg.) Freeman Hosp. Newc.; SHO (Psychiat.) Maidstone Kent Greenwich Hosp. Lond.

STANOWSKI, Robert Tollgate Health Centre, 220 Tollgate Road, London E6 5JS Tel: 020 7474 7709 Fax: 020 7445 7715 — MB BS 1984 Lond.

STANSBIE, David Leslie Bristol Royal Infirmary, Department of Chemical Pathology, Bristol BS2 8HW; 6 Charlotte St. S., Bristol BS1 5QB — MB ChB 1968 Leeds; PhD Bristol 1977, BSc 1973; MRCPath 1977. (Leeds) Cons. Chem. Path. Bristol Roy. Infirm. Prev: Sen. Lect. (Med. Biochem.) Welsh Nat. Sch. Med. Cardiff.

STANSBIE, Mr John Michael (retired) Walsgrave Hospital, Clifford Bridge Road, Coventry CV2 2DX Tel: 024 76 538966 — BM BCh Oxf. 1966; MA Oxf. 1966; FRCS Eng. 1972. Prev: Cons. ENT Surg. Walsgrave Hosps. NHS Trust.

STANSBY, Mr Gerard Patrick 24 Grangewood, Potters Bar EN6 1SH — MB BChir 1982 Camb.; BA, MB BChir Camb. 1982; FRCS Eng. 1987.

STANSFIELD, Alfred Gimson (retired) Brewhouse Cottage, Wild Hill, Hatfield AL9 6DS Tel: 01707 642610 — MB BChir 1941 Camb.; MA 1941, MB BChir Camb. 1941; FRCPath 1964. Hon. Cons. Histopath Imperial Cancer Research Fund. Prev: Rdr. & Cons. Histopath. St. Bart. Hosp. Lond.

STANSFIELD, Jean Mary (retired) Brewhouse Cottage, Wild Hill, Hatfield AL9 6DS Tel: 01707 642610 — MB ChB 1948 Ed. Prev: Asst. GP Hatfield, Herts.

STANSFIELD, Professor Stephen Alfred Department of Pychiatry, Barts and the London Queen marys school of Medicine, and Dentistry, Medical sciences building, Mile end Road, London E14NS Tel: 0207 882772517 Fax: 0207 8827924 Email: s.a.stansfeld@qmul.ac.uk; 10 Woodberry Crescent, London N10 1PH Tel: 020 8883 6524 — MB BS 1975 Lond.; PhD Lond. 1989, MB BS 1975; MRCP (UK) 1978; MRCPsych. 1982. Hons cons. Psychiat. E. Lond. & the city Health NHS Trust; Prof. of Pschiatry, Barts and the Lond. Qu. Mary Sch. of Med. and Dentistry. Socs: Roy. Soc. Med. (Vice Pres. Psychiat. Sect.). Prev: Reader (Social & Environm. Psychiat. Univ coll.med.Sch.; Vis. Prof. Preven. Med. Univ. Toronto, Canada; Sen. Regist. Maudsley Hosp. Lond.

STANSFIELD, Alison Jane 4 Cheyney Close, Steeple Morden, Royston SG8 0LT Tel: 01763 852177 Email: struby@ibm.net — MB ChB 1989 Leic.; MRCPsych 1996. Specialist Regist. (Learning

Disabil.) Hinchingbrooke Health Care Trust Huntingdon; Specialist Regist. (Learning Disabil. & Gen. Psychiat.) Yorks. Deanery. Prev: Regist. (Psychiat.) Hinchingbrooke Health Trust Huntingdon; SHO Rotat. (Psychiat.) Camb. Train. Scheme.

STANSFIELD, Damian Anthony 7 Hassness Close, Hawkley Hall, Wigan WN3 5RL — MB BS 1996 Lond.

STANSFIELD, David Phillip 2 Cresta House, 12 Ireton St., London E3 4XP Tel: 020 8983 3852 — MB BS 1989 Lond.; BSc (Physiol.) Lond. 1988. Regist. (Anaesth.) St. Bart. Hosp. Lond. Prev: Regist. (Anaesth.) Moorfields NHS Trust Lond.; SHO (Anaesth.) Milton Keynes NHS Trust & Watford Gen. Hosp.

*STANSFIELD, Francesca** 31 Woodside Drive, Bingley BD16 1RG — MB ChB 1998 Manch.; MB ChB Manch 1998.

STANSFIELD, Janet Mary 89 Recreation Road, Reading RG30 4UB — MB BS 1994 Lond.; BSc Lond. 1991; MRCP (Lond.) 1997. (UMDS) SHO (Anaesth.) Roy. Berks. Hosp. Reading.

STANSFIELD, Margaret Helen West End Medical Practice, 21 Chester Street, Edinburgh EH3 7RF Tel: 0131 225 5220 Fax: 0131 226 1910; 42 Comiston Drive, Edinburgh EH10 5QR Tel: 0131 447 6826 — MB BS 1969 Lond.; MRCS Eng. LRCP Lond. 1969. (St. Thos.) Prev: Regist. (Path.) Groote Schuur Hosp. Univ. Cape Town, S. Africa; Ho. Surg. St. Nicholas Hosp. Lond.; Ho. Phys. Lewisham Hosp. Lond.

STANSFIELD, Rosamund Eileen North Tyneside General Hospital, Newcastle upon Tyne NE29 8NH Tel: 0191 259 6660 Ext: 2386 Fax: 0191 293 2796 Email: r_stansfield@hotmail.com — MB BS 1983 Newc.; FCRpath 1998. (Newcastle uon Tyne) Cons. Microbiologist N. Tyneside Gen. Hosp. N.umbria Healthcare NHS Trust NE29 8NH. Socs: Assn. of Med. Microbiologists; Hospsital Infec. Soc.; Brit. Infec. Soc. Prev: Regist. (Microbiol.) W.. Gen. Hosp. Edin.; SHO (Path.) N.. Gen. Hosp. Sheff.; Sen. Regist. (Microbiol.) W.. Gen. Hosp. Edin.

STANSFIELD, Victoria Charlotte Standish Tel: 01865 881206 — MB BS 1986 Lond.; DRCOG 1992. GP Princip., Eynsham Med. Centre. Prev: GP Retainer Scheme N. Oxf. Med. Centre Oxf.

STANTON, Alan Spencer Solihull Healthcare, 20 Union Road, Solihull B91 3EF Tel: 0121 711 7171 Fax: 0121 711 7212; 45 Goodby Road, Moseley, Birmingham B13 8RH Email: alan@spencerstanton.freeserve.co.uk — MB BS 1981 Lond.; MSc Lond. 1994, BSc 1979; MRCP (UK) 1987; DCH RCP Lond. 1985. Cons. Community Paediat. Solihull Healthcare; Hon. Sen. Vis. Clin. Lect. Univ. Warwick 1997; Hon. Sen. Clin. Lect. Univ. Birm. 1997. Prev: Regist. (Paediat.) S. Birm. HA.

STANTON, Alice Veronica Department of Clinical & Cardiovascular Pharmacology, Imperial College School of Medicine, St Mary's Hospital, London W2 1NY Tel: 020 7594 3448 Fax: 020 7594 3411 Email: a.stanton@ic.ac.uk — MB BCh BAO 1984 NUI; PhD NUI 1993; BSc NUI 1986; MRCPI 1987. Sen. Lect. Hon. Cons. Clin. Pharm. & Therap. Dept. Clin. & Cardiovasc. Pharm. Nat. Heart Lung Inst. Imperial Coll. Sci. Technol. & Med. Prev: Lect. (Clin. Pharmacol.) Imperial Coll. Sch. Med. Lond.; Lect. (Therap.) Roy. Coll. Surg. Irel. Dub.

***STANTON, Andrew Ewing** Top Right Flat, 227 Wilton St., Glasgow G20 6DE — MB ChB 1998 Glas.; MB ChB Glas 1998.

STANTON, Anthony John, OBE Secretariat for London LMCs, BMA House, Tavistock Square, London WC1H 9HT Tel: 020 7387 7418 Fax: 020 7388 2080; 4 Southbank Gardens, Lambourn, Hungerford RG17 7LW — MB BS 1964 Lond.; MRCS Eng. LRCP Lond. 1964; DObst RCOG 1971. (Westm.) Sec. Lond. Local Med. Comms.; Dir. GPFC Ltd. Prev: SHO (O & G) Roy. Hants. Co. Hosp. Winchester; Ho. Phys. W.m. Childr. Hosp.; Surg. Lt. RN.

STANTON, Anthony Walter Burgin Division of Physiological Medicine (Dermatology), Department of Medicine, St George's Hospital Medical School, London SW17 0RE Tel: 020 8725 5438 Fax: 020 8725 3297 Email: a.stanton@sghms.ac.uk — MB BCh 1980 Wales; PhD Lond. 1989; BSc (Hons.) Wales 1977. Research Fell. (Physiol.) St. Geo. Hosp. Med. Sch. Lond. Socs: Brit. Microcirculat. Soc.

STANTON, Arthur Peter Flat 49, Ivy Lane, Headington, Oxford OX3 9DT — MB BS 1986 Sydney.

STANTON, Eleanor Frances Marshfield Road Surgery, 4647 Marshfield Road, Chippenham SN15 1JU Tel: 01249 654466 Fax: 01249 462320 — MB ChB 1991 Manch. Trainee GP Stockport.

STANTON

STANTON, Elinor Claire Ruth 45 Goodby Road, Moseley, Birmingham B13 8RH — BM 1988 Soton. Prev: SHO (Paediat.) New Cross Hosp. Wolverhampton.

***STANTON, Ian David Paul** 38 Mayfield Road, Hasbury, Halesowen B63 1BQ — MB BS 1994 Lond.

STANTON, Jean Rosina Dunstable Road Surgery, 163 Dunstable Road, Luton LU1 1BW Tel: 01582 23553 — MB BS 1983 Lond.

STANTON, Jennifer Anne Yeadon Health Centre, 17 South View Road, Yeadon, Leeds LS19 7PS Tel: 0113 295 4040 Fax: 0113 295 4044; 10 Netherfield Road, Guisley, Leeds LS20 9HE Tel: 01943 873284 Fax: 01943 870627 — MB ChB 1976 Sheff.

STANTON, Jeremy Simon 6 Gun Lane, Knebworth SG3 6AU — MB BChir 1990 Camb.

STANTON, John Albert 143 Derwen Fawr Road, Swansea SA2 8ED Tel: 01792 207935 — MB BCh 1949 Wales; BSc 1946, MB BCh Wales 1949. (Cardiff) Col. RAMC T. & AVR. Prev: Ho. Phys. Child Health, Dermatol. & Neurol. Depts Roy. Infirm.; Cardiff; Capt. RAMC.

STANTON, Josephine Anne 13 Canons Drive, Edgware HA8 7RB Tel: 020 8952 1503 — MB BS 1962 Lond.; MRCS Eng. LRCP Lond. 1962; BA Open Univ. 1995. (Middlx.) Med. Adviser Benefits Agency DSS. Prev: Princip. GP; Med. Off. Blood Transfus. Serv.; Occupat. Health Phys. Edgware Gen. Hosp.

STANTON, Joy Margaret Airedale General Hospital, Steeton, Keighley BD20 6TD Tel: 01535 652511 Fax: 01535 655129 — MB ChB 1975 Leeds; FFA RCS Eng. 1984; DA Eng. 1977; 1994 Dip. Health Serv. Mngmt. York. Cons. Anaesth. Airedale NHS Trust. Prev: Sen. Regist. (Anaesth.) Yorks. RHA.

STANTON, Judith Rose 28 Braemar Court, Ashburnham Road, Bedford MK40 1DZ — MB BS 1989 Lond.; MRCGP 1993; T(GP) 1993; DGM RCP Lond. 1993; Cert. Family Plann. JCC 1992; DRCOG 1991.

STANTON, Julie Catherine Crossbrook Surgery, 126 Crossbrook Street, Cheshunt, Waltham Cross EN8 8JY Tel: 01992 622908 Fax: 01992 624756; 89C Kelvin Road, London N5 2PL — MB BS 1986 Lond.; MRCGP 1993.

STANTON, Linda Marian (retired) 16 The Callanders, Heathbourne Road, Bushey, Watford WD23 1PU Tel: 020 8950 7760 — MB BS (Univ. Medal Hons. Path., Obst. & Gyn. & Therap.) Lond. 1961; MA Lond. 1990; MRCGP 1974. Chairp. Barnet LMC; Chairp. Barnet GP Commiss.ing Gp. Prev: GP Barnet.

STANTON, Mr Martin Barry North London Nuffield Hospital, Calvell Drive, Uplands Park Road, Enfield EN2 7NR Tel: 020 8366 2122 Fax: 020 8367 8032 — MB BS 1955 Lond.; BA Open 1991; FRCS Eng. 1963; MRCS Eng. LRCP Lond. 1955; DLO Eng. 1958. (Middlx.) Socs: Fell. Roy. Soc. Med. (Mem. Sects. Otol. & Laryng.); Brit. Assn. Otol. Prev: Cons. Surg. (ENT) Enfield Hosp. Gp.; Sen. Regist. Roy. Ear & Univ. Coll. Hosps. Lond. & (ENT) Roy. Berks. Hosp. Reading; Regist. Roy. Nat. Throat, Nose & Ear Hosp. Lond.

STANTON, Michael Philip 33 Mayfair Gardens, Banister Park, Southampton SO15 2TW — MB BS 1994 Lond.

STANTON, Morris Burmantofts Health Centre, Lincoln Green Road, Leeds LS9 7ST Tel: 0113 248 0321 — MB ChB 1943 Leeds; MB ChB (Hons.) Leeds 1943. (Leeds) Prev: Capt. RAMC, Asst. Med. Off. S. Wales Sanat.; Ho. Phys. Lincoln Co. Hosp.

STANTON, Richard Alan Hillview Lodge, Royal United Hospital Bath, Combe Down, Bath BA1 3NG Tel: 01225 324208 — MB BS 1988 Lond.; MRCPsych 1993. Cons. (Psychiat. Gen. Adult & Rehabil.) Roy. United Hosp. Bath. Prev: Sen. Regist. (Psychiat.) Univ. Coll. Hosp. Lond.; Clin. Research Fell. & Regist. (Psychiat.) Roy. Lond. Hosp.

STANTON, Robert John The Surgery, High Street, Cheslyn Hay, Walsall WS6 7AB Tel: 01922 701280; Slack Terrace Farm, Dick Edge Lane, Cumberworth, Huddersfield HD8 8YE Tel: 01484 681029 — MB ChB 1979 Sheff.

STANTON, Professor Stuart Lawrence Richard Flat 10, 43 Wimpole St., London W1G 8AE Tel: 020 7486 0677 Fax: 020 7486 6792 Email: sstantonwimpole@yahoo.com; 1 Church Hill, Wimbledon, London SW19 7BN Tel: 020 8879 1678 Fax: 020 8944 5177 — MB BS 1961 Lond.; FRANZCOG 2001; FRCS Eng. 1967; FRCS Ed. 1967; MRCS Eng. LRCP Lond. 1961; FRCOG 1987, M 1969; DObst RCOG 1963. (Univ. Lond. & Lond. Hosp.) Cons. Gyn. &Prof.St. Geo. Hosp. Lond.; Prof. Pelvic Reconstruc. & Urogyn. St. Geo. Hosp. Lond.; Asst. Edr. Internat. Urogyn. Jl; Examr. RCOG.

Socs: Assoc. Mem. BAUS; Blair Bell Res. Soc.; Fell. Roy. Soc.Med. Prev: Regist. (Surg.) Roy. Masonic Hosp. Lond.; Sen. Regist. St. Geo. Hosp. Lond.; Research Fell. Inst. Urol. Lond.

STANTON, Susan Margaret Warden Lodge Surgery, Albury Ride, Cheshunt, Waltham Cross EN8 8XE Tel: 01992 622324 Fax: 01992 636900 — MB ChB 1978 Bristol; DCH RCP Lond. 1985.

STANTON, Timothy James (retired) 5 North Mill Place, Halstead CO9 2FA Tel: 01787 479003 — MB BS 1952 Lond.; LMSSA Lond. 1952; DObst RCOG 1954; FFA RCS Eng. 1958; DA Eng. 1955. Prev: Cons. Anaesth. Crawley and Horsham Hosp.s.

STANTON, Tony 2R 3 Trefoil Avenue, Glasgow G41 3PD — MB ChB 1996 Glas. SHO (Gen. Med.) CrossHo. Hosp. Kilmarnock.

STANTON-KING, Kevin David Nene Valley Medical Centre, Clayton, Orton Goldhay, Peterborough PE2 5GP Tel: 01733 366600 Fax: 01733 370711 — MB ChB 1984 Leic.

STANWAY, Andrew Tadeusz 22 Portland Square, London E1W 2QR Tel: 020 7481 3500 Fax: 020 7481 3502 Email: panda@stanways.freeserve.co.uk — MB BS 1968 Lond.; MRCP (UK) 1971; MRCS Eng. LRCP Lond. 1968. (King's Coll. Hosp.) Psychosexual & Marital Phys. Surrey. Socs: Fell. Roy. Soc. Med. Prev: Med. Edr. Update Pub.ations Ltd.; Regist. (Med.) King's Coll. Hosp. Lond.

STANWAY, Penelope Ann 8 Woodhyrst Gardens, Kenley CR8 5LX — MB BS 1969 Lond.; MRCS Eng. LRCP Lond. 1969. (King's Coll. Hosp.) Socs: Assoc. Mem. BPA. Prev: Sen. Med. Off. Croydon AHA.

***STANWAY, Susannah Jane** 41 Clarence Place, Bristol BS2 8DD — MB ChB 1998 Bristol.

STANWAY, Tania Lea 29 Kingsway, Frodsham, Warrington WA6 6RU — MB ChB 1988 Liverp.; MRCPsych 1992.

STANWELL, Patricia Mary (retired) Candytuft, Beeding, Steyning BN44 3WN Tel: 01903 813216 — MRCS Eng. LRCP Lond. 1946.

STANWELL SMITH, Rosalind Elaine PHLS - Communicable Diseases, Surveillance Centre, 61 Colindale Avenue, London NW9 5EQ Tel: 020 8200 6868 Fax: 020 8200 7868 Email: rssmith@phls.co.uk; 60 Agamemnon Road, London NW6 1EH — MB BCh 1974 Wales; MRCOG 1980; FFCHM 1994. (Wales) Cons. Epidemiol. PHLS Communicable Dis. Surveillance Centr.; Edr. (Health & Hyg.); Hon. Sen. Lect. Lond.; Sch. of Hyg. & Trop. Med. Prev: Med. Off. Environmen. Health, Bristol; Sen. Regist. (Epidemiol.) PHLS Communicable Dis. Surveillance Centr.; Mem. Scientif. Staff MRC Epidemiol. & Med. Care Unit N.wick Pk. Hosp. Harrow.

STANWORTH, Andrew Ward Kings Road Surgery, 67 Kings Road, Harrogate HG1 5HJ Tel: 01423 875875 Fax: 01423 875885 — MB ChB 1978 Leeds. GP Harrogate.

STANWORTH, Mr Peter Antony, TD Walsgrave Hospital, Clifford Bridge Road, Coventry CV2 2DX Tel: 024 7660 2020; Long Meadow Farm, Hob Lane, Burton Green, Kenilworth CV8 1QB Tel: 024 7646 6524 Fax: 024 7646 6524 Email: pete.stanworth@cwcom.net — BM BCh 1968 Oxf.; MA (Physics) Oxf. 1967, BA (Physics) 1962, BM BCh 1968; FRCS Eng. 1973; DCH Eng. 1971. (Oxf.) Cons. Neurosurg. Walsgrave Hosp. Coventry; Lt. Col. RAMC (V). Prev: Cons. Neurosurg. Inst. Neurol. Sc. Glas.; Sen. Regist. (Neurosurg.) Manch. Roy. Infirm. & Radcliffe Infirm Oxf.

STANWORTH, Shirley Elizabeth (retired) Rockcliffe, Castle Road, Wemyss Bay PA18 6AN Tel: 01475 520488 Fax: 0145 522566 — MB ChB 1959 Manch. Assoc. Specialist (Cytol.) Inverclyde Roy. Hosp. Greenock. Prev: Assoc,. Specialist (Cytol.) Inverclyde Roy. Hosp. Greenock.

STANWORTH, Simon Jonathan 15 Ledborough Wood, Beaconsfield HP9 2DJ — BM BCh 1987 Oxf.; MRCPath 2001; BA Oxf. 1984; MRCP (UK) 1990. Specialist Regist. (Haemat.) Lond. Prev: Wellcome Fell. Inst. Molecular Med. Univ. Oxf.; SHo Rotat. Bristol & Stoke on Trent.; Specialist Regist. (Haemat.) Manch.

STAPLE, Gordon 14 Ffordd Dryden, Killay, Swansea SA2 7PA — MB ChB 1994 Manch.

STAPLES, Brian North Cheshire Health, Lister Road, Astmoor West Est, Runcorn WA7 1TW — MB ChB 1988 Liverp.; BSc (1st. cl. Hons. Phys.) Lancaster 1981; MPH Liverp. 1991; MFPHM RCP (UK) 1996; DRCOG 1997; DFFP 1998. Cons. (Pub. Health Med.). Prev: GP Princip.; GP Regist.; Sen. Regist. (Pub. Health) N. Chesh.

STAPLES, Derrick (retired) 80 Sorby Way, Wickersley, Rotherham S66 1DR — MB ChB Sheff. 1960. Prev: Asst. Cas. Off. & Ho. Surg. (ENT) Roy. Infirm. Sheff.

STAPLES, Emma Tavistock Clinic, 120 Belsize Lane, London NW3 — MB BS 1988 Lond.; MRC Psych. 1994. Sen. Regist. Psych. Tavistock Clinic. Prev: Regist. (Psychiat.) Maudsley Hosp. Lond.

STAPLES, Emma Jane 45 Millbeck Green, Collingham, Wetherby LS22 5AG — MB BS 1996 Lond.

STAPLES, Susan Ann 15 Blakeney Close, Eaton, Norwich NR4 7QP Tel: 01603 504158 — MB BS 1977 Lond.; MRCS Eng. LRCP Lond. 1977; DRCOG 1979. (Guy's)

STAPLES, Vincent John Water's Edge, Mill Lane, Govilon, Abergavenny NP7 9SA — MB BCh 1985 Wales.

***STAPLETON, Andrew James** 24 The Drive, East Preston, Littlehampton BN16 1QL — MB BS 1998 Lond.; MB BS Lond 1998.

STAPLETON, Clare Department of Anaesthesia, Frechay Hospital, Bristol BS16 1LE Tel: 0117 970 2020 — MB BS 1988 Lond.; MRCP (UK) 1993; FRCA 1995. (The London Hospital Medical College) Cons. Anaesth., Frenchay Hosp., Bristol. Socs: BMA; Assn. of Anaesth.s of Gt. Britain & Irel. Prev: SPR Anaesth., S.-W. Region; Fell. in Anaesth., St Michaels Hosp., Toronto, Canada; Clin. Research Fell., Univ. of Bristol.

STAPLETON, Edward Mark Claremont Bank Surgery, Claremont Bank, Shrewsbury SY1 1RL Tel: 01743 357355; River House, 43 Berwick Road, Shrewsbury SY1 2LS — MB BS 1985 Lond.; BSc Immunol. Lond. 1982; MRCGP 1989; DCH RCP Lond. 1989.

STAPLETON, Geoffrey Arthur Gillard The Surgery, The Coppice, Herne Lane, Rustington, Littlehampton BN16 3BE Tel: 01903 783178 Fax: 01903 859027; 24 The Drive, East Preston, Littlehampton BN16 1QL Tel: 01903 785040 Email: 100304.115@compuserve.com — MB BS 1964 Lond.; MRCS Eng. LRCP Lond. 1964; FFA RCS Eng. 1972; DA Univ. W. Indies 1968; DObst RCOG 1966. (Lond. Hosp.) Prev: Regist. Lond. Hosp. (Whitechapel) & Chase Farm Hosp. Enfield; P.ss Margt. Hosp. Nassau, Bahamas.

STAPLETON, Mr Simon Robert St John Department of Neurosurgery, Atkinson Morley's Hospital, Wimbledon, London SW20 0NE Tel: 020 8725 4179 Fax: 020 8947 8389; Rosevine, Ockham Road N., Ockham, Woking GU23 6NW — MB BS 1985 Lond.; BSc Lond. 1982, MD 1994; FRCS (SN) 1994; FRCS Eng. 1989. Cons. Neurosurg. Atkinson Morley's Hosp. Lond.

STAPLETON, Siobhan 212 Greenford Avenue, London W7 3QT — MB BCh BAO 1992 Dub.

STAPLETON, Thomas The Foundry Cottage, Lane End, High Wycombe HP14 3JS Tel: 01494 881257 — BM BCh Oxf. 1943; MA Oxf. 1945, DM 1953; FRCP Lond. 1970, M 1947; FRACP 1975; DCH Eng. 1944. (Oxf.) Emerit. Prof. Child Health Univ. Sydney & Overseas Fell. Ch.ill Coll. Camb. Socs: Hon. FRCPCH; FRCPCH (Hon.); Hon Mem. Paediat. Sect.. Roy.Soc.Med. Prev: Sec-Gen. Internat. Pediat. Assn.; Asst. Dir. Paediat. Unit St. Mary's Hosp. Med. Sch. Lond.; Tutor (Child Health) Univ. Sheff.

STAPLEY, Alison Mary East Surrey Hospital, Canada Drive, Redhill RH1 5RH Tel: 01737 768511; 16 Lavender Close, Redhill RH1 5LP — MB BS 1996 Lond. SHO GP VTS E. Surrey Hosp. Redhill.

STAPLEY, Margaret Lawson High Road Surgery, 114 High Road, South Woodford, London E18 2QS Tel: 020 8491 3310 Fax: 020 8491 3307 — MB ChB 1966 Liverp.; DCH Eng. 1970; DObst RCOG 1968. (Liverp.) Prev: Regist. (Anaesth.) Lond. Hosp.; Regist. (Paediat.) Windsor Gp. Hosps.; SHO (O & G) BRd.green Hosp. Liverp.

STAPLEY, Miss Sarah Ann, Surg. Lt.-Cdr. RN 25 Rosedale Close, Crawley RH11 8NQ Email: sas04@globalnet.uk — MB ChB 1989 Glas.; FRCS Eng. 1996. Specialist Regist. (Orthop.) P'boro Dist. NHS Trust. Prev: Specialist Regist. (Orthop.) Roy. Hosp. Haslar, Gosport.; Dep. Princip. M.O. HMS Illustrious.

***STARBUCK, Daniel Augustus** Hurst Bank, Hodder Court, Knowles Brow, Stonyhurst, Clitheroe BB7 9PP — MB ChB 1998 Sheff.; MB ChB Sheff 1998.

STARBUCK, David Paul New Pond Row Surgery, 35 South Street, Lancing BN15 8AN Tel: 01903 752265 Fax: 01903 851634 — MB ChB 1979 Leeds; MRCGP 1983.

STARBUCK, Martin John Shiregreen Medical Centre, 492 Bellhouse Road, Sheffield S5 0RG Tel: 0114 245 6123 Fax: 0114 257 0964; 53 Ranmoor Crescent, Ranmoor, Sheffield S10 3GW — MB ChB 1982 Sheff.; MRCGP 1995; DRCOG 1987. (Sheff.)

STARBUCK, Mary Joan (retired) 48 St Lawrence Forstal, Canterbury CT1 3PA Tel: 01227 765832 — MB BS Lond. 1952; FRCS Eng. 1959; MRCS Eng. LRCP Lond. 1952; FRCOphth 1988; DO Eng. 1956; DObst RCOG 1954. Prev: Cons. Ophth. Surg. Canterbury & Thanet & SE Kent Health Dists.

***STARCK, Alan Lee** 5 Watson Close, Bury St Edmunds IP33 2PG — MB BS 1996 Lond.

STARCK, Gordon Philip St Chad (retired) 74 Hempstead Road, Watford WD17 4ER — MA, MB BChir Camb. 1954; MRCS Eng. LRCP Lond. 1954; DObst RCOG 1959. Prev: Regist. (Paediat.) Salisbury Gen. Hosp.

STARCZEWSKA, Mrs Maria (retired) 90 Iveagh House, Loughborough Road, London SW9 7SF Tel: 020 7326 4830 — MB ChB 1949 Polish Sch. of Med.

STARCZEWSKI, Anthony Roman Glan Aber, Red Wharf Bay, Pentraeth LL75 8PZ — MB ChB 1976 Manch.; BSc (Hons.) (Med. Biochem.) Manch. 1973, MB ChB (Hons.) 1976; MRCP (UK) 1982. Cons. Phys. (Geriat. Med.) Ysbyty Gwynedd, Bangor. Prev: Sen. Regist. (Geriat. Med.) The Maelor Gen. Hosp. Wrexham; Regist. (Gen. Med.) War Memor. Hosp. Wrexham; SHO (Gen. Med.) Univ. Manch. Hope Hosp. Salford.

STARER, Fritz Lawnswood, 8 Green Lane, Oxhey, Watford WD19 4NJ Tel: 01923 23420 — LRCP LRCS 1949 Ed.; LRCP LRCS Ed. LRFPS Glas. 1949; FRCP Ed. 1971, M 1954; FRCR 1975; FFR 1960. Cons. Radiol. W.m. Hosp. Lond.

STAREY, Nigel Harvey Leonard Hall Farm, Hollington, Ashbourne DE6 3GB Tel: 01335 361090 Email: n.starey@derby.ac.uk — MRCS Eng. LRCP Lond. 1977; BSc (Hons.) Lond. 1972, MB BS 1977; MRCGP 1983. (Char. Cross) GP Princip.; Dir. Centre for Primary Care Univ. Derby. Prev: GP Burnham on Crouch.; Med. Adviser, N. W. Anglia Health Auth.

***STARFORD, Helen** 2 Farley Drive, Middlesbrough TS5 8QT — MB ChB 1994 Leeds.

STARITA, Carla 15 Norfolk House, Regency St., London SW1P 4BD — State Exam 1991 Naples.

STARK, Agnes Macfarlane (retired) 7 Thorp Avenue, Morpeth NE61 1JT Tel: 01670 512737 — MB ChB 1945 Glas.; MD (Commend.) Glas. 1972; FRCOG 1981, M 1951, DObst 1948. Prev: Dir. (BrE. Diag.) & Asst. (Gyn. Oncol.) Qu. Eliz. Hosp. Gateshead.

STARK, Allistair Neil Department of Haematology, Dumfries & Galloway Royal Infirmary, Bankend Road, Dumfries DG1 4AP Tel: 01387 241441 Fax: 01387 241344 — MB ChB 1980 Glas.; MRCPath 1989; MRC (UK) 1983. (Glasgow) Cons. Haemat. Dumfries & Galloway Roy. Infirm. NHS Trust. Socs: Brit. Soc. Haematol. & Assn. Clin. Path.; Fell. Roy. Coll. Pathologists; Fell. Roy. Coll. ??? (Glas.). Prev: Sen. Regist. (Haemat.) N.. RHA.

STARK, Mr Andrew Douglas Flat 3/2, 15 Haugh Road, Glasgow G3 8TX Tel: 0141 579 2368 Fax: 0141 579 2368 Email: a.stark@which.net — MB ChB 1993 Glas.; BSc (Hons.) Glas. 1990; FRCS Ed. 1997. Specialist Regist. -Orthop. W. of Scotl. Rotat. Prev: SHO (Orthop.) Glas. Roy. Infirm.; SHO (Gen. Surg.) Glas. Roy. Infirm.; SHO Rotat. (Surg. & Orthop.) W.. Infirm. Glas.

STARK, Cameron Ross 2 Scorguie Road, Inverness IV3 8QJ — MB ChB 1985 Glas.; MFPHM RCP (UK) 1994; MPH Glas. 1991; MRCPsych 1990. Cons. Pub. Health Ayrsh. & Arran HB. Prev: Regist. (Psychiat.) S.. Gen. & Levendale Hosps.

STARK, Daniel Peter Harry Dept of Med.Oncology, St James hospital., Bechett St., Leeds LS9 7TF Tel: 0113 243 3144 Fax: 0113 246 0136 Email: csjds@concerned.leeds.ac.uk — MB BChir 1993 Camb.; MRCP 1995. (Cambridge) Specialist Regist. Med. Oncol.Yorks. Rotat. Socs: Assoc.Cancer.Phys.

STARK, Edmund George 11 Wycome Road, Hall Green, Birmingham B28 9EN — MB ChB 1988 Leeds; MRCGP 1995.

STARK, Gail Lisa Dept. of Haematology, Royal Victoria Infirmary, Queen Victoria Rd, Newcastle upon Tyne NE1 Tel: 0191 232 5131 — BMedSci (Hons.) Nottm. 1992; 2001 DipRCPath; BM BS Nottm. 1994; MRCP (Lond.) 1997. Regist. (Haemat.) Roy. Vict. Infirm. Newc. u. Tyne. Prev: SHO (Med.) Newc.

STARK, Gavin Peter Victoria Street Medical Group, 7 Victoria Street, Aberdeen AB10 1QW Tel: 01224 641930 Fax: 01224 644081; 6 Ferryhill Place, Aberdeen AB11 7SE — MB ChB 1978 Aberd.; MRCGP 1990. Med. Asst., Dept. of Plastic Surg., Aberd. Roy. Infirm. Prev: Facilitator (Gen. Med. Pract.) Grampian HB.

STARK, Gordon David (retired) Craigard, Aberfeldy PH15 2LB Tel: 01887 830529 — MB ChB 1960 Ed.; FRCP Ed. 1972, M 1964; DCH RCP Lond. 1964; DObst RCOG 1963; FRCPCH 1997. Cons.

STARK

Paediat. Roy. Hosp. for Sick Childr. Edin. & St. John's Hosp. Livingston; Hon. Sen. Lect. (Child Life & Health) Univ. Edin. Prev: Cons. Paediat. (Neurol.) King Faisal Specialist Hosp. & Research Centre Riyadh, Saudi Arabia.

STARK, Isobel Mary Webster (retired) 22 Drumlin Drive, Milngavie, Glasgow G62 6LN Tel: 0141 956 2288 — MB ChB Glas. 1947; DObst RCOG 1951.

STARK, Professor James Marshall (retired) 179 Adventurers Quay, Cardiff Bay, Cardiff CF10 4NS Tel: 029 20 492581 Fax: 029 20 492621 — MB ChB Glas. 1953; MD (Commend.) Glas. 1969; FRCPath 1977, M 1965; DPath Eng. 1960. Prev: Prof. & Hon. Cons. Med. Microbiol. Univ. Wales Coll. Med. Cardiff.

STARK, Mr Jaroslav Great Ormond Street Hospital for Children NHS Trust, London WC1N 3JH Tel: 020 7831 7593 Fax: 020 7430 1281 — MD 1958 Prague; CSc Prague 1968; LAH Dub. 1970; FRCS Eng. 1980; FACC 1978; FACS 1978. (Charles Univ. Prague) Cons. Cardiothoracic Surg. Hosp. Sick Childr. Gt. Ormond St. Lond. Socs: Eur. Assn. Cardiothoracic Surg.; Hon. Mem. Amer. Assn. Thoracic Surg. Prev: Asst. (Paediat. Surg.) Chas. Univ. Prague; Sen. Regist. (Surg.) Hosp. Sick Childr. Gt. Ormond St. Lond.; Research Fell. (Cardiol.) Harvard Med. Sch. Boston, USA.

STARK, Jeremy Paul 40 Weigall Road, London SE12 8HE — MB BChir 1975 Camb.; MA Camb. 1974. Sen. Regist. (Pub. Health Med.) SE Thames RHA. Prev: GP Ryde I. of Wight; SCMO (Community Child Health) Lewisham & N. S.wark HA.

STARK, John (retired) 151 Burngreave Road, Sheffield S3 9DL Tel: 0114 272 2094 — MRCS Eng. LRCP Lond. 1953. Prev: Cas. Off. & Ho. Phys. Roy. Hosp. Sheff.

STARK, John Emanuel (retired) The Old School, Llanigon, Hereford HR3 5QA — MB BChir 1959 Camb.; MD Camb. 1967; FRCP Lond. 1975, M 1961. Prev: Sen. Lect. & Hon. Cons. Phys. St. Bart. Hosp. Lond.

STARK, Margaret Mary The Forensic Medicine Unit, St George's Hospital Medical School, Cranmer Terrace, Tooting, London SW17 0RE Tel: 020 8725 0015 Fax: 020 8725 0017 Email: stark@deam.demo.co.uk — MB BS 1981 Lond.; DGM RCP 1989; DAB Lond. 1982; DMJ (Clin.) Soc. of Apothecaries 1992; LLM Wales 1996. (Westminster) Hon. Sen. Lect., Clin. Research Fell., The Forens. Med. Unit, St Geo.'s Hosp. Medicial Sch.

***STARK, Michael John** (2F1) 15 Bernard Terrace, Edinburgh EH8 9NU — MB ChB 1996 Ed.

STARK, Philip John 11 Wycombe Road, Hall Green, Birmingham B28 9EN — MB ChB 1982 Leeds.

STARK, Robert Alexander (retired) Twelve Trees, Bare Lane, Ockbrook, Derby DE72 3RG — MB ChB 1952 Glas.; DObst RCOG 1954.

STARK, Ronald David Hill of Park House, Drumoak, Banchory AB31 5HJ Tel: 01330 811400 Fax: 01330 811409 Email: ronstsrk@mistral.co.uk — MB ChB 1965 Aberd.; PhD Aberd. 1969; MD Birm. 1973; FRCP Lond. 1985; MRCP (UK) 1973; FFPM RCP (UK) 1989. (Aberd.) Indep.Cons. Pharm.Med.; Examr. Fac. Pharmaceut. Med.; Hon. Sen. Lect. Med. & Therap. Univ. Aberd. Socs: Physiol. Soc.; Brit. Pharm. Soc.; Brit.Hypertens..Soc. Prev: Clin. Research Fell. (Med.) Univ. Birm.; Canad. MRC Research Fell. & Lect. (Pharmacol.) Univ. Manitoba, Winnipeg, Canada; Chief.Phys.ZenecaPharmaceuts.Alderley PK.

STARK, Roy Fraser (retired) Willowmead, Sutton-on-the-Forest, York YO61 1DW Tel: 01347 810489 — MB ChB St. And. 1952. Prev: Clin. Asst. (Orthop.) York Dist. Hosp.

STARK, Vida Jessie McFarlane (retired) Kivernell House, Kivernell Road, Milford on Sea, Lymington SO41 0PQ — MD 1938 Glas.; MD (Commend.) Glas. 1938, MB ChB 1925, DPH 1933. Prev: PMO Matern. & Child Welf., Liverp. Pub. Health Dept.

STARKE, Ian Douglas University Hospital Lewisham, Lewisham High St., London SE13 6LH Tel: 020 8333 3000 Fax: 020 8333 3381; Flat 11, Queen's Court, 25/27 Earl's Court Square, London SW5 9BY — MB BS 1972 Lond.; MB BS (Hons.) Lond. 1972; MD Lond. 1985, MSc 1980, BSc (1st. cl. Hons.) 1969; FRCP Lond. 1993; MRCP (UK) 1974; MRCS Eng. LRCP Lond. 1972. (Guy's) Cons. Phys. & Sen. Lect. (Med. for Elderly) Univ. Hosp. Lewisham & Guys, Kings & St. Thomas' Med. Sch.s Lond. Socs: Brit. Geriat. Soc. & Brit. Thoracic Soc. Prev: Sen. Regist. (Gen. & Geriat. Med.) Guy's Hosp. Lond.

STARKEY, Caroline Nicola Department of General Practice and Primary Care, St George's Hospital Medical School, Cranmer Terrace, London SW17 0RE Tel: 020 8725 0056 Fax: 020 8767 7697 Email: cstarkey@sghms.ac.uk; 7 Lattimer Place, London W4 2UD — MB BS 1985 Lond.; MSc Lond. 1994, BSc (Hons.) 1982; MRCGP 1990; DCH RCP Lond. 1989; DRCOG 1987. (Guys Hospital Medical School) Clin. Lect., Dept. of Gen. Pract., St Geo.'s Hosp. Med. Sch.; Non-Princip. GP.

STARKEY, Colin Woodlands, Nertherghyll Lane, Cononley, Keighley BD20 8PB — MB ChB 1971 Ed.; FFA RCS Eng. 1976.

STARKEY, Graham Bedlingtonshire Medical Group, The Health Centre, Glebe Road, Bedlington NE22 6JX Tel: 01670 822695 — MB BS 1989 Newc.; 1996 MRCGP; 1996 DRCOG. (Newc. u. Tyne) GP Princip. Bedlington N.d.; Clin. Asst. Gen. Surg. Wansbeck Gen. Hosp. Ashington; PCG Prescribing Lead Centr. PCG, N.d.; Vice Chair, Wawsbeck and Community Prescribing SubComm.

STARKEY, Ian Richard Department of Cardiology, Western General Hospital, Crewe Road S., Edinburgh EH4 2XU Tel: 0131 537 1844 Fax: 0131 537 1844 Email: ian.starkey@luht.scot.nhs.uk; 24A Cairnmuir Road, Corstorphine, Edinburgh EH12 6LP Tel: 0131 334 2755 Fax: 0131 334 7948 Email: ianstarkey1@compuserve.com — MB ChB 1975 Ed.; FRCP Ed. 1989; MRCP (UK) 1977. (Ed.) Cons. Cardiol. W.. Gen. Hosp. Edin. Socs: Brit. Cardiac Soc.; Scott. Cardiac Soc.; Brit. Cardiovasc. Interven. Soc. Prev: Sen. Regist. (Cardiol.) N.. Gen. Hosp. Sheff.

STARKEY, Katherin Gisela Bedlington Medical Group, Glebe Road, Bedlington NE22 6JX Tel: 01670 822695 Fax: 01670 531860 — MB BS 1977 Newcastle; MB BS Newc. 1977. (Newcastle) GP Bedlington, N.d.

STARKEY, Mrs Mary Rosina 8 Carlton Road, Ainsdale, Southport PR8 2PG — MB ChB 1967 Birm. (Birm.)

STARKIE, Carol Margaret (retired) Huntroyd, 27 Manor Road N., Edgbaston, Birmingham B16 9JS Tel: 0121 242 2497 — MB ChB 1963 Birm.; BSc (Hons. Anat.) Birm. 1960; MRCS Eng. LRCP Lond. 1963; FRCPath 1991, M 1979; DCH Eng. 1967. Prev: Cons. Histopath. Selly Oak Hosp. Birm.

STARKIE, Colin (retired) 142 Sutton Park Road, Kidderminster DY11 6JQ Tel: 01562 823338 — MD Manch. 1938, BSc Manch. (Anat. & Physiol.) 1928; MB ChB Manch. 1932, DPH 1933; MRCS Eng. LRCP Lond. 1931. Prev: MOH Boro. Kidderminster.

STARKIE, David William Health Centre Practice, Bromsgrove Street, Kidderminster DY10 1PG Tel: 01562 822077 Fax: 01562 823733; 47 Staite Drive, Cookley, Kidderminster DY10 3UA Tel: 01562 850132 Email: starkie.mcclung@compuserve.com — BM BS 1985 Nottm.; BMedSci Nottm. 1983; MRCGP 1989. Clin. Asst. (Rheum.) Kidderminster Gen. Hosp.; Tutor (Gen. Pract.) Kidderminster.

STARKIE, John 16 North Rise, Greenfield, Oldham OL3 7ED Tel: 0161 557 0456 — MRCS Eng. LRCP Lond. 1934; MB ChB Manch. 1936, DPH 1937; MFCM 1972. (Manch.) Prev: SCM (Child Health) Oldham AHA; Clin. Asst. Monsall Hosp. Manch.

STARKS, John Michael (retired) Strathyre, Kings Cross, Whiting Bay, Brodick KA27 8RG — MRCS Eng. LRCP Lond. 1944.

STARLEY, Mr Ian Francis 3 Railway View, Croston, Preston PR26 9RY — MB BS 1989 Lond.; MSc (Surgic. Scis.) Lond. 1995, BSc (Hons.) Microbiol. & Genetics 1984; FRCS Eng. 1995. Regist. (Plastic Surg.) Roy. Preston Hosp. Prev: SHO Rotat. (Orthop. & Surg.) Derriford Hosp. Plymouth.; Demonst. (Anat.) & Cas. Off. Univ. Coll. Hosp. Lond.; Ho. Surg. Univ. Coll. Hosp. & Middlx. Hosp.

STARLING, Andrew James Meridian Surgery, Meridian Way, Peacehaven BN10 8NF Tel: 01273 581999 Fax: 01273 589025 — MB BS 1985 Lond.; MRCGP 1991. Gen. Pract. Princip.; Clin. Asst. Demetology; Peacehaven Clinic, Brighton Health Trust. Socs: CICP; CMF.

STARR, David Ralph Plume 11 Frank Dixon Way, Dulwich, London SE21 7ET Tel: 020 8693 6696 Email: david.starr@ukgateway.net — MRCS Eng. LRCP Lond. 1956; MB BS Lond. 1956, DPH 1966; DCH Eng. 1962. (Middlx.) Socs: BMA. Prev: Ho. Phys. Middlx. Hosp. Lond.; Asst. Pathol. Bland-Sutton Inst. Middlx. Hosp. Med. Sch. Lond.; Capt. RAMC.

STARR, Dolores Ramona (retired) 71 Queens Reach, Hampton Court, East Molesey KT8 9DE — MB ChB Sheff. 1962. JP. Prev: Ho. Surg. & Ho. Phys. City Gen. Hosp. Sheff.

STARR, Mr Donald Gordon Oral and Facial Surgery, Hull Royal Infirmary, Hull HU3 2JZ Tel: 01482 675774 Fax: 01482 675064 — MB ChB 1988 Glas.; BDS Manch. 1979; FRCS (Max-Fac.) 1996; FRCS Ed. 1993; FDS RCS Eng. 1983. (Glas.) Cons. (Oral & Maxillofacial Surg.) Roy. Hull Hosp.; Hon. Cons. (Oral & Maxillofacial Surg.) York Dist. Hosp. Socs: Fell. Brit. Assn. Oral & Maxillofacial Surg.; BMA; Eur. Assn. Cranio-Maxillo. Surg. Prev: Sen. Regist. (Maxillofacial Surg.) Leeds Dent. Inst. & Gen. Infirm. Leeds; Sen. Regist. Rotat. (Maxillofacial Surg.) N.. Region; Regist. (Maxillofacial Surg.) Middlesbrough Gen. Hosp. & Newc. Gen. Hosp.

STARR, Harry (retired) 71 Queens Reach, Hampton Court, East Molesey KT8 9DE — MB ChB 1962 Sheff.; DObst RCOG 1964. Hosp. Practitioner Demat. Old Ch. Hosp. Romford Essex. Prev: Indust. Med. Off. Allied Brewery Romford Essex.

STARR, John Michael 36 Steele Road, Isleworth TW7 7HN — MB BS 1984 Lond.

STARR, Kathryn Janet Royal Cornhill Hospital, Cornhill Road, Aberdeen AB25 2ZH Tel: 01224 681818; 29 B Roadhaven Road, Old Portlethen Vill., Aberdeen AB12 4NR Tel: 01224 780556 — MB ChB 1972 Aberd.; MRCPsych 1983; MRCGP 1980; DA Eng. 1978; DObst RCOG 1974. Sen. Regist. (Psychiat.) Roy. Cornhill Hosp. Aberd.

STARR, Lesley Margaret Porch Surgery, Beechfield Road, Corsham SN13 9DL Tel: 01249 712232 Fax: 01249 701389; Tel: 01225 744195 — BM BCh 1979 Oxf.; MA 1978; MRCGP 1983; DRCOG 1982. (Cambridge & Oxford) Prev: Asst. GP Corsham & St. Jas. Surg. Bath; Trainee GP Bristol VTS.; Clin. Asst. (Endoscopy) Roy. United Hosp. Bath.

STARR, Matthew Jonathan 63 Harley Street, London W1N 1DD — MB BChir 1993 Camb.; MA Camb. 1993.

STARR, Perry Louise 612 Stannington Road, Stannington, Sheffield S6 6AE Email: perry.starr@ukonline.co.uk — MB BS 1994 Lond.; BSc (Hons.) Lond. 1991. (Univ. Coll. & Middlx. Sch. Med.) Clin. Research Fell., Centre for Reproductive Med. Walsgrave Hosp. Coventry. Prev: Specialist Regist. (O & G) Solihull Hosp.; SHO (O & G) St. James Hosp. Leeds; SHO (O & G) John Radcliffe Hosp. Oxf.

STARR, Mr Philip Alan John 63 Harley Street, London W1G 8QX Tel: 020 7636 4326 Fax: 020 7436 2046 — MRCS Eng. LRCP Lond. 1956; MD Birm. 1965, MB ChB 1956; FRCSC 1978; FRCS Eng. 1963; FRCS Ed. 1963; LMCC 1957; FRCOphth 1988; DO Sydney 1961. (Birm.) Cons. Ophth. Surg. Roy. N. Hosp. & Roy. Free Hosp. Lond. Socs: Fell. Roy. Soc. Med.; Counc. UK Implant Soc.; Counc. InDepend. Doctors Forum. Prev: Chief Clin. Asst. Moorfields Eye Hosp. Lond.; Sen. Regist. St. Mary's Hosp. Lond.; Regist. Sydney Hosp. NSW, Austral.

STARR, Rebecca Louise 17 Grand Avenue, Camberley GU15 3QJ Tel: 01276 61981 — MB ChB 1989 Leic. SHO (O & G) Geo. Eliot Hosp. Nuneaton.

STARRITT, David Raynor The Surgery, Ailsa Muir, The Market Stance, Tarland, Aboyne AB34 4UB Tel: 01339 881281 Fax: 01339 881077; Bonnington, Melgum Road, Tarland, Aboyne AB34 4YL Tel: 0133 98 81489 — MB BS 1980 Lond.; BSc (Hons.) Lond. 1976; DRCOG 1982.

STARRITT, Mary Patricia Dundallan, 32 Gravelly Hill, Birmingham B23 7PF Tel: 0121 327 1401 — MB BCh BAO 1946 Dub.; MA Dub. 1954, BA 1942, MB BCh BAO 1946; LM Coombe 1946. (T.C. Dub.)

***STARRITT, Nicola Elizabeth** Flat 1F1, 51 Marchmont Road, Edinburgh EH9 1HT — MB ChB 1996 Ed.

START, Neil John Sett Valley Medical Centre, Hyde Bank Road, New Mills, Stockport SK22 4BP Tel: 01663 743483; 133 Buxton Old Road, Higher Disley, Stockport SK12 2BX Tel: 01663 762889 Email: njstart@gpiag-asthma.org — MB ChB Liverp. 1985; AFOM RCP Lond. 1994; MRCGP 1989; DRCOG 1987; DGM RCP Lond. 1987. GP Princip.; HSE Lead Apptd. Doctor. Socs: Soc. of Occupat. Med. Prev: Trainee GP Walton & Fazakerley Hosps. Liverp. VTS.

START, Roger David Department of Histopathology, Chesterfield & North Derbyshire Royal Hospital, Calow, Chesterfield S44 5BL Tel: 01246 277271 Ext. 2277 — MB ChB 1988 Sheff.; MD Sheff. 1996; BMedSci Sheff. 1987; MRCPath 1995, D 1992. (Sheff.) Cons. Histopath. Chesterfield & N. Derbysh. Roy. Hosp. NHS Trust. Prev: Lect. (Path.) Sheff. Univ. Med. Sch.; Regist. Rotat. (Histopath.) Sheff.; SHO (Histopath.) N.. Gen. Hosp. Sheff.

START, Susan Ann 6 Silver Birch Avenue, Sheffield S10 3TA — MB ChB 1988 Sheff.; MRCGP 1882. (Sheff.)

STASSEN, Mr Leo Francis Anna Sunderland Royal Hospital, Kayll Road, Sunderland SR4 7TP Tel: 0191 565 6256 Fax: 0191 569 9231 Email: leostassen@aol.com; 19 Westfield Avenue, Gosforth, Newcastle upon Tyne NE3 4YH Tel: 0191 284 4284 Fax: 0191 246 1040 Email: leostassen@aol.com — MB BCh BAO 1980 Dub.; MA Dub. 1980, BA 1977; BDentSc TC Dub. 1977; FRCS Ed. 1984; FDS RCS Eng. 1985; Dip. Managem. Admin. UK 1995. (Trinity College Dublin) Cons. (Oral & Maxillofacial Surg.) Sunderland Roy. Hosp. & S. Tyneside Gen. Hosp. Socs: Fell. Brit. Assn. Oral & Maxillofacial Surg. (Hon. Edr. and Counc. Mem.); Craniofacial Soc.; Eur. Assn. Oral & Maxillo. Surg. Prev: Sen. Regist. (Maxillofacial Surg.) Canniesburn Hosp. Glas. & Glas. Dent. Hosp. & Sch.

STASTNY, Dusan (retired) Community Drug Service, Paget House, 2 West St., Leicester LE1 6XP Tel: 0116 247 0200 — MUDr 1967 Charles Univ. Prague; MRCPsych 1972. Cons. Psychiat. Leicester HA. Prev: Sen. Regist. (Psychiat.) St. Thos. Hosp. Lond.

STATEN, Paul The Red House Surgery, 241 Queensway, Bletchley, Milton Keynes MK2 2EH Tel: 01908 375111 — MB BS 1979 Lond.; MA Camb. 1976; MRCGP 1984; DRCOG 1984.

STATHAM, Alison Mary Latham House Surgery, 31 Lord Street, Burscough, Ormskirk L40 4BZ; 25 Emmanuel Road, Churchtown, Southport PR9 9RP Tel: 01704 231814 — MB ChB 1987 Liverp.; MRCGP 1993; DFFP 1992; DRCOG 1991; DGM RCP Lond. 1990; DCH RCP Lond. 1989. Clin. Asst. - G.U. Med. Prev: Trainee GP S.port.

STATHAM, Barry Nigel Singleton Hospital, Skelly Lane, Swansea SA2 8QA Tel: 01792 285038 Email: barry.stratham@swansea-tr.nhs.wales.uk — MB BCh 1975 Wales; FRCP 1997 Lond; MRCP (UK) 1977. Prev: Sen. Regist. (Dermat.) Leeds Gen. Infirm.; Regist. (Dermat.) Univ. Hosp. Wales Cardiff; Rotating Regist. (Med.) Univ. Hosp. Wales.

STATHAM, Helen Claire 10 The Pantiles, Bickley, Bromley BR1 2BX — MB BS 1990 Lond.; BSc Lond. 1987. SHO (Anaesth.) Bromley Hosp.

STATHAM, John Anthony 6 Hurstwood, Waverton, Chester CH3 7QJ Tel: 01244 336498 Email: Jastat@aol.com; 6 Hurstwood, Waverton, Chester CH3 7QJ Tel: 01244 Email: jastat@aol.com — MB BS 1975 Newc.

STATHAM, Neil Anthony Beechwood Surgery, 371 Chepstow Road, Newport NP19 8HL Tel: 01633 277771 Fax: 01633 290631 — MB BCh 1981 Wales; MRCGP 1985; DRCOG 1985. Prev: Trainee GP Newport VTS.; Ho. Off. (Med.) Neath Gen. Hosp.; Ho. Off. (Surg.) Llandough Hosp. Cardiff.

STATHAM, Mr Patrick Francis Xavier Western General Hospital, Crewe Road, Edinburgh EH4 2XU Tel: 0131 5372101/6 Fax: 0131 537 1133 Email: patrick.statham@ed.ac.uk; 76 Belgrave Road, Edinburgh EH12 6NQ Tel: 0131 476 9209 Email: pfxstatham@netscape.net — MB BS 1980 Lond.; FRCS Surg. Neurol. 1991; FRCS Ed. 1985; FRCS Eng. 1986. (St Bartholomews London) Cons. Neurosurg. (Clin. Neurosci.) W. Gen. Hosp. Edin.; Sen. Lect. Dept. Clin. Neurosci.s Univ. of Edin. Socs: Soc. Brit. Neurosurg. (Counc. Mem.); Cervical Spine Soc.; Europ. Skull Base Soc. Prev: Sen. Regist. (Neurosurg.) Dept. Clin. Neurosci. W.. Gen. Hosp. Edin.; Regist. (Neurosurg.) Inst. Neurol. Sci. Glas.

STATHAM, Rita (retired) 11 Platt Court, Deganwy Road, Conwy LL31 9DG — MB ChB Manch. 1956; MRCOG 1963; MFFP 1993. Clin. Asst. (Obst.) City Hosp. Nottm. Prev: SCMO & Instruc. Doctor (Family Plann.) Nottm. HA.

STATHAM, Roy 24 Victoria Crescent, Nottingham NG5 4DA Tel: 01159 607338 — MB ChB 1958 Manch. (Manch.) Emerit. Cons. Genitourin. Med. Trent RHA. Socs: Fell. Manch. Med. Soc.; (Ex-Chairm.) Reg. Adv. Sub-Comm. Genitourin. Med. Prev: Med. Off. Trent Regional Blood Trans. Serv.m.; Cons. Genitourin. Trent RHA; Med. Asst. (Venereol.) Sheff. RHB.

STATHER-DUNN, Brenda Lois Seaview, Wisemans Bridge, Saundersfoot SA69 9AU Tel: 01834 812918 Email: bsthatherdunn@compuserve.com — BM BCh Oxf. 1953; DLO Eng. 1958. (Oxf. & St. Bart.) Prev: Assoc. Specialist (Psychiat.) St. David's Hosp. Carmarthen.

STATHER-DUNN, Michael Taylor (retired) Seaview, Wisemans Bridge, Saundersfoot SA69 9AU — MB BS 1953 Lond.; MB BS

STATTER Lond. 1953.; DPM Eng. 1959. Prev: Cons. Psychiat. St. David's Hosp. Carmarthan.

STATTER, Neil Richard The Park Surgery, 4 Alexandra Road, Great Yarmouth NR30 2HW Tel: 01493 855672 — MB ChB 1973 Sheff.; FRCGP 1997, MRCGP 1977; DObst RCOG 1976. Course Organiser Gt. Yarmouth VTS. Prev: Ho. Phys. Roy. Hosp. Sheff.; Ho. Surg. Roy. Infirm. Sheff.; Trainee Gen. Pract. Doncaster Vocational Train. Scheme.

STATTERS, Deborah Jane Manchester Health Centre, Manchester Royal Infirmary, Oxford Rd, Manchester M13 9WL Tel: 0161 276 1234 Email: deborah.statters@mhc.cmht.nwest.nhs.uk; 45 Barry Court, Palatine Rd, Withington, Manchester M20 3LQ Tel: 0161 438 0339 Fax: 0161 446 1443 — BM BCh 1987 Oxf.; MA Oxf. 1987; MRCP (UK) 1992. Electrophysiol. Fell., Manch. Heart Centre. Socs: Jun. Cardiac Club; NASPE; BCS. Prev: Regist. (Cardiol.) Good Hope Hosp.Birm; Jun. Research Fell. Brit. Heart Foundat. St. Geo. Hosp. Med. Sch. Lond.; Regist. (Cardiol.) Qu. Eliz. Hosp. Birm.

STAUGHTON, Richard Charles David Lister Hospital, Chelsea Bridge Rd, London SW1W 8RH Tel: 020 7730 8308 Fax: 020 7823 5541 Email: rstaughton@lineone.net; 131 Elgin Crescent, London W11 2JH Tel: 020 7727 6989 Fax: 020 7221 7993 — MB BChir Camb. 1970; BA Camb. 1967, MA 1970; FRCP Lond. 1986; MRCP (UK) 1973. (Camb. & St. Bart.) Hon. Cons. Dermat. Roy. Hosp. Chelsea, Brompton Hosp. Lond. & King Edwd. VII Hosp. for Offs. Lond.; Cons. Dermat. Chelsea & W.m. Hosp. Lond. Socs: (Ex-Pres.) St. Johns Dermat. Soc.; (Ex-Pres.) Derm. Sec. RSM Roy. Soc. Med.; (Ex-Pres.) Dowling Club. Prev: Cons. Dermat. Addenbrooke's Hosp. Camb.; Regist. Skin Dept. St. Thos. Hosp. Lond.; Ho. Phys. St. Bart. Hosp. Lond.

STAUNTON, Avril Felicity (Schneider) Classical Homeopath and Complementary Medicine, British Embassy, USMR 5, BFPO 2; 4115 N. Ridgeview Road, McLean VA 22101, USA Email: dravrilus@aol.com — MRCS Eng. LRCP 1978 Lond.; MB ChB (Hons.) Liverp. 1978; MD Munich 1984. (Liverpool) Accreditation procedures for cl.ical Homeopath and Complementary Med., Virginia, USA. Prev: Capt. RAMC GMO Hameln, Acting SMO Detmold; Sen. Regist. Equivalent Obst. and Gyn., Univ. of Munich, Grosshadern; Lect. in Obst. and Gyn., Univ. of Munich, II Frauenklinik, Grosshadern, Univ. of Munich.

STAUNTON, Carmel Rose (retired) 204 Kennington Lane, London SE11 5DN Tel: 020 7735 1770 — MB BCh BAO 1952 NUI. Prev: GP Lond.

STAUNTON, Donal The Surgery, 32 Queen Street, Louth LN11 9AU Tel: 01507 602421 Fax: 01507 601700; 54 Westgate, Louth LN11 9YD Tel: 01507 602421 Fax: 01507 601700 — MB BS 1980 Lond.; MA (Physiol. Sci.) Oxf. 1983; DRCOG 1982. Prev: SHO (Paediat.) W. Chesh. Hosp.; SHO (O & G) Norf. & Norwich Hosp.; Ho. Surg. Amersham Gen. Hosp.

STAUNTON, Eamon Bernard Fordingbridge Surgery, Bartons Road, Fordingbridge SP6 1RS Tel: 01425 652123 Fax: 01425 654393 — MB BS 1979 Lond.; MRCGP 1986; DCH RCP Lond. 1986.

STAUNTON, Mr Michael Douglas Mary (retired) 25 Regent's Park Road, London NW1 7TL Tel: 020 7267 6171 — MB BCh BAO Dub. 1949; MA, BA Dub. 1948, LLD 1993, MCh 1962; FRCS Ed. 1957; FRCS Eng. 1957. Mem. Med. Appeal Tribunal. Prev: Cons. Surg. St. Bart. & Homerton Hosps. Lond.

STAUNTON, Michael Henry (retired) Landscape, South Bank Road, Northchurch, Berkhamsted HP4 1LL Tel: 01442 3912 — MB BS 1954 Lond. Prev: Clin. Asst. Roy. N.. Hosp. Lond.

STAUNTON, Neville John Crouch Oak Family Practice, Station Road, Addlestone, Weybridge KT13 2BH Tel: 01932 840123; The Beeches, Guildford Road, Effingham, Leatherhead KT24 5QL Tel: 01372 459236 — MB 1979 Camb.; BChir 1978. (St.Geo.) Prev: Asst. Diabetes St. Peter's Hosp. Ottershaw.

STAUNTON, Ruth Mary (retired) 29 Porson Road, Cambridge CB2 2ET — MB ChB 1960 Liverp.; MA Camb. 1977; DPH 1964 Liverp; DPM Eng. 1973.

STAUNTON, Thomas (retired) 7 Park Road, Runcorn WA7 4PU — MB BCh BAO 1945 NUI. Prev: GP Runcorn.

STAUNTON, Thomas Henry Francis Aldersbrook House, 88 Aldersbrook Road, Manor Park, London E12 5DH — MB BS 1957 Lond.; MRCS Eng. LRCP Lond. 1957.

STAVELEY, Catharine Diana Tawstock Medical Centre, 7 High Street, Chard TA20 1QF Tel: 01460 67763 Fax: 01460 66044; Knapp House, Waterlake Road, Tatworth, Chard TA20 2SZ Tel: 01460 220460 — MB BS 1986 Lond. (Roy. Free)

STAVERT-DOBSON, Adrian John 68 Lound Side, Chapeltown, Sheffield S35 2UR — MB ChB 1997 Leic.

STAVRI, Mr George Theodore Dept. Cardiothoracic Surgery, Hammersmith Hospital, Du Cane Road, London W12 0HS; 34, Linton House, 11, Holland Park Avenue, London W11 3RL — MB BS 1986 Lond.; MS 1996 Lond.; FRCS Eng. 1991. Specialist Regist., Cardiothoracic Surg., Hammersmith Hosp., Lond. Prev: Regist. (Rotat.) (Gen. Surg.) Univ. Wales Coll. Med.; Vasc. Research Fell., King's Coll. Hosp.

STAVRON, Karim John 21 Blenkarne Road, London SW11 6HZ — MB ChB 1993 Liverp.

STAVROPOULOS, Nikolaos Room 254, West Wing Nurses Home, Guys Hospital, St Thomas St., London SE1 9RT — Ptychio Iatrikes 1985 Thessalonika.

STAVROU, Margaret (retired) 31 Merton Hall Road, London SW19 3PR Tel: 020 8540 7082 — MB BS 1965 Lond.; MRCS Eng. LRCP Lond. 1963; FRCPath 1984, M 1972. Prev: Cons. (Histopath.) Qu. Mary's Hosp. Roehampton. 1978-96.

STAWARZ, Marek Jerzy Cedars Surgery, 8 Cookham Road, Maidenhead SL6 8AJ Tel: 01628 620458 Fax: 01628 633270 — MB BS 1987 Lond. Trainee GP/SHO Ealing Hosp. VTS. Prev: Regist. (Child Psychiat.) N.wick Pk. Hosp. Harrow.

STAYTE, Dennis John (retired) 636 Magdalen Yard Road, Dundee DD2 1AL Tel: 01382 642161 — MB ChB 1960 Bristol; MRCGP 1975; DLO Eng. 1964. Prev: Princip. GP Lond.

STAYTE, Wendy Mary Erme House, Mr Gould Hospital, Plymouth PL4 7QD Tel: 01752 272317 Fax: 01752 272361; Port Meadow, 2 Seymour Villas, Totnes TQ9 5QR Tel: 01803 868305 Email: wendysayte@mailcity.com — MB 1966 Camb.; BA Camb. 1962, MB 1966, BChir 1965; MRCPsych 1972; DPM Eng. 1969; DCH Eng. 1967. Cons. Child. Psychiat. Plymouth Hosps. Trust. Socs: ACPP Scientif. & Med. Network; Roy. Soc. Med. Prev: Cons. Child Psychiat. Pk.side Clinic Lond.; Sen. Regist. (Child Psychiat.) Tavistock Clinic Lond.

STAZIKER, Ann Christine 50 Menzieshill Road, Dundee DD2 1PU Tel: 01382 642612 — MB ChB 1968 St. And.; FFA RCS Eng. 1973. (St. And.) Cons. Anaesth. Ninewells Hosp. Dundee.

STEAD, Alan Lawrence (retired) Bryn Awel, Holyhead LL65 2TF Tel: 01407 2073 — MB ChB 1948 St. And.; MD St. And. 1954, MB ChB 1948; FFA RCS Eng. 1954; DA Eng. 1952. Prev: Cons. Anaesth. United Liverp. Hosps. & Liverp. Regional Hosp. Bd.

STEAD, Barbara Elizabeth 5 Springfield Close, Burton on the Wolds, Loughborough LE12 5AN — MRCS Eng. LRCP Lond. 1957; FRCS Eng. 1971; DLO Eng. 1960. (Leeds) Prev: Supernum. Sen. Regist. (ENT) Nottm. Gen. Hosp.; Regist. Metrop. ENT Hosp. Lond.; Otol. Jt. MRC/NPL Working Gp. on Indust. Noise & Hearing.

STEAD, Brian Roy, TD (retired) 3 Hamilton Road, Newmarket CB8 0NQ Tel: 01638 662454 — MB ChB 1956 Ed.; FFA RCS Eng. 1963; DA Eng. 1958. Prev: Cons. Anaesth. Gen. Hosp. Newmarket, W. Suff. Hosp. Bury St. Edmunds &Addenbrooke's Hosp. Camb.

STEAD, Catherine Anne 35 Rugby Road, Brighton BN1 6EB — MB ChB 1986 Sheff.

STEAD, Christina Ellis Caldwell (retired) Bryn Awel, Gors Avenue, Holyhead LL65 1PB Tel: 01407 2073 — LRCP LRCS 1949 Ed.; LRCP LRCS Ed. LRFPS Glas. 1949. Clin. Med. Off. Sch. Health Serv. Liverp.; Sch. Med. Off. Liverp. AHA.

STEAD, Graham William 8 Oakleigh View, West Lane, Baildon, Shipley BD17 5TP — MB ChB 1975 Dundee.

STEAD, Harry West Grove, Bramley, Leeds LS13 1HD — MB ChB 1942 Leeds. (Leeds) Prev: RAMC; Med. Regist. Halifax Roy. Infirm.

STEAD, Janet Elizabeth Roche Products Ltd., PO Box 8, Welwyn Garden City AL7 3AY Tel: 01707 367833; 2B Prospect Road, St Albans AL1 2AX — BM BS 1986 Nottm.; BMedSci Nottm. 1984; MRCP (UK) 1990; MRCGP 1994. Pharmaceut. Phys. Roche Products Ltd. Welwyn Garden City. Prev: Regist. (Dermat.) Glas. Roy. Infirm.; SHO (Dermat.) Univ. Hosp. Nottm.; SHO (Med.) City Hosp. Nottm.

STEAD, Jonathan William Wyndham House Surgery, Fore Street, Silverton, Exeter EX5 4HZ Tel: 01392 860034 Fax: 01392 861165; 17 Cranford Avenue, Exmouth EX8 2HT Tel: 01395 225654 — MB

BS 1974 Lond.; MPhil Lond. 1993, MB BS 1974; MRCGP 1979; DRCOG 1978.

STEAD, Matthew Sumner Carnewater Practice, Dennison Road, Bodmin PL31 2LB Tel: 01208 72321 Fax: 01208 78478; Kingberry, 38 Rhind St, Bodmin PL31 2EL — BM BCh 1981 Oxf.; MA Oxf. 1987, BM BCh 1981; MRCGP 1986; Dip. IMC RCS Ed. 1991.

STEAD, Robert John Macclesfield District General Hospital, Victoria Road, Macclesfield SK10 3BL Tel: 01625 661350 Fax: 01625 663150 — MB ChB 1977 Birm.; FRCP Lond. 1994; MRCP (UK) 1980. (Birm.) Cons. Phys. Macclesfield Dist. Gen. Hosp.; Postgrad. Clin. Tutor. Socs: Brit. Thorac. Soc.; NW Thoracic Soc.; Nat. Assn. Clin. Tutors. Prev: Sen. Regist. (Gen. & Respirat. Med.) Yorks. RHA; Lect. (Thoracic Med.) Cardiothoracic Inst. Lond.; Regist. (Gen. Med. Endocrinol.) Soton. Gen. Hosp.

***STEAD, Tanya Louisa** 10 Whyteleafe Road, Caterham CR3 5EE — MB ChB 1998 Bristol.

STEADMAN, Alison Fay 26 Vitre Gardens, Lymington SO41 3NA — MB ChB 1992 Leic.

STEADMAN, James Richard (retired) 1 Ashton Way, Woodburn Est., Whitley Bay NE26 3JH Tel: 01632 524208 — MB BS 1943 Durh. Prev: Cons. Anaesth. Tynemouth Vict. Jubilee Infirm. & Preston Hosp. N.

STEADMAN, Karen Elaine 8 Crispin Close, Locks Heath, Southampton SO31 6TD — MB ChB 1989 Leic.; MRCGP 1994; DRCOG 1993; DCH RCP Lond. 1993. Sen. Regist. (Palliat. Med.) Countess Mt.batten Hse. Soton. Prev: Trainee GP Kettering VTS.

STEADMAN, Philip William Melvyn St Nicholas Centre, 79b Tewson Road, London SE18 1BB; 55 Shrewbury Lane, London SE18 3SE — MB BS 1989 Lond.; MSc Managem. Sci. Lond. 1984, BSc (Hons.) 1974; MRCPsych 1994. Cons. Psychiat. Socs: BMA; Roy. Soc. Med.

STEAN, Martin Leslie Priory Road Surgery, Priory Road, Park South, Swindon SN3 2EZ Tel: 01793 521154 Fax: 01793 512562; Wellview Cottage, Broad Hinton, Swindon SN4 9PA Tel: 01793 731071 — MB BS 1985 Lond.; MRCGP 1996; DCH RCP Lond. 1988; DRCOG 1988; Cert. Family Plann. JCC 1988. (King's Coll.) Tutor (Gen. Pract.) Swindon; Lect. (Gen. Pract.) Bath Univ.

STEANE, Patricia Ann, OBE Singleton Hospital, Swansea NHS Trust, Sketty, Swansea SA2 8QA Tel: 01792 285259 Fax: 01792 285260; White Lodge, 279 Gower Road, Sketty, Swansea SA2 7AA Tel: 01792 205396 — MB BS 1962 Lond.; MRCS Eng. LRCP Lond. 1962; FFA RCS Eng. 1971; DA Eng. 1964. (Roy. Free) Med. Dir. Cons. Anaesth. Singleton Hosp. Swansea. Socs: Assn. Anaesth. & Obst. Anaesth. Assn. Prev: Cons. Anaesth. Morriston Hosp. Swansea; Sen. Regist. (Anaesth.) Singleton & Morriston Hosps. Swansea.

STEARE, Alison Louise 15 Wellmans Meadow, Kingsclere, Newbury RG20 5HJ — MB BS 1984 Lond.; MRCGP 1989; DRCOG 1987. (Char. Cross)

STEARE, Stephen Eric Bayer plc, Strawberry Hill, Newbury RG15 1JA Tel: 01635 563052 — MB BS 1985 Lond.; MD Lond. 1994; MRCP (UK) 1988. Head Clin. Developm. Bayer plc Newbury. Prev: Clin. Lect. Univ. Coll. Lond.; Regist. (Clin. Cardiol.) Hammersmith Hosp. Lond.

STEARMAN, Andrew Steven Lee 322 Old Shoreham Road, Hove BN3 7HA — MB BS 1992 Lond.

***STEARN, Alison Claire** 19 Aubrey Road, London E17 4SL — BM 1995 Soton.

STEARN, Margaret Ruth 5 Leckford Place, Oxford OX2 6JB — BM BCh 1972 Oxf.; MRCP (U.K.) 1976; FRCP 1998.

STEARNES, Graham Nigel Touchwood, Hill Farm Road, Taplow Village, Maidenhead SL6 0EY Tel: 01628 666173; 60 West Drayton Road, Hillingdon, Uxbridge UB8 3LA Tel: 020 8573 7674 — MB BS 1975 Lond.

STEARNS, Anthony Herbert (retired) Madrono, 341 Maidstone Road, Chatham ME5 9SE — MB ChB 1953 Sheff. Prev: Regist. (Med.) Croydon Gen. Hosp.

STEARNS, Elizabeth Jane Elford Coroner's Court, Queens Road, Walthamstow, London E17 8QP Tel: 020 8520 7247; Hill Farm, Watling St, Radlett WD7 7HP Tel: 01923 856354 — MRCS Eng. LRCP Lond. 1974; MB BS Lond. 1974, BDS (Hons.) 1970; LDS RCS Eng. 1969; Barrister 1997. (Guy's) HM Coroner for the E.ern Dist. of Gt.er Lond. Prev: Dep. Coroner N.ern Dist. Gt.er Lond.

STEARNS, Mr Michael Patrick Suite 14, 30 Harley St., London W1G 9PN Tel: 020 7631 4448 Fax: 0207 637 7606; Hill Farm, Watling St, Radlett WD7 7HP Tel: 01923 856354 — MRCS Eng. LRCP Lond. 1974; MB BS Lond. 1974, BDS (Hons.) 1970; FRCS Eng. 1978. (Guy's) Cons. ENT Surg. Roy. Free Hosp. & Barnet Hosp. Lond.; Roy. Nat. Ear, Nose and Throat Hosp., Lond. Prev: Fell.sh. Facial Plast. Surg. Portland Oregon, USA.; Sec. Europ. Acad. of Facial Plastic Surg. 1989-94.

STEARS, Anna Jane 11 Cherry Close, Dinas Powys CF64 4RG — MB BS 1992 Lond.

STEBBING, Birgit Middlefield, Hinton Way, Great Shelford, Cambridge CB2 5AN — MB BS 1968 Lond.

STEBBING, Jane Elizabeth The Alresford Surgery, Station Road, Alresford SO24 9JL Tel: 01962 732345; 11 Fair View, Alresford SO24 9PR Tel: 01962 735384 — MB BS 1984 Lond.; MA Camb. 1985, BA 1981; DCH RCP Lond. 1989; DRCOG 1988. (Guy's) Prev: Trainee GP/SHO Hants. Co. Hosp. Winchester VTS; SHO (Med.) Ipswich Hosp.; SHO (A & E) Lewisham Hosp. Lond.

STEBBING, Mr John French Royal Surrey County Hospital, Egerton Road, Guildford GU2 7XX Tel: 01483 571122 Fax: 01483 464157 Email: jstebbing@uk-consultants.co.uk — MB BS 1987 Lond.; MA Camb. 1988; FRCS Eng. 1991; MS Lond. 1997; FRCS (Gen.) 1998. Cons. (Surg.) Roy. Surrey Co. Hosp. Guild. Prev: Sen. Regist. (Gen. Surg.) S. W. Region; MRC Clin. Research Fell. Univ. Oxf.; Regist. Rotat. (Surg.) SW Thames.

STEBBING, Miss Margaret Anne North Hampshire Hospital, Aldermaston Road, Basingstoke RG24 9NA Tel: 01256 313566 Fax: 01256 313512; Two Ponds, Crondall Road, Crookham Village, Fleet GU51 5SZ Email: anne.stebbing@tesco.net — MB BS 1981 Lond.; MA Camb. 1982; MD Lond. 1993; FRCS Eng. 1986; FRCS Ed. 1986; T(S) 1993. (Guy's) Cons. Surg. N. Hants. Hosp. Basingstoke. Socs: Hon Sec Surg. Sect. RSM; BASO; Fell. ASGBI. Prev: Sen. Regist. (Surg.) St. Geo. Hosp. Lond.; Regist. (Surg.) Frimley Pk. Hosp.; SHO (Surg.) Roy. Surrey Co. Hosp. Guildford.

STEBBINGS, Neville Eric The Nottingham Nuffield Hospital, Mansfield Road, Woodthorpe, Nottingham NG5 3FZ Tel: 0115 993 2015 Fax: 0115 967 3005; Munden House, 2 Fairlawn Place, Private Road, Sherwood, Nottingham NG5 4DD Tel: 0115 960 5638 Fax: 0115 960 5638 — MB BS Lond. 1950; MRCS Eng. LRCP Lond. 1950. (St. Bart.) Med. Dir. Center Parcs UK Ltd.; Company Doctor Carlton Television Studios E. Midl.; Theatre Doctor Roy. Centre Nottm. Socs: Fell. Roy. Soc. Med. Prev: Clin. Asst. City Hosp. Nottm.; Capt. RAMC.

STEBBINGS, Mr William Stanley Lewis Tel: 01603 286423 Fax: 01603 286423 Email: denise.batchelor@norfolk-norwich.thenhs.com — MB BChir 1977 Camb.; MChir Camb. (Distinc.) 1988; FRCS Eng. 1981. (Camb. & St. Bart.) Cons. Gen. Surg. (Coloproctol.) Norf. & Norwich Hosp.; Hon. Sen. Lect. Univ. E. Anglia; Progr. co-ordinator for Higher Surgic. Train., E. Anglia Region. Socs: Fell. Roy. Soc. Med. Prev: Resid. Surg. Off. St. Mark's Hosp. Lond.; Sen. Regist. (Gen. Surg.) St. Bart. Hosp. Lond.; Regist. (Surg.) N. Middlx. Hosp. Lond.

***STECHMAN, Michael James** 45 Oakwood Avenue, Purley CR8 1AR — MB ChB 1994 Birm.

STECKLER, Thomas Horst Wolfgang 53 Eland Edge, Ponteland, Newcastle upon Tyne NE20 9AY — State Exam Med 1990 Berlin.

STEDDON, Simon John Ashdown, 48 Rayleigh Road, Hutton, Brentwood CM13 1AD — MB BS 1993 Lond.

STEDEFORD, Averil (retired) 71 Sandfield Road, Headington, Oxford OX3 7RW Tel: 01865 762383 — MB BS 1955 Lond.; MRCPsych 1976; DPM Eng. 1975; DCH Eng. 1958; DObst RCOG 1958. Prev: Cons. Psychol. Med. Sir Michael Sobell Hse. Oxf.

STEDEFORD, Judith Clare Flat 5, Chelholm, Lansdown Road, Cheltenham GL51 6PU — MB BS 1993 Lond.; MRCP (UK) 1996. (St. Bart. Med. Coll. Lond.)

STEDEFORD, Mr Roland David (retired) 23 High Street, Ascott-under-Wychwood, Chipping Norton OX7 6AW — BM BCh 1956 Oxf.; PhD Lond. 1960; MA, BM BCh Oxf. 1956; FRCS Eng. 1961. Prev: Cons. Surg. Havering Hosps. Trust.

STEDMAN, Alan Ernest Weybridge Health Centre, 22 Church Street, Weybridge KT13 8DW Tel: 01932 853366 Fax: 01932 844902 — MB BS 1967 Lond.; MRCS Eng. LRCP Lond. 1967; MRCGP 1984; DObst RCOG 1970. (St. Geo.) Prev: Ho. Off. Gen.

STEDMAN

Med. St. Chas. Hosp. Lond.; Res. Obst. Asst. & Ho Surg. St. Geo. Hosp. Lond.

*STEDMAN, Alan Jeffrey 60 Victoria Road, Clacton-on-Sea CO15 6BJ — BM 1994 Soton.

STEDMAN, Brian 82 Canon Street, Winchester SO23 9JQ — MB BS 1994 Lond.

STEDMAN, Caroline Jane Sophia 82 Canon Street, Winchester SO23 9JQ — MB BS 1994 Lond.; BSc (Hons.) Lond. 1993. SHO (Med.) N.wick Pk. Hosp. Lond. Prev: Ho. Phys. (Med.) Roy. Free Hosp. Sch. Med.; Ho. Surg. N. Staffs. Roy. Infirm.

STEDMAN, Hamish Gordon Blair Manchester Road Surgery, 63 Manchester Road, Swinton, Manchester M27 5FX Tel: 0161 794 4343 Fax: 0161 736 0669 — MB ChB 1978 Manch.; BSc St. And. 1975. Clin. Asst. (O & G) Salford HA; Med. Off. St. Ann's Hospice.

STEDMAN, Juliet Kate The Park Medical Centre, 691 Coventry Road, Small Heath, Birmingham B10 0JL; 36 Clarence Road, Harbone, Birmingham B17 9LG Tel: 01214 261018 — MB ChB 1993 Birm.; DCH 1996. (Birmingham) p/t GP Retainer The Pk. Med. Centre, Small Heath. Socs: Med. Protec. Soc.; BMA; MSS. Prev: GP/Regist. Worcs VTS; SHO Worcester Roy. Infirm. VTS; Ho. Off. (Gen. Med.) Alexandra Hosp. Redditch & Qu. Eliz. Hosp. Birm.

STEDMAN, Sarah Anne Whitelands, Hyde Road, Long Sutton, Basingstoke RG29 1SP — MB BS 1978 Lond.; DRCOG 1983; DCH RCP Lond. 1982. (Lond. Hosp.)

STEDMAN, Stephen Roger 36 Clerence Road, Birmingham B17 9LG Email: roger@drstad.demon.co.uk — MB ChB 1993 Birm.; ChB Birm. 1993; FRCA. (Birmingham) Specialist Regist. (Anaest.) Birm Univ Hosp.

STEDMAN, Susan Lynda Layer Road Surgery, Layer Road, Colchester CO2 9LA Tel: 01206 546494 Fax: 01206 369912 — MB ChB 1974 Sheff.

STEDMAN, Vanessa Ruth — MB BS 1991 Lond.; MRCP (UK) 1995. GP. Socs: Med. Defence Union. Prev: Regist. (ITU & Med.) Sydney, Austral.

STEDMAN, William John 9 Nethercroft Drive, Packington, Ashby-de-la-Zouch LE65 1WT Tel: 01530 412704 — MB ChB 1945 Ed.; DObst RCOG 1949. Prev: Ho. Surg. Chalmers' Hosp. Edin.

STEDMAN, Yvonne Florence Dingle Barn, Dingle Road, Leigh, Worcester WR6 5JX Tel: 01886 833039 — MB BS 1975 Newc.; MFFP 1993; MRCGP 1979; DGM RCP Lond. 1992; DRCOG 1978. (Newcastle upon Tyne) Cons. Family Plann. & Reproduc. Health Care S. Worcs. Community NHS Trust; Hon. Sen. Clin. Lect. (Obst. & Gyn.) Univ. Birm. Socs: Chairm. W. Midl. Assn. Family Plann. Doctors. Prev: SCMO Mancunian Community Health Care.

STEED, Andrew John Pathology Laboratory, Halifax General Hospital, Salterhebble, Halifax HX3 0PW Tel: 01422 57171; 11 High Court, Slack Top Heptonstall, Hebden Bridge HX7 7HA Tel: 01422 845119 — MB ChB 1973 Manch.; BSc (Hons.) Manch. 1969, MSc 1971; FRCP (1997); FRCPath (1997). (Manch.) Cons. Haemat. Calderdale HA.

STEED, Andrew John 27 Thornleigh, Newry Road, Armagh BT60 1HT — MB ChB 1986 Manch.; BSc (Med. Sci.) St. And. 1983. Med. Off. (Occupat. Health Serv.) Belf.; Clin. Asst. (Cas.) Armagh Community Hosp. Socs: Soc. Occupat. Med. Prev: Partner Boness Rd. Pract. Grangemouth; Trainee GP Alness; SHO (Psychiat.) St. Lukes Hosp. Armagh.

STEED, Elizabeth Ann Pontcae Surgery, Georgetown, Merthyr Tydfil CF48 1YE; 55 Chester Close, Heolgerrig, Merthyr Tydfil CF48 1SW — MB ChB 1983 Liverp.; MRCGP 1987; DRCOG 1985. Prev: Trainee GP Merthyr Tydfil VTS; Ho. Off. (Surg. & Med.) Mid Glam. HA.

STEED, Joan Margaret Dr Martys and Partners, Darley Dale Medical Centre, Two Dales, Matlock DE4 2SA Tel: 01629 733205; Falkland House, 10 New Road, Youlgreave, Bakewell DE45 1WP Tel: 01629 636195 — MB BS 1978 Lond.; DRCOG 1982. (Kings Coll. Hosp. Med. Sch. Lond.) Retainer GP. Prev: Retainer GP Drs Dave and Craven, Allen St., Cheadle, Staffs.; Partner at Dr Middleton & Partners Storer Rd Surg. LoughBoro. Leics.

STEED, Sarah Sylvia Shelford Health Centre, Ashen Green, Great Shelford, Cambridge CB2 5EY Tel: 01223 843661 Fax: 01223 844569 — MB BChir 1983 Camb.; MA Camb. 1984; MRCGP 1987; DRCOG 1986. (Camb. & St. Thos.) p/t Princip. GP. Prev: Trainee GP Camb. VTS; SHO (A & E) St. Thos. Hosp. Lond.; SHO (O & G) St. Thos. Hosp. Lond.

STEEDE, Francis Desmond FitzGerald (retired) 32 Oak Close, Ottery St Mary EX11 1BB Tel: 01404 815077 — MB BCh BAO 1938 Dub.; DPH Leeds 1950; MFCM 1972. Prev: DCP Swindon HA & MOH Thamesdown Boro. & Kennet Dist. Councs.

STEEDEN, Andrew Louis Honicknowle Green Medical Centre, Honicknowle Green, Plymouth PL5 3PY Tel: 01752 704364 Fax: 01752 789130; 6 Park Road, Lower Compton, Plymouth PL3 5DR — MB ChB 1987 Glas.

STEEDMAN, Gail Great Barr Group Practice, 912 Walsall Road, Great Barr, Birmingham B42 1TG Tel: 0121 357 1250 Fax: 0121 358 4857 — MB BS 1974 Lond.; MRCP (UK) 1979; DRCOG 1987; DCH Eng. 1977; DTM & H Eng. 1978.

*STEEDS, Charlotte Emma 21 Canynge Square, Clifton, Bristol BS8 3LA — MB BS 1996 Lond.

STEEDS, John Harold, MBE (retired) Orchard End, Whitehouse Lane, West Bergholt, Colchester CO6 3ET Tel: 01206 241491 — MRCS Eng. LRCP Lond. 1942; MB BChir Camb. 1946; MA Camb. 1946; FRCGP 1981; DCH Eng. 1946. Med. Off. Univ. Essex. Prev: Regist. (Paediat.) & Ho. Surg. (Midw. & Gyn.) & Regist. Middlx. Hosp.

*STEEL, Alan William Flat 3, 20 Porten Road, London W14 0LZ — MB BS 1996 Lond.

STEEL, Andrew 189 Arundel Drive, Poulton-Le-Fylde, Blackpool — MB BS 1981 Newc.; MRCP (UK) 1984; FRCP Lond. 1997. Cons. Integrated Med. Kettering Gen Hosp NHS Trust. Prev: Sen. Regist. (Geriat. & Gen. Med.) W. Midl. Regional Train. Scheme; Oesoph. Cancer Research Appeal Fell.; Regist. (Gen. Med.) Good Hope Gen. Hosp. Sutton Coldfield.

STEEL, Andrew Christopher 49C Dartmouth Park Road, Dartmouth Park, London NW5 1SU — MB BS 1996 Lond.; BSc Lond. 1993. (St. Bartholomew's Hospital Medical College) SHO Rotat. (Gen. Med.) Roy. Free Hosp. Hampstead Lond. Prev: Ho. Phys. St. Bart. Hosp.; Ho. Surg. Bristol Roy. Infirm.

STEEL, Andrew Michael Alderman Jack Cohen Health Centre, Springwell Road, Sunderland SR3 4HG Tel: 0191 522 9908 Fax: 0191 528 8294 — MB BS 1985 Newc.; MRCGP 1989. Prev: SHO (Paediat.) S. Shields Gen. Hosp.; SHO (Cas.) Ingham Infirm. S. Shields; SHO (Geriat. Med.) Shotley Bridge Gen. Hosp.

STEEL, Mr Anthony Edgar London Otological Centre, 66 New Cavendish St., London W1G 8TD Tel: 020 7637 5111; Studland Cottage, Belvedere Road, Burnham-on-Crouch CM0 8AJ Tel: 01621 784093 — MRCS Eng. LRCP Lond. 1949; FRCS Eng. 1961. (St. Mary's) Hon. Cons. ENT Surg. S.end Health Dist.; ENT Adviser (RCS) NE Thames RHA. Socs: Fell Roy. Soc. Med. (Mem. Sects. Otol. & Laryng.). Prev: Cons. ENT Surg. S.end Health Dist.; Regist. St. Mary's Hosp. Lond. & Hammersmith Hosp.; Lt.-Col. RAMC, TA.

STEEL, Anthony Macpherson (retired) West Street Surgery, 12 West St., Chipping Norton OX7 5AA Tel: 01608 642529 Fax: 01608 645066 — MB ChB Ed. 1963; FRCGP 1982, M 1969. Prev: Med. Off. Nat. Childr. Homes Chipping Norton.

STEEL, Charles Nicholas 60 Chestnut Avenue, Esher KT10 8JF — MRCS Eng. LRCP Lond. 1974.

STEEL, Professor Christopher Michael School of Biological & Medical Science, University of St Andrews, Bute Medical Building, St Andrews KY16 9TS Tel: 01334 463558 Fax: 01334 463482 Email: cms4@st-and.ac.uk; 3A The Scores, St Andrews KY16 9AR Tel: 01334 472877 — MB ChB 1965 Ed.; MB ChB (Hons.) Ed. 1965; FRSE 1994; PhD Ed. 1972, BSc (Hons. Physiol.) 1962, DSc 1988; FRCS Ed. 1994; FRCPath 1992, M 1982; FRCP Ed. 1990, M 1968. (Ed.) Prof. Med. Sci. Univ. St And.; Hon. Cons. Phys. Lothian HB; Mem. UK Cancer Family Study Gp.; Mem. UK Gene Ther. Advis. Comm. Socs: Fell. Roy. Soc. Med.; BMA. Prev: Dep. Dir. MRC Human Genetics Unit W.. Gen.; MRC Trav. Research Fell. (Path.) Kenyatta Nat. Hosp. Nairobi, Kenya; Research Fell. (Med.) W.. Gen. Hosp. Edin.

STEEL, Claire Suzanne 1 The Orchard, Hepscott, Morpeth NE61 6HT — MB BS 1989 Newc.; DRCOG 1992; MRCGP 1993. (Newcastle) Prev: GP Bristol.

STEEL, Mr David Henry William Sunderland Eye Infirmary, Queen Alexandra Road, Sunderland SR2 9HP Email: dhwsteel@hotmail.com — MB BS 1989 Newc.; FRCOphth 1993. (Newcastle Upon Tyne) p/t Cons. Ophthalmologist, Sunderland eye Infirm.

STEEL, Dennis Eightlands Road, Dewsbury WF13 2P Tel: 01924 465929 — MB BS 1961 Lond.; MRCS Eng. LRCP Lond. 1961.

STEELE

(King's Coll. Hosp.) Prev: Ho. Surg. & Ho. Phys. Dulwich Hosp.; Ho. Surg. Obst. St. Lukes' Hosp. Bradford.

STEEL, Eleanor Judith Les Hunguets Farm, La Route Des Blicqs, St Andrews — MB BS 1974 Newc.; DObst. RCOG 1976. GP Guernsey. Prev: GP Welwyn Gdn. City.

***STEEL, Elizabeth Anne** Cumberhead Farm, Lesmahagow, Lanark ML11 0HN — MB ChB 1994 Glas.

***STEEL, Elizabeth Anne** 21 Berkeley Precinct, Hunters Bar Ecclesall Rd, Sheffield S11 8PN — MB ChB 1997 Sheff.

STEEL, George Mark Ann Burrow Thomas Health Centre, South William Street, Workington CA14 2ED Tel: 01900 603985 Fax: 01900 871131 — MB BS 1987 Newc.; MRCGP 1992.

STEEL, Graham 17 Warren Road, Orpington BR6 6JF — MB BCh 1992 Wales.

***STEEL, Graham Fulton** 11- Corsebar Road, Paisley PA2 9PY — MB ChB 1996 Glas.

STEEL, Helen Clare North Oxford Medical Centre, 96 Woodstock Road, Oxford OX2 7NE Tel: 01865 311005 Fax: 01865 311257 — MB BS 1982 Lond.; MA Oxf. 1983; MRCGP 1986; DRCOG 1986. (Oxf. & Univ. Coll. Hosp.)

STEEL, Helen Mary HIV & Opportunistic Infections, Therapeutic Development Group, Glaxo Wellcome, Greenford Road, Greenford UB6 0HE Tel: 020 8966 3673 Fax: 020 8864 9599; 31 New Cross Road, London SE14 5DS — MB BS 1982 Lond.; BSc Lond. 1979, MD 1994; MRCPath 1990; FRCPath 1998. (St. Geo. Hosp.) Sen. Clin. Research Phys. Glaxo Wellcome plc & Hon. Lect. (Virol.) St. Geo. Hosp. Med. Sch. Lond. Prev: Sen. Regist. (Virol.) St. Geo. Hosp. Lond. & Kingston Hosp. Surrey.

STEEL, James Roger 352A Old Ford Road, London E3 5TA — MB BS 1990 Lond.

STEEL, Jonathan Andrew Paul The Street Surgery, 42 The Street, Uley, Dursley GL11 5SY; Cotswold House, Pitt Court, North Nibley, Dursley GL11 6EH — MB ChB 1985 Bristol; MRCP (UK) 1988; T (GP) 1991. Prev: Trainee GP/SHO (Paediat.) Cheltenham HA VTS.

STEEL, Judith Margaret, MBE Department of Diabetes, Victoria Hospital, Kirkcaldy KY2 5AN Tel: 01592 643355 Fax: 01592 647090; 3A The Scores, St Andrews KY16 9AR Tel: 01334 472877 Fax: 01334 472877 Email: mandjsteel@aol.com — MB ChB 1965 Ed.; MB ChB (Hons.) Ed. 1965; FRCP Ed. 1981, M 1968; Cert. JCC Lond. 1976. (Ed.) Assoc. Specialist (Diabetes) Vict. Hosp. Kirkcaldy; Hon. Sen. Lec. Univ. St. Andrews. Socs: BMA & Brit. Diabetic Assn. Prev: Sen. Regist. & Regist. Diabetic Dept. Roy. Infirm. Edin.; SHO (Endocrin.) & Ho. Phys. W.. Gen. Hosp. Edin.

STEEL, Kiki Carolyn Mary James Street Surgery, 2 James Street, Boston PE21 8RF Tel: 01205 362556 Fax: 01205 359050; 2 St Andrews, Grantham NG31 9AE Tel: 01476 590522 Fax: 01476 590522 — MB ChB 1989 Glas.; DRCOG 1993. (Glas.) Co. Surg. of St John Ambul. Lincs.; Mem. of Lincs. Integrated Volun. Emerg. Serv.; Mem. of Brit. Assn. of Immediate Care. Prev: Trainee GP Grantham.

STEEL, Margaret Rachel (retired) 6 School Lane, Hampton Wick, Kingston upon Thames KT1 4DF Tel: 020 8977 4357 — MB BS 1953 Lond.; MRCS Eng. LRCP Lond. 1953; T(OM) 1991; DPH Eng. 1965. Prev: Med. Adviser Surrey CC.

STEEL, Mark Dominic University Medicine, Southampton General Hospital, Tremona Road, Southampton SO16 6YD Tel: 02380 777222 Ext: 4155 Email: mds68@soton.ac.uk — MB BS 1993 Lond.; MA Oxf. 1996, BA 1990; MRCP (UK) 1996. (Char. Cross and Westm.) Clin. Res. Fell. (Respir. Med.) Soton. Gen. Hosp. Socs: Brit. Thorac. Soc. Prev: Regist. (LAT in Respirat. & Gen. Med.) Mayday Hosp. Croydon; Regist. (LAT in Respirat. & Gen. Med.) Medway Hosp. Gillingham, Kent; SHO (Int. Care) Qu. Eliz. Hosp. Birm.

STEEL, Martin Robert Blackpool Victorial Hospital, Whinney Keys Road, Blackpool FY3 8NR Tel: 01253 303653 Email: martinsteel@doctors.net.uk; 288 Queens Promenade, Blackpool FY2 9AZ Email: martinsteel@doctors.net.uk — MB BS 1982 Lond.; BA Oxf. 1979; MRCGP 1986; MRCOG 1989, D 1986; MObstG Liverp. 1991. Cons. O & G Blackpool Vict. Hosp. Socs: Brit. Soc. Gyn. Endoscopy. Prev: Sen. Regist. SE Thames Region; Regist. (O & G) St. Davids Hosp. Cardiff & Liverp. Matern. Hosp.; Trainee GP Cleveland VTS.

STEEL, Maxwell 23 Honister Avenue, Newcastle upon Tyne NE2 3PA — MB BS 1983 Newc.

STEEL, Michael Arthur Pharmacia & Upjohn Ltd, Davy Avenue, Knowhill, Milton Keynes MK5 8PH Tel: 01908 603017 Fax: 01908 603950 Email: michael.steel@eu.pnu.com; Linden Tree House, 23 Bow Brickhill Road, Woburn Sands, Milton Keynes MK17 8QD — MB BS 1983 Lond.; BSc (Hons.) Lond. 1980; MRCGP 1987; DRCOG 1987. Med. Adviser Pharmacia & Upjohn Ltd. Milton Keynes. Prev: GP Lond.; Occupat. Health Phys. Char. Cross Hosp. Lond.; Trainee GP/SHO Vict. HA VTS.

STEEL, Nicholas Trinity Street Surgery, 1 Trinity Street, Norwich NR2 2BG Tel: 01603 624844 Fax: 01603 766829; 189 Earlham Road, Norwich NR2 3RG Email: n.steel@uea.ac.uk — MB ChB 1988 Bristol; MRCGP 1993; T(GP) 1993; DRCOG 1993. (Univ. Bristol) GP; Research Fell. Health Policy & Pract. Unit Univ. of Anglia Norwich. Socs: BMA.

STEEL, Nigel Richard Department of Medicine for the Elderly, Hull Royal Infirmary, Anlaby Road, Hull HU3 2JZ Tel: 01482 674739 Fax: 01482 674026 — BM BCh 1977 Oxf.; FRCP Lond. 1995; MRCP (UK) 1979. (Oxford) Cons. Geriat. (Med. for Elderly) Hull Roy. Infirm., Hull. Socs: Brit. Geriat. Soc.; Brit. Diabetic Assn. Prev: Sen. Regist. (Med. & Geriat.) Hull Roy. Infirm.; MRC Train. Fell. Endocrine Unit (Med.) Roy. Vict. Infirm. Newc.; Regist. (Med.) N. Tees Gen. Hosp. Stockton-on-Tees.

STEEL, Peter Cecil, MBE (retired) The Nook, Withyham Road, Groombridge, Tunbridge Wells TN3 9QP Tel: 01892 863326 — MB BChir Camb. 1951; MA Camb. 1951. Prev: Ho. Surg. St. Bart. Hosp.

STEEL, Robby Michael University of Edinburgh, Department of Psychiatry, Kennedy Tower, Royal Edinburgh Hospital, Edinburgh EH10 Tel: 0131 537 6265 Email: r.steel@ed.ac.uk; 12 Ross Gardens, Newington, Edinburgh EH9 3BS — MB ChB 1993 Glas.; MA Camb. 1990; MRCPsych. 1997. Lect. in Psychiat. Univ. of Edin.; Hon. Specialist Regist. Roy. Edin. Hosp. Prev: SHO Rotat. (Psychiat.) S.. Gen. Hosp. Glas.

STEEL, Robin Easton, MBE (retired) St Johns House Surgery, 28 Bromyard Road, St. Johns, Worcester WR2 5BU Tel: 01905 423612 Fax: 01905 740003 — MB BS 1956 Lond.; MRCS Eng. LRCP Lond. 1956; FRCPsych 1996, M 1994; FRCGP 1973, M 1968; DObst RCOG 1964; DPM Eng 1959. Treas. W. Midl. LMC. Prev: Chairm. RCGP Ethics Comm. 1989-1992.

STEEL, Sarah Frances Mary Child Development Unit, 40 Upton Road, Norwich NR4 Tel: 01603 508937 Email: sarah.steel@doctors.org.uk — MB ChB 1988 Bristol; 2000 MSC USA; BSc Bristol 1985; MRCP (UK) 1993. (Bristol) p/t Cons. Paediat. Norwich Coy Primary Care Trust Childr.s Sevices Norwich; Med. Adviser Adoption and Family Finding Unit. Prev: Sen; Regist. Norwich Community Health Partnership.

STEEL, Shirley Ann Peterborough Hospitals NHS Trust, Peterborough PE3 6DA Tel: 01733 874000; 15 Pingle Lane, Northborough, Peterborough PE6 9BW Tel: 01733 253114 Fax: 01733 252203 — MB BS 1980 Lond.; FRCOG 1998. (St Bartholomews Hospital Medical College) Cons. O & G PeterBoro. Hosps. NHS Trust.

STEEL, Stanley Joseph (retired) 23 Grove Road, Bournemouth BH1 3AS Tel: 01202 552785 — MB BS Lond. 1944; MD Lond. 1949; FRCP Lond. 1974, M 1950; MRCS Eng. LRCP Lond. 1944. Hon. Cons. Phys. Lond. Chest Hosp.; Hon. Sen. Lect. Nat. Heart & Lung Inst. Prev: Cons. Phys. Barking, Havering & Brentwood Dist. Hosps.

STEEL, Stephen 17-19 Heaton Road, Newcastle upon Tyne NE6 15A Tel: 0191 265 3361 Fax: 0191 276 6085; 14 Montagu Avenue, Newcastle upon Tyne NE3 4JH Tel: 0191 285 5108 — MB BS 1959 Durh.; MRCGP 1978. (Newc.) Clin. Asst. (Radiother.) Newc. Gen. Hosp. Socs: BMA; MRCGP. Prev: Trainer (Gen. Pract.) Newc. AHA; Tutor (Family Med.) Univ. Newc.; Ho. Phys. (Paediat.) Newc. Gen. Hosp.

STEEL, Mr William Matthew (retired) Grove House, 11 King St., Newcastle ST5 1EH Tel: 01782 614174 Fax: 01782 714957 — MB ChB 1957 Ed.; FRCS Eng. 1992; FRCS Ed. 1962. Prev: Cons. Orthop. Surg. N. Staffs. Hosp. Centre Stoke-on-Trent.

STEELE, Adrian Paul Hawthorn 29 Mount Ephraim Lane, London SW16 1JE — MB BChir 1988 Camb.; BA Camb. 1985, MB BChir 1988; MRCP (UK) 1991. SHO (Anaesth.) St. Bart. Hosp. Lond. Prev: Regist. (Med.) St. And. Hosp. Lond.; SHO (Med.) Roy. Lond. Hosp.; Lect. (Physiol.) Lond. Hosp. Med. Coll.

STEELE

STEELE, Alison Mary Paediatric Department, Queen Elizabeth Hospital, Sheriff Hill, Gateshead NE9 6SX Tel: 0191 487 8989 — BM 1985 Soton.; MRCP (UK) 1990. Cons. (Paediat.) Gateshead Health Trust.

STEELE, Ann Helen Garthhill, 10 Ferryhills Road, North Queensferry, Inverkeithing KY11 1HE — MB ChB 1980 Ed.; BSc. (Med. Sci.) Ed. 1977, MB ChB 1980; MRCGP 1984; DRCOG 1983; DCCH RCP Ed. 1985.

STEELE, Annette Christa Portobello Medical Centre, 14 Codrington Mews, London W11 2EH Tel: 020 7727 5800/2326 Fax: 020 7792 9044 — MB BS 1986 Lond.; BSc Lond. (1st cl. Hons.) 1983, MB BS 1986; DRCOG 1988; Dip. Ther. 1997; Cert. Family Plann. JCC 1988. (St. Mary's Hosp.) GP; Tutor (Gen. Pract.) & Clin. Asst. (A & E) St. Mary's Hosp. Lond.; Hon. Med. Ref. Brit. Sub Aqua Club.

STEELE, Anthony Simon Vanpraagh 9 Garnett Road, London NW3 2XN Tel: 020 7586 5067 — MB BS 1956 Lond.; PhD Camb. 1964; MRCGP 1971; DTM & H RCP Lond. 1976. (Univ. Coll. Hosp.) Prev: Med. Off. Usutu Pulp Co. Swaziland; Med. Off. Govt. Seychelles; Med. Off. Govt. St. Lucia.

STEELE, Mr Arthur David McGowan 22 Seymour Walk, London SW10 9NF Tel: 020 7351 3064 Fax: 020 7351 5429 — MB BS 1960 Melbourne; FRCS Eng. 1971; FRCOphth 1988 Hon 2000; FRACO 1979, M 1977; DO Eng. 1970. Consg. Ophth. Moorfields Eye Hosp. Lond. Socs: Fell. Roy. Soc. Med. Prev: Cons. Ophth. Moorfields Eye Hosp. Lond.; Lect. Dept. Clin. Ophth. Moorfields Eye Hosp. & Inst. Ophth. Lond.; SHO Croydon Eye Unit.

STEELE, Barbara Denise 27 Redcastle Crescent, Broughty Ferry, Dundee DD5 3NF — MB BCh 1985 Witwatersrand.

STEELE, Caroline Anne 1 Broom Grove, Watford WD17 4RY — MB ChB 1979 Leeds; FRCS Ed. 1984.

STEELE, Christopher 29 Parkmount Gardens, Larne BT40 1QN — MB BCh BAO 1993 Belf.

STEELE, Christopher Bodey Medical Centre, 363 Wilmslow Road, Fallowfield, Manchester M14 6XU Tel: 0161 248 6644 Fax: 0161 224 4228; 14 Belfield Road, Didsbury, Manchester M20 6BH Tel: 0161 445 3410 Fax: 0161 445 3423 — MB ChB 1968 Manch. Med. Dir. Stop Smoking Clinic Univ. Hosp. S. Manch.; Med. Presenter 'This Morning Progr.' ITV; Managing Dir. Smokequitters Manch. Socs: Manch. Med. Soc. & Brit. Med. & Dent. Hypn. Soc. Prev: Cons. Smoking Cessation for DERBY FHSA.

STEELE, Elizabeth Sandra Maybole Health Centre and Day Hospital, 6 High Street, Maybole KA19 7BY Tel: 01655 882278 Fax: 01655 889616; 17 Kilnford Crescent, Dundonald, Kilmarnock KA2 9DW Tel: 01563 850801 — MB ChB 1973 Ed. GP Maybole CMO Family Plann. Ayrsh. & Arran HB. Prev: GP Troon.

STEELE, Emma Kristine Royal Jubilee Maternity Service, Grosvenor Road, Belfast BT12 6BJ Tel: 02890 894633 — MB BCh BAO 1992 Belf.; MD 2000; MRCOG 1997. (Queen's University) SPR (O & G) Roy. Jubilee Matern. Serv., Belf. Socs: BMA; Roy. Coll. Obst. & Gyn.; Ulster Obst. & Gyn. Soc. Prev: SPR (O & G) Craigavon Area Hosp.; SPR, (O & G) Altnagelvin Hosp. - L'derry; SPR (O & G) Roy. Matern. Hosp. Belf.

***STEELE, Gavin John** 35C Ommaney Road, New Cross, London SE14 5NS Tel: 020 7358 1384 — MB BS 1997 Lond.

STEELE, George Alfred, TD (retired) Westwood, Guard Hill, Sandside, Milnthorpe LA7 7JU Tel: 01524 761079 — MB ChB 1948 Manch.; BA Open. 1984; MRCS Eng. LRCP Lond. 1948; DPH Lond. 1951. Prev: Fact. Med. Off. H. J. Heinz Co. Ltd.

STEELE, Gillian Jane Bynack, 35 Nunholm Road, Dumfries DG1 1JW — MB ChB 1978 Aberd.

STEELE, Graham Arthur Parkfields, 220 Duffield Road, Derby DE22 1BL Tel: 01332 342263 Fax: 01332 342263 — MB ChB 1957 Manch.; FRCR 1995; DMRD Eng. 1962. Cons. Radiol. Derbysh. Roy. Infirm. Socs: Brit. Soc. Interven. Radiol.; Brit. Inst. Radiol. & Fac. Radiol. Prev: Sen. Regist. (X-Ray) Manch. Roy. Infirm.

STEELE, Herbert Desmond Loughview Surgery, 2 Main Street, Kircubbin, Newtownards BT22 2SP Tel: 028 4273 8532 Fax: 028 4273 8070 Email: d.steele@p283.gp.n-i.nhs.uk; Shore Cottage, Portaferry Road, Greyabbey, Newtownards BT22 2RU Email: dsteele@doctors.org.uk — MB BCh BAO 1975 Belf.

STEELE, Ian Conrad Department of Healthcare for the Elderly, Royal Victoria Hospital, Grosvenor Road, Belfast BT12 6BA Tel: 01232 263320 Fax: 01232 263159; 3 Campbell Chase, Hawthornden Way, Belfast BT4 3LA Tel: 01232 654061 — MB BCh BAO 1988 Belf.; MD 1996; MRCP (UK) 1991. Cons. Phys. (Geriat. Med.) Roy. Vict. Hosp. Belf.

STEELE, Mr James Alexander Accident & Emergency dept, Altnageluin Area Hospital, Glenshane Road, Londonderry BT47 6SB Tel: 01504 345171 Fax: 01504 611245 Email: jsteel@alt.n-i.nhs.uk — MB BCh BAO 1987 Belf.; FRCS Ed. 1991. Cons., A&E Dept., Altnagelin Area Hosp., Lond.derry.

STEELE, James Wallace Birtley Medical Group Practice, Birtley Medical Group, Durham Road, Birtley, Chester-le-Street DH3 2QT Tel: 0191 410 3421 Fax: 0191 410 9672; 16 Larchwood, Harraton, Washington NE38 9BT Tel: 0191 417 4865 — MB ChB 1972 Ed.; BSc (Med. Sci. & Bact., Hons.) Ed. 1972, MB ChB 1975. GP Birtley. Prev: Trainee Gen. Pract. Bournemouth & Poole Vocational Train Scheme; Ho. Off. (Gen. Med.) & Ho. Off. (Gen. Surg.) Bangour Gen. Hosp.; Broxburn.

STEELE, Jan Mairi Boyd 58 Hollingbourne Road, London SE24 9ND — MB BS 1992 Lond.

STEELE, Jeremy Peter Charles Department of Medical Oncology, St. Bartholomew's Hospital, West Smithfield, London EC1A 7BE Tel: 0207 3777 700 Fax: 020 7601 7577 Email: j.p.steele@mds.qmw.ac.uk — MB BS 1989 Lond.; MRCP (UK) 1994; DA (UK) 1992. (St. Geo. Hosp. Lond.) Specialist Regist. (Med. Oncol.) St. Barts. Hosp. Lond. Socs: Assn. Cancer Phys.; Amer. Soc. Clin. Oncol.; Internat. Mesothelioma Interest Gp. Prev: Vis. Lect. New Eng. Med. Center Boston, USA 1992; Research Fell. (Med.) Roy. Marsden Hosp. & Inst. Cancer Research Sutton; Regist. (Neuro-oncol.) Roy. Marsden Hosp. Lond. & Surrey.

STEELE, John Douglas Torrance (retired) Bynack, 35 Nunholm Road, Dumfries DG1 1JW Tel: 01387 53986 — MB ChB 1942 Ed.; BSc Ed., MB ChB (Hons.) 1942; FRCP Ed. 1972, M 1948. Prev: Res. Med. Off. Raigmore Hosp. Inverness.

STEELE, Katrine 27 Send Road, Send, Woking GU23 7ET — BM 1993 Soton.

STEELE, Lynne Colquhoun 2 Farmhouse, Springbank farm, Monkton, Prestwick KA9 2SW — MB ChB 1995 Glas.

STEELE, Mary Christine North Sheen, South St., West Rainton, Houghton-le-Spring DH4 6PA — MB BS 1969 Lond.; MRCS Eng. LRCP Lond. 1969. (Roy. Free) Assoc. Specialist (Dermat.) N. Durh. Acute Hosps. Trust.

STEELE, Michael (retired) 9 Broadwood, Bolton BL6 4PD Tel: 01204 843317 — MB ChB St. And. 1952; DObst RCOG 1954.

STEELE, Michael Alan Fowler Way Health Clinic, Fowler Way, Ballywalter, Newtownards BT22 2PY Tel: 02842 758292 Fax: 02842 758540; 156 Groomsprot Road, Bangor BT20 5PF Tel: 02891 274559 Fax: 02842 758540 — MB ChB 1982 Ed.; MRCP (UK) 1994; MRCGP 1986; DRCOG 1984. GP Princip. Ballywalter Health Clinic. Socs: Roy. Coll. Phys.

STEELE, Nicholas Anthony 29 Murvagh Close, Cheltenham GL53 7QX — MB BS 1994 Lond.; BSc (Hons.) Lond. 1989. SHO (A & E) Roy. Lond. Hosp. & Homerton Hosp. Lond. Socs: BMA (N. Thames JDC); MDU. Prev: Ho. Off. (Med.) Homerton Hosp. Lond.; Ho. Off. (Renal) St. Bart. Hosp. Lond.; Ho. Off. (Surg.) Whipps Cross Hosp. Lond.

STEELE, Nicholas James The Health Clinic, Weeping Cross, Bodmin Avenue, Stafford ST17 0HE Tel: 01785 662505 Fax: 01785 661064 — MB ChB 1990 Birm.; ChB Birm. 1990; MRCGP 1994.

STEELE, Peter Raynor Macdonald 52 Earlsway, Curzon Park, Chester CH4 8AZ Tel: 01244 676932 — MB BChir 1973 Camb.; PhD Camb. 1970, MA 1969; FRCPath 1991, M 1979. (Middlx.) Cons. Path. Countess of Chester Hosp. Prev: Lect. (Path.) Univ. Camb.; Fell. Qu.'s Coll. Camb.

STEELE, Phyllis Sharon 25 Ballylenaghan Road, Belfast BT8 6WT — MB BCh BAO 1991 Belf.; MRCP (UK) 1994.

STEELE, Raymond Geoffrey 18 Glebe Road, Norwich NR2 3JG — MB BS 1991 Melbourne.

STEELE, Richard Thompson Wythall Health Centre, May Lane, Hollywood, Birmingham B47 5PD Tel: 01564 822642 — MB ChB 1959 Ed.; MRCGP 1989.

STEELE, Professor Robert James Campbell Department of Surgery and Molecular Oncology, Ninewells Hospital & Medical School, Dundee DD1 9SY Tel: 01382 660111 Fax: 01382 641795 Email: r.j.c.steele@dundee.ac.uk; Redgarth, 11 Rockfield Crescent, Dundee DD2 1JE Tel: 01382 667411 — MB ChB 1977 Ed.; BSc

(Hons.) Ed. 1974, MD 1983; FRCS Eng. 1996; FRCS Ed. 1984. Prof. Surgic. Oncol. Univ. Dundee; Chairm. Scott. Cancer Trials Colorectal Gp.; Chairm.Sign Colorectal Cancer Focus Gp.; Chairm. Colorectal Caner Gp.. Critical Standards for Scotl. Socs: Assn. Coloproctol.; Assn. Surg.; Brit. Soc. Gastroenterol. Prev: Convenor Educat. Comm. RCS Ed.

STEELE, Russell John Frederick St. Leonard's Medical Practice, 34 Denmark Road, Exeter EX1 1SF Tel: 01392 201790; 23 Doriam Close, Exeter EX4 4RS Email: russell.steele@rustle.cix.co.uk — MB ChB 1971 Birm.; FRCGP 1991, M 1975; DObst RCOG 1973. Assoc. Adviser Devon & Cornw.; Lect. Univ. Exeter Dept. Gen. Pract. Prev: Med. Panel Examrs.; Course Organiser.

STEELE, Mr Simon Craig Dept of Obstetrics & Gynaecology, Sunderland Royal Hospital, Kayll Road, Sunderland SR4 7TP Tel: 0191 569 9781 Fax: 0191 569 9218 Email: craig.steele@chs.northy.nhs.uk; 32 Fern Avenue, Jesmond, Newcastle upon Tyne NE2 2QX Tel: 0191 281 1995 Email: sc.steele@btinternet.co.uk — MB ChB 1981 Leeds; MRCOG 1989. (Leeds University Medical School) cons. O & G Sunderland Roy. Hosp. Sunderland.

STEELE, Sinclair (Joseph Ekow) 18 Girton Avenue, London NW9 9SX — BM BCh 1998 Oxf.

***STEELE, Sine** 17 Muirden Road, Maryburgh, Dingwall IV7 8EJ — MB ChB 1997 Glas.

STEELE, Mr Stuart James 10 Harley Street W1g 9PF Tel: 0207 467 8312; 35 Tring Avenue, London W5 3QD Tel: 020 8992 2113 Fax: 020 8992 2113 — MB Camb. 1957, BChir 1956; MA Camb. 1957; FRCS Eng. 1962; MRCS Eng. LRCP Lond. 1956; MFFP 1993; FRCOG 1975, M 1964; DObst RCOG 1958. (Camb. & Middlx.) Emerit. Reader (O & G) Univ. Coll. Lond. Med. Sch.; Hon. Cons. (Paediat. Gyn.) Gt. Ormond St. Hosp. Sick Childr.; Hon. Cons. Margt. Pyke Centre Lond. Socs: Fell. Roy. Soc. Med.; Blair Bell Res. Soc.; Brit. Fertil. Soc. Prev: Dir. (O & G) Middlx. Hosp. Med. Sch. Lond.; Res. Med. Off. Qu. Charlotte's Hosp. Lond.; Hon.Cons(Obst&Gyn)UCL Hosps.

STEELE, Susan Margaret Accident & Emergency Department, Ninewells hospital & medical school, Dundee DD1 9SY Tel: 01382 667411; Redgarth, 11 Rockfield Cresent, Dundee DD2 1JE Tel: 01382 667411 — MB ChB 1978 Ed. Tayside Univ. Hosp. NHS trust. Prev: Staff Grade Pract. Qu. Med. Centre (NHS Trust) Univ. Hosp. Nottm.

STEELE, Tony 8 Fraser Street, Bristol BS3 4LY — MB ChB 1983 Sheff.

STEELE, William Keith Dunluce Avenue Surgery, 1-3 Dunluce Avenue, Belfast BT9 7AW Tel: 028 9024 0884; 19 Lougherne Road, Hillsborough BT26 6NL Tel: 01846 638660 — MB BCh BAO 1978 Belf.; MD Belf. 1987; MICGP 1987; FRCGP 1996, M 1983; DCH NUI 1983. (Qu. Univ. Belf.) Sen. Lect. (Gen. Pract.) Qu. Univ. Belf. Socs: Assn. Univ. Teach. Gen. Pract. Prev: Janet Nash Trav. Fell.sh. RSM 1989; Princip. Tutor (Gen. Pract.) (RCGP) Qu. Univ. Belf.

STEELE, William Murray Saltoun Surgery, 46 Saltoun Place, Fraserburgh AB43 9RY Tel: 01346 514154 Fax: 01346 517680; 33 Buchan Road, Fraserburgh AB43 9WE Tel: 01346 518243 — MB ChB 1971 Aberd.; DObst RCOG 1974. (Aberd.) Clin. Asst. (Diabetes) Fraserburgh Hosp.; Hosp. Med. Dir. Fraserburgh Hosp. Socs: Aberd. M-C Soc.; (Chairm. & Sec.) Fraserburgh Postgrad. Med. Soc. Prev: Trainee GP Aberd. VTS; Ho. Off. Roy. N.. Infirm. Inverness.

STEELE, Yvette Elizabeth Grosvenor Road Surgery, 17 Grosvenor Road, Paignton TQ4 5AZ Tel: 01803 559308 Fax: 01803_ 526702; Chy-Ang-Wheal, Bridgetown Hill, Totnes TQ9 5BA — MB ChB 1987 Aberd.; MRCGP 1992; DRCOG 1992. (Aberd.) Prev: Asst. GP Trawden, Lancs.; SHO (Paediat.) Burnley Gen. Hosp.; Trainee GP Guide Post Health Centre N.d.

STEELE-PERKINS, Anthony Peter, Surg. Capt. RN Retd. Brincil Cottage, Kingsdon, Somerton TA11 7LA — MB BS Lond. 1968; MSc Lond. 1979; MRCS Eng. LRCP Lond. 1968; FFOM RCP Lond. 1994, MFOM 1983; DAvMed Eng. 1976. (St. Thos.) Occupat. Phys. Health Servs. BMI. Socs: Fell. Roy. Soc. Med.; Soc. Occupat. Med. Prev: Dir. Med. Personnel (Navy); Chief Staff Off. (Health & Safety) to Flag Off. Naval Aviat.; MoD Staff of Surg. Gen.

STEELE-PERKINS, Professor Peter Edward (retired) Earlsland Cottage, Bradninch, Exeter EX5 4QP Tel: 01392 881500 — MRCS Eng. LRCP Lond. 1942; BA Camb. 1938. Prev: Specialist Venereol. RAMC.

STEEN, Benjamin Meyer 19 Bishopsgate, Wellknowle Place, Glasgow G74 5AX — LRCP LRCS 1945 Ed.; LRCP LRCS Ed. LRFPS Glas. 1945; FRFPS Glas. 1947; MRCP Glas. 1962.

STEEN, Caryle Ann (retired) 35 Cholmeley Park, London N6 5EL Tel: 020 8340 1122 Fax: 020 8340 9879 — MB BS 1958 Lond.; MRCS Eng. LRCP Lond. 1958; FRCGP 1992, M 1972. Hon. Clin. Asst. (Obst.) & Hon. Sen. Clin. Lect. (Gen. Pract.) Univ. Coll. Hosp. Lond. Prev: GP Lond.

STEEN, Heather Jean Cupar Street Clinic, Falls Road, Belfast BT13 2LJ Tel: 01232 327613; Killyloob, 85 Old Kilmore Road, Moira, Craigavon BT67 0NA — MB BCh BAO 1978 Belf.; MRCP (UK) (Paediat.) 1984; DCH RCP Glas. 1981. Cons. Paediat. Roy. Belf. Hosp. Sick Childr. N. & W. Belf. H & SS Trust. Socs: BMA & Brit. Paediat. Soc.; Irish Thoracic Soc.

STEEN, Jillian Sara Muriel Medicines control Agency, Market Towers, 1 Nine Elms Road, London SW8 5NQ Tel: 020 7273 0260 Fax: 020 7273 0554 — MB BS 1967 Lond.; MBA Lond. 1986; MB BS (Hons.) Surg. Lond. 1967; FFPM 1990; Dip Pharm Med RCP (UK) 1979. (Lond. Hosp.) Sen. Med. Off. Med. Control Agency. Socs: Fell. Fac. Pharmaceut. Phys. Prev: Regist. (Anaesth.) & Ho. Surg. Surgic. Unit. Lond. Hosp.; Med. Adviser Ciba-Geigy UK Ltd.; Commercial Affairs Manager IMS Clin. Servs.

STEEN, Leslie (retired) 7 St Mary's Road, Prestwich, Manchester M25 1AQ — LRCP LRCS Ed. LRFPS Glas. 1950; MRCPsych 1971; DPM Eng. 1959. Prev: Cons. Psychiat. Stockport Dist. HA & Prestwich Hosp.

STEENE, Laura St Helen's Medical Centre, 151 St. Helens Road, Swansea SA1 4DF Tel: 01792 476576 Fax: 01792 301136 — MB BCh 1985 Wales.

STEEP, Elke Doctors Residence, Macclesfield District General Hospital, Victoria Road, Macclesfield SK10 3BL — State Exam Med. Berlin 1990.

STEER, Brian Oldways End, 28 Upper Carlisle Road, Eastbourne BN20 7TN Tel: 01323 722314 — MB BS 1967 Lond.; MRCS Eng. LRCP Lond. 1967; FFA RCS Eng. 1972. (Univ. Coll. Hosp.) Cons. Anaesth. E.bourne Health Dist. Socs: BMA & E.bourne Med. Soc. Prev: Sen. Regist. Char. Cross Hosp. Lond.; Regist. Nat. Hosp. Nerv. Dis. & Char. Cross Hosp. Lond.

STEER, Charles (retired) Ballacreg, Dreemskerry, Ramsey IM7 1BA Tel: 01624 815148 Fax: 01624 815148 Email: chasteer@which.net — MB BS Lond. 1950; MRCGP 1957. Prev: Sen. Ho. Phys. (O & G) Cornelia Gen. Hosp. Poole.

STEER, Charles Gabriel The Surgery, 15 Brackendale, 25 Gloucester Road, Kingston upon Thames KT1 3RL Tel: 020 8546 8864 Fax: 020 8541 0217; 26 Cranes Park, Surbiton KT5 8AD Tel: 020 8399 8008 — MB BS 1978 Lond.; BA (2nd cl. Hons. Eng. Sci.) Oxf. 1970, MA 1980; MLCOM 1992; DRCOG 1980. (Univ. Coll. Hosp.)

STEER, Christopher Richard Paediatric Department, Victoria Hospital, Hayfield Road, Kirkcaldy KY2 5AH Tel: 01592 261155; 14 Bellhouse Road, Aberdour, Burntisland KY3 0TL Tel: 01383 860738 — FRCPCH 1997; BSc (Hons. Physiol.) Ed. 1969, MB ChB 1971; FRCP Ed. 1986; MRCP (UK) 1976; DCH RCPS Glas. 1974. (Ed.) Cons. (Paediat.) Vict. Hosp. Kirkcaldy Fife; Clin. Dir. (Obst. & Gyn. & Paediat.) Acute Unit Fife HB; Hon. Clin. Tutor Dept. Child Life & Health Edin. Univ.; Hon. Sen. Lect. Child Life & Health Aberd. Univ.; Hon. Sen. Lect. Preclin. Studies St. And. Univ. Socs: Brit. Paediat. Assn.; Scott. Paediat. Soc.; Roy.Soc. of Med. Prev: Sen. Regist. (Paediat. Neurol.) & Regist. (Paediat.) Roy. Hosp. Sick; Childr. Edin.; SHO Infec. Dis. Unit City Hosp. Edin.

STEER, Christopher Victor Orpington Hospital, Quebec Ward, Cararod Wing, Sevenoaks Road, Orpington BR6 9JU.Tel: 01689 815277 Fax: 01689 815279 Email: csteer@bromley.tcom.co.uk; Oakenhill, Hosey Hill, Westerham TN16 1TB — MB ChB 1982 Birm.; MD Birm. 1993; MRCOG 1985. (Birm) Cons. O & G FarnBoro. Hosp.

STEER, Graham Lansley 20 Primrose Hill, Brentwood CM14 4LT — MB ChB 1969 Bristol; FFA RCSI 1976; DA Eng. 1971. Cons. Anaesth. Havering Hosp. Trust; Hon. Cons. Anaesth. Italian Hosp. Lond. & St. Luke's Hosp. for Clergy Lond. Prev: Sen. Regist. St. Mary's Hosp. Lond.

STEER

STEER, Mr Howard William Bush House, Romsey Road, East Wellow, Romsey SO51 6BG — MB BS 1970 Lond.; PhD Lond. 1968, BSc 1965; FRCS Eng. 1975; MRCS Eng. LRCP Lond. 1970. (St. Thos. Hosp.) Cons. Surg. Soton. Gen. Hosp. Prev: Reader (Surg.) Oxf. Univ.

STEER, Jane Anne Royal Free Hampstead NHS Trust, Pond St, London WC1E 6BD Tel: 020 7794 0500 — MB BS 1990 Lond.; MSc Lond. 1994; MRCPath 1999. p/t Cons. Roy. Free Hosp. Prev: Sen Regist (Clin Medicol) Univ Coll. Lond Hosp; Research Fell. (Clin. Microbiol.) Univ. Coll. Hosp. Lond.; Regist. (Clin. Microbiol.) Univ. Coll. Lond. Hosps.

STEER, Janet Mary Blackthorn Surgery, 73 Station Road, Netley Abbey, Southampton SO31 5AE Tel: 023 8045 3110 Fax: 023 8045 2747 — BM BCh 1980 Oxf.; BSc Lond. 1966, MSc 1969; MFFP 1994; DRCOG 1984; Cert. Family Plann. JCC 1982. (St Thomas's and Oxford) Sen. Clin. Med. Off. (Family Plann.) Soton. Family Plann. Serv.

STEER, Keith Alistair 132 Weston Park, Hornsey Vale, London N8 9PN Tel: 01563 574237 Email: jeremystirling@aol.com — MB BS 1987 Lond.; FRCP 2000; PhD Lond. 1982; MSc Soton. 1979; BSc (Hons.) Leeds 1978; MRCP (UK) 1991. (Middlx.) Cons. Metabol. Med. N.wick Pk. Hosp. Harrow. Socs: Brit. Diabetic Assn. (Med. & Scientif. Sect.); Soc. for Endocrinol. Brit. Thyroid Assoc. Prev: Lect. (Med., Diabetes & Endocrinol.) Univ. Bristol; Regist. (Med., Diabetes & Endocrinol.) N.wick Pk., Edgware Gen. & St. Mary's Hosps. Lond.; Regist. (Chem. Path.) Univ. Coll. & Middlx. Sch. Med.

STEER, Professor Philip James Academic Department Obstetrics & Gynaecology, Chelsea & Westminster Hospital, 369 Fulham Road, London SW10 9NH Tel: 020 8846 7892 Fax: 020 8846 7880 Email: p.steer@ic.ac.uk; 48 Langley Avenue, Surbiton KT6 6QR Tel: 020 8390 3913 — MB BS 1971 Lond.; BSc (1st cl. Hons.) Lond. 1968, MD 1986; MRCS Eng. LRCP Lond. 1971; FRCOG 1989, M 1977; T(OG) 1991. (Guy's & King's Coll. Hosps.) Head Dept Matern. Fetal Med. Imp. Coll. Sch. Med. Lond.; Prof. Roy. Soc. Med. Foundat. 1995. Socs: Blair Bell Res. Soc.; (Pres.) Brit. Assn. Perinatal Med.; Fell. Roy. Soc. Med. Prev: Prof. & Head Dept. Char. Cross & W.m. Med. Sch. Lond.; Sen. Lect. (Obst.) St. Mary's Hosp. Lond.; Ch.ill Fell. 1981.

STEER, Sophia Elizabeth Dept. of Rheumatology, Guy's Hospital, St Thomas' St, London SE1 9RS — MB BS 1993 Lond.; MRCP (UK) 1996. (Guy's) ARC Clin. Lect., Dept. of Rheum., Guy's Hosp., Lond.

STEERE, Christopher Edwin The Surgery, 10 Liverpool Road, Neston, Wirral CH63 9JP; Delsany, 286 Telegraph Road, Heswall, Wirral CH60 7SQ — MB ChB 1980 Liverp.

STEERS, Mr Alfred James Wanklyn 16 Cammo Crescent, Edinburgh EH4 8DZ — MB BS 1967 Lond.; FRCS Eng. 1972. (Middlx.)

STEFAN, Marcus Aurelius 25 Park Avenue, Gateshead NE11 9QE Tel: 0191 604735 — MD 1938 Prague.

STEFAN, Martin David 41 Telford House, Tiverton St., London SE1 6NY — MB BS 1989 Lond.

STEFANI, Terence Antony Whitstable Health Centre, Harbour Street, Whitstable CT5 1BZ Tel: 01277 263033 Fax: 01277 771474; Brookfield, 127 South St, Whitstable CT5 3EL Tel: 263949 — MB ChB Sheff. 1970; MRCP (UK) 1973; DObst RCOG 1973; DCH Eng. 1972. Hosp. Pract. (Paediat.) Kent & Canterbury Hosp. Socs: Chairm. 1st aid Train. panel Roy. Nat. Life Boat Inst.; BMA & Mem. Brit. Paediat. Assn. Prev: SHO (Gen. Med./Gen. Paediat./ Neonat.) Dudley Rd. Hosp.; SHO (Anaesth.) Cheltenham Hosp.

STEFANUTI, Eric (retired) 4 Silverdale Close, Sheffield S11 9JN Tel: 0114 236 9219 Email: eric@stfnt.demon.co.uk — MB ChB 1959 Sheff.

STEFANUTTO, Tiscia Bernadette 21 Park Avenue, The Mumbles, Swansea SA3 4DU — MB ChB 1993 Cape Town.

STEFFEN, Gundula Margarete 12 St Vincent Road, Wallasey CH44 8BJ — State Exam Med 1991 Munster. SHO (Anaesth.) Roy. L'pool Univ. Hosp.

STEGEN, Gerti Adult Department, Tavistock & Portman NHS Trust, 120 Belsize Lane, London NW3 5BA Tel: 020 7435 7111 — State Exam Med 1989 Hamburg; State Exam. Med. Hamburg 1989; MD Hamburg 1989; MRCPsych 1995. (Hamburg, Germany) Sen. Regist. (Psychother.) Adult Dept. Tavistock Clinic Lond. Prev: Regist. (Psychiat.) Oxf. Train. Scheme; SHO (Nesurol. & Neuropsychiat.) W.. Gen. Hosp. Edin.

STEGER, Mr Adrian Churchill 74 Croxted Road, London SE21 8NP — MB BS 1977 Lond.; MS Lond. 1990, MB BS 1977; FRCS Glas. 1982; FRCS Eng. 1998. (St Thomas's) Cons. Surg. Univ. Hosp. Lewisham; Hon. Sen. Lect. (Surg.) United Med. & Dent. Schs. of Guys & St Thos. Socs: Fell. Roy. Soc. Med.; Brit. Soc. Gastroenterol.; Surg. Research Soc. Prev: Sen. Regist. (Surg.) King's Coll. Hosp. Lond.; Clin. Lect. Univ. Coll. Hosp.; Regist. (Surg.) Roy. Postgrad. Med. Sch. & Hammersmith Hosp. Lond.

STEGER-LEWIS, Valerie May Eastney Health Centre, Highland Road, Southsea PO4 9HU Fax: 023 9273 4900; 10 Craneswater Park, Southsea PO4 0NT Tel: 01705 731107 Email: bandvs-1.demon.co.uk — MB BS 1962 Lond.; MRCS Eng. LRCP Lond. 1962. (King's Coll. Hosp.)

STEGGALL, Emily Anne 11 Woodland Road, Weston Super Mare BS23 4HF — MB BS 1998 Lond.

***STEGGALL, Margaret Anne** 266 Heeley Road, Selly Oak, Birmingham B29 6EN — MB ChB 1998 Birm.; ChB Birm. 1998.

STEGGLES, Mr Brian George Higher Newton, Metherell, Callington PL19 PL17 8D Tel: 01579 350154 Email: bstegg@doctors.net.uk — MB BS 1970 Lond.; 2001 FIMC RCS Ed.; BDS Lond. 1962; FRCS Ed. 1994; MRCS Eng. LRCP Lond. 1970; LDS RCS Eng. 1962; Dip. IMC RCS Ed. 1995. (King's Coll. Hosp.) p/t Gen. Pract. Locum; Hon. Lect. Plymouth Postgrad. Med. Sch.; Chairm. Fac. Pre-Hosp. Care RCS Edin. Socs: Resusc. Counc.; Examr. Advis. Bd. Immediate Med. Care Roy. Coll. Surg. Edin.; Plymouth Med. Soc. Prev: Regist. (Oral Surg.) Roy. Free Hosp.; Lect. (Oral Surg.) King's Coll. Hosp.

STEIGER, Christine Ann Alder Hey Royal Liverpool Childrens Hospital, Eaton Road, Liverpool L12 2AP Tel: 0151 228 4881; Tel: 0151 342 4667 — MB BS 1983 Newc.; MRCP (UK) 1986. Cons. Paediat. (Community Child Health) Alder Hey Hosp. Liverp. Prev: Sen. Regist. (Community Child Health) Alder Hey Hosp. Liverp.; Sen. Regist. (Community Child Health) N.wick Pk. Hosp. & Nottm.

STEIGER, Malcolm Jonathan Walton Hospital for Neurology & Neurosurgery, Liverpool L9 7LJ Tel: 0151 525 3611 Fax: 0151 529 5500 Email: ms@wcnn.co.uk — MB BS 1983 Newc.; FRCP 1999; MD Newc. 1995; MRCP (UK) 1986. (Newcastle-upon-Tyne) Cons. Neurol. Walton Hosp. Neurol. & Neurosurg. Liverp. Prev: Research Fell. Inst. Neurol. Nat. Hospital Nerv. Disorders Lond.; Sen. Regist. (Neurol.) Nat. Hosp. Neurosurg. & Neurosurg. Lond.; Regist. (Med.) Nottm. AHA.

STEIL, Helga The Conquest Hospital, The Ridge, St Leonards-on-Sea TN37 7RD — State Exam 1987 Gottingen.

STEIN, Professor Alan Leslie Department Psychiatry, University of Oxford, Wareford Hospital, Oxford OX3 7JX Tel: 01865 223911 Fax: 01865 226384 Email: alan.stein@psych.ox.ac.uk; Tel: 020 7447 3735 Fax: 020 7447 3733 — MB BCh 1979 Witwatersrand; FRCPsych 1996, M 1984. Prof. of Child Health & Adolesc. Psychiat. Prev: Prof. of Child Family Ment. Health, Roy. Free Univ. Coll. Med. Sch., UCL, Tavistock Clinic; Leopold Muller Prof. Child & Family Ment. Health.

STEIN, Alexander Geoffrey 65 Marlborough Mansions, Cannon Hill, London NW6 1JS — MB BS 1973 Lond.; MRCS Eng. LRCP Lond. 1973.

STEIN, Andrew George 14 Kingsdown Avenue, South Croydon CR2 6QF — BM BS 1984 Nottm.; MRCP (UK) 1988.

STEIN, Claudia Elisabeth World Health Organisation, GPE/EBD, 20 Avenue Appice, 1211 Geneva, Switzerland Tel: +41 22 7913234 Fax: +41 22 7914328 Email: pheath@dorset.swest.nhs.uk, steino@who.int; 4 Blencowe Drive, Chandlers Ford, Eastleigh SO53 4LZ Tel: 01703 275571 Email: phealth@dorset.swest.nhs.uk — State Exam Med 1989 Essen; PhD (Epidemiol.) Soton. 1997; MSc (Pub. Health) Lond. 1997; DLSHTM (Pub Health) Lond 1998; MFPHM London 2000. (Univ. Essen, Germany) Med. Office Epidemiologist; Consulant to WHO, Geneva. Socs: Fell. Roy. Soc.Med.; BMA; Chamber Phys. (Germany). Prev: MRC Research Fell. (Environm. Epidemiol.) Soton. Univ.; Sen. Regist. in Pub. Health, Wessex Roation; SHO Rotat. (Med.) Soton. Univ. Hosps.

STEIN, David Dawson (retired) 15 Stamford Avenue, Hayling Island PO11 0BJ Tel: 02392 468296 — MB ChB Ed. 1945. Surg. Lt. RNVR. Prev: Ho. Phys. Roy. Hants. Co. Hosp. Winchester & Perth Roy. Infirm.

STEIN, Emma Leonore (retired) 16 The Paddocks, Wembley HA9 9HH Tel: 020 8904 3872 — MB BS 1947 Lond.; 1947 MB BS

STEINER

Lond.; 1951 DMRD Eng.; 1946 Deans Medal Clin.Med. Prev: GP S. Harrow.

STEIN, Fiona Caroline Glendaruel, Picklers Hill, Abingdon OX14 2B — MB BS 1982 Nottm.; MRCGP 1987; DRCOG 1987.

STEIN, Gaby Flat 2, Peace Court, 8 Swynford Gardens, London NW4 4XL — MB ChB 1989 Cape Town.

STEIN, George Willowbrook Medical Practice, Brook St., Sutton-in-Ashfield NG17 1ES — MRCS Eng.; LRCP 1962 Lond.; MRCS Eng. LRCP Lond. 1962. Chairm. Mem. Dep. Coop.; JMC Mem. Socs: BMA. Prev: Clin. Asst. (Psychiat.) King's Mill Hosp. Sutton-in-Ashfield.

STEIN, George Stanley 25 Beadon Road, Bromley BR2 9AS — MB BS Lond. 1968; M Phil 1979; MRCP (UK) 1972; FRCPsych 1995; MRCPsych 1976; DCH Eng. 1973. (UCH) Cons. Psychiat. Cane Hill & FarnBoro. Hosp. Orpington Kent; Hon. Sen. Lect. KCH Lond.; Asst. Edr. Brit. Jl. Psychiat. Prev: Regist. Maudsley Hosp. Lond.; Regist. (Med.) Hackney Hosp. Lond.

STEIN, Harry 48 Finchley Park, London N12 9JL Tel: 020 8446 4913 — MB BCh 1949 Witwatersrand; FRCP Ed. 1972; FRCPC 1973; MRCP Ed. 1952; DCH Eng. 1952.

STEIN, Jennifer Ann 18A Buttermarket, Thame, Oxford OX9 3EP Tel: 01865 260150 Fax: 01865 260150 — MB BCh BAO 1987 NUI; PhD Newc. 1978; BSc Lond. 1974; MRCPsych 1992. (Univ. Coll. Cork, N.U.I.) Cons. Psychiat. Psychoth. The Univ. of Oxf. Counselling Serv. for Stud.s Oxf.; Cons. Psychiatric Psychotherapist Aylesbury Vale Ment. Health Care Trust Aylesbury; Cons. Psychiatric Psychotherapist and Jungian Analyst in Private Pract. Oxf. Socs: Exec. Comm. for Psychother. Fac. Roy. Coll. of Psychiat.s; Soc. of Analyt. Psychol. Prev: Cons. Psychiat. Psychoth.Rockingham Forest NHS Trust Kettering.

STEIN, Professor John Frederick Magdalen College, Oxford OX1 4AU Email: john.stein@physiol.ox.ac.uk — BM BCh 1966 Oxf.; MSc, MA Oxf. 1965; MRCP Lond. 1968; FRCP Lond. 1999. (St Thomas's Hosp.) Lect. (Neurophysiol.) Oxf. Univ.; Fell. & Tutor (Med.) Magdalen Coll. Socs: Physiol. Soc.; Assn. Brit. Neurol.; Brit. Dyslexia Assn. (Scientif. Adv.).

STEIN, Kenneth William Thomas 7 Esplanade Terrace, Joppa, Edinburgh EH15 2ES — MB ChB 1987 Bristol.

STEIN, Linda (retired) Careston Manse, Brechin DD9 6SA Tel: 01356 630366 — MB ChB 1973 Manch.; MRCP (UK) 1978; DCH Eng. 1975; DObst RCOG 1975.

STEIN, Penelope Effie Department of Haematology, Cambridge Institute for Medical Research, University of Cambridge, Cambridge CB2 2XY Tel: 01223 762660 Fax: 01223 336788 Email: penny@mrc_imb.cam.ac.uk; 27 Hinton Avenue, Cambridge CB1 7AR Tel: 01223 520646 — MB BChir 1983 Camb.; PhD Camb. 1990; MSc Lond. 1987; BMedSci Nottm. 1980. Wellcome Sen. Fell. (Clin. Sci.) Univ. of Camb. Prev: Research Assoc. Univ. Alberta; Lister Fell. (Haemat.) Univ. Camb.

STEIN, Robert Colin Ludwig Institute for Cancer Research, 91 Riding House St., London W1P 8BT Tel: 020 7878 4060 Fax: 020 7878 4040 Email: rstein@ludwig.ucl.ac.uk; 20 Walcot Square, Kennington, London SE11 4TZ — MB BChir Camb. 1982; PhD Camb. 1978, MA 1978; MRCP (UK) 1986. Clin. Scientif. Fell. & Sen. Lect. & Hon. Cons. Med. Oncol. Ludwig Inst. for Cancer Research & Dept. Oncol. Univ. Coll. Lond. Med. Sch. Prev: Lect. & Hon. Sen. Regist. (Med. Oncol.) St. Geo. Hosp. Med. Sch. Lond.; Sen. Regist. (Med. Oncol.) Middlx. & Univ. Coll. Hosps. Lond.; Regist. (Gen. Med.) Whipps Cross Hosp. Lond.

STEIN, Rose Ellen Chelsea House, Haywood Close, Pinner HA5 3LQ Tel: 020 8866 5757 — MB BS 1963 Lond.; MRCS Eng. LRCP Lond. 1963. (St. Mary's) Clin. Asst. (Radiol.) Edgware Gen. Hosp. Prev: Ho. Off. (Med.) King Edwd. VII Hosp. Windsor; Ho. Off. (Surg.) Mt. Vernon Hosp. N.wood.

STEIN, Samuel Mark Family Consultation Clinic, Dunstable Health Centre, Priory Gardens', Dunstable LU6 3SU Tel: 01582 707660 Fax: 01582 707659 Email: sbcht1@business.ntl.com — MB BCh 1986 Witwatersrand; BA (Criminol.) 1994; MRCPsych. (Witwatersrand) Cons. (Child, Adolesc. & Family Psychiat.) S. Beds. Comm. Health Care Trust. Prev: SHO & Regist. Train. Oxf.; Specialist Regist. Train. St Mary's Hosp. Imperial Coll. Lond.

STEIN, Tarrant Robert East Oxford Health Centre, Manzil Way, Cowley Road, Cowley, Oxford OX4 1XD Tel: 01865 242109; 19 Abberbury Road, Iffley, Oxford OX4 4ET Tel: 01865 777989 — MB BS 1966 Lond.; MRCS Eng. LRCP Lond. 1966; MRCGP 1974; DObst RCOG 1968. (King's Coll. Hosp.)

STEINBERG, Benjamin 7 Saxholm Dale, Bassett, Southampton SO16 7GZ Tel: 023 8076 0177 — MB ChB BAO Belf. 1946; MD Belf. 1955; FRCPsych 1974, M 1971; DPM Lond. 1951. Emerit. Cons. Psychiat. Soton. & SW Hants. Health Dist. Socs: Soton. Med. Soc. (Ordinary Mem.); Wessex Psychother. Soc. Prev: Cons. & Clin. Asst. (Psychiat.) Knowle Hosp. Fareham; Sen. Regist. WhitCh. Hosp. Cardiff.

STEINBERG, Derek Ticehurst House Hospital, Ticehurst, Wadhurst TN5 7HU Tel: 01580 200391 Fax: 01580 201006; 14 Devonshire Place, London W1N 1PB Tel: 020 7935 0640 Fax: 020 7224 6256 — MB BS Lond. 1965; MPhil Lond. 1972; MRCS Eng. LRCP Lond. 1965; FRCPsych 1979, M 1972; DPM Eng. 1968. (Lond. Hosp.) Cons. Psychiat. & Vis. Sen. Tutor Ticehurst Hse. Hosp. Sussex; Trustee Bethlem Roy. & Maudsley Hosp. Art & Hist. Collections Trust. Socs: Fell. Roy. Soc. Med.; Exec. Comm. S. and S. W. Div. Roy. Coll. Psychiat.; Arts & Health Forum, King's Fund. Prev: Cons. Maudsley & Bethlem. Roy. Hosps.; Sen. Regist. Pk. Hosp. Childr. Oxf.; Regist. Maida Vale Hosp. Nerv. Dis. Lond.

*STEINBERG, Mark Westbury Medical Centre Tel: 020 8346 6919 Fax: 020 8346 6919 — MB ChB 1995 Manch.; DRCOG 1997.

STEINBERG, Myer (retired) 12 Charles Street, Herne Bay CT6 5JF — MB BCh BAO Dub. 1941.

STEINBERG, Stanley Westbury Medical Centre, 205 Westbury Avenue, Wood Green, London N22 6RX Tel: 020 8888 3021 Fax: 020 8888 6898 — MB BCh BAO Dub. 1960; BA Dub. 1959. (TC Dub.) Prev: Ho. Phys. & Ho. Surg. Dr. Steevens' Hosp. Dub.; SHO (Cas. & Orthop.) Roy. Vict. Hosp. Bournemouth; Resid. Med. Off. Bearsted Memor. Hosp. Hampton.

STEINBERG, Stanley Victor Castlemilk Health Centre, 71 Dougrie Drive, Glasgow G45 9AW Tel: 0141 531 8585 Fax: 0141 531 8596; 6 Berryhill Drive, Giffnock, Glasgow G46 7AS Tel: 0141 638 7828 Fax: 0141 638 7828 — MB ChB 1970 Glas.; BSc (Hons.) Glas. 1968. (Glas.) Prev: Ho. Surg. S.. Gen. Hosp. Glas.; Ho. Phys. Raigmore Hosp. Inverness.

STEINBERG, Stephen David 13 Howard Walk, London N2 0HB Tel: 020 8455 1587 — MB BS 1983 Lond. Socs: Fell. Roy. Soc. Med.; Brit. Acupunc. Soc. Prev: Clin. Asst. (Rheum.) Chase Farm Hosp. Hosp. Enfield; SHO Char. Cross Hosp. Lond.; SHO (Rheum.) P.ss Alexandra Hosp. Harlow.

STEINBERG, Victor Leonard 22 Holne Chase, London N2 0QN Tel: 020 8458 2764 — MB BS 1951 Lond.; FRCP Lond. 1988; FRCP Ed. 1971, M 1957; DPhysMed. Eng. 1958. (St. Bart.) Socs: Fell. Roy. Soc. Med. (Ex-Pres. Sect. Rheum. & Rehabil.); Brit. Soc. Rheum. Prev: Cons. Rheum. Wembley Hosp.; Hon. Cons. Rheum. Centr. Middlx. Hosp.; Phys. Dept. Physical Med. & Regional Rheum. Centre Chase Farm Hosp. Enfield.

STEINBERGS, Gerardo Gustavs Fullwell Cross Health Centre, 1 Tomswood Hill, Barkingside, Ilford IG6 2HG Tel: 020 8500 0231 Fax: 020 8491 1598; 95 Queens Road, Buckhurst Hill IG9 5BW — MB BS 1982 Lond.; MRCGP 1987; DRCOG 1984; Cert. Family Plann. JCC 1985. Princip. GP Fullwell Cross Health Centre Barkinside Essex; Club Med. Off. W. Ham United Football Club. Socs: Sec. of Ilford Med. Soc. Prev: Assoc. Course Organiser Redbridge VTS. 1990-1993; Sec. of Ilford Med. Soc. 1986-1996.

STEINBRECHER, Mr Henrik Alex Department of Paediatric Surgery, Southampton University NHS Trust, Southampton General Hospital, Tremona Road, Southampton SO16 6YD Tel: 02380 798464 Fax: 02380 794750 Email: henniksteinbrecher@hotmail.com — MB BS 1986 Lond.; FRCS Eng. 1990; MS Soton. 1995; FRCS Paediat. 1997. Cons. (Paediat. Surg.) Soton. Univ. NHS Trust Soton Gen Hosp.

STEINER, David Arthur The Old Vicarage, Christchurch, Coleford GL16 7NS Tel: 01594 835330 Fax: 01594 837555 — MB ChB 1972 Liverp.; T(GP) 1993. Prev: GP Jersey, CI; Med. Off. St. Francis Hosp., Zambia; Ho. Off. Ormskirk & Dist. Gen. Hosp. Ormskirk.

STEINER, Eduard Samuel Roundwood Surgery, Wood Street, Mansfield NG18 1QQ Tel: 01623 648880 Fax: 01623 631761; La Corbiere, Cauldwell Drive, Mansfield NG18 4SL Tel: 01623 653615 Fax: 01623 653615 Email: steiners1@aol.com — MB ChB 1974 Liverp.; DTPC Nottm. 1996; DCH RCPS Glas. 1976. GP Princip.; PCG Chairm. Prev: Regist. (Paediat.) Nottm. City Hosp.; Regist. & SHO (Paediat.) King's Mill Hosp. Mansfield.

STEINER

STEINER, Eleanor Margaret (retired) Atlantic House, Ellenabeich, Isle of Seil, Oban PA34 4RF Tel: 01852 300593 — MB ChB Aberd. 1961; MICGP 1984; MRCGP 1976; MFCM 1972; DPH Aberd. 1966; FRSH 1997. Prev: Mem. Indep. Tribunal Serv.

STEINER, Gerhard Martin (retired) Sheffield Childrens Hospital, Western Bank, Sheffield S10 2TH Tel: 0114 271 7000 Fax: 0114 271 7514 Email: martin@fulwoody@EMON.co.uk — MB BS Lond. 1956; FRCP Lond. 1980, M 1962; MRCS Eng. LRCP Lond. 1956; FRCR 1980; FFR 1967; DMRD 1965; DObst RCOG 1960; DCH Eng. 1959. Hon. Clin. Lect. Sheff. Univ.; Cons. Radiol. Sheff. Childr. Hosp. Prev: Instruc. (Radiol.) Yale Univ. Med. Sch., USA.

STEINER, Hans 30 Elm Grove, Killingworth, Newcastle upon Tyne NE12 7AN — MB ChB 1959 Bristol; MD Bristol 1974.

STEINER, Helen Rebecca 584 Fulwood Road, Sheffield S10 3QE Tel: 0114 230 4943 — MB BS 1990 Lond.; BSc Lond. 1987; DObst Auckland 1992. Prev: Trainee GP/SHO Auckland Area HB, NZ.

STEINER, Jane 155 Risca Road, Newport NP20 3PP — MB BCh 1977 Wales.

STEINER, Janice Ann Oxford Therapeutics Consulting Ltd., Magdalen Centre, Oxford Science Park, Oxford OX4 4GA Tel: 01865 784874 Fax: 01865 784874 Email: jansteiner@oxrx.com — DPhil Oxf. 1980; MB BS Sydney 1969; FRACP 1975. (Sydney) Dir. Oxf. Therap. Cons. Ltd. Socs: Brit. Pharm. Soc; Fell. Fac. of Pharmaceut. Med.; Brit. Assn. of Pharmaceut. Phys. Prev: Europ. Med. Dir. Gensia Europe Ltd; Head of Clin. Support, Roche Products Ltd; Dir. of Clin. Pharmacol. Searle Research & Developm. UK.

STEINER, John 28 Park Drive, London NW11 7SP Tel: 020 8458 8303 — MB ChB 1958 New Zealand; PhD Camb. 1964; FRCPsych. 1981, M 1971; DPM Lond. 1967. (Otago) Socs: Brit. Psychoanal. Soc. Prev: Cons. Psychother. Tavistock Clinic Lond.; Cons. Psychiat. Maudsley Hosp. Lond.

STEINER, Marion Ruth Southmead Health Centre, Ullswater Road, Bristol BS10 6DF; 57 Ravenswood Road, Redland, Bristol BS6 6BP — MB BS 1985 Lond.; MFFP 1995; MRCGP 1989; DRCOG 1989; LFHom 1997. (London) GP Bristol. Prev: Princip. GP Newc.

STEINER, Michael Charles 28 Park Drive, London NW1 7SP — MB BS 1990 Lond.

STEINER, Nicholas Brian Michael The Hollies Surgery, The Green, Great Bentley, Colchester CO7 8PJ Tel: 01206 250691 Fax: 01206 252496; Rectory Lodge, Rectory Road, Weeley Heath, Clacton-on-Sea CO16 9BH Tel: 01255 830379 — MB ChB 1972 Bristol.

STEINER, Mr Robert Emil, CBE 12 Stonehill Road, London SW14 8RW Tel: 020 8876 4038 — MD 1957 NUI; MB BCh BAO 1941; FRCS Eng. 1982; FRCP Lond. 1965, M 1959; FRCR 1975; FFR 1952; DMR Eng. 1945; Hon. FACR 1965; Hon. FRACR 1971; Hon. FFR RCSI 1972. (Univ. Coll. Dub.) Emerit. Prof. Radiol. Univ. Lond. At Postgrad. Med. Sch. Hammersmith Hosp. Socs: FRCR (Ex-Pres. & Warden); Brit. Inst. Radiol. (Ex-Pres. & Edr. Brit. Jl. Radiol.). Prev: Civil Cons. Radiol. to Med. Dir. Gen. (Naval); Cons. Adviser (Radiol.) DHSS; Pres. & Warden Roy. Coll. Radiols.

STEINER, Roy Raymond Woodbridge Road Surgery, 165-167 Woodbridge Road, Ipswich IP4 2PE Tel: 01473 256251; 59 Linksfield, Rushmere St. Andrew, Ipswich IP5 1BA — MB BS 1983 Lond.; MRCGP 1988; DFFP 1993; DRCOG 1987; DCH RCP Lond. 1987. (Westm.) Prev: Trainee GP Harold Hill Essex; Trainee Community Paediat. HornCh.; Clin. Med. Off. (Family Plann. & Child Health) HornCh.

STEINER, Timothy John Division of Neuroscience and Psychological Medicine, Imperial College School of Medicine, St Dunstan's Road, London W6 8RP Tel: 020 8846 1191 Fax: 020 8741 7808 Email: t.steiner@ic.ac.uk — MB BS 1976 Lond.; LLM Wales 1991; BSc (Hons.) Lond. 1969, PhD 1975; MFPM RCP (UK) 1994; MA Wales 1997; FFPM RCP (UK) 1998. (Char. Cross) Reader (Clin. Physiol.) Imperial Coll. Sch. of Med. Lond.; Hon. Cons. Clin. Physiol. Char. Cross Hosp. Lond. Socs: Internat. Headache Soc. Mem. Exec. Comm. (Chairm. Ethics Comm., Mem. Clin.Trials Comm.); Eur. Headache Federat. (Pres., UK Bd. Mem. & Chairm. PR Comm.); Brit. Assn. for the Study of Headache (Mem. Exec. Comm.). Prev: Sen. Lect. (Clin. Physiol.) Char. Cross & W.m. Med. Sch. Lond.; Lect. (Experiment. Neurol.) Char. Cross & W.m. Med. Sch. Lond.

STEINERT, Jack 30 Vicarage Road, East Sheen, London SW14 8RU Tel: 020 8876 9505 — MB ChB 1956 Birm.; FRCPsych 1977, M 1971; DPM Eng. 1965. (Birm.) Vis. Cons. Psychiat. Roehampton Priory Hosp. Lond.; Hon. Sen. Clin. Lect. Imperial Coll Lond. Socs: BMA. Prev: W. Lond. Healthcare Trust Ealing; Cons. Psychiat. Springfield Hosp. Lond.; Sen. Regist. St. Geo. Hosp. Lond. & Springfield Hosp. Lond.

STEINGOLD, Harry Castlemilk Health Centre, 71 Douglas Drive, Cadtlemilk, Glasgow G45 9AW Tel: 0141 531 8500; 5 Humbie Gate, Newton Mearns, Glasgow G77 5NH Tel: 0141 639 8321 — MB ChB 1950 Glas. (Glas.)

STEINGOLD, Mr Raymond Frank The Warren, 3 Sketchley Old Village, Burbage, Hinckley LE10 3HT Tel: 01455 633054 — MB ChB 1971 Manch.; FRCS Eng. 1978. Cons. Orthop. Surg. Nuneaton. Socs: Fell. Brit. Orthop. Assn. Prev: Sen. Regist. (Orthop.) Harlow Wood Hosp. & Leic. Roy. Infirm.; Tutor & Hon. Regist. (Orthop.) Univ. Dept. Orthop. Hope Hosp. Manch.; Orthop. Regist. Preston Roy. Infirm.

STEINHARDT, Stephen Ian Steinhardt and Partners, The Surgery, 5A Brookfield Road, Hucclecote, Gloucester GL3 3HB Tel: 01452 617295 Fax: 01452 617296; Springfield House, Little Witcombe, Gloucester GL3 4TU — MB ChB 1973 Bristol; MRCGP 1978; D.Occ.Med. RCP Lond. 1995; DObst RCOG 1976. Prev: SHO (Cas. & Orthop.) Cheltenham Gen. Hosp.; SHO (Obst.) S.mead Hosp. Bristol; SHO (Paediat.) Cheltenham Childr. Hosp.

STEINLECHNER, Mr Colin Wolfgang Brett Frimley Park Hospital; Email: colin@steinlechner.fsnet.co.uk — MB BS 1992 Lond.; BSc (Hons) Lond. 1989; FRCS Eng 1996. Specialist Regist. (Trauma & Orthop.) S. W. Thames Rotat.

STEKELMAN, Sharon 237 Alexandra Park Road, London N22 7BJ Tel: 020 8888 9428 Fax: 020 8888 9428 Email: sharonos@hotmail.com — MB BS 1962 Lond.; MRCS Eng. LRCP Lond. 1962; DPM Eng. 1971. (King's Coll. Lond. & St. Geo.) Socs: Brit. Psychoanal. Soc. Prev: Clin. Asst. Portman Clinic & Centre Psychother. Lond.; Sen. Regist. Earls Ct. Child Guid. Unit; Regist. (Psychiat.) Halliwick Hosp. Lond.

STELFOX, Dora Elizabeth Church Street Surgery, 1 Church Street, Newtownards BT23 4FH Tel: 028 9181 6333 Fax: 028 9181 8805; 3 Old Belfast Road, Newtownards BT23 4SG Tel: 01247 819647 — MB BCh BAO 1979 Belf.; MRCGP 1984; DRCOG 1983; DCH 1981. Socs: BMA & Ulster Med. Soc.

STELL, Ian Michael 96 Arran Road, London SE6 2NN — MB BS 1984 Lond.; FRCS Ed. 1995; MRCP (UK) 1988; MRCGP 1989; Dip. Epid. FPHM RCP (UK) 1994; DTM & H RCP Lond. 1990; DCH RCP Lond. 1987; DRCOG 1987. Cons. (A & E Med.) Bromley NHS Trust. Prev: Lect. (A & E) Guy's Hosp. Lond.

STELL, Professor Philip Michael 69 The Village, Haxby, York YO32 2JE Tel: 01904 761469 — MB ChB 1958 Ed.; ChM Liverp. 1976; FRCS Eng. 1966; FRCS Ed. 1962. (Ed.) Prof. Emerit. Otorhinolaryng. Univ. Liverp. Socs: Fell. Roy. Soc. Med. (Ex-Pres. Sect. Laryngol.); (Ex-Pres.) Liverp. Med. Inst.; German Acad. Prev: Fell. Washington Univ. St. Louis, USA.

STELLAKIS, Michael Laurence Constantine Basement Flat, 6 Vyvyan Terrace, Bristol BS8 3DF — MB ChB 1991 Bristol.

STELLER, Philip Harold 23 Marle Croft, Whitefield, Manchester M45 7NB — MB ChB 1972 Manch.; FFA RCS Eng. 1978. Cons. Anaesth. N. Manch. Gen. Hosp.

STELLMAN, Rose Margaret Fraser (retired) 7 Finch Court, 10 Lansdown Road, Sidcup DA14 4EN Tel: 020 8309 9522 — MB ChB Aberd. 1939. Prev: PMO (Child Health) Bexley Health Dist.

STELLON, Anthony John Abbey Practice, 107 London Road, Temple Ewell, Dover CT16 3BY Tel: 01304 821182 Fax: 01304 827673; 125 Whitstable Road, Canterbury CT2 8EQ Tel: 01227 453086 Email: stellon@btinternet.com — MB BS 1977 Lond.; MRCP (UK) 1980; MRCS Eng. LRCP Lond. 1977; Dip. Med. Acupunc. 1995; Dip. Occ Med. 1999. (Roy. Free Hosp. Lond.) Hosp. Pract. (Gastroenterol.) Buckland Hosp. Dover. Socs: Brit. Med. Acupunct. Soc. Prev: Regist. (Med.) Liver Unit King's Coll. Hosp. Lond.; SHO Rotat. (Gen. Med.) N.. Gen. Hosp. Sheff.; Ho. Surg. Barnet Gen. Hosp.

STENHOUSE, Craig William St. Werburghs House, Wood Lane, Hanbury, Burton-on-Trent DE13 8TG — MB ChB 1986 Leic.

STENHOUSE, Emily Jane Whinfell House, 5 Claremont Drive, Bridge of Allan, Stirling FK9 4EE — MB ChB 1996 Glas. SHO (O & G) Glas.

STEPHEN

STENHOUSE, George (retired) 166 Southbrae Drive, Jordanhill, Glasgow G13 1TX Tel: 0141 954 9594 — MB ChB 1966 Glas.; PhD Glas. 1973, BSc (Hons.) 1963; FRCR 1980. Prev: Lect. (Physiol.) Univ. Glas.

***STENHOUSE, Grant** 2/2, 23 Pitfour St., Dundee DD2 2NY — MB ChB 1998 Dund.; MB ChB Dund 1998.

STENHOUSE, Jeremy Nicol Health Centre, Faringdon SN7 7EZ Tel: 01367 242388 — MB BChir 1958 Camb.; MA, MB Camb. 1958, BChir 1957; DObst RCOG 1961. (Camb. & Oxf.) Prev: Anaesth. Regist. Launceston Gen. Hosp. Tasmania; Ho. Surg. & Ho. Phys. Radcliffe Infirm. Oxf.; Obst. Ho. Surg. Ch.ill Hosp. Oxf.

***STENHOUSE, Peter Granger** 7 Beech Avenue, Bearsden, Glasgow G61 3EU — MB ChB 1998 Glas.; MB ChB Glas 1998.

STENHOUSE, Philip Daniel 91A Friern Road, London SE22 0AZ — MB BS 1993 Lond.; BDS Lond. 1985.

STENHOUSE, Robin Balfour (retired) Karoo, 10 Sandybed Lane, Scarborough YO12 5LH — MB BChir Camb. 1960; DPM Eng. 1968; DObst RCOG 1965. Clin. Asst. (Psychiat.) St. Mary's Hosp. ScarBoro. Prev: Surg. Lt. RN.

STENHOUSE, Shirley McLean The Surgery, 46 Annan Road, Gretna DG16 5DG — MB ChB 1987 Glas.; MRCGP 1991. Prev: Trainee GP Crieff Health Centre; SHO (O & G & Med.) Stirling Roy. Infirm.; SHO (Psychiat.) Bellsdyke Hosp. Larbert.

STENHOUSE, Thomas Grove Road Surgery, 3 Grove Road, Solihull B91 2AG Tel: 0121 705 1105 Fax: 0121 711 4098; 6 The Crescent, Solihull B91 1JP Tel: 0121 705 1821 — MB ChB 1976 Birm.; MRCGP 1984; DRCOG 1980.

STENNER, Jonathan Maurice Crathorne 77 High Street, Buckden, St Neots, Huntingdon PE19 5TA — BChir 1990 Camb.

STENSON, Benjamin James Consultant Neonatologist, Simspon Memorial Maternity Pavilion, Edinburgh Email: stensonb@telemedicine.clh.ed.ac.uk — MB ChB 1986 Ed.; MRCP (UK) 1990; MD Ed. 1997; FRCPCH 1998. Cons. Neonatologist. Prev: Research Fell. & Hon. Regist. (Neonat. Paediat.) Univ. Edin.

STENSON, Keith, TD The Surgery, Torton Hill Road, Arundel BN18 9HG Tel: 01903 882517/882191 Fax: 01903 884326 — MB BS Lond. 1965; MRCS Eng. LRCP Lond. 1965; MRCGP 1975; DObst RCOG 1971. (Westm.) Hosp. Pract. (Geriat.) Worthing & S.lands NHS Trust; Col. RAMC(V). Socs: Hon. Progr.. Sec. Med. Off. Sch.Assn. Prev: Ho. Phys. Roy. Vict. Hosp. Bournemouth; Ho. Surg. W.m. Hosp. Lond.

***STENSON, Susan Laura** Sandygate, Church St., East Markham, Newark NG22 0SA Tel: 01777 871036 — MB BS 1998 Lond.; MB BS Lond 1998.

STENT, Venetia Mary 50 Fir Road, Hanworth, Feltham TW13 6UJ Tel: 020 8898 0253 Fax: 020 8893 3864 — MB BS 1980 Lond.; MRCGP 1985. (St Bartholomews)

STENTIFORD, Norman Henry (retired) The Oaks, Strawmoor Lane, Oaken, Codsall, Wolverhampton WV8 2HY Tel: 01902 761557 Email: bim@stent.eu.org — MB ChB 1960 Bristol; FRCP Lond. 1980, M 1963. Cons. Phys. Russells Hall Hosp. Dudley. Prev: Cons. Phys. Burton Rd. Hosp. Dudley.

***STENTON, Kay Jeanette** 18 Lowburn Road, Richmond, Sheffield S13 8DH — MB ChB 1995 Sheff.

STENTON, Mark John, Surg. Lt. RN 64 Yarrow Way, Locks Heath, Southampton SO31 6XD Tel: 01489 570162 — MB BS 1992 Lond. Surg. Lt. RN.

STENTON, Samuel Christopher Department of Respiratory Medicine, Royal Victoria Infirmary, Newcastle upon Tyne NE1 4LP Tel: 0191 232 5131 Fax: 0191 227 5224 — MB BCh BAO 1981 Belf.; BSc Belf. 1978; FRCP (UK) 1999; MFOM RCP Lond. 1995. Cons. Phys. Roy. Vict. Infirm. & Assoc. Hosps. NHS Trust; Sen. Lect. (Med.) Univ. Newc. Prev: Lect. (Med.) Univ. Newc.; Regist. (Med.) Newc. HA.

STEPANEK, Peter Andrew 4 Vernon Park, Galgate, Lancaster LA2 0LP — MB ChB 1987 Manch.

STEPHAN, Talal Fouad Mansfield Community Hospital, Stockwell Gate, Mansfield NG18 5QJ Tel: 01623 785151 Fax: 01623 785180; Cornerstone Lodge, 72 Main St, Papplewick, Nottingham NG15 8FE Tel: 0115 964 0099 — MB ChB 1971 Baghdad; FRCP Glas.; FRCPI; Dip. Cardiol. Lond 1983. Cons. Rehabil. Med. Mansfield Community Hosp.; Exec. Comm. Mem. - Mansfield Primary Care Trust. Socs: BMA; Brit. Soc. Rehabil. Med. Prev: Sen. Regist. (Rehabil. Med.) Derbysh. Roy. Infirm.; SCMO (Rehabil. Med.)

Haywood Hosp. Stoke-on-Trent; Career Regist. (Gen. & Geriat. Med.) W. Midl. RHA.

STEPHEN, Alan James Lower Ericstane, 7A West Montrose St., Helensburgh G84 9NF — MB ChB 1974 Glas.

STEPHEN, Alexander Kynoch (retired) Ivycroft, 153 Redcar Lane, Redcar TS10 2DZ — MB ChB Aberd. 1951.

STEPHEN, Andrew Alexander Linden Medical Group, Linden Medical Centre, Linden Avenue, Kettering NN15 7NX Tel: 01536 512104 Fax: 01536 415930; The Spinney, 16B Harrington Road, Loddington, Kettering NN14 1JZ Tel: 01536 711993 — MB ChB Sheff. 1969; MRCGP 1980; DCH Eng. 1973; DObst RCOG 1971. (Sheff.) Gen. Med. Practitioner; Med. Off. SATRA (Shoe & Allied Trades Research Assoc.) Kettering. Socs: BMA. Prev: SHO (Paediat.) Sheff. Childr. Hosp.; SHO (Obst.) Jessop Hosp. Sheff.; Ho. Off. (Med.) N.. Gen. Hosp. Sheff.

STEPHEN, Annie Margaret (retired) Broad Reach, Inchberry Road, Fochabers IV32 7QA Tel: 01343 821637 — MB ChB Aberd. 1940.

STEPHEN, Mr Arthur Buchan Orthopaedic Department, Queens Medical Centre, Clifton Boulevard, Nottingham NG7 2UH Tel: 0115 924 9924 — MB BS 1993 Lond.; BSc Lond. 1990, MB BS 1993; FRCS (Eng) 1997. (Univ. Coll. & Middx. Hosp. Med. Sch.)

STEPHEN, Catherine Margaret 99 Rannoch Drive, Bearsden, Glasgow G61 2ER — MB ChB 1986 Aberd. (Univ. Aberd.) Prev: Liaison Phys. (c/o Elderly) Newc. City Trust; Trainee GP Dumfries & Galloway HB; SHO Rotat. (Med.) Newc. Gen. Hosp.

STEPHEN, Doris Leonora (retired) 40 Denhill Park, Newcastle upon Tyne NE15 6QH Tel: 0191 273 3809 — MB ChB Aberd. 1949. Assoc. Specialist Blood Transfus. Centre Newc.

STEPHEN, Elizabeth Daphne Storey (retired) Royal Oak House, Royal Oak Mews, Mayfield TN20 6AL Tel: 01435 872632 — MB ChB 1942 St. And.; FFA RCS Eng. 1954; DA Eng. 1945. Hon. Cons. Anaesth. Maidstone & Tunbridge Wells Health Dist. & Kent HA. Prev: Cons. Anaesth. Maidstone & Tunbridge Wells Health Dist.

STEPHEN, George Portlethen Group Practice, Portlethen Health Centre, Bruntland Road, Portlethen, Aberdeen AB12 4QL Tel: 01224 780223 Fax: 01224 781317; 53 Crollshillock Place, Newtonhill, Stonehaven AB39 3RF Tel: 01569 30511 — MB ChB 1970 Aberd.; MRCGP 1976. Prev: Resid. Ho. Off. (Med. & Surg.) Aberd. Roy. Infirm.; Trainee GP Aberd. VTS.

STEPHEN, George Willson The Health Centre, Trenchard Avenue, Thornaby, Stockton-on-Tees TS17 0DD Tel: 01642 762636 Fax: 01642 766464; Lewins, Fieldhouse Lane, Kirklevington, Yarm TS15 9LS Tel: 01642 781110 — MB ChB 1961 Aberd.; MRCGP 1982; DA Eng. 1972; DObst RCOG 1964. Socs: BMA. Prev: Anaesth. S. Teesside Hosp. Gp.; Ship's Surg. Roy. Fleet Auxil. Serv.

STEPHEN, George Wilson 30 Flanchford Road, London W12 9ND — MB ChB 1956 Aberd.; FFA RCSI 1962; FFA RCS Eng. 1963. (Aberd.)

STEPHEN, Helen Janet The Old School Surgery, The Old School, The Square, Tarves, Ellon AB41 7GX Tel: 01651 851777 Fax: 01651 852090 — MB ChB 1969 Aberd.; MRCP (UK) 1979; DCH Glas. 1977.

STEPHEN, Mr Ian Bruce Murray New Barn, 39A Grange Road, Broadstairs CT10 3ER Tel: 01843 867848 Fax: 01843 868536 — MB BChir Camb. 1968; FRCS Eng. 1973; MRCS Eng. LRCP Lond. 1968. (Camb. & St. Bart.) Cons. Orthop. Surg. E. Kent Hosps. NHS Trust; Cases Comm. Mem. Med. Protec. Soc. Socs: Fell. BOA & Roy. Soc. Med.; Pres. 2000/2001 Brit. Orthop. Foot Surg. Soc.; Expert Witness Inst. Prev: Sen. Regist. (Orthop.) P.ss Eliz. Orthop. Hosp. Exeter; Regist. (Orthop.) Bristol Roy. Infirm.; Research Fell. (Orthop.) McGill Univ. Montreal, Canada.

STEPHEN, Joanna Ruth 51 Pontcanna Street, Pontcanna, Cardiff CF11 9HR Tel: 029 2039 4155 — MB ChB 1994 Dundee. SHO (Basic Surg. Train.) Univ. Hosp. Wales Cardiff. Prev: Demonst. (Anat.) Univ. Dundee.

STEPHEN, John Francis (retired) 25 Vivian Terrace, Davidsons Mains, Edinburgh EH4 5AW — MB ChB Ed. 1950; DObst RCOG 1954.

STEPHEN, Mr John Gordon 12 The Willows, Bishop Auckland DL14 7HH — MB BChir 1970 Camb.; MA Camb. 1970, MChir 1984; FRCS Eng. 1973. Cons. Surg. Bishop Auckland Gen. Hosp.; Hon. Clin. Lect. (Surg.) Univ. Newc. Socs: Brit. Soc. Gastroenterol.; Assn. Surg.

STEPHEN

STEPHEN, John Robert 21 Verlands Road, Preston, Weymouth DT3 6BY — MB ChB 1994 Dundee; BA Oxf. 1984.

STEPHEN, Linda Jane Epilepsy Unit, Western Infirmary, Dumbarton Road, Glasgow G11 6NT; Ground Right Flat, 6 Dryburgh Gardens, Glasgow G20 6BT — MB ChB 1989 Glas.; MRCGP 1994; DFFP 1997; T(GP) 1994; DCH 1993; DRCOG 1992. Dep. Dir. & Epilepsy Unit W.. Infirm. Glas.

STEPHEN, Margaret Elizabeth (retired) Parkside, 124B South Street, Armadale, Bathgate EH48 3JU Tel: 01501 730700 — MB ChB 1967 Aberd. Prev: Res. Ho. Surg. Woodend Gen. Hosp. Aberd.

STEPHEN, Mark James By The Way, Mingoose Vale, Mount Hawk, Truro TR4 8RY — MB ChB 1994 Manch.

STEPHEN, Mary Ross Royal Infirmary, Department of Pathology, 84 Castle St., Glasgow G4 0SF Tel: 0141 211 4738 Fax: 0141 211 4884 — MB ChB 1971 Glas.; MRCPath 1994. (Glasgow) Cons. Cytopath. Roy. Infirm. Glas.

STEPHEN, Robert Strachan Aultoun Croft, Aquharney, Hatton, Peterhead AB42 5BN — MB ChB 1977 Aberd.

***STEPHEN, Samantha Jane** Tiverton, Lyne Close, Virginia Water GU25 4EA — MB BS 1998 Lond.; MB BS Lond 1998.

STEPHEN, Stewart Anderson (retired) 1 East Campbell Court, Longniddry EH32 0NW Tel: 01875 853470 — MB ChB 1950 St. And.; FRCP Ed. 1973, M 1956. Prev: Cons. Phys. (Geriat.) Sanderson Hosp. Galashiels.

STEPHEN, Thomas Barker (retired) — MB BS Lond. 1953; MRCS Eng. LRCP Lond. 1953. Prev: Ho. Surg. & Ho. Phys. Guy's Hosp.

STEPHEN, Walter Taylor Woodside Medical Group A, 80 Western Road, Woodside, Aberdeen AB24 4SU Tel: 01224 492631 Fax: 01224 276173 — MB ChB 1973 Aberd.; MRCGP 1977.

STEPHEN, William (retired) 19 Newton Road, Lindfield, Haywards Heath RH16 2NB Tel: 01444 484577 — MB ChB 1942 Aberd.; MRCPsych 1971. Prev: PMO HM Prison Serv.

STEPHEN, William John (retired) 27 New Street, Wells BA5 2LE Tel: 01749 672642 — MB ChB 1956 Bristol; DObst RCOG 1960; MRCP 1996. Prev: RCGP/Stanning Trav. Fell. 1980.

STEPHEN, William Simpson Younie Albyn Medical Practice, 30 Albyn Place, Aberdeen AB10 1NW Tel: 01224 586829 Fax: 01224 213238; 172 Deeside Gardens, Aberdeen AB15 7PX Tel: 01224 325024 — MB ChB 1973 Aberd.; MRCGP 1979. Hon. Clin Tutor Dept. Gen. Pract. Univ. Aberd.

STEPHENS, Adrian David Kings College Hospital, Demark Hill, London SE5 9RS Tel: 020 7346 4598 Fax: 020 7346 3514; 54 Telfords Yard, Wapping, London E1W 2BQ Tel: 020 7680 1474 — MRCS Eng. LRCP Lond. 1963; MD Lond. 1980, MB BS 1963; FRCPath 1988, M 1976. (St. Bart.) Cons. Haemat. Kings Coll. Hosp. Lond. Socs: Brit. Soc. Haematol. Prev: Cons. Haemat. St. Bart. Hosp. Lond.; Lect. (Med.) St. Bart. Hosp. Med. Coll. Lond.; Sen. Regist. (Haemat.) & Ho. Surg. St. Bart. Hosp. Lond.

STEPHENS, Alison Rhona (retired) 28 High Street, Eynsham, Witney OX29 4HB — MB ChB Ed. 1958; MFFP 1993; DCH RCPS Glas. 1961; DObst RCOG 1960. Prev: Asst. GP Oxf.

STEPHENS, Andrew David Elm Hayes Surgery, High Street, Paulton, Bristol BS39 7QJ Tel: 01761 413155 Fax: 01761 410573 Email: andrew.stephens@gp-l81059nhs.uk; 1 Sawmill Gardens, Chilcompton, Bath BA3 4FE Tel: 01761 233947 — MB BS 1990 Lond.; MRCGP 1998; DFFP 1997; DRCOG 1996; BSc 1987 Lond. (Middlx. Hosp. Med. Sch. Lond.) GP Princip., Dr. Roy and Partners, Elm Hayes Surg., High St., Paulton. Socs: BMA; RCGP. Prev: GP Princip., Dr. Slade and Partners, Irnham Lodge Surg., Minehead, Som. TA24 5RG.

***STEPHENS, Angela** 26 Manor Crescent, Stapleton, Leicester LE9 8JQ — MB BS 1993 Lond.; MB BS Lond 1993.

STEPHENS, Brian Alexis Fenwick (retired) Tollgate House, Wing, Leighton Buzzard LU7 0PW — MRCS Eng. LRCP Lond. 1942; MRCGP 1962. Med. Off. StockGr. Pk. Sch. Prev: Clin. Asst. Med. Roy. Bucks. Hosp. Aylesbury.

STEPHENS, Caroline Jane Bridge Street Surgery, 67 Bridge Street, Cambridge CB2 1UR Tel: 01223 355060 Fax: 01223 460812; 43 Herbert Street, Cambridge CB4 1AG Tel: 01223 321320 — BM 1981 Soton. Dep. Police Surg. Camb. Socs: LMC.

STEPHENS, Caroline Susan 12 Kirkintilloch Road, Bishopbriggs, Glasgow G64 2AX — MB ChB 1986 Glas.

STEPHENS, Carys Llywella Brynawel, 10 Parc-yr-Afon, Carmarthen SA31 1RL — MB BS 1962 Lond.; DA Eng. 1967. (Cardiff) Regist. (Anaesth.) Merthyr & Aberdare Hosp. Gp.

STEPHENS, Catherine Joan Myfanwy Poole Hospital NHS Trust, Longfleet Road, Poole BH15 2JB Tel: 01202 665511; Sancroft House, Canford Magna, Wimborne BH21 3AF — MB BS 1981 Lond.; MRCP (UK) 1984; FRCP (UK) 1998. Cons. Dermat. Poole Hosp. Prev: Sen. Regist. (Dermat.) St. John's Dermat. Centre Lond.; Regist. (Dermat.) St. Thos. Hosp. Lond.

STEPHENS, Catriona Alison 28 High Street, Eynsham, Witney OX29 4HB — MB BS 1993 Lond.

STEPHENS, Charles Philip Church Cottage, Church Hill, Marnhull, Sturminster Newton DT10 1PU — MB BS 1992 Lond.

STEPHENS, Christine Tel: 01332 513283; Tel: 01283 711077 — MB ChB 1986 Sheff. GP Retainer Micklover, Derby.

STEPHENS, Christopher Roman Victor Street Surgery, Victor Street, Shirley, Southampton SO15 5SY Tel: 023 8077 4781 Fax: 023 8039 0680 — MB BS 1979 Lond.; MRCGP 1983; DRCOG 1985; DCH RCP Lond. 1984. (Guy's) Sen. Lect. (Primary Med. Care) Sch. Med. Soton. Univ.

STEPHENS, Clare Alice Torrington Park Health Centre, Torrington Park, North Finchley, London N12 9SS Tel: 020 8445 7261 Fax: 020 8343 9122; 16 The Ridgeway, London N3 2PH — MB BS 1990 Lond.; MRCGP 1995; DRCOG 1994. Clin. Lect. (Primary Care) Univ. Coll. Lond. Prev: Regist. (Gen. Pract.) Lond.; SHO Rotat. (Obst.) Univ. Coll. Hosp. Lond.

STEPHENS, Cyril Joakim (retired) Whitefriars, Carmel St., Great Chesterford, Saffron Walden CB10 1PH Tel: 01799 530612 Fax: 01799 531584 — MRCS Eng. LRCP Lond. 1953; BA Camb. 1949; FFA RCS Eng. 1962; DA Eng. 1955. Prev: Cons. Anaesth. W. Essex Dist.

STEPHENS, David Elm Lodge Surgery, 2 Burbage Road, London SE24 9HJ Tel: 020 7733 3073 Fax: 020 7924 0710 — MB BS 1977 Lond.; MRCS Eng. LRCP Lond. 1977; MRCGP 1982; DRCOG 1982. Trainer (Gen. Pract.) SE Thames Region; Tutor (Gen. Pract.) KCH Lond.; GP Cons. Lambeth, S.wark & Lewisham Health Commisss. Socs: Socialist Med. Assn. Prev: SHO (O & G) Greenwich Dist. Hosp. Lond.; SHO (Med. & Paediat.) Guy's Hosp. Lond.; Ho. Phys. Addenbrooke's Hosp. Camb.

STEPHENS, David Beverley Low Cedars, Westerland, Paignton TQ3 1RR Tel: 01803 556795 — MB ChB 1959 Sheff. (Sheff.) SCMO Torbay Health Auth. Prev: Ho. Phys. City Gen. Hosp. Sheff.; Asst. Cas. Off. Roy. Hosp. Sheff.; Obst. Ho. Off. Hull Matern. Hosp.

STEPHENS, David Edward Orchard Lea, 23 Mount St, Bishops Lydeard, Taunton TA4 3AN — LMSSA Lond. 1962; Dip. Med. Acupunc.

STEPHENS, David Francis Fisk (retired) Mary Potter Health Centre, Gregory Blvd, Hyson Green, Nottingham NG5 4DB Tel: 0115 960 8882 — LRCP LRCS 1948 Ed.; LRCP LRCS Ed. LRFPS Glas. 1948; MRCGP 1966; Cert Contracep. & Family Plann. RCOG & RCGP. JP City of Nottm. Prev: Ho. Phys. Roy. Edin. Hosp. Ment. Disorders.

STEPHENS, David John (retired) Downham Cottage, Lechlade GL7 3DL Tel: 01367 252075 — MB ChB 1949 Leeds; MRCGP 1959; DObst RCOG 1953. Prev: GP Lechlade.

STEPHENS, David Samuel Pendennis, 13 Park Road, Barry CF62 6NW Tel: 01446 4439 — MB BS 1957 Lond. (St. Geo.) Socs: BMA & Barry Med. Soc. Prev: Ho. Surg. St. Geo. Hosp.; Res. Obst. Asst. N. Middlx. Hosp. Lond.; Ho. Phys. Fulham Hosp.

STEPHENS, Derek Dillwyn Ty Heulog, Love Lane, Brightlingsea, Colchester CO7 0QQ Tel: 01206 302711 — BM BCh 1949 Oxf.; BM BCh Oxon. 1949.

STEPHENS, Douglas Alan (retired) 43 Greystoke Park, Gosforth, Newcastle upon Tyne NE3 2DZ Tel: 0191 217 0409 Fax: 0191 217 0409 Email: alapat@ukonline.co.uk — MB ChB 1956 Birm.; FRCPsych 1977, M 1971; DPM Eng. 1961. Med. Mem. N.. Ment. Health Review Tribunal Nottm.; Second Opinion Apptd. Doctor Ment. Health Act Commiss. Nottm. Prev: Direct. Clin. Serv. (Psychiat.) N. Tyneside Gen. Hosp.

***STEPHENS, Elizabeth Angela** Morley Rectory, Deopham Road, Morley St Botolph, Wymondham NR18 9DA — MB BS 1998 Newc.; MB BS Newc 1998.

STEPHENS, Elizabeth Ann 28 Enfield Avenue, Liverpool L23 0SZ Tel: 0151 476 9174 — MB BS 1993 Lond.; BSc Lond. 1990; DRCOG 1995; DFFP 1995.

STEPHENS, Emily Christdasi Peters 73 Pollard Lane, Bradford BD2 4RW Tel: 01274 636273 — LMS 1951 Punjab; LAH Dub. 1968; LMS Ludhiana Punjab India 1951. Hosp. Pract. (Genitourin. Med.) St. Lukes Hosp. Bradford.

STEPHENS, Enid Winifred Brett (retired) 5 Sherrardspark Road, Welwyn Garden City AL8 7JW Tel: 01707 324069 — LRCP LRCS 1944 Ed.; LRCP LRCS Ed. LRFPS Glas. 1944. Prev: GP Hertford.

STEPHENS, Fraser Renfree Hillside, Ladock, Truro TR2 4NG — MB ChB 1991 Aberd. Trainee GP N. Devon. Healthcare Trust Barnstaple.

STEPHENS, Frederick Graham 15 Forth-an-Nance, Portreath, Redruth TR16 4NQ — MB BS 1965 Lond.; MRCS Eng. LRCP Lond. 1965.

STEPHENS, Geoffrey Paul Holmes Chapel Health Centre, London Road, Holmes Chapel, Crewe CW4 7BB — MB ChB 1971 Otago.

STEPHENS, Helen Elizabeth 17 Kestrel Avenue, Staines TW18 4RU — MB BS 1988 Lond.

STEPHENS, Henry Michael Alcwyn Thomson and Partners, The Medical Centre, Oak Street, Lechlade GL7 3RY Tel: 01367 252264 — MB BS 1983 Lond.; MRCP (UK) 1986; MRCGP 1989; Dip. Pract. Dermat. Wales 1991; DRCOG 1989.

STEPHENS, Imogen Freya Dawn Argyll & Clyde NHS Board, Ross House, Hawkhead Road, Paisley PA2 7BN Tel: 0141 842 7200 Fax: 01436 820376 Email: imogen.stephens@achb.scot.nhs.uk — MB ChB 1983 Ed.; BSc (Hons.) Ed. 1980, MD 1994; MPH Glas. 1995; MFFP 1994; MRCOG 1988; MFPHM 1998. (Edin.) p/t Cons. (Pub. Health Med.) Argyll & Clyde NHS Bd. Prev: Sen. Regist. (Pub. Health Med.) Argyll & Clyde HB; Specialist Wom. Health Glas.; CRC Research Fell. Gyn. Oncol.

STEPHENS, Janice Mary City Walls Medical Centre, St. Martin's Way, Chester CH1 2NR Tel: 01244 357800; Flaxyards Cottage, Rhuddal Heath, Tarporley CW6 9HJ — MB ChB 1987 Leic.; MRCGP 1992; DRCOG 1991; DCH RCP Lond. 1990.

STEPHENS, Jason Spencer The Woodlands, Kingsford Lane, Wolverley, Kidderminster DY11 5SB — MB BS 1990 Lond.

STEPHENS, Jeffrey Wayne Dept of Endocrinology, Middlesex Hospital, UCL Hospitals, London W1N 8AA Email: jwstephens@tingworld.co.uk; Email: jwstephens@tingworld.co.uk — MB BS 1994 Lond.; BSc (Hons.) Lond. 1993; MRCP (UK) 1997; Dip. ALS 1996. (St. Mary's Hosp. Med. Sch. Lond.) Specialist Regist. (Endocrinol. Diabetes/Gen. Med.) Middlx. Hosp. Lond. Socs: Soc. of Endocrinol.; Diabetes UK. Prev: SHO Rotat. (Med.) N.wick Pk. Hosp. Harrow; Ho. Off. St. Mary's Hosp. & Ealing Hosp.; Specialist Regist. (Endocrine / Diabetes) Roy. Free Hosp. Lond, UCL Hosp. Lond., Chase Farm Hosp. Enfield.

STEPHENS, Jessica Northfield House, Turweston, Brackley NN13 5JX Tel: 01280 705378 — MB BS 1984 Lond.; DRCOG 1987.

STEPHENS, Joan (retired) 1 The Glebe, Cumnor, Oxford OX2 9QA Tel: 01865 864660 — MB BS 1948 Durh.; MFFP 1993. Div. Surg. St. John Ambul. Brig. Prev: Sen. Med. Off. Croydon HA.

STEPHENS, John 44 Beech Way, Blackmore End, Wheathampstead, St Albans AL4 8LY Tel: 01438 833333 Fax: 01438 833536; 44 Beech Way, Blackmore End, Wheathampstead, St Albans AL4 8LY Tel: 01438 833333 Fax: 01438 833536 Email: johnstephen@totalise.co.uk — MB BS 1973 Lond.; MRCS Eng. LRCP Lond. 1973; DRCOG 1976.

STEPHENS, John David 29 Crossways, Shenfield, Brentwood CM15 8QY; 93 Harley Street, London W1N 1DF — MB BS 1967 Lond.; MD Lond. 1979; FRCP Lond. 1993; MRCP (UK) 1970; MRCS Eng. LRCP Lond. 1967. (Guy's) Cons. Cardiol. Barking Havering & Riedbridge NHS Trust; Hon. Cons. Cardiol. Barts & the Lond. Hosps. NHS Trust. Socs: Brit. Cardiac Soc. Prev: Sen. Regist. (Cardiol.) St. Bart. Hosp. Lond.; Regist. (Cardiol.) Brompton Hosp. Lond.; Med Research Fell. (Cardiol.) Harvard Univ. Med. Sch. & Peter Bent Brigham Hosp. Boston, USA.

STEPHENS, John Patrick St Ann's Hospital, 69, Haven Road, Poole BH13 7LN Tel: 01202 492084 Fax: 01202 707628 — MB BS 1990 Lond.; MRCPsych 1995. (St. Mary's Hosp. Lond.) Cons. Psychiat. St Ann's Hosp. Poole Dorset; ASM Lond. 1990. Socs: Roy. Coll. of Psychiat.s. Prev: Sen. Regist. (Liaison Psychiat.) St. Geo. Hosp. Tooting; Sen. Regist. (Gen. Ad. Psychiat.) Grayling Well Hosp. Chichester; Regist. (Forens. Psychiat.) Shaftsbury Clinic & (Liaison Psychiat.) St. Geo. Hosp. Lond.

STEPHENS, John Richard Dynevor The Harvey Practice, Magna House, 81 Merley Lane, Wimborne BH21 3BB Tel: 01202 841288 Fax: 01202 840877; Stour Cottage, High St, Spetisbury, Blandford Forum DT11 9DW Email: johnstephens@btinternet.com — BM 1986 Soton.; MRCP (UK) 1990; MRCGP 1993; DFFP 1993; DRCOG 1992; DCH 1991. (Univ. Soton.)

***STEPHENS, Katharine** 27 Commondale, Putney, London SW15 1HS — MB ChB 1997 Bristol.

STEPHENS, Mr Keith MacGregor, Brigadier (retired) Palmer House, Moulton, Richmond DL10 6QG Tel: 01325 377937 Email: brigkim@aol.com — MB BS 1964 Lond.; FRCS Ed. 1974. Prev: Commanding Off. Duchess of Kent Hosp.

***STEPHENS, Laura Catherine Rebecca** The Laurels, 12 Venn Gardens, Hartley, Plymouth PL3 5PW — MB BCh 1996 Wales.

STEPHENS, Laurence Spencer (retired) 11 Windsor Road, Droitwich WR9 7BZ — MB ChB 1944 Birm.; MFCM 1972; DObst RCOG 1945; DPH Liverp. 1950. Prev: SCMO Worcester HA.

STEPHENS, Marjory Stevenson Kilsyth Medical Partnership, Kilsyth Health Centre, Burngreen Park, Kilsyth, Glasgow G65 0HU Tel: 01236 822081 Fax: 01236 826231 — MB ChB 1975 Dundee.

STEPHENS, Mark Department of Histopathology, Central Pathology Laboratory, Hartshill Road, Hartshill, Stoke-on-Trent ST4 7PA Tel: 01782 716662 — MB BCh 1982 Wales; MRCPath 1988. Cons. Histopath. Centr. Path. Laborat. Stoke-on-Trent. Prev: Sen. Regist. (Histopath.) Univ. & City Hosps. Nottm.; Regist. (Histopath.) Univ. Hosp. Wales Cardiff; SHO (Path.) Univ. Hosp. Wales Cardiff.

***STEPHENS, Matthew Francis Tamour** Flat 1, 1 Malvern Road, Stoneygate, Leicester LE2 2BH — MB ChB 1994 Leic.

STEPHENS, Michael Redford 13 Windmill Close, Llantwit Major, Vale of Glamorgan, Cardiff CF14 9BL Tel: 01446 792465 Email: redfordstephens@aol.com — MD 1975 Bristol; MB ChB 1963; FRCP Ed. M 1969. (Bristol) Cons. Cardiol. Univ. Hosp. Wales Cardiff; Lect. (Cardiol.) Welsh Nat. Sch. Med. Cardiff.

STEPHENS, Myles David Buckingham (retired) 49 Kings Court, Bishop's Stortford CM23 2AB Tel: 01279 652719 Fax: 01279 466572 Email: stephmdb@onetel.net.uk — MRCS Eng. LRCP Lond. 1956; MD Lond. 1985, MB BS 1956; MRCGP 1971; FFPM RCP (UK) 1990; DMJ (Clin.) Soc. Apoth. Lond. 1970; DObst RCOG 1958; Dip Pharm Med RCP (UK) 1978. Cons. WHO Uppsala Mt.ing Centre (UMC); Pharmaceut. Cons. Bishop's Stortford. Prev: GP Minehead.

STEPHENS, Mr Neville Aubrey (retired) 19 Bakehouse Hill, Dullingham, Newmarket CB8 9XJ Tel: 01638 508221 — MB BS Lond. 1948; FRCS Eng. 1953. Cons. Surg. Dartford & Gravesham Health Dist. Prev: Regist. (Urol.) & Sen. Regist. (Surg.) King's Coll. Hosp. Lond.

STEPHENS, Nicola Gay Maesycoed, Gwbert Road, Cardigan SA43 1PH — MB BCh 1990 Wales.

***STEPHENS, Nicola Jane** 56 Ladythorn Road, Bramhall, Stockport SK7 2EY — MB ChB 1998 Liverp.; MB ChB Liverp 1998.

STEPHENS, Nigel Graham Dept. of Cardiology, Northwick Park Hospital, Harrow HA1 3UJ Tel: 020 8869 3182 Fax: 020 8869 3176; Email: nigel@nigelstephens.demon.co.uk — MB BS 1988 Lond.; PhD Lond. 1985; MRCP (UK) 1991. Cons. Cardiol. & Dir. Cardiol. N.wich Pk. Hosp. Harrow. Socs: Brit. Cardiac Soc.; Brit. Cardiovasc. Interven. Soc. Prev: Sen. Regist. (Cardiol.) Addenbrooke's & Papworth Hosps. Camb.; Lect. (Med.) Camb. Univ.; Regist. (Cardiol.) Hammersmith Hosp. Lond.

***STEPHENS, Paul Charles** 1 Brae Grove, Ballygowan, Newtownards BT23 5TP — MB ChB 1998 Glas.; MB ChB Glas 1998; BSc (Hons) Glas. 1996.

STEPHENS, Peter John 31 Llys Gwyn, Caernarfon LL55 1EN — MB ChB 1978 Liverp.

STEPHENS, Robert Charles Meredith 7 Archer Road, Penarth CF64 3HW Tel: 01222 702346 — MB BS 1993 Lond.; BA Oxf. 1990. SHO (Anaesth.) Kingston Hosp. Surrey.

STEPHENS, Rosemary (retired) Green Court, Orley Farm Road, Harrow HA1 3PG Tel: 020 8422 3175 — MB BS 1948 Lond.; FRCP Lond. 1977, M 1959; MRCS Eng. LRCP Lond. 1948; DCH Eng. 1950; FRCPCH 1996. Prev: Cons. Paediat. Hosp. Sick Childr. Gt. Ormond St. & N.ampton & Kettering Hosps.

STEPHENS

STEPHENS, Rowan Elizabeth 8 Dale Lodge Road, Ascot SL5 0LY — MB ChB 1980 Otago; T(GP) 1991.

STEPHENS, Sheila Joan (retired) Downham Cottage, Lechlade GL7 3DL Tel: 01367 252075 — MB ChB 1951 Leeds; DObst RCOG 1953. Assoc. Specialist (Path.) P.ss Margt. Hosp. Swindon. Prev: Med. Asst. (Cytol.) Swindon & Cirencester Hosp. Gp.

STEPHENS, Professor Simon Dafydd Glyn Welsh Hearing Institute, University Hospital of Wales, Cardiff CF14 4XW Tel: 029 2074 3474 Fax: 029 2073 3563 Email: stephensd@cf.ac.uk; Pen y Bryn, Llan-maes, Llanilltud Fawr, Llantwit Major CF61 2XR Tel: 01446 792403 Email: dafydda/glyn@lineone.net — MB BS Lond. 1965; MPhil Lond. 1973, BSc (Special Physiol.) 1962; FRCP Lond. 1994; MRCP (UK) 1984; MRCS Eng. LRCP Lond. 1965; DHMSA 1980. (Char. Cross) Dir. Welsh Hearing Inst.; Hon. Prof. Univ. Wales Coll. Med.; Audiol. Phys. Univ. Hosp. of Wales, Cardiff. Socs: (Pres.) Internat. Assn. Phys. Audiol.; (Pres.) Internat. Collegium of Rehabil. Audiol.; (Exec. Comm.) Internat. Soc. Audiol. Prev: Cons. Audiol. Med. Roy. Nat. ENT Hosp. Lond.; Clin. Research Fell. Inst. Sound & Vibration Research Univ. Soton.; Psychoacousticist MRC Applied Psychol. Unit Camb. & Nat. Physical Laborat.

STEPHENS, Suzanne Emma Dept. Ophthalmology, Royal Hallamshire Hospital, Glossop Rd, Sheffield S10 2JF Tel: 0114 271 2223 — MB BS 1992 Lond.; MRCP (UK) 1996. Specialist Regist. (Paediat.) S. Thames Rotat. Socs: MRCPCH.

STEPHENS, Virginia Joan The Bell Surgery, York Road, Henley-on-Thames RG9 2DR Tel: 01491 843250 Fax: 01491 411295; Mole End, Crowsley Road, Lower Shiplake, Henley-on-Thames RG9 3LD Tel: 0118 940 4058 — MB BS 1978 Lond.; MRCS Eng. LRCP Lond. 1978; DRCOG 1996. (St. Bart.)

***STEPHENS, Wendy Jean** 57 Hartopp Road, Leicester LE2 1WG — MB ChB 1997 Leic.

STEPHENS, William Philip — MB BS 1972 Lond.; MD Lond. 1982; FRCP Lond. 1991; MRCP (UK) 1976; MRCS Eng. LRCP Lond. 1972; DObst RCOG 1975; DCH Eng. 1975; AKC. (Westm.) Cons. Phys. Trafford Gen. Hosp. Davyhulme Manch. & Alexandra Hosp. Cheadle; Chief Med. Off. Friends Provident Life Off. Socs: Fell. Manch. Med. Soc.; Brit. Diabetic Assn.; BMA. Prev: Sen. Regist. (Med.) Manch. Roy. Infirm.; Lect. (Med.) Univ. Manch.; Ho. Off. W.m. Hosp. Lond.

STEPHENSON, Mr Andrew James Northern General Hospital, Herries Road, Sheffield S5 7A — MB ChB 1990 Birm.; FRCS Glas. 1996.

STEPHENSON, Mr Brian Mark Woodsdale, St. Brides Netherwent, Penhow, Newport NP26 3AS Tel: 01633 400850 Fax: 01633 234252 — MB BS 1983 Lond.; BSc (Hons.) Lond. 1980, MB BS 1983; MSc Lond. 1992, MS 1992; FRCS 1987. (St. Barth.) Cons. Gen. & Colorect. Surg. Roy. Gwent Hosp. Newport. Prev: Sen. Regist. (Surg.) Univ. Hosp. Wales Cardiff Roy. Infirm. & Newport Hosp.; Clin. Research Fell. (Surg.) Leeds Gen Infirm.; Regist. Rotat. (Surg.) Univ. Hosp. Wales.

STEPHENSON, Caroline Mary Elizabeth 22 The Fairway, Bar Hill, Cambridge CB3 8SR; 205 Hills Road, Cambridge CB2 2RN Tel: 01223 214925 — MB BChir 1990 Camb.; PhD Camb. 1984; BSc (Experim. Psychol.) Sussex 1980; MRCPsych 1997; MRCGP 1994; DRCOG 1993.

STEPHENSON, Catherine Jane The Great Barn, Howsham, York YO60 7PH — MB ChB 1994 Ed.; Dip. Of Child Health, Univ. of Otago, 1997; Dip. Of Obst, Otago, 1998.

STEPHENSON, Catherine Mary 40 Tredegar Drive, Oakwood, Derby DE21 2RA — MB ChB 1990 Manch.; BSc Manch. 1987; MRCP (UK) 1993; DFFP 1995; DRCOG 1995. (Manch.) Locum GP. Prev: GP Princip. Charnwood Surg. Derby; Trainee GP Stoke-on-Trent VTS; SHO (Gen. Med.) N. Staffs. Hosp. Centre Stoke-on-Trent.

STEPHENSON, Charles Roger Brooklea Clinic, Wick Road, Bristol BS4 4HU; Mill House, Woollard, Pensford, Bristol BS39 4HX Tel: 01761 490352 — MB ChB 1973 Ed.; MRCP (UK) 1976; MRCGP 1977; DRCOG 1977.

STEPHENSON, Charmian Louise Paula 38 Lebanon Park, Twickenham TW1 3DG Email: rnorth@globalnet.co.uk — BM BCh 1992 Oxf.; MA Camb. 1993; MRCGP 1996; DFFP 1996. (Oxf.) Career Break. Socs: BMA; Mem. of RCGP. Prev: Regist. (Gen. Pract.) St. John's Health Centre Woking; Trainee GP/SHO St. Peter's Hosp. NHS Trust; Asst. GP Chiswick Health Centre ('97-'98).

STEPHENSON, Christopher John 11 Cragside, Sedgfield, Stockton-on-Tees TS21 2DU — MB ChB 1989 Sheff.

STEPHENSON, Clare 50 Birkdale Gardens, Belmont, Durham DH1 2UJ Tel: 0191 384 2904 — BM BS 1995 Nottm.; BMedSci Nottm. 1993, BM BS 1995. Socs: MPS. Prev: SHO (Surg.) Newc.Gen.; SHO (Med.) Ayr; (Anat. Demonst., Newc. Med. Sch.).

STEPHENSON, Clare Anne 4 Highlands, Ashtead KT21 2SD — MB BS 1980 Lond.; MRCP (UK) 1983; MRCGP 1993.

STEPHENSON, Clare Judith (Smith) Oxford National Health Centre, 3 Church Cowley Road, Oxford OX4 3JR Tel: 01865 715615; Oxford National Health Centre, 3 Church Cowley Road, Oxford OX4 3JR Tel: 01865 715615 Email: clare@cholsey.fsworld.co.uk — BM BCh 1988 Oxf.; LicAc MBAcC 1998 (Licentiate in Acupunc. Mem. of Brit. Acupunc. Cou); MA Camb. 1982; MRCP (UK) 1991; MRCGP 1994; MSc (Pub. Health Med.) Lond. 1997. (Camb/Oxf.) p/t Acupunc. in Private Pract.; Lect. in Clin. Med., Coll. of Integrated Chinese Med., Oxf. Socs: BMA; Roy-Coll. Phys.; Roy. Coll. Gen. Pract. Prev: Specialist Regist. (Pub. Health Med.) Oxf.; Trainee GP Oxf.; SHO (Psychiat.) Tindal Centre, Aylesbury.

STEPHENSON, Daniel Timothy 193 Popes Lane, London W5 4NH Tel: 020 8579 0592 — MB ChB 1995 Manch.; BSc (Hons.) Manch. 1992. SHO (Med.) N.ern Gen. Hosp. Sheff. Prev: SHO (A & E) Hope Hosp. Salford.

STEPHENSON, David Kenneth Department of Anaesthesia, Derbyshire Royal Infirmary NHS Trust, London Road, Derby DE1 2QY Tel: 01332 347141; Tel: 01543 472672 — MB ChB 1971 Manch.; FFA RCS Eng. 1977. (Manch.) Staff Grade Anaesth. Derbysh. Roy. Infirm.; Emerit. Cons. Anaesth. N. Notts. HA. Socs: Assn. Anaesth. GB & Irel.; PANG; BSOA. Prev: Cons. Anaesth. & Pain Control Centr. Notts. HA; Lect. (Anaesth.) Manch. Univ.; Sen. Regist. (Anaesth.) Manch. AHA (T).

STEPHENSON, Deborah Angela Eli Lilly & Company Ltd, Dextra Court, Chapel Hill, Basingstoke RG21 5SY Tel: 01256 315000, 01256 401719 Email: debs@lilly.com; 14 Mitcham Park, Mitcham CR4 4EG — MB BS 1985 Lond.; MRCPsych 1990; AFPM RCP Lond. 1994. (St. Geo.) Sen. Clin. Research Phys., Eli Lilly & Co., Basingstoke. Prev: Hon. Assoc. Psychiat. Chelsea & W.m. Hosp.; Europ. Clin. Research Phys. Lilly Research Centre Windlesham Surrey; Regist. Rotat. (Psychiat.) St. Geo. Hosp. Lond.

***STEPHENSON, Gemma Elizabeth Catherine** 34 Newport View, Leeds LS6 3BX — MB ChB 1997 Leeds.

STEPHENSON, Geoffrey Victoria Road Health Centre, Victoria Road, Washington NE37 2PU Tel: 0191 416 2578 Fax: 0191 416 6091 Email: geoffrey.stephenson@ecss4.sunderland.northy.nhs.uk; Whyteleafe, 10 Underhill Road, Cleadon Village, Sunderland SR6 7RS — MB BS 1974 Newc.; MRCGP 1978. (Newc. u. Tyne) Clin. Governance Lead, Sunderland W. Pct; Bd. Mem. Sunderland W. Pct.

STEPHENSON, Iain 6 Granby Croft, Bakewell DE45 1ET; 4 Langton House Cottages, Main St, Tur Langton, Leicester LE8 0PJ Email: istephen@globalnet.co.uk — MB BChir 1993 Camb.; BA (Hons.) Camb. 1991; MRCP Ed. 1997. (Addenbrookes) Specialist Regist. (Infec. Dis.s) Leicester Roy. Infirm. Socs: Brit. Infect. Soc. Prev: Regist. (Infec. Dis.s) N. Staffs. Hosp. Stoke on Trent.

STEPHENSON, James Reginald 4 Highlands, Ashtead KT21 2SD — MB BS 1980 Lond.; MSc Lond. 1986, MB BS 1980; MA Oxf. 1985; MRCPath 1986. Cons. Med. Microbiol. St Helier NHS Trust Carshalton.

STEPHENSON, Jane Tracy Church View Surgery, Market Hill, Hedon, Hull HU12 8JE Tel: 01482 899348 — MB ChB 1993 Birm.; MRCGP 1993; MRCGP (distinchin). GP Regist. Ch. View Surg. E. Yorks. GP Princip.-. Socs: MRCGP.

***STEPHENSON, Janet Margaret** 2 Hurstwood, Waverton, Chester CH3 7QJ — MB ChB 1995 Dundee.

STEPHENSON, Jeffrey Benjamin Grainger Southampton General Hospital, Tremona Road, Shirley, Southampton SO16 6YD — MB BChir 1994 Camb.; MRCP (UK) 1997. SHO Rotat. (Med.) Soton. Univ. Hosps. Trust. Socs: BMA; Med. Protec. Soc. Prev: Ho. Phys. Addenbrooke's Hosp. Camb.; Ho. Surg. Hinchingbrooke Hosp. Huntingdon.

STEPHENSON, Jennifer Ann Walkley House Medical Centre, 23 Greenhow Street, Sheffield S6 3TN Tel: 0114 234 3716; Stannington Medical Centre, Uppergate Road, Stannington, Sheffield

S6 6BX Tel: 0114 234 5303 Fax: 0114 234 3113 — MB ChB 1981 Sheff.; MRCGP 1985; DRCOG 1985; DCH RCP Lond. 1984; Cert. Family Plann. JCC 1984. (Sheff.) Trainer (Gen. Pract.) Sheff. VTS specialising in flexible train.; Mem. Sheff. LMC; GP Represen. Cervical Cytol. Working Party; GP Represen. Local Diabetes Servs. Advis. Gp.; G.P. Rep. Health Improvement Grp of the PCT. Socs: BMA; RCGP. Prev: Trainee GP/SHO Barnsley VTS; Ho. Off. (Med. & Dermat.) Roy. Hallamsh. Hosp. Sheff.; Ho. Off. (Orthop.) N.. Gen. Hosp. Sheff.

STEPHENSON, Jeremy David Lower Road Surgery, 17 Lower Road, Fetcham, Leatherhead KT22 9EL Tel: 01372 378166 Fax: 01372 374734 — BM BS 1989 Nottm.

STEPHENSON, Professor John Burdett Primmer Fraser of Allander Neurosciences Unit, Royal Hospital Sick Children, Yorkhill, Glasgow G3 8SJ Tel: 0141 201 0141 Fax: 0141 201 9270; 27 Charles Crescent, Lenzie, Glasgow G66 5HH Tel: 0141 776 5589 Email: jbps@jbpstephenson.demon.co.uk — BM BCh Oxf. 1960; MA Oxf. 1960; DM Oxf. 1991; FRCP Glas. 1984, M 1982; FRCP Lond. 1979, M 1965; FRCPCH 1996; DCH Eng. 1965; HonFRCPCH 2000. (Oxf. & St. Thos.) Hon. Prof. Med. Paediat. Neurol. Univ. Glas. Not Retd. Socs: Assn. Brit. Neurol.; Brit. Paediat. Neurol. Assn.; Internat. Child Neurol. Assn. Prev: Retd. Cons. Paediat. Neurol. Roy. Hosp. Sick Childr. Glas.; Sen. Regist. (Med. Paediat. & Neurol.) Roy. Hosp. Sick Childr. Glas.; Fell. (Neurol.) Hosp. Sick Childr. Toronto, Canada.

STEPHENSON, John David Green Lane Surgery, 2 Green Lane, Belper DE56 1BZ Tel: 01773 823521 Fax: 01773 821954 — MB ChB 1986 Leeds; DRCOG 1992; DCH RCP Lond. 1991. Prev: SHO (Paediat.) York Dist. Hosp.

STEPHENSON, Judith Mary DEPT STD, UCL Medical school, Mortimer Market Centre, Off Capper St., London WC1E 6AU Email: jstephen@gum.ucl.ac.uk; 66 Trinity Church Square, London SE1 4HT — MD 1994 Lond.; MSc 1991, MB BS 1985; MA Oxf. 1993; MRCP (UK) 1988; FFPHM RCP (UK) 1998. Sen. Lect. (Epidemiol.) UCL Med. Sch. Lond.

***STEPHENSON, Kay Ann** 7 Gowland Drive, Cannock WS11 1TG — MB ChB 1996 Liverp.

STEPHENSON, Kenneth Dowson (retired) 185 Coniscliffe Road, Darlington DL3 8DE Tel: 01325 468247 — MB BS 1952 Durh.; DA Eng. 1957. Hosp. Pract. (Anaesth.) Darlington Memor. Hosp. Prev: Ho. Phys. & Ho. Surg. Roy. Vict. Infirm. Newc.

STEPHENSON, Kevin Silksworth Health Centre, Silksworth, Sunderland SR3 2AN Tel: 0191 521 0252 — MB ChB 1986 Leeds.

STEPHENSON, Lauren Kristina Oak Lodge Medical Centre, 234 Burnt Oak Broadway, Edgware HA8 0AP Tel: 020 8952 1202 Fax: 020 8381 1156; 70 Friern Barnet Lane, Friern Barnet, London N11 3NB — MB BChir 1988 Camb.; MA Camb. 1990; MRCGP 1992; DRCOG 1992. (Cambridge) Prev: Trainee GP/SHO Edgware Gen. Hosp. VTS; Ho. Off. (Med.) QE II Hosp. Welwyn Garden City; Ho. Off. (Surg.) Newmarket Gen. Hosp.

STEPHENSON, Margaret Anne (retired) 185 Coniscliffe Road, Darlington DL3 8DE Tel: 01325 468247 — MB BS 1954 Durh. Clin. Asst. (Venereol.) Darlington Memor. Hosp.; Clin. Asst. in ENT Darlington Memor. Hosp. Prev: Sen. Surgic. Ho. Off. & Ho. Phys. Darlington Memor. Hosp.

STEPHENSON, Matthew George 40 Tredegar Drive, Oakwood, Derby DE21 2RA — MB ChB 1991 Bristol; MRCGP 1995; DFFP 1994; DRCOG 1994. (Bristol)

STEPHENSON, Matthew Thomas 1 Blackheath Park, London SE3 9RN — MB BS 1987 Lond.

STEPHENSON, Michael Roy c/o Doctor Ryan's Secretary, Community Mental Health, Manor Road, Beverley HU17 7BZ — MB ChB 1991 Leeds; BSc (Hons.) Leeds 1988; MRCPsych 1996. Sen. Regist. (Psychiat.) Community Ment. Health N. Humberside.

STEPHENSON, Patricia Mary Central Health Clinic, Mulberry St., Sheffield S1 Tel: 0114 271 6790; 33 Dore Road, Sheffield S17 3NA Tel: 0114 235 2508 — MB ChB 1975 Leeds; DFFP 1994; DCH RCP Lond. 1977. Clin. Med. Off. (Family Plann. & Reproduc. Health) Sheff.

STEPHENSON, Paul Seamus Christmas Maltings Surgery, Camps Road, Haverhill CB9 8HF Tel: 01440 702203 Fax: 01440 712198; Wheel Cottage, The St, Great Wratting, Haverhill CB9 7HQ — BM BCh 1987 Oxf.; MA Oxf. 1984; MRCGP 1991; DGM RCP Lond.

1990; DRCOG 1989. Edr.ial Bd. Mem. Primary Care Resp. Jl. Prev: Trustee, Nat. Asthma Campaign.

STEPHENSON, Peter (retired) Flat One, Dockendale Hall, Whickham, Newcastle upon Tyne NE16 4EN — MB BCh 1952 Witwatersrand; FRCP Lond. 1974, M 1960. Cons. Phys. Gateshead & Dist. Hosp. Gp. Prev: Research Asst. Cardiol. Roy. Vict. Infirm. Newc.

STEPHENSON, Philip Bernard Ommanney Eynsham Medical Group, Conduit Lane, Eynsham, Witney OX29 4QB Tel: 01865 881206 Fax: 01865 881342; Woodlands, Green Lane, North Leigh, Witney OX29 6TW — MB BChir 1984 Camb.; MA Camb. 1985, MB BChir 1984; MRCGP 1988; DRCOG 1987; DCH RCP Lond. 1987. (Cambridge and St Thomas') Prev: Ho. Surg. St. Thos. Hosp. Lond.; Cas. Off. Poole Gen. Hosp.; Trainee GP Reading VTS.

STEPHENSON, Ralph Harry, TD Rowcroft Medical Centre, Rowcroft Retreat, Stroud GL5 3BE Tel: 01453 764471 Fax: 01453 755247 — MB BS 1967 Lond.; MRCS Eng. LRCP Lond. 1967; DA Eng. 1973; DObst RCOG 1969. (King's Coll. Hosp.) p/t Anaesth. Stroud Gen. Hosp. Prev: SHO (Anaesth.) Gloucester Roy. Hosp.; SHO (Obst.) Redhill Gen. Hosp.; Ho. Surg. & Ho. Phys. King's Coll. Hosp.

STEPHENSON, Richard Hudson Bicester Health Centre, Coker Close, Bicester OX26 6AT Tel: 01869 249333 Fax: 01869 320314; Upper Aynho Grounds, Aynho, Banbury OX17 3AY Tel: 01869 810607 Fax: 01869 320314 — MB BChir 1967 Camb.; MA, MB Camb. 1967, BChir 1966; FRCGP 1997; DMRD Eng. 1969; DObst RCOG 1969. (St. Thos.) Socs: Brit. Inst. Radiol.; RCGP. Prev: Regist. (Radiol.) St. Thos. Hosp. Lond.; Ho. Off. St. Peter's Hosp. Chertsey; Ho. Off. (Surg.) Lambeth Hosp.

STEPHENSON, Mr Richard Neal Department of Urology, Western General Hospital, Crewe Road S., Edinburgh EH4 2XU Tel: 0131 537 1581; 79 Orchard Brae Avenue, Edinburgh EH4 2UR — MB ChB 1982 Bristol; FRCS (Urol.) 1994; FRCS Eng. 1988. Sen. Regist. (Urol.) Lothian HB. Socs: Assoc. Mem. BAUS. Prev: Lect. (Urol.) Univ. Edin.; Research Regist. (Renal Transpl.) Univ. Sheff.; Regist. (Urol.) P.ss Roy. Hosp. Hull.

STEPHENSON, Robert John Toft Road Surgery, Toft Road, Knutsford WA16 9DX Tel: 01565 632681 — MB BS 1983 Lond.; BA Camb. 1980; MRCGP 1988; D.Occ Med. RCP Lond. 1995; DRCOG 1988. (Roy. Free (Clinical) Camb. Univ. (Pre-clinical)) GP Partner Toft Rd. Surg. Knutsford Chesh.; Company Doct. Ilford Mobberley. Prev: Trainee GP Macclesfield VTS.

STEPHENSON, Robert Vivian (retired) Pentland House, Bradford Road, Sherborne DT9 6BP Tel: 01935 814173 — MB BChir Camb. 1957; BA Camb. 1957; FRCOG 1974, M 1961; MA Camb 1997. Prev: Cons. O & G Yeovil Dist. Hosp. & Yeatman Hosp. Sherborne.

STEPHENSON, Roger Hill Side, Henley Road, Thornhill, Dewsbury WF12 0JL Tel: 01924 465343 — MRCS Eng. LRCP Lond. 1959. (St. Thos.) Clin. Asst. in Anaesth. Dewsbury, Batley & Mirfield Hosp. Prev: Ho. Surg. (Orthop.) Memor. Hosp. PeterBoro.; Ho. Phys. (Paediat.) Gen. Hosp. Dewsbury; Ho. Off. (O & G) Staincliffe Hosp. Dewsbury.

STEPHENSON, Roger Edwin Fair Park Surgery, Fair Park, Bow, Crediton EX17 6EY Tel: 01363 82333 Fax: 01363 82841 — MB BS 1980 Lond.; MA Camb. 1981; MRCGP 1987.

***STEPHENSON, Rosalind** The Gables, Rodridge Lane, Station Town, Wingate TS28 5HB Tel: 01429 837648 — MB ChB 1996 Glas.

STEPHENSON, Ruth Nicole Anaesthetics Department, Aberdeen Royal Infirmary, Aberdeen AB25 2ZN Tel: 01224 681818; 83 Fountainhall Road, Aberdeen AB15 4EA — MB ChB 1987 Ed.; FRCA 1993; FFA RCSI 1992. Sen. Regist. (Anaesth.) Aberd. Roy. Infirm.

STEPHENSON, Sarah Jane Ansley Mill, Ansley, Nuneaton CV10 0QT Tel: 01676 41557 — MB BS 1983 Lond.; MRCGP 1988; DRCOG 1986. GP Liverp.

STEPHENSON, Professor Terence John Academic Division of Child Health, School of Human Development, University of Nottingham, Nottingham NG7 2UH Tel: 0115 970 9255 Fax: 0115 970 9382 Email: terence.stephenson@nottingham.ac.uk — BM BCh 1983 Oxf.; BSc (1st cl. Hons.) Bristol 1979; DM Nottm. 1992; FRCP Lond. 1995; MRCP (UK) 1986; FRCPCH Lond. 1997. (Oxf.) Prof. Child Health & Dep. Head, Sch. of Human Developm. Univ. Nottm.; Hon. Cons. Paediat. Qu. Med. Centre Nottm. Socs: Neonat. Soc.; Paediat. Research Soc.; Fell. Roy. Coll. of Paediat. and Child Health.

STEPHENSON

Prev: Sen. Lect. & Lect. (Child Health) Univ. Nottm.; SHO Nat. Hosp. Nerv. Dis. Lond.; Ho. Phys. Profess. Med. Unit Oxf.

STEPHENSON, Timothy John Department of Histopathology, Royal Hallamshire Hospital, Glossop Road, Sheffield S10 2JF Tel: 0114 271 2213 Fax: 0114 271 2200 Email: tim.stephenson@sth.nhs.uk — MB ChB 1981 Sheff.; MB ChB (Hons.) Sheff. 1981; MA Camb. 1982, BA (1st cl. Hons.) 1978; MD Sheff. 1995; FRCPath 1996, M 1988; Dip. Health Serv. Mgt. Open 1996; MBA Open 1999. Cons. Sheff.Teachg.. Hosps. NHS Trust & Hon. Clin. Sen. Lect. Sheff. Univ. Socs: Fell. Roy. Soc. Med.; Postgrad Educat. Sec Assn. Clin. Path.; Internat. Acad. Path. Prev: Sen. Lect. (Path.) Univ. Sheff.; Ho. Off. Profess. Med. & Profess. Surg. Units Roy. Hallamsh. Hosp. Sheff.

STEPHENSON, Mr Timothy Patrick Department of Urology, University Hospital of Wales, Heath Park, Cardiff CF14 4XW — MB BS 1963 Lond.; MS Lond. 1977; FRCS Eng. 1970.

STEPHENSON, Tony 12 The Cloisters, Newcastle upon Tyne NE7 7LS — MB BS 1986 Lond.; MRCGP 1990.

STEPHENSON, Trevor Buteland Terrace Health Centre, Buteland Terrace, Newbiggin-by-the-Sea NE64 6NS Tel: 01670 816796 Fax: 01670 818797; 15 Southgate Wood, Southgate, Morpeth NE61 2EN — MB BS 1965 Durh.; DCH RCPS Glas. 1969. (Newc.) Socs: BMA. Prev: SHO (O & G) & (Paediat.) W. Cumbld. Hosp.

***STEPHENSON, Victoria Jane** Doghurst Cottage, Doghurst Lane, Chipstead, Coulsdon CR5 3PL Tel: 01737 556548; Doghurst Cottage, Doghurst Lane, Chipstead, Coulsdon CR5 3PL — MB ChB 1998 Leeds.

STEPHENSON, Mr Walter Henry (retired) 82 Chiltern Road, Sutton SM2 5QY Tel: 020 8642 6708 — MRCS Eng. LRCP Lond. 1936; FRCS Ed. 1947. Prev: Hon. Cons. Orthop. Surg. Hammersmith Hosp. Lond.

STEPP-SCHUH, Kerstin Kirchroder, Tremorvah Crescent, Truro TR1 1NL Tel: 01872 271014 Email: steppschuh@compuserve.com — State Exam Med. Bonn 1991.

STEPTOE, Adele Marjorie Ashington House, Ashington Way, Westlea, Swindon SN5 7XY Tel: 01793 614840 Fax: 01793 491191 — MB BCh 1987 Wales; MRCGP 1993; DRCOG 1992; DGM Lond. 1992. (Univ. Wales Coll. Med.) GP Princip. Socs: BMA. Prev: Trainee GP Trowbridge; Trainee GP/SHO Roy. United Hosp. Bath; GP Princip. Cheltenham.

STERA, Hanna 131 Eastcote Road, Ruislip HA4 8BJ — LMSSA 1993 Lond.

STERGIDES, Anthimos Char Scartho Medical Centre, 26 Waltham Road, Grimsby DN33 2QA Tel: 01472 871747 Fax: 01472 276050; 7 Scartho Road, Grimsby DN33 2AB Tel: 01472 878651 — Ptychio latrikes 1973 Athens, Greece; Ptychio latrikis Athens, Greece 1973. Clin. Asst. (Gastroenterol.), Grimsby Dist. Gen. Hosp. Prev: Regist. & SHO (Gen. Med.) Grimsby Dist. Gen. Hosp.; SHO (Med. & ITU.) Staffs. Gen. Infirm.

STERLAND, John Helmerow Helmford House Surgery, 283 High Street, London Colney, St Albans AL2 1EL Tel: 01727 823245; 23 Juniper Gardens, Shenley, Radlett WD7 9LA — MB BS 1982 Lond. (Roy. Free) Prev: Trainee GP N. Uist; SHO (Geriat., Orthop. & Cas.) Maidstone Hosp.

STERLAND, Mairi Elizabeth (retired) Amberside, Pentrich, Ripley, Derby DE5 3RH Tel: 01773 743216 — MB ChB 1949 Aberd. Prev: Ho. Surg. O & G St. Martin's Hosp. Bath.

STERLING, Graham Murray (retired) General Hospital, Tremona Road, Southampton SO16 6YD Tel: 02380 777222 — MRCS Eng. LRCP Lond. 1960; MD Camb. 1969, MB 1961, BChir 1960; FRCP Lond. 1977, M 1964. Cons. Phys. Soton. Univ. Hosps. Trust; Hon. Clin. Sen. Lect. (Med.) Univ. Soton. Prev: Sen. Lect. (Med.) Univ. Soton.

STERLING, (IJ) Nuala, CBE (Bradbury) Southampton General Hospital, Southampton SO16 6YD Tel: 02380 794656 Fax: 02380 796965; Vermont House, Withers Lane, E. Boldre, Brockenhurst SO42 7WX Tel: 01590 612378 — MB BS 1960 Lond.; FRCP Lond. 1982, M 1971; MRCS Eng. LRCP Lond. 1960. (St. Geo.) Cons. Phys. Geriat. Med. Soton. Univ. Hosp. Trust; Mem. Independant review pannel for advertising of Med.s 2000; Vice Chairm. S.. RAC (Distinc. Awards) 2000-02. Socs: Med. Wom. Federat. (Pres. 1989-90) & Brit. Geriat. Soc. (Counc. Mem. 1987-89). Prev: Mem. (Ex-Chairm.) Standing Med. Advisory Comm.; Lect. (Geriat. Med.) Univ. Soton.; Lect. (Med.) Univ. Calif. San Francisco, USA.

STERLING, Jane Carolyn Department of Dermatology, Box 46, Addenbrooke's Hospital, Hills Road, Cambridge CB2 2QQ Tel: 01223 216459 Fax: 01223 216863 Email: jcs12@mole.bio.cam.ac.uk; 17 Norwich Street, Cambridge CB2 1ND — MB BChir 1978 Camb.; PhD Camb. 1991, MA 1980; FRCP Lond. 1997, M 1981. (Camb.) Lect. (Dermat.) Camb. Univ. & Hon. Cons. Dermat. Addenbrooke's Hosp. Camb. Socs: Brit. Assn. Dermat.; Soc. Gen. Microbiol.; Brit. Soc. Investig. Dermat. Prev: Hon. Sen. Lect. St. John's Inst. Dermat. Lond.; Hon. Cons. Dermat. St. John's Dermat. Centre St. Thos. Hosp. Lond.; MRC Clin. Scientist Fell. Camb.

STERLING, Victor James (retired) Dromore, 23 Larchfield Park, Newcastle BT33 0BB Tel: 028437 23668 — MB BCh BAO Belf. 1942.

STERN, Adam Bernard The Whapping Health Centre, 22 Wapping Lane, London; Tel: 020 7354 3242 — MB BS 1988 Lond.; MRCGP 1996. (King' Coll. Lond.) Prev: Trainee GP Lond.; SHO (Paediat., O & G & Geriat. Med.) Newham Gen. Hosp.

STERN, Colin Michael Macleod St. Thomas's Hospital, London SE1 7EH Tel: 020 7928 9292 Fax: 020 7960 5631 Email: colin.stern@gstt.sthames.nhs.uk; 24 Clearwater Place, Long Ditton, Surbiton KT6 4ET Tel: 020 8398 2676 — PhD Lond. 1978; MA, MB Camb. 1967, BChir 1966; FRCP Lond. 1983, M 1969; DCH Eng. 1970; FRCPCH 1997. (St. Thos.) p/t Cons. Paediat. St. Thos. Hosp. Lond.; Assoc. Regional Dean of Postgrad. Med., Lond. Socs: Roy. Soc. of Med. Lond., Vice-Chairm., Acad. Bd. Prev: Sen. Lect. (Immunol.) Roy. Postgrad. Med. Sch. Lond.; Hon. Cons. (Paediat.) Hammersmith Hosp. Lond.; Postgrad. Subdean UMDS Guy's & St. Thos. Hosp. Lond.

STERN, David (retired) — MRCS Eng. LRCP Lond. 1942. Hon. Cons. Path. E. Dorset Health Dist. Prev: Dir. Haemophillia Centre Roy. Vic. Hosp. Bournemouth.

STERN, David Michael Manor Surgery, Osler Road, Headington, Oxford OX3 9BP Tel: 01865 762535 — MRCS Eng. LRCP Lond. 1969; FRCGP 1999; BSc Lond. 1966, MB BS 1969; MRCGP 1984. (Lond. Hosp.) GP Headington; Clin. Tutor (Gen. Pract.) Univ. Oxf.

STERN, Mr David Michael, CBE (retired) 32 Thames Point, Fairways, Teddington TW11 9PP — MB BChir 1929 Camb.; FRCS Eng. 1932; MRCS Eng. LRCP Lond. 1928; FRCOG 1942. Prev: Prof. (Obst.) Univ. Khartoum.

STERN, Gerald Malcolm Woolavington Wing, The Middlesex Hospital, Mortimer St., London W1T 3AA Tel: 020 7376 0627 Fax: 020 7937 0438 — MB BS 1954 Lond.; MD Lond. 1965; FRCP Lond. 1970, M 1958. (Lond. Hosp.) Emerit. Cons. Neurol. Univ. Coll. Lond. Hosp. & Nat. Hosp. for Neurol. & Neurosurg. Qu. Sq. Lond. Socs: Assn. Brit. Neurols. & Assn. Phys. GB & Irel. Prev: 1st Asst. Dept. Neurol. Univ. Newc.; Sen. Regist. (Neurol.) Lond. Hosp.; Research Assoc. (Neurol.) Columbia Univ., New York.

STERN, Gillian 42 Southwood Avenue, London N6 5RZ Tel: 020 8348 1351 Fax: 020 8348 1357 — MB ChB 1971 Witwatersrand; BSc (Med.) Witwatersrand 1967; MRCPsych 1989. Cons. Child & Adolesc. Psychiat. Haringey Health Care, Lond. Socs: BMA; Roy. Coll. Psychiat.; Assoc. Brit. Assn. Psychotherapists.

STERN, Glenn Marvin The Surgery, 939 Green Lanes, Winchmore Hill, London N21 2PB Tel: 020 8360 2228 Fax: 020 8360 5702 — BSc Lond. 1966, MB BS 1969; MRCP (UK) 1973; DObst RCOG 1973; DCH Eng. 1971. (Univ. Coll. Hosp.) Treasury Med. Off. Socs: Roy. Soc. Med. Prev: Ho. Phys. Evelina Childr. Hosp. (Guy's Hosp.) Lond.; SHO (Med.) Poole Gen. Hosp.; SHO (O & G) Whittington Hosp. Lond.

STERN, Professor Harold 16 Hill Rise, Hampstead Garden Suburb, London NW11 6NA Tel: 020 8458 3966 — MB ChB 1946 Glas.; PhD Glas. 1953; FRCPath 1971, M 1964. Emerit. Prof. Virol. Univ. Lond. & St. Geo. Hosp. Med. Sch. Socs: Hon. Mem. Path. Soc. GB & Irel. Prev: Cons, Virol. St. Geo. Hosp. Lond.; MRC Schol. (Bact. & Chem.) Univ. Glas.; Postgrad. Med. Federat. Trav. Fell., USA.

STERN, Jeremy Samuel PET Neuroscience Group, MRC Cyclotron Unit, Hammersmith Hospital, Du Cane Road, London W12 0NN Tel: 020 8383 3162 Fax: 020 8383 2029 Email: jeremystern2000@hotmail.com — MB 1991 Camb.; MB BChir Camb. 1991; MA Camb. 1992; MRCP (UK) 1994; DHMSA 1995. (Christ's Coll. Camb. & Univ. Coll. Lond.) Research Fell. Hon. Specialist Regist. (Neurol.) MRC Cyclotron Unit, Hammersmith

Hosp.; Trustee of the Tourette Syndrome (UK) Assoc.; Asst. Sec. Assoc. of Brit. Neurol. Trainees. Prev: Elected Mem. (For Eng.) GMC.

STERN, Julian Michael Royal London Hospital (St. Clements), 2A Bow Road, London E3 4LL Tel: 020 7377 7966; St. Marks Hospital, Watford Road, Harrow HA1 3UJ Tel: 020 8235 4017 — MB ChB 1985 Cape Town; MRCPsych 1991. Cons. (Psychother.) Roy. Lond. Hosp.; Cons. St. Marks Hosp. Lond. Prev: Sen. Regist. Maudsley Hosp.

STERN, Manfred 69 Wayland Avenue, Brighton BN1 5JL Tel: 01273 506038 — MB BS 1954 Lond.; LMSSA Lond. 1952. (Lond. Hosp.) Clin. Asst. Roy. Lond. Homoeop. Hosp. Socs: Assoc. Fac. Homoeop. Prev: Sen. Regist. (Med.) E. Ham. Hosp. Gp.; Sen. Ho. Phys. High Wycombe & Dist. War Memor. Hosp.; Ho. Phys. Hove Gen. Hosp.

STERN, Martin Adam Leicester General Hospital, Gwendolen Road, Leicester LE5 4PW — BM BCh 1965 Oxf.; MSc (Immunol.) Birm. 1973; MA Oxf. 1965, BA 1962, BM BCh 1965; FRCP Lond. 1989; MRCP (UK) 1971. Cons. Clin. Immunol. Leics. AHA (T). Socs: Brit. Soc. Immunol. & Brit. Soc. Allergy & Clin. Immunol. Prev: Ho. Surg. & Ho. Phys. Radcliffe Infirm. Oxf.; Clin. Research Fell. Med. Research Counc.; Research Sen. Regist. Dept. Med. Guy's Hosp. Med. Sch. Lond.

STERN, Morag Campbell 23 Stoughton Drive S., Oadby, Leicester LE2 2RJ Tel: 0116 270 7978 — MB ChB 1966 St. And.; MD (Hons.) Dundee 1971; MRCP (UK) 1973; MFPHM RCP (UK) 1992. (Dundee) Cons. Pub. Health Med. & Med. Adviser Coventry HA. Prev: Sen. Regist. (Pub. Health Med.) Trent RHA.; Asst. Phys. Midl. Asthma & Allergy Treatm. Centre Derby; GP Leicester.

STERN, Myra 10 Beaufort Drive, London NW11 6BU — MB ChB 1985 Cape Town; MRCP (UK) 1992; PhD Cape Town 1992. Sen. Regist. & Research Fell. Roy. Brompton Hosp. Nat. Heart & Lung Inst.

STERN, Peter Max High Street, 16 High Street, Great Baddow, Chelmsford CM2 7HQ; 14 Lister Tye, Chelmsford CO12 9LS — MB BS 1984 Lond.; MRCGP 1990.

STERN, Richard Stephen (cons. rooms), St. Anthony's Hospital, London Road, North Cheam, Sutton SM3 9DW Tel: 020 8337 6691 Fax: 020 8337 0816 Email: sternrichard@hotmail.com; Springfield Hospital, 61 Glenburnie Road, London SW17 7DJ — MB BS 1967 Lond.; MD Lond. 1972; MRCS Eng. LRCP Lond. 1967; FRCPsych 1986, M 1972; DPM Eng. 1970. (Char. Cross) Vis. Cons., Priory Hosp., Priory La., Roehampton SW15 5JJ. Prev: Cons. Psychiat. St. Geo. & Springfield Hosps. Lond. & St. Helier Hosp. Carshalton; Sen. Lect. Inst. Psychiat. Lond.; Lect. (Psychol. Med.) Med. Coll. St. Bart. Hosp. Lond.

STERN, Sidney The Chalthorpe Clinic, 4 Arthur Road, Edgbaston, Birmingham B15 2UL Tel: 021 455 7585; 3 Oakwood Avenue, Borehamwood WD6 1SP Tel: 020 8953 9140 — MB ChB Glas. 1957; FRCOG 1981, M 1966. Socs: Brit. Menopause Soc. Prev: Vis. Cons. Dept. Gyn. Manor Ho. Hosp. Golders Green; Sen. Cons. O & G Murtala Mohammed Hosp. Kano, Nigeria; Regist. (O & G) Solihull & E. Birm. Hosp.

STERN, Simon Carl Maxim Deparment of Haematology, East Surrey Hospital, Canda Avenue, Redhill RH1 5RH Tel: 01737 768511 Fax: 01737 231694 Email: simon.stern@sysx-tr.shcare-tr.sthames.nhs.uk; Dept. of Cardiology, 2nd Floof B block, Hammersmith Hospital, London W12 0HS Tel: 01737 789139 Email: simonstern10@hotmail.com — MB BS 1987 Lond.; MRCP (UK) 1992; MRCPath 1998. (St. Geos. Hosp. Lond.) Cons. Haematologist, Surrey and Sussex Healthcare NHS Trust, E. Surrey Hosp., Redhill Surrey, RH1 5RH. Prev: Sen. Regist. (Haemat.) Chelsea & W.minster Hosp. Lond.; Sen. Regist. (Haemat.) Hammersmith Hosp. Lond.; Lect. & Hon. Sen. Regist. (Haemat.) Char. Cross Hosp. Lond.

STERN, Steven Richard The Surgery, Brede Lane, Sedlescombe, Battle TN33 0PW Tel: 01424 870225 — MB ChB 1978 Bristol; BSc (Hons.) Bristol 1975, MB ChB 1978; MRCP (UK) Paediat. 1982; Cert. Family Plann. JCC 1988; DRCOG 1988. Prev: Trainee GP Hastings VTS; SHO (O & G) Buchanan Hosp. Hastings; Sen. Regist./Regist. (Paediat.) Roy. Hosp. Sick Childr. Edin.

STERNBERG, Alexander Justin 57 Woodlands Avenue, New Malden KT3 3UH — MB ChB 1991 Bristol; BSc Bristol 1988; MRCP (UK) 1996. (Bristol University) Specialist Regist. (Haemat.) John Radcliffe Hosp. Oxf. Prev: SHO (Haemato-Oncol.) Roy. Marsden Hosp. Fulham Rd.; SHO (Gen. Med.) Taunton; SHO (A & E) Frenchay.

STERNBERG, Michael Paul (retired) (cons. rooms), 2 Clifton Park, Bristol BS8 3BS Tel: 0117 906 4217 — MRCS Eng. LRCP Lond. 1958; LMSSA Lond. 1958; DPM Eng. 1966; MRCPsych 1972. Prev: Cons. Psychiat. Bristol & W.on HA.

STERNBERG, Simon 187 Mendip House, Market Square, Edmonton, London N9 0TD Tel: 020 8803 9638 — MB BS 1948 Lond.; MRCS Eng. LRCP Lond. 1948. (Lond. Hosp.) Assoc. Specialist St. Michael's Hosp. Enfield. Prev: Med. Asst. St. Michael's Hosp. Enfield; SHO Infec. Dis. & Chest Units Plaistow Hosp.; Capt. RAMC.

STERNDALE BENNETT, (Winifred) Anne (retired) E12 Tower Lane, Bearstead, Maidstone ME14 4JJ Tel: 01622 737921 Fax: 01622 737921 — MB BS 1947 Lond.; MRCS Eng. LRCP Lond. 1947; DO Eng. 1953. Prev: Ophth. Kent CC.

STERNE, Adrian Patrick The Country Medical Centre, 122 Ballinlea Road, Armoy, Ballymoney BT53 8TY Tel: 028 2075 1266 Fax: 028 2075 1122; 4 Semicock Road, Ballymoney BT53 6PX Tel: 01265 665604 — MB BCh BAO 1984 Belf.; MRCGP Ed. 1988; DCH RCPSI 1989; DRCOG 1987.

STERNE, Austin John 127 Swanshurst Lane, Birmingham B13 0AS — MB ChB 1991 Birm.; ChB Birm. 1991.

STERRICK, Mark James Millar 10 Abbotsford Park, Edinburgh EH10 5DX Tel: 0131 466 2130 Fax: 0131 446 2148; 29 Houstoun Gardens, Uphall, Broxburn EH52 5SH Tel: 01506 853543 — MB ChB 1985 Leic.; DFM Glas. 1988; T(GP) 1991. (Leic. Univ.) Assoc. Specialist (Ment. Handicap) Abbotsford Pk. Socs: Founder Mem. Scott. Soc. of Clin. Epileptologists. Prev: Staff Grade (Ment. Handicap.) Gogarburn Hosp. Edin.; Clin. Asst. (Psychiat.) Edin.; GP/Regist. Alness.

STERRY, Mark Julian Gwyn Grove Surgery, 3 Grove Road, Solihull B91 2AG Tel: 0121 705 1105 Fax: 0121 711 4098 — MB BCh 1990 Wales; MRCGP 1994; DRCOG 1995; T(GP) 1994; DFFP 1993; Dip. Palliat. Med. 1997. (UWCM) Med. Off. Marie Curie Centre, Warren Pearl, Solihull. Prev: Trainee GP/SHO Wolverhampton VTS.

STEUER, Alan Department of Rheumatology, Charing Cross Hospital, Fulham Palace Road, London W6 8RF; 49 Foscote Road, London NW4 3SE — MB BS 1991 Lond.; BSc Lond. 1988; MRCP (UK) 1994. Specialist Regist. (Rheum. & Gen. Med.) Char. Cross Hosp.

STEUER, Lara Rachelle 49 Foscote Road, London NW4 3SE — MB BChir 1992 Camb.

STEVEN, Mr Alastair Matthew 16 Kyle Drive, Giffnock, Glasgow G46 6ES Email: alastair.steven@virgin.net — MB ChB 1992 Glas.

STEVEN, Carolyn Margaret 7 Dora Road, London SW19 7EZ Tel: 020 8947 6314 Fax: 020 8947 6314 — MB ChB Glas. 1968; FFA RCS Eng. 1976; DA Eng. 1971. (Glas.) Cons. (Anaesth.) St. Helier Hosp. Carshalton; Hon. Sen. Lect. St. Geo. Hosp. Med. Sch. Lond. Socs: Obst. Anaesth. Assn.; Brit. Assn. Day Surg.; BMA & Assn. Anaesth. Gt. Brit. & Irel. Prev: Sen. Regist. (Anaesth.) St. Thos. Hosp. Lond.; Regist. (Anaesth.) Glas. Roy. Infirm. & St. Thos. Hosp. Lond.

STEVEN, Colin Alexander 9 Ainslie Close, Aylestone Hill, Hereford HR1 1JH — MB BS 1968 Lond. Prev: Med. Off. Brit. Petroleum Abu Dhabi Marine Areas, V.A.E.; Med. Off. Lockheed Aircraft Internat. Riyadh, Saudi Arabia.; Med. Off. Exxon Oil Tripoli N. Africa.

STEVEN, Colin Monteith, MBE (retired) Rossland, Wigtown, Newton Stewart DG8 9DZ Tel: 01988 402395 — MB ChB. Glas. 1939.

STEVEN, Grace Campbell (retired) 29 Strathview Terrace, Balfron, Glasgow G63 0PU — MB ChB 1949 Glas.

STEVEN, John Douglas King's Park Hospital, Polmaise Road, Stirling FK7 9JH Tel: 01786 451669; 10 Dargai Terrace, Dunblane FK15 0AU Tel: 01786 823664 Email: john.steven@frah.scot.nhs.uk — MB ChB Ed. 1970; FRCOG 1989, M 1976. Cons. (O & G) Stirling Roy. Infirm. Prev: Sen. Regist. (O & G) Ninewells Hosp. Dundee; Regist. (O & G) W.. Gen. Hosp. Edin.

STEVEN, John Mark 47A Roman Road, Bearsden, Glasgow G61 2QP — MB ChB 1992 Glas.

STEVEN, Karen 2 Brora Road, Bishopbriggs, Glasgow G64 1HX — MB ChB 1990 Glas.

STEVEN

STEVEN, Malcolm Monteith Raigmore Hospital, Inverness IV2 3UJ Tel: 01463 704000 Fax: 01463 705640 — MB ChB 1974 Aberd.; MD Aberd. 1985; FRCP Ed. 1995; FRCP Glas. 1988; MRCP (UK) 1977. Cons. Phys. (Med. & Rheum.) Highland Acute Hosps. Trust; Hon. Clin. Sen. Lect. Univ. Aberd. Socs: (Counc.) Brit. Soc. of Rheum.; Brit. Soc. of Rheum.; Scott. Soc. Phys. Prev: Sen. Regist. Centre for Rheum. Dis. Glas.; Regist. (Gen. Med.) Aberd. Teach. Hosps.; Regist. (Gen. Med.) Clin. Research Unit Walter & Eliza Hall Inst. Med. Research Melbourne.

STEVEN, Neil Matthew Institute for Cancer Studies, University of Birmingham, Edgbaston, Birmingham B15 2TA Tel: 0961 199219 Fax: 0121 414 3263 Email: n.m.steven@bham.ac.uk; 12 Elmcroft Road, Birmingham B26 1PJ Tel: 0121 784 8677 — MB BS 1986 Lond.; PhD Birm. 1998; BA (Hons.) Camb. 1983; MRCP (UK) 1990; DTM & H RCP Lond. 1993; PhD 1998. MRC Clin. Scientist. Inst. Of Cancer Studies, Univ. of Birm. Socs: Assn. Cancer Phys. Prev: CRC Lect. (Med. Oncol.) Univ. Birm.; MRC Train. Fell. (Infect. & Cancer Studies) Univ. Birm.; Regist. (Infect. & Trop. Med.) Birm. Heartlands Hosp.

STEVEN, Robert Edward 35 Osmaston Road, Stourbridge DY8 2AL — MB ChB 1993 Liverp.

STEVEN, Rukshana Ramzan 16 Kyle Drive, Giffnock, Glasgow G46 6ES — MB ChB 1993 Glas.

STEVENS, Andrea Mary — MB BS 1991 Lond.; FRCR 1999; MRCP (UK) 1994. Regist. (Clin. Oncol.) Birm. Oncol. Centre. Prev: SHO Rotat. (Med.) Glos. Roy. Hosp.; SpR W. Midl.s Clin. Oncol. Train. Progr.

STEVENS, Professor Andrew John Henrik Department of Public Health and Epidemiology, The University of Birmingham, Edgbaston, Birmingham B15 2TT Tel: 0121 414 6768 Fax: 0121 414 7878 — MB BS 1983 Lond.; MSc Lond. 1986; BA Camb. 1975; FFPHM RCP (UK) 1995; MFCM RCP (UK) 1989. Prof. Pub. Health Med. Univ. Birm. Prev: Sen. Lect. (Pub. Health Med.) Wessex Inst. Pub. Health Med.; Cons. Pub. Health Med. Lewisham & N. S.wark HA.

STEVENS, Angela Felicity The Maudsley Hospital, Denmark Hill, London SE5; 1 Park Farm Cottages, 32 Leonard Avenue, Offord, Sevenoaks TN14 5RB — MB BS 1992 Lond.; PhD Microbiol. Leics. 1985; BSc (Hons.) Microbiol. & Virol. Warwick Univ 1981.

STEVENS, Mrs Ann Wyn Sunset, Old Carnon Hill, Carnon Downs, Truro TR3 6LF Tel: 01872 862975 — MB ChB 1962 Liverp. (Liverp.) Med. Off. (Occupat. Health) Roy. Cornw. Hosp. Trust. Truro. Prev: Ho. Surg. & Ho. Phys. David Lewis N.. Hosp. Liverp.

STEVENS, Anna Miranda Hamlyn 4 Roman Grove, Leeds LS8 2DT — MB BChir 1993 Camb.

STEVENS, Anthony Baxter Occupational Health Unit, Royal Hospitals Trust, Grosvenor Road, Belfast BT12 6BB Tel: 01232 894611 Fax: 01232 263163 Email: tony.stevens@royalhospitals.n-i.nhs.uk — MB BCh BAO 1982 Belf.; MD Belf. 1991; FRCP 1997; MRCP (UK) 1985; FFOM 1997; MFOM RCP Lond. 1991, AFOM 1989. (Qu. Univ. Belf.) Cons. Occupat. Med. Roy. Hosps. Trust Belf.; Sen. Hon. Lect. (Occupat. Med.) Qu. Univ. Belf.; Director Risk and Occupat. Health Serv.s Roy. Hosp. Belf. Socs: Fell. Ulster Med. Soc.; Soc. Occupat. Med.; Brit. Occupat. Hyg. Soc. Prev: Cons. Occupat. Med. EHSSB; Sen. Regist. (Occupat. Med.) EHSSB; Research Fell. (Med.) Qu. Univ. Belf.

STEVENS, Anthony Edward (retired) The Somerfield Hospital, London Road, Maidstone ME16 0DU Tel: 01622 686581 Fax: 01622 674706 — MB BS 1952 Lond.; FRCP Lond. 1975, M 1958. Prev: Cons. Phys. The Maidstone Hosp.

STEVENS, Anthony George (private rooms), Fardel Manor, Ivybridge PL21 9HT Tel: 01752 892353 Fax: 01752 893039; 2 Tambrook Court, 9 Holbein Place, London SW1W 8NR Tel: 020 7750 6320 — BM BCh 1963 Oxf.; BA (Hons.) Oxf. 1959; BA (Hons.) Reading 1955; MRCPsych 1996; MA Oxf. 1965, DM 1975; DPM Eng. 1969. (Oxf. & Char. Cross) Socs: Fell. Roy. Soc. Med. Prev: Sen. Regist. Horton Hosp. Epsom; Ho. Surg. Roy. Surrey Co. Hosp. Guildford; Research Fell. Qu. Anna Maria Inst. Child Health Athens.

STEVENS, Anthony John (retired) 42 Chiswick Quay, London W4 3UR Tel: 020 8995 1222 Fax: 020 8995 1222 Email: anaes@johnstevens.co.uk — MB BS Lond. 1963; MRCS Eng. LRCP Lond. 1963; FANZCA 1992; FFARCS 1970; DA (UK) 1965. Private Pract. Prev: Cons. Anaesth. Hammersmith Hosp. Trust.

***STEVENS, Arabella Paula** Latchetts, Wellgreen Lane, Kingston, Lewes BN7 3NS — MB ChB 1998 Manch.; MB ChB Manch 1998.

STEVENS, Claire Elizabeth Appletree Medical Practice, 47a Town Street, Duffield, Belper DE56 4GG Tel: 01332 841219, 01332 844200 — BM BS 1984 Nottm.; MRCGP 1990; DRCOG 1987. GP Duffield Derby.

***STEVENS, Clare Valentine** 45 Lockesfield Place, London E14 3AJ — MB BS 1997 Lond.

STEVENS, David Brook Nobles Hospital, Douglas IM1 4QA Tel: 01624 642144 Fax: 01624 642144 Email: isleofmandbs@hotmail.com; Ashley, Ekorora Drive, Douglas IM2 3NN Tel: 01624 675063 Fax: 01624 673549 Email: islelfmandbs@hotmail.com — MB ChB 1969 Ed.; BSc Ed. 1966; DMRD Ed. 1974. (Ed.) Cons. Radiol. Noble's Hosp. I. of Man; Dir. I. of Man Motorsport Med. Servs. Socs: Roy. Coll. Radiol. & BASICS; Mem. Fac. of Pre-Hosp. Immediate Care Roy. Coll. Surg. Edin.

STEVENS, David George, Wing Cdr. RAF Med. Br. Retd. Green Lane Hospital, Devizes SN10 9DS Tel: 01380 731325; Tel: 01249 815537 Email: dgspsych@eclipse.co.uk — MB BS 1978 Lond.; BSc Lond. 1972; MRCPsych. 1989; MRCGP 1983; Cert. Family Plann. JCC 1982. (St. Bartholomews) Cons. Psychiat. Wilts. Ment.. Health Care Trust. Prev: Cons. Psychiat. P.ss Alexandra RAF Wroughton; Regist. Highfield Adolesc. Unit Warneford Hosp. Oxf.; Regist. Felix Post Unit Maudsley Hosp. Lond.

STEVENS, David James Waller 8 Lavant Road, Chichester PO19 4RH Tel: 01243 527264 — MB 1972 Camb.; BChir 1971; DRCOG 1976; DA Eng. 1974. (Middlx.)

STEVENS, David Laurence Department Neurology, Gloucestershire Royal Hospital GL1 3NN; Springfield Lawn, The Park, Cheltenham GL50 2SD Tel: 01242 237921 Fax: 01242 522424 Email: david-stevens@springfield-lawn.demon.co.uk — MB BS 1961 Lond.; MD Lond. 1977; FRCP Ed. 1997; FRCP Lond. 1980, M 1966; MRCS Eng. LRCP Lond. 1961. (Guy's) Cons. NeUrol. in Private Pract.; Trustee, Variant Crentzfeld & Jakob Dis. Trust, UK; Cons. NeUrol. Gloucestershire Roy. Hosp., Cheltenham Gen. Hosp., Bristol. Socs: World Federat. Neurol. Research Comm. Huntington's Chorea (Sec.Gen.); World Federate. Neurol Finance Comm. (Mem.); Assn. of Brit. Neurol. Topics. Prev: Cons. Neurol. Glos. Roy. Hosp., Cheltenham Gen. Hosp. & Frenchay Hosp. Bristol; Ho. Surg. & Ho. Phys. St. Olave's Hosp. Lond.; Sen. Regist. (Neurol.) Gen. Infirm. Leeds.

STEVENS, Mr David Michael (retired) 6 Ogbourne, Colerne, Chippenham SN14 8DJ — MB BS 1944 Lond.; FRCS Ed. 1952; MRCS Eng. LRCP Lond. 1943; DLO Eng. 1948. Cons. ENT Surg. Bath Clin. Area. Prev: Sen. ENT Regist. United Cardiff Hosps.

STEVENS, David William Paediatric Dept, Glorcestershire Royal Hospital, Glorcester GH 3NW; 51B Turnberry Drive, Wilmslow SK9 2QW Tel: 01625 520084 Email: david.stevens@bristol.ac.uk — MB BS 1963 Lond.; FRCPCH 1997; FRCP Lond. 1989; MRCP (UK) 1970; MRCS Eng. LRCP Lond. 1963; DCH Eng. 1971. (Westm.) Cons. Paediat. Glos. Roy. Hosp.; Sen. Lect., Univ. of Bristol Dept of Child Health. Prev: Sen. Regist. Roy. Hosp. for Sick Childr. Bristol.

STEVENS, Deborah St. Julia's Hospice, Trelissick Road, Hayle TR27 4JA Tel: 01736 751216 Fax: 01736 751355; Elm Cottage, Relubbus, Penzance TR20 9EP Tel: 01736 763417 — MB BS 1982 Lond. Med. Direct. St. Julia's Hospice St. Michael's Hosp. Cornw.; Hon. Cons. (Palliat. Med.) Roy. Cornw. Hosps Trust.

STEVENS, Diana Claire The New Surgery, Lindo Close, Chesham HP5 2JN Tel: 01494 782262; Stavacre, Bellingdon, Chesham HP5 2XW — MB BS 1979 Lond.; MRCGP 1986; DCH RCP Lond. 1984; Cert. Family Plann. RCOG & RCGP 1984. GP Chesham. Socs: BMA & Med. Protec. Soc. Prev: Clin. Med. Off. W. Lambeth HA; SHO (Paediat.) Char. Cross Hosp. Lond.

STEVENS, Dominic John Charles 86 Numa Court, Brentford Dock, Brentford TW8 8QF — MB ChB 1964 Bristol; MSc (Clin. Trop. Med.) Lond. 1983; MRCGP 1977. (Bristol) GP Bolton. Prev: Dist. Med. Off. Luapula Province, Zambia; SHO (Ment. Health) Bristol Roy. Infirm.; Ho. Surg. & Ho. Phys. King's Lynn Gen. Hosp.

STEVENS, Eileen Denise Trafford General Hospital, Moorside Road, Davyhulme, Manchester M41 5SL; 90 Bollington Road, Stockport SK4 5ES — MB ChB 1985 Manch.; MRCP (UK) 1988. p/t Clin. Asst. (Med. & Geriat.) Trafford Gen. Hosp. Manch. Socs: Brit. Geriat. Soc.; Roy. Soc. Med; Mem. Med. Soc. Prev: Regist. (Geriat.)

Salford HA; Regist. (Med.) Trafford Dist. Gen. Hosp.; SHO (Gen. Med.) N. Manch. Gen. Hosp.

STEVENS, Fiona Maureen Department of Medicine, University College Hospital, Galway, Republic of Ireland Tel: 00 353 91 524222 Fax: 00 353 91 750540; 36 Manton Hollow, Marlborough SN8 1RR Tel: 01672 53219 — MB BS 1965 Lond.; MD NUI 1993; FRCP Lond. 1988; MRCP (UK) 1970; MRCS Eng. LRCP Lond. 1965. (St. Geo.) Lect. (Med.) Galway Regional Hosp.

STEVENS, Graham Colin 42 High Street, Harrington, Northampton NN6 9NU — MB ChB 1994 Leic.; BSc (Hons.) Leic. 1992. SHO (A & E) Kettering Gen. Hosp.

STEVENS, Gwyneth Mary (retired) 3 Rodney Close, Rodney Road, New Malden KT3 5AA — MRCS Eng. LRCP Lond. 1950; DCH Eng. 1955.

STEVENS, Howard Martin Kennoway Medical Group, Jordan Lane, Kennoway, Leven KY8 5JZ Tel: 01333 350241 Fax: 01333 352884; 4 Lundin View, Leven KY8 5TL Tel: 01333 421 589 Email: howard@hms60.freeserve.co.uk — MB ChB 1983 Aberd. (Aberdeen) Clin. Asst. (Geriat.) Glenrothes. Socs: Roy. Coll. Gen. Pract.; BMA; Brit. Med. Accupuncture Soc. Prev: SHO (ENT) Aberd. Roy. Infirm.; SHO (O & G) P.ss of Wales Hosp. Bridgend; Trainee GP Bridgend M. Glam.

STEVENS, Howard Peter South Wing, Bramfield House, Hertford SG14 2QT Tel: 01992 584447 — MB BS 1988 Lond.; MRCP (UK) 1991; ma (Oxon) 1983; PhD (Lond) 1998. Cons. Dermatolgist (F/T) - Barnet & Chase Farm Gen. Hosp. Prev: Wellcome Research Train. Fell.sh. & Hon. Sen. Regist. Roy. Lond. Hosp. Lond.; Regist. (Dermat.) Roy. Free Hosp. Lond.; Regist. (Gen. Med.) Watford Gen. Hosp.

STEVENS, Isobel Mary (retired) 29 Woolsington Park S., Woolsington, Newcastle upon Tyne NE13 8BJ Tel: 0191 286 3001 — MB ChB Glas. 1950. Prev: Clin. Asst. (Med.) Newc. AHA (T).

STEVENS, Jacqueline Ann John Tasker House Surgery, 56 New Street, Dunmow CM6 1BH — MB BS 1992 Lond. (St. Georges) p/t Gen. Practitioner, Asst. Gt. Dunmold. Prev: SHO Rotat. N. Hants. Hosp. Basingstoke; GP Regist. Alton Health Centre, Hants. Locum GP - N. Essex.

***STEVENS, James Clement** Glenfield, 24 The Crescent, Northwich CW9 8AD — MB BS 1998 Lond.; MB BS Lond 1998.

***STEVENS, Jane** 13 Kinderton Avenue, Withington, Manchester M20 1AL — MB ChB 1996 Manch.

STEVENS, Jane Frances 3 Clarendon Street, Cambridge CB1 1JU Tel: 01223 316046 Fax: 01223 500248 Email: jfsterons@compuserve.com — MB BS 1976 Lond.; MRCP (UK) 1979; MFOM 1990; DIH Eng. 1983. (Univ. Coll. Lond.) Cons. Occupat. Health. Socs: Soc. Occupat. Med. & Roy. Soc. Med. Prev: Head of Occupat. Health Glaxo Research & Developm. Greenford; Regist. (Gen. Med.) St. Stephen's Hosp. Lond.; SHO (Thoracic Med.) Brompton Hosp. Lond.

STEVENS, Jeremy David Anaesthetic Department, Royal Hospital Trust, Calow, Chesterfield S44 5BL Tel: 01246 277271; Sparrow Busk Cottage, Clowne Road, Barlborough, Chesterfield S43 4EN Tel: 01246 570358 Fax: 01246 570229 — MB BS 1982 Lond.; FFA RCSI 1989. (St. Bart.) Cons. Anaesth. Roy. Hosp. Trust. Chesterfield. Socs: Med. Protec. Soc.; HCSA; Pain Soc. Prev: Sen. Regist. & Regist. Roy. Hallamsh. Hosp. Sheff.; Regist. (Anaesth.) & Research Regist. (Acute Pain) York Dist. Hosp.

STEVENS, John Edwin 13 All Saints Road, Headington, Oxford OX3 7AU — MB BS 1974 Lond.; FFA RCS Eng. 1979. Cons. Anaesth. & Direct. of Paediat. IC, John Radcliffe Hosp., Headington, Oxf..

STEVENS, John Robert David South West London & St George's Mental Health Trust, Department of Psychotherapy, Harewood House, Springfield Hospital, London SW17 7DJ Tel: 020 8682 6682 Fax: 020 8682 6476 Email: jstevens@swlstg-tr.nhs.uk; 'Earnsdale', 2 Whitepost Hill, Redhill RH1 6BD Tel: 01737 277706 Fax: 01737 277709 — MB BS 1976 Lond.; MRCPsych 1980; T(Psych) 1991. (Char. Cross) Cons. Psychother. Springfield Hosp. S. W. Lond. & St Geo.'s Ment. Health. NHS Trust; Cons. Psychother. Surrey Oaklands NHS Trust. Socs: Assn. Psychoanalyt. Psychother. NHS. Prev: Cons. Psychiat. Gender Identity Clinic (Psychiat.) Char. Cross Hosp. Lond.; Cons. Psychiat. (Psychother.) P.ss Roy. Hosp. Haywards Heath; Sen. Regist. (Psychol. Med.) Univ. Coll. Hosp. Lond.

STEVENS, Jonathan Paul 88 Carleton Gardens, Brecknock Road, London N19 5AQ — MB ChB 1989 Manch.; BSc Hons. Manch. 1986. Research Fell. & Hon. Regist. Roy. Postgrad. Med. Sch. Lond.; RMO Portland Hosp. for Wom. & Childr. Lond. Socs: Fell. Roy. Soc. Med. Prev: Interne (Neonatol.) Clinique Port Roy., Paris.; SHO (Paediat.) Hammersmith Hosp. & Hosp. Sick Childr. Lond.

STEVENS, Judith Mary Wessex Renal and Transplant Unit, St. Mary's Hospital, Milton Road, Portsmouth PO3 6AD Tel: 02392 866113 Fax: 02392 866108 — MB BS 1981 Newc.; MD Newc. 1991; FRCP Lon. 2000. Cons. Nephrol. & Gen. Med. St. Mary's Hosp. Portsmouth. Prev: Sen. Regist. (Nephrol.) St. Mary's Hosp. Portsmouth; Regist. (Renal) Qu. Eliz. Hosp. Adelaide.; Research Fell. Roy. Postgrad. Med. Sch. Lond.

STEVENS, Mr Julian Douglas Moorfields Eye Hospital, City Road, London EC1V 2PD Tel: 020 7253 3411 Fax: 020 7253 4696 Email: 100437.663@compuserve.com; John Saunders Suite, Bath St, London EC1V 9EL Tel: 020 7566 2699 Fax: 020 7566 2608 Email: julianstevens@compuserve.com — MB 1983 Camb.; BChir 1982; MA Oxf. 1985, BA 1980; FRCS Eng. 1988; MRCP (UK) 1986; FRCOphth 1988; DO RCS Eng. 1988. (Univ. Camb.) Cons. Ophth. Moorfields Eye Hosp. Lond. Socs: Eur. Soc. Cataract & Refractive Surgs.; Soc. Cataract & Refractive Surgs. UK & Irel.; Amer. Soc. Cataract & Refractive Surgs. Prev: Corneal & Refractive Fell. Moorfields Eye Hosp. Lond.; Sen. Regist. (Ophth.) Moorfields Eye Hosp. Lond.; Regist. (Ophth.) Oxf. Eye Hosp.

STEVENS, Katharine Lindsey Haughton Accident & Emergency Department, St. Helier's Hospital, Wrythe Lane, Carshalton SM5 1AA Tel: 020 8296 2276 Fax: 020 8288 1837 — MB BChir 1979 Camb.; MA Camb. 1978; FRCP Lond. 1994; MRCP (UK) 1983; FFAEM 1993. (Univ. Camb. & Middlx. Hosp.) Clin. Dir. A & E Servs. St Helier's Hosp. Carshalton; NHS Assessor; Hon. Sen. Lect. St. Geo. Hosp. Med. Sch. Univ. Lond.; Advanced Trauma Life Support Instruc.; Paediat. Advanced Life Support Instruc.; Dep. Dist. Surg. St. Johns Ambul.; Examr. FRCS (A & E). Socs: Fell. Roy. Soc. Med. (Edit. Represen. Accid. & Emerg. Sect.); Brit. Assn. Accid. & Emerg. Med. Prev: Cons. Manager A & E St. Geo. Hosp. Lond.

STEVENS, Kathleen Mary (retired) 19 Moore Avenue, Harton, South Shields NE34 6AA Tel: 0191 456 0539 — MB BS Durh. 1945, CPH 1947. Prev: Princip. Community Clinician Durh. AHA.

STEVENS, Kathryn Jane City Hospital, Hucknall Road, Nottingham NG5 1PJ Tel: 0115 969 1169; 34 Torvill Drive, Wollaton, Nottingham NG8 2BU Tel: 0115 928 1223 — MB BS 1989 Lond.; BSc Lond. 1986. Regist. (Radiol.) City Hosp. Nottm. Prev: SHO Rotat. Nottm.; Demonst. (Anat.) Camb. Univ.

STEVENS, Lesley Carol Connaught House, Royal Hampshire County Hospital, Romsey Road, Winchester SO22 5DG Tel: 01962 825128 — MB BS 1986 Lond.; MRCPsych 1991. (St. Bart. Hosp. Lond.) Cons. (Psychiat.).

STEVENS, Liam Francis Newtown Surgery, 147 Lawn Avenue, Great Yarmouth NR30 1QP Tel: 01493 853191 Fax: 01493 331861; 147 Lawn Avenue, Great Yarmouth NR30 1QP — MB BS 1982 Lond.; MRCGP 1986; DRCOG 1985. (St. Mary's) Prev: Ho. Surg. King Edwd. VII Hosp. Windsor; Ho. Phys. St. Chas. Hosp. Lond.

STEVENS, Linda Eileen Whetstone Lane Health Centre, 44 Whetstone Lane, Birkenhead CH41 2TF Tel: 0151 647 9613 Fax: 0151 650 0875 — MB ChB 1974 Liverp.; MRCGP 1979; DCH Eng. 1978; DObst RCOG 1976. Prev: GP Nottm.

STEVENS, Louise Anne Rose Cottage, Lower St., Great Bealings, Woodbridge IP13 6NH — MB BS 1990 Lond.; DRCOG 1993.

***STEVENS, Lydia Mary** 62 Dukes Avenue, London W4 2AF — BM 1995 Soton.

STEVENS, Lyndon Robert 2 Main Road, Gilberdyke, Hull HU15 2UP — MB BCh 1972 Wales; DObst RCOG 1976. Princip. Med. Off. (Forens. Med. Serv.) Hull.

***STEVENS, Mark** 46 Yarningale Road, Coventry CV3 3EL — MB BS 1997 Lond.

STEVENS, Mark Andrew John Malvern House, 41 Mapperley Road, Nottingham NG3 5AQ Tel: 0115 841 2006 Fax: 0115 841 2006 — BChir Camb. 1981; MRCGP 1987; DRCOG 1985. Prev: Trainee GP Aylesbury VTS; SHO (Paediat.) St. Thos. Hosp. Lond.

STEVENS, Mark Norton Frambury Lane Surgery, Frambury Lane, Newport, Saffron Walden CB11 3PY; 6 Pond Cross Farm, High St,

STEVENS

Newport, Saffron Walden CB11 3RW Tel: 01799 541848 — MB BS 1972 Lond. (St. Thomas')

STEVENS, Martin John 55 Elfindale Road, Herne Hill, London SE24 9NN Tel: 020 7274 7558 — MB BCh 1983 Wales; MRCP (UK) 1986. Research Fell. Diabetic Dept. Kings Coll. Hosp. Lond. Prev: Regist. (Med.) Roy. S. Hants. Hosp. Soton.; SHO OldCh. Hosp. Romford.

STEVENS, Martin John Minsmere House, The Ipswich Hospital, Heath Road, Ipswich IP4 5PD Tel: 01473 704202; 55 Henley Road, Ipswich IP1 3SJ Tel: 01473 251265 — MRCS Eng. LRCP Lond. 1967; FRCP Lond. 1995; MRCP (UK) 1972; FRCPsych 1986, M 1975. (St. Thos.) Cons. Psychiat. (Geriat. Psychiat.) Ipswich Hosp. Socs: Brit. Geriat. Soc. & Europ. Assn. Geriat. Psychiat.; Internat. Psychogeriat. Assn. Prev: Sen. Regist. (Psychol. Med.) Newc. Univ. Hosp.; Regist. (Gen. Med.) Gen. Hosp. Burton on Trent; Ho. Phys. (Psychol. Med.) St. Thos. Hosp. Lond.

STEVENS, Mary MacTaggart 10 Charles Court, Knighton Drive, Stoneygate, Leicester LE2 3HB — MB ChB 1938 Glas. (Glas.)

STEVENS, Matthew James 170 Mayals Road, Mayals, Swansea SA3 1HF — MB BCh 1995 Wales. SHO (O & G) GPVTS Scheme. Socs: BMA cl.ic; MDU. Prev: SHO Elderley Med. 6 mths. Australia (Orthop. Anaesth.); SHO A&E; Ho. Off. Gen. Surg.

***STEVENS, Matthew Thomas** 9 Strangeways, Larkhill, Salisbury SP4 8LN — BM 1996 Soton.

STEVENS, Maxine Danny House, New Way Lane, Hurstpierpoint, Hassocks BN6 9BB — MB ChB 1959 Manch.; DPH Lond. 1962.

STEVENS, Michael Charles Garston Birmingham Children's Hospital, NHS Trust, Birmingham B4 6NH Tel: 0121 333 8412 Fax: 0121 333 8241 Email: mikestevens@bhamchildrens.wmids.nhs.uk — MD 1983 Lond.; MB BS (Hons.) 1974; FRCP Lond. 1992; MRCP (UK) 1976; FRCPCH 1997. (St. Mary's) Cons. Paediatric Oncologist Birm. Childr.'s Hosp. NHS Trust. Socs: Internat. Soc. of Paediat. Oncol.; UK Childr.'s Cancer Study Gp. Prev: Med. Dir. Birm. Childr.'s Hosp. NHS Trust; Chairm. UK Childr.s Cancer Study GP.

STEVENS, Michele Ann 16 Wyndham Road, London W13 9TE Tel: 0208 840 4595 Email: mike.michelle@virgin.net; Email: mike.michele@virgin.net — MB BS 1990 Lond.; FRCA 1997. (St. Bartholow's Hospital, London) Spr (Anaest) Green Charlottes & Chelsea. Hosp. Lond. Prev: SHO (Anaesth.) Chelsea & W.m. Hosp. Lond.; SHO (Cardiothoracic Surg.) St. Bart. Hosp. Lond.; Regist. (Anaesth.) Chelsea & W.m. Hosp. Lond.

STEVENS, Monica Rosemary Clare Northgate Practice, Northgate, Canterbury CT1 1WL — MB BS 1988 Lond.; DFFP. (St. Mary's Medical School) p/t Trainee GP Medway VTS., GP Retainer; CMO Family Plann., Canterbury. Prev: Ho. Surg. Bucklands Hosp. Dover; Ho. Phys. Kent & Canterbury Hosp.; Med.s VTS.

STEVENS, Nigel Bradley, Surg. Lt.-Cdr. RN Windsor Crescent Surgery, 6 Windsor Crescent, Val Plaisant, St Helier, Jersey JE2 4TB Tel: 01534 32341 Fax: 01534 870635; 12 Le Feugerel, Le Mont de la Pulente, St Brelade, Jersey JE3 8HB — MB BCh 1982 Wales; MRCGP 1987.

STEVENS, Paul Edward, Squadron Ldr. RAF Med. Br. Retd. Department of Renal Medicine, Kent & Canterbury Hospital, Ethelbert Road, Canterbury CT1 3NE Tel: 01227 766877 Fax: 01227 783073 Email: paul.stevens@kch_tr.sthames.nhs.uk; Milestone Barn, Hode Lane, Bridge, Canterbury CT4 5DL — MB BS 1980 Lond.; BSc (Hons.) Lond. 1977, MB BS 1980; MRCP (UK) 1985; FRCP 1996. (London Hospital Medical College) Cons. Nephrol. & Dir. Renal Servs. Kent & Canterbury Hosp. Socs: Eur. Dialysis & Transpl. Assn.; Renal Assn. Prev: Cons. Phys. & Nephrol. P.ss Mary's RAF Hosp. Halton; Lect. & Hon. Sen. Regist. (Gen. Med. & Nephrol.) Char. Cross Hosp. Lond.; Sen. Regist. (Renal Med.) P.ss Mary's Hosp. Halton.

STEVENS, Paul George Cathcart Practice, 8 Cathcart Street, Ayr KA7 1BJ Tel: 01292 264051 Fax: 01292 293803; 3 Ewenfield Park, Ayr KA7 2QG Tel: 01292 265442 — MB ChB 1976 Glas.; DRCOG 1977. (Glasgow) Specialist (Genito-Urin. Med.) Heathfield Clinic Ayr.

STEVENS, Peter John Newbold Surgery, Windermere Road, Chesterfield S41 8DU Tel: 01246 277381 Fax: 01246 239828 — MB ChB 1969 Ed.; FRCGP 1994, M 1977; DObst RCOG 1972. (Ed.) Prev: SHO (Obst.) W.. Gen. Hosp. Edin.; Med. Off. St. Kitts, W. Indies.

STEVENS, Peter John, OBE (retired) South Orchard, College Lane, East Grinstead RH19 3JR Tel: 01342 325963 Fax: 01342 325963 Email: stevens.pj@doctors.org.uk — MB ChB 1949 Birm.; MD Birm. 1968; DCP Lond 1955; FRCPath 1972, M 1964; DTM & H Eng. 1960. Prev: Cons. Path. Qu. Vict. Hosp. E. Grinstead.

STEVENS, Philip Harold (retired) The Surgery, Bissoe Road, Carnon Downs, Truro TR3 6JD Tel: 01872 863221 — MRCS Eng. LRCP Lond. 1961. Prev: Regist. (Gen. Med.) Sefton Gen. Hosp. Liverp.

STEVENS, Philip John Washington House Surgery, 77 Halse Road, Brackley NN13 6EQ Tel: 01280 702436; 5 Broad Lane, Evenley, Brackley NN13 5SF Tel: 01280 702879 — MB BCh 1978 Wales; MRCGP 1984; DRCOG 1983.

STEVENS, Richard Charles Harrisson Orchard Court Surgery, Orchard Court, Orchard Road, Darlington DL3 6HZ Tel: 01325 465285 Fax: 01325 284034; The Surgery, Orchard Court, Darlington DL3 6HZ Tel: 01325 465285 Fax: 01325 284034 — MB BS 1987 Newc.; MRCGP 1993; DRCOG 1993; DFFP 1993. (Newc. u. Tyne) Clin. Asst. (Asthma) Darlington Memor. Hosp. Prev: Stud. Health Off. Hawkes Bay Polytechnic, NZ; Trainee GP Cleveland VTS.

STEVENS, Richard Frederic 243 Brooklands Road, Manchester M23 9HF Tel: 0161 969 4151 Fax: 0161 905 3451 — MB ChB 1973 Birm.; BSc (Hons.) Birm. 1970; FRCP Lond. 1991; MRCP (UK) 1976; FRCPath 1996, M 1981; FRCPCH 1997. Cons. Haemat. Manch. Childr. Hosps. Prev: Cons. Haemat. Manch. Roy. Infirm. & Blood Transfus. Serv. Manch.; Sen. Regist. (Haemat.) Manch. Roy. Infirm.; Regist. (Clin. Haemat.) Manch. Roy. Infirm.

STEVENS, Richard Jeffrey The Heberden Unit, Amersham Hospital, Amersham HP7 0JD Tel: 01494 734079 Fax: 01494 734504 — MB BS 1984 Lond.; FRCP 2001 (UK); BSc Lond. 1981; MRCP (UK) 1988. (St. Mary's Hosp. Med. Sch. Lond.) Cons. Rheum. S. Bucks. NHS Trust. Prev: Sen. Regist. St. Thos. Hosp. Lond.

STEVENS, Richard Murray East Oxford Health Centre, Manzil Way, Cowley Road, Cowley, Oxford OX4 1XD Tel: 01865 791850 Fax: 01865 727358; Tel: 01865 512580 — BM BCh 1980 Oxf.; 1980 MA; MRCGP 1984; DRCOG 1983; FRCGP 1998. Hosp. Pract. (Gastroenterol.) John Radcliffe Hosp. Oxf. Socs: Chairm. Primary Care Soc. For Gastroenterol.

STEVENS, Robert Hartley 23 Egerton Road, Whitefield, Manchester M45 7FU Tel: 0161 796 6773 — MB BCh BAO 1987 Belf.; MSc Manch. 1993; BSc Belf. 1984. Sen. Regist. (Pub. Health Med.) NW RHA. Socs: Fac. Pub. Health Med. Prev: SHO (Path.) N. Manch. Gen. Hosp.; Ho. Off. (Med. & Surg.) Roy. Lancaster Infirm.

***STEVENS, Robert John** 21 Greenside, Maidstone ME15 7RU — MB ChB 1994 Birm.

STEVENS, Robert William Arrowe Park Hospital, Arrowe Park Road, Upton, Wirral CH49 5PE Tel: 0151 678 5111 — MB ChB 1974 Liverp.; MB ChB (Hons.) Liverp. 1974; BSc (Hons. Biochem.) Liverp. 1971; FFA RCS Eng. 1979. Cons. Anaesth. Wirral Hosp. NHS Trust. Prev: Sen. Regist. (Anaesth) Notts. AHA (T); Regist. (Anaesth.) Liverp. AHA (T).

STEVENS, Roger John Roborough Surgery, 1 Eastcote Close, Southway, Plymouth PL6 6PH Tel: 01752 701659 Fax: 01752 773181; Gaillac, Yelverton PL20 6DW Tel: 01822 855560 — MB BS 1966 Lond.; MRCS Eng. LRCP Lond. 1965. (King's Coll. Hosp.) Prev: SHO (Psychol. Med.) St. Pancras Hosp. Lond.; Resid. Med. Off. King Edw. VII Memor. Hosp. Bermuda; Ho. Phys. & Ho. Surg. King's Coll. Hosp. Lond.

STEVENS, Rosemary Frances 35 Princess Gardens, Holywood BT18 0PN — MB BCh BAO 1980 Belf.

STEVENS, Rosemary Jane 27 Ford Park Road, Mutley Plain, Plymouth PL4 6RD — MB BS 1965 Lond.; MB BS Lond. 1966; MRCS Eng. LRCP Lond. 1965; AKC. (King's Coll. Hosp.) Prev: Clin. Asst. (Child Psychiat.) Nuffield Clinic Plymouth; Ho. Surg. King's Coll. Hosp. Lond.

STEVENS, Roy 13 Balmoral Road, Lytham St Annes FY8 1ER — MB ChB 1976 Liverp.; FRCP Lond. 1995; MRCP (UK) 1980; FRCPCH 1996. Cons. Paediat. Vict. Hosp. Blackpool.

STEVENS, Sarah Anne 20 Catherines Close, Great Leights, Chelmsford CM3 1RX — MB BS 1990 Lond.

STEVENS, Thomas Guy 21 Prince's Rise, London SE13 7PP — MB BChir 1991 Camb.

STEVENS, Vivian John Rodier The Avenue Surgery, 14 The Avenue, Warminster BA12 9AA Tel: 01985 846224 Fax: 01985 847059 Email: vjrs@ictus.demon.co.uk — MB BS 1980 Lond.; MRCS Eng. LRCP Lond. 1980; BA (Open) 1998; MRCGP 1988;

DRCOG 1987; BSc Lond. 1976. (Char. Cross) Socs: Clin. Soc. of Bath. Prev: Clin. Asst. (Psychogeriat.) Warminster.

STEVENS, William James 1 Hillside Drive, Old Road E., Gravesend DA12 1NY Tel: 01474 566470 — MRCS Eng. LRCP Lond. 1942; FFA RCS Eng. 1954; DA Eng. 1943. (Guy's) Prev: Cons. Anaesth. Dartford & Gravesham Health Dist.; Chief Asst. Edgware Gen. Hosp.; Anaesth. Guy's Hosp.

***STEVENS-KING, Angela** 31 Kenton Park Road, Harrow HA3 8UB — MB ChB 1994 Sheff.

STEVENSON, Alan David St James Medical Centre, 9 Herbert Street, Pontardawe, Swansea SA8 4EB Tel: 01792 830089 Fax: 01792 830089; 281 Clasemont, Morriston, Swansea SA6 6BT — MB BS 1988 Lond.

STEVENSON, Alastair Gordon Moffat 11 Netherhouse Avenue, Lenzie, Kirkintilloch, Glasgow G66 5NF — MB ChB 1997 Glas. (Glasgow University)

STEVENSON, Alison Wendy Craig Dunain Hospital, Inverness IV3 8JR Tel: 01463 242860; Hollybank, Station Road, Evanton, Dingwall IV16 9YW — MB ChB 1986 Glas. (Glas.)

STEVENSON, Allan John Murray Department of Radiology, Western General Hospital, Crewe Road, Edinburgh EH4 2XU Tel: 0131 537 2054 — MB ChB 1979 Ed.; MRCP (UK) 1982; FRCR 1988; DMRD Ed. 1986. Cons. Radiol. W.ern Gen. Hosps. NHS Trust Edin. Prev: Cons. Radiol. E. & W.. Gen. Hosps. Edin.; Sen. Regist. (Radiol.) Roy. Infirm. Edin.; Regist. (Radiol.) Roy. Infirm. Edin.

STEVENSON, Angela Margery 270 Merville Garden Village, Newtownabbey BT37 9TT — MB BCh BAO 1969 Belf.

STEVENSON, Ann Iwan North Cardiff Medical Centre, Excalibur Drive, Thornhill, Cardiff CF14 9BB Tel: 029 2075 0322 Fax: 029 2075 7705 — MB BCh 1966 Wales; MRCGP 1983. GP Llanishen.

STEVENSON, Anna Elizabeth 28 Racton Road, London SW6 1LP — MB ChB 1993 Otago.

STEVENSON, Anne Grant Bangholm Medical Centre, 21-25 Bangholm Loan, Edinburgh EH5 3AH Tel: 0131 552 7676 Fax: 0131 552 8145; 18A Merchiston Park, Edinburgh EH10 4PN — MB ChB 1980 Aberd.; MRCGP 1984; DRCOG 1982. Hosp. Practitioner (Genitourin. Med.) Roy. Infirm. Edin.

STEVENSON, Anthony John Maxwell, OBE 6 Ingleside Crescent, Lancing BN15 8EN — MRCS Eng. LRCP Lond. 1941.

STEVENSON, Beryll Janette (retired) Alt Tigh, Rosemount, Tain IV19 1ND Tel: 01862 893996 — MB ChB Glas. 1959. Prev: Assoc. Specialist Yorks Reg. Blood Transfus. Serv. Leeds.

STEVENSON, Brian John (retired) The Surgery, Highwood Road, Brockenhurst SO42 7RY Tel: 01590 622272 Fax: 01590 624009 — MB BS Lond. 1958; BSc (Physiol.) Lond. 1956; FRCGP 1981, M 1975; DCH Eng. 1962; DObst RCOG 1960. Prev: SHO Qu. Eliz. Hosp. Childr. Lond.

STEVENSON, Brian John Psychopharmacology Unit, School of Medical Sciences, University Walk, Bristol BS8 1TD Email: brian.stevenson@bristol.ac.uk; 14 Cornwallis Avenue, Bristol BS8 4PP Email: brian_j.stevenson@virgin.net — MB ChB Leic. 1992; MA Hons (II) in Physics Oxford; MSc in Digial Electronics, Lond. Research Fell.; Hon. Regist. Avon Alcohol Serv.

***STEVENSON, Christopher David** 13 Beacon Road, Woodhouse Eaves, Loughborough LE12 8RN — MB ChB 1994 Liverp.

STEVENSON, Christopher James (retired) 16 Kingsland, Jesmond, Newcastle upon Tyne NE2 3AL Tel: 0191 281 2959 — MB BS 1945 Lond.; MD Lond. 1952; FRCP Lond. 1971, M 1947; MRCS Eng. LRCP Lond. 1945; MFOM RCP Lond. 1981. Hon. Cons. Dermat. Newc. HA. Prev: Cons. Phys. Brit. Gas. N..

STEVENSON, Christopher John Infirmary Drive Medical Group, Consulting Rooms, Infirmary Drive, Alnwick NE66 2NR Tel: 01665 602388 Fax: 01665 604712 — MB BS 1978 Newc.; MRCGP 1983; DCH RCPS Glas. 1982.

STEVENSON, Claire Elizabeth 14 Gibbet Hill Road, Coventry CV4 7AJ Tel: 024 7641 9047 — MB ChB 1982 Manch.; DRCOG 1986. Prev: Trainee GP Warks. & Coventry VTS.

STEVENSON, Claire Winchester South Acre, Dalmuinzie Road, Bieldside, Aberdeen AB15 9EB — MB ChB 1972 Glas.

STEVENSON, Colin Horace (retired) Nettlebury, 4 White Lovington, Bere Regis, Wareham BH20 7NF — BM BCh 1971 Oxf.; BA Oxf. 1968, MA 1977; MRCGP 1977; FFPHM RCP (UK) 1995, M 1989; MFCM RCP (UK) 1985. Prev: Dirtector Pub. Health N. Staffs. HA.

STEVENSON, David Castlehill Health Centre, Castlehill, Forres IV36 1QF Tel: 01309 672233; West Park House, Forres IV36 1HB Tel: 01309 672883 — MB ChB 1982 Glas.; MRCGP 1999 Edin.; 1986 DRCOG (Birmingham). (Glas.) GP Princip. Socs: Highland Med. Soc.; Hon. Life Mem. Glas. Univ. MC Soc.; Moray Med. Soc. Prev: SHO (O & G) Raigmore Unit Highland Health Bd.; SHO (ENT & Ophth.) Raigmore Unit.; GP Trainee, Foyers Invernesshire.

STEVENSON, David James 92 Hillview Drive, Clarkston, Glasgow G76 7JD — MB ChB 1994 Glas.

STEVENSON, David John Douglas Public Health Sciences, University of Edinburgh Medical School, Teviot Place, Edinburgh EH8 9AG Tel: 0131 650 3228 Fax: 0131 650 6909 Email: david.stevenson@ed.ac.uk; 22 Blacket Place, Edinburgh EH9 1RL Tel: 0131 667 3748 — MB ChB 1957 Glas.; MA Camb. 1958; MD Glas. 1965; FFPHM RCP (UK) 1993; DPH Glas. 1964; DTM & H Liverp. 1961. (Glas.) Hon. Fell. Pub. Health Sci. Univ. Edin. Socs: Life Mem. Freshwater Biol. Assn.; Soc. Scientif. Exploration; Roy. Soc. Trop. Med. & Hyg. (Comm. Mem. Scott. Br.). Prev: Sen. Lect. (Internat. Community Health) Liverp. Sch. Trop. Med.; Govt. Med. Off. Malawi; Research Adviser Tribhuwan Univ., Nepal.

STEVENSON, Douglas Kirkwood (retired) Piper's Croft, 1 Beverley Rise, Ilkley LS29 9DB Tel: 01943 436521 — MB ChB (Commend.) St. And. 1942; FRCP Ed. 1968, M 1948. Prev: Cons. Chest Phys. Bradford.

STEVENSON, Ede (retired) Brynmoor House, Harpers Lane, Bolton BL1 6HR Tel: 01204 41052 Fax: 01204 841052 — MB ChB 1961 Manch.; DObst RCOG 1963; DCH Eng. 1964.

STEVENSON, Gary Ferryhill Medical Practice, Durham Road, Ferryhill DL17 8JJ Tel: 01740 651238 Fax: 01740 656291; 2 Walkworth Lane, Spennymoor DL16 6UY Tel: 01388 812455 — BM 1984 Soton.

STEVENSON, Gary Scot Tel: 01334 652611 Fax: 01334 653950 Email: garystevenson@fife=pct.scot.nhs.uk — MB ChB 1990 Glas.; BSc (Hons.) Glas. 1987; MRCPsych 1996; M.Phil (Ed.) 1997; Dip. FMSA 1999. Cons. Psychiat. (Old Age). Socs: Med. & Dent. Defence Union Scotl. Prev: Specialist Regist. (Psychiat.); Regist./SHO (Psychiat.) SE Scotl. Train. Scheme; SHO Dunedin Pub. Hosp., NZ.

STEVENSON, Geoffrey Roy East Quay Medical Centre, East Quay, Bridgwater TA6 5AZ Tel: 01278 423474 — MB BS 1953 Lond.; MRCS Eng. LRCP Lond. 1953; DObst RCOG 1957.

STEVENSON, George Telford Southampton General Hospital, Tremona Road, Southampton SO16 6YD Tel: 02380 777222 Fax: 02380 704061; 9 Meadowhead Road, Bassett, Southampton SO16 7AD Tel: 02380 769092 — MB BS 1955 Sydney; DPhil Oxf. 1965; MD Sydney 1962; FRCPath 1993. (Sydney) Prof. Immunochem. Univ. Soton; Dir. Tenovus Research Laborat. Gen. Hosp. Soton.; Hon. Cons. Immunol. Soton. & SW Hants. HA. Prev: Resid Med. Off. Sydney Hosp.; Research Fell. (Med.) Univ. Sydney; Nuffield Demonst. (Biochem.) Oxf.

STEVENSON, Graham Charlton 24 Headlam Road, Darlington DL1 4UY Tel: 01325 282660 — MB BS 1970 Newc.

STEVENSON, Guy Newcastle Clinic, 4 Tower Ave, Jesmond, Newcastle upon Tyne NE2 3QE Tel: 0191 281 2393; 10 Otterburn Terrace, Jesmond, Newcastle upon Tyne NE2 3AP Tel: 0191 281 7437 — MB BS 1977 Newc.; MLCOM 1987; MSc (Sports Med) 1997. Specialist (Orthop. Med.) Newc. u. Tyne. Socs: Brit. Assn. Sport & Med.; Brit. Inst. Manip. Med. Prev: Surg. Lt. Cdr. RN.

***STEVENSON, Helen Lenore** 93 Park Road, Formby, Liverpool L37 6AD — MB ChB 1997 Liverp.

STEVENSON, Mr Howard Morris (retired) 2 Church Close, Ballylesson, Belfast BT8 8JX Tel: 01232 826437 — MB BCh BAO 1943 Belf.; FRCS Ed. 1948. Cons. Thoracic Surg. Roy. Vict. & Forster Green Hosps. Belf. Prev: Surg. Regist. Roy. Vict. Hosp. Belf.

STEVENSON, Mr Ian Michael 34 St Michaels Road, Crosby, Liverpool L23 7UN — MB ChB 1966 Liverp.; FRCS Eng. 1971; FRCS Ed. 1971 (Liverp.). Cons. Surg. Walton Hosp. Liverp. & Fazakerley Hosp. Liverp.; Surg. Tutor RCS Eng. Socs: Liverp. Med. Inst. & Vasc. Soc. Gt. Brit. & Irel. Prev: Sen. Surgic. Regist. Walton Hosp. Liverp. & David Lewis. N.. Hosp.; Liverp.

STEVENSON, Ian Neil Brown The Parish Fields Practice, The Health Centre, Mount St., Diss IP22 4WG Tel: 01379 642023 Fax: 01379 643320; Willow Farm, Thrandeston Great Green, Diss IP21 4BP Tel: 01379 783560 Email: n.stevenson@notional.demon.co.uk — MB BS Lond. 1965; MSc

STEVENSON

Pub. Health Lond. 1995; DPhil Oxf. 1976; MRCS Eng. LRCP Lond. 1965; Acad. Dipl. Social Anthropol. Univ. Lond. 1969. (King's Coll. Hosp.) Norf. Dis. Cancer Lead. Socs: BMA; NHS Primary Care Gp Alliance. Prev: Research Off. Oxf. Univ.

STEVENSON, Ilbury Hugh The Poplars Surgery, 17 Holly Lane, Erdington, Birmingham B24 9JN Tel: 0121 373 4216 Fax: 0121 382 9576 — MB BS 1959 Lond.; DObst RCOG 1964. (St. Mary's) Prev: Govt. Med. Off. Gibraltar; Ho. Surg. (Obst.) Cheltenham Matern. Hosp.; Clin. Asst. & Hosp. Pract. Jaffray Hosp. Birm.

STEVENSON, Mr James 3 Hillside Cottages, Dalry KA24 4DP — MB ChB 1983 Glas.; FRCS Ed. 1987; DA (UK) 1989.

STEVENSON, James Duncan Cedar lodge, 36 Lakeside Road, Branksome Park, Poole BH13 6LS Tel: 01202 761464 — MB BS 1971 Lond.; BSc Lond. 1968, MB BS 1971; FRCR 1980. Cons. Radiol. E. Dorset Health Care Dist. Prev: Sen. Regist. (Radiol.) St. Geo. Hosp. Lond.; Ho. Phys. (Neurol.) St. Thos. Hosp. Lond.; Med. Regist. Kingston Hosp.

STEVENSON, James Gordon 21 Kilmahew Avenue, Cardoss, Dumbarton G82 5NG — MB ChB 1971 Glas.; MRCP (UK) 1973.

STEVENSON, Janet Audrey Margaret Morris (retired) Causewell Cottage, The Street, Darsham, Saxmundham IP17 3QA Tel: 017228 668369 — MRCS Eng. LRCP Lond. 1943; DPH Lond. 1947. Prev: Train. Med. Off. FPA.

STEVENSON, Janet Elaine 27 Rankin Road, Edinburgh EH9 3AW — MB BS 1988 Lond. Sen. Regist. (Pub. Health Med.) N. RHA. Prev: SHO (Pub. Health Med.) Centr. Birm. HA.

STEVENSON, Jean Grange Road Surgery, Grange Road, Bishopsworth, Bristol BS13 8LD Tel: 0117 964 4343 Fax: 0117 935 8422 — MB BS 1969 Newc.

STEVENSON, Jean Frances 9 Briant's Close, Pinner HA5 4SY — MB ChB 1975 Leeds; BSc (Pharmacol.) St. And. 1970.

***STEVENSON, Joanne Catherine** 3 Lyric Way, Thornhill, Cardiff CF14 9BP — MB BCh 1998 Wales.

STEVENSON, John (retired) Alt Tigh, Rosemount, Tain IV19 1ND Tel: 01862 893996 — MB ChB 1952 Glas.; FRCP Ed. 1968, M 1958; FRFPS Glas. 1958; FRCP Glas. 1969, M 1962. Cons. Phys. Infec. Dis. Dept. Seacroft Hosp. Leeds; Sen. Clin. Lect. Univ. Leeds. Prev: Regist. Med. Glas. Roy. Infirm.

STEVENSON, John (retired) 1 Bramble Edge, Broadmayne, Dorchester DT2 8HE — MRCS Eng. LRCP Lond. 1945. Prev: Ho. Surg. King's Coll. Hosp.

STEVENSON, John Curtis Endocrinology & Meatabolic Medicine, Imperial College School of Medicine, St Mary's Hospital, Praed Street, London W2 1NY Tel: 020 7886 1678 Fax: 020 7886 1790 Email: j.stevenson@ic.ac.uk; Holyrood, Police Station Road, Hersham Village, Walton-on-Thames KT12 4JQ — MB BS 1972 Lond.; FRCP Lond. 1993; MRCP (UK) 1979; FESC 1997. (Kings Coll. Hosp.) Reader Fac. of Med. Imperial Coll. Lond.; Hon. Cons. Phys. Roy. Brompton Hosp. Lond.; Hon. Cons. Phys. St Mary's Hosp. Lond.; Hon. Med. Off., Esher RFC. Socs: Endocrine Soc. USA; Fell. Europ. Soc. Cardiol.; Exec. Comm. Mem. Internat. Menopause Soc. Prev: Dir. Wynn Inst.. Imperial Coll. Lond.; Cons. Endocrinol. Wynn Inst. for Metab. Research Lond.; Lect., Research Fell & Regist. Endocrine Unit Roy. Postgrad. Med. Sch. Hammersmith Hosp. Lond.

STEVENSON, John Erskine David Health First Medical Group, King George Surgery, 135 High Street, Stevenage SG1 3HT Tel: 01438 361111 Fax: 01438 361227; The Bury, Rectory Lane, Stevenage SG1 4DA — MB 1977 Camb.; BA Camb. 1973, MB 1977, BChir 1976; MRCGP 1980; DRCOG 1978. Clin. Governance Lead, Stevenage PCG. Socs: Herts. Medico-Legal Soc. Prev: Clin. Asst. (Diabetes), Lister Hosp., Stevenage.

STEVENSON, Mr John Howard 38 Ruskin Park, Hillsborough Old Road, Lisburn BT27 Tel: 0184 62 70458 — MB BCh BAO 1973 Belf.; FRCS Ed. 1977; DObst RCOG 1976.

STEVENSON, John James The Spinney, Ottery St Mary EX11 1LE Tel: 01404 822525 Email: john@exrays.freeserve.co.uk — MB ChB 1941 Ed.; MD Ed. 1950; FFR RCSI 1962; DMR Lond 1945. (Ed.) Prev: Dir. Diag. X-Ray Roy. Marsden Hosp. & St. Peter's Hosp. Gp. (Inst. Urol.).

STEVENSON, John Laing Stotfold Bury, Stotfold, Hitchin SG5 4NU Tel: 01462 730966 — MB BS 1952 Lond.; MRCS Eng. LRCP Lond. 1952; DObst RCOG 1957. (St. Mary's) Prev: O & G Ho. Surg. Geo. Eliot Hosp. Nuneaton; Capt. RAMC; Ho. Phys. & Ho. Surg. Harold Wood Hosp.

STEVENSON, John Michael 14 Carsington Crescent, Allestree, Derby DE22 2QZ — MB ChB 1957 Sheff.; FFA RCS Eng. 1966; DObst RCOG 1962. (Sheff.) Prev: Cons. Anaesth. Derby Hosp. Gp.; Sen. Regist. (Anaesth.) Derbysh. Roy. Infirm.; Regist. (Anaesth.) United Sheff. Hosps.

STEVENSON, John Samuel (retired) 20 Belbrough Lane, Huton Rudby, Yarm TS15 0HY Tel: 01642 700603 — LRCP LRCS Ed. LRFPS Glas. 1944. Prev: SHO Ballochmyle Hosp. Mauchline.

STEVENSON, John Stevenson Kennedy (retired) 30 Moston Terrace, Newington, Edinburgh EH9 2DE Tel: 0131 667 4405 — MB ChB Glas. 1955; FRCGP 1972, M 1964; DObst RCOG 1957. Prev: Sen. Lect. Dept. Gen. Pract. Univ. Edin.

STEVENSON, Katherine Elizabeth PO Box 12650, London SE3 9ZZ Tel: 020 8852 8522 Fax: 020 8852 8522 Email: eyes@dbcg.co.uk — BM 1979 Soton.; DO RCS Eng. 1983; FRCS Eng. (Ophth.) 1984. Cons. Ophth. W. Kent Eye Centre FarnBoro. Hosp. Prev: Sen. Regist. Moorfields Eye Hosp. Lond.; Regist. (Ophth.) Oxf. Eye Hosp.; SHO (Ophth.) Soton. Eye Hosp.

STEVENSON, Kirsteen Morag Child & Family Therapy Service, Battenburg Avenue Clinic, Battenburg Avenue, North End, Portsmouth PO2 0TA Tel: 023 92 653433 — MB BS 1981 Lond.; MRCPsych 1987. Cons. Child & Adolesc. Psychiat. Portsmouth City Primary Care Trust. Prev: Sen. Regist. (Child Psychiat.) Lond. Hosp.

STEVENSON, Laura Vyvian 1 Drummond Place, Edinburgh EH3 6PH — MB ChB 1992 Ed.

STEVENSON, Lee 181 Langley Hall Road, Solihull B92 7HB — MB ChB 1989 Sheff.

***STEVENSON, Madeline Claire** 3 Victoria Drive, Troon KA10 6EN — MB ChB 1998 Glas.; MB ChB Glas 1998.

STEVENSON, Margarita Carmeno 14 First Street, Chelsea, London SW3 2LD Tel: 020 7584 0658 Fax: 020 7225 0518; 14 First Street, Chelsea, London SW3 2LD Tel: 020 7584 0658 Fax: 020 7225 0518 — MB BS 1962 Lond.; MRCS Eng. LRCP Lond. 1962; MRCOG 1968, DObst 1965; FRCOG; MBBS 1962; MRCS Eng LRCP Lond. 1962; DOBT 1965; MRCOG 1968; FRCOG 1978. (St. Bart. & Char. Cross) State Nures Gyn. Lond. Socs: Roy. Soc. Med.; Fell.Med. Soc. Lond.; Worshipful Soc. Apoth. Lond. Prev: Sen. Med. Off. Home Office; Resid. Obst. Providence Hosp. Seattle America; Hon. Cons. Gyn. S.gate Hosp. Lond.

STEVENSON, Marian Pearl 77 Athlestan Way, Stretton, Burton-on-Trent DE13 0XT — MB BS 1969 Lond.

STEVENSON, Mary Elizabeth Cedar Lodge, 36 Lakeside Road, Branksome Park, Poole BH13 6LS Tel: 01202 761464 Fax: 01202 761464 — MB BS 1972 Lond.; DObst RCOG 1974. (St. Thos.) Clin. Asst. (Anaesth.) Roy. Bournemouth Hosp. & Poole Gen. Hosp. Socs: Assn. Anaesth.; BMA; Roy. Soc. Med. Prev: Regist. (Anaesth.) Poole Gen. Hosp. & Kingston Gen. Hosp.; SHO & Regist. (Anaesth.) St. Thos. Hosp. Lond.

STEVENSON, Mary J Ardinning, Moor Road, Strathblane, Glasgow G63 9EX Tel: 0141 70308 — MB ChB 1967 Glas.; FRCR 1985. Cons. Radiol. Roy. Alexandra Hosp. Paisley.

STEVENSON, Mary Margaret Department of Genitourinary Medicine, Guest Hospital, Tipton Road, Dudley DY1 4SE Tel: 01384 244856 Fax: 01384 244826 — MB ChB 1987 Glas.; MRCP (UK) 1992; DTM & H RCP Lond. 1991. Cons. (Genitourin. Med.) Guest Hosp. Dudley. Prev: Sen. Regist. (Genitourin. Med.) Gen. Hosp. Birm.; Regist. (Genitourin. Med.) Gen. Hosp. Birm.

STEVENSON, Maureen Michaela Maghera Health Centre, 3 Church Street, Maghera BT46 5EA Tel: 028 7964 2579 Fax: 028 7964 3002; 11 Ardmoneen Court, Magherafelt BT45 5NX Tel: 01648 301179 — MB BCh BAO 1988 Belf.; MRCGP 1992; DCH RCPSI 1991; DRCOG 1991. Prev: Ho. Off. Ipswich Gen. Hosp. Qu.sland, Austral.

STEVENSON, Michael Denis Seascale Health Centre, Seascale CA20 1PU Tel: 01946 728101; The Old Rectory, Bootle, Millom LA19 5TH Email: mdstevenson@doctors.net.uk — MB BS 1982 London; BDS 1974 Univ. Birmingham; MRCGP London. (Royal Free Hosp. School of Medicine) GP; Scheme Organiser, W. Cumbria V.T.S. Socs: BMA.

STEVENSON, Nicola Jane 69 Quarry Street, Liverpool L25 6HA — MB ChB 1994 Liverp.

STEVENSON, Nicola Jane Lowther Medical Centre, 1 Castle Meadows, Whitehaven CA28 7RG Tel: 01946 692241 Fax: 01946 590617; 1 Victoria Villa, Moor Row CA24 3JX Tel: 01946 813112

— MB ChB 1985 Birm.; MRCGP 1992; DRCOG 1991. Prev: Trainee GP W. Cumbld. Hosp. Whitehaven VTS; SHO (Ophth.) Birm. Eye Hosp.; Temp. Lect. (Anat.) Univ. Birm.

STEVENSON, Pamela 5 Drummond Avenue, Auchterarder PH3 1NX — MB ChB 1967 Ed.

STEVENSON, Pamela Susan Castleside Unit, Centre for the Health of the Elderly, Newcastle General Hospital, Newcastle upon Tyne NE4 6BE Tel: 0191 273 8811; 4 Scalby Close, Whitebridge Park, Gosforth, Newcastle upon Tyne NE3 5LJ Tel: 0191 284 8795 — MB BS 1979 Newc.; MRCPsych 1986; Cert. JCPTGP 1984. Specialist Regist. Old Age Psychiat. Newc. Gen. Hosp. Newc.

STEVENSON, Paul Anthony 8 Lyndhurst Road, Wallasey CH45 6XA — MB ChB 1963 Bristol; FRCPath 1990. Cons. Haemat. Walton Hosp. Liverp. Prev: Research Regist. (Leukaemia) Bristol Childr. Hosp.

STEVENSON, Pauline Frances (retired) Swallowfield, Wheeler's Lane, Linton, Maidstone ME17 4BN Tel: 01622 743392 Email: tpwaters@freenet.name — MB ChB 1956 Bristol; MRCPsych 1976; DPM Eng. 1977; DTM & H Liverp. 1962; DCH Eng. 1959. Cons. Child & Adolesc. Psychiat. Maidstone, Kent; Mem. Inst. Gp. Anal. 1982. Prev: Cons. Child & Adolesc. Psychiat. N. Wilts.

STEVENSON, Peter Robert 37 Coedyfron, Holywell CH8 7UJ Tel: 01352 716886 — MB ChB 1979 Liverp.; MRCGP 1987; DRCOG 1985; MFPHM 1997. Cons. (Pub. Health Med.) N. Wales Health Auth.

STEVENSON, Philip George 9 Meadowhead Road, Southampton SO16 7AD — BChir 1990 Camb.; MRCP 1993.

STEVENSON, Robert 270 Melville Garden Village, Whitehouse, Newtownabbey BT37 9TT — MB BCh BAO 1966 Belf.; DObst RCOG 1968. (Belf.)

STEVENSON, Robert Duncan Ardinning, Moor Road, Strathblane, Glasgow G63 9EX Tel: 014170308 — MD 1978 Glas.; MB ChB (Commend) 1967; MRCP (U.K.) 1971. (Glas.) Cons. Gen. & Respirat. Med. Glas. Roy. Infirm. & Stobhill Gen. Hosp. Glas. Prev: Sen. Regist. (Med. & Respirat. Dis.) W.. Infirm. Glas. & Glas. Roy. Infirm.; Lect. (Med.) W.. Infirm. Glas.

STEVENSON, Robert Newton Department of Cardiology, Huddersfield Royal Infirmary, Huddersfield HD3 3EA Tel: 01484 22191; 104 Main Gate, Hepworth, Huddersfield HD9 1TJ — MB BS 1983 Lond.; BSc Lond. 1980, MD 1993; MRCP (UK) 1986; FRCP Lond. 1998. (London Hospital) Cons. Phys. (Cardiol & Med.) Huddersfield Roy. Infirm. Socs: Brit. Cardiac Soc. Prev: Research Fell. Regist. (Cardiol.) Lond. Chest Hosp.; Regist. (Med.) Univ. Coll. Hosp. Lond.

STEVENSON, Robert Rowan (retired) 60 Northwold Avenue, West Bridgford, Nottingham NG2 7JD Tel: 0115 981 9053 — MB ChB 1945 St. And.; BSc. 1942, MB ChB St. And. 1945; MRCGP 1960. Prev: Ho. Surg. & Regist. (Med.) Roy. Infirm. Dundee.

STEVENSON, Mr Ronald Yates (retired) Clare Corner, Tiverton EX16 6NH Tel: 01884 252217 — MB BS Lond. 1937; FRCS Ed. 1947; MRCS Eng. LRCP Lond. 1937. Prev: Cons. Surg. Tiverton Hosps.

***STEVENSON, Sarah Jane** Random Patch, Little Clifton, Workington CA14 1YR — MB BS 1997 Newc.

STEVENSON, Thomas (retired) 4 Lonsdale Road, Newton Abbot TQ12 1DT — MB ChB 1942 Glas.

STEVENSON, Thomas Charles (retired) Brymoor House, Harpers Lane, Smithills, Bolton BL1 Tel: 01204 41052 — MB ChB 1957 Manch.; FRCOG 1977, M 1963. Prev: Cons. O & G Bolton & Dist. Hosp. Gp.

STEVENSON, Thomas Henry 59 Strangford Road, Downpatrick BT30 6SL — MB BCh BAO 1974 Dub.

***STEVENSON, Thomas Roger** 72 Bloomfield Road, Bangor BT20 4XA — MB BCh BAO 1994 Belf.

STEVENSON, Timothy Richard Thomas Northbourne Medical Centre, Eastern Avenue, Shoreham-by-Sea BN43 6PE Tel: 01273 464640; 67 The Green, Southwick, Brighton BN42 4FX — MB BCh BAO 1984 NUI; MRCGP 1988; DRCOG 1987. Prev: SHO (Paediat.) Edgware Gen. Hosp.; Trainee GP Lond.; SHO Edgware Gen. Hosp. VTS.

STEVENSON, Valerie Lynne NMR Research Unit, Institute of Neurology, Queen Square, London WC1N 3BG Tel: 020 7837 3611 Email: v.stevenson@ion.ucl.ac.uk; Flat M, 11 Mattock Lane, Ealing, London W5 5BG — MB BS 1991 Newc.; MRCP (UK) 1994. (Newc. u. Tyne) Research Fell. Inst. Neurol. Lond.

***STEVENSON, Victoria Jane** Flat 3, 15 Eckstein Rd, London SW11 — BM 1996 Soton.

STEVENSON, William (retired) 1 Vivian Park Drive, Aberavon, Port Talbot SA12 6RT — MB BCh 1944 Wales; BSc Wales 1941, MB BCh 1944. Prev: Surg. Regist. Morriston Gen. Hosp. Swansea.

STEVENSON, William John Consett Medical Centre, Station Yard, Consett DH8 5YA Tel: 01207 216116 Fax: 01207 216119; 17 Blackwood, Coalville LE67 4RG Tel: 01207 509047 — MB BCh BAO 1977 Belf. (Queens)

STEVENSON, William Thomas John 6 Flowerfields, Catterall, Preston PR3 1YU Tel: 01995 600593 Email: wtjs@compuserve.com — MRCS Eng. LRCP Lond. 1980; BM BCh Oxf 1981. Cons. (Radiol.) Vict. Hosp. Blackpool. Prev: Cons. Radiol. W. Wales Hosp. Carmarthen.; Cons. Radiol. P.ss Roy. Hosp. Telford.

STEVENTON, David Michael Hawthorn House, 2 Walton Lane, Brocton, Stafford ST17 0TT — MB BS 1986 Lond.

STEVENTON, Nicholas Barrie 2 Railway Cottages, Itchen Abbas, Winchester SO21 1BA — MB BChir 1991 Camb.

STEVENTON, Paul Nigel Integrated Care Partnership, Fitznell Manor Surgery, Chessington Road, Ewell, Epsom KT17 1TF Tel: 020 8394 1471 Fax: 020 8393 9753 — MB BS 1977 Lond.; MRCGP 1983; DRCOG 1983; DCH RCP Lond. 1981. GP Princip., IT Specialist, Integrated Care Partnership, Ewell, Epsom, Surrey; Chairm. Doctors Indep. Network. Socs: Roy. Soc. of Med. (Fell.). Prev: Sen. Med. Off. (RDF) N.. Irel.

STEWARD, Colin Graham Oncology Day Beds, Bristol Royal Hospital for Children, Upper Maudlin St., Bristol BS2 8BJ Tel: 0117 342 8523 Fax: 0117 342 8628 — BM BCh 1984 Oxf.; PhD Bristol 1994; MA Camb. 1985; MRCP (UK) 1987. Cons. & Sen. Lect. Bone Marrow Transpl. Roy. Hosp. Sick Childr. Bristol. Socs: Fell. Roy. Coll. Paediat. & Child Health; Roy. Coll. Phys. Prev: Regist. (Oncol.) Bristol Childr. Hosp.; Regist. (Paeadiat.) Addenbrooke's Hosp. Camb.; Regist. Hosp. Sick Childr. Gt. Ormond St. Lond.

STEWARD, John Aubrey Welsh Cancer Intelligence and Surveillance Unit, 14 Cathedral Road, Cardiff CF11 9LJ Tel: 029 2037 3500 Fax: 029 2037 3511 Email: jstewa@pipex.dial.com; 21 Augustan Close, Caerleon, Newport NP18 3DJ Tel: 01633 421240 — MB BCh 1970 Wales; MSc Math. Statistics & Computing Wales 1984; PhD Wales 1995; BA (Hons.) Open 1982; MFPHM 1986. (Cardiff) Dir. Welsh Cancer Intelligence & Surveillance Unit (Velinde NHS Trust). Prev: Cons. (PHM) Gwent 1990; Asst. Dir. Welsh BrE. Screening Serv.; Sen. Lect. (Pub. Health Med.) UWCM 1989.

STEWARD, Kathleen Anne Hillfoot Surgery, 126 Owlcotes Road, Pudsey LS28 7QR Tel: 0113 257 4169 Fax: 0113 236 3380 — MB BS 1984 Newc.; BA (Hons.) Camb. 1981; MRCGP 1989; DRCOG 1987.

STEWARD, Mr Mark Arnold 157 Hartshead Lane, Hartsead, Liversedge WF15 8AJ — MB ChB 1988 Leeds; FRCS Ed. 1996. Specialist Regist. (Gen. Surg.) N. W.ern Deanery. Prev: Clin. Surgic. Research Fell. (BrE. Cancer) Leeds Gen. Infirm.; SHO (O & G) St. Jas. Univ. Hosp. Leeds; SHO Rotat. (Surg.) Leeds Gen. Infirm.

STEWARD, Mark Rider Potterells Medical Centre, Station Road, North Mymms, Hatfield AL9 7SN Tel: 01707 273338 Fax: 01707 263564; 28 The Shaws, Welwyn Garden City AL7 2HR Tel: 01707 884552 Email: m_c.steward@virgin.net — MB BS 1991 Lond. Princip. GP N. mymms Herts.

STEWARD, Rebecca Jane Batten, Haileybury College, Hertford SG13 7NU — MB BS 1982 Lond.

STEWARD, Ronald Edgar (retired) Adams, Wrotham Road, Meopham, Gravesend DA13 0JH Tel: 01474 813586 — MB ChB 1959 Ed. Prev: Regist. (Cas.) & SHO (Gen. Surg.) W. Hill Hosp. Dartford.

STEWARD, Sarah Elizabeth The Cottage, Wilmington, Polegate BN26 5SJ — MB BS 1985 Lond.; MRCGP 1991.

STEWARD, Professor William Patrick Department of Oncology, Leicester Royal Infirmary, Leicester LE1 5WW Tel: 0116 258 7597 Fax: 0116 258 7599 Email: wps1@ie.ac.uk; 65 Burnmill Road, Market Harborough LE16 7JG — MB ChB 1977 Manch.; PhD Manch. 1988; FRCPC 1995; FRCP Glas. 1992; MRCP (UK) 1979. (Manch.) Prof. Med. Oncol. Univ. Leicester. Prev: Prof. Oncol. Qu. Univ. Kingston Ont., Canada; Sen. Lect. (Med. Oncol.) Beatson

STEWART

Oncol. Centre Glas.; Lect. CRC Dept. Clin. Oncol. Christie Hosp. Manch.

STEWART, Adrian John The Willows, 2 Common Road, Witchford, Ely CB6 2HY — MB BS 1986 Lond.

STEWART, Adrian John 49 St Margarets Street, Rochester ME1 1UG — MB BCh BAO 1985 Belf.; MRCP (UK) 1988.

STEWART, Adrian Johnston 2 Aberfoyle Park, Belfast BT10 0DY — MB BCh BAO 1983 Belf.

STEWART, Adriel Lyndthorpe, 3 Waringmore, Moira, Craigavon BT67 0LG — MB BS 1992 Lond.

STEWART, Agnes Campbell (retired) Woodlands, Inverdruie, Aviemore PH22 1QH Tel: 01479 811765 — MB ChB 1961 Ed.; BSc. OU 1998; Dip. Clin Hyp. Sheffield. Staff Grade (Dermat.) Barnsley Dist. Gen. Trust Hosp. Prev: GP Barnsley.

STEWART, Aileen Joy 21 Edenside, Cumbernauld, Glasgow G68 0ER — MB ChB 1990 Aberd.; DFFP 1994; MRCGP 1994; DCCH RCGP 1996; DRCOG 1992. Staff Grade (Community Paediat.) Hamilton, Lanarksh. Healthcare NHS Trust. Prev: SHO (Community Paediat.) Dumfries & Galloway Community NHS Trust; SHO (Paediat. & Cas.) Dumfries & Galloway Roy. Infirm.; SHO (Psychiat.) Crichton Roy. Hosp. Dumfries.

STEWART, Alasdair Garnett Chest Clinic, Medway Hospital, Gillingham ME7 5NY Tel: 01634 830000 Fax: 01634 833837 Email: alaisdairstewart@melway-tr.sthames.nhs.uk; Cooling House, Main Road, Cooling, Rochester ME3 8DH — MB BChir 1982 Camb.; MA Camb. 1983, MD 1993; MRCP (UK) 1986. Cons. Phys. (Thoracic Med. & Allergy) Medway Hosp. Gillingham. Socs: Brit. Thorac. Soc.; Eur. Soc. Clin. Respirat. Physiol.; Brit. Soc. Allergy & Clin. Immunol. Prev: Sen. Regist. (Med.) Addenbrooke's Hosp. Camb.; Lect. (Med.) Univ. Sheff.; Regist. (Med.) Roy. Hallamsh. Hosp. Sheff. & Lincoln Co. Hosp.

STEWART, Alan Charles (cons. rooms), 30 The Drive, Hove BN3 3JD Tel: 01273 487003 Fax: 01273 487576; The Coach House, Malling Deanery, Church Lane, Lewes BN7 2JA — MB BS 1976 Lond.; MRCP (UK) 1979; MRCS Eng. LRCP Lond. 1976. (Guy's) Indep. Cons. Pract. Nutrit. & Homoeop. Hove; Med. Adviser Wom. Nutrit. Advis. Serv. Lewes. Prev: Informat. Off. Brit. Soc. Nutrit Med.

STEWART, Alan Douglas Wayside House, Clare, Sudbury CO10 8NP Tel: 01787 277638 — MB ChB 1946 Bristol; DObst RCOG 1950. (Bristol) Prev: Ho. Surg. Bristol Roy. Infirm.; O & G Ho. Surg. Wom. Hosp. Wolverhampton; Ho. Phys. Worcester Roy. Infirm.

STEWART, Alan John Church Street Surgery, 30 Church Street, Dunoon AB15 5NB — MB ChB 1990 Ed.; MRCGP 2001. (Ed.) GP Princip.

STEWART, Alan Keith (retired) — MB ChB 1966 Manch.; MSc Manch. 1963; MRCP Lond. 1969.

STEWART, Alan Leslie 3 Priestnall Road, Heaton Mersey, Stockport SK4 3HR — MD 1981 Aberd.; MB ChB 1975; FRCR 1985. Cons. Radiother. & Oncol. Christie Hosp. & Holt Radium Inst. Manch. Prev: Sen. Regist. (Radiother.) Christie Hosp. & Holt Radium Inst. Manch.; Research Fell. & Regist. (Clin. Pharmacol.) Christie Hosp. & Holt Radium Inst. Manch.

STEWART, Alastair Fulton Struthers 51 St Patricks Road N., St. Annes on Sea, Lytham St Annes FY8 2HB Tel: 01253 712185 — MB BS 1960 Lond.; DObst RCOG 1965. (St. Bart.) Prev: Cas. Off. Paddington Gen. Hosp.; Ho. Surg. Sutton & Cheam Hosp.; Ho. Phys. Bethnal Green Hosp. Lond.

STEWART, Alastair Ian 23 Blardenon Drive, Cumbernauld, Glasgow G68 9BE — MB ChB 1984 Ed.

STEWART, Alexander Market Street Health Centre, Market Street, Ullapool IV26 2XE Tel: 01854 612015/612595 Fax: 01854 613025 — MB ChB 1974 Glas.; MRCGP 1979.

STEWART, Alexander Bryce (retired) 18 Dorset Lake Avenue, Lilliput, Poole BH14 8JD Tel: 01202 708557 — MB BS 1941 Durh.; LRCP LRCS Ed. LRFPS Glas. 1942; FRCGP 1978, M 1959. Prev: Sen. Med. Off. MoH.

STEWART, Alexander George CDSC (NW), Vernon Pritchard CT, 57a Upper Northgate Street, Chester CH1 4EF Tel: 01244 665300 Fax: 01244 665309 Email: astewart@liv.ac.uk — MB ChB 1974 Glas.; DRCOG 1976; DTM & H RCP Lond. 1976; MPH Liverpool 2000. (Glas.) Specialist Regist. Pub. Health, Merseyside; Problem based learning Tutor, Med. Fac., Liverp. Univ. Socs: Soc. for Environm. GeoChem. & Health, Bd. Mem.; Europ. Assn. for Cancer

Educat., Vice Pres.; Brit. Thyroid Assn., Mem. Prev: GP Aman Clinic, Khapalu Pakistan; Research Fell., Dept of Health care Educat., Univ. of Liverp.

STEWART, Alexander Ian, TD Worston Hall, Great Bridgeford, Stafford ST18 9QA Tel: 01785 282203 — MB ChB 1971 Birm.; BSc (Physiol. Hons.) Birm. 1968; FFA RCS Eng. 1976. Cons. Anaesth. N. Staffs. Hosp. Prev: Sen. Regist. (Anaesth.) W. Midl. RHA.

STEWART, Alexander Macrae (retired) Fair Oak, 5 Woodlands Drive, Thelwall, Warrington WA4 2EU Tel: 01925 261968 Fax: 01925 261968 — MB ChB Liverp. 1953; MFOM RCP Lond. 1978; DIH Soc. Apoth. Lond. 1963. Prev: Gp. Med. Off. Simon Engin. Ltd. Cheadle Heath.

STEWART, Alexander Rae 35 Morningside Park, Edinburgh EH10 5HD — MB ChB 1958 Glas.

STEWART, Alice Mary Evenlode Cottage, Fawler, Charlbury, Oxford OX7 3AQ Tel: 01993 891667; 4 Ferndale Court, 109 Metchley Lane, Birmingham B17 0JH Tel: 0121 527 5867 Fax: 0121 414 3630 — MB BChir 1935 Camb.; MA, MD Camb. 1937; FRCP Lond. 1946, M 1936; MRCS Eng. LRCP Lond. 1932. (Camb. & Lond. Sch. Med. Wom.) Prof. Med. Birm. Univ. Socs: RSM. Prev: Reader (Social Med.) Univ. Oxf.

STEWART, Alisdair George (retired) 4 Margaret Road, Harrogate HG2 0JZ Tel: 01423 569480 — MB ChB 1960 St. And.; FRCP Lond. 1980, M 1966; FRCP Ed. 1976, M 1965; LMCC 1962. Cons. Phys. Harrogate HA. Prev: Research Fell. (Med.) McGill Univ.

STEWART, Alison 55 Proctors Road, Wokingham RG40 1RP — BM BS Nottm. 1983; BMedSci Nottm. 1981. (Nottm.) Clin. Asst. Psychiat. Barkham Day Hosp. Workingham; Clin. Asst. Subst. Abuse. Neutral Zone. Reading. Prev: Clin. Asst. (Psychiat.) Walsgrave Hosp. Coventry, Clin. Asst. Reading; Regist. & SHO (Psychiat.) Walsgrave Hosp. Coventry; Ho. Off. (Gen. Med. & Gen. Surg.) S. Cleveland Hosp.

***STEWART, Alison Jane** 2FL 144 St Stephen Street, Edinburgh EH3 5AA — MB ChB 1998 Ed.; MB ChB Ed 1998.

STEWART, Alison Jill 123 Morningside Drive, Edinburgh EH10 5NP — MB BS 1991 Lond.; MB BS (Hons.) Lond. 1991; BSc (Hons.) Lond. 1988; DCH RCP Lond. 1995; DFFP 1998; MRCGP 1998. (Roy. Free Hosp. Sch. Med.) SHO (Palliat. Med.) Marie Currie Centre, Fairmile Edin. Prev: Trainee GP Roy. Devon & Exeter Hosp.; SHO (Paediat.) Glos. Roy. Hosp.; SHO (Anaesth. & A & E) Taunton & Som. Hosp.

STEWART, Alison Lesley Stonehaven Medical Group, Stonehaven Medical Centre, 32 Robert Street, Stonehaven AB39 2EL Tel: 01569 762945 Fax: 01569 766552; 84 Arduthie Road, Stonehaven AB39 2EH Tel: 01569 65533 — MB ChB 1979 Dundee; DRCOG 1983; DCH Glas. 1981.

STEWART, Alison Margaret Western Infirmary, Dumbarton Road, Glasgow G11 6NT Tel: 0141 211 2000 Ext: 3389; 27 Rosemont, Westerwood, Cumbernauld, Glasgow G68 0HL Email: astewart27@aol.com — MB ChB 1991 Glas.; MRCP (UK) 1994. (Glas.) Specialist Regist. (Endocrin.) W.ern Infirm. Glas. Socs: Brit. Diabetic Assn.; Caledonian Soc. Endocrinol.; Soc. For Endocrin. Prev: Specialist Regist. (Gen. Med., Diabetes & Endocrinol.) S.. Gen. Hosp. NHS Trust Glas.; Specialist Regist. Stirling Roy. Infirm.

STEWART, Alison Martin 1500 Warwick Road, Knowle, Solihull B93 9LE Tel: 01564 772010 Fax: 01564 771224; 10 Diddington Lane, Hampton-in-Arden, Solihull B92 0BZ Tel: 01675 442832 — BM 1976 Soton.; MRCP (UK) 1980; MRCGP 1983.

***STEWART, Alistair Bryce** Bush Cottage, Bisterne Close, Burley, Ringwood BH24 4AU — BM 1998 Soton.; BM Soton 1998.

STEWART, Alistair George 15 St John's Court, New Road, Radcliffe, Manchester M26 1NH — MB ChB 1982 Manch.; MRCPsych 1986. Sen. Regist. (Psychother.) Manch. Roy. Infirm.

STEWART, Amanda Grace Elizabeth Mary Frinton Road Surgery, 68 Frinton Road, Holland-on-Sea, Clacton-on-Sea CO15 5UW — MB ChB 1983 Glas. GP; SHO (A & E) Colchester Gen. Hosp. Prev: SHO (Accid. & Orthop.) S.. Gen. Hosp. Glas.; Ho. Off. (Med.) S.. Gen. Hosp. Glas.; Ho. Off. (Surg.) Hairmyres Hosp. E. Kilbride.

STEWART, Amanda Louise Department of Medicine, Bishop Auckland General Hospital, Cockton Hill Road, Bishop Auckland DL14 6AD — MB ChB 1989 Dundee. Regist. (Med.) Health Waikato, NZ. Socs: BMA & Roy. Soc. Med. Prev: Regist. (med.) Lakeland Heath; Ho. Off. Prof. Med. Unit. Univ. Dundee.

STEWART

*****STEWART, Amy Alexander** 27 Hairmyres Park, East Kilbride, Glasgow G75 8SS — MB ChB 1997 Glas.

STEWART, Andrea Diane 58 Waddington Avenue, Coulsdon CR5 1QF — MB ChB 1992 Birm.

STEWART, Mr Andrew 1 Derwent Close, Claygate, Esher KT10 0RF — MB BS 1986 Lond.; BDS Lond. 1979; FRCS Glas. 1990; FDS RCS Eng. 1985. (King's College Hospital London) Cons. Oral & Maxillofacial Surg. Qu. Mary's Hosp. Lond. & St. Helier Hosp. Carshalton. Prev: Sen. Regist. (Oral & Maxillofacial Surg.) Qu. Vict. Hosp. E. Grinstead; Sen. Regist. (Oral & Maxillofacial Surg.) Univ. Coll. Hosp. Lond.; Regist. (Oral & Maxillofacial Surg.) Qu. Mary's Hosp. Lond.

*****STEWART, Andrew David** 12 Burnside Gardens, Stonehaven AB39 2FA — MB ChB 1998 Aberd.; MB ChB Aberd 1998.

STEWART, Andrew Draycott Flat 2, Trident House, 14 West St., Portsmouth PO1 2JW — MB ChB 1978 Manch.; BSc (Psychol.) Manch. 1975, MB ChB 1978; MRCP (UK) 1982; FRACP 1988; DCH RCP Lond. 1982; DObst 1981. Cons. Paediat. Gisborne Hosp. New Zealand.

*****STEWART, Andrew Hugh Robert** 742 Saintfield Road, Carryduff, Belfast BT8 8AT — BChir 1995 Camb.

STEWART, Andrew James Department of Haematology, Royal Infirmary, Lauriston Place, Edinburgh EH3 9YW Tel: 0131 536 1000; 1 Cramond Glebe Terrace, Cramond, Edinburgh EH4 6NR Tel: 0131 312 8891 — MB ChB 1988 Ed.; BA Oxf. 1985; MRCP (UK) 1991; Dip. RCPath. 1995. (Oxford and Edinburgh) Lect. in Haemat. Edin. Univ. Prev: Regist. (Nephrol.) Leeds Gen. Infirm.; Regist. (Haemat.) Roy. Infirm. Edin.

STEWART, Andrew Norman The Surgery, 6 College Road, Eastbourne BN21 4HY Tel: 01323 735044 Fax: 01323 417705 — MB ChB 1986 Aberd.; MRCGP 1990; DCH RCPS Glas. 1989. (Aberd.) GP Princip. Socs: E.bourne Med. Soc. Prev: Trainee GP E.bourne HA VTS.

STEWART, Andrew Peter Orchard Health Centre, The Orchard, Gunnislake PL18 9JZ Tel: 01822 836241 Fax: 01822 833757; Barnwell, Bealbury Farm, St. Mellion, Saltash PL12 6RX Email: d0101951@infotrade.co.uk — MB BS 1974 Lond.; MRCGP 1980; DRCOG 1976. (Char. Cross) Ment. Health Lead E. Cornw. PCG; Mem. Cornw. & Isles of Scilly LMC. Socs: BMA; Assn. BRd.casting Doctors; Roy. Coll. Gen. Pract. Prev: Regist. (Geriat. Med.) Barncoose Hosp. Redruth; SHO (Obst.) W. Lond. Hosp.; Ho. Phys. (Gen. Med.) Char. Cross Hosp. Lond.

*****STEWART, Andrew Peter** 5 Lambert Drive, Sale M33 5WP — MB ChB 1998 Aberd.; MB ChB Aberd 1998.

STEWART, Andrew Peter Owen (retired) 22 Pennine Grove, Huntroyde, Burnley BB12 9AB Tel: 01282 772389 — MB BS 1953 Lond. Prev: Ho. Phys. Guy's Hosp.

STEWART, Angela Jane 15 Park Road, Winchester SO22 6AA Tel: 01962 852172 Fax: 01962 852172 Email: angla@bafled.f.snet — MB BS 1966 Lond.; MB BS (Hons.) Obst. Lond. 1966; MRCS Eng. LRCP Lond. 1966; MFFP 1993; DObst RCOG 1969; MFFP. (Roy. Free) SCMO Soton. Community Health Trust; Sen. Clin. Med. Off. Loddon N. Hants. Community Trust. Socs: Assoc. Mem. Inst. Psychosexual Med. Prev: Med. Off. Brit. Rail; GP Eltham; SHO FarnBoro. Hosp. Kent.

STEWART, Angus John 56 Trumpington Street, Cambridge CB2 1RG Tel: 01223 361611 Fax: 01223 356837; Little Wynyard, 6 Orchard Close, Harston, Cambridge CB2 5PT Tel: 01223 872077 — MA Camb. 1983, MB BChir 1982; MRCGP 1986; AFOM 1990; DCH RCP Lond. 1986; DRCOG 1985. Med. Off. John Lewis Partership; Div. Med. Off. CIBA Gregy Plastics; Sch. Med. Off. Leys Sch.

STEWART, Ann Lindsay (retired) Department of Paediatrics, The Rayne Institute, University College London, 5 University St., London WC1E 6JJ Tel: 020 7209 6117 Fax: 020 7209 6103 Email: a.stewart@ucl.ac.uk — MB ChB Bristol 1955; MRCP (UK) 1994; FRCPCH 1997; DCH Eng. 1958; FRCP 1999. Hon. Sen. Lect. (Paediat.) Univ. Coll. Lond. Med. Sch.; Hon. Sen. Lect. (Psychol. Med.) Inst. Psychiat. Lond. Prev: Human Biochem. Genetics Unit. Univ. Coll. Lond.

*****STEWART, Ann-Marie** 37A Westbourne Road, Sheffield S10 2QT — MB ChB 1994 Sheff.

STEWART, Anne Highfield Family & Adolescent Unit, Warneford Hospital, Warneford Lane, Oxford OX3 7JX Tel: 01865 226280 Fax: 01865 226381 — MB BS 1978 Lond.; BSc Lond. 1975; MRCPsych 1985; DCH RCP Lond. 1985. (St. Bart.) Cons. Child & Adolesc. Psychiat. Highfield Family & Adolesc. Unit Oxf. Prev: Sen. Lect. Wellington Sch. Med., NZ.

STEWART, Anne Briar 284 Telegraph Road, Heswall, Wirral CH60 7SG — MB ChB 1978 Ed.; MRCP (UK) 1983. Cons. Emerg. & Ambulatory Paediat. Alder Hey Childr. Hosp. Liverp.

STEWART, Anne Elizabeth St Lukes Hospice, Turnchapel, Plymouth PL9 9XA; North Beneknowle, Diptford, Totnes TQ9 7LU — MB BS 1983 Lond.; BSc Lond. 1981, MB BS 1983; MRCGP 1987. Staff Grade (Palliat. Care) St Lukes Hospice Turnchapel Plymouth. Prev: Trainee GP Plymouth VTS.

STEWART, Anne Linn 9 Abbotsford Avenue, Rutherglen, Glasgow G73 3NX Tel: 0141 647 3422 — MB ChB 1960 Glas.

STEWART, Anne Rosemarie Chorley Road Surgery, 65 Chorley Road, Swinton, Manchester M27 4AF Tel: 0161 794 6287 Fax: 0161 728 3415 — MB BCh BAO 1978 NUI. (Univ. Coll. Dub.) Prev: SHO (Paediat. Surg.) Duchess of York Hosp. Babies Manch.; Intern. (Med.) & Intern. (Surg.) St. Michael's Hosp. Dun Laoghaire.

STEWART, Audrey Elizabeth (retired) 55 Broad Street, Portsmouth PO1 2JD Tel: 01705 823045 Fax: 01705 295961 — MB ChB. Manch. 1949; DObst. RCOG 1951. Prev: Sen. Dept. Med. Off. City Portsmouth Health Dept.

STEWART, Barbara Enid (retired) Annickbank, Irvine KA11 4HS Tel: 01294 272173 — MB BS Lond. 1947. Assoc. Specialist Chest Unit Ayrsh. & Arran HB.

STEWART, Barbara Jane Armstrong Brick Kiln Cottage, 3 Bow End, Stanford in the Vale, Faringdon SN7 8JB; Department of Community Paediatrics, 3 Craven Road, Reading RG31 5LF Tel: 0118 986 2277 ext 2288 Fax: 0118 975 0297 — MB BS 1985 Lond.; BA Camb. 1982; MRCP (UK) 1989; Dip. Epidemiol. RCP (UK) 1993. Cons. Paediat. (Community Child Health). Prev: Sen. Regist. (Paediat. & Community Child Health) Ch.ill Hosp. Oxf.; Research Fell. (Community Paediat.) Radcliffe Infirm. Oxf.

STEWART, Barbara Janet Clare 201 Braid Road, Edinburgh EH10 6HT — MB ChB 1992 Ed.

STEWART, Belinda Rosemary 20 Christchurch Road, Malvern WR14 3BE Tel: 01684 564008 — MB BCh 1990 Wales; MRCGP 1995. GP Trainee Brecon. Prev: Trainee GP Abergavenny; Vocat. Train. Abergavenny.

STEWART, Bruce Alexander 111 Brim Hill, London N2 0EZ — MB ChB 1990 Cape Town. (Univ. Cape Town) Socs: S. Afr. Med. & Dent. Counc.; Coll. Med. S. Afr. Prev: SHO (O & G) St. Jas. Univ. Hosp. Leeds; SHO (Gen. Med.) Wolverhampton HA.

STEWART, Bruce Alexander Dept. of Microbiology, East Surrey Hospital, Canada Avenue, Redhill RH1 5RH Tel: 01737 768511 Email: bruce@doctors.org.uk — MB ChB 1989 Birm.; MRCP UK 1993; MSC, Lond, 1996; MRCPath, 1999. (Birmingham) Cons. Microbiologist Surrey & Sussex Healthcare Trust. Socs: BMA; Brit. Soc. For Antimicrobial Chemo.; Assn of Med. Microbiologists.

STEWART, Carol Calsayseat Medical Group, 2 Calsayseat Road, Aberdeen AB25 3UY Tel: 01224 634345 Fax: 01224 620210 — MB ChB 1988 Dundee.

STEWART, Carol Margaret Bathgate Health Centre, Mid St, Bathgate EH48 1PT; 25 Saltcoats Gardens, Bellsquarry S., Livingston EH54 9JD Tel: 01506 419439 — MB ChB 1990 Ed.; BSc Ed. 1988, MB ChB 1990; MRCP (UK) 1994; MRCGP 1997; DRCOG 1995. Retainee GP. Bathgate Heath Centre. Bathgate. Prev: SHO Marie Curie Centre Fairmile Edin.; SHO (Med.) N.. & W.. Gen. Hosps. Edin.

STEWART, Charles Douglas (retired) 8A Quay Road, Ballycastle BT54 6BH Tel: 0126 57 62206 — MB BCh BAO 1939 Belf. Prev: RAMC.

*****STEWART, Charles Glyndwr** 29 Sandy La, Caldicot, Newport NP26 4NA — MB BCh 1997 Wales.

STEWART, Charles Hall (retired) 18 Portglenone Road, Randalstown, Antrim BT41 3BE Tel: 01849 472891 — MB BCh BAO Belf. 1956. Prev: Dep. Police Surg. Antrim Sub-Div. Roy. Ulster Constab.

STEWART, Charles Malcolm Dundas Park Farm, Elmsted, Ashford TN25 5JW — MB BS 1970 Lond.; T(OG) 1991; MRCOG 1981. Clin. Research Fell. Hon. Sen. Regist. Dept. O & G St.; Med. Sch. Lond.

STEWART, Charles Peter (retired) 35 Woodside Walk, Hamilton ML3 7JD Tel: 01698 281590 — MB ChB 1951 Glas.

STEWART

STEWART, Charles Rodger University Hospitals of Leicester NHS Trust, Leicester General Hospital, Gwendolem Road, Leicester LE5 4PW Tel: 0116 258 4833; Bardon Croft, 4 Knighton Rise, Oadby, Leicester LE2 2RE Tel: 0116 270 6230 — MB ChB 1965 Glas.; FRCOG 1982, M 1970; T(OG) 1991. (Glas.) Cons. - Obstetrics and Gyn. Leicester Gen. Hosp.; Hon. Clin. Lect. Univ. Leicester. Socs: BMA (Sec. Leics. & Rutland Div.); N. Eng. Obst. Soc.; Birm. and Midl.s Obsterical Soc. Prev: Sen. Lect. Univ. Leicester Med. Sch.; Sen. Lect. Univ. Otago & Hon. Cons. (Gyn.) N. Canterbury Hosp. Bd., NZ.

STEWART, Charles Teasdale Trades Lane Health Centre, Causewayend, Coupar Angus, Blairgowrie PH13 9DP Tel: 01828 627318 — MB ChB 1984 Glas.

STEWART, Christopher David The Taymount Surgery, 1 Taymount Terrace, Perth PH1 1NU Tel: 01738 627117 Fax: 01738 444713 — MB BCh BAO 1988 Belf.; MB BCh Belf. 1988.

STEWART, Clare Isobel Louise Glaxo Day Hospital, Ashludie Hospital, Monifieth, Dundee DD5 4HQ Tel: 01382 527831 Fax: 01382 527852; 22 Cedar Road, Broughty Ferry, Dundee DD5 3BB — MB ChB 1988 Dundee; DGM RCPS Glas. 1994. Staff Grade Phys. (Med. for Elderly) Glaxo Day Hosp. Monifieth.

STEWART, Clyne Robert Bruce (retired) 18 Sandringham Court, Porthill, Shrewsbury SY3 8LL Tel: 01743 355743 — MB ChB Aberd. 1947.

STEWART, Colin John Reid Strathwood, Milndavie Road, Strathblane, Glasgow G63 9EN — MB ChB 1983 Glas.

STEWART, Colin Peter Urquhart The Pines, 38 Seafield Road, Broughty Ferry, Dundee DD5 3AN Tel: 01382 779513 Fax: 01382 480194 Email: cstewart@dth.scot.nhs.uk — MB ChB 1973 Dundee; MD Dundee 1986; DMedRehab Eng. 1979. (Dundee) Assoc. Specialist (Prosth. & Orthotics) Murdoch Centre, Ninewells Hosp, Dundee; Vis. Lect. & Examr. Nat. Centre for Train. Prosth. & Orthop. Strathclyde Univ. Glas; Hon. Lect. Dundee Univ. Socs: Fell. Internat. Soc. Prosth.s & Orthotics; Amputee Rehabil. Med. Soc. (Hon. Treas.); BMA (Chairm. NCCG Sub Comm. SCHMS). Prev: Regist. (Prosth. & Orthotics) Dundee Limb Fitting Centre Broughty Ferry; Regist. (Geriat. Rehabil.) Ashludie Hosp. Monifieth.

STEWART, Dan (retired) 16 Eversley Crescent, London N21 1EJ Tel: 020 8360 1512 — MB BS 1951 Lond.; MRCGP 1977; DObst RCOG 1955. Prev: GP Staff Wood Green & S.gate Hosps. & Enfield War Memor. Hosp.

STEWART, David Manchester Childrens Hospitals NHS Trust, Royal Manchester Childrens Hospital, Department Intens. Care Med., Hospital Road, Pendlesbury, Manchester M27 4HA Tel: 0161 727 2468 Fax: 0161 727 2198 Email: david.stewart@man.ac.uk — MB ChB 1986 Leic.; BSc (Hons.) Manch. 1981; MRCP (UK) 1991; FRCPCH. Cons. Paediat. Intens. Care Manch. Childr. Hosps. NHS Trust; Lead Clinician Train. & Clin. Pract. Developm.; Lead Clinician High Dependency Unit. Socs: Paediat. Intens. Care Soc.; Soc. Critica Care Med. Prev: Clin. Fell. (Paediat. Critical Care) Toronto Hosp. for Sick Childr.; Sen. Regist. Rotat. W. Midl. RHA; Regist. Rotat. (Paediat.) W. Middlx. Univ. Hosp. & W.m. Childr. Hosp.

STEWART, David, Maj. RAMC 16 Gratton Drive, Windsor SL4 4AS Tel: 01753 62192 — MB BS 1976 Lond. Regtl. Med. Off. Ho.hold Cavalry. Prev: SHO (A & E) Redhill Gen. Hosp.; SHO (ENT) & (Paediat.) Roy. Surrey Co. Hosp. Guildford.

STEWART, David Andrew 143 Woodstock Avenue, Glasgow G41 3SE — MB ChB 1986 Glas.; MRCGP 1990.

STEWART, David Armour 9 Dornoch Avenue, Griffnock, Glasgow G46 6QH — MB ChB 1981 Glas.; MRCP (UK) 1985.

STEWART, David George Telford 37 Main Street, Castlerock, Coleraine BT51 4RA — MB BCh BAO 1979 Belf.; MSc (Community Med.) Ed. 1983; FFPHM RCP (UK) 1994; MFCM RCP 1984. Dir. (Pub. Health) EHSSB Belf.

STEWART, David Graeme Department of Dermatology, University Hospital Birmingham, Raddle Barn Road, Birmingham B29 6JD Tel: 0121 627 1627 Fax: 0121 627 8765 — MB ChB 1985 Aberd.; FRCP 2001; MRCP (UK) 1991. Cons. (Dermatol.) Univ. Hosp. Birm. Prev: Sen. Regist. (Dermatol.) Univ. Hosp. Birm.; Regist. The Birm. Skin Hosp.

STEWART, David Hamilton 7 Glenwater Close, Axmouth, Seaton EX12 4BT — MB ChB 1952 Cape Town; FRCOG 1973, M 1959. (Cape Town)

STEWART, David John (retired) Wayside, South Stoke, Bath BA2 7DJ Tel: 01225 832031 — MB ChB Glas. 1944; LM Rotunda 1957. Prev: Clin. Med. Off. Bath Health Dist.

STEWART, David John NMGH, Delaunays Road, Crumpsall, Manchester M8 5RL Tel: 0161 795 4567; 33 Alder Road, Mansewood, Glasgow G43 2UU — MB ChB 1997 Manch.; BSc St And 1993. SHO (IC) NMGH Crumpsall Manch. Socs: BMA; MDU; MPS.

STEWART, David Patrick Edward 12 Meenaleck Walk, Londonderry BT48 8HL — MB BCh BAO 1990 Belf.

STEWART, David Patterson Dr MacLean and Partners, Monifieth Health Centre, Victoria Street, Monifieth, Dundee DD5 4LX Tel: 01382 534301 Fax: 01382 535959 — MB ChB 1988 Dundee; MRCGP 1992; DRCOG 1990.

STEWART, David Winterburn Wishaw Health Centre, Kenilworth Avenue, Wishaw ML2 7BQ Tel: 01698 373341 — MB ChB 1973 Glas.; DObst RCOG 1976. (Glas.)

STEWART, Denis John Alexander The Health Centre, Station Road, Bawtry, Doncaster DN10 6RQ Tel: 01302 710210 Fax: 01302 710261; 9 Arundel Drive, Ranskill, Retford DN22 8PG Tel: 01302 710210 — MB ChB 1980 Dundee; BSc St. And. 1976; DRCOG 1982.

STEWART, Donald Norman, OStJ, TD (retired) High Down, Mount Pleasant, Bishop's Tawton, Barnstaple EX32 0BS Tel: 01271 374548 — MRCS Eng. LRCP Lond. 1942; DLO Eng. 1963. Prev: Asst. ENT Surg. Croydon Gp. Hosps.

STEWART, Mr Douglas James Consultant Surgeon, Royal Preston Hospital, 11 Moor Park Avenue, Preston PR1 6AS Tel: 01772 251507; 14 Uplands Chase, Fulwood, Preston PR2 7AW Tel: 01772 865009 — MB ChB 1969 Aberd.; ChM Aberd. 1979, MB ChB 1969; FRCS Ed. 1973. (Aberdeen) Cons. Gen. Surg. Preston Acute Hosp. NHS Trust. Socs: Assn. of Surg. of GB & Irel.; Assn. of Coloproctol. of GB & Irel.

STEWART, Duncan Bernard The Surgery, 28 Wilbury Road, Hove BN3 3JP Tel: 01273 733830 Fax: 01273 207424 — MB BS 1967 Lond.; MRCS Eng. LRCP Lond. 1967; DObst RCOG 1969. (Guy's) Med. Off. Roedean Sch. Brighton & Harewood Ct. RMBI Home. Socs: Brighton & Sussex M-C Soc.

STEWART, Duncan John 51 Cavell Court, Block C23, Queen's Medical Centre, Nottingham NG7 2UH Tel: 0115 924 9924 Ext: 43129; 30 Maple Walk, Pucklechurch, Bristol BS16 9RJ Tel: 0117 937 2963 — MB ChB 1997 Sheff. (Sheff.) SHO Basic Surg. Train. Rotat. Prev: SHO (Cardio.) Nottm City Hosp.; Ho. Off. (Gen. Med.) Doncaster Roy. Infirm.; Ho. Off. (Gen. Surg.) DRI Doncaster.

STEWART, Edmund Central Health Centre, North Carbrain Road, Cumbernauld, Glasgow G67 1BJ Tel: 01236 737214 Fax: 01236 781699 — MB ChB 1991 Glas.

STEWART, Elaine Oenone (retired) The Lawn, Holybourne, Alton GU34 4ER — MB BS University College London; MD Lond. 1928, MB BS 1926; MRCS Eng. LRCP Lond. 1926. Prev: Med. Off. Basingstoke Family Plann. Clinic.

STEWART, Eleanor Janet 295 Merville Garden Village, Newtownabbey BT37 9TY — MB BCh BAO 1981 Belf.; FRCS Ed. 1986.

STEWART, Elizabeth Helen Craig (retired) 12 Charles Clore Court, Appleford Road, Reading RG30 3NT — LRCP LRCS Ed. LRFPS Glas. 1942; Dip. Audiol. Manch. 1971. Prev: SCMO Berks. AHA.

STEWART, Elizabeth Jane Colhoun Department Dermatology, Royal Berkshire Hospital, Reading RG1 5AN Tel: 01734 877417; 25 Woodward Close, Winnersh, Wokingham RG41 5NW — MB ChB 1980 Glas.; MRCP (UK) 1983; MRCGP 1988; DRCOG 1989. Regist. (Dermat.) Roy. Berks. Hosp. Prev: GP Wokingham; Trainee GP Cumbernauld VTS; Regist. (Dermat.) Roy. & Vict. Infirms. Glas.

STEWART, Elizabeth Mary (retired) 4 Margaret Road, Harrogate HG2 0JZ Tel: 01423 569480 — MB ChB 1960 St. And. Prev: SCMO (Community Child Health) Harrogate Health Care Trust.

STEWART, Elspeth Jane 24 Durbin Park Road, Clevedon BS21 7EU — MB ChB 1977 Glas.

STEWART, Esther Caroline Ann 7 The Pines, Hillsborough BT26 6NT Tel: 01846 683835 Email: carolinestewart@characterlink.net; Kilgole House, Bridgetown, Laghey, Donegal, Republic of Ireland Tel: 0173 34058 — MB BCh BAO 1990 Belf.; MRCPI (Paediat.) 1995; DCH RCPS Glas. 1992.

STEWART

(Qu. Univ. Belf.) Specialist Regist. (Paediat.) Roy. Belf. Hosp. for Sick Childr.; Community Paediat. Belf.

STEWART, Ewen Andrew Rose Garden Medical Centre, 4 Mill Lane, Edinburgh EH6 6TL Tel: 0131 554 1274 Fax: 0131 555 2159 — MB ChB 1991 Ed.; BSc MedSci (Bacteriol.) Ed. 1989; MRCGP 1995; DFFP 1995. Asst. Primary Care Facilitator (HIV/AIDS) Lothian Health. Prev: Regist. Kobler Centre Chelsea & W.m. Hosp. Lond.; Hosp. Pract. (Diabetes) EGH.

STEWART, Fiona Jane Department of Medical Genetics, Level A, Belfast City Hospital, Lisburn Road, Belfast BT9 7AB Tel: 01232 329241 Fax: 01232 236911; The Gables, 229 Ballymoney Road, Ballymena BT43 5HQ Email: 106330.3017@compuserve.com — MB BS 1985 Lond.; MRCP (UK) 1989; MA Belf. 1997. Cons. Med. Genetics Belf. City Hosp. Socs: Brit. Paediat. Assn. & Clin. Genetics Soc. Prev: Sen. Regist. (Med. Genetics) Belf. City Hosp.

STEWART, Fiona Karen Orchard House Psychogeriatric Day Hospital, Union St., Stirling FK8 1NY Tel: 01786 474161; 92 Thriepland Wynd, Perth PH1 1RH Tel: 01738 630643 — MB ChB 1986 Dundee. Clin. Asst. (Old Age Psychiat.) Orchard Hse. Psychogeriat. Day Hosp. Stirling.

STEWART, Frances Ellen 5 Archery Road, Leamington Spa CV31 3PT — MB ChB 1979 Glas.

STEWART, Frances Maria Apartment 2/L, 107 Crown Road North, Glasgow G12 9HS — MB BCh BAO 1995 Belf.

STEWART, Frank Ian Tel: 01506 423800 Fax: 01506 460757; Tel: 01506 653428 — MB ChB 1965 Ed.; FRCGP 1995, M 1971; DCH RCPS Glas. 1969. Gen. Practitioner; Hosp. Pract. (Paediat.) W. Lothian NHS Trust.

STEWART, Gareth Alexander 10 (3F2) Brougham Place, Edinburgh EH3 9HW — MB BCh BAO 1993 Belf.

STEWART, Gavin Davidson Fair Oak, 5 Woodlands Drive, Thelwall, Warrington WA4 2EU Tel: 01925 261968 Fax: 01925 261968 Email: stewart@aol.com; 7 Lapworth Oaks, Station Lane, Lapworth, Solihull B94 6L6 Tel: 01564 785091 Fax: 01564 785093 Email: stewartgd@aol.com — MB BS 1985 Newc.; MB BS (Hons.) Newc. 1985; BA (1st cl. Hons.) Lond. 1979; MRCP Lond. 1988; FRCR 1991. Cons. Radiol. (Diagn. Radiol.) Warwick Dist. Gen. Hosp. Prev: Sen. Regist. & Regist. Rotat. (Diagn. Radiol.) Manch. Roy. Infirm.; SHO Rotat. (Med.) Leicester Roy. Infirm.

STEWART, George Edward Stanforth, MBE Mount Pleasant Farm, Croes-ny-Pant, Mamhilad, Pontypool NP4 0JD Tel: 01495 785781 — MB ChB 1933 Ed.; DTM & H Eng. 1938. Prev: Sen. Med. Off. P & O Gp.; Med. Supt. Brit. India SN Co. Ltd. Bombay & Lond.; Lt.-Col. IMS (Ret.).

STEWART, George MacLeod (retired) 4 Ashview Close, Ashford TW15 3RF Tel: 01784 255162 — MB ChB Aberd. 1959; FFPHM RCP (UK) 1994; MFCM RCP (UK) 1972; DIH Eng. 1970; DPH Aberd. 1969; DTM & H Eng. 1964. Prev: Cons. Communicable Dis. Control & Princip. Med. Off. Control Unit Lond. (Heathrow) Airport.

STEWART, Georgina Houston (retired) — MB ChB Glas. 1962; FRCP 1996; FFCM 1988, M 1980; DIH Soc. Apoth. Lond. 1986; DTM & H Liverp. 1975; Dip. Community. Med. Ed. 1977.

STEWART, Gillian Elizabeth Glencree, 68 Old Mountfield Road, Omagh BT79 1EH — MB ChB 1992 Aberd.

STEWART, Mr Gordon Ayr Hospital, Ayr KA6 6DX Tel: 01292 610555; 'Alyth', 63 Monument Road, Ayr KA7 2UE Tel: 01292 880610 — MB ChB 1973 Glas.; BSc (Hons. Physiol.) Glas. 1971, MD 1985, MB ChB 1973; FRCS Glas. 1978. (Glas.) Cons. Gen. Surg. & Vasc. Surg. Ayrsh. & Arran Acute Hosps. NHS Trust. Socs: Vasc. Soc. GB & Irel. & Assn. Surgs. GB & Irel.; Eur. Vasc. Soc.; Venous Forum RSM. Prev: Lect. (Surg.) & Sen. Regist. St. Thos. Hosp. Lond.; Sen. Specialist Surg. Cade Unit PM RAF Hosp. Halton.

STEWART, Gordon Duff (retired) Lammasfield, Baring Road, Cowes PO31 8DW — LRCP LRCS 1955 Ed.; LRCP LRCS Ed. LRFPS Glas. 1955; FRCPsych 1990, M 1971; DPM Eng. 1965. Prev: Sen. Med. Off. HM Prison Pk.hurst.

STEWART, Professor Gordon Thallon 29/8 Inverleith Place, Edinburgh EH3 5QD Tel: 0131 5522648 Email: g.stewart@gifford.co.uk; 3 Lexdon Terrace, Tenby SA70 7BJ Tel: 01834 844772 Fax: 01834 849198 Email: g.stewart@gifford.co.uk — MD (High Commend.) 1949; MB ChB Glas. 1942; BSc Glas. 1939; FRCP Glas. 1975, M 1972; FFCM 1972; FRCPath 1963; DTM & H Liverp. 1947. (Glas.) Emerit. Prof. Pub. Health Univ. Glas. Socs: Emerit. Fell. Infec. Dis. Soc., USA; Fell. Med. Soc. Lond.; Fell. Roy.

Statistical Soc. Prev: Cons. (Epidemiol.) WHO; Cons. Phys. Gtr. Glas. HB; Vis. Prof. Dow Med. Coll. Karachi, Pakistan 1953-54 & Cornell Univ. Med. Coll. New York City, USA 1970-72.

STEWART, Gordon Walker Rayne Institute, University College & Middlesex Med. School, University St., London WC1E 6JJ Tel: 020 7209 6193 Fax: 020 7209 6211 Email: g.stewart@ucl.ac.uk; Tel: 01753 880428 — MD 1984 Ed.; MSc Lond. 1989; BSc Sussex 1971; MB ChB 1976 Ed.; MRCP (UK) 1978; FRCP 1996. (Edin.) Sen. Lect. & Hon. Cons. Phys. Univer. Coll. & Middlx. Hosps. Prev: Wellcome Sen. Fell. (Clin. Sci.) Rayne Inst. Univ. Coll. Lond.; Lect. (Med.) St. Marys Hosp. Med. Sch. Lond.

STEWART, Graham Royal Alexandra Hospital NHS Trust, Paisley PA2 9PN Tel: 0141 887 9111 Fax: 0141 580 4364 Email: g.stewart@rah.scot.nhs.uk; Tel: 0141 334 2704 — MB ChB 1982 Ed.; MRCP (UK) 1988; FRCPCH; FRCP Glasgow 2000. Cons. Paediat. Argyll & Clyde Acute Hosp.s NHS Trust. Socs: Neantol. Soc.; Brit. Assn. Permatal Med.

STEWART, Graham Alexander 21 Edenside, Cumbernauld, Glasgow G68 0ER — MB ChB 1991 Glas.; MRCP (UK) 1995. Research Fell. (Nephrol.) W.ern Infirm. Glas. Prev: SHO (Med.) & Ho. Off. (Surg.) Dumfries & Galloway Roy. Infirm.; Ho. Off. (Med.) Glas. Roy. Infirm.; SHO (Renal Med.) W.. Infirm. Glas.

STEWART, Gregor St John Angus 49 Lynn Grove, Gorleston, Great Yarmouth NR31 8AR — MB ChB 1962 Glas.; DA Eng. 1965; DObst RCOG 1965. Prev: GP Gt. Yarmouth.

STEWART, Gregory (retired) — MB 1963 Camb.; MA Camb. 1972, MB 1963, BChir 1962; MRCP Lond. 1966; FRCPsych 1986, M 977. Sen. Lect. (Developm. Psychiat.) Univ. Coll. & Middlx. Hosp. Lond.; Cons. Horizon Trust & Bloomsbury Community Trust Lond.

STEWART, Grizel D'Rastricke Springhall Farm, Sheriff Mountain, Londonderry BT47 — MB BCh BAO 1946 Belf. (Belf.) Med. Asst. N.W. Special Care Serv. N. Irel. Prev: Regist. (Psychiat.) Lancaster Moor Hosp.

STEWART, Harold Markinch Medical Centre, 19 High Street, Markinch, Glenrothes KY7 6ER Tel: 01592 610640 Fax: 01592 612089 — MB BCh BAO 1979 Belf.

STEWART, Harold 16 Ferncroft Avenue, Hampstead, London NW3 7PH Tel: 020 7435 8696 — MB BS 1947 Lond.; MRCS Eng. LRCP Lond. 1947; FRCPsych 1978, M 1971. (Univ. Coll. Hosp.) Socs: Brit. Psychoanal. Soc. Prev: Cons. Psychother. Adult Dept. Tavistock Clin.; Cons. Phys. & Cons. Psychiat. Paddington Centre for Psychotherap.; Clin. Asst. (Psychol. Med.) Univ. Coll. Hosp. Lond.

STEWART, Harold Charles, CBE, KStJ 41 The Glen, Green Lane, Northwood HA6 2UR Tel: 01923 824893 — MB BChir 1931 Camb.; FRSE; PhD Lond. 1942; MA Camb. 1934, MD 1936; FRCP Lond. 1968, M 1949; FFA RCS Eng. 1969. (Univ. Coll. Hosp.) Emerit. Prof. Pharmacol. Univ. Lond.; DL; Chairm. Buttle Trust for Childr.; Pres. Sir Halley Stewart Trust for Research; Patron Med. Counc. on Alcoholism; Vice-Pres. St. Christophers Hosp. Terminal Cases. Socs: Physiol. & Pharmacol. Socs.; Hon. Vice-Pres. Stewart Soc. Prev: Head Pharmacol. St. Mary's Hosp. Med. Sch.; Dir.-Gen. St. John Ambul. Assn.; Hon. Med. Adviser & Mem. Commonw. Counc., Brit. Commonw. Ex-Servs. League.

STEWART, Hazel Elizabeth Coleraine Health Centre, Castlerock Road, Coleraine BT51 3HP Tel: 028 7034 4834 Fax: 028 7035 8914; 10 Rectory Road, Ballyrashane, Coleraine BT52 2LR — MB BCh BAO 1976 Belf.; MRCGP 1983.

STEWART, Helen Susan 34 Crescent Road, Hale, Altrincham WA15 9NA — MB BCh 1988 Wales; MRCP (UK) 1991. Specialist Regist. (Clin. Genetics.) St. Mary's Hosp. Manch. Prev: Regist. (Paediat.) Leic. Roy. Infirm.; Regist. & SHO (Haemat.) Birm. Childr. Hosp.; SHO (Paediat.) Univ. Hosp. Wales.

STEWART, Helen Valerie Ann Mursdale Surgery, Mursdale, Tarbert PA29 6XG Tel: 01583 421206; Glenralloch Cottage, Tarbert PA29 6XX Tel: 01330 820052 Email: drstewart@aol.com — MB ChB 1985 Glas.; MRCP (UK) 1988; MRCGP 1990; DCCH RCP Ed. 1992. (Glas.) Assoc. GP.

STEWART, Herbert James 4 Royal Oaks, Kesh Road, Maze, Lisburn BT27 5RP Tel: 01846 622732 Email: dfbstewart@aoc.com — MB BCh BAO 1986 Belf.; DRCOG 1991; DFFM 1997. (Queens University, Belfast) Locum GP; Primary Care Pract. A & E Dept. Master Infirmorum Host, Belf. Socs: Ulster Med. Soc.; BMA.

STEWART, Mr Hugh Donald Royal Lancaster Infirmary, Orthopaedic Department, Ashton Road, Lancaster LA1 4RP; 151

STEWART

Brookhouse Road, Brookhouse, Lancaster LA2 9NX — MB BS 1974 Lond.; FRCS Eng. 1979. (Lond. Hosp.) Cons. Traum. & Orthop. Surg. Lancaster & Kendal. Prev: Cons. Orthop. St. Vincents Hosp. Melbourne, Austral.; Sen. Regist. (Orthop.) Derbysh. Roy. Infirm. & Harlow Wood Orthop. Hosp. Mansfield; Regist. (Orthop.) Derbysh. Roy. Infirm.

STEWART, Hugh Vaughan Dryburn Hospital, North Road, Durham DH1 5TW Tel: 0191 3332 333; 9 Larches Road, Durham DH1 4NL Tel: 0191 383 1301 — MB ChB 1984 Univ. Zimbabwe; MSc Trop. Med. Liverp. 1995; MRCP (UK) 1992. Cons. (Paediat.) Dryburn Hosp. Durh. Socs: Roy. Coll. Paediat. & Child Health.

STEWART, Mr Iain 220 Moss Heights Avenue, Cardsnald, Glasgow G52 2UB; 17 Mertylfarm View, Braunton EX33 1QH Email: iain@croyde52.freeserve — MB ChB 1990 Glas.; FRCS Ed. 1994; DRCOG 1997; MRCGP 1998. (Glas.) GP Locum; GP Regist. Warwick Pract. Prev: SHO Anaesth., N. Devon Dist. Hosp.; GP Regist. N.am Pract.

STEWART, Iain Douglas 240 Bennett Street, Long Eaton, Nottingham NG10 4HH — MB ChB 1981 Glas.

STEWART, Iain Macphail (retired) 25 Boclair Road, Bearsden, Glasgow G61 2AF Tel: 0141 942 1615 — MB ChB 1958 St. And.; MFCM 1973; DPH St. And. 1964; DIH Dund 1968. Prev: Community Med. Specialist (Gt.er Glas. Health Bd.).

STEWART, Ian MacDonald 16 Stanley Road, Lytham St Annes FY8 5QX Tel: 01253 736739 — MB ChB 1968 St. And.; FRCP 1991; FRCP Ed. 1991; MRCP (UK) 1972. (St. And.) Cons. Rheum. Vict. Hosp. Blackpool & Wrightington Hosp. Prev: Sen. Regist. (Rheum.) Manch. AHA (T).

STEWART, Ian McLennan (retired) Manor Farm House, Sessay, Thirsk YO7 3BE Tel: 01845 501521 — LMSSA 1952 Lond.; MRCPsych 1971; DPM Eng. 1962. Cons. Forens. Psychiat. Stockton Hall Psychiat. Hosp. Prev: Cons. Psychotherap. Guernsey, CI.

STEWART, Mr Ian Park Derriford Hospital, Derriford, Plymouth PL6 8DH — MB ChB 1962 Bristol; BSc Bristol 1959, MB ChB 1962; FRCS Eng. 1969. (Bristol) Cons. A & E Dept. Plymouth Gen. Hosp. (Freedom Fields Br.). Socs: BMA. Prev: Surgic. Regist. United Sheff. Hosps.; Surg. Regist. Plymouth Gen. Hosp.; Surg. Regist. Birm. Accid. Hosp.

STEWART, Ian Smith Flat 12, Beechgrove, 149 Crown Road S., Glasgow G12 9DP — MB ChB 1974 Glas.; FRCR 1981; DMRD Eng. 1979.

STEWART, Iris Dorothy Margaret 69 Brookfield Avenue, Poynton, Stockport SK12 1JE — MB ChB 1963 Manch.; MSc Manch. 1980, MB ChB 1963; MFCM RCP Lond. 1982; DO Eng. 1973; Cert JCC Lond. 1977. Socs: Manch. Med. Soc.; Fell. Roy. Inst. Pub. Health & Hyg.

STEWART, Isabella (retired) 74 The Common, Parbold, Wigan WN8 7EA Tel: 01257 462173 — MB ChB 1957 Glas.

STEWART, Isaiah Casey Medical Assessment Unit, Royal Infirmary of Edinburgh, Lauriston Place, Edinburgh EH3 9YW Tel: 0131 536 1000 Fax: 0131 536 1001; Lyndhurst, 5 Brae Park, Edinburgh EH4 6DJ — MB ChB 1978 Ed.; BSc (Med. Sci.) Ed. 1975; MBChB Ed. 1978; MRCP (UK) 1980; MD 1987; FRCP Ed. 1994.

STEWART, Isobel Douglas (retired) Molendinar, 3 Ferryfield Road, Connel, Oban PA37 1SR Tel: 01631 710324 — MB ChB Glas. 1945. Prev: SCMO Community Health Gtr. Glas. Health Bd.

STEWART, Jacqueline Linda 6 Cavendish Drive, Newton Mearns, Glasgow G77 5NY Tel: 0141 639 3610 — MB ChB Glas. 1994.

STEWART, James Alexander David Glenfield Hospital, Groby Road, Leicester LE3 9QP; 2 Cedar Cottages, Rolleston Road, Skeffington, Leicester LE7 9YD Tel: 0116 259 6430 Email: james.stewart@uhl-tr.nhs.uk — MB ChB 1991 Leic.; LLM 2000 Cardiff; MRCP (UK) 1994. Cons. Phys. & Gastroenterologists, Univ. Hosps. of Leicester. Socs: Brit. Soc. of Gastroenterologists; Soc. of Acute Med.; Brit. Assn. of Parenteral & Enternal Nutrit. Prev: SHO Rotat. (Med.) Leicester & P'boro.; Specialist Regist. (Med. & Gastroenterol.) Leicester Roy. Infirm.

STEWART, James Bryson 7 Johnshaven, North Barr, Erskine PA8 6EH — MB ChB 1992 Glas.

STEWART, James Douglas Meeks Road Surgery, 10 Meeks Road, Falkirk FK2 7ES Tel: 01324 619930 Fax: 01324 627266; The Stable House, Braco, Dunblane FK15 9RA Tel: 01786 880204 — MB ChB 1968 Dundee; FRCPath 1986, M 1974; MRCGP 1979. (Dundee) Prev: Regist. Path. Stirlingsh. Area Laborat. Serv.; Jun. Ho. Off.

(Med. & Surg.) Stirling Roy. Infirm.; Sen. Regist. (Path.) Glas. Roy. Infirm.

STEWART, James Francis Norman Health Centre, 14 Market Place, Carluke ML8 4AZ Tel: 01555 752150 Fax: 01555 751703; 27 Quarry Road, Lawhill, Carluke ML8 5HB — MB ChB 1980 Glas.; MRCGP 1984; DFFP 1993; DRCOG 1984.

STEWART, James Frederick Garfield c/o Department of Ophthalmology, Western Infirmary, Dumbarton Road, Glasgow G11 6NT — MB ChB 1982 Otago.

STEWART, James Ian McKay Department of Anaesthetics, Queen's Medical Cantre, University Hospital, Nottingham NG7 2UH — MB BS 1989 Newc.; FRCA 1995. Regist. (Anaesth.) Welsh Train. Scheme.

STEWART, James Martin (retired) 13A Davenant Road, Oxford OX2 8BT Tel: 01865 553067 — MB BCh BAO Dub. 1944.

STEWART, James Sinclair (retired) 2 Calderwood Court, Montpellier Parade, Cheltenham GL50 1UA Tel: 01242 578070 — MB BS 1955 Lond.; MD Lond. 1970; FRCP Lond. 1975, M 1960. Hon. Cons. Phys. (Gastroenterol.) W. Middlx. Univ. Hosp. Isleworth & Teddington Memor. Hosp.; Hon. Sen. Lect. Char. Cross & W.m. Med. Sch. Lond.; Edx-Examr. RCP Lond. Prev: Tutor & Sen. Regist. (Med.) Roy. Postgrad. Med. Sch. Lond. & Hammersmith Hosp.

STEWART, James Wallace (retired) Hatherleigh, Tower Road, Hindhead GU26 6SP Tel: 01428 604770 — MB BS 1944 Lond.; FRCP Lond. 1980, M 1973; MRCS Eng. LRCP Lond. 1944; FRCPath 1963. Prev: Cons. Haemat. Lond. Clinic.

STEWART, Jane Alison 11 Rectory Terrace, Gosforth, Newcastle upon Tyne NE3 1XY — MB ChB 1988 Ed.

STEWART, Jeanie (retired) 49 Bryansglen Park, Bangor BT20 3RS Tel: 01247 461528 — MB BCh BAO 1949 Belf.

STEWART, Jennie Patterson (retired) 1/30 Claycot Park, Ladywell Avenue, Corstorphine, Edinburgh EH12 7LG Tel: 0131 334 4768 — MB ChB 1930 St. And. Prev: Ho. Surg. & Obstetr. Redlands Hosp. Wom. Glas.

STEWART, Jill Amanda Northamptonshire Centre For Oncology, Northampton Gen NHS Trust, Northampton NN1 5BD Tel: 01604 545238 — MB BS 1973 Lond.; FRCR 1979. (Middlx.) Clin. Oncologist, N.amptonshire Centre For Oncol. N.ampton Gen NHS Trust N.ampton NN1 5BD. Prev: Sen. Regist. & Regist. (Radiother.) Ch.ill Hosp. Oxf.

STEWART, Mrs Joan Elizabeth 13 Howard Place, St Andrews KY16 9HL — MB ChB 1946 St. And. Prev: Med. Off. W. Scotl. Blood Transfus. Serv.; Ho. Surg. Dundee Roy. Infirm. & Roy. Hosp. Sick Childr. Edin.; Jun. Hosp. Med. Off. King's Cross Hosp. Dundee.

STEWART, John (retired) Bentink Crescent, Troon Tel: 01292 314110 — MB ChB 1945 Glas.; MB ChB (Commend.) Glas. 1945; FRCPath 1971, M 1964. Prev: Cons. Pathol. Ayrsh. Hosp. Gp.

STEWART, John Alan 2 Peartree Court, Old Orchards, Lymington SO41 3TF Tel: 01590 672411 — MB ChB 1954 Ed.; FRCP Ed. 1977, M 1962; MRCPsych 1971; DPM Eng. 1960. (Ed.) Prev: Cons. Psychiat. Hellingly Hosp. Hailsham, Qu Vict. Hosp. E. Grinstead & Community Ment. Health Centre, Uckfield.

STEWART, John Alexander Bannatyne Plandons, Long Melford, Sudbury CO10 9ET — MB BS 1949 Lond.; MRCS Eng. LRCP Lond. 1949; DObst RCOG 1954. (St. Thos.) Prev: Ho. Phys. Salisbury Gen. Infirm.; Ho. Phys. & Cas. Off. Lambeth Hosp.; Obst. Ho. Surg. Roy. Berks. Hosp. Reading.

STEWART, John Alexander Mackenzie (retired) Sunnylaw, 42 Bonhard Road, Scone, Perth PH2 6QB Tel: 01738 52454 — MB ChB 1949 Glas.; MRCGP 1960. Prev: Ho. Surg. Glas. Roy. Infirm.

STEWART, John Angus 89 Wyke Road, Weymouth DT4 9QN Tel: 0130 575681 — MB BS 1948 Lond.; LMSSA Lond. 1947. (Guy's) Prev: Ho. Surg. Torbay Hosp. Torquay; Capt. RAMC.

STEWART, John Barrie (retired) 20 The Gables, Oxshott, Leatherhead KT22 0SD Tel: 01372 843378 Fax: 01372 844497 Email: dr.iain@stewart1482.freeserve.co.uk — MB ChB 1957 Ed.; FRCPath 1981, M 1969; DRCPath 1967; DTM & H Lond 1961. Prev: Cons. Histopath. Epsom Gen. Hosp.

STEWART, John Charles Marshall Marshallstown, Downpatrick BT30 8AL; Efamol Ltd., Woodbridge Meadows, Guildford GU1 1BA — MB ChB 1978 Dundee; PhD (Chem.) Camb. 1969; BSc Belf. 1966; MFPM 1990. Med. Dir. Scotia Pharmaceut. Guildford.

STEWART, Mr John Dawson Macrae (retired) The Sherburne Hospital, 78 Broyle Road, Chichester PO19 4BE Tel: 01243 775952

STEWART

Fax: 01243 536108 — MB BChir 1959 Camb.; MA Camb. 1959; FRCS Eng. 1966; MRCS Eng. LRCP Lond. 1958. Indep. Cons. Surg. Orthop. & Medico-Legal Adviser Chichester. Prev: Cons. Surg. (Orthop.) Chichester HA.

STEWART, John Gordon (retired) 1 Wallings Lane, Silverdale, Carnforth LA5 0SA Tel: 01524 701325 Email: doc@gordon3.freeserve.co.uk — MB ChB 1951 Glas. Prev: GP Atherstone.

STEWART, John Gordon Hume Argyll Street Surgery, 246 Argyll Street, Dunoon PA23 7HW Tel: 01369 702067 Fax: 01369 706680 — MB ChB 1973 Glas.; MRCGP 1977. (Glas.)

STEWART, John Hatrick The Health Centre, 73 Main Street, Stoneyburn EH47 8BY — MB ChB 1983 Dublin; 1988 MRCGP Edin. (Trinity College, Dublin)

STEWART, John Hirst (retired) Dorter House, Buccleuch St., Melrose TD6 9LD — MB ChB 1950 Glas.; MRCGP 1980. Prev: GP Glas.

STEWART, John Hubert Hall, OBE (retired) 43 Coolsythe Road, Randalstown, Antrim BT41 3HF Tel: 01849 472801 — MB BCh (Hons.) BAO Belf. 1952. Additional Dep. Forens. Med. Off. Antrim Sub-Div. Roy. Ulster Constab; JP. Prev: Resid. Ho. Off. Roy. Vict. Hosp. Belf. & Roy. Belf. Hosp. Sick Childr.

STEWART, John Lumsdaine (retired) Apartment 36, Hometay House, 2 High St., Monifieth, Dundee DD5 4BN Tel: 01382 533555 — MD 1955 Ed.; MB ChB 1945; MFCM 1974. Prev: SCMO Norf. AHA.

STEWART, John Malcolm The Anchorage, Green Road, Thorpe, Egham TW20 8QN Tel: 01344 843185 Fax: 01344 843185 — MB ChB 1956 St. And.; DTM & H Eng. 1964. (St. And.) Cons. Adviser BAMSTA. Prev: Sen. Med. Off. Brit. Airways Health Serv.; Regtl. Med. Off. Life Guards; GP Portsmouth.

STEWART, John Matthew Archibald Craig (retired) 1 Villiers Crescent, Eccleston, St Helens WA10 5HP Tel: 01744 23810 — MB ChB 1950 Birm.; BSc Birm. 1947; MRCPsych 1971; DPM Eng. 1955. Prev: Cons. Psychiat., Sen. Hosp. Med. Off. & Sen. Regist. (Psychiat.) Rainhill Hosp.

STEWART, Mr John Oscar Reginald (retired) 2 Northgate, Lincoln LN2 1QS Tel: 01522 523231 — MB BCh BAO 1945 Belf.; MB BCh BAO (Hons.) Belf. 1945; FRCS Eng. 1951; DHMSA 1990. Prev: Cons. Surg. Co. Hosp. Lincoln & Horncastle War Memor. Hosp.

STEWART, John Owen (retired) 26 Conway Mews, Brompton, Gillingham ME7 5BD Tel: 01634 403880 Fax: 01634 403880 — MRCS Eng. LRCP Lond. 1965; BSc (Anat.) Lond. 1960, MB BS 1965; FRCPath 1986, M 1974; DObst. RCOG 1967. Prev: Cons. Path. Dist. Laborat. Severalls Hosp. Colchester.

STEWART, John Simon Watson, Bt Dept of Radiotherapy, Charing Cross Hospital, London W6 8AF — MB BS 1980 Lond.; BSc Lond. 1977, MB BS 1980; FRCP Lond. 1994; MRCP (UK) 1983; FRCR 1986. Cons. Radiother. & Oncol. St. Mary's Hosp. Lond. & Sen. Lect. (Radiother. & Oncol.) Imperial Sch. of Med. Socs: ASCO; ESTRO; RAD Soc. Prev: Clin. Research Fell. Imperial Cancer Research Fund.

STEWART, John Stewart Simpson 74 The Common, Parbold, Wigan WN8 7EA — MB ChB 1951 Glas.

STEWART, John Theophile Berry 4 Penyfai Lane, Llanelli SA15 4EN — MRCS Eng. LRCP Lond. 1950; MA Camb. 1951, MB BChir 1950. (Westm.)

STEWART, John Tytler (retired) 4 Larch Road, Glasgow G41 5DA Tel: 0141 427 2832 — MB ChB 1955 Glas.; FRCOG 1978, M 1964. Prev: Cons. O & G Stobhill Gen. Hosp. Glas.

STEWART, Mr Jonathan 20 Claverdon Drive, Sutton Coldfield B74 3AH — MD 1986 Leeds; MB ChB 1978; FRCS Ed. 1982; FRCS Eng. 1982; T(S) 1991. Prev: Cancer Research Campaign Fell. MRC Camb.

STEWART, Jonathan 269 Craigie Drive, Dundee DD4 7UE — MB ChB 1992 Dundee.

STEWART, Joseph Gordon The Highlands, 4 Highlands Gardens, St Leonards-on-Sea TN38 0HT Tel: 01424 433234 — MB ChB 1952 Glas.

STEWART, Julia Louise 14 The Coaches, Holywood BT18 0LE — MB BCh BAO 1988 Belf.

STEWART, Karen Rosalind 2 Queensway, Grantham NG31 9QD — MB ChB 1991 Leicester.

STEWART, Kathleen Heyland (retired) 9 Prior Bolton Street, London N1 2NX Tel: 020 7359 1862 — MB BCh BAO 1943 Belf.; DObst RCOG 1947.

STEWART, Kay 17 Vicar Lane, Woodhouse, Sheffield S13 7JH — MB ChB 1994 Glas.; BSc (Hons.) Glas. 1992. SHO (Med.) N. Gen. Hosp. Sheff. Prev: SHO (Med.) Airedale Gen. Hosp. Keighley.

STEWART, Keith Ramsay Kent Paediatric Audiology Service, Cobtree, Preston Hall, Maidstone ME20 7NJ Tel: 01622 225703; 3 Park House, 41 East Street, Faversham ME13 8AU Tel: 01795 534559 Fax: 01795 534559 Email: keith.kpas@lineone.net — MRCS Eng. LRCP Lond. 1969; MSc Manch. 1993; DObst RCOG 1971. (Guy's) Assoc. Special. community Paediat. Audiol. Socs: Fell. Roy. Soc. Med.; Brit. Soc. Audiol.; Brit. Assoc. Communtiy DRS in Audiol. Prev: Ho. Surg. (ENT) Guy's Hosp. Lond.; Ho. Phys. Guy's Hosp. Gp.; Gen. Practitioner Huntingdon 1974-1999.

STEWART, Mr Kenneth John — MB ChB 1990 Aberd.; MD 1999; 2001 FRCS Ed. Plast.; BMedBiol Aberd. 1989; FRCS Ed. 1995. (Aberdeen) SpR Plastic Surg., Edin. Socs: Fell. Roy. Coll. Surgs. Ed.; Brit. Assoc. Plastic Surg. Trainee Assoc.; Brit. Assoc. Head & neck Oncologists. Assoc. Prev: Research Regist. (Plastic & Reconstructr. Surg.) St. Geo. Hosp. Sydney, Austral.; SpR Plastic Surg., Aberd. Roy. Infirm.; Cranicracial Fell. Chelsea & W. Minster Hosp.

STEWART, Kenneth Macbeth (retired) 4 Holt Drive, Kirby Muxloe, Leicester LE9 2EX Tel: 0116 239 3542 — MB ChB 1953 Ed.; DTM & H Liverp. 1957. Prev: Ho. Phys. & Ho. Surg. (Obst.) Bangour Hosp.

STEWART, Kenneth McLauchlan Woodlands, Inverdale, Aviemore PH22 1QH — MB ChB 1958 Ed.

STEWART, Mr Kenneth Sloan Four Winds, Loftbrae, Gargunnock, Stirling FK8 3DH Tel: 01786 73776 — MD Ed. 1977, MB ChB 1962; FRCS Ed. 1969; FRCOG 1983, M 1969, DFM 1988, DObst. 1966. (Ed.) Cons. Obst. Stirling Roy. Infirm. Prev: Sen Research Fell. Univ. Rhodesia & Cons. Harari Hosp. Salisbury; Sen. Regist. & Clin. Tutor Qu. Eliz. Med. Centre Birm.; Regist. Aberd. Roy. Infirm.

STEWART, Mr Kenneth Sutherland (retired) 5 Gainsborough Drive, Gunton Park, Lowestoft NR32 4LX Tel: 01502 584934 Fax: 01502 584934 — LRCP LRCS Ed. LRFPS Glas. 1944; FRCS Ed. 1952. Prev: Cons. Orthop. Surg. Gt. Yarmouth & Waveney HA.

STEWART, Kevin Owen Royal Hampshire County Hospital, Romsey Road, Winchester SO22 5DG Tel: 01962 825569 Fax: 01962 825570 — MB BCh BAO 1982 Belf.; FRCP 1997, MRCP (UK) 1985. Cons. Phys. Roy. Hants. Co. Hosp. Winchester. Prev: Cons. Phys. Newham HA; Sen. Regist. (Geriat. Med.) Whittington & Roy. N.. Hosps. Lond.; Sen. Regist. (Geriat.) Islington & Bloomsbury HA.

STEWART, Laura 26 Scotstoun Park, South Queensferry EH30 9PQ — MB ChB 1991 Ed.; MRCP (UK) 1994. (Univ. Edin.) Specialist Regist. Paediat. Roy. Hosp. for Sick Childr. Yorkhill Glas. Prev: Regist. (Paediat.) Ninewells Hosp. Dundee.

STEWART, Mr Laurence Herbert BUPA Murrayfield Hospital, 122 Corstorphine Road, Edinburgh EH12 6UD Tel: 0131 441 7112; Bonaly Tower, 65 Bonaly Road, Edinburgh EH13 0PB — MB ChB 1982 Aberd.; MD Aberd. 1994; FRCS Ed. 1986. (Aberd.) Cons. Urol. W.. Gen. Hosp. Edin. Socs: Internat. Continence Soc.; Brit. Assn. Cancer Research; Assoc. Mem. BAUS. Prev: Sen. Regist. (Urol.) Cardiff Roy. Infirm. Wales & Aberd. Roy. Infirm.; Sen. Regist. (Urol.) ChristCh. Pub. Hosp., NZ.

STEWART, Lawrence Guthrie (retired) 39 Kings Road, Elderslie, Johnstone PA5 9LY Tel: 01505 22060 — MB ChB 1958 Glas.

STEWART, Lesley Jane Benview, off Culterhouse Road, Peterculter AB14 0NT — MB ChB 1968 Aberd.; DCH RCPS Glas. 1979.

STEWART, Lesley MacDonald (retired) 178 Ayr Road, Newton Mearns, Glasgow G77 6DX Tel: 0141 639 1069 — MB ChB 1947 Glas. JP. Prev: Assoc. Specialist Mearnskirk Hosp. & Vict. Infirm. Chest Clin. Glas.

STEWART, Linda Bryson Department of Neuroanaesthesia, Institute of Neurological Sciences, Southern General Hospital, 1345 Govan Road, Glasgow G51 4TF — MB ChB 1987 Glas.; FRCA 1991. (Univ. Glas.) Cons. Neuroanaesth. S.. Gen. Hosp. Glas. Prev: Sen. Regist. (Anaesth.) Roy. Infirm. Ed.; Research Fell. (Neuroanaesth. & Neurosurg.) Glas. Univ.

STEWART

STEWART, Lucy Margaret Flat 3 The Rowans, Prince Edwards Road, Lewes BN7 1BD — MB ChB 1988 Bristol; MRCPC (Paed.) 1995; MRCGP 1992. (Bris. Univ.)

STEWART, Margaret Pathology Department, Royal Lancaster Infirmary, Ashton Road, Lancaster LA1 4RB Tel: 01524 583793 — MB BS 1975 Lond.; BSc 1972 Lond.; MRCPath 1986. (Lond. Hosp.) Cons. Histopath. Lancaster Acute Hosps. NHS Trust. Prev: Sen. Regist. (Histopath.) Derby Roy. Infirm., City Hosp., Univ. Hosps. Nottm. & Lancaster Moor Hosp.; Regist. (Path.) Leeds Gen. Infirm.

STEWART, Margaret Elizabeth Hairmyres Hospital, East Kilbride, Glasgow G75 8RG Tel: 01355 572640 — MB ChB 1974 Aberd.; BMedBiol Aberd. 1971; FRCP Glas. 1989; MRCP (UK) 1978. Cons. Phys. (Geriat. Med.) Hairmyres Hosp. Socs: Brit. Soc. for Rehabil. Med.; Brit. Geriat. Soc.; Pk.inson's Dis. Soc. Prev: Cons. Phys. (Geriat. Med.) Law Hosp. Carluke; Sen. Regist. (Geriat. Med.) Gtr. Glas. Health Bd. W.. Dist.; Regist. (Med. & Haemophilia) Glas. Roy. Infirm.

STEWART, Margaret Helen Department of Community Health, Udston Hospital, Hamilton ML3 9LA — MB ChB 1974 Glas.

STEWART, Margaret Jean Winter (retired) The Anchorage, Green Road, Thorpe, Egham TW20 8QN Tel: 01344 843185 Fax: 01344 843185 Email: mjwstewart@msn.com — MB ChB St. And. 1956; FFPHM RCP (UK) 1990; MFCM 1974; DPH Eng. 1971. Prev: Dir. Health Purchasing & Pub. Health SW Surrey HA Guildford.

STEWART, Margaret Laird The Danders, 5 Main St., Livingston Village, Livingston EH54 7AF Tel: 01506 411306 Fax: 01506 460757 — MB ChB 1967 St. And.; BSc St. And. 1963. Med. Off. Howden Occupat. Health Serv. Livingston.

STEWART, Margaret McGregor (retired) 9 Bartholomew Terrace, Exeter EX4 3BW Tel: 01392 431732 — MB ChB Glas. 1945. Prev: Clin. Med. Off. (Community Health) SW Surrey & NE Hants. HAs.

STEWART, Margaret Roberta (retired) 13A Davenant Road, Oxford OX2 8BT Tel: 01865 553067 — MB BCh BAO 1943 Belf.

STEWART, Margaret Sheila Wayside, South Stoke, Bath BA2 7DJ — MB ChB 1989 Manch. SHO (Ophth.) Ayr. Hosp.

STEWART, Mr Mark Department of Surgery, Darent Valley Hospital, Dartford DA2 8DA Tel: 01322 428100 Fax: 01322 428635 Email: mark.stewart@dag-tr.sthames.nhs.uh; The White House, Green Lane, Under River, Sevenoaks TN15 0SB — MB BS Lond. 1970; MS Lond. 1984; FRCS Eng. 1977; MRCS Eng. LRCP Lond. 1970. Cons. Surg. & Urol. Joyce Green Hosp. Dartford Kent. Socs: Assn. Surg. & Assoc. Mem. Brit. Assn. Urol. Surg.; AUGIS; Assoc. Of Colo-Rectal Surg.s (ACPGBI). Prev: Cons. Surg. & Sen. Lect. Baragwanath Hosp. & Univ. Witwatersra Johannesburg, S. Afr.

STEWART, Martin Joseph Knockavally, Rossglass Road, Killough, Downpatrick BT30 7Q — MB BCh BAO 1982 Belf., MB BCh Belf. 1982.

STEWART, Mary Dickson Cameron 3F1, 29 Springvalley Terrace, Edinburgh EH10 4PZ — MB ChB 1991 Aberd.

STEWART, Mrs Mary Donaldson (retired) 7 Roseland Crescent, Marton, Middlesbrough TS7 8AH Tel: 01642 313814 Email: mds@roseland.u-net.com — MB ChB Glas. 1945. Prev: Cytol. Progr. Co-ordinator S. Tees HA.

STEWART, Mary Elizabeth Fife Primary Care NHS Trust, Whyteman's Brae Hospital, Whyteman's Brae, Kirkcaldy KY1 2ND Tel: 01592 643355 Fax: 01592 643790 — MB ChB 1981 Aberd.; MRCPsych 1986; T(Psychiat.) 1992. Cons. Gen. Adult Psychiat. Fife Primary Care NHS Trust Whyteman's Brae Hosp. Kirkcaldy. Prev: Sen. Regist. (Psychiat.) Roy. Edin. Hosp.; Research Regist. Crichton Roy. Hosp. Dumfries; Regist. (Psychiat.) Glas. HB.

STEWART, Mrs Mary Felicity Department of Clinical Biochemistry, Salford Royal Hospitals NHS Trust, Stott Lane, Salford M6 8HD Tel: 0161 787 4971 Fax: 0161 788 7443 Email: fstewart@fs1.ho.man.ac.uk — MB BS 1980 Lond.; BSc (Biochem.) Lond. 1977, MD 1992; MRCPath 1993. (Univ. Coll. Hosp.) Cons. Chem. Path. Salford Roy. Hosp.s NHS Trust Salford. Socs: Assn. Clin. Biochem.; Brit. Hyperlipid. Assn.; Soc. Endocrinol. Prev: Sen. Regist. (Chem. Path.) Manch. Roy. Infirm. & Salford Roy. Hosp.s NHS Trust Salford; Regist. (Chem. Path.) Wythenshawe Hosp. Manch.

STEWART, Mary Patricia Dunlop 10 Meeks Road, Falkirk FK2 7ES Tel: 01324 619930; The Stable House, Feddal, Braco FK15 9RA Tel: 01786 880204 — MB ChB 1968 Glas. Prev: Jun. Ho. Off. (Med. & Surg.) Stirling Roy. Infirm.

STEWART, Mary Wendover St James Road Surgery, 22 St. James Road, Torpoint PL11 2BH Tel: 01752 812404 Fax: 01752 816436 — MB ChB 1970 Cape Town; MB ChB 1970 Cape Town.

***STEWART, Melissa** Morham Burn, Haddington EH41 4LQ — MB BS 1996 Lond.

STEWART, Michael David, Surg. Lt. RN 10 Moody Road, Fareham PO14 2BP — MB ChB 1987 Manch. Regist. (Med.) RNH Haslar Gosport. Prev: Med. Off. RN Air Station Culdrose; Med. Off. RN Submarine Escape Train. Unit; SHO (Med.) Derriford Hosp. Plymouth.

STEWART, Michael John James Cook University Hospital, Middlesbrough TS4 3BW Tel: 01642 854623 Fax: 01642 854190 Email: michael.stuart@email.stahnst.northy.nhs.uk — MB ChB 1986 Ed.; MD Ed. 1997; MRCP (UK) 1989; FCRP 2000. Cons. Cardiol. James Cook Univ. Hosp. Middlesbrough. Socs: Brit. Hypertens. Soc. Brit. Cardiac. Soc. Prev: Sen. Regist. Cardiovasc. Med. S.. Gen. Hosp. Glas.; Career Regist. (Cardiol.) Glas. Roy. Infirm.; Brit. Heart Fondat. Jun. Research Fell. Dept. Cardiol. W. Gen. Hosp. Edin.

STEWART, Lt. Col. Michael Peter MacGregor, Lt.-Col. RAMC Department of Orthopaedic Surgery, Bishop Auckland General Hospital, Cockton Hill Road, Bishop Auckland DL14 6AD Tel: 01988 454090; Beckwath, Romaldkirk, Barnard Castle DL12 9EE Fax: 01833 650917 — MB ChB 1979 Aberd.; FRCS (Orth.) 1994; FRCS Glas. 1988. (Aberd.) Cons. Orthop. Trauma Surg. S. Durh. NHS Trust Bishop Auckland Gen. Hosp. Bishop Auckland; Cons. Adviser (Orthops. & Trauma) Dir. Gen. Army Med. Servs. Socs: Fell. BOA; Brit. Shoulder & Elbow Soc.; Brit. Trauma Soc. Prev: Cons. Orthop. & Trauma Surg. The Friarage Hosp. N.allerton N. Yorks.

STEWART, Moira Connell Department of Child Health, Institute of Clinical Science, Grosvenor Road, Belfast BT12 6BJ; 5 The Point, Groomsport, Bangor BT19 6JN Tel: 01247 464701 — MB BCh BAO 1977 Belf.; MD Belf. 1986; FRCP Lond. 1994; MRCP (UK) 1982; DCH Dub. 1981. Cons. Paediat. & Sen. Lect. Inst. Clin. Sci. Belf. Socs: Brit. Paediat. Assn.; Brit. Assn. Community Child Health; (Sec.) Ulster Paediat. Assn.

STEWART, Monnica Charlotte (retired) 7 Station Road, Kintbury, Hungerford RG17 9UP Tel: 01488 658615 Fax: 01488 658688 — MB BS 1950 Durh.; DObst RCOG 1953. Prev: Princip. Med. Off. (Adult Health) Basingstoke & N. Hants. HA.

STEWART, Morag Elmbank Group, Foresterhill Health Centre, Westburn Road, Aberdeen AB25 2AY Tel: 01224 696949 Fax: 01224 691650 — MB ChB 1994 Aberd. (Univ. Aberd.) Socs: BMA; Assoc. Mem. RCGP.

STEWART, Mr Murray 5 King Edward Road, Jordanhill, Glasgow G13 1QW — MB ChB 1986 Aberd.; FRCS Ed. 1994; FRCS Glas. 1990. Career Regist. (ENT) Roy. Alexandra Hosp. Paisley; Clin. Asst. (A & E) W.. Infirm. Glas. Socs: Assoc. Mem. Brit. Assn. Otolaryngol. Head & Neck Surgs.; Otolaryngol. Research Soc. Prev: SHO Rotat. (Surg.) W. Scotl. Train. Scheme.

STEWART, Murray Willis 6 Woodlands Grange, Forest Hall, Newcastle upon Tyne NE12 9DF — BM 1984 Soton.; BM Soton 1984; DM Soton. 1995; MRCP (UK) 1989. Cons. Phys. (Diabetes & Endocrinol.) Newc.; Hon. Sen. Lect. Newc. Univ. Prev: MRC Lect. & Sen. Regist. (Diabetes & Endocrinol.) Newc. Univ.; Regist. (Med., Diabetes & Endocrinol.) Roy. Vict. Infirm. Newc. u. Tyne; Regist. (Med.) CrossHo. Hosp. Kilmarnock.

***STEWART, Myra Judith** 47 Brackendale, Potters Bar EN6 2LP — MB ChB 1996 Birm.

STEWART, Neil Andrew Russell 1 Rose Cottages, Chelmsford Road, Great Waltham, Chelmsford CM3 1AG — MB ChB 1989 Aberd.; MRCP (UK) 1992; DTM & H RCP Lond. 1993.

STEWART, Neil Grant Laurelview, St Mary's Drive, Dunblane FK15 0HB — MB ChB 1993 Ed.

STEWART, Nicholas Church Lane Medical Centre, Orchid Rise, Off Church Lane, Scunthorpe DN15 7AN Tel: 01724 864341 Fax: 01724 876441 — MB ChB 1986 Sheff. Trainee GP Lancaster VTS. Prev: Ho. Off. (Gen. Med.) York Dist. Hosp.; Ho. Off. (Gen. Surg.) Pontefract Gen. Infirm.

STEWART, Mr Owen Gavin Low Barn, Brocket View, Acaster Malbis, York YO23 2PY Tel: 01904 707493 Email: owenstewart@fsmail.net — MB BS 1993 Newc.; FRCOphth 1997. Specialist Regist. Ophth. Yorks. Rotat. Leeds Gen. Infirm. Socs: MDU. Prev: SHO (Ophth.) St. Jas. Univ. Hosp. Leeds; SHO (Ophth.)

STEWART

Bradford Roy. Infirm.; SHO (Ophth.) N. Riding Infirm. Middlesbrough.

STEWART, Pamela Doris Beckwath, Romaldkirk, Barnard Castle DL12 9EE — MB ChB 1985 Cape Town. (Univ. Cape Town)

STEWART, Patricia Antonia East Aquhorthies Farmhouse, Inverurie AB51 5JL — BM 1982 Soton.; DIP EIN Mirco, Lond. Hosp. Med. Coll 1987; MRCPath 1998. Prev: Sen. Regist. In Med. MicroBiol. P/T, Soton. Gen. Hosp.

STEWART, Patricia Jean Martin, Barr and Stewart, Eastwick Park Avenue, Great Bookham, Leatherhead KT23 3ND Tel: 01372 452081 Fax: 01372 451680; 4 Sayers Close, Fetcham, Leatherhead KT22 9PE Tel: 01372 450485 — MB ChB St. And. 1968; DObst RCOG 1971.

STEWART, Patrick Carlin 23 Eastleigh Drive, Belfast BT4 3DX — MB BCh BAO 1992 Belf.

STEWART, Paul Alexander Bromsgrove Street, Kidderminster DY10 1PH — MB ChB 1978 Birm. GP Medico-Legal Advisor Independ. Med.; Hon. Med. Adviser Wyre Forest Athletics Assn.; Med. Off. Brit. Sugar Kidderminster. Prev: Regist. (Radiother. & Oncol.) Velindre Hosp. WhitCh. Cardiff; Regist. (Med.) New Cross Hosp. Wednesfield Wolverhampton; SHO (O & G) Wordsley Hosp. Stourbridge.

STEWART, Professor Paul Michael Department of Medicine, Queen Elizabeth Hospital, Edgbaston, Birmingham B15 2TH Tel: 0121 627 2380 Fax: 0121 627 2384 Email: p.m.stewart@bham.ac.uk; Broadlands, Salter Street, Hockley Heath, Solihull B94 6BY — MB ChB 1982 Ed.; F Med Sci 1999; FRCP Lond. 1995; MD Ed. 1989; MRCP (UK) 1985. (Edinburgh) Prof. of Med. & Hon. Cons. Phys. Birm.; Prof. Med. Socs: Endocrine Soc.; Soc. for Endocrinol.; Acad. of Med. Sci. Prev: Lect. & Hon. Sen. Regist. (Med.) Qu. Eliz. Hosp. Birm.; Sir Stanley Davidson Lect. (Med.) Univ. Edin.; MRC Train. Fell.

STEWART, Pauline Mary Drymen Road Surgery, 96 Drymen Road, Bearsden, Glasgow G61 2SY Tel: 0141 942 9494; 24 Station Road, Bearsden, Glasgow G61 4AL — MB ChB 1978 Glas.; MRCGP 1987. Prev: Trainee GP Guildford VTS.

STEWART, Peter 20 Whiteley Wood Road, Sheffield S11 7FE — BM BCh 1971 Oxf.; MRCOG 1979. Cons. O & G Sheff. Health Auth.

STEWART, Philippa Jane 1 Borrowdale Close, Gamston, Nottingham NG2 6PD — MB BCh 1993 Wales.

STEWART, Rebekah Angela Louise 66 The Causeway, Edinburgh EH15 3PZ — MB BChir 1990 Camb.; FRCS 1994; FRCR 1997.

STEWART, Rhona Margaret Royal Hospital, Calow, Chesterfield S44 5BL Tel: 01246 277271 — MB BS 1973 Lond.; FRCP Lond. 1992; MRCP (UK) 1978; FRCPath 1992, M 1981. (Middlx.) Cons. Haemat. Roy. Hosp. Chesterfield. Prev: Cons. Haemat. Scunthorpe & Goole Hosps.

STEWART, Mr Richard James Department Paediatric Surgery, University Hospital, Queens Medical Centre, Nottingham NG7 2UH Tel: 0115 942 1421; Meadow View, 73 Tollerton Lane, Tollerton, Nottingham NG12 4FS Tel: 0115 937 2434 — MD 1988 Belf.; MB BCh BAO 1980; FRCS Ed. 1984. Cons. Paediat. Surg. Univ. Hosp. Qu. Med. Centre & City Hosp. Nottm. Socs: Fell. Roy. Coll. Surg. (Paediat.) 1992; Brit. Assn. Paediat. Surg. & BMA. Prev: Sen. Regist. Roy. Belf. Hosp. for Sick Childr. & Roy. Childr. Hosp. Melbourne Austral.

***STEWART, Robert Charles** (4F2) 9 Warrender Park Terrace, Edinburgh EH9 1JA — MB ChB 1996 Ed.

STEWART, Robert Clifford, Lt.-Col. RAMC c/o Ulster Bank, Shaftesbury Square, Belfast BT2 — MB BCh BAO 1949 Belf.; FRCPath 1976, M 1964; DTM & H Eng. 1961. Asst. Prof. Path. RAM Coll. Millbank. Socs: Assn. Clin. Pathols. & Path. Soc. Gt. Brit.

STEWART, Robert Curle Park Medical Centre, Shavington Avenue, Newton Lane, Chester CH2 3RD Tel: 01244 324136 Fax: 01244 317257; Rock House, Village Road, Christleton, Chester CH3 7AS Tel: 01244 332657 — MB ChB 1979 Manch.; MRCGP 1991; DRCOG 1981. Clin. Asst. (Coloscopy) Chester. Prev: Trainee GP Cheadle Hulme Health Centre Manch.; SHO (Paediat.) Booth Hall Childr. Hosp. Manch.; SHO (O & G) St. Mary's Hosp. Manch.

STEWART, Robert Evan (retired) 9C/1 Merchiston Park, Edinburgh EH10 4PW Tel: 0131 229 7717 — MB ChB 1949 Glas.; FRCGP 1981, M 1963; DObst RCOG 1953. Prev: Med. Off. & Princip. Lect. (Health Educat.) Moray Ho. Coll. Edin.

STEWART, Robert Gregor 26 Westfield Grove, Wakefield WF1 3RS Tel: 01924 2344 — MB ChB 1946 Glas. (Univ. Glas.) Prev: Capt. RAMC; Cas. Off. Manor Hosp. Walsall; Ho. Surg. Whiston Co. Hosp. Whiston.

STEWART, Robert Howard Mackenzie Donkleywood House, Donkleywood, Hexham NE48 1AQ Tel: 01434 240303 — MB ChB 1940 Liverp.; MD Liverp. 1948; FFCM 1972. (Liverp.) Prev: Sen. Admin. Med. Off. Newc. RHB; WHO Consult. 1966.

STEWART, Robert Ian Child Guidance Clinic, Tanner St., Winchester SO23 8AD Tel: 01962 855477; Morecroft, Muss Lane, King's Somborne, Stockbridge SO20 6PE — MB ChB 1977 Glas.; BA (Hons.) N. Carolina 1972; MRCPsych. 1981. Cons. Child & Family Psychiat. Roy. Hants. Co. Hosp. Winchester.

STEWART, Robert James Section of Epidemiology, Institute of Psychiatry, De Crespigny Park, Denmark Hill, London SE5 8AF — MB ChB 1991 Leeds; MSc 2000 London. Socs: Roy. Coll. Psychiat.

STEWART, Robert More The Surgery, Old Road, Elham, Canterbury CT4 6UH Tel: 01303 840213 Fax: 01303 893817; White Gate House, Acrise, Folkestone CT18 8JU — MB BS 1978 Lond.; MRCS Eng. LRCP Lond. 1978; DRCOG 1980. GP Princip.; Chairm. Shepway PCG. Socs: Local Med. Comm. (Kent.). Prev: Regist. (Psychiat.) Hammersmith & St. Bernards Hosp.; SHO (Obst.) W. Lond. & Char. Cross Hosp. Lond.; SHO (Paediat.) Whipps Cross Hosp. Lond.

STEWART, Roberta Aitchison (retired) 17 Framingham Road, Sale M33 3ST Tel: 0161 973 2876 — MB ChB Manch. 1946. Prev: Gen. Practitioner,Wythen Shawe Manch.

STEWART, Roderick James Ballenmuir, Newbold, Forres IV36 — MB ChB 1963 St. And.; DObst RCOG 1966.

STEWART, Ronald Dawson Miller Maryhill Practice, Elgin Health Centre, Maryhill, Elgin IV30 1AT Tel: 01343 543788 Fax: 01343 551604 — MB ChB 1978 Aberd.; MRCP (UK) 1981; MRCGP 1984; DRCOG 1983. Prev: Regist. (Med.) S. Grampian Health Dist.; Research Fell. (Med.) Univ. Aberd.; SHO (Obst.) Bellshill Matern. Hosp.

STEWART, Rorie John Gordon Old Machar Medical Practice, 526 King Street, Aberdeen AB24 5RS Tel: 01224 480324 Fax: 01224 276121; 25 Tarvit Avenue, Cupar KY15 5BN — MB ChB 1987 Dundee; BMSc (Hons.) Dund 1984; MRCGP 1991.

STEWART, Rosamund Chad Hanwell Health Centre, 20 Church Road, Hanwell, London W7 1DR Tel: 020 8579 7337 Fax: 020 8579 7337; 5 Park Avenue, London SW14 8AT Tel: 020 8878 7114 — MBBS 1978 Lond.; DRCOG 1981. (Char. Cross)

STEWART, Rosemary Ann 2FL, 29 Spottiswoode St., Edinburgh EH9 1DQ — MB ChB 1987 Ed.

STEWART, Rosemary Anne 98A Galgorm Road, Ballymena BT42 1AA — MB BCh BAO 1992 Belf.

STEWART, Rosemary Jean 4390 Comanche Drive, Boulder CO 80303, USA Tel: 00 1 303 4942903 Fax: 00 1 303 4923674; 8 Dean Terrace, Edinburgh EH4 1ND — MB ChB 1988 Ed.; MRCGP 1995; DRCOG 1991. Consultancy Research Assoc. Univ. Colarado, Boulder, USA. Prev: GP/Regist. Links Med. Centre Edin.

STEWART, Sheila Christine (retired) Cormorants, Channel Way, Fairlight, Hastings TN35 4BP Tel: 01424 813676 — MB BS Lond. 1962; MRCS Eng. LRCP Lond. 1961; MRCPsych 1978; DObst RCOG 1965; DPM Eng. 1974.

STEWART, Sheila Constance Anne (retired) Hill House, Loch Striven, Dunoon PA23 8RG Tel: 01369 820228 — MB ChB 1952 Glas. Prev: Anaesth. Greenock & Dist. Hosps.

STEWART, Sheila Louise Elvang, Queenshaugh, Riverside, Stirling FK8 1XH — MB ChB 1987 Glas.; FRCR 1993. Cons. (Radiol.) S.ern Gen. Hosp. Glas. Prev: Cons. (Radiol.) Falkirk & Dist. Roy. Infirm.; Sen. Regist. (Radiodiag.) Roy. Infirm. Edin.; Regist. (Radiodiag.) S.. Gen. Hosp. Glas.

***STEWART, Shelagh Fraser** 8 Fairview Avenue, Alsager, Stoke-on-Trent ST7 2NW — MB ChB 1995 Aberd.

STEWART, Susan Department of Pathology, Papworth Hospital, Papworth Everard, Cambridge CB3 8RE Tel: 01480 830541 Fax: 01480 831192 — MB BChir 1979 Camb.; MB BChir Camb. 1978; MA Camb. 1979; FRCPath 1996, M 1984. Cons. Histopath. Papworth Hosp. Camb.; Assoc. Lect. (Path.) Univ. Camb.

STEWART, Suzanne Dorothy Liskey House, 12 Myrtle Road, Victoria Bridge, Strabane BT82 8QB — MB BS 1993 Lond.

STEWART

STEWART, Sylvia (retired) Orchard Wall, Earleswood, Cobham KT11 2BZ Tel: 01932 864233 — MB BS 1947 Lond.; MRCS Eng. LRCP Lond. 1947; FFA RCS Eng. 1954; DA Eng. 1950. Prev: Cons. Anaesth. Reading Gp. Hosps.

STEWART, Mr Terence James The Ulster Hospital, Dundonald, Belfast BT16 1RH Tel: 02890 484511 Fax: 02890 571368; Lake House, Holly Park Road, Killinchy, Newtownards BT23 6SN Tel: 02897 542662 Fax: 02897 542662 — MB BCh BAO 1964 Belf.; FRCS Eng. 1971. (Qu. Univ. Belf.) Cons. Otolaryngol. Ulster Hosp. Belf.; Cons. Otolaryngol. Belf. City Hosp. Socs: Mem. Of Brit. Assoc of Otorhinolaryngologists - Head & Neck Surg.s; Mem. Of Irish otoLaryngol. Soc. Prev: Sen. Regist. Eye & Ear Clinic Roy. Vict. Hosp. Belf.; Research & Clin. Fell. Mass. Eye & Ear Infirm. Boston, USA; on Staff Mass. Eye & Ear Infirm. & Instruc. Harvard Med. Sch.

STEWART, Thomas Wilfred (retired) 3 Aughton Road, Southport PR8 2AF Tel: 01704 566088 Fax: 01704 566088 — MB ChB 1955 Manch.; FRCP Ed. 1973, M 1963. Prev: Cons. Dermat. Roy. Liverp. Hosp., S.port & Formby DGH & Ormskirk & Dist Gen. Hosp.

STEWART, Timothy Dennis Stanley 44 Wyke Avenue, Ash, Aldershot GU12 6EA — MB ChB 1986 Cape Town.

***STEWART, Victoria Rosalind** 2 Montpelier Villas, Brighton BN1 3DH — BM BS 1998 Nottm.; BM BS Nottm 1998.

STEWART, Walter, MBE, Col. late RAMC Retd. 59 Burgh Road, Aylsham, Norwich NR11 6AT Tel: 01603 732383 — MB ChB 1934 Aberd.; MFCM 1972; DPH Eng. 1948. Prev: Med. Off. Norf. AHA.

STEWART, Wendy Adele Dept of Biomollecular sciences, University of Manchester Institute of science and Technology, Sackville St., Manchester M60 1QD Email: wendy.stewart@stud.umist.ac.uk; 15 Elm Grove, Manchester M20 6PQ — MB ChB 1995 Manch.; MRCP (LOND) 1998. Haemat. Research Assoc., U.M.I.S.T, Manch. Prev: SHO in Med., Manch. Roy. Infirm. AUG 1997-Oct 1998; SHO in Med. Roy. Bolton Hosp. AUG 1996- AUG 1997.

STEWART, Wilfred Ewart Garvary Rectory, Killyuilly, Enniskillen — MB BCh BAO 1961 Belf.; MRCOG 1967, DObst 1963. (Belf.) Cons. (O & G) Erne Hosp. Enniskillen. Prev: Med. Off. Jubilee Matern. Hosp. Belf.; Sen. Tutor (Obst.) Ulster Hosp. for Wom. & Childr. Dundonald; Sen. Regist. (O & G) Jubilee Mat. Hosp. Belf.

STEWART, William The Stables, Craigie Village, Kilmarnock KA1 5LY — MB ChB 1993 Glas.

STEWART, William Bryce (retired) Ringans Well, Raitloan, Nairn IV12 5SA Tel: 01667 453211 — MB ChB 1958 Glas.; DObst RCOG 1960. Prev: Ho. Phys. S.. Gen. Hosp. Glas. & Lennox Castle Matern. Hosp.

STEWART, William Gordon Argyle House, 3 Lady Lawson St., Edinburgh EH3 0QH Tel: 0131 222 5301 — MB ChB 1983 Dundee. Med. Adviser Benefits Agency Edin.; Med. Off. Glenrothes RFC. Prev: SHO (Psychiat.) Stratheden Hosp. Cupar.; SHO (Paediat.) Vict. Hosp. Kirkealdy; Princip. GP, Possil Pk. Glas.

STEWART, William Kinnear (retired) Stanmore, 18 Station Crescent, Invergowrie, Dundee DD2 5DT Tel: 01382 562755 — MB ChB 1948 St. And.; MB ChB (Distinc.) St. And. 1948; PhD Dundee 1980; MD (Hons.) St. And. 1972; FRCP Lond. 1974, M 1953; FRCP Ed. 1970, M. 1966.

STEWART, William Muir, OBE, Brigadier late RAMC Retd. The Moat House, 21 Victoria Road, Holywood BT18 9BA Tel: 01232 2371 — MB BCh BAO 1935 Belf.; DPH Eng. 1950.

STEWART-BROWN, Sarah Lynette Health Services Research Unit, Department of Public Health, Oxford University, Institute of Health Sciences, Old Road, Headington, Oxford OX3 7LF Tel: 01865 226717 Fax: 01865 226711 Email: sarah.stewart-brown@dphpc.ox.ac.uk — BM BCh 1974 Oxf.; PhD Bristol 1989; FRCP Lond. 1995; MRCP (UK) 1979; FFPHM RCP (UK) 1995; MFCM 1986. (Westm.) Dir. Health Servs. Research Unit Dept. Pub. Health & Primary Care Univ. Oxf.; Hon. Cons. Oxon. DHA; Reader in Health Servs. Research Univ., of Oxf. Prev: Cons. Pub. Health Med. Worcester & Dist. HA; Hon. Sen. Lect. (Social Med.) Birm. Univ.; Sen. Lect. Community Med., Bristol Univ.

STEWART-JONES, John Halkett Place Surgery, 84 Halkett Place, St Helier, Jersey JE1 4XL Tel: 01534 36301 Fax: 01534 887793; L'Arc en Ciel, 4 Clos du Parcq, Richmond Road, St Helier, Jersey JE2 3GL Tel: 01534 737119 Fax: 01534 504987 — MB BS 1974 Lond.; MRCGP 1978; DRCOG 1977. (Lond. Hosp. Med. Coll.) Prev: SHO (Chest & Gen. Med. & Paediat.) St. Woolos Hosp. Newport; SHO (O & G) Roy. Gwent Hosp. Newport.

STEYN, Anne Marjory Meltham Road Surgery, 9 Meltham Road, Lockwood, Huddersfield HD1 3UP Tel: 01484 432940 Fax: 01484 451423; 168 Woodside Road, Beaumont Park, Huddersfield HD4 5JG Tel: 01484 658628 — MB ChB 1987 Aberd. (Aberdeen) GP Huddersfield. Socs: BMA. Prev: Trainee GP Port Glas. VTS; SHO Aberd. Matern. Hosp.; SHO (Geriat.) Bridge of Weir Hosp.

STEYN, Mr John Hofmeyr, CStJ Albyn Hospital, 21-24 Albyn Place, Aberdeen AB10 1RW Tel: 01224 595993 Fax: 01224 584797; 3 Louisville Avenue, Aberdeen AB15 4TT Tel: 01224 318450 — MB ChB Cape Town 1952; PhD Aberd. 1967; FRCS Ed. 1973; FRCS Eng. 1957. (Cape Town) Chairm. Albyn Hosp. Aberd.; Emerit. Cons. Urol. Aberd. Roy. Infirm. Socs: Brit. Assn. Urol. Surgs.; Hon. Mem. S. Afr. Urol. Assn. Prev: Cons. i/c Dept. Urol. Aberd. Roy. Infirm.

STEYN, John Peter Blackhall Medical Centre, 51 Hillhouse Road, Edinburgh EH4 3TH Tel: 0131 332 7696 Fax: 0131 315 2884 — MB ChB 1979 Aberd.; FRCGP 1996, M 1984.

STEYN, Michael Paul 118C Moulsham Street, Chelmsford CM2 0JW Email: sunways@ukgateway.net — MB ChB 1984 Aberd.; MSc Aberd. 1995; FFA RCSI 1991; MRCGP 1988; DRCOG 1986. Cons. Anaesth. Socs: Association of Burns & Reconstruc. Anaesth.s; Brit. Burns Assn.; Europ. Club of Paediatric Burns. Prev: Trainee GP Dumfries & Galloway Health Bd. VTS.; Sen. Regist. (Anaesth.) Grampian HB.; Const. Anaesth. Mid Essex Hosps. Trust.

STEYN, Mr Richard Stephen The Cardiothoracic Centre, Thomas Drive, Liverpool L14 3PE Tel: 0151 228 1616; 8 Harrison Hey, Liverpool L36 5YR — MB ChB 1984 Aberd.; FRCS Ed. 1991; MRCGP 1991; Dip. IMC RCS Ed. 1996; T(GP) 1991; DRCOG 1990. (Aberdeen) Specialist Regist. (Cardiothoracic Surg.) Cardiothoracic Centre Liverp. Socs: Soc. Cardiothoracic Surg. GB & Irel.; BASICS.

STEYNOR, Gillian Rowland 16 Byron Crescent, Bedford MK40 2BD — MB BS 1974 Lond.; MRCS Eng. LRCP Lond. 1974; DRCOG 1976. (Roy. Free) Prev: GP Bedford; SHO (Paediat.) P.ss Alexandra Hosp. Harlow; Ho. Surg. Roy. Free Hosp. Lond.

STHYR, Leslie Valdemar c/o Midland Bank, 39 Tottenham Court Road, London W1 — MRCS Eng. LRCP Lond. 1942; MD Lond. 1950, MB BS 1948; FRCP Lond. 1973, M 1953. (Middlx.) Socs: Brit. Geriat. Soc. Prev: Phys. Supt. & Cons. Geriat. St. John's Hosp. Battersea; Asst. Phys. (Geriat.) Buckinghamsh. Area; Sen. Regist. Qu. Mary's Roehampton Hosp.

STIBBE, Rev. Hazel Mary (retired) 8 Church Hill Road, Tettenhall, Wolverhampton WV6 9AT Tel: 01902 746089 Fax: 01902 746089 — MB BChir 1960 Camb.; MRCS Eng. LRCP Lond. 1959; FRCOG 1978, M 1965; DCH Eng. 1962. Prev: Cons. O & G New Cross Hosp. Wolverhampton.

STIBE, Catharina Magdalene Helen 23 Meadowbrook, Oxted RH8 9LT — MRCS Eng. LRCP Lond. 1983. (Sheff.)

STIBE, Eva 161A Southgate Road, Islington, London N1 3LE — MB BCh 1987 Wales; FRCS Ed. 1993.

STIBY, Emma Katherine The Red House, Sanderstead Road, South Croydon CR2 0AG — MB ChB 1989 Leic. SHO (A & E) Belf. City Cas.

STICKLAND, Jane Katherine Duchess of kent House, Dellwood Hospital, Liebenraod Road, Reading Tel: 0118 958 8952 — BM 1987 Soton.; MRCGP 1995; DRCOG 1992. Clin. Asst. (Palliat. Med.) Duchess of Kent Hse. Reading.

STICKLEY, Eileen Angela 3 Blenheim Road, Wakefield WF1 3JZ — MB BCh BAO 1973 Dub.

STIDOLPH, Mr Neville Edsell, Wing Cdr. (retired) 15 Tretawn Park, Mill Hill, London NW7 4PS — BM BCh Oxf. 1937; BA Cape Town 1932; BA Oxf. 1937; FRCS Eng. 1947. Med. Chairm. War Pens. Appeal Tribunals Eng. & Wales; Mem. Ct.. Examrs. & Penrose May Tutor in Clin. Surg. RCS Eng. Prev: Surg. & Urol. Whittington Hosp.

STIDOLPH, Paul Neville IIAC Secretariat (CMG), 6th Floor, The Adelphi, 1-11 John Adam St., London WC2N 6HT Tel: 020 7962 8412 Fax: 020 7712 2330 Email: paul.stidolph@dwp.gov.uk; Tel: 020 8783 0326 Fax: 020 8783 0326 Email: paul@candoc.fsnet.co.uk — MRCS Eng. LRCP Lond. 1979; MSc (Occupat. Med.) Lond. 1990; MA Camb. 1981, BA Med. Scs. 1976; LDS RCS Eng. 1974; DRCOG 1983. (Addenbrooke's, Cambridge) Med. Sec. to the Indust. Injuries Advisory Counc. (IIAC), Dept. for

Work & revisions, Lond., WC2N 6HT. Socs: Fell.Amer. Acad. of Disabil. Evaluating Phys.s; Europ. Union of Med. Ass. & Social Sec. (EUMASS); Coun. Mem. Assur. Med. Soc. (AMS). Prev: CMO's Represen. to the Appeals Serv.; Med. Policy Manager, Med. Policy Gp. DSS Lond.; Sen. Med. Off. BAMS DSS Lond. (N.) Region.

***STIDOLPH, Paula Anne Marie** 11 Delamere Close, Sothall, Sheffield S20 2QE — MB ChB 1994 Sheff.; MRCGP Dec 1998; DFFP 1998.

STIER, Susan The Surgery, Parkwood Drive, Warners End, Hemel Hempstead HP1 2LD Tel: 01442 250117 Fax: 01442 256185; Tel: 01442 250117 — MB ChB 1991 Leeds.

STIERLE, Cornelia 45 Sydney Road, Sheffield S6 3GG Tel: 0114 268 0112 — State Exam Med. Heidelberg 1988.

STIFF, Graham Howard St Marys Road Surgery, St. Marys Road, Newbury RG14 1EQ Tel: 01635 31444 Fax: 01635 551316 — MB BS 1988 Lond.; 2000 (Dist) Cert Med Education; BSc Physiol. Lond. 1983; 1996 MRCGP. (St. Mary's) GP Princip. St Marys Rd. Newbury; Clin. Asst. (A & E) Newbury Dist. Hosp.; Vocational Trainer. Socs: Fell. Roy. Soc. Med.; Brit. Assn. Accid. & Emerg. Med. Prev: GP/Regist. Manor Surg. Oxf.; Regist. (Med.) & SHO (Anaesth.) Roy. Berks. Hosp. Reading; SHO (Paediat.) Radcliffe Hosp. Oxf.

STIFF, James Howard The Surgery, 382 Upminster Road North, Rainham RM13 9RZ Tel: 01708 553120 Fax: 01708 553120 — MRCS Eng. LRCP Lond. 1959; FRCGP 1981, M 1968; DFFP 1993; Cert. Family Plann. JCC 1975. (St. Mary's) Socs: Barking & Havering Med. Audit Advis. Gp. & LMC; (Ex-Provost) NE Lond. Fac. Roy. Coll. Gen. Practs.; BMA (Ex-Chairm. NE Thames Regional Counc.).

STIGGELBOUT, Hendrik Jan Shotton Lane Surgery, 38 Shotton Lane, Shotton, Deeside CH5 1QW Tel: 01244 812094 Fax: 01244 811728 — Artsexamen 1984 Amsterdam; MRCGP 1989.

STILES, Mark Andrew Speedwell Surgery, 1 Speedwell Street, Paddock, Huddersfield HD1 4TS Tel: 01484 531786 Fax: 01484 424249; Croft Cottage, 36 Greenhill Bank Road, New Mill, Holmfirth HD9 1ER Tel: 01484 681360 — MB ChB 1985 Leeds; MRCGP 1989; DRCOG 1990; DCH RCP Lond. 1990. (Leeds) Prev: Trainee GP Clitheroe Health Centre.

STILES, Mr Peter James Hawks View, 5 Fairway, Merrow, Guildford GU1 2XG Tel: 01483 562296 Fax: 01483 562296 — MB BS 1956 Lond.; FRCS Eng. 1961; MRCS Eng. LRCP Lond. 1956. (Guy's) Emerit. Orthop. Surg. Roy. Surrey Co. Hosp. Guildford; Orthopaedic Adviser, various aid organisations. Socs: Fell. Roy. Soc. Med.; Fell. BOA; World Orthopaedic Concern. Prev: Cons. Orthop. Surg. SW Surrey Dist.; Chief Asst. & Sen. Regist. (Orthop. Surg.) St. Bart. Hosp. Lond.; Cons. Orthop. Surg. Rowley Bristow Orthop. Hosp.

STILGOE, Jemima Rya 47 Dryburgh Road, London SW15 1BN; 6 East Shrubbery, Redland, Bristol BS6 6SX — MB BS 1993 Lond.; DRCOG 1995; DCH 1997; MRCGP 1999. (St mary Hosp.)

STILL, Mabel Alexandra 10 Abbey Water, Romsey SO51 8EJ — MB BCh 1966 Wales; MRCGP 1981; DA Eng. 1969. GP N. Baddesley.

STILL, Ronald McKinnon (retired) 9/5 Whistlefield Court, 2 Canniesburn Road, Bearsden, Glasgow G61 1PX Tel: 0141 942 3097 — MB ChB 1956 Glas.; FRCOG 1976, M 1963. Cons. Gyn. Glas. Nuffield Hosp. & Ross Hall Hosp. Glas.; Health Care Internat. Med. Centre Beardmore St. Glas. Clydebank. Prev: Cons. Gyn. Stobhill Gen. Hosp. Glas. & Cons. Obst. Roy. Matern. Hosp.

STILL, Sarah 15 East Hill, Oxted RH8 9AF — BM 1995 Soton.; DRCOG 1998; DCH 1999. (Soton) GP Regist. Riverside Pract., Winch. Prev: SHO GP VTS Roy. Hants Co. Hosp. Winch.

STILLEY, Dores (retired) 5 Ainslie Place, Edinburgh EH3 6AR — MB ChB 1948 Ed. Prev: Med. Adviser Derby Diocesan Adoption Comm.

STILLMAN, Kim Canterbury Health Centre, 26 Old Dover Road, Canterbury CT1 3JB — MB ChB 1982 Liverp. Trainer GP Canterbury; Police Surg. Hosp. Pract. (Venereol.) Canterbury.; Course organiser, Canterbury VTS.

STILLMAN, Paul Leacroft Medical Practice, Ifield Road, Ifield, Crawley RH11 7BS Tel: 01293 526441 Fax: 01293 619970; Claybrooke Haywards, Pound Hill, Crawley RH10 3TR Tel: 01293 882100 — MB ChB 1969 Bristol; DObst RCOG 1974. Course Organiser Crawley & Horsham VTS. Prev: Trainee GP Cirencester VTS; Chairm. SW Thames Regional Audio Visual Gp & Crawley & Horsham Med. Soc.; Ho. Surg. & Cas. Off. S.mead Hosp. Bristol.

STILLMAN, Richard Huntley (retired) Caldy Manor, Caldy Wood, Wirral CH48 2HY — MRCS Eng. LRCP Lond. 1943. Prev: Squadron Ldr. RAF Div. Surg. St. Johns Ambul.

STILLWELL, Jennifer Margaret Swan House, 12A Cuxham Road, Watlington OX49 5JW — MRCS Eng. LRCP 1962 Lond.; MRCS Eng LRCP Lond. 1962; MFCH 1989. SCMO Wycombe HA.

STILLWELL, Mark Douglas The Surgery, Welbeck Street, Creswell, Worksop S80 4HA Tel: 01909 721206; Manor Lodge, Worksop Road, Whitwell, Worksop S80 4ST — MB ChB 1987 Sheff.; DRCOG 1991; DCH RCP Lond. 1990. GP Princip. Prev: Trainee GP Worksop VTS.

STILLWELL, Susan Manor Lodge, Worksop Road, Whitwell, Worksop S80 4ST — MB ChB 1987 Sheff.; MRCOG 1992; DRCOG 1991; DCH RCP Lond. 1990. Clin. Asst. (Gyn.) & Clin. Med. Off. (Family Plann.) Notts.

STILWELL, Mr John Harry 81 Longmeadow Road, Knowsley Village, Prescot L34 0HW Tel: 0151 548 6094 Fax: 0151 545 0975 Email: jhshand@aol.co.uk — BM BCh 1972 Oxf.; BSc (Biochem., Hons.) Liverp. 1967; FRCS Eng. 1977; LMSSA Lond. 1972. (Oxf.) Cons. Hand Surg. Wrightington Hosp., Wigan & Alder Hey Childr. Hosp. Liverp. Socs: Brit. Assn. Plastic Surg.; Brit. Soc. Surg. Hand. Prev: Cons. Plastic Surg. Whiston Hosp. Prescot; Fell. Hand Surg. Univ. Louisville, Kentucky, USA; Sen. Regist. (Plastic Surg.) Whiston Hosp. Prescot.

STILWELL, Ray (retired) Two Gates, Fore St., Wylye, Warminster BA12 0RQ Tel: 01985 248363 — MB BS 1961 Lond.; MRCS Eng. LRCP Lond. 1961; MRCGP 1973; DObst RCOG 1963; DA Eng. 1963. Med. Mem. - Appeals Serv. Prev: Med. Advisor Benefits Agency DSS.

STIMMLER, Anthony The Surgery, 60 Chadwick Road, London SE15 4PU Tel: 020 7639 9622 Fax: 020 7639 0489; 68 Flower Lane, Mill Hill, London NW7 2JL Tel: 020 8959 2269 — MB BS 1982 Lond.; D.Occ.Med. RCP Lond. 1995; Cert. Family Plann. JCC 1984; DRCOG 1984. (Lond. Hosp.) p/t Occupat. Health Phys. Lewisham & N. S.wark HA. Socs: Soc. Occupat. Med. Prev: SHO (Psychiat.) Goodmayes; SHO (Obst.) Newham Matern. Hosp.; SHO (Paediat.) Newham Gen. Hosp.

STIMMLER, Leo 31 Westhall Park, Warlingham CR6 9HS Tel: 01883 624522 — MRCS Eng. LRCP Lond. 1954; MD Lond. 1966, MB BS 1954; FRCP Lond. 1974, M 1960. (Guy's) Cons. Paediat. Guy's Hosp. Lond. Socs: Brit. Paediat. Assn. Prev: Sen. Research Fell. Inst. Child Health Birm.; Lect. in Paediat. Univ. Birm.; Research Fell. Univ. Colo. Denver, USA.

STIMPSON, Graham George Blackberry Hill Hospital, Fishponds, Bristol BS16 2EW Tel: 0117 965 6061; 12 Challoner Court, Bristol BS1 4RG — MB BS 1965 Lond.; MRCS Eng. LRCP Lond. 1965; MRCPsych 1972; DPM Eng. 1969. (Guy's) Cons. Psychother. Blackberry Hill Hosp. Bristol; Clin. Lect. (Ment. Health) Bristol Univ.

STIMPSON, Victor Barry (retired) 265 Chells Way, Stevenage SG2 0HN Tel: 01438 313001 Fax: 01438 362322 — MB ChB 1958 Ed.

STINCHCOMBE, Claire Elizabeth 5 Cherry Close, Shillingford, Wallingford OX10 7HG — MB ChB 1993 Birm.

STINCHCOMBE, Simon John Connacht House, Cotton Mill Lane, Farnsfield, Newark NG22 8EJ — MB BS 1982 Nottm.; BMedSci 1980; FRCR 1990; T(R)(CR) 1992. Cons. Radiol. King's Mill Centre Sutton-in-Ashfield. Prev: Sen. Regist. & Regist. (Radiol.) Nottm. Hosps.

STINSON, Deborah Mary S. W. London & St Georges Mental Health NHS Trust, St. Helier, Sutton Hospital, Cotswold Road, Sutton SM2 5NF Tel: 020 8296 4342 Fax: 020 8296 4342 Email: dstinson@sthelier.sghms.ac.uk; 5 Palace Road, East Molesey KT8 9DJ — MB BCh BAO 1981 Belf.; MRCPsych 1986. Cons. Psychiat. Sutton Hosp. Surrey.

STINSON, Ian Rodney The Parklands Medical Practice, Park Road, Bradford BD5 0SG Tel: 01274 227575 Fax: 01274 693558; The Medical Centre, 30 Buttershaw Lane, Bradford BD6 2DD Tel: 01274 678464 Fax: 01274 693558 — BSc (Hons.) Leeds 1985, MB ChB (Distinc. Path.) 1988; MRCGP 1993; T(GP) 1993; Cert Family Plann JCC 1992; DCH RCP Lond. 1982. Socs: BMA; MRCGP.

***STINSON, Pauline Gladys** 82 Derryfubble Road, Dungannon BT71 7PW — MB BCh BAO 1996 Belf.

STINSON, Mr Robert (retired) Cloghmore, 8 Greystone Road, Antrim BT41 1HD Tel: 01849 428367 Fax: 01849 428367 — MB

STINSON

BCh BAO Belf. 1947; FRCS Ed. 1962. Hon: Cons. Surg. Antrim Area Hosp. N. Health & Social Servs. Bd. Ballymena. Prev: Cons. Surg. Massereene Hosp. Antrim & Waveney Hosp. Ballymena.

STINSON, Sara Isabel (retired) 2 Lavenham Road, Grimsby DN33 3EX — MB ChB Leeds 1946; DCH Eng. 1953; DObst RCOG 1950. Prev: GP Humberside FPC.

***STINSON, Victoria Louise** 4 Hermitage Court, Saughall, Chester CH1 6QP — MB ChB 1998 Sheff.; MB ChB Sheff 1998.

STIRK, Nicola Jane 148 Chorley New Road, Heaton, Bolton BL1 4NX — MB ChB 1986 Manch.

STIRLAND, Alison Margaret Womens Community Health Services, CELFACS, St Leonard's Hospital, Nutall St., London N1 5LZ Tel: 020 7601 7100 Fax: 020 7601 7903 — MB ChB 1987 Ed.; MFFP 1995; MRCGP 1991; DRCOG 1991. Clin. Asst. Archway Sexual Health Clinic Whittington Hosp. Lond. Socs: Scientif. Study of VD. Prev: CMO (Family Plann. & Genitourin. Med. in Community) Open Doors Sexual Health Project; SCMO St. Bart. Hosp. & CMO City & Hackney Community Servs. NHS Trust.

STIRLAND, Emma Prospect House, Bulls Cross, Sheepscombe, Stroud GL6 7HU — MB BS 1980 Lond.

STIRLAND, Hilary (retired) Swithland, Hazelwood Lane, Chipstead, Coulsdon CR5 3QZ — MB BS Lond. 1960; FRCPCH 1997; MFCM RCP (UK) 1983; FFCM 1988; DObst RCOG 1961. Cons. Pub. Health Med. Cesol S. Thames W.; Hon. Sen. Lect. St. Geo. Hosp. Med. Sch. Lond. Prev: Dir. of Pub. Health Med. Merton Sutton & Wandsworth HA.

STIRLAND, John David 56 Holymoor Road, Holymoorside, Chesterfield S42 7DX Tel: 01246 566723 — MRCS Eng. LRCP Lond. 1956; BA Camb. 1953, MB 1957, BChir. 1956; FRCPsych 1985, M 1971; DPM Eng. 1960. (St. Mary's) Cons. Psychiat. Chesterfield Hosp. Prev: Regist. Shenley Hosp. St. Albans; Sen. Regist. Dept. Psychiat. United Sheff. Hosps.

STIRLAND, Robert Mandell (retired) 16 Corn Mill Court, West Road, Saffron Walden CB11 3DE Tel: 01799 522415 — MB BChir 1954 Camb.; MA Camb. 1954, MD Camb. 1963; FRCPath 1977, M 1965. Prev: Cons. Bact. Manch. Roy. Infirm. & Sen. Lect. (Clin. Bact.) Univ. Manch.

STIRLING, Mr Alistair John 7 Chad Road, Edgbaston, Birmingham B15 3EN Tel: 0121 454 2991 Fax: 0121 454 9008; 119 Gough Road, Edgbaston, Birmingham B15 2JG Tel: 0121 440 3157 — MB ChB 1977 Birm.; FRCS Ed. 1981. Cons. Orthop. Surg. Roy. Orthop. Hosp.; Hon. Sen. Lect. Univ. Birm. Socs: Brit. Scoliosis Soc. Exec. Comm.; Brit. Assn. of Spinal Surg.; Soc. for Back Pain Research. Prev: MRC Research Fell. Univ. Leeds; Lect. (Orthop.) Univ. Leeds.

***STIRLING, Amanda Jane** Dr McElhone and Partners, Townhead Surgery, 6-8 High St., Irvine KA12 0AY Tel: 01294 273131 Fax: 01294 312832; 3 Old Hillfoot Road, Ayr KA7 3LW — MB ChB 1989 Ed.; BSc Ed. 1988, MB ChB 1989; MRCGP 1994; DRCOG 1992.

STIRLING, Andrew Mark 46 Findhorn Place, Grange, Edinburgh EH9 2NS — MB ChB 1991 Glas.

STIRLING, Anne Whitehead Cumberland House, Jordangate, Macclesfield SK10 1EG Tel: 01625 428081 Fax: 01625 503128 Email: anne.stirling@gp-n81062.nhs.uk — MB ChB 1968 Glas.; Dip. Prescri Sci. 2000 Liverpool; MRCP (UK) 1975; DCH RCPS Glas. 1970. (Glas.) Prescribing Lead. E.ern Chesh. P.C.G. Socs: BMA; BMS (Brit. Menopause Soc.); AFMS (Anglo-French Med. Soc.). Prev: Regist. (Paediat. Med.) Roy. Hosp. Sick Childr. Glas.; SHO (Gen. Med.) S.. Gen. Hosp. Glas.; Ho. Off. Roy. Infirm. Glas.

STIRLING, Carol Ann 9 Shawfarm Apartments, Newtonlea Avenue, Newton Mearns, Glasgow G77 5QF — MB ChB 1989 Glas.; MRCP (UK) 1993.

STIRLING, Catherine Mary Flat 1/L, 150 Fergus Drive, Glasgow G20 6AX — MB ChB 1990 Glas.; MRCP (UK) 1993.

STIRLING, Christina Fionna Margaret Whiteoak, 3 West Common Close, Harpenden AL5 2LJ Tel: 01582 764166 — MB BS 1984 Lond.; MA Camb. 1985; MRCP (UK) 1989. (Guy's) Prev: SHO (O & G) Mayday Hosp. Croydon; SHO (Paediat.) City Gen. Hosp. Stoke on Trent; SHO (Paediat.) Qu. Eliz. Hosp. Childr. Lond.

STIRLING, Gavin Mair (retired) 1 Inch Avenue, Dovecot Park, Aberdour, Burntisland KY3 0TF Tel: 01383 860295 — MB ChB 1928 Glas.

STIRLING, George Anthony (retired) 50 Cyprus Road, Mapperley Park, Nottingham NG3 5EB — MB BS 1952 Durh.; MD Durh. 1958; FRCPath 1974.

STIRLING, George Scott 12 Albany Place, Dumfries DG1 1JN — MB ChB 1949 Aberd.; FRCP Glas. 1986, M 1984; FRCPsych 1977, M 1971; DPM Eng. 1954. Prev: Cons. Psychiat. & Med. Admin. Crichton Roy. Hosp. Dumfries; RAF; Mem. Parole Bd. Scotl.

STIRLING, Heather Fiona Department of Paediatrics, Walsgrave Hospital NHS Trust, Clifford Bridge Road, Walsgrave, Coventry CV2 2DX Tel: 024 76 602020 Fax: 024 76 622197; 101 Ullenhall Road, Knowle, Solihull B93 9JH Tel: 01564 773468 — MB ChB 1981 Liverp.; BSc (Hons.) Liverp. 1978; MD Liverp. 1995; MRCP (UK) 1985; DCCH RCP Ed. 1986; FRCP Lond. 1997. (Liverpool University) Cons. Paediat. Walsgrave Hosp. Coventry.

STIRLING, Iain Boyd Queens Road Medical Grp, 6 Queens Rd, Aberdeen AB15 4NU Tel: 01224 641560 Fax: 01224 642773; Lochwood Cottage, Drumoak, Aberdeen AB31 5HE Tel: 01330 811952 — MB BS 1983 Lond.; BSc (Hons.) Chem. Lond. 1977; MRCGP 1989; DRCOG 1987. (Roy. Free) Prev: SHO (Psychiat., O & G, Anaesth. & Paediat.) Roy. Shrewsbury Hosp.

STIRLING, James Beattie Murcar, 56 Bailie Drive, Bearsden, Glasgow G61 3AH Tel: 0141 942 2120 — MB ChB 1945 Glas.; DA Eng. 1953. (Glas.) Socs: Scott. Soc. Anaesths. & Assn. Anaesth. Gt. Brit. & Irel. Prev: Cons. Anaesth. Stobhill Gen. Hosp. & Roy. Hosp. Sick Childr. Glas.; Flight Lt. RAFVR; Sen. Regist. Anaesth. W.. Infirm. Glas.

STIRLING, Jennifer Stewart The Balfron Practice, Skimped Hill Health Centre, Skimped Hill Lane, Bracknell RG12 1LH Tel: 01344 306613 Fax: 01344 306614; Courthorpe, Longhill Road, Chavey Down, Bracknell RG12 9UB — MB ChB 1977 Glas.

STIRLING, Jeremy Mowat 132 Weston Park, Hornsey Vale, London N8 9PN, 01563 574237, jeremystirling@aol.com — MB ChB 1987 Leeds; MRCPsych 1992. Cons. (Addic. & Gen. Psychiat.) Ayrsh. & Arran.

STIRLING, Joanne Louise 14 Croy Avenue, Newton Mearns, Glasgow G77 5SG Tel: 0141 639 7295 — MB ChB 1994 Manch.; BSc St. And. 1991. SHO (Paediat.) Roy. Hosp. Sick Childr. Glas..; Regist. Paediat. New childr. Hosp. Sydney, Austral. Prev: SHO (A & E) Vict. Hosp. Blackpool; Ho. Surg. Glas. Roy. Infirm.; Ho. Off. (Med.) Vict. Hosp. Blackpool.

STIRLING, John Grime 7 Nursery Gardens, Beverley HU17 8NS — MB BCh BAO 1980 Dub.

STIRLING, Jonathan Agnew Templepatrick Surgery, 80 Castleton, Templepatrick, Ballyclare BT39 0AZ Tel: 028 9443 2202 Fax: 028 9443 3707; 56A Ballybentragh Road, Dunadry, Antrim BT41 2HJ Tel: 01849 433348 — MB BCh BAO 1982 Dub.; MB BCh BAO Belf. 1982; BSc (1st cl. Hons.) Belf. 1979; MRCGP 1986; DCH Dub. 1985; DRCOG 1985.

STIRLING, Julie Allison Fax: 01620 860204; Violet Bank, Duke Street, Belhaven, Dunbar EH42 1NT — MB ChB 1990 Ed. GP E. Linton.

STIRLING, Kenneth Whyte Alloa Health Centre, Marshiil, Alloa FK10 1AQ Tel: 01259 216476; 27 Benview Terrace, Devon Village, Fishcross, Alloa FK10 3AR — MB ChB 1981 Glas.; FRCP Glas. 1994; MRCP (UK) 1984; MRCGP 1987; DRCOG 1988. Prev: Regist. (Cardiac Med.) W.. Infirm. Glas.

STIRLING, Lucy Caroline Molecular Nociception Group, Department of Biology, University College London, London WC1E 6BT Tel: 020 7679 7943; Flat 23, 1 Prince of Wales Road, London NW5 3LW Tel: 020 7284 0917 — MB BS 1987 Lond.; MRCGP 1993; MSc 1999. Research Fell., Molecular Nociception, Univ. Coll. Lond.; Sen. Registar, Palliat. Med., Roy. Marsden Hosp. Fulham Rd. Lond. SW4. Socs: Assn. Palliat. Med.; Roy. Soc. Of Med. Prev: Sen. Regist. (Palliat. Med.) Whipps Cross Hosp. Leytonstone, Lond.; Sen. Regist. (Palliat. Med.) Roy. Free Hosp. & Edenhall Marie Curie Centre Lond.

STIRLING, Pauline Williamina Margaret Catherine (retired) 15 Willowbed Avenue, Chichester PO19 2JE Tel: 01243 785300 — MB ChB 1932 Ed.; DPM Eng. 1937. Prev: Cons. Psychiat. Friern & Halliwick Hosps. Lond.

STIRLING, Mr Richard John 64 Park Road, Buxton SK17 6SN Email: stirling@btinternet.com — MB ChB 1986 Leic.; BSc (Hons.) Leic. 1984, MB ChB 1986; FCOphth 1991, M 1990. Cons. Ophth. Darlington Memor. Hosp.

STOCKDALE

STIRLING, Robert Wilson — MB ChB 1977 Glas.; FRCPath 1996, M 1986. Wansbeck Gen. Hosp., Ashington, N.umberland (Changing Jan 2002 to here). Prev: Cons. Histopath. W. Middlx. Univ. Hosp. Isleworth.

*STIRLING, Sarah Louise Crosshouse Hospital, Kilmarnock KA2 0BE Tel: 01563 521133; 9 Stamperland Drive, Clarkston, Glasgow G76 8HD — MB ChB 1994 Glas.

STIRLING, Susanna Clare 115 Craigleith Road, Edinburgh EH4 2EH — MB ChB 1992 Sheff.; MSC (MCH) UCL 1997; DCH Coll Paeds, S Afr 1995. Specialist Regist. Pub. Health Med., S. W.ern Deanery.

STIRLING, Thomas Boyd (retired) 25 Longwood Road, Aldridge, Walsall WS9 0TA Tel: 01922 452470 Fax: 01922 452551 — MB ChB 1946 Birm.

STIRLING, Valda Anne 7 Nursery Gardens, Beverley HU17 8NS — MB BS 1976 Adelaide; MFCM 1987.

STIRLING, Mr William John Craigavon Area, Hospital Group Trust, 68 Lurgan Road, Craigavon BT63 5QQ; 71 Drumnacanvy Road, Portadown, Craigavon BT63 5LY — MB BCh BAO 1970 Belf.; FRCS Ed. 1975. Cons. Surg. Craigavon Area Hosp.

STIRLING, William Neil (retired) Westmead, 24 Ladygates, Betley, Crewe CW3 9AN — MB ChB 1950 Glas.; MRCGP 1959. Prev: Police Surg., City of Stoke on Trent.

STIRRAT, Mr Allan Norman Department of Orthopaedics, Sunderland District General Hospital, Kayll Road, Sunderland SR4 7TP Tel: 0191 565 6256 — MB ChB 1979 Dundee; FRCS Ed. 1984. Cons. Orthop. Surg. Sunderland HA. Socs: Brit. Orthop. Assn. & Brit. Soc. Surg. Hand.; Brit. Elbow & Shoulder Soc. Prev: Sen. Regist. (Orthop.) St. Mary's Hosp. Paddington & Roy. Nat. Orthop.Hosp. Stanmore; Regist. (Orthop.) N.wick Pk. Hosp. Harrow; Sen. Resid. (Orthop.) Mass. Gen. Hosp. Boston, USA.

STIRRAT, Fiona Wallace 48 Ashburnham Gardens, South Queensferry EH30 9LB Fax: 0131 319 2361 Email: istirrat@aol.com — MB ChB 1981 Glas.; MRCGP 1986; DRCOG 1985. (Glasgow University) Asst. GP.

STIRTON, Rosalind Fiona (retired) Westcotes House, Westcotes Drive, Leicester LE3 0QU — BM BS 1981 Nottm.; BMedSci Nottm. 1979, BM BS 1981; MRCPsych 1986. Locum Cons. Child & Adolesc. Psychiat. Leics. NHS Trust. Prev: Cons. Child & Adolesc. Psychiat. Leic. NHS Trust.

STIRZAKER, Ljuba Oxfordshire Health Authority, Richards Building, Old Road, Headington OX3 7LG Tel: 01865 227186 Fax: 01865 226894 Email: ljuba.stirzaker@oxon-ha.anglox.nhs.uk; 4 Wellington Place, Oxford OX1 2LD — BM BCh 1981 Oxf.; MA 1989; MSc Community Med. Lond. 1990; MFPHM RCP (UK) 1993. Cons. Pub. Health Med. Oxf.shire Health Auth.. Prev: Cons. Pub. Health Med. Glos. Health Auth.; Sen. Regist. PHM Oxf. RHA.

STITSON, Mr David James, Squadron Ldr. RAF Med. Br. Department of Orthopaedic, Royal Cornwall Hospital, Treliske, Truro Tel: 01872 250000; 6 Charlton Crescent, Crownhill, Plymouth PL6 5EQ Tel: 01752 768173 — MB BS 1991 Lond.; FRCS Eng. 1996. (St. Bart. Hosp. Lond.) Specialist Regist. (Orthop. & Travia) Derriford Hosp. Plymouth. Socs: Brit. Orthop. Train. Assn.

STITSON, Richard Norman Michael 25 Swift Way, Thurlby, Bourne PE10 0QA Email: dr.stitson@wavenet.co.uk — MB ChB 1992 Aberd.; BMedBiol. (Hons.) 1990. SHO (Histopath.) QMC, Nottm. Prev: SHO3 (Haemat.) WGH, Edin.; MRC Clin. Train. Fell. (Genetics) Univ. Camb.

STITT, Geoffrey Woodford Grosvenor House Surgery, 6 Warwick Square, Carlisle CA1 1LB Tel: 01228 525041 Fax: 01228 515786; Woodend, Heads Nook, Carlisle CA8 9AE Tel: 01228 560426 — MB BS 1965 Durh.; MRCGP 1972; DObst RCOG 1969. Socs: BMA.

*STIVAROS, Stavros Michael Woodfield House, Hill Rd, Penwortham, Preston PR1 9XH — MB ChB 1997 Manch.

STOATE, Howard Geoffrey Alvan Albion Surgery, Pincott Road, Bexleyheath DA6 7LP Tel: 020 8304 8334 Fax: 020 8298 0408; 36 Heathclose Road, Dartford DA1 2PU — MB BS 1977 Lond.; MSc Gen. Pract. Lond. 1989; FRCGP 1993, M 1981; DRCOG 1979. Tutor (Gen. Pract.) Qu. Mary's Hosp. Sidcup. Prev: Clin. Asst. (Respirat. Med.) Brook Gen. Hosp. Lond.; Trainer (Gen. Pract.) Kent; Chair Research Ethics Comm. Bexley HA.

STOBART, James Andrew Harley Honeyhurst, Oast View, Hormonden, Tonbridge TN12 8LE — MB ChB 1989 Sheff.; BMedSci 1986; MRCGP 1994; DRCOG 1993.

STOBBS, Ian Peter The Health Centre, Testwood Lane, Totton, Southampton SO40 3ZN Tel: 023 8086 5051 Fax: 023 8086 5050 — MB ChB 1968 Manch.

STOBIE, Fiona Jane 24 Dronachy Road, Kirkcaldy KY2 5QL — MB ChB 1992 Glas.

STOCK, Anthony Ian 54 Long Acre, Bingham, Nottingham NG13 8AH — MB BS 1984 Lond.; MRCOG 1990. Vis. Lect. Chinese Univ. Hong Kong.

STOCK, David 7 Chestnut Tree Close, Radyr, Cardiff CF15 8RY Tel: 029 2084 2603 — MB ChB 1979 Liverp.; MRCPath 1986. Cons. Histopath. E. Glam. Gen. Hosp. Socs: Roy. Coll. Path. & Internat. Acad. Path. Prev: Sen. Regist. (Histopath.) Middlesbrough Gen. Hosp. & Roy. Vict. Infirm. Newc.; Regist. (Path.) BRd.green Hosp. & Alder Hey Childr. Hosp. Liverp.

STOCK, David James 13C Weston Park, London N8 9SY Tel: 020 8342 9957 — MB BS 1990 Lond.; BSc Lond. 1989.

STOCK, Mr Douglas Graham, Brigadier RAMC Retd. Guy's Nuffield House, Newcomen St., London SE1 1YR Tel: 0207 955 5000 Ext: 5978 Fax: 0207 955 4754; Greenshaw House, Wrotham Road, Meopham Green, Gravesend DA13 0AU Tel: 01474 815859 Fax: 01474 815889 — MB BS 1962 Lond.; FRCS Eng. 1967; MRCS Eng. LRCP Lond. 1963; T(S) 1991. (Char. Cross) Cons. Orthop. Surg. Defence Secondary Care Agency. Socs: Fell. BOA; BMA. Prev: Ho. Surg. & Ho. Phys. & Cas. Off. Mt. Vernon Hosp.; Cons. Advisor Orthop. Surg. D.G.A.M.S.

STOCK, Jeremy Guy Louis Conquest Hospital, The Ridge, St Leonards-on-Sea TN37 7RD Tel: 01424 755255; Blackthorne House, The Thorns, Guestling, Hastings TN35 4LR Tel: 01424 814851 — MB ChB 1977 Sheff.; FFA RCS Eng. 1981. Cons. Anaesth. Hastings & Rother NHS Trust. Socs: Assn. Anaesth. & BMA. Prev: Cons. Anaesth. Sheff. HA; Sen. Regist. (Anaesth.) Wessex RHA; Lect. (Anaesth.) Univ. Calgary Alberta, Canada.

STOCK, Penelope Margaret 32 Copleston Road, Ipswich IP4 5HB — MB ChB 1988 Leeds; DRCOG 1992. (Leeds)

STOCK, Peter Royston (retired) 3 Kellaway Crescent, Westbury-on-Trym, Bristol BS9 4TE Tel: 0117 924 3131 — MB ChB 1957 Bristol.

STOCK, Richard David Crouch End Health Centre, 45 Middle Lane, Crouch End, London N8 8PH; 5 Horse Shoe Lane, London N20 8NJ Tel: 020 8446 0401 — MB BS 1980 Lond.; MRCGP 1984; Cert. Family Plann. JCC 1984. Prev: Trainee GP N.wick Pk. Hosp. Harrow VTS; Ho. Phys. & Ho. Surg. St. Mary's Hosp. Lond.

*STOCK, Sarah Jane Elizabeth 9 Union Place, Montrose DD10 8QB — MB ChB 1998 Manch.; MB ChB Manch 1998.

STOCK, Mr Simon Everitt Bishop Auckland General Hospital, Bishop Auckland DL14 6AD Tel: 01388 454000 Fax: 01388 454135; Spence House, Hamsterley, Bishop Auckland DL13 3QF Tel: 01388 488468 Email: simon@sphouse.freeserve.co.uk — MD 1988 Newc.; MB BS 1980; FRCS Eng. 1985; FRCS Ed. 1985. Cons. Surg. Bishop Auckland Gen. Hosp. Socs: Christ. Med. Fell.sh.; Assn. Surg.; Brit. Soc. of Gastroenterol. Prev: Sen. Regist. (Surg.) N.. RHA.

STOCKDALE, Andrew David Coventry Radiotherapy & Oncology Centre, Walsgrave Hospital, Clifford Bridge Road, Coventry CV2 2DX Tel: 024 76 602020 Fax: 024 76 538900 — MB BS 1979 Lond.; BSc 1976 Lond.; MRCP (UK) 1982; FRCR 1985. (Westm.) Cons. Clin. Oncol. Walsgrave Hosp. Coventry.; Vis. Cons. Clin. Oncol. Solihull Hosp., W. Midl.s. Prev: Sen. Regist. (Radiother.) St. Lukes Hosp. Guildford; Sen. Regist. & Regist. (Radiother.) W.m. Hosp. Lond.

*STOCKDALE, Anna Victoria Kate 21 Vale Road, Wilmslow SK9 5QA — MB ChB 1997 Manch.

STOCKDALE, Elizabeth Joan Noel Department of Diagnostic Radiology, Royal Aberdeen Childrens Hospital, Cornhill Road, Aberdeen AB25 2ZG Tel: 01224 681818 Fax: 01224 840659; 1 Grant Road, Banchory AB31 5UW Tel: 01330 823096 Email: e.stockdale@abd.ac.uk — MB ChB 1971 Aberd.; MBA Strathclyde 1995; FRCPCH 1997; FRCR 1979; DMRD Eng. 1977. (University of Aberdeen) Cons. Aberd. Roy. Hosps. Trust; Clin. Sen. Lect. Univ. Aberd. Socs: Eur. Soc. Paediat. Radiol.; Brit. Med. Ultrasound Soc.; Brit. Paediat. Radiol. & Imaging Gp. Prev: Sen. Regist. St. Geo. Hosp. Lond.; Regist. Roy. Nat. Orthop. Hosp. Lond.; SHO (Surg.) Profess. Surg. Unit. Hosp. Sick Childr. Gt. Ormond St. Lond.

*STOCKDALE, Helen Elizabeth 318 Tadcaster Road, York YO24 1HF — MB ChB 1996 Birm.

STOCKDALE

STOCKDALE, Nicholas Alex John Arden Cottage, Earlswood Common, Earlswood, Solihull B94 5SQ Tel: 01564 702506 — MB BCh 1994 Wales. SHO (Orthop. & Trauma) Worcester Roy. Infirm.

STOCKDALE, Robert Christopher Grove Road Surgery, 3 Grove Road, Solihull B91 2AG Tel: 0121 705 1105 Fax: 0121 711 4098; Arden Cottage, The Common, Earlswood, Solihull B94 5SQ Tel: 01564 702506 — MB ChB 1967 Birm. (Birm.) Prev: Regist. (Gen. Surg. & Thoracic Surg.) Qu. Eliz. Hosp. Birm.; Regist. (Cas.) Gen. Hosp. Birm.

STOCKDALE, Walter Trevor 6 Peckitt Street, York YO1 1SF Tel: 01904 639171 Fax: 01904 633881; 318 Tadcaster Road, York YO24 1HF Tel: 01904 705217 — MB ChB 1966 Leeds; DObst RCOG 1968. (Leeds) Prev: Ho. Off. (Surg. & Med.) York Co. Hosp.; Ho. Off. (Obst.) Matern. Hosp. York.

STOCKDILL, George Tower Cottage, Darnick, Melrose TD6 9AQ — MB ChB 1969 Glas.; FRCP Glas. 1985; MRCP (UK) 1972; FRCPath 1989, M 1979. (Glas.) Cons. Haemat. Borders Gen. Hosp. Melrose. Prev: Cons. Haemat. W.. Gen. Hosp. Edin.; Sen. Regist. (Haemat.) W.. Gen. Hosp. Edin.; Regist. (Haemat.) Glas. Roy. Infirm.

STOCKER, Catherine Anne Rhynern, Station Road, Bere Ferrers, Yelverton PL20 7JS — MB BS 1989 Lond.; MRCGP 1994.

STOCKER, David Ian Department of Genitourinary Medicine, Central Outpatients Department, Hartshill Road, Stoke-on-Trent ST4 7PW; 54 Booth Street, Audley, Stoke-on-Trent ST7 8EP — MB ChB 1975 Birm.

STOCKER, John Charles 30 Sundial House, Les Rocquettes, Alderney 6Y9 3TF Tel: 01481 822077 Fax: 01481 823900 — MB BS 1978 Lond.; DRCOG 1984. (Lond. Hosp. Med. Coll.) Socs: Alderney Med. Assn. Prev: Resid. Med. Off. K. Edwd. VII Hosp. for Offs.

***STOCKER, Judith** 4 Melbourne Street, York YO10 5AQ — MB ChB 1998 Leeds.

STOCKER, Mary Elizabeth The Coach House, Bickleigh, Plymouth PL6 7AL — MB ChB 1995 Bristol.

STOCKILL, Giles Raymond 6 Carleton Road, Pontefract WF8 3ND — MB ChB 1988 Liverp.

STOCKILL, Ruth Antonia 6 Carleton Road, Pontefract WF8 3ND — MB ChB 1988 Liverp.

STOCKING, Anthony John Hubert The Coatham Surgery, 18 Coatham Road, Redcar TS10 1RJ Tel: 01642 483495 Fax: 01642 487520 — MB BS 1975 Lond.; DRCOG 1980.

STOCKINGS, Frieda Eveline (retired) Wheal Rose, Winterborne Houghton, Blandford Forum DT11 0PE — MRCS Eng. LRCP Lond. 1961; FFA RCS Eng. 1972; DA Eng. 1965; DObst RCOG 1963. Prev: Cons. Anaesth. Centr. Hosp. St. Vincent., W. Indies.

STOCKLEY, Andre George Ings (retired) 27 Campden Road, South Croydon CR2 7ER Tel: 020 8688 3089 — MB BS 1945 Lond.; LMSSA Lond. 1944. Prev: Ho. Surg. Guy's Hosp.

STOCKLEY, Andrew Thomas Whitefields Surgery, Hunsbury Hill Road, Camp Hill, Northampton NN4 9UW Tel: 01604 760171 Fax: 01604 708528; 16 Beech Close, Bugbrooke, Northampton NN7 3RB Tel: 01604 831370 — BM BCh 1979 Oxf.; MA Oxf. 1979; MRCGP 1984. (Oxford)

STOCKLEY, Mr Ian Connaghyn, 239 Graham Road, Ranmoor, Sheffield S10 3GS Tel: 0114 263 0646 Fax: 0114 263 0686 Email: i.stockley@sheffield.ac.uk — MD 1994 Sheff.; MB ChB 1979; FRCS Eng. 1983. Cons. Orthop. Surg. N. Gen. Hosp. Sheff. Socs: Brit. Orthop. Research Soc. & Brit. Orthop. Foot Surg. Soc.; Brit. Hip. Soc.; Europ. Hip Soc. Prev: Sen. Regist. (Orthop.) N.. Gen. Hosp. Sheff.; Clin. Fell. Mt. Sinai Hosp. Toronto, Canada; Sir Harry Platt Research Fell. Hope Hosp. Salford.

STOCKLEY, Jane Manuela Worcester Royal Infirmary, Castle St., Worcester WR1 3AS Tel: 01905 760177 Fax: 01905 22343; Ryall Hill, Ryall Lane, Upton Upon Severn, Worcester WR8 0PN — MB ChB 1981 Birm.; FRCPath 1997, M 1989. Cons. Microbiol. Worcester Roy. Infirm. Worcester Acute Hosp.s NHS Trust.

***STOCKLEY, Richard Arthur** 6 Tennyson Street, Leicester LE2 1HS — MB ChB 1995 Leic.

STOCKLEY, Robert Andrew 10 Swarthmore Road, Selly Oak, Birmingham B29 4JR — MD 1978 Birm.; DSc Birm. 1986, MD 1978, MB ChB 1971; FRCP Lond. 1984; MRCP (UK) 1973. Prof. Med. Qu. Eliz. Hosp. Birm.; Edit. Bd. Europ. Respirat. Jl. & Internat. Jl. Biochem.; Wolfson Research Fell. RCP. Socs: Brit. Lung Foundat. Research Comm.; (Chairm. Chest Research Comm.) Chest, Heart &

Stroke Assn.; Assn. Phys. Prev: Lect. (Med.) Univ. Birm.; Chairm. Nat. Asthma Campaign Reseach Comm. 1995.

STOCKLEY, Simon Nicholas The Health Centre, Sunningdale Drive, Eaglescliffe, Stockton-on-Tees TS16 9EA Tel: 01642 780113 Fax: 01642 791020; 189 Durham Road, Stockton-on-Tees TS19 0PX — MB ChB 1985 Birm.; MRCGP 1992; Dip. IMC RCS Ed. 1991. (Birmingham)

STOCKLEY, William David Kenmore Medical Centre, 60-62 Alderley Road, Wilmslow SK9 1PA Tel: 01625 532244 Fax: 01625 549024 — MB BS 1963 Lond.; MRCGP 1976; DCH RCPS Glas. 1966; DObst RCOG 1965. (King's Coll. Hosp.) Hosp. Pract. (Paediat.) Wythenshawe Gen. Hosp. Manch.

***STOCKMAN, Alan** 27 Fenaghy Road, Galgorm, Ballymena BT42 1HW — MB BCh 1998 Belf.; MB BCh Belf 1998.

***STOCKMAN, Neil Joseph Thomas** 46 Cotswold Avenue, Belfast BT8 6NA — MB BCh BAO 1995 Belf.

STOCKMAN, Paul Kennedy Western General Hospital, Crewe Road, Edinburgh EH4 2XU Tel: 0131 537 1903 Fax: 0131 537 1172 — MB ChB 1991 Ed.; PhD Ed. 1988, BSc 1982. (Edinburgh) Specialist Regist. (Haemat.) LUNHS.TRUST, Edin.

STOCKPORT, John Christopher 5 Glen View, Rhyd-y-Foel, Abergele LL22 8EB — MB ChB 1996 Manch. Surg. SHO Glan Clwyd Hosp. Denbighsh.

STOCKS, David Allen 4 Garth Avenue, Collingham, Wetherby LS22 5BJ — MB BS 1975 Lond.; AFOM RCP Lond. 1981; DRCOG 1983; DIH Eng. 1980.

STOCKS, Gary Mark Dept. of Microbiology, Queen Elizabeth Hospital, Edgbaston Tel: 0121 472 3311 — MB BS 1991 Lond.; BSc Lond. 1988; FRCA 1996. (St. Geo. Hosp. Med. Sch. Lond.) Cons. Anaesth., Hammersmith Hosp.s NHS Trust. Socs: Obsteric Anaesthetic Assn. Prev: Regist. Rotat. (Anaesth) UCH & Middlx.Hosps.Lond.

STOCKS, Nigel Phillip Walford House, The Street, Frampton on Severn, Gloucester GL2 7EA — MB BS 1986 Adelaide; FRACGP 1992. Clin. Lect. (Primary Care) Bristol.

STOCKS, Philippa Jane Department of Pathology, Kettering General Hospital, Rothwell Road, Kettering NN16 8UZ Fax: 01623 26575 — MB BS 1974 Lond.; MRCS Eng. LRCP Lond. 1974; FRCPath 1996, M 1985. (St. Bart.) Cons. (Histopath.) Kettering Gen. Hosp. NHS Trust. Socs: Assn. Clin. Pathologists. Prev: Cons. (Histopath.) King's Mill Centre; Sen. Regist. (Histopath.) Soton. Gen. Hosp. & Leicester Roy. Infirm.

STOCKS, Richard John Mill House, Mill Lane, Corton, Lowestoft NR32 5HZ — MB BS 1973 Lond.; FRCP Lond. 1995; MRCP (UK) 1977; FRCPCH 1996; DCH Eng. 1976. (St. Bart.) Cons. Paediat. Jas. Paget Hosp. Gt. Yarmouth; Clin. Dir. Jas. Paget Healthcare NHS Trust; Clin. Teach. Univ. Camb. Socs: & Paediat. Research Soc.; Brit. Soc. Paediat. Gastroenterol. & Nutrit.; Fell. Roy. Coll. Paediat. and Child Health. Prev: Regist. (Paediat.) Soton. Gen. Hosp.; Lect. (Child Health) Univ. Leicester; Hon. Sen. Regist. (Paediat.) Leicester Roy. Infirm.

***STOCKTON, Emma Fiona** Department of Anaesthetics, Northampton General Hospital, Cliftonville, Northampton NN1 5BD — MB BS 1997 Lond.

STOCKTON, Glyn 13 Hazel Street, Leicester LE2 7JN — MB ChB 1997 Leic. (Leicester) SHO (Surg.) PeterBoro. Hosps. NHS Trust PeterBoro. Prev: Ho. Off. (Med.) Geo. Eliot Hosp. Nuneaton; Ho. Off. (Surg.) Geo. Eliot Hosp.; SHO (Urol.) PeterBoro. Hosp. NHS Trust.

STOCKTON, Martyn Graham Princes Park Health Centre, Wartling Road, Eastbourne BN22 7PF Tel: 01323 744644 Fax: 01323 736094; 19A Upland Road, Eastbourne BN20 8EN Tel: 01323 735361 — MB ChB 1976 Birm.

STOCKTON, Michael Ronald St. Gemma's Hospice, Harrogate Road, Moortown, Leeds LS17 6QD Tel: 0113 269 3231; The Lodge, Cookridge Lane, Cookridge, Leeds LS16 7LG — MB ChB 1988 Leeds; MRCGP 1992. Cons. (Palliat. Med.) St. Gemma's Hospice Leeds.

STOCKTON, Paul Anthony 17 Matlock Close, Great Sankey, Warrington WA5 3PZ — MB ChB 1993 Liverp. SHO (Med.) Whiston Hosp. Merseyside. Prev: Ho. Off. Whiston Hosp. Merseyside.

STOCKWELL, Angela Jane Royal Cornwall Hospital, Treliske, Truro TR1 3LJ; Chyverton Castle, Zelam, Truro TR1 3LJ — MB BS 1974 Lond.; MRCS Eng. LRCP Lond. 1974; FRCS (Ophth.) Ed. 1985;

FCOphth. Lond. 1988. Cons. Ophth. Roy. Cornw. Hosp. Trust Treliske Hosp. Truro.

STOCKWELL, Joanna Claire 9 Elm Close, South Croydon CR2 7AH — BM BCh 1994 Oxf. SHO (anaesth.) Roy. United Hosp. Avon.

STOCKWELL, Margaret Caldwell 41 Abercrombie Drive, Bearsden, Glasgow G61 4RR Tel: 0141 942 5755 Email: maggie.stockwell@btinternet.com — MB ChB 1969 Glas.; FFA RCS Eng. 1975; DA Eng. 1972; DObst RCOG 1971. Cons. Anaesth Glas. Roy. Infirm. Prev: Cons. Anaesth. S.. Gen. Hosp. Glas.; Sen. Regist. & Regist. (Anaesth.) Glas. Roy. Infirm.

STOCKWELL, Martin Andrew Department of Anaesthesia, St Helier Hospital, Wrythe Lane, Carshalton SM5 1AA Tel: 020 8644 4343 Fax: 020 8296 2951; 45 Chatsworth Avenue, Wimbledon Chase, London SW20 8JZ — MB BS 1981 Lond.; FFA RCS Eng. 1986. Cons. ANaesth. & ITU St. Helier NHS Trust Lond. Socs: Assn. Anaesth & Intens. Care Soc.

STOCKWELL, Robert Charles Radiology Department, Chorley & South Ribble District General Hospital, Chorley PR7 1PP Tel: 01257 245878; The Old Barn, Pickup Bank, Hoddlesden, Darwen BB3 3QQ — MB ChB 1987 Manch.; FRCR 1994. (St. And. & Manch.) Cons. Radiol. Chorley & S. Ribble Dist. Gen. Hosp. Prev: Sen. Regist. & Regist. (Radiol.) N.. Region; SHO (Gen. Surg.) Halton Dist. Hosp.

STOCKWELL, William Stephen (retired) 13 Cardean Way, Balgeddie, Glenrothes KY6 3PW Tel: 01592 743733 — MB ChB 1969 Glas.; MRCPath 1976; FRCPath 1988.

STODDARD, Alan (retired) 23 Tollhouse Close, Chichester PO19 1SF Tel: 01243 780734 — MB BS 1943 Lond.; MRCS Eng. LRCP Lond. 1942; DPhysMed Eng. 1947. Prev: Phys. i/c Physical Med. Dept. Brook Hosp. Lond.

STODDARD, Mr Christopher James 12 Slayleigh Lane, Fulwood, Sheffield S10 3RF Tel: 0114 230 9284 Fax: 0114 230 7107; 12 Slayleigh Lane, Fulwood, Sheffield S10 3RF Tel: 0114 230 9284 Fax: 0114 230 7107 — MD 1977 Sheff.; MB ChB 1971; FRCS Eng. 1976. (Sheff.) Cons. Surg. Sheff. HA; Regional Specialty Adviser (Gen. Surg.) Trent; Trent Rep. Counc. of Upper GI Surgs. Socs: Surg. Research Soc. & Brit. Soc. Gastroenterol.; Assn. Upper G.I. Surg.; Assn. ColoProctol. Prev: Sen. Lect. (Surg.) Univ. Liverp.; Lect. (Surg.) Univ. Sheff.; Clin. Fell. (Surg.) McMaster Med. Centre Hamilton, Canada.

STODDARD, David Royston 10 Chestnut Close, Duffield, Derby DE56 4HD — MB BS 1968 Lond.; MRCS Eng. LRCP Lond. 1968. (Roy. Free)

STODDART, Andrew Patrick Birds Kitchen, Main St., Peasmarsh, Rye TN31 6YA Tel: 01797 230370 — BM 1983 Soton.; FRCA 1991; DA (UK) 1986. Cons. Anaesth. Conquest Hosp. St. Leonards-on-Sea. Prev: Sen. Regist. (Anaesth.) Oxf.; Instruc. Anaesth. Univ. Calif., Irvine; Regist. (Anaesth.) Addenbrooke's Hosp. Camb.

STODDART, Bethan Ceri 20 Corisande Road, Birmingham B29 6RH — BM BS 1996 Nottm.

STODDART, Clare Angela 28 Manor Orchard, Harbury, Leamington Spa CV33 9LZ — MB ChB 1994 Leeds; DECOG 1998; DFFP 1998.

STODDART, Mr David 65 Powdermill Brae, Gorebridge EH23 4HY; 33 Marywood Square, Strathbungo, Glasgow G41 2BN — MB ChB 1992 Manch.; FFAEM 2000; FRCS Ed. 1996. Locum Cons. A&E CrossHo. Hosp. Prev: SHO (A & E & Orthop.) Addenbrooke's Hosp. Camb.; SHO (A & E) Roy. Lancaster Infirm.; SHO (Med.) W.morland Gen. Hosp.

STODDART, Donald George Shettleston Health Centre, 420 Old Shettleston Road, Glasgow G32 7JZ Tel: 0141 531 6220 Fax: 0141 531 6206; The Hollies, 16 Richmond Drive, Cambuslang, Glasgow G72 8BH Tel: 0141 641 1183 Email: donaldstoddart@compuserve.com — MB ChB 1980 Glas.; BSc Glas. 1979; DRCOG 1984. (Glas.)

STODDART, Fiona Helen 38 Sandy Lane, Sutton SM2 7PQ — MB ChB 1993 Bristol.

STODDART, Helen Division of Primary Health, University of Bristol, Canynge Hall, Whiteladies Road, Bristol BS8 2PR Tel: 0117 928 7313 Email: helen.stoddart@bristol.ac.uk — MRCGP 1998; BSc Lond. 1981, MB BS 1984; DCH RCP Lond. 1987; DRCOG 1987; MFPHM 1994. Clin. Lect. Primary Health Care, Univ. of Bristol; GP Princip., Alma Rd. Surg., Bristol. Socs: Mem. Roy. Coll. of Gen.

Practitioners.; Brit. Med. Assn. Prev: Trainee GP Portslade Health Centre; Trainee GP Univ. Coll. Hosp. Lond. VTS.

***STODDART, James William Anderson** 18 Dee Place, Dundee DD2 4JH — BM BCh 1998 Oxf.; BM BCh Oxf 1998.

STODDART, Joseph Charles 3 Kingsland, Newcastle upon Tyne NE2 3AL Tel: 0191 232 5131 — MD 1965 Newc.; MB BS Durh. 1956; FRCP Lond. 1994; FRCA 1993. (Newc.) Cons. Anaesth. Roy. Vict. Infirm. Newc. u. Tyne; Cons. i/c Intens. Ther. Unit Roy. Vict. Infirm. Newc. u.Tyne; Civil Cons. Anaesth. RAF; Cons. Intens. Ther. N.. RHA. Socs: Anaesth. Research Gp. & Intens. Care Soc.; (Counc.) Roy. Coll. Anaesth. Prev: Regist. (Anaesth.) Roy. Vict. Infirm. Newc.; Med. Off (Research) RAF Inst. Aviat. Med. FarnBoro. Hants.; 1st Asst. (Anaesth.) Univ. Newc.

STODDART, Mark Grainger 92 Woodbine Road, Gosforth, Newcastle upon Tyne NE3 1DE — MB ChB 1985 Aberd.; BMedBiol. 1985; FRCOphth 1993. Regist. Rotat. (Ophth.) Roy. Vict. Infirm. Newc. u. Tyne. Socs: BMA & N. Eng. Ophth. Soc. Prev: SHO (Ophth.) Roy. Vict. Infirm. Newc.; SHO (Ophth.) Cheltenham Gen. Hosp.; SHO (Neurosurg.) Univ. Hosp. Wales Cardiff.

STODDART, Norman (retired) 7 St Wilfrids Square, Calverton, Nottingham NG14 6FP Tel: 0115 965 2294 Fax: 0115 965 5898 — MB BS 1961 Lond.; MRCS Eng. LRCP Lond. 1961; MRCGP 1990. Prev: ICI Computer Fell. RCGP.

STODDART, Patricia Elizabeth Burns Watling Street Surgery, 162 Watling Street East, Towcester NN12 6DB — MB ChB 1974 Aberd.; MRCGP 1980; DObst RCOG 1976.

STODDART, Peter Anthony Anaesthetic Department, The Royal Hospital for Sick Children, St Michaels Hill, Bristol BS2 8ET Tel: 0117 928 5203 — MB BS 1984 Lond.; BSc Lond. 1981; MRCP (UK) 1989; FCAnaesth 1991; DA (UK) 1987. Cons. Paediat. Anaesth. The Roy. Hosp. for Sick Childr. Bristol. Prev: Regist. (Anaesth.) Gt. Ormond St. Hosp. Lond.; Asst. Prof. Univ. Virgina, USA.

STODDART, Peter Gavin Pilditch Tableland, Burton Row, Brent Knoll, Highbridge TA9 4BW — MD 1987 Bristol; BA Oxf. 1974; MB BS Lond. 1977; FRCR 1983; DMRD Eng. 1982. Cons. Diag. Radiol. W.on Health Trust.

STODDART, Peter Ronald 108 Queens Road, Leicester LE2 3FL Tel: 0116 707067 — MB BCh 1968 Wales. (Cardiff) Socs: BMA.

STODELL, Malcolm Anthony Luton and Dunstable Hospital, Luton LU4 0DZ Tel: 01582 497233; Chestnut Tree Farm, Ampthill Rd, Maulden, Bedford MK45 2DP — MB BS 1972 Lond.; FRCP Lond. 1994; MRCP (UK) 1976; MRCS Eng. LRCP Lond. 1972. (Guy's) Cons. Phys. Rheum. & Gen. Med. Luton & Dunstable Hosp. Luton. Socs: Brit. Soc. Rheum. Mem. Prev: Sen. Regist. Rotat. (Rheum.) W.m., Char. Cross & St. Stephen's Hosps. Lond.; Regist. (Gen. Med.) St. Helier Hosp. Carshalton.

STOECKER, Holger Rhynern, Station Road, Bere Ferrers, Yelverton PL20 7JS — State Exam Med 1992 Munster.

STOHLNER, John 9 Scholars Court, West St., Yarm TS15 9SQ — MB ChB 1944 St. And.; DObst RCOG 1948. (St. And.) Prev: Res. Obst. Off. Sunnyside Matern. Hosp. Cheltenham; O & G Ho. Surg. Harrogate & Dist. Gen. Hosp.; Temp. Capt. RAMC.

***STOJKOVIC, Stevan George** 7 Ashdene Court, Cullingworth, Bradford BD13 5JR — MB ChB 1994 Sheff.

STOKELL, Richard Alexander The Strand Medical Centre, 272 Marsh Lane, Bootle L20 5BW Tel: 0151 922 1600; 45 Waterpark Road, Birkenhead CH42 8PN — MB ChB 1984 Manch.; MRCGP 1988; DRCOG 1986. Prev: Trainee GP Ormskirk & Dist. Gen. Hosp. VTS.

***STOKER, Alex Patrick** 6A Blackheath Park, London SE3 9RR — MB BS 1998 Lond.; MB BS Lond 1998.

STOKER, Catherine Jane War Memorial Health Centre, Crickhowell NP8 1AG Tel: 01873 810255 — MB BS 1982 Lond.; MRCGP 1986; DRCOG 1985.

STOKER, Mr David Lawson Department of Surgery, North Middlesex Hospital, Sterling Way, London N18 1QX Tel: 020 8887 2461 Fax: 020 8887 2369 Email: dls@dr.com; Tel: 020 8372 7095 Fax: 020 8360 3146 Email: dls@dr.com — MB ChB 1979 Ed.; BSc (Med. Sci.) Ed. 1976, MD 1990; FRCS Eng. 1984; FRCS Ed. 1983. (Edinburgh University Medical School) Cons. Gen. Surg. N. Middlx. Hosp. Lond.; Assoc. Med. Dir. N. Middlx. Hosp. Lond; Clin. Assoc. Prof. St. Geo. Sch. of Med. Grenada; Lead Clinician - Surg. Socs: Assn. Endoscopic Surgs.; Brit. Soc. Gastroenterol.; Fell. Assn. Surgs.

STOKER

Prev: Sen. Regist. (Gen. Surg.) St. Bart. Hosp. Lond. & N. Middlx. Hosp. Lond.; Regist. (Gen. Surg.) Homerton & St. Bart. Hosps. Lond.; Research Fell. (Gastroenterol.) RN Hosp. Haslar Gosport.

STOKER, Dennis James Royal National Orthopaedic Hospital, 45-51 Bolsover St., London W1W 5AQ; 3 Pearces Orchard, Henley-on-Thames RG9 2LF Tel: 01491 575756 Fax: 01491 575756 — MB BS Lond. 1951; FRCS Eng. 1992; FRCP Lond. 1976, M 1958; MRCS Eng. LRCP Lond. 1951; FRCR 1975; FFR 1971; DMRD Eng. 1969. (Guy's) p/t Cons Radiol Roy Nat Omlop Hosp; Cons. Radiol Frimley Pk. Hosp. (frimley sy.). Socs: Fell. (Ex-Dean & Vice-Pres.) Roy. Coll. Radiol.; Fell. Roy. Soc. Med.; Founder Mem. Internat. Skeletal Soc. Prev: Dean Inst. Orthop. Univ. Lond.; Cons. Phys. RAF.

***STOKER, Jeffrey Alan** 41 Settrington Road, Scarborough YO12 5DL — MB ChB 1994 Leeds.

STOKER, John Brandon Sowood House, The Green, Ossett WF5 0AL Tel: 01924 274122 — MB ChB 1961 Leeds; BSc, MB ChB Leeds 1961; FRCP Lond. 1980, M 1967. Cardiol. St. Jas. & Killingbeck Hosps. Leeds.

STOKER, Kathryn Elizabeth Anne Sowood House, The Green, Ossett WF5 0AL — MB ChB 1992 Leeds.

STOKER, Nigel Richard Brandon Broomlea, Old Church Road, Cullen, Buckie AB56 4UZ — MB ChB 1992 Leeds.

STOKER, Mr Thomas Alan Mayfield 6A Blackheath Park, London SE3 9RR Tel: 020 8852 2669 — MB BChir 1962 Camb; MD Camb. 1969, MA; FRCS Eng. 1967; MRCS Eng. LRCP Lond. 1962. (Guy's) Cons. Surg. Qu. Eliz. NHS Trust Lond. SE18; Cons. Surg. Greenwich Dist. Hosp. Socs: Fell. Assn. of Surg.s; Ex-Pres. W. Kent M-C Soc.; Brit. Soc. Surg. Oncols. Prev: Lect. (Surg.) W.m. Hosp. Lond.; Res. Surg. Off. Roy. Marsden Hosp Lond.; Ho. Surg. Guy's Hosp. Lond.

STOKES, Cathryn Elizabeth Saxonbury House Surgery, Croft Road, Crowborough TN6 1DL Tel: 01892 652266 Fax: 01892 668607 — BM BS 1986 Nottm.; 2000 D.Occ.Med; MPhil Nottm. 1984, BMed Sci 1983; MRCGP 1991; DRCOG 1990; DGM RCP Lond. 1989; DFFP 1997. (Nottm.) Socs: BMA.

STOKES, Christopher Simon Gowan Brae, Station Road, Staveley, Kendal LA8 9NB — MB ChB 1986 Bristol; BSc Bristol 1983; MRCP (UK) 1990; DRCOG 1992.

STOKES, E. Joan (retired) Ossicles, Newnham Hill, Henley-on-Thames RG9 5TL Tel: 01491 641526 — MB BS 1937 Lond.; MB BS (Hons.) Lond. 1937; FRCP Lond. 1958, M 1939; MRCS Eng. LRCP Lond. 1937; FRCPath 1963. Cons. Clin. Bacteriol. Univ. Coll. Hosp. Lond. Prev: Pub. Health Bacteriol. Sector IV Watford.

STOKES, Elizabeth Louise Monkspath Surgery, 27 Farmhouse Way, Monkspath, Shirley, Solihull B90 4EH Tel: 0121 711 1414 Fax: 0121 711 3753; 16 Manton Croft, Dorridge, Solihull B93 8TD — MB BS 1989 Lond.

STOKES, Iain Michael Nevill Hall Hospital, Brecon Road, Abergavenny NP7 7EG Tel: 01873 732146 Fax: 01873 732147 Email: iain.stokes@gwent.wales.nhs.uk; Ashlea, 72 Hereford Road, Abergavenny NP7 6AB Tel: 01873 859950 Fax: 01873 859950 — MB BCh 1971 Wales; FRCOG 1989; MRCOG 1977. Cons. O & G Nevill Hall Hosp. Abergavenny; Lead Clin. Dir. (Obst. & Gyn.) Gwent Healthcare NHS Trust. Prev: Sen. Regist. (O & G) Univ. Hosp. of Wales, +St Davids Hosp. Cardiff & Roy. Gwent Hosp. Newport.

STOKES, Jacqueline Margaret Glenfinlas, Whitchurch Road, Horrabridge, Yelverton PL20 7TZ Tel: 01822 853068 Fax: 01822 853068 — MB ChB Bristol 1983; DA (UK) 1989; DRCOG 1987. (Bristol) Clin. Asst. (Anaesth.) Tavistock & Plymouth. Prev: Princip. Stannary Surg. Tavistock Devon; SHO (Anaesth.) Roy. Devon & Exeter Hosp.; SHO (O & G) MusGr. Pk. Hosp. Taunton.

STOKES, John Fisher Ossicles, Newnham Hill, Henley-on-Thames RG9 5TL Tel: 01491 641526 — MB BChir 1937 Camb.; MD Camb. (Prox. Acc. Raymond Horton-Smith Prize) 1947; FRCP Ed. 1975; FRCP Lond. 1947, M 1939; MRCS Eng. LRCP Lond. 1937. (Camb. & Univ. Coll. Hosp.) Consg. Phys. Univ. Coll. Hosp. Socs: Assn. Phys. Prev: Lt.-Col. RAMC; Examr. for MRCP (UK); Examr. for Various Univs.

STOKES, Judith Mary 5 Finney Bank Road, Sale M33 6LR — MB ChB 1989 Manch.; BSc (Hons.) 1984. SHO (Prosth.s) Manch. Roy. Infirm.

STOKES, Julian Edward Terence Marches Surgery, Westfield Walk, Leominster HR6 8HD Tel: 01568 614141 Fax: 01568 610293 — MB BS 1974 Lond.; MB BS (Hons.) Lond. 1974; MRCP (UK) 1977; MRCS Eng. LRCP Lond. 1974; Dip. Pract. Dermat. Wales 1995; Dip. Ther. Cardiff 1994; DRCOG 1979. (Guy's Hosp. Lond.) Socs: Full Mem. Brit. Md. Acupunc. Soc.; Assoc. Mem. Inst. Psycho-Sexual Med.

STOKES, Mary Louise (retired) 4 Lorn Road, Stockwell, London SW9 0AD Tel: 020 7274 2649 — MRCS Eng. LRCP Lond. 1948; FRCOG 1977, M 1963; DObst RCOG 1950. Cons. Mission Hosp. Iran. Prev: Cons. Gyn. & Obst. St. Jas. Hosp. Balham, S. Lond. Hosp. & St. Geo. Hosp. Lond.

STOKES, Mathew James The Shamba, Wotton Crescent, Wotton-under-Edge GL12 7JZ; 7 High Street, Wotton-under-Edge GL12 7DE — MB ChB 1990 Pretoria; BSc Witwatersrand 1985.

STOKES, Mr Maurice Anthony Department of Surgery, Daisy Hill Hospital, 5 Hospital Road, Newry BT35 8DR Tel: 01693 65511 Fax: 01693 68869; Lisnegar, 23 Well Road, Warrenpoint, Newry BT34 3RS Tel: 016937 52998 Email: maurice.a.stokes@lineone.net — MB BCh BAO 1980 NUI; BSc (Anat.) NUI 1982; MCh NUI 1991; FRCSI 1986. (Univ. Coll. Dub.) Cons. Surg. (Gen. Surg.) Daisy Hill Hosp. Newry. Socs: Fell. Surg. GB & Irel.; RAMI; BASO. Prev: Sen. Regist. (Gen. Surg.) Irish Train. Scheme; Lect. (Surg.) Univ. Auckland, NZ; Regist. (Surg.) Hosp. Hosp. Salford & Roy. Hosp. Wolverhampton.

STOKES, Michael John Horsefair Practice, Horse Fair, Rugeley WS15 2EL Tel: 01889 582244 Fax: 01899 582244 — MB ChB 1988 Birm.; DFFP Birm.; DRCOG Birm. (Birmingham) GP Horsefair, Rugeley, Staffs.; Family Plann. Med. Off., 1st Community Health, Stafford.

STOKES, Michael John 39 The Green, Barton under Needwood, Burton-on-Trent DE13 8JD — MB ChB 1962 Birm.; MRCP (UK) 1973; DCH Eng. 1966. Cons. (Paediat.) S.E. Staffs. Health Dist. Prev: Sen. Regist. (Paediat.) King's Coll. Hosp. Lond.; Regist. (Paediat.) Copthorne Hosp. Shrewsbury; Regist. (Paediat.) United Newc. Hosps.

STOKES, Monica Anne Department of Anaesthesia, University of Birmingham, Edgbaston, Birmingham B15 2TH — BM BS 1981 Nottm.; BMedSci Nottm. 1979; FFA RCS Eng. 1986. Sen. Lect. (Anaesth.) Univ. Birm.; Hon. Cons. Birm. Childr. Hosp. NHS Trust. Prev: Lect. (Anaesth.) Univ. Birm.

STOKES, Paul Robert Alexander 18 Meadowhead Road, Southampton SO16 7AD Tel: 02380 767902 Email: xsy76@dial.pipex.com — MB ChB 1997 Birm.; BSc (Hons) Birm. (Birmingham University) SHO in A&E, John Radcliffe Hosp., Oxf. Prev: Ho. Off. Surg., Alexandra Hosp., Redditch; Ho. Off. Med./ Cardology, Qu. Eliz. Hosp., Birm.

STOKES, Peter John Alresford Surgery, Station Road, Alresford SO24 9JL Tel: 01962 732345 Fax: 01962 736034 — MB BS 1984 Lond.; BSc (Basic Med. Sci. & Physiol.) Lond. 1981, MB BS 1984; MRCGP 1991. (Westm.) Prev: Regist. & SHO (Med.) Roy. Devon & Exeter Hosp. Exeter; SHO (Obst.) Freedom Fields Hosp. Plymouth; SHO (A & E) St. Helier Hosp. Surrey.

STOKES, Robert Andrew Tottington Health Centre, 16 Market Street, Tottington, Bury BL8 4AD Tel: 01204 885106 Fax: 01204 887717 — MB ChB 1986 Manch.; MRCGP 1990; DRCOG 1990.

***STOKES, Sian Michelle** 133 Trevelyan Road, London SW17 9LP — MB BS 1998 Lond.; MB BS Lond 1998; BSc Lond. 1997.

STOKES, Stephen Alan Kinsey Brightonwater Farm, Cardingham, Bodmin PL30 4DL — MB ChB 1945 Bristol.

STOKES, Thomas Christopher 87 Kidbrooke Grove, Blackheath, London SE3 0LQ — MD 1981 NUI; MSc Lond. 1979; MB BCh BAO NUI 1971; MRCPI 1976; FRCP Lond. 1989; MRCP (UK) 1974. Cons. Phys. Qu. Eliz. Hosp. Woolwich; Hon. Cons. Phys. St. Thos. Hosp. Lond. Prev: Sen. Regist. (Respirat. Med.) Addenbrookes Hosp. Camb. & Papworth; Hosp.; Clin. Lect. Cardiothoracic Inst. & Brompton Hosp.

STOKES, Timothy Newman Department General Practice & Primary Health Care, University of Leicester, Leicester General Hospital, Gwendolen Road, Leicester LE5 4PW Tel: 0116 258 4873 Fax: 0116 258 4982 Email: tns2@le.ac.uk — MB ChB 1989 Ed.; MPH 1987 Notts.; MPhil 1987 Camb.; MA 1989 Oxf.; BA 1985 Oxf.; MRCGP 1993. p/t Sen. Lect. Gen. Pract. Univ. of Leicester; GP E. Leics. Med. Pract., Leics. Prev: Trainee GP Airedale HA.; Ho. Off. (Surg.) York Dist. Hosp.; Ho. Off. (Med.) City Hosp. Edin.

STOKES, Victoria Valerie Lyndhurst Surgery, 2 Church Lane, Lyndhurst SO43 7EW Tel: 01703 282689 Fax: 01703 282918; 63A

Southampton Road, Lymington SO41 9GH Tel: 01590 670401 — MB ChB 1993 Leeds. GP Regist, Lyndhurst Surg. Hants. Prev: SHO Rotat. (Med.) Huddersfield Roy. Infirm. Huddersfield, W. Yorks.

STOKES-LAMPARD, Helen Jayne Department of Primary Care & General Practice, The Medical School, University of Birmingham, Birmingham B15 2TT Email: stokesh@medgp1.bham.ac.uk; 14 Holte Drive, Four Oaks, Sutton Coldfield B75 6PR Email: stockesh@medgp1.bham.ac.uk — MB BS 1996 Lond.; DRCOG 2000; DFFP 1998. (St. Geo.) Acad. GP Regist. Univ. of Birm.; GP Regist.; Hon. Research Fell. Univ. of Birm. Socs: BMA. Prev: Regist. Observ. RCGP Counc.; SHO (O & G) Singleton Hosp. Swansea.

STOKKEREIT, Colin Redlands, Mount Tavy Road, Tavistock PL19 9JL; 50 Benson Road, Grays RM17 6DL — MB BS 1994 Lond.; BSc (Biochem.) Lond. 1991. Prev: SHO (A & E) Lister Hosp. Stevenage; Ho. Off. (Surg.) Lister Hosp. Stevenage; Ho. Off. (Gen. Med.) King Geo. Hosp. Goodmayes.

STOKOE, David 9 Linkside, Higher Bebington, Wirral CH63 5PE — MB ChB 1987 Liverp.

STOKOE, David Jeremy 23 Guffitts Rake, Wirral CH47 7AH — MB ChB 1985 Liverp.

STOKOE, Eric (retired) 9 Hall Farm, Shincliffe, Durham DH1 2UE Tel: 0191 386 4807 — MA Camb. 1952, MB BChir 1951; MRCS Eng. LRCP Lond. 1950; DIH Soc. Apoth. Lond. 1961. Prev: GP Durh. City.

STOKOE, Margaret Ann The Rookery, Giddeahall, Chippenham SN14 7EP — MB ChB 1983 Dundee; DRCOG 1990; Cert. Family Plann. JCC 1990; Cert. Prescribed Equiv. Exp. JCPTGP 1989; DCH RCP Lond. 1986.

STOKOE, Norman Leslie (retired) 26 Morningside Place, Edinburgh EH10 5EY Tel: 0131 447 8966 — MB ChB 1945 Ed. Edinburgh; MB ChB Ed. 1945 Edinburgh; FRCS Ed. 1953 Edinburgh; FRACS 1958 Melbourne; FRCOphth 1988 London; DO Eng. 1951 London. Prev: Cons. Ophth. Surg. E. Fife Hosp. & Edin. Roy. Infirm.

STOLAR, Mark 91 Palmerston Road, Walthamstow, London E17 6PU Tel: 020 8520 7115; 27 Nevin Drive, Chingford, London E4 7LL Tel: 020 8529 1271 — MRCS Eng. LRCP Lond. 1959; DM Cairo 1954, MB BCh 1950. Prev: Med. Regist. Wanstead Hosp. Lond.; Clin. Asst. (Gen. Med.) Battersea Gen. Hosp.; Clin. Asst. (Neurol.) Qu. Mary's Hosp. for E. End. Lond.

STOLKIN, Colin 30 Talfourd Road, London SE15 5NY Tel: 020 7701 1321 — BM BCh 1969 Oxf.; MA. Lect. Dept. Anat. King's Coll. Lond. Prev: Sen. Research Fell. (Ment. Health Foundat. & Research Trust) MRC; Neuro-immunol. Project Dept. Zool. Univ. Coll. Lond.; MRC Jun. Research Fell. Dept. Neuropath. Inst. Psychiat. Lond.

STOLL, Basil Arnold 5 Milton Court, Highfield Road, London NW11 9LY — MRCS Eng. LRCP Lond. 1939; FRCR 1975; FFR 1951; DMRD Eng. 1948; DMR Lond 1948; DMRT Eng. 1947; DTM & H Eng. 1946. (Westm.) Hon. Cons. Dept. Radiother. St. Thos. Hosp. & Roy. Free Hosp. Lond.; Vis. Prof. Univ. Witwatersand S. Afr.; Edr. Revs. on Endocrine-Related Cancer; Dep. Edr. Clin. Oncol.; Clin. Edr. BioTher. Socs: Brit. BrE. Gp. Prev: Cons. Radiotherap. Cancer Inst. Melb. & Lect. in Radiother. Monash & Melb. Univs.; Hon. Radiotherap. P. Henry's Hosp. Melb.

STOLL, Henry (retired) 2 Spencer Close, Regents Park Road, Finchley, London N3 3TX Tel: 020 8346 1848 — MRCS Eng. LRCP Lond. 1937. Prev: Chairm. Hampstead Div. BMA.

STOLL, Lionel Julian 27 Hollycroft Avenue, Hampstead, London NW3 7QJ Tel: 020 7435 2656 — MRCS Eng. LRCP Lond. 1933; FRCGP 1971. (Guy's) Socs: Fell. BMA (Ex-Pres. & Chairm. Metrop. Cos. Br.); Fell. Hunt. Soc.; Osler Club. Prev: Clin. Asst. Metrop. ENT Hosp. Lond.; Squadron Ldr. RAF; Phys. CharterHo. Rheum. Clinic.

STOLLARD, Mr Gordon Edmund, RD Harrogate District Hospital, Lancaster Park Road, Harrogate HG2 7SX Tel: 01423 885959 Fax: 01423 881168; Randabel, 6 Throstle Nest Drive, Harrogate HG2 9PB Tel: 01423 872249 Email: stollge@aol.com — MB BS Lond. 1965; FRCS Eng. 1972; MRCS Eng. LRCP Lond. 1965. (Univ. Coll. Hosp.) Cons. Surg. (Orthop. & Trauma) Harrogate Health Care Trust. Socs: Fell. BOA; BMA; HCSA. Prev: Sen. Regist. (Orthop.) P.ss Eliz. Orthop. Hosp. Exeter; Regist. (Surg.) & Ho. Phys. & Ho. Surg. Univ. Coll. Hosp. Lond.

STOLLERY, Nigel Alexander Smeeton Road Health Centre, Smeeton Road, Kibworth, Leicester LE8 0LG Tel: 0116 279 3308 Fax: 0116 279 3320 — MB BS 1989 Lond.

STONAWSKI, Boguslaw 77 Track Road, Batley WF17 7AB Tel: 01924 474466 — Med. Dipl. Cracow 1938.

STONE, Adam Francis Minto 5 Deepdene Mansions, Rostrevor Road, Fulham, London SW6 5AQ Tel: 020 7731 5395 — MB BChir 1991 Camb.; MA Camb. 1992; MRCP (UK) 1994. Regist. SW Thames RHA.

STONE, Alan Kenneth 4/5 Avondale Court, Onchan, Douglas IM3 1AD Tel: 01624 676212; 43 Cronk Avenue, Birchill, Onchan, Douglas IM3 3DE Tel: 01624 623557 — MB ChB 1979 Aberd.; MRCGP 1986. Gen. Med. Pract.

STONE, Alan Martin Kings Road Surgery, 180 Kings Road, Canton, Cardiff CF11 9DQ Tel: 029 2034 1547 Fax: 029 2064 0499 — MB BS Lond. 1984; MRCGP 1988; DRCOG 1988; DCH RCP Lond. 1987.

STONE, Alexander, SBStJ Cranford, Hillside Drive, Woolton, Liverpool L25 5NS Tel: 0151 428 2155 Fax: 0151 421 1070 — MB ChB Liverp. 1944; MRCS Eng. LRCP Lond. 1943; FRCGP 1969, M 1952. (Liverp.) Hon. Lect. (Gen. Pract.) Univ. Liverp. Prev: Dir. Studies (Gen. Pract.) Univ. Liverp.; Corps Surg. St. John Ambul. Brig.

STONE, Alexander George Henry Hill Cottage, Church Hill, Godshill, Ventnor PO38 3HY — MB BS 1994 Lond. SHO (Anaesth.) Whipps Cross Hosp. Lond. Prev: SHO (A & E) Roy. Lond. & Homerton Hosps.; Ho. Off. (Gen. Med.) St. Bart. & Homerton Hosps. Lond.; Ho. Off. (Gen. Surg. & Urol.) S.end Gen. Hosp.

STONE, Alison Louise Rosemount, 31 Main Road, Portskewett, Newport NP26 5SA — MB BS 1984 Lond.

STONE, Andrew Brian 30 Eton Rise, Eton College Road, London NW3 2DF — MB BS 1996 Lond.; BSc (Hons) Lond. 1993 (Physiol).

STONE, Andrew David Royston Church Street Surgery, Church Street, Spalding PE11 2PB Tel: 01775 722189 Fax: 01775 712164 — MB BS 1984 Lond.; DRCOG 1988; DGM RCP Lond. 1987; AKC 1984. (Kings Coll. Hosp. Med. Sch.) Prev: Ho. Off. (Surg.) King's Coll. Hosp. Lond; SHO (Paediat. & O & G) All St.s Hosp. Chatham Kent.; SHO (Obst & Gyn.) Chatham Kent & Trainee GP Canterbury.

***STONE, Anna Mary** 15 Rodbourne Road, Harborne, Birmingham B17 0PN — MB ChB 1995 Birm.

STONE, Anthony Royston 23 Cross Street, Ystrad, Pentre CF41 7RF — MB ChB 1993 Manch.

STONE, Anthony William 23 The Close, Cleadon, Sunderland SR6 7RG — MB ChB 1987 Leeds; MRCGP 1994; DRCOG 1992.

STONE, Audrey Mary (retired) The Manor House, Tollerton, York YO61 1QQ Tel: 01347 838454 Fax: 01347 838454 — MRCS Eng. LRCP Lond. 1957; DA Eng. 1960. Clin. Asst. (Anaesth.) York Dist. Hosp. Prev: Instruc. in Anaesth. Johns Hopkins Hosp. Baltimore, U.S.A.

STONE, Barnet Stoneacre, Paris Farm, Common Road, Lingfield RH7 6BZ Tel: 01342 833816 — MB ChB 1931 Manch. (Manch.)

STONE, Beryl Cynthia Keymer House, West Hill, Ottery St Mary EX11 1UW — MB BS 1951 Lond. (King's Coll. Hosp.)

STONE, Brian Edwin Shanklin Medical Centre, 1 Carter Road, Shanklin PO37 7HR Tel: 01983 862245 Fax: 01983 862310 — MRCS Eng. LRCP Lond. 1961; DObst RCOG 1964. (St. Bart.) Prev: Asst. Co. Med. Off. I. of Wight; Ho. Surg. Redhill Gen. Hosp.; Ho. Phys. & Ho. Surg. (O & G) St. Mary's Hosp. Newport.

***STONE, Carol Anne** Flat 02, 4 Vinicombe Street, Glasgow G12 8BG — MB ChB 1997 Glas.

STONE, Christine Janet Health Promotion Unit, Beckenham Hospital, 379 Croydon Road, Beckenham BR3 3QL Tel: 020 8289 6658 Fax: 020 8282 3242 — MRCS Eng. LRCP Lond. 1965. (St. Mary's) Primary Care Ment. Health Facilitator Bromley Health. Prev: Ho. Phys. Prospect Pk. Hosp. Reading; Ho. Surg. Roy. Berks. Hosp. Reading.; Partner W. Wickham.

STONE, Mr Christopher Anthony 2 Barton Mews, Exton, Exeter EX3 0PP Email: c.a.stone@btinternet.com — MB ChB 1990 Manch.; MSc Lond. 1996; FRCS Eng. 1994; FRCS Ed. 1994. (Manch.) Specialist Regist. (Plastic Surg.) Roy. Devon & Exeter Hosp.; Instruc. in Emerg. Managem. of Severe Burns. Socs: Brit. Burns Assn.; Assoc. Mem. Brit. Assn. Plastic Surgs. Prev: SHO (Gen. Surg.) Wythenshawe Hosp.; SHO (Plastic Surg.) Radcliffe Infirm.; SHO (Orthop.) Mt. Vernon Hosp.

STONE, Christopher Michael 87A St Georges Drive, Pimlico, London SW1 4DB — MB BS 1983 Lond.

STONE, Christopher William Department of Psychological Medicine, Hope Hospital, Stott Lane, Salford M6 8HD Tel: 0161 789

STONE

7373 — MB ChB 1975 Dundee; MPhil Ed. 1986; MRCP (UK) 1980; MRCPsych 1982. Cons. Psychiat. Hope Hosp. Salford; Hon. Assoc. Lect. Univ. Manch.

STONE, Mr Colin David Payne Crawley Hospital, West Green Drive, Crawley RH11 7DH Tel: 01293 600325 Fax: 01293 600341 — MB ChB 1971 Ed.; BSc (Hons.) Ed. 1968; FRCS Ed. 1976. (Ed.) Cons. Orthop. Surg. Crawley Hosp. New E. Surrey Hosp. Redhill. Socs: Brit. Orthop. Assn.; Brit. Soc. Surg. Hand. Prev: Sen. Regist. (Orthop.) W. Midl. RHA; Regist. (Orthop.) Lothian HB.

STONE, David Gordon Harvey (retired) Flowers Court Coach House, Pangbourne, Reading RG8 8ES Tel: 0118 984 1510 — MB BS Lond. 1943; FRCP Lond. 1972, M 1948; MRCS Eng. LRCP Lond. 1943. Prev: Cons. Paediat. W. Berks. HA.

STONE, Professor David Hope Department of Child Health, Yorkhill Hospital, Glasgow G3 8SJ Tel: 0141 201 0178 Fax: 0141 201 6943 — MB ChB 1972 Ed.; MRCP (UK) 1974; MD Ed. 1982; FRCPCH 1997; FFCM 1987, MFCM 1979; FRCP Glas. 1990. Dir. (Paediat. Epidemiol. & Community Health) Univ. Glas.; Sen. Lect. (Paediat. Epidemiol.) Univ. Glas.; Hon. Cons. Paediat. Epidemiol. Yorkhill NHS Trust. Prev: Lect. (Community Med.) St. Thos. Hosp. Med. Sch. Lond.; Sen. Lect. (Epidemiol.) B.G. Univ. Negev, Israel.; Hon. Cons. Pub. Health Med. Gtr. Glas. HB.

STONE, David Lewis Papworth Hospital, Papworth Everard, Cambridge CB3 8RE Tel: 01480 364361; 12 Wooton Way, Cambridge CB3 9UX Tel: 01223 357147 Email: dls27@cam.ac.uk — MB BS 1971 Lond.; BSc Lond. 1968; MD Lond. 1985; FRCP Ed 1997; FRCP Lond. 1992; MRCS Eng. LRCP Lond. 1971. (Charing Cross Hosp.) Cons. Cardiol. Papworth & W. Suff. Hosp. Trusts; Assoc. Dean Camb. Sch. Clin. Med.

STONE, Derek William George 1 Dean Lane, Southville, Bristol BS3 1DE Tel: 0117 966 3149 — MB ChB 1952 Bristol.

STONE, Diana Rachel 3 Irlam Road, Sale M33 2BH — BM BS 1992 Nottm.

STONE, Elizabeth Jeanne Theale Medical Centre, Englefield Road, Theale, Reading RG7 5AS Tel: 0118 930 2513 Fax: 0118 930 4419; Pine Paddock, Whitchurch Hill, Reading RG8 7PB Tel: 0118 984 4345 — MB BS 1967 Lond.; DRCOG 1993. (King's Coll. Hosp.) Socs: BMA. Prev: Trainee GP W.. Elms Surg. Reading; SHO (O & G) Roy. Berks. Hosp. Reading; CMO E. Berks. Health Auth.

STONE, Frances 719 Walmersley Road, Bury BL9 5JN — MB ChB 1975 Manch.

STONE, Professor Frederick Hope, OBE 14A Hamilton Avenue, Glasgow G41 4JF Tel: 0141 427 0115 — MB ChB 1945 Glas.; FRCP Lond. 1971, M 1950; FRCP Glas. 1967, M 1962; FRFPS Glas. 1949; FRCPCH 1997; FRCPsych 1971. (Univ. of Glas.) Prof. Emerit. Child & Adolesc. Psychiat. Univ. Glas.; Pres. Young Minds. Socs: BMA. Prev: Paediat. Psychiat. & Act. Dir. Lasker Centre of Hadassah, Jerusalem; Cons. Child Psychiat. Roy. Hosp. Sick Childr. Glas.

STONE, George Francis (retired) 17 Tree Tops, Sydney Road, Woodford Green IG8 0SY Tel: 020 8505 9623 — MRCS Eng. LRCP Lond. 1952; DObst RCOG 1953. Prev: Sen. Ho. Off. (O & G) Gen. Hosp. Leicester.

STONE, Gordon Victor The Carn, Flichity, Inverness IV2 6XD Tel: 01808 521401 — MB ChB 1969 Aberd.; FFCM 1987, M 1977; Dip. Community. Med. Ed. 1976. Gen. Manager. Highland HB; Hon. Sen. Lect. (Community Med.) Univ. Aberd. Socs: Fac. Community Health (Irel.). Prev: Chief Med. Off. & Dir. Pub. Health Highland HB; Specialist (Community Med.) Grampian HB; Flight Lt. RAF Med. Br.

STONE, Ian Mitchell Falmouth Road Surgery, 78 Falmouth Road, London SE1 4JW Tel: 020 7407 4101/0945 Fax: 020 7357 6170 — MB 1980 Camb.; BChir 1979.

STONE, James Ciaran Waterside Health Centre, Glendermot Road, Londonderry BT47 6AU Tel: 028 7132 0100 Fax: 028 7134 9323; 8 Glenaden Hill, Altnagelvin, Londonderry BT47 2LJ — MB BCh BAO 1972 Belf.; FRCGP 1996; MRCGP 1977. GP Commiss.er WHSSB.

***STONE, James Michael** 425 Seaside, Eastbourne BN22 7RT — MB BS 1997 Lond.

STONE, Jaqueline Carey 1 Martineau Road, London N5 1NG — MB ChB 1989 Cape Town.

STONE, Jennifer Ann Stracey Castle Street Surgery, 67 Castle Street, Salisbury SP1 3SP Tel: 01722 322726 Fax: 01722 410315; 7 Queensberry Road, Salisbury SP1 3PH Tel: 01722 326220 — MB BS 1968 Lond.; MRCS Eng. LRCP Lond. 1968; DObst RCOG 1971. (King's Coll. Hosp.) Socs: BMA. Prev: GP with Newton, Dunn & Partners; Med. Off. Quarriers Homes; Clin. Asst. (Psychiat.) Dykebar Hosp. Paisley.

STONE, John Peter William Sheet Street Surgery, 21 Sheet Street, Windsor SL4 1BZ Tel: 01753 860334 Fax: 01753 833696; 12 Ruston Way, Ascot SL5 8TG Tel: 01344 873720 — MB BS 1986 Lond. (Roy. Free Hosp. Sch. Med.) Mem. Berks. LMC. Socs: Windsor Med. Soc.

STONE, Jonathan Department of Clinical Nevrosciences, Western General Hospital, Crewe Rd, Edinburgh EH4 2XU Tel: 0131 537 1000 Email: jstone@skull.dcn.ed.ac.uk — MB ChB 1992 Ed.; MRCP (UK) 1995. Research Fell. (Neurol.) W.. Gen. Hosp. Edin. Socs: Brit. Neuropsychiat. Assn.; Assoc. of Brit. Neurols. Prev: SHO (Psych.) Roy. Vict. Infirm. Newc.; Regist. (Gen. Med.) Waikato Hosp., Hamilton, NZ; Regist. (Neurol.) Newc. Gen. Hosp.

***STONE, Julian Philip** 1 Park Street, Maidenhead SL6 1SN — MB BS 1994 Lond.

STONE, Karen Elizabeth 4 Westwood Rise, Ilkley LS29 9SW — MB ChB 1990 Birm.; MRCP (UK) 1995. (Birm.) Specialist Regist. (Paediat.) Yorks. Region. Prev: Regist. (Paediat.).

***STONE, katherine Peta** 37 Napoleon Avenue, Farnborough GU14 8LZ — BM BCh 1998 Oxf.; BM BCh Oxf 1998.

STONE, Kenneth Arrowsmith, TD, OStJ (retired) 2 School Close, Cottingwood Lane, Morpeth NE61 1DY Tel: 01670 517411 — MB BS 1950 Durh.; MRCGP 1974. Clin. Asst. (Psychiat.) St. Geo. Hosp. Morpeth.

STONE, Mr Kenneth Harold (retired) North London Nuffield Hospital, Cavell Drive, Enfield EN2 7PR Tel: 020 8440 0157 — MB BS 1950 Lond.; FRCS Eng. 1956; MRCS Eng. LRCP Lond. 1950. Indep. Cons. Surg. (Orthop.) N. Lond. Nuffield Hosp.; Hon. Lect. Inst. Orthop. Prev: Cons. Surg. (Orthop.) Barnet, Enfield & Haringey HAs.

STONE, Kenneth Michael (retired) 138 Leamington Road, Coventry CV3 6JY Tel: 01203 413338 — LMSSA 1951 Lond. Prev: SHO (Orthop.) Vict. Hosp. Burnley.

STONE, Mr Laurence Donald Bootle Health Centre, Park St., Bootle L20 3RF; 1 Almacs Close, Blundellsands, Liverpool L23 6XT Tel: 0151 924 3752 — MB BS 1980 Lond.; FRCS Eng. 1984; MRCS Eng. LRCP Lond. 1980; DCH RCP Lond. 1987; DRCOG 1987. (Westm.) Research Assoc. Dept. Gen. Pract. Univ. Liverp. Prev: Profess. Regist. (Surg.) Roy. Marsden Hosp. Lond.; Profess. Regist. (Surg.) Roy. Liverp. Hosp.

STONE, Leslie David 13 Queensmead, St. John's Wood Park, London NW8 6RE — MRCS Eng. LRCP Lond. 1935. (Manch.) Prev: Med. Regist. Ancoats Hosp. Manch.; Asst. Med. Off. Withington Hosp. Manch. & Lambeth Hosp. (LCC).

STONE, Malcolm St Mary's Surgery, Church Close, Andover SP10 1DP Tel: 01264 341424 Fax: 01264 336792; 9 Cottage Green, Goodworth Clatford, Andover SP11 7RZ — MB BS 1984 Lond.; MRCGP 1988; DRCOG 1987. Princip. GP Andover Hants.

STONE, Mr Martin Ye Olde Forge, Llanmartin, Newport NP18 2EB Tel: 01633 413073 Fax: 01633 411148 Email: marjam@globalnet.co.uk — MB ChB Liverp. 1968; MD Liverp. 1979; FRCOG 1986, M 1973. (Liverp.) Cons. O & G Roy. Gwent Hosp. Newport. Socs: BMA; (Ex-Treas.) Welsh Obst. & Gyn. Soc.; (Ex-Pres.) Gwent Med. Soc. Prev: Sen. Regist. (O & G) St. Geo. Hosp. Lond. & Soton. Gen. Hosp.; Regist. (O & G) Char. Cross Hosp. Lond.; Ho. Surg. (O & G) United Liverp. Hosps.

STONE, Mr Martin Hope Department of Orthopaedic Surgery, The General Infirmary, Leeds LS1 3EX Tel: 0113 392 6902 Fax: 0113 392 3770; Glenroyd, 1 West Park Grove, Roundhay, Leeds LS8 2HQ Tel: 0113 266 0481 — MB ChB 1979 Glas.; MPhil Strathclyde 1987; FRCS Eng. 1997; FRCS Ed. 1983. Cons. Orthop. & Trauma Surg. Gen. Infirm. Leeds. Socs: Fell. BOA; Brit. Hip Soc. (Exec. Comm.). Prev: Sen. Regist. (Orthop.) Soton. Gen. Hosp.; Regist. (Orthop. Surg.) Glas. Roy. Infirm.

STONE, Melanie Ann 231 Vandyke Road, Leighton Buzzard LU7 3HS Email: melanie.stone5@virgin.net — MB BS 1994 Lond.; FRCS Eng 1999; FRCS Ed 1999.

STONE, Michael Christopher Cuffley Village Surgery, Maynards Place, Cuffley, Potters Bar EN6 4JA Tel: 01707 875201 Fax: 01707 876756 — MB BS 1987 Lond.; MRCGP 1991. Prev: Trainee GP Pilgrim Gen. Hosp. VTS.

STONEHILL

*STONE, Michael David 7 Headlands Road, Bramhall, Stockport SK7 3AN — MB ChB 1994 Dundee.

STONE, Michael Derek Bone Research Unit, Llandough Hospital, Academic Centre, Penlan Road, Penarth CF64 2XX Tel: 01222 716957 Fax: 01222 707628 Email: stonemd@cardiff.ac.uk; 78 TreeTops, Portskewett, Newport NP26 5RT Tel: 01291 421988 Email: mikestone6@compuserve.com — MB BS 1984 Lond.; BA Oxf. 1981; MRCP (UK) 1987; DM Nottm. 1997; FRCP (UK) 1998. (Oxford University and London Hospital) Cons. Phys. Med. (c/o the Elderly) Llandough Hosp. Penarth; Dir. of Bone Research. Socs: Med. Adviser Nat. Osteoporosis Soc.; Bone & Tooth Soc.; Brit. Geriat. Soc.

STONE, Michael John Trafford Training Centre, Birch Road, off Isherwood Road, Carrington, Manchester M30 4BH Tel: 0161 868 8750 Fax: 0161 868 8853 Email: mike.stone@manutd.co.uk; 11 Chiltern Close, Hazel Grove, Stockport SK7 5BQ Tel: 0161 285 9328 — MB ChB 1974 Manch.; MRCP (UK) 1980; DRCOG 1976. Club doctor, Manch. United. Socs: Brit. Assn. of Sport and Exercise Med.; Roy. Soc. of Med.; Manch. Med. Soc. Prev: Gen. Practitioner, Beech Ho.. Hazel Gr.

STONE, Michele Patricia Whitehead Health Centre, 17B Edward Road, Whitehead, Carrickfergus BT38 9RU Tel: 028 9335 3454 Fax: 028 9337 2625; 19 Old Shore Road, Trooperstone, Greenisland, Carrickfergus BT38 8PF Tel: 01960 369951 — MB BCh BAO 1986 Belf.; MRCGP 1990; Cert. Family Plann. JCC 1991; DRCOG 1989.

STONE, Natalie Marie Royal Gwent Hospital, Cardiff Road, Newport NP20 2UB — MB BS 1992 Lond.; MRCP (UK) 1995.

STONE, Nicola Doctors' Mess, Kent and Sussex Hospital, Mount Ephraim, Tunbridge Wells TN4 8AT — BM BS 1995 Nottm.

STONE, Patricia Ann Department of Respiratory Physiology, North West Lung Centre, Wythenshawe Hospital, Southmoor Road, Manchester M23 9LT Tel: 0161 291 2493 Fax: 0161 291 5020; 17 Ogden Road, Bramhall, Stockport SK7 1HJ — MB ChB 1975 Manch. (Manchester) Assoc. Specialist (Sleep Laborat.) Wythenshawe Hosp. Manch. Socs: Fell. Manch. Med. Soc.; Brit. Thorac. Soc.; Brit. Sleep Soc. Prev: Research Fell. (Respirat. Physiol.) Wythenshawe Hosp. Manch.; Med. Off. Nat. Blood Transfus. Serv.; Research Asst. (Respirat. Med.) Manch. Roy. Infirm.

STONE, Patrick Charles 74 Lambton Road, London SW20 0LP — MB BChir 1991 Camb.; MA Camb. 1990, MB BChir 1991; MRCP (UK) 1993. MacMillan Lect. (Palliat. Med.) Roy. Lond. Hosp. Socs: Assn. Palliat. Med.

STONE, Pauline Ann The Western Infirmary, Dumbarton Road, Glasgow G11 6NT Tel: 0141 211 2069; 6 Turnberry Avenue, Glasgow G11 5AQ — MB ChB 1981 Leeds; FFARCS 1988; FRCS Ed. 1985. Cons. Anaesth. W.. Infirm. Glas.; Hon. Clin. Sen. Lect. Prev: Sen. Regist. (Anaesth.) Cardiff; Regist. (Surg.) & SHO (Anaesth.) Roy. Infirm. Edin.

STONE, Peter Gordon Department of Anaesthesia, Scarborough Hospital, Woodlands Drive, Scarborough YO12 6QL Tel: 01723 342394 Fax: 01723 342637; East Farm, Scalby Nabs, Scarborough YO13 0SL Email: peter.stone@virgin.net — MB BS 1985 Lond.; MA Camb. 1986, BA 1982; MRCP (UK) 1988; FRCA 1992. Cons. in Anaesth. & Intens. Care Med. ScarBoro. & N. E. Yorks. Healthcare NHS Trust. Socs: Intens. Care Soc.; BMA; AAGBI. Prev: Sen. Regist. (Anaesth.) Oxf. & S. Bucks.; Fell. Critical Care Med. Harvard Med. Sch. Boston, USA; Regist. & SHO Rotat. (Gen. Med.) Roy. Lond. Hosp.

STONE, Philip Thomas 51 Tradescant Drive, Meopham, Gravesend DA13 0EL Email: ptstone@btinternet.com — MB BS 1972 Lond.; DMRD 1980; AKC. (Westm.) Cons. Radiol. To HM Prison Serv. Prev: Sen. Regist. & Regist. (Radiol.) Lond. Hosp. Whitechapel; Regist. (Radiol.) Qu. Mary's Hosp. Roehampton.

STONE, Richard Jeremy BUPA, Provident House, Essex St., London WC2R 3AU Tel: 020 7353 5212; 5 Spillers & Bakers, Schooner Way, Atcamtic Wharf, Cardiff CF10 4BX Tel: 01222 499544 — MB BCh 1989 Wales; DMS Keele Univ. 1993; DA (UK) 1993. Assoc. Med. Dir. BUPA Lond.

STONE, Richard Malcolm Ellis Forth Floor, Barkat House, 117 - 118 Finshley Road, London NW3 5HT Tel: 0870 755 0509 — MA (Jurisprudence) Oxf. 1963, BM BCh 1970; MRCGP 1975; DObst RCOG 1972. p/t Medico-Legal Practitioner; Mem. Of Lond. Mayor's Cabinet. Prev: Sen. Partner Garway Rd. Med. Centre Lond.

*STONE, Richard Philip 19 Thelbridge House, Bruce Road, London E3 3HT — MB BS 1994 Lond.

STONE, Richard Vernon (retired) Boundary Cottage, Boundary Lane, Over Peover, Knutsford WA16 8UJ Tel: 01625 861204 — MB BChir 1943 Camb.; MA Camb. 1943, MD 1950; FRCP Lond. 1972, M 1945. Prev: Hon. Cons. Phys. Trafford AHA.

STONE, Robert Hellesdon Medical Practice, 343 Reepham Road, Hellesdon, Norwich NR6 5QJ Tel: 01603 486602 Fax: 01603 401389 — MB ChB 1977 Sheff.; Dip Health Science UEA 2000.

STONE, Robert Anthony Taunton & Somerset Hospital, Musgrove Park, Taunton TA1 5DA Tel: 01823 333444 Fax: 01823 336877 Email: robert.stone@tauntonsom-tr.swest.nhs.uk — MB BS 1983 Lond.; PhD Lond. 1993; BSc Lond. 1980, MB BS 1983; MRCP (UK) 1986; FRCP 1999. (St. Thos.) Cons. Phys. Gen. & Respirat. Med. Taunton & Som. Hosp. Taunton. Prev: Sen. Regist. (Gen. & Respirat. Med.) St. Bart. & Whipps Cross Hosps. Lond.

STONE, Robert Campbell Applecross, Melford Road, Cavendish, Sudbury CO10 8AA Tel: 01787 282505 — MB BS 1982 Lond.

STONE, Ruth Lloyd 5 Church Road, Whitchurch, Cardiff CF14 2DX — MB BS 1985 Lond.; MRCGP 1994.

STONE, Sally Ann Orchard Court Surgery, Orchard Court, Orchard Road, Darlington DL3 6HS Tel: 01325 465285 Fax: 01325 284034; Dibdale House, Dibdale Road, Neasham, Darlington DL2 1PG — MB BS 1987 Newc.; MRCGP 1993; MRCP 1990. (Newcastle) GP; Clin. Asst. BrE. Clinic; Primary Care Bd. Mem.

STONE, Sheldon Paul Department of Medicine for Elderly People, Royal Free Hospital, Pond St., London NW3 2QG — MB BS 1980 Lond.; BSc (Hons.) Lond. 1977, MB BS 1980; MRCP (UK) 1984. Lect. (Gen. & Geriat. Med.) Hackney, Homerton, Whipps Cross & St. Bart. Hosps. Lond. Socs: Brit. Geriat. Soc. & Med. Disabil. Soc. Prev: Regist. (Neurol.) Char. Cross Hosp. Lond.; Regist. (Med.) Mt. Vernon Hosp. N.wood.

*STONE, Timothy David 12 Paxhill La, Twyning, Tewkesbury GL20 6DU — MB ChB 1997 Birm.

STONE, Weland Dinnis (retired) The Manor House, Tollerton, York YO61 1QQ Tel: 01347 838454 Fax: 01347 838454 — DM Oxf. 1968, BM BCh 1956; FRCP Lond. 1977, M 1960. Cons. Phys. York Health Dist. Prev: Sen. Regist. Dudley Rd. Hosp. Birm.

STONEBRIDGE, Mr Peter Arno Department of Surgery, Ninewells Hospital, Dundee DD1 9SY Tel: 01382 60111 — MB ChB 1980 Manch.; ChM Manch. 1991, MB ChB 1980; FRCS Ed. 1986. Cons. Surg. Ninewells Hosp. Dundee.

STONEHAM, John Russell Ewhurst Lodge, Windfall Wood Common, Blackdown, Haslemere GU27 3BX Tel: 01428 708066 Fax: 01428 707350 Email: jrs@hive.demon.co.uk; Roundals Farm, Roundals Lane, Hambledon, Godalming GU8 4EA Tel: 01428 682708 Fax: 01428 683575 — MB BS Lond. 1969; MRCS Eng. LRCP Lond. 1969; FFA RCS Eng. 1973; DA Eng. 1971. (Guy's) Cons. Anaesth. S.W. Surrey (Guildford) Health Dist. Prev: Res. (Anaesth.) Vancouver Gen. Hosp.; Sen. Regist. (Anaesth.) Guy's Hosp. Lond.; Regist. (Anaesth.) St. Lukes Hosp. Guildford & Farnham Hosp.

STONEHAM, Mark David, Surg. Lt. RN Retd. Nuffield Department of Anaesthesia, Oxford Radcliff NHS Hospital, Oxford OX3 9DU Tel: 01865 221590 Fax: 01865 220077 Email: mark.stoneham@nda.ok.ac.uk; Email: mark@stonehaml.freeserve.co.uk — MB BChir 1987 Camb.; MA Camb. 1987; FRCA 1994; Dip. Med. Care Catastrophies Soc. Apoth. Lond. 1995. Cons. (Anaesth.) Oxf. Prev: Vis. Instruc. Univ. Michigan Med. Center, USA; Anaesth. Regist. Bristol, Exeter.

STONEHAM, Michael David Millbarn Medical Centre, 34 London End, Beaconsfield HP9 2JH Tel: 01494 675303 Fax: 01494 680214; 113 Brands Hill Avenue, High Wycombe HP13 5PX — MB BS 1971 Lond.; BSc Lond. 1968; MRCS Eng. LRCP Lond. 1971; MRCGP 1976. (Roy. Free) Research GP Unit of Healthcare Clin. Epidemiol. Oxf. Socs: Chiltern Med. Soc. Prev: Trainee GP High Wycombe VTS; Ho. Surg. New End Hosp. Lond. (Roy. Free); Ho. Phys. Stoke Mandeville Hosp. Aylesbury.

STONEHILL, Edward 138 Harley Street, London W1N 1AH Tel: 020 7935 0554; Hornbeams, The Bishops Avenue, London N2 0BJ Tel: 020 8458 2237 Fax: 020 8455 1996 Email: mhs-p@dipcon.co.uk — MRCS Eng. LRCP Lond. 1961; MD Lond. 1972, MB BS 1961; FRCPsych 1978, M 1971; DPM Eng. 1965. (Middlx.) Emerit. Med. Director, Florence Nightingale Hosps., Lond.; Emerit.

STONEHOUSE

Cons. Psychiat. Centr. Middlx. Hosp. Lond. Socs: (Ex-Pres.) Soc. Psychosomatic Res.; Fell. RSM; BMA. Prev: Cons. Psychiat. Centr. Middlx. Hosp. Lond. & Shenley Hosp.; Cons. Psychiat. Imperial Coll. Sc. & Tech. Lond; Research Fell., Hon. Lect. & Hon. Sen. Regist. Acad. Dept. Psychiat. St. Geo. Hosp. Lond.

***STONEHOUSE, Judith Lynn** 4 Grosvenor Road, Chandlers Ford, Eastleigh SO53 5BW — MB ChB 1998 Birm.

STONEHOUSE, Mary Patricia Newton Lodge Farm, Austrey Lane, No Mans Heath, Tamworth B79 0PE — MB BS 1986 Lond.; MRCGP 1990; DRCOG 1990; MRCP 1997; MRCPCH 1997. (Guy's) Specialist Regist. Paediatics, W. Midl. Prev: SCMO (Family Plann.) Nottm. Community Unit; Staff Paed, Good Hope Hospe.

STONEHOUSE, Walter Patrick Bowman (retired) 82 Mossley Road, Grasscroft, Oldham OL4 4HA Tel: 0145 77 874951 — MRCS Eng. LRCP Lond. 1938; DPH Leeds 1950. Prev: Sen. Ho. Surg. & Cas. Off. N. Riding Infirm.

STONELAKE, Angela Virginia Lindisfarne, Gubeon Wood, Tranwell Woods, Morpeth NE61 6BH — BM BS 1993 Nottm.; DTM & H Liverp. 1996; MRCPCH Lond. 1999. SHO (Paediat.) Univ. Hosp. QMC Nottm.; SHO (Paediat.) Huddersfield Roy Infirm. Prev: SHO (Paediat.) City Hosp. Nottm.; SHO (Obst.) City Hosp. Nottm.; SHO (A & E) Wythanshawe Manch.

STONELAKE, Paul Anthony 85 Belmont Road, Uxbridge UB8 1QU Tel: 01895 255472 — BM BS 1993 Nottm.; BMedSci Nottm. 1991. SHO (Anaesth.) Derbysh. Roy. Infirm. NHS Trust.

STONELAKE, Mr Paul Simeon City Hospital NHS Trust, Dudley Road, Birmingham B18 7QH Tel: 0121 554 5755 Fax: 0121 507 5568; 45 Beauty Bank, Cradley Heath, Cradley Heath B64 7HZ Email: p.s.stonelake@bham.ac.uk — BM BS 1985 Nottm.; DM Nottm. 1996, BMedSci (Hons.) 1983; FRCS Ed. 1990; FRCS Eng. 1990. (Nottingham) Cons. Surg. City Hosp. Birm.; Hon. Sen. Lect. Univ. Birm. Socs: Brit. Assn. Surgic. Oncol.; Assn. Coloproctol.; Surg. Research Soc. Prev: Lect. (Surg.) Univ. Birm. & Hon. Sen. Regist. W. Mild. RHA; Career Regist. (Gen. Surg.) W. Midl. Higher Surgic. Train. Scheme; Ho. Off. Profess. Med. Unit Qu. Med. Centre Nottm.

STONEMAN, Margaret Elizabeth Riley (retired) 9 Trapfield Close, Bearsted, Maidstone ME14 4HT Tel: 01622 737039 — MB ChB Manch. 1947; MD Manch. 1959; FRCP Lond. 1977, M 1963; FRCPCH 1997; DCH Eng. 1950. Prev: Cons. Paediat. Maidstone & Medway Health Dists.

STONER, Bryan Anthony (retired) Combe Water, Periton Road, Minehead TA24 8DU Tel: 01643 705330 Email: bstone@btinternet — MB BS 1967 Lond.; MRCS Eng. LRCP Lond. 1967; MRCGP 1976. Prev: GP Minehead.

STONER, Edward Alexander 207 Plough Way, South Dock Marina, London SE16 7FN Email: ed.sarah@dial.pipex.com — MB ChB 1990 Manch.; MRCP (UK) 1993. Regist. Rotat. (Gastroenteol.) Newham Gen. Hosp. & Lond. Hosp.; Specialist Regist. Roy. Lond. Hosp. Prev: Res. Fell. Roy. Lond. Hosp.

STONER, Harry Berrington (retired) 131 Spring Clough, Chatsworth Road, Worsley, Manchester M28 2WR — MB ChB (1st cl. Hons.) Sheff. 1942; BSc Sheff. (1st cl. Hons.) 1939, MD 1946; FRCS Eng 1982; FRCPath 1978, M 1966. Prev: Dir. MRC Trauma Unit Manch. Univ. Med. Sch.

STONER, Jill Mary 475 Manchester Road, Bury BL9 9SH — MB BS 1985 Lond.; MRCGP 1989; DRCOG 1988.

STONER, Katherine Barbara Jarvis Breast Screening Centre, Stoughton Road, Guildford GU1 1LJ Tel: 01483 783200 — MB ChB 1982 Cape Town; BSc (Med.) 1978; FFRAD (D) (SA) 1989; FRCR 1993. Cons. Radiol. Jarvis BrE. Screening Centre Guildford; Cons. Radiol. Epsom Gen. Hosp.

STONER, Sarah Jane 5 Watlington Road, Harlow CM17 0DX — MB BS 1992 Lond.

STONES, Lawrence 102 Westbourne Road, Sheffield S10 2QT Tel: 0114 266 0864 — MB ChB 1961 Sheff.; LDS 1951. (Sheff.) Socs: BMA. Prev: Ho. Phys. Rotherham Hosp.; Ho. Surg. Roy. Hosp. Sheff.

STONES, Martina Mary 11 Annieslea Avenue, Stepps, Glasgow G33 6DR — MB ChB 1989 Glas.

STONES, Nigel Anthony Priorslegh Medical Centre, Civic Centre, Park Lane, Poynton, Stockport SK12 1GP Tel: 01625 872299 — MB ChB 1980 Manch.; MRCP (UK) 1983; MRCGP 1986; DRCOG 1985. Hosp. Pract. (Endocrinol.) Univ. Hosp. S. Manch.

STONES, Robert William University Department of Obstetrics & Gynaecology, Princess Anne Hospital, Coxford Road, Southampton SO16 5YA Tel: 02380 796033 Fax: 02380 786933 — MB BS 1979 Lond.; MD Lond. 1994; MRCOG 1988; DTM & H RCP Lond. 1981. Sen. Lect. (O & G) Univ. Soton. Prev: Lect. (O & G) Univ. Soton. & St. Mary's Hosp. Med. Sch. Lond.; Research Fell. (Anat.) Univ. Coll. Lond.

STONES, Robin Nicholas, SBStJ Manchester Road Medical Centre, 27 Manchester Road, Knutsford WA16 0LZ Tel: 01565 633101 Fax: 01565 750135; 20 Rockford Lodge, Knutsford WA16 8AH — MB ChB 1983 Manch.; MRCGP 1987; DRCOG 1986; Cert. Family Plann. JCC 1986. (Manchester) GP Princip.; Hosp. Pract. (Dermat.) Trafford Gen. Hosp. Manch. Socs: BMA. Prev: Trainee GP Lancaster VTS; SHO (ENT) Beaumont Hosp. Lancaster; Ho. Off. (Orthop. & Gen. Surg.) Roy. Preston Hosp.

STONEY, Mr Philip John Furness General Hospital, Dalton Lane, Barrow-in-Furness LA14 4LF Tel: 01229 870870 — MB ChB 1978 Glas.; BSc (Hons.) Glas. 1975; FRCS (ENT) 1986; FRCS Ed. (Gen.) 1983. Cons. Otolaryngol. Furness Gen. Hosp. Barrow-in-Furness.

STONHAM, Joseph 133 Lennard Road, Beckenham BR3 1QR — MB BS 1973 Lond.; FFA RCS Eng. 1979. Sen. Regist. (Anaesth.) Avon AHA. Prev: Regist. (Anaesth.) Soton. Gen. Hosp. Vis. Asst. Prof. Anaesth. Univ.; Texas S. W.. Med. Sch. Dallas Texas, U.S.A.; Regist. (Anaesth.) Soton. Gen. Hosp.

STONIER, Professor Peter David Hoechst Marion Roussel Ltd., Broadwater Park, Denham, Uxbridge UB9 5HP Tel: 01895 837629 Fax: 01895 837740 Email: peter.stonier@hmrag.com — MB ChB 1974 Manch.; PhD Sheff. 1969; BSc Birm. 1966; FRCP Ed. 1993; MRCPsych 1995; FFPM RCP (UK) 1989; FRCP 1998. (Manchester) Med. Dir. Hoechst Marion Roussel Ltd. (UK); Vis. Prof. (Pharmaceutical Med.) Univ. Surrey 1992-; Vis. Prof. (Pharmaceutical Med.) Univ. Lond. 1998-. Socs: Chairm. Brit. Assn. Pharmaceut. Phys. 1988-90; Roy. Soc. Med. (Ex-Pres. Pharmaceut. Med. & Research Sect.); Pres. Fac. (Pharmaceutal Med.) RCP (UK) 1997-. Prev: Med. Dir. Hoechst UK Ltd. Pharmaceut. Div.; SHO (Surgic. & Cas.) Leicester Roy. Infirm.

STOODLEY, Mr Brian John 21 Lushington Road, Eastbourne BN21 4LG Tel: 01323 410441 Fax: 01323 410978 Email: lushington_clinic@lineone.net; Tuckvar, West St, Alfriston, Polegate BN26 5UX Tel: 01323 870443 — MB BChir Camb. 1963; MChir Camb. 1973, MA 1963; FRCS Eng. 1967; MRCS Eng. LRCP Lond. 1962. (St. Bart.) p/t Hon. Cons. Surg. Dist. Gen. Hosp. E.bourne & Uckfield Hosp. Socs: Fell. Roy. Soc. Med.; Fell. Assn. Surgs.; Fell Assn. Coloprctol. Prev: Sen. Regist. (Surg.) St. Bart. Hosp. Lond.; RSO (Surg.) St. Mark's Hosp. Lond.

STOODLEY, Katharine Joanna 83 Pickmere Road, Sheffield S10 1GZ — MB ChB 1993 Sheff.

STOODLEY, Neil Gordon Cardiff and Vale NHS Trust, Department of Neuroradiology, University Hospital of Wales, Heath Park, Cardiff CF14 4XW — BM BCh 1985 Oxf.; FRCS Eng. 1989; FRCR 1997. Cons. (NeuroRadiol.) Univ. Hosp. Wales. Socs: Brit. Soc. Neuroradiologists; Europ. Soc. of NeuroRadiol. Prev: Sen. Regist. (Diagnostic Radiol.) John Radcliffe Hosp. Oxf.; Sen. Regist. (Neuroradiol.) Radcliffe Infirm. Oxf.; Regist. (Diag. Radiol.) Soton. Gen. Hosp.

STOOT, Christopher John, Surg. Lt. RN 60 South Court Avenue, Dorchester DT1 2BZ — MB BS 1979 Lond.

STOPPARD, Elizabeth Rosemary Flat 2, 17 Brook Rd, Fallowfield, Manchester M14 6UE Tel: 0161 225 9113 — MB ChB 1997 Manch.; BSc (Hons) St And 1994.

STOPPARD, Miriam 173 Clarence Road, Windsor SL4 5AP — MD 1966 Newc.; MB BS Durh. 1961; MRCP Lond. 1964. (Newc.) Socs: Fell. Roy. Soc. Med.; Assoc. Mem. Heberden Soc. Prev: Managing Dir. Syntex Pharmaceut. Ltd. Maidenhead; Med. Dir. Syntex Pharmaceut. Ltd. Maidenhead; Sen. Regist. (Dermat.) Bristol Roy. Hosp.

STORAH, Peter Kenneth (retired) Yew Tree Cottage, Stafford Avenue, Halifax HX3 0BH Tel: 01422 356513 Fax: 01422 356513 — MB BCh BAO 1948 Dub.; MD Dub. 1965; FFA RCSI 1962; DA RCPSI 1952; DObst RCOG 1950. Prev: Cons. Anaesth. Roy. Halifax Infirm. & Halifax Gen. Hosp.

STORE, Frederick Robert c/o The Royal Bank of Scotland plc, Kirkland House, Whitehall, London SW1A 2EB — MRCS Eng. LRCP Lond. 1933.

STORRING

STORER, David The General Infirmary, Great George St., Leeds LS1 3EX Tel: 0113 292 3204 Fax: 0113 292 6771 — MB ChB Sheff. 1967; FRCPsych 1988, M 1972; DPM Eng. 1970. (Sheff.) Cons. Psychiat. Leeds Gen. Infirm.; Sen. Clin. Lect. Univ. Leeds.

STORER, James Ivan 10 Heathland Crescent, Boldmere, Sutton Coldfield B73 5EP — MB ChB 1970 Birm.; MRCGP 1975; DRCOG 1972. GP Sutton Coldfield.

STORER, John Richard (retired) Westfield House, Westbrook St, Blewbury, Didcot OX11 9QA Tel: 01235 850651 Email: jgstorer@care4free.net — MB ChB 1960 Birm.; DObst RCOG 1963. Prev: Princip., GP.

STORER, Nigel Raymond Bewbush Medical Centre, Bewbush Place, Bewbush, Crawley RH11 8XT Tel: 01293 519420 — BM 1982 Soton.; MRCGP 1986; DRCOG 1985.

STORES, Professor Gregory University of Oxford, Park Hospital for Children, Old Road Headington, Oxford OX3 7LQ Tel: 01865 226515 Fax: 01865 762358 Email: gregory.stores@psych. ox.ac.uk; North Gate House, 55 High St, Dorchester-on-Thames, Wallingford OX10 7HN Tel: 01865 34115 — MB ChB 1967 Manch.; MA Oxon 1988; MD 1977; BA 1960 (Hons. Psychol.) Manch.; BA (Hons.) (Psychol.) Manch. 1960, MD 1977; FRCP Lond. 1983; MRCP (UK) 1970; FRCPsych 1981, M 1972; DPM Eng. 1971. (Manch.) Prof. of Developm. NeuroPsychiat., Univ. of Oxf.; Hon. Cons. Oxf. HA; Fell. of Linacre Coll., Univ. of Oxf. Socs: Roy. Coll. Psychiat. (Child Psychiat. Sec.); Brit. Paediat. Neurol. Assn.; Fell.Roy.Coll.Phys. Prev: Cons. Neuropsychiat. & EEG Pk. Hosp. Childr. Oxf.; Lect. (Developm. Med.) Univ. Dept. Psychiat. & Pk. Hosp. Childr. Oxf.; Clin.Reader.Child & Adult Psychiat.Univ.Oxf.

STORES, Olga Patricia Rahma 445 Streetsbrook Road, Solihull B91 1QZ — MB ChB 1967 Manch. (Manch.) Prev: Research Fell. Dept. Regius Prof. Med. Radcliffe Infirm. Oxf.; Clin. Asst. Oxf. Univ. Dept. Psychiat. Warneford Hosp. Oxf.; Regist. (Psychiat.) Bootham Pk. & Naburn Hosps. York.

STOREY, Alan Brett Darwen Health Centre, Union St., Darwen BB3 0DA Tel: 01254 771315; 5 Spinningfield Way, Heywood OL10 2LF — MB BS 1985 Lond.; DRCOG 1989. Prev: Trainee GP Manch.; SHO (A & E & Gen. Med.) Goldcoast Hosp., Austral.; SHO (Psychiat.) Fairfield Gen. Hosp. Bury.

STOREY, Dawn Flat 3F1, 207 Bruntsfield Place, Edinburgh EH10 4DH Tel: 0131 447 1312 — BM BS 1995 Nottm.; BMedSci Nottm. 1993; DRCOG 1997. (Nottm.) SHO (Clin. Oncol.) W.ern Gen. Hosp. Edin. Prev: SHO (Med.) St Johns Hosp. Livingston; SHO (Anaesth.) St Johns Hosp. Livingston; SHO (O & G) St. Johns.

***STOREY, Elizabeth Clare** 29 Thurlow Road, Clarendon Park, Leicester LE2 1YE — MB ChB 1998 Leic.; MB ChB Leic 1998.

STOREY, Geoffrey Oldroyd (retired) Pine Grove, Kentsford Rd, Grange-over-Sands LA11 7BB Tel: 015395 34483 — MD 1956 Camb.; MB BChir 1942; FRCP Lond. 1971, M 1948; DPhysMed Eng. 1953. Prev: Cons. Rheumat. Hackney & Lond. Hosps.

***STOREY, Imogen Clare** Townend, Farleton, Carnforth LA6 1PB — MB ChB 1998 Birm.

STOREY, John Loftus 21 Michel Grove, East Preston, Littlehampton BN16 2SX Tel: 01903 783687 — MB BS 1957 Lond.; BDS Lond. 1964; MRCS Eng. LRCP Lond. 1957; LDS RCS Eng. 1964.

STOREY, Mark Edward The Surgery, Kirk Road, Houston, Johnstone PA6 7AR Tel: 01505 613240 Email: storey_mark@hotmail.com — MB ChB 1993 Glas.; BSc (Hons) Physiol. 1990. (Glasgow) LHCC Mutual Health Lead.

STOREY, Neil David The Coach House, 3 Kennedy Drive, Helensburgh G84 9AP — MB ChB 1991 Glas.

STOREY, Nicola 125 Ashby Road, Burton-on-Trent DE15 0NU — BM 1986 Soton.

STOREY, Peter Brett (retired) 2 Brunswick Square, Penrith CA11 7LL Tel: 01768 865006 — MB BS 1953 Lond.; MD Lond. 1970; FRCP Lond. 1973, M 1959; FRCPsych 1975, M 1971; DPM Lond. 1963. Hon. Cons. Psychiat. St. Geo. & Springfield Hosps. Lond. Prev: Med. Administr. Springfield Hosp. Lond.

STOREY, Robert Frederick 46 Wharncliffe Road, Ilkeston DE7 5GF — BM 1989 Soton.

STOREY, Robert George Nixon 20 Ballyclander Road, Downpatrick BT30 7DZ — MB BCh BAO Belf. 1970; FRCOG 1991. Cons. O & G Downe Hosp. Downpatrick Matern. Hosp. & Belf. City Hosp. Socs: Ulster Obst. & Gyn. Soc.; BSCCP; TENS Soc. Prev: Sen. Regist. (O & G) Belf. City Hosp.; Regist. (O & G) Roy. Matern. Hosp. Belf.; Lect. (O & G) Univ. Nairobi, Kenya.

STOREY, Susan Mary Islington Child & Family Consultation Service (CFCS), Northorn Health Centre, 594 Holloway Road, London N7 6LB Tel: 0207 445 8150 — MB ChB 1988 Bristol; BSc Bristol 1985; MRCPsych 1993. (Bristol) p/t Cons. In Child & Adolesc. Psychiat. Islington CFCS, Lond. Prev: Sen. Regist. (Child & Adolesc. Psychiat.) Tavistock Clinic Lond.

STOREY, Victor Charles Marks Gate Health Centre, Lawn Farm Grove, Chadwell Heath, Romford RM6 5LL Tel: 020 8590 7066; 130 Harley Street, London W1N 1AH — MB BS 1953 Lond.; LMSSA Lond. 1952. (St. Bart.)

STORK, Ann Frances 52 The Sanctuary, Cardiff CF5 4RX — BM BS 1990 Nottm.

STORK, Sheila Tel: 020 8745 3359 — MB BS Lond. 1985; DAvMed. Fac. Occupat Med.; MFOM for Occupational Medicine 1998; Accredit Specialist Aviat & Occupat Med 1998. Chief Med. Off., Nat. Air Traffic Serv.s; Med. Examr. CAA; Med. Examr. JOA; Med. Examr. FOA. Socs: Fac. Occupat. Med.; Soc. of Occupat.al Med.; Roy. Agronautical Soc. Prev: Head of Aeromed. Centre and Occupat.al Health Serv.s for the Civil Aviat. Auth.; Head of Aeromed. Sect. CAA.

STORM, Marion Croft House, Maynestone Road, Chinley, High Peak SK23 6AH — MB ChB 1983 Ed. Socs: Roy. Coll. Psychiat.

STORMONT, Fiona Claire Flat 5, 27 Warrington Crescent, London W9 1ED — MB BS 1989 Lond.

STORR, Bernard Stanley Harold (retired) Copse End, Chart Road, Chart Sutton, Maidstone ME17 3RB Tel: 01622 843881 — MRCS Eng. LRCP Lond. 1944; BA Camb. 1941; DMRD Eng. 1949. Prev: Cons. Radiol. Brighton & Mid-Downs HAs.

STORR, Catherine (retired) 12 Frognal Gardens, London NW3 6UX Tel: 020 7435 9275 — MRCS Eng. LRCP Lond. 1944. Prev: Asst. Psychiat. Middlx. Hosp.

STORR, Charles Anthony (retired) 45 Chalfont Road, Oxford OX2 6TJ Tel: 01865 553348 Fax: 01865 316013 Email: anthony.storr@green.oxford.ac.uk — MB BChir 1944 Camb.; FRCP Lond. 1975, M 1946; FRCPsych 1971; DPM Eng. 1950. Hon. Cons. Psychiat. Oxon. HA. Prev: Clin. Lect. (Psychiat.) Univ. Oxf.

STORR, John Nicholas Paul The Cumberland Infirmary, Newtown Road, Carlisle CA2 7HY Tel: 01228 523444; The Manor Stables, Great Corby, Carlisle CA4 8NE Email: johnstorr@compuserve.com — MD 1989 Cape Town; MB ChB 1976; FRCP 1997; FRCPCH 1997. (Cape Town) Cons. Paediat. Cumbld. Infirm. Carlisle. Prev: Sen. Regist. (Paediat.) Selly Oak Hosp. Birm.

STORR, Teresa Mary Swallows Waite, Seaville, Silloth, Carlisle CA7 4PT Tel: 016973 61156 — MB BS 1982 Newc.; MRCGP 1986; DRCOG 1984. Clin. Asst. (Haemat. & Oncol.) Cumbld. Infirm. Carlisle.

STORRAR, David Allan Helsby Street Medical Centre, 2 Helsby Street, Warrington WA1 3AW Tel: 01925 637304 Fax: 01925 570430; 4 Marlborough Crescent, Grappenhall, Warrington WA4 2EE — MB ChB 1984 Manch.; BSc Hons. (Biochem.) St. And. 1977. Princip. GP Warrington.

STORRIE, Marion Pettigrew Newbyres Medical Group, Gorebridge Health Centre, Gorebridge EH23 4TP Tel: 01875 820405 Fax: 01875 820269 — MB ChB 1977 Edinburgh; MB ChB Edin 1977. (Edinburgh) GP Edin.

STORRING, Ferdinand Karl (retired) 5 Cliffside, Penarth CF64 5RG Tel: 01222 701081 — MD 1931 Kiel; MB BS Durh. 1951; FRCPath 1971, M 1964. Prev: Cons. Path. Llandough Hosp. Penarth.

STORRING, Patrick Lindsay National Institute for Biological Standards & Control, Blanche Lane, South Mimms, Potters Bar EN6 3QG Tel: 01707 654753 Fax: 01707 646730 Email: pstorring@nibsc.ac.uk — MB BCh Wales 1962; PhD, MA Camb. 1972, BA 1967; MRCS Eng. LRCP Lond. 1962. (Cardiff) Princip. Sci. Div. of Endocrinol., Nat. Inst. Biol. Standards & Control. Socs: Soc. Endocrinol. & Biochem. Soc. Prev: Mem. of Scientif. Staff, Nat. Inst. for Med. Research; Fell. Damon Runyon Memor. Fund for Cancer Research Biochem. Dept. Univ. Chicago, USA; MRC Jun. Research Fell. Biochem. Dept. Univ. Camb.

STORRING, Roderick Alexander 42 Felstead Road, Wanstead, London E11 2QJ Tel: 020 8989 5853 — MB BS 1966 Lond.; FRCP Lond. 1986, M 1969. Cons. Phys. Barking Hosp. & King. Geo.

STORROW

Hosp. Ilford. Prev: Med. Regist. St. Geo. Hosp. Lond.; Ho. Phys. Brompton Hosp. Lond.

STORROW, Kim Johanna Peverell Park Surgery, 162 Outlands Road, Peverell, Plymouth PL2 3PR Tel: 01752 791438 Fax: 01752 783623 — MB BCh 1982 Wales; DCH RCP Lond. 1987. GP Peverell Pk. Surg. Plymouth. Socs: Local Med. Comm. Represent. Prev: GP Plympton Health Centre Plymouth.

STORRS, Charles Nicholas (retired) Warwick Hospital, Lakin Road, Warwick CV34 5BW Tel: 01926 495321 — MB BChir 1964 Camb.; MB Camb. 1964, BChir 1963; FRCP Lond. 1985, M 1969; DCH Eng. 1967. Cons. Paediat. Warwick Hosp. Prev: Sen. Regist. (Paediat.) Ch.ill Hosp. Oxf.

STORRS, Mr Thomas John Chequers, Nackington Park, Nackington Road, Canterbury CT4 7AX Tel: 01227 454441 Fax: 01277 454150 Email: storrs@netlineuk.net — MB BS Lond. 1970; BDS (Hons.) 1966; MRCS Eng. LRCP Lond. 1970; FDS RCS Eng. 1972, L 1966. (Guy's) Cons. Maxillofacial Surg. Kent & Canterbury Hosp. Socs: Fell. Brit. Assn. Maxillofacial Surg.; BMA; Centr. Cons. & Specialists Comm.

STORRS-FOX, Peter (retired) Glebe House, 22 Station Road, South Cave, Brough HU15 2AA Tel: 01430 422855 — MRCS Eng. LRCP Lond. 1934; FRCGP 1969. Prev: Off. i/c St. Luke's Hosp. Ummedpur.

STORY, Clive Alwyn The Surgery, Grasmere Drive, High Bentham, Lancaster LA2 7JP Tel: 01524 261202 Fax: 01524 262222905 — MB BS 1966 Newc.

STORY, Doris (retired) 14 Ferndene Court, Moor Road S., Newcastle upon Tyne NE3 1NN — MB BS 1953 Durh.; MFCM 1972; DPH Durh. 1958. Prev: SCM (Child Health) N. Tyneside HA.

STORY, Peter 7 Dene Road, Northwood HA6 2AE Tel: 01923 823928 — MRCS Eng. LRCP Lond. 1942; MD Lond. 1950, MB BS 1947; FRCPath 1969, M 1963. (St. Bart.) Consg. Haemat. St. Bart. Hosp. Lond. Prev: Lt.-Col. RAMC; Brit. Postgrad. Med. Federat. Trav. Fell. (Haematol.) Washington Univ.St. Louis, USA; Cons. Haemat. Inst. Orthop. Roy. Nat. Orthop. Hosps. Stanmore.

STORY, Peter Sean The Medical Centre, Gun Lane, Strood, Rochester ME2 4UW Tel: 01634 290655 — MB BS 1971 Newc.; MRCGP 1980; DObst RCOG 1975.

STORY, Philipa Alice 167 Gladstone Street, Nottingham NG7 6HX — MB ChB 1988 Otago.

STORY, Thomas William 29 Parker Street, Barrow-in-Furness LA14 5RN — MB BS 1980 Lond.

STORY, Timothy Simon 1 Fore Street, St Germans, Saltash PL12 5NR Tel: 01503 230257 — MB BS 1992 Lond.; BSc (Clin. Pharmacol.) Lond. 1989; DCH RCP Lond.; DRCOG. (St. Geo. Hosp. Lond.) GP Regist. Portview Surg. Higher Portview Saltash Cornw. Prev: SHO (O & G) Derriford Hosp. Plymouth; SHO (Paediat.) St. Richards Hosp. Chichester; SHO (A & E) St. Geo. Hosp. NHS Trust Lond.

STOSSEL, Mr Clifford Alain Flagstones, Millbank, Headcorn, Ashford TN27 8JG Tel: 01622 890702 Fax: 01622 891636 — MB BS 1961 Lond.; FRCS Eng. 1970; FRCS Ed. 1968; MRCS Eng. LRCP Lond. 1962. (St. Mary's) Cons. Orthop. Surg. Maidstone Health Dist. Socs: Fell. BOA; BMA. Prev: Sen. Regist. (Orthop.) St. Mary's & Roy. Nat. Orthop. Hosps. Lond.; Regist. (Surg.) W. Herts. Hosp. Hemel Hempstead.

STOTESBURY, Stanley Neville (retired) 40 Malmains Drive, Frenchay, Bristol BS16 1PJ Tel: 0117 956 7984 — MRCS Eng. LRCP Lond. 1948. Prev: Ho. Surg. (Orthop.) W.m. Hosp.

STOTHARD, Mr John Consultant Hand & Orthopaedic Surg., Middlesbrough General Hospital, Ayresome Green Lane, Middlesbrough TS5 5AZ Tel: 01642 854214 Fax: 01642 854375 — MB ChB 1971 Ed.; MD Ed. 1980; FRCS Ed. (Orth.) 1981; FRCS Ed. 1976. (Ed.) Cons. Hand Surg. S. Tees Acute Unit NHS Trust; Vis. Prof. Sch. Health Univ. Teesside; Hon. Clin. Lect. Fac. of Med. Univ. Newc. Prev: Cons. Orthop. Surg. N. Tees Health NHS Trust; Sen. Regist. (Orthop. Surg.) N. RHA; Research Assoc. MRC Decompression Sickness Research Team.

STOTHER, Mr Ian George Glasgow Nuffield Hospital, Beaconsfield Road, Glasgow G12 0PJ Tel: 0141 334 9441 Fax: 0141 339 1352; 13 Moncrieff Avenue, Lenzie, Glasgow G66 4NL Tel: 0141 776 5330 — MB BChir 1970 Camb.; MA Camb. 1970; FRCS Glas. 1981; FRCS Ed. 1974. (St. Geo.) Cons. Orthopaedic Surg. & Clin. Director Trauma & Orthapaedics N. Glas. Univ. Hosp.

NHS Trust; Cons. Orthop. Surg. Glas. Roy. Infirm.; Hon. Sen. Clin. Lect. Univ. Glas.

STOTHERS, James 14 Darvel Crescent, Ralston, Paisley PA1 3EF — MB ChB 1956 Glas.

STOTT, Caroline Jayne Emperor's Gate Centre for Health, First Floor, 49 Emperors Gate, London SW7 4HJ Tel: 020 8237 5333 Fax: 020 8237 5344; 28 Stamford Brook Avenue, Stamford Brook, London W6 0YD Tel: 020 8563 2026 — BM BS 1989 Nottm.; BMedSci Nottm. 1987; MRCGP 1994; DRCOG 1993. (Univ. Nottm.) GP. Socs: Brit. Med. Acupunc. Soc. Prev: Trainee GP/SHO (Psychiat.) Lond.

STOTT, Mrs Catherine Mary Ware Road Surgery, 77 Ware Road, Hertford SG13 7EE Tel: 01992 587961; 20 Harwood Close, Tewin, Welwyn AL6 0LF — MB BCh BAO 1965 NUI. (Cork) Clin. Asst. (Paediat.) Hertford Co. Hosp. Prev: Intern Regional Gen. Hosp. Limerick; Clin. Asst. (Psychiat.) & SHO (Paediat.) Qu. Eliz. II Hosp. Welwyn Gdn. City.

STOTT, Christopher Simon Tel: 020 8460 4611 Fax: 020 8460 9450 — MB BS 1982 Lond.; DMJ 2001; DRCOG 1984. (Charing Cross) GP Princip.; Princip. Forens. Med. Examr. (Police Surg.) Lond. Metrop. Police. Socs: Assn. Police Surg.; BMA.

STOTT, David Brian (retired) Thatched Cottage, Kerry Lane, Eccleshall, Stafford ST21 6EJ Tel: 01785 850271 — MB ChB Manch. 1947; MRCS Eng. LRCP Lond. 1947. Prev: Ho. Surg. Manch. Roy. Infirm.

STOTT, Professor David James Academic Section of Geriatric Medicine, Royal Infirmary, Glasgow G4 0SF Tel: 0141 211 4976 Fax: 0141 211 4944 Email: d.j.stott@clinmed.gla.ac.uk; 15 South Erskine Park, Bearsden, Glasgow G61 4NA Tel: 0141 942 7341 — MB ChB 1981 Glas.; MD Glas. 1988; FRCP (Ed.) 1997; FRCP Glas. 1994; MRCP (UK) 1984. David Cargill Prof. Geriat. Med. Univ. Glas. (1994-); Hon. Cons. Geriat. Med. Glas. Roy. Infirm. (1994-). Socs: Med. Res. Soc. & Brit. Geriat. Soc. Prev: Sen. Lect. & Hon. Cons. Geriat. Med. Univ. Glas.; Sen. Regist. (Geriat. & Gen. Med.) Gtr. Glas. HB.

STOTT, David Rowland Patel and Partners, Broom Lane Medical Centre, 70 Broom Lane, Rotherham S60 3EW Tel: 01709 364470 Fax: 01709 820009; Glengarth Surgery, Doncaster Road, Rotherham S65 1DT Tel: 01709 365522 — MB ChB 1980 Sheff.; BSc. Sheff. 1976, MB ChB 1980. Hosp. Pract. (A & E) N. Gen. Hosp., Sheff.

STOTT, Denise Gaye Department of Anaesthetics, Stoke Mandeville Hospital, Mandeville Road, Aylesbury HP21 8AL Tel: 01296 315262; Keepers Cottage, 5 Burts Lane, Long Crendon HP18 0SB — MB ChB 1982 Sheff.; FRCA 1988. (Univ. Sheff. Med. Sch.) Cons. Anaesth. Stoke Mandeville Hosp. Prev: Cons. Anaesth. Withington Hosp. Manch.; Regist. (Anaesth.) Withington Hosp. Manch. & Stepping Hill Hosp. Stockport; Sen. Regist. (Anaesth.) NW RHA.

STOTT, Donald Verney (retired) 35 Tavistock Road, Crownhill, Plymouth PL5 3AF — MB BS 1940 Lond.; MRCS Eng. LRCP Lond. 1940. Prev: Clin. Asst. Orthop. Dept. Sheff. Roy. Infirm.

***STOTT, Ian Mark** 2 Andover Court, Andover Road, Cheltenham GL50 2QX — BM BS 1998 Nottm.; BM BS Nottm 1998.

STOTT, Janet Elizabeth Stockton Heath Medical Centre, The Forge, London Road, Stockton Heath, Warrington WA4 6HJ Tel: 01925 604427 Fax: 01925 210501; 15 Edenbridge Gardens, Appleton, Warrington WA4 5FH Email: janet@edenbridge.unet.com — BM BS 1983 Nottm.; BMedSci Nottm. 1981. Prev: SHO (Med., O & G & Paediat.) Warrington Dist. Gen. Hosp.

STOTT, Jenefer Anne Vaughan Parklands Surgery, 4 Parklands Road, Chichester PO19 3DT Tel: 01243 786827; 25 Lyndhurst Road, Chichester PO19 2LE Tel: 01243 784157 — MB BS 1989 Lond.; DRCOG 1993. Prev: SHO (Geriat.) St. Richard's Hosp. Chichester; SHO (Psychiat.) S.lands Hosp. Worthing.

STOTT, John Richard Ravenscourt Surgery, 36-38 Tynewydd Road, Barry CF62 8AZ Tel: 01446 733515 Fax: 01446 701326; Gwynfryn Private Surgery, 34 Tynewydd Road, Barry CF62 8HB Tel: 01446 733047 — MB BCh BAO 1970 NUI; MRCGPI 1987. (Univ. Coll. Cork) Princip. in Gen. Pract., Barry, S. Wales; Bro Taf Drug & Therap Comm.; Bro Taf Local Med. Comm.; Med. Off., Barry Town Football Club.; Bd. Mem. of Nat. Obesity Forum; Exec. Bd., Local Health Gp. Socs: Brit. Soc. Experim. & Clin. Hypn.

STOTT, John Richard Rollin Centre for Human Sciences, DERA, Farnborough GU14 0LX Tel: 01252 394406 Fax: 01252 392097

Email: jrrstott@dera.gov.uk; Well Lane House, Well Lane, Lower Froyle, Alton GU34 4LP Tel: 01420 23783 — MRCS Eng. LRCP Lond. 1963; MB Camb. 1964, BChir 1963; MA Camb. 1964; MRCP Lond. 1969; DAvMed FOM RCP Lond. 1985; DCH Eng. 1965; DIC 1974. (Middlx.) Princip. Med.Off.DERA Centre for Human Sci.s. Socs: Aerospace Med. Assn. & Biol. Engin. Soc. Prev: Sen. Regist. (Clin. Measurem.) W.m. Hosp. Lond.; Ho. Phys. & Cas. Med. Off. Middlx. Hosp. Lond.

*STOTT, Linda 23 Briarwood, Dudley, Cramlington NE23 7DN — MB ChB 1998 Dund.; MB ChB Dund 1998.

STOTT, Mr Mark Anthony Department of Urology, Royal Devon & Exeter Hospital (Wonford), Barrack Road, Exeter EX2 5DW — MD 1990 Bristol; MB ChB 1980; FRCS Eng. 1985. Cons. Urol. Exeter HA. Prev: Sen. Regist. (Urol.) E. Anglian RHA; Research Regist. (Urol.) Ham Green Hosp. Bristol.

STOTT, Professor Nigel Clement Halley Llanedeyrn Health Centre, Maelfa, Llanedeyrn, Cardiff CF23 9PN Tel: 029 2073 1671 Fax: 029 2054 0129; Coastguard Cottage, Oxwhich, Swansea SA3 1LS Tel: 01792 390 0746 Fax: 01222 540129 Email: nstottoxwich@sparticus.net — MB ChB 1966 Ed.; BSc (Hons.) Ed. 1964; FRCP Ed. 1980 M 1969; FRCGP 1987, M 1979; T(GP) 1991. (Univ. Ed.) Prof. Gen. Pract. Univ. Wales Coll. Med. Cardiff; Chairm. Liaison Comm. Roy. Coll. Wales; Chairm. MRC Gen. Pract. Research Framework Coordinating Comm.; MRC HSPRB 1998-2002. Socs: Acad. of Med. Sci.; BMA; Cardiff Med. Soc. (Mem.). Prev: Prof. Primary Med. Care Univ. Soton.; Vis. Prof Univ. Singapore 1994-1999; Sen. Lect. Welsh Nat. Sch. Med. Cardiff.

STOTT, Peter Charles The Surgery, 1 Troy Close, Tadworth Farm, Tadworth KT20 5JE Tel: 01737 362327 Fax: 01737 373469 — MB 1975 Camb.; BChir 1974; FRCGP 1989, M 1979; DCH Eng. 1977; DRCOG 1976; Cert JCC Lond. 1976.

STOTT, Richard Anthony Philip Old Cottage Hospital Surgery, Alexandra Road, Epsom KT17 4BL Tel: 01372 724434 Fax: 01372 748171; 52 Manor Green Road, Epsom KT19 8RN Tel: 01372 728692 — MB BS 1972 Lond.; FRCP Ed. 1992; MRCP (UK) 1979; DCH Eng. 1975. (St. Thos. Hosp. Lond.)

STOTT, Robin Bradley 15 Egerton Drive, Greenwich, London SE10 8JS Tel: 020 8692 4667 Email: stott@dircon.co.uk — MB BChir 1967 Camb.; MA Camb. 1967; FRCP Lond. 1981, M 1969; MRCS Eng. LRCP Lond. 1967. Cons. Phys. Lewisham Trust.; Sub-Dean, Guys, Kings & St Thos. Sch. of Med. & Dent. Prev: Cons. Phys. Lewisham Hosp. Lond.; Sen. Lect. (Med.) Univ. Zimbabwe.

STOTT, Shiona Margaret Department of Anaesthetics, Stobhill Hospital, Balornock Road, Glasgow G21 3UW Tel: 0141 201 3005; 15 South Erskine Park, Bearsden, Glasgow G61 4NA Tel: 0141 942 7341 — MB ChB 1984 Glas.; FRCA 1989. Cons. Anaesth. Stobhill Hosp. Glas. Prev: Sen. Regist. (Anaesth.) W.. Infirm. Glas.; Regist. (Anaesth.) Roy. Infirm. Glas.

STOTT, Stephen Alexander Department of Anaesthetics, Aberdeen Royal Infirmary, Foresterhill, Aberdeen AB25 2ZN — MB ChB 1985 Bristol.

STOTT, William Bethune (retired) 43 Kingsway Court, Hove BN3 2LQ — LRCP LRCS 1921 Ed.; LRCP LRCS Ed. LRFPS Glas. 1921; DPH Camb. 1925. Prev: MOH Cuckfield RD & Cuckfield & Burgess Hill UDs.

STOTTER, Miss Anne Department of General Surgery, Glenfield General Hospital, Groby Road, Leicester LE3 9QP Tel: 0116 287 1471 Fax: 0116 255 6841 — MB BS 1978 Lond.; MA Camb. 1974, PhD 1975; FRCS Ed. 1982; FRCS Eng. 1982. Cons. Gen. Surg. Glenfield Gen. Hosp. Leics. Prev: Sen. Regist. (Surg.) St. Mary's Hosp. Lond.; Clin. Fell. (Surg. Oncol.) MD Anderson Cancer Center Houston, USA.

STOUT, Alan William 22a Bridge Road, Helens Bay, Bangor BT19 1TH — MB BCh BAO 1995 Belf.

STOUT, Alastair John Burnside, Dulnain Bridge, Ballieward, Grantown-on-Spey PH26 3PA — MB ChB 1992 Aberd.

*STOUT, David Brian 24 Brailswood Road, Poole BH15 2JW — MB ChB 1997 Leeds.

STOUT, Edward Laverick (retired) 49 Hesligton Lane, York YO10 4HN Tel: 01904 623050 — BA Camb. 1948; MRCS Eng. LRCP Lond. 1953. Prev: Clin. Asst. (Anaesth.) York Dist. Hosp.

STOUT, Ian Hugh Department of Psychiatry of Later Life, Meadowbrook, Stott Lane, Salford M6 8DD Tel: 0161 772 3766 Fax: 0161 772 3772; 25 Warwick Drive, Hale, Altrincham

WA15 9EA — MB ChB 1974 Manch.; MB ChB (Hons.) Manch. 1974; MSc (Psychiat.) Manch. 1981; FRCPsych 1995, M 1978. Cons. Psychogeriat. Ment. Health Servs. Salford NHS Trust; Hon. Clin. Lect. (Psychiat.) Manch. Univ. Prev: Sen. Regist. (Psychiat.) Tameside Gen. Hosp.; Clin. Research Fell. (Psychiat.) Univ. Manch.; Sen. Regist. (Psychiat.) Univ. Hosp. S. Manch.

STOUT, John Clark Peterhead Group Practice, The Health Centre, Peterhead AB42 2XA Tel: 01774 474841 Fax: 01774 474848; Kirkton House, Markethill, Longside, Peterhead AB42 4TD — MB ChB 1983 Dundee; MRCGP 1987; DRCOG 1985.

STOUT, Robert James (retired) 113 Imperial Road, Gillingham ME7 5PH Tel: 01634 307793 — MB BS 1943 Lond.; MRCS Eng. LRCP Lond. 1941; FFA RCS Eng. 1954; DA Eng. 1942. Prev: Cons. Anaesth. Medway Health Dist.

STOUT, Professor Robert William Department of Geriatric Medicine, Whitla Medical Building, 97 Lisburn Road, Belfast BT9 7BL Tel: 01232 335777 Fax: 01232 325839; 3 Larch Hill Drive, Craigavad, Holywood BT18 0JS Tel: 01232 422253 Fax: 01232 428478 — MB BCh BAO 1965 Belf.; MB BCh BAO (Hons.) Belf. 1965; DSc Belf. 1989, MD Belf. 1970; FRCPS Glas. 1995; FRCP Ed. 1988; FRCP Lond. 1979, M 1967; FRCPI 1989. (Belf.) Prof. Geriat. Med. Qu. Univ. Belf.; Cons. Phys. Belf. City Hosp.; Dean Fac. Med. & Health Sci. Qu. Univ. Belf. Socs: Assn. Phys., Brit. Geriat. Soc.; Pres. Ulster Med. Soc. Prev: Sen. Lect. (Med.) Qu. Univ. Belf.; Brit. Heart Foundat. Sen. Research Fell. (Med.) Qu. Univ. Belf.; Eli Lilly MRC Trav. Fell. & Vis. Scientist Dept. Med. Univ. Washington, Seattle, USA.

STOUT, Ronald Christie Hospital NHS Trust, Withington, Manchester M20 4BX Tel: 0161 446 3000 Fax: 0161 446 3352; 9 Fairfax Avenue, Didsbury, Manchester M20 6AJ Tel: 0161 434 6596 — MB ChB 1973 Liverp.; FRCP 1996; FRCR 1980. (Liverpool) Cons. Radiother. & Oncol. Christie Hosp. & Holt Radium Inst.; Hon. Lect. Univ. Manch. Inst. Cancer Studies. Socs: BMA; Fell. Roy. coll. Phys. Eng.; Fell. Roy. Coll. Radiol.

STOUT, Thomas Vincent Caerphilly District Miners' Hospital, St. Martin's Road, Caerphilly CF83 2WW Tel: 029 2085 1811 — MB BS 1963 Lond.; MRCOG 1971, DObst 1967; DCMT Lond. 1966. (Univ. Coll. Hosp.) Cons., Caerphilly Miners Hosp. Prev: Sen. Regist. (O & G) St. David's Hosp. Bangor; Regist. (O & G) Torbay Hosp. Torquay; Regist. (O & G) N.. Gen. Hosp. Sheff.

STOVES, Catherine 16 Hillston Close, Naisberry Park, Hartlepool TS26 0PE Tel: 01429 260755 — MB BS 1968 Newc.; DA Eng. 1970.

STOVES, John 29 Rutland Road, Wallsend NE28 8QL — MB ChB 1991 Ed.

STOVES, Robert The Health Centre, Alfred Squire Road, Wednesfield, Wolverhampton WV11 1XU Tel: 01902 575033 Fax: 01902 575013 — BM BS 1991 Nottm. Trainee GP/SHO (Obst.) Sandwell Dist. Gen. Hosp. Socs: MDU.

STOVIN, Oliver John The Surgery, Glpathorne Road, Oundle, Peterborough PE8 4JA Tel: 01832 273408; 135 Glapthorne Road, Oundle, Peterborough PE8 5BA Tel: 01832 274493 — MB BS 1983 Lond.; BA Oxf. 1980; MRCGP 1988; DRCOG 1986. Prev: Trainee GP Camb. VTS; SHO (Med.) Jas. Paget Hosp. Gt. Yarmouth.

STOVIN, Patricia Helen The Surgery, 32 Queen Street, Louth LN11 9AU Tel: 01507 602421 Fax: 01507 601700; Grove House, 54 Westgate, Louth LN11 9YD Tel: 01507 602421 — MB BS 1980 Lond.; DRCOG 1982. (St. Mary's Hosp. Lond.)

STOVIN, Peter George Ingle (retired) 307 Hills Road, Cambridge CB2 2QS — MB BChir 1950 Camb.; MRCP Lond. 1952; FRCPath 1973, M 1963. Prev: Cons. Pathol. Papworth & Hinchingbrooke Hosps.

STOVIN, Sybille Elizabeth (retired) 307 Hills Road, Cambridge CB2 2QS — MB BS 1950 Lond.; MRCS Eng. LRCP Lond. 1950. Prev: SCMO (Family Plann.) Camb. HA.

STOW, Pamela Jean (retired) 6 Harrow Road, Knockholt, Sevenoaks TN14 7JT — MB BS 1957 Lond.; FFA RCS Eng. 1967; DA Eng. 1959. Cons. Anaesth. Croydon & Warlingham Pk. Hosp. Gp. Prev: Ho. Phys. Univ. Coll. Hosp.

*STOW, Rachael Elizabeth 32 Moorcroft Dr, Sheffield S10 4GW — MB ChB 1997 Dundee.

STOW, Sophia Luise Low Farm, Wilden Road, Colmworth, Bedford MK44 2NN — MB BS 1993 Lond.

STOWE, Helen Elizabeth Rose Cottage,, 4, Alexandra Terrace,, Kelsall, Tarporley CW6 0RW Tel: 01829 751396 — MB BS 1993 Newc.; 2001 Dip Fam. Plan.; DRCOG 1997. (Newc. u. Tyne) Socs: BMA. Prev: Locum GP 1998-2001; SHO QEQM Hosp. Margate, c/o the Elderly.

STOWE, Roy (retired) 1 Pilgrims Way, Canterbury CT1 1XS Tel: 01227 471441 — MB BS 1953 Lond. JP. Prev: Ho. Phys. Univ. Coll. Hosp.

STOWELL, Gillian Margaret Ide Lane Surgery, Ide Lane, Alphington, Exeter EX2 8UP Tel: 01392 439868 Fax: 01392 493513; 14 Marlborough Road, Exeter EX2 4TJ Tel: 01392 437364 — MB ChB 1976 Bristol; MRCGP 1981. (Univ. Bristol)

STOWELL, Patricia Anne 13 Queens Terrace, Otley LS21 3JE — MB BChir 1983 Camb.; BSc Lond. 1976; BA Camb. 1981, MB BChir 1983.

STOWELL, Thomas Eldon Scott (retired) 3 The Grange, Grange Court, Bognor Regis PO21 4XR Tel: 01243 826330 Fax: 01243 826330 Email: testowell@aol.com — BM BCh 1943 Oxf.; MA Oxf. 1943, BA (Hons.) 1940; FRCGP 1975, M 1952. Prev: Squadron Ldr. Orthop. Specialist RAF.

STOWER, Mr Michael John York District Hospital, York YO31 8HE Tel: 01904 453601 Fax: 01904 453078 Email: michael.j.stower@excha.yhs-tr.northy.nhs.uk; Bramble End, Derwent Lane, Dunnington, York YO19 5RR Tel: 01904 489312 Email: mjstower@aol.com — MB ChB 1975 Bristol; DM Nottm. 1983; FRCS Eng. 1979. (Bristol) Cons. Urol. York. Socs: Brit. Assn. Urol. Surg.; BMA; Brit. Prostate Gp. Prev: Sen. Regist. S W. RHA; Regist. (Surg.) Nottm. & Derby.

STOYLE, Mr Thomas Frederick 15 Roundhill Close, Syston, Leicester LE7 1PP Tel: 0116 260 2729 Fax: 0116 246 1076; Broadmead, 12 Southernhay Road, Leicester LE2 3TJ Tel: 0116 270 8654 — MB BS 1953 Lond.; FRCS Eng. 1961; LMSSA Lond. 1953; DObst RCOG 1955. (St. Geo.) Emerit. Cons. Orthop. Surg. Leicester Roy. Infirm. & Glenfield Gen. Hosp. Leicester. Socs: Fell. BOA; Brit. HIV Soc.; Brit. Soc. Childr. Orthop. Surg. Prev: Sen. Regist. (Orthop.) Sheff. Roy. Infirm.; Regist. (Orthop.) St. Bart. Hosp. Lond.; Ho. Off. (Orthop.) & Cas. St. Geo. Hosp. Lond.

STRACEY, Doreen Mary Josephine (retired) 15 Mortlake House, 512 High Road, Chiswick, London W4 5RH Tel: 020 8995 2880 — MB BS 1930 Punjab; MRCOG 1949. Prev: GP Lond.

STRACEY, Pamela Mary (retired) 59 Hazel Avenue, Acland Park, Braunton EX33 2EZ Tel: 01271 815469 — MB BS 1958 Lond.; MRCS Eng. LRCP Lond. 1958; T(Anaesth) 1991; FFA RCS Eng. 1963; DA Eng. 1960. Cons. Anaesth. Eliz. G. Anderson Hosp. Lond. & Moorfields Eye Hosp. Lond. Prev: Specialist Anaesth. Univ. NSW, Austral.

STRACH, Mr Erich Hugo (retired) 7 Tower Way, Woolton Park, Liverpool L25 6EB Tel: 0151 428 3806 Email: hugmarg@kemplend.freeserve.co.uk — MD 1938 Prague; FRCS Eng. 1951; MChOrth. Liverp. 1952. Prev: Cons. Orthop. Surg. St. Helens Hosp. & Whiston Hosp.

STRACHAN, Alasdair Neil 194 Queensway, Cheadle SK8 3HH — MB ChB 1989 Sheff.; MRCGP 1993; DTM & H Lond. 1993; DRCOG 1991.

***STRACHAN, Alexander Gregory** 23 Cherry Orchard Road, Lisvane, Cardiff CF14 0UD Tel: 0114 763072 — MB ChB 1996 Sheff.

***STRACHAN, Alexandra Mary Jane** 28 Chalcot Square, London NW1 8YA — MB BS 1994 Lond.

STRACHAN, Bruce Taylor 6 Glendale Road, Peterhead AB42 1AE — MB ChB 1993 Aberd.

STRACHAN, Bryony Katharine Nottingham City Hospital, Nottingham NG5 1PB; 89 Wilsthorpe Road, Breaston, Derby DE72 3EA Tel: 01332 875772 — MB ChB 1987 Sheff.; MRCOG 1995. Clin. Lect. Dept. of Human Developm. Univ. of Nottm. Prev: Specialist Regist. (O & G) Nottm.

STRACHAN, Charles Douglas Scott Low Moor House, 167 Netherlands Avenue, Low Moor, Bradford BD12 0TB Tel: 01274 606818 Fax: 01274 691684; Lime House, Simm Carr Lane, Shibden, Halifax HX3 7UL — MB ChB 1986 Aberd.; MRCGP 1994; DCH RCP Lond. 1990. (Aberd.) GP Bradford.

STRACHAN, Mr Colin John Logan (cons. rooms), The Hove Nuffield, 55 New Church Road, Hove BN3 4BG Tel: 01273 720217/627053 Fax: 01273 220919 Email: gibson.maggie@talk21.com; Braidlea, Beacon Road, Ditchling, Hassocks BN6 8UL Tel: 01273 842984 Fax: 01273 846864 Email: colin.strachan@btinternet.com — MB ChB Glas. 1966; MD Birm. 1979; FRCS Eng. 1996; FRCS Glas. 1987; FRCS Ed. 1970. Cons. Surg. Brighton Acute Health Care Trust; Arris & Gale Lect. RCS; Revalidation Dir. RCS Edin; Lead Assessor. GMC Performance Assessm. in Surg.; Bound Maker, Intercollogists Speciality Bd., Gen. Surg. Socs: Assn. Surg.; (Counc.) RCS Edin.; Vasc. Surg. Soc. Prev: Sen. Lect. (Surg.) Qu. Eliz. Hosp. Birm.; MRC Research Fell. (Vasc. Surg.) King's Coll. Hosp. Lond.; Regist. (Surg.) W.. Infirm. Glas.

STRACHAN, David Andrew Shebburn Surgery, Main Street, New Abbey, Dumfries DG2 8BY Tel: 01387 850263 Fax: 01387 850468; Gillfoot Farm, New Abbey, Dumfries DG2 8HD Tel: 01387 850225 Email: daveandsue@medix-uk.com — MB ChB 1985 Aberd. (Aberd.) Prev: Trainee GP/SHO Dumfries & Galloway VTS; Ho. Off. (Med.) Aberd. Roy. Infirm.; Ho. Off. (Surg.) Dumfries & Galloway Roy. Infirm.

STRACHAN, David Buchan (retired) Southville, Stanningley, Pudsey, Leeds Tel: 0113 270361 — MB ChB 1948 Aberd. Prev: Ho. Surg. N. Ormesby Hosp. Middlesbrough.

STRACHAN, David Grant (retired) 20 Denham Green Terrace, Edinburgh EH5 3PD Tel: 0131 552 3178 — MB ChB 1957 Ed.; DObst RCOG 1961. Prev: Ho. Surg. (ENT) Roy. Infirm. Edin.

STRACHAN, Professor David Peter Department of Public Health Sciences, St. George's Hospital Medical School, Cranmer Terrace, London SW17 0RE Tel: 020 8725 5429 Fax: 020 8725 3584 Email: d.strachan@sghms.ac.uk; 157 Hayes Chase, West Wickham BR4 0JD — MB ChB 1981 Ed.; MD (Dist.) Ed. 1990; MSc (Dist.) (Epidemiol.) Lond. 1986; FRCP Lond. 1996; MRCP (UK) 1985; FFPHM RCP (UK) 1995, M 1989; MRCGP 1985. Prof. (Epidemiol.) St. Geo. Hosp. Med. Sch. Lond.; Hon. Cons. Pub. Health Med. Wandsworth HA. Prev: Sen. Lect. (Epidemiol.) St. Geo. Hosp. Med. Sch. Lond.; Lect. (Epidemiol.) Lond. Sch. Hyg. & Trop. Med.; Wellcome Research Train. Fell. (Clin. Epidemiol.) Dept. Community Med. Univ. Edin.

STRACHAN, Mr David Richard ENT Department, Bradford Royal Infirmary, Duckworth Lane, Bradford BD9 6RJ Tel: 01274 364439 Fax: 01274 366549 Email: drstrachan@cs.com — MB ChB 1986 Leeds; FRCS (ORL.) 1997; FRCS Ed. 1992; FRCS Eng. 1992; Dip. HSM York 1997. Cons. ENT Surg.; Cons. Ear Nose & Throat Surg. The Yorks. Clinic Bradford Rd. Bingley BD16 1TW. Socs: Assoc. Mem. Brit. Assn. Otorhinol. Head & Neck Surgs.; Eur. Acad. Facial Plastic Surg.; Roy. Soc. Med. Prev: Regist. (Otolaryngol.) Leeds, Yorks. & Hull; Trainee Geo. Portmann Foundat. Bordeaux, France; Sen. Regist. (Leeds, Bradford, Hull).

STRACHAN, David Selby (retired) 75 Marwood Drive, Great Ayton, Middlesbrough TS9 6PD Tel: 01642 723800 Email: davidzena@doctors.org.uk — MB ChB 1949 Glas.; FRCGP 1979, M 1960; DObst RCOG 1958. GP MiddlesBoro. Prev: Ho. Surg. W.. Dist. Hosp. Glas.

STRACHAN, Eric James (retired) 29 Chadvil Road, Cheadle SK8 1NX Tel: 0161 428 7343 — MB ChB Aberd. 1934.

STRACHAN, Fiona Margaret Flat 10, Howburn Court, 173 Hardgate, Aberdeen AB11 6YA Tel: 01224 573065 — MB ChB 1991 Aberd.; MRCP (UK) 1994. Career Regist. (Diabetes & Endocrinol.) Aberd. Roy. Infirm.

STRACHAN, Mr George Mathieson 4 Frederick Street, Inverallochy, Fraserburgh AB43 8XU — MB ChB 1976 Aberd.; FRCS Ed. 1994; FRCS Glas. 1993. Staff Grade (A & E) Roy. Vict. Infirm. Newc. u. Tyne.

STRACHAN, Gillian 2/L 2 Garrioch Drive, Glasgow G20 8RP — MB ChB 1991 Dundee.

STRACHAN, Gordon Robert Henrietta Street Health Centre, 109A Henrietta Street, Girvan KA26 9AN Tel: 01465 713343 Fax: 01465 714591 — MB ChB 1993 Manch.

STRACHAN, Hilary Margaret Christine Crown Avenue Surgery, 12 Crown Avenue, Inverness IV2 3NF Tel: 01463 710777 Fax: 01463 714511 — MB ChB 1984 Aberd.

STRACHAN, Mr Ian MacDonald (retired) 1 Beech Hill Road, Sheffield S10 2SA Tel: 0114 268 4242 — MB ChB 1959 St. And.; FRCS Ed. 1965; FCOphth 1990; DO Eng. 1963. Cons. Ophth. Centr. Sheff. Childr. Hosp. Trust. Prev: Sen. Regist. Dundee Roy. Infirm.

STRACHAN, James (retired) Lower Lime House, Simm Carr Lane, Shibden, Halifax HX3 7UL — MB ChB Aberd. 1950. Prev: Clin. Asst. (Rheum.) Halifax Gen. Hosp.

STRACHAN, James Christopher Marnan Health Clinic, 407 Main Road, Dovercourt, Harwich CO12 4ET Tel: 01255 201299 Fax: 01255 201270; 7 Queens Road, Dovercourt, Harwich CO12 3TH Tel: 01255 506420 — MB BS 1964 Lond.; FRCS Ed. 1971. (Westm.) GP Surg. Harwich & Dist. Hosp.; Clin. Asst. (Surg.) Colchester Gp. Hosps. Socs: Colchester Med. Soc.; BMA & Colchester Med. Soc. Prev: Rotating Regist. (Surg.) United Sheff. Hosps.; Regist. (Gen. Surg.) Lincoln Co. Hosp.; Ho. Surg. W.m. Hosp. Lond.

STRACHAN, James Gerrit Tel: 0131 537 6438 Fax: 0131 537 6117 Email: james.strachan@lpct.scot.nhs.us — MB ChB 1973 Ed.; MPhil Ed. 1979, BSc (Med. Sci.) 1970; FRCPysch 1993, M 1977. (University of Edinburgh) Cons. Psychiat. Roy. Edin. Hosp.; Hon. Sen. Lect. Univ. Edin. Socs: Chairm. Scott. Sec.Gen. Psych. RCPsych. 1996 - 2000; Union Européenne des médesins Spécialistes - Sect. of Psychol. 2001. Prev: Lect. Univ. Utrecht, Netherlands; Cons. Psychiat. Min. Justice Pieter Baan Centre Utrecht.

STRACHAN, James Wallace 40 The Avenue, Girvan KA26 9DS Tel: 01465 3343 — MB ChB 1962 Glas.; DObst RCOG 1964. (Glas.) Prev: Ho. Off. (Med. & Surg.) Glas. Roy. Infirm.

STRACHAN, John Alan Churchill Department of Anaesthesia, Plymouth General Hospital, Plymouth PL4 7JJ — MB ChB 1956 Bristol; FFA RCS Eng. 1966. Cons. Anaesth. Plymouth Hosps.

STRACHAN, Mr John Charles Haggart 126 Harley Street, London W1N 1AH Tel: 020 7935 0142; 28 Chalcot Square, London NW1 8YA — MB BS 1961 Lond.; FRCS Eng. 1966; FRCS Ed. 1966; MRCS Eng. LRCP Lond. 1961. (St. Mary's) Cons. Orthop. Surg. S. Hammersmith (Char. Cross) Health Dist. (T); Cons. Orthop. Surg. Roy. Ballet Co. Socs: Fell. Roy. Soc. Med. & Brit. Orthop. Assn. Prev: Sen. Orthop. Regist. St. Mary's Hosp. Lond.; SHO Roy. Nat. Orthop. Hosp. Lond.; Ho. Surg. & Cas. Off. St. Mary's Hosp. Lond.

STRACHAN, Mr John Robert South Warwickshire General Hospitals NHS Trust, Lakin Road, Warwick CV34 5BW Tel: 01926 495321 Fax: 01926 482602; Oak Farm House, Ufton Fields, Ufton, Leamington Spa CV33 9NZ Tel: 01926 612237 — MB BS 1977 Lond.; MS Lond. 1990; FRCS Eng. 1982; T(S) 1991. (University of London) Cons. Urol. S. Warks. Gen. Hosp.s NHS Trust. Prev: Sen. Regist. St. Mary's Hosp. Lond.; Sen. Regist. Roy. Marsden Hosp. Lond.; Research Regist. Inst. Urol. & King's Coll. Hosp. Lond.

***STRACHAN, Katherine Anne** 28 Beacon Road, Ditchling, Hassocks BN6 8UL — MB ChB 1996 Glas.

STRACHAN, Kenneth Alexander Boyd Peterhead Group Practice, The Health Centre, Peterhead AB42 2XA Tel: 01774 474841 Fax: 01774 474848; Ravenscraig Cottage, Inverugie, Peterhead AB42 3DS — MB ChB 1979 Aberd.

STRACHAN, Kenneth Flory The Village Farm, Offchurch, Leamington Spa CV33 9AP Tel: 01926 435239 — MB BS Lond. 1941. (St. Mary's) Prev: RAMC 1942-47; Ho. Phys. Harefield EMS Hosp.; Ho. Surg. Staines Co. Hosp.

STRACHAN, Kerry Jane 41 Ratcliffe Road, Sheffield S11 8YA Tel: 0114 268 1938 — MB ChB 1992 Sheff.; BSc Sheff. 1987; DRCOG 1995; MRCGP 1997. (Sheff.) Prev: Trainee GP/SHO (Psychiat.) N.lands Day Hosp. Sheff.

STRACHAN, Mark William John 107 Candlemaker's Park, Edinburgh EH17 8TL Tel: 0131 664 6059 Email: mark.strachan@ed.ac.uk — MB ChB 1992 Ed.; BSc (Hons.) Ed. 1990; MRCP (UK) 1995. (Univ. Ed.) Specialist Regist. (Diabetes, Endo, Gen. Med.) W.ern Gen. Hosp. Edin. Socs: Brit. Diabetic Assn.; Eur. Assn. Study Diabetes; Caledonian Endocrine. Soc. Prev: SHO (Gen. Med.) Stirling Roy. Infirm.; SHO (Cardiothoracic & A & E) Roy. Infirm. Edin.; Clin. Research Fell., Roy. Infirm. Edin.

STRACHAN, Michael Charles Tel: 01622 752345 Fax: 01622 758133 — MB BS 1980 Lond.; MRCGP 1985; DRCOG 1984. GP Trainer Maidstone.

STRACHAN, Pauline Anne Cedar Lodge, 64 Springfield Avenue, Aberdeen AB15 8JB — MB ChB 1984 Aberd.; MRCGP 1988.

STRACHAN, Robert Alexander Hawthorns Surgery, 331 Birmingham Road, Sutton Coldfield B72 1DL Tel: 0121 373 2211 Fax: 0121 382 1274; 57 Somerville Road, Sutton Coldfield B73 6HJ — MB ChB 1966 Aberd.; FRCGP 1986, M 1972; DObst RCOG

1970. Partner GP; Assoc. Adviser (Gen. Pract.) W. Midl. RHA. Prev: GP Course Organiser W. Midl. RHA.

STRACHAN, Mr Roger David Department of Neurosurgery, Middlesbrough General Hospital, Ayresome Green Lane, Middlesbrough TS5 5AZ Tel: 01642 854413 Fax: 01642 854118; Tel: 01642 723803 — MB ChB 1979 Ed.; BSc (Med. Sci.) Ed. 1976, MD 1995; FRCS (SN) 1994; FRCS Ed. 1986. Cons. Neurosurg., Dept. of Neurosurg. Middlesbrough Gen. Hosp., Middlesbrough. Socs: Soc. Brit. Neurol. Surg.; Soc. Research into Hydrocephalus and Spina Bifida (SRHSB); Internat. Neuromodulation Soc. Prev: Sen. Regist. (Neurosurg.) Manch. Roy. Infirm. & Hope Hosp. Salford; Regist. (Neurosurg.) Middlesbrough Gen. Hosp.; Research Regist. (Surg.) Univ. Newc.

STRACHAN, Ronald Hamilton Medical Group, 4 Queen's Road, Aberdeen AB15 4ZT Tel: 01224 622345 — MB ChB 1972 Aberd.

STRACHAN, Stephanie Ruth 9 Glen Hazel, Wyatts Green, Brentwood CM15 0PE — BM BS 1996 Nottm. SHO (Med.) Qu.'s Med. Centre Nottm.

STRACHAN, Mr William Ellis (retired) — MB ChB 1954 Aberd.; FRCS Ed. 1962. Prev: Sen. Regist. (Surgic. Neurol.) Roy. Infirm. Edin.

STRADLING, Andrew James c/o 31 Field Barn Drive, Weymouth DT4 0EE — MB BS 1996 Lond. (University College London) SHO (Neurosurg.) Addenbrooke's Hosp. Camb.; SHO (A & E) UCL.

STRADLING, Hugh Alan The Health Centre, Banks Road, Haddenham, Aylesbury HP17 8EE Tel: 01844 291874 Fax: 01844 292344 — MB BS 1973 Lond.; BSc Lond. 1970, MB BS 1973; MRCP (UK) 1976; MRCGP 1978; Dip. Palliat. Med. Wales 1994; DRCOG 1979.

STRADLING, Professor John Reginald Oxford Centre for Respiratory Medicine, Churchill Hospital, Oxford OX3 7LJ Tel: 01865 225236 Fax: 01865 225221 Email: john.stradling@orh.nhs.uk; The Ridings, High St, Beckley, Oxford OX3 9UU Tel: 01865 351623 — MB BS 1976 Lond.; BSc Lond. 1973, MD Lond. 1981; FRCP Lond. 1992; MRCP (UK) 1978. (Middlx.) Cons. Respirat. & Sleep Med. Ch.ill Hosp. Oxf.; Prof. for Respirat. Med., univ Oxf. Socs: Brit. Thorac. Soc. & Sleep Res. Soc. Prev: MRC Trav. Fell. (Med.) Univ. Toronto, Canada; Sen. Regist. Oxf. Hosps.; Regist. Hammersmith Hosp. Lond.

STRADLING, Patricia Ann Walnut Corner, 27B The Gables, Haddenham, Aylesbury HP17 8AD — MB BS 1973 Lond.; BSc Lond. 1970, MB BS 1973; DA Eng. 1976.

STRADLING, Peter (retired) Apple Acre, Sampford Brett, Taunton TA4 4LB Tel: 01984 632545 — MB BS 1942 Lond.; MD Lond. 1947; FRCP Lond. 1966, M 1947; MRCS Eng. LRCP Lond. 1942. Prev: Dir. Chest Clinic & Sen. Lect. (Respirat. Dis.) Roy. Postgrad. Med. Sch. Hammersmith Hosp. Lond.

STRAFFEN, Anne Mary Tel: 01226 730000 Ext: 2772, 01226 777762 Ext: 2772 Fax: 01226 777769 Email: ann.straffen@bdgh-tr.trent.nhs.uk — MB BS 1983 Lond.; MRCPath 1991; BSc 1980. Cons. Chem. Pathologist, Barnsley DGM, Barnsley.

STRAHAN, Mr Jack (retired) Skerry, Drumgay, Enniskillen BT74 4GH Tel: 01365 323498 — MB BCh BAO 1956 Belf.; MCh Belf. 1971, MB BCh BAO 1956; FRCS Ed. 1962; DObst RCOG 1958. Prev: Cons. Surg. Erne Hosp. Enniskillen.

STRAIN, Anne Geraldine 9 Tudor Grove, Omagh BT78 1HJ Tel: 01662 245713; 44 Derrybard Road, Fintona, Omagh BT78 2JH — MB BCh BAO 1989 Belf.; DMH Belf. 1991; T(GP) 1993. SHO St. Luke's Hosp., Armagh. Prev: Trainee GP/SHO S. Tyrone Hosp. Dungannon.

STRAIN, Ethel Olivia (retired) 12 South Drive, Hartlepool TS26 8NQ Tel: 01429 272650 — MB BCh BAO Dub. 1946. Prev: Clin. Med. Off. (Hartlepool) Retd.

STRAIN, George Andrew (retired) 12 South Drive, Hartlepool TS26 8NQ Tel: 01429 272650 — MB ChB St. And. 1933. Prev: Flight Lt. RAFVR.

STRAIN, Graham Barbour Cumbernauld Road Surgery, 804 Cumbernauld Road, Glasgow G33 2EH Tel: 0141 770 5234 Fax: 0141 770 0850 — MB ChB 1981 Glas. Prev: Trainee GP New Galloway VTS; GP Cascais, Portugal.

STRAIN, Gregory John 36 Pencombe Drive, Wolverhampton WV4 5EW — MB BS 1986 Lond.

STRAIN, Harriet Anne 1 Downes Road, Marshalswick, St Albans AL4 9NS — MB BS 1986 Lond.; MRCGP 1990.

STRAIN

STRAIN, John William, DFM Broadfield, Egremont CA22 2NG Tel: 01946 820300 — MRCS Eng. LRCP Lond. 1952. (Lond. Hosp.) SBStJ. Prev: Sen. Med. Off. Brit. Nuclear Fuels Ltd.; Ho. Surg. & Ho. Phys. Lond. Hosp.

STRAIN, Thomas Bertram Humphrey (retired) 32 Meadow Hill Road, King's Norton, Birmingham B38 8DD Tel: 0121 458 1399 Email: tbhstrain@barclays.net — MB ChB 1952 N.Z.; FFA RCS Eng. 1970; DA Eng. 1968. Cons. Anaesth. Selly Oak Hosp. Birm. Prev: Regist. (Anaesth.) N. Canterbury Hosp. Bd. & W.M. RHA.

***STRAIN, William David** 10 St Johns Avenue, Walton, Liverpool L9 2BS — MB ChB 1996 Liverp.

STRAITON, John Alexander Department of Neuroradiology, Leeds General Infirmary, Leeds LS1 3EX Tel: 0113 392 3683 Fax: 0113 392 5196 Email: jstrai@ulth.northy.nhs.uk — MB ChB 1981 Glas.; FRCP Glas. 1995; MRCP (UK) 1984; T(R) (CR) 1991; FRCR 1988. Cons. Neuroradiol. Leeds Gen. Infirm.

STRAITON, John Michael Culver Farm, Old Compton Lane, Farnham GU9 8EJ Tel: 01252 724924 Fax: 01252 724924 — MB BS 1955 Lond.; MRCS Eng. LRCP Lond. 1955; MRCOphth 1992; DO Eng. 1959; DA (UK) 1957. (Char. Cross) Assoc. Specialist Moorfields Eye Hosp. Socs: Fac. Ophth. RCS Eng.; Fac. Anaesth. RCS Eng. Prev: Chief Clin. Asst. Moorfields Eye Hosp.; Asst. Med. Off. Moorfields Eye Hosp.; Resid. Anaesth. Char. Cross Hosp.

STRAITON, Nicholas 6 Colin Road, Paignton TQ3 2NR — MB BS 1979 Lond.

STRAKER, Diana Mary Norden House Surgery, Avenue Road, Winslow, Buckingham MK18 3DW Tel: 01296 713434; Homefield, Oving, Aylesbury HP22 4HN Tel: 01296 641737 — MB ChB 1985 Manch.; MRCGP 1990; DRCOG 1988. Socs: Buckingham & Dist. Med. Soc. Prev: Trainee GP/SHO Aylesbury VTS; Ho. Off. (Gen. Surg.) Oldham Dist. Hosp.; Ho. Off. (Gen. Med.) Altrincham Gen. Hosp.

STRANDERS, Alan Patrick O'Connell Davenport House Surgery, Bowers Way, Harpenden AL5 4HX Tel: 01582 767821 Fax: 01582 769285; 34 Park Hill, Harpenden AL5 3AT Tel: 01582 713159 — MB BS 1972 Lond.; MRCS Eng. LRCP Lond. 1972; DObst RCOG 1975. (Middlx.)

STRANEX, Stephen Belvior Park Hospital, Northern Ireland Radiotherapy Centre, Hospital Road, Belfast BT8 8JR Tel: 01232 491942; 10 Hampton Court, Holywood BT18 OHU Tel: 01232 425992 — MB BCh BAO 1977 Belf.; FFR RCSI 1984. Cons. N. Irel. Radiother. Centre Belf.

STRANG, Alison Kathleen Gladys Sundial House, 29 High St., Skelton-in-Cleveland, Saltburn-by-the-Sea TS12 2EF Tel: 01287 654175 Fax: 01287 654075 — MB ChB 1973 Glas.; MRCGP 1979. Managem. Cons. Cert.d Trainer of NLP; Psychother. Cleveland. Socs: UKCP. Prev: Princip. Gen. Pract.s Redcar; Occupat. Health Physics.

STRANG, Cecil Duncan (retired) Strathlyn, Kilmahog, Callender FK17 8HD Tel: 01877 330074 Email: duncan@istrang.freeserve.co.uk — MB ChB Glas. 1957; MRCGP 1970; DObst RCOG 1959. Prev: GP Strathclyde.

STRANG, Christopher The Granary, Dalton, Newcastle upon Tyne NE18 0AA Tel: 01661 886470 — MD Durh. 1949, MB BS (Hnrs.) 1941; FRCP Lond. 1965. M 1947. (Durh.) Hon. Cons. Phys. Newc. HA. Socs: Assn. Phys. Gt. Brit. & Irel. & Thoracic Soc. Prev: Clin. Lect. Med. Univ. Newc.; Sen. Med. Regist. Roy. Vict. Infirm. Newc.; Surg. Lt. RNVR.

STRANG, Christopher James Ballantyne Mortimer Surgery, Victoria Road, Mortimer Common, Reading RG7 1HG Tel: 0118 933 2436 Fax: 0118 933 3801; Wisteria House, Mortimer Lane, Mortimer, Reading RG7 3AJ Tel: 01734 332572 — MB BS 1981 Lond.; MRCGP 1987; DRCOG 1986. Socs: BMA & Reading Med. Soc. Prev: Med. Off. Save The Childr. Sudan; Trainee GP Windsor VTS; SHO Roy. Cornw. Hosp. Truro.

STRANG, Mr Francis Alexander Manchester Royal Infirmary, Oxford Road, Manchester M13 9WL — MB 1960 Camb.; BA Camb. 1956, MB 1960, BChir 1959; FRCS Eng. 1964. (Camb. & St. Bart.) Sen. Cons. Neurosurg. Manch. Roy. Infirm.; Hon. Lect. Neurosurg. Univ. Manch. Prev: Lect. Neurosurg. Univ. Manch. & Hon. Cons. Manch. Roy. Infirm.; Sen. Regist. Dept. Neurosurg. Qu. Eliz. Hosp. Birm.; Regist. Dept. Neurol. Surg. St. Bart. Hosp. Lond.

STRANG, Gladys Elsa McArthur (retired) 26 Malcolmson Close, Edgbaston, Birmingham B15 3LS Tel: 0121 454 8335 — MB ChB St. And. 1937; MRCPsych 1973; DPM Eng. 1964. Hon. Cons. Highcroft Hosp. Birm. Prev: Retited.

STRANG, Graham Duncan Macgregor The Medical Centre, 4 Bracklinn Road, Callander FK17 8EJ Tel: 01877 331001 Fax: 01877 331720; The Orchard, Kilmahog, Callender FK17 8HD Tel: 01877 331669 — MB ChB 1983 Glas.; DRCOG 1992. Med. Mem. Nursing Home Inspection Team for Forth Valley HB; Exec. Mem. NW Forth Valley Locality. Prev: SHO (Cardiothoracic) W.. Infirm. Glas.; SHO (Thoracic Med.) Hairmyres Hosp. E. Kilbride; Trainee GP Argyll.

STRANG, Ian Guthrie (retired) 29 Moorside Road, Eccleshill, Bradford BD2 2HB Tel: 01274 636433 — LMSSA Lond. 1960.

STRANG, Ian William 2 Kelvinside Gardens, Glasgow G20 6BB; 31 Borestone Place, Stirling FK7 0PP — MB ChB 1967 Aberd.; FFPHM 1989, M 1977; Dip. Soc. Med. Ed. 1973. Indep. Computing & Health Informat. Cons. Scottl. Socs: Soc. Social Med. & BMA. Prev: SCM Forth Valley HB;.; Epidemiol. MRC Head Injury Progr.; Lect. Bio-Engin. Unit Univ. Strathclyde Glas.

STRANG, Isabella 4 Dunchurch Road, Paisley PA1 3JW — MB ChB 1972 Glas.; FFA RCSI 1978; DObst RCOG 1974.

STRANG, James Ian George c/o La Salle, Bristol Rd, Frenchay, Bristol BS16 1LQ — MB BS 1969 Lond.; MRCS Eng. LRCP Lond. 1969; MRCP (UK) 1972.

STRANG, Jeffrie Ritchard North Yorkshire Health Authority, Ryedale Building (4th Floor), 60 Piccadilly, York YO1 9PE Tel: 01904 825238 Fax: 01904 825245 Email: jeffrie.strang@nyorks-ha.northy.nhs.uk; Midnight Lodge, Scawton, Thirsk YO7 2HG Tel: 01845 597454 — MB ChB 1972 Glas.; MPH Harvard 1977; MFPHM 1992. Cons. Pub. Health Med. N. Yorks. HA. Prev: Sen. Regist. (Pub. Health Med.) N.. RHA; GP Redcar; Research Assoc. Dept. Community Med. Univ. Camb.

STRANG, Professor John Stanley National Addiction Centre, 4 Windsor Walk, Denmark Hill, London SE5 8AF — MB BS 1973 Lond.; MRCS Eng. LRCP Lond. 1973; MRCPsych 1977; MD 1995; FRCP 1993. (Guy's Hosp.) Prof. Psychiat. of Addic. & Dir. Addic. Research Unit Nat. Addic. Centre Lond. Prev: Cons. Psychiat. Drug Depend. Manch.; Regist. & Sen. Regist. Maudsley & Bethlem Roy. Hosps.

STRANG, Louis 87 Bidston Road, Birkenhead CH43 6TS — M.B., Ch.B. Glas. 1944. (Glas.) Prev: Paisley.

STRANG, Robert Archibald 69 Elms Lane, Wembley HA0 2NS — MB ChB 1933 Glas.; DPH 1937.

STRANG, Timothy Iain Email: timstrang@doctors.org.uk — MB ChB 1986 Manch.; FCAnaesth 1991; DCH RCP Lond. 1988. Cons. Anaesth. Univ. Hosp. of S. Manch. Socs: Difficult Airway Soc.; ACTA. Prev: Sen. Regist. (Anaesth.) NW RHA; Attend. Phys. Univ. Calif., Irvine, USA; SHO (Paediat. & Anaesth.) Booth Hall Hosp. Manch.

STRANGE, David James 28 Bassetts Way, Orpington BR6 7AE — MB BS 1991 Lond.; BSc Lond. 1988, MB BS 1991. SHO (Paediat.) Qu. Mary's Sidcup Hosp. Prev: SHO (Med.) King's Coll. Hosp. Lond.

STRANGE, Mr Frederick Griffiths St Clair (retired) Church Hill House, Harbledown, Canterbury CT2 9AB Tel: 01227 463660 — MRCS Eng. LRCP Lond. 1934; FRCS Eng. 1939. Prev: Hon. Civil Cons. Orthop. Roy. Herbert Hosp. 1967-1976.

STRANGE, Julian William Nevill 26 Kingsgate Road, Winchester SO23 9PG — MB ChB 1994 Bristol.

STRANGE, Stephen William Sarehole Surgery, 60 Colebank Road, Hall Green, Birmingham B28 8EY Tel: 0121 777 1315 Fax: 0121 777 0865 — MB ChB 1983 Birm.; BSc (Hons) Birm. 1980; MRCGP 1995; DGM RCP.; Dip Occ. Med. Roy. Coll. Phys.; Dip. Ther. (Wales). Socs: Birm. Local Med. Comm.; Small Pract.s Assn. (SPA).

STRANGEWAYS, Janet Edna Margaret Merton, Sutton & Wandsworth Health Authority, The Wilson, Cranmer Road, Mitcham CR4 4TP Tel: 020 8687 4529 Fax: 020 8687 4565; 22 Hamilton Way, Finchley, London N3 1AN Tel: 020 8346 0196 — MB BS Lond. 1966; FRCPath 1986, M 1973; MRCS Eng. LRCP Lond. 1966. (Roy. Free) Cons. Communicable Dis. Control Merton, Sutton & Wandsworth HA; Hon. Sen. Lect. (Microbiol.) St. Geo. Hosp. Med. Sch. Lond. Socs: Brit. Infec. Soc.; Hosp. Infec. Soc.; BMA. Prev: Cons. Med. Microbiol. St. Geo. Healthcare NHS Trust Lond.; Regist. (Path.) Radcliffe Infirm. Oxf.; Trainee Bact. Pub. Health Laborat. Portsmouth.

STRANGEWAYS, Peter Robert Furrows, 101 Sutton Veny, Warminster BA12 7AW Tel: 01985 840403 Fax: 01985 840403 Email: pstrangeways@doctors.org.uk — MB BChir Camb. 1963; MA Camb. 1964. (St. Thos.) Hon. Med. Adviser, Wessex MS Ther. Centre Warminster, Wilts; Mem., Bath & Dist. Community Health Counc. Socs: Brit. Med. Assn.; Med. Equestrian Assn. Prev: Med. Advisor Glos. FHSA; GP Warminster; Med. Off. Qu. Eliz. Hosp., Barbados.

STRANKS, Mr Geoffrey John The North Hampshire Hospital, Aldermaston Road, Basingstoke RG24 9NA Tel: 01256 473202; Mulberry Corner, Ibworth Road, Hannington, Tadley RG26 5TL Tel: 01256 782820 — MB BS 1983 Lond.; BSc Lond. 1980; FRCS (Orth.) 1995; FRCS Ed. 1988. (St. Geo.) Cons. Orthop. Surg. N. Hants. Hosp. Basingstoke.

STRANKS, Sarah Jane 7 Watlow Gardens, Buckingham MK18 1GQ — MB ChB 1990 Dundee; DRCOG 1993. Clin. Asst. (A & E) Wycombe Gen. Hosp.

STRANTZALIS, George Department of Neurosurgery, Walsgrave Hospital, Clifford Bridge Road, Walsgrave, Coventry CV2 2DX — Ptychio latrikes 1981 Athens.

STRATFORD, Andrew John The Health Centre, Elm Grove, Mengham, Hayling Island PO11 9AP Tel: 023 9246 6224; 38 Beach Road, Hayling Island PO11 0JG Tel: 01705 463826 — MB BS 1970 Lond.; MRCS Eng. LRCP Lond. 1969; DObst RCOG 1971. (Char. Cross) Clin. Asst. (Ment. Subn.) Hants. AHA (T).

STRATFORD, Gillian Ann 79 Rosebery Crescent, Jesmond Vale, Newcastle upon Tyne NE2 1EX — MB ChB 1987 Manch.

STRATFORD, Karen Anne Llynfi Surgery, Llynfi Road, Maesteg CF34 9DT Tel: 01656 732115 Fax: 01656 864451 — MB BCh 1988 Wales; BSc Wales 1983, MB BCh 1988; MRCGP 1992; DGM RCP Lond. 1991.

STRATFORD, Maria 56 Pondcroft Road, Knebworth SG3 6DE Tel: 01438 811040 — Lic Med. New U. Lisbon 1978.

STRATH, Donald John 1 Bishops Place, Paignton TQ3 3DZ Tel: 01803 559421 Fax: 01803 663381 — MB BS 1960 Lond.; MRCS Eng. LRCP Lond. 1959; MRCGP 1974; DObst RCOG 1960. (King's Coll. Hosp.) Socs: Fell. Roy. Soc. Med.; Exeter Med. Soc. Prev: Med. Pract. Silverton, Devon; Capt. RAMC 23 Parachute Field Ambul. Aldershot.

STRATH, Iain Douglas The Health Centre, 2 The Tanyard, Cumnock KA18 1BF Tel: 01290 422723 Fax: 01290 425444; 5 Langmuir Avenue, Perceton, Irvine KA11 2DR Tel: 01294 222255, 01444 440950 Fax: 01444 440950 Email: deekini@yahoo.co.uk — MB ChB 1985 Aberd.; MRCGP 1992; DRCOG 1991; DCH RCPS Glas. 1989.

STRATHDEE, Geraldine Mary 113 Hayes Chase, West Wickham BR4 0HY — MB BCh BAO 1977 Belf. Regist. Maudsley Hosp. Beckenham.

***STRATHERN, Colin Holmes Coats** 99 Fenwick Road, Griffnock, Glasgow G46 6JA — MB ChB 1995 Glas.

STRATHERN, Hugh Murray Altnabreac, Kilmacolm PA13 4AZ — MB ChB 1950 Glas.; FRCR 1975; FFR 1964; DMRD Eng. 1957; DObst RCOG 1954. (Glas.) Cons. Radiol. i/c Inverclyde Roy. Hosp. Greenock, Dunoon Gen. Hosp. & Vict. Hosp. Rothesay. Socs: Brit. Inst. Radiol. & BMA. Prev: Cons. Radiol. i/c Hairmyres & Assoc. Hosps. E. Kilbride.

STRATON, Rae Hervey (retired) The Paddocks, 1 Provost St., Fordingbridge SP6 1AY Tel: 01425 652391 — M.B., Ch.B. Bristol 1945.

STRATON, Thomas (retired) The Paddocks, 1 Provost St., Fordingbridge SP6 1AY Tel: 01425 652391 — MB ChB 1945 Bristol. Prev: Ho. Phys. Bristol Roy. Infirm.

STRATTON, David Dept of Child Health, Salisbury District Hospital, Salisbury SP2 8BJ Tel: 01722 425272 Fax: 01722 425284 Email: dr.d.stratton@shc-tr.swest.nhs.uk; Matrimony Farmhouse, Charlton-All-Saints, Salisbury SP5 4HA Tel: 01722 329720 Email: davidstratton100@hotmail.com — MB BS 1967 Lond.; MRCP (UK) 1972; MRCS Eng. LRCP Lond. 1967; FRCPCH 1998; DCH Eng. 1971; DObst RCOG 1971. (Guy's) Cons. Paediat. Salisbury Dist. Hosp. Socs: BMA Royl coll. Paed. & Child Health. Prev: Regist. (Paediat.) Lond. Hosp.; Lect. Child Health Lond. Hosp. Med. Sch. & Univ. Bristol; Sen. Regist. (Paediat.) Ahmadu Bello Univ. Hosp. Zaria, Nigeria.

STRATTON, Fred Queensgate, 74 Clumber Road, Poynton, Stockport SK12 1NW — MD 1944 Manch.; DSc Manch. 1957, MD 1944, MB ChB 1937, DPH 1939; FRCP Lond. 1966, M 1960; FRCPath 1963. (Manch.) Hon. Research Cons. Blood Serv. Manch.; Prof. Emerit. Human Serology Univ. Manch. Prev: Dir. of Research Blood Transfus. Serv. Manch.

STRATTON, Frederick Justin Department of Pathology, Birch Hill Hospital, Rochdale OL12 9QB Tel: 01706 377777 Email: fjstratton@orangenet.co.uk — MB ChB 1974 Manch.; MBA Manch. 1993; MHSM 1994; FRCPath 1992, M 1980. Cons. Chem. Path. Rochdale Healthcare NHS Trust & Bury Health Care NHS Trust; Clin. Teach. (Med.) Univ. Manch. Prev: Med. Dir. Rochdale Healthcare NHS Trust; Sen. Regist. (Chem. Path.) Manch. AHA (T).

STRATTON, Jonathan David Renal Unit, Lister Hospital, Stevenage SG1 4AD Tel: 01705 240410; 12 Rucklers Lane, Kings Langley WD4 8AU Email: jon.stratton@ntlworld.com — MB BS 1992 Lond.; MRCP (UK) 1995. Regist. (Nephrol.) St. Mary's Hosp. Lond.; Research Regist. Lister Hosp. Stevenage. Prev: SHO (Med.) St. Mary's Hosp. Portsmouth; Renal Regist. Lister Hosp. Stevenage; Med. Regist. Wexham Pk. Slough.

STRATTON, Michael Rudolf 6 Creighton Road, London NW6 6ED Tel: 020 8918 4087 — MB BS 1982 Lond.; PhD 1989; BA Oxf. 1979; MRCPath 1991. Prof. Cancer Genetics; Hon. Cons. Roy. Marsden Hosp. Lond. Prev: Sen. Regist. (Neuropath.) Inst. Psychiat. Lond.; MRC Research Fell. Inst. Cancer Research Lond.; Regist. (Histopath.) Hammersmith Hosp. Lond.

STRATTON, Paul Newark Road Surgery, 501 Newark Road, South Hykeham, Lincoln LN6 8RT Tel: 01522 537944 Fax: 01522 510932 — MB BS 1971 Lond.; MRCGP 1977; DCCH RCP Ed. 1984; DCH Eng. 1974; Cert JCC Lond. 1974; DObst RCOG 1973; FRCGP 1997. (Lond. Hosp.) Prev: Ho. Phys. St. Helen's Hosp. Hastings; Ho. Off. (Obst.) W. Chesh. Matern. Hosp.; SHO (Paediat.) Chester City Hosp.

STRATTON, Richard John Rheumatology Department, The Royal Free Hospital, London NW3 2QG Tel: 020 7794 0500 — MB BS 1988 Lond.; MA Oxf. 1985; MRCP Lond. 1991; MD Lond. 1999. Sen. Regist. (Rheumatol.) Roy. Free Hosp. Lond.; PhD Stud. (Vasc. Biol.) King's Coll. Lond.; Regist. (Rheumatol. & Gen. Med.) Guy's Hosp. Lond. Prev: Research Regist. Roy. Free Hosp. Lond.

STRAUGHAN, Donald William, OBE (retired) 9 Beaufort West, Bath BA1 6QB Tel: 01225 789926 Fax: 01225 789926 Email: donald.w.straughan@btinternet.com — MB BS (Hons.) Lond. 1961; PhD Lond. 1959, BSc (Hons.) 1956; MRCS Eng. LRCP Lond. 1961. Prev: Sen. Lect. (Pharmacol.) Univ. Edin.

STRAUGHAN, John Kenmore British Rubber Manufacturers Association Ltd., Health Research Unit, Scala House, Holloway Circus, Birmingham B1 1EQ Tel: 0121 643 9269 Fax: 0121 631 3297; Cleeton Court, Cleeton St Mary, Cleobury Mortimer, Kidderminster DY14 0QZ Tel: 01584 823379 — MB BS Durh. 1962; FFOM RCP Lond. 1994 MFOM 1983. Med. Dir. Health Research Unit Brit. Rubber Manufacturers Assn. Socs: Soc. Occupat. Med. & Fac. Occupat. Med. Prev: Chief Med. Adviser OcciDent. Oil of Libya; Chief Med. Adviser Berec Gp. Lond.; Sen. Med. Adviser Brit. Aircraft Corp.

STRAUGHAN, Stephen James Bramblehaies Surgery, College Road, Cullompton EX15 1TZ Tel: 01884 33536 Fax: 01884 35401; 44 Fore Street, Bradninch, Exeter EX5 4NN Tel: 01392 881904 — MB ChB 1980 Leeds; MRCGP 1987; DA (UK) 1985. Clin. Asst. (Anaesth.) Roy. Devon & Exeter Trust. Socs: GP Assn. Matern. Care; Med. Off. Sch. Assn.; Soc. Orthop. Med.

STRAUSS, Julian Paul The Health Centre, St. Mary's Road, Ferndown, Wimborne BH21 9HB Tel: 01202 897200 — BM 1980 Soton.; BM Soton 1980; MRCGP 1984; MRCPsych 1988; DCH RCP Lond. 1984; DRCOG 1984. GP Ferndown Health Centre Dorset.

***STRAW, Robert George** Flat 12, Janeleigh Court, 193 Fosse Rd S., Leicester LE3 0FY — MB ChB 1996 Leic.

STRAWBRIDGE, Ms Louise Catherine Barent Gen. Hospital, Wellhouse Lane, Barnet CB3 0NE Tel: 0208 216 4000 — MB ChB 1993 Ed. Specialist Reg. In Obst. and Gyn.

STRAWBRIDGE, Walter Glyndwr Caradoc 1 Tyfica Road, Pontypridd CF37 2DA Tel: 01443 3273 — MB BCh 1958 Wales; MD Wales 1958, BSc, MB BCh 1953; Dip. Bact. Lond 1961; FRCPath 1974, M 1963. (Cardiff) Socs: Roy. Soc. Health; BMA. Prev: Dep. Dir. Pub. Health Laborat. Birm.; Asst. Bacteriol. Centr.

STRAWFORD

Pub. Health Laborat. Colindale; Asst. Clin. Path. Welsh Nat. Sch. Med. Cardiff.

STRAWFORD, Gillian Rosemarie Medical Defence Union, 192 Altrincham Road, Sharston, Manchester M22 4RZ Tel: 0161 428 1234 Fax: 0161 491 3301 — MB BS 1985 Lond.; MRCGP 1991; DRCOG 1989. Medicolegal Adviser The Med. Defence Union Ltd. Socs: (Asst. Sec.) Med. Defence Union.

STRAWFORD, Ian David Jackson and Partners, Glastonbury Surgery, Feversham Lane, Glastonbury BA6 9LP Tel: 01458 833666 Fax: 01458 834536; 66 Barton House, Butleigh, Glastonbury BA6 8TH — MB ChB 1985 Birm.; MRCGP 1990; DCH RCP Lond. 1989.

STRAWFORD, Julie Upton Medical Partnership, 18 Sussex Place, Slough SL1 1NS Tel: 01753 522713 Fax: 01753 552790 — MB ChB 1976 Bristol.

STRAY, Colin Michael 20 Guildford Road, Stoneygate, Leicester LE2 2RB Tel: 0116 270 6106 Email: c.m.stray@carnewas.fsnet.co.uk — MB BS 1967 Lond.; FFA RCS Eng. 1972. (Westm.) Cons. Anaesth. Leicester Univ. Hosp.s Trust. Socs: BMA. Prev: Sen. Regist. (Anaesth.) Birm. AHA (T); Regist. (Anaesth.) Bristol Roy. Infirm.; SHO (Anaesth.) Soton. Hosp. Gp.

STREAHORN, David 23 Bush Road, Bushvale, Dungannon BT71 6QE — MB BCh BAO 1971 Belf.

STREATHER, Christopher Paul 38B Charteris Road, London N4 3AB — MB BS 1987 Lond.; MA Oxf. 1994; MRCP (UK) 1990. Sen. Research Fell. & Hon. Clin. Lect. (Renal Med.) King's Coll. Hosp. Lond. Socs: Renal Assn.; Eur. Dialysis & Transpl. Assn. Prev: Regist. (Renal Med.) King's Coll. Hosp., Roy. Sussex Co. Hosp. & St Thos. Hosp. Lond.

STREDDER, David Hugh 2 Maddison Street, Southampton SO14 2BN — MB ChB 1978 Leeds; MRCP (UK) 1983; MRCGP 1996; MFPM RCP (UK) 1989; DFFP (RCOG) 1997; DRCOG 1997; Dip. Pharm. Med. RCP (UK) 1986. (Leeds)

STREET, David Frank (retired) 6 Oast Court, Yalding, Maidstone ME18 6JY Tel: 01622 814495 — MB BS Lond. 1943; MRCS Eng. LRCP Lond. 1943; DMRD Eng. 1957. Prev: Cons. Radiol. Orsett, Basildon & St. And. Hosps.

STREET, Edmund Warren (retired) Bracken House, Brasted Chart, Westerham TN16 1LU Tel: 01959 63561 — MRCS Eng. LRCP Lond. 1942; MRCS Eng., LRCP Lond. 1942. Prev: Cons. Chest Phys. Bromley AHA.

STREET, Gillian Lesley Whiston Hospital, Dragon Lane, Liverpool Tel: 0151 426 1600; 8 Shrewsbury Road, Sale, Manchester M33 3TP Tel: 0161 976 3363 — MB ChB 1986 Liverp. Clin. Asst. (Dermat.) St. Helens Hosp. & Whiston Hosp. Merseyside & Knowsley HA.

***STREET, Karen Nicola** 71 Woodcote Avenue, Kenilworth CV8 1BG — BM BCh 1994 Oxf.

STREET, Mark Nicholas 39 Peartree Avenue, Newhall, Burton-on-Trent — MB BS 1985 Lond.

STREET, Martin Kinman Coorparoo, Bridgelands Barcombe, Lewes BN8 5BW — MB ChB 1978 Birm.; FFA RCS Eng. 1983; FFA RCSI 1983.

STREET, Murray John The Surgery, 21 Queens Road, Brighton BN1 3XA Tel: 01273 328080 Fax: 01273 725209; 20 East Drive, Queens Park, Brighton BN2 2BQ Tel: 01273 603538 — MB BCh 1980 Wales; BSc Wales 1975; MRCGP 1985; DRCOG 1982. (University Wales)

STREET, Miss Patricia Department of Obstetrics, Royal Berkshire Hospital, Cravon Road, Reading RG1 5AN Tel: 01189 878117; Halsinger Farm, Halsinger, Braunton EX33 2NL Tel: 01271 814504 Fax: 01271 816139 — MRCS Eng. LRCP Lond. 1974; FRCOG 1997; MRCOG 1982. (Roy. Free Sch. Med. Lond.) Cons. Obst. Roy. Berks. Hosp. Reading; Dep. Police Surg. Thames Valley Police Reading. Socs: Cert. Mem. BSCCP; Soc. Police Surg. Prev: Assoc. Specialist (O & G) Roy. Berks. Hosp. Reading; Regist. (O & G) Roy. Berks. Hosp. Reading; Regist. (O & G) N. Manch. Gen. Hosp.

STREET, Roger Geoffrey (retired) Tilford, Yealm Road, Newton Ferrers, Plymouth PL8 1BQ Tel: 01752 872073 — MB BChir Camb. 1964; MA Camb. 1964; DObst RCOG 1970. Prev: Principle in Gen. Pract.,Warminster, Wilts.

STREET, Simon Haswell Kidlington Health Centre, Exeter Close, Oxford Road, Kidlington OX5 1AP Tel: 01865 841941 — MB ChB 1974 Birm.; MCI Sc 1991; MRCGP 1978; DRCOG 1977. Prev: Tutor (Pub. Health & Primary Care) Univ. Oxf.; Trainee GP Oxf. VTS; Ho. Phys. Gen. Hosp. Birm.

STREET, Simon Quentin Ingarfield 6 St Mary's Road, Poole BH15 2LH — MB ChB 1988 Birm.; ChB Birm. 1988; MRCGP 1995; DCH RCP Lond. 1995; DRCOG 1995. (Birm.) Staff Paediat. (Community Child Health) Poole.

***STREETEN, Naomi Clare** Knowle Hill, Newick Lane, Mayfield TN20 6RD — MB BS 1997 Lond.

STREETER, Graham Stuart Tel: 01622 831257 — MB BS 1982 Lond.; MRCGP 1986; DRCOG 1986; DCH RCP Lond. 1985. (Charing Cross Hospital) GP Trainer Maidstone VTS.

STREETER, Helen Louise Cransley Hospice, St. Mary's Hospital, London Road, Kettering NN15 7PW; Eddonelea, Church Lane, East Haddon, Northampton NN6 8DB — MB BS 1989 Lond.; MRCGP 1993; DRCOG 1994; DCH RCP Lond. 1993. (Roy. Free Hosp. Sch. Med.) Clin. Asst. (Palliat. Med.) Cransley Hospice Kettering.

STREETLY, Allison Bexley and Greenwich Health Authority, 221 Erith Road, Bexleyheath DA7 6HZ Tel: 020 8298 6171 Fax: 020 8298 6183 Email: allisonstreetly@ics.bexgreen-ha.sthames.nhs.uk; Department of Public Health Medicine, UMDS, Capital House, 42 Weston St, London SE1 Tel: 020 7955 4945 Email: allison.streetly@kcl.ac.uk — MB BChir 1985 Camb.; MSc Lond. 1989; BA (Hons.) Camb. 1981; MFPHM RCP Lond. 1992. Acting Dir. Pub. Health Bexley & Greenwich; Sen. Lect. (Pub. Health Med.) UMDS. Prev: Sen. Regist. (Pub. Health Med.) SE Thames RHA.

STREETLY, Matthew James 99 Glyndebourne Gardens, Corby NN18 0QA — BM BS 1994 Nottm.

STREETS, Carole Ann Derriford Hospital, Plymouth PL6 8PH Tel: 01752 777111 Email: carole.streets@phnt.swest.nhs.uk; 2 Bradford Cottages, Buckland Monachorum, Yelverton PL20 6ES Tel: 01822 853473 Email: 2cstreets@2bradroh.freeserve.co.uk — MB ChB 1992 Bristol; BSc (Hons.) Bristol 1989; MRCP (UK) 1996. (Univ. Bristol) SHO (Anaesth.) Derriford Hosp. Plymouth. Socs: BMA; Assoc. of Anaesth. Of GB & Ire.; Roy. Coll. Phys. Prev: SHO (Med.) Derriford Hosp. Plymouth; SHO (A & E) & Ho. Off. (Med.) Roy. United Hosp. Bath; Ho. Off. (Surg.) Frenchay Hosp. Bristol.

STREETS, Mr Christopher George, Surg. Lt.-Cdr. RN Royal Hospital Haslar Gosport, Gosport PO12 2AA Tel: 01705 584255; 2 Bradford Cottages, Buckland Monachorum, Yelverton PL20 6ES Tel: 01822 853473 Email: 2cstreets@2bradcott.freeserve.co.uk — MB ChB 1992 Bristol; BSc (Hons.) Biochem. Bristol 1989; MRCS 1998. (Bristol) Reg. (Gen. Sur.), Rh Haslar. Prev: SHO (Gen. Surg.) MDHU Derriford Plymouth; SHO (Plastics) MDHU Derriford Plymouth; SHO (Neurosurg) MDHU Derriford Plymouth.

STREFFORD, Teresa Isabel 24 Carlton Road, Northwich CW9 5PN — MB ChB 1997 Leeds.

STREHLE, Eugen-Matthias 5 Trotwood, Limes Farm, Chigwell IG7 5JN — State Exam Med 1990 Munich; MD Munich 1993. SHO (Paediat., Paediat. Neurol. & Neonatol.) Roy. Preston Hosp. & Sharoe Green Hosp. Prev: SHO (Hosp. & Community Paediat.) Birch Hill Hosp. Rochdale; SHO (Paediat. & Neonatol.) City & Heartlands Hosp. Birm. & Solihull Hosp.

STREIT, Catherine Elizabeth Longrigg Medical Centre, Leam Lane Estate, Felling, Gateshead NE10 8PH Tel: 0191 469 2173 Fax: 0191 495 0893 — Dip Fed 1981 Switzerland. GP Gateshead, Tyne & Wear.

STRELAU-SOWINSKA, Jadwiga 31 Thornway, Bramhall, Stockport SK7 2AQ — MB BCh BAO 1958 NUI; MRCPsych 1971. Cons. (Child Psychiat.) Stockport AHA.

STRELITZ, Norma Sylvia White House, Slateway, Pitton, Salisbury SP5 1ED Tel: 01722 712236 — MB ChB Liverp. 1955; DMRT Liverp. 1961. (Liverp.)

STRELLING, Malcolm Keith (retired) Sarnia, Westella Road, Yelverton PL20 6AS Tel: 01822 853219 — MB BS 1953 Lond.; FRCP Lond. 1976; FRCP Ed. 1975; FRCPCH 1996; DRCOG 1958; DCH RCP Lond. 1958. Prev: Cons. Paediat. Plymouth.

STRETCH, Richard Frederick Orrell Road Practice, 84 Orrell Road, Orrell, Wigan WN5 8HB Tel: 01942 222321 Fax: 01942 620327 — MB ChB 1974 Manch.; MRCGP 1982. Prev: Ho. Off. (Gen. Surg. & Gen. Med.) Roy. Albert Edwd. Infirm. Wigan.

STRETTON, Christopher Martin Barnwood Road Surgery, 51 Barnwood Road, Gloucester GL2 0SE Tel: 01452 523362 Fax: 01452 387931 — MB ChB 1964 Birm.; MMedSc Leeds 1985;

MRCS Eng. LRCP Lond. 1964; MRCGP 1980; DObst RCOG 1966. (Birm.)

STRETTON, Trevor Bannister (retired) 12 Hill Top Avenue, Cheadle Hulme, Cheadle SK8 7HN Tel: 0161 485 1361 — MB ChB 1955 Manch.; FRCP Lond. 1972, M 1957. Med. Chairm. Pens. Appeal Tribunals Lond. Prev: Cons. Phys. Manch. Roy. Infirm. & Sen. Lect. (Med.) Univ. Manch.

STREULE, Michael John (retired) Broomfield Cottage, Broomfield Hill, Great Missenden HP16 9PD Tel: 01494 863940 — MB BS Lond. 1959; LMSSA Lond. 1959; DObst RCOG 1961. Prev: GP, Bucks.

STREVENS, Maurice John 187 Upton Road, Bexleyheath DA6 8LY — MB BCh 1969 Wales; MRCP (U.K.) 1973.

STRICH, Sabina Jeannette (retired) 1 Folly Bridge Court, Oxford OX1 1SW Tel: 01865 251741 Email: sabina@strich.demon.uk — BM BCh Oxf. 1949; DM Oxf. 1956; MRCP Lond. 1967; FRCPsych 1980, M 1973; MRCPath 1963. Prev: Cons. Child Psychiat. Croydon.

STRICK, Miss Margaret Joy Royal Victoria Infirmary, Queen Victoria Road, Newcastle upon Tyne NE1 4LP Tel: 0191 232 5131; Hauplands Farm, Ardrossan KA22 8PL Tel: 01294 829533 — MB BCh 1989 Witwatersrand; FRCS Glas. 1995. (Witwatersrand) Specialist Regist. (Plastic Surg.) Roy. Vict. Infirm. Newc. Prev: Ho. Phys. Perth Roy. Infirm; SHO (Plastic Surg.); W. Norwich Hosp.

***STRICKLAND, Andrew David** Springfield, Yarm Way, Leatherhead KT22 8RQ — BM BS 1995 Nottm.

STRICKLAND, Ian David Kingston Hospital, Kingston upon Thames KT2 7QB Tel: 020 8546 7711 Fax: 020 8547 1786; Court Cottage, 23 Catherine Road, Surbiton KT6 4HA Tel: 020 8399 7995 Fax: 020 8287 0885 Email: i_d_strickland@compuserve.com — MB Camb. 1967, BChir 1966; FRCP Lond. 1984, M 1968. (Lond. Hosp.) Cons. Phys. Kingston Hosp. Surrey. Socs: Brit. Soc. Gastroenterol. Prev: Sen. Regist. & Lect. (Med.) Lond. Hosp.; Ho. Off. (Surg.) & Ho. Phys. Lond. Hosp.

STRICKLAND, John Esse Talbot (retired) Sizergh, Le Pont Vaillant Lane, Vale, Guernsey GY6 8BN Tel: 01481 55771 — MB BS 1946 Lond.; MRCS Eng. LRCP Lond. 1939. Prev: Venereol., Special Treatm. Clinic Bd. of Health Guernsey.

STRICKLAND, Nicola Hilary Department of Imaging, Hammersmith Hospital, Imperial College School of Medicine, Du Cane Road, London W12 0NN Tel: 020 8383 4956 Fax: 020 8383 3121 Email: n.stickland@ic.ac.uk; Flat 88 Millbank Court, 24 John Islip St, London SW1P 4LQ Tel: 020 7828 9186 — BM BCh 1984 Oxf.; MA (Hons.) Oxf. 1985, BM BCh 1984; MRCP (UK) 1987; FRCR 1991; FRCP UK 2000. (Oxf.) Cons. & Sen. Lect. (Radiol.), Hammersmith Hosp., Imperial Coll. Sch. Med. Lond. Socs: Pres. Europacs Soc.; Pres. Anglo-French Med. Soc. Prev: Sen. Regist. (Radiol.) Hammersmith Hosp. Lond.; SHO (Cardiol. & Thoracic Med.) Brompton Hosp. Lond.; SHO (Med. ITU) St. Thos. Hosp. Lond.

STRICKLAND, Paul, OBE 2 Stonehill Road, E. Sheen, London SW14 8RW Tel: 020 8876 0568 Fax: 020 8876 7842; Northwood Consulting Rooms, 25B Green Lane, Northwood HA6 2XJ Tel: 0192 74 26948 — MB BS Lond. 1943; FRCP Lond. 1975, M 1952; MRCS Eng. LRCP Lond. 1943; FRCR 1975; FFR 1952; DMR Lond 1947. (King's Coll. Lond.) Med. Manager (Imaging) Mt. Vernon Hosp. N.wood. Socs: Fell. Linnean Soc. Prev: Cons. Radiother. Mt. Vernon Hosp. & Radium Inst. N.wood; Vis. Radiother. Hillingdon Hosp., Hertford Co. Hosp., Herts. & Essex Gen. Hosp. & Wexham Pk. Hosp. Slough.

STRICKLAND, Paul John Elmham Surgery, Holt Road, Elmham, Dereham NR20 5JS — MB ChB 1982 Bristol; MRCGP 1986; DCH RCP Lond. 1985; DRCOG 1984.

STRICKLAND, Paul Laurence Department of Psychiatry, Meadowbrook, Stott Lane, Salford M6 8DD Tel: 0161 772 3730 Fax: 0161 772 3715 Email: p.strickland@man.ac.uk — MB ChB 1986 Manch.; BSc (Hons.) (Physiol.) Manch. 1983, MB ChB 1986; MMedSc. Leeds 1992; MRCPsych 1990. (Manch.) Lect. Hon. Cons. Psychiat. Univ. Manch. & Salford Ment. Health Trust. Socs: Manch. Med. Soc.; Soc. Psychosomatic Research. Prev: Clin. Research Fell. (Psychiat.) Univ. Manch. Withington Hosp. Manch.; Sen. Regist. (Gen. Psychiat.) Univ. Hosp. S. Manch. & Withington Hosp.Manch.; Regist. (Gen. Psychiat.) St. Jas. Hosp. Leeds.

STRIDE, Amanda 5 Bowring Mead, Moretonhampstead, Newton Abbot TQ13 8NP Tel: 01647 440278 — MB ChB 1995 Birm.; MB ChB (Hons.) Birm. 1995. (Univ. Birm.) SHO (Gen. Med.) Roy. Devon & Exeter Hosp. (Wonford). Prev: HO. (Gen. Med.) Manor Hosps. Walsall; Ho. Off. (Orthop. & Gen. Surg.) MusGr. Pk. Hosp. Taunton.

STRIDE, Jean Gray (retired) 123 Sussex Road, Petersfield GU31 4LB Tel: 01730 264314 — MB BS Lond. 1954; DCH Eng. 1958. Prev: GP Petersfield.

STRIDE, John Stanley Charles Portobello Medical Centre, 14 Codrington Mews, London W11 2EH Tel: 020 7727 5800/2326 Fax: 020 7792 9044; 7 Stonehill Close, London SW14 8RP — MB BS 1976 Lond.; MRCS Eng. LRCP Lond. 1974; LFHom Lond. 1996; Cert. Family Plann. JCC 1980. (Char. Cross) Prev: Regist. (Psychiat. & Community Med.) P. of Wales Hosp. Sydney, Austral.; SHO (Paediat.) Wexham Pk. Hosp. Slough; Ho. Phys. Char. Cross Hosp. Lond.

***STRIDE, Jonathan David** 74 Lower Northam Road, Hedge End, Southampton SO30 4FT — MB ChB 1995 Birm.

STRIDE, Peter Charles Department of Anaesthetics, Cumberland Infirmary, Carlisle CA2 7HY — MB ChB 1980 Birm.; FFA RCS Eng. 1986. Cons. Anaesth. Cumbld. Infirm. Carlisle.

STRIESOW, Mrs Hannah Hedwig (retired) (Surgery), 138 Claremont Road, London E7 0PX Tel: 020 8472 5873 — Staatsexamen, Halle 1932. Prev: Ho. Surg. Lond. Jewish Hosp.

STRIGNER, Andrew Ernest 17 Harley Street, London W1G 9QH Tel: 020 7935 4543 Fax: 020 7436 8819 — MB BS 1952 Lond.; MFHom 1954. (Guy's) Socs: Vice-Pres. McCarrison Soc.; Fell. Roy. Soc. Med.; Med. Soc. Lond. Prev: Mem. Counc. Inst. Study & Treatm. Delinq.; Honeyman Gillespie Lect. (Mat. Med.) Roy. Lond. Homoeop. Hosp.; Asst. Phys. Paediat. & Cardiol. Out-pat. Depts. Roy. Lond. Homoeop. Hosp.

STRIGNER, Peter Bernard Tel: 01899 220383 Fax: 01899 221583; Garden Cottage, Kirkwood, Biggar ML12 6PP Tel: 01899 220731 — MB BS 1975 Lond.; MRCS Eng. LRCP Lond. 1975; MRCP (UK) 1982; DRCOG 1978. (Guy's) GP Princip./Partner Biggar Med. Pract. Socs: Regional Fell., Roy. Soc. of Med.; Scott. McCarrison Soc. Prev: Full-time Dep., Healthcall, Edin.; GP Princip./Partner Llangollen Health Centre; GP Trainer Wrexham VTS.

STRIKE, Philip Christopher 3 Woodland Grove, Pontefract WF7 7EP — MB BS 1991 Lond.; MRCP (UK) 1995.

STRINA, Piero Flat 1, The Maples, QEH Residentials, Gayton Road, King's Lynn PE30 4ET — State Exam 1990 Mainz.

***STRINATI, Mair** 3 Broomgrove Road, London SW9 9TL — MB BS 1997 Lond.

STRINGER, Bevyl Margaret The Deanery, The College, Ely CB7 4DN Tel: 01353 662432; Mid Anglia Community Health Trust, Child Health Centre, Hospital Road, Bury St Edmunds IP33 3ND Tel: 01284 775071 — MB BS Lond. 1967; MRCS Eng. LRCP Lond. 1967; DObst RCOG 1969; DCH Eng. 1971. (Roy. Free) SCMO Mid Anglia Community Health Trust. Socs: Brit. Paediat. Assn. Prev: SCMO Blackburn Hyndburn & Ribble Valley HA; Deptm. Med. Off. W. Riding CC; Clin. Med. Off. Wilts. AHA.

STRINGER, Emma Charlotte Walnut Tree Cottage, High St., Streatley, Reading RG8 9HY — MB BS 1988 Lond.

STRINGER, Jane The Health Centre, Greenside, Cleckheaton BD19 5AN Tel: 01274 872200; Toothill Cottage, Tooothill Lane, Rastrick, Brighouse HD6 2SE — MB ChB 1980 Leeds; MRCGP 1984; DRCOG 1983.

STRINGER, Joan Karen Breidden, Calcott Lane, Bicton, Shrewsbury SY3 8EX — MB BCh 1987 Wales; MRCGP 1991; Cert. Family Plann. JCC 1990; DRCOG 1990. (Welsh Nat. Sch. Med.) Prev: SHO (ENT) Shrewsbury; SHO (Psychiat.) NW Hosp. Denbigh; SHO (Cas.) Shrewsbury.

STRINGER, Jonathan The Group Practice Surgery, Chester Road, Whitby, Ellesmere Port, South Wirral CH65 6TG Tel: 0151 355 6144; 16 Liverpool Road, Chester CH2 1AE — MB ChB 1981 Liverp.; MRCS Eng. LRCP Lond. 1981.

STRINGER, Julian Roy Riverside Medical Practice, Roushill, Shrewsbury SY1 1PQ Tel: 01743 352371 Fax: 01743 340269 — MB BCh 1987 Wales; MRCGP 1991; Cert. Family Plann. JCC 1990; DRCOG 1989. Prev: Trainee GP Rossett Chesh. & Welshpool Powys; SHO (Psychiat.) NWH Denbigh; SHO (ENT) Shrewsbury.

STRINGER, Kathryn Rachael Flat 8, 130-132 Talbot Road, London W11 1JA Tel: 020 7792 9501 — BM BS 1992 Nottm.; BMedSci Nottm. 1990; MRCP (UK) 1995. Specialist Regist. (Anaesth.) N. W. Thames Region.

STRINGER

STRINGER, Mr Mark David Children's Liver & G.I. Unit, Gledhow Wing, St James's University Hospital, Leeds LS9 7TF Tel: 0113 206 6689 Fax: 01132066691 — MB BS 1980 Lond.; BSc Lond. 1977, MS 1990; FRCPCH 1998; FRCP Lond. 1996; FRCS (Paediat.) 1993; FRCS Eng. 1985; MRCP (UK) 1984. (Guy's Hosp.) Cons. Paediatric Hepatobiliary/Transpl. Surg. Leeds Teachg. Hosp. NHS Trust. Socs: Fell. Roy. Soc. Med.; Int. Pediatr. Transpl. Assn.; Brit. Assn. Paediat. Hepatol. Surgs. Prev: Lect. (Paediat. Surg.) King's Coll. Hosp. Lond.; Sen. Regist. (Paediat. Surg.) Hosp. Sick Childr. Lond.

STRINGER, Rhona (retired) Park Lodge, Brigg DN20 9LD — MRCS Eng. LRCP Lond. 1955; FRCOG 1975, M 1962; DObst RCOG 1956. Hon. Cons. O & G Scunthorpe & Goole NHS Trust. Prev: Hon. Cons. Colposcopy & Laser N.. Gen. Hosp. Sheff.

STRINGER, Romola Mary Sprint Mill, Burneside, Kendal LA8 9AQ Tel: 01539 725168 — MB BChir 1975 Camb.; DRCOG 1979.

STRINGFELLOW, Helen Frances Dept. of Hisopathology, Royal Preston Hospital, Sharoe Green Lane, Preston PR2 9HT Tel: 01772 710149 — MB ChB 1991 Manch.; BSc (Hons) 1989; MRCPath 1998. (Manch.) Cons. (Pathol.) Roy. Preston Hosp. Socs: Int. Acad. Of Pathol.; BMA; Assoc. Clin. Pathologists.

STRINGFELLOW, Michael John Shirley Avenue Surgery, 1 Shirley Avenue, Shirley, Southampton SO15 5RP Tel: 023 8077 3258/1356 Fax: 023 8070 3078; 58 Shirley Avenue, Southampton SO15 5NJ Tel: 02380 704109 — BM 1982 Soton.; MRCP (UK) 1986; MRCGP 1990. (Southampton University) GP Shirley Avenue Surg. Soton.

STRITCH, William Alan 7 Hindley Close, Fulwood, Preston PR2 9UG Tel: 01772 704272 — MB ChB Ed. 1962. Med. Off. DHSS Norcross Blackpool. Prev: SCMO ScarBoro. HA.

STRIVENS, Edward Chapel Farm, Dilham, North Walsham NR28 9PZ Tel: 01692 536483 Fax: 01692 535318 — MB BS 1993 Lond.; BSc Jordan 1992. (Char. Cross) Prev: SHO Roy. Lond. Hosp.; Ho. Surg. Norf. & Norwich Hosp.; Ho. Phys. Chelsea & W.m. Hosp. Lond.

STRIVENS, Thomas Edward Alan (retired) Chapel Farm, Dilham, North Walsham NR28 9PZ Tel: 01692 536483 Fax: 01692 535318 — MB BS 1955 Lond.; DA Eng. 1974; DObst RCOG 1964. Prev: GP Norf.

STROBEL, Professor Stephan Immunobiology Unit, Institute of Child Health &, Great Ormond Street Hospital for Children NHS Trust, 30 Guilford St., London WC1N 1EH Tel: 020 7242 9789 Fax: 020 7242 8437 — MD 1972 Frankfurt; FRCPCH 1996; PhD Ed. 1984; FRCP Lond. 1994; MRCP (UK) 1990. Vice Dean for Educat. - Train. Inst. Child Health Lond.; Prof. Paediat. & Clin. Immunol. UCL. Prev: Prof. Paediat. Univ. Frankfurt, Germany.

STRODE, Christopher Edmund (retired) 96 Kennington Road, Kennington, Oxford OX1 5PE Tel: 01865 735594 — BM BCh 1953 Oxf.; DObst RCOG 1958. Prev: Ho. Phys. Childr. Dept. United Oxf. Hosps.

STRODE, Michael (retired) Flat 6, The Red House, Warrs Hill Road, North Chailey, Lewes BN8 4JE — MB BS 1946 Lond.; MRCS Eng. LRCP Lond. 1946. Prev: Assoc. Specialist (Paediat.) Chailey Heritage Craft Sch. & Hosp. Chailey.

STRODE, Patricia Ann 148 Baslow Road, Sheffield S17 4DR; Anselm, White Edge Drive, Baslow, Bakewell DE45 1SJ — MB ChB 1980 Sheff.; DRCOG 1983.

STROMBERG, Peter 21 Woodside, Craigends, Houston, Johnstone PA6 7DD — MB ChB 1973 Glas.; BSc (Pharmacy) (1st cl. Hons.) Strathclyde 1969; MRCPath 1981; MRSC, CChem 1977; MCB 1980. Cons. Clin. Biochem. Argyll & Clyde Health Bd. Prev: Regist. & Sen. Regist. (Clin. Biochem.) Glas. Roy. Infirm.

STROMMER, Thomas Rochus Staunton Group Practice, 3-5 Bounds Green Road, Wood Green, London N22 8HE Tel: 020 8889 4311 Fax: 020 8826 9100; 30 Braydon Road, Stamford Hill, London N16 6QB Tel: 020 8802 9577 — State Exam Med. Heidelberg 1989.

STRONACH, Anita Jane 23 Brooke Avenue, Chester CH2 1HQ — MB ChB 1990 Birm.; ChB Birm. 1990.

STRONACH-HARDY, Sally 43 King's Road, Sherborne DT9 4HX — MB BS 1967 Lond.

STRONG, Alastair Martin Priory Road Surgery, Priory Road, Park South, Swindon SN3 2EZ Tel: 01793 521154 Fax: 01793 512562; 8 Magdalen Road, Wanborough, Swindon SN4 0BG Tel: 01793 790934 — MB ChB 1988 Sheff.; MRCGP 1994. (Sheff.) Prev: Trainee GP Swindon VTS.

STRONG, Alexandra McMillan Millar Craigie Lea, 6 St Andrew's Avenue, Bothwell, Glasgow G71 8DL Tel: 0141 852221 — MB ChB 1972 Glas.; MRCP (UK) 1976; FRCP Glas. 1989. (Glas.) Cons. Dermatolgist Monklands Hosp. Airdrie. Prev: Sen. Regist. (Dermat.) Roy. Infirm. Glas.

STRONG, Professor Anthony John King's College Hospital, Denmark Hill, London SE5 9RS — MB ChB 1966 Ed.; MA Oxf. 1979, BA 1963, DM 1995; FRCS Ed. 1970. (Edinburgh) Cons. Neurosurg. Guy's, King's Coll. & Maudsley Hosps.; Prof. of Neurosurg., King's Coll. Lond. Prev: Reader (Neurosurg.) Univ. Newc.; MRC Fell. Inst. Neurol. Lond.; Sen. Regist. (Neurosurg.) Nat. Hosp. Nerv. Dis. Lond.

STRONG, Clare Karola Tamale, Jenkins Lane, St Leonards, Tring HP23 6NW — MB ChB 1979 Bristol; MRCP (UK) 1985.

***STRONG, Daniel Peter** 5 Nursery Barns, Woodborough, Pewsey SN9 5PF — MB ChB 1995 Birm.

STRONG, David Alan The Deanery, 19 The Front, Middleton One Row, Darlington DL2 1AS Tel: 01325 332241 — MB BChir 1956 Camb.; MA, MB Camb. 1956, BChir 1955. (Univ. Coll. Hosp.) Prev: Med. Asst. A & E Dept. Watford Gen. Hosp.

STRONG, Emma Patricia Homoeopathy & Comp. Med. Centre, 28 Wilkinson St., Sheffield S10 2GB Tel: 0114 276 9500; Tel: 01623 860493 Fax: 01623 860493 — MB BS 1966 Calcutta; MFHom 1997. (Calcutta Med. Coll. Lond.) p/t Clin. Asst. Gen. Pract. Bilsthrope, Nottm; Private Homoeop. Pract. Socs: Fac. Homoeopath. Prev: GP Sheff.; Med. Adviser For Benefits Agency Nottm.

STRONG, Professor John Anderson, CBE (retired) 12 Lomond Road, Edinburgh EH5 3JR Tel: 0131 552 2865 — MB BCH BAO DUB. 1937; FRCGP ad eundem 1982; FRSE; MA, MD Dub. 1967, BA 1937; FRCP Lond. 1962, M 1946; FRCP Ed. 1957, M 1954; Hon. FRCP Ed. 1994; Hon. FRCPI 1980; Hon. FCPP 1981; Hon. FACP 1980. Hon. Lt.-Col. RAMC; Hon. Fell. Trinity Coll. Dub. 1982; Fell. Roy. Soc. of Edin., FRSE. Prev: Pres. Roy. Coll. Phys. Edin.

STRONG, Mr John David Eugene (retired) Golwg-y-Mynydd, Llangorse, Brecon LD3 7UG Tel: 01874 658292 — MB BChir 1951 Camb.; MB BChir Cambl. 1951; MA Camb. 1951; FRCS Eng. 1971; DO Eng. 1956. Cons. Ophth. P.ss Margt. Hosp. Swindon & Savernake Hosp. MarlBoro. Prev: Sen. Regist. (Ophth.) Roy. Vict. Infirm. Newc.

STRONG, John Edward 4 Riverside, Church Road, Holywood BT18 9DB Tel: 028 9042 3568 — MB BCh BAO 1970 Belf.; FFA RCSI 1976; DObst RCOG 1974. Cons. Anaesth. Belf. City Hosp. Prev: Regist. (Anaesth.) Ulster Hosp. Dundonald; Ho. Off. Roy. Vict. Hosp. Belf.; Regist. Lagan Valley Hosp. Lisburn.

STRONG, Mr Nicholas Patrick Department of Ophthalmology, Royal Victoria Infirmary, Newcastle upon Tyne NE1 4LP Tel: 0191 282 4736 Fax: 0191 282 5525 Email: nickstrong2@nuth.north.nhs.uk; Deneholme, Allendale Road, Hexham NE46 2DH Tel: 01434 606511 Email: n.p.strong@ncl.ac.uk — MB 1984 Camb.; PhD (Physiol.) Calif. 1981; BChir 1983; FRCS Glas. 1987; FCROphth. 1989. Cons. Roy. Vict. Infirm. Newc. u. Tyne. Prev: Sen. Regist. (Ophth.) Leicester Roy. Infirm.; Regist. (Ophth.) Moorfields Eye Hosp.; SHO (Ophth.) King Edwd. VII Hosp. Windsor.

STRONG, Patrick Martin Bolton Radiology, 57 Chorley New Road, Bolton BL1 4QR Tel: 01204 23270; Sandford, 8 Carlton Road, Heaton, Bolton BL1 5HU Tel: 01204 43591 — MB BCh 1977 Wales; FRCR 1985; DMRD Eng. 1981. Cons. Radiol. Bolton HA. Socs: Manch. Med. Soc. & Bolton Med. Soc. Prev: Sen. Regist. (Diag. Radiol.) Manch. Hosps.; Regist. (Diag. Radiol.) Manch. Hosps.; SHO (Neurosurg.) Plymouth Gen. Hosps.

STRONGE, Kenneth Alfred Newtownards Health Centre, Frederick Street, Newtownards BT23 4LS — MB BCh BAO 1978 Belf.; DRCOG Lond. 1980. GP Newtownards Health Centre.

STRONKHORST, Carolina Heleentje The Flat, Perridge House, Pilton, Shepton Mallet BA4 4EN — Artsexamen 1991 Amsterdam.

STROOBANT, John Lewisham Childrens Hospital, High St., Lewisham, London SE13 6LH Tel: 020 8333 3136 Fax: 020 8690 1963; 33 Holbrook Lane, Chislehurst BR7 6PE Email: stroo@dircom.co.uk — MB BS 1973 Sydney; FRCP Lond. 1993; FRCPCH 1997; MRCGP 1979; DRCOG 1978; DCH Eng. 1976. (Sydney) Cons. Paediat. Childr. Hosp. Lond. Prev: Staff Neonat. Roy. Hosp. for Wom., Sydney; Cons. Paediat. Whipps Cross Hosp. Lond.; Research Fell. Hosp. Sick Childr. Lond.

STROSS, Josefine (retired) Parkwood House, Elsworthy Road, London NW3 Tel: 020 7586 5949 — LRCP LRCS 1940 Ed.; LRCP LRCS Ed. LRFPS Glas. 1940; MD Vienna 1925. Prev: Paediatr. The Hampstead Child Ther. Course & Clinic.

STROSS, William Paul Department of Haematology, St Richard's Hospital, Chichester PO19 4SE Tel: 01243 831651 Fax: 01243 831413 Email: paul.stross@rws-tr.ienws.nhs.uk; 12 The Avenue, Chichester PO19 4PU Tel: 01243 530245 Email: paul.stross@btinternet.com — MB ChB 1981 Bristol; MRCP (UK) 1984; MRCPath 1992; FRCP 1999. Cons. Haemat. St. Richard's Hosp. Chichester; Cons. Haemotologist King Edwd. VII Hosp. Midhurst. Prev: Sen. Regist. (Haemat.) John Radcliffe Hosp. Oxf.; Regist. (Haemat.) Sheff. HA; SHO (Med.) S. W.. RHA.

***STROUD, Catherine Rachel** 5 Holmewood Drive, Rowlands Gill NE39 1EL — MB ChB 1996 Sheff.

STROUD, Sir Charles Eric 84 Copse Hill, Wimbledon, London SW20 0EF — MB BCh 1945 Wales; BSc Wales 1945, MB BCh (Distinc. Pub. Health &; For. Med., Path. & Bact., Surg, Obst. & Gyn.) 1948; FRCP Lond. 1968, M 1955; DCH Eng. 1955. (Cardiff) Hon. Med. Dir. Childr. NAtionwide Med. Research Fund; Hans Sloane Fell. Overseas Off. RCP; Emerit. Prof. Child Health King's Coll. Univ. Lond. Socs: Brit. Paediat. Assn.; (ex-Pres.) Club de Pediatrie Sociale d'Europe. Prev: Prof. Child Health King's Coll. Sch. Med. & Dent.; Asst. to Dir., Dept. Paediat. Guy's Hosp. Lond.; Hon. Lect. Univ. E. Africa, Kampala & Med. Off. Uganda Govt.

STROUD, David Stuart 12 Walnut Grove, Worlington, Bury St Edmunds IP28 8SF — MB ChB 1995 Sheff.

***STROUD, Joanna Elizabeth** 4 Oakfield Cr, Tonteg, Pontypridd CF38 1NG — MB BCh 1997 Wales.

STROUD, Michael Adrian, OBE Institute of Human Nutrition, Southampton General Hospital, Tremona Road, Southampton SO16 6YD Tel: 02380 796317 Fax: 02380 796317 Email: mikestr@globalnet.co.uk; Mole House, Langley, Liss GU33 7JP — MB BS 1979 Lond.; BSc Lond. 1976, MD 1996; MRCP (UK) 1984; MD 1996; FRCP Lond. 1994; FRCP (Ed) 1994. Sen. Lect. (Med. Gastro. Nutrit.); Hon. Cons. Phys. Socs: BSG. Prev: Chief Scientist (Physiol.) DRA Centre for Human Sci.s FarnBoro. Hants.; Sen. Regist. (Gastroenterol.) & Research Fell. (Nutrit.) Soton. Gen. Hosp.

STROUD, Ronald Alan Kirkstead, Green Lane, Pangbourne, Reading RG8 7BG Tel: 0118 984 2931 — MB BS 1955 Lond.; MB BS (Hons. Midw. & Gyn., & Applied Pharmacol. & Therap.) Lond. 1955; DObst RCOG 1961. (St. Bart.) Socs: Reading Path. Soc. Prev: GP Pangbourne; Ho. Surg. & Ho. Phys. St. Bart. Hosp.; Ho. Surg. Marston Green Matern. Hosp. & Hosp. Wom. Birm.

STROUDLEY, Jessica Lisa 95 Langthorne Street, Fulham, London SW6 6JU — MB BCh 1982 Wales; FRCR 1994. Cons. Radiol., Ealing Hosp. Lond.

STROUHAL, Peter David Hedgerow Cottage, Chapel Lane, Wythall, Birmingham B47 6JX — MB BS 1994 Lond.; BSc (Hons.) Lond. 1991; FRCR Pt 1 Lond. 1998. (Univ. Coll. Lond. Med. Sch.) Specialist Regist. (Radiol.) W. Midls. Rotat. (City Hosp., Birm.). Prev: SHO (Gen. Med.) Barnet Gen. Hosp.; SHO (Transpl. Med.) Harefield Hosp.; SHO (A & E) & Ho. Off. (Gen. Med.) Whittington Hosp. Lond.

***STROUTHIDIS, Nicholas Gabriel** 14 Clavering Walk, Cooden, Bexhill-on-Sea TN39 4TN — MB BS 1997 Lond.

STROUTHIDIS, Theodore Department of Medicine for the Elderly, Conquest Hospital, St Leonards-on-Sea TN37 7RD Tel: 01424 755255 Fax: 01424 846183 — MB ChB 1962 Alexandria; LMSSA Lond. 1970; FRCP Lond. 1982, M 1969. (Alexandria) Cons. Phys. (Geriat.) Hastings & Rother NHS Trust; Cons. Med. Adviser Internat. Med. Rescue Lond. Socs: BMA; Brit. Geriat. Soc. Prev: Sen. Regist. (Geriat.) Guy's Hosp. Lond.; Ho. Phys. St. Helier Hosp. Carshalton.

STROUTHOS, Marios 42 Cissbury Ring N., Woodside Park, London N12 7AH Tel: 020 8445 4824 Email: marios@the.forthnet.gr — MB BS 1987 Lond.; MRCPsych 1992; MSC (Ment. Health Sc.) 1994. (University of London & St Mary's Hospital Medical School) Socs: RCPsych.

STROVER, Alister Roger Matthew Cumberland Infirmary, Newton Road, Carlisle CA2 7HY Tel: 01228 523444; Bank House, Kirkoswald, Penrith CA10 1DQ Tel: 01768 898658 — MB BS 1994 Lond. SHO (Paediat.). Socs: Med. Protec. Soc.; BMA; Protec. Soc. Prev: GP Regist. St Pauls Sq. Carlisle; SHO (Psychiat.) Argyll & Bute Hosp.; 1st Year Ho. Surg. Wellington Hosp., New Zealand.

STROVER, Mr Angus Everett Droitwich Knee Clinic, St. Andrews Road, Droitwich WR9 8YX Tel: 01905 794858 Fax: 01905 795916 Email: strovknee@aol.com; 10 Hengrave Road, Honor Oak, London SE23 3NW Tel: 020 8699 5778 Fax: 020 8291 5139 — MB ChB 1962 Cape Town; FRCS Ed. 1979. Cons. Knee Clinic Droitwich Private Hosp.; Edr. Isokinetics & Exercise Sci. Socs: Brit. Assn. Surg. Knee; Internat. Soc. Arthroscopy, Knee Surg. & Orthop. Med. (ISAKOS). Prev: Cons. Trauma & Orthop. Surg. Alexandra Hosp. Redditch.

STROVER, Sheila Margaret ftmg Associates LTD, Old Cornstore, Rosemundy, St Agnes TR5 0LD Tel: 01872 553102 Fax: 01872 554060 Email: ashgrove@kneeguru.co.uk — MB BCh Witwatersrand 1974; BSc (Hons.) Witwatersrand 1971; MBA Warwick 1994. (Witwatersrand) Med. Managem. Cons. Ftmg Assoc. Ltd. Prev: Dir. United Surg. Servs. Ltd.; Dir. Droitwich Knee Clinic Ltd.; Dir. ftmg Assocs. Ltd.

STROWBRIDGE, Nicholas Foster, Lt.-Col. RAMC Medical Reception Station, Ypres Road, Colchester CO7 7NL Tel: 01206 782947 Email: mfscolchester@army.mod.uk.net; Weeping Ash Cottage, Ardleigh Road, Great Bromley, Colchester CO7 7TL — MB BS 1977 Lond.; DFFP 1995; DA (UK) 1980. (St. Thos.) Sen. Med. Off. M.R.S. Colchester. Prev: SHO (Anaesth.) Guy's Hosp. Lond.

STROWGER, Timothy Benjamin Clive 16 Westholme, Letchworth SG6 4JB — MB BS 1994 Lond.

STRUBBE, Patricia Anna Maria Josepha St. Elizabeth Hospice, 565 Foxhall Road, Ipswich IP3 8LX Tel: 01473 727776 Fax: 01473 274717 Email: doctors@gtelizabethhospice.org.uk; Regency House, Lower St, Great Bealings, Woodbridge IP13 6NL Tel: 01473 735325 Email: patricia.wyard@btinternet.com — MD 1983 Ghent; MRCGP 1994; Dip. Palliat. Med. Wales 1995. (State University Ghent Belgium) p/t Dep. Med. Dir. St. Eliz. Hospice Ipswich; Hon. Cons. Palliat. Med. Ipswich Hosp. NHS Trust. Prev: GP Suff.

STRUBE, Allen George (retired) 33 Goffs Park Road, Crawley RH11 8AX Tel: 01293 612900 — MB 1956 Camb.; BChir 1955; MRCP Lond. 1968; DObst RCOG 1961. Prev: GP Audit Facilitator W. Sussex.

STRUBE, Gillian 33 Goffs Park Road, Crawley RH11 8AX Tel: 01293 612900 — MB BS Lond. 1958; MRCS Eng. LRCP Lond. 1958; DCH Eng. 1960. (Guy's) Asst. GP Burgess Hill W. Sussex; Med. Expert Witness. Prev: Med. Adviser W. Sussex Family Health Servs. Auth. Chichester; GP Crawley; Ho. Phys. Lewisham Hosp. & Evelina Childr. Hosp. of Guy's Hosp. Lond.

STRUBE, Patrick John South Bucks Trust, Wycombe Hospital, Queen Alexandra Rd, High Wycombe HP11 2TT — MB ChB 1975 Leeds; FRCA. 1982; DRCOG 1978. Cons. Anaesth. & Intens. Care S. Bucks. NHS Trust Hosps. Prev: Sen. Regist. Middlx. Hosp., Brompton Hosp. & N.wick Pk. Hosp.; Sen. Med. Off. King Edwd. VIII Hosp. Durban S. Africa.

STRUDLEY, Martin Robert Upper Gordon Road Surgery, 37 Upper Gordon Road, Camberley GU15 2HJ Tel: 01276 26424 Fax: 01276 63486 — MB BS 1980 Lond.; MRCP (UK) 1984; DCH RCP Lond. 1984.

STRUDWICK, Richard Harold Kingston Lodge, 18 Avenue Road, Leamington Spa CV31 3PQ Tel: 01926 831139 — MB ChB 1944 Birm.; MFPHM RCP (UK) 1989; MFCM 1973; DPH Lond. 1958; DTM & H (Medal Trop. Med.) Liverp. 1946. (Birm.) Chief Med. Off. Div. of Family Health WHO Geneva, Switz. Socs: Fell. Roy. Soc. Trop. Med. & Hyg. Prev: Asst. Dir. Health Servs. S.E. Asia Region WHO; WHO Pub. Health Adviser Afghanistan & Ghana.

***STRUGNELL, Madeline Jane** 4 The Orchard, Badswell Lane, Appleton, Abingdon OX13 5LF — BM 1995 Soton.

STRUIK, Siske Sybrich 94 Avondale Road, Liverpool L15 3HF — Artsexamen 1993 Utrecht; Artsexamen Utrect 1993.

STRUNIN, Professor Leo Anaesthetics Unit, The Royal London Hospital, Whitechapel, London E1 1BB Tel: 020 7377 7119 Fax: 020 7377 7126 — MB BS 1960 Durh.; MD Newc. 1974; FRCPC 1980; FFA RCS Eng. 1964. BOC Prof. Anaesth. St. Bart. & Roy. Lond. Hosp. Sch. Med. & Dent.; Pres. Roy. Coll. Anaesth. Prev: Prof. & Head Dept. Anaesth. Univ. Calgary, Canada.

STRUTHERS, Agnes Dykes Southside Road Surgery, 43 Southside Road, Inverness IV2 4XA Tel: 01463 710222 Fax: 01463 714072 — MB ChB 1980 Glas.; MRCGP 1984; DRCOG 1982.

STRUTHERS, Professor Allan David Department Clinical Pharmacology and Therapeutics, Ninewells Hospital, Dundee

STRUTHERS

DD1 9SY; Bech na Mara, 5 Riverview, Newport-on-Tay DD6 8QX — MB ChB 1977 Glas.; MB ChB (Hons.) Glas. 1977; BSc (Hons.) Glas. 1973, MD 1984; FRCP Lond. 1992; FRCP Glas. 1990; FCRP Ed. 1990; MRCP (UK) 1980; FESC 1994; DCH Glas. 1979. Prof. & Cons. Phys. Ninewells Hosp. Med. Sch. Dundee. Prev: Sen. Regist. (Med.) Roy. Postgrad. Med. Sch. & Qu. Charlotte's Matern. Hosp. Lond.; Regist. (Med.) Stobhill Hosp. Glas.; SHO (Child Health) Roy. Hosp. Sick Childr. Glas.

STRUTHERS, Charles Alexander Clouds Hill House, St. George, Bristol BS6 7LD — MB ChB 1977 Bristol.

STRUTHERS, Gavin Douglas North Ormesby Health Centre, Elizabeth Terrace, North Ormesby, Middlesbrough TS3 6EN Tel: 01642 247196; 33 Fearnhead, Marton, Middlesbrough TS8 9XN — MB ChB 1978 Glas.; BSc Glas. 1975; MRCGP 1983; DRCOG 1981. Socs: Soc. Occupat. Med.

STRUTHERS, George Robert Bromson Hall, Ashorne, Warwick CV35 9AD Tel: 01926 651046 Email: gstruthers@doctors.org.uk; 5 Davenport Road, Earlsdon, Coventry CV5 6QA Tel: 02476 672997 — MB 1974 Camb.; FRCP Lond. 1994; MRCP (UK) 1977. (King's Coll. Hosp.) Cons. Rheum. Univ. Hosp.s of Coventry and Warks. NHS Trust. Socs: Fell. Roy. Soc. Med.; Midl. Rheum. Soc.; Brit. Soc. Rheum. Mem. of Counc. 2000. Prev: ARC Michael Mason Research Fell. & Hon. Lect. St. Geo. Hosp. Kogarah & Univ. New S. Wales Sydney; Sen. Regist. (Med. Rheum.) Qu. Eliz. Hosp. Birm.; Regist. (Med.) MusGr. Pk. Hosp. Taunton.

STRUTHERS, Ian Robertson Struthers and Partners, 436 Mosspark Boulevard, Glasgow G52 1HX Tel: 0141 882 5494 Fax: 0141 883 1015; 14 Falkland Street, Glasgow G12 9PR — MB ChB 1976 Glas.; BSc Glas. 1974; MRCP (UK) 1979; MRCGP 1983; DRCOG 1982.

STRUTHERS, James Edgar (retired) Mayfield, Pennal, Machynlleth SY20 9DP Tel: 01654 791268 — MB ChB 1935 Glas.; FFPHM 1989; FFCM 1974; FRCGP 1971. Prev: PMO Dept. Health & Social Security.

STRUTHERS, James Keith 2 Campden Way, Handforth, Wilmslow SK9 3JA — MB ChB 1988 Witwatersrand; MRCPath 1993.

STRUTHERS, Jean Orr (retired) 17 Douglas Avenue, Langbank, Port Glasgow PA14 6PE Tel: 01475 540661 — MB ChB Glas. 1954; MD Glas. 1967; FRCOG 1973, M 1958. Prev: Cons. O & G Roy. Alexandra Hosp. Paisley.

STRUTHERS, John Langford (retired) 27 Kellett Road, Southampton SO15 7PS Tel: 01703 772226 — MB BChir 1955 Camb. Prev: GP Soton.

STRUTHERS, Linda Jane 97 Nethercraigs Road, Paisley PA2 8SG — MB ChB 1990 Dundee. (Univ. Dundee) Specialist Regist. (Paediat.) Whipps Cross Hosp. Lond. Prev: SHO (Paediat.) Qu. Eliz. Hosp. Childr. Lond.; SHO (Paediat.) St. Mary's Hosp. Lond. & Qu. Med. Centre Nottm.

STRUTHERS, Mark William Albion House Surgery, 22 Heneage Road, Grimsby DN32 9ES Tel: 01472 345411; Cordeaux House, 15 Cooks Lane, Great Coates, Grimsby DN37 9NW — MB ChB 1981 Sheff.; DRCOG 1985.

STRUTHERS, Richard Alexander 20 Gamekeepers Park, Edinburgh EH4 6PA — MB ChB 1992 Bristol.

STRUTHERS, Simon Langford 2 Seamans Cottage, Seamans Lane, Minstead, Lyndhurst SO43 7FU — MB ChB 1992 Leic.

STRUTT, Kristina Leila 10 Buxton Old Road, Macclesfield SK11 7EL — MB BS 1984 Lond.; MA Camb. 1985; MRCP (UK) 1988; MFPHM 1993; Dip. Pharm. Med. 1991. (The Middlesex Hospital Medical School) Med. Adviser (Oncol.) Zeneca Pharmaceut. Prev: Regist. (Med.) Roy. Berks. Hosp. Reading.

STRUTT, Matthew David 73 Pier Avenue, Herne Bay CT6 8PG Tel: 01227 367206 — MB BS 1994 Lond.; MSc Lond. 1991, BSc 1989. (St. Bartholomew's) Regist. Virol./Microbiol. Dulwich/Kings Coll. Hosp. Prev: Regist. Med. Microbiol. Greenwich Dist. Hosp.

STRUTTE, Lesley Janet Fraser Brookside Farmhouse, Pitney, Langport TA10 9AQ Tel: 01458 250126 Fax: 01458 250126 — MB BS Lond. 1970; MFHom 1989; DObst RCOG 1973. (St. Geo.)

STRYCHARCZYK, Kazimierz Julian Crouch End Health Centre, 45 Middle Lane, Crouch End, London N8 8PH — MB BS 1986 Lond.; BSc Lond. 1983, MB BS 1986; MRCGP 1991; DRCOG 1990.

STRYJAKIEWICZ, Eugene Glenn 4 Colston Crescent, Wilford Hill, West Bridgford, Nottingham NG2 7FT — MB ChB 1980 Sheff.

STRYMOWICZ, Christine Green Woods, 3 Essenden Road, Sanderstead, South Croydon CR2 0BW Tel: 020 8657 0141 — LRCP LRCS Ed. LRCPS Glas. 1971; MB Wroclaw 1963. (Med. Acad. Wroclaw) Regist. St. Thos. Hosp. Lond. Socs: BMA.

STRZELECKA, Maria Jozefa Richmond Road Medical Centre, 95 Richmond Road, Kingston upon Thames KT2 5BT Tel: 020 8546 1961 Fax: 020 8974 9008; 107 Coombe Lane, London SW20 0BD — MB BCh BAO Dub. 1961; MA Dub. 1961. Socs: Trinity Coll. Dub. Alumni Assn.; Kingston Hosp. Postgrad. Med. Assn.; Polish Med. Assn.

STUART, Alan Graham Childrens Heart Unit, Bristol Children's Hospital, St Michaels Hill, Bristol BS2 8BJ Tel: 0117 928 3324 Fax: 0117 928 3341 Email: graham.stuart@ubht.nhs.uk — MB ChB 1982 Dundee; MRCP (UK) 1985; FRCPCH 1997; FRCP Lond. 1998. (Univ. Dundee) Cons. Cardiol. (Congen. Heart Dis.) United Bristol Combined Hosp. Trust; Hon. Sen. Lect. (Med.) Bristol Univ. Socs: Brit. Paediat. Assn.; Brit. Paediat. Cardiac Assn.; Brit. Cardiac. Soc. Prev: Cons. (Congen. Heart Dis.) Univ. Hosp. of Wales; Sen. Regist. (Cardiol. & Paediat.) W. Midl. RHA; Hon. Sen. Regist. & Research Fell. (Child Health) Univ. Newc. u. Tyne.

STUART, Alexander Barclay Bridge of Allan Health Centre, Fountain Road, Bridge of Allan, Stirling FK9 4EU Tel: 01786 833210; 1 Allanwater Gardens, Bridge of Allan, Stirling FK9 4DW Tel: 01786 833210 — MB BChir 1980 Camb.; BSc (Hons.) St. And. 1974; DRCOG 1983. Med. Off. i/c H.M. Inst. Cornton Vale Stirling.

STUART, Andrew Brian Douglas The Park End Surgery, 3 Park End, South Hill Park, London NW3 2SE Tel: 020 7435 7282 — MB BS 1991 Lond.; MRCGP 1995; DRCOG 1994. (Univ. Coll. Middlx. Hosps.) GP. Prev: Hon. Sen. Lect. Acad. Fell. GP Regist.

STUART, Angus Erskine (retired) Ardshiel, Isle Ornsay, Isle of Skye IV43 8QS — MB ChB 1948 Glas.; FRS Ed. 1970, PhD 1959; FRCP Ed. 1970, M 1959. Prev: Prof. (Path.) Univ. Newc.

STUART, Anthony Leslie Gordon 2 Regents Court, Balcombe Road, Poole BH13 6DY Tel: 0202 757081 — MRCS Eng. LRCP Lond. 1943. (St. Mary's) Prev: Med. Off. Lond. Airport (Heathrow).

STUART, Brenda Margaret Mid Sussex NHS Trust, The Princess Royal Hospital, Haywards Heath RH16 4EX Tel: 01444 441881 — MB BS 1988 Lond.; MRCP (UK) 1992. (St Georges Hospital Medical School) Cons. (Rheum.) Mid Sussex NHS Trust, P.ss Roy. Hosp., Haywards Heath. Prev: Sen. Regist. (Rheum.) Poole, Bournemouth & ChristCh. Hosps.; Regist. Soton. Gen. Hosp.; Regist. (Med.) Roy. S. Hants. Hosp. & Salisbury Dist. Gen. Hosp.

STUART, Brian Sansom Craigievar, Ford Road, Newton Mearns, Glasgow G77 5AB Tel: 0141 639 5300 — MB ChB 1969 Aberd.; MPhil 1998 Glas.; FFA RCS Eng. 1974. (Aberd.) Cons. (Anaesth.) Vict. Infirm. Glas. Prev: Sen. Regist. Dept. Anaesth. W.. Infirm. Glas.; Research Fell. Dept. Surg. W.. Infirm. Glas.; Regist. (Anaesth.) Vict. Infirm. Glas.

STUART, Catriona Anne The White House, 11 Claremont Drive, Bridge of Allan, Stirling FK9 4EE — MB BS 1977 Lond.

STUART, Mr David Wallington (retired) St. Mary's, 1 Poolfield Avenue, Keele Road, Newcastle ST5 Tel: 01782 619260 — MB BS 1945 Lond.; FRCS Eng. 1959; FRCS Ed. 1959; DLO Eng. 1953. Cons. ENT Surg. N. Staffs. Roy. Infirm. Stoke-on-Trent; Mem. Midl. Inst. Otol.; Mem. N. Staffs. Med. Inst. Prev: Wing Cdr. RAF Med. Br., ENT Specialist.

STUART, Donald William (retired) Threeways, Canny Hill, Newby Bridge, Ulverston LA12 8NY Tel: 01448 31505 — MRCS Eng. LRCP Lond. 1927. Prev: Ho. Surg. Qu.'s Hosp. Childr. Hackney.

STUART, Douglas (retired) 491 Nuthall Road, Nottingham NG8 5DD Tel: 0115 978 3156 — MB ChB 1954 Aberd. Prev: Gen. Practitioner Nottm.

STUART, Elizabeth Morrice Dounby Surgery, Dounby, Orkney KW17 2HT; Kewing, Rendall, Orkney KW17 2HA — MB ChB 1979 Aberd.; D.Occ.Med. RCP Lond. 1995. Occupat. Health Phys. Orkney HB. Socs: BMA (Sec. Orkney Div.).

***STUART, Elsa Anita** 61 Hazel Crescent, Kidlington OX5 1EJ — MB ChB 1998 Bristol.

STUART, Emma Louise Southview House, Catherine Hill, Olveston, Bristol BS35 4EN; Polepit Cottage, Fearn Close, East Horsley, Leatherhead KT24 6AJ — BM BCh 1991 Oxf.; MA Camb. 1992. Ho. Off. Rotat. (Surg.) Mt. Isa Base Hosp. Qu.sland.

***STUART, Fiona Elizabeth** Oak Cottage, London Road, Woore, Crewe CW3 9RQ — MB ChB 1996 Birm.

STUART

STUART, Fiona Margaret Ottershaw Surgery, 3 Bousley Rise, Ottershaw, Chertsey KT16 0JX Tel: 01932 875001 Fax: 01932 873855; 12 Wilson Drive, Ottershaw, Chertsey KT16 0NT — MB BS 1987 Lond.; DRCOG 1991.

STUART, Forbes MacKenzie 23 Keirsbearth Court, Kingseat, Dunfermline — MB ChB 1974 Aberd.; MRCGP 1978; DRCOG 1977.

STUART, Gillian 34 West Stonebridge, Orton Malborne, Peterborough PE2 5LU; 34 West Stonebridge, Orton Malborne, Peterborough PE2 5LU — MB ChB 1964 Birm.; BSc. Birm. 1961, MB ChB 1964; MRCP Lond. 1968; DFFP 1993. (Birm.)

STUART, Gillian Kathleen (retired) 2 The Old Orchard, Ebrington, Chipping Campden GL55 6PA — MB BS 1960 Durh.

STUART, Gordon William Rosemary, Royal Esplanade, Ramsgate CT11 0 Tel: 01843 591450 — M.B., Ch.B. Aberd. 1944. (Aberd.) Mem. (Ex. Chairm.) Kent Family Pract. Comm. (FCP) & Kent Local Med. Prev: R.A.M.C.; Ho. Surg. & Res. Anaesth. King Geo. Hosp. Ilford.

***STUART, Heather Catherine** 34 West Stonebridge, Orton Malborne, Peterborough PE2 5LU — BM BS 1997 Nottm.

STUART, Helen Mary Runwell Hospital, Wickford SS11 9QE Tel: 01268 735555 — MB BS 1984 Lond.; BSc Lond. 1981, MB BS 1984; MRCPsych 1989. Cons. Psychiat. Runwell Hosp. Prev: SHO (A & E) St. Thos. Hosp. Lond.; Ho. Surg. Qu. Alexandra Hosp. Portsmouth; Ho. Off. (Med.) St. Thos. Hosp. Lond.

STUART, Ian (retired) Lagavaigh, 14 Brothock Meadows, Letham Grange, Arbroath DD11 4QN Tel: 01241 890488 — MB ChB 1955 Aberd.; DObst RCOG 1957.

STUART, Ian Michael Giffard Doctors Surgery, 68 Giffard Drive, Cove, Farnborough GU14 8QB Tel: 01252 541282 Fax: 01252 372159 — MB ChB 1981 Leeds; MRCGP 1987; DRCOG 1984. Chair., Black Water Valley Doctors CoOperat.; Bd. Mem., Blackwater Valley PCG.

STUART, Ian Mitchell (retired) Snushalls, 135 Old London Road, Hastings TN35 5LY Tel: 01424 420768 — MB BS 1957 Lond.; DObst RCOG 1963.

STUART, Ian Peter Derby City General Hospital, Uttoxeter Road, Derby DE22 3NE — MB BS 1985 Lond.; MA Camb. 1986; MRCOG 1990. Sen. Regist. (O & G) Derby City Gen. Hosp. Prev: Regist. P.ss Anne Hosp. Soton.; Regist. Groote Schuur Hosp. Cape Town.

STUART, Irvine Renfrew Blythe Practice, 1500 Warwick Road, Knowle, Solihull B93 9LE Tel: 01564 779280 Fax: 01564 772010 Email: irvinestuart@blythepractice.co.uk — MB BS 1974 Newc.; BDS Newc. 1969; MRCGP 1978; DRCOG 1976. (Newc.) Course Organiser Solihull VTS.

STUART, Jack Macfarlane (retired) Blythways, Coleshill, Birmingham B46 1AH Tel: 01675 463301 — MB ChB 1942 Birm.; MRCGP 1952; DCH Eng. 1947; DObst RCOG 1950. Prev: GP Coleshill.

STUART, Jacqueline Mary Elizabeth Teasdale Cottage, Slaley, Hexham NE47 1TT — MB BS 1986 Newc.; MRCGP 1990.

STUART, James Douglas South Queensferry Group Practice, The Health Centre, Rosebery Avenue, South Queensferry EH30 9HA Tel: 0131 331 1396 Fax: 0131 331 5783; 1 Essex Road, Edinburgh EH4 6LF Tel: 0131 339 0894 — MB ChB 1971 Ed.; BSc (Med. Sci.) Ed. 1968; MRCGP 1975; Dip. Occ. Med. 1996; DObst RCOG 1975. Prev: Ho. Phys. Roy. Infirm. Edin.; Ho. Surg. Roy. Hosp. Sick Childr. Edin.; SHO (Neurol.) N.. Gen. Hosp. Edin.

STUART, James MacNaughton CDSC (SW), Public Health Laboratory, Gloucestershire Royal Hospital, Gloucester GL1 3NN Tel: 01452 413080 Fax: 01452 412946 Email: jstuart@phls.org.uk; Tankard Spring House, High St, Chalford, Stroud GL6 8DW — MB 1975 Cantab.; MA Cantab BChir 1974; MFCM 1988; T(PHM) 1991; DCH RCP Lond. 1979; DRCOG 1979. (Camb. Middlx. Hosp.) Cons. Epidemiol. PHLS, Gloucester. Socs: Fell. Fac. of Pub. Health Med.; Internat. Epidemiol. Assn. Prev: Princip. Med. Off. (Epidemiol.) DoH, Kwazulu.; Cons. Pub. Health Med. Glos. HA; Med. Supt. Ekombe Hosp., Kwazulu.

STUART, Professor John (retired) 12 Brueton Avenue, Solihull B91 3EN Tel: 0121 705 1443 — MD 1971 Ed.; MB ChB 1960; FRCP Ed. 1972, M 1965; FRCPath 1979, M 1972. Prof. Haemat. Univ. Birm. Prev: Cons. Haemat. Qu. Eliz. Hosp. Birm.

STUART, John Paton (retired) 3 Clifton House, Queen Parade, Harrogate HG1 5PW Tel: 01423 521025 — MB ChB Leeds 1946, DPH 1967; MFCM 1972. Prev: Div. Med. Off. W. Riding CC.

STUART, Joyce Cameron Department of Anaesthetics, Victoria Hospital, Kirkcaldy KY2 5AH Tel: 01592 643355; 19 Mayfield Road, Ulverston LA12 0DU Tel: 01229 584154 Email: david@allan-ulv.freeserve.co.uk — MB ChB 1986 Aberd.; MPhil 2000 Medical Law & Ethics, University of Glasgow; FRCA 1990. (Aberd.) p/t Cons. (Anaesth.) Vict. Hosp. Kirkcaldy. Prev: Sen. Regist. (Anaesth.) Edin. Roy. Infirm.; Regist. (Anaesth.) Vict. Infirm. Glas.; SHO (Anaesth.) Ninewells Hosp. Dundee.

STUART, Kenneth Crichton (retired) 2 Waterside Close, Darley Abbey, Derby DE22 1JT Tel: 01332 550206 Fax: 01332 550206 — MB ChB 1956 Ed.; MRCGP 1966; DObst RCOG 1962.

STUART, Sir Kenneth Lamonte (retired) The Barbados High Commission, 1 Great Russell St., London WC1B 3JY Tel: 020 7631 4975 Fax: 020 7323 6872 — MB BCh BAO 1948 Belf.; DSc (Hon.) Belf. 1986, MD 1952; FRCP Lond. 1965, M 1952; FRCP Ed. 1960, M 1952; FFPHM RCP (UK) 1995; FFPM RCP (UK) 1991; FACP 1977. Hon. Med. & Scientif. Adviser Barbados High Commiss. Lond.; Gresham Prof. Physic Gresham Coll. Lond.; Mem. Counc. King's Coll. Lond. Prev: Prof. & Head, Dept. Med. & Dean Med. Fac. Univ. W. Indies, Jamaica.

STUART, Lynda Maria 3 The Garth, Cobham KT11 2DZ — MB BS 1993 Lond.

STUART, Margaret Anne Evelyn (retired) Lych Gate, Bakeham Lane, Englefield Green, Egham TW20 9TZ Tel: 01784 432724 — MRCS Eng. LRCP Lond. 1952; DCH Eng. 1971. Clin. Asst. (Paediat.) Ashford Hosp. Middlx. Prev: Ho. Phys. Mile End Hosp.

STUART, Mary Helen The Surgery, 18 Hove Park Villas, Hove BN3 6HG Tel: 01273 776245 Fax: 01273 324202 — MB ChB 1976 Aberd.; BSc Aberd. 1971, MB ChB 1976; DCH Eng. 1980; DRCOG 1979. GP Princip. Hove.

STUART, Michael Hillier Queensway Surgery, 75 Queensway, Southend-on-Sea SS1 2AB Tel: 01702 463333 Fax: 01702 603026; Fair Havens Hospice, 126 Chalkwell Avenue, Westcliff on Sea SS0 8HN Tel: 01702 344879 — MB ChB 1962 Leeds. (Leeds) Hon. Med. Dir. Fair Havens Hospice W.cliff on Sea. Socs: Founder Mem. Assn. Palliat. Med.; Assur. Med. Soc. Prev: Regist. (ENT) S.end Gen. Hosp.; Resid. Aural Off. Gen. Infirm. Leeds; SHO (Accid. & Orthop.) Roy. Halifax Infirm.

STUART, Nancy (retired) 15 Oak Tree Lodge, Harlow Manor Park, Harrogate HG2 0HH — MB ChB Manch. 1950. Prev: Clin. Med. Off. (Community Child Health) Leeds E. Dist. HA (T).

STUART, Nicholas Simon Andrew Department of Oncology, Ysbyty Gwynedd, Penrhosgarnedd, Bangor LL57 2PW Tel: 01248 384150 Fax: 01248 384505 Email: nick.stuart@nww_tr.wales.nhs.uk; Coedlan, Llangoed, Beaumaris LL58 8NR Tel: 01248 490062 — BM 1979 Soton.; DM Soton. 1991; MRCP (UK) 1983; T(M) 1991; FRCP 1998. Cons. Med. Oncol. Ysbyty Gwynedd; Hon. Cons. Med. Oncol. Clatterbridge Centre for Oncol. Wirral; Hon. Sen. Lect. Univ. Bangor. Prev: ICRF Clin. Research Fell. Ch.ill Hosp. Oxf.; Sen. Regist. Qu. Eliz. Hosp. Birm.; Regist. Burton-on-Trent Hosps.

STUART, Olivia Mary Christmas Cottage, Little Longstone, Bakewell DE45 1NN — MB ChB 1993 Birm.

STUART, Patricia Joy 4 Marine Crescent, Great Yarmouth NR30 4ER Tel: 01493 855672 — MB ChB 1955 Leeds; MRCGP 1968.

STUART, Mr Paul Robert Freeman Hospital, Freeman Road, Newcastle upon Tyne NE7 7DN Tel: 0191 284 3111 Email: prstuart@compuserve.com — MB BS 1983 Newc.; FRCS Eng. 1987; FRCS Ed. 1987. Cons. Orthop. (Hand & Upper Limb Surg.) Freeman Hosp. Newc. u. Tyne; Hon. Clin. Lect. Univ. Newc. Socs: Brit. Soc. Surg. Hand; Brit. Orthop. Assn.; NE Medico-Legal Soc. Prev: Hand Fell. Trent RHA; Research Fell. Mayo Clinic Rochester, Minnesota, USA; Sen. Regist. (Orthop.) N.. RHA.

STUART, Pauline Cameron 6 Leslie Place, 2FR, Edinburgh EH4 1NQ — MB ChB 1987 Ed.

STUART, Peter, ERD Pejong, 74 Longlands Road, Carlisle CA3 9AE Tel: 01228 525718 — MB ChB Glas. 1949; FFA RCS Eng. 1955; DA Eng. 1954. (Glas.) Cons. Anaesth. Carlisle & E. Cumbld. Hosp. GP.; Lt.-Col. RAMC, T & AVR, Cons. in Anaesth. Socs: BMA & Assn. Anaesths. Gt. Brit. & Irel. Prev: Sen. Regist. Anaesth. Glas. Roy. Infirm.; Vis. Instruc. in Anaesth. Univ. Rochester & Vis. Fell. in Anaesth.; Strong Memor. Hosp. Rochester, New York.

STUART

STUART, Ranald McKenzie Department of Radiology, Royal Perth Hospital, Wellington Street, Perth 6008, Western Australia, Perth, Australia; 35 Honister Avenue, High West Jesmond, Newcastle upon Tyne NE2 3PA — MB ChB 1991 Ed.; FRCS 1999; BSc Ed. 1989. (Ed.) Radiol. Fell., Roy. Perth Hosp., Perth, Australia. Prev: SpR in Radiol., Newc. upon Tyne Hosps. Trust; SHO (Med.) Roy. Infirm., W. Gen. Hosp. Edin. & New Cross Hosp. Wolverhampton; Ho. Off. W. Gen. Hosp. & Roy. Infirm. Edin.

STUART, Richard Alexander Oakwood, Bushell Road, Neston, South Wirral CH64 9QB — MB ChB 1993 Liverp.; DROGG 1998; BSc (Hons) 1984.

STUART, Mr Robert Cornelius 5 Kylepark Crescent, Uddingston, Glasgow G71 7DQ — MB BCh BAO 1982 NUI; MCh NUI 1993, MB BCh BAO 1982; FRCSI (Gen.) 1995; FRCSI 1987. Sen. Lect. & Hon. Cons. (Upper Gastrointestinal Surg.) Glas. Roy. Infirm. Prev: Sen. Regist. (Surg.) St. Jas. Hosp. Dub.; Vis. Lect. (Surg.) P. Wales Hosp. Shatin, Hong Kong.

STUART, Robert Darrell 4 Kings Court, Kings Avenue, Buckhurst Hill IG9 5LU — MB ChB 1994 Leeds.

STUART, Ruth (retired) 2 Waterside Close, Darley Abbey, Derby DE22 1JT Tel: 01332 550206 Fax: 01332 550206 — MB ChB 1956 Ed.

STUART, Susan Heaton Road Surgery, 41 Heaton Road, Heaton, Newcastle upon Tyne NE6 1TP Tel: 0191 265 5509 Fax: 0191 224 1824; 21 Northumberland Avenue, Forest Hall, Newcastle upon Tyne NE12 9NR — MB BS 1969 Newc. (Newc.)

STUART, Terence Michael Old Hall Grounds Health Centre, Old Hall Grounds, Cowbridge CF71 7AH Tel: 01446 772237 Fax: 01446 775883 — MB BCh 1979 Wales; MRCGP 1983; DRCOG 1982.

STUART, Wendy Hazel 4 Marine Crescent, Great Yarmouth NR30 4ER — MB BS 1987 Lond.; FRCA 1995; DRCOG 1989.

STUART, Wesley Paul 12 Balgreen Avenue, Edinburgh EH12 5ST — MB ChB 1991 Ed.

STUART, William Edgar (retired) 5 Crossways, Craigends, Houston, Johnstone PA6 7DG Tel: 01505 614765 — MB BS 1944 Durh.

STUART-BUTTLE, Charles Derek George Dunorlan Medical Group, 64 Pembury Road, Tonbridge TN9 2JG Tel: 01732 352907 Fax: 01732 367408 Email: charles.stuart-buttle@gp-g82042.nhs.uk; 9 Holden Road, Tunbridge Wells TN4 0QG — MB BS 1980 Lond.; DRCOG 1983. (St. Bartholemews) Partner. Prev: Dir. of Read Code Developm. NHS Centre for Coding & cl.ification, GP Tadworth.

***STUART-COLE, Elizabeth** 22 Manchester Road, Shuttleworth, Ramsbottom, Bury BL0 0DH — MB ChB 1996 Liverp.

STUART MORROW, Carol 22 Devonshire Place, London W1G 6JA Tel: 020 7935 9366 Fax: 020 7935 9366; 9 Blandford Close, Hampstead Garden Suburb, London N2 0DH Tel: 020 8455 6544 — MB ChB 1964 Liverp.; Dip Forens Pyschother 1996. (Liverp.) Indep. Specialist (Psychosexual Med.) Lond. Socs: Inst. Psychosexual Med.; BAP; BMA. Prev: Instruct. Sen. Med. Off. Margt. Pyke Centre Study & Train.; Ho. Phys. Poole Gen. Hosp.; Ho. Surg. King Edwd. VII Hosp. Windsor.

STUART-SMITH, Deryk Aubrey 30 Dolphin Road, Maxwell Park, Glasgow G41 4DZ Tel: 0141 423 2430 — MD 1971 Glas.; BSc Glas. 1952, MD (Hons.) 1971, MB ChB 1957; FRCP Ed. 1973, M 1961; FRCP Glas. 1976, M 1973. Dir. Bone Metab. Research Unit & Sen. Lect. Dept. Med. W.. Infirm. Glas. Socs: Assn. Phys. Gt. Brit. & Irel. Prev: MRC Research Asst. & Lect. Dept. Med. W.. Infirm. Glas.

STUART-SMITH, Karen Dept. of Anaesthesia, Birmingham Heartlands Hospital, Bordesley Greean East, Birmingham B9 5SS Tel: 0121 424 3438 Email: stuart@heartsd.wmids.nhs.uk — MD 1990 Glas.; BSc (Hons.) Glas. 1982, MB ChB 1985; FRCA 1991. (University of Glasgow) Cons. Anaesth., Birm. Heartlands Hosp. Prev: Post-Doctoral Research Fell. (Physiol.) Mayo Clinic Rochester, USA; SHO (Anaesth.) Vict. Infirm Glas.; Attend. Anaesthesiol. John Hopkins Hosp. Baltimore, Maryland, USA.

STUART-SMITH, Sara Elizabeth Department of Haematology, Hammersmith Hospital, Du Cane Road, London W12 Tel: 020 8383 0000; Email: sarass@tinyworld.co.uk — MB BS 1996 Lond.; BSc 1995 Lond; MRCP 1999 Lond. (Royal Free Hospital School of Medicine) Haemat. Specialist Regist., Hammersmith Hosp., Lond. Socs: Roy. Coll. of Phys.s, Lond.

STUART-SMITH, Susan Jane The Tavistock Clinic, 120 Belsize Lane, London NW3 5BA; The Barn, Serge Hill, Abbots Langley WD5 0RY — MB BS 1989 Lond.; MRC Psych 1997; MA Camb. 1982. (Univ. Coll. Hosp. Lond.) p/t Specialist Regist. Tavistock Clinic. Prev: Regist. Rotat. Oxf.

STUART TAYLOR, Malvena Elizabeth Dept Anasethetics, Southampton General Hospital, Tremonia Road, Southampton SO16 6YD Tel: 023 8079 6135 Fax: 023 8079 4348 Email: malvena.st.@lineone.net — MB BS 1978 Lond.; BSc Lond. 1975; FRCA 1985. (Roy. Free) p/t Cons. Anaesth. Soton. Gen. Hosp. Socs: BMA; Soc. Computing & Technol. in Anaesth.; Pain Soc. Prev: Sen. Regist. & Regist. (Anaesth.) Soton. Gen. Hosp.; Resid. Med. Off. (Cardiol.) Nat. Heart Hosp. Lond.

STUBBENS, Gillian Church Street Practice, 8 Church Street, Southport PR9 0QT Tel: 01704 533666 Fax: 01704 539239 — MB ChB 1982 Bristol; MRCGP 1986; DRCOG 1984; Cert. Family Plann. JCC 1984. GP S.port. Prev: GP Barnsley; Clin. Med. Off. Barnsley HA; Trainee GP St Ives, Camb. VTS.

STUBBINGS, Clive Alan Exmouth Health Centre, Claremont Grove, Exmouth EX8 2JF Tel: 01395 273001 Fax: 01395 273771; Tolpedn, 23 Cranford Avenue, Exmouth EX8 2HU Tel: 01395 274473 — MB BChir 1974 Camb.; MB Camb. 1974, BChir 1973; MA Camb. 1974; MRCP (UK) 1975; MRCGP 1977. (Univ. Coll. Hosp.) GP Princip. Prev: Course Organiser (Gen. Pract.) Exeter Postgrad. Med. Sch. Exeter VTS; Research Fell. (Gen. Pract.) Univ. Exeter.

STUBBINGS, Martin Andrew Gosford Hill Medical Centre, 167 Oxford Road, Kidlington OX5 2NS Tel: 01865 374242 Fax: 01865 377826; 63 Bicester Road, Kidlington OX5 2LD Tel: 01865 376185 — MB BS 1977 Lond.

STUBBINGS, Ronald (retired) 85 Dovercourt Road, Dulwich, London SE22 8UW — MB BS 1959 Lond.; AFOM RCP Lond. 1979; DHMSA 1979. Prev: Med. Off. BP Co. Ltd. Lond.

STUBBINGS, Susan Margaret Exmouth Health Centre, Claremont Grove, Exmouth EX8 2JF Tel: 01395 273001 Fax: 01395 273771; Tolpedn, 23 Cranford Avenue, Exmouth EX8 2HU Tel: 01395 274473 Email: clivestubb@eclipse.co.uk — MB BS 1973 Lond.; BSc Lond. 1970, MB BS 1973; MRCGP 1978. (Univ. Coll. Hosp.)

STUBBINGTON, Hayley Louise Trinity Hill, Bungalown, Trinity Hill, Medstead, Alton GU34 5LT — MB BS 1992 Lond.

STUBBINS, John Haydn (retired) Hathaway, 4 Dynevor Avenue, Neath SA10 7AG Tel: 01639 644671 — MB ChB 1962 Ed.; MFCM 1973; DPH Wales 1966. Prev: Cons. Pub. Health Med. M. Glam. HA.

STUBBS, Arthur (retired) Myrtle Cottage, The Street, Kirkby-Le-Soken, Frinton-on-Sea CO13 0EG — MB ChB 1959 Sheff.; DObst RCOG 1962.

STUBBS, Benjamin Herbert Rex — MB BS 1994 Lond.; MRCGP 2000; BSc Birm. 1995; MSc Lond. 1986.

STUBBS, Emma Jane Darenth Dene, Shoreham Road, Otford, Sevenoaks TN14 5RP — MB BS 1993 Lond.

STUBBS, John Richard Campion (retired) 13 Victoria Road, Dumfries DG2 7NU Tel: 01387 255343 — MB BS 1958 Durh.; FFA RCS Eng. 1967. Prev: Cons. Anaesth. Dumfries & Galloway Roy. Infirm.

STUBBS, Lesley Anne 2 Cathedral Drive, Fairfield, Stockton-on-Tees TS19 7JT — MB BS 1981 Newc. Clin. Med. Off. (Child Health) S. Tees HA.

***STUBBS, Martin Campbell** 11 Broadlands, Carnoustie DD7 6JY — MB ChB 1994 Dundee.

STUBBS, Paul Gerard Pontardawe Health Centre, Pontardawe, Swansea SA8 4JU Tel: 01792 863103 Fax: 01792 865400 — MB BCh 1979 Wales; MRCGP 1984; DRCOG 1985.

STUBBS, Peter Damian Hartcliffe Health Centre, Hareclive Road, Bristol BS13 0JP Tel: 0117 964 2839 Fax: 0117 964 9628 — MB ChB 1971 Bristol; MRCGP 1975; DObst RCOG 1973.

STUBBS, Peter John 22 St Georges Road, Richmond TW9 2LE — MB BS 1982 Lond.; MRCP (UK) 1987; MRCPI 1986. Med. Regist. W. Middlx. Univ. Hosp. Isleworth. Prev: SHO (Nephrol.) St. Peter's Gp. of Hosps. Lond.; Ho. Off. (Cardiol.) Roy. Free Hosp. Lond.

STUBBS, Robert Paul Tickle and Stubbs, 28 West Street, Earls Barton, Northampton NN6 0EW Tel: 01604 810219 Fax: 01604 810401; 48 Northampton Road, Earls Barton, Northampton NN6 0HE — MB ChB 1986 Sheff.; MRCGP 1990; DRCOG 1989.

STUBBS, Valerie Margaret Myrtle Cottage, 80 The Street, Kirby-le-Soken, Frinton-on-Sea CO13 0EG Tel: 01255 677954; Myrtle

STURGEON

Cottage, 80 The St, Kirby-le -Soken, Frinton-on-Sea CO13 0EG Tel: 01255 677954 — MB ChB 1961 Sheff. (Sheff.)

STUBGEN, S O The Coach House Surgery, 27 Canterbury Road, Herne Bay CT6 5DQ Tel: 01227 374040 — MB ChB 1985 Pretoria; MB ChB 1985 Pretoria. Gen. Med. Practitioner.

STUBINGTON, Mr Simon Richard Department of Urology, Nottingham City Hospital, Hicknall Road, Nottingham NG5 1PB Tel: 0115 969 1169 Fax: 0115 962 7791; 19 Greet Park Close, Southwell NG25 0EE Email: stubinggton@cwcom.net — MB BS 1987 Lond.; BSc Lond. 1984; FRCS Ed. 1992; FRCS Eng. 1992; Dm Nottm 1999; FRCS (Urol) 1999. (St. Thos. Hosp. Lond.) Specialist Regist. (Urol.) Nottm. City Hosp. Socs: Fell. Roy. Soc. Med.; Brit. Transpl. Soc.; Assoc. Mem. BAUS. Prev: Transpl. Research Fell. (Surg.) Nottm. City Hosp.; Regist. (Surg.) Nottm. City Hosp.; SHO (Surg.) Leeds Gen. Infirm.

STUBLEY, Michael Walter Aughton Surgery, 19 Town Green Lane, Aughton, Ormskirk L39 6SE Tel: 01695 422384 — MB BS 1976 Lond.; MRCS Eng. LRCP Lond. 1976.

STUCKE, Sally Kathleen Nevill Hall Hospital, Brecon Road, Abergavenny NP7 7EG Tel: 01873 732485 Email: sally.stucke@gwent.wales.nhs.uk — MB BS 1987 Lond.; MA Camb. 1983; MRCP 1993 Lond. (UK); FRCPCH 1997 Lond. Cons. Paediat. (Community Child Health) Gwent Healthcare Trust. Socs: Fell. Roy. Coll. Paediat. & Child Health; Brit. Assn. Community Child Health; Welsh Paediat. Soc. Prev: Regist. (Paediat.) Bristol; Regist. (Neonat.) Bristol; Regist. (Community Child Health) Bristol.

STUDD, Clive Department of Anaesthetics, Royal Sussex County Hospital, Brighton — MB ChB 1969 Leeds; FFA RCS Eng. 1975. (Leeds) Cons. Anaesth. Roy. Sussex Co. Hosp. Brighton. Prev: Sen. Regist. (Anaesth.) Bristol Roy. Infirm.; Specialist in Anaesth. P.ss Alexandra's RAF Hosp. Wroughton; SHO Anaesth. Leeds Gen. Infirm.

STUDD, Professor John William Winston Lister Hospital, Chelsea Bridge Road, London SW1W 8RH Tel: 020 7730 5433 Fax: 020 7823 6108 Email: lister@studd.co.uk; 27 Blomfield Road, London W9 1AA Tel: 020 7266 0058 Fax: 020 7266 2663 Email: laptop@studd.co.uk — MB ChB Birm. 1962; DSc Birm. 1994, MD 1971; FRCOG 1986, M 1967. (Birm.) Prof. Of Gynaecol. Chelsea & W.m. Hosp. Lond.; Dir. Fertil. & Endocrinol. Centre Lister Hosp. Lond.; Examr. Univs. Lond., Birm., Nottm. & Camb. & RCOG; Chairm. Menopause & PMS Trust; Pub.ats. Off. RCOG; Vice Pres. - Nat. Osteoporosis Soc. Socs: Fell. Roy. Soc. Med. (Pres. Sect. Obst. & Gyn.); (Pres.) Internat. Soc. Reproduc. Med.; (Chairm.) Nat. Osteoporosis Soc. Prev: Cons. O & G King's Coll. & Dulwich Hosp.; Sen. Lect. & Cons. (O & G) Univ. Nottm.; Lect. & Sen. Regist. (O & G) Univ. Birm.

***STUDDARD, Gareth Lincoln** 41 Clive Road, Pattingham, Wolverhampton WV6 7DJ — MB ChB 1998 Birm.

STUDDS, Christopher John 47 Ecton Avenue, Macclesfield SK10 1RD — MB BS 1986 Lond.

STUDDY, John Denman (retired) 86 Braiswick, Colchester CO4 5AY Tel: 01206 853487 — MB BS 1950 Lond.; MRCPsych 1971. Prev: Cons. Psychiat. Bridge Hosp. Witham.

STUDDY, Peter Robert Harefield Hospital, Harefield, Uxbridge UB9 6JH Tel: 01895 823737 — MD 1983 Lond.; FRCP Lond. 1989. (Roy. Free) Cons. Phys. Roy. Brompton & Harefield NHS Trust & W. Herts NHS Trust.

STUDHOLME, Katrine Madge 10 Park Road, Abingdon OX14 1DS Tel: 01235 530722 — MRCS Eng. LRCP Lond. 1955; MB Camb. 1956, BChir 1955; MRCGP 1979. (Lond. Hosp.) p/t Indep. Psychotherapist Abingdon. Prev: GP 1960-1990.

STUDHOLME, Thomas James 432 Springvale Road, Crookes, Sheffield S10 1LQ — MB ChB 1993 Otago.

STUDLEY, Mr John George Noel James Paget Hospital NHS Trust, Lowestoft Road, Gorleston, Great Yarmouth NR31 6LA Tel: 01493 452452 — MB BS 1973 Lond.; MS Lond. 1986; FRCS Eng. 1978. (Middlx.) Cons. Gen. Surg. Jas. Paget Hosp. Gt. Yarmouth. Prev: Sen. Regist. (Gen. Surg.) N.ampton Gen. Hosp., Hammersmith Hosp. & Roy. Postgrad. Med. Sch.; Regist. Rotat. (Gen. Surg.) Bloomsbury HA; Research Fell. (Surg.) State Univ. N.Y., Buffalo.

STUMBLES, Dorothy Edith 41 Gretton Court, Girton, Cambridge CB3 0QN Tel: 01223 277617 — MB ChB Birm. 1938. (Birm.) Socs: BMA. Prev: Anaesth. P.ss Eliz. Orthop. Hosp. Exeter; Hon. Anaesth. Roy. Hosp. Wolverhampton; Resid. Anaesth. Gen. Hosp. Birm.

STUMPER, Oliver Friedrich Wilhelm The Heart Unit, Children's Hospital, Steelhouse Lane, Birmingham B4 6NH Tel: 0121 333 9442 Fax: 0121 333 9441 Email: oliver.stumper@bhamchildrens.wmids.nhs.uk — State Exam Med. Bonn 1988; PhD Rotterdam 1991 University Rotterdam, NL; MD Bonn 1988 University Bonn. (Bonn, Germany) Cons. Paediat. Cardiol.; Hon. Sen. Lect. Univ. Birm.; Hon. Cons. Cardiol. Qu. Eliz. Hosp. Birm. Socs: Brit. Paediat. Cardiol. Assn.; Eur. Soc. Cardiol. Prev: Sen. Regist. (Paediat. Cardiol.) Birm. Childrs. Hosp.; Sen. Research Fell. Hosp. Necker, Paris.

STUMPFLE, Richard 29 Clockhouse Place, London SW15 2EL — MB ChB 1997 Ed.; BSc Ed. 1995.

STUPPLE, Jeremy Mark Gifford The Medical Centre, 15 Cawley Road, Chichester PO19 1XT Tel: 01243 786666/781833 Fax: 01243 530042; Kilindi, Itchenor, Chichester PO20 7DH Tel: 01243 511304 Fax: 01243 514780 — MB BS 1983 Lond.; MRCGP 1986; DCH RCP Lond. 1986; DRCOG 1986.

STURDEE, David William Department Obstetrics and Gynaecology, Solihull Hospital, Solihull B91 2JD Tel: 0121 424 5390 Fax: 0121 424 5389 Email: sturded@heartsol.wmids.nhs.uk; 44 Mirfield Road, Solihull B91 1JD Tel: 0121 705 1759 — MB BS Lond. 1969; MD Birm. 1979; DA Eng. 1972; FRCOG 1988, M 1975; DObst 1971. (St. Thos.) Cons. O & G Solihull & Birm. Heartlands Hosp.; Sen. Clin. Lect. Univ. Birm.; Co-Edr. in Chief Jl. Internat. Menopause Soc. - The Climacteric 1997-. Socs: BMA (Ex. Chairm. Solihull Div.); (Ex-Chairm.) Brit. Menopause Soc.; Brit. Soc. Colpos. & Cerv. Path. Prev: Edr. Diplomate 1993-9; Sen. Regist. (O & G) Walsgrave Hosp. Coventry & Birm. Matern. Hosp.; Research Fell. (O & G) Univ. Birm.

***STURDEE, Simon Williams** 529 Meanwood Road, Meanwood, Leeds LS6 4AW — MB ChB 1996 Leeds.

STURDY, Mr David Eric Rothesay, 22 Stow Park Circle, Newport NP20 4HF Tel: 01633 264646 — MB BS 1950 Lond.; MS Lond. 1960, MB BS 1950; FRCS Eng. 1956. (Guy's) Surg. Roy. Gwent Hosp.; Urol. St. Woolos Hosp. Newport. Socs: Brit. Assn. Urol. Surgs.; Assn. Surg. Prev: Sen. Regist. (Surg.) Roy. Infirm. Preston & Hosp. Sick Childr. Gt. Ormond St.; Regist. Roy. Marsden Hosp. Lond.

STURDY, John Laurence 91 Gledhow Lane, Leeds LS8 1NE — MB ChB 1978 Liverp. Clin. Asst. Leeds Community & Ment. Health Trust High Royds Hosp.

STURDY, Maxine Lida Leonie Farnham Health Centre, Brightwells, Farnham GU9 7SA Tel: 01252 723122; 7 Old Farnham Lane, Farnham GU9 8JU — MB 1969 Camb.; BChir 1968; DObst RCOG 1970. (Camb. & St. Thos.) Socs: Farnham Med. Soc.; BMA. Prev: GP Chelmsford & Tonbridge.

STURDY, Roger Elston High Noon, Ladock, Truro TR2 4PW Tel: 01726 882386 — MB 1973 Camb.; MA Camb. 1976, MB 1973, BChir 1972; MRCPsych 1979. Prev: Sen. Regist. (Child Psychiat.) Lond. Hosp.; Asst. Dir. Lond. Med. Gp. & Soc. Study Med. Ethics; Regist. (Psychol. Med.) Hosp. Sick Childr. Lond.

STURGE, Joan Claire 45 Eaton Rise, London W5 2HE Tel: 020 8997 8972 — MPhil Lond. 1972, MB BS 1965; MRCPsych 1971; DPM Eng. 1970; DCH RCPS Glas. 1967. (Middlx.) Cons. Child Psychiat. N.wick Pk. Hosp. & Gayton Child & Family; Serv. Harrow.

STURGE, Richard Arthur 45 Eaton Rise, London W5 2HE Tel: 020 8997 8972 Fax: 020 8997 4427 Email: sturgera@aol.com — MB BS Lond. 1965; FRCP Lond. 1986; MRCP (UK) 1971. (Guy's) Cons. Rheum. Barnet & Chase Farm Hosp.s NHS Trust. Socs: BMA & Brit. Soc. Rheum. Prev: SHO MRC Rheum. Unit Taplow; Med. Regist. Guy's Hosp. Lond.; Sen. Regist. (Gen. Med. & Rheum.) Char. Cross & St. Stephens Hosps.

STURGEON, David Alexander Department Psychological Medicine, University College Hospital, Gower St., London WC1E Tel: 020 7387 9300 Ext: 8585 Fax: 020 7387 1710 — BM BCh 1971 Oxf.; MA Oxf. 1971; FRCPsych 1986, M 1976. Cons. Liaison. Psychiat. & Hon. Sen. Lect. (Fac. Clin. Sci.) Univ. Coll. Lond. Socs: Fell. Internat. Coll. Psychosomatic Med. (Treas.). Prev: Sen. Lect. (Ment. Health) Univ. Coll. Lond.; Hon. Cons. (Psychiat.) Univ. Coll. Hosp. Lond.; Leverhulme Research Fell. Univ. Coll. Hosp. Med. Sch. Lond.

STURGEON, James Liddell Motherwell Health Centre, 138-144 Windmill Street, Motherwell ML1 1TA Tel: 01698 265193 Fax: 01698 253324 — MB ChB 1968 Glas. (Glas.)

STURGES

STURGES, Margaret (retired) 5 Allen Court, Hauxton Road, Trumpington, Cambridge CB2 2LU — MRCS Eng. LRCP Lond. 1925. Prev: SPG Med. Miss. Chota Nagpur Diocese, India.

STURGESS, Mr Dale Anthony 7 Bowerfield Avenue, Hazel Grove, Stockport SK7 6HZ — MB ChB 1981 Manch.; FRCS Ed. 1991; FRCOphth 1991. Socs: Fell. Roy. Coll. Surg. Edin.; Fell. Roy. Coll. Ophth.; BMA. Prev: SHO (Ophth.) Stepping Hill Hosp. Stockport; SHO (Neurol. & Neurosurg.) Midl. Centre for Neurol. & Neurosurg.; SHO (Ophth.) Wolverhampton Eye Infirm.

STURGESS, Hugh Failsworth Health Centre, Ashton Road W., Failsworth, Manchester M35 0HN Tel: 0161 682 6297; 8 North Nook, Austerlands, Saddleworth, Oldham OL4 3QR — MB ChB 1981 Manch.; MRCGP 1986; DRCOG 1986. Local Med. Off. Civil Serv.; Dep. Police Surg.

STURGESS, Ian 24 Ethelbert Road, Canterbury CT1 3NE — MB ChB 1982 Leeds.

***STURGESS, Lucy Bethan** 27 Margravine Gardens, London W6 8RL — MB BS 1998 Lond.; MB BS Lond 1998.

STURGESS, Michael John Hayes Court, 50 Hayes Lane, Kenley CR8 5LA — MB BCh 1971 Wales.

STURGESS, Richard Patrick 47 Rose Mount, Oxton, Birkenhead CH43 5SQ — MB BS 1984 Lond.; BSc Lond. 1981; MD Lond. 1996; MRCP (UK) 1987. (Middlx.) Cons. Phys. (Gen. Med. & Gastroenterol.) Aintree Hosps. Liverp. Socs: Brit. Soc. Gastroenterol. Prev: Sen. Regist. Roy. Liverp. Univ. Hosps.; Research Fell. St. Thos. Hosp. Lond.; Regist. Inst. Liver Studies King's Coll. Hosp.

STURGISS, Stephen Noel Department of Obstetrics & Gynaecology, Royal Victoria Infirmary, Newcastle upon Tyne NE1 4LP Tel: 0191 232 5131; 61 Whinfell Road, Darras Hall, Newcastle upon Tyne NE20 9EW — MB ChB 1982 Manch.; MD Newc. 1993; MRCOG 1988. Cons. Obst. & Fetal Med. RUI Newc.

STURLEY, Rachel Helen Royal Devon & Exeter Hospital (Heavitree), Gladstone Road, Exeter EX1 2ED Tel: 01392 405049 Fax: 01392 405061 — MB ChB 1980 Sheff.; MD Sheff. 1994; MRCOG 1985. Cons. O & G Roy. Devon & Exeter Hosp. Socs: Brit. Diabetic Assn.; BSCCP. Prev: Sen. Regist. (O & G) Roy. Devon & Exeter Hosp.; Regist. (O & G) S.mead Hosp. Bristol; Research Regist. (Obst. & Diabetes) Roy. United Hosp. Bath.

***STURMAN, Daniel Robert** 4 Aspen Close, Laughterton, Lincoln LN1 2LQ Tel: 01427 8389 — MB ChB 1998 Sheff.; MB ChB Sheff 1998.

STURMAN, Janette May Carmel Surgery, Nunnery Lane, Darlington DL3 8SQ Tel: 01325 463149; 23 Brompton Walk, Darlington DL3 8RT Tel: 01325 488541 — MB ChB 1984 Glas.; DRCOG 1988. (Glas.) Socs: BMA. Prev: Trainee GP Stokesley VTS & GuisBoro.

***STURMAN, Jon Mark** 8c Elsington Terrace, Jesmond, Newcastle upon Tyne NE2 4RJ — MB BS 1993 Newc.

STURMAN, Stephen George Department of Neurology, City Hospital NHS Trust, Dudley Road, Winson Green, Birmingham B18 7QH Tel: 0121 554 3801 — MB ChB 1983 Birm.; FRCP 1997, M 1986. Cons. Neurol. & Rehabil. Med. City Hosp. & QE. Hosp. Birm.; Hon. Sen. Clin. Lect. (Neurol.) Univ. Birm. Socs: Assn. Brit. Neurol.; Brit. Soc. Rehabil. Med. Prev: Lect. (Neurol.) Univ. Birm.

STURMER, Heidi Louise 2 Mansfield Avenue, Quorn, Leicester LE12 8BD; 2 Mansfield Avenue, Quorn, Leicester LE12 8BD — MB BS 1993 Lond.; BSc (Intercalated) Lond. 1990; 1997 MRCGP; DRCOG; DFFP; DCH RCP Lond. 1995. (Charing Cross and Westminster)

STURRIDGE, Bernadette Frances 72 Margaret Road, Barnet EN4 9NX — MB BS 1988 Lond.

STURRIDGE, Mr Marvin Francis (retired) The Middlesex Hospital, Mortimer St., London W1T 3AA Tel: 020 7636 8333 — MB BS 1952 Lond.; MS Lond. 1965; FRCS Eng. 1958. Archiv. Middlx. Hosp. Prev: Cons. Thoracic Surg. Middlx. Hosp.

***STURRIDGE, Sabastian Newdigate** Flat 3, The Beeches, 9/17 Trinder Road, London N19 4QT — MB BS 1998 Lond.; MB BS Lond 1998; BSc (Psychology) 1995.

STURROCK, Alison Margaret 2 Harrow Street, Dundee DD2 1TG — MB ChB 1993 Ed.

STURROCK, Angela Mary Blackwoods Medical Centre, 8 Station Road, Muirhead, Glasgow G69 9EE Tel: 0141 779 2228 Fax: 0141 779 3225 — MB ChB 1993 Glas.; MRCGP 1997. GP Partner. Prev: SHO (Gyn.) W.. Univ. NHS Trust Glas.

STURROCK, David (retired) Lanemead, Common Road, Corston, Malmesbury SN16 0HL Tel: 01666 823429 Fax: 01666 826484 Email: david_sturrock@mdix-uk.com — MB ChB 1950 Glas.; MSc Lond. 1965. Prev: Home Off. Insp. Animals (Scientif. Procedures) Act 1986.

STURROCK, Mr George Douglas West of England Eye Infirmary, Magdalen St., Exeter EX2 4HT — MB 1967 Camb.; BChir 1966; FRCS Eng. 1974.

STURROCK, Maureen Margaret Douglas Inch Centre, 2 Woodside Terrace, Glasgow G3 7UY Tel: 0141 211 8000 Fax: 0141 211 8005 — MB ChB 1974 Aberd.; MRCPsych 1979; T(Psych) 1991; DObst RCOG 1976. Cons. Forens. Psychiat. Gtr. Glas. Community & Ment. Health Servs. Trust. Prev: Cons. Forens. Psychiat. Mersey RHA.

STURROCK, Nigel David Crighton Nottingham City Hospital NHS Trust, Hucknall Road, Nottingham NG5 1PB Tel: 0115 969 1169 Fax: 0115 962 7959 Email: nsturroc@ncht.trent.nhs.uk — MD 1994 Dundee; FRCP (UK) 2001; MB ChB 1988, BMSc (Hons.) 1985; MRCP (UK) 1991. Cons. (Diabetes & Endocrinol.) City Hosp. Nottm.; Clin. Director, acute Med., city Hosp., Nottm. Socs: Soc. for Endocrinol.; Nottm. M-C Soc.; Diabetes UK. Prev: Sen. Regist. (Diabetes Mellitus & Endocrinol.) City Hosp. Nottm.; Regist. (Med.) QMC Nottm.; Research Fell. (Clin. Pharmacol.) Univ. Dundee.

STURROCK, Professor Roger Davidson Centre for Rheumatic Diseases, University Department of Medicine, Royal Infirmary, 10 Alexandra Parade, Glasgow G31 2ER Tel: 0141 211 4687/8 Fax: 0141 211 4878 Email: rdsturrock@cliasmed.gla.ac.uk — MRCS Eng. LRCP Lond. 1969; MD Lond. 1977, MB BS 1969; FRCP Glas. 1983; FRCP Lond. 1985; MRCP (UK) 1971. (Westm.) McLeod/ARC Chairm. Rheum. Univ. Glas. Socs: Fell. Roy. Soc. Med.; Brit. Soc. Rheum.; Brit Soc Rheumatol. (Ex-Pres.). Prev: Sen. Lect. & Cons. Phys. Centre Rheum. Dis. Roy. Infirm. Glas.; Lect. (Rheum. & Med.) Centre for Rheum. Dis. & Univ. Dept. Med. Glas. Roy. Infirm.; Research Asst. (Rheum.) W.m. Hosp. Lond.

STURROCK, Susan Marjory 11 Craster Drive, Arnold, Nottingham NG5 8SL — MB ChB 1988 Dundee; DRCOG 1997; DFFP 1998. GP. Prev: SHO (O & G) City Hosp. Nottm.; GP/Regist. Bakersfield Med. Centre Nottm.; SHO (Psychiat.) Qu.s Med. Centre. Nottm.

STURT, Tessa Mary Albion Health Centre, 333 Whitechapel Road, London E1 1BU Tel: 020 7247 1730 Fax: 020 7247 2589 — MB BS 1984 Lond.; MRCGP 1992; DRCOG 1990.

STURTON, Edwin William (retired) 32A Skinner Street, Creswell, Worksop S80 4JH Tel: 01909 721535 — BM BCh 1956 Oxf.; MRCGP 1978; DObst RCOG 1958. Prev: Ho. Phys. & Ho. Surg. (ENT) Radcliffe Infirm. Oxf.

STURTON, Peter Richard Abbey Medical Practice, 95 Monks Road, Lincoln LN2 5HR Tel: 01522 530334 Fax: 01522 569442; The Coach House, Weir St, Lincoln LN5 8DU Tel: 01522 529763 — MB ChB 1983 Dundee. Prev: Trainee GP Chesterfield VTS; Ho. Off. (Med.) King's Cross Hosp. Dundee; Ho. Off. (Orthop.) Dundee Roy. Infirm.

STURZAKER, Mr Hugh Gerard Coastal Clinic, 4 Park Road, Gorleston, Great Yarmouth NR31 6EJ Tel: 01493 601770 Fax: 01493 442430 Email: hsturzaker@aol.com; Hobland House, Hobland, Great Yarmouth NR31 9AR Tel: 01493 665287 Email: hsturzaker@aol.com — BM BCh 1966 Oxf.; BM BCh. Oxf. 1966; MA Oxf. 1966; FRCS Eng. 1972; FRCS Ed. 1971; MRCS Eng. LRCP Lond. 1966. (Oxf. & Guy's) Cons. Surg. Jas. Paget Hosp. Gorleston, Gt. Yarmouth. Socs: Fell. Roy. Soc. Med.; BMA; Assn. Surg.. (Counc. Mem.). Prev: Sen. Regist. (Surg.) Guy's Hosp. Lond.; Ho. Surg. Guy's Hosp.; Research Fell. (Surg.) St. Mark's Hosp. Lond.

STUTCHFIELD, Peter Roy Glan Clwyd District General Hospital, Rhyl LL18 5UJ Tel: 01745 583910; Glas Coed, Pen-yr-Allt, Whitford, Holywell CH8 9DD — MB BS 1977 Lond.; BSc (Hons. Genetics) Lond. 1974; FRCP Lond. 1995; MRCP (UK) 1981. (Univ. Coll. Hosp.) Cons. Paediat. Glan Clwyd Hosp. Rhyl; Clin. Lect. Univ. Liverp.; Clin. Teach. Child Health Univ. of Wales Coll. of Med. Socs: Brit. Soc. Paediat. Endocrinol.; Brit. Assn. Perinatal Med.; Roy. Coll. Paediat. and Child Health. Prev: Sen. Regist. (Paediat.) Roy. Liverp. Hosp. Alder Hey; Regist. (Paediat.) Birm. Childr. Hosp.; SHO (Paediat. Respirat. & Intens. Care) Hosp. Sick Childr. Gt. Ormond St. Lond.

STUTELY, Julie Debra Grantham Health Clinic, St. Catherine Road, Grantham NG31 8GH Tel: 01476 590805; 37 Webster Way, Gonerby Hill Foot, Grantham NG31 8GH Tel: 01476 592074 — MB

BS 1984 Newc.; DCH RCP Lond. 1998. (Newc. u. Tyne) Assoc. Specialist (Community Paediat.) Pilgrim NHS Trust Boston Lincs. Socs: BMA; RCPCH; MDU.

STUTLEY, Jennifer Elizabeth Radiology Department, St. Mary's Hospital NHS Trust, Newport PO30 5TG Tel: 01983 524081 Fax: 01983 821331 — MB ChB 1979 Bristol; MRCP (UK) 1982; FRCR 1988; DRCOG 1985; ACR 1995. (Univ.Bristol) Cons. Radiol. St Marys hosp. Newport. Socs: BMA & Coll. Radiol. Prev: Asst. Prof. Med. Univ. S. Carolina USA; Fell.Radiol.Univ.Toronto.Canada; Sen.Regist. (Radiol.) St. Geo.s Hosp. Lond.

***STUTT, Marcus** Royal Bournemouth Hospital, Residences, Room 27 Block 2, Castle Lane E., Bournemouth BH7 7DW Tel: 01202 303626 — BM 1997 Soton.

STUTTAFORD, Irving Thomas 8 Devonshire Place, London W1N 1PB Tel: 020 7935 5011 Fax: 020 7486 7166; 36 Elm Hill, Norwich NR3 1HG Tel: 01603 615133 — MRCS Eng LRCP Lond 1959. (Oxf. & W. Lond) Med. Columnist 'The Times'; Sen. Lect., Keele Univ., Staffs. Research Fell. in Gen. Pract., Regional GP Unit, Birm.; Med. Adviser to C.E. andersons & Sons Ltd., Barclays Bank Ltd. & other Cos.; Primary Care Phys. (UK & abRd.); Vis. Cons. Learning Assessm. Centre, Horsham, W. Sussex; HP. Rshit S.port; HS RSCH Guildford; RAF Med. Pract. Prev: Visit.Phys.BUPA Med.Centre; Clin. Assist. (Venerol.) Lond. Hosp.

STUTTARD, Ana Maria 37A Burghley Road, London N8 — Lic Med. Lisbon 1977.

STUTTARD, Carl Albert Smugglers Lane Surgery, Smugglers Lane, Reepham, Norwich NR10 4QT Tel: 01603 870271 Fax: 01603 872995 — MB ChB 1977 Liverp.; MRCGP 1982.

STUTTARD, Susan South Milford Surgery, High St., South Milford, Leeds LS25 5AA Tel: 01977 682202 Fax: 01977 681628; Prebendal House, Church Lane, Monk Fryston, Leeds LS25 5ES Tel: 01977 681207 — BM BS 1987 Nottm.; BMedSci Nottm. 1985; MRCGP 1992. (Nottingham) Socs: BMA; POWAR. Prev: Trainee GP Nottm.; SHO (Psychiat.) Leics.

STUTZ, Joanna Alexandra 23 Pondfield Road, Orpington BR6 8HJ — MB BChir 1989 Camb.

STYLE, Anne Marion (retired) Muncaster House, Loweswater, Cockermouth CA13 0RU Tel: 01900 85318 — MB BS 1950 Lond.; MRCS Eng. LRCP Lond. 1950. SCMO W. Cumbria DHA. Prev: Ho. Surg. Fulham Hosp.

STYLES, Caroline Jane 40 Crockerton Road, London SW17 7HG — MB BChir 1993 Camb.

STYLES, Caroline Louise Bristol Royal Infirmary, Marlborough St., Bristol BS2 8HW Tel: 0117 923 0000; Flat 3, 15 Victoria Square, Clifton, Bristol BS8 4ES Tel: 0117 973 3711 — MB BChir 1990 Camb.; MA Camb. 1991; MRCP (UK) 1993; FRCR 1997. Specialist Regist. Bristol Roy. Infirm. Prev: Regist. (Radiol.) Qu. Med. Centre Nottm.; SHO (Med.) City Hosp. Nottm. & Newham Gen. Hosp. Lond.

STYLES, Hilary Frances Lower Mitton Farm, Mitton, Penkridge, Stafford ST19 5QW Tel: 01785 780507 — MB ChB 1964 Manch.; DObst RCOG 1967. (Manch.) Prev: Ho. Surg. Univ. Dept. Orthop. Manch. Roy. Infirm.; Ho. Phys. Salisbury Gen. Infirm.; SHO O & G Epsom Dist. Hosp.

STYLES, John Trevor (retired) Lower Mitton Farm, Mitton, Penkridge, Stafford ST19 5QW Tel: 01785 780507 — MB BS 1964 Lond.; MB BS (Hons., Distinc. Obst. & Gyn.) Lond. 1964; BSc (Hons. Anat.) Lond. 1961; MRCS Eng. LRCP Lond. 1964; FFA RCS Eng. 1968. Cons. Anaesth. Roy. Wolverhampton Hosps. NHS Trust. Prev: Sen. Regist. (Anaesth.) United Birm. Hosps.

STYLES, Mary Elise Child Health Bureau, Graylingwell Hospital, PO Box 115, Chichester PO19 4YT Tel: 01243 815400 — BM 1985 Soton.; BM Soton 1985; DCH RCP Lond. 1990; DGM RCP Lond. 1988; MSc Lond. 1997. Staff Grade Paediat. Chichester.

STYLES, Richard John Whitchurch Surgery, Bell Street, Whitchurch RG28 7AE Tel: 01256 892113 Fax: 01256 895610 — MB ChB 1974 Bristol; FRCGP 1995, M 1978; DRCOG 1976. Course Organiser Mid Wessex VTS Examr. RCGP; RCGP Convenor of Jt. Hosp. Vis. Wessex Region. Prev: Trainee GP Univ. Bristol VTS; SHO (O & G) S.mead Hosp. Bristol.

STYLES, Rosemary Vere Woodbury, 22 Dunkeld Road, Bournemouth BH3 7EN Tel: 01202 766878 — LRCPI & LM, LRSCI & LM 1949; LRCPI & LM, LRCSI & LM 1949.

STYLIANIDES, Labrini The Old Rectory, Rectory Rd, Tolleshunt Knights, Maldon CM9 8EZ — MB BS 1990 Lond.

SU, Mr Archibald Paul Ching Chung Rivermead, Creekview Road, South Woodham Ferrers, Chelmsford CM3 5YL Email: q-z-su@doctors.net.uk — MB BS 1964 Lond.; FRCS Eng. 1973. (Univ. Coll. Hosp.) Cons. ORL & Head & Neck Surg. Basildon & Thurrock Gen. Hosp.s NHS Trust. Socs: Fell. Roy. Soc. Med.; Mem. BMA; Brit. Assoc. of Otorhinolaryngologists Head & Neck Surg.s. Prev: Sen. Regist. (Otolaryng.) Nottm. Univ. Hosp.; Regist. (Otolaryng.) S.end Gen. Hosp.; Ho. Surg. Roy. Ear Hosp. (Univ. Coll. Hosp.) Lond.

SU, Robin Chee Wei 87 Colwith Road, Hammersmith, London W6 9EZ — MB BS 1985 Lond.

***SUALLY, Donald Dilveer Singh** 92 St Helens Street, Ipswich IP4 2LB — MB BS 1998 Lond.; MB BS Lond 1998.

SUARES, M Woodlands Surgery, Pilch Lane, Huyton, Liverpool L14 0JE Tel: 0151 489 1806 Fax: 0151 489 0920.

SUAREZ, Richard — MB BS 1976 Lond.; FRCR 1984; DMRD Eng. 1982. (Lond. Hosp.) Cons. Radiol. Staffs.Gen. Hosp. Prev: Sen. Regist. (Radiol.) N. Staffs. Hosp. Centre Stoke-on-Trent; SHO Neurosurg. Unit Lond. Hosp.; Demonst. Anat. Lond. Hosp. Med. Coll.

SUAREZ, Valerie Willow Cottage, Milwich, Stafford ST18 0ET Tel: 01889 505224 — MB BS 1979 Lond.; BSc Lond. 1976; FRCPath 1997; MRCPath 1986. (Lond. Hosp.) Cons. Histopath. Mid. Staffs Gen. Hosps. Trust.

SUBAK-SHARPE, Robert John County Hospital, Hereford HR1 2ER Tel: 01432 355444; The Poppies, Shelwick, Hereford HR1 3AL Tel: 01432 356054 — MB ChB 1979 Glas.; MRCOG 1986; FRCOG 1998. Cons. O & G Co. Hosp. Hereford. Prev: Sen. Regist. Rotat. (O & G) Wales; In Vitro Fertilisation Co-ordinator & Research Regist. Roy. Postgrad. Med. Sch. Hammersmith Hosp. Lond.; Regist. (O & G) Walton & Fazakerley Hosps. Liverp.

SUBANANDAN, P Green Street Surgery, 48 Green Street, Enfield EN3 7HW Tel: 020 8804 3200 Fax: 020 8443 2615 — MB BS 1973 Sri Lanka; MB BS 1973 Sri Lanka.

SUBASH CHANDRAN, Rajagopalan 34 Belmont Road, Bangor LL57 2LL Tel: 01248 364251 Email: subash@hotmail.com — MB BS 1973 Madras; MD Madras 1976; MRCP (UK) 1990. Trust Specialist Phys. (Med. & c/o Elderly) Ysbyty Gwynedd Bangor. Prev: Clin. Asst. (c/o Elderly) & Regist. (Geriat. Med.) Ysbyty Gwynedd Bangor; SHO (Gen. Med.) Watford Gen. Hosp.; SHO (Geriat. Med.) Doncaster.

SUBASH CHANDRAN, Srinivasan Sandling House, Sandling Lane, Sandling, Maidstone ME14 3AH — MB BS 1974 Madras.

SUBASINGHE, Suranganie Zita Augusta Eye Unit, Southend General Hospital, Prittlewell Chase, Westcliff on Sea SS0 0RY Tel: 01702 390359 Email: subusinghe@aol.com; 20 Cranley Avenue, Westcliff on Sea SS0 8AH Tel: 01702 390359 — MB BS 1967 Ceylon; MS (Ophth.) Colombo 1988; FRCS Ed. 1976; FRCOphth 1989; DO Eng. 1970. Cons. Ophth. Surg. S.end Gen. Hosp. W.cliff-on-Sea Essex. Socs: MRCOphth.; (Counc.) Coll. Ophth. Sri Lanka.; BMA. Prev: Cons. Ophth. Sri Jayewardena Pura Gen. Hosp., Sri Lanka; Cons. Ophth. MoH, Kuwait; Sen. Regist. (Ophth.) Roy. Lond. Hosp. & Moorfields Eye Hosp. Lond.

SUBBERWAL, Kamini Windermere Gardens Surgery, 49 Windermere Gardens, Redbridge, Ilford IG4 5BZ Tel: 020 8550 9195 Fax: 020 8550 3746 — MB BS 1971 Rayishankar U; MB BS 1971 Rayishankar U.

SUBBIAH, Shanmugam Ribblesdale House Medical Centre, Market Street, Bury BL9 0BU Tel: 0161 764 7241 Fax: 0161 763 3557; 74 Rudgwick Drive, Bury BL8 1YE — LRCP LRCS 1979 Ed.; LRCP LRCS Ed. LRCPS Glas. 1979; MRCGP 1983; DRCOG 1982.

SUBBIAH, Sundaram 173 Wembley Hill Road, Wembley HA9 8EL Tel: 020 8904 5784 — MB BS 1958 Madras. (Stanley Med. Coll. Madras) Regist. (Surg.) Manor Hse. Hosp. Lond.; Assoc. Specialist (Gen. Surg.) Manor Hse. Hosp. Lond. Prev: SHO (Surg.) Reedyford Memor. Hosp. Nelson; SHO (Surg.) Hartlepool Hosp.; Hon. Asst. Phys. Govt. Gen. Hosp. Madras.

SUBBU, Venkata Subramanyam Morrison Road Surgery, Morrison Road, Port Talbot SA12 6TH Tel: 01639 887790 Fax: 01639 888093; The Croft, 99 Penycae Road, Port Talbot SA13 2EG — MB BS 1967 Andhra; DA Eng. 1971. (Andhra Med. Coll. Visakhapatnam) Prev: Regist. (Anaesth.) Neath Gen. Hosp.

SUBESINGHE

SUBESINGHE, Nyanissara 52 Traps Lane, New Malden KT3 4SA Tel: 020 8942 8812 — MB BS 1971 Ceylon; MRCP (UK) 1981.

SUBHANI, Javaid Mahmood Royal Free Hospital, Pond St., London NW3; 8 Ashley Walk, Mill Hill, London NW7 1DU Tel: 020 8346 9717 — MB BChir 1989 Camb.; MRCP Lond. 1992. Regist. (Gastroenterol.) St. Geo. Hosp. Lond.

SUBHANI, Mahmud Alhambra, Stonegate, Thorne, Doncaster DN8 Tel: 01405 812160 — MB BS 1958 Karachi; BSc (Hons.), MB BS Karachi 1958. (Dow Med. Coll.)

SUBHANI, Moinuddin Wyken Medical Centre, Brixham Drive, Coventry CV2 3LB Tel: 024 7668 9149 Fax: 024 7666 5151; The Garden House, Lower Road, Barnacle, Coventry CV7 9LD Tel: 024 76 604793 — MB BS 1962 Karachi; MRCGP 1977. (Dow Med. Coll.) Princip. GP. Socs: BMA; MBMAS. Prev: SHO, Ho. Surg. & Ho. Phys. I. of Thanet Hosp. Gp.; Resid. Med. Off. Holywell Hosp. Watford.

SUBHANI, Sapna Oak Lodge Medical Centre, 234 Burnt Oak Broadway, Edgware HA8 0AP Tel: 020 8952 1202 Fax: 020 8381 1156; 8 Ashley Walk, Mill Hill, London NW7 1DU Tel: 020 8346 9717 — BChir 1988 Camb.; BA (Hons.) Oxf. 1986; MRCGP 1993; DRCOG 1992; DCH RCP Lond. 1991. SHO (Gen. Med.) Whittington Hosp. Lond. VTS. Prev: Trainee GP/SHO Whittington Hosp. VTS; SHO (Geriat.) Welwyn Gdn. City; Ho. Off. (Surg.) RAF Hosp. P.ss of Wales Hosp Ely.

SUBHEDAR, Nimish Vasant NICU Liverpool Womens Hospital, Crown St., Liverpool L8 7SS Tel: 0151 708 9988 Email: nvsubhedar_lwh@yahoo.com; 40 Village Road, Oxton, Birkenhead CH43 6TY — MB ChB 1988 Bristol; MRCP (UK) 1991; MD (liverpool) 1998. (Bristol) Cons. Neonat. Paediat., Liverp. Wom.s Hosp. Socs: RCPCH.

SUBHIE, Naseem 15 Carlton Avenue, Handsworth, Birmingham B21 8AN — MB BS 1934 Lucknow.

SUBOTSKY, Fiona Eleanor Department of Child & Family Psychiatry, King's Collge Hospital, Denmark Hill, London SE5 9RS Tel: 020 7346 3219 Fax: 020 7346 3221 — MB BS 1966 Lond.; BSc (Psychol.) Lond. 1971; MRCPsych 1975. (St. Bart.) Cons. Child & Adolesc. Psychiat. S. Lond. & Maudsley Trust Lond. Socs: Fell. Roy. Coll. Psychiats.; Fell. Med. Woms. Federat. (Past Treas. Lond. Assn. of MWF); BMA. Prev: Med. Dir. Bethlem & Maudsley Trust; Cons. Child Psychiat. King's Coll. Hosp. Lond. & Brixton Child Guid. Unit; Sen. Regist. (Psychol. Med.) Hosp. Sick Childr. Gt. Ormond St. Lond.

SUBRAHMANYAM, Pasapula Chinna Ordnance Road Surgery, 171 Ordnance Road, Enfield Lock, Enfield EN3 6AD Tel: 01992 761185 Fax: 01992 760938; 5 Dickins Close, Cheshunt, Waltham Cross EN7 6BG Tel: 01992 27797 — MB BS 1969 Sri Venkateswara. (Kurnool Med. Coll.) GP Enfield. Prev: Regist. & SHO St. Geo. Hosp. Lincoln; SHO (Surg.) Co. Hosp. Louth; SHO W. Kent Gen. Hosp. Maidstone & Kent & Canterbury Hosp.

SUBRAMANIAM, Kumari Pushpa 22 North Drive, Stoke Mandeville Hospital, Aylesbury HP21 9AN — MB BS 1985 Rani Durgavati; MRCP (UK) 1993.

SUBRAMANIAM, Muruga Kumar Rushden Medical Centre, Parklands, Wymington Road, Rushden NN10 9EB Tel: 01933 396000 — MB BS 1976 (Hons.) Sri Lanka; LMSSA Lond. 1989; T(GP) 1994. (University of Ceylon) Clin. Asst. (Ophth.) Kettering Gen. Hosp.

SUBRAMANIAM, Sickan 358 Marfleet Lane, Hull HU9 5AD — MB BS 1975 Madras.

SUBRAMANIAM, Sri Dharan 18 Brooklands Court, Brooklands Avenue, Cambridge CB2 2BP — BM BCh 1996 Oxf.

SUBRAMANIAM, Mr Srinivasan Kings Mill Hospital, Mansfield Road, Sutton-in-Ashfield NG17 4JL; 15, 53 Stoney Street, Nottingham NG1 1LX — MB BS 1984 Mysore; FRCS Glas. 1990; FRCOphth 1990. Cons. Ophthalm. Kings Mill hosp. Socs: BMA. Prev: Fell.Med.Retinal.Serv.Moofields Eye.Hosp; Fell.anteria segmentServ.moorfields Eye hosp.; Specialist Regist. N Thames Rotat.

SUBRAMANIAN, Mr Anantasivan c/o Staff Residences, Glan Glwyd Hospital, Sarn Lane, Bodelwyddan, Rhyl LL18 5UJ — MB BS 1988 Bombay; FRCS Glas. 1993.

SUBRAMANIAN, Geeta c/o Old Church Hospital, Oldchurch Road, Romford RM7 0BE; 53 Great Cullings, Romford RM7 0YJ — MB BS 1980 Madras; MRCP (UK) 1981; DCH RCP Lond. 1980. (Jipmer, Pondicherry, India) Cons. Paediat. Havering Hosp. Trust Romford. Socs: Brit. Paediat. Assn. Prev: Cons. Neonat. King Abdulaziz Hosp. Jeddah, Saudi Arabia.

SUBRAMANIAN, Mr Kodaganallur Ananthakrishnier 1 Harlow Road, Rainham RM13 7UP Tel: 01708 552072 Fax: 01708 524408 — MB BS 1969 Madras; MS; DFFP; FRCS Glas.; FRCS Ed. (Madras University) Socs: BMA.

SUBRAMANIAN, Pallipuram Bharathan Hurst Road Health Centre, Hurst Road, Walthamstow, London E17 3BL Tel: 020 8503 6710 Fax: 020 8521 8293 — MB BS 1958 Madras. (Stanley Med. Coll.) Prev: Regist. (Cas.) & Regist. (Orthop.) Whipps Cross Hosp. Lond.; SHO W. Cumbld. Gp. Hosps.

SUBRAMANIAN, Shobha Dept. of Paediatrics, Pinderfields Hospital, Aberford Road, Wakefield WF1 4EE Tel: 01924 201688 — MB BS 1986 Bombay; MD Bombay 1989; MRCP 1993. (Grant Medical College, Bombay) Sen. Regist. (Paediat.) Pinderfields Hosp., Aberford Rd., Wakefield; Cons. Community Paediat., P.ss Roy. Hosp. Huddersfield. Socs: BMA. Prev: Sen. Regist. (Paediat.) S. Tyneside NHS Trust.

SUBRAMANIAN, Thiruppathy 15 Maple House, King's Mill Hospital, Mansfield Road, Sutton-in-Ashfield NG17 4NY — MB BS 1984 Madras.

SUBRAMANYAM, M Cranbury Surgery, 16 Cranbury Avenue, Southampton SO14 0LQ Tel: 023 8022 2660 Fax: 023 8022 2660 — MB BS 1963 Mysore; MB BS 1963 Mysore.

SUBRAMANYAM, Pisipati Varsha Gemini Vale, 3 Birchwood Grove, Hampton TW12 3DU Tel: 020 8941 5882 — MB BS 1965 Madras; MRCOG 1973, DObst 1968. Asst. Prof. (O & G) King Abdul Aziz Hosp. Univ. Riyadh, Saudi. Prev: SHO Ashford Hosp. Middlx.; Ho. Surg. Edgware Gen. Hosp.; Ho. Off. Watford Gen. Hosp.

SUBZPOSH, Mr Syed Yafis Ali 80 Whitmore Road, Harrow HA1 4AH Tel: 020 8248 1790 — MB BS 1979 Aligarh; MB BS Aligarh Muslim Un 1979; MCh (Orth.) Liverp. 1989.

SUCH, Agnes 30 Hallgate, Cottingham HU16 4DJ — MD 1984 Debrecen.

SUCHAK, Kirtikumar Kalyanji Centre Point Surgery, Centre Point, Fairstead, King's Lynn PE30 4SR Tel: 01553 772063 Fax: 01553 771463 — MB BS 1971 Sambalpur; LRCP LRCS Ed. LRCPS Glas. 1975. (S.S. Med. Coll. Burla) Socs: BMA. Prev: SHO Accid., Emerg. & Orthop. Dept. Ashington Gen. Hosp.; SHO (Gen. Med.) Dunston Hill Hosp. Gateshead; SHO (Chest Dis.) Kelling Hosp. Holt.

SUCHAK, Vinesh Mansukh 113 Central Road, Worcester Park KT4 8DU — MB BCh 1993 Wales; BSc (Physiol.) Wales 1990. (Univ. Wales Coll. Med.) GP Trainee.

SUCHDEV, Mr Manjit Singh 7-8 Croxdale Terrace, Pelaw, Gateshead NE10 0RR Tel: 0191 469 2337; 43 Callander, Ouston, Chester-le-Street DH2 1LG Tel: 0191 410 9446 — MB BS 1975 Punjab; MS Punjab 1978, MB BS 1975; FRCS Ed. 1983; MRCGP 1989; DRCOG 1985. GP Gateshead.

SUCHETT-KAYE, Robert Anthony William Shotfield Health Centre, Shotfield, Wallington SM6 Tel: 020 8647 0031 — MRCS Eng. LRCP Lond. 1974; BSc (Biochem.) Lond. 1971, MB BS 1974; DObst. RCOG 1980. (Roy. Free) Prev: GP VTS Croydon. Regist. (Haemat.) St. Geo. Hosp. Lond.; SHO (Path.) W.m. Hosp. Lond.

SUCHY, Katja Christina 6 Londrina Terrace, Berkhamsted HP4 2NA — State Exam Med. Munich 1991.

SUCKLE, Norman Edward Blantyre Health Centre, 64 Victoria Street, Blantyre, Glasgow G72 0BS Tel: 01698 823260; Gleniffer House, Braehead Road, Thorntonhall, Glasgow G74 5AQ Tel: 0141 644 3833 — MB ChB 1962 Glas.; DObst RCOG 1964.

SUCKLING, Heather Cullenbel (retired) 93 Ribblesdale Avenue, London N11 3AQ Tel: 020 8368 6130 Email: heathers@doctors.org.uk — MB BS Lond. 1963; FRCGP 2001; DObst RCOG 1965. p/t Cons. to BIS Healthcare, advising on Educat. for Primary Care in Macedonia. Prev: Course Organiser St. Bart. & Homerton VTS (1981-1996).

SUCKLING, Ian Gerard Sandsend Surgery, East Row, Sandsend, Whitby YO21 3SU Tel: 01947 895356 Fax: 01947 895581; (branch Surgery) Hazeldene, 9 Coach Road, Sleights, Whitby YO22 5AA Tel: 01947 810775 Fax: 01947 810667 — MB ChB 1983 Liverp.; MRCGP 1990; DGM RCP Lond. 1993. Prev: Cas. Off. RN Hosp. StoneHo.; Sen. Med. Off. RM Poole Dorset.

***SUCKLING, Rebecca Jo** 75 Festing Road, London SW15 1LW — MB BS 1996 Lond.

SUCKLING, Rupert John Rotherham Health Authority, Rotherham SG5 2QU Email: rupert.suckling@exs.rotherham-h.a.trent.nhs.uk — MB ChB 1992 Ed. Specialist Regist. Pub. Health, Rotherham HA.

SUD, Suman Kumar 711 Alum Rock Road, Alum Rock, Birmingham B8 3JA Tel: 0121 328 1746 — MB ChB 1975 Leeds; BChD Leeds 1983; LDS RCS Eng. 1983. Prev: Trainee GP Coventry & Birm. VTSs.

SUDAN, Sandeep 81 Park Road, Hendon Central, London NW4 3PA — MB BS 1993 Lond.; BSc 1990. (Kings College London) Specialist Regist (Anaesth.) William Harvey Hosp. Ashford Kent.

***SUDARSANAM, Padhmavathi** 1 Duchess Grove, Knighton Lane, Buckhurst Hill IG9 5HA Tel: 020 8498 9766 Fax: 020 8498 9766 — LRCP LRCS 1986 Ed.; LRCP LRCS Ed. LRCPS Glas. 1986; MFFP 1994.

SUDARSHAN, Catherine Dushyanthy 9 Alverton Drive, Newton Aycliffe DL5 7PP — BM 1991 Soton. SHO (A & E) Tameside Gen. Hosp. Ashton-under-Lyne. Prev: Ho. Off. (Cardiol. & Gen. Med.) Hull Roy. Infirm.; Ho. Off. (Cardiothoracic Med.) N.. Gen. Hosp. Sheff.

SUDARSHAN, Gururau 6 Sheldon Grove, Newcastle upon Tyne NE3 4JP — MB BS 1981 New Delhi, India; FCAnaesth. 1990; FFA RCSI 1989.

***SUDARSHI, Sonali** 7 Garland Way, Hornchurch RM11 2SX — MB BS 1998 Lond.; MB BS Lond 1998.

SUDBURY, John Roger (retired) Malvern, Cameron Close, Ingatestone CM4 9HA Tel: 01277 356006 — BM BCh 1948 Oxf.; MA Oxf. 1950, BM BCh 1948; MRCP Lond. 1952; DObst RCOG 1950. Prev: Jun. Med. Regist. & Res. Accouch. Lond. Hosp.

SUDBURY, Peter Russell Wexham Park Hospital, Slough SL2 4HL Tel: 01753 633000 — BM BCh 1986 Oxf.; MA Camb. 1985, BA (Natural Sci.) 1982; MRCPsych 1990; MBA Oxf. Brookes 1996. (Oxf.) Cons. (Psychiat. & Addic.s) Wexham Pk. Hosp. Slough. Socs: BMA; Soc. Study Addic.

***SUDDER, Jennifer Ailsa** 9 Battock Terrace, Torphins, Banchory AB31 4JD — MB ChB 1997 Aberd.

SUDDERICK, Mr Robert Malcolm Mount Alvernia Hospital, Harvey Road, Guildford GU1 3LX Tel: 01483 451460 Fax: 01483 451459; Meadow View House, 15 Warwicks Bench, Guildford GU1 3SZ Tel: 01483 450480 — MB BS 1983 Lond.; BDS Liverp. 1974; FRCS Eng. 1988; FRCS Ed. 1988; FDS RCS Eng. 1978. Cons. Otolaryngol. Roy. Surrey Co. Hosp. Guildford. Socs: Brit. Assn. Otol.; BMA; Roy. Soc. Med. Prev: Sen. Regist. (Otolaryngol.) Char. Cross Hosp. Lond. & Mayday Hosp. Croydon; Regist. (Otolaryngol.) Char. Coss Hosp. Lond.; SHO (Otolaryngol.) Univ. Hosp. Qu. Med. Centre Nottm.

SUDDERUDDIN, Ameena Pretoria Road Surgery, 1 Pretoria Road, Leytonstone, London E11 4BB Tel: 020 8539 3232 — MB BS 1973 Dacca.

SUDDES, Kevin Paul The Coach House, Boycott Manor, Dadford Road, Buckingham MK18 5JZ — MB ChB 1982 Leeds.

SUDDICK, Evelyn Mabel 25 South Drive, Fulwood, Preston PR2 9SR Tel: 01772 862674 — MB ChB 1962 Liverp.; DObst RCOG 1964; DTM & H Liverp. 1964. Community Child Health Doc. Blackpool Wyre, rfylde Community NHS Trust. Prev: SCMO (Child Health & Audiometry) Chorley & S. Ribble HA.

SUDDLE, Abid Raza 59 Clarendon Rise, London SE13 5EX — MB BS 1993 Lond.

SUDDLE, Asim Nadeem 75 Old Ford End Road, Bedford MK40 4LY — MB ChB 1992 Glas.

SUDELL, Anthony John North West Lancashire Health Authority, Wesham Park Hospital, Derby Road, Wesham, Preston PR4 3AL Tel: 01253 306371 — MB BS 1981 Lond.; MSc Manch. 1988; MA Oxf. 1983; MFPHM 1989. (St. Mary's) Cons. Pub. Health Med. NW Lancs. HA. Prev: Sen. Regist. (Community Med.) N. W.. RHA.

SUDELL, Christopher Joseph Meden Vale Medical Centre, Egmanton Road, Meden Vale, Warsop, Mansfield NG20 9QN Tel: 01623 845694 Fax: 01623 844550; 24 St. Peter's Avenue, Church Warsop, Mansfield NG20 0RZ — MB ChB 1986 Sheff.; BSc Lond. 1981. Prev: SHO (O & G) Doncaster Roy. Infirm.; Trainee GP Sheff.; SHO (Paediat.) Childr. Hosp. Sheff.

SUDELL, Joanna Mary 67 St James Lane, London N10 3QY — MB BS 1985 Lond.; MRCGP 1989; DRCOG 1988; DCH RCP Lond. 1988.

SUDELL, Raymond Paul Meden Vale Medical Centre, Egmanton Road, Meden Vale, Warsop, Mansfield NG20 9QN Tel: 01623 845694 Fax: 01623 844550 — MB ChB 1988 Sheff.; MRCGP 1992.

SUDELL, William Alexander Hamilton Road Surgery, 201 Hamilton Road, Felixstowe IP11 7DT Tel: 01394 283197 — MB BS 1978 Lond.; BSc (Hons.) Lond. 1975; MRCS Eng. LRCP Lond. 1978; AFOM RCP Lond. 1992; DRCOG 1982; OFFP 1993. (Guy's) Med. Advisor Cranes Fluid Systems. Socs: BMA; Soc. Occupat. Med. Prev: Trainee GP Brighton VTS; Ho. Phys., Ho. Surg. & SHO (Med. & Cardiol.) Guy's Hosp. Lond.

SUDHA, Immaneni Kanaka Cranham Health Centre, 117 Marlborough Gardens, Upminster RM14 1SR Tel: 01708 222722 Fax: 01708 640961; 45 Viking Way, Brentwood CM15 9HY Tel: 01277 219963 — MB BS 1975 Sri Venkateswara; MRCP (UK) 1987; MRCGP 1990; DCH 1986; DRCOG 1987. (Sri Venkateswara Univ.) GP Trainer Upminster; B & H MAAG Co-Chairm.

SUDHAKAR, Chundarathil 27 Norman Avenue, South Croydon CR2 0QH Tel: 020 8660 5393 Fax: 020 8239 92450 Email: c.sudhakakar@btinternet.com — MB BS 1967 Andhra. (Andhra Med. Coll. Vizag) GP Tutor S. Croydon; Sen. Tutor (Gen. Pract.) St. Geo. Hosp. Med. Sch. Lond. Prev: SHO (Surg.) St. Chas. Hosp. Lond. & Vict. Hosp. Worksop; SHO (Surg. & Urol.) Kent & Canterbury Hosp.

SUDHAKAR, Mr Joseph Ebenezer Norht Tees General Hosptial, Dept. of Orthopaedics, Hardwick, Stockton-on-Tees TS19 8PE Tel: 01642 617617 Fax: 01642 624902; 2 School Lane, Barbon, Carnforth LA6 2LP Tel: 015242 76388 Fax: 015242 76316 Email: joesudhakar@btinternet.com — MB BS 1987 Kerala; FRCS Eng. 1993. Specialist Regist. In Orphopaedic Suregy. Socs: BMA; BOA; MDU.

SUDHAKAR, K St John's Surgery, 2 Greenfield Walk, Huyton, Liverpool L36 0XP Tel: 0151 489 9067.

SUDHAKAR, Madhwapathi c/o Department of Anaesthetics, Prince Charles Hospital, Merthyr Tydfil CF47 9DT — MD BS 1986 Sri Venkateswara.

SUDHAKAR KRISHNAN, Vidya 15 Main Street, Thorner, Leeds LS14 3DX — MB ChB 1994 Leeds.

SUDHAKAR RAO, Settipalli 17 Applewood Close, St Leonards-on-Sea TN37 7JS — MB BS 1980 Osmania.

***SUDHAKARAN, Nadarajan** 21 Westbourne Gardens, Hove BN3 5PL — MB BCh 1995 Wales.

SUDHEER, Kondaveeti 4 Thompson Close, Folkestone CT19 5UA — MB BS 1973 Sri Venkateswara.

SUDLOW, Catherine Lucy Moore Clinicial Trial Service Unit and Epidemiogical Studies Unit, Radcliffe Infirmary, Oxford OX2 6HE Tel: 01865 404855 Fax: 01865 404849 Email: cathie.sudlow@ctsu.ox.ac.uk; 5 Cumberland Street, Se Lane, Edinburgh EH3 6RU Tel: 0131 557 1499 — BM BCh 1991 Oxf.; MSc (Epidemiol.) Lond. 1997; BA (Hons.) Med. Sci. Camb. 1988; MRCP (UK) 1994. (Oxf.) Clin. Research Fell. Clin. Trial Serv. Unit & Epidemiol. Studies Unit, Oxf. Univ.; Hon. Regist. (Neurol.) Radcliffe Infirm. NHS Trust, Oxf. Socs: Steering Comm. - Antithrombotic Ther. Trialists Collaboration; Assn. Brit. Neurols.; Cochrane Stroke Gp. Prev: Regist. (Med. Neurol.) W.. Gen. Hosp. Edin.; Regist. (Gen. Med.) Worthing Hosp. W. Sussex.; SHO Rotat. (Gen. Med.) W.. Gen. Hosp. Edin.

SUDLOW, Christopher Mark Department of Medicine, The Medical School, University of Newcastle, Newcastle upon Tyne NE2 4HH Tel: 0191 222 6000 Fax: 0191 222 0723; 110B St Georges Terrace, Jesmond, Newcastle upon Tyne NE2 2DP Tel: 0191 281 7991 — BM BCh 1990 Oxf.; MA Camb. 1992; MRCP (UK) 1993. MRC Train. Fell. (Health Servs. Research) Univ. Newc. Socs: Brit. Geriat. Soc.

SUDLOW, Elizabeth Mary 58 Craigleith View, Edinburgh EH4 3JY Tel: 0131 337 2022 — MB BS 1964 Lond. (St. Thos.) SCMO Lothian Region Family Plann. Serv.; Clin. Asst. Colposcopy Unit Roy. Infirm. Edin. Prev: Ho. Surg. St. Thos. Hosp. Lond.; Ho. Phys. N. Staffs. Roy. Infirm. Stoke-on-Trent.

SUDLOW, Michael Frederick 58 Craigleith View, Edinburgh EH4 3JY Tel: 0131 337 2022 — MB BS 1964 Lond.; FRCP Lond. 1983, M 1967; FRCP Ed. 1982. (St. Thos.) Cons. Phys. & Hon. Sen. Lect. (Med.) Roy. Infirm. Edin. Prev: Ho. Phys. St. Thos. Hosp. Lond.; Ho. Surg. Qu. Eliz. Hosp. Birm.

SUDLOW

SUDLOW, Mr Robin Andrew 82 Burnham Road, Leigh-on-Sea SS9 2JS — MB BS 1972 Lond.; FRCS Eng. 1979. (Lond. Hosp.) p/t Cons. Orthop. Surg. S.end Gen. Hosp. Socs: Fell. Brit. Orthop. Assn.; Fell. Roy. Soc. of Med. Prev: Lect. The Lond. Hosp.; Sen. Regist. (Orthop.) Notley Hosp.; Sen. Regist. Roy. Nat. Orthop. Hosp. Lond.

SUDLOW, Sheila Staithe Road Surgery, Staithe Road, Ludham, Great Yarmouth NR29 5AB Tel: 01692 678611 Fax: 01692 678295; Rosecroft, Church Road, Catfield, Great Yarmouth NR29 5AX Tel: 01692 580646 — MB ChB 1977 Manch.; MRCGP 1981; DRCOG 1979. Prev: GP Stalham.

SUDWORTH, Helen Muriel TY LLWYD, 60 Castle Street, Caergwrle, Wrexham LL12 9DS Email: helen.sudworth4@net.ntl.com — MB BS 1996 Lond. (Lond. Hosp. Med. Coll.) SHO Med. / GP Trainee. Socs: CMF.

SUE-LING, Mr Henry Michael Leeds General Infirmary, Great George St., Leeds LS1 3EX Tel: 01132 923467 Fax: 01132 923635; St Catherine's, College Farm Lane, Linton, Wetherby LS22 4HR — MB ChB 1980 Leeds; MD Leeds 1986; FRCS Glas. 1986; FRCS Eng. 1987. Cons. Surg. Leeds Gen. Infirmay. Socs: BMA; Assn. Surg.; Brit. Soc. Gastroenterol.

***SUETT, Mark James** Crantock, Westgate, Bridgnorth WV16 5BL — MB ChB 1997 Birm.

SUFFERN, Margaret Alison (retired) 6 Cundall Way, Harrogate HG2 0DY Tel: 01423 503142 — MB ChB 1943 Leeds. Prev: Matern. & Child Welf. Off. Leeds.

SUFFERN, Walter Sefton (retired) 6 Cundall Way, Harrogate HG2 0DY Tel: 01423 503142 — MB ChB 1942 Leeds; MD Leeds 1947; FRCP Lond. 1970, M 1948; MRCS Eng. LRCP Lond. 1942. Prev: Cons. Phys. Harrogate Gen. Hosp. & Ripon Hosp.

SUFFIELD, Mervyn John Trinity Care, 15 Musters Road, West Bridgeford, Nottingham NG2 7PP Tel: 01159 455485 Email: mervynsuffield@trinitycare.co.uk; The Cottage, Winchester Road, Waltham Chase, Southampton SO32 2LG — MB BS Newc. 1975. Dir. of Care. Socs: Coll. Occup. Health. Prev: Princip. Gen. Pract. Occupat. Health Specialty.

***SUFFLING, Hannah** 20 Spur Hill Avenue, Parkstone, Poole BH14 9PH — MB ChB 1998 Bristol.

SUFFLING, Norford John (retired) 20 Spur Hill Avenue, Parkstone, Poole BH14 9PH — MB BS Lond. 1963; MRCPsych 1975; DPM Eng. 1973; FRCPsych 1998. Prev: Cons. Psychiat. E. Dorset Health Dist.

SUFRAZ, Reshad Bowden House Clinic, London Road, Harrow HA1 3JL Tel: 020 8966 7000 Fax: 020 8864 6092 — MB BS 1988 Lond.; MA (Clin. Psychol.) Pepperdine 1996; BSc Lond. 1985; MRCPsych 1994. (Univ. Coll. Hosp.) Assoc. Specialist (Psychiat.) Bowden Ho. Clinic Harrow; Resid. Med. Off. Bowden Ho. Clinic. Socs: BMA; MPS; Roy. Coll. Psychiats.

SUGANTHI, Damal Pathangi Queens Hospital FPC Unit, 200 Pawsons Road, Croydon CR0 2QF Tel: 020 8664 9002 Fax: 020 8664 9003; 8 Sprucedale Gardens, Shirley, Croydon CR0 5HU Tel: 020 8654 5049 — MB BS 1964 Madras; MRCOG 1974, DObst 1967. Clin. Asst. (Obst.) Mayday Hosp. Thornton Heath Surrey. Socs: Fell. Roy. Soc. Med.; BMA. Prev: SHO (O & G) Beckenham Matern. Hosp., Greenwich Dist. Hosp. & Lewisham Gp. Hosps.

SUGARMAN, Mr Ian David 17 Bernards Close, Christchurch BH23 2EH; The Old Methodist School Room, Marston Road, Tockwith, York YO26 7PR — MB ChB 1985 Leeds; FRCS Ed. 1991.

SUGARMAN, Philip Ashley The Trevor Gibbens Unit, Maidstone Hospital, Hermitage Lane, Maidstone ME16 9NN Tel: 01622 723106 Fax: 01622 720820 — MB ChB 1983 Liverp.; MSc Manch. 1990; MRCPsych 1987. Cons. Forens. Psychiat. Invicta Community Care NHS Trust; Sen. Lect. Guys & St. Thomas Med. Sch.; Regional Adviser Forens. Psychiat. S. E. Region NHS Exec.; Clin. Dir. Kent Forens. Psychiat. Serv. Prev: Sen. Regist. Reaside Clinic Birm.

SUGARMAN, Mr Philip Morris 3 Leamington Avenue, Manchester M20 2WQ — MB BS 1988 Lond.; BSc Lond. 1985, MB BS 1988; FRCS Ed. 1994. Specialist Regist. (A&E) Mersey Deanery.

SUGARS, Kenneth Hugh, Surg. Capt. RN Retd. 11 Waudby Close, Walkington, Beverley HU17 8SA Tel: 01482 861056 — MB ChB 1965 Ed.; MRCGP 1971. (Ed.) Occupat. Health Phys. Hull HA; Company Med. Off. Brit. Aerospace Brough; Occupat. Health Phys. Med. Indust. Servs. Ltd. E.bourne. Socs: Soc. Occupat. Med. Prev: Dir. Med. Personnel Med. Directorate Gen. (Naval); Adviser Gen. Pract. to Med. Dir. Gen. (Navy).

SUGATHADASA, Jean Evangeline Conkers, 14 Westfield Road, Toftwood, Dereham NR19 1JB — MB BS 1971 Ceylon; DCCH RCP Ed. 1990; DCH Ceylon 1976. (Colombo - Sri-Lanka) Staff Grade Community Paediat. Norwich Health Care Community Trust.

SUGDEN, Mr Brian Anthony 8 Balcomie Crescent, Troon KA10 7AR Tel: 01292 311009 — MB BS 1970 Newc.; FRCS Glas. 1976. Cons. Surg. CrossHo. Hosp. Kilmarnock.

SUGDEN, Brian David Sugden and Ndirika, The Health Centre, Curtis Street, Hucknall, Nottingham NG15 7JE Tel: 0115 963 3580 Fax: 0115 963 3733 — MB BS 1973 Lond.; MRCGP 1977. GP Hucknall; Clin. Tutor Gen. Pract. Univ. Nottm.

SUGDEN, Christopher John St Andrew's Hospice, Henderson Street, Airdrie ML6 6DJ Tel: 01236 766957 Fax: 01236 748786 Email: hospice@btcomed.com; 59 Lubnaig Road, Newlands, Glasgow G43 2RX — MB ChB 1976 Aberd.; FFA RCS Eng. 1980. Med. Dir. St. And.Hospice Airdrie Lanarksh.; Cons. Anaesth. Lanarksh. Acute Hosp.s NHS Trust. Prev: Cons. Anaesth. S. Gen. Hosp. NHS Trust.

SUGDEN, Elaine Margaret Department of Radiotherapy & Oncology, Churchill Hospital, Oxford OX3 7LJ Tel: 01865 741841; 36 North Hinksey Village, Oxford OX2 0NA Tel: 01865 728128 — BM BCh 1972 Oxf.; MA Oxf. 1972; DCH Eng. 1975; FCR Eng 1975. Cons in Clin. Onocol. Socs: Chair St Hilda's Med. Soc. Oxf.

SUGDEN, Jacqueline Janet Chenies, Lakeview Road, Furnace Wood, Felbridge, East Grinstead RH19 2QB — BM 1995 Soton.

SUGDEN, Joanna Helen Rosedale, Bluntisham Rd, Colne, Huntingdon PE28 3LY — BChir 1996 Camb.; MB BChir Camb. 1996; DTM & H Liverp 1998. (Camb.) GP Regist. Foundry La. Surg. Leeds. Prev: SHO (Rheumat.) Leeds United Teachg. Hosps.; SHO (A&E) S. Manch. Univ. Hosps. Trust; Ho. Off. (Gen. Surg.) Ipswich Hosp.

SUGDEN, John Christopher Hawthorne Farm, Little Fenton, South Milford, Leeds LS25 6HF Tel: 0193781 7462 — MB ChB 1968 Leeds; MB ChB (Hons.) Leeds 1968; BSc (Hons.) Leeds 1965; FFA RCS Eng. 1972. Cons. Anaesth. Leeds Gen. Infirm. & Sen. Clin. Lect. Univ. Leeds.

SUGDEN, John Harrison (retired) Hingabank Farm, Deepdale Dent, Sedbergh LA10 5RD Email: john@sugden.dial.lakesnet.co.uk — MB ChB 1963 St. And.; DPM Leeds 1974. Prev: Regist. (Psychiat.) Lynfield Mt. Hosp. Bradford.

SUGDEN, John Samuel 50 Totley Brook Road, Dore, Sheffield S17 3QT — MRCS Eng. LRCP Lond. 1954; MRCGP 1965; DObst RCOG 1957.

SUGDEN, Kenneth Heaver (retired) Holly Bank, Rogues Hill, Penshurst, Tonbridge TN11 8BQ — MRCS Eng. LRCP Lond. 1936; MRCS Eng., LRCP Lond. 1936. Prev: Asst. Co. Med. Off.

SUGDEN, Kenneth John Macclesfield, Pinfold Lane, Scarisbrick, Ormskirk L40 8HR Tel: 01704 840350 Email: jsbrbkbuff@aol.com — MB BS Lond. 1959; MRCS Eng. LRCP Lond. 1959; Cert FPA 1974; DObst RCOG 1963. (St. Bart.) Socs: MRCGP; BMA. Prev: Managing Dir. On Call Ltd.

SUGDEN, Mary (retired) 35 Gill Bank Road, Ilkley LS29 0AU Tel: 01943 601480 — MB ChB 1951 Leeds; DCH Eng. 1954.

***SUGDEN, Paul Elliot** 52 Pirie Road, Congleton CW12 2EF — MB ChB 1994 Manch.

SUGG, David James Berriedale, Mayfield Lane, Wadhurst TN5 6JE Tel: 01892 782959 — MB ChB 1988 Manch.; MRCGP 1996; DRCOG 1991. Prev: GP/Regist. HildenBoro, Med. Gp. Tonbridge; GP Kawana Waters 7 Day Med. Centre Minyama Qu.sland, Austral.; SHO (A & E & ENT) Roy. Preston Hosp.

SUGGETT, Nigel Ross 2 Fernwoods, Bartley Green, Birmingham B32 3RL — BM BCh 1994 Oxf.; FRCS (Eng.) 1998. Specialist Regist. (Gen. Surg.) W. Midl. Rotat. Prev: SHO Rotat. (Surg.) Birm. Heartlands Hosp.; SHO (Gen. Surg.) Sandwell Gen. Hosp.; SHO (Gen. Surg.) Qu.'s Hosp., Burton-on-Trent.

SUGHRA, Ghulam 19 Surig Road, Canvey Island SS8 9EP Tel: 01268 695331 — MB BS 1971 Punjab.

SUGRUE, David Charles 6 Bownder Dowr, Hayle TR27 6JA Tel: 01736 757582 — MB BS 1988 Lond.; MRCGP 1992. (Char. Cross and Westm.) Police Sug. Devon & Cornw. Constab. Prev: Trainee GP Truro VTS.

SUGRUE, Mr Denis Lambert (retired) 2 Fieldway, Trentham, Stoke-on-Trent ST4 8AQ Tel: 01782 657953 — MCh NUI 1953,

MB BCh BAO 1950; DLO Eng. 1953. Prev: Cons. Phys. Genitourin. Med. N. Staffs Hosp. Centre & Dist. Gen. Hosps.tafford.

***SUGUMAR, Kanagalingam** 27 Hamond Close, South Croydon CR2 6BZ — LRCP LRCS Ed. LRCPS Glas. 1995.

SUGUNAKARA RAO, Mr Yalamanchili Venkata Krishna 8 Bronte Close, Kettering NN16 9XN — FRCS Glas. 1984; FRCSI 1984.

SUHAIL, Mohammed 6 Reaper Crescent, Highgreen, Sheffield S35 3FH — MB ChB 1993 Dundee.

SUHARWARDY, John Mohammed Ally 12 Breamore Crescent, Dudley DY1 3DA — MB ChB 1986 Manch.

SUKHDEO, Marlene Kalawatee 14 Fane Way, Maidenhead SL6 2TL — MB BS 1990 West Indies.

SUKHIA, Viraf Dara 6 Fulmer Way, London W13 9XQ Tel: 020 8840 4259 — MB BS 1966 Poona; DCH Eng. 1969; DObst RCOG 1968. (B.J. Med. Coll.) Prev: Regist. (Paediat.) King Edwd. Hosp. Ealing & Perivale Matern. Hosp.; SHO Paediat. Soton. Childr. Hosp.; SHO Neonat. Paediat. Whittington Hosp. Lond.

SUKUMAR, Pathmajani Dove Dale, 22 Over Hill Road, Wilmslow Park, Wilmslow SK9 2BE Tel: 01625 539659 — LMSSA 1993 Lond. SHO (c/o the Elderly) Univ. Hosp. S. Manch.; GP Regist. Prev: SHO (Paediat.) Macclesfield D.G.H.

SUKUMARAN, Othayoth Sukumaran, Jupiter House Surgery, Sunderland Road, Horden, Peterlee SR8 4NN Tel: 0191 587 2488 Fax: 0191 586 1995 — MB BS 1966 Kerala.

SUKUMARAN, Suparna 149 Saltram Crescent, London W9 3JT Tel: 020 8960 6771 — MB ChB 1989 Liverp.; MRCPsych 1996; DCCH RCGP 1993. (Liverp.) Cons. Child & Adolesc. Psyhiatrist W. Lond. Ment. Health Trust. Socs: BMA; Roy. Soc. of Med. Prev: SHO & Regist. Rotat. (Psychiat.) UMDS Lond.; SHO Rotat. (Paediat.) Char. Cross & W.m. Hosps. Lond.; SHO Rotat. (Med.) Roy. Liverp. Hosp.

SUKUMARAN, Suryagopal Obulisamy The Frank Swire Health Centre, Nursery Lane, Ovenden, Halifax HX3 5TE Tel: 01422 355535 — MB BS 1970 Madras; MFCH Lond. 1989; JCPTGP Lond. 1982; DCH RCPSI 1977. GP. Socs: Med. Protec. Soc.; Fac. Community Health.

SUKUMARAN NAIR, Cheripadi Lakshmi, Park Farm Villas, South Newsham, Blyth NE24 4HA — MB BS 1974 Mysore; BSc, MB BS Mysore 1974. (Kasturba Med. Coll.) SHO Wharfedale Gen. Hosp. Otley. Prev: SHO (Med.) Gen. Hosp. Chester-le-St.; SHO (Geriat.) Wharfedale Gen. Hosp. Otley.

SUKUMARAN NAIR, Parameswara Kurup Frimley Park Hospital NHS Trust, Portsmouth Road, Frimley, Camberley GU15 5UJ Tel: 01276 604604; 13 Falmouth Close, Camberley GU15 1EA — MB BS 1974 Kerala; Dip. Thoracic Med. Lond 1988; DCH RCPSI 1985; Dip. Respirat. Med. RCPSI 1989. Staff Grade (Paediat. Med.) Frimley Pk. Hosp. NHS Trust.

SUKUMARAN NAIR, Sethulekshmy Frimley Park Hospital NHS Trust, Portsmouth Road, Frimley, Camberley GU16 7UJ; 13 Falmouth Close, Camberley GU15 1EA — MB BS 1974 Kerala; MD Kerala 1979; MRCOG 1991. Staff Gyn. & Obst. Frimley Pk. Hosp. NHS Trust.

SULAIMAN, H M Riverside Centre for Health, Park Street, Liverpool L8 6QP Tel: 0151 706 8306.

SULAIMAN, Mohamed Zubayr Careem c/o Department GU Medicine, Gloucester Royal Hospital, Great Western Road, Gloucester GL1 3NL Tel: 01452 394462 Fax: 01452 394466; 3 Ellesmere Grove, Cheltenham GL50 2QQ Tel: 01242 252576 — MB ChB 1972 St. And.; FRCOG 1996, M 1981. (Univ. of St. Andrews) Cons. Phys. (Genitourin. Med.+ HIV Med.) Gloucester; Cons. Phys. (Genitourin. Med + HIV Med.) Cheltenham. Socs: Med. Soc. Study VD; Brit. Soc. Colpos. & Cerv. Path. Prev: Cons. Phys. (Genitourin. Med.) Gt. Yarmouth & Waveney HA; Sen. Regist. (Genitourin. Med.) Roy. Hallamsh. Hosp. Sheff. & Gen. Hosp. Nottm.

SULAIMAN, Mr Shah Khalid Dept of Orthopaedic, Walsall Manor Hospital NHS Trust, Moat Rd, Walsall WS2 9PS; 160 The Mall, Fendon, Pinner HA5 9TH — MB BS 1977 Karachi; FRCS Ed. 1982; MRCS Eng. LRCP Lond. 1979; FRCS (Orth). Cons (Orthop) Surg. Socs: BFO; BMA.

***SULAIMAN, Syed Ayaz Lutfi** 49 Castle Road, Colne BB8 7AR — MB ChB 1997 Liverp.

SULAIMAN, Syed Mahmood Urfi 49 Castle Road, Colne BB8 7AR — MB ChB 1992 Leeds.

SULAIVANY, Taha-Ismail Abbo Ground Floor Flat, 123 Hamilton Place, Aberdeen AB15 5BD — MB ChB 1978 Mosul; MRCP (UK) 1989; MRCPI 1989.

SULCH, David Antony 1 Winston Drive, Isham, Kettering NN14 1HS — MB BS 1986 Lond.

SULE, Bamidele Adebola 129 Mowbray Road, Cambridge CB1 7SP — MB ChB 1984 Obafemi Awolowu U, Nigeria.

SULE, Hem Dattatray Moss Side Medical Practice, 16 Moss Side Way, Leyland, Preston PR26 7XL Tel: 01772 466004 Fax: 01772 622897 — MB BS 1968 Jiwaji.

SULE, Kuldip Kaur 163 Dunstable Road, Luton LU1 1BW — MB BS 1986 Lond.; MRCGP 1992.

SULE, Sulabha Hem Moss Side Medical Practice, 16 Moss Side Way, Leyland, Preston PR26 7XL Tel: 01772 466004 Fax: 01772 622897 — MB BS 1970 Jiwaji; MRCOG 1984.

SULE SUSO, Josep Staffordshire Oncology Centre, North Staffs Hospital Trust, Princes Road, Stoke-on-Trent ST4 7LN; 80 Dartmouth Avenue, Westlands, Newcastle ST5 3PA — LMS Autonoma Barcelona 1988. Clin. Asst. (Oncol.) Staffs. Oncol. Centre N. Staffs. Hosp. Trust. Prev: Research Fell. (Experim. Oncol.) Nat. Cancer Inst. Milan, Italy; SHO (Oncol. Radiolther.) N. Staffs Roy. Infirm. Stoke-on-Trent.

SULEMAN, Abdulrahim Eaglestone Health Centre, Standing Way, Eaglestone, Milton Keynes MK6 5AZ Tel: 01908 679111 Fax: 01908 230601 — MB BCh 1972 Wales; DObst RCOG 1974.

SULEMAN, Adil Shabaz 44 Sunderland Road, Bradford BD9 4QJ — MB ChB 1994 Dundee.

SULEMAN, Bilqis Akhtar Warrington Hospital NHS Trust, Lovely Lane, Warrington WA5 1QG — MB BS 1969 Peshawar; MRCPath 1984.

SULEMAN, Mohammad Ishaque Manor Park Medical Centre, High St., Polegate BN26 5DJ Tel: 01323 482301 Fax: 01323 484848; 7 Weatherby Close, Park Lane, Eastbourne BN21 2XB Tel: 01323 502041 — MB BS 1961 Karachi. (Dow. Med. Coll. Karachi) Hosp. Pract. Diabetic & Cardiac Clinics Dist. Gen. Hosp. E.bourne. Socs: BMA; E.bourne Med. Soc. Prev: Regist. (Med.) E.bourne Hosp. Gp.; SHO (Med. & Paediat.) St. Helen's Hosp. Hastings; Ho. Off. (Paediat.) Evelina Childr. Hosp. Guy's Hosp. Lond.

***SULEMAN, Mohammed Hanif Jamal** 10 Poole Street, Blackburn BB1 3JS — MB ChB 1998 Sheff.; MB ChB Sheff 1998.

SULEMAN, Nawshad Akberali Brooklands, Coleshill Road, Birmingham B37 7HL — MB BS 1977 Osmania; MRCPsych 1985.

SULEMAN, Mr Shamshudeen Karmali Epsom General Hospital, Epsom KT8 7EG Tel: 01372 735735 Fax: 01372 745351 Email: ssuleman@steliev.sghms.ac.uk — LRCPI & LM, LRSCI & LM 1958; FRCS Ed. 1965; FFAEM 1996. Cons. A & E Med. Epsom Gen. Hosp. Socs: RSM Fell.; BAEM Fell. Prev: Sen. Orthop. Specialist MoH Kenya; Assoc. Prof. Orthop. Univ. Agakhan Karachi, Pakistan.

***SULEMAN, Subeena Tubussum** 99 Thornbury Road, Birmingham B20 3DE — MB ChB 1997 Glas.

***SULEMAN, Zora** 78 Third Avenue, Bordesley Green, Birmingham B9 5RL — MB ChB 1994 Leeds.

SULH, Jaswinder Singh 29 Park Lane, Slough SL3 7PG — MB ChB 1987 Manch.; MRCGP 1993; DCH RCP Lond. 1991; DRCOG 1992.

SULIMAN, Abdel Moneim Hussein Cardiology Department, Newham General Hospital, Glen Road, Plaistow, London E13 8SL Tel: 020 7476 4000 Fax: 020 7363 8350; 239 Prince Regent Lane, Plaistow, London E13 8SD Tel: 020 7474 7307 — MB BS 1976 Khartoum; MB BS Khartoum Sudan 1976; MSc Cardiovasc. Studies Leeds 1988; MRCPI 1989; DTCD Wales 1984.

SULIMAN, Mohamed El Ghazali Rahmtalla The Endocrine Unit, Q Floor, Royal Hallamshire Hospital, Glossop Road, Sheffield S10 2JF — MB BS 1985 Khartoum; MRCP (UK) 1993.

SULIMAN, Mr Mohamed Tayfoor Mohamed 1 Red Wood Croft, Nuneaton CV10 7HY — MB BS 1981 Khartoum; FRCS Glas. 1994.

SULISTIO, Edy 14 Birley Park, Didsbury, Manchester M20 2TL — BM BS 1991 Nottm.

SULKE, Alfred Neil Department of Cardiology, Eastbourne General Hospital, Kings Drive, Eastbourne BN21 2UB Tel: 01323 423747 — BM 1983 Soton.; BSc (Hons. Biochem.) Sussex 1977; DM Soton. 1991; MRCP (UK) 1986; FACC 1995. Cons. (Cardiol.) E.bourne Gen. Hosp. & St. Thos. Hosp. Lond. Socs: Brit. Pacing &

SULLIVAN

Electrophysiol. Gp.; N. Amer. Soc. Pacing & Electrophys.; Fell. Amer. Coll. Cardiol. Prev: Sen. Regist. (Cardiol.) Guy's Hosp. Lond.; Research Regist. & Regist. (Cardiol.) Guy's Hosp. Lond.; SHO Rotat. Soton. Univ. Hosps.

SULLIVAN, Aline (retired) 21 Saffrons Court, Compton Place Road, Eastbourne BN21 1DX — MRCS Eng. LRCP Lond. 1951.

SULLIVAN, Angela Jane Northcroft Surgery, Northcroft Lane, Newbury RG14 1BU Tel: 01635 31575 Fax: 01635 551857; Frogmill, Pound Lane, Burghclere, Newbury RG20 9JR Tel: 01635 278541 — MB ChB 1975 Leeds; MRCP (UK) 1980; MRCGP 1983; DCH Eng. 1978; DRCOG 1977. Prev: Regist. (Gen. Med.) Roy. Berks. Hosp. Reading; SHO (Med.) Radcliffe Infirm. Oxf.; SHO (O & G) & (Paediat.) Soton. Gen. Hosp.

SULLIVAN, Anita Louise 23 Watling Street, Bury BL8 2JD — MB ChB 1994 Manch.

SULLIVAN, Ann 23 John Street, Hamilton ML3 7EU Tel: 01698 427923 — MB ChB 1991 Glas.

SULLIVAN, Ann Kathleen 264 Trinity Road, London SW18 3RQ — MB BS 1988 Tasmania; MRCP (UK) 1995.

SULLIVAN, Anne Cestria Health Centre, Whitehill Way, Chester-le-Street DH2 3DJ Tel: 0191 388 7771 Fax: 0191 387 1803; 173 Gilesgate, Durham DH1 1QH — MB BS 1971 Lond.; MRCS Eng. LRCP Lond. 1971; DObst RCOG 1973.

SULLIVAN, Brendan Anthony St. Georges Lodge, 123 Fronks Road, Dovercourt, Harwich CO12 4EF Tel: 01255 502909 — MB 1978 Camb.; MA Camb. 1978, MB 1978, BChir 1977; MLCOM 1989.

SULLIVAN, Brian Anthony Pantysgawen Farm, Thornhill Road, Cardiff CF14 9UA Tel: 029 2062 3054 — MB BCh 1974 Wales; FRCR 1979. Cons. Radiol. Roy. Gwent Hosp. Newport. Socs: Brit. Soc. Skeletal Radiol.; Eur. Soc. Skeletal Radiol.; Brit. Soc. Interven. Radiol.

SULLIVAN, Carol Linda Singleton Hospital, Sketty, Swansea SA2 8QA Tel: 01792 205666 Fax: 01792 285244 Email: carol.sullivan@swansea-tr.nhs.uk; 15 Roger Beck Way, Sketty, Swansea SA2 0JF — BM BCh 1987 Oxf.; BA (Hons.) Oxf. 1984; MRCP (UK) 1991; FRCPCH 1997. (Oxf.) Cons. Paediat. Singleton Hosp. Swansea. Prev: Sen. Regist. (Paediat.) Nottm. & Derby Hosps.; Regist. (Paediat.) Bristol & Exeter; SHO (Paediat. Cardiol.) Childr. Hosp. Birm.

SULLIVAN, Caroline Frances 18 Midland Avenue, Nottingham NG7 2FD — MB ChB 1982 Liverp.; MRCPsych 1987.

SULLIVAN, Caroline Mary 481C Hulloway Road, London N19 4DD Tel: 020 7272 8004 — MB ChB 1996 Manch. SHO (A & E) UCLH Lond.

SULLIVAN, Charles Anthony (retired) 35 Urney Road, Strabane BT82 9DA — LAH Dub. 1951.

SULLIVAN, Charlotte Anne Flat 3 Balmonac Court, 1 Scotland St., Birmingham B12 1RR — MB BS 1992 Lond.; BSc (Hons.) Lond. 1991; FRCOphth 1996. (St. George's Hosp. Med. Sch. Lond.) Specialist Regist. (Ophth.): Socs: Fell. Roy. Coll. Of Ophthal.

SULLIVAN, Christine June The Health Centre, 80 Knaresborough Road, Harrogate HG2 7LU Tel: 01423 883212; 6 Stone Rings Close, Harrogate HG2 9HZ Tel: 01423 872737 — MB ChB 1978 Bristol; DRCOG 1981.

SULLIVAN, Christobel Jean 5 Elston Hall, Elston, Newark NG23 5NP Tel: 01636 525657 — MB BS 1965 Lond.; MB BS (Hons. Surg.) Lond. 1965; MRCS Eng. LRCP Lond. 1965. Asst. Specialist Dermat. Grantham Hosp. & INCS. Socs: Lincoln Med. Soc. Prev: GP Newark; Hon. Surg. Newmarket Gen. Hosp.; Hon. Phys. Brit. Milit. Hosp. Singapore.

SULLIVAN, Dorothy Beatrice 1 Fergusson Place, St Andrews KY16 9NF — MB ChB 1980 Glas.; MRCGP 1987; DRCOG 1985; MSc (Med. Sci.) Glas. 1997. GP Princip.

SULLIVAN, Francis Michael Blantyre Health Centre, Victoria St., Blantyre, Glasgow G72 0BS Tel: 0141826331; 124 Kylepark Drive, Uddingston, Glasgow G71 7DE — MB ChB 1980 Glas.; MB ChB (Hons.) Glas. 1980; PhD (Clin. Epidemiol.) Glas. 1991; FRCP Glas. 1994; MRCP (UK) 1983; MRCGP 1984. Sen. Lect. (Gen. Pract.) Glas. Prev: Lect. (Gen. Pract.) Univ. Glas.; Cons. Phys. Seychelles.

SULLIVAN, Frederick Donald The Fountain Medical Centre, Sherwood Avenue, Newark NG24 1QH; 5 Elston Hall, Top St., Elston, Newark NG23 5NP — MB BS 1964 Lond.; MRCS Eng. LRCP Lond. 1964; FFA RCS Eng. 1971; DA Eng. 1966. (Westm.) Socs: Assn. Anaesths. Prev: Sen. Regist. (Anaesth.) N. Staffs. Gp. Hosps.; Specialist in Anaesth. RAF; Ho. Phys. W.m. Hosp. Lond.

SULLIVAN, Gary North Glamorgan NHS Trust, St. Tydfil's Hospital, Merthyr Tydfil CF47 0SJ Tel: 01685 723244 Email: gary.sullivan@nglam-tr.wales.nhs.uk — MB BCh 1982 Wales; MSc (Psychiat.) Wales 1995; BSc (Hons. Chem. & Biochem.) Wales 1976; MRCPsych 1993; MRCGP 1987; MBA (Open) 1999. (Univ. Wales Coll. Med.) Cons. (Psychiat) St. Tydfils Hosp. Prev: Sen. Regist. Rotat. (Psychiat.) S. Wales; SHO (Psychiat.) Gwent Train. Scheme; Trainee GP E. Glam. Hosp. VTS.

SULLIVAN, Geoffrey (retired) 16 Kingsway, Penwortham, Preston PR1 0AP Tel: 01772 742365 — MB ChB 1950 Manch. Prev: Cons. Radiol. Preston & Chorley.

SULLIVAN, Graham Howell (retired) 2 Freemantle Road, Leicester LE2 2EL Tel: 0116 270 5276 — MB BS Lond. 1952. Prev: Jun. Specialist Dermat. RAMC.

SULLIVAN, Jillian Valerie Health Clinic, 407 Main Road, Dovercourt, Harwich CO12 4ET Tel: 01255 201299 Fax: 01255 201270; St. Georges Lodge, 123 Fronks Road, Dovercourt, Harwich CO12 4EF — MB BS 1976 Lond.; MRCS Eng. LRCP Lond. 1976; DRCOG 1979.

SULLIVAN, John Marcus Moorside Surgery, 1 Thornbridge Mews, Bradford BD2 3BL Tel: 01274 626691; 7 Fairfax Grove, Yeadon, Leeds LS19 7WA Tel: 0113 250 7236 — MB ChB 1987 Leeds; MRCGP 1992; T(GP) 1992; DRCOG 1991. Prev: Trainee GP Bradford VTS.

SULLIVAN, Mr Jonathan Gerald Bristol Urological Institute, Southmead Hospital, Bristol BS10 5NB; 9 Julian Road, Sneyd Park, Bristol BS9 1NQ Tel: 0117 962 6130 — MB BS 1989 Lond.; FRCS Eng. 1995. (Kings Coll. Hosp. Lond.) Clin. Research Fell. (Urol.) S.mead Hosp. Bristol. Prev: SHO (Gen. Surg./Urol.) Cheltenham Gen. Hosp.; SHO (Urol.) Inst. of Urol. Middlx. Hosp. Lond.

SULLIVAN, Lynne Frances 35 Hengist Road, Erith DA8 1HB — MB BS 1991 Lond.

SULLIVAN, Marianne Antoinette Louise The Practice Of Health, 31 Barry Road, Barry CF63 1BA Tel: 01446 700350 Fax: 01446 420795; Home Farm, Sully, Penarth CF64 5UF Tel: 01222 530263 — MB BCh 1975 Wales; Cert. Family Plann. JCC 1977. Socs: Barry Med. Soc.

SULLIVAN, Mark Lemon Street Surgery, 18 Lemon Street, Truro TR1 2LZ Tel: 01872 73133 Fax: 01872 260900; 2 Creekside View, Tresisclan, Truro TR2 4BS Tel: 01326 240123 Email: sullivan@cht.swest.nhs.uk — MB ChB 1976 Birm.; MRCGP 1987; MFHom 1991. (Birm.) GP; Homoeop. Phys. Cornw. Socs: BMA. Prev: GP Mullion Cornw.; SHO (Med.) Walsgrave Hosp. Coventry; SHO (Obst.) Roy. Cornw. Hosp. Truro.

SULLIVAN, Mr Mark Edward 40 The Avenue, Worminghall, Aylesbury HP18 9LE — MB BS 1989 Lond.; FRCS Ed. 1993.

SULLIVAN, Martin James Kingsway surgery, 37 The Kingsway, Swansea SA1 5LP Tel: 01792 650716 Fax: 01792 456902; Email: mjsullivan@btinternet.com — BM 1994 Soton.; MRCGP 1998; DRCOG 1997. GP Princip. Kingsway Surg. Swansea. Socs: Chairm. Gt.er Swansea GP Co-op. Prev: GP Regist. Kingsway Surg. Swansea.

SULLIVAN, Mr Michael Francis Consulting Rooms, The Princess Grace Hospital, 42-52 Nottingham Place, London W1U 5NY Tel: 020 7486 4970 Fax: 020 7935 5467; 12 Gloucester Crescent, London NW1 7DS Tel: 020 7485 4473 Email: mfsullivan@aol.com — MB Camb. 1962, BChir 1961; FRCS Eng. 1967; MRCS Eng. LRCP Lond. 1961. (Camb. & St. Mary's) Cons. Orthop. Surg. Roy. Nat. Orthop. Hosp. Lond. Socs: Fell. (Counc.) BOA; BMA; (Pres.) Europ. Spine Soc.

SULLIVAN, Michael John Llwyn Brwydrau Surgery, 3 Frederick Place, Llansamlet, Swansea SA7 9RY Tel: 01792 771465 — MB BCh 1979 Wales; DRCOG 1983. Exam. Med. Off. & Exam. Med. Phys. DHSS. Socs: BMA.

SULLIVAN, Navina 2A Jennings Road, St Albans AL1 4NT — MB ChB 1989 Natal; MSc (Mother & Child Health) Lond. 1992; DCH RCPI 1994. Socs: BMA. Prev: Trainee GP/SHO (Gen. Med.) P.ss Alexandra Hosp. Harlow; Regist. (O & G) S. Afr.

SULLIVAN, Patricia Mary 51 Twmpath Road, Pontypool NP4 6AQ — MB BCh 1957 Wales; FFA RCS Eng. 1968; DA Eng. 1961.

SULLIVAN, Paul Andrew Sullivan, Hart and Jones, Ringland Health Centre, Ringland Circle, Newport NP19 9PS Tel: 01633

277011 Fax: 01633 290706 — MB BS 1982 Lond.; MRCGP 1987; Dip Ther 1999. (St. Mary's Hosp. Lond.)

SULLIVAN, Paul Major Patrick Moorfield Eye Hospital, London EC1V 2PD; 5 Tolmers Ave, Cuffley, Potters Bar EN6 4QE — MB BS 1984 Lond.; MD Lond. 1991; FCOphth 1992. Cons. Moorfields Eye Hosp. Lond. Socs: Brit. Diabetic Assn.; Brit. Ophth. Photogr. Assn. Prev: Sen. Regist. & Fell. Moorfields Eye Hosp. Lond.; Regist. Soton. Eye Hosp.; Research Fell. Hammersmith Hosp. Lond.

SULLIVAN, Peter Bernard Department of Paediatrics, John Radcliffe Hospital, Oxford OX3 9DU Tel: 01865 220934 Fax: 01865 220479; Bridge House, Oaksmere, Appleton, Abingdon OX13 5JS — MB ChB 1980 Manch.; MA Oxf. 1994; BSc Manch. 1975, MD 1991; FRCP Lond. 1997, M (UK) 1985; FRCPCH 1997; DRCOG 1984. Univ. Lect. & Hon. Cons. Paediat. John Radcliffe Hosp. Oxf. Socs: Chairm. Commonw. Assn. Paediat. Gastroenterol. & Nutrit.; Brit. Soc. Paediat. Gastroenterol. & Paediat. Research Soc.; Eur. Soc. Paediat. Gastroenterol. & Nutrit. Prev: Sen. Lect. (Paediat.) Chinese Univ., Hong Kong; Lect. (Child Health) Char. Cross & W.m. Med. Sch. Lond.; Clin. Research Fell. Dunn Nutrit. Laborat. Univ. Camb.

SULLIVAN, Peter Michael Ballyferriter, 81 Compton Road, Wolverhampton WV3 9QH Tel: 01902 423047 — MB ChB 1953 Birm. Prev: GP Bilston W. Midl.s.

SULLIVAN, Ralph The Surgery, Grasmere Drive, High Bentham, Lancaster LA2 7JP Tel: 01524 261202 Fax: 01524 262222905; 2 Richmond House, Hawes Road, Ingleton, Carnforth LA6 3AN Tel: 015242 41885 Fax: 015242 41825 Email: ralph@giffard.demon.co.uk — MB ChB 1977 Manch.; MRCGP 1984; DRCOG 1983; Dip Ther. Newc. 1996. (Manch.)

SULLIVAN, Raymond Patrick 35 Preston Ave, Newhall, Sutton Coldfield B76 1HS Tel: 01902 307999 Email: md@lexmedicus.com; 35 Preston Avenue, Newham, Sutton Coldfield B76 1HS — MB BCh BAO 1987 NUI; DCH 1990. Private Practitioner. Socs: PgDL UCE 2000.

***SULLIVAN, Richard** Whitney House, London Road, Hartley Whitney, Basingstoke RG27 8RN — MB BS 1993 Lond.

SULLIVAN, Shona Clare Pantysgawen Farm, Thornhill Road, Cardiff CF14 9UA Tel: 029 2062 3054 — MB BCh 1974 Wales; FRCS Eng. 1979; FCOphth 1984. Cons. Ophth.Roy. Glam. Hosp.; Llantrisant; Mem. Oxf. Congr. Socs: Eur. Soc. Oculoplastic & Reconstruc. Surg. Prev: Sen. Regist. Univ. Hosp. Wales Heath Pk. Cardiff.

SULLIVAN, Stephen Kevan Lowther Medical Centre, 1 Castle Meadows, Whitehaven CA28 7RG Tel: 01946 692241 Fax: 01946 590617; Brackenwray Farm, Kinniside, Cleator CA23 3AG Tel: 01946 862604 Email: brakenwray@aol.com — MB BS 1969 Lond.; DObst RCOG 1972.

SULLIVAN, Terence James Nochestnut House, Pollard Road, Morden SM4 6EG Tel: 020 8640 4773; PO box 760, Morden SM4 3QS Tel: 020 8640 8640 Fax: 020 8640 8640 — MB BS 1975 Lond.; Primary 88A; MRCS Eng. LRCP Lond. 1975; DA (UK) 1982. (St. Mary's London) Indep. Anaesth. (Day Care Dent.) Surrey. Socs: Assn. Anaesth. - Elected; Soc. Advancem. Anaesth. in Dent.; Dent. Sedation Teach.s Gp. Prev: Cons. Anaesth., Libya.

SULLIVAN, Thomas James (retired) 69 Corinium Gate, Cirencester GL7 2PX — MB BChir 1949 Camb.; PhD Lond. 1960; MA Camb. 1950, MB BChir 1949. Prev: Sen. Lect. Pharmacol. & Therap. St. Thos. Hosp. Med. Sch. Lond.

SULLIVAN, Valerie Joan Flatt Walks Health Centre, 3 Castle Meadows, Catherine Street, Whitehaven CA28 7QE Tel: 01946 692173 Fax: 01946 590406; Brakenwray Farm, Kinniside, Cleator CA22 2TB Tel: 01946 862604 — MB BS 1971 Lond.; BSc Lond. 1966. (St. Geo. Hosp.)

SULLIVAN, Vera Alma (retired) Rus-in-Urbe, 6 Beechcote Avenue, Portadown, Craigavon BT63 5DG Tel: 028 2833 3709 — MD Belf. 1955, MB BCh BAO 1946; MRCPsych 1971; DPM Dub. 1949. Cons. Psychiat. Learning Disabilty S.. Health & Social Servs. Bd.; Cons. Psychiat. Ment. Handicap Serv. S.. Health & Social Servs. Bd.

SULLIVAN, William Roy The Surgery, Abbey End, Kenilworth, Coventry CV8 1LF Tel: 01926 52576 — MB ChB 1959 Ed.

SULLMAN, Barry 118 Second Avenue, Manor Park, London E12 6EL — MB ChB 1988 Dundee.

SULLY, Mr Lance Department Plastic Surgery, City Hospital, Nottingham NG5 1PB Tel: 0115 969 1169 Ext: 46790 Fax: 0115 962 7939; 11Regent Street, Nottingham NG1 5BS Tel: 0115 947 5475 Fax: 0115 924 1606 — MB 1966 Camb.; BChir 1965; FRCS Eng. 1973. (St. Geo.) Cons. Plastic Surg. Nottm. HA.

SULTAN, Helen Yasmin 22 St Ronan's Road, Harrogate HG2 8LE — BChir 1996 Camb.

SULTAN, Khalida House F-8, Residences, Princess of Wales Hospital, Coity Road, Bridgend CF31 1RQ Tel: 0165 662166 — MB BS 1973 Jammu & Kashmir.

SULTAN, M S The Surgery, 226 Mitcham Road, Tooting, London SW17 9NN Tel: 020 8672 7868 Fax: 020 8672 8630 — MB BS 1973 Madras; MB BS 1973 Madras.

SULTAN, Mahmoud Gamal El-Din Riyadh Military Hospital, D161, PO Box 7897, Riyadh 11159, Saudi Arabia Tel: 00 966 1 4625209 Fax: 009661 462509 Email: m.sultan@prime.net.sa; 98 Redgrove Park, Cheltenham GL51 6QZ Tel: 01242 512451 — MB BCh 1969 Ain Shams; FRCOG 1997, MRCOG 1982. Cons. Obst. & Gyn. Riyadh Milit. Hosp., Saudi Arabia.; Asst. Director of Obst. Riyadh Milit. Hosp. Saudi Arabia.

SULTAN, Mohammad Lower Broughton Health Centre, Great Clowes Street, Salford M7 1RD; 20 Sefton Drive, Worsley, Manchester M28 2NQ — MB BS 1967 Punjab; BSc Punjab (Pakistan) 1966, MB BS 1967; DCH RCPSI 1972. (King Edwd. Med. Coll. Lahore) Socs: Fell. Manch. Med. Soc.; BMA. Prev: SHO (Gen. Surg.) Mayo Hosp. Lahore, Pakistan; SHO (Paediat. Infec. & Chest Dis.) Castle Hill Hosp. Cottingham; SHO (Paediat.) Bradford Gp. Hosps.

SULTAN, Mohammed 116 Dorchester Way, Coventry CV2 2LX — MB BS 1990 Lond.; MRCPI 1994.

SULTAN, Nighat Accident and Emergency Department, Glasgow Royal Infirmary, 84 Castle Street, Glasgow G4 0SF — MB BS 1996 Newc.

SULTAN, Vimala 21 West Way, Carshalton SM5 4EN — MB BS 1975 Madras.

SULTANA, Afzal Mohi Uddin Woodside Lodge, 12 Victoria Avenue, Sunderland SR2 9PZ — MB BS 1985 Karachi; MRCOG 1993.

SULTANA, Ayesha Ashma The Surgery, 1 Boundary Court, Snells Park, Edmonton, London N18 2TB; Tel: 020 8889 0383 — MB BS 1971 Calcutta; DGO 1973; DRCOG 1979. GP Lond.; Clin. Asst. Diabetic Centre, N. Middlx. Hosp., Sterling Way, Edmonton.

SULTANA, Khurshid 39 Braemar Avenue, Wood Green, London N22 7BY Tel: 020 8889 3790 — MB BS 1958 Karachi; DObst RCOG 1966. CMO City & Hackney Health Dist.

SULTANA, Kishwar 19 Romilly Crescent, Canton, Cardiff CF11 9NP — MB BCh 1991 Wales.

SULTANA, Razia 2 Llanddennis Road, Roath Park, Cardiff CF23 6EF Tel: 029 2075 5555 — MB BS 1969 Dacca.

SULTANA, Mr Stefan 3 Howeywood Close, Canterbury CT1 1XF — MD 1984 Malta; LRCP LRCS Ed. LRCPS Glas. 1989; FRCS Ed. 1992.

SUMANASURIYA, Rudrani Champa Wexham Park Hospital, Slough SL2 4HL Tel: 01753 633166 Fax: 01753 691343; 152 Old Woking Road, Woking GU22 8LE — MB BS 1980 Colombo; MRCS Eng. LRCP Lond. 1987; MRCP (UK) 1986.

SUMARIA, Mahendra Kumar Mulchand Brierley Hill Health Centre, Albion Street, Brierley Hill DY5 3EE Tel: 01384 77382 Fax: 01384 483931 — MB BS 1972 Saurashtra; MRCGP 1977. (M. P. Shah Med. Coll.) Prev: Trainee Gen. Pract. Dudley Vocational Train. Scheme; Ho. Off. (Gen. Med.) & Ho. Off. (Gen. Surg.) Dudley AHA.

***SUMATHIPALA, Sanjeewa** 2 West Green Close, Edgbaston, Birmingham B15 2LA — MB ChB 1995 Birm.

SUMBWANYAMBE, Nawa Wilfred X-Ray Department, Diana, Princess of Wales Hospital, Scartho Road, Grimsby DN33 2BA Tel: 01472 874111 Ext. 7758 Fax: 01472 875450 Email: nawa.sumbwanyambe@nelincs-tr.trent.nhs.uk; Mundawanga, 218A Station Road, New Waltham, Grimsby DN36 4PH Tel: 01472 828907 — MB ChB 1982 Zambia; FRCR 1990; T(R)(CR) 1991; DMRD Ed. 1988. Cons. Radiol. Dist. & Gen. Hosp. Grimsby. Socs: Fell. Roy. Coll. Radiol.; Brit. Med. Ultrasound Soc.; Brit. Inst. Radiol. Prev: Sen. Regist. (Radiol.) Hull Roy. Infirm.; Regist. (Radiol.) Roy. Infirm. Edin.

SUMERAY, Mark Stephen Ethicon Ltd, PO BOX 408, Bankhead Ave, Edinburgh E11 4HE Tel: 0131 442 5563 Email: msumeray@ethgb.jnj.com — MS 1998 Lond.; MB BS Lond. 1990; BSc (1st cl. Hons.) Lond. 1987; FRCS Ed. 1994; FRCS Eng. 1994.

SUMERLING

(University College and Middlesex School of Medicine) Vice Pres. Clin. Trials, Ethicon. Socs: Roy. Soc. Med. Prev: Brit. Heart Foundat. Jun. Research; Fell. (Cardiothoracic Surg.) Middlx. Hosp. Lond.; Specialist Regist. (Cardiothorac Surg.) E. Lond. Rotat.

SUMERLING, Michael Derek (retired) Brockencote, Riding Mill NE44 6HX Tel: 01434 682305 — MB ChB 1948 Leeds; BSc Leeds 1948, MB ChB (2nd Cl; Hnrs.) 1951; FRCP Ed. 1970, M 1967; MRCP Lond. 1956; FRCR 1959; DMRD Eng. 1957. Prev: Cons. Radiol. Regional Cardiothoracic Centre Freemans Hosp. Newc.

SUMIRA, Roman Peter Studfall Medical Centre, Studfall Avenue, Corby NN17 1LG Tel: 01536 401371 Fax: 01536 401300 — MB ChB 1985 Leic.

SUMITRA, John Vijayakumar Department of Community Paediatrics, Royal Berkshire Hospital NHS Trust, 3 Craven Road, Reading RG1 5LF Tel: 0118 986 2277 Fax: 0118 975 0297; 11 Longworth Avenue, Tilehurst, Reading RG31 5JU Tel: 0118 941 0525 — MB BS 1969 Bangalore; M.D. (Paediat.); MSc Community Paediat. Lond. 1991; DCCH RCP Ed. 1983; MRCPCH 1997. SCMO (Child Health) Roy. Berks. Hosp. NHS Trust. Socs: Fac. Comm. Health. Prev: Clin. Med. Off. Norwich HA; Regist. (Paediat.) Brown Memor. Hosp. Ludhiana, India; Asst. Paediat. ETCM Hosp. Kolar, India.

***SUMMER, Mick** 14 Croyde Close, Leicester LE5 4WG — MB ChB 1995 Leic.

SUMMERELL, Joan Mary (retired) 7 Hill Crest, Langland, Swansea SA3 4PW — MB BCh 1956 Wales; FRCPath 1982, M 1970; DCP Lond 1968. Cons. Morbid Anatomist W. Glam. AHA.

SUMMERFIELD, Brian John The Surgery, The Limes, Hawley Street, Margate CT9 1PU Tel: 01843 227567 Fax: 01843 230167; Balcombe House, 11A Ave. Gardens, Cliftonville, Margate CT9 3BD Fax: 01843 292407 Email: bjsummerfield@doctors.org.uk — MB ChB Sheff. 1972; DRCOG 1976. Prev: Regist. (Med.) N.. Gen. Hosp. Sheff.; SHO (Obst.) St. John's Hosp. Chelmsford.

SUMMERFIELD, Derek Anton Medical Foundation for Care of Victims of Torture, 96 Grafton Road, London NW5 3EJ Tel: 020 7813 7777 Fax: 020 7813 0011; 55 Denman Road, London SE15 5NS — MB BS 1977 Lond.; BSc (Hons.) Cape Town 1970; MRCPsych 1985. Psychiat. Med. Found. For c/o Victims of Torture.; Hon. Sen. Lect. (Psychiat.) St. Geo. Hosp. Med. Sch. Lond.; Research Assoc. Refugee Studies Progr., Oxf. Univ. Prev: Sen. Regist. (Psychiat.) St. Geo. Hosp. Lond.

SUMMERFIELD, Hilary Ann (retired) 29 Brent Way, West Finchley, London N3 1AJ Tel: 020 8349 2351 — MB BCh 1970 Oxf.; MRCP (UK) 1972. CMO Family Plann. & Well Wom. Serv. Barnet Community Healthcare Trust.

SUMMERFIELD, Professor John Arthur Department of Medicine, Imperial College School of Medicine at St Mary's, London W2 1PG Tel: 020 7886 6365 Fax: 020 7724 9369; 25 Kildare Terrace, London W2 5JT — MB BS 1979 Lond.; MB BS Lond. 1970; MD Lond. 1976; FRCP Lond. 1985; MRCP (UK) 1972. (Lond. Hosp.) Prof. Med. Imperial Coll. Sch. Med. Lond.; Clin. Dir. Of Med. St Mary's NHS Trust. Socs: Assn. Phys.; Brit. Soc. Gastroenterol.; Eur. Assn. Study Liver Prev: Wellcome Trust Sen. Fell. & Hon. Cons. Phys. Roy. Free Hosp. Lond.; MRC Clin. Research Fell. Roy. Free Hosp. Lond.; Lect. (Med.) Roy. Free Hosp.

SUMMERFIELD, Karen Elizabeth St Peters Street Medical Practice, 16 St Peters Street, London N1 8JG Tel: 020 7226 7131 Fax: 020 7354 9120 — MB BChir 1990 Camb.; MA Camb. 1990, MB BChir 1990; MRCGP 1993; DCH RCP Lond. 1991; DRCOG 1992. GP.

***SUMMERFIELD, Oliver John** 25 Kildare Terrace, London W2 5JT — MB BS 1998 Lond.; MB BS Lond 1998.

SUMMERFIELD, Richard John West Wood House, Church Lane, Sparsholt, Winchester SO21 2NJ — MB BChir 1974 Camb.; MA Camb. 1973; FRCA 1981.

SUMMERHAYES, John Lionel Vickery (retired) Brocklands Cottage, Ridgeway Lane, Lymington SO41 8AA Tel: 01590 674060 — MB BS 1949 Lond.; MRCP Lond. 1952; MRCS Eng. LRCP Lond. 1948; MRCGP 1968; DObst RCOG 1956. Prev: Regist. (Med.) King's Coll. Hosp. Lond.

SUMMERHAYES, Julius Wilfrid (retired) Vince Cottage, Kingsdown, Deal CT14 8DX Tel: 0130 45 373512 — MB BChir 1931 Camb.; MA Camb. 1943; BA Camb. 1928; DTM Liverp. 1936, DTH 1937. Prev: Lt.-Col. late RAMC, Med. Specialist.

SUMMERHAYES, Michael Wilfred (retired) Alma Road Surgery, Alma Road, Romsey SO51 8ED Tel: 01794 513422 Fax: 01794 518668 — MB 1966 Camb.; BChir 1965.

SUMMERHAYES, Peter James Sandown Medical Centre, Melville Street, Sandown PO36 8LD Tel: 01983 402464 Fax: 01983 405781 — MB BS 1973 Lond.

SUMMERHAYS, Beatrice Gabrielle Community Child Health Department, Dunsbury Way, Leigh Park, Havant PO9 5BG Tel: 01705 482154 Fax: 01705 471892 — MB BS 1979 Lond.; BSc Lond. 1976. (Westm.) SCMO (Community Child Health) Portsmouth Healthcare NHS Trust; Sen. Doctor (Child Protec.) Portsmouth & SE Hants. HA. Socs: Roy. Coll. Paediat. & Child Health. Prev: GP W. Bromwich W. Midl.; Trainee GP Braintree; Clin. Med. Off. (Community Child Health) Havant.

SUMMERLY, Myrtle Enid (retired) 6 Airdall Spinney, Stone ST15 8AZ Tel: 01785 615938 — MB ChB 1955 Birm.; FFCM 1985, M 1980; DCH Eng. 1960. Prev: Dir. Pub. Health N. Staffs. HA.

SUMMERS, Alison Rael Child Health Department, Kidderminster Health Centre, Bromsgrove St., Kidderminster DY10 1PG Tel: 01562 820091; Lineholt Grange, Lyth Lane, Lineholt, Ombersley, Droitwich WR9 0LG Tel: 01905 621670 — MB ChB 1972 Birm. Community Paediat. Kidderminster Healthcare NHS Trust; Clin. Asst. (Ear, Nose & Throat).

SUMMERS, Andrew Hendford Lodge Medical Centre, 74 Hendford, Yeovil BA20 1UJ Tel: 01935 470200 Fax: 01935 470202; Sheepslake House, Longlands Lane, East Coker, Yeovil BA22 9HN — MB BS 1977 Lond.; MRCGP 1985; DRCOG 1983.

SUMMERS, Andrew Paul Millfield House, 27 Selby Road, Riccall, York YO19 6QP — MB ChB 1989 Leeds. Trainee GP Leeds VTS.

SUMMERS, Beatrice Anne Department of Neurology, Staffordshire General Hospital, Weston Road, Stafford ST16 3SA Tel: 01785 230238 Fax: 01785 230237 — BChir Camb. 1974; MB 1975; MA Camb. 1975; FRCP 1997 M (UK) 1977. (Univ. Coll. Hosp.) Cons. Neurol. M. Staffs. Gen. Hosp. NHS Trust. Socs: Brit. Pharm. Soc. Prev: Sen. Regist. (Neurol.) Inst. Psychiat. Lond.; Regist. Nuffield Dept. Clin. Med. John Radcliffe Hosp. Oxf.; SHO (Neurol.) Nat. Hosp. Nerv. Dis. Qu. Sq.

SUMMERS, Mr Bruce Neville Department of Orthopaedics, The Princess Royal Hospital, Telford TF1 6TF Tel: 01952 641222 Email: bruce.summers@prt-tr.wmid.nhs.uk; Cheswell House, Cheswell, Newport TF10 9AD — MB BS 1976 Lond.; FRCS Eng. 1981; T(S) 1991. (Middlx.) Cons. Orthop. Surg. P.ss Roy. Hosp. Telford. Prev: Sen. Regist. (Orthop.) Middlx. Hosp. Lond.; Regist. (Orthop.) Robt. Jones & Agnes Hunt Orthop. Hosp. OsW.ry.

SUMMERS, Miss Claire Lucy 9 Dalton Gardens, Davyhulme, Manchester M41 5TH Tel: 0161 747 6376 — MB ChB 1983 Manch.; FRCS Glas. 1988; FFAEM 1994; DCH RCP Lond. 1990. Cons. A & E Med. Trafford Gen. Hosp. Manch. Prev: Sen. Regist. (A & E Med.) Addenbrooke's Hosp. Camb. & Norf. & Norwich Hosp.

SUMMERS, David Michael 408 Morningside Road, Edinburgh EH10 5HY — MB ChB 1993 Ed.

SUMMERS, Donald William Bates Health Centre, Llanfairfechan LL33 0NH Tel: 01428 680021; Hafod y Bryn, Mount Road, Llanfairfechan LL33 0HD Tel: 01428 680500 — MRCS Eng. LRCP Lond. 1958. (Char. Cross)

SUMMERS, Douglas Joseph The Gables Health Centre, 26 St Johns Road, Bedlington NE22 7DU Tel: 01670 829889 Fax: 01670 820841 — MB ChB 1988 Sheff. GP Bedlington, N.d.

SUMMERS, Dylan Jeremy Bennett Johns House, Burnley General Hospital, Casterton Avenue, Burnley BB10 2PQ — MB ChB 1997 Manch.

SUMMERS, Edward James The Coatham Surgery, 18 Coatham Road, Redcar TS10 1RJ Tel: 01642 483495 Fax: 01642 487520; 26 Saltscar, Redcar TS10 2PH — MB ChB 1984 Leeds; MRCGP 1988; DRCOG 1988. Prev: Trainee GP Boston VTS.

SUMMERS, Elizabeth Mary (retired) 8 Alderwood Grove, Edenfield, Ramsbottom, Bury BL0 0HQ Tel: 01706 826655 — MB ChB 1959 Liverp.; MB ChB (Hons. cl. 2, Distinc. Surg.) Liverp; DObst RCOG 1961. Prev: SCMO Salford HA.

SUMMERS, Geoffrey David Kidderminster General Hospital, Bewdley Road, Kidderminster DY11 6RJ Tel: 01562 823424; The Little Oak, Far Forest, Kidderminster DY14 9EA — MB BChir 1974 Camb.; MA Camb. 1974; FRCP Lond. 1992; MRCP (UK) 1976; T(M) 1991. Cons. Phys.Worchestershire Acute Hosps. NHS Trust. Socs:

SUMMERTON

Midl. Thoracic Soc. & Brit. Thoracic Soc. Prev: Lect. (Med.) St. Thos. Hosp. Med. Sch. Lond.; Regist. (Med.) Centr. Middlx. Hosp. Lond.; SHO (Med.) Walton Hosp. Liverp.

SUMMERS, Gillian Denise Sandy Health Centre Medical Practice, Northcroft, Sandy SG19 1JQ; Alwyn House, 17 St Neots Road, Sandy SG19 1LE Tel: 01767 681171 Fax: 01767 681171 — MB BCh 1977 Wales; MRCGP 1984; DRCOG 1983. Prev: Dep. Police Surg. N. Beds.

SUMMERS, Graham Taybank Medical Centre, 10 Robertson Street, Dundee DD4 6EL Tel: 01382 461588 Fax: 01382 452121; 23 Hill Street, Monifieth, Dundee DD5 4DE Tel: 01382 535711 Email: gsum.msum@cableinet.co.uk — MB ChB 1987 Dundee. Socs: Forfarshire Med. Assn. Prev: Trainee GP Tayside HB VTS; Ho. Off. (Med.) Ninewells Hosp. Dundee; Ho. Off. (Surg.) Stracathro Hosp. Angus.

SUMMERS, Gregory Dominic Department of Rheumatology, Derbyshire Royal Infirmary, London Road, Derby DE1 2QY Tel: 01332 347141 Fax: 01332 254989 Email: greg.summers@sdah-tr.trent.nhs.uk; Pine Cottage, Heage Lane, Etwall, Derby DE65 6LS Tel: 01283 734345 Email: summers@bearwardcote.freeserve.co.uk — MB ChB 1976 Manch.; BSc Manch. 1973, MD 1987; FRCP Lond. 1995; MRCP (UK) 1979.

SUMMERS, Henry Arthur Hamilton (retired) 8 Princes Avenue, Walsall WS1 2PH Tel: 01922 27047 — MB BCh BAO 1942 Belf.; DPH Belf. 1948. Prev: SCM (Environment Health) Walsall AHA.

SUMMERS, Isobel Margaret Rosemary 125 Newmarket Road, Cambridge CB5 8HA Tel: 01223 64116; 9 Adams Road, Cambridge CB3 9AD Tel: 01223 61805 — MB 1974 Camb.; BChir 1973.

SUMMERS, John Woodilee Hospital, Lenzic, Glasgow G66 4UG Tel: 0141 777 8000 — MB BChir 1985 Camb.

SUMMERS, Judith Alison East Lancashire Health Authority, 31-33 Kenyon Road, Lomeshaye Estate, Nelson BB9 5SZ Tel: 01282 610215 — MB ChB 1979 Leeds; MRCPsych 1998; MFPHM 1990; DTM & H Liverp. 1981. p/t Cons. Pub. Health Med. E. Lancs. HA; Specialist Regist. in Psychiat. Guild Trust Preston. Socs: Fac. Pub. Health Med.; Roy. Coll. of Psychiat.s.

SUMMERS, Judith Ann The Old Orchard, Village St., Hexton, Hitchin SG5 3JB — MB BS 1977 Lond.; MRCS Eng. LRCP Lond. 1977.

SUMMERS, Lesley Ann Haleacre Unit, Amersham Hospital, Whileden St., Amersham HP7 0JD; 42 Stubbs Wood, Amersham HP6 6EX — MB BS 1981 Lond. Clin. Asst. (Psychiat.) Amersham Hosp. Prev: Clin. Asst. (Psychiat.) Drug Dependency Clinic Amersham Hosp. Bucks.; Regist. (Psychiat.) The Lond. Hosp.

SUMMERS, Lucinda Kate Mary Department of Endocrinology, Diabetes & Metabolic Medicine, St Thomas' Hospital, Lambeth Palace Road, London SE1 7EH Tel: 020 7928 9292 Fax: 020 7928 4458 Email: l.summers@umds.ac.uk; 24 Lee Road, London SE3 9RT Tel: 020 8852 8214 — MB BS 1990 Lond.; BSc Lond. 1987; MRCP (UK) 1993; Dphil Oxford, 1998. (University Hospital London & King's College Sch. Med. & Dent) Lect. (Med.) Dept. of Endocrinol., Diabetes & Metab. Med. St Thos. Hosp. Lond.; Hon. Regist. St Thos. Hosp. Lond. Socs: Endocrine Soc.; Brit. Diabetic Assn. (Med. & Scientif. Sect.); Eur. Assn. for Study Diabetes. Prev: Research Regist./Hon. Regist. Oxf. Radcliffe Infirm.; Regist. (Med.) Middlx. Hosp., Regist. (Med.) Basildon Hosp. Essex.

SUMMERS, Lucy Jane Overbridge Surgery, 135 Worting Road, Basingstoke RG22 6NJ — MB BChir 1969 Camb.; MRCP (UK) 1981; DRCOG 1987; DCH Eng. 1971. (Guy's).

SUMMERS, Lynne Worthen Sentry Hill, Henley Road, Marlow SL7 2DQ Tel: 01628 486444 Fax: 01628 476560 Email: lynne@sentryhill.demon.co.uk; 12 Dartmouth Court, South Embankment, Dartmouth TQ6 9DG Tel: 01803 834238 — MB BS 1976 Lond.; MRCS Eng. LRCP Lond. 1976. Socs: Chiltern Med. Soc. & BMA.

SUMMERS, Margaret Windsor 128 Coventry Road, Nuneaton CV10 7AD — MB ChB 1965 Sheff. (Sheff.)

SUMMERS, Maria (retired) 1 St Margaret's Drive, Leire, Lutterworth LE17 5HW — MB BCh BAO NUI 1952; MD NUI 1967; DPM 1961 Manch. Prev: Cons. Child Psychiat. Clatterbridge Hosp. Bebington & Dir. Child Guid. Clin. Ellesmere Port.

SUMMERS, Philip David 10 Ravensdon Street, London SE11 4AR — MB BS 1993 Lond.

SUMMERS, Richard Thomas Fern House Surgery, 125-129 Newland Street, Witham CM8 1BH Tel: 01376 502108 Fax: 01376 502281; Schills Barn, Lanham Green Road, Cressing, Braintree CM7 8DR — MB BS 1989 Lond. (St. Bart. Lond.)

SUMMERS, Roderick Olaf Cheney Knight House, Wolverley, Kidderminster DY11 5XD — MB 1963 Camb.; MA Camb. 1965, MB 1963, BChir 1962; MRCP Lond. 1967; MRCGP 1978; DObst RCOG 1964. (Camb.) Socs: BMA. Prev: Ho. Phys. Gen. Hosp. Birm.; Ho. Surg. Gen. Hosp. Hereford; Med. Regist. Gen. Hosp. Birm.

SUMMERS, Ronald (retired) 353 Arbroath Road, Dundee DD4 7SQ Tel: 01382 456682 — MB ChB St. And. 1943; DTM & H Liverp. 1949. Prev: Squadron Ldr. R. Aux. AF.

SUMMERS, Sarah Helen Sheepslake House, Longlands Lane, East Coker, Yeovil BA22 9HN — MB BS 1978 Lond.; BSc (Hons.) Biochem. Lond. 1975, MB BS 1978; DRCOG 1982.

SUMMERS, Stephen Paul The Park Medical Group, Fawdon Park Road, Newcastle upon Tyne NE3 2PE Tel: 0191 285 1763 Fax: 0191 284 2374; 10 Belle Grove W., Spital Tongues, Newcastle upon Tyne NE2 4LT — MB ChB 1984 Manch.; MRCGP 1988; DRCOG 1988.

SUMMERS, Stephen Robert Gayton Road Health and Surgical Centre, Gayton Road, King's Lynn PE30 4DY Tel: 01553 762726 Fax: 01553 696819; 323 Wootton Road, King's Lynn PE30 3AX — MB BS 1979 Lond.; FRCGP 1997, M 1986; MFHom 1995; MRCGP 1986; DRCOG 1983; Cert. Family Plann. RCOG & RCGP 1983; Dip. Med. Acupunct. 1997. GP King's Lynn. Prev: Med. Off. Providenciales Health Centre Turks & Caicos Is.; SHO (A & E) & (Paediat.) Qu. Eliz. Hosp. King's Lynn.

SUMMERS, Susan Katharine Mount Chambers Surgery, 92 Coggeshall Road, Braintree CM7 9BY Tel: 01376 553415 Fax: 01376 552451; Schills Barn, Lanham Green Road, Cressing, Braintree CM7 8DR — MB BS 1989 Lond. (St. Bart. Lond.)

SUMMERS, William Brown 27 Ashfield Road, Clarkston, Glasgow G76 7TX Tel: 0141 644 1599 — MB ChB 1938 Glas.; DPH Glas. 1946. (Glas.) Chest Phys. Belvedere Hosp.

SUMMERS, Yvonne Jane Christie Hospital NHS Trust, Department of Medical Oncology, Wilmslow Road, Withington, Manchester M20 2BX Tel: 0161 446 3000; 55 Northenden Road, Sale M33 2DG — MB ChB 1993 Manch.; MRCP (UK) 1996; BSc 1990. (St. Andrews and Manchester) Clin. Lect. (Med. Oncol.) Christie Hosp. Manch.

SUMMERS, Zelda c/o Mrs Horton, Hafaneydd, Gwern-y-Steeple, Peterson-Super-Ely, Cardiff CF5 6LG; Department of Liaison Psychiatry, St Codacs Hospital, Lodge Road, Caerleon, Newport NP18 3XQ — MB BS 1987 Lond.

SUMMERSCALES, Adrian Alvaston Medical Centre, 14 Boulton Lane, Alvaston, Derby DE24 0GE Tel: 01332 571322; 16 Main Street, Ambaston, Derby DE72 3ES — BM BS 1987 Nottm. Socs: Derby Med. Soc.; Brit. Assn. Sport & Med.

SUMMERSKILL, Shirley Catherine Wynne (retired) 58 Compayne Gardens, London NW6 3RY Tel: 020 7328 4774 — BM BCh 1958 Oxf.; MA Oxf. 1958. Prev: Med. Off. Blood Transfus. Serv.

SUMMERSKILL, William Storith Markham EBS Teaching Coordinator, NHS South Region, Department of Medical Education, University of Bristol, Bristol; Pincott Farm, Coopers Hill, Upton St Leonards, Gloucester GL4 3RX — MB BS 1986 Lond.; MSc 2000 (Oxon.); DFFP 1996; MRCGP 1990; DCH RCP Lond. 1990; DRCOG 1988. (St. Mary's) Prev: Trainee GP/SHO Portsmouth VTS; Ho. Surg. Qu. Alexandra Hosp. Portsmouth; Ho. Phys. Roy. United Hosp. Bath.

SUMMERTON, Ailie Mary 7 Hall Walk, Welton, Brough HU15 1PN — BM BCh 1984 Oxf.; MA Camb. 1985. Sen. Regist. (Chem. Path.) Sheff. HA. Prev: Regist. (Chem. Path.) Roy. Hallamsh. Hosp. Sheff.; SHO Rotat. (Path.) N. Staffs. HA; SHO & Ho. Off. (Med.) N. Staffs. HA.

SUMMERTON, Christopher Barry Trafford General Hospital, Moorside Road, Davyhulme, Manchester M41 5SL Tel: 0161 746 2846 Fax: 0161 746 2378 Email: chris.summerton@tfaffdhc-tr.nwest.nhs.uk; 24 Parsonage Road, Heaton Moor, Stockport SK4 4JR Tel: 0161 291 9047 Fax: 0161 291 9048 — MB BChir 1983 Camb.; BA Camb. 1979, MA 1983; MRCS Eng. LRCP Lond. 1982; MRCP (UK) 1986; MD Camb. 1992; FRCP Ed 1999; FRCP (Lond.) 2000. (Camb. Univ.) Cons. (Gastro. & Gen. Med.) Trafford Gen. Hosp.; Hon. Cons. (Phys.) Hope Hosp. Salford; Hon. Lect. in

SUMMERTON

Med., Uni. Of Manch. Socs: Brit. Soc. Gastroenterol.; Brit. Assn. Study Liver; Brit. Assn. Paren. & Ente. Nutrit. Prev: Sen. Regist. (Gastroenterol. & Gen. Med.) N. Manch. Gen. Hosp.; Sen. Regist. (Gastroenterol. & Gen. Med.) Manch. Roy. Infirm.; Research Regist. & Regist. (Med.) Addenbrooke's Hosp. Camb.

SUMMERTON, Mr Duncan John, Surg. Cdr. RN Department of Urology, Royal Hospital Haslar, Gosport PO12 2AA Tel: 02392 584255 Ext: 2757 Email: djsummerton@clara.net — MB ChB 1987 Leic.; FACS 2000 (Urol.); BSc Leic. 1984; FRCS Eng. 1994; FRCS Ed. 1994. (Leic.) Cons. Urol., Solent Dept. of Urol., Portsmouth. Socs: Brit. Assn. of Urological Surg.s (BAVS); Ex-Hon. Sec. of the Specialist Urological Regist.s Gp. (Surg); Roy. Naval Med. Soc. Prev: Specialist Regist. (Urol.) RN Hosp. Haslar; Sen. Regist., Inst. of Urol., Lond.; Specialist Regist. (Wexxex Rotat.).

SUMMERTON, Nicholas The Surgery, Manlake Avenue, Winterton, Scunthorpe DN15 9TA Tel: 01724 732202 Fax: 01724 734992 — BM BCh 1984 Oxf.; MA Oxf. 1986, BA 1981; MPH Leeds 1994; MFPHM RCP (UK) 1995; MRCGP 1988; DRCOG 1987. (Oxford) Clin. Sen. Lect. (Primary Care Med.) Univ. Hull. Prev: Sen. Regist. (Pub. Health) Huddersfield; Regist. (Pub. Health) Bradford HA; GP Skelman Thorpe Huddersfield.

SUMMORS, Andrew Charles Anaesthetics Department, Norfolk & Norwich Hospital, Brunswick Road, Norwich NR1 3SR — MB BS 1990 Queensland.

SUMMORS, Rachel Emma Fonmon Cottage, Station Road, Llantwit Major CF61 1ST Tel: 01446 794251 — MB BS 1989 Lond.; DRCOG 1995; MRCGP 1997. GP Longterm Locum at present.

SUMNALL, Andrew Gordon Dyneley House Surgery, Newmarket Street, Skipton BD23 2HZ Tel: 01756 799311 Fax: 01756 707203; 21 Gainsborough Court, Skipton BD23 1QG Tel: 01756 791510 — BM BCh 1986 Oxf.; BA Camb. 1983; MRCGP 1990; DRCOG 1988. (Oxford) Clin. Asst. (Geriat.) Skipton Gen. Hosp. Prev: Trainee GP Cambs. VTS.

SUMNER, Alexander Harold 15 Market Street, Ramsbottom, Bury BL0 0JQ; 61 Cromwell Avenue, Highgate, London N6 5HP — MB ChB 1988 Liverp. SHO (A & E)St. Bart. Hosp. Lond. Prev: SHO Regional Thoracic Unit Fazakerley Hosp. Liverp.

SUMNER, Alfred William (retired) 24 The Shrubberies, Cannon Hill Road, Coventry CV4 7EF Tel: 01203 416842 — MB ChB St. And. 1949.

SUMNER, Colin (retired) 7 Barncroft Drive, Hempstead, Gillingham ME7 3TJ Tel: 01634 379140 Fax: 01634 379140 — MRCS Eng. LRCP Lond. 1953; MRCGP 1970; DObst RCOG 1968. Prev: Adj. Med. Pract. & Chairm. DSS Appeal Cases.

SUMNER, David James The Surgery, 30 Old Road West, Gravesend DA11 0LL Tel: 01474 352075/567799 Fax: 01474 333952 — MB ChB 1980 Sheff.; DCH RCP Lond. 1984.

SUMNER, David William, TD (retired) Flat 2, Gledhow Manor, 350 Gledhow Lane, Leeds LS7 4NH Tel: 0113 266 4024 — MB ChB 1950 Manch.; BSc Manch. 1947; FRCP Ed. 1982; FRCP Lond. 1974, M 1958. Mem. Med. Appeal Tribunal. Prev: Cons. Neurol. & Hon. Clin. Lect. (Neurol.) Univ. Leeds.

SUMNER, Deborah Wycombe General Hospital, High Wycombe HP11 2TT Tel: 01494 526161; Barracks House, Barracks Hill, Coleshill, Amersham HP7 0LN — MB BS 1980 Lond.; FRCS Eng. 1985; MRCOG 1988. Cons. O & G Wycombe Gen. Hosp. Prev: Sen. Regist. (O & G) Pembury Hosp. & St. Thos. Hosp. Lond.; SHO (Gen. Surg.) Reading Hosps.; SHO (O & G) Qu. Charlotte's & Chelsea Hosps. Lond.

SUMNER, Deborah Jane Hollies Surgery, Elbow Lane, Liverpool L37 4AF Tel: 01704 877600 Fax: 01704 833811 — MB ChB 1984 Liverp.; MRCGP 1992.

SUMNER, Edward 49 Gordon Mansions, Torrington Place, London WC1E 7HG Tel: 020 7637 0968 Fax: 020 7829 8866 — BM BCh 1966 Oxf.; MA Oxf. 1966; FRCA 1971. (Univ. Coll. Hosp.) Cons. Anaesth. Hosp. Sick Childr. Gt. Ormond St. Lond.; Edr.-in-Chief Paediat. Anaesth. Prev: Sen. Regist. (Anaesth.) St. Thos. Hosp. Lond.; Regist. (Anaesth.), Ho. Surg. & Ho. Phys. Univ. Coll. Hosp. Lond.

SUMNER, Helen Mary 3 Laurel Bank, Foxhouses Road, Whitehaven CA28 8AD Tel: 01946 692750 — MB ChB 1962 Aberd.

SUMNER, Ian James 35 Lansdowne Road, Atherton, Manchester M46 9HL — MB ChB 1982 Sheff.

SUMNER, Keith Robert (Surgery), 53 Borough St., Castle Donington, Derby DE74 2LB Tel: 01332 810241 Fax: 01332 811748; 35 Towles Pastures, Castle Donington, Derby DE74 2RX Tel: 01332 810241 — MB ChB 1975 Birm.; MRCGP 1980; DRCOG 1981; DCH Eng. 1978. (Birm.) Trainer (Gen. Pract.) Nottm. VTS.

SUMNER, Margaret Anne Ellen (retired) Flat 2, Gledhow Manor, 350 Gledhow Lane, Leeds LS7 4NH Tel: 0113 266 4024 — MB ChB 1954 Manch.; DA Eng. 1957. Prev: Clin. Med. Off. (Vaccination & Immunisation) Leeds E. HA.

SUMNER, Mary Clare (retired) 21 Berwick Drive, Blundellsands, Liverpool L23 7UH — MB ChB 1955 Liverp.; MRCS Eng. LRCP Lond. 1955; DMRD Liverp. 1961.

SUMNER, Michael (Surgery), 69 Bury Road, Gosport PO12 3P; 50 Parson Street, Congleton CW12 4ED — MB ChB 1980 Birm.; MRCGP 1985; DRCOG 1985. Prev: Trainee GP Centr. Birm. VTS.

SUMNER, Michael John Centeon Limited, Centeon House, Market Place, Haywards Heath RH16 1DB Tel: 01444 447424; Myrtle Cottage, The Common, Dunsfold, Godalming GU8 4LE Tel: 01483 200570 — MB BS 1990 Lond.; MRCP (UK) 1993; Dip Pharm. Med. 1996. Clin. & Med. Affairs Manager Centeon Ltd.

SUMNER, Tina Louise Heywood and Partners, 119 Wren Way, Farnborough GU14 8TA Tel: 01252 541884 Fax: 01252 511410 — MB BS 1995 Lond.

SUMNERS, David George Albany Lodge, Church Crescent, St Albans AL3 5JF Tel: 01727 834330 Fax: 01727 834182 — MB BS 1978 Lond.; FRCPsych 2001; BSc (Hons.) Lond. 1974; MRCPsych 1983. (Univ. Coll. Hosp.) Cons. Psychiat. W. Herts. Community Trust; Cons. Psychiat. The Brain Injury Rehabil. Trust. Socs: BMA & Brit. Soc. Rehabil. Med. Prev: Cons. Psychiat. & Med. Dir. Barnet Healthcare NHS Trust; Sen. Regist. (Psychiat.) Middlx. Hosp. Lond.; Regist. (Psychiat.) Guy's Hosp. Lond.

SUMNERS, Susan Mary Watling Medical Centre, 42 London Road, Stanmore HA7 4NU Tel: 020 8958 4237 Fax: 020 8905 4809 — MB BS 1976 Lond.; MRCS Eng. LRCP Lond. 1976; MRCGP 1981. (Roy. Free)

SUMPTER, Katherine Anne Royal Marsden Hospital, Sutton SM2 5PT; 4 Weltie Road, Hammersmith, London W6 9TG — MB BS 1992 Lond.; MRCP 1995. (St. Bartholomew's) Research Fell.

SUMPTION, Catherine Anne 16 Creighton Road, London NW6 6ED — MB BS 1986 Lond.

SUMPTION, John Carlyon 3 Windsor Avenue, Radyr, Cardiff CF1 8BW Tel: 02920 842291 — MB BS 1950 Lond.; MRCS Eng. LRCP Lond. 1949; FFA RCS Eng. 1954; DA Eng. 1951. (St. Mary's) Cons. Anaesth. E. Glam. Gen. Hosp. Pontypridd. Prev: Sen. Regist. Anaesth. United Birm. Hosps.; Regist. Anaesth. United Cardiff Hosps.; Specialist Anaesth. RAMC.

SUMPTION, Nanno Joyce Corris House, Radyr, Cardiff Tel: 029 2084 2291 — MB BCh 1949 Wales; BSc, MB BCh Wales 1949. (Cardiff) Clin. Med. Off. S. Glam. AHA (T).

SUMPTON, John Roy (retired) One Hundred, Austin Fields, King's Lynn PE30 1RS — MB BS 1958 Lond.

SUMRA, Rupinder 19 Campion Road, Leamington Spa CV32 5XF — MB ChB 1990 Manch.; MRCGP 1995; DFFP 1995; DRCOG 1995; DCH RCP (UK) 1993.

SUN, Kai Fai 11 Trueman Gardens, Nottingham NG5 6QT — BM BS 1988 Nottm. Ho. Off. (A & E) N. Staffs. Roy. Infirm. Stoke.

SUN WAI, Wong Yen Seng 16A Vicarage Road, London E10 5EA Tel: 0208 925 7433; 18 Cook Street, Port Louis, Mauritius Tel: 00 230 21 22027 — MB BCh BAO 1988 NUI; FRCA 1995. Clin. Research Phys. Internat. Clin. Trials Lond. Prev: Acting Sen. Regist. & Regist. Rotat. Roy. Lond. Hosp. & Whipps Cross Hosp. Lond.

SUNAK, Yashvir The Surgery, 34 Raymond Road, Upper Shirley, Southampton SO15 5AL Tel: 023 8022 7559 Fax: 023 8033 4028; 21 Spindlewood Close, Glenwood Avenue, Bassett, Southampton SO16 3QD Tel: 02380 767002 — MB ChB 1974 Liverp.; DRCOG 1976. (Liverp.) GP Soton.; Clin. Asst. (Learning Disabil.) Soton. Community NHS Trust; Med. Mem. of Indep. Tribunal Serv.; Occupat. Health Phys. John Lewis partnership. Socs: Soc. Occupat. Med.; Soton. Med. Soc. Prev: Trainee GP Aldermoor Health Centre & Victor St. Surg.; SHO (O & G) Soton. Gen. Hosp.; SHO (Paediat.) Alder Hey Childr. Hosp. Liverp.

SUNDAR, Mr Manthravadi Sivakama 5 Broadhalgh, Rochdale OL11 5LX — MB BS 1976 Andhra; MCh (Orthop.) Liverp. 1991; FRCS Ed. 1985.

SUNDAR ESWAR, Dr 185 Machon Bank Road, Netheredge, Sheffield S7 1PH — MB BS 1989 Madras; MRCOG 1994.

SUNDAR RAO, Mr Praveen 40 Magdalen Road, Thornton-Cleveleys FY5 3EF — MB BS 1988 Madras; FRCS Glas. 1992.

***SUNDARALINGAM, Janaki** 56 Compton Road, London SW19 7QD — MB BS 1998 Lond.; MB BS Lond 1998.

SUNDARALINGAM, Jeyanthi 43 Alwyne Road, London SW19 7AE — MB BS 1994 Lond.; BA (Hons.) Camb. 1991. SHO (Gyn. & Oncol.) Hammersmith Hosp. Lond. Prev: Ho. Off. (Surg.) Chelsea & W.m. Hosp. Lond.; Ho. Off. (Med.) Mayday Hosp. Lond.

SUNDARALINGAM, Sinnappu 19 Fareham Close, Fulwood, Preston PR2 8FH — MB BS 1972 Sri Lanka; FFA RCSI 1983.

SUNDARALINGAM, Visvalingam The Surgery, 111 Wennington Road, Rainham RM13 9TH Tel: 01708 552461; 34 Millwell Crescent, Chigwell IG7 5HY Tel: 020 8500 3050 — MB BS 1963 Ceylon. (Ceylon) GP.

SUNDARAM, Krishna Kumar — MB BS 1992 Lond.; BSc (Hons.) Lond. 1989; MRCP (UK) 1995. Specialist Regist. (Gastroenteriol.) S. W. Thames Region.

SUNDARAM, Shanti 54 Hindmans Road, London SE22 9NG — MB BCh BAO 1984 NUI. Lect. Dept. Toxicol. St. Bart. Hosp. Lond. Prev: SHO (Med.) St. Bart. Hosp. Rochester.

SUNDARARAJAN, Kolappa (retired) 7 Larkin Close, Old Coulsdon, Coulsdon CR5 2LS — MB BS Madras 1954; DPM Eng. 1969. Prev: Cons. Psychiat. Surrey.

SUNDARARAJAN, Prabhavati Thursby Surgery, 2 Browhead Road, Burnley BB10 3BF Tel: 01282 422447 Fax: 01282 832575 — MB BS 1973 Bombay; MB BS 1973 Bombay.

SUNDARESAN, Maryse Lakshmi Department of Histopathology, North Middlesex Hospital, Sterling Way, London N18 1QX — MB BS 1982 Lond.; MRCPath 1994. (Guy's Hospital Medical School) Cons. Histopath. N. Middlx. Hosp. Prev: Sen. Regist. (Histopath.) King's Coll. Hosp. Lond.; Regist. (Histopath.) Hammersmith Hosp. Lond.

SUNDARESAN, Rathiranie Fairfield, Oxhey Lane, Pinner HA5 4AN Tel: 020 8421 2109 — MB BS 1955 Ceylon; DPH Lond. 1967. (Colombo) SCMO Harrow HA. Socs: BMA. Prev: MOH Dehiwela, Ceylon.

SUNDARESAN, Thirunavukkarasu The Health Centre, London Road, Tilbury RM18 8EB Tel: 01375 842504; Fairfield, Oxhey Lane, Pinner HA5 4AN Tel: 020 8421 2109 — MB BS 1954 Ceylon; DCH RCPS Glas. 1968. Socs: BMA. Prev: SHO (O & G) PeterBoro. Hosp.; SHO (Psychiat.) Hillingdon Hosp.; GP Badula, Ceylon.

SUNDARESAN, Vasiharen Molecular Microbiology, MRC Centre 4th Floor, Guy's Hospital Campus, London SE1 1HL Tel: 020 7955 5000 ext. 3142 Fax: 020 7403 8883 Email: v.sundaresan@umds.ac.uk; Department of Histopathology, St. Thomas' Hospital, Lambeth Palace Road, London SE1 7EH Tel: 020 7928 9292 — MB BS 1981 Lond.; PhD Lond. 1993, MB BS 1981; MRCP (UK) 1984; FRCPath 1998; MRCPath 1989. Sen. Lect. (Histopath.. Path.) Hon. Cons. Guys St Thomas Hosp. Kings Coll. Lond. Prev: MRC Clin. Scientist Fell., MRC, Camb.; Clin. Research Fell. Cancer Research Campaign Univ. & MRC Clin. Oncol. Radiother. Units Camb.; Regist. (Histopath.) Addenbrooke's Hosp. Camb. & Char. Cross Hosp. Lond.

SUNDERLAND, Anne Renfrew Health Centre, 103 Paisley Road, Renfrew PA4 8LL Tel: 0141 886 3535 Fax: 0141 885 0098; Kirkton Lodge, Northview Road, Bridge of Weir PA11 3EX Tel: 01505 24297 — MB ChB 1979 Glas.; DRCOG 1982. Prev: Trainee GP Paisley VTS.

SUNDERLAND, Mr Graham Thomas Department of Surgery, Southern General Hospital NHS Trust, 1345 Govan Road, Glasgow G51 4TF Tel: 0141 201 1655 Fax: 0141 201 1674 Email: gtsunderland@compuserve.com — MB ChB 1980 Glas.; BSc (1st cl. Hons.) Physiol. Glas. 1977, MD 1988, MB ChB 1980; FRCS Glas. 1984. Cons. Surg. S.. Glas. Hosps. NHS Trust. Prev: Sen. Regist. Rotat. (Gen. Surg.) Glas.; Research Fell. Univ. Dept. Surg. Glas. Roy. Infirm.; Lect. Univ. Surg. Chinese Univ. Hong Kong.

SUNDERLAND, Mr Henry (retired) 1 Rose Hill Court, Bessacarr, Doncaster DN4 5LY — MB BChir 1951 Camb.; MChir Camb. 1961,

MB BChir 1951; FRCS Eng. 1957. Prev: Cons. Gen. Surg. Doncaster Roy. Infirm.

SUNDERLAND, John Robert Towcester Medical Centre, Link Way, Towcester NN12 6HH Tel: 01327 359953 Fax: 01327 358929 — MB ChB 1975 Leeds; MRCGP 1981; DRCOG 1979.

SUNDERLAND, Lesley Anne (retired) The Street Lane Practice, 12 Devonshire Avenue, Leeds LS8 1AY Tel: 0113 295 3838 Fax: 0113 295 3842 — MB ChB 1987 Sheff.; Cert. Family Plann. JCC 1990; DRCOG 1989.

SUNDERLAND, Michael Henry (retired) 3 Elgin Mews S., London W9 1JZ Tel: 020 7289 1330 — MB ChB 1952 Leeds; MRCPsych 1972; DPM Eng. 1958. Prev: Assoc. Specialist Psychiat. & Psychother. St. Geo. Hosp. & Springfield Hosp. Lond.

SUNDERLAND, Robert Birmingham Childrens Hospital, Steelhouse Lane, Birmingham B4 6NH Tel: 0121 333 8168 — MB ChB 1974 Ed.; MD 1982 Ed.; MRCP (UK) 1977; FRCP (L) 1996; FRCPCH 1997. (Edinburgh) Cons. Paediat. Birm. Childr. Hosp.; Hon. Sen. Clin. Lect. (Child Health) Birm. Univ. Prev: Sen. Regist. (Paediat.) W. Midl. RHA; Regist. (Paediat. Path.) Childr. Hosp. Sheff.; Regist. Childr. Hosp. Sheff. & St. Finbarr's Hosp. Cork.

***SUNDERLAND, Robin** Woodlands, Penn St., Amersham HP7 0PX — MB BS 1998 Lond.; MB BS Lond 1998.

SUNDKVIST, Torbjorn Per Henrik 14 Harrowdene Court, 6 Belvedere Drive, London SW19 7BY — Lakarexamen 1975 Lund.

SUNDLE, Marcus Mortimer (retired) 72 Millway, London NW7 3QY Tel: 020 8959 8227 — MB BCh BAO 1953 Belf.; FRCGP 1981, M 1965. Clin. Asst. (Dermat.) N.wick Pk. Hosp. Harrow. Prev: Regist. (Med.) Acton Hosp.

SUNGUM-PALIWAL, Sobharani Park View Clinic, 60 Queensbridge Road, Moseley, Birmingham B13 8QE Tel: 0121 243 2000 Fax: 0121 243 2010 — MD 1980 Marseilles; MRCPsych 1985; DTM & H Marseilles 1980. (Faculty of Medicine, Marseille) Cons. Child & Adolesc. Psychiat. & Hon. Sen. Clin. Lect. (Paediat. & Child Health) Birm. Childr.s Hosp. Socs: BMA; Assn. Child Psychol. & Psychiat.; Brit. Psychol. Soc. Prev: Sen. Regist. (Child & Adolesc. Psychiat.) W. Midl. RHA; Regist. (Psychiat.) Nottm. Train. Scheme.

SUNIL BABU, Velikkakathu Springfield University Hospital, London SW17 7DJ Tel: 020 8682 6325 Fax: 020 8682 6868; 2 Southwood Avenue, Coulsdon CR5 2DT — MB BS 1985 Kerala; MRCPsych 1993. Cons. (Psychiat.) S. Merton Elderly Team Springfield Hosp. Lond.; Hon. Sen. Lect. (Psychiat.) St. Geo. Hosp. Med. Sch. Lond. Socs: Brit. Neuropsychiat. Assn. Prev: Sen. Regist. Sutton Hosp. Sutton.

SUNMAN, Wayne Department of Care of the Elderly, City Hospital, Hucknall Road, Nottingham NG5 1PB Tel: 0115 969 1169 Fax: 0115 960 8409 Email: wsunman@ncht.org.uk — MB ChB 1983 Ed.; MD Liverp. 1998; MRCP (UK) 1986; BSc Ed. 1981. (Ed.) Cons. (Geriat. & Gen. Med.) Nottm. Socs: Med. Res. Soc.; Brit. Geriat. Soc. Prev: Sen. Regist. (Geriat. & Gen.) Oxf.; Hon. Sen. Regist. (Therap.) Liverp. Univ.; Clin. Research Fell. (Therap.) St. Mary's Hosp. Lond.

SUNTER, James Peter Causey Bridge End Farm, Marley Hill, Newcastle upon Tyne NE16 5EG — MD 1981 Newc.; MB BS 1971; FRCPath 1992, M 1980; DMJ Path.) Soc. Apoth. Lond. 1985. Home Off. Path.; Hon. Cons. Histopath Gateshead Hosp. NHS Trust; Hon. Lect. Univ. Newc.; Assn. Clin. Path. & Brit. Assn. Forens. Med. Socs: Path. Soc.

SUNTHA, Sinnathurai Orrell Road Practice, 84 Orrell Road, Orrell, Wigan WN5 8HB Tel: 01942 222321 Fax: 01942 620327 — MD 1971 Moscow; MD Peoples Friendship Univ. Moscow 1971; LRCP LRCS Ed. LRCPS Glas. 1977; DCH RCPSI 1978; DRCOG 1977. Prev: Regist. (Chest & Infec. Dis.) Ayrsh. & Arran Health Bd.; SHO (Paediat.) Seafield Childr. Hosp. Ayr; SHO (A & E) Kilmarnock Infirm.

SUNTHANKAR, Gita Clapham Park Surgery, 72 Clarence Avenue, Clapham, London SW4 8JQ — MB BCh 1989 Wales; MSc (Publ. Health) 1996; BSc (Hons) Wales 1985; DRCOG (Bristol) 1992; DTM & H Liverp. 1992. (Univ. Hosp. Wales) GP Princip. Socs: BMA. Prev: Assoc. Profess. Offs. Scheme ODA Cambodia.

SUNTHARALINGAM, Ganeshalingam 69 Hillside Ave, Worthing BN14 9QT — MB BChir 1990 Camb.; BA Camb. 1988, MB BChir 1990.

SUNTHARALINGAM, Murugasu 69 Hillside Avenue, Worthing BN14 9QT — MB BS 1964 Ceylon; MRCP 1973 Lond.; FRCP Lond. 1988. (Colombo) Cons. Phys. (Geriat. Med.) Worthing Health Dist.

SUNTHARALINGAM

Socs: Brit. Geriat. Soc. & BMA. Prev: Sen Regist. (Geriat. Med.) Ipswich Hosp.; Regist. (Geriat. Med.) W. Middlx. Hosp. Isleworth.

*SUNTHARALINGAM, Shiamala 7 Brangwyn Crescent, London SW19 2UA — MB BS 1997 Lond.

SUNTHARANATHAN, Ariamalar 10 Marvell Close, Pound Hill, Crawley RH10 3AL Tel: 01293 512273 — MB BS 1977 Sri Lanka; MB BS Sri Lanka Ceylon 1977.

SUPER, Maurice Clinical Genetics Unit, Royal Manchester Childrens Hospital, Manchester M27 4HA Tel: 0161 727 2335 Fax: 0161 727 2333 Email: maurice.super@man.ac.uk; 120 Fog Lane, Didsbury, Manchester M20 6SP Tel: 0161 445 4927 Fax: 0161 445 4927 Email: maurice.super@man.ac.uk — MB BCh 1959 Witwatersrand; MSc Ed. 1979; MD Cape Town 1978; FRCP Lond. 1992; FRCP Ed. 1977, M 1965; DCH RCPS Glas. 1965; FRCPCH 1997. (Witwatersrand) p/t Cons. Paediat. Geneticist & Hon. Lect. Roy. Manch. Childr. Hosp. Socs: (Counc.) Manch. Med. Soc.; Brit. Hum. Genetic Soc.; Roy. Coll. Paediat. & Child Health. Prev: Cons. Paediat. S. W.. Afr. Admin.

SUPER, Patricia Abbey Medical Centre, 87-89 Abbey Road, London NW8 0AG; Flat 1, 91 Cranfield Gardens, London NW6 3EA — MB ChB 1992 Stellenbosch; DFFP 1997; DRCOG 1997. GP Regist. Abbey Med. Centre. Socs: BMA. Prev: SHO (O & G) Roy. Free Hosp. Lond.; SHO (Anaesth.) Guy's Hosp. Lond.

SUPER, Mr Paul Anthony Birmingham Heartlands & Solihull NHS Trust, Bardesley Green E., Birmingham B9 5SS Tel: 0121 766 6611; 109 Old Station Road, Hampton in Arden, Solihull B92 0HE Email: sup3r@aol.com — MB BS 1987 Lond.; BSc Glas. 1982; FRCS Eng. 1991; FRCS (Gen.) 1998. (Royal Free. Hosp.) Cons. (Surg.) Upper GI & Gen. Surg. Birm. Heartlands & Solihull NHS Trust. Prev: Sen. Regist. N.ern Gen. Hosp. Sheff.; Sen. Regist. Roy. Hallamshire Hosp. Sheff.; Lect. (Surg.) St. Mary's Hosp. Med. Sch. Lond.

SUPPLE, David Lincoln Preston Park Surgery, 2a Florence Road, Brighton BN1 6DP Tel: 01273 559601/566033 Fax: 01273 507746; 35 Rugby Road, Brighton BN1 6EB — MB BS 1983 Lond.; MRCGP 1989.

SUPPLE, Mohammed Arif Towcester Medical Centre, Link Way, Towcester NN12 6HH; 73 West End, Silverstone, Towcester NN12 8UY Tel: 01327 858147 — MB BS 1982 Lond.; MRCGP 1989; DRCOG 1987.

SUPPLE, Neelam Tahseen 4 Avondale Road, Lillington, Leamington Spa CV32 7ES — MB BS 1984 Lond.; BSc (Hons.) Lond. 1981, MB BS 1984.

SUPPREE, David Alastair (retired) Hampstead Medical Practice, 91 Heath Street, London NW3 6SS Tel: 020 7435 5055 Fax: 020 7794 4101 — MB ChB 1975 Liverp. Princip. Family Practitioner.

SUPRAMANIAM, Ganesan Watford General Hospital, Vicarage Road, Watford WD18 0HB Tel: 01923 217695 Fax: 01923 217841; 11 Macdonald Close, Chesham Bois, Amersham HP6 5LZ Tel: 01494 728523 Fax: 01494 434458 Email: supramaniam@lineone.net — MB BS 1971 Ceylon; FRCPCH 1996; FRCP Lond. 1992; MSc (Nutrit.) Lond. 1978; MRCP (UK) 1977; DCH Eng. 1975. (Colombo) p/t Cons. Paediat. Watford Gen. Hosp. Socs: BMA; Roy. Coll. of Paediat. & Child Health; Sec. Gen. Commonw. Assoc. for Ment. Handicap & Developm.al Disabilities (CAMHADD). Prev: Sen. Regist. (Paediat.) St. Mary's Hosp. Lond.; Regist. (Paediat.) Dept. Child Health St. Geo. Hosp. Lond.; SHO (Paediat.) N. Middlx. Hosp. & St. Mary's Hosp. Lond.

*SUPRIA, Surinderpal Kaur 92 Evington Lane, Leicester LE5 5PP — MB BS 1998 Lond.; MB BS Lond 1998.

SUR, Sujit Kumar Birleywood Health Centre, Birleywood, Skelmersdale WN8 9BW Tel: 01695 723333 Fax: 01695 556193; 56 Elmers Green, Skelmersdale WN8 6SB — MB BS 1967 Calcutta.

SURALIWALA, Khushroo Homi Surgical Directorate, Ormskirk & District General Hospital, Wigan Road, Ormskirk L39 2AZ Tel: 01695 656164 Fax: 01695 656878 Email: helenfynn@mail.soh.t12.newst.nhs.uk — MB BS 1980 Gujarat; MS (Orthop.) Gujarat 1983; MChOrth Liverp. 1990. (B. J. Med. Coll. Ahmedabad, India & Univ. Liverp.) Cons. Orthop. Surg. Ormskirk Dist. & Gen. Hosp.; Hon. Sen. Lect. (Sports Rehabil.) Univ. of Salford. Socs: Brit. Assn. Surg. Knee; Brit. Orthop. Assn.; Brit. Orthop. Foot Surg. Soc.

SURAWY, Andrzej Jerzy The Surgery, 17 Battersea Rise, London SW11 1HG Tel: 020 7228 0195 Fax: 020 7978 5119 — MB BS 1971 Lond.; MRCS Eng. LRCP Lond. 1977; MRCGP 1984. (Westm.)

SURAWY, Jerzy (retired) Dromquinna, Birchall Close, Leek ST13 5RQ — MB BCh BAO 1952 NUI; MRCPsych 1971; DPM Eng. 1963. Prev: Cons. Psychiat. Stallington Hosp. Blythe Bridge.

*SURDHAR, Harminderjeet Singh 10 Grafton Road, Birmingham B21 8PL — MB BS 1996 Lond.

SURENDRA KUMAR, Dhushyanthan 46 Kelburn Close, Northampton NN4 0RA — MB ChB 1993 Bristol. SHO (Med.) Bristol Roy. Infirm.; Chairm. SW Jun. Doctors' Comm.

SURENDRA KUMAR, Rajasundram Meadow View, Roman Park, Little Aston Park, Sutton Coldfield B74 3AF Tel: 0121 360 7360 Fax: 0121 366 6977 — MB BS 1967 Ceylon. (Peradeniya) Hosp. Pract. St. Margt. Hosp. Gt. Barr & N.croft Hosp. Birm.; Police Surg. Birm. Prev: Clin. Asst. (Rheum.) Selly Oak Hosp. Birm.

SURENDRAKUMAR, Sylvia Mathiraratnam Meadow View, 1 Roman Park, Roman Lane, Sutton Coldfield B74 3AF — MB BS 1967 Ceylon; Dip. Community Paediat. Warwick 1983. SCMO (Child Health) Walsall AHA. Prev: Clin. Med. Off. (Child Health) Walsall AHA.

SURENTHIRAN, Sabaratnam 19 Pickhurst Park, Bromley BR2 0UE — MB BS 1982 Colombo; MB BS Colombo Sri Lanka 1982; MRCP (UK) 1989.

SURENTHIRAN, Sangaralingam Shanmuga 68 Westmount Road, London SE9 1JE — MB BS 1985 Lond.

SURESH, Cheriyil Gangadhara Kurup Department of Cardiology, Royal Oldham Hospital, Rochdale Road, Oldham OL1 2JH Tel: 0161 627 8492 Fax: 0161 627 8474 Email: britmed@aol.com — MD 1987 Kerala; MB BS Kerala 1983; MRCP (UK) 1990. Assoc. Specialist (Cardiol.).

SURESH, Dorairaj c/o Drive T. Sivakumar, 154 Uppingham Avenue, Stanmore HA7 2JU — MB BS 1977 Madras.

SURESH, Krishnmurthy c/o Drive P. P. Jana, 9 Tamarind Close, Hempstead, Gillingham ME7 3ST — MB BS 1988 Madras; MRCP (UK) 1992.

SURESH, Tharayil Royal Scottish National Hospital, Central Scotland Health Care NHS Trust, Larbert FK5 4SD Tel: 01324 570700; 2 Skelmorlie Place, Stenhousemuir, Larbert FK5 4UU Tel: 01324 562484 — MB BS Kerala 1969; DPM Leeds 1980. Assoc. Specialist (Psychiat.) Roy. Scott. Nat. Hosp. Centr. Scotl. Health Care NHS Trust. Socs: Affil. Mem. Roy. Coll. Psychiat; BMA. Prev: Cons. Psychiat. Govt. Ment. Hosp. Calicut, India; Regist. (Psychiat.) Stanley Royd Hosp. Wakefield & St. Luke's Hosp. Huddersfield.

SURESH BABU, Mr Gokarakonda Department of Urology, James Paget Hospital, Great Yarmouth NR31 6LA Tel: 01493 452452; 15 Winstanley Road, Thorpe St. Andrew, Norwich NR7 0YH Tel: 01603 439212 Email: sgokor@aol.com — MB BS 1978 Nargarjuna; MB BS Nagarjuna 1978; MS (Gen. Surg.) Chandigarh 1982; FRCS Ed. 1986. (Guntur Medical College A.P. India) Cons. Urol. James Paget Hosp. Gt. Yarmouth. Socs: Med. Defence Union; BAUS; RCS Edin. Prev: Regist. (Urol.) N. Manch. Gen. Hosp.

SURESH BABU, Pillanna 129 Humberston Avenue, Humberston, Grimsby DN36 4ST — MB BS 1981 Mysore.

SURESH SHETTY, Vorvady 1 Eastacombe Rise, Heanton, Barnstaple EX31 4DG — MB BS 1974 Mysore.

SURESHKUMAR, Thambipillai 23 Milton Road, London E17 4SP — MB BS 1982 Colombo.

SURI, Anil Kumar Ferndale Unit, Fazakerley Hospital, Longmoor Lane, Liverpool L9 7AL Tel: 0151 529 3206 — MD 1977 Panjab; MB BS 1970; MRCPsych 1974. (Govt. Med. Coll. Patiala) Cons. Psychiat. Fazakerley Hosp. Liverp.; Hon. Clin. Lect. (Psychiat.) Univ. Liverp. Prev: Lect. (Psychiat.) Univ. Liverp.

SURI, Avinash Chander New North Road Surgery, 563 New North Road, Hainault, Ilford IG6 3TF Tel: 020 8500 3054 Fax: 020 8501 3025 — MB BS 1971 Aligarh Muslim; MB BS 1971 Aligarh Muslim; MRCS Eng. LRCP Lond. 1981 London.

SURI, Avtar Singh Birchills Health Centre, 23-27 Old Birchills, Walsall WS2 8QH Tel: 01922 614896 Fax: 01922 35073 — MB BS 1972 All India Inst. Med. Sci.; MB BS All India Inst. Med.Sci. 1972.

SURI, Deepak Institute of Hepatology, University College London, 69-75 Chenies Mews, London WC1E 6HX Email: d.suri@ucl.ac.uk — MB BS 1992 Lond.; BSc Lond. 1989, MB BS 1992. (UCL) Clin. Res. Fell. (Hepat.) Inst. of Hepat. Lond. Prev: Regist. Guy's Hosp. Lond.; SHO St. Geo.'s Hosp. Lond.

SURI, Harminder Singh, Air Commodore RAF Med. Br. The Surgery, 25 Greenwood Avenue, Beverley HU17 0HB Tel: 01482

881517 Fax: 01482 887022 — MB BS 1977 Lond.; BSc Guru Nanak Dev 1972; LMSSA Lond. 1985. Police Surg.

SURI, Ranjan 118 Canterbury Road, Harrow HA1 4PB Tel: 020 8723 6412 — MB ChB 1994 Manch.; MRCPaed. 1997. (Manchester) Paediat. Regist. N.wick Pk. Hosp. Harrow. Socs: RCPCH.

SURI, Shailesh 118 Canterbury Road, Harrow HA1 4PB — MB ChB 1992 Birm.

SURI, Shobha Burscough Health Centre, Stanley Court, Lord Street, Burscough, Ormskirk L40 4LA Tel: 01704 894997 — MB BS 1972 Gauhati.

SURI, Shubhada Sanjay Rotherham District General Hospital, Moorgate Road, Oakwood, Rotherham S60 2UD Tel: 01709 820000 Email: tanmay@mcmail.com; 11 Woolgreaves Avenue, Sandal, Wakefield WF2 6DX Tel: 01924 259648 — MB BS 1986 Univ. Poona; MRCP (UK) 1995. (Byramjee Jeejeebhoy) Staff Grade (c/o Elderly). Socs: BMA.

SURI, Sushil Burscough Health Centre, Stanley Court, Lord Street, Burscough, Ormskirk L40 4LA Tel: 01704 894997; 3 Backmoss Lane, Burscough, Ormskirk L40 4BD — MB BS 1968 Delhi.

SURI, Yash Pal Memorial Hospital, Holyhurst Road, Darlington DL3 6HX Tel: 01325 380100 Fax: 01325 743622 — MB BS 1958 Agra; BSc Agra 1953, MB BS 1958; FRCP Ed. 1991; FRCP Glas. 1988; MRCP (UK) 1973; ECFMG 1965; DTM & H Liverp. 1969. Cons. Phys. Geriat. Med. Memor. Hosp. Darlington & Richardson Hosp. Bernard Castle; Vis. Prof. Czechoslovakia Fac. of Med. Univ. Bratislava. Socs: Nat. Exec. Comm. & Div. Chairm. UK Overseas Doctors Assn.; Eur. Tissue Repair Soc. Prev: Sen. Regist. (Geriat. Med.) S. Cleveland HA; Regist. (Gen. Med.) Leigh Infirm.

SURIYA, Anar 6 Thornhill Close, Blackpool FY4 5BR — MB ChB 1991 Dundee.

SURRIDGE, John Giles c/o Department of Endoscopy, The Royal Bournemouth Hospital, Castle Lowe E., Bournemouth BH1 1DW Tel: 01202 303626; Koyana, 224 Sanbanks Road, Poole BH14 8HA Tel: 01202 700688 Fax: 01202 706544 — BM BCh 1960 Oxf.; MA Oxf. 1960; DObst RCOG 1965. (St. Thos.) Assoc. Specialist (Med.) Roy. Vict. Hosp. Bournemouth. Socs: BMA. Prev: GP Bournemouth; Sen. Med. Off. (Cas.) St. Thos. Hosp. Lond.

SURRIDGE, Julia Mary 224 Sandbanks Road, Poole BH14 8HA — MB BS 1990 Lond.; DRCOG 1994; DCH 1997. (St. Bartholomew's London) Community Paediat. SHO Brighton. Socs: MPS. Prev: Trainee GP Chichester VTS; Paediat. SHO Brighton; Paediat. SHO Portsmouth.

SURRIDGE, Nicholas John Bellingham Green Surgery, 24 Bellingham Green, London SE6 3JB Tel: 020 8697 7285 Fax: 020 8695 6094; 87 Bromley Road, London SE6 2UF — MB BS 1980 Lond.; BSc (1st cl. Hons.) Lond. 1977; LMSSA 1980. (King's Coll. Hosp.)

SURTEES, Ann Curliss House, Corby Glen, Grantham Tel: 0147 684251 — MB ChB 1953 Leeds. (Leeds) Prev: Ho. Surg. O & G Hosp. Wom. & Matern. Hosp. Leeds.

SURTEES, Helen Frances Anne (Cotton) Studholme Medical Centre, 50 Church Road, Ashford TW15 2TU; 143 Church Street, Staines TW18 4XZ — MB BS 1987 Lond.

SURTEES, John Keith Hucclecote, Glasnakille, Elgol, Broadford, Isle of Skye IV49 9BQ — MB ChB 1976 Manch.; MSc Clin. Trop. Med. Lond. 1984, BSc (Hons.) Lond. 1970; DTM & H Liverp. 1983; AKC 1970. Socs: Fell. Roy. Soc. Trop. Med. & Hyg.; Coll. Primary Care Phys.s of Zimbabwe (MCPCPZ). Prev: Phys. ALERT Addis Ababa, Ethiopia; Med. Off. Howard Mission Hosp. Zimbabwe; SHO (O & G) Middlx. Hosp. Lond.

SURTEES, Kathryn Jane 26 Medlar Lane, Kirkham, Preston PR4 3HR Tel: 01253 836613 — MB ChB 1993 Manch. Socs: Diplomate Fac. of Family. Prev: GP Regist. Preston VTS.

SURTEES, Ridley Alexander (retired) Curliss House, Corby Glen, Grantham — MB ChB 1954 Leeds; MRCGP 1968.

SURTEES, Robert Alexander Harrison Institute of Child Health, 30 Guilford St., London WC1N 1EH; 134 Victoria Road, London N22 7XQ — BM BCh 1980 Oxf.; PhD Lond. 1992; MA, 1980; FRCP Lond. 1995; FRCPCH 1997. (Oxf.) Sen. Lect. (Paediat. Neurol.) Inst. Child Health Univ. Lond.; Hon. Cons. Neurol. Hosp. Sick Childr. Gt. Ormond St. Lond.

SURTEES, Stanley John Postgraduate Medical Centre, District General Hospital, Eastbourne BN21 2UD Tel: 01323 417400 Fax:

01323 414932 — MB ChB 1952 Liverp.; FRCP Ed. 1982, M 1960; FRCPath 1976, M 1964; DHMSA 1992; DTM & H Liverp. 1960. (Liverp.) Hon. Cons. Path. Clin. Chem., Med. Archiv. E.bourne Hosp. Trust. Socs: Assn. Clin. Biochem.; Path. Soc.; Assn. Clin. Path. Prev: Sen. Lect. (Path.) & Erasmus Wilson Demonst. RCS Eng.; Regist. (Path.) St. Jas. Hosp. Lond. & Walton Hosp. Liverp.

SURY, Michael Roy Joseph Great Ormond Street Hospital for Children, Great Ormond St., London WC1A 7AS Tel: 020 7829 8865 Fax: 020 7829 8866 — MB BS 1980 Lond.; FFA RCS Eng. 1985; DA Eng. 1982. Cons. Anaesth. Gt. Ormond St. Hosp. for Child. NHS Trust.; Clin. Dir. & Med. & Urol. Directorate, Gt. Ormond St.

SURYANARAYAN SETTY, Raja Seetharamaiah, MBE The Royal Oldham Hospital, Rochdale Road, Oldham OL1 2JH Tel: 0161 624 0420 Fax: 0161 627 8694; 34 Epping Close, Chadderton, Oldham OL9 9ST Tel: 0161 678 7009 Fax: 0161 345 6704 — MB BS Bangalore 1970; BSc Mysore 1958; Cert. Family Plann. JCC 1996; DTM & H Liverp. 1973. (Bangalore Med. Coll.) Assoc. Specialist Oldham AHA. Socs: Fell. Roy. Soc. Med. Prev: SHO Sheff. & Bradford HA.

SURYAVANSHI, Vijay Singh c/o Weybridge Medical (UK) Ltd., Freepost KT4605, Weybridge KT13 8BR — MB BS 1974 Jiwaji.

SUSHILA, Sivathanu 11 Arthur Road, Farnham GU9 8PB Tel: 01252 710490 — MB BS 1954 Madras; FRCP Ed. 1994; MRCP Ed. 1959; DCH Eng. 1957. (Madras Med. Coll.) Socs: BMA. Prev: Reader (Paediat.) Madras Med. Coll.; Regist. Liverp. RHB.

SUSMAN, Maurice Daniel (retired) 13 Canons Drive, Edgware HA8 7RB Tel: 020 8952 1503 — MB ChB 1951 Manch.; FFPHM 1991; DPH Eng. 1965. Med. Ref. W. Herts Crematorium Watford Herts. Prev: Cons. Communicable Dis. Control Barnet HA.

SUSMAN, Rachel Davida 13 Canons Drive, Edgware HA8 7RB Tel: 020 8952 1503 Fax: 020 8952 1503 — MB BS 1994 Lond. Research Fell. Roy.Hosp.For Wom. Sydney Australia.

SUSNERWALA, Shabbir Saifuddin Radiotherapy Department, Royal Preston Hospital, Sharve Green Lane, Fulwood, Preston PR2 9HT Tel: 01772 710903 Fax: 01772 710955; 47 Mellor Brow, Mellor, Blackburn BB2 7EX Tel: 01254 812613 — MB BS 1983 Bombay; FRCR 1995; DMRT Lond. 1994. Cons. Clin. Oncol.

SUSSAMS, Roger William (retired) 349 Wrotham Road, Istead Rise, Gravesend DA13 9EF Tel: 0147 483 2494 — MB BS 1962 Lond.; MFOM RCP Lond. 1980; DIH Eng. 1981. Prev: Occupat. Phys. Wellcome Foundat. Ltd. Gp. Occupat. Health Serv.

SUSSEX, Janet Elisabeth North Street House Surgery, 6 North Street, Emsworth PO10 7DD Tel: 0143 373538 — MB BS 1972 Lond.; DCH Eng. 1976; DObst RCOG 1975. (St. Mary's Hosp. Lond.)

SUSSKIND, Werner (retired) 1B Ramsay Court, Eaglesham Road, Newton Mearns, Glasgow G77 5DJ Tel: 0141 639 3265 Fax: 0141 639 3265 Email: wsusskind@msn.com — MB ChB Glas. 1956; FRCP Ed. 1976, M 1963; FRCP Glas. 1972, M 1962; T(M) 1991. Prev: Cons. Dermat. Vict. Infirm. Glas.

SUSSMAN, Helen Sarah Greenmantle, 3 Washington Close, Reigate RH2 9LT — MB BS 1975 Lond.; BSc (Hons.) Lond. 1971; FFPM RCP (UK) 1994. Prev: Med. Manager Ciba-Geigy Ltd Horsham; Med. Adviser Farmitalia Carlo Erba Ltd Barnet.

SUSSMAN, Jonathan David Greater Manchester Neuroscience Centre, Hope Hospital, Stott Lane, Salford M6 8HD Tel: 0161 787 4591 Fax: 0161 787 2933 — MB ChB 1986 Leeds; PhD (Cantab.) 1998; MRCP (UK) 1989. Cons. Neurol. Prev: Research Asst. MRC Centre for Brain Repair Camb.; Lect. (Neurol.) Univ. of Sheff.; Regist. (Med.) Univ. Hosp. of Wales Cardiff.

SUTARIA, Nilesh 2 Akehurst Close, Copthorne, Crawley RH10 3QQ — MB ChB 1990 Leeds.

SUTARIA, Mr Praful Dahyabhai Blackheath Hospital, Lee Terrace, Blackheath, London SE3 9UD Tel: 020 8318 7722 Fax: 020 8318 2542; 106 St. Georges Road, London SE1 Tel: 020 7261 9165 — MB BS 1965 Nagpur; FRCS Ed. 1968. (Nagpur) Cons. Surg. Orthop. Greenwich Dist. Hosp. Socs: Fell. Brit. Soc. Surg. Hand.; Fell. BOA. Prev: Sen. Regist. (Orthop.) Char. Cross Hosp. Lond., N.wick Pk. Hosp. Harrow & Roy. Nat. Orthop. Hosps.

SUTCLIFF, John Robert Harvey Lee House Surgery, Eves Corner, Danbury, Chelmsford CM3 4QA Tel: 01245 225522 Fax: 01245 222196; Melroyd End, Bicknacre, Chelmsford CM3 4HA — MB BS 1966 Lond.; MRCP (UK) 1973; FRCGP 1994, M 1977; DObst RCOG 1974. (St. Bart.) Trainer (Gen. Pract.) Essex FPC; Med. Off. Hosp. &

SUTCLIFFE

Homes St. Giles. Socs: (Ex-Hon. Sec. & Ex-Pres.) Chelmsford Med. Soc. Prev: Regist. (Med.) United Norwich Hosps.

SUTCLIFFE, Alastair Gordon Royal Free & University College Medical School, University College London, London NW3 5QG Tel: 020 7830 2049 Fax: 020 7830 2049; 17 Eastholm, London NW11 6LR Tel: 020 8201 9244 — MB ChB 1987 Manch.; MD; FRCPCH; MRCP (UK) 1992. Sen. Lect. (Paediat.) Roy. Free & Univ. Coll. Med. Sch. Lond.; Hon. Cons. Paediat. Socs: Brit. Paediat. Assn.; BMA; Assn. Research Infant & Child Developm. Prev: Lect. (Child Health) Roy. Free Hosp. Lond.; Sen. Regist. (Paediat.) Roy. Free Hosp. & Moorfields Eye Hosp. Lond.; Lect. (Child Health) Univ. Manch.

SUTCLIFFE, Alistair Paul Moor Lodge, Brackenhill Lane, Eskdaleside, Whitby YO22 5ER — MB ChB 1993 Aberd.; MB ChB (Hons.) Aberd. 1993; BSc (1st cl. Hons.) Lond. 1987; DFFP 1996; MRCGP 1998; DRCOG 1997. (Aberd.) Prev: SHO (Med.) John Radcliffe Hosp. Oxf.; SHO (O & G) Raigmore, Aberd.; SHO (Paediat.) Aberd.

SUTCLIFFE, Anne Josephine 36 Brueton Avenue, Solihull B91 3EN Tel: 0121 704 2925 Email: asutcli793@aol.com — MB ChB 1974 Birm.; BSc (Hons.) Birm. 1971; FFA RCS Eng. 1979; FFA RCSI 1978. (Birm.) Lead Clinician Neuroscis. Critical Care Area; Ruscoe Clark Memor. Lect. Socs: Assn. Anaesth. (Ex-Mem. Counc.); (Ex-Brit. Rep.) Internat. Trauma Anaesth. & Critical Care Soc. (Chairm., Finance Comm.). Prev: Cons. Anaesth. Birm. Accid. Hosp.

SUTCLIFFE, George Raymond Moorse 12A Green Lane, Buxton SK17 9DX — MB BS 1938 Durh.; DPhysMed. Eng. 1949. (King's Coll. Newc.) Med. Off. Buxton Hosp. Socs: Foundat. Mem. Coll. GP; Fell. Manch. Med. Soc. Prev: Med. Regist. Newc. Gen. Hosp. & Devonshire Roy. Hosp. Buxton.

SUTCLIFFE, Gordon Edward (retired) Heathfield, Sandy Way, Maybury, Woking GU22 8BB Tel: 01483 773178 — MB BS 1943 Lond.; MRCS Eng. LRCP Lond. 1942.

SUTCLIFFE, Ian Michael Respiratory Medicine, Leeds General Infirmary, St Georges St, Leeds Tel: 0113 243 2799; 84 Shakespeare Tower, Leeds LS9 7UG Tel: 0113 235 1773 Email: csutcliff@hotmail.com — MB BS 1991 Lond.; MRCP (UK) 1996. Specialist Regist. (Respirat. Med.) Leeds Gen Inf. Socs: BMA; Brit. Thorac. Soc. Prev: Specialist Regist. (Respir. Med.) Dewsbury Hosp.; Regist. & SHO OldCh. Hosp. Romford.

SUTCLIFFE, James Edward Lawrence (retired) Seskinore, 49 Shore Road, Carrickfergus BT38 8UA Tel: 01232 862241 — MB BCh BAO 1950 Belf.; MRCGP 1968; DObst RCOG 1952. Prev: Ho. Off. Roy. Vict. Hosp. Belf.

SUTCLIFFE, Mr John Christopher The London Spine Clinic, 119 Harley Street, London W1G 6AU Tel: 020 7616 7200 Fax: 020 7486 4601 — MB ChB 1983 Ed.; FRCS (SN) 1992; FRCS Ed. 1988. Cons. Neurosurg. Roy. Lond. Hosp. & Harley St. Lond. Socs: Brit. Neurol. Surg. Soc. Prev: Sen. Regist. (Neurosurg.) Roy. Lond. Hosp.; Regist. (Neurosurg.) Roy. Hallamsh. Hosp. Sheff.

SUTCLIFFE, Mr Jonathan Richard 102 Waterloo Road, Southport PR8 3AY Tel: 01704 575615 — MB ChB 1991 Leeds; FRCS 1998. SHO Postgrad. Surgic. Train. Scheme St. Jas. Univ. Hosp. Leeds.

SUTCLIFFE, Lesley Kathleen Glenfields, Blind Lane, Isle Abbotts, Taunton TA3 6RH Tel: 01460 281205 — MB BS 1976 Lond.; MFFP 1993; T(GP) 1991; DRCOG 1978. (Lond. Hosp.) Clin. Asst., Gyn, Taunton Somerset. Part - time; Clin. Asst. Gen. Med., Sen. family Plann. doctor, Tanton, p/t.

SUTCLIFFE, Mr Martin Logan Rockleigh, 51 Roman Bank, Stamford PE9 2ST Tel: 01780 63728 — MB ChB 1969 Sheff.; FRCS Eng. 1974. (Sheff.) Cons. Orthop. Surg. P'boro. Dist. Hosp., Edith Cavell Hosp., Co. Hosp. Doddington, Fitzwilliam Hosp. P'boro. & Stamford & Rutland Memor. Hosp.; Recognised Clin. Teach. Univ. Camb.; Hon. Clin. Tutor Univ. Leicester. Socs: Fell. BOA; BMA. Prev: Sen. Regist. Sheff. AHA (T); Regist. Rotat. (Surg.) Roy. Hosp. Sheff.; Regist. (Orthop.) King Edwd. VII Orthop. Hosp. Sheff.

SUTCLIFFE, Melanie Kate Sheffield Children's Hospital, Western Bank, Sheffield S10 2TH Tel: 0114 271 7000; 33 Wyston Brook, Hilton, Derby DE65 5JB Tel: 730448 Email: msutcliffe@doctorsnet.org.uk — MB BS 1997 Lond.; BSc (Ost.) 1992 CNNA. (St. George's Hosp. Med. Sch.)

SUTCLIFFE, Mr Michael Matthew Lister (retired) Underwood, Waterhouse Lane, Kingswood, Tadworth KT20 6HT Tel: 01737 832532 — MB BS 1954 Lond.; FRCS Eng. 1963. Prev: Cons. Surg. Mayday Healthcare Croydon.

SUTCLIFFE, Moira Caroline Fishponds Health Centre, Beechwood Road, Fishponds, Bristol BS16 3TD Tel: 0117 908 2365 Fax: 0117 908 2377 — MB ChB 1985 Bristol. Trainee GP Bristol VTS. Prev: SHO (ENT) MusGr. Pk. Hosp. Taunton.

SUTCLIFFE, Neil 102 Roundwood Road, Northenden, Manchester M22 4AB — MB ChB 1987 Leic.

SUTCLIFFE, Nicholas Peter Health Care International, Beardmore St., Clydebank G81 4HX Tel: 0141 951 5611 Fax: 0141 951 5603 — MB ChB 1982 Manch.; BSc Manch. 1979; MRCP (UK) 1985; FCAnaesth 1989. Sen. Regist. (Anaesth.) Roy. Liverp. Hosp. Prev: Regist. (Anaesth.) Glas. Roy. Infirm.; Regist. (Renal Med.) Glas. Roy. Infirm.

SUTCLIFFE, Norman Howard (retired) 16 Burnham Road, Leigh-on-Sea SS9 2JU Tel: 01702 74724 — MB BS 1960 Lond.; MRCS Eng. LRCP Lond. 1959. Prev: SHO (Obst.) & Ho. Phys. City Hosp. Derby.

SUTCLIFFE, Nurhan (retired) Bloomsbury Rheumatology Unit, 4th Floor, Arthur Stanley House, 40-50 Tottenham St., London W1T 4NJ Tel: 020 7380 9230 Fax: 020 7380 9278 — Tip Doktoru 1987 Istanbul; MD 2001; MRCP (UK) 1993. p/t Specialist Regist. (Rheum.) Middlx. Hosp. Lond. Prev: Regist. Hope Hosp. Manch.

SUTCLIFFE, Penelope Jane 42 Petworth Road, Haslemere GU27 2HX — MB BS 1992 Lond.

SUTCLIFFE, Rachel Christine 359 Wheatley Lane Road, Fence, Burnley BB12 9QA — BChir 1992 Camb.

SUTCLIFFE, Richard Lawrence Guy, DFC (retired) 5 Berkeley Close, Green Park, Northampton NN1 5BJ Tel: 01604 638501 — MB BS Lond. 1953; FRCP Ed. 1975, M 1967; MRCS Eng. LRCP Lond. 1953. Prev: Cons. Phys. (Geriat. Med.) N.ampton HA & St. And. Hosp. N.ampton.

SUTCLIFFE, Roderick Ian Academic Unit of Primary Care, 20 Hyse Terrace, University of Leeds, Leeds LS2 9LN Tel: 0113 233 4193 Fax: 0113 233 4181 Email: r.i.sutcliffe@leeds.ac.uk; Raw End Cottage, Raw End Road, Warley, Halifax HX2 7SR Tel: 01422 882082 — MB ChB 1976 Liverp.; MMedSci Sheff. 1995; FRCGP 1994, M 1980; DRCOG 1980. (Liverp.) Sen. Lect. in Primary Care Teachg. Leeds; GP Princip. Leeds. Prev: Cons. Primary Med. Care Sheff. Health; Course Organiser Calderdale VTS; GP Sheff. Halifax & Hebden Gp. Pract.

***SUTCLIFFE, Sarah Jane** 10 The Brambles, Thorpe Willoughby, Selby YO8 9LL — MB ChB 1998 Birm.

SUTCLIFFE, Veronica Anne The Surgery, Ardingly Court, 1 Ardingly Street, Brighton BN2 1SS Tel: 01273 688333 Fax: 01273 671128 — MB BS 1990 Lond.; BSc Lond. 1987; MRCGP 1995; DCH RCP Lond. 1995; DRCOG 1994; DTM & H RCP Lond. 1992. (UCL) p/t GP Brighton. Prev: Trainee GP/SHO Brighton VTS; Ho. Surg. Roy. Sussex Co. Hosp. Brighton; Ho. Phys. W. Norwich Hosp.

SUTER, Catherine Mary Willingham Surgery, 52 Long Lane, Willingham, Cambridge CB4 5LB Tel: 01954 260230 Fax: 01954 206204; 71 Cottenham Road, Histon, Cambridge CB4 9ET Tel: 01223 565326 — MB BS 1980 Lond.; BSc (Hons.) Lond. 1975; DRCOG 1982. (Univ. Coll. Hosp.)

***SUTERIA, Yasmin** 1 Bentham Close, Bury BL8 3DL — BM 1995 Soton.

SUTHERBY, Elizabeth Kim Maudsley Hospital, Denmark Hill, London SE5 8AZ Tel: 020 7703 6333 — MB BS 1986 Lond.; MRCPsych 1992. Sen. Regist. (Psychiat.) Maudsley Hosp. Lond. Socs: BMA.

SUTHERLAND, Aeneas Rose (retired) 8 Grange Road, St Andrews KY16 8LF Tel: 01334 73747 — MB ChB 1943 Ed.; DA Eng. 1954. Prev: Cons. Anaesth. Law Hosp. Carluke.

SUTHERLAND, Mr Alasdair George 288 Broomhill Road, Aberdeen AB10 7LQ Email: ort025@abdn.ac.uk — MB ChB 1990 Aberd.; FRCS Ed. 1994; FRCS Ed (Tr&Orth) 1999. Lect. (Orthop) Univ. pf Hordeun. Socs: Assoc. Fell. BOA; Socute Inst. Orthopeche et de Traumatol. (SICOT). Prev: SHO Rotat. (Surg.) Aberd. Hosps.; Regist (Orthop Roy Infirm.

SUTHERLAND, Alastair Mackie 12 Newtonlea Avenue, Newton Mearns, Glasgow G77 5QA Tel: 0141 639 1434 — MB ChB 1959 Glas.

SUTHERLAND, Andrew Sharp Kelso Medical Group Practice, Health Centre, Inch Road, Kelso TD5 7LF Tel: 01573 224424 Fax:

SUTHERLAND

01573 226388; Goshen Bank, Edenside Road, Kelso TD5 7BS — MB ChB 1979 Ed.; MRCGP 1993; DRCOG 1981.

SUTHERLAND, Anne Bryson (retired) 48 Ravelston Gardens, 48 Ravelston Gardens, Edinburgh EH4 3LF Tel: 0131 337 3921 — MB ChB 1951 Ed.; MD Ed. 1958; FRCS Ed. 1963. Prev: Cons. Plastic Surg. Plastic & Maxillofacial Unit SE Region Scotl.

SUTHERLAND, Anthony Michael Leemont, Le Bequet Road, Village de Putron, St Peter Port, Guernsey — MB BS 1993 Newc. SHO (A & E) Guernsey. Socs: BMA.

SUTHERLAND, Bruce 35 Springfield Gardens, Aberdeen AB15 7RX — MB ChB 1976 Aberd.

SUTHERLAND, Cassandra Jane The Old Vicarage, Mabe, Penryn TR10 9JG — MB ChB 1987 Liverp.; FRCA 1994. Cons. (anaesth.) Roy. Cornw. Hosp. Truro. Prev: Clin. Research Fell. (Anaesth.) Derriford Hosp. Plymouth.; Specialist Regist. SW Sch. Anaesth.

*SUTHERLAND, Ceri Jane 68A Downhham Road, London N1 5BG — MB ChB 1992 Ed.

SUTHERLAND, Charles George Grant Department of Pathology, Royal Alexandra Hospital, Paisley PA2 9PN Tel: 0141 580 4162 Fax: 0141 580 4164 Email: charles.sutherland@rah.scot.nhs.uk — MB ChB 1979 Dundee; MRCPath 1987. Cons. Histopath. Roy. Alexandra Hosp. Paisley.

SUTHERLAND, Christine Annette Hastings 23 Norwood Drive, Giffnock, Glasgow G46 7LS — MB ChB 1991 Glas.; MRCPsych 1995. (Glasgow) Staff Grade Psychiat. Gt.er Glas. Primary Care Trust. Prev: SHO S. Sector Psychiat. Serv. Community & Ment. Health Unit Gt.er Glas.

*SUTHERLAND, Claire 1 Hay Avenue, Bishopton PA7 5LL — MB ChB 1998 Glas.; MB ChB Glas 1998.

SUTHERLAND, David Findlay Woodside Health Centre, Barr Street, Glasgow G20 7LR Tel: 0141 531 9556 Fax: 0141 531 9555; 46A Dalziel Drive, Glasgow G41 4HY — MB ChB 1982 Aberd.; MRCGP 1986; DRCOG 1984. Prev: Trainee GP W.. Infirm. Glas. VTS.

SUTHERLAND, David Thompson (retired) 26 Dallam Drive, Sandside, Milnthorpe LA7 7LL — MB ChB 1947 Aberd.

*SUTHERLAND, Derek James 10 Woodside Drive, Sanquhar, Forres IV36 2UF — MB ChB 1994 Aberd.

SUTHERLAND, Donald Hall, DFC (retired) 5 Kinnaber Road, Hillside Montrose DD10 9HE Tel: 01674 830285 — MB ChB 1951 Glas.; DMRD Eng. 1959. Cons. Radiol. Stracathro Hosp. Brechin; Hon. Sen. Lect. Univ. Dundee. Prev: Sen. Regist. Dept. Radiodiag. Roy. Infirm. Aberd.

SUTHERLAND, Dorothy Anne (retired) 13 Clayton Drive, Prestatyn LL19 9RW — MB ChB 1950 Aberd.; DCH Eng. 1955. Assoc. Specialist Paediat. Glan Clwyd Hosp.

SUTHERLAND, Edmond McIntosh (retired) 12 Runcorn Close, Greenlands, Redditch B98 7PU — BM BCh 1964 Oxf.; BA Oxf. 1960, BM BCh 1964; MRCPsych 1972; DPM Eng. 1968. Prev: Research Sen. Regist. Oxf. RHB.

SUTHERLAND, Elisabeth (retired) Mill House, Grinton, Richmond DL11 6HL Tel: 01748 84279 — MB ChB 1951 Sheff.; MRCGP 1974. Prev: Ho. Phys. Sheff. Roy. Infirm. & Childr. Hosp.

SUTHERLAND, Eric Lynton (retired) Mill House, Grinton, Richmond DL11 6HL Tel: 01748 884279 — MB ChB 1951 Sheff.; FRCPsych 1980; DPM Eng. 1958. Prev: Cons. Psychiat. Winterton Hosp.

SUTHERLAND, Fraser Tullis 14 Atholl Gardens, Kilwinning KA13 7DQ; 270 Queen's Road, Aberdeen AB15 8DR Tel: 01224 318157 — MB ChB 1989 Aberd.

SUTHERLAND, George Pottinger (retired) 8 Inchberry Place, Fochabers IV32 7QL Tel: 01343 820333 — MB ChB Aberd. 1945. Prev: Jun. Hosp. Med. Off. Anaesth. Stracathro Hosp. Brechin.

SUTHERLAND, George Roberton (retired) 22 Montrose Drive, Bearsden, Glasgow G61 3LG Tel: 0141 942 7802 — MB ChB (Distinc.) Ed. 1955; FRCP Glas. 1986; FRCP Ed. 1971, M 1959; MRCP (Glas.) 1984; FRCR 1975; FFR 1967; DMRD Ed. 1965. Prev: Cons. Nuffield Hosp. & Bon Ssecour Hosp. Glas.

SUTHERLAND, George Ross 25 Howard Place, Edinburgh EH3 5JY — MB ChB 1972 Ed.; MRCP (UK) 1975. Head of Cardiac Ultrasound Thorax Center Ziekenhuis Dijrzegt, Rotterdam, The Netherlands. Prev: Cons. Paediat. Cardiol. Soton. Gen. Hosp.

SUTHERLAND, Glenys Ann The Harlequin Surgery, 160 Shard End Crescent, Shard End, Birmingham B34 7BP — MB ChB Leeds 1974; MRCGP 1981.

SUTHERLAND, Gordon Archibald Directorate of Anaesthesia, Royal Infirmary, Alexandra Parade, Glasgow G31 3ER; 45 Laxton Drive, Lenzie, Glasgow G66 5LX — MB ChB 1974 Glas.; FRCA 1980. Cons. (Anaesth.) Glas. Roy. Infirm. Prev: Clin. Fell. (Anaesth.) McGill Univ. Montreal Canada.

SUTHERLAND, Graeme Munro Abbey Health Centre, East Abbey Street, Arbroath DD11 1EN Tel: 01241 870307 Fax: 01241 431414 — MB ChB 1978 Glas.

SUTHERLAND, Graham Crieff Health Centre, King Street, Crieff PH7 3SA Tel: 01764 652456 Fax: 01764 655756; Schiehallion, 27 Strathearn Terrace, Crieff PH7 3BZ Tel: 01764 655459 — MB ChB 1990 Ed.; MRCGP 1995.

SUTHERLAND, Hamish Watson (retired) Redstones, 9 Marchbank Road, Bieldside, Aberdeen AB15 9DJ Tel: 01224 867017 — MB ChB 1957 St. And.; FRCOG 1976, M 1964; DObst RCOG 1960. Hon. Cons. O & G Aberd. Roy. Hosps. Trust; Hon. Clin. Reader (Obst. & Gyn.) Univ. Aberd. Prev: Cons. O & G Aberd. Roy. Hosps. Trust.

SUTHERLAND, Helen Bruce (retired) Park Towers, 30 Marlborough Road, Ryde PO33 1AB Tel: 01983 611644 — MB ChB 1920 Glas.; DPH Lond. 1930. Prev: Anaesth. Roy. I. of Wight Co. Hosp. Ryde.

SUTHERLAND, Helen Claire 2 Park Lane, Hale, Altrincham WA15 9JS — BM BS 1993 Nottm.

SUTHERLAND, Hugh (retired) 23 Dunvegan Drive, Bishopbriggs, Glasgow G64 3LB — MB ChB 1955 Glas. Prev: SCMO (Child Health) Gtr. Glas. HB.

SUTHERLAND, Iain Alasdair Keith Chastleton, Newton Drive, Framwellgate Moor, Durham DH1 5BH Tel: 01385 46171 — MB 1972 Camb.; BChir 1971; DObst RCOG 1976; DCH Eng. 1973.

SUTHERLAND, Iain Alexander Pembroke House, 32 Albert Road, N.E. Lincolnshire, Cleethorpes DN35 8LU Tel: 01472 691033 Fax: 01472 291516 — MB ChB 1967 Aberd.; DRCOG 1972.

SUTHERLAND, Ian Alexander Tel: 01875 320302 Fax: 01875 320494; Tel: 01578 750325 — MB ChB 1978 Ed. GP Princip. Pathhead Midlothian EH37 5PP. Socs: MRCGP.

SUTHERLAND, Ian Alexander 10 Waverley Road, Farnborough GU14 7EY — MB BS 1965 Lond.; MRCS Eng. LRCP Lond. 1965; FFA RCS Eng. 1970; DA Eng. 1967. (Guy's) Cons. Anaesth. Frimley Pk. Hosp. Prev: Sen. Regist. (Anaesth.) Char. Cross Hosp. Lond.; Staff Anaesth. St. Radboud Ziekenhuis Nijmegen Univ., Netherlands; Regist. (Anaesth.) Guy's Hosp. Lond.

SUTHERLAND, Ian Boyd (retired) Flat 1, 8 Chesterfield Road, Eastbourne BN20 7NU Tel: 01323 739777 — MB ChB Ed. 1949, DPH 1953; FRCP Ed. 1983, M 1982; FFCM 1972. Prev: Regional Med. Off. S. W.. RHA.

SUTHERLAND, Ian Crawford (retired) Green Meadows, Prinsted, Emsworth PO10 8HS Tel: 01243 372504 Email: sutherland.i@virgin.net — MRCS Eng. LRCP Lond. 1957; FFA RCS Eng. 1968; DA Eng. 1964; DObst RCOG 1962. Cons. Anaesth. Portsmouth & S.E. Hants. HA. Prev: Cons. Anaesth. Portsmouth & S.E. Hants. HA.

SUTHERLAND, Ian Ross Sturry Surgery, 53 Island Rd, Sturry CT2 0EF — MB ChB 1988 Aberd.; MRCGP 1996. GP Princip., Dr Molony & Partners, Sturry Surg., Sturry, Kent. Prev: Locum GP Qu.sland, Australia; Locum GP Montpellier Health Care, Cheltenham; GP Trainee, Shipston-on-Stour.

SUTHERLAND, James Alexander Medicine for The Elderly, St James University Hospital, Beckett St., Leeds LS9 7TF — MB BS 1986 Melbourne.

SUTHERLAND, James Andrew The New Surgery, 209 Sheffield Road, Killamarch, Sheffield S21 8DZ Tel: 01909 770347 — MB BS 1981 Newc.; MRCGP 1986.

SUTHERLAND, Jamie 26 Furze Hill Drive, Poole BH14 8QL — BM 1990 Soton.

SUTHERLAND, Jane Katriona Royal Edinburgh Hospital, Morningside Park, Edinburgh EH10 5HF — MB ChB 1993 Ed.

SUTHERLAND, Janet Shirley (retired) 8 Grange Road, St Andrews KY16 8LF Tel: 01334 73747 — MB ChB 1958 Glas. Prev: Clin. Med. Off. (Family Plann.) Ninewells Hosp. Dundee.

SUTHERLAND

SUTHERLAND, Joanne (retired) Strathard, Drumnadrochit, Inverness IV63 6XP Tel: 01456 450230 — MB ChB Ed. 1957; DCH RFPS Glas. 1962; MRCPsych 1984. Prev: Clin. Asst. (Psychiat. Research) Highland Psychiat. Research Gp. Craig Dunain Hosp. Inverness.

SUTHERLAND, John (retired) Fernbank, Miller Avenue, Wick KW1 4DF Tel: 01955 5326 — MB ChB 1952 Glas. Prev: Ho. Surg. Law Hosp. Carluke & Overtoun Matern. Hosp. Dumbarton.

SUTHERLAND, John Douglas (retired) Craig Ben Cottage, Kinlochspelve, Isle of Mull PA62 6AA Tel: 0168 04 224 — MB ChB 1956 Ed.

SUTHERLAND, John Forbes Wilson, MBE (retired) 25 MacDonald Drive, Knockothie, Ellon AB41 8BD Tel: 01358 723801 — MB ChB Glas. 1955; DObst RCOG 1957. Prev: GP Peterhead.

SUTHERLAND, John Graham 107 Sunnyside Road, Aberdeen AB24 3LT — MB ChB 1994 Aberd.

SUTHERLAND, John Hugh (retired) Glan y Mor Surgery, Poles, Dornoch IV25 3HZ — MB ChB 1951 Ed.; MRCGP 1969.

***SUTHERLAND, Karen Elizabeth** Birch Rock, Craig na Gower Avenue, Aviemore PH22 1RW — MB ChB 1998 Glas.; MB ChB Glas 1998.

SUTHERLAND, Mrs Kathryn Anne 25 Bangholm Loan, Edinburgh EH5 3AH Tel: 0131 552 7676 Fax: 0131 552 8145; 25 Howard Place, Edinburgh EH3 5JY — MB ChB 1974 Ed.; MRCP (UK) 1977. (Edinburgh) Gen. Practitoner. 25 Bangholm Loan, Edin.; Clin. Asst. Lipid Clinic (Cardiol.) Roy. Infirm. Edin.; Hosp. Practitioner, Lipid Clinic (Cardiol.) Roy. Infirm. Edin. Socs: Brit. Hyperlipid. Assn.; SHARP.

SUTHERLAND, Linda Mary Jasmine Park (ward 6), City Hospital, Aberdeen Tel: 01224 663131; 77 Fountainhall Road, Aberdeen AB15 4EA Tel: 01224 644170 — MB ChB 1979 Aberd. Clin. Asst. (Med. for Elderly) City Hosp. Aberd. Prev: Sessional Med. Off. Aberd. & NE Scotl. Blood Transfus. Serv.; Clin. Asst. (Psychogeriat.) Farnham Rd. Hosp. Guildford; Regist. Rotat. (Psychiat.) Aberd.

SUTHERLAND, M Shona McPhail Kirkton Cottage, Kirkton of Auchterhouse, Dundee DD3 0QS — MB ChB 1988 Glas.; FRCOphth 1997. Specialist Regist. (Ophth.) Ninewells Hosp. Dundee.

SUTHERLAND, MacKenzie Stewart 70 Chestnut Drive, Marton, Middlesbrough TS7 8BX Tel: 01642 273332 — MB ChB Aberd. 1962; MRCPsych 1973; Dip. Psychother. Aberd. 1970; DPM Ed. & Glas. 1967. Indep. Cons. Psychiat.; Hon. Cons. N. Tees Gen. Hosp. Stockton. Socs: Fell. Roy. Soc. Med. Prev: Sen. Regist. NE (Scotl.) RHB; Regist. Profess. Unit Ross Clinic Aberd.; Exchange Regist. (Psychiat.) Univ. W. Indies.

SUTHERLAND, Mary Veronica (retired) 18 Cantley Manor Avenue, Cantley, Doncaster DN4 6TN — MB ChB St. And. 1956. Prev: GP Tickhill.

SUTHERLAND, Paul Dudley Southampton General Hospital, Tremona Road, Southampton SO16 6YD; 43 Beech Grange, Landford, Salisbury SP5 2AL Email: pauldsutherland@hotmail.com — BM BCh 1991 Oxf.; FRCA 1996. (Oxford) Cons. Anaesth.

SUTHERLAND, Peter (retired) Strathard, Drumnadrochit, Inverness IV63 6XP Tel: 014562 450230 — MB ChB Ed. 1957. GP Inverness; Civil Serv. Med. Off. Prev: SHO (Paediat.) S. Shields Gen. Hosp.

SUTHERLAND, Rachel Jane 1 The Drive, Adel, Leeds LS16 6BG — MB ChB 1990 Leeds. Trainee GP N. Worcs. HA VTS.

SUTHERLAND, Robert William 35 Dalhousie Terrace, Edinburgh EH10 5PD — MB ChB 1986 Ed.; FRCA 1992; DA (UK) 1990. (Ed.) Cons. Anaesth. W.. Gen. Hosp. NHS Trust Edin.

SUTHERLAND, Sandra Jane The Surgery, St. Couan Crescent, Kirkcowan, Newton Stewart DG8 0HH Tel: 01671 830206 Fax: 01671 404163 — MB ChB 1984 Aberd.; MRCGP 1989; DCCH RCP Ed. 1989; DRCOG 1986.

SUTHERLAND, Lady Sheena (retired) — MB ChB 1963 Aberd.; MRCPath 1982. Hon. Cons. Roy. Infirm. Edin. NHS Trust. Prev: Cons. Virol. Dulwich PHL King's Coll. Hosp. & Hon. Sen. Lect. King's Coll. Sch. Med. & Dent.

SUTHERLAND, Sheilah Dorothy Dunrobin, Offerton Old Road, Stockport SK2 5HH Tel: 0161 427 2081 — MD Manch. 1963, MB ChB 1957. (Manch.) Socs: Fell. Manch. Med. Soc.; Hon. Fell. Soc. Chiropodists. Prev: Sen. Lect. Anat. Univ. Manch; Ho. Surg. & Ho. Phys. Manch. Roy. Infirm.; JP.

SUTHERLAND, Sinclair Stewart (retired) 32 Dunlop Street, Strathaven ML10 6LA Tel: 01357 29752 — MB ChB 1955 Aberd.; FRCPsych 1983, M 1971; DPM Eng. 1963. Prev: Phys. Supt. Hartwood Hosp. Shotts.

SUTHERLAND, Stephanie Claire Claro House, Stratton Chase Drive, Chalfont St Giles HP8 4NS Tel: 01494 874647 Fax: 01494 874605 — MB BS 1991 Newc. SHO (Paediat.).

SUTHERLAND, Thomas Worsley (retired) 70 Batley Road, Alverthorpe, Wakefield WF2 0AD Tel: 01924 372857 — MD 1953 Leeds; MB ChB 1940; FCPath 1966. Reader & Sen. Lect. (Path.) Univ. Leeds. Prev: Hon. Cons. Pathol. Gen. Infirm. Leeds.

SUTHERLAND, William Gordon Macintyre The Brewery Lane Surgery, 18 Brewery Lane, Thornhill Lees, Dewsbury WF12 9DZ Tel: 01924 458787 Fax: 01924 458040; 2 Betula Way, Lepton, Huddersfield HD8 0ET Tel: 01484 608405 — MB ChB 1978 Aberd. Prev: SHO (O & G) Stathcliffe Gen. Hosp.

SUTHERST, John Richard Centre for Urotherapy & Research, BUPA Murrayfield Hospital, Thingwall, Wirral CH61 1AU Tel: 0151 648 0561 Fax: 0151 648 7864; 20 Bath Street, Waterloo, Liverpool L22 5PS Tel: 0151 920 0791 Fax: 0151 928 7821 Email: bathst@cableinet.co.uk — MB ChB 1963 Sheff.; MD Sheff. 1980; FRCOG 1980, M 1967. Cons. O & G & Med. Dir. Centre for Urother. & Research Murrayfield Hosp.; Cons.Gyn.(Urol.n) Liverp. Wom.Hosp. Socs: Internat. Continence Soc.; Assoc. Mem. BAUS; Internat. Urogyn. Assn. Prev: Reader (Clin. O & G) Univ. Liverp. & Hons. Cons. (Obst. & Gyn.) Liverp. HA; Sen. Lect. (O & G) Univ. Liverp.; Regist. & Sen. Regist. Jessop Hosp. Wom. Sheff.

SUTLIEFF, Patricia Ann Foster House Surgery, 23 Cockett Road, Langley, Slough SL3 7TQ Tel: 01753 580484 Fax: 01753 580501 Email: pat.sutlieff@k81612.nhs.uk — MB BS 1973 Lond.; BSc Lond. 1970; Cert. Family Plann. JCC 1977; DRCOG 1976; DA Eng. 1976. (St. Geo.) GP Langley Berks. Prev: GP Hayes & Slough; SHO (Obst. & Anaesth.) N.wick Pk. Hosp. Harrow.

SUTTIE, Gillian Mary (retired) Braeside, Fenwick Park, Hawick TD9 9PB Tel: 01450 372979 — MB ChB 1962 Aberd.

SUTTIE, Keith Young 3 Kilspindie Road, Dundee DD2 3JP Tel: 01382 611472 — MB ChB 1991 Dundee. Regist. (O & G) Walsgrave Hosp. Coventry.

***SUTTLE, Theresa Jane** 44 St James Gardens, Penicuik EH26 9DU — MB ChB 1995 Aberd.

SUTTON, Adrian Graham Lyndale, 90 Woodford Road, Bramhall, Stockport SK7 1PB — MB BS 1977 Lond.; BSc (Hons.) (Psychol.) Lond. 1974, MB BS 1977; FRCPsych 1994, M 1981. (Univ. Coll. Hosp.) Cons. Child & Family Psychiat. Winnicott Centre Centr. Manch. Health Care Trust; Hon. Assoc. Lect. Vict. Univ. Manch. Prev: Sen. Regist. Child Guid. Train. Centre & Whitting Hosp. Lond.; Sen. Regist. (Child & Family) Tavistock Clin. Lond.; Regist. (Psychol. Med.) Univ. Coll. Hosp. Lond.

SUTTON, Alan Roade Medical Centre, 16 London Road, Roade, Northampton NN7 2NN Tel: 01604 862218 Fax: 01604 862129; 9 Lodge Avenue, Collingtree, Northampton NN4 0NQ Tel: 01604 766804 — MB ChB 1967 Sheff.; DObst RCOG 1970. Clin. Asst. Grafton Manor Brain Injury Unit. Prev: Lect. (Health Educat.) N.ampton Boro.; Ho. Off. (Surg. & Paediat.) & SHO (O & G) N.ampton Gen. Hosp.

SUTTON, Amanda Tel: 020 8883 9149 Fax: 020 8883 0194 — MB ChB 1986 Bristol; MRCGP 1990; DRCOG 1989; Cert. Family Plann. JCC 1989. (Bristol) p/t Partner in Gen. Pract., Dukes Avenue Pract., Lond. N10. Prev: Trainee GP St. Johns Way Lond.

SUTTON, Andrew Gordon Charles 45 Algarth Road, Pocklington, York YO42 2HL — MB BChir 1993 Camb.; MA Camb. 1994; MRCP (UK) 1996. (Addenbrooke's Clin. Sch. Camb.) Research Regist. (Cardiol.) S. Cleveland Hosp. Middlesbrough.

SUTTON, Andrew Nicholas Sullivan Way Surgery, Sullivan Way, Scholes, Wigan WN1 3TB Tel: 01942 243649 Fax: 01942 826476; The Old School House, 254 Withington Lane, Aspull, Wigan WN2 1JA Tel: 01942 492904 — MB ChB 1982 Manch.

SUTTON, Ann Mary Yorkhill NHS Trust, Glasgow G3 8SJ Tel: 0141 201 0557 Fax: 0141 201 9352 — MB BS 1974 Lond.; FRCP Glas. 1988; MRCP (UK) 1980; DCH Eng. 1976; FRCPCH 1997. (King's Coll.) Cons. Paediat. Yorkhill NHS Trust Glas.; Hon. Sen. Lect. Glas. Univ.

SUTTON, Anthony John (retired) Hazel Cottage, Whinburgh, Dereham NR19 1QR — MB BS 1956 Lond. Prev: Ho. Surg. Lond. Hosp.

SUTTON, Beverly Anne St. George's Hospital, Blackshaw Road, Tooting, London SW17 0RE Tel: 020 8672 1255; Headland House, 3 Avenue Road, Belmont, London SW2 6JE Tel: 020 8642 7520 — MB BS 1986 Lond.; FRCA 1990. (St. Geo. Hosp. Lond.) Cons. Anaesth. St. Geo. Hosp. Lond. & Atkinson Morleys Hosp. Prev: Sen. Regist. St. Geo. Hosp. Lond.

SUTTON, Caroline Judith 1 The Avenue, South Moulescoomb, Brighton BN2 4GF; 26 St. Leonards Gardens, Hove BN3 4QB — MB BS 1979 Lond.; MRCP (UK) 1986; DCH RCP Lond. 1983.

SUTTON, Christopher Derek 8 Acorn Way, Wigston LE18 3YA — MB BCh 1993 Wales.

SUTTON, Professor Christopher James Gabert Guildford Nuffield Hospital, Stirling Road, Guildford GU2 7RF Tel: 01483 555833 Fax: 01483 555835 Email: csutton@uk-consultants.co.uk; Gunner's Farm, Stringers Common, Guildford GU4 7PR — MB BChir Camb. 1967; 1987 FRCOG; MA 1967 Trinity College, Cambridge. (St. Mary's) Cons. Gyn. Roy. Surrey Co. Hosp. Guildford; Prof. Of Gynaecol. Surg. Uni. Of Surrey, Guildford; Hon. Lect. Roy. Lond. Hosp. Univ. Lond.; Clin. Tutor Imperial Coll. Sch., Uni. Lond. Socs: Brit. Soc. Of Gynaecol. Endoscopy; Euro. Soc. Of Gynaecol. Endoscopy; Gynaecol. Club of GB & Ire. Prev: Cons. O & G St. Luke's Hosp. Guildford; Sen. Regist. Addenbrooke's Hosp. Camb. & St. Mary's Hosp. Lond.; Cons. Lautoka Hosp., Fiji.

***SUTTON, Claire Helen** 40 Corvedale Road, Selly Oak, Birmingham B29 4LQ — MB ChB 1998 Leeds.

SUTTON, David (retired) 21 Meadowbank, Primrose Hill Road, London NW3 3AY Tel: 020 7586 4473 — MD Manch. 1949, MB ChB 1942; FRCP Lond. 1964, M 1952; FRCR 1975; FFR 1953; DMRD Eng. 1947. Prev: Cons. Radiol. St. Mary's Hosp. & Nat. Hosps. Nerv. Dis. Lond.

SUTTON, David Alfred Owen Department of Medicine for the Elderly, Llandough Hospital, Penarth CF64 2XX Tel: 01222 711711 Fax: 01222 700877 — MB ChB 1962 Bristol; MA Wales 1993; FRCP Lond. 1991; MRCP (UK) 1973. (Bristol) Cons. Phys. Llandough Hosp. NHS Trust. Prev: Sen. Regist. (Geriat. Med.) Bournemouth & E. Dorset & Char. Cross Hosps.; Regist. (Gen. Med.) Roy. Gwent Hosp. Newport.

***SUTTON, David Nicholas** 2A Ashleigh Grove, West Jesmond, Newcastle upon Tyne NE2 3DL — MB ChB 1995 Liverp.

SUTTON, David Nigel Shackleton Department of Anaesthetics, Southampton General Hospital, Tremona Road, Southampton SO16 6YD Tel: 02380 796135 Fax: 02380 794348 Email: david.sutton@suht.swest.nhs.uk — BM 1978 Soton.; FFA RCS Eng. 1985; DA Eng. 1983. Cons. Anaesth. Soton. Univ. Hosps. NHS Trust. Socs: Assn. of GB & Irel.; BASICS; Roy. Coll. Anaesth. Prev: Clin. Servs. Director, Critical Care; Sen. Regist. (Anaesth. & IC) Soton. Gen. Hosp.; Resid. Anaesth. King Edwd. VII Memor. Hosp., Bermuda.

SUTTON, Derek Richard (retired) 17 Kirk Lane, Walkington, Beverley HU17 8SN — MB BS 1964 Lond.; MD Lond. 1972; FRCP Lond. 1982, M 1968; MRCS Eng. LRCP Lond. 1964. Prev: Phys. & Gastroenterol. Hull Roy. Infirm.

SUTTON, Dorothy Everett Lancashire Paediatric Audiology Service, 4 Lytham Road, Preston PR2 8JB Tel: 01772 716066; Walker Lane Barn, Snape Raike Lane, Goosnargh, Preston PR3 2EU Tel: 01995 640655 — MB ChB 1967 St. And.; MSc Audiol. Med. Manch. Univ. 1990. SCMO (Audiol.) Preston HA.

SUTTON, Elizabeth Joan (retired) 29 Halsall Lane, Formby, Liverpool L37 3NN — MRCS Eng. LRCP Lond. 1949; FFCM RCP (UK) 1984, M 1972; DPH Liverp. 1961; DCH . Lond. 1953. Prev: Community Phys. (Child Health) Sefton HA.

SUTTON, Emma Jane 28 Crossland Road, Chorlton, Manchester M21 9DG — BM BS 1991 Nottm.

***SUTTON, Emma Michelle** 30 Hill Top Avenue, Cheadle Hulme, Cheadle SK8 7HY — MB ChB 1994 Bristol.

***SUTTON, Emma Victoria** 11 Beech Hill, Hexham NE46 3AG — MB BS 1997 Newc.

SUTTON, Fay Julie Castle Mead Medical Centre, Hill Street, Hinckley LE10 1DS Tel: 01455 637659 Fax: 01455 238754; The Old Rectory, Church St, Sapcote, Leicester LE9 4FG Tel: 0116 23451 — MB ChB 1974 Bristol; DRCOG 1976. Lect. (Gen. Pract.) Leicester Univ.

SUTTON, Mr Frederick Raymond (retired) 2 Blunts Hall Drive, Witham CM8 1LZ Tel: 01376 513614 — MB BS 1943 Lond.; FRCS Eng. 1949; MRCS Eng. LRCP Lond. 1943. Prev: Sen. Surg. Rush Green Hosp. Romford.

SUTTON, Gaius Backholer (retired) Kirkiboll House, Tongue, Lairg IV27 4XL Tel: 01847 611255 — MB ChB 1957 Bristol; DCH RCP Lond. 1961; DA (UK) 1961; DObst RCOG 1959. Prev: GP Highland HB.

SUTTON, Mr George Augustine 38 Harborne Road, Edgbaston, Birmingham B15 3HE Tel: 0121 452 1083 Fax: 0121 455 8485 — MB BCh BAO 1967 NUI; FRCS Ed. 1977; FRCOphth 1989; DCH NUI 1969. (Univ. Coll. Dub.) Ophth. Birm. & Midl. Eye Hosp. & Good Hope Hosp.; Cons. Ophth. Birm. HA; Clin Tutor Birm. Univ. Socs: Fell. Roy. Soc. Med.; UK IOL Soc.; Europ. Soc. (Oculoplastic) Surg.s.

SUTTON, George Christopher 6 The Ridings, Cobham KT11 2PT Tel: 01372 843335 — MA, MD Camb. 1971, MB BChir 1958; FRCP Lond. 1977, M 1962. (Univ. Coll. Hosp.) Sen. Lect. Nat. Heart & Lung Inst. Imp. Coll. Sch. Med. Lond.; Hon. Cons. Roy. Brompton & Nat. Heart Hosp. Lond. & Harefield Hosp. Middlx. Socs: Fell. Amer. Coll. Cardiol.; Brit. Cardiac Soc. Prev: Sen. Regist. (Cardiol.) Brompton Hosp. Lond.; Ho. Phys. & Ho. Surg. Univ. Coll. Hosp. Lond.; Regist. (Med.) Addenbrooke's Hosp. Camb.

SUTTON, Graham Cunningham Wakefield Health Authority, White Rose House, Wakefield WF1 1LT Tel: 01924 213035 Fax: 01924 814401 — MB ChB 1975 Ed.; PhD Ed. 1981; MSc (Human Genetics) Ed. 1977; FFPHM RCP (UK) 1996, M 1986. Cons. Pub. Health Wakefield HA.

SUTTON, Mr Graham Leslie James The Anchorage, Lands End Road, Old Burlesdon, Southampton SO31 8DN Tel: 02380 402385 — BM 1978 Soton.; MS Soton. 1989; FRCS Ed. 1982; FRCS Eng. 1982. (Soton.) Cons. Vasc. Surg. Qu. Alexandra Hosp. Portsmouth. Socs: BMA. Prev: Sen. Clin. Vasc. Fell. St. Mary's Hosp. Lond.; Sen. Regist. (Surg.) Wessex RHA.

SUTTON, Harold Braham (retired) Leylands, Soulbury, Leighton Buzzard LU7 0BY Tel: 01525 270266 — MB BCh BAO 1935 Dub.; MD Dub. 1939.

SUTTON, Helen Ersy (retired) Manderley, 34 Bower Gardens, Shady Bower, Salisbury SP1 2RL Tel: 01722 323902 — MB BS 1956 Lond.; MSc Nuclear Med. Lond. 1983; BA 2000 Winchester. Prev: Sen. Med. Off. DHSS.

SUTTON, Helen Joan (retired) 119 Moor End Road, Mellor, Stockport SK6 5PT Tel: 0161 427 2550 — MRCS Eng. LRCP Lond. 1954; BA Camb. 1951, MB BChir 1956. Prev: Assoc. Specialist (Geriat.) Barnes Hosp. & Manch. Roy. Infirm.

SUTTON, Ian John 33 St Helena Way, Horsford, Norwich NR10 3EA — MB ChB 1992 Birm.

SUTTON, Isaac 40 Holne Chase, Hampstead Garden Suburb, London N2 0QQ Tel: 020 8455 0825; 40 Holne Chase, Hampstead Garden Suburb, London W2 0QQ Tel: 020 8455 0825 — BSc Manch. 1928, MD 1947, MB ChB 1931, DPM 1938; MRCS Eng. LRCP Lond. 1931; FRCPsych 1971. (Manch.) Hon. Cons. Psychiat. Friern, Halliwick & Highlands Hosps. Lond.; Hon. Cons. Psychiat. Gr.lands Priory Hosp. S.gate. Lond.; Hon. Lt.-Col. RAMC, Specialist Psych. Med. Socs: Fell. Roy. Soc. Med. Prev: Phys. Supt. & Cons. Psychiatt. Friern Hosp. Lond. & Menston. Ment.; Hosp. Leeds; Ho. Surg. Manch. Roy. Infirm.

SUTTON, Jacqueline Frances 14A Finney Drive, Chorlton, Manchester M21 9DS — MB BS 1993 Lond.

***SUTTON, James Francis** 120 Poplar Road, Dorridge, Solihull B93 8DQ — MB ChB 1994 Leic.

SUTTON, Jane Cecilia (retired) The Health Centre, Whyteman's Brae, Kirkcaldy KY1 2NA Tel: 01592 641203 — MB ChB 1959 Liverp. Prev: Ho. Off. Childr. Hosp. Liverp.

SUTTON, Jean Margaret Park Road Surgery, 25 Park Road, St Helens WA9 1DG Tel: 01744 738735 Fax: 01744 454624; Lonsdale, 14 Laurel Road, West Park, St Helens WA10 4AX Tel: 01744 24285 — MB ChB 1989 Liverp.; DRCOG 1992. (Univ. Liverp. Med. Sch.) Princip. GP. Socs: Med. Defence Union; BMA; Christians in Caring Professions. Prev: Trainee GP/SHO (Psychiat.) Fazakerley Hosp. & (Paediat. & Cas.) Alder Hey Hosp. Liverp.

SUTTON, John Andrew Clinical Pharmacology Unit, Royal Surrey County Hospital, Egerton Road, Guildford GU2 7XX Tel: 01483 51122 Fax: 01483 455375; The Cedars, Vanzell Road, Easebourne, Midhurst GU29 9BA Tel: 01730 817150 Email: asjs@compuserve.co.uk — MB BS Lond. 1966; MD Lond. 1989; FFA RCSI 1976; DObst RCOG 1968. Dir. Clin. Pharmacol. Unit

SUTTON

Guildford. Socs: Brit. Pharm. Soc.; Brit. Assn. Pharmaceut. Phys. Prev: Head Clin. Pharmacol. Units Roussel Beecham.

SUTTON, John Baden The Surgery, 141 Long Causeway, Adel, Leeds LS16 8EX Tel: 0113 293444 Fax: 0113 295 3440 — MB ChB 1975 Leeds; BSc (Pharmacol.) Leeds 1973; DRCOG 1977; Cert. JCC Lond. 1977. Gen. Practitioner Princip. Leeds. Socs: GP Airways Gp. Prev: SHO (A & E) Gen. Infirm. Pontefract; SHO (O & G) & Ho. Surg. St. Jas. Hosp. Leeds; Ho. Phys. Leeds Gen. Infirm.

SUTTON, Jonathan Department of Pathology, The General Infirmary, Leeds LS1 3EX Tel: 0113 392 7836 Fax: 0113 392 7839 — MB BS 1977 Lond.; BA 1971 CANTAB; MRCPath 1985.

SUTTON, Julian Kingsley 30 Hill Top Avenue, Cheadle Hulme, Cheadle SK8 7HY Tel: 0161 485 3668 — BM BCh 1994 Oxf.; BA (Hons. Physiol. Sci.) Oxf. 1991. (Oxford University Medical School)

SUTTON, Juliet Clare Poplar Grove Surgery, Meadow Way, Aylesbury HP20 1XB Tel: 01296 482554 Fax: 01296 398771 — BSc (Hons.) Lond. 1985, MB BS 1988; MRCGP 1992; DCH RCP Lond. 1990. Prev: Trainee GP Hemel Hempstead; SHO (Psychiat.) Hill End Hosp. St. Albans; Ho. Off. (Surg.)& (Med.) Hemel Hempstead.

SUTTON, Katherine Jane Meadway Health Centre, Meadway, Sale M33 4PS Tel: 0161 905 2880 — MB ChB 1985 Ed.; MRCGP 1991; T(GP) 1991; Cert. Family Plann. JCC 1990; DRCOG 1988. Prescribing & Coronary Heart Dis. Lead, Trafford S. PCT. Socs: Roy. Med. Soc. Edin.

SUTTON, Keith Henry (retired) Foxgloves, Holt Forest, Wimborne BH21 7DU Tel: 01258 840832 — MB BS 1954 Lond.; MRCGP 1976; DObst RCOG 1964. Prev: GP Lond. & Bournemouth.

SUTTON, Laurence Neil Main X-Ray, Royal Halifax Infirmary, Free School Lane, Halifax HX1 2YP Tel: 01422 357222; Century House, 2 Heath Avenue, Manor Heath Road, Halifax HX3 0EA Tel: 01422 360253 — MB ChB 1979 Leeds; BSc (Hons.) (Pharmacol.) Leeds 1976, MB ChB 1979; FRCR 1988; MRCP (UK) 1983. Cons. Diag. Radiol. Halifax Hosps. Socs: Roy. Coll. Phys. Lond. Prev: Sen. Regist. (Radiol.) Leeds.

SUTTON, Lisa Jayne 18 Minster Close, Off Churchfields, Barry CF63 1FL Tel: 01446 700731 — MB BS 1986 Lond. Clin. Med. Off. Welsh Blood Transfus. Serv. Prev: SHO A & E Colchester Gen. Hosp.; Trainee GP Colchester.

SUTTON, Lynne Joanne 7 Thorney Close, Lower Earley, Reading RG6 3AF — BMedSci 1993 Nottm.; BM BS Nottm. 1995. (Nottingham) SHO (Med.) St. Richards Hosp. Chichester. Socs: BMA; MPS.

SUTTON, Margaret Amelia Winifred (retired) Foxgloves, Holt Forest, Wimborne BH21 7DU Tel: 01258 840832 — MB ChB 1956 Liverp. Prev: SCMO (Adult Health) Newham Health Dist.

SUTTON, Mary Elizabeth Bitterne Health Centre, Commercial St., Southampton SO18 6BT Tel: 02380 420420 Fax: 02380 448920; North Ridge, Edinburgh Road, Kings Worthy, Winchester SO23 7NY Tel: 01962 883649 Fax: 01962 883649 — MB BS 1973 Lond.; DCH Eng. 1976; FRCPCH 1997. (Lond. Hosp.) Cons. Paediat. (Community Child Health) Soton. Community Serv. NHS Trust. Socs: Brit. Assn. Community Child Health; FRCPCh. Prev: SCMO (Community Child Health) Soton. Community Serv. NHS Trust; Regist. (Paediat.) Basingstoke & Dist. Hosp. & Soton. Gen. Hosp.; SHO (Paediat.) Qu. Eliz. Hosp. Childr. Lond.

SUTTON, Mr Michael Cheltenham General Hospital, Cheltenham GL53 7AN Tel: 01242 272361 Fax: 01242 272403; Lansdown Lodge, Lansdown Road, Cheltenham GL51 6QL Tel: 01242 520900 Fax: 01242 253816 — BM BCh 1967 Oxf.; MA Oxf. 1967; FRCS Eng. 1973; FRCOG 1990, M 1977. (Oxf. & Guy's) Cons. O & G Cheltenham Hosps. Prev: Sen. Regist. & Regist. (O & G) W.m. Hosp. Lond.; Maj. RAMC.

SUTTON, Paul Adrian Riverside Surgery, Barnard Avenue, Brigg DN20 8AS Tel: 01652 650131 Fax: 01652 651551; Beechwood Lodge, 10 Scawby Lodge, Broughton, Brigg DN20 0AF Tel: 01652 658857 Email: ji_pasutton@compuserve.com — MB ChB 1978 Leeds; MRCGP 1988. GP Brigg N. Lincs.; Bd. Mem. & Clin. Governance Lead N. Lincs PCG. Prev: Clin. Research Fell. (Pub. Health Med.) Univ. Hull.; Med. Adviser E. Riding HA; GP Winterton Scunthorpe.

SUTTON, Mr Paul Mark Northern General Hospital, Herries Road, Sheffield S5 7AU Tel: 014 226 6251; 8 Cadland Court, Channel Way, Ocean village, Southampton SO14 3GP — MB ChB 1990

Sheff.; FRCS 1999; FRCS Eng. 1994; FRCS Ed. 1994. Cons. Orthopeadic Sugeon. Socs: Treas. BRIT. Orth. Train.s Assn. Prev: SHO Rotat. (Gen. Surg.) Leeds Gen. Infirm.; Regist. (Orthop.) Yorks. Regional Train. Scheme.

SUTTON, Penelope Anne 12 Hall Walk, Cottingham HU16 4RL — MB ChB 1994 Liverp.; MB ChB (Hons.) Liverp. 1994; MRCP (UK) 1997. (Liverpool) Specialist Regist. Clatterbridge Centre for Oncol. Wirral, Merseyside.

SUTTON, Peter Douglas (retired) Lamont, Southdown Road, Seaford BN25 4HU Tel: 01323 898560 — MB BS 1945 Lond.; FRCR 1975; FFR 1962; DMRD Eng. 1954. Hon. Civil Cons. (Radiol.) RAF. Prev: Cons. Advisor Radiol. RAF.

SUTTON, Peter Morgan (retired) Manderley, 34 Bower Gardens, Shady Bower, Salisbury SP1 2RL Tel: 01722 323902 — MB BS 1956 Lond.; BSc (Hons. Anat.) Lond. 1953; FRCPath 1976, M 1964. Prev: Dir. Pub. Health Laborat. Serv. Centre Applied Microbiol. & Research Porton Down.

SUTTON, Peter Robert Beverley Road Surgery, 840 Beverley Road, Hull HU6 7HP Tel: 01482 853270; 12 Hallwalk, Snuffmill Lane, Cottingham HU16 4RL Tel: 01482 848162 — MB ChB 1968 Leeds. Clin. Asst. (Dermat.) P.ss Roy. Hosp. Hull. Prev: SHO (Paediat. & Obst.) & Ho. Off. Wakefield Hosp. Gp.

SUTTON, Philip Henry 27 Bure Way, Aylsham, Norwich NR11 6HL Tel: 01263 733272 — MRCS Eng. LRCP Lond. 1940; BSc Lond. 1937, MD 1947, MB BS 1940; FRCP Lond. 1973, M 1947. (Westm.) Prev: Cons. Chest Phys. Norwich Health Dist.; Ho. Phys. Radcliffe Infirm. Oxf.; R.A.F. Med. Br. 1941-46.

SUTTON, Philip Percy University Hospital of Hartlepool, The General Hospital, Hartlepool TS24 9AH Tel: 01429 266654 Fax: 01429 235389; West View House, West Park Lane, Sedgefield, Stockton-on-Tees TS21 2BX Tel: 01740 620140 — MB BS 1975 Newc.; BSc Newc. 1973, MD 1984; FRCP Lond. 1993; FRCP Ed. 1991. Cons. Phys., N.Tees & Hartlepool NHS Trust; Hon. Clin. Lect., Univ. of Newc. Socs: Brit. Thorac. Soc. Prev: Sen. Regist. Aberd. Roy. Infirm.; Lect. Roy. Free Hosp. Sch. Med. Lond.; Regist. Ninewells Hosp. Dundee.

SUTTON, Pylotis Gan Stuart 11 Bexley Lane, Sidcup DA14 4JW Tel: 020 8300 8548 — MRCS Eng. LRCP Lond. 1948. (Middlx.) Prev: Ho. Surg. Co. Hosp. Hereford; Res. Anaesth. Roy. United Hosp. Bath; Ho. Surg. O & G Manor Hosp. Walsall.

***SUTTON, Rebecca Sian** 9 Moorside Road, West Cross, Swansea SA3 5EY — MB ChB 1997 Manch.

SUTTON, Richard 149 Harley Street, London W1G 6DE Tel: 020 7935 4444 Fax: 020 7935 6718 — FAHA 2000; MB BS Lond. 1964; DSc (Med.) Lond. 1988; FRCP Lond. 1983, M 1967; MRCS Eng. LRCP Lond. 1964; FESC 1989; FACC 1975. (King's Coll. Hosp.) p/t Cons. Cardiol. Roy. Brompton Hosp. Lond. & Chelsea & W.m. Hosp.; Hon. Cons. Cardiol. St. Luke's Hosp. Lond.; Edr.-in-Chief EUROPACE 1998-. Socs: (Sub. Comms.) N. Amer. Soc. Pacing & Electrophysiol.; BMA; Brit. Cardiac Soc. Prev: Chairm. Europ. Working Gp. Cardiac Pacing of the Europ. Soc. Cardiol.; Cons. Cardiol. W.m. Hosp. Lond.; Sen. Regist. & Dir. Cardiac Catheterisat. Laborat. Nat. Heart Hosp. Lond.

SUTTON, Richard James 17 Kirk Lane, Beverley HU17 8SN — MB BS 1990 Lond.

SUTTON, Mr Robert Department of Surgery, Royal Liverpool University Hospital, Daulby St., Liverpool L69 3GA Tel: 0151 706 4170 Fax: 0151 706 5826 Email: r.sutton@liverpool.ac.uk — MB BS 1980 Lond.; BA (Anthropol. & Psychol.) (Hons.) Durh. 1974; DPhil Oxf. 1989; FRCS (Gen.) 1992; FRCS Eng. 1984. (King's Coll. Hosp.) Reader (Surg.) Univ. Liverp., Hon. Cons. Surg., Roy. Liverp. Univ. Hosp.; Hunt. Prof. RCS Eng. (1990-91). Socs: Pancreatic Soc. of GB and Irel.; Assoc. Surg. GB and Irel.; Soc. Acad. Res. Surg. Prev: Sen. Lect. (Surg.) Univ. Liverp.; Clin. Lect. (Surg.) John Radcliffe Hosp. Oxf.

SUTTON, Roger Barrie Owen 212 Anerley Road, Penge, London SE20 8TJ — MB BS 1972 Lond.; BDS Lond. 1966, MB BS 1972; FDS RCS Eng. 1974, L 1966.

SUTTON, Roger Malcolm Havant Health Centre Suite C, PO Box 44, Civic Centre Road, Havant PO9 2AT Tel: 023 9247 4351 Fax: 023 9249 2524; 2 Taswell Road, Southsea PO5 2RG Tel: 01705 756926 — BM 1983 Soton.; MRCGP 1989; DRCOG 1988. (Southampton) Socs: Christian Med. Soc. Prev: SHO (O & G) St.

SWAIN

Mary's Hosp. Portsmouth; SHO (ENT/Geriat./Cas.) Qu. Alexandra Hosp. Portsmouth.

SUTTON, Mr Ronald Arthur Beechfield, 11 Beech Hill, Hexham NE46 3AG Tel: 01434 602021 Fax: 01434 602021 — MB BS 1963 Durh.; FRCS Ed. 1969. (Durh.) Cons. Orthop. Surg. Hexham Gen. Hosp. Socs: Inter. Med. Soc. Paraplegia. Prev: Sen. Regist. & Regist. (Orthop. Surg.) Roy. Vict. Infirm. Newc.; Sen. Regist. (Orthop. Surg.) Univ. Dept. Orthop. Nuffield Orthop. Hosp.

SUTTON, Ruth Helen Harvey House Surgery, 13-15 Russell Avenue, St Albans AL3 5ES Tel: 01727 831888 Fax: 01727 845520; 31 Alma Road, St Albans AL1 3AT — MB ChB 1991 Leic.; MRCGP 1995; DFFP 1995.

SUTTON, Stanley Edward (retired) 9 Richard Road, Crosby, Liverpool L23 8TD — MB ChB Manch. 1950. Prev: Capt. RAMC.

SUTTON, Stanley Grahame 35 Montagu Gardens, Wallington SM6 8EP Tel: 020 8647 1135 — MB BChir 1957 Camb.; MRCS Eng. LRCP Lond. 1954; DA (UK) 1961; DCH Eng. 1959; DObst RCOG 1959. (Camb.) Socs: Sutton Med. Soc.; Internat. Organisat. Mycoplasmol.; Brit. Med. Laser Assn. Prev: SHO (Anaesth.) Ronkswood Hosp. Worcester; SHO (Paediat.) W. Pk. Hosp. Macclesfield; SHO (Infec. Dis.) Cherry Tree Hosp. Stockport.

SUTTON, Timothy Mark 9 Lodge Avenue, Collingtree, Northampton NN4 0NQ Tel: 01604 766804 Fax: 01604 766804 Email: docalsu@aol.com — MB ChB 1992 Bristol; BSc Bristol 1989; MRCP (UK) 1996. Specialist Regist. (Cardiol.) Auckland, New Zealand. Prev: SHO (Med.) N.ampton Gen. Hosp.; Ho. Off. (Med.) Bristol Roy. Infirm.; Ho. Off. (Surg.) Bristol Roy. Infirm.

SUTTON, Vera Estelle 40 Holne Chase, Hamstead Garden Suburb, London N2 0QQ Tel: 020 8455 0825 Fax: 020 8458 7188 Email: vera@provid.demon.co.uk; 40 Holne Chase, Hampstead Garden Suburb, London N2 0QQ Tel: 020 8455 0825 Fax: 020 8458 7188 — MB ChB Leeds 1957. (Leeds) Med. Off. to Various Life Insur. Companies. Socs: Affil. RCPsych; Fell. Roy. Soc. Med. & Med. Soc. Lond.; Assur. Med. Soc. & Roy. Coll. Psychiat. Prev: Hon. Clin. Asst. Friern & Halliwick Hosps. Lond.; Med. Off. Marie Stopes Clinic Lond.; Ho. Phys. & Ho. Surg. (O & G) St. Jas. Hosp. Leeds.

SUTTON, Wendy Elizabeth 15 Tregaron Avenue, Cosham, Portsmouth PO6 2JU — MB BChir 1994 Camb.; MRCGP 1997; DRCOG 1996.

SUTTON COULSON, Thomas (retired) Graylings, Bascombe Road, Churston Ferrers, Brixham TQ5 0JX Tel: 01803 842703 — MA, BM BCh Oxf. 1939; MRCS Eng. LRCP Lond. 1939. Prev: RAMC 1939-45.

SUVARNA, Jeremy Rafe, Squadron Ldr. RAF Med. Br. Retd. 19 Rufus Isaacs Road, Caversham, Reading RG4 6DD Tel: 01189 472403 Email: rsuvarna@rsuvarna.demon.co.uk — MB BS 1988 Lond.; BSc (Hons.) Lond. 1985; Dip. IMC RCS Ed. 1995; DAvMed FOM RCP Lond. 1992. (Roy. Free Hosp.) Med. Adviser Boehringer Ingelheim Ltd. Bracknell Berks.

SUVARNA, Simon Kim Department of Histopathology, Northern General Hospital, Herries Road, Sheffield S5 7AU Tel: 0114 271 4942 Fax: 0114 261 1034 Email: s.k.suvarna@sheffield.ac.uk — MB BS 1984 Lond.; BSc (Hons.) Lond. 1981; MRCP (UK) 1987; FRCPath 1993. (Middlx.) Cons. Histopath. & Cytopath. N. Gen. Hosp. NHS Trust. Prev: Sen. Regist. (Histopath.) Sheff.; Regist. (Histopath.) St. Mary's Hosp. Lond.; SHO (Histopath.) Univ. Coll. Hosp. Lond.

SUXENA, Shesh Raj Audley Health Centre, Church St., Audley, Stoke-on-Trent ST7 8EW Tel: 01782 721345 Fax: 01782 723808 — MB BS 1955 Osmania; MRCP (UK) 1965.

SUZUKI, Hisaharu Derriford Hospital, Derriford Road, Plymouth PL6 8DH; 18 Longpark Drive, Woolwell, Plymouth PL6 7QE — MB ChB 1991 Bristol. SHO (Med.) Plymouth HA. Prev: Ho. Off. (Med., Cardiol., Neurol. & Gen. Med.) Bristol Roy. Infirm.; Ho. Off. (Gen. Surg. & Urol.) S.mead Hosp.

*SUZUKI, Iris Ingeborg 13 Wicker Street, London E1 1QF — MB BS 1993 Lond.

*SVASTI-SALEE, Derek 9 Bruges Place, London NW1 0TE — MB BS 1998 Lond.; MB BS Lond 1998.

SVENNE, Mr Dzintars 15 Downhills Way, London N17 6AN Tel: 020 8888 4269; 62 Woodland Drive, Berry Hill, Mansfield NG18 4JL — MB BS 1963 Lond.; FRCSI 1966; LRCPI & LM, LRCSI & LM 1958; DMRD Eng. 1969. (RCSI) Cons. Radiol. Centr. Notts. Health Dist. Socs: Fell. Roy. Soc. Med.; Assn. Surgs. E. Afr. Prev:

Sen. Regist. (Radiol.) & Clin. Tutor Nottm. Univ. Hosp. Gp.; Sen. Regist. (Neurosurg.) & Hon. Clin. Lect. Dept. Surg. Mulago Hosp.; (Makerere Univ.) Kampala, Uganda.

SVENSSON, William Edward X-Ray, Ealing Hospital Trust, Uxbridge Road, Southall UB1 3HW Tel: 020 8967 5658 Fax: 020 8967 5449 Email: bsvensson@eht.org.uk; 1 High Park Road, Richmond TW9 4BL Tel: 020 8876 0997 — LRCPI & LM, LRSCI & LM 1974; LRCPI & LM, LRCSI & LM 1974; FRCSI 1979; FRCR 1988. (Ireland) Cons. Radiol. Ealing Hosp. Trust; Hon. Sen. Lect. Hammersmith Hosp. Socs: Fell. Roy. Soc. Med.; Brit. Inst. Radiol. Prev: Sen. Regist. (Nuclear Med. & Ultrasound) Roy. Marsden Hosp. Lond.; Regist. (Diag. Radiol.) Roy. Free Hosp. Lond.

SVERRISDOTTIR, Anna 21 Ranmoor Cliffe Road, Ranmoor, Sheffield S10 3HA — Cand Med et Chir 1984 Reykjavik; FRCS Ed. 1993.

SVOBODA, Daniel 17 Cherry Tree Avenue, Scarborough YO12 5DX — MB ChB 1990 Otago.

SVOBODA, Vladimir Henry John (retired) 92 Heath Road, Petersfield GU31 4EL Tel: 01730 264884 Fax: 01730 264884 Email: v.h.j.svoboda@btinternet.com — MUDr Prague 1955; LMSSA Lond. 1972; FFR 1970; DMRT Eng. 1969. Prev: Cons. Radiother. St. Mary's Gen. Hosp. Portsmouth.

SWABY, Donald Saint Antonious 63 Ellen Street, Birmingham B18 7LE — MB BS 1990 Lond.

SWABY, Martin John Manston Surgery, 72-76 Austhorpe Road, Leeds LS15 8DZ Tel: 0113 264 5455 Fax: 0113 232 6181; Carlton House, 149 Primrose Lane, Leeds LS15 7QZ — MB ChB 1974 Leeds; DRCOG 1977.

SWADDLE, Margaret Brooklyn, Corchester Terrace, Corbridge NE45 5NS — MB BS Lond. 1968; MRCS Eng. LRCP Lond. 1968; DObst RCOG 1970. (Roy. Free)

SWADE, Shelley Naomi St Quintins Health Centre, St. Quintin Avenue, London W10 6NX Tel: 020 8960 5677 Fax: 020 8968 5933 — MB ChB 1975 Cape Town; MSc Lond. 1999; Dip. Ven. Soc. Apoth. Lond. 1981; Dip. Ther. Lond. 1997.

SWAEBE, Clare Isobel 1 Cotswold Way, Ashby-de-la-Zouch LE65 1ET — MB ChB 1992 Leeds.

SWAGE, Thoreya Hananne 20 Edward Road, Farnham GU9 8NP Tel: 01252 726432 Fax: 01252 726432 Email: t.swage@btinternet.com — MB BS 1985 Lond.; MA Oxf. 1993. Cons. in Healthcare Managem. Prev: Dir. Primary Care Developm. W Surrey HA; Locality Manager Ealing, Hammersmith & Hounslow HA; Area Manager Ealing, Hammersmith & Hounslow FHSA.

SWAI, Elishita Andrews c/o Department of Anaesthesia, South Tyneside District Hospital, Harton Lane, South Shields NE33 Tel: 0191 202 4046 Fax: 0191 202 4046; 62 Murrayfields, West Allotment, Newcastle upon Tyne NE27 0RF Tel: 0191 270 9007 Fax: 0191 270 9007 — MB ChB 1970 E. Afr.; FRCA 1974. (Unvi. Of Makerere. Uganda) S. Tyneside NHS Trust; Assoc. Specialist. Socs: BMA; NE Soc. Anaesth. Prev: Cons. Anaesth.Al-Amiri Hosp. Kuwait.

SWAIN, Alison Jane Hockley Medical Practice, 247 South Road, Hockley, Birmingham B18 5JS Tel: 0121 554 1757 Fax: 0121 554 1757; 133 Wentworth Road, Harborne, Birmingham B17 9SU — MB ChB 1986 Birm.; DRCOG 1990. Prev: Trainee GP Birm. VTS; SHO Dudley Rd. Hosp. VTS; SHO (Med.) Selly Oak Hosp. Birm.

SWAIN, Anna Victoria 201 Sandyford Road, Sandyford, Newcastle upon Tyne NE2 1NP — MB BS 1998 Newc.; MB BS Newc 1998.

SWAIN, Anne Frances 41 Willow Road, London NW3 1TN — MB BS 1973 Lond.; FRCP Lond. 1993; MRCP (UK) 1976; MRCS Eng. LRCP Lond. 1973. (Roy. Free) Cons. Dermat. Luton & Dunstable Hosp. Luton.

SWAIN, Archana 16 Royal Lodge Road, Belfast BT8 7UL — MB BS 1970 Urkal.

SWAIN, Catherine Mary 25 Brookside Way, Wall Heath, Kingswinford DY6 9AW — MB ChB 1985 Birm.; MRCGP 1995.

SWAIN, Christopher Paul 41 Willow Road, Hampstead, London NW3 1TN — MRCS Eng. LRCP Lond. 1971; BA Oxf. 1964; MD Lond. 1986, BSc 1968, MB BS 1972; FRCP Lond. 1990; MRCP (UK) 1974. (St. Bart.) Cons. & Sen. Lect. (Gastroenterol.) Lond. Hosp. Prev: Sen. Regist. St. Geo. Hosp. Lond.

SWAIN, David Geoffrey Department Elderly Med., Arden Lodge Annexe, Yardley Green Hospitalt, Yardley Green Road, Birmingham

SWAIN

B5 9PX Tel: 0121 766 6611 Fax: 0121 753 0653; 133 Wentworth Road, Birmingham B17 9SU — MB BS 1981 Lond.; BSc Lond. 1978, MB BS Lond. 1981; MRCP (UK) 1984; FRCP 1998. (Roy. Free) Cons. Phys. Elderly Med. - Birm. Heartlands. Hosp. Prev: Sen. Regist. (Geriat.) Sandwell Hosp. Birm.

SWAIN, David Leslie, LVO, QHP, Surg. Capt. RN Royal Naval Hospital, Haslar, Gosport PO12 2AA Tel: 01705 584255 — MB ChB 1964 Bristol; FRCA Eng. 1975; DA Eng. 1972; DObst RCOG 1971. (Bristol) Cons. Adviser Anaesth. RN Hosp. Haslar. Prev: Med. Off. i/c RN Hosp. Plymouth; Dir. Naval Offs. Appointing (Med.); Cons. Adviser (Anaesth.) Med. Directorate Gen. (Naval).

SWAIN, Mr Debadutta Rabinandan 75 Carnleigh Drive, Brooklands, Sale M33 3PT — MB BS 1974 Patna; FRCS Glas. 1983; FRCS Ed. 1982.

SWAIN, Elizabeth Doctors Surgery, 18 Union Street, Kirkintilloch, Glasgow G66 1DJ Tel: 0141 776 1238 Fax: 0141 775 2786; 7 Woodilee Cottages, Lenzie, Glasgow G66 3UA Tel: 0141 776 3879 — MB ChB 1973 Dundee; MRCGP 1981; DTM & H Liverp. 1981; DObst RCOG 1975. Prev: Med. Supt. Ch. of Christ Centr. Nigeria Alushi Med. Centre Plateau State, Nigeria.

SWAIN, Kiran Behari Oldpark Road Surgery, 460 Oldpark Road, Belfast BT14 6QG Tel: 028 9074 6535 Fax: 028 9074 7768; 16 Royal Lodge Road, Belfast BT8 7UL Tel: 01232 746535 — MB BS 1971 Utkal; PhD Qu. Univ. Belf. 1996; MICGP 1985. Research Fell. (Cardiac) Ulster Hosp.

SWAIN, Rosemary Anne Hamilton St Pauls Medical Centre, St. Pauls Square, Carlisle CA1 1DG Tel: 01228 524354 Fax: 01228 616660; 12 Portland Square, Carlisle CA1 1PY Tel: 01228 24354 — MB BS 1980 Lond.; MRCGP 1984; DRCOG 1985.

SWAIN, Mr William David Department of Orthopaedics, Royal Victoria Hospital, Grovuenor Road, Belfast BT12 6BA Tel: 028 9089 4762 — MB BCh BAO 1986 Belf.; BSc 1983 Belf.; FRCS 1997 (Orth.); FRCSI 1990. (Queen's University Belfast) Cons. Orthop. Surg. Prev: SHO Rotat. (Gen. Surg.) Lisburn Co. Antrim.

SWAINE, Christina Anne 5 Mushroom Field, Kingston, Lewes BN7 3LE — MB BS 1993 Lond.; BSc (Hons.) Physiol. Lond. 1988.

SWAINE, Christopher Norman Anaesthetic Department, Royal Sussex County Hospital, Eastern Road, Brighton BN2 5BE — MB BS 1979 Lond.; MA, MB BS Lond. 1979.

SWAINE, David John The Surgery, School Hill House, High Street, Lewes BN7 2LU — BSc Lond. 1988, MB BS 1991; DCH RCP Lond. 1994; DFFP 1993; DRCOG 1992. Trainee GP Riverside VTS.

SWAINE, Josephine Mary (retired) 15 Loom Lane, Radlett WD7 8AA — MB BCh 1963 Wales; DObst RCOG 1965. SCMO (Family Plann. & Reproduc. Health Care) W. Herts.Community Health (NHS) Trust St. Albans. Prev: SCMD (Family Plann. & Reproduc. Health Care) NW Herts Community Trust (NHS).

SWAINSBURY, Joanna Shaw Nuffield House Surgery, The Stow, Harlow CM20 3AX Tel: 01279 425661 Fax: 01279 427116 — MB BS 1978 Lond. GP Harlow.

SWAINSON, Catherine Jane 6 Connor Way, Gatley, Cheadle SK8 4HF — MB BS 1986 Newc.; FRCS Ed. 1990; FRCR 1994. Cons. Radiol. The Roy. Oldham Hosp. Oldham. Prev: Sen. Regist. (Diag. Radiol.) Manch. RHA.

SWAINSON, Charles Patrick Lothian University Hospitals NHS Trust, 1 Lauriston Place, Edinburgh EH3 9YW Tel: 0131 536 3008 Fax: 0131 536 2559 Email: charles.swainson@luht.cot.who.uk — MB ChB 1971 Ed.; FRCP Ed. 1985; MRCP (UK) 1974. (Edinburgh) Med. Dir., Cons. Phys. & Hon. Sen. Lect. (Med.) Roy. Infirm. Edin. Socs: Internat. Soc. Nephrol.; Renal Assn.; Brit. Assn. of Med. Managers. Prev: Sen. Lect. (Med.) Univ. Otago ChristCh., NZ.

SWAINSON, Susanna Monica Arbory Street Surgery, Arbory Street, Castletown IM9 1LN; 23 Victoria Road, Castletown IM9 1EN Tel: 01624 823686 Fax: 01624 823686 Email: john.bell@mail.enterprise.net — MB BCh BAO 1977 Belf.

SWAINSTON, David George L'Aumone Surgery, Castel GY5 7RU Tel: 01481 256517 Fax: 01481 251190 — MB BS Durh. 1965; DA Eng. 1970. GP. Prev: Med. Off. Drug Concern Clinic.

SWAINSTON, Ruth Morag 6 Newlands Lane, Nayland, Colchester CO6 4JJ — MB ChB 1996 Birm.; ChB Birm. 1996. SHO c/o the Elderly, Colchester Gen. Hosp.

SWALE, Jim 3 Cranmore Way, London N10 3TP — MB BS 1945 Lond.

SWALE, Nicholas Frederick Holyoake 5 St Thomas Terrace, Wells BA5 2XG — BM 1995 Soton. SHO (Med.) Roy. Hants. Co. Hosp. Winchester.

SWALE, Victoria Jane Royal London Hospital, Dept of Dermatology, London E2 Tel: 0207 377 7383 — BM 1992 Soton.; MRCP (UK) 1995. (Soton.) SPR BWA's & the Lond. NHS Trust. Prev: SHO (Dermat.) Guy's & St. Thos. Hosp. Trust Lond.; SHO (Med.) Qu. Alexandra Hosp. Portsmouth; SHO (Oncol. & Radiother.) Cheltenham Gen. Hosp.

SWALES, Brian Geoffrey (retired) 6 Palmaston Close, Haverbreaks, Lancaster LA1 5BS Tel: 01524 69682 — MRCS Eng. LRCP Lond. 1961; FFA RCS Eng. 1972; DA Eng. 1965; DObst RCOG 1963. Prev: Cons. Anaesth. Lancaster Acute Hosps. NHS Trust & W.morland Hosps. NHS Trust.

SWALES, Caroline Louise 6 Palmaston Close, Haverbreaks, Lancaster LA1 5BS — MB ChB 1988 Leeds. Trainee Phys. (Occupat. Health) ICI Runcorn.

SWALES, Hilary Anne Southampton General Hospital, Tremora Rd, Southampton SO16 6YD — MB ChB 1986 Leeds; FRCA 1993. Cons. (Anaesth.) Soton. Gen. Hosp. Prev: SHO (Anaesth.) York Dist. Hosp. & Leeds Gen. Infirm.; Ho. Off. Profess. Med. Unit St. Jas. Hosp. Leeds; SHO (A & E) Leeds Gen. Infirm.

SWALES, Professor John Douglas Department of Medicine, Clinical Sciences Building, Royal Infirmary, Leicester LE2 7LX Tel: 0116 252 3181 Fax: 0116 252 5847 Email: jds12@le.ac.uk; 21 Morland Avenue, Leicester LE2 2PF Tel: 0116 270 7161 — MB BChir Camb. 1961; MD Camb. 1971; FRCP Lond. 1977, M 1964; MRCS Eng. LRCP Lond. 1960; F Med Sci 1998. (Camb. & Westm.) Prof. Med. Univ. Leicester; Roy. Soc. Med. Vis. Prof. Amer. Heart Assn.; Sir Arthur Hall Lect. Sheff. Univ 2000. Socs: Fell. (Counc.) High Blood Pressure Research of Amer. Heart Assn.; Fell. Austral. Counc. for High Blood Pressure Research; (Chairm.) Federat. Assn. Clin. Profs. 1987. Prev: Sen. Lect. (Med.) Manch. Roy. Infirm.; Dir. Research & Developm. NHS 1996-1998; Regist. (Med.) W.m. Hosp. Lond.

SWALES, Mr John Saunders Tel: 01304 373341 Fax: 01304 372864; The Haven, Church Path, Great Mongeham, Deal CT14 0HH — MB ChB 1979 Sheff.; FRCS Eng. 1983; DRCOG 1986. Prev: Regist. (Gen. Surg.) Leicester Roy. Infirm.

SWALES, Miss Nola Vanessa Flat 2, 18 Vernon Road, Edgbaston, Birmingham B16 9SH Tel: 0121 454 9128; XX, The Common, Goathland, Whitby YO22 5AN Tel: 01947 896257 — MB ChB 1992 Dundee; FRCS Ed. 1996. Regist. (Gen. Surg.) Hereford Co. Hosp. Socs: BMA. Prev: Sen. SHO Birm.; SHO Rotat. Heartlands & Solihull.

***SWALES, Philip Patrick Richard** 21 Morland Avenue, Leicester LE2 2PF; 6 Orlando Road, Clarenton Park, Leicester LE2 1WN Tel: 0116 270 6104 — MB BS 1997 Lond.; BSc Lond. 1994.

SWALES, Valerie Susan Elm Lane Surgery, 104 Elm Lane, Sheffield S5 7TW Tel: 0114 245 6994 Fax: 0114 257 1260; The Briers, 28 Victoria Road, Sheffield S10 2DL Tel: 0114 266 8090 — MB ChB 1982 Sheff.; MRCGP 1989.

***SWALLOW, Elizabeth Bryony** Chestnut Tree Cottage, Willows Green, Chelmsford CM3 1QH — MB BS 1997 Lond.

SWALLOW, Hugh Malcolm Streatley Hall, Sharpenhoe Road, Streatley, Luton LU3 3PS Tel: 01582 881680; 19 Cardiff Road, Luton LU1 1PP Tel: 01582 31831 Fax: 01582 454142 — MB BS 1955 Lond.; MRCS Eng. LRCP Lond. 1955; DObst RCOG 1959. (St. Geo.) Hosp. Pract. (ENT) Luton & Dunstable Hosp.; Med. Off. S. Beds. Hospice.

SWALLOW, James Howard (retired) Chestnut Tree Cottage, Willows Green, Chelmsford CM3 1QH Tel: 01245 361472 — MB BChir 1952 Camb.; FRCP Lond. 1974, M 1959; MRCS Eng. LRCP Lond. 1952. Prev: Cons. Phys. Mid-Essex HA.

SWALLOW, James William Wellington Health Centre, Chapel Lane, Wellington, Telford TF1 1PZ Tel: 01952 242304; The Grange, Upton Magna, Shrewsbury SY4 4TZ Tel: 01743 709386 — MB ChB 1989 Birm.

SWALLOW, Janice (retired) 2 Trowbridge Cottages, Pilley, Lymington SO41 5QP Tel: 01590 677298 — LMSSA 1960 Lond. Prev: Med. Dir. Oakhaven Hospice Lymington.

SWALLOW, Julia (retired) The Cedars, Cholesbury Road, Wigginton, Tring HP23 6JQ — BSc (Hons. Physiol.) Leeds 1959, MB

SWAN

ChB 1961. SCMO S.W. Herts. Dist. Prev: Clin. Med. Off. Derbysh. AHA & Leics AHA(T).

SWALLOW, Malcolm Bryan Market Surgery, Warehouse Lane, Wath-On-Dearne, Rotherham S63 7RA Tel: 01709 877524 Fax: 01709 875089 Email: malcolm.swallow@gp-c87029.nhs.uk; 89 Rockingham Road, Swinton, Mexborough S648EE — MB BS 1982 Lond.; MRCGP 1988; DRCOG 1987; DCH RCP Lond. 1986.

SWALLOW, Michael David Northgate Village Surgery, Northgate Avenue, Chester CH2 2DX Tel: 01244 390396; 58 Greenfield Crescent, Waverton, Chester CH3 7NH Tel: 01244 332250 — MB ChB 1961 Sheff. (Sheff.) Prev: Regist. (Med.) N.. Gen. Hosp. Sheff.; Sen. Ho. Phys. Chesterfield Roy. Hosp.; Ho. Phys. & Ho. Surg. Roy. Infirm. Sheff.

SWALLOW, Michael William, OBE (retired) 15 Deramore Drive, Belfast BT9 5JQ Tel: 01232 669042 Fax: 01232 669042 — MB BS 1952 Lond.; FRCP Lond. 1972, M 1958. Neurol. Roy. Vict. Hosp. Prev: Sen. Regist. (Neurol.) Univ. Coll. Hosp.

SWALLOW, Patricia Diana Margaret Rose (retired) Chestnut Tree Cottage, Willows Green, Chelmsford CM3 1QH Tel: 01245 361472 Fax: 0243 360774 Email: di.swallow@btinternet.com — FRCA 1969; MB BS Lond. 1962; MRCS Eng. LRCP Lond. 1962. Prev: Cons. Anaesth. St. And. Centre Broomfield Hosp. Chelmsford.

***SWALLOW, Peter Nigel** 100 High Street, Olney MK46 4BE — MB BS 1998 Lond.; MB BS Lond 1998.

SWALLOW, Rodney Alan Tel: 024 7633 6542/2636 Fax: 024 7633 7353; 1 Holbeche Crescent, Fillongley, Coventry CV7 8ES Tel: 01676 541261 Email: rodney@swallowpcg.freeserve.co.uk — MB BChir 1972 Camb.; MA Camb. 1972. (Camb.) Chairm. Coventry N. PCG.

***SWALLOW, Rosemary Alexandra** Chestnut Tree Cottage, Willows Green, Chelmsford CM3 1QH Tel: 01245 361472 Fax: 01245 361472 — MB BS 1994 Lond.; MRCP UK 1997.

SWAMI, Atul Bhai Addenbrooke's Hospital, Box 93, Hills Road, Cambridge CB2 2QQ Tel: 01223 245151 Fax: 01223 216066; 96 Cotelands, Chichester Road, Croydon CR0 5UF — MB BCh 1984 Wales; MRCP (UK) 1987; FRCA 1990. Cons. Neurosci. Critical Care Unit Addenbrookes Hosp. Camb. Prev: Cons. Anaesth. & Ex-Dir. Neuroanaesth. Servs. Addenbrooke's Hosp. Camb.; Sen. Regist. (Anaesth.) Roy. Free Hosp. Lond. & Nat. Hosp. Neurol.; SHO (Anaesth.) Univ. Coll. & Middlx. Hosps. Lond.

SWAMI, Mr Kuchibhotla Satyanarayana Aberdeen Royal Infirmary, Ward 44, Aberdeen AB25 2ZN Tel: 01224 554629 Fax: 01224 840726 Email: uroswams@aol.com; 2 Primrose Bank Drive, Cults, Aberdeen AB15 9PF — MB BS 1977 Andhra; FRCS (Urol.) 1994; FRCS Ed. 1987; Dip. Urol. Lond 1990. (Andhra Med. Coll., India) Cons. Urol. Surg. Aberd. Roy. Infirm.; Cons. Urol. Surg. Albyn Hosp., Aberd. Socs: Brit. Assn. Urol. Surg.; Eur. Assn. Urol.; Société Internat. D'Urologie. Prev: Sen. Regist. (Urol.) Aberd. Roy. Infirm.; Clin. Research Fell. Bristol Urol. Inst.; Regist. (Urol.) S.mead Hosp. Bristol.

SWAMI, Manohar Lal Russell Street Surgery, 79 Russell Street, Reading RG1 7XG Tel: 0118 959 2131 Fax: 0118 959 3112; 5 Goodwin Close, Calcot, Reading RG31 7ZW — MB BS 1970 Rajasthan; MRCPI 1981. Thames Valley Police Surg. (Newbury & Didcot.). Prev: Med. Off. Univ. Leeds; SHO & Regist. (Gen. Med.) N.gate Hosp. Gt. Yarmouth; SHO (Gen. Med.) Cromer & Dist. Hosp. Norf.

SWAMI, Pinakiprasad Maganbhai Oak Road Surgery, 1 Oak Road, Canvey Island SS8 7AX Tel: 01268 692211 — MB BS 1960 Baroda. (Baroda)

SWAMI, Sadhana Russell Street Surgery, 79 Russell Street, Reading RG1 7XG Tel: 0118 959 2131 Fax: 0118 959 3112 — MB BS 1973 Rajasthan.

SWAMINATHAN, Muthuswamy Burton District Hospital Centre, Bewedere Road, Burton-on-Trent DE13 0RB Tel: 01283 66333; Garden House, Fishpond Lane, Egginton, Derby DE65 6HJ — MB BS 1981 Madras; LRCP LRCS Ed. LRCPS Glas. 1988. Acting Regist. (Orthop. & A & E) Burton Dist. Hosp. Centre. Prev: SHO Burton Dist. Hosp. Centre.

***SWAMPILLAI, Janice Suhanthi** The Steps, Boxford, Sudbury CO10 5HP — MB BS 1997 Lond.

SWAMY, Gowri Narayana The Medical Centre, The Strand, Kirkholt, Rochdale OL11 2JG — MB BS 1975 Madras.

SWAMY, Master Shivalingappa Associate Specialist, Department Health & Care of the Elderl, 1 Lpapford Close, Mapperley, Nottingham NG3 5SQ Tel: 0115 920 9419 — MB BS 1955 Mysore. (Mysore Med. Coll.) Assoc. Specialist Nottm. HA.

SWAN, Alberta Isabel (retired) 23 Southgate Spinneys, South Rauceby, Sleaford NG34 8QF Tel: 01529 488292 — MB BS 1934 Lond.; MRCS Eng. LRCP Lond. 1934.

SWAN, Alexander Julian Newton Medical Practice, Park St., Newtown SY16 1EF Tel: 01686 626221; Pinefields, Pines Gardens, Llanidloes Road, Newtown SY16 1EY Tel: 01686 629733 — MB BS 1988 Lond.; MRCGP 1992; DRCOG 1991. Prev: Trainee GP/SHO (Psychiat.) N.ampton Gen. Hosp. VTS; Ho. Off. (Gen. Med.) Burton on Trent Gen. Hosp.; Ho. Off. (Gen. Surg.) St. Thos. Hosp.

SWAN, Charles Henry James Mencom House, 2 Gower St, Newcastle-under-Lyme ST5 1EH — MB ChB Birm. 1961; MD Birm. 1969; FRCP Ed. 1994; FRCP Lond. 1979, M 1967. (Birm.) Socs: Brit. Soc. Gastroenterol. (Mem. Comm. Endoscopy Sect.- Mem. Counc. & Vice-Pres. Endoscopy); Assn. Phys. Prev: Cons. Phys. (Gastroenterol.) N. Staffs. Hosp. Centre Stoke-on-Trent; Sen. Regist. Gen. Hosp. Birm.; US Pub. Health Serv. Research Fell. New York Med. Coll., USA.

SWAN, Diana Shoreside, St. Margaret's Hope, Orkney KW17 2TQ — MB BS 1969 Lond.; MRCS Eng. LRCP Lond. 1969. (Westm.) Care Serv. Manager Orkney Health Unit. Prev: GP Orkney; Ho. Off. (Surg.) W. Herts. Hosp. Hemel Hempstead; Ho. Off. (O & G) Luton & Dunstable Hosp.

SWAN, Elspeth Anne Street House, Westward, Wigton CA7 8AF — MB BS 1988 Newc.; MA Camb. 1989; MRCGP 1992. Prev: Asst. GP Cumbria.

SWAN, Ethne 6 Rosedene Close, Birchill, Onchan, Douglas IM3 3HU Tel: 01624 76218 — MB ChB Glas. 1963; MFFP 1993. Family Plann. Clin. Med. Off.; Asst. Gen. Pract.

SWAN, Frances Ann Arran, 40 Admiral Street, Glasgow G41 1HU Tel: 0141 429 2626 Fax: 0141 429 2331; 16 Florence Drive, Glasgow G46 6UN — MB ChB 1986 Glas.; MRCGP 1990; DRCOG 1988.

SWAN, Harold Thomas (retired) 4 Albert Terrace, Edinburgh EH10 5EA Tel: 0131 447 1167 — MB ChB 1944 Ed.; DLitt Sheff. 1992; MD Ed. 1961; FRCP Ed. 1985; FRCP Lond. 1974, M 1949; FRCPath 1973, M 1963; DCH Eng. 1951. Hon. Lect. (Hist. of Med.) Univ. Sheff. Prev: Clin. Dean Fac. Med. Univ. Sheff.

SWAN, Mr Iain Ruairidh Cameron Department of Otolaryngology, Royal Infirmary, Glasgow G31 2ER Tel: 0141 211 4695 Fax: 0141 552 8411 Email: iain@ihr.gla.ac.uk; 3 Manor Road, Jordanhill, Glasgow G14 9LG Tel: 0141 959 5586 — MB ChB 1976 Glas.; MD Glas. 1985; FRCS Ed. 1980. (University of Glasgow) Sen. Lect. (Otolaryngol.) Univ. Glas.; Cons. Otol. MRC Inst. Hearing Research (Scott. Sect.) Roy. Infirm. Glas; Hon. Cons. Otolaryngol. Roy. Infirm. Glas.

SWAN, Ian Robert 60 Bradford Road, Trowbridge BA14 9AR Tel: 01225 754255; Little Priory, Bathwick Hill, Bath BA2 6LA — MB ChB 1974 Glas.; Dobst RCOG 1976 1976; Dip. Astmma 1997; MRCGP 1981; DFFP 1997. (Glasgow) GP; GP Trainee.

SWAN, Ingrid Louise Hamilton Blackhouse, Eyemouth TD14 5LR — MB ChB 1980 Glas.; MRCPsych 1988; MRCGP 1985; DRCOG 1982. Assoc. Specialist Dingleton Hosp. Melrose.

SWAN, John David (retired) 42 Linkswood, Compton Place Road, Eastbourne BN21 1EF Tel: 01323 731397 — LRCP LRCS 1938 Ed.; LRCP LRCS Ed. LRFPS Glas. 1938; MRCGP 1952. Prev: Capt. RAMC 1940-46.

SWAN, John Horatio (retired) 32 Ranelagh Road, London W5 5RJ — MRCS Eng. LRCP Lond. 1939; MRCGP 1970. Prev: Clin. Asst. Med. Out-pats. King Edwd. Memor. Hosp. Ealing.

SWAN, Jonathan William Cardiology Department, North Manchester General Hospital, Manchester M8 6RL Tel: 0161 795 4567 Email: jws1@bigfoot.com; Barleywell Cottage, Castle Mill Lane, Ashley, Altrincham WA15 0QU — MB ChB 1983 Manch.; MD Manch. 1994; MRCP (UK) 1988; DRCOG 1985. Cons. Cardiol. N. Manch. Gen. Hosp. Prev: Sen. Regist. (Cardiol.) Manch. Roy. Infirm.; BMS Cardiovasc. Research Fell. Brompton Hosp. Lond.; Regist. (Cardiol.) Harefield Hosp. & Kings Coll. Hosp. Lond.

SWAN, Joseph 12 Snaefell Crescent, Onchan, Douglas IM3 4NJ Tel: 01624 75444 — MB ChB 1963 Glas.; DPH 1966.

SWAN

SWAN, Katharine Olive 29 Gortin Park, Belfast BT5 7EQ — MB BCh BAO 1990 Belf.; MB BCh Belf. 1990.

SWAN, Kathleen Mary Sundon Medical Centre, 142-144 Sundon Park Road, Sundon Park, Luton LU3 3AH Tel: 01582 571130 Fax: 01582 564452; 44 Kingsdown Avenue, Luton LU2 7BU — MB ChB 1977 Sheff.

SWAN, Lorna Level 4 Cardiology, Western Infirmary, Glasgow G11 6NT Tel: 0141 211 2987 Fax: 0141 339 2800 Email: ls11n@clinmed.gla.ac.uk; 82 Micklehouse Road, Springhill, Baillieston, Glasgow G69 6TG — MB ChB 1992 Glas.; MRCP (UK) 1995. Clin. Research Fell. (Med. & Therap.) W.. Infirm. Glas.

SWAN, Marc Christopher Withermore House, Stourbridge Road, Wombourne, Wolverhampton WV5 9BN Email: swanmarc@hotmail.com — MB BS 1996 Lond.; BSc (Neurosci.) Lond. 1993. (St. Mary's Hosp. Med. Sch.) SHO (Vasc. Surg.) St. Mary's Hosp. Lond. Prev: SHO (Orthop.) St. Mary's Hosp. Lond.; SHO (A & E Med.) St. Mary's Hosp. Lond.; SHO Transpl. Surg. Freeman Hosp. Newc.

SWAN, Marion PO Box 43, Windermere LA22 0GR Tel: 015394 31025 Fax: 01642 785620 Email: 101641.3650@compuserve.com — MB BS 1972 Newc.; FRCPsych 1997; MRCPsych 1977. Indep. Forens. Psychiat. Cumbria. Prev: Cons. Forens. Psychiat. N.. RHA; Sen. Regist. (Forens. Psychiat.) N.. RHA; Sen. Regist. (Psychiat.) St. Luke's Hosp. Middlesbrough.

SWAN, Melanie Jane 14 Larch Way, Ferndown, Wimborne BH21 9SS — MB BS 1987 Lond.; MRCP (UK) 1991.

SWAN, Philippa Ann (retired) The River House, Tarrant Rushton, Blandford Forum DT11 8SD Tel: 01258 452403 — MB ChB 1946 Ed.; DObst RCOG 1949. Prev: Ho. Phys. & Ho. Surg. Deaconess Hosp. Edin.

SWAN, Sandra Elizabeth The New Surgery, Victoria Road, Wargrave, Reading RG10 8BP Tel: 0118 940 3939 Fax: 0118 940 1357; 4 Holly Cross, Crazies Hill, Wargrave, Reading RG10 8QB Tel: 01734 403483 — MB ChB 1968 St. And.; DObst RCOG 1970. (St. And.)

SWAN, Timothy Fraser Wesleyan Chapel, Barningham, Richmond DL11 7DU — MB ChB 1991 Liverp.; BSc (Hons) Biochem. Liverp. 1986. HM Forces Doctor.

SWAN, William Gordon Dunblane Medical Practice, Well Place, Dunblane FK15 9BQ Tel: 01786 822595 Fax: 01786 825298 — MB ChB 1972 Aberd.; DObst RCOG 1975.

SWANI, Mohan Singh 265 Baldwins Lane, Hall Green, Birmingham B28 0RF Tel: 0121 744 1290; 37 Brueton Avenue, Solihull B91 3EN Tel: 0121 704 2321 — MB ChB Sheff. 1958; MB ChB Sheff. 1958; DObst RCOG 1962; DObst RCOG 1962. (Sheff.)

SWANN, Alan Bedford Imperial College Health Centre, Watts Way, London SW7 1LU Tel: 020 7594 9401 Fax: 020 7594 9407 Email: a.swann@ic.ac.uk — BM 1978 Soton.; AFOM RCP Lond. 1988. (Southampton) Dir. Occupat. Health Imperial Coll. of Sci. Technol. & Med. Lond. Prev: GP Princip. Imperial Coll. Med. Partnership Lond.; Trainee GP Willesden; SHO Cent. Middlx. Hosp. Lond.

SWANN, Alan George Castleside Unit, Newcastle General Hospital, Westgate Road, Newcastle upon Tyne NE4 6BE Tel: 0191 273 6666; 1 Bridge End Cottage, Warden, Hexham NE46 4SH — MB BCh BAO 1983 Dub.; MRCPI 1986; MRCPsych 1990; MRCGP 1987. Cons. Old Age Psychiat. Castleside Unit Newc. Gen. Hosp.; Clin. Director.

SWANN, Alison Rosehill Surgery, 189 Manchester Road, Burnley BB11 4HP Tel: 01282 428200 Fax: 01282 838492; Witton Lodge, School Lane, Simonstone, Burnley BB12 7HR Tel: 01282 771711 — MB ChB 1973 Dundee; MRCGP 1977; Dip. Pract. Dermat. Wales 1991; DObst RCOG 1975. (St Andrews) Prev: Clin. Med. Off. Burnley HA; SHO (Anaesth.) Roy. Hosp. Sick Childr. Edin.; SHO (Obst.) Elsie Inglis Matern. Hosp. Edin.

SWANN, Cynthia Mary 32 Abbotts Way, Highfield, Southampton SO17 1NS — MB ChB 1972 Leeds; MRCGP 1976. Prev: Univ. Phys. Univ. Health Serv. Univ. Soton.; Lect. (Primary Med. Care) Univ. Soton.

SWANN, David Graham Department of Anaesthetics, Royal Infirmary of Edinburgh, Lauriston Place, Edinburgh EH3 9YW Tel: 0131 229 2477 Fax: 0131 519 5400 — MB ChB 1980 Bristol; BSc Bristol 1977; FRCA 1989. Cons. Anaesth. Roy. Infirm. Edin.

SWANN, Debra Elizabeth 1 Fairway, Clifton, York YO30 5QA — MB BS 1990 Lond. SHO (A & E) Yorks.

SWANN, Mr Ian James Kirklea, 7 Campsie Road, Strathblane, Glasgow G63 9AB — MB BS 1971 Newc.; FRCS 1976 Eng.; DFM 1989 Glas.; FFAEM 1993; FFAEM 1993; FRCS Eng. 1976; DFM Glas. 1989. (Newc. u. Tyne) Cons. Admin. Charge of A & E Glas. Roy. Infirm.; Hon. Clin. Sen. Lect. Glas. Univ. Prev: Clin. Dir. (A & E Med.) Glas.; Sen. Regist. (A & E) Glas. Roy. Infirm.; Regist. Rotat. (Gen. Surg.) Newc. AHA (T).

SWANN, Ian Lonsdale Burnley General Hospital, Casterton Avenue, Burnley BB10 2PQ Tel: 01282 474167 Fax: 01282 474156; Witton Lodge, School Lane, Simonstone, Burnley BB12 7HR Tel: 01282 71711 — MB ChB 1970 St. And.; FRCP (UK) 1997; FRCP Ed. 1985; FRCPCH 1997; DCH Eng. 1976. (St. And.) Cons. Paediat. N. W.. RHA; Clin. Dir. Burnley Health Care Trust; Hon. Lect. Univ. Liverp. Med. Sch; Prin. Regional Examr. NW. Region RCPCH. Socs: Fell. Manch. Med. Soc.; FRCPCh.; Roy. Coll. Paedia. & Child Health. Prev: Sen. Regist. (Paediat.) Univ. Hosp. Wales Cardiff; Regist. (Neonat. Paediat.) Simpson Memor. Matern. Pavil. Edin.; Regist. (Paediat. Med.) Roy. Hosp. Sick Childr. Edin.

SWANN, James Cyprian (retired) 104 Hayes Way, Beckenham BR3 6RT Tel: 020 8650 3673 — MB BS 1959 Lond.; FRCR 1975; FFR 1965; DMRD Eng. 1963; DObst RCOG 1961. Cons. Radiol. BMI Sloane Hosp. Beckenham & Chelsfield Pk. Hosp. Prev: Cons. Radiol. & Sen. Regist. (Radiodiag.) & Ho. Off. (Gen. Med. & Surg.) Lond. Hosp.

SWANN, John David Grosvenor Street Surgery, 4 Grosvenor Street, St Helier, Jersey JE1 4HB Tel: 01534 30541 Fax: 01534 887948 — MB BCh BAO 1964 Belf.; DObst RCOG 1967. (Belf.)

SWANN, Kenneth John Whitley Road Health Centre, Whitley Road, Whitley Bay NE26 2ND Tel: 0191 253 1113; 36 Arden Court, Hadrian Park, Wallsend NE28 9YB Tel: 0191 263 7626 — MB BS 1983 Newc.; MRCGP 1987.

SWANN, Mr Malcolm (cons. rooms), 9 Beaumont Road, Windsor SL4 1HY Tel: 01753 863063 Fax: 01753 850128; 3 Chantry Place, Kingstable St., Eton, Windsor SL4 6RH Tel: 01753 840328 Email: malcomswann@btinternet.com — MB BS 1955 Lond.; FRCS Eng. 1960; MRCS Eng. LRCP Lond. 1955. (Westm.) Cons. Orthop. Surg. Heatherwood & Wexham Pk. Hosp. Trust. Socs: Fell. Roy. Soc. Med. (Ex-Pres. Orthop. Sect.); Fell. BOA. Prev: Sen. Regist. Roy. Nat. Orthop. Hosp. Lond.; Hon. Sec. Brit. Orthop. Assn.; Ho. Surg. Roy. Marsden Hosp.

SWANN, Margaret Alice 27 Hawthornden Road, Belfast BT4 3JU Tel: 01232 651825 Fax: 01232 651825 — MB BCh BAO 1968 Belf.; MD Belf. 1989; DCH RCPSI 1970. (Belf.) Indep. Med. Pract. Belf. Prev: SCMO S. & E. Belf. Community Trust.

SWANN, Richard Ivan Adair West Kent HA, Preston Hall, Aylesford ME20 7NJ — MA, MB Camb. 1968, BChir 1967; MRCGP 1976; MFPHM 1990; DObst RCOG 1970. (Camb. & St. Thos.) Cons. Pub. Health Med. W. Kent. HA. Prev: Cons. Pub. Health Med. SE Thames RHA; Sen. Regist. (Community Med.) SE Thames RHA; GP Sutton Valence.

SWANN, Roy Andrew Clinical Microbiology and Public Health Laboratory, Level 5 Sandringham Building, Leicester Royal Infirmary, Leicester LE1 5WW Tel: 0116 258 6505; 15 Chapel Close, Houghton on the Hill, Leicester LE7 9HT — BM BCh 1976 Oxf.; MA Camb. 1976; FRCPath 1994, M 1982. Cons. Med. Microbiol. Roy. Infirm. Leic. NHS Trust.

SWANNACK, Robert Yorkley Health Centre, Bailey Hill, Yorkley, Lydney GL15 4RS Tel: 01594 562437 — MB BS 1974 Lond.

SWANNELL, Anthony John (retired) The City Hospital, Hucknall Road, Nottingham NG5 1PJ Tel: 0115 969 1169 Fax: 0115 962 7709 — MB 1963 Camb.; MB Camb. 1962, BChir 1963; FRCP Lond. 1979, M 1967. Cons. Rheum. Nottm. City Hosp. Trust (T); Clin. Teach. Univ. Nottm. Prev: Sen. Regist. (Rheum.) Canad. Red Cross Memor. Hosp. Taplow & Hammersmith Hosp. Lond.

SWANSON, Mr Alexander James Grenville (retired) Fernbrae Hospital, 329 Perth Road, Dundee DD2 1LJ Tel: 01382 667203 — MB ChB 1966 St. And.; FRCS Ed. 1974. Hon. Sen. Lect. Univ. of Dundee. Prev: Sen. Lect. (Orthop. & Trauma Surg.) Univ. Dundee.

SWANSON, Fiona Margaret 3 Arnprior Place, Alloway, Ayr KA7 4PT — MB ChB 1987 Manch.; BSc (Med. Sci.) St. And. 1984. BrE. Phys. / Screening Ayrsh. Centr. Hosp, Irvine; Staff Grade (Comm. Paediat.) Ayrsh. Centr. Hosp, Irvine. Prev: SHO (Psychiat.)

St. Mary's Hosp. N.d.; SHO (Child Psychiat.) Qu. Eliz. Hosp. Gateshead; SHO (Paediat. & Comm. Paediat.) Qu.s Pk. Hosp. Blackburn.

SWANSON, Gilbert Herbert (retired) Tigh na Creige, Crarae, By Minard, Inveraray PA32 8YA — MB ChB 1949 Glas. Prev: Clin. Asst. (ENT) Hull Roy. Infirm.

SWANSON, Iain Melvin Spindrift, 19 Seaview, Dunure, Ayr KA7 4LX — MB ChB 1982 Glas.

SWANSON, Lynn 17 Honister Avenue, Jesmond, Newcastle upon Tyne NE2 3PA — MB BS 1988 Newc.; DA (UK) 1992.

SWANSON, Maureen Ann South Cheshire Health Authority, 1829 Building, Countess of Chester Health Park, Liverpool Road, Chester CH2 1UL Tel: 01244 650330 Fax: 01244 650396 — MB ChB 1976 Liverp.; DRCOG 1979. Med. Dir. (Primary Care) S. Chesh. HA.

SWANSON, Noel Christopher Paul Child & Family Therapy, 2nd Floor, Osborn Clinic, Osborn Road, Fareham PO16 7ES Tel: 01329 822220 Fax: 01329 282136; Tel: 01329 282829 Fax: 01329 282829 — BM 1982 Soton.; MRCPsych 1987. (Southampton) p/t Cons. Child & Adolesc. Psych. Child & Fam. Ther. Clinic, Hants. Prev: Fell. Psychiat. Dalhousie Univ. Halifax Nova Scotia, Canada; Psychiat. Belize City Hosp., Belize; SHO (Psychiat.) Middlx. Hosp. Lond.

SWANSON, William Cameron (retired) Strathmore House, Newtyle, Blairgowrie PH12 8TP Tel: 01828 646293 — MB ChB Glas. 1936; FRCR 1975; DMR Ed. 1940. Prev: Consult. Radiother. Ninewells Hosp. Dundee.

SWANSTON, Alice Catherine Nelson (retired) Flat 14 Yewdale, 196 Harborne Park Road, Harborne, Birmingham B17 0BP Tel: 0121 427 9414 — MRCS Eng. LRCP Lond. 1933; DPH Lond. 1946; DIH Soc. Apoth. Lond. 1946. Prev: Sen. Med. Off. DHSS.

SWANSTON, James Kelly (retired) Tillypronie, Helmsley, York YO62 5DQ Tel: 01439 770670 — LRCP LRCS Ed. LRFPS Glas. 1934; MRCGP 1962.

SWANSTON, John Stephen Kelly, OStJ, Col. late RAMC Royal Hospital Chelsea, London SW3 4SR Tel: 020 7370 0161 — MB ChB 1966 Liverp. (Liverpool) Asst. Phys. (Gen. Pract.) Roy. Hosp. Chelsea. Socs: BMA; Roy. Soc. Med. Prev: Cdr. (Med.) HQ Lond. Dist.; Med. Adviser NATO Forces, Norway; Sen. Med. Off. Episcopi Garrison Cyprus.

***SWANTON, Alexander Graham** 5 Pennsylvania Close, Exeter EX4 6DJ — MB BS 1998 Lond.; MB BS Lond 1998.

SWANTON, Angus Richard (retired) 20 Marsham Lodge, Marsham Lane, Gerrards Cross SL9 7AB Tel: 01753 886302 — MRCS Eng. LRCP Lond. 1947. Prev: Med. Off. Civil Aviat. Auth.

SWANTON, Robert Howard 42 Wimpole Street, London W1g 8yf Tel: 020 7486 7416 Fax: 020 7487 2569; 10 Dover Park Drive, Roehampton, London SW15 5BG Email: rhswanton@easynet.co.uk — MB BChir 1970 Camb.; MA, MD Camb. 1980; FRCP Lond. 1984; MRCP (UK) 1971. (St. Thos.) Socs: BMA; Pres. Brit. Cardiac Soc. (1998-2001); Fell. Europ. Soc. Cardiol. Prev: Sen. Regist. (Cardiol.) Nat. Heart Hosp. Lond.; Regist. (Cardiac) & Ho. Phys. St. Thos. Hosp. Lond.

SWANWICK, Maelie Victoria 34 Leeds Road, Rawdon, Leeds LS19 6HA — MB ChB 1991 Leeds; BSc (Hons.) Leeds 1988, MB ChB 1991.

SWANWICK, Timothy High Street Surgery, 87 High Street, Abbots Langley WD5 0AJ Tel: 01923 262363 Fax: 01923 267374 — MB BS 1986 Lond.; MA Camb. 1983; MRCGP 1990; DCH RCP Lond. 1990; DRCOG 1989. Examr. RCGP; Dep. Dean of Postgrad. Gen. Pract. Educat., Lond.; Dept. of Postgradate Med. and Dent. Educat.

SWAPP, Helen Garden Sunnybank House Medical Centre, Towngate, Wyke, Bradford BD12 9NG Tel: 01274 424111 Fax: 01274 691256 — MB ChB 1987 Aberd.; MRCGP 1993. (Aberdeen) Prev: Trainee GP Leeds W.. HA; SHO (Anaesth.) Roy. Hallamsh. Hosp. Sheff.; SHO Gold Coast Hosp. Qu.sland, Austral.

SWARBRICK, Edwin Thornton Coppice Green, Shifnal TF11 8PB Tel: 01952 462226 — MB BS 1968 Lond.; MB BS (Hons.) Lond. 1968; MD Lond. 1980; FRCP Lond. 1985; MRCP (UK) 1971. (St. Geo.) Cons. Phys. & Gastroenterol. New Cross & Roy. Hosps. Wolverhampton; Hon. Reader (Gastroenterol.) Univ. Wolverhampton. Socs: Fell. Roy. Soc. Med.; Brit. Soc. Gastroenterol. Prev: Research Fell. St. Bart. Hosp. Lond.; Regist. (Med.) St. Mark's Hosp. Lond.; Regist. Roy. Lond. Hosp.

SWARBRICK, John Gerard Stanley Road Surgery, 204 Stanley Road, Bootle L20 3EW Tel: 0151 922 5719; 37 Prescot Road, Ormskirk L39 4TG Tel: 01695 572882 — MB ChB 1985 Dundee; MRCGP 1989. Socs: Guild Catholic Doctors. Prev: GP Poulton-le-Fylde.

SWARBRICK, Mr Michael John Department of Radiology, Royal Hallamshire Hospital, Glossop Road, Sheffield S10 2JF Tel: 0114 276 6222 Fax: 0114 271 3766; 4 Bishopdale Drive, Ridgeway, Sheffield S20 5PH Tel: 0114 248 7811 — BM BCh 1986 Oxf.; MA Oxf. 1988, BA 1983; FRCS Eng. 1991; FRCR 1994. Sen. Regist. (Radiol.) Roy. Hallamsh. Hosp. Sheff. Prev: Regist. (Radiol.) Roy. Hallamsh. Hosp. Sheff.; SHO (Gen. Surg.) Roy. Infirm & Gen. Hosp. Leicester; SHO (Cardiothoracic Surg.) Glenfield Gen. Hosp. Leics.

SWARBRICK, Peter John Benefits Agency, Medical Services, Argyle House, Lady Lawson St., Edinburgh EH3 0QL Tel: 0131 222 5775; 32 West Werberside, Crewe Road S., Edinburgh EH4 1SZ Tel: 0131 332 1931 — MB ChB Ed. 1962; FRCGP 1993, M 1969. (Ed.) Med. Adviser Benefits Agency Edin.; Hon. Fell. Rehabil. Studies Unit Univ. Edin. Socs: Fell. Roy. Soc. Med. Edin.; Scott. Soc. Rehabil. Prev: Princip. GP Livinston; SHO P.ss Margt. Rose Orthop. Hosp. & W.. Gen. Hosp. Edin.; Ho. Surg. Roy. Infirm. Edin.

SWARBRICK, Philomena Mary The Old Vicarage, Colton, Ulverston LA12 8HF — MB ChB 1984 Manch.; BSc (Hons. Anat.) Manch. 1981; MRCP (UK) 1993; MRCGP (Distinc.) 1995; DRCOG 1994; DFFP 1994. (Manchester) Socs: BMA. Prev: Trainee GP Milnthorpe, Cumbria.; Partner GP Cumbria; Med. Off. to Hospice.

SWARBRICK, Ruth Hanna Homestead, Rew St., Cowes PO31 8NP — MB BS 1991 Lond.; BSc (Hons.) Lond. 1986, MB BS 1991; E.

SWAROOP, Mukul Brook Medical Centre, Ecton Brook Road, Northampton NN3 5EN Tel: 01604 401185 Fax: 01604 403268; Wendover, 512 Wellingborough Road, Northampton NN3 3HX Tel: 01604 402787 — MB BS 1969 Agra; DCH Delhi 1972. (S.N. Med. Coll. Agra) Hosp. Pract. (Paediat.) N.ampton Gen. Hosp.

SWART, Christopher Fleming Priory House, Priest Lane, Cartmel, Grange-over-Sands LA11 6PU — MB BS 1990 Lond.

SWART, Michael Leslie Department of Anaesthesia, Torbay Hospital, Newton Road, Torquay TQ2 7AA — MB BS 1987 Lond.

SWART, Sonia Sylvia Northampton General Hospital, Cliftonville, Northampton NN1 5BD Tel: 01604 545839 Fax: 01604 545933 Email: sonia.swart@ngh-tr.anglox.uk; Northampton General Hospital, Cliftonville, Northampton NN1 5BD Tel: 01858 545465 Email: sonia.swart@btinternet — MB BChir 1977 Camb.; FRCPath 1992; FRCP 1993; MD Camb. 1986, MA, MB 1977, BChir 1976; MRCP (UK) 1979; MRCPath 1986. Cons. Haemat. N.ampton Gen. Hosp. NHS Trust. Prev: Lect. Haemat. Dept. of Pharmacol. & Therap. Univ. Leicester.; Cons. Haemat. N. Warks. HA & Rugby HA.

SWARTZ THIRLWALL, Marianne Birgitta c/o Major D. Thirlwall, HQ Joint Services Medical Unit BFPO 1 — Lakarexamen Goteburg 1979.

SWARUP, Namita Department of Paediatrics, John Radcliffe NHS Trust, Oxford OX3 9DU — MB BS 1989 Ibadan; MRCP (UK) 1995.

SWASH, Professor Michael Neurological Department, The Royal London Hospital, London E1 1BB Tel: 020 7377 7472 Fax: 020 7377 7318 Email: mswash@mds.qmw.ac.uk; 88 Woodwarde Road, Dulwich, London SE22 8UT Tel: 020 8693 6574 — MB BS 1962 Lond.; MD Lond. 1973; FRCP Lond. 1977, M 1969; FRCPath 1991, M 1982. (Lond. Hosp.) Prof. Neurol. St. Bart. & the Roy. Lond. Hosp. Coll. of Med. & Dent.; Cons. Neurol. Roy. Lond. Hosp.; Prof. Neurol. St. Bart., Roy. Lond. Hosp. Coll. Med. & Dent. & Qu. Mary W.field Coll; Hon. Cons. Neurol. St. Mark's & St. Luke's Hosp. for Clergy Lond.; Neurol. (Adjunct Staff) Cleveland Clinic Foundat. Ohio, USA; Chief Med. Off. Swiss ReInsur. (UK) Ltd.; Chairm. Research Ethics Comm. of E. Lond. City HA; Trustee Motor Neurone Dis. Assn. Socs: (Ex-Sec.) Assn. Brit. Neurol.; Hon. Mem. Austral. Assn. Neurols.; Chairm. Motor Neurone Dis. Assn. Prev: Sen. Regist. (Neurol.) Lond. Hosp.; Resid. (Neurol.) Univ. Hosps. Cleveland Case-W.. Reserve Univ. USA; Med. Dir.

SWATKINS, Sandra Substance Misuse Team, 27/29 Hallchurch Road, Holly Hall, Dudley DY2 0TQ Tel: 01384 457373 Fax: 01384 244903 Email: sandra.swatkins@dudleyph-tr.wmids.nhs.uk — MB ChB 1980 Birm.; MRCPsych 1984. Cons. Psychiat. (Drug & Alcohol Misuse) Dudley Priority Health NHS Trust.

SWAYNE, Jeremy Michael Deneys Greys, Ditcheat, Shepton Mallet BA4 6RB Tel: 01749 860662 Fax: 01749 860530 Email:

SWAYNE

jem.swayne@btinternet.com — BM BCh Oxf. 1967; BA Oxf. 1963; MRCS Eng. LRCP Lond. 1966; FFHom 1991, M 1983; MRCGP 1974; DObst RCOG 1969. (Oxf. & St. Geo.) Dean, Fac. Homeop. Lond.; Homoeop. Phys. SW Region. Prev: Sen. Med. Coding Cons. NHS Centre for Coding & cl.ification; Homoeop. Phys. Bristol Homoeop. Hosp.; GP Yeovil & Coleford.

SWAYNE, Philippa Salisbury District Hospital, Salisbury SP2 8BJ Tel: 01722 336262; Lower Nunton Farm House, Nunton, Salisbury SP5 4HP — MB ChB 1982 Bristol; MB ChB (Hons.) Bristol 1982; MRCGP 1989; FFA RCS Eng. 1988; DRCOG 1986. Cons. Anaesth. Salisbury Dist. Hosp. Socs: Assn. Anaesth.; Obst. Anaesth. Assn. Prev: Sen. Regist. (Anaesth.) Bristol & Salisbury; Regist. (Anaesth.) P.ss Margt. Hosp. Swindon & Oxf. HA.

SWEATMAN, Catherine Mary The Surgery, 134 Baffins Road, Portsmouth PO3 6BH Tel: 023 9282 7132 Fax: 023 9282 7025; 7 Hamilton Close, Langstone, Havant PO9 1RP — BM 1985 Soton.; MRCGP 1990; DRCOG 1988. Prev: Trainee GP Portsmouth VTS.

SWEATMAN, Martin Charles Michael Mount Vernon Hospital, Northwood HA6 2RN Tel: 01923 844393 Fax: 01923 844168 — MB BS 1976 Lond.; BSc (Hons.) Lond. 1973; FRCP Lond. 1995; MRCP (UK) 1980; MRCS Eng. LRCP Lond. 1976. (St. Bart.) Cons. Phys. Mt. Vernon Hosp. N.wood. Socs: Assoc. Mem. Brit. Thoracic Soc.; Brit. Geriat. Soc. Prev: Sen. Regist. St. Thos. & Kent & Canterbury Hosp.; Clin. Research Fell. Cardiothoracic Inst. Brompton Hosp. Lond.

SWEDAN, Hisham Ibrahim Hurst Road Health Centre, Hurst Road, Walthamstow, London E17 3BL Tel: 020 8520 4095 Fax: 020 8520 4894; 8 Felstead Road, Wanstead, London E11 2QJ — MB BCh 1972 Cairo; DGM RCP Lond. 1985.

SWEDAN, Mr Mohamed Ibrahim 93A Harley Street, London W1N 1DF Tel: 020 7935 9370 Fax: 020 7487 4298; 218 Sussex Gardens, London W2 3UD Tel: 020 7723 3693 — MRCS Eng. LRCP Lond. 1978; DS Cairo 1966, MB BCh 1964; FRCS Eng. 1976; FRCS Ed. 1974. (Cairo) Surg. P.ss Grace Hosp. & Harley St. Clinic. Socs: Fell. Roy. Soc. Med. Prev: Clin. Asst. St. Mark's Hosp. Lond.; Regist. (Surg.) W.m. Hosp. Lond. & Connaught Hosp. Lond.

SWEDAN, Sawsan Kamel Selim Lord Lister Health Centre, 121 Woodgrange Road, Forest Gate, London E7 0EP Tel: 020 8250 7530 Fax: 020 8250 7535; 8 Felstead Road, Wanstead, London E11 2QJ — MB BCh 1974 Cairo; MRCS Eng. LRCP Lond. 1982; DObst. RCPSI 1980. GP City & E. Lond. FPC.

SWEENEY, Anthony Martin Tang Hall Surgery, 190 Tang Hall Lane, York YO10 3RL Tel: 01904 411139 Fax: 01904 431224 — MB ChB 1981 Liverp.

SWEENEY, Anthony Niall The Grange, Highfield Road, Hemsworth, Pontefract WF9 4DP Tel: 01977 610009 Fax: 01977 617182 — MB ChB 1981 Liverp.; MRCGP 1989. GP Hemsworth.

SWEENEY, Bernard John Gerard 108 Ifield Road, London SW10 9AD — MB BCh BAO 1986 NUI; MRCPI 1988.

SWEENEY, Brendan The Crescent Medical Practice, 12 Walmer Crescent, Glasgow G51 1AT Tel: 0141 427 0191 Fax: 0141 427 1581 — MB ChB 1972 Glas.; MA Glas. 1966, MB ChB 1972; FRCGP 1986, M 1976; DObst RCOG 1974.

SWEENEY, Brian Edward Fintona Medical Centre, 33 Dromore Road, Fintona, Omagh BT78 2BB Tel: 028 8284 1203 Fax: 028 8284 0545 — MB BCh BAO 1987 NUI; LRCPSI 1987.

***SWEENEY, Catherine Marie** 1 Ridgeway, Epsom KT19 8LD — MB BS 1997 Lond.

SWEENEY, Clare Mary Clanrye Surgery, Newry Health Village, Monaghan Street, Newry BT35 6BW Tel: 028 3026 7639 Fax: 028 3025 7414 — MB BCh BAO 1990 Belf.; MB BCh Belf. 1990.

SWEENEY, Clodagh Margaret 6 Fortfield, Maypole Hill, Dromore BT25 1DD — MB BCh BAO 1993 Belf.; BSc (Hons.) Pathol. 1991; MRCPI (Paediat.) Dublin 1997. (Queen's Belfast) Socs: Ulster Paediat. Soc.

SWEENEY, Cormac James Erne Health Centre, Erne Hospital, Cornagrade Road, Enniskillen BT74 6AY Tel: 028 6632 5638; Health Centre, Cornagrade Road, Enniskillen BT74 Tel: 01365 325638 Fax: 01365 329446 — MB BCh BAO 1973 NUI; MICGP 1986. (University College Dublin) GP Enniskillen. Prev: Regist. (Med.) Altnagelvin Hosp. Lond.derry; SHO (Paediat.) St. Anthony, Newfld.; Ho. Phys. & Ho. Surg. Altnagelvin Hosp. Lond.derry.

SWEENEY, David The Grange Clinic, Westfield Avenue, Malpas, Newport NP20 6EY Tel: 01633 855521 Fax: 01633 859490 — BM BS 1981 Nottm.; BMedSci Nottm. 1979; MRCGP 1985; DRCOG 1983.

SWEENEY, Denis Oldpark Road Surgery, 460 Oldpark Road, Belfast BT14 6QG Tel: 028 9074 6535 Fax: 028 9074 7768 — MB BCh BAO 1979 Belf.

SWEENEY, Desmond 20 Buchanan Drive, Rutherglen, Glasgow G73 3PE Tel: 0141 647 1824 — LRCP LRCS 1973 Ed.; LRCP LRCS Ed. LRFPS Glas. 1944 FACA 1973; Dip. Amer. Bd. Anesth. 1968. (Anderson Coll. Glas.) Cons. Anesth. Auburn Gen. Hosp. Washington USA; Sen. Instruct. Dept. Anaesth. Univ. Hosp. Seattle, Washington. Socs: Fell. Roy. Soc. Med.; King Co. Med. Soc.; Fell. Internat. Anesth. Research Soc. Prev: Chief Resid. (Anesth.) King Co. Hosp. Seattle, U.S.A.; Resid. (Anesth.) Washington Hosp. Center, U.S.A.; Capt. RAMC.

SWEENEY, Elizabeth 49 Covertside, Wirral CH48 9UH — MB ChB 1993 Bristol.

SWEENEY, Gary Alan Ranworth Surgery, 103 Pier Avenue, Clacton-on-Sea CO15 1NJ Tel: 01255 421344 Fax: 01255 473581; 22 Holland Road, Clacton-on-Sea CO15 6EQ Tel: 01255 429041 Fax: 01255 473581 — MRCS Eng. LRCP Lond. 1978; MRCGP 1987; FFA RCSI 1985. (St. Bart.) GP Princip.; Hosp. Pract. (Anaesth.) Colchester Hosp.; Med. Adviser N. Essex HA. Socs: Brit. Assoc. of Med. Managers; Colchester Med. Soc. Prev: Regist. (Anaesth.) Coventry HA; SHO (Anaesth.) S.end Hosp. NE Thames HA; SHO (Paediat. & O & G) St. John's Hosp. Chelmsford.

SWEENEY, Helen Ruth The Surgery, 2 Great Wood Road, Small Heath, Birmingham B10 9QE Tel: 0121 766 8828 Fax: 0121 773 0091 — MB BS 1989 Newc.

SWEENEY, Jennifer Margaret 209 Glasgow Road, Dumbarton G82 1DP — MB ChB 1993 Glas.

SWEENEY, John Nicholas 168 Almond Brook Road, Standish, Wigan WN6 0SS Email: john.n.sweeney@btinternet.com — MB ChB 1983 Sheff.; FRCP 1999; Dip. Gum. (Dist.) 1994 Soc. of Apoth. Lond.; MRCP (UK) 1988. Cons. Phys. (G U Med.) Blackpool Vict. & Roy. Preston Hosps. Prev: Cons. Phys. (G U Med.) Roy. Lond. Hosp.; Sen. Regist. (G U Med.) Roy. Lond. Hosp.; Hon. Sen. Regist. (Immunol.) St. Bart. Med. Coll. Lond.

SWEENEY, Jonathan Edmon 484 West Road, Newcastle upon Tyne NE5 2ET — MB ChB 1978 Liverp.

SWEENEY, Kathleen Mary Majella Marblearch Terrace Surgery, 1 Marblearch Terrace, Florence Court Demesne, Enniskillen BT92 1EF Tel: 028 6634 8275; Moybrone, Letterbreen, Enniskillen BT92 — MB BCh BAO 1985 NUI; MRCGP 1989; DRCOG 1992. (Univ. Coll. Galway) SHO (Dermat.) Roy. Alexandra Hosp. Paisley. Socs: Sligo GP Soc.; Fermanagh GP Assn. Prev: Trainee GP Cumnock Ayrsh.; SHO (O & G) S.mead Gen. Hosp. Glas.; SHO (Paediat.) Booth Hall Manch.

SWEENEY, Kevin Thomas 1016 Great Western Road, Glasgow G12 0NP — LRCP LRCS 1942 Ed.; LRCP LRCS Ed. LRFPS Glas. 1942. Socs: Roy. M-C Soc. Glas. & BMA.

SWEENEY, Kieran Gerard St. Leonard's Medical Practice, 34 Denmark Road, Exeter EX1 1SF Tel: 01392 201790 Fax: 01392 201796; 1 Robins Court, Upton Pyne, Exeter EX5 5HZ Tel: 01392 841639 — MB ChB 1978 Glas.; MA Glas. 1971, MB ChB 1978; MRCGP 1982; MPhil Exeter 1996. (Glasgow) GP Exeter; Lect. Health Serv. Research RDSU Roy. Devon Exeter NHS Trust; Lect. (Gen. Pract.) Univ. of Exeter. Socs: Fell. Roy. Soc. Of Arts. Prev: Harkness Fell. Commonw. Fund New York 1991; Vis. Fell. Univ. Washington, Seattle, USA.

SWEENEY, Louise Evelyn X-Ray Department, Royal Belfast Hospital for Sick Children, 180 Falls Road, Belfast BT12 6BE — MB BCh BAO 1976 Belf.; FRCR 1983; DCH RCPS Glas. 1978; DMRD Eng. 1980. Cons. Radiol. Roy. Belf. Hosp. Sick Childr. & Roy. Vict. Hosp. Belf.

SWEENEY, Margaret Mary (retired) 20 Parkway, Ilford IG3 9HU Tel: 020 8599 0776 — MRCS Eng. LRCP Lond. 1945.

SWEENEY, Mark Gerard Knightsbridge Medical Centre, 71-75 Pavilion Road, London SW1X 0ET Tel: 020 8237 2600; 24 Friars Place Lane, Acton, London W3 7AP Tel: 020 8740 7808 — MB BS 1984 Lond.; MRCGP Lond. 1988; DRCOG 1989; Dip. Clin. Hypn. Lond. 1997. GP Princip.; GP Tutor Chelsea & W.m. Hosp.; Chairm. K.C.W. Clin. Audit Advis. Gp.

SWEENEY, Mary Elizabeth 5 Linden Avenue, Liverpool L23 8UL — MB ChB 1990 Liverp.

SWEETNAM

SWEENEY, Michael Thomas 8 Harbern Close, West Derby, Liverpool L12 8SR — MB ChB 1984 Liverp.

SWEENEY, Oliver James 7 Worcester, North Hampshire Hospital, Aldermaston Road, Basingstoke RG24 9NA — MB BS 1998 Lond.; MB BS Lond 1998.

SWEENEY, Patrick Laurie (retired) Fintona Medical Centre, 33 Dromore Road, Fintona, Omagh BT78 2BB Tel: 028 8284 1203 Fax: 028 8284 0545 — LRCPI & LM, LRSCI & LM 1962.

SWEENEY, Peter Martin Red House Surgery, 124 Watling Street, Radlett WD7 7JQ Tel: 01923 855606 Fax: 01923 853577; 9 King Harry Lane, St Albans AL3 4AS Tel: 01727 848072 — MB BS 1986 Lond.; MRCGP 1991; DRCOG 1990; DA (UK) 1988.

SWEENEY, Richard Charles Dr Moss and Partners, 28-38 Kings Road, Harrogate HG1 5JP Tel: 01423 560261 Fax: 01423 501099 — MB ChB 1979 Leeds; FRCGP 1995, M 1984; DRCOG 1982; Cert. Family Plann. RCOG 1982. (Leeds)

***SWEENEY, Sineaid Rosalie** 98 Marchmont Crescent, Edinburgh EH9 1HD — MB ChB 1998 Ed.; MB ChB Ed 1998.

SWEENEY, Thomas Kevin, QHP (retired) Tresanton, Wych Hill Way, Woking GU22 0AE Tel: 01483 828199 — MB BCh BAO Univ. Coll. Dub. 1949; FFPHM RCP (UK) 1989; FFCM 1983, M 1972; TDD Wales 1959; DTM & H Eng. 1954. Prev: Sen. Med. Off. DHSS.

SWEENIE, Alan Christopher 1/R, 1 Cathkin Road, Langside, Glasgow G42 9UB Tel: 0141 636 6129 — MB ChB 1993 Glas. SHO (Anaesth.) Victor A. Infirm. Glas. Prev: SHO (Anaesth.) Hairmyres Hosp. E. Kubride; SHO (A & E) Roy. Alexandra Hosp. Paisley.; SHO (A & E & Orthop.) S.. Gen. Hosp. Glas.

SWEENIE, John Fraser Crown Avenue Surgery, 12 Crown Avenue, Inverness IV2 3NF Tel: 01463 710777 Fax: 01463 714511; Tendore Farm, North Kessock, Inverness IV1 0XD — MB ChB 1981 Glas.; MRCP (UK) 1988; MRCGP 1990; Dip Pract. Dermat. Wales 1993. Hon. Lect. (Gen. Pract.) Dundee Univ.

SWEERTS, Michele Irene Edith c/o Watercress Cottage, 1 Oldbury Lane, Wick, Bristol BS15 5QG — MB ChB 1975 Cape Town.

***SWEET, Amanda Jane** 55 Whittington Road, Cheltenham GL51 6BT — MB BCh 1998 Wales.

SWEET, David Gordon The Gables, 15 Ormiston Park, Belfast BT4 3JT Tel: 02890 580373 Email: dsweet@ntlworld.com; The Gables, 15 Ormiston Park, Belfast BT4 4JT Email: dsweet@ntworld.com — MB BCh BAO 1990 Belf.; MRCPCH 1996; MRCPI 1995. (Qu. Univ. Belf.) Specialist Regist. (Train. Paediat.) Belf.; Maj. RAMC (Territorial Army).

SWEET, David John Stratton Medical Centre, Hospital Road, Stratton, Bude EX23 9BP Tel: 01288 352133 — MB 1974 Camb.; BChir 1973; DA 1981; DRCOG 1979. GP Bude; Hon. Doctor Bude Surf Club.

SWEET, Elizabeth Mary (retired) Dunwhillan, 3 Fullarton Crescent, Troon KA10 6LL Tel: 01292 314325 — MB ChB 1950 Ed.; FRCP Ed. 1968, M 1954; FRCP Glas. 1983, M 1981; FRCR 1975; FFR 1962; DMRD 1959; DCH Eng. 1953. Prev: Cons. Radiol. Roy. Hosp. Sick Childr. & Qu. Mother's Hosp. Glas.

SWEET, Hector Struthers (retired) Gothic Cottage, Lamb Corner, Dedham, Colchester CO7 6DX Tel: 01206 322391 — MB ChB 1939 Glas.; DOMS Eng. 1950.

SWEET, Peter Thomas Maes Mawr, 61 First Avenue, Charmandean, Worthing BN14 9NP Tel: 01903 209192 — MB BS 1975 Lond.; MRCS Eng. LRCP Lond. 1975; FFA RCS Eng. 1979. Cons. Anaesth. Worthing HA. Prev: Sen. Regist. St. Mary's Hosp. Lond. W2; Regist. St. Bart. Hosp. Lond.

***SWEET, Petra Louise** 23 Callaghan Cottages, Lindley St., London E1 3AZ — MB BS 1997 Lond.

SWEET, Pia Rebecca 7 Ballast Quay, Greenwich, London SE10 9PD — MB ChB 1985 Leic.; FRCA 1994. Cons. (anaesth.) Qu. Mar Hosp. Sidcup.

SWEET, Robert Douglas (retired) Dormer Cottage, Chollacott Lane, Tavistock PL19 9DD Tel: 01822 613066 — MB BChir 1942 Camb.; FRCP Lond. 1968, M 1947. Prev: Cons. Dermat. Plymouth Gen. Hosp.

SWEET, Stephen Charles Mayne (retired) La Ferme du Pignon, Route des Sages, Torteval, Guernsey GY8 0LB Tel: 01481 263273 Fax: 01481 263905 Email: s.sweet@lineone.net — MB ChB 1973 Bristol; DA Eng. 1976; DObst RCOG 1976. Prev: Clin. Asst. (Psychogeriat. Med.) Catel Hosp. Guernsey.

SWEET-ESCOTT, Michael William (retired) Moor Cottage, Guiting Power, Cheltenham GL54 5UE Tel: 01451 850357 — BM BCh 1951 Oxf.; MA Oxf. 1951; MRCGP 1962. Prev: GP Skipton; .

SWEETEN-SMITH, Beverley Ann Adelaide Medical Centre, 111 Adelaide Road, London NW3 7RY Tel: 020 7722 4135 — MB BS 1985 Lond.; BSc Nottm. 1980; MRCGP 1990; DTM & H RCP Lond. 1996; DRCOG 1990. (Univ. Coll. Lond.) GP Princip. Prev: GP Wantage Oxon.; Trainee GP John Radcliffe Hosp. VTS; Flt. Lt. RAF.

SWEETENHAM, Dileas Mary Combe House, Lynbrook Lane, Entry Hill, Bath BA2 5NB Tel: 01225 427110 Fax: 01225 423110 — MB BS 1956 Lond.; DCH Eng. 1958. (Roy. Free) Socs: Med. Off. Sch. Assn.; Clin. Soc. Bath. Prev: Med. Off. The Roy. Sch. Bath; Resid. Med. Off. Roy. Free Hosp.

SWEETENHAM, Ian Arthur 75 Ermine Street, Huntingdon PE29 3EZ Tel: 01480 453038; 12 Church Road, Brampton, Huntingdon PE28 4PW Tel: 01480 355454 — MB BChir 1988 Camb.; MA Camb. 1989; MRCGP 1992. GP Tutor Huntingdon; Clin. Asst. (Med. for Elderly) Huntingdon.

SWEETING, Audrey Evelyn (retired) Low Banks, Banks Lane, Riddlesden, Keighley BD20 5BD Tel: 01535 607972 — MB ChB 1957 Leeds; BSc (Gen. & Hons.) Lond. 1952 & 1953; DPM Leeds 1978. Prev: Assoc. Specialist (Psychogeriat. & Psychiat.) Airedale Gen. Hosp. Keighley.

SWEETING, Keith William (retired) Low Banks, Banks Lane, Riddlesden, Keighley BD20 5BD — MRCS Eng. LRCP Lond. 1957. Prev: GP Keighley.

SWEETLAND, Helen Margaret Department of Surgery, University of Wales College of Medicine, Heath Park, Cardiff CF14 4XN Tel: 029 2074 2896 Fax: 029 2076 1623; 4 Gateside Close, Cardiff CF23 8PB Tel: 029 2073 3697 — MB ChB 1983 Sheff.; MD Sheff. 1992; FRCS Ed. 1988. Sen. Lect. (Surg.) Univ. Wales Coll. Med. Prev: Sen. Regist. Rotat. (Gen. Surg.) N. Trent Region; Lect. (Surg.) Univ. Sheff. & N. Gen. Hosp. Sheff.; Regist. Rotat. (Surg.) Roy. Hallamsh. Hosp. Sheff.

SWEETMAN, Anne Cecilia Portugal Place Health Centre, Portugal Place, Wallsend NE28 6RZ Tel: 0191 262 5252 Fax: 0191 262 0241 Email: anne.sweetman@ppn6.nant-ha.northy.nhs.uk; 26 Rosebery Crescent, Jesmond, Newcastle upon Tyne NE2 1EU Tel: 0191 281 6808 — MB BS 1975 Newc.; MRCGP 1979; DRCOG 1978.

SWEETMAN, Bernard Stewart (retired) 9 Westpoint, 49 Putney Hill, London SW15 6RU Tel: 020 8788 7088 — MB BS 1944 Lond.; MRCS Eng. LRCP Lond. 1944. Prev: Local Treasury Med. Off. Med. Adviser Thresher & Co.

SWEETMAN, Brian John Morriston Hospital, Swansea SA6 6NL Tel: 01792 703103 Fax: 01792 703632 — MD 1986 Lond.; PhD Lond. 1981, MB BS 1968; FRCP Lond. 1994; MRCP (UK) 1972. (St. Thos.) Cons. Phys. Rheum. Morriston, Singleton, Neath & LLa.lli Hosps. Socs: Brit. Soc. Rheum.; Soc. Back Pain Research. Prev: Research Assoc. & Sen. Regist. Guy's Hosp. Lond.

SWEETMAN, Julian Andrew Pontllandffraith Health Centre, Blackwood Road, Blackwood NP12 2YU Tel: 01495 227156 Fax: 01495 220311 — MB ChB 1991 Bristol; BSc (Hons.) Bristol 1988.

SWEETMAN, Stella Muriel (retired) 9 Westpoint, 49 Putney Hill, London SW15 6RU — LRCPI & LM, LRSCI & LM 1941; LRCPI & LM, LRCSI & LM 1941. Prev: Capt. RAMC.

SWEETNAM, Anthony Thomas 9 Redesdale Gardens, Adel, Leeds LS16 6AT Tel: 0113 267 8591 — MRCS Eng. LRCP Lond. 1963; DA Eng. 1970. (Leeds) Clin. Asst. (Anaesth.) Harrogate Gen. Hosp.

SWEETNAM, Cecil Wallis (retired) 127 North Road, Bourne PE10 9BU Tel: 01778 422249 — MB BCh BAO 1944 Dub.; LM Rotunda 1949; DObst RCOG 1947. Prev: Sen. Clin. Clerk Rotunda Hosp. Dub.

SWEETNAM, Mr David Ian Staveley 6 Dunstable Mews, Devonshire St., London W1G 6BT Tel: 020 7935 5004 Fax: 020 7935 5004 Email: davidsweetnam@msn.com — MB BS 1987 Lond.; FRCS Eng. 1991; FRCS 1996; Dip. Sports Med. RCS Ed. (The Middlesex Hospital Medical School) Sen. Regist. The Roy. Nat. Orthop. Hosp. Trust Stanmore. Socs: Brit. Orthop. Assn.; Roy. Soc. Med.; Brit. Hip Soc.

SWEETNAM, Sir (David) Rodney, KCVO, CBE Went House, 25 Woodlands Road, Bushey WD23 2LS Tel: 01923 223161 Fax:

SWENY

01923 223161 — MB BChir Camb. 1950; MA Camb. 1951, BA 1947; FRCS Eng. 1955; Hon. FRCS (Glas.) 1997; Hon. FRCS (Irel.) 1997; Hon. FACS 1998; Hon. FCM (SA) 1998; Hon. FDS RCS 1998. (Camb. & Middlx.) Cons. Orthop. Surg. Emerit. The Middlx. Hosp. Lond. & Kings Edwd. VII Hosp. for Offs. Lond.; Fell. UCL; Pres. Roy. Med. Benevocent Fund. Socs: Hon. Fell. BOA; Fell. Roy. Soc. Med.; Fell. Roy. Coll. Surg. Eng. Prev: Orthop. Surg. to the Qu.; Pres. Roy. Coll. of Surgs. Eng.; Pres. Brit. Orthop. Assn.

SWENY, Paul Renal Transplant Unit, Royal Free Hospital, London NW3 2QG Tel: 020 7794 0500 — MB BChir 1970 Camb.; MA, MD Camb. 1979, MB 1970, BChir 1969; FRCP Lond. 1986; MRCP (UK) 1972. Cons. & Sen. Lect. (Nephrol. & Transpl.) Roy. Free Hosp. Lond.

SWERDLOW, Anthony John Epidemiological Monitoring Unit, London School of Hygiene & Tropical Medicine, Keppel St., London WC1E 7HT — BM BCh 1975 Oxf.; PhD Glas. 1985; MA Oxf. 1990, DM 1990; MA Camb. 1976; MFCM 1980; FFPHM RCP (UK) 1994, M 1989; T(PHM) 1991. Reader (Epidemiol.) Lond. Sch. Hyg. & Trop. Med. Univ. Lond.; Head Epidemiol. Monitoring Unit Lond. Sch. Hyg. & Trop. Med. Univ. Lond. Prev: Sen. Lect. (Epidemiol.) Lond. Sch. Hyg. & Trop. Med.; Sen. Med. Statistician Off. Populat. Censuses & Surveys; Sen. Lect. (Comm. Med.) Univ. Glas.

SWERDLOW, Mark 2 Broomleigh, Booth Road, Altrincham WA14 4AU Tel: 0161 928 6673 — MD 1951 Manch.; MSc Manch. 1958, BSc 1939, MD 1951, MB ChB 1942; FFA RCS Eng. 1953; DA Eng. 1948. (Manch.) Socs: Hon. Mem. Internat. Assn. for Study of Pain; Hon. Mem. The Pain Soc.; Assn. Anaesth. Gt. Brit. Prev: Dir. NW Regional Pain Relief Centre; Adviser WHO Cancer Unit; Cons. Anaesth. Salford Roy. Hosp., Roy. Manch. Childr. Hosp. & Hope Hosp. Univ. Manch.

SWIERCZYNSKI, Stanislaw 9 White Court, 200 West Hill, London SW15 3JB — Lekarz 1955 Lublin; Clin. Dip. Endocrinol. Warsaw 1968; Clin. Dip. Paediat. Warsaw 1963. Clin. Asst. (Ment. Handicap) Botleys Pk. Hosp. Chertsey Surrey. Prev: Regist. (Psychiat.) FarnBoro. Hosp. Kent; Clin. Asst. Ment. Handicap Area, Cornw.

SWIESTOWSKI, Ignacy The Black County Family Practice, Health Centre, Queens Road, Tipton DY4 8PH Tel: 0121 557 6397 Fax: 0121 557 1662; 36 Woodcroft Avenue, Tipton DY4 8AE Tel: 0121 557 2446 — LRCPI & LM, LRSCI & LM 1957; LRCPI & LM, LRCSI & LM 1957; DObst RCOG 1959. (RCSI)

SWIETOCHOWSKI, John Patrick Gerard The Doctors House, Victoria Road, Marlow SL7 1DN Tel: 01628 484666 Fax: 01628 891206 — MB ChB 1977 Dundee.

SWIFT, Mr Andrew Cree Department of Otolarynology, Head & Neck Surgery, University Hospital Aintree, Aintree NHS Trust, Fazakerley, Liverpool L9 7AL Tel: 0151 529 5258 Fax: 0151 529 5263; 64 Knowsley Road, Cressington Park, Grassendale, Liverpool L19 0PG Tel: 0151 427 6377 Fax: 0151 427 6377 — MB ChB 1977 Sheff.; ChM Sheff. 1989; FRCS Ed. 1984; FRCS Eng. 1981. (Sheffield) Cons. ENT Surg. Univ. Hosp. Aintree Liverp.; Clin. Lect. Univ. Liverp. Socs: BAOL - HNS Full Mem.; RSM Full Mem.; N. Eng. Otolaryngol. Soc. Prev: Lect. & Sen. Regist. (ENT) Mersey RHA; MRC Research Fell. Univ. Liverp.; Regist. (ENT) Liverp. HA.

***SWIFT, Benjamin** 11 Famona Road, Carlton Colville, Lowestoft NR33 8JU — MB ChB 1998 Leic.; MB ChB Leic 1998.

SWIFT, Professor Cameron Graham Department of Health Care of the Elderly, Kings College School of Medicine & Dentistry, Kings College Hospital (Dulwich), London SE22 8PT Tel: 020 7346 6076 Fax: 020 7346 6476; 8 Spencer Road, Bromley BR1 3SU — MB BS 1969 Lond.; PhD Dundee 1984; FRCP Lond. 1988; MRCP (UK) 1974; MRCS Eng. LRCP Lond. 1969. (St. Bart.) Prof. Health c/o Elderly & Cons. Phys. King's Coll. Hosp. Lond.; Prof. Health c/o Elderly Univ. Kent. Socs: Brit. Pharm. Soc.; Brit. Geriat. Soc. (Chairm. Scientif. Comm.). Prev: Sen. Lect. & Cons. Phys. (Geriat. Med.) Univ. Wales Coll. of Med. Cardiff; Cons. Phys. (Med. for the Elderly) & Postgrad. Clin. Tutor Hull HA; Trustbank Vis. Prof. ChristCh. Sch. Med. NZ 1994.

SWIFT, Ephraim Frank Flat 24, The Willows, Beechfield Gardens, Southport PR8 2SW — MRCS Eng. LRCP Lond. 1948. (Liverp.)

SWIFT, Gillian Lesley Llandough Hospital, Penlan Road, Penarth CF64 2XX Tel: 01222 711711 — MB BCh 1986 Wales; BSc Wales 1983; MD Wales 1992; MRCP (UK) 1989; FRCP 1999. (UWCM) Cons. Phys. (Gastroenterol. & Gen. Med.) Llandough Hosp. Cardiff. Socs: Brit. Soc. Gastroenterol.; Nutrit. Soc.; Eur. Assn. Gastroenterol. & Endoscopy. Prev: Sen. Regist. (Gastroenterol.) Llandough Hosp. Cardiff; Regist. (Med.) Cardiff Roy. Infirm.; Research Regist. (Gastroenterol.) Univ. Hosp. Wales Cardiff.

SWIFT, Graham Roger (retired) The Surgery, Park Lane, Woodstock, Oxford OX20 1UB Tel: 01993 811452 — MB BS 1956 Lond.; MRCS Eng. LRCP Lond. 1956; DObst RCOG 1959; Family Plann. Cert RCOG 1981. Apptd. Fact. Doctor. Prev: Ho. Surg. & Ho. Phys. Whittington Hosp. Lond.

SWIFT, Joseph Louis Windyside Mill Hill, Shenfield, Brentwood CM15 8EU Tel: 01277 848996 Fax: 01277 848997 — MB BS 1951 Lond.; MRCS Eng. LRCP Lond. 1951; FRCPsych 1979, M 1971; DPM Eng. 1954. (Middlx.) Child & Family Consultation Serv. Socs: Fell. Roy. Soc. Med.; Assoc. Mem. Brit. Psychoanalyt. Soc. Prev: Med. Dir. Romford Child Guid. Clinic; Cons. Psychiat. Community Ment. Health & Child Guid. Lond. Boro. Newham; Psychiat. Portman Clinic Lond.

SWIFT, Margaret Rosemary Brook Lane Surgery, 27 Brook Lane, Bromley BR1 4PX Tel: 020 8461 3333 Fax: 020 8695 5567; 8 Spencer Road, Bromley BR1 3SU Tel: 020 8460 3215 — MB BS 1969 Lond. GP Bromley.

SWIFT, Michael Andrew The Surgery, Branksomewood Road, Fleet GU51 4JX Tel: 01252 613624 Fax: 01252 816489; Little Orchard, School Lane, Ewshot, Farnham GU10 5BN — MB ChB 1976 Bristol; DA Eng. 1979.

SWIFT, Nicholas David 50 Wallasey Village, Wallasey CH45 3NL Tel: 0151 691 2088 Fax: 0151 637 0146 Email: ndswift@ aol.com; 42 Mount Road, Upton, Wirral CH49 6JB Tel: 0151 604 1934 Email: ndswift@aol.com — MB ChB 1986 Manch.; DRCOG 1990. Forens. Med. Examr. Merseyside Police A (Wirral) Div. Socs: Assn. Police Surg.

***SWIFT, Pauline Anne** Stravithie Mill, St Andrews KY16 8LT — MB BS 1994 Lond.

SWIFT, Peter George Furmston Leicester Royal Infirmary Children's Hospital, Leicester LE1 5WW Tel: 0116 254 1414 Fax: 0116 258 7637; 21 Westminster Road, Leicester LE2 2EH Tel: 0116 221 7376 Email: peterswift@webleicester.co.uk — MB Camb. 1969, BChir 1968; MA Camb. 1969; FRCP Lond. 1984; MRCP (UK) 1971; MRCS Eng. LRCP Lond. 1968; DCH Eng. 1972; FRCPCH 1996. (Camb. & Guy's) Cons. Paediat. & Endocrinol. Leicester Roy. Infirm. Socs: Roy. Coll. Paediat. & Child Health; (Ex-Sec.) Brit. Soc. Paediat. Endocrinol. & Diabetes; (Ex-Counc.) Internat. Soc. Paediat. & Adolesc. Diabetes. Prev: Sen. Regist. (Paediat.) Bristol Hosp. Sick Childr.; Regist. (Paediat.) Sheff. Childr. Hosp.; SHO (Neonat. Paediat.) Univ. Coll. Hosp. Lond.

SWIFT, Robert Ian 33 Seymour Avenue, East Ewell, Epsom KT17 2RS — MB BS 1983 Lond.; BSc (Hons.) Lond. 1981; MS Lond. 1995; FRCS Lond. 1985; FICS 1995. (Kings Coll. Lond.) Cons. Surg. (Colorectal) Mayday Univ. Hosp. Croydon; Hon. Cons. Surg. Roy. Marsden Hosp. Socs: Assn. Coloproctol.; Assn. Surg.; AESGBT.

SWIFT, Sarah Elizabeth St Jame's University Hospital, Beckett St, Leeds LS9 7TF Tel: 0113 206 5231; 127 East Parade, Henworth, York YO31 7YD Tel: 01904 431524 — MB BChir 1991 Camb.; MA, MB BChir (Hons.) Camb. 1991; MRCP (UK) 1993; FRCR 1996. (Emmanuel College, Camb./ St. Bartholomew's Hospital Medical Sch, Lond.) Cons. Radiol., St Jame's Uni. Hosp. & Cookridge Hosp., Leeds. Prev: Specialist Regist., Leeds/Bradford, Radiol. Train. Scheme; SHO (Med.) N.wick Pk. Hosp.; Ho. Phys. St. Bart. Hosp. Lond.

SWIFT, Timothy David Speedwell Surgery, 1 Speedwell Street, Paddock, Huddersfield HD1 4TS Tel: 01484 531786 Fax: 01484 424249; Surat Cottage, 2 Meal Hill, Slaithwaite, Huddersfield HD7 5UR Tel: 01484 842983 — MB BS 1978 Lond.; MA Camb. 1979, BA 1975; MRCGP (Distinc.) 1982; Dip. Pract. Dermat. Wales 1991; DRCOG 1980. Clin. Asst. (Dermat.) Huddersfield. Socs: BMA; RCGP.

SWINBURN, Christopher Ralph Taunton And Somerset NHS Trust, Taunton TA1 5DA Tel: 01823 342146 Fax: 01823 343709; 2 The Avenue, Taunton TA1 1EA Tel: 01823 289295 — MB BChir 1978 Camb.; FRCP 1994; MD Camb. 1985; MRCP (UK) 1980. (St. Thos.) Cons. Phys. Thoracic & Gen. Med. Taunton & Som. Hosp. (MusGr. Pk. Br..). Socs: Fell. Roy. Coll. Phys. (Lond.); Brit. Thorac. Soc. Prev: Sen. Regist. (Thoracic Med.) Freeman Hosp. Newc.; Sir

Jules Thorn Research Fell. & Regist. (Med.) Middlx. Hosp. Med. Sch.; SHO (Cardiol. & Neurol.) St. Geo. & Atkinson Morley's Hosp.

SWINBURN, Helen Mary 40 The Pavillions, 140 Cambridge Road, Southend-on-Sea SS1 1HP — BM 1984 Soton. Regist. (Haemat.) S.end Hosp. Essex.

SWINBURN, Jonathan Murray Amyatt Department of Cardial Research, Northwick Park Hospital, Watford Road, Harrow HA1 3UJ Tel: 020 8869 2547 Fax: 020 8864 0075 Email: jonswinburn@compuserve.com — MB BS 1994 Lond.; MA Camb. 1995, BA 1991; MRCP 1997. (Char. Cross & Westm.) Clin. Research Fell. (Cardiol.) N.wick Pk. Hosp. Prev: Research Regist. (Cardiol.) N.wick Pk. Hosp.; SHO (ITU) Birm. City Hosp.; SHO (Med.) N.wick Pk. Hosp.

SWINBURN, Ralph Teasdale (retired) 45 Woodcroft Road, Wylam NE41 8DH Tel: 01661 852113 — MB BS 1948 Durh.; DObst RCOG 1952. Prev: Ho. Phys. Chase Farm Hosp. Enfield.

SWINBURNE, Anita Priory Lane Surgery, Priory Lane, Prestatyn LL19 9DH Tel: 01745 854496; 18 Bryneithin Avenue, Prestatyn LL19 9LS Tel: 01745 853219 Email: aswinburne@aol.com — MB ChB 1987 Liverp.; MRCGP 1992. (Liverp.) Socs: Assn. Police Surg. Prev: Trainee GP Abergele VTS.

SWINBURNE, Kenneth Arthur McLeod Cairns Owen (retired) 16 Foxhill Crescent, Leeds LS16 5PD — MB BChir 1956 Camb.; DMRD Eng. 1966; GI Biol. 1995. Cons. (Diag. Radiol.) St. Jas. Univ. Hosp. Leeds & Wharfedale Gen.; Hosp. Sen. Clin. Lect. in Diag. Radiol. Univ. Leeds. Prev: Sen. Regist. Diag. Radiol. Gen. Infirm. Leeds.

SWINBURNE, Margaret Layinka 16 Foxhill Crescent, Leeds LS16 5PD — MB ChB 1951 Leeds; BSc Leeds 1948; FRCP Lond. 1976, M 1957; FRCPath 1975, M 1964; DCH Eng. 1954; GI Biol. 1995. Prev: Cons. Path. St. Jas. Hosp. Leeds.; Sen. Regist. (Path.) St. Jas. Hosp. Leeds; Jun. Asst. (Path.) Univ. Camb.

***SWINBURNE, Paul** 30 Canberra Road, Marton-in-Cleveland, Middlesbrough TS7 8EU — MB ChB 1997 Ed.

SWINBURNE, Robert Miles Audley Mills Surgery, 57 Eastwood Road, Rayleigh SS6 7JF Tel: 01268 774981; Wades, Creeksea Ferry Road, Canewdon, Rochford SS4 2EX — MB BS 1959 Lond.; MRCS Eng. LRCP Lond. 1959; DObst RCOG 1961. (Lond. Hosp.) Prev: Receiv. Room Off. Lond. Hosp.; Ho. Surg. Gen. Hosp. Rochford.

SWINDALE, Flora Elisabeth 22 Cooper Road, Guildford GU1 3LY Tel: 01483 32306 — MD 1938 Basle. (Bonn, Berlin & Basle) Socs: BMA.

SWINDALL, Hilary Jane East Quay Medical Centre, East Quay, Bridgwater TA6 5YB Tel: 01278 444666 Fax: 01278 445448 — MB ChB 1977 Sheff.; MRCGP 1999; DRCOG 1979.

SWINDELL, Pamela Joy The Health Centre, Beeches Green, Stroud GL5 4BH Tel: 01453 763980 — MB BS 1975 Newc.; MB BS (Hons.) Newc. 1975; MRCP (UK) 1978. Prev: Research Regist. (Microbiol.) S.mead Hosp. Bristol; SHO (Med. & Path.) S.mead Hosp. Bristol.

SWINDELLS, Ann Craigard, Evening Hill, Thursby, Carlisle CA5 6PU Tel: 01228 710944 — MB ChB 1971 Bristol. Clin. Med. Off. E. Cumbria HA.; Staff Grade Paediat. (Audiol.) - N. I. Healthcare Trust.

***SWINDELLS, Kirsty Joanna** 2F2, 17 Marchmont Road, Edinburgh EH9 1HY — MB ChB 1997 Ed.

SWINDELLS, Robin Fraser Cawley Wigton Group Medical Practice, Half Moon Lane, Wigton CA7 9NQ Tel: 016973 42254 Fax: 016973 45464; Craigard, Evening Hill, Thursby, Carlisle CA5 6PU Tel: 01228 710944 — MB ChB 1971 Bristol; MRCGP 1975; DObst RCOG 1974.

SWINDELLS, Stephen Robert 36 Hookstone Drive, Harrogate HG2 8PP Tel: 01423 880948 — MB ChB 1976 Ed.; BSc (Med. Sci.) (Hons.) Ed. 1973, MB ChB 1976; FFA RCS Eng. 1981. (Edin.) Cons. Anaesth. St. Jas. Univ. Hosp. Leeds; Hon. Tutor Univ. Leeds. Prev: Regist. (Anaesth.) St. Jas. Univ. Hosp. Leeds; Lect. (Anaesth.) Chinese Univ., Hong Kong.

***SWINDEN, Josephine Anne** 96 Windy Arbour, Kenilworth CV8 2BB — MB BS 1996 Lond.

SWINDEN, Stephen John Darnall Health Centre, 2 York Road, Sheffield S9 5DH Tel: 0114 244 1681 Fax: 0114 242 1160 — MB ChB 1975 Manch.

SWINDLEHURST, Amanda Louise The Riverside Surgery, Waterside, Evesham WR11 6JP Tel: 01386 40121 Fax: 01386 442615; Little Orchard, Kersoe, Pershore WR10 3JD Tel: 01386 710607 — MB BS 1988 Lond.; MRCGP 1994; DCH RCP Lond. 1993; DA (UK) 1992. Prev: Trainee GP Cheltenham.

***SWINDLEHURST, Ruth Alys** 20 Woodland Avenue, Lymm WA13 0BJ — MB ChB 1998 Leic.; MB ChB Leic 1998.

SWINDLEHURST, Deborah Anne 85 Leopold Road, Ipswich IP4 4RN Tel: 01473 728144 Email: d.swinglchurst@ic.ac.uk — MB BS 1993 Lond.; MA Camb. 1994; DCH RCP Lond. 1996; DGM RCP Lond. 1995; DRCOG Lond. 1997; MRCGP Lond. 1998. (Univ. Camb. Jesus Coll. & St. Mary's Hosp. Lond.) GP Researcher, Imperial Coll. Sch. Of Med.; GP Locum. Prev: GP Regist. Lattice Barn Surg. Ipswich; SHO (Med.) Ipswich Gen. Hosp. VTS; SHO (A & E & c/o Elderly) N.ampton Gen. Hosp.

***SWINGLHURST, Paul Anthony** 18 Windsor Street, Barrow-in-Furness LA14 5JR — MB ChB 1997 Liverp.

SWINGLHURST, Peter John (retired) 11 Thorpe Road, Staines TW18 3EA Tel: 01784 490786 Fax: 01784 441244 — MB BChir 1960 Camb.; DObst RCOG 1963. Princip. in Gen. Med. Pract. Prev: Ho. Off. (O & G) Farnham Hosp.

SWINGLER, Mr Gordon Richard Church House, Frampton-on-Severn, Gloucester GL1 2LY Tel: 01452 740306 & profess. 0452 423601 — MB ChB 1968 Bristol; FRCS Ed. 1976; MRCOG 1974. Cons. O & G Gloucester Roy. Hosp. Prev: Sen. Regist. (O & G) Avon & Bath AHA; Regist. (O & G) Univ. Hosp. S. Manch.; Temp. Lect. in Path. Univ. Manch.

SWINGLER, Rebecca 30 Birch Road, Southville, Bristol BS3 1PF Tel: 0117 966 8360 Email: rebeccaswingler@hotmail.com — MB ChB 1994 Ed. SSHO O & G.

SWINGLER, Robert James Department of Neurology, Ninewells Hospital, Dundee DD1 9SY Tel: 01382 660111 Fax: 01382 425739 Email: roberts@tuht.sco.nhs.uk — MB BS 1980 Lond.; BSc (Hons.) Lond. 1977, MD 1990; MRCP (UK) 1983; T(M) 1991; FRCP Ed. 1998; FRCP 1999. (Guy's) Cons. Neurol. Dundee Teachg. Hosps. NHS Trust; Hon. Sen. Lect. Dundee Univ. Socs: Ord. Mem. BMA; Ord. Mem. ABN; Corr. Assoc. AAN. Prev: Sen. Regist. (Neurol.) Dundee Gen. Hosps.; MRC Trav. Fell.sh. CB Day Laborat. Mass. Gen. Hosp. E. Charle Mass., USA; Lect. (Med. Neurol.) Univ. Edin.

SWINHOE, Alexandra Louise Anaesthetic Department, Royal Hallamshire Hospital, Sheffield S10 2JF Tel: 0114 271 2381; 9 Salt Box Grove, Sheffield S35 8SG Tel: 0114 245 9061 — MB ChB 1991 Birm.; ChB Birm. 1991; FRCA 1997. (Birm. Univ.) Specialist Regist. Rotat. (Anaesth.) N. Trent Sheff. Prev: SHO (Anaesth.) Halifax; SHO (Paediat.) Wordsley; Ho. Off. (Surg.) Russell Hall Hosp. Dudley.

SWINHOE, Crispin Francis Anaesthetic Department, Barnsley District General Hospital, Barnsley S75 2EP Tel: 01226 730000 Fax: 01226 777976; 47 Hawthorne Way, Shelley, Huddersfield HD8 8PX Tel: 0114 245 9061, 01484 608992 — MB BS 1979 Lond.; MRCGP 1985; FRCA 1993; DA (UK) 1988. (St. Mary's) Cons. Anaesth. Barnsley Dist. Gen. Hosp.; Clin. Head of Serv. Critical Care. Socs: Intens. Care Soc.; Anaesth. Res. Soc. Prev: Sen. Regist. (Anaesth.) Roy. Hallamsh. Hosp. Sheff.; Clin. Research Fell. (Anaesth.) Sheff. Univ.; Ho. Phys. (Med.) RNH Haslar.

SWINHOE, David John Elmwood Medical Centre, 7 Burlington Road, Buxton SK17 9AY Tel: 01298 23019; Crossview Cottage, 147 Green Lane, Buxton SK17 9DG — MB ChB 1980 Manch.; MRCGP 1990; MRCOG 1985. Prev: Regist. (O & G) Qu. Mothers Hosp. Glas.

SWINHOE, June Rose 23 Wood Lane, Highgate, London N6 5UE Tel: 020 8883 1591 — MRCS Eng. LRCP Lond. 1971; MD Lond. 1985, MB BS 1971; FRCOG 1989, M 1975. (Roy. Free) Cons. O & G King Geo. Hosp. Goodmayes. Socs: Fell. Roy. Soc. Med. Prev: Sen. Regist. Roy. Free Hosp. Lond.; Regist. (O & G) United Liverp. Hosp.; SHO (O & G) Qu. Charlottes & Chelsea Hosps.

SWINHOE, Peter Harrison, OBE, CStJ, Brigadier late RAMC Retd. (retired) The Retreat, Bonchurch Shute, Bonchurch, Ventnor PO38 1NX — MB Chir Camb. 1952; MA Camb. 1952; MRCS Eng. LRCP Lond. 1951; MFCM 1973; DTM & H Eng. 1968; DObst RCOG 1954. Prev: Hon. Phys. to HM Qu.

SWINHOE, Peter Joseph Irwin Road Health Centre, St Helens WA9 3UG Tel: 01744 816889 Fax: 01744 850483 — MB BS 1982 Lond.; MRCGP 1989; DRCOG 1986.

SWINN, Mr Michael James 15A Radway Road, Shirley, Southampton SO15 7PT — MB BS 1991 Lond.; BSc (Hons.) Lond.

SWINNEY

1988; FRCS Eng. 1996. Regist. (Uroneurol.) & Lect. (Urol.). Prev: Nat. Hosp. Neurol. & Neurosurg. & Inst. of Urol. Lond.

SWINNEY, George Ewen (retired) 1 Deanston View, Doune FK16 6AS Tel: 01786 841294 — MB ChB 1941 Aberd.; MA (Hnrs.) Aberd. 1936, MB ChB (Hnrs.) 1941; DPM Lond. 1951. Prev: Phys. Supt. Woodilee Hosp. Lenzie.

SWINSCOE, Anthony William Cedar House Surgery, 14 Huntingdon Street, St. Neots, Huntingdon PE19 1BQ Tel: 01480 406677 Fax: 01480 475167; Stilton Cottage, 18 Alberman St, Eaton Socon St Neots, Huntingdon Tel: 01480 212596 — MB ChB 1979 Sheff.; DRCOG 1983; MRCGP 1983.

SWINSCOE, Brian David The Surgery, Bottesford, Nottingham NG13 0AN Tel: 01949 842325 — BM BS 1981 Nottm.; BSc (Hons.) Cranwell 1971; BMedSci (Hons.) Nottm. 1979, BM BS 1981.

***SWINSON, Brian David** 131 Mountsawdel Road, Coleraine — MB BCh 1998 Belf.; MB BCh Belf 1998.

***SWINSON, Daniel Edmund Bryan** 155 Wigan Road, Standish, Wigan WN6 0AG — MB BS 1996 Lond.

SWINSON, David Robert Wrightington Hospital, Appley Bridge, Wigan WN6 9EP Tel: 01257 256239 Fax: 01257 256375 Email: david.swinson@btinternet.com; 155 Wigan Road, Standish, Wigan WN6 0AG Tel: 01257 421003 — MB BS Lond. 1965; FRCP Lond. 1984; MRCP (UK) 1970; MRCS Eng. LRCP Lond. 1965; DPhysMed Eng. 1974. (King's Coll. Hosp.) Cons. Rheum. & Rehabil. Wrightington Hosp. NHS Trust & Wigan & Leigh NHS Trust. Socs: Fell. Roy. Soc. Med.; Fell. Manch. Med. Soc.; Brit. Soc. Rheum.

***SWINSON, Sophie Elizabeth** 24 College Lane, Hurstpierpoint, Hassocks BN6 9AQ — MB BS 1998 Lond.; MB BS Lond 1998; BA (Hons) Cantab 1995.

SWINSTEAD, Peter Duncan (retired) East Wing, North Wells, Ducie Avenue, Bembridge PO35 5NF — MRCS Eng. LRCP Lond. 1939; M.B., B.S. Lond. 1939; FRCPath 1963. Prev: Cons. Pathol. St. Mary's Hosp. Newport, I. of Wight.

SWINTON, Susan McLean 82 Springfield Road, Linlithgow EH49 7JW Tel: 01506 843855 — MB ChB 1997 Aberd. (Aberdeen) SHO (Anaesth.) Monklands Hosp. Airdrie. Socs: Med. Defence Union. Prev: SHO (A & E) S.ern Gen. Hosp. Glas.; SHO (Ortho. Surg.) S.ern Gen. Hosp. Glas.; SHO (Med.) Raigmore Hosp. Inverness.

SWINYARD, Peter William Phoenix Surgery, Dunwich Drive, Toothill, Swindon SN5 8SX Tel: 01793 600440 Fax: 01793 600410 — MB BS 1979 Lond. (St. Thos.) Prev: Trainee GP Colchester VTS.

SWIRE, Herbert Churchfields Surgery, Recreation Road, Bromsgrove B61 8DT Tel: 01527 872163 — MB ChB 1968 Birm.; MA Camb. 1964. Indep. Clin. Asst. BromsGr. Socs: BromsGr. & Redditch Med. Soc. Prev: GP BromsGr..

SWIRE, Nina Palliative Care Team, 26 Nassau St., London W1N 7RF Tel: 020 7380 9236; 37 Ninehams Road, Caterham-on-the-Hill, Caterham CR3 5LN Tel: 020 8660 9264 — MB ChB 1984 Leeds; MRCP (UK) 1992. Sen. Regist. (Palliat. Med.) Camden & Islington NHS Community Trust.

SWIRSKY, David Michael Leeds General Infirmary, Great George St., Leeds LS1 3EX Tel: 0113 392 6285 Fax: 0113 392 6286 — MB BS 1975 Lond.; FRCP Lond. 1993; MRCPath 1987. (Univ. Coll. Hosp. Med. Sch. Lond.) Cons. Haematologist Leeds Gen. Infirm. Socs: Brit. Soc. Haematol. Prev: Sen. Lect. & Hon. Cons. Haemat. Hammersmith Hosp. Lond.; Leukaemia Research Fund Train. Fell. (Haemat. Med.) Camb.; Sen. Regist. Hammersmith Hosp. Lond.

SWITALSKI, Boleslaw Jan Dingley Dell, 443 Barnsley Road, Sandel, Wakefield WF2 6BJ Tel: 01924 250988 — MB ChB 1942 Polish Sch. of Med. (Poznan & Polish Sch. of Med.) Prev: Ho. Surg. Roy. Infirm. Edin.; Cas. Off. & Ho. Phys. Chesterfield Roy. Hosp.; Capt. Polish Army Med. Corps. 1942-8.

SWITHINBANK, David Winthrop Stokes Medical Centre, Braydon Avenue, Little Stoke, Bristol BS34 6BQ Tel: 01454 616767 Fax: 01454 616189; 20 Woodland Grove, Stoke Bishop, Bristol BS9 2BB. Tel: 0117 968 4400 — MB BS 1976 Lond.; MRCGP 1983; DRCOG 1981. Occupat. Phys. Hewlett Packard Ltd. Bristol.

SWITHINBANK, Ian Milne Camborne/Redruth Community Hospital, Barncoose Terrace, Redruth TR15 3ER Tel: 01209 881645 — MB BChir 1975 Camb.; MRCP (UK) 1977. Cons. Phys. (s/i in Elderly) Camborne/Redruth Community Hosp. Cornw. Prev: Sen. Regist. (Geriat. & Gen. Med.) Dudley Rd., Gen. & Selly Oak Hosps.;

Regist. (Neurol.) Frenchay Hosp. Bristol.; Ho. Phys. St. Thos. Hosp. Lond.

SWITHINBANK, Lucy Victoria 20 Woodland Grove, Stoke Bishop, Bristol BS9 2BB — MB BS 1977 Lond. Clin. Asst. (Urodynamics) S.mead Hosp. Bristol.

SWOFFER, Steven John Oak Hall Surgery, 41-43 High Street, New Romney TN28 8BW Tel: 01797 362106 Fax: 01797 366495 — MB BS 1982 Lond.; DRCOG 1986. Hon. Med. Off. Littlestone-on-Sea Lifeboat.

SWORD, Andrew James Alton Health Centre, Anstey Road, Alton GU34 2QX Tel: 01420 84676 Fax: 01420 542975; Oakbank, East Worldham, Alton GU34 3AT — MB ChB 1982 Manch.; MRCGP 1987. Prev: SHO (O & G) St. Mary's Hosp. Manch.; SHO (A & E) Stockport Infirm.; SHO (Paediat.) N. Manch. Gen. Hosp.

SWORD, Annie Carmichael (retired) Stourvale, 2 Bridge Place, Northbourne, Bournemouth BH10 7EA — MB ChB 1926 Ed.; DPH Lond. 1930. Prev: Asst. Co. Med. Off. Lindsey (Lincs.) CC.

SWORD, David 7 Drybridge Road, Dundonald, Kilmarnock KA2 9HA — MB ChB 1994 Glas.

SWORD, Linda 7 Drybridge Road, Dundonald, Kilmarnock KA2 9HA — MB ChB 1994 Aberd.

SWORD, Lindsay Jean Watercress Medical Group, Dean Surgery, Ropley, Alresford SO24 0BQ Tel: 01962 772340 Fax: 01962 772551; Oakbank, East Worldham, Alton GU34 3AT — MB ChB 1982 Manch.; DRCOG 1986.

SWORDS, Jacqueline Greenford Road Medical Centre, 591 Greenford Road, Greenford UB6 8QH Tel: 020 8578 1764 Fax: 020 8578 8347; 16 Altenburg Avenue, Ealing, London W13 9RN — MB ChB 1989 Dundee; MRCGP 1993; DRCOG 1992; DCH RCP Lond. 1991. Prev: Trainee GP Lond. VTS.

SWORDS, Patrick Joseph Kevin Winterton Hospital, Sedgefield, Stockton-on-Tees TS21 3EJ — LRCP LRCS 1963 Ed.; LRCP LRCS Ed. LRCPS Glas. 1963; LAH Dub. 1958; MRCPsych 1974; DPM RCPSI 1972; DCH NUI 1970; DObst RCOG 1966; LM Coombe 1965. (Galway)

SWORN, Michael John (retired) Heronfield, West Somerton NR29 4DJ — MRCS Eng. LRCP Lond. 1965; LLB Lond. 1985, MB BS 1965; FRCPath 1983, M 1971; Cert BA 1992. Prev: Lect. Path. Univ. Sheff.

SYADA, Mr Mounir 152 Harley Street, London W1N 1HH Tel: 020 7935 8868 Fax: 020 7224 2574; Romany, 414 Fulham Palace Road, London SW6 6HX Tel: 020 7385 1184 Fax: 020 7385 1184 — MD 1971 Damascus; FRCS Glas. 1982. Cons. Gen. Surg. Cromwell Hosp. & Lond. Bridge Hosp. Lond.; Sec. W. Lond. M-C Soc., Postgrad. Centre Char. Cross Hosp. Lond. Socs: Fell. Roy. Soc. Med.; Sec. W. Lond. Medico-Chirurgical Soc. Prev: Cons. Gen. Surg. Whittington & Roy. N.. Hosp. Lond.; Regist. (Gen. Surg.) St. Stephen's & Roy. Masonic Hosps. Lond.; SHO (Gen. Surg., Urol., Orthop. & Cardiovasc.) Char. Cross, St. Mary's & Hammersmith Hosps.

SYAM, Velayudham Stuart Road Surgery, Stuart Road, Pontefract WF8 4PQ Tel: 01977 703437 Fax: 01977 602334; 46 Dulverton Rise, Pontefract WF8 2PY — MB BS 1980 Kerala; MRCP (UK) 1989; MRCGP 1992; DRCOG 1991. GP Pontefract W. Yorks.

SYDENHAM, David John Taylor and Partners, The Surgery, Hexton Road, Barton-le-Clay, Bedford MK45 4TA Tel: 01582 882050 — MB BS 1970 Lond.; MRCS Eng. LRCP Lond. 1970; DObst RCOG 1973. (Char. Cross)

SYDENHAM, Johanna Evamarie Bridget, Maj. RAMC Retd. (retired) 54 Sparrow Close, Brampton, Huntingdon PE28 4PY — BM 1987 Soton.; MRCGP 1994; DFFP 1995; DRCOG 1993.

SYDNEY, John Paul Martin Sydney and Partners, St Mary's Medical Centre, Rock St, Oldham OL1 3UL Tel: 0161 620 6667 Fax: 0161 626 2499 — MB ChB 1975 Manch.; MRCGP Lond. 1981; DCH Eng. 1979. GP Oldham.

SYDNEY, Margaret Mary (retired) 11 Barnfield Close, Thornton-Cleveleys FY5 2AF — MB BCh BAO 1969 Dub.; MA Dub. 1968. Med. Policy Adviser DSS HQ's Lancs. Prev: Med. Adviser War Pens. Agency & Med. Off. Benefits Agency Blackpool.

SYDNEY, Michael Aidan Flatt Walks Health Centre, 3 Castle Meadows, Catherine Street, Whitehaven CA28 7QE Tel: 01946 692173 Fax: 01946 590406 — MB ChB 1967 Manch.; MB ChB (Hons.) Manch. 1970; BSc (Hons. Physiol.) Manch. 1967; MRCP (UK) 1973; MRCGP 1977.

SYKES

SYDNEY, Ronald 30 Glamis Drive, East Kilbride, Glasgow G74 4EF — MB ChB 1994 Manch.; BSc (Med. Sci.) St. And. 1991. Regist. (Gen. Pract.) Denny Health Stirlingsh. Prev: SHO (Psychiat. Geriat. Med. & O & G).

SYED, A A Kingsdowne Surgery, 34 Kingsdowne Road, Surbiton KT6 6LA Tel: 020 8399 9032 Fax: 020 8390 2122.

SYED, Aamir Bakhtiar Syed, Dibdin and Asker, 511 Fox Hollies Road, Hall Green, Birmingham B28 8RJ Tel: 0121 777 1180 Fax: 0121 777 6265; 157 Swanshurst Lane, Moseley, Birmingham B13 0AS — MB BS 1984 Lond.; MRCGP 1991; DRCOG 1988.

SYED, Mr Altaf Hussain 14 Craigleith Hill Gardens, Edinburgh EH4 2JJ — MB BS 1977 Kashmir; FRCS Ed. 1991.

SYED, Attiya 192 Lavender Hill, Enfield EN2 8NP Tel: 020 8367 3815 — MB BS 1965 Punjab. (Fatima Jinnah Med. Coll.) Clin. Asst. (Accid.) Chase Farm Hosp. Enfield.

***SYED, Ghufran Mahmood** 38 Gainsborough Road, New Malden KT3 5NU — BM 1995 Soton.

SYED, Iftikhar Ali Manchester Road Surgery, 187 Manchester Road, Burnley BB11 4HP Tel: 01282 420680 Fax: 01282 832031; Oaklands, 332 Burnley Road, Holme in Cliviger, Burnley BB10 4ST — MB BS 1958 Karachi; DPH Manch. 1966.

***SYED, Imran Anwaar** 55 Hamilton Avenue, Romford RM1 4RP — MB BS 1994 Lond.

SYED, Junaid Ali Kingsdowne Surgery, 34 Kingsdowne Road, Surbiton KT6 6LA Tel: 020 8399 9032 Fax: 020 8390 2122; 11 Thornhill Road, Surbiton KT6 7TW Tel: 020 8390 1706 — MB BS 1991 Lond.; MRCGP 1996. (Char. Cross & Westm.) Socs: BMA. Prev: Trainee GP Roehampton VTS.

SYED, M F Prenton Medical Centre, 516 Woodchurch Road, Prenton, Birkenhead CH43 0TS Tel: 0151 608 7666 — MBBS Lond.; MRCOG Lond.; 1996 MFFP-RCOG Lond. Socs: BMA; MDU; Roy. Coll. of AP.

SYED, Naila Yasmin Northwood Medical Centre, 10/12 Middleton Hall Road, Kings Norton, Birmingham B30 1BY Tel: 0121 458 5507 — MB ChB 1990 Bristol; MRCGP 1994; DRCOG 1996. (Univ. Bristol)

SYED, Naveed Akhtar Avon Health Authority, Public Health Department, King Square House, King Square, Bristol BS2 8EE Tel: 0117 900 2670 Fax: 0117 900 2571; 24 Almeda Road, St. George, Bristol BS5 8RZ Tel: 0117 904 0195 — MB ChB 1993 Manch. Specialist Regist. (Pub. Health Med.) Avon Health Auth. Bristol. Prev: SHO (Oncol.) St. Jas. Univ. Hosp. Leeds; SHO (Dermat.) Hope Hosp. Univ. of Manch. Salford; SHO (Gen. Med.) Blackburn Roy. Infirmary.

SYED, Onn Abbas 14 Greenford Road, Manchester M8 0NW — MB BCh 1993 Wales.

***SYED, Rakshan** 68 Basing Hill, Wembley HA9 9QR — MB BS 1996 Lond.

***SYED, Rizwan Ul Hoda** 33 Norborough Road, Wheatley, Doncaster DN2 4AT — BM 1996 Soton.

SYED, Samira Batul 30 Saddleback Road, Ramleaze, Shaw, Swindon SN5 5RL — MB BS 1982 Lond.; DCH RCP Lond. 1990; DCCH RCP Ed. RCGP & FCM 1987. (Univ. Coll. Hosp.) Staff Grade Paediat. Gt Ormond St. Hosp. Lond. Socs: Univ. Coll. Hosp. Old Stud.'s Assn.; BMA. Prev: SHO (O & G) P.ss Margt. Hosp. Swindon; Regist. & SHO (Paediat.) P.ss Margt. Hosp. Swindon; SHO (Neonates) S.mead Hosp. Bristol.

SYED, Shahid Hussain Oldham Health Authority, Department Public Health Medicine, Westhulme Avenue, Oldham OL1 2PN Tel: 0161 624 0420; 1 Dunlin Close, Bamford, Rochdale OL11 5PZ Tel: 01706 523005 — MB BS 1965 Punjab; FRIPHH 1983. SCMO (Adult Health) Dept. Pub. Health Oldham; Non-Exec. Bd. Mem. Rochdale HA. Socs: BMA (Exec. Mem. Oldham Div.); Fac. Comm. Health.; Assn. Local Auth. Med. Advisers. Prev: Med. Off. Provin. Health Servs. Punjab, Pakistan.

SYED, Shamshad Ullah 81 Bridgewater Road, Wembley HA0 1AQ Tel: 020 8903 2737 — MB BS 1968 Calcutta. (Calcutta)

SYED, Shamsun Nahar 13 Fern Bank Close, Stalybridge SK15 2RZ; 13 Fernbank Close, Stalybridge SK15 2RZ — MB BS 1966 Dacca. (Dacca Med. Coll.) Assoc. Specialist in Anaesth. N. W.. RHA.

***SYED, Shamsuzzoha Babar** 39 Park Avenue, Mitcham CR4 2ER — MB BS 1996 Lond.

***SYEDAH, Najam Anwar** 55 Hamilton Av, Romford RM1 4RP — MB BS 1997 Lond.

SYERS, Graham Ernest 55 Starbeck Avenue, Newcastle upon Tyne NE2 1PB — MB BS 1994 Newc.

SYKES, Alan John Oxgang Farm, 92 Main St., North Frodingham, Driffield YO25 8AZ — MB ChB 1978 Dundee; MRCGP 1986; DRCOG 1984; DA Eng. 1982.

SYKES, Alison Elizabeth 38 Queen Street, Steeton, Keighley BD20 6NX — MB ChB 1996 Leeds.

SYKES, Andrew 41 Hill Drive, High Ackworth, Pontefract WF7 7LQ — MB ChB 1989 Sheff.; BSc Sheff. 1984, MB ChB 1989.

SYKES, Andrew Sykes and Menzies, Littlebury Medical Centre, Fishpond Lane, Holbeach, Spalding PE12 7DE Tel: 01406 22231 Fax: 01406 425008 — BM BCh 1977 Oxf.

SYKES, Andrew John Christie Hospital, Wilmslow Road, Manchester M20 4BX Tel: 0161 446 3000 Fax: 0161 446 3270; 5 Broom Road, Hale, Altrincham WA15 9AR Tel: 0161 941 5425 Email: andrew.sykes@virgin.net — MB ChB 1989 Birm.; MRCP (UK) 1992; FRCR 1996. (Univ. Birm.) Cons. (Clin. Oncol.) Christie Hosp. Manch.

***SYKES, Andrew John** 1F2 132 Comiston Road, Edinburgh EH10 5QN — MB ChB 1998 Ed.; MB ChB Ed 1998.

SYKES, Anne Charlotte Jenner Health Centre, 201 Stanstead Road, Forest Hill, London SE23 1HU Tel: 020 8690 2231; 32 Manor Way, Beckenham BR3 3LJ — BM BCh 1980 Oxf.; MA Camb. 1981; MRCGP 1984; Cert. Family Plann. JCC 1984. Socs: BMA. Prev: GP Leeds & Sydenham Green Lond.; Trainee GP Airedale Health Dist.

***SYKES, Annemarie** Barnwell House, Skirmett Road, Fingest, Henley-on-Thames RG9 6TH — MB BS 1998 Lond.; MB BS Lond 1998.

SYKES, Caroline Frances Gordon Brown's Farm, Milkingpen Lane, Old Basing, Basingstoke RG24 7DE Tel: 01256 475839 Fax: 01256 474469 Email: cfgsykes@aol.com — MB BS 1983 Lond.; MA Oxf. 1978; MRCGP 1988; DRCOG 1986.

SYKES, Catherine Joanne Ladywell medical centre, Edinburgh EH12 7TB — MB ChB 1988 Ed.; MRCGP 1993; DRCOG 1992; DCCH RCP Ed. 1994. Prev: Trainee GP York VTS.

SYKES, Catherine Margaret 58 Kirby Road, Dunstable LU6 3JH Tel: 01582 602927; 41 Seamons Close, Dunstable LU6 3EQ Tel: 01582 603359 — MB BS 1979 Lond.; MRCS Eng. LRCP Lond. 1979; DRCOG 1981. (Char. Cross) Gen. Practitioner, Dunstable, Beds; Occupat. Phys. Marks & Spencer (& other companies); Family Plann. Clin. Sector. Socs: BMA. Prev: Univ. Luton Stud. Health Doctor.

SYKES, Colin Alexander The Villa, Mount Pleasant, Greenodd, Ulverston LA12 7RG Tel: 01229 861459 — MB BS 1967 Lond.; FRCP Lond. 1986; MRCP (U.K.) 1972; MRCS Eng. LRCP Lond. 1967; DCH Eng. 1971; DA Eng. 1970; DObst RCOG 1969. (St. Bart.) Cons. Gen. Phys. Morecambe Bay NHS Trust. Socs: Brit. Cardiac Soc.; BMA; HCSA. Prev: Sen. Regist. (Med.) Clatterbridge Hosp. Bebington, Roy. Liverp. Hosp. & Liverp. Roy. Infirm.

SYKES, Mr David (retired) Mullions, Aston Road, Chipping Campden GL55 6HG Tel: 01388 849100 — MB ChB 1956 Liverp.; MD Liverp. 1960, ChM 1964; FRCS Eng. 1961. Lect. (Clin. Surg.) Univ. Liverp. Prev: Cons. Gen. Surg. Walton, Waterloo & Fazakerley Hosps. Liverp.

***SYKES, David** 27 Longford Road, Bradway, Sheffield S17 4LP — MB BS 1996 Newc.

SYKES, David Allan 10 Llwynupia Road, Lisvane, Cardiff CF4 — MB BChir 1979 Camb.; MRCS Eng. LRCP Lond. 1979.

SYKES, David Paul 2 Second Avenue, Dalton, Huddersfield HD5 9SJ — MB ChB 1984 Leeds.

SYKES, David William (retired) Eastcliff, 14 Marine Parade, Budleigh Salterton EX9 6NS — MB ChB 1959 Bristol; FRCOG 1982, M 1969; DObst. 1964. Cons. O & G Roy. Devon. & Exeter Hosp. Prev: Lect. (O & G) & Hon. Sen. Regist. Roy. Free Hosp. Lond.

***SYKES, Eliot** 39 Rectory Park, Morpeth NE61 2SZ — MB BS 1996 Newc.

SYKES, Elizabeth Mary 24 Bury Road, Alverstoke, Gosport PO12 3UD — MB ChB 1974 Dundee. Clin. Med. Off. Portsmouth & SE Hants. HA.

SYKES

SYKES, George William 7 Avenue Road, Stratford-upon-Avon CV37 6UW — MB BChir 1947 Camb.; MA Camb. 1947; MRCGP 1962. (Camb. & Manch.)

SYKES, Hannah Ruth Southport NHS Trust, Town Lane, Kew, Southport PR8 6PN Tel: 01704 547471; 15 The Birches, Formby, Liverpool L37 7HX Tel: 0170 48 76269 — MB BS 1986 Lond.; BSc Lond. 1983, MB BS 1986; MRCP (UK) 1989; FRCP 1998. Cons. Phys. & Rheumatol. S.port Hosp. Socs: BSR. Prev: Sen. Regist. (Med. & Rheum.) Mersey RHA; Regist. Rotat. (Rheum. & Med.) N.. RHA; SHO (Med.) Newc. HA.

SYKES, Helen Department of Haematology, Kingston Hospital, Galsworthy Road, Kingston upon Thames KT2 7QB Tel: 020 8547 0887 — MB BS 1970 Lond.; FRCPath 1989, M 1977. Cons. (Haemat.) Kingston Hosp. Surrey. Prev: Sen. Research Assoc. (Leukaemia Research Fund Fell.) Dept. Haemat.; Med. Univ. Camb.; Lect. (Haemat.) St. Geo. Hosp. Med. Sch. Lond.; Regist. (Clin. Path.) Roy. Marsden Hosp. Lond.

SYKES, Helen Elaine 18 Tynybedw Street, Treorchy, Cardiff CF42 6RA Tel: 01443 774484 — MB BCh 1994 Wales. SHO (A & E) E. Glam. Hosp. Prev: Ho. Off. (Gen. Med.) P. Chas. Hosp. Merthyr Tydfil; Ho. Off. (Gen. Surg.) W. Wales Gen. Hosp. Carmarthen.

SYKES, Ian Richard Oakham Surgery, 213 Regent Road, Tividale, Oldbury B69 1RZ Tel: 01384 252274 Fax: 01384 240088 — MB ChB 1987 Birm.; BSc (Hons.) Birm. 1984; MRCGP 1992; T(GP) 1992; DRCOG 1991; DCH RCP Lond. 1990. (Birmingham) Gen. Practitioner. Prev: SHO (Psychiat.) Rubery Hill Hosp. Birm.; SHO (Paediat., Geriat. & A & E) Selly Oak Hosp. Birm.

SYKES, Jennifer Anne Glaxo Wellcome Research & Development, Stockley Park W., Uxbridge UB11 1BT Tel: 020 8990 8016 Fax: 020 8990 8140; 14 Ranelagh Road, Ealing, London W5 5RJ Tel: 020 8840 4469 — MB ChB 1983 Manch.; MRCP (UK) 1988; Cert. Av. Med. 1991. (Univ. Manch.) Med. Strategy Head (Internat. Respirat. Med.) Glaxo Wellcome Research & Developm. Uxbridge; Hon. Clin. Asst. Hammersmith Hosp. Lond. Socs: Brit. Assn. Pharmaceut. Phys.; Brit. Assn. Sport & Med.; Brit. Assn. Lung Res. Prev: Sen. Med. Adviser Allen & Hanbury's Ltd.; Med. Off. (Aero Med. Evacuations) Mondial Asst. (UK) Ltd.; Regist. (Respirat. Med. & Infec. Dis.) Hammersmith Hosp. Lond.

SYKES, Jeremy James William The Office of Medical Director General, HM Naval Base, Portsmouth PO1 3LS Tel: 023 92 24592; 24 Bury Road, Gosport PO12 3UD — MB ChB 1973 Dundee; MSc Lond. 1980; FFOM RCP Lond. 1992, M 1985; FRCP RCP Lond. 1996. Dir. of Health (Navy); Acad. Regist. Fac. Occupat. Med. Socs: Soc. Occupat. Med.; Eur. Undersea Biomed. Soc. Prev: Head Undersea Med. Inst. of Naval Med.; RN Exchange Med. Off. Naval Med. Research Inst. Bethesda MD, USA; Princip. Med. Off. HM Naval Base Rosyth.

SYKES, Joanna Vivienne The Hollies, Burley Gate, Hereford HR1 3QR — MB BS 1987 Lond.

SYKES, John Anthony 30 Pollard Way, Gomersal, Cleckheaton BD19 4PR — MB ChB 1977 Bristol; DRCOG 1979.

SYKES, John Edmondson Smithkline Beecham International, SB House, Great West Road, Brentford TW8 9BD Tel: 020 8975 3302 Fax: 020 8975 4489 Email: john.e.sykes@sb.com; Tel: 020 7267 1002 Fax: 020 7267 1002 Email: jsykes4500@aol.com — MB BS 1976 Lond.; BSc Lond. 1973, MB BS 1976; FFA RCS Eng. 1983. Dir. & Vice Pres. (Clin. Developm. & Med. Affairs) Smithkline Beecham Internat. Socs: Fell. Fac. of Pharmaceutical Phys.; Fell. Roy. Fac. Anaesth.s. Prev: Med. Dir. Smithkline Beecham Australia; Regional Med. Dir. S. E. Asia Beecham Internat.

SYKES, John Reginald 243 Wilmslow Road, Heald Green, Cheadle SK8 3BQ — MB ChB 1981 Sheff.; MRCPsych 1985. Cons. Psychiat. for the Elderly Walton Hosp. Chesterfield.; Med. Director Community Health Care Serv. (N. Derbysh.) HNS Trust. Prev: Lect. N.. Gen. Psychiat. Unit Sheff.

***SYKES, Kathryn Louise** 3 Octavia Street, London SW11 3DN Tel: 020 7652 0550 Email: kathrynsykes@csi.com — BM BCh 1997 Oxf.; BSc (1st cl) Ed. 1994; MRCP 1999.

SYKES, Kenneth Bryan Sandringham Practice, Sandringham Road Health Centre, Sandringham Road, Intake, Doncaster DN2 5JH Tel: 01302 321521 Fax: 01302 761792; 106 Stoops Lane, West Bessacarr, Doncaster DN4 7RY Tel: 01302 370759 — MB ChB 1974 Birm.; MRCGP 1980 DRCOG 1979; Dip. Therapeut UWCH 1997. (University of Birmingham) Prev: Trainee GP Doncaster VTS; SHO (Gen. Med.) Good Hope Hosp. Sutton Coldfield & Coventry AHA; Ho. Phys. Gen. Hosp. Birm.

SYKES, Linda Worsbrough Health Centre, Oakdale, Worsbrough, Barnsley S70 5EG Tel: 01226 204090 Fax: 01226 771966; 29 Mount Vernon Road, Barnsley S70 4DH Tel: 01226 207237 Email: lshw@globalnet.uk — MB ChB 1978 Ed.; MRCGP 1995; DRCOG 1983; DA Eng. 1981. Tutor (Gen. Pract.) Barnsley. Socs: Fac. Anaesth. RCS.

***SYKES, Lisa-Jane** 123 Staincross Common, Mapplewell, Barnsley S75 6ND — MB ChB 1997 Leic.

SYKES, Professor Sir Malcolm Keith 10 Fitzherbert Close, Iffley, Oxford OX4 4EN Tel: 01865 771152 — MB BChir 1949 Camb.; MA Camb. 1951; FFA RCS Eng. 1955; Hon. FCA (SA) 1989; Hon. FRANZA 1978; DA Eng. 1953. (Univ. Coll. Hosp.) Emerit. Prof. Anaesth. Univ. Oxf. Prev: Prof. Clin. Anaesth. Roy. Postgrad. Med. Sch. Lond.; Fell. (Anaesth.) Mass. Gen. Hosp. Boston, USA; Rickman Godlee Trav. Fell. Univ. Coll. Hosp. Med. Sch. 1954.

SYKES, Michael Hugh (retired) Hazelwood, 5 Hawksdown, Walmer, Deal CT14 7PH Tel: 01304 373341 — MB BS 1958 Lond.; MRCS Eng. LRCP Lond. 1958. Prev: Ho. Surg. W.m. Hosp. Lond.

SYKES, Muriel Grace 85 Mainway, Alkrington, Middleton, Manchester M24 1LL — MB ChB Liverp. 1955.

***SYKES, Nicholas Fenton** 23 Thornville Street, Leeds LS6 1RP — MB ChB 1994 Leeds.

SYKES, Nigel Philip St. Christopher's Hospice, Lawrie Park Road, London SE26 6DZ — BM BCh 1980 Oxf.; MA Oxf. 1981; FRCGP 1995, M 1984. Cons. Palliat. Med. St. Christopher's Hospice Lond.; Hon. Cons. Palliat. Med. Guy's, St. Thos. & Lewisham Hosps.; Hon. Sen. Lect. Palliat. Med. King's Coll. Lond. Socs: Assn. Palliat. Med. (Mem. Ethical Comm.). Prev: Macmillan Lect. (Palliat. Med.) Univ. Leeds; Sen. Regist. St. Christopher's Hospice Lond.

SYKES, Oliver Mark The Paddock, Wallings Lane, Silverdale, Carnforth LA5 0RZ — MB BS 1987 Newc.; MRCGP 1993; DRCOG 1993; DCH RCPS Glas. 1992.

SYKES, Peter (retired) Brook Farmhouse, Brinkhill, Louth LN11 8QX Tel: 01507 253 — MB ChB Sheff. 1953; LMSSA Lond. 1953; FRCPsych 1976, M 1971; DPM Eng. 1958. Prev: Mem. Ment. Health Review Tribunal Nottm.

SYKES, Mr Peter Antony Dept. Surgery, Trafford General Hospital, Moorside Road, Davyhulme M42; 40 Carrwood Avenue, Bramhall, Stockport SK7 2PY Tel: 0161 440 9644 — MB ChB 1966 Manch.; MD Manch. 1975; FRCS Eng. 1972; FRCS Ed. 1971. p/t Cons. Surg.; Reviewer for Commiss. of Health Improvement. Socs: Fell. Manch. Med. Soc.; Assn. Surg. Prev: Sen. Regist. (Surg.) Univ. Hosp. S. Manch.; Regist. (Surg.) Manch. Roy. Infirm.

SYKES, Peter Hugh Wowham, Lansdown Road, Bath BA1 5RB — MB ChB 1985 Bristol.

SYKES, Peter Hugh The Surgery, The Corn Stores, 12 Nargate Street, Littlebourne, Canterbury CT3 1UH Tel: 01227 721515; 5 Park Cottages, Park Lane, Preston, Canterbury CT3 1DS — MB BS 1984 Lond.; DRCOG 1988.

SYKES, Mr Philip John, OBE St Joseph's Hospital, Harding Avenue, Malpas, Newport NP20 6ZE Tel: 01633 820357 Email: l.bellamy.plas.surg@talk21.com; Applecote, Applethwaite, Keswick CA12 4PP Tel: 017687 75027 Email: sykes.keswick@virgin.net — BA 1961 Camb.; FRCS Edin. AdHominem 2001; 1964 MB Bchir Camb. 1964; MA Camb. 1964; FRCS Eng. 1970; T(S) 1991. (Middlx.) p/t Cons. Expert Priv. Medico-legal Pratice Plast. & Hand Surg. St Joseph's Hosp. Newport. Socs: Brit. Soc. Surg. Hand; Brit. Assn. Plastic Surg. Prev: cons.plastic surg.Morrison Hosp.Swansea; Sen. Regist. (Plastic Surg.) Stoke Mandeville Hosp.; Regist. (Surg.) N.ampton Gen. Hosp.

SYKES, Phyllis May (retired) 50 Buckingham Place, Downend, Bristol BS16 5TN — MB ChB Leeds 1938.

SYKES, Rachel Anne Parkhill Road Surgery, 40 Parkhill Road, Bexley DA5 1HU Tel: 01322 522056 Fax: 01322 521345; 7 Walton Road, Sidcup DA14 4LJ — BM BS 1977 Nottm.; MRCGP 1981; DRCOG 1981.

SYKES, Rachel Sarah The Surgery, Field Road, Stainforth, Doncaster DN7 5AF Tel: 01302 841202; The Firs, Hay Green, Fishlake, Doncaster DN7 5JY Tel: 01302 844905 — MB ChB 1987 Liverp.; MRCGP 1992; DRCOG 1991. (Liverp.) GP; Med. Off. Youth

Clinic; Hon. Clin. Tutor Sheff. Univ.; GP Trainer. Prev: Trainee GP Doncaster VTS.

SYKES, Richard Vernon (retired) Carrantuohill, Bare Lane, Ockbrook, Derby DE72 3RG Tel: 0332 280852 — MB ChB Manch. 1948.

SYKES, Robert Andrew Sunrise Cottage, Barrack Hill, Kingsthorne, Hereford HR2 8AY — MB BS 1995 Lond.; DRCOG 1997. (Roy. Lond. Hosp.) GP Regist. - Much Birch Surg. Heref.

SYKES, Robin Alastair Morecambe Health Centre, Hanover Street, Morecambe LA4 5LY Tel: 01524 418418 Fax: 01524 832584 — MB ChB 1985 Manch.; MRCGP 1991; DRCOG 1988. (Manch.) Socs: Assoc. Mem. Brit. Acupunc. Soc. Prev: Trainee GP Bolton VTS; Ho. Off. (Surg.) Vict. Hosp. Blackpool; Ho. Off. (Med.) Bolton Gen. Hosp.

SYKES, Robin George, TD (retired) Low Bridges, Stocksfield NE43 7SF Tel: 01661 842319 — BM BCh 1942 Oxf.; MA Oxf. 1942; FFA RCS Eng. 1953; DA Eng. 1949. Cons. Anaesth. N. Regional Thoracic Surg. Centre, Freeman Hosp. Newc. Prev: Hon. Surg. to H.M. The Qu.

SYKES, Roger Andrew David Ravenscraig Hospital, Inverness Road, Greenock PA16 9HA Tel: 01475 633777; The Mill, Swinbrook, Burford OX18 4DY Tel: 01993 823108 — MB ChB 1978 Glas.; MRCPsych 1984; FRCPsych 1999. Cons. Psychiat. Ravenscraig Hosp. Greenock.

SYKES, Rupert 52 Broadway, Bramhall, Stockport SK7 3BU Tel: 0161 439 1823 — MB BS 1932 Lond.; BSc Lond. 1926, MD 1935; FRCP Lond. 1969, M 1934; MRCS Eng., LRCP Lond. 1932. (Manch.) Fell. Manch. Med. Soc. Prev: Cons. Phys. Stepping Hill Hosp. Stockport; Cons. Phys. Manch. N.. Hosp.; Res. Med. Off. Manch. Roy. Infirm.

SYKES, Seth Alexander Greer Wainfleet Road Surgery, Wainfleet Road, Burgh Le Marsh, Skegness PE24 5ED Tel: 01754 810205; 66 Station Road, Burgh Le Marsh, Skegness PE24 5EL Tel: 01754 810275 — MB ChB 1965 Edin.

SYKES, Sheila Grace (retired) Carrantuohill, Bare Lane, Ockbrook, Derby DE72 3RG Tel: 01332 280852 — MB ChB Manch. 1955; DCH Eng. 1960; DPH Ed. 1959; DObst RCOG 1958. Prev: Retd. GP.

SYKES, Steven John Danks, Smith, Sykes and Farrell, 134 Beeston Road, Beeston Hill, Leeds LS11 8BS Tel: 0113 276 0717 Fax: 0113 270 3727 — MB ChB 1980 Leeds; MRCGP 1984; DRCOG 1983. Prev: SHO & Ho. Off. Airedale Gen. Hosp. Steeton.

SYKES, Mr Timothy Charles Freeman Pembroke House, Old Mill Lane, Oldbury, Bridgnorth WV16 5EY Tel: 01746 764 3060 Email: sykesburke@online.rednet.co.uk — MB BCh 1991 Wales; BSc (Physiol.) Wales 1988; FRCS Eng. 1995. (Univ. Wales Coll. Med.) Regist. (Gen. Surg.) Worcester Roy. Infirm. Prev: Regist. (Gen. Surg.) Heartlands Hosp. Birm.; SHO Rotat. (Surg.) S. Birm.; SHO (Urol.) Roy. Marsden Hosp.

SYLVESTER, Anna Rachel 45 Reddings Road, Birmingham B13 8LW — MB ChB 1994 Leeds.

SYLVESTER, Mr Bernard Simon 15 Bruntwood Lane, Cheadle SK8 1HS Tel: 0161 832 7780 — MB BS 1969 Lond.; FRCS Eng. 1974. (Lond. Hosp.) Cons. Orthop. Surg. N. Manch. Health Dist. Socs: Orthop. Research Soc.; Brit. Orthop. Assn. Prev: Regist. (Orthop.) Hammersmith Hosp. Lond.; Regist. (Orthop.) St. Mary's Hosp. Lond.; Lect. Orthop. Surg. Hope Hosp. Salford.

SYLVESTER, Derek George Holden (retired) Almondsbury Field, Tockington Lane, Lower Almondsbury, Bristol BS32 4EB Tel: 01454 613178 — MB BS 1946 Lond; MB BS Lond. 1946; MD Lond. 1952; MRCGP 1968. Prev: Occupat. Health Phys. Univ. Bristol.

SYLVESTER, Gillian Mary Doctors Surgery, 2 Danson Crescent, Welling DA16 2AT Tel: 020 8303 4204 Fax: 020 8298 1192; 12 Mottingham Gardens, London SE9 4RL Tel: 020 8857 4019 — MB BS 1961 Lond.; MRCS Eng. LRCP Lond. 1961; DObst RCOG 1966. (Roy. Free)

SYLVESTER, Nigel Charles Friarsgate Practice, Friarsgate Medical Centre, Friarsgate, Winchester SO23 8EF Tel: 01962 853599 Fax: 01962 849982; Windy Ridge, Cliff Way, Compton Down, Winchester SO21 2AP — MB BS 1977 Newc.; MRCGP; DRCOG 1979.

SYLVESTER, Mr Paul Andrew 12 Cothale Vale, Cotham, Bristol BS6 6HR — MB ChB 1990 Bristol; FRCS Lond. 1994.

SYLVESTER, Peter Kirwan The Cedars, Makeney Road, Duffield, Belper DE56 4BD Tel: 01332 840448 — MB BS 1950 Lond.; MRCS

Eng. LRCP Lond. 1948; FFPHM RCP (UK) 1989; FFCM RCP (UK) 1978, M 1974; DPH Lond. 1957; DObst RCOG 1952; DCH Eng. 1951. (Westm.) Emerit. Cons. S.ern Derbysh. HA. Socs: Hon.Mem. BMA; Hon. Mem. Derby Med. Soc. Prev: Dist. Med. Off. S.. Derbysh. HA; Area Med. Off. Derbysh. HA; Dep. Co. MOH & Dep. Princip. Sch. Med. Off. Derbysh. CC.

SYLVESTER, Stephen Houghton Henry The Surgery, Tennant Street, Stockton-on-Tees TS18 2AT Tel: 01642 613331 Fax: 01642 675612; Greenways, 9 Teesbank Avenue, Eaglescliffe, Stockton-on-Tees TS16 9AY Email: s.sylvester@btinternet.com — MB ChB 1981 Cape Town; MRCP (UK) 1985; DRCOG 1986; Dip. Med. Educat. Dund 1994; FRCGP 1998. GP Princip. Stockton on Tees; GP Tutor.

SYLVESTER, Susan Elizabeth Westbourne Medical Centre, Milburn Road, Bournemouth BH4 9HJ Tel: 01202 752550 Fax: 01202 769700 — MB BCh Wales 1974.

SYM, Jessie Crawford Broun (retired) 10A Morningside Place, Edinburgh EH10 5ER Tel: 0131 447 2735 — MB ChB 1924 Ed.; MD (High Commend.) Ed. 1928; DPH Ed. 1931.

SYM, Ruth Audrey 8 Beaumont Avenue, Southwell NG25 0BB — MB ChB 1990 Glas.

SYMCOX, Helen Ann Shay Lane Medical Centre, Shay Lane, Hale, Altrincham WA15 8NZ Tel: 0161 980 3835 Fax: 0161 903 9848 — MB ChB 1988 Liverp.; BSc Liverp. 1988; MRCGP 1992; DRCOG 1991.

SYME, Adam Iain Cameron Riverside Medical Practice, Ballifeary Lane, Inverness IV3 5PW Tel: 01463 715999 Fax: 01463 718763 — MB ChB 1982 Ed.; FRCGP; MRCGP 1988; MRCP (UK) 1985; DRCOG 1987. GP Princip.

SYME, Mr Brian Allan 10 Glen Orrin Avenue, Kilmarnock KA2 0LR — MB ChB 1991 Glas.; FRCS Ed. 1996. Specialist Regist. Orthop. Vict. Infirm.

SYME, David McBride Killin Medical Practice, Laggan Leigheas, Ballechroisk, Killin FK21 8TQ Tel: 01567 820213 Fax: 01567 820805 — MRCGP 1982; DCH RCPS Glas. 1981. GP Killin.

SYME, Mr Ian George 19 Beech Crescent, Newton Mearns, Glasgow G77 5BN — MB ChB 1975 Glas.; FRCS Ed. 1979. Cons. Ophth. Surg. StoneHo. Gen. Hosp. Lanarksh.

SYME, Paul David Borders General Hospital, Melrose, Roxburghshire, Melrose TD6 9BS; Ashtrees, Gattonside, Melrose TD6 9LZ — MB ChB 1981 Ed.; BSc Hons 1979, MBCNB 1981; FRCP Ed 1997. Cons. Phys.; Sen. Lect., Edin. Univ.

SYME, Mr William Smith (retired) North Carthat, Collin, Dumfries DG1 3SA — MB ChB Glas. 1957; FRCS Ed. 1965; FRCS Glas. 1964; LMCC 1960. Prev: Cons. Orthop. Surg. Dumfries & Galloway Roy. Infirm.

SYMEONAKIS, Argyrios 9 Castle Canyke Road, Bodmin PL31 1DY — Ptychio Iatrikes 1987 Athens.

SYMERS, Dorothy Annie (retired) La Meule, Rue Du Moulin, St Martin, Jersey JE3 6AH Tel: 01534 851582 — MB BS Lond. 1945. Prev: Med. Off. J. Lyons & Co. Ltd.

SYMES, Clare (retired) Tudor Cottage, The Street, Brent Eleigh, Sudbury CO10 9NU Tel: 01787 247354 — MB ChB 1974 Manch.; MRCGP 1978. Prev: GP Sudbury.

SYMES, David Millman Camster House, 7 Beechdene, Tadworth KT20 5EA Tel: 01737 814714 Fax: 01737 819807 — MB BS 1955 Lond.; MRCS Eng. LRCP Lond. 1955; Dip. Dermat. Wales 1992. (St. Mary's) Hon. Clin. Tutor (Dermat.) St. Geo. Hosp. Med. Sch.; Hon. Asst. Specialist (Dermat.) Kingston Hosp.; Med. Adviser Disablem. Tribunal & Examg. Med. Pract. DSS. Socs: Fell. Roy. Soc. Med.; Soc. Occupat. Med.; BMA. Prev: Hon. Hosp. Pract. (Dermat.) St. Geo. Hosp. Lond.; Sen. Med. Cons. Whittaker Life Scs. Ltd.; Med. Cons. John Brown Engin. & Construc. Ltd.

SYMES, Janet Elizabeth Woodside Barn, Back Lane, Heath Charnock, Chorley PR6 9DJ — MB ChB 1983 Manch.; Cert. Family Plann. JCC 1987; DRCOG 1986.

SYMES, John Bernard Lloyd Horsmans Place, Instone, Dartford DA1 2JP Tel: 01322 228363 — MD 1973 Malta; MRCOG 1979; M.A. (Med. Ethics and Law) Lond. 1997. Prev: Regist. (O & G) W.m. & St. Stephens Hosps. Lond.; Regist. (O & G) Edgware Gen. Hosp.; SHO (Obst.) Univ. Coll. Hosp. Lond.

SYMES, Mr John Mayland Crossways, Church Road, Binstead, Ryde PO33 3TA — MRCS Eng. LRCP Lond. 1964; MS Lond. 1978, MB BS 1964; FRCS Eng. 1970. (Char. Cross) Cons. Surg. I. of Wight

SYMES

AHA. Prev: Ho. Surg. St. Jas. Hosp. Balham; Lect. in Surg. Lond. Hosp. Med. Coll.; Sen. Regist. Vasc. Surg. Lond. Hosp.

SYMES, Michael Harvey (retired) 21 Priors Court, Back of Avon, Tewkesbury GL20 5US Tel: 01684 290081 — MB BS 1949 Lond.; LMSSA Lond. 1948; MRCPsych 1971; DPM Eng. 1963.

SYMES, Michael Herbert Archibald Cromer Group Practice, 48 Overstrand Road, Cromer NR27 0AJ Tel: 01263 513148 — MB BS 1968 Lond.; MRCS Eng. LRCP Lond. 1968; DObst RCOG 1976; DA Eng. 1971. (Westm.)

SYMES, Michael Oliver 242 Shirehampton Road, Bristol BS9 2EH — MD 1963 Bristol; MB ChB 1959. (Bristol) Cons. Sen. Lect. in Surg. Univ. Bristol; Hon. Cons. Immunol. Avon AHA (T).

***SYMES, Michelle Antoinette** 18 Beckenham Road, West Wickham BR4 0QT — MB BS 1994 Lond.

SYMES, Steven Roy Woodside Barn, Back Lane, Heath Charnock, Chorley PR6 9DJ — MB ChB 1983 Manch.; Cert. Family Plann. JCC 1987.

SYMINGTON, Alan John Forsyth ThE Elizabeth Courtauld Surgery, Factory Lane West, Halstead CO9 1EX Tel: 01787 475944 Fax: 01787 474506 — MB Camb. 1977, BChir 1976; MRCGP 1981; DCH RCP Lond. 1981; DRCOG 1978; FRCGP 1998. (Cambridge) GP Princip.; GP Tutor Braintree PCG.

SYMINGTON, Lady (Esther Margaret) (retired) Green Briar, 2 Lady Margaret Drive, Troon KA10 7AL Tel: 01292 3157 — MB ChB 1942 Glas. Clin. Asst. (Geriat.) Ayrsh. Centr. Hosp. Irvine. Prev: Clin. Asst. (Geriat.) Cuddington Hosp. Sutton.

SYMINGTON, Ian Stevenson Glasgow Occupational Health, 20 Cochrane St., Glasgow G1 1DD Tel: 0141 287 4422 Fax: 0141 287 4133 Email: Ian.Symington@northglasgow.scot.nhs.uk; 10 Buchanan Street, Milngavie, Glasgow G62 8DD — MB ChB Glas. 1969; FRCP Lond. 1994; FRCP Glas. 1983, M 1973; FFOM RCP Lond. 1985, MFOM 1983; DObst RCOG 1971; DIH Soc. Apoth. Lond. 1977. (Glas.) Dir. Occupat. Health Servs. & Cons. Occupat. Health Stobhill NHS Trust; Hon. Cons. Univ. Strathclyde; Hon. Sen. Clin. Lect. Univ. Glas. Socs: (Ex-Pres.) Soc. Occupat. Med. Prev: Sen. Employm. Med. Adviser EMAS Lond.; Employm. Med. Adviser EMAS Dundee; Regist. (Respirat. Med.) W.. Infirm. Glas.

SYMINGTON, James Joseph Mark Coleraine Hospital, 28A Mountsandal Road, Coleraine BT52 1JA Tel: 01265 44177; 21 Old Coleraine Road, Portstewart, Londonderry BT55 7PZ Tel: 01265 835298 Email: msymington@aol.com — MB BCh BAO 1985 Belf.; FFA RCSI 1990. Cons. (Anaesth.) Coleraine Hosp. Prev: Sen. Regist. (Anaesth.) Craigavon Area Hosp.

***SYMINGTON, Stuart Kevin** 248 Coalisland Road, Dungannon BT71 6EP — MB BCh BAO 1991 Belf.

SYMINGTON, Sir Thomas Green Briar, 2 Lady Margaret Drive, Troon KA10 7AL Tel: 01292 315707 — MB ChB 1941 Glas.; FRS Ed.; BSc (Hons.) Glas. 1936, MD (Hons.) 1950, MB ChB 1941; FRCP Glas. 1962; FRFPS Glas. 1958; FRCPath 1964. (Glas.) Socs: FRIC; Fell. Roy. Soc. Med.; Path. Soc. Prev: Dir. Inst. Cancer Research Roy. Cancer Hosp. Chester Beatty; Research Inst. Lond. & Prof. Pathol. Inst. Cancer Research Roy. CancerHosp.

SYMMERS, Eleanor 81 St Albans Road, Edinburgh EH9 2PQ Tel: 0131 667 1716 Email: eleanorsymmers@dial.pipex.com — MB ChB 1965 Glas. Indep. Counselling Psychother. Edin.; Med. Mem. Appeals. Serv; Hosp. Pract. Med. Rehab. Prev: Research Fell. BrE. Unit Dept. Clin. Surg. Roy. Infirm. Edin.; Regist. (Psychiat.) Roy. Edin. Hosp.; Regist. Psychiat. Univ. Coll. Hosp. Lond.

SYMMERS, William St Clair Howdenhall Surgery, 57 Howden Hall Road, Edinburgh EH16 6PL Tel: 0131 664 3766 Fax: 0131 672 2114; 81 St. Alban's Road, Edinburgh EH9 2PQ Tel: 0131 667 1716 — MB BS 1967 Lond.; MB BS (Hons. Obst. & Gyn.) Lond. 1967; BSc (Hons.) Physiol. Lond. 1964; MSc (Med. Sci.) Glas. 1983; MRCS Eng. LRCP Lond. 1967; MRCGP 1984. (Univ. Coll. Hosp. Med. Sch.) GP Adviser Roy. Infirm. Edin. NHS Trust. Prev: Head of WHO MONICA Proj. Univ. Edin. & Hon. Research Fell. (Cardiovasc. Epidemiol. Unit) Univ. Dundee.

SYMMONS, Professor Deborah Pauline Mary ARC Epidemiology Research Unit, University of Manchester Medical School, Oxford Road, Manchester M13 9PT Tel: 0161 275 5044 Fax: 0161 275 5043 — MB ChB 1977; MD Birm. 1987, MB ChB 1977; FRCP Lond. 1994; MRCP (UK) 1980; MD 1987 Birm.; MFPHM 1999. Dep. Dir. ARC Epidemiol. Unit Univ. Manch. Med. Sch.; Cons. Rheum. Macclesfield Dist. Gen. Hosp.; Prof. of Rheum.

and Musculoskeletal Epidermiology, Univ. of Manch. Prev: Lect. (Rheum.) Univ. Birm.; Regist. (Rheum. & Med.) Guy's Hosp. Lond.

SYMON, David Nicholas Kidd University Hospital of Hartlepool, Hartlepool TS24 9AH Tel: 01429 522802 Fax: 01429 522738 Email: david.symon@nth.northy.nhs.uk — MB ChB 1973 Glas.; BSc Glas. 1971; FRCP Lond. 1995; FRCP Ed. 1991; FRCP Glas. 1989; FRCPCH 1997. Cons. Paediat. Univ. Hosp. of Hartlepool. Socs: Internat. Headache Soc.Mem. of Paediatric Sub Comm.; Brit. Assn. Study Headache Sec.; Mem.. Anglo-Dutch Migraine Assn. Prev: Lect. (Child Health) Univ. Aberd.; Regist. (Med. Paediat.) Roy. Hosp. Sick Childr. Glas.; Regist. Rotat. (Med.) W.. Infirm. Glas.

SYMON, Professor Lindsay, TD, CBE (retired) Maple Lodge, Rivar Road, Shalbourne, Marlborough SN8 3QE Tel: 01672 870501 Fax: 01672 870501 — MB ChB (1st cl. Hons.) Aberd. 1951; FRCS Eng. 1959; FRCS Ed. 1957; Hon. FACS 1994. Prev: Prof. Neurol. Surg. Univ. Lond. Inst. Neurol. Lond. 1978-95.

SYMON, Margaret Allison South Cleveland Hospital, Marton Road, Middlesbrough TS4 3BW Tel: 01642 850850; Tigh an Achadh, Stockton Road, Castle Eden, Hartlepool TS27 4SD Tel: 01429 836612 — MB ChB 1982 Aberd.; FRCP Glas. 1995; MRCP (UK) 1985; FRCA 1989; DA (UK) 1988. Cons. Anaesth. S. Tees Acute Hosps. NHS Trust. Prev: Sen. Regist. (Anaesth.) Newc. Teach. Hosps.; Regist. (Gen. Med.) Aberd. Teach. Hosps.; Clin. Tutor Univ. Aberd.

SYMON, Michaela Anne Invergowire House, Dundee DD2 1UA — MB ChB 1994 Dundee.

SYMON, Rosemary Buckland House, Oxford St., Eddington, Hungerford RG17 0ET Tel: 01488 682658; High Street, Ramsbury, Marlborough SN8 2QT Tel: 01672 20366 — MB BS 1980 Lond.; MRCGP 1985; DRCOG 1982; Cert. Family Plann. JCC 1982. (St. Thos. Hosp. Med. Sch. Lond.) Prev: Trainee GP Reading VTS; Clin. Asst. (Ophth.) P.ss Margt. Hosp. Swindon; SHO (Anaesth.) St. Thos. Hosp. Lond.

SYMON, Thomas, Lt.-Col. RAMC Medical Centre, Army Foundation College, Harrogate H63 0SE Email: tomsymon@madasafish.com; Parkwood, Lartington, Barnard Castle, Republic of Ireland Email: tomsymon@madasafish.com — MB ChB 1966 Glas.; DFFP 1995. (Glas.) Sen. Med. Off.,Army Foundat. Coll., Harrogate. Socs: Assoc. RCGP; BMA. Prev: Chief Med. Off. UN Peacekeeping Force Cyprus; Chief Med. Off. Rotyal Brunei Armed Forces SMO ITC Catterick.

SYMONDS, Professor Edwin Malcolm Scchool of Human Development & Midwifery, Floor D, East Block, University Hospital, Queen's Medical Centre, Nottingham NG7 2UH Tel: 0115 970 9240 Fax: 0115 970 9234; Nursery Cottage, The Green, Car Colston, Nottingham NG13 8JE — MB BS 1957 Adelaide; MD Adelaide 1970; FFPHM (Distinc.) RCP (UK) 1996; FRCOG 1971, M 1962; FACOG; FRANZOG. (Adelaide) Foundat. Prof. O & G Univ. Nottm.; Edr-in-Chief Curr. Obst. & Gyn. Socs: Fell. Amer. Gyn. & Obst. Soc.; Fell. Hungarian Gyn. Soc.; (Counc.) Med. Defence Union. Prev: Commiss.er of Commonw. Schol.sh. Commiss.; Sen. Regist. (O & G) Univ. Liverp.; Sen. Lect. & Reader (O & G) Univ. Adelaide.

SYMONDS, Ian Martin Derby City General Hospital, Uttoxeter Road, Derby DE22 3NE Tel: 01332 625633 Fax: 01332 625634 Email: ian.symonds@nottingham.ac.uk; 46 Appledore Avenue, Wollaton, Nottingham NG8 2RW Tel: 0115 916 5732 — BM BS 1983 Nottm.; DM Nottm. 1995; BMedSci. Nottm. 1981; MRCOG 1995. (Nottm.) Sen. Lect. (O & G) Univ. Nottm. Socs: Eur. Assn. for Cancer Research; Brit. Gyn. Cancer Soc. Prev: Lect. (O & G) Univ. Nottm.; Regist. (Gyn.) Birm. Wom. Hosp.; Regist. (O & G) Birm. Matern. Hosp.

SYMONDS, Jane Marion 12 Dowles Close, Selly Oak, Birmingham B29 4LE Tel: 0121 475 8991 — MB ChB 1972 Bristol; MRCPath 1979. Cons. Med. Microbiol. Dudley Gp. Hosps. NHS Trust; Sen. Clin. Lect. Univ. Birm. Prev: Sen. Regist. (Med. Microbiol.) Qu. Eliz. Hosp. Birm.; SHO (Path.) S.mead Hosp. Bristol; Temp. Lect. (Path.) Univ. Manch.

SYMONDS, Miss Katherine Elizabeth Accident & Emergency Department Dept, Hereford General Hosp, Nelson Street, Hereford HR1 2PA Tel: 01432 355444; The Steppes, Checkley, Hereford HR1 4ND Tel: 01432 850922 — MB ChB 1975 Liverp.; FFAEM 1996; FRCS Ed. 1981. Cons. A & E Surg. Hereford Gen. Hosp. Prev: Clin. Asst. (A & E) Hereford Gen. Hosp.; Regist. N. Manch. Gen.

Hosp. & Roy. Manch. Childr. Hosp.; Cons. A & E Surg. (Paediat. Trauma) Birm. Childr. Hosp.

SYMONDS, Raymond Paul, TD Department of Oncology, Leicester Royal Infirmary, Leicester LE1 5WW Tel: 0116 258 6294 Fax: 0116 258 5942 Email: psymonds@uhl.trent.nhs.uk; 11 Alvington Way, Market Harborough LE16 7NF Tel: 01858 461018 — MB BS 1972 Newc.; MD Newc. 1981; FRCP Glas. 1989; MRCP (UK) 1975; FRCR 1982. Reader in Oncol., Leicester Univ.; Vis. Prof. Hahnemann Med. Coll. Philadelphia, USA 1981; Hon. Cons. Leicester Roy. Infirm. Prev: Cons. Radiother. & Oncol., Beatson Oncol. Centre, W.ern Infirm. Glas.; MRC Fell. (RadioBiol.), Regist. & Hosp. Office (Radiol.) Roy. Vict. Infirm. Newc.

SYMONDS, Richard Leonard Medway Hospital, Windmill Road, Gillingham ME7 5NY Tel: 01634 830000 Fax: 01634 830082 Email: mens.sana@virgin.net; 141 Butchers Lane, Mereworth, Maidstone ME18 5QD Tel: 01622 812425 Email: r.symonds@virgin.net — MB ChB 1967 Birm.; FRCPsych 1989, M 1972; DPM Eng. 1971. Cons. Psychiat. Thames Gateway NHS Trust, Medway Maritime Hosp.; Recognised Teach. United Med. & Dent. Sch. 1988; Cons. Psychiat. Medway Hosp.; Hon. Sen. Lect. Univ. of Kent at Canterbury. Socs: BMA (Exec. Comm. Local Div.); NHSCA. Prev: Cons. Psychiat. Tunbridge Wells HA & Sen. Lect. Kings Coll. Hosp.; Lect. (Psychol. Med.) Welsh Nat. Sch. Med. Cardiff; Sen. Regist. (Psychiat.) WhitCh. Hosp. Cardiff.

SYMONDSON, Alicia Millicent (retired) Landscape, Kinnerley, Oswestry SY10 8DU Tel: 01691 682577 — MB BChir 1939 Camb.; MA, MB BChir Camb. 1939. Prev: Ho. Phys. Burslem, Haywood & Tunstall Memor. Hosp.

SYMONS, Audrey Jean Cunningham (retired) 6A Thornly Park Avenue, Paisley PA2 7SB Tel: 0141 884 2034 — MB ChB 1950 Glas.; FFA RCS Eng. 1964; DA Eng. 1959. Prev: Cons. Anaesth. Roy. Alexandra Infirm. Paisley.

SYMONS, Gareth Vize Yule House, Kew Gdns. Road, Kew, Richmond Tel: 020 8940 4223 — MB BS 1964 Lond.; FFA RCSI 1973; FFA RCS Eng. 1973. (St. Mary's) Cons. Anaesth. St. Mary's Hosp. Teach. Gp. Prev: Capt. RAMC.

SYMONS, Hugh Francis Brady (retired) 6 Rockhampton Close, London SE27 0NG Tel: 020 8769 5862 — MRCS Eng. LRCP 1942 Lond.; MRCS. Eng. LRCP Lond. 1942; DphysMed. Eng. 1950. Prev: Cons. Phys. Rheum. & Rehabil. St. Geo. Hosp. Lond.

SYMONS, Iris Elizabeth Department of Anaesthetics, Barnet General Hospital, Wellhouse Lane, Barnet EN5 3DJ — MB ChB 1972 Bristol; BSc 1968 (Hons.) Bristol; FFA RCS Eng. 1977; DObst RCOG 1974. Cons. Anaesth. Barnet and Chase Farm Hosp.s Trust Barnet, Herts. Socs: BMA & Assn. Anaesth.; Assn. of Paediat. Anaesth. Prev: Underlaker Thoraxanestesi Karolinska Hosp. Stockholm.; Sen. Regist. (Anaesth.) Addenbrooke's Hosp. Camb.; Regist. (Anaesth.) Hosp. Sick Childr. Gt. Ormond St.

SYMONS, John Charles Colchester General Hospital, Turner Road, Colchester CO4 5JL Tel: 01206 853535; Moors Farm, Assington, Colchester CO10 5NE Tel: 01787 227379 — MB BChir 1962 Camb.; MA Camb. 1962; FRCP Lond. 1971; DCH Eng. 1965; DObst RCOG 1964. (St. Thos.) Cons. Paediat. Essex Co. Hosp. Colchester; Paediat. Dir. NEE HA. Socs: Brit. Paediat. Assn.; BMA. Prev: Hon. Clin. Asst. Brompton Hosp. Lond.; Ho. Surg. St. Thos. Hosp.; Sen. Regist. (Paediat.) Jenny Lind Hosp. Norwich & Brompton Hosp. Lond.

SYMONS, Kenneth William, VRD Symons Medical Centre, 25 All Saints Avenue, Maidenhead SL6 8EL Tel: 01628 26131; Oaktree House, Cannon Hill, Bray, Maidenhead SL6 2EW Tel: 01628 624575 Fax: 01628 410051 — MB BChir Camb. 1944; MA Camb. 1944; MRCS Eng. LRCP Lond. 1944. (Camb. & St. Geo.) Med. Ref. & Other Insur. Cos. Socs: Hon. Mem. (Ex-Pres.) Windsor Med. Soc. Prev: Ho. Phys. St. Geo. Hosp.; Surg. Lt.-Cdr. RNR; Assoc. Specialist (Dermat.) K. Edwd. VII Hosp. (Windsor) & Heatherwood Hosp. Ascot.

SYMONS, Lorraine Claire Warwick House Medical Centre, Holway Green, Upper Holway Road, Taunton TA1 2QA — BM BS 1989 Nottm.; BMedSc Nottm. 1987; MRCGP 1994; DRCOG 1992; DGM RCP Lond. 1991.

SYMONS, Michael (retired) 26 Town Walls, Shrewsbury SY1 1TN Tel: 01743 362173 — MB BChir 1944 Camb.; MA Camb. 1946, MB BChir 1944; FRCP Lond. 1975, M 1946; MRCS Eng., LRCP Lond. 1944; FRCPath 1964. Prev: Cons. Path. Salop. AHA.

SYMONS, Nicola Jane Howsman Bradford Hospital Trust, Extension Block, St Luke's Hospital, Bradford BD5 0NA Tel: 01274 365028 Fax: 01274 365127; Little Broom Ing, Calverley Lane, Calverley, Leeds LS28 5QQ — MBChB 1975; DCH 1985; DCCH 1986; FRCPCH 1997. (Leeds) Cons. Community Paediat. Bradford Hosp. Trust. Socs: BMA; RCPCH.

SYMONS, Rory Charles Francis The Symons Medical Centre, 25 All Saints Avenue, Maidenhead SL6 6EL Tel: 01628 626131 Fax: 01628 410051 — MB BS 1982 Lond.; MRCGP 1986; DCH RCS Lond. 1986. (St. Mary's) Clin. Asst. (Rheum.) Wycombe & Amersham Hosps. Prev: Trainee GP Kentish Town Health Centre Lond.; SHO (A & E, Paediat. & Psychiat.) Univ. Coll. Hosp. Lond.

SYMONS, Sean Benjamin Vize 192 Portnall Road, London W9 3BJ — MB BS 1995 Lond.

***SYMONS, Stephanie Jennifer** 17 Hall Road, Rusholme, Manchester M14 5HN — MB ChB 1995 Manch.

SYN, Thant Department of Child Health, Mansfield Community Hospital, Mansfield NG18 5QJ Tel: 01623 785176 Fax: 01623 424062; 6 Pineview Close, Mansfield NG18 4PQ Tel: 01623 421054 — MB BS 1984 Med. Inst. (II) Rangoon; MPH Univ. Mahodol, Bangkok 1990; MRCPI & E Paediatrics 1999. Staff Community Paediat. (Child Health Servs.) Mansfield Community Hosp.; Staff Paediat. (On-Call) King's Mill Centre Sutton-in-Ashfield; Cert. Educat. Commiss. for Foreign Med. Grads. (USA). Socs: BMA; Assoc. Mem. RCPCH; Brit. Assn. Community Child Health.

***SYN, Wing-Kin** Flat 6 Room 1, Block 1, Royal Hallamshire Hospital Residences, 5 Beech Hill Road, Sheffield S10 2RA — MB ChB 1998 Sheff.; MB ChB Sheff 1998.

SYNDIKUS, Isabella Maria Clatterbridge Centre for Oncology, Bebington, Wirral CH63 4JY Tel: 0151 334 1155 Fax: 0151 482 7675 — MD 1986 Munich; State Exam Med. Munich 1986; FRCP Lond. 1992; MRCP (UK) 1989. Cons. Clin. Oncol. Clatterbridge Hosp. Liverp. Prev: Sen. Regist. (Clin. Oncol.) Middlx. Hosp. Lond.; Regist. (Radiother.) Roy. Marsden Hosp. Sutton; SHO (Gen. Med.) Addenbrooke's Hosp. Camb.

SYNEK, Miroslav H-Villa, Coldeast Hospital, Southampton SO31 7YJ Tel: 01489 570799 Fax: 01489 578490; 39 Corvette Avenue, Warsash, Southampton SO31 9AN — MUDr 1982 Charles Univ. Prague; MUDr Charles U, Prague 1982; MD Soton. 1995. (Fac. Med.) Staff Grade (Community Paediat.) Portsmouth Health Care Trust. Prev: Research Fell. Univ. Med. Univ. Soton.

SYNGE, Jessie 24 Merrivale, Oakland, London N14 4SL — MB 1951 Calcutta.

SYNNOTT, Mary Bernadette North Staffs Health Authority, Heron House, Grove Road, Stoke-on-Trent ST4 4LX Tel: 01782 298134 Fax: 01782 298135; 5 Hallahan Grove, Hartshill, Stoke-on-Trent ST4 7SL — MB BCh BAO 1974 NUI; MD NUI 1985; FRCPI 1996, M 1978. (Univ. Coll. Dub.) SCMO (Pub. Health Med.) N. Staff. HA. Socs: BMA. Prev: Clin. Lect. (Med. Microbiol.) Univ. Birm.; Intern & SHO (Med.) St. Vincent's Hosp. Dub.; SHO (Clin. Path.) Qu. Eliz. Hosp. Birm.

SYNNOTT, Mary Eithna 11 Greenpark Road, Rostrevor, Newry BT34 3EY Tel: 01693 738333 Fax: 01693 739454 — MB BCh BAO 1979 NUI. Prev: Chief Med. Off. Oke-Offa Hosp., Ibadan; Chief Med. Off. St. Brendan's Hosp., Nigeria.

SYRED, John Ralph Syred, Brantgarth, Guldrey Lane, Sedbergh LA10 5DS Tel: 015396 20239 — MB BS 1969 Lond.; MRCS Eng. LRCP Lond. 1972; MRCGP 1978; DA Eng. 1972; DObst RCOG 1972. (St. Bart.)

SYSON, Anneregine Department of Genitourinary Medicine, West Wing, Cardiff Royal Infirmary, Cardiff — MB ChB 1968 Leeds; Dip GUM Soc. Apoth. 1989. Assoc. Specialist (Genitourin. Med.) Cardiff Roy. Infirm.

SYYED, Raheel 319 Albert Drive, Pollockshields, Glasgow G41 5EA Tel: 0141 423 4977 — MB ChB 1993 Glas.; MB ChB Glasgow 1993; MRCP Glasgow 1998. (Glas.) SHO (Med.) Hairmyers Hosp. E. Kilbride. Socs: MRCP (Glas.). Prev: SHO (Med.) StoneHo. Hosp.; SHO (A & E) Stobhill Gen. Hosp. Glas.; SHO (Geriat. Med.) Vict. Geriat. Unit.

SZABADI, Professor Elemer Division of Psychiatry, B Floor, Medical School University Hospital, Queen's Medical Centre, Nottingham NG7 2UH Tel: 0115 970 9336 Fax: 0115 919 4473 Email: elemer.szabadi@nottingham.ac.uk — MD 1964 Budapest; DSc Manch. 1983; PhD Ed. 1978; FRCPsych 1981, M 1974; Dip.

SZABOLCSI

Neurol. Budapest 1968. (Budapest) Prof. Psychiat. Univ. Nottm. & Hon. Cons. Psychiat. Qu. Med. Centre Nottm. Socs: (Ex-Comm. & Edit. Bd.) Brit. Pharm. Soc.; Brit. Assn. Psychopharmacol. Prev: Reader (Psychiat.) Univ. Manch.; Sen. Lect. (Psychiat.) Univ. Manch. & Lect. (Neurol.) Univ. Budapest; Lect. (Psychiat.) Univ. Edin.

SZABOLCSI, Anna Eva The Surgery, 55 Wimpole Street, London W1M 7DG Tel: 020 7935 9795 Fax: 020 7486 3934; 21 Hermitage Lane, London NW2 2EY — MD 1972 Budapest; MRCS Eng. LRCP Lond. 1982. (Semmelweiss) Licenciate in Acupunc. Socs: Brit. Med. Acupunct. Soc.; Primary Care Rheum. Soc.; BMA. Prev: Trainee GP Hampstead; Regist. (Rheumat.) Roy. Free Hosp. Lond.; Regist. Wexham Pk. Hosp.

SZAFRANSKI, Jan Stanislaw 3 Crescent Road, Rowley Park, Stafford ST17 9AW — BM BS 1985 Nottm.

SZAMOCKI, Mrs Janina Zofia Maria Brookfields, Green Barns Lane, Little Hay, Lichfield WS14 0QN Tel: 01543 480970 — MB ChB 1950 Aberd. (Aberd.) Indep. Homoeop. Pract. Staffs.

SZANTO, Stephen Francis (retired) 39 Kensington Drive, Woodford Green IG8 8LP — PhD Lond. 1969; LAH Dub. 1962; FRCPI 1982, M 1964. Prev: Cons. Phys. in Geriat. Forest & Thames Gps. Hosps. Lond.

SZAREWSKI, Anne Marie Imperial Cancer Research Fund, PO Box 123, Lincoln Inn Fields, London WC2A 3PX Tel: 020 7269 3160 Fax: 020 7269 3429 Email: a.szarewski@icrf.icuef.uk; 5 Priory Terrace, London NW6 4DG Tel: 020 7624 7170 Fax: 020 7372 7510 — MB BS 1982 Lond.; PhD 1997 Lond.; MFFP 1993; Cert. Family Plann. JCC 1984; DRCOG 1984. (Middlx. Hosp. Med. Sch. Lond.) Sen. Clin. Research Fell. Imperial Cancer Research Fund Lond.; Instruc. Doctor (Family Plann.) Margt. Pyke Centre Lond. Prev: Clin. Asst. Lydia Dept. St. Thos. Hosp. Lond.; Clin. Asst. (Colposcopy) Roy. N.. Hosp. Lond.

SZCZESNIAK, Leszek Andrzej Sussex Road Surgery, 125 Sussex Road, Southport PR8 6AF Tel: 01704 536778 Fax: 01704 532838 — MB ChB 1976 Leeds.

SZEKELY, Frances Helen M.D.U., 3 Devonshire Place, London W1G 6HE; 207 Mill Road, Cambridge CB1 3AN Tel: 01223 722257 Fax: 01222 722258 Email: fszekely@dial.pipex.com — MB BS 1980 Lond.; MRCGP 1990. Prev: Trainee GP Pilgrim Hosp. Boston VTS; SHO (A & E) Whittington Hosp. Lond.; Research Asst. (Radiol.) Whittington Hosp. Lond.

SZEKELY, Gabor 2 Prentis Road, Streatham, London SW16 1XU Tel: 020 8769 5002 Fax: 020 8677 1800; 43 The Chase, Norbury, London SW16 3AE Email: gab.szekely@virgin.net — MB BS 1980 Lond.; BSc Lond. 1977; MRCGP 1984; DGM RCP Lond. 1993; DRCOG 1982; DFFP 1998. (St. Geo.) Prev: Clin. Asst. (Med. for the Elderly) Whittington Centre Streatham.

SZEKELY, John Michael George Clare Surgery, Swan Drive, New Road, Chatteris PE16 6EX Tel: 01354 695888 Fax: 01354 695415 — MB BS 1980 Lond.; BSc Lond. 1977; MRCGP 1984. Prev: Trainee GP Boston VTS.

***SZEKI, Iren Katalin** 34 Brackenfield Road, Gosforth, Newcastle upon Tyne NE3 4DY — MB BS 1996 Lond.

SZEMIS, Andrzej Hubert The Willows, Cordelia Close, Leicester LE5 0LE Tel: 0116 246 0988 Fax: 0116 246 1368 — Lekarz 1961 Warsaw. Assoc. Specialist in Psychiat. Socs: Affil. Roy. Coll. of Psychiat.s. Prev: Staff Grade (Psychiat.) Leicester.

SZILAGYI, Roman Zsolt c/o Easty, 59 Arcadia Square, Old Castle St., London E1 7TD — State Exam Med 1989 Cologne.

***SZLOSAREK, Piotr Wojciech** 32 Devonshire Road, London N13 4QX — MB BS 1994 Lond.

SZOFINSKA, Barbara Barlow Medical Centre, 8 Barlow Moor Road, Didsbury, Manchester M20 6TR Tel: 0161 445 2101 Fax: 0161 445 9560 — MB ChB 1990 Manch.; MRCGP 1994; DFFP 1993. (Manch.) Prev: Trainee GP Manch. VTS.

SZOLACH, Mrs Maria Regina The Surgery, 127 Trinity Road, Tooting, London SW17 7HJ Tel: 020 8672 3331 — MRCS Eng. LRCP Lond. 1990. GP Lond. Socs: BMA; Polish Med. Assn. Prev: Trainee GP/SHO Centr. Middlx. Hosp. NHS Trust VTS; Ho. Off. (Med.) OldCh. Hosp.; Ho. Off. (Surg. & Orthop.) Mayday Univ. Hosp.

SZOLLAR, Judit Havering Hospitals, Romford RM7 0BE Tel: 01708 345 5331 Ext: 3273; 66 Savernake Road, London NW3 2JR Tel: 020 7284 1336 Fax: 020 7284 1336 — MD 1968 Budapest; PhD Tncsis Budapest 1981; Paediatrics & Neonatology 1979; Human Genetics 1979. (Simmclwcis University Budapest) Cons. Paediat.

with s/i in Paediatric Diabetes and Endocrinol., OldCh. and Harold Wood Hosps. Socs: Roy. Coll. Paediat. and Child Health; Assoc. Mem. of Roy. Coll. of Pathologists Clincal Genetics Soc. Prev: Sen. Lect. (Paediat. & Neonat.) Univ. Semmelweis Budapest, Hungary.

SZULEC, Zdzislaw Jan (retired) 1 The Meadow, Bryants Farm, Lostock, Bolton BL1 5XN Tel: 01204 493053 — MB ChB 1947 Polish Sch. of Med. Corps. Surg. St. John Ambul. Brig. N. W. Area.

SZULECKA, Teresa Krystyna St. James University Hospital, Department of Psychiatry, Beckett St., Leeds LS9 7FT Tel: 0113 243 3144 Fax: 0113 234 6856; 7 Oaklea Hall Close, Adel, Leeds LS16 8HB — Lekarz Krakow 1970; MD Brussels 1986; MRCPsych 1979. Cons. Psych.Harrogate clinic, Mid Yorks. Nuffield Hosp. Socs: Brit. Neuropysch. Assn. Prev: Cons. Psychiat. Bassetlaw Dist. Gen. Hosp. Worksop.; Cons. Psychiat. Doncaster Roy. Infirm.; Cons. Psychiat. St. James' Univ. Hosp. Leeds.

SZWEDZIUK, Peter 4 Stanley Road, Chatham ME5 8LN — MB BS 1985 Lond.

SZYPRYT, Mr Edward Paul 34 Regent Street, Nottingham NG1 5BT Tel: 0115 956 1300 Fax: 0115 956 1314 — MB BS 1978 Lond.; FRCS Eng. 1983. (Royal London Hosp.) Cons. (Orthop. & Trauma Surg.) Univ. Hosp. NHS Trust Nottm. Socs: Fell. BOA; Brit. Orthop. Research Soc.; Fell. Roy. Coll. Surg. Eng. Prev: Sen. Regist. (Trauma & Orthop.) Univ. Hosp. & Harlow Wood Orthop.Hosp. Nottm.; NCB Spinal Research Fell. Harlow Wood Orthop. Hosp. Nottm.; Regist. (Trauma & Orthop.) P. of Wales & St. Geo. Hosp. Sydney, Australia.

SZYSZKO, Janina Maria Southfield Medical Centre, 89 Southfield Road, Chiswick, London W4 1BB — MB BS 1986 Lond.; BSc (Basic Med. Scis. with Anat.) Lond. 1983; MRCGP 1990; DRCOG 1988. Prev: Trainee GP Chiswick; SHO (A & E & Psychiat.) Hillingdon Hosp.; SHO (Geriat. & O & G) Qu. Mary's Univ. Hosp. Roehampton.

TA, Thuan Chi 120 Rosebery Street, Swindon SN1 2ES — MB BS 1992 Lond.

TAAFFE, Patrick Islwyn, Glandwr, Barmouth LL42 1TG — LAH Dub. 1955.

TAAFFE, William Gerald 93 Queens Drive, Mossley Hill, Liverpool L18 1JL — MB ChB 1941 Liverp.; DPH 1947.

TAAMS, Mr Karel Otto Derriford Hospital, Plastic Surgery & Burns Unit, Plymouth PL6 8DH Tel: 01752 777111 — Artsexamen 1988 Groningen; MMed (Plastic & Reconstruc. Surg.) Witwatersrand 1994; FCS(SA) 1994. (Artsexamen Groningen) Cons. Plastic Surg. Derriford Hosp. Plymouth. Socs: BAPS; Craniofacial Soc. Prev: Cons. Plastic Surg. Acad. Hosp. Rotterdam, Netherlands.

TABANDEH, Mr Homayoun 30 Palace Court, London W2 4HZ — MB BS 1985 Lond.; MS Lond. 1996; FRCS Glas. 1990; MRCP (UK) 1990; FCOphth 1990; DO RCS Glas. 1989. Sen. Regist. Moorfields Eye Hosp. Lond.

TABAQCHALI, Professor Soad (retired) Department of Medical Microbiology, St. Bartholomew's & Royal London School Med. & Dent., St Bartholomew's Hospital, Smithfield, London EC1A 7BE Tel: 020 7601 8401 Fax: 020 7601 8409 — MB ChB St. And. 1958; FRCP Lond. 1993; MRCP (UK) 1990; FRCPath 1986, M 1974. Prof. & Head Dept. Med. Microbiol. St. Bart. & Roy. Lond. Sch. Med. & Dent.; Hon. Cons. Roy. Hosps. NHS Trust; Clin. Dir. (Med. Microbiol.) & Chairm. Infec. Control Comm. Roy. Hosps. NHS Trust Lond. Prev: Reader & Sen. Lect. (Med. Microbiol.) St. Bart. Hosp. Med. Coll. Lond.

TABB, Peter Asquith Knights, Billingshurst — MB ChB St. And. 1969; DCH RCPS Glas. 1972. Prev: GP Billingshurst; Regist. (Paediat.) Dundee Health Dist.; SHO (Med.) Roy. Salop Infirm. Shrewsbury.

TABBARA, Mr Zeid Bahjat Westminster Children's Hospital, Vincent Square, London SW1; 94 Grosvenor Road, London SW1V 3LF — MB ChB 1969 Liverp.; FRCS Eng. 1977; FRCS Ed. 1976. Acting Cons. Surg. W.m. Childr. Hosp. Lond.; Clin. Asst. (Paediat. Surg.) St. Thos. Hosp. Lond.; Surg. to Harley Dean & Assocs. Prev: Resid. Surg. Off. W.m. Childr. Hosp. Lond.; Regist. (Surg.) Weymouth & Dist. Gen. Hosp.; Rotat. SHO (Surg. Specialties) Norwich.

TABBERER, Helen Judith The Surgery, Alexandra Road, Lowestoft NR32 1PL Tel: 01502 574524 Fax: 01502 531526; 3 Coastguard Cottages, Battery Green, Lowestoft NR32 1DY — MB BS 1984 Lond.; MRCGP 1988; DCH RCP Lond. 1989; DRCOG 1987; Cert. Family Plann. JCC 1987. (Char. Cross) Prev: Clin. Med. Off. (Child

Health) Greyfriars Clinic Gt. Yarmouth; Trainee GP Jas. Paget Hosp. Gorleston, Gt. Yarmouth VTS; Ho. Phys. Mt. Vernon Hosp. N.wood.

TABERNER, Catherine Ruth 2 La Bertozerie, George Road, St Peter Port, Guernsey GY1 1BD — MB ChB 1987 Sheff.

TABERNER, David Allan 20 Cogshall Lane, Comberbach, Northwich CW9 6BS — BM BCh 1970 Oxf.; MRCP (U.K.) 1973; MRCPath 1978. Cons. (Haemat.) Withington Hosp. Manch. Socs: Brit. Soc. Haemat.; Fell. Manch. Med. Soc. Prev: Sen. Regist. United Manch. Hosps.; SHO (Cardiol.) Brompton Hosp. Lond.; SHO IC Unit St. Thos. Hosp. Lond.

TABERT, James Edward Keir, MBE Castle Street Surgery, 39 Castle Street, Luton LU1 3AG Tel: 01582 729242 Fax: 01582 725192 — MB BS 1960 Lond.; DObst RCOG 1962. (St. Bart.) Prev: Ho. Surg. Swindon Matern. Hosp.; Ho. Surg. & Ho. Phys. Sutton & Cheam Hosp.

TABET, Naji Toufic Institute of Psychiatry, Kings College, London SE5 8AZ — LMSSA 1994 Lond.; LRCS Eng. LRCP Lond. 1994.

TABNER, James Anthony Grove Surgery, Charlotte Street, Wakefield WF1 1UJ Tel: 01924 372596 Fax: 01924 200913; 125 Thornes Road, Wakefield WF2 8QD Tel: 01924 374000 — MB ChB 1983 Leic.; MRCGP 1988. Prev: Trainee GP Wakefield VTS; SHO (Community Med.) Stockport HA VTS.

TABNER, Shirley Anne 66 Wrenthorpe Lane, Wrenthorpe, Wakefield WF2 0PT Tel: 01924 290908 — MB BS 1981 Lond.; DRCOG 1983. Clin. Med. Off. (p/t) Family Plann. Wakefield & Ponefract Community Trust. Prev: Mem. Wakefield VTS; Ho. Surg. & Ho. Phys. Pinderfields Gen. Hosp. Wakefield.

TABONE-VASSALLO, Mr Mario 10 Harley Street, London W1N 1AA Tel: 020 7467 8300 Fax: 020 7467 8312; Dwejra, 80 Vicarage Terrace, Romford Road, London E15 4EE — MD Malta 1971; FRCS Eng. 1977; FRCS Ed. 1976; FFAEM 1994. Socs: Roy. Soc. Med. (Founder & Ex-Pres. & Sec. Sect. Accid. & Emerg. Med.); Founding Fell. Europ. AERO Med. Inst. (Ex-Vice-Pres.); Liveryman Worshipful Soc. Apoth. Prev: Clin. Dir. (A & E) Med. Servs. Malta; Cons. Surg. i/c A & E Dept. Greenwich Dist. Hosp.; Cons. Surg. i/c A & E Dept. N. Middlx. Hosp.

TABONY, Winifred Mary Mains Medical Centre, Park Mains Post Office, 300 Mains Drive, Erskine PA8 7JQ Tel: 0141 812 3230 Fax: 0141 812 5226; 23 Pendicle Road, Bearsden, Glasgow G61 1PT — MB ChB 1974 Glas.; MRCGP 1978.

TABOR, Arthur Shand 5 Woodland Drive, Hove BN3 6DH Tel: 01273 557779 — MB BS Lond. 1958. (St. Bart) Prev: Ho. Phys. & Ho. Surg. St. Bart. Hosp.; Ho. Surg. Mayday Hosp.; Squadron Ldr. RAF Med. Br.

TABOR, John Edward Kildonan House, Ramsbottom Road, Horwich, Bolton BL6 5NW Tel: 01204 468161 Fax: 01204 698186; 2 Manor Road, Horwich, Bolton BL6 6AR Tel: 01204 694503 — MB BS 1982 Lond.; MA Oxf. 1982; MRCGP 1987; DRCOG 1987.

TABRIZI, Sarah Joanna 11 Rupert House, 54 Nevern Square, London SW5 9PL — MB ChB 1992 Ed.; PhD 2000 UCL; MRCP (UK) 1995; BSc (Hons) 1986. Specialist Regist. Neurol., Nat. Hosp. For Neurol. and Neurosurg., Lond. Socs: ABN. Prev: Specialist Regist. (Neurol.) Roy Free Hosp. Lond.; Regist. (Med.) St. Thos. Hosp. Lond.

TABRY, Helena 56 Shirley Park Road, Southampton SO16 4FU — MB ChB 1994 Liverp.; FRCS (Eng) 1999.

TACCHI, Derek, TD (retired) 2 Oakfield Road, Gosforth, Newcastle upon Tyne NE3 4HS Tel: 0191 285 2945 Fax: 0191 285 2945 — MB BS Durh. 1948; MD Durh. 1961; FRCOG 1965, M 1954. Prev: Cons. O & G Roy. Vict. Infirm. & P.ss Mary Matern. Hosp. Newc.

TACCHI, Mary Jane Crisis Assessment and Treatment Team, St Nicholas Hospital, Gosforth, Newcastle upon Tyne NE3 3XT; 60 Elmfield Road, Gosforth, Newcastle upon Tyne NE3 4BD — MB BS 1986 Lond.; MRCPsych 1991. (Westminster) Cons. (Adult Psychiat.); Clin. Lect. (Psychiat.) Newc. Univ. Socs: BMA; RCPsych.

TACCONELLI, Franco Flat 23, Fletcher Buildings, Martlett Court, London WC2B 5EU — MB BS 1996 Lond.; BSc Lond. 1986; AKC Lond. 1986; PhD Lond. 1992. Trainee GP.

TACHAKRA, Mr Spitman Savak Accident & Emergency Department, Central Middlesex Hospital, Acton Lane, London NW10 7NS Tel: 020 8453 2250 Fax: 020 8453 2764; 83 Barn Hill, Wembley HA9 9LN Tel: 020 8904 0642 Email: sapal.tachakra@tinyworld.co.uk — MB BS 1964 Bombay; MS Bombay 1967; FRCS Ed. 1972; FFAEM 1994. Cons. A & E Med.

Nat. W. Lond. Hosp.s NHSTrust; Hon. Clin. Sen. Lect. (A & E Med.) Imperial Coll. Lond.; Hon Cons. A&E Med. St. Mary's Hosp. Lond. Socs: Roy. Soc. Med. (Sec. Telemed Forum & Mem. Counc. Accid. & Emerg. Med.). Prev: Undergrad. Sub-Dean St Mary's Hosp. Med. Sch. Lond.; Mem. Exec. Comm. Brit. Assn. of A & E Med.

TACKLEY, Roger Malcolm Anaesthetic Department, Torbay General Hospital, Torquay TQ2 7AA Tel: 01803 614567 Fax: 01803 654312; Redmayes, 42 Parkhurst Road, Torquay TQ1 4EP Tel: 01803 316 091 Email: r.tackley@scata.org.uk — MRCS Eng. LRCP Lond. 1977; MB BS 1977 Lond.; BSc 1973 (Pharmacol. Hons.) Lond; FRCA 1982 Eng. (St. Bart.) p/t Cons. Anaesth. Torbay HA. Socs: Chairm. Of Soc. For Computing and Technol. in Anaesth. (SCATA).

TADPATRIKAR, Miland Hari 19 Brockenhurst Road, Mansfield NG19 6TX — BM BS 1996 Nottm.

TADROS, Amir 8 Whitegale Close, Hitchin SG4 9LP — MB ChB 1996 Leic.

TADROS, Mr Athanassius Naguib Royal Eye Infirmary, Dorset County Hospital, Williams Avenue, Dorchester DT1 2JY Tel: 01305 255387 Fax: 01305 255374; Grace Land, Red Hill Lane, Worcester WR5 2JL Tel: 01905 350344 — MB BCh Ain Shams 1977; FRCOphth 1990; FRCS (Ophth.) Glas. 1990; DO RCPSI 1987. Cons. Ophth. Surg. Roy. Eye. Infirm. Dorset Co. Hosp.; Cons. Ophth. Surg., Yeovil Dist. Hosp., Yeovil; At Winterbourne Hosp., Herringston Rd., Dorchester, DT1 2DR. Socs: Mem. of Amer. Acad. of Ophth.; Mem. of Europ. Soc. of Cataract and Refractive Surg.; Mem. of Med. Protec. Soc.

TADROS, Fayez Farid 6 Burnaston Crescent, Shirley, Solihull B90 4LT — MB ChB 1970 Alexandria.

TADROS, Osama Ibrahim 8 Whitegale Close, Hitchin SG4 9LP Tel: 01462 36686 — MB BCh 1963 Cairo; DS Cairo 1966, MB BCh 1963, DGO 1971.

TADROS, Samuel Shafik Mikhail Flat 6, Wylye House, Odstock Hospital, Salisbury SP2 8BJ Tel: 01722 336262 — MB ChB 1971 Alexandria; DLO RCS Eng. 1979.

TADROS, Victor Rafla 48 The Avenue, Branksome Park, Poole BH13 6LL Tel: 01202 761569 — MRCS Eng. LRCP Lond. 1942. (St. Bart.) Prev: Resid. Med. Off. High Wycombe War Memor. Hosp.; Ho. Surg. (Gyn.) Roy. Vict. & W. Hants. Hosp. Bournemouth.

TADROS, Wadie Samaan c/o Lloyds Bank, 407-409 Coventry Road, Birmingham B10 0SP — LMSSA 1973 Lond.; MB BS Khartoum 1969; DCH RCPSI 1973; ECFMG Cert 1973. (Khartoum) Supervising Phys. & Sen. Phys. (Intern. Med.) Tapline-Badanah Hosp. Saudi Arabia. Prev: Regist. (Gen. Med.) Bolton Roy. Infirm.

TADROS-ATTALLA, Mr Samir Gorgy (retired) Pengarth, 55 Falmouth Road, Truro TR1 2HL Tel: 01872 2663 — MB ChB 1958 Alexandria, Egypt; FRCS Ed. 1966; LMSSA Lond. 1967. Indep. Med. Pract. Truro. Prev: Assoc. Specialist (A & E) Roy. Cornw. Hosp. Truro.

TADROS-CAUDLE, Maria Ernest Villa Sheradrosa, Nelson Avenue, Minster on Sea, Sheerness ME12 3SF — LRCP LRCS Ed. LRCPS Glas. 1976.

TADROSS, Mr Alphonse Atallah James Paget Hospital, Lowestoft Road, Gorlesdon, Great Yarmouth NR31 6LA Tel: 01493 600611; Lotus Villa, New Road, Fritton, Great Yarmouth NR31 9HP — MB ChB 1973 Assiut; FRCS Ed. 1988. Assoc. Specialist (Surg.) Jas. Paget Hosp. Gt. Yarmouth. Prev: Regist. (Surg.) Cheltenham Gen. Hosp.

TADROSS, Mr Tamer Samir Fawzy Sunderland General Hospital, Sunderland; 19 Delaval Terrace, Gosforth, Newcastle upon Tyne NE3 4RT Tel: 0191 213 1954 — MB BCh 1982 Ain Shams; MSc (Orth.) Lond. 1995; FRCS Ed. 1991. Knee Fell. (Orthop.) OldCh. Hosp. Romford; Sen. Regist. (Orthop.) N.. & Yorks. Train. Progr. Socs: BMA; BOA.

TADROUS, Paul Jospeh Department of Histopathology, Northwick Park & St Mark's NHS Trust, Northwick Park Hospital, Watford Road, Harrow HA1 3UJ — MB BS 1992 Lond.; MSc. Image Anal. in Histol. (Distinct.) Lond. 1994. (Lond. Hosp. Med. Coll.) Specialist Regist. in Histopath. Socs: Path. Soc.; Train. Mem. Assn. Clin. Path.

TAEGTMEYER, Anne Barbara Keeper's Cottage, Headington Hill, Oxford OX3 0BT — BM BCh 1997 Oxf.

TAEGTMEYER, Miriam Keeper's Cottage, Headington Hill, Headington, Oxford OX3 0BT — BM BCh 1994 Oxf.

TAFFINDER

TAFFINDER, Adrian Paul Health Centre, Poplar Avenue, Gresford, Wrexham LL12 8EP Tel: 01978 852208; 69 Wynnstay Lane, Marford, Wrexham LL12 8LH Tel: 0197 885 2492 — MB BCh 1976 Wales; MRCGP 1980; DRCOG 1978. Course Organiser S. Clwyd VTS. Prev: Trainee GP Wrexham VTS; Ho. Phys. Singleton Hosp. Swansea; Ho. Surg. Roy. Gwent Hosp. Newport.

TAFFINDER, Gaenor Ann Canolfan Iechyd Llay Health Centre, School Rd, Wrecsam LL1 6TR Tel: 01978 852206; 69 Wynnstay Lane, Marford, Wrecsam LL12 8LH Tel: 0197 885 2492 — MB BCh 1976 Wales; MRCGP 1980; DRCOG 1979. Prev: SHO (Cas.) War Memor. Hosp. Wrexham; Trainee Gen. Pract. Wrexham Vocational Train. Scheme; Ho. Surg. & Ho. Phys. Roy. Gwent Hosp. Newport.

TAFFINDER, Lawrence David (Surgery), Main Road, Stickney, Boston PE22 8AA Tel: 01205 480237; Pennycress, Chapel Lane, Sibsey, Boston PE22 0SN Tel: 01205 750496 — MB BCh 1971 Wales; MRCGP 1977; Dip. Pract. Dermat. Wales 1992; Cert. Family Plann. JCC 1977; DObst RCOG 1973. Trainer GP Boston. Prev: Trainee GP Wolverhampton VTS; Ho. Phys. & Ho. Surg. Nottm. Gen. Hosp.

TAFFINDER, Mr Nicholas James Academic Surgical Unit, St Mary's Hospital, Praed St., London W2 1NY; 104 Coldershaw Road, London W13 9DT Tel: 020 8579 0317 Email: nicktaff@msn.com — MB BChir 1990 Camb.; FRCS Eng. 1993. Regist. (Gen. Surg.) St Mary's Hosp. Lond. Prev: SHO Jean Verdier Hosp., Paris, St Mary's Hosp. Lond. & Qu. Alexandra Hosp. Portsmouth.

TAGBOTO, Senyo Komla 12 Smore Slade Hills, Oadby, Leicester LE2 4UX — MB ChB 1987 Ghana; MRCP (UK) 1994. Regist. (Nephrol.) Leicester Gen. Hosp. Prev: Regist. (Nephrol. & Gen. Med.) P'boro. Dist. Hosp.

TAGELDIN, Mr Mohamed Elhosseini 23 Byron Road, London NW7 4AH — MB ChB 1960 Alexandria; FRCS Eng. 1978. (Alexandria) Prev: Regist. (Gen. Surg.) Bishop Auckland Gen. Hosp.; SHO (Gen. Surg.) & Med. Assoc. (Orthop.) W. Suff. Hosp.

TAGG, Catherine Elizabeth Brill View, Woodperry Road, Beckley, Oxford OX3 9UZ — MB BS 1996 Lond.

TAGG, Gillian Valerie St. James University Hospital, Beckett St., Leeds LS9 7TF Tel: 0113 206 4068 Fax: 0113 206 4085 — MB ChB 1968 Leeds; FRCPsych 1995, M 1978; DPM Leeds 1977; DObst RCOG 1970. Cons. Child & Adolesc. Psychiat. Leeds Community Ment. Health Trust; Sen. Lect. (Psychiat.) Univ. Leeds. Prev: Sen. Regist. (Child & Adolesc. Psychiat.) Yorks. RHA; Regist. (Psychiat.) St. Jas. Univ. Hosp. Leeds; SHO (Psychiat.) Glenside Hosp. Bristol.

TAGGART, Allister James Department of Rheumatology, Musgrave Park Hospital, Stockman's Lane, Belfast BT9 7JB Tel: 01232 669501 Fax: 01232 683191; 65 Richmond Court, Lisburn BT27 4QX Tel: 01846 664832 — MB BCh BAO 1975 Belf.; MD Belf. 1982; FRCP Lond. 1994; FRCP Ed. 1989. Dep. Med. Dir. GreenPk. Healthcare Trust. Socs: Fell. Ulster Med. Soc.; Brit. Soc. Rheum.; (Hon. Sec.) Irish Soc. Rheum. Prev: Cons. Phys. & Sen. Lect. (Therap. & Pharmacol.) Qu. Univ. Belf.

TAGGART, Catherine Mary 22 Newtonbreda Road, Belfast BT8 6AS — MB BCh BAO 1995 Belf.

TAGGART, Mrs Christina Rose Flat 18D, Burnwood Court, Buchanan Drive, Newton Mearns, Glasgow G77 6QN — MB ChB 1984 Aberd.

TAGGART, Christopher Michael Woodside Medical Centre, Jardine Crescent, Coventry CV4 9PL Tel: 024 7669 4001 Fax: 024 7669 5639; The Mill Barn, Ivy Farm Lane, Coventry CV4 7BW Tel: 024 76 416321 — MB ChB 1981 Manch.; MRCGP 1985; DRCOG 1984. (Manchester) Princip. GP; Postgrad. Tutor (Gen. Pract.) Coventry & Warks. Hosp.; GP Bd. Mem. W. Coventry PCG; Mem. Coventry Local Med. Comm. Socs: BMA; Christ. Med. Fell.sh. Prev: Trainee GP Lancaster VTS; Ho. Off. (Med.) Roy. Lancaster Infirm.; Ho. Off. (Surg.) Macclesfield Infirm.

TAGGART, Curphey Clague The Surgery, Mill Road, Ballasalla IM9 2EA Tel: 01624 823243 Fax: 01624 822947; Hunters Lodge, Bridge Road, Ballasalla IM9 3DQ Tel: 01624 822815 — MB ChB 1976 Liverp.; MRCGP 1984; DRCOG 1979.

TAGGART, Mr David Paul Peter Oxford Heart Centre, John Radcliffe Hospital, Oxford OX3 Tel: 01865 221121 Fax: 01856 220244 Email: david.taggart@orh.nhs.uk; Solway, Badger Lane, Oxford OX1 5BL — MB ChB 1981 Glas.; PhD 1999 Glas; MD (Hons.) Glas. 1989; FRCS Glas. 1985. Cons. Cardiothoracic Surg. John Radcliffe Hosp. Oxf. Prev: Sen. Regist. Roy. Brompton Nat. Heart & Lung Hosp.

TAGGART, George Edward Crouch Farmhouse, Long Mill Lane, Crouch, Borough Green, Sevenoaks TN15 8QD — MB BS 1991 Lond.

TAGGART, Hugh Francis 37 Newlands Road, Glasgow G43 2JG — MB ChB 1951 Glas.

TAGGART, Hugh McAllister Department of Health Care for The Elderly, Belfast City Hospital, Lisburn Road, Belfast BT9 7AB Tel: 01232 329241 Fax: 01232 263946 Email: hugh.taggart@bchn-i.nhs.uk; 1 Crawfordsburn Wood, Crawfordsburn, Bangor BT19 1XB Email: hugh.taggart@nirland.com — MB BCh BAO 1973 Belf.; MD Belf. 1979; FRCP Glas. 1997, Lond. 1991; MRCP (UK) 1977. (Belf.) Cons. Phys. (Health Care for Elderly) Belf. City Hosp. Socs: Fell. Ulster Med. Soc.; Brit. Geriat. Soc.; Amer. Soc. Bone & Mineral Research. Prev: Sen. Lect. (Geriat. Med.) Qu's. Univ. Belf.; Resid. Fell. (Geriat. Med.) Univ. Washington, Seattle, USA.

TAGGART, Ian 252 Nithsdale Road, Dumbreck, Glasgow G41 5AH — MB ChB 1983 Aberd. Cons. Plastic Surg. Cannisburn Hosp.

TAGGART, Lucy Petronilla 164 Turney Road, London SE21 7JJ — MB BS 1985 Lond.; MRCGP 1991.

TAGGART, Michael Borough Green Medical Practice, 34 Maidstone Road, Borough Green, Sevenoaks TN15 8BD; Crouch Farm House, Long Mill Lane, Borough Green, Sevenoaks TN15 8QD Tel: 01732 3161 — MB BChir 1958 Camb.; BA Camb. 1958; DObst RCOG 1959. (Camb. & St. Thos.)

TAGGART, Patrick Campbell Millar 378 Higham Lane, Nuneaton CV11 6AP — MB BS 1971 Lond.; BSc (Hons. Physiol.) Lond. 1968; FFA RCS Eng. 1978; DCH Eng. 1974; DObst RCOG 1974. (King's Coll. Hosp.) Cons. Anaesth. Geo. Eliot Hosp. NHS Trust Nuneaton.

TAGGART, Peter Irwin 12 Blandford Road, Bedford Park, Chiswick, London W4 1DU Tel: 020 8994 8547 — MD Lond. 1976, MB BS 1957; FRCP Lond. 1985, M 1964; MRCP Ed. 1964. (St. Bart.) Reader (Cardiol.) Dept. Med. Middlx. Hosp. Lond. Socs: Brit. Cardiac Soc. & Physiolog. Soc. Prev: Med. Regist. King's Coll. Hosp. Lond.; Leverhulme Research Schol. & Brit. Heart Foundat. Research Fell. & Hon. Sen. Regist. Dept. Cardiol. Middlx. Hosp. Lond.

TAGGART, Simon Department of Clinical Neurophysiology, Regional Neurosciences Centre, Newcastle General Hospital, Newcastle upon Tyne NE3 1DB Tel: 0191 273 8811; 4 Badsworth Close, Guisborough TS14 785 — MB BS Newc. 1993; BMedSc Newc. 1992. Specialist Regist. Clin. Neurophysiol. Regional Neurosci. Centre Newc. Gen. Hosp.

TAGGART, Simon Charles Ormandy Robin Hood Cottage, Great Staughton, Huntingdon PE19 4BB — MB ChB 1989 Manch.; MRCP (UK) 1992; MD Manchester 1996. (St Andrews and Manchester) Sen. Regist. (Thoracic & Gen. Med.). Socs: Affil. Mem. Amer. Thoracic Soc.; BMA; Exec. Comm. Brit. Lung Foundat.

TAGGART, Thomas Frederick Ormandy 25 Oxford Street, Liverpool L15 8HX — MB ChB 1991 Liverp.

TAGGART-JEEVA, Sakib 47 Colinmander Gardens, Ormskirk L39 4TE — MB ChB 1997 Liverp.

TAGHIPOUR, Jahangir Royal Berkshire & Battle NHS Trust, London Road, Reading RG1 5AN Tel: 0118 987 7022; 132 Chaplin Road, Wembley HA0 4UT Tel: 020 8900 2977 — MD 1979; MRCS Eng. LRCP Lond. 1990; DRCOG 1996; DFFP 1995; Dip. Thorac. Med. Lond. 1987. Staff Grade Reading. Prev: Regist. (A & E) Good Hope Hosp. N. Birm. HA.

TAGHIZADEH, Abdosamad Department of Pathology, Oldchurch Hospital, Romford RM7 0BE — MD 1958 Tehran; PhD Lond. 1965. Cons. Histopath. OldCh. Hosp. Romford.

TAGHIZADEH, Mr Arash Kusha 27A Cyril Mansions, Prince of Wales Drive, London SW11 4HP — MB BS 1992 Lond.; BSc Lond. 1989; FRCS (Eng) 1997.

TAGORE, N K Westminster Medical Centre, Aldams Grove, Liverpool L4 3TT Tel: 0151 922 3510 Fax: 0151 902 6071.

TAHA, Ali Said Assa'd Division of Medicine & Gastroenterology, Eastbourne General Hosptial, Eastbourne BN21 2UD Tel: 01323 417400; 22 Ashburnham Road, Eastbourne BN21 2HX — MRCS Eng. LRCP Lond. 1982; PhD Glas. 1993, MD 1990; MRCP (UK) 1987; MRCPI 1986. (Bristol) Cons. Gastroenterol. E.bourne Gen. Hosp. Socs: Internat. Mem. Amer. Gastroenterol. Assn.; Brit. Soc.

Gastroenterol. Prev: Sen. Regist. (Gastroenterol. & Gen. Med.) S.. Gen. Hosp. Glas.; Regist. (Gastroenterol.) Glas. Roy. Infirm.; Regist. (Med.) Falkirk & Dist. Roy. Infirm.

TAHA, Hassan Mohamed Westbrook Centre, Margate CT9 5DD Tel: 01843 255466 Fax: 01843 232181; 72 Rochester Ave, Canterbury CT1 3YE — MB BS 1976 Khartoum, Sudan; DPM RCPSI 1997; DCP 1996. (Fac. Med. Univ. Khartoum) Staff Grade.(Adult Psychiat.) E. Kent Comm Trust. Socs: BMA; MDU; Sudan Med. Assn. Prev: Staff Grade Doctor Old Age Psychiat. Rotherham Dist. Gen. Hosp. Rotherham.

***TAHA, Riem** 44 Chepstow Road, London W2 5BE — MB ChB 1998 Leic.; MB ChB Leic 1998.

TAHALANI, R P Whiston Road Surgery, 219 Kingsland Rd, London E2 8AN Tel: 020 7739 8625 — MB BS 1973 Patna Med. Coll. India.

TAHBAZ, Arash Flat 3, 25 De Vere Gardens, London W8 5AN — MB ChB 1992 Bristol.

TAHERI, Sepideh Great Ormond Street Hospital for Children, London WC1N 3JH Tel: 020 7405 9200; 104 Bankton Park E., Livingston EH54 9BN Tel: 01506 433277 Fax: 01506 433277 Email: staheri@cherub.demon.co.uk — MB ChB 1989 Ed.; MRCP (UK) 1994. Regist. (Paediat. Nephrol.) Gt. Ormond St. Hosp. Lond. Socs: Roy. Coll. Paediat. & Child Health; Health Promotion. Prev: Regist. (Paediat.) Basildon Hosp.; Regist. (Paediat. Nephrol.) Guy's Hosp. Lond.; SHO (Paediat.) Guy's Hosp. Lond.

TAHERI, Shahrad Department of Endocrinology, Imperial College School of Medicine, The Hammersmith Hospital, Du Cane Road, London W12 0HS Tel: 020 8743 2030; 41 Windermere Avenue, London SW19 3EP Tel: 020 8542 2272 — MB BS 1994 Lond.; MB BS (Hons.) Lond. 1994; MSc (Human Biol.) Oxf. 1989; BSc (Hons.) Lond. 1987; MRCP (Lond.) 1997. (Barts, Lond.) Wellcome Research Fell. Hammersmith Hosp. Lond. Socs: BMA. Prev: Specialist Regist. (Endocrinol.) Hammersmith Hosp. Lond.; Regist. (Gen. Med. & Cardiol.) Ashford Hosp. Middlx.; Research Regist. Hammersmith Hosp. Lond.

TAHERZADEH, Omeed 66F Blomfield Road, Little Venice, London W9 2PA Tel: 020 7266 4315 — MB BS 1993 Lond.; BSc Lond. 1989. (Univ. Coll. Hosp.) SHO (Plastics) Morriston Hosp. Swansea. Prev: SHO (Gen. Surg.) Qu. Eliz. Qu. Mother's Hosp. Margate; SHO (Urol.) Kent & Canterbury Hosp.; SHO (Orthop.) St. Peter's Hosp. Chertsey.

TAHGHIGHI, Jason Payman 1 Lyne Walk, Hackleton, Northampton NN7 2BW — MB ChB 1991 Manch.; DFFP 1995; DRCOG 1995. SHO (A & E Med.) Trafford Gen. Hosp. Manch. Prev: SHO (O & G) Trafford Gen. Hosp.; SHO Intens. Care Unit Roy. Preston Hosp.; SHO (Neurol.) Roy. Preston Hosp.

TAHIR, Hasan Iman Syed 53 Wembley Park Drive, Wembley HA9 8HE — MB BS 1996 Lond.

TAHIR, Mohammad Zakariya 58 Vicarage Road, West Bromwich B71 1AQ — MB BS 1964 Punjab; MB BS Punjab (Pakistan) 1964; DLO Eng. 1976; DA Eng. 1968. (King Edwd. Med. Coll. Lahore)

TAHIR, Muhammad Cameron-Mowat and Partners, Manford Way Health Centre, 40 Foremark Close, Hainault, Ilford IG6 3HS Tel: 020 8500 9938 Fax: 020 8559 9319; 3 Nelmes Crescent, Emerson Park, Hornchurch RM11 2PX — MB BS 1988 Newc.; MRCGP 1992.

TAHIR, Saad Sabeh Radiotherapy Department, St. Lukes Hospital, Warren Road, Guildford GU1 3NT; 7 Gill Avenue, Guildford GU2 7WW Tel: 01483 571122 — MB ChB 1974 Baghdad; FRCR 1986. Sen. Regist. (Clin. Oncol.) St Luke's Hosp. Guildford.

TAHIR, Shahed Mehmood 24 Queens Road, Wheatley, Doncaster DN1 2NQ — MB ChB 1995 Leeds.

TAHIR, Tayyeb Ahmed 36 Cavendish Gardens, Withington Hospital, West Didsbury, Manchester M20 1LA — MB BS 1991 Punjab.

TAHMASSEBI, Ali 48 West Street, Yarm TS15 9BU — MB BS 1993 Newc.

TAHMASSEBI, Maryam Jacklin 13 Lowick Court, Newcastle upon Tyne NE3 1YQ — MB BS 1987 Newc. SHO (Paediat.) Luton & Dunstable Hosp. Prev: Cas. Off. (A & E) Qu. Eliz. Hosp. Gateshead.

TAHZIB, Farhang 4 The Spinney, Haywards Heath RH16 1PL — MB ChB 1976 Aberd.

TAI, Chen-Chin Christ's College, Cambridge CB2 3BU — BChir 1995 Camb.

TAI, Grace Kee Ling 1 Stroud Park Road, Plymouth PL2 3NL — MB BCh BAO 1987 NUI; LRCPSI 1987.

TAI, Nigel Richard Mason University Department of Surgery, Royal Free Hospital, Pond Street, Hampstead, London NW3 2QG Tel: 020 7794 0500 Ext: 3938 Fax: 020 7435 5342 — MB BS 1991 Lond.; FRCS (Eng.) 1996. (The Middlesex Hospital Medical School) Research Fell. Dept of Surg. Roy. Free Hosp. Sch. of Med. Prev: SHO (Surg.) Chase Farm Hosp.; SHO (Orthop.) Ealing Hosp.; Med. Off. (Surg.) Frere Hosp. E. Lond., S. Africa.

TAI, Yeoman Michael Arthur Heath Lane Consulting Rooms, 7/9 Heath Lane, Oldswinford, Stourbridge DY8 1RF Tel: 01384 396146; The Chaucer Hospital, Nackington Road, Canterbury CT4 7AR Tel: 01227 455466 — LRCPI & LM, LRSCI & LM 1961; LRCPI & LM, LRCSI & LM 1961; LAH Dub. 1961; FFA RCSI 1967; DObst RCOG 1963; DA Eng. 1963. (RCSI) Cons. Pain Relief & Palliat. Care E. Kent Pain Managem. Serv. Margate. Socs: Assn. Anaesths.; Intractable Pain Soc. Prev: Cons. Anaesth. & Dir. Pain Relief Unit Dudley HA; Sen. Regist. (Anaesth.) United Birm. Hosps. & Birm. RHB; Ho. Surg. & Ho. Phys. & Regist. (Anaesth.) Adelaide Hosp. Dub.

***TAIBJEE, Saleem Mustafa** 375 New Bedford Road, Luton LU3 2AB — MB ChB 1998 Birm.

TAIG, Carole Eileen Mary Dunvorist Cottage, Drumstrudy Road, Kingennie, Broughty Ferry, Dundee DD5 3RE — MB ChB 1992 Ed.

TAIG, Christine Stobswell Medical Centre, 163 Albert Street, Dundee DD4 6PX Tel: 01382 461363 Fax: 01382 453423 — MB ChB 1967 St. And. (St. And.)

TAIG, David Retson Coldside Medical Practice, 129 Strathmartine Road, Dundee DD3 8DB Tel: 01382 826724 Fax: 01382 884129 — MB ChB 1967 St. And. (St. And.)

TAILBY, Christine Helen Bridge Cottage, 120 Bridge Lane, Frodsham, Warrington WA6 7HZ Tel: 01928 739562 — MB ChB 1988 Dundee. SHO (Anaesth.) BRd.green Hosp. NHS Trust Liverp. Socs: Christ. Med. Fell.sh. Prev: SHO (Anaesth.) Hull Roy. Infirm.

TAILOR, Anilkumar Jayantilal Norther Lynaecological Oncology Centre, Queen Elizabeth Hospital, Sheriff Hill, Gateshead NE9 6RX Tel: 0191 4036154 Email: anil@tailoruk.freeserve.co.uk; 9 Bishops Drive, Ryton NE40 3NY Tel: 0191 4139938 — MB BS 1991 Lond.; BSc (Hons.) Lond. 1988; MRCOG 1998. (Kings Coll Hosp.) Gynaecologial Oncol. Fell., Qu. Eliz. Hosp. Gateshead. Prev: Specialist Regist. (O & G) S.end Gen. Hosp.; Research Regist. & SHO (O & G) King's Coll. Hosp. Lond.; SHO (O & G) Greenwich Dist. Hosp.

TAILOR, Harshad North Street Health Centre, North Street, Ashby-de-la-Zouch LE65 1HU Tel: 01530 414131 — MB ChB 1989 Dundee; MMedSci Birm. 1994; AFOM RCP Lond. 1997; MRCGP 1995; DRCOG 1993. GP Leicester; Occupat. Phys.

TAILOR, Manubhai Dahyabhai The Surgery, Worcester Road, Great Witley, Worcester WR6 6HR Tel: 01299 896370 Fax: 01299 896873; Shivam, Worcester Road, Great Witley, Worcester WR6 6HR Tel: 01299 896660 — MB ChB 1962 Birm. (Birm.)

TAILOR, Rajesh 95 Hertford Road, E. Finchley, London N2 9BX — MB ChB 1984 Dundee.

TAILOR, Rekha Anil John Tasker House, 56 New St., Great Dunmour, Dunmow CM6 1BH; 24 West Hayes, Hatfield Heath, Bishop's Stortford CM22 7DH — MB ChB 1989 Manch.; MRCGP 1995; DRCOG 1993; DFFP 1992. (Manch.) GP Retainee. Prev: GP Princip.

TAILOR, Vijay Gulab Hillcrest Surgery, 337 Uxbridge Road, Acton, Wembley W3 9RA Tel: 0208 993 0982 Email: vijaytailor@gp-e855028.nhs.uk — MB ChB 1993 Leic.; Bsc (Hons.) MBchB DRCOG. Gen. Pract. Princpal.

TAINE, Diana Landon Greensands Medical Practice, Brook End Surgery, Potton, Sandy SG19 2QS Tel: 01767 260260 Fax: 01767 261777; 18 Gamlingay Road, Waresley, Sandy SG19 3DB — MB BS 1984 Lond.; MRCGP 1988.

TAINSH, John Alexander Department of Radiology, Stracathro Hospital, Brechin DD9 7QA Tel: 0135 664 7291 Ext: 321; 'Tanglewood', 1A Viewfield Road, Arbroath DD11 2BS Tel: 01241 876210 — MB ChB 1977 Aberd.; BMedBiol (Commend.) Aberd. 1974, MB ChB 1977; FRCP 1998; FRCR 1985; DMRD Ed. 1983. (Aberdeen) Cons. (Radiol.) Tayside Health Bd. Prev: Sen. Regist. (Radiol.) Tayside Health Bd.; Regist. (Radiol.) Lothian Health Bd. (Edin.); Regist. (Gen. Med.) Grampian Health Bd. (Aberd.).

TAIT

TAIT, Alan Christopher 9 Ley Hey Road, Marple, Stockport SK6 6PQ — MB ChB 1972 Birm.; MRCPsych 1977. Cons. Psychiat. Tameside AHA, Tameside Gen. Hosp. & Community Ment.; Health Centre Hyde. Socs: Assn. Family Therapists.

TAIT, Allan Christie (retired) 56A Craigmillar Park, Edinburgh EH16 5PT — MB ChB 1941 Glas.; DPH 1947; FRCP Ed. 1969, M 1965; FRCPsych 1971; DPM Lond. 1948. Prev: Phys. Supt. & Cons. Psychiat. Crichton Roy., Dumfries.

TAIT, Charles Robert Sabine The Loddon Vale Practice, Hurricane Way, Woodley, Reading RG5 4UX Tel: 0118 969 0160 Fax: 0118 969 9103; Woodvale House, Spencers Wood, Reading RG7 1AE Tel: 01734 883296 — MB BS 1968 Lond.; MRCS Eng. LRCP Lond. 1968; DCH Eng. 1970; DObst RCOG 1970. (St. Bart.) Clin. Asst. (Paediat.) Roy. Berks. Hosp. Reading. Socs: BMA; Reading Path. Soc. Prev: SHO (Paediat.) Roy. Berks. Hosp. Reading.

TAIT, Clare Penelope c/o Prof. P. Haggett, 5 Tunbridge Close, Bristol BS40 8SU — MB BS 1985 Lond.; MB BS (Hons.) Lond. 1985; MRCP (UK) 1988. Prev: SHO (Med.) Whittington Hosp. & Hammersmith Hosp. & Brompton Hosp. Lond.

TAIT, Colin Michael Busby Road Surgery, 75 Busby Road, Clarkston, Glasgow G76 7BW Tel: 0141 644 2666 Fax: 0141 644 5171; 26 Church Road, Giffnock, Glasgow G46 6LT — MB ChB 1973 Glas.; FRCP Glas. 1991; DObst RCOG 1976. Prev: Regist. (Gen. Med.) Vict. Infirm. Glas.; SHO (O & G) Paisley Matern. Hosp.; SHO (Paediat. Med.) Roy. Hosp. Sick Childr. Glas.

TAIT, David Hamilton Hay Murray Royal Hospital, Perth PH2 7BH Tel: 01738 621151 Fax: 01738 440431 Email: david.tait@tpct.scot.nhs.uk — MB ChB 1974 Ed.; MBA Stirling 1998; FRCPsych 1993, M 1978; BA Open 1986; BSc Ed. 1971. (Ed.) Cons. Psychiat. and Psychotherapist; Hon. Sen. Lect. Univ. Dundee; Librarian, Roy. Coll. of Psychiat.s, Lond. Socs: Fell., Roy. Coll. of Psychiat.s; Fell., Roy. Soc. of Med.; Mem., Scott. Inst. of Human Relations. Prev: Sen. Regist. Aberd. Teach. Hosps.; Regist. Roy. Edin. Hosp.

TAIT, Deborah 15 Byng Road, Barnet EN5 4NW — MB ChB 1998 Leeds.

TAIT, Diana Mary Royal Massden Hospital, Dauns Road, Sutton SM2 5PT Fax: 0207 661 3365 Email: diana.tait@rmh.nthames.nhs.uk — MB ChB 1975 Ed.; MD Ed. 1988; MRCP (UK) 1978; FRCR 1984; FRCP 1998. Cons. Clin. Oncol. Roy. Marsden NHS Trust Sutton & Lond.; Hon. Sen. Lect. Univ. Lond.

TAIT, Elizabeth Ann (retired) Ham Glebe, Church Road, Ham, Richmond TW10 5HG Tel: 020 8940 8629 — MB BS 1960 Lond.; DObst RCOG 1961. Prev: GP Lond.

TAIT, Frank George (retired) Jays Cottage, Tisbury Row, Tisbury, Salisbury SP3 6RZ Tel: 01747 870209 — MB BS 1947 Melbourne; MRCPsych 1972; DPM Eng. 1954. Prev: Sen. Med. Off. DHSS.

TAIT, Mr Gavin Robert Crosshouse Hospital, Kilmarnock KA2 0BE Tel: 01563 577333 Fax: 01563 577976 — MB ChB 1980 Ed.; FRCS Glas. 1984. (Edinburgh) Cons. Orthop. Surg. CrossHo. Hosp. Kilmarnock. Socs: Brit. Assn. Surg. Knee; Brit. Elbow & Shoulder Soc. Prev: Wellcome Research Asst. Qu. Univ. Belf.; Sen. Regist. (Orthop. Surg.) Vict. Infirm. Glas.

TAIT, Godfrey Beckwith (retired) 16 Crowlees Road, Mirfield WF14 9PJ Tel: 01924 497867 — MD 1947 Ed.; MB ChB 1939; FRCP Ed. 1958, M 1947. Hon. Cons. Gen. Med. Dewsbury Area Hosps. Prev: Sen. Med. Regist. Huddersfield Roy. Infirm.

TAIT, Graeme William Dumfries & Galloway Royal Infirmary, Bankend Road, Dumfries DG1 4AP Tel: 01387 246246 Fax: 01387 241192; Cairnlynns, Kingholm Road, Dumfries DG1 4AX Tel: 01387 253142 Fax: 01387 250592 Email: gwtait@aol.com — MB ChB 1982 Ed.; MD Ed. 1996; MRCP (UK) 1987. (Univ. Ed.) Cons. Phys. & Cardiol. Dumfries & Galloway Roy. Infirm. Prev: Clin. Lect. (Med. Cardiol. & Path. Biochem.) Univ. Glas.

TAIT, Hamish Adie Tait and Partners, 68 Pipeland Road, St Andrews KY16 8JZ Tel: 01334 476840 Fax: 01334 472295; 1 Aikman Place, St Andrews KY16 8XS Tel: 01334 473909 Email: hamish.tait@bigfoot.com — MB ChB 1971 Glas.; MRCGP 1978; DCH RCPS Glas. 1974; DObst RCOG 1973. (Glasgow University)

TAIT, Ian Greville (retired) Westfields, 45 Park Road, Aldeburgh IP15 5EN Tel: 01728 452114 — MB BChir 1954 Camb.; MD Camb. 1981; MA, MB Camb. 1954, BChir 1953; FRCGP 1977, M 1960; DCH Eng. 1957. Prev: GP Aldeburgh Suff.

TAIT, Ian James Nunwell Surgery, 10 Pump Street, Bromyard HR7 4BZ Tel: 01885 483412 Fax: 01885 488739; Ashfields House, Hereford Road, Bromyard HR7 4ET Tel: 01885 482872 — MB ChB 1982 Birm.; MRCGP 1987; DRCOG 1986. (Birm.)

TAIT, Isobel Anne (retired) 4/4 Advocates Close, 357 High Street, Edinburgh EH11 PS Email: anne.tait@cressington.force9.co.uk — MD 1982 Ed.; MB ChB 1959; DObst RCOG 1962; Dip Ven 1980; Dip Palliat Med 1999 Cardiff. Prev: Cons. Genitourin. Med. Liverp. & Wirral HAs.

TAIT, Mr Ivan Ballantyne, TD, KStJ (retired) 6 Lennox Row, Edinburgh EH5 3HN Tel: 0131 552 9329 — MB ChB 1951 Ed.; FRCS Glas. 1984; FRCS Eng. 1958; FRCS Ed. 1957. Prev: Cons. i/c Genitourin. Med. Servs. of W. Scotl. Roy. Infirm. Glas.

TAIT, Jacqueline 17 Station Road, Mintlaw, Peterhead AB42 5EE — MB ChB 1983 Aberd.

TAIT, James 109 Western Boulevard, Nottingham NG8 3NX — LRCPI & LM, LRSCI & LM 1939; LRCPI & LM, LRCSI & LM 1939.

TAIT, James Stephen Smithy Cottage, Lighthorne, Warwick CV35 0AU — MB BS 1998 Lond.

TAIT, Mrs Janet Felicity Westfields, 45 Park Road, Aldeburgh IP15 5EN Tel: 01728 452114 Fax: 01728 454070 — MB BS 1954 Lond.; Cert. FPA JCC 1960. (St. Bart.) Med. Off. Family Plann. Clinics Local Health Partnerships NHS Trust Ipswich. Prev: GP Aldeburgh; Asst. MOH E. Suff. CC; Fell. (Med.) St. Luke's Hosp. New York.

TAIT, Janis Tel: 01343 820247 Fax: 01343 820132; Lairg, Old Mills, Fochabers IV32 7HJ Tel: 01343 820373 — MB ChB 1978 Glas.

TAIT, Karen Fiona 28 Currock Mount, Carlisle CA2 4RF — MB ChB 1997 Leeds.

TAIT, Margaret Caroline (retired) Cruan, Firth, Finstown, Orkney KW17 2NY Tel: 01856 761692 — MB ChB 1941 Ed.; BSc Ed. 1943.

***TAIT, Nicholas Karl** 224 Banner Dale Road, Ecclesall, Sheffield S11 9FE — MB ChB 1995 Birm.

TAIT, Nicholas Paul 1 Rectory Park, Morpeth NE61 2SZ — MB 1979 Camb.; BChir 1978.

TAIT, Robert Campbell Department of Haematology, MacEwan Building, Royal Infirmary, Glasgow G4 0SF Tel: 0141 211 5168 Fax: 0141 211 4931 Email: campbell.tait@northglasgow.scot.nhs.uk — MB ChB 1984 Glas.; BSc (Hons.) Glas. 1981, MB ChB 1984; FRCP Glas. 1997; MRCP (UK) 1987; MRCPath 1993; FRCPath 2001. (Univ. Glas.) Cons. Haemat. Glas. Roy. Infirm.

TAIT, Sheila Angela Elizabeth Tel: 01506 670027; 66 Bells Burn Avenue, Linlithgow Tel: 01506 840181 — MB ChB 1992 Aberd.; MRCGP 1996; DRCOG 1995. (Aberd.) GP. Socs: BMA. Prev: Clin. Research Phys. Inveresk Clin. Research Edin.; GP Princip. Kingsgate Med. Centre Bathgate; GP Regist. S. Qu.sberry Health Centre.

TAIT, Sheila Kathleen Springbank Surgery, York Road, Green Hammerton, York YO26 8BN Fax: 01423 331433; Carlton Farm, Nun Monkton, York YO26 8EJ — MB ChB 1976 Aberd.; MRCGP 1985; MRCOG 1981.

TAIT, Timothy John Department of Rheumatology, Grimsby Hospital, Scartho Road, Grimsby DN33 2BA Tel: 01472 874111 Fax: 01472 875483; Burwell Manor, Burwell, Louth LN11 8PR — MB BS 1987 Lond.; BSc Lond. 1984; MRCP (UK) 1991. Cons. Rheum. Grimsby Hosp. Prev: Sen. Regist. (Rheum) York Dist. Hosp.

TAIT, William Miller (retired) 79 Shaftesbury Avenue, Blackpool FY2 9TT Tel: 01253 592052 — MB ChB Glas. 1957; DA S. Afr. 1978; DObst RCOG 1961. Prev: Med. Advsr War Pens. Agency Norcross Blackpool.

TAIT, Winifred Beech House, Beech Avenue, Hazel Grove, Stockport SK7 4QR Tel: 0161 483 6222; 54 Ladythorn Road, Bramhall, Stockport SK7 2EY Tel: 0161 439 1343 — MB ChB 1959 Aberd.

TAIT, Winifred Anne Regional Infections Diseases Unit, Western General Hospital, Crewe Road, Edinburgh EH4 2XU Tel: 0131 537 2855 Fax: 0131 537 2878 — MB BChir 1979 Camb.; Mem. , Scott. Assn. of Psychoanalytical Psychotherapists 1993; MRCPsych 1985. Cons. Psychiat. Regional Infec. Dis. Unit. W.. Gen. Hosp. Edin. Prev: Sen. Regist. (Psychiat.) Roy. Edin. Hosp.

TAIWO, Mr Claudius Bola 4 Chestnut Avenue, Gainsborough DN21 1EU — MB BS 1980 Ibadan; MB BS Ibadan, Nigeria 1980; FRCS Eng. 1989; FRCS Ed. 1988. Hosp. Surg. (Gen. Surg.) John

Coupland Hosp. GainsBoro. Socs: FICS; Med. Defence Union. Prev: Tutor (A & E) Univ. Leeds.

TAJUDDIN, Meraj Lichfield Street Surgery, 267 Lichfield Street, Fazeley, Tamworth B78 3QF Tel: 01827 289512 Fax: 01827 262244 — MB BS 1993 Lond.

TAK, Abdul Momin 24 Sunley Gardens, Perivale, Greenford UB6 7PE — MB BS 1987 Kashmir.

TAK, Mr Vinay Manohar 9 Raleigh Close, Eaton Sucan, St Neots, Huntingdon PE19 8NN — MB BS 1985 Calcutta; FRCS Ed. 1992.

TAKEDA, Scott 6 Missenden Close, Bedfont Lane, Feltham TW14 9XN — MB BS 1992 Lond.

TAKES, Hendricka Margaret The Karis Medical Centre, Waterworks Road, Edgbaston, Birmingham B16 9AL Tel: 0121 454 0661 Fax: 0121 454 9104; 36 Stirling Road, Edgbaston, Birmingham B16 9BG — MB ChB 1985 Birm.; MRCGP 1989; DRCOG 1988.

TAKEUCHI, Elena Erina 10 Westbury Ave, Sale M33 4WQ Tel: 0161 973 4057 — MB ChB 1998 Manch.

TAKHAR, Amrit Pal Singh Wansford Surgery, Yarwell Road, Wansford, Peterborough PE8 6PL Tel: 01780 782342 Fax: 01780 783434; Springfield House, 21 Roman Drive, Stibbington, Peterborough PE8 6LL Tel: 01780 783575 Fax: 01780 784088 Email: amrit@btinternet.com — MB ChB 1983 Birm.; BSc (Hons.) Birm. 1980; MRCGP 1987; DCH RCP Lond. 1986; DRCOG 1986. (Birmingham)

TAKHAR, Baldeep 32 Grovewood Hill, Coulsdon CR5 2EL — MB ChB 1990 Manch.; DRCOG 1994; DFFP 1994; DCH RCP Lond. 1993. GP Tutor Nottm. Univ. Prev: SHO (Psychiat.) Derby City Hosp.; Trainee GP Purley; SHO (Paediat.) N. Middlx. Hosp.

TAKHAR, Gurpreet Singh 130 Princes Gardens, London W3 0LL — MB BS 1989 Lond.; BSc (Immunol.) Lond. 1986; MBA (INSEAD) 1994; MRCGP 1993. Director of World-wide Business Developm. GlaxoSmithKline; Ex-Internat. Off. BMA Assoc. Gp. Comm.; Vis. Fac. Imperial Coll. Health; Managem. Progr.. Socs: Roy. Coll. of Gen. Practitioners. Prev: Trainee GP St. Bart. Lond. VTS.

TAKHAR, Kuljeet 7 Parkway, Uxbridge UB10 9JX — MB ChB 1997 Dundee.

TAKLA, Ashraf Fouad Shawky The Crescent Surgery, 2 The Crescent, Northampton NN1 4SD Tel: 01604 713434 Fax: 01604 717689; 23 The Fairoaks, Wakes Meadow, Northampton NN3 9UZ Tel: 01604 416226 — MB BCh 1981 Ain Shams; DFFP 1993.

TAKTAK, Mr Sabah George 7 Broomgrove Gardens, Edgware HA8 5SH Tel: 020 8951 3871 — MB ChB 1959 Baghdad; FRCS Ed. 1979; LMSSA Lond. 1969. (Baghdad) Regist. (Orthop.) Lister Hosp. Stevenage. Prev: Regist. (Orthop.) W. Lond. Hosp., Roy. N.. Hosp. Lond. & Roy. Free; Hosp. Lond.

TAKYI, Alfred 30 Cadewell Park Road, Torquay TQ2 7JU Tel: 01803 615171; 11Cadewell Park, Clayhall, Ilford IG5 0JL Tel: 020 8550 6354 — MUDr 1971 Charles Univ. Prague; MUDr Charles U. Prague 1971; Dip. Postgrad. Cert. Psychiat. Budapest 1985. SCMO (Psychiat.) Newham Health Care Trust Lond. Socs: Fell. Roy. Soc. Med. Prev: Staff Grade (Psychiat.) Newham Healthcare Trust Lond.; Clin. Asst. (Psychiat.) Torquay; Regist. (Psychiat.) Dorchester & Lincoln & Torquay.

TALAT, Mahe The Surgery, 49 Tottenham Lane, Hornsey, London N8 9BD — MB BS 1969 Sind. (Liaquat Med. Coll.) Prev: SHO (Gen. Med.) Moyle Hosp. Larne; Trainee GP Whitehead Health Centre.

TALATI, Freni (retired) 392 Southcroft Road, London SW16 6QX Tel: 020 8677 2614 — MB BS 1950 Bombay; BSc Bombay 1944.

TALATI, Mr Vrandavan Ratilal Chesterfield Royal Hospital, Chesterfield Tel: 01246 77271 — MB BS 1963 Gujarat; MS Gujarat 1967, MB BS 1963; FRCS Ed. 1977; DLO Eng. 1973. (B.J. Med. Coll. Ahmedabad) Cons. ENT Surg. Chesterfield Roy. Hosp. Prev: Sen. Regist. (ENT) Hallamsh. Hosp. Sheff.; Sen. Regist. (ENT) Leicester Roy. Infirm.; Regist. (ENT) Bradford Roy. Infirm.

TALAVLIKAR, Prakash Hari 59 The Ridgeway, Chatham ME4 6PB Tel: 01634 43466 — MD 1964 Bombay; MB BS 1962; FRCP Ed. 1986, M 1968. (Grant Med. Coll.) Cons. Phys. c/o Elderly N. Kent Healthcare NHS Trust. Socs: Roy. Soc. Med.; Brit. Geriat. Soc. & Indian Cardiol. Soc. Prev: Regist. (Med.) St. Bart. Hosp. Rochester & (Cardiac) W.. Gen. Hosp. Edin.; Sen. Regist. (Geriat. Med.) Univ. Hosp. S. Manch.

TALBERT, Alison Wendy Audrey Mvumi Hospital, PO Box 32, Mvumi, Dodoma, Tanzania; c/o 28 Pine Grove, Eccles, Manchester M30 9JL — MB BS 1983 Lond.; BA (Hons.) Physiol. Sci. Oxf. 1980; MRCP (UK) 1986. Miss. Doctor Mvumi Hosp. Tanzania. Prev: SHO Hosp. Trop. Dis. Lond.; Ho. Phys. Lond. Hosp.; Ho. Surg. Amersham Gen. Hosp.

TALBOT, Alison Jane Tilehurst Surgery, Tylers Place, Pottery Road, Tilehurst, Reading RG30 6BW Tel: 0118 942 7528 Fax: 0118 945 2405 — BM 1986 Soton.; BM Soton 1986; MRCGP 1990; DCH RCP Lond. 1990; DRCOG 1990.

TALBOT, Andrew William East House, 38 St John's Avenue, Bridlington YO16 4NG Tel: 01262 401921 Fax: 01262 400161 — MB ChB 1982 Leeds; MRCPsych 1987. (Univ. Leeds) Cons. Psychiat. Bridlington & Dist. Hosp. N. Humberside. Prev: Sen. Regist. (Psychiat.) W. Midl. RHA; Tutor (Psychiat.) Univ. Leeds; Regist. Rotat. Leeds Train. Scheme.

TALBOT, Mr Clifford Heyworth (retired) Moorlands Farm, Moorlands Lane, Froggatt, Calver, Hope Valley S32 3ZH Tel: 01433 631876 — MB BChir 1948 Camb.; MA Camb. 1950, MChir 1957, MB BChir 1948; FRCS Eng. 1953. Prev: Cons. Surg. Roy. Hallamsh. Hosp. Sheff.

TALBOT, Mr David 84 Woodbine Road, Gosforth, Newcastle upon Tyne NE3 1DE — MB BS 1982 Newc.; MD Newc. 1988; FRCS Ed. 1989; PhD 2000 Newcastle. Cons. Surg. Freeman Hosp. Newc. u. Tyne; Hon. Lect. (Surg.) Univ. Newc. Socs: Eur. Soc. Organ Transpl.; Eur. Liver Transpl. Assn.; Assoc. Mem. Brit. Assn. Paediat. Surgs. Prev: Vis. Fell. Hepatobiliary Unit Qu. Eliz. Hosp. Birm.; Sen. Regist. (Renal Transpl.) Newc. u. Tyne.

***TALBOT, Deborah** 48 Chesterfield Road, Lichfield WS13 6QW — MB ChB 1998 Birm.

TALBOT, Denis Charles University of Oxford, ICRF Medical Oncology Unit, Churchill Hospital, Headington, Oxford OX3 7LJ Tel: 01865 226183 Fax: 01865 226179 Email: dtalbot@icrf.icnet.uk; 33 Butts Road, Horspath, Oxford OX33 1RJ Tel: 01865 87542 — MB BChir 1981 Camb.; PhD Lond. 1978; MA Oxf. 1996; MA Camb. 1983; BSc Liverp. 1974; FRCP Lond. 1996; MRCP (UK) 1985. (Camb.) Cons. Med. Oncol. Oxf. HA & Imperial Cancer Research Fund; Sen. Clin. Lect. Univ. Oxf. Socs: Assn. Cancer Phys.; Amer. Soc. Clin. Oncol.; Amer. Assn. Cancer Research. Prev: Sen. Regist. (Med.) Roy. Marsden Hosp. Lond. & Sutton; Regist. (Med. Oncol.) St. Bart. & Homerton Hosp. Lond.; Regist. (Gen. Med.) Newmarket Gen. Hosp.

TALBOT, Mr Ernest Mark Eye Department, Royal Preston Hospital, Sharoe Green Lane, Preston PR2 9HT; 38 Higher Bank Road, Fulwood, Preston PR2 8PE — MB ChB 1980 Dundee; FRCS Ed. 1985; FRCOphth 1988; DOphth Dub. 1983. Cons. Ophth. Roy. Preston Hosp.; Hon. Sen. Lect. Univ. Centr. Lancs. Prev: Sen. Regist. Tennent Inst. Glas.; Regist. & SHO (Ophth.) St. Paul's Eye Hosp. Liverp.

TALBOT, Heather 94 Ashdell Road, Sheffield S10 3DB Tel: 0114 266 0404 — MB BS Lond. 1967; MRCS Eng. LRCP Lond. 1967; FFA RCS Eng. 1977; DA Eng. 1972; DObst RCOG 1969. (Roy. Free) Assoc. Specialist (Anaesth.) Roy. Hallamsh. Hosp. Sheff. Prev: Regist. (Anaesth.) Nottm. City Hosp.

TALBOT, Professor Ian Charles Academic Department of Pathology, St. Mark's Hospital, Northwick Park, Watford Road, Harrow HA1 3UJ Tel: 020 8235 4221 Fax: 020 8235 4277 Email: i.talbot@icrf.icnet.uk; 34 Belitha Villas, London N1 1PD — MB BS 1964 Lond.; MD Lond. 1979; FRCPath 1983, M 1971. (King's Coll. Hosp.) Cons. Histopath. St. Mark's Hosp.; Prof. Histopath. Imperial Coll. Sch. Med. Socs: Path. Soc.; Brit. Soc. Gastroenterol.; Fell. Roy. Soc. Med. Prev: Reader Univ. Leicester & Hon. Cons. Pathol. Leics. HA; Sen. Lect. (Morbid Anat.) King's Coll. Hosp. Med. Sch. Lond.; Regist. (Morbid Anat.) Hammersmith Hosp. Lond.

TALBOT, Joanna Louise Rock House, New Road, Penkridge, Stafford ST19 5DN — MB BCh 1994 Wales.

TALBOT, Mr John FitzRoy Royal Hallamshire Hospital, Glossop Rd, Sheffield S10 2JF Tel: 0114 271 3056; Daggers House, Hope, Hope Valley S33 6RH Tel: 01433 620323 — MB BS 1970 Lond.; FRCS Eng. 1978; MRCS Eng. LRCP Lond. 1970; FRCOphth 1988. Cons. Ophth. Roy. Hallamsh. Hosp. Sheff.; Hon. Lect. Sheff. Univ. Med. Sch.; Vice Pres. Roy. Coll. of Ophth.s. Prev: Sen. Regist. Moorfields Eye Hosp.; Lect. Inst. Ophth.

TALBOT, John Michael Bicester Health Centre, Coker Close, Bicester OX26 6AT Tel: 01869 249333 Fax: 01869 320314; The Barn House, Souldern, Bicester OX6 9JP Tel: 01869 345555 — BM

TALBOT

BCh 1968 Oxf.; MA, BM BCh Oxf. 1968; FRCGP 1997, M 1977; DObst RCOG 1974. (Oxf.) Prev: Regist. Dept. Paediat. & Child Health Univ. Cape Town Red Cross Hosp.; Cape Town S. Africa; Ho. Phys. & Surg. Radcliffe Infirm. Oxf.; SHO Accid. Serv. United Oxf. Hosps.

TALBOT, John Michael (retired) 3 Whitegates Close, Canns Lane, Hethersett, Norwich NR9 3JG Tel: 01603 811709 — MB BS 1945 Lond.; MD Lond. 1952; FRCPath 1968, M 1963; Dip. Bact. Lond. 1952. Prev: Med. Dir. Priscilla Bacon Lodge (Palliat. Care Unit) Norwich.

TALBOT, John Storey Trehafod, Waurnarlydd Road, Sketty, Swansea SA2 0GB Tel: 01792 582139 Fax: 01792 585220 — MB ChB 1978 Liverp.; MRCS Eng. LRCP Lond. 1978; MRCPsych 1983. Cons. Child & Adolesc. Psychiat. Child & Family Clinic Port Talbot.; Vis. Cons. Psychiat. to Hillside Secure Unit, Neath. Socs: Chairm. Div. Psychiat. Swansea; Welsh Regional Represen. Child & Adolesc. Psychiat., Roy. Collgege of Psychiat.s. Prev: Sen. Regist. (Child & Adolesc. Psychiat.) Alder Hey Hosp. Liverp. & Young People's Centre Countess of Chester Hosp.; Regist. (Psychiat.) Roy. Liverp. Hosp.

TALBOT, John Stuart Salford Trafford HA, Peel House, Albert St., Eccles, Manchester M30 0NJ Tel: 0161 787 0128 — MB ChB 1965 Manch.; MRCGP 1976; DObst RCOG 1969. (Manch.) Med. Adviser Salford & Trafford HA.

TALBOT, Kevin Andrew University Dept of Clinical Neurology, Radcliffe Infirmary, Woodstock Rd, Oxford OX2 6HE — MB BS 1990 Lond.; BSc Lond. 1989; MRCP (UK) 1993; Dphil (Oxon) 1999. (Char Cross and Westminster) Clin Lect.. Dept of Clin Neurol. Univ of Oxf.; Hon. Regist. (Clin. Neurol.) Radcliffe Infirm. Oxf. Prev: Med. Research Counc. Clin. Train. Fell. (Genetics) Univ. Oxf.; SHO Hammersmith Hosp. & Nat. Hosp. for Neurol. & Neurosurg. Lond.

TALBOT, Margaret Anne 5 Beeston Close, Bollington, Macclesfield SK10 5RQ — MB ChB 1986 Manch.; DRCOG 1991. Trainee GP Chesh.

TALBOT, Mark Shoghi New Cross Hospital, Royal Wolverhampton Hospitals, Wolverhampton WV10 0QP — MB BS 1990 Lond.; MRCP (UK) 1995.

TALBOT, Martin David Royal Hallamshire Hospital, Glossop Road, Sheffield S10 2JF — MED (Medical Educ.); MB ChB 1972 (Hons. Dist. Pharmacol. & Obst. & Gyn.) Liverp.; Liverp. 1972; FRCP Lond. 1989; MRCP (UK) 1976. Director of UnderGrad. Med. Educat., Sheff. Teachg. Hopitals.; Hon. Sen. Clin. Lect. Univ. Sheff.; Cons. Phys. (Genitourin. Med.) Roy. Hallamshire Hosp. Socs: Med. Soc. Study VD; Assn. Med. Educat.; Assn. Humanistic Psych. Prev: Sub-Dean Fac. Med. Univ. Sheff.; Regist. (Med.) David Lewis N. Hosp. Liverp.; Ho. Phys. Liverp. Roy. Infirm.

TALBOT, Mr Nicholas John The Old Dairy, Fore St., Silverton, Exeter EX5 4HP Tel: 01392 861344 — BM BCh 1994 Oxf.; BA (Hons.) Oxf. 1991; FRCS (Eng) 1998. (Oxf.) SHO Rotat. (Surg.) Roy. Devon & Exeter Hosp.; SHO (Orthop. & Trauma) Roy. Devon & Exeter Hosp. Prev: Med. Demonst. (Physiol.) Univ. Bristol; Ho. Phys. (Chest & Gen. Med.) Roy. Devon & Exeter Hosp.; Ho. Surg. (Gen., BrE. & Urol. Surg.) John Radcliffe Hosp. Oxf.

TALBOT, Paul Richard Department of Neurology, Manchester Royal Infirmary, Oxford Road, Manchester M13 9WL; Heath Barn, The Heath, Glossop SK13 7QF Email: paultalbot@doctors.org.uk — MB ChB 1987 Manch.; MD 1996; MRCP (UK) 1990. Cons. Neurol. - Gt.er Manch. Neurosci. Unit, Hope Hosp., Salford. Socs: Assn. Brit. Neurol. Prev: Sen. Regist. (Neurol.) Manch. Roy. Infirm.; Research Fell. (Neurol.) Manch. Roy. Infirm.; Regist. (Neurol.) N. Manch. Gen. Hosp.

TALBOT, Mr Peter Albert James Talbot, Ward, Seery and Ahmad, Gardenia Surgery, 2A Gardenia Avenue, Luton LU3 2NS Tel: 01582 572612 Fax: 01582 494553; 355 Old Bedford Road, Luton LU2 7BL — MB ChB 1972 Liverp.; FRCS Ed. 1977; MRCGP 1988. Prev: Regist. (Gen. Surg.) Whiston Hosp. Prescot Merseyside; Regist. (Orthop.) Roy. S.. Hosp. Liverp.

TALBOT, Peter Stanley Winsor House, Belfast City Hospital, Lisburn Road, Belfast BT9 7AB Tel: 01232 335791 Fax: 01232 324543 Email: peter.talbot@newscientist.net; 90 Ballinderry Road, Ballinderry Upper, Lisburn BT28 2NS Tel: 01846 621713 — MB ChB 1984 Bristol; MRCPsych 1997; DMH Belf. 1996; DA (UK) 1989. (Univ. of Bris. Med. Sch.) Specialist Regist. (Gen. Psychiat.) Windsor Ho. Belf. City Hosp.; Sen. Tutor, Qu.'s Univ. Belf. Socs: Brit. Assn. Psychopharmacol.; Ulster Med. Soc. Prev: Research Fell.

(Ment. Health) Holywell Hosp. Antrim; SHO (Gen. Psychiat.) Knockbracken Healthcare Pk. Belf.; SHO (Ment. Handicap) Muckamore Abbey Hosp. Antrim.

TALBOT, Mr Robert William Poole General Hospital, Longfleet Road, Poole BH15 2 Tel: 01202 675100; 1 Beaucroft Road, Wimborne BH21 2QW Tel: 01202 887579 Fax: 01202 442615 — MB BS 1974 Lond.; MS Lond. 1984, MB BS 1974; FRCS Eng. 1978; T(S) 1991. (King's Coll. Hosp.) Cons. Gen. Surg. Poole Gen. Hosp. Socs: Fell. Roy. Soc. Med.; Assoc. of ColoProctol. Prev: Vis. Scientist Mayo Clinic Rochester, USA; RSO St. Marks Hosp. Lond.

TALBOT, Ruth Mary The Grange, The Street, Waltham St. Lawrence, Reading RG10 0JJ — BA Camb. 1978, MB BChir 1981; MRCPsych 1987; DCH RCP Lond. 1983. Indep. Cons. Child and Adolesc. Psychiat. Prev: Cons. Child & Adolesc. Psychiat. Merton Child Guid. Serv. Mitcham.; Sen. Regist. (Child Psychiat.) St. Geo. Hosp. Lond.; SHO & Regist. (Rotat.) (Psychiat.) St. Geo. Hosp. Tooting.

TALBOT, Sarah 22 Newberry Road, Weymouth DT4 8LW — BM BCh 1997 Oxf.

TALBOT, Sheelagh Bradley and Partners, 30 Woodland Avenue, Luton LU3 1RW Tel: 01582 572239 Fax: 01582 494227; 30 Woodlands Avenue, Luton LU3 1RW — MB ChB 1972 Liverp.

TALBOT, Stephen Laurel Farm, Pitney, Langport TA10 9AF Tel: 01458 252266 — MB BS 1963 Lond.; BA (Hons.) Open 1993; MRCP Lond. 1966; MRCS Eng. LRCP Lond. 1963; DRCOG 1965. (Guy's) Indep. Phys. Som. Socs: BMA; Med. Protec. Soc. Prev: Sen. Regist. Sheff. HA & Hammersmith Hosp. Lond.; Regist. Qu. Eliz. Hosp. Birm.; Regist. MusGr. Pk. Hosp. Taunton.

TALBOT-SMITH, Alison Jane 112 Kynaston Avenue, Aylesbury HP21 9DS — MB BS 1993 Newc.

TALBUTT, Arthur James (retired) 34 Westbroke Gardens, Romsey SO51 7RQ — MB BS 1953 Durh. Prev: Ho. Surg. W. Norf. & King's Lynn Gen. Hosp.

TALEB, Sidi Mohammed Taleb and Partners, The Surgery, Burton Road, Woodville, Swadlincote DE11 7JG Tel: 01283 217036 Fax: 01283 552308 — MRCS Eng. LRCP Lond. 1976.

TALERMAN, Harold Joseph 152 Harley Street, London W1N 1HH Tel: 020 7935 8868 — MB BCh 1959 Witwatersrand; DO Eng. 1968; DO RCPSI 1968. (Witwatersrand) Clin. Asst. Moorfields Eye Hosp. Lond. Socs: Ophth. Soc. UK. Prev: Cons. Eye Surg. Provin. Hosp. & Livingstone Hosp. Port. Eliz., S. Afr.

TALKHANI, Mr Imtiyaz Suleman 1 Osborne Cottage, Highfield, Wrexham LL11 4US — MB BS 1986 Karnatak; FRCS Glas. 1992.

TALLACH, Cameron Rowanlea, 5A Upper Breakish, Breakish, Isle of Skye IV42 8PY — MB ChB 1968 Aberd. Socs: Hong Kong Med. Soc. & Hong. Kong Coll. Gen. Pract.

TALLACH, James Ross Free Presbyterian Manse, Isle of Raasay, Kyle IV40 8PB Tel: 01478 660216 Fax: 01478 660216 Email: jamesross@tallach.fnet.co.uk; Free Presbyteriam Manse, Isle of Raasay, Kyle IV40 8PB Email: jamesross@tallach.fsnet.co.uk — MB ChB 1967 Aberd. p/t GP Raasay. Socs: Brit. Med. Assoc. Prev: Med. Off. Mbuma Mission Hosp. Nkai, Zimbabwe.

TALLACK, Faye Vivien (retired) 18 Parkfield, Horsham RH12 2BG Tel: 01403 252810 — BM BCh 1949 Oxf.; MA Oxf. 1952; DO Eng. 1953. Prev: Assoc. Specialist (Ophth.) Sutton Hosp.

TALLACK, Fenella Evelyn Riverside Substance Misuse Service, 69 Warwick Road, London SW5 Tel: 020 8846 7777 — MB 1983 Camb.; MA Camb. 1984, MB 1983, BChir 1982; MRCPsych 1990. Staff Grade Team Dir. Subst. Misuse Community Team Riverside HA. Socs: BMA. Prev: Regist. (Psychiat.) Kingston Gen. Hosp.; SHO (Psychiat.) PeterBoro. Dist. Hosp.; SHO (Psychiat.) Roy. Edin. Hosp.

TALLACK, John Aidan (retired) Machaon, Swallows Cross, Mountnessing, Brentwood CM15 0SS Tel: 01277 353206 Email: jtallack@msn.com — MB ChB Aberd. 1949. Prev: Assoc. Specialist Phys. OldCh. & Rush Green Hosps. Romford.

TALLANT, Neil Peter Barn Surgery, Christchurch Medical Centre, Purewell Cross Road, Christchurch BH23 3AF Tel: 01202 486456 Fax: 01202 486678; 84 Walcott Avenue, Christchurch BH23 2NG Tel: 01202 479856 — BM 1983 Soton.; MRCGP 1987; DRCOG 1987. GP. ChristCh..; Clin. Asst. Thoracic Med. Bournemouth Gen. Hosp. Prev: Trainee GP I. of Wight VTS.

TALLANTYRE, Helen Myfanwy Espley Cottage, Espley, Morpeth NE61 3DJ — MB ChB 1997 Sheff.

TALLANTYRE, Patricia Margaret The Gables Health Centre, 26 St. Johns Road, Bedlington NE22 7DU Tel: 01670 829889 Fax: 01670 820841; Espley Cottage, Espley, Morpeth NE61 3DJ Tel: 01670 513396 — MB BChir 1967 Camb.; BA Camb. 1964. (Camb. & St. Thos.) Socs: BMA. Prev: SHO Essex Co. Hosp. Colchester; SHO (Paediat.) Flemming Memor. Hosp. Newc.; SHO (O & G) P.ss Mary Matern. Hosp. Newc.

TALLENT, David Neill The Medical Suite, Renaissance Hotel Gatwick, Gatwick Airport, Horley RH6 0BE Tel: 01293 776996 Fax: 01293 823 6498 Email: david.tallent@srg.caa.co.uk; 26 Grasslands, Smallfield, Horley RH6 9NU Tel: 01342 844952 Email: david.tallent@btinternet.com — MB ChB 1981 Sheff.; AFOM RCP Lond. 1995; MRCGP 1989; DAvMed FOM RCP Lond. 1992. Aviat. Med. Off. Civil Aviat. Auth. Gatwick. Prev: Company Aeromed. Specialist Dan-Air Serv. Ltd. Horley.

TALLENTS, Mr Christopher John, TD Eye Department, Kidderminster General Hospital, Bewdley Road, Kidderminster DY11 6RJ Tel: 01562 823424 Fax: 01562 513062; The White Cottage, Kinlet, Bewdley DY12 3BD Tel: 01299 841238 Fax: 01299 841482 — MB BS 1964 Lond.; LMCC 1973; FRCS 1969 Eng.; BSc (Hons.) 1961 Lond.; DO 1967 Eng.; BSc (Hons.) Lond. 1961; FRCS Eng. 1969; DO Eng. 1967; LMCC 1973. (Middlx.) Cons. Ophth. Kidderminster Gen. Hosp. Socs: BMA. Prev: Sen. Regist. (Ophth.) King's Coll. Hosp. Lond.; Regist. (Ophth.) Sussex Eye Hosp.; SHO (Ophth.) Leeds Gen. Infirm.

TALLETT, Paul Ronald Inwoods Farm, Five Ashes, Mayfield TN20 6JA — MB BS 1976 Lond.; DRCOG 1978; FRCR 1982. (King's Coll. Hosp.) Cons. (Radiol.) Kent & Sussex Hosp. & Nuffield Hosp. Tunbridge Wells.

TALLIS, Patricia Mary Child Adolescent Mental Health Service, Bristol Royal Hospital for Children, Paul O'Gorman Building, Upper Maudlia St., Bristol BS2 8BJ — MB ChB 1988 Liverp.; MRCPsych 1994. (Univ. Liverp.) p/t Sen. Regist. (Child & Adolesc. Psychiat.) Bristol. Prev: Regist. Rotat. (Psychiat.) Liverp. Train. Sch.; SHO Rotat. (Psychiat.) Liverp. VTS.

TALLIS, Professor Raymond Courtenay Clinical Sciences Building, Hope Hospital, Eccles Old Road, Salford M6 8HD Tel: 0161 787 7164 Fax: 0161 787 5578 Email: rtallis@fs1.ho.mau.ar.uk; 5 Valley Road, Bramhall, Stockport SK4 2BZ Tel: 0161 439 2548 — BM BCh 1970 Oxf.; DLITT 1997; FRCP Lond. 1988, M 1976. Prof. Geriat. Med. Univ. Manch.; Hon. Cons. Phys. (Geriat. Med.) Hope & Ladywell Hosps. Salford. Socs: Sec. 1942 Club; Med. Pilgrams. Prev: Sen. Lect. (Geriat. Med.) Roy. Liverp. Hosp.

TALLON, Carole Anne 147 St Leonards Road, Leicester LE2 3BZ — MB ChB 1990 Leic.

TALLON, Grainne Mary 111 Ballylenaghan Park, Primrose Hill, Belfast BT8 6WR; 111 Ballylenaghan Park, Primrose Hill, Belfast BT8 6WR — MB BCh BAO 1994 Belf.; MRCP (Glasgow) 1999.

TALLON, Julian Griffith John Mitchell and Partners, The Park Surgery, Old Tetbury Road, Cirencester GL7 1US Tel: 01285 654733 Fax: 01285 641408 — MB BCh 1985 Wales; DCH RCP Lond. 1991. Community Paediat. E. Wilts. Socs: BMA. Prev: Trainee GP Stroud, Glos.; SHO (Paediat.) E. Glam. Hosp. Pontypridd; Dep. Doctor Melbourne, Austral.

TALLURI, Satish Chandra c/o Dr P.B. Gopal, Department of Anaesthesia, Darlington Memorial Hospital, Holyhurst Road, Darlington DL3 6HX — MB BS 1984 Andhra; MRCPI 1993.

TALMUD, Juli Clair 26 Richborough Road, London NW2 3LX — MB ChB 1998 Leeds.

TALPAHEWA, Sudath Parakrama Dundee Teaching Hospitals, Dundee DD1 9SY Tel: 01224 649995; 27 Lytton Grove, Lytton St, Dundee DD2 — MB BS 1993 Sri Lanka; LRCP LRCS Ed. LRCPS Glas. 1996.

TALPUR, Hyder Ally Hanford Health Clinic, New Inn Lane, Hanford, Stoke-on-Trent ST4 8EX Tel: 01782 658047; 3 Sark Close, Newcastle ST5 3LN — MB BS 1970 Sind; MRCP (UK) 1982; ECFMG Cert. 1976; Cert. Prescribed Equiv. Exp. JCPTGP 1983. (Liaquat Med. Coll. Hyderabad) Prev: Regist. & SHO (Geriat. Med.) City Gen. Hosp. Stoke-on-Trent; SHO (Chest Med.) Halifax Gen. Hosp.

TALUKDER, Ranadhir High Street Medical Practice, The Health Centre, High Street, Winsford CW7 2AS Tel: 01606 862767 Fax: 01606 550876; 3 Partridge Close, Swanlow Park, Over, Winsford CW7 1PY Tel: 01606 861618 — MB BS Univ. Dacca 1967; LRCP LRCS Ed. LRCPS Glas. 1979; DTM & H Eng. 1975. (Chittagong Med. Coll. Dacca) Socs: N.wich Med. Soc.; BMA; Overseas Doctors Assn. Prev: Regist. (Gen. Med.) Leeds Gen. Infirm.; Regist. (Gen. Med.) Scunthorpe Gen. Hosp.; SHO (Gen. Med.) Bishop Auckland Gen. Hosp.

TALUKDER, Mr Shyam Benode c/o Dr S. D. Ghosh, Flat 2, Singleton Hospital, Sketty, Swansea SA2 8QA — MB BS 1960 Calcutta; FRCS Ed. 1971; DLO RCS Eng. 1967.

TALWAR, Meenakshi 177 Sorrel Bank, Linton Glade, Croydon CR0 9LZ — MB BS 1994 Lond. (Univ. Coll. Lond.) SHO Chelsea & W.m. Hosp. Lond.

***TALWAR, Sandeep** 8 Yeading Avenue, Harrow HA2 9RN — BM 1987 Soton.

TALWAR, Suneel Leicester Royal Infirmary, Infirmary Square, Leicester LE1 5WW Tel: 0116 254 1414 — MB BS 1991 New Delhi; MRCP Ed. 1996.

TALWATTE, Beatrice Yuletine 7 Highview Gardens, Finchley, London N3 3EX Tel: 020 8346 4574 — MB BS 1960 Ceylon; DPM Eng. 1974; DTM & H Eng. 1972; DPH Eng. 1968. (Colombo) Regist. & Assoc. Specialist (Psychiat.) Harperbury Hosp. Shenley. Prev: Med. Off. Outpat. Dept. Gen. Hosp. Colombo, Ceylon; Sch. Med. Off. Ceylon; Med. Off. (Matern. & Child Health) Kandy, Ceylon.

TALWATTE, Dhesa Bandu Bandare 7 High View Gardens, Finchley, London N3 3EX — MB BS 1958 Ceylon; FFA RCS Eng. 1972; DA Eng. 1968; DObst RCOG 1968. (Colombo) Cons. Anaesth. N. Middlx. Hosp. Lond. Socs: Ceylon Med. Assn. Prev: Cons. Anaesth. St. Albans City Hosp. & Gen. Hosp. Kandy, Ceylon; Sen. Regist. (Anaesth.) Roy. Free Hosp. Lond.

TAM, Barbara Sau Man 61 Alma Court, Bristol BS8 2HJ — MB ChB 1992 Bristol.

TAM, Carmen Ka Man Royal Hospital for Sick Children, Edinburgh EH9 1LF; 24/16 East Parkside, Edinburgh EH16 5XN Tel: 0131 662 4456 — MB ChB 1998 Ed. SHO. Roy Hosp for Sick Childr. Prev: JHO. Roy Infirm of Edin.

TAM, Darwin Jaffe and Partners, Belmont Health Centre, 516 Kenton Lane, Kenton, Harrow HA3 7LT Tel: 020 8427 1213; 11 Ridgeway Court, 1 The Avenue, Hatch End, Pinner HA5 4UT — MB BCh 1990 Wales; MRCGP 1995; DRCOG 1994; DCH RCP Lond. 1994. GP Princip.

TAM, Frederick Wai-Keung Renal Unit, Imperial College School of Medicine, Hammersmith Hospital, Du Cane Road, London W12 0NN Tel: 020 8740 3152 Fax: 020 8383 2062 Email: ftam@rpms.ac.uk; 43 Cotswold Gardens, London NW2 1QT — MB BChir 1985 Camb.; PhD Lond. 1996; MA Camb. 1986, BA 1982; MRCP (UK) 1987. Sen. Research Fell. Nat. Kidney Research Fund. Prev: MRC Train. Fell.; Regist. Rotat. (Med.) Hammersmith & Hillingdon Hosps. Lond.; SHO (Neurol.) St. Jas. Univ. Hosp. Leeds.

***TAM, Nicolette Lai Kay** Kewins, Newtons Hill, Hartfield TN7 4DH Tel: 01892 770231; 83 Middle Way, Summertown, Oxford OX2 7LE Tel: 01865 511726 — BM BCh 1998 Oxf.; BM BCh Oxf 1998.

TAM, Philip Gordon Emmanuel 28 Montgomerie Terrace, Skelmorlie PA17 5DT — MB BS 1996 Lond.

TAM, Thomas Chris Flat 11 Straffon Lodge, 1 Belsize Grove, London NW3 4XE — MB ChB 1993 Leic.

TAM, Wing Kwong Majumder, Roy and Tam, Greenock Health Centre, 20 Duncan Street, Greenock PA15 4LY Tel: 01475 724477 Fax: 01475 727140 — MD 1947 Shantung Christian U. (Shantung Christian U) GP Greenock, Renfrewsh.

TAM-LIT, Johnson Wha-Suen Calypso Farm, Low Farm, Bishop Monkton, Harrogate HG3 7QN — MB BCh BAO 1987 NUI; LRCPSI 1987.

TAMALE SSALI, Mr Edward Gasterfson 66 Park Hall Road, London SE21 8BW — MB ChB 1974 Makerere; FRCS Ed. 1982; MRCS Eng. LRCP Lond. 1977; MRCOG 1982, D 1979. (Makerere Med. Sch. Kampala) Cons. O & G Kuwait Oil Co. Prev: Regist. (O & G) Scarsdale Hosp. Chesterfield; SHO (Gyn.) Newton Abbot Hosp. Devon; SHO (O & G) Nottm. Hosp. Wom.

TAMAYO, Brando Christian Craig, Surg. Lt. RN HMS Repulse (STBD) BFPO 372 Tel: 01436 674321 Fax: 01436 674321 — MB ChB 1993 Dundee. Submarine Med. Off. RN; Apptd. Doctor Diving Hse. Socs: BMA.

TAMBAKOPOULOS

TAMBAKOPOULOS, Dimitrios 36 Leonard Court, Edwardes Square, London W8 6NN — Ptychio Iatrikes 1980 Thessalonika.

TAMBAR, Mr Balvir Krishan Burnley District Hospital, Barnsley — MB BS 1966 Delhi; FRCS Eng. 1974. (Maulana Azad Med. Coll. New Delhi) Regist. (Gen. Surg.) Barnsley Dist. Gen. Hosp. Prev: Regist. (Urol.) Ballochmyle Hosp. Mauchline; SHO (Gen. Surg.) Leicester Gen. Hosp. & W. Wales Gen. Hosp.; Carmarthen.

***TAMBER, Pritpal Singh** 87 Romway Road, Evington, Leicester LE5 5SE — MB ChB 1998 Birm.

TAMBIAH, Jeymi 28 Wykeham Hosp, Chaucer Place, Off North Rd, Wimbledon, London SW19 1HU Email: j.tambiah@ic.ac.uk — MB ChB 1993 Manch.; BSc (Hons.) St. And. 1990; FRCS 1993; FRCS 1998. SHO (Intens. Care) Qu. Mary's Hosp. Sidcup; Research Regist. (Vasc. Surg.) Char Cross. Lond. Prev: SHO.(Cardio Surg.) St Thomas Hosp. Lond.

TAMBYRAJA, Andrew Laksman 58 Heron Drive, Lenton, Nottingham NG7 2DF — BM BS 1998 Nottm.; BM BS Nottm 1998.

TAMHNE, Rashmin Chandrakant Children's Directorate, Leisestershire and Rutland Healthcare NHS Trust, 10/12 University Road, Leicester LE1 7RG Tel: 0116 255 9600 Fax: 0116 254 4051 Email: rct3@leicester.ac.uk; 16 Shanklin Avenue, Knighton, Leicester LE2 3RE Tel: 0116 270 4364 Fax: 0116 244 8319 — MB BS 1976 Lond.; MB BS Baroda 1976; MD (Pediat.) Baroda 1980; FRCP Lond. 1995; FRCP Ed. 1994; MRCP (UK) 1984; FRCPCH 1997; DCH RCP Lond. 1981. Cons. Paediat. Leics. & Rutland Healthcare NHS Trust Leicester; Jt. Edr. Ambulatory Child Health. Socs: Brit. Paediat. Neurol. Assn.; Brit. Assn. for Community Child Health; Assn. Child Psych. & Psych. Chairm. Leicester Br. 1997-99. Prev: Sen. Regist. (Community Paediat.) Camb. HA; Research Assoc. (Child Health) Univ. Newc.; SHO (Neonat. Paediat.) City Hosp. Nottm.

TAMIMI, Nihad Asad Mohammad Kent & Canterbury Hospital, Ethelbert Road, Canterbury CT1 3NG Tel: 01227 766877 Fax: 01227 783073; 24 Cowdrey Place, Canterbury CT1 3PD Tel: 01227 785932 — MB BS 1982 Punjab; MRCP (UK) 1991; MSc Cantab. 1998. Assoc. Specialist (Renal Med.) Kent & Canterbury Hosp.; Mem. Jordanian Med. Counc. Specialist Regist. Socs: Eur. Renal Assn.; Brit. Renal Assn. Prev: Research Regist. (Renal) Canterbury; Regist. (Renal) Canterbury; Regist. (Renal) Kuwait.

TAMIN, Jacques Sin Fat, TD MTL Medical Services, 24 Hatton Gardens, Liverpool L3 2AN Tel: 0151 227 1873 Fax: 0151 236 5857; 10 Leicester Road, Sale M33 7DU Tel: 0161 905 2024 — MB ChB 1980 Manch.; LLM Univ. Wales 1993; MFOM RCP Lond. 1994, AFOM 1991; MRCGP 1984; Dip. Pract. Dermat. Wales 1990; DRCOG 1983. (Manch.) Chief Occupat. Phys. MTL Med. Servs. Liverp.; Cons. Occupat. Health Ciba Specialty Chem. UK. Socs: Soc. Occupat. Med. & Medichem.; Chairm. Soc. of Occupat. Med., N.W. Gp. Prev: Cons. Occupat. Health Salford Community Healthcare Trust; Cons. Occupat. Health Ashworth Hosp.; Clin. Asst. (Occupat. Health) N. Manch. HA.

TAMIN, Sylvio Kin Fat 8 Fern Avenue, Flixton, Manchester M41 5RZ Tel: 0161 746 9579 — MB ChB 1983 Manch. Clin. Research Phys. Medeval Ltd. Univ. Manch. Prev: Clin. Asst. Antenatal Clinic Tameside.

TAMIZIAN, Onnig Derby City Hospital, Uttoxter Rd, Derby DE22 3NE Tel: 01332 340131; 27 Balmoral Drive, Bramcote Hills, Nottingham NG9 3FU Tel: 0115 925 8371 Email: onnig.tamizian@dial.pipex.com — BM BS 1993 Nottm.; BMSc (1st cl. Hons.) Nottm. 1991. SHO.(Geriats.) Roy Vic Hosp. Edin. Prev: Specialist Regist. (O & G) Mid Trent Rotat.; Ho. Off. (Med.) Nottm. City Hosp.; Ho. Off. (Surg. & Gyn.) Qu. Med. Centre Nottm.

TAMKIN, Elaine Jean Springfield House, New Lane, Patricroft, Eccles, Manchester M30 7JE — MB ChB 1976 Manch.

TAMKIN, William Patrick Borchardt Medical Centre, 62 Whitchurch Road, Withington, Manchester M20 1EB Tel: 0161 445 7475 Fax: 0161 448 0466 Email: bill.tamkin@gp-p840101.nhs.uk — MB ChB 1976 Manch.; MMedSc (Gen. Pract.) Leeds 1987; MRCGP 1983.

TAMLYN, Geoffrey William (retired) Lancaster House, Springfield Road, Chelmsford CM2 6BP Tel: 01245 357457 — MB BS 1954 Lond.; BA Open 1996; MRCGP 1971; DA Eng. 1959; DObst RCOG 1956. Prev: Med. Off. New Hall Sch.

TAMLYN, Gregory John The Health Centre, Cakeham Road, East Wittering, Chichester PO20 8BH Tel: 01243 673434 Fax: 01243 672563 — MB BS 1978 Lond.; MRCGP 1986; DRCOG 1981. (Guy's)

TAMLYN, Roger Stanley Pelham, MBE Warren House, 1 Leven House, Talbot Woods, Bournemouth BH4 9LH Tel: 01202 766493 Mobile: 07850 506971 — MB BS 1966 Lond.; FRCA; MRCS Eng. LRCP Lond. 1965; FFA RCS Eng. 1977. (King's Coll. Hosp.) On sabbatical; Sen. Cons. & Head Dept. Anaesth. Resusc. Qu. Eliz. Hosp. Lond. Socs: BMA; Assoc. Anaesth. Prev: Head (Anaesth. / Resusc. & Intens. Care) BM8 Rinteln BAOR; Head (Anaesth. / Resusc. & Intens. Care) Camb. Milit. Hosp.; Head (Anaesth. / Resusc. & Intens. Care) Duchess of Kent Hosp.

TAMMA, Mr Suryanarayana Goodhope Hospital, Rectory Road, Sutton Coldfield B75 7RR Tel: 0121 378 2211; 3 Clark Way, Heston, Hounslow TW5 9EG — MB BS 1977 Berhampur; FRCS Ed. 1987.

TAMMES, Bruin 14 Fitzjohn's Avenue, London NW3 Tel: 020 7435 1840 — MB ChB 1957 Ed.

TAMPI, Suresh Chandran 1 Millars Croft, Adlington St., Macclesfield SK10 1BD — MB BS 1973 Madras. (Jawaharlal Inst. Postgrad. Med. Pondicherry) Staff Surg. (A & E) Macclesfield Dist. Gen. Hosp.

TAMPIYAPPA, Tennent Nirushan 22 Harwood Avenue, Bromley BR1 3DU — MB BS 1994 Lond.

TAMS, Jonathan Tang Hall Surgery, 190 Tang Hall Lane, York YO10 3RL Tel: 01904 411139 Fax: 01904 431224; Church End House, Cow Catton, York YO41 1EA Tel: 01759 372777 — MB ChB 1976 Dundee; MRCGP 1982. Trainer (Gen. Pract.) York VTS.

TAMVAKOPOULOS, George Spiros 210 Herne Hill Road, London SE24 0AE — MB BS 1998 Lond.

TAN, Anton Tiauw-Lok 85 Highfield S., Birkenhead CH42 4ND — State Exam Med 1987 Dusseldorf.

TAN, Boon Bing 90 Meadow Road, Wolston, Coventry CV8 3JP — MB BS 1987 Lond.; MRCP (UK) 1991.

TAN, Boon Chong Flat 38 Block 6, Phase 3 Residence, Walsgrave General Hospital, Clifford Bridge Road, Coventry CV2 2DX — MB ChB 1993 Aberd.

TAN, Carol 3 Vyvyan Ter, Bristol BS8 3DF — MB ChB 1997 Bristol.

TAN, Chin Yau The Birmingham Skin Centre, Sheldon Block, City Hospital NHS Trust, Dudley Road, Birmingham B18 7QH Tel: 0121 554 3801 Fax: 0121 507 6644 — MB BS 1972 Malaysia; FRCP Lond. 1994; MRCP (UK) 1978. Cons. Dermat. Birm. Skin Centre City Hosp. NHS Trust; Hon. Cons. Dermat. Dent. Hosp. Birm.; Hon. Sen. Clin. Lect. Univ. Birm. Socs: BMA & Brit. Assn. Dermat. Prev: Sen. Regist. (Dermat.) N. Staffs. Hosp. Centre Stoke-on-Trent; Clin. Research Off. Welsh Nat. Sch. Med. Cardiff; Regist. (Dermat.) Univ. Hosp. Wales Cardiff.

TAN, Garry Daniel 18 Wragby Close, Bury BL8 1XD — MB ChB 1993 Manch.; MRCP (UK) 1996; DTM & H Lond. 1997.

TAN, Garryck Shern-Shih 58 Jalan SS 22/27, Damansara Jaya, Selangor 47400, Malaysia; 4 Lockesfield Place, Westferry Road, London E14 3AH — BM BS 1993 Nottm. SHO (Med.) Medway Hosp., Gillingham; SHO (A & E) Barnet Gen. Hosp. Socs: BMA. Prev: Med. Off. (Surg.) Klwang Dist. Hosp. Johor, Malaysia.

TAN, Geraldine Morriston Hospital, Morriston, Swansea SA6 6NL Tel: 01792 702222; 107 Wymering Mansions, Wymering Road, London W9 2NE — MB BCh 1994 Wales; MRCP (UK) 1997. (University of Wales College of Medicine) SHO (Gen. Med.) N. Middlx. Hosp. Lond.; Specialist Regist. (Elderly Care & Int. Med.) Roy. Lond. Hosp. Socs: BMA; Med. Protec. Soc.; MSS. Prev: SHO (Gen. Med.) Morriston Hosp. Swansea; Ho. Off. (Gen. Med.) Bronglais Hosp.; Ho. Off. (Gen. Surg. & Urol.) Morriston Hosp. Swansea.

TAN, Jessica Cheng-Ghim 2 Hill Place, Edinburgh EH8 9DS Tel: 0131 662 1105; 144B Jalan Utama, Pulau Pinang 10450, Malaysia Tel: 00 60 4 281118 — MB ChB 1985 Dundee; MRCP (UK) 1994; DCH RCPS Glas. 1990. Prev: GP Malaysia.

TAN, Mr John Bu Leong Quarter Jack Surgery, Rodways Corner, Wimborne BH21 1AP Tel: 01202 882112 Fax: 01202 882368 — MB ChB 1985 Bristol; FRCSI 1992; MRCGP 1993; DFFP 1995; DRCOG 1994. Prev: Trainee GP Bournemouth; SHO (Obst. & Gyn.) Poole; SHO (Paediat.) Yeovil.

TAN, Ju Le 16 Radcliffe Road, Croydon CR0 5QE — MB BS 1993 Newc.; MRCP. 1996. (Newc.) SHO (Med.) S. Cleveland Hosp. Prev: SHO Rotat. (Med.) S. Tyneside Dist. Hosp.

TAN, Kai Lee 4 Clearwater Way, Lakeside, Cardiff CF23 6DJ — MB BCh 1993 Wales; MBA Wales 1996; MRCP 1999. (Univ. Wales Coll. of Med.) Regist. (Med.) E. Glam. Gen. Hosp. Prev: SHO (Med.) P.ss of Wales Hosp. Bridgend; SHO (Med.) Caerphilly Dist. Miner's Hosp.

TAN, Kathryn Choon Beng 4 Wilde Place, Palmers Green, London N13 6DU — MB BCh 1984 Wales; MRCP (UK) 1987.

TAN, Kay-Sin Department of Neurology, Pinderfields General Hospital, Wakefield WF1 4DG — MB BS 1994 Melbourne; Dip. Med. Lond 1996; MRCP (UK) 1997. (Melbourne, Australia) Specialist Regist. (Neurol.) Pinderfields Gen. Hosp. Wakefield. Socs: Roy. Coll. Phys. Edin.; Liverp. Med. Inst.; Univ. Melbourne Med. Soc. Prev: SHO Rotat. (Med.) Roy. Liverp. Univ. Hosp.

TAN, Kee Sun Holywood Arches Health Centre, Westminster Avenue, Belfast BT4 1NS Tel: 028 9056 3354 Fax: 028 9065 3846; 17 Massey Avenue, Belfast BT4 2JT Tel: 01232 760200 — MRCS Eng. LRCP Lond. 1968.

TAN, Kelvin Hiang-Vee 20 Bruce Street, Cardiff CF24 4PJ — MB BCh 1993 Wales.

TAN, Mr Keng Kooi Yorkhill NHS Trust Hospital, Yorkhill Court, Block 7, Yorkhill, Glasgow G3 8SG — MB BS 1987 Lond.; FRCS Glas. 1993. SHO (Cardiothoracic) Papworth Hosp. Camb.

TAN, Khor Heng 91 Travellers Way, Bath Road, Hounslow TW3 — MB BS 1965 Queensland; MRCOG 1973. Prev: Regist. (O & G) Eliz. G. Anderson Hosp. Lond.; Ho. Off. Paediat., Gen. Surg. & O & G Govt. Hosps. Singapore.

TAN, Kia Meng Lister II, Plaistow Hospital, Samson Street, Plaistow, London E13 9EH Tel: 020 8586 6419 Fax: 020 8586 6420; 41 Colvestone Crescent, London E8 2LG — MB ChB 1982 Glas.; MSc Lond. 1991; MRCP (UK) 1987. (Univ. Glas.) Cons. Paediat. (Community Child Health) Newham Community Health Servs. NHS Trust.

TAN, Kia Soong 19 Blackness Avenue, Dundee DD2 1ET — MB ChB 1989 Glas.; MRCP (UK) 1994.

TAN, Kim-Heung 309 Cinnamon Wharf, Shad Thames, London SE1 2YJ — MB BS 1986 Lond.; MD Lond. 1995; MRCP (UK) 1989. (Middlx. Hosp. Med. Sch.) Sen. Regist. (Cardiol.) Guy's Hosp. Lond. Socs: Brit. Cardiac Soc.

TAN, Ko Yih Flat 10, 6 Riverview Place, Glasgow G5 8EB — MB ChB 1994 Ed.

TAN, Kristinn Siew-Wei 11 Grays Lane, Downley, High Wycombe HP13 5TZ — MB ChB 1998 Sheff.

TAN, Kuok Chuin Eddie 5 Hinchin Brook, Lenton, Nottingham NG7 2EF — BM BS 1997 Nottm.

TAN, Mr Lam Chin Flat 1, York House, Queen Alexandra Hospital, Southwick Hill Road, Cosham, Portsmouth PO6 3LY — MB ChB 1987 Ed.; FRCS Ed. 1992.

TAN, Lan Aik Rectory Road Surgery, 41 Rectory Road, Hadleigh, Benfleet SS7 2NA Tel: 01702 558147 — MB BS 1988 Lond. Regist. Rotat. (O & G) Whipps Cross Hosp., St. Bart. & Homerton Hosp. Lond. Prev: SHO (O & G) Chelsea & W.m. Hosp. & Univ. Coll. Hosp. Lond.

TAN, Li Tee Oncoloy Centre, Addenbrooke's NHS Trust, Hills Road, Cambridge CB2 2QQ Tel: 01223 216555 Fax: 01223 216589 Email: itant@doctors.org.uk; Email: litee.tan@which.net — MB BS 1985 Lond.; MRCP (UK) 1988; FRCR 1992. (Charing Cross and Westm.) Cons. Clin. Oncol. Addenbrooke's NHS Trust Camb.; Cons. Clin. Oncol. Hinchingbrooke Hospm Huntingdon, Cambs.; Cons. Cli. Oncol. PeterBoro. Dist. Gen. Hosp..

TAN, Lip-Bun Room G188, Jubilee Wing, Leeds General Infirmary, Leeds LS1 3EX Tel: 0113 392 5401 Fax: 0113 932 5395 — MB BChir 1980 Camb.; DPhil Oxf. 1977, BSc (Hons.) 1973; FRCP Lond. 1995; MRCP (UK) 1983; FESC 1994. (Oxford and Cambridge) Brit. Heart Foundat. Mautner Sen. Lect. (Cardiovasc. Med.) Univ. Leeds; Hon. Cons. Cardiol. St Jas. Univ. Hosp. & Gen. Infirm. at Leeds. Socs: Hon. Sec. Brit. Assn. of Cardiac Rehabil. Prev: Lect. (Cardiovasc. Med.) John Radcliffe Hosp. Oxf.; MRC Trav. Fell. Cardiovasc. Inst. Michael Reese Hosp. Chicago, USA; Regist. (Cardiol.) E. Birm. Hosp.

TAN, Maw Pin Nottingham City Hospital, Hucknall Rd, Nottingham NG5 1PB Tel: 0115 969 1169 — BM BS 1998 Nottm.; BMedSci Nottm. 1996. SHO. (Med.) Nottm City Hosp. Prev: Pre Regist HO. Derby City Gen. Derby.

TAN, Melanie Wai Ling St Edmunds College, Cambridge CB3 0BN — MB BS 1996 Melbourne.

TAN, Michael Chor Soon Flax Centre, Ardoyne Avenue, Belfast BT14 7AD; 7 Avonvale, Circular Road, Belfast BT4 2WA — MB BCh BAO 1986 Belf.; MRCGP 1990; DCH Dub. 1989.

TAN, Mr Michael Meng Say 11 Aylsham Mews, Swinton, Manchester M27 0LS — MB ChB 1982 Glas.; FRCS Ed. 1994.

***TAN, Nicholas Chien Lee** 10 Chatham Street, London SE17 1NY Email: drnicktan@yahoo.com — MB BS 1998 Lond.; MB BS Lond 1998; BSc (Hons) Lond. 1995.

TAN, Patrick Swee Teong Marcham Road Family Health Centre, Marcham Road, Abingdon OX14 1BT Tel: 01235 522602 Email: patrick.tan@gp-k84041.nhs.uk — BM BCh 1992 Oxf.; MRCGP 1996; DRCOG 1995; DCH RCP Lond 1994. (Oxford)

TAN, Peng Chiong Royal Free Hospital, Pond St, London NW3 2QG; 78 Avondale Ave, London N12 8EN — MB BS 1989 Lond.; MRCOG 1996; CCST COBS & GYNAE 1998. (Univ. Coll. & Middlx. Hosp.) Specialist Regist. (O & G) Roy. Free Hosp. Lond.; Research Fell.(Obs & Gyn.) Roy Free Hosp. Prev: Specialist Regist. Barnet Gen. Hosp. Lond.; Specialist Regist. Homerton Hosp. Lond.; Specialist Regist. St. Barth. Hosp. Lond.

TAN, Peng Hong Montrose, 3 Hendon Avenue, London N3 1UL Tel: 020 8349 4861 Fax: 020 8343 0694 Email: phtani@aol — MB BS 1995 Lond. (St Mary's Hosp. Med. Sch.) SHO Basic Surg. Rotat. W. Suff. Hosp. Bury St. Edmunds Suff.

TAN, Robert Seng-Hoon Orleigh Mount, St. Stephens Road, Lansdown, Bath BA1 5PN Tel: 01225 313488 — MB 1965 Camb.; BChir 1964; MA 1969 Camb.; FRCP Lond. 1983, M 1969. (St. Thos.) p/t Cons. Dermatol. Roy. United Hosp. Bath. Prev: Sen. Regist. (Dermat.) W.m. Hosp. Lond.; Regist. (Dermat.) St. Thos. Hosp. Lond.; Regist. (Med.) Poole Gen. Hosp.

TAN, Professor Seang Lin Department of Obstetrics & Gynaecology, McGill University, Royal Victoria Hospital, Women's Pavilion, 687 Pine Avenue West, Montreal H31 1A1, Canada Tel: 00 1 514 8431658 Fax: 00 1 514 8431678; The London Women's Clinic, 113/115 Harley St, London W1G 6AP Tel: 0207 487 5050 Fax: 0207435 5850 — MB BS 1977 Singapore; MMed (Obst. & Gyn.) Singapore 1982; FRCSC 1995; FRCOG 1995, M 1983; T(OG) 1991. James Edmund Dodds Prof. & Chairm. Dept. Obst. & Gyn. McGill Univ. & Obst. & Gyn. in Chief Roy. Vict. Hosp. Montreal, Canada. Socs: Fell. Roy. Soc. Med.; Amer. Fertil. Soc.; Eur. Soc. Human Reproduc. & Embryol. Prev: Cons. & Sen. Lect. (Obst. & Gyn.) King's Coll. Sch. Med. & Dent. Lond.; Sen. Research Fell. Dept. Obst. & Gyn. King's Coll. Sch. Med. & Dent. Lond.; Sen. Regist. Kandau Karbau Hosp., Singapore.

TAN, Sen Hean 217 Gammons Lane, Watford WD24 5JJ — MB BCh BAO 1966 NUI.

TAN, Shani 37 Mount Pleasant Road, Brondesbury Park, London NW10 3EG Tel: 020 8459 3680; 70 Fernhill Road, Singapore 1025, Singapore — MB BS 1982 Singapore; FFA RCS Eng. 1988. Hon. Sen. Regist. Hosp. for Sick Childr. Lond.; Clin. Teach. (Anaesth.) Fac. Med. Nat. Univ. Singapore. Socs: Singapore Soc. Anaesthesiol. Prev: Sen. Regist. (Anaesth.) Singapore Gen. Hosp.; Regist. (Anaesth.) Hammersmith Hosp. Lond.

TAN, Si-Yen 23 Buttermere Drive, London SW15 2HW — MB ChB 1984 Ed.; MD Ed. 1996; MRCP (UK) 1987. Cons. Nephrol. King's Coll. Hosp. Lond. Socs: Eur. Dialysis & Transpl. Assn.; Internat. Soc. Nephrol.; Renal Assn. Prev: Sen. Regist. & Hon. Lect. (Renal) Hammersmith Hosp. Lond.; Research Fell. & Hon. Sen. Regist. Hammersmith Hosp. Lond.; Regist. (Renal) Roy. Infirm. Edin.

TAN, Sil Yee c/o Dr Peter Godfrey, Charlotte Keel Health Centre, Seymore Road, Easton, Bristol BS5 0UA; PO Box 44, Seri Complex 2600, Brunei Darussalam — MB ChB 1991 Bristol.

TAN, Simon 47 Vista Road, Clacton-on-Sea CO15 6DG — MB BS 1994 Lond.

TAN, Stella Veronica Su-Ming Neuromuscular Unit, Department of Neurology, Charing Cross Hospital, London W6 8RF — MB BS 1986 Lond.; BSc (Infec. & Immunity, 1st cl. Hons.) Lond. 1983, MB BS 1986; MRCP (UK) 1989. Research Regist. (Neurol.) Char. Cross & Chelsea & W.m. Hosps. Lond. Prev: Regist. (Neurol.) Atkinson Morley's Hosp. Lond.

TAN

TAN, Su-Yen 481C Holloway Road, London N19 4DD — MB ChB 1996 Manch.

TAN, Suan Cheng Room 2/10, 30 Pembridge Gardens, London W2 4DX — MB BS 1998 Lond.

TAN, Susern Flat 4, 377 Crookesmoor Road, Sheffield S10 1BD — MB ChB 1994 Sheff.

TAN, Swee Wan Elm Lodge, 64 Elm Grove, London SE15 5DE Tel: 020 8692 2209 — MB BS 1964 Lond.; DObst RCOG 1969. (St. Thos.)

TAN, Swee Yaw 8/7 West Powburn, Edinburgh EH9 3EN — MB ChB 1998 Ed.

TAN, Wee Ming Westgate Practice, Greenhill Health Centre, Church St., Lichfield WS13 6JL; 30 Peak Close, Thirlmere Park, Armitage, Rugeley WS15 4TY — MB ChB 1989 Sheff. Trainee GP Lichfield VTS. Prev: SHO (Gen. Med.) Burton Gen. Hosp.

TAN, Wei Beng CF2 Rosemount Hall, Farmer's Hall Lane, Aberdeen AB25 4XF — MB ChB 1998 Aberd.

TAN, Wen-Hann Room 39 Block C11, Curie Court, Queens Medical Centre, Derby Road, Nottingham NG7 2UH — BM BS 1998 Nottm.

TAN, Wie-Tiong 8 Vicarage Lane, Kings Langley WD4 9HR — LRCP LRCS 1960 Ed.; LRCP LRCS Ed. LRFPS Glas. 1960; DMRD Ed. 1964.

TAN, Yan Mei Darlington Memorial Hospital, Hollyhurst Road, Darlington DL3 6HX Tel: 01325 380100; 12 Lorong 14/37B, Petaling Jaya, Selangor 46100, Malaysia Tel: 01 06 03 7560096 — MB ChB 1990 Glas.; MRCP (UK) 1994. SHO Darlington Memor. Hosp. S. Durh. HA. Prev: SHO Castle Hill Hosp. E. Yorks. HA.

TAN, Yeh Mao 8 Sycamore Dr, Chesterfield S44 5DX Tel: 01246 277271 Ext: 3937 Fax: 01246 277271 X3937 Email: ymtan@doctors.org.uk; 395H Taman Nam Seng, Kg Lapan, 75200 Melaka, Malaysia Tel: 00 60 6 282 8970 — MB ChB 1993 Aberd. SHO (Gen. Surg.) Chesterfield & N. Derbysh. Roy. Hosp. Socs: MDU; Fell. Manch. Med. Soc.; BMA. Prev: SHO Rotat. (Surg.) Blackburn Roy. Infirm.; SHO (A & E) Trafford Gen. Hosp. Manch.; SHO (Gen. Surg.) Lorn & Is.s DGH, oban.

TAN, Yoke Khim Balmoral Court, Flatt 22, 20 Queens Terrace, London NW8 6DW — MB BS 1986 Singapore.

TAN ENG LOOI, Carolyn 22 Downsview Road, London SE19 3XB — MB BS 1980 Malaya; FRCS Ed. 1985; FRCS Glas. 1985.

TAN HARK HONG, Kenneth Department of Paediatrics, Rotherham District General Hospital, Moorgate Road, Rotherham S60 2UD — MB BS 1991 Melbourne.

TAN PHOAY LAY, Christina The Health Centre, 120 Bedford Hill, Balham, London SW12 9HS Tel: 020 8673 1720 — MB BS 1985 Lond.; MRCGP 1993; DRCOG 1989. (Lond. Hosp.) Prev: SHO (O & G) The Lond. Hosp.

TAN SWEE CHUAN, Mr Peter c/o Vascular Research Division, Brigham & Women's Hospital, 221 Longwood Avenue, LMRC Room 401, Boston MA 02115, USA; 30 Falsgrave Crescent, Burton Stone Lane, York YO30 7AZ Tel: 01904 630091 — BM 1989 Soton.; FRCS Eng. 1993. SHO Rotat. (Surg.) York Dist. Hosp.

TAN TONG KHEE, Dr Ilford Cottage, Clifton St., Laugharne, Carmarthen SA33 4QG — MB BS 1986 Singapore; FFA RCSI 1995.

TANAKA, Hiro 6 Treherbert Street, Cathays, Cardiff CF24 4JN Tel: 029 2038 7190 — MB BCh 1994 Wales. Resid. Med. Off. BUPA Hosp. Pentwyn. Prev: Ho. Off. (Haemat.) Univ. Hosp. Wales Cardiff; Ho. Off. (Gen. Med. & Gen. Surg.) Llandough Hosp.

TANDAY, Jashpal Singh The Thorndike Centre, Longley Road, Rochester ME1 2TH Tel: 01634 817217 — MB BCh 1975 Wales; MRCGP 1980; DRCOG 1978. GP Tutor Medway.

TANDON, Anand Prakash Calderdale Royal Hospital, Salterhebble, Halifax HX3 0PW Tel: 01422 224231 Fax: 01422 224471; Heath Lodge, Heath Lane, Halifax HX3 0BZ Tel: 01422 369960 — MD (Med.) Lucknow 1968, MB BS 1964; FRCP Lond. 1988; MRCP (UK) 1973. p/t Cons. Cardiol., Calderdale Roy. Hosp.; Clin. Dir. Acute Med. Socs: Brit. Cardiac Soc. & Brit. Pacing & Electrophys. Gp. Prev: Tutor (Med.) Univ. Leeds; Sen. Regist. (Cardiol.) Leeds Gen. Infirm.; Cons. Phys. & Cardiol. Roy. Halifax Infirm. & Halifax Gen. Hosp.

TANDON, Asha The Surgery, 62 Southend Road, Rainham RM13 7XJ Tel: 01708 52510 — MB BS 1956 Lucknow; FFA RCS Eng. 1969; DA Eng. 1960. (King Geo. Med. Coll.) Socs: BMA (Exec. Comm. Havering Div.). Prev: Ho. Surg. Dept. O & G King Geo. Med. Coll. Lucknow; SHO (Anaesth.) Ipswich & E. Suff. Hosp. Ipswich; Anaesth. Regist. OldCh. & Rush Green Hosps. Romford.

TANDON, Bhaskar 4 Deene Close, Grimsby DN34 5XB — MB BS 1969 Delhi.

TANDON, Dinesh Kumar 19 Locksley Close, Stockport SK4 2LW — MB BS 1966 Lucknow; DA Eng. 1973. (G.S.V.M. Med. Coll. Kanpur)

TANDON, H P Penketh Health Centre, Honiton Way, Penketh, Warrington WA5 2EY Tel: 01925 725644 Fax: 01925 791017 — MB BS 1963 Vikram; MB BS 1963 Vikram.

TANDON, Kopal 4 The Drive, Longton, Preston PR4 5AJ — BM BCh 1997 Oxf.

TANDON, Mr Mahendra Kishore Frimley Park Hospital, Portsmouth Road, Frimley, Camberley GU16 7UJ Tel: 01276 692777; 5 Orchard End, Rowledge, Farnham GU10 4EE Tel: 0125 125 4452 — MB BS 1963 Lucknow; FRCS Ed. (Ophth.) 1976; DO RCPSI 1970. (K.G.M. Coll. Lucknow) Cons. Ophth. Surg. Frimley Pk. Hosp. & Farnham Hosp. Prev: Sen. Regist (Ophth.) Kent Co. Ophth. Hosp. Maidstone; Regist. (Ophth.) Centr. Middlx. Hosp. Lond.; Out-Pat. Off. Moorfields Eye Hosp. Lond.

TANDON, Naresh Kumar 161 Woodlands Road, Sparkhill, Birmingham B11 4ER — MB ChB 1993 Dundee.

TANDON, Pradip Kumar Tandon, 71 Grove Road, Wallasey CH45 3HF Tel: 0151 639 4616 Fax: 0151 637 0182; 18 Woodbank Park, Oxton, Birkenhead CH43 9WN Tel: 0151 652 7659 Fax: 0151 637 0182 — MB BS 1969 Lucknow; DTM & H Liverp. 1980. Community Paediat. Merseyside; Med. Adviser, Wirral Unified Housing. Socs: (Dep. Treas.) Overseas Doctors Assn.; BMA. Prev: SCMO Manch.

TANDON, R Tandon, 71 Grove Road, Wallasey CH45 3HF Tel: 0151 639 4616 Fax: 0151 637 0182 — Dip Ven. Liverpool 1993; DCH 1971; MBBS 1970. (Kanpur, India)

TANDON, Mr Roop Kishore New Cross Hospital, The Royal Wolverhampton Hospitals NHS Trust, Wolverhampton WV10 0QP Tel: 01902 642965; 17 Addisland Court, Holland Villas Road, London W14 8DA Tel: 020 7603 6667 — MB BS Andhra 1961; FRCS Ed. 1970. Cons. Orthop. Roy. Hosp. Wolverhampton. Socs: Brit. Orthop. Assn. Prev: Regist. Heatherwood Hosp. Ascot & Roy. Postgrad. Med. Sch. Hammersmith Hosp. Lond.

TANDON, Sankalap 14 Squirrel Way, Loughborough LE11 3GP — BM BS 1998 Nottm.; BM BS Nottm 1998.

TANDON, Sneh Lata Rochester Health Centre, Delce Road, Rochester ME1 2EL Tel: 01634 401111; 127 Wilson Avenue, Rochester ME1 2SL Tel: 01634 812064 — MB BS 1966 Lucknow; BSc, MB BS Lucknow 1966. (G.S.V.M. Med. Coll. Kanpur) Family Plann. Assn. & IUCD Instruc. Prev: Trainee GP Brent & Harrow VTS; SHO (Surg.) Ulster Hosp. Belf.; SHO (O & G) P. of Wales Gen. Hosp. Lond.

TANDON, Mr Subash Chander Royal Hospital, Cleveland Rdl., Wolverhampton Tel: 01902 307999; 6 Rowallane Close, Bangor BT19 7SS Tel: 01247 274508 — MB BCh BAO 1988 Belf.; FRCSI 1992. Regist. (Orthop.) Roy. Hosp. Wolverhampton. Socs: BMA & Brit. Orthop. Assn. Prev: SHO (Cas.) E. HB; Ho. Off. Belf. City Hosp.

TANDON, Urmila Rani 161 Woodlands Road, Sparkhill, Birmingham B11 4ER — MB ChB 1994 Leic.

TANDY, Andrew David Department of Child Health, Musgrove Park Hospital, Taunton TA1 5DA Tel: 01823 342690 Fax: 01823 333 6877 — MB BS 1981 Lond.; BSc (Hons.) Lond. 1978; MRCP (UK) 1990; FRCPCH 1997; MRCGP 1985; T(M) (Paediat.) 1993; T(GP) 1991; DCH RCP Lond. 1985; DRCOG 1983. (Univ. Coll. Hosp.) Cons. Paediat. Taunton & Som. Hosp. Socs: BMA; SW Paediat. Club; Brit. Assn. Community Child Health. Prev: Lect. & Hon. Sen. Regist. (Child Health) Univ. Nottm.; Regist. Roy. United Hosp. Bath; Ho. Phys. Univ. Coll. Hosp. Lond.

TANDY, Catherine Lucia 23 Temple Row Close, Leeds LS15 9HR — MB ChB 1996 Leeds.

TANDY, George Graham Byways, Stockswell Road, Hough Green, Widnes WA8 — MRCS Eng. LRCP Lond. 1952. (Liverp.)

TANDY, Jane Catherine 17 Poyner Close, Prices Lodge, Fareham PO16 7YQ — MB ChB 1983 Ed.; MRCP (UK) 1986. Cons. c/o Elderly Qu. Alexandra Hosp. Portsmouth.

TANEGA, Kara Rosemary McKenna Ferryview Health Centre, 25 John Wilson Street, Woolwich, London SE18 6PZ Tel: 020 8319 5400 Fax: 020 8319 5404 — MB BS 1988 Lond.

TANEJA, Ashok West End Clinic, West End Lane, Rossington, Doncaster DN11 0PQ Tel: 01302 865865 Fax: 01302 868346 — MB BS 1981 Delhi; MRCGP 1991.

TANG, Alan Leong Fai The Florey Unit, Royal Berkshire Hospital, Reading RG1 5AN Tel: 0118 987 7205 Fax: 0118 987 7211 Email: alan.tang@rbbh-tr.anglox.nhs.uk — MB BS 1983 Lond.; FRCP 1996; DFFP 1996; Dip. GU Med. Soc. Apoth. Lond. 1988. (King's Coll.) Cons. Phys. Genitourin. Med. Roy. Berks. Hosp. Reading; Vis. Cons., HMYOI & RC Reading, Forbury Rd, Reading. Socs: BMA (Hon. Sec. W. Berks. Div.); Assn. Genitourin. Med.; Med. Soc. Study VD, Counc. Mem. Prev: Cons. Phys. Genitourin. Med. Greenwich Dist. Hosp. Lond.; Sen. Regist. (Gen. & Genitourin. Med.) St. Thos. Hosp. Lond.; SHO (Med.) Whittington Hosp. Lond.

TANG, Mr Augustine Tak-Ming Dept. of Cardiothoracic Surgery, Southampon General Hospital, Tremona Rd, Southampton SO16 6YD Tel: 02380 777222 — BM BS 1990 Nottm.; BMedSci (Hons.) Nottm. 1988; FRCS Ed. 1994; DM Nottm. 1998. Specialist Regist. (Cardiol Surg.) Wessex.; Hon Surg Research Fell. Liverp. Univ. Hosps. NHS Trust. Socs: Soc. Of Cardiothoracic Surg.s of GB & Irel.; Europ. Assn. For Cardiothoracic Surg.; Cardiac Surgic. Research Club. Prev: Brit. Heart Foundat. Research Fell. (Cardiothoracic Surg.) Manch. & Liverp.

TANG, Bruce Yew Wai Annfield Medical Centre, 16 Annfield Place, Glasgow G31 2XE Tel: 0141 554 2989 Fax: 0141 550 3965; 9 Sandfield Avenue, Milngavie, Glasgow G62 8NR Tel: 0141 956 6270 — MB ChB 1984 Dundee; MRCGP 1990; DRCOG 1990.

***TANG, Carol Pui-Yi** 128 Lauriston Road, London E9 7LH — MB BCh 1998 Wales.

TANG, Carol Wei Man 37 High Street, Cricklade, Swindon SN6 6AY — MB BCh 1997 Wales. (University of Wales College of Medicine) GP VTS P.ss of Wales Hosp. Bridgend. Prev: Pre-Regist. Ho. Off. E. Glam. Hosp. Ch. Village & Glan Clwyd Hosp. Bodelwyddan Rhyl.

TANG, Christopher Yeong Kee 97 Waterloo Road, Romford RM7 0AA — MRCS Eng. LRCP Lond. 1971.

TANG, Mr Daniel Tung Shing 16 Moorfield Road, Bingley BD16 1PS — MB ChB 1982 Sheff.; FRCS Ed. 1991. (Sheff.) Cons. Orthop. Surg. Airedale Gen. Hosp. W. Yorks. Socs: BMA.

TANG, Dannis Wing Kuen Suite 5, Egmont House, 116 Shaftesbury Avenue, London W1V 7DJ — MB ChB 1984 Sheff.; MRCP Paediat. (UK) 1987; DCH RCPS Glas. 1992; DRCOG 1990; MD Sheffield 1997. (Sheffield) Research Fell. Qu. Charlotte's & Chelsea Hosp. Lond.

TANG, Joseph Gordon 200 Richmond Road, Kingston upon Thames KT2 5HE — BChir 1987 Camb.

TANG, Kare Hung 174 Balgores Lane, Romford RM2 6BS — BM 1991 Soton.

TANG, Kim Man Morrill Street Health Centre, Morrill Street, Holderness Road, Hull HU9 2LJ Tel: 01482 323398 Fax: 01482 217957 — MB ChB 1980 Manch. (Manch.)

TANG, Kwok Hung 172 Balgores Lane, Gidea Park, Romford RM2 6BS — MB ChB 1991 Ed.; MRCP (UK) 1995. Specialist Regist. Rotat. (Gastroenterol.) S. Thames Region. Prev: Regist. (Gastroenterol. & Gen. Med.) Greenwich Lond.; Ho. Off. Roy. Infirm. Edin. & City Hosp.

TANG, Reginald Zhen-Guo 26 Windermere Crescent, Belfast BT8 6XY — MB BCh BAO 1991 Belf.

TANG, Sek Cheung 79 Brim Hill, London N2 0EZ — MB BS 1978 Lond.; MRCS Eng. LRCP Lond. 1978.

TANG, Siu Cheung 28A Egerton Road, Hartlepool TS26 0BW — MB BS 1977 Hong Kong; T(S) 1991.

TANG, Sui Yuen 2 Foreman Place, Merthyr Tydfil CF47 0EJ — MB BS 1998 Lond.

TANG, Thomas Man Hay G/R, 1 Naseby Avenue, Glasgow G11 7JQ — MB ChB 1990 Aberd. SHO Ill Bellstall Matern. Hosp. Prev: SHO (O & G) Grampian HB.

TANG, Wing Yu 9 Triscombe Drive, Llandaff, Cardiff CF5 2PN — MB BCh 1998 Wales.

TANG, Yew Cheen Salcombe Gardens, 8 Salcombe Gardens, Mill Hill, London NW7 2NT Tel: 020 8959 6592 Fax: 020 8959 0112 — BM 1982 Soton.

TANG, Yuen-Tsang Katherine 26 Woodberry Way, London N12 0HG — MB BS 1956 Hong Kong.

TANG, Yuet Yee Mary Orchard Surgery, Christchurch Medical Centre, Purewell Cross Road, Christchurch BH23 5ET Tel: 01202 481902 Fax: 01202 486887 — MB ChB 1991 Manch.; MRCGP 1996. (Univ. Manch.)

TANG ING CHING, John Cottage 42, Inverclyde Royal NHS Trust, Larkfield Road, Greenock PA16 0XN — MB BS 1990 Queensland.

TANG SIP SHIONG, Sylvia Dept of Psychiatry, Royal Free Hospital, Pond St, London NW3 — MB BS 1992 Lond.; MRCPsych 1997. Specialist Regist. (Psychiat) Roy Free Hosp. Lond.

TANGANG, Vivian Ngwu Flat 10, Emmanuel House, Distin St., London SE11 6QL — MB BS 1997 Lond.

TANGNEY, Anne-Marie c/o Chemistry Department, Lensfield Road, Cambridge CB2 1E — MB ChB 1990 Auckland; T(GP) 1994.

TANGNEY, David Joseph High Street Surgery, 1st Floor, 97-101 High Street, Fort William PH33 6DG Tel: 01397 703773 Fax: 01397 701068 — MB BCh BAO 1985 NUI.

TANGRI, Arun Kumar Riverlyn Medical Centre, Station Road, Bulwell, Nottingham NG6 9AA Tel: 0115 927 9214 Fax: 0115 977 0971; 37 Gunnersbury Way, Nuthall, Nottingham NG16 1QD Tel: 0115 975 4323 — MB BS 1975 Poona; MRCS Eng. LRCP Lond. 1989. (Armed Forces Med. Coll. Poona, India)

TANGRI, Charu Derby Royal Infirmary, London Road, Derby DE1 2QY; 37 Gunnersbury Way, Nuthall, Nottingham NG16 1QD Tel: 0115 975 4323 — MB BS 1979 Delhi; LRCP LRCS Ed. LRCPS Glas. 1986; DO RCPSI 1985. Staff Grade (Psychiat.) Derby Roy. Infirm.

TANGYE, Sheila Royse (retired) 89 Lonsdale Road, Barnes, London SW13 9DA Tel: 020 8748 4574 — BM BCh 1943 Oxf.; MA Oxf. 1947, DM 1951; MRCPsych 1971; DCH Eng. 1947, DPM 1960. Prev: Cons. Psychiat. Roy. Albert Hosp. Lancaster.

TANKARD, Justin Graham Deansgate Health Centre, Deansgate, Bolton BL1 1HQ — BM BS 1990 Nottm.; BMedSci. (Hons.) Nottm. 1988; MRCGP 1995. Prev: GP/Regist. W. Houghton; SHO (O & G & Paediat.) Bolton Gen. Hosp.

TANKEL, Mr Henry Isidore, OBE (retired) 26 Dalziel Drive, Glasgow G41 4PU Tel: 0141 423 5830 Fax: 0141 424 3648 — MB ChB (Commend.) Glas. 1948; MD (Commend.) Glas. 1958; FRCS Ed. 1954; FRFPS Glas. 1962. Cons. Surg. Glas. Prev: Cons. Surg. S.. Gen. Hosp. Glas.

TANKEL, Jeremy William Lanceburn Health Centre, Clarendon Surgery, Churchill Way, Salford M6 5QX Tel: 0161 736 4529 Fax: 0161 736 2724 — MB ChB 1979 Glas.; DMJ 1998; MRCGP 1986; FRCS Glas. 1983. Partner Gen. Pract.; Police Surg.; Hon. Lect. Gen. Pract. Univ. of Manch.

***TANN, Carolyn Julie** 35 Grange Road, Shrewsbury SY3 9DG Email: callytann@hotmail.com — MB ChB 1997 Birm.

TANN, Oliver Richard Thanet House, High St., Chalford, Stroud GL6 8DH — MB BS 1998 Lond.

TANNA, Amratlal Gokaldas 351 London Road, Stoneygate, Leicester LE2 3JX Tel: 0116 270 7086 — MB BS 1966 Baroda; DPM Eng. 1975.

TANNA, Aruna Dhirendra Upton Surgery, Waggon Lane, Upton, Pontefract WF9 1JS Tel: 01977 647521; 3 Rosslyn Close, Ackworth, Pontefract WF7 7QF Tel: 01977 610308 — MB BS 1969 Bombay. (Grant Med. Coll.)

TANNA, Dhirendra Ranchhoddas (retired) Upton Surgery, Waggon Lane, Upton, Pontefract WF9 1JS Tel: 01977 647521 — MB BS 1972 Bombay. Clin. Asst. (Psychogeriat.) Pontefract HA.

TANNA, Kirit Harold Hill Centre, Gooshays Drive, Romford RM3 9JP Tel: 01708 343815 Fax: 01708 379790 — MB BS 1979 Gujarat; MB BS 1979 Gujarat.

TANNA, Meeta 4 Winchester Mews, 12A Winn Road, Southampton SO17 1ET — BM 1997 Soton. SHO (Paediat.) Soton. Gen. Hosp. Socs: BMA; MPS. Prev: PRHO (Med.) Soton.; PRHO (Surg.) Dorchester.

TANNA, Natwarlal Keshavji Flat 6, Cedar Grange, 50 Ducks Hill Road, Northwood HA6 2SU Tel: 01923 450815 Fax: 01923 450815 — MB BS 1962 Bombay; DA Eng. 1968.

TANNA, Rajendra 392 Greenlane Road, Leicester LE5 4NE — MB ChB 1995 Leic.

TANNA, Sandeep Natwarlal 55 Riverside Walk, Wickford SS12 0DU — MB BS 1986 Lond.; MRCP (UK) 1989.

TANNA

TANNA, Shobhana Amritlal 351 London Road, Stoneygate, Leicester LE2 3JX Tel: 0116 270 7086 — MB BS 1964 Baroda; DPM Lond. 1974. (Baroda) SCMO (Community Med.) Leics. HA.

TANNA, Vikram Narandas Morarji Clarendon Medical Practice, Clarendon Street, Hyde SK14 2AQ Tel: 0161 368 5224 Fax: 0161 368 4767 — MB BS 1978 Lond.; MSc 1999 Univ. of Manchester; FRCGP 1997; MRCGP 1983; DRCOG 1981; MA Oxf. 1974. (Middlx.) Gen. Med. Practitioner; GP Postgrad. Tutor Tameside. Socs: Fell. Manch. Med. Soc. Prev: Trainee GP Bramhall Health Centre; SHO Preston VTS; Ho. Surg. Christie Hosp. Manch.

TANNA, Viral The Barnard Medical Practice, 43 Granville Road, Sidcup DA14 4TA — MB BS 1989 Lond.; DRCOG 1993; DFFP 1993.

TANNAHILL, Professor Andrew James Health Education Board for Scotland, Woodburn House, Canaan Lane, Edinburgh EH10 4SG Tel: 0131 536 5500 Fax: 0131 536 5501 — MB ChB 1977 Glas.; MB ChB (Hons.) Glas. 1977; MSc (Community Med.) Ed. 1982; FRCP Ed. 1996; FFPHM RCP (UK) 1992; MFCM RCP (UK) 1985; FRCP (Glas.) 1999. (Univ. Glas.) Chief Exec.Health Educat. Bd. Scotl.; Vis. Prof. (Centre for Exercise Sci. & Med.) Univ. Glas.; Hon. Sen. Lect. (Epidemiol. & Pub. Health) Univ. Dundee; Hon. Sen. Lect. (Pub. Health) Univ. Glas.; Hon. Fell. (Pub. Health Scis.) Univ. Edin. Prev: Sen. Lect. (Pub. Health Med.) Univ. Glas. & Hon. Cons. Pub. Health Med. Gtr. Glas. HB; Specialist Community Med. E. Anglian RHA & Assoc. Lect. (Community Med.) Univ. Camb.

TANNAHILL, Mary Mabel (retired) 12 The Wigdale, Hawarden, Deeside CH5 3LL Tel: 01244 520321 Email: tanjo@doctors.org.uk — MB ChB 1957 Glas.; FRCPsych 1979, M 1971; DPM Eng. 1962; DPH Lond. 1960. Cons. Psychiat. N. Wales Hosp. Denbigh. Prev: Sen. Lect. (Psychol. Med.) St. Thos. Hosp. Lond.

TANNER, Andrew Roger North Tees General Hospital, Hardwick, Stockton-on-Tees TS19 8PE Tel: 01642 617617 Fax: 01642 624089 — MB BChir 1973 Camb.; BA Camb. 1969, MA, MB BChir 1973; DM Soton. 1982; FRCP Lond. 1991; FRCP Ed. 1989; MRCP (UK) 1975; FRACP 1979. (Camb. & Guy's) Cons. Phys. N. Tees Gen. Hosp. Socs: Brit. Soc. Gastroenterol. Prev: Lect. (Med.) Soton. Gen. Hosp.; Lect. (Med.) Univ. Qu.sland & Brisbane, Austral.; Sen. Regist. Roy. Brisbane Hosp. Austral.

TANNER, Carless Paul (retired) Rosegarth, Backcrofts, Rothbury, Morpeth NE65 7XY Tel: 01669 21032 — MB BS 1945 Durh.; FRCGP 1976, M 1958. Prev: Course Organiser Regional Postgrad. Inst. Med. Sch. Newc.

TANNER, Colin Cedric Frimley Green Medical Centre, 1 Beech Road, Frimley Green, Camberley GU16 6QQ Tel: 01252 835016 Fax: 01252 837908; 5 Henley Drive, Frimley Green, Camberley GU16 6NE — MB BS 1981 Lond.; DRCOG 1985. (St. Geo.)

TANNER, Elizabeth Irene (retired) 3 Netheravon Road, Salisbury SP1 3BJ Tel: 01722 322933 — MB BChir 1954 Camb.; Dip. Bact. Lond 1961; FRCPath 1976, M 1964. Prev: Cons. Bacteriol. Pub. Health Laborat. Epsom.

TANNER, Gregory Peter Gerrard Taunton Road Medical Centre, 12-16 Taunton Road, Bridgwater TA6 3LS Tel: 01278 444400 Fax: 01278 423691; Crossways Barn, Main Road, Middlezoy, Bridgwater TA6 3LS Tel: 01278 444158 — MB BS 1989 Lond.; BSc (Chem.) Lond. 1984, MB BS 1989; MRCGP 1994; DFFP 1994; DGM RCP Lond. 1993. GP. Med Centre. Bridgwater.

TANNER, Helena Taunton Road Medical Centre, 12-16 Taunton Road, Bridgwater TA6 3LS Tel: 01278 444400 Fax: 01278 423691; Crossways Barn, Main Road, Middlezoy, Bridgwater TA7 0PD — MB BS 1989 Lond.

TANNER, James Mourilyan Stentwood Coach house, Dunkeswell, Honiton EX14 4RW Email: jgtanner@aol.com — MB BS 1944 Lond.; MD Penna. 1944; PhD Lond. 1953, DSc 1957; FRCP Lond. 1972, M 1963; FRCPsych 1971; DPM Lond. 1946. (St. Mary's & Univ. Penna., Philadelphia) Emerit. Prof. Child. Health & Growth Univ. Lond. Socs: Soc. Study Human Biol.; BMA. Prev: Sen. Lect. (Physiol.) St. Thos. Hosp. Med. Sch.; Ho. Phys. Johns Hopkins Hosp. Baltimore; Demonst. (Human Anat.) Oxf.

TANNER, John Albert Oving Clinic, Church Lane, Oving, Chichester PO20 6DG Tel: 01243 773167 Fax: 01243 530567; Tangmere Cottage, Tangmere, Chichester PO20 6HW Tel: 01243 537435 — MB BS 1977 Lond.; BSc (Psychol.) Lond. 1973; Dip. Musculoskell Med. Soc. Apoth. Lond. 1993; Dip. Sports Med. Lond 1993. (Lond. Hosp.) Indep. Orthop. & Sports Phys. & Staff Grade Pain Clinic Odstock Rehabil. Hosp. Salisbury; Mem. Brit. (Treas. Counc.) Inst. Musculoskeletal Med.; Mem. Phys. (Chairm.) Research Foundat. (UK). Socs: Pain Soc.; Brit. Assn. Sport & Med.; Internat. Intradiscal Ther. Soc. Prev: Med. Staff King. Edwd. VII Hosp. Bermuda; Dir. Milton Keynes Sports Injury Clinic.

TANNER, John Gwyn Silverbrook, Rhiwsaeson, Pontyclun CF7 — MB BCh 1970 Wales. (Welsh Nat. Sch. Med.)

TANNER, John Winton (retired) 119 Stafford Road, Bloxwich, Walsall WS3 3PG Tel: 01922 476089 — MB ChB 1951 Birm.; MRCGP 1964. Prev: GP Walsall.

TANNER, Kirsty Jayne 149 Ship Lane, Farnborough GU14 8BJ — MB BS 1998 Newc.

TANNER, Professor Malcolm Stuart Division of Child Health, University of Sheffield, The Children's Hospital, Western Bank, Sheffield S10 2TH Tel: 01142 717228 Fax: 01142 755364 Email: m.s.tanner@sheffield.ac.uk — MB BS Lond. 1969; MSc (Biochem.) Lond. 1977, BSc (1st cl. Hons.) (Pharmacol.) 1966; FRCP Lond.1986; MRCP (UK) 1974; MRCS Eng. LRCP Lond. 1969; DCH Eng. 1972. (King's Coll. Hosp.) Prof. Paediat. Univ. Sheff.; Non-Exec. Dir. Sheff. Childr. Hosp. NHS Trust. Socs: Brit. Soc. Gastroenterol.; Roy. Coll. Paediat. & Child Health; Eur. Soc. Paediat. Gastroenterol. & Nutrit. Prev: Sen. Lect. (Child Health) Univ. Leicester.

TANNER, Mark Hertford County Hospital, North Road, Potters Bar SG14 1LP — MB BCh 1983 Wales; LLM 1999; MRCPsych 1994. Cons. (Psychiat.) Herford Co. Hosp.; Barrister 1986 Middle Temple. Prev: Regist. (Psychiat.) St. Bernard's Hosp. Ealing; Clin. Research Fell. St. Mary's Hosp. Lond.; Sen. Regist., St Clements Hosp., Lond.

TANNER, Mark Antony 45a Hampstead High Street, Hampstead, London NW3 1QG — MB BS 1997 Lond.

TANNER, Michael Thomas Greystead, High St., Kinver, Stourbridge DY7 6HG Tel: 01384 872200 — MB ChB 1961 Birm. (Birm.)

TANNER, Mr Norman Stuart Brent BUPA Hospital Tunbridge, Fordcombe Road, Fordcombe, Tunbridge Wells TN3 0RD Tel: 01892 740044 Fax: 01892 740085 Email: brenttanneer@brenttannner.co.uk; The Oasts, Broadreed Farm, Criers Lane, Five Ashes, Mayfield TN20 6LG Tel: 01825 830409 Fax: 01825 830367 — MA, MB Camb. 1970, BChir 1969; FRCS Eng. 1974; MRCS Eng. LRCP Lond. 1969. (Camb. & St. Thos.) Hon. Cons. Plastic Surg. Qu. Vict. Hosp. E. Grinstead; Bupa Hopital Tunbridge Wells, Kent; The Sussex Nuffield Hosp.; The N. Downs Hosp., Surrey; Cons. Plastic and Reconstruc. Surg., Gatwick Pk. Hosp., Horley, Surrey. Socs: Brit. Assn. Plastic Surg.; Brit. Assn. Aesthetic Plastic Surgs.; Roy. Coll. of Surg.s. Prev: Sen Regist. (Plastic Surg.) Canniesburn Hosp. Glas.; Research Fell. (Head & Neck Unit) Roy. Marsden Hosp. Lond.; Ho. Off. Surg. St. Thos. Hosp. Lond.

TANNER, Patricia Mary (retired) Ashmount, 13 Woodlands Rise, Ilkley LS29 9BU Tel: 01943 608064 — MB ChB Ed. 1947. Prev: Ho. Phys. Lond. Chest Hosp. & Radcliffe Infirm.

TANNER, Peter Archibald Stuart Witchings, Bakers Hill, Barnet EN5 5QL Tel: 020 8447 0817 — MB BS 1979 Lond.; MRCPath 1987. Cons. Histopath. King Geo. & Barking Hosps. Socs: Brit. Div. Internat. Acad. Path.; Assn. Clin. Path. Prev: Sen. Regist. (Histopath.) W.m. & St. Stephens Hosp. Lond.; Regist. (Histopath.) Barnet Gen. Hosp.; Med. Adviser 'The Human Body' published 1986.

TANNER, Robert Michael Llangollen Health Centre, Regent Street, Llangollen LL20 8HL Tel: 01978 860625 Fax: 01978 860174; Pendraw Garth Isa, Garth, Glyn Ceiriog, Llangollen LL20 7LY — BM BCh 1992 Oxf.; BA (Hons.) Oxf. 1989; MRCGP 1996. Prev: GP/Regist. Aylesbury VTS; SHO (Obst.) Hammersmith Hosp. Lond.; Ho. Surg. John Radcliffe Hosp. Oxf.

TANNER, Simon John 5 Ullswater Grove, Alresford SO24 9NP — BM 1981 Soton.; MSc Lond. 1994; MRCGP 1986; DCH RCP Lond. 1985; DRCOG 1984; MFPHM 1996. Cons. (Pub. Health Med.) N. & Mid Hants. Health Auth. Prev: GP Alresford, Hants.

TANNER, Stephanie Peta 107 Camberwell Grove, London SE5 8JH — MB BS 1993 Lond.

TANNER, Mr Vaughan Royal Berkshire Hospital, London Road, Reading RG1 5AN — MB BS 1990 Lond.; BSc (Hons. Med. Sci.) Lond. 1987; FRCOphth 1994. (St. George's Hosp. Lond.) Cons. Oputhalmic Surg. Roy. Berks. Hosp. Reading; Cons. Oputhalmic

Surg., P. Chas. Eye Unit, King Edwd. VII Hosp. Windsor. Socs: MDU; RCOphth; Amer. Acad. Of Ophth. Prev: Regist. (Ophth.) P. Chas. Eye Unit King Edwd. VII Hosp. Windsor; Specialist Regist (Ophth.) Oxf. Eye Hosp.; Vitreo- retinal Fell. St. Thomas's Hosp. Lond.

TANNETT, Peter Geoffrey 5 Lilac Oval, Hillam, Leeds LS25 5HQ — MB ChB 1958 Leeds; FRCA Eng. 1975; DObst RCOG 1965; DA Eng. 1964. (Leeds) p/t Locum Cons. Anaesth. Pinderfields Pontefract Hosp. NHS Trust. Socs: Yorks. Soc. Anaesth.; BMA; Assn. Anaesth. Prev: Sen. Regist. (Anaesth.) Yorks. RHA; Ho. Phys. & Cas. Off. Gen. Infirm. Leeds.

TANNOCK, Timothy Charles Ayrton (retired) Conservative Central Office, 32 Smith Square, London SW1P 3HH Tel: 0207 984 8235 Fax: 0207 984 8292 Email: ctannock@europal.eu.int — MB BS 1983 Lond.; MA Oxf. 1993, BA (Hons.) 1980; MRCPsych 1988; T(Psych) 1994. Mem. of the Europ. Parliament (Lond. Region - Conserv.). Prev: Cons. (Psychiat.) Univ. Coll. Hosp. & Middlx. Hosp. Lond.

TANQUERAY, Andrew Baron 46 West Street, Rochford SS4 1AJ — MB 1978 Camb.; BChir 1977; MRCP (UK) 1980; FRCR 1986. Cons. Radiol. S.end Hosp. Prev: Sen. Regist. St. Thos. Hosp.

TANQUERAY, John Frederic Harlestone Road Surgery, 117 Harlestone Road, Northampton NN5 7AQ Tel: 01604 751832 Fax: 01604 586065; Mulberry House, The Green, Hardingstone, Northampton NN4 7BU Tel: 01604 761876 — MB BChir 1985 Camb.; MRCGP 1989; DCH RCP Lond. 1988; DRCOG 1987. (Cambridge) Gen. Practitioner, N.ampton. Socs: Pres. N.ants. Medico-Legal Soc.; Soc. of Expert Witnesses. Prev: GP Ipswich.

TANSER, Anthony Raymond (retired) Middle Barn, Hunstrete, Pensford, Bristol BS39 4NT Tel: 01761 490655 — MD Lond. 1970, MB BS 1956; FRCP Lond. 1975, M 1961; MRCS Eng. LRCP Lond. 1956. Prev: Cons. Phys. Bath Health Dist.

TANSER, Susan Jane, Surg. Lt.-Cdr. RN 1 Garfield Road, Netley Abby SO19 4DA Email: sjtanser@yahoo.com — MB BS 1990 Lond.; DA; FRCA 1997. (St. Bartholomew's)

TANSEY, Alexandra Katherine Philomena (retired) Daventry Road Surgery, 281 Daventry Road, Coventry CV3 5HJ Tel: 024 7650 3485 Fax: 024 7650 5730 — LRCPI & LM, LRSCI & LM 1960; DObst RCOG 1963. Prev: Ho. Off. (Obst.) & Ho. Phys. Paediat. N.ampton Gen. Hosp. & Ho.

TANSEY, Bernard John Low Waters Medical Centre, 11 Mill Road, Hamilton ML3 8AA Tel: 01698 283626 Fax: 01698 282839; 4 Carnoustic Court, Bothwell, Glasgow G71 8UB Tel: 01698 853351 — MB ChB 1966 Glas. (Glas.) Med. Off. Philips Elec., Safeway (W. of Scotl.), & Lawrence Scott, Hamilton. Prev: Ho. Phys. Falkirk & Dist. Roy. Infirm.; Ho. Surg. Hairmyres Hosp. E. Kilbride; Ho. Surg. (Obst.) Falkirk Roy. Infirm.

TANSEY, David James 2A Oaklea Road, Wirral CH61 3US — BM BS 1989 Nottm.

TANSEY, John Michael Trent Meadows Medical Centre, 87 Wood Street, Burton-on-Trent DE14 3AA Tel: 01283 845555 Fax: 01283 845222 Email: johntansey@btinternet.com — MB ChB 1983 Leic.; DPMC Keele 1991. Prev: Trainee GP Leic. VTS.; Regist. & SHO (Psychiat.) Carlton Hayes Hosp. Leics.

TANSEY, Margaret Therese Low Waters Medical Centre, 11 Mill Road, Hamilton ML3 8AA Tel: 01698 283626 Fax: 01698 282839; 4 Carnoustie Court, Bothwell, Glasgow G71 8UB Tel: 01698 853351 — MB ChB 1965 Glas.; DObst RCOG 1967. (Glas.) Med. Off. (Obst.) Bellshill Matern. Hosp. Socs: E. Kilbride Med. Soc. Prev: Ho. Surg. Glas. Roy. Infirm. & Glas. Roy. Matern. Hosp.; Ho. Phys. Belvedere Hosp. Glas.

TANSEY, Mr Michael Alfred Lambert (retired) Manor Farm, Old Milverton, Leamington Spa CV32 6SA Tel: 01926 39495 — LRCPI & LM, LRSCI & LM 1960; FRCS Ed. 1969. Cons. Orthop. Surg. S. Warks. Gp. Hosps. Prev: Res. Surg. Off. Hallam Hosp. W. Bromwich.

TANSEY, Michael James Byron Cromwell Cottage, 9-11 Mill St., Gamlingay, Sandy SG19 3JW Tel: 01767 50719 — MD 1981 Cape Town; BSc. St. And. 1970; MB ChB Manch. 1973.

TANSEY, Mr Patrick Alfred Harbison 10 Norwood Avenue, Heaton, Newcastle upon Tyne NE6 5RA — MB BCh BAO 1990 NUI; FRCS Ed. 1994; LRCPSI 1990.

TANSEY, Patrick Joseph 1382 Dumbarton Road, Glasgow G14 9EY — MB ChB 1973 Glas.; FRCP Glas. 1989; MRCP (UK) 1976; FRCPath. 1992,M 1980.

TANSEY, Susan Patricia Servier Research & Development Unit, Fulmer Hall, Windmill Hill, Slough SL3 6HH Tel: 01753 666345 Fax: 01753 664408 — MB ChB 1988 Manch.; DPM 2000; MRCP (UK) 1994; DCH RCP Lond. 1992. Clin. Research Manager Servier R & D. Socs: MRCPCH. Prev: SP Reg.Paediat.Roy.Liverp.Childr.s.Hosp; Research Fell.Antenatal TRH Trial Wom..Hosp.Liverp.

TANSLEY, Miss Anne Patricia Cairn Cottage, Montgomery Hill, Frankby, Wirral CH48 1NF — MB ChB 1992 Liverp.; FRCS Ed. 1997. (Liverpool) Specialist Regist. (Gen. Surg.) Mersey Region. Socs: WIST; BMA; ASIT.

TANSLEY, Mr Anthony Gerard The Marches Medical Practice, Mill Lane, Buckley CH7 3HB — MB ChB 1986 Liverp.; FRCS Ed. 1992. Prev: SHO (Plastic SUrg.) Qu. Mary's Hosp. Roehampton & Whiston Hosp.

TANSLEY, Elizabeth Jane Tansley and Partners, Chalkhill Health Centre, Chalkhill Road, Wembley HA9 9BQ Tel: 020 8904 0911 — MB BS Lond. 1966; MRCS Eng. LRCP Lond. 1966. (St. Mary's) Trainer (Gen. Pract.) Middlx. Socs: BMA. Prev: Clin. Tutor (Gen. Pract.) Middlx. Hosp. Lond.; Ho. Surg. Paddington Green Childr. Hosp.; Ho. Phys. Chase Farm Hosp. Enfield.

TANSLEY, Margaret Catherine Parkside Family Practice, Eastleigh Health Centre, Newtown Road, Eastleigh SO50 9AG Tel: 023 8061 2032 Fax: 023 8062 9623 — MB BS 1970 Lond.; MRCGP 1976; DObst RCOG 1972. (St. Geo.) Prev: Civil. Med. Pract. to Army Tidworth Garrison; Ho. Phys. St. Geo. Hosp. Lond.; Ho. Surg. Salisbury Gen. Infirm.

TANSLEY, Patrick David Thomas 1 Gullet Lane, Kirby Muxloe, Leicester LE9 2BL Tel: 0116 238 6315 — MB BChir 1994 Camb.; MB BChir Camb. 1995; BSc Lond. 1992. Socs: Brit. Assn. Clin. Anat.; Roy. Soc. Med.

TANSLEY, Robert Giles 9 South Hill, Guildford GU1 3SY — MB BS 1989 Lond.; MPhil Camb. 1994; MRCOG 1995. Med. Assessor MCA. Prev: Med. Affairs Sanofi Winthrop Guildford; Regist. Rotat. Camb. & P'boro.

TANT, Darryl Roderic The Surgery, 37 Castle Street, Luton LU1 3AG Tel: 01582 726123 Fax: 01582 731150; Algonquin, 30 Roundwood Park, Harpenden AL5 3AF Tel: 01582 763362 Email: tant@zoom.co.uk — MB BChir 1967 Camb.; MA Camb. 1967; MRCS Eng. LRCP Lond. 1967; FRCGP 1982, M 1975. (Camb. & Middlx.) GP; Examr. MRCGP Exam. Prev: Course Organiser Luton & Dunstable Hosp. VTS; Tutor (Gen. Pract.) Luton & Dunstable Hosp. Postgrad. Med. Centre; Resid. (Internal Med.) Sunnybrook Hosp. Univ. Toronto, Canada.

TANT, Martin Charles Otto 10 Admiralty Cottages, Halliday Close, Gosport PO12 4TT — MB BS 1990 Lond.

TANTAM, Professor Digby John Howard Centre for Psychotherapeutic Studies, University Sheffield, 16 Claremont Crescent, Sheffield S10 2TA Tel: 0114 222 2979 Fax: 0114 275 0226 Email: o.tantam@sheffield.ac.uk — BM BCh 1972 Oxf.; PhD Lond. 1986; BA Open 1985; MA, BA Oxf. 1966; FRCPsych 1991, M 1977; MPH Harvard 1977. Clin. Prof. Psychother. Univ. Sheff. & Hon. Cons. Psychotherapist (Community Health) Sheff.; Sen. Lect. (Psychiat.) & Hon. Cons. Psychiat. UHSM.; Prof. Psychother. Univ. Warwick & Hon. Cons. Psychotherapist Coventry 1990-95; Vis. Prof. Univ. Zambia; Lect. Inst. Psychiat. Prev: MRC Train. Fell. Inst. Psychiat. Lond.; Sen. Regist. (Psychiat.) Maudsley Hosp. Lond.; Clin. Fell. (Psychiat.) Harvard Med. Sch., USA.

TANTI, Geoffrey John Llwyn Ygroes Psychiatric Unit, Wrexham Maelor Hospital, Wrexham Technology Park, Wrexham LL13 7TD — MD 1986 Malta; MRCPsych 1994; MSc 1999. Cons. Psychiat., Wrexham; Cons. Psychiat. in Learning Disabilities.

TANWEER, Kishwer (retired) 36 Woodbourne Avenue, London SW16 1UU Tel: 020 8677 4618 — MB BS Karachi 1963. Prev: Clin. Med. Off. (Child Health) Sutton Community NHS Trust.

TAO, Miriam Third Floor, 60 Cadogan Square, London SW1X 0EE — MB BS 1984 Lond. (Char. Cross Hosp.) SHO (Med.) P.ss Margt. Hosp. Swindon. Socs: BMA. Prev: SHO (Cas.) Hillingdon Hosp. Lond.; SHO (Oncol.) St. Geo. Hosp. Lond.; Ho. Phys. Char. Cross Hosp. Lond.

TAOR, Jennifer Helen 3 Roberts Close, Southwater, Horsham RH13 7BJ — MB BS 1975 Lond.; MRCGP 1981; DObst. RCOG 1981; DCH 1980. (Char. Cross Hosp.) SHO (Neonat. Paediat.) Whittington Hosp. Lond. Prev: Regist. (Geriat.) Char. Cross Hosp.

TAOR

Lond.; SHO (Paediat.) Torbay Hosp.; SHO (Obst.) Heavitree Hosp. Exeter.

TAOR, Lesley Patricia Muriel The Beeches, Packhorse Road, Bessels Green, Sevenoaks TN13 2QP — MRCS Eng. LRCP Lond. 1973; DRCOG 1977. (Char. Cross) Prev: Trainee GP Medway VTS; Ho. Surg. (Orthop.) & Ho. Phys. (Geriat. Psychiat. & Dermat.) Char. Cross Hosp. Lond.

TAOR, Pamela Jane (Surgery), 7A Welbeck Road, West Harrow, Harrow HA2 0RQ Tel: 020 8422 3021; Highlands, London Road, Harrow-on-the Hill, Harrow HA1 3JJ Tel: 020 8422 3260 — MB BS 1963 Lond.; BA (Phil.) Lond. 1986, MB BS 1963. (Char. Cross) Hosp. Pract. Edgware Gen. Hosp. Prev: Regist. (Psychiat.) Edgware Gen. Hosp.

TAOR, Mr William Stewart Flat 19, Harmont House, 20 Harley St., London W1G 9PH; Highlands, London Road, Harrow HA1 3JJ Tel: 020 8422 3260 Fax: 020 8422 7979 — BSc Lond. 1960, MB BS 1962; FRCS Eng. 1967; LLB 2000. (Char. Cross) Medico-Legal Cons.; Hon. Med. Adviser & Orthop. Surg. Badminton Assn. of Eng. & Internat. Badminton Federat. Socs: Fell. BOA. Prev: Cons. Orthop. Surg. Pk.side Health Dist.; Sen. Regist. Roy. Nat. Orthop. Hosp. & Char. Cross Hosp. Lond.; Cons. Orthop. Surg. Manor Ho. Hosp.

TAPLEY, Michael Philip 7 Mottram Old Road, Stalybridge SK15 2TG — MB BS 1985 Lond. Clin. Asst. (Genitourin. Med.) Roy. Oldham Hosp. Socs: BMA. Prev: SHO (Anaesth.) Tameside Gen. Hosp. Ashton-under-Lyne Lancs. & W.m. Hosp. Lond.; SHO (A & E) Qu. Mary's Hosp. Lond.

TAPP, Andrew John Singleton Royal Shrewsbury Hospital, Mytton Oak Road, Shrewsbury SY3 8XQ Tel: 01743 261000 — MB BS 1982 Lond.; MRCOG 1989. Cons. O & G Roy. Shrewsbury Hosp. Prev: Sen. Regist. St. Geo. & Mayday Hosp. Lond.

TAPP, Edmund Foxdenton House, Sytchampton, Stourport-on-Severn Tel: 01905 621657 Fax: 01905 621657; Foxdenton House, Sytchampton, Stourport-on-Severn Tel: 0190 562 1657 Fax: 0190 562 1657 — MB ChB (Hons.) Liverp. 1959; MD Liverp. 1964; MRCS Eng. LRCP Lond. 1959; FRCPath 1978, M 1968. (Liverp.) p/t Indep. Forens. Pathologist to the Home Office. Socs: Liverp. Med. Inst.; Palaeopath. Assn.; Liverp. Med. Inst. Prev: Cons. Path. (Morbid Anat. & Histopath.) Roy. Preston Hosp.; Cons. Path. (Morbid Anat. & Histol.) Withington Hosp. Manch.; Lect. (Path.) & Hon. Lect. (Orthop. Path.) Liverp. Univ.

TAPP, Gwendolyn Rosemary (retired) Mallards, 36 Sea Drive, Felpham, Bognor Regis PO22 7NB Tel: 0124 369 582252 — MB BS 1950 Lond.; MRCS Eng. LRCP Lond. 1950; MFCM 1974; DCH Eng. 1952, DPH 1956. Prev: Sen. Med. Off. (Child Heath) E. Surrey Health Dist.

TAPP, Martin James Franklin 129 New Road, Brixham TQ5 8DB — MB ChB 1998 Bristol.

TAPPER, Geoffrey William The Mount, Salisbury Road, Shaftesbury SP7 8NL Tel: 01747 852872 Fax: 01747 851463 — MB BS 1955 Lond.; DObst RCOG 1961. (Middlx.) Examp. Med. Practitioner, Benefit Agency. Prev: Chairm., Thomas Hardy Soc.; Chairm., Dorset Social Servs. Com.; Ldr. Dorset Co. Counc.

TAPPER, Roger John Frogmill, Pound Lane, Burghclere, Newbury RG20 9JR — MB BS 1968 Lond.; DObst RCOG 1970. (St. Thos.)

TAPPER-JONES, Lorna Maureen Penylan Road Surgery, 100 Penylan Road, Cardiff CF2 5HY Tel: 029 2046 1100 Fax: 029 2045 1623; Maes-y-Coed, 59 Heath Pk Avenue, Cardiff CF14 3RG Tel: 029 2075 1306 — MB BCh 1977 Wales; MD Wales 1986, BDS 1972; FRCGP 1992, M 1982; MFFP 1993; DCH (UK) 1981; DRCOG 1980. (Wales) GP Princip.; Sen. Lect. (Gen. Pract.) Univ. Wales Coll. Med. Cardiff; GP Trainer S. Glam. VTS; Examr. Roy. Coll. Gen. Practs. Socs: Cardiff Med. Soc.; Primary Care Dermat. Soc.; Primary Care Rheum. Soc. Prev: Trainee GP S. Glam. VTS; Lect. (Oral Med.) Welsh Nat. Sch. Med.; Clin. Med. Off. S. Glam. HA.

TAPPIN, Alan Robert (retired) Knapwood House, Littlewick Road, Knaphill, Woking GU21 2JU Tel: 01483 474122 — MB BS 1959 Lond.; FFA RCS Eng. 1966; DA Eng. 1962; DObst RCOG 1961. Prev: ons. Anaesth. N.W. Surrey Gp. Hosp.

TAPPIN, David Michael Yorkhill NHS Trust, Royal Hospital for Sick Children, Glasgow G3 8SJ Tel: 0141 201 0176 Fax: 0141 201 0837 Email: goda11@udcf.gla.ac.uk; 31 Shawhill Road, Glasgow G41 3RW Tel: 0141 632 6412 — MB BS 1981 Lond.; MPH (Glas) 1998; MRCP (UK) 1986; MD Lond. 1996. (Middlesex Hospital) Sen. Lect. (Community Child Health) Glas. Univ.; Cons. Paediatrican

(Hon.) Roy. Hosp. For Sick Childr., Glasg. Socs: MRCPCH; Fell. Roy. Coll. Phys. & Surg. Glas. Prev: Canterbury Cot Death research fell. ChristCh. New Zealand; Sen lect. Scott Cot Death Trust.

TAPPIN, John Alexander Homewood, Stanley Avenue, Higher Bebington, Wirral CH63 5QE — MD 1981 Liverp.; BSc (Hons.) Liverp. 1970, MD 1981, MB ChB 1973; FRCP Lond. 1992; MRCP (UK) 1977. Cons. Haemat. Whiston Hosp. Prescot.

TAPPIN, Michael James Knapwood House, Little Wick Road, Knaphill, Woking GU21 2JU — MB BS 1990 Lond.

TAPPING, Peter John Vine Medical Centre, 69 Pemberton Road, East Molesey KT8 9LJ Tel: 020 8979 4200 Fax: 020 8941 9827; Tandrup, Hill View Road, Claygate, Esher KT10 0TU — MB BS 1983 Lond.; MRCGP 1988. GP E. Molesey. Prev: Trainee GP Frimley Pk. Hosp.; Ho. Off. (Med.) Newham Gen. Hosp.; Ho. Off. (Surg.) Lond. Hosp.

TAPPOUNI, Faiz Raphael The Eye Academy, 114A Harley St., London W1N 2EL Tel: 020 7722 6638 Fax: 020 7722 6638; 114A Harley Street, London W1N 1DG Tel: 020 7935 0052 Fax: 020 7935 0072 — MB ChB 1963 Baghdad; MD Baghdad 1973; FRCOphth 1989. p/t Cons. Ophth. Eye Acad. Lond.; Mem. Amer. Acad. Ophth.; Mem. Pan Arab Congr. Ophth.; Co-Edr. Afro-Asian Jl. Ophth. Socs: Eur. Soc. Cataract & Refractive Surgs. Prev: Cons. Ophth. Surg. Al Haitham Hosp.

TAPSELL, Sam Henry John High Noon, 11 Middle St., Nether Heyford, Northampton NN7 3LL — MB BS 1998 Newc.

TAPSFIELD, William George Collingwood Surgery, Hawkeys Lane, North Shields NE29 0SF Tel: 0191 257 1779 Fax: 0191 226 9909 — MB ChB 1978 Ed.

TAPSON, John Stephen Freeman Hospital, Newcastle upon Tyne NE7 7DN Tel: 0191 284 3111 Fax: 0191 213 0370 Email: john.tapson@tfh.nuth.northy.nhs.uk; Hollybush House, Robshenge, Newcastle upon Tyne NE20 0JQ Tel: 01661 886443 — MB BS 1976 MB BS; BSc (Hons.) Lond. 1973.; MD Newc. 1988; FRCP (UK) 1994; MRCP (UK) 1980; MRCS Eng. LRCP Lond. 1976. (Guy's, London) Cons. Nephrol. Freeman Hosp. Newc. u. Tyne. Prev: Sen. Regist. (Nephrol.) Roy. Vict. Infirm. Newc.

TARABA, Pam The Surgery, 118 Old Oak Road, London W3 7HG Tel: 020 8740 7328 Fax: 020 8743 2235 — MUDr Prague 1960; MRCS Eng. LRCP Lond. 1973; DPM Eng. 1975. (Charles Univ. Prague) Clin. Asst. in Psychiat. W. Middlx. Hosp.

TARALA, Mrs Christine Thelma Maltings Green Road Surgery, 64 Maltings Green Road, Layer de la Haye, Colchester CO2 0JJ — MB ChB 1975 Glas.; DRCOG 1978. (Glasgow)

TARAPHDAR, S East Street Surgery, 1 East Street, Rochdale OL16 2EG — MB BS 1970 Calcutta; MB BS 1970 Calcutta.

TARAR, Mr Moazzam Nazeer 34 South Oswald Road, Edinburgh EH9 2HG Tel: 0131 668 3535 — MB BS 1985 Punjab; FRCS Eng. 1990.

TARBUCK, Mr David Thomas Henrich (retired) Tanglewood, 11 South Lynn Drive, Eastbourne BN21 2JF — MB BS 1967 Lond.; FRCS Eng. 1975; FRCOphth 1988; MRCS Eng. LRCP Lond. 1967; DO Eng. 1971. Prev: Cons. Opth. Surg. E.bourne NHS Trust.

TARELLI, Stephen Vincent 4 Greencroft Close, Darlington DL3 8HW — MB ChB 1968 Ed.

TARFF, Peter James Catbells Cottage, 42 Marsh Road, Upton, Norwich NR13 6BS — MB BS 1977 Lond.; MSc Lond. 1993, BSc 1974, MB BS 1977; DMJ(Path) Soc. Apoth. Lond. 1988. Socs: Fell. Brit. Acad. Forens.; Fell. Roy. Soc. Med. Prev: SHO Rotat. (Psychiat.) Char. Cross Hosp. Lond.; Lect. (Forens. Med.) Univ. Lond. & Sheff.

TARGETT, Mr John Peter Geoffrey Orthopaedic Department, Basildon Hospital, Nether Mayne, Basildon SS16 5NL Tel: 01268 533911; Hartswood House, Hartswood Road, Great Warley, Brentwood CM14 5AG — MB BS 1983 Lond.; FRCS (Orth.) 1995; FRCS Eng. 1988. (St. Mary's Hosp. Med. Sch. Lond.) Cons. Trauma & Orthop. Basildon Hosp. Essex. Socs: Fell. BOA; FRSM - Orthopaedic Sect. & Sports Med. Prev: Sen. Regist. & Regist. Rotat. (Orthop.) St. Geo. Hosp. Lond.; Regist. (Gen. Surg. & Orthop.) Basildon Hosp. Essex.

TARGETT, Katherine Lesley 19 Tofts Close, Low Worsall, Yarm TS15 9QA — BM BCh 1993 Oxf.

TARGOSZ, Sarah Alexandra Woodlands, 53 Strathblane Road, Milngavie, Glasgow G62 8HA — MB ChB 1998 Manch.

TARIN, Mr Mohammad Kamran c/o Abdul Quyum, 36 Cemetry Road, Oldbury, Oldbury B68 8SP — MB BS 1986 Peshawar; FRCS Ed. 1993.

TARIN, Pamela Joan Amersham Health Centre, Chiltern Avenue, Amersham HP6 5AY Tel: 01494 434344; Oak Tree House, Hervines Road, Amersham HP6 5HS — BM BCh 1963 Oxf.; BSc (1st cl. Hons. Anat.) Leeds 1961. Clin. Asst. (Paediat.) Wycombe Gen. Hosp. High Wycombe. Prev: Lect. (Anat.) Univ. Leeds Med. Sch.; Ho. Surg. Radcliffe Infirm. Oxf.; Ho. Phys. Amersham Gen. Hosp.

TARIQ, Shahid Latif 112 Lode Lane, Solihull B91 2HN — MB BS 1986 Punjab; FFA RCSI 1994.

TARJUMAN, Mr Muhammad 83 Nickleby Road, Chelmsford CM1 4XG — MD 1971 Damascus; FRCS Glas. 1986. Regist. (Gen. Surg.) Broomfield Hosp. Chelmsford. Prev: Regist. (Gen. Surg.) Walsgrave Hosp. Coventry.

TARLETON, David Edward Balliol Ridingleaze Medical Centre, Ridingleaze, Bristol BS11 0QE Tel: 0117 982 2693 Fax: 0117 938 1707; 43A Nore Road, Portishead, Bristol BS20 6JY — MB ChB 1972 Birm.

TARLO, Leonard 28 Lyttelton Road, Droitwich WR9 7AA Tel: 01905 773315 — MB BCh BAO 1951 Dub.; BA Dub. 1948, MB BCh BAO 1951; FRCPsych. 1981, M 1971; DPM Eng. 1954. (T.C. Dub.) Hon. Cons. St. Luke's Hosp. for the Clergy Lond. Prev: Cons. Psychiat. Mid. Worcs. Gp. Hosps.; Hon. Clin. Tutor Univ. Birm.; Asst. Psychiat. W. Pk. Hosp. Epsom.

TARLOW, Jonathan Holloway Road Surgery, 94 Holloway Road, London N7 8JG Tel: 020 7607 2323; 16 Greenhalgh Walk, London N2 0DJ Tel: 020 8455 8680 Fax: 020 8458 0182 — MB BS 1965 Lond.; MRCS Eng. LRCP Lond. 1965; DObst RCOG 1967. (Lond. Hosp.) Prev: Ho. Phys. & Obst. Ho. Surg. Qu. Eliz. II Hosp. Welwyn Gdn. City; Ho. Surg. Whittington Hosp. Lond.

TARLOW, Michael Jacob (retired) 43 Silhill Hall Road, Solihull B91 1JX Tel: 0121 681 9656 Fax: 0121 681 9657 Email: tarlowmj@aol.com — MB BS 1962 Lond; MB BS Lond. 1962; MSc (Biochem.) Lond. 1965; FRCP Lond. 1982, M 1968; FRCPCH 1997; L.L.M. 2000 Univ. of Wales. Prev: Sen. Lect. (Paediat. & Child Health) Univ. Birm.

TARLOW, Samuel Holloway Road Surgery, 94 Holloway Road, London N7 8JG Tel: 020 7607 2323 — MRCS Eng. LRCP Lond. 1937. (Univ. Coll. Hosp.)

TARN, Anne Carolyn Department Chemical Pathology, Mayday University Hospital, London Road, Croydon CR7 7YE; 15 Church Way, Hurst Green, Oxted RH8 9EA Tel: 01883 722953 — MB BS 1978 Lond.; MSc (Clin. Biochem.) Univ. Surrey 1990; MD Lond. 1996, MB BS 1978; MRCPath 1996; MRCS Eng. LRCP Lond. 1978; MRCP Lond. 1982. (St. Bart.)

TARN, Mark, Maj. RAMC 28 Swanstead, Basildon SS16 4PE Tel: 01268 474268 — BM 1990 Soton. (Southampton)

TARNESBY, Georgia Miriam Susannah 68 Ossulton Way, London N2 0LB Tel: 020 8883 0224 — MB BChir 1988 Camb.; MA Camb. 1989, BA 198; MBA (INSEAD) 1994; MRCP (UK) 1991. (St. Thomas. Hosp., UMDS) Prev: Regist. (Cardiol.) N.wick Pk. Hosp. Lond.; SHO (Neurol.) Roy. Free Hosp. Lond.; SHO (Renal & Transpl.) Guy's Hosp. Lond.

TARNOKY, Joan Maureen (retired) 12 Whitby Drive, Reading RG1 5HW Tel: 0118 986 0299 Fax: 0118 986 0299 — MB BS Durh. 1950; FRCPCH; DCH Eng. 1953. Prev: Assoc. Specialist & Regist. (Paediat.) Roy. Berks. Hosp. Reading.

TARNOW-MORDI, William Odita Department of Child Health, University of Dundee, Dundee DD1 9SY Tel: 01382 660111 Fax: 01382 645783 Email: w.o.tarnow-mordi@dundee.ac.uk; 11 West Park Road, Dundee DD2 1NU — MB 1976 Camb.; MB BChir Camb. 1976; MRCP (UK) 1977; DCH Eng. 1978. Reader (Neonat. Med. & Perinatal Epidemiol.) & Hon. Cons. Paediat. Ninewells Hosp. & Med. Sch. Dundee. Socs: Roy. Coll. Paediat. & Child Health; Neonat. Soc.; Brit. Assn. Perinatal Med. Prev: Research Fell. & Hon. Sen. Regist. John Radcliffe Hosp. Oxf.; SHO (Paediat.) Univ. Coll. Hosp. Lond.; SHO Hosp. Sick Childr. Gt. Ormond St.

TARPEY, Joseph Jarlath Department of Anesthestics, Warwick Hospital, Lakin Road, Warwick CV34 5BW Tel: 01926 495321 Fax: 01926 403715 — MB BCh BAO 1985 NUI; FFA RCSI 1991. Cons. Anaesth. Warwick Hosp. Prev: Vis. Asst. Prof. Oregon Health Sci.s Univ.

TARR, Gillian 25 Penygraig Road, Ystradowen, Cwmllynfell, Swansea SA9 2YP — MB BCh 1984 Wales.

TARR, Katherine Elizabeth 25 Hampden Road, Malvern WR14 1NB — MB BS 1992 Lond.

TARR, Terence John Ashlea, 37 Thurstaston Road, Heswall, Wirral CH60 6SB Tel: 0151 342 7087 — MB BS 1980 Lond.; FRCA. 1986. (Guy's) Cons. Anaesth. Arrowe Pk. Hosp. Wirral. Prev: Lect. & Hon. Sen. Regist. (Anaesth.) Univ. Liverp.; Regist. (Anaesth.) Qu. Vict. Hosp. E. Grinstead; Regist. (Anaesth.) Guy's Hosp. Lond.

TARRANT, Catharine Jane 18 Gertrude Road, West Bridgford, Nottingham NG2 5BY; Department of Psychiatry, Duncan MacMillan House, Porchester Road, Nottingham NG3 6AA Tel: 0115 969300 Ext: 40766 Email: jane.tarrant@nottingham.ac.uk — BM BS 1992 Nottm.; MRCPsych 1996. (Nottingham) Clin. Research Worker/Research Fell. Univ. of Nottm.

TARRANT, Mrs Deborah Anne The Surgery, 215 Lower Kirkgate, Wakefield WF1 1JJ Tel: 01924 371331; 67 Ruskin Avenue, Wrenthorpe, Wakefield WF1 2BG Tel: 01924 366997 — MB BChir 1985 Camb.; MA Camb. 1987, MB BChir 1985; MRCGP 1990; DRCOG 1990. Socs: BMA. Prev: Trainee GP Wakefield VTS.

TARRANT, Kevin Nigel Brigstock Medical Centre, 141 Brigstock Road, Thornton Heath CR7 7JN Tel: 020 8684 1128 Fax: 020 8689 3647; Hawthorns, 26 Burcott Road, Purley CR8 4AA — MB BS 1982 Nottm.; Dip Occ Health & Safety 1999; BMedSci (Hons.) Nottm. 1980, MB BS 1982; MRCGP 1986; DRCOG 1985. p/t Clin. Asst. (Rheum.) Mayday Hosp. Croydon.; Hosp. Practitioner (Rheun). Prev: Clin. Asst. (Diabetes) Mayday Hosp. Croydon.

TARRANT, Paul Douglas 129 Mains Drive, Erskine PA8 7JJ Tel: 0141 812 6033 Fax: 0141 561 3033; 129 Mains Drive, Erskine PA8 7JJ Fax: 0141 561 3033 Email: drptarrant@aol.com — MB ChB 1976 Glas.; MRCGP 1979; DRCOG 1979. Director Nazarene Compassionate Ministries - Europe; Adviser Care Counselling for Scotl.; Regist. Nazarene Health Care Fell.sh.; Mem. Med. Advis. Comm. Ch. of the Nazarene Internat. Socs: Christian Med. Fell.sh. Prev: Mem. Renfrew Dist. Med. Comm.; Mem. GP Sub. Comm. Argyll & Clyde Area Med. Comm.

TARRY, Jennifer Elizabeth Edward House, Humberdine Close, Worcester WR5 2DD Fax: 01905 351214; 104 Battenhall Road, Worcester WR5 2BT Email: jennifertarry@hotmail.com — MB ChB 1973 Birm.; MRCPsych 1981. (Birmingham) Cons. Psychiat. i/c Elderly Worcs. Community Ment. Health NHS Trust. Prev: Cons. Psychiat. i/c Elderly Co. Hosp. Durh.

TARSH, Evelyn June (retired) 15 Hillcrest Avenue, London NW11 0EP Tel: 020 8458 7783 — MB ChB Liverp. 1958; MRCS Eng. LRCP Lond. 1958. Prev: Asst. GP. Ruislip.

TART, Christopher John — MB BS 1973 Lond.; BSc Lond. 1970; FFA RCS Eng. 1979. (Univ. Coll. Lond. & Westm.) EMP in Med. Servs.; SEMA Disabil. Med. Prev: Med. Off. Gosport War Memor Hosp.; Trainee GP Wessex VTS.; Regist. (Anaesth.) Magill Dept. Anaesth. W.m. Hosp. Lond.

TARUVINGA, Margaret Gravesend & North Kent Hospital, Bath St., Gravesend DA11 0DG — MB BS 1985 W. Indies.

TARVER, David Stephen Dept. of Radiology, Poole Hospital, Longfleet Road, Poole BH15 2JB Tel: 01202 716908 Email: dtarver@email.com — MB BS 1982 Lond.; MRCP (UK) 1985; MRCGP 1988; FRCR 1993. Cons. Radiologist, Pool Hosp., Poole, Dorset.

TARVET, Faye The Cooperage, Mid Shore, Pittenweem, Anstruther KY10 2NW — MB ChB 1997 Ed.

TARZI, Michael David 39 Charlock Way, Guildford GU1 1XY — MB BS 1997 Lond.

TARZI, Naji 5 Belle Vue Close, Staines TW18 2HY — LMSSA 1962 Lond.

TARZI, Ruth Margaret Flat 21 Corfton Lodge, Corfton Rd, Ealing, London W5 2HU — BM BCh 1994 Oxf.; MA 1995; MRCP 1997. Specialist Regist. (Nephrol.) St Mary's Hosp. Lond. Prev: SHO (Haemat.) Kings Coll. Hosp.; SHO (Neurol.) Radcliffe Infirm. Oxf.; SHO (Renal Med.) Hammersmith Hosp. Lond.

TASHARROFI, Ramin 2 Thackeray Close, Eastbourne BN23 7TJ — MB ChB 1993 Liverp.

TASKER, Angela Doreen Papworth Hospital, Department of Radiology, Papworth Everard, Cambridge CB3 8RE — MB BChir 1984 Camb.; MA Camb. 1985, BA (Hons.) 1981; MRCP (UK) 1986; FRCR 1992. Cons. (Radiol.) Papworth Hosp. Camb. Prev: Sen.

TASKER

Regist. (Radiol.) John Radcliffe Hosp. Oxf.; Regist. (Radiol.) John Radcliffe Hosp. Oxf.; Regist. Rotat. (Med.) St. Thos. Hosp. Lond. & Medway Hosp. Kent.

TASKER, Bronwyn Elizabeth Glenpark Medical Centre, Ravensorth Road, Dunston, Gateshead NE11 9AD — MB BS 1988 Newc.; MRCGP 1992; DCH RCP Lond. 1991; Dip. Therap. 1998. (Newcastle upon Tyne) Prev: Trainee GP N.d. VTS.

TASKER, Claire Mary Grey House, High St., Beckeley, Oxford OX3 9UU — MB ChB 1969 Birm.

TASKER, Mr David Gordon Ravenscourt Surgery, 36-38 Tynewydd Road, Barry CF62 8AZ Tel: 01446 733515 Fax: 01446 701326; 8 Minehead Avenue, Sully, Penarth CF64 5TH — MB BCh 1972 Wales; FRCS Eng. 1978; MRCGP 1990. Prev: Regist. (Surg.) Addenbrookes Hosp. Camb. & Llandough Hosp.; SHO Profess. Surg. Unit Univ. Hosp. Wales Cardiff.

TASKER, Geraldine Lynn 35A Boundary Close, Woodstock OX20 1LR — MB ChB 1992 Cape Town.

TASKER, Gillian Dallas Magnolia House Practice, Magnolia House, Station Road, Ascot SL5 0QJ Tel: 01344 637800 Fax: 01344 637823; Tall Trees House, Winchfield Road, Ascot SL5 7EX Tel: 01344 876648 — MB BS 1982 Lond.; MRCGP 1986; DCH RCP Lond. 1987; DRCOG 1985. (Char. Cross) p/t Clin. Asst. BrE. Clinic King Edwd. VII Hosp. Windsor. Socs: Windsor Med. Soc. Prev: Clin. Med. Off. St. Thos. Hosp. Lond.; Trainee GP Windsor VTS; SHO (Med., Paediat., A & E & O & G) Heatherwood Hosp. Ascot.

TASKER, Heather Yvonne 72 Lowther Road, London SW13 9NU — BM BS 1997 Nottm.

TASKER, Ian Thomas 64 Thirlmere Road, Partington, Manchester M31 4PT — MB ChB 1991 Sheff.; MRCGP Lond. 1997; DRCOG Lond. 1996. (Sheff.) GP Partnership Swinton Manch.

TASKER, John Anthony West Bar Surgery, 1 West Bar Street, Banbury OX16 9SF Tel: 01295 256261 Fax: 01295 756848; Saddlers Cottage, Main St, North Newington, Banbury OX15 6AJ Tel: 01295 730531 — BM BCh 1977 Oxf.; MA, DPhil Oxf. 1978; MRCP (UK) 1980; FRCGP 1996, M 1982; DRCOG 1981; DCH RCP Lond. 1980. (Oxf.) Chair PCG; Tutor (Gen. Pract.) Banbury.

TASKER, John Rendel 6 Milton Court, Milton Malsor, Northampton NN7 3AX Tel: 01604 858545; 21 The Drive, Northampton NN1 4RY Tel: 01609 711222 — MD 1951 Camb.; MB BChir 1940; FRCP Lond. 1963, M 1943. (Lond. Hosp.) Prev: Cons. Phys. Gen. Hosp. & Cynthia Spencer Hospice N.ampton; Examr. Med. ConJt. Bd. & Extern. Examr. Med. Univ. Baghdad, Iraq; Sen. Regist. (Med.) & Phys. (Cas.) Lond. Hosp.

TASKER, Laura Jane Willowbrook, Coldwell Lane, Stonehouse, Kings Stanley, Stonehouse GL10 3PR — MB BCh 1993 Wales.

TASKER, Margaret Silver Birches, 110 Rawlinson Lane, Heath Charnock, Chorley PR7 4DE — MB ChB 1976 Ed.; MRCOG 1981, D 1978.

TASKER, Mr Paul Richard Siebert 157 Worsley Road, Worsley, Manchester M28 2SJ — MB BS 1973 Lond.; FRCS Eng. 1981. (St. Geo.) Sen. Regist. (Surg.) Morriston & Singleton Hosps. Swansea. Socs: Fell. Manch. Med. Soc.; BMA. Prev: Hon. Surg. Regist. & Markland Research Fell. Dept. Gastroenterol.; Manch. Roy. Infirm; Regist. Rotat. (Surg.) Whittington & Roy. Free; Hosp. Lond.; SHO Rotat. (Surg.) St. Geo. & Roy. Marsden Hosps. Lond.

TASKER, Peter Roy William St James House Surgery, County Court Road, King's Lynn PE30 5SY Tel: 01553 774221 Fax: 01553 692181; Doomsday House, Hall Lane, South Wootton, King's Lynn PE30 3LQ Tel: 01553 673260 Email: doct@globalnet.co.uk — MB BS 1971 Lond.; MRCS Eng. LRCP Lond. 1971; FRCGP 1989, M 1979; DRCOG 1978; DCH Eng. 1977. Prev: SHO & Ho. Phys. Profess. Dept. Med. & Ho. Surg. Char. Cross Hosp. Lond.

TASKER, Robert Charles Department of Paediatrics, University of Cambridge, School of Clinical Medicine, Addenbrookes Hospital, Hills Building, Cambridge CB2 2QQ — MB BS 1983 Lond.; MA Camb. 1983; MRCP (UK) 1986; DCH RCP Lond. 1985. Univ. Lect. (Paediat. IC) Camb. Univ.; Hon Cons. Phys. (IC) Addenbrooke's Hosp. Camb. Prev: Cons. Phys. (IC) Hosp. for Sick Childr. Gt. Ormond St. Lond.; Fell. (Critical Care & Anaesth.) John Hopkins Hosp. USA; Research Regist. Respirat. Unit Hosp. Sick Childr. Gt. Ormond St.Lond.

TASKER, Robert Lucian Hewitt (retired) 21 Willow drive, Clench Warton, King's Lynn PE34 4EN — MRCS Eng. LRCP Lond. 1948. Prev: Flight Lt. RAF Med. Br.

TASKER, Timothy Charles Gadsden SmithKline Beecham Pharmaceuticals, New Frontiers Science Park, Third Avenue, Harlow CM19 5AW — MB BS 1978 Lond.; BA Oxf. 1974; MRCP (UK) 1981; FFPM RCP (UK) 1994, M 1990. (Univ. Coll. Hosp.) Dir. & Vice-Pres. Clin. Pharmacol. (Europe) SmithKline Beecham Pharmaceut. Research & Developm. Socs: Brit. Assn. Pharmaceut. Phys. & Brit. Assn. Psychopharmacol. Prev: Clin. Pharmacol. Beecham Pharmaceuts.; Phys. i/c Clin. Pharmacol. Beecham Pharmaceut. Harlow; Research Fell. King's Coll. Hosp. Lond.

TASKER, Mr Timothy Patrick Beaumont Winfield Hospital, Tewkesbury Road, Longford, Gloucester GL2 9WH Tel: 01452 331111; Gloucestershire Royal Hospital, Great Western Road, Gloucester GL1 3P — MB ChB 1972 Cape Town; FRCS Ed. 1977. Cons. Orthop. Surg. Gloucester Roy. Infirm. Socs: Fell. BOA; Fell. Brit. Assn. for Study of Knee Surg.

TASKER, William John Angel Hill Surgery, 1 Angel Hill, Bury St Edmunds IP33 1LU Tel: 01284 753008 Fax: 01284 724744 — MB BS 1986 Lond. SHO (Health Care for Elderly) Dulwich Hosp. Lond. Prev: SHO (A & E) Hinchingbrooke Hosp. Huntingdon; SHO (A & E) Qu. Mary's Hosp. Sidcup Kent.

TASLIMUDDIN, Abu Siddique Mohammad 43 Barley Lane, Goodmayes, Ilford IG3 8XE — MB BS 1958 Dacca; MB BS Dacca 1958. Prev: GP Dagenham.

TASOU, Anthony London Road Surgery, 49 London Road, Canterbury CT2 8SG Tel: 01227 463128 Fax: 01227 786308 — MB BS 1984 Lond.; DRCOG 1990. (St. Bart.) GP Canterbury.

TASSADAQ, Mr Tariq 123 Murray Road, Rugby CV21 3JR — MB BS 1985 Punjab; FRCS Ed. 1989.

TASSI, Lesley Ann 29 Richmond Gardens, Redhill, Nottingham NG5 8JS — MB BS 1987 Lond.

***TASSONE, Peter** 22 Manor Road, London Colney, St Albans AL2 1PL — MB ChB 1995 Birm.

TATAM, Margaret Elizabeth Kingsway Surgery, 20 Kingsway, Waterloo, Liverpool L22 4RQ Tel: 0151 920 9000 Fax: 0151 928 2411; 17 Eshe Road N., Blundellsands, Liverpool L23 8UE Tel: 0151 924 3286 — MB ChB 1973 Ed.; BSc (Med. Sci.) Ed. 1970; DCH Eng. 1976. (Edin.) Socs: SPA Comm. Mem. Prev: Trainee GP Sighthill Health Centre Edin.; SHO (Anaesth.) Leicester Roy. Infirm.; SHO (Paediat.) W.. Gen. Hosp. Edin.

TATE, Alexandra Rowena 71 Dyke Road Avenue, Hove BN3 6DA — MB BS 1994 Lond.

TATE, Andrew Lawson Kilburn Park Medical Centre, 12 Cambridge Gardens, London NW6 5AY Tel: 020 7624 2414 Fax: 020 7624 2489 — MB BS 1990 Lond.; MRCGP 1995.

TATE, Ann de Carteret Horsenden House, Little Bealings, Woodbridge IP13 6LX — MB BS 1967 Lond.; FRCS Ed. 1972; MRCS Eng. LRCP Lond. 1967; FRCR 1975; FFR 1974; DMRD Eng. 1972. (Guy's) Cons. Radiol. Ipswich Hosp. Prev: Sen. Regist. (Radiol.) Ipswich Hosp. & Univ. Coll. Hosp. Lond.; Regist. (Radiol.) Univ. Coll. Hosp. Lond.

TATE, Anne Teresa Palliative Care Team, St. Bartholomews Hospital, West Smithfield, London EC1A 7BE Tel: 020 8601 8500; 15 Park Avenue N., London N8 7RU — MB BS 1974 Lond.; FRCP Lond. 1997; MRCS Eng. LRCP Lond. 1974; FRCR 1981. (Roy. Free Hosp.) Med. Adviser Marie Curie Cancer Care, Lond.; Cons. Palliat. Med. & Hon. Sen. Lect. St. Bart. Hosp. Lond.; Hon. Cons. Palliat. Med. Homerton Hosp. Lond. Prev: Clin. Instruc. (Radiat. Oncol.) Univ. Calif. San Diego, USA; Regist. (Radiother.) St. Bart. & Roy. Free Hosps. Lond.; Cons. Palliat. Med. Whipps Cross Hosp., Lond.

TATE, Bernard Stanley Hillside, Chester Road, Alpraham, Tarporley CW6 9JA — MB ChB 1961 Sheff.; DObst RCOG 1963.

TATE, Ddavid William 70 Southfield Road, Nailsea, Bristol BS48 1SE — MB ChB 1995 Leeds.

TATE, Mr Geoffrey Thompson (retired) 65 Kent Road, Harrogate HG1 2NH — MB ChB 1952 Leeds; FRCS Ed. 1959; FRCS Eng. 1963. Surg. Harrogate Health Dist.

TATE, Graham Harry Austin The Priory Hospital Marchwood, Hythe Road, Marchwood, Southampton SO40 4WU Tel: 023 8084 0044 Fax: 023 8020 7554 Email: austintate@.prioryhealthcare.co.uk; 9 Warwick Road, Southampton SO15 7PF Tel: 023 8077 3785 Fax: 023 8090 6819 Email: tate@zoo.co.uk — MB ChB 1964 Birm.; MRCS Eng. LRCP Lond. 1964; FRCPsych 1994, M 1972; DPM Eng. 1971. (Birm. Univ.) Cons. Psychiat. & Med. Dir. Marchwood Priory Hosp.; Gp. Med. Dir.,

Priory Healthcare.; Chairm. UK Alcohol Forum. Prev: Cons. Psychiat. King Khalid Nat. Guard Hosp. Jeddah, Saudi Arabia; Cons. Psychiat. Roy. S. Hants., Hosp. Soton; Maj. RAMC.

TATE, Janice 8A Marshall Road, Hayling Island PO11 9NH — BM 1990 Soton.

TATE, Mr Jeremy James Thompson Department of Surgery, Royal United Hospital, Bath BA1 3NG Tel: 01225 824543 Email: jeremy.tate@ruh-bath.swest.nhs.uk — MB BS 1980 Lond.; MS Soton. 1989; FRCS Eng. 1985; FRCS Ed. 1984. Cons. Gen. Surg. Roy. United Hosp. Bath. Socs: Assn. Endoscopic Surg. (Counc. Mem. 1998-1999). Prev: Sen. Regist. (Gen. Surg.) Roy. Free Hosp. Lond.; Lect. Chinese Univ. Hong Kong, Shatin.

TATE, Judith 3 Torquay Gardens, Gateshead NE9 6XB — MB BS 1987 Lond.; BSc (Physiol.) Lond. 1984, MB BS 1987; MRCGP 1992; DA (UK) 1990.

TATE, Mary Elsbeth (retired) 91 Hartswood Road, Brentwood CM14 5AG Tel: 01277 226086 — MB BS Lond. 1961; MRCS Eng. LRCP Lond. 1961. Prev: Med. Off. Barking, Havering & Brentwood DHA.

TATE, Michael John Middlewich Road Surgery, 6 Middlewich Road, Sandbach CW11 1DL Tel: 01270 767411 Fax: 01270 759305; Townend Barn, Marsh Green Farm, Vicarage Lane, Sandbach CW11 3BU Tel: 01270 764320 — MB ChB 1980 Liverp.; MRCGP 1984. (Liverpool) GP; GP Trainer.

TATE, Patricia Ann East Barnwell Health Centre, Ditton Lane, Cambridge CB5 8SP Tel: 01223 728900 Fax: 01223 728901; 109 Grantchester Meadows, Cambridge CB3 9JN — MB BChir 1982 Camb.; MA Camb. 1983; MRCGP 1987; DCH RCP Lond. 1985; DGM RCP Lond. 1985; DRCOG 1984. (Addenbrookes Cambridge) Examr MRCGP; Hon. Clin .Asst. Psychother. Socs: (Mem. Counc.) Balint Soc.

TATE, Patricia Mary The Surgery, Carisbrooke House, Stockleigh Road, St Leonards-on-Sea TN38 0JP Tel: 01424 423190/432925 Fax: 01424 460473 — MB BS 1970 Lond.; BSc Lond. 1966, MB BS 1970. (Middlx.) Prev: Ho. Phys. Middlx. Hosp. Lond.; Ho. Surg. St. Albans City Hosp.; Ho. Off. (Obst.) Hackney Hosp.

TATE, Paul Andrew Oldchurch Hospital, Waterloo Road, Romford RM7 0BE — MB BS 1993 Lond.

TATE, Peter Howard Lovel Marcham Health Centre, Marcham Road, Abingdon OX14 1BT Tel: 01235 522602; The Clock House, High St, Culham, Abingdon OX14 4NA Tel: 01235 528052 Fax: 01235 539291 — MB BS 1968 Newc.; FRCGP 1983, M 1974. Trainer (Gen. Pract.) Abingdon; VIDEO Convenor MRCGP Exam. Socs: BMA & Oxf. Med. Soc. Prev: Surg. P & O Lines.

TATE, Rachel Mary (retired) 18 Beaulieu Close, Champion Hill, London SE5 8BA — MB ChB 1945 Birm.; DObst RCOG 1948; DCH Eng. 1950. Prev: Sen. PMO DHSS.

TATE, MR Robert James The Ipswich Hospital, Heath Road, Ipswich IP4 5PD Tel: 01473 703205 Fax: 01473 703158 Email: tate.sec@irish-tr.anglox.nhs.uk; Horsenden House, Little Bealings, Woodbridge IP13 6LX Tel: 01473 622995 Fax: 01473 622995 — MB BS 1968 Lond.; BDS Lond. 1964; MRCS Eng. LRCP Lond. 1968; LDS RCS Eng. 1963, F 1970. (Guy's) Cons. Oral & Maxillofacial Surg. Ipswich & W. Suff. Hosps. Socs: Brit. Assn. Oral Surgs. & BMA; HCSA; Brit. Dent. Assn. Prev: Sen. Regist. (Oral Surg.) W.m. Gp. Hosps.; Lect. (Oral Surg.) Univ. Coll. Hosp. Lond.; Ho. Surg. (ENT) Guy's Hosp. Lond.

TATE, Rodney Temple 71 Dyke Road Avenue, Hove BN3 6DA Tel: 01273 501542 — MB BS 1962 Lond.; DObst RCOG 1964. (St. Mary's) Socs: BMA.

TATE, Stephen 5 Strandview Street, Stranmillis, Belfast BT9 5FF — MB BCh BAO 1995 Belf.

TATE, Stephen Richard Holmes Chapel Health Centre, London Road, Holmes Chapel, Crewe CW4 7BB — MB BS 1983 Newc.; MRCP (UK) 1986; MRCGP 1989; Dip. Occ. Med. 1996.

TATEK, Josef 17 St Andrews Drive, Bridge of Weir PA11 3HS Tel: 01505 614168 — MD 1962 Prague; LRCP LRCS Ed. LRCPS Glas. 1971. (Chas. Univ. Prague) Assoc. Specialist (Orthop.) Roy. Alexandra Infirm. Paisley. Prev: Regist. (Orthop.) Roy. Alexandra Infirm. Paisley. SHO (Surg.) Gen.; Hosp. Tabor, Czechoslovakia; Regist. (Orthop.) 1st Orthop. Clinic Prague, Czechoslovakia.

TATEOSSIAN, Miss Jasmine Krikor Hammersmith Hospital (Cytology Department), 150 Du Cane Road, London W12 0HS Tel: 020 8383 3931; 24 Langside Avenue, Roehampton, London SW15 5QT Tel: 020 8876 5974 — MB BS 1965 Lond.; MRCS Eng. LRCP Lond. 1963. (Roy. Free) Assoc. Specialist (Histopath.) Hammersmith & Qu. Charlotte's & Chelsea Hosps. Prev: Regist. Chelsea Hosp. Wom.; SHO Gyn. Guy's Hosp. Gp. Obst. Off. Roy. Free Hosp. Lond.

TATFORD, Edgar Patrick Wylie, MBE, TD 38 Stone Road, Bromley BR2 9AU Tel: 020 8460 1061 — MB BS 1951 Lond.; MRCS Eng. LRCP Lond. 1951; FRCOG 1973, M 1960; DCH Eng. 1961; DObst 1957. (Guy's) Cons. O & G Bromley Hosp. Gp.; Col. late RAMC (V), OC 217 (L) Gen. Hosp. RAMC (V). Socs: Fell. Roy. Soc. Med. Prev: Sen. Regist. (O & G) Guy's Hosp. Lond.; Jun. Lect. (Anat.) St. Bart. Hosp. Lond.; Resid. Med. Off. Chelsea Hosp. Wom. & Qu. Charlotte's Hosp. Lond.

TATHAM, Margaret Elizabeth Goodinge Health Centre, Goodinge Close, North Road, London N7 9EW Tel: 020 7530 4940 — MB BS 1981 Lond.; BA (Hons.) (Physiol.) Oxf. 1978; BA (Hons.) (Hist.) Toronto 1970; MRCP (UK) 1984.

TATHAM, Pamela Charity The Garth, 79 Hallgarth St., Durham DH1 3AY Tel: 0191 384 6242; 52 Mitchell Avenue, Jesmond, Newcastle upon Tyne NE2 3LA Tel: 0191 281 0193 — MB BS 1949 Lond. (Univ. Coll. Hosp.) Socs: Brit. Assn. Allergy & Environm. Med.; (Comm.) Inst. Psionic Med.; Assoc. Mem. Fac. Homoeop. Prev: Clin. Med. Off. Sunderland HA; Med. Off. Colon. Med. Serv. Malaya & N. Borneo.

TATHAM, Peter Frank Baxter Farm, Willoughby-on-the-Wolds, Loughborough LE12 6SY Tel: 01509 880975 — MB BS 1966 Lond.; MRCS Eng. LRCP Lond. 1966; FFA RCS Eng. 1970. (St. Bart.) Cons. Anaesth. Nottm. City Hosp. Prev: Sen. Regist. (Anaesth.) St. Bart. Hosp. Lond.; Dir. of Anaesth. Papua New Guinea; Regist. (Anaesth.) Hosp. Sick Childr. Gt. Ormond St.

TATHAM, Peter Heathcote Maynards, Cornworthy, Totnes TQ9 7HB Tel: 01803 732733 — MB BChir 1959 Camb.; MA Camb. 1959; Dip. Analyt. Psychol. C.G. Jung Inst. Zürich 1978; DObst RCOG 1966. (St. Thos.)

TATHAM, Richard Hugh Benjamin 4 Elim Terrace, Peverell, Plymouth PL3 4PA Tel: 01752 260202; The Old Hall, Harberton, Totnes TQ9 7SQ — MB BS 1987 Lond.; BSc (Hons.) Biochem. Lond. 1984. SHO (Med.) Derriford Hosp. Plymouth. Prev: Trainee GP Saltash Cornw.; SHO (Special Care Baby Unit) & Med. Rotat. Derriford Hosp.

TATLA, Taranjit 52 Portland Street, Derby DE23 8QB — MB BS 1996 Lond.

TATMAN, Maybelle Alice Epidemiology and Biostatistics Unit, Institute of Child Health, 30 Guilford St., London WC1N 1EH Tel: 020 7242 9789; 34 Cobden Road, Brighton BN2 2TJ Tel: 01273 684381 — MB BS 1984 Lond.; MSC (Community Paediat.) Lond. 1990; MRCP (UK) 1987. Research Fell. Inst. Child Health Lond. Socs: Brit. Paediat. Assn. Prev: Regist. (Paediat.) Roy. Lond. Hosp.

TATMAN, Peter John 85 Goldington Avenue, Bedford MK40 3DB; 107 Warwick Avenue, Bedford MK40 2DH — MBBS; MRCGP 1983; DRCOG 1982. (London Middlesex Hosp.) Gen. Med. Practitioner.

TATNALL, Frances Melanie 71 Cholmeley Crescent, London N6 5EX — MB BS 1978 Lond.; MD Lond. 1991; MRCS Eng. LRCP Lond. 1978; FRCP 1996, MRCP (UK) 1980. (Roy. Free Hosp.) Cons. Dermat. Watford Gen. Hosp.

TATNALL, Sarah Kate Royal Manchester Children's Hospital, Manchester M27 4HA; 125 Swinton Park Road, Salford M6 7PB — BM BS 1995 Nottm. SHO (Paediat.) Roy. Manch. Childr. Hosp.

TATTAN, Theresa Maria Goretti Cossham Hospital, Lodge Road, Kingswood, Bristol BS15 1LQ — MB BS 1988 Lond.; MSc Manch. 1996; MRCPsych 1994. (Royal Free Hospital School of Medicine) Sen. Regist. (Psychiat.).

TATTARI, Ms Christalleni 144 Harley Street, London W1G 7LD Tel: 0207 935 0023 Fax: 0207 935 5972; 13 Bancroft Avenue, London N2 0AR Tel: 0208 340 0777 — Ptychio latrikes 1970 Athens; MRCS Eng. LRCP Lond. 1975; FRCS Lond. 1979; T(S) 1994. (Univ. Athens) Indep. Pract. (Plastic Surg.) Nuffield Hosp. Lond.; InDepend. Cosmetic and Aesthetic Surg., King's Oak Hosp. Chase Farm (N.side). Socs: Europ. Acad. Facial Surg.; BMA. Prev: Cons. Plastic Surg. & Head of Plastic Surg. Unit Tembisa Hosp. Olifansfontein, S. Afr.

TATTERSALL, Anne Elizabeth Clifton Lodge Surgery, 7 Clifton Lane, Meltham, Huddersfield HD9 4AH Tel: 01484 852073 Fax:

TATTERSALL

01484 854760 — MB BS 1970 Lond.; MRCS Eng. LRCP Lond. 1970; DCH Eng. 1972. (Roy. Free)

TATTERSALL, Christopher William 121 Clifton Drive S., Lytham St Annes FY8 1DX — MB BS 1970 Lond. GP Blackpool.

TATTERSALL, Deborah Jane 10 Bare Avenue, Morecambe LA4 6BE; 16 Silver St, Chacombe, Banbury OX17 2JR Tel: 01295 710612 — MB ChB 1991 Manch.; BSc (Hons.) Manch. 1988; MRCP (UK) 1994; FRCE (UK) 1998. Regist. (Radiol.) John Radcliffe Hosp. Oxf. Prev: SHO (Med.) S.mead Hosp. Bristol.

TATTERSALL, Edward Paul Dove River Practice, Gibb Lane, Sudbury, Ashbourne DE6 5HY Tel: 01283 812455 Fax: 01283 815187; Threeways, Rolleston on Dove, Burton-on-Trent DE13 9BD Tel: 01283 813532 Email: thetats@inrolleston.fsnet.co.uk — MB BS 1983 Lond.; MRCGP 1987; DRCOG 1986; Cert. Family Plann. JCC 1986. (Roy. Free) Socs: BMA; Dispensing Doctors Assn. Prev: Trainee GP Burton on Trent VTS.

TATTERSALL, Hilary Jane Pen y Maes Health Centre, Beech Street, Summerhill, Wrexham LL11 4UF Tel: 01978 756370 Fax: 01978 751870 — MB BCh 1977 Wales; DFFP 1994; DRCOG 1981; Cert. Family Plann. JCC 1981; MRCGP 1981. (WNSM)

TATTERSALL, James Erskine 42 Thrush St, Sheffield S6 5BQ Tel: 01142 322432 Email: jamestattersall@compuserve.com — MB BS 1980 Lond.; MD 1995 Lond.; MRCP 1985 Lond. (Charing Cross Hospital) p/t Hon. Cons. Renal Unit Basildon Dist. Gen. Hosp.; Med. Director Software Developm. Mediqal Ltd Stevenage. Socs: RCP. Prev: Staff Grade Nephrol. N.. Gen. Hosp. Sheff.; Clin. Scientist, Lister Hosp. Stevenage; Research Regist.,Nephrol. St Bart Hosp.,Lond.

TATTERSALL, Jill Marjorie (retired) 1 Brackenbarrow Cottages, Smithy Hill, Lindale, Grange-over-Sands LA11 6LT Tel: 015395 34872 — MB ChB 1956 Sheff.; DCH Eng. 1959; DObst RCOG 1959; MFFP RCOG 1995. Prev: Head Family Plann. & Well Wom. Servs. Community & Ment. Health Trust S. Cumbria HA.

TATTERSALL, Joan Mary (retired) 10 North Grange Mews, North Grange Road, Leeds LS6 — MB 1936 Leeds; MB, ChB Leeds 1936. Prev: Asst. Med. Off. Dept. Stud. Health Univ. Leeds.

TATTERSALL, Joseph Pen y Maes Health Centre, Beech Street, Summerhill, Wrexham LL11 4UF Tel: 01978 756370 Fax: 01978 751870 — MB BCh 1976 Wales; AFOM 1999; D.Occ.Med. 1995; MRCGP 1981; DRCOG 1980; Cert Family Plann 1980. (WNSM)

TATTERSALL, Louise Jane CMHT Victorial House, 28 Alexandra Road, Lowestoft NR32 1P Tel: 01502 532 2100; 12a The Street, South Walsham, Norwich NR13 6AH Tel: 01603 270020 — MB ChB 1987 Leic. Staff Psychiat. Norf. Ment. Health Care (NHS) Trust; Director of Med. Progr. Newmarket Ho. Clinic, Norwich Centre for Treatm. of eating disorders. Prev: Regist. Rotat. (Psychiat.) Merseyside RHA.; Staff Psychiat. E. Chesh. NHS Trust Macclesfield.

TATTERSALL, Mark Lincoln Huntercombe Manor, Huntercombe Lane S., Taplow, Maidenhead SL6 0PQ Tel: 01628 667881 Fax: 01628 603398 — MB BS 1981 Lond.; MRCPsych 1989; MRCPsych 1989. (Westm. Hosp. Med. Sch.) Cons. Adolec. & Adult Eating Disorders Huntercombe Manor Hosp. Taplow; Hon. Cons. Eating Disorders St. Geo. Hosp. Lond. Prev: Hon. Cons. Eating Disorders Gt. Ormond St. Childr Hosp. Lond.; Cons. Kingston Hosp. Kingston-upon-Thames; Sen. Regist. St. Geo. Hosp. Lond.

TATTERSALL, Michael Paul Swindon & Marlborough NHS Trust, Princess Margaret Hospital, Okus Road, Swindon SN1 4JU Tel: 01793 536231 — MB BS 1975 Lond.; FFA RCS Eng. 1980. (St Thomas's Hospital London) p/t Cons. Anaesth. Swindon & MarlBoro. NHS Trust. Prev: Sen. Regist. (Anaesth.) Nuffield Dept. Anaesth. Oxf.; Regist. (Anaesth.) Bristol Roy. Infirm.; SHO (Clin. Measurem.) W.m. Hosp. Lond.

TATTERSALL, Nigel Manchester Road Surgery, 187 Manchester Road, Burnley BB11 4HP Tel: 01282 420680 Fax: 01282 832031; Shephers Clough Farm, Dean Lane, Lumb, Rossendale — MB ChB 1985 Aberd.; BSc (Hons.) Aberd. 1980. Prev: Clin. Asst. (Genitourin.) Burnley Health Care NHS Trust.

TATTERSALL, Philip Heap Claypath Medical Practice, Claypath House, 65 Claypath, Durham DH1 1QU Tel: 0191 386 3848; 8 Ravensworth Terrace, Durham DH1 1QP Tel: 0191 384 3699 — MB ChB 1955 Leeds; MRCGP 1963. Prev: Hosp. Pract. (ENT) Durh. Health Dist.; Ho. Phys. Dept. Dermat. Leeds Gen. Infirm.; Ho. Surg. (Obst.) St. Mary's Hosp. Leeds.

TATTERSALL, Rachel Scarlett 4 Oakwood Mount, Leeds LS8 2JG — MB ChB 1995 Sheff.; BMedSci Sheff. 1992. SHO (Gen. Med.) St. Jas. Univ. Hosp. Leeds.

TATTERSALL, Professor Robert Booth Curzon House, Curzon St, Gotham, Nottingham NG11 0HQ — MD Camb. 1975, MB 1968, BChir 1967; FRCP Lond. 1980; MRCP (U.K.) 1970. Specialist Prof. Human Metab. Nottm. 1998; Prof. Clin. Diabetes Nottm. Prev: Prof. Clin. Diabetes Nottm.; Sen. Lect. St. Bart. Hosp. Lond.; Sen. Regist. Diabetic Dept. King's Coll. Hosp. Lond.

TATTERSALL, Toby Spa Road Surgery, Spa Road East, Llandrindod Wells LD1 5ES Tel: 01597 824291 / 842292 Fax: 01597 824503 — MB BS 1988 Lond.; MRCGP 1993; DRCOG 1991.

TATTERSFIELD, Professor Anne Elizabeth Division of Respiratory Medicine, Clinical Sciences Building, City Hospital, Hucknall Road, Nottingham NG5 1PB Tel: 0115 840 4772 Fax: 0115 840 4771 Email: anne.tattersfield@nottingham.ac.uk; Priory Barn, The Hollows, Thurgarton, Nottingham NG14 7GY Tel: 01636 830378 — MB BS Durh. 1963; MD Newc. 1970; FRCP Lond. 1979, M 1966. (Newc.) Prof. Respirat. Med. City Hosp. Nottm. Socs: Brit. Thoracic Soc. (Past Pres.); Acad. of Med. Sci.s; Assn. of Physcillaris. Prev: Sen. Lect. & Reader (Med.) Soton.; Sen. Regist. Lond. Hosp.; Regist. Hammersmith Hosp.

TATTERSFIELD, Helen Grace Oakview Family Practice, 190 Shroffold Road, Downham, Bromley BR1 5NJ Tel: 020 8695 6485 Fax: 020 8695 0830; 29 Stone Road BR2 9AX Tel: 0208 460 9993 — MB BS 1984 Lond.; MA Oxf. 1984; MRCGP 1990; DRCOG 1989; DCH RCP Lond. 1989; DFFP 1996. (King's Coll. Lond.) Primary Care Phys., Lewisham Hosp.; Bd. Mem., S. lewisham PCG.

TATTERSFIELD, Mr James Frederick 30 Sauncey Avenue, Harpenden AL5 4QJ Tel: 01582 762919 — MB BS Lond. 1957; FRCS Ed. 1967; DO Eng. 1964. (Middlx.) Cons. Ophth. Surg. Luton & Dunstable Hosp. & St. Albans City Hosp. Socs: FRCOphth. Prev: Sen. Regist. (Ophth.) Nat. Hosp. Nerv. Dis. Maida Vale & Roy. Free Hosp.; Clin. Asst. Moorfields Eye Hosp.; Regist. St. Mary's Hosp. & W. Ophth. Hosp. Lond. & Addenbrooke's Hosp.

TATTON, Pamela Upholme, Blackamoor Crescent, Dore, Sheffield S17 3GL Tel: 0114 236 0339 — MB ChB 1977 Sheff.

TATTUM, Christine Mary The Tardis Surgery, 9 Queen Street, Cheadle, Stoke-on-Trent ST10 1BH Tel: 01538 753771 Fax: 01538 752557 — MB ChB 1980 Manch.; MRCGP 1986; DRCOG 1984. Asst. Occupat. Phys. Stroke-on-Trent. Prev: Trainee GP/SHO N. Staffs. HA VTS.

TATTUM, Keith Thomas Baddeley Green Surgery, 988 Leek New Road, Stoke-on-Trent ST9 9PB Tel: 01782 533777 Fax: 01782 533333; 988 Leek New Road, Stockton Brook, Stoke-on-Trent ST9 9PB — MB ChB 1980 Manch.; BA (Hons.) Hull 1974; FRCGP 1993, M 1986; DFFP 1994; DRCOG 1984. Clin. Lect. Keele Univ.; Course Organiser N. Staffs. VTS. Prev: Lect. (Med.) Sch. Univ. Manch.; SHO (A & E) Wythenshawe Hosp. Univ. Manch. Sch. Med.; Trainee GP N. Staffs. VTS.

TAUB, Pierre-Stanislas Antoine 209 Harrow Road, London W2 5EG Tel: 020 7266 6000 — MB BCh 1990 Wales; T (GP) 1994; MRC Psych 1997. (University of Wales, College of Medicine) Cons. Psychiat., Paterson Centre for Ment. Health, Lond.

TAUBE, Mr Martin West Wales General Hospital, Carmarthen SA31 2AF Tel: 01267 227514 Fax: 01267 227514; 21 Swiss Valley, Llanelli SA14 8BS Tel: 01554 774096 Fax: 01554 774096 Email: mtaute8642@aol.com — MRCS Eng. LRCP Lond. 1975; BSc Lond. 1972, MS 1988, MB BS (Hons.) 1975; FRCS Eng. 1979. (Westm.) Cons. (Urol.) W. Wales Gen Hosp. Carmathen. Prev: Ho. Surg., Regist., Sen. Regist. & Lect. W.m. Hosp. Lond.; Cons. Surg. & Urol. P. Philip Hosp. LLa,lli; Marks & Spencer Fell. RCS 1980.

TAUBEL, Jorg Charterhouse Clinical Research, The Stamford Hospital, Ravenscourt Park, London W6 0TN Tel: 020 8741 7170 Fax: 020 8741 5986 Email: jt@c-house.demon.co.uk — MD 1989 Frankfurt; State Exam Med. Frankfurt 1987. MD CharterHo. Clin. Research Unit Lond. Prev: Head Med. Dept. Clin. Pharmacol. Parexel Berlin.

TAUBMAN, Rachel Lucy 101 Westfield Lane, St Leonards-on-Sea TN37 7NF — MB BS 1993 Lond.

TAUDEVIN, Elizabeth Jeanne Elm Grove Surgery, Silver St., Calne SN11 0JD Tel: 01249 812305; 60 Trinity Park, Calne SN11 0QD — MB BChir 1993 Camb.; MRCGP 1996; DRCOG 1995. (Camb.) GP

Calne. Prev: Trainee GP/SHO (Psychiat.) Roy. United Hosp. Bath VTS.

TAULKE-JOHNSON, Timothy Desmond c/o Newlands Medical Clinic, Chorley New Road, Bolton BL1 5BP — MB BS 1977 Lond.; MRCS Eng. LRCP Lond. 1977.

TAUSSIG, David Christopher 52 Arthur Road, Wimbledon, London SW19 7DS Tel: 020 8946 0316; 20 Mina Road, Old Merton Park, London SW19 3AU — MB BS 1993 Lond.; MRCPath 2001; BSc (Basic Med. Scis. & Pharmacol.) Lond. 1990; MRCP (UK) 1996. (Char. Cross & Westm. Med. Sch.) Specialist Regist. (Haemat.) Roy. Lond. Hosp.; ICRF Translational Research Fell., Stem cell Laborat. Room 504, ICRF, 44 Lincoln's Inn Fields, Lond. Prev: SHO (Intens. Care) St. Geo. Hosp. Lond.; SHO (Infec. Dis.) St. Geo. Hosp. Lond.; SHO (Gen. Med. with Cardiol.) E. Surrey Hosp. Redhill.

TAUSSIG, Jo-Ann 57 Vainor Road, Wadsley, Hillsborough, Sheffield S6 4AP — MB BS 1998 Lond.; MB BS Lond 1998.

TAUZEEH, Shah Mohammad Finchley Memorial Hospital, Granville Road, London N12 0JE — MB BS 1981 Calcutta.

TAVABIE, Abdolah The Surgery, 108 Chislehurst Road, Orpington BR6 0DW Tel: 01689 826664 Fax: 01689 890795 — MD 1975 Jondishapour; MRCGP; FRCGP 1993. (Jondishapour Univ.) GP; Dean of Postgrad. GP Educat. S. Thames (E.).

TAVABIE, Jacqueline Ann The Surgery, 108 Chislehurst Road, Orpington BR6 0DW — MB BS 1981 Lond.; BSc (Biochem.) Lond. 1978; MRCGP 1995; DRCOG 1994. (Guy's) GP Orpington.

TAVADIA, Hosie Byram (retired) Department of Pathology, Stirling Royal Infirmary, Stirling FK8 2AU Tel: 01786 434000 — MB ChB 1964 Aberd.; FRCPath 1982, M 1971; DObst RCOG 1966. Prev: Lect. (Path.) Roy. Infirm. Glas.

TAVADIA, Sherine Menzies Byram 3F1, 7 Hovelock St., Glasgow G11 5JB — MB ChB 1993 Glas.; MRCP(UK) 1996.

TAVAKKOLI, Aryandokht — MB BS 1991 Lond.; MRCP (UK) 1994. (St. Bartholomews, London) Cons., Repiratory/Gen. Med., Dartford. Socs: BMA & Med. Defence Union; Brit. Thorac. Soc.; RCP. Prev: Specialist Regist. Guy's Hosp. Lond.; Specialist Regist. King's Coll. Hosp.; Regist. St. Thos. Hosp.

TAVAKKOLIZADEH, Ali Floor 3, Room 14, Parkstone House, 35 Parkstone Road, Poole BH15 2NG — MB BS 1993 Lond.

TAVARE, Alison Jane The Surgery, 60 Falcondale Road, Westbury-on-Trym, Bristol BS9 3JY Tel: 0117 962 3406 Fax: 0117 962 1404 — MB ChB 1985 Bristol.

TAVARE, Stephen Myles Sawston Health Centre, Link Road, Sawston, Cambridge CB2 4LB Tel: 01223 832711 Fax: 01223 836096 — MB 1977 Camb.; BChir 1976; DRCOG 1979; MRCGP 1981.

TAVARES-MOTT, Nicola Esseuvolon 138 Selwyn Road, Birmingham B16 0HN — MB BS 1994 Lond.; BSc Lond. 1991.

TAVERNER, Deborah Mary Queen Elizabeth II Hospital, Welwyn Garden City; Winston Cottage, Rectory Road, Gillingham NR34 0HH — MB ChB 1982 Leic.; MRCGP 1986; T(GP) 1991; DRCOG 1984. p/t Clin. Asst. BrE. Clinic Hertford Co. Hosp. And QE 11 Hosp. Prev: Asst. GP E. Barnet Lond.; SHO (Paediat.) Centr. Middlx. Hosp. Lond.; SHO (A & E) & (O & G) Middlx. Hosp. Lond.

TAVERNER, John Patrick (retired) 96 Dorridge Road, Dorridge, Solihull B93 8BS Tel: 01564 775575 — MB BCh 1970 Wales; MRCGP 1975; DObst RCOG 1974. Prev: SHO (Allergy & Asthma) St. Davids Hosp. Cardiff.

TAVERNOR, Rosalyn Mary Elizabeth Department of Forensic Psychiatry, Nottingham Healthcare NHS Trust, Duncan Macmillan House, Nottingham NG3 6AA — MB ChB 1988 Leeds; MRCPsych 1994. Lect. (Forens. Psychiat.) Liverp. Univ. & Hon. Sen. Regist. Ashworth Hosp.

TAVERNOR, Simon James Department of Psychiatry, B Floor South Block, Queens Medical Centre, Derby Road, Nottingham NG7 2UH Tel: 0115 924 9924 — MB ChB 1987 Ed.; BSc (Hons.) Ed. 1985; MRCPsych 1993. Cons. (Psychiat.) Univ. Hosp. Nottm.; Clin. Teach., Nottm. Univ. Socs: Brit. Neuropsychiat. Assn.; Brit. Assn. for PsychoPharmacol. Prev: Clin. Lect. (Psychiat.) Nottm. Univ.; Sen. Regist. Rotat. (Gen. Adult Psychiat.) Mid Trent; Regist. Rotat. (Psychiat.) Gtr. Manch.

TAW, Harry 6 Hillside Road, Southall UB1 2PD — MB BS 1975 Med. Inst. (I) Rangoon.

TAWFIK, Rihab Fathi Pinderfields General Hospital, Wakefield WF1 4DG Tel: 01924 201688 Fax: 01924 814864 Email: rihab.tawfik@panp-tr.northy.nhs.uk — MB ChB Baghdad 1969; MRCP (UK) 1979; FRCPCH 1996; DCH Baghdad 1976; FRCP 1999. (Baghdad, Iraq) Cons. Paediat. Pinderfields Hosp. Wakefield. Socs: Brit. Soc. Paediat. Gastroenterol. & Nutrit.; Yorks. Regional Paediat. Soc. Prev: Sen. Regist. (Paediat. Gastroenterol.) Booth Hall Hosp. Manch.

TAWIA, Anmor 46 Strand Park, Cloughmills, Ballymena BT44 9LL — LRCPI & LM, LRSCI & LM 1963; LRCPI & LM, LRCSI & LM 1963.

TAWIAH, Alexander Lamptey (retired) 110 Wergs Road, Wolverhampton WV6 8TH Tel: 01902 752923 — LRCPI & LM, LRSCI & LM 1958; LRCPI & LM, LRCSI & LM 1958; LAH Dub. 1958; MCOphth 1990; DO RCS Eng. 1965.

TAWN, David Julian Department Diagnostic Radiology, Royal Bournemouth Hospital, Castle Lane E., Bournemouth BH7 7DW Tel: 01202 303626; Elgam House, 32 Arnewood Road, Southbourne, Bournemouth BH6 5DH Tel: 01202 428776 — MB ChB 1980 Bristol; FRCR 1988. Cons. Radiol. Roy. Bournemouth & ChristCh. Hosps. NHS Trust. Prev: Sen. Regist. (Radiodiag.) Bristol Roy. Infirm. & Plymouth Hosp.

TAWODZERA, Percy Bobo-Changadeya Peter c/o Professor Middlemiss, Department of Radiodiagnosis, Bristol Royal Infirmary, Bristol BS2 8HW Tel: 0117 922041 — MB ChB 1974 Birm.; FRCR 1982; DMRD Eng. 1981. (Rhodesia)

TAWS, Elizabeth Roxborough — MRCS Eng. LRCP Lond. 1968; FRCPsych 1985, M 1972; DPM Eng. 1971. (Sheff.) Prev: Cons. Psychiat. Goodmayes Hosp. Ilford; Cons. Psychiat. Norf. Ment. Health Care Trust.

TAWSE, Bernadette Marie Pudsey Health Centre, 18 Mulberry Street, Pudsey LS28 7XP Tel: 0113 257 6711 Fax: 0113 236 3928; 101 Holt Lane, Leeds LS16 7PJ — MB ChB 1972 Aberd.

TAWSE, Stephen Barclay The Health Centre, North Road, Stokesley, Middlesbrough TS9 5DY Tel: 01642 710748 Fax: 01642 713037; 12 The Avenue, Stokesley, Middlesbrough TS9 5ET Tel: 01642 711365 — MB BS 1987 Lond.; BSc Lond. 1984; MRCGP 1993; DRCOG 1992; DA (UK) 1991. Prev: Trainee GP Leyburn; SHO (Psychiat.) Darlington; SHO (Paediat.) N.allerton.

TAY, Clement Chong Kheng Simpson Memorial Maternity Pavilion, Royal Infirmary, Lauriston Place, Edinburgh EH3 9YW Tel: 0131 536 1000 Email: clement.tay@luht.scot.nhs.uk; Tel: 0131 664 1669 — MB ChB 1980 Glas.; MSc (Med. Sci.) Glas. 1984; FRCS Glas. 1988; MRCOG 1988; FRCOG 2000 London. Cons. O & G Simpson Memor. Matern. Pavilion Roy. Infirm. Lauriston Pl. Edin. Prev: Subspeciality Train. Fell. (Reproduc. Med.) & Sen. Regist. (O & G) Roy. Infirm. Edin.; WHO Clin. Research Fell. (Reproduc. Med.) Centre for Reproduc. Biol. Univ. Edin.; Regist. Qu. Mother's Hosp. & W.. Infirm. Glas.

TAY, Eugene Sheng Wei Flat 167, Defoe House, Barbican, London EC2Y 8ND — MB BS 1997 Lond.

TAY, Hua Hui 156 Bensham Lane, Thornton Heath, Croydon CR0 2R — MB BS 1981 Lond.; MRCP (UK) 1984.

TAY, Mr Huey Ling ENT Department, Freeman Hospital, High Heaton, Newcastle upon Tyne NE7 7DN; 203 Elmwood House, Melville Grove, Newcastle upon Tyne NE7 7AZ — BM BCh Oxf. 1985; FRCS Eng. 1993; FRCS Ed. 1989.

TAY, Jacqueline I-Yen Department Obstetrics and Gynaecology, Gledhow Wing, St James's University Hospital, Beckett St., Leeds LS9 7TF — MB ChB 1986 Leic.; MRCOG 1992. Lect. (O & G) St. Jas. Univ. Hosp. Leeds. Prev: Research Regist. Assisted Conception Unit Leeds Gen. Infirm.

TAY, Kem Sing The Evergreen Practice, Skimped Hill Health Centre, Skimped Hill Lane, Bracknell RG12 1LH Tel: 01344 306936 Fax: 01344 306966 — LRCP LRCS 1982 Ed.; LRCP LRCS Ed. LRCPS Glas. 1982. Socs: BMA & Brit. Med. Acupunc. Soc.

TAY, Keng Yeow Room 18 Doctors' Residence, Glasgow Royal Infirmary, 91 Wishart St., Glasgow G31 2ER — MB BS 1997 New South Wales.

TAY, Paul Yee Siang Flat 6, Eden Court, 79 Clarkehouse Road, Sheffield S10 2LG Tel: 0114 267 0665 — MB BCh BAO 1992 Belf.; MRCOG. 1996. SHO (O & G) Roy. Vict. Hosp. Belf.; Clin. Fell. Sheff. Fertil.. Sheff. Prev: SHO (O & G) Ulster Hosp. Dundonald & Roy. Vict. Hosp.; SHO (O & G) Roy Vict Hosp. Belf.; SHO (O & G) Belf. City Hosp. Belf.

TAY, Teck Wah 18 Kensington Manor, Dollingstown, Craigavon BT66 7HR — MB BCh BAO 1992 Belf.

TAY MCGARRY

TAY MCGARRY, Guek Siang 9 The Plateau, Piney Hills, Belfast BT9 5QP — MB BCh BAO 1969 Belf.

TAY ZA AUNG, Dr New Health Centre, Third Avenue, Canvey Island SS8 9SU Tel: 01268 683758 Fax: 01268 684057; 85 Long Road, Canvey Island SS8 0JB — MB BS 1957 Rangoon; MRCGP 1974; DObst RCOG 1967; DPH Bristol 1961. (Rangoon) Prev: SHO S.end & Rochford Gen. Hosps. & Co. Hosp. Griffithstown; Med. Off. Sea & Airport Rangoon, Burma.

TAYABALI, Mujtaba 14 Hauxton Road, Little Shelford, Cambridge CB2 5HJ — MB ChB 1962 St. And.

TAYAL, Mr Nilema 5 East Court, Wembley HA0 3QJ Tel: 020 8904 3590 — FRCS Ed. 1986.

TAYAL, Surupchand Aminchand 21 Angram Drive, Sunderland SR2 7RD Tel: 0191 564 2513 Fax: 01642 854328 Email: s.taylor8144@aol.com — MB BS 1977 Gujarat; MD Gujarat 1980; MRCPI 1990. Cons.(Genitourin Med.) Middlesbourough Gen Hosp. Socs: Soc. Study VD. Prev: Sen. Regist. (Genitourin. Med.) Newc. Gen. Hosp.

TAYAR, René St Helier Hospital NHS Trust, Wrythe Lane, Carshalton SM5 1AA Tel: 020 8644 4343; 45 Epsom Lane S., Tadworth KT20 5TA Tel: 01737 813582 — MD 1980 Malta; MD Malta 1969; FRCR 1980. Cons. Radiol. St. Helier NHS Trust Carshalton Surrey; Hon. Sen. Lect. St. Geo. Hosp. Med. Sch. Lond.; Hon. Sec. MRRA (UK). Socs: MRRA (UK). Prev: Sen. Regist. & Regist. United Bristol Hosps.

TAYEBJEE, Muzahir Hassan Aberdeen Royal Infirmary, Polwarth Building, Foresterhill, Aberdeen AB25 2ZD — MB ChB 1998 Aberd.

*TAYIB, Shahila 128/3 Nicolson Street, Edinburgh EH8 9EH; No 6, Jalan Taman Bandar Baru, Taman Bandar Baru, Sungat Lalang, Bedong, Kedah 08100, Malaysia Tel: 006 04 4582752 Email: syarq@hotmail.com — MB ChB 1997 Ed.

TAYLER, David Holroyd Royal Sussex County Hospital, Eastern Road, Brighton BN2 3EW — MB BS 1981 Lond.; FFA RCS Eng. 1986. Cons. Anaesth. Roy. Sussex Co. Hosp. Brighton. Prev: Sen. Regist. (Anaesth.) King's Coll. Hosp. Lond.

TAYLER, David Ian Lawson Road Surgery, 5 Lawson Road, Broomhill, Sheffield S10 5BU Tel: 0114 266 5180; 225 Ringinglow Road, Bents Green, Sheffield S11 7PT Email: d.tayler@shef.ac.uk — BM 1977 Soton.; BSc (Engin) (1st cl. Hons.) 1972; MRCP (UK) 1979; MRCGP 1986; DRCOG 1986. Hosp. Pract. (Cardiol.) N.. Gen. Hosp. Sheff. Socs: Sheff. MC Soc. Prev: Research Fell. Cardiol. N.. Gen. Hosp. Sheff.; Regist. (Cardiol. & Gen. Med.) King's Coll. Hosp. Lond. & Roy. Sussex.Co. Hosp.

TAYLER, Deborah Jayne Cherry Trees, Buckland Monachorum, Yelverton PL20 7NL — MB BCh 1985 Wales; BSc (Physiol.) Wales 1980; MRCGP 1989; DRCOG 1987.

TAYLER, Elizabeth Mary C/O FCO (ABUJA), King Charles Street, London SW1A 2AH Email: l-tayler@dfid.gov.uk — BM BCh 1988 Oxf.; MRCP (UK) 1991; MFPHM 1999. Health Adviser DFID Nigeria. Prev: ODA Fell. Tuberc. Unit WHO Geneva; Sen. Regist., Pub. health, Oxf. health Auth.

TAYLER, Michael John The Surgery, Margaret Street, Thaxted, Dunmow CM6 2QN Tel: 01371 830213 Fax: 01371 831278; Oakhurst, Park St, Thaxted, Dunmow CM6 2NE Tel: 01371 831059 — MB 1980 Camb.; BChir 1979; MRCGP 1985; Dip. IMC RCS Ed. 1993; DRCOG 1983. Prev: Trainee GP Addenbrooke's Hosp. VTS Camb.; Ho. Surg. Addenbrooke's Hosp. Camb.; Ho. Phys. W. Suff. Hosp. Bury St. Edmunds.

TAYLER, Peter James Fairfield Centre, 12 Portland Square, Carlisle; 24 Woodcroft Road, Wylam NE41 8DH Tel: 01661 852464 Fax: 01661 854044 — BM BCh 1976 Oxf.; MA Camb. 1977; MRCP (UK) 1978; FRCPsych 1997; MRCPsych 1985. Cons. Adolesc. Psychiat. Fairfield Centre Carlisle; Cons. Adolesc. Psychiat. Lindisfarne Suite Nuffield Private Hosp. Clayton Rd. Jesmond, Newc.-u-Tyne. Prev: Sen. Regist. (Child Adolesc. Psychiat.) Nuffield Child Psychiat. Unit Newc.; Cons. Adolesc. Psychiat. Sir Martin Roth. Young People's Unit Newc. Gen. Hosp.; Regist. (Paediat.) W.m. Childr. Hosp.

TAYLER, Robert George Opie (retired) Merlebank, Church Hill, Merstham, Redhill RH1 3BJ Tel: 01737 643178 — MB BChir 1948 Camb.; MA Camb. 1946, MB BChir 1948; DObst RCOG 1951. Prev: Clin. Asst. (Surg.) Redhill E. Surrey Hosp.

TAYLER, Timothy Martin Brooks Lane Surgery, 233a Brook Lane, Sarisbury, Southampton SO31 6DQ Tel: 01489 575191 Fax: 01489 570033; 60 Brook Lane, Warsash, Southampton SO31 9FG Tel: 01489 584297 — MB ChB 1981 Bristol; MRCP (UK) 1984. Prev: SHO (Neurol., Cardiol. & Gastroenterol.) Soton. Gen. Hosp.; SHO (Chest Med.) Hall Green Hosp. Bristol.

TAYLOR, Adam David 1 Meadow Close, Hove BN3 6QQ — MB ChB 1993 Aberd.

TAYLOR, Adrian 21 Chelford Avenue, Astley Bridge, Bolton BL1 7AY — MB ChB 1989 Aberd.

TAYLOR, Adrian Howard The Fosse, Pheasant Copse, Fleet GU51 4LP — MB BS 1992 Lond.

TAYLOR, Adrian Vincent Garratt Acres End Barn, Barton Hartshorne, Buckingham MK18 4JX — MB BS 1982 Lond.; MRCP (UK) 1993; DRCOG 1988; DCH RCP Lond. 1986; MPhil 2000; FRCP 2000. Cons. Phys. & Endocrinol. Horton Gen. Hosp. Banbury; Cons. Obstetric Phys., John Radcliffe Hosp., Oxf.. Prev: Sen. Regist. (Endocrinol.) Char. Cross Hosp. Lond.

TAYLOR, Adrienne Laurel Farm, 20 St Andrew's Road, Old Headington, Oxford OX3 9DL — BM BCh 1967 Oxf.; MA, BM BCh Oxf. 1967. (Oxf.)

TAYLOR, Aileen Euphemia Macdonald Department of Dermatology, Royal Victoria Infirmary, Queen Victoria Road, Newcastle upon Tyne NE1 4LP Tel: 0191 232 5131; 40 Reid Park Road, Jesmond, Newcastle upon Tyne NE2 2ES — MB ChB 1976 Ed.; MRCP (UK) 1980; FRCP 1998. (Edin.) Cons. Dermat. Newc. Hosps. NHS Trust.

TAYLOR, Alan Pathology Laboratory, Furness General Hospital, Barrow-in-Furness LA14 4LF Tel: 01229 491257 Fax: 01229 491044 Email: alan.taylor@b.bay-tr.nwest.nhs.uk — MB ChB 1977 Liverp.; FRCPath 1996, M 1984; MA Oxon 1990; BA (Hons.) Oxf. 1970. Cons. Chem. Path. Roy. Infirm., Lancaster; Cons. Chem. Path. Wedmorland Gen. Hosp. Kendal; Hon. Lect. Biochem. Dept. Univ. Lancaster. Socs: Assn. Clin. Biochems.; Brit. Hyperlipidaemia Assn. Prev: Ho. Off. Liverp. Roy. Infirm.; Sen. Regist. (Clin. Chem.) Univ. Hosp. Nottm.; Regist. (Clin. Biochem.) Addenbrookes Hosp. Camb.

TAYLOR, Alan David — MB BS 1991 Lond.; DPhil (Chem.) Sussex 1986, BSc (Chem.) 1983; MRCP (UK) 1995. (St. Bart. Hosp. Med. Sch.) Specialist Regist. (Cardiol.) Derriford Hosp. Plymouth. Socs: MDU. Prev: Regist. (Cardiol.) Roy. Devon & Exeter Hosp.; SHO (Med.) Singleton Hosp. Swansea; SHO (Gen. Med.) Cheltenham Gen. Hosp.

TAYLOR, Alan Richard, BEM (retired) 12 Culloden Road, Enfield EN2 8QB — MB BS Lond. 1950; MRCGP 1964; DTM & H Eng. 1959; DObst RCOG 1952. Prev: Med. Supt. Med. Serv. & Clinic Chittagong, E. Pakistan.

TAYLOR, Mr Alan Robert Stoke Mandeville Hospital NHS Trust, Mandeville Rd, Ailesbury HP01 8AL Tel: 01296 315197 Fax: 01296 315199; Elmhurst, 23 School Lane, Weston Turville, Aylesbury HP22 5SG Tel: 01296 613201 Fax: 01296 615401 — MB BS 1969 Newc.; FRCS Eng. 1975; FRCS Ed. 1975. Cons. Gen. Surg. Stoke Mandeville Hosp. Socs: Brit. Assn Of Research Surg.; Assoc. Of Surg.s GB + Irel.; Soc. Of Acad. and Research surg. Prev: Lect. (Surg.) Univ. Liverp.; Sen. Regist. (Surg.) Roy. Liverp. Hosp. & BRd.green Hosp. Liverp.; Wellcome Research Fell. & Tutor (Surg.) Roy. Postgrad. Med. Sch.

TAYLOR, Alexander James, OBE Grampian Healthcare NHS Trust, Westholme, Woodend Hospital, Aberdeen AB15 6LS Tel: 01224 663131 Fax: 01224 840790 Email: staff@ghc.wintermute.co.uk; Beechwood, Fyvie, Turriff AB53 8PB Tel: 01651 891349 Fax: 01651 891706 — MB ChB Aberd. 1950; FRCGP 1978, M 1963. Chairm. Grampian Healthcare NHS Trust Woodend Hosp. Aberd.; Hon. Sen. Lect. Univ. Aberd.; Med. Examr. Civil Aviat. Auth. Prev: Lect. (Gen. Pract.) Univ. Aberd.; GP Fyvie, Turriff; Med. Off. Shapinsay, Orkney.

TAYLOR, Alexandra 30 Bonchurch Road, Southsea PO4 8RZ — MB BS 1993 Lond.

TAYLOR, Alexandra Jayne 12 Haileybury Road, West Bridgford, Nottingham NG2 7BJ — MB BS 1993 Lond.

TAYLOR, Alfred Butler 26 Church Street, Cawthorne, Barnsley S75 — LMSSA 1939 Lond.

TAYLOR, Mr Alfred Roy (retired) 4 Watchcroft Drive, Buckingham MK18 1GH Tel: 01280 823551 — MB BS 1957 Lond.; FRCS Eng. 1964; MRCS Eng. LRCP Lond. 1957. Assoc. Surg. Nuffield Orthop. Centre Oxf. Prev: Cons. Orthop. Surg. Aylesbury Gp. Hosps. & Oxf. Regional Rheum Research Centre Stoke Mandeville Hosp. Aylesbury.

TAYLOR

TAYLOR, Aliki Joanna Public Health Department, Worcestershire Health Authority, Isaac Maddox House, shrub Hill Rd, Worcester WR4 9RW Tel: 01905 760093 Email: aliki.a.t.taylor@solihull-ha.wmids.nhs.uk; 123 Crabtree Lane, Bromsgrove B61 8PQ Tel: 01527 870768 Email: aliki@nationwideisp.net — MB BS 1994 Lond.; BSc Anthropology (Lond.) 1989; DFPHM 1999. (Lond.) Specialist Regist. (Pub. Health) W. Midl. Prev: SHO (Med.) Cheltenham Gen. Hosp.; SHO (Geriat.) Delancey Hosp. Cheltenham; SHO (Gastroenterol.) Norwich Gen. Hosp.

TAYLOR, Alison Elizabeth 10 St Georges Avenue, Timperley, Altrincham WA15 6HE — MB ChB 1994 Manch.

TAYLOR, Alison Mary Cameron The Central Hove Surgery, 3 Ventnor Villas, Hove BN3 3DD Tel: 01273 744911 Fax: 01273 744919 — MB BS 1989 Lond.; MRCGP 1994; DRCOG 1991. (St. Barts. Hosp. Lond.) GP Centr. Ho. Surg. Hove. Prev: Trainee GP Hove.

TAYLOR, Alison Patricia QEDH, Mindelsohn Way, Edgbaston, Birmingham B15 2QZ — MB ChB 1988 Manch.; BA Liverp. 1978; MMedSci (Psychiat.) Birm. 1996; MRCPsych 1992. p/t Cons. (Old Age Psychiat.) S. Birm. Ment. Health Trust. Prev: Sen. Regist. (Psychiat.) W. Midl. RHA; Regist. Rotat. (Psychiat.) S. Birm. DHA; SHO (Psychiat.) Lancaster Moor Hosp. & Midl. Nerve Hosp. Birm.

TAYLOR, Alistair John The Health Centre, Bank St., Faversham ME13 8QR Tel: 01795 533296 — MB ChB 1981 Bristol; MRCGP 1985; DRCOG 1984.

TAYLOR, Amanda Jane Whetstone Lane Health Centre, 44 Whetstone Lane, Birkenhead CH41 2TF Tel: 0151 647 9613 Fax: 0151 650 0875; Beacon Cottage, Moorland Close, Heswall, Wirral CH60 0EL — MB ChB 1986 Liverp.; DRCOG 1988.

TAYLOR, Amanda Jane Biggleswade Health Centre, Saffron Road, Biggleswade SG18 8DJ — MB BS 1992 Lond.

TAYLOR, Amanda Jane 27 Robertson Close, Shenley, Church End, Milton Keynes MK5 6EB — MB ChB 1992 Manch.

TAYLOR, Amanda Victoria Wessex Regional Forensic Psychiatric Services, Ravenswood House, The Knowle Hospital, Fareham PO17 5NA Tel: 01329 836198 Fax: 01329 834780 — MB BS 1985 Lond.; BSc Lond. 1982, MB BS 1985; MRCPsych 1991. (Middlesex)

TAYLOR, Andrea Jane Town Medical Centre, 25 London Road, Sevenoaks TN13 1AR Tel: 01732 454545/458844 Fax: 01732 462181; 22 Annetts Hall, Borough Green, Sevenoaks TN15 8DY — MB ChB 1982 Leeds; BSc (Chem. Path.) Leeds 1979, MB ChB 1982; MRCGP 1986; DRCOG 1985.

TAYLOR, Andrew 42A Camperdown Street, Broughty Ferry, Dundee DD5 3AB — MB ChB 1989 Dundee.

TAYLOR, Andrew Alexander 23A Akenside Terrace, Newcastle upon Tyne NE2 1TN — MB BS 1993 Newc.

TAYLOR, Mr Andrew Barrie Wilson Easter Cornhill, South Creake, Fakenham NR21 9LX Tel: 01328 560 — MB ChB 1964 Ed.; FRCS Ed. 1971; FRCOG 1983, M 1970, DObst 1967. (Ed.) Cons. O & G Qu. Eliz. Hosp. King's Lynn Norf. Socs: Brit. Soc. Colposcopy; Fell. Edin. Obst. Soc.; Fell. Roy. Soc. Med. Prev: Sen. Regist. & Clin. Tutor Hammersmith Hosp. Lond.; Regist. (Gen. Surg.) Peel Hosp. Galashiels; SHO Simpson Memor. Matern. Pavil., Roy. Infirm. Edin.

TAYLOR, Andrew Damian Hull Royal Infirmary, X-Ray Department, Anlaby Road, Hull HU3 2JZ Tel: 01482 28541 — MB ChB 1977 Bristol; FRCR 1986. Cons. Diag. Radiol. Hull & E. Yorks. HA. Socs: Brit. Med. Ultrasound Soc.; Roy. Coll. of Radiologists; Brit. Soc. Of Skeletal Radiologists. Prev: Sen. Regist. (Diag. Radiol.) Char. Cross Hosp. Lond.

TAYLOR, Andrew Frederick 347 Green Lane, Chertsey KT16 9QS — MB BS 1996 Lond.; BSc (Lond.) 1993, MB BS 1996. SHO (Anaesth.) Redhill & St. Hellier Hosps. Surrey.

TAYLOR, Andrew Harry William Harvey Hospital, Kennington Road, Willesborough, Ashford TN24 0LZ — MB ChB 1988 Cape Town.

TAYLOR, Mr Andrew John Nigel 21 St Anthony's Road, Blundellsands, Liverpool L23 8TN — MB BS 1991 Lond.; BSc Lond. 1988; FRCS Eng. 1995.

TAYLOR, Andrew Kevin Spencer 15 Brighton Close, Wigston LE18 1EF — MB ChB 1997 Leic.

TAYLOR, Andrew Lionel Johnson St James Medical Centre, 11 Carlton Road, Tunbridge Wells TN1 2HW Tel: 01892 541634 Fax: 01892 545170 — MB BS 1975 Lond.; MRCGP 1981; DCH RCP Lond. 1979; DRCOG 1977. (St. Bartholomews Hosp., Lond.) Socs: Christian Med. Fell.sh. Prev: Med. Off. Africa Inland Ch. Kapsowar Hosp., Kenya.

TAYLOR, Andrew Mark Maudsley Hospital, London SE5 8AF — MB BS 1988 Lond.

TAYLOR, Andrew Mayall 82 Russell Road, Wimbledon, London SW19 1LW — BM BCh 1992 Oxf.; BA Camb. 1989; MRCP (UK) 1995. (Camb./Oxf.) Clin. Research Fell. MR Unit Roy. Brompton Hosp. Lond.

TAYLOR, Andrew Michael 160 The Dashes, Harlow CM20 3RU — BM 1992 Soton.; BSc Sheff. 1988.

TAYLOR, Mr Andrew Michael Keld Head, Keld, Penrith CA10 3QF — MB BS 1990 Lond.; FRCS Eng. 1994. Socs: Brit. Orthop. Train. Assn.

TAYLOR, Andrew Philip 71 Flixborough Road, Burton-upon-Stather, Scunthorpe DN15 9HB — MB ChB 1990 Leeds.

TAYLOR, Andrew Richard Beech Tree Surgery, 68 Doncaster Road, Selby YO8 9AJ Tel: 01757 703933 Fax: 01757 213473 — MB ChB 1988 Birm. (Birm.) Clin. Asst. (A & E) Selby War Memor. Hosp. N. Yorks.

TAYLOR, Andrew Spencer Taylor, Parsons, Donnelly, Kuruvilla and Mulrine, Woolton House Medical Centre, 4/6 Woolton Street, Woolton, Liverpool L25 5JA Tel: 0151 428 4184 Fax: 0151 428 4598; 5 Sunnygate Road, Liverpool L19 9BS — MB ChB 1977 Liverp.; MRCGP 1988. Med. Off. Liverp. Marie Curie Centre. Socs: Liverp. LMC.

TAYLOR, Andrew William Leesbrook Surgery, Mellor Street, Lees, Oldham OL4 3DG Tel: 0161 621 4800 Fax: 0161 628 6717; 38 Summershades Lane, Grasscroft, Saddleworth, Oldham OL4 4ED Tel: 01457 878570 Fax: 01457 874894 Email: drat@msn.com — MB ChB 1970 Manch. Clin. Asst. (Urodynamics) Oldham HA. Prev: Regist. (Surg.) Preston Roy. Infirm.; SHO Rotat. (Surg.) Manch. Roy. Infirm.; SHO (Urol.) Crumpsall Hosp. Manch.

TAYLOR, Angela Valerie (retired) 30 Trafalgar Road, Birkdale, Southport PR8 2HE Tel: 01704 568800 Email: angelataylor@msn.com — MB ChB 1960 Liverp. Med. Mem. of APPEALS Serv. Prev: Princip. in Gen. Pract.

TAYLOR, Anita Jane Central Health Clinic, 1 Mulberry St., Sheffield S1 2PJ Tel: 0114 271 6790 Fax: 0114 271 6791; 74 Townend Street, Sheffield S10 1NN — MRCS Eng. LRCP Lond. 1971; MFFP 1993. SCMO Community Health Sheff. NHS Trust. Socs: Fac. Community Health; Inst. Psychosexual Med.

TAYLOR, Anne Elizabeth 14 Main Street, Weston Turville, Aylesbury HP22 5RR — MB ChB 1971 Glas.; DObst RCOG 1973.

TAYLOR, Anne Kathryn 8 Swann Grove, Cheadle Hulme, Cheadle SK8 7HW — MB ChB 1991 Manch.

TAYLOR, Anthony Department of Physiology, Charing Cross & Westminster Medical School, Fulham Palace Road, London W6 8RF Tel: 020 8846 7593 Fax: 020 8846 7338 Email: ragboo5@s1.cxwms.ac.uk — MB BS 1954 Lond.; BSc Lond. 1951. (Lond. Hosp.) Prof. Emerit. & Sen. Research Fell. (Physiol.) Char. Cross & W.m. Med. Sch. Lond. Prev: Hon. Cons. & Prof. of Physiol. United Med. Dent. Sch. Guy's & St. Thos. Hosps. Head Div. Phys.

TAYLOR, Anthony James 9 Bowers Croft, Cambridge CB1 8RP — MB BS 1993 Lond.

TAYLOR, Anthony John, CBE (retired) Tir-an-Og, Brooklands, Sarisbury Green, Southampton SO31 7EE Tel: 01489 583199 — MB BChir Camb. 1958; MA Camb. 1981, BA 1955. Prev: Co. Med. Off. Cyanamid GB Ltd.

TAYLOR, Anthony John 67 Cleveland Road, North Shields NE29 0NW — MB ChB 1985 Leic.; FRCA 1994. Sen. Regist. Rotat. (Anaesth.) Newc. u. Tyne.

TAYLOR, Anthony Martin 17 Rookery Avenue, Ashton-in-Makerfield, Wigan WN4 9PE — MB ChB 1993 Leeds.

TAYLOR, Anthony St John Willow Street Medical Centre, 81-83 Willow Street, Oswestry SY11 1AJ Tel: 01691 653143 Fax: 01691 679130; Hamilton House, Trefonen, Oswestry SY10 9DG Tel: 01691 653417 — MB ChB 1975 Birm.; DRCOG 1985. Socs: BMA. Prev: Regist. (Surg.) Centr. Birm. Dist. HA; Regist. (Orthop.) E. Birm. Hosp.; Regist. (Surg.) Co. Hosp. Hereford.

TAYLOR, Antonia Jane 40 Mountside, Guildford GU2 4JE — BM BS 1991 Nottm.; DRCOG 1996; DCH 1998.

TAYLOR

TAYLOR, Arthur William Outram Saltoun Hall, Pencaitland, Tranent EH34 5DS Tel: 01875 340262 — MB ChB Ed. 1939; FRCP Ed. 1972, M 1947. (Univ. Ed.) Prev: Ho. Phys. Leith Hosp.; T/Lt.-Col. RAMC.

TAYLOR, Mr Barry Anthony Warrington Hospital NHS Trust, Lovely Lane, Warrington WA5 1QG Tel: 01925 662076 Fax: 01925 662042; Lilac Cottage, Pickerings Lock, Crewood Common, Crowton, Northwich CW8 2TX Tel: 01928 788503 — BM BCh 1978 Oxf.; MA Camb. 1979; MCh Oxf. 1986; FRCS Eng. 1982. (Oxford) Cons. Gen. Surg. Warrington Dist. Gen. Hosp.; Moynihan Trav. Fell. Assn. Surgs. GB & Irel. Socs: Ord. Mem. Surg. Research Soc.; Brit. Soc. Gastroenterol.; Assn. Coloproctol. (Counc. Mem.). Prev: Sen. Lect. (Surg.) & Hon. Cons. Surg. BRd.green & Roy. Liverp. Univ. Hosps.; Lect. & Hon. Sen. Regist. (Surg.) Univ. Wales Coll. Med. Cardiff; Fell. (Colon & Rectal Surg.) Mayo Clinic Rochester, USA.

TAYLOR, Mr Benjamin Anthony The Scoliosis Unit, Royal National Orthopaedic Hospital Trust, Brockley Hill, Stanmore HA7 4LP Tel: 020 8954 2300 Fax: 020 8954 8964 Email: btaylor@rnoh-tr.nthames.nhs; Fax: 01442 891318 — MB BS 1980 Lond.; MCh (Orthop.) Liverp. 1990; FRCS Eng. 1986; FRCS Ed. 1985. (Univ. Coll. Hosp.) Cons. Orthop. Surg. Roy. Nat. Orthop. Hosp. Trust Stanmore. Socs: Fell. BOA; Founder Mem. Brit. Cervical Spine Soc.; Brit. Scoliosis Soc. Prev: Sen. Regist. (Orthop.) Middlx. Hosp. Lond.; Regist. (Orthop.) Univ. Coll. Hosp. Lond.; Demonst. St. Thos. Hosp. Med. Sch.

TAYLOR, Berenice Penelope (retired) 43 Ridgeway Gardens, Hornsey Lane, Highgate, London N6 5NH — MB ChB 1968 Sheff.; DObst RCOG 1970. Prev: Med. Assessor with the Indep. Tribunal Serv.

TAYLOR, Bernard 3/5 Merchant Street, London E3 4LJ Tel: 020 8980 3676; (private), 7 Sharon Gardens, London E9 7RX Tel: 020 8985 1657 — MB BS 1949 Lond.; FRCGP 1979, M 1957. (Guy's) Socs: Lond. Jewish Hosp. Med. Soc. & Israel Med. Assn. Brit. Fell.sh. Prev: Capt. RAMC; Ho. Phys. Dudley Rd. Hosp. Birm. & Connaught Hosp. Walthamstow.

TAYLOR, Miss Brenda Anita (retired) 12 Park View, Wootton Bridge, Ryde PO33 4RJ — MRCS Eng. LRCP Lond. 1949; M.B., B.S. Lond. 1949; FRCOG 1976, M 1959. Prev: Cons. O & G I. of Wight Hosp. Gp.

TAYLOR, Brenda Esther (retired) Cleveley Mere House, Cleveley Bank Lane, Forton, Preston PR3 1BY Tel: 01524 791702 — BSc (Hons., Special Anat.) Lond. 1956, MD 1969, MB; BS (Hons. Surg.) 1959; FRCP Lond. 1979, M 1963; MRCS Eng. LRCP Lond. 1959. Prev: Cons. Phys. Preston Health Dist.

TAYLOR, Brian Oscar Treweek Burches, 4 The Green, Colne Engaine, Colchester CO6 2EZ Tel: 01787 224876 Fax: 01787 224897 Email: ptaylor762@aol.com; 19 Hamilton Road, Cambridge CB4 1BP Tel: 01223 312020 — MRCS Eng. LRCP Lond. 1945; MFHom 1971; MRCGP 1964. (St. Thos.) Hon. Med. Off. Halstead Hosp. Socs: Colchester Med. Soc. Prev: Asst. Med. Off. Essex Co. Hosp. Black Notley; Ho. Phys. Roy. Surrey Co. Hosp. Guildford; Resid. Med. Off. High Wycombe & Dist. War Memor. Hosp.

TAYLOR, Bruce Lindsay Department of Intensive Care Medicine, Queen Alexandra Hospital, Cosham, Havant PO9 6BX Tel: 01705 281844 Fax: 01705 286967; Puriton Lodge, Scant Road E., Hambrook, Chichester PO18 8UG Tel: 01243 573675 — MB ChB 1979 Manch.; BSc St. And. 1976; FFARCS Eng. 1984; FANZCA 1990, FFICANZCA 1990. (St. Andr./Manch.) Cons. (Intens. Care Med.) Cons. Anaesth. Qu. Alexandra Hosp. Cosham Hants. Socs: Intens. Care Soc.; Paediat. Intens. Care Soc.; Assn. Anaesth. Prev: Regist. (Paediat. Intens. Care) Roy. Childrs. Hosps. Melbourne Austral.; Sen . Regist. (Anaesth.) S.W. Rec. Rotat.; Regist. (Anaesth.) Addenbrooke's Hosp. Camb.

TAYLOR, Bruce Weir Claughton Medical Centre, 161 Park Road North, Birkenhead CH41 0DD Tel: 0151 652 1688 Fax: 0151 670 0565; Heathfield, Telegraph Road, Caldy, Wirral CH48 1NZ Tel: 0151 625 6337 — MB BS 1982 Nottm.; MRCGP 1986; DRCOG 1985.

TAYLOR, Bryce Leighton Road Surgery, 1 Leighton Road, Linslade, Leighton Buzzard LU7 1LB Tel: 01525 372571 Fax: 01525 850414; 36 Creslow Way, Stone, Aylesbury HP17 8YW Tel: 01296 747980 — MB ChB 1978 Manch.; MRCGP 1984; Dip. Pract. Dermat. Wales 1991; DRCOG 1981; DCH RCP Lond. 1981.

TAYLOR, Caecilia Jane Anne Kneesworth House Hospital, Bassingbourne-Cum-Kneesworth, Royston SG8 5JP Tel: 01763 255700 Fax: 01763 255718 — MB BS 1982 Lond.; BSc Med. Sociol. Lond. 1979; MRCPsych 1986; Dip. Forens. Psychiat. Lond. 1995. (Roy. Free) Cons. Forens. Psychiat. Kneesworth Ho. Hosp. Bassingbourne-Cum-Kneesworth; Research Fell. Inst. of Criminology Univ. of Camb., Camb. Socs: Roy. Coll. Psychiat.; Brit. Med. Assn.; Internat. Assn. of Forens. Psychother. Prev: Sen. Lect. Dept. Forens. Psychiat. Inst. of Psychiat. & BRd.moor Hosp.; Research Psychiat. Genetics Sect. Inst. Psychiat. Lond.; SHO Rotat. (Psychiat.) Roy. Free Hosp. Lond.

TAYLOR, Carl Lucien 33 High Street, Ivinghoe, Leighton Buzzard LU7 9EP — MB BS 1979 Lond.; MRCPsych 1984. (Roy. Free) Cons. Psychiat.Milton Keynes Hosp.s. Prev: Cons. Psychiat. W. Cumbld. Hopital Whitehaven; Sen. Regist. (Psychiat.) Fulbourn Hosp. Camb.; Sen. Regist. St. Clements Hosp. Ipswich.

TAYLOR, Caroline Anita The Health Centre, Manor Way, Lee-on-the-Solent PO13 9JG Tel: 02392 550220; 70 Woodrush Crescent, Locks Heath, Southampton SO31 6UP Tel: 01489 602263 — BM 1994 Soton.; MRCGP 1998; DRCOG 1996; DFFP 1997. GP Princip.; CMO Family Plann. & Reproductive Health, S.ampton & Portsmouth.

TAYLOR, Caroline Grace 16 Tabor Grove, Wimbledon, London SW19 4EB — MB BS 1989 Lond.; MRCP (UK) 1993; FRCR 1997. (St. Thos. Hosp. Med. Sch. (UMDS)) Regist. (Radiol.) Char. Cross Hosp. Lond. Hammersmith NHS Trust. Prev: Regist. (Med.) St. Mary's Hosp. Lond.; SHO (Med.) Medway Hosp. Kent; SHO (A & E) St. Geo. Hosp. Lond.

TAYLOR, Caroline Louise Crown Dale Medical Centre, 61 Crown Dale, London SE19 3NY Tel: 020 8670 2414 Fax: 020 8670 0277; Fairmount, 2A Mount Ephraim Lane, Streatham, London SW16 1JG Tel: 020 8769 5631 — MB BS 1983 Lond.; DRCOG 1987. (St. Geo.) Prev: Trainee GP Lond. VTS.

TAYLOR, Caroline Louise 38 Heath Crescent, Halifax HX1 2PR — MB ChB 1992 Leeds. Trainee GP York VTS.

TAYLOR, Caroline Margaret Lawton House Surgery, Bromley Road, Congleton CW12 1QG Tel: 01260 275454 Fax: 01260 298412; Brackenrigg, Crouch Lane, Timbersbrook, Congleton CW12 3PT Tel: 01260 276898 — MB ChB 1986 Manch.; MRCGP 1990; DRCOG 1988. Socs: BMA; RCGPs & Anglo-German Soc. Prev: SHO/Trainee GP Hope Hosp. Salford VTS; Ho. Surg. & Ho. Phys. Manch. Roy. Infirm.

TAYLOR, Caryl 51 Kimberley Road, Penylan, Cardiff CF23 5DL — MB BS 1987 Lond.

TAYLOR, Catherine Elizabeth Duffryn Road, Rhydyfelin, Pontypridd CF37 5RW Tel: 01443 400940 Fax: 01443 492900; 43 Parc-y-Bryn, Creigiau, Cardiff CF15 9SE Tel: 029 2089 2396 Email: catherin.e.taylor@care4free.net — MB ChB 1981 Birm.; MRCGP 1986. (Birmingham) Prev: Sen. Med. Off. (Ophth.) Centr. Hosp. Honiara; Clin. Asst. (Ophth.) E. Glam. Gen. Hosp.

TAYLOR, Catherine Jane 144 Stannington View Road, Sheffield S10 1SS — MB ChB 1997 Sheff.

TAYLOR, Catherine Mary Ferndale, New Road, Henley-in-Arden, Solihull B95 5HY — MB ChB 1993 Birm.; MRCEP. 1998; DRCOG 1997; DFFP. 1997. (Birmingham) GP. Locum. Prev: SHO (A & E) Worcester Roy. Infirm.; SHO (Ophth.) Worcester Roy. Infirm. VTS; Ho. Off. (Surg.) Qu. Eliz. Hosp. Birm.

TAYLOR, Cecil Frederick (retired) Medical Department, British Steel, Port Talbot Works, Port Talbot SA13 2NG Tel: 01637 872000 Fax: 01639 872560 — MB ChB Birm. 1965; FFOM RCP Lond. 1991, MFOM 1981; DIH Soc. Apoth. Lond. 1977. Occupat. Phys. Prev: Chief Med. Off. Brit. Steel plc. (Tinplate).

TAYLOR, Cecilia (retired) Health Centre, Walesmoor Avenue, Kiveton Park, Sheffield S26 5RF Tel: 01909 770213 — MB ChB 1943 Leeds; DCH Eng. 1943.

TAYLOR, Chadwick Richard 5 Morninton Road, Sale M33 2DA — MB ChB 1990 Manch.

TAYLOR, Charles Edmunds Darby (retired) Alnwick House, High St., Little Shelford, Cambridge CB2 5ES Tel: 01223 842115 — MB BChir Camb. 1946; MA Camb. 1948, BA 1944, MD 1956; FRCPath 1970; Dip. Bact. Lond 1955. Prev: Dir. Regional Pub. Health Laborat. Camb., Hon. Cons. Microbiol. Camb. HA & Assoc. Lect. Univ. Camb.

TAYLOR, Charles Matheson (retired) Barnards, Redricks Lane, Sawbridgeworth CM21 0RL — MB ChB Aberd. 1945; Dip. Psychol. Lond. 1990. Prev: Ho. Phys. (Paediat.) Whipps Cross Hosp.

TAYLOR, Charles Murray (retired) Moss Cottage, Ledaig, North Connel, Oban PA37 1RX — MB ChB 1954 Ed.; BSc (Hons.) Glas. 1942, MB ChB Ed. 1954; DObst RCOG 1956. Prev: Ho. Phys. & Ho. Surg. Roy. Infirm. Edin.

TAYLOR, Charles Peter Brannams Medical Centre, Brannams Square, Kiln Lane, Barnstaple EX32 8AP Tel: 01271 329004 Fax: 01271 346785 — MB BS 1986 Lond.

TAYLOR, Charlotte Jane 15 Birch Tree Court, West St., Hoole, Chester CH2 3PH — MB BS 1992 Newc.

TAYLOR, Chimene Mary The Surgery, Duns Road, Greenlaw, Duns TD10 6XJ Tel: 01361 810216 Fax: 01361 810799; Kennington House, Greenlaw, Duns TD10 6XX Tel: 01361 810509 — BM 1990 Soton.; Cert. Prescribed Equiv. Exp. JCPTGP 1995. Asst. GP Greenlaw Surg. Duns. Socs: BMA; Assoc. Mem. RCGP. Prev: GP Regist. Coldstream Health Centre; SHO (Psychiat.) St. John's Hosp. Howden Livingstone; Trainee GP Berwick-on-Tweed.

TAYLOR, Miss Christine Jean Accident & Emergency Department, Queen Mary's Hospital, Frognal Avenue, Sidcup DA14 6LT Tel: 020 8302 2678 Email: chris@cjt.co.uk — State Exam Med 1982 Bonn; FRCS Ed. 1987. Dir. Emerg. Care Qu. Mary Hosp. Sidcup.

TAYLOR, Christopher Bryan Directorate of Sexual Health, King's Healthcare, 15-22 Caldecot Road, London SE5 9RS Tel: 020 7346 3478 Fax: 020 7346 3486 — MB BS 1986 Lond.; MRCP (UK) 1992. Cons. Phys. (HIV & Genitourin. Med.) King's Healthcare Lond.

TAYLOR, Professor Christopher John Sheffield Children's Hospital, Department of Paediatrics, Sheffield S10 2TH Tel: 0114 276 1111 Fax: 0114 275 5364; 315 Cantaknowle Road, Sheffield S11 9FY Tel: 0114 235 1015 — MB ChB 1973 Liverp.; MD Liverp. 1986; FRCP (UK) 1978; DCH RCPS Glas. 1975. Prof. (Paediat. Gastroenterol.) Univ. Sheff.; Hon. Cons. Paediat. Sheff. Childr. Hosp. Socs: Brit. Paediat. Assn.; Brit. Soc. Gastroenterol. Prev: Sen. Lect. (Paediat.) Alder Hey Childr. Hosp.

***TAYLOR, Christopher John** 69 Oakley Close, Holbury, Southampton SO45 2PJ Tel: 02380 894868 — MB BS 1996 Lond.

TAYLOR, Christopher Mark Birmingham Children's Hospital, Birmingham B4 6NH Tel: 0121 333 9233 Fax: 0121 333 9231; 65 Salisbury Road, Moseley, Birmingham B13 8LB Tel: 0121 449 4838 — MB ChB 1971 Birm.; FRCP Lond. 1991; MRCP (UK) 1975; DCH Eng. 1973. Cons. Paediat. & Nephrol. Birm. Childr. Hosp.; Sen. Clin. Lect. Univ. Birm. Prev: Lect. (Paediat. & Nephrol.) Birm. Childr. Hosp. & E. Birm. Hosp.; Research Asst. (Renal Unit) Birm. Childr. Hosp.; Sen. Regist. Univ. Hosp. W. Indies Jamaica.

TAYLOR, Christopher Michael St. James's University Hospital, Roundhay Wing, Beckett St., Leeds LS9 7TF Tel: 0113 243 3144 Fax: 0113 234 6856; 42 The Drive, Adel, Leeds LS16 6BQ Tel: 0113 226 4463 Fax: 0113 226 4463 Email: chris.taylor@cwcom.net — MB BChir 1977 Camb.; MA (Hons.) Camb. 1973; MRCPsych 1982. Hon. Clin. Lect. Univ. Leeds; Cons. Psychiat. St. Jas. Univ. Hosp. Leeds.

TAYLOR, Christopher Paul Haslemere Health Centre, Church Lane, Haslemere GU27 2BQ Tel: 01483 783023 Fax: 01428 645065; Fridays Hill House, Fernhurst, Haslemere GU27 3DX Tel: 01428 643480 — MB BS 1974 Lond.; DRCOG 1977; DA Eng. 1977. (St. Thos.) GP. Socs: Chairm. Haslemere Med. Soc. Prev: Clin. Asst. in Rehabil. Young Severely Disabled Unit Godwin Unit Haslemere Hosp.; SHO (Anaesth.) St. Thos. Hosp. Lond.; SHO (O & G & Paediat.) Ashford Hosp. Middlx.

TAYLOR, Claire Louise 7 Taironen, Cowbridge CF71 7UA — MS BS Lond. 1991.

TAYLOR, Claire Margaret 56 Lindale Mount, Wakefield WF2 0BH — MB ChB 1991 Leeds.

TAYLOR, Clare 65 Sommerville Road, Bristol BS7 9AD — MB ChB 1990 Bristol.

TAYLOR, Clare Helen Firs House Surgery, Station Road, Histon, Cambridge Tel: 01223 234286; Email: jon.clare@jsphipps.fsnet.co.uk — MB ChB 1989 Bristol; BSc (Hons.) Cell Path. Bristol 1989; MRCGP 1996; DRCOG 1995. p/t GP Retainee Firs Ho. Surg. Histon Camb.

TAYLOR, Clare Louise 36 Habberley Road, Kidderminster DY11 5PE — MB ChB 1998 Manch. SHO.(Gen Med.) Roy Lanc Infirm. Lanc. Prev: HO. (Surg.) Roy Lanc Infirm. Lanc.; HO. (Med.) Roy Lanc Infirm. Lanc.

TAYLOR, Clare Petronella Florence Dept of Haematology, The Royal Free Hospital, Pond St, Hampstead, London NW3 2QG Tel: 020 7794 0500 Ext: 8462 Fax: 0207 830 2092 Email: clare.taylor@rfh.nthames.nhs.uk; 35 Tanza Road, London NW3 2UA Tel: 020 7435 7715 — MB BS 1985 Lond.; PhD Lond. 1995; MRCP (UK) 1988; MRCPath 1998. Cons & Hon Sen Lect. (Haemat. & Transfus Med.) Roy Free Hampstead NHS Trust. Lond.; Cons., Nat. Blood Serv., N. Lond.. Socs: Brit. Soc. of Haemat.; Brit. Blood Transfus. Soc. Prev: Sen. Regist. (Clin. Haemat.) Roy. Free Hosp. Lond.; Clin. Research Fell. Imperial Cancer Research Fund Lond.; Regist. (Haemat.) St. Mary's Hosp. Lond.

TAYLOR, Colette 24 Foxlands Drive, Penn, Wolverhampton WV4 5NA Tel: 01902 339107 — MB ChB 1959 Liverp.; DObst RCOG 1961. SCMO Wolverhampton HA.

TAYLOR, Colette Lydie Barn Cottage, Back Road, Apperknowle, Dronfield S18 4AR Tel: 01246 412259 — MB BS Lond. 1949; FFA RCS Eng. 1954; DA Eng. 1952. (Roy. Free) Anaesth. Sheff. Sch. Dent. Serv. Prev: Anaesth. Regist. Hosp. Sick Childr. Gt. Ormond St. Lond.; Res. Anaesth. Roy. Free Hosp. Lond.

TAYLOR, Colin George (retired) 11 Bumbles, 3 Station Road, Little Houghton, Northampton NN7 1AJ Tel: 01604 891452 — MB BS 1956 Lond.

TAYLOR, Colin George Dept. Of Haematology, Pembury Hospital, Pembury, Tunbridge Wells TN2 4QJ Tel: 01892 823535; 5 Waverley Drive, Sandown Park, Tunbridge Wells TN2 4RX — MB BS 1965 Lond.; FRCP 1999; MRCS Eng. LRCP Lond. 1965; FRCPath 1984, M 1974. Cons. Haemat. Pembury Hosp. Tunbridge Wells. Socs: Assn. Clin. Path.; Brit. Soc. Haemat. Prev: Regist. & Lect. Kings Coll. Hosp. Lond.

TAYLOR, Craig James Charles 69 Vicarage Road, Harborne, Birmingham B17 0SR — MB ChB 1993 Ed.

TAYLOR, Daniel John Evelina Childrens Hospital, Guys Hospital, St Thomas St, London SE1; Flat 1, 12 Christchurch Rd, London N8 9QL — MB ChB 1996 Liverp.; MRCPCH. 1999. Regist. (Paediat IC.) Guys Hosp. Lond.

TAYLOR, David 27 Heath Huost Road, London NW3 2RU — MB BS Lond. 1970; MRCP (UK) 1972; FRCPsych 1989, M 1976. (UCHMS) Cons. Psychother. Tavistock Clin. Lond. Socs: Brit. Psychoanal. Soc.; Fell. Roy. Coll. Psychiat. Prev: Hon. Sen. Regist. Maudsley Hosp. Lond.; Research Worker Inst. Psychiat. Lond.; Sen. Regist. Nat. Hosp. Nerv. Dis. Qu. Sq. Lond.

TAYLOR, David Alexander South Buckinghamshire NHS Trust (from 18/02/2002), Wycombe Hospital, Queen Alexandra Rd, High Wycombe HP11 2TT Tel: 01494 526161; 14 Kensington Place, London W8 7PT Tel: 020 7243 0085 — MB BS 1990 Lond.; MD Lond. Univ. 2000; BSc (Hons.) Lond. 1987; MRCP (UK) 1994. (St Mary's Hospital) Cons. Respirat. & Gen. Phys. Wycombe Hosp. High Wycombe, as from 18/02/2002. Socs: Brit. Thoracic Soc. Prev: Clin. Research Fell. Nat. Heart & Lung Inst.; Clin. Research Phys. (Clin. Pharmacol.) Wellcome Research Laborat. Beckenham; SHO (Gen. Med.) N.wick Pk. Hosp. Lond.

TAYLOR, David Anthony Rosegarth Surgery, Rothwell Mount, Halifax HX1 2XB Tel: 01422 353450/350420 — MB ChB 1992 Leeds.

TAYLOR, David Bryan Stuart, TD, CStJ (retired) Easingwold, 498 Chorley New Road, Bolton BL1 5DR Tel: 01204 843406 — MB ChB 1948 Manch.; MRCS Eng. LRCP Lond. 1949; MRCGP 1978; DObst RCOG 1964. Prev: Ho. Surg. Ancoats Hosp. Manch. & Matern. Hosp. Hull.

TAYLOR, Professor David Charles Pentre Grange, Llanover, Abergavenny NP7 9EW Fax: 01873 880340 — MD 1969 Lond.; MB BS 1960, DPM 1965; FRCP Lond. 1982, M 1976; FRCPCH (Hon.) 1997; FRCPsych 1973, M 1971; T(Psych) 1991. (Char. Cross) Vis. Prof. Paediat. Neuropsychiat. Hosp. Sick Childr. Gt. Ormond St. Lond.; Vis. Psychiat. David Lewis Centre for Epilepsy & St. Piers Lingfield.; Cons. Pysch. Epilepsy Surg. Program Beaumont Hosp. Dub. Prev: Prof. Child & Adolesc. Psychiat. Univ. Manch.; Sen. Research Off. Human Developm. Research Unit Univ. Oxf.; Research Asst. Guy's Maudsley Neurosurg. Unit.

TAYLOR, David Donaldson George Street Surgery, 99 George Street, Dumfries DG1 1DS Tel: 01387 253333 Fax: 01387 253301;

TAYLOR

Oakfield, Newbridge, Dumfries DG2 0QX Tel: 01387 720122 — MB ChB 1976 Aberd.; MRCGP 1980; DRCOG 1979.

TAYLOR, Professor David Ernest Meguyer, TD Department of Mechanical Engineering, Brunel University, Uxbridge UB8 3PH Tel: 01895 274000 Fax: 01895 256392; 35 Maswell Park Road, Hounslow TW3 2DL — MB ChB 1952 Ed.; FRSE; FRCS Eng. 1978; FRCS Ed. 1957. Research Prof. Brunel Univ. Uxbridge; Hon. Cons. St. Mary's Hosp. Med. Sch. Lond. Socs: Soc. Thoracic & Cardiovasc. Surgs.; Physiol. Soc. Prev: Prof. Applied Physiol. & Surg. Sc. (Univ. Lond.) RCS Eng.; Hon. Cons. Thoracic Surg. Unit Roy. Infirm. Edin.

TAYLOR, David Geoffrey Barrie Woodland Road Surgery, 57 Woodland Road, Northfield, Birmingham B31 2HZ Tel: 0121 475 1065 Fax: 0121 475 6179 — MB ChB 1978 Bristol; MRCP Ed. 1982; DRCOG 1984. Princip. GP N.field.

TAYLOR, David George 21 Phoenix Lodge Mansions, Brook Green, London W6 7BG — MB BCh BAO 1986 Belf.; MRCPsych 1990. Cons. Psychiat. W. Lond. Healthcare NHS Trust. Prev: Sen. Regist. (Psychiat.) Char. Cross & W.m. Higher Train. Scheme.; Research Train. Fell. (Psychiat. Neuropath.) Ment. Health Foundat. Roy. Free Hosp. Lond.; Regist. (Psychiat.) Roy. Free Hosp. Lond.

TAYLOR, David Henry Victoria House, Newry Road, Banbridge BT32 3HF — MB BCh BAO 1995 Belf.

TAYLOR, David John Lochmaben Medical Group, The Surgery, 42-44 High Street, Lochmaben, Lockerbie DG11 1NH Tel: 01387 810252 Fax: 01387 811595; Merrick, 2 Rankine Heights, Marjoriebanks, Lochmaben, Lockerbie DG11 1LJ Tel: 01387 811376 Email: djtaylor01@aol.com — MB ChB 1977 Aberd.; MRCGP 1982; DRCOG 1980. p/t Assoc. Advisor (Med. Educat. IT & Audit) Dumfries & Galloway. Prev: Trainee GP VTS Dumfries & Galloway Roy. Infirm.; Research Fell.sh. Univ. Aberd.; Med. Manager, Dumfries & Galloway After Hours Med. Serv. (OG Med.).

TAYLOR, Professor David John Department of Obstetrics & Gynaecology, Clinical Sciences Building, Leicester Royal Infirmary, Leicester LE2 7LX Tel: 0116 252 3161 Fax: 0116 252 3154 Email: djt131@le.ac.uk; Yew Lodge, 8 Chapel Lane, Leicester LE2 3WE — MB BS 1970 Newc.; MD Newc. 1983; FRCOG 1988, M 1975. Prof. & Head Dept. O & G Univ. Leicester Sch. Med.; Clin. Dir. & Hon. Cons. (Obst. & Gyn.) Leicester Roy. Infirm. Prev: Reader (O & G) Univ. Dundee; Scientif. Staff, MRC Reproduc. & Growth Unit P.ss Mary Matern. Hosp. Newc.; Ho. Surg. & Ho. Phys. Roy. Vict. Infirm. Newc.

TAYLOR, David Lynton Siam Surgery, Sudbury CO10 1JH Tel: 01787 370444 Fax: 01787 880322; 10 White Hall Close, Great Waldingfield, Sudbury CO10 0XU — LMSSA 1981 Lond.; MA Camb. 1982, MB ChB 1982; MRCGP 1987; DRCOG 1987.

TAYLOR, David McIntyre Inverkeithing Medical Group, 5 Friary Court, Inverkeithing KY11 1NU Tel: 01383 413234 Fax: 01383 410098 — MB ChB 1971 Glas.; MRCGP 1975.

TAYLOR, David Robert Queen Camel Health Centre, Queen Camel, Yeovil BA22 7NG Tel: 01935 850225 Fax: 01935 851247 — MB BS 1984 Lond.; MRCGP 1990; DRCOG 1988; DCH RCP Lond. 1988.

TAYLOR, David Russell Department of Dermatology, New Cross Hospital, Wolverhampton WV10 0QD — MB BChir 1971 Camb.; MB Camb. 1971, BChir 1970; MRCP (UK) 1974; DObst RCOG 1972. (St. Bart.) Cons. Dermat. Roy. Wolverhampton Hosps. Socs: Fell. Roy. Soc. Med. Prev: Sen. Regist. (Dermat.) St. Helier Hosp. Carshalton; Regist. (Dermat.) Univ. Coll. Hosp. Lond.; SHO (Gen. Med.) Brook Gen. Hosp. Lond.

TAYLOR, Mr David Samuel Bethany, 14 Leadhall Way, Harrogate HG2 9PG — MB ChB 1964 Manch.; FRCS Ed. 1973; DCH Eng. 1966; FRCOG 1983, M 1970, DObst 1967. Cons. O & G Harrogate Health Dist. Prev: Tutor (O & G) Manch. Univ.; Sen. Regist. (O & G) & Regist. (Gyn. Path. & Cytol.) St. Mary'sHosp. Manch.

TAYLOR, Mr David Samuel Irving Consulting Rooms, 234 Great Portland Street, London W1W 5QT Tel: 020 7935 7916 Fax: 020 7323 5430 Email: eyeclinic.234gps@btinternet.com; 23 Church Road, Barnes, London SW13 9HE Tel: 020 8878 0305 Fax: 020 8878 1125 — MB ChB 1967 Liverp.; FRCP Lond. 1984; FRCS Eng. 1973; MRCP (UK) 1972; FCOphth 1990; DO RCS Eng. 1970; FRCPCH 1998; DSc 2001. (Liverp.) Cons. Ophth. Hosp. Sick Childr. Gt. Ormond St. Lond. & Hon. Sen. Lect. Inst. Child Health Lond. Socs: Internat. Mem. Amer. Assn. Paediat. Ophth. & Strabismus; Counc. Mem. Roy. Lond. Soc. Blind; Roy. Soc. Med. & Brit.

Orthoptic Bd. Prev: Fell. Neuroophthol. Univ. Calif. Med. Centre San Francisco, USA; Research Fell. Hosp. Sick Childr. Gt. Ormond St. Lond.; Cons. Ophth. Nat. Hosp. Nerv. Dis. Lond.

TAYLOR, David Stephen Honeysuckers, 36 White Hart Lane, Hockley SS5 4DW Tel: 01302 203083 — MB BS 1986 Lond.; MRCGP 1991.

TAYLOR, David William Oakswood, Wingfield Road, Oakerthorpe, Alfreton DE55 7LH — MB ChB 1980 Liverp.

TAYLOR, Dawn Anne 22 Alloway Drive, Newton Mearns, Glasgow G77 5TG — MB ChB 1992 Glas.

TAYLOR, Dawn Margaret Southern Medical Group, 322 Gilmerton Road, Edinburgh EH17 7PR Tel: 0131 664 2148 Fax: 0131 664 8303 — MB ChB 1980 Dundee; MRCGP 1984; DRCOG 1982. GP Edin.

TAYLOR, Deborah Anne 141 Dewhirst Road, Syke, Rochdale OL12 9TX — BM BS 1993 Nottm.

TAYLOR, Deborah Hannah College Road Surgery, 50/52 College Road, Maidstone ME15 6SB Tel: 01622 752345 Fax: 01622 758133; Smartswell, Willow Wents, Mereworth, Maidstone ME18 5NF Tel: 01622 814991 — MB BS 1986 Lond.; MRCGP 1989; DRCOG 1991. (Lond. Hosp.)

TAYLOR, Derek 8 Clochranhill Road, Alloway, Ayr KA7 4PZ — MB ChB 1975 Glas.; BSc (Hons.) Glas. 1971, MB ChB 1975; MRCP (UK) 1978; DCH Eng. 1977.

TAYLOR, Mr Desmond Gerard (retired) Barn Cottage, Back Road, Apperknowle, Dronfield S18 4AR Tel: 01246 412259 Fax: 01246 292213 — MB BCh BAO 1948 Belf.; FRCS Eng. 1952. Hon. Lect. (Thoracic Surg.) Univ. Sheff. Prev: Thoracic Surg. United Sheff. Hosps. & City Gen. Hosp. Sheff.

TAYLOR, Diane Michele Tel: 0151 355 6144 Fax: 0151 355 6843; 19 Sutton Hall Drive, Little Sutton, South Wirral CH66 4UQ — MB ChB 1981 Liverp.; DRCOG 1984. Gen. Practitionor Princip.; Family Plann. Clinic Modical Off.

TAYLOR, Dorothy Linda Playfield House, Stratheden Hospital, Cupar KY15 5RR — MB BS 1975 Lond.; MRCPsych 1983; DCH Eng. 1978. Cons. Child & Family Psychiat. Stratheden Hosp. Cupar. Prev: Sen. Regist. Dept. Child & Family Psychiat. Roy. Hosp. Sick Childr.; Glas.

TAYLOR, Edith (retired) Dolcrwm, Roe Wen, Conwy LL32 8TE Tel: 01492 650311 — MB BS Lond. 1946; MRCS Eng., LRCP Lond. 1939; DObst RCOG 1943. Prev: Ho. Phys. King's Coll. Hosp. & Qu.'s Hosp. Childr.

TAYLOR, Edward Ian Russell 378 Chester Road, Birmingham B36 0LE Tel: 0121 770 3035 — MB ChB 1958 Ed. Socs: BMA. Prev: Ho. Surg. (Orthop.) & Ho. Phys. Stracathro Hosp. Brechin; Squadron Ldr. RAF Med. Br.

TAYLOR, Edward Philip Martin 21 Harrop Road, Hale, Altrincham WA15 9DA — MB ChB 1992 Manch.

TAYLOR, Eithne Gayle Dewsbury & District Hospital, Healds Road, Dewsbury WF13 4HS Tel: 01924 465105 Fax: 01924 816286; 27 The Drive, Roundhay, Leeds LS8 1JQ — MB ChB 1987 Bristol; BSc Bristol 1984; MRCP (UK) 1990. (Univ. Bristol) Cons. Dermat. Dewsbury Dist. Hosp. Socs: Brit. Assn. Dermat.; Brit. Assn. of Paediat. Dermatol.; Dowling Club. Prev: Sen. Regist. (Dermat.) Leeds Gen. Infirm.; Regist. (Dermat.) Roy. Berks. Hosp. Reading; Regist. (Dermat. & Gen. Med.) Wycombe Gen. Hosp.

TAYLOR, Eleanore 4 Allington Road, London NW4 3DJ Tel: 020 8203 1347 — MB BS 1989 Lond. Staff Grade Med. Off. Regional Rehabil. Unit N.wick Pk. Hosp. Lond. Prev: Trainee GP Watford Gen. Hosp. VTS; Trainee GP St. Geo. Lodge Lond.

TAYLOR, Elizabeth Helen 46 Fernleigh Cr, Up Hatherley, Cheltenham GL51 3QL Email: liztaylordoc@hotmail.com — MB ChB 1997 Birm.; BSc (1st cl Hons.) Birm. 1994, MB ChB 1997. (Birm.)

TAYLOR, Elizabeth Jane Elm Farm, Horpit, Lower Wanborough, Swindon SN4 0AT — MB BS 1977 Lond.; DRCOG 1980.

TAYLOR, Elizabeth Mary (retired) Department Paediatrics, University of Sheffield, The Children's Hospital Western Bank, Sheffield S1 2GY Tel: 0114 272 6380 Fax: 0114 275 5364 — MD 1984 Sheff.; MB ChB 1956. Hon. Cons. Community Paediat. Univ. Sheff.

TAYLOR, Elizabeth Patricia 45 Pasture Hill Road, Haywards Heath RH16 1LY — MB ChB 1988 Cape Town.

TAYLOR, Elizabeth Rutherford (retired) Charnston B, Charney Road, Grange-over-Sands LA11 6BP Tel: 015395 35230 — MB

BChir Camb. 1950. Prev: Cas. Off. N. Lonsdale Hosp. Barrow-in-Furness.

TAYLOR, Ella Storey Cottage, Kirkby Overblow, Harrogate HG3 1HD Tel: 01423 871607 — MB ChB Aberd. 1946; DPH Glas. 1952. (Aberd.)

TAYLOR, Elsie Gladys (retired) 8 Milton Road, Mill Hill, London NW7 4AX Tel: 020 8959 8820 — MB BCh BAO 1951 Belf.; DObst RCOG 1954; DCH Eng. 1953.

TAYLOR, Emily Clare 56 Woolwich Road, Belvedere DA17 5EN — MB BS 1996 Lond.

TAYLOR, Miss Emma Jane South Malling Cottage, Lewes Road, Haywards Heath RH16 2LF Tel: 01273 891286 — MB BS 1994 Lond.; FRCS Eng. 1998. (UMDS) Specialist Regist. (Orthop.) S. E. Thames Rotat. Prev: SHO (Surg.) Roy. Sussex Co. Hosp. Brighton.

TAYLOR, Emma Jane Stewart Longreach, Crampshaw Lane, Ashtead KT21 2UF Tel: 01372 273506 — MB BS 1992 Lond.; DA (UK) 1996. SHO (Anaesth.) Epsom Gen. Hosp. Prev: SHO (Neonates) St. Geo. Hosp. Lond.; SHO (Anaesth.) Roy. Hants. Co. Hosp. Winchester.

TAYLOR, Mrs Enid (Wheldon) 148 Harley Street, London W1G 7LG Tel: 020 7935 1207; 60 Wood Vale, London N10 3DN Tel: 020 8883 6146 Email: tomt.anaes.uk@cablei.net.co.uk — MB BChir Camb. 1957; MA Camb. 1969, BA 1954; FRCS Eng. 1965; FRCOphth 1993. (Lond. Hosp.) Cons. Ophth. Surg. N. Middlx. Hosp. Lond. Socs: Fell. Roy. Soc. Med.; BMA; Jun. Warden The Worshipful Soc. of Apoth. of Lond. Prev: Cons. Ophth. Surg. Eliz. G. Anderson Hosp. Lond.; Sen. Regist. (Ophth.) St. Bart. Hosp. Lond.; Regist. (Ophth.) St. Jas. Hosp. Balham & N. Middlx. Hosp.

TAYLOR, Professor Eric Andrew MRC Unit in Child Psychiatry, Institute of Psychiatry, De Crespigny Park, London SE5 8AF Tel: 020 7703 5411 Fax: 020 7708 5800 — MA, MB Camb. 1968, BChir 1968; FRCP Lond. 1986; MRCP (UK) 1973; FRCPsych 1988, M 1975. (Middlx.) Prof. Child & Adolesc. Psychiat. Inst. of Psychiat. Lond.; Hon. Cons. (Child & Adolesc. Psychiat.) Bethlem Roy. & Maudsley Hosp. & KCH. Prev: Prof. Developm. Neuropsychiat. Inst. Psychiat. King's Coll. Lond.; Sen. Regist. (Child & Adolesc. Psychiat.) Bethlem Roy. & Maudsley Hosps. Lond.; Clin. & Research Fell. (Psychiat.) Mass. Gen. Hosp.

TAYLOR, Eric Hilton (retired) Crab Cottage, Ridley Hill, Kingswear, Dartmouth TQ6 0BY Tel: 01803 752349 — MB BS 1946 Lond.; MRCS Eng. LRCP Lond. 1944; DTM & H Liverp. 1963. Prev: Med. Off. N.. Territory Austral.

TAYLOR, Mr Eric William Inverclyde Royal Hospital, Greenock PA16 0XN Tel: 01475 633777 Fax: 01475 656139; 5 Langbank Rise, Kilmacolm PA13 4LF Tel: 01505 872722 Email: e-w-taylor@yahoo.co.uk — MB BS 1967 Lond.; FRCS Glas. 1986; FRCS Eng. 1974; MRCS Eng. LRCP Lond. 1967. (St. Mary's) Cons. Surg. Inverclyde Roy. Hosp., Greenock., Argyll and Clyde Acute NHS Trust; Hon. Clin. Sen. Lect. Univ. Glas.; Cons. Gen. Surg. RN Scotl.; Edr. Surgic. Infec. Socs: Fell. Assn. Surgs.; Surg. Infec. Soc.; Hosp. Infec. Soc. Prev: Surg. Cdr. RN & Cons. Surg. RN Hosp. Haslar; Sen. Regist. (Surg.) Profess. Surg. Unit S. Grampian (Aberd.) Health Dist.

TAYLOR, Ethel Gertrude (retired) 27 Earlsfort, Moira, Craigavon BT67 0LY Tel: 01846 612203 — MA Dub. 1952, MB BCh BAO 1951; FFCM 1985, M 1973; DPH Belf. 1962. Prev: Community Phys. E. Health & Social Servs. Bd. N.I.

TAYLOR, Evelyn Anne The Old Farm, 26 Meriden Road, Hampton-in-Ardon, Solihull B92 0BT Tel: 01675 442765 Fax: 01675 443901; Anaesthetic Department, Walsgrave NHS Trust, Clifford Bridge Road, Walsgrave, Coventry CV2 2DX Tel: 01203 602020 — MB ChB Birm. 1970; FFA RACS (Intens. Care) 1982; FFA RCS Eng. 1975; DA Eng. 1972. Cons. Anaesth. & IC Walsgrave Hosp. Coventry. Prev: Regist. Roy. Perth. ICU W. Australia; Asst. Dir. ICU & Cons. Anaesth. Wellington Hosp. New Zealand.

TAYLOR, Evelyn June Wycombe General Hospital, High Wycombe HP11 2TT — MB BS 1972 Lond.; MRCS Eng. LRCP Lond. 1972; FFA RCS Eng. 1977; T(Anaesth) 1991; DObst RCOG 1974. (Roy. Free) Cons. Anaesth. Wycombe Gen. Hosp. Socs: Assn. Anaesth.; BMA. Prev: Sen. Regist. (Anaesth.) W. Midl. & Oxf. HAs; Regist. (Anaesth.) N.wick Pk. Hosp. Harrow; SHO (Anaesth.) Roy. Sussex Co. Hosp. Brighton.

TAYLOR, Fiona Ann Dept of Community Child Health, Grampian University Hosp, Berry Den Rd, Aberdeen AB25 3; 29 Binghill Road, Milltimber, Aberdeen AB13 0JA — MB ChB 1989 Aberd. Staff Grade Community Paediat. Grampian Univ Hosp NHS Trust.

TAYLOR, Fiona Clare 57A Loom Lane, Radlett WD7 8NX — MB BS 1994 Lond. SHO (O & G) St. Johns of Howden Hosp. Livingstone.

TAYLOR, Fiona Gillian Mary Long Reach, Crampshaw Lane, Ashtead KT21 2UF Tel: 01372 273506; Long Reach, Crampshaw Lane, Ashtead KT21 2UF — MB BS 1996 Lond. (Roy. Lond. Hosp.) SHO (Surgic.). Prev: SHO (A & E); SHO (Orthop.).

TAYLOR, Fiona Janet 31A Queens Crescent, Edinburgh EH9 2BA — MB ChB 1982 Aberd. SHO (Psychiat.) Dingleton Hosp. Melrose. Prev: SHO (Psychiat.) Bilbohall Hosp. Elgin.

TAYLOR, Frank (retired) Larchwood, Kerves Lane, Horsham RH13 6ET Tel: 01403 54794 — MB BS 1936 Lond.; MRCS Eng. LRCP Lond. 1935. Prev: on Med. Staff Horsham Hosp.

TAYLOR, Frank (retired) 98 Sudbury Court Drive, Harrow HA1 3TF Tel: 020 8908 1177 — MB BS Lond. 1948; MD Lond. 1952; DObst RCOG 1952; DCH Eng. 1952. Hosp. Pract. (Infec. Dis.) St. John's Hosp. Uxbridge. Prev: Regist. (Paediat.) Hillingdon Hosp.

TAYLOR, Frank John Barron (retired) Hartford Bridge House, Bedlington NE22 6AQ Tel: 01670 823260 — MB BChir 1961 Camb.; MRCS Eng. LRCP Lond. 1960. Clin. Asst. N.d. Ment. Health NHS Trust. Prev: GP Blyth.

TAYLOR, Frank Richard Taylor and Partners, The Surgery, Hexton Road, Barton-le-Clay, Bedford MK45 4TA Tel: 01582 528700 Fax: 01582 528714; Taymer House, Luton Road, Silsoe, Bedford MK45 4QP Tel: 01525 860245 Fax: 01525 861889 — LRCPI & LM, LRSCI & LM 1962. (RCSI)

TAYLOR, Frank Thomas Barnt Green Surgery, 82 Hewell Road, Barnt Green, Birmingham B45 8NF Tel: 0121 445 1704 Fax: 0121 447 8253 — MB ChB 1981 Birm.; MRCGP 1986; DRCOG 1984. (Birmingham) GP Barnt Green.

TAYLOR, Frederick Gerard Invergare, Glenarn Road, Helensburgh G84 8LL Tel: 01436 821432 Fax: 01436 821452 — MB ChB 1961 Glas.; MSc (Occupat. Med.) Lond. 1976; FRCP Lond. 1993; FFOM RCP Lond. 1987, MFOM 1981; MRCGP 1974; DIH Eng. 1976; DObst RCOG 1963. Cons. Occupat. Phys. Lond.; Corporate Health Adviser Citibank NA. Socs: Fell. Roy. Soc. Med. (Ex-Pres. Occupat. Med. Sect.); (Ex-Pres. & Treas.) Soc. Occupat. Med. Prev: Chief Med. Off. & Head of Health & Welf. Servs. Marks & Spencer plc.

TAYLOR, Gareth Henry Fisher Little St John Street Surgery, 7 Little St. John Street, Woodbridge IP12 1EE Tel: 01384 382046 — MB BCh 1986 Witwatersrand.

TAYLOR, Gavin Beddie (retired) 26 Blackhouse Terrace, Peterhead AB42 1LQ Tel: 01779 472345 — MB ChB 1954 Aberd.; MRCGP 1965. Prev: GP Aberd.sh.

TAYLOR, Geoffrey Arnold Northfield Road Surgery, Northfield Road, Blaby, Leicester LE8 4GU Tel: 0116 277 1705; 13 Willoughby Road, Countesthorpe, Leicester LE8 5UA Tel: 0116 277 1428 — MB BChir 1951 Camb.; MA, MB BChir Camb. 1951; DObst RCOG 1957. (Guy's) Prev: Asst. Ho. Surg. & Ho. Phys. Guy's Hosp. Lond.; Ho. Surg. (Gyn. & Obst.) Roy. United Hosp. Bath.

TAYLOR, Mr Geoffrey James Wycombe General Hospital, Queen Alexandra Road, High Wycombe HP11 2TT Tel: 01494 426421; Sladmore Farm House, Cryers Hill Road, Cryers Hill, High Wycombe HP15 6LL — MB ChB 1977 Birm.; FRCS (Orthop.) Ed. 1988; FRCS Ed. 1982; FRCS Eng. 1982. (Brimingham) Cons. Orthop. & Trauma Surg. Wycombe HA. Socs: Fell. BOA; BMA; Brit. Elbow & Shoulder Soc. Prev: Sen. Regist. (Orthop.) Guy's & St. Thos. Hosp. Lond.; Regist. (Orthop.) N.wick Pk. Hosp. Harrow; Regist. Rotat. (Orthop.) Roy. Free Hosp. & Windsor HA.

TAYLOR, George (retired) Redbrook, Brookledge Lane, Adlington, Macclesfield SK10 4JU Tel: 01625 829834 — MRCS Eng. LRCP Lond. 1930; DIH Eng. 1949. Cons. Med. Adviser Hawker Siddeley Aviat. Ltd.

TAYLOR, George Abel (retired) 5 Campsie Place, Aberdeen AB15 6HL Tel: 01224 319602 — MB ChB Aberd. 1958; FRCGP 1991, M 1972.

TAYLOR, George Benjamin 18 Palmerston Road, Buckhurst Hill IG9 5LT Tel: 020 8504 1552 — MB BS 1950 Lond.; DObst RCOG 1954; MRCS Eng. LRCP Lond. 1949; DCH Eng. 1955. (St. Bart.) Mem. Staff Forest Hosp. Buckhurst Hill.

TAYLOR, George Browne Guidepost Health Centre, Willow terrace Road, University of Leeds, Leeds LS2 9JT Tel: 01670 822071 Fax: 01670 531068 Email: g.b.taylor@doctors.org.uk; 41 Clayton

TAYLOR

Road, Jesmond, Newcastle upon Tyne NE2 4RQ Tel: 0191 281 1728 Fax: 0191 281 8268 — MB BS 1972 Newc.; Ed. D. (Newc.) 2000; FRCGP 1986, M 1976; MICGP 1987; DObst RCOG 1975. Prev: Course Organiser N.umbria VTS; Trainee GP Newc. VTS; Ho. Phys. Child Health & Ho. Surg. Roy. Vict. Infirm. Newc.

TAYLOR, George Rowland (retired) 2 Branksome Court, 5 Western Road, Canford Cliffs, Poole BH13 7BD Tel: 01202 709014 — MB BS 1936 Lond.; MRCS Eng. LRCP Lond. 1935; MFPHM RCP Lond. 1972; DPH Lond. 1939. Prev: Dist. Community Phys. Herts. AHA.

TAYLOR, George Swan (retired) Eden Holme, Haltwhistle NE49 0AF Tel: 01434 320376 — MB ChB 1945 Ed. Prev: Ho. Surg. Orthop. Hosp. Larbert.

TAYLOR, Gerald Gershom 53 Gervis Road, Bournemouth BH1 3DQ Tel: 01202 25154 — MRCS Eng. LRCP Lond. 1941. (King's Coll. & Char. Cross)

TAYLOR, Gillian Mairi Flat G/2, 56 Fortrose St., Glasgow G11 5LP — MB ChB 1998 Glas.

TAYLOR, Gordon James 12 Old Vicarage Lane, Quarndon, Derby DE22 5JB — MB ChB 1956 Sheff.; MRCS Eng. LRCP Lond. 1956; FFA RCS Eng. 1960; DA Eng. 1958. Cons. Anaesth. Nottm. HA. Socs: Intrac. Pain Soc. GB & Irel. (Ex-Hon. Sec.). Prev: Sen. Regist. Anaesth. W.. Infirm. Glas.; Sen. Ho. Off. Anaesth. Roy. Hosp. Sheff.; Regist. Anaesth. United Sheff. Hosps.

TAYLOR, Gordon William, MBE (retired) 97 Hildens Drive, Tilehurst, Reading RG31 5JA Tel: 01189 411752 — MB ChB 1952 Manch.; FRCGP 1983, M 1962; DObst RCOG 1953. JP Supplm.. List. Prev: Hosp. Pract. (Med.) Roy. Berks. Hosp. Reading.

TAYLOR, Graeme Roy 47 Crowtree Lane, Louth LN11 9LL — MB ChB 1986 Sheff.

TAYLOR, Graham Albert William (Surgery), Ecclesbourne, 1 Warwick Terrace, Lea Bridge Road, London E17 9DP Tel: 020 8539 2077 Fax: 020 8556 1723; 8 Ashfields, Loughton IG10 1SB — MB BS 1966 Lond.; MRCS Eng. LRCP Lond. 1966. (Guy's)

TAYLOR, Graham David Heathcroft, Back Lane, Letchmore Heath, Watford WD25 8EF Email: grahamt@nildram.co.uk — MB BS 1980 Lond.; BSc (Hons.) Lond. 1977; MRCGP 1988; MBA 1999. (Char. Cross Hosp.)

TAYLOR, Graham Errington Budleigh Salterton Medical Centre, 1 The Lawn, Budleigh Salterton EX9 6LS Tel: 01395 441212 Fax: 01395 441244; Greyfriars, Westfield Road, Budleigh Salterton EX9 6SS Tel: 01395 442498 — MB ChB 1971 St. And. Prev: SHO (O & G) Roy. Devon & Exet Hosp. (Heavitree); Ho. Off. (Med.) Maryfield Hosp. Dundee; Ho. Off. (Surg.) Roy. Infirm. Dundee.

TAYLOR, Graham Malcolm St James University Hospital, Beckett St, Leeds LS9 7TF; 19 The Village, Thorp Arch, Wetherby LS23 7AR — MB ChB 1993 Manch. Lect. (Obst & Gyn.) St James Univ Hosp. Leeds. Prev: Specialist Regist. (O & G) Ninewells Hosp. Dundee.

TAYLOR, Graham Paul Royal Cornwall Hospital (Treliske), Gloweth, Truro TR1 3LJ Tel: 01872 252716 Fax: 01872 252017 Email: graham.taylor@rcht.swest.nhs.uk — MB BS 1972 Lond.; FRCPCH 1997; FRCP Lond. 1994; MSc (Immunol.) Lond. 1988; MRCP (UK) 1977; DCH Eng. 1976; DObst RCOG 1976. (St. Geo.) Cons. Paediat. Roy. Cornw. Hosp. Truro. Socs: BMA. Prev: Sen. Regist. (Paediat.) W.m. & W.m. Childr. Hosps. Lond.; Research Fell. & Hon. Sen. Regist. Roy. Postgrad. Med. Sch. Hammersmith Hosp. Lond.; Regist. (Paediat.) St. Mary's Hosp. Lond.

TAYLOR, Graham Philip Wright Fleming Institute, Acad. Department of Genitourinary Medicine & Communicable Di, Imperial College School of Medicine at St Mary's, Norfolk Place, London W2 1PG Tel: 020 75943910 Fax: 020 75943910 Email: g.p.taylor@ic.ac.uk; 43 Parc-y-Bryn, Creigiau, Cardiff CF15 9SE Tel: 029 2089 2396 — MB ChB 1981 Birm.; MRCP (UK) 1987. (University of Birmingham Medical School) Sen. Lect./Hon. Cons., Genitourin. Med. Communicable Dis.s, Imperial Coll./St Mary's Hosp. Lond. Socs: Brit. Infec. Soc.; BHIVA; Roy. Soc. Trop. Med. & Hyg. Prev: Hon. Sen. Regist. (Genitourin. Med. Communicable Dis.) St. Mary's Hosp. Lond.; Chief Med. Off. Centr. Hosp. Honiara, Solomon Is.; Regist. (Med.) Mid. Glam. HA.

TAYLOR, Graham Roy Maryhill Practice, Elgin Health Centre, Maryhill, Elgin IV30 1AT Tel: 01343 543788 Fax: 01343 551604 — MB ChB 1985 Aberd.; MRCGP 1989; DRCOG 1988.

TAYLOR, Mr Grahame John Saint Clair Department of Orthopaedics, The Glenfield Hospital, Groby Road, Leicester LE3 9QP Tel: 0116 287 1471 Ext: 3448 — MB ChB 1981 Ed.; FRCS (Orth.) 1995; FRCS Ed. 1987. (Univ. Ed.) Cons. Orthop. Surg. Glenfield Hosp. Leicester. Socs: Brit. Orthopaedic Assn.; Brit. Orthopaedic Research Soc. Prev: Lect. (Orthop.) Surg. Leicester Univ.

TAYLOR, Grainne Cait Benvon 5 Beach Lane, Penarth CF64 4LQ — MB ChB 1997 Liverp.

TAYLOR, Guinevere Sarah Emily 490 Manchester Road, Rochdale OL11 3EL — MB ChB 1997 Leeds.

TAYLOR, Gwyneth Yvette West Bar Surgery, 1 West Bar, Banbury OX16 9SF Tel: 01295 256261 — DFFP 1998; MB BS Lond. 1993; DRCOG 1997; DCH 1996; MRCGP. (St. Georges) GP Princip.; Clin. Med. Off. (Family Plann.). Prev: Trainee GP Horton Gen. Hosp. Oxf. VTS.

TAYLOR, Heath Philip 171 St Ann's Hill, London SW18 2RX — MB BS 1994 Lond.; BSc (Physiol.) Lond. 1991.

TAYLOR, Helen 22 Charlemont Road, Walsall WS5 3NG Tel: 01922 626280 — MB ChB 1994 Leeds.

TAYLOR, Helen Denise Clifton Medical Centre, 571 Farnborough Road, Clifton, Nottingham NG11 9DN Tel: 0115 921 1288 — MB ChB 1986 Liverp.; DRCOG 1991. Trainee GP Tutbury Health Centre. Prev: SHO (O & G) Univ. Hosp. Nottm.; SHO (Paediat.) Good Hope. Hosp. Sutton Coldfield.

TAYLOR, Helen Elizabeth Anne 4 Vane Road, Thame OX9 3WG — MB ChB 1984 Birm.

TAYLOR, Helen Frances (retired) 7 Hampole Balk, Skellow, Doncaster DN6 8LF — MB ChB 1953 Sheff.; MRCS Eng. LRCP Lond. 1954.

TAYLOR, Helen Louise 9 Sumatra Road, London NW6 1PS — MB BChir 1993 Camb.

TAYLOR, Helen Louise Hinchingbrooke Hospital, Huntingdon PE29 6NT Tel: 01480 416132 — MB BS 1988 Lond.; MRCP (UK) 1992; FRCR 1995. Cons. Radiol.

TAYLOR, Helen Mary St. David's Foundation, Cambrian House, St John's Road, Newport NP19 8GR — MB ChB 1980 Liverp.; MRCGP 1995. Cons. Palliat. Med. St. David's Foundat. Newport Gwent.

TAYLOR, Helen Mary 66 Strouden Road, Chairminster, Bournemouth BH9 1QN — MB ChB 1995 Birm.

TAYLOR, Helen Murray Hawkhill, Lunan Bay, Arbroath DD11 4UX — MB ChB 1990 Glas.

TAYLOR, Helen Patricia Derwent Practice, Norton Road, Malton YO17 9RF Tel: 01653 600069 Fax: 01653 698014; Maris Otter House, West St, Swinton, Malton YO17 6SP — MB ChB 1986 Sheff. Clin. Asst. Ophth.

TAYLOR, Helena Scott Lauder Saltoun Hall, Pencaitland, Tranent EH34 5DS Tel: 01875 340262 — MB ChB 1939 Ed.; DPH 1941. (Ed.) Prev: Asst. MOH & Asst. Sch. Med. Off. Co. Boro. Ipswich; Ho. Phys. Roy. Hosp. Sick Childr. Edin.

TAYLOR, Henry John Hunter 79 Woodman Road, Brentwood CM14 5AU — MB BS 1993 Lond.; FRCR 2001; BSc Lond. 1990; MRCP 1997. SpR (Clin. Oncol.) Roy. Marsden Hosp. Lond. Prev: SHO (Med.) Whipps Cross Hosp. Lond.; Specialist Regist. (Clin. Oncol.) St Bartholomews Hosp. Lond.

TAYLOR, Hilary Elizabeth 119 Main Street, Menston, Ilkley LS29 6HT; 3 Kingfield, Guiseley, Leeds LS20 9DZ — MB ChB 1984 Leic. Prev: Trainee GP Stockport VTS.

TAYLOR, Hilary Jane 5 Wynbreck Dr, Keyworth, Nottingham NG12 5FY — MB BS 1997 Newc. SHO (Med.) Lister Hosp. Stevenage.

TAYLOR, Hugh Fraser Ongar Health Centre, Bansons Lane, Ongar CM5 9AR Tel: 01277 363028 Fax: 01277 365264 Email: hugh.taylor@gp-f81049.nhs.uk; 57 Coopers Hill, Marden Ash, Ongar CM5 9EF — MB BS 1976 Lond.; BSc (Psychol.) Lond. 1973; MRCP (UK) 1981; DRCOG 1983. (Lond. Hosp.) Clin. Asst. (Gastroenterol.) P.ss Alexandra Hosp. Harlow; Hosp. Pract. P.ss Alexandra Hosp. Harlow. Prev: Regist. (Med.) St. Margt.s Hosp. Epping; Regist. (Med.) Lond. Hosp. Whitechapel.

TAYLOR, Hugh William Granby Place Surgery, Granby Place, 1 High Street, Northfleet, Gravesend DA11 9EY Tel: 01474 352447/362252; 3 Old Road W., Gravesend DA11 0LH Tel: 01474 333228 — MB BS 1982 Lond.; MRCGP 1987; DRCOG 1985.

TAYLOR, Mr Hugo Wheldon Rowntree Basildon Hospital, Nether Mayne, Basildon SS16 5NL Tel: 01268 533911; Little Styles Cottage, MargarettingTye, Ingatestone CM4 9JX Tel: 01277 840618

TAYLOR

Fax: 01277 841339 — MB BS 1983 Lond.; FRCS Eng. 1989; FRCS (Gen.) 1997. Cons. (Gen. Surg. ColoProctol. & BrE. Surg.) Basildon Hosp. Socs: Worshipful Soc. Apoth.; Brit. Assn. Surg. Oncol. Prev: Sen. Regist. (Gen. Surg.) Roy. Free Hosp. Lond.; Regist. (Gen. Surg.) The Lond. Hosp., Basildon & Roy. Free Hosp.; SHO Pre-Fell.sh. Rotat. (Surg.) St. Bartholomews Hosp. Lond.

TAYLOR, Iain Neil Rowan Cottage, Monktonhill Road, Prestwick KA9 1UJ — MB ChB 1982 Aberd.; FFA RCSI 1989. Sen. Regist. (Anaesth.) Vict. Infirm. Glas. Prev: Regist. (Anaesth.) Glas. Roy. Infirm.; SHO (Anaesth.) Falkirk & Dist. Roy. Infirm.

TAYLOR, Ian, OBE Windmill Grange, 90 Windmill Lane, Histon, Cambridge CB4 9JF — MD 1948 Lond.; FRCP Lond. 1966; MRCS Eng. LRCP Lond. 1929; DPH Eng. 1931. (King's Coll. Hosp.) Prev: Med. Off. LCC Fever Hosps.; Epidemiol. GLC & Min. of Health; Edr. Brit. Jl. Soc. Med.

TAYLOR, Ian Arthur Mansion House Surgery, Abbey Street, Stone ST15 8YE Tel: 01785 815555 Fax: 01785 815541; 87 Lichfield Road, Stone ST15 8QD Tel: 01785 815060 — MB ChB Birm. 1968; DCH Eng. 1971; DObst RCOG 1970. (Birm.) Prev: SHO (Psychiat.) Bristol Roy. Infirm.; SHO (Obst.) Birm. Matern. Hosp.; Ho. Phys. Qu. Eliz. Hosp. Birm.

TAYLOR, Ian Christie Department Health Care for Elderly People, Ulster Hospital, Dundonald, Belfast BT16 1RH Tel: 01232 484511 Fax: 01232 550415 Email: it@netcomuk.co.uk — MB BCh BAO 1975 Belf.; BSc (Hons.) Belf. 1972, MD 1980; FRCP Lond. 1995; FRCP Ed. 1994; FRCP Glas. 1993; MRCP (UK) 1979. Cons. Phys. (Geriat. Med.) Ulster Hosp. Dundonald. Socs: Brit. Geriat. Soc. & Ulster Med. Soc. Prev: Cons. Phys. (Geriat. Med.) Roy. Vict. Hosp. Belf.

TAYLOR, Professor Ian Galbraith, CBE (retired) Croft Cottage, Cinder Hill, Whitegate, Northwich CW8 2BH Tel: 01606 882119 — MB ChB Manch. 1948; MD (Gold Medal) Manch. 1962; FRCP Lond. 1977, M 1973; FRCPCH; DPH Manch. 1954. Prev: Ellis Llwyd Jones Prof. of Audiol. & Educat. of Deaf Univ. Manch.

TAYLOR, Ian Hammond 39 Stanhope Road, Darlington DL3 7AP Tel: 01325 462593 — MB BCh BAO 1956 Belf. Socs: Assoc. Mem. Fac. Homoeop.

TAYLOR, Ian Hayes (retired) 226 Cantley Lane, Doncaster DN4 6QT Tel: 01302 536419 — MB BS 1958 Durh.; FFA RCS Eng. 1965. Prev: Cons. Anaesth. Doncaster Roy. Infirm.

TAYLOR, Ian Keith Sunderland Royal Hospital, Kayll Road, Sunderland SR4 7TP Tel: 0191 565 6256 ext 47348 Fax: 0191 569 9292; 36 Runnymede Road, Ponteland, Newcastle upon Tyne NE20 9HG — MB BS 1983 Lond.; BSc (Upper 2nd cl. Hons.) Lond. 1979, MB BS 1983; MRCP (UK) 1986; FRCP 1997. (St. Mary's) Cons. Phys. (Gen. & Respirat. Med.) Sunderland Roy. Hosp. Kayll Rd. Sunderland. Socs: Brit. Thorac. Soc.; Eur. Respirat. Soc.; Amer. Thoracic Soc. Prev: Sen. Lect. (Hon. Cons. Phys.); Nat. Heart & Lung Inst. & Roy. Postgrad. Med. Sch.

TAYLOR, Ian Robert Southampton General Hospital, Tremona Road, Southampton SO16 6YD Tel: 02380 796720; Tel: 01243 372161 Fax: 020 8906 8217 Email: henry@nouiel.freeserve.co.uk — MB ChB 1992 Bristol; DA (UK) 1995; FRCA 1998. (Bristol) Specialist Regist. Rotat. (Anaesth.) Wessex. Socs: Obstetric Anaesth.s Assn.; Brit. Ophth. Anaesth.s Soc. Prev: SHO (Anaesth.) Qu. Alexandra Hosp. Portsmouth; SHO (Med.) St. Mary's Hosp. Portsmouth; SHO (Anaesth.) Barnstaple.

TAYLOR, Ian William 5 Sycamore Drive, Marlow Bottom, Marlow SL7 3NL — MB ChB 1991 Manch.; PhD Surrey 1981; BSc Manch. 1977. Head of unit, Clin. Pharm. Unit, Glaxo-Wellcome.

TAYLOR, Professor Irving Department of Surgery, Royal Free and University College Medical School, Charles Bell House, 67-73 Riding House St., London W1W 7EJ Tel: 020 7679 9312 Fax: 020 7636 5176 Email: j.stumcke@ucl.ac.uk; 43 Ridgeway Gardens, Hornsey Lane, Highgate, London N6 5NH Tel: 020 7263 8086 Fax: 020 7263 8085 — F.MedSci 2000; FRCPS 2001 (Hon.) Glas.; MB ChB Sheff. 1968; ChM Sheff. 1978, MD (Distinc.) 1975; FRCS Eng. 1972. (Sheff.) Prof. Surg. Univ. Coll. Lond.; Hon. Cons. Univ. Coll. Lond. Hosps. NHS Trust; Edr.-in-Chief Europ. Jl. Surgic. Oncol. Socs: Assn. Surg. (Ex-Educat. Sec.); (Ex-Sec.) Surgic. Research Soc.; Brit. Assn. Surg. Oncol. (ex-Pres.). Prev: Prof. Surg. Univ. Soton.; Sen. Lect. & Cons. Surg. BRd.green Hosp. Liverp. & Roy. Liverp. Hosp.; Sen. Regist. (Surg.) Roy. Hosp. Sheff.

TAYLOR, Isabel Robertson Hazel Cottage, 63 King Street, Duffield, Belper DE56 4EU — MB ChB 1985 Sheff.; DCH RCP Lond. 1988; DRCOG 1987.

TAYLOR, J D M Seymour Road, Easton, Bristol BS5 0UA — MB ChB 1973 Bristol; MB ChB 1973 Bristol.

TAYLOR, Jack Andrew (retired) Ropewalk Cottage, Bruton BA10 0DW Tel: 01749 813440 — MRCS Eng. LRCP Lond. 1939; LMSSA Lond. 1938; MRCGP 1952. Prev: Sen. Resid. Med. Off. Middlesbrough Gen. Hosp.

TAYLOR, Jack Lorimer Aboyne Health Centre, Bellwood Road, Aboyne AB34 5HQ Tel: 01339 886345; Craigston, Birsemore, Aboyne AB34 5EP Tel: 013398 86297 Email: jack_taylor@virgin.net — MB ChB 1975 Aberd.; DRCOG 1977; MRCGP 1979; FRCGP 1998. (Aberdeen) Princip. Gen. Pract.; Cas. Off. Aboyne Hosp.; Med. Dir. Aboyne Hosp.; Clin. Tuor Aberd. Univ.; Trainer Gen. Pract.

TAYLOR, Jacqueline 120E Brondesbury Park, London NW2 5JR — MB BS 1987 Newc.

TAYLOR, James 12 Park Hall Road, Reigate RH2 9LH — MB BS 1993 Lond.; BDS Glas. 1983; FDS RCS Eng. 1988. Socs: Char. Cross Dent. Soc. Prev: Regist. (Oral & Maxillofacial Surg.) St. Margt. Epping & Roy. Lond. Hosp.

TAYLOR, James Aitken Vennel Street Health Centre, 50 Vennel Street, Dalry KA24 4AG Tel: 01294 832523 Fax: 01294 835771; 8 Saint Palladius Terrace, Dalry KA24 5AX Tel: 01294 833621 Email: j_a_taylor@compuserve.com — MB ChB 1976 Dundee; MRCGP 1980; DRCOG 1978. Company Med. Adviser Roche Products Ayrsh. Socs: (Treas.) Anglo-French Med. Soc.

TAYLOR, James Calbeck (retired) 52 Cleveley Road, Meols, Wirral CH47 8XR Tel: 0151 632 4332 — MB ChB 1949 Liverp.; MD Liverp. 1962, MB ChB 1949, DPH 1955. Prev: SCMO (Community Child Health Serv.) Liverp. HA.

TAYLOR, James Christopher The Middlesex Hospital, London W1P 9PG; 50 George Lane, Lewisham, London SE13 6HL Tel: 020 8697 4072 Email: jaime-taylor@msn.com — MB BS 1990 Lond.; MRCP Lond. 1993. Specialist Regist. (Research Fell.) Osteoperosis.; Specialist Regist. (Rheum & Gen Med.). Socs: BMA; BSR; ASBR.

TAYLOR, James Francis Nuttall Cardiac Wing, Great Ormond Street Hospital for Children, NHS Trust, Great Ormond St., London WC1N 3JH Tel: 020 7430 2987 Fax: 020 7430 2995; 10 Arragon Court, 62 The Avenue, Beckenham BR3 5LA Tel: 020 8650 884 Fax: 020 8663 3309 — MB BChir Camb. 1962; MA Camb. 1962, MD Camb. 1976; FRCP Lond. 1978, M 1966; MRCS Eng. LRCP Lond. 1962; FRCPCH 1996; DCH Eng. 1964. (St. Thos.) Cons. Paediat. Cardiol. Gt. Ormond St. Hosp. Childr. Lond.; Sen Lect. Inst. of Child Health UCL. Socs: Brit. Cardiac Soc.; Brit. Paediat. Cardiol. Assn.; Assn. Europ. Paediat. Cardiol. Prev: Sen. Regist. (Med.) & Ho. Phys. Thoracic Unit Hosp. Sick Childr. Gt. Ormond St. Lond.; Regist. (Med.) St. Thos. Hosp. Lond.

TAYLOR, James Fraser (retired) Rosehaugh, Rhynie, Huntly AB54 4LJ Tel: 01464 861325 — MB ChB 1954 Aberd.; FFOM RCP Lond. 1990; DPH Ed. 1965; DIH Eng. 1965. Prev: Sen. Med. Off. Chloride GP plc.

TAYLOR, James Graham (retired) Karassy, Westwood Road, Windlesham GU20 6LS Tel: 01344 22437 — MB ChB Birm. 1940; FFOM RCP Lond. 1979; FFOM RCPI 1977. Cons. in Aviat. & Occupat. Med. to Brit. Airways; Health Screening Phys. P.ss Margt. Hosp. Windsor. Prev: Dir. Med. & Safety Serv. Brit. Airways.

TAYLOR, James Michael 2 North Road, Peterhead AB42 1BL — MB ChB 1955 Aberd.

TAYLOR, James Patrick Thursby Surgery, 2 Browhead Road, Burnley BB10 3BF Tel: 01282 422447 Fax: 01282 832575 — MB ChB 1978 Manchester; MB ChB 1978 Manchester.

TAYLOR, James William 5 Wentworth Drive, Messingham, Scunthorpe DN17 3TZ — MB BS 1981 Lond. Sen. Med. Off. Roy. Fleet Aux.

TAYLOR, Jane Ann Claremont Surgery, 56-60 Castle Road, Scarborough YO11 1XE Tel: 01723 375050 Fax: 01723 378241; 11 Holbeck Hill, Scarborough YO11 2XE Tel: 01723 373557 — MB BS 1981 Lond.; Dip Occ Med 1999 London; Dip. Therap. Newc. 1998. (Guy's Hospital) G.P; Clin. Asst. (Cardiol.).; O.H.P. Prev: Clin. Asst. (Diabetes).

TAYLOR, Jane Charmian Gordon Wilson 28 Craigmount Park, Corstorphine, Edinburgh EH12 8EE — MB ChB 1987 Glas. Med. Off. Scott. Nat. Blood Transfus. Serv. Glas.

TAYLOR

TAYLOR, Jane Hunt Wallacetown Health Centre, 3 Lyon Street, Dundee DD4 6RF Tel: 01382 459519 Fax: 01382 453110 — MB ChB 1982 Aberd.; MRCGP Ed. 1987.

TAYLOR, Jane Rosemary Chrisp Street Health Centre, 100 Chrisp St., Poplar, London E14 6PG Tel: 020 7515 4860; 5 Alloway Road, Bow, London E3 5AS — MB ChB 1976 Manch.; MRCGP 1981. GP Lond.

TAYLOR, Janet Irene Hobcroft House, Hobcroft Lane, Mobberley, Knutsford WA16 7QS — MB BCh BAO 1958 Dub. (T.C. Dub.) Prev: Asst. Psychiat. Regist. Hope Hosp. Eccles, Salford Roy. Hosp. & Bridgewater Hosp. Eccles.

TAYLOR, Janet Margaret Old Hall Grounds Health Centre, Old Hall Grounds, Cowbridge CF71 7AH Tel: 01446 772383 Fax: 01446 774022; Crud-y-Gwynt, Love Lane, Llanbleddian, Cowbridge CF71 7JQ Tel: 01446 772295 — MB BCh 1975 Wales; Diploma in Clinical Hypnosis 2001 (University College London; Diploma in Counselling (University of Wales, Swansea). (Welsh School of Medii) Gen. Practitioner, Dr. R. D. Jones & Partners, The Health Centre, Cowbridge Vale of Glam. CF31 1RQ; Counsellor and Med. Hypnotherapist, The Bridgend Clinic, P.ss of Wales Hosp., City Rd., Bridgend, Mid Glam. CF31 1RQ. Socs: Brit. Soc. of Med. and Dent. Hypn.; Brit. Soc. of Experim. and Clin. Hypn. Prev: Trainee GP M. Glam. VTS; SHO (O & G) S. Glam. HA (T); SHO (Psychiat.) Morgannwg Hosp. Bridgend.

TAYLOR, Jason Leslie Warley Hospital, Warley Hill, Brentwood CM14 5HQ — MB BS 1977 Lond.; MRCS Eng. LRCP Lond. 1977; MRCPsych 1982; MSc (Econ.) 1997. (Roy. Free) Cons. Psychiat. Warley Hosp. Brentwood. Prev: Sen. Regist. (Psychiat.) Friern, Whittington & Roy Free Hosps. Lond.; Clin. Asst. & Regist. (Psychiat.) Roy. Free Hosp. Lond.

TAYLOR, Jean (retired) 18 Lions Hall, St Swithun St., Winchester SO23 9HW Tel: 01962 841303 — LRCP LRCS Ed. LRFPS Glas. 1945.

TAYLOR, Jean Elizabeth Culduthel Road Surgery, Ardlarich, 15 Culduthel Road, Inverness IV2 4AG Tel: 01463 712233 Fax: 01463 715479 — MB ChB 1965 Aberd.; DObst RCOG 1967.

TAYLOR, Jeffrey Panteg Health Centre, Kemys Street, Griffithstown, Pontypool NP4 5DJ Tel: 01495 763608 Fax: 01495 753925 — MB BCh 1984 Wales.

TAYLOR, Jennifer Princess Royal Community Health Centre, Huddersfield; Mollicar House, Lumb Lane, Almondbury, Huddersfield HD4 6SZ — MB ChB 1978 Dundee. Clin. Med. Off. Family Plann. Prev: Trainee GP Huddersfield VTS.; GP.

TAYLOR, Jennifer Geraldine 17 Littleworth Grove, Walmley, Sutton Coldfield B76 2XF — MB BCh 1988 Wales. SHO (Cas.) Roy. Hosp. Wolverhampton. Prev: Ho. Off. (Med.) W. Wales Gen. Hosp.; Ho. Off. (Surg.) Neath Gen. Hosp.

TAYLOR, Jennifer Louise 32 Busby Road, Carmunnock, Clarkston, Glasgow G76 9BN — MB ChB 1998 Aberd.

TAYLOR, Jeremy David The Old Farm House, Epsom Road, Guildford GU4 7AB — MB BS 1998 Lond.

TAYLOR, Jillian (retired) Carr Bank Cottage, Gawthwaite, Ulverston LA12 8EU — MB ChB 1958 Sheff. Prev: Research Asst. in Med. (Univ. Sheff.) & Ho. Surg. Roy. Hosp. Sheff.

TAYLOR, Joan (retired) 2 Broadlands Road, London N6 4AS — MRCS Eng. LRCP Lond. 1927; BSc Lond. 1924, MB BS 1927; FRCPath 1963; DPH Eng. 1929. Fell. Univ. Coll. Lond. Prev: Asst. Dep. Clin. Pathol. Univ. Coll. Hosp.

TAYLOR, Joanna Karen Elizabeth Tir-Na-Og, Brooklands, Sarisbury Green, Southampton SO31 7EE — BM BS 1986 Nottm.

TAYLOR, Joanne Denyse 3 Beeches Walk, Carshalton SM5 4JS — MB BS 1994 Lond.

TAYLOR, Joanne Elizabeth Renal Unit, Dorset County Hospital, Williams Avenue, Dorchester DT1 2JY Tel: 01305 255269 Fax: 01305 254756 — MB BChir 1984 Camb.; MB BChir Camb. 1985; BSc St. And. 1982; MD Camb. 1992; MRCP (UK) 1987. (Camb.) Dir. (Renal Servs.) Dorset. Prev: Sen. Regist. Nottm. City Hosp.; Regist. Qu. Eliz. Hosp. Birm.

TAYLOR, Joanne Lisa 23 Thornville Street, Leeds LS6 1RP — MB ChB 1993 Leeds.

TAYLOR, Joby 38 Thirlestane Road, Edinburgh EH9 1AW — MB ChB 1998 Ed.

TAYLOR, John (retired) Ardgowan Medical Practice, 2 Finnart Street, Greenock PA16 8HW Tel: 01475 888155 Fax: 01475 785060 — MB ChB 1958 Aberd.; MRCGP 1972.

TAYLOR, John St Giles Road Surgery, St. Giles Road, Watton, Thetford IP25 6XG Tel: 01953 889134/881247 Fax: 01953 885167 — MB ChB 1969 Liverp.; DObst RCOG 1972; DA Eng. 1972.

TAYLOR, John Rockhaven, 30 Georges Lane, Horwich, Bolton BL6 6RT — MB ChB 1968 Ed.

TAYLOR, John Arnold 20 Downesway, Alderley Edge SK9 7XB — MB ChB 1966 Manch. (Manch.)

TAYLOR, John Brian (retired) Greenbank, Riverside Road, Dittisham, Dartmouth TQ6 0HS Tel: 01803 722380 — MB BCh BAO 1948 Belf.; FRCGP 1970; DObst RCOG 1951; DCH Eng. 1952. Prev: Ho. Phys. & Sen. Extern. Surg. Roy. Vict. Hosp. Belf.

TAYLOR, John Christopher, Lt.-Col. RAMC Glencairn, Reidhaven St., Elgin IV30 1QH — MB ChB 1981 Aberd.; FFA RCS Eng. 1988. Cons. Anaesth. Dr Gray's Hosp. Elgin. Prev: Cons. Anaesth. Brit. Army; Sen. Regist. (Anaesth.) Brit. Army; Regist. (Anaesth.) Aberd. Roy. Infirm.

TAYLOR, John Christopher Kneesworth House Hospital, Bassingbourn-cum-Kneesworth, Royston SG8 5JP Tel: 01763 255600 Fax: 01763 246115 — MRCS Eng. LRCP Lond. 1972; FRCPsych 1993, M 1981; DObst. RCOG 1975. (Guy's) Med. Dir. Partnerships In Care Ltd. Prev: Cons. Forens. Psychiat. Roy. Free, Friern Hosps. Lond. & Wessex RHA; Sen. Regist. (Forens. Psychiat.) Roy. Free Hosp. & HM Prison Holloway.

TAYLOR, Mr John Desmond Renal Unit, Guy's Hospital, Guy's Tower, St Thomas St., London SE1 9RT Tel: 020 7955 4818 Fax: 020 7407 6370 Email: johndtaylor@kcl.ac.uk; 182 Shakespeare Tower, Barbican, London EC2Y 8DR Tel: 020 7382 9048 Email: johnatguys@aol.com — MB BChir 1978 Camb.; MA Camb. 1978; MD Leicester 1989; MRCS Eng. LRCP Lond. 1977; FRCS Ed. 1982. (Camb. & Guy's) Cons. Transpl. Surg. Guy's Hosp. Lond.; Hon. Cons. Transpl. Surg., Kent and Canterbury Hosp.; Hon. Cons. Transpl. Surg. - King's Healthcare, Lond.; Hon. Cons. Transpl. Surg., Gt. Ormond St Hosp. Lond. Socs: Roy. Soc. Med.; Brit. Transpl. Soc.; Assn. Surg. Prev: Sen. Regist. (Gen. Surg.) & Regist. Roy. Liverp. Hosp.; Research Fell. (Surg.) Univ. Leics.

TAYLOR, John Edward (retired) 9 Pine Meadows, Kirkella, Hull HU10 7NS Tel: 01482 656366 Email: john@jetaylor11.fsnet.co.uk — MRCS Eng. LRCP Lond. 1953; LDS Leeds 1960. Prev: Ho. Phys. Pinderfields Hosp. Wakefield.

TAYLOR, Mr John Frederic (retired) 34 South Road, Grassendale Park, Liverpool L19 0LT Tel: 0151 427 1148 Fax: 0151 427 1148 Email: johnftaylor@compuserve.com — MB ChB 1958 Liverp; MB ChB Liverp. 1958; MD Liverp. 1965, MChOrth 1971; FRCS Eng. 1966; DTM & H Liverp. 1963. Prev: Cons. Orthop. Surg. Alder Hey Childr. Hosp. Liverp.

TAYLOR, John Frederick, CBE 45 Canonbury Road, London N1 2DG Tel: 020 7359 2548; Burthallan House, Burthallan Lane, St Ives TR26 3AB Tel: 01736 796577 — MB BS 1957 Lond.; FRCP Lond. 1992; FFOM RCP Lond. 1985, MFOM 1978; DIH Soc. Apoth. Lond. 1960; DObst RCOG 1959. (St. Geo.) p/t Med. Adviser, Pub. Carriage Office, Lond. Socs: Fell. Roy. Soc. Med. Prev: Chairm. Transport Comm. Med. Commissn on Accid. Preven.; Chief Med. Off. Dept. of Transport; Sen. Med. Off. Driver & Vehicule Licensing Centre (DVLC).

TAYLOR, Mr John Gibson, VRD (retired) Hill Farm, Downham, Wymondham NR18 0SD Tel: 01603 810462 — FRCS Eng. 1947; MB BS 1941 Lond.; MRCS Eng. LRCP Lond. 1941. Prev: Cons. Orthop. Surg. Norf. & Norwich Hosp. & Rheum. Unit St. Michael's Hosp. Aylsham; 1st Asst. Accid. Serv. Radcliffe Infirm. Oxf.

TAYLOR, Mr John Harvey Queens Hospital, Belvedere Road, Burton-on-Trent DE13 0RB Tel: 01283 566333 Fax: 01283 593041 — MB BS Lond. 1957; FRCSC 1968; FRCS Eng. 1966; FACS 1971. (Lond. Hosp.) Cons. Palliat. Med. SE Staffs. HA. Prev: Med. Dir. St. Giles Hospice Whittington.

TAYLOR, John Henry Keevil (retired) Talisker, Moor Court, Amberley, Stroud GL5 5DA Tel: 01453 873151 — MB BS 1955 Lond.; DObst RCOG 1959. Prev: GP Middlx.

TAYLOR, John Jarvis States Laboratory, St Helier, Jersey Tel: 01534 59000 — MB BS 1955 Lond.; FRCPath 1978, M 1966; DMJ Soc. Apoth. Lond. 1982. (Char. Cross) Dir. States Laborat. Jersey.

Prev: Ho. Phys. & Ho. Surg. Char. Cross Hosp.; Res. Clin. Pathol. Qu. Eliz. Hosp. Birm.

TAYLOR, Mr John Lang Birmingham Heartlands & Solihull NHS Trust, Bordesley Green E., Birmingham B9 5SS Tel: 0121 424 2000 Fax: 0121 424 0442; Breakway, 108 School Road, Hockley Heath, Solihull B94 6RB Tel: 01564 784959 — MB BS 1977 Lond.; MS Lond. 1989; FRCS Ed. 1982. (St. Thos.) Cons. Surg. Birm. Heartlands & Solihull NHS Trust; Hon. Sen. Clin. Lect. (Surg.) Univ. Birm. Socs: (Ex-Pres.) Assn. Surg. in Train. Prev: Sen. Regist. (Surg.) W. Midl.; Sheldon Clin. Research Fell.sh. 1984; Regist. (Surg.) Roy. Hosp. Wolverhampton & Walsgrave Hosp. Coventry.

TAYLOR, John Langton (retired) 3 Linnet Hill, Rochdale OL11 4DA Tel: 01706 524242 — BSc Manch. 1940, MB ChB 1943; FRCP Lond. 1970, M 1948; MRCS Eng. LRCP Lond. 1943. Prev: Cons. Phys. Rochdale & Dist. Gp. Hosps.

TAYLOR, John Leahy (retired) 18 Thameside, Riverfield Road, Staines TW18 2HA Tel: 01784 452331 Fax: 01784 452331 — MB BS 1957 Lond.; MRCS Eng. LRCP Lond. 1944; MRCGP 1953; DMJ Soc. Apoth. Lond. 1964. Prev: Sec. Med. Protec. Soc.

TAYLOR, John Mark Stuart Road Surgery, Stuart Road, Pontefract WF8 4PQ Tel: 01977 703437 — MB ChB 1984 Sheff.

TAYLOR, John Nicholas Health Centre, Pen y Bont, The Roe, St Asaph LL17 0LU Tel: 01745 583208 Fax: 01745 583748; Perth-y-Terfyn, 51 Mount Road, St Asaph LL17 0DH Tel: 01745 583734 — MB ChB 1971 Liverp. Prev: Med. Regist. Mersey RHA; SHO Roy. Liverp. Childr. Hosp.

TAYLOR, John Robert Florence Street Resource Centre, 20-60 Florence St., Glasgow G5 0YZ Tel: 0141 429 2878 — MB ChB 1987 Ed.; MPhil Ed. 1996, MB ChB Ed. 1987; MRCPsych 1992. Cons. Psychiat. Levendale Hosp. Glas. Prev: Regist. (Psychiat.) Dingleton Hosp. Melrose.; Sen. Regist. N. Mersey Community Trust Liverp.

TAYLOR, John Salsbury Chester Lodge, Austen Road, Guildford GU1 3N Tel: 01483 64578 — MB BS 1947 Lond.; MRCS Eng. LRCP Lond. 1950; DObst RCOG 1949. (Lond. Hosp.) SBStJ. Socs: BMA. Prev: Res. Accouch., Res. Anaesth. & Ho. Surg. Lond. Hosp.

TAYLOR, John Stephen Pinfold House, Gillamoor, York YO62 7HX Tel: 01751 31665 — MB BS 1969 Lond. (St. Thos.) Prev: Med. Regist. Dorset Co. Hosp. Dorchester.

TAYLOR, John Stephen Garratt Palmerston Road Surgery, 18 Palmerston Road, Buckhurst Hill IG9 5LT Tel: 020 8504 1552 — MB BS Lond. 1978.

TAYLOR, John Stewart (retired) Oakroyd, Moray Place, Elgin IV30 1NN Tel: 01343 543595 — MB ChB 1951 Aberd. Prev: Ho. Phys. Roy. Infirm. & City Hosp. Aberd.

TAYLOR, John Victor Kings Cross Surgery, 199 King Cross Road, Halifax HX1 3LW Tel: 01422 330612 Fax: 01422 323740; 41 Savile Park, Halifax HX1 3EX — BM BS 1984 Nottm.; BMedSci (Hons.) 1982; MRCGP 1988. Princip GP Halifax.

TAYLOR, Mr John Vincent 18 Fontburn Road, Seaton Delaval, Whitley Bay NE25 0BH Tel: 0191 237 0733; 75 News Lane, Rainford, St Helens WA11 7JY — MB ChB 1993 Liverp.; BSc (Hons.) Liverp. 1990; FRCS Ed. 1997. (Liverp.) SHO (Surg.) Warrington Hosp. Chesh. Socs: Liverp. Med. Inst.; Assn. Liverp. Med. Sch.; Assn. Surg. Train. Prev: Price Surgic. Research Fell. Univ. of Louisville Kentucky, USA; SHO (Surg.) Warrington Hosp. Chesh.; SHO (Orthop.) Fazakerley Hosp. Liverp.

TAYLOR, Jonathan Breck Park Slope Surgery, 32 Stoke Road, Blisworth, Northampton NN7 3BT Tel: 01604 858237 Fax: 01604 859437; Grey House, 5 Baker St, Gayton, Northampton NN7 3EZ — MB BS 1986 Lond.; DRCOG 1991. (Westm.)

TAYLOR, Jonathan Michael 3 Apple Tree Close, Church St., Boston Spa, Wetherby LS23 6DG — MB ChB 1982 Leeds; DRCOG 1986.

TAYLOR, Josephine 29 Merton Hall, Wimbledon, London SW19 3PR — MB BS 1985 Lond.

TAYLOR, Judith O'Mara 106 Harley Street, London W1N 1AF; 8 Prince Albert Road, London NW1 7SR — BM 1979 Soton.; MRCP (UK) 1985. p/t Locum Cons. Paediatric Nephrologist Guys Hosp. Lond.

TAYLOR, Julia Christine 131 Leys Lane, Frome BA11 2JS — MB BS 1990 Lond.

TAYLOR, Julia Marion Ward End Medical Centre, 794A Washwood Heath Road, Ward End, Birmingham B8 2JN Tel: 0121 327 1049 Fax: 0121 327 0964 — MB ChB 1978 Manch.; MRCGP 1983; DRCOG 1983.

TAYLOR, Julia Mary National Blood Service Leeds Blood centre, Bridle path, Leeds LS15 7TW Tel: 0113 2148646 Email: julia.taylor@nbs.nhs.uk — MB ChB 1980 Sheff.; MRCP 1983; FRCPath 1998. (Sheff.) Cons. in Transfus. Med., Nat. blood Serv., Leeds. Prev: Sen. Regist. Char. Cross & W.minster Hosps. Lond.; Regist. Leicester Roy. Infirm.

TAYLOR, Julie Ann Newbold Verdon Medical Practice, St. George's Close, Newbold Verdon, Leicester LE9 9PZ Tel: 01445 822171 Fax: 01445 824968 — BM BS 1986 Nottm.; BMedSci Nottm. 1984; DRCOG 1989. Gen. Practitioner Leics. Prev: Trainee GP Warks.

TAYLOR, Justin Stanley William 15 Royal Close, Henbury, Bristol BS10 7XF Tel: 0117 950 5415; Eaton Close, Eaton Hill, Baslow, Bakewell DE45 1SB Tel: 01246 582144 — BM BS 1995 Nottm. SHO (Med.) Bristol Roy. Infirm. Prev: Ho. Off. (Med. & Surg.) Qu. Med. Centre Nottm.

TAYLOR, Karen Margaret 5 Westerham Close, Trentham, Stoke-on-Trent ST4 8JW — MB ChB 1993 Birm.

TAYLOR, Karey Anne 53 Langley Close, Headington, Oxford OX3 7DB — BM BCh 1985 Oxf.

TAYLOR, Kathleen Anne Benoran, Torr Road, Bridge of Weir PA11 3BE — MB ChB 1985 Glas.; MRCGP 1990; DCCH RCP Ed. 1989; DRCOG 1988. Trainee GP Edin. VTS.; GP Retainer Scheme. Prev: Clin. Asst. Merchiston Hosp. Johnstone; GP Princip. Battersea Lond.; SHO (Psychiat.) Warlingham Pk. Hosp.

TAYLOR, Kathrine Nena The Stables, Ibsley, Ringwood BH24 3PP — BM 1986 Soton.

TAYLOR, Kathryn Alison 25 Granada Road, Hedge End, Southampton SO30 4AL — MB BS 1987 Lond.

TAYLOR, Kay Vivienne Park Road Health Centre, Park Road, Tarporley CW6 0BE Tel: 01829 732401 Fax: 01829 732404 — MB ChB 1977 Manch.

TAYLOR, Keith John 15 Northdene Drive, Rochdale OL11 5NH — MD 1990 Manch.; MB ChB 1977; MRCP (UK) 1983. Cons. Phys. Respirat. Med. Glan Clwyd Dist. Gen. Hosp. Rhyl Denbish.

TAYLOR, Keith William Department of Medicine, Royal London Hospital, Whitechapel, London E1 1BB; 18 Lion Street, Rye TN31 7LB Tel: 01797 222512 — MB BChir 1955 Camb.; PhD Camb. 1960, MA 1955; FRCP Lond. 1994. (King's Coll. Hosp.) Emerit. Prof. Biochem. Lond.; Cons. Med. Roy. Lond. Hosp. Prev: Hon. Cons. Diabetic Med. King's Coll. Hosp. Lond.; Prof. Biochem. Lond. Hosp. Med. Coll.; Prof. Biochem. & Cons. Chem. Path. Univ. Sydney, Austral.

TAYLOR, Kenneth Clifford Gordon (retired) Mulberry Cottage, Horringer, Bury St Edmunds IP29 5SA — MRCS Eng. LRCP Lond. 1948; MA, MB BChir Camb. 1948. Prev: Med. Off. to WRNS.

TAYLOR, Kenneth George The Diabetes & Endocrinology Unit, City Hospital, Dudley Road, Birmingham B18 7QH Tel: 0121 507 4592 Fax: 0121 507 4988; Redstacks, 1 Priory Road, Halesowen B62 0BZ Tel: 0121 602 2142 Fax: 0121 602 2142 — MB BS Lond. 1970; MD Lond. 1978; FRCP Lond. 1987; MRCP (UK) 1973; MRCS Eng. LRCP Lond. 1970. (St. Bartholomew's Hospital Medical School) Cons. Phys. City Hosp. Birm.; Hon. Sen. Clin. Lect. Univ. Birm. Socs: Diabetes UK; Brit. Hyperlipidaemia Assoc. Prev: Sen. Regist. (Med.) Birm. Gen. Hosp.; Hon. Sen. Regist. & Research Fell. St. Bart. Hosp. Lond.

TAYLOR, Professor Kenneth MacDonald Cardiothoracic Surgical Unit, Imperial College School of Medicine, Hammersmith Hospital, Ducane Road, London W12 0NN Tel: 020 8383 3214 Fax: 020 8740 7019 Email: scarroll@ic.ac.uk; 129 Argyle Road, Ealing, London W13 0DB — MD Glas. 1979, MB ChB 1970; FRCS Eng. 1984; FRCS Glas. 1974. Brit. Heart Foundat. Prof. Cardiac Surg. Univ. Lond.; Prof. Cardiac Surg. Imperial Coll. Sch. of Med. at Hammersmith Hosp. Lond. Socs: Surg. Research Soc. & Soc. Thoracic & Cardiovasc. Surgs.; FSA 1977; FESC 1995. Prev: Sen. Lect. (Cardiac Surg.) Univ. Glas.; Hall Tutorial Fell. in Surg. Univ. Glas.

TAYLOR, Kenneth Mark 8 Egmanton Close, Oakwood, Derby DE21 2EL — MB ChB 1987 Sheff.

TAYLOR, Kobina Arba 47 Linchmere Road, Lee, London SE12 0NB — MB BChir 1952 Camb.; MA, MB BChir Camb. 1952. (Univ. Coll. Hosp.) Prev: SHMO S. Wing Bedford Gen. Hosp.; Res.

TAYLOR

Surg. Off. Roy. Hosp. Chesterfield; Surg. Regist. PeterBoro. Gen. Hosp.

TAYLOR, Lakhbir Kaur Boxworth End Surgery, 58 Boxworth End, Swavesey, Cambridge CB4 5RA Tel: 01954 230202 Fax: 01954 206035 — MB BS 1982 Lond.; BSc. (Hons.) Lond. 1979. (St. Bart.)

TAYLOR, Laura Bradley 122 The Ridgeway, Enfield EN2 8JN — MB BS 1998 Lond.

TAYLOR, Mr Lee James The Firs, 47 Lavant Road, Chichester PO19 4RD Tel: 01243 527287 — MB BS 1977 Lond.; FRCS Eng. 1981. (Middlx.) Hunt. Prof. RCS. Prev: Cons. Orthop. Surg. St. Richards Hosp. Chichester; Sen. Regist. Middlx. Hosp. & Roy. Nat Orthop. Hosps.; Regist. (Orthop.) St. Geo. Hosp. Lond.

TAYLOR, Liam Paul Gerard The Grange Clinic, Westfield Avenue, Malpas, Newport NP20 6EY Tel: 01633 855521 Fax: 01633 859490 — MB BCh BAO 1990 Belf.; MRCGP 1995; DRCOG 1994; DGM RCPS Glas. 1993; DCH Dub. 1993. GP Princip. Prev: Regist. (Pub. Health Med.) & Cornw. Isles of Scilly Health Auth.; SHO Altnagelvin Hosp. Lond.derry; Ho. Off. Mater Hosp. Belf.

TAYLOR, Liane Celia Regina Bertha Hornsey Rise Health Centre, Hornsey Rise, London N19 3YU Tel: 020 7530 2484 — MB BS 1977 Lond.; MRCS Eng. LRCP Lond. 1977; MRCGP 1983; Cert. Prescribed Equiv. Exp. JCPTGP 1982; Cert. JCC Lond. 1980; DRCOG 1980. (Roy. Free)

TAYLOR, Lilian (retired) — MB ChB 1959 Manch. Prev: Clin. Asst. Dept. Path. High Wycombe Gen. Hosp.

TAYLOR, Lillious McLellan (retired) c/o Purvis, 2 Dalmellington Court, Kittoch Field, East Kilbride, Glasgow G74 4XD Tel: 01355 263602 — MA Glas. 1949, MB ChB 1960; DObst RCOG 1962; DCH RCPS Glas. 1967. Prev: Assoc. Specialist (Dermat.) Vict. Infirm. Glas.

TAYLOR, Linda Elizabeth 4 Beech Close, Highnam, Gloucester GL2 8EG — MB BCh BAO 1979 Belf.; MRCGP 1988; DCH Dub. 1982; DCCH Ed. 1989. Clin. Med. Off. (Child Health) Glos.

TAYLOR, Lorna Anne 63-65 Garstang Road, Preston PR1 1LJ Tel: 01772 253554; Moor Hall Cottage, Lower Bartle, Preston PR4 0RU Tel: 01772 723274 — MB BCh 1979 Wales; BSc (Hons.) St. And. 1976. GP Preston.

TAYLOR, Lorna Margaret Mayfield Road Surgery, 125 Mayfield Road, Edinburgh EH9 3AJ Tel: 0131 668 1095 Fax: 0131 662 1734; 33 Kingsknowe Drive, Edinburgh EH14 2JY Tel: 0141 443 5590 — MB ChB 1978 Ed.; MRCGP 1982; DRCOG 1980.

TAYLOR, Louise Deborah The Flat, Maxstoke Castle, Castle Lane, Coleshill, Birmingham B46 2RD Tel: 01675 465474 — MB ChB 1991 Leic.; MRCGP 1996; DCH 1996; DRCOG 1995; DFFP 1996. Socs: Fam. Plann. Comm.

TAYLOR, Magnus John Avecia LTD, PO BOX 521, Leeds Rd, Huddersfield HD2 1GA Tel: 01484 433946 Email: magnus.taylor@avecia.com; 112 Huddersfield Road, Brighouse HD6 3RN — MB ChB 1976 Manch.; FRCP Lond. 1999; FFOM RCP Lond. 1993, M 1986; MRCP (UK) 1981. Regional Specialty Adviser Occupat. Med. Socs: Mem. Soc. of Occupat.al Med. Prev: Sen. Occupat. Health Phys. ICI BioSci.s Huddersfield; Chairm. Soc. Occupat. Med. (Yorksh. Br.); Lect. (Occupat. Med.) Manch. Univ.

TAYLOR, Malcolm Bernard Oakeswell Health Centre, Brunswick Park Road, Wednesbury WS10 9HP Tel: 0121 556 2114; 53 Broadway, Walsall WS1 3EZ — MB ChB 1969 Birm.; DObst RCOG 1973. Prev: SHO (O & G) Marston Green Matern. Hosp. Birm.; Ho. Phys. Qu. Eliz. Hosp. Birm.; Ho. Surg. Gen. Hosp. Birm.

TAYLOR, Malcolm Peter (retired) 20 Saxton Avenue, Doncaster DN4 7AX Tel: 01302 370927 — MB ChB 1955 Birm.; FRCGP 1974. Prev: GP Doncaster.

TAYLOR, Marcus Ben Depart. Of Diagnostic Radiology, Christie Hospital NHS Trust, Wilmslow Road, Withington, Manchester M20 4BX Tel: 0161 446 3980; Clifton Cross, Asbourne DE6 2DH Tel: 0161 432 7382 — MB ChB 1991 Sheff.; FRCR 1999; MRCP (UK) 1994. (Sheffield) Cons. Radiologist, Christie Hosp. NHS Trust, Manch. Prev: SHO Rotat. (Med.) City Hosp. Birm.; Specialist Regist. Rotat. (Diagn. Radiol.) Manch.

TAYLOR, Margaret (retired) 7 Marina Drive, South Shields NE33 2NH — MB ChB 1957 Bristol; FRCPCH; FRCP Ed. 1980, M 1965; DCH Eng. 1960; DObst RCOG 1961. Cons. Paediat. S. Shields Hosp. Gp.

TAYLOR, Margaret Alexander 17 Greenacres, Fulwood, Preston PR2 7DA — MB ChB 1943 Liverp. (Liverp.)

TAYLOR, Margaret Elizabeth Ty Nant, 13 Hermitage Meadow, Snow Hill, Clare, Sudbury CO10 8QQ — MB BS 1961 Lond.; MRCS Eng. LRCP Lond. 1961. (Roy. Free) Socs: BMA. Prev: Gyn. Ho. Surg. Roy. Free Hosp. Lond.; Ho. Phys. Qu. Mary's Hosp. Sidcup.

TAYLOR, Margaret Elspeth Jubilee Surgery, Barry's Meadow, High St., Titchfield, Fareham PO14 4EH Tel: 01329 844220; 56A West Street, Titchfield, Fareham PO14 4DF Tel: 01329 847209 — MB ChB 1965 Liverp. (Liverp.)

TAYLOR, Margaret Jean (retired) 16 Broadmead, Broadmayne, Dorchester DT2 8EE — LRCP LRCS 1953 Ed.; LRCP LRCS Ed. LRFPS Glas. 1953. Asst. (Path.) W. Dorset Gp. Hosps.

TAYLOR, Margaret Joan 86 Rennets Wood Road, Eltham, London SE9 2NH Tel: 020 8850 0990 — MB ChB 1962 Sheff.; MRCPsych 1978.

TAYLOR, Margaret Lilian (retired) 25 The Beeches, Plas Newton Lane, Chester CH2 1PE — MB ChB 1943 Liverp. Prev: Sen. Med. Off. Chesh. AHA.

TAYLOR, Margery Winifred Whitmoor, The Street, Puttenham, Guildford GU3 1AT Tel: 01483 810490 — MRCS Eng. LRCP Lond. 1948. (W. Lond.) Socs: BMA; Rowhook Med. Soc.

TAYLOR, Marian Ann (retired) The Birches, Huntington Lane, Ashford Carbonel, Ludlow SY8 4DG — MRCS Eng. LRCP Lond. 1955; DO Eng. 1982; DCH Eng. 1960.

TAYLOR, Marion Haddo Medical Group, The Old School, The Square, Tarves AB41 7GX Tel: 01651 851777; 3 Vogue Court, 107-109 Widmore Road, Bromley BR13AF Tel: 01358 721631 — MB ChB 1992 Aberd.; MRCGP 1996. (Aberd.) Gen. Practitioner Haddo Med. Gp. Prev: Locum Gen. Practioner Aberd.; Locum Gen. Practioner Hereford; Med. Off. St. Michael's Hospice Hereford.

TAYLOR, Marjory Frances Shettleston Health Centre, Shettleston Health Centre, 420 Old Shettleston Road, Glasgow G32 7JZ Tel: 0141 531 6250 Fax: 0141 531 6216; 187 Sandy Hills Road, Mount Vernon, Glasgow G32 9NB — MB ChB 1988 Glas. Prev: SHO (Geriat.) Roy. Alexandra Hosp. Glas.; SHO (A & E) W.. Infirm. Glas.; SHO (Med.) Glas. Roy. Infirm.

TAYLOR, Mark Alexander 21 Seventree Road, Londonderry BT47 5QH — MB BCh BAO 1994 Belf.

TAYLOR, Mark Andrew The Surgery, Marsh Gardens, Honley, Huddersfield HD9 6AG Tel: 01484 303366 Fax: 01484 303365; Mollicar House, Lumb Lane, Almondbury, Huddersfield HD4 6SZ — MB ChB 1981 Leeds; MRCGP 1985. Socs: Huddersfield Med. Soc. Prev: Trainee GP Huddersfield VTS; Ho. Phys. Chapel Allerton Hosp. Leeds.; Ho. Surg. Leeds Gen. Infirm.

TAYLOR, Mark Bartholomew Longacre House, Crapstone, Yelverton PL20 7PF — MB BS 1978 Lond.; FFA RCS Eng. 1983. (St. Bart.) Cons. Dept. Anaesth. & Pain Relief Clinic, Derriford Hosp. Plymouth. Prev: Sen. Regist. (Anaesth.) Hammersmith & Char. Cross Hosps. Lond.; Regist. (Anaesth.) Hosp. Sick Childr. Lond.; Fell. Toronto Gen. Hosp.

TAYLOR, Mark Buchanan 131 Brewery Road, Plumstead, London SE18 1NE — MB BS 1979 Lond.; PhD Kent 1984; MA Camb. 1977; MRCPath 1993. Lect. (Med. Microbiol.) Lond. Hosp. Med. Coll. Prev: Wellcome Train. Fell. St. Mary's Hosp. Lond.; Ho. Surg. Roy. Ear Hosp. Lond.

TAYLOR, Mark Conroy Hill House Surgery, Aspatria, Carlisle CA7 3NG Tel: 016973 20209 Fax: 016973 22333; Teesdale House, High Scale, Aspatria, Carlisle CA7 3NG — MB BS 1980 Newc.; MRCGP 1984; DRCOG 1984.

TAYLOR, Mark Lees 75 The Balk, Walton, Wakefield WF2 6JX; 2 The Cottage, Manse Brae, Croy, Inverness IV2 5PU Tel: 01967 43332 — MB ChB 1991 Birm. Socs: MRCGP.

TAYLOR, Mark Stuart Magna House Medical Centre, 81 Merley Lane, Merley, Wimborne BH21 3BB Tel: 01202 841288 Fax: 01202 840877 Email: doctors@merleysurgery.freeserve.co.uk; Greenholm, Arrowsmith Road, Canford Magna, Wimborne BH21 3BD Tel: 01202 693366 Email: mark.taylor5@virgin.net — MB BS 1975 Lond.; MRCGP 1989. (Guy's) GP Princip. Magna Ho. Med. Centre; GP Trainer Dorset; Course Organiser Dorset VTS. Prev: Examr. RCGP; RNLI Med. Off.; Clin. Asst. Opht.

TAYLOR, Martin, Capt. 38 Summershades Lane, Grasscroft, Oldham OL4 4ED Email: martintaylor999@hotmail.com — MB ChB 1998 Leeds. (Leeds) SHO. (A&E.) PeterBoro. Gen Hosp. Socs: RAMC - Capt. Prev: PRHO. Derriford Hosp Plymouth.; PRHO. Leeds Gen Infirm.

TAYLOR, Martin Charles 7 Westfield Road, Lymington SO41 3PZ — MB BS 1985 Lond.; MRCP (UK) 1994. Regist. (Diabetes & Endocrinol.) Soton. Gen. Hosp. Prev: Regist. (Diabetes & Endocrinol.) Roy. Bournemouth Hosp.; Regist. Gen. Hosp. Jersey.

TAYLOR, Mr Martin Christopher King's Mill Centre for Healthcare Services, Mansfield Road, Sutton-in-Ashfield NG17 4JL Tel: 01623 622515; 38 Main Street, Woodborough, Nottingham NG14 6EA Tel: 0115 965 5654 — MB ChB 1971 Sheff.; FRCS Ed. 1977. (Sheff.) Cons. Urol. King's Mill Hosp. Mansfield; Clin. Director of Surg. King's Mill Hosp. Mansfield. Prev: Clin. Dir. (Urol.) City Hosp. Nottm.; Cons. Urol. Dist. Gen. Hosp. Rotherham; Sen. Regist. City Hosp. Nottm.

TAYLOR, Martin George 4 Bankfield Drive, Shipley BD18 4AD — MB BS 1978 Newc. SHO (Gen. Med.) Darlington Memor. Hosp. Prev: Ho. Off. (Gen. Med. & Surg.) Darlington Memor. Hosp.

TAYLOR, Martin John Marylebone Road Health Centre, Marylebone Road, March PE15 8BG Tel: 01354 606300 Fax: 01354 656033; Willow Farm, 129 Knight's End Road, March PE15 8QD Tel: 01354 652611 — MB ChB 1985 Sheff.; MRCGP 1989.

TAYLOR, Mary (retired) Elm Cottage, Mill Road, Shiplate, Henley-on-Thames RG9 3LW Tel: 0118 940 3046 — MB ChB BAO Belf. 1961; DObst RCOG 1963. Prev: Assoc. Specialist (Anaesth. & IC) Roy. Berks. Hosp. Reading.

TAYLOR, Mary Buchanan Aboyne Health Centre, Bellwood Road, Aboyne AB34 5HQ Tel: 01339 886345; Aboyne Medical Practice, The Health Centre, Aboyne AB34 5HQ Tel: 013398 86345 — MB ChB 1974 Aberd.; MRCGP 1979; DCH RCPS Glas. 1976; DRCOG 1978. Partner in Gen. Pract. Socs: Country Mem. Liverp. Med. Inst.; Co-organiser Upper Deeside Med. Gp.

TAYLOR, Mary Caroline Greencroft Medical Centre (South), Greencroft Wynd, Annan DG12 6GS Tel: 01461 202244 Fax: 01461 205401 — MB ChB 1977 Glas.; MRCGP 1981; DRCOG 1979.

TAYLOR, Mary Helen Department of Anaesthetics, Birmingham Heartlands Hospital, Bordesley Green E., Birmingham B9 5SS Tel: 0121 766 6611; 65 Salisbury Road, Moseley, Birmingham B13 8LB Tel: 0121 449 4838 — MB ChB 1971 Birm.; FFA RCS Eng. 1975; DA Eng. 1974; DObst RCOG 1973. Cons. Anaesth. Birm. Heartlands Hosp. Prev: Sen. Regist. (Anaesth.) W. Midl. RHA; Sen. Regist. (Anaesth.) Univ. Hosp. Kingston, Jamaica; Regist. (Anaesth.) Walsgrave Hosp. Coventry.

TAYLOR, Mary Honor Westcotes House, Westcotes Drive, Leicester LE3 0QU — BM 1981 Soton.; MRCP (UK) 1984; MRCPsych 1997.

TAYLOR, Matthew Adam 3 Archery Close, Wickersley, Rotherham S66 1DT — MB ChB 1998 Manch.; MB ChB Manch 1998.

TAYLOR, Matthew Alvin 24 Woodland Park, Ynystawe, Swansea SA6 5AR — MB BS 1988 W. Indies.

TAYLOR, Matthew James The Rectory, Well Meadow, Church Road, Newbury RG14 2DR — MB BS 1991 Lond.

TAYLOR, Mavis Gloria Spencer (retired) 78 Kimberley Road, Little Wakering, Southend-on-Sea SS3 0JP Tel: 01702 219279 — MB BS (Hons. Surg.) Lond. 1958. Prev: Ho. Surg. Char. Cross Hosp.

TAYLOR, Melvyn Roy Lakeside Practice, The Health Centre, Off Station, Askern, Doncaster DN6 0JB Tel: 01302 700212 Fax: 01302 707370; 3 The Orchards, Campsall, Doncaster DN6 9AQ Tel: 01302 700837 — MB ChB 1970 Sheff. (Sheff.) Prev: SHO (ENT) Sheff. Roy. Hosp.; Ho. Off. (Gen. Med.) Doncaster Roy. Infirm.; Ho. Off. (Orthop.) Sheff. Roy. Infirm.

TAYLOR, Michael Leverndale Hospital, 510 Crookston Rd, Glasgow G53 7TU Tel: 0141 211 6531 — MB ChB 1991 Glas.; MPhil (Glas) 2000; MRCPsych 1996. (Glas.) Cons. Psychiat., Leverndale Hosp. Glas. Prev: Specialist Regist. (Psychiat.) Douglas Inch Centre Glas.

TAYLOR, Michael Park Road West Surgery, 11 Park Road West, Crosland Moor, Huddersfield HD4 5RX Tel: 01484 642020/642044 Fax: 01484 460774 — MB ChB 1978 Leeds.

TAYLOR, Michael Anthony 1 Windle Grove, Windle, St Helens WA10 6HN — MB BChir 1991 Camb.

TAYLOR, Michael Antony Rollin 5 Drumblefield, Chelford, Macclesfield SK11 9BT — MB BS 1966 Lond.; MRCS Eng. LRCP Lond. 1966; FRCP Lond. 1986; MRCP (U.K.) 1971. Cons. Phys. Macclesfield Hosp. Prev: Sen. Med. Regist. St. Jas. Univ. Hosp. Leeds & Univ. Hosp. W. Indies; Kingston Jamaica.

TAYLOR, Michael Arkwright (retired) Eskdale, 112 Sutton Park Road, Kidderminster DY11 6JG — MRCS Eng. LRCP Lond. 1961; DObst RCOG 1964.

TAYLOR, Michael Eric The White House, Llangenny, Crickhowell NP8 1HA — MB BS 1960 Lond.; BSc Lond. 1957, MB BS 1960; MRCP Lond. 1965; FRCR 1975; FFR 1969; DMRD Eng. 1967. Cons. Phys. St. Geo. Hosp. Lond. Socs: Fell. Roy. Soc. Med. Lond.; Brit. Soc. Allergy & Environm. Med. Prev: Sen. Regist. (Radiol.) Univ. Coll. & Middlx. Hosp. Lond. & Hosp. Sick Childr. Gt.Ormond St. Lond.; Regist. (Med.) Roy. Brompton Nat. Heart & Lung Hosp. Lond.; Ho. Surg. Middlx. Hosp. Lond.

TAYLOR, Mr Michael Francis Scott Department of Orthopaedics, Broomfield Hospital, Court Road, Chelmsford CM1 7ET Tel: 01245 514604 Fax: 01245 574644 — MB ChB 1983 Bristol; FRCS (Orth.) 1992; FRCS Ed. 1987. Cons. Orthop. Surg. Broomfield Hosp. Chelmsford & Black Notley Hosp. Braintree.

TAYLOR, Michael James Yatton Family Practice, 155 Mendip Road, Yatton, Bristol BS49 4ER Tel: 01934 832277 Fax: 01934 876085; Stablegrove, West Hay Road, Wrington, Bristol BS40 5NR Tel: 01934 863504 Fax: 01934 863599 Email: michael.j.taylor@btinternet.com — MB BS 1985 Lond.; MA Camb. 1982; MRCGP 1989; DRCOG 1988. Socs: BMA.

TAYLOR, Michael John Clayton Health Centre, 89 North Road, Clayton, Manchester M11 4EJ Tel: 0161 223 9229 Fax: 0161 223 1116 — MB ChB 1961 Manch.; DObst RCOG 1962. (Manch.)

TAYLOR, Michael Stuart 34 Bramwith Road, Nethergreen, Sheffield S11 7EZ Tel: 0114 230 8352 — MB ChB 1994 Manch. SHO (Med.) N. Derbysh. Roy. Hosp. Chesterfield.

TAYLOR, Michael William Calsayseat Medical Group, 2 Calsayseat Road, Aberdeen AB25 3UY Tel: 01224 634345 Fax: 01224 620210; 46 Newlands Crescent, Aberdeen AB10 6LH Tel: 01224 315202 — MB ChB 1975 Aberd.; BSc Aberd. 1970; FRCP Ed. 1993; MRCP (UK) 1977; FRCGP 1992, M 1980. Dir. of Post Grad. Gen. Pract. Educat. Post Grad. Centre Aberd. Roy. Infirm.; Sen. Lect. Dept. Gen. Pract. & Primary Care Foresterhill Health Centre W.burn Rd. Aberd.

TAYLOR, Moira Elizabeth Stockport NHS Trust, Department of Microbiology, Department of Laboratory Medicine, Stepping Hill Hospital, Poplar Grove, Stockport SK2 7JE — MB ChB 1985 Manch.; MSc (Molecular Microbiol) Manch. 1993; MRCPath 1994. (Manchester) p/t Cons. (Microbiologist) Stockport NHS Trust Stockport.

TAYLOR, Murray George (retired) Beaconscroft, Peak Lane, Compton Dundon, Somerton TA11 6NZ Tel: 01458 274284 — MB BS Lond. 1952; DObst RCOG 1957. Prev: Regist. (Med.) Weymouth & Dist. Hosp.

TAYLOR, Myles James Overton 18 Quarry Hollow, Headington, Oxford OX3 8JR — BM BCh 1989 Oxf.

TAYLOR, Neil Malcolm 51 Munnings Drive, College Town, Sandhurst GU47 0FN — MB BS 1985 West. Australia; FRCA 1993. Sen. Regist. (Anaesth.) St. Geo. Hosp. Healthcare. Prev: Research Fell. (Anaesth.) St. Geo. Hosp. Med. Sch. Lond.

TAYLOR, Neil Michael Caius Hill Farm, Heggatt, Horstead, Norwich NR12 7AZ — BM 1987 Soton.

TAYLOR, Nia Jane 3 Beddoes Drive, Bayston Hill, Shrewsbury SY3 0BU — BM BCh 1998 Oxf.

TAYLOR, Nicholas Charles Gwion Castle, Llandysul SA44 4LE — MB ChB 1971 St. And.; MRCP (UK) 1976; DCH Eng. 1973. Cons. Phys. & Cardiol. W. Wales Hosp. Carmarthen. Socs: Brit. Cardiac Soc. Prev: Hon. Sen. Regist. Papworth Hosp. Camb.; Regist. Nat. Heart Hosp. Lond.

TAYLOR, Nicholas Howard 97 London Road, Gloucester GL1 3HH Tel: 01452 522079 Fax: 01452 387884; 12 Clarement Road, Bishopston, Bristol B57 8DQ — MB BS 1978 Lond.; MRCGP 1983; DRCOG 1982. (St. Geo.)

TAYLOR, Nicholas John, Maj. RAMC Almond Road Surgery, Almond Road, St. Neots, Huntingdon PE19 1DZ Tel: 01480 473413 Fax: 01480 406906; The Priory, 26 West St, Godmanchester, Huntingdon PE29 2HG — MB BChir 1983 Camb.; MA Camb. 1983; MRCGP 1988; DRCOG 1987. Prev: Regtl. Med. Off. 1st Bn. Green Howards Osnabruck BAOR; SHO (Med.) Camb. Milit. Hosp. Aldershot; Ho. Phys. (Neurol.) St. Bart. Hosp. Lond.

TAYLOR, Nicholas Mark 246 Meadow Head, Sheffield S8 7UH — MB ChB 1985 Leeds.

TAYLOR

TAYLOR, Nicholas Patrick, Maj. RAMC Dr Moss and Partners, 28-38 Kings Road, Harrogate HG1 5JP Tel: 01423 560261 Fax: 01423 501099; 14 St. James Drive, Harrogate HG2 8HT — MB BS 1985 Newc.; MRCGP 1991; DCH RCP Lond. 1991. Prev: Ho. Off. (Gen. Med.) Dryburn Gen. Hosp. Durh.; Ho. Off. (Gen. Surg.) Cumbld. Infirm. Carlisle.; Unit Med. Off. 35RE.

TAYLOR, Nicholas Robert 20 Lightborne Road, Sale M33 5EA — MB ChB 1998 Bristol.

TAYLOR, Nigel Geoffrey Hebden Bridge Health Centre, Hangingroyd Lane, Hebden Bridge HX7 6AG Tel: 01422 842333 Fax: 01422 842404 — MB BS 1991 Lond.; DFFP 1996. (King's Coll. Sch. Med. & Dent.)

TAYLOR, Nigel William Gervase Bradgate Surgery, Ardenton Walk, Brentry, Bristol BS10 6SP Tel: 0117 959 1920 Fax: 0117 983 9332 — MB BS 1978 Lond.; BA Camb. 1973; MRCGP 1982; DRCOG 1981. (Westm.)

TAYLOR, Nora Louise (retired) 6 London Road, Uppingham, Oakham LE15 9TJ — LRCP LRCS Ed. LRFPS Glas. 1951; DFFP 1993.

TAYLOR, Norman Henry Lancaster (retired) Northside, 15 Eastfield, Westbury-on-Trym, Bristol BS9 4BH Tel: 0117 962 2163 — MB BS Lond. 1959; DObst RCOG 1963. Prev: Ho. Surg. (Orthop.) St. Geo. Hosp. Lond.

TAYLOR, Norval Richard William (retired) 258 Staines Road, Twickenham TW2 5AR Tel: 020 8894 2342 — MB ChB Ed. 1947; MRCP Ed. 1956; MFPHM RCP (UK) 1974; FRCP Ed. 1997. Prev: Sen. Med. Off. Dept. Health & Social Security.

TAYLOR, Ormond Hargreaves (retired) 47 Crowtree Lane, Louth LN11 9LL Tel: 01507 603685 — MB ChB 1947 St. And.; DObst RCOG 1951. Prev: Ho. Surg. Vict. Hosp. Burnley & Hull Matern. Hosp.

TAYLOR, Mr Ormond Mark Kettering General Hosptial NHS Trust, Rothwell Road, Kettering NN16 8UZ — MB ChB 1983 Sheff.; MD Sheff. 1995; FRCS (Gen.) 1996; FRCS Ed. 1990. (Sheff.) Cons. Gen. Surg. Kettering Gen. Hosp. NHS Trust. Prev: Sen. Regist. (Gen. Surg.) Yorks.; Research Fell. Univ. Dept. Surg. Leeds Gen. Infirm.

TAYLOR, Pamela Ann Flat 4, 71 Chalton St., London NW1 1HY — MB ChB 1987 Ed. Regist. Rotat. (Psychiat.) St. Mary's Hosp.

TAYLOR, Professor Pamela Jane Tel: 020 7848 0123 Fax: 020 7848 0754; Broadmoor Hospital, Crowthorne RG45 7EG Tel: 01344 754398 Fax: 01344 754385 — MB BS Lond. 1971; MRCP (UK) 1974; MRCS Eng. LRCP Lond. 1971; FRCPsych 1989, M 1976. Prof. Special Hosp. Psychiat. Dept. Forens. Psychiat. Inst. Psychiat. Univ. Lond.; Hon. Cons. Psychiat. Bethlem & Maudsley Hosps. & BRd.moor Hosp.; Chairm. Roy. Coll. of Psychiat.s Working Gp. on Treatm. in Security. Socs: Amer. Psychiat. Assn.; RSM. Prev: Head of Med. Servs. Special Hosps. Serv. Auth. Lond.; Sen. Lect. (Forens. Psychiat.) Inst. Psychiat. & Hon. Cons. Psychiat. Bethlem Roy. & Maudsley Hosps.; Clin. Dir. Denis Hill Secure Unit Bethlem Roy. Hosp.

TAYLOR, Patricia Anne Summerleaze House, Kilmington, Axminster EX13 7RA — MB BS 1986 Lond.; DA (UK) 1989. (King's College Hospital London) SCMO (Anaesth.) Exeter Community Trust. Prev: Regist. (Anaesth.) Yeovil Dist. Hosp.; SHO (Anaesth.) Roy. Devon & Exeter Hosp.; SHO (Neonat. Paediat.) S.mead & Bristol Matern. Hosps.

TAYLOR, Patrick Keith (retired) 35 Glebe Road, Long Ashton, Bristol BS41 9LJ — MRCS Eng. LRCP Lond. 1966; FRCOG 1989; MRCOG 1971, DObst 1969. Prev: Cons. (GU Med.) Bristol Roy. Infirm.

TAYLOR, Paul Alexander Colville 2 St Werburghs Road, Chorlton-cum-Hardy, Manchester M21 0TN Tel: 0161 881 6721; 11 Hilary Road, Taunton TA1 5BH Tel: 01823 333915 — MB ChB 1987 Manch.; BSc (Hons.) Manch. 1985; MRCGP 1992; DRCOG 1991.

TAYLOR, Paul Anthony Hanham Surgery, 33 Whittucks Road, Hanham, Bristol BS15 3HY Tel: 0117 967 5201 Fax: 0117 947 7749; 17 Sunnyvale Drive, Longwell Green, Bristol BS30 9YH — MB BS 1987 Lond.; MRCGP 1991; DCH RCP Lond. 1992; DRCOG 1991. GP Bristol.

TAYLOR, Paul Francis Tinshill Lane Surgery, 8 Tinshill Lane, Leeds LS16 7AP Tel: 0113 267 3462 Fax: 0113 230 0402; 4 Highfield Drive, Rawdon, Leeds LS19 6EY Tel: 0113 250 7664 — MB ChB 1969 Leeds; DObst RCOG 1975.

TAYLOR, Paul Martin Department of Clinical Radiology, Manchester Royal Infirmary, Manchester M13 9WL Email: ptaylor@central.cmht.nwest.nhs.uk; Bell in The Thorn, 111 Belthorn Road, Belthorn, Blackburn BB1 2NY — MB ChB 1977 Manch.; MRCP (UK) 1981; FRCR 1985; FRCP 2000. Cons. Radiol. Centr. Manch. Healthcare Trust; Hon. Clin. Sen. Lect. Univ. Manch. Prev: Sen. Lect. (Diagn. Radiol.) Univ. Manch.

TAYLOR, Paul Richard Philip 5a Thornsett Road, Sheffield S7 1NA — MB ChB 1992 Sheff.

TAYLOR, Pauline Felicity (retired) 4 Vicarage Close, Vicarage Way, Ringmer, Lewes BN8 5LF Tel: 01273 813660 — MB ChB 1950 St. And. Prev: Med. Off. L/c St. Luke's Hosp. Chabua, India & St. Luke's Hosp.

TAYLOR, Penelope Rose Anne Royal Victoria Infirmary, Newcastle upon Tyne NE1 4LP Tel: 0191 232 5131 Fax: 0191 230 0651; 41 Clayton Road, Jesmond, Newcastle upon Tyne NE2 4RQ Tel: 0191 281 1728 Fax: 0191 281 8268 — MB BS 1972 Newc. Assoc. Specialist (Haemat.) Roy. Vict. Infirm. Newc. u. Tyne. Prev: Regist. (Haemat.) Roy. Vict. Infirm. Newc.; Ho. Phys. & Profess. Ho. Surg. Roy. Vict. Infirm. Newc. u. Tyne.

TAYLOR, Peter (retired) Carr Bank Cottage, Gawthwaite, Ulverston LA12 8EU — MB ChB 1953 Sheff.; FRCP Ed. 1983, M 1960; FCOphth 1988; DO Eng. 1958. Prev: Cons. Ophth. Roy. Preston Hosp.

TAYLOR, Peter Anthony Airlea, Crapstone, Yelverton, Plymouth — MB BS 1965 Lond.; MRCS Eng. LRCP Lond. 1964; FFA RCS Eng. 1968. (Lond. Hosp.) Cons. (Anaesth.) Plymouth Gen. Hosp. Socs: BMA & Assn. Anaesths. Prev: SHO (Anaesth.) St. Margt.'s Hosp. Epping; Regist. (Anaesth.) Char. Cross Hosp Lond.; Sen. Regist. (Anaesth.) St. Thos. Hosp. Lond.

TAYLOR, Peter Bruce (retired) 14 Dunearn Street, Broughty Ferry, Dundee DD5 3NP Tel: 01382 738978 Email: peterbrucetaylor@tinyonline.co.uk — MB ChB Aberd. 1967; FFA RCS Eng. 1975. Examr. to St. And.Ambul. Brig. Prev: Cons. Anaesth. Ninewells Hosp.

TAYLOR, Peter Charles Department of Rheumatology, Charing Cross Hospital, Fulham Palace Road, London W6 8RF — BM BCh 1985 Oxf.; PhD Lond. 1996; BA Camb. 1982; MRCP (UK) 1988. Sen. Lect. (Rheum.) Char. Cross Hosp. Lond. Prev: Lect. (Rheum.) Char. Cross Hosp. Lond.; Research Fell. (Arthritis & Rheum.) Kennedy Inst. Rheum. Lond.; Regist. & SHO Rotat. (Gen. Med.) N. Staffs. HA.

TAYLOR, Mr Peter Charles Andrew The Clementine Churchill Hospital, Sudbury Hill, Harrow HA1 3RX; 55 Woodfield Road, Ealing, London W5 1SR — MRCS Eng. LRCP Lond. 1975; FRCSI (ENT) 1984. Cons. ENT Surg. N. W. Lond. NHS Trust; Hon. Cons. ENT Surg. Roy. Postgrad. Med. Sch. Hammersmith Hosp. Lond. Socs: Fell. Internat. Coll. Surgs.; Hunt. Soc. Prev: Regist. (ENT Surg.) United Bristol Hosps. & S.mead Hosp.; SHO (ENT Surg.) St. Mary's Hosp. Lond.; Cas. Off. St. Mary's Hosp. Lond.

TAYLOR, Peter Christopher Department of Haematology, Rotherham District General, Rotherham S60 2UD Tel: 01709 820000 Fax: 01709 830694; Mootings, Sitwell Grove, Rotherham S60 3AY — MB ChB 1977 Sheff.; MRCP (UK) 1982; MRCPath 1986. Cons. Haemat., Rotherham Dist. Gen. Hosp. Socs: Assn. Clin. Paths.; Brit. Soc. Haemat. Prev: Sen. Regist. (Haemat.) Roy. United Hosp. Bath; Regist. (Haemat.) Roy. Hallamsh. Hosp. Sheff.; Regist. (Med.) Rotherham Dist. Gen. Hosp.

TAYLOR, Mr Peter David 33 Shiphay Avenue, Torquay TQ2 7ED; 9 Ridgewood Gardens, South Gosforth, Newcastle upon Tyne NE3 1SB Tel: 0191 284 0984 — MB ChB 1984 Glas.; FRCS Ed. 1989. Regist. (Gen. Surg.) Newc. HA.

TAYLOR, Peter John 5 Royal Chase, Dringhouses, York YO24 1LN — MB ChB 1987 Leeds; MRCGP 1992; DRCOG 1991. Med. Adviser for Civil Serv. Leeds. Prev: SHO (O & G) P.ss Roy. & Hull Matern. Hosps.; SHO (ENT Surg. & Infec. Dis.) Seacroft Hosp. Leeds; SHO (Med. for Elderly) St. Jas. Hosp. Leeds.

TAYLOR, Mr Peter John, Surg. Lt.-Cdr. RN Dept. Vascular Surgery, Roy. United Hospital, Combe Park, Bath BA1 3NG Tel: 01225 824761 Fax: 01225 825366 Email: p.taylor@bath.ac.uk; 28 Symes Park, Weston, Bath BA1 4PA Tel: 01225 471534 Email: p.taylor@bath.ac.uk — MB BS 1987 Lond.; DTMH, Liverpool. 1996; FRCS Eng. 1992; DA (UK) 1990. (Lond. Hosp. Med. Coll.) Specialist Regist., Gen. Vasc. Surg., Roy.Navy. Socs: Affil. Mem., Vasc. Surg.

Soc. Of Brit. And N. Ire.; Affil. Mem., Europ. Soc. Of Vasc. + EndoVasc. Surg. Prev: Regist. (Gen. Surg.) Raigmore Hosp. NHS Trust; Regist. (Gen. Surg.) Aberd. Roy. Hosps. NHS Trust; Cons.Surg. Kisiizi Hosp. Uganda.

TAYLOR, Peter Leon 514 Scott Hall Road, Leeds LS7 3RA Tel: 0113 620780 — MB ChB 1953 Leeds.

TAYLOR, Peter Neil The Dairy House, Stratton, Dorchester DT2 9RU — MB BS 1983 Lond.; MRCP (UK) 1986; FRCR 1991. Cons. Radiol. W. Dorset Gen. Hosps. NHS Trust. Prev: Sen. Regist. (Radiol.) Leeds.

TAYLOR, Mr Peter Richard Department of Surgery, Guy's & St. Thomas Hospital Trust, Lambeth Palace Road, London SE1 7EH Tel: 020 7403 3893 Fax: 020 7403 2323 Email: taylorvasc@aol.com — MB BChir 1980 Camb.; MChir Camb. 1990, MA, MB 1980, BChir 1979; FRCS Eng. 1983. (Cambridge) Cons. (Vasc. Surg.) Guy's St. Thos. Hosp. Trust; Hon. Cons. Vasc. Surg. KCH; Hon. Cons. Vasc. Surg. Univ. Hosp. Lewisham. Socs: Vasc. Surg. Soc. & Europ. Vasc. Surg. Soc.; Assn. Surg.; Internat. Soc. of Endovasulan Specialists. Prev: Sen. Lect. & Hon. Cons. Surg. (Vasc. Surg.) Guy's & Lewisham Hosps.; Sen. Regist. (Gen. Surg.) Guy's Hosp. Lond.; Sen. Fell. (Vasc.) St. Mary's Hosp. Lond.

TAYLOR, Philip James Ralph St Thomas Court Surgery, St. Thomas Court, Church Street, Axminster EX13 5AG Tel: 01297 32126 Fax: 01297 35759 — MB BS 1984 Lond.; MA Oxf. 1981; T(GP) 1991; MRCGP 1989. Med. Audit Advis. Gp. Coordinator Exeter Dist.

TAYLOR, Philip James Steevens Denton Turret Medical Centre, 10 Kenley Road, Slatyford, Newcastle upon Tyne NE5 2UY Tel: 0191 274 1840; 14 Highlaws, South Gosforth, Newcastle upon Tyne NE3 1RQ Tel: 0191 284 7775 — MB BS 1984 Newc.; MRCGP 1988; Cert. Family Plann. JCC 1988; DRCOG 1987.

TAYLOR, Philip John 16 Belvedere Court, Putney, London SW15 6HY — MB BCh BAO 1971 Dub.; FRCA 1980. Prev: Ho. Off. Meath Hosp. Dub.

TAYLOR, Mr Philip John The James Cook Hospital, Marton Road, Middlesbrough TS4 3BW Tel: 01642 854891 Fax: 01642 854830; Spring House, Great Broughton, Stokesley, Middlesbrough TS9 7HX Tel: 01642 778389 — MB ChB 1970 Sheff.; MRCOG 1985; MRACOG 1983; FRACGP 1979; FRCOG 2000. Cons O & G S. Cleveland Hosp. Prev: Lect. (O & G) Univ. Aberd.; Regist. Roy. Infirm. Ed.; Regist. (O & G) Newc., Austral.

TAYLOR, Philip Joseph (retired) 19 College Avenue, Great Crosby, Liverpool L23 0SS Tel: 0151 928 4000 — MB ChB Liverp. 1944; FRCPath 1971, M 1964.

TAYLOR, Phillip West House, 30 Southlands Mount, Riddlesden, Keighley BD20 5HH — BM BCh 1988 Oxf.; BA Oxf. 1986, BM BCh 1988. SHO (Anaesth.) Norf. & Norwich Hosp.

TAYLOR, Phillipa Anne London Lane Clinic, Kinnaird House, 37-39 London Lane, Bromley BR1 4HB Tel: 020 8460 2661 Fax: 020 8464 5041 — MRCGP; MB BCh 1983 Witwatersrand.

TAYLOR, Phyllis 53 Gervis Road, Bournemouth BH1 3DQ Tel: 01202 555154 Fax: 01202 555154 Email: gp@fatcat12.fsnet.co.uk — MB BS 1947 Lond.; DCH Eng. 1949. (Roy. Free) Gen. Practitioner (Private).

TAYLOR, Rachel Ann Close Farm Surgery, 47 Victoria Road, North Common, Bristol BS30 5JZ — MB BCh 1992 Wales; MRCGP 1996; T(GP) 1996; DCH RCP Lond. 1995; DFFP 1995; DRCOG 1994. (Univ. Wales Coll. Med.) GP N. Common Bristol. Prev: SHO Gwent HA.

***TAYLOR, Rachel Elizabeth** Yew Lodge, 8 Chapel Lane, Knighton, Leicester LE2 3WE Tel: 0116 270 7180; Yew Lodge, 8 Chapel Lane, Knighton, Leicester LE2 3WE Tel: 0116 270 7180 — MB ChB 1997 Manch.

TAYLOR, Rachel Sarah 31 Thirlmere Road, Hinckley LE10 0PE; 111 Mayola Road, Clapton, London E5 0RG — MB BS 1994 Lond.

TAYLOR, Rachel Sophie 43 Newport Road, Edgmond, Newport TF10 8HQ Tel: 01952 812511 Email: rdoling@aol.com — MB ChB 1993 Sheff.; MRCGP. 1997; DFFP. 1997. (Sheffield) Prev: GP. Worcester.

TAYLOR, Ralph Ernest (retired) Fortescue, 2 Granville Close, Benfleet SS7 1HR Tel: 01268 793265 — MB BS 1955 Lond.; MRCGP 1966. Prev: Ho. Surg. King. Geo. Hosp. Ilford.

TAYLOR, Ralph Lionel 86 Rennets Wood Road, Eltham, London SE9 2NH Tel: 020 8850 0990 — MB ChB Sheff. 1960; FRCR 1975; FFR 1973; DMRD Eng. 1971; DObst. RCOG 1962. Cons. Radiologist, Blackheath Hosp., Lond. SE3 9UD; Hon. Cons. Radiol. Qu. Eliz. Hosp. (NHS Trust) Lond. SE18 4QH. Prev: Sen. Regist. (Radiol.) St. Bart. Hosp. Lond.; Regist. (Radiol.) Lond. Hosp.; Asst. Cas. Off. & ENT Ho. Surg. Roy. Infirm. Sheff.

TAYLOR, Raphael 14 Braemore Court, Kingsway, Hove BN3 4FG Tel: 01273 720390 — MRCS Eng. LRCP Lond. 1940; AFOM RCP Lond. 1978. (Middlx.) Med. Ref. Pruden. Assur. Co. Prev: Resid. Med. Off. Min. of Pens. Hosp. Stoke Mandeville; Asst. Med. Off. St. Geo-in-the-E. (LCC) Hosp. Wapping; Capt. RAMC, Graded Specialist in Venereol.

TAYLOR, Reginald David Park Surgery, Hursley Road, Chandlers Ford, Eastleigh SO53 2ZH Tel: 01703 267355 Fax: 01703 265394 — MB BCh 1958 Dublin; MB BCh Dub. 1958. (Dublin) GP E.leigh, Hants.

TAYLOR, Rhoda Margaret (retired) Alastrean House, Tarland, Aboyne AB34 4TA Tel: 013398 81162 — MB ChB 1937 Ed.; MRCPath 1964.

TAYLOR, Richard 2 Haigh Head, Hoylandswaine, Sheffield S30 6JJ Tel: 01226 765827; Walderslade, Elsecar, Barnsley S74 9LJ Tel: 01226 743221 — MB ChB 1975 Liverp.; MRCGP 1981. Clin. Asst. (Genito-Urin. Med.) Barnsley Dist. Gen. Hosp. Prev: Trainee Gen. Pract. Barnsley Vocational Train. Scheme; SHO (Endocrine Path.) Jessop Hosp. Wom. Sheff.; SHO (O & G) St. Catherine's Hosp. Birkenhead.

TAYLOR, Richard Andrew Stephen The Surgery, High Street, Fenny Compton, Leamington Spa CV47 2YG Tel: 01295 770855 Fax: 01295 770858; 1 Brook Street, Fenny Compton, Leamington Spa CV47 2YH — BM BCh 1981 Oxf.; MA Camb. 1982; MRCGP 1985; DCH RCP Lond. 1985; DRCOG 1984.

TAYLOR, Richard Charles Henry The Surgery, Sandy Lane, Brewood, Stafford ST19 9ES Tel: 01902 850206 Fax: 01902 851360; Westgate, Dean St., Brewood, Stafford ST19 9BU Tel: 01902 850594 — MB BS 1968 Lond.; MRCS Eng. LRCP Lond. 1968; DObst RCOG 1973. (Guy's) Prev: Ho. Surg. Guy's Hosp.; Ho. Phys. St. Olave's Hosp. Lond.; SHO Harari Gen. Hosp. Salisbury, Rhodesia.

TAYLOR, Richard Geoffrey Taylor and Partners, Shirehampton Health Centre, Pembroke Road, Shirehampton, Bristol BS11 9SB Tel: 0117 916 2233 Fax: 0117 930 8246; 5 Cotham Grove, Cotham, Bristol BS6 6AL — MB ChB 1976 Birm.; AFOM 1999; D.Occ.Med. RCP Lond. 1995; MRCGP 1981; DRCOG 1979. GP Bristol; Occupat. Phys. SITA Contract Serv.

TAYLOR, Richard John Alexander School Health Department, Ulverston Health Centre, Victoria Road, Ulverston LA12 0EW Tel: 01229 583238; 17 Hallfield, Ulverston LA12 9TA Tel: 01229 587611 — BSc (Hons.) Newc. 1969, MB BS 1972; MRCGP 1976; DCH RCPS Glas. 1975; DObst RCOG 1974. Socs: Hon. Treas. Local BMA Div.. Prev: GP Chelmsford Essex; Trainee GP E. Cumbria VTS.

TAYLOR, Richard Matthew 703 Shadwell Lane, Leeds LS17 8ET — BM BCh 1989 Oxf.; BA (Hons.) Oxf. 1986, BM BCh 1989.

TAYLOR, Richard Thomas (retired) 11 Church Walk, Kidderminster DY11 6XY Tel: 01562 60010 Fax: 01562 748371 — MB Camb. 1960, BChir 1959; FRCP Lond. 1979, M 1965. Prev: Cons. Phys. Kidderminster Gen. Hosp.

TAYLOR, Richard Waring (retired) White House Farm, Main St., Keyham, Leicester LE7 9JQ Tel: 0116 259 5415 — MB BChir 1964 Camb.; MRCGP 1973; DObst RCOG 1965. Prev: GP Leicester.

TAYLOR, Richard Winston Martin 107 Weavers Way, London NW1 0XG — MB BS 1990 Lond.; BSc (Hons.) Lond. 1987; MRCPsych 1996. (Univ. Coll. Lond.) Regist. (Psychiat.) Maudsley Hosp. Lond.

TAYLOR, Robert Bryce 11 Eccleston Gardens, St Helens WA10 3BN — MRCS Eng. LRCP Lond. 1937; MRCPsych 1972; DPM Eng. 1948. (Lond. Hosp.)

TAYLOR, Robert Capel (retired) Westerton, Balloch, Alexandria G83 8NA Tel: 01389 753064 — MB ChB Glas. 1952; DA Eng. 1956. Prev: Cons. Anaesth. Vict. Infirm. Glas.

TAYLOR, Robert Henry Paediatric Intensive Care Unit, Royal Belfast Hospital for Sick Children, 180 Falls Road, Belfast BT12 6BE Tel: 01232 263056 Email: drbobtaylor@compuserve.com; 57 Ballyhanwood Road, Belfast BT5 7SW Tel: 01232 487303 — MB BCh BAO 1982 Belf.; MA (Med. Ethics and Law) Belf. 1997; FFA RCS Dub. 1986. Cons. Paediat. Anaesth. & Paediat. Intens. Care

TAYLOR

Roy. Belf. Hosp. for Sick Childr. Prev: Clin. Fell. (Paediat. Anaesth.) Hosp. for sick Child. Toronto.

TAYLOR, Mr Robert Horace Eye Department, York District Hospital, Wigginton Road, York YO31 8HE Tel: 01904 631313 Fax: 01904 453397 Email: rtaylor@yorkeyes.demon.co.uk — MB BS 1985 Lond.; FRCS Glas. 1990; MRCS Eng. LRCP Lond. 1984; FRCOphth 1993; DO RCS Eng. 1989. (Guy's) Cons. Ophth. York Dist. Hosp. Socs: Int. Mem. Amer. Assoc. Paediat. Ophthl. & Strabismus Surg.s; UK & Irel. Soc. Cataract & Refractive Surg.s; Oxf. Ophth. Congr. Prev: Fell. Paediat. Ophth. Toronto Canada; Sen. Regist. Roy. Hallamsh. Hosp. Sheff.; Regist. (Ophth.) Birm. & Midl. Eye Hosp.

TAYLOR, Mr Robert Murray Ross, CBE (retired) Croft House, Slaley, Hexham NE47 0AA Tel: 01434 673322 — MB ChB 1956 Glas.; ChM Glas. 1968; FRCS Eng. 1965; FRCS Ed. 1964; DObst RCOG 1960. Hon. Lect. (Transpl.) Univ. Newc. u Tyne; Chairm. Transpl. Pats. Trust GB. Prev: Cons. Surg. Roy. Vict. Infirm. Newc. u Tyne.

TAYLOR, Mr Robert Stewart The Ashtead Hospital, The Earren, Ashtead KT21 2SB Tel: 01372 276874 Fax: 01372 276874; 10 Catherine Court, Lake Road, Wimbledon, London SW19 7EW — MS Lond. 1973, MB BS 1957; FRCS Ed. 1962; FRCS Eng. 1962; MRCS Eng. LRCP Lond. 1957. Cons. Vasc. Surg. & Hon. Sen. Lect. St. Geo. Hosp. Lond.; Hon. Cons. Surg., Epsom.; Gen. Hosp., Epsom, Surrey. Socs: Fell. Assn. Surgs.; Internat. Cardiovasc. Soc. & Vasc. Surg. Soc. GB & Irel.; GP & Ire. Vasc. Surg. Soc. - Counc. Mem. Prev: Sen. Regist. (Surg.) Lond. Hosp.; Cons. Gen. & Vasc. Surg. Epsom Gen.; Cons. Gen. & Vasc. Surg. St Geo.'s.

TAYLOR, Roderick Gordon Calderdale Royal Hospital, Halifax HX3 0PW — MB BS 1975 Lond.; BSc (1st cl. Hons.) Lond. 1972, MD 1986; FRCP Lond. 1994; MRCP (UK) 1978. (Roy. Free) Cons. (Gen. & Respirat. Med.) Calderdale & Huddersfield NHS Trust. Socs: Brit. Thorac. Soc. Prev: Lect. (Thoracic Med. & Physiol.) Roy. Free Hosp. Sch. Med. Lond.; Research Regist. (Respirat. Unit) Roy. Postgrad. Med. Sch.; SHO (Thoracic Med.) Brompton Hosp.

TAYLOR, Rodney Geoffrey George (retired) 66 Pares Way, Ockbrook, Derby DE72 3TL — MB ChB 1947 Bristol.

TAYLOR, Professor Rodney Hemingfield Ealing Hospital NHS Trust, Uxbridge Road, Southall UB1 3HW Tel: 020 8967 5120 Fax: 020 8967 5990 Email: Rodney.Taylor@ehs.nhs.uk — MB BS 1972 Lond.; MBA OUBS 1996; DPhilMed 1994; BSc Bristol 1965; MD Lond. 1984; FRCP Lond. 1987; MRCP (UK) 1976; MRCS Eng. LRCP Lond. 1972; DHMSA 1992; FRIPHH 2001. (Univ. Coll. Hosp.) Med. Dir. & Cons. Phys. & Gastroenterol. Ealing Hosp.; Vice-Pres., Fac. Hist. Phil. Med, Soc. Apoth. Lond.; Examr. Hist. Med. Soc. Apoth. Lond. Socs: Med. Res. Soc.; (Treas.) Brit. Soc. Gastroenterol.; Fell. Med. Soc. Lond. Prev: Wellcome Sen. Research Fell. Clin. Sc. & Sen. Lect. (Gastroenterol.) Centr. Middlx. Hosp. & Middlx. Hosp. Med. Sch. Lond.; RCP/RN Prof. Med & Assoc. Postgrad. Dean RDMC; Research Assoc. Univ. Laborat. Physiol. Oxf.

TAYLOR, Roger David Thamesbridge Surgery, Portsmouth Road, Thames Ditton KT7 0HA Tel: 020 8398 7171 Fax: 020 8398 7111; 6 Westville Road, Thames Ditton KT7 0UJ Tel: 020 8398 1355 — MB BS 1966 Lond.; MB BS (Hons.) Lond. 1966; MRCS Eng. LRCP Lond. 1966. (King's Coll. Hosp.) Lect. & Examr. Brit. Red Cross. Socs: Brit. Assn. Immed. Care Schemes. Prev: Regist. (Accid. & Orthop.) St. Thos. Hosp. Lond.; Regist. (Gen. Surg. & Urol.) Roy. Sussex Co. Hosp. Brighton; Ho. Off. King's Coll. Hosp. Lond.

TAYLOR, Roger Edward Cookridge Hospital, Leeds LS16 6QB Tel: 0113 267 3411; 8 Adel Park Close, Adel, Leeds LS16 8HR Tel: 0113 267 0557 — MB BS 1976 Lond.; MA Oxf. 1973; FRCP Ed. 1992; MRCP (UK) 1979; FRCR 1984; FRCP 1998. (St. Bart.) Cons. Clin. Oncol. Cookridge Hosp. Leeds. Socs: UK Childr. Cancer Study Gp. & Internat. Soc. Paediat. Oncol. Prev: Sen. Lect. & Hon. Cons. Radiat. Oncol. Univ. Edin. & W.. Gen. Hosp. Edin.; I.C.R.F. Research Fell. & Hon. Sen. Regist. (Clin. Oncol.) W., Gen. Hosp. Edin.; Regist. (Radiother. & Oncol.) Lond. Hosp. Whitechapel.

TAYLOR, Roger George Fairways, Dudley Avenue, Westgate-on-Sea CT8 8PT Tel: 01843 831675 Email: rogertaylor99@aol.com — MB BS 1958 Lond.; DObst RCOG 1959.

TAYLOR, Rosalind Ann Hospice of St Francis, 27 Shrublands Road, Berkhamsted HP4 3HX Tel: 01442 862960 Fax: 01442 877685; Low House, 33 High St, Ivinghoe, Leighton Buzzard LU7 9EP Tel: 01296 668266 Fax: 01296 668266 Email: carl.taylor4@virgin.net — MB BChir 1980 Camb.; MA Camb. 1981; MRCGP 1986; DRCOG 1984. (Westm.) Med. Dir. Hospice of St. Frances, Berkhamsted. Prev: Asst. Phys. (Palliat. Med.) W. Cumbld. Hosp.; GP Cockermouth.; GP St. Neots Cambs.

TAYLOR, Ross Jenkins University of Aberdeen, Dept. U General Practice, Foresterhill Health Centre, Westburn Road, Aberdeen AB25 2AY Tel: 01224 553972; Westburn Medical Group, Foresterhill Health Centre, Westburn Road, Aberdeen AB25 2AY Tel: 01224 559595 — MB ChB 1966 Aberd.; FRCP Edin 2001; MD Aberd. 1981; FRCGP 1982, M 1972; DCH Lond. 1970. (Aberdeen 1966) Sen. Lect. (Gen. Pract.) Univ. Aberd. Socs: Assn. Study Med. Educat. & Nutrit Soc.

TAYLOR, Rowena Frances Halstead The Chest Clinic, Whipps Cross Hospital, Whipps Cross Road, London E11 1NR Tel: 020 8539 5522 — MB BS 1981 Lond.; MD Lond. 1996; MRCP (UK) 1984. Cons. Phys. (Thoracic & Gen. Med.) Whipps Cross Hosp. Lond. Prev: Sen. Regist. Whipps Cross Hosp. Lond.; Clin. Tutor & Research Regist. (Cystic Fibrosis) Roy. Brompton Hosp. Lond.; Regist. (Med.) Lond. Chest Hosp. & Whittington Hosp.

TAYLOR, Professor Roy Department of Medicine, Medical School, Framlington Place, Newcastle upon Tyne NE2 4HH Tel: 0191 232 5131 Fax: 0191 222 0723; 40 Reid Park Road, Jesmond, Newcastle upon Tyne NE2 2ES — MB ChB 1976 Ed.; BSc (Hons.) (Bacteriol.) Ed. 1973, MD 1985; FRCP Ed. 1991; FRCP Lond. 1989. (Ed.) Prof. Med. & Metab. & Hon. Cons. Phys. Roy. Vict. Infirm. Newc. Socs: Soc. Magnetic Resonance; Brit. Diabetic Assn.; Assn. Phys. Prev: 1st Asst. (Med.) Freeman Hosp. Newc.; Vis. Prof. Med. Yale Univ. 1990-91; Regist. (Med.) Newc. AHA.

TAYLOR, Roy Charles (retired) Hill House, Cheney Hill, Rodmersham, Sittingbourne ME9 0AH — MB BS 1954 Lond.; MRCS Eng. LRCP Lond. 1954; DObst RCOG 1956. Prev: O & G Ho. Surg. Lewisham Hosp.

TAYLOR, Russell John (retired) 17 Outwoods Road, Loughborough LE11 3LX Tel: 01509 267456 Email: russell.j.taylor@cwcom.net — MB ChB Leeds 1957. Prev: GP Princip., Bridge St. Med. Pract. LoughBoro.

TAYLOR, Ruth Alice Richmond 60 Gervase Road, Burnt Oak, Edgware HA8 0EP — MB ChB 1970 St. And.; MFHom 1982; MRCGP 1980; Cert Contracep. & Family Plann. RCOG, RCGP &; Cert FPA 1975; DA Eng. 1974. Prev: Asst. Roy. Lond. Homeop. Hosp.; Med. Off. Brook Advis. Clinics; Clin. Med. Off. (Family Plann.) Pk.side HA.

TAYLOR, Ruth Diana 21 Cunningham Hill Road, St Albans AL1 5BX — MB BS 1992 Lond.

TAYLOR, Ruth Elizabeth Dept. of Psychiatry, Institute of Psychiatry, De Crepigny Park, London SE5 8AF Tel: 020 7848 0757 Fax: 020 7848 0757 Email: spjurut@iop.ucl.ac.uk — MB ChB 1985 Manch.; MB ChB Manch. 1988; BSc (1st. cl. Hons.) Psych. Manch. 1985; MRCPsych 1993. Res. Fell. Inst. Of Psych.; Hon. Clin. Asst. (Neuropsychiat.) Nat. Hosp. Neurol. & Neurosurg. Qu. Sq. Lond. Prev: Regist. (Psychiat.) Manch. Roy. Infirm.; SHO (A & E Med.) St. Bart. Hosp. Lond.; Ho. Off. (Gen. Med.) Salford Roy. & Hosp. Hosps. Salford.

TAYLOR, Ruth Louise Arden Cottage, King St., Silverton, Exeter EX5 4JG — MB BS 1996 Lond.

TAYLOR, Sadie Louise 17 Cwm Cwddy Drive, Bassaveg, Newport NP10 8JN — BM 1992 Soton.

TAYLOR, Sally Margaret Paddington Green Health Centre, 4 Princess Louise Close, London W2 1LQ Tel: 020 7887 1600 Fax: 020 7887 1635 Email: sallytaylor@gp-e87008.nhs.uk; 13 Manstone Road, Cricklewood, London NW2 3XH — MB ChB 1982 Manch.; MRCGP 1989; Cert. Family Plann. JCC 1987; DRCOG 1986. (Manch. & St. And.) GP Trainer; GP Trainer Lond. Prev: Trainee GP. Kentish Town Health Centre Lond. VTS; Resid. (Gen. Med. & Paediat.) UHWI Kingston, Jamaica; SHO (Gyn.) Univ. Coll. Hosp. Lond.

TAYLOR, Samuel Geoffrey (retired) 23 Rusham Park Avenue, Egham TW20 9LZ Tel: 01784 432448 — MB BChir 1957 Camb.; BA Camb. 1957; MRCS Eng. LRCP Lond. 1956; DObst RCOG 1958. Prev: Ho. Surg. (Obst.) King Edwd. VII Hosp. Windsor.

TAYLOR, Sandra Jane Theatre Royal Surgery, 27 Theatre Street, Dereham NR19 2EN Tel: 01362 852800 Fax: 01362 852819; Sunset View, Fakenham Road, Horningtoft, Dereham NR20 5DP —

MB ChB 1979 Ed.; MRCGP 1983; DCH Lond. 1982. (Edinburgh) GP; Clin. Asst. GU Med. Norf. & Norwich Hosp.

TAYLOR, Sandra Jean Mawbey Brough Health Centre, 39 Wilcox Close, London SW8 2UD Tel: 020 7622 3827 Fax: 020 7498 1069 — MB ChB 1989 Bristol; 1999 (Dist.) MRCCeP; T(GP) 1994; DFFP 1994. GP. Prev: Dist. Med. Off. Luapula Province, Zambia.

TAYLOR, Sara Dillwyn 68 Hammersmith Grove, London W6 7HA — LRCPI & LM, LRSCI & LM 1976; LRCPI & LM, LRCSI & LM 1976.

TAYLOR, Sarah Anissa 27 Crosbie Road, Birmingham B17 9BG — MB ChB 1998 Liverp.

TAYLOR, Sarah Catryn 14 High Laws, Newcastle upon Tyne NE3 1RQ — MB BS 1984 Newc.

TAYLOR, Sarah Jane X Ray Department, Princess Margaret Hospital, Okus Road, Swindon SN1 4JU Tel: 01793 536231; 1 Silver Close, Minety, Malmesbury SN16 9QT Tel: 01666 860728 — MB BS 1981 Lond.; BSc Lond. 1978; FRCR 1987. (St. Bart.) Cons. Radiol. P.ss Margt. Hosp. Swindon. Prev: Clin. Fell. (Radiol.) McMaster Univ. Hamilton Ontario, Canada; Sen. Regist. (Radiol.) Stoke City Gen. Hosp. & N. Staffs. Infirm.; Regist. Birm. Hosps.

TAYLOR, Sarah Jane 17 Whitfield Park, Ringwood BH24 2DX — MB BS 1990 Lond.; MRCGP 1994; Dip. Occ. Med. Lond. 1998. Specialist Regist., Occupat. Med. Soton. Univ. Hosp. NHS Trust. Socs: SOM.

TAYLOR, Sarah Jane 741 Woodbridge Road, Ipswich IP4 4NB — MB ChB 1996 Dundee.

***TAYLOR, Sarah Katherine** St Georges Medical Centre, Field Rd, Wallasey CH45 5LN Tel: 0151 630 2080; 55 Brimstage Road, Heswall, Wirral CH60 1XE Tel: 0151 342 3599 — MB BS 1992 Lond.; DRCOG 1998.

TAYLOR, Sarah Louise Birmingham Health Authority, St Chads Court, Edgbaston, Birmingham B15 9RG Tel: 0121 695 2416 Email: sarah.taylor@hq.birminghamha.wmids.nhs.uk; 135 Lordswood Road, Harborne, Birmingham B17 9BL Tel: 0121 427 3583 — MB BS 1980 Newc.; MFPHM RCP (UK) 1990; FFPHM. Cons. Pub. Health Med. Birm. HA.

TAYLOR, Sarah Lucy 18 Kings Drive, Heaton Moor, Stockport SK4 4DZ — MB ChB 1991 Birm.; MRCGP 1995; DFFP 1995; DCH RCP Lond. 1994. (Birmingham) p/t GP Locum.

TAYLOR, Mr Scott Garry Flat 31, 22 Cleveland St, Glasgow G3 7AE — MB ChB 1993 Glas.; FRCS RCPS (Glas.) 1997. Research Fell. Univ. Dept. of Surg. W.ern Infirm. Glas. Prev: SHO Rotat. (Surg.) Monkland Dist. Gen. Hosp. Airdrie.

TAYLOR, Sharon Elisa 80 Holmfield Court, Belsize Grove, London NW3 4TU — MB BS 1992 Lond.

TAYLOR, Simon Christopher, Capt. Tel: 0121 4556 2894 Email: simonc8@hotmail.com; Flat 5, 9 York Road, Edgbaston, Birmingham B15 9MX Tel: 0121 456 2894 Email: simonc8@hotmail.com — MB BCh 1997 Wales. (University of Wales) GP. Brit. Army; SHO Orthop. Socs: Haywood Club. Prev: SHO Orthop., Frimley Pk. Hosp.; SHO A&E, Lewisham Hosp.

TAYLOR, Simon Wheldon 1 Pump Court, Temple, London EC4Y 7AA Tel: 020 7827 4000 Fax: 020 7827 4100; September Cottage, Monks Lane, Wadhurst TN5 6EN — MB BChir 1987 Camb.; MA Camb. 1987. Barrister-at-Law. Socs: BMA; Liveryman Worshipful Soc. Apoth. Prev: Ho. Off. Lond. Hosp.

TAYLOR, Stanley Howard Aberford Court, Aberford, Leeds LS25 3AH Tel: 0113 813237 Fax: 01132 813654 — PhD Leeds 1977; BSc (Hons.) Birm. 1950, MB ChB 1953; FRCP Ed. 1973, M 1962; MRCS Eng. LRCP Lond. 1953; FACC 1984. (Birm.) Cons. Cardiol. Leeds AHA (T); Sen. Lect. & Dep. Dir. Dept. Cardiovasc. Studies Univ. Leeds. Socs: Brit. Cardiac Soc. & Med. Research Soc. Prev: Sen. Lect. (Med.) Dept. Med. Univ. Edin.; Lect. (Med.) Dept. Med. Univ. Birm.; MRC Fell. (Clin. Research) Dept. Med. Roy. Postgrad. Med. Sch. Lond.

TAYLOR, Stephanie Jane Caroline Dept of General Practice and Primary Care, St Barts Royal London School of Med. & Dentistry, University of London, London E1 4NS; 15 Courtnell Street, London W2 5BU — MB BS 1984 Lond.; MSc Lond. Sch. Hyg. & Trop. Med. Lond. 1993; MFPHM RCP (UK) 1996; MRCGP 1989; DRCOG 1989; DCH RCP Lond. 1986. (Roy. Free) Sen. Clin. Lect. in Health Serv.s Research & Developm., St Barts.; Hon. Cons. Pub. Health Med. Havering Hosp. NHS Trust, Essex.

TAYLOR, Stephen 37 Villiers Street, Leamington Spa CV32 5YH Tel: 01926 833188 Fax: 01926 833265 Email: staylor.inet@court.co.uk — MB ChB 1992 Leic.; MRCP (UK) 1996; DTM & H RCP Lond. 1994. (Leicester) Specialist Regist. (Genitourin. Med.) Birm. Heartlands Hosp. Socs: BMA, MSSVD & BHIVA. Prev: SHO (Infec. Dis. & Trop. Med.) Birm. Heartlands Hosp.; SHO (Infec. Dis. & Trop. Med.) Birm. Heartlands Hosp.

TAYLOR, Stephen Anselm Willis (retired) 25 Boscobel Road, Walsall WS1 2PL Tel: 01922 628366 Fax: 01922 627 607 Email: osawtaylor@cs.com — MB BS Lond. 1957.

TAYLOR, Stephen Carl 103 Dogfield Street, Cathays, Cardiff CF24 4QN — MB BCh 1992 Wales; BSc (Hons.) Physiol. 1989.

TAYLOR, Stephen Charles (retired) The Staploe Medical Centre, Brewhouse Lane, Soham, Ely CB7 5JD Tel: 01353 624123 — MB 1971 Camb.; BChir 1970; DObst RCOG 1974. Prev: Ho. Surg. King's Coll. Hosp. Lond.

TAYLOR, Stephen Gordon The Long House, 73-75 East Trinity Road, Edinburgh EH5 3EL Tel: 0131 552 4919; 16 West Ferryfield, Edinburgh EH5 2PU Tel: 0131 551 2620 — MB ChB 1984 Ed.; MRCGP 1989; DCH RCP Glas. 1987; DRCOG 1986. (Edinburgh)

TAYLOR, Stephen James 3 Mosswook Park, Manchester M20 5QW — MB ChB 1989 Manch. (Manchester) Socs: MRCGP.

TAYLOR, Mr Stuart Alexander Netley House, Gravel Hill, Wombourne, Wolverhampton WV5 9HA Tel: 01902 892135 Email: stuartataylor@virgin.net — MS Lond. 1980, MB BS 1968; FRCS Eng. 1972; MRCS Eng. LRCP Lond. 1966. (King's Coll. Hosp.) Cons. Surg. The Roy. Wolverhampton Hosps. NHS Trust. Prev: Sen. Surg. Regist. King's Coll. Hosp. Lond.; Ho. Surg. & Ho. Phys. Kings Coll. Hosp. Lond.

TAYLOR, Stuart Andrew 8 Chapel Drive, Balsall Common, Coventry CV7 7EQ — MB BS 1994 Lond.

TAYLOR, Stuart Watson Chadwick (retired) Health Environment & Safety Services, Courtaulds plc, PO Box 111, 72 Lockhurst Lane, Coventry CV6 5RS Tel: 01203 688771 Fax: 01203 638369 — MB BS 1960 Lond.; MSc Lond. 1978; FFOM RCP Lond. 1994, MFOM 1981; DIH Eng. 1977; DObst RCOG 1962. Prev: Chief Med. Off. Ct.aulds Gp.

TAYLOR, Susan Aline Park Surgery, Aline Park, Lochaline, Morvern, Oban PA34 5XT Tel: 01967 421252 Fax: 01967 421303 — MB ChB 1985 Glas.

TAYLOR, Susan Glenfield Hospital, Groby Road, Leicester LE3 9QP Tel: 0116 287 1471; 9 Swithland Court, Brand Hill, Woodhouse Eaves, Loughborough LE12 8SS Tel: 01509 890971 — MB BS 1971 Lond.; MRCS Eng. LRCP Lond. 1971; FFA RCS Eng. 1980; DA Eng. 1974. (Roy. Free) Cons. Anaesth. Glenfield Hosp. Leicester. Prev: Sen. Regist. (Anaesth.) Leicester AHA; Regist. (Anaesth.) Roy. Nat. Throat, Nose & Ear Hosp. Lond.; Regist. (Anaesth.) Roy. Free Hosp. Lond.

TAYLOR, Susan Barrie George Street Surgery, 99 George Street, Dumfries DG1 1DS Tel: 01387 253333 Fax: 01387 253301; Tel: 01387 720122 — MB ChB 1976 Aberd.; MRCGP 1980; DRCOG 1978.

TAYLOR, Susan Diane Holly Tree House, 278 Church Road, Frampton Cotterell, Bristol BS36 2BH — MB ChB 1971 Sheff.; FFA RCS Eng. 1976.

TAYLOR, Susan Doris Dickson (retired) 86 Heathcote Grove, Chingford, London E4 6SF Tel: 020 8529 2527 — MB BCh BAO Belf. 1941. Prev: Med. Off. Cytol. Clinics Redbridge & Waltham Forest AHA. Late Med.

TAYLOR, Susan Elizabeth 9 Turf Lane, Cullingworth, Bradford BD13 5EJ — BM 1989 Soton. SHO (O & G) Roy. United Hosp. Bath. Prev: Regist. (Psychiat.) Roy. S. Hants. Hosp. Soton.

TAYLOR, Susan Jane Rotherfield Surgery, Rotherfield, Crowborough TN6 3QW Tel: 01892 852415/853288 Fax: 01892 853499; Brook Health Centre, Crowborough Hill, Crowborough TN6 2ED Tel: 01892 652850 — MB BS 1980 Lond.; Dip. Pract. Dermat. Wales 1994; DRCOG 1983. Prev: Clin. Asst. (Dermat.) Kent & Sussex Hosp. Tunbridge Wells; GP Sittingbourne; Trainee GP Crawley VTS.

TAYLOR, Susan Mary Rudrashetty and Partners, Mary Potter Health Centre, Gregory Boulevard, Hyson Green, Nottingham NG7 5HY — BM BS 1987 Nottm.; MRCGP 1991; DRCOG 1991; DCH RCP Lond. 1990. Trainee GP/SHO Nottm. HA & Qu. Med. Centre Nottm.

TAYLOR

TAYLOR, Terence Anthony Health Centre, Pier Road, Tywyn LL36 0AT Tel: 01654 710238 Fax: 01654 712143 — MB BCh BAO 1985 NUI; MRCGP 1989. GP Tywyn.

TAYLOR, Thomas Beech Glade, Doubleton Lane, Penshurst, Tonbridge TN11 8JA Tel: 01892 870476 — MB BS 1948 Lond.; MRCS Eng. LRCP Lond. 1945; MFOM 1981; DPH Lond. 1959; DIH Eng. 1959. (St. Bart.) Occupat. Health Phys. Lewisham NHS Trust Occupat. Health Serv., FarnBoro. Hosp., Kent.; Apptd. Doctor Health & Safety Exec. Socs: BMA; Fell. Roy. Soc. Med. Prev: Sen. Med. Off. Centr. Electricity Generating Bd. SE Region; Asst. Dir. Urban Servs. Dept., Hong Kong; Flight Lt. RAFVR Med. Br.

TAYLOR, Thomas Cochrane, KStJ (retired) 19 Redcar Road, Marske-by-the-Sea, Redcar TS11 6BS Tel: 01642 485138 — MB BS Durh. 1945; DLO Eng. 1952. Chair. BMA S. Tees Div.

TAYLOR, Thomas Gilchrist 39 Midmills Road, Inverness IV2 3NZ — MB ChB 1965 Aberd.; MRCPath 1974.

TAYLOR, Thomas Henry (retired) 60 Wood Vale, London N10 3DN Tel: 020 8883 6146 Email: tomt.anaes.uk@cableinet.co.uk — MB BS Lond. 1954; FRCA 1992; FFA RCS Eng. 1960. Prev: Cons. Anaesth. Roy. Lond. Trust.

TAYLOR, Thomas Lauder Outram Wellington Health Centre, Chapel Lane, Wellington, Telford TF1 1PZ Tel: 01952 244740 — MB ChB 1968 Ed.; MRCOG 1977; Cert JCC Lond. 1979. Prev: Regist. (O & G) Wythenshawe Hosp. Manch.; Ho. Phys. & Ho. Surg. Roy. Infirm. Edin.; Surg. Lt. RN (Gen. Serv. Medal).

TAYLOR, Thomas William Department of Clinical Radiology, Ninewells Hospital, Dundee DD1 9SY Tel: 01382 660111 — MB ChB 1984 Ed.; BSc (Hons.) Ed. 1982; FRCR 1991; DMRD Ed. 1990. Cons. Radiol. Tayside Univ. Hosps. NHS Trust. Prev: Sen. Regist. (Radiol.) Roy. Infirm. & W.. Gen. Hosp. Edin.

TAYLOR, Timothy Chadwick (retired) The Spinney, Brooklands, Hammerwood, East Grinstead RH19 3QA Tel: 01342 322494 — MB BChir 1960 Camb.; MA, MB Camb. 1960, BChir 1959; DObst RCOG 1964. Prev: GP Lingfield, Surrey.

TAYLOR, Timothy Mackford St Richards Hospital, Spitalfield Lane, Chichester PO19 4SE Tel: 01243 788122; Three Anchor Bay, 2 Downview Road, Barnham, Bognor Regis PO22 0EE — MB BS 1984 Lond.; BSc Lond. 1981, MB BS 1984; MRCP (UK) 1989. Cons. Paediat. St. Richards Hosp. Chichester. Prev: Sen. Regist. St. Geo. Hosp. Lond.

TAYLOR, Timothy Michael Winn Taunton Road Medical Centre, 12-16 Taunton Road, Bridgwater TA6 3LS Tel: 01278 444400 Fax: 01278 423691 — MB 1987 Camb.; BChir 1986; MA Oxf. 1988.

TAYLOR, Tom Horsfield (retired) 211 Brodie Avenue, Liverpool L19 7NB Tel: 0151 427 1494 — MRCS Eng. LRCP Lond. 1926; MRCS Eng., LRCP Lond. 1926. Prev: Hon. Surg. Out-pats. Beckett Hosp. Barnsley.

TAYLOR, Mr Trevor Childs Royal Belfast Hospital for Sick Children, Belfast BT12 6BE Tel: 028 9024 0503; 27 Hawthornden Road, Belfast BT4 3JU Tel: 028 9065 6302 Fax: 028 9065 1825 Email: tctaylor@dnet.co.uk — MB BCh BAO 1968 Belf.; FRCS Eng. 1995; FRCS Ed. 1972. (Belf.) Cons. Orthop. Surg. Roy. Hosps. Trust Belf. Socs: Fell. BOA; Ulster Med. Soc. Prev: Tutor (Surg.) Qu. Univ. Belf.; Clin. Orthop. Study Fell. Hosp. Sick Childr. Toronto, Canada; Cons. Bloorview Childr. Hosp. Willowdale, Canada.

TAYLOR, Valerie Eileen 27 Orchard Street, Aberdeen AB24 3DA — MB ChB 1995 Aberd.; BSc Med. Sci. (Hons.) Aberd. 1993. SHO Aberd. Roy. Hosps. NHS Trust.

TAYLOR, Valerie Margaret 24 West Drive, Harrow Weald, Harrow HA3 6TS — MB ChB 1978 Glas.; FFA RCS Eng. 1982. Cons. Anaesth. Roy. Nat. Orthop. Hosp. Stanmore.

TAYLOR, Vernon Rostron The Surgery, 74A Worcester Road, Hagley, Stourbridge DY9 0NH Tel: 01562 882474; Windover Cottage, Field Lane, Clent, Stourbridge DY9 0JA Tel: 01562 884529 — MB ChB 1958 Liverp.

TAYLOR, Victor Norman (retired) 86 Heathcote Grove, Chingford, London E4 6SF — MB BCh BAO Belf. 1941. Prev: Orthop. Ho. Surg. & Cas. Off. Kent & Sussex Hosp.

TAYLOR, Vivien Mary 31 Wimbolt Street, London E2 7BX — BM 1977 Soton.; MSc Lond. 1989; MRCGP 1982; DRCOG 1980.

TAYLOR, Walter Noel Alexander (retired) 6 London Road, Uppingham, Oakham LE15 9TJ Tel: 01572 822802 — MB BS Lond. 1951; MRCS Eng. LRCP Lond. 1951; DObst RCOG 1959. Prev: Surg. Lt. RN.

TAYLOR, Walter Robert John 26 Pitchford Road, Heath Farm, Shrewsbury SY1 3HS — MB BS 1981 Lond.; MRCP (UK) 1988.

TAYLOR, Wendy Barbara NCCT, Newcastle General Hospital, Newcastle upon Tyne NE4 6BE Tel: 0191 219 4279; 12 Boundary Gardens, High Heaton, Newcastle upon Tyne NE7 7AA — MB BS Newc. 1979; BMedSc Newc. 1976, MD 1987; MRCP (UK) 1982; FRCR 1990. (Univ. Newc. u. Tyne) Cons. Clin, Oncol. Newc. Gen. Hosp. Socs: Brit. Gyn. Cancer Soc. Prev: Sen. Regist. & Regist. (Radiother. & Oncol.) Newc. Gen. Hosp.; Research Regist. (Clin. Pharmacol.) Univ. Newc.

TAYLOR, Wendy Jane Taybank Medical Centre, 10 Robertson Street, Dundee DD4 6EL Tel: 01382 461588 Fax: 01382 452121; Windrush Cottage, 13 Bonfield Road, Strathkinners KY16 0DA Tel: 01334 850710 — MB ChB 1989 Dundee; MRCGP 1995.

TAYLOR, Wendy Jane 17 Lawford Road, London W4 3HS — MB ChB 1981 Bristol; MSc Lond. 1988; MRCP (UK) 1984; FRCR 1989. Sen. Regist. Neuroradiol. Hosp. Sick Childr. & Nat. Hosp. Neurol. & Neurosurg. Prev: Sen. Regist. (Radiol.) Roy. Free Hosp. Lond.

TAYLOR, William Flat 10, 48 Handsworth Wood Road, Birmingham B20 2DT — MB ChB 1964 Birm.; BSc (Physiol.) Birm. 1961, MB ChB 1964; MRCP Lond. 1969.

TAYLOR, William 2 Hollytree Road, Liverpool L25 5PA — MB ChB Liverp. 1969; MRCPath 1978; DObst RCOG 1971. Cons. Histopath. & Gastrointest. Endoscopist Univ. Hosp. Aintree, Liverp.

TAYLOR, William (retired) 5 Priory Gardens, St Andrews KY16 8XX Tel: 01334 478522 — MB ChB 1951 Glas.; MRCGP 1974; DObst RCOG 1960. p/t Med. Ref. Dundee Benefits Agency. Prev: GP Ardrie.

TAYLOR, Mr William Arthur Stewart — MB ChB 1984 Glas.; FRCS Glas. 1988. Cons. Neurosurg., S.ern Gneral Hopitsl, Glas. Prev: Regist. Rotat. (Surg.) W. of Scot.; Sen. Regist. (Neurosurg.) Atkinson Morley's Hosp. Wimbledon.

TAYLOR, William Douglas White Lodge Practices, 21 Grosvenor Street, St Helier, Jersey JE1 4HA Tel: 01534 873786; Clairfield, Maufant, St Saviour, Jersey JE2 7HQ Tel: 01534 861441 — MB ChB 1960 Glas. Prev: Ho. Phys. & Ho. Surg. Ballochmyle Hosp. Mauchline; Ho. Surg. Matern. Hosp. Swindon.

TAYLOR, William Edwin Elmbank Group, Foresterhill Health Centre, Westburn Road, Aberdeen AB25 2AY Tel: 01224 696949 Fax: 01224 691650; 63 Cairnlee Avenue E., Cults, Aberdeen AB15 9NU Tel: 01224 861642 — MB ChB 1979 Aberd.; FRCGP 1994, M 1983; DCH RCP Lond. 1983; DRCOG 1983. (Aberd.) Dir. Quality Assur. Initiatives RCGP Scotl.; Med. Off. Liberty Aberd. Socs: Soc. Occupat. Med.; Aberd. M-C Soc. Prev: Trainee GP Dumfries & Galloway; Ho. Phys. Aberd. City Hosp.; Ho. Surg. Aberd. Roy. Infirm.

TAYLOR, William Gledhill (retired) 7 Bridge Close, Burniston, Scarborough YO13 0HS Tel: 01723 870547 — MB ChB 1953 Leeds; MFOM RCP Lond. 1978; DIH Soc. Apoth. Lond. 1973. Prev: Sen. Med. Off. Imperial Chem. Industries plc.

TAYLOR, Mr William Gordon Tel: 01978 291100; Bywell, Chester Road, Rossett, Wrexham LL12 0HN — MB ChB 1980 Leeds; FRCOG 2000; MRCOG 1988; Dip. Obst. Ultrasound RCOG 1992; MObstG Liverp. 1990. Cons. Obst. Gyn. Wrexham Maelor Hosp. Socs: Brit. Med. Ultrasound Soc. Prev: Sen. Regist. Liverp. Matern. Hosp.; Regist. Newc. u. Tyne Gen. Hosp. & Roy. Liverp. Hosp.

TAYLOR, William Halstead Department of Medical Microbiology, Duncan Building, Royal Liverpool Hospital, Prescot St., Liverpool L7 8XW Tel: 0151 706 2000; Clare House, 16 Salisbury Road, Cressington Park, Liverpool L19 0PJ Tel: 0151 427 1042 Email: drwhtaylor@hotmail.com — BM BCh Oxf. 1948; MA Oxf. 1949; BA (1st cl. Hons. Animal Physiol.) 1946; DM 1957; FRCP Lond. 1971, M 1950. (Oxf.) Emerit. Cons. Liverp. HA & Emerit. Cons. Metabol. Med. Halton Gen. Hosp. Runcorn. Socs: Assn. Clin. Path. & Med. Research Soc. Prev: Cons. Chem. Path. & Head of Dept. Liverp. HA; Dir. Mersey Regional Unit Metabol. Investig.; Fell. & Tutor (Natural Sc.) St. Peter's Coll., Univ. Oxf.

TAYLOR, William Nigel 182 Church Road, Litherland, Liverpool L21 5HE Tel: 0151 949 0281 Fax: 0151 949 0271 — MB ChB 1983 Liverp.; BSc (Hons.) Liverp. 1978; DFFP 1993; T(GP) 1991. (Univ. Liverp.) Salaried PMS GP, Bootle and Litherland PCT. Socs: N. W. Soc. of Family Plann. Prev: Trainee GP Bridge of Allan VTS; SHO (O & G) Ninewells Hosp. Dundee; SHO (Gen. Surg.) Hexham Gen. Hosp. N.d.

TAYLOR, William Reginald (retired) 61 Efflinch Lane, Barton-under-Needwood, Burton-on-Trent DE13 8EU Tel: 01283 712356 — MB ChB 1956 Sheff. Prev: GP Burton-on-Trent.

TAYLOR, Willson Davidson Tithe House, Sadberge, Darlington DL2 1RP Tel: 01325 332040 Fax: 01325 332040 Email: wdt@tayderm.demon.co.uk — MB ChB 1969 Aberd.; FRCP Lond. 1989; FRCP Ed. 1985; MRCP (UK) 1974. (Aberd.) Cons. Dermat. Glaxo Dept. Dermat. S. Cleveland Hosp. Middlesbrough.

TAYLOR, Yvonne Thornliebank Health Centre, 20 Kennishead Road, Thornliebank, Glasgow G46 8NY Tel: 0141 531 6901 Fax: 0141 638 7554; Tel: 0141 632 9293 — MB ChB 1963 Glas.; FRCP Glas. (Glas.) Prev: Regist. Inst. Radiotherap. Glas.

TAYLOR, Zoe Leigh The Hainin, Aberfeldy PH15 2LB — MB ChB 1998 Aberd.

TAYLOR-BARNES, Kathryn Shere Surgery, Gomshall Lane, Shere GU5 9DR Tel: 01483 202066 — MB BCh BAO Dublin; DCH 2001; LRCPI Dublin. Gen. Pract. Regist., Shere Surg., Shere.

TAYLOR BROWN, Mary 3 Hampton Terrace, Murrayfield, Edinburgh EH12 5JD — MB ChB 1941 Ed.; FRCP Ed. 1971, M 1953. (Ed.) Insole Schol. Research On VD 1961-2; Cons. Phys. VD Dept. Roy. Infirm. Edin.; Lect. Edin. Univ. & to Nurses Roy. Infirm. Edin. & Edin. S.. Gp. Hosps. Socs: New York Acad. Sc. & Soc. Study VD. Prev: Ho. Surg., Ho. Phys. & Asst. Anaesth. Ballochmyle Hosp.

TAYLOR-HELPS, Douglas Frederick Derwent Practice, Norton Road, Malton YO17 9RF Tel: 01653 600069 Fax: 01653 698014 — MB ChB 1980 Manch.; MRCGP 1985.

TAYLOR-ROBERTS, Matthew Giles William Westcourt, 12 The Street, Rustington, Littlehampton BN16 3NX Tel: 01903 784311 Fax: 01903 850907; Yew Tree Cottage, Warningcamp, Arundel BN18 9QJ — MB BS 1980 Lond.; DRCOG 1985; Cert. Family Plann. JCC 1985.

TAYLOR-ROBERTS, Timothy David The Surgery, 35A High Street, Wimbledon, London SW19 5BY Tel: 020 8946 4820 Fax: 020 8944 9794 — MB BS 1971 Lond.; BSc Lond. 1967; DObst RCOG 1975. Prev: Ho. Phys. St. Mary's Hosp. Lond.

TAYLOR-ROBINSON, Professor David Department of Genitourinary Med., Winston Churchill Wing, Imperial College School of Medicine, St Mary's Hospital, Paddington, London W2 1PG Tel: 020 594 3901 Fax: 020 594 3906; 6 Vache Mews, Vache Lane, Chalfont St Giles HP8 4UT Tel: 01494 580324 Fax: 01494 580324 — MB ChB 1954 Liverp.; MD (NE Roberts Prize) Liverp. 1958; MRCP (UK) 1996; FRCPath 1977, M 1965. Emerit. Prof. Genitourin. Microbiol. & Med. Imperial Coll. Sch. Med. St. Mary's Hosp. Lond. Socs: Soc. Gen. Microbiol.; Med. Soc. Study VD; Path. Soc. Prev: Head Div. Sexually Transm. Dis. MRC Clin. Research Centre Harrow; Mem. Scientif. Staff MRC Common Cold Unit Salisbury; Christiana Hartley Fell. (Bact.) Univ. Liverp.

TAYLOR-ROBINSON, David Carlton 97 Menlove Avenue, Liverpool L18 3HP — MB ChB 1998 Leeds.

TAYLOR-ROBINSON, John Winston Belle Vale Health Centre, Hedgefield Road, Liverpool L25 2XE Tel: 0151 487 0514 Fax: 0151 488 6601; 97 Menlove Avenue, Calderstones, Liverpool L18 3HP Tel: 0151 722 1681 — MRCS Eng. LRCP Lond. 1971. (Liverp.) Prev: Ho. Surg. & Ho. Phys. St. Helens Gen. Hosp.; Ho. Off. (Obst.) Liverp. Matern. Hosp.

TAYLOR-ROBINSON, Katharine 32 Dacre Road, Hitchin SG5 1QJ — MB ChB 1998 Leeds.

TAYLOR-ROBINSON, Simon David Gastroenterology Section, Division of Medicine (Medicine A), Imperial College School of Medicine, Hammersmith Hospital, Du Cane Road, London W12 0HS Tel: 020 8383 3266 Fax: 020 8749 3436 — MB BS 1984 Lond.; MD 1996 Lond; FRCP 2001 UK; MRCP (UK) 1989. Sen. Lect. Med. (Gastroenterol. & Hepat.) Hon. Cons. Hammersmith & St. Mary's Hosp. & Imperial Coll. Sch. of Med. Lond. Prev: Sen. Regist. (Gastroenterol.) Hammersmith Hosp. Lond.; Research Fell. (Gastroenterol.) NMR Unit, Roy. Postgrad. Med. Sch., Hammersmith Hosp., Lond.; Regist. (Gastroenterol.) Roy. Free Hosp. Lond.

TAYLOR-SHEWRING, Mrs Dorothy A (retired) 37 Fox Hill, Selly Oak, Birmingham B29 4AG Tel: 0121 472 2857 — M.B., Ch.B. Liverp. 1923.

TAYLOR-SMITH, Robert George The Gables, 12 Albany House, 85 Manor Drive, Wembley HA9 8DJ — MB BS 1992 Lond.

***TAYLOR-SMITH, Sarah Rachael** Bramble Wood, 63 Brighton Road, Godalming GU7 1NT — BM 1997 Soton.

TAYOB, Yunus St. Albans & Hemel Hempstead Trust Hospitals, St. Albans City Hospital, Waverley Road, St Albans AL3 5PN Tel: 01727 866122 Fax: 01727 841390; 4 Douglas Road, Harpenden AL5 2EW Fax: 01442 219251 Email: yunus@globalnet.co.uk — MB BCh BAO 1977 Dub.; MA 1979, MB BCh BAO Dub. 1977; MRCOG 1983; MFFP. Cons. O & G St. Albans City & Hemel Hempstead Hosps.; Examr. RCOG & PLAB & United Examg. Bd. Socs: Inst. Obst. & Gyn. Irel.; Blair Bell Res. Soc.; Nat. Assn. Family Plann. Doctors. Prev: Lect. & Hon. Sen. Regist. Roy. Free Hosp. Lond.; Regist. Middlx. Hosp. Lond.; Research Fell. Margt. Pyke Centre Lond.

TAYTON, Mr Keith John Jeremy Stoneycroft House, Shirenewton, Chepstow NP16 6RQ Tel: 01291 641747 Fax: 01291 641747 — MB BS Lond. 1968; FRCS Eng. 1973; MRCS Eng. LRCP Lond. 1968. (Roy. Free) Cons. Orthop. Surg. Roy. Gwent Hosp., Newport. Socs: Fell. BOA.; BMA. Prev: Sen. Lect. (Traum. & Orthop. Surg.) Welsh Nat. Sch. Med. Cardiff; Sen. Regist. (Orthop.) S. Glam. AHA (T); Regist. (Orthop.) Nuffield Orthop. Centre Oxf.

TAYTON, Robert Geoffrey The Health Centre, Bath Road, Thatcham, Newbury RG18 3HD Tel: 01635 867171 Fax: 01635 876395 — MB BS 1970 Lond.; MRCS Eng. LRCP Lond. 1970; MRCGP 1975; DCH Eng. 1974; DObst RCOG 1973; AKC. (King's Coll. Hosp.) Prev: Trainee GP Tunbridge Wells VTS; Ho. Phys. King's Coll. Hosp. Lond.; Ho. Surg. Kent & Sussex Hosp. Tunbridge Wells.

TAYYAB, Mohammad 17 New Haeth Close, Wednesfield, Wolverhampton WV11 1XX — MB BS 1984 Bahauddin Zakariya U Pakistan; MRCPI 1994; MRCOG 1994.

TAYYEBI, Gulam Ali Russell Medical Centre, Upper Russell Street, Wednesbury WS10 7AR Tel: 0121 556 5470 Fax: 0121 505 1157 — MB BS 1969 Vikram.

TAYYIB, Mr Muhammad 1 Blake Close, Welling DA16 3NS — LRCP LRCS 1983 Ed.; BSc Punjab 1974, MB BS 1979; FRCS Glas. 1986; FRCS Ed. 1986; LRCP LRCS Ed. LRCPS Glas. 1983; DO RCS Eng. 1985.

TCHAMOUROFF, Stephan Elias 18 Palmeira Avenue, Hove BN3 3GB Tel: 01273 736285 — LMSSA 1961 Lond.; FRCOG 1987, M 1970; DObst 1967. (St. Bart.) Cons. Genitourin. Med. Brighton HA. Socs: Med. Soc. Study VD; Internat. Union Against Venereal Dis. & Treponematoses; Assoc. Mem. Inst. Psycho-Sexual Med. Prev: Sen. Regist. (Genitourin. Med.) Univ. Coll. Hosp. Lond.

TEAGO, Philippa Jane Health Centre, Purbeck, Stentonbury, Milton Keynes MK14 2LB Tel: 01908 318989; 14 The Meadway, Loughton, Milton Keynes MK5 8AN Tel: 01908 200680 — MB ChB 1984 Manch.

TEAGUE, Emma Mary Rydon House, Paignton Road, Stoke Gabriel, Totnes TQ9 6SP — MB ChB 1995 Bristol; DRCOG 1998; DFFP 1999.

TEAGUE, Gillian Department of Paediatrics, Vowden Hall, Torbay Hospital, Totnes TQ2 7AA Tel: 01803 614567; Rydon House, Stoke Gabriel, Totnes TQ9 6SP Tel: 01803 782547 — MB ChB Bristol 1968; DCH Eng. 1972. Clin. Asst. (Paediat.) Torbay Hosp. Torquay.

TEAGUE, Isabel The Surgery, Worcester Road, Great Witley, Worcester WR6 6HR Tel: 01299 896370 Fax: 01299 896873; 43 Eardiston, Tenbury Wells WR15 8JJ Tel: 01584 881240 Fax: 01584 881353 — MB BS 1991 Lond.; BSc Lond. 1988; MRCGP 1995; DFFP 1994. (Univ. Coll. and Middl. Sch. of Med.) Clin. Med. Off. Family Plann. (p/t). Socs: BMA; RCGP. Prev: Trainee GP Worcs.; SHO (Paediat.) Worcester Roy. Infirm.; Bd. Mem. Malvern Hills PCG.

TEAGUE, Robin Harry Torbay Hospital, Lawes Bridge, Torquay TQ2 7AA Tel: 01803 614567 Fax: 01803 654896; Rydon House, Stoke Gabriel, Totnes TQ9 6SP Tel: 01803 782547 Fax: 01803 782955 — MB ChB Bristol 1968; MD Bristol 1976; FRCP Lond. 1986; MRCP (UK) 1974; MRCS Eng. LRCP Lond. 1968. Cons. Phys. Torbay Hosp. Torquay. Socs: Brit. Soc. Gastroenterol. Prev: Cons. Sen. Lect. Univ. Liverp.

TEAHON, Catherine Department of Gastroenterology, Nottingham City Hospital Trust, Hucknall Road, Nottingham NG5 1PB — MB BCh BAO 1981 NUI; MD NUI 1991, MMedSci 1985; MRCPI 1984.

TEALE, Charles Department of Medicine for the Elderly, Seacroft Hospital, York Road, Leeds LS14 6UH Tel: 0113 264 8164; 3 Lidgett Park Road, Leeds LS8 1EE Tel: 0113 266 1123 — BM 1983 Soton.; FRCP 1998; MD Leeds 1992; MRCP (UK) 1986. Cons. Phys. (Elderly) Seacroft aand St James Hosp. Leeds; Sen. Clin. Lect. Fac. Med. Leeds Univ. Socs: Brit. Geriat. Soc.; Brit. Thorac. Soc. Prev: Sen. Regist. Leeds Hosps.; Regist. Leeds Hosps.

TEALE

TEALE, Glyn Robert Birmingham Women's NHS Trust, Edgbaston, Birmingham B15 2TG; 6 Swiss Farm Road, Copthorne, Shrewsbury SY3 8XB — MB BS 1989 Lond.; BSc Biochem. Lond. 1986, MB BS (Hons.) 1989; MRCP (UK) 1993. Research Fell., Birm. Wom.'s NHS Trust.

TEALE, Katherine Frances Helen Department of Anaesthetics, Manchester Royal Infirmary, Oxford Road, Manchester M13 9WL — MB ChB 1987 Ed.; FRCA. 1992; DA (UK) 1989. Prev: SHO (Anaesth.) Stobhill Hosp. Glas.

TEALE, Teresa Elizabeth The Surgery, 4 Station Road, Frimley, Camberley GU16 5HF Tel: 01276 62622 Fax: 01276 683908; 1 Chestnut Avenue, Camberley GU15 1LT Tel: 01276 24693 — MB ChB 1967 Glas.; DObst RCOG 1970. (Glas.) Prev: SHO (O & G) Roy. Matern. Hosp. Belf.

TEALL, Angela Jane Greenwich District Hospital, Vanbrugh Hill, Greenwich, London SE10 9HE Tel: 020 8858 8141; 12 Garlies Road, Forest Hill, London SE23 2RT Tel: 020 8699 0386 — MB BS 1977 Lond.; MA (Univ. of Surrey) 2001 (Wimbledon School of AA); MSc Lond. 1984; MRCP Lond. 1981; MRCPath 1984; BA Lond. Inst. 1998. p/t Cons. Microbiol. Greenwich Healthcare NHS Trust. Socs: BMA; Brit. Soc. of Antimicrobial Chemother.; Hosp. Infec. Soc. Prev: Sen. Regist. (Microbiol.) Univ. Coll. & Middlx. Hosp.

TEALL, John Graham Church Grange, Bramblys Drive, Basingstoke RG21 8QN Tel: 01256 29021 — MRCS Eng. LRCP Lond. 1957; LMSSA Lond. 1955; DObst RCOG 1957; DA Eng. 1959. (Birm.) Clin. Asst. (Dermat.) Basingstoke & N. Hants. Health Dist.; Med. Cons. Automobile Assn., Lancia SpA (Competitions) Turin & Fed. Internat. de l'Automobiliste. Socs: BMA. Prev: Clin. Research Asst. St. John's Hosp. Lond. Ho. Surg. & Ho. Phys.; Manor Hosp. Walsall; Obst. Ho. Phys. & Ho. Anaesth. Roy. Hants. Co. Hosp. Winchester.

TEANBY, Mr David Nigel Whiston Hospital, Prescot L35 5DR Tel: 0151 426 1600 Fax: 0151 430 1094 — MB ChB 1980 Liverp.; FRCS (Orth.) 1995; FRCS Eng. 1988. Cons. Orthop. Surg. Whiston Hosp. Merseyside. Socs: Hon. Fell. BOA; Brit. Trauma Soc.; Brit. Assn. Surg. Knee. Prev: Sen. Regist. Hope Hosp. Salford.

TEARE, Celia Margaret Lila Wantage Health Centre, Church Street Practice, Wantage OX12 7AY Tel: 01235 770245 Fax: 01235 770727; 60 Newbury Street, Wantage OX12 8DF — MB BS 1971 Lond.; MRCGP 1976.

TEARE, Erica Louise Chelmsford Public Health Laboratory, New Writtle St., Chelmsford CM2 0YX Tel: 01245 513312 Fax: 01245 492496 Email: l.teare@btinternet.com; Smallfields, Mill Road, Stock, Ingatestone CM4 9LL Tel: 01277 840524 — MB BS 1977 Lond.; MSc Lond. 1982, BSc (Hons.) 1974; MRCS Eng. LRCP Lond. 1977; FRCPath 1996, M 1983. (St. Geo.) Cons. Med. Microbiol. & Dir. Pub. Health Laborat. Chelmsford. Socs: (Counc.) Roy. Soc. Med.; (Counc.) Hosp. Infec. Soc.; Assn. Med. Microbiol. Prev: Asst. Med. Microbiol. Pub. Health Laborat. Dulwich; Lect. (Med. Microbiol.) W.m. Hosp. Lond.; Regist. (Med. Microbiol.) & SHO (Path.) W.m. Hosp. Lond.

TEARE, Helen Caroline Woodlands, Lezayre Road, Ramsey IM8 2LN — MB BS 1989 Lond.

TEARE, Julian Paul GI Unit, St Mary's Hospital, Paddington, London W2 1NY Tel: 0207 886 1072 Fax: 0207 886 6871; Tel: 0208 987 8548 — MB BS 1984 Lond.; MD Lond. 1995; MRCP (UK) 1988; FRCP 2000. Cons. Gastroenterol. St. Mary's Hosp. Lond.; Mem. Med. Counc. on Alcoholism. Socs: Brit. Soc. Gastroenterol.; Amer. Gastoenterol. Assn. Prev: Sen. Regist. (Gen. Med. & Gastroenterol.) St. Mary's Hosp. Lond.; Regist. (Gen. Med. & Gastroenterol.) St. Thos. Hosp. Lond.; Regist. (Med.) Canterbury Hosp.

TEARE, Lara Jane 26 Temple Road, Dorridge, Solihull B93 8LF — MB ChB 1998 Bristol.

TEASDALE, Andrew Richard Department of Anaesthetics, Royal Devon & Exeter Hospital, Barrack Road, Exeter EX2 5DW Tel: 01392 402474 Fax: 01392 402473 Email: andrew@teardale100freeserve.co.uk — MB ChB 1984 Zimbabwe; LRCP LRCS Ed. LRCPS Glas. 1986; FCAnaesth. 1989. Cons. in Anaesth. Roy. Devon & Exeter Healthcare Trust Exeter. Prev: Regist. (Anaesth.) Soton. Gen. Hosp.; Asst. Prof. (Anaesth.) UWMC Seattle; Sen. Regist. (Anaesth.) Leeds Gen. Infirm.

TEASDALE, Mr Colin Derriford Hospital, Derriford Road, Plymouth PL6 8DH Tel: 01752 777111 Fax: 01752 763436; Nuffield Hospital, Derriford Road, Plymouth PL6 8BG Tel: 01752 775861 Fax: 01752 768969 — MB BS 1969 Lond.; BSc Lond. 1966, MS 1983, MB BS 1969; FRCS Eng. 1974. (Lond. Hosp.) Cons. Gen. Surg. Plymouth HA. Socs: Brit. Assn. Surg. Oncol.; Fell. Assn. Surgs. Prev: Sen. Regist. (Surg.) Bristol Health Dist. (T); Lect. (Surg.) & Hon. Sen. Regist. Welsh Nat. Sch. Med. Cardiff; Cancer Research Campaign Fell. (Surg.) Welsh Nat. Sch. Med. Cardiff.

TEASDALE, Mr Derek Hall (retired) 8 Mytchett Heath, Mytchett, Camberley GU16 6DP Tel: 01252 546859 — MB BS 1942 Lond.; FRCS Eng. 1949; MRCS Eng. LRCP Lond. 1942. Hon. Cons. Surg. Rochdale Infirm. & Birch Hill Hosp. Rochdale; Penrose May Teach. RCS. Prev: Surg. Adviser RCS Eng. NW RHA.

TEASDALE, Diane Elizabeth Larwood Health Centre, 56 Larwood, Worksop S81 0HH Tel: 01909 500233 Fax: 01909 479722 — MB ChB 1992 Sheff.; Dip Palliat Care 1999. (Sheffield) GP; Med Off. Hospice of Good Shephard.Retford.

TEASDALE, Eric Leslie AstraZeneca, Global Safety, Health and Environment, 15 Stanhope Gate, London W1K 1LN Tel: 01625 512510 Fax: 01625 517824 Email: eric.teasdale@astrazeneca.com; Badgers Bend, 5 Eaton Drive, Alderley Edge SK9 7RA Tel: 01625 585854 Email: eric.teasdale@astrazeneca.com — MB ChB 1972 Aberd.; FFOM RCP Lond. 1993, MFOM 1983, AFOM 1979; FRCGP 1993, M 1976; DIH Soc. Apoth. Lond. 1979; CIH Dund. 1979; Cert. Family Plann. JCC 1975; FRCP 1999; FACOEM 2000; FIOSH.RSP 1999. Gp. Chief Med. Off. AstraZeneca; Dir. Global SH & E Strategy; Mem. Internat. Commiss. Occupat. Health. Socs: Soc. Occup. Med.; MIEMA. Prev: Chief Med. Off. Zeneca; Trainee GP Aberd. VTS; Div. Med. Off. ICI.

TEASDALE, Professor Graham Michael University Department Neurosurgery, Institute of Neurological Sciences, Southern General Hospital, Glasgow G51 4TF Tel: 0141 201 2019 — MB BS 1963 Durh.; FRSE 2001; FRCS 2001 (Eng.); MRCP Lond. 1966; FRCS Glas. 1981; FRCS Ed. 1971; T(S) 1991; F Med Sci 1999. (Durham) Prof. Neurosurg. Univ. Glas.; Hon. Cons. Neurosurg. S. Gen. Hosp. Glas.; Chairm. Europ. Brain Injury Consortium. Socs: Soc. Brit. Neurol. Surg.; Internat. Neurotrauma Soc. Prev: Pres.Soc. of BrE. Neurol. Surg.

TEASDALE, Katherine 15 Denleigh Gardens, Thames Ditton KT7 0YL — MB ChB 1989 Sheff.; MRCP (UK) 1993; DTM & H Liverp. 1994.

TEASDALE, Kathryn Jane 4 The Hawthorns, Common Road, Malmesbury SN16 0HS — MB BS 1991 Lond.; DRCOG 1995; DFFP 1995; MRCGP 1996. (St. Geo. Hosp. Med. Sch.) Prev: Trainee GP Epsom, Surrey.

TEATHER, Stephen John Richmond House Surgery, Richmond Terrace, Station Road, Whitchurch SY13 1RH Tel: 01948 662870; 52 Pear Tree Lane, Whitchurch SY13 1NQ — MB ChB 1975 Birm.; DCH Eng. 1978; DRCOG 1977.

TEBAY, Kathryn Elena 7 Harold Street, Woodholde, Leeds LS6 1PL — MB ChB 1993 Leeds.

TEBB, James Barry Tunstall Washway Road Medical Centre, 63-65 Washway Road, Sale M33 7SU Tel: 0161 962 4354 Fax: 0161 962 0046 — MB ChB 1968 Manch. Prev: SHO (Cardiac Surg.) Manch. Roy. Infirm.; SHO (Orthop. & Cas.) Pk. Hosp. Davyhulme; Ho. Off. (Surg.) Unit. Manch. Roy. Infirm.

TEBBETT, John Ernest (retired) 122 Urmston Lane, Stretford, Manchester M32 9BQ — MB ChB 1949 Birm. Ex-Officio Mem. Trafford LMC Chairm.; Mem. Trafford Family Pract. Comm. Prev: Ho. Surg. Gen. Hosp. Birm.

TEBBIT, Anne 19 Pennine Rise, Scissett, Huddersfield HD8 9JE — MB BS 1991 Lond.

TEBBOTH, Louise Ina Joan 24 Cleveland Way, London E1 4UF — MB ChB 1998 Sheff.; MB ChB Sheff 1998. (Sheffield) GP St Thomas + Guys. Prev: PRHO. (Med + Surg Rotat.).

TEBBS, Elizabeth Mary Department of Health, Room 606A Skipton House, 80 London Road, Elephant & Castle, London SE1 6LW Tel: 020 7972 5030 Fax: 020 7972 5138; 6 Parkholme Road, Hackney, London E8 3AD Tel: 020 7275 7539 — MB ChB 1972 Leeds; MSc (Pub. Health) Lond. 1997; DRCOG 1976. (St Geos. Hosp. Med. Sch.) Sen. Med. Off. Health Protec. Div. DoM. Prev: RMO DoH; GP York.

TEBBS, Veronica Margaret — MB BS 1980 Newc.; MRCGP 1984; FFPM RCP 2001 (UK). Assoc. Med. Dir. 3M Health Care Ltd & Europ. Clin. Developm. Manager, Basal Cell Carcinoma Project; Clin. Asst., Dept. of Dermat., Qu.s Med. Centre, Nottm. Prev: Head

Drug Safety Copenhagen; Head (Med.) Milton Keynes; Head (Rheum. & Consumer Med.) Nottm.

TEBBUTT, Isabel Helen Harold Wood Hospital, Gubbins Lane, Romford RM3 0BE Tel: 01708 345533; Walletts, Great Warley St, Great Warley, Brentwood CM13 3JE Tel: 01277 227557 — MB BS 1977 Lond.; FRCOG 1995, M 1982; DCH Eng. 1980. (St. Geo.) Cons. O & G Harold Wood Hosp. Romford. Prev: Cons. O & G Stoke Mandeville Hosp. Aylesbury; Sen. Regist. (O & G) Hammersmith Hosp. Lond.; Hon. Clin. Tutor (O & G) W. Chesh. Hosp.

TEBBUTT, Niall Christopher 15 Wimbledon Drive, Stourbridge DY8 2PQ — BM BCh 1989 Oxf.

TEBBY, Susan Jane Norwood, 57 Elworth St., Sandbach CW11 1HA Tel: 01270 763454 — MB ChB 1986 Manch.; BSc (Hons.) Pharm. Med. Manch. 1983; MRCP (UK) 1990; FRCR 1997. Specialist Regist. (Diag. Radio.) N. Staffs. Hosp. Prev: Regist. Rotat. (Med.) N. Staffs. Roy. Infirm. & City Gen. Hosp Stoke-on-Trent.; Regist. Rotat. (Diag. Radiol.) N. W. RHA.

TECKHAM, Paul Ng Soon Harold Wood Hospital, 14 Hospital Crescent, Gubbins Lane, Romford RM3 0BJ — MB ChB 1982 Leeds.

TEDBURY, Michael John St Johns Medical Centre, 62 London Road, Grantham NG31 6HR Tel: 01476 590055 Fax: 01476 400042 — MB BS 1976 Newc.; MRCGP 1980. (Lond.)

TEDD, Clive Barron Saltaire Medical Centre, Richmond Road, Shipley BD18 4RX Tel: 01274 593101 Fax: 01274 772588 — MRCS Eng. LRCP Lond. 1970; DA Eng. 1973.

TEDD, Rachael Jane 7 Craven Cl, Fulwood, Preston PR2 9PU — MB ChB 1997 Glas.

TEDDERS, Brian Claudy Health Centre, Irwin Crescent, Claudy, Londonderry BT47 4AB Tel: 028 7133 8371 — MB BCh BAO 1978 NUI; LRCPI & LM, LRCSI & LM 1978.

TEDDERS, Raphael Andrew The Health Centre, Cemmaes Road, Machynlleth SY20 8LB; Brickfield House, Brickfield St, Machynlleth SY20 — MB BCh BAO 1979 NUI; LRCPI & LM, LRCSI & LM BAO 1979.

TEDDY, Mr Peter Julian Department of Neurological Surgery, The Radcliffe Infirmary, Oxford OX2 6HE Tel: 01865 224941 Fax: 01865 224898; St. Peters College, Oxford OX1 2DL Tel: 01865 278900 — BM BCh 1972 Oxf.; MA, DPhil, BSc 1972; FRCS Eng. 1977. Cons. Neurosurg. Radcliffe Infirm. Oxf. & Nat. Spinal Injuries Centre Stoke Mandeville Hosp. Aylesbury; Sen. Research Fell. St. Peter's Coll. Oxf.; Clin. Lect. Univ. Oxf. Med. Sch. Socs: Soc. Brit. Neurol. Surg. & Internat. Assn. Study of Pain; Internat. Med. Soc. Paraplegia; Brit. Cervical Spine Soc. Prev: Dir. Clin. Studies Univ. Oxf. Med. Sch.; Asst. Edr. Brit. J. Neurosurg.; Clin. Director (Neurosci.), Radcliffe Infirm., Oxf..

TEDSTONE, Ian Keith Newthorpe Medical Practice, Eastwood Clinic, Nottingham Road, Eastwood, Nottingham NG16 3GL Tel: 01773 760202 Fax: 01773 710951 — BM BS 1994 Nottm.

TEE, Dudley Edward Handbury (retired) 1 St Aubyns Mead, Rottingdean, Brighton BN2 7HY Tel: 01273 302635 — MB BS 1954 Lond.; FRCPath 1976, M 1965. Prev: Head of Immunol. King's Coll. Sch. Med. & Dent.

TEE, George Harry (retired) Hannaford House, Poundsgate, Newton Abbot — MRCS Eng. LRCP Lond. 1944; PhD 1953; MA Camb. 1944; FRCPath 1964. Prev: Director Pub. Health Laborat. Dorchester.

TEE, Michael Kevin John Tasker House Surgery, 56 New Street, Great Dunmow, Dunmow CM6 1BH Tel: 01371 873774 Fax: 01371 873793 Email: miketee@jth.demon.co.uk; Meadow Cottage, High St, Widdington, Saffron Walden CB11 3SG Tel: 01799 542626 — MB BChir 1985 Camb.; BSc (Hons.) St. And. 1980; MRCGP 1990; DRCOG 1989; DLO RCS Eng. 1988. Clin. Asst. (Ear, Nose & Throat). Socs: LMC; Vice-chair. PCT.

TEEBAY, Linda Evelyn (retired) 32 Saddler's Rise, Priory Grange, Runcorn WA7 6PG — MB ChB 1983 Liverp. Staff Grade (Paediat. A & E) Roy. Liverp. Childr.'s Hosp.

TEEBAY, Peter French Millwood Road Surgery, 95 Millwood Road, Liverpool L24 2UR Tel: 0151 425 3717 Fax: 0151 425 3233; 17 Hale Road, Hale Village, Liverpool L24 5RB Tel: 0151 425 3742 Fax: 0151 425 3742 — MB ChB 1956 Liverp.; MRCS Eng. LRCP Lond. 1956; MRCGP 1971; Dip Ad Educat Liverp. 1971. (Liverp.) Lect. (Gen. Pract.) Liverp. Univ.; Vis. Gen. Pract. Sir Alfred Jones

Memor. Hosp. Garston. Socs: BMA. Prev: Clin. Asst. (Psychiat.) Rainhill Hosp. Prescot; SHO (O & G) Harrogate Gen. Hosp.; Ho. Phys. & Ho. Surg. (Orthop.) Roy. Liverp. Childr. Hosp.

TEECE, Stewart Conway 40 Beverley Road, Nunthorpe, Middlesbrough TS7 0HN — MB ChB 1995 Glas.

TEED, Alison Rhona Wellspring Surgery, St. Anns Health Centre, St. Anns, Well Road, Nottingham NG3 3PX Tel: 0115 9505907/8 Fax: 0115 988 1582 — MB BCh 1985 Wales; DRCOG 1990. Prev: GP Newport, Gwent; SHO (Urol. & A & E) Cardiff Roy. Infirm.; SHO (Geriat. & O & G) Llandough Hosp. Cardiff.

TEED, Henry (retired) 466 Loose Road, Maidstone ME15 9UA Tel: 01622 743948 — MB BS 1957 Lond.; DCH Eng. 1961; DObst RCOG 1960. Prev: Ho. Surg. (O & G) St. Mary Abbot's Hosp. Kensington.

TEELOCK, Boodhun 49 Newlands Court, Forty Avenue, Wembley HA9 9LZ — MB ChB 1950 Ed.

TEENAN, Mr Robert Paul 1 Erskine Avenue, Glasgow G41 5AL — MB ChB 1981 Glas.; MD Glas. 1990; FRCS (Gen.) 1995; FRCS Glas. 1985. Cons. Surg. Glas. Roy. Infirm.

TEES, Ernest Carroll 6 Templars Place, St. Peter St., Marlow SL7 1NU Tel: 016284 71113 — MB BCh BAO 1953 Dub.; MA Dub. 1939, MB BCh BAO 1953. (T.C. Dub.) Socs: Brit. Allergy Soc. Prev: Ho. Off. City & Co. Hosp. Lond.derry; Capt. Middlx. Regt.

TEGNER, Henry The Surgery, 1 Forest Hill Road, London SE22 0SQ Tel: 020 8693 2264 Fax: 020 8299 0200 — MB BS 1969 Lond.; MSc Lond. 1993; FRCGP 2000; DObst RCOG 1973. (Lond. Hosp.) Course Organiser Lewisham VTS. Prev: Ho. Phys. Mile End. Hosp.; Ho. Surg. Lond. Hosp.; Squadron Ldr. RAF Med. Br.

TEGOS, Thomas 9 Craven Hill Gardens, London W2 3ES — Ptychio Iatrikes 1989 Thessalonika.

TEH, Corina Poh Ling 1 Foxes Close, Hermitage Walk, The Park, Nottingham NG7 1PG; Flat 3, Tower Mansions, 86/87 Grange Road, London SE1 — BM BS 1987 Nottm.; BMedSci. (Hons.) 1985; MRCP (UK) 1992; MRCGP 1993; DFFP 1994; DRCOG 1993.

TEH, Hui-Pin (retired) St. John's Hospital, Livingston EH54 6PP Tel: 01506 419666 — MB BCh BAO 1964 Dub.; FFA RCS Eng. 1968. Cons. Anaesth. St. John's Hosp. Livingston W. Lothian. Prev: Cons. Anaesth. Bangour Gen. & City Hosps. Edin.

TEH, James Lip Ze 109 Coningham Road, London W12 8BU — MB BS 1991 Lond.; BSc (Hons.) Psychol. Lond. 1987; MRCP (UK) 1994. Specialist Regist. (Radiol.) Lond.

TEH, Lee Gek Whitevale Medical Group, 30 Whitevale Street, Glasgow G31 1QS — MB ChB 1978 Aberd.

TEH, Lee-Suan Department of Rheumatology, Ward 13, Level 5, Blackburn Royal Infirmary, Bolton Road, Blackburn BB2 3LR Tel: 01254 294484 Fax: 01254 294423 Email: lsteh@btinternet.com; 28 cholmondeley Road, Salford M6 8NH Tel: 0161 7430392 Email: lstch@btinternet.com — MB ChB 1984 Aberd.; MB ChB (Commend.) 1984; MRCP (UK) 1987; MD Aberd. 1994; FRCP Glas. 1997; FRCP Lon. 2000. (Univ. Aberd. Med. Sch.) Cons. Rheum. Blackburn Roy. Infirm. Socs: BMA; Brit. Soc. of Rheum.; Brit. Soc. of Immunol. Prev: Sen. Regist. (Rheum.) Manch.; Research Fell. Arthritis & Rheum. Counc.; Regist. (Rheum.) Univ. Hosp. Wales.

TEH, Rosalind Kin Kin 28 Juniper Way, Grimsby DN33 2BQ — BM BS 1996 Flinders.

TEHAN, Brian Edwin Department of Anaesthesia, Glan Clwyd Hospital, Bodelwyddan, Rhyl LL18 5UJ Tel: 01745 583910 Fax: 01745 583143 Email: drbrian.tehan@glanclwyd.tr.wales.nhs.uk; Ty Canol, Copthorn Road, Upper Colwyn Bay, Colwyn Bay LL28 5YP Tel: 01492 531284 Email: brian.tehan@virgin.net — MB BCh BAO 1986 NUI; FFA RCSI 1992; Spec. Accredit. Anaesth. RCSI (Fac. Anaesth.) 1995. Cons. Anaesth. & Intens. Care Glan Clwyd Hosp. Socs: Welsh Soc. Anaesth.; Sec. Welsh Intens. Care Soc.; Intens. Care Soc. Prev: Sen. Regist. (Anaesth.) & Fell. Cardiothoracic Anaesth. Leeds Gen. Infirm.; SHO (Anaesth.) St. Jas. Univ. Hosp. Leeds.

TEILLOL-FOO, Weng Lee Melvyn Pharmarcia & UpJohn Pharmaceuticals, 4-3-13 Toranomon, Toyko, Minato-KU 163-1350, Japan; 55 Ashworth Place, Church Langley Way, Harlow CM17 9PU — MB ChB 1984 Sheff.; FRCA 1991; FFA RCSI 1989; Dip. Pharm. Med. RCP (UK) 1994; DA (UK) 1987. (Sheff.) Director Clin. Pharmacol.. Socs: Brit. Assn. Pharmaceut. Phys. Prev: Assoc. Director (Clin. Pharmacol.) SmithKline Beecham Pharmaceut. Harlow;

TEIMORY

Business Manager Pharmaco Leicester Clin. Research Centre Ltd.; Sen. Phys. Leicester Clin. Research Centre Ltd.

TEIMORY, Masoud Worthing Hospital, Park Avenue, Worthing BN11 2DH — MB ChB 1986 Bristol; FRCOphth 1991.

TEIRNEY, Raewyn Doctors Quarters, University Hospital, Queens Medical Centre, Nottingham NG7 2UH — MB ChB 1994 Auckland.

TEJANI, Sakkar (retired) 107 Cadogan Gardens, South Woodford, London E18 1LY Tel: 020 8989 7974 — MB BS 1956 Bombay; MRCGP 1966.

TEJURA, Bindu Albert Einstein Medical Centre, 5501 Old York Road, Philadelphia PA 19141, USA Tel: 215 456 7890 Fax: 215 473 7566 Email: btejura@aol.com; 88 Trinity View, Caerleon, Newport NP18 3SW — MB BCh 1992 Wales; BSc (Hons) Pharmacology. (Wales)

TEJURA, Harsit 88 Trinity View, Caerleon, Newport NP18 3SW — MB BCh 1993 Wales.

TEK, Vinod 95 Grosvenor Road, Ilford IG1 1LB — LMSSA 1997 Lond.

TEKLE, Iyassu Ashurst Health Centre, Lulworth, Ashurst, Skelmersdale WN8 6QS Tel: 01695 732468 Fax: 01695 555365 — MB BCh 1979 N U Ireland; MB BCh 1979 N U Ireland.

TEKRIWAL, Alok Kumar Department of Ophthalmology, County Hospital, Lincoln LN2 5QY — MB BS 1988 Patna; FRCOphth 1994.

TELANG, Shammohan Maharudra Gray Hill Surgery, Woodstock Way, Caldicot, Newport NP26 5AB; Momon's Folly, Wedgwood Drive, Portskewett, Newport NP6 4TL Tel: 01291 420252 — MB BS 1955 Poona. (B. J. Med. Coll. Poona) Apptd. Fact. Doctor. Prev: Regist. (Orthop.) Cardiff Roy. Infirm.; SHO (Cas.) Sassoon Hosp. Poona; Ho. Surg. St. Woolos Hosp. Newport.

TELESZ, Ann Marysia Health Centre, Handsworth Avenue, Highams Park, London E4 9PD Tel: 020 8527 0913 Fax: 020 8527 6597 — MB BS 1980 Lond.; MA Oxf. 1978, BA (Biochem.) 1975; MRCGP 1985; DRCOG 1984. (Univ. Coll. Hosp.) Trainer; Course Organiser Whipps Cross Hosp. VTS.

TELFER, Aileen Hazel 34 Grange Terrace, Edinburgh EH9 2LE — MB ChB 1990 Ed. SHO (Gen. Med. & Infec. Dis.) Castle Hill Hosp. Hull.

TELFER, Alexander Borland Meikle (retired) Kinmuir, 167 Mugdork Road, Milngavie, Glasgow G62 8NB Tel: 0141 956 1371 — MB ChB 1956 Glas.; FRCP Glas. 1984, M 1982; FFA RCS Eng. 1963. Cons. Anaesth. Glas. Roy. Infirm.; Hon. Clin. Lect. Anaesth. Univ. Glas. Prev: Sen. Regist. Univ. Dept. Anaesth. & Ho. Off. (Anaesth.) Glas. Roy.Infirm.

TELFER, Carol Ann Linda 14 Sorbie Drive, Stonehouse, Larkhall ML9 3NL — MB ChB 1987 Glas.

TELFER, Ian Dept of Psychiatry, Tameside Central Hosp, Fountain St, Ashton-under-Lyne OL6 9RW Tel: 0161 331 5094 — MB ChB 1979 Liverp.; MRCPsych 1985. Cons.(Psychiat.) W. Pennine Health Auth.. Socs: MDU.

TELFER, James Robert Mill Road Surgery, Mill Road, Market Rasen LN8 3BP Tel: 01673 843556 Fax: 01673 844388 — MB BS 1984 Lond.; MA Camb. 1992; MRCGP 1988.

TELFER, Mr John Robert Currie 78 Hainburn Park, Fairmilehead, Edinburgh EH10 7HJ — MB ChB 1985 Ed.; FRCS Glas. 1991. Specialist Regist. (Plastic Surg.) St. John's Hosp. at Howden Livingstone. Prev: SHO (Plastic Surg.) Char. Cross Hosp., St. Geo. Hosp. & Qu. Mary's Univ. Hosp. Lond.

TELFER, John Robin (retired) Ellenthorpe, Church Road, Lympstone, Exmouth EX8 5JT — MB BS 1965 Lond.; DObst RCOG 1968; DCH Eng. 1967. Prev: SHO (O & G & Paediat.) Freedom Fields Hosp. Plymouth.

TELFER, June Mary 10 Woodburn Gardens, Aberdeen AB15 8JA — MB ChB 1994 Ed.

TELFER, Mr Martin Ronaldson Tel: 01904 453756 Fax: 01904 454468; Beech House, Warthill, York YO19 5XW — MB BS 1985 Lond.; BDS 1977; FRCS Ed. 1988; FDS RCS Eng. 1985. Cons. Oral & Maxillofacial Surg. York Dist. Hosp.; Lead Head and Neck Cancer Clinician - N. Yorks.; Dep. Lead Cancer Clinician - York Trust.

TELFER, Nicholas Roland Dermatology Centre, Hope Hospital, Stott Lane, Salford M6 8HD Tel: 0161 787 1010 Fax: 0161 962 2054 Email: nrtelfer@aol.com — MB ChB 1981 Manch.; MRCP (UK) 1984; FRCP Lond. 1998. Cons. Dermat. & Dermat. Surg. Dermat. Centre Manch. Socs: Brit. Assn. Dermat.; Fell. Amer. Coll. of MOHS Micrographic Surg. & Cutaneous Oncol.; Fell. Amer. Soc.

Dermatologic Surg. Prev: Asst. Prof. & Fell. MOHS & Dermat. Surg. Div. Dermat. Univ. Calif. Los Angeles, USA; Sen. Regist. (Dermat.) Skin Hosp. Manch.

TELFER, Paul Trevor 156 Warren Crescent, Shirley, Southampton SO16 6AX — BM BCh 1986 Oxf.; MRCP (UK) 1989. Regist. (Haemat.) Roy. Free Hosp. Lond.

TELFER, Mr Robert Currie, Surg. Capt. RN Retd. (retired) Eastwood House, Fushiebridge, Gorebridge EH23 4QH Tel: 01875 822367 — MB ChB 1957 Ed.; FRCS Ed. 1968. Prev: Head Orthop. RNH Haslar.

TELFER, Trevor Percival (retired) Cob End, Oast Court, Yalding, Maidstone ME18 6JY — MB BS 1948 Melbourne; FRCP Lond. 1988, M 1957; FRCP Ed. 1983, M 1957; FRCPath 1972, M 1964; MCPA 1958; DPath. Eng. 1955. Cons. Path. St. Bart. Hosp. Rochester. Prev: Regist. (Clin. Path.) Univ. Coll. Hosp.

TELFER BRUNTON, William Andrew Truro Public Health Laboratory, Penventinnie Lane, Treliske, Truro TR1 3LQ Tel: 01872 254900 Fax: 01872 222198 Email: atb@dial.pipex.com — MB ChB 1973 Ed.; BSc (Hons.) (Bact.) Ed. 1970; FRCPath 1982, M 1980; FRCP Ed. 1998. (Ed.) Cons. Microbiol., Dir. Pub. Health Laborat. Truro; JP. Socs: Assn. Clin. Path.; Brit. Soc. Study of Infec.; Assn. Med. Microbiol. Prev: Lect. (Bact.) & (Clin. Chem.) Univ. Edin.

TELFORD, Anne Marie Tower Hill, Armagh BT61 9DR Tel: 01861 410041 Fax: 01861 414551; 11 Rosemary Park, Belfast BT9 6RF — MB BCh BAO 1975 Belf.; MD Belf. 1982; MRCP (UK) 1980; FFPHM RCP (UK) 1994, M 1988; FRCP (UK) 1999. (Queens University Belfast.) Dir. Pub. Health SHSSB. Prev: Cons. Pub. Health Med. NHSSB; Sen. Regist. (Community Med.) NHSSB Ballymena.

TELFORD, David Ronald Department of Microbiology, Royal Lancaster Infirmary, Ashton Road, Lancaster LA1 4RP Tel: 01524 583770 Fax: 01524 583798 Email: david.telford@1.bay-tr.nwest.nhs.uk; Aldcliffe, Carr Bank, Milnthorpe LA7 7LB Tel: 01524 761529 — MB ChB 1971 Manch.; FRCPath. 1990, M 1978; Dip. Bact. Manch. 1978. (Manchester) Cons. Microbiol. Morecambe Bay Hosps. NHS Trust; Cons. Communicable Dis. Control Morecambe Bay HA; Hon. Reader (Biol. Sci.) Lancaster Univ.; Dep. Med. Dir. Morcambe Bay Hosps. NHS Trust. Prev: Cons. Microbiol. Leeds Pub. Health Lab.; Sen. Regist. (Microbiol.) Manch. AHA; Tutor (Communicable Dis.) Manch. Univ.

TELFORD, Karen Jane 4 Friars Court, Coleraine BT51 3JH — MB ChB 1991 Bristol.

TELFORD, Michael Edwin Fournier Pharmaceuticals Ltd, 22-23 Progress Business centre, Whittle Parkway, Slough SL1 6DG Tel: 01753 740400 Fax: 01753 740444 Email: m.telford@fournier.fr — MB BS 1983 Lond.; Dip. Pharm. Med. RCP (UK) 1997; T(GP) 1987; AFPM RCP Lond. 1998. (St. Mark's Hospital Medical School) Med. Director, Fournier Pharmaceut. Ltd., Slought. Socs: Brit. Assn. Pharmaceut. Phys. - Mem. Exec. Comm.; Fell. Roy. Soc. of Med. Prev: Sen. Med. Affairs Phys., Bayer plc, Newbury; Med. Adviser Yamanouchi Pharma Ltd. W. Byleet; GP Hampton.

TELFORD, Richard Jonathan 9 Barton Close, Exton, Exeter EX3 0PE — MB BS 1981 Lond.; BSc (Hons.) Lond. 1978, MB BS 1981; FFA RCS Eng. 1985. (St. Bart.) Cons. Anaesth. Roy. Devon & Exeter Hosps. Prev: Sen. Regist. (Anaesth.) St. Geo. Hosp. Lond.; Regist. (Paediat. Anaesth.) Roy. Liverp. Childr. Hosps.; Regist. (Anaesth.) Guy's Hosp.

TELFORD, Rosemary Margaret The Robert Darbishire Practice, Walmer Street, Rusholme, Manchester M14 5NP Tel: 0161 225 6699 Fax: 0161 248 4580 — MB ChB 1983 Manch.; MRCGP 1988; DCH RCP Lond. 1987; DRCOG 1986. (Manch.) Hon. Lect. (Gen. Pract.) GP Tutor. Prev: Dist. Med. Off. Katherine N. Terr., Austral.; GP Chippenham; Trainee GP N.wick Pk. Hosp. Harrow VTS.

TELFORD, Sydney Bruce (retired) Channel Farm, Oakridge, Winscombe BS25 1NJ Tel: 01934 843247 Email: btel682804@aol.com — MB BCh BAO 1949 Dub.; FFCM 1986, MFCM 1974; DTM & H Eng. 1960. Prev: SCM S. W.. RHA & Avon HA.

TELLECHEA ELORRIAGA, Francisco Javier 11 Simpson Street, Crosshouse, Kilmarnock KA2 0BD — LMS 1989 Basque Provinces.

TELLER, Richard Henry Marshall Finchley Road Surgery, 682 Finchley Road, Golders Green, London NW11 7NP Tel: 020 8455 9994 — MB BS 1988 Lond.; MA Oxf. 1982; MRCGP 1992.

TELLING, Jeremy Philip The Priory Surgery, 326 Wells Road, Bristol BS4 2QJ Tel: 0117 949 3988 Fax: 0117 778250 — MB ChB 1956 Bristol; DObst RCOG 1961. Prev: Act. Maj. RAMC.

TELLIS, Michael McDonald (retired) Measham Medical Unit, High Street, Measham, Swadlincote DE12 7HR Tel: 01530 270667 Fax: 01530 271433 — MB ChB 1960 Ed.; FRCGP 1978, M 1971; DObst RCOG 1962.

TELLO ARENAS, Eduardo 9 Eastbury Court, 37 Lyonsdown Road, New Barnet, Barnet EN5 1LD — LMS 1991 Cordoba.

TELLWRIGHT, Joseph Michael (retired) Manor Farm, Hunsterson, Nantwich CW5 7RB Tel: 01270 520353 — MB 1956 Camb.; BChir 1955.

TEMBE, Mr Dinkar Parashuram Charnley Farm House, 19 Clancutt Lane, Coppull, Chorley PR7 4NR Tel: 01257 791216 — MB BS 1957 Poona; FRCS Ed. 1970; LMSSA Lond. 1971; MRCGP 1976; DLO Eng. 1961. Clin. Asst. (ENT Surg.) Roy. Albert Edwd. Infirm. Wigan. Socs: Brit. Soc. Med. & Dent. Hypn.; Assoc. Mem. N. Eng. Otolaryng. Soc. Prev: Regist. (Otolaryngol.) Roy. Albert Edwd. Infirm. Wigan & Selly Oak Hosp. Birm.

TEMME, Christine Patricia Severn NHS Trust, Rikenel, Montpellier, Gloucester GL1 1LY Tel: 01452 891022 Fax: 01452 891020; 10 Canters Leaze, Wickwar, Wotton-under-Edge GL12 8LX Tel: 01454 294660 — MB BS 1965 Lond.; MRCS Eng. LRCP Lond. 1965. (St. Mary's) SCMO Gloucester HA. Socs: BMA; RCPCH. Prev: Clin. Med. Off. Glos. HA; Med. Off. Warks. CC; SHO (Anaesth.) & Ho. Phys. Altrincham Gen. Hosp.

TEMPERLEY, Christine The Medical Centre, 4 Craven Avenue, Thornton, Bradford BD13 3LG Tel: 01274 832110/834387 Fax: 01274 831694; 32 Lidget, Oakworth, Keighley BD22 7HH Tel: 01535 642008 — MB ChB 1989 Leeds. GP. Prev: Trainee GP York VTS; SHO (Psychiat.) Lynfield Mt. Hosp. Bradford.

TEMPERLEY, David Edward Royal Albert Edward Infirmary, Wigan Lane, Wigan WN1 2NN Tel: 01942 244000; 67 Framingham Road, Sale, Manchester M33 3RH Tel: 0161 972 0004 — MB BCh BAO 1984 Dub.; MB BCh BAO (Dub.) 1984; MRCPI 1986; FRCR 1991. Cons. Radiol. Wigan & Leigh NHS Trust. Prev: Regist. (Radiol.) N. W.. RHA.

TEMPERTON, Helen Clair 6 Clifton House, 131 Cleveland St., London W1T 6QE — MB BCh 1995 Wales.

TEMPEST, Heidi Victoria 19 Langham Road, Cambridge CB1 3SD — BChir 1996 Camb.

TEMPEST, Janet Elizabeth The Surgery, 14 Manor Road, Beckenham BR3 5LE Tel: 020 8650 0957 Fax: 020 8663 6070 — MB BS 1982 Lond.; MRCGP 1986. GP Beckenham.

TEMPEST, Lynda Carole Hamilton Road Surgery, 201 Hamilton Road, Felixstowe IP11 7DT Tel: 01394 283197 Fax: 01394 270304; 31 Foxgrove Lane, Felixstowe IP11 7JU — MB ChB 1975 Sheff.; DRCOG 1977. (Sheffield) Prev: Trainee Gen. Pract. Sheff. Vocational Train. Scheme; Ho. Phys. & Ho. Surg. Doncaster Roy. Infirm.

TEMPEST, Pernell Kate 34 Chyandor Close, St. Blazey, Par PL24 2LP — MB BS 1992 Lond.

TEMPLE, Mr Adrian James 1a Marsh Road, Weymouth DT4 8JD Tel: 01305 774466 Fax: 01305 760538 — MB BS 1968 Lond.; FRCS Eng. 1975; MRCS Eng. LRCP Lond. 1968. (St. Geo.) p/t Private practitioner, Weymouth, Dorset & Clin. Assist. (Rheumat.). Prev: GP, Weymouth, Dorset.

TEMPLE, Mr Andrew John Lovington Grange, Lovington Lane, Lower Broadheth, Worcester WR2 6QQ Tel: 01905 640992 — MB BS 1994 Lond.; BSc Lond. 1991; FRCS Lond. 1998. Specialist Rotat. (Orthop.) W. Midl. Prev: SHO Rotat. (Surg.) Roy. Berks. Hosp.

***TEMPLE, Andrew Richard** 19 Welland Vale Road, Leicester LE5 6PX — MB ChB 1994 Leeds.

TEMPLE, Celia Margaret Rose Garden Medical Centre, 4 Mill Lane, Edinburgh EH6 6TL Tel: 0131 554 1274 Fax: 0131 555 2159 — MB ChB 1984 Sheff.; MRCGP 1988.

TEMPLE, Dean Russell Orchard Medical Practice, Innisdoon, Crow Hill Drive, Mansfield NG19 7AE Tel: 01623 400100 Fax: 01623 400101; Ashworth, 2 St. Chads Close, Mansfield NG18 4DS Tel: 01623 654177 — MB ChB 1987 Leic. Prev: SHO (Geriat. & A & E) Kings Mill Hosp. Sutton-in-Ashfield; Trainee GP/SHO Mansfield VTS.

TEMPLE, Isabel Karen Wessex Clinical Genetic Service, Department of Child Health, Princess Anne Hospital, Coxford Road, Southampton SO16 5YA Tel: 02380 796625 Fax: 02380 794346; South Ploverfield, Long Lane, Bursledon, Southampton SO31 8DA — MB ChB 1981 Birm.; FRCP Lond. 1995; MRCP (UK) 1984. Cons. Clin. Genetics Soton. Gen. Hosp.; R & D Soton. Univ. Hosps. Trust; Hon. Sen. Lect. Univ. of Soton. Socs: (Comm.) Clin. Genetics Soc. Prev: Sen. Regist. (Genetics) Hosp. for Sick Childr. Gt. Ormond St.

TEMPLE, John Darcus The Surgery, 292 Derby Road, Lenton, Nottingham NG7 1QG Tel: 0115 947 4002 Fax: 0115 924 0783 — MB BChir 1970 Camb.; MB BChir. Camb. 1969; MA Camb. 1970; MRCGP 1976; Dip. Med. Educat. Dund 1995; DObst RCOG 1973. (Middlx.) GP Nottm.; Lect. (Gen. Pract.) Univ. Nottm. since 1981. Prev: Trainee GP Teeside VTS; SHO (Psychiat.) Lond. Hosp.; Ho. Phys. W. Middlx. Hosp.

TEMPLE, Professor John Graham Wharncliffe, 24 Westfield Road, Edgbaston, Birmingham B15 3QG Tel: 0121 454 2445 Fax: 0121 454 2445 — MB ChB (Hons.) Liverp. 1965; ChM Liverp. 1977; FRCS Eng. 1970; FRCS Ed. 1969; MRCS Eng. LRCP Lond. 1966; FRCP 1999; F med Sci 1998. (Liverp.) Postgrad Dean Birm. Univ. & W. Midl. Region; Prof. Surg. Birm. Univ.; Examr. RCS Edin.; Chairm. COPMED; Special Adviser to CMO (Postgrad. Educat.). Socs: BMA & Surgic. Res. Soc.; Roy. Soc. Med.; (Counc.) Roy. Coll. Surgs. Edin. Prev: Sen. Lect. (Surg.) Univ. Manch.; Hon. Cons. Surg. Salford AHA (T); Regist. (Surg.) Liverp. Roy. Infirm.

TEMPLE, Jonathan Mark Fraser Gwent Health Authority, Mamhilad, Pontypool NP4 0QN Email: mtemple@pha2.demon.co.uk — MB BChir 1980 Camb.; DRCOG 1981; MRCGP 1983; Cert. Family Plann. JCC 1982. Regist. (Pub. Health) Gwent HA. Prev: GP Glynneath W. Glam.

TEMPLE, Mr Leslie Joseph (retired) 4 King Charles Court, Watertower St., Chester CH1 2AW — MB BS 1948 Lond.; MB BS (Hnrs.) Lond. 1948; FRCS Eng. 1941; MRCS Eng. LRCP Lond. 1939. Prev: Dir. of Studies (Cardiothoracic Surg.) Univ. Liverp.

TEMPLE, Louis Norman Department of Histopathology, Epsom District Hospital, Dorking Road, Epsom KT18 7EG — MB BS 1972 Lond.; MRCS Eng. LRCP Lond. 1972; MRCPath 1985. (St. Bart.) Cons. Histopath. Epsom Dist. Hosp.

TEMPLE, Margaret Eleanor 33 Mountsandel Road, Coleraine BT52 1JE — MB BCh BAO 1953 Dub.; DA Eng. 1956.

TEMPLE, Margaret Jillian Leighton Wharncliffe, 24 Westfield Road, Edgbaston, Birmingham B15 3QG Tel: 0121 454 2445 Fax: 0121 454 2445 — MB ChB Liverp. 1965; MRCS Eng. LRCP Lond. 1966; MFFP 1993. (Liverp.) SCMO Birm. Socs: Foundat. Mem. Fac. Family Plann. & Reproduc. Healthcare; W Midl. Family Plann. Doctors; Fac. Pub. Health Med. Prev: Med. Off. (Family Plann.) Sefton AHA; Asst. Div. Med. Off. Lancs. CC; Ho. Off. BRd.green Hosp. Liverp.

TEMPLE, Melanie Jayne Dept. Mental Health, University Hospital of North Tees, Hardwick, Stockton-on-Tees TS19 8PE Tel: 01642 624316 Email: meljaynetemple@aol.com; The Mill House, Church Row, Mewonby, Richmond DL11 6HL Tel: 01325 718421 Email: familytemple@aol.com — MB ChB 1994 Glas. SpR (Gen. Psychiat.) Dept. Ment. Health, N. Tees Hosp., Stockton. Socs: MRCPsych. Prev: SHO (Gen. Psychiat.) Duchess of Kent Hosp. Catterick.

TEMPLE, Nicholas Owen Thomas Tavistock Clinic, 120 Belsize Lane, London NW3 5BA Tel: 020 7435 7111 Fax: 020 7447 3709 Email: chairman@tavi-port.org; Stanfield House, 86 Hampstead High St, London NW3 1RE Tel: 020 7794 1259 — MB ChB 1969 Bristol; BSc (Hons. Anat.) Bristol 1966, MB ChB 1969; FRCPsych 1991, M 1973; DPM Scot. 1972. (Bristol) Cons. Psychiat. Pyschother.Tavistock Clin.; Med. Director Tavistock and Portman NHS Trust; Chairm. Profess. Comm. Tavistock Clinic; Chairm. Tavistock Clinic Found. Med. Dir. Socs: Brit. Psychoanal. Soc. Prev: Cons. Psychother. Maudsley Hosp. Lond., King's Coll. Hosp. & Portman Clinic Lond.

TEMPLE, Paul Ian Accident & Emergency Department, Kings Mill Centre for Health Care Services NHS Trust, Sutton-in-Ashfield NG17 4JL Tel: 01623 622515; 14 Charnwood Lane, Arnold, Nottingham NG5 6PE Tel: 0115 926 4332 — MB ChB 1987 Sheff.; BSc Sheff. 1984; MRCGP 1995; DFFP 1995; Dip. IMC RCS Ed. 1995. Staff Grade (A & E) Kings Mill Centre Notts. Prev: Trainee GP Mansfield VTS.

TEMPLE, Mr Robert Hartley 24 Grange Avenue, Hale, Altrincham WA15 8ED Tel: 0161 904 8953 — MB ChB 1991 Sheff.; 2000 FRCS Ed. ORL-HNS; FRCS Ed. (Orl.) 1995. Specialist Regist. (OtoLaryngol.) Manch. Socs: Forum Mem. Roy. Soc. Med.; BAO - HNS. Prev: SHO Rotat. (Otolarnyngol.) Roy. Liverp. Hosp.

TEMPLE

TEMPLE, Robert Mark Department of Renal Medicine, Birmingham Heartlands Hospital, Bordesley Green E., Birmingham B9 5SS Tel: 0121 424 2157 — MB ChB 1982 Birm.; MD Birm. 1992; MRCP (UK) 1986. Cons. Nephrol. Birm. Heartlands Hosp. Socs: FRCP Edin.; FRCP Lond. Prev: Sen. Regist. (Nephrol.) Portsmouth; Wellcome Lect. (Med.) Univ. Edin.; Regist. (Nephrol.) Edin.

TEMPLE, Robert Wilbur (retired) Sandelford, 33 Mountsandel Road, Coleraine BT52 1JE — MB BCh BAO Dub. 1938; BA Dub. 1938; FRCP Lond. 1972, M 1948; FRCPI 1969, M 1948. Prev: Phys. Coleraine Hosp. Gp.

TEMPLE, Rosemary Christine Norfolk and Norwich Hospital, Brunswick Road, Norwich NR1 3SR Tel: 01603 286771 Fax: 01603 287320; 8 Montague Road, Cambridge CB4 1BX Tel: 01223 311360 — MB BS 1977 Lond.; FRCP (UK) 1999; MRCP (UK) 1980; MA Camb. 1977. Cons. Endocrinol. & Diabetes Norf. & Norwich Hosp. Socs: Eur. Assn. for Study Diabetes; Brit. Diabetic Assn. Prev: SCMO (Endocrinol. & Diabetes) Norf. & Norwich Hosp.; Sen. Regist. (Endocrinol.) Addenbrooke's Hosp. Camb.; Lect. (Endocrinol. & Metab.) Lond. Hosp.

TEMPLE, Sarah Elizabeth Basement Flat, 86 Disraeli Road, London SW15 2DX — MB BChir 1986 Camb.

TEMPLE-MURRAY, Anne Pauline Upton Village Surgery, Wealstone Lane, Upton, Chester CH2 1HD Tel: 01244 382238 — BM BS 1984 Nottm.; BMedSci Nottm. 1982. GP Chester Retainer Scheme. Prev: GP Beeston, Nottm.

TEMPLETON, Professor Allan Department of Obstetrics & Gynaecology, University of Aberdeen, Foresterhill, Aberdeen AB25 2ZD Tel: 01224 840590 Fax: 01224 684880 Email: allan.templeton@abdn.ac.uk; Templeton, Knapperna House, Udny, Ellon AB41 6SA Tel: 01651 842481 — MB ChB 1969 Aberd.; MRCOG 1974; MD (Hons.) Aberd. 1982, MB ChB 1969; FRCOG 1987, M 1974. (Aberdeen) Prof. O & G Univ. Aberd.; Hon. Sec. Roy. Coll. of Obst. & Gyn. Socs: Brit. Fertil. Soc.; Soc. for Study of Fertil.; ESHRE. Prev: Sen. Lect. (O & G) Univ. Edin.

TEMPLETON, Andrew Martin (Surgery), 90 Emscote Road, Warwick CV34 5QJ Tel: 01926 492311; 1 Farm Road, Lillington, Leamington Spa CV32 7RP — MB BS 1967 Lond.; MRCS Eng. LRCP Lond. 1967; DObst RCOG 1973. (Univ. Coll. Hosp.) Prev: Resid. Obst. Brit. Milit. Hosp. Rinteln; Garrison Med. Off. Hemer.

TEMPLETON, Ann Reid Pill Box, Pill Creek, Truro TR3 6SE — MB ChB 1952 Glas. (Glas.) Chest Phys. Tehidy Hosp. Camborne. Socs: FRSM. Prev: Ho. Phys. Brompton Hosp. Lond.; Med. Dir. Mass Radiog. Serv. Devon.

TEMPLETON, David James 5 Brownside Avenue, Cambuslang, Glasgow G72 8BL — MB ChB 1995 Aberd.

TEMPLETON, Hilary Margaret (retired) 73 Newberries Avenue, Radlett WD7 7EL — MB BCh 1973 Wales. Prev: GP Watford.

TEMPLETON, James Douglas (retired) 72 Castlebury Court, Largs KA30 8DP Tel: 01475 673815 — MB ChB 1954 Glas.; FRCPsych 1982, M 1971. Prev: Cons. Psychiat. & Psychotherap. Dept. S.. Gen. Hosp. Glas.

TEMPLETON, Professor John The Beeches, 170 Oulton Road, Stone ST15 8DR — MB BCh BAO Belf. 1961; FRCS Glas. 1993; FRCS Eng. 1991; FRCSC 1970. (Belfast) Prof. Traum. Orthop. Surg. Keele Univ.; Cons. Orthop. Surg. N. Staffs. Roy. Infirm., Stoke on Trent. Socs: Fell. BOA; Girdlestone Orthop. Soc. Prev: Dean Fac. of Health, Keele Univ.; Cons. Orthop. Surg. Roy. Vict. Hosp. & Musgrave Pk. Hosp. Belf.; Asst. Prof. Surg. McGill Univ. Montreal, Canada.

TEMPLETON, John Stewart (retired) 62a South St, Perth PH2 8PD — MB ChB Glas. 1957. Prev: Europ. Regional Med. Dir. A.H. Robins Co.

TEMPLETON, Lisa Kim Melbury Lodge, Royal Hampshire County Hospital, Romsey Road, Winchester SO22 5DG — BM BS 1990 Nottm. Regist. Rotat. (Psychiat.) Oxf. Prev: SHO (Psychiat.) Fairmile Hosp. Wallingford; SHO (Geriat. Med.) Newc. Gen. Hosp.; Ho. Off. (Surg. & Urol.) Derbysh. Roy. Infirm.

TEMPLETON, Lynn Margaret Clydebank Health Centre, Kilbowie Road, Clydebank G81 2TQ Tel: 0141 952 2080; 9 Sandfield Avenue, Milngavie, Glasgow G62 8NR — MB ChB 1985 Glas.; MRCGP 1989.

TEMPLETON, Mr Peter Alexander Leeds General Infirmary, Great George St, Leeds LS1 3EX; 5 Lammas Court, Scarcroft, Leeds

LS14 3JS — MB BCh BAO 1987 Belf.; FRCS (Eng) 1991; FRCS (Orth) 1996. (Queen's Univeristy Belfast) Cons. (Trauma & Orthop.) Leeds Gen Infirm. Leeds; Sen Clin Lect. Univ. Leeds.

TEN HOEVE, Wilhelmina Johanna 8 Sirenia Close, Brightstone, Newport PO30 4BH — Artsexamen 1992 Rotterdam.

TENANT-FLOWERS, Melinda Directorate of Sexual Health, The Caldecot Centre, King's Healthcare NHS Trust, 15-22 Caldecot Road, London SE5 9RS Tel: 020 7346 3453 Fax: 020 7346 3486; Flat 2, 37 Richborne Terrace, London SW8 1AS Tel: 020 7735 1732 — MB BChir 1982 Camb.; BSc (Hons.) Durham. 1976; MRCPI 1987. (Newc. u. Tyne & Camb.) Cons. Sexual Health Kings Healthcare Lond. Socs: BMA; Assn. Sexual Health Med.; Soc. Study VD. Prev: Sen. Lect. (Sexual Health Med.) Sydney Hosp., Austral.; Clin. Lect. (Genitourin. Med.) Middlx. Hosp. Lond.; Sen. Regist. (Genitourin. Med.) W.m. & St. Stephens Hosps. Lond.

TENCH, Colin Mark 7 Tyndale Terrace, Islington, London N1 2AT — MB BChir 1992 Camb. Specialist Regist. (Rheum.) N. Thames Region. Socs: RCP; RSM; Brit. Soc. Rheum.

TENCH, David William Park House, Manchester Mental Health Partnership, Gen. Hospital, Delaunays Road,, Manchester M8 5RL Tel: 0161 720 2421; 59 Moorfield Road, Salford, Manchester M6 7EY Tel: 0161 737 1086 Email: tenchie@eggconnect.net — MB ChB 1984 Manch.; MSc Manch. 1993, MB ChB 1984; MRCPsych. 1989. Cons. Psychiat. For The Elderly, Manch. Ment. Health Partnership. Socs: Fell. Of Manch. Med. Soc. Psychiat. Sec.; Of the Fac. of Old Age Psychiat., Roy. Coll. Of Psychiat. Prev: Sen. Regist. (Psychiat.) Withington Hosp. Manch.; Research Fell. (Psychiat.) Hope Hosp. Salford.; Cons. Psychiat. The Roy. Oldham Hosp.

TENDALL, John David 1 Hillside, London NW5 1QT — MB BS 1973 Lond.

TENGKU ISMAIL, Tengku Saifudin Flat 1/2, 18 Cornwall St., Glasgow G41 1AQ — MB ChB 1995 Glas.

TENNANT, Allan William The Firs, Cadney Road, Howsham, Market Rasen LN7 6LA — BM 1985 Soton.

TENNANT, Barry Desmond Gloucester House Medical Center, 17 Station Road, Urmston, Manchester M41 9JS Tel: 0161 748 7115; 62 Lock Lane, Partington, Manchester M31 4PP — MB ChB 1961 Manch. (Manch.)

TENNANT, David X-Ray Department, North Tyneside General Hospital, Rake Lane, North Shields NE29 8NH Tel: 0191 293 2512 Fax: 0191 293 2541; 6 Beechways, Durham DH1 4LG — MB ChB 1978 Ed.; BSc Ed. 1975; MRCP (UK) 1983; FRCR 1991; DCH RCP Lond. 1983. (Edinburgh) Cons. Radiol. N. Tyneside Hosp. N. Shields. Socs: Fell. Roy. Coll. Radiol.; Brit. Inst. Radiol.; BMA. Prev: Cons. Radiol. Dryburn Hosp. Durh.

TENNANT, Francesca Dorothy Bournewood Community NHS Trust, Trust HQ, Goldsworth Park Centre, Woking GU21 3LQ Tel: 01483 728201; 16 Well Close, Horsell, Woking GU21 4PT Tel: 01483 765613 — MB ChB 1980 Liverp.; Dip. Community Paediat. Warwick 1993; DCH RCP Lond. 1988. Community Med. Off. (Child Health) Bournewood Community NHS Trust; Assoc. Specialist (Paediat. Audiol.) Woking. Socs: Brit. Assn. Community Child Health; Brit. Assn. Community Drs in Audiol.

***TENNANT, Michael Ian,** Surg. Lt. RN 3 Bridgwater Avenue, Auchterarder PH3 1DQ — MB BS 1994 Newc.

TENNANT, Nicola Jayne Tamara, 3A Duff Avenue, Elgin IV30 1QS — MB ChB 1997 Aberd.

TENNANT, Rachel Caroline Flat 2, 10 Henfield Road, London SW19 3HU — MB BS 1996 Lond.

TENNANT, Sally Jane 40 Ashmore Road, Maida Vale, London W9 3DF; 40C Ashmore Road, Maida Vale, London W9 3DF — MB BS 1993 Lond.; FRCS 1997. (St Marys Hospital Medical School)

TENNANT, Mr William George E Floor, West Block, University Hospital, Queens Medical Centre, Nottingham NG7 2UH Fax: 0115 970 9150 Email: billt@qmcvascular.demon.co.uk — MB ChB Ed. 1982; BSc (Med. Sci.) Ed. 1979, MD 1993; FRCS (Gen.) 1994; FRCS Ed. 1987. (Edinburgh) Cons. Vasc. & Gen. Surg. Qu. Med. Centre Nottm.

TENNEKOON, Mahinda Forest Road Medical Centre, 354-358 Forest Road, Walthamstow, London E17 5JL Tel: 020 8520 6060 Fax: 020 8521 6505; 12B Sinnot Road, London E17 Tel: 020 8527 2512 — MB BS 1962 Ceylon; DCH Eng. 1966. GP Redbridge & Waltham Forest FPC. Socs: Med. Protect. Soc. Prev: Regist.

(Paediat.) Whipps Cross Hosp. Lond.; SHO (Med.) Barking Hosp.; SHO (Paediat., Neurol. & Rheumat.) P.ss Alex. Hosp. Harlow.

TENNEKOON, Milinda Satyajith 16 Roseacres, Sawbridgeworth CM21 0BU — MB BS 1991 Lond.

TENNENT, Thomas Duncan 6 Viscount Close, Friern Barnet, London N11 3PX Email: duncantennent@freeserve.co.uk — MB BS 1992 Lond.; BSc (Hons) Essex 1987; FRCS (Eng) 1996. (St. Bart's Hosp.) Specialist Regist. Roy. Nat. Orthop. Hosp. Rotat. Socs: Roy. Soc. Med.; RCS (Eng.).

TENNENT, Thomas Gavin Church Farm, Church Lane, Harwell, Didcot OX11 0EZ — BM BCh 1961 Oxf.; DM Oxf. 1970; FRCPsych 1979, M 1971; DPM Eng. 1967.

TENNET, Hilary Mary 39A Malone Park, Belfast BT9 6NL — MB BCh BAO 1973 NUI.

TENNICK, Jane Rachel No-64 (TFL) Findhorn Place, Edinburgh EH9 2NW Tel: 0131 667 8482; Luxmoore House, 16a The Precincts, Canterbury CT1 2DS Tel: 01227 595515 — MB ChB 1996 Ed.; DCH Ed 1998. Gen. Vocational Train. Scheme; St. John's Hosp. Livingston, Nr. Edin. Socs: MDDUS; Med. Sickness Soc. Prev: SHO Med. St. John's Hosp., Livingston Scotl.; SHO Paeds. St. John's Hosp., Livingston Scotl.; SHO (A&E) St. John's Hosp., Livingston Scotl.

TENNISON, Barry Roy West Hertfordshire Health Authority, Tonman House, 63-77 Victoria St., St Albans AL1 3ER Tel: 01727 812929 Fax: 01727 792800 Email: barry.tennison@nospam.ha.wherts-ha.nthames.nhs.uk; Holmdale, 35 Baldock Road, Royston SG8 5BJ Tel: 01763 241456 Email: barry.tennison@nospam.dial.pipex.com — MB BChir 1983 Camb.; PhD Camb. 1973, MA 1972; MSc (Community Med.) Lond. 1987; FFPHM RCP (UK) 1994, M 1989; T(PHM) 1992. Dir. (Pub. Health) W. Herts. HA; Hon. Sen. Lect. Pub. Health Policy Roy. Sch. Hyg. Trop. Med. Prev: Dir. of Infomation Camb. Dist. HA; Fell. Sidney Sussex Coll. Camb.; Asst. Lect. (Mathematics) Univ. Camb.

TENTERS, Michael Teodors The Surgery, Park Lane, Stubbington, Fareham PO14 2JP Tel: 01329 664231 Fax: 01329 664958; 31 Skylark Meadows, Fareham PO15 6TJ — MB BS 1983 Lond.; BSc (Hons.) (Physiol.) Lond. 1980, MB BS 1983; MRCGP 1988; MRCOG 1986.

TEO, Andrew Chien Wei 11 Celandine Court, Yateley GU46 6LP — MB BS 1992 Lond.

TEO, Cuthbert Eng-Swee Department of Forensic Medicine, Guy's Hospital, London SE1 9RT Tel: 020 7407 0378 Fax: 020 7403 7292 — MB BS 1988 Singapore; MB BC Singapore 1988; DMJ (Path.) Soc. Apoth. Lond. 1993. Hon. Clin. & Research Assoc. (Forens. Med.) UMDS Lond. Socs: Brit. Acad. Forens. Sci.; Assn. Police Surg.

TEO, Ho Teck Ho Tit Christopher 73 Brynland Avenue, Bishopston, Bristol BS7 9DZ — MB ChB 1979 Glas.

TEO, Hong-Giap Trafford General Hospital, Moorside Road, Manchester M41 5SL Tel: 0161 748 4022; Apartment 24, Whitworth House, 53 Whitworth St, Manchester M1 3WS Tel: 0161 236 7523 Email: hgteo@clara.net — MB ChB 1995 Sheff. (Sheffield University) SHO (Gen. Med.) Trafford Gen. Hosp. Moorside Rd. Manch. Socs: Med. Protec. Soc.

TEO, Hoon Seong Department of Anaesthetics, West Suffolk Hospital, Hardwick Lane, Bury St Edmunds IP33 2QZ; 107 Dudley Road, Manchester M16 8BW — MB ChB 1991 Bristol.

TEO, Lee Na 239 Minster Court, Liverpool L7 3QH — MB ChB 1988 Liverp.

TEO, Nee Beng Flat 23, Forrestburn Court, Monkscourt Avenue, Airdrie ML6 0JS — MB ChB 1994 Glas.

TEO, Roderick Eng Chee Medical Residencies, Block 20 Room 24, Pilgrim Hospital, Sibsey Road, Boston PE21 9QS — MB ChB 1992 Bristol.

TEO, Swee Guan 79 Burgoyne Road, London N4 1AB — MB BS 1996 New South Wales; MB BS (1st Cl. Hons) New South Wales 1996; BSc Med. 1996. (The University of New South Wales, Australia) SHO (Med.) The Whittington Hosp. Lond.

TEO, Mr Tiew-Chong The Queen Victoria Hospital, Holtye Road, East Grinstead RH19 3DZ Tel: 01342 410210 Fax: 01342 315512 Email: tc.teo@gvh-tr.sthames.nhs.uk; 3 Meridian Way, East Grinstead RH19 3GB Tel: 01342 410210 — MB ChB 1982 Aberd.; MD (Hons.) Aberd. 1991; FRCS (Plast) 1995; FRCS Ed. 1987. Sen. Regist. (Plastic Surg.) Qu. Vict. Hosp. E. Grinstead. Socs: Med. Protec. Soc. Prev: Sen. Regist. St. Thos. Hosp. Lond.; Regist.

Wexham Pk. Hosp. Slough; Research Fell. Harvard Univ. Boston, USA.

TEODORCZUK, Andrew Michael 72 Mallard Pl, Twickenham TW1 4SR — MB ChB 1997 Ed.

TEOH, Chia-Meng Flat 10, 6 Riverview Place, Glasgow G5 8EB — MB ChB 1994 Ed.

TEOH, Joo Ee 44 Russell Bank Road, Sutton Coldfield B74 4RQ — MB BS 1990 New South Wales; DRCOG 1992.

TEOH, Leok-Kheng Kristine 79 Eyre Court, Finchley Road, London NW8 9TX — MB BChir 1991 Camb.; BA Camb. 1988; FRCS Eng. 1996. RSO (Cardiothoracic Surg.) Lond. Chest Hosp. Prev: Sen. SHO (Gen. Surg.) Roy. Surrey Co. Hosp. Guildford.

TEOH, Robin Elizabeth c/o 11 Marshall Road, Godalming GU7 3AS — MB ChB 1980 Bristol; MRCGP 1986; DRCOG 1986; DA Eng. 1984. Prev: Lect. (Primary Care Med.) Malaysia; Med. Off. Leics. Hospice.

TEOH, Siew Koon 44 Clarence Terrace, Regents Park, London NW1 4RD — MB BS 1982 Lond. SHO (Med.) (Rotat.) Camb. HA.

TEOH, Tiong Ghee St Marys Hospital, Dept of Obstetrics & Gynaecology, Praed St, London W2 1NY Tel: 020 7886 6691 Fax: 020 7886 2169; 3A Victoria Grove Mews, Notting Hill, London W2 4LN — MB BCh BAO 1987 NUI; MRCPI 1993; LRCPSI 1987; MRCOG 1992; MD 1996. Cons. (Obst & Gyn.) St Marys Hosp. Lond. Socs: RSM. Prev: Serv. Dir. Obst.

TEOH, Yee Ping Trust Office, Law Hospital NHS Trust, Carluke ML8 5ER — MB BS 1996 Melbourne.

TEOH, Yin Yin 76 Hawthorn Avenue, Glasgow G61 3NQ — MB BCh BAO 1993 Belf.

TEOTIA, Narendra Pal Singh Mill Lane Surgery, 135 Mill Lane, Chadwell Heath, Romford RM6 6RS Tel: 020 8599 6835 Fax: 020 8983 8063 — MB BS 1969 Lucknow.

TEPPER, Rachel 1a Hanover Gardens, Salford, Manchester M7 4FQ Tel: 0161 773 2354 — MB ChB 1940 Manch. (Manch.) Prev: Clin. Med. Off. N. Manch. HA; GP Crawley; Ho. Phys. Booth Hall Hosp. Childr. Manch. & Crumpsall Hosp. N. Manch.

TER HAAR, Reynier Gerrit c/o Cromford Court, Matlock Bath, Matlock DE4 3PY Tel: 01629 583973 — MB ChB 1989 Orange Free State.

TER MORSHUIZEN, Roderick Ernst Iwan The Ayr Hospital, Dalmellington Road, Ayr KA6 6DX — Artsexamen 1992 Free U Amsterdam; Artsexamen Free Univ Amsterdam 1992.

TERIBA, Aderemi Hakeem Health Services Department, University of Lagos, Lagos, Nigeria; 3 Wareham House, Fentiman Road, London SW8 1AZ — MB BS 1972 Ibadan; MMedSci (Gen. Pract.) Leeds 1988; MRCGP 1989. Director (Health Serv.) Univ. Lagos. Prev: SHO (Paediat.) E. Birm. Hosp.; SHO (Geriat.) Newc. Gen. Hosp.

TERLESKI, Michelle Jane 2 Bro Llwyn, Yr Ala, Pwllheli LL53 5HW — MB BS 1981 Lond.; BSc Lond. 1978, MB BS Lond. 1981; MRCGP 1986. Prev: GP BasCh. Shewsbury; Trainee GP Shrewsbury VTS; Ho. Surg. Char. Cross Hosp.

TERLEVICH, Ana 1 Bradrushe Fields, Cambridge CB3 0DW — MB ChB 1997 Bristol.

TERRELL, Clare (retired) Manor House, Alderton, Woodbridge IP12 3BL Tel: 01394 411334 — MB BS Lond. 1960; FFR 1972; DMRT Eng. 1968; DCH Eng. 1966. Cons. Palliat. Med. Guy's Hosp. Lond. Prev: Med. Dir. St. Eliz. Hospice Ipswich.

TERRELL, Emily Sarah 19 Springfield, Kegworth, Derby DE74 2DP — BM 1997 Soton.

TERRELL, Helen Mary 52 Midsummer Road, Snodland ME6 5RP — MB ChB 1994 Birm.

TERRELL, John Davidson (retired) 47 Longlands Road, Carlisle CA3 9AE Tel: 01228 525986 Fax: 01228 525986 — MB ChB Glas. 1951, DPH 1957; FFCM 1981, M 1973; DCH Eng. 1956. Prev: DMO W. Cumbria Health Auth.

TERRELL, Victoria 27 Queens Road, Wimbledon, London SW19 8NW Tel: 020 8946 1172 — LMSSA 1975 Lond.

TERREROS BERRUETE, Orlando 47 Vicarage Gardens, Scunthorpe DN15 7BA — LMS 1988 Basque Provinces.

***TERRIERE, Emma Charlotte** 624 Brighton Road, Purley CR8 2BA; 89 Kinghorne St, Arbroath DD11 2LZ Tel: 01241 879909 — MB ChB 1998 Dund.; MB ChB Dund 1998; BMSc Dund. 1995.

TERRILL

TERRILL, Lisa Maria Stone Cottage, 12 High Road, Manthorpe, Grantham NG31 8NG — MB BS 1991 Lond.

TERRIS, Alexander James McDonnell Purvis and Partners, The Hart Surgery, York Road, Henley-on-Thames RG9 2DR Tel: 01491 843200 Fax: 01491 411296; Harpsden Gate, Harpsden Way, Henley-on-Thames RG9 1NS Tel: 0149157 574691 — MB BS 1968 Lond.; MRCP (UK) 1971. (St. Mary's) GP Princip. Hart Pract. Henley Oxon.; Med. Off. Shiplake Coll. Prev: Med. Off. Shiplake Coll.; Regist. (Med.) Amersham Hosp.; SHO (Neurol.) Soton. Gp. Hosps.

TERRIS, Mark Grampian University Hospital Trust, Aberdeen Royal Infirmary, Forresthill, Aberdeen AB25 2YA; 63 Clifton Road, Aberdeen AB24 4RN — MB ChB 1998 Aberd.; MB ChB Aberd 1998. SHO.(Med Paediat.) Roy Aberd Childr Hosp. Prev: HO. (Gen Surg & Orthop.); HO. (Rheum & Cardio.).

TERRY, Anne Elizabeth Ashurst Morris Crisp, 5 Appold St, London EC2A 2HA — MB BS 1991 Lond.; DRCOG 1995.

TERRY, Catherine Margaret Twin Oaks Medical Centre, Ringwood Road, Bransgore, Christchurch BH23 8AD Tel: 01425 672741 Fax: 01425 674333; Trevaylor, Hightown Hill, Ringwood BH24 3HG Tel: 01425 476338 Fax: 01425 674333 — BM 1984 Soton.; MSc Surrey 1971; BSc Soton. 1968; DFFP 1993; DRCOG 1988; Cert. Family Plann. JCC 1988; DGM RCP Lond. 1987. (Soton.) Socs: Brit. Med. Acupunct. Soc.; BMA. Prev: SHO (A & E) Roy. Hants. Co. Hosp. Winchester.

TERRY, Dennis Arthur 41 High Street, Colney Heath, St Albans AL4 0NS Tel: 01727 565 — MB BS 1964 Lond.; MRCS Eng. LRCP Lond. 1964; MRCPsych 1976; DPM Eng. 1974. (Univ. Coll. Hosp.)

TERRY, Diana Margaret Susan Sir Humphry Davy Department Anaesthesia, Bristol Royal Infirmary, Bristol BS2 8HW Tel: 0117 923 0000 Fax: 0117 928 2098 Email: diana.terry@ubht.swest.nhs.uk; 16 Sion Hill, Bath BA1 2UJ Tel: 01225 313374 Fax: 01225 447846 Email: diana.terry@ubht.swest.nhs.uk — MB BS 1975 Lond.; FFA RCS Eng. 1980; FFA RCSI 1979. (King's Coll. Hosp.) p/t Cons. Anaesth. Bristol Roy. Infirm. Socs: (Counc.) Assn. Dent. Anaesth.; (Counc.) Soc. Analgesia and Anxiety Control in Dent. (SAAD); Resusc. Counc. UK. Prev: Sen. Regist. (Anaesth.) Middlx. Hosp. Lond.

TERRY, Dorothy 1 Rutland Avenue, Pontefract WF8 3RD Tel: 01977 702270 — MB ChB 1928 Leeds. Socs: BMA & Med. Wom. Federat. Prev: Ho. Phys. Leeds Gen. Infirm.; Ho. Surg. Hosp. Wom. Leeds & Roy. Matern. & Wom. Hosp. Glas.

TERRY, Gordon 'Westaways', Lowes Barn Bank, Durham DH1 3QP — MB BS 1966 Durh.; FRCP Ed. 1985; FRCP Lond. 1982, M 1970. Cons. Phys. Dryburn Hosp. Durh.; Hon. Clin. Lect. Univ. Newc. Socs: Brit. Cardiac Soc. Prev: Sen. Regist. (Med.) Newc. Univ. Gp. Hosps.; Regist. (Med. & Cardiol.) Aberd. Roy. Infirm.; SHO Roy. Infirm. Edin.

TERRY, Helen Jane Department of Elderly Medicine, St. Luke's Hospital, Bradford; 2 Goodrick Close, Harrogate HG2 9EX — BM BCh 1986 Oxf.; MA Camb. 1987; MRCP (UK) 1989. Cons. Geritrician, Bradford Hosp.s NHS Trust, Bradford. Prev: Sen. Regist. (Geriat. & Gen. Med.) & Regist. (Gen. Med.) Univ. Hosp. Nottm.; SHO (Gen. Med.) Univ. Hosp. Nottm.; Sen. Regist. (Geriat. & Gen. Med.) St. Jas. Hosp., Leeds.

TERRY, Jack 4 Bennett's Copse, Wood Drive, Chislehurst BR7 5SG Tel: 020 8467 7271 — MB BS 1951 Lond.; MRCS Eng. LRCP Lond. 1951. (King's Coll. Hosp.)

TERRY, Miss Julia Marion Park Surgery, Hursley Road, Chandlers Ford SO53 — MB BS 1991 Lond.; MRCGP 1999; DFFP 1999; BSc (Hons.) (Path.) 1988; FRCS Eng. 1995. (The Royal Lond. Hosp.) GP, Chandlers Ford, Hants. Prev: GP Locum, W.Sussex; GP Regist. The Med. Centre, Cawley Rd., Chichester.

TERRY, Kathryn Jane 1 Complins, Holybourne, Alton GU34 4EH — MB BS 1994 Lond.

TERRY, Patrick Michael St Quintin Aldermoor Surgery, Aldermoor Close, Southampton SO16 5ST Tel: 02380 241000 Fax: 02380 241010 — MB BS 1980 Lond.; MRCOG 1986; MRCGP 1994; MFFP 1994; T (GP) 1994; T (M) 1991; MRCGP 1994; MFFP 1994; MRCOG 1986; T(M) 1991; T(GP) 1994. Princip. Gen. Pract. Prev: Princip. & Clin. Teach. Primary Med. Care Gp. Univ. Soton.

TERRY, Paula Miriam 51 Rushton Drive, Middlewich CW10 0NJ Tel: 01606 833007 Email: polly@embedded.demon.co.uk — MB ChB 1991 Manch.; DA (UK) 1995. Staff Phys. Leighton Hosp. Crewe.

TERRY, Mr Peter Brian 60 Forest Road, Aberdeen AB15 4BP Tel: 01224 317560 — MD 1987 Ed.; MB ChB 1976; FRCS Ed. 1981; FRCOG 1994, M 1981. Cons. & Hon. Sen. Lect. (O & G) Aberd. Matern. Hosp. Socs: Blair Bell Res. Soc. Prev: Sen. Lect. & Hon. Cons. (O & G) Aberd. Matern. Hosp.; Sen. Regist. (O & G) Aberd. Matern. Hosp.; Regist. (O & G) Dudley Rd. Hosp. Birm.

TERRY, Robert Sidney (retired) Mill Cottage, Gladestry, Kington HR5 3NY — MB BS 1960 Lond. Asst. Gen. Practitioner Prev: Paediat. Ho. Phys. Worcester Roy. Infirm.

TERRY, Robin Eric Richmond House Surgery, Richmond Terrace, Station Road, Whitchurch SY13 1RH Tel: 01948 662870 — MB ChB 1975 Birm.; DRCOG 1979.

TERRY, Roger Walter Patrick (retired) The Ledges, Redbrook Road, Monmouth NP25 3LZ Tel: 01600 715725 — MB ChB 1967 Birm. Prev: Regist. (Orthop.) S. Warks. Hosp. Gp.

TERRY, Mr Roland Mark ENT Department, Farnborough Hospital, Farnborough Common, Orpington BR6 8ND Tel: 01689 814257; 13 Park Farm Road, Bromley BR1 2PF Fax: 020 8467 6218 — MB BS 1978 Lond.; FRCS Eng. 1982. Cons. ENT. Surg. Bromley HA. Socs: Fell. Roy. Soc. Med.; Brit. Assn. Otol. Head & Neck Surg. Prev: Sen. Regist. Yorks RHA; Research Fell. Univ. Leeds.

TERRY, Roland Mervyn Stanley (retired) 7 Tower Close, Orpington BR6 0SP — MB 1944 Calcutta; DMRD Eng. 1950.

TERRY, Susan Hazel (retired) 47 Mill Lane, Dorridge, Solihull B93 8NN — MRCS Eng. LRCP Lond. 1965; MRCOG 1971, DObst 1966; DPM Eng. 1975. Prev: Cons. Adult Ment. Handicap Coventry, N. Warks. & S. Warks. HAs.

TERRY, Sydney Walter Wellington (retired) 67 Minster Way, Bath BA2 6RJ Tel: 01225 466430 — MB BS 1941 Madras; MFCM 1972; DTM & H Eng. 1947; DPH Lond. 1948. Prev: SCM Wilts. AHA.

TERRY, Mr Timothy Robin Leicester General Hospital, Gwendolen Road, Leicester LE5 4450 Tel: 0116 258 4450 — MRCS Eng. LRCP Lond. 1975; BSc (Hons.) Lond. 1972, MS 1987, MB BS 1975; FRCS Eng. 1980. (King's Coll. Lond. & St. Geo.) Cons. Urol. & Hon. Clin. Tutor Leicester Univ. Hosps. Socs: Brit. Assn. Urol. Surgs.; Corres. Mem. Amer. Urol. Assn. Prev: Sen. Regist. Leeds Univ. Hosps.; Regist. Rotat. (Urol.) Char. Cross Hosp. Lond. & E.bourne Hosp.; Wellcome Surg. Research Regist. Profess. Surg. Unit St. Geo. Hosp. Lond.

TERVIT, Nicola Margaret 37 Marchbank Drive, Balerno EH14 7ER — MB ChB 1994 Glas.

TERZIS, George Flat 4, 145A Wells Road, Bath BA2 3AL — Ptychio Iatrikes 1986 Athens; T(S) 1994.

TESCHKE, Caroline Jean 20 Manor Farm Road, Dorchester-on-Thames, Oxford OX10 7HX — MB BS 1979 Newc.; BA (Hons.) Lond. 1968; MRCP (UK) 1985.

TESFAYE, Solomon Royal Hallamshire Hospital, Floor P, Glossop Road, Sheffield S10 2JF Tel: 0114 271 2709 Fax: 0114 271 3708; 4 Cherry Tree Road, Sheffield S11 9AA Tel: 0114 250 7696 — MB ChB 1984 Bristol; FRCP 2001; MD Bristol 1994; MRCP (UK) 1988. (Bristol University Medical School) Hon. Sen. Clin. Lect. Univ. of Sheff. Socs: Brit. Diabetic Assn.; BMA; Internat. Diabetes Federat. Prev: Cons. Phys. & Diabetol. Roy. Hallamsh. Hosp. Sheff./ Hon. Sen. Clin. Lect. (Univ. of Sheff.); Sen. Regist. (Diabetes & Endocrinol.) Roy. Liverp. Hosp.; Research Regist. (Diabetes) Roy. Hallamsh. Hosp. Sheff.

TESFAYOHANNES, Mr Biniam Northern General Hospital NHS Trust, Herries Road, Sheffield S5 7AU Tel: 0114 243 4343 Fax: 0114 256 0472 Email: t.biniam@sheffield.ac.uk — MB ChB 1982 Sheff.; FRCS Ed. 1988; FFAEM 1994. Cons. A & E N. Gen. Hosp. NHS Trust Sheff.

TESH, Anne Elizabeth Christina Bridge Farm, Sweffling, Saxmundham IP17 2BA — MB ChB 1995 Sheff.

TESH, Dorothy Eileen (retired) 20 Hillgrove Crescent, Kidderminster DY10 3AP — MB ChB 1965 Birm.; MRCPsych 1984. Prev: Cons. (Ment. Handicap) Lea Castle Hosp. Kidderminster.

TESTA, Professor Humberto Juan The Alexandra Hospital, Mill Lane, Cheadle SK8 2PX Tel: 0161 428 3656 Fax: 0161 491 3867; 27 Barcheston Road, Cheadle SK8 1LJ Tel: 0161 428 6873 — MD 1979 Buenos Aires; PhD Manch. 1972; Medico 1962; FRCP Lond. 1986; FRCR 1988. Cons. (Nuclear Med.) Priv. Pract. The Alexandra Hosp. Cheadle.

TETLEY, Giles Holdenhurst Road Surgery, 199 Holdenhurst Road, Bournemouth BH8 8DF Tel: 01202 558337 — MB BS 1972 Lond.; FFA RCS Eng. 1977; DA Eng. 1975; DObst RCOG 1974. (Univ. Coll. Hosp.) Prev: Regist. (Anaesth.) Roy. Berks. Hosp. Reading; SHO (Paediat.) N.ampton Gen. Hosp.

TETLOW, Stanley 3 Highbury Close, Springwell, Gateshead NE9 7PU Tel: 0191462532 — MB BS 1958 Durh. (Durh.) Prev: Ho. Phys. & Ho. Surg. Roy. Vict. Infirm. Newc.

TETSTALL, Ann Philippa Rivermead Gate Medical Centre, 123 Rectory Lane, Chelmsford CM1 1TR Tel: 01245 348688 Fax: 01245 458800 — MB BS 1978 Lond.; MRCP (UK) 1981.

TETTELAAR, Maxim 86 Shrubbery Avenue, Worcester WR1 1QP — Artsexamen 1990 Groningen.

TETTENBORN, Michael Adrian Frimley Children's Centre, Church Road, Frimley, Camberley GU16 5AD Tel: 01483 782861 Fax: 01483 782998; Email: mtettenborn@doctors.org.uk — MB ChB 1971 Bristol; FRCP Lond. 1994; FRCPCH 1996; DRCOG 1976; DCH Eng. 1973. (Bristol) Cons. Child Health Surrey Hants. Borders NHS Trust. Prev: Cons. (Child Health) E.bourne & Co. NHS Trust; Sen. Regist. (Paediat.) Guy's Hosp. Lond.; Regist. (Paediat.) John Radcliffe Hosp. Oxf.

TETTMAR, Richard Eden (retired) Chelmsford Public Health Laboratory, New Writtle St., Chelmsford CM2 0YX — MB BS 1972 Lond.; MRCS Eng. LRCP Lond. 1972; FRCPath 1991, M 1979; DPath Eng. 1977.

TEUNISSE, Frank Surgery Gord, Levenwick, Shetland ZE2 9HX Tel: 01950 422240; Glenlea, Southpunds, Levenwick, Shetland ZE2 9HX Tel: 01950 422427 — Artsexamen 1988 Amsterdam; Artsexamen Free Univ Amsterdam 1988; MRCGP 1993; T(GP) 1993. Prev: Trainee GP Inverness.

TEUTEN, Anthony Robert (retired) 5 Beaufort Road, Ealing, London W5 3EB Tel: 020 8997 2884 — MB BS Lond. 1949. Prev: GP Lond.

TEVENDALE, Mr James Victoria Hospital, Hayfield Road, Kirkcaldy KY2 5AH Tel: 01592 643355 Fax: 01592 202248; Newton House, Newton of Falkland, Ladybank, Cupar KY15 7RZ Tel: 01337 857291 — MB ChB 1952 Glas.; FRCS Ed. 1959. Cons. ENT Surg. Vict. Hosp. Kirkcaldy; Hon. Sen. Lect. Univ. St. And. Socs: Scott. Otol. Soc. & Brit. Soc. Audiol. Prev: Sen. Regist. Edin. N.. Gp. Hosps.

TEVERSON, Eric Fern House Surgery, 125-129 Newland Street, Witham CM8 1BH Tel: 01376 502108 Fax: 01376 502281; Barnardiston House, 35 Chipping Hill, Witham CM8 2DE Tel: 01376 502266 — MB BS 1978 Lond.; DRCOG 1982. Prev: GP Kings Lynn VTS; Ho. Phys. Kingston Hosp.; Ho. Surg. Lond. Hosp.

TEW, Christopher John Lister Hospital, Coreys Mill Lane, Stevenage SG1 4AB Tel: 01438 314333 Fax: 01438 781147 — MB BS 1976 Lond.; BSc Lond. 1973, MB BS 1976; MRCP (UK) 1982; MRCPath 1985; FRCP (London) 2000. Cons. Haemat. Lister Hosp. Stevenage. Prev: Lect. (Haemat.) Char. Cross & W.m. Med. Sch. Lond.; Sen. Regist. (Haemat.) W.m. Hosp. Lond.; Regist. (Gen. Med.) Redhill Gen. Hosp.; Regist. (Haemat.) St. Bart. Hosp. Lond. Regist. (Haemat.) St. Bart. Hosp. Lond.

TEW, David Neil Princess Margaret Hospital, Okus Road, Swindon SN1 4JU — MB BS 1984 Lond.; FRCA. 1989.

TEW, Elizabeth The Windsor Road Surgery, Windsor Road, Garstang, Preston PR3 1ED Tel: 01995 603350 Fax: 01995 601301; Blencathra, Cabus Nook Lane, Cabus, Preston PR3 1AA Tel: 01524 791146 — MB BS 1972 Newc.; DCCH RCP Ed. 1984. GP Garstang. Socs: Fac. Fam. Plann. & Reproduc. Health Care. Prev: Ho. Surg. & Ho. Phys. Newc. Gen. Hosp.; Trainee GP Newc. VTS.

TEW, Jeremy Simon Touraj Westminster And Pimlico General Practice, 15 Denbigh Street, London SW1V 2HF Tel: 020 7834 6969 Fax: 020 7931 7747 — MB BS 1992 Lond.

TEW, John Anthony The Windsor Road Surgery, Windsor Road, Garstang, Preston PR3 1ED Tel: 01995 603888 Fax: 01995 601301; Blencathra, Cabus Nook Lane, Cabus, Preston PR3 1AA Tel: 01524 791146 — MB BS 1972 Newc.; MRCGP 1976. Hosp. Pract. (Psychiat.) Roy. Preston Hosp. Prev: Trainee Gen. Pract. Newc. Vocational Train. Scheme; Ho. Surg. & Ho. Phys. Newc. Gen. Hosp.

TEW, Josephine Hewgill 94 Inkerman Street, Luton LU1 1JD Tel: 01582 415381; Ansley House, Woburn, Milton Keynes MK17 9PU Tel: 01525 290656 — BM BCh 1952 Oxf.; DCH Eng. 1958. (St. Bart.) Socs: Brit. Paediat. Assn. & Soc. Pub. Health. Prev: SCMO

Beds. HA; Ho. Phys. St. Martin's Hosp. Bath & SHO Roy. United Hosp. Bath; Ho. Surg. (Obst.) City of Lond. Matern. Hosp.

*****TEW, Robert Patrick** Limeleigh Medical Group, 434 Narborough Road, Leicester LE3 2FS Tel: 0116 282 7070 Fax: 0116 289 3805 — MB ChB 1988 Leic.

*****TEW, Rosalind Evelyn** Ansley House, London End, Woburn, Milton Keynes MK17 9PU Tel: 01525 290656 — MB ChB 1994 Manch.

TEWARI, Rohini Mira 19 Station Road, Cippenham, Slough SL1 6JJ — MB BS 1993 Lond.

TEWARI, Sidhartha Lea Castle, Wolverley, Kidderminster DY10 3PP Tel: 01562 850461 — MB BS 1982 Ranchi; MRCPsych 1992; Dip. Psychiat. Ed. 1991. Cons. Psychiat. Worcs.

TEWARI, Sushil Kumar 87 St Albans Avenue, Hartshead, Ashton-under-Lyne OL6 8XN Tel: 0161 339 9547 — MB BS 1970 Jiwaji.

TEWARI, V K Trentham Road Surgery, 37 Trentham Road, Kirkby, Liverpool L32 4UB Tel: 0151 546 3711 Fax: 0151 548 4265 — MBBS; MD (Dip. Clinic Hypnosia) Sheffield. (I.M.S. Banaras Hindu Univ., India) Gen. Practitioner with Cardiol. interest; Private for Acupunc. and Hypn. in Kirkby, Liverp. L32 4UB. Socs: BMA; IMA UK; Brit. Med. and Dent. Hypnotic Soc.

TEWARY, Mr Ashok Kumar Walsall Hospital Trust, Moat Road, Walsall WS2 9PS — MB BS Panjab 1978; FRCS Eng. 1990; FRCS Ed. 1988; MS Panjab; FRCS.

TEWSON, Edward Timothy Cayley, GM (retired) The Manor, Ickford, Aylesbury HP18 9HS Tel: 01844 339255 — BM BCh 1951 Oxf.; DObst RCOG 1953. Prev: Ho. Phys. Radcliffe Infirm. Oxf.

TEWSON, Gillian Rosemary The Surgery, Norwich Road, Saxlingham Nethergate, Norwich NR15 1TP Tel: 01508 499208; Skeets Hill Farm House, Shotesham St Mary, Norwich NR15 1UR — MB BS 1980 Lond.; MRCGP 1985; DRCOG 1983.

TEWSON, Jocelyn Manor, Ickford, Aylesbury HP18 9HS Tel: 01844 339255 — MB BS 1949 Lond.; MRCGP 1975; DCH Eng. 1954. Prev: Sen. Ho. Phys. Ch.ill Hosp. Oxf.; Paediat. Ho. Phys. & Surgic. Ho. Surg. Radcliffe Infirm. Oxf.

TEWSON, Penelope Jane Hall Farm House, High St., Great Abington, Cambridge CB1 6AE — MB BS 1968 Lond.; DCH Eng. 1971; DObst RCOG 1970. (Roy. Free) GP Linton Cambs. Prev: Regist. (Paediat.) P.s Margt. Hosp. Swindon; SHO (Paediat.) Radcliffe Infirm. Oxf.; Ho. Phys. Roy. Free Hosp.

THA, Zan Crabbs Cross Surgery, 38 Kenilworth Close, Crabbs Cross, Redditch B97 5JX Tel: 01527 544610 Fax: 01527 540286 — MB BS 1973 Med. Inst. (I) Rangoon; ECFMG (USA) 1979; MRCGP 1981; MICGP 1985; DCCH RCP Ed. 1984; DRCOG 1981. (Rangoon, Burma) Princip. GP Crabbs Cross Surg. Redditch. Socs: BMA; Burmese Doctors Assn.

THACKER, Andrew Jonathan 168 Causeway Green Road, Oldbury, Oldbury B68 8LJ — MB ChB 1988 Birm.; ChB Birm. 1988. SHO (A & E) Dudley Rd. Hosp. Birm. Prev: Ho. Off. Sandwell Dist. Gen. Hosp.; Ho. Off. Gen. Hosp. Birm.

THACKER, Betty Victoria 24 Rugby Close, Newcastle ST5 3JN — MB ChB 1955 Birm.; LRCP 1955 Lond.; MRCS Eng.; FFA RCS Eng. 1961; DObst. RCOG 1957; DA Eng. 1958. (Birm.) Cons. Anaesth. Stoke-on-Trent Gp. Hosps. Socs: BMA. Prev: Regist. (Anaesth.) United Birm. Hosps.; Sen. Regist. (Anaesth.) Roy. Hosp. Wolverhampton; Cons. Anaesth. Dudley Rd. Hosp. Birm.

THACKER, Bharat Gunvantray The Medical Centre, 144-150 High Road, Willesden, London NW10 2PT Tel: 020 8459 5550; 59 Morley Crescent E., Stanmore HA7 2LG — MB ChB 1989 Glas.; MRCGP 1993; Cert. Family Plann. JCC 1992; DRCOG 1991. Clin. Asst. Willesden Gen. Hosp. Socs: BMA. Prev: Trainee GP Paisley; Trainee GP Rendrewsh. VTS; Ho. Off. (Surg.) Dumfries & Galloway Hosp. Ho. Off. (Med.) Roy. Aberd. Hosp.

THACKER, Mr Charles Robert 15 Bincleaves Road, Weymouth DT4 8RS Tel: 01305 785891 — MB BS 1974 Lond.; FRCS Eng. 1979; MRCS Eng. LRCP Lond. 1974. (St. Mary's) Cons. Orthop. Surg. W. Dorset Gen. Hosps. NHS Trust. Socs: Fell. BOA; BMA. Prev: Sen. Regist. (Orthop. & Trauma) Soton. & Portsmouth HAs; Regist. (Surg.) St. Mary's & Qu. Alexandra Hosp. Portsmouth; SHO (Orthop. & Trauma) Roy. United Hosp. Bath.

THACKER, Elizabeth Julie Royal Cornwall Hospital, Treliske, Truro TR1 3LJ; Helnoweth Farm, Gulval, Penzance TR20 8YP — MB BS 1985 Lond. Staff Grade (Nephrol.) Renal Unit. Roy. Cornw. Hosp. Truro.

THACKER

THACKER, Justin Gray McDougall 15 Rowcroft, Hemel Hempstead HP1 2JF — MB ChB 1992 Ed.; MRCP (UK) 1996; MRCOG 1994; DTM & H 1998. SHO (Paediat. Surg.) Edin. Socs: Med. & Dent. Defence Union Scotl. Prev: SHO (Med. Paediat.) Edin.

THACKER, Michael Puttrell Arnewood Practice, Milton Medical Centre, Avenue Road, New Milton BH25 5JP Tel: 01425 620393 Fax: 01425 624219; Far Forest, South Drive, Ossemsley, New Milton BH25 5TN — MB BS 1972 Lond.; MRCS Eng. LRCP Lond. 1972; MRCGP 1977. (Westm.) Prev: Trainee GP Bournemouth & Poole VTS; Ho. Surg. W.m. Hosp. Lond.; Ho. Phys. Gen. Hosp. Nottm.

THACKER, Richard Henry Lister House Surgery, 35 The Parade, St Helier, Jersey JE2 3QQ Tel: 01534 36336 Fax: 01534 35304; Melrose, St. Clement Inner Road, St Helier, Jersey JE2 6QP Tel: 01534 35285 Fax: 01534 25659 — MRCS Eng. LRCP Lond. 1965; LMCC Canada 1970; DObst 1970. Prev: GP Squamish BC, Canada; Flight Lt. RAF Med. Br.

THACKER, Sarah Lucia 225 Broad Lane, Coventry CV5 7AQ — MB BS 1990 Lond.

THACKER, Simon John Marazion Surgery, Gwallon Lane, Marazion TR17 0HW Tel: 01736 710505 Fax: 01736 711205; Helnoweth Farm, Gulval, Penzance TR20 8YP — MB BS 1985 Lond.; DCH RCP Lond. 1988.

THACKER, Simon Philip Derby City General Hospital, Uttoxeter Road, Derby DE22 3NE Tel: 01332 625553; 5 Hardy Close, Barton under Needwood, Burton-on-Trent DE13 8HG Email: sptha@easynet.co.uk — MB ChB 1988 Birm.; MB ChB (Hons.) Birm. 1988; BSc (Hons.) Birm. 1987; MRCPsych 1993; CCST 1997. Cons. (Old Age Psychiat.) Derby City Gen. Hosp. Socs: BMA; RCPsych. Prev: Sen. Regist. Rotat. (Old Age Psychiat.) Nottm.; Regist. Rotat. (Psychiat.) Birm.; SHO (Med.) Dudley Rd. Hosp. Birm.

THACKRAY, Mr Alan Christopher 67 Hillway, London N6 6AB Tel: 020 8340 2642 — MB BChir 1940 Camb.; MD Camb. 1946, MA, MB BChir 1940; FRCS Eng. 1968; MRCS Eng. LRCP Lond. 1939; FRCPath 1964. (Camb. & Middlx.) Emerit. Prof. (Morbid Histol.) Univ. Lond. Socs: Fell. Roy. Soc. Med.; Path. Soc. Prev: Prof. (Morbid Histol.) Bland-Sutton Inst. & Hon. Cons. Pathol. Middlx. Hosp. Lond.

THACKRAY, Colin Peter Rhoslan Surgery, 4 Pwllycrochan Avenue, Colwyn Bay LL29 7DA Tel: 01492 532125 Fax: 01492 530662 — MB ChB 1982 Liverp.; MRCGP 1987; DGM RCP Lond. 1986; DRCOG 1984.

THACKRAY, Jennifer Erdmuthe 24 Vincent Gardens, London NW2 7RP — MB BS 1994 Lond.

THACKRAY, Peter Oak Tree Lodge, 157 West Ella Road, Kirk Ella, Hull HU10 7RN Tel: 01482 658161 Email: 106515.1144@compuserve.com — MB BS 1962 Durh.; FFPM RCP (UK) 1989; DObst RCOG 1966. (Durh.) Socs: Brit. Assn. Pharmaceut. Phys. Prev: Dir. Med. Research Europe/Africa Div. Vick Internat. Egham; Med. Supt. Wenchi Methodist Hosp., Ghana; Flight Lt. RAF Med. Br.

THACKRAY, Simon Dominic Rhodes 157 Westella Road, Kirkella, Hull HU10 7RN Tel: 01482 658161 Email: simonthackray@lineone.net — MB BS 1993 Lond.; MRCP Lond. 1998. (St Geos.) Research Regist. (Cardio.) Univ of Hull. Prev: Specialist Regist. PeterBoro. & Papworth Hosp.; Med. Regist. Rotat. Roy. P. Alfred Hosp. Sydney, Australia; Med. SHO Rotat. Hull Roy. Infirm.

THACKSTONE, Stanley Irvine (retired) Cremorne, Roughcote Lane, Cookshill, Caverswall, Stoke-on-Trent ST11 9EG Tel: 01782 392561 — MB ChB 1956 Leeds; MRCGP 1965. Prev: Ho. Phys. Seacroft Gen. Hosp. Leeds.

THADANI, Helen Dept of Chemical Pathology and Endocrinology, St Thomas Hospital, Lambeth Palace Rd, London SE1 7EH Tel: 020 7928 9292 Ext: 3542 Email: helen.thadani@kd.ac.uk; 34 South Lodge Drive, Oakwood, London N14 4XP — MB BChir 1995 Camb.; BSc (Hons.) Camb. 1990. Specialsit Regist. Guys & St Thomas's Hosp NHS Trust. Lond. Prev: Specialist Regist. Oxf. Deanery John Radcliffe Hosp. Oxf.; Hon. Research Regist. King's Coll. Sch. Med. & Dent. Lond.; SHO (Clin. Chem., Endocrinol. & Metab. Med.) King's Coll. Hosp. Lond.

THAIN, Alexander Buchan (retired) Castle Coach House, Inverugie, Peterhead AB42 3DN Tel: 01779 838274 Email: sandyabt@inverugie.freeserve.co.uk — MB ChB 1959 Aberd.; CIH Dund 1974; MFOM RCP Lond. 1984; DObst RCOG 1966. Prev: Head Occupat. Health ADCO Abu Dhabi, UAE.

THAIN, Annie (retired) Minfield, Pipegate, Market Drayton TF9 Tel: 0163 081418 — MB ChB 1921 Aberd.; MB ChB (1st Cl. Hnrs.) Aberd. 1921. Prev: Ho. Phys. W.m. Hosp.

THAKAR, Bharati Ranee 6 Berystede, Kingston upon Thames KT2 7PQ — MB BS 1988 Karnatak, India; MRCOG 1994. Clin. Research Fell. Middlx. Socs: Fac. Fam. Plann.; Med. Protec. Soc. Prev: Regist. Mayday Univ. Hosp.; Regist. Worcester Roy. Infirm.; Regist. Alexandra Hosp. Redditch.

THAKE, Ann Isobel Smith The Laurie Pike Health Centre, 95 Birchfield Road, Handsworth, Birmingham B19 1LH Tel: 0121 554 0621 Fax: 0121 554 6163; 47 Somerville Road, Sutton Coldfield B73 6HH — MD 1987 Sheff.; MB ChB 1969; DObst RCOG 1971. Lect. Dept. Gen. Pract. Birm. Univ. Prev: Clin. Asst. Genetics W. Midl. RHA.

THAKER, Chandrakant Shankerlal Burgess Road Surgery, 357a Burgess Road, Southampton SO16 3BD Tel: 023 8067 6233 Fax: 023 8067 2909; 10 Spindlewood Close, Bassett, Southampton SO16 3QD Tel: 02380 767645 — MB BS 1974 Bombay. (Grant Med. Coll.)

THAKER, Dilesh Arrowe Park Hospital, Arrowe Park Road, Wirral CH49 5PE — MB ChB 1998 Liverp.

THAKER, Kantilal Kalidas Knowsley Medical Centre, 9-11 Knowsley St., Bury BL9 0ST Tel: 0161 764 1217 Fax: 0161 764 6155; 9 Rothbury Close, Bury BL8 2TT — MB BS 1971 Gujarat.

THAKER, Pinakin Kumarbhai The Surgery, 65 Church Street, Cannock WS11 1DS — MB BS 1971 Gujarat. (B.J. Med. Coll. Ahmedabad)

THAKERAR, Jayendra Gordhandas The Surgery, 192 Tudor Drive, Kingston upon Thames KT2 5QH Tel: 020 85490061 Fax: 020 8549 9488; Ham Clinic, Ashburnham Road, Ham, Richmond TW10 7NF Tel: 020 8940 9442 — MB BS 1971 Bombay. Med. Off. Family Plann. Clinic W. Molesey. Socs: Roy. Soc. Med.; Overseas Doctors Assn.; BMA. Prev: Clin. Asst. (Rheum.) Croydon Gen. Hosp.; Sessional Med. Off. Family Plann. Clinic Richmond.

THAKKAR, Bhalchandra Chhaganlal The Clinic, Barbers Avenue, Rawmarsh, Rotherham S62 6AD Tel: 01709 526277 Email: bhalthakkar@gpc87024nhs.uk; 8 Broom Lane, Rotherham S60 3EL Tel: 01709 305309 Fax: 01709 305309 Email: bhal1wk@yahoo.co.uk — MB BS 1960 Calcutta; BSC Baroda India. (National Medical College) B.O.C. Med. Adviser.

THAKKAR, Chandrashekhar Hirjibhai The London Hospital (Whitechapel), Neuro X-Ray Department, Whitechapel Road, London E1 1BB Tel: 020 7377 7165 Fax: 020 7377 7165; St. Bartholomew's Hospital, Neuro X-Ray Department, Q.E. Block, Ground Floor, West Smithfield, London EC1A 7BE Tel: 020 7601 8301 Fax: 020 7601 8323 — MB BS 1972 Bombay; MD Bombay 1975; FRCR 1979; DMRD Lond. 1977. Cons. Radiol. The Roy. Lond. Hosp. Whitechapel,Lond.; Cons. Neuroradiol. St. Barts. Hosp. Lond.; Cons. Neuroradiol. The Lond. Imaging Centre., Lond.; Cons. Neuroradiol., The Lond. Clinic. Lond. Socs: Fell. Roy. Coll. Radiol. Prev: Cons. Neuroradiol. Bombay Hosp. India; Sen. Regist. The Lond. Hosp. Whitechapel. Lond.

THAKKAR, Mr Dilipkumar Ramoobhai 53 Russell Road, Moor Park, Northwood HA6 2LP Tel: 01923 835638 Fax: 01923 835638 — MS Orth. 1974 Bombay; DOrth 1974 Bombay; FCPS 1975 Bombay (Orth.); FRACS 2000 UK (Tr & Orth); MChOrth 1978 Liverpool; MB BS 1972 Bombay. (Bombay) Cons. Orthopaedic Surg., Hewham Gen. Hosp.; Staff Orthopaedic Surg., Old Ch., Essex. Socs: Overseas Fell. Brit. Orthop. Assn.; Mem. Indian Orthop. Assn. Prev: Hon. Asst. Prof. (Orthop.) Topiwala Nat. Med. Coll. Univ., Bombay; Lect. (Orthop) Univ. Sheff.; Regist. (Orthop.) Roy. Liverp. Hosp.

THAKKAR, Mr Dushyant Hirjibhai Hexham General Hospital, Corbridge Road, Hexham NE46 1QJ Tel: 01923 835638; 53 Russell Road, Moor Park, Northwood HA6 2LP Tel: 01923 835638 Fax: 01923 835638 — MB BS 1972 Bombay; FRCS 2000 (Tr&Orth) UK; MS Orth. Bombay 1975; FRCS (Tr & Orth) UK 2000; DOrth. Bombay 1974; FCPS Bombay (Orth.) 1975; MChOrth Liverp. 1978. (Bombay) Cons. Orthopeadic Surg., Hexham Gen. Hosp., Corbridge Rd., Hexham NE46 1QJ. Socs: Overseas Fell. BOA; Indian Orthop. Assn. Prev: Staff Orthopaedic Surg., Old Ch., Essex; Regist. (Orthop.) Roy. Liverp. Hosp.; Hon. Asst. Prof. (Orthop.) Topiwala Nat. Med. Coll. Univ. Bombay.

THAKKAR, Ila Dushyant 53 Russell Road, Northwood HA6 2LP Tel: 01923 835638 Fax: 01923 835638 — MB BS 1976 Gujarat; DA (UK) 1987; DA Eng. 1981; DGO TC Dub. 1979. Gen. Practitioner, Barnet Health Auth. Prev: Regist. (Anaesth.) Morriston Hosp. Swansea.; Regist. (Anaesth.) N.wick Pk. Hosp., Harrow & Harefiled Hosp.

THAKKER, Bishan Department of Bacteriology, Lister Building, Royal Infirmary, Castle St., Glasgow G12 0SF Tel: 0141 211 4640 — MB ChB 1985 Ed.; MRCPath 1993. Cons. Bacteriol. Roy. Infirm. Glas.

THAKKER, Pradumal 18 Westmorland Gardens, Peterborough PE1 5HU — MB BS 1989 Newc.

THAKKER, Professor Rajesh Vasantlal Molecular Endocrinology, Nuffield Dept of Medicine, University of Oxford, John Radcliffe Hospital, Oxford OX3 9DU Tel: 01865 222043 Fax: 01865 222047 Email: rajesh.thakker@ndm.ox.ac.uk — MB BChir 1981 Camb.; FMedSci 1999; FRCPath 1998; FRCP Ed. 1997; MD Camb. 1994, MA 1981, BA 1977; FRCP Lond. 1993; MRCP (UK) 1983. May Prof. of Med., Univ. of Oxf., Oxf., and Consulatant Phys. and Endocrinologist at John Radcliffe Hosp., Oxf.. Socs: Assn. Phys.; (Ex-Chairm.) N. Amer. Paediat. Bone & Mineral Working Gp.; Amer. Soc. of Bone & Mineral Research. Prev: Prof. Med & Cons Phy/ Endocrin & MRC Clin. Scientist ImperialColl. Sch. of Med., Lond.; Hon. Cons. Phys. (Endocrinol.) N.wick Pk. Hosp. Harrow; MRC Train. Fell. & Hon. Sen. Regist. Middlx. Hosp. Med. Sch. Lond.

THAKKER, Yogini Department of Child Health, Milton Keynes PCT, Standing Way, Eaglestone, Milton Keynes MK6 5LD — MB ChB 1982 Manch.; MRCP (UK) 1989; DCH RCP Lond. 1986; DRCOG 1985. Cons. Community Paediat. Milton Keynes PCT.

THAKOR, Ranjit Sinh The Surgery, 2-4 Halsbury Street, Leicester LE2 1QA Tel: 0116 273 0044 Fax: 0116 249 0810; 30/32 Loughborough Road, Leicester LE4 5LD Tel: 01162 268 2727 Fax: 01162 261 1223 — MB ChB 1974 Birm.; MRCGP 1978; DRCOG 1977. (Birmingham) Prev: Trainee GP Kettering Vocations Train. Scheme; Ho. Surg. Dudley Rd. Hosp. Birm.; Ho. Phys. Gen. Hosp. Birm.

THAKOR, Surendra Balwantray 8 Starfield Avenue, Littleborough OL15 0NG Tel: 01706 41409 — MB BS 1962 Gujarat; DA Gujarat 1963. (B.J. Med. Coll. Ahmedabad) Hosp. Pract. (Anaesth.) Burnley, Pendle, Rossendale AHA. Prev: Clin. Asst. (Anaesth.) Burnley, Pendle, Rossendale AHA; Regist. (Anaesth.) Burnley Health Dist.

THAKORE, Jogin Hemant Academic Department of Psychological Medicine, 3rd Floor, Alexandra Wing,, The Royal London Hospital, London E1 1BB Tel: 020 7377 7344 Fax: 020 7377 7343 Email: j.h.thakore@mds.qmw.ac.uk — MB BCh BAO 1986 Dub.; PhD Lond. 1995; MRCPsych 1993. Sen. Lect. (Psychol. Med.) St. Barth. & The Roy. Lond. Sch. of Med. & Dent. Socs: Inst. Soc. Psychoneuroendocrinol.; Brit. Neuroendocrine Gp.; Brit. Assn. Psychopharmacol. Prev: Lect. (Psychol. Med.) St. Bart. Hosp. Lond.

THAKORE, Mr Shobhan Bansidhar 9 Clovis Duveau Drive, Dundee DD2 5JA — MB ChB 1992 Dundee; BMSc (Hons.) Dund 1989; FRCS Ed. 1996; DRCOG 1994. Specialist Regist. (A&E.) Ninewells Hosp. Dundee. Prev: SHO (Intens. Care) Qu. Margt. Hosp. Dunfermline.

THAKRAR, Arita 251 Chesterfield Road, Sheffield S8 0RT Tel: 0114 255 1164; 18 Adelaide Road, Nether Edge, Sheffield S7 1SQ Tel: 0114 258 0685 — BM 1985 Soton.; MRCGP 1990; DCCH RCGP 1991; DRCOG 1990. Retainer Scheme (Gen. Pract.) Sheff. Socs: BMA. Prev: Clin. Med. Off. (Community Child Heath) Sheff.; Trainee GP Rotherham Dist. Gen. Hosp.

THAKRAR, Diviash Narendra Northwood Health Centre, Neal Close, Acre Way, Northwood HA6 1TH Tel: 01923 820844 Fax: 01923 820648 — MB BS 1993 Lond.

THAKRAR, Jayshree Prabhudas 42 Christchurch Avenue, Kenton, Harrow HA3 8NJ Tel: 020 8907 0936 — Artsexamen 1991 Utrecht.

THAKRAR, Navinchandra Amarshi Holly Road Medical Centre, 2A Holly Road, Chiswick, London W4 1NU Tel: 020 8994 0976 Fax: 020 8994 3685; 34 Lea Gardens, Wembley HA9 7SE Fax: 020 8994 3685 — MB BS 1972 Bombay. (Grant Med. Coll.) GP Lond.; Mem. Ealing, Hammersmith & Hounslow LMC; Sec. Overseas Doctor's Assn.

THAKRAR, Pankaj Mohanlal Havant Health Centre Suite C, PO Box 44, Civic Centre Road, Havant PO9 2AT Tel: 023 9247 4351 Fax: 023 9249 2524 — BM 1987 Soton.; MRCGP 1993; DRCOG 1991; DCH RCP Lond. 1990. Prev: Trainee GP Leicester & Market HarBoro..

THAKUR, Baleshwar Plungington Road Surgery, 100 Plungington Road, Preston PR1 7UE Tel: 01772 250574 — MB BS 1962 Patna. (Patna) Clin. Asst. Sharoe Green Hosp. Fulwood.

THAKUR, Eileen c/o The Indian YMCA, 41 Fitzroy Square, London W1P 6AQ — MB BS 1960 Patna.

THAKUR, Indra Mohan Department of Paediatrics, Darlington Memorial Hospital, Hollyhurst Road, Darlington DL3 6HX Tel: 01325 380100; 100 Cleveland Avenue, Darlington DL3 7BE Tel: 01325 281427 — MB BS 1979 Patna; FRCPI 1992. Cons. Paediat. Darlington Memor. Hosp. Co. Durh.

THAKUR, Makhan Chandra Dias and Thakur, Silver Lane Surgery, 1 Suffolk Court, Yeadon, Leeds LS19 7JN Tel: 0113 250 5988 Fax: 0113 250 3298; 62 West End Lane, Horsforth, Leeds LS18 5EP Tel: 0113 258 4664 Fax: 0113 250 3298 — MB BS 1963 Gauhati; DPM Leeds 1972. (Assam Med. Coll. Dibrugarh) Socs: BMA.

THAKUR, Meenakshi 498 Uxbridge Road, Pinner HA5 4SL — MB BS 1988 Lond.; MRCGP 1993; DCH RCP Lond. 1992.

THAKUR, S C Speke Health Centre, North Parade, Speke, Liverpool L24 2XP Tel: 0151 486 1695.

THAKUR, Miss Shakti Birmingham & Midland Eye Centre City Hospital, Dudley Road, Birmingham — MB BS 1990 Lond.; FRCS Ed. 1995; FRCOphth 1996. (University of London, St. George's Hospital Medical School) Specialist Regist. (Ophth.) W. Midl.s. Prev: SHO (Cas.) St. Geo. Hosp. Lond.; SHO (Ophth.) N. Middlx. Hosp. Lond. & Edgware Gen. Hosp.; SHO (Ophth.) Centr. Middx Hosp.

THALAKOTTUR, Joy Mathew Purbeck Health Centre, Purbeck, Stantonbury, Milton Keynes MK14 6BL Tel: 01908 318989 Fax: 01908 319493 — MB BS Bangalore 1972; DORCS (Lond.) 1985; DORCP&S (Dublin) 1985. (Bangalore Medical College) Gen. Med. Practitioner; Ophth. Med. Practitioner. Prev: Clin. Asst. Ophth.

THALANGE, Nandu Kumar Sidramappa 42 Regent Road, Lostock, Bolton BL6 4DQ; Marion Cottage, 68 London Road, Stone, Dartford DA2 6AN Tel: 01322 292659 — MB BS 1988 Lond.; MRCP (UK) 1992. Prev: SHO (Paediat.) King's Coll. Hosp. Lond. & S.end Hosp.

THALAYASINGAM, Balasingam 16 Middlewood Road, Lanchester, Durham DH7 0HL Tel: 01207 520693; 16 Middlewood Road, Lanchester, Durham DH7 0HL — MB BS Durh. 1960; MRCP (U.K.) 1970; MRCS Eng. LRCP Lond. 1961; FRCP Lond. 1988; FRCP Ed. 1987; FRCPCH 1997; DObst RCOG 1964; DCH Eng. 1964. (Newc.) Hon. Cons., N. Durh. Univ. Hosp.; Examr. MRCP (UK) RCP of Edin. & Lond.; Examr. PLAB; Examr. R.C.P.C.H; Locum Cons. Paediat., S. Tyneside health NHS Trust, Palmers Community Hosp. Socs: BMA; Fell. Roy. Soc. Med. Prev: Sen. Regist. (Rheum. & Med.) City Hosp. Nottm.; Fell. (Gastroenterol.) St. Christopher's Hosp. Childr. (Temple Univ.) Philadelphia, USA; Fell. (Neonatol.) Wayne State Univ. Michigan, USA.

THALAYASINGAM, Marie Edna Laleeni Westbourne Surgery, Kelso Grove, Shiney Row, Houghton-le-Spring DH4 4RW Tel: 0191 385 2512 Fax: 0191 385 6922 — MB BS 1971 Ceylon; DFFP 1993; DCH RCPS Glas. 1982. (Peradeniya) GP Princip.; W.bookne Surg. Kelso Gr. Shiney Row Tyne & Wear. Socs: BMA; MDU; DFFP. Prev: SHO (Paediat.) S. (Manch.) Health Dist. (T); Ho. Off. (Paediat.) & Ho. Off. (O & G) Gen. Hosp. Kandy, Sri Lanka.; N.ernbia Vocational Train. for Gen. Pract.

THALLER, Mr Vladimir Theodor Royal Eye Infirmary, Apsley Road, Plymouth PL4 6PL Tel: 01752 203167 Fax: 01752 254162 — BM BS 1976 Nottm.; BMedSci 1973; FRCS Eng. 1984; FRCOphth. (Nottingham University) Cons. Ophth. Surg. Plymouth HA. Socs: Fell. Roy. Coll. Ophth.; Eur. Soc. Oculoplastic & Reconstruc. Surg. Prev: Resid. & Oculoplastic Fell. Moorfields Eye Hosp.

THALLON, Angeli Jaya 16 Tradescant Road, London SW8 1XE Tel: 020 7582 4651 — MB BS 1994 Lond. SHO (O & G) Guy's & St. Thos. Hosps. Flexible Trainee. Prev: SHO (O & G) Guy's & St. Thos. Hosp. Lond.; Ho. Off. (Gen. Med.) Guy's Hosp. Lond.; Ho. Off. (Surg.) Greenwich.

THALLON, David Frank Edmonstone (Surgery), Rothschild House, Chapel St., Tring HP23 6PU Tel: 01442 822468 Fax: 01442 825889; The Laurels, 14 Station Road, Tring HP23 5NG Tel: 01442 823172 — MB BChir 1961 Camb.; MA, MB Camb. 1961, BChir 1960; DObst RCOG 1961. (St. Thos.) Socs: BMA; Roy. Soc. Med.

Prev: Ho. Surg. St. Thos. Hosp. Hydestile; Ho. Phys. (O & G) St. Thos. Hosp. Lond.; Resid. Med. Off. Burton Gen. Hosp.

*THAM, Lawrence Chiew Hong 49 The Chare, Burnopfield, Newcastle upon Tyne NE1 4DD — MB BS 1988 Newc.

THAM, Nirangalie Cockfosters Medical Centre, Heddon Court Avenue, Cockfosters, Barnet EN4 9NB Tel: 020 8441 7008 — MB BS 1983 Lond.; DRCOG 1986.

THAM, Siew Wan Division of Disability, Department of Mental Health Services, St. Georges Hospital, Jenner Wing, Cranmer Terrace, London SW17 0RE; 9 Barnes Avenue, Barnes, London SW13 9AA Tel: 020 8741 7631 — MB BChir 1990 Camb.; BA Camb. 1987, MB BChir 1990; MA Camb. 1991. Regist. (Psychiat.) St. Geo. Hosp. Lond.; Regist. (Disabil.) Dept. Ment. Health Sci. St. Geo. Hosp. Lond. Prev: SHO (Psychiat.) Roy. Lond. Hosp.

THAM, Tony Chiew Keong Ulster Hospital, Dundonald, Belfast BT16 1RH Tel: 02890 561344 Fax: 02890 561396 Email: ttham@ktvinternet.com; 43 New Forge Lane, Belfast BT9 5NW Tel: 02890 280620 — MB BCh BAO 1985 Belf.; MD Belf. 1990; MRCP (UK) 1988; FRCP 2000; FRCPI 2000. (Queens University Belfast) Cons. Phys. & Gastroenterol. Ulster Hosp. Dundonald Belf. Socs: Brit. Soc. Gastroenterol.; Ulster Soc. Gastroenterol.; Ulster Soc. Internal Med. Prev: Gastroenterol. Fell. Brigham & Wom.s Hosp. Harvard Med. Sch. Boston, Mass., USA; Sen. Regist. & Sen. Tutor (Gastroenterol.) Inst. Clin. Sci. Qu.s Univ. & Roy. Vict. Hosp. Belf.; Regist. (Gen. Internal Med.) & Sen. Home Off., Belf. Teachg.. Hosp.

THAMAN, Rajesh 91 Princes Avenue, Surbiton KT6 7JW — MB BS 1994 Lond.

THAMBAPILLAI, Mr Augustus Jayaseelan Dept. of Audiological Medicine, St Ann's Hospital, St Ann's Road, London N15 3TH Tel: 0205 442 6523 Fax: 0208 442 6769; 13A Heather Bank, Beaumont Road, Petts Wood, Orpington BR5 1JL — MB BS 1972 Ceylon; FRCS Ed. 1987; DLO RCS Eng. 1986; MSc 1994. (Ceylon) Cons. (Audiological Med.). Socs: BMA; BAAP; IAAP. Prev: Sen. Regist. in Audiogical Med., Roy. Nat. Throat Nose & Ear Hospatl; Staff Surg. ENT, N. Riding Infirm., MiddlesBoro.

THAMBAPILLAI, Ravindraseelan St. Elmo, 201 Church Hill Road, Barnet EN4 8PQ — MB BS 1973 Sri Lanka; MRCP (UK) 1984; DCH RCP Lond. 1983. (Colombo)

THAMBAR, Isaac Vanniasingham (retired) Department of Genitourinary Medicine, Royal Infirmary, Blackburn BB2 3LR Tel: 01254 687304 — MB BS 1960 Ceylon; FRCP Lond. 1994; FRCP Ed. 1991; MRCP (UK) 1976. Prev: Cons. Genitourin. Med. Roy. Infirm. Blackburn Gen. Hosp. Burnley & Gen. Hosp. Bury.

THAMBIRAJAH, Gladstone Ravindraraj Chesterfield & North Derbyshire Royal Hospital, Chesterfield S44 5BL Tel: 01246 277271; 9 Hockley Lane, Wingerworth, Chesterfield S42 6QG — MB BS 1979 Peredeniya; LRCP LRCS Ed. LRCPS Glas. 1987; MRCOG 1995. Staff Grade (O & G) Chesterfield Roy. Hosp. NHS Trust.

THAMBIRAJAH, Muthusamy Subramaniam Child & Family Consultation Centre, 161 Eccleshall Road, Stafford ST16 1PD Tel: 01785 222708; 8 Thelsford Way, Solihull B92 9NR Tel: 0121 705 8388 — MB BS 1967 Ceylon; LMSSA Lond. 1985; MRCPsych 1987. Cons. Child & Adolesc. Psychiat. Child & Family Consult. Centre Stafford.

THAMBIRAJAH, Sharmini Anaesthetics Department, Rotherham District General Hospital, Moorgate Road, Rotherham S60 2UD — MB BS 1979 Peradeniya; MB BS Peradeniya, Sri Lanka 1979.

THAMBYRAJAH, Jeetendra 18 Eachway, Rubery, Rednal, Birmingham B45 9DQ — BM BS 1993 Nottm.; BMedSci Nottm. 1991.

THAMIZHAVELL, Mr Ramasamy Chakravarthy Accident & Emergency Department, Kettering General Hospital, Kettering NN16 8UZ — MB BS 1975 Madras; FRCS Glas. 1990. Cons. A & E Kettering Gen. Hosp. Prev: Staff Grade (A & E) Bedford Hosp.

THAMMANNA, Dr 60 Keward Avenue, Wells BA5 1TS Tel: 01749 75036 — MB BS 1970 Mysore. (Mysore Med. Coll.) Clin. Asst. in Psychiat. Mendip Hosp. Wells. Prev: Regist. (Psychiat.) High Royds Hosp. Menston.

THAMMONGKOL, Kokeo 22 Redington Road, London NW3 7RG — MRCS Eng. LRCP Lond. 1969.

THAMPI, Annette Adult Mental Health Services, Claydon Community Mental Health Service, Claydon, Melbourne Vic. 3168, Australia; 3 Coolsara Park, Lisburn BT28 3BG Tel: 01846 679066 — MB ChB 1991 Bristol; MRCPsych 1995. (Univ. Bristol) Sen.

Regist. (Psychiat.) Melbourne. Austral. Socs: BMA; Ulster Med. Soc.; Roy. Coll. Psychiat. Prev: Sen. Regist. (Psychiat.) Holywell Hosp. Antrim; Sen. Regist. Jt. Research Holywell Hosp. Antrim.; SHO (Psychiat.) Windsor Hse. Belf. City Hosp.

THAMPY, Reshma Sreekumaran 9 Lorne Crescent, Bishopbriggs, Glasgow G64 1XU — MB ChB 1998 Glas.

THAN, Min The Surgery, 62/64 Church St., Bilston WV14 0AX Tel: 01902 496065 Fax: 01902 496384; Tinacre Top, 40 Tinacre Hill, Wightwick, Wolverhampton WV6 8DA Tel: 01902 579279 — MB BS 1981 Rangoon; DGM RCP Lond. 1992; DTCD Wales 1987. Prev: Regist. (Gerontol.) Medway Hosp. Gillingham.

THAN, Myint Anaesthetic Department, Broomfield Hospital, Court Road, Broomfield, Chelmsford CM1 7ET; 74(A) Nalla Gardens, Chelmsford CM1 4AX — MB BS 1978 Rangoon; DA (UK) 1993; FRCA 1996. Staff Grade (Anaest.). Socs: MDU; Assn. Anaesths.; BMA.

THAN, Nilar Flat 4, 23 Bainbrigge Road, Leeds LS6 3AD Tel: 0113 274 7285; 24 Buttermere Drive, Kendal LA9 7PA Tel: 01539 733807 — MB ChB 1993 Leeds; MB ChB (Hons.) Leeds 1993; BSc (Hons.) Leeds 1990; MRCP UK. Specialist Regist. (Renal Med.) Leeds Gen. Infirm. Socs: BMA; MDU; Eur. Dialysis & Transpl. Assn.

THAN, Soe Room 28, Tyndall House, Southmead Health Services NHS Trust, Southmead Hospital, Southmead Road, Westbury-on-Trym, Bristol BS10 5NB — MB BS 1987 Med. Inst. (I) Rangoon; MRCP (UK) 1995.

THAN HTAY, Dr 11 Love Lane, Halifax HX1 2BQ Tel: 01422 356609 — MB BS 1973 Med. Inst. (I) Rangoon; DA (UK) 1983. Assoc. Specialist (Anaesth.) Halifax Roy. Infirm. Prev: Clin. Asst. & Regist. (Anaesth.) Halifax Roy. Infirm.; SHO (Anaesth.) E.bourne Gen. Hosp.

THAN KYAW, Dr 155 Manchester Road, Swinton, Manchester M27 4FH Tel: 0161 794 6901 Fax: 0161 728 4877; 37 Granary Lane, Worsley, Manchester M28 7PH Tel: 0161 794 7363 — MBBS 1972 Burma; MFCH; MSc.

THAN NYUNT, Martin Paul Accident Emergency Department, Royal Infirmary of Edinburgh, Lauriston Place, Edinburgh EH3 9YW Tel: 0131 229 2477; Middle House, High St, Harby, Newark NG23 7EB Tel: 01522 703456 — MB BS 1991 Lond. SHO (A & E Med.) Roy. Infirm. Edin. Socs: Brit. Assn. Accid. & Emerg. Med.

THAN THAN SWE, Dr 283 Queslett Road, Birmingham B43 7HB — MB BS 1971 Rangoon; MB BS Med Inst (I) Rangoon 1971.

THANABALASINGHAM, Balamurali 125 Green Lane, Edgware HA8 8EL — BChir 1996 Camb.; MB Camb. 1997.

THANABALASINGHAM, Sri Thalayasingham Health Control Unit, Terminal 3 Arrivals, Heathrow Airport, Hounslow TW6 1NB Tel: 020 8745 7208 Fax: 020 8745 6181 Email: st.hcu@virgin.net; Jesmin, 18 Sheridan Gardens, Kenton, Harrow HA3 0JT Tel: 020 8907 3814 — MB BS Ceylon 1972; MRCPI 1986; DTM & H RCP Lond. 1986; FRCP (Ireland) March 2000. (Univ. Ceylon, Peradeniya, Sri Lanka) Clin. Dir. & Port Med. Off. Health Control Unit Terminal 3 Arrivals Heathrow Airport, Hounslow; Sen. Clin. Med. Off. (Gen. Med. & Infec. Dis.) W. Middlx. Univ. Hosp. Isleworth; Assoc. Specialist (Chest Med.) Hillingdon Hosp. Hillingdon. Socs: Brit. Med. Assn. Prev: Regist. (Infec. Dis. & Trop. Med.) W. Middlx. Univ. Hosp. Isleworth; SHO (Gen. Med.) N. Tyneside Gen. Hosp.; Ho. Off. (Gen. Med.) Gen. Hosp. Colombo, Sri Lanka.

THANABALASINGHAM, Yasothara Department of ENT, Northwick Park Hospital, Harrow HA1 3UJ Tel: 020 8864 3232; Jesmin, 18 Sheridan Gardens, Kenton, Harrow HA3 0JT Tel: 020 8907 3814 — MB BS 1976 Sri Lanka; MB BS Univ. Sri Lanka 1976; LMSSA Lond. 1990; DLO RCS Eng. 1984. Clin. Asst. (ENT) N.wick Pk. Hosp. Harrow & Centr. Middlx. Hosp. Pk. Roy. Prev: SHO (ENT) W. Middlx. Unit. Hosp. Isleworth & N. Tyneside Gen. Hosp.; Ho. Off. (Gen. Med.) Gen. Hosp. Kurunegala, Sri Lanka.

THANDA, Khin Myo Tel: 01772 401930 Fax: 01772 886567 — DRCOG Lond.; MB BS 1975 Med Inst (I) Rangoon; MB BS 1975 Med Inst (I) Rangoon. (Institute of Medicine (I) Rangoon, Burma)

*THANDI, Himat Singh Flat 3, 22 Rutland Sq, Edinburgh EH1 2BB Tel: 0131 229 5053 — MB ChB 1997 Ed.

THANDI, Karamvir Singh 46 Wadhurst Road, Birmingham B17 8JE — MB ChB 1992 Birm.

THANDI, Rajvir Singh — MB ChB 1994 Birm.; MRCGP 1998; DRCOG 1997. (Birmingham) Princip. Gen. Practitioner, N.brook Gp.

THAVAPALAN

Pract., 93 N.brook Rd, Olton, Solihull B90 3LX, W. Midl.s. Prev: GP Regist., Monkspath Surg., Solihull.

THANE, Htun Room 42, Elm House, Stepping Hill Hospital, Poplar Grove, Stepping Hill, Stockport SK2 7JE Tel: 0161 419 5142 — MB BS 1981 Med. Inst. Rangoon; MRCP (UK) 1993.

THANGA, Vakees 30 Shelton Road, Merton Park, London SW19 3AT — MB BS 1986 Lond.; DCH RCP Lond. 1989. Trainee GP Lond. VTS. Socs: MDU. Prev: SHO (Paediat.) Hammersmith Hosp. Lond.; SHO (A & E) Lewisham Hosp.; SHO (Geriat.) St. Geo. & Rushgreen Hosps.

THANGARAJ, Irene Latha 38 Redbourne Avenue, Finchley, London N3 2BS — MB BS 1986 Madras; MRCP (UK) 1996. Sen. Regist. (Gen. & Geriat. Med.) Watford Gen. Hosp. Prev: Regist. (c/o Elderly) Barnet Gen. Hosp.; SHO (c/o Elderly & Gen. Med.) Barnet Gen. Hosp.

THANGARAJASINGAM, Vythialingam (retired) 328 Pickhurst Rise, West Wickham BR4 0AY — MB BS 1956 Ceylon; DCH RCP Lond. 1962; DTM & H Liverp. 1962. Prev: Clin. Asst. (Family Plann.) FarnBoro. Hosp. Orpington.

THANGKHIEW, Irene Hospital of St Cross, Barby Road, Rugby CV22 5PX Tel: 01788 572831 Fax: 01788 545159; 29 Stareton Close, Coventry CV4 7AU Tel: 01203 419857 — MB BS 1966 Gauhati; MSc (Bact.) Manch. 1970; MRCPath 1994; Dip. Bact. Lond 1968. Assoc. Specialist Med. Microbiol. Socs: BMA; Brit. Soc. Antimicrob. Chemother.

THANKEY, Kishorchandra Lalji The Surgery, Riversley Road, Nuneaton CV11 5QT Tel: 024 7638 2239/7664 2409 Fax: 024 7632 5623 — MB BS 1973 Rajasthan.

THANOON, Manal Younis 171 Duddingston Drive, Kirkcaldy KY2 6XQ — MB ChB 1981 Mosul; MRCP (UK) 1990.

THANT, Moe 5 Chaffinch Close, Skippingdale, Scunthorpe DN15 8EL; Anaesthetic Department, Scunthorpe General Hospital, Scunthorpe DN16 — MB BS 1985 Med. Inst (I) Rangoon; DA Lond. 1994. Staff Grade Anaesth.

THAPA, Shailendra 31 Golding Throughfare, Chelmsford CM2 6TU Tel: 01245 608854 — MB BS 1988 Bahauddin Zakariya Univ. Clin. Research. Instit of Psychiat. Socs: MRCPsych.

THAPA, Than Bahadur The Machylilleth Health Centre, Forge Road, Machynlleth SY20 8EQ Tel: 01654 702601 Fax: 01654 3688; Maes-y-Gynesh, Garth Road, Machynlleth SY20 8HQ Tel: 01650 702601 Fax: 01654 3688 — MB BS Gauhati 1959; MRCP (UK) 1970; DTM & H Ed. 1967; DPH Calcutta 1963; FRCP Ed 1998. GP; Clin. Asst. Bro Ddyfi Community Hosp. Prev: Regist. (Med.) P.ss Margt. Hosp. Swindon.

THAPAR, Ajay Kumar Department of General Practice, Rusholme Health Centre, Walmer St., Rusholme, Manchester M14 — MB ChB 1984 Dundee; BSc (Hons.) Physiol. Dund 1980; MRCGP 1990; DRCOG 1989; DCH RCP Lond. 1988. Lect. (Gen. Pract.) Univ. Manch. Prev: Lect. (Gen. Pract.) Univ. Wales Coll. Med.; GP Aberbargoed, M. Glam.

THAPAR, Professor Anita Dept of Psychological Medicine, University of Wales College, Heath Park, Cardiff CF14 4XN Tel: 029 2074 3241 — MB BCh 1985 Wales; PhD Wales 1995; MRCPsych 1989. Prof. (Child & Adolesc. Psychiat.) Univ of Wales Coll of Med. Prev: Sen. Lect. (Child & Adolesc. Psychiat.) Univ. Manch.; MRC Research Fell. Univ. Wales Coll. Med. Cardiff; Sen. Regist. Rotat. (Child & Adolesc. Psychiat.) S. Wales.

THAPAR, Nikhil — BM 1993 (Hons.) Soton.; BSc (Hons) 1992; MRCP (UK) 1997; MRCPCH 1997. Specialist Regist. in Paediat. Gastroenterol., Gt. Ormond St. Hosp., Lond. Prev: Specialist Regist. in Paediatric Gastroenterol., St Bartholemew's and the Roy. Lond. Hosp.; Specialist Regist. in Paediat., St Marys Hosp. Portsmouth.

THAPAR, Rama Silver Street Medical Centre, 159 Silver Street, London N18 1PY Tel: 020 8807 1057 Fax: 020 8345 5259 — MB BS 1970 Delhi; Cert. Family Plann. JCC 1972. (Delhi)

THAPAR, Vineet Oak Hill Health Centre, Oak Hill Road, Surbiton KT6 6EN Tel: 020 8399 6622 Fax: 020 8390 4470 — BM 1986 Soton.; MRCGP 1991; DRCOG 1989. Socs: BMA; Brit. Med. Acupunct. Soc. Prev: Regist. (Med.) Qu. Eliz. II Hosp. Brisbane, Austral.; SHO (Paediat.) Wexham Pk. Hosp. Slough; SHO (O & G) Heatherwood Hosp. Ascot.

THARAKAN, Parayil Mohan Brenkley Avenue Health Centre, Brenkley Avenue, Shiremoor, Newcastle upon Tyne NE27 0PR Tel: 0191 219 5708 — MB BS 1974 Kerala. (Kerala) GP Newc.

THARIAN, Bridget Savannah, Pitfold Avenue, Haslemere GU27 1PN — MB BS 1955 Punjab.

THARMARAJAH, Pritam 42 Lucerne Road, Thornton Heath, Croydon CR7 7BA — MB BS 1996 Lond.

THARMARATNAM, Anand Kumaresh 21 Iverna Court, Wrights Lane, London W8 6TY Email: 106056.2037@compuserve.com — MB BS 1992 Lond. (University College London) Res. Phys. Quintiles Transnat. Lond. Prev: SHO (Anaesth.).

THARMARATNAM, Dushen 243 High Kingsdown, Bristol BS2 8DG — MB ChB 1998 Bristol.

THARMARATNAM, Jeyarany 113 Flemming Avenue, Leigh-on-Sea SS9 3AU — MB BS 1982 Sri Lanka; MRCS Eng. & LRCP Lond. 1987.

THARMARATNAM, Suresh Tel: 028 9026 813 — MB BS 1987 Lond.; DAdv Obst. Ultrasound 1998; MRCOG 1992. (Char. Cross & Westm. Med. Sch.) Cons. (O & G) Belf. City Hosp. Belf.; Cons. (O&G) Roy. Jubilee Matern. Hosp. Belf. Socs: Ulster Obst. & Gyn. Soc.; Brit. Med. Ultrasound Soc.; BMA. Prev: Sen. Regist. (O & G) Ant. Area Hosp. Antrim; Lect./Sen. Regist. (O & G) Roy. Matern. Hosp. Belf.; Regist. (O & G) St. Bart. & King Geo. Hosps. Lond.

THARMASEELAN, Kanagasingam 19 Cheriton Avenue, Bromley BR2 9DL Tel: 020 8464 1577 — MB BS 1974 Sri Lanka; MRCS Eng. LRCP Lond. 1986; FCOphth 1990; DO RCS Glas. 1987. Staff Grade Ophalmologist, Essex Co. Hosp., Colchester. Socs: FRCO. Prev: Clin. Med. Off., Roy. Eye Infirm., Plymouth.

THARUMARATNAM, Devika Bosede 23 Gainsborough Gardens, Edgware HA8 5TA — MB BS 1994 Lond.

THATCHER, Mr Matthew James Medicines Control Agency, Market Towers, 1 Nine Elms Lane, London SW8 5NQ — MB BS 1977 Lond.; MB BS (Hons.) Lond. 1977; FRCS Eng. 1982; FRCS Ed. 1982; DRCOG 1988; DMRD 1984. Sen. Med. Off. Med. Control Agency.

THATCHER, Professor Nicholas Department Medical Oncology, Christie Hospital, Manchester M20 4BX Tel: 0161 446 3745 Fax: 0161 446 3299 — MB BChir 1971 Camb.; PhD Manch. 1980; FRCP Lond. 1984; MRCP (UK) 1972; DMRT Eng. 1974; DCH Eng. 1973. Prof. & Cons. Med. Oncol. Christie Hosp. Manch. Prev: Chairm. MRC Lung Cancer Working Party; Chairm. UK Coordinating Comm. on Cancer Research (Trials).

THATCHER, Peter Graham 46 Cornflower Lane, Shirley Oaks, Croydon CR0 8XJ — MB BS 1993 Lond.

THAUNG, Caroline May Hla Medical Centre, Harwell, Didcot OX11 0RO Email: cthaung@har.mrc.ac.uk — MB ChB 1992 Glas.; BSc Glas. 1989; Dip. Forens. Med. Glas 1996; FRCOphth 1998. Clin. Research Fell. in Ophth. MRC Harwell. Prev: SHO (Opthalmology) S. Gen. Hosp. Glas.; Senir Health Off. (Ophth.) MusGr. Pk. Hosp. Taunton.

THAVA, Vallipuram Raja Department of Radiology, Lincoln County Hospital, Greetwell Road, Lincoln LN2 5QY Tel: 01522 573457/573266 Fax: 01522 573241 Email: raj.thava@ulh.nhs.uk; Paddock House, Old Mulberry Court, Welbourne, Lincoln LN5 0TB Tel: 01400 272572 Fax: 01522 573241 Email: drvthava@hotmail.com — MB BS 1974 Sri Lanka; MRCS Eng. LRCP Lond. 1985; T(R) (CR) 1992; FRCR 1990. Cons. Radiol. Lincoln Hosps. NHS Trust. Prev: Cons. Radiol. Grimsby Hosp. NHS Trust; Sen. Regist. (Radiol.) W. Midl. RHA.

THAVABALAN, Ponnappa Bobby Essex County Hospital, Essex Rivers Healthcare Trust, Lexden Road, Colchester CO3 3NB Tel: 01206 834558 — MB BS 1962 Ceylon; FRCP Lond. 1994; FRCP Ed. 1989; Dip. Dermat. Lond. 1968. (Ceylon) Cons. Genitourin. Med. Colchester. Socs: BMA; Assn. GU Med. Prev: Sen. Regist. (Venereol.) W.m. Hosp. Lond.; Regist. (Dermat. & Venereol.) Univ. Coll. Hosp. Lond.

THAVAPALAN, Muruganandan Thavapalan and Partners, 55 Little Heath Road, Bexleyheath DA7 5HL Tel: 01322 430129 Fax: 01322 440949 Email: m.thavapalan@gp_g83033.nhs.uk; Tel: 01322 559942 Email: m.tharapalan@ftinternet.com — MB BS 1974 Sri Lanka; MRCS Eng. LRCP Lond. 1982; MRCGP 1992. Prev: Clin. Asst. (Thoracic Med.) Brook Hosp. Lond.; Clin. Asst. (Dermat.) Brook Hosp. Lond.

THAVAPALAN, Nandani Dora 18 Heathwood Walk, Bexley DA5 2BP Tel: 01322 559942 Email: myresh@msn.com — MB BS 1973 Sri Lanka; MRCPsych 1986. Assoc. Specialist (Psychiat.) Greenwich Dist. Hosp. Lond.

THAVARAJ

THAVARAJ, Manchulaa 23 Lyndhurst Crescent, Swindon SN3 2RW — MB ChB 1998 Dund.

THAVARAJAH, Vaithilingam Muthusamy Nobles Hospital, Westmoreland Road, Douglas — MB BS 1974 Sri Lanka; LRCP LRCS Ed. LRCPS Glas. 1987.

THAVASOTHY, Murali 31 Stivichall Croft, Coventry CV3 6GP — MB BS 1990 Lond.

THAVASOTHY, Rajaratnam Coventry Mental Health Unit, Walsgrave Hospital, Clifford Bridge Road, Coventry CV2 2TE Tel: 02476 602020; 31 Stivichall Croft, Coventry CV3 6GP Tel: 02476 414275 Fax: 02476 538920 — MB BS 1959 Ceylon; MRCP (UK) 1971; MRCPsych 1972; DPM Eng. 1969. (Ceylon) Cons. Psychiat. Coventry Ment. Health Unit; Hon. Sen. Clin. Lect. (Clin. Psychiat.) Univ Birm. Prev: Sen. Regist. Fulbourn Hosp. & United Camb. Hosps.; Vis. Cons. Psychiat., Univ. of Warwick.

THAWDA WIN, Dr 10 Mapledale Avenue, Croydon CR0 5TA — MB BS 1976 Med. Inst. (I) Rangoon.

THAYALAN, Aingarapillai Samuel Occupational Health Department, Kingston Hospital, Galsworthy Road, Kingston upon Thames KT2 Tel: 020 8546 7711; 45 High Drive, New Malden KT3 3UD Tel: 020 8546 7711 — MB BS 1982 Peradeniya, Sri Lanka; MRCS Eng. LRCP Lond. 1987; MRCP (UK) 1990; AFOM RCP (UK) 1993. Cons. Occupat. Phys. Epsom Health Care Trust Kingston Hosp. NHS Trust. Socs: Soc. Occupat. Med.; BMA. Prev: Sen. Regist. (Occupat. Med.) Freeman Hosp. Newc.; Trainee GP/SHO Newcross Hosp. Wolverhampton.

THAYALAN, Sumathy 45 High Drive, New Malden KT3 3UD Tel: 020 8408 0368 — LRCP LRCS 1993 Ed.; MBBS LRCP LRCS Ed. LRCPS Glas. 1993; DCH 1997. GP Regist. Epsom.

THÉ, Ing Thay (retired) 7 Queen Elizabeth Street, London SE1 2LP Tel: 020 7407 1069 — MB BS 1944 Lond.; DTM & H Eng. 1948. Prev: Ho. Phys. Postgrad. Med. Sch. Lond. & Guy's Hosp. FarnBoro.

THEAKER, Jeffrey Michael Litton Lodge, Clifton Road, Winchester SO22 5BP — MB BS 1980 Lond.; MA Oxf. 1982; MD 1987; MRCPath 1986. Cons. Histopath. Soton. Univ. Hosp. Prev: Clin. Lect. Nuffield Dept. Path. & Bacteriol. John Radcliffe Hosp. Oxf.

THEAN, See Yin Lennard Harold No 03-55 Mayer Mansion, 55 Devonshire Road, Singapore 239855, Singapore Email: ithean@mbox4.singnet.com.sg; 22 Holybank Court, 193 London Road, Leicester LE2 1ZF — MB ChB 1990 Leic.; FRCS Ed. 1997. Specialist Regist. Singapore Nat. Eye Centre.

THEANO, Ginette South London and Maudsley NHS Trust, The Crescent Res. Centre, Salcot Crescent, New Addington,, Croydon CR0 0JJ — LMS 1965 Madrid; 1966 Licenciatura in Medicina (Madrid); FRCPsych 1989,; DPM Eng. 1970; Dip. Psychiat. Madrid 1967; MRCPsych 1972. (Madrid) Cons. Psychiat. S. Lond. and Maudsley NHS Trust. Socs: Brit. Assn. Psychopharmacol.; Croydon Medico-Legal Soc.; Roy. Coll. of Psychiat.s. Prev: Sen. Regist. (Psychol. Med.) Guy's Hosp. Lond.; Regist. Croydon AHA; SHO Runwell Hosp. Essex.

THEAR-GRAHAM, Michael Robert Parc-y-Bont, Newport Road, Llantarnam, Cwmbran NP44 3AF Tel: 01633 33166 Fax: 01633 33166; 14 Longhouse Grove, Henllys, Cwmbran NP44 6HQ Tel: 01633 864919 Fax: 01633 864919 — MB ChB 1985 Ed. Indep. Dispensing GP Gwent.

THEBE, Phaudaraj Raj Department of Pathology, Dartford & Gravesham NHS Trust, Joyce Green Hospital, Dartford DA1 5PL Tel: 01322 227242 Fax: 01322 283532; 40 Lamorbey Close, Sidcup DA15 8BA Tel: 020 8302 3814 — MB BS 1979 Jiwaji; MRCPath 1993; DCP Lond 1988. Cons. Histopath. & Cytopath. Dartford & Gravesham NHS Trust. Socs: IAP (Brit. Div.); BSCC.

THEBRIDGE, Peter Jonathan Yardley Green Medical Centre, 73 Yardley Green Road, Bordesley Green, Birmingham B9 5PU Tel: 0121 773 3838 Fax: 0121 506 2005; 45 Kingslea Road, Solihull B91 1TQ Tel: 0121 704 9608 — MB ChB 1981 Manch.; MRCGP 1985; DRCOG 1984.

***THEIN, Michael** 647 Great West Road, Osterley, Isleworth TW7 4PZ — MB BS 1998 Lond.; MB BS Lond 1998.

THEIN, Myint Parnwell Medical Centre, Peterborough PE1 4YL Tel: 01733 896112 Fax: 01733 892286 — MB BS 1975 Rangoon; MB BS Med. Inst. (I) Rangoon 1975; DTM UK Liverp.

THEIN, Professor Swee Lay Dept. of Molecular Haematology, GKT School of Medicine, King's Denmark Hill Campus, Bessemer Road, London SE5 9PJ Tel: 020 7346 1682, 020 7346 1689 Fax: 020 7346 1681 Email: se.thein@kcl.ac.uk — MB BS 1975 Malaya; MRCP (UK) 1977; MRCPath (Haemat.) 1981; FRCPath 1993; FRCPA 1998; DSc 1999. Prof. in Haematology & Hon. Cons. King's Healthcare Trust, Lond. Prev: Wellcome Sen. Research Fell. & Hon. Cons. Oxf. RHA.

THEIN THEIN WYNN, Dr 10 Longdean Park, Chester-le-Street DH3 4DF — MB BS 1965 Med. Inst. (I) Rangoon; MRCP (UK) 1971. SCMO (Elderly) Newc. City Health Trust. Socs: Fac. Community Health; Brit. Geriat. Soc.

THEIVENDRA, Muttiah Town Surgery, 37 Cecil Road, Enfield EN2 6TJ Tel: 020 8342 0330 Fax: 020 8342 0330 — MB BS 1975 Sri Lanka; LRCP LRCS Ed. LRCPS Glas. 1984.

THEKEKARA, Abraham George Flat 1, 28 Great Ormond St., London WC1N 3JE — MB BS 1984 Punjab, India; MB BS Punjabi, India 1984; MRCP (UK) 1993; MRCPI 1990.

THELWALL-JONES, Hugh (retired) 89 Harley Close, Telford TF1 3LF Tel: 01952 247182 Fax: 01952 247183 Email: hugh.t@virgin.net — MRCS Eng. LRCP 1965 Lond.; MB BChir 1966 Camb.; MA Camb. 1966; FRCOG 1983, M 1970; T(OG) 1991; DObst 1968. Prev: Gp. Med. Dir. Brit. United Provident Assn.

THELWELL, Christine Margaret 49 Wolds Drive, Keyworth, Nottingham NG12 5FT — MB ChB 1990 Glas.

THELWELL, John Reginald (retired) 49 Eaton Mews, Handbridge, Chester CH4 7EJ — MB ChB Manch. 1959. Prev: Ho. Off. (Obst.) Withington Hosp. Manch.

THEMEN, Mr Arthur Edward George Department of Orthopaedics, Royal Berkshire Hospital, Reading Tel: 01734 871555; Whitley Glebe, 11 Glebe Road, Reading RG2 7AG Tel: 01734 752097 — MB 1965 Camb.; MA Camb. 1968; FRCS Eng. 1969; FRCS Ed. 1969. Cons. Orthop. Surg. Roy. Berks. Hosp. Reading. Socs: Fell. BOA. Prev: SHO Postgrad. Med. Sch.; Sen. Regist. (Orthop.) Roy. Nat. Orthop. Hosp. Stanmore; Regist. (Orthop.) St. Mary's Hosp. Lond.

THEN, Kong Yong 45 Tudor Court, Princes Riverside Road, London SE16 5RH Tel: 020 7231 1502 — MB BS 1995 Lond. (St. Geo. Hosp. Med. Sch. Lond.) SHO (Ophth.) Birm. & Midl. Eye Centre City Hosp. Socs: Med. Defense Union; BMA. Prev: SHO (Ophth.) Roy. Eye Infirm. Plymouth; Ho. Off. (ENT & Surg.) Manor Hosp. Walsall; Ho. Off. (Med.) Yeovil Hosp. Som.

THENUWARA, Charitha 14 Blendon Road, Bexley DA5 1BW — MB BS 1998 Lond.

THENUWARA, Clarence Dayasiri The Surgery, 118 Restons Crescent, Eltham, London SE9 2JJ Tel: 020 8859 7941 Fax: 020 8859 2382 — MB BS 1967 Ceylon. Socs: Mem. Brit. Acupunture Counc.; Mem. Brit Med. Acupunture Soc.

THEOBALD, Andrew John Bedgrove Surgery, Brentwood Way, Aylesbury HP21 7TL Tel: 01296 330330 Fax: 01296 399179; Hundred Acre Wood, Ashendon Farm Barns, Ashendon, Aylesbury HP18 0HB Tel: 01296 651869 Email: theo@bucksnet.co.uk — MB ChB 1987 Dundee; MRCGP 1991; T(GP) 1991; DCCH RCP Ed. 1990; DRCOG 1989. (Dundee) Clin. Asst. Cancer Care & Chemother. Unit Stoke Mandeville Hosp. NHS Trust Aylesbury. Prev: Trainee GP Aylesbury VTS; Ho. Off. (Med.) Stoke Mandeville Hosp.; Ho. Surg. Amersham Gen. Hosp.

THEOBALD, Janet Louisa Mary — MB ChB 1993 Aberd.; MB ChB 1993 (Hons) Aberd.; BSc Leeds 1981. (Aberdeen) Socs: Austral. Med. Assn.; BMA. Prev: Regist. (Psychiat.) Alfred Gp. Hosps. Melbourne, Austral.

THEOBALD, John Arthur (retired) 2A Retreat Road, Topsham, Exeter EX3 0LF Tel: 01392 875498 — MB BS Lond. 1957; MRCS Eng. LRCP Lond. 1956; MFCM 1974; DPH Lond. 1961. Prev: Sen. Med. Off. (Pub. Health Med.) Exeter & N. Devon HA.

THEOBALD, Nicholas John Anthony Chelsea & Westminster Hospital SW10 9NH Tel: 020 8846 6149 Email: nicktheobald@chelwest.nhs.uk; Tel: 020 7371 1871 — MB BS 1983 Lond.; MRCGP 1987; DRCOG 1985; Dip GU Med. 1997. (Guy's) GP Fell. Community Liaison HIV Team Chelsea & W.m. Hosp. Lond. Prev: GP Swindon; Trainee GP Rotat. Swindon VTS; Ho. Surg. Roy. Devon & Exeter Hosp.

THEOBALD, Paul Wycombe Hospital, Queen Alexandra Rd, High Wycombe HP11 2TT; Whittaborough House, Whittaborough Farm, Plympton, Plymouth PL7 5ES Tel: 01752 839762 — MB BS 1998 Lond. (UCLMS) SHO Rotat.

THEOBALDS, John Richard (retired) The Tithebarn, Yealand Redmayne, Carnforth LA5 9TA Tel: 01524 781413 — MRCS Eng. LRCP Lond. 1947; FRCPsych 1986, M 1971; DPM Eng. 1960. Hon. Cons. Psychiat. Lanc. Moor Hosp. Prev: Regist. (Psychiat.) Pk. Prewett Hosp. Basingstoke.

THEODORE, Cecelia Maria 27 Methley Street, Kennington, London SE11 4AL Tel: 020 7582 2448 — MB BCh BAO 1985 Dub.; BA Dub. 1985; MRCP (UK) 1991; DFFM 1995; Dip. GU Med. Soc. Apoth. Lond. 1992. Cons. GU & HIV Med. Mayday Univ. Hosp. Croydon. Socs: Med. Soc. Study VD; Assn. GU Med.; Brit. Soc. Colposc. & Cervic. Pathol. Prev: Sen. Regist. (Genitourin. Med. & HIV) Char. Cross Hosp. Lond.; MRC Research Fell. Roy. Lond. Hosp.

THEODOROU, Maria 124 Woodside Road, London N22 5HS — MB BS 1998 Lond.

THEODOROU, Mr Nikitas Alfred Flat 22, Holst Mansions, 96 Wyatt Drive, London SW13 8AJ — MRCS Eng. LRCP Lond. 1972; MS Lond. 1985, MB BS 1972; FRCS Ed. 1977; FRCS Eng. 1977. (Char. Cross) Cons. Surg. Char. Cross Hosp. Lond. & W. Middlx. Hosp.; Cons. Sugreon, Hammersmith Hosp.s NHS Trust, Dept. of Gastrointeatinal Surgey Charin Cross Hosp. Prev: Sen. Regist. (Surg.) Char. Cross Hosp. Lond.; Regist. (Surg.) Mt. Vernon Hosp. N.wood; SHO (Anaesth.) Char. Cross Hosp. Lond.

THEODOROU, Stanley 14 Acre End Street, Eynsham, Witney OX29 4PA — MB BS 1985 New South Wales; MRCPsych 1994.

THEODOSIOU, Catherine Anne 5 Morningside Park, Edinburgh EH10 5HD — MB ChB 1997 Ed.

THEODOSIOU, Louise Joyce 5 Morningside Park, Edinburgh EH10 5HD Tel: 0131 452 8669 — MB ChB 1997 Manch.; BSc (Hons.) St. And. SHO. (Psychiat.) Withington Hosp. Socs: MDU. Prev: Ho. Off. Manch. Roy. Infirm.

THEODOSSI, Andrew 26 Roedean Crescent, London SW15 5JU Tel: 020 8876 6346 Fax: 020 8401 3495 — MB BS 1971 Lond.; MD Lond. 1985; FRCP Lond. 1986; MRCP (UK) 1974. Cons. Phys. (Gastroenterol.) Mayday Hosp. Lond. Socs: Fell. Roy. Soc. Med.; Brit. Soc. Gastroenterol. Prev: Sen. Regist. (Gen. Med. & Gastroenterol.) W.m. Hosp. Lond.; Clin. Research Fell. Liver Unit King's Coll. Hosp. Lond.

THEODOSSIADIS, Alexander North Manchester General Hospital, Crumpsall, Manchester M8 5RB Tel: 0161 720 2037 Fax: 0161 720 2073 — Ptychion Iatrikis Athens 1968; MRCS Eng. LRCP Lond. 1971; FRCPsych 1996, M 1973; DPM Eng. 1972. Cons. Psychiat. N. Manch. Gen. Hosp. Socs: Fell. Manch. Med. Soc. Prev: Sen. Regist. (Psychiat.) Manch. AHA (T); Regist. (Psychiat.) Bristol Health Dist. (T); SHO (Psychiat.) Profess. Unit Glenside Hosp. Stapleton.

THEODOULOU, Georgios Steliou 5 Gibbins Road, Selly Oak, Birmingham B29 6PG — MB ChB 1997 Birm. Old Age Pschiat. Litte Bromich Eldery Ment. Centre. Prev: Gen Adult Pschiat. Solihull Ment. Health Trust.

THEODOULOU, Megan Tara 24 Aston Street, Oxford OX4 1EP — MB BS 1989 Lond.

THEOLOGIS, Timoleon Nuffield Orthopaedic Centre, Old Road, Headington, Oxford OX3 7LD; 117 Kingston Road, Oxford OX2 6RW — Ptychio Iatrikes 1985 Athens.

THEOPHANOUS, Markos 17 Erylmore Road, Liverpool L18 4QS — MB ChB 1991 Liverp.

THEOPHILOPOULOS, Nicky 4 Congleton Close, Alderley Edge SK9 7AJ — Ptychio Iatrikes 1968 Athens; Ph D 1992; MD 1985. Cons. Psychiat. Tameside Gen. Hosp. Ashton u. Lyne. Socs: Mem. Roy. Coll. Psychiatr.; Mem. Brit. Pharmacol. Soc. Prev: Lect. Univs. Manch. & Liverp.

THEOPHILUS, Mary Neelamala 121 Rosemallion House, Treliske Hospital, Treliske, Truro TR1 3LJ — MB ChB 1998 Ed.

THEOPHILUS, Padmini 8-12 University Road, Leicester LE1 7RG; Inglewood, 32 Ratcliffe Road, Leicester LE2 3TD Tel: 0116 270 7429 — MB BS 1956 Madras. (Christian Med. Coll. Vellore) Sen. Med. Off. (Community Med.) Leics. AHA (T). Prev: Clin. Med. Off. (Community Med.) Birm. AHA (T).

THEOPHILUS, Samuel Wilfred Jyotichandra (retired) Leicester Royal Infirmary Hospital Trust, Leicester LE1 5WW Tel: 0116 254 1414 Fax: 0116 258 6174 — MB BS 1956 Madras; FFA RCSI 1974; DA Eng. 1967. Prev: Cons. Anaesth. Leicester Roy. Infirm.

THERAPONDOS, Georgios Panayiotis 3/5 Gilmour's Entry, Edinburgh EH8 9XL — MB ChB 1992 Ed.; BSc Med. Sci. (Hons.) Ed. 1991; MRCP (UK) 1996. Clin. Research Fell. (Med.) Roy. Infirm. Edin.

THERKILDSEN, Mr Lance Karl Hyde The Royal London Hospital, Dept. of Oral Omaxillofacial Surgery, 3rd Floor Alex House, Whitechapel, London E1 1BB Tel: 01708 688344, 020 7377 7051 Fax: 020 7377 7095 — MB BS 1961 Lond.; FRCS Eng. 1971; DObst. RCOG 1963. (St. Bart.) p/t Cons. Orthop. Surg. P.ss Alexandra Hosp. Harlow. Socs: Brit. Orthopaedic Assn.; Roy. Coll. of Surg.s; Brit. Med. Assn. Prev: Cons. Orthop. Surg. St. Margt. Hosp. Epping.; Sen. Regist. (Orthop.) St. Bart. Hosp. Lond. & Hosp. Sick Childr. Gt. Ormond St. Lond.

THERON, Johanna Susanna 8 Harefield Close, Enfield EN2 8NQ — MB ChB 1987 Stellenbosch.

THET TUN, Dr The Surgery, Elm Lodge, The Cricket Green, Mitcham CR4 4LB Tel: 020 8648 5030 — MB BS 1955 Rangoon. Prev: Hosp. Pract. (Obst.) St. Helier Hosp. Carshalton; Sen. Med. Off. Burma Rlys.; Cas. Off. Hertford Co. Hosp.

THET WIN, Dr 22 Tyrley Close, Compton, Wolverhampton WV6 8AP — MB BS 1973 Med. Inst. Mandalay; DO RCPSI 1983.

THETFORD, David Ernest Allan 53 Main Street, Doune FK16 6BW; Department of Respiratory Medicine, Aberdeen Royal Infirmary, Foresterhill, Aberdeen AB25 2ZN Tel: 01224 681818 — MB ChB 1989 Glas.; MRCP (UK) 1993. Specialist Regist. (Respirat. Med.) Aberd. Roy. Infirm. Prev: SHO (Respirat. Med.) Raigmore Hosp. Inverness.

THETHRAVUSAMY, Mr Joseph Aloysius 43 Stayton Road, Sutton SM1 1QY — MB BS 1949 Madras; FRCS Eng. 1960.

THETHY, Ragbir Singh 629 Kings Road, Birmingham B44 9HW — MB ChB 1990 Manch.

THEVA, Rajalakshmi 5 Silver Lane, Purley CR8 3HJ — MB BS 1969 Ceylon; MRCPsych 1985; DPM Eng. 1984. (Ceylon) Cons. Psychiat. Surrey Oaklands NHS Trust. Prev: Cons. Psychiat. Croydon Ment. Handicap Unit.

THEVASAGAYAM, Mahilravi Samuel 139 Freedom Road, Sheffield S6 2XB — MB ChB 1992 Sheff.

THEVATHASAN, Mr Lionel Jeyakumar 41 Bushey Road, London SW20 8TE Email: lionelthe@hotmail.com — MB BS 1994 Lond.; FRCS (Eng.) 1998. (St. Bartholomew's London) Research Fell. (Neurosurg.) Addenbrooke's Hosp. Camb.

THEVATHASAN, Muthuveloe Court House Practice, Tonyfelin Surgery, Bedwas Road, Caerphilly CF83 1XN Tel: 029 2088 7316 — MB BS 1954 Ceylon; DPH Eng. 1962; DTCD Wales 1961.

THEVATHASAN, Pravin Asrajit 5 Mayfield Park, Shrewsbury SY2 6PD — MB BS 1988 Lond.

THEVENDRA, Sabaratnam Forum Health Centre, 1A Farren Road, Wyken, Coventry CV2 5EP Tel: 024 7626 6370 Fax: 024 7663 6518 — MB BS Ceylon; MRCOG 1977.

THEW, David Charlton Naisbitt 1 Eleanor Crescent, Stapleford, Nottingham NG9 8BH — MB ChB 1975 Birm.; DTM & H Liverp. 1988; DRCOG 1980.

THEW, Melanie Elizabeth Barn 1 Hall Farm, Westhorpe, Southwell, Nottingham NG2 0NG Tel: 01636 815102 — BM BS 1994 Nottm.; BMedSci Nottm. 1992. (Nottm.) SHO (Anaesth.) Roy. Devon & Exeter Hosp. Prev: SHO (Med.) Torbay Hosp. Torquay; SHO (A & E) Roy. United Hosp. Bath.

THEW, Ronald James Latham House Medical Practice, Sage Cross Street, Melton Mowbray LE13 1NX Tel: 01664 854949 Fax: 01664 501825; 16 Asfordby Place, Asfordby, Melton Mowbray LE14 3TG Tel: 01664 813771 Fax: 01664 501825 Email: rjthew@aol.com — MB BS 1968 Lond.; MRCS Eng. LRCP Lond. 1968; FRCGP 1987, M 1979; DA Eng. 1971; DCH Eng. 1970; DObst RCOG 1970. (St. Bart.) Chair Melton PCG. Socs: Leic. Med. Soc. Prev: SHO (Anaesth.) Poole Gen. Hosp.; SHO (Paediat.) Redhill Gen. Hosp.; Ho. Off. (Obst.) Redhill Gen. Hosp.

THEWLES, Michael John Manchester Road Surgery, 484 Manchester Road, Sheffield S10 5PN Tel: 0114 266 8411 — MB ChB 1977 Sheff.; MRCGP 1981.

THEXTON, Penelope Jane St Bartholomew's Sexual Health Centre, St Bartholomew's Hospital, West Smithfield, London EC1A 7BE Tel: 020 7601 8092 Fax: 020 7601 8601; 36 Albert Street, London NW1 7NU Tel: 020 7387 7370 Email: 101605.243@compuserve.com — MB BS 1986 Lond.; BA Camb. 1976; MRCGP 1990; DCH RCP Lond. 1989. Clin. Asst. Dgum St. Bart. Hosp. & Med. Off. Med. Express Clinic. Lond.

THEXTON

THEXTON, Robina 41 Hillcroft Crescent, Ealing, London W5 2SG Tel: 020 8997 1748 — MB BS 1951 Lond.; MRCS Eng. LRCP Lond. 1950. (Roy. Free) Instruc. Med. Off. (Family Plann.) Ealing Health Dist. Socs: Inst. Psychosexual Med. Prev: Ho. Surg. Roy. Lond. Homoep. Hosp.; Ho. Phys. Roy. Free Hosp.

THIAGALINGAM, Namasivayam Mayday University Hospital, London Road, Croydon CR7 7YE Tel: 020 8401 3000; Flat 4, 19 Poppy Close, Wallington SM6 7HD Tel: 020 8773 0930 Fax: 020 8773 0930 — MB BS 1985 Colombo. Regist. (A & E).

THIAGARAJAH, Mr Kadampamoorthy Amaranath North Middlesex Hospital, Stirling Way, London N18 1QX Tel: 020 8887 2466 Fax: 020 8887 2256; 23 Houndsden Road, London N21 1LU Tel: 020 8360 9532 Fax: 020 8360 9532 Email: k.a.t.hound@btinternet.com — MB BS Ceylon 1970; FRCS Ed. 1982; FRCOpth 1989. (Peradeniya) Cons. Ophth. N. Middlx. Hosp. Lond. Socs: Oxf. Ophth. Congr.; Internat. Mem. Amer. Acad. Ophth.; Fell. RSM. Prev: Cons. Ophth. King Khaliy Hosp., Saudi Arabia; Sen. Regist. (Ophth.) Roy. Hallamsh. Hosp. Sheff.; Regist. (Ophth.) Derbysh. Roy. Infirm. Derby.

THIAGARAJAH, Sivakkolunthar Greenacres, Homefield Road, Worthing BN11 2HS Tel: 01903 843888 Fax: 01903 843889 — MB BS 1971 Ceylon; BCPsych Lond. 1992. (Faculty of Medicine University of Ceylon) Assoc. Specialist (Psychiat.) Worthing Priority Care NHS Trust.

THIAGARAJAN, Jayaraman Department of Anaesthesia, Frenchay Hospital, Frenchay Park Road, Bristol BS16 1LE — MB BS 1985 Madras; FCAnaesth 1991; DA (UK) 1988.

THIAGARAJAN, Manickam Cleveleys Health Centre, Kelson Avenue, Thornton-Cleveleys FY5 3LF; 31 Shore Green, Thornton-Cleveleys FY5 2LT Tel: 01253 822649 — MB BS 1992 Lond.; MB BS Karnatak 1966. (Kasturba Med. Coll.)

THIBAUT, R E Parsons Heath Medical Practice, 35A Parsons Heath, Colchester CO4 3HS Tel: 01206 864395 Fax: 01206 869047 — MB BS 1977 London; MB BS 1977 London.

THICK, Anthony Patrick Great North Road Surgery, 164 Great North Road, Gosforth, Newcastle upon Tyne NE4 5AB Tel: 0191 285 2460 — MB BS 1976 Lond. (Royal London) GP Princip. Newc. & N. Tyneside Health Auth. Socs: Soc. Occupat. Med. Prev: Div. Med. Off. Thames Water Plc.

THICKETT, Charles Roy (retired) 6 Ladderbanks Lane, Baildon, Shipley BD17 6RX Tel: 01274 598490 — MB ChB 1950 Sheff.; MRCGP 1960. Prev: Capt. RAMC.

THICKETT, David Richard 26 Hall Drive, London SE26 6XB — MB BS 1992 Lond.

THICKETT, Kathleen Mary 15 West View, Chesterfield S44 6LJ — MB ChB 1991 Leeds.

THICKETT, Margaret Anne 22 Elmete Avenue, Leeds LS8 2QN — MB ChB 1983 Bristol; FFA RCSI 1989; DA (UK) 1986. Cons. Anaesthetist, Dewbury Gen. Hosp. Halifax Rd. Dewsbury. Prev: Sen. Regist. (Anaesth.) Yorks. RHA.; Regist. (Anaesth.) Sheff. Hosps. & St. Jas. Univ. Hosp. Leeds; SHO (Neonat.) Jessop Hosp. for Wom. Sheff.

THICKNES, Philip John Lyon (retired) 8 Woodside Avenue, Corbridge NE45 5EL Tel: 01434 632082 Fax: 01434 634416 Email: philipthick@doctors.org.uk — MB BChir Camb. 1964; MA Camb. 1964; MRCGP 1975; DObst RCOG 1966. Prev: Princip., Riversdale Surg., Wylam N.umberland.

THIEDE, Mrs Brenda (retired) Great Ghyll, West Scrafton, nr henburn, Consett DH8 4AT Tel: 01969 640670 — MB ChB 1957 Leeds.

THILAGANATHAN, Mr Baskaran Fetal Medicine Unit, St Georges Hospital Medical School, Cranmer Terrrace, Harrow HA3 9RD Tel: 020 8725 0079 — MS BS Lond. 1988; BSc (Hons.) Basic Med. Scs. Lond. 1985, MD 1995; MRCOG 1995. Dir. of Fetal Med. St Geo.s Hosp. Med. Sch. Lond. Prev: Regist. (O & G) St. Bart. & Homerton Hosps. Lond.; Research Fell. Harris Birthright Research Centre for Fetal Med. Kings Coll. Hosp Med Sch Lond; Lect. & Sen. Regist. (O & G) St. Bart. & Homerton Hosps. Lond.

THILAGARAJAH, Mr Kanagasabai, TD Queen Mary's Sidcup NHS Trust, Sidcup DA14 6LT Tel: 020 8302 2678 Fax: 020 8308 3041; 5 Regents Place, Blackheath, London SE3 0LX Tel: 020 8853 1392 — MB BS 1959 Ceylon; FRCS Ed. 1969; FRCS Eng. 1972; MRCS Eng. LRCP Lond. 1974. (Colombo, Univ. Ceylon) Clin. Dir. (A & E) Qu. Mary's Hosp. Sidcup. Socs: Milit. Surg. Soc.; W Kent. M-C Soc.; Roy. Soc. Med. Prev: Cons. A & E N. Middlx. Univ. Hosp.; Regist. (Thoracic Surg.) Preston Hall Hosp. Maidstone; Regist. (A & E, Orthop. & Gen. Surg.) Croydon Gp. Hosps.

THILAGARAJAH, Mr Michael 5 Regents Place, Blackheath, London SE3 0LX — MB BS 1992 Lond.; FRCS Eng. 1997; MSc Lond. 1998. (Char. Cross & Westm.) Specialist Regist. In Orthop., SE Thames Region; Specialist Regist. in Orthop. & Trauma - Guy's & St. Thomas' Hosp., Lond. Socs: Brit. Orthop. Assn. Prev: S. E. Thames Spr Rotat.; MSc Research fell. (Surgic. Sci.), Hammersmith.

THILAGARAJAH, Mr Ranjan 37 Deanhill Court, Upper Richmond St W., East Sheen, London SW14 7DJ Tel: 020 8878 9952 Fax: 020 8858 4425 Email: ranjan@dhet.netkonect.co.uk — MB BS 1990 Lond.; FRCS Eng. 1995. Specialist Regist. (Urol.) Cen Middlx. Hosp. Socs: Fell. Roy. Soc. Med. Prev: Specialist Regist. (Urol.) Colchester Hosp.; Research Regist. (Urol.) St. Mary's Hosp. Lond.; SHO (Urol.) Whittington Hosp. Lond.

THILAKAWARDHANA, Wellala Don Punyasena Princess Margaret Hospital, Okus Road, Swindon SN1 4JU Tel: 01793 36231 — MB BS 1973 Sri Lanka; DA Eng. 1982.

THILLAIAMBALAM, Navathevi 2 Greenlands Close, Simpson Cross, Haverfordwest SA62 6EZ — MB ChB 1998 Sheff.

THILLAINADARAJAH, Pandaram 2 Sporhams, Lee Chapel S., Basildon SS16 5TS — MB BS 1970 Ceylon; MRCPsych 1985; DPM RCPSI 1986. Regist. (Psychiat.) St. Cadoc's Hosp. Caerleon. Prev: Regist. (Psychiat.) Runwell Hosp. Wickford.

THILLAINATHAN, Sinnadurai Brownlow Medical Centre, 140 Brownlow Road, Southgate, London N11 2BD Tel: 020 8888 7775 Fax: 020 8888 3450 — MB BS 1972 Sri Lanka; LMSSA Lond. 1986.

THILLAINAYAGAM, Andrew V. Gastroenterology Unit, Hammersmith Hospital, Du Cane Road, London W12 0NN Tel: 020 8383 3266 (Academic), 0208 846 1945 (NHS) Fax: 0208 749 3436, 0208 846 1975; Tel: 0208 741 4074 — MB ChB 1984 Manch.; MD 1995; FRCP Lond. 2001; MRCP 1987 (UK). Cons. (Gastroenterol.) Hammersmith Hosps. NHS Trust; Hon. Sen. Lect. Imperial Coll. Sch. of Med. Lond.; Hon. Cons., John Radcliffe Hosp., Oxf. Socs: Fell. Roy. Soc. Med.; Brit. Soc. Gastroenterol.; Amer. Gastroenterological Assn. Prev: Sen. Regist. John Radcliffe Hosp. Oxf.; RMO St. Marks Hosp. Lond.; Regist. & Hon. Lect. Med. Coll. St. Bart. Hosp. Lond.

THILLAIVASAN, Kathiravelpillai Department of Anaesthesia, The Edith Cavell Hospital, Bretton Gate, Peterborough PE3 6QR Tel: 01733 330777; 47 Walkers Way, Milton Gate, South Bretton, Peterborough PE3 9AX Tel: 01733 332449 — MB BS 1971 Ceylon; DA (UK) 1983. (Colombo) Clin. Med. Off. (Anaesth.) Edith Cavell Hosp. PeterBoro.. Prev: Regist. (Anaesth.) PeterBoro. Dist. Hosp.; Clin. Asst. (Anaesth.) Pboro. Dist. Hosp.

THILO, Julia Belinda Parkside Family Practice, Green Road Surgery, 224 Wokingham Road, Reading RG6 1JT Tel: 0118 966 3366 Fax: 0118 926 3269 — MB BS 1990 Lond.; MRCGP 1995; DRCOG 1994; DFFP 1994. Clin. Asst. Genitourin. Clinic Roy. Berks. Hosp. Prev: Trainee GP Reading Scheme; SHO Frimley Pk. Hosp.

THIMMEGOWDA, Hanume Mountain Road Medical Centre, Thornhill, Dewsbury WF12 0BS Tel: 01924 522100 Fax: 01924 522102 — MB BS Karnatak 1967. (Karnatak Med. Coll. Hubli) GP Dewsbury. Prev: Regist. (Geriat. Med.) St. Luke's Hosp. Huddersfield.

THIN, Mairead Jane Blackwood, North Kessock, Inverness IV1 3XD — MB ChB 1998 Aberd.

THIN, Robert Nicol Traquair, OBE 13 Park Avenue, Bromley BR1 4EF Tel: 020 8464 9278 — MB ChB 1959 Ed.; MD Ed. 1968; FRCP 1988; FRCP Ed. 1973, M 1964. (Ed.) Clin. Asst., Dept. of Genitourin. Med., Beckham Hosp., Beckham, Kent. Socs: Fell. Roy. Soc. Med.; (Ex-Pres.) Med. Soc. Study VD; (Ex-Chairm.) Assn. for Genitourin. Med. Prev: Phys. (Genitourin. Med.) St. Thos. Hosp. Lond.; Cons. (Venerol.) St. Peter's Hosps. Lond.; Phys. (Genital Med.) St. Bart. Hosp. Lond.

THIN KYU, Dr 177 Cheltenham Road, Bristol BS6 5RH — MB BS 1968 Rangoon.

THIN THIN AYE, Dr Radiology Department, Walsgrave Hospital, Coventry CV2 2DX — MB BS 1965 Med. Inst. (I) Rangoon; BSc Univ. Rangoon 1958; FRCR 1975; DMRD Eng. 1970. (Inst. Med. (I) Rangoon) Cons. Radiol. Walsgrave Hosp. Coventry, Coventry & Warks. Hosp. &; Geo. Eliot Hosp. Nuneaton. Socs: Brit. Inst. Radiol.

Prev: Civil Asst. Surg. Rangoon Gen. Hosp., Burma; Civil Asst. Surg. Mandalay Gen. Hosp., Burma; Head Dept. Radiol. Magwe Div. Hosp., Burma.

THIN THIN SAING, Dr 6 Smitham Bottom Lane, Purley CR8 3DA — MB BS 1982 Med. Inst. Rangoon; MRCP (UK) 1994. Staff Grade (Paediat.) Law Hosp. Carluke. Prev: SHO (Paediat.) Plymouth; SHO (Paediat.) Oxf.

THIND, Indra 40 Brookside, Great Barr, Birmingham B43 5DB — MB ChB 1995 Leic.

THIND, Jaishree Castle Hill Hospital, Castle Road, Cottingham HU16 5JQ — MB BS 1983 Madras; FRCA 1992. Cons. Anaesth. Castle Hill Hosp. Cottingham. Socs: Assn. Anaesth. of Gt. Britain & N.ern Irelans; Brit. Assn of Day Surg.; Intens Care Soc. Prev: Specialist Regist. (Anaesth.) Oxf. Redcliffe Hosp.; Locum Cons., Hillingdon Hosp., Uxbridge, Middlx.; Clin. Fell., Obstetric Anaesth., W.chester Co. Med. Center, Valhalla, New York, USA.

THING, John Rhodes 1 Cambridge Road, Owlsmoor, Sandhurst GU47 0UB Tel: 01344 777015 Fax: 01344 777226 — MB ChB 1972 Cape Town; BSc S. Afr. 1968; MRCGP 1978; Cert. Family Plann. JCC 1977. (Univ. Cape Town) GP; Clin. Asst. (Sports Med.) Frimley Pk. Hosp.

THIRILOGANATHAN, Somasundram (retired) Northowram Hospital, Halifax HX3 7SW Tel: 01422 201101 — MB BS 1964 Ceylon; MRCPsych 1984. Cons. Psychogeriat. Calderdale Healthcare NHS Trust.

THIRKELL, Claire Elizabeth Heathgate Surgery, The Street, Poringland, Norwich NR14 7JT Tel: 01508 494343; 11A The St, Brooke, Norwich NR15 1JW Tel: 01508 550264 — MB BChir 1984 Camb.; BSc (Hons.) St. And. 1981; MRCGP 1990. GP Princip. Heathgate Surg. Poringland.

THIRKETTLE, James Leslie (retired) 1 Old Horsham Road, Crawley RH11 8PD — MB BS Lond. 1955; FRCP Lond. 1978, M 1961. Prev: Cons. Phys. Crawley Hosp.

THIRLAWAY, Barbara May (retired) Ziarat, 18 Speen Lane, Newbury RG14 1RW — MB BS Punjab 1941. Prev: Clin. Med. Off. Hants. CC 1964-84.

THIRLWALL, Miss Andrea Simone, Level 1 11 Holiday St, Berkhamsted HP4 2EE Tel: 01442 864079 — BM BS 1993 Nottm.; FRCS CSIG. 1998; FRCS OUT. 1998. Specialist Regist. (ENT.) Oxf. Region. Socs: MPS; FRS; BAOHNS.

THIRLWALL, Michael Meadowcroft Surgery, Jackson Road, Aylesbury HP19 9EX Tel: 01296 425775 Fax: 01296 330324 Email: drmikethirlwall@gp-k82018.nhs.uk; Tel: 01844 292143 Email: thirlwalls@mintons.fsbusiness.co.uk — MB BS 1971 Lond.; MRCS Eng. LRCP Lond. 1971; FRCGP 1987, M 1975; DObst RCOG 1973. (Char. Cross) p/t Examr. (RCGP). Prev: Course Organiser Aylesbury Health Dist. VTS.

THIRLWALL, Pamela Jane 11 Ripon Road, Killinghall, Harrogate HG3 2DG — MB ChB 1969 Leeds. (Leeds)

THIRLWELL, Christina The Mallards, The Causeway, Occold, Eye IP23 7PP — MB BS 1997 Lond.

THIRU, Mr Chittampalam Naranapillai (retired) 158 Anson Road, London NW2 6BH Tel: 020 8452 0170 — MB BS Ceylon 1962; FRCS Ed. 1974. Examg. MO. Prev: GP.

THIRU, Nallasivam 95 Parkhall Road, Walsall WS5 3HS — MB BS 1969 Kerala.

THIRU, Yamuna Department Paediatrics, Level 7, QEQM, St Mary's Hospital, South Wharf Road, London W2 1NY Tel: 020 7886 6377 Fax: 020 7886 6284 Email: y.thiru@ic.ac.uk; Mews Flat, Milne House, 3 Norfolk Square, London W2 1RU — MB ChB 1990 Leeds; BSc (Hons.) Leeds 1987, MB ChB 1990; MRCP (UK) 1993; DCH (UK) 1994. (Leeds University)

TIRUCHELVAM, Angeeta Conway Medical Centre, Westbourne Road, Luton LU4 8JD Tel: 01582 429953 Fax: 01582 487500 — MB ChB 1991 Leeds.

THIRUCHELVAM, Nikesh 90 Cliff Lane, Ipswich IP3 0PJ — MB BS 1996 Lond.

THIRUCHELVAM, Timonthy Rajiv 113 Worple Way, Rayners Lane, Harrow HA2 9SW — MB ChB 1996 Liverp.

THIRUMALA KRISHNA, Mamidipudi c/o Dr A. H. Deshpande, 24 Midgley Drive, Four Oaks, Sutton Coldfield B74 2TW; University Medicine, Level D, Centre Block, Southampton General Hospital, Tremona Road, Southampton SO16 6YD Tel: 01703 794155 Fax: 01703 701771 Email: mtk@soton.ac.uk — MB BS 1989 Madras; MRCP (UK) 1992; Dip Nat. Bd. Med. Examiners (Gen. Med.) New Delhi 1997; PhD Soton. Postdoctoral Clin. Research Fell. Dept. of Med. Univ. of Soton.; Hon. Regist. (Med./Respirat. Med.) Soton. Univ. Hosps. NHS Trust. Socs: Roy. Coll. Phys.; Brit. Assn. Lung Res. Prev: Sen. Resid. (Med. & Cardiol.) Vijaya Health Centre, Madras.

THIRUMAMANIVANNAN, Mr Govindan 3 Shelley Avenue, Manor Park, London E12 6SP — MB BS 1982 Madras; FRCS Glas. 1994.

THIRUMAVALAVAN, Mr Vallur Sivaprakasam 20 Milford Gardens, Wembley HA0 2AR Tel: 020 8903 2402 — MB BS 1977 Madras; MS (Gen. Surg.) Madras 1983; FRCS Glas. 1985; FRCS Ed. 1985; Dip. Urol. Lond 1989.

THIRUNATHAN, Jegathesvary 18 Laurel Park, Harrow HA3 6AU — MB BS 1968 Ceylon.

THIRINAVUKARASU, Ratnasabapathy (retired) 30 Ennerdale Avenue, Stanmore HA7 2LD Tel: 020 8907 8942 — MB BS 1955 Ceylon.

THIRUNAVUKKARASU, Sathiamalar Department of Pathology, Cambridge University, Tennis Court Road, Cambridge CB2 1QP Tel: 01223 217163; Department of Pathology, Addenbrookes Hospital, Cambridge CB2 2QQ — MB ChB 1964 Leeds; MA Camb. 1977; FRCP Lond. 1990; MRCP (UK) 1970; FRCPath 1988, M 1974; Dip. Amer. Bd. Clin. Anat. Path. 1976. Sen. Lect. Dept. of Path., Univ. of Camb.; Hon. Cons. Path. Addenbrookes Hosp. Camb. Socs: Fell. Roy. Coll. Phys.; Fell., Roy. Coll. of Path. Prev: Cons. Path. Beth Israel Hosp. Boston, USA; Clin. Fell. Harvard Med. Sch. Boston, U.S.A.; Clin. Lect. Sch. of Clin. Med. Univ. Camb.

THIRUNAWARKARISU, Kankanamalage Susitha St. Davids Hospital, Carmarthen SA31 3HB Tel: 01267 237481 — Vrach 1970 Moscow; Vrach Peoples Friendship U, Moscow 1970.

THIRUVUDAIYAN, Ponnampalam 1 Thorndene Avenue, London N11 1ET — MB BS 1972 Sri Lanka; MRCP (UK) 1986.

THISTLETHWAITE, David Burnley General Hosptial, Casterton Avenue, Burnley BB10 2PQ Tel: 01282 425071; 160 Ightenhill Park Lane, Burnley BB12 0LS Tel: 01282 39148 — MB ChB 1966 Ed.; FRCPCH 1997; FRCP Ed. 1985; FRCP Lond. 1984; DCH RCPS Glas. 1969. Sen. Cons. Phys. Burnley Gen. Hosp. Socs: Manch. Paed. Club; BMA; Brit. Assn. for Paediat. Endocrinol. Prev: Lect. (Child Life & Health) Univ. Edin.; Ho. Phys. (Neonat. Paediat.) Memor. Matern. Pavil. Edin.; Ho. Phys. Roy. Hosp. Sick Childr. Edin.

THISTLETHWAITE, Jill Elizabeth Medical Education Unit, The Medical School, University of Leeds, Leeds LS2 9LN Tel: 0113 233 4179 — MB BS 1981 Lond.; BSc (Hons.) Lond. 1978; MRCGP (Distinc.) 1985; DRCOG 1984. Sen. Lect. (Community-Based Teachg.) Med. Sch. Univ. Leeds.

THIT THIT, Dr 93 Shakespeare Road, Luton LU4 0HT Tel: 01582 580946 — MB BS 1982 Med. Inst. (I) Rangoon; MRCP (UK) 1995. Staff Grade (Med. for Elderly) Luton & Dunstable Hosp. Socs: BMA; Brit. Geriat. Soc.

THIYAGARAJAN, Chinnaya Asari 2 Marlborough Road, Aylesbury HP21 8AU — MB BS 1975 Madras.

THOBURN, Charles Royston Flat 76, Boss House, Boss St., London SE1 2PT — MB BS 1994 Lond.

THOM, Alexander Anderson Parkhead Hospital, 81 Salamanka St, Glasgow G31 5ES Tel: 0141 211 8300; Tel: 01355 579947 — MB ChB 1991 Glas.; BSc (Hons) Glas. 1988; MRCPsych. 1997. Specialist Regist.(Adult Gen Psychiat.) W. Scotl., Cons. Gen. Psychiat., Pk.head Hosp., Glas.

THOM, Alexander William Rose (retired) 24 Marina Court, Alfred St., Bow, London E3 2BH Tel: 020 8981 1508 — LRCP LRCS Ed. LRFPS Glas. 1947.

THOM, Barry Thornton (retired) 6 Glen Rise, Brighton BN1 5LP Tel: 01273 558177 — MB BS Lond. 1956; Dip. Bact. 1965; FRCPath 1978, M 1966. Prev: Dir. Pub. Health Laborat. Roy. Sussex Co. Hosp. Brighton.

THOM, Carolyn Margaret Harrison 82 Warren Road, Blundellsands, Liverpool L23 6UG — MB ChB 1971 Ed.; MRCOG 1979. Cons. (O & G) Mill Rd. Matern. Hosp. & Roy. Liverp. Hosp.

THOM, Christopher Henry The Maidstone Hospital, Hermitage Lane, Maidstone ME16 9QQ Tel: 01622 224819 Fax: 01622 224018 Email: chris_thom@lineone.net; Old Hill House, Old Loose Hill, Loose, Maidstone ME15 0BN — MB 1982 Camb.; BChir 1981 Camb.; MRCP (UK) 1985; FRCP (Lond)1999; FRCP (Lond) 1999. (Camb.) Cons. Phys. c/o the Elderly The Maidstone Hosp. Socs:

THOM

BMA; Brit. Geriat. Soc. Prev: Sen. Regist. (Geriat. & Gen. Med.) St. Thoms. Hosp Lond.; Sen. Regist. (Geriat. & Gen. Med.) Kent & Canterbury Hosp.; Lect. (Med.) Univ. Maiduguri Nigeria.

THOM, Duncan Edward 115 Seedhill Road, Paisley PA1 1RD — MB ChB 1994 Glas.

THOM, Margaret Helen 212-214 Great Portland Street, London W1W 5QN Tel: 020 7387 8686 Fax: 020 7387 3773 — MB BS 1973 Lond.; FRCOG 1990, M 1978. (King's Coll. Hosp.) Cons. O & G 212-214 Gt. Portland St. Lond. Socs: Fell. Roy. Soc. Med.; Blair Bell Res. Soc. Prev: Cons. O & G Guy's Hosp. Lond.; Sen. Regist. (O & G) Qu. Charlotte's Matern. Hosp. & Chelsea Hosp. for Wom.

THOM, Margaret Vivien Martin House Hospice for Children, Grove Rd, Clifford, Wetherby LS23 6TX Tel: 01937 844836 — MB BCh BAO 1984 Belf.; MRCGP 1988; Dip. Palliat. Med. Cardiff 1994; DCH Dub. 1987; DRCOG 1987; DGM RCP Lond. 1986. Clin. Asst. Amrtin Ho. Hospice for Childr. Prev: Cons. Palliat. Med. P. if Wales Hospice & Pontefract Hosp NHS Trust; Med. Director P. of Wales Hospice Pontefract.

THOM, Martin George 116 Scotland Road, Carlisle CA3 9EY — MB ChB 1998 Dund.

THOM, Norman Klaus 31A Waterloo Road, Penylan, Cardiff CF23 9BG — State Exam Med 1991 Erlangen.

THOM, Peter McGregor Van Den Bergh Foods Ltd., Brooke House, Manor Royal, Crawley RH10 9RQ Tel: 01293 648299 Fax: 01293 648900; Conifers, 3 Birdhaven, Wrecclesham, Farnham GU10 4PB Tel: 01252 725667 — MB ChB 1970 Aberd.; Assoc. Fac. Occupat. Med. RCP Lond. 1980. (Aberd.) Foods Med. Adviser Unilever (UK) Crawley. Socs: Soc. Occupat. Med. Prev: Med. Off. Brit. Steel Corp. Motherwell.

THOM, Ruth Balami Old Hill House, Old Loose Hill, Loose, Maidstone ME15 0BN Tel: 01622 744833 — LMSSA 1997; LMSSA LRCP LRCS Lond. 1997; MSC Lond. 1993; MBBS. 1988.

THOM, Simon Alasdair McGillivray The Peart-Rose Clinic, St. Mary's Hospital, London W2 1NY Tel: 020 7886 1172 Fax: 020 7886 6145 Email: s.thom@ic.ac.uk; 26 Kingswood Avenue, Queens Park, London NW6 6LL — MB BS 1976 Lond.; MD Lond. 1992; FRCP Lond. 1996; MRCP (UK) 1979. (St. Mary's) Sen. Lect. & Hon. Cons. Phys. (Clin. Pharmacol. & Therap.) St. Mary's Hosp. & Med. Sch. Lond. Socs: Brit. Hypertens. Soc.; Brit. Pharm. Soc. Prev: Regist. (Med.) St. Mary's Hosp. Lond.; SHO Rotat. (Med.) Newc. AHA (T).

THOM, William Flockhart Yealm Medical Centre, Yealmpton, Plymouth PL8 2EA — MB BChir 1985 Camb.; MA Camb. 1985; MRCGP 1988. (Camb. Univ. Westm. Hosp.) Princip. Gen. Pract.; Course Organiser Plymouth GPVTS. Socs: BMA; Plymouth Med. Soc.; RCGP. Prev: GP S.wold; Trainee GP Plymouth VTS.

THOM, William Francis John Maxwell (retired) 51 Gunters Mead, 37 Copsem Lane, Esher KT10 9HJ Tel: 01372 849588 — LRCP LRCS Ed. LRFPS Glas. 1940; DPH Ed. 1948; DTM & H Eng. 1947; DCH Eng. 1947. Prev: Hon. Lt.-Col. IMS, IAMC (Mentioned in Dispatches).

THOM, William Reid 9 Kitchener Street, Wishaw ML2 7JQ — MB ChB 1981 Aberd.

THOM, William Tod, OBE (retired) Wanda Cottage, Station Road, Eddleston, Peebles EH45 8QN Tel: 01721 730277 — MB ChB 1940 Ed.; FFCM 1979, M 1974; DTM & H Ed. 1950. Prev: Dir. Med. Servs. Somaliland, Protectorate.

THOMAS, A G St Laurence's Medical Centre, 32 Leeside Avenue, Kirkby, Liverpool L32 9QU Tel: 0151 549 0000 Fax: 0151 547 4747.

THOMAS, Abraham 2 Fairholme Close, Saughall, Chester CH1 6AH — MB BS 1979 Nigeria; MRCPI 1990.

THOMAS, Adrian Graham Booth Hall Childrens Hospital, Charlestown Road, Blackley, Manchester M9 7AA Tel: 0161 795 7000 Fax: 0161 220 5072 Email: agthomas@manu.demon.co.uk — MB ChB 1981 Manch.; BSc (Physiol.) (Hons.) Manch. 1978, MD 1991, MB ChB 1981; FRCP (Ed.) 1997; MRCP (UK) 1984. (Manch.) Cons. Paediat. Gastroenterol. Booth Hall Childr. Hosp. Manch. Socs: Eur. Soc. Paediat. Gastroenterol. & Nutrit.; Co-Chairm. Quality of Life Working Gp.; Europ. Soc. Paediatric Gastroenterol. & Nutrit. Prev: Hon. Sen. Regist. Hosp. Sick Childr. Lond.; Tutor (Child Health) Univ. of Manch.

THOMAS, Adrian Llewellyn 19 Lingwood Close, Bassett, Southampton SO16 7GB — MB ChB 1956 Birm.; DObst RCOG 1959. Prev: SHO O & G & Ho. Phys. Solihull Hosp.

THOMAS, Adrian Mark Kynaston X-Ray Department, Bromley Hospital, 17 Cromwell Avenue, Bromley BR2 9AJ Tel: 0208 289 7083 Fax: 0208 289 7003; 3 Cedar Copse, Bickley, Bromley BR1 2NY Tel: 0208 467 6808 Email: adrian.thomas@btinternet.com — MB BS 1978 Lond.; BSc (Hons.) Lond. 1975; FRCP Lond. 1996; MRCP (UK) 1981; FRCR 1984. (Univ. Coll. Lond. & Univ. Coll. Hosp.) Cons. Radiol. Bromley Hosps. NHS Trust. Socs: BMA (Vice-Chairm. Bromley Div.); Fell. Roy. Soc. Med. (Mem. Counc. Sect. Radiol.); Hon Sec. Brit. Inst. of Radiol. Prev: Sen. Regist. (Radiol. & Diagn. Imaging) Hammersmith Hosp. & Hillingdon Hosp. Uxbridge; Regist. (Radiol. & Diagn. Imaging) Hammersmith Hosp.; SHO (Paediat.) Hillingdon Hosp. Uxbridge.

THOMAS, Alan Donald Consultant Anaesthetist, Stracathro Hospital, Brechin DD9 7QA Tel: 01356 647291; 3 Finavon Castle, Finavon, Forfar DD8 3PX Email: d.thomas@doctors.org.uk — MB ChB 1981 Bristol; FFA RCSI 1989; MSc 2000 Robert Gordon Uni. Aberdeen. Cons. Anaesth. Tayside Hosps. NHS Trust (Stracathro & Dundee). Socs: N. E. of Scotl. Soc. of Anaesth.s (Hon. Sec.). Prev: Sen. Regist. (Anaesth.) Aberd. Roy. Hosp. NHS Trust; Med. Off. Brit. Antarctic Survey Aberd.; Regist. Rotat. (Anaesth.) Sheff. HA.

THOMAS, Alan Jeffrey 13 Stamfordham Close, Rudchester Park, Wallsend NE28 8ER — MB ChB 1989 Manch.

THOMAS, Alan John Crud Yr Awel, Penrhyndeudraeth LL48 6NG — MB ChB 1992 Sheff.

THOMAS, Alastair Lloyd 52 Long Copse Lane, Emsworth PO10 7UR Tel: 01243 373434 — MB BS 1967 Lond.; FRCP Lond. 1990; MRCP (UK) 1972; MRCS Eng. LRCP Lond. 1967. (Guy's) Cons. Rheum. Portsmouth & S.E. Hants. HA. Socs: BMA. Prev: Sen. Regist. (Rheum.) Univ. Hosp. Wales, Cardiff; Research Fell. Univ. Michigan Hosp. Ann Arbor, USA; Regist. (Med.) Cardiff. Roy. Infirm.

THOMAS, Alec Jeremy 34 Church Street, Oswestry SY11 2SP Tel: 01691 652929; Croeswylan Way, Croeswylan Lane, Oswestry SY10 9PT Tel: 01691 670181 — MB BS 1959 Lond.; MRCS Eng. LRCP Lond. 1959; Cert. Family Plann. JCC 1976; DObst RCOG 1961. (St. Mary's) Hosp. Pract. (O & G) Shrewsbury Gp. Socs: BMA. Prev: Resid. Med. Off. Qu. Charlotte's Hosp. Lond.; Cas. Off. & Resid. Off. (O & G) St. Mary's Hosp. Lond.

THOMAS, Alexandra Jane 74 Wheatlands Park, Redcar TS10 2PF Tel: 01642 471952 — MB ChB 1994 Dundee; DRCOG 1996. (Dundee) Trainee GP Garth Surg. GuisBoro. Cleveland. Socs: BMA. Prev: SHO (Gen. Med.) Middlesbrough Gen. Hosp.; SHO (ENT & Ophth. & Dermat.) N. Riding Infirm.; SHO (A & E) Middlesbrough Gen. Hosp.

THOMAS, Aleyamma Lalita Department of Histopathology, Greenwich District Hospital, Vanburgh Hill, London SE10 9HE Tel: 020 8312 6023; 10 Eastlands Crescent, London SE21 7EG Tel: 020 8693 2424 Fax: 020 8693 2424 — MB BS 1970 Panjab; MD 1975; FRCPath 1990. (Christian Med. Coll.) Cons. Histo/cytopath. Greenwich Dist. Hosp. Lond. Prev: Lect./Sen. Regist. Path. Qus. Med. Centre Nottm.; Regist. Path. Qu. Mary's Univ. Hosp. Roehampton.

THOMAS, Alfred Arthur Llewellyn Haslemere Health Centre, Church Lane, Haslemere GU27 2BQ Tel: 01428 653881 Fax: 01428 645065; High Garth, High Lane, Haslemere GU27 1BD Tel: 01428 644418 Email: alfred.thomas@btinternet.com — MB BS Lond. 1956; DObst RCOG 1958. (St. Thos.) Hosp. Pract. (Med.) Haslemere Hosp. Socs: BMA.

THOMAS, Alfred Evan 18 Villiers Road, Woodthorpe, Nottingham NG5 4FB Tel: 0115 960 9264 — MB ChB 1944 Manch.; BSc Manch. 1941, MB ChB (Hons.) 1944; FRCP Lond. 1972, M 1949. (Manch.) Cons. Phys. City Hosp. Nottm. Prev: Surg. Lt. RNVR; Med. Regist. Manch. Roy. Infirm.; Sen. Med. Regist. Sheff. Roy. Infirm.

THOMAS, Mr Alfred Keith St. George's House, 56 Billing Road, Northampton NN1 5DB Tel: 01604 626211 Fax: 01604 631211; Pear Tree Cottage, Pitsford, Northampton NN6 9AR Tel: 01604 880402 — MB BS Lond. 1962; FRCS Eng. 1968; MRCS Eng. LRCP Lond. 1962. (St. Bart.) Cons. Otolaryngol. N.ampton Gen. Hosp. NHS Trust; Examr. DLO (RCS Eng.) Part 2. Socs: Fell. Roy. Soc. Med.; Brit. Assn. Otol. Prev: Chief Asst. ENT Dept. St. Bart. Hosp. Lond.; Sen. Regist. Roy. Nat. Throat, Nose & Ear Hosp. Lond.; Lect. (Anat.) St. Bart. Hosp. Med. Coll.

THOMAS, Alfred Theophilous 41 Garden Avenue, Mitcham CR4 2EE Tel: 020 8648 9371 — Vrach 1974 Odessa; MRCP (UK) 1983; DTM & H Liverp. 1978.

THOMAS, Alison Jane Holly Lodge, London Road, Addington, Maidstone ME16 0LP — MB BS 1991 Lond.; MRCGP 1995. (Char. Cross & Westm.)

THOMAS, Alison Jane 47 Coleraine Road, London SE3 7PF Tel: 020 8852 9975 — MB ChB 1992 Birm. Cas. Off. Gosford Hosp. NSW, Austral. Prev: SHO Qu. Eliz. Hosp. Birm.; Ho. Off. (Med.) Good Hope Hosp.

THOMAS, Alison Michaela 34 Waungron Road, Cardiff CF5 2JJ — MB ChB 1993 Bristol.

THOMAS, Allan Eric (retired) 67 Thornhill Road, Plymouth PL3 5NG Tel: 01752 672412 — MRCS Eng. LRCP Lond. 1945.

THOMAS, Alun Hugh William Brown Centre, Manor Way, Peterlee SR8 5TW Tel: 0191 554 4544 Fax: 0191 554 4552 Email: hugh.thomas@gp-a83012.nhs.uk — MB BChir 1978 Camb.; MA Camb. 1978; MRCGP 1982.

THOMAS, Alyn Keith 121 Joel Lane, Gee Cross, Hyde SK14 5LF — MRCS Eng. LRCP Lond. 1946. (St. Thos.)

THOMAS, Amanda Jane Hart Community Paediatrics, St James's University Hospital, Beckitt St., Leeds LS9 7TF Tel: 0113 206 5923 Fax: 0113 206 4877 Email: amanda.thomas@gw.sjsuh.northy.nhs.uk; Derry Gariff, Northfield Lane, Askham Bryan, York YO23 3FX — MB BS 1982 Lond.; MMed. Sci. Leeds 1998; DCH RCP Lond. 1985. Cons. Community Paediat., St James Univ. Hosp., Leeds; Full Time (Child Protect.) Leeds Community & Ment. Health Trust. Socs: BMA; RCPCH; BACCH. Prev: SCMO (Child Protec. & Audiol.) LCMHT; Clin. Med. Off. (Child Health & Family Plann.) York HA & E. Surrey HA; Trainee GP Carshalton Surrey.

THOMAS, Andrew 3 Shelsley Close, Penkridge, Stafford ST19 5EF — MB ChB 1982 Liverp.; MRCOG 1988. (Liverp.) Princip. GP. Prev: Regist. (O & G) St. Mary's Hosp. Portsmouth.

THOMAS, Mr Andrew Martin Charles The Royal Orthopaedic Hospital, Woodlands, Northfield, Birmingham B31 2AP Tel: 0121 685 4005 Fax: 0121 685 4100 — MB BS 1977 Lond.; FRCS Eng. 1983; FRCS Ed. 1982. (London Hospital Medical College) Cons. Orthop. Surg. Roy. Orthop. Hosp. Birm. & Univ. Hosp. Birm.; Med. Dir. Roy. Orthop. Hosp. Birm.; Hon. Sen. Lect. Univ. Birm. Socs: Brit. Orthop. Research Soc.; Internat. Soc. Study Lumbar Spine; Rheumatoid Arthritis Surg. Soc. Prev: Hon. Research Fell. Physiol. Univ. Birm.; Sen. Regist. Roy. Orthop. Hosp. Birm.; Regist. (Neurosurg.) Qu. Eliz. Hosp. Birm.

THOMAS, Mr Andrew Philip Wolverhampton Nuffield Hospital, Wood Road, Tettenhall, Wolverhampton WV6 8LE Tel: 01527 835166 Fax: 01527 835166 — MB BChir 1976 Camb.; FRCS Ed. (Orth.) 1986; FRCS Eng. 1980.

THOMAS, Angela Eleine Royal Hospital for Sick Children, Sciennes Road, Edinburgh EH9 1LF Tel: 0131 536 0433 Fax: 0131 536 0430 Email: scp@ed.ac.uk — MB BS 1980 Lond.; PhD Lond. 1995; FRCPCH 1997; FRCP Ed. 1994; MRCP (UK) 1983; FRCPath 1996. (St. Bart.) Cons. Haemat. (Paediat.) Roy. Hosp. Sick Childr. Edin. Prev: Hon. Sen. Regist. (Haemat.) Char. Cross Hosp. Lond.; Clin. Research Fell. Centre for the Genetics of Cardiovasc. Disorders Rayne Inst. Lond.; Sen. Regist. (Haemat.) St. Bart. Hosp. Lond.

THOMAS, Anita Jane Derriford Hospital, Plymouth PL6 8DH — MB ChB 1975 Bristol; MB ChB (Distinc. Clin. Path.) Bristol 1975; PhD Soton. 1991; FRCP Lond. 1992; MRCP (UK) 1978. (Bristol) p/t Cons. Phys. in Gen. & Geriat. Med. & Assoc. Med. Dir. (Med. Educat.); Clin. Subdean (Plymouth) Peninsula Med. Sch.; Lead Assessor GMC Professional Perform. Procedures; Mem. DH Expert Gp. on Vit.s & Minerals; Mem. DH/FSA Scientif. Advis. CHEE on Nutrit.; Mem. DH COMA Panel on Novel Foods; Examr. RCP. Socs: Brit. Geriat. Soc.; Nutrit. Soc.; Nat. Assn. Clin. Tutors. Prev: Mem. (Counc.) Roy. Coll. Phys. (Hon. Sec. Comm. Med. Educat., Train. & Staffing) Gen. Internal Med. Comm.; Sen. Lect. (Geriat. Med.) & Hon. Cons. Phys. Univ. Soton.; MRC/AFRC Special Train. Fell. Nutrit. 1985-1987.

THOMAS, Ann (retired) Longdale, 20 The Rise, Llanishen, Cardiff CF14 0RD — MB BCh 1954 Wales; MSc Manch. 1978; BSc Wales 1951, MB BCh 1954; FCMI 1988, M 1979; MFCM 1982; DObst RCOG 1957. Prev: Cons. Pub. Health Med. S. Glam.

THOMAS, Ann Elizabeth Isca General Practice Unit, Cadoc House, High Street, Caerleon, Newport NP18 1AZ Tel: 01633 423886 Fax: 01633 430153 — MB BCh 1977 Wales; BSc 1972 (Hons.) Wales. Princip. GP Gwent.

THOMAS, Anna Kathryn Tel: 029 2088 Ext: 1994 Fax: 029 2085 3114; Gwaun Gledyr Uchaf, Penrhos, Nantgarw, Cardiff CF15 7UN Tel: 029 2088 9221 — MB BCh 1975 Wales; LLM Wales 1997; MRCPsych 1987; DCH Eng. 1980; DRCOG 1977. (Wales) Cons. Forens. Psychiat. for People with Learning Disabilities; Med. Director InDepend. Community Living Ltd Caerphilly S.Wales. Socs: Wales Medico-Legal Soc. Prev: Cons. Forens. Psychiat. Caswell Clinic Bridgend; Sen. Regist. Psychiat. of Learning Disabil., Forens. Psychiat.; Sen. Med. Off. Welsh Off. Cardiff.

THOMAS, Anna Margaret The Groes, Hope Mountain, Caergwrle, Wrexham LL12 9HF — MB BCh 1995 Wales.

THOMAS, Anna May 4 Kings Court, Kings Avenue, Buckhurst Hill IG9 5LU — MB BS 1996 Lond.

THOMAS, Anne Gwendolen Glenview, Glasllwch Lane, Newport NP20 3PS Tel: 01633 62517 — MB BCh 1950 Wales; BSc Wales 1947, MB BCh 1950; DObst RCOG 1952. (Cardiff) Sen. Med. Off. Gwent Health Auth. Prev: Res. Pathol. Mass. Gen. Hosp. Boston; Asst. Clin. Pathol. Univ. Wales; Res. Clin. Pathol. Radcliffe Infirm. Oxf.

THOMAS, Anne Louise Department of Oncology, Leicester Royal Infirmary, Leicester LE1 5WW Tel: 0116 258 7597 Fax: 0116 258 7599; 3 The Barns Wold Farm, Kinoulton Lane, Nottingham HG12 3EQ Tel: 01949 81822 — BM 1991 Soton.; MRCP (UK) 1994; Phd. 1999. (Univ. Soton.) Specialist Regist. (Med. Oncol.) Leicester Roy. Infirm. Prev: Clin. Research Fell. (Med. Oncol.) City Hosp. Nottm.; Med. Regist. QMC Nottm.

THOMAS, Anne Margaret The Surgery, White Cliff Mill Street, Blandford Forum DT11 7BH Tel: 01258 452501 Fax: 01258 455675; Tilhayes, Church Hill, Iwerne Minster, Blandford Forum DT11 8LS Tel: 01747 811658 — MB BS 1978 Lond.; MB BS (Hons. Med.) Lond. 1978; MRCP (UK) 1981; MRCGP 1983; DRCOG 1984; DCH 1981. (St. Bart.) Prev: Trainee GP Islington VTS Lond.; SHO Hosp. Sick Childr. Gt. Ormond St.; SHO (Obst.) Mothers Hosp. Lond.

THOMAS, Anne Myfanwy Institute of Neurological Sciences, Glasgow G51 4TF Tel: 0141 201 2490 Fax: 0141 201 2510; 27 Rowallan Gardens, Broomhill, Glasgow G11 7LH Tel: 0141 339 7988 Fax: 0141 339 7988 — MD Lond. 1985, MB BS 1968; FRCP Glas. 1989; DCH RCPS Glas. 1971; FRCP 1998. (Roy. Free) Cons. Neurol. Inst. Neurol. Sci. Glas.; Hon. Sen. Clin. Lect. Univ. Glas. Socs: Mem. Brit. Neuropsychiatric Assn. Prev: Sen. Regist. (Neurol.) Inst. Neurol. Sci. Glas.; Regist. (Neurol.) Qu. Eliz. Hosp. Birm.; Regist. (Neurol. & Neuropath.) Inst. Neurol. Scs. Glas.

THOMAS, Anne Stella Mary Cardiff Road Medical Centre, Cardiff Road, Taffs Well, Cardiff CF15 7YG Tel: 029 2081 0260 Fax: 029 2081 3002 — MRCS Eng. LRCP Lond. 1965.

THOMAS, Anthony (retired) Radiology Department, Norfolk & Norwich Hospital, St. Stephen's Road, Norwich NR1 3SR Tel: 01603 286094 — MB BS 1963 Lond.; MB BS (Hons.) Lond. 1963; MRCS Eng. LRCP Lond. 1963; FRCR 1975, FFR 1972; DMRD Eng. 1969; DObst RCOG 1965. Cons. Radiol. Norf. & Norwich Health Care NHS Trust. Prev: Sen. Regist. (Radiol.) St. Mary's Hosp. & Nat. Hosp. Nerv. Dis. Lond.

THOMAS, Anthony Bainbridge The Wynd Surgery, 9 The Wynd, Marske-by-the-Sea, Redcar TS11 7LD Tel: 01642 477133 Fax: 01642 475150; Sundon, 2 Windsor Road, Saltburn-by-the-Sea TS12 1BQ Tel: 01287 622393 — MB BS 1966 Durh.; DObst RCOG 1969. Prev: SHO (O & G) Preston Hosp. N. Shields; SHO (Paediat.) Qu. Eliz. Hosp. Gateshead; Ho. Phys. & Ho. Surg. Middlesbrough Gen. Hosp.

THOMAS, Anthony Leonard 14 Linkway Avenue, Ashton-in-Makerfield, Wigan WN4 8XE — MB ChB 1989 Sheff.

THOMAS, Anthony Mark Roderic 1 Archway Road, Poole BH14 9AY — MB BS 1991 Lond.

THOMAS, Antony 60 Walmesley Road, Leigh WN7 1XN — MB BS 1988 Madras; MRCP (UK) 1994.

THOMAS, Antony Noel Department Anaesthesia, Hope Hospital, Eccles Old Road, Salford M6 8HD; 38 Hillington Road, Sale M33 6GP — MB BS 1982 Lond.; FFA RCS Eng. 1987. Cons. Anaesth. Hope Hosp. Salford.

THOMAS, Antony Russell 38 Fabis Drive, The Grove, Nottingham NG11 8NZ — MB ChB 1990 Leeds.

THOMAS, Archibald Lloyd (retired) 149 Stoddens Road, Burnham-on-Sea TA8 2DE Tel: 01278 4172 — LMSSA 1930 Lond.;

THOMAS

MRCS Eng. LRCP Lond. 1931; DIH Eng. 1947. Prev: Med. Off. Roy. Arsenal Woolwich.

THOMAS, Arnallt Ty-Gwyn, 382 Pentregethin Road, Gendros, Swansea SA5 8AH — LMSSA 1960 Lond.

THOMAS, Arnold Owen West House, Westgate, Cowbridge CF7 — MB BCh 1952 Wales.

THOMAS, Arthur Glannrafon Surgery, Glannrafon, Amlwch LL68 9AG Tel: 01407 830878 Fax: 01407 832512 — MB ChB 1967 Liverp. Socs: BMA.

THOMAS, Arthur Richard Pinfold Health Centre, Field Road, Bloxwich, Walsall WS3 3JP Fax: 01922 775132; Oakwood, Roman Road, Little Aston Park, Sutton Coldfield B74 3AQ — MB ChB 1962 Birm.; DA Eng. 1965; DObst RCOG 1965. (Birm.) Socs: BMA. Prev: SHO Anaesth. Dudley Rd. Hosp. Birm.; Sen. Ho. Surg. ENT Dept. Qu. Eliz. Hosp. Birm.; Ho. Surg. Heathfield Rd. Matern. Hosp. Birm.

THOMAS, Arthur Robinson, MBE, VRD (retired) Upper Gulmswell, Combe-in-Teignhead, Newton Abbot TQ12 4RE Tel: 01626 873420 — MB BChir 1958 Camb.; MA Camb. 1931; MRCS Eng. LRCP Lond. 1928; DMRE 1933. Prev: Hon. Radiol. Newton Abbot Hosp.

THOMAS, Barbara Ann, OBE (retired) Jarvis Screening Centre, Stoughton Road, Guildford GU1 1LJ Tel: 01483 783200 Fax: 01483 783299 — MB BChir 1960 Camb.; MA Camb. 1960; MRCR 1988; DObst RCOG 1960. Mem. - Margt. Gp. - BrE. Cancer Screening - Age Trial. Prev: Director - Jarvis BrE. Cancer, Screening, Diagnostic and Nat. Train. Centre, Guildford.

THOMAS, Barbara Elizabeth (retired) 116 Newmarket Road, Norwich NR4 6SA Tel: 01603 452394 — BM BCh 1948 Oxf.; BM BCh Oxf.; MA Oxf. 1950; FFA RCS Eng. 1954. Prev: Assoc. Specialist (Anaesth.) Norf. & Norwich Hosp.

THOMAS, Barbara Elsie Clark Avenue Surgery, Clark Avenue, Pontnewydd, Cwmbran NP44 1RY Tel: 01633 482733 Fax: 01633 867758 — MB BCh 1966 Wales. (Cardiff) Prev: Ho. Surg. & Ho. Phys. E. Glam. Hosp. Pontypridd.

THOMAS, Benny 53 Chaucer Avenue, Cranford, Hounslow TW4 6NA — MB BS 1987 Lond.; DRCOG Lond.; MRCP Lond. 1995. (Royal Free Hospital London) Regist. (Neurol.) Morriston Hosp. Swansea.

THOMAS, Bernard 70 Everton Road, Liverpool L6 2EW — MB ChB 1988 Manch.; MRCGP 1992; DRCOG 1991. GP Liverp. Prev: Assoc. GP. NWRHA.

THOMAS, Beryl Irene Evans Church Surgery, Portland St., Aberystwyth SY23 2DX Tel: 01970 4855; Orlandon, 31 North Parade, Aberystwyth SY23 2JN Tel: 01970 623808 — MB BCh 1959 Wales; MFCM 1972; DPH Lond. 1964; DCH Eng. 1961. (Cardiff) Prev: Dep. MOH Cards. CC; Ho. Phys. Maelor Hosp. Wrexham; SHO (Paediat.) Neath Gen. Hosp.

THOMAS, Brett Morgan Grosvenor Avenue Surgery, 20 Grosvenor Avenue, Hayes UB4 8NL Tel: 020 8845 7100 Fax: 020 8842 4401; 34 Rickmansworth Road, Harefield, Uxbridge UB9 6JX — MB BS 1980 Lond. (Char. Cross) Clin. Asst. (Gastroenterol.) Mt. Vernon Hosp. Prev: SHO (Thoracic Surg.) Harefield Hosp.; SHO (ENT) Mt. Vernon & Hillingdon Hosps. N.wood.

THOMAS, Brian Michael (retired) 35 Alderney Ave, Hounslow TW5 0QN Tel: 020 8570 2926 — MB BS 1958 Lond.; FRCP Lond. 1981, M 1962; MRCS Eng. LRCP Lond. 1958; FRCR 1975; FFR 1967; DMRD Eng. 1965. Prev: Cons. Radiol. Univ. Coll. Hosp. & St. Marks Hosp.

THOMAS, Bronwen Ellen 27 Strange Road, Garswood, Ashton-in-Makerfield, Wigan WN4 0RX — MB ChB 1972 Liverp.

THOMAS, Bronwen Neilson (retired) Fay Cottage, 37 Penyfai Lane, Llanelli SA15 4EN — MB BCh 1951 Wales; BSc, MB BCh Wales 1951. JP. Prev: Sen. Hosp. Med. Off. LLa.lli Chest Centr.

THOMAS, Carin Mary 24 Silloth Street, Carlisle CA2 5UR — MB ChB 1984 Manch.

THOMAS, Carol Adelaide Portswood Road Surgery, 186-188 Portswood Road, Portswood, Southampton SO17 2NJ Tel: 023 8055 5181 Fax: 023 8036 6416; 16 Blenheim Avenue, Southampton SO17 1DU — MB BS 1979 Lond.; T (GP) 1992; DFFP 1995. (Middlesex Hospital University of London) GP Soton.; Clin. Asst. (BrE. Surg.) Soton. Univ. Hosp. Trust. Roy. S. Hants. Hosp. Prev: Regist. (Haemat.) Guy's Hosp. Lond.

THOMAS, Caroline Frances Louise Barons Farm, Plantation Rd, Turton, Bolton BL7 0BZ — MB ChB 1993 Dundee.

THOMAS, Caroline Lucy 12C Bernard Island House, Royal United Hospital, Bath BA1 3NG; 59 Western Road, Hagley, Stourbridge DY9 0JX — BM 1992 Soton. Ho. Off. Roy. United Hosp. Bath.

THOMAS, Caroline Margaret Jean Lletymaelog, Llandeilo SA19 7HY Tel: 01558 823541 Email: carolthomas@nextcall.net — MB BS 1969 Lond.; FRCP (UK) 1997, MRCP 1979; MRCS Eng. LRCP Lond. 1969; DCH Eng. 1975; DObst RCOG 1972. (Roy. Free Hosp.) Cons. Community Paediat. P. Philip Hosp. LLa.lli. Socs: Fell. Roy. Soc. Med.; Brit. Paediat. Assn.; Welsh Paediat. Soc. Prev: Sen. Regist. Llaudough Hosp. Cardiff.

THOMAS, Carys Wyn Merrywood, 31 Deepdene Wood, Dorking RH5 4BE Tel: 01306 882482; Merrywood, 31 Deepdene Wood, Dorking RH5 4BE Tel: 01306 882482 — MB BS 1998 Lond.; MA Camb 1999; BA Camb 1995. (Univ Coll + Middlesex School of Med.) Socs: BMA; MS; MDU.

THOMAS, Catherina Myfanwy Wicken Wood, 49 Hinton Way, Great Shelford, Cambridge CB2 5AZ — MB BS 1980 Lond.; MRCGP 1985; DRCOG 1984; DCH RCP Lond. 1984; DOH 1998. (Royal Free Hospital School of Medicine) Prev: GP Camb.

THOMAS, Cathryn Patricia Ley Mill Surgery, 228 Lichfield Road, Sutton Coldfield B74 2UE Tel: 0121 308 0359 Fax: 0121 323 2682 — MB ChB 1984 Birm.; FRCGP 1995, M 1989. (Birmingham) Sen. Lect. (Gen. Pract.) Univ. of Birm. Prev: Lect. (Gen. Pract.) Univ. Birm.

THOMAS, Cecilia Elizabeth Brynderwen Surgery, Crickhowell Road, St. Mellons, Cardiff CF3 0EF Tel: 029 2079 9921 Fax: 029 2077 7740; 14 Lake Road E., Roath Park, Cardiff CF23 5NN — MB BCh 1978 Wales; 1999 PCR - Univ. Of Bath; DFFP 1995; Dip. Palliat. Med. Wales 1992; MRCGP 1982. p/t Hon. Lect. Gen. Pract. Univ. of Wales Coll. of Med.; Trainer in Family Plann.

THOMAS, Cenydd William Gorwel, Pendine, Carmarthen SA33 4PQ — MB BS 1998 Lond.

THOMAS, Charles Ernest Allen (retired) Trefusis, Buttermilk Lane, Pembroke SA71 4TL Tel: 01646 682912 — MRCS Eng. LRCP Lond. 1954; LMSSA Lond. 1950. Prev: SHO (Anaesth.) Chelmsford Hosp. Gp.

THOMAS, Christine Margaret 7 Varlian Close, Ormskirk L40 6HJ Tel: 01695 574170 — MB ChB 1983 Liverp.

THOMAS, Christine Suzanne 110 Elthorne Park Road, London W7 2JJ — MB BS 1989 Lond. Specialist Regist. (Anaesth.) Middlx. Hosp.

THOMAS, Mr Christopher David 24 Briarsmount, Heaton Mersey, Stockport SK4 2EB Tel: 0161 442 1421 Fax: 0161 442 1421 Email: christhomas1@compuserve.com — MB ChB 1992 Manch.; FRCS Eng. 1997. (Manch.) Specialist Regist. (Orthop.) N. W. Region. Socs: Manch. Med. Soc.; BMA. Prev: Research Fell. Orthop. Surg. Manch. Roy. Infirm.

THOMAS, Christopher Elwyn 12 Brickmarkers Lane, Colchester CO4 5WP — MB ChB 1993 Ed.

THOMAS, Christopher James County Hospital, Hereford HR1 2ER Tel: 01432 355444; Paradise House, Lower Paradise Frm., Marden, Hereford HR1 3EN — MB BS 1972 Lond.; MRCP (UK) 1976; MRCS Eng. LRCP Lond. 1972; MRCPsych 1977. Cons. Psychiat. Hereford Co. Hosp. Prev: Cons. Liaison Psychiat. Leicester Roy. Infirm.

THOMAS, Christopher Peter Alma Road Surgery, Alma Road, Romsey SO51 8ED Tel: 01794 513422 Fax: 01794 518668; Brackenwood Cottage, Rudd Lane, Michelmersh, Romsey SO51 0NG — MB BS 1984 Lond.; MRCGP 1988; DRCOG 1987.

THOMAS, Christopher Stuart Department of Psychiatry, Laurente House, Wythenshawe Hospital, Manchester M23 9LT Tel: 0161 291 6925 Fax: 0161 291 6907 — MD 1992 Wales; MRCPsych 1984; T(Psych) 1991. Cons. Psychiat. & Hon. Lect. Univ. Hosp. S. Manch. Prev: Sen. Lect. (Psychiat. Med.) Univ. Otago, NZ.

THOMAS, Christopher William (retired) Garian, 4 Dinglewood Close, Westbury-on-Trym, Bristol BS9 2LL Tel: 0117 968 3726 Fax: 0117 968 3726 Email: chris@dinglewood.freeserve.co.uk — MB ChB Ed. 1957. Prev: Ho. Phys., Ho. Surg. & SHO (Cas.) Roy. Gwent Hosp. Newport.

THOMAS, Claire 84 Brookfield Road, Grimsby DN33 3JL — BM BS 1994 Nottm.

THOMAS, Claire Daphne Royal Shrewbury Hospital, Mytton Oak Road, Mytton Oak, Shrewsbury SY3 8XQ Tel: 01743 261000 Email:

cdthomas@doctors.org.uk; 25 Bull St, Harborne, Birmingham B17 0HH Tel: 0121 426 2018 — MB ChB 1993 Birm.; MRCPCH 1998. (Birmingham) Ho. Off. (Paediat.) Mackay Base Hosp. Mackay, Austral. Prev: Ho. Off. & Resid. Med. Off. (O & G) Mt. Isa Base Hosp., Austral.; Ho. Off. (Med.) Birm. Heartlands Hosp.

THOMAS, Claire Philippa Hope House, 17 Kings Road, Alton GU34 1PZ Email: claireptpt@hotmail.com — MB BS 1994 Lond.; Dphil (Oxon.) 1991; MBBS 1994.

THOMAS, Colin Charles 11 Woodbank Avenue, Gerrards Cross SL9 7PY — MB BChir 1983 Camb.; MA Camb. 1983; MFOM RCP Lond. 1994, A 1990. Sen. Med. Off. BBC TV. Prev: Cons. Occupat. Phys. S.end Hosp.; Med. Off. Ford Motor Co. Dagenham; Ho. Phys. New Addenbrooke's Hosp. Camb.

THOMAS, Colin Hugh West Heights, Uphampton, Ombersley, Droitwich WR9 0JS Tel: 01905 620203 Fax: 07092 270561 Email: colin.thomas@doctors.org.uk — MB ChB 1968 Birm.; FFA RCS Eng. 1972. (Birm.) Cons. Anaesth. Birm. InDepend. Pract. Prev: Cons. Anaesth. Birm. Accid. Hosp.; Cons. Anaesth: Roy. Orthop Hosp. Birm.

THOMAS, Cyril Geoffrey Arthur (retired) 116 Newmarket Road, Norwich NR4 6SA Tel: 01603 452394 — BM BCh 1948 Oxf.; MA Oxf. 1949; FRCP Lond. 1987, M 1952; FRCPath 1970. Prev: Cons: Microbiol. Norf. & Norwich Hosp.

THOMAS, Dafydd Huw Vaughan The Health Centre, Hermitage Road, St John's, Woking GU21 1TD Tel: 01483 723451 Fax: 01483 751879 — MB BCh 1980 Wales; MRCGP 1986; DRCOG 1985.

THOMAS, Dafydd Wyn Department of Anaesthesia and Intensive Care, Morriston Hospital, Swansea SA6 6NL Tel: 01792 703468 Fax: 01792 703470; Cynghordy, Salem, Abertawe, Swansea SA6 6PD Tel: 01792 842598 Email: dafydd@cynghordy.demon.co.uk — MB BCh 1978 Wales; FFA RCS Eng. 1984. Cons. (Anaesth. & IC) Swansea. Socs: Soc. Anaesth. of Wales; Counc. Mem. Autologous Transfus. s/i Gp.; Dep. Regional Advisor for Anaesth. Wales.

THOMAS, Damion Block 9 Southampton General Hospital, Tremona Road, Southampton SO16 6YD — BM 1998 Soton.

THOMAS, Daniel Ashley Gorwel, Welsh Hook Road, Hayscastlecross, Haverfordwest SA62 5NY — MB ChB 1968 Liverp.; FFA RCS Eng. 1975; DObst RCOG 1970. Cons. (Anaesth.) Withybush Hosp. HaverfordW..

THOMAS, Daniel Lewis Charles Hereford House, 51 Westerfield Road, Ipswich IP4 2UU Tel: 01473 254555 — MB BS 1945 Lond.; MD Lond. 1953 MB BS 1945, DPM 1950; MRCPsych 1971. (Lond. Hosp.) Socs: BMA. Prev: Cons. Psychiat. Suff. Ment. Hosps.; Sen. Hosp. Med. Off. Runwell Hosp.; Sen. Regist. Dept. Psychiat. St. Geo. Hosp. Lond.

THOMAS, Daniel Phillip Pennant, Rhosmaen, Llandeilo SA19 6NP — MB BS 1990 Lond.

THOMAS, David 31 Lizban Street, Blackheath, London SE3 8SS — MB BS 1975 Lond.; FFA RCS Eng. 1980. Sen. Regist. (Anaesth.) Lond. Hosp.

THOMAS, David Adrian 4 The Paddock, Ockbrook, Derby DE72 3RS Email: 100425.3262@compuserve.com — MB ChB 1981 Birm.; MRCP (UK) 1987; DCH RCP Lond. 1986. Cons. Paediat. & Intensivist Qu.s Med. Centre Nottm. Socs: Paediat. Intens. Care Soc. Prev: Sen. Regist. (Paediat.) City Hosp. & Qu. Med. Centre Nottm.

THOMAS, David Arthur Long Lane Surgery, 15 Long Lane, Liverpool L19 6PE Tel: 0151 494 1445; 121 Alder Road, Liverpool L12 2BA — MB ChB 1954 Liverp.; BSc (Hons. Physiol.) Liverp. 1951. Socs: Liverp. Med. Inst.

THOMAS, David Brynmor Bute Medical Buildings, Queens Terrace, St Andrews KY16 9TS Tel: 01334 76161 — MB BS 1956 Lond.; FRS Ed.; DSc Birm. 1976; BSc (Special) Lond. 1952, MB BS 1956; FRCP Ed. 1984; FRCPath 1977, M 1974; FIBiol. 1976. (Univ. Coll. Lond. & Univ. Coll. Hosp.) Bute Prof. Anat. & Experim. Path. Univ. St. And. Socs: Fell. Roy. Soc. Med. Prev: Master, United Coll. St. Salvator & St. Leonard St. Andrews; Sen. Lect. Histol. & Cellular Biol. Univ. Birm.; Nuffield Lect. Path. Univ. Oxf.

THOMAS, David Charles 36 Granville Road, Oxted RH8 0DA Tel: 01883 712423 — MB ChB 1983 Sheff.; DA 1986; DRCOG 1991.

THOMAS, David Colwyn West Winds, Caswell Road, Newton, Swansea SA3 — MB BS 1947 Lond.; MRCS Eng. LRCP Lond. 1942. (St. Bart.) Mem. Min. of Pens. & Nat. Insur. Med. Bds. Socs: BMA.

Prev: Phys. & Anaesth. EMS Hosp. Morriston; Ho. Surg. Swansea Gen. & Eye Hosp.; Capt. RAMC.

THOMAS, David Derek Maendy Place Medical Centre, 1 Maendy Place, Weatherall Street, Aberdare CF44 7AY Tel: 01685 872146 Fax: 01685 884767 — MB BCh 1976 Wales; DRCOG 1978.

THOMAS, Mr David Fraser Morgan Department of Paediatric Surgery & Urology, Clinical Sciences Building, St James's University Hospital, Leeds LS9 7TF Tel: 0113 243 3144 Fax: 0113 283 6972 Email: d.f.m.thomas@leeds.ac.uk — MB BChir 1971 Camb.; MA Camb. 1971; FRCP Lond. 1997; FRCP Ed. 1997; FRCS Eng. 1976; MRCP (UK) 1973; FRCPCH 1997. (Camb./Guys) Cons. Paediat. Urol. St. Jas. Univ. Hosp. & Gen. Infirm. Leeds; Hon. Reader Paediat. Surg. Univ. Leeds. Socs: Exec. Counc. Brit. Assn. Paediat. Surg.; Exec. Counc. Brit. Assn. Urol. Surg.; Exec. Counc. Eur. Soc. Paediat. Urol. Prev: Sen. Clin. Lect. Univ. Leeds; Sen. Regist. Hosp. Sick Childr. Gt. Ormond St. Lond.; Wellcome Research Fell. Inst. Child Health Lond.

THOMAS, David Gareth Green Close Surgery, Green Close, Kirkby Lonsdale, Carnforth LA6 2BS Tel: 015242 71210 Fax: 015242 72713 — MB BS 1971 Bombay. (Bombay) GP Carnforth, Lancs.

THOMAS, David Gareth 2 Lambourn Avenue, Eastbourne BN24 5PQ — BM 1998 Soton.

THOMAS, David Gareth Hughes let Wen, Morfa Nefyn, Pwllheli LL53 6AR — MB BCh 1949 Wales; BSc MB BCh Wales 1949. (Cardiff) Sen. Med. Off. Roy. Fleet Auxil. Prev: Ho. Surg. Llandough Hosp. Cardiff; RN; Res. Med. Off. H.M. Stanley Hosp. St. Asaph.

THOMAS, David Gary 4 Brookfield Park Road, Cowbridge CF71 7HJ — MB BCh 1981 Wales; FFA RCS Lond. 1985. Cons. Anaesth. P.ss of Wales Hosp. Bridgend. Prev: Sen. Regist. (Anaesth.) Cardiff & Swansea; Regist. (Anaesth.) St. Mary's Hosp. Lond.; SHO (Anaesth.) Swansea.

THOMAS, David George Chastleton, Newton Drive, Framwellgate Moor, Durham DH1 5BH Tel: 0191 384 6171 Email: thomas@brancepath.freeserve.co.uk; 5 Goodwell Lea, Brancepeth, Durham DH7 8EN Tel: 0191 378 4465 — MB BCh 1993 Wales. (Univ of Wales.)

THOMAS, David Geraint BUPA Occupational Health, PO Box 15, Gresty Road, Crewe CW2 6BT Tel: 01270 532386 Fax: 01270 533167 Email: thomas.bupaoh@ems.rail.co.uk; 14 Nevis Drive, Crewe CW2 8UH Tel: 01270 214241 Email: thomascrewe@aol.com — MRCS Eng. LRCP Lond. 1974; AFOM RCP Lond. 1995. Med. Off. Brit. Railways Crewe. Socs: Fell. Roy. Soc. Med.; Soc. Occupat. Med. Prev: SHO (Surg.) Manch. Roy. Infirm. & Sharoe Green Hosp. Preston.

THOMAS, David Gerard Department of Anaesthesia, Dryburn Hospital, North Road, Durham DH1 5TW Tel: 0191 386 4911; 10 Richmond Crescent, Vicars Cross, Chester CH3 5PB — MB BS 1980 Newc.; FFA RCSI 1990; Dip. Obst. Auckland 1988. Cons. Anaesth. Dryburn Hosp. Durh. Socs: Assn. Anaesth.; Obst. Anaesth. Assn.

THOMAS, Professor David Glyndor Treharne The National Hospital for Neurology & Neurosurgery, Queen Square, London WC1N 3BG Tel: 020 7837 3611 Fax: 020 7278 7894 Email: neurological.surgery@ion.ucl.ac.uk; 14 Montagu Square, London W1H 2LD Tel: 020 7486 8566 — MA Camb. 1968, BA 1963, MB 1967, BChir 1966; FRCP Glas. 1985; FRCS Ed. 1972; MRCP (UK) 1970; MRCS Eng. LRCP Lond. 1966; FRCS Eng 1998. (St. Mary's) Prof. Neurosurg. Nat. Hosp. Neurol. & Neurosurg. Lond.; Sen. Lect. Inst. Neurol. Lond.; Cons. Neurosurg. Nat. Hosps. Nerv. Dis. Lond. & N.wick Pk. Hosp. Socs: Fell. Roy. Soc. Med.; Soc. Brit. Neurol. Surgs.; Pres. Europ. Soc. Stereotactic & Func.al Neurosurg. Prev: Sen. Regist. (Neurosurg.) Inst. Neurol. Scs. S.. Gen. Hosp. Glas.; SHO (Neurol.) St. Mary's Hosp. Lond.; Asst. Lect. (Anat.) St. Mary's Hosp. Med. Sch. Lond.

THOMAS, David Gordon Borough Green Medical Practice, Quarry Hill Road, Borough Green, Sevenoaks TN15 8BE Tel: 01732 883161 Fax: 01732 886319 — MB BChir 1969 Camb.; MRCGP 1989; DCH Eng. 1971. (Camb. & Guy's) Prev: Regist. (Paediat.) Pembury Hosp. Tunbridge Wells; Ho. Phys. Roy. Devon & Exeter Hosp.; Ho. Surg. Guys Hosp. Lond.

THOMAS, Mr David Gwyn 3 Haugh Lane, Sheffield S11 9SA — MB BS 1962 Lond.; FRCS Eng. 1967; FRCP 1999. (Middlx.) Cons. Urol. Surg. Spinal Injuries Unit N.ern Gen. Hosp., Sheff.; Hon. Clin. Lect. Urol. Univ. Sheff. Prev: Hon. Clin. Lect. Spinal Injuries Univ. Sheff.; Sen. Regist. Dept. Urol. Sheff.

THOMAS

THOMAS, David Hugh (retired) 61 Stakesby Road, Whitby YO21 1JF — MB ChB 1956 Leeds; DObst RCOG 1961. Local Treasury Med. Off. Prev: GP Whitby.

THOMAS, David Hywel Llwyn-y-Piod, Peniel, Carmarthen SA32 7AA — BM BS 1997 Nottm.

THOMAS, David Ian 18 Pilkington Avenue, Sutton Coldfield B72 1LA — MB ChB 1981 Birm.; FCAnaesth. 1990; DA (UK) 1985.

THOMAS, David Ieuan (retired) 21 Church Street, Market Deeping, Peterborough PE6 8AN Tel: 01778 343219 — MB ChB 1961 St. And.; DObst RCOG 1961. Prev: GP P'boro.

THOMAS, David Iorwerth (retired) 34 Widewell Road, Roborough, Plymouth PL6 7DW — MRCS Eng. LRCP Lond. 1941. Prev: Ho. Surg. N.ampton Gen. Hosp. & Selly Oak Hosp. Birm.

THOMAS, Mr David James Department Urology, Freeman Hospital, Newcastle upon Tyne; 2 Cadaway House, Greenside, Ryton NE40 4SH — MB BS 1985 Lond.; FRCS Eng. 1990; FRCS Ed. 1989. Research Regist. (Urol.) Freeman Hosp. Newc. u. Tyne. Prev: Regist. (Surg.) St. Mary's Hosp. Portsmouth; Regist. (Surg.) Qu. Alexandra Hosp. Cosham Portsmouth; SHO Rotat. (Surg.) Bristol Roy. Infirm.

THOMAS, David James 31 Smith Street, Chelsea, London SW3 4ER Tel: 020 7352 5899 — MB BS 1943 Lond.; MD 1947 Lond.; DCH 1944 Eng.; MRCP 1946 Lond.; MRCS 1942 Eng.; LRCP 1942 Lond.; MRCGP 1960; MD Lond. 1947; MRCP Lond. 1946; MRCS Eng. LRCP Lond. 1942; MRCGP 1960; DCH Eng. 1944. (St. Mary's) Socs: BMA (Late Chairm. Local Br.). Prev: Clin. Asst. Vict. Hosp. Childr. Tite St.; Ho. Phys. King Edwd. Memor. Hosp. Ealing.

THOMAS, Mr David Jeffrey Glan Clwyd Hospital, Rhyl LL18 5UJ Tel: 01745 583910 Fax: 01745 583143; Plas Ffordd Ddwr, Llandyrnog, Denbigh LL16 4ET Tel: 01824 790316 — MB BS 1965 Lond.; FRCS Ed. 1970; MRCS Eng. LRCP Lond. 1964; FRCOG 1983, M 1970. (St. Mary's) Cons. O & G Clwyd N. Health Dist. Socs: Fell. N. Eng. Obst. & Gyn. Soc.; Welsh Obst. & Gyn. Soc. Prev: Sen. Regist. (O & G) W.m. Hosp. Lond.; Ho. Surg. (Gyn.) Samarit. Hosp. Lond.; Ho. Surg. (Obst.) St. Mary's Hosp. Lond.

THOMAS, David John Woolletts, Cherry Tree Lane, Fulmer, Slough SL3 6JE Tel: 01753 662147 Fax: 01753 664023 — MB BChir Camb. 1970; MD Birm. 1977; MA Camb. 1970; FRCP Lond. 1985; MRCP (UK) 1972. (Camb. & Birm.) Cons. Neurol. St. Marys Hosp. Lond.; Sen. Lect. Inst. Neurol. & Hon. Cons. (Neurol.) Nat. Hosp. Neurol. & Neurosurg. & Chalfont Centre for Epilepsy. Socs: Trustee Stroke Assn.; Stroke Counc. of Amer. Heart Assn.; Governor Nat. Soc. for Epilepsy. Prev: Research Fell. St. Thos. Hosp. Lond. & Nat. Hosp. Nerv. Dis. Qu. Sq. Lond.; Sen. Regist. (Neurol.) Qu. Eliz. Hosp. Birm. & Midl. Centre Neurosurg.; Cons.Neurol.King Edwd. VII Hosp.Windsor, Heatherwood Hosp, Ascot, St Mark's Hosp Maidenhead P. Chas. Eye Unit.

THOMAS, David John Bowen 4 Chandos Close, Buckhurst Hill IG9 5HS Tel: 020 8505 0421 — MD 1978 Lond.; MB BS 1971; FRCP Lond. 1993; MRCP (UK) 1974. (St. Thos.) Cons. Phys. Mt. Vernon & Hillingdon Hosps.; Sen. Regist. Med. Unit St. Bart. Hosp. Lond. Socs: Brit. Diabetic Assn.; Med. Res. Soc. Prev: Sen. Regist. Whipps Cross Hosp. Lond.; Regist. Basingstoke Dist. & Soton. Univ. Hosp.; Wessex Research Fell.

THOMAS, David Kermac Macmeikan (retired) The White Cottage, Braywood, Oakley Green, Windsor SL4 4QF Tel: 01628 621250 — MB BS 1953 Lond.; MRCGP 1963; DObst RCOG 1957. Prev: Ho. Surg. Univ. Coll. Hosp.

THOMAS, David Lewis Royal Gwent Hospital, Cardiff Road, Newport NP20 2UB — MB BCh 1976 Wales; FFA RCS Eng. 1980. Cons. Anaesth. Roy. Gwent Hosp. Newport.

THOMAS, David Malcolm University Hospital of Wales, Heath Park, Cardiff CF14 4WZ Tel: 029 2074 6645 Fax: 029 2074 6661 — MB BChir 1984 Camb.; MD Camb. 1994; FRCP 2000. Clin. Director of Med., Cardiff & the Vale NHSTrust; Cons. Phys. (Nephrol.) Univ. Hosp. Wales.

THOMAS, David Michael Marlow and Partners, The Surgery, Bell Lane, Minchinhampton, Stroud GL6 9JF Tel: 01453 883793 Fax: 01453 731670 — MB BS 1983 Lond.; MRCP Lond. 1986; DA (UK) 1988.

THOMAS, Mr David Michael Dept. of ENT, Gloucester Royal Hospital, Gloucester GL1 3NN Tel: 01452 394186 Fax: 01452 394432; 39 The Burgage, Prestbury, Cheltenham GL52 3DL Email: mtent60@hotmail.com — MB BS 1987 Lond.; BSc Cardiff 1982; FRCS (Otol.) 1993; FRCS Eng. 1991; FRCS (Orl.) 1997. (Char. Cross & Westm.) Cons. (Otolaryngol.) Cheltenham Gen Gloucester Hosp.& Gloucester Roy. Hosp.; Lect. Univ. of Bristol. Socs: BAO; H+NS; BAHNO. Prev: Sen. Regist. (ENT) S.mead Hosp. Bristol; Regist. (ENT) St. Mary's Hosp. Lond.; Sen. Regist. (ENT) Roy. Devon & Exeter Hosp.

THOMAS, Mr David Michael Department of Urology, Queen's Hospital NHS Trust, Belvedere Road, Burton-on-Trent DE13 0RB Tel: 01283 566333 Ext: 4011 Fax: 01283 593087; (cons. rooms), 181 Rolleston Road, Burton-on-Trent DE13 0LD Tel: 01283 563045 — MB BChir 1971 Camb.; MA Camb. 1971; FRCS Eng. 1975. (Middlesex Hospital) Cons. Urol. Burton Hosp. NHS Trust. Socs: BAUS. Prev: Sen. Regist. (Urol.) Middlx. Hosp. & St. Peters Hosp.

THOMAS, David Michael Spa Medical Centre, Snowberry Lane; 1 Garfield Road, Netley Abby SO19 4DA Email: sjtanser@yahoo.com — MB BS 1990 Lond.; MRCGP 1995; DRCOG 1994. GP Princip. Melksham Wiltire. Socs: MDU & BMA. Prev: GPUTS, St Albans.

THOMAS, David Michael Marryat, Kippington Road, Sevenoaks TN13 2LH — MB BS 1975 Lond.; BSc (Hons.) Lond. 1972; MRCS Eng. LRCP Lond. 1975. (Guy's)

THOMAS, David Owen Goldacre Farm, Farway, Colyton EX24 6DH — MB ChB 1991 Sheff.

THOMAS, David Rhys Lowfield Road, 5 Lowfield Road, Shaw Heath, Stockport SK2 6RW Tel: 0161 480 8249 Fax: 0161 474 0290; 27 Heath Road, Stockport SK2 6JJ Tel: 0161 419 9001 — MB BS 1964 Lond.; MRCP Lond. 1967; MRCS Eng. LRCP Lond. 1964.

THOMAS, David Richard Bryn Villa, Gorslas, Llanelli SA15 5AT — MB BS 1978 Lond.; MA Camb. 1978; MRCS Eng. LRCP Lond. 1978.

THOMAS, Mr David Richard (retired) 6 North Avenue, Ashbourne DE6 1EZ Tel: 01335 345800 Email: d.thomas@pobox.com — MB BS Lond. 1961; FRCS Eng. 1967; MRCS Eng. LRCP Lond. 1961. Cons. Surg. Derbysh. Roy. Infirm. & Derbysh. Childr. Hosp.; Clin. Teach. Univ. Nottm.; DL Derbysh. Prev: Ho. Phys. (Med.) & Ho. Surg. (Surg.) St. Geo. Hosp. Lond.

THOMAS, David Richard Brynmor Messers Herbert Smith, Exchange House, Primrose St., London EC2A 2HS Tel: 020 7374 8000 Fax: 020 7374 0888; Old Orchard, The St, Plaxtol, Sevenoaks TN15 0QG Tel: 01732 811070 — MB ChB 1987 Ed. (Univ. of Edin.) Solicitor Messers Herbert Smith Lond. Socs: Fell. Roy. Soc. Med. Prev: Ho. Surg. Vasc. Surg. Unit. Glas. Roy. Infirm.; Ho. Phys. Med. Unit Roy. Infirm. Edin.; SHO (A & E) Glas. Roy. Infirm.

THOMAS, David Richard Tudor Swallowfield Medical Practice, The Surgery, Swallowfield, Reading RG7 1QY Tel: 0118 988 3134 Fax: 0118 988 5759 — MB BS 1987 Lond.; DRCOG 1992.

THOMAS, David Roger 14 Lake Road E., Roath Park, Cardiff CF23 5NN — MB BCh 1978 Wales; MRCPsych 1984. Cons. Forens. Psychiat., Bro Morgannwg Trust, Glanrhyd Hosp., Bridgend.

THOMAS, David Vaughan Philipps (Surgery), 83 Grove Road, Sutton SM1 2DB Tel: 020 8642 1721; 51 Southway, Carshalton Beeches, Carshalton SM5 4HP Tel: 020 8642 8973 — MRCS Eng. LRCP Lond. 1971; DFFP 1994. (Guy's) Socs: Brit. Assn. Sport & Med. Prev: Regist. Accid. & Orthop. Dept. St. Peter's Hosp. Chertsey; Cas. Off. Guy's Hosp.; Asst. Med. Off. Brookfield Cott. Hosp. Newfoundld., Canada.

THOMAS, David William Phillip (retired) 26 Rhiwbina Hill, Cardiff CF14 6UN Tel: 029 2062 7741 — MB BChir 1956 Camb.; MA Camb. 1956; MRCS Eng. LRCP Lond. 1956; MRCGP 1965; DObst RCOG 1959.

THOMAS, Debbie Bevan Ty-Elli Group Practice, Ty Elli, Llanelli SA15 3BD Tel: 01554 772678 / 773747 Fax: 01554 774476; 10 Squirrel Walk, Fforest, Pontarddulais, Swansea SA4 1UH — MB BCh 1988 Wales; MRCGP 1992; DRCOG 1991. Clin. Asst. GU Med.

THOMAS, Deborah Jane 5 Clovelly Road, Emsworth PO10 7HL — MB BS 1987 Lond.

THOMAS, Deborah Jane 12 Brickmakers Lane, Colchester CO4 5WP — MB ChB 1993 Ed. SHO (O & G) Colchester.

THOMAS, Deborah Karen 18 Fosse Way, London W13 0BZ — MB BS 1993 Lond.

THOMAS, Derek Thomas (retired) 21 Orchard Lane, Hutton, Driffield YO25 9PZ — MRCS Eng. LRCP Lond. 1940. Prev: Treasury Med. Off.

THOMAS

THOMAS, Dhanesvari Northampton General Hospital, The Eye Department - Singlehurst Ward, Cliftonville, Northampton NN1 5BD — MB ChB 1991 Natal.

THOMAS, Diana Kernick 34 Woodlane, Falmouth TR11 4RF — MB BCh 1962 Wales.

THOMAS, Dianne Claire 85 Heol-y-Deri, Cardiff CF14 6HE — MB BCh 1994 Wales.

THOMAS, Digby Patrick Chisholm West Denburn Medical Practice, West Wing, Denburn Health Centre, Rosemount Viaduct, Aberdeen AB25 1QB Tel: 01224 642955 Fax: 01224 637736; 11 Whitehall Terrace, Aberdeen AB25 2RY Tel: 01224 643157 — MB ChB 1984 Ed.; MSc Ed. 1993; MRCGP 1988; DFFP 1993. Princip. Gen. Pract. Denburn W. Med. Gp. Aberd. (p/t); Clin. Teach. Fell. (Gen. Pract.) Univ. Aberd. Socs: Fell. Roy. Med. Soc. Edin. Prev: Hon. Fell. (Gen. Pract.) Univ. Edin.; SHO (Pub. Health Med.) Som. HA; Med. Off. Tristan da Cunha.

THOMAS, Donald Alexander (retired) 64 Hutton Village, Hutton, Brentwood CM13 1RU — MRCS Eng. LRCP Lond. 1956; FFA RCS Eng. 1967; DA Eng. 1961. Cons. Anaesth. Havering Health Dist. Prev: Sen. Regist. (Anaesth.) Barnet Gen. Hosp.

THOMAS, Donald Glynne Department of Occupational medicine, Royal Liverpool University NHS Trust, Liverpool L14 Tel: 0151 282 6765 Fax: 0151 282 6815; 5 Church Farm Court, Neston Road, Willaston, South Wirral CH64 2XP — MB ChB Liverp. 1968; Assoc. Fac. Occupat. Med. RCP Lond. 1979. (Liverp.) Clin. Dir. (Occupat. Med.) Liverp. Trusts, Univ. Hosps., Mersey Regional Bd. & Nat. Blood Transfus. Serv.; Cons. Anaesth. Mersey RHA. Socs: Liverp. Soc. Anaesth. & Soc. Occupat. Med.; Fell. Roy. Soc. Med. Prev: Med. Asst. (A & E) Chester Roy. Infirm.; Regist. (Radiol.) Robt. Jones & Agnes Hunt Orthop. Hosp. OsW.ry; Regist. (Anaesth.) Clatterbridge Hosp. Bebington.

THOMAS, Donald John, MBE, KStJ 22 Bowham Avenue, Bridgend CF31 3PA Tel: 01656 653130 — MB BCh 1954 Wales; BSc Wales 1951; FFOM RCP Lond. 1985, MFOM 1978; Specialist Accredit. (Occupat. Med.) RCP Lond. 1978. (Cardiff) Socs: Soc. Occupat. Med.; BMA (Exec. Mem. Mid-Glam. Div.); Cardiff PG Fed.Chest Dis. Prev: Company. Assoc. Brit. Ports. Swansea & Cardiff; Med. Off. i/c Radiol. Servs. S. Wales Area Nat. Coal Bd. & Nat. Smokeless Fuels Ltd.; SHO Miners' Chest. Dis. Treatm. Centre Llandough Hosp.

THOMAS, Dorothy Spencer Windyridge, Swaines Road, Bembridge PO35 5XS — MB BS 1921 Lond.; MRCS Eng. LRCP Lond. 1921. (King's Coll.) Prev: Med. Off. Knowle Hosp. Fareham; Clin. Asst. Neurol. Dept. & Obst. Ho. Surg. King's Coll. Hosp.

THOMAS, Douglas Gordon 388 Westdale La, Mapperley, Nottingham NG3 6ES — MB ChB 1997 Birm.

THOMAS, Mr Douglas Wilfred Glyder, Gwaelodygarth Close, Merthyr Tydfil CF47 8DX — MRCS Eng. LRCP Lond. 1943; BA Camb. 1940; FRCS Eng. 1949. (Camb. & Westm.)

THOMAS, Duncan Porter (retired) The Old Barn, North Green, Kirtlington, Kidlington OX5 3JZ Tel: 01869 350930 Email: dpt@patrol.i-way.co.uk — MB BS Lond. 1954; MSc Oxf. 1952, DPhil 1958; MD Lond. 1964; FRCPath 1980, M 1973. Prev: Head Div. Haemat. Nat. Inst. Biol. Standards & Control Potters Bar.

THOMAS, Earlando Oliver 53 Cecil Avenue, Southampton SO16 4GP — MB BS 1986 West Indies.

THOMAS, Edna June (retired) (Surgery), 5 Strawberry Place, Glyn Mefus, Morriston, Swansea SA6 7AQ Tel: 01792 771072 — MB ChB 1958 Birm. Prev: Ho. Surg. & Ho. Phys. Morriston Hosp. Swansea.

THOMAS, Edward Gwyn 32 Cedar Avenue, Hazlemere, High Wycombe HP15 7DW Tel: 01494 712065 Email: thomasg@war.wyeth.com — MB BCh 1974 Wales; FFPM RCP (UK) 1995.

THOMAS, Edward Hartley (retired) 2 Cranford Gardens, Marple, Stockport SK6 6QQ Tel: 0161 427 3500 — MB ChB 1960 Manch.; MRCGP 1968; DA Eng. 1962; DObst RCOG 1961. Prev: GP Stockport.

THOMAS, Elaine 2 Melbourne Crescent, Beaconside, Stafford ST16 3JU — MB ChB 1985 Leeds; Dip. Community Paediat. Warwick 1993; DRCOG 1989. Staff Grade Doctor Premier Health NHS Trust.

THOMAS, Eleanor Elizabeth 13 Southernhay Road, Stoneygate, Leicester LE2 3TN Tel: 0116 270 8058 — MB BS 1993 Lond.; BSc Hons 1990; MRCP 1998. (St Marys Hosp. NHS Sch.) SHO (Community Paediat.) Frencham Hosp. Bristol. Prev: SHO (Neonat.) St Michaels Hosp. Bristol; SHO (Paediat.) Australia; SHO (Paediat.) Lewisham Hosp. Lond.

THOMAS, Eleri Wyn 57 Porset Close, Caerphilly CF83 1PQ — MB BCh 1998 Wales.

THOMAS, Elfyn Owen Heulfryn, Ty Mawr, Lon Pentraeth, Menai Bridge LL59 5HR — MB BS 1990 Lond.

THOMAS, Elizabeth Ann Irnham Lodge Surgery, Townsend Road, Minehead TA24 5RG Tel: 01643 703289 Fax: 01643 707921 — MB BCh 1982 Wales.

THOMAS, Elizabeth Ann The Dewerstone Surgery, Hampton Avenue, St Marychurch, Torquay TQ1 3LA Tel: 01803 323123/314240 Fax: 01803 322001; Iona, 27 Shiphay Avenue, Torquay TQ2 7ED Tel: 01803 605359 — MB BS 1983 Lond.; MRCGP 1991; DRCOG 1990. Prev: Trainee GP Ivybridge Health Centre Devon; Regist. (Gen. Med.) Plymouth Gen. Hosp.; SHO (O & G & A & E) Plymouth Gen. Hosp.

THOMAS, Elizabeth Margaret 10 Airbles Drive, Motherwell ML1 3AS — MB ChB 1976 Glas.; MRCGP 1980; DCH Eng. 1980; DRCOG 1979.

THOMAS, Emily Jane Bridge Ways, Little Bookham St., Bookham, Leatherhead KT23 3HR — BM BCh 1998 Oxf.; BM BCh Oxf 1998.

THOMAS, Emma Elizabeth 26 Brentford Avenue, Crosby, Liverpool L23 2UZ — MB ChB 1993 Birm.

THOMAS, Emrys Cadwaladr, OBE (retired) Inverard, 46/31 Inverleith Gardens, Edinburgh EH3 5QF Tel: 0131 551 5607 — LRCP LRCS Ed. LRFPS Glas. 1929. Med. Miss.

THOMAS, Professor Eric Jackson Department Obstetrics & Gynaecology, The Princess Anne Hospital, Coxford Road, Southampton SO16 5YA Tel: 02380 796044 Fax: 02380 786933 — MD 1987 Newc.; MB BS 1976; MRCOG 1983. Prof. (O & G) Univ. Soton. & Hon. Cons. Obst. Soton. Univ. Hosps.Trust & Dean (Med., Health & Biological Sci.s) Univ. Soton.; William Blair Bell Memor. Lect. RCOG 1987; Chairm. Scientif. Advis. Comm. Socs: Fell. Acad. Med. Sci.s; RCOG. Prev: Head Sch. Med. Univ. Soton.; Sen. Lect. Univ. Newc. & Cons. O & G Newc. HA; Lect. & Research Fell. (O & G) Univ. Sheff. Jessop Hosp. for Wom.

THOMAS, Eric Jackson 23 Westbourne Terrace, Shiney Row, Houghton-le-Spring DH4 4QT Tel: 0191 852512; 7 High Friarside, Burnopfield, Newcastle upon Tyne NE16 6AN Tel: 01207 71624 — MB BS 1949 Durh. (Durh.) Mem. Med. Bd. Min. of Social Security; Div. Med. Off. St. John Ambul. Brig. Socs: BMA. Prev: Ho. Surg. Roy. Vict. Infirm. Newc.; Ho. Phys. Stobhill Hosp. Glas.

THOMAS, Eryl Ann James Paget Hospital NHS Trust, Lowestoft Road, Gorleston NR14 6EP Tel: 01493 452400 — MB ChB 1982 Bristol; MRCP (UK) 1985; FRCR 1989. Cons. Radiol. Jas. Paget NHS Trust Gt. Yarmouth. Socs: Roy. Coll. of Radiologists; Roy. Coll. of Phys.s; JPH Ethics Advis. Gp. Prev: Cons. Radiol. BRd.green Hosp. NHS Trust Liverp.; Sen. Regist. (Radiol.) Bristol Roy. Infirm. & Plymouth Gen. Hosp.

THOMAS, Essillt Balgay, Grange Lane, Alvechurch, Birmingham B48 7DJ — MB ChB 1959 Liverp.

THOMAS, Ewan Llywelyn Gerafon Surgery, Benllech, Llandudno — MB ChB 1982 Manch.

THOMAS, Ewart Royston (retired) Four Winds, Bynea, Llanelli SA14 9PR Tel: 01554 59597 — MRCS Eng. LRCP Lond. 1955. Prev: Ho. Surg. & Ho. Phys. St. And. Hosp. Bow.

THOMAS, Ffion Jones Bryn-y-Mor Farm, Pembrey Mountain, Burry Port SA16 0BX — MB BCh 1989 Wales.

***THOMAS, Fiona Ena** Walsgrave Hospital, Clifford Bridge Road, Walsgrave, Coventry CV2 2DX Tel: 024 76 602020; 16 Rothley Drive, Brownsover, Rugby CV21 1TS — MB ChB 1996 Birm.

THOMAS, Frank Melville York Medical Practice, St John's Health Centre, Oak Lane, Twickenham TW1 3PA Tel: 020 8744 0220 Fax: 020 8892 6855; Lansdowne, 187 Percy Road, Twickenham TW2 6JS — MB BS 1978 Lond.; BDS Wales 1972; LDS RCS Eng. 1973; Cert. Family Plann. JCC 1984. (Char. Cross University of Wales) Socs: Fell. Roy. Soc. Med.; BMA. Prev: Trainee GP W. Middlx. Hosp. VTS; SHO & Demonst. (Anat.) Char. Cross. Hosp. Lond.; Ho. Surg. (Urol., ENT & Oral Surg.) Char. Cross Hosp. Lond.

THOMAS, Gail Golygfa Hardd, Caerbryn Square, Penygroes Road, Ammanford SA18 — MB BCh 1989 Wales; MRCGP 1993.

THOMAS

THOMAS, Gareth Boxbush, 243 Rushmere Road, Ipswich IP4 3LU Tel: 01473 712088 Fax: 01473 712088 — MB BS 1969 Lond.; LLM Wales 1996; MD Lond. 1979; MRCS Eng. LRCP Lond. 1969; FRCOG 1987, M 1974. (St. Mary's) Cons. (O & G) Ipswich Hosp.; Dep. Med. Dir. Ipswich Hosp. NHS Trust. Socs: BMA; Eur. Assn. Gyn. & Obst.; Ipswich Medico-Legal Soc. Prev: Sen. Regist. John Radcliffe Hosp. Oxf.; Lect. (O & G) Univ. Coll. Hosp. Lond.; Resid. Med. Off. Qu. Charlotte's Matern. Hosp. Lond.

THOMAS, Gareth Andrew Osbert Department of Gastroenterology, University Hospital of Wales, Heath Park, Cardiff CF4 4QW Tel: 029 2074 4880; 1 The Avenue, Llandaff, Cardiff CF5 2LP — MB BS 1988 Lond.; BSc (1st cl. Hons.) Lond. 1985, MD 1995; MRCP (UK) 1991. (St. Bart.) Cons. Phys. & Gastroenterol. Univ. Hosp. Wales Cardiff. Socs: Brit. Soc. Gastroenterol. Prev: Sen. Regist. (Gastroenterol.) & Regist. (Med.) Univ. Hosp. Wales Cardiff.

THOMAS, Mr Gareth Edward Melbourne (retired) 9 Forest Road, Branksome Park, Poole BH13 6DQ — MB BS 1952 Lond.; FRCS Ed. 1959; MRCS Eng. LRCP Lond. 1951. Hon. Cons. ENT Surg. Bournemouth & E. Dorset Hosp. Gp. Prev: Sen. Regist. (ENT) Cardiff Roy. Infirm.

THOMAS, Gareth Lewis 50 The Coverdales, Gascoigne Estate, Barking IG11 7JY — BM BS 1994 Nottm.

THOMAS, Gareth Lewis c/o 1 Newtondale, Guisborough TS14 8EY — MB BS 1994 Newc.; BMedSc (Hons.) Newc. 1993; MRCP (UK) 1998. (Newcastle) SHO Rotat. (Anaesth./IC) Roy. Oldham Hosp. & Stepping Hill+ Hosp. Stockport. Prev: Ho. Phys. Roy. Vict. Infirm. Newc.; Ho. Surg. Newc. Gen. Hosp.; SHO Rotat. (Med.) Roy. Vict. Infirm. & Freeman Hosp. Newc. u. Tyne.

*THOMAS, Gareth Owen 9 Tocil Croft, Cannon Park, Coventry CV4 7DZ — MB ChB 1996 Birm.

THOMAS, Gareth Rees Victoria Gardens Surgery, Victoria Gardens, Neath SA11 1HW Tel: 01639 643786 Fax: 01639 640018 — MRCS Eng. LRCP Lond. 1975.

THOMAS, Gavin David Peggottys, Little Cheney, Dorchester DT2 9AN — MB BS 1996 Lond.

THOMAS, Gaynor (retired) 24 St John's Road, Hazel Grove, Stockport SK7 5HG Tel: 0161 483 2724 — MB ChB 1957 Manch.; DA Eng. 1960. Prev: Assoc. Specialist Stepping Hill Hosp. Stockport & Stockport Infirm.

THOMAS, Gaynor Caroline Cherrytree Cottage, Broadfield, Saundersfoot SA69 9DG — MB BCh 1998 Wales.

THOMAS, George Douglas Hylton Department of Pathology, Calderdale Royal Hospital, Salterhebble, Halifax HX3 0PW Tel: 01422 224885 — MB ChB 1973 Liverp.; FRCPath 1994; MRCPath 1981. Cons. Histopath. & Morbid Anat. Yorks. RHA. Prev: Sen. Regist. (Histopath.) Yorks, RHA.

THOMAS, George Martin Old Hall, Stainburn, Workington CA14 1SY Tel: 01900 602660 — MB ChB 1957 Ed.; FRCGP 1984, M 1969; DObst RCOG 1962. (Ed.)

THOMAS, Geraint Huw Northgate Surgery, 9 Woolborough Road, Crawley RH10 8EZ Tel: 01294 547315 Fax: 01293 613439; Long Acre, Effingham Road, Crawley RH10 3HY Tel: 01342 713893 — MB BCh 1987 Wales.

THOMAS, Gerald Vaughan 37 Heol-y-Bryn, Rhiwbina, Cardiff CF14 6HX — MB BCh 1980 Wales.

THOMAS, Geraldine (retired) Connetts Cottage, Halsfordwood Lane, Nadderwater, Exeter EX4 2LD Tel: 0139 281384 — MB BS 1958 Lond.; MRCS Eng. LRCP Lond. 1958. Prev: GP Exeter.

THOMAS, Gillian Dawn Department of Clinical Oncology, Derbyshire Royal Infirmary, London Road, Derby DE1 2QY — MB BS 1980 Lond.; MRCS Eng. LRCP Lond. 1980; T(R) (CO) 1992; FRCR 1987; MD 1996. (Char. Cross Hosp.) Cons. (Clin Oncol.) Derbysh. Roy Infirm. Derby. Prev: Clin. Research Fell. (Immunol.) Univ. Birm.; SHO/Regist. (Radiother.) Velindre Hosp. Cardiff VTS.; Sen. Regist. (Radiother./Oncol.) Clin. Acad. Unit. Roy. Marsden Hosp. Sutton.

THOMAS, Glenna (retired) Swn-y-Mor, Overton, Gower, Swansea SA3 1NR Tel: 01792 391244 — MB BCh 1952 Wales; DObst RCOG 1956.

THOMAS, Gordon Oswald (retired) 30 Western Road, Abergavenny NP7 7AD Tel: 01873 857711 Fax: 01873 857711 — MB BS 1961 Lond.; FRCP Lond. 1981, M 1965; MRCS Eng. LRCP Lond. 1961; FCCP 1995. Prev: Cons. Phys. (Gen. & Thoracic Med.) Nevill Hall Hosp. Abergavenny.

THOMAS, Gordon Robert Williams The Surgery, Trentham Mews, New Inn Lane, Trentham, Stoke-on-Trent ST4 8PX Tel: 01782 657159 — MB ChB 1980 Birm.

THOMAS, Graham David Castellfryn Surgery, Castellfryn, Star, Gaerwen LL60 6AS — MB ChB 1993 Aberd. GP Castellfryn Surg., Star. Prev: Trainee GP Powys.

THOMAS, Graham Edgar (retired) 243 Forest Road, Tunbridge Wells TN2 5HT Tel: 01892 526503 — MB BS Lond. 1965; MD Lond. 1977; FRCP Lond. 1992; MRCP (UK) 1970; MRCS Eng. LRCP Lond. 1965. Prev: Phys. Nuffield Hosp. Tunbridge Wells Kent.

THOMAS, Graham Evelyn (retired) 4 Queenswood Close, Wellington, Hereford HR4 8BQ Tel: 01432 830448 — MRCS Eng. LRCP Lond. 1942; MA Camb. 1943, MB BChir 1947; FRCPath 1964. Prev: Cons. Path. Greenwich Dist. Hosp.

THOMAS, Gregory Patrick Lorne North Farm House, High Road, Loughton IG10 4JJ — BM BCh 1998 Oxf.; MA 1995. (Oxford) Surg. John Radcliff Hosp. Oxf. Prev: Phys. Milton Keynes Gen Hosp.

THOMAS, Gruffydd John The Queen Edith Medical Practice, 59 Queen Ediths Way, Cambridge CB1 8PJ Tel: 01223 247288 Fax: 01223 213459 — MB ChB 1992 Bristol; MRCGP 1996; DRCOG 1996. (Bristol) GP Qu. Edith Med. Pract. Prev: Trainee GP/SHO Roy. Devon & Exeter NHS Trust.

THOMAS, Gwenyth Old Road Surgery, Old Road, Llanelli SA15 3HR Tel: 01554 775555 Fax: 01554 778868; Bwthyn Trebuan, 7 Trebuan, Felinfoel, Llanelli SA15 4LH Tel: 01554 756034 Fax: 01554 756034 — MB BCh 1984 Wales; DRCOG 1987. (Univ. Wales Sch. of Med. Cardiff) Prev: Trainee GP W. Wales Gen. Hosp. Carmarthen.

THOMAS, Gwyn David (retired) 22 Court Crescent, Bassaleg, Newport NP10 8NH Tel: 01633 251541 — MB BS 1956 Lond.; MRCS Eng. LRCP Lond. 1956; FFA RCS Eng. 1965; DA Eng. 1964. Prev: Cons. Anaesth. Glan Hafren NHS Trust.

THOMAS, Gwynallt Watkins (retired) Meadow Cottage, Alpington, Norwich NR14 7NG — MB BS 1960 Lond.; MRCS Eng. LRCP Lond. 1960; FFA RCS Eng. 1968; DA Eng. 1965; DObst RCOG 1962. Prev: Cons. Anaesth. Norwich Health Dist.

THOMAS, Hannah Mari (retired) Ystrad Isa, Denbigh LL16 4RL Tel: 01745 812550 Fax: 01745 813345 Email: gwyn.thomas@ystrad-isa.co.uk — MB BCh 1956 Wales. GP Denbigh. Prev: Med. Ref. Welsh Office.

THOMAS, Hawys Olwen 23 Hammond Way, Penylan, Cardiff CF23 9BB — MB BCh 1993 Wales.

THOMAS, Hayley Rebecca 8 Eardley Road, Heysham, Morecambe LA3 2PH — MB ChB 1997 Manch.

THOMAS, Heather Mary 34 Gillespie Crescent, Edinburgh EH10 4HX — MB ChB 1982 Ed.

THOMAS, Helen Catherine Lisson Grove Medical Centre, 3-5 Lisson Grove, Mutley, Plymouth PL4 7DL Tel: 01752 205555 Fax: 01752 205558; 24 Thorn Park, Mannamead, Plymouth PL3 4TD Tel: 01752 666133 — MB ChB 1986 Birm.; ChB Birm. 1986; DRCOG 1989.

THOMAS, Helen Joan Roycroft, Madden and Thomas, Chelford Surgery, Elmstead Road, Chelford, Macclesfield SK11 9BS Tel: 01625 861316 Fax: 01625 860075 — MB ChB 1989 Liverp.; MRCGP 1993. (Liverpool) Clin. Asst. (Gen. Med.) E. Chesh. Trust.

THOMAS, Helen Joanna 15 Wayland Close, Adel, Leeds LS16 8LT Tel: 0113 267 0388 — MB ChB 1987 Leic.; MRCGP 1992; DCCH 1996; DGM RCP Lond. 1991; DRCOG 1989; DCCH 1997. (Leic.)

THOMAS, Helen Lucy 34 Poplar Avenue, Putnoe, Bedford MK41 8BL Tel: 01234 346551 Email: h.l.thomas@btinternet.com — BM 1990 Soton.; MSc (Med. Anthropol.) Brunel Univ. 1998. Prev: Locum CMO Community Paediat. Richmond Twickenham & Roehampton; Researcher Centre for Social Research & Educat. Bogota Colombia; Grade 8 Dr Dept. of Epidemiol. Colombian Nat. Inst. of Health Bogota Colombia.

THOMAS, Helen Mair 57 Milton Road, London SW14 8JP — MB BS 1986 Lond.; DRCOG 1993. Prev: Trainee GP Lond.; SHO (O & G) Bristol; SHO (A & E) Lond.

THOMAS, Helen Ruth 68 St Guthiac St, Hereford HR1 2EX — MB ChB 1998 Manch. SHO. Hereford Hosp. Prev: PRHO. (Med & Surg.) City Gen Hosp. Stoke-On-Trent.

THOMAS, Hilary Department of Clinical Oncology, Hammersmith Hospital, Du Cane Road, London W12 0NN Tel: 020 8740 3059 Fax: 020 8743 8766 Email: hthomas@rpms.ac.uk — MB BS 1984

Lond.; MA Camb. 1985; MRCP (UK) 1987; FRCR 1991. (Univ. Coll. Hosp.) Sen. Lect. (Clin. Oncol.) Hammersmith Hosp. Lond. Socs: Med. Wom. Federat. Prev: Clin. Research Fell., ICRF; Regist. (Clin. Oncol.) Hammersmith Hosp. Lond.; SHO (Neurol.) Roy. Free Hosp. Lond.

THOMAS, Professor Howard Christopher Department of Medicine, St. Mary's Hospital, London W2 1PG Tel: 020 7886 6454 Fax: 020 7724 9369 Email: h.thomas@ic.ac.uk — MB BS 1969 Newc.; MB BS (Hons.) Newc. 1969; PhD Glas. 1975; BSc (Hons.) Newc. 1966; FRCP Lond. 1979; FRCPS Glas. 1978; FRCPath 1986, M 1981. Prof. Med. Imperial Coll. Sch. Med. St. Mary's Hosp. Lond.; Cons. Phys. & Hepatol. St. Mary's Hosp. Lond. Socs: Fell. Roy. Soc. Med.; Counc. Europ. Assn. Study of Liver.; (Trustee) Brit. Liver Trust. Prev: Prof. Med. Roy. Free Hosp. Med. Sch. Lond.

THOMAS, Howard Glyn North Swindon Practice, Home Ground Surgery, Thames Avenue, Haydon Wick, Swindon SN25 1QQ Tel: 01793 705777 — MB ChB 1972 Ed.; MRCGP 1980.

THOMAS, Mr Howard James Watkins (retired) Station Road Surgery, 46 Station Road, New Barnet, Barnet EN5 1QH Tel: 020 8441 4425 Fax: 020 8441 4957 — MB BS 1965 Lond.; FRCS Eng. 1974; FRCS Ed. 1971; MRCS Eng. LRCP Lond. 1964. Prev: Resid. Surg. Off. Barnet Gen. Hosp.

THOMAS, Hugh Alistair Barton, Horn Lane, Plymstock, Plymouth PL9 9BR Tel: 01752 407129; Bridge Park Cottage, 117 Goutsford, Ermington, Ivybridge PL21 0NY Tel: 01548 830192 — MB BS 1975 Lond.; MRCS Eng. LRCP Lond. 1975. GP Plymstock, Devon.

THOMAS, Hugh Falcon College Road Surgery, 6 Colleger Road, Eastbourne BN1 4HY Tel: 01323 735044; Tel: 01323 411956 — MB ChB 1986 Leic.; MSc Aston 1978; BSc (Hons.) (Environm. Sci.) Salford 1973; MFPHM RCP (UK) 1994; Cert. Av. Med. 1988. Gen. Practitioner. Prev: Epidemiologist MRC Epidemiol. Unit Llandough Hosp. Penarth; Sen. Regist. (Pub. Health Med.) Wessex RHA; Regist. (Community Med.) Canterbury & Thanet HA.

THOMAS, Mr Hugh James McKim 9 Lucknow Avenue, Mapperley Park, Nottingham NG3 5AZ Tel: 0115 960 7823; 34 Regent Street, Nottingham NG1 5BT Tel: 0115 956 1304 Fax: 0115 956 1314 — MB BCh Wales 1955; FRCS Eng. 1963. (Cardiff) Cons. Orthop. Surg. Univ. Hosp. Nottm. & Nottm. City Hosp. Socs: Fell. Brit. Orthop. Assn.; Brit. Soc. Childr. Orthop. Surg.; Brit. Cervical Spine Soc. Prev: Lect. in Orthop. Surg. Univ. & Roy. Infirm. Manch.; Hon. Cons. Orthop. Surg. Robt. Jones & Agnes Hunt Hosp. OsW.ry; Orthop. Regist. Roy. Nat. Orthop. Hosp. Lond.

THOMAS, Hugh Williams (retired) 31 Fairway, Trentham, Stoke-on-Trent ST4 8AS Tel: 01782 657539 — MB ChB 1949 Glas.; FRCGP 1978, M 1960.

THOMAS, Huw Brian Watcyn TFL, 11 Lutton Pl, Edinburgh EH8 9PD — MB ChB 1997 Ed.

THOMAS, Huw Daniel 50 Victoria Road, Penarth CF64 3HZ — MB BCh 1998 Wales.

THOMAS, Huw Gerwyn Irnham Lodge Surgery, Townsend Road, Minehead TA24 5RG Tel: 01643 703289 Fax: 01643 707921; Woodcombe Farm House, Woodcombe, Minehead TA24 8SB — MB BCh 1983 Wales; MRCGP 1990; DRCOG 1989.

THOMAS, Huw Glyn Merrywood, Deepdene Wood, Dorking RH5 4BE — MB BS 1996 Lond.

THOMAS, Huw Jeremy Wyndham Department of Gastroenterology, St. Mary's Hospital, Praed St., London W2 1NY Tel: 020 7886 1208 Fax: 020 7886 1138; 66 Harley Street, London W1N 1AE Tel: 020 7631 0966 Fax: 020 7631 5341 — MB BS 1982 Lond.; PhD Lond. 1991; MA Camb. 1982; FRCP (1997), MRCP (1985). (Camb. & Lond. Hosp.) Cons. Phys. & Gastroenterol. St. Mary's Hosp. Lond.; Hon. Cons. (Phys. & Gastroenterol.) King Edwd. VII Hosp. Lond.; Sen. Lect. & Hon. Cons. Phys. ICRF Colorectal Unit St. Mark's Hosp. Harrow.

THOMAS, Huw Morgan Department of General Paediatrics, Southmead Hospital, Westbury-on-Trym, Bristol BS10 5NB Tel: 0117 959 5582 Fax: 0117 959 5282 Email: Thomas_H@southmead.swest.nhs.uk — MB BS 1983 Lond.; BSc Lond. 1980; MRCP (UK) 1989; FRCPCH 1997. (Univ. Coll. Hosp. Lond.) Cons. Paediat. S.mead Hosp. Bristol; Cons. Respirat. Paediat.Bristol Roy. Hosp. for Childr. Socs: Roy. Coll. of Paediat. and Child Health; Brit. Thoracic Soc. Prev: Sen. Regist. (Paediat.) Roy. Hosp. for Sick. Childr. Bristol.

THOMAS, Mr Huw Owen 31 Rodney Street, Liverpool L1 9EH Tel: 0151 709 8522; Pinwydden, 18 Pine Walks, Prenton, Prenton CH42 8NE Tel: 0151 608 3909 Fax: 01515132494 Email: verstapp@aol.com — MB BCh 1966 Wales; MChOrth Liverp. 1973; FRCS Eng. 1972; FRCS Ed. 1971; ECFMG Cert 1966. Medico-Legal Cons. Socs: Low Friction Soc.; Med. Appeal Tribunal; Liverp. Med. Inst. Prev: Late Capt. TAVR; Sen. Cons. Orthop. Surg. Arrowe Pk., Clatterbridge Hosps. Wirral & BUPA Murrayfield Hosp. Wirral; Sen. Regist. (Orthop.) Liverp. Roy. Infirm. & Wrightington Hosp. Appley Bridge.

THOMAS, Hywel Gwyn X Ray Department, Musgrave Park Hospital, Taunton TA1 5DA Tel: 01823 342347; 5 Gatchell Meadow, Trull, Taunton TA3 7HY Tel: 01823 330148 Fax: 01823 343907 — MB ChB 1983 Birm.; MRCP (UK) 1987; FRCR 1990. (Birmingham) Cons. Diag. Radiol. MusGr. Pk. Hosp. Taunton. Socs: Assoc. Mem. Med. Defence Union; Inst. Radiol.; Brit. Soc. Interven. Radiol. Prev: Sen. Regist. & Regist. (Diag. Radiol.) John Radcliffe Hosp. Oxf.; SHO (Neurosurg.) Walsgrave Hosp. Coventry.

THOMAS, Hywel Lloyd Profiad Ltd., 20-24 Vachel Road, Reading RG1 1NY Tel: 0118 951 0707 Fax: 0118 951 0606 Email: h.thomas@profiad.com; Goodwood, Boulston, Haverfordwest SA62 4AG Tel: 01437 768794 Fax: 01437 763517 — MB BS 1981 Lond.; MRCGP 1985; DCH RCP Lond. 1987; DRCOG 1984. (St. Bart.) Managing Dir. Profiad Ltd.; Comp. Sec. Rifleman Research Ltd. Prev: GP HaverfordW.

THOMAS, Ian McDougall Llynyfran Surgery, Llynyfran Road, Llandysul SA44 4JX Tel: 01559 363306 Fax: 01559 362896; Glancwerchyr, Maesllyn, Llandysul SA44 5LD Tel: 01239 851505 — MB BCh 1976 Wales; DRCOG 1980. (Cardiff)

THOMAS, Illtyd Richard John 43 New Road, Cockett, Swansea SA2 0GA — MB BChir 1992 Camb.; BA (Hons.) 1989, MB BChir Camb. 1992.

THOMAS, Mr Iowerth Huw 17 Holmfield Road, Leicester LE2 1SD — MD 1983 Newc.; MB BS 1974; FRCS Ed. 1980.

THOMAS, Ivor Gareth Queen Margaret Hospital, Whitefield Road, Dunfermline KY12 0SU Tel: 01383 623623 Fax: 01383 627044; 50 The Muirs, Kinross KY13 8AU — MB ChB Ed. 1984; MRCPsych 1989. Cons. Old Age Psychiat. Fife HB Dunfermline. Prev: Sen. Regist. (Psychiat.) N. Region; Regist. (Psychiat.) Aberd.

THOMAS, Iwan Richard, TD Crinnis House, Les Bois, Layer de la Haye, Colchester CO2 0EX Tel: 01206 738273 Email: ir.thomas@virgin.net — MB BS Lond. 1965; MSc Surrey 1971; AFOM RCP Lond. 1995. (Middlx.) Indep. p/t. Occupat. Phys. Socs: Fell. Roy. Soc. Med.; Soc. Occupat. Med. Prev: Area.Med.Advis,Post Office EHS; RMO 22nd Special Air Serv. Regt.; Ho. Surg. & Ho. Phys. St. And. Hosp. Billericay.

THOMAS, Jacob Department of Psychiatry, Pilgrim Hospital, Sibsey Road, Boston PE21 9QS Tel: 01205 364801 Ext: 3506; Karimparampil, Tiruvalla 5, PO Kerala State, India — MB BS 1973 Mysore; BSc (Chem.) Kerala 1963; FRCPsych 1993, M 1978; Dip. Health Serv. Managem. York 1992; DPM Eng. 1977. (Kasturba Med. Coll. Mangalore) Cons. Psychiat. Pilgrim Hosp. Boston. Prev: Sen. Regist. St. Bart. & N. Middlx. Hosps. Lond. & Goodamyes Hosp. Ilford.

THOMAS, Jacqueline Quinton Goodmayes Hospital, Barley Lane, Ilford IG3 8XJ Tel: 020 8983 8000 — MB BS 1961 Lond.; DA Eng. 1963. (Char. Cross) Clin. Asst. (Psychiat.) Goodmayes Hosp. Ilford. Prev: Clin. Asst. (Anaesth.) Whittington Hosp. & Friern Hosp. Lond.; Regist. (Anaesth.) Whittington Hosp. Lond.

THOMAS, James Alexander 53 Main Street, Embsay, Skipton BD23 6RD — MB BS 1994 Lond.

THOMAS, Mr James Andrew 70 St Ambrose Road, Heath, Cardiff CF14 4BH Tel: 029 2061 2919 — MB BCh 1987 Wales; FRCS Eng. 1992. Cons. (Urol.) Bridgend & Dist. NHS Trust. Socs: Assoc. Mem. BAUS; BMA; MDU. Prev: Specialist Regist. (Urol.) S Wales Train. Scheme; Regist. Rotat. (Surg.) Cardiff.

THOMAS, James Clannie 19 Somersham Road, Bexleyheath DA7 4SA — MB BCh BAO 1971 NUI.

THOMAS, Mr James Nigel ENT Department, King's College Hospital, Denmark Hill, London SE5 9RS Tel: 020 7346 5338 Fax: 020 7346 5337; ENT Department, Bromley Health Trust, Farnborough Hospital, Farnborough Common, Orpington BR6 8ND Tel: 01689 814285 — BM BCh Oxf. 1968; MA Oxf. 1968; FRCS Eng. 1974. Cons. Surg. ENT Dept. King's Coll. Hosp. Lond. Prev:

THOMAS

Cons. Surg. ENT Dept. Groote Schuur Hosp. Capetown; 1st Asst. ENT Dept. Radcliffe Infirm. Oxf.

THOMAS, James Picton Douglas (retired) Ty Cornel, Rudry, Caerphilly CF83 3DD Tel: 01222 754765 — MD 1956 Camb.; BA Camb. 1944, MD 1956, MB BChir 1948; FRCP Lond. 1970, M 1953. Hon. Cons. Phys. Univ. Hosp. Wales Cardiff. Prev: Sen. Lect. (Med.) Welsh Nat. Sch. Med.

THOMAS, James Roger Leighton 28 Maresfield Gardens, London NW3 5SX Tel: 020 7435 4737 Fax: 020 7433 1334 — MB BS 1966 Lond.; MRCS Eng. LRCP Lond. 1965; DObst RCOG 1968. (St. Thos.) Med. Adviser Ernst & Young OcciDent. Internat. Oil Inc., Morgan Crucible Company Ltd; Internat. Maritime Organisation, Lond. Docklands Developm. Corp. & Solaglas Ltd; Examg. Phys. United Nations Lond. Socs: Assoc. Fac. Occupat. Med. Prev: Ho. Surg. St. Thos. Hosp. Lond.; Ho. Phys. Lewisham Hosp. & P.ss Louise Kensington Hosp. Childr. Lond.

THOMAS, James Stephen Idris Bryn-Villa, Gorslas, Llanelli SA14 7LP — MB BS 1981 Lond.

THOMAS, Jane Elizabeth Goodwood, Boulston, Haverfordwest SA62 4AG Tel: 01437 763517 — MB ChB 1982 Bristol; DA (UK) 1988; DCH RCP Lond. 1987.

THOMAS, Jane Margaret 12 Ardwick Road, London NW2 2BX — MB ChB 1987 Liverp.

THOMAS, Jane Mary 84 Wyresdale Road, Lancaster LA1 3DY Tel: 01524 382682; 34 Bury Old Road, Whitefield, Manchester M45 6TF — MB ChB 1987 Manch. Primary Health Care Adviser for Develop. Countries Working with Non-Govt.al Aid Organisations. Socs; Fell. Roy. Soc. of Trop. Med. & Hyg.

THOMAS, Janet Department of Clinical Haematology, Royal United Hospital, Combe Park, Bath BA1 3NG; 15 Park Hill, Shirehampton, Bristol BS11 0UH — MB BS 1966 Lond.; MRCS Eng. LRCP Lond. 1966; FRCPath 1972. (Roy. Free) Assoc. Specialist (Haemat.) Roy. United Hosp. Bath. Prev: Sen. Regist. (Haemat.) Kingston Hosp. Kingston-upon-Thames & St. Thos.Hosp. Lond.

THOMAS, Janet Rhondda NHS Trust, Albert Road, Pontypridd CF37 1LA Tel: 01443443789 Fax: 01443 443791; Bedford Falls, 24 Danygraig Drive, Talbot Green, Pontyclun CF72 8AQ Tel: 01443 223385 Fax: 01443 223385 — MB BCh 1969 Wales; MFFP 1993. (Cardiff) Cons. (Family Plann. & Reproduct. Health Care); Progr. Co-ordinator for Gwent; Treas. Welsh Family Plann. Doctors Gp.; Cervical Screening Wales. Socs: Treas. Welsh Family Plann. Doctors Gp.; Fac. Community Health; Fac. Fam. Plann. Prev: GP Pontyclun & Kenilworth; SHO (O & G) Walsgrave Hosp. Coventry; Ho. Off. (Paediat.) Gulson Rd. Hosp. Coventry.

THOMAS, Janet Beynon Ty Maen Cottage, South Cornelly, Bridgend CF33 4RE Tel: 01656 746404 — MB BS Lond. 1965; MRCS Eng. LRCP Lond. 1965; DTM & H RCP Lond. 1986.

THOMAS, Janet Mary 92 Ulleswater Road, Southgate, London N14 7BT — MB ChB 1978 Bristol; DCH Eng. 1982; DRCOG 1980.

THOMAS, Jean Alero Department of Infectious & Tropical Diseases, London School of Hygiene & Tropical Medicine, Keppel St., London WC1E 7HT Tel: 020 7927 2289 Fax: 020 7927 2303 Email: a.thomas@lshtm.ac.uk — MSc Oxf. 1976; MB BS Lond. 1970; MRCPath 1991. (St Mary's Hospital London) Sen. Clin. Lect.

THOMAS, Jeffery Llewellyn Edward Watson (retired) Rectory Lodge, Cosheston, Pembroke Dock SA72 4UJ — MB BS 1958 Lond.; MRCS Eng. LRCP Lond. 1958; FFA RCS Eng. 1963; DA Eng. 1962, DTM & H 1961. Prev: Cons. Anaesth. W. Glam. HA.

THOMAS, Jenkyn Powell 60 Cemetery Road, Porth CF39 0BL — MB BS 1955 Lond.

THOMAS, Jennifer Kingswood Villa, Mynyddygarreg, Kidwelly SA17 4RA — MB BCh 1993 Wales.

THOMAS, Jennifer Anne Tudor Lea, Sutton Close, Cookham, Maidenhead SL6 9QU Tel: 01628 524859 — MB BS 1996 Lond. (Charing Cross and Westminster Medical School) SHO (Med.) Soton. Gen. Hosp.

THOMAS, Jeremy Gwynfryn 23/3 Parkside Terrace, St. Leonards, Edinburgh EH16 5XW Tel: 0131 662 0810 — MB ChB 1988 Ed.; FRCA 1994. Career Regist. (Anaesth.) Roy. Infirm. Edin.

THOMAS, Jeremy Simon 14 Cleeve Lawns, Bristol BS16 6HJ — MB BCh 1992 Wales.

THOMAS, Jeremy St John Department of Histopath, Western General Hospital NHS Trust, Crewe Road, Edinburgh EH4 2XU Tel: 0131 537 1961 Fax: 0131 537 1013 Email: jeremy.thomas@ed.ac.uk — MB BS 1978 Lond.; FRCPath 1997; MA Oxf. 1980, BA 1975; FRCP Glas. 1994; FRCP Ed. 1992; MRCP (UK) 1981; MRCS Eng. LRCP Lond. 1978; MRCPath 1986; T(Path) 1991. (St. Thos.) Cons. Histopath. & Cytol. W. Gen. Hosp. Edin. Socs: Internat. Acad. Pathol. (Brit. Div.); Path. Soc. Prev: Sen. Regist. (Path.) W.. Infirm. Glas.; SHO (Gen. Med.) W.. Infirm. Glas.; Ho. Surg. St. Thos. Hosp. Lond.

THOMAS, Joan (retired) 76 Wimmerfield Avenue, Killay, Swansea SA2 7DA — MB BCh 1944 Wales; BSc, MB BCh Wales 1944; DObst RCOG 1946. Prev: GP Swansea.

THOMAS, Joan Margaret 1 The Courtway, Bone Mill Lane, Enborne, Newbury RG20 0EU — MB BS 1973 Lond.; MRCP (UK) 1977. (Univ. Coll. Hosp.) Assoc. Specialist (Med.) Battle Hosp. Reading.

THOMAS, Joanna Clare Plas Ffordd Ddwr, Llandyrnog, Denbigh LL16 4ET — MB ChB 1998 Liverp.

THOMAS, John Glynneath Surgery, Bodfeddyg, 102 High Street, Glynneath, Neath SA11 5AL Tel: 01639 722431 — MB BCh 1963 Wales. (Cardiff) Prev: SHO (Gen. Med.) St. David's Hosp. Cardiff; Regist. (Chest & Gen. Med.) Llangwyfan Hosp.; SHO (O & G) H. M. Stanley Hosp. St. Asaph.

THOMAS, Mr John Alun Beynon West Hill, 26 Fairwater Road, Llandaff, Cardiff CF5 2LE Tel: 029 2056 2763 — MB BCh 1937 Wales; BSc, MB BCh Wales 1937; FRCS (Orl.) Eng. 1949; DLO Eng. 1943. (Cardiff) Socs: (Ex-Pres.) S. W. Otolaryngol. Soc. Prev: Cons. Otol. MRC Inst. Hearing Research (Welsh Sect.) Univ. Hosp. Wales; Fell. Roy. Soc. Med. (Ex-Pres. Sect. Laryngol.); Cons. ENT Surg. Univ. Hosp. Wales Cardiff.

THOMAS, John Berian (retired) Tan-y-Castell, Llanmill, Narberth SA67 8UE Tel: 01834 860435 — MRCS Eng. LRCP Lond. 1943. Cons. Accid. Surg. Pembroke Co. War Memor. Hosp. HaverfordW.. Prev: Clin. Asst. Orthop. Surg. PeterBoro. & Dist. Memor. Hosp.

THOMAS, John Berwyn (retired) The Cottage, Buttons Farm, Wadhurst TN5 6NW Tel: 01892 782848 — MB BCh 1955 Wales; FFA RCS Eng. 1965; DA Eng. 1961. Cons. Anaesth. Tunbridge Wells Health Dist. Prev: Sen. Regist. W.m. & Brompton Hosps. Lond.

THOMAS, John Bruce Trevelyan 2 Clarendon Road, Bournemouth BH4 8AH Tel: 01202 764136; Lilliput House, Alington Road, Parkstone, Poole BH14 8LX Tel: 01202 707478 — MRCS Eng. LRCP Lond. 1942; MA Camb. 1942; DOMS Eng. 1948. (Camb. & Cardiff) Ophth. Med. Ref. Civil Serv. Commiss. Socs: Ophth. Soc. U.K. & S. Ophth. Soc. Prev: Clin. Asst. &outpat. Off. Moorfields Eye Hosp.; Ophth. Clin. Asst. Swansea Gen. & Eye Hosp.; Capt. RAMC, Graded Surg.

THOMAS, John Delwyn (retired) 33 Edyvean Close, Bilton, Rugby CV22 6LD Tel: 01788 817236 — MB BCh Wales 1949; BSc Wales 1945.

THOMAS, John Derek, OBE Corbett House, Stroud GL5 2HP Tel: 01453 759793 — MB BS 1952 Lond.; MRCS Eng. LRCP Lond. 1950; MFOM RCP Lond. 1978; DIH Soc. Apoth. Lond. 1960; Specialist Accredit. (Occupat. Med.) RCP Lond 1978. (St. Thos.) Indep. Cons. Occupat. Med. Glos.; Co. Commr. (Pool) St. John Ambul. Brig. Socs: Soc. Occupat. Med. Prev: Sen. Med. Off. Brit. Steel Corp.; Capt. RAMC; Ho. Phys. & Ho. Surg. (Orthop.) St. Thos. Hosp. Lond.

THOMAS, John Geraint Penarth Health Centre, Stanwell Road, Penarth CF64 3XE Tel: 029 2070 0911 — MB BCh 1971 Wales; DObst RCOG 1974.

THOMAS, John Gethin Marsham Street Surgery, 1 Marsham Street, Maidstone ME14 1EW Tel: 01622 752615/756129 — MB BS 1977 Lond.; DRCOG 1981.

THOMAS, John Glyn 12 Beresford Road, Birkenhead CH43 1XG — MB BS 1968 Liverp.; MRCS Eng. LRCP Lond. 1967.

THOMAS, John Gwyn (retired) Ystrad Isa, Denbigh LL16 4RL Tel: 01745 812550 Fax: 01745 813345 Email: gwyn.thomas@ystrad-isa.demon.co.uk — MB BCh 1956 Wales; BSc Wales 1952; FRCGP 1974, M 1965; DCH Eng. 1961; DObst RCOG 1960. Approved Med. Off. Ment. Health Act EMP Wales. Prev: Mem. Advis. Body (Gen. Pract.) Welsh Med. Comm.

THOMAS, John Hirwain (retired) 134 Victoria Avenue, Porthcawl CF36 3HA — MRCS Eng. LRCP Lond. 1940; FRCP Lond. 1975, M 1950; DCH Eng. 1950. Prev: Cons. Phys. Geriat. Bridgend Gen. Hosp. & Morgannwg Ment. Hosps.

THOMAS, John Lumley (retired) 5 Meridian Way, Newcastle upon Tyne NE7 7RU Tel: 0191 266 2504 — MB BS 1955 Durh.; DPH Newc. 1968. Prev: GP Wallsend.

THOMAS, John Montague (retired) Eirianell, Springfield Road, Carmarthen SA31 1EA Tel: 01267 237580 — MRCS Eng. LRCP Lond. 1947. Prev: Ho. Surg. Neurosurg. Dept. & Receiv. Room Off. Lond. Hosp.

THOMAS, John Norman (retired) 1 Beechwood Avenue, Neath SA11 3TD Tel: 01639 644471 — MRCS Eng. LRCP Lond. 1937. Asst. Surg. W. Glam. St. J; Regional Med. Adviser Manor Ho. Hosp. Lond. Prev: Mem. Glam. Local Med. Comm.

THOMAS, John Samuel Bryn-Coed, 114 Sketty Road, Swansea SA2 0JX Tel: 01792 208626; Arosfa, Llangoedmôr, Cardigan SA43 2LT — MB BCh Wales 1966; FFA RCS Eng. 1971; DA Eng. 1971; DObst RCOG 1969. (Welsh National School of Medicine) Cons. Anaesth. W. Glam. HA Swansea. Socs: BMA & Assn. of Anaesth. Gt. Brit. & Irel.; BMA. Prev: Ho. Phys. & Ho. Surg. Morriston Hosp. Swansea; SHO (Anaesth.) Nuffield Dept. Anaesth. Radcliffe Infirm. Oxf.; Sen. Regist. (Anaesth.) Univ. Hosp. of Wales Cardiff.

THOMAS, Jonathan Mark Greenbank Road Surgery, 29 Greenbank Road, Liverpool L18 1HG Tel: 0151 733 3224 Fax: 0151 734 5147; 4 Penhale Close, Aigburth, Liverpool L17 5BT Tel: 0151 726 0915 — MB ChB 1987 Liverp. (Liverp.)

THOMAS, Jonathan Martin 47 Old Road, Llanelli SA15 3HR — MB ChB 1993 Manch.

THOMAS, Jose Caerphilly District Miners Hospital, St. Martin's Road, Caerphilly CF83 2WW Tel: 029 2080 7268 Fax: 029 2080 7269; 13 Millwood, Lisvane, Cardiff CF14 0TL Tel: 029 2075 6720 Fax: 01222 764288 Email: jose.thomas@virgin.net — MB BS 1981 Kerala; MD Inst. Med. Sci. India 1981; MRCP (UK) 1987. Cons. Phys. (Thoracic Med.) Caerphilly Dist. Miner's Hosp.; Hon. Cons. Phys. Llandough Hosp. Penarth. Socs: Brit. Thorac. Soc.; Welsh Thoracic Soc.; Soc. Phys. in Wales. Prev: Regist. (Thoracic Med.) Llandough Hosp. S. Glam. HA; Lect. Univ. Wales Coll. Med.

THOMAS, Joseph Kuzhiamplaril 34 Wood Lane, Falmouth TR11 4RF Tel: 01326 312091; 11 St Antony way, Falmouth TR11 4EG Tel: 01326 318795 — MB BS 1971 Karnatak. (Kasturba Med. Coll.)

THOMAS, Mr Joseph Meirion The Lister Hospital, Chelsea Bridge Road, London SW1W 8RH Tel: 020 7631 4498 Fax: 020 7259 9552 — MB BS 1969 Lond.; MS Lond. 1979; FRCS Eng. 1975; FRCP 1998. (wESTM.) Cons. Surg. Oncol. Roy. Marsden Hosp. Lond. & Chelsea & W.m. Hosp. Lond. Prev: Resid. Surgic. Off. St. Mark's Hosp. Lond.; Sen. Regist. (Surg.) St. Geo. Hosp. St. Jas. Hosp. Lond. & Roy. Marsden Hosp. Sutton.

THOMAS, Joyce Lilian, OBE (retired) 72 East Dulwich Grove, Dulwich, London SE22 8PS — MD Liverp. 1978, MB ChB 1948; FFPHM RCP (UK) 1988; FFCM 1982, M 1978; DCH Eng. 1970. Hon. Cons. Pub. Health Med. W. Glam. DHA; Sen. Lect. Sch. Postgrad. Studies Med. & Health Care Swansea.

THOMAS, Judith Anne The Deepings Practice, Godsey Lane, Market Deeping, Peterborough PE6 8DD Tel: 01778 579000 Fax: 01778 579009; 194 Eastgate, Deeping St. Jas., Peterborough PE6 8RD Tel: 01778 346098 — MB ChB 1982 Leic.; MRCGP 1986; DRCOG 1986.

THOMAS, Judith Clatterbridge Hospital, Bebington CH63 4JY Tel: 0151 334 4000; Pinwydden, 18 Pine Walks, Prenton, Birkenhead CH42 8NE Tel: 0151 608 3909 Fax: 0151 513 2494 Email: verstapp@aol.com — MB ChB 1975 Liverp.; BA 2001 (Hons) Open; Cert Family Planning 1986 JCC; BSc (Hons.) Liverp. 1972, MB ChB 1975. (Liverpool) p/t Clin. Asst. (Diag. Ultrasound) Clatterbridge Hosp., Bebington & Arrowe Pk. Hosp. Upton Wirral. Prev: SHO (Med.) & Ho. Off. BRd.green Hosp. Liverp.; Sessional Screening BUPA Murrayfield Med. Centre.

THOMAS, Judith Barbara Department of Public Health Medicine, Sunderland Health Authority, The Childrens Centre, Durham Road, Sunderland Tel: 0191 565 6256; 18 Berwick Chase, Peterlee SR8 1NQ — MB BChir 1978 Camb.; MSc Newc. 1989; MA Camb. 1978; MFPHM RCP (UK) 1990. Dir. (Pub. Health) Sunderland Health Auth.

THOMAS, Judith Mary Longwater Lane Medical Centre, Longwater Lane, Old Costessey, Norwich NR8 5AH Tel: 01603 742021 Fax: 01603 740271; Talisker, Tuttles Lane W., Wymondham NR18 0DZ Tel: 01953 606532 — MB BS 1974 Newc. (Newcastle-upon-Tyne) GP Princip.; Dep. Police Surg. Norf. Constab.; Clin. Med. Off. Well Wom. Clinic Norwich.

THOMAS, Julia Elizabeth Trevithick Surgery, Basset Road, Camborne TR14 8TT Tel: 01209 716721 Fax: 01209 612488 — MB BS 1994 Lond.

THOMAS, Julia Susanne 12 Dalebury Road, London SW17 7HH Tel: 020 8682 9742 — MB ChB 1990 Manch. (Manchester) Prev: Trainee GP/SHO Ealing Hosp. VTS.

THOMAS, Julian Edward Institute of Child Health, Royal Victoria Infirmary, Queen Victoria Road, Newcastle upon Tyne NE1 4LP Tel: 0191 202 3033 Fax: 0191 202 3022 Email: j.e.thomas@ncl.ac.uk — MB BS 1982 Newc.; MRCP (UK) 1985; MD 1998 Newcastle. Ann Coleman Sen. Lect. in Paediatric Gastroenterol. and Nutrit., Univ. of Newc. Prev: Clin. Research Fell. Dunn Nutrit. Laborat. Camb.

THOMAS, Julie Greenmount, Bradford Road, Sherborne DT9 6BP Tel: 01935 813977 — MB BS 1998 Lond.; MB BS Lond 1998. PRHO. (Gen Surg.) Colchester Gen Hosp.) Colchester. Essex. Prev: PRHO. (Med.) Dorset Co. Hosp. Dorchester.

THOMAS, June Margaret Winslade, Lower Priory, Milford Haven SA73 3UB — MB BS 1981 Lond.; MRCS Eng. LRCP Lond. 1981; DRCOG 1983.

THOMAS, Kannankara Mathew Harraton Surgery, 3 Swiss Cottages, Vigo Lane, Harraton, Washington NE38 9AB Tel: 0191 416 1641 — MB BS 1974 Kerala. (Kerala) GP Washington Tyne & Wear.

THOMAS, Karen Elizabeth 10 Sowbury Park, Chieveley, Newbury RG20 8TZ — MB BS 1986 Lond.

THOMAS, Karen Elizabeth Copsen, Knoll Road, Frith Hill, Godalming GU7 2EL Email: karenthomas5@yahoo.com — BM BCh 1990 Oxf.; MA Camb. 1991, B 1987; MRCP (UK) 1993. Cons. Radiologist, Hosp. for sick Childr., Toronto, Ontario. Prev: Cons. Radiologist, St Mary's Hosp. and Gt. Ormond St. Hosp., Lond.

THOMAS, Karen Jane Dunorlan Medical Group, 64 Pembury Road, Tonbridge TN9 2JG Tel: 01732 352907 Fax: 01732 367408; Rosenlaui, 3 Higham Gardens, Tonbridge TN10 4HZ — MB BS 1985 Lond.; DFFP 1994; DRCOG 1989. (St. Thos.) Prev: Trainee GP Redhill VTS.

THOMAS, Katherine Eleanor 53 Main Street, Embsay, Skipton BD23 6RD — MB BS 1994 Lond.

THOMAS, Kathleen Anne The Laser Centre, Frenchay Hospital, Frenchay, Bristol BS16 1LE Tel: 0117 975 3807; 7 Collingwood Road, Redland, Bristol BS6 6PB — MB ChB 1983 Bristol; MRCGP 1989; DRCOG 1987. Staff Grade, Laser Centre, Frenchay Hosp., Bristol. Prev: Gen. Pract., Asst., Bristol.

THOMAS, Kathleen Mary (retired) 18 Kings Avenue, Woodford Green IG8 0JA — MB BS 1963 Queensland; MRCPath 1972. Cons. Histopath. Whipps Cross Hosp. Lond.

THOMAS, Kathleen Mary (retired) Sails, West St, Seaview PO34 5ER Tel: 01983 612679 — MB BCh BAO 1947 Dub.; BA Dub. 1947; DO Eng. 1961. Prev: Med. Off. Oji River Settlem. Nigeria Leprosy Serv.

THOMAS, Kathrin Jane Margaret Thompson Medical Centre, 105 East Millwood Road, Speke, Liverpool L24 6TH Tel: 0151 425 3331 Fax: 0151 425 2272 — MB ChB 1986 Leic.; MRCGP 1994; DRCOG 1994.

THOMAS, Kathryn Mary Jane St. Thomas Medical Group, Cowick St., Exeter EX4 1HJ Tel: 01392 676606 Fax: 01392 264424 Email: k.m.thomas@exeter.ac.uk; 14 Bagshot Avenue, Exeter EX2 4RN — MB BS 1981 Lond.; MRCGP 1986; DRCOG 1985; DA Eng. 1984. (Royal Free Hospital School of Medicine, London) GP St Thomas Med. Gp.; Princip. Med. Off. Univ. Exeter. Prev: Trainee GP Tiverton VTS; SHO (Paediat. & Anaesth.) Roy. Devon & Exeter Hosp.

THOMAS, Kathryn Patricia Abbotswood Medical Centre, Defford Road, Pershore WR10 1HZ Tel: 01386 552424 — MB ChB 1983 Leeds; DCH 1986 RCP, Lond; DRCOG 1986; MRCGP 1987; DFFP 1986. (Leeds University Medical School) p/t GP.

THOMAS, Kathryn Samantha 18 The Whimbrels, Rest Bay, Porthcawl CF36 3TR — MB BS 1989 Lond.

THOMAS, Kay 27 Kenyon Street, London SW6 6JZ — MB BS 1994 Lond.

THOMAS, Keith Microbiology Department, Chesterfield & North Derbyshire Royal Hospital, Calow, Chesterfield S44 5BL Tel: 01246

THOMAS

552270; 15 Elm Tree Drive, Wingerworth, Chesterfield S42 6QD Tel: 01246 200199 — MB BCh 1974 Wales; FRCPath 1993, M 1981. Cons. Microbiol. Roy. Hosp. Chesterfield.

THOMAS, Keith Heathbridge House, The Old Bridge, Kenfig Hill, Bridgend CF33 6BY Tel: 01656 740359 Fax: 01656 745400; Gwalia House, 4 Oaklands Drive, Bridgend CF31 4SH Tel: 01656 668433 — MRCS Eng. LRCP Lond. 1955. (Lond. Hosp.) Prev: Ho. Surg. Orthop. & Accid. Dept. Lond. Hosp.; Ho. Phys. Anaesth. Div. RAF Hosp. Ely; JHMO Paediat. & Obst. Dept. N.ampton Gen. Hosp.

THOMAS, Keith David 30 Howecroft Croft, Eastmead Lane, Bristol BS9 1HJ — BM BCh 1993 Oxf.

THOMAS, Keith Lewis Salop House Surgery, Salop House, Chapel Street, Tregaron SY23 6HA Tel: 01974 298218 Fax: 01974 298207; Rhandir, Lampeter Road, Tregaron SY25 6HG — MB BS 1983 Lond.; DRCOG 1987; DCH RCP Lond. 1986; DGM RCP Lond. 1985; MRCGP 1987. Clin. Asst. Geriat. Med. Dyfed.

THOMAS, Mr Kelvin Einstein Brook Cottage, Rodsley, nr. Brailsford, Ashbourne DE6 3AL Tel: 01335 330471 Email: k.e.t@usa.net — MB BS Lond. 1955; BA Johns Hopkins Univ. 1950; FRCS Eng. 1962; DLO Eng. 1960. (Guy's) Emerit. Cons. ENT Surg. Univ. Hosp. Nottm. Socs: Fell. Roy. Soc. Med. (Mem. Sect. Otol. & Laryngol.); Fell. Roy. Soc. Arts; BMA & Med. Art Soc. Prev: Sen. Regist. (ENT) & Asst. Ho. Phys. & Ho. Surg. Guy's Hosp. Lond.; Sen. Regist. (ENT) Addenbrooke's Hosp. Camb.

THOMAS, Kenneth Bruce (retired) 4 Glen Eyre Road, Southampton SO16 3FZ Tel: 01703 586701 — MRCS Eng. LRCP Lond. 1943; MD Liverp. 1972, MB ChB 1943. Prev: GP Waterlooville.

THOMAS, Keri Vivien Chapelthorpe Surgery, Hall Lane, Chapelthorpe, Wakefield WF4 3JE Tel: 01924 255166 Fax: 01924 257653; The Rectory, 2 Westgate, Almondbury, Huddersfield HD5 8XE Tel: 01484 421753 Fax: 01484 421753 — MB BS 1980 Lond.; MRCGP 1985; Dip. Palliat. Med. Wales 1993; DRCOG 1983; Cert. Family Plann. JCC 1983. GP Wakefield; Macmillan GP Facilitator in Cancer & Palliat. Care for Calderdale & Kirklees HA; Staff Grade Kirkwood Hospice Huddersfield. Socs: RCGP; Assn. Palliat. Med.; Brit. Med. Acupunc. Assoc. Prev: Clin. Asst. (Palliat. Med.) Kirkwood Hospice Huddersfield; GP Dewsbury & Cleckheaton; SHO (Palliat. Med.) Leeds.

THOMAS, Kerry Wynn Bron-y-Garn Surgery, Station St., Maesteg CF34 9AL Tel: 01656 733262; Sisial-y-Nant, 18B Yr-Ysfa, Maesteg CF34 9AG — MB BCh 1983 Wales.

THOMAS, Kevin 38 Dan-y-Coed, Aberystwyth SY23 2HD — MB ChB 1991 Liverp.

THOMAS, Mr Kevin James 4 Sybil Street, Clydach, Swansea SA6 5EU — MB BS 1985 Lond.; FRCS Ed. 1993. (St. Bart. Hosp. Lond.) Sen. Regist. (Urol.) Univ. Hosp. Wales.

THOMAS, Kevin Ross Pontcae Surgery, Dynevor Street, Georgetown, Merthyr Tydfil CF48 1YE Tel: 01685 723931 Fax: 01685 377048; 7 Lon y Brynnau, Brynna Farm, Cwmdare, Aberdare CF44 8PU — MB ChB 1989 Manch.; MB ChB (Hons.) Manch. 1989; MRCGP 1993; DRCOG 1993; Dip. IMC RCS Ed. 1992. (Manchester) LHG Clin. Governance Lead & Exec. Bd. Mem. Prev: SHO (A & E Med. & O & G) P. Chas. Hosp. Merthyr Tydfil.

THOMAS, Kim Louise 26 Cae Braenar, Holyhead LL65 2PN — MB ChB 1998 Manch.

THOMAS, Kizhakkekara Thomas 36 Norford Way, Rochdale OL11 5QS Tel: 01706 344454 — MB BS 1968 Kerala; MRCPsych 1976. Cons. Psychiat. (Learning Disabil.) Lancs.; Mem. Med. Specialists Comm.; Mem. Clin. Care Team & Head Learning Disabil. Servs.

THOMAS, Lee Spencer 13 Eshelby Close, Liverpool L22 3XT — MB ChB 1998 Dund.

THOMAS, Mr Lewis Philip (retired) Glenview, Glasllwch Lane, Newport NP20 3PS Tel: 01633 243001 — MB BCh 1944 Wales; BSc Wales 1941, MCh 1959, MB BCh 1944; FRCS Eng. 1947. Prev: Cons. Surg. Roy. Gwent Hosp. Newport.

THOMAS, Linzi Ann 1 Richmond Park Road, Clifton, Bristol BS8 3AS Tel: 0117 973 7698; Landfall, 6 Marytwill Lane, Langland, Swansea SA3 4RB Tel: 01792 368532 — MB BCh 1988 Wales; MRCP (UK) 1991. Regist. (Med.) S. W.. RHA. Prev: SHO (Med.) W. Glam. HA.

THOMAS, Louis Glynne (retired) Doire, Garth Avenue, Surby, Port Erin IM1 3JW — MRCS Eng. LRCP Lond. 1927; DPH Liverp. 1931. Prev: Obst. Off. Birkenhead Matern. Hosp.

THOMAS, Lynda Joan Cottage Hospital, Birmingham Road, Sutton Coldfield B72 1QH Tel: 0121 255 4032 Fax: 0121 321 1299; The Dell, 33 Hartopp Road, Four Oaks, Sutton Coldfield B74 2QR Tel: 0121 308 6344 — MB ChB 1973 Birm.; MRCPCH 1996; Dip. Community Paediat. Warwick 1985; MSc Comm. Child Health Warwick 1999. (Birm.) SCMO NBC Community Health Trust & Good Hope Hosp. Socs: Fac. Community Health.

THOMAS, Lynn Marie 15 London Road, Cowplain, Waterlooville PO8 8DE — MB BS 1992 Lond.

***THOMAS, Mair** Croesawdy, Llandre, Bow St., Aberystwyth SY23 5BZ Tel: 01970 828726 — MB BCh 1997 Wales.

THOMAS, Mair Eleri Morgan (Livingstone) 21 Park Avenue, London NW11 7SL Tel: 020 8455 7600 — BSc Ed. 1941; MFCM RCP (UK) 1972; FRCPath 1963; MFPHM RCP (UK) 1989; DPH Eng. 1947. (Univ. Ed.) Emerit. Cons. Microbiol. Univ. Coll. Lond. Hosp. NHS Trust. Socs: Fell. Path. Soc.; Fell. Roy. Soc. Med.; Internat. Organisat. Mycoplasmol. Prev: Cons. Epidemiol. Centr. Publ. Health Laborat. Colindale; Cons. Microbiol. & Hon. Sen. Lect. Univ. Coll. Hosp.; Cons. Path. Eliz. G. Anderson Hosp. Lond.

THOMAS, Malcolm Glaxo Wellcome Research & Development, Greenford Road, Greenford UB6 0HE Tel: 020 8422 3434 — MB BCh 1968 Wales; MB BCh Wales 1968.; FRCP Lond. 1994. Internat. Dir. Clin. Pharmacol. Greenford. Prev: SHO (Gen. Med.) Singleton Hosp. Swansea; Ho. Surg. & Ho. Phys. Cardiff Roy. Infirm.

THOMAS, Malcolm David 51 Laws Street, Pembroke Dock, Pembroke Tel: 01646 683113 — MB BCh 1969 Wales; DObst RCOG 1971. (Cardiff)

THOMAS, Malcolm Ian Guidepost Health Centre, North Parade, Guidepost, Choppington NE62 5RA Tel: 01670 822071 Fax: 01670 531068; Hemmel House, West Farm Steadings, Nedderton, Bedlington NE22 6AR — MB BChir 1982 Camb.; MA Camb. 1984, MB BChir 1982; MRCGP 1988; DRCOG 1986. (Cambridge) Course Organiser N.umbria VTS for Gen. Pract.

THOMAS, Maliakal Cherian 9 Tranby Lane, Analby, Hull HU10 7DR — MB BS 1965 Kerala.

THOMAS, Maliampurackal Sebastian (retired) 38 Hutton Close, Westbury-on-Trym, Bristol BS9 3PT Tel: 0117 968 5486 Fax: 0117 968 5486 — MB BS 1968 Kerala; BSc Kerala 1963. Clin. Asst. Rehabil. Unit Ham Green Hosp. Bristol; Clin. Asst. (Genitourin. Med.) P.ss Margt. Hosp. Swindon. Prev: Clin. Asst. (A & E) Bristol Roy. Infirm.

THOMAS, Marcus James 4 Cody Road, Clapham, Bedford MK41 6ED Tel: 01234 217659 — MB ChB 1986 Manch.; Cert. Prescribed Equiv. Exp. JCPTGP 1991. Staff Grade Doctor Child & Family Consult. Serv. N.ants. HA. Socs: Affil. Roy. Coll. Psychiat.

THOMAS, Margaret Carlin Corby Knowe, Rowantreehill Road, Kilmacolm PA13 4NW Tel: 01505 874159 — MB ChB 1967 Glas.; FFA RCS Eng. 1973; DA Eng. 1970; DObst RCOG 1969. Cons. Anaesth. Argyll & Clyde Health Bd. Prev: Cons. Anaesth. Tabuk Saudi Arabia; Cons. Anaesth. Ayrsh. & Arran Health Bd.

THOMAS, Margaret David (retired) 39 Heathpark Avenue, Cardiff CF14 3RF Tel: 02920 756524 Email: gethyn@tinyworld.co.uk — MB BCh 1956 Wales. Prev: Clin. Asst. Dept. Child Health S. Glam. HA (T).

THOMAS, Margaret Louise The Surgery, St. Mary's Road, Newbury RG14 1ES Tel: 01189 883134; 23 Cheviot Close, Newbury RG14 6SQ Tel: 01635 40246 Fax: 01635 35069 Email: m.l.thomas@lineone.net — MB ChB 1977 Sheff.; DRCOG 1985; MFFP 1995; Mem. Inst. Psychosexual Medicine. GP. Socs: Fac. Fam. Plann. & Reproduc. Health Care; IPM. Prev: Cons. in Family Plann. & Reproductive Health Care.

THOMAS, Margaret Marsh The Surgery, Astonia House, High Street, Baldock SG7 6BP Tel: 01462 892458 Fax: 01462 490821; Newstead, Oaks Close, Hitchin SG4 9BN Tel: 01462 433258 Fax: 01462 433258 — MB BS 1968 Lond.; MRCS Eng. LRCP Lond. 1968; DObst RCOG 1970. (Roy. Free) Socs: RSM.

THOMAS, Margaret Susan Bradgate Surgery, Ardenton Walk, Brentry, Bristol BS10 6SP Tel: 0117 959 1920 Fax: 0117 983 9332 — MB ChB 1970 Bristol; DPM Eng. 1974; DObst RCOG 1971. (Bristol) GP Bristol. Prev: Sen. Regist. (Child Psychiat.) Bristol Roy. Hosp. Sick Childr.

THOMAS, Margaret Wylie (retired) Gean Cottage, 11 Harelaw Road, Edinburgh EH13 0DR Tel: 0131 441 3242 — MD 1931 Glas.; MD (High Commend.) Glas. 1931, MB ChB (Hnrs.). Prev: Med. Off. Belvidere Fev. Hosp., Mearnskirk Hosp. Childr. & Matern. &.

THOMAS, Margot Ross Flat 2, 101 St Johns Way, Archway, London N19 3RG — MB BS 1984 Lond.

THOMAS, Margot Vivienne Gelli, Idole, Carmarthen SA32 8DG — MB BCh BAO 1960 Dub.; MA Dub. 1960. (TC Dub.) Clin. Asst. (Adult Psychiat.) W. Wales. Prev: Med. Off. Serv. Childr. Schs. JHQ Rhinedahlen, BAOR BFPO 40; Clin. Asst. (Med.) LoughBoro. Gen. Hosp.; Clin. Asst. (Psychiat.) Coney Hill Hosp. Gloucester.

THOMAS, Marian Berwyn, Pentraeth Road, Menai Bridge LL59 5RR Tel: 01248 712794 — MB ChB Manch. 1965; SR 1998. (Manch.) SCMO Gwynedd AHA. Socs: Fac. Comm. Health. Prev: Clin. Med. Off. Gwynedd AHA; Ho. Surg. ENT Dept. Manch. Roy. Infirm.; Ho. Phys. Sefton Gen. Hosp. Liverp.

THOMAS, Marion Green Bank, Rose Lane, Mynydd Isa, Mold CH7 6UA — MB ChB 1991 Birm.

THOMAS, Marjorie Mitchell Seafield, Cardross, Dumbarton G82 5LD Tel: 01389 841342 — MB ChB 1965 Ed.; DObst RCOG 1967. Assoc. Specialist (A & E) Vale of Leven Hosp. Alexandria. Prev: Asst. & Assoc. Specialist (Surg.) Vale of Leven Hosp. Alexandria.

THOMAS, Marjorie Paula (retired) 5 Lawnt y Pentre, Flint Mountain CH6 5UN Tel: 01352 761951 Fax: 01352 730233 Email: paulathom@aol.com — MB ChB Manch. 1957; BSc Open Univ. 1996; FRCS Ed. 1967; FRACS 1972. Prev: Princip. GP Manch.

THOMAS, Mark Countisbury Avenue Surgery, 152 Countisbury Avenue, Llanrumney, Cardiff CF3 5YS Tel: 029 2079 2661 Fax: 029 2079 4537 — MB BCh 1980 Wales.

THOMAS, Mark Edward Renal Unit, Leicester General Hospital, Gwendolyn Road, Leicester LE5 4PW Tel: 0116 249 0490; 23 Wimborne Road, South Knighton, Leicester LE2 3RQ — MB BS 1983 Lond.; BSc Lond. 1980; MRCP (UK) 1988. (Westm. Med. Sch. Univ. Lond.) Sen. Regist. (Nephrol.) Leicester Gen. Hosp. Prev: Sen. Regist. (Med.) Leicester Roy. Infirm.; Research Fell. Washington Univ. St. Louis USA; Research Fell. (Nephrol.) Roy. Free Hosp. Lond.

THOMAS, Mark Greenslade 54 Southmoor Road, Walton Manor, Oxford OX2 6RD — MB ChB 1977 Auckland.

THOMAS, Mark Lloyd Dept. Anaesthesia, Great Ormond St. Hospital, London WC1N 3JH Tel: 023 8077 7222; Dept of Anaesthesia, Great Ormond St Hospital, London WC1 — MB BChir 1989 Camb.; BSc Lond. 1987; FRCA 1994. Regist. Rotata. (Anaesth.) Char. Cross Hosp. Lond. Prev: SHO (Anaesth.) Hinchingbrooke Hosp. & Roy. Lond. Hosp.; SHO (Cardiol. & Cas.) Roy. Adelaide Hosp., Austral.; Regist. Rotat. (Anaesth.) Char. Cross Hosp. Lond.

THOMAS, Mark Richard 11 Frederick Square, London SE16 5XR — MB BS 1993 Lond.; BSc (Hons.) Sociol. Applied to Med. Lond. 1991; MRCP (UK) 1997. (Lond. Hosp. Med. Coll.) Specialist Regist. (Neonatology) St. Geo.'s Hosp. Lond. Prev: SHO (Paediat. Oncol.) Roy. Marsden Hosp.; SHO (Paediat.) St. Geo. Hosp. Lond.; SHO (Paediat.) Whittington NHS Trust.

THOMAS, Mark Stephen Llynyfran Surgery, Llynyfran Road, Llandysul SA44 4JX Tel: 01559 363306 Fax: 01559 362896 — MB BS 1987 Lond.; DFFP 1996. (St. Geos. Lond.)

THOMAS, Martin Murmur-Y-Coed, Bethesda Bach, Llanwnda, Caernarfon LL54 5SG — MB ChB 1996 Liverp.; BSc (Hons.) Liverp. 1991. (Liverpl.) GP Regist. Gwynedd VTS. Prev: Ho. Off. Med. & Surg. S.port & Forming NHS Trust.

THOMAS, Martin David 23B Southview Road, Southampton SO15 5JD — BM 1992 Soton.

THOMAS, Mr Martin Harford The Runnymede Hospital, Guildford Road, Chertsey KT16 0RQ Tel: 01932 877831 Fax: 01932 877832 Email: marthinthomas@veinsurgeon.co.uk; The Holme, Clay Lane, Headley, Epsom KT18 6JS Fax: 01372 375581 Email: martinthomas@veinsurgeon.co.uk — MB BS Lond. 1969; MS Lond. 1980; FRCS Eng. 1974; MRCS Eng. LRCP Lond. 1969. (St. Thos.) Cons. Surg. St. Peter's Hosp. Chertsey. Socs: Fell. Roy. Soc. Med.; Vasc. Surg. Soc.; Ass. Surg. GBI. Prev: Sen. Regist. (Surg.) St. Thos. Hosp. Lond.; Clin. Research Fell. Scripps Clinic, Calif. USA; Research Fell. (Surg.) King's Coll. Hosp. Med. Sch. Lond.

THOMAS, Martin John Llwynbedw Medical Centre, 82/86 Caerphilly Road, Birchgrove, Cardiff CF14 4AG Tel: 029 2052 1222 Fax: 029 2052 2873; The Nook, 22 Westbourne Crescent, Cardiff CF14 2BL Tel: 029 2069 2227 — MB BCh 1975 Wales; BSc (Med. Biochem.) (Hons.) Wales 1972; MRCGP 1980. (Cardiff)

THOMAS, Martin Paul 17 Marsdale Drive, Nuneaton CV10 7DE — MB ChB 1992 Leic.

THOMAS, Martin Peter Thomas and Partners, 3 High Street, Pontypool NP4 6EY Tel: 01495 752444 Fax: 01495 767820 — MB BS 1983 Lond.; MRCGP 1990.

THOMAS, Martin Richard (retired) Ladypark, Dousland, Yelverton PL20 6NF Tel: 01822 853412 — MB BS 1931 Lond.; MD Lond. 1934; FRCP Lond. 1970, M 1934; MRCS Eng. LRCP Lond. 1930; FRCPath 1963. Cons. Path. Plymouth Gen. Hosp. Prev: Clin. Asst. (Path.) Plymouth Gen. Hosp.

THOMAS, Martyn Geoffry The Riverside Practice, The Health Centre, Marylebone Road, March PE15 8BG Tel: 01354 661922 Fax: 01354 650926 Email: martyn.thomas@gp-d81603.nhs.uk — MB BS 1983 Lond.; BSc Lond. 1980; MRCGP 1988; DFFP 1998; DGM RCP Lond. 1991; DRCOG 1986. (Roy. Free) Prev: SHO (Paediat.) Whipps Cross Hosp. Lond.; Ho. Surg. Basildon Gen. Hosp.; Ho. Phys. Whipps Cross Hosp.

THOMAS, Martyn Rhys c/o Dept of Cardiology, Kings College Hospital, Denmark Hill, London SE6 9RS Tel: 020 8346 3748 Fax: 020 7346 3489; 43 Canadian Avenue, Catford, London SE6 3AU Tel: 020 8690 3003 Email: mttwins@aol.com — MD 1993 Lond.; MB BS 1982; FRCP 1999; MRCP (UK) 1985. Cons. Cardiol. King's Coll. Hosp. Lond. Prev: Research Regist. (Cardiol.) Kings Coll. Hosp. Lond.; Sen. Regist. (Med. & Cardiol.) Kings Coll. Hosp. Lond.; Regist. Med. Unit. St. Mary's Hosp. Lond.

THOMAS, Mary Bowie (retired) Chorad, Little Bay, Kingarth, Rothesay PA20 9NP Tel: 01700 831228 — MB ChB Glas. 1944. Prev: Regist. Bellshill Matern. Hosp. & William Smellie Matern. Hosp. Lanark.

THOMAS, Mary Frances 27 Cornes Close, Winchester SO22 5DS — MB BS 1968 Lond.; MRCS Eng. LRCP Lond. 1968; MRCOG 1976, DObst. 1970. (St. Mary's) SCMO (Adult Servs.) Winchester Health Auth. Prev: Regist. (O & G) Roy. Hants. Co. Hosp. Winchester; Paediat. Regist. St. Mary's Hosp. Portsmouth.

THOMAS, Mary Parker Smith, MBE 31 Fairway, Trentham, Stoke-on-Trent ST4 8AS Tel: 01782 657539 — MB ChB 1949 Glas. (Glas.) Prev: Med. Off. Matern. Sect. Ayrsh. Centr. Hosp. Irvine; Med. Off. Stobhill Hosp. Glas. & Ballochmyle Hosp.

THOMAS, Mathew Koduvathrail Birmingham Heartlands Surgery, Gray Street, Bordesley Village, Birmingham B9 4LS Tel: 0121 772 2020 — MB BS 1965 Panjab; DCH Eng. 1968. (Christian Med. Coll. Ludhiana) Prev: Clin. Med. Off. (Child Health) Birm. AHA; Regist. (Geriat. & Med.) St. Luke's Hosp. Huddersfield; SHO (Gen. Med. & Paediat.) Horton Gen. Hosp. Banbury.

THOMAS, Matthew Department of Medicine for the Elderly, Poole Hospital, Longfleet Road, Poole BH15 2JB Tel: 01202 448160 Fax: 01202 442993 — MB BS 1988 Lond.; MRCP (UK) 1991; FRCP 1999. (London Hospital Medical College) Cons. Phys. (Med. for Elderly) Poole Hosp. Socs: Brit. Geriat. Soc. Prev: Research Fell. & Hon. Sen. Regist. Roy. Bournemouth Hosp.; Sen. Regist. Rotat. (Geriat. Med.) Wessex; Regist. Rotat. Jersey & Soton.

THOMAS, Matthew James Colman 15 (1F2) Spottiswoode Street, Edinburgh EH9 1EP — MB ChB 1996 Ed.

THOMAS, Miss Medi Angharad West Wales General Hospital, Carmarthen SA31 2AF Tel: 01267 227585 — MB BS 1985 Lond.; FRCS (ORL-HNS). (Roy. Lond. Hosp. Med. Coll.) Cons. ENT Surg. W. Wales Gen. Hosp. Carmarthen.

THOMAS, Megan Ruth Blenheim House Child Development Centre, 145-147 Newton Drive, Blackpool FY3 8LZ Tel: 01253 397006 Fax: 01253 397008; 52 Albany Road, Lytham St Annes FY8 4AS Tel: 01253 738371 Fax: 01253 738371 — MB ChB 1988 Manch.; BSc St. And. 1985; MRCP Paediat. Glas. 1992; DRCOG 1991. (St Andrews and Manchester) Cons. (Community Paediat.) Blenheim Hse. Child Developm. Centre Blackpool. Socs: FRCPCH. Prev: Sen. Regist. (Paediat.) Blackpool Vict. Hosp.; Sen. Regist. (Paediat.) Ninewells Hosp. & Med. Sch. Dundee; Regist. (Paediat.) Mater Misercordiae Hosp. Brisbane, Australia.

THOMAS, Mr Michael 9 Beaumont Road, Windsor SL4 1HY Tel: 01753 620810 Fax: 01753 850128 Email:

THOMAS

mikethomas@ukdoctors.com — MB BS 1980 Lond.; FRCS (Orth.) 1993; FRCS Eng. 1986; FRCS Ed. 1984. Cons. Orthop. Heatherwood & Wexham Pk. Hosp. Trust. Socs: Fell. BOA; BESS; RASS. Prev: Sen. Regist. (Orthop.) St. Mary's Hosp. Lond.; Regist. (Orthop.) Char. Cross Hosp. Lond.; Regist. (Orthop.) Univ. Cape Town, S. Afr.

THOMAS, Michael Copsen, Knoll Road, Frith Hill, Godalming GU7 2EL Tel: 01483 422949 — MB BChir 1966 Camb.; MA Camb. 1960, MD 1966; FRCP Lond. 1977, M 1962. (St. Mary's) Cons. Cardiol. King Edwd. VII Hosp. Midhurst; Hon. Phys. Roy. Brompton Hosp. Lond. Socs: Brit. Cardiac Soc. Prev: Mem. Scientif. Staff & Cons. Phys. MRC Cardiovasc. Research Unit Roy.; Postgrad. Med. Sch. Hammersmith Hosp. Lond.; Ho. Phys. (Med.) St. Mary's Hosp.

THOMAS, Michael Albert 85 Pentre Road, Pontardulais, Swansea SA4 1HR — MB BCh 1992 Wales.

THOMAS, Michael David Guardian Medical Centre, Guardian Street, Warrington WA5 1UD Tel: 01925 650226; 25 Woodbridge Close, Appleton, Warrington Tel: 01925 601518 — MB ChB 1961 Manch.; BSc (Anat. Hons.) Manch. 1959; FRCGP 1995, M 1974; DObst RCOG 1966; DA Eng. 1965. GP Partner. Prev: Course Organiser Chester VTS.

THOMAS, Mr Michael Graham The Department of Surgery, The 4th Floor, The Bristol Royal Infirmary, Marlborough St., Bristol BS2 8NW Tel: 0117 9283066 Fax: 0117 925 2786 Email: NGTBristol@aol.com; 87 Park Grove, Henleaze, Bristol BS9 4NY — MB BS 1984 Lond.; MS Lond. 1994, BSc (1st cl. Hons.) 1981; FRCS (Gen.) 1996; FRCS Ed. 1989; FRCS Eng. 1989. (Middlx. Hosp. Med. Sch.) Cons. Colorectal Surg.. Bristol NHS Trust. Socs: Brit. Soc. Gastroenterol.; Assn. Coloproctol.; Surgic. Rese. Soc. Prev: Lect. (Surg.) Univ. Liverp.

THOMAS, Michael Harford (retired) Coppice House, Bradford-on-Avon — MB ChB 1942 Bristol. Prev: Ho. Surg. & Cas. Off. Bristol Roy. Infirm.

THOMAS, Michael John Evan 219 Inverness Place, Cardiff CF24 4RY — MB BCh 1993 Wales.

THOMAS, Michael John Glyn, Col. late RAMC Retd. Fieldfare, North Heath Close, Horsham RH12 5PH Tel: 01403 262652 Fax: 01403 262657 Email: michaeljgthomas@compuserve.com; 12 Winchfield Court, Winchfield Hurst, Hook RG27 8SP Tel: 01252 842740 Fax: 01252 843736 — MB BChir 1963 Camb.; MA Camb. 1963; LMSSA Lond. 1962; DTM & H RCP Lond. 1964; FRCP Ed 1997. (St. Bart.) p/t Clin. Dir. Blood Care Foundat.; Chairm. Data & Satety Monitoring Bd. Hemclinicintern. Clin. Trials; Med. Cons. to Dideco - Blood Managem. & Zeal Med.; Indep. Cons. Transfus. Med. Hook. Socs: Fell. BMA; Brit. Blood Transfus. Soc.; Internat. Soc. Blood Transfus. Prev: Dir. Army Blood Transfus. Serv. Aldershot.

THOMAS, Michael Richard Martin The Old Bakehouse, High St., Chieveley, Newbury RG20 8UX — MB ChB 1993 Bristol.

THOMAS, Miles Alexander 28 Harnwood Road, Salisbury SP2 8DB Tel: 01722 320893 — MB BS 1983 Lond. GP Shrewton, Wilts.

THOMAS, Millicent Anne Department of Pathology, Inverclyde Royal Hospital, Larkfield Road, Greenock PA16 0XN; 12 Mosspark Road, Milngavie, Glasgow G62 8NJ — MB ChB 1978 Ed.; MRCPath 1987. Cons. Path. Inverclyde Roy. Hosp. Greenock. Prev: Cons. Cytopath. Glas. Roy. Infirm.

THOMAS, Mivart Gwynrudd West 121 Harley Street, London W1N 1DH Tel: 020 7224 0402 Fax: 020 7224 0403; 30 Red Post Hill, Dulwich, London SE24 9JQ Tel: 020 7274 6599 — MRCS Eng. LRCP Lond. 1965; MA Camb. 1965; MRCPsych 1971. (Camb. & St. Bart.) Cons. Psychiat. Charter Nightingale Hosp. Lond. Socs: Fell. Med. Soc. Lond.; Amer. Psychiat. Assn. Prev: Asst. Prof. Clin. Psychiat. New Jersey Med. Sch. USA; Dir. Dept. Psychiat. Jersey City Med. Center, USA; Asst. Prof. Psychiat. Rutgers Univ. New Jersey, USA.

THOMAS, Moira Jean Department of Immunology, Queens Medical Centre, Nottingham NG7 2UH — MB ChB 1987 Glas.

THOMAS, Molliamma 23 Ontario Way, Lakeside, Cardiff CF23 6HB — MB BS 1989 Kerala.

THOMAS, Nancy Elizabeth Saffron Lane Health Centre, 612 Saffron Lane, Leicester LE2 6TD Tel: 01162 911212 Fax: 01162 910300 — MB BS 1977 Newc.; MRCGP 1982.

THOMAS, Neil Howard Mailpoint 021, Department of Child Health, Southampton General Hospital, Tremona Road, Southampton SO16 6YD Tel: 023 8079 4457 Fax: 023 8079 4962 Email: neil.thomas@suht.swest.nhs.uk; Denbigh, Shepherds Lane, Compton, Winchester SO21 2AD — MB BChir 1983 Camb.; FRCP 1999; FRCPCH 1997; MRCP (UK) 1987; DCH RCP Lond. 1987; MA Camb. 1983. (King's Coll. Hosp.) Cons. Paediat. Neurol. Soton. Gen. Hosp. Prev: Sen. Regist. (Paediat.) Guy's Hosp. Lond.; Research Fell. (Paediat.) Roy. Postgrad. Med. Sch. Lond.; Regist. (Paediat.) Hammersmith Hosp.

THOMAS, Neil Martin 34 Cheriton Grove, Tonteg, Pontypridd CF38 1PF — MB ChB 1992 Liverp.

THOMAS, Mr Neil Philip The Hampshire Clinic, Basing Road, Basingstoke RG24 7AL Tel: 01256 819222 Fax: 01962 761152 — MB BS 1974 Lond.; BSc (Hons.) Lond. 1971; FRCS Eng. 1978. Cons. Orthop. Surg. N. Hants. Hosp., The Hants. Clinic & Wessex Nuffield Hosp. Socs: Fell. Roy. Soc. Med.; Fell. BOA (Counc. 1999-2001); (Ex-Sec.) Brit. Assn. Surg. of Knee (BASK). Prev: Sen. Regist. Rotat. (Orthop.) Univ. Coll. Hosp. & W.m. Hosp. Lond.; Regist. (Gen. Surg.) Univ. Coll. Hosp. Lond.; SHO Rotat. (Surg.) N.wick Pk. Hosp. Harrow.

THOMAS, Neil Rhys Arden House, 9-10 Launceton Close, Winsford CW7 1LY Tel: 01606 861200 — MB BCh 1983 Wales; DRCOG 1990; MRCGP 1988.

THOMAS, Mr Nicholas Wake Macmeikan Kings College Hospital, Denmark Hill, London SE5 9RS Tel: 0207 346 3288 Fax: 0207 346 3280; 3 Radlet Avenue, Forest Hill, London SE26 4BZ Tel: 0208 291 7739 Email: nwm.thomas@virgin.net — MB BS 1988 Lond.; FRCS Glas. 1992; FRCS Eng. 1992; FRCS (SN) 1997. (Roy. Lond. Hosp.) Cons. Neurosurg. Kings Coll. Hosp. Lond. Socs: Fell. Roy. Soc. Med.; BMA. Prev: Spinal Fell. (Neurosurg.) Ohio State Univ. Ohio, USA; Regist. (Neurosurg.) Atkinson Morley Hosp.; Sen. Regist. (Neurosurg.) Gt. Ormond St. Hosp. & Nat. Hosp. for Neurol & Neurosurg. Qu. Sq. Lond. & Atkinson Morley's Hosp. Lond.

THOMAS, Nicola Frances c/o LT Col. Parsons, Land Operations BFPO 50; 74 Powisland Drive, Derriford, Plymouth PL6 6AD — MB BS 1983 Lond.; FRCA 1989.

THOMAS, Nicola Frances 235 Liverpool Road, Haydock, St Helens WA11 9RT — MB ChB 1997 Manch.

THOMAS, Professor Nigel Brett North Manchester General Hospital, Delaunays Road, Crumpsall, Manchester M8 5RB Tel: 0161 795 4567; 10 Juniper Close, Sale M33 6JT — MRCS Eng. LRCP Lond. 1981; BSc (Hons.) Lond. 1978, MB BS 1981; FRCR 1987. (St. Bart.) Cons. (Radiol.) N. Manch. Gen. Hosp.; Hon. Vis. Prof., Univ. of Salford.

THOMAS, Nigel Eugene (retired) Cottage View, Stonewalls, Burton, Rossett, Wrexham LL12 0LG Tel: 01244 571436 — MB ChB Liverp. 1958; DPH Eng. 1962; DCH Eng. 1961.

THOMAS, Noel Bell Bron-y-Garn Surgery, Station Street, Maesteg CF34 9AL Tel: 01656 733262 Fax: 01656 735239; Bron-y-Garn, Maesteg CF34 9AL — MB ChB 1968 Ed.; MA Camb. 1965; MFHom 2000; DCH Eng. 1972; DObst RCOG 1970. (Camb. & Ed.) GP (NHS). Prev: Ho. Phys. Edin. Roy. Infirm.; SHO Paediat. Amersham Gen. Hosp.

THOMAS, Norman Armsden The Surgery, Caerffynnon, Dolgellau LL40 1LY Tel: 01341 422431 — MB ChB 1945 Birm.; DObst RCOG 1950. (Birm.) Med. Off. Dolgellau & Barmouth Dist. Hosp. Prev: Ho. Surg. Dudley Rd. Hosp. Birm.; Ho. Surg. MRC Burns Unit Birm. Accid. Hosp.; Hon. Maj. RAMC.

THOMAS, Norman Spencer (retired) 25 Alvechurch Highway, Lydiate Ash, Bromsgrove B60 1NZ — MB BS Lond. 1951; MRCS Eng. LRCP Lond. 1951; FFA RCS Eng. 1962; DA Eng. 1957. Prev: Cons. Anaesth. Selly Oak Hosp. Birm.

THOMAS, Olive Mary (retired) Perivale, Higher Metherell, Callington PL17 8DD Tel: 01579 350737 Email: oandg@ukgateway.net — MB ChB Manch. 1950; DPH Manch. 1954. Prev: Med. Off. (Family Plann.) Wigan HA.

THOMAS, Osmond Leopold 110 Westcotes Drive, Leicester LE3 0QS — MB BS 1985 West Indies.

THOMAS, Owain Rhys 35 Parc Castell-y-Mynach, Creigiau, Cardiff CF15 9NW — MB BCh 1997 Wales.

THOMAS, Owen Gethin Maesgwyn, 75 Pengam Road, Ystrad Mynach, Hengoed CF82 8AB Tel: 01443 813248 — MB BS 1948

Lond. (St. Bart.) Prev: Lt. RAMC; Ho. Surg. Accid. Unit & Cas. Off. St. David's Hosp. Cardiff.

THOMAS, Owen Maelgwyn (retired) 65 Sandringham Road, Swindon SN3 1HT — MB ChB 1956 Leeds. Prev: Ho. Phys. & Ho. Surg. Swansea Gen. Hosp.

THOMAS, Mr Palakuzhyil Thomas 6 Sunningdale Close, Kirkham, Preston PR4 2TG Tel: 01772 672722 — MB BS 1968 Aligarh Muslim, India; FRCSI 1986. Assoc. Specialist (Gen. Surg.) Blackpool Vict. Hosp.

THOMAS, Pamela Jill Everton Road General Practice, 70 Everton Road, Liverpool L6 2EW Tel: 0151 260 5050 — MB ChB 1986 Manch.; Dip. Ther. 1997; DFFP 1993; MRCGP 1991. GP (p/t). Prev: Trainee GP Harpenden; Trainee GP Rugby VTS.

THOMAS, Patricia Anne (retired) 43 Monument Lane, Rednal, Birmingham B45 9QQ Tel: 0121 453 2964 — MB ChB St. And. 1957; MCOphth 1990; DO Eng. 1965. Prev: Assoc. Specialist (Ophth.) BromsGr. & Redditch Health Dist.

THOMAS, Patricia Catherine Garburn House, Westmorland General Hospital, Burton Road, Kendal LA9 7RG Tel: 01539 795253 Fax: 01539 795361; Verandah Cottage, Nether Burrow, Kirby Lonsdale, Carnforth LA6 2RJ Tel: 015242 74223 — MB ChB 1974 Birm.; MRCPsych 1978. Cons. Psychiat. Bay Community Trust. Prev: Sen. Regist. (Psychiat.) Univ. Coll. Hosp. Lond.; Research Fell. (Psychiat.) Univ. Coll. Hosp. Med. Sch. Lond.; Regist. (Psychiat.) Shelton Hosp. Shrewsbury.

THOMAS, Patrick Jonathan Minffordd, Pennal, Machynlleth SY20 9DP Tel: 01654 791607 — MD 1968 Bristol; MB ChB 1962. Emerit. Reader (Pharmacol.) King's Coll. Lond. Prev: Demonst. Pharmacol. Univ. Bristol; Research Fell. in Pharmacol. Chelsea Coll. Univ. Lond.; Reader (Pharmacol.) Chelsea Coll. Univ. Lond.

THOMAS, Paul 9 Victoria Avenue, Forest Hall, Newcastle upon Tyne NE12 8AX — MB BS 1988 Newc.; MRCP (UK) 1994. SHO (anaesth.) Dryburn Hosp.

THOMAS, Mr Paul Anthony Department of Surgery, Whipps Cross Hospital, London E11 1NR Tel: 020 8535 6606; 22 King's Avenue, Buckhurst Hill IG9 5LP Tel: 020 8505 3203 — MB BS 1968 Lond.; BSc Lond. 1965, MS 1977; FRCS Eng. 1973. (Lond. Hosp.) Cons. Gen. & Gastrointestinal Surg. Whipps Cross Hosp. Lond.; Undergrad. Tutor Whipps Cross Hosp. Lond.; CME Tutor RCS Eng.; Regional Adviser Surg. NE Thames; Edr. Brit. Jl. Hosp. Med.; Chairm. Higher Surg. Train. Comm. NE Thames; Mem. Exam. Comm. RCS Eng.; Mem. Edit. Bd. FRCS Supplm. Socs: Surg. Research Soc.; Brit. Soc. Gastroenterol.; Assn. Endoscopic Surgs. Prev: Organiser Whipps Cross Hosp. Advanced Surgic. Course Lond.; Tutor (Surg.) RCS; Chairm. Physiol. Sect: Appl: Basic Sci Exam. RCS.

THOMAS, Paul David Taunton and Somerset NHS Trust, Husgrove Park, Taunton TA1 5DA Tel: 01823 333444 — MB BChir 1988 Camb.; 2001 MD (Lond.); MRCP (UK) 1992; DTM & H Liverp. 1993. Cons. Phys./Gastroenterologist, Taunton & Som. Hosp. Prev: Research Fell. St. Mark's & St. Thos. Hosps.; Regist. Chelsea & W.m. Hosp. Lond.

THOMAS, Paul David Gipping Valley Practice, Norwich Road, Barham, Ipswich IP6 0DJ Tel: 01473 832832 Fax: 01473 830200 — MB BS Lond. 1984; MSc (Ergonomics) Loughborough 1975; BSc (Hons. Physiol.) Dund 1974; MRCGP 1988. (Roy. Free) Socs: BASICS; Disp. Doctors Assn. (Mem. Nat. Comm.). Prev: Trainee GP Ipswich VTS; Research Off. MRC Div. Bioeng. Harrow.

THOMAS, Paul Rhodri Department Primary Care & General Practice, Imperial College School Of Medicine, St Mary's Campus, Norfolk Place, London W2 1PG Tel: 020 7402 7457 Email: p.r.thomas@ic.ac.uk; 13 Kingsgate Road, West Hampstead, London NW6 4TD Tel: 020 7419 4391 — MB ChB 1979 Bristol; DCH Lond. 1983. Sen. Lect. Dept. Primary Health Care & Gen. Pract. Socs: BMA; MRCGP.

THOMAS, Mr Paul Roderick Spensley St. Helier Hospital, Carshalton SM5 1AA Tel: 020 8644 4343 — MB BS 1978 Lond.; MS Lond. 1991; FRCS Eng. 1982. (Bart.) Cons. Surg. (Gen. & Vasc. Surg.) St. Helier Hosp. Carshalton. Socs: (Ex-Counc.) Vasc. Surgic. Soc.; Surgic. Research Sc.

THOMAS, Paul Stephen 92 Chesterfield Road, Liverpool L23 9TS — MB ChB 1992 Liverp.

THOMAS, Paul Winston 2FF, 9 Windsor Terrace, Clifton, Bristol BS8 4LW Tel: 0117 929 7542 — MB BS 1991 Lond.; DCH RCP Lond. 1995. Regist. Rotat. (Anaesth.) Bristol. Prev: SHO (SCBU & Paediat. Intens. Care Unit) Bristol Childr. Hosp.; SHO (Anaesth.) Roy. United Hosp. Bath; SHO (Anaesth.) Roy. Lond. Hosp.

THOMAS, Mrs Pauline Julia (retired) 6 Hunter Place, Louth LN11 9LG Tel: 01507 603473 — MB ChB 1959 St. And. Prev: Clin. Med. Off. N. Lincs. DHA.

THOMAS, Pauline Mary Ann 16 Frankland Terrace, Emsworth PO10 7BA Tel: 01243 378870 — MB BS Lond. 1954. (Roy. Free) SCMO Portsmouth Healthcare Trust.

THOMAS, Peter Bowden Flat 3, 57 Arlingford Road, London SW2 2ST — MB BS 1992 Lond.

THOMAS, Mr Peter Brian Macfarlane Department of Postgraduate Medicine, Thorn Burrow Drive, Hartshill, Stoke-on-Trent ST4 7QB Tel: 01782 716857; Rock Cottage, Mordiford, Hereford HR1 4LR Tel: 01432 870448 — MB BS 1975 Lond.; FRCS Eng. 1981; FRCS Ed. 1981. (St. Thos.) Cons. & Sen. Lect. (Orthop. Surg.) Keele; Cons. Orthop. Surg. N. Staffs. Roy. Infirm. Socs: Fell. Orthop. Assn. & Brit. Hand Soc. Prev: Sen. Regist. Robt. Jones & Agnes Hunt Orthop. Hosp. OsW.ry; Research Fell. (Orthop.) St. Luke's Episcopal Hosp. & Methodist Hosp. Houston, Texas; Regist. (Surg.) Univ. Hosp. Wales Cardiff.

THOMAS, Peter Cadwalladr 55 Trinity Road, Hoylake, Wirral CH47 2BS — MB ChB 1981 Liverp.

THOMAS, Peter Daniel Spence (retired) The Hill, Baldersby, Thirsk YO7 4PH Tel: 01765 640332 — MB BChir 1950 Camb.; MA Camb. 1950; MRCS Eng. LRCP Lond. 1950; DCH Eng. 1973. Prev: Gen. Practitioner, Bedale, N. Yorks.

THOMAS, Peter George 70 Fairlawn, Liden, Swindon SN3 6EU; Old School House, Pen-Yr-Aber, Solva, Haverfordwest SA62 6UR Tel: 01437 721300 — MRCS Eng. LRCP Lond. 1965.

THOMAS, Peter Howard Lower Farm House, Llysworney, Cowbridge CF71 7NQ Tel: 01446 772450 — MB BCh 1944 Wales; MD Wales 1955; FRCGP 1969; Pres. Medal RCGP 1998. (Cardiff) Morgan E. Williams Award 1955; Hon. Curator, Museum RCGP. Socs: Counc. (Ex-Pres.) Hist. Med. Soc. Wales; Convener S. Wales Fac. Hom. (Bristol & SW Br.). Prev: Ho. Phys. Welsh Nat. Sch. Med.

THOMAS, Professor Peter Kynaston, CBE Inst. Of Neurology, Queen Square, London WC1N 3BG Tel: 020 7837 3611; 33 West Hill Park, Merton Lane, London N6 6ND Tel: 020 8340 3365 Email: pkt.hotline@virgin.net — MB BS Lond. 1950; DSc Lond. 1971, BSc (1st cl. Hons.) 1947, MD 1957; FRCP Lond. 1967, M 1956; MRCS Eng. LRCP Lond. 1950; FRCPath 1990. (Univ. Coll. Lond. & Univ. Coll. Hosp.) Emerit. Prof. Roy. Free Hosp. Sch. Med. & Inst. Neurol. Lond.; Hon. Cons. Neurol. Roy. Free Hosp., Nat. Hosp. Neurol. Neurosurg. Qu. Sq. & Roy. Nat. Orthop. Hosp. Lond. Socs: Assn. Brit. Neurol.s; Assn. Phys.; Hon. Mem. Amer. Neurol. Assn. Prev: Asst. Prof. Neurol. McGill Univ. Montreal; Sen. Regist. Acad. Unit, Nat. Hosp. Qu. Sq.; Regist. (Neurol.) Middlx. Hosp. Lond.

THOMAS, Peter Leslie Portswood Road Surgery, 186-188 Portswood Road, Portsmouth, Southampton SO17 2NJ Tel: 023 8055 5181 Fax: 023 8036 6416; 16 Blenheim Avenue, Southampton SO17 1DU — MB BS 1980 Lond.; BSc Lond. 1980; FRCS (Orl.) Eng. 1987; T(GP) 1990. (Middlx.) GP Soton.; Occupat. Phys. Soton. City Counc., GEC Marconi Infrared Ltd, Phillips Electronics Lrd, Soton. Container Terminals. Socs: Small Pract.s Assoc.; Primary Care Spec. Gp. of Brit. Computer Soc.; GP Asthma Gp. (Regional Coordinator). Prev: Regist. (ENT Surg.) Roy. Gwent Hosp.

THOMAS, Peter Leslie Bupa Wellness Centre, Centurian Court, 64 London Road, Reading RG1 5AS Tel: 01189 062800 Fax: 01889 062801 Email: thomas@bupa.com — MB BS 1969 Lond.; Dip. Sports Med. Scott. Roy. Coll. 1997; DObst RCOG 1972. (St. Thos.) Sen. Orthopaedic and Sports Phys.; Med. Off. Brit. Olympic Med. Centre; Med. Commiss. Mem. FISA. Prev: Team Doctor GB Rowing Team; Maj. RAMC.

THOMAS, Peter Walter Vaughan Red Bank Group Practice, Red Bank Health Centre, Unsworth Street, Radcliffe, Manchester M26 3GH Tel: 0161 724 0777 Fax: 0161 724 8288; Woodthorpe, 28 South Downs Road, Hale, Altrincham WA14 3HW Tel: 0161 928 0668 — MB ChB 1980 Manch.; MRCGP 1987; DCH RCP Lond. 1986; DRCOG 1985. (Manchester) p/t Occupat. Health Phys. Rochdale Hosp. NHS Trust & Salford Univ. Sch. of Nursing; Vice-Chairm. & Commiss.ing Lead Bury S. PCG; Med. Off. Bury Hospice. Prev: Paediat. Dubai-Lond. Clinic, Dubai, UAE; Trainee GP Barlow Med. Centre Manch.; SHO & Ho. Off. S. Manch. Hosps.

THOMAS

THOMAS, Philip Andrew Heath Lane Surgery, Earl Shilton, Leicester LE9 7PB Tel: 01455 844431 Fax: 01455 442297; The Lodge, Station Road, Earl Shilton, Leicester LE9 4LU — MB ChB 1974 Manch.

THOMAS, Philip David St. Davids, Lower Road, Hockley SS5 5JU — MB BCh BAO 1972 Dub.; BSc (Hons.) Wales 1968; BA.

THOMAS, Philip Desmond 38 West Cross Lane, West Cross, Swansea SA3 5LS — MB BS 1978 Lond.; DLSHTM 1997; FRCPath 1995; MRCPath 1985; MSc Lond. 1982; MRCS Eng. LRCP Lond. 1978. (Westminster, London) Hon. Cons. W. Glam. HA; Cons. Med. Microbiol. Pub. Health Laborat. Serv.

THOMAS, Philip Fredric Department of Social & Economic Studies, University of Bradford, Richmond St., Bradford BD7 1DP Email: p.thomas@bradford.ac.uk; Lane Head Farm Cottage, Heptonstall, Hebden Bridge HX7 7PB — MB ChB 1972 Manch.; MPhil. Ed. 1984; FRCPsych 1995, M 1980; DPM Eng. 1978; MD Manch 2000. (Manch.) Cons. Psychiat. Bradford Community Health Trust & Sen. Research Fell. Dept. of Social & Economic Studies Univ. Bradford. Prev: Cons. Psychiat. Ysbyty Gwynedd & Manch. Roy. Infirm.; Lect. & Hon. Sen. Regist. (Psychiat.) Roy. Edin. Hosp.

THOMAS, Mr Philip James Dept. of Urology, Sussex House, 1 Abbey Road, Brighton BN2 1H Tel: 01273 696955 Email: philipthomas@brighton_healthcare.nhs.uk; The Gables, 56 Southover High St., Lewes BN7 1JA — MB BS 1981 Lond.; FRCS (Urol.) 1992; FRCS Lond. 1986. Cons. (Urol.) Brighton Health Care Trust; Cons. Urol. (Urol.) Char. Cross Hosp. Lond. Prev: Sen. Regist. (Urol.) Guy's Hosp. Lond.

THOMAS, Phillip Morriston Hospital, Morriston, Swansea SA6 6NL Tel: 01792 703889; The Coach House, Penmaen, Swansea SA3 2HA — MB BCh 1979 Wales; FRCP Lond. 1996; MRCP (UK) 1982. Cons. Cardiol. Morriston Hosp. Swansea. Prev: Cons. Cardiol. Singleton Hosp. Swansea; Lect. & Hon. Sen. Regist. St. Mary's Hosp. Lond. & N.wick Pk. Hosp. Harrow.

THOMAS, Phyllis Marion (retired) 49 Cilddewi Park, Johnstown, Carmarthen SA31 3HP — MB BCh 1957 Wales. Prev: Assoc. Specialist St. Davids Hosp. Carmarthen.

THOMAS, Phyllis Menna 45 Westbury Road, Northwood HA6 3DB Tel: 01923 823712 — MB BCh 1952 Wales; BSc (Chem.) Wales 1944, MB BCh 1952. (Cardiff) Clin. Asst. (Dermat.) Mt. Vernon Hosp. & Edgware Gen. Hosp. Prev: Ho. Phys. Roy. Infirm. Cardiff; SHO (Psychiat.) Fulbourn Hosp. Camb.; Beal Research Fell. Stanford Med. Sch. San Francisco, USA.

THOMAS, Mr Puthenparampil George Parkgate Medical Centre, Netherfield Lane, Parkgate, Rotherham S62 6AW Tel: 01709 514500 Fax: 01709 514490 — MB BS 1980 Panjab; FRCS Ed. 1987. GP. Prev: Regist. (Orthop.) Qu. Eliz. Hosp. Gateshead.

THOMAS, Rachel Gillian 190 Jarrom Street, Leicester LE2 7DF — MB ChB 1997 Leic.

THOMAS, Mr Ravi Department of Rehabilitation, Raigmore Hospital, Inverness IV2 3UJ Tel: 01463 234151; 2 Inshes View, Westhill, Inverness IV2 5DS Tel: 01463 793458 — MB BS 1970 Kerala; MS (Orthop.) Panjab 1974. (Med. Coll. Trivandrum) Med. Off. (Rheum. & Rehabil.) Raigmore Hosp. Inverness. Prev: Regist. (Orthop.) Raigmore Hosp. Inverness.

THOMAS, Rebecca Elizabeth 177 Kingshayes Road, Walsall WS9 8RZ — MB BS 1997 Lond.

THOMAS, Rhian Princess Street Surgery, Princess Street, Gorseinon, Swansea SA4 4US Tel: 01792 895681 Fax: 01792 893051; The Gnoll, 2 Bryntywod, Llangyfelach, Swansea SA5 7LE Tel: 01792 792343 — MB BS 1985 Lond.; DCH RCP Lond. 1990; MRCGP 1993. (St Bartholomew's Hospital) GP.

THOMAS, Mr Rhidian de Winton Melbourne Department of Orthopaedics, Charing Cross Hospital, Fulham Palace Road, London SW8 Tel: 020 8846 1475 Fax: 020 8967 5625 Email: rhidian.thomas@ic.ac.uk — MB BS 1986 Lond.; BSc 1983; FRCS Ed. 1991; MS 1998; FRCS (Orth) 1997. (St Bart. Hosp. Med. Sch.) Cons., Orthop., Char. Cross Hosp. Lond.; Hon. Sen. Lect., Imperial Coll. Sch. of Med., Lond. Socs: BOA; BOSTA; BMA.

THOMAS, Mr Rhys Hywel Tricoed, 35 St Gowan Avenue, Heath, Cardiff CF14 4JX — MB BS 1990 Lond.; FRCS Glas. 1995. (Univ. Coll. Hosp.)

THOMAS, Richard Charles 14 West Street, Titchfield, Fareham PO14 4DH — MB BS 1991 Lond.; FRCA 1996; DA (UK) 1996; FRCA 1998. (St. Mary's) Regist. (Anaesth. & Intens. Ther.) Wessex Rotat.

THOMAS, Richard Cherian 9 Tranby Lane, Anlaby, Hull HU10 7DR — MB BS 1996 Newc.

THOMAS, Richard David Radiology Department, Royal Devon & Exeter Hospital (Wonford), Barrack Road, Exeter EX2 5DW — MB ChB 1985 Liverp.; MRCP (UK) 1988; FRCR 1991. Cons. Radiol. Roy. Devon & Exeter Hosp. (Wonford). Prev: Sen. Regist. (Radiol.) Soton. Univ. Hosps.; Regist. (Radiol.) Soton. Gen. Hosp.; SHO (Med.) Truro Hosps.

THOMAS, Richard Gerwyn Tanyfron Surgery, 7-9 Market Street, Aberaeron SA46 0AS Tel: 01545 570271 Fax: 01545 570136; Brynhyfryd, Crossways, Ffosyffin, Aberaeron SA46 0HD — MB BS 1982 Lond.; MRCGP 1986.

THOMAS, Richard Huw 19 Smithies Avenue, Sully, Penarth CF64 5SS — MB ChB 1985 Manch.

THOMAS, Richard John Rooftops, Pyle Road, Nottage, Porthcawl CF36 3TF — BM 1993 Soton.; DGM RCP Lond. 1995. SHO (O & G) Portsmouth NHS Trust.

THOMAS, Richard John 9 Beckett Road, Worcester WR3 7NH Tel: 01905 451034 — MB BS 1973 Lond.; MRCS Eng. LRCP Lond. 1973. Prev: Clin. Asst. (Thoracic Med.) Worcester Roy. Infirm.; GP Droitwich, Worcs.

THOMAS, Mr Richard Stephen Alban BUPA Hospital, Leicester LE2 2FF Tel: 01162 653650 Fax: 01162 653651; The Oaks, 6 Main St., Queiniborough, Leicester LE7 3DA — MA, MB BChir Camb. 1964; FRCS Eng. 1970. (St. Bart.) Cons. Otolaryngol. Leicester AHA (T). Socs: Sect. Roy. Soc. Med. & Examr. Otolaryngol. RCS Eng.; BMA; FRCS. Prev: Sen. Regist. (ENT) St. Bart. Hosp. & Roy. Marsden Hosp. Lond.; Sen. Regist. Roy. Nat. Throat, Nose & Ear Hosp. Lond.; Ho. Phys. & Ho. Surg. (ENT) St. Bart. Hosp. Lond.

THOMAS, Richard Stephen Lloyd Heath Hill Practice, Heath Hill Road South, Crowthorne RG45 7BN Tel: 01344 777915 — MB BS 1974 Lond.; MRCGP 1981; DCH Eng. 1980; DRCOG 1979; Cert JCC Lond. 1980. (Char. Cross)

THOMAS, Robert James 12 Philadelphia Road, Porthcawl CF36 3DP — MB ChB 1984 Leic.; MRCP (UK) 1988. Regist. (Oncol. & Radiother.) Middlx. Hosp. Lond.

THOMAS, Robert Jesse Greystones, Kidmore Lane, Denmead, Portsmouth PO6 6NN Tel: 023 92 482148 — MB BS 1955 Lond.; BSc Lond. 1952, MB BS 1955; FRCGP 1981, M 1975. (Univ. Coll. Hosp.) Regional Adviser Gen. Pract. Univ. Soton. & Wessex RHA; Civil Cons. Gen. Pract. RN. Prev: Ho. Surg. Surgic. Unit & Ho. Phys. Univ. Coll. Hosp. Lond.

THOMAS, Robert Stephen Rainbow Medical Centre, 333 Robins Lane, St Helens WA9 3PN Tel: 01744 811211 — MB ChB 1978 Liverp.; MSc Aberystwyth 1998; BA Open 1989; DRCOG 1982.

THOMAS, Roderic David The Cardiac Centre, Royal United Hospital, Combe Park, Bath BA1 3NG Tel: 01225 428331 Fax: 01225 825441; Rowley House, Combe Hay, Bath BA2 7EF Tel: 01225 832188 — MB BChir 1968 Camb.; MD Camb. 1978, MA 1969; FRCP Lond. 1986; MRCP (UK) 1970. (St. Thos.) Cons. Phys. & Cardiol. Roy. United Hosp. Bath. Socs: Brit. Cardiac Soc. Prev: Sen. Regist. (Med. & Cardiol.) Leeds Gen. Infirm. & Killingbeck Hosp.; Regist. (Med.) St. Thos. Hosp. Lond.

THOMAS, Roderick Lister Barn Surgery, Christchurch Medical Centre, Purewell Cross Road, Christchurch BH23 3AF Tel: 01202 486456 Fax: 01202 486678 — MB BS 1976 Lond.; MRCS Eng. LRCP Lond. 1976; D.Occ.Med. RCP Lond. 1995. (Westm.) Med. Off. (Occupat. Health) Roy. Bournemouth Hosp.; Chairm. ChristCh. PCG. Prev: SHO (Med.) Kent & Canterbury Hosp.; SHO (Med.) Roy. Vict. Hosp. Bournemouth; Ho. Phys. (Radiother.) W.m. Hosp. Lond.

THOMAS, Roger David Medical Policy Group Office of the Chief Medical Adviser, Department of Social Security, 1-11 John Adam St, London WC2N 6HT Tel: 020 7712 2003 Email: r.thomas@ade003.dss.gov.uk; Allambi, Long Hill, Seale, Farnham GU10 1NQ — MB BS 1973 Lond.; DRCOG 1977. (St. Mary's Hosp.) Med. Policy Adviser DSS Lond.

THOMAS, Roger Walwyn Old Road Surgery, Old Road, Llanelli SA15 3HR Tel: 01554 775555 Fax: 01554 778868; Y Graig, Caswell St, Llanelli SA15 1BS Tel: 01554 759500 Fax: 01554 759500 — MB BCh BAO 1970 Dub. Exam. Med. Off. Attendance Allowance Bd. & Co-op. Insur. Company; Company Doctor S. Wales Region Thysseu GB Ltd.

THOMAS

THOMAS, Rosemary Ann Natalie Torrington Health Centre, New Road, Torrington EX38 8EL Tel: 01805 622247 Fax: 01805 625083 — MB ChB 1984 Bristol; MRCGP Lond. 1989; Cert. Family Plann. JCC 1989; DRCOG Lond. 1988. Prev: Trainee GP Taunton VTS; SHO (Geriat. Med., A & E & O & G) Som. HA.

THOMAS, Roslyn Margaret Northwick Park and St Marks Hospital, Watford Road, Harrow HA1 3UJ Tel: 020 8869 3941 Fax: 020 8869 2923; 40 Chiswick Quay, Hartington Road, Chiswick, London W4 3UR Tel: 020 8994 6982 — MB BS 1970 Queensland; FRCP Lond. 1993; MRCP (UK) 1975; FRCPCH. (University of Queensland) Cons. Paediat. N.wick Pk. & St. Marks Hosp. with s/i Neonatol. Socs: Hon. Sec. Thames Reg. Perinatal Gp.; Neonat. Soc.; Brit. Assn. Perinatal Med. Prev: Sen. Regist. (Paediat.) Univ. Coll. Hosp. Lond.

THOMAS, Rosser Ian Heol Fach Surgery, Heol Fach, North Cornelly, Bridgend CF33 4LD Tel: 01656 740345 Fax: 01656 740872; 5 Church View, Laleston, Bridgend CF32 0HF Tel: 01656 654077 — MB BCh 1978 Wales; MRCGP 1981; DRCOG 1981.

THOMAS, Ruth Cameron (retired) Meadow Cottage, Alpington, Norwich NR14 7NG — BM BCh 1965 Oxf.; MA Oxf. 1966, BM BCh 1965; FFA RCS Eng. 1969. Prev: Cons. Anaesth. Norwich Health Dist.

THOMAS, Ruth Elizabeth 15 Lon Cadog, Sketty, Swansea SA2 0TS — MB BCh 1993 Wales.

***THOMAS, Ruth Ellen** 19 Nightingale Road, Rickmansworth WD3 7DE — MB BS 1988 Lond.

THOMAS, Mr Ryland James Department of Orthopaedic Surgery, New Cross Hospital, Wolverhampton WV10 0QP Tel: 01902 642961; Hillcrest, Hopstone, Claverley, Wolverhampton WV5 7BW — MB BS Lond. 1966; FRCS Eng. 1971; MRCS Eng. LRCP Lond. 1966; DObst RCOG 1968. (Lond. Hosp.) Cons. Orthop. Surg. Roy. Wolverhampton NHS Hosps. Trust. Socs: BMA; BOA.

THOMAS, Sally Christina The Firs, Tiverton, Tarporley CW6 9NB — MB BS 1992 Lond.

THOMAS, Samuel Jeffrey Isca General Practice Unit, Cadoc House, High Street, Caerleon, Newport NP18 1AZ Tel: 01633 423886 Fax: 01633 430153 — MB BCh 1981 Wales; BSc 1972 Wales; PhD 1976 Wales; DRCOG 1985. GP Caerleon.; Med. Dir. Cadoc Health Care.

THOMAS, Sarah Family Doctor Unit Surgery, 92 Bath Road, Hounslow TW3 3LN Tel: 020 8577 9666 Fax: 020 8577 0692; 20 St. Pauls Close, Hounslow TW3 3DE Tel: 020 8572 0158 Fax: 020 8572 0158 — MB BS 1985 Lond.; DCH RCP Lond. 1992; DRCOG 1988.

THOMAS, Sarah Elizabeth Barnsley District General Hospital, Gawber Road, Barnsley S75 2EP Tel: 01226 777874 Fax: 01226 777941; Tapton Heights, 29 Taptonville Road, Broomhill, Sheffield S10 5BQ — MB ChB 1975 Sheff.; MB ChB (Hons.) Sheff. 1975; MRCP (UK) 1978; DTM & H Liverp. 1979. Cons. Dermat. Barnsley Dist. Gen. Hosp.; Assoc. Postgrad. Dean Univ. Sheff.

THOMAS, Sarah Emma Maesymeillion, Crundale, Haverfordwest SA62 4DG — MB BCh 1993 Wales.

THOMAS, Shan Elizabeth Mary Ashleigh Surgery, Napier Street, Cardigan SA43 1ED Tel: 01239 621227 — MB BCh 1981 Wales; DCH RCP Lond. 1985; DRCOG 1983.

THOMAS, Shanthi Eucharista Antonita Princess Alexandra Hospital, Hamstel Road, Harlow CM20 1QX Tel: 01279 444455 Fax: 01279 416846; The Orchard, Much Hadham SG10 6BS Tel: 01279 842556 Fax: 01279 843623 — MB BS 1971 Ceylon; MBA 1998; MSc Lond. 1984, MD 1990; FRCPath 1995, M 1983. Cons. Chem. Path. W. Essex HA. Socs: Fell. Roy. Soc. Med. Prev: Lect. Inst. Child Health Hosp. for Sick Childr. Lond.; Sen. Regist. St. Mary's Hosp. Lond.; Sen. Regist. N.wick Pk. Hosp. Harrow.

THOMAS, Sheena Dawn 'Islwyn', 9 Plas Cadwgan Road, Ynystawe, Swansea SA6 5AG — MB BCh 1997 Wales.

THOMAS, Sheena Diane Department of Palliative Care, Salisbury District Hospital, Salisbury SP2 8BJ Tel: 01722 336262; The Briars, 78 Campbell Road, Salisbury SP1 3BG Tel: 01722 332322 — MB BCh 1976 Wales. Sessional Clin. Asst. (Palliat. Care) Salisbury Dist. Hosp. Prev: SHO Univ. Hosp. Wales & E. Glam. Hosp.; Clin. Med. Off. S. Glam. & Leicester HA.

THOMAS, Shona Alison 13 Stamfordham Close, Rudchester Park, Wallsend NE28 8ER — MB ChB 1989 Manch.; MRCGP 1994; T(GP) 1994. Trainee GP Blackburn.

THOMAS, Sian Beaumont Villa Surgery, 23 Beaumont Road, St Judes, Plymouth PL4 9BL Tel: 01752 663776; The Forge, Dorsley Barns, Old Plymouth Road, Totnes TQ9 6DN Tel: 01803 863892 — MB BS 1988 Lond.; DRCOG 1991; MRCGP 1992. (Royal Free Hospital School of Medicine) GP Princip.

THOMAS, Sian Elizabeth Sydenham Green Group Practice, 26 Holmshaw Close, London SE26 4TH Tel: 020 8676 8836 Fax: 020 7771 4710; 90 Barn Mead Road, Beckenham BR3 1JD Tel: 020 8676 8836 Fax: 020 7771 4710 — MB BS 1981 Lond.; MRCGP 1986; DRCOG 1984.

THOMAS, Sian Rachel 43 Patrickhill Road, Glasgow G11 5BY Tel: 0141 339 0585 — BM 1991 Soton.; MRCP (UK) 1995. Lect. Neurol. S.ern Gen. Hosp. Glas.

THOMAS, Simon Hugh Lynton Wolfson Unit of Clinical Pharmacology, University of Newcastle upon Tyne, Claremont Place, Newcastle upon Tyne NE1 4LP Tel: 0191 222 5644 Fax: 0191 261 5733 Email: simon.thomas@ncl.ac.uk; 28 Elmfield Road, Gosforth, Newcastle upon Tyne NE3 4BA — MB BS 1981 Lond.; BSc (Hons.) Lond. 1978, MD 1991; MRCP (UK) 1984; FRCP 2000. Cons. Phys. & Sen. Lect. Freeman Hosp. & Univ. Newc. Socs: Brit. Pharm. Soc.; Amer. Soc. Clin. Pharmacol. & Therap.; Brit. Toxicology Soc. Prev: Sen. Regist. (Med. & Clin. Pharmacol.) Freeman Hosp. Newc.; Regist. (Med.) & Lect. St. Thos. Hosp. Lond.; SHO Lond. Chest Hosp., Brompton Hosp. & Roy. Free Hosp. Lond.

THOMAS, Simone Yvette Anne Cheddar Medical Centre, Roynon Way, Cheddar BS27 3NZ Tel: 01934 742061 Fax: 01934 744374 — MB BS 1987 Lond. (Roy. Free Hosp. Lond.)

THOMAS, Stanley Long Byre, Hay Hedge Lane, Bisley, Stroud GL6 7AN — MD 1956 Wales; MB ChB 1949. (Cardiff) Emerit. Prof. Physiol. Manch. Univ.

THOMAS, Stephen David Dept Of Anaesthesia, The Cardiothoracic Centre, Thomas Drive, Liverpool L14 3PE Tel: 0151 228 1616; Pinelodge, 1 Hanson Park, Oxton, Prenton CH43 9JN Tel: 0151 652 7656 — MB ChB 1984 Liverp.; FCAnaesth. 1991; DA (UK) 1990. (Liverp.) Cons.(Anaesth.) The Cardio Centre. Liverp. Socs: Jun. Mem. Liverp. Soc. Anaesth.; Train. Mem. Assn. AnE.h. Prev: Sen. Regist. Rotat. (Anaesth.) Merseyside; Clin. Lect. (Anaesth.) Univ. Liverp.; Regist. Rotat. Merseyside.

THOMAS, Stephen Mark Kings College Hospital, London SE5 9RS; 56 Selkirk Road, Twickenham TW2 6PX — BM 1986 Soton.; MRCP (UK) 1989.

THOMAS, Stephen Michael 85 Castle Lane, Bournemouth BH7 Tel: 01202 522622 — MB BS 1972 Lond.; DObst RCOG 1976. (St. Thos.) Prev: SHO (Paediat.) Poole Gen. Hosp.; SHO (Med.) Roy. Nat. Hosp. Bournemouth; Ho. Phys. & Ho. Surg. Salisbury Gen. Hosp.

THOMAS, Stephen Rhys Department of Cystic Fibrosis, Royal Brompton Hospital, London SW3 6NP; 53 Chatsworth Avenue, Merton Park, London SW20 8JZ Tel: 020 8543 2507 — MB BS 1988 Newc.; MRCP Ed. 1991. Research Fell. & Hon. Regist. (Cystic Fibrosis) Roy. Brompton Hosp. Lond. Socs: Brit. Thorac. Soc. Prev: Regist. Rotat. (Respirat. & Gen. Med.) SE Scott.; SHO (Med.) City Hosp. Edin. & Christie Hosp. Manch.

THOMAS, Steven Guy Dolhaul, Llangoedmor, Cardigan SA43 2LH — MB ChB 1991 Leeds.

THOMAS, Steven John 79 St Albans Road, Bristol BS6 7SQ — MB BCh 1996 Wales.

THOMAS, Steven Mark Department of Radiology, Northern General Hospital, Herries Road, Sheffield S7 5AU Tel: 0114 243 4343 Fax: 0114 271 4747 Email: s.m.thomas@sheffield.ac.uk — MB BS 1988 Lond.; FRCR 1995; MRCP 1991 UK; MSc 2000 Sheffield. Clin. Sen. Lect. and Hon. Cons. Radiologist, Univ. of Sheff. Socs: Brit. Soc. Interven. Radiol.; Cardiovasc. & Interven. Radiol. Soc. Europe; Soc.Cardiovasc & Interven.al Radiol. Prev: Sen. Regist. Rotat. (Diagn. Radiol.) St. Geo. Hosp. Lond.; Regist. Rotat. (Diagn. Radiol.) St. Geo. Hosp. Lond.; EndoVasc. Fell., N.ern Gen. Hosp. Sheff.

THOMAS, Steven Noel 61 Walkley Road, Sheffield S6 2XL Email: mdp97snt@sheffield.ac.uk — MB ChB 1993 Sheff.; MRCGP 1997. SHO (Med.) Sheff.

THOMAS, Stuart Alan 107 St Austell Avenue, Broken Cross, Macclesfield SK10 3NY — MB ChB 1989 Birm.; MRCGP 1993; DFFP 1993; DCH RCP Lond. 1993.

THOMAS, Stuart Ian Merlins, 63 Shepherds Lane, Beaconsfield HP9 2DU — BM 1998 Soton.; BM Soton 1998.

THOMAS

THOMAS, Stuart Kynaston (Surgery), 7 South Parade, Llandudno LL30 2LN Tel: 01492 876969; Dursley, 9A Whitehall Road, Rhos-on-Sea, Colwyn Bay LL28 4HW Tel: 01492 540775 — MB ChB 1970 Liverp.; MB ChB (Hons.) Liverp. 1970; DObst RCOG 1972.

THOMAS, Stuart Winston Wellspring Medical Centre, Park Road, Risca, Newport NP11 6BJ Tel: 01633 612438 Fax: 01633 615958; Ffynon Oer Farm, Panylan Road, Bassaleg, Newport NP1 9RW — MB BCh 1981 Wales; MRCGP 1987; DRCOG 1985. (University Hospital Wales)

THOMAS, Mr Sunil Soloman West Midlands Regional Plastic Surgery Unit, Wordsley Hospital, Stourbridge DY8 5QX Tel: 01384 401401 Fax: 01384 244436; 9 Crookham Close, Harborne, Birmingham B17 8RR Tel: 01384 244322 — MB BS 1981 Panjab; MS Punjab 1985; FRCSI 1996. (Christian Med. Coll. Ludhiana, Punjab) Staff (Plastic Surg.) Good Hope & Wordsley Hosps. W. Midl. Socs: BMA; Eur. Wound Managem. Soc.; Assn. Surgs. India.

THOMAS, Susan Dinas Powys Health Centre, 75 Cardiff Road, Dinas Powys CF64 4JT Tel: 029 2051 2293 Fax: 029 2051 5318 — MB BCh 1979 Wales; DRCOG 1982. (Welsh Nat. Sch. Med.) Socs: Cardiff Med. Soc.

THOMAS, Susan Beverley 40 Manor Way, Cardiff CF14 1RH — MB BCh 1983 Wales.

THOMAS, Susan Joan Regional Child Development Centre, St James's University Hospital, Leeds LS9 7TF Tel: 0113 206 5870 — MB BS 1975 Newc.; MRCP (Paediat.) (UK) 1982. Cons. Paediat. St Jas. Univ. Hosp. Leeds.

THOMAS, Susan Marguerite Lilliput Surgery, Elms Avenue, Lindisfarne, Poole BH14 8EE Tel: 01202 741310 Fax: 01202 739122; Wyke Lodge, 74 Canford Cliffs Road, Poole BH13 7AB — MB BS 1981 Lond.; MRCGP 1985; DRCOG 1985. (St. Thos.)

THOMAS, Susan Mary Tindal Centre, Bierton Road, Aylesbury HP20 1HU Tel: 01296 393363 Fax: 01296 399332; The Chiltern Hospital, London Road, Great Missenden HP16 0EN Tel: 01494 890890 Fax: 01494 890250 — MB BS 1982 Lond.; MRCPsych 1988. (Roy. Free) Cons. Psychiat. Aylesbury Vale Community Healthcare NHS Trust. Prev: Sen. Regist. (Psychiat.) Maudsley Hosp. Lond.; Regist. (Psychiat.) Fulbourn Hosp. Camb.

THOMAS, Susanna Jane 11 Fane Road, Oxford OX3 0RZ — BM BCh 1990 Oxf.

THOMAS, Tabitha Sophie Low Birks, Sedbergh LA10 5HQ — BChir 1996 Camb.

THOMAS, Teresa Angela 20 Hillcrest, Chedgrave, Norwich NR14 6HX — MB BChir 1988 Camb.

THOMAS, Thekanady Mathew Cedar House Surgery, 14 Huntingdon Street, St. Neots, Huntingdon PE19 1BQ Tel: 01480 406677 Fax: 01480 475167 — MB BS 1986 Lond.

THOMAS, Thelma Margaret 3 Montpelier Road, London W5 2QS Tel: 020 8998 3567 — MB BS 1969 Lond.; MRCP (UK) 1972; MRCGP 1983; MFCM 1979. (St. Mary's) GP. Prev: Mem. Clin. Scientif. Staff MRC Epidemiol. & Med. Care Unit.

THOMAS, Thomas 4 Carlton Close, Rushden NN10 9EL — MB BS 1975 Nagpur, India.

THOMAS, Mr Thomas Glyn 4 Redditch Close, Wirral CH49 2QJ — MB ChB 1990 Liverp.; FRCS Eng. 1994.

THOMAS, Mr Thomas Glyn (retired) Manyara, Bushy Ruff, Ewell Minnis, Dover CT16 3EE Tel: 01304 822321 Fax: 01304 367036 — MB BS 1951 Lond.; FRCS Eng. 1959. Prev: Cons. Orthop. Surg. S.E. Kent and Canterbury Hosp.

THOMAS, Thomas Peter Lloyd Llys-y-Coed, Llanddarog, Carmarthen SA32 8NU — MB BS 1973 Lond.; FRCP 1992, M 1976; MRCS Eng. LRCP Lond. 1973; T (M) 1991. (St. Mary's) Cons. Phys. P. Philip Hosp. Dyfed.

THOMAS, Thomas Richard Suite D, Havant Health Centre, Civic Centre Road, Havant PO9 2AP Tel: 023 9247 5010 Fax: 023 9249 2392; Pentwyn, Ferry Road, Hayling Island PO11 0BY — BSc (Hons., Anat.) Wales 1969, MB BCh 1972. (Welsh National School of Medicine) p/t Med. Off. (Family Plann., Vasectomies) St. Mary's Hosp. Family Plann. Clinic Portsmouth.

THOMAS, Tina Elisabeth Tynewydd, Vinegar Hill, Undy, Magor, Newport NP26 3BW — MB BCh 1989 Wales.

THOMAS, Tom Dulyn Llewelyn (retired) Plas-y-Wern, New Quay SA45 9ST Tel: 01545 580230 — MB ChB 1952 Liverp.; MD Liverp. 1966; MFCM 1973; DPH Liverp. 1956.

THOMAS, Trevor Anthony 14 Cleeve Lawns, Downend, Bristol BS16 6HJ — MB ChB 1964 St. And.; FFA RCS Eng. 1969. Cons. Anaesth. United Bristol Healthcare Trust; Hon. Clin. Lect. Univ. Bristol. Socs: Obst. Anaesth. Assn. (Ex. Pres., Ex Hon. Sec.); Soc. of Anaesth.s of the S. W.. Region (Ex. Pres., Ex Hon. Sec. and Ex-Edr. Anaesth. Points W.; Roy. Soc. of Med. Sect. of Anaesth. (Ex Monorary Sec.). Prev: Chairm. Div. Anaesth. Brist. Health Dist.; Chairm. Hosp. Med. Comm. Bristol & W. HA; Research Asst. Univ. Toronto, Canada.

THOMAS, Tudor Huw 10 Bryn Castell, Radyr, Cardiff CF15 8RA — MB BS 1989 Lond.

THOMAS, Mr Tudor Lloyd Turner Rise Consulting Rooms, 55 Turner Road, Colchester CO4 5JY Tel: 01206 752888 Fax: 01206 752223 — MRCS Eng. LRCP Lond. 1971; MB BS Lond. 1971, BDS 1966; FRCS Eng. 1976. (Middlx.) Cons. Orthop. Surg. Colchester & Roy. Lond. Hosps.; Regional Adviser, N. Thames E.; Regional Speciality Adviser; Trauma and Orthop.

THOMAS, Valerie Anne Department of Cellular Pathology, St Georges Hospital, Blackshaw Road, Tooting, London SW17 0RE Tel: 020 8725 2448 Fax: 020 8767 2984 — MB BS 1986 Lond.; PhD Lond. 1984, BSc 1980; MRCPath 1991. (St. George's HMS) Cons. Cytopath. and Histiopath St. Geo. Hosp. Lond.; Hon. Sen. Lect. St. Geo. Hosp. Lond. Prev: Lect. & Hon. Sen. Regist. (Histopath.) Roy. Free Hosp. Lond.

THOMAS, Vaughn Llewellyn Farne House, Armstrong Road, Brockenhurst SO42 7TA — LRCP LRCS 1978 Ed.; MB ChB 1978; LRCP LRCS Ed. LRCPS Glas. 1978; FFARCS Eng. 1983; DCH RCP Lond. 1984. (Univ. Rhodesia)

THOMAS, Vivian, Group Capt. RAF Med. Br. Sedgwick medigold, Health Consultancy, Preston Lodge Court, Preston Deanery, Northampton NN7 2DS — MB BCh 1970 Wales; AFOM RCP Lond. 1980; MRCGP 1976; DAvMed Eng. 1978; DObst RCOG 1972. (Cardiff) Sen. Occupat. Phys. Sedgwick Noble Lowndes Health Consult. N.ampton; Med Dir medigold Health Consultancy. Prev: PMAN 5 (RAF); Pres. Med. Bd. OASc; Oc Med. Wing RAF Wegberg.

THOMAS, Vivien Joy Ensom Magill Department of Anaesthetics, Chelsea & Westminster Hospital, Fulham Road, London SW10 9NH Tel: 020 8746 8026 Fax: 020 8746 8801; The Holme, Clay Lane, Headley, Epsom KT18 6JS — MB BS Lond. 1969; FFA RCS Eng. 1974. (St. Mary's) Cons. Anaesth. Chelsea & W.m. Hosp. Lond. Socs: Assn. Anaesth.; Assn. Paediatric Anaesth. Prev: Sen. Regist. (Anaesth.) W.m. Hosp. Lond. & St. Geo. Hosp. Lond.; SHO (Anaesth.) St. Thos. Hosp. Lond.

THOMAS, Vivienne Rachel 23 Shftesbury Way, Twickenham TW2 5RN — MB BS 1991 Lond.

THOMAS, Walter Hugh Muriau Cadarn, Llan-Talyllyn, Brecon LD3 7TG Tel: 01874 658344 — MB BS 1960 Lond.; MD Connecticut 1967; FRCSC 1968; FRCS 1963; MRCS Eng. LRCP Lond. 1960. (St. Mary's) Cons. Surg. P. Chas. Gen. Hosp. Merthyr Tydfil; Hon. Surgic. Teach. Welsh Nat. Sch. Med. Prev: Cons. Surg. St. Catherines Canada; Cons. Surg. RAMC; Research Assoc. (Surg.) Yale Univ. USA.

THOMAS, William Alfred 18 Villiers Road, Woodthorpe, Nottingham NG5 4FB; South Woodville, St. Margaret's Road, Bowdon, Altrincham WA14 2AW — MB ChB 1973 Sheff.; FFA RCS Eng. 1979. Cons. Anaesth. Wythenshawe Hosp. Manch. Prev: Sen. Regist. (Anaesth.) St. Bart. Hosp. Lond.; Regist. (Anaesth.) Hosp. Sick Childr. Gt. Ormond St. Lond.

THOMAS, William Cledwyn Teilo, MBE, KStJ, TD Fay Cottage, 37 Penyfai Lane, Llanelli SA15 4EN Tel: 01554 2678; 6 Brynfield Court, Swansea SA3 4TF Tel: 01792 369753 — MRCS Eng. LRCP Lond. 1950. (St. Bart.) DL Dyfed; Police Surg. (A Div.) Dyfed Powys Police; Occupat. Health Phys. & Clin. Asst. (Haemat.) P. Phillip Hosp. Lla.lli. Prev: Venereologist W. Wales Hosp. Carmarthen; Regtl. Med. Off. 4th Bn. RRW TAVR Lt. Col.; Surg. Lt. RNVR.

THOMAS, Mr William Ernest Ghinn Royal Hallamshire Hospital, Glossop Road, Sheffield S10 2JF Tel: 0114 271 3142 Fax: 0114 271 3512; Ash Lodge, 65 Whirlow Pk Road, Whirlow, Sheffield S11 9NN Tel: 0114 262 0852 Fax: 0114 236 3695 Email: thomas@wegt.freeserve.co.uk — MB BS 1972 Lond.; BSc Lond. 1969, MS 1980; FRCS Eng. 1977; MRCS Eng. LRCP Lond. 1972; AKC 1969. (St. Geo.) Hon. Sen. Lect. Sheff. Univ.; Ct. of Exam. RCS; Surgic. Skills Tutor RCS Eng.; Intercollegiate Speciality Bd. Panel of Examrs.; Gen. Med. Counc. Phase 2 Assessor. Socs: Fell.

Assn. Surg.; Brit. Soc. Gastroenterol.; Surg. Research Soc. Prev: Sen. Regist. (Surg.) United Bristol Hosps.; Cons. Surg. & Clin. Dir. Surg. Roy. Hallamsh. Hosp. Sheff.; Regist. (Surg.) Addenbrooke's Hosp. Camb.

THOMAS, Mr William Gareth Morvah Farmhouse, Saltash PL12 5AB — MB BS 1973 Lond.; BSc (Biochem.) Lond. 1970; FRCS Eng. 1980; FRCS Ed. 1979; MRCS Eng. LRCP Lond. 1973. (Lond. Hosp.) Cons. Orthop. Surg. Plymouth HA. Socs: Brit. Scoliosis Soc.; Brit. Assn. Surg. Knee; Brit. Elbow & Shoulder Soc. Prev: Sen. Regist. (Orthop.) Soton. Gen. Hosp.; Regist. (Surg.) St. Thos. Hosp. Lond.; SHO (Surg.) Bristol Roy. Infirm.

THOMAS, William Gethyn (retired) 39 Heath Park Avenue, Cardiff CF14 3RF Tel: 02920 754 6524 — MB BCh 1956 Wales. Prev: Phys. i/c Res. Staff. & Stud.s Univ. Hosp. Wales & Univ. Wales Coll. Med.

THOMAS, William Ifor Thyge Enevoldson Springfield Surgery, Springfield Way, Brackley NN13 6JJ Tel: 01280 703431 Fax: 01280 703241 — MB BS 1957 Lond.; DObst RCOG 1962. (Middlx.) Med. Off. Nat. Childr. Home Evenley Hall. Socs: BMA. Prev: Ho. Phys. & Ho. Surg. Middlx. Hosp. Lond.; Flight Lt. RAF Med. Br.

THOMAS, William Ioan 16 Heol Gwys, Upper Cwmtwrch, Swansea SA9 2XQ — MB BCh 1997 Wales.

THOMAS, William Kenneth Aylesbury Partnership, Aylesbury Medical Centre, Taplow House, Thurlow Street, London SE17 2XE Tel: 020 7703 2205 — MB BS 1959 Lond.; MRCS Eng. LRCP Lond. 1959. (King's Coll. Hosp.) Socs: S. Lond. Obst. Soc. Prev: Ho. Phys. St. And. Hosp. Bow; Ho. Surg. Obst. St. Giles' Hosp. Lond.; Outpat. Off. Roy. Nat. Throat, Nose & Ear Hosp. Lond.

THOMAS, Mr William Michael Leicester General Hospital, Gwendolen Road, Leicester LE5 4PW Tel: 0116 249 0490; The Willows, Wartnaby Road, AB Kettleby, Melton Mowbray LE14 3JJ — MB BCh 1982 Wales; DM Nottm. 1991; FRCS Ed. 1987. Cons. Gen. Surg. Leicester Gen. Hosp. Prev: Sen. Regist. (Gen. Surg.) Leicester Hosps.; MRC Research Fell. (Surg.) Nottm. Univ.

THOMAS, Mr William Robert Griffith 5 Dyffryn Road, Gorseinon, Swansea SA8 3BX — MB BCh 1957 Wales; FRCS Ed. 1965; FRCS Eng. 1965. Cons. Surg. W. Wales Gen. Hosp. Carmarthen.

THOMAS, Wilson 13 The Copse, Marple Bridge, Stockport SK6 5QQ — MB BS 1981 Punjab; MD (Gen. Med.) Punjab 1985; MRCP (UK) 1987.

THOMAS GIBSON, Siwan Colestocks House, Colestocks EX14 3JR Email: datsrde@hotmail.com — MB BS 1992 Lond.; BSc (Hons.) Lond. 1991; MRCP (UK) 1995. (St. Mary's Hosp. Med. Sch.) p/t Specialist Regist (Gstroenterology) W Thames. Socs: RSM; Brit. Soc. Gastroenterol.; Amer. Soc. Gastroenterol. Prev: SpR (Gathro) St Mark's, Harrow; SpR (Gathro) Hillingdon; SpR (Gathro) St Mary's, Paddington.

THOMASON, Mr Andrew James Stephen Flat 2, Colebrook House, Royal Hampshire County Hospital, Romsey Road, Winchester SO22 5DG — MB BS 1989 Lond.; FRCSI 1994.

THOMASON, Frederic William Lower Crows Nest Farm, Kiln Lane, Milnrow, Rochdale OL16 3TR — MB ChB 1976 Manch.; DRCOG 1978.

THOMASON, Janie Keith Medical Group, Health Centre, Turner St, Keith AB55 5DJ Tel: 01542 882244 Fax: 01542 882317; Cockmuir House, Longmorn, Elgin IV30 8SL — MB ChB 1980 Aberd.; MRCGP 1984; DCH RCP Glas. 1983. Clin. Asst. (Diabetes) Dr. Gray's Hosp. Elgin.

THOMASSON, David Ian 34 Coope Road, Bollington, Macclesfield SK10 5AE — MB ChB 1990 Manch.

THOMASSON, Jane Elizabeth Rachel The Dairy House, Stratton, Dorchester DT2 9RU — MB ChB 1986 Bristol; FRCA 1992. Clin. Asst. (Anaesth.) W. Dorset Gen. Hosps. NHS Trust. Prev: Regist. (Anaesth.) Yorks. Region Train Scheme; Regist. (Anaesth.) Plymouth Gen. Hosps.

THOMASSON, Ruth Elizabeth 2A Hesketh Lane, Tarleton, Preston PR4 6UB — MB BS 1997 Newc.

THOMERSON, Derek George (retired) 55 Mountfield, Hythe, Southampton SO45 5AQ Tel: 02380 844088 — MB BS Lond. 1959; LMSSA Lond. 1956. Prev: Port Health Med. Off. Soton.

THOMERSON, Myfanwy Celia Rosalind 55 Mountfield, Hythe, Southampton SO45 5AQ — MB ChB Manch. 1952; DRCOG 1958; Dip. Med. Acupunc. 1997. (Manch.) Socs: Brit. Med. Acupunct. Soc.

THOMLINSON, John — MB ChB 1963 Birm.; FRCOG 1980; FRCOG 1980, M 1967; DObst 1965. Cons. Gynaecologist, Dewsbury Dist. Hosp. Prev: Sen. Regist. (O & G) Hammersmith Hosp. Lond.; Regist. (O & G) Roy. Hants. Co. Hosp. Winchester & Dudley Rd.; Hosp. Birm.

THOMPSELL, Amanda Ann Bence 41 Vine Street, London EC3N 2AA — MB BS 1982 Lond.; MRCPsych 1997; DGM RCP Lond. 1986; DRCOG 1985. (Char. Cross) Regist. (Psychiat.) Roy. Free Hosp. Lond. Prev: Clin. Asst. (Med. for Elderly) Roy. Free Hosp. Lond. & Diagn. Unit Eliz. Garrett Anderson.

THOMPSETT, Caroline 40 Tavistock Court, Tavistock Square, London WC1H 9HG — MB BS 1985 Lond.; FRCA 1991. (Roy. Free) Sen. Regist. (Anaesth.) St. Mary's Hosp. Lond.

THOMPSON, Adam Mathias Magpie Cottages, 5 Rakeham Hill, Torrington EX38 8JE — MB BS 1994 Lond.

THOMPSON, Mr Adrian Charles ENT Department, Queen's Hospital, Burton-on-Trent DE13 0RB Tel: 01283 566333 Fax: 01283 593004 — MB ChB 1982 Leeds; FRCS (Orl.) 1993; FRCS Eng. 1988; FRCS Ed. 1986. (Leeds) Cons. ENT Surg. Burton Hosps. NHS Trust. Socs: Brit. Assn. Otol. Head & Neck Surg.; Brit. Assn. Head & Neck Oncol.; Brit. Assn. of Endocrine Surgs. Prev: Sen. Regist. Rotat. (ENT) Nottm. & Derby Train. Scheme; Regist. (ENT) Univ. Hosp. Nottm. & Vict. Infirm. Glas.; SHO (Plastic Surg.) St. Luke's Hosp. Bradford.

THOMPSON, Aidan William 18 Corrina Park, Dunmurray, Belfast BT17 0HA — MB BCh BAO 1995 Belf.

THOMPSON, Alan Brian Robert The Surgery, 20 Lee Road, Blackheath, London SE3 0PE Tel: 020 8852 1235 Fax: 020 8297 2193; Tel: 020 8853 0415 — MB BS 1979 Lond.; MRCS Eng. LRCP Lond. 1979; MRCP (UK) 1983; MRCGP 1988; DCH RCP Lond. 1985. (St. Mary's)

THOMPSON, Mr Alan Clive 14 Osborne Close, Harrogate HG1 2EF — MB BS 1985 Lond.; BSc (Hons.) Lond. 1982, MB BS 1985; FRCS Eng. 1991. Regist. (Surg.) Roy. Lond. Hosp.

THOMPSON, Professor Alan James Institute of Neurology, Queen Square, London WC1N 3BG Tel: 020 7837 3611 Fax: 020 7813 6505 Email: a.thompson@ion.ucl.ac.uk — MD 1985 Dub.; MB BCh BAO 1979; FRCP Lond. 1994; FRCPI 1995. Garfield W.on, Prof. of Clin. Neurol. and Neurorehabilitaion; Cons. Neurol. s/i in Disabil., Nat. Hosp. for Neurol. & Neurosug.; Director of Research and Developm.; Assoc. Clin. Director. Socs: Assn. Brit. Neurol; Amer. Neurol. Assn.; Pres., Europ. Comm. for Treatm. and Research in MS. Prev: Sen. Lect. Inst. of Neurol.; Reader (Clin. Neurol.) Univ. Dept. Clin. Neurol. Inst. of Neurol.; Cons. Neurol. Whittington Hosp.

THOMPSON, Alan James 189 Cooden Sea Road, Bexhill-on-Sea TN39 4TH — BM 1998 Soton.

THOMPSON, Alan Richard 189 Cooden Sea Road, Cooden, Bexhill-on-Sea TN39 4TH — MB BS 1969 Lond.; FFA RCS Eng. 1975; DA Eng. 1973. (Univ. Coll. Hosp.) Cons. (Anaesth.) Hastings Health Dist. Prev: Sen. Regist. (Anaesth.) Soton. & S.W. Hants. Health Dist. (T); Regist. (Anaesth.) Univ. Coll. Hosp. Lond.; Ho. Surg. & Ho. Phys. Metrop. Hosp. Lond.

THOMPSON, Mr Alastair Mark Dept of Surgery, Ninwells Medical School, Dundee DD1 9SY Tel: 01382 66011 Email: amthompson@ninewells.dundee.ac.uk — MB ChB 1984 Ed.; FRCS (Gen.) 1995; FRCS Ed. 1991; MD. 1991; BSc (Hons) 1982. Reader, Univ. Dundee; Hon Cons. Surg. Socs: Assn. of Surg.s of Gt. Britain & Irel.; Brit. Oncological Assn.; Brit. Assn. for Cancer Research. Prev: Hon. Regist. Univ. Dept. Surg. Roy. Infirm. Ed. Lothian HB; Regist. (Surg.) Raigmore Hosp. Inverness; SHO W.. Infirm. Glas.

THOMPSON, Mr Albert Edward The Consulting Rooms, York House, 199 Westminster Bridge Road, London SE1 7UT Tel: 020 7928 3019 Fax: 020 7928 3019 — MB BS 1955 Lond.; MS Lond. 1966; FRCS Eng. 1959. (St. Mary's) Prev: Cons. Surg. St. Thos. Hosp. & Roy. Marsden Hosp. Lond.; Asst. Dir. Surgic. Unit St. Mary's Hosp. Lond.; Sen. Regist. (Surg.) St. Mary's Hosp. Lond.

THOMPSON, Alexander John 61 St Clares Court, Lower Bullingham, Hereford HR2 6PY Tel: 01432 343062 Email: docajt@aol.com — MB BS 1994 Lond.; DRCOG 1996. (Roy. Lond. Hosp. Med. Coll.) GP Non-Princip.; Health Promotion Off. Heref. HA. Prev: SHO Hereford Hosps. NHS Trust VTS; Ho. Off. (Med.) King Geo. Hosp. Ilford; Ho. Off. (Surg.) Epsom.

THOMPSON, Alice Mary Susan Park Lane Cottages, Hawstead, Bury St Edmunds IP29 5NX Tel: 01284 753296 — MB BS 1966

THOMPSON

Lond.; MRCP (UK) (Paediat.) 1984; MRCS Eng. LRCP Lond. 1966; DObst RCOG 1975; DCH Eng. 1971. (St. Bart.) Cons. Paediat. W. Suff. Gen. Hosp. Bury St Edmunds.; Dep. Police Surg. Suff. Prev: Assoc. Specialist (Paediat.) W. Suff. Gen. Hosp. Bury St Edmunds.

THOMPSON, Mr Alistair Graham 81 Harborne Road, Edgbaston, Birmingham B15 3HG Tel: 0121 455 9496 — MB ChB Birm. 1965; FRCS Eng. 1995; FRCS Ed. 1972; T(S) 1991. (Birm.) Cons. Orthop. Surg. Roy. Orthop. Hosp.; Hon. Sen. Lect. (Orthop. Surg.) Univ. Birm.; Corr. Foreign Fell. Scoliosis Research Soc., USA; Hon. Cons. Birm. Childr.'s Hosp. NHS Trust. Socs: Fell. BOA (Counc. Mem. 1997-2000); Int. Fell. Scoliosis Res. Soc. (US) 1992-; Fell. Brit. Scoliosis Soc. (Med. Exec. Comm. 19996-2001). Prev: Sen. Regist. Roy. Orthop. Hosp. Birm.; Lect. (Orthop. Surg.) Univ. Hong Kong; Research Fell. (Surg.) Univ. Calif., San Diego.

THOMPSON, Alistair Robin Tytler Seven Brooks Medical Centre, 21 Church Street, Atherton, Manchester M46 9DE Tel: 01942. 882799 Fax: 01942 873859 — MB ChB Glas. 1970; FRCGP 1996. (Glas.) GP Assoc. Dir. Salford & Trafford HA. Socs: BMA; RCGP. Prev: SHO (Obst.) Paisley Matern. Hosp.; SHO (Anaesth.) Glas. Roy. Infirm.

THOMPSON, Allan Christopher Division of Psychiatry, North Tees General Hospital, Hardwick, Stockton-on-Tees TS19 8PE — BM 1979 Soton.

THOMPSON, Andrea Meloney 7 Wye Close, Bletchley, Milton Keynes MK3 7PJ — MB BS 1997 Lond.

THOMPSON, Mr Andrew 20 Limefield Ave, Lymm WA13 0QB Tel: 01925 756940 — MB ChB 1991 Manch.; FRCS Eng. 1995. Specialist Regist. (Urol.) NW Region. Socs: BAUS (Jun. mem.). Prev: SHO (Surg.) Wythenshawe Hosp. Manch.; SHO (A & E & Orthop.) Roy. Liverp. Univ. Hosp.; Demonst. (Anat.) Univ. Leeds.

THOMPSON, Andrew 121 Humber Road S., Beeston, Nottingham NG9 2EX — MB BS 1996 Lond.

THOMPSON, Andrew Leech Meadow Cottage, Sheinton, Cressage, Shrewsbury SY5 6 — MB BS 1998 Lond.

THOMPSON, Andrew Christopher 22 Southfield Drive, Hazlemere, High Wycombe HP15 7HB — MB ChB 1998 Bristol.

THOMPSON, Andrew James 10 Adelaide Avenue, Belfast BT9 7FY Tel: 01232 208805 — MB BCh BAO 1989 Belf.; MB BCh Belf. 1989; MRCP. (Queens University Belfast) Socs: MRCPCH.

THOMPSON, Andrew Jeffrey Stafford Road Surgery, 60 Stafford Road, Cannock WS11 2AG Tel: 01543 503332 Fax: 01543 503010; Squirrel's Leap, Denefield, Penkridge, Stafford ST19 5JF Email: ajtho@lineone.net — MB ChB 1979 Liverp.; DRCOG 1982. GP Cannock. Socs: Cannock & Mid Staffs. Med. Socs.; BMA.

THOMPSON, Andrew John 119 Main Street, Menston, Ilkley LS29 6HT Tel: 01943 872113; 152 Bradford Road, Menston, Ilkley LS29 6ED Tel: 01943 872583 — MB ChB 1980 Leeds; MRCGP 1984.

THOMPSON, Andrew Joseph Department of Radiology, Kettering General Hospital, Kettering NN16 8UZ Tel: 01536 492000 Fax: 01586 492473; 6 Boardman Road, Kettering NN15 7DH Tel: 01536 515495 — MB ChB 1971 Liverp.; FRCR 1977; DMRD Liverp. 1975. (Liverpool) Cons. Radiol. Kettering Gen. Hosp.

THOMPSON, Andrew Keith Dept of Histopathology, The Medical School, University of Birmingham, Birmingham B15 2TT Tel: 0121 414 4016; 7 Cornfield Croft, Sutton Coldfield B76 1SN Tel: 0121 378 2342 — MB ChB 1988 Leeds. Specialist Regist. Histopath. W. Midl. Regional Traning Scheme. Prev: Ho. Off. (Gen. Surg.) Bradford Roy. Infirm.; Ho. Off. (Gen. Med.) Huddersfield Roy. Infirm.

THOMPSON, Andrew Maurice The Strand Practice, 2 The Strand, Goring-by-Sea, Worthing BN12 6DN Tel: 01903 243351 Fax: 01903 705804; Whiteridge, 12 Longlands, Charmandean, Worthing BN14 9NT Tel: 01903 231568 — MB BS 1990 Lond.; MRCGP 1994; DRCOG 1993; DFFP 1993. (Guy's Hospital)

THOMPSON, Andrew Paul The Surgery, 174 Rookery Road, Handsworth, Birmingham B21 9NN Tel: 0121 554 0921; 114 West Avenue, Handsworth Wood, Birmingham B20 2LY Tel: 0121 686 5461 Fax: 07000 329362 — MB ChB 1989 Birm.; MRCGP 1993; DFFP 1993; DGM RCP Lond. 1991. (Birmingham) Socs: Fell. Roy. Soc. Med. Prev: Trainee GP Birm.; SHO (O & G) Dist. Gen. Hosp. W. Bromwich; SHO (Geriat. & A & E) & Ho. Off. (Med.) Russells Hall Hosp. Dudley.

THOMPSON, Andrew Philip Westerhope Medical Group, 377 Stamfordham Road, Westerhope, Newcastle upon Tyne NE5 2LH

Tel: 0191 243 7000 Fax: 0191 243 7006 — MB BS 1987 Newc.; MRCGP 1994; DA (UK) 1989. (Newcastle upon Tyne) GP Princip. W.erhope Med. Gp. Prev: Trainee GP N.d. VTS; SHO (Paediat. & Med.) Qu. Eliz. Hosp. Gateshead; SHO (Anaesth.) Newc. u. Tyne.

THOMPSON, Angela North Warwickshire NHS Trust, Child Health Services, 5 Pool Bank St., Nuneaton CV11 5DB Tel: 01203 351333 Fax: 01203 350509; 17 Hargrave Close, Oak Farm, Binley, Coventry CV3 2XS Tel: 01203 448351 — MB ChB 1980 Liverp.; DCCH RCP Ed. 1984; DCH RCP Lond. 1983. SCMO (Child Health) Warks. HA. Socs: Brit. Paediat. Assn.; Brit. Assn. Community Child Health; RCPCH. Prev: Clin. Med. Off. (Child Health) Coventry HA.

***THOMPSON, Angela Claire** 36 Sherwood Drive, Marske, Redcar TS11 6DR — MB ChB 1996 Liverp.; DGH - RCPCH 1999.

THOMPSON, Angela Mary Stewart 6 Highgate Road, Altrincham WA14 4QZ Tel: 0161 928 4862 — MB ChB Liverp. 1960; DObst RCOG 1962. (Liverp.) Clin. Med. Off. Trafford AHA. Socs: Fac. Community Health; Assoc. Mem. Brit. Paediat. Soc. Prev: Ho. Surg. & Ho. Phys. BRd.green Hosp. Liverp.; Ho. Surg. Mill Rd. Matern. Hosp. Liverp.

THOMPSON, Angus James Radiology Department, Woodend Hospital, Aberdeen AB15 6XS Tel: 01224 663131; 48 Camperdown Road, Aberdeen AB15 5NU Tel: 01224 633804 — MB ChB 1980 Aberd.; FRCR 1986; DMRD Aberd. 1984. Head Radiol. Woodend Hosp., Aberd. Prev: Cons. Radiol. Dundee Hosps. & Carlisle Hosps.; Vis. Prof. Kwong Wah Hosp. Kowloon Hong Kong 1991; Sen. Regist. (Diagn. Radiol.) Roy. Surrey Co. Hosp. Guildford.

THOMPSON, Ann Veronica 30 Cleveland Road, South Woodford, London E18 2AL Tel: 020 8530 4917 Fax: 020 8530 4917 — MB BChir 1974 Camb.; Dobst RCOG 1975; MA 1974 Camb.; MA Camb. 1974; DObst RCOG 1975. Hosp. Practitioner Chingford Osteoporosis Clinic Lond. Prev: GP Oxf.; Research Regist. (Community Med. & Gen. Pract.) Univ. Oxf.

THOMPSON, Anne Elizabeth Child, Adolescent & Family Services, Moore House, 10/11 Lindum Terrace, Lincoln LN2 5RS — MB BS 1985 Newc.; MRCP (UK) 1988; MRCPsych 1991. Cons. (Child & Adolesc. Psychiat.) Lincoln. Prev: Lect. (Child & Adolesc. Psychiat.) Univ. Nottm.; Sen. Regist. N.. RHA; Regist. Rotat. (Psychiat.) Newc.

THOMPSON, Anne Mary The Surgery, 48 Mulgrave Road, Belmont, Sutton SM2 6LX Tel: 020 8642 2050; 5 Lymbourne Close, Sutton SM2 6DX — BM 1978 Soton.; DFFP 1995.

THOMPSON, Anne Rosemary Robinson, Ashton, Leung, Solari and Thompson, James Preston Health Centre, 61 Holland Road, Sutton Coldfield B72 1RL Tel: 0121 355 5150; The Grange, 7 The Orchards, Four Oaks, Sutton Coldfield B74 2PP — MB ChB 1980 Birm.; MRCGP 1984. (Birm.)

THOMPSON, Anne Tait Avon Medical Centre, Academy Street, Larkhall ML9 2BJ Tel: 01698 882547 Fax: 01698 888138; Garngour, 22 Hill Road, Stonehouse, Larkhall ML9 3EA — MB ChB 1983 Glas.; MRCGP 1987; DRCOG 1986. GP StoneHo. Socs: BMA.

THOMPSON, Anthony Baird Tamarisk, Frogspool, Truro TR4 8RU — MB ChB 1989 Liverp.

THOMPSON, Anthony Michael 30 Myrtlefield Park, Belfast BT9 6NF Tel: 01232 665094 Email: amt@myrtlfld.dnet.co.uk; 6 Heathmount, Portstewart BT55 7AP Tel: 01265 833845 — MB BCh BAO 1976 Belf.; FFR RCSI 1985; DRCOG 1978. Cons. Radiol. Downe Hosp. Downpatrick & Roy. Vict. Hosp. Belf. Socs: Roy. Coll. Radiol. & Fell. Ulster Med. Soc.; Brit. Med. Ultrasound Soc.; Amer. Röentgen Ray Soc. Prev: Sen. Regist. Univ. Hosp. Nottm.; Regist. (Radiol.) Roy. Vict. Hosp. Belf.; SHO & Ho. Off. Craigavon Area Hosp.

THOMPSON, Ashley George Gyton (retired) c/o Westminster Bank, 62 Victoria St., London SW1 — MB BCh 1914 Camb.; MA (Nat. Sc. Trip.) Camb. 1911, MD 1924, MB BC DPH. Prev: MOH Boro. Lambeth.

THOMPSON, Barbara (retired) Heathcliffe, 14 Green Head Road, Utley, Keighley BD20 6EA Tel: 01535 602875 — MB ChB 1963 Sheff.; DObst RCOG 1966. Prev: SCMO Airedale HA.

THOMPSON, Barbara Clare (retired) Newlands, Whitchurch Hill, Reading RG8 7PN — MB BS Lond. 1962; MRCS Eng. LRCP Lond. 1962. Prev: Community Paediat. (Presch. Audiol.) Roy. Berks. & Battle Hosp. NHS Trust Reading.

THOMPSON, Basil Ainsworth (retired) 28 Tarvin Road, Littleton, Chester CH3 7DG Tel: 01244 336215 — MB ChB 1952 Sheff.;

MRCS Eng. LRCP Lond. 1953; AFOM RCP Lond. 1990; MRCGP 1961; DIH Soc. Apoth. Lond. 1963.

THOMPSON, Mr Blair Alexander (retired) Burnside, Innerleithen EH44 6HY Tel: 01896 830372 — MB ChB 1942 Ed.; FRCS Ed. 1948. Prev: Cons. Surg. Scott. Borders Hosps.

THOMPSON, Brenda Mildred (retired) 705 Aylestone Road, Leicester LE2 8TG Tel: 0116 283 2325 — MB BS 1961 Lond.; MRCS Eng. LRCP Lond. 1961. Prev: Ho. Surg. & Ho. Phys. Gt. Yarmouth & Gorleston Hosp.

THOMPSON, Brian Christopher Basement Flat, Granville Court, 31 West St., Southcliff, Scarborough YO11 2QR — MB ChB 1991 Leeds.

THOMPSON, Bryan Eykyn Lombe, MBE (retired) 60A London Road, Kilmarnock KA3 7DD — MB BChir 1951 Camb.; LMSSA Lond. 1949. Prev: Med. Supt. St. Luke's Hosp. PO Hiranpur, Dist. Pakur, Bihar, India.

THOMPSON, Caroline Creed Taunton & Somerset Hospital, Musgrove Park, Taunton TA1 5DA Tel: 01823 333444 Fax: 01823 342411; Welham Rise, Charlton Mackrell, Somerton TA11 7AJ Fax: 01458 224219 — MB ChB 1983 Birm.; DLO 2000; MRCGP 1992; DRCOG 1989; DA (UK) 1985. p/t Staff Grade Surg. ENT Dept., Taunton & Som. Hosp. Socs: BMA; MDU. Prev: GP Principle, Glastonbury.

THOMPSON, Carolyn Irene Royal Infirmary of Edinburgh, Lauriston Place, Edinburgh — MB ChB 1980 Ed.; FRCRP (Ed.); MRCP (UK) 1983. Cons. in Gum, NHS Lothian, Edin. Prev: Cons. in Gum, Fife Acute Hosp.s NHS Trust.

THOMPSON, Catherine Susannah Bottom Cross, Chew Stoke, Bristol BS40 8XD — MB BS 1990 Lond.; BSc Lond. 1987, MB BS 1990. SHO (Med. & Clin. Oncol.) Bristol Roy. Infirm.

THOMPSON, Catriona 25 Knoll Park, Alloway, Ayr KA7 4RH — MB ChB Ed. 1960; FFA RCS Eng. 1970; DA (Eng.) 1963. Cons. Anaesth. Ayrsh. & Arran HB. Prev: Cons. Anaesth. N. W.. RHA; Cons. Anaesth. Harare Hosp., Zimbabwe; Hon. Lect. (Anaesth.) Univ. Zimbabwe.

THOMPSON, Catriona Jane Kwinchens, Old High Road, Brightwell-cum-Sotwell, Wallingford OX10 0QF — BM 1995 Soton.

THOMPSON, Cecil Hamilton (retired) 83 Southworth Road, Newton-le-Willows WA12 0BL — MB ChB 1947 Manch.

THOMPSON, Cecilia Mary Hill Lane Surgery, 162 Hill Lane, Southampton SO15 5DD Tel: 023 8022 3086 Fax: 023 8023 5487; Tel: 023 8025 3225 — MB BS 1976 London; MRCP 1980 Lond. (London) p/t GP Soton. Socs: RCGP; BMA.

THOMPSON, Cedric Francis Derek Kelvedon & Feerine Health Centre, 46 High Street, Kelvedon CO5 9AE Tel: 01376 572906 Fax: 01376 572484 Email: cedric.thompson@gp-f81011.nhs.uk; 6 Brockwell Lane, Kelvedon CO5 9BB Tel: 01376 570660 — MB BS 1975 Lond.; MRCGP 1981; DRCOG 1979. (Westminster)

THOMPSON, Mr Charles Edward Rosslyn (retired) 138 Spilsby Road, Boston PE21 9PE Tel: 01205 364387 — MB BChir 1958 Camb.; MA Camb. 1958; FRCS Ed. 1964. Prev: Cons. Surg. S. Lincs. Health Dist.

THOMPSON, Charles Kevin Wordsworth Surgery, 97 Newport Road, Cardiff CF24 0AG Tel: 029 2049 8000 Fax: 029 2045 5494; 36 Lake Road W., Cardiff CF2 5NN — MB BCh 1978 Wales; MRCGP 1982.

THOMPSON, Christine Louise Chipping Surgery, 1 Symn Lane, Wotton-under-Edge GL12 7BD Tel: 01453 842214; 23 Hawkesbury Road, Hillesley, Gloucester GL2 7RE Email: christine.gordon@btinternet.com — MB ChB 1986 Bristol; DRCOG 1991. (Bristol) GP. Prev: Trainee GP Bath VTS; SHO (Infec. Dis. & Respirat. Med.) Ham Green Hosp. Bristol.

THOMPSON, Christine Mary 52 Boston Place, London NW1 6ER Tel: 020 7402 3550 Fax: 020 7402 3550; 11 Blackwell Scar, Darlington DL3 8DL Tel: 01325 464914 Fax: 01325 464914 — MB BS Lond. 1955; MFOM RCP Lond. 1979; Spec. Accredit. (Occupat. Med.) RCP Lond 1979; DIH Eng. 1968; DPH Lond. 1967. (St. Bart.) p/t Med Adviser Penguin Books Ltd. Harmondsworth Middlx. Socs: Fell. Roy. Soc. Med.; BMA.

THOMPSON, Professor Christopher University of Southampton, Department of Psychiatry, Royal South Hampshire Hospital, Brinton's Terrace, Southampton SO14 0YG Tel: 02380 825533 Fax: 02380 234243 — MD 1987 Lond.; MRCGP 2000; MPhil Lond. 1984, BSc 1974, MB BS 1977; FRCP 1995; FRCPsych. 1991, M 1982. (Univ. Coll. Lond.) Prof. Psychiat. Fac. Med. Health & Biological Sci. Univ. Soton.; Head of the Sch. of Med. Socs: Assoc. Fell. Brit. Psychol. Soc.; Fell. Collegium Internat.e Neuropsychopharmacologicum (CINP); Founder Int. Soc. Affective Disorders. Prev: Sen. Lect. Char. Cross & W.m. Med. Sch. Lond.

THOMPSON, Claire Lorraine 6 Castle Street, Inner Avenue, Southampton SO14 6HA — MB ChB 1990 Sheff.

THOMPSON, Claire Louise Ravenstone, The Park, Cheltenham GL50 2RP Tel: 01242 234504 — MB ChB 1995 Birm.

THOMPSON, Craig Antony Pavilion Flat, University Road, Aberdeen AB24 3DR — MB ChB 1986 Aberd.; BMedBiol. Aberd. 1985. SHO (Accid. Emerg. & Gen. Surg.) Hairmyres Hosp. E. Kilbride Glas. Prev: SHO (Thoracic Surg.) Hairmyres Hosp. E. Kilbride Glas.; SHO (Orthop. A & E) StoneHo. Hosp. StoneHo.; SHO (A & E) Roy. Sussex Co. Hosp. Brighton.

THOMPSON, Craig Stephen County Hospital, North Road, Durham DH1 4ST Tel: 0191 333 3434 — MB BS 1991 Newc. Staff Grade (Gen. Psychiat). Gen. Hosp. Durh. Prev: Regist. (Gen. Psychiat.) St. Luke's Hosp. Middlesbrough.

THOMPSON, Damien Harold Michael 13 Rectory Square, London E1 3NQ — MB BS 1994 Lond.

THOMPSON, Daniel Owl End, Newfield Lane, Sheffield S17 3DB — MB BS 1998 Lond.

THOMPSON, Daniel Stenhouse Luton & Dunstable Hospital, Luton LU4 0DZ Tel: 01582 491122 Fax: 01582 497388 Email: dan.thompon@ldh-tr.anglox.nhs.uk; 16 Hollybush Lane, Harpenden AL5 4AT Tel: 01582 460739 — MB BS 1965 Lond.; BSc (Physiol.) Lond. 1962; MRCS Eng. LRCP Lond. 1965; FRCPath 1984, M 1972. (Univ. Coll. Hosp.) Cons. Haemat. Luton & Dunstable Hosp. Socs: Brit. Soc. Haematol.; Assn. Clin. Path. Prev: Sen. Regist. (Haemat.) Univ. Coll. Hosp. Lond.; Sen. Regist. (Haemat.) Roy. Perth Hosp., W. Austral.; Ho. Phys. Univ. Coll. Hosp.

THOMPSON, Mr David Hope Hospital, Stott Lane, Salford, Manchester M6 8HD; Squirrel Chase, Heighley Castle Way, Madeley, Crewe CW3 9HF Tel: 01782 750778 — MB BS 1991 Lond.; FRCS Eng. 1996. (Guy's Hosp. Lond.) Specialist Regist. In Radiol., N. W. Rotat., Hope Hosp. Manch. Prev: SHO Rotat. (Surg.) Kent & Canterbury Hosp.; SHO (Urol.) Harold Wood Hosp. Romford; SHO(Surg)Roy. Hants. Co. Hosp.

THOMPSON, David Charles The Priory Hospital, Priory Lane, London SW15 5JJ Tel: 020 8876 8261; Pitt Cottage, Bowling Green Close, London SW15 3TE Tel: 020 8788 7815 — MRCS Eng. LRCP Lond. 1950; MRCPsych 1972; FRANZCP 1978, M 1966; DPM Eng. 1964. (Univ. Coll. Hosp.) Cons. Psychiat. The Priory Roehampton; Hon. Psychiat. P. of Wales's Hosp. Sydney; Vis. Cons. Psychiat. Repatriation Dept. Austral. Govt. Socs: BMA & Roy. Soc. Med. Prev: Res. Med. Off. Univ. Coll. Hosp. Lond.; Ho. Phys. Brompton Hosp. Lond.; Med. Regist. Roy. Masonic Hosp. Lond.

THOMPSON, David Frederick John Westby House Farm, Rawcliffe Road, St Michaels, Garstang, Preston PR3 0UE — MRCS Eng. LRCP Lond. 1957; DObst RCOG 1959. (St. Mary's) Dir. BUPA Manch. Med. Centre. Socs: Fell. Manch. Med. Soc.; Soc. Occupat. Health. Prev: Med. Dir. BUPA Manch. Med. Centre; Regist. (O & G) Sharoe Green Hosp. Preston.

THOMPSON, David George Department of Medicine, Hope Hospital, Salford M6 8HD Tel: 0161 787 4363 Fax: 0161 787 4364 — MB BS 1972 Lond.; BSc Lond. 1969, MD 1980; FRCP Lond. 1992; MRCP (UK) 1974. Prof. & Hon. Cons. Med. & Gastroenterol. Hope Hosp. Socs: Amer. Gastroenterol. Assn.; (Sec.) Brit. Soc. Gastronterol.; Physiol. Soc. Prev: Wellcome Trust Sen. Lect. (Med.) Lond. Hosp. Med. Coll.; Lect. (Med.) Lond. Hosp.; SHO Hammersmith Hosp.

THOMPSON, David John Headquarters, The Masion, Mansion Park, Tongue Lane, Leeds LS6 4QT Tel: 0113 231 6716 Fax: 0113 231 6718 — MB BS 1970 Lond.; MSc Manch. 1980; FRCPsych 1991. (Middlx.) Cons. Psychiat. Malham Hse. Day Hosp. Leeds; Sen. Clin. Lect. Univ. Leeds. Prev: Cons. Psychiat. Airedale Gen. Hosp. Keighley; Sen. Regist. (Psychiat.) Withington Hosp. Manch.

THOMPSON, David Robert Peter Newtownstewart Medical Centre, 5 Millbrook Street, Newtownstewart, Omagh BT78 4BW Tel: 028 8166 1333 Fax: 028 8166 1883; Brandon House, Newtownstewart, Omagh — MB BCh BAO 1974 Belf.

THOMPSON, David Sheraton 14 St Margaret's Street, Rochester ME1 1TR — MB 1972 Camb.; BChir 1971; FRCP Lond. 1989;

THOMPSON

MRCP (UK) 1973. Cons. Phys. & Cardiol. Medway HA; Hon. Cons. Cardiol. St. Thos. Hosp. Lond. Prev: Sen. Regist. St. Thos. Hosp. Lond.; Ho. Phys. St. Bart. & Brompton Hosps. Lond.

THOMPSON, David Theodore 14 Green Lane, Oxhey, Watford WD19 4NJ — MB BChir 1966 Camb.; MA, MB Camb. 1966, BChir 1965. (Middlx.) Clin. Research Asst. Dept. Urol. Middlx. Hosp. Socs: Fell. Med. Soc. Lond. Prev: Surgic. Regist. Lond. Hosp., Willesden Gen. & Hitchin Hosps.

THOMPSON, Denys Ridley Southview, Lower St., Whiteshill, Stroud GL6 6AR Tel: 01453 751581 — BM BCh Oxf. 1965.; BSc, Leeds 1963; MRCGP 1978; DObst RCOG 1972. (Leeds & Oxf.) Prev: SHO Accid. Serv., Ho. Surg. & Ho. Phys. Radcliffe Infirm. Oxf.; Ho. Off. (Obst.) Ch.ill Hosp. Oxf.

THOMPSON, Desmond George The Surgery, 20 Lee Road, Blackheath, London NW7 1LJ Tel: 020 8852 1235 Fax: 020 8297 2193; 83 Guibal Road, Lee, London SE12 9HF — MB BS 1983 Lond.; Dip Sports Med 2001 Bath Univ.; MRCGP 1989; DRCOG 1986. (St. Bart.) GP Princip. Prev: GP Lewisham & S.wark VTS; Ho. Surg. Hackney Hosp. Lond.; Ho. Phys. St. Bart. Hosp. Lond.

THOMPSON, Dinah Deborah (retired) Saunders, Church St., Coggeshall, Colchester CO6 1TX Tel: 01206 561245 — MB BChir 1949 Camb.; MA Camb. 1950; DPM Eng. 1968. Prev: Cons. Psychiat. Severalls Hosp. Colchester.

THOMPSON, Mr Dominic Nolan Paul Department of Neurosurgery, Great Ormond Street Hospital for Children, NHS Trust, London WC1N 3TH Email: dominic.thompson@gosh-tr-nthames.nhs.uk; 28 Brodrick Road, London SW17 7DY — MB BS 1986 Lond.; BSc (Anat.) Lond. 1983, MB BS 1986; FRCS (SN) 1997; FRCS 1990; FRCS Eng. 1990. (Char. Cross & Westm. Med. Sch.) Cons. Paediat. Neurosurg. Gt. Ormond St. Hosp. For Childr. NHS Trust; Hon. Cons. Neurosurg.; Nat. Hosp. for Neurol. and Neurosurg., Qu. Sq. Lond.. Prev: Sen. Regist. (Neurosurg.) Atkinson Morley's Hosp. & Nat. Hosp. Qu. Sq.; Research Fell. (Neurosurg. & Craniofacial) Hosp. Sick Childr. Gt. Ormond St. Lond.; Regist. (Neurosurg.) Nat. Hosp. Qu. Sq. Lond.

THOMPSON, Edward Eustace Michael (retired) Tregenna, Brooks Drive, Hale Barns, Altrincham WA15 8TR Tel: 0161 980 4113 — MB ChB 1959 Liverp.; FFA RCS Eng. 1967; DObst RCOG 1964. Cons. Anaesth. S. Manch. Health Dist. (T). Prev: Sen. Regist. (Anaesth.) United Manch. Hosps.

THOMPSON, Professor Edward John Institute of Neurology, National Hospital, Queen Square, London WC1N 3BG Tel: 020 7837 3611 Fax: 020 7837 8553 Email: e.thompson@ion.ucl.ac.uk — MD 1968 Rochester; PhD Lond. 1966, DSc 1992; FRCP Lond. 1996; FRCPath 1989, M 1979; MRCP Lond. 1999. (Univ. Rochester, USA) Prof. & Hon. Cons. Chem. Path. Inst. Neurol. Nat. Hosp. for Neurol. & Neurosurg. Lond. Prev: on Staff Zool. Dept. Univ. Coll. Lond., Nat. Inst. Health Bethesda, USA.

THOMPSON, Eleanor Ada (retired) 78 Bellemoor Road, Upper Shirley, Southampton SO15 7QU Tel: 01703 782242 — MRCS Eng. LRCP Lond. 1942.

THOMPSON, Elinor Mary South and West Devon Health Authority, The Lescaze Offices, Dartington, Totnes TQ9 6JE — MB ChB 1983 Bristol; MFCM 1989. Cons. Pub. Health Med. S. & W. Devon HA.

THOMPSON, Elizabeth Anita Bristol Homeopathic Hospital, Cotham Hill, Bristol BS6 6AX — MB BS 1987 Lond.; MRCP (UK) 1991; MFHom 1995. Cons. Homeopathic Phys.

THOMPSON, Elizabeth Ann 27 Moor Park Road, Northwood HA6 2DL Tel: 01923 827361 — MB BChir 1966 Camb.; MA Camb. 1966. (Camb. & St. Mary's) Prev: SHO (Anaesth.) & Ho. Surg. Hillingdon Hosp. Uxbridge; Ho. Phys. St. Mary's Hosp. Lond.

THOMPSON, Elizabeth Claire 69 Valley Drive, Kirk Ella, Hull HU10 7PW — MB ChB 1991 Liverp.

THOMPSON, Elizabeth Georgina Emily 1 Hackwood Park, Hexham NE46 1AX — MB ChB 1998 Manch.

THOMPSON, Elizabeth Hildred St Margaret's Somerset Hospice, Heron Drive, Bishops Hull, Taunton TA1 5HA Tel: 01823 259394 Fax: 01283 345900; Green End, Rowford, Cheddon Fitzpaine, Taunton TA2 8JY Tel: 01823 451529 — MB ChB 1971 Manch.; Dip. Pallial. Med. 1995. Sen. Med. Off. (Palliat. Med.) St. Margt. Som. Hospice Taunton.

THOMPSON, Elizabeth Jacqueline 36 Park Road, Ipswich IP1 3SU — MB ChB 1964 Ed.; FFA RCS Eng. 1972.

THOMPSON, Elizabeth Mary Department of Histopathology, St. Mary's Hospital, London W2 1NY Tel: 020 7886 1770 Fax: 020 7886 6068 Email: m.thompson@ic.ac.uk; 88 Grange Road, London W5 3PJ — MB BChir 1977 Camb.; MA Camb. 1977; MD Camb. 1993; MRCP (UK) 1980; FRCPath 1995, MRCPath 1983. (Camb. & Middlx.) Cons. Histopath. St. Mary's Hosp. Lond. Socs: Assn. Clin. Path.; Renal Assn.; Internat. Acad. Path. Prev: Sen. Lect. (Histopath.) Roy. Postgrad. Med. Sch. Lond.; MRC Train. Fell. Roy. Postgrad. Med. Sch. Lond.; Sen. Regist. (Histopath.) Hammersmith Hosp. Lond. & N.wick Pk. Hosp. Harrow.

THOMPSON, Elizabeth Mary Mater Informorum Hospital, Crumlin Road, Belfast BT14 6AB Tel: 01232 741211; 39 Carnreagh, Hillsborough BT26 6LJ Tel: 01846 682482 — MB BCh BAO 1976 Belf.; FFA RCS Eng. 1981. Cons. Anaesth. Mater Informorum Hosp. Belf.

THOMPSON, Emma Carol Margaret Frenchay Healthcare Trust, Blackberry Hill Hospital, Manor Road, Fishponds, Bristol BS16 2EW; 91 Richmond Road, Montpelier, Bristol BS6 5EP — MB ChB 1983 Bristol; MRCPsych 1991; MRCGP 1988; DRCOG 1986; Dip. Psychoan Observat. Studies East. Lond. Clin. Asst. in Psychoth. 1 session per week Frenchay Healthcare Trust. Prev: Staff Grade, Regist. & SHO (Psychiat.) United Bristol Healthcare NHS Trust; Trainee GP Avon VTS.

THOMPSON, Eric John Bertha House, 71 Malone Road, Belfast BT9 6SB — MB BCh BAO 1947 Belf. Prev: Ho. Surg. & Ho. Phys. W. Norf. & King's Lynn Gen. Hosp.

THOMPSON, Euan James 70/4 St Leonard's Street, Edinburgh EH8 9RA — MB ChB 1996 Ed.

THOMPSON, Fiona Charlotte 10 Old Downs, Hartley, Longfield DA3 7AA — BM BS 1996 Nottm.

THOMPSON, Fiona Hilary 22 Southfield Drive, Hazlemere, High Wycombe HP15 7HB — MB ChB 1997 Bristol; BSc (Hons.) Bristol 1994.

THOMPSON, Fiona Jane Department of Pediatrics, Northampton General Hospital, Cliftonville, Northampton NN1 5BD Tel: 01604 545522 Fax: 01604 545640 Email: fionathompson@ngh-tr.anglox.nhs.uk; Meadowbrook, 12/13 Lower Harlestone, Northampton NN7 4EW Tel: 01604 820840 Email: kenthompson@compuserve.com — MB BS 1987 Lond.; MRCP (UK) 1991; FRCPCH; DCH RCP Lond. 1991. (Med. Coll. St. Bart. Hosp. Univ. Lond.) Cons. Paediat. N.ampton Gen. Hosp. Socs: Neonat. Soc. Prev: Research Fell. (Paediat.) King's Coll. Hosp. Lond.; Sen. Regist. (Paediat.) N.ampton Gen. Hosp. & John Radcliffe Hosp. Oxf.

THOMPSON, Fiona Jane 237 London Road, Wokingham RG40 1RB — MB ChB 1997 Leeds.

THOMPSON, Frank Derek 27 Moor Park Road, Northwood HA6 2DL — MB 1965 Camb.; BChir 1964; FRCP Eng. 1983; MRCP (U.K.) 1971. (Camb. & St. Mary's) Cons. (Nephrol.) St. Peter's Hosp. Lond. Harefield & Mt. Vernon Hosp.; Hon. Cons. (Nephrol.) Nat. Heart Hosp. Lond. N.wood; Hon. Sen. Lect. Inst. Urol Lond. Prev: Renal Regist. St. Philip's Gp. Hosps.; Lect. in Nephrol. Inst. Urol. Lond.; Ho. Surg. St. Mary's Hosp.

THOMPSON, Gary Halliday 22 Malone Heights, Belfast BT9 5PG — MB BCh BAO 1987 Belf.

THOMPSON, Gaynor Louise 24 Woods Grove, Burniston, Scarborough YO13 0JD — MB BS 1991 Newc.

THOMPSON, Geoffrey Robert Royal Shrewsbury Hospital, North Mytton Oak Road, Copthorne, Shrewsbury SY3 8BR Tel: 01743 231122; The Old Barn, Great Ness, Shrewsbury SY4 2LE — MB ChB 1966 Manch.; FFA RCS Eng. 1972. (Manch.) Cons. Anaesth. Salop AHA. Socs: Fell. Manch. Med. Soc. Prev: Sen. Regist. & Regist. (Anaesth.) Manch. Roy. Infirm.; Regist. (Anaesth.) Ashton-under-Lyne Gen. Hosp.

THOMPSON, Geoffrey Stuart (retired) 6 Highgate Road, Altrincham WA14 4QZ Tel: 0161 928 4862 — MB BChir Camb. 1951; MA Camb. 1954, MD 1965; FRCP Lond. 1974, M 1960. Prev: Cons. Phys. Wythenshawe Hosp. Manch.

THOMPSON, Professor Gilbert Richard Metabolic Medicine Imperial College, Hammersmith Hospital, Ducane Road, London W12 0NN Tel: 020 8383 2322 Fax: 020 8383 2322 Email: g.thompson@ic.ac.uk; 3 Queen Anne's Gardens, London W4 1TU Tel: 020 8994 6143 Email: gthompson@ic.ac.uk — MB BS Lond. 1956; MD Lond. 1963; FRCP Lond. 1973, M 1959. (St. Thos.) Sen. Research Investigator, Imperial Coll., Lond.; Emerit. Prof. Clin.

THOMPSON

Lipidol. Imperial Coll. 1998; Hon. Con. Phys. Hamersmith Hopital Lond. 1998. Socs: (Ex-Chairm.) Brit. Hyperlipidaemia Assn.; Ex-(Chairm.) Brit. Atherosclerosis Soc. Prev: Research Fell. Harvard Med. Sch. & Mass. Gen. Hosp. Boston, USA; Asst. Prof. Baylor Coll. Med. & Methodist Hosp. Houston, USA; Vis. Prof. McGill Univ. & Roy. Vict. Hosp. Montreal, Canada.

THOMPSON, Gillian 48A Loanends Road, Nutts Corner, Crumlin BT29 4YW — MB BCh 1998 Belf.

THOMPSON, Gillian Mary The Health Centre, Main Road, Radcliffe-on-Trent, Nottingham NG12 2GD Tel: 0115 933 3737; 360 Musters Road, West Bridgford, Nottingham NG2 7DA — MB ChB 1977 Manch.; MRCGP 1981.

THOMPSON, Gordon (retired) 157 Reads Avenue, Blackpool FY1 4HZ Tel: 01253 627061 Fax: 01253 627061 Email: gordon.thompson@virgin.net — MB ChB 1959 Sheff.; DIH Soc. Apoth. Lond. 1966. Prev: Med. Off. DHSS Blackpool.

THOMPSON, Gordon Henry Health Centre, Forum Way, Cramlington NE23 6QN Tel: 01670 712821 Fax: 01670 730837; 28 Easedale Avenue, Melton Park, Gosforth, Newcastle upon Tyne NE3 5TB Tel: 01632 2182 — MB BS 1965 Durh.; DObst RCOG 1971.

THOMPSON, Graham David Donnington Medical Practice, Wrekin Drive, Donnington, Telford TF2 8EA Tel: 01952 605252 Fax: 01952 677010; The Lees, Potters Bank, Red Lake, Telford TF1 5EP — MB BS 1968 Lond.; MRCS Eng. LRCP Lond. 1968; DCH Eng. 1972; DObst RCOG 1970. (St. Bart.) Prev: Regist. (Paediat.) Wolverhampton AHA; Regist. (Med.) Cheltenham.

THOMPSON, Mr Graham Michael Department of Ophthalmology, St. George's Hospital, Tooting, London SW17 0QT Tel: 020 8725 2062 Fax: 020 8725 3026; Parkside Hospital, Wimbledon, London SW19 5NX Tel: 020 8971 8000 Fax: 020 8971 8002 — MB BS 1973 Lond.; FRCS Eng. 1979; FRCOphth 1989; DO Eng. 1976. Cons. Ophth. St. Geo. Hosp. Lond.; Hon. Sen. Lect. St. Geo. Hosp. Med. Sch. Lond. Prev: Sen. Regist. (Ophth.) St. Barts. Hosp. Lond.; Sen. Regist. & Regist. Moorfields Eye Hosp. Lond.

THOMPSON, Harold Wellesley Karl (retired) 307 London Road, Appleton, Warrington WA4 5JB Tel: 01925 264211 — MB BCh BAO 1953 Belf. Med. Off. Laporte Chem.s & other Cos. Prev: Sen. Extern. Ho. Surg. Roy. Vict. Hosp. Belf.

THOMPSON, Harry Edwin George Street Surgery, 16 George Street, Alderley Edge SK9 7EP Tel: 01625 584545/6; Davenport House Farm, Upcast Lane, Wilmslow SK9 6EH Tel: 01625 590337 — MB ChB 1983 Dundee; BSc Dund 1979; MRCGP 1987; DRCOG 1985. (Dundee)

THOMPSON, Helen Macfarlane, MBE (retired) 60A London Road, Kilmarnock KA3 7DD — MB ChB Glas. 1947; DObst. 1951.

THOMPSON, Henry (retired) 7 Clarry Drive, Four Oaks Est., Sutton Coldfield B74 2RA Tel: 0121 323 2549 — MD 1954 Glas.; MB ChB 1948; FRCPath 1975. Reader (Path.) Univ. Birm.; Cons. Pathol. Gen. Hosp. Birm. Prev: Ho. Surg. Glas. Roy. Infirm.

THOMPSON, Hilary Frances Brooklands Medical Practice, 594 Altrincham Road, Brooklands, Manchester M23 9JH Tel: 0161 998 3818 Fax: 0161 946 0716; Woodlawn, Belmont Road, Hale, Altrincham WA15 9PT Tel: 0161 928 2535 — MB BS 1972 Lond.; BSc Lond. 1969, MB BS (Hons. Med.) 1972; MRCP (UK) 1975; MRCGP 1992; DRCOG 1976; DCH Eng. 1975. Princip. Gen. Pract. Prev: Trainee Gen. Pract. Lond. (Whittington Hosp.) Vocational Train.; Scheme; Ho. Phys. & Ho. Surg. Lond. Hosp.

THOMPSON, Howard Michael Brayford House Farm, Fen Lane, East Keal, Spilsby PE23 4AY Tel: 01790 752618 Email: hmthompson@msn.com — MB ChB 1988 Birm.; FRCA 1994. Cons. (Anaesth. & Pain Managem.) Pilgrim Hosp. Boston. Socs: Assn. Anaesth.; Pain Soc. Prev: Sen. Regist. Leicester; Regist. (Anaesth.) Leicester; SHO (Anaesth.) S. Warks. Hosp. Warwick.

THOMPSON, Hudson Taylor, MBE (retired) 9 Cotswold Way, Trenewydd Park Est., Risca, Newport NP11 6QT Tel: 612797 — MRCS Eng. LRCP Lond. 1950.

THOMPSON, Mr Hugh Hilary Lister Hospital, Coreys Mill Lane, Stevenage SG1 4AB Tel: 01438 781103 Fax: 01438 781267; Priory Cottage, Charlton, Hitchin SG5 2AA Tel: 01462 431409 — MB BS 1971 Lond.; MS Lond. 1982, BSc (1st cl. Hons. Anat.) 1968; MB BS (Hons. Distinc. Med.) Lond. 1971; FRCS Eng. 1977. (Lond. Hosp.) Cons. Surg. Lister Hosp. Stevenage. Socs: Assn. Surg.; Assn. Coloproctol.; Assn. Endoscopic Surgs. Prev: Sen. Lect. Surg. Lond.

Hosp. Med. Coll.; Fell. Dept. Surg. UCLA Los Angeles, USA; Ho. Off. Birm. Accid. Hosp.

THOMPSON, Ian Mill Street Medical Centre, Mill Street, St Helens WA10 2BD Tel: 01744 23641 Fax: 01744 28398; 47 Eccleston Gardens, St Helens WA10 3BJ Tel: 01744 602162 — MRCS Eng. LRCP Lond. 1968.

THOMPSON, Ian Davenport (retired) 63 St Martin's Road, Finham, Coventry CV3 6FD Tel: 01203 411522 — MB ChB Birm. 1956; FFA RCS Eng. 1962; DA Eng. 1959. Prev: Cons. Anaesth. Coventry Hosp. Gp.

THOMPSON, Ian David 63 Harlow Moor Drive, Harrogate HG2 0LE; 4 Randolph Crescent, Edinburgh EH3 7TH — MB ChB 1977 Ed.; MRCP (UK) 1982. Sen. Regist. City Hosp. Edin.

THOMPSON, Mr Ian Duncan (retired) 17 Cookstown Road, Moneymore, Magherafelt BT45 7QF Tel: 028 8674 8209 — MB BCh 1947 BAD; MD Belf. 1952; FRCS Eng. 1956; DMRD Eng. 1961. Prev: Temp. Lect. (Physiol.) Qu.'s Univ. Belf.

THOMPSON, Ian George Chestnuts Surgery, 70 East Street, Sittingbourne ME10 4RU Tel: 01795 423197 Fax: 01795 430179; 205 Borden Lane, Sittingbourne ME9 8HR — MB BS 1966 Durh.; MRCGP 1973; DObst RCOG 1968. (Newc.)

THOMPSON, Ian McKim 36 Harborne Road, Birmingham B15 3AJ Tel: 0121 456 1402 — MB ChB 1961 Birm. Dep. Sec. BMA. Socs: Hon. Mem. Med. Colls. of Spain. Prev: Mem. GMC.

THOMPSON, Ian Philip Cousley 17 Cookstown Road, Moneymore, Magherafelt BT45 7QF — MB BCh BAO 1988 Belf.; MRCGP 1995; DRCOG 1992. Clin. Asst. (ENT) Downe Hosp. Belf. Prev: SHO (ENT) Ulster Hosp.

THOMPSON, Ian Richard Norfolk House, Restell Close, Vanbrugh Hill, London SE3 7UN — MB BS 1998 Lond.

THOMPSON, Ian Wallace 29 Brownlow Lane, Cheddington, Leighton Buzzard LU7 0SS — MB ChB 1978 Ed.

THOMPSON, Irene Margaret (retired) 2 Cedar Park, Bleary, Portadown, Craigavon BT63 5LL — MB BCh BAO Belf. 1947; MD Belf. 1952; MFCM 1972; DPH Belf. 1949. Prev: Sen. Med. Off. Down Co. Health Comm.

THOMPSON, Ivan Horden Group Practice, The Health Centre, Peterlee SR8 1AD Tel: 0191 587 0808 Fax: 0191 587 0700; 3 Woodfield, Peterlee SR8 1DB Tel: 0191 586 8218 Fax: 0191 586 8218 — MB ChB Bristol 1957; MRCGP 1968. (Bristol) Co. Surg. St. John Ambul. Brig. Socs: Fell. Roy. Soc. Med.

THOMPSON, Jacqueline 9 Woodside, Madeley, Crewe CW3 9HA — MB ChB 1996 Leeds; BSc (Hons.) Leeds 1994.

THOMPSON, Jacqueline Mary Holmgarth House, Carthorpe, Bedale DL8 2LF — MB ChB 1985 Leic.; MRCGP 1994; DRCOG 1989.

THOMPSON, Jacqueline Russell Daudsons Mains Medical Centre, 5 Quality St, Edinburgh EH4 5BP Tel: 0131 336 2291 Fax: 0131 336 1886 Email: jacquelinethompson@orange.net; 615 Gosford Place, Edinburgh EH6 4BJ Tel: 0131 530 1185 — MB ChB 1993 Ed.; MRCGP; DRCOG. 1998; DFFP. 1999. GP Princip., Daudsons Mains Med. Centre, Edin..; SHO (O&G), S.mead, Bristol. Prev: SHO. (A & E.) Frenehay Hosp. Bristol.; SHO. (Psychiat.) Cornw..; SHO. (Med.) Cornw..

THOMPSON, Jacqueline Susan Park Medical Centre, 164 Park Road, Peterborough PE1 2UF Tel: 01733 552801 Fax: 01733 425015; 51 Thorpe Park Road, Peterborough PE3 6LJ Tel: 01733 203601 — MB BS 1980 Lond.; LMSSA Lond. 1980; DRCOG 1985.

THOMPSON, James 73 Kiltaire Crescent, Ivertowers Grange, Airdrie ML6 8JG — MB ChB 1974 Glas.; DObst RCOG 1976; DFFP 1997.

THOMPSON, James Francis Webster The Old Vicarage, South St., Roxby, Scunthorpe DN15 0BJ — MB BS 1975 Lond.; BA (Physics) Oxf. 1970; FFA RCS Eng. 1979. Cons. Anaesth. Scunthorpe Gen. Hosp.

THOMPSON, James Reid The Surgery, 5 Kensington Place, London W8 7PT Tel: 020 7229 7111 Fax: 020 7221 3069 — MB BCh BAO 1988 Belf.; MRCGP 1996. (Qu. Univ. Belf.) GP. Prev: Trainee GP Char. Cross Hosp. Lond. VTS; SHO (Genitourin. Med.) Chelsea & Wesm. Hosp. Lond.; SHO (Med.) Hammersmith Hosp. Lond. & Harefield Hosp.

THOMPSON, Jane Louise Tel: 01256 762125 Fax: 01256 760608; Kinsale, Pines Road, Fleet GU51 4NL Tel: 01252 615121 — MB BS 1968 Lond.; DFFP 1993. (Middlx.) Socs: Christ. Med.

THOMPSON

Fell.sh. Prev: Clin. Med. Off. W. Surrey & NE Hants. HAs; Ho. Surg. (Gyn. & Obst.) & Ho. Phys. (Paediat.) Middlx. Hosp. Lond.; Ho. Phys. Mayday Hosp. Thornton Heath.

THOMPSON, Jane Maureen (retired) 12 Margetts Place, Lower Upnor, Rochester ME2 4XF — MB BCh BAO 1964 Dub.; BA Dub. 1962, MB BCh BAO 1964; DCH RCPSI 1966.

THOMPSON, Jane Sarah Chatham House, Doncaster Gate, Rotherham S65 1DW Tel: 01709 304808 Fax: 01709 304886 — MB ChB 1987 Sheff. Staff Grade Doctor (Child & Adolesc. Psychiat.) Chatham Hse. Rotherham. Prev: Clin. Asst. (Adolesc. Unit) N.. Gen. Hosp. Sheff.

THOMPSON, Jean Burns The Royal Well Surgery, 1 Royal Crescent, Cheltenham GL50 3DB Tel: 01242 521070; 14 Carisbrooke Drive, Charlton Kings, Cheltenham GL52 6YA — MB BS 1958 Durh.

THOMPSON, Jennifer Lucinda 23 Horwood Close, Headington, Oxford OX3 7RF; 23 Horwood Close, Headington, Oxford OX3 7RF — MB ChB 1993 Leic.; Primary FRCA 1997; Final FRCA 1999. (Leicester) Specialist Regist. (Anaest.) Oxf.. Prev: Regist. (Anaesth.) Oxf. Radcliffe Hosps. Trust; SHO (Anaesth. & ITU) N.ampton Gen.; SHO (Anaesth.) Broomfield Hosp. Chelmsford.

THOMPSON, Jeremy Charles St Martins Practice, 319 Chapeltown Road, Leeds LS7 3JT Tel: 0113 262 1013 Fax: 0113 237 4747 — MB ChB 1983 Leeds; MRCGP 1990; DRCOG 1987. Socs: Nat. Inst. Med. Herbalists.

THOMPSON, Jeremy Neil Trelawney Avenue Surgery, 425 Trelawney Avenue, Langley, Slough SL3 7TT Tel: 01753 775545 Fax: 01753 775545; 39 Burroway Road, Langley, Slough SL3 8EH Tel: 01753 541047 — MB BS 1975 Newc.; MRCP (UK) 1978; MRCGP 1983.

THOMPSON, Mr Jeremy Nowell Department of Surgery, Chelsea & Westminster Hospital, 369 Fulham Road, London SW10 9NH Tel: 020 8746 8463 Fax: 020 8746 8282 Email: gisurg@chelwest.org; 88 Grange Road, London W5 3PJ — MB BChir 1977 Camb.; MChir Camb. 1988, BA 1974; FRCS Eng. 1980. Cons. Surg. Chelsea & W.m. Hosp. & Roy. Marsden Hosp. Lond. Socs: Fell. Assn. Surgs.; Surgic. Research Soc.; Brit. Soc. Gastroenterol. Prev: Cons. Surg. Ealing & Hammersmith Hosp. Lond.; Sen. Lect. (Surg.) Roy. Postgrad. Med. Sch. Lond.; Lect. Acad. Surg. Unit St. Mary's Hosp. Lond.

THOMPSON, Joanna Jane Wansbeck House, Kirkwhelpington, Newcastle upon Tyne NE19 2RT — MB BS 1987 Newc.

THOMPSON, Joanne 9 Westerdale Road, Seaton Carew, Hartlepool TS25 2AE — MB BChir 1988 Camb.

THOMPSON, Joanne 11 Manor Way, Beckenham BR3 3LH — MB BS 1997 Lond.

Thompson, Joanne Helen The Surgery, Vicarage Lane, Walton on the Naze CO14 8PA Tel: 01255 674373 Fax: 01255 851005 — MB BS 1988 Lond.; DRCOG 1993.

THOMPSON, John (retired) PO Box 1428, Glasgow G52 3QS — MD 1964 Glas.; MB ChB 1943; DPH 1948.

THOMPSON, John (retired) Crossways, Frodesley, Shrewsbury SY5 7HA Tel: 01694 731262 — MB ChB 1950 Liverp.; DObst RCOG 1955. Prev: GP Wirral.

THOMPSON, John 1 Lichfield Close, Denshaw, Oldham OL3 5SF — MB ChB 1991 Manch.

THOMPSON, John Andrew Spring Gardens Health Centre, Providence Street, Worcester WR1 2BS Tel: 01905 681681 Fax: 01905 681699; 15 Yew Tree Close, London Road, Worcester WR5 2LH — MB ChB 1972 Bristol; DObst RCOG 1976; DA Eng. 1975. Prev: Ho. Surg. Bristol Roy. Infirm.; SHO (Paediat.) Bristol Childr. Hosp.; SHO (Anaesth.) Roy. Devon & Exeter Hosp. (Wonford) Exeter.

THOMPSON, John Beck (retired) 40 Castle Gardens, Richhill, Armagh BT61 9QL — MB BCh 1948 Belf.; MB BCh BAO Belf. 1948, LRCP LRCS Ed. LRFPS Glas. 1948. Prev: Ho. Off. Lagan Valley Hosp. Lisburn.

THOMPSON, John Brian The Health Centre, 20 Duncan Street, Greenock PA15 4LY Tel: 01475 724477 Fax: 01475 727140; Suilven, 7 Hilltop Crescent, Gourock PA19 1YW — MB ChB 1975 Glas.; DA Eng. 1979; DRCOG 1977.

THOMPSON, John Bruce Mount Farm Surgery, Lawson Place, Bury St Edmunds IP32 7EW Tel: 01284 769643 Fax: 01284 700833; Park Lane Cottages, Hawstead, Bury St Edmunds IP29 5NX — MB BChir 1968 Camb.; BA Camb. 1964; MRCP (UK) 1970. (St. Bart.)

THOMPSON, John Charles Barnshaw Bodnant, Water St., Penygroes, Caernarfon LL54 6LU Tel: 01286 880203 Fax: 01286 880629 Email: jcbthompson@compuserve.com — MB ChB 1969 St. And.; MRCGP Distinc. 1974; DObst RCOG 1971. GP & Clin. Asst. (Psychiat.) Gwynedd HA. Socs: BMA & Welsh Psychiat. Soc. Prev: SHO (O & G) Robroyston Hosp. Glas.; Ho. Surg. Dunfermline & W. Fife Hosp.; Ho. Phys. Bangour Gen. Hosp. Broxburn.

THOMPSON, John Clifford Seven Brooks Medical Centre, 21 Church Street, Atherton, Manchester M46 9DE Tel: 01942 882799 Fax: 01942 873859 — MB ChB 1979 Liverp.; DRCOG 1980.

THOMPSON, Mr John Douglas (retired) 3 Mayfield Drive, Cleadon Village, Sunderland SR6 7QN — MRCS Eng. LRCP Lond. 1943; FRCS Eng. 1959; FRCS Ed. 1958.

THOMPSON, John Edgar 2B Manor Street, Cardiff CF14 3PU — MB BS 1984 West. Austral.

THOMPSON, Mr John Frederick Royal Devon & Exeter Hospital (Wonford), Barrack Road, Exeter EX2 5DW; Email: jflsuig@hotmail.com — MB BS 1982 Lond.; MS Soton. 1990; FRCS Ed. 1986; FRCS Eng. 1986. Cons. Surg. Roy. Devon & Exeter Hosps. Socs: Vasc. Surg. Soc. of GB & Irel.; Assn. Surg.; Jt. Vasc. Research Gp. (Treas.). Prev: Lect. & Sen. Regist. Univ. Bristol & Bristol Roy. Infirm.; Wessex Research Fell. Soton. Univ. Hosps.; SHO & Demonst. (Anat.) Char. Cross & W.m. Med. Sch. Lond.

THOMPSON, John Mark 121 Dalkeith Road, Edinburgh EH16 5AJ — MB BS 1998 Newc.

THOMPSON, John Michael Hazel Cottage, School Lane, Pirbright, Woking GU24 0JW — MB BS 1982 Lond.; MRCS Eng. LRCP Lond. 1981.

THOMPSON, John Tytler (retired) Carrick House, Firs Road, Over Hulton, Bolton BL5 1HB Tel: 01942 877394 — MB ChB 1940 Glas.

THOMPSON, Professor John Warburton 1 Hackwood Park, Hexham NE46 1AX Tel: 01434 608552 Fax: 01434 608552; 1 Hackwood Park, Hexham NE46 1AX Tel: 01434 608552 Fax: 01434 608552 — MB BS 1948 Lond.; MB BS (Hons.) Surg., Hyg. & Forens. Med. Lond. 1948; Dip. Med. Acupunc. 1995; FRCP Lond. 1981, M 1977; PhD Lond. 1960. (Lond. Hosp.) Hon. Phys. & Hon. Cons. in Med. Studies, St. Oswald's Hospice, Newcatle upon Tyne (Palliat. Med., especially the control of Chronic Pain).; Emerit. Prof. Pharmacol. Univ. Newc. u. Tyne; Emerit. Cons. Clin. Pharm. Newc. HA; Cons. in Pain Managem. with special Refer. to mechanisms and Managem. of chronic pain problems (Private Pract.). Socs: Brit. Pharm. Soc.; Internat. Assn. Study of Pain; Assn. Palliat. Med. Prev: Prof. Pharmacol. Univ. Newc.; Sen. Lect. (Pharmacol.) Inst. Basic Med. Scs. RCS Eng. & St. Geo. Hosp. Med. Sch. Lond.; Research Asst. (Applied Pharmacol.) Univ. Coll. & Univ. Coll. Hosp. Med. Sch.

THOMPSON, Jonathan Andrew Richard West Kirby Health Centre, Grange Road, Wirral CH48 4HZ Tel: 0151 625 9171 Fax: 0151 625 9171; Millyea, 47 Farr Hall Drive, Lower Heswall, Wirral CH60 4SE — MB ChB 1985 Liverp.; Dip Primary Care Therapeutics 1999. (Liverpool)

THOMPSON, Jonathan Lee 33 Old Lansdowne Road, Manchester M20 2PA — BM BS 1986 Nottm.; BMedSci (Hons.) Nottm. 1984.

THOMPSON, Jonathan Paul Whytecote Cottage, 21 Station Road, Littlethorpe, Leicester LE9 5HS — MB ChB 1988 Leic.; BSc (Med. Sci.) Leic. 1986; FRCA 1994. Lect. & Hon. Sen. Regist. (Anaesth.) Leicester Univ. Dept. Anaesth.

THOMPSON, Joseph Anderson Tanyfron, Seven Sisters, Neath Tel: 01639 360 — MB 1932 Belf.; MB, BCh BAO Belf. 1932. (Qu. Univ. Belf.) Apptd. Fact. Doctor. Socs: (Ex-Pres.) Neath Med. Soc.; BMA (Mem. Exec. Mid-Glam. Div.). Prev: Ho. Phys. & Ho. Surg. Co. Hosp. Bedford.

THOMPSON, Josephine Amanda Temple Sowerby Medical Practice, Temple Sowerby, Penrith CA10 1RZ Tel: 017683 61232 Fax: 017683 61980; Nunwick Hall, Great Salkeld, Penrith CA11 9LN — MB BCh 1989 Wales; DRCOG 1994; DCH RCP Lond. 1993; DFFP 1993. Off. (Family Plann.) Penrith Dist.; Trainee GP Penrith Retainer Scheme. Prev: SHO (Cas.) Greenwich Lond. VTS; Ho. Off. (Gen. Med.) E. Glam. Gen. Hosp. Pontypridd; Ho. Off. (Neurosurg. & Gen. Surg.) Univ. Hosp. Wales Cardiff.

THOMPSON, Judith Ann Sunnyside Doctors Surgery, 150 Fratton Road, Portsmouth PO1 5DH Tel: 023 9282 4725 Fax: 023 9286 1014; St. Andrews, 9 Eastern Parade, Southsea PO4 9RA Tel: 023

92 756938 Fax: 01705 756438 — MB ChB 1970 Bristol; DObst RCOG 1972. (Bristol) Clin. Asst. BrE. Clinic Qu. Alexandra Hosp. Portsmouth. Socs: Nat. Assn. Family Plann. Doctors; BMA (Mem. Social Sec. Portsmouth & SE Hants. Div.). Prev: Trainee GP Portsmouth & SE Hants. HA; SCMO (Family Plann.) Portsmouth & SE Hants. HA.

THOMPSON, Julian Barton de Courcy Vye House, The Street, Ash, Canterbury CT3 2EW — MB BS 1993 Lond.

THOMPSON, Julie Ann Croft Cottage, 98 Leeds Road, Liversedge WF15 6AA — MB ChB 1998 Leeds.

THOMPSON, Juliet Anne St. Paul's Surgery, Oram's Mount, Winchester SO22 5DD Tel: 01962 853599 — BM BS 1990 Nottm.; MRCGP 1994; DRCOG 1993. (Nottingham)

THOMPSON, Juliet Anne 5 Drake Road, Grays RM16 6PS — MB BS 1990 Lond.; BSc Lond. 1987, MB BS 1990.

THOMPSON, Justin Rhys Health Building Surgery, 1 Bentsbrook Close, North Holmwood, Dorking RH5 4HY Tel: 01306 885802 — BMedSci Nottm. 1983, BM BS 1985; MRCGP 1990; DCH RCP Lond. 1990. GP E.bourne.

THOMPSON, Karen Jill Wellway Medical Group, Wellway, Morpeth NE61 1BJ Tel: 01670 517300; The Cottage, Threeways, Tranwell Woods, Morpeth NE61 6AQ Tel: 01670 511286 — MB BS 1990 Lond.; MRCGP 1994; DRCOG 1993. Prev: SHO (Gen. Med. & Geriat.) Qu. Eliz. Hosp. Gateshead; SHO (O & G) Hexham Gen. Hosp.; SHO (Paediat.) N. Tyneside Hosp.

THOMPSON, Katherine Mary 28 Holmwood Gardens, Westbury-on-Trym, Bristol BS9 3EB — MB BS 1979 Newc.

THOMPSON, Kenneth John 25 Shandon Park, Ballymena BT42 2ED Tel: 01266 652854; 16 Collins Crescent, St. Davids Harbour, Dalgety Bay, Dunfermline KY11 9FG Tel: 01383 820354 — MB ChB 1988 Dundee. (Dundee) Princip. Gen. Pract. Prev: SHO (O & G) Forth Pk. Matern. Hosp. Kirkcaldy.; SHO (Cardiothoracic Surg.) Roy. Infirm. Edin.

THOMPSON, Kenneth Robin Bangor Health Centre, Newtownards Road, Bangor BT20 4LD Tel: 028 9146 9111 — MB BCh BAO 1971 Belf.

THOMPSON, Kenneth Whitton Newland Clinic, Borough Road, Middlesbrugh TS4 2EJ Tel: 01642 247401 Fax: 01642 223803 Email: K.thompson@lineone.net; 11 Southwood, Coulby Newham, Middlesbrough TS8 0UE Tel: 01642 593554 Fax: 0870 130 9903 Email: k.thompson@lineone.net — MB ChB Ed. 1960. (Edinburgh) p/t Indust. Med. Off.

THOMPSON, Kerry Coral Old Dairy Cottage, Clay Lane, Cross Bush, Arundel BN18 9RS — BM 1987 Soton.; BSc (1st cl. Hons.) Psych. & Physiol. Soton. 1983; MRCP (UK) 1991; PhD 1998. (Southampton) p/t Cons. Phys./Gastroenterlogist, Worthing and S.lands NHS Trust, Worthing Hosp., Worthing. Prev: SpR Gastroenterol., Roy. Hants. Co. Hosp., Winchester.

THOMPSON, Kevin Orion Thorpe Wood Surgery, 140 Woodside Road, Norwich NR7 9QL Tel: 01603 701477 Fax: 01603 701512; The Paddock, 2 Meadows Lane, Thorpe St. Andrew, Norwich NR7 0QX Tel: 01603 701220 Fax: 01603 701512 Email: k.thompson@netcom.co.uk — MB BChir 1973 Camb.; MB Camb. 1973, MA, BChir 1972; MRCS Eng. LRCP Lond. 1971. (Camb. & Guys) Socs: BMA. Prev: Med. Regist. Norf. & Norwich Hosp.; SHO (O & G) Norf. & Norwich Hosp.

THOMPSON, Lawrence Edward Crumlin Medical Practice, 5 Glenavy Road, Crumlin BT29 4LA Tel: 028 9442 2209 Fax: 028 9442 2233 — MB BCh BAO 1973 Belf.; MRCGP 1981; DObst RCOG 1975.

THOMPSON, Linda 17 Maria Square, Belmont, Bolton BL7 8AF — MB ChB 1985 Liverp.

THOMPSON, Lucy Victoria Lovemead Group Practice, Roundstone Surgery, Polebarn Circus, Trowbridge BA14 7EH — MB BS 1989 Lond.; MRCP (UK) 1993. Prev: Trainee GP/SHO Bath VTS.; SHO Rotat. (Med.) Bournemouth & Poole Hosps.

THOMPSON, Mabel Mary Helen (retired) 8 Manor Way, Blackheath, London SE3 9EF Tel: 020 8852 4938 — MB BCh BAO 1950 Dub.; BA Dub. 1947, MB BCh BAO 1950. Prev: GP Lond.

THOMPSON, Malcolm Charles 18 Greenhill Main Road, Greenhill, Sheffield S8 7RD — MB ChB 1977 Manch.; DCH (RCP Lond.) 1994; FRCA 1997; MLCOM 1993; MRCGP 1985; MRNZCOG 1985; MRCOG 1983, D 1980; DGM RCP Lond.1989; DA (UK) 1995; DCH RCP Lond. 1994. Socs: Brit. Med. Acupunct. Soc.; Pain.

Soc. Prev: Specialist Regist. Rotat. (Anaesth.) SE Thames; GP Buller, NZ.

THOMPSON, Malcolm Charles Friarage Hospital, Northallerton DL6 1JG Tel: 01607 779911 — MB ChB 1973 Manch.; FFA RCS Eng. 1981; DCH Eng. 1976; DRCOG 1977. Cons. Anaesth. Friarage Hosp. N.allerton. Socs: Assn. Anaesth. Gt. Brit. & Irel.; Intens. Care Soc. Prev: Sen. Lect. (Milit. Anaesth.) Brit. Army; Sen. Regist. (Anaesth.) Guy's Hosp. Lond.; Trainee GP King's Lynn VTS.

THOMPSON, Malcolm George (retired) Rotherhurst, 3 The Avenue, Orpington BR6 9AS Tel: 01689 824240 — MB BS 1950 Lond.; MRCS Eng. LRCP Lond. 1950. Prev: Hosp. Pract. (Surg.) Orpington Hosp.

THOMPSON, Margaret Elizabeth 51 St. Vincent Place, Albert Park 3206, Victoria, Australia Tel: 0136 998044; Abbots Mead, Crown Lane, Farnham Royal, Slough SL2 3SF — MB ChB 1955 Ed.; FRACGP 1973. (Ed.)

THOMPSON, Margaret Jane Johnston Ashurst Hospital, Lyndhurst Rd, Southampton SO40 7AR Tel: 02380 743030 Fax: 02380 743033 Email: mtl@soton.ac.uk; 3 Sandy Lane, Titchfield, Fareham PO14 4ER Tel: 01329 847234 Fax: 01329 847236 — MB ChB 1970 Glas.; FRCP Glas. 1988; MRCP (UK) 1975; FRCPsych 1994, M 1979; DObst RCOG 1973; DCH RCPS Glas. 1972; FRCHCP 1999. (Glas.) Child Psychiat.; Clin. Sen. Lect.; Cons. Child Pyschiat. Socs: Assn. Child Psychol. & Psychiat.; Brit. Paediat. Assn.; Maru Soc. Prev: Sen. Regist. Wessex RHA; Lect. (Child & Adolesc. Psychiat.) Univ. Glas.; Hon. Sen. Regist. (Child & Family Psychiat.) Roy. Hosp. Sick Childr. Glas.

THOMPSON, Mark Adrian The Coach House, Post Office Lane, Fernhill Heath, Worcester WR3 8RB; Ty Uchaf, Llanwrin, Machynlleth SY20 8QH — MB BS 1990 Lond.

THOMPSON, Mark Graham 25 Cotswold View, Bath BA2 1HA Email: thompson@wanderers70.freeserve.co.uk — MB ChB 1994 Bristol; DRCOG 1999. GP VTS Bath. Socs: BMA. Prev: SHO (Anaesth.); SHO (Acc. & Emerg.); SHO (O & G).

THOMPSON, Mark John Thornbury Health Centre, Eastland Road, Thornbury, Bristol BS35 1DP Tel: 01454 412167 Fax: 01454 419522 — MB ChB 1991 Bristol.

THOMPSON, Mark Kennedy 6 Rowell Way, Oundle, Peterborough PE8 4HX — MB BS 1996 Lond.

THOMPSON, Mark Wakefield Greenway Street Medical Centre, Greenway Street, Handbridge, Chester CH4 7JS Tel: 01244 680169 Fax: 01244 680162; 7 Hoole Park, Hoole, Chester CH2 3AN Tel: 01244 313103 — MB BS 1983 Lond.; MA Camb. 1984. Prev: Trainee GP Chester VTS; Trainee GP E.. Suburbs VTS Melbourne; Family Plann. ChristCh. N.Z.

THOMPSON, Mary Adela (retired) Shankill Health Centre, 135 Shankill Parade, Belfast BT13 1SD Tel: 01232 247181 — MB BCh BAO 1960 Belf.

THOMPSON, Mary Dymock 84 Moorside N., Newcastle upon Tyne NE4 9DU Tel: 0191 273 8637 — MD 1947 Durh.; MB BS 1940, DPH 1960. (Durh.) Prev: Childh. Tuberc. Phys. Newc.; Paediat. Regist. Qu. Charlotte's Hosp.; Res. Med. Off. Babies Hosp. Newc.

THOMPSON, Matthew Graham Park Lane Cottages, Hawstead, Bury St Edmunds IP29 5NX — BM 1993 Soton. (Southampton)

THOMPSON, Matthew James Central Microbiologial Laboratories, Western General Hospital, Crewe Road, Edinburgh EH4 2XU — MB ChB 1989 Glas.

THOMPSON, Mr Matthew Merfyn Department of Surgery, Clinical Sciences Building, Leicester Royal Infirmary, Leicester LE2 7LX Tel: 01533 523142 Fax: 01533 523179; 23 Guilford Road, Leicester LE2 2RD — MD 1994 Leicester; MA Camb. 1988; MD (Distinc.) Leicester 1994; MB BS Lond. 1987; FRCS Eng. 1994; FRCS 1998. (St Barts.) Cons.(Vascul EndoVasc. Surg.) Leics Roy Infirm.; Lect. (Surg.) Univ. Leicester.

THOMPSON, Maureen Kerry Judith 39 Mountsandel Road, Coleraine BT52 1JE Tel: 01265 51151 — MB ChB 1994 Manch. (Manchester)

THOMPSON, Michael Alan River Lodge Surgery, Malling Street, Lewes BN7 2RD Tel: 01273 472233 Fax: 01273 486879 — MB BS 1987 Lond.; DRCOG 1992; DCH RCP Lond. 1992.

THOMPSON, Michael Alexander Gateways, Church Lane, Stanway, Colchester CO3 5LR — MB BS 1970 Lond.; MRCP (U.K.) 1975; MRCS Eng. LRCP Lond. 1970; FFA RCS Eng. 1976. (Guy's)

THOMPSON

Cons. Dept. Anaesth. Guy's Hosp.; Fell. Roy. Soc. Med. & Med. Soc. Lond. Prev: Regtl. Med. Off. 3rd Bn. Roy. Regt. of Fusiliers; Trainee (Anaesth.) Brit. Milit. Hosp. Rinteln; Specialist in Anaesth. Roy. Herbert Hosp. Woolwich.

THOMPSON, Michael Ernest 21 Gardenfield, Skellingthorpe, Lincoln LN6 5SP Tel: 01522 684084 — MB ChB 1968 Sheff.; FFOM RCP Lond. 1994, MFOM 1982, AFOM 1980; MRCGP 1975; DIH Eng. 1982; DObst RCOG 1970. Cons. Occupat. Phys. Socs: Soc. Occupat. Med. Prev: Cons. Occupat. Med. Lincoln Hosps. NHS Trust; Area Med. Off. Brit. Rail Doncaster; Clin. Asst. (Diabetes) Doncaster Roy. Infirm.

THOMPSON, Mr Michael Harrison Department of Surgery, Southmead Hospital, Southmead, Bristol BS10 5NB Tel: 0117 950 5050 — MB BS 1968 Newc.; MD Newc. 1979, MB BS 1968; FRCS Eng. 1973. Cons. Surg. S.mead Hosp. Bristol. Socs: Brit. Soc. Gastroenterol.; Assn. Surg.; Eur. Assn. Endoscopic Surgs. Prev: Lect. (Surg.) Univ. Bristol.

THOMPSON, Michael Hugh Luton & Dunstable Hospital, Dunstable Road, Luton LU4 0DZ Tel: 01582 491122 Fax: 01582 497280; 8 Green Close, Stanbridge, Leighton Buzzard LU7 9JL Tel: 01525 210478 Email: mikeht@aol.com — BM BCh 1973 Oxf.; FRCP; MRCP (UK) 1977; FRCPCH; DCH Eng. 1977. (Oxf.) Cons. Paediat. Luton & Dunstable Hosp. Prev: Sen. Regist. (Paediat.) Roy. Alexandra Childr. Hosp. Brighton; Sen. Regist. (Paediat.) King's Coll. Hosp. Lond.

THOMPSON, Michael Joseph Glebe House Surgery, 19 Firby Road, Bedale DL8 2AT Tel: 01677 422616 Fax: 01677 424596 — MB ChB 1985 Leic.; MRCGP 1989; DRCOG 1989; Cert. Family Plann. JCC 1989.

THOMPSON, Mr Michael Reginald Queen Alexandra, Cosham Hospital, Portsmouth Tel: 023 92 286710 Fax: 02392 286710 Email: michael.thomson@qmail01.porthosp.swest.nhs.uk; St. Andrews, 9 Eastern Parade, Southsea PO4 9RA Tel: 023 92 756938 Fax: 01705 838170 — MB ChB Sheff. 1966; MD Sheff. 1980; FRCS Eng. 1971. (Sheff.) Cons. Surg. Qu. Alexandra Hosp. Portsmouth. Socs: Fell. (Counc. Mem.) Roy. Soc. Med. (Sec. Sect. Coloproctol.); Brit. Soc. Gastroenterol. (Sec); Assn of ColoProctol. GB+I (Sec). Prev: Sen. Regist. (Gen. Surg.) Bristol Roy. Infirm.; Regist. (Surg.) Roy. Infirm. Sheff.; Lect. (Surg.) Univ. Manch.

THOMPSON, Michael Robert Northland Surgery, 79 Cunninghams Lane, Dungannon BT71 6BX Tel: 028 8772 752 Fax: 028 8772 7696; 7 Riverdale, Tamnamore, Dungannon BT71 6PZ Tel: 01868 723126 Email: mthom80931@aol.com — MB BCh BAO 1984 Belf.; MB BCh Belf. BAO 1984; MRCGP 1991.

THOMPSON, Michael William Benedict Portslade Health Centre, Church Road, Portslade, Brighton BN41 1LX Tel: 01273 422525 Fax: 01273 413510 — MB BS 1987 Lond.; MRCGP 1992; T(GP) 1993; DTM & H 1993; DRCOG 1991; DCH 1990. (Char. Cross & Westm. Med. Sch. Lond.) Socs: Internat. Comm. RCGP.

THOMPSON, Michelle Jean 22 Livingstone Place, Marchmont, Edinburgh EH9 1PD — MB ChB 1985 Aberd.; FRCS Ed. 1991. Regist. (Cardiothoracic Surg.) Roy. Infirm. Edin. Prev: Regist. (Orthop. Surg.) P.ss Margt. Rose Hosp. Edin.; Regist. Rotat. (Gen. Surg.) Roy. Infirm. Edin.; SHO (Trauma Team III & Burns Unit) Birm. Accid. Hosp.

THOMPSON, Morounfolu Olaleye CDS, South Cleveland Hospital, Marton Road, Middlesbrough TS4 3BW — MB BS 1982 Ibadan.

THOMPSON, Mr Neill Stuart 8 Greystown Avenue, Belfast BT9 6UJ — MB BCh BAO 1990 Belf.; FRCS Ed. 1994.

THOMPSON, Nichola Jane Magrathea, 51 Woodham Waye, Woking GU21 5SJ — MB ChB 1974 Bristol; DCH Eng. 1980.

THOMPSON, Nicholas Montgomery House Surgery, Piggy Lane, Bicester OX26 6HT Tel: 01869 249222; 22 West End, Launton, Bicester OX26 5DF Tel: 01869 321366 Fax: 01869 249888 Email: nickthompson@pgec-horton.demon.co.uk — MB BS 1972 Lond.; MRCGP 1978; DCH Eng. 1975; DObst RCOG 1974; FRCGP 1999. (Middlx.) Course Organiser Banbury VTS Oxf. Region.

THOMPSON, Nicholas Paul Dept. of Medicine, Freeman Hospital, Newcastle upon Tyne NE7 7DN Tel: 0191 284 3111 Fax: 0191 223 1249 Email: nick.thompson@tfh.nuth.northy.nhs.uk — MB BS 1987 Lond.; FRCP 2001; MD Lond. 1996; MRCP (UK) 1990. (St. Bart.) Cons. (Gastroenterol. & Gen. Phys.) Newc. Upon Tyne. Socs: Brit.

Soc. Gastroenterol. Prev: Clin. Research Fell. Roy. Free Hosp. Med. Sch.; Sen. Regist. (Gastroenterol.) Newc.

THOMPSON, Nicola 18 Whinny fold, by Cruden Bay, Peterhead AB42 0QH — MB BCh BAO 1989 Belf.; FRCA 1994.

THOMPSON, Norris Ferguson Doctors Surgery, 18 Union Street, Kirkintilloch, Glasgow G66 1DJ Tel: 0141 776 1238 Fax: 0141 775 2786; Glengyle, 4 Douglas Avenue, Lenzie, Kirkintilloch, Glasgow G66 4NU Tel: 0141 776 2778 — MB ChB 1965 Glas.; FRCGP 1994, M 1974. (Glas.) Assoc. Adviser (Gen. Pract.) Glas.; Hon. Clin. Sen. Lect. Univ. Glas. Prev: Ho. Phys. & Ho. Surg. W.. Infirm. Glas.

THOMPSON, Patricia Ann Criffel House, Water Lane, Frisby-on-the-Wreake, Melton Mowbray LE14 2NP Tel: 01664 434012 Email: patfrisby@lineone.net — MB BS 1962 Lond.; MRCS Eng. LRCP Lond. 1962; MFFP 1995. Sen. Clin. Med. Off. Fosse Health Trust Leic.

THOMPSON, Patricia Diane 218 Christchurch Road, Newport NP19 8BJ — MRCS Eng. LRCP Lond. 1964. (Sheff.) Prev: GP Caerphilly M. GLam.; Ho. Phys. & Ho. Surg. Rotherham Hosp.

THOMPSON, Patricia Mary (retired) 1 Embankment Gardens, London SW3 — MRCS Eng. LRCP Lond. 1952; MRCS Eng. LRCP Lond. (Feb.) 1952.

THOMPSON, Paul Consultant Psychiatrist, Argyll and Bute Hospital, Lochgilphead PA31 8LD — MB 1987 Camb.; PhD Leeds 1982, BSc (Hons.) 1978; BChir 1986; MRCPsych 1993.

THOMPSON, Paul Northumberland House, 4337 Stourport Rd, Kidderminster DY11 7BL; 12 Imperial Avenue, Kidderminster DY10 2RA — MB BS 1994 Lond.; MRCCGP; DRCOG. (London Hospital)

THOMPSON, Paul Warren Department of Rheumatology, Poole General Hospital, Poole BH15 2JB Tel: 01202 442123 Fax: 01202 660147 Email: xad90@dial.pipex.com — MD 1990 Lond.; MB BS 1977; MRCP (UK) 1982; FRCP 1996. Cons. Rheum. & Rehabil. Poole Gen. Hosp.; Hon. Sen. Lect. Roy. Lond. Hosp. Med. Coll. Socs: Brit. Soc. Rheum.; Amer. Coll. Rheum.; Roy. Soc. Med. Prev: Sen. Lect. (Rheum.) Lond. Hosp. Med. Coll. Lond.; Sen. Regist. (Rheum.) Lond. Hosp. Whitechapel.; ARC Research Fell. (Lond. Hosp.).

THOMPSON, Penelope Jane Bell House, Grand Bouet, St Peter Port, Guernsey GY1 2SB; Seawood House, Colborne Road, St. Peter Port, Guernsey — MB ChB 1980 Sheff.; MRCP (UK) 1984; MRCPsych 1989. Cons. Child & Adolesc. Psychiat. States of Guernsey. Prev: Cons. Child & Adolesc. Psychiat. Pk. Hosp. Oxf.

THOMPSON, Peter c/o Ellison Unit, Bensham Hospital, Bensham, Gateshead NE8 4YL Tel: 0191 402 6680 — MB BS 1980 Newc.; FRCPsych 1995, M 1984. Cons. Psychiat. (Psychogeriat.) N. RHA; Hon. Clin. Lect. Univ. Newc. Socs: BMA. Prev: Sen. Regist. (Psychiat.) N.. RHA; Regist. & SHO (Psychiat.) Newc. HA.

THOMPSON, Peter Brian French Weir Health Centre, French Weir Avenue, Taunton TA1 1NW Tel: 01823 331381 — MB ChB 1971 Manch.; MRCGP 1975.

THOMPSON, Peter David 7 Park View, Kingsmark, Chepstow NP16 5NA Tel: 01291 623643 Email: thomopd@aol.com — MB ChB 1966 Bristol; MRCGP 1976; DObst RCOG 1968. (Bristol) Prev: SHO (Thoracic Surg.) Frenchay Hosp. Bristol; Ho. Phys. Bristol Roy. Infirm.

THOMPSON, Peter John 154 Grand Drive, Raynes Park, London SW20 9LZ — MB BS 1985 Lond.; MRCOG 1993. Sen. Regist. (O & G) Roy. Free Hosp. Lond. Prev: MRC Research Fell. (Pennatol.) Kings Coll. Hosp. Lond.

THOMPSON, Peter John St Melor Surgery, St Melor House, Edwards Road, Amesbury, Salisbury SP4 7LT Tel: 01980 622474 Fax: 01980 622475 — MB BS 1976 Lond.; BDS Lond. 1968; MRCS Eng. LRCP Lond. 1976; FDS RCS Eng. 1972; DRCOG 1980. (Univ. Coll. Hosp.) Socs: BMA. Prev: SHO (O & G) Plymouth Gen. Hosp.; Ho. Phys. Bromley Hosp.; Ho. Surg. FarnBoro. Hosp. Kent.

THOMPSON, Mr Peter John McKim Wier Cottage, Millbank, Fladbury, Pershore WR10 2QA — MB ChB 1992 Birm.; FRCS 1997. (Birm.) Specialist Regist. (Orthop.) NW Thames Rotat. Prev: SHO N.wick Pk. Hosp. Harrow; Neurosurg. SHO Qu. Sq. Lond.; Gen. Surg. SHO Chase Farm Hosp. Enfield.

THOMPSON, Mr Peter Kenneth 50 Gloucester Terrace, London W2 3HH Tel: 020 7723 0517; Pitt Cottage, Bowling Green Close, Putney Heath, London SW15 3TE Tel: 020 8788 7815 — MB BS 1990 Lond.; BSc (Hons.) Lond. 1987; FRCS Ed. 1994. (Lond. Hosp.

THOMPSON

Med. Coll.) Clin. Fell. (Intrathoracic Transpl.) St. Geo. Hosp. Lond. Socs: Med. Protec. Soc.; Roy. Soc. Med. Prev: SHO (Cardiothoracic) Middlx. Hosp. Lond.; SHO (Vasc. Surg.) St. Mary's Hosp. Lond.; Ho. Phys. (Cardiol. & Gen. Med.) Roy. Lond. Hosp. Whitechapel.

THOMPSON, Mr Peter Melville, RD Department of Urology, Kings College Hospital, Denmark Hill, London SE5 9ZS; 7 Crescent Place, London SW3 2EA Tel: 020 7352 1301 Fax: 020 7352 1310 Email: mptsurgery@aol.com — MB BS 1970 Lond.; FRCS Eng. 1975; MRCS Eng. LRCP Lond. 1970. (Kings Coll. Hosp.) Cons. Urol. Surg. Kings Health Care Trust Hosps. Socs: Fell. Roy. Soc. Med.; Brit. Assn. Urol. Surgs.; Int. Loltinence Soc. Prev: Sen. Regist. (Urol.) King's Coll. Hosp. Lond.; Sen. Regist. (Surgic.) Baragwanath Hosp. Johannesburg, S. Afr; Regist. (Surg.) King's Coll. Hosp. Lond.

THOMPSON, Peter Wentworth, MBE (retired) 2 Lakeside Drive, Cardiff CF23 6DD Tel: 02920 754134 Fax: 0222 755926 — MB BChir Camb. 1949; MRCS Eng. LRCP Lond. 1949; FRCA. 1953; DA Eng. 1953. Prev: Cons. Anaesth. Univ. Hosp. Wales Cardiff.

THOMPSON, Petrie Bourne 119 Haberdasher Street, London N1 6EH Tel: 020 7608 2965; 71 Oldfield Road, London N16 0RR Tel: 020 7249 3725 — MB BS 1976 Lond.; MRCPsych 1983. (Univ. Coll. Hosp.) Psychiat. Adviser Inner City Centre Lond. Prev: Sen. Regist. Cassel Hosp.; Regist. Maudsley Hosp.

THOMPSON, Philip Michael 3 Queen Anne's Gardens, London W4 1TU — MB BS 1996 Lond.; MRCP. 1999; MA. 1999. Specialist Regist. (Radiol.).

THOMPSON, Rachel Elizabeth (retired) Thornleigh, 28 Tarvin Road, Littleton, Chester CH3 7DG — MRCS Eng. LRCP Lond. 1952. Prev: GP Chester.

THOMPSON, Rachel Elizabeth Beatrice 9 Riverview Avenue, Coleraine BT51 3JA — MB BCh BAO 1955 Belf.

THOMPSON, Ralph Cecil William (retired) 37 Marine Parade, Dovercourt, Harwich CO12 3RG Tel: 01255 502791 — MB BS Lond. 1944; FFA RCS Eng. 1954; DA Eng. 1952. Hon. Cons. Char. Cross Hosp. Lond. Prev: Cons. (Anaesth.) Roy. Masonic Hosp. Lond.

THOMPSON, Richard Charles Fernyhough Priory Medical Group, Cornlands Road, Acomb, York YO24 3WX Tel: 01904 781423 Fax: 01904 784886 — BM BS 1989 Nottm.

THOMPSON, Richard Damian 37 Grange Hill Road, Birmingham B38 8RE — MB BS 1992 Lond.; BSc (Physiol.) Lond. 1989; MRCP (UK) 1995. (London) MRC Clin. Fell. Hammersmith Hosp. Lond.

THOMPSON, Richard James The Old Rectory, Stapleford Tawney, Romford RM4 1TD — BM BS 1993 Nottm.; BMedSci 1991; FRCS Eng. 1997.

THOMPSON, Richard John Glenview, 341 Crystal Palace Road, E. Dulwich, London SE22 9JL — BM BCh 1987 Oxf.; MRCP (UK) 1994. Research Fell. (Paediat.) Univ. Coll. Lond. Med. Sch. Socs: Brit. Paediat. Assn. Prev: Lect. (Paediat.) UCL Med. Sch. 1994-1995.

THOMPSON, Richard John Bridgewater Family Medical Practice, Drumcarrig, Bridgwater St., Whitchurch SY13 1QH Tel: 01948 662128 Fax: 01948 666550; Heatherfield House, Hollins Lane, Tilstock, Whitchurch SY13 3NT Tel: 01948 880480 Email: r.thompson@freeuk.com — MB ChB 1979 Birm.; MRCGP 1984; DRCOG 1982; Cert. Family Plann. JCC 1982. Hosp. Pract. Shrops. HA; Med. Adviser WhitCh. Community Hosp.; Dep. Police Surg. W. Mercia Police.

THOMPSON, Richard Norman John Lisburn Road Surgery, 10-12 Lisburn Road, Belfast BT9 6AA Tel: 028 9032 3035 — MB BCh BAO 1985 Belf.

THOMPSON, Richard Paul Hepworth (cons. rooms), York House, 199 Westminster Bridge Road, London SE1 7UT Tel: 020 7928 5485 Fax: 020 7928 3748; 36 Dealtry Road, London SW15 6NL Tel: 020 8789 3839 Fax: 020 8788 3492 — BA 1962 Oxford; BM BCh Oxf. 1964; MA, DM Oxf. 1971; FRCP Lond. 1979, M 1966. (Oxf. & St. Thos.) p/t Cons. Phys. St. Thos. Hosp. Lond.; Phys. to HM the Qu.; Hon. Phys. King Edwd. VII Hosp. Offs.; Hon. Cons. & Sen. Lect. Liver Unit KCH Lond. Prev: Phys. to HM Ho.hold; MRC Clin. Research Fell. & Hon. Lect. Med. Liver Unit Kings Coll. Hosp. Lond.; Research Asst. Gastroenterol. Unit Mayo Clinic Rochester, USA.

THOMPSON, Richard Stewart The Old Laundry, Neatishead, Norwich NR12 8AD — MRCS Eng. LRCP Lond. 1969.

THOMPSON, Richard William Graham St Thomas Surgery, Rifleman Lane, St. Thomas Green, Haverfordwest SA61 1QX Tel: 01437 762162 Fax: 01437 776811; Fox Hollow, RHOS, Haverfordwest SA62 4AU — ChB Birm. 1986; MRCGP 1993; Cert. Family Plann. JCC 1992; DRCOG 1992; DCH RCP Lond. 1989. Socs: Roy. Coll. Gen. Practitioners.

THOMPSON, Robert John (retired) The Plough, The Street, Guston, Dover CT15 5ET — MRCS Eng. LRCP Lond. 1971; FFA RCS Eng. 1975. Prev: Regist. (Anaesth.) Salisbury Health Dist.

THOMPSON, Robert Martin The Kennels, Middle Lane, Hutton Buscel, Scarborough YO13 9LS Tel: 01723 863594 — MB BS 1980 Lond.; DRCOG 1982.

THOMPSON, Robert Miles Hawthorn, New Road, Old Snydale, Pontefract WF7 6HE — MB BS 1977 Lond.

THOMPSON, Robert Noel Department of Rheumatology, Aintree Hospitals NHS Trust, Liverpool L9 7AL Tel: 0151 529 3341; 12 Riverbank Road, Heswall, Wirral CH60 4SG Tel: 0151 342 8457 — MB BCh BAO 1973 NUI; FRCP Lond. 1992; MRCP (UK) 1980. Cons. Rheum. Univ. Hosp. Aintree Liverp.; Clin. Dir. (Rheum.) Univ. Hosp. Aintree Liverp. Socs: Brit. Soc. Rheum. Prev: Fell. Rheum. Univ. Alberta, Canada; Sen. Regist. (Rheum. & Rehabil.) Manch. Univ. Rheum. Dis. Centre, Hope, Withington & Roy. Infirm. Manch.

THOMPSON, Robert Stronnar 4 Ranelagh Drive N., Liverpool L19 9DS — MB ChB 1928 Ed. (Ed.)

THOMPSON, Robert Tester The Surgery, 59 Sevenoaks Road, Orpington BR6 9JN Tel: 01689 820159; 59 Sevenoaks Road, Orpington BR6 9JN Tel: 01689 20159 — MB BS 1978 Lond.; MRCGP 1983; DRCOG 1982. (Guy's)

THOMPSON, Rodney Julian Wesley The Grange, 7 The Orchards, Four Oaks, Sutton Coldfield B74 2PP — MB ChB 1976 Birm.; MRCGP 1983.

THOMPSON, Roger Woodseats Medical Centre, 4 Cobnar Road, Woodseats, Sheffield S8 8QB Tel: 0114 274 0202 Fax: 0114 274 6835; Owl End, Dore Moor Est., Newfield Lane, Sheffield S17 3DB — MB ChB 1971 Sheff.

THOMPSON, Roger Humphrey Leech Meadow Cottage, Sheinton, Cressage, Shrewsbury SY5 6DN — MB BS 1967 Lond.; MRCGP 1981; AFOM 1982. (Lond. Hosp.) Prev: Regist. (Gen. Med.) Aberd. Gen. Hosps.; Ho. Surg. (O & G) Mile End Hosp.

THOMPSON, Roger Martin Drs Thompson, Stokes, Knight, Fisher, Knight & Edwards, Marches Surgery, Westfield Walk, Leominster HR6 8HD Tel: 01568 614141; Pound House, Brockmanton, Leominster HR6 0QU Tel: 01568 760606 — MB BS 1973 Lond.; MRCGP 1977; DObst RCOG 1975. (Lond. Hosp.) Prev: Trainee GP Preston VTS; Ho. Surg. (Cardiothoracic Surg. Lond. Hosp.; Ho. Phys. Bethnal Green Hosp.

THOMPSON, Professor Ronald Augustine, MBE, TD (retired) 37 Grange Hill Road, Kings Norton, Birmingham B38 8RE Tel: 0121 458 3549 Email: rthompson9434@aol.com — MB BS 1958 Lond.; BSc (Anat.) Lond. 1955; FRCP Lond. 1979, M 1963; MRCS Eng. LRCP Lond. 1958; FRCPath 1981, M 1971. Prev: Cons. Immunol. E. Birm. Hosp.

THOMPSON, Ronald Bolton (retired) 84 Moorside N., Newcastle upon Tyne NE4 9DU Tel: 0191 273 8637 — MD 1943 Durh.; MD (Hons.) Durh. 1943, MB BS 1941; FRCP Lond. 1960, M 1942. Prev: Cons. Phys. Roy. Vict. Infirm. Newc.

THOMPSON, Ronald Leslie Ernest 3 Stoneypath, New Buildings, Londonderry BT47 2AF — MB BCh BAO 1981 Belf.

THOMPSON, Ruth Elizabeth 7 Callender Road, Liverpool L6 8NT — MB ChB 1997 Dundee.

THOMPSON, Sara Anne Station Road Surgery, 24 Station Road, Long Buckby, Northampton NN6 7QB Tel: 01327 842360 Fax: 01327 842302; Bridge House, Murcott, Long Buckby, Northampton NN6 7QR Tel: 01327 842850 — MB BS 1982 Newc.; MRCGP 1986; DRCOG 1986. (Newc.) Trainer GP N.ampton.

THOMPSON, Sara Jane 6 Greenacres, Stainton, Middlesbrough TS8 9BN — MB ChB 1998 Manch.

THOMPSON, Sharon Elizabeth 38 Kilnford Drive, Dundonald, Kilmarnock KA2 9ET — MB ChB 1995 Aberd.

THOMPSON, Shirley Margaret Creighton Cherry Cottage, 5 The Square, Kenilworth CV8 1EF Tel: 01926 59996 — MB BS 1950 Durh. (Durh.) Clin. Asst. (Psychiat.) S. Warks. Hosp. Gp. Prev: Med. Off. Leeds Corp.; Asst. Med. Off. Durh. CC; SHO Orthop. Unit Bridge of Earn Hosp.

THOMPSON, Simon Abington Health Complex, Doctors Surgery, 51A Beech Avenue, Northampton NN3 2JG Tel: 01604 791999 Fax:

THOMPSON

01604 450155 — MB ChB 1982 Aberd.; MRCGP 1986; DRCOG 1986. Socs: BMA.

THOMPSON, Simon David Risca Surgery, St. Mary Street, Risca, Newport NP11 6YS Tel: 01633 612666 — MB BS 1979 Lond.; MRCGP 1984.

THOMPSON, Simon Gower Amersham Health Centre, Chiltern Avenue, Amersham HP6 5AY Tel: 01494 434344; 54 Hogg Lane, Holmer Green, High Wycombe HP15 6PZ — MRCS Eng. LRCP Lond. 1972; MRCGP 1979. (Guy's)

THOMPSON, Simon Patrick Ringwood Health Centre, The Close, Ringwood BH24 1JY Tel: 01425 478901 Fax: 01425 478239; 24 Gravel Lane, Ringwood BH24 1LN — MB BS 1981 Lond.; DRCOG 1986. (St Thomas') Prev: Trainee GP Salisbury; SHO (Cas. Orthop.) Derby Roy. Infirm.; Ho. Phys. Salisbury Gen. Infirm.

THOMPSON, Mr Stanley Graham, RD (retired) Abbey House, Great Massingham, King's Lynn PE32 2JG Fax: 01485 520254 — MB BS 1953 Lond.; FRCS Eng. 1961. Prev: Cons. Surg. W. Norf. & Wisbech HA.

THOMPSON, Stephen John 2 St Nicholas Drive, Whitesmocks, Durham DH1 4HH — MB BS 1985 Newc. Regist. (Histopath.) Newc. Gen. Hosp.

THOMPSON, Mr Stephen Keith Fairfield Cottage, Croft Drive E., Caldy, Wirral CH48 1LS Tel: 0151 625 9081 — MB ChB 1968 Liverp.; MChOrth Liverp. 1976; FRCS Ed. 1973. (Liverp.) Cons. Orthop. Surg. Roy. Liverp. Hosp. & Warrington Dist. Gen.; Regist. (Orthop. Surg.) Liverp. AHA (T).

THOMPSON, Stephen William Iona, Course Lane, Newburgh, Wigan WN8 7UB — MB ChB 1991 Manch.

THOMPSON, Mr Stuart David 35 Bridle Road, Wollaston, Stourbridge DY8 4QE — MB BS 1989 Lond.; FRCS Ed. 1994. Clin. Research Fell. (Surg.) Univ. Hosp. Edgbaston.

THOMPSON, Susan Mary 16 Meadow Brook Road, Birmingham B31 1NE — MB ChB 1972 Birm.; FRCOphth 1992; FRCS Eng. 1981. Cons. Ophth. Dudley & Sandwell HAs.

THOMPSON, Susan Mary 144-150 High Road, Willesden, London NW10 2PT Tel: 020 8459 5550; 27 Asmuns Hill, London NW11 6ES Tel: 020 8455 1731 — MB BS 1980 Lond.; MRCGP 1985.

THOMPSON, Sylvia Ann Sussex Place Surgery, 63 Sussex Place, Bristol BS2 9QR Tel: 0117 955 6275 Fax: 0117 955 8666 — MB BCh BAO 1984 Belf.; MB BCh Belf. 1984; MRCGP 1990.

THOMPSON, Terence Joseph 2 Shelley Grove, Southport PR8 6HA — MB BCh BAO 1984 NUI.

THOMPSON, Thomas Roy (retired) East House, Shoreston Hall, Seahouses NE68 7SX Tel: 01665 720052 — MB BS 1952 Durh. Prev: Mentioned in Despatches 1955.

THOMPSON, Timothy Mark The Health Centre, Bath Road, Thatcham, Newbury RG18 3HD Tel: 01635 67171 — MB BS 1973 Lond.; MRCGP 1977; DObst RCOG 1975.

THOMPSON, Trevor David Barnes 20 Milner Road, Glasgow G13 1QL Tel: 0141 954 9326 Email: doctortrev@bigfoot.com — MB BS 1990 Lond.; BA Oxf. 1986; MFHom 1996; MRCGP 1995; DRCOG 1992. (Oxford and St. Mary's) Higher Professional Train. Fell. Univ. of Glas.; Dir. MIRTH! Internet Consultancy Phys. (Homoeopathy). Prev: Clin. Researcher Glas. Homoeop. Hosp.; SHO (Homoeop.) Glas. Homoeop. Hosp.

THOMPSON, Trevor Henry Raymond Ely Bridge Surgery, 23 Mill Road, Ely, Cardiff CF5 4AD Tel: 029 2056 1808 Fax: 029 2057 8871 — MB BCh 1981 Wales; MRCGP 1986; DRCOG 1984.

THOMPSON, Trevor John 10 Rosslea Gardens, Limavady BT49 0TJ — MB BCh 1998 Belf.

THOMPSON, Trevor Joseph 30 Rathmena Avenue, Ballyclare BT39 9HX — MB BCh BAO 1990 Belf.; MB BCh Belf. 1990.

THOMPSON, Valerie The Barn, Church Walks, Christleton, Chester CH3 7AF — LLB 1975 Southampton; MB ChB Liverp. 1996. (Liverpool) GP Regist. Bunbury Med. Pract. Prev: SHO Rotat. (Surg.) Liverp. & Chester.

THOMPSON, Valerie Mary (retired) The Fieldings, Papermill Lane, South Moreton, Didcot OX11 9AH — MB BS Lond. 1948; FRCOG 1969, M 1953; FRCS Eng. 1958; MRCS Eng. LRCP Lond. 1948. Prev: Cons. Gyn. Roy. Free Hosp.

THOMPSON, Mr Walter Turton (retired) Southview, Lamlash, Brodick KA27 8LE Tel: 01770 600327 — MRCS Eng. LRCP Lond. 1940; MD Leeds 1950, MB ChB (2nd Cl. Hons.) 1940; FRCS Eng. 1942; FICS 1952; Amer. Bd. Certification (Gen. Surg.) 1959; Dip. Nat. Bd. Med. Examr. USA 1954. Prev: Surg. John N Norton Memor. Infirm. & Childr. Hosp. Louisville USA.

THOMPSON, Wendy Christine Ruby 31 Girdlers Road, London W14 0PS — MB BS 1986 Lond.

THOMPSON, William 14 Avon Close, The Bryn Estate, Pontllanfraith, Blackwood NP12 2GB — MB BCh 1983 Wales.

THOMPSON, William Department Obstetrics & Gynaecology, Institute of Clinical Science, Grosvenor Road, Belfast BT12 6BJ Tel: 01232 894600 Fax: 01232 328247 Email: w.thompson@qub.ac.uk — MB BCh BAO (Hons.) 1961; BSc (Hons.) Belf. 1958, MD 1975; FRCOG 1980, M 1967; DObst RCPI 1963. (Qus. Univ. Belf.) Prof. O & G Qu. Univ. Belf.; Cons. Obst. Roy. Matern. Hosp. Belf.; Cons. Gyn. Roy. Vict. Hosp. Belf.; Cons. Obst. & Gyn. Belf. City Hosp. Socs: Treas. Internat. Federat. Fertil. Soc.; Brit. Fertil. Soc.; Brit. Menopause Soc. Prev: Lect. (O & G) Kandang Kerbau Hosp., Univ. Singapore.

THOMPSON, Mr William Arthur Lisle, TD (retired) 22 Fford Llechi, Rhosneigr LL64 5JY Tel: 01407 810505 — MChOrth Liverp. 1956, MB ChB 1947; FRCS Ed. 1955. Prev: Cons. Orthop. Surg. Walton & Fazakerley Hosps. Liverp.

THOMPSON, William Bruce Church Walk Surgery, 28 Church Walk, Lurgan, Craigavon BT67 9AA Tel: 028 3832 7834 Fax: 028 3834 9331; 3 Solitude Demesne, Lurgan, Craigavon BT67 9GN — MB BS 1985 Lond.; MRCGP 1990; Dip. Sports Med. Scotl. 1993; DRCOG 1990; DCH Dub. 1989. (St. Barts. Hosp.) Clin. Asst. Orthops. & Sports Med. Craigavon Area Hosp. Portadown. Socs: Soc. Orthopaedic Med. Lond. 1997; Amer. Coll. Sports Med.; Soc. of Orthop. Med.

THOMPSON, William David North Tees General Hospital, Stockton-on-Tees TS19 8PE Tel: 01642 617617 — MB BS 1980 Newc.; FRCP Ed. 1995; MRCP (UK) 1983; FRCR 1987. (Newc. u. Tyne) Cons. Radiol. Cleveland. Socs: Brit. Med. Ultrasound Soc. Prev: Sen. Regist. & Regist. (Radiol.) Newc.

THOMPSON, William Douglas Department of Pathology, Medical School, Aberdeen Royal Infirmary, Aberdeen AB25 2ZD Tel: 01224 681818 Fax: 01224 663002; East Law, Durno, Pitcaple, Inverurie AB51 5EU Tel: 0146 76 681401 — MB ChB 1970 Glas.; PhD Glas. 1981; DSc Aberd. 1996; FRCPath 1990, M 1978. Sen. Lect. (Path.) Aberd. Roy. Infirm. Socs: Path. Soc.; Brit. Atherosclerosis Soc.; Internat. Fibrinogen Research Soc. Prev: Lect. (Path.) Glas. Roy. Infirm.

THOMPSON, William Joseph (retired) The Margaret Thompson Medical Centre, 105 East Millwood Road, Speke, Liverpool L24 6TH Tel: 0151 425 3339 Fax: 0151 425 2272 — MB ChB Liverp. 1961; DTM & H 2000 Liverpool. Prev: Ho. Surg. & Ho. Phys. & SHO (O & G) Walton Hosp. Liverp.

THOMPSON, William Michael Cardiff Community Healthcare Trust, Ely Hospital, Cowbridge Road W., Cardiff CF2 5DW Tel: 029 2056 2323 Fax: 029 2055 5047 — MB BCh 1989 Wales. Sen. Regist. (Learning Disabilities) Cardiff Community Healthcare Trust.

THOMPSON, William Stanley (retired) 395 Sandyfields Road, Lower Gornal, Dudley DY3 3DJ Tel: 01902 882938 — LRCP LRCS Ed. LRFPS Glas. 1951.

THOMPSON, Winifred Maude (retired) 162 Leicester Road, Loughborough LE11 2AQ Tel: 01509 263303 — MB BS 1938 Lond.; MRCS Eng. LRCP Lond. 1938; MRCGP 1963. Prev: Clin. Asst. Hastings Ho. Hosp. Loughboro.

THOMS, Gavin Malcolm Macthomas Department of Anaesthesia, Manchester Royal Infirmary, Oxford Road, Manchester M13 9WL Tel: 0161 276 4551 Fax: 0161 273 5685 Email: gavin.thoms@man.ac.uk; 1 Hungry Lane, Bradwell, Hope Valley S33 9JD — MB ChB 1971 Ed.; MSc Manch. 1985; MFPHM 1985; FRCA 1976; DCH Eng. 1973; FFPHM 1998. (Ed.) Cons. Anaesth. Manch. Roy. Infirm.; Hon. Sen. Research Fell. (Anaesth.) Manch. Univ. Socs: Assn. of Anaesth.s; Soc. Computing & Technol. in Anaesth.; Assn. Anesth. Clin. Directors. Prev: Sen. Research Fell. Manch. Univ.; Director of Pub. Health Manch. Health Auth.; Sen. Med. Off. Dept. of Health Leeds.

THOMSITT, Mr John (cons. rooms), 4 Manston Terrace, Exeter EX2 4NP Tel: 01392 435053 Fax: 01392 435301 — MB BS 1960 Lond.; FRCS Eng. 1969; FRCOphth 1988. Cons. Ophth. Eng. W. of

Eng. Eye Unit Roy. Devon & Exeter Hosp. Wonford. Prev: Sen. Lect. (Clin. Ophth.) Univ. Lond. Moorfields Eye Hosp. Lond.

THOMSON, Mr Adrian Alexander Gordon Department of Surgery, Birch Hill Hospital, Rochdale OL12 9QB Tel: 01706 377777; Underbank House, Charlestown, Hebden Bridge HX7 6PE Tel: 01422 844355 — MB BChir 1969 Camb.; MA Camb. 1967; FRCS Eng. 1975. Cons. Gen. Surg. Rochdale HA, Birch Hill Hosp., Rochdale. Socs: Assn. Surg.; Brit. Assn. of Surgic. Oncol.; Assn. Endoscopic Surgs. Prev: Dir. (Surg.) K. Abdul Aziz Naval Gen. Hosp. Saudi Arabia.

THOMSON, Alan Robert The Maltings Family Practice, 10 Victoria Street, St Albans AL1 3JB Tel: 01727 853296 Fax: 01727 862498 — MB BChir 1986 Camb.; MA Camb. 1989, BA 1984, MB BChir 1986.

THOMSON, Alan Roderick 41 Braeside Avenue, Aberdeen AB15 7ST — MB ChB 1990 Aberd.

THOMSON, Alan Sinclair Castlehill Health Centre, Castlehill, Forres IV36 1QF Tel: 01309 672233 Fax: 01309 673445; Montana, Nelson Road, Forres IV36 1DR Tel: 01309 673023 — MB ChB 1984 Aberd.; BSc Aberd. 1978; MRCGP 1988.

THOMSON, Alan Walter Argyll Street Surgery, 246 Argyll Street, Dunoon PA23 7HW Tel: 01369 703279 Fax: 01369 704430 — MB ChB 1976 Ed.; FFARCSI 1985; MRCGP 1986.

THOMSON, Alasdair James 34 Riversdale, Gravesend DA11 8SR — MB ChB 1979 Aberd.

THOMSON, Alastair Grant Old Town Surgery, 13 De la Warr Road, Bexhill-on-Sea TN40 2HG Tel: 01424 219323 Fax: 01424 733940; The Tall House, Heatherdune Road, Bexhill-on-Sea TN39 4HB Tel: 01424 214385 — MB ChB 1979 Bristol; MRCGP 1984; DRCOG 1984; DCH RCP Lond. 1983.

THOMSON, Alastair James Western General Hospital, Crewe Road South, Edinburgh EH4 2XU Email: a.j.thomson@aol.ac.uk — MB ChB 1993 Ed.; MRCP (UK) 1996; FRCA 1999. (Edinburgh) Specialist Regist. (Anaesth.) Edin.; Research Fell. Dept. of Med. Sci. Univ. of Edin. Prev: SHO (Anaesth.) Glas.; SHO (Med.) Edin.

THOMSON, Alastair Matheson 15 Kingsford Avenue, Glasgow G44 3EU — MB ChB 1950 Glas.

THOMSON, Alexander Colin Peter Duguid, MC (retired) Beech Wood, Perrotts Brook, Cirencester GL7 7BS — MB ChB 1939 Ed.; DMR Ed. 1946. Prev: Cons. Radiol. Bath Clin. Area.

THOMSON, Alexander McFarlane 53 New Abbey Road, Dumfries DG2 7LZ — MB ChB 1998 Manch.

THOMSON, Alison Jean Abbotswood, Gattonside, Melrose TD6 9NS Tel: 0189 682 2754 — MB ChB 1966 Ed.; FRCP Ed. 1984; MRCP (UK) 1972; DObst RCOG 1968. (Edin.) Socs: Scott. Paediat. Soc. & Brit. Paediat. Soc. Prev: Sen. Regist. (Paediat.) Roy. Aberd. Childr. Hosp.; Regist. (Paediat.) Edin. N.. Hosp. Gp.; Resid. Hosp. Sick Childr. Toronto, Canada.

THOMSON, Alison Jean Marin Ancrum Medical Centre, 12-14 Ancrum Road, Dundee DD2 2HZ Tel: 01382 669316 Fax: 01382 660787; Beach Cottage, 71 Beach Crescent, Broughty Ferry, Dundee DD5 2BG Tel: 01382 730321 — MB ChB 1981 Dundee; DRCOG 1984. GP Tayside. Prev: Med. Off. E. Scotl. Blood Transfus. Serv. Dundee.

THOMSON, Alison Joyce Midlock Medical Centre, 7 Midlock Street, Glasgow G51 1SL Tel: 0141 427 4271 Fax: 0141 427 1405 — MB ChB 1984 Glas.; MRCGP 1989. Gen. Practitioner - Princip.

THOMSON, Alistair David 26 Primrose Street, Dumfries DG2 7AU — MB ChB 1981 Glas.; MRCGP 1984; DFFP 1993; Cert. Family Plann. JCC 1988; Cert. Prescribed Equiv. Exp. JCPTGP 1986. Socs: Assn. Course Organisers.

THOMSON, Alistair Park (retired) 1 Albion Terrace, Saltburn-by-the-Sea TS12 1JW — MB ChB 1959 Glas.; MFOM RCP Lond. 1980; DIH Soc. Apoth. Lond. 1979; CIH Dund 1978. Prev: Wilton Area Med. Off. Teeside Operat. ICI, C & P plc Cleveland.

THOMSON, Alistair Peter James Leighton Hospital, Crewe CW1 4QJ Tel: 01270 612289; 2 The Avenue, Alsager, Stoke-on-Trent ST7 2AN Tel: 01270 873569 — MB BChir 1977 Camb.; MD Camb. 1991; FRCP Lond. 1994; MRCP (UK) 1981; DCH Eng. 1980; DRCOG 1979; FRCPCH 1997. (King's Coll. Hosp.) Cons. Paediat. Mid Chesh. Hosps. NHS Trust, Leighton Hosp. Crewe; Hon. Cons. Paediat. Roy. Liverp. Childr. Hosp.; Hon. Clin. Lect. Univ. Liverp.; PostGrad. Clin. Tutor and Director of Med. Educat., Mid Chesh. Hosps & NHS Trust, Crewe.; Hon. Lect. Dept. Med. Micro.Univ.

Liverp. Socs: Paediat. Research Soc.; Nat. Assn. Clin. Tutors (Chair). Prev: Sen. Regist. Rotat. (Paediat.) Mersey RHA; Research Fell. & Hon. Regist. St. Thos. Hosp. Lond.; Regist. St. Thos. Hosp. Lond. & Pembury Hosp.

THOMSON, Allan David 64 Lee Park, London SE3 9HZ — PhD Ed. 1971, BSc 1961, MB ChB 1963; FRCP Lond. 1993; FRCP Ed. 1984; MRCP (UK) 1973; ECFMG Cert 1966. (Ed.) Hon. Sen. Lect. (Med.) KCH Lond.; Emerit. Edr. Alcohol & Alcoholism; Hon. Cons. Gastroenterol. Greenwich Dist. Hosp.; Hon. Sen. Lect. Kims\ Canterbury. Socs: Amer. Assn. Study Liver Dis.; Brit. Soc. Gastroenterol.; Med. Counc. on Alcoholism. Prev: Asst. Prof. Internal Med., Instruc. in Med. & Nat. Inst. Health; Post-Doctoral Research Fell. Coll. Med. & Dent New Jersey, USA.

THOMSON, Andrew (retired) High Corrie, Stanley, Perth PH1 4PG Tel: 01738 828540 — MB ChB Ed. 1950; MRCGP 1967; DObst RCOG 1960. Prev: GP Stanley.

THOMSON, Andrew John University Department of Obstetrics and Gynaecology, Glasgow Royal Infirmary, 10 Alexandra Parade, Glasgow G31 2ER Tel: 0141 211 4706 Fax: 0141 553 1367 Email: ajt3w@udcf.gla.ac.uk — MB ChB 1989 Glas.; MB ChB Glasgow 1989; MRCOG 1994; BSc Hons (Pharmacy) 1986; MD Hons Glasgow 1999. (Glasgow) Clin. Lect. in O & G; Specialist Regist.

THOMSON, Andrew McLean MRC Molecular Haematology Unit, Institute of Molecular Medicine, John Radcliffe Hospital, Oxford OX3 9DS Tel: 01865 222395 Fax: 01865 222500 Email: athomson@worf.molbiol.ox.ac.uk; September Cottage, 69B North St, Middle Bacon, Chipping Norton OX7 7BZ Tel: 01869 347649 — MB ChB 1990 Glas.; DPhil Oxf. 1997; BSc (Hons.) Glas. 1987. MRC Post Doctoral Research Fell. MRC Molecular Haemat. Unit Inst. Molecular Med. Univ. Oxf. Prev: Specialist Regist. (Virol.) St. Mary's Hosp. Lond.; SHO (Path.) Stirling Roy. Infirm.; Ho. Off. (Surg.) Stirling Roy. Infirm.

THOMSON, Andrew McMurray Paterson 7 Rannoch Avenue, Bishopbriggs, Glasgow G64 1BU — MB ChB 1947 Glas. (Glas.) Asst. Phys. Stobhill Gen. Hosp. Glas.

THOMSON, Andrew Scott The Atherstone Surgery, 1 Ratcliffe Road, Atherstone CV9 1EU Tel: 01827 713664 Fax: 01827 713666; The Firs, Shadows Lane, Congerstone, Nuneaton CV13 6NF — MB ChB 1987 Ed.; MRCGP 1993. Prev: SHO (Gen. Pract.) Nuneaton VTS; SHO (Gen. Med.) Geo. Eliot Hosp. Nuneaton.

THOMSON, Angus John Malcolm Arrowe Park Hospital, Upton, Wirral CH49 5PE Tel: 0151 678 5111; 1 Quarry Road West, Heswall, Wirral CH60 6RE Tel: 0151 342 6493 Email: gus@doctors.org.uk — MB ChB 1993 Liverp.; MRCOG 1999; DFFP 1997. Specialist Regist. O & G, Mersey Region. Socs: Brit. Fertil. Soc. Prev: Specialist Regist. (O & G) Mersey Deanery N. W. Region.

THOMSON, Anne Helen Department of Paediatrics, John Radcliffe Hospital, Headington, Oxford OX3 9DU Tel: 01865 221496 — MD 1987 Aberd.; MB ChB 1976; FRCP Lond. 1994. Cons. Paediat. Respirat. Dis. John Radcliffe Hosp. Oxf. Prev: Lect. (Child Health) Univ. Leic.; Research Fell. (Neonat. Respirat.) Hammersmith Hosp. Lond.

THOMSON, Archibald McLellan Wright, TD (retired) 44 Netherblane, Blanefield, Glasgow G63 9JW Tel: 01360 770041 — MB ChB 1932 Glas.; MD (Commend.) Glas. 1947; FRFPS Glas. 1936; FRCP Glas. 1964, M 1962; FCOphth 1988; DOMS Eng. 1935. Prev: Surg. Glas. Eye Infirm.

THOMSON, Brian James 22 Lymington Road, London NW6 1HY — MB ChB 1980 Ed.; PhD CNAA 1992; MRCP (UK) 1983. MRC Train. Fell. Nat. Inst. for Med. Research Lond.; MRC Clin. Sci. Fell. Addenbrooke's Hosp. Camb. Prev: Regist. (Med.) Roy. Infirm. Edin.

THOMSON, Bruce Ewan (retired) Knoweside, Ferntower Road, Crieff PH7 3DH Tel: 01764 653048 Fax: 01764 653048 — MB BS 1962 Lond.; MA Oxf. 1980; MRCS Eng. LRCP Lond. 1962; MRCGP 1977; DObst RCOG 1965.

THOMSON, Bruce Forsyth Morrison Lincluden Surgery, 53 Bellshill Road, Uddingston, Glasgow G71 7PA Tel: 01698 813873; 10 Gleneagles Park, Bothwell, Glasgow G71 8UT Tel: 01698 852856 — MB ChB 1981 Glas.; MRCGP 1985; DRCOG 1984.

THOMSON, Carl Craggs Farm House, Little Broughton, Cockermouth CA13 0YG Tel: 01900 825244 Fax: 01900 829354 Email: carlthomson@doctors.org.uk — MB ChB 1967 Ed.; MRCP (UK) 1970. (Ed.) Prev: Cons. Phys. W. Cumbld. Hosp. Hensingham 1997-1998.

THOMSON

THOMSON, Carolyn Margaret 9 Milton Crescent, Edinburgh EH15 3PF — MB ChB 1985 Aberd.

THOMSON, Catherine Robertson Health Centre, Park Drive, Stenhousemuir, Larbert FK5 3BB Tel: 01324 570570 Fax: 01324 553632 — MB ChB 1977 Glasgow. (Glasgow) GP Larbert.

THOMSON, Catriona Woodside, Copperas Lane, Haigh, Wigan WN2 1PB — MB ChB 1989 Manch.

THOMSON, Charles Wilson (retired) The Pound, 32 Brookfield Road, East Budleigh, Budleigh Salterton EX9 7EL Tel: 01395 446008 — MB BS 1953 Durh.; FFA RCS Eng. 1961.

THOMSON, Christopher Bruce (retired) 584 Bath Road, Bristol BS4 3LE Tel: 0117 971 2132 — MRCS Eng. LRCP Lond. 1956; FFOM RCP Lond. 1982, MFOM 1979; DIH Dund 1970. Prev: Sen. Employm. Med. Adviser Health & Safety Exec.

THOMSON, Clare Mary Moody Street Medical Centre, 23-25 Moody Terrace, Congleton CW12 4AW Tel: 01260 272331 Fax: 01260 277964 — MB ChB 1979 Manch.; BSc St. And. 1976.

THOMSON, Colin Buchanan (retired) 24 Longdean Park, Hemel Hempstead HP3 8BZ Tel: 01442 64273 — MB ChB 1922 Ed.

THOMSON, Colin Charles Buchanan 24 Longdean Park, Hemel Hempstead HP3 8BZ — BM BCh 1998 Oxf.

THOMSON, Colin Hugh (retired) Troisdorf, Hereford Road, Weobley, Hereford HR4 8SW — MB ChB 1952 Ed. Prev: Ho. Surg. & Ho. Phys. Cumbld. Infirm. Carlisle.

THOMSON, Daniel Ferguson 1 Ledcameroch Crescent, Bearsden, Glasgow G61 4AD Tel: 0141 942 7513 — MB ChB 1964 Glas.; FFA RCS Eng. 1968. (Glas.) Cons. (Anaesth.) Vict. Infirm. Glas. Prev: Sen. Regist. Glas. Roy. Infirm.; Sen. Specialist Natal Provin. Hosp. Admin. S. Africa.

THOMSON, David Alexander, OBE (retired) Evendine House, Colwall, Malvern WR13 6DT Tel: 01684 540948 — MB ChB Glas. 1938; MRCOG 1948; MRCGP 1958.

THOMSON, David James Ramsay Gibb 31 Fitzroy Square, London W1P 5HH Tel: 020 7387 5798; 52 Rawstorne Street, London EC1V 7NQ Tel: 020 7278 9251 Email: clerks@barnards_inn_chambers.co.uk — MB ChB 1985 Sheff.; LLM (Hons.) 1993; LLB (Hons.) 1992. Barrister at Law; GP Retainer Scheme; Regt.. Surg. Inns of Ct. & City of Lond. Yeomanry. Socs: Fell. Roy. Soc. Med.; Med. Pract. Union.; Soc. Doctors in Law. Prev: GP Lond.; SHO (Surg.) Brompton & Roy. Marsden Hosps.; Demonst. & Lect. Leeds Med. & Dent. Sch.

THOMSON, Mr David Stewart 35 Champion Hill, London SE5 8BS — MB ChB 1977 Manch.; BSc St. And. 1974; FRCS Eng. 1981. Head Clin. Research Lorex Synthelabo (UK).

THOMSON, Deborah Jane 2 Hockley Mill, Church Lane, Twyford, Winchester SO21 1NT Tel: 01967 711424 — MB BChir 1981 Camb.; MA Oxf. 1986, BA 1979. Pract. of Traditional Chinese Acupunc. Winchester. Socs: Brit. Acupunc. Soc. Prev: Clin. Asst. (Pub. Health) N. & Mid Hants. HA; Clin. Asst. (Haemat.) Winchester HA; Trainee GP Winchester VTS.

THOMSON, Derek Adam Haltwhistle Health Centre, Greencroft Avenue, Haltwhistle NE49 9AP Tel: 01434 320077 Fax: 01434 320674; Sholl, Fairholme, Comb Hill, Haltwhistle NE49 9EX Tel: 01434 321182 — MB BS 1983 Newc.; MRCGP 1988. Chairm. W. N.umberland PCG.

THOMSON, Donald Mark Melven (retired) Pinkacre, Leigh on Mendip, Bath BA3 5LX Tel: 01373 812230 — MB ChB 1954 Bristol. Prev: Med. Off. Uganda Med. Dept.

THOMSON, Donald McDonald McKenzie Medical Centre, 20 West Richmond Street, Edinburgh EH8 9DX Tel: 0131 667 2955; 72 Craighall Road, Edinburgh EH6 4RG Tel: 0131 552 5069 — MB ChB 1971 Ed.; BSc Ed. 1968; FRCP Ed. 1990; MRCP (UK) 1973; FRCGP 1990, M 1975. Sen. Lect. (Gen. Pract.) Univ. Edin.; Assoc. Dean (Admissions) Fac. Med. Univ. Edin. Prev: Lect. (Gen. Pract.) Univ. Edin.

THOMSON, Douglas John The Park Medical Centre, Maine Drive Clinic, Maine Drive, Chaddesden, Derby DE21 6LA Tel: 01332 665522 Fax: 01332 678210 — MB ChB 1975 Glas.

THOMSON, Mr Douglas Stormonth (retired) 38 Christ Church Road, Cheltenham GL50 2PW Tel: 01242 515932 — MB BS Durh. 1945; FRCS Ed. 1960; DOMS Eng. 1950. Prev: Cons. Ophth. Surg. N. Glos. Clin. Area.

THOMSON, Duncan George c/o 15 Spylaw Bank Road, Colinton, Edinburgh EH13 0JW — MB ChB 1987 Aberd.

THOMSON, Edith Agnes Craston (retired) 11 Wester Coates Avenue, Edinburgh EH12 5LS Tel: 0131 337 2304 — MB ChB St. And. 1942. Prev: Ho. Surg. Roy. Hosp. Sick Childr. & Roy. Matern. & Wom. Hosp. Glas.

THOMSON, Elaine Sheila Wallacetown Health Centre, 3 Lyon Street, Dundee DD4 6RF Tel: 01382 459519 Fax: 01382 453110 Email: ethomson@green.org.finix.co.uk; Bellfield, 3 Bank St, Newport-on-Tay DD6 8AU — MB ChB 1992 Dundee; MRCGP 1996; DRCOG 1995; DFFP 1995.

THOMSON, Elizabeth Jean (retired) 114 West King Street, Helensburgh G84 8DQ Tel: 01436 672673 — MB ChB 1963 Glas.; FRCPath 1982, M 1969; DObst RCOG 1964. Cons. Microbiol. Monklands Hosp. Airdrie. Prev: Cons. Bact. Belvidere Hosp. Glas.

THOMSON, Emma Cassandra 11 Kelvin Dr, Glasgow G20 8QG — MB ChB 1997 Glas.

THOMSON, Fiona Jane Dept. Of Medicine for the Elderly, Hull Royal Infirmary, Anlaby Road, Hull HU3 2JZ Tel: 01482 676301 Fax: 01482 676138 — MB ChB 1984 Manch.; BSc St. And. 1981; MD Manch. 1992; FRCP 1998. Cons. Phys. (Geriat. Med.) Hull and E. Yorks. Hosps. Trust. Prev: Sen. Regist. (Gen. & Geriat. Med.) Roy. Oldham, Hope & Ladywell Hosps. Salford; Tutor (Gen. & Geriat. Med.) Manch. Roy. Infirm.; SHO (Gen. Med.) Hope Hosp. Salford.

THOMSON, Gail Lindsay Brownlee Centre, Gartnavel General Hospital, Glasgow; 11/5 Queenshill, South Groathill Avenue, Edinburgh EH4 2LL — MB ChB 1994 Ed. SHO (Infect. Dis.) Gartnavel Hosp. Glas.

THOMSON, Mr Gary George John Bonnyrigg Health Centre, High Street, Bonnyrigg EH19 2DA Tel: 0131 663 7272 — MB ChB 1977 Ed.; FRCS Ed. 1983. (Edinburgh)

THOMSON, George Alexander Diabetes Unit, The Kings Mill Centre for Health Care Services, Mansfield Road, Sutton-in-Ashfield NG17 4JL Tel: 01623 622515 Ext: 3272 Fax: 01623 672332; 50B Roland Avenue, Nuthall, Nottingham NG16 1BB Tel: 0115 975 7266 Email: george@thoms1.freeserve.co.uk — MB ChB 1988 Glas.; MB ChB (Commend.) Glas. 1988; MRCP (UK) 1991; FRCS (Edinburgh)1999. Cons. Phys. (Diabetes & Endocrinol.) The Kings Mill Centre for Health Care Servs. Nottm. Socs: Collegiate Mem. Roy. Coll. Phys & Surg. Glas.; FRCP Edin.; Diabetes UK. Prev: Sen. Regist. (Med., Diabetes & Endocrinol.) Univ. Hosp. Nottm.; Sen. Regist. (Med., Diabetes & Endocrinol.) Derbysh. Roy. Infirm.; Career Regist. (Diabetes & Endocrinol.) S.. Gen. Hosp. Glas.

THOMSON, George Douthwaite Moore House Lodge, Whalton, Morpeth NE61 3UX — MB BS 1962 Durh. (Durh.)

THOMSON, George Edward Brookside Health Centre, Brookside Road, Freshwater PO40 9DT Tel: 01983 753433 Fax: 01983 753662 — MB BS 1976 Lond. Clin. Asst. (Rheum.) St. Mary's Hosp. Newport, IOW.

THOMSON, George Jeremy (retired) Ravenswood, Tighnabruaich PA21 2EE Tel: 01700 811603 — MB ChB 1957 Glas. Prev: Ho. Phys. Roy. Infirm. Glas.

THOMSON, Mr George John Lyle Royal Preston Hospital, Sharoe Green Lane, Fulwood, Preston PR2 9HT Tel: 01772 716565 Fax: 01772 710315; 16 Oakley Park, Heaton, Bolton BL1 5XL Tel: 01204 843693 Email: geo_thomson@hotmail.com — MB ChB 1977 Glas.; MD Glas. 1989; FRCS Glas. 1982. (Glasgow) Cons. Surg. Roy. Preston Hosp. Socs: Manch. Med. Soc.; Vasc. Surg. Soc. GB & Irel.; Assn. Surg.

THOMSON, Graeme Arthur Department of Haematology, Chelsea & Westminster Hospital, 369 Fulham Road, London SW10 9NH Tel: 0208 746 8201 Fax: 0208 746 8202; 24 Fairmount Road, London SW2 2BL Tel: 020 8678 0473 Fax: 020 8 4883378 Email: gthomson@xtrabox.com — Artsexamen 1990 Amsterdam; BSc (Hons.) Immunol. Glas. 1981. Lect. & Hon. Sen. Regist. (Haemat.) Roy. Postgrad. Med. Sch. Hammersmith Lond.; Sen. Regist. (On Call Rota) Char. Cross Hosp. Lond. & Chelsea W.minster Hosp.; Assoc. Specialist (Hematology) Chelsea & W.minster Hosp. Lond.. Socs: Fell. Roy. Soc. Med.; Brit. Soc. Haematol.; Brit. Soc. Immunol. Prev: Regist. (Blood Transfus.) NE Scotl. Blood Transfus. Centre Roy. Infirm. Aberd.; Regist. (Haemat.) Roy. Devon & Exeter Hosp. (Wonford); SHO (Haemat.) Char. Cross Hosp. Lond.

THOMSON, Mr Hamish Gray The Chiltern Hospital, London Road, Great Missenden HP16 0EN Tel: 01494 890890; Alscot Cottage, Alscot Lane, Longwick, Princes Risborough HP27 9RU Tel: 01844 343382 — MB BS 1981 Lond.; FRCS Ed. 1985; FRCS Eng. 1987;

THOMSON

T(S) 1991. (St. Bart.) Cons. Otolaryngol. Wycombe Gen. Hosp. High Wycombe & Amersham Hosp. Socs: BMA & BAOL. Prev: Sen. Regist. (ENT) W. Midl. Train. Scheme; Regist. (ENT) Roy. Nat. Hosp. Lond.; SHO Rotat. (Gen. Surg.) Bristol.

THOMSON, Harry Robbins (retired) The Warren, Rhosneigr, Anglesey LL64 5QT Tel: 01407 811282 — MB BS 1941 Lond.; MD Lond. 1949; FRCP Lond. 1975, M 1948. Prev: Cons. Phys. (Geriat.) Coventry & N. Warks.

THOMSON, Helen W (retired) 24 Rowan Road, Dumbreck, Glasgow G41 5BZ Tel: 0141 427 0771 — MB ChB Glas. 1964. Prev: SCMO Community Child Health Servs. Gtr. Glas. Health Bd.

THOMSON, Mr Henry Harron Clementine Churchill Hospital Cons. Rooms, Sudbury Hill, Harrow HA1 3RX Tel: 020 8422 3464; 9 Deerings Drive, Eastcote, Pinner HA5 2NZ Tel: 020 8429 1482 — MB BS 1952 Lond.; FRCS Eng. 1966; MRCS Eng. LRCP Lond. 1952; FRCOG 1980, M 1964, DObst 1957. (St. Geo.) Gyn. Surg. Centr. Middlx. Hosp. Lond.; Gyn. Willesden Gen. Hosp. Socs: Chelsea Clin. Soc.; Hunt. Soc. Prev: Chief Asst. Dept. O & G St. Bart. Hosp. Lond.; Obst. Regist. Hillingdon Hosp. Uxbridge; Orthop. Ho. Surg. St. Geo. Hosp. Lond.

THOMSON, Hilary Ann Burnham Health Centre, Minniecroft Road, Burnham, Slough SL1 7DE Tel: 01268 5333; Woodlands, 12 Claremont Gardens, Marlow SL7 1BS — MB BS 1981 Lond.; MRCGP 1986; DRCOG 1986. (Lond.)

THOMSON, Horace Norman Michaelson (retired) Denville, Coulardbank Road, Lossiemouth IV31 6ED Tel: 01343 813865 Fax: 01343 813865 Email: horacenm@msn.com — MB ChB 1944 Aberd.; DPH Glas. 1965. Prev: Med. Off. & Lect. (Health Educat.) Aberd. Coll. of Educat.

THOMSON, Hugh Eric Gordon (retired) 24 Woodlands Grove, Stockton Lane, York YO31 1DL Tel: 01904 424530 — MB ChB St. And. 1957. GP York. Prev: ENT Ho. Surg. Ho. Phys. Bridge of Earn Hosp.

THOMSON, Mr Hugh James Department of Surgery, Heartlands Hospital, Birmingham B9 5SS Tel: 0121 766 6611 Fax: 0121 773 6897; 18 Hampshire Drive, Birmingham B15 3NZ Tel: 0121 455 7327 — MB ChB 1977 Aberd.; ChM Aberd. 1984; FRCS Ed. 1981; FRCS Eng. 1981. Cons. Surg. Heartlands Hosp. Birm.; Hon. Clin. Lect. (Surg.) Univ. Birm. Socs: Christ. Med. Fell.sh.; Brit. Soc. Gastroenterol.; BMA. Prev: Sen. Regist. (Surg.) Addenbrooke's Hosp. Camb.; Regist. (Surg.) W.. Gen. Hosp. Edin.; Regist. (Surg.) Aberd. Roy. Infirm.

THOMSON, Ian Andrew Thomson and Partners, The Medical Centre, Oak Street, Lechlade GL7 3RY Tel: 01367 252264 — MB BS 1979 Lond.

THOMSON, Ian Bruce Clackmannan and Kincardine Medical Practice, Health Centre, Main Street, Clackmannan FK10 4JA Tel: 01259 723725 Fax: 01259 724791; 3 Linnmill Cottage, Clackmannan, Alloa FK10 3PY Tel: 01259 723975 — MB ChB 1980 Dundee. Prev: Trainee GP Greenock & Gourock VTS; SHO (Surg.) Perth Roy. Infirm.; SHO (Med.) Stracathro Hosp.

THOMSON, Ian Copland (retired) Tanera House, Riccall, York YO19 6PT Tel: 01757 248319 — MB ChB 1959 Ed.; DObst RCOG 1961. Prev: Princip., Gen. Pract., Beech Tree Surg., Selby, N. Yorks.

THOMSON, Ian George 5 The Empire, Grand Parade, Bath BA2 4DF — BM BCh 1955 Oxf.; MA, BM BCh Oxf. 1955; FRCPsych 1984, M 1971; DPM Eng. 1966. (Oxf. & Middlx.) Prev: Cons. Psychiat. I. of Wight Hosp. DHA; Dist. Surg. S. Africa.

THOMSON, Ian Howie, OStJ 51 Heatherwood, Seafield, Bathgate EH47 7BX Tel: 01506651070 — MB ChB 1947 Ed.; AFOM RCP Lond. 1982. (Univ. Ed.) Med. Adviser Centre for Marine & Indust. Safety Technol. Heriot-Watt Univ Edin. Socs: Brit. Soc. Med. & Dent. Hypn. & Soc. Occupat. Med. Prev: Sen. Med. Off. Brit. Steel Corpn. Scotl.; GP Broxburn; Ho. Surg. & Ho. Phys. Roy. Infirm. Edin.

THOMSON, James Burt Department of Anaesthesia, Wishaw General Hospital, Wishaw ML21 0DP — MB ChB 1973 Ed.; BSc (Med. Sci.) Ed. 1970; FFA RCS Eng. 1977. (Edinburgh) Cons. Anaesth. Wishaw Gen. Hosp. Socs: Europ. Soc. of Regional Anaesth.-Life Mem.; Brit. Soc. of Orthopaedic Anaesth.s.

THOMSON, James Ewing Inverclyde Royal Hospital, Greenock PA16 0XN Tel: 01475 633777; Raasay, 14 Douglas Avenue, Langbank, Port Glasgow PA14 6PE — MB ChB 1970 Glas.; FRCP Ed. 1988; FRCP Glas. 1983; MRCP (UK) 1973. Cons. Phys. Inverclyde Roy. Hosp. Greenock.

THOMSON, James Laing Gordon (retired) Little Begbrook, Begbrok Park, Frenchay, Bristol BS16 1NF Tel: 0117 957 0161 — MD Lond. 1950, MB BS 1945; FRCP Lond. 1971, M 1952; FRCR 1975; DMRD Eng. 1948. Prev: Cons. Radiol. Frenchay Hosp. & Roy. Infirm. Bristol.

THOMSON, James Laing Spalding (retired) 17 Seaforth Gardens, Winchmore Hill, London N21 3BT Tel: 020 8886 7188 — MB ChB 1932 Aberd.; MRCGP 1963. Prev: Mem. Med. Staff, Wood Green & S.gate Hosp.

THOMSON, James Morris Dott 9 Morgan Street, Dundee DD4 6QE — MB ChB 1969 St. And.; BSc St. And. 1966; DObst RCOG 1974.

THOMSON, Mr James Phillips Spalding Master' Lodge, Charterhouse, Chaterhouse Square, London EC1M 6AN Tel: 020 7253 0272 — MB BS Lond. 1962; DM Lambeth 1987; MS Lond. 1974; FRCS Eng. 1969; MRCS Eng. LRCP Lond. 1962; DObst RCOG 1964. (Middlx.) Emerit. Cons. Surg. St. Marks Hosp. for Intestinal & Colorectal Disorders NW Lond. NHS Trust; Hon Civil. Cons. Surg. RAF; Emerit. Cons. - Surg. RN; Hon. Cons. Surg. St. Luke's Hosp. For the Clergy. Socs: Fell. Roy. Soc. Med.; Assn. Coloproctol.(Sec. 1990-92); Honterian Soc. - Pres. 2001/2. Prev: Lect. (Surg.) Studies Middlx. Hosp. Med. Sch. Lond.; Resid. Surg. Off. St. Mark's Hosp. Dis. of Rectum Lond.; Demonst. (Anat.) Middlx. Hosp. Med. Sch. Lond.

THOMSON, Janet McMurray Glen 8 Bath Street, Stonehaven AB39 2DH — MB ChB 1978 Glas.; MRCGP 1984. GP Glas.

THOMSON, Janette Kennedy 1 Ledcameroch Crescent, Bearsden, Glasgow G61 4AD Tel: 0141 942 7513 — MB ChB 1966 Glas. (Glas.) GP Clydebank Health Centre.

THOMSON, Janice The Old Station Surgery, Heanor Road, Ilkeston DE7 8ES Tel: 0115 930 1055; 50B Roland Avenue, Nuthall, Nottingham NG16 1BB Tel: 0115 975 7266 — MB ChB 1990 Dundee; MRCGP 1994; DFFP 1993; DRCOG 1993. Prev: Trainee GP Vict. Infirm. VTS.

THOMSON, Jean The Anaesthetic Department, Royal Halifax Infirmary, Free School Lane, Halifax HX1 2YP — MB ChB 1973 Birm.; FFA RCS Eng. 1977; DRCOG 1979.

THOMSON, Jennifer Clair 7 Naworth Drive, Carlisle CA3 0DD — MB ChB 1998 Manch.

THOMSON, Jennifer Rosalind LR1 Staff Residences, Walnut St., Leicester LE2 7GJ — MB BS 1994 Lond.; BSc Genetics (1st cl. Hons.) 1991; MRCP (UK) 1997. (UMDS Lond.) SHO (Paediat.) Roy. Alxandra Childr.'s Hosp. Brighton. Prev: SHO (Renal) Roy. Sussex Co. Hosp. Brighton; SHO (Respirat.) Hove Gen. Hosp.; SHO (Elderly Care) Brighton Gen. Hosp.

THOMSON, Joan Hairmyres Hospital, Eaglesham Road, East Kilbride, Glasgow G75 8RG — MB ChB 1970 Ed.; BSc (Med. Sci.) (Hons. Bact.) Ed. 1968, MD 1980; FRCPsych 1992, M 1974; DPM Ed. 1973. Cons. Gen. Psychiat. Hairmyres Hosp. E. Kilbride.

THOMSON, Joan Elizabeth 7 Low Road, Castlehead, Paisley PA2 6AQ — MB ChB 1983 Glas.; MRCPsych. 1988. Sen. Regist. Tayside HB.

THOMSON, Joan Elizabeth Govan Health Centre, 5 Drumoyne Road, Glasgow G51 4BJ Tel: 0141 440 1212; 21 Russell Drive, Bearsden, Glasgow G61 3BB — MB ChB 1968 Glas.; DA Eng. 1970.

THOMSON, John Kintore, 24 Rowan Road, Dumbreck, Glasgow G41 5BZ Tel: 0141 427 0771 Fax: 0141 427 0771 — MB ChB 1960; MD Glas. 1973; FChs Soc. Chirop & Podiat Lond. 1996; FRCP Ed. 1992; FRCP Glas. 1973, M 1965; DObst RCOG 1962. Cons. (Dermat.) Glas. Roy. Infirm. (Retd.).

THOMSON, John Alexander (retired) 13 Russell Drive, Bearsden, Glasgow G61 3BB Tel: 0141 942 6302 — MB ChB Glas. 1956; PhD Glas. 1974; MD Glas. 1970; FRCP Lond. 1975; FRCP Glas. 1968; MRCP Lond. 1961; FRFPS Glas. 1961. Prev: Reader (Med.) & Cons. Phys. Univ. Dept. Med. Roy. Infirm. Glas.

THOMSON, John Blackwood (retired) 10 Carnoustie Gardens, Glenrothes KY6 2QB Tel: 01592 755268 — MB ChB Manch. 1959.

THOMSON, John Duncan Ross The Barn, High St., Waddington, Lincoln LN5 9RF — BM BS 1993 Nottm.; MRCP (UK) 1996.

THOMSON, John Richard (retired) No. 11, John Murray Court, Motherwell ML1 2QW Tel: 01968 252798 — MB ChB Glas. 1950. Prev: Med. Off. RAAMC.

THOMSON

*THOMSON, John Stewart St. Clair House, 34 Hutcheon St., Aberdeen AB25 3TB Email: john.t@psionworld.net — MB ChB 1995 Aberd.

THOMSON, John Young (retired) Walton Hospital, Rice Lane, Liverpool L9 — MB ChB Liverp. 1964; MRCGP 1978. Cons. (A & E) Walton Hosp.

THOMSON, Joseph Howard Crumlin Medical Practice, 5 Glenavy Road, Crumlin BT29 4LA Tel: 028 9442 2209 Fax: 028 9442 2233; Park House, Crumlin BT29 4BW Tel: 0184 94 52209 — MB BCh BAO 1973 Belf.; MRCGP 1980; DObst RCOG 1975. Prev: Sen. Med. Off. Harbour Breton Newfld.

THOMSON, Julia 3a Alexandra Grove, Finsbury Park, London N4 2LG — BM 1997 Soton. SHO (Paediat.) Roy Free.

THOMSON, Julie Primary Care Centre, Whitburn Road, Bathgate EH48 1PT Tel: 01506 655155; Annacht, 1 Simpson Crescent, Bathgate EH48 1BL Tel: 01506 654688 — MB ChB 1982 Ed.; MRCGP 1987. (Edinburgh)

THOMSON, Keith Derek Department of Anaesthesia, North Hampshire Hospital, Aldermaston Road, Basingstoke RG24 9NA Tel: 01256 313461 Fax: 01256 354224; Brookside Farm, Winkfield Road, Ascot SL5 7LT Tel: 01344 886147 Email: keith.t2@ukonline.co.uk — MB BS 1976 Lond.; DRCOG 1982; FFA RCS Eng. 1981; DA Eng. 1979; BSc Ed. 1969. (University College Hospital London) Cons. Anaesth. N. Hants. Hosp. Basingstoke Hants.

THOMSON, Keith Thomas Engleton House, 1A Engleton Road, Coventry CV6 1JF Tel: 024 7659 2012 Fax: 024 7660 1913; 42 Dencer Drive, Kenilworth CV8 2RU Tel: 01926 852880 — MB ChB 1975 Leeds.

THOMSON, Kenneth Fletcher Malcolm, TD, OStJ (retired) 41 Heslington Lane, York YO10 4HN Tel: 01904 622159 — BM BCh 1951 Oxf.; DLO Eng. 1954. Prev: Area Surg. St. John Ambul. Brig. (Off. Brother).

THOMSON, Kevin James 26 Seaforth Road, Golspie KW10 6TJ — MB ChB 1997 Glas.

THOMSON, Kirsty Jane 15 Spylaw Bank Road, Edinburgh EH13 0JW — MB ChB 1989 Aberd.

THOMSON, Kirsty Jane 4 Buccleuch Terrace, Edinburgh EH8 9ND — MB ChB 1996 Ed.

THOMSON, Lawrence Mackinnon (retired) 49 Westland, Martlesham Heath, Ipswich IP5 3SU Tel: 01473 612188 — MB BS 1962 Lond. Prev: GP Ipswich.

THOMSON, Lesley Fiona 21 Hunts Mead, Billericay CM12 9JA — MB ChB 1986 Leeds.

THOMSON, Lindsay Dorothy Greig Department of Psychiatry, The University of Edinburgh, Kennedy Tower, Morningside Park, Edinburgh EH10 5HF Tel: 0131 537 6509 Fax: 0131 537 6508 Email: l.d.g.thomson@ed.ac.uk — MB ChB 1987 Ed.; MD 2000 Ed.; MPhil Ed. 1994; MRCPsych 1991. (Ed.) Sen. Lect. (Forens. Psychiat.) Univ. Edin.; Hon. Cons. Forens. Psychiat. The State Hosp. Carstairs Lanark. Prev: Sen. Regist. (Adult Psychiat. & Forens. Psychiat.) Roy. Edin. Hosp.; Research Fell. (Psychiat.) Univ. Edin.; Regist. Rotat. (Psychiat.) Roy. Edin. Hosp. Lothian HB.

THOMSON, Lucy Anne Baronscourt Surgery, 89 Northfield Broadway, Edinburgh EH8 7RX Tel: 0131 657 5444 Fax: 0131 669 8116; Kilfinan, 19 Glenesk Crescent, Eskbank, Dalkeith EH22 3BW — MB BS 1990 Lond.; MRCGP (Distinc.) 1995; DFFP 1995; DRCOG 1994. (Univ. Coll. Hosp. Middlx.)

THOMSON, Lucy Elizabeth Victoria Park Health Centre, Bedford Avenue, Berkenhead, Merseyside; 11 Harringay Avenue, Mossley Hill, Liverpool L18 1JE Tel: 0151 734 0432 — MB ChB 1993 Liverp.; DRCOG 1996; DFFP 1997. (Liverp.) GP Retainer. Prev: GP Regist.

THOMSON, Margaret Shah and Thomson, Bute House Medical Centre, First Floor, Grove Road, Luton LU1 1QJ Tel: 01582 729428 Fax: 01582 417762 Email: margaretthompson@gp-e81048.nhs.uk — MB ChB 1971 Ed.

THOMSON, Mrs Margaret Ann Sonning Common Health Centre, Wood Lane, Sonning Common, Reading RG4 9SW Tel: 01734 722188 Fax: 01734 724633; The Strip, Shepherds Green, Rotherfield Greys, Henley-on-Thames RG9 4QW — BM BCh 1964 Oxf.; MA Oxf. 1964, BM BCh 1964; MRCP (UK) 1970; DCH RCP Eng. 1967. Prev: Med. Off. (Paediat.) Radcliffe Infirm. Oxf.; Sen.

Regist. (Haemat.) Roy. Postgrad. Med. Sch. Hammersmith Hosp. Lond.

THOMSON, Margaret Anne Rees Ward 37/38, Ninewells Hospital & Medical School, Dundee DD1 9SY Tel: 01382 660111 Fax: 01382 632096 Email: margaret.a.r.thomson@tuht.scot.uk; 1 Whitefauld Road, Dundee DD2 1RH Tel: 01382 566622 Email: robert.smith3@which.net — MB ChB 1974 Dundee; FRCOG 1994 M 1979. Cons. O & G & Hon. Sen. Lect. Ninewells Hosp. & Med. Sch. Dundee. Prev: Sen. Med. Off. Scott. Off. Home & Health Dept. Edin.

THOMSON, Marion Taylor 4 Grove House, The Grove, Epsom KT17 4DJ Tel: 01372 742743 — MB ChB 1939 Glas.; DPH 1943; MFCM 1972. (Glas.) Prev: SCMO Som. HA; Med. Off. Min. of Pens. Unit, MusGr. Pk. Hosp. Taunton; Res. Med. Off. Belvidere Fev. Hosp. Glas.

THOMSON, Mary Forsyth (retired) 19 Stokesley Road, Marton, Middlesbrough TS7 8DT Tel: 01642 275691 Email: m.f.veitch@gunrgate.demon.co.uk — MB ChB Glas. 1952.

THOMSON, Mary Janette (retired) 35 Newland Park Drive, York YO10 3HR Tel: 01904 423992 — MB ChB Ed. 1963; DObst RCOG 1965. Prev: GP York & Bromley.

THOMSON, Matilda Kennedy (retired) 11 Orchard Toll, Edinburgh EH4 3JF Tel: 0131 315 2747 — MB ChB Glas. 1939.

THOMSON, Mr Matthew Perekkatt 10 Levaghery Close, Portadown, Craigavon BT63 5HL Tel: 01762 336579 — MB BS 1958 Kerala; FRCS Ed. 1977; DLO Eng. 1967. Cons. ENT Surg. Craigavon Area Hosp. Gp. Trust.

THOMSON, Melvyn Fyffe Denmuir Farm, Newburgh, Cupar KY14 6JQ — MB ChB 1970 Glas.; FFA RCSI 1977. Cons. Anaesth. & Hon. Sen. Lect. Univ. Dundee.

THOMSON, Merran Ann Department of Paediatrics, Hammersmith Hospital, Du Cane Road, London W12 0NN Tel: 020 8383 3270 Fax: 020 8740 8281 Email: merran.thomson@ic.ac.uk; 3 The Woodlands, London Road, Harrow HA1 3JG Tel: 020 8864 3939 Fax: 020 8864 3939 — MB ChB 1982 Manch.; MRCP (UK) 1988. (Manchester and St Andrews) Cons. (Perinatology) Neonat. Units Hammersmith & Qu. Charlotte Hosps. Lond. Socs: Eur. Soc. Paediat. Research; Fell. Roy. Coll. Paediat. and Child Health; Neonat. Soc. Prev: Cons. & Hon. Clin. Lect. (Perinatol.) Neonat. Unit Hope Hosp. Salford; Sen. Regist. & Hon. Clin. Lect. (Paediat.) Neonat. Unit Birm. Matern. Hosp.; Clin. Research Fell. & Hon. Regist. (Paediat.) Dept. Child Health Univ. Liverp.

THOMSON, Michael Little Shannon, 87 Crock Lane, Bridport DT6 4DH Tel: 01308 458133; PO Box 20, Murambinda Mission Hospital, Muranbinda, Zimbabwe Tel: 01308 458133 Fax: 01308 458133 Email: michael.thomson2@virgin.net — MB BS Lond. 1965; FRCGP 1993, M 1975; DObst RCOG 1967. (Guy's) p/t Locum GP. Prev: Ho. Surg. & Ho. Phys. Orpington Hosp.; Ho. Surg. (Obst.) Boscombe Hosp.

THOMSON, Michael Andrew University Department of Paediatric Gastroenterology, Royal Free Hospital, Pond St., London NW3 2QG Tel: 020 7830 2781 Fax: 020 7830 2146 Email: mthomson@rfhsm.ac.uk; Tanera House, Riccall, York YO19 6PT — MB ChB 1985 Aberd.; MRCP (Paediat.) UK 1990; FRCPCH 1997; DCH Lond. 1987. (Aberd.) Cons. Paediat. (Gastroenterol. & Nutrit.) Roy. Free Hosp. Lond.; Hon. Sen. Lect. (Paediat. Gastroenterol.) Roy. Free Hosp. Sch. Med. Lond. Socs: Brit. Paediat. Assn.; Brit. Soc. Paediat. Gastroenterol. & Nutrit.; BMA. Prev: Lect. Liver Transpl. Birm. Childr. Hosp.

THOMSON, Michael David (retired) Little Pednavounder, Coverack, Helston TR12 6SE Tel: 01326 280140 — MB ChB 1944 St. And.

THOMSON, Michael Roy Burnham Medical Centre, Love Lane, Burnham-on-Sea TA8 1EU Tel: 01278 795445 Fax: 01278 793024; Burnham Medical Centre, Love Lane, Burnham-on-Sea TA8 1EU Tel: 01278 782283 — MB ChB 1972 Bristol; BSc Bristol 1969, MB ChB 1972; MRCP (U.K.) 1975; MRCGP 1980; DRCOG 1977.

THOMSON, Morven Elizabeth Priory Hospital, Priory Lane, London SW15 5JJ Tel: 0208 876 8261; 30 Roehampton Close, London SW15 5LU Tel: 020 8876 3979 — MB ChB 1950 Glas.; MRCPsych 1978; DPM Eng. 1978. (Glas.) Vis. Cons. Psychiat. Priory Hosp. Lond. Prev: Cons. Psychiat. Sutton Hosp. (Chiltern Wing); Sen. Regist. The Priory Roehampton.

THOMSON

THOMSON, Professor Neil Campbell Department of Respiratory Medicine, Western Infirmary, Glasgow G11 6NT Tel: 0141 211 3241 Fax: 0141 211 3463 Email: n.c.thomson@clinmed.gla.ac.uk; Gryffe Lodge, Florence Drive, Kilmacolm PA13 4JN — MD 1980 Glas.; MB ChB 1972; FRCP Lond. 1990; FRCP Glas. 1986; MRCP (UK) 1975. Prof. of Respirat. Med. Univ. Glas.; Hon. Cons. W.ern Infirm. Glas. Socs: Brit. Thorac. Soc.; Amer. Thoracic Soc.; Assoc. of Phys. Prev: Research Fell. McMaster Univ. Hamilton Canada; Jun. Doctor Glas. Teach. Hosps.; Hon. Prof. Univ. Glas.

THOMSON, Nigel Stuart, TD Fax: 01379 641673 Email: nigel.thomson@gp-d82022.nhs.uk; Folly Farm, Bressingham, Diss IP22 2AS — MB ChB 1976 Manch.; FRCP 2001; MRCP (UK) 1980. (Manchester) Prev: Tutor (Child Health) Univ. Manch.

THOMSON, Ninian Omand Saltcoats Health Centre, 17-19 Raise Street, Saltcoats KA21 5LX Tel: 01294 605141 Fax: 01294 466041 — MB ChB 1979 Manch; BSc St. And. 1976; MFHom RCP Lond. 1993; MRCGP 1983. Princip. GP & Homoeop. Phys. Saltcoats. Prev: Clin. Asst. Regional Homoeop. Serv. Mossley Hill Hosp. Liverp.

*****THOMSON, Noah Dominic** Allfrey House, Bolney Rd, Cowfold, Horsham RH13 8AZ Tel: 01403 865345 — MB BS 1997 Lond.; BSc (Hons.) Lond. 1994.

THOMSON, Patricia Helen Gibb 14 Crosbie Court, Craigend Road, Troon KA10 6ES — MB ChB 1967 Glas.; DCH RCPS Glas. 1974. SCMO (Child Health) Ayrsh. & Arran.

THOMSON, Penelope Jane Foxmoor Nurseries, Wellington TA21 9PH — MB BS 1982 Lond.

THOMSON, Penelope Jane 49 Wroxham Gardens, Potters Bar EN6 3DJ Email: penny.thomson@virgin.net — MB BS 1983 Lond. Staff Grade in Dermat., Barnet Hosp., Barnet.

THOMSON, Peter Gifford Greyswood Practice, 238 Mitcham Lane, London SW16 6NT Tel: 020 8769 0845/8363 Fax: 020 8677 2960 — BSc Lond. 1982, MB BS 1985; MRCGP 1990; DCH RCP Lond. 1988. (Westminster)

THOMSON, Peter Gordon 8 Galachlaw Shot, Edinburgh EH10 7JF Tel: 0131 445 1001 — MB ChB 1970 Ed.; MRCOG 1976. Cons. O & G St. John's Hosp. Livingston.

THOMSON, Professor Peter James Department of Oral & Maxillofacial Surgery, The Dental School, Framlington Place, Newcastle upon Tyne NE2 4BW Tel: 0191 222 8290 — MB BS 1988 Newc.; PhD Manch. 1997; MSc Manch. 1993, BDS 1982; FRCS Ed. 1992; FDS RCS Eng. 1990; FFD RCSI 1990. Prof. Oral & Maxillofacial Surg. Univ. Newc. u. Tyne. Socs: Fell. of the Brit. Assn. of Oral & Maxillofacial Surg.; Brit. Assn. of Head & Neck Oncol.; Brit. Assn. of Day Surg. Prev: Lect. (Maxillofacial Surg.) Univ. Manch.

THOMSON, Rachel Wildway, Clarendon Drive, Dundee DD2 1JU — MB ChB 1998 Aberd.

THOMSON, Ralph Menzies (retired) 9 Balgonie Woods, Paisley PA2 6HW Tel: 0141 884 5090 — MB ChB 1942 Glas.; BSc, MB ChB Glas. 1942; FRFPS Glas. 1949; FRCP Glas. 1964, M 1962. Prev: Cons. Phys. & Cardiol. Roy. Infirm. Glas.

THOMSON, Richard Geoffrey 25 Jesmond Park W., High Heaton, Newcastle upon Tyne NE7 7BU Email: richard.thomson@ncl.ac.uk — BM BCh Oxf. 1982; BA Oxf. 1979; MD Newc. 1990; FRCP Lond. 1996; MRCP (UK) 1985; FFPHM RCP (UK) 1996, M 1990. Sen. Lect. & Cons. Pub. Health Med. Newc. Univ. Med. Sch. Prev: Dir. Health Strategy N.. RHA; Sen. Regist. (Community Med.) N. RHA; Duncan Flockhart Research Fell. Univ. Newc. u. Tyne.

THOMSON, Richard Kerr The Royal Bournemouth Hospital, Castle Lane E., Bournemouth BH7 7DW Email: rkt@soton.ac.uk — MB BChir 1989 Camb.; BA (1st. cl. Hons.) Camb. 1986, MA 1990; MRCP (UK) 1992. Specialist Regist. (Gastroenterol. & Gen. Med.) The Roy. Bournemouth Hosp. Socs: Brit. Soc. Immunol.; Brit. Assn. Study Liver Dis.; Brit. Soc. Gastroenterol. Prev: BDF Clin. Research Train. Fell. & Hon. Regist. Soton. Gen. Hosp.; Regist. (Gen. Med. & Gastroenterol.) Bristol Roy. Infirm.; SHO (Gen. Med.) MusGr. Pk. Hosp. Taunton.

THOMSON, Richard Simon Greenheart, Highfields, East Horsley, Leatherhead KT24 5AA — MB ChB 1996 Ed.

THOMSON, Robert Cunningham Glen Meadowbank Health Centre, 3 Salmon Inn Road, Falkirk FK2 0XF Tel: 01324 715446 Fax: 01324 717986; 37 St. Ninians Road, Linlithgow EH49 7BN Tel: 01506 842679 — MB ChB 1978 Ed.

THOMSON, Mr Robert George Nighy Friarscroft, 31 Highgate Avenue, Fulwood, Preston PR2 8LN Tel: 01772 719515 — MB BS 1960 Lond.; FRCS Eng. 1966; MRCS Eng. LRCP Lond. 1960. (St. Bart.) Cons. Urol. Preston & Chorley Hosp. Gp. Socs: Fell. Roy. Soc. Med.; Brit. Assn. Urol. Surgs. Prev: Research Fell. To Merseyside Assn. Kidney Research; Ho. Surg. Midw. & Gyn. Dept. St. Bart. Hosp. Lond.; Demonst. Anat. Lond. Hosp.

THOMSON, Robert John Tanera House, Riccall, York YO19 6PT — MB BS 1989 Newc. Regist. (Community Psychiat.) Wiakato HB Hamilton, NZ.

THOMSON, Robert McNeill Woodside, Copperas Lane, Haigh, Wigan WN2 1PB Tel: 01942 831047 — MB ChB 1949 Manch.; FRCOG 1971, M 1955, DObst 1951; DCH Eng. 1952. (Manch.) Cons. O & G Wigan & Leigh Hosp. Gp.; Chairm. Med. Exec. Comm. & Cons. Staff Comm.; Cons. Mem. DMT Wigan DHA. Socs: Fell. Manch. Med. Soc.; N. Eng. Obst. & Gyn. Soc. Prev: Lect. (O & G) Univ. Manch.; 1st Asst. O & G St. Mary's Hosps. Manch.; Sen. Ho. Surg. (Obst.) Qu. Charlotte's Matern. Hosp. Lond.

THOMSON, Robert Scott Cathcart Practice, 8 Cathcart Street, Ayr KA7 1BJ Tel: 01292 264051 Fax: 01292 293803; 8 Blackburn Road, Ayr KA7 2XQ Tel: 01292 266407 Fax: 01292 280824 — MB ChB 1963 Glas.; DObst RCOG 1965. (Glas.) Prev: Clin. Asst. (Psychiat.) Ayrsh. & Arran HB.

THOMSON, Roderick David Anthony 10 Bedford Road, Chiswick, London W4 1JJ Tel: 020 8747 8801 — MB BS 1989 W. Indies; DCH RCP Lond.; DFFP 1998.

THOMSON, Rodney Gordon 4 Redthorne Way, Cheltenham GL51 3NW Tel: 01242 251310 — MRCS Eng. LRCP Lond. 1971. Prev: Regist. (O & G) Riyadh; GP Austral.

THOMSON, Roger Geoffrey Trumpington House, 56 High Street, Dulverton TA22 9DW Tel: 01398 323333 Fax: 01398 324030 — MB BS 1983 Lond.; MRCGP 1989; DCH RCP Lond. 1990. (Char. Cross Hosp. Lond.) Socs: RSM. Prev: Sen. Med. Off. N.ants.

THOMSON, Ruth Ballantine Rowena, 53 Glebe St., Dumfries DG1 2LZ — MB ChB 1968 Ed.; FRCP Glas. 1985; MRCP (UK) 1975; DObst RCOG 1972; DCH Eng. 1971. (Ed.) Cons. (Paediat.) Dumfries & Galloway Roy. Infirm. Dumfries. Socs: Brit. Soc. Study Infec.; Brit. Paediat. Assn. Prev: Sen. Regist. & Regist. (Paediat.) Roy. Hosp. Sick Childr. Glas.; Regist. (Infec. Dis.) Belvidere Hosp. Glas.

THOMSON, Samuel Alastair Braids Medical Practice, 6 Camus Avenue, Edinburgh EH10 6QT Tel: 0131 445 5999; Braids Medical Practice, 6 Camus Avenue, Edinburgh EH10 6QT Tel: 0131 445 5999 — MB ChB 1978 Aberd.; MRCP (UK) 1980; MRCGP 1985.

THOMSON, Samuel Wood (retired) Mansfield, Easter St., Duns TD11 3DW Tel: 01361 882963 — MB BS 1945 Lond.; MRCS Eng. LRCP Lond. 1945; MRCGP 1968; DOMS Eng. 1948; DObst RCOG 1948; DTM & H Liverp. 1949. Prev: Mem. Nigerian Med. Counc.

THOMSON, Sarah Renata Sitwell and Partners, Little Common Surgery, 82 Cooden Sea Road, Bexhill-on-Sea TN39 4SP Tel: 01424 845477 Fax: 01424 848225; The Tall House, Heatherdune Road, Bexhill-on-Sea TN39 4HB Tel: 01424 214385 — MB ChB 1980 Bristol; MB ChB (Hons.) Bristol 1980; MRCGP 1984; DRCOG 1983.

THOMSON, Sean Douglas 12 Cedar Close, Borehamwood WD6 2ED — MB ChB 1992 Otago.

THOMSON, Sheila (retired) 25A Davidson Road, Edinburgh EH4 2PE Tel: 0131 332 7945 — MB ChB 1932 Aberd.; MFCM 1972; MMSA Lond. 1936; DPH Aberd. 1935. Prev: Sen. Med. Off. Matern. & Child Welf. Renfrew CC.

THOMSON, Sheila Evelyn Gordon (retired) 24 Woodlands Grove, Stockton Lane, York YO31 1DL Tel: 01904 424530 — MB ChB 1956 St. And. Clin. Asst. Special Centre Epilepsy Neuro-Psychiat. Unit Bootham Pk. Hosp. York. Prev: Med. Adviser to Macmillan Nurses York.

THOMSON, Sheila Mairi Jean (retired) 62 Countesswells Road, Aberdeen AB15 7YE Tel: 01224 316387 — MB ChB Aberd. 1946. Prev: Community Phys. Grampian HB.

THOMSON, Sheila Margaret Paisley Road West Surgery, 1808 Paisley Road West, Glasgow G52 3TS Tel: 0141 211 6660 Fax: 0141 211 6662 — MB ChB 1970 Glas.

THOMSON, Simon LR1 Staff Residences, Walnut St., Leicester LE2 7GJ — MB BS 1994 Lond.; BSc (Human Biol.) Lond. 1991. Ho. Off. (Gen. Surg.) Roy. Sussex Co. Hosp. Brighton; Ho. Off. (Gen. Med.) St. Thos. Hosp. Lond.

THOMSON

THOMSON, Mr Simon David Charing Cross Hospital, Fulham Palace Road, London W6 8RF — MB ChB 1989 Manch.; BSc (Hons.) Anat. Manch. 1987; FRCS Ed. 1993. Regist. (Gen. Surg.) Char. Cross Hosp. Prev: Regist. (Gen. Surg.) Bedford Hosp.; SHO (Gen. Surg.) Qu. Alexandra Hosp. Portsmouth; Sen. Demonst. (Anat.) Liverp. Univ.

THOMSON, Simon James Tanners, Highfields Lane, Kelvedon, Colchester CO5 9BE — MB BS 1983 Lond.; FFA RCS Eng. 1988. Cons. Anaesth. Basildon & Thurrock Hosp. Trust. Socs: Pres. of Internat. Neuromodulation Soc. (UK).

THOMSON, Stanley Andrew (retired) 46 Love Lane, Stourbridge DY8 2LD Tel: 01384 394333 — M.B., Ch.B. Glas. 1945. Med. Off. Swinford Old Hall, Stourbridge; Chairm. Dudley Local Med. Comm.; Mem. Dudley FPC. Prev: Ho. Surg. Roy. Infirm. Glas.

THOMSON, Stephen Paul Sturrock 17 Portland Road, Bowdon, Altrincham WA14 2PA — MB BS 1991 Newc. SHO (Ophth.) Gateshead. Prev: SHO (Ophth.) Sunderland Eye Infirm. & N. Riding Eye Infirm. Middlesbrough; SHO (A & E) Sunderland Dist. Gen. Hosp.

THOMSON, Tanya Kim 110 Egerton Road, Bristol BS7 8HP — BSc Lond. 1985, MB BS 1988; MRCGP 1993; DRCOG 1992; DCH RCP Lond. 1991. GP & Clin. Asst. (Ophth.) Bristol. Prev: SHO (A & E) S.mead Hosp. Bristol.

THOMSON, Sir Thomas James, KBE, CBE, OBE (retired) 1 Varna Road, Jordanhill, Glasgow G14 9NE Tel: 0141 959 5930 — MB ChB 1945 Glas.; Hon. LLD Glas. 1988; FRCPI 1983; FRCP Ed. 1981; FRCP Glas. 1964, M 1962; FRCP Lond. 1969, M 1950; FRFPS Glas. 1949; Hon. FACP 1983. Prev: Chairm. Gtr. Glas. HB.

THOMSON, William Tawelfan, Llanegwad, Nantgaredig, Carmarthen SA32 7NJ Tel: 01267 290578 — MB ChB 1975 Liverp.; FFA RCS Eng. 1982. Cons. Anaesth. Carmarthen & Dist. NHS Trust. Prev: Sen. Regist. (Anaesth.) N. W.. RHA; Regist. (Anaesth.) Cardiff Hosps.; SHO (Anaesth.) Nottm. Hosps.

THOMSON, William Black Govan Health Centre, 5 Drumoyne Road, Glasgow G51 4BJ Tel: 0141 531 8400 Fax: 0141 531 8404; Westfield Health Centre, 71 Hillington Road S., Glasgow G52 2AE Tel: 0141 882 2222 Fax: 0141 882 4321 — MB ChB 1975 Glas.; MRCGP 1979; DRCOG 1977.

THOMSON, William Bruce (retired) Chantry House, Vicarage Close, Cookham, Maidenhead SL6 9SE Tel: 01628 528022 — MB BS 1951 Lond.; MB BS (Hons.) Lond. 1951; BSc Lond. 1948, MD (Med.) 1952; FRCP Lond. 1972, M 1954. Prev: Cons. Phys. Chiltern AMI Hosp. Gt. Missenden Bucks.

THOMSON, William George (retired) 19 Chinthurst Park, Shalford, Guildford GU4 8JH Tel: 01483 565627 Fax: 01483 565627 Email: bill@wgthomson.freeserve.co.uk — MB ChB 1947 Aberd.; MFOM RCP Lond. 1978; DMJ (Clin.) Soc. Apoth. Lond. 1969, DIH 1967; Specialist Accredit. (Occupat. Med.) RCP Lond. 1978; Cert. Av Med. RCP Lond. & CAA 1978. Med. Adviser Legal & Gen. Assur. in Pre-Retirement Educat.; Med. Adviser Retirement Counselling Serv. Prev: Cons. Phys. H. Shepherd & Co. Ltd. (Engin.).

THOMSON, Mr William Hamish Fearon Gloucester Royal Hospital, Great Western Road, Gloucester GL1 3NN Tel: 01452 528555 Fax: 01452 394813 — MB BS Lond. 1961; MS Lond. 1975; FRCS Eng. 1967. (St. Bart.) Cons. Surg. Gloucester AHA. Socs: Assn. Surg.; Assn. Coloproctol. Prev: Sen. Regist. (Surg.) Soton. Univ. Hosp.

THOMSON, William John (retired) Nelson, Little Court, Elie, Leven KY9 1AU — MB ChB 1955 St. And. Prev: GP Fife.

THOMSON, Mr William Old 1 Brownside Avenue, Cambuslang, Glasgow G72 8BL Tel: 0141 641 1220; Department of Surgery, Hairmyres Hospital, East Kilbride, Glasgow G72 8RG — MB ChB 1971 Glas.; FRCS Glas. 1976. (Glas.) Cons. Surg. Hairmyres Hosp. E. Kilbride.

THOMSON, William Oliver (retired) 7 Silverwells Court, Bothwell, Glasgow G71 8LT — MB ChB 1947 Glas.; MD (Commend.) Glas. 1958; FRCP Glas. 1988; MRCP (UK) 1986; FFCM 1977, M 1974; DIH Soc. Apoth. Lond. 1958; DPH Glas. 1951, DPA 1956; Dip. Scott. Counc. Health Educat. 1979. Prev: Chief Admin. Med. Off. Lanarksh. HB.

THOMSON, William Stenhouse Taylor (retired) Ar Dachaidh, Mid-Letters, Strachur, Cairndow PA27 8DP — MB ChB 1945 Glas.; PhD Glas. 1954, BSc (Hons. Biochem.) 1951, MB ChB; FRCP Glas. 1972, M 1970; FRCPath 1973, M 1970. Prev: Cons. Biochem. S.. Gen. Hosp. Glas.

THOMSON, Winifred Isobel (retired) Colinton Surgery, 296B Colinton Road, Edinburgh EH13 0LB Tel: 0131 441 4555 Fax: 0131 441 3963 — MB ChB 1961 Ed.

THOMSSEN, Henrike Kennedy Institute of Rheumatology, Sunley Division, 1 Lurgan Avenue, London W6 8LW Tel: 020 8741 8966 Fax: 020 8563 0399 — State Exam Med 1988 Munich; State Exam Med. Munich 1988; MD Munich 1989.

THONET, Mr Robert Gustave Nicholas Kingston and Queen Mary's Hospitals, Galsworthy Road, Kingston upon Thames KT2 7QB Tel: 020 8355 2027 Fax: 020 8355 2871; Devon Lodge, 17 Portsmouth Avenue, Thames Ditton KT7 0RU Tel: 020 8398 0046 Fax: 020 8398 0046 — MB BS 1971 Lond.; FRCS Eng. 1977; FRCS Ed. 1977; MRCS Eng. LRCP Lond. 1971; MRCOG 1979; FRCOG 1991. (Westm.) Cons. O & G Qu. Mary's Univ. Hosp. Lond. Socs: N. Eng. Obst. & Gyn. Soc.; Brit. Menopause Soc.; Brit. Fertil. Soc. Prev: Sen. Regist. (O & G) Univ. Hosp. S. Manch.; Regist. (O & G) Camb. HA; Resid. Med. & Surg. Off. Qu. Charlotte's & Chelsea Hosp. for Wom. Lond.

THONG, Kok Foon MacMillan Surgery, 10 Dulas Road, Kirkby, Liverpool L32 8TL Tel: 0151 546 2908 Fax: 0151 548 0704; 13 Stanley Avenue, Birkdale, Southport PR8 4RU Tel: 01704 66205 — MB BS 1980 Newc.; MRCPI 1987. Socs: Roy. Coll. Phys. Irel.; Roy. Soc. Med. Lond. Prev: Regist. (Cardiol.) Centr. Middlx. Hosp. Lond.; Med. Rotat. Univ. Aberd.

THONG, Kok Joo 10 Coventry Gardens, Grainger Park, Newcastle upon Tyne NE4 8DX — MB BS 1983 Newc. SHO (Gyn.) Roy. Vict. Infirm. Newc.; SHO (Obst.) P.ss Mary Matern. Hosp. Newc. Prev: Ho. Surg. S. Shields Gen. Hosp. Tyne & Wear; Ho. Phys. S. Cleveland Hosp. Middlesbrough.

THOO, Chee Kong 62 Queens Drive, Mossley Hill, Liverpool L18 0HF — MB ChB 1988 Liverp.; DTM & H Liverp. 1991.

THOPPIL, Joseph Philip 106 Ancrum Street, Spital Tongues, Newcastle upon Tyne NE2 4LR — MB BS 1998 Newc.

***THOPPIL, Mathew Philip** 106 Ancrum Street, Newcastle upon Tyne NE2 4LR — MB BS 1997 Newc.

THORBURN, Douglas TL,22 Caird Drive, Glasgow G11 5DT Tel: 0141 334 5378 Email: dougie@dthorburn.freeserve.co.uk — MB ChB 1990 Glas.; MRCP (UK) 1993. Lect. (Med. & Gastroenterol.) Univ. Glas.

THORBURN, John Stuart 548 Meanwood Road, Leeds LS6 4JN Tel: 0113 741313 — MD 1949 Leeds; MB ChB 1943. (Leeds) Med. Off. T. Walls & Son Leeds Area. Prev: Regist. Dermat. Dept. Leeds Gen. Infirm.; Capt. RAMC.

THORBURN, Pamela Joyce 38 Pendicle Road, Bearsden, Glasgow G61 1EE — MB ChB 1990 Glas.; MRCGP 1994.

THORBURN, Robert Anthony Frederick Holmes Chapel Health Centre, London Road, Holmes Chapel CW4 7BB Tel: 01477 533100 Fax: 01477 532563; 87 Portree Drive, Holmes Chapel, Crewe CW4 7JF — BM BCh 1990 Oxf.; MA Camb 1992; MRCP (UK) 1994. Gen. Practitioner, Holmes Chapel Health Centre. Prev: SHO Rotat. (Med.) N. Staffs. Hosp.; Trainee GP N. Staffs. VTS.

THORBURN, Robert Norval Colvend, 6 Firbeck, Harden, Bingley BD16 1LP — MB ChB 1948 Glas. (Glas.)

THORBURN, Rosalind Jane Community Child Health, Guardian House, Warrington WA5 1TP Tel: 01925 405713 Fax: 01925 405725; 15 Portland Road, Bowdon, Altrincham WA14 2PA Tel: 0161 928 1748 Fax: 0161 926 8436 — MB BS 1971 Lond.; MRCP (UK) 1975; MRCS Eng. LRCP Lond. 1971; FRCPCH 1997. Cons. Paediat. (Community Child Health) Warrington Community NHS Trust. Socs: FMRCPCH. Prev: Cons. Paediat. Community Child Health Addenbrooke's Hosp. Camb.; Sen. Regist. (Paediat.) Addenbrooke's Hosp. Camb.; Lect. (Paediat.) Univ. Coll. Hosp. Lond.

THORBURN, Terence Guy Tilhurst, Thursley, Godalming GU8 6QD — BM BS 1997 Nottm.

THORBURN, William (retired) 5 Craigton Cottages, Craigton, Milngavie, Glasgow G62 7HQ Tel: 0141 956 5813 — MB ChB Glas. 1943. Prev: Ho. Phys. W.. Infirm. Glas.

THORBURN, William Stuart Farfield Group Practice, St. Andrew's Surgeries, West Lane, Keighley BD21 2LD Tel: 01535 607333 Fax: 01535 611818 — MB ChB 1975 Leeds; BSc (Hons. Physiol.) Leeds 1972, MB ChB 1975.

THORES, Orison Alistair 5 Haven's Edge, Old Golf Course, Limekilns, Dunfermline KY11 3LJ — MB ChB 1960 Aberd.; FRCP Canada 1972; AFOM RCP Lond. 1983; FFCM 1979; DCH RCPS Glas. 1963; DObst RCOG 1963. (Aberd.) Sen. Med. Off. Scott. Home & Health Dept. Prev: Community Med. Specialist Fife Health Bd.; Research Fell. Univ. Brit. Columbia; Sen. Med. Cons. Min. Health Ontario.

THORIS, Sigrid 1 Doune Gardens, Glasgow G20 6DJ — Cand Med et Chir Reykjavik 1989.

THORLEY, Anthony Philip Bath Addictions Service, Camden House, Bath Mental Health Care Trust, Bath NHS House, Combe Park, Bath BA1 3QE — MRCS Eng. LRCP Lond. 1970; MA, MB BChir Camb. 1970; FRCPsych 1984, M 1974. (Univ. Coll. Hosp.) Cons. Psychiat. Newc. Healthcare Trust Newc. u. Tyne; Sen. Med. Off. (Addic.) DoH; Hon. Cons. Psychiat. Bethlem Roy. & Maudsley Hosps. Lond. Prev: Dir. Centre for Alcohol & Drug Studies St. Nicholas Hosp. Newc. u.Tyne; Research Psychiat. Addic. Research Unit Inst. Psychiat. Lond.; Sen. Regist. & Regist. Bethlem Roy. & Maudsley Hosps. Lond.

THORLEY, Arnold Stanley (retired) 19 Barn Meadow Lane, Great Bookham, Leatherhead KT23 3HJ Tel: 01372 54646 — MRCS Eng. LRCP Lond. 1932; MD Lond. 1939, MB BS 1934; FRCPsych 1971; DPM Eng. 1936. Prev: Psychiat. Consult. Belmont Hosp. Sutton & Out-Pats. Dept. Wimbledon Hosp.

THORLEY, Claire Hamilton 1 Parkfield Close, Hartlebury, Kidderminster DY11 7TW — MB ChB 1987 Birm.; BSc (Hons. Anat.) Birm. 1984; MRCGP 1992; T(GP) 1992; DRCOG 1991. (Birm.) GP Asst. Ombersley Med. Pract. Prev: GP Asst. Davenal Ho. Surg. BromsGr.; GP Asst. The Med. Centre Chaddesley Corbett.

THORLEY, Clive Graham Health Centre Practice, Bromsgrove Street, Kidderminster DY10 1PG Tel: 01562 822077 Fax: 01562 823733; 1 Parkfield Close, Hartlebury, Kidderminster DY11 7TW — MB ChB 1987 Birm.; BSc (Hons. Anat.) Birm. 1984; MRCGP 1992; T(GP) 1992. (Birm.) Prev: Trainee GP Hay-on-Wye; SHO (Med., Psychiat., Paediat. & O & G) Worcester Roy. Infirm.; Ho. Off. (Surg.) Qu. Eliz. Hosp. Birm.

THORLEY, Helen Black Firs, Birks Drive, Ashley heath, Market Drayton TF9 4PQ — MB BS 1977 Lond.; MRCPsych. 1983; Dip. Psychother. Univ. Liverp. 1994. Cons. Psychiat. City Gen. Hosp. Stoke-on-Trent. Prev: Cons. Psychiat. St. Geo. Hosp. Stafford.

THORLEY, John Newlyn Treleaver, Mithian Downs, St Agnes TR5 0PY — MB BS 1970 Lond.; MRCS Eng. LRCP Lond. 1970; DA Eng. 1976. (St. Mary's)

THORLEY, Kevan John Higherland Surgery, 3 Orme Road, Poolfields, Newcastle ST5 2UE Tel: 01782 717044 Fax: 01782 715447 — MB BChir 1977 Camb.; MB Camb. 1977, BChir 1976; MA Camb. 1976; MRCGP 1985; Dip. Occ. Med. 1995; DRCOG 1978. (Camb./Middlx. Hosp.) GP Trainer, Higherland Surg. Newc.-u-Tyne. Socs: Internat. Soc. Perinatal Med. & Psychol.; Brit. Holistic Med. Assn. (Chairm. N. Midl. Div.).

THORLEY, Nicola Jane (Carpenter) Manor House Surgery, Manor Street, Glossop SK13 8PS — BM BCh 1994 Oxf.; MA 1991 Cantab.; DRCOG 1997; DFFP 1998. GP.

THORLEY, Rosemary Ann Windrush Health Centre, Welch Way, Witney OX28 6JS Tel: 01993 702911 Fax: 01993 700931 — MB BS 1985 Lond.

THORMAN, Christopher Andrew Laird Wymondham Medical Partnership, Postmill Close, Wymondham NR18 0RF Tel: 01953 602118 Fax: 01953 605313; Greenfields, Dykebeck, Wymondham NR18 9PL Tel: 01953 607211 — BMedSci. Nottm. 1978, BM BS 1980; MRCGP 1985; DRCOG 1984; DCH RCP Lond. 1983. (Nottingham)

THORMAN, Neil Anthony 80A Leader Road, Sheffield S6 4GH — MB ChB 1994 Sheff.

THORMOD, Clare Elisabeth 20 Alberta House, Blackwall Way, London E14 9QH — MB BS 1987 Lond.; MRCGP 1991. Occupat. Health Phys., Marks and Spencer.

THORN, Christopher Charles Flat 14, The Merchant's House, 66 North St., Leeds LS2 7PN — MB BS 1998 Lond.

THORN, David Roger Lakenham Surgery, 24 Ninham Street, Norwich NR1 3JJ Tel: 01603 765559 Fax: 01603 766790; 6 Poplar Avenue, Norwich NR4 7LB — MB ChB 1970 Leeds; T(GP) 1991. Prev: SHO (Obst.) Norf. & Norwich Hosp.; Ho. Phys. & Ho. Surg. St. Jas. Hosp. Leeds.

THORN, Jennifer Beatrice 1 Burnbrae, Maybury Drive, Edinburgh EH12 8UB — MB BS 1970 Lond.; MRCS Eng. LRCP Lond. 1970. Chief Med. Off. (Family Plann. & Psychosexual Counselling) Lothian Health Bd. Family Plann. & Well Wom. Servs.

THORN, John Leslie 7 Champions Way, South Woodham, Chelmsford CM3 5NJ — MB ChB 1975 Bristol; FFA RCS 1981.

THORN, Vivienne Mary Barton Surgery, Lymington House, Barton Hill Way, Torquay TQ2 8JG Tel: 01803 323761 Fax: 01803 316920; Inchcolme, 5 St Margarets Road, St Marychurch, Torquay TQ1 4NW Tel: 01803 311325 Fax: 01803 326691 — MB ChB 1979 Ed.; BSc (Med. Sci.) Ed. 1976, MB ChB 1979; MRCGP 1988.

THORNBER, Andrew John 14 Greystoke Close, Berkhamsted HP4 3JJ; 5 Hawsley Road, Beesonend, Harpenden AL5 2BL — MB ChB 1991 Liverp.; BSc (Hons.) Microbiol. 1986. Trainee GP Qu. Eliz. II Hosp. Welwyn Gdn. City VTS.

THORNBER, Doreen Rosemary St. James Hospital, Portsmouth; Child & Family Therapy Service, Havant Health Centre, Petersfield Road, Havant PO9 2AG — MB BS 1956 Lond.; DMP 1965 Eng.; MRCPsych 1972. (St. Mary's) Cons. Child Psychiat. Wessex Unit for Parents & Childr. & Hants. Child Guid. Serv. Prev: Ho. Surg. Hertford Co. Hosp.; Ho. Phys. Cuckfield Hosp.

THORNBER, Mark Merryhills, Rumbling Bridge, Kinross KY13 0PX — MB ChB 1990 Glas.

THORNBER, Stephen Heath House Surgery, Free School Lane, Halifax HX1 2PS Tel: 01422 365533 Fax: 01422 345851; 19 Rocks Road, Halifax HX3 0HR Tel: 01422 352923 — MB ChB 1967 St. And.

THORNBERRY, Cyril Joseph (retired) 12 Canons Close, Bishopsteignton, Teignmouth TQ14 9RU Tel: 01626 770104 — LRCPI & LM, LRSCI & LM 1941; LRCPI & LM, LRCSI & LM 1941; LM Rotunda 1946; FRCOG 1968, M 1953, DObst 1948. Prev: Cons. O & G N. Wirral HA.

THORNBERRY, Mr David John Disablement Services Centre, 1 Brest Way, Off Morlaix Drive, Derriford, Plymouth PL6 5XW Tel: 01752 792777; Lane End, Oak Tree Lane, Whitchurch, Tavistock PL19 9DA Tel: 01822 614848 — MB BChir 1974 Camb.; MA Camb. 1974; FRCS Eng. 1980; MRCS Eng. LRCP Lond. 1974. (Camb. & St. Thos.) Cons. Rehabil. Med. Derriford Hosp. Plymouth. Socs: Brit. Soc. Rehabil. Med.; Internat. Soc. Prosth.s & Orthotics; Posture & Mobility Gp. of Eng. & Wales. Prev: Med. Off. & Hon. Cons. Prosth. Rehabil. Disablem. Servs. Centre P.ss Eliz. Orthop. Hosp. Exeter; Med. Off. Artific. Limb Centre Qu. Mary's Hosp. Roehampton; Regist. Wolverhampton Hosps.

THORNBERRY, Elizabeth Anne Dept. of Anaesthetics, Gloucestershire Royal Hospital, Great Western Road, Gloucester GL1 3NN Tel: 01452 394812 Fax: 01452 394485 Email: eannet@doctors.org.uk; Email: eannet@doctors.org.uk — MB BS 1977 Lond.; FFA RCS Eng. 1982. (King's Coll. Hosp.) Cons. Anaesth. Glos. Roy. NHS Trust. Socs: Obst. Anaesth. Assn.; Soc. for Educat. in Anaesth. UK; Brit. Soc.y of Orthopaedic Anaesth. Prev: Cons. Anaesth. Portsmouth Hosps. NHS Trust; Sen. Regist. Soton. HA; Regist. Bristol Roy. Infirm.

THORNBURGH, Imogen Lucy Forge Cottage, 2 Linton Rd, Loose, Maidstone ME15 0AE — BM BS 1997 Nottm.; BMedSci Nottm. 1995. SHO (Paediat.) Qu.s Med. Centre. Nottm.

THORNBURY, Gail Donna 274 Saintfield Road, Belfast BT8 6PD — MB BCh BAO 1985 Belf.; MRCP (UK) 1989; FRCR 1990. Sen. Regist. (Radiol.) Roy. Vict. Hosp. Belf.

THORNBURY, Keith Douglas 2 Riverview Street, Belfast BT9 5FD — MB BCh BAO 1982 Belf.; MB BCh Belf. 1982.

THORNE, Alison Alice Cottage, 2 The Green, Culham, Abingdon OX14 4LZ — MB ChB 1993 Manch.

THORNE, Mrs Anne Kathryn Churton House, Church Pulverbatch, Shrewsbury SY5 8BZ Tel: 0174 373270 — MB BCh 1969 Wales; DObst RCOG 1971. (Lond.) GP W.bury Salop Wom.'s Retainer Scheme. Prev: Govt. Med. Off. Dominica, W. Indies; Govt. Med. Off. Solomon Is.

THORNE, Bernadette Mary Harcourt Medical Centre, Crane Bridge Road, Salisbury SP2 7TD Tel: 01722 333214 Fax: 01722 421643; 3 Wrenscroft, Salisbury SP2 8ET — MB BS 1981 Lond.; MRCS Eng. LRCP Lond. 1981; MRCGP 1985; DRCOG 1985. (Char. Cross) GP Princip.

THORNE

THORNE, Christopher Paul Mount Pleasant Health Centre, Mount Pleasant Road, Exeter EX4 7BW Tel: 01392 55262 Fax: 01392 270497 — BM BS 1984 Nottm.; MRCGP 1988.

THORNE, Deborah Michelle 9 Lower Farm, Brownley Green Lane, Hatton, Warwick CV35 7ER — MB ChB 1996 Birm.; ChB Birm. 1996. Trainee GP S. Warks. Hosps. NHS Trust.

THORNE, Mrs Dorothy Helen (retired) The Gin Case, Castle Hill, Hayton, Brampton CA8 9JA Tel: 01228 670749 — MRCS Eng. LRCP Lond. 1943; BA Camb. 1937.

THORNE, Mr John Anthony 11 Ashfield Road, Cheadle SK8 1BB — MB BS 1990 Lond.; BSc Lond. 1987; FRCS Eng. 1994. Specialist Regist. (Neurosurg.) Manch. Roy. Infirm. & Hope Hosp. Salford.

THORNE, Martin Geoffrey (retired) Brookhouse, Ringmore Road, Shaldon, Teignmouth TQ14 0EP Tel: 01626 872212 — MD 1953 Camb.; MB BChir 1945; FRCP Lond. 1969, M 1949. Prev: Cons. Phys. Torbay Hosp. Torquay.

THORNE, Napier Arnold Hospital of St John & St Elizabeth, 60 Grove End Road, London NW8 9NH Tel: 020 7286 5126 Fax: 020 7266 2316; 3 Rosewood, Pk Road, Haslemere GU27 2NJ Tel: 01428 644224 — MB BS Lond. 1945; MD Lond. 1949; FRCP Lond. 1972, M 1949; MRCS Eng. LRCP Lond. 1945. (St. Bart.) Cons. Dermat. Hosp. St. John & Eliz. Lond. Socs: Fell. Roy. Soc. Med.; Brit. Assn. Dermat.; Fell. Roy. Soc. Arts. Prev: Cons. Dermat. Roy. Lond. Hosp., P. of Wales Hosp. & St. Ann's Gen. Hosp.; Sen. Regist. (Med.) Whipps Cross Hosp. & (Skin) Lond. Hosp.

THORNE, Pamela Mary Tarr Steps, 21 Back Lane, Bilbrough, York YO23 3PL Tel: 01937 531819 — MRCS Eng. LRCP Lond. 1956; MCOphth 1989; DO Eng. 1961; DObst RCOG 1958. (Leeds) Clin. Asst. (Ophth.) Co. Hosp. York. Socs: NOTB Assn.; York Med. Soc. Prev: Regist. (Ophth.) K. Edwd. VII Hosp. Windsor; SHMO (Ophth.) Sheff. RHB.; Resid. Surg. Off. Roy. Eye Hosp. Lond.

THORNE, Richard John Thorne Farend, Faringdon Rd, Abingdon OX14 1BB — MB BChir 1965 Camb. (Oxf.) Socs: BMA. Prev: Demonst. (Human Anat.) Oxf. Univ.; SHO (Accid. Serv.), Ho. Phys. & Ho. Surg. Radcliffe Infirm. Oxf.

THORNE, Rosemary Jane Rother House Medical Centre, Alcester Road, Stratford-upon-Avon CV37 6PP Tel: 01789 269386 Fax: 01789 298742; Aldeen House, Lighthorne Road, Kineton, Warwick CV35 0JL Tel: 01926 640767 — MB BS 1974 Lond. (Middlx.)

THORNE, Sara Angela Queen Elizabeth Hopsital, Edgbaston, Birmingham B15 2TH Tel: 0121 627 2959 Fax: 0121 627 2862 — MB BS 1986 Lond.; MD Lond. 1993; MRCP (UK) 1989. (Royal Free) Cons. Cardiol. & Hon. Sen. Lect. Qu. Elzabeth Hosp. Birm.. Prev: Cons (Cardio.) Roy Brompton Hosp. Lond.; Lect. (Cardiol.) Roy. Brompton Hosp. Lond.; Regist. (Cardiol.) Gt. Ormond St. Hosp. Lond.

THORNE, Simon James 21 Woodfield Park, Amersham HP6 5QH — MB ChB 1996 Leeds.

THORNE, Theophilus Crowhurst, MC (retired) 2 St Andrews Road, Rochford SS4 1NP Tel: 01702 544181 — MRCS Eng. LRCP Lond. 1940; FFA RCS Eng. 1954; DA Eng. 1947; FRCA Eng. 1992. Prev: Cons. Anaesth. Rochford & S.end Gen. Hosps.

THORNE, William Ivor John Churton House, Church Pulverbatch, Shrewsbury SY5 8BZ; Churton House, Church Pulverbatch, Shrewsbury SY5 8BZ Tel: 0174 373270 — MB ChB 1969 Ed.; MA Oxf. 1966; BSc Ed. 1966, MB ChB 1969; MRCGP 1982; DTM & H Liverp. 1972. Clin. Asst. Roy. Shrewsbury Hosp. Prev: Dist. Med. Off., Dominica W. Indies; Chief Med. Off., Solomon Is.s.

THORNELEY, Christopher William The Old Stables, Swanton Morley Road, Worthing, Dereham NR20 5HS — MB BS 1997 Lond.

THORNELOE, Mr Michael Hugh Woodburn, Wood Lane, Parkgate, South Wirral CH64 6QZ — MB BCh BAO 1970 Dub.; FRCS Eng. 1975.

THORNETT, Andrew Martyn Dept. of Psychiatry, University of Southampton, Royal South Hants Hospital, Southampton SO14 0YG — MB BCh 1993 Wales. Clin. Research Fell. Dept. Psychiat., Univ. S.ampton. Prev: SHO Rotat. (Psychiat.) Chichester.

THORNETT, Judith Ann Well Lane Surgery, Well Lane, Stow on the Wold, Cheltenham GL54 1EQ Tel: 01451 830625 Fax: 01451 830693; Chestnut Court, College Farm, Wyck Rissington, Cheltenham GL54 2PN Tel: 01451 810991 Fax: 01451 810991 Email: thornett@wyckrssington.freeserve.co.uk — MB ChB 1984 Birm.; MRCGP 1990; DCH RCP Lond. 1989; DRCOG 1989. p/t Partner Gen. Pract. Stow-on-the-Wold, Glos. Prev: GP Kidderminster.

THORNHAM, John Rodger Norton Medical Centre, Harland House, Norton, Stockton-on-Tees TS20 1AN Tel: 01642 360111 Fax: 01642 558672; Morton Grange Cottage, Church Lane, Nunthorpe, Middlesbrough TS7 0PE Tel: 01642 320092 — MB BS 1971 Newc.; FRCGP 1986, M 1976; DObst RCOG 1976. Assoc. Adviser (Gen. Pract.) Univ. Newc. u. Tyne.; Chairm. PCG.

THORNHILL, John David Stenhouse Medical Centre, Furlong Street, Arnold, Nottingham NG5 7BP Tel: 0115 967 3877 Fax: 0115 967 3838; 51 Burlington Road, Sherwood, Nottingham NG5 2GR — MB ChB 1980 Sheff.; MRCGP 1986. (Sheff.) Trainer (Gen. Pract.) Nottm.

***THORNHILL, Professor Martin Hope** St Barts. and The Royal London Oral Disease Research Centre, Clinical Sciences Building, 2 Newark St., London E1 2AD Tel: 020 7295 7154, 020 7882 7154 Fax: 020 7295 7159, 020 7882 7159 Email: m.h.thornhill@mds.qmw.ac.uk; Tel: 020 8850 4171 Fax: 020 8850 4171 — MB BS 1978 Lond.; BDS Lond. 1982, PhD 1990, MSc 1986; FFD RCSI 1992; FDS RCS Ed. 1988; T(S) 1992.

THORNHILL, Robert John Birmingham Children's Hospital, Steelhouse Lane, Birmingham B13 8BU Tel: 0121 333 9999; Well Cottage, Newcastle Road South, Sandbach CW11 1SA Email: rjthorn@btinternet.com — MB ChB 1995 Birm. (Univ. Birm.) Clin. Fell. PICU: Birm. Childr.s Hosp. Socs: Assn. Anaesth.; Obst. Anaesth. Assn.; Intens. Care Soc. Prev: Ho. Off. (Surg.) Birm. Heartlands Hosp.; Ho. Off. (Med.) N. Staffs. Hosp.; SHO (Anaesth. & IC) Birm. Heartlands Hosp.

THORNHILL, Suzanne Jane 6 Oriel Close, Walkington, Beverley HU17 8YD — MB ChB 1986 Bristol; MRCGP 1990. Trainee GP Abbey Surg. Tavistock VTS.

THORNHILL, Mr William Cecil (retired) Rookwood, 110 Pearson Lane, Bradford BD9 6BE — LRCPI & LM, LRSCI & LM 1945; LRCPI & LM, LRCSI & LM 1945; FRCS Eng. 1959; DO Eng. 1952. Prev: Sen. Cons. Ophth. Bradford Roy. Infirm.

THORNICROFT, Professor Graham John Section of Community Psychiatry (PRiSM), Health Services Dep., Institute of Psychiatry, De Crespigny Park, London SE5 8AF — MB BS 1984 Lond.; MSc 1989 Lond.; MRCPsych 1988; MA 1980 Camb.; Phd 1995 Lond.; PhD Lond. 1995; MSc (Epidemiol.) Lond. 1989; MA Camb. 1980; MRCPsych 1988; MFPM 1999; FRCPsych 2000. Cons. Psychiat. S. Lond. Maudsley NHS Trust (SL&M); Prof. & Dir. Sect. of Community Psychiat.; Head, Helath Serv.s Research Dept, Inst. of Psychiat.; Director of R&D (SL&M); (PRiSM).

THORNICROFT, Sylvia Gill (retired) 8 Caversfield Close, Littleover, Derby DE23 7SR Tel: 01332 510090 — MB ChB 1958 Sheff.; MRCP Ed. 1968; DCH Eng. 1961.

THORNILEY-WALKER, Edward George Anthony Aitken, Thorniley-Walker, Lombard and Booth, Medical Centre, Gibson Court, Boldon Colliery NE35 9AN Tel: 0191 519 3000 Fax: 0191 519 2020; 34 Hawthorn Road, South Gosforth, Newcastle upon Tyne NE3 4DE Tel: 0191 284 7136 — MB BS 1985 Newc.; MRCGP 1994; DRCOG 1990. Prev: GP Kirkbymoorside; Trainee GP Gr. Med. Gp. Gosforth; SHO (Paediat.) S. Shields Gen. Hosp.

***THORNING, Geoffrey Phillip** 58 Elderfield Road, London E5 0LF; 58A Granby Road, Eltham, London SE9 1EN Tel: 020 8319 0317 — MB BS 1996 Lond.; BA Camb. 1991.

THORNINGTON, Roger Edgar Department of Anaesthesia, Royal Liverpool Childrens Hospital, Alder Hey, Eaton Road, Liverpool L12 2AP Tel: 0151 228 4811 Fax: 0151 252 5460 Email: ret@liv.ac.uk; Quarrystones, 166 Quarry St, Liverpool L25 6DZ Tel: 0151 428 4518 Fax: 0151 252 5460 — MB BS 1968 Lond.; FFA S. Afr. 1976; FRCA 1991. Cons. Paediat. Anaesth. Liverp. HA. Socs: Liverp. Soc. Anaesth.; Assn. Paediat. Anaesth. Prev: Cons. Anaesth. Red Cross War Memor. Childr. Hosp. Cape Town.

THORNLEY, Andrew Peter 85 Guywood Lane, Romiley, Stockport SK6 4AW; 8 Hadfield Place, Glossop SK13 8JE Tel: 01457 860671 — MB ChB 1996 Leeds.

THORNLEY, Barbara Ann Department of Anaesthetics, Horton Hospital, Oxford Road, Banbury OX16 9AL Tel: 01295 275500 Fax: 01295229067; Holly Tree House, 48A Main Road, Middleton Cheney, Banbury OX17 2LT — MB BS 1966 Lond.; MRCS Eng. LRCP Lond. 1966; FFA RCS Eng. 1972; DA Eng. 1969. (Roy. Free) Cons. Anaesth. Horton Hosp. Banbury; Assoc. Dir. of Postgrad.

Med. Educat. Oxf. Deanery. Socs: BMA; Assn. Anaesth.; R.S.M. Prev: Sen. Regist. (Anaesth.) Roy. Berks. Hosp. Reading; Sen. Regist. & Regist. (Anaesth.) Radcliffe Infirm. Oxf.

THORNLEY, Craig Norman 39 Upton Dene, Grange Road, Sutton SM2 6TA — MB ChB 1992 Otago.

THORNLEY, Nan The Bell House, Arddleen, Oswestry — MB ChB 1995 Sheff.

THORNLEY, Philip Courtside Surgery, Kennedy Way, Yate, Bristol BS37 4DQ — MB ChB 1982 Sheff.; DRCOG 1985. Socs: Doctors Accid. Rescue Team; S. Yorks. Medico-Legal Soc. Prev: SHO (A & E) Rotherham Dist. Gen. Hosp.

THORNLEY, Sarah Kate Maryport Group Practice, Alneburgh House, Ewanrigg Road, Maryport CA15 8EL Tel: 01900 815544 Fax: 01900 816626; Bridge End, Deanscales, Cockermouth CA13 0SL Tel: 01900 827378 — MB ChB 1989 Leeds; MRCGP 1994; DCCH RCP Ed. 1994. (Leeds) GP Princip. Prev: Trainee GP W. Cumbld. Hosp. Cumbria VTS.

THORNS, Andrew Roger 59 Vale Road, Claygate, Esher KT10 0NL — MB BS 1989 Lond.; MRCGP 1995; DCH RCP Lond. 1992.

THORNS, Rosemary Feldon Lane Surgery, Feldon Lane, Halesowen B62 9DR Tel: 0121 422 4703; Locksley Cottage, Belbroughton, Stourbridge DY9 0DG — MB BS 1985 Newc.; DRCOG 1990; Cert. Family Plann. JCC 1988; DGM RCP Lond. 1988.

THORNTON, Albert John The Glen, Summerhill, Kingswinford, Brierley Hill — MB ChB 1963 Birm.; MRCS Eng. LRCP Lond. 1963. (Birm.)

THORNTON, Andrew Moor End, Irton, Holmrook CA19 1YQ — MB ChB 1967 Manch.; MRCS Eng. LRCP Lond. 1967; DA Eng. 1972.

THORNTON, Andrew Chalbury Unit, Weymouth Community Hospital, Melcombe Avenue, Weymouth DT4 7TB Tel: 01305 762522 Fax: 01305 762526 Email: andrew.thornton@dorset-tr.swest.nhs.uk — MB ChB 1986 Leeds; MRCPsych 1992. Cons. Psychiat. for the Elderly, Weymouth Community Hosp. Weymouth. Prev: Regist. Rotat. (Psychiat.) Camb. VTS.; Sen. Regist. in Gerontology & Old age Psychiat., N. W. TS.

THORNTON, Andrew Joseph 790 Edenfield Road, Norden, Rochdale OL12 7RB — MB ChB 1985 Birm. Trainee GP Lancs. Prev: Regist. (Histopath.) Stirling Roy. Infirm.

THORNTON, Andrew Shepherd Northlands Surgery, North Street, Calne SN11 0HH Tel: 01249 812091 Fax: 01249 815343 — MB BS 1977 Lond.; MA Camb. 1975; MRCGP 1983; DCH RCP Lond. 1981. (Lond. Hosp.)

THORNTON, Anna Sara Constance 5 Sloane Street, London SW1 — MB BS 1975 Lond.; FRCR 1983; DMRD Eng. 1980. (Middlx.) Cons. Radiol. Newham Gen. Hosp. Lond. Socs: FRCR. Prev: Sen. Regist. Univ. Coll., Gt. Ormond St., Maida Vale & Lond. Hosps.; Regist. W.m. Hosp. Lond.

THORNTON, Barbara Ann Four Winds, Glenmore Rd E., Crowborough TN6 1RE — MB ChB 1976 Manch.

THORNTON, Basil Muschamp (retired) 2 Navariono Court, High St., Lymington SO41 9AE Tel: 01590 672825 — BM BCh 1937 Oxf.; BA, BM BCh Oxon. 1937; FRCGP 1973. Prev: Cas. Off., Ho. Surg. & Ho. Phys. Roy. Vict. & W. Hants. Hosp.

THORNTON, Catherine Walker (retired) Fasgadh, Kilmichael, Glassary, Lochgilphead PA31 8QJ Tel: 0154 65 226 — MB ChB 1945 Glas. Prev: Anaesth. Walsall Gp. Hosps.

THORNTON, Catriona Margaret Burn Parade Surgery, The Parade, Liskeard PL14 6AF Tel: 01379 342667 — MB BS 1987 Lond.; BSc Lond. 1984; MRCGP 1992; DRCOG 1991; DGM RCP Lond. 1990. (Guy's Hosp.)

THORNTON, Claire Maureen Histopathology Department, Institute of Clinical Science, Royal Group of Hospitals Trust, Grosvenor Road, Belfast BT12 6BA Tel: 01232 240503 Fax: 01232 233643; 38 Ranfurly Avenue, Bangor BT20 3SJ Tel: 01247 467049 — MB BCh BAO 1983 Belf.; MRCPath 1990. (Queen's University Belfast) Cons. Perinatal/Paediat. Path. Roy. Vict. Hosp. Belf.

THORNTON, Daniele Alexandra Allesley Park Medical Centre, Whitaker Road No.2, Coventry CV5 9JE Tel: 024 7667 4123 Fax: 024 7667 2196; Orchard House, Banbury Road, Kineton, Warwick CV35 0JY Tel: 01926 642515 — MB ChB Leeds 1988; MRCGP 1993; DFFP 1992; T(GP) 1992. (Leeds)

THORNTON, Daphne Parkway Medical Centre, 2 Frenton Close, Chapel House Estate, Newcastle upon Tyne NE5 1EH Tel: 0191 267 1313 Fax: 0191 229 0630 — MB BS 1986 Newc.; MRCGP 1992; DRCOG 1992.

THORNTON, David John Queensview Medical Centre, Thornton Road, Northampton NN2 6LS Tel: 01604 713315 Fax: 01604 714378 — MB ChB 1968 Bristol.

THORNTON, David Mark 13 Avondale Road, Chesterfield S40 4TF Tel: 01246 277879 — MB ChB 1987 Birm. (Birm.) Staff Grade (A & E) Chesterfield Roy. Hosp. Calow Chesterfield. Socs: Ordinary Mem. Roy. Soc. Med. Prev: SHO (A & E) Kings Mill Hosp. Mansfield Notts.; GP/Regist. CNDRH VTS.

THORNTON, David Michael 8 Glenhurst Road, Nab Wood, Shipley BD18 4DZ — MB ChB 1982 Sheff.; BSc Sheff. 1979, MB ChB 1982.

THORNTON, Eric John, Air Commodore RAF Med. Br. c/o DDMed Pers, DGMS (RAF), HQPTC, RAF Innsworth, Gloucester GL3 1EZ — MB ChB 1972 Dundee; MFOM RCP Lond. 1989; DAvMed. Eng. 1981.

THORNTON, Helen Louise 22 Bloomfield Drive, East Rainton, Houghton-le-Spring DH5 9SF — MB BS 1993 Newc.

THORNTON, Helena Mary Jane Saddleworth Vicarage, Station Road, Uppermill, Oldham OL3 6HQ Tel: 01457 872412 Fax: 01457 872412 — MB ChB 1978 Birm.; DRCOG 1981. (Birm.) GP Princip.; Forens. Phys. St. Mary's Centre, Manch. Socs: Assn. Police Surg.; Roy. Soc. Med.

THORNTON, James Grant Department of Obstetrics & Gynaecology, Leeds General Infirmary, Clarendon Wing, Leeds LS2 9NS Tel: 0113 243 2799 Fax: 0113 231 6479; 19 Claremont Drive, Leeds LS6 4ED Tel: 0113 278 9359 — MB ChB 1977 Leeds; MD Leeds 1988; MRCOG 1986; DTM & H Liverp. 1982. Reader Lect. & Hon. Cons. O & G Leeds. Gen. Infirm. Prev: Hon. Sen. Regist. (O & G) St. Jas. Univ. Leeds; Lect. (O & G) Univ. Wales Coll. Med. Cardiff.; Med. Off. Chogoria Hosp., Kenya.

THORNTON, John Andrew (retired) 8 Beaumond Green, Winchester SO23 8GF Tel: 01962 851574 — MB BS 1951 Lond.; MD Lond. 1969; MRCS Eng. LRCP Lond. 1951; FFA RACS 1983; FFA RCS Eng. 1954; DA Eng. 1953. Prev: Prof. & Head Dept. Anaesth. & Intens. Care Chinese Univ. of Hong Kong Shatin NT, Hong Kong.

THORNTON, John Douglas (retired) 2 Green Hill Road, Leeds LS12 3QA Tel: 0113 263 9099 — MB ChB 1947 Leeds.

THORNTON, John Noel Dickson Copnor Road Surgery, 111 Copnor Road, Portsmouth PO3 5AF Tel: 023 9266 3368 Fax: 023 9278 3203; 18 Craneswater Park, Southsea PO4 0NT — MB ChB 1985 Birm.; MRCGP 1989; DRCOG 1988. GP Portsmouth. Prev: SHO BromsGr. & Redditch VTS; Ho. Surg. Birm. Accid. Hosp.; Ho. Phys. Good Hope Hosp. Sutton Coldfield.

THORNTON, John Richard Ashford & St Peter's Hospitals NHS Trust, Ashford Hospital, London Road, Ashford TW15 3AA Tel: 01784 884239 Fax: 01784 884017; The Princess Margaret Hospital, Osborne Road, Windsor SL4 3SJ Tel: 01753 743434 Fax: 01753 743435 — MD 1982 Bristol; MB ChB (Hons.) 1974; FRCP 1997. Cons. Phys. Ashford Hosp. Middlx. & St Peter's Hosp. Surrey. Socs: Brit. Soc. Gastroenterol. Prev: Lect (Med.) St. Jas. Hosp. & Gen. Infirm. Leeds; Clin. Regist. & MRC Research Fell. (Med.) Bristol Roy. Infirm.

THORNTON, Leonard Countess of Chester Hospital, Liverpool Road, Chester CH2 1UL — MB ChB 1980 Glas.; MRCPsych 1984. Cons. Child & Adolesc. Psychiat. Countess of Chester Hosp. Prev: Cons. Adolesc. Psychiat. Preswich Hosp. Manch.

THORNTON, Leslie Stuart Hugh (retired) Fairoak, Taplow Common Road, Burnham, Slough SL1 8LP — MB ChB 1940 Glas.

THORNTON, Margaret Elizabeth (retired) 23 Shelsley Drive, Moseley, Birmingham B13 9JU Tel: 0121 449 0531 — MB ChB Birm. 1951; FFA RCS Eng. 1961; DCH Eng. 1954, DA 1955. Prev: Cons. Anaesth. & Pain Relief W. Birm. HA.

THORNTON, Mark Julian Radiology Dept, Southmead Hosp, Westbury, Bristol BS10 5NB; 10 Royal Park, Clifton, Bristol BS8 3AW Tel: 0117 946 7885 — MB ChB 1987 Bristol; MRCP (UK) 1991; FRCR 1995. Cons.(Radiol.). Socs: Fell. Roy. Soc. Med. Prev: Sen. Regist. Rotat. (Clin. Radiol.) SW Region; Regist. (Clin. Radiol.) Bristol; SHO (Neurosurg., Neurol. & Med.) Frenchay Hosp.

THORNTON

THORNTON, Martin Robert The Dairy, Grunge Farm, Lutleyy Lane, Halesowen B63 1EZ — MB ChB 1997 Liverp.

THORNTON, Maureen (retired) 54 Deramore Park S., Belfast BT9 5JY Tel: 01232 660186 — MB BCh BAO 1955 Belf.

THORNTON, Michael Campion (retired) Turnstones, 36 Salford, Audlem, Crewe CW3 0BJ Tel: 01270 811621 — MB BChir Camb. 1952; DObst RCOG 1957. Prev: Cas. Off. St. Geo. Hosp. Lond.

THORNTON, Patrick Dominic 6 North Link, Glen Road, Belfast BT11 8HW — MB BCh BAO 1991 Belf.; MB BCh Belf. 1991.

THORNTON, Paul Elmwood Health Centre, Huddersfield Road, Holmfirth, Huddersfield HD9 3TR Tel: 01484 683138 Fax: 01484 689711; Wood Farm, Wood Lane, Holmfirth, Huddersfield HD9 3JB Tel: 01484 688614 — MB BS 1985 Lond.; DCCH RCP Ed. 1989. Prev: Trainee GP Huddersfield.

THORNTON, Paul George Newsome 43 Granby Hill, Bristol BS8 4LS Tel: 0117 929 9113 Email: paul.thornton@which.net — MB ChB 1970 Bristol; FFA RCS Eng. 1975; DA Eng. 1972. Cons. (Anaesth.) united Britol Healthcare Trust. Prev: Sen. Regist. (Anaesth.) Avon AHA (T); Regist. (Anaesth.) Bristol Health Dist. (T); SHO (Anaesth.) Alder Hey Childr. Hosp. Liverp.

THORNTON, Peter John The Surgery, 20-22 Westdale Lane, Carlton, Nottingham NG4 3JA Tel: 0115 961 9401 — MB ChB 1970 Leeds.

THORNTON, Peter William Carnoustie Medical Group, The Health Centre, Dundee Street, Carnoustie DD7 7RB Tel: 01241 859888 Fax: 01241 852080; Rimuhau, 49 Carlogie Road, Carnoustie DD7 6EW — MB ChB 1972 Ed.; BSc Ed. 1969; MFFP 1994; FRCGP 1995, M 1978; DA Eng. 1975; DObst RCOG 1975. (Edinburgh) GP Princip. Carnoustie Med. Gp.; Mem. GP Clin. Advis. Panel Med. & Dent. Defence Union of Scotl. Socs: BMA. Prev: SHO (Paediat. & Plastic Surg.) Perth Roy. Infirm.; Ho. Surg. Roy. N.. Infirm. Inverness; Ho. Phys. Deaconess Hosp. Edin.

THORNTON, Rebecca Jane The Lodge, Manor Farm, Shropham, Attleborough NR17 1DX — MB ChB 1991 Leeds.

THORNTON, Richard John 45 Steep Hill, Lincoln LN2 1LU — MB BS 1971 Lond.; FFA RCS Eng. 1976.

THORNTON, Robert, Col. late RAMC Ministry of Defence, Whitehall, London SW1A 2HH Tel: 0207 807 0363; Tel: 0980 670449 — MD 1988 Ed.; MSc (Occupat. Med.) Lond. 1984; MB ChB 1974; MFOM 1985, A 1981; DIH Soc. Apoth. Lond. 1984; DAvMed FOM RCP Lond. 1979; FFOM 1999. Asst. Dir. Med. Plans MOD. Socs: Fell. Aerospace Med. Assoc. Prev: Assit Dir Med Policy MOD; Cons. Adviser Aviat. Med. HQ DAAC; Research Med. Off. Inst. Aviat. Med. FarnBoro.

THORNTON, Robert David Bewicke Health Centre, 51 Tynemouth Road, Wallsend NE28 0AD Tel: 0191 262 3036 Fax: 0191 295 1663; 41 The Links, Whitley Bay NE26 1TD Tel: 0191 252 7019 — MB BS 1978 Newc.; MRCGP 1982.

THORNTON, Robert John 26 Arran Hill, Thrybergh, Rotherham S65 4BH — BM BS 1998 Nottm.

THORNTON, Sandra Joy Elmwood Health Centre, Huddersfield Road, Holmfirth, Huddersfield HD9 3TR Tel: 01484 688614 Fax: 01484 689711; Wood Farm, Wood Lane, Holmfirth, Huddersfield HD9 3JB Tel: 01484 688614 — MB BS 1984 Lond.; DCH RCP Lond. 1986. Prev: Trainee GP Huddersfield.

THORNTON, Sarah Jane 24 Mount Pleasant, Nangreaves, Bury BL9 6SP — MB ChB 1991 Leeds. Regist. (Anaesth.) Hope Hosp. Salford. Socs: BMA; Train. Mem. Assn. Anaesth.; Manch. Med. Soc. Prev: SHO (ICU & Neurosurg.) N. Manch. Gen. Hosp.; SHO (Anaesth.) Huddersfield Roy. Infirm.; SHO (Anaesth.) Stepping Hill Hosp. Stockport.

THORNTON, Sarah Jane The Granary, Whinfell, Kendal LA8 9EQ — MB ChB 1994 Leic. SHO (Gen. Med.) Roy. Lancaster Infirm.; SHO (Paediat.) Roy. Lancaster Infirm. Prev: SHO (Med.) Kendal; SHO (O & G) Leicester; Ho. Off. (Med.) Leicester.

THORNTON, Sarah Jane 22 Mitton Avenue, Barrowford, Nelson BB9 6BD — MB BS 1998 Lond.

THORNTON, Simon John CARE at the Park, The Park Hospital, Sherwood Lodge Drive, Nottingham NG5 8RX Tel: 0115 967 1670 Fax: 0115 967 3542 Email: info@care-ivf.com — MB BChir 1981 Camb.; MA Camb. 1983; MD Melbourne 1990; MRCOG 1986. Med. Dir. CARE, The Pk. Hosp. Nottm. Socs: Brit. Fertil. Soc.; Amer. Soc. Reproduc. Med. Prev: Med. Dir. NURTURE Qu.s Med. Centre

Nottm.; Sen. Regist. (Reproduc. Med.) Jessop Hosp. Sheff.; IVF Co-ordinator Roy. Wom. Hosp. Carlton, Vict., Austral.

THORNTON, Professor Steven Department Biological Sciences, University of Warwick, Coventry CV4 7AL Tel: 024 76 572747 Fax: 024 76 523568 Email: Sthornton@bio.warwick.ac.uk — BM 1983 Soton.; DM Soton. 1989; MRCOG 1989. (Soton.) Prof. (O & G) Univ. Warwick. Socs: Soc. Endocrinol.; Physiol. Soc. Prev: Lect. Hon. Cons. (Materno-fetal Med.) Rosie Matern. Hosp. Camb.; MRC Clin. Sci. Camb.; Birthright Train. Fell.

THORNTON, Susan Mary Brook House, Dam Lane, Leavening, Malton YO17 9SF Tel: 01653 658249 — BM BS 1985 Nottm.; BMedSci Nottm. 1983; MRCGP 1990; DCH RCP Lond. 1989; DRCOG 1989. (Nottingham) Asst. GP Derwent Surg. Malton Retainer Scheme.

THORNTON, Timothy James Pickering Surgery, Southgate, Pickering YO18 8BL; Middleton Hall, Middleton, Pickering YO18 8NX Tel: 01751 472283 — MB BChir 1977 Camb.

THORNTON, Timothy John Health Centre, 80 Knaresborough Road, Harrogate HG2 7LU Tel: 01423 883212 — MB BS 1974 Lond.; MRCS Eng. LRCP Lond. 1974; MRCGP 1980; DRCOG 1979. (Guy's) Princip. in Gen. Pract. Harrogate. Prev: Squadron Ldr. Med. Off. RAF.

THORNTON, Vyvian Granville Four Winds, Glenmore Road E., Crowborough TN6 1RE — MB BS 1977 Lond.; MRCS Eng. LRCP Lond. 1977.

THORNTON, William Dickson, CB, QHP (retired) 54 Deramore Park S., Belfast BT9 5JY Tel: 01232 660186 — MB BCh BAO Dub. 1954; MD Dub. 1968; FFPHM RCP (UK) 1989; FFCM RCP (UK) 1979, M 1974. Prev: Dep. Chief Med. Off. DHSS N. Irel.

THORNTON-CHAN, Eddie Wing Cheong Clarendon Medical Practice, Clarendon Street, Hyde SK14 2AQ Tel: 0161 368 5224 Fax: 0161 368 4767; Grove End Farm, Blossoms Lane, Woodford, Stockport SK7 1RF — MB ChB 1983 Dundee. Prev: SHO (Paediat.) Bury Gen. Hosp.; SHO (Gen. Med.) Salford HA.

THORNTON-SMITH, Alexander Nathan 101 Roseberry Road, Epsom Downs, Epsom KT18 6AB — MB BS 1996 Lond.; BSc Lond. 1993. (King's College School Medicine and Dentistry)

THOROGOOD, Alan 71 Endsleigh Court, Colchester CO3 3QW Tel: 01206 575915 — MRCS Eng. LRCP Lond. 1951; FFA RCS Eng. 1957; DA Eng. 1955. (Westm.) Cons. Anaesth. Colchester Hosp. Gp. Socs: Assn. Anaesths. & Intractable Pain Soc.; BMA. Prev: Sen. Regist. (Anaesth.) Qu. Vict. Hosp. E. Grinstead; Instruc. (Anaesth.) Univ. Wash. & Staff Anaesth. Veteran's Admin. Hosp. Seattle, USA.

THOROGOOD, Christopher The Medical Centre, Badgers Crescent, Shipston-on-Stour CV36 4BQ Tel: 01608 661845 Fax: 01608 663614; Walnut Cottage, Upper Brailes, Banbury OX15 5AZ Tel: 01608 685581 Fax: 01608 685191 Email: chris@walnutcott.demon.co.uk — MB BS 1975 Lond.; MRCS Eng. LRCP Lond. 1975; FRCGP 1997, M 1979; DRCOG 1978; DCH Eng. 1977. (Roy. Free) GP Warks. HA; Course Organiser Banbury Dist. Oxf. Region; Examr. Roy. Coll. Gen. Pract.

THOROGOOD, Simon Vernon Department of Radiology, Royal Cornwall Hospitals Trust, Truro TR1 3LT Tel: 01872 250000 Fax: 01872 225314 Email: simon.thorogood@rcht.swest.nhs.uk; Greenacre, St. Clement, Truro TR1 1SZ Tel: 01872 278023 Email: simon@sthorogood.freeserve.co.uk — MB BS 1987 Lond. Cons. Radiol. Roy. Cornw. Hosps. Trust. Socs: FRCR; RCP. Prev: Sen. Regist. (Radiol.) Bristol Roy. Infirm.; Regist. (Radiol.) Plymouth Gen. Hosp.; Regist. (Gen. Med.) Poole Hosp.

THORP, Jennifer Susan Audley Mills Surgery, 57 Eastwood Road, Rayleigh SS6 7JF Tel: 01268 774981; 14 Hall Park Avenue, Westcliff on Sea SS0 8NR Tel: 01702 77330 Fax: 01268 770176 — MB ChB 1967 Sheff.; DObst RCOG 1969. Prev: Ho. Surg. (O & G) & Ho. Phys. OldCh. Hosp.; Romford.

THORP, Josephine Mary 32 Middleton Drive, Milngavie, Glasgow G62 8HT — MB ChB (Hons.) Leeds 1970; MRCP (UK) 1973; FRCA 1976. Cons. Anaesth.Lanarksh. Seute Hosp.s NHS Trust.

THORP, Julie Kathryn Pine Lodge, The Green, Carleton, Pontefract WF8 3NJ — MB ChB 1998 Leeds.

THORP, Margaret Elsie 19 Lower Strines Road, Marple, Stockport SK6 7DL — MB ChB 1947 Manch.; DPH Leeds 1950. (Manch.)

THORP, Nicola Jayne Maria Louise Clatterbridge Centre for Oncology, Bebington, Wirral CH63 4JY Tel: 0151 334 4000 Fax: 0151 482 7675; 33 Cheltenham Avenue, Liverpool L17 2AR Tel:

0151 733 5272 Email: ia50@rapid.co.uk — FRCR 1998; MB ChB Leic. 1990; MRCP (UK) 1994. Regist. (Clin. Oncol.) Clatterbridge Centre for Oncol. Wirral.

THORP, Roland Hunter Deep Syke Head, West Linton EH46 7AY Tel: 01968 747 — LRCP LRCS 1950 Ed.; LRCP LRCS Ed., LRFPS Glas. 1950. (Ed.) Maj. RAMC RARO. Socs: Founder Mem. Brit. Blood Transfus. Soc.; M-C Soc. Edin. Prev: Extern. Examr. Applied Anat. & Physiol. Edin. Univ.; Ho. Surg. Surgic. Out-pats. Dept. Edin. Roy. Infirm.; Ho. Phys. (Med.) & Ho. Surg. (O & G) Bangour Hosp.

***THORP, Suzanne Louise** 50 Danford Lane, Solihull B91 1QG Tel: 0121 711 3422 — MB ChB Birm. 1995.

THORP, Tom Anthony John (retired) Harcombe House, Harcombe, Sidmouth EX10 0PR Tel: 01395 597480 — MB ChB Manch. 1949; MRCOphth 1990; DO Eng. 1960; DPH Liverp. 1952. Prev: Ophth. Med. Pract. Chesh. FPC.

THORP, Tom Anthony Simon Royal Sussex County Hospital, Eastern Road, Brighton BN2 5BE Tel: 01273 609060 Fax: 01273 609060; 11 Crown Hill, Seaford BN25 2XJ Tel: 01323 873416 Fax: 01323 873416 — MB ChB 1980 Liverp.; 2001 MRCA; FFA RCSI 1988; DA (UK) 1985. Cons. Anaesth. & Pain Relief Brighton Health Care NHS Trust. Socs: Assn. Anaesth.; Pain Soc.; Roy. Soc. Med. Lond. Prev: Hon. Cons. Pain Relief Guy's Hosp. Lond.; Sen. Regist. (Anaesth.) Qu. Med. Centre Nottm.

THORP-JONES, Daryl John 4 Northmead, Ledbury HR8 1BE — MB BS 1998 Lond.; MB BS Lond 1998.

THORPE, Mr Andrew Christopher Department of Urology, City Hospitals, Sunderland SR4 7TP Tel: 0191 565 6256; 4 Ivy Road, Gosforth, Newcastle upon Tyne NE3 1DB — MB BCh 1981 Wales; MS Wales 1993; FRCS (Urol) 1994; FRCS Ed. 1985. Cons. Urol. City Hosps. Sunderland. Prev: Sen. Regist. (Urol.) Freeman Hosp. Newc.; Regist. (Paediat. Surg.) Lond. Hosp.; Regist. (Urol.) & Research Fell. Roy. Lond. Hosp.

THORPE, Mr Anthony Peter Department of Radiology, Royal Aberdeen Hospital, Westburn Road, Aberdeen AB25 2ZG Email: p.thorpe@abdn.ac.uk; Foresters Croft, McGray Hill, Stonehaven AB39 3QA — MB ChB 1984 Birm.; BSc (Hons.) Birm. 1981, MB ChB 1984; FRCS Eng. 1989; FRCR 1994; MRad (D) 1996. (Birm.) Cons. Radiol. Prev: Fell. in Interview. Radiol. Glas.; Regist. (Emerg. Med.) Fremantle, W.. Austral; SHO (Orthop.) Nottm. HA.

THORPE, Anthony Wilfred (retired) 53 Church Street, Emley, Huddersfield HD8 9RP Tel: 01924 840127 — MB ChB Leeds 1957. Prev: GP Wakefield.

THORPE, Christopher Michael 28 Beaufort Avenue, Langland, Swansea SA3 4NU — MB BS 1985 Lond.; FRCA 1992. Sen. Regist. (Anaesth.) Edin.

THORPE, Elizabeth Jane 12 Grosvenor Court, Brighton Road, Sutton SM2 5BL — MB BS 1997 Lond.

THORPE, Frederick Graham (retired) Haslams Cottage, High Lane Farm, 71 Falkland Road, Ecclesall, Sheffield S11 7PN Tel: 0114 266 6692 — MB ChB 1952 Sheff.; FRCPsych 1978, M 1971; DPM Eng. 1957. Prev: Cons. Childr. Psychiat. Sheff. HA (T).

THORPE, George William (retired) 10 Parkfields, Arden Drive, Dorridge, Solihull B93 8LL Tel: 01564 772768 — MB ChB 1950 Birm.; MB ChB (Hnrs.) Birm. 1950; MRCP Lond. 1952; MRCS Eng. LRCP Lond. 1950; FRCGP 1983, M 1972. Prev: Regional Adviser (Gen. Pract.) W. Midl. RHA & Univ. Birm.

THORPE, Gerald William The Shambles, Moxons Lane, Waddington, Lincoln LN5 9QF — MB BS 1977 Lond.; FRCR 1983; DCH RCP Lond. 1980. Cons. Radiol. Lincoln Hosps NHS Trust. Prev: Sen. Regist. (Radiol.) Manch. HA; SHO (Med.) Doncaster Roy. Infirm.; SHO (Paediat.) Leic. Gen. Hosp. & P'boro. Dist. Hosp.

THORPE, Graham John (retired) 36 Barnbrook Road, Sarisbury Green, Southampton SO31 7BQ Tel: 014899 480181 Email: thorpeatgraham@yahoo.co.uk — MB BS 1956 Lond.; FRCP Lond. 1977, M 1962; DTM & H (Warrington Yorke Medal) Liverp. 1961. Prev: Cons. Phys. (Palliat. Med.) Countess Mt.batten Hse. Moorgreen Hosp. Soton.

THORPE, Mr James Andrew Charles Department of Cardiothoracic Surgery, Leeds General Infirmary, St George St., Leeds Tel: 0113 392 5897 Fax: 0113 392 5092; The Poplars, 22 Fink Mill, Morsforth, Leeds LS18 4DH Tel: 0113 281 9349 Email: athorpe@suflink.co.uk — MB ChB 1972 Leeds; FECTS 1998; FRCS Eng. 1977; FRCS Ed. 1976. Cons. Thoracic Surg. Leeds Gen. Infirm. Socs: Soc. of Thoracic & Cardiovasc. Surg.; Eur. Soc. Pneumonol.;

Eur. Assn. Cardioth. Surg. Prev: Cons. Cardiothoracic Surg. Roy. Hallamsh. Hosp. & N.. Gen. Hosp. Sheff.; Sen. Regist. (Cardiothoracic Surg.) Birm. Hosps.; Regist. (Surg.) Papworth Hosp. Camb.

THORPE, Joanna Brentry Hospital, Phoenix NHS Trust, Bristol BS10 6JH; 42 Homefield, North Yate, Bristol BS37 5US Tel: 01454 329403 Email: joannathorpe@hotmail.com — MB ChB 1991 Leic. Clin. Asst. Learning Disabil. Brentry Hosp. Bristol. Socs: BMA. Prev: Regist. Rotat. (Old Age Psychiat.) Bristol Train. Scheme; Regist. (Child Psychiat.) Limetrees Unit York; Regist. & SHO (Gen. Adult Psychiat.) Bodiham Pk. Hosp. York.

THORPE, John Wainwright Department of Neurology, National Hospital for Neurology & Neurosurgery, Queen Square, London WC1N 3BG Tel: 020 7837 3611 Email: john@nmr.ion.bpmf.ac.uk; 12 Pepys Road, London SE14 5SB Email: thorpeje@aol.com — MB BS 1988 Lond.; BA (Hons.) Oxf. 1985; MRCP (UK) 1991. Regist. (Neurol.) Nat. Hosp. Qu. Sq. Lond. Socs: Assoc. Mem. Assn. Brit. Neurol. Prev: Regist. (Neurol.) St. Thos. Hosp. Lond.; Research Fell. Inst. Neurol. Qu. Sq. Lond.; Regist. & SHO (Med.) Ipswich Hosp.

THORPE, Kim Fionna, Flight Lt. RAF Med. Br. Retd. (retired) Tamarisk Cottage, Church Road, Penn, Buckingham HP10 8NX — MB ChB 1984 Sheff.; DRCOG 1994. Civil Regist. (Path.) IPTM RAF Halton. Prev: Regist. (Path.) IPTM RAF Halton MoD.

THORPE, Margaret Oatway (retired) Flat 2, 49 Westbourne Villas, Hove BN3 4GG Tel: 01273 722055 — MD Toronto 1932; MCPS Alta. 1937; DObst RCOG 1944. Prev: Asst. Venereol. H.M. Prison Holloway.

THORPE, Maric John Langridge 32 Steventon, Daresbury Park, Sandymoor, Runcorn WA7 1UB — MB ChB 1993 Liverp.

THORPE, Mark Adrian, Maj. RAMC Retd. Smallbrook Surgery, 48 Boreham Road, Warminster BA12 9JR Tel: 01985 846700 Fax: 01985 846700 — MB BS 1983 Lond.; MRCGP 1987.

THORPE, Michael Hamilton (retired) 28 Beaufort Avenue, Langland, Swansea SA3 4NU Tel: 01792 368780 — MB ChB Sheff. 1958; FFA RCS Eng. 1963. Prev: Cons. Anaesth. Singleton Hosp. Swansea.

THORPE, Mr Nigel Christopher Hillcrest, 11 Church Farm Road, Heacham, King's Lynn PE31 7JB — MB BS 1981 Lond.; FRCS Ed. 1988; FRCS Eng. 1988.

THORPE, Mr Paul Lawrence Patrick South West (Northern) Specialist Registrar Rotation, Bristol; 42 Homefield, North Yate, Bristol BS37 5US Tel: 01454 329403 Fax: 01454 329403 Email: plpjt@hotmail.com — MB ChB 1991 Leic.; FRCS Ed. 1996. Specialist Regist. (Orthop.) S. W. Rotat.; Chairm. S. W. Jun. Doctors Comm. Socs: Brit. Orthop. Train. Assn.; Med. Network Amnesty Internat.; BMA Nat. Jun. Doctors Comm. Exec. Mem. Prev: SHO Rotat. (Surg.) Frenchay Hosp. Bristol; SHO (Orthop. & A & E) Roy. Hallamsh. Hosp. Sheff.; Demonst. (Anat.) St. Luke's Hosp. for Clergy & Univ. Lond.

THORPE, Penelope Anne Department of Histopathology, West Middlesex University Hospital, Isleworth TW7 6AF Tel: 020 8565 5860 Fax: 020 8565 5516; Email: anne.thorpe@wmuh-tr.nthames.nhs.uk, drthorpe@dircon.co.uk — MB BS 1980 Lond.; 1997 FRCpath; PhD Camb. 1975; BSc (Hons.) Ed. 1971; MRCPath 1986. (Royal Free) Cons. Histopath. W. Middlx. Univ. Hosp.

THORPE, Richard William Jamieson, Thorpe and Burgess, Moulton Medical Centre, High St, Moulton, Spalding PE12 6QB Tel: 01406 370265 Fax: 01406 373219 — MB ChB 1985 Sheff.; MMedSci Nottm. 1996. Clin. Asst. (Geriat.) Welland Hosp. Spalding; Med. Off. Holbeach Hosp. Socs: BMA; Roy. Soc. Med.

THORPE, Ronald Stanley Gostelyns, Stoke Holy Cross, Norwich NR14 8LW Tel: 01508 2288 — MB ChB 1942 Birm.; FRCR 1975; DMRD Eng. 1947. (Birm.) Sen. Cons. Radiol. Norwich Health Dist. Socs: Norwich M-C Soc. Prev: Ho. Surg. Burntwood EMS Hosp; Regist. (Radiol.) Birm. United Hosp; Capt. RAMC 1943-47.

THORPE, Russell John The Old Links Surgery, 104 Highbury Road East, Lytham St Annes FY8 2LY Tel: 01253 713621; Haymon, 150 St Annes Road E., Lytham St Annes FY8 23HW Tel: 01253 712481 — MB ChB 1982 Liverp. Prev: Trainee GP Wirral HA VTS; Ho. Off. S.port Gen. Infirm.

THORPE, Sheila Christine (retired) Meadowside, Ropley, Alresford SO24 0DS Tel: 01962 773202 — MB ChB 1952 Glas.; MRCGP 1974; DObst RCOG 1962. Prev: Regist. (O & G) Fulham Hosp. & Fulham Matern. Hosp.

THORPE

THORPE, Susan Sheila Standerton, Seymour Road, Mannamead, Plymouth PL3 5AT — MB BS 1984 Lond. Regist. (O & G) Lewisham & Guy's. Hosps. Lond. Prev: SHO (O & G) St. Mary's Hosp. Portsmouth; SHO (O & G) King's Coll. & Dulwich Hosps. Lond.

THORPE-BEESTON, John Guy Chelsea and Westminster Hopspital, Fulham Road, London SW10 9NH — MB BChir 1984 Camb.; FRCOG 2001; MA Camb 1985, MD 1991; MRCOG 1989. Cons. O & G Chelsea & W.m. Hosp. Lond. Prev: Sen. Regist. (O & G) St. Mary's Hosp. Lond.; SHO (O & G) Kings Coll. Hosp. Lond.; SHO (Surg.) Hammersmith Hosp. Lond.

THOULD, Anthony Keith (retired) Idless Mill, Idless, Truro TR4 9QS Tel: 01872 272593 — MD Lond. 1960, MB BS (Hnrs.) 1954; FRCP Lond. 1974, M 1958. Cons. Rheum. Roy. Cornw. Hosp. (City) Truro; Surg. Lt. Cdr. RNR. Prev: Sen. Regist. (Med.) & Ho. Surg. St. Bart. Hosp. Lond.

THOULD, Geoffrey Robert South & West Devon Health Authority, The Lescaze Offices, Shinner's Bridge, Dartington, Totnes TQ9 6JE Tel: 01803 866665 — MB BS 1986 Lond.; MB BS (Distinc.) Lond. 1986; MSc (Pub. Health) Lond. 1995; BSc (Hons.) Durham. 1981; MFPHM 1998. Cons., Communicable Dis. Control (Pub. Health Med.), S & W Devon Health Auth.. Prev: Sen. Regist. (Pub. Health Med.) S. & W. RHA; Regist. (Pub. Health Med.) SE Thames RHA; Regist. (Microbiol.) Bristol Roy. Infirm.

THOUNG, Mehm Tin 8 Church Green, Roxwell, Chelmsford CM1 4NZ — MB BS 1985 Western Australia; FRCA 1993.

THOW, Jonathan Charles Department of Medicine, York District Hospital, Wiggington Road, York YO31 8ZZ Tel: 01904 453453 — MD 1991 Newc.; MB BS 1982; MRCP (UK) 1985; FRCP Lond. 1998. (Newcastle upon Tyne) Cons. Phys. Diabetes & Endocrinol. York Dist. Hosp. Prev: Sen. Regist. (Med.) Manch. Roy. Infirm.; Regist. (Gen. Med.) Newc. Gen. Hosp.

THOW, Mary Elizabeth (retired) Sighthill Health Centre, Calder Road, Edinburgh EH11 4AU Tel: 0131 453 5335 — MB BS 1957 Lond. Prev: GP Princip. Sighthill Health Centre Edin. EH11 4AU.

THRASHER, Adrian James Department Molecular Immunology, Institute of Child Health, 30 Guilford St., London WC1N 1EH; 54 Haydon Park Road, London SW19 8JY Tel: 020 8540 6925 — MB BS 1986 Lond.; PhD Lond. 1995; MRCP (UK) 1989. Wellcome Clin. Scientist Fell. & Lect. Inst. Child Health; Hon. Sen. Regist. UCL Sch. Med. & Gt. Ormond St. Hosp. Lond. Prev: Clin. Lect. & Hon. Regist. Rayne Inst. Univ. Coll. Hosp. Lond.; Lect. (Molecular Med.) & Regist. (Gen. Med.) Univ. Coll. Hosp.

THREEPURANENI, Gopichand 22 Holder Drive, Cannock WS11 1TL — MB ChB 1995 Leic.

THREFALL, Simon Jeremy 36 Allens Avenue, Norwich NR7 8EP — MB BS 1983 Lond.; MA Camb. 1980.

THRELFALL, Alexandra Katherine Walnut Tree House, Oxford Road, Old Marston, Oxford OX3 0PH Tel: 01865 242071 — BM Soton. 1977; MRCGP 1984; DCH RCP Lond. 1981; DRCOG 1979.

THRELFALL, Alison Louise Testvale Surgery, 12 Salisbury Road, Totton, Southampton SO40 3PY Tel: 023 8086 6999/6990 Fax: 023 8066 3992; 3 Blackwater House, Emery Down, Lyndhurst SO43 7FJ Tel: 02380 283022 — MB ChB 1981 Birm.; MRCGP 1985; DRCOG 1985; FPA 1985. (Birmingham)

THRELFALL, Ann Elizabeth Edenfield Road Surgery, Cutgate Shopping Precinct, Edenfield Road, Rochdale OL11 5AQ Tel: 01706 344044 Fax: 01706 526882; 110 Bury Road, Edenfield, Ramsbottom, Bury BL0 0ET — MB ChB 1981 Manch.

THRELFALL, James Anthony 8 Pinewood Close, Ashton-with-Stodday, Lancaster LA2 0AD — BM BS 1997 Nottm.

THRES, Grace Veronica The Hazard, Widemouth Bay, Bude EX23 0AQ — MB ChB 1945 Bristol; DPH Eng. 1958. (Bristol & Univ. Tulane)

THRIPPLETON, Lucy Kate 25 Grove Street, Wantage OX12 7AB — MB BS 1997 Lond.

THRIPPLETON, Sean Arthur 4 Chestnut Grove, Calverley, Pudsey LS28 5TN — MB BS 1987 Lond.; MRCGP 1992; DRCOG 1991.

THROSSELL, Jane Ann Lynfield Mount Hospital, Heights Lane, Bradford BD9 6DP Tel: 01274 494194 Fax: 01274 483494 — MB BS 1974 Newc.; MRCPsych 1978; DPM Leeds 1977. Cons. Psychiat. Bradford Community Health Trust.

THROWER, Andrew James 14 Cliffside Gardens, Leeds LS6 2HA — MB ChB 1998 Leeds.

THROWER, Arthur Leslie (retired) 33 Hatchett Lane, Stonely, Huntingdon Tel: 01480 860328 — MB BS 1945 Lond.; MRCS Eng. LRCP Lond. 1942; MFCM RCP (UK) 1974; DPH 1952. Prev: Dist. Community Phys. St. Thos. Health Dist. (T).

THROWER, Dorothy Frances (retired) 2 Highfields, Warsash Road, Warsash, Southampton SO31 9JE Tel: 01489 579168 Email: dthrower@300m.co.uk — MB ChB 1955 Bristol; DCH Eng. 1957, DPH 1966; DObst RCOG 1958. Prev: Clin. Med. Off. (Community Health) Portsmouth & SE Hants. HA.

THROWER, Michelle Mary 33 The Kyles, Ravenscraig, Kirkcaldy KY1 2QG Tel: 01592 205699 — MB ChB 1990 Dundee; MRCGP 1994. Prev: Trainee GP Fife.

THROWER, Patricia Ann St Georges Medical Centre, 7 Sunningfields Road, Hendon, London NW4 4QR Tel: 020 8202 6232 Fax: 020 8202 3906; Links Cottage, Holders Hill Crescent, London NW4 1NE Tel: 020 8203 2217 — MB BS 1974 Lond.; FRCP 2001. (St. Bart.) GP Princip.; Clin. Director Barnet PCT. Prev: Sen. Regist. (Gen. Med. & Rheum.) St. Bart. Hosp. Lond.

THROWER, Stephanie Mary (Surgery), Wadeslea, Elie, Leven KY9 1EA Tel: 01333 330302; The Manse, Pittenweem, Anstruther KY10 2LR Tel: 01333 311255 — MB ChB 1963 St. And. Prev: Clin. Asst. Playfield Ho. Cupar & PDU Vict. Hosp. Kirkcaldy; Asst. Med. Off. Falmouth Hosp. Trelawny Jamaica.

THRUSH, David Cyril Little Beacon, Court Road, Newton Ferrers, Plymouth PL8 1DA Tel: 01752 872503 — MD Camb. 1973, MB 1966, BChir 1965; FRCP Lond. 1982, M 1968. (Camb. & St. Geo.) Cons. Neurol. Devon AHA. Socs: Assn. Brit. Neurol. & W. Country Phys. Assn.

THRUSH, Roger Pinfold Health Centre, Field Road, Bloxwich, Walsall WS3 3JP Fax: 01922 775132; 9 St. Margaret's, Streetly, Sutton Coldfield B74 4HU Tel: 0121 353 8858 — MB BS 1968 Lond.; MRCGP 1972; DObst RCOG 1970; DCH RCP Lond. 1971. (St. Bart.) Prev: Trainee GP Newc. VTS; Ho. Off. (Med.) Rochford Gen. Hosp.; Ho. Surg. Dept. Orthop. St. Bart. Hosp. Lond.

THRUSH, Steven 9 St Margarets, Sutton Coldfield B74 4HU — MB BS 1992 Lond.

THUL, Dorothea Margaretha Leicester General Hospital, 32 Jackson House, Gwendolen Road, Leicester LE5 4PW; Flat 3, 16 Alexandra Road, Leicester LE2 2BB — State Exam Med 1992 Heidelberg.

THULBOURNE, Mr Terence Rivendell, Auchterhouse, Dundee DD3 0RF — MB ChB 1960 Sheff.; MB ChB (Hnrs.) Sheff. 1960; FRCS Eng. 1969. (Sheff.) Cons. Orthop. Dundee Roy. Infirm. Socs: Brit. Orthop. Assn. Prev: Sen. Orthop. Regist. Tayside Health Bd.; Orthop. Regist. King's Coll. Hosp. Lond.; Orthop. Clin. Research Fell. Hosp. Sick Childr. Toronto, Canada.

THULUVATH, Paul Joseph Department of Gastroenterology, Charing Cross Hospital, Fulham Palace Road, London W6 8RF Tel: 020 8846 1234 Fax: 020 8846 1111; 9 Brook Avenue, Edgware HA8 9XF Tel: 020 8958 9804 — MD 1990 Sheff.; MB BS Bangalore 1980; MRCP (UK) 1984; T(M) 1991. Sen. Regist. (Gen. Med. & Gastroenterol.) Char. Cross & W.m. Hosps. & W. Middlx. Univ. Hosp. Socs: Brit. Soc. Gastroenterol. & Brit. Assn. Study of Liver. Prev: Regist. (Med. & Gastroenterol.) Addenbrooke's Hosp. Camb.; Research Regist. (Hepatol.) Univ. Dept. Med. Roy. Hallamsh. Hosp. Sheff.

THUM, Annabel Maxine Elizabeth Highgate Group Practice, 4 Notrh Hill, Highgate, London N6 4QH Tel: 0208 340 6628; 14 Denewood Road, Highgate, London N6 4AJ Tel: 0208 341 2558 — MB ChB 1987 Bristol; MRCGP 1991; DRCOG 1990. p/t Retainee in Gen. Pract., Highgate, N6; Clin. Assist. Gyn., Whittington Hosp. Lond. N19. Prev: Trainee GP Capelfield Surg. Claygate; SHO (A & E) Kingston Hosp. Kingston u. Thames; SHO (Psychiat.) The Priory Roehampton.

THUMPSTON, Marjorie Bernelle 50 Burges Road, Thorpe Bay, Southend-on-Sea SS1 3AX Tel: 01702 588948 — MB BS 1937 Rangoon; DCH Eng. 1940.

THURAIRAJ, Thillairaj 6 The Pastures, Bixley Farm, Ipswich IP4 5UQ Tel: 01473 715108 — MB BS 1980 Sri Lanka. SCMO (Psychiat. for Elderly) Minsmere Hse., St. Clements & Gen. Hosp. Ipswich. Prev: Staff Grade (Psychiat. for Elderly) Barnet Gen. & Napsbury Hosp. Herts.

THURAIRAJA, Ramesh 24 Malcolm Drive, Surbiton KT6 6QS — BM 1998 Soton.

THURAIRAJAH, Adrian 32 St John's Road, Wembley Central, Wembley HA9 7JQ Tel: 020 8902 0118 — MB BS 1954 Ceylon.

THURAIRAJAH, Guhaeni York Road Surgery, Ilford IG1 3AF Tel: 020 8514 0906 Fax: 020 8553 3323 — MB BS 1971 Ceylon.

THURAIRAJAH, Krishni 92 Helmsdale Avenue, Dundee DD3 0NW — MB ChB 1993 Dundee; DRCOG 1996; MRCGP 1998. GP.

THARAIRAJASINGAM, Sornaghandimalar (retired) 8 Fir Tree Avenue, Worsley, Manchester M28 1LP — MB BS 1953 Ceylon; FRCR 1975; FFR 1969; DMRD Eng. 1962. Cons. Radiol. Salford AHA (T).

THURAIRATNAM, Della Norris 54 Somertrees Avenue, London SE12 0BY — MB BS 1996 Lond.

THURAISINGAM, Adrian Ivo 24 Castle Bank, Stafford ST16 1DJ — MB ChB 1995 Manch.

THURAISINGAM, Chelliah Paul (retired) 24 Castle Bank, Stafford ST16 1DJ Tel: 01785 241040 — MB BS 1950 Ceylon; DTM & H Ceylon 1953. Prev: GP Stafford.

THURAISINGHAM, Jeyasingham Chittambalam 26B Chesterfield Road, London W4 3HG — MB BS 1955 Ceylon; DTM & H Ceylon 1970. Prev: Mem. Med. Comm. Asian Football ConFederat..

THURAISINGHAM, Raj Chandran West Hill Hospital, Dartford Tel: 01322 23223; 83 Lavender Sweep, London SW11 1EA — MB BS 1987 Lond.

THURGOOD, Michael Clive Fairwater Medical Centre, Fairwater Square, Fairwater, Cwmbran NP44 4TA Tel: 01633 869544 — MB BCh 1992 Wales; DRCOG 1997; MRCGP 1996. GP. Socs: Roy. Coll. Gen. Pract.; BMA. Prev: Trainee GP Cardiff; SHO (O & G) Cardiff.

THURKETTLE, Alison Jayne City Medical Practice, 60, Portland St, Lincoln LN5 7LB Tel: 01522 876800 Fax: 01522 876803; Fax: 01522 543573 — MB ChB 1984 Leeds; DRCOG 1987. (University of Leeds) p/t Asst. GP Lincoln.

THURLBECK, Sarah Margaret St. George's Hospital, Blackshaw Road, London SW17 0QT Tel: 020 8725 3648 Fax: 020 8725 3938 Email: sthurlbe@sghms.ac.uk — MB BS 1980 Lond.; MRCP (UK) 1983; FRCPC 1990. Cons. Paediat. St. Geo. Hosp. Lond.

THURLEY, Patricia Ann (Surgery), 3 Cape Road, Warwick CV34 4JP Tel: 01926 499988; 33 Blacklow Road, Warwick CV34 5SX Tel: 01926 491673 — MRCS Eng. LRCP Lond. 1967. (Liverp. & Birm.) Prev: Ho. Surg. & Ho. Phys. Warneford Gen. Hosp. Leamington Spa.

THURLEY, Patricia Elizabeth X-Ray Department, Whipps Cross Hospital, Leytonstone, London E11 Tel: 020 8539 5522; 16 Grove Hill, South Woodford, London E18 2JG Tel: 020 8989 0623 Email: pethurley@aol.com — MB BS 1970 Lond.; BSc (Special) Lond. 1967; MRCS Eng. LRCP Lond. 1970; FRCR 1981; DMRD Eng. 1974; DCH Eng. 1972. (Westm.) Cons. Radiol. Whipps Cross Hosp. Lond. Prev: Clin. Asst. (Radiol. & Ultrasound) Whipps Cross Hosp. Lond.; Regist. (Radiol.) W.m. Hosp. Lond.

THURLOW, Alexander Cresswell Department of Anaesthesia, St. George's Hospital, Blackshaw Road, London SW17 0QT Tel: 020 8672 1255; 17 Belvedere Drive, London SW19 7BU Tel: 020 8946 0240 — MB BS 1964 Lond.; MRCS Eng. LRCP Lond. 1964; FFA RCS Eng. 1968. (St. Mary's) Cons. Anaesth. St. Geo. Hosp. Lond. Socs: BMA; Assn. Anaesths. Prev: Sen. Regist. (Anaesth.) St. Thos. Hosp. Lond. & Hosp. Sick Childr. Gt. Ormond St.; Regist. (Anaesth.) St. Geo. Hosp. Lond.

THURLOW, Bettie Pendril Longsight, Western Road, Crediton EX17 3NF — MB BS Lond. 1943. (Lond. Sch. Med. Wom.)

THURLOW, Beverley Anne Beatrice 214 Moss Delph Lane, Aughton, Ormskirk L39 5BJ Tel: 01695 422067 — MB ChB 1963 Liverp.; MRCOG 1970, DObst 1965. (Liverp.) Assoc. Specialist - Child Health Alder Hey Childrs. Hosp. NHS Trust. Prev: Clin. Med. Off. S. Sefton HA.; Clin. Asst. Ultrasound Dept. Fazakerley Hosp. Liverp.; Regist. (O & G) Walton Hosp. Liverp.

THURLOW, John Horning Road Surgery, Horning Road West, Hoveton, Norwich NR12 8QH Tel: 01603 782155 Fax: 01603 782189; Church Farm, Upper St, Horning, Norwich NR12 8NL — MB BS 1969 Lond.; MRCS Eng. LRCP Lond. 1969; DCH Eng. 1971. (St. Bart.) Prev: SHO Ipswich & E. Suff. Hosps.; SHO (Obst.) Roy. Berks. Hosp. Reading; Ho. Surg. St. Bart. Hosp. Lond.

THURLOW, Susan Kristina Grosvenor Avenue Surgery, 20 Grosvenor Avenue, Hayes UB4 8NL Tel: 020 8845 7100 Fax: 020 8842 4401 — MB BS 1989 Lond.; MRCGP 1994; DRCOG 1993.

THURNELL, Mr Christopher Alain 20 Eton Court, Hornby Lane, Liverpool L18 3HG Email: christhurnell@hotmail.com; 49 Thames Street, St Albans, Christchurch, New Zealand Email: chricthurnell@hotmail.com — MB ChB 1990 Manch.; 2001 (FRANZCOG); 1998 MRNZCOG; MRCOG 1999; BSc (Hons.) Manch. 1984, MB ChB 1990. (Manchester) p/t Cons. (O & G) Rotorua Hosp. Rotorua, New Zealand. Prev: Regist. (O & G), Countess of Chester, Chester; Regist. (O & G) Cheltenham Hosp. Cheltenham; Demonst. (Anat.) Univ. Manch.

THURRELL, Wendy Pamela Nutshell, Stelling Minnis, Canterbury CT4 6BE — MB BS 1983 Lond.; MRCPath 1992.

THURSBY-PELHAM, Anna Katherine 2 Woodlands Avenue, New Malden KT3 3UN — MB ChB 1996 Dundee.

THURSBY-PELHAM, Fergus William Vaughan 2 Woodlands Avenue, New Malden KT3 3UN — MB BS 1998 Lond.

THURSBY-PELHAM, Helen Gunn (retired) Swallow Hill, Baldwins Gate, Newcastle ST5 5ES Tel: 01782 680354 — MB ChB 1950 Manch. Prev: Med. Off. Stoke-on-Trent & Dist. Family Plann.

THURSFIELD, Sian Rhiannon 40A Lichfield Road, London NW2 2RG — MB BS 1993 Lond.

THURSFIELD, William Reginald Ritchie (retired) Red Cross Cottage, Salterns, Seaview PO34 5AG Tel: 01983 613115 — MB BS 1946 Lond.; MRCS Eng. LRCP Lond. 1945; LMCC 1954; DMRD Eng. & Lond 1950. Cons. Radiol. I. of Wight & Portsmouth Hosp. Gp. Prev: Asst. Radiol. X-Ray Dept. Vict. Hosp. Lond., Canada.

THURSTAN, John Whieldon Holywell House Surgery, Holywell Street, Chesterfield S41 7SD Tel: 01246 273075 Fax: 01246 555711; Wych Cottage, Common Lane, Cutthorpe, Chesterfield S42 7AN — MB ChB 1979 Sheff.; DRCOG 1983. Socs: MRCGP.

THURSTAN, Nigel David Antony Chard Road Surgery, Chard Road, Plymouth PL5 2UE Tel: 01752 363111; 62 Windemere Crescent, Plymouth PL6 5HX — MB ChB 1971 Manch.

THURSTON, Mr Andrew Vernon Consultant Urologist, St Albans City Hospital, St Albans AL3 5PN Tel: 01721 897116; Email: andrew.thurlton@tesco.net — MB BChir 1978 Camb.; MA Camb. 1978; FRCS Eng. 1982. Cons. Urol. W. Herts Hosp.s. Socs: Brit. Assn. Urol. Surgs. & Brit. Prostate Gp.; Amer. Urological Assn. Prev: Regist. (Urol.) Portsmouth HA; Demonst. (Anat.) Camb. Univ.; Cons. (Urol.) Doncaster.

THURSTON, Anne Marguerite Dr J M Beck and Partners, 21 Beaufort Road, Southbourne, Bournemouth BH6 5AJ Tel: 01202 433081 Fax: 01202 430527; The Glen, Beckley, Christchurch BH23 7ED — MB BS 1981 Lond.; MRCGP 1985; DCH RCP Lond. 1986; DRCOG 1984. (Guy's) Socs: BMA. Prev: Trainee GP Guy's Hosp. VTS; Clin. Med. Off. & Ho. Phys. Guy's Hosp. Lond.

THURSTON, Brian John Lisson Grove Medical Centre, 3-5 Lisson Grove, Mutley, Plymouth PL4 7DL Tel: 01752 205555 Fax: 01752 205558; Clinkland Farm House, Ermington, Ivybridge PL21 9JY Email: brianthur@aol.com — MB BChir 1979 Camb.; DRCOG 1986; DCH RCP Lond. 1986. (Cambridge & Westminster) Prev: SHO (A & E) Torbay Hosp. Torquay; SHO (Paediat.) Roy. Devon & Exeter Hosp. Exeter; SHO (O & G) Camb. HA.

THURSTON, Caroline (retired) Corner House, Plump Rd, Tharston, Norwich NR15 2YR — MB ChB 1989 Sheff.; BSc (Hons.) Soton. 1983; FFARCSI (Pt. II) 1994; FRCA (Pt. I) 1993.

THURSTON, David Wingrave Donnington Health Centre, 1 Henley Avenue, Oxford OX4 4DH Tel: 01865 774844 — MB BS 1972 Lond.; MRCPsych 1978; MRCGP 1979.

THURSTON, Eric Wistan, OStJ (retired) 11 Ryder Seed Mews, Pageant Road, St Albans AL1 1NL Tel: 01727 856112 — MB BS Lond. 1948. Prev: Capt. RAMC.

THURSTON, Professor Herbert University of Leicester, Leicester Warwick Med. Sch., School of Medicine, Robert Kilpatrick Clinical Sciences Building, Leicester Royal Infirmary, PO Box 65, Leicester LE2 7LX Tel: 0116 252 3183 Fax: 0116 252 3188; Linden House, Loddington Road, Tilton-on-the Hill, Leicester LE7 9DE — MB ChB 1966 (Hons.) Manch.; BSc (Hons.) Manch. 1964, MD 1980; FRCP Lond. 1981; MRCP (UK) 1970. Prof. Med. & Cons. Phys. Univ. Leicester & Leicester Roy. Infirm. Socs: Assn. Phys. & Med. Research Soc.; Internat. Soc. of Hypertens.; Cardiac Soc. Research Assn. Prev: SHO Profess. Med. Unit & Ho. Phys. & Ho. Surg. Manch. Roy. Infirm.; Lect. (Med.) Univ. Manch.

THURSTON, Hilary Ann Sefton Health Authorities, Burlington House, Crosby Road N., Waterloo, Liverpool L22 0QB Tel: 0151 920

THURSTON

5056 Fax: 0151 920 1035 — MB ChB 1983 Liverp.; MPH Liverp. 1991; MRCGP 1989; DRCOG 1986; MFPHM 1998. Socs: BMA. Prev: Sp. Regist. (Pub. Health Med.) Mersey RHA; Trainee GP Merseyside VTS; RMO (Psychiat.) Vict., Austral.

THURSTON, John Gavin Bourdas Tel: 01322 428135 Fax: 01322 428161; Vessels, Bessels Green Road, Sevenoaks TN13 2PT Tel: 01732 458367 — MB BS 1961 MB BS Lond.; MRCP Lond. 1967; MRCS Eng. LRCP Lond. 1961; FFAEM 1993. (Guy's) Hon. Med. Off. RFU Twickenham; Hon. Phys. Grand Order Water Rats. Socs: Fell. Roy. Soc. Med. (Ex-Pres. Sect. Accid. & Emerg.); BMA; Fell. (Previously Regist.) Fac. A & E Med. Prev: Cons. Phys. i/c A & E Dept. Qu. Mary's Hosp. Roehampton; Sen. Regist. (Gen. Med. & Cardiol.) W.m. Hosp. Lond.; Ho. Phys. Guy's & Brompton Hosps.

THURSTON, John Vernon (retired) Actons Cottage, Buckholt La, Bexhill-on-Sea TN39 5AX Tel: 01424 830415 — MB BS 1948 Lond.; MRCS Eng. LRCP Lond. 1945; DObst RCOG 1950.

THURSTON, Julia Sarah The New Surgery, Victoria Road, Wargrave, Reading RG10 8BP Tel: 0118 940 3939 Fax: 0118 940 1357 — MB BS 1981 Lond.; MRCGP 1985; DRCOG 1984. (Guy's) Socs: BMA. Prev: Trainee GP Guy's Hosp. VTS Lond.

THURSTON, Kenneth The Surgery, Lydford Mews, 23 High Street, East Hoathly, Lewes BN8 6DR Tel: 01865 840943 Fax: 01865 841309; Hollyhocks Thomas Turner Drive, East Hoathly, Lewes BN8 6QF — MRCS Eng. LRCP Lond. 1974. (Sheff.) Prev: SHO (A & E Orthop. & Gen. Surg.) Leicester Roy. Infirm.; Demonst. (Anat.) Univ. Leicester; Ho. Phys. (Cardiol. & Gen. Med.) N.. Gen. Hosp. Sheff.

THURSTON, Nicola Garden Cottages, Trewsbury House, Coates, Cirencester GL7 6NY — MB BS 1994 Lond.

THURSTON, Stephen Charles Wymondham Medical Partnership, Postmill Close, Wymondham NR18 0RF; 33 Wood Avens Way, Wymondham NR18 0XP — MB ChB 1985 Leic.; DRCOG 1989. Prev: Trainee GP Leicester VTS.

THURSTON, Timothy John New Milton Health Centre, Spencer Road, New Milton BH25 6EN Tel: 01425 621188 Fax: 01425 620646; The Glen, Beckley, Christchurch BH23 7ED — BSc Lond. 1979, MB BS 1982; MRCGP 1986; DCH RCP Lond. 1986; DRCOG 1985. (Guy's) Prev: GP Trainee Sidcup VTS; Ho. Phys. Guy's Hosp. Lond.; Ho. Surg. Greenwich Dist. Hosp. Lond.

THURSZ, Mr Anthony David Standing Stones, Kinniside, Cleator CA23 3AQ Tel: 01946 861415 Fax: 01946 861415; Standing Stones, Kinniside, Cleator CA23 3AQ Tel: 01946 861415 Fax: 01946 861415 — MA, MB BChir Camb. 1953; FRCS Ed. 1963; MRCS Eng. LRCP Lond. 1953; FRCOG 1976, M 1963, DObst 1956. (King's Coll. Hosp.) Socs: Fell. Manch. Med. Soc. & N. Eng. Obst. & Gyn. Soc. Prev: Cons. O & G Vale of Leven Hosp. Alexandria; Cons. O & G W. Cumbld. Hosp. Gp.; Sen. Regist. (O & G) Newc. Gen. Hosp.

THURSZ, Mark Richard Imperial College School of Medicine, Department of Medicine, St Mary's Hospital, Praed St., London W2 1PG Tel: 020 7594 3641 Fax: 020 7724 9369 Email: m.thursz@ic.ac.uk; Heath Cottage, Little Heath Lane, Potten End, Berkhamsted HP4 2RY Tel: 01442 876062 — MB BS 1986 Lond.; MRCP (UK) 1989; MD Lond. 1997. Sen. Lect. & Hon. Cons. (Med. & Gastroenterol.) St. Mary's Hosp. Med. Sch. Imperial Coll. Lond. Socs: Brit. Soc. Gastroenterol.; Eur. Assn. Study Liver; Assn. of Phys.s. Prev: Regist. (Med. & Gastroenterol.) N.wick Pk. Hosp.

THURTLE, Owen Anthony Woodbridge Road Surgery, 165-167 Woodbridge Road, Ipswich IP4 2PE Tel: 01473 256251; 43 Cowper Street, Ipswich IP4 5JA Tel: 01473 278022 — MB BS 1973 Newc.; MRCP (UK) 1977; MRCGP 1985; T (GP) 1991; T (M) 1991; DRCOG 1984. Prev: Sen. Regist. (Rheum & Rehabil.) Soton. & Portsmouth; Regist. (Med.) York Health Dist.

THUSE, Mr Makarand Ganesh Manor Hospital, Moat Road, Walsall WS2 9PS Tel: 01922 721172; 29 Carlton Croft, Streetly, Sutton Coldfield B74 3JT — MB BS 1969 Bombay; MS (Gen. Surg.) Bombay 1972; FRCS Eng. 1975; FRCS Ed. 1975; FRCR 1983; DMRD Eng. 1981; Dip. Orthop. CPS Bombay 1972. (Seth G.S. Med. Coll.) Cons. Radiol. Walsall Heath Dist. Manor, Little Aston Hosps. Prev: Sen. Regist. (Radiol.) W. Midl. RHA; Regist. (Surg.) Gravesend & N. Kent Hosp. & Dartford & Gravesham Health Dist.; Regist. (Surg.) Qu. Mary's Hosp. Sidcup.

THWAITE, Dawn Sarah Trem-Y-Bryn, Carreghofa Lane, Llanymynech SY22 6LA; Trem-Y-Bryn, Carreghofa Lane, Llanymynech SY22 6LA Tel: 01691 830083 — MB BS 1994 Lond.; BSc Basic Med. Scs. & Physiol. (1st cl. Hons.) Lond. 1991; MRCP Pt. I 1996; DRCOG. 1998; DFFP. 1998. GP Regist. Montgomery Med Pract. Powys. Prev: SHO (GUM & HIV) Chelsea & W.minster Hosp.; SHO (O & G) FarnBoro. Hosp. Kent; SHO Rotat. (Med.) Kings Coll. Hosp. Lond.

THWAITE, Erica Louise 95 Avon Road, Billinge, Wigan WN5 7SF — MB BS 1991 Lond.; MRCP 1994; FRCRI 1996; DMRD 1997. (King's College London) Specialist Regist. (Radiol.) Mersey Region.

THWAITE, Linda Jane 364 Hale Road, Halebarns, Altrincham WA15 8SY — MB ChB 1989 Sheff.; DRCOG 1992; MRCGP 1995. (Sheffield)

THWAITES, Alison Jane 47 Lonsdale Road, Birmingham B17 9QX — MB ChB 1988 Birm.; ChB Birm. 1988.

THWAITES, Barnaby Christopher 71 Low Stobhill, Morpeth NE61 2SQ Tel: 01670 513501 — MB BS 1979 Lond.; BSc (Genetics & Biol.) Manch. 1974; MRCP (UK) 1982. (Roy. Free) Cons. Phys. & Cardiol. Wansbeck Hosp. N.d.; Hon. Cons. Cardiol. Freeman Hosp. Newc. Socs: Brit. Pacing & Electrophysiol. Gp.; Brit. Cardiac Soc. Prev: Cons. Phys. & Cardiol. Holberton Hosp. Antigua, W. Indies.; Regist. Nat. Heart Hosp. Lond.

THWAITES, Ian Guy Marlhurst, Southwater, Horsham RH13 7BY Tel: 01403 730153 — MB BChir 1967 Camb.; MLCOM 1991; DMS Med. 1993; DCH Eng. 1970. (St. Thomas' Hospital Lond.) Indep. Phys. (Musculoskeletal Med.) Horsham. Socs: (Counc.) Brit. Inst. Musculoskeletal Med. Prev: GP Horsham, Sussex.

THWAITES, Richard John Department of Paediatrics, St. Mary's Hospital, Portsmouth PO3 6AD Tel: 023 92 286000 Fax: 023 92 866101 — MB BS 1985 Lond.; MRCP 1991 UK; BA 1982 Camb.; BA Camb. 1982; MRCP (UK) 1991. Cons. Paediat. St. Mary's Hosp. Portsmouth. Prev: Lect. (Neonatol.) United Med. Sch. Guy's & Thos. Hosp. Lond.; Lect. (Child Health) Med. Coll. St. Bart. Hosp. Lond.

THWAITES, Rosemary North View, Copt Hewick, Ripon HG4 5BY — MB ChB 1994 Manch.

THWAITES, Sheila Margaret 5 Arlington Close, Goring-by-Sea, Worthing BN12 4ST Tel: 01903 244265 — MB BS 1960 Lond.; MRCS Eng. LRCP Lond. 1960; DObst RCOG 1964.

THWAITES, Susan Valerie Millway Medical Practice, Hartley Avenue, Mill Hill, London NW7 2HX Tel: 020 8959 0888 Fax: 020 8959 7050 — MB BS 1971 Lond.; MRCS Eng. LRCP Lond. 1971; MRCGP 1984; DObst RCOG 1973. (Char. Cross)

THWAY, Yi Histopathology Department, Chelmsford & Essex Centre, New Writtle St., Chelmsford CM2 0PT Tel: 01245 513468 Fax: 01245 513464 — MB BS 1972 Inst. Med. Rangoon; MRCPath 1983; FRCPath 1995. Cons. Pathol. Chelmsford & Essex Hosp. Socs: Internat. Acad. Path. & BMA. Prev: Regist. Shrodells Hosp. Watford; Lect. & Hon. Sen. Regist. W.m. Med. Sch. Lond.

THYNE, Douglas Hamish Scott 2nd Flat, 17 Comley Bank St, Edinburgh EH4 1AP — MB ChB 1996 Ed. SHO. (Geriats.) Edin. Socs: BMA. Prev: Surg. Ho. Off. Dumfries & Galloway Roy. Infirm. Dumfries; Med. Ho. Off. Cumbld. Infirm. Carlisle; Paediat. SHO Perth Roy. Infirm. Perth.

THYVEETIL, Mable Das Department of Histopathology, Wexham Park Hospital, Slough SL2 4HL Tel: 01753 633457; 3 Edenham Close, Lower Earley, Reading RG6 3TH Tel: 0118 966 9678 Email: 100677.1106@compuserve.com — MB BS 1983 Kerala; MB BS Kerala 1981; BSc (Zool.) Lond. 1975; MRCPath 1993. Assoc. Specialist (Histopath.) Wexham Pk. Hosp. Slough; Mem. Internat. Acad. Path. (Brit. Div.). Socs: Med. Defence Union. Prev: Staff Grade & Regist. (Histopath.) Wexham Pk. Hosp.

TIAH, Howard Anthony 7 Benson Street, Linthorpe, Middlesbrough TS5 6JQ — MB BCh BAO 1983 NUI.

TIARKS, John Christopher Grianan Surgery, Grianan, Isle of Eigg, Arisaig PH42 4RL Tel: 01687 482427 Fax: 01687 482493 — MB BChir 1964 Camb.; MA, MB Camb, 1964, BChir 1963; FRCGP 1997. (St. Thos.) GP Small Isles. Socs: BMA & Lochaber Med. Soc. Prev: SHO (Radiother.) W.m. Hosp. Lond.; Regist. (Med.) Willesden Gen. Hosp.; SHO (Med.) Croydon Gen. Hosp.

TIBBALLS, Jonathan Mark Radiology Department, Royal Free Hospital, Pond St., Hampstead, London NW3 2QG Tel: 020 78302170 Fax: 020 7830 2316 Email: jonathan.tibballs@rfh.nthames.nhs.uk — MB BS 1987 Lond.; MRCP (UK) 1990; FRCR 1994; FRACR 1998. Cons.(Radiol & Hon Sen

Lect.). Prev: SHO (Gen. Med., Neurol. & Gasteroenterol.) OldCh. Hosp. Romford.

TIBBATTS, Lucy Margaret 240 Longmore Road, Shirley, Solihull B90 3ES — BChir 1996 Camb.; MB BChir Camb. 1996; MA Camb. 1998. SHO (Gen. Med.) Norwich.

TIBBITS, John Christopher Nigel (retired) 144 Middleton Hall Road, Kings Norton, Birmingham B30 1DL Tel: 0121 458 2597 — MB ChB 1951 Birm.; MRCPsych 1971; DPM Eng. 1954. Prev: Vis. Consult. Uffculme Clinic Birm.

TIBBITT, Elizabeth Anne (retired) PO Box 52, Liskeard PL14 4YN Fax: 01579 345055 Email: frasier@freenet.co.uk — MB BCh BAO 1976 Belf.; MRCPsych 1982; T(Psychiat.) 1991. Indep. Practitioner & Cons. Psychiat. Liskeard. Prev: Cons. Psychiat. ADUR Community Ment. Health Team Worthing HA.

TIBBITTS, Adrian Richard Haytons Bent, Nett Road, Shrewton, Salisbury SP3 4HB — MB 1969 Camb.; BChir 1968. (St. Thos.) Barrister-at-Law Middle Temple. Socs: BMA. Prev: Ophth. Ho. Surg. St. Thos. Hosp.; Ho. Phys. Chapel Allerton Hosp. Leeds.

TIBBLE, Helen Clare 7 Nicholas Crescent, Fareham PO15 5AQ — MB ChB 1990 Leic.

TIBBLE, Jeremy Alexander 96 Hamlets Way, Mile End, Bow, London E3 4SY; Department of Gastroenterology, King's College Hospital, Denmark Hill, London SE5 Tel: 020 7346 6044 — MB BS 1990 Lond.; MRCP (UK) 1993; MSc (Distinction) Lond. 1999. Research Fell. (Gastroenterol.) King's Coll. Hosp. Lond. Prev: Regist. Rotat. (Gastroenterol.) King's Coll. Hosp. Lond.; SHO Rotat. (Med.) Newham Gen. Hosp.

TIBBLE, Michael John Kenneth St Peters Street Medical Practice, 16 St Peters Street, London N1 8JG Tel: 020 7226 7131 Fax: 020 7354 9120 — MB BS 1965 Lond.; MRCS Eng. LRCP Lond. 1965. (Westminster) Socs: MDU.

TIBBLE, Rachel Katherine The Quest, Bendarroch Road, West Hill, Ottery St Mary EX11 1TS — MB ChB 1992 Leic.

TIBBOTT, Christopher William Downing Street Surgery, 4 Downing Street, Farnham GU9 7NX Tel: 01252 716226 Fax: 01252 322338; Millington, 37 Echo Barn Lane, Farnham GU10 4NG Tel: 01252 716075 — MB BS 1973 Lond.; BSc (Hons.) Lond. 1970; MRCGP 1980; DRCOG 1977; AKC. (King's Coll. Hosp.)

TIBBS, Christopher Joceyln St George's Hospital, Blackshaw Road, London SW17 0QT Tel: 020 8674 1255 Fax: 020 8780 2338 Email: cjtibbs@netcomuk.co.uk; Bunchfield, Lynchmere Ridge, Haslemere GU27 3PP — MB BS 1984 Lond.; MA Oxf. 1979; FRCP 1999. (Univ. Oxf. & St. Thos. Hosp. Med. Sch.) Cons. Gastroenterol. St. Geo.'s Hosp. Lond.; Cons. Gastoenterology Qu. Mary's Roehampton. Socs: Brit. Soc. Gastroenterol.; Brit. Assn. Study Liver (Comm. Mem.); Eur. Assn. Study Liver Dis. Prev: Lect. Inst. Liver Studies King's Coll. Hosp. Lond.; Regist. (Med.) St. Richard's Hosp. Chichester & St. Thos. Hosp. Lond.

TIBBS, Mr David John, MC (retired) 31 Davenant Road, Oxford OX2 8BU Tel: 01865 515259 Fax: 01865 438344 Email: davidtibbs@compuserve.com — MB BS Lond. 1943; MA Oxf. 1965; MS Lond. 1959; FRCS Eng. 1948; MRCS Eng. LRCP Lond. 1942. Hon. Cons. Surg. John Radcliffe Hosp. Oxf. Prev: Reader (Surg.) Univ. Durh.

TIBBS, Philip Graydon North Street House Surgery, 6 North Street, Emsworth PO10 7DD Tel: 0143 373538; Mays Coppice Farm House, Rowlands Castle, Havant PO9 5NE Tel: 01705 413239 — BM BCh 1980 Oxf.; MA Oxf. 1982, BA 1977, BM Bch 1980; MRCGP 1984; DRCOG 1982. Prev: Trainee GP Portsmouth VTS; Ho. Phys. John Radcliffe Hosp. Oxf.; Ho. Surg. Roy. United Hosp. Bath.

TIBBUTT, David Arthur c/o U.P.M.B., PO Box 4121, Kampala, Uganda Tel: 00 256 41 270788 Fax: 00 256 41 341413 Email: lcme@infocom.co.ug; Perry Point, 4 Whittington Road, Worcester WR5 2JU Tel: 01905 355451 — BM BCh 1967 Oxf.; MA Oxf. 1967, DM 1977; FRCP Lond. 1983; MRCP (UK) 1971. (Oxf.) Co-ordinator for Continuing Med. Educat. Min. of Health Uganda. Socs: Brit. Cardiac Soc.; BMA; W Midl. Region Phys. Assn. Prev: Cons. Phys. Worcester Roy. Infirm.; Clin. Director (Med.) Worcester Roy. Infirm; Sen. Regist. (Gen. Med.) Radcliffe Infirm. Oxf.

TIBBY, Shane Martin Paediatric Intensive Care, Guy's Hospital, London SE1 9RT; 69 Cornhill Avenue, Hockley SS5 5BY — MB ChB 1987 Otago; MRCP (UK) 1994.

TIBREWAL, Mr Sheo Bhagwan Greenwich District Hospital, London SE10 9HE Tel: 020 8312 6099 Fax: 020 8312 6152; The Blackheath Hospital, Lee Terrace, London SE3 9UD Tel: 020 8295 5795 Fax: 020 8295 5795 — MB BS 1973; FRCS Eng. 1980; FICS 1990; T(S) 1991. Cons. Orthop. Surg. Greenwich HA. Socs: Fell. Roy. Soc. Med.; Fell. BOA; Hunt. Soc. Prev: Lect. (Orthop. Surg.) Univ. Newc.; Sen. Regist. (Orthop. Surg.) St. Bart. Hosp. Lond.; Regist. (Orthop. Surg.) Nuffield Orthop. Centre Oxf.

TIBREWAL, Suresh Prasad The Surgery, 119 Richmond Road, London E8 3AA Tel: 020 7254 2298 — MB BS 1978 Ranchi; LMSSA 1984; DRCOG 1989; DCH RCPS Glas. 1985. Prev: SHO (O & G) N. Middlx. Hosp. Lond.; SHO (A & E) Chase Farm Hosp. Enfield; SHO (Paediat.) Roy. Berks. Hosp. Reading.

TICE, Mr John William Sunley Trauma & Orthopaedic Directorate, Southampton General Hospital, Tremona Road, Southampton SO16 6YD Tel: 02380 796249; The Old Rectory, Southampton SO32 1JH Tel: 01489 860866 — MB BS 1988 Lond.; MA (Engin. Sci.) Oxf. 1983; FRCS (Tr & Orth); FRCS Eng. 1993. Cons. Orthopaedic Surg., S.ampton gen.Hosp.; Regist.Rotat (Orthop) St Geo.Hosp.Lond. Socs: Brit. Orthop. Assn.; Roy. Soc. Med.; Brit. Trauma Soc. Prev: SHO Rotat. (Surg.) St. Mary's Hosp. Lond.; Asst. Lect. (Anat.) Med. Coll. St. Bart. Hosp. Lond.; Ho. Surg. Homerton Hosp. Lond.

TICEHURST, Arthur Christopher, QHS, Maj.-Gen. late RAMC Retd. (retired) c/o Lloyds Bank Ltd, 19 Obelisk St., Camberley GU15 3SE Tel: 01249 444661 Email: arthur.ticehurst@virgin.net — MB BS 1956 Lond.; MRCS Eng. LRCP Lond. 1956; FFPHM 1990; MFCM 1977. Prev: Cdr. Med. HQ (UK) Land Forces.

TICEHURST, Henry Michael 51 Beech Road, Chorlton-cum-Hardy, Manchester M21 9FD — MB ChB 1992 Manch.

TICEHURST, Peter Rowland Ampleforth Surgery, Back Lane, Ampleforth, York YO62 4EF Tel: 01439 788215 Fax: 01439 788002; 50 Bondgate, Helmsley, York YO62 5EZ Tel: 01439 770098 — MB BS Lond. 1969; MRCS Eng. LRCP Lond. 1969. (Guy's) Med. Off. Thos. The Baker Helmsley; Med. Off. Ampleforth Coll. & Jun. Sch. Socs: Med. Off. Sch. Assn. Prev: Ho. Surg. Qu. Mary's Hosp. Sidcup; Ho. Phys. Pembury Hosp.

TICEHURST, Mr Richard Norman (retired) Kingswood, Starvecrow Lane, Peasmarsh, Rye TN31 6XN Tel: 01424 882575 — MB BChir 1943 Camb.; MChir Camb. 1952, MA, MB BChir 1943; FRCS Eng. 1948; MRCS Eng. LRCP Lond. 1942. Prev: Cons. Gen. Surg. & Urol. Hastings Gp. Hosps.

TICKLE, Caroline 22 Dunholme Road, Newcastle upon Tyne NE4 6XE — MB BS 1998 Newc.

TICKLE, Elaine Kirsty Tyn Gadlas, Waynfawr, Caernarfon LL55 4BZ Tel: 01286 650031 — MB ChB 1996 Liverp.; BSc (Hons.) Liverp.1993, MB ChB 1996. (Liverpool) SHO. (GP UTS.). Prev: MO (Gen. Duty).

TICKLE, Simon Andrew Tickle and Stubbs, 28 West Street, Earls Barton, Northampton NN6 0EW Tel: 01604 810219 Fax: 01604 810401; 142 Ardington Road, Northampton NN1 5LT Tel: 01604 635258 — MB ChB 1982 Manch.; BSc St. And. 1979; MRCGP 1987. Socs: BMA; Med. Protec. Soc. Prev: Trainee GP Chester VTS; Ho. Phys. Tameside Gen. Hosp.; Ho. Surg. Salford Roy. Hosp.

TICKTIN, Stephen Jan Flat 29 Church Garth, Pemberton Gardens, London N19 5RN — MD 1973 Toronto; MA Toronto 1969; MRCPsych 1982. Indep. Psychiat. Lond.; Vis. Lect. Sch. Psychother. & Counselling Regent's Coll. Lond. Prev: Clin. Asst. (Child & Adolesc. Psychiat.) Centr. Middlx. Hosp. Lond.; Regist. N.gate Clinic Lond.; SHO Roy. Free & Friern Hosps. Lond.

TIDBURY, Penelope Jane Dept. of Cellular Pathology, Princess margaret Hospital, Okus Road, Swindon SN1 4JU Fax: 01793 426617; 202 Old Frome Road, Bath BA2 5RH — MB BS 1980 Lond.; MRCPath 1997. Cons. Cylo and Histiopathologist. P.ss Margt. Hosp. Swindon. Prev: Sen. Regist. (Histopath.) Bloomsbury & Islington DHA; Lect. Chinese Univ. Hong Kong, Shatin.

TIDESWELL, David James Hillside, High St., Bloxham, Banbury OX15 4LT — MB BS 1998 Newc.

TIDLEY, Michael Gwyn Department of Occupational Health, Princess of Wales Hospital, Cotty Road, Bridgend CF31 — MB ChB 1989 Bristol; MFOM 1999; AFOM 1997. Cons. in Occupat.al Med., Bro Borgannwg NHS Trust, Bridgend. Socs: Soc. of Occupat.al Med.; Assn. of NHS Occupat.al Phys.s. Prev: Specialist in Occupat.al Med. - BMI Health Servs.; Specialist Regist. in Occupat.al Med. - Civil Serv./BMI Health Servs.

TIDMAN

TIDMAN, Jill Sheelagh Maureen Slateford Road Surgery, 79 Slateford Road, Edinburgh EH11 1QW Tel: 0131 313 2211; 30 Greenhill Gardens, Edinburgh EH10 4BP Tel: 0131 447 1102 — MB BS 1978 Lond.; MRCS Eng. LRCP Lond. 1977; MRCGP 1982; T(GP) 1991; DRCOG 1980. (Guy's) Prev: GP Carshalton; Trainee GP Guy's Hosp. Lond. VTS.

TIDMAN, Michael John Department of Dermatology, The Royal Infirmary, Lauriston Place, Edinburgh EH3 9YW Tel: 0131 536 2051; 30 Greenhill Gardens, Edinburgh EH10 4BP Tel: 0131 447 1102 — BSc (Hons) Lond. 1974, MD 1986, MB BS 1977; FRCP Ed. 1991; MRCP (UK) 1979; MRCS Eng. LRCP Lond. 1977. (Guy's) Cons. Dermat. Roy. Infirm. Edin. Prev: Sen. Regist. Dermat. Guy's Hosp. Lond.; MRC Train. Fell. Inst. Dermat. Lond.; Hon. Regist. St. John's Hosp. Dis. Skin Lond.

TIDMARSH, David (retired) — MB BChir Camb. 1958; MD Camb. 1977; FRCPsych 1992; DPM Eng. 1964. Prev: Cons. Psychiat. BRd.moor Hosp. Crowthorne.

TIDMARSH, Mark Douglas Cumberland Infirmary, Carlisle CA2 7HY — MB ChB 1988 Leic.; MB ChB (Hons.) Leic. 1988; BSc (Biochem.) Liverp. 1982; FRCA 1994. Regist. Rotat. (Anaesth.) Leicester & Derby; Cons. Anaesth. Carlisle. Prev: SHO Rotat. (A & E Gen. Med. & Endocrinol.) Leicester Roy. Infirm.; Ho. Off. (Surg.) P'boro. Dist. Gen. Hosp.

TIDNAM, Peter Frederick (retired) Brougham House, 7 Scotton St., Wye, Ashford TN25 5BU Tel: 01233 813582 — MB BS 1963 Lond.; MRCS Eng. LRCP Lond. 1963; FFA RCS Eng. 1971; DA Eng. 1966. Prev: Cons. Anaesth. W.m. Hosp. Lond. & Qu. Mary's Hosp. Roehampton.

TIDSWELL, Alexander Thomas 7 Plumian Way, Balsham, Cambridge CB1 6EG — MB BChir 1992 Camb.

TIDSWELL, Andrew Thomas Harrison Herbert Avenue Surgery, 268 Herbert Avenue, Poole BH12 4HY Tel: 01202 743333 Fax: 01202 738998 — MRCS Eng. LRCP Lond. 1975; DRCOG 1981. Med. Direct. (Occupat. Health) Employm. Med. Servs. Poole. Socs: Soc. Occupat Med.

TIDSWELL, Philip Royal Preston Hospital, Sharoe Green Lane N., Fulwood, Preston PR2 9HT Tel: 01772 716565 Fax: 01772 710162; 56 Stubbins Street, Ramsbottom, Bury BL0 ONL Tel: 01706 828001 Fax: 01706 828001 — MB BS 1984 Lond.; MA Camb. 1984; MRCP (UK) 1987; FRCP 1999. (Cambridge; London) Cons. Neurol. Roy. Preston Hosp. & Blackburn Roy. Infirm. Socs: Assn. Brit. Neurol.; N. Eng. Neurol. Assn. Prev: Sen. Regist. & Regist. Rotat. (Neurol.) Leeds Gen. Infirm. & St Jas. Univ. Hosp. Leeds; Research Regist. (Neurol.) Roy. Hallamsh. Hosp. Sheff.

TIDY, Colin Richard Jericho Health Centre, Walton Street, Oxford OX2 6NW Tel: 01865 311234 Fax: 01865 311087 — MB BS 1983 Lond.; MRCP (UK) 1991; MRCGP 1989; DCH RCP Lond. 1991. (Guy's) GP Oxf.

TIDY, Gerald The Portmill Surgery, 114 Queen Street, Hitchin SG4 9TH Tel: 01462 434246 — MRCS Eng. LRCP Lond. 1969. (St. Mary's) Prev: SHO (Med.) Cheltenham Gen. Hosp.; Psychiat. Resid. St. Brendan's Hosp. Bermuda; SHO (O & G) Qu. Eliz. II Hosp. Welwyn Gdn. City.

TIDY, John Anthony Clinical Sciences Centre, Northern General Hospital, Herries Road, Sheffield S5 7AU Tel: 0114 271 4745 — MB BS 1982 Lond.; BSc Lond. 1979, MD 1991; MRCOG 1989. Sen. Lect. (Gyn. Oncol.) N. Gen. Hosp. Sheff.; Clin. Fell. (Obst. & Gyn.) Beth Israel Hosp. Harvard Med. Sch. Boston, USA. Prev: Subspecialty Fell. (Gyn. Oncol.) & Sen. Regist. St. Mary's Hosp. Med. Sch. Lond.; Clin. Research Fell. Ludwig Inst. Cancer Research St. Mary's Hosp. Med. Sch. Lond.

TIEN, Paul Hak Shun 25 Winchester Road, Shirley, Southampton SO16 6UN — BM 1980 Soton.

TIERNAN, Diarmuid Gerard Mary 7 Old Town Way, Hunstanton PE36 6HE — MB BCh BAO 1982 NUI. Clin. Asst. (c/o Elderly & Rheum.) Qu. Eliz. Hosp. King's Lynn, Norf. Prev: GP Birtley, Tyne & Wear & Hunstanton, Norf.

TIERNEY, Christopher John Appleton Village Surgery, 2-6 Appleton Village, Widnes WA8 6DZ Tel: 0151 423 2990 Fax: 0151 424 1032; 28 Knowsley Road, Liverpool L19 0PG — MB ChB 1977 Manch.; MRCGP 1983; DRCOG 1979. (Manchester) Med. Adviser Liverp. FHSA.

***TIERNEY, Dawn Maria** 71 Ely Road, Littleport, Ely CB6 1HJ — MB BS 1994 Lond.

TIERNEY, Edward The Medical Centre, Market St., Whitworth, Rochdale OL12 8QS Tel: 01706 852238 Fax: 01706 853877 — LRCPI & LM, LRSCI & LM 1964; LRCPI & LM, LRCSI & LM 1964; MRCGP 1975. (RCSI) Med. Off. Buckley Hall Prison. Socs: BMA; IMA; Assn. Police Surg. Prev: Police Surgs. Rochdale; Ho. Surg. Richmond Hosp. Dub.; SHO (Anaesth.) Rochdale Hosp. Gp.

TIERNEY, Francis Benbecula Medical Practice, Griminish Surgery, Griminish, Isle of Benbecula HS7 5QA Tel: 01870 602215 Fax: 01870 602630 — MB ChB 1984 Sheff.; MRCGP 1990; DA (UK) 1991; DRCOG 1987; DFFP 1996. (Sheffield) p/t Ltd. Specialist (Anaesth.) Uist and Barra Hosp., Isle of Benbecwa. Prev: SHO (Anaesth.) Trent RHA; Trainee GP Portree I. of Skye VTS; SHO (Paediat., Gen. Med. & O & G) Highland HB.

TIERNEY, Gillian Maria 12 Stanhope St, Stanton-By-Dale, Ilkeston DE7 4QA — BM BS 1991 Nottm.; BMedSci (Hons.) Nottm. 1989; FRCS Eng. 1995; DM 1999.

TIERNEY, Jacqueline Naomi 70 The Crest, Birmingham B31 3QA — MB ChB 1993 Liverp.

TIERNEY, Mr John Department of Surgery, Hammersmith Hospital, Du Cane Road, London W12 0NN — MB BCh BAO 1987 NUI; FRCSI 1991.

TIERNEY, John Patrick 28 Regents Court, Coalisland, Dungannon BT71 4SB — MB BCh BAO 1993 Belf.

TIERNEY, Nicholas Mark 1 Wentworth Drive, Sale M33 6PW — MB ChB 1982 Manch.

TIERNEY, Patrick Brendan Clontiloret, Shawforth, Rochdale — LRCPI & LM, LRSCI & LM 1969; LRCPI & LM, LRCSI & LM 1969.

TIERNEY, Patrick Thomas Francis New Pond Row, 35 South St., Lancing BN15 8AN Tel: 01903 752265 Fax: 01903 851634 — MB BS 1975 Lond.; Cert. Prescribed Equiv. Exp. JCPTGP 1981. (Univ. Coll. Hosp.) Prev: Ho. Phys. Stoke Mandeville Hosp. Aylesbury; Ho. Surg. Univ. Coll. Hosp. Lond.

TIERNEY, Mr Paul Alexander Dept. of ENT Surgery, Southmead Hospital, Bristol — BM BCh 1989 Oxf.; FRCS (Oto-Hns) 1999; BA (Physiol.) Oxf. 1986; FRCS Eng. 1993. Cons. Ear Nose & Throat S.mead Hosp. & W.on Hosp., Bristol. Socs: BAO.

TIERNEY, Richard 71 Hangleton Road, Hove BN3 7GH — MB BS 1993 Lond.

TIFFIN, Nicholas John 3 Arthur Street, Penrith CA11 7TT — MB BCh 1995 Wales.

TIFFIN, Paul Alexander University Dept of Psychiatry, Royal Victoria Infirmary, Newcastle upon Tyne NE1 Email: p.a.tiffin@1town2.newcastle.ac.uk — MB BS 1997 Newc.; B.Med.Sci (Hons). Newc. 1994. SHO. (Psychait Rotat.) N.ern Deanery.

TIFFIN, Peter Arnold Crawford 28 Lethnot Street, Broughty Ferry, Dundee DD5 2QS — MB BS 1987 Newc.

TIGCHELAAR, Eibert Frank St James House Surgery, County Court Road, King's Lynn PE30 5SY Tel: 01553 774221 Fax: 01553 692181 — Artsexamen 1988 Rotterdam.

TIGG, Alison 25 Grummock Avenue, Ramsgate CT11 0RP — MB BS 1989 Lond.; MRCP (UK) 1995.

TIGHE, Brian Stanley 33 Honister Road, Moston, Manchester M9 4LW — MB BS 1996 Lond.; BSc (Hons) Lond. 1991; BCH Lond. 1998. (Char. Cross & Westm. Med. Sch.)

TIGHE, Jane Elizabeth Tel: 01224 681818 Fax: 01224 840714 Email: j.e.tighe@arh.grampian.scot.nhs.uk; Fax: 01224 790557 — MB BS 1985 Lond.; PhD Lond. 1995, BSc 1982; MRCP (UK) 1988; MRCPath 1995, D 1993; FRCP Ed 2000. (St. Thomas's Hospital Medical School) Cons. Haemat. Aberd. Roy. Infirm. Socs: Brit. Soc. Haematol. Prev: Sen. Regist. (Haemat.) Univ. Coll. Hosp. Lond.; MRC Research Fell. (Haemat.) RPMS Lond.; Regist. (Haemat.) Hammersmith Hosp. Lond.

TIGHE, Professor John Richard 9 Eden Park Close, Batheaston, Bath BA1 7JB Tel: 01225 859425 — MD 1962 Wales; BSc Wales 1950, MD 1962, MB BCh 1953; FRCP Lond. 1974, M 1958; FRCP Ed. 1971, M 1958; FRCPath 1975, M 1963. (Cardiff) Emerit. Prof. Histopath. Univ. Lond. Guy's and St Thomas's Hosp. Med. Sch. Socs: Fell. Roy. Soc. Med. (Ex-Pres. & Hon. Mem. Path. Sect.); Path. Soc. Gt. Brit. Prev: Prof. Histopath. UMDS Lond.; Hon. Cons. Histopath. to Army; Regist. & Vice-Pres. RCPath.

TIGHE, Karen Elaine Dept. of Anaesthetics, Leicester Royal Infirmary, Leicester LE1 5WW Email: k.tighe@ghl.trent.nhs.uk — MB ChB 1986 Manch.; DA (UK) 1989; MRCP (UK) 1990; FRCA

1993. Cons. Anaesth. Leicester Roy. Infirm. Prev: Sen. Regist. Rotat. Nottm. & E. Midl.; Regist. Derby City Hosp. & Nottm. Univ. Hosp.; Regist. (Anaesth.) Qu.s Med. Centre Univ. Hosp. Nottm.

TIGHE, Mary Department of Haematology, Musgrove Park Hospital, Taunton TA1 5DA Tel: 01823 271049; 22 Holway Avenue, Taunton TA1 3AR Tel: 01823 271049 — MB ChB 1973 Ed.; MRCP (UK) 1978; DRCOG 1976. Assoc. Specialist (Haemat. & Oncol.) Taunton & Som. NHS Trust. Prev: Med. Off. Taunton & Som. Hosp. MusGr. Pk. Br. Married Wom. Doctors Retainer Scheme; SHO Taunton & Som. Hosp. (MusGr. Pk. Br.); Ho. Off. Norf. & Norwich Hosp. & W. Norwich Hosp.

TIGHE, Michael Richard Woodlands House, West Norwich Hospital, Bowthorpe Road, Norwich — MB BS 1984 Lond.; MD Lond. 1994; MRCP (UK) 1987.

TIGHE, Nicola Jane The Coach House, South Woodville, St Margarets Rd, Altrincham WA14 2AW — MB ChB 1997 Liverp.

TIGHE, Robert John (retired) 1 Law Court, Wygate Park, Spalding PE11 3FG Tel: 01775 767322 — MRCS Eng. LRCP Lond. 1946. Prev: Ho. Surg. Gen. Hosp. Birm.

TIGHE, Sean Quentin Miles, Surg. Cdr. RN Retd. Anaesthetic Department, Countess of Chester Hospital NHS Trust, Chester CH2 1UL Tel: 01244 365461 Fax: 01244 365435; 38 Glan Aber Park, Chester CH4 8LF Tel: 01244 683086 Email: sean_tighe@msn.com — MB BS 1978 Lond.; MRCS Eng. LRCP Lond. 1978; FFA RCS Eng. 1984. (Guy's) Cons. Anaesth. Countess of Chester Hosp. NHS Trust. Socs: Intens. Care Soc.; Assn. Anaesth.; BMA. Prev: Cons. Anaesth. & Head Dept. RNH Plymouth; Cons. Anaesth. & Sen. Lect. RNH Haslar; Hon. Sen. Regist. Glas. Roy. Infirm.

TIGHE, Shelagh Maureen (retired) 9 Eden Park Close, Batheaston, Bath BA1 7JB — MD Sheff. 1963, MB ChB 1952; FRCP Lond. 1977, M 1958; MRCS Eng. LRCP Lond. 1952; DCH Eng. 1954. Prev: Cons. Dermat. Ashford Hosp. Middlx. & Teddington Memor.

TIJSSELING, Andreas Charles Ferryhill Medical Practice, Durham Road, Ferryhill DL17 8JJ Tel: 01740 651238 — Artsexamen 1986 Amsterdam. (Amsterdam) GP Ferryhill, Co. Durh.; Clin. Asst. Dermat. BAG Hosp. (p/t).

TILAK-SINGH, Deepa C-7 Maryfield Terrace, Dumfries DG1 4UG — MB BS 1987 Poona.

TILBURY, Jonathan Gregory 104 Strathmore Avenue, Coventry CV1 2AF — MB ChB 1975 Birm.

TILDESLEY, Geoffrey Cadzowbank, 19 Coniscliffe Road, Hartlepool TS26 0BT — MB ChB 1962 Birm.; MRCP Lond. 1966; FRCP Lond. 1982, M 1966. Cons. Phys. Hartlepool Gp. Hosps. Prev: Sen. Regist. (Gen. Med.) Welsh Hosp. Bd. & United Cardiff Hosps.; Ho. Phys. Qu. Eliz. Hosp. Birm.

TILDSLEY, Gemma Jane Department of Histopathology, Princess Royal Hospital, Lewes Road, Haywards Heath RH16 — MB BS 1984 Lond.; MRCPath 1991. (Westm.) Cons. Histopath. P.ss Roy. Hosp. Haywards Health Sussex.

TILEY, Christopher George Westchester, Huntingdon Road, Cambridge CB3 0LG Tel: 01223 276331 — MB BS 1992 Lond.; BSc Lond. 1989; MRCP (UK) 1996.

TILEY, June Elizabeth 5 Sandybrook Close, Fulwood, Preston PR2 5QX — MB ChB 1983 Liverp. Clin. Asst. (Child & Adolesc. Psychiat. & Drug Abuse) Preston & Blackburn. Prev: Regist. (Psychiat.) Preston HA.

TILEY, Michael John Harperhall, Elsrickle, Biggar ML12 6QZ — MB ChB 1973 Aberd.; DObst RCOG 1976.

TILFORD, Maureen Patricia Tilford, Preston and Burrell, Health Centre, Lawson Road, Norwich NR3 4LE Tel: 01603 427096 Fax: 01603 403704; Mulberry House, 3 Newmarket Road, Cringleford, Norwich NR4 6UE Tel: 01603 504710 — MB ChB 1972 Glas.; Cert. Family Plann. JCC 1988. Socs: Doctor-Healer Network; Brit. Soc. for Med. & Dent. Hypn. Prev: Trainee GP Twickenham; SHO (Cas.) W. Middlx. Hosp.; SHO (Paediat.) Hillingdon Hosp. Middlx.

TILFORD, Trevor John (retired) 12 Newmarket Road, Cringleford, Norwich NR4 6UE Tel: 01603 452540 — MB BS 1965 Lond.; MRCS Eng. LRCP Lond. 1964; DObst RCOG 1968. Prev: GP Norwich.

TILL, Mr Anthony Stedman (retired) Holwell House, Burford, Oxford OX18 4JS Tel: 0199 382 3162 — MB BChir 1936 Camb.; MA Oxf. 1957; MA Camb. 1936, MChir 1947; FRCS Eng. 1936; MRCS Eng. LRCP Lond. 1934. Prev: Temp. Maj. RAMC.

TILL, Arthur Michael Hadwen Medical Practice, Glevum Way Surgery, Abbeydale, Gloucester GL4 4BL Tel: 01452 529933; Yew Trees, 12 Larkspear Close, Gloucester GL1 5LN Tel: 01452 525141 — MB BS 1962 Lond.; DObst RCOG 1964. (Middlx.) Prev: Ho. Surg. (ENT) Middlx. Hosp. Lond.; Ho. Off. (O & G) Roy. Lancaster Infirm.; Maj. RAMC (Specialist O & G).

TILL, Christopher Brian Wright The Chase, Highknott Road, Arnside, Carnforth LA5 0AW — BM 1987 Soton.; FRCA 1993. Cons. Anaesth. Lancaster Acute NHS Trust. Socs: Manch. Med. Soc.; Intens. Care Soc.

TILL, Janice Anne Department of Paediatrics, Royal Brompton Hospital, Sydney St., London SW3 6NP Tel: 020 7351 8546 Fax: 020 7351 8622; 179 Engadine Street, Southfields, London SW18 5DU — MB BS 1982 Lond.; BSc (Immunity & Infec.) Lond. 1979; MD Lond. 1994. (St Bart. Hosp. Med. Sch.) Cons. Paediat. Electrophysiol. Roy. Brompton & Harefield NHS Trust; Hon. Sen. Lect. Nat. Heart & Lung Inst. Socs: BMA; Paediat. Electrophysiol. Gp.; N. Amer. Pacing & Electrophysiol. Gp. Prev: Research Regist. (Paediat. Cardiol.) Brompton Hosp. Lond.; Lect. (Paediat. Electrophysiol.) Roy. Brompton Hosp.

TILL, Mr Kenneth Reed's Court, Lydeard St Lawrence, Taunton TA4 3RX Tel: 01984 667388 Fax: 01984 667388 Email: 106036.3500@compuserve.com — MB BChir Camb. 1946; MA Camb. 1945; FRCS Eng. 1953; MRCS Eng. LRCP Lond. 1944; Hon. FRCPCH. (St. Geo.) Hon. Cons. Neurol. Surg. Hosp. Sick Childr. Gt. Ormond St. & Univ. Coll. Hosp. Lond.; Hon. Civil Cons. RAF. Socs: Internat. Soc. Paediat. Neurosurg.; Soc. Brit. Neurol. Surgs.; Internat. Assoc. Mem. Amer. Assn. of Neurol. Surg. Prev: Neurol. Surg. Univ. Coll. Hosp. Lond.; Sen. Regist. (Neurosurg.), Cas. Off. & Res. Anaesth. St. Geo. Hosp.

TILL, Morwenna Margaret (retired) Reed's Court, Lydeard St Lawrence, Taunton TA4 3RX Tel: 01984 667388 Fax: 01984 667388 Email: 106036.3500@compuserve.com — MB BChir Camb. 1944; BA Camb. 1941; DCH Eng. 1946. Prev: Sen. Research Fell. (Haemat.) Inst. Child Health Lond. Clin. Research.

TILL, Noorjahan (retired) 26A Campbell Road, Southsea PO5 1RN Tel: 01705 817732 — MB BS 1966 Bihar; MB AcC Brit. Coll. Acupunc. Lond. 1995; DPM Eng. 1979. Prev: Assoc. Specialist St. Jas. Hosp. Portsmouth.

TILL, Richard James Ashley Roundhay Road Surgery, 209 Roundhay Road, Leeds LS8 4HQ Tel: 0113 249 0504 Fax: 0113 248 0330 — MB ChB 1965 Leeds; DObst RCOG 1967. (Leeds)

TILL, Richard John Wright 17 Upper Pines, Banstead SM7 3PU — MB ChB 1981 Birm.

TILL, Sarah Johanne 174 Stallington Road, Blythe Bridge, Stoke-on-Trent ST11 9PA — MB BCh 1995 Wales.

TILL, Simon Harold Royal Hallamshire Hospital, Department of Rheumatology, Beech Hill Road, Sheffield S10 2JF Tel: 0114 271 1941 Fax: 0114 271 1844 Email: s.till@sheffield.ac.uk; 7 Grove Road, Dore, Sheffield S17 4DJ — MB ChB 1989 Sheff.; MRCP (UK) 1992. Cons. (Rheum & Sport Med.). Prev: Sen Regist. (Gen. Med. & Rheum.) Chesterfield Roy. Hosp.

TILLEARD-COLE, Professor Richard Reginald Rupert, OBE, Col. colonel Professor R.R.R. Tilleard-Cole, (cons. rooms), 5 Walton St., Oxford OX1 2HG Tel: 01865 554754; Roubartelle Abbas, Clifton Hampden, Abingdon OX14 3EQ Tel: 01865 407722 — MA 1954 Oxford; BM BCh 1954 Oxford; FRCPsych 1976 M.1971; BA 1950 Oxford; DPM 1960 London. (Oxf., St. Bart., Brunswick & Hanover) Cons. Psychiat. & Dir. Oxf. Inst. Psychiat. Oxf.; Hon. Cons. St. And. Hosp. N.ampton; May & Baker Prof. Psychiat. & Hon. Fell. Worcester Coll. Oxf. (Oxf.); Pres. Oxf. Postgrad. Fell.sh. of Psychiat.; Dep. Hon. Col. & Master Oxf. Univ. Off's Train. Corps.; Pres.; Tilleard-Cole Med. Soc. Worcester Coll. Oxf. Socs: Liveryman Soc. of Apoth. Lond.; Fell. Brit. Soc. Med. & Dent. Hypn.; Oxf. Soc. Of Med. Prev: Tutor (Neuro-Anat.) Univ. Oxf. (Worcester Coll.); Psychiat. Warneford Hosp. Oxf.; Col. Wilts. Regt.

TILLER, Gillian 79 Grayswood Drive, Mytchett, Camberley GU16 6AS — MB BS 1981 Lond.

TILLER, Jane Margaret South London & Mandsley NHS Trust, Denmak House, London SE5 8AZ — MB ChB 1986 Glas.; MRCPsych. Cons. Adult Psychiat. & Clin. Direct. S.rah. Prev: Researcher & Hon. Sen. Regist. (Psychiat.) Inst. Psychiat. Lond.

TILLETT

TILLETT, Angela Jane 17 St Bernard Road, Colchester CO4 4LE Tel: 01206 845103 Email: lawr@globalnet.co.uk; 39 Ettrick Haugh Road, Selkirk TD7 5AX Tel: 01206 742158 — MB BS 1987 Lond.; MRCGP 1994; DCH RCP Lond. 1992; DRCOG 1991; MRCP (UK) 1994. Prev: Regist. (Paediat.) Ipswich Hosp.

TILLETT, David Robin Fraser Bennett House, Coombe Park, Kingston upon Thames KT2 7JB Tel: 020 8546 5983 Fax: 020 8547 3603 — MRCS Eng. LRCP Lond. 1962; FFA RCS Eng. 1971; DA Eng. 1969. (St. Geo.) United Kingdom Progr. Director Amer. Univeristy of The Caribbean, St Maarten Netherland Antilles. Socs: BMA. Prev: Sen. Regist. (Anaesth.) St. Thos. Hosp. Lond.; Regist. (Anaesth.) St. Mary's Hosp. Portsmouth & Roy. Childr. Hosp. & Roy. Wom. Hosp. Melb.; Cons. Anaesth. Kingston Hosp.

TILLETT, Richard Ian Laccohee Wonford House Hospital, Exeter EX2 5AF Tel: 01392 403446 — MB BS Lond. 1969; MRCPsych 1977; FRCPsych 1998. Cons. Psychiat. & Psychother. Exeter & Dist. Community NHS Trust. Prev: Sen. Regist. (Psychiat.) Glenside Hosp. Bristol.

TILLEY, Alison Jane Dept. of Occupational Health, Whitefriars, Leurins Nead, Bristol BS1 2NT Tel: 01179 282223 — MB BS 1988 Lond.; DOM 1999; MRCGP 1994; DRCOG 1993. (Middlx. Hosp. Med. Sch.) p/t Clin. Asst. in Occupat.al Health. Prev: Locum GP Bristol.

TILLEY, Elisabeth Ann Turret Lodge, 29 Slipper Road, Emsworth PO10 8BS; Turret Lodge, 32 Havant Road, Emsworth PO10 7JG — BSc (2nd cl. Hons. Physiol.) Lond. 1977, MB BS 1980; MRCP (UK) 1983; FRCR 1986. (St. Mary's) Cons. Radiol. Qu. Alexandra Hosp. Portsmouth. Prev: Sen. Regist. (Radiol.) St. Geo. Hosp. Lond.

TILLEY, Emma Jane Westcourt, 12 The Street, Rustington, Littlehampton BN16 3NX Tel: 01903 784311 Fax: 01903 850907; 6 Ruston Park, Rustington, Littlehampton BN16 2AB Tel: 01903 775487 — MB BS 1988 Lond.; DRCOG 1994; DCH RCP Lond. 1993. (St. Bart. Hosp. Med. Coll.) GP. Socs: BMA. Prev: Regist. (Med. Diabetes & Endocrinol.) Worcester Roy. Infirm.; SHO (Paediat.) Cheltenham Gen. Hosp.

TILLEY, James Howey MacDonald (retired) 7 The Avenue, Nunthorpe, Middlesbrough TS7 0AA Tel: 01642 316412 — MB BChir Camb. 1944; MA (Hons. Chem.) Camb. 1938; MFCM 1973; DPH Liverp. 1946. Prev: Area Specialist (Pub. Health Med.) Cleveland HA.

TILLEY, Jane Anne Appleby House, Kingston Bagpuize, Abingdon OX13 5AP — MB BCh 1995 Wales.

TILLEY, Jane Marie Flat B, 3 Manstone Road, Cricklewood, London NW2 3XH — MB BS 1994 Lond. Socs: Med. Defence Union; BMA.

TILLEY, John Stewart The Surgery, 35 Great Pulteney Street, Bath BA2 4BY Tel: 01225 464187 Fax: 01225 485305 — MB BS 1975 Lond.; MRCS Eng. LRCP Lond. 1974; MRCGP 1990.

TILLEY, Marelle Margaret Ellen Motherwell Health Centre, 138-144 Windmill Street, Motherwell ML1 1TB Tel: 01698 266688 Fax: 01698 253230; 1 Thanes Gate, Bothwell, Glasgow G71 7HS — MB ChB 1986 Glas.; MRCGP 1992; DRCOG 1991. Socs: BMA.

TILLEY, Nicola Jane 226 Barton Road, Kettering NN15 6RZ — MB ChB 1992 Birm.

TILLEY, Peter John Boston Neurology Department, Middlesbrough General Hospital, Middlesbrough TS5 5AZ Tel: 01642 850222 — MB BS 1967 Newc.; FRCP Lond. 1984; MRCP (U.K.) 1971. (Newc.) Cons. Neurol. N. RHA. Socs: BMA & Assn. Brit. Neurol. Prev: Sen. Regist. (Neurol.) Newc. Gen. Hosp.; Fell. (Neurol.) Mayo Clinic Rochester USA; Regist. (Neurol.) Roy. Vict. Infirm. Newc.

TILLEY, Rebecca Elizabeth 21 Ireton Road, Colchester CO3 3AT Tel: 01206 543423 — MB BS 1996 Lond.; BSc (Hons.) Hist. Med. Lond. 1993. (Univ. Coll. Lond.)

TILLEY, Rosalinde Caron 15 Bellew Street, Tooting, London SW17 0AD Tel: 020 8946 6053 Fax: 0870 054 8423 Email: ros@bellew.demon.co.uk — MB BS (Hons.) Lond. 1992; BSc (Sociol. Appl. Med. & Basic Med. Sci.) Lond. 1989; FRCA 1998. Specialist Regist. (Anaesth.) S. W. Thames Rotat. Socs: Intens. Care Soc.; Anaesth. Assn.; Obst. Anaesth. Assn. Prev: Regist. & SHO (ITU) Roy. Brompton Hosp. Lond.; SHO (Respirat. Med.) Roy. Brompton Hosp. Lond.; SHO (Anaesth.) Whittington Hosp. Lond.

TILLING, Keith John (retired) Tregate, West End, Cholsey, Wallingford OX10 9LW — MB BS 1955 Lond.; MRCPsych 1971; DPM Eng. 1959. Prev: Cons. Psychiat. Fair Mile Hosp. Wallingford & Roy. Berks. Hosp. Reading & Eldon Day Hosp. Reading.

TILLMAN, David McGill Department of Dermatology, Western Infirmary, Dumbarton Road, Glasgow G11 6NT — MB ChB 1981 Glas.; PhD (Biochem.) Glas. 1976; FRCP Glas. 1994; MRCP (UK) 1984. Sen. Lect. (Dermat.) Univ. Glas.; Hon. Cons. (Dermat.) Gtr. Glas. HB. Prev: Regist. (Dermat.) W. Infirm. Glas.; Clin. Scientist/Hon. Med. Regist. MRC Blood Pressure Unit. W.. Infirm. Glas.

TILLMAN, Mr Roger Michael Royal Orthopaedic Hospital, Bristol Road S., Northfield, Birmingham B31 2AP Tel: 0121 685 4150 Fax: 0121 685 4146 — MB ChB 1984 Manch.; FRCS (Orth.) 1993; FRCS Ed. 1988. Cons. Orthop. Surg. Roy. Orthop. Hosp. Birm.; Hon. Sen. Clin. Lect. in Surg. Univ. of Birm. Socs: Brit. Orthop. Oncol. Soc.; Brit. Assn. Surg. Knee; Brit. Orthop. Assoc. Prev: Sen. Regist. Wrightington Hosp., Roy. Preston Hosp. & Manch. Roy. Infirm.; Demonst. (Anat.) Univ. Bristol.

TILLOTSON, Doreen Mary (retired) Flat 28, Dukes Drive, Leicester LE2 1TP Tel: 0116 270 4435 — MB ChB 1928 Leeds. Prev: Sch. Med. Off. Leicester City.

TILLOTT, Rebecca Claire 63 Illingworth, Windsor SL4 4UP — MB ChB 1998 Manch.

TILLSON, Christopher Bodnant Surgery, Menai Avenue, Bangor LL57 2HH Tel: 01248 364567 Fax: 01248 370654 — MB BS 1976 Lond.; DRCOG Lond. 1981; MRCGP Lond. 1981 FP Cert. 1981. (St. Thos.)

TILLU, Abhay Bhalchandra 61 Staff Residences, James Paget Hospital, Lowestoft Road, Great Yarmouth NR31 6LA — MB BS 1984 Bombay; MB BS Bombay India 1984.

TILLY, Adam 72 Northumberland Avenue, Gidea Park, Hornchurch RM11 2HP — MB BS 1986 Lond.; DCH RCP Lond. 1992. (St. Bart. Hosp. Med. Sch.) Staff Grade (Community Child Health) City & Hackney HA. Socs: Brit. Assn. of Community Doctors in Audiol.; Brit. Soc. of Audiol. Prev: SHO (Paediat.) OldCh. Hosp.; SHO (Paediat.) Riverside H.A.; SHO (Paediat.) Char. Cross Hosp. Lond.

TILLY, Helen Victoria Saffrons, Gables Road, Church Crookham, Fleet GU52 6QZ Tel: 01252 621430 — MB BS 1988 Lond.

TILNEY, Henry Simon St Richards Hospital, Spitalfield Lane, Chichester PO19 4SE; Rowlane Farm House, Rowlane, Dunsden, Reading RG4 9PT Tel: 01189 472392 — MB BS 1997 Lond. (St Barts, London) SHO. (Surg Rotat.) St Richards Hosp, Chichester.

TILSED, Mr Jonathan Victor Thomas 15 Cross Road, Wimbledon, London SW19 1PL Email: j.v.tilsed@mds.qmw.ac.uk — MB BS 1988 Lond.; FRCS Eng. 1993; FRCG (Gen Surg) 1999. (St. Mary's) Clin. Lect. (Surg.) St Bart. & The Roy. Lond. Sch. ofMed.and Dent.; Hon. Specialist Regist. (Gen. Surg.) Roy. Lond. Hosps. NHS Trust. Socs: Fell. Roy. Soc. Med.; Affil. Fell. Assn. Surg. GB & Irel.; Assoc. Fell. Assoc. of ColoProctol. GB & Irel. Prev: RCS Research Fell. Inst. of Cancer Research; Specialist Regist. (Gen. Surg.) SE Thames Regional Higher Train. Scheme; SHO Rotat. (Surg.) Leicester.

TILSEN, Elizabeth Mary (retired) Priors Gate, 92B Tettenhall Road, Wolverhampton WV6 0BX — MB ChB 1954 Birm.; MRCP Lond. 1966; DCH Eng. 1958; DObst RCOG 1956. Prev: Sen. Regist. & Cons. Phys. (Geriat. Med.) New Cross Hosp. Wolverhampton.

TILSLEY, David William Owen 15 Greenways, Beckenham BR3 3NG — MB BS 1983 Lond.

TILSLEY, George Nigel Wykeham (retired) Dodington House, Dodington, Nether Stowey, Bridgwater TA5 1LF Tel: 01278 741238 — MB ChB 1952 Sheff.; MRCS Eng. LRCP Lond. 1952. Prev: GP Sheff.

TILSLEY, Timothy Mark Mill Street Surgery, Mill Street, North Petherton, Bridgwater TA6 6LX Tel: 01278 662223 Fax: 01278 663727; Dodington House, Dodington, Nether Stowey, Bridgwater TA5 1LF — MB ChB 1982 Sheff. Clin. Forens. Phys. Som. Prev: Trainee GP Milnthorpe VTS; SHO (Geriat.) Lancaster Roy. Infirm.; SHO (Orthop. & Cas.) Roy. Hallamsh. Hosp. Sheff.

TILSTON, Mr Michael Paul Grimbsy Health NHS Trust, Scartho Road, Grimsby DN33 2BA Tel: 01472 874111; Brinkhill House, Main St, Fulstow, Louth LN11 0XF — MB BS 1980 Lond.; FRCS Ed. 1984. Cons. Surg. Grimsby Gen. Hosp.

TILSTON, Stephanie Jane The Coach House, Braeside Gardens, York YO24 4EZ — MB ChB 1998 Dund.

TILZEY, Anthea Jane Department of Virology, St Thomas' Hospital, London SE1 7EH Tel: 020 7922 8167 Fax: 020 7922

8387 — MB BS 1978 Lond.; MA Oxf. 1980; MRCP (UK) 1983. Cons. (Virol.) Guys & St. Thos. Trust Lond.; Hon. Sen. Lect. United Med. & Dent. Schs. Guy's & St Thos. Hosp. Socs: Eur. Soc. Clin. Virol.; Soc. Gen. Microbiol. Prev: Assoc. Specialist (virol.) Guys & St. Thos. Trust. Lond.; Sen. Regist. (Virol.) St. Thos. Hosp. Lond.; Regist. (Med. & Genitourin Med.) St. Thos. Hosp. Lond.

TILZEY, Susan Elizabeth 42 Corrance Road, London SW2 5RH — MB 1985 Camb.; BChir 1984.

TIMANS, Anita Rita Psycological therapies service, Leonard lodge, Leonard rd, Croydon Tel: 020 8700 8832; 129 Auckland Rise, London SE19 2DY Tel: 020 8653 7958 — MB BS 1984 Lond.; MRCPsych 1990. Cons. Psychotherapist S. Lond. & Muadsley NHS trust. Socs: Hon. Mem. Latvian Psychiat. Assn. Prev: Sen. Regist. (Psychother.) Pathfinder Trust Springfield Hosp. Tooting Bec; Sen. Regist. (Psychiat.) St. Geo.'s Hosp. Lond.; Regist. & SHO Rotat. (Psychiat.) St. Geo. Hosp. Lond.

TIMBERLAKE, Anthony Herbert 13 Shrubbery Avenue, Worcester WR1 1QN — MB ChB 1962 Birm.

TIMBERLAKE, Carolyne Marie Foxleigh, Kings End, Powick, Worcester WR2 4RA — MB BS 1989 Lond.

TIMBERLAKE, Timothy The Gate House, 54-56 Pinewood Road, Ferndown BH22 9RR; Orchard Farm, Leigh Common, Wincanton BA9 8LF Tel: 01747 841207 Fax: 01747 840088 Email: timothytimberlake@aol.com — MB BS Lond. 1966; MRCS Eng. LRCP Lond. 1966; DObst RCOG 1968. (Westm.) Sen. Med. Assoc. Eurodor Ltd.; Lect. SeleroTher. E. Midl.s Coll.; Lect. SeleroTher.. The Glace Sch. Socs: GP Writers Assn. Prev: Sen. Partner, Tumberlake. Blackurore, Ladd, Jenkins, W. Moors, Dorest.; Med. Off. i/c Troops Petroleum Centre W. Moors; Resid. Obst. Asst. Kingston Hosp.

TIMBURY, Morag Crichton (retired) 22 Monckton Court, Strangways Terrace, Holland Park Road, London W14 8NF Tel: 020 7602 3345 — MB ChB 1953 Glas.; FRSE 1979; PhD Glas. 1966, MD 1960; FRCP Lond. 1994; FRCP Glas. 1974, M 1972; FRCPath 1976, M 1964. Prev: Dir. Centr. Pub. Health Laborat. Lond.

TIMLIN, Clive Edward Underwood Surgery, 139 St. Georges Road, Cheltenham GL50 3EQ Tel: 01242 580644 Fax: 01242 253519; 2 Yew Tree Close, Shipton Oliffe, Cheltenham GL54 4JT — MB BS 1972 Lond. (St. Mary's)

TIMLIN, Mark Andrew 35 Northwick Avenue, Kenton, Harrow HA3 0AA — BM 1995 Soton.

TIMLIN, Nicholas Anthony Patrick 96 Drummond Terrace, North Shields NE30 2AG — MB ChB 1984 Manch.; DCH RCP Lond. 1988. SHO (O & G) N. Tyneside Gen. Hosp. N. Shields. Prev: SHO (Community Paediat.) N. Tyneside Gen. Hosp. N. Shields; SHO (Psychiat.) S. Shields Gen. Hosp.; Ho. Surg. & Ho. Phys. N. Manch. Gen. Hosp.

TIMMINS, Alan James H.M. Young Offenders Centre, Glen Parva, Tigers Road, Wigston, Leicester LE18 4TN — MB ChB 1974 Birm. Sen. Med. Off. Health Care Serv. for Prisoners Wigston. Prev: Regist. & SHO (Psychiat.) Highcroft Hosp. Birm.; Ho. Phys. Birm. Gen. Hosp.

TIMMINS, Andrew Clive 18 Willoughby Road, Chelmsford CM2 6UT — MB ChB 1981 Birm.

TIMMINS, Bryan Christopher Kemsley Division, National Centre for Brain Injury Rehabilitation, St Andrews Hospital, Billing Road, Northampton NN1 5DG Tel: 01604 629696 Email: woodforrdmanor@aol.com — MB ChB 1986 Leeds; MRCP (UK) 1996; MRCPsych 1992. (Leeds) Cons. (Brain Injury Rehabil.) Kemsley Unit, N.ampton. Prev: Cons. DKMH Catterick, N. Yorks.; Regist. Posts Cardiol. QEMH Lond.; Sen. Specialist (Psychiat.) QEMH Lond. & Maudsley Hosp. Lond.

TIMMINS, David John Grant Southwell House Surgery, Southwell House, Back Lane, Rochford SS4 1AY Tel: 01702 545241 Fax: 01702 546390; Botelers, Hall Road, Rochford SS4 1NN Tel: 01702 545241 — MB BS 1970 Lond.; FRCGP 1985, M 1975; DFFP 1993; DObst RCOG 1974; Cert. Family Plann. RCOG & RCGP 1974. (Middlx.)

TIMMINS, Derek John 8 Douglas Road, West Kirby, Wirral CH48 6EB; Royal Liverpool and Broadgreen University Hospital, Prescot St, Liverpool L7 8XP Tel: 0151 706 2630 Fax: 0151 706 5821 — MB ChB 1977 Liverp.; LLM 1999 Cardiff; MBA 2000 Open; FRCP 1999 Ed; Dip. Occ. Med. 1998; FRCP Lond. 1995; MRCP (UK) 1985; MFFP 1996; MRCGP 1982; DRCOG 1982; Dip. Psychosexual Med. 1997; Cert. Family Plann. JCC 1982; Dip. Ven.

Liverp. 1986. (Liverp.) Cons. Phys. Liverp. HA; Hon. Lect. (Genitourin Med.) Univ. Liverp. Socs: Med. Soc. Study VD; Brit. Soc. of Colposcopists; Counc. Memb. MSSVD 2001-2004. Prev: Sen. Regist. (Genito-urin. Med.) Middlx. Hosp. Lond.

TIMMINS, S F Newington Road Surgery, 100 Newington Road, Ramsgate CT12 6EW Tel: 01843 595951 Fax: 01843 853387 — Artsexamen 1991 Utrecht; Artsexamen 1991 Utrecht.

TIMMINS, William Leonard (retired) Roswen, 22 Western Terrace, Falmouth TR11 4QP Tel: 01326 314922 — MB BS 1950 Lond.; MRCS Eng. LRCP Lond. 1949; DObst RCOG 1951; MRCGP 1968. Prev: Ho. Surg. St. Bart. Hosp.

TIMMIS, Adam David London Chest Hospital, Bonner Road, London E2 9JX Tel: 020 8983 2413 Fax: 020 8983 2279; 19 Lonsdale Square, London N1 1EN Tel: 020 7607 6410 — MD 1983 Camb.; MA Camb. 1975, MD 1983, MB 1974, BChir 1973; FRCP Lond. 1993; MRCP (UK) 1976; FESC 1994. Cons. Cardiolroy.Hosp.NHS Trust Lond.; Hon. Sen. Lect. Lond. Hosp. Med. Sch. Socs: Brit. Cardiac Soc. Prev: Sen. Regist. (Cardiol.) Guy's Hosp. Lond.; Research Fell. Massachusett's Gen. Hosp. Boston, USA; Regist. (Cardiol.) King's Coll. Hosp. Lond.

TIMMIS, Christopher Grant Eastcote Health Centre, Abbotsbury Gardens, Eastcote, Pinner, Ruislip HA5 1TG Tel: 020 8866 0121 Fax: 020 8866 8382; 54 Waxwell Lane, Pinner HA5 3EN — MB 1977 Camb.; BChir 1976; MA Camb. 1976; MRCGP 1983; DRCOG 1981. GP Trainer Pinner. Socs: Roy. Coll. Gen. Pract.

TIMMIS, John Benjamin 12 Ringwood Avenue, London N2 9NS — MB BS 1975 Lond.; FRCR 1982; DMRD Eng. 1982. Cons. (Radiol.) Whittington & Roy. N. Hosps. Lond.

TIMMIS, Paul Kenneth 54A Victoria Park Road, London E9 7NB Tel: 020 8533 5986 — MB ChB 1986 Sheff.; DA (UK) 1992; FRCA 1994. Cons. Anaesth. Whipps Cross Hosp. Lond. Prev: Regist. Rotat. (Anaesth.) St. Bartholomews Hosp. Lond.; SHO (Med.) Hereford Co. Hosp.; SHO (Anaesth.) Colchester.

TIMMIS, Mr Peter (retired) Cherry Trees, Shootersway Lane, Berkhamsted HP4 3NP Tel: 01442 863727 — MB BS 1948 Lond.; FRCS Eng. 1954; MRCS Eng. LRCP Lond. 1946. Prev: Cons. ENT Surg. Luton & Dunstable Hosp. & W. Herts. Hosp. Hemel Hempstead.

TIMMIS, Robert Gerald The Hadleigh Practice, Hadleigh House, 20 Kirkway, Broadstone BH18 8EE Tel: 01202 692269; 4 Wickham Drive, Corfe Mullen, Wimborne BH21 3JT — MB BS 1988 Lond.; MRCGP 1992; DRCOG 1991. (Univ. Coll. & Middlx. Sch. Med.) Prev: Trainee GP Brighton HA VTS; Ho. Off. (Med.) Mt. Vernon Hosp.; Ho. Off. (Surg.) Stoke Mandeville Hosp.

TIMMONS, James Anthony 76 Caledonia Road, Saltcoats KA21 5AP — MB ChB 1974 Glas.; DRCOG 1976.

TIMMONS, Maria Therese Grace No.8 Dovecote Farm, Waldridge Lane, Chester-le-Street DH2 2NQ — MB BCh BAO 1983 NUI.

TIMMONS, Mr Michael John Department of Plastic Surgery, Bradford Royal Infirmary, Bradford BD9 6RJ — MB BChir 1974 Camb.; MChir Camb. 1988, MA 1974; MB Camb. 1974, BChir (Distinc. Obst. & Gyn.) 1973; FRCS Eng. 1978. (Camb. & Guy's) Cons. Plastic Surg. Bradford & Airedale NHS Trusts. Socs: Brit. Soc. Surg. Hand; Brit. Assn. Plastic Surg. Prev: Regist. (Surg.) Addenbrooke's Hosp. Camb.; Regist. (Plastic Surg.) Mt. Vernon Hosp. N.wood; Sen. Regist. (Plastic Surg.) Leeds & Bradford HAs.

TIMMONS, Michael Joseph London Road Medical Practice, 12 London Road, Kilmarnock KA3 7AD Tel: 01563 523593 Fax: 01563 573552 — MB ChB 1981 Ed.; MSc Glas. 1973, BSc 1969; BSc (Med. Sci.) St. And. 1978; DRCOG 1983. Lect. (Aviat. Med.) Brit. Aerospace Flying Coll. Prestwick; Clin. Asst. (Cardiol.) CrossHo. Hosp. Kilmarnock. Socs: Assoc. Mem. RCGP.; BMA. Prev: Regist. (Geriat. Med.) N. Ayrsh. Dist. Gen. Hosp.; SHO (Orthop., A & E) N. Ayrsh. Dist. Gen. Hosp.; SHO (Paediat.) N. Ayrsh. Dist. Gen. Hosp.

TIMMS, Celia Mary Joyce West Pikefish Farmhouse, Pike Fish La, Laddingford, Maidstone ME18 6BH — MB ChB 1997 Bristol.

TIMMS, Damian Patrick 4 Park Crescent, Emsworth PO10 7EA — MB ChB 1976 Bristol; MRCGP 1984; DRCOG 1982; DA Eng. 1981. Regist. (Anaesth.) RN. Hosp. Haslar. Prev: Regist. (Anaesth.) Qu. Alexandra's Hosp. Cosham; SHO (Cas.) RN Hosp. Haslar Gosport.

TIMMS, Ian George Oliver The Basement Flat, 12 Cambridge St., London SW1V 4QJ — MB BS 1994 Lond.

TIMMS

TIMMS, Josephine Wihelmina Martina 23 Hadrian Drive, Exeter EX4 1SR — Artsexamen 1993 Utrecht.

TIMMS, Matthew Adam John Lingmel, Thurstaton Rd, Heswall, Wirral L60 6RY — MB ChB 1997 Bristol.

TIMMS, Mr Michael Steven ENT Dept, Blackdown Royal Infirmary, Bolton Road, Blackburn BB79pQ Tel: 01254 294409; Great Mitton Hall, Great Mitton, Clitheroe BB7 9PQ Tel: 01254 826150 — MB ChB 1980 Leeds; FRCS Eng. 1987; FRCS Ed. 1986; T(S) 1992. Cons. Otolaryngol. Blackburn Roy. Infirm. & Burnley Gen. Hosp. Socs: Brit. Assn. of Otorhinolatyngologists / Head and Neck Surg.s; Europ. Acad. of Facial Plastic Surg. (Joseh Soc.). Prev: Sen. Lect. (Otorhinolaryng.) NW RHA.

TIMMS, Philip Wingrave Guy's, King's and St thomas's School of Medicine, Start Team, Master's House, London SE11 4TH Tel: 020 840 0653 Fax: 020 840 0657; Email: philip.timms@virgin.net — MRCS Eng. LRCP Lond. 1976; MRCPsych 1985. (Guy's) Sen. Lect. (Community Psychiat.) Guy's, King's & St Thomas's Sch. of Med.; Hon. Cons.; S. Lond. & Maudsley Trust. Prev: Sen. Regist. (UMDS Psychiat.) Guy's Hosp. Lond.

TIMMS, Roger Francis Acle Medical Centre, Bridewell Lane, Acle, Norwich NR13 3RA Tel: 01493 750888 Fax: 01493 751652; Rose Farmhouse, Broad Road, Fleggburgh, Great Yarmouth NR29 3DD Tel: 01493 368273 — MB BS 1980 Lond. (King's Coll. Med. Sch.) Hosp. Practitioner (Dermat.) Jas. Paget Hosp. Norf. Socs: BMA; Norf. & Norwich Medico-Chirurgical Soc. Prev: Trainee GP Leicester VTS; Ho. Surg. King's Coll. Hosp. Lond.; Ho. Phys. St. Helen's Hosp. Hastings.

TIMMS, Ronald Lionel Thundersley Hall, 192 Church Road, Thundersley, Benfleet SS7 4PL Tel: 01268 792583 — MRCS Eng. LRCP Lond. 1948. (Guy's)

TIMNEY, Aidan Patrick Irish Street, 17 Irish Street, Whitehaven CA28 7BU Tel: 01946 693412 Fax: 01946 592046; Elvet, Low Moresby, Whitehaven CA28 6RX Tel: 01946 694257 Fax: 01946 694257 — MB BS 1964 Durh.; DIH Eng. 1979.

TIMOL, Sulaiman Ahmed Moor House, Station Town, Wingate TS28 5HA — MB BS 1965 Med. Inst. (I) Rangoon. (Med. Inst. I Rangoon) Assoc. Specialist (Psychiat.) Winterton Hosp. Sedgefield. Socs: Affil. RCPsych. Prev: SHO, Regist. (Psychiat.). & Asst. Psychiat. Winterton Hosp. Sedgefield.

TIMONEY, Mr Anthony Gerard Mary Bristol Urological Institute, South Mead Hospital, Bristol BS37 9XE Tel: 0117 959 5154 Fax: 0117 950 2229 Email: anthony-timothy@bui.ac.uk; Northend Farm, Wotton Road, Iron Acton, Bristol BS37 9XE — MB BCh BAO 1981 NUI; MCh 1995; FRCS Ed. 1985; FRCSI 1985. (Dub.) Cons. Urol. N. Bristol NHS Trust Bristol. Socs: BAUS; BMA; Brit. Soc. EndoUrol.

TIMONEY, Norma 150 Park Hill Road, Birmingham B17 9HD — MB ChB 1992 Bristol; BA (BDen Sc) Dub. 1981; FRCS Eng. 1995; FDS RCS Eng. 1986. (Bristol) Regist. Rotat. (Plastic Surg.) Higher Specialist Train. W. Midl. Socs: Brit. Craniofacial Soc. Prev: Regist. & SHO (Plastic Surg.) Roy. Devon & Exeter Hosp.; SHO (Plastic Surg.) Frenchay Hosp.; SHO Rotat. (Gen. Surg.) MusGr. Pk. Hosp. Taunton.

TIMOTHY, Adrian Robert Department of Radiotherapy & Oncology, Guy's and St Thomas NHS Trust, St Thomas Hospital, London SE1 7EH Tel: 020 7928 9292 Fax: 020 7928 9968 — MB BS 1969 Lond.; FRCP Lond. 1988; MRCS Eng. LRCP Lond. 1969; FRCR 1976; DMRT Eng. 1974. (Westm.) Cons. Radiother. & Oncol. St. Thos. Hosp. Lond. Prev: Gordon Hamilton Fairley Fell. St. Bart. Hosp. Lond.; Fell. Radiat. Therap. Harvard Med. Sch. Boston USA; Sen. Regist. (Radiother.) St. Bart. Hosp. Lond.

TIMOTHY, Elizabeth Molly 22 Parkwood Avenue, Roundhay, Leeds LS8 1JW — MB BS 1959 Madras; MFCM 1986; DPH Leeds 1970; DCH Eng. 1964; DObst RCOG 1963. (Christian Med. Coll. Vellore) Specialist in Community Med. Child Health Plann. & Informat. Dewsbury Dist. HA. Socs: BMA & Assn. Community Phys. Prev: Sen. Regist. (Community Med.) Leeds Gen. Infirm.; SCMO Leeds AHA; Asst. Med. Off. Wakefield Co. Boro.

TIMOTHY, Huw Richards 18 Keele Walk, Blackburn BB1 1EH — MB BS 1983 Lond.; MRCGP 1990. GP Trainer S. Yorks. Socs: Fell. Roy. Soc. Health.

TIMOTHY, Irene (retired) 6 Millrace Drive, Fullers Drive, Wistaston, Crewe CW2 6XG Tel: 01270 665242 — MB BS Madras 1957; MFFP 1994; MRCOG 1980; DObst RCOG 1966. Prev: Assoc. Specialist Mid Chesh. Hosps. Trust.

TIMOTHY, Mr Jacob Department of Neurosurgery, Leeds General Infirmary, Leeds LS1 — MB BS 1991 Lond.; FRCS Eng. 1996. Specialist Regist. (Neurosurg.) Leeds Gen. Infirm. Prev: SHO (Gen. Surg.) Kent & Canterbury Hosp.; SHO (Orthop.) Greenwich Hosp.; SHO (Cardiothoracic) Roy. Brompton Hosp.

TIMOTHY, John Ivor (retired) Flat 36, Andorra Court, widmore road, Bromley BR1 3AE Tel: 0208 460 3308 — MB BS 1940 Lond.; MRCS Eng. LRCP Lond. 1939; MRCPsych 1971; DPM Eng. 1947. Prev: Cons. Psychiat. St. Matthew's Hosp. Burntwood.

TIMOTHY, John Richards, Maj. RAMC 10th PMO Gurkha Rifles, Gallipoli Lines BFPO 1 — MB BS 1986 Lond.; BSc Lond. 1983, MB BS 1986; MRCGP 1993. Regtl. Med. Off. 10th PMO Gurkha Rifles. Prev: Med. Off. 4th Armoured Field Ambul., BMH Rinteln & IRS (OP Eranby).

TIMPANY, Margaret Mary (retired) Home Breeze House, Beach St, Bare, Morecambe LA4 6BT Tel: 0180 420772 — MB ChB Ed. 1943; DPH Birm. 1947. Prev: Clin. Med. Off. Lancaster Health Dist.

TEMPERLEY, Andrew Colin 8 Middleton Way, Leasingham, Sleaford NG34 8LN — MB ChB 1990 Leeds.

TIMPERLEY, Mr Andrew John 2 The Quadrant, Wonford Road, Exeter EX2 4LE Tel: 01392 437070 Email: jtimperley@bigfoot .com — MB ChB 1981 Manch.; FRCS Ed. 1986. Cons. Orthop. & Trauma Exeter.

TIMPERLEY, Jane Clare 2 Lochside Road, Castle Douglas DG7 1EU Tel: 01556 503259 Email: jctimperle@aol.com — MB ChB 1987 Dundee; MRCGP 1993; FRCA (UK) 1998; DA (UK) 1989. Staff Doctor in Anaesth. Dumfries & Galloway Roy. Infirm. Dumfries.

TIMPERLEY, Jonathan 9 Welton Mount, Leeds LS6 1ET — MB ChB 1994 Leeds.

TIMPERLEY, Lorretta Rose Holly Tree Cottage, Ashiestiel, Galashiels TD1 3LJ; Borders Community Health Services, Dingleton Hospital, Melrose TD6 9HN Tel: 01896 822727 Fax: 01896 823807 — MB ChB 1991 Dundee; MA (Hons.) Ed. 1969; PhD Ed. 1977. Staff Grade (Psychiat.). Prev: SHO (Psychiat.) Crichton Roy. Hosp. Dumfries.

TIMPERLEY, Malcolm Richard — MB ChB 1980 Liverp.; MRCPsych 1987. Cons. Psychiat. Tees & NE Yorks. NHS Trust.

TIMPERLEY, Professor Walter Richard — BM BCh Oxf. 1961; MA Oxf. 1961, DM 1970; FRCPath 1981, M 1969. (Oxf.) Cons. Neuropath. & Hon. Clin. Lect. (Path.) United Sheff. Hosps. & Univ. Sheff. Socs: Pres. Assn. Clin. Path.; Sec. Gen. World Assn. of Soc. Path.; RCPath. Prev: Lect. (Path.) Manch. Univ.; Regist. (Path.) W.. Infirm. Glas.; Ho. Phys. & Ho. Surg. Radcliffe Infirm. Oxf.

TIMSON, Ian Roe Lee Surgery, 367 Whalley New Road, Blackburn BB1 9SR Tel: 01254 680075 Fax: 01254 695477 — MB ChB 1985 Manch.; T(GP) 1991; MRCGP 1989. Prev: Trainee GP Clitheroe VTS.

TIN, Nyan Kyaw Leacroft Medical Practice, Ifield Road, Ifield, Crawley RH11 7BS Tel: 01293 526441 Fax: 01293 619970 — MB BS 1976 Rangoon; MB BS Med Inst (I) Rangoon 1976; MRCGP 1988. GP Gambrill & partners.

TIN LOI, Shay Fho 34A Little Norsey Road, Billericay CM11 1BL — MB BS 1976 Lond.; MRCP (UK) 1979; MRCS Eng. LRCP Lond. 1976; FFA RCS Eng. 1983.

TIN MIN OHN, Dr River House, Gulson Road Hospital, Gulson Road, Coventry CV1 2HR — MB BS 1973 Med. Inst. (I) Rangoon.

TINCELLO, Aileen Joyce 10 Raven Meols Lane, Formby, Liverpool L37 4DF — MB ChB 1988 Ed.; DRCOG 1994. (Ed.) GP S.port Retainer Scheme.

TINCELLO, Douglas Gordon University Dept Obstecrics & Gynaelogy, Liverpool Women's Hospital, Crown St., Liverpool L8 7SS Tel: 0151 702 4114 Fax: 0151 702 4024 Email: dgt@surfaid.org; 11 Elson Road, Formby, Liverpool L37 2EG Email: tincello@liv.ac.uk — MB ChB 1989 Ed.; BSc (Med. Sci.) Ed. 1987, MD 1995; MRCOG 1995. (Ed.) Clin. Lect. Univ of Liverp. Socs: Internat. Continence Soc.; (Sec.) Mem. Mersey Urogynaecol. Soc.; Internat. Pelvic Floor DysFunc. Soc. Prev: Research Regist. Liverp. Wom.'s Hosp.; Specialist Regist. (O & G) Mersey Deanery.

TINCKLER, Mr Laurence Francis, TD Maelor General Hospital, Wrexham Tel: 01978 291100; Priddbwll Bonc, Farm Llansilen, Oswestry SY10 7QB Tel: 0169 791455 Fax: 01691 791455 Email: ltinckler@aol.com — MB ChB (Hons.) Liverp. 1945; MD Liverp. 1962, ChM 1955; FRCS Eng. 1950; FACS 1966; MRCS Eng. LRCP Lond. 1946; DTM & H Liverp. 1959. (Liverp.) Cons. Gen. & Urol. Surg. Maelor Gen. Hosp. Wrexham; Head of Dept. Surg. Riyadh Al-

Kharj Milit. Hosp. Saudi Arabia; Chief of Urol. K. Fahad Hosp. Al Baha, Saudi Arabia; Hon. Research Assoc. Dept. Surg. Univ. Liverp.; Lt. Col. RAMC(V) O.C. Surgic. Div. 203 (Welsh) Gen. Hosp.; Med. Dir. Curnow Shipping Ltd. Socs: Fell. Roy. Soc. Med.; Brit. Assn. Urol. Surgs.; BMA. Prev: Cons. Surg. K. Edwd. Memor. Hosp. Falkland Is.s; Prof. Surg. Univ. Singapore & Hon. Cons. Surg. Brit. Milit. Hosp. Singapore; Vis. Prof. Surg. Univ. Calif. Los Angeles.

TINCOMBE, Michael Robert Park Surgery, 278 Stratford Road, Shirley, Solihull B90 3AF Tel: 0121 241 1700 Fax: 0121 241 1821 — MRCS Eng. LRCP Lond. 1975 London; MRCS Eng. LRCP Lond. 1975 London.

TINDAL, Margaret Taylor 30 Newlands Road, Glasgow G43 2JD Tel: 0141 632 1583 — MB ChB 1926 Glas.; MD (Commend.) 1933; FRCP Glas. 1983, M 1962; FRFPS Glas. 1931. Prev: Muirhead Research Schol. Roy. Hosp. Sick Childr. Glas.; Extra Disp. Phys. Glas. Roy. Infirm.; Hon. Disp. Phys. Roy. Hosp. Sick Childr. Glas.

TINDALL, Hilary Department of Diabetes, North Middlesex Hospital, Sterling Way, London N18 1QX — MD 1983 Leeds; MB ChB 1972; FRCP Ed. 1997; FRCP Lond. 1994; MRCP (UK) 1977.

TINDALL, Mark Julian 26 Swanmore Road, Littleover, Derby DE23 7SD — MB ChB 1997 Sheff.

TINDALL, Nicholas John Wellington Road Surgery, Wellington Road, Newport TF10 7HG Tel: 01952 811677 Fax: 01952 825981; 22 Newport Road, Edgmond, Newport TF10 8HQ Tel: 01952 814668 — MB ChB 1980 Birm.; DRCOG 1983. (Birmingham) Med. Off. Lilleshall Sports Injury Centre Newport. Prev: Trainee GP N. Staffs. HA VTS.

TINDALL, Mr Stuart Frederick Laurel Bank, West End, Winteringham, Scunthorpe DN15 9NS — MB ChB 1969 Sheff.; MCh 1985 Sheff.; FRCS Eng. 1974. (Sheff.) Cons. Urol. Scunthorpe & Grimsby Hosps.; Div.al Director Surg., N.. Lincs. & Goole Hosps., NHS Trust. Socs: BMA; Assoc. Mem. BAUS; Assn. of Surg. GB & Irel. Prev: Sen. Regist. (Gen. Surg.) Hallamsh. Hosp. Sheff.; Research Asst. Dept. Surg. Sheff. Univ.; Rotating Surg. Regist. Sheff. Roy. Infirm.

TINDALL, Professor Victor Ronald, CBE 4 Planetree Road, Hale, Altrincham WA15 9JJ Tel: 0161 904 8222 Fax: 0161 904 8333 — MB ChB Liverp. 1951; MSc Manch. 1976; MD Liverp. 1962; FRCS Eng. 1991; FRCS Ed. 1961; FRCOG 1974, M 1961; DObst RCOG 1955. (Liverp.) Emerit. Prof. O & G Univ. Manch. Socs: Fell Roy. Soc. Med. Prev: Cons. O & G Univ. Hosp. Wales Cardiff & Welsh Hosp. Bd.; Sen. Lect. Welsh Nat. Sch. Med. Cardiff; Wellcome Vis. Prof. S. Afr. 1986.

TINDLE, John Edward (retired) Gwernant, Tanygroes, Cardigan SA43 2JS Email: jtindle@compuserve.com — MB BS Lond. 1956; MRCS Eng. LRCP Lond. 1956. Designated Examr. Austral. High Commiss. Prev: Med. Adviser Old Ct. Hosp. Lond.

TINEGATE, Hazel Nancy Todridge Farm, Middleton, Morpeth NE61 4RE — MB BS 1975 Lond.; MRCP (UK) 1979; MRCPath 1983; T(Path) 1991. Cons. Haemat. N. Tyneside Gen. Hosp. Prev: Sen. Regist. (Haemat.) Freeman Hosp. Newc.

TINER, Richard Stephen Association of the British Pharmaceutical Industry, 12 Whitehall, London SW1A 2DY Tel: 020 7747 1404 Fax: 020 7747 1400 Email: rtiner@abpi.org.uk — MB BS 1974 Lond.; MFPM 1999; DRCOG 1977. (Middlx. Hosp.) Med. Dir. Assn. Brit. Pharmaceut. Industry Lond. Socs: Roy. Soc. Med.; BMA; Brit. Assn. of Pharmaecutical Phys.s. Prev: GP French Weir Health Centre Taunton & Trainee GP Taunton VTS; SHO Kettering Gen. Hosp. N.ants.

TING, Alison Yih-Hua 14/8 East Parkside, Edinburgh EH16 5XL — MB ChB 1997 Ed.

TING, Mr Philip Yuen Cho Flat 62, Good Hart Place, Limehouse Basin, London E14 8EQ — MB BS 1989 Lond.; FRCS Ed. 1994.

TING, Simon Chow Hwa 300 Bellhouse Road, Shiregreen, Sheffield S5 0RE — MB ChB 1996 Sheff.

TINGEY, Mr William Robert The Chiltern Hospital, London Road, Great Missenden HP16 0EN Tel: 01494 890890; Flat 4, Teal House, The Millstream, London Road, High Wycombe HP11 1AE Tel: 01494 539939 Fax: 01494 539939 Email: wrtinge@uk-consultants.co.uk — MB BS 1969 Lond.; FRCS Eng. 1975; MRCS Eng. LRCP Lond. 1969; FRCOG 1992, M 1977. (St. Bart.) Cons. Gyn., Private Pract.; Examr. DRCOG Course Guys & Thomas's; Examr. Univeristy of Lond. MBBS Guy's and Thomas's; Examr. FRCOG Course Guys &

Thomas's. Socs: Hysteroscopy Soc.; Europ. Endoscopy Soc.; Pelvic Floor Soc. Prev: S. Bucks NHS Trust; Cons. Obsterician & Gynaecologist; Sen. Regist. (O & G) Oxf. & N.ampton.

TINGLEY, Paul Granville Reed Stamford, 128 Eccles Old Road, Salford M6 8QQ Tel: 0161 736 1972; 494 Liverpool Street, Salford M6 5QZ Tel: 0161 736 1972 — MB BChir 1960 Camb.; MRCS Eng. LRCP Lond. 1959. (Camb. & St. Thos.) Prev: Ho. Off. (Surg.) Stamford & Rutland Gen. Hosp.; Ho. Off. (Midw. & Gyn.) W. Pk. Hosp. Macclesfield.

TINKER, Andrew The Rayne Institute, Room 325, Department of Medicine, Cruciform Project, 5 University Street, University College London, London WC1E 6JJ Tel: 020 7209 6174 Fax: 020 7823 2846 Email: a.tinker@ucl.ac.uk; 34 Green End Dell, Green End Road, Boxmoor, Hemel Hempstead HP1 Tel: 01442 216902 Fax: 01442 216902 — MB BS Lond. 1987; PhD Lond. 1993; BA Oxf. 1984; MRCP (UK) 1990. (Roy. Free Hosp. Med. Sch.) Wellcome Sen. Research Fell. (Clin. Sci.), Sen. Lect. & Hon. Cons. (Clin. Pharmacol.) Univ. Coll. Lond. Prev: Postdoctoral Research Fell. Univ. Calif., San. Francisco; MRC Train. Fell. Nat. Heart & Lung Inst. Lond.; Regist. (Med.) Epsom Dist. Hosp.

TINKER, Andrew James 9 Greystone Close, Burley in Wharfedale, Ilkley LS29 7RS Tel: 01943 865587 Email: andytinker@aol.com — MB ChB 1987 Leic.; MB ChB Leics. 1987; MRCP (UK) 1990. (Leics.) Clin. Asst. (Med.) Whiston Hosp.; Clin. Asst. (Cardiol.) Fazakerley Hosp. Prev: Regist. (Med.) S.end Hosp., New Zealand; Regist. (Med.) Whiston Hosp.; SHO (Med.) E. Birm. Hosp.

TINKER, Gladys Mary Llandough Hospital NHS Trust, Ymddiriedolaeth NHS Ysbyty Llandochau, Llandough Hospital, Penlan Road, Penarth CF64 2XX Tel: 01222 711711 Fax: 01222 708973; 7 Cae Garn, Heol-y-Cyw, Bridgend CF35 6LD — MB ChB 1969 Ed.; MSc Wales 1994; BSc (Med. Sci.) Ed. 1966; FRCP Ed. 1993; MRCP (UK) 1976; Dip. Palliat. Med. Wales 1992. Cons. Phys. (Geriat. Med.) Llandough Hosp. NHS Trust. Prev: Sen. Regist. W. Wales Hosp. Carmarthen; Regist. St. David's Hosp. Cardiff; SHO (Geriat. Unit) Univ. Hosp. of Wales Cardiff.

TINKER, Jack The Royal Society of Medicine, 1 Wimpole St., London W1G 0AE Tel: 020 290 3920 Fax: 020 290 2977 Email: jack.tinker@roysocmed.ac.uk; 1 Rectory Road, Barnes, London SW13 0DU — BSc, MB ChB Manch. 1960; FRCP Lond. 1980, M 1969; FRCS Glas. 1966; DIC 1971. (Manch.) Dean The Roy. Soc. of Med.; Emerit. Cons. Phys. Univ. Coll. Hosps.; Edr. in Chief Hosp. Med.; Med. Adviser Rio Tinto plc. Socs: Fell. Roy. Soc. Med.; Fell. Roy. Soc. of Arts. Prev: Dean & Postgrad. Med. Univ. Lond. & NW Thames; Postgrad. Sub-Dean Middlx. Hosp. Med. Sch.; Unit. Gen. Manager & Dir. of ITU Middlx. Hosp. Lond.

TINKER, Michael David The Health Centre, The Surgery, Bowholm, Canonbie DG14 0UX Tel: 01387 371313 Fax: 01387 381211; Hillside, 1 Hillside Crescent, Langholm DG13 0EE — MB ChB 1969 Ed.; MRCGP 1985; DObst RCOG 1971. (Ed.) Course Organiser E. Cumbria VTS; N.. Region Summatire Assessm. Coordinator.

TINKER, Noel Richard 2 Northfield Close, South Lane, Brough HU15 2EW — MB ChB 1993 Liverp.

TINKER, Rachel Mary Moss Valley Medical Practice, Gosber Road, Eckington, Sheffield S21 4BZ — MB BS 1987 Lond.; MRCGP 1995; DRCOG 1993. (Char. Cross & Westm. Med. Sch.)

TINKLER, Anne Marie Brockley House, Pilgrims Way, Guildford GU4 8AD — MB ChB 1983 Manch.; MRCGP 1987; DRCOG 1986.

TINKLER, George Geoffrey Portway Surgery, 1 The Portway, Porthcawl CF36 3XB Tel: 01656 304204 Fax: 01656 772605; 128 West Road, Nottage, Porthcawl CF36 3RY — MB BCh 1972 Wales; MRCGP 1976; Cert. Family Plann. JCC 1977; DObst RCOG 1974. Clin. Asst. (Behaviour Ther.) Morganwg Hosp. Bridgend; GP Trainer Porthcawl.

TINKLER, Joanna Mary Hope Cove, Cuddington Way, Sutton SM2 7HY Tel: 020 8661 1996; First Floor Flat, 52 Hamilton Rd, Wimbledon, London SW19 1JF — MB BS 1993 Lond.; DCH RCP Lond. 1996; DRCOG 1996; MRCPCH Lond. 1999. SHO (Paediat.) Qu. Marys Childr Hosp. Surrey. Prev: SHO (Neonates.) St Helier Hosp. Surrey.; SHO (Paediat.) Roy Surrey Co. Hosp. Guildford.; Med Regist. ChristCh.. NZ.

TINKLER, Richard Frederick William The Surgery, 34 Teme Street, Tenbury Wells WR15 8AA Tel: 01584 810343 Fax: 01584 819734; Kitchen Hill, Orleton, Ludlow SY8 4HP Tel: 01568 780369

TINKLER

— MB BS 1973 Lond.; BSc West. Austral. 1968; DA Eng. 1977; DCH Eng. 1975. (St. Geo.) Hosp. Pract. (Anaesth.) & Clin. Asst. (Cas.) Tenbury & Dist. Hosp. Socs: Assn. Anaesth. Prev: SHO (Paediat., O & G & Anaesth.) N. Staffs. Hosp. Centre Stoke-on-Trent.

TINKLER, Robert 713 Yardley Wood Road, Birmingham B13 0PT Tel: 0121 444 3597; 95 Hither Green Lane, Abbey Park, Redditch B98 9BN — MB ChB 1955 Birm. (Birm.)

TINKLER, Sandra Dawn 70 Broomfield Avenue, Battlehill Estate, Wallsend NE28 9AE — MB ChB 1984 Dundee; MSc (Clin. Oncol.) Ed. 1991; MRCP (UK) 1988; FRCR 1992. Cons. Clin. Oncol. Wessex Radiother. Centre Roy. S. Hants. Hosp. Prev: Sen. Regist. (Radiat. Oncol.) Newc. Gen. Hosp.; Regist. (Radiat. Oncol.) W.. Gen. Hosp. Edin.

TINKLIN, Tracy Susan 40 Bucknalls Lane, Garston, Watford WD25 9JQ — BM 1988 Soton.; MRCP (UK) 1993.

TINLINE, Colin Carmichael — MB ChB 1971 Ed.; FRCPsych 1993, M 1977; DPM Eng. 1977. Cons. & Adolesc. Psychiat., PearTree Centre, Redditch. Prev: Sen. Regist. Nuffield Child Psychiat. Unit Newc.; Regist. (Psychiat.) Newc. HA; SHO Centr. Hosp. Warwick.

TINNION, Shirley Anne Meadowcroft Surgery, Jackson Road, Aylesbury HP19 9EX Tel: 01296 425775 Fax: 01296 330324; 4 Willow Rise, Haddenham, Aylesbury HP17 8JR — BSc (Hons.) Lond. 1984, MB BS 1987; MRCGP 1991; DRCOG 1990; DCH RCP Lond. 1990. Trainee GP Stoke Mandeville Hosp. Aylesbury. Prev: Ho. Phys. Stoke Mandeville Hosp. Aylesbury; Ho. Surg. Amersham Hosp.

TINSA, Jazwinder Singh 7 Elwells Close, Bilston WV14 9YH — MB ChB 1992 Aberd.

TINSLAY, Pamela Ivy 4 Romney Chase, Emerson Park, Hornchurch RM11 3BJ — MB BS 1959 Lond.; MRCS Eng. LRCP Lond. 1959; MFCM 1972; DPH Glas. 1967. (Roy. Free) Hon. Cons. Pub. Health Med. Barking & Havering HA. Prev: Cons. Communicable Dis. Control Barking & Havering HA; Dist. Community Phys. Havering Health Dist.

TINSLEY, Ellis George Frederick (retired) Brooklands, Carleton Road, Skipton BD23 2BE Tel: 01756 792338 — MB Camb. 1957, BChir 1956; FRCPath 1976, M 1964. Prev: Cons. Path. Airedale Gen. Hosp. Keighley.

TINSLEY, Helen Margaret Meyer Street Surgery, 20 Meyer Street, Cale Green, Stockport SK3 8JE Tel: 0161 480 2882 Fax: 0161 480 0583; 20 Harrisons Drive, Woodley, Stockport SK6 1JY — MB ChB 1974 Manch.; MFFP 1994; ECFMG Cert 1975. (Manchester) Socs: Fac. Fam. Plann. & Reproduc. Health; Brit. Menopause Soc.; BDA.

TINSLEY, Michael John, Col. late RAMC Clifton, 76 Main St., Keyworth, Nottingham NG12 5AD — MB ChB 1966 Manch.; BSc Manch. 1963; MRCGP 1976; DObst RCOG 1970. (Manch.) Cdr. Med. 2 (UK) Div. E Dist. Prev: IFOR Theatre Surg.; Med. Advis. Allied Forces NW Europ.; Cdr. Med. BMH Iserlohn.

TINSON, Ruth Elizabeth 30 Links Way, Eden Park, Beckenham BR3 3DQ — MB BS 1998 Lond.

TINSTON, Caroline 111 Bracadale Drive, Stockport SK3 8RY — MB ChB 1992 Manch.

TINT LWIN, Dr 74 Elliott Avenue, Ruislip HA4 9LZ — MB BS 1972 Rangoon.

TINTO, Barbara Anne Oakbank, Lamlash, Brodick KA27 8LH — MB ChB 1976 Glas.; DRCOG 1978.

TINTO, Elizabeth Isabella London Street Practice, 70 London Street, Reading RG1 4SL Tel: 0118 957 4640 Fax: 0118 959 7613; 5 Fallowfield Close, Cavesham, Reading RG4 8NQ Tel: 01734 470253 — MB ChB 1977 Aberd.; DRCOG 1982.

TINTO, Richard Graham Lamlash Medical Centre, Lamlash, Brodick KA27 8NS Tel: 01770 600516 Fax: 01770 600132; Oakbank, Lamlash, Brodick KA27 8LH Tel: 0177 06 00517 — MB ChB 1971 Glas.; MRCP (UK) 1978; MRCGP 1981. (Glas.) Prev: Regist. (Med.) Hairmyres Hosp. E. Kilbride; Med. Off. All St.s' Hosp. Transkei, S. Afr.

TINTO, Sujaee Asoka Samarasekara (retired) 5 Carnoustie Court, Bothwell, Glasgow G71 8UB — MB BS 1965 Ceylon; MRCGP 1977; DSM Ed. 1969.

TINTON, Marilyn Margaret Longcroft Clinic, 5 Woodmansterne Lane, Banstead SM7 3HH Tel: 01737 359332 Fax: 01737 370835; 37 Ewell Downs Road, Ewell, Epsom KT17 3BT — MB BS 1973 Lond.; DCH Eng. 1977; DRCOG 1976.

TIONG, Ho Yee 27 Lower Road, Beeston, Nottingham NG9 2GT — BM BS 1997 Nottm.

TIPLADY, Peter North Cumbria Health Authority, 4 Wavell Drive, Rosehill, Carlisle CA1 2SE Tel: 01228 603500 Fax: 01228 603612; The Arches, The Green, Wetheral, Carlisle CA4 8ET Tel: 01228 561611 Email: petertiplady@ncha.demon.co.uk — MB BS 1965 Durh.; FFPHM RCP (UK) 1986; MRCGP 1972. Dir. (Pub. Health) N. Cumbria HA. Socs: BMA.

TIPLADY, Trevor John (retired) Evelyn House, Ramsbury, Marlborough SN8 2PA Tel: 01672 520288 — MB BS 1955 Lond.; MRCS Eng. LRCP Lond. 1955; DObst RCOG 1959. Prev: Clin. Asst. (Obst.) & Stroke Rehabil. Unit Savernake Hosp. MarlBoro.

TIPPER, Rebecca Jane 46 Marchmont Road, Edinburgh EH9 1HX — MB ChB 1988 Ed.; MRCGP 1996. SHO (Psychiat.) Dingleton Hosp. Melrose. Prev: GP/Regist. Edin.; SHO (Geriat. & Gen. Med.) Haddington.

TIPPETT, Richard Jonathan Downside House, St. Boniface Rd, Ventnor PO38 1PJ — MB BS 1997 Lond.

TIPPETT, Susan Anne Nightingale Surgery, Greatwell Drive, Cupernham Lane, Romsey SO51 7QN Tel: 01794 517878 Fax: 01794 514236; 22 The Thicket, Whitenap, Romsey SO51 5SZ Tel: 01794 516028 — MB ChB 1975 Leeds; MRCGP 1980; DRCOG 1977.

TIPPETTS, Alice Elizabeth Ekams, PO 216, Kununurra WA 6743, Australia Tel: 08 91 681288; 8 Oakfield Street, Heavitree, Exeter EX1 2QT Tel: 01392 424704 — BM 1988 Soton.; MRCGP 1994; DRCOG 1992; Austral Med Counc 1999. (Soton.) Med. Off. (GP) in Aboriginal Health in rural Australia. Prev: Sen. Med. Off. Carnarvon Aboriginal Med. Serv. Austral.; Long Term GPO Locum Exeter; Trainee GP Exeter VTS.

TIPPETTS, Ranette 22 Sitwell Villas, Morton, Alfreton DE55 6GX Tel: 01246 864602; 12 Deighton Close, St Ives, Huntingdon PE27 3JJ Tel: 01480 463704 — MB ChB 1995 Birm.; ChB Birm. 1995. SHO Neonatology, Addenbrookes Hosp. Prev: SHO (Paediat.) Birm. Heartlands; SHO (A & E) Bristol Roy. Infirm.; PRHO (Surg.) City Hosp. Birm.

TIPPING, Conal Gerard 1 Inglewood, Lurgan, Craigavon BT67 9LS — MB BCh 1998 Belf.

TIPPING, Jonathan Peter Netherfields, Broadway, Ilminster TA19 9RB — MB BCh 1988 Wales; MRCGP 1993.

TIPPING, Kathryn Elizabeth 31 Bramley Road, Bramhall, Stockport SK7 2DW — MB BS 1993 Lond.

TIPPING, Philip James 24 Penine Avenue, Riddings, Alfreton DE55 4AE Tel: 01773 602707; Crofters Barn, Knowts Hall Farm, Golden Valley, Riddings, Alfreton DE55 4ES Tel: 01773 749058 — MB ChB 1988 Liverp.; Cert. Family Plann. JCC 1991. Prev: SHO (Paediat.) Chester; SHO (O & G) Whiston; SHO (Geriat.) Chester.

TIPPING, Thelma Ruth Royal Glamorgan Hospital, Ynysmaery, Llantrisant, Pontypridd CF72 8XR Tel: 01443 443443 Fax: 01443 443248; 10 Clinton Road, Penarth CF64 3JB Tel: 02920 712673 — MB BCh 1979 Wales; BSc (Hons.) (Maths) Wales 1973, MB BCh 1979; FFA RCSI 1985. (Welsh National School of Medicine) Roy. Glamprgan Hosp. Llantrisant. Prev: Cons. Anaesth. Manor Hosp. Walsall.

TIPPLE, Berndine Gesiene Everest House Surgery, Everest Way, Hemel Hempstead HP2 4HY Tel: 01442 240422 Fax: 01442 235045 — BM 1983 Soton.; DRCOG 1986; Cert. Family Plann. JCC 1986. Socs: BMA. Prev: Trainee GP Harpenden VTS; SHO (O & G & Gen. Med.) Luton & Dunstable Hosp.

TIPPLE, Ronald Whitaker, Surg. Capt. RN Cree, Crapstone, Yelverton PL20 7PG — MB BCh 1938 Wales; BSc, MB BCh Wales 1938; DLO Eng. 1947. (Cardiff)

TIPPLES, Melanie Kate 20 Nella Road, London W6 9PB — MB BS 1992 Lond. SHO (O & G) St. Thos. Hosp. Lond.

TIPPU, Naveed Iqbal Park Avenue Surgery, 27 Park Avenue, Dover CT16 1ES Tel: 01304 206463 Fax: 01304 216066; 74 Archers Court Road, Whitfield, Dover CT16 3HU Tel: 01304 826766 Email: tippu@lineone.net — MB BS Oshanir 1980; LRCP LRCS Ed. LRCPS Glas. 1983; MRCP (UK) 1988; Dip. Addict Behaviour St. George's Med. Sch. 1995; LFHOM (Licenciete Fellow in Homeopathy) Royal London Homoeopathic Hospital 1998. Princip. Gen. Pract. Socs: Roy. Coll. Phys.; Fac. Homoeop. Prev: Regist. (Gen. Med.) Basildon Hosp.; SHO Rotat. (Gen. Med.) Gen. Hosp. & Ingham Infirm. S. Shields.

TIWARI

TIPTAFT, Mr Richard Charles 42 Gloucester Circus, Greenwich, London SE10 8RY — MB BS 1972 Lond.; BSc (Hons. Physiol.) Lond. 1969, MB BS 1972; FRCS Eng. 1976. Cons. Urol. St. Thos. Hosp. Lond. Prev: Sen. Lect. Urol. & Hon. Cons. Surg. Urol. Lond. Hosp.; Hon. Cons. Urol. Newham HA; Resid. (Urol.) Yale New Haven Med. Centre USA.

TIPTON, Carolyn Mary Crieff Health Centre, King Street, Crieff PH7 3SA Tel: 01764 652456 Fax: 01764 655756; Newra House, 63 Willoughby St, Crieff PH5 2AE — MB BS 1988 Lond.; DRCOG 1991; MRCGP 1992. GP Crieff Retainer Scheme.; GP Princip.

TIPTON, Richard Henson (retired) Gyfres Farm, Bucks Hill, Chipperfield, Kings Langley WD4 9BR Tel: 01923 267664 Email: rht1@ndirect.co.uk — MB BS 1960 Lond.; MD Sheff. 1971; FRCOG 1978, M 1965; DObst RCOG 1963. Prev: Cons. O & G Watford Gen. Hosp.

TIRUNAWARKARISU, Kanawadi Pillai St. David's Hospital, Carmarthen SA31 3HB Tel: 01267 237481; Brynawelon, 2 Alltycnap Road, Johnstown, Carmarthen SA31 3QY — MB BS 1971 Ceylon; MRCPsych 1984. (Ceylon) Regist. (Psychiat.) St. David's Hosp. Carmarthen. Prev: Regist. (Child Psychiat.) Bod Difyr Clinic Colwyn Bay; Regist. & SHO Winwick Hosp. Warrington.

TIRUPATHI-RAO, Marada Tonypandy Health Centre, Winton Field, Tonypandy CF40 2LE Tel: 01443 433284 Fax: 01443 436848 — MB BS 1972 Andhra. (Andhra) GP Tonypandy, M. Glam.

TISCHKOWITZ, Mark Derek Karl-Eugen White's Farmhouse, Upp End, Manuden, Bishop's Stortford CM23 1BT — MB ChB 1993 Liverp.

TISDALE, John Bartholomew Tregony Road Surgery, Tregony Road, Probus, Truro TR2 4JZ; The Surgery, Mill Lane, Grampound, Truro TR2 4RU — MB ChB 1976 Liverp.

TISDALL, Jennifer Mary (retired) The Red House, 23 Furzehatt Road, Plymstock, Plymouth PL9 8QX Tel: 01752 402356 Fax: 01752 402366 Email: jentisdl@netcomuk.co.uk — MB BS Lond. 1956. Prev: SCMO (Family Plann.) Devon AHA.

TISDALL, Michael Walter (retired) The Red House, 23 Furzehatt Road, Plymstock, Plymouth PL9 8QX Tel: 01752 402356 — MB Camb. 1956, BChir 1955; DObst RCOG 1959; DCH Eng. 1958; BA 1955 Middlesex Hospital.

TISH, Keith Neil 1 Druids Park, Liverpool L18 3LJ Tel: 0151 722 2917 — MB ChB 1988 Leeds; MRCP (UK) 1992. Regist. (Med.) Dunedin Hosp. NZ.

TISI, Mr Paul Vincent Department Vascular Surgery, Southampton General Hospital, Tremona Road, Southampton SO16 6YD Tel: 02380 798801 Fax: 02380 798911; 105 Cheltenham Gardens, Hedge End, Southampton SO30 4UE — MB BS 1988 Lond.; MB BS (Hons.) Obst. & Gyn. Lond. 1988; FRCS Ed. 1992. Specialist Regist. (Vasc. Surg.) Soton. Gen. Hosp. Soton. Socs: Eur. Soc. Vasc. Surg. Prev: Specialist Regist. (Surg.) St. Richard's Hosp. Chichester; Research Fell. (Vasc. Surg.) Roy. S. Hants. Hosp. Soton.; Regist. (Gen. Surg.) Qu. Alexandra Hosp. Portsmouth.

TISI, Roger Bernard Valkyrie Road Surgery, 20 Valkyrie Road, Westcliff on Sea SS0 8BX Tel: 01702 331255 Fax: 01702 437050 — MB BS 1984 Lond.; MRCGP 1989; DRCOG 1988. Assoc. Course Organiser Basildon & S.end VTS.

TISSAINAYAGAM, Melwyn Balendra Jeganathan (retired) 15 Meadowvale, Darras Hall, Ponteland, Newcastle upon Tyne NE20 9NF — MB BS Ceylon 1964; MRCOG 1976. Prev: Med. Off. DSS Newc.

TITCHMARSH, Michael Reid (retired) 24 Castlegate, York YO62 5AB Tel: 01439 771860, 01439 770620 — MB ChB 1965 Liverp.; DObst RCOG 1967.

TITCOMB, Daniel Robert 27 Woodland Gr, Bristol BS9 2BD — MB ChB 1997 Bristol; BSc (Hons) UCL 1993.

TITCOMB, Josephine Ann Paediatric Medical Unit, Southampton General Hospital, Southampton SO16 6YD Tel: 02380 796492 Fax: 02380 794750 — MB ChB 1976 Bristol; MRCPsych 1983; DRCOG 1978. Cons. Child Psychiat. Soton. Prev: Sen. Regist. (Child & Adolesc. Psychiat.) Bristol Childr. Hosp.

TITCOMB, Margaret Louise 22 Kingsway Gardens, Chandler's Ford, Eastleigh SO53 1FE — MB BS 1982 Lond.; MRCGP 1988. p/t GP.

TITCOMBE, Donald Hereward Macalister 9 Harefield Drive, Wilmslow SK9 1NJ Tel: 01625 27396 — MB ChB 1940 Manch; MB ChB (2nd cl. Hons., Distinc. in Surg.) Manch. 1940. (Manch.) Socs:

Fell. Manch. Med. Soc. Prev: Ho. Surg. & Clin. Asst. Aural Dept. Manch. Roy. Infirm.

TITCOMBE, Jane Louisa Mary Ware Road Surgery, 77 Ware Road, Hertford SG13 7EE Tel: 01992 587961 — MB ChB 1977 Dundee; MRCGP 1984. (Dundee) Clin. Asst. (Dermat.) Qu. Eliz. II Hosp. Welwyn Gdn. City. Socs: Scott. Dermat. Soc.; Dowling Club. Prev: Regist. (Gen. Med.) Perth Roy. Infirm.; Regist. (Dermat.) Tayside HB; SHO (Dermat.) Ninewells Hosp. Dundee.

TITE, Lorraine Jean 20 Chanctonbury Chase, Redhill RH1 4BB — MB BS 1998 Lond.

TITFORD, Joan Elvira (retired) 1 Tollers Lane, Coulsdon CR5 1BE — MRCS Eng. LRCP Lond. 1943. Prev: Regist. (O & G) New End Hosp. Hampstead.

TITHERIDGE, Katherine Louise Cornerways, 62 Epsom Road, Guildford GU1 3PB — BM BS 1997 Nottm.

TITHERIDGE, Ruth Elsie 3 Chapman Lane, Flackwell Heath, High Wycombe HP10 9AZ Tel: 01628 523972 — MB BS 1983 Lond.; MRCGP Lond. 1987; DCH RCP Lond. 1987; DRCOG 1987. (Char. Cross Hosp. Med. Sch.) Prev: GP Bedford.

TITLEY, Guy Jonathan 15 King's Drive, Midhurst GU29 0BL — MB BS 1993 Lond.

TITLEY, Jeremy Victor East Hill Farm, West Knoyle, Warminster BA12 6AN — MB BS 1968 Lond.

TITLEY, Mr Oliver Garth Sellyoak Hospital, University Hospital Birmingham NHS Trust, Raddlebarn Road, Sellyoak, Birmingham B29 6JD Tel: 021 627 8602; 43 Woodville Road, Harborne, Birmingham B17 9AR Tel: 0121 427 1432 Email: gtilley@btinternet.com — MB ChB 1986 Birm.; CCST 1999; FRCS 1998 (Plast); MSc Birm. 1992; FRCS Eng. 1992. Cons. Plastic Surg., Unversity Hosp., Birm.; Cons. Plastic Surg., Good Hope Hosp., Sutton Coldfield. Socs: Full BAPS; Assoc. BSSH. Prev: SHO (Plastic Surg.) Wexham Pk. Hosp. Slough; SHO (Plastic Surg.) W. Midl. Regional Plastic & Jaw Surg. Unit; SHO Rotat. (Gen. Surg.) Leicester.

TITLEY, Roger George The Surgery, 20 Southwick Street, Southwick, Brighton BN42 4TB Tel: 01273 592723/596077; 7 Mill Hill, Shoreham-by-Sea BN43 5TG Tel: 01273 455247 — MB BS 1965 Lond.; MRCS Eng. LRCP Lond. 1964; DObst RCOG 1967. (St. Mary's) Police Surg. Shoreham by Sea; Port Med. Off. HMA Shoreham by Sea Lifeboat. Prev: Ho. Surg. (O & G) Odstock Hosp. Salisbury; Ho. Surg. & Ho. Phys. Salisbury Infirm; Ho. Surg. (Orthop.) Paddington Gen. Hosp.

TITMAS, Gordon John (retired) 7 The Bull Meadow, Streatley-on-Thames, Reading RG8 9QD Tel: 01491 874057 — MB BS Newc. 1968; MRCGP 1975; Dip. Palliat. Med. Wales 1991; DObst RCOG 1972.

TITMAS, John Michael (retired) 706 Finchley Road, London NW11 7ND Tel: 020 8458 7371 — MB BS Lond. 1949; MRCS Eng. LRCP Lond. 1947; DPH Lond. 1963. Prev: Civil. Ophth. Specialist RAF Centr. Med. Estab. Lond.

TITMUSS, John 59 Nottingham Road, Trowell, Nottingham NG9 3PJ — MB BS 1993 Newc.; BMedSci (Hons.) 1990.

TITMUSS, Sarah Jane The Old Rectory, Madresfield, Malvern WR13 5AB Tel: 01425 403413, 01684 572495 Fax: 01425 402032 — MB BS 1982 Lond.; BSc (Hons.) Lond. 1977; DCH RCP Lond. 1988; DRCOG 1985. (University College Hospital London)

TITORIA, Manoj Wrightington Hospital, Hall Lane, Appley Bridge, Wigan WN6 9EP Tel: 01257 256244; The Beeches, 2 Normanhurst, Ruff Lane, Ormskirk L39 4UZ Tel: 01695 581001 Fax: 01695 581001 — MB BS Lucknow 1967; DA Lond. 1972. Socs: Fell. Assoc. Anaesth. GB & Irel.; Assn. Obst. Anaesth.; BMA. Prev: Cons. Anaesth. Ormskirk & Dist. Gen. Hosp.; Cons. Anaesth. Wrightington Hosp.

TITTERINGTON, Mary Barbara 7 Horseshoe Lane, Brackagh, Portadown, Craigavon BT62 3RS Tel: 01762 840415 — MB BCh BAO 1974 Dub. Clin. Med. Off. Health Centre Portadown.

TIVY-JONES, Mr Peter North West Wales Hospitals Trust, Bangor LL57 2PW — MB BS 1970 Lond.; FRCS Ed. 1975; MRCS Eng. LRCP Lond. 1970; MRCOG 1976. (Westm.) Cons. N. W. Wales Hosp.sTrust. Socs: BMA; HCSA. Prev: Sen. Regist. St. David's Hosp. Bangor; Regist. (O & G) St. Mary's & Samarit. Hosps. Lond.; Resid. Med. Off. Qu. Charlotte's Hosp. Wom. Lond.

TIWARI, Alok 42 Pollards Green, Chelmsford CM2 6UH — MB BS 1996 Lond.

TIWARI

TIWARI, Indrajit Department of Gatroenterology, Broomfield Hospital, Chelmsford CM1 7ET Tel: 01245 514097 Fax: 01245 514864 Email: itiwari@hotmail.com; Email: itiwari@hotmail.com — MBBS; MD 1975 India; MRCP 1980 Royal College of Physicians, Ireland; FRCP 1990 Royal College of Physicians, Ireland. (MLN Medical College, Allahabad, India, 1971) Assoc. Specialist Gatroentrlogy, Broomfield Hosp. Chelmsford. Socs: Mem. Brit. Soc. of Gastroenterol.; Fell. Roy. Soc. of Med. (1993); Mem. Saudi Gastroenterol. Assn. Prev: Cons. Gastroenterologist Milit. Hosp. S.. Region, Saudi Arabia; Regist. Med. Cumbld. Infirm. Carlisle; Regist. Med. Univ. Hosp. NHS, Cardiff.

TIWARI, Mr Indu Bhushan, Group Capt. RAF Med. Br. Retd. (retired) 66 A Arundell, Ely CB6 1BQ — MB BS 1961 Nagpur; FRCS Ed. 1969. Prev: Regist. (Surg.) W. Cumbld. Hosp. Hensingham.

TIWARI, Kala 87 St Alban's Avenue, Hartshead, Ashton-under-Lyne OL6 8XN Tel: 0161 339 9547 Fax: 0161 223 7282 — MB BS 1968 Banaras Hindu; BSc (Hons.) Banaras Hindu 1962. Clin. Med. Off. (Family Plann.) Stockport HA.

TIWARI, Ninawatie Vimal Wrafton House Surgery, Wrafton House, 9-11 Wellfield Road, Hatfield AL10 0BS Tel: 01707 265454 Fax: 01707361286 — MB ChB 1975 Aberd.; MRCGP 1987; DCH RCP Lond. 1986; DRCOG 1979; Cert. Family Plann. JCC 1978. (Aberdeen) Sstaff Screde Community Prediatrician, W. Herts Trust. Prev: Clin. Med. Off. Dacorum & St. Albans Community NHS Trust.; Trainee GP St. Mary's Hosp. Lond. VTS; Hosp. Med. Off. Shenley Hosp.

TIWARI, Mr Pari North Staffordshire Royal Infirmary, Princes Road, Hartshill, Stoke-on-Trent ST4 7LN Tel: 01782 55285 Email: paciuk@mailexcit.com — MB BS 1986 Lond.; FRCS Eng. 1991; FRCR 1996. (The London Hospital Whitechapel) Specialist Regist. (Radiol.) N. Staffs. Roy. Infirm. Stoke-on-Trent; Radiol. Fell.sh. St Pauls Hosp. Vancouver Canada 1998-1999.

TIWARI, Prem Prakash The Surgery, Deep Croft, 21 Croft Road, Edwalton, Nottingham NG12 4BW.

TIWARI, Ram Krishna Nelson Health Centre, Cecil Street, North Shields NE29 0DZ Tel: 0191 257 1191 Fax: 0191 258 4961 — MB BS 1972 Lucknow. (Lucknow) GP N. Shields Tyne & Wear.

TIWARI, Ravindra Butetown Health Centre, Loudown Square, Docks, Cardiff CF10 5UZ Tel: 029 2046 2347 Fax: 029 2045 3080.

TIWARI, Shobhi Rani The Surgery, Deep Croft, 21 Croft Road, Edwalton, Nottingham NG12 4BW.

TIWARY, Ram Nain 504 New Cross Road, London SE14 6TJ — MRCS Eng. LRCP Lond. 1968; MSc (Med. Sci.) 1985 Glas.; MSc (Med. Sci.) Glas. 1985.

TIZARD, Eleanor Jane Childrens Renal Unit, Bristol Royal Hospital for Children, Upper Maudlinst, Bristol BS2 8BJ Tel: 0117 342 8881 Email: jane.tizard@bht.swest.nhs.uk; 32 Waverley Road, Redland, Bristol BS6 6EX — MB BS 1979 Lond.; MRCP (UK) 1981; FRCP. (Middlesex) Cons. Paediatric Nephrologist S.mead Hosp. Bristol. Socs: Liveryman Soc. Apoth. Lond.; Fell. Roy. Coll. Paediat. & Child Health; Brit. Assn. Paediat. Nephrol.

TIZZARD, Simon Peter Lamport, Stowe, Buckingham MK18 5AB — MB BS 1996 Lond.; BA Cantab 1993.

TJANDRA, Mr Janwar Joe Department of Surgery, University Hospital of Wales, Heath Park, Cardiff CF4 4XN Tel: 029 2074 2756 — MB BS 1981 Melbourne; FRCS Eng. 1986; FRCS Glas. 1985; FRACS 1989. Sen. Lect. & Cons. Surg. Univ. Hosp. Wales. Socs: Amer. Soc. Colon & Rectal Surg. Prev: Clin. Assoc. Cleveland Clinic Foundat., USA; Sen. Regist. Roy. Melbourne Hosp. Austral.

TJON FONG KWIE, Robertus Tjon Joe Ten South Warwickshire Hospital, Lakin Road, Warwick CV34 5BW — Artsexamen 1994 Amsterdam.

TLUSTY, Peter John The Belgravia Surgery, 24-26 Eccleston Street, London SW1W 9PY Tel: 020 7590 8000 Fax: 020 7590 8010; Tel: 020 8874 4286 Fax: 020 8877 1851 — MB BS 1980 Lond.; BSc Lond. 1977; FRCS Ed. 1986; MRCS Eng. LRCP Lond. 1980. (Char. Cross Hosp.) Sen. Partner Gen. Pract. Prev: SHO (Obst.) W.m. Hosp. Lond.; SHO (Surg.) St. Jas. Hosp. Lond.; Resid. Med. Off. (Obst.) Qu. Charlottes Hosp. Lond.

TO, Meekai Stephanie 45 Farnes Drive, Romford RM2 6NT Tel: 01708 760043 — BM BS 1994 Nottm.; BMedSci 1992. Research Fell. Harris Birthright Centre Kings Coll. Hosp. Lond. Socs: RSM. Prev: SHO Qu. Charlottes & Chelsea Hosp.

TO, Mr Shun Suen Princess Margaret Hospital, Okus Road, Swindon SN1 4JU — MB ChB 1974 Ed.; FRCS Ed. 1979; FRCS Eng. 1982; DLO Eng. 1981. (Ed.) Cons. ENT Surg. P.ss Margt. Hosp. Swindon. Prev: Sen. Regist. (ENT) W. Midl. RHA; Regist. (Gen. Surg.) Burton-on-Trent Gen. Hosp.; Regist. (Gen. Surg.) Nazareth Hosp. (EMMS), Israel.

TO, Ting Hoi Cross Deep Surgery, 4 Cross Deep, Twickenham TW1 4QP Tel: 020 8892 8124 Fax: 020 8744 9801; 30 Ravensbourne Road, Twickenham TW1 2DQ Tel: 020 8892 2805 — MB BS 1978 Lond.; DRCOG 1979. (Roy. Free)

TOAL, Brendan Jude Donegall Road Surgery, 293 Donegall Road, Belfast BT12 5NB Tel: 028 9032 3973 — MB BCh BAO 1982 Belf.; MB BCh Belf. 1982.

TOAL, Elizabeth May Wester Deanhead, Dunfermline KY12 0SG — MB ChB 1967 Glas.

TOAL, Martin John Biogen Ltd, 5D Roxborough Way, Foudation Park, Maidenhead SL6 3UD Tel: 01628 501000; 10 Larchmoor Park, Gerrards Cross Rd, Stoke Poges, Slough SL2 4EY Tel: 01753 662198 — MB BCh BAO 1988 Belf.; MSc (Pub. Health) Newc. 1997; DPH Belf. 1995; DMH Belf. 1992; MFPHMI. 1998; MFPHM 1999. Med. Dir., Biogen Ltd. Socs: (Counc.) BMA (Ex-Chairm. N. Irel. Jun. Doctors Comm.) (Chairm. Pub. Health; BMA Counc. Mem. Prev: Regional Med. Adviser, Bristol- Myers Lauss Pharaceutics Lts; SHO (Psychiat.) Tyrone & Fermanagh Hosp. Omagh; SHO Rotat. (Psychiat.) N. Irel.

TOAL, Patrick Anthony Tattykeel House, 126 Doogary Road, Omagh BT79 0BN — MB BCh BAO 1993 Belf.; DRCOG 1996; DCH Dub. 1996; DGM RCPS Glas. 1995. GP/Regist. Foyleside Med. Pract. Derry. Prev: SHO (O & G Paediat. & Med.) Altnagelvin Hosp. Derry.

TOAL, Surgeon Captain Patrick Francis, SBStJ, Surg. Capt. RN Retd. (retired) Willow End, 1B Glebe Park Avenue, Bedhampton, Havant PO9 3JR Tel: 02392 479363 — MB BCh BAO 1949 NUI; DPH (Hnrs.) 1965; MFOM RCP 1980; FFCM 1979, M 1974; DIH Dund 1969; Specialist Accredit. (Occupat. & Community Med.). Prev: Dir. Health & Research (Navy).

TOALE, Eamon 15B Windsor Road, London W5 3UL — MB BCh BAO 1991 NUI.

TOASE, Peter David Huntingdon Road Surgery, 1 Huntingdon Road, Cambridge CB3 0DB Tel: 01223 364127 Fax: 01223 322541 — MB BS 1972 Lond.; MRCGP 1977; DCH Eng. 1975; DObst RCOG 1975. (St. Thos.) Prev: Trainee GP Wessex VTS; Ho. Phys. St. Peter's Hosp. Chertsey; Ho. Surg. Brook Gen. Hosp. Lond.

TOBERT, Alexandra 7 Cotman Close, London NW11 6QD — MB BS 1944 Lond.; DCH Eng. 1949. (Lond. Sch. Med. Wom.) Socs: Inst. Psychosex. Med.; Hon. Life Mem. Nottm. Medico Chir. Soc. Prev: Clin. Asst. & Lect. (Psycho-Sexual Med.) Dept. Gyn. City Hosp. Nottm.

TOBEY, Ilona West Street Surgery, 16 West Street, Newport PO30 1PR Tel: 01983 522198 Fax: 01983 524258 — MB ChB 1970 Bristol; DCH Eng. 1973.

TOBIANSKY, Robert Ian Colindale Hospital, Silkstream Unit, Colindale Avenue, London NW9 5HG Tel: 020 8200 1555 Fax: 020 8205 8911 — MB BCh 1986 Witwatersrand; MRCPsych 1992. Cons. Old Age Psychiat. Colindale Hosp. Lond.

TOBIAS, Andrew John Tel: 01903 753279 Fax: 01903 851339; 11 Browning Road, Lancing BN15 ORY Tel: 01903 761088 — BM BS 1980 Nottm.; BMedSci 1978 Nottm.; MRCGP 1984; DRCOG 1984; Cert. Av. Med. 1993. Authorised Aviat. Med. Trauma for UK, Civil Aviat. Auth. Prev: Hosp. Practitioner, Urol., Worthy & S.ends, NHS Trust, S.

TOBIAS, Anthony Richard 3 Sefton Ave, Mill Hill, London NW7 3QB Tel: 020 8959 0369 — MB ChB 1991 Manch.; BSc St. And. 1988; MRCGP 1996; DRCOG 1994; DFFP. NHS GP Princip., Barnet HA, Mill Hill, N. Lond. Prev: GP Regist. E. Kilbride; SHO (Gen. Med.) Ayr Hosp.; SHO (Paediat.) CrossHo. Hosp.

TOBIAS, Catherine Mary Royal Manchester Childrens Hospital, Pendlebury, Manchester M27 4HA — MB BS 1987 Newc.; MRCPsych 1995; MRCGP 1991. Prev: Trainee GP N.umbria VTS; Research Regist. Univ. Manch.; Sen. Regist. Rotat. (Child & Adult Psychiat.) Manch.

TOBIAS, Edward Spencer Dunca Guthrie Institute, Yorkhill Hospital, Glasgow G3 8SJ Tel: 0141 201 0365 Email: gbcv55@udcf.gla.ac.uk — MB ChB 1991 Glas.; PhD Glas. 1997;

TOD

MB ChB (Commend) Glas. 1990; BSc (Hons.) Molecular Biol. Glas. 1987; MRCP (UK) 1993. (Univ. Glas.) Specialist Regist. (Med. Genetics) Duncan Guthrie Inst., Yorkhill Hosp. Glas. Socs: RCPS Glas.; Brit. Soc. Human Genetics. Prev: Clin. Research Sci. Beatson Inst. for Cancer Research Glas.; MRC Train. Fell. (Biochem. & Molec. Biol.) Univ. Glas.; SHO Rotat. (Med.) W.. Infirm. Glas.

TOBIAS, Gabriela Jill The Surgery, 52B Well Street, London E9 7PX Tel: 020 8985 2050 Fax: 020 8985 5780; 48 Northchurch Road, London N1 4EJ Tel: 020 7249 2326 — MB BS 1973 Lond.; MRCGP 1978; DCH Eng. 1977. Cochair Exec., City & Hackney PCT. Prev: Clin. Fell. in Med. Mass. Gen. Hosp. Boston, U.S.A.; Regist. (Geriat.) St. Thos. Hosp. Lond.; Ho. Phys. Univ. Coll. Hosp. Lond.

TOBIAS, Jeffrey Stewart Meyerstein Institute of Oncology, Middlesex Hospital, London W1 Tel: 020 7637 1214 Fax: 020 7637 1201 Email: j.tobias@uclh.org; 48 Northchurch Road, London N1 4EJ Tel: 020 7249 2326 — MB BChir 1972 Camb.; BA Camb. 1968, MD 1977, MA, MB 1972, BChir 1971; FRCP Lond. 1990; MRCP (UK) 1973; FRCR 1979. (St. Bart.) p/t Cons. Radiother. & Oncol. Univ. Coll. Hosp. & Middlx. Hosp. Lond.; Hon. Sen. Lect. Univ. Coll. & Middlx. Sch. Med. Socs: Founder Mem. (Ex-Hon. Sec.) Brit. Oncol. Assn.; Counc. RCRadiol. Prev: Clin. Dir. Meyerstein Inst. Oncol. Middlx. Hosp. Lond.; Lect. (Radiother. & Oncol.) Roy. Marsden Hosps. Lond.; Fell. (Med. Oncol.) Harvard Med. Sch. Boston, USA.

TOBIAS, John Avrom Elmwood Avenue Surgery, 3 Elmwood Avenue, Newton Mearns, Glasgow G77 6EH Tel: 0141 639 2478 Fax: 0141 639 6708 — MB ChB 1986 Glas.; MRCGP 1990; Cert. Family Plann. JCC 1989. (Glasgow) Hon. Clin. Sen. Lect. Dept. Gen. Pract. Univ. Glas. Socs: RCGP. Prev: GP Aberd. VTS.

TOBIAS, Jonathan Harold Rheumatology Unit, Bristol Royal Infirmary, Bristol BS2 8HW Tel: 0117 928 2907; 33 Carnarvon Road, Bristol BS6 7DS Tel: 0117 923 2537 — MB BS 1984 Lond.; PhD Lond. 1994, MD 1991; MA Camb. 1985; MRCP (UK) 1987; FRCP (UK) 1999. Cons. Sen. Lect. (Rheum.) Univ. Bristol & United Bristol Hosp. Trust. Socs: Brit. Soc. Rheum.; Amer. Soc. Bone & Mineral Research; Bone & Tooth Soc. (Comm. Mem.). Prev: ARC Clin. Research Fell. & Hon. Sen. Regist. (Rheum.) St. Geo. Hosp. Med. Sch. Lond.; MRC Research Train. Fell. St. Geo. Hosp. Med. Sch. Lond.; Regist. (Med.) St. Richard's Hosp. Chichester & St. Geo. Hosp. Lond.

TOBIAS, Lazarus (retired) 1 Hough Lane, Wilmslow SK9 2LG Tel: 01625 530851 — MB ChB Glas. 1938. Prev: Sen. Res. Med. Off. Manor Ho. Hosp. Golders Green.

TOBIAS, Martin P/o Box 304/2, Kilburn, London NW6 42Q Mobile: 0771 433 5820; 18 Marston Close, Swiss Cottage, London NW6 4EU Tel: 020 7328 2092 — MB ChB 1954 Manch.; DObst RCOG 1957. Indep. GP Lond. Prev: Med. Off. Esso Petroleum Co. Ltd. Lond.; SHO (Surg.) Ashton-under-Lyne Gen. Hosp.; Flight Lt. RAF Med. Br.

TOBIAS, Michael Avalon, Swiss Hill, Alderley Edge SK9 7DP Tel: 01625 583815 Fax: 01625 583815 Email: mike_tobias@hotmail.com — MB ChB Manch. 1963; FRCA. Eng. 1968; DA Eng. 1965; DObst RCOG 1965. (Manch.) Cons. Anaesth. Wythenshawe Hosp. Manch. Socs: Fell. Manch. Med. Soc.; BMA; N. W. Regional Pain Gp. Prev: Instruc. (Anaesth.) Mass. Gen. Hosp. Boston, USA; Sen. Regist. (Anaesth.) Univ. Hosp. W. Indies, Jamaica; SHO (Anaesth.) St. Bart. Hosp. Lond.

TOBIAS, Myer (Surgery) 49 Belle Vale Road, Liverpool L25 Tel: 0151 487 8660; 157 Menlove Avenue, Calderstones, Liverpool L18 3EE Tel: 0151 722 2384 — LRCP LRCS 1954 Ed.; LRCP LRCS Ed. LRFPS Glas. 1954. (Glas.) SCMO Liverp. AHA (T); Instruc. Doctor Jt. Comm. Contracept. Lond. Prev: Ho. Phys., Ho. Surg. & Ho. Off. (O & G) Sharoe Green Hosp. Preston.

TOBIAS, Naomi Frances The Health Centre, Park Road, Tarporley CW6 0BE Tel: 01829 3456 — MB ChB 1979 Manch.; MRCGP 1983; DRCOG 1982.

TOBIN, Caoimhin Padraig The White Rose Surgery, Exchange Street, South Elmsall, Pontefract WF9 2RD — MB BCh BAO 1990 NUI; Diploma in Practical Dermat., Cardiff 2000; DCH RCPSI 1993; DObst RCPI 1993. GP Trainer. Prev: Trainee GP Som.

TOBIN, David Edward The Grayshott Surgery, Boundary Road, Grayshott, Hindhead GU26 6TY Tel: 01428 604343 — MB BS 1979 Lond.; MRCS Eng. LRCP Lond. 1979; DRCOG 1984; DA (UK) 1982. Prev: Trainee GP Windsor VTS.

TOBIN, Francis Anthony Law Street Surgery, 49-51 Laws Street, Pembroke Dock SA72 6DJ Tel: 01646 683113 / 682002 Fax: 01646 622273 — MB BCh BAO 1987 NUI.

TOBIN, Geoffrey Brian Tobin, Redwood and Lalli, 25 Alms Hill, Bourn, Cambridge CB3 7SH Tel: 01954 719313 Fax: 01954 718012; Ave. House, High St, Madingley, Cambridge CB3 8AB — MRCS Eng. LRCP Lond. 1974; BSc Lond. 1971, MB BS 1974; MRCP (UK) 1977. (Guy's) Prev: Regist. (Med.) Addenbrookes Hosp. Camb.; SHO Brompton Hosp. Lond.; Resid. Med. Off. Nat. Heart Hosp. Lond.

TOBIN, Gerald William 7 Manor Park, Redland, Bristol BS6 7HJ Tel: 0117 907 1720; United Bristol Healthcare NHS Trust, Bristol BS1 3NU Tel: 0117 928 6314 — MD 1987 Dub.; MB BCh BAO 1977; FRCPI 1992, M 1980; FRCP Lond. 1998. Cons. Phys. c/o Elderly United Bristol Health Care NHS Trust.

TOBIN, Jean Margaret Department of Genitourinary Medicine, St. Mary's Hospital, Milton Road, Portsmouth PO3 6AD Tel: 02392866796 Fax: 02392 866769 Email: jean.tobin@porthosp.swest.nhs.uk — MB BS Lond. 1968; MRCS Eng. LRCP Lond. 1968; MFFP 1995; FRCOG 1989, M 1973. (Roy. Free) Cons. Genitourin. Med. St. Mary's Hosp. Portsmouth.; Cons. Civil. Adviser in GU Med. to the Roy. Navy. Socs: Sec. Brit. Federat. against Sexually Transm. Dis.s; Dep. Chairm. BMA Dermato-Venerology sub-comm.

TOBIN, John O'Hara (retired) 4 Gladstone Road, Headington, Oxford OX3 8LJ Tel: 01865 750926 — BM BCh 1942 Oxf.; MA, DM Oxf. 1991, BM BCh 1942; FRCP Lond. 1979, M 1971; FRCPath 1970, M 1963; Dip. Bact. Manch. 1948. Prev: Dir. Pub. Health Laborat. Oxf.

TOBIN, Judith Ann Heathfield Medical Centre, Lyttelton Road, Hampstead Garden Suburb, London N2 0EE Tel: 020 8458 9262 Fax: 020 8458 0300; 39 Southway, London NW11 6RX Tel: 020 8458 4617 Email: judith54-39@hotmail.com — MB BCh 1978 Wales; MRCGP 1984; DCH Eng. 1981; DRCOG 1980.

TOBIN, Martin Damian c/o Mr M. J. Rogers, 46 Wilga Road, Welwyn AL6 9PS — MB ChB 1988 Leic.

TOBIN, Michael John William Ringmead Medical Practice, Great Hollands Health Centre, Great Hollands Square, Bracknell RG12 8WY Tel: 01344 454338 Fax: 01344 861050; Lynton House, Lower Wokingham Road, Crowthorne RG45 6BT Tel: 01344 774080 — MRCS Eng. LRCP Lond. 1973; DObst RCOG 1975. (Leeds)

TOBIN, Michael Vincent Pinderfields Hospital, Aberford Road, Wakefield WF1 4DG Tel: 01924 212519; 5 Fennel Court, Carr Lane, Sandal, Wakefield WF2 6TS Tel: 01924 256378 — MB BCh BAO 1979 NUI; FRCP 1998; MD NUI 1991; MRCP (UK) 1983. Cons. Phys. Gastroenterol. Pinderfields Hosp. Wakefield. Prev: Sen. Regist. (Med. & Gastroenterol.) Walton Hosp. Liverp.; Research Fell. (Med.) Hope Hosp. Salford; Sen. Regist. BRd.green & Walton Hosps. Liverp.

TOBIN, Robert 16 Invergordon Avenue, Newlands, Glasgow G43 2HP — MB ChB 1992 Glas.; FRCS Glas. 1996; FRCS Ed. 1997. (Univ. Glas.) GP Regist. Glas. Socs: MDDUS; BMA; Fell. RCS Ed.

TOBIN, Simon David Manning Norwood Avenue Practice, 11 Norwood Avenue, Southport PR9 7EG Tel: 01704 226973 Fax: 01704 505758 — MB BS 1989 Lond.; BSc (Hons.) Lond. 1986; MRCGP 1994; DRCOG 1993; DCH RCP Lond. 1992.

TOBIN, Tracy Ann c/o Mr M. J. Rogers, 46 Wilga Road, Welwyn AL6 9PS — MB ChB 1989 Leic.

TOBY, John Paxton, CBE Chinkwell House, Great Brington, Northampton NN7 4HY Tel: 01604 770292 Email: johntobyuk@cs.com — MB Camb. 1965, BChir 1964; MRCP (U.K.) 1969; FRCGP 1980, M 1972. (St. Bart.) Assoc. Regional Adviser GPVTS Oxf. HA. Socs: Chairm. of Counc. Roy. Coll. of GPs. Prev: Hosp. Pract. (Gen. Med.) N.ampton Gen. Hosp.; Course Organiser Gen. Pract. Train. N.ampton Health Dist.; Regist. (Med.) N.ampton Gen. Hosp.

TOCEWICZ, Mr Krzysztof 11 Orchard Close, Newcastle upon Tyne NE12 6YZ — MD 1979 Warsaw; PhD Warsaw 1987; FRCS Glas. 1992. Regist. (Cardiothoracic. Surg.) Freeman Hosp. Newc. u. Tyne.

TOD, Edward David Macrae, OBE APCET Tel: 020 8665 1138 Fax: 020 8665 1118; The Firs, Budiam Road, Sandhurst TN18 5JY — MB ChB 1952 Ed.; FRCGP 1993, M 1971; Dip. Criminol. Lond. 1984. (Ed.) p/t Ed. PCG NHS; Cons. Scorpio Ltd.; JP; Chief Exec.

TOD

APCET. Socs: Fell. Med. Soc. Lond.; Liveryman Soc. Apoth.; Med. Jl.ists Assn. Prev: Dir. Forum for Indep. Research in Health Keele Univ.; Hon. Research Fell. (Clin. Epidemiol. & Social Med.) St. Geo. Hosp. Med. Sch.

TODD, Ian Alexander Arthur Upper Eden Medical Practice, The Medical Centre, Brough CA17 4AY Tel: 017683 41294 Fax: 017683 41068 — MB BS 1977 Newc.; MRCGP 1981; DRCOG 1980.

TODD, Alastair Stewart (retired) 10 Gillies Terrace, Broughty Ferry, Dundee DD5 3LF Tel: 01382 477758 — MB BS Durh. 1949; MD Durh. 1961; FRCPath 1976, M 1964. Prev: Cons. Haemat. Ninewells Hosp. Dundee.

TODD, Alison Agnes Jean Flat 11, Magnolia Lodge, 73 Chingford Avenue, London E4 6SX — MB ChB 1988 Aberd.; BA Durham. 1993.

TODD, Alistair William Hill House, Braehead, Avoch IV9 8QL — MB ChB 1981 Dundee; MRCP (UK) 1984; FRCR 1987. Cons. Radiol. Raigmore Hosp. Inverness. Prev: Regist. (Radiol.) Newc. HA.

TODD, Alwyn Edward Brooklands, 303 Belstead Road, Ipswich IP2 9EH — MB ChB 1960 Leeds.

TODD, Andrew James The Old Rectory, St. Mary Church, Cowbridge CF71 7LT — MRCS Eng. LRCP Lond. 1961. (W. Lond.) Sen. Med. Off. Home Office; Hon. Clin. Asst. (Psychiat.) Univ. Wales.

TODD, Andrew Martin 9 Colquhoun Drive, Bearsden, Glasgow G61 4NQ — MB ChB 1995 Aberd.

TODD, Ann-Marie 53 Glendevon Way, Broughty Ferry, Dundee DD5 3TG — MB ChB 1995 Dundee.

TODD, Barras James (retired) 12 Gravel Hill, Croydon CR0 5BB Tel: 020 8654 6406 Email: barras.todd@virgin.net — MB BS 1952 Lond.

TODD, Mr Brian David Stepping Hill Hospital, Poplar Grove, Stockport SK2 7JE Tel: 0161 483 1010 Email: brian.todd.@btinternet.com; Croft House, Maynestone Road, Chinley, High Peak SK23 6AH Tel: 01663 750568 — MB ChB 1980 Ed.; FRCS Ed. (Orth.) 1991; FRCS Ed. 1984. (Edinburgh) Cons. Trauma & Orthop. Surg. Stockport HA; Surg. Tutor RCS Eng. Socs: Brit. Orthop. Assn.; NW Spine Gp.; Manch. Med. Soc. Fell. Prev: Sen. Regist. (Orthop.) Sheff. Hosps.; Regist. (Orthop.) Roy. Sussex Co. Hosp. Brighton & St. Thos. Hosp. Lond.

TODD, Mr Bryan Seymour Accident Department, John Radcliffe Hospital, Headington, Oxford OX3 9DU — MB BChir 1979 Camb.; DPhil Oxf. 1989, MA 1982; FRCS Eng. 1984. Clin. Asst. (A & E Med.) John Radcliffe Hosp.; Research Off. (Neonat. Telemonitoring) Oxf. Univ. Prev: Research Fell. Progr. Research Gp. Oxf. Univ.; Regist. (Gen. Surg.) P.ss Margt. Hosp. Swindon.

TODD, Catherine Anne Margaret Loaningbank, Menstrie FK11 7EB — MB ChB 1988 Leic.; MRCGP 1992; DTM & H Liverp. 1994; DRCOG 1991. Prev: Regist. (Emerg. Med.) Auckland Hosp., NZ; Trainee GP/SHO Leeds Gen. Infirm. VTS.

TODD, Catherine Louise Mowbray House, 277 North End, Northallerton DL7 8DP Tel: 01609 775281 Fax: 01609 778029; Harewood House, 28 Harewood Lane, Northallerton DL7 8BQ Tel: 01609 773198 — MB ChB 1982 Leeds; MRCGP 1988; DO RCS Eng. 1986. (Leeds)

TODD, Ceri 23 Duffryn Street, Pontlottyn, Bargoed CF81 9RQ — MB BCh 1992 Wales.

TODD, Charles (retired) 5 Richmond Crescent, Bangor BT20 5QD Tel: 01247 472758 — MB BCh BAO Belf. 1964.

TODD, Christopher (retired) West Acre, 2 The Street, Morston, Holt NR25 7AA Tel: 01263 740118 — MRCS Eng. LRCP Lond. 1945; DA Eng. 1957. Prev: Asst. Lect. Dept. Physiol. St. Bart. Hosp. Med. Sch.

TODD, Colin Eric Campbell Kingston Hospital, Galsworthy Road, Kingston upon Thames KT2 7QB Tel: 0208 546 7711 Fax: 0208 934 3291; 15 Elm Road, Chessington KT9 1AF — MB BS 1979 Lond.; FRCS Ed. 1984; FRCR 1990. (Roy. Free) Cons. Radiol. Kingston Hosp. Trsut, Kingston Upon Thames. Prev: Sen. Regist. (Radiol.) Guy's Hosp. Lond.; Regist. (Radiol.) W.m. Hosp. Lond.; SHO (Cardiothoracic Surg.) Soton. Gen. Hosp.

TODD, David 1 Riverside Gardens, Barrow-in-Furness LA13 0DD Tel: 01229 821032 Fax: 01229 824689 — MB BS 1967 Lond. (Char. Cross) Med. Dir. Morecambe Bay Occupat. Health Serv. Barrow-in-Furness; Med. Adviser Kimberley Clark Barrow & N.fleet, Brit. Gas. HRL, Ashley Rock Ltd. & T. Brady & Son. Ltd. Socs: Soc.

Occupat. Med.; Roy. Soc. Med. Prev: Ho. Surg. W. Hill Hosp. Dartford; Ho. Phys. Joyce Green Hosp. Dartford.

TODD, David Anthony 38 Arundel Close, New Milton BH25 5UH — MB BS 1998 Sydney.

TODD, David Bryan 17 Orford Gardens, Strawberry Hill, Twickenham TW1 4PL Email: mpmdbt@bath.ac.uk — MB BChir 1984 Camb.; MA Oxf. 1982; FRCA 1994; MRCGP 1990; DA (UK) 1992; DCH RCP Lond. 1989; DRCOG 1988. GP; Sports Med. Course. Socs: BMA; Frenchay Hosp. Triathlon Club. Prev: Regist. Rotat. (Anaesth.) S. W.ern RHA.

TODD, Mr Denis Oliver University Health Service, 5 Lennoxvale, Belfast BT9 5BY Tel: 028 9033 5551 Fax: 028 9033 5540 — MB BCh BAO 1977 Belf.; FRCS Ed. 1981; MFOM RCPI 1986; MFOM RCP Lond. 1987, A 1985; MRCGP 1983; DObst 1980; Cert. Av. Med. 1987; FFOM RCPI 1997; FFOM RCP Lond. 1998. Sen. Med. Off. Qu. Univ. Belf. Socs: Pres. Soc. Occupat. Med. (UK); (Ex Gp. Chairm.) Occupat. Med.; BMA. Prev: GP Cherryvalley & Med. Off. DHSS (N.. Irel.).

TODD, Derick Morris Flat 6, 229 Marsland Road, Sale M33 3NR Email: dericktodd@compuserve.com; 7 Corsehill Park, Ayr KA7 2UG Tel: 01292 267366 — MB ChB 1991 Ed.; BMedSci (Hons.) Ed. 1989; MRCP Ed. 1994. Regist. Rotat. (Cardiol.) Trent Region.; Research Regist. Manch. Heart Centre. Prev: SHO Rotat. (Med.) Lothian HB Edin.

TODD, Elizabeth Anne 7 Cathedral Rise, Lichfield WS13 7LP — MB ChB 1984 Manch.

TODD, Elizabeth Jane Bradley Stoke Surgery, Brook Way, Bradley Stoke North, Bristol BS32 9DS Tel: 01454 616262 Fax: 01454 619161 — MB ChB 1979 Bristol; BSc (Hons.) Lond. 1968, PhD 1974; Cert Prescribed Equiv. Exp. JCPTGP 1987; Cert. Family Plann. JCC 1985. (Bris.) GP Bristol. Socs: Soc. Occupat. Med.

TODD, Miss Felicity Nicola A&E Dept, Bradford Royal Infirmary, Duckworth Lane, Bradford BD9 6RJ Tel: 01274 364457 Email: felicity.todd@bradfordhospitals.nhs.uk — MB ChB 1987 Liverp.; FRCS Ed. 1994; FFAEM 1998. Cons.(A&E.) Brad Roy Infim. Socs: Brit. Assn. Accid. & Emerg. Med.; Assn. Study Med. Educat.; Eur. Resusc. Counc. Prev: Regist. (A & E) N. Trent Doncaster; Sen. Regist.. Yorks. Deanery 1996-1998.

TODD, Geoffrey Robert George Moyle Hospital, Larne BT40 1RP — MB BCh BAO 1975 Belf.; MRCP (UK) 1979. Cons. Phys. Moyle Hosp. Larne.

TODD, Mr George Buchanan Coniston Broad Chalke, Salisbury SP5 5DH Tel: 01722 780595 — MB BChir 1966 Camb.; FRCS Eng. 1970; MRCS Eng. LRCP Lond. 1965. (Univ. Coll. Hosp.) Cons. Surg. (ENT) Salisbury NHS Health Care Trust. Socs: Roy. Soc. Med. (Mem. Otol. & Laryngol. Sects.). Prev: Sen. Regist. (ENT) St. Thos. Hosp. Lond.; Sen. Surg. Off. Roy. Nat. Throat, Nose & Ear Hosp. Lond.; Sen. Lect. W. Indies Jamaica.

TODD, Gillian Bees 6th Floor, Churchill House, Churchill Way, Cardiff CF10 2TW Tel: 029 2022 6216 Fax: 029 2023 0106; 20 High Fields, Cardiff CF5 2QA Tel: 029 2057 8244 — MB BCh Wales 1966; FFPHM 1987. Chief Exec. Bro Taf HA. Prev: Chief. Exec. S. Glam. DHA; Chief Exec. S. Birm. Acute Unit; Dist. Gen. Manager Centr. Notts. HA.

TODD, Graham Philip Anthony 1 Alexandra Road, Brookvale, Basingstoke RG21 7RG — MB ChB 1994 Sheff.; BMedSci Sheff. 1993. Ho. Surg. (Emerg.) Middlemore Hosp. Auckland, NZ. Prev: SHO (Orthop.) Auckland; SHO (A & E) Winchester; SHO (Geriat.) Bradford.

TODD, Iain Charles Astley Ainslie Hospital, 133 Grange Loan, Edinburgh EH9 2HL Tel: 0131 537 9087 Fax: 0131 537 9087; 48 The Green, Pencaitland, Tranent EH34 5HE Tel: 01875 340832 Fax: 0131 537 9080 — MD 1991 Ed.; BSc Ed. 1976, MD 1991, MB ChB 1979; MRCP (UK) 1982. Cons. (Rehabil. Med.) Astley Ainslie Hosp. Edin. Socs: Brit. Cardiac Soc.; Brit. Soc. For Rehab. Med.; Brit. Assoc. of Stroke Phys.s. Prev: Sen Regist. (Rehabil. Med.) Astley Ainslie Hosp. Edin.; Regist. (Gen. Med.) Vict. Infirm. Glas.; Regist. & SHO (Gen. Med. Rotat.) Hull.

TODD, Iain Mathieson 2 Gartness Court, Drymen, Glasgow G63 0AX — MB ChB 1948 Glas.; MRCGP 1973. (Univ. Glas.) Prev: Ho. Surg. W.. Infirm. Glas.; Obst. Ho. Surg. Stobhill Hosp. Glas.

TODD, Ian Douglas Hutchinson (retired) 455 Parrs Wood Road, Didsbury, Manchester M20 5NE Tel: 0161 445 9497 — MB ChB 1950 Aberd.; FRCP Lond. 1975, M 1958; FRCR 1975; FFR 1962;

DMRT Eng. 1960. Prev: Dep. Dir. (Radiother.) & Cons. (Radiother. & Oncol.) Christie Hosp. & Holt Radium Inst. Manch.

TODD, Ian Michael 14 St Peters Avenue, Weston Super Mare BS23 2JU — BM BCh 1983 Oxf.

TODD, Sir Ian Pelham, KBE (retired) 4 Longmead Close, Farleigh Road, Norton St Philip, Bath BA2 7NS Tel: 01373 834081 Fax: 01373 834081 — MRCS Eng. LRCP Lond. 1944; MD Toronto 1945, MS 1956; FRCS Eng. 1949; Hon. FRCS Glas.; Hon. FRCSC; Hon. FACS; Hon. FRACS; Hon. FCS (SA); DCH Eng. 1947. Prev: Dir. Overseas Doctors Higher Train. Scheme RCS Eng.

TODD, James Andrew 1 Crag View, Sutton-in-Craven, Keighley BD20 7QE Tel: 01535 631852 — MB ChB 1993 Manch. (Manchester) SHO. (Psychiat.) Leeds. Prev: SHO. (Psychiat.); GP Regist. Springfield Med Cen. Bingley.; SHO. (Psychiat.) Airedale Gen Hosp. Keighley/.

TODD, James Gordon Eastfield, Tandlehill Road, Kilbarchan, Johnstone PA10 2DQ — MB ChB 1975 Glas.; FFA RCS Eng. 1979. Cons. Anaesth. W.. Infirm. Glas. & Inst. Neurol. Sci. Glas. Socs: Assn. Anaesth. Gt. Brit. & Irel.; Anaesth. Research Soc. Gt. Brit. Prev: Sen. Regist. (Anaesth.) W.. Infirm. Glas.; Regist. (Anaesth.) Roy. Infirm. Glas.; Sen. Regist. (Anaesth.) Palmerston N., N.Z.

TODD, James Peter (retired) The Red House, 47 Clayton Road, Jesmond, Newcastle upon Tyne NE2 4RQ Tel: 0191 281 5425 — MB BS Durh. 1960; DObst RCOG 1964.

TODD, Jennifer Ann 3 Longbeach Road, Battersea, London SW11 5SS Tel: 020 7585 0991 — MB ChB 1990 Manch.; BSc St. And. 1987; MRCGP 1994; DRCOG 1993. (St Andrews) Specialist Regist. (Palliat. Med.) S. Thames Rotat. Socs: APM; RCGP. Prev: SHO (Palliat. Med.) St. Ann's Hospice Manch.

TODD, John Bedlington Medical Group, Glebe Road, Bedlington NE22 6JX Tel: 01670 822695 Fax: 01670 531860; 13 Sweethope Dene, Morpeth NE61 2DZ — MB ChB 1985 Leeds; BSc (Hons.) Physiol. Leeds 1982; MRCGP 1989.

TODD, John Archibald 53 Glendevon Way, Broughty Ferry, Dundee DD5 3TG — MB ChB 1995 Dundee.

TODD, Mr John Kirkland (retired) 9 Colquhorn Drive, Bearsden, Glasgow Tel: 0141 942 0908 — MD 1962 Glas.; BSc Glas. 1955, MD (Hons.) 1962, MB ChB 1958; FRCS Ed. 1963; FRCS Glas. 1963. Prev: Cons. Surg. Roy. Infirm. Glas.

TODD, John Neild (retired) 20 Highfields, Cardiff CF5 2QA Tel: 029 2057 8244 — MB BS 1952 Lond.; FFCM 1985, MFCM 1982. Prev: Dir. Pub. Health Sheff. HA.

TODD, John Ovenstone, Wing Cdr. RAF Med. Br. Retd. Moray Health Services, Doctor Gray's Hospital, Elgin IV30 1SN Tel: 01343 543131; Kyle Lodge, Lochiepots Road, Miltonduff, Elgin IV30 8WL Email: 106731.3026@compuserve.com — MB ChB 1979 Aberd.; MRCGP 1990; AFOM RCP Lond. 1992; MRCPsych 1985; DAvMed 1991; T(GP) 1991; T(Psych) 1991. Cons. Psychiat. Doctor Gray's Hosp. Elgin. Prev: Sen. Med. Off. RAF St. Athan; Hon. Regist. Warneford Hosp. Oxf.; Clin. Assoc. Psychogeriat. Maudsley Hosp. Lond.

TODD, John Reynard Comrie 1 Barnton Park Dell, Edinburgh EH4 6HW Tel: 0131 476 0024 Email: john.todd2@virgin.net — MB ChB St. And. 1966; DObst RCOG 1968. Prev: SHO (O & G) Dundee Roy. Infirm.; Anaesth. Centr.lasarett Uddevalla, Sweden; Research Fell. (Ophth.) Univ. Toronto, Canada.

TODD, Jonathan James 70 Rofant Road, Northwood HA6 3BA — MB BS 1994 Lond.

TODD, June Lorraine Red Reap Surgery, 31 Coton Road, Nuneaton CV11; 29 Seneschal Road, Chelesmore, Coventry CV3 5LF — MB ChB 1972 Sheff.; MRCGP 1977; DObst RCOG 1974.

TODD, Katharine Hilda Lesley (retired) Spindle Tree, Pant Lane, Austwick, Lancaster LA2 8BH — MRCS Eng. LRCP Lond. 1961; MA Oxf. 1939; DObst RCOG 1965. Prev: Clin. Asst. Cas. & Accid. Dept. Bradford Roy. Infirm.

TODD, Kathryn Helen Collum House, 214 Leckhampton Road, Cheltenham GL53 0AW — MB BS 1992 Lond.

TODD, Killingworth Richard (retired) 18 Bshop Road, Nether Stowey, Bridgwater TA5 1NP — MB BS Lond. 1942. Prev: Cas. Surg. Regist. Edgware Gen. Hosp.

TODD, Kim Paula Knight, Todd, Jackson and Gilliland, Hawthorn House Medical Centre, 28-30 Heaton Road, Newcastle upon Tyne NE6 1SD Tel: 0191 265 5543/6246 Fax: 0191 276 2985; 41

Manor Fields, Benton, Newcastle upon Tyne NE12 8AG — BM BS 1981 Nottm.; MRCGP 1986.

TODD, Mairi Jane Alleyn Queensbridge Group Practice, 24 Holly Street, London E8 3XP Tel: 020 7254 1101 Fax: 020 7923 1541 — MB BS 1984 Lond.; MRCGP 1989. (St. Bart.) Partner in Gen. Pract. Lond. Socs: Med. Pract. Union; BMA; Soc. Wom. in Med. Prev: GP Halesworth; Trainee GP Lond. VTS.

TODD, Margaret Mary The Gables, 3 Main Road, Biddenham, Bedford MK40 4BB Tel: 01234 353357 — MB BCh BAO 1951 NUI; LM Coombe 1953. (Univ. Coll. Dub.) Prev: GP Bedford; JHMO Cas. Dept. Hillingdon Hosp. Uxbridge; Orthop. Regist. St. And. Hosp. Billericay.

TODD, Marie Colette Springburn Health Centre, 200 Springburn Way, Glasgow G21 1TR Tel: 0141 531 9681 Fax: 0141 531 6705; 9 Colquhoun Drive, Bearsden, Glasgow G61 4NQ Tel: 0141 942 0908 — MB ChB 1965 Glas.; DA Eng. 1969. (Glas.) GP Glas. Prev: Late Anaesth. Krankenhaus Wattwil, Switz..

TODD, Neil James Department of Microbiology, St. James' University Hospital, Beckett St., Leeds LS9 7TF Tel: 01532 433144 Fax: 01532 837085; Lynn Dene, Back Lane, Barkston Ash, Tadcaster LS24 9PL — MB ChB 1984 Bristol; BA Oxf. 1981; MRCPath 1991. Cons. Microbiol. St. Jas. Univ. Trust Hosp.; Hon. Sen. Lect. (Microbiol.) Univ. Leeds. Prev: Sen. Regist. (Microbiol.) Yorks. RHA.

TODD, Neville Barras Totnes Hospital, Coronation Road, Totnes TQ9 5GH Tel: 01803 862622 — MB BS 1978 Lond.; MRCPsych 1988; MRCGP 1982; DRCOG 1980. Cons. (Old Age Psychiat.) S. Devon Healthcare Trust Torbay. Prev: Sen. Regist. (Psychiat.) St. Lawrences Hosp. Bodmin; Sen. Regist. (Psychiat.) Moorhaven Hosp. Plymouth.

TODD, Mr Nicholas Vyner Department of Neurosurgery, Regional Neurosciences Centre, Newcastle General Hospital, Newcastle upon Tyne NE4 6BE Tel: 0191 273 8811 Fax: 0191 273 0117; Foulmartlaw, Gallowmill, Morpeth NE61 3TZ Tel: 01661 881694 — MD 1987 Lond.; MB BS 1978; FRCS Eng. 1982. (Guy's) Cons. Neurosurg. Regional Neurosci. Centre Newc. u. Tyne. Prev: Sen. Regist. (Neurosurg.) Inst. Neurosci. Glas.; MRC Research Fell.

TODD, Norman Alexander 16 Ormonde Drive, Glasgow G44 3SJ — MB ChB 1951 Glas.; FRCP Ed. 1976, M 1961; FRCPsych 1979, M 1972; DPM Eng. 1959. (Glas.) Socs: BMA. Prev: Regist. Psychiat. Unit, Stobhill Hosp. Glas.; Ho. Surg. Roy. N.. Infirm. Inverness; SHO Robroyston Hosp. Glas.

TODD, Olive Isobel (retired) 18 Bishop Road, Nether Stowey, Bridgwater TA5 1NP — MRCS Eng., LRCP Lond. 1947. Prev: Ho. Surg. Roy. Salop. Infirm. Shrewsbury.

TODD, Oliver Rowland The Gables, 3 Main Road, Biddenham, Bedford MK40 4BB Tel: 01234 353357 — MRCS Eng. LRCP Lond. 1952. (King's Coll. Hosp.) Prev: GP Bedford; Ho. Phys. Brook Hosp. Woolwich; Ho. Surg. (Obst.) St. And. Hosp. Billericay.

TODD, Pamela Margaret Box 46 Department of Dermatology, Addenbrookes NHS Trust, Hills Road, Cambridge CB2 2QQ — MB BS 1984 Lond.; FRCP 2000; BSc Lond. 1981; MRCP (UK) 1987. Cons. Dermatol., Addenbrooke Hosp., Camb.; Assoc. Lect. Univ. of Camb. Med. Sch. Socs: Brit. Med. Assoc.; Melanoma study Gp.; Brit. Soc for Study of Vulval Dis. Prev: Regist. (Dermat.) Glas. Roy. Infirm.; Dermat. Sen. Regist. Roy. Hosps., Lond.; Dermat. Regist. Kings Coll. Hosp., Lond.

TODD, Peter Graham (retired) Redbourn, The Spinney, Bassett, Southampton SO16 7FW Tel: 01703 768763 — MD Lond. 1941, MB BS (Hons. Surg. & Path.) 1939; FRCP Lond. 1964, M 1940; MRCS Eng. LRCP Lond. 1939; DCH Eng. 1944. Prev: Phys. Roy. S. Hants. Hosp., Soton. Gen. Hosp. & Hythe Hosp.

TODD, Peter James Sunnymount, 10 Oldfield Way, Heswall, Wirral CH60 6RG — MB BS 1973 Lond.; FRCP Lond. 1990; MRCP (UK) 1975; DCH Eng. 1978. (Middlx.) Cons. (Paediat.) Arrowe Pk. Hosp. Merseyside. Prev: Sen. Regist. (Paediat.) Roy. Liverp. Childr. Hosp. & Alder Hey Childr.; Hosp.

TODD, Rebecca Grace 10 Pentland Crescent, Edinburgh EH10 6NP — MB ChB 1993 Ed.

TODD, Richard George The Shrubbery, 65A Perry Street, Northfleet, Gravesend DA11 8RD Tel: 01474 356661 Fax: 01474 534542; 84 Whitehill Road, Gravesend DA12 5PH — MB BS 1981 Newc.; MRCGP 1985; DRCOG 1984.

TODD

TODD, Richard William 18 Sandy Lane, Chester CH3 5UL — MB ChB 1992 Birm.

TODD, Mr Robert Marshall 9 Oaklands Drive, Bishop's Stortford CM23 2BZ Tel: 01279 53166 — MB ChB 1956 Glas.; FRCS Ed. 1971. Cons. Ophth. Herts. & Essex Gen. Hosp. Bishop's Stortford. Prev: Cons. in Ophth. RAF Hosp. Cosford.

TODD, Robert McLaren (retired) 17 Beauclair Drive, Liverpool L15 6XG Tel: 0151 722 2218 — MA Camb. 1941, MD 1946, MB BChir 1940; MRCS Eng. LRCP Lond. 1940; FRCP Lond. 1965, M 1945; DCH Eng. 1943. Prev: Reader in Child Health. Univeristy of Liverp..

TODD, Mr Ronald Stanley 29 Boundary Drive, Moseley, Birmingham B13 8NY Tel: 0121 442 2672 — MB ChB 1954 Liverp.; FRCS Eng. 1961; FRCS Ed. 1960; DObst RCOG 1956. Mem. Ct.. Examrs. RCS Eng. Socs: Liverp. Med. Inst. Prev: Cons. Surg. Clwyd HA; Hon. Sen. Surg. Regist. Liverp. Roy. Infirm. & BRd.green Hosp.; Demonst. (Anat.) & Lect. (Surg.) Univ. Liverp.

TODD, Rose Miriam (retired) The Red House, 47 Clayton Road, Jesmond, Newcastle upon Tyne NE2 4RQ Tel: 0191 281 5425 — MB BS Durh. 1960.

TODD, Ruth Louise 4 Canterbury Road, Brotton, Saltburn-by-the-Sea TS12 2XG — MB BS 1993 Newc.; DRCOG 1996. (Newcastle) SHO (Palliat. Med.) Teesside Hospice Middlesbrough.

TODD, Sarah Elizabeth 87 Allensbank Road, Cardiff CF14 3PP — MB BCh 1990 Wales.

TODD, Stephen Andrew 30 Rutherglen Park, Bangor BT19 1DD — MB BCh BAO 1997 Belf.

TODD, Virginia Ann Lakeside Health Centre, Tavy Bridge, Thamesmead, London SE2 9UQ Tel: 020 8310 3281 — MB BS 1966 Lond.; FRCP Canada 1974; DObst RCOG 1971; DCH Eng. 1971.

TODD, William Health Centre, Linwood, Johnstone PA5 7DG Tel: 01505 21051; 9 Crossways, Houston, Johnstone PA6 7DG Tel: 01505 613729 — MB ChB 1947 Glas. (Glas.) Socs: BMA. Prev: Chief Med. Off. Nchanga Consolidated Copper Mines Ltd. (Broken Hill; Div.) Kabwe, Zambia; Med. Supt. Miss. Hosp. Jalna, India.

TODD, William George 4 Merchiston Crescent, Edinburgh EH10 5AN Tel: 0131 229 5400 — MB ChB 1943 Aberd.

TODD, William Taylor Andrew Infectious Diseases Unit, Monklands Hospital, Monkscourt Avenue, Airdrie ML6 0JS Tel: 01236 712241 Fax: 01236 712449; 17 Crosshill Drive, Rutherglen, Glasgow G73 3QT Tel: 0141 647 7288 Email: andrew@todds.demon.co.uk — MB ChB 1977 Ed.; BSc (Hons.) Ed. 1974. MB ChB 1977; FRCP Glas. 1990; FRCP Ed. 1988; T(M) 1991. Cons. Phys. Gen. Med. & Communicable Dis. Monklands Dist. Gen. Hosp. Socs: Roy. Medicochirurgical Soc. Glas.; Scott. Soc. Phys.; Coun. Mem. Brit. Infec. Soc. Prev: Sen. Regist. (Communicable Dis.) City Hosp. Edin.; Lect. (Med.) Harare, Zimbabwe; Regist. (Gen. Med. Endocrinol.) Roy. Infirm. Edin.

TODD-POKROPEK, Cecilia Jane 2 Links Gardens, London SW16 3JW — MB ChB 1997 Liverp.

TODES, Cecil Jacob (retired) 38 Clifton Hill, London NW8 0QG Tel: 020 7624 4533 — MRCS Eng. LRCP Lond. 1960; BDS Witwatersrand 1953; FRCPsych 1985, M 1971; FDS RCS Eng. 1956; DPM Eng. 1965. Prev: Cons. Child Psychiat. Paddington Centre for Psychother.

TODMAN, Elaine Garden 8, 21 Fernbank Road, Redland, Bristol BS6 6PZ — MB ChB 1996 Bristol.

TODMAN, Rodney Claud Frederick (retired) 14 Dovehouse Court, Grange Road, Olton, Solihull B91 1EW Tel: 0121 705 8685 — MB ChB Ed. 1944. Prev: GP Druids Heath Birm.

TODMAN, Roger Herbert Department of Child Health, Willows Child Development Centre, Pedders Lane, Ashton, Preston PR2 2TR Tel: 01772 401472 Fax: 01772 768122; 6 Ascot Road, Thornton-Cleveleys FY5 5HN Tel: 01253 866150 — MB ChB 1976 Liverp.; DCCH RCP Ed. 1991. SCMO (Child Health) Guild Community Health Care Preston. Socs: Fac. Community Health.

TOEG, Daniel Caversham Practice, 4 Peckwater Street, London NW5 2UP Tel: 020 7530 6500 Fax: 020 7530 6530 — MB ChB 1985 Manch.; DFFP 1998; T(GP) 1992; MRCGP 1992; MRCP (UK) 1988; BSc (Hons.) Manch. 1982. (Manchester University) PCG Bd. Mem., S. Camden PCG. Prev: Trainee GP Highams Pk. Lond.; SHO Rotat. (Med.) S.end Gen. Hosp.

TOELLNER, Christoph Barthold Weavers Lane Surgery, 1 Weavers Lane, Whitburn, Bathgate EH47 0QU Tel: 01501 740297 Fax: 01501 744302 — State Exam Med 1986 Bonn; MD Bonn 1988. (Bonn) GP Whitburn. Socs: BMA; Roy. Coll. Gen. Pract.; Med. Protec. Soc.

TOES, Norman Antony (retired) 56 Mayfield Road, Writtle, Chelmsford CM1 3EL Tel: 01245 421729 — MB BS 1949 Lond.; MRCS Eng. LRCP Lond. 1949; DObst RCOG 1954. Prev: Sen. Med. Off. Prison Med. Serv. Home Office.

TOFF, Nicholas James 12 St Annes Close, Winchester SO22 4LQ — MB BS 1981 Lond.; BSc (Hons.) Lond. 1977; FRCA 1988; DRCOG 1983; Cert. Av. Med. 1987. (Charing Cross) Prev: Regist. (Anaesth.) Bristol Extended Train. Scheme; SHO (Anaesth.) S.mead Hosp. Bristol; SHO (Anaesth.) Roy. Hants. Co. Hosp.

TOFF, Penelope Rebecca 20 Chatham Road, Oxford OX1 4UY Tel: 01865 721495 — MB BS 1986 Lond.; BSc Basic Med. Scs. & Psychol. Lond. 1983. SHO (Paediat.) Oxf. Radcliffe Hosp. Trust. Prev: SHO (A & E) Oxf. Radcliffe Hosp. Trust; SHO (Genitourin. Med.) St. Mary's Hosp. Trust Lond.; SHO & Clin. Med. Off. (Family Plann. & Wom. Health) Lothian HB.

TOFF, William Daniel Tilcocks, 4 West Hill, Aspley Guise, Milton Keynes MK17 8DN — MB BS 1981 Lond.; BSc (Hons.) Lond. 1978. (Univ. Coll. Hosp.)

TOFT, Anthony Douglas, CBE Endocine Clinic, Royal Infirmary, Edinburgh EH3 9YW Tel: 0131 536 2093 Fax: 0131 536 2091 — BSc Ed. 1966, MD 1976, MB ChB 1969; Hon. FACP 1993; Hon. FRACP 1993; MRCP (UK) 1971; FRCS Ed. 1993; FRCP Glas. 1993; FRCPI 1993; FRCP Lond. 1992; FRCP Ed. 1980; Hon. FFPharm Med. 1994; Hon. FRCPC 1994; Hon. FRCGP 1994. Cons. Phys. Roy. Infirm. Edin. Socs: Assn. Phys. Prev: Ho. Surg. & Ho. Phys. Roy. Infirm. Edin.

TOFT, Kristan Celia 36 Paddock Close, Radcliffe-on-Trent, Nottingham NG12 2BX — MB ChB 1989 Leeds.

TOFT, Neil John 20 Craighouse Terrace, Edinburgh EH10 5LJ — MB ChB 1994 Ed.

TOFTE, Barclay Clemence Bedford Cottage, Egley Road, Woking GU22 0AT Tel: 01483 22685 — MB ChB 1980 Stellenbosch.

TOFTS, Elizabeth Jane Finsbury Health Care, 5 London Wall Buildings, Finsbury Circus, London EC2M 5NS Tel: 0207 638 0909; 21 East Sheen Avenue, East Sheen, London SW14 8AR Tel: 020 8876 5067 — MB BS 1987 Lond.; MA Camb. 1987, BA (Hons.) 1984; DRCOG 1993. (Camb. & Roy. Free) GP Partner (p/t).

TOFTS, Louise Jane The Bays, West Edge, Marsh Gibbon, Bicester OX27 0HA — MB BS 1998 Lond.

TOGHILL, Peter James (retired) 119 Lambley Lane, Burton Joyce, Nottingham NG14 5BL Tel: 0115 931 2446 Fax: 0115 931 2446 Email: ptoghill@dialstart.net — MB BS Lond. 1955; MD Lond. 1966; FRCP Lond. 1975; FRCP Ed. 1973, M 1961; MRCP (UK) 1962; MRCS Eng. LRCP Lond. 1955; DObst RCOG 1959. Emerit. Cons. Phys. Univ. Hosp. Nottm. Prev: Censor Roy. Coll. Phys. Lond.

TOGOBO, Ambrose Kofi Whipps Cross Hospital, Whipps Cross Road, Leytonstone, London E11 1NR Tel: 020 8539 5522; 59 King's Road, Leytonstone, London E11 1AU Tel: 020 8558 4171 Fax: 020 8539 5552 — Vrach 1971 Lvov Med Inst., USSR; Vrach Lvov Med. Inst., USSR 1971; Cert. Family Plann. JCC 1986; DA (UK) 1981; DTM & H Liverp. 1973. Assoc. Specialist & Clin. Asst. (Anaesth.) Whipps Cross Hosp. Lond. Socs: BMA; Med. Protec. Soc. Prev: SHO (Anaesth.) Basildon Hosp.; SHO (Anaesth. & O & G) King's Mill Hosp.; SHO (Obst.) Firs Matern. Hosp. Nottm.

TOH, Chee Tse Accident & Emergency Department, Central Middlesex Hospital NHS Trust, Acton Lane, Park Royal, London NW10 7NS — MB BS 1990 Lond.; BSc (Hons.) (Pharm. with Basic Med. Sc.) 1987.

TOH, Cheng Hock Royal Liverpool University Hospital, Prescot St., Liverpool L7 8XP Tel: 0151 706 4322 Fax: 0151 706 5810 Email: toh@liverpool.ac.uk — MB ChB 1985 Sheff.; MB ChB (Hons.) Sheff. 1985; MD Sheff. 1995; MRCP (UK) 1988; MRCPath 1994; FRCP (UK) 1999. (Univ. Sheff.) Sen. Lect. (Haemat.) Roy. Liverp. Hosp. Socs: Brit. Soc. Haematol.; Brit. Soc. Haematol. & Thrombosis; Amer. Soc. Haematol. Prev: Sen. Regist. (Haemat.) Sheff. Hosps.; Post-Doctoral Fell. (Haemat.) Qu. Univ. Kingston, Canada; Regist. (Haemat.) Roy. Hallamsh. Hosp. Sheff.

TOH, Khay-Wee 38 Burr Close, London E1W 1NB — MB BS 1994 Lond.

TOH, Mr Simon Khay Chuan Southampton General Hospital, Tremona Road, Southampton SO16 6YD Tel: 02380 777222 Fax: 02380 794020; 14 Victoria Avenue, Surbiton KT6 5DW Tel: 020 8390 5475 Email: simon_toh@compuserve.com — MB BS 1986 Lond.; FRCS Eng. 1991; FRCS (Gen.Surg) Intercoll Spec Exam. Intercoll Bd.Gen.Surg. Ed.1999. (UMDS Guy's Hosp. Lond.) Specialist Regist. Gen.Surg.N.Hamp.Hosp.Basingstoke. Socs: AUGIS; Mem. AESGBI; Mem. ASIT. Prev: Surg.Regist.Roy.Adelaide.Hosp.Austr.; Specialist Regist. in Surg. Univ.Soton.; Advanced Surgic. Regist. Roy. Adelaide Hosp. Australia.

TOHANI, Vinod Kumar Southern Health and Social Services Board, Tower Hill, Armagh BT61 9DR Tel: 01861 41004 Fax: 01861 414551 — MB BCh BAO 1976 Dub.; FFPHM 2001; FFPHM 2001; BA Dub. 1974, MA 1977; MSc (Community Med.) Univ. Lond. 1982; MFPHM RCPI 1992; MFCM RCP (UK) 1986; MICGP 1984. Cons. Communicable Dis. Control SHSSB Craigavon; Chairm. Pub. Health Med. & Community Health N. Irel.; Mem. of NI Food Standard Advisery Comm. 2000-2003. Socs: BMA; Soc. for Social Med.; Travel Assn. Prev: SCM WHSSB; Specialist (Community Med.) Burnley, Pendle & Rossendale HA.

TOHILL, John 100 Somerton Road, Belfast BT15 4DE — MB BCh BAO 1949 Belf.; BA Lond. 1938; BComSc Belf. 1942; DPH 1955. (Belf.)

TOHILL, John Gerard Diamond Medical Centre, Meeting Street, Magherafelt BT45 6ED Tel: 028 7930 2902 Fax: 028 7930 1891; 5 Dunard Park, Magherafelt BT45 6EG Tel: 028 7963 1479 — MB BCh BAO 1974 Belf.; MRCGP 1978. (Queens University Belfast)

TOHILL, Martin 47 Derramore Heights, Magherafelt BT45 5RX Tel: 02879 301575 Email: martintohill@occupationalhealth.fsnet.co.uk — MB BCh BAO 1989 Belf.; 2000 Docc Mel; MRCGP 1994; DFFP 1993; DRCOG 1992. Occupat.al Phys.; Med. Ref.; GP Locum. Socs: BMA; BMAS; SOM. Prev: Trainee GP/SHO (Paediat.) Ulster Hosp. Dundonald; SHO (Psychiat.) Tyrone & Fermanagh; SHO (Med.) & Ho. Off. Mid Ulster Hosp.

TOHILL, Mel Patrick 5 Dorchester Park, Belfast BT9 6RH — MB BCh BAO 1997 Belf.

TOKE, Eric (Surgery), 2 Radnor Place, Liverpool L6 4BD Tel: 0151 263 3100; (home), 5 Dudlow Gardens, Liverpool L18 2HA Tel: 0151 722 1871 — MB ChB 1950 Liverp.; FRCGP 1987. JP; Clin. Asst. (Psychiat.) & Clin. Med. Off. Liverp. DHA; Local Med. Off. Civil Serv. Socs: Liverp. Med. Inst.; Merseyside Med.-Legal Soc.

TOLAN, Damian John Michael St James Univ. Hospital, Leeds LS9 7TP — MB ChB 1997 Leeds. Sen Ho. Off., St James' Univ. Hosp. Leeds.

TOLAN, Emma Louise 13 Euxton Cl, Bury BL8 2HY — MB ChB 1997 Leeds.

TOLAN, Mr Michael Jude Wessex Cardiothoracic Unit, Southampton General Hospital, Tremona Road, Southampton SO16 6YD — MB BCh BAO 1985 NUI; FRCSI 1992; MRCPI 1988.

TOLAN, Shaun Paul 58 Albion Street, St Helens WA10 2HD — MB BCh 1997 Wales.

TOLAND, Jane Mary Paula 8 Stockmans Drive, Belfast BT11 9AU — MB BCh BAO 1988 Belf.; MB BCh Belf. 1988.

TOLAND, Mary Waterside Health Centre, Glendermot Road, Londonderry BT47 6AU Tel: 028 7132 0100 Fax: 028 7134 9323; 110 Caw Hill Park, Londonderry BT47 6XX — MB BCh BAO 1986 NUI; MRCP (UK) 1989; MRCGP 1992; DRCOG 1991; DCH NUI 1990.

TOLAND, William James Whiteabbey Health Centre, 95 Doagh Road, Newtownabbey BT37 9QN Tel: 028 9086 4341 Fax: 028 9086 0443 — MB BCh BAO 1971 Belf.; DObst 1973.

TOLANEY, Mohan Dulahinomal 3 Woodstock Drive, Worsley, Manchester M28 2NP — MB BS 1965 Bombay.

TOLANEY, Padma Moham 3 Woodstock Drive, Worsley, Manchester M28 2NP — MB BS 1965 Bombay.

TOLBA, Mr Mahmoud Abd-Allah Orchard House, High Halden, Ashford TN26 3BS Tel: 01580 240333 — MB BCh 1972 Cairo; MSc Cairo 1980; MRCOG 1993. Assoc. Specialist (Gyn.) Benenden Hosp. Cranbrook. Socs: Exec. Comm. Brit. Soc. (Psychosomatics in Obst. & Gyn.); Eur. Assn. Obst. & Gyn.

TOLCHER, Rosamond Anne Family Planning Service, Central Health Clinic, East Park Terrace, Southampton SO14 0YL Tel: 02380 902506 Fax: 02380 902600; Beech House, 123B Newton Road, Warsash, Southampton SO31 9GY Tel: 01489 578324 — BM 1985 Soton.; BM (Hons. Distinc.) Clin. Med. & Med. Sci. Soton. 1985; MFFP 1994; DRCOG 1987. (Soton.) Cons. (Family Plann. & ReProduc. Health). Prev: SHO (A & E & Paediat.) Soton. Gen. Hosp.; SHO (O & G) P.ss Anne Hosp. Soton.

TOLE, Derek Michael 2 Helme Lodge, Burton Road, Natland, Kendal LA9 7QA; 3 Middleton Hall, Belford NE70 7LF — MB ChB 1982 Manch.; MRCGP 1988; DRCOG 1985; DGM 1987. GP Belford. Prev: Trainee GP S.W. Cumbria VTS.

TOLEDANO, Helen 21 Florence Street, London NW4 1QG Tel: 020 8203 0742 — MB ChB 1993 Manch.; BSc (Hons.) Anat. Manch. 1990. (Manch.)

TOLEMAN, Susan Elizabeth Portchester Health Centre, West Street, Portchester, Fareham PO16 9TU Tel: 023 9237 6913 Fax: 023 9237 4265 — BM 1977 Soton.

TOLHURST, Professor David Erskine Guy's Nuffield House, Newcomen St.,, London SE1 1YR Tel: 020 7955 4761; 47 Aylesford Street, London SW1V 3RY — MB ChB New Zealand 1959; FRCS Lond. 1966; PhD Rotterdam 1988. (Otago University, New Zealand) Cons. Plastic Surg. Guy's Nuffield Ho. Lond.; Co-Edr. Europ. Jl. of Plastic Surg. Socs: Brit. Assn. Plastic Surg.; Historian Europ. Assn. of Plastic Surg. Prev: Marks Fell. & Sen. Regist. Qu. Vict. Hosp. E. Grinstead; Cons. Plastic Surg. Wellington Hosp. New Zealand; Prof. (Plastic Surg.) Leiden Univ. Netherlands.

TOLHURST, Jacqueline Crook Log Surgery, 19 Crook Log, Bexleyheath DA6 8DZ Tel: 020 8304 3025 Fax: 020 8298 7739; 27 Spring Vale, Bexleyheath DA7 6AR Tel: 01322 523918 — MB ChB 1986 Ed.; MRCGP Lond. 1996; DCH RCP Lond. 1989. (Ed.) GP Princip. Bexleyheath; Community Med. Off. Greenwich Healthcare Trust & Oxleas NHS Trust. Prev: GP/Regist. Eltham; SHO (Paediat.) Borders Gen. Hosp. Melrose; SHO (O & G) Simpsons Matern. Memor. Hosp. Edin.

TOLHURST, St John Michael Alexander 129 Durleigh Road, Bridgwater TA6 7JF Tel: 01278 422963 — MB BS Lond. 1941; MRCS Eng. LRCP Lond. 1941; DObst RCOG 1947. (Guy's Hosp.) Socs: BMA.

TOLHURST-CLEAVER, Christopher Lewis Maugerhay, 17 West Road, Bowdon, Altrincham WA14 2LD — MB ChB 1971 Sheff.; FRCA Eng. 1977; DObst RCOG 1976. Cons. (Anaesth.) S. Manch. Univ. Hosp.; Hon. Clin. Lect. Vict. Univ. Manch.; Pres. Anaes Sect. Manch. Med. Soc. Socs: Europ. Soc. Regional Anaesth.; Assn. Anaesth. GB & Irel.; Plastic Surg. & Burns Anaesth. Prev: Sen. Regist. (Anaesth.) Brompton & W.m. Hosps. Lond.; Vis. Asst. Prof. (Anaesth.) Univ. Texas, Dallas; Regist. (Anaesth.) Sheff. AHA (T).

TOLIA, Mr Jitendra Jayantilal BUPA Hospital, Abrose Lane, Harpenden AL5 4BP Tel: 01582 763191 Fax: 01582 497329; 7 Bedford Road, Moor Park, Northwood HA6 2BA Tel: 01923 841677 Fax: 01923 841977 Email: jiten.tolia@btinternet.com — MB ChB 1975 Glas.; FRCOphth 1992; FRCS Ed. (Ophth.) 1980. (Univ. Glas.) Cons. Ophth. Luton & Dunstable Hosp. Socs: FRCOphth. Prev: Cons. Ophth. Ysbyty Gwynedd Bangor; Sen. Regist. Qu. Med. Centre Nottm.; Hon. Lect. Nottm. Univ.

TOLIA, Kusum Jagdish Barking Medical Group Practice, 130 Upney Lane, Barking IG11 9LT Tel: 020 8594 4353/5709 Fax: 020 8591 4686 — MRCGP 1987 RCGP; MB BCh 1979 N U Ireland; MB BCh 1979 N U Ireland. (Royal College of Surgeons Dublin, Ireland)

TOLIAS, Mr Christos 46 Weymoor Road, Harbourne, Birmingham B17 0RY Email: christostolias@compuserve.com — Ptychio latrikes 1988 Greece; FRCS Eng. 1994. Specialist Regist. (Neurosurg.). Prev: Specialist Regist. (Neurosurg.) Liverp.; Research Regist (Neurosurg.) Walsgrave Hosp. Coventry.

TOLLAND, Elizabeth Mary Child Health, Mid Anglian Community Health Trust, Hospital Road, Bury St Edmunds IP33 3ND Tel: 01284 775075; Spencers Farm, Polstead Heath, Colchester CO6 5BD Tel: 01787 210503 Email: tollwick@aol.com — MB BS 1974 Newc.; DFFP RCOG 1993. (Newcastle upon Tyne) Med Off. (Paediat) Suufolk.; Family Plann. Doctor. Socs: MRCPCH; Brit. Assn. Community Child Health. Prev: Community Med. Off. W. Suff. HA.

TOLLAND, John (retired) 10 Skottowe Crescent, Great Ayton, Middlesbrough TS9 6DS Tel: 01642 723513 — LRFPS 1938 Ed.; LRCP LRCS Ed. LRFPS Glas. 1938; MFCM 1973; DPH Belf. 1947. Prev: Dist. Community Phys. S. Tees Health Dist.

TOLLAND, Julia Patricia 5 Whiterock Road, Killinchy, Newtownards BT23 6PR; Apartment 4, Osbourne Park House, 64

TOLLAST

Osbourne Park, Belfast BT9 6JP Tel: 0789 305565 — MB BCh 1998 Belf. (Queens University Belfast) Pre Regist. (Gen Med.) Belf. City Hosp.

TOLLAST, Anthony Richard Sunnyside Doctors Surgery, 150 Fratton Road, Portsmouth PO1 5DH Tel: 023 9282 4725 Fax: 023 9286 1014; Tel: 023 9282 4725 Fax: 01705 861014 Email: anthony@tollastuk.freeserve.co.uk — BM 1983 Soton.; MRCGP 1987; Dip. Pract. Dermat. Wales 1993; DRCOG 1986; Cert. Family Plann. JCC 1985. Clin. Asst. (Dermat.) St. Mary's Hosp. Portsmouth. Prev: Trainee GP Portsmouth VTS; Ho. Surg. & Ho. Phys. St. Mary's Hosp. Portsmouth.

TOLLER, Ruth Anne Royal Victoria Hospital, Jedburgh Road, Dundee DD2 1SP Tel: 01382 423181; 3 Duffus Court, Dundee DD4 9BU — MB BS 1976 Newc.; MRCGP 1980. Clin. Med. Off. (Community c/o Elderly) Tayside Health Bd.

TOLLETT, Barbara Joan Fleet Medical Centre', Churh Rd, Fleet GU51 4PE — MB ChB 1981 Birmingham.

TOLLEY, Mr David Anthony Murrayfield Hospital, Corstorphine Road, Edinburgh EH12 6UD Tel: 0131 334 0363 Fax: 0131 334 7338; Loquhariot Farm, Gorebridge EH23 4PB Tel: 01875 820860 — MB BS 1970 Lond.; FRCS Ed. 1983; FRCS Eng. 1975; MRCS Eng. LRCP Lond. 1970. (Kings Coll. Hosp.) Cons. Urol. Surg. W.. Gen. Hosp. Edin.; Dir. Scott. Lithotriptor Centre W.. Gen. Hosp.; Hon. Sen. Lect. Univ. Edin. Socs: Counc. Roy. Coll. of Surg.s Edin.; (Counc.) Brit. Assn. Urol. Surgs.; Soc. Internat.e d'Urologie, Europ. Prev: Sen. Regist. (Urol.) Gen. Infirm. Leeds; Sen. Regist. (Urol.) Kings Coll. Hosp. Lond.; Regist. (Urol. & Transpl.) Hammersmith Hosp. Lond.

TOLLEY, Ian Philip Hellesdon Medical Practice, 343 Reepham Road, Hellesdon, Norwich NR6 5QJ Tel: 01603 408275 Fax: 01603 401389 — MB ChB 1985 Leic.; MRCGP 1989; DRCOG 1989. GP Norwich.

TOLLEY, Jennifer Mary Manor Park Surgery, Bell Mount Close, Leeds LS13 2UP Tel: 0113 257 9702 Fax: 0113 236 1537 — MB BS 1974 Newc.; DRCOG 1976. GP Leeds. Prev: SHO (O & G) Airedale Gen. Hosp.; SHO (Gen. Med.) Darlington Memor. Hosp.; SHO (O & G) Roy. Berks. Hosp. Reading.

TOLLEY, Martin Stephen Bellevue Medical Centre, 26 Huntingdon Place, Edinburgh EH7 4AT Tel: 0131 556 2642 Fax: 0131 557 4430 — MB BS 1982 Lond.; MA Camb. 1978, BA 1974; MRCGP 1988; DCH RCP Lond. 1985. Clin. Asst. P.ss Alexandra Eye Pavil. Roy. Infirm. Edin. Prev: Trainee GP Sheff. VTS; Ho. Phys. St. Bart. Hosp. Lond.; Ho. Surg. Whipps Cross Hosp. Lond.

TOLLEY, Michael Edward Carlton House, 17 High Green, Great Shelford, Cambridge CB2 5EG — MRCS Eng. LRCP Lond. 1964; BSc Lond. 1961, MB BS 1964; FFA RCS Eng. 1969; DA Eng. 1967. (Univ. Coll. Hosp.) Cons. Anaesth. Addenbrookes Hosp. Camb. Prev: Sen. Regist. (Anaesth.) Addenbrooke's Hosp. Camb.; Regist. (Anaesth.) United Camb. Hosps.; SHO (Anaesth.) Soton. Hosps. Gp.

TOLLEY, Mr Neil Samuel St Mary's Hospital, Praed St., Paddington, London W2 1NY Tel: 020 7886 1091 Fax: 020 7886 1847 — MB BCh 1982 Wales; MD Wales 1988; FRCS Eng. 1989; FRCS Ed. 1988; DLO RCS Eng. 1987. (Cardiff) Cons. ENT & Head & Neck Surg. St. Mary's & Ealing NHS Trust; Regional Adviser in Otolaryngol., Roy. Coll. of Surg.s (Eng.). Socs: Eur. Acad. Facial Surg.; Brit. Assn. Otorhinol.; Brit. Assn. Paediatric Otolaryngologists. Prev: Sen. Regist. Roy. Nat. Throat, Nose & Ear Hosp.; Jun. Cons. Groote Schuur Hosp. Cape Town, S. Afr.; Sen. Regist. Sir Chas. Gairdner Hosp. Perth, W.. Austral.

TOLLEY, Peter Frederick Richmond 23 Beechcroft Drive, Ellesmere Port, South Wirral CH65 6PD — MB ChB 1973 St. And.

TOLLIDAY, John Douglas Lyngford Park Surgery, Fletcher Close, Taunton TA2 8SQ Tel: 01823 333355 Fax: 01823 257022 — MB ChB 1978 Manch.; MRCGP 1986. Prev: Ho. Phys. & Ho. Surg. Stepping Hill Hosp. Stockport; Trainee GP Exeter VTS.

TOLLINS, Alan Peter Elsdale Street Surgery, 28 Elsdale Street, London E9 6QY Tel: 020 8985 2719 — MB BS 1983 Lond.

TOLLINTON, Hugh John 29 Copse Hill, Harlow CM19 4PN — BM BCh 1959 Oxf.; MRCPsych 1972; DPM Eng. 1964; Dip Psychother. Aberd. 1966. Cons. Psychiat. Harlow Health Dist. Prev: Leverhulme Fell. in Psychother. Univ. Aberd.

TOLLISS, David Arthur Robert 29 Apple Grove, Enfield EN1 3DA Email: 100603.1541@compuserve.com — MB ChB 1991 Sheff.; MRCGP 1996. GP Bollington. Socs: Med. Protec. Soc.; BMA. Prev: SHO (O & G) Tameside Hosp. Ashton under Lyne; SHO (Psychiat.) Withington Hosp. Manch.; SHO (Gen. Med.) Mid Chesh. Hosps. Trust Crewe.

TOLMAN, Cae Jonathan 11 Holtdale Drive, Leeds LS16 7RT — MB ChB 1997 Leeds.

TOLMIE, John Lorimer Duncan Guthrie Institute of Medical Genetics, Yorkhill Hospitals, Yorkhill, Glasgow G3 8SJ Tel: 0141 339 8888; 85 Hughenden Lane, Hyndland, Glasgow G12 9XN — MB ChB 1980 Glas.; BSc (Hons.) Glas. 1977; FRCP Glas. 1994; MRCP (UK) 1983. Cons. Clin. Genetics Yorkhill Hosp. Glas. Socs: Clin. Genetics Soc.

TOLUFASHE, Ezekiel Ajibola 67 Framfield Road, Mitcham CR4 2AW — MB BS 1977 Lagos; MRCP (UK) 1987. Staff Grade Phys. Chase Farm Hosp. Enfield.

TOM, Joan Pearson (retired) 66 Ravensfield Gardens, Ewell, Epsom KT19 0SR Tel: 020 8393 5426 — MB BS 1940 Sydney; BSc Sydney 1935, MB BS 1940; DCH Eng. 1951. Prev: Dept. Med. Off. Lond. Boro. Merton.

TOM, Patrice Ann Kim Flat 28, Shore Court, Shore Lane, Sheffield S10 3BW — MB ChB 1994 Sheff.

TOMA, Mr Abbad 15A Westfield Park, Redland, Bristol BS6 6LX Tel: 0117 908 3088 Email: 101463.2725@compuserve.com — MB BCh BAO 1986 NUI; FRCS Ed. 1994; LRCPSI 1986; FRCS (ORL) 1997.

TOMAN, Andrew 239 Aylesbury Close, Tytherington, Macclesfield SK10 2LE — MB ChB 1982 Manch.; BSc (Hons.) Manch. 1979, MB ChB 1982; MRCP (UK) 1985. Regist. (Gen. Med.) N. Staffs. Hosp. Centre Stoke-on-Trent. Prev: SHO (Gen. Med.) N. Staffs. Hosp. Centre Stoke-on-Trent.

TOMAR, Surendra Singh College Street Health Centre, College Street, Leigh WN7 2RD Tel: 01942 671085 Fax: 01942 680477 — MB BS 1971 Indore.

TOMB, Joseph John 96 Crwafordsburn Road, Newtownards BT23 4UH — MB BCh BAO 1947 Belf. (Belf.)

TOMBLESON, Philip Michael John, MBE Health Centre, Lewes Road, Ditchling, Hassocks BN6 8TT Tel: 01273 842570; Little Ash, 30 Lewes Road, Ditchling, Hassocks BN6 8TU Tel: 01273 844099 Fax: 01273 845747 — MB BS 1960 Lond.; MRCS Eng. LRCP Lond. 1960; FRCGP 1989, M 1968; DObst RCOG 1962; DA Eng. 1962. (Guy's) Prev: Course Organiser Mid-Sussex Vocational Train. Scheme; Convenor of Panel Examnrs. MRCGP Exam.

TOMBLIN, Maeve Philomena Mary Worle Health Centre, 125 High St, Worle, Weston Super Mare BS22 6HB Tel: 01934 510510 Fax: 01934 522088 — MB BCh BAO 1981 NUI; DObst RCPI 1985.

TOMBOLINE, David Spencer The Health Centre, Milman Road, Reading RG2 0AY Tel: 01734 862285; 5 Hartsbourne Road, Earley, Reading RG6 5PX — MB BS 1986 Lond.; DCH RCP Lond. 1990; DRCOG 1989; T (GP) 1991.

TOMBS, David George 3 The Paddock, Winshill, Burton-on-Trent DE15 0BB — MB ChB 1982 Birm.; MMedSci Leeds 1989; MRCPsych 1987. Cons. Psychiat. Pastures Hosp. Derby. Socs: Derby Med. Soc. Prev: Lect. Univ. Leeds.

TOME DE LA GRANJA, Maria Begona 80 Lewisham Way, London SE14 6NY — LMS 1991 Basque Provinces.

TOMEI, Louise Dawn Quercus, Parkwood Road, Nutfield, Redhill RH1 4HD — MB ChB 1991 Leic.; BSc (Hons.) Lond. 1986; DRCOG. 1995; DFFP. 1996; MRCGP. 1996.

TOMES, Doris Helen (retired) c/o National Westminster Bank, 18 Cromwell Place, London SW7 — MRCS Eng. LRCP Lond. 1927. Prev: Asst. Co. Med. Off. Devon C.C.

TOMES, Joanna Susan Heatherside, Prestwick Lane, Grayswood, Haslemere GU27 2DU — MB BS 1987 Lond.

TOMETZKI, Andrew John Peter Bristol Royal Hospital For Children, Upper Maudlin Street, Bristol BS2 8BJ Tel: 0117 342 8853 Email: andrew.tometzki@ubht.swest.nhs.uk — MB ChB 1985 Sheff.; MRCP (UK) 1991. (Sheffield Medical School) Cons. and Hon. Lect. in Paediatric Cardiol.; Hon. Cons., Roy. United Hosp. Bath; Hon. Cons. Roy. Devon & Exeter Hosp.; Hon. Cons. Torbay Hosp. Devon. Socs: Roy. Coll. Paediat. & Child Health; MRCP, Lond.; Brit. Cardiac Soc. Prev: Regist. (Paediat. Cardiol.) Roy. Liverp. Childr. Hosp. & Roy. Hosp. Sick Childr. Glas.; ECMO Research Fell.; Sen. Regist. (Paediat. Cardiol.) Roy. Hosp. Sick Childr. Edin.

TOMIAK, Richard Henry Herbert Merck, Sharpe & Dohme, Hertford Road, Hoddesdon EN11 9BU Tel: 01992 467272 Fax:

TOMLINSON

01992 451066; 12 Hartington Road, Chiswick, London W4 Tel: 020 8995 5629 — MB BChir 1981 Camb.; MA Camb. 1982, MB BChir 1981; Dip. Pharm. Med. RCP UK. 1987; MFPM 1989. Dir. Med. Affairs Merck, Sharpe & Dohme Hoddesdon. Prev: Sen. Med. Adviser Syntex Pharmaceut.

TOMIC, Damian Anton Fyffe, Northfield Avenue, Pinner HA5 1AR — MB BS 1990 Lond.

TOMINEY, Damian Paul Tominey, 17 Upper Lattimore Road, St Albans AL1 3UD Tel: 01727 839617 Fax: 01727 839617 — MB BS 1971 Lond.; BSc (Hons.) Lond.; T(GP) 1991; DObst RCOG 1974. (Univ. Coll. Hosp.) p/t Indep. Med. Pract. St. Albans; Exec. Med. Off. DHSS. Socs: Soc. Apoth.; BMA.

TOMISON, Arden Randall Fromeside Clinic, Blackberry Hill Hospital, Stapleton, Bristol BS16 1ED Tel: 0117 958 3678 — MB ChB 1979 Dundee; M 1984; FRCPsych 1997; FRCPsych 1997, M 1984. Cons. Forens. Psychiat. & Head Forens. Psychiat. Avon & Wilts. Ment. Health NHS Trust. Prev: Sen. Regist. (Forens. Psychiat.) Langdon Hosp.; Clin. Dir. (Ment. Health) Frenchay Healthcare NHS Trust.

TOMKINS, Professor Andrew Mervyn Centre for International Child Health, Institute of Child Health, University College London, 30 Guildford Street, London WC1N 1EH Tel: 0207 905 2123 Fax: 0207 404 2062 Email: a.tomkins@ich.ucl.ac.uk; 11 Moreton Avenue, Harpenden AL5 2EU Tel: 01582 768121 — MB BS 1966 Lond.; FRCP 1981; MRCP Lond. 1969; MRCS Eng. LRCP Lond. 1966; FFPHM 1996; FRCPCH 1997. (Middlx.) Hon. Cons. Paediat. Hosp. for Childr. Gt. Ormond St. Lond.; Hon. Cons. Phys. Hosp. Trop. Dis. & UCH. Prev: Sen. Lect. (Clin. Nutrit.) Lond. Sch. Hyg. & Trop. Med. Lond.; Sen. Regist. (Med.) Ahmadu Bello Univ. Zaria, Nigeria; Clin. Sci. MRC Fajara, The Gambia, W. Afr.

TOMKINS, Christine Margaret Paris House, The Rocks Road, E. Malling, West Malling ME19 6AU — MB BCh 1980 Manch.; MB BCh (Hons.) Manch. 1980; BSc Manch. 1977; MBA Lond. 1997; FRCS Eng. 1984; FCOphth 1989; DO RCS Eng. 1983. Professional Servs. Dir. Med. Defence Union. Prev: Regist. (Ophth.) & SHO (Ophth.) St. Thos. Hosp. Lond.; Hon. Lect. (Anat.) Univ. Manch.; SHO (Ophth.) Char. Cross Lond.

TOMKINS, John Garrick Usherwood, Sutton Place, Abinger Hammer, Dorking RH5 6RP Tel: 01306 730214 — MB BCh 1947 Wales; BSc Wales 1943, MB BCh 1947. (Cardiff) Med. Dir. Surrey Chest X-Ray Serv. Prev: Jun. Specialist (Med.) RAMC; Regist. (Med.) Bridgend Gen. Hosp.; Asst. Med. Dir. SW Lond. Mass X-Ray Serv.

TOMKINS, Michael James 9 Hawkesbury Road, Shirley, Solihull B90 2QR — MB BS 1988 Lond.; MRCP (UK) 1993.

TOMKINS, Stephen Flat 38B, Sandcotes Road, Poole BH14 8PA — BM 1992 Soton.

TOMKINS, Susan Elizabeth Institute of Medical Genetics, University Hospital of Wales, Cardiff CF4 4XW Tel: 029 2074 4058 Fax: 029 2074 7603 Email: tomkins@cardiff.ac.uk; 35 Ilton Road, Penylan, Cardiff CF23 5DU — MB ChB 1988 Leic.; MRCP (Paediat.) (UK) 1994.

TOMKINSON, Alun Kenbrook, Upper Canning Street, Ton Pentre, Pentre CF41 7HG — MB BCh 1987 Wales.

TOMKINSON, John Spencer 36 Redgates, Walkington, Beverley HU17 8TS — BM BS 1978 Nottm.; BMedSci (Hons.) Nottm. 1975; MRCPsych 1982. Cons. Psychiat. Dales Hse. Hull; Hon. Clin. Lect. Univ. Leeds. Prev: Sen. Regist. (Psychiat.) Yorks. RHA; Regist. (Psychiat.) Nottm. HA.

TOMKINSON, Julian Stuart The Barn, 17 Oaks Lane, Bradshaw, Bolton BL2 3BR — MB ChB 1995 Manch.

TOMLIN, Pamela Irene Royal Preston Hospital, Sharoe Green Lane, Preston PR2 9HT Tel: 01772 710246; 13 Billinge Avenue, Blackburn BB2 6SD — MB 1972 Camb.; BChir 1971; FRCP Lond. 1992; MRCP (UK) 1977; FRCPCH 1997; DCH RCP Lond. 1973. Cons. Paediat. Neurol. Roy. Preston Hosp. N. W.. RHA.

TOMLIN, Peter James (retired) Radnor House, The Headlands, Downton, Salisbury SP5 3HJ — MB BS 1957 Lond.; FFA RCS Eng. 1962. Prev: Sen. Regist. Hammersmith Hosp. Lond.

TOMLINS, Christopher David Corbett 13 Bath Road, Reading RG1 6HH Tel: 0118 955 3461 Fax: 0118 958 5928; Hazeldene, Wolverton Common, Tadley RG26 5RY Tel: 01635 298719 — MB BS Lond. 1969; MRCS Eng. LRCP Lond. 1969; BDS Lond. 1964; FDS RCS Eng. 1973, LDS 1963. (Guy's) Cons. Oral Surg. Roy. Berks. Hosp. Reading. Socs: Fell. RCS Eng.; Fell. Brit. Assn. Oral &

Maxillofacial Surg.; BMA. Prev: Sen. Regist. (Oral Surg.) W.m. Hosp. Gp.; Regist. (Oral Surg.) E.man Dent. Hosp. Lond.; Ho. Surg. (Orthop.) Guy's Hosp.

TOMLINS, Frank Geoffrey 14 Alderton Hill, Loughton IG10 3JB — MB BChir 1948 Camb.; MA MB BChir Camb. 1948. (Univ. Coll. Hosp.) Prev: Ho. Surg. Obst. Unit Univ. Coll. Hosp.; Ho. Phys. W. Kent Gen. Hosp. Maidstone; Asst. Med. Off. Brit. Rlys. W.. Region.

TOMLINSON, Alan McNeal, TD (retired) Little Firs, The Avenue, Ascot SL5 7LY — M.B., Ch.B. Manch. 1934. JP. Prev: Maj. RAMC TA att. 137th Field Regt. RA TA.

TOMLINSON, Andrew Alan Directorate of Anesthesia, City General, North Staffs Hospital, Newcastle Road, Stoke-on-Trent ST4 6QG Tel: 01782 715444; 2 Granville Avenue, Newcastle ST5 1JH — MB BS 1975 Lond.; MRCS Eng. LRCP Lond. 1975; FRCA 1980. (Roy. Free) Cons. Anaesth. N. Staffs. Hosp. Prev: Sen. Regist. (Anaesth.) Soton. HA; Staff Anaesth. Shanta Bhawan Hosp. Kathmandu, Nepal; Regist. (Anaesth.) Sheff. HA.

TOMLINSON, Anne Patricia Bromborough Village Road, Bromborough, Wirral CH62 7EU Tel: 0151 343 9437; 15 West Drive, Upton, Wirral CH49 6JX Tel: 0151 677 1605 — MB BCh 1977 Wales; MRCGP 1981; DRCOG 1980; DCH Eng. 1979. Prev: Clin. Med. Off. Wirral HA. NHS Trust; Trainee GP Clatterbridge VTS.

TOMLINSON, Sir Bernard Evans, CBE Greyholme, Wynbury Road, Low Fell, Gateshead NE9 6TS Tel: 0191 491 3468 — MB BS 1943 Lond.; MD Lond. 1962; Hon. MD Newc. 1993; FRCP Lond. 1965, M 1944; MRCS Eng. LRCP Lond. 1943; FCPath 1964. (Univ. Coll. Hosp.) Hon. Emerit. Prof. Path. Univ. Newc.; Hon. Cons. Neuropath. Gen. Hosp. Newc.; Hon. Mem. MRC Unit Neurochem. Path. Gen. Hosp. Newc. Socs: (Counc.) Assn. Clin. Path.; Hon. Mem. Amer. Neurol. Assn.; (Counc.) Roy. Coll. Path. Prev: Chairm. N.. RHA; Pres. Brit. Neuropath. Soc.; Cons. Neuropath. Gen. Hosp. Newc.

TOMLINSON, Brian (retired) 7 Clwyd Avenue, Prestatyn LL19 9NG Tel: 01745 857040 — MB ChB Leeds 1952. Prev: GP Prestatyn.

TOMLINSON, Christopher James 31 Yorton Cottage, Shrewsbury SY4 3EU — BM BS 1993 Nottm.; BMedSci Nottm. 1991.

TOMLINSON, Clare Jacqueline 26 Willow Drive, Droitwich WR9 7QE Tel: 01905 796461 — BM 1985 Soton. SHO (O & G) Worcester Roy. Infirm. VTS; Ref. & Adjudicating Med. Pract. for Benefits Agency Med. Servs. Prev: SHO (Psychiat.) Worcs. Community Healthcare Trust; SHO (Med.) & Ho. Off. (Med. & Surg.) P.ss Margt. Hosp. Swindon.

TOMLINSON, David Robert 21 Holmsdale Avenue, London SW14 7BQ — MB BS 1985 Lond.

TOMLINSON, David Robert 11 Kempson Avenue, Wylde Green, Sutton Coldfield B72 1HJ Tel: 0121 355 6893 — BM 1995 Soton.; BM (Hons.) Soton. 1995; BSc Soton. 1994.

TOMLINSON, Diane Church Farm House, Arminghall, Norwich NR14 8SG — MB BS 1981 Lond.; MRCGP 1986; DRCOG 1987.

TOMLINSON, Ellen Oi-Lun High Gable, 62 Banks Road, Pound Hill, Crawley RH10 7BP Tel: 01293 526509 — MB BChir Camb. 1984; BSc (Hons.) St. And. 1982; MRCPI 1986; MRCGP 1993; DRCOG 1990. Prev: Trainee GP Lewisham VTS; SHO Rotat. (Med.) St. Jas. Hosp. Leeds.

TOMLINSON, Frank Edwin (retired) 89 Westgate, Tranmere Park, Guiseley, Leeds LS20 8HH Tel: 01943 872927 — MB ChB 1957 Leeds; DObst RCOG 1961. Prev: GP Shipley, W. Yorks.

TOMLINSON, Garry Nelson The Health Centre, Bridge Street, Thorne, Doncaster DN8 5QH Tel: 01405 812121 Fax: 01405 741059; Wrancarr Mill, Wrancarr Lane, Moss, Doncaster DN6 0DP — MB ChB 1974 Auckland; DRCOG 1979; DPM Eng. 1981. (Auckland) GP Doncaster AHA. Prev: Regist. (Psychiat.) Fair Mile Hosp. Wallingford; SHO (O & G) Odstock Hosp. Salisbury; Trainee GP Liphook.

TOMLINSON, Geoffrey Charles Glenbourne, Momaix Drive, Dernford, Plymouth PL6 5AF Tel: 01752 761 3120; Rose Wollas, Rose, Truro TR4 9PH Tel: 01872 573583 Email: gtomlinson@doctors.org.uk — MB BCh 1974 Wales; MRCPsych 1979; DPM Leeds 1977. Cons. Psychiat. Glenbourne Community Trust 1999; Psychiat. Adviser to Centre for Ment. Health Servs. Developm. Socs: Brit. Assn. Behavioural & Cognitive Psychother.; Roy. Coll. Psychiats. Prev: Cons. Psychiat. N.. Birm. Ment. Health Trust; Cons. Psychiat. Trengweath Ment. Health Unit Redruth; Sen. Regist. (Psychiat.) Mapperley Hosp.

TOMLINSON

TOMLINSON, Ian Philip Mark 7 New Road, Reading RG1 5JD — BM BCh 1992 Oxf.; PhD Camb. 1988, MA 1989, BA 1985; MRC Path 1999. Head, Molecular & Populat. Genetics Laborat., ICRF, Lond. Prev: Sen. Clin. Res. Fell., Oxf.; Sen. Clinician Research Fell. Inst. Cancer Research Sutton; Research Fell. Cancer Genetics Laborat. Imperial Cancer Research Fund Lond.

TOMLINSON, Ian Walter Castle Hill Hospital, Castle Road, Cottingham HU16 5JQ Tel: 01482 875875; 7 Allanhall Way, Kirkella, Hull HU10 7QU Tel: 01482 654291 — MD 1982 Lond.; MB BS 1971; FRCP Lond. 1993; MRCP (UK) 1977. (Kings London) Cons. Rheum.Hull & E. Yorks. Hosp. NHS Trust. Prev: Cons. Rheum. E. Yorks. & ScarBoro. Hosp. Trusts.; Regist. (Gen. Med.) Leicester Gen. Hosp.; Lect. (Rheum.) Univ. Manch.

TOMLINSON, Isobel Mary Moorcroft Medical Centre, Butteslon Street, Hanley, Stoke-on-Trent ST1 3NJ; Holmlea, Moor Lane, Rowton, Chester CH3 7QW Tel: 01244 332231 — MB BS 1975 Lond.; MRCS Eng. LRCP Lond. 1975; MRCGP 1984; DRCOG 1977. (Roy. Free) p/t GP Princip. Prev: GP Newc. Staffs.; Trainee GP Wessex VTS; Clin. Asst. Shanta Bhawan Hosp. Kathmandu, Nepal.

TOMLINSON, Jean Mowat 3 Long Acres Close, Coombe Dingle, Bristol BS9 2RF Tel: 0117 968 2079 — MRCS Eng. LRCP Lond. 1948. (Univ. Coll. Lond. & W. Lond. Hosp.) Prev: Lady Med. Off. Seremban & Penang, Malaya.

TOMLINSON, John David Leicestershire Health, Gwendolen Road, Leicester LE5 4QF Tel: 0116 273 1173 Fax: 0116 258 8577 — MB ChB 1980 Liverp.; MFPHM RCP (UK) 1994; MRCGP 1986; DRCOG 1985. Cons. Pub. Health Med. Leics. Health; Clin. Tutor Leicester Univ. Med. Sch., Nottm. Univ. Med. Sch. & Nottm. Sch. Pub. Health.

TOMLINSON, John Fielding Fartown Health Centre, Huddersfield HD2 2QA Tel: 01484 544318 — MB ChB 1952 Manch. (Manch.) Socs: Huddersfield Med. Soc.

TOMLINSON, John Howard Rosegarth House, Clifton Road, Tettenhall, Wolverhampton WV6 9AP — MB ChB 1974 Manch.; FFA RACS 1982. Cons. (Anaesth.) Wolverhampton DHA.

TOMLINSON, John Montgomery Royal Hampshire County Hospital, Romsey Road, Winchester SO22 5DG Tel: 01962 824443 Fax: 01962 824443; Clays Farm, East Worldham, Alton GU34 3AD Tel: 01420 82210 Fax: 01420 543060 — MB BS 1959 Lond.; FRCGP 1984, M 1965; DObst RCOG 1962. (Middlx.) p/t Clinician (Men's Sexual Health) Roy. Hants. Co. Hosp. Winchester; Cons. (Men's Sexual Health) Sarum Rd. Hosp. Winchester SO22 5HA. Socs: BMA; Soc. Study Androgen Defic. in Adult Male (the Audiopause Soc.). Prev: Hon. Sen. Lect. (Primary Med. Care) Univ. Soton. Med. Sch.; Sen. Partner, Tomlinson & Partners Alton; Assoc. Adviser Profess. Developm. Wessex Region.

TOMLINSON, Jonathon 2 Wool House Gardens, Codford, Warminster BA12 0PS — MB BS 1996 Lond.

TOMLINSON, Joy Elizabeth Mary 83 Milton Road, Kirkcaldy KY1 1TP — MB ChB 1993 Glas.

TOMLINSON, Kenneth Mills 4 Cook's Place, Newent GL18 1TR Tel: 01531 821129 — MB BS 1949 Lond.; MRCS Eng. LRCP Lond. 1940. (St. Thos.) Prev: JP; Dermat. Warwick Hosp.; Regist. Skin Dept. Coventry & Warw. Hosp.

TOMLINSON, Kerry Celina Nottingham City Hospital, Nottingham NG5 1PB Tel: 0115 969 1169; Flat 3, 6 Harlaxton Drive, Lenton, Nottingham NG7 1JA — BM BCh 1993 Oxf.; MRCP (UK). 1996; PhD Nottm. 1989. (Oxford) Specialist Regist. (Nephrol.).

TOMLINSON, Laurie Alexandra 28A Hoyle Road, London SW17 0RS — MB BS 1998 Lond.

TOMLINSON, Marjorie Jane Bristol Oncology Centre, Horfield Road, Bristol BS2 8ED Tel: 0117 923 0000; Arden, 33 Cambridge Road, Clevedon BS21 7DN — MB ChB 1977 Liverp.; MRCP (UK) 1981; FRCR 1995. Cons. (Clin. Oncol.) W.on Gen. Hosp., W.on-Super-Mare and Bristol Oncol. centre.

TOMLINSON, Mr Mark Antony Clinical Research Unit, Ingleby House, St. George's Hospital, Blackshaw Road, Tooting, London SW17 0QT Tel: 020 8725 0177 — MB BS 1990 Lond.; FRCS Eng. 1995. (St. Geo. Hosp.) Research Regist. (Vasc. Surg.) St. Geo. Hosp. Lond. Prev: SHO (Colorectal Surg. & Cardiothoracic Surg.) St. Geo. Hosp. Lond.; SHO (Plastic Surg.) Salisbury Dist. Hosp.; SHO (Gen. Surg.) St. Helier Hosp. Carshalton.

TOMLINSON, Mark John 1 Onslow Street, Guildford GU1 4YS; Email: rsimcock@doctors.org.uk — MB BCh 1985 Wales; AFPM 2001; MRCGP 1989; Dip. Pharm. Med. RCP (UK) 1996; DRCOG 1988. Head Of Med. Affairs, SANOFI - Synthelabo, Guildford.; Assoc. Dir. (Cardiovasc.) Bristol-Myers Squibb, P.ton, New Jersey. Prev: Med. Manager Sanofi Winthrop Ltd. Guildford; GP Wilts.; Asst. GP Cohuna Vict., Austral.

TOMLINSON, Patricia Outram (retired) Clay's Farm, East Worldham, Alton GU34 3AD Tel: 01420 82210 Fax: 01420 543060 — MB BS 1957 Lond.; MRCS Eng. LRCP Lond. 1957; DCH Eng. 1961. Prev: Sch. Med. Off. Lord Mayor Treloar Coll. for Disabled Boys & Girls.

TOMLINSON, Paul Alexander Department of Anaesthesia, City Hospital, Hucknall Road, Nottingham NG5 1PB — MB ChB 1973 Bristol; FFA RCS Eng. 1981.

TOMLINSON, Piers Sunnymead, Tring Road, Long Marston, Tring HP23 4QL — BM 1994 Soton.

TOMLINSON, Rachel Jane The Health Centre, Victoria Street, Marsden, Huddersfield HD7 6DF Tel: 01484 844332 Fax: 01484 845779 — MB ChB 1988 Leeds.

TOMLINSON, Mr Richard John Rostron 8 Church Street, Southport PR9 0QT Tel: 01704 533666 — MB ChB 1970 Manch.; FRCS Eng. 1974.

TOMLINSON, Robert Cyril Green Cottage, Moor Lane, Kirk Ireton, Ashbourne DE6 3JE — MB ChB 1995 Liverp.

TOMLINSON, Robert James (retired) Brackley, 15 Crooklands Drive, Garstang, Preston PR3 1JH Tel: 01995 603752 — MB BS 1962 Lond.; MRCS Eng. LRCP Lond. 1962; DObst RCOG 1964. Prev: SHO (O & G) St. Mary's Hosp. Kettering.

TOMLINSON, Simon David 9 Glendale Grove, Spital, Wirral CH63 9FP — MB ChB 1991 Birm.; ChB Birm. 1991.

TOMLINSON, Professor Stephen Dean's Office, Faculty of Medicine, University of Manchester, Oxford Road, Manchester M13 9PT Tel: 0161 275 5027 Fax: 0161 275 5584 — MB ChB (Hons.) Sheff. 1968; MD Sheff. 1976; FRCP Lond. 1982; MRCP (UK) 1971. (Sheff.) Prof. Med. Univ. Manch.; Hon. Cons. Phys. Manch. Roy. Infirm.; Dean Fac. Med. Dent. & Nursing Univ. Manch. Socs: Exec. Sec. Counc. Heads Med. Sch.s; Chairm. Assn. Clin. Profs. Med.; Chairm. Fed. Assn Clin. Prof. Prev: Reader (Med.) & Wellcome Trust; Sen. Lect. Univ. Sheff. Med. Sch.; Hon. Cons. Phys. Sheff. HA.

TOMLINSON, Stewart John Medwyn Surgery, Moores Road, Dorking RH4 2BG Tel: 01306 882422 Fax: 01306 742280; 16 Burlington Place, Reigate RH2 9HT Tel: 01737 222542 — MB BS 1994 Lond.; BSc. (Hons.) Lond. 1991, MB BS 1994; MBBS 1994 Lond.; DROG 1997Lond.; DFFP 1997 Lond.; MRCAP (DUTINC.) 1998 Lond. GP Princip. Dorking Surrey. Socs: RCGP; RCOG.

TOMLINSON, Sydney Brian (retired) Springfield, Wharfeside Avenue, Threshfield, Grassington, Skipton BD23 5BS — MB ChB 1944 Leeds; MRCGP 1953. Prev: Regist. Dept. Paediat. & Child Health Gen. Infirm. Leeds.

TOMMEY, Martin Frederick Miller Street Surgery, Miller Street, Off Kings Street, Newcastle ST5 1JD Tel: 01782 711618 Fax: 01782 713940 — MB BS 1971 Lond.; MRCS Eng. LRCP Lond. 1971.

TOMMINS, Kathryn Sarah Morrill Street Health Centre, Holderness Road, Hull HU9 2LJ Tel: 01482 320046; 18 Hambling Drive, Beverley HU17 9GD — MB ChB 1978 Manch.; MRCGP 1982. GP Hull.

TOMNAY, Joyce 16 Mansion House Road, Glasgow G41 3DN — MB ChB 1973 Aberd.

TOMOS, Hywel Wynn New Cross Surgery, 48 Sway Road, Morriston, Swansea SA6 6HR Tel: 01792 771419; Port Reath, Balaclava Road, Glais, Swansea SA7 9HH — MB BCh 1991 Wales; MRCGP 1995.

TOMPKIN, David Michael Bankes Woodlands Surgery, 5 Woodlands Road, Redhill RH1 6EY Tel: 01737 761343 Fax: 01737 770804; 5 Cronks Hill Road, Redhill RH1 6LY Tel: 01737 247659 — MB BS 1974 Lond.; MRCS Eng. LRCP Lond. 1974. (St. Thos.) Prev: Med. Off. Port Saunders Hosp. Newfld.; Ho. Off. (Orthop.) & SHO (O & G) St. Thos. Hosp. Lond.

TOMPKINS, David Stewart Leeds Public Health Laboratory, Bridle Path, York Road, Leeds LS15 7TR Tel: 0113 264 5011 Fax: 011320 603655 — MB ChB 1976 Birm.; FRCPath 1994, M 1982. Cons. Microbiol. Pub. Health Laborat. Leeds.; Hon. Cons. Leeds Teachg. Hosp.s NHS Trust. Socs: Assn. Med. Microbiol.; Hon. Sec. Assn. of Med. Microbiologists 1995-1997; Vice-Pres. Acd. Clin.

Microbiologists (India). Prev: Cons. Microbiol. Bradford; Lect. Univ. Leeds.

TOMPKINS, Geoffrey David (retired) The Thatched cottage, Chignal Smealy, Chelmsford CM14SX Tel: 01245 441034 Fax: 01245 441034 Email: tompkins@tinyworld.co.uk — MB BS 1955 Lond. JP.; Dep. Coronor E. Dist. Gt Lond. Area. Prev: Ho. Surg. Hillingdon Hosp.

TOMPKINS, Josephine Charlotte Rozanne Somers Town Health Centre, Blackfriars Close, Portsmouth Tel: 023 92 851202 Fax: 023 92 296380 — MB BS 1964 Lond.; MRCS Eng. LRCP Lond. 1965; DCH Eng. 1967. (St. Bart.) Hosp. Practitioner, Dermat., St. Mary's Hosp., Portsmouth. Prev: Ho. Surg. & Ho. Phys. S.end Gen. Hosp.; Ho. Phys. Eliz. G. Anderson Hosp. Lond.

TOMPKINSON, John Michael Ripley Medical Centre, Derby Road, Ripley DE5 3HR Tel: 01773 747486; 20 Chevin Road, Belper DE56 2UW Tel: 01773 820498 — BM BS 1988 Nottm.; BMedSci (Hons.) Nottm. 1995. (Nottm.)

TOMPSETT, Mary Josephine St Raphael's Hospice, London Road, North Cheam, Sutton SM3 9DX Tel: 020 8337 7475 Fax: 020 8335 3089; 21 Tamar Gardens, West End, Southampton SO18 3LR — MB BS 1992 Lond.; MRCP (UK) 1997. (St George's Hospital London) Regist. (Palliat. Med.) St Raphael's Hospice N. Cheam Surrey; Hon. Regist. (Palliat. Med.) St Heliers Hosp. Carshalton Surrey. Socs: BMA; MDU.

TOMS, Mr Andoni Paul 77 Station Road, Impington, Cambridge CB4 9NP — MB BS 1991 Lond.; FRCS Eng. 1995. Regist. (Radiol.) Addenbrooke's NHS Trust Camb.

TOMS, Andrew David Royal Shrewsbury Hospital, Shrewsbury SY3 8XQ; 26 Acton Burnell, Shrewsbury SY5 7PQ — MB ChB 1992 Birm.

TOMS, David Anthony 2 Regent Street, Nottingham NG1 5QB Tel: 0115 947 4755 Fax: 0115 950 8174; The Manor House, Main St, Aslockton, Nottingham NG13 9AL Tel: 01949 850374 — MB BS 1960 Lond.; MRCP Lond. 1967; MRCS Eng. LRCP Lond. 1960; FRCPsych. 1982, M 1972; DObst RCOG 1962; DCH Eng. 1963; DPM 1968. (Univ. Coll. Hosp. Lond.) Indep. Psychiat. Notts.; Emerit. Cons. Psychiat. N. HA. Socs: Soc. Psychosomatic Research. Soc.; Nottm. M-C Soc. Prev: Sen. Regist. (Psychiat.) St. Geo. Hosp. Lond.; Regist. (Psychiat.) Claybury Hosp. Woodford Bridge, Essex; Ho. Phys. Univ. Coll. Hosp. Lond.

TOMS, Elaine Stella Greenwood and Sneinton Family Medical Centre, 249 Sneinton Dale, Sneinton, Nottingham NG3 7DQ Tel: 0115 950 1854 Fax: 0115 958 0044; 12 Nuthall Grove, Glen Parva, Leicester LE2 9HU — MB ChB 1982 Birm.; MB ChB (Hons.) Birm. 1982; MRCP (UK) 1985; MRCGP 1989. Prev: Regist. Rotat. (Med.) Kettering & Leicester Hosps.; SHO (Rotat.) City Hosp. Nottm.

TOMS, Graham Christopher Oldchurch Hospital, Romford RM7 0BE Tel: 01708 746090; 47 Beacontree Road, Leytonstone, London E11 3AX — MD 1989 Manch.; MB ChB 1979; MRCP (UK) 1982. Lect. (Metab. & Endocrinol.) Lond. Hosp. Med. Coll.

TOMS, Graham Ralph Parade Surgery, The Parade, Liskeard PL14 6AF Tel: 01579 342667 Fax: 01579 340650; Tremellick Cottage, St. Cleer, Liskeard PL14 6RP Tel: 01579 343306 — MB BS 1984 Lond.; MRCGP 1988; DA (UK) 1990; DRCOG 1987. Prev: Trainee GP Chertsey VTS; Ho. Surg. Univ. Coll. Hosp. Lond.; Ho. Phys. Roy. Devon & Exeter Hosp.

TOMS, Julian Stanley Martyn Portree Medical Centre, Portree IV51 9BZ Tel: 01478 612013 Fax: 01478 612340; Creag-a-Charran, Staffin Road, Portree IV51 9HP Tel: 01478 612961 — MA Camb. 1971, MB BChir 1970; FRCP Ed. 1997; MRCP (UK) 1984; MRCGP 1974; DFFP 1996; DObst RCOG 1973; DCH Eng. 1972. (Camb. & St. Bart.) GP Portree, Isle of Syke; Clin. Asst. Portree Hosp.; GP Trainer, Portree Med. Centre. Prev: SHO (Psychiat.) Craig Dunain Hosp. Inverness; SHO (Paediat.) Roy. Cornw. Hosp. Truro; SHO (Neurol.) Dundee Roy. Infirm.

TOMS, Mark Edwin 43 Woburn Av, Farnborough GU14 7HQ — MB ChB 1997 Sheff.

TOMS, Rhinedd Margaret The Lakes Mental Health Centre, Turner Road, Colchester CO4 5JL Tel: 01206 228740 Fax: 01206 844182; 45 Oaks Drive, Colchester CO3 3PS Tel: 01206 549547 — MB BChir 1967 Camb.; BChir 1967; MA Camb. 1968; MRCS Eng. LRCP Lond. 1967; FRCPsych 1993, M 1981. (Camb. & Westm.) Cons. Psychiat. N. Essex Ment. Health Partnership NHS Trust; Hon. Cons. Psychiat. St. Luke's Hosp. for Clergy Lond. Socs: BMA. Prev: Sen. Regist. (Psychiat.) Severalls Hosp. Colchester; Supernum. Regist. (Psychiat.) Severalls Hosp. Colchester; Med. Off. (Staff Health) Lambeth Lewisham & S.wark AHA.

TOMS, Walter Hewitt (retired) 1 Temple, Underbank, Hebden Bridge HX7 6PS — MB ChB 1941 Ed. Prev: PMO Lond. Boro. Redbridge.

TOMSON, Charles Richard Vernon Department of Renal Medicine, Southmead Hospital, Bristol BS10 5NB Tel: 0117 959 5225 Fax: 0117 950 8677 Email: tomson_c@southmead.swest.nhs.uk; 40 Caledonia Place, Bristol BS8 4DN — MB BCh 1981 Oxf.; DM Oxf. 1990; MRCP (UK) 1984; FRCP (UK). (Oxford) Cons. Nephrol. S.mead Hosp. Bristol. Socs: Educ. Sec. Renal Assn.; Mem., Renal Assn. Train. Educat. & Research Subcomm.; Mem., Roy. Coll. Phys.s (Lond.) CPD Advisery Gp. Prev: Cons. Nephrol. St. Bart. Hosp. Lond.; Lect. (Med.) Leicester Univ.; MRC Train. Fell. RVI Newc. u. Tyne.

TOMSON, Christopher Mark Calder Blackthorn Surgery, 73 Station Road, Netley Abbey, Southampton SO31 5AE Tel: 023 8045 3110 Fax: 023 8045 2747; 33 Old Priory Close, Hamble, Southampton SO31 4QP Tel: 02380 457950 Fax: 01703 457950 Email: marktomson@compuserve.com — MB BS 1985 Lond.; MRCGP 1993.

TOMSON, David Peter Carey Collingwood Surgery, Hawkeys Lane, North Shields NE29 0SF Tel: 0191 257 1779 Fax: 0191 226 9909; 20 Rothbury Terrace, Heaton, Newcastle upon Tyne NE6 5XH Email: d.p.c.tomson@ncc.ac.uk — BM BCh 1985 Oxf.; BA (Hons.) Camb. 1982; MRCGP 1990. GP Partner; Hon. Lect. Newc. Med. Sch.; Vice-Chairm. Riveside PCG.

TOMSON, Michael John Francis 72 Southgrove Road, Sheffield S10 2NQ — MB BS 1982 Lond.; BA Camb. 1979; MRCGP 1989; Cert. Family Plann. JCC 1987; DRCOG 1987; DCH RCP Lond. 1986. (Univ. Camb. & Lond. Hosp.) GP; CME Tutor. Prev: Regist. (Child Psychiat.) Tavistock Clinic Lond.; SHO (Paediat. & Community Paediat.) Paddington & N. Kensington HA; SHO Rotat. (Med.) Romford.

TOMSON, Peter Riley Vernon (retired) The Abbots House, Abbots Langley WD5 0AR Tel: 01923 264946 Email: peter.tomson@btinternet.com — MB BChir 1950 Camb.; FRCGP 1973, M 1961; DObst RCOG 1954. Prev: Capt. RAMC.

TONER, Christopher Charles 3 Ridgeway Crescent Gardens, Orpington BR6 9QH — BM 1986 Soton.

TONER, Geraldine Gertrude 3 Laurel Park, Randalstown, Antrim BT41 3HJ — MB BCh BAO 1975 Belf.; DCH Eng. 1979. Prev: GP. Antrim Health Centre Antrim.

TONER, Janet Anna Altnagelvin Hospital, Londonderry BT52 1JE Tel: 01504 45171; 16 Dalboyne Park, Lisburn BT28 3BU — MB BCh BAO 1995 Belf. (Qu. Univ. Belf.) SHO (Gen. Med.) Coleraine Hosp. Socs: BMA. Prev: Ho. Off. Coleraine Hosp. 1996 - 1999.

TONER, Mr Joseph Gerard 3 Myrtleland Park, Belfast BT9 6NE — MB BCh BAO 1979 Belf.; FRCS Ed. 1983. Cons. (Otolaryngol.) Ulster Hosp. Dundonald, Belf. City Hosp. Prev: Sen. Regist. (Otolaryngol.) Belf. City Hosp.

TONER, Joseph Michael St Woolos Hospital, Newport NP20 4SZ Tel: 01633 238317; 13 Dorallt Close, Henllys, Cwmbran NP44 6EY Tel: 01633 480256 — MB BS 1977 Lond.; BSc (Hons.) Lond. 1974; FRCP (UK) 1997, M 1980. Cons. Phys. Roy. Gwent & St. Woolos Hosp. Newport. Prev: Cons. Geriat. Med. St. Woolos Hosp. Newport.

TONER, Professor Peter Gilmour Department of Pathology, Royal Hospital Trust, Grosvenor Road, Belfast BT12 6BL Tel: 01232 240503 Fax: 01232 312265 — MB ChB 1965 Glas.; DSc Glas. 1972, MB ChB (Hons.) 1965; FRCP Glas. 1984, M 1982; FRCPath 1984, M 1971. (Glas.) Cons. Path. Roy. Vict. Hosp. Trust Belf.; Edr. in Chief Jl. Path. Socs: Comm. Mem. Path. Soc. GB & Irel. Prev: Musgrave Prof. Path. Qu. Univ. Belf.; Prof. (Path.) Univ. Glas.; Vis. Prof. (Path.) Univ. Colorado Med. Centre Denver USA.

TONES, Brian John Fontana and Partners, Silsden Health Centre, Elliott Street, Silsden, Keighley BD20 0DG Tel: 01535 652447 Fax: 01535 657296; Low Shann Farm, High Spring Gardens Lane, Keighley BD20 6LN Tel: 01535 600001 — MB ChB 1973 Birm.; MRCGP 1978. (Birmingham) GP; Course Organiser Airedale VTS; Clin. Asst. (Cardiol.).

TONG, David Radiotherapy Department, Guy's Hospital, St Thomas St., London SE1 9RT Tel: 020 7955 4406 Fax: 020 7955 4828; 18

TONG

Selborne Road, Sidcup DA14 4QY Tel: 020 8300 1032 — MRCS Eng. LRCP Lond. 1966; BSc (Hons.) Anat. 1963, MB BS Lond. 1966; FRCP Lond. 1992; MRCP (UK) 1972; FRCR 1976; DMRT Eng. 1974. (Guy's) Cons. (Radiother. & Oncol.) Guy's & St Thomas' Hosp. NHS Trust. Socs: BMA. Prev: Sen. Regist. (Radiother.) Guy's Hosp. Lond.; Regist. (Med.) Research Asst. BrE. Clinic Guy's Hosp. Lond.

TONG, Grant Ying Kit 21 Craigbarnet Road, Milngavie, Glasgow G62 7RA — MB ChB 1989 Glas.; FRCA 1997; FRCS 1995 Glas.; FRCS Glas. 1995; FRCA 1997. Specialist Regist. (Anaesth.) Glas. Prev: SHO (Anaesth.) Glas.; SHO (Surg.) Monklands Hosp. Airdrie; SHO (A & E) W.. Infirm. Glas.

TONG, Hiu Nam Manchester Royal Infirmary, Manchester M13 9WL — MB BS 1992 Lond.; BSc Lond. 1989. Clin. Fell., Emerg. Med. Manch. Roy. Infirm. Prev: SHO (Med.) Ulster Hosp. Dundonald.

TONG, Jeffrey Leighton, Maj. RAMC Frimley Park Hospital, Portsmouth Rd, Camberley GU16 7UJ Tel: 01276 604604; 2 Elton House, Rodney Place, Clifton, Bristol BS8 4HZ Tel: 0117 923 8691 — MB ChB 1991 Birm.; DA (UK) 1996; FRCA (UK) 1998. (Birm.) Specialist Regist. (Anaest.) Frimley Pk. Hosp. Surrey. Socs: Med. Defence Union; Train. Mem. Assn. AnE.h.; BPAS. Prev: Specialist Regist. (Anaesth.) John Radcliffe Hosp. Oxf.; Specialist Regist. (Anaesth.) Bristol Roy. Infirm.; SHO (Anaesth.) Frimley Pk. Hosp. Camberley.

TONG, Nigel Anthony The Barn, Back Lane, Aughton, Ormskirk L39 6SX — MB ChB 1986 Liverp.

TONG, Peter Chun-Yip Department of Medicine, Medical School, University of Newcastle upon Tyne, Framlington Place, Newcastle upon Tyne NE2 4HH — MB BS 1988 Newc.; BPharm Bradford 1982; MRCP (UK) 1991; PhD Newc. 1998. Peel Med. Research Trust Trav. Fell.sh. Prev: Sen. Regist. (Gen. Med., Diabetes & Endocrine) N.. RHA; MRC Clin. Train. Fell.sh.

TONG, Terence 4 Neville Drive, London N2 0QR Tel: 020 8455 4488 — MB BCh BAO 1983 NUI; LRCPI & LM, LRCSI & LM 1983. Socs: BMA. Prev: Ho. Off. (Urol. & Surg.) Oldham Roy. Infirm.; Ho. Off. (Med.) Oldham & Dist. Gen. Hosp. & Oldham Roy. Infirm.

TONG, Timothy 4 Neville Drive, London N2 0QR — MB BS 1992 Lond.

TONG, William The Binfield Practice, Binfield Health Centre, Terrace Road North, Binfield, Bracknell RG42 5JG Tel: 01344 425434 Fax: 01344 301843; 7 Caswall Close, Binfield, Bracknell RG42 4EF Tel: 01344 422734 Email: willtong@mcmail.com — MB BS 1982 Lond.; BSc (Hons.) Biochem. Lond. 1977. (Westm. Hosp.) Company Occupat. Health Phys. Bracknell. Socs: Brit. Assn. Sport & Med.; Brit. Med. Acupunct. Soc.; Assoc. Mem. Soc. Occupat. Med.

TONGE, Ann Elizabeth 118 Banstead Road S., Sutton SM2 5LJ — MB ChB 1981 Bristol.

TONGE, Anne Rogerson 8 Dartford Road, Sevenoaks TN13 3TQ Tel: 01732 452046 — MB ChB 1959 Birm. Indep. Analyt. Psychother. Kent.

TONGE, Barbara Lesley (retired) Heathfield, Tarvin Road, Littleton, Chester CH3 7DF Tel: 01244 335059 — MB BS 1955 Lond.; MRCS Eng. LRCP Lond. 1955; DCH Eng. 1963. Prev: GP Chester.

TONGE, Gillian Margaret Peterloo Medical Centre, 133 Manchester Old Road, Middleton, Manchester M24 4DZ Tel: 0161 643 5005 Fax: 0161 643 7264 — MB ChB 1992 Manch.; MRCGP 1996; DRCOG 1995; DCH RCP Lond. 1995. Trainee GP Birch Hill Hosp. Rochdale VTS.

TONGE, Helen Wilson (retired) 32 Eslington Terrace, Newcastle upon Tyne NE2 4RN Tel: 0191 281 1816 — MB ChB Ed. 1943. Prev: Clin. Med. Off. S. Tyneside HA.

TONGE, Hilda Margaret Royal United Hospital, Combe Park, Bath BA1 3NG Tel: 01225 428331 Email: maggit.tonge@ruh-bath.nhs.uk; 2 Widcombe Crescent, Bath BA2 6AH — MB BS 1978 Lond.; FRCOG 2000; PhD Rotterdam 1987; MRCOG 1988. Cons. O & G Roy. United. Hosp. Bath. Socs: BMA & Brit. Med. Ultrasound Soc. Prev: Sen. Regist. (O & G) Roy. United Hosp. Bath & Bristol; Research Regist. Qu. Charlotte's Matern. Hosp. Lond.; Regist. (O & G) Bristol Matern. Hosp.

TONGE, Jennifer Louise House of Commons, Westminster, London SW1A 0AA Tel: 020 7219 4596 Fax: 020 7219 4596 Email: tonge@cix.co.uk; 28 Kew Gardens Road, Richmond

TW9 3HD Tel: 020 8948 1649 Email: j.tonge@cix.co.uk — MB BS Lond. 1964; MFFP 1993. (Univ. Coll. Hosp.) MP. Socs: FRSPHH; Fac. Fam. Plann. Prev: Sen. Managem. Community Health Servs. W. Lond. Healthcare Trust; Clin. Asst. W.m. Hosp. Obst. Unit Qu. Mary's Hosp. Roehampton; SCMO (Wom. Servs.) Ealing HA Lond.

TONGE, Jeremy Marcus Adrian 13 Brook Avenue N., New Milton BH25 5HE Tel: 01425 613399 Email: louisejeremy@hotmail.com — MB BS 1993 Lond.; DRCOG 1995; DFFP 1995; MRCOG 1998. (St Mary's) Sen. SHO. (Obst & Gyn.) Chichester; SHO (Obst. & Gyn.) Basingstoke.; SHO (Obst. & Gyn.) Winchester NHS Trust. Prev: SHO (Paediat. & Neonates) Poole NHS Trust; SHO Capital Coast Health, NZ; SHO (O & G) Soton. NHS Trust.

TONGE, John Churchgate Surgery, 15 Churchgate, Retford DN22 6PA Tel: 01777 706661 Fax: 01777 711966; Longacre, 69 Town St, Lound, Retford DN22 8RT Tel: 01777 817982 — MB ChB 1973 Sheff.; MRCP (UK) 1978. GP Princip.; Non-Exec. Dir. Bassetlaw Hosp. & Community Serv. Trust. Prev: Regist. (Med.) Roy. Infirm. Sheff.

TONGE, Kathryn Anne The Hillingdon Hospital, Pield Heath Rd, Uxbridge UB8 3NN Tel: 01895 238282 Fax: 01895 279215; Tel: 02 8560 4693 — MB BS 1988 Lond.; MA (Hons.) Oxf. 1989, BA (Hons.) 1985; MRCP (UK) 1991. (Univ. Oxf. & St. Mary's Hosp. Med. Sch.) Cons. (Gastroenterol.) The Hillingdon Hosp. Uxbridge. Prev: Sen Regist. Chelsea & W.minster & St Marks Hosp.

TONGE, Keith Angus Dept. Radiology, St Thomas' Hospital, London SE1 7EH Tel: 020 7928 9292 Ext: 2436 Fax: 020 7261 0405 Email: keith.tonge@gstt.sthames.nhs.uk; 5 Bush Road, Kew, Richmond TW9 3AN Tel: 0208 948 1649 Fax: 0208 948 1649 — MB BS 1965 Lond.; BSc Lond. 1962; MRCS Eng. LRCP Lond. 1965; FRCR 1975; FFR 1973; DMRD Eng. 1970. (Univ. Coll. Hosp.) p/t Cons. Radiol. Guy's & St. Thos. Hosp. Trust. Socs: RSM Sect. Radiol. Counc.lor. Prev: Research Fell. Roy. Marsden Hosp. Lond.; Sen. Regist. (Radiol.) United Birm. Hosps.

TONGE, Mary Francella Rebecca 85 Yvonne Road, Redditch B97 5HT — MB ChB 1978 Birm.

TONGE, Vincent (retired) Heathfield, Tarvin Road, Littleton, Chester CH3 7DF Tel: 01244 335059 — MB ChB 1954 Liverp.; DTM & H Liverp. 1976; DObst RCOG 1958.

TONI, Eric Edward The Surgery, 106 Cowper Road, Rainham RM13 9TS Tel: 01708 550276 Fax: 01708 552620 — MB BS 1977 London; MB BS 1977 London.

TONKIN, Lisa Vivyan Minster Cottage, Highmoor Hill, Caldicot, Newport NP26 5PF — MB BCh 1998 Wales.

TONKIN, Ralph William (retired) 11 Muirton, Aviemore PH22 1SF — MB ChB 1945 Ed.; FRCP Ed. 1979, M 1976; FRCPath 1974, M 1963. Prev: Sen. Lect., Dept. Bacteriol. Univ. Edin. Roy. Infirm. Edin.

TONKIN, Richard Douglas (retired) 66 Noel Road, Islington, London N1 8HB Tel: 020 7359 1279 — MB BS 1939 Lond.; MD Lond. 1946; FRCP Lond. 1955, M 1945; MRCS Eng. LRCP Lond. 1939. Pres. Research Counc. for Complementary Med. Prev: Dir. Diagn. Unit Lond. Clinic.

TONKS, Alison Mary BMJ Editorial, BMA House, Tavistock Square, London WC1H 9JR Tel: 020 7383 6347 Fax: 020 7383 6418; 70 Chesterfield Road, St Andrews, Bristol BS6 5DP Tel: 0117 924 3356 Email: atonks@bmj.com — MB ChB 1985 Bristol; FRCA 1990. Asst. Edr. BMJ Lond.; Sen. Er Stud. BMJ.

TONKS, Clive Malcolm (retired) 10 Anselm Road, Pinner HA5 4LJ Tel: 020 8428 3894 Fax: 020 8621 4764 Email: cmtonk@aol.com — MB ChB Leeds 1955; FRCP Lond. 1980, M 1959; FRCPsych 1974, M 1971; DPM Lond. 1962. Prev: Cons. Psychiat. St. Mary's Hosp. & Med. Sch. Lond.

TONKS, Joyce Margaret (retired) 10 Anselm Road, Pinner HA5 4LJ Tel: 020 8428 3894 Fax: 020 8621 4764 — MB ChB 1957 Leeds. Prev: SCMO Harrow DHA.

TONKS, Wendy Stella Saltaire Medical Centre, Richmond Road, Shipley BD18 4RX Tel: 01274 593101 Fax: 01274 772588; 52 Moorland Avenue, Baildon, Shipley BD17 6RW — MB BS 1981 Newc.; MRCGP 1996; DRCOG 1986.

TONNESMANN, Margarete Elisabeth Hedwig Pauline 41A Aberdare Gardens, London NW6 3AL Tel: 020 7624 5688 — MD 1958 Kiel; State Exam. Med. Hamburg 1951. (Gottingen, Bonn, Dusseldorf & Hamburg) Hon. Cons. Psychother. & Med. Sociologist King's Coll. Hosp. Lond. Socs: Assoc. Mem. Brit. Psychoanal. Soc.

TONUCCI, Daniela Francesca Maria 26 Windsor Road, London N3 3SS — MB ChB 1995 Bristol.

TOO-CHUNG, Mr Michael Arthur (retired) 3 Tythe Close, Stewkley, Leighton Buzzard LU7 0HD Tel: 01525 240609 Fax: 01525 240609 Email: toochung@btinternet.com — MB ChB 1965 Ed.; FRCS Ed. 1970. Prev: Cons. ENT Surg. Stoke Mandeville Hosp. NHS Trust & Oxf. Radcliffe Infirm. NHS Trust.

TOOBY, David John 34 The Ridgeway, Chatham ME4 6PD Tel: 01634 45979 — MRCS Eng. LRCP Lond. 1959; BSc Lond. 1956, MB BS 1959; DObst RCOG 1962. (St. Bart.)

TOOBY, Hugh Alaric The Ridge Medical Practice, 3 Paternoster Lane, Great Horton, Bradford BD7 3EE Tel: 01274 502905 Fax: 01274 522060 — MB ChB 1985 Ed.; MA Camb. 1986, BA 1982; T(GP) 1991; DA (UK) 1988. (Ed.)

TOOGOOD, Andrew Alan 10 Finbury Close, Olton, Solihull B92 8DH — MB ChB 1987 Manch.; MRCP (UK) 1991. Clin. Research Fell. (Hon. Regist.) Christie Hosp. NHS Trust Manch. Socs: Soc. Endocrinol. & Growth Hormone Research Soc.

TOOGOOD, Carolyn Maud Hillstaed Cottage, 186 Hinton Way, Great Shelford, Cambridge CB2 5AN — MB ChB 1988 Birm.; MRCGP 1993; DRCOG 1991.

TOOGOOD, Mr Giles John St James University Hospital, Leeds LS9 7TF; 81 North Lane, Roundhay, Leeds LS8 2QJ — BM BCh 1986 Oxf.; FRCS Ed. 1990; DM 1995; FRCS (Gen) 1996. Cons. (Surg.).

TOOGOOD, Shirley Joyce 31 Kendal End Road, Barnt Green, Rednal, Birmingham B45 8PY Tel: 0121 445 2627 — MB BS 1956 Lond. (King's Coll. Hosp.) Dist. Med. Off. W. Birm. HA. Prev: SCM Birm. HA; Sen. Clin. Med. Family Plann. & Health Educat. Birm. AHA (T); Clin. Asst. (Psychiat.) Rubery Hill Hosp. Birm.

TOOHER, Carmel Jane 27 Woodville Street, Farington, Preston PR25 4QE — MB ChB 1987 Manch.

TOOKE, Professor John Edward Peninsula Medical School, ITTC Building, Tamar Science Park, Davy Rd, Plymouth PL6 8BX Tel: 01752 764262 Fax: 01752 764226 — BM BCh 1974 Oxf.; DM Oxf. 1982, MA, MSc 1974; FRCP Eng. 1993; MRCP (UK) 1977; MRCS Eng. LRCP Lond. 1974; DSC Oxon. 1998. (Oxford) Dean, Penninsula Med. Sch.; Hon. Cons. Phys., Roy. Devon And Exeter Hosp.; Prof. Of Vasc. Med., Uni. Of Exeter. Socs: Pres. Brit. MicroCirc. Soc.; Chairm. Prof. Sec.s Coordinating Comm. Brit. Diabetic Assoc.; Pres. Europ. Soc. Microcirc. Prev: Wellcome Sen. Lect. Char. Cross & W.m. Med. Sch. Lond.; Hon. Cons. Phys. Endocrine Unit Char. Cross Hosp. Lond.; Lect. (Med.) Leeds Gen. Infirm.

TOOKMAN, Adrian Jeffrey 2C Wolverton Road, Stanmore HA7 2RN Tel: 020 8954 5345 — MB BS 1976 Lond.; MRCS Eng. LRCP Lond. 1976; MRCPI 1982. (Char. Cross) Regist. (Radiother. & Oncol.) Roy. Free Hosp. Lond. Prev: Regist. (Rheum.) Whittington Hosp. Lond.; Resid. Med. Off. Roy. N.. Hosp. Lond.; SHO (Med. Ophth.) St. Thos. Hosp. Lond.

TOOLEY, Mr Alan Hunter (retired) 26 The Avenue, Linthorpe, Middlesbrough TS5 6PD Tel: 01642 818750 Fax: 01642 822949 Email: aht@linthorpe75.freeserve.co.uk — MB BS 1953 Lond.; FRCS Eng. 1957; MRCS Eng. LRCP Lond. 1953. Prev: Cons. Surg. S. Tees Acute Trust Hosps.

TOOLEY, Deborah Ann Department of Anaesthetics, St. James University Hospital, Beckett St., Leeds LS9 7TF; The Lodge, Potterton, Barwick in Elmet, Leeds LS15 4NN Tel: 0113 281 1186 Fax: 0113 281 1186 Email: debs@taytoo.demon.co.uk — MB ChB 1990 Auckland; MB ChB Auckland 1989; Dip. Obs. Auckland 1993; DA (Eng.) 1996. (Auckland) Specialist Regist. (Anaesth.) St. James Univ. Hosp. Leeds. Socs: Assn. Anaesth.; Intens. Care Soc. Prev: SHO (Anaesth.) W. Yorks.; Regist. (A & E) UK & New Zealand; SHO (O & G) New Zealand.

TOOLEY, Ian Russell Littlewick Medical Centre, 42 Nottingham Road, Ilkeston DE7 5PR Tel: 0115 932 5229 Fax: 0115 932 5413 — MB BS 1983 Newc.; MRCGP 1987; DRCOG 1986. Trainee GP N.umbria VTS.

TOOLEY, James Ross 7 River Walk, Great Yarmouth NR30 4BZ Email: jim@caves.demon.co.uk — MB BS 1993 Lond.; MRCP (UK) 1996. Specialist Regist. (Paediat.) Addenbrookes Hosp. Camb. Prev: Regist. (Paediat.) Nor. & Norwich Hosp.; SHO (Paediat.) Roy. Brompton Hosp. Lond.; SHO (Paediat.) King's Coll. Hosp. Lond. & Norf. & Norwich Hosp.

TOOLEY, Peter John Hocart PT Pharma Consultancy (Gernsey) Ltd., Les Miellles, L'Ancresse, Vale, Guernsey GY3 5AZ Tel: 01481 242607 Fax: 01481 242505 Email: tooleyp@aol.com; Les Mielles, L'Ancresse, Vale, Guernsey GY3 5AZ Tel: 01481 244543 Email: tooleyp@aol.com — MB BS Lond. 1964; LLM (Wales) 1994; MRCS Eng. LRCP Lond. 1963; MRCGP 1971; DMJ Soc. Apoth. Lond. 1981; DObst RCOG 1965. (Lond. Hosp.) Cons. Pharmaceut. Med.; Contract Med. Dir. Sankyo Pharma (UK); Contract Med. Adviser Janssen-Cilag Ltd (UK); Contract Med Dir.Alliance Pharmaceut.; Contract Med. Dir., Faulding Pharmaceut. PLC. Socs: Fell. Roy. Soc. Med.; BMA; Brit. Acad. Forens. Sci. Prev: Head of Med. Affairs Janssen-Cilag Ltd (UK); GP Twyford.

TOOLIS, Francis Haematology Department, Dumfries & Galloway Royal Infirmary, Bankend Road, Dumfries DG1 4AP Tel: 01387 246246 Fax: 01387 241344 Email: f.toolis@dgri.scot.nhs.uk — MB ChB 1972 Ed.; FRCP (E,G,L), FRCPath, MBA. Cons. Haemat. Dumfries & Galloway Roy. Infirm. Socs: Coll. of Amer. Pathologists; Amer. Soc. of Hematology; Europ. Soc. of Haemat.

TOOMEY, Henry 14 North Close, Drayton Parslow, Milton Keynes MK17 0JQ — MB BS 1993 Lond.; DRCOG 1995; DFFP 1997. (University College London) GP Princip. The Surg. 29 Bassett Rd., Leighton Buzzard. Prev: GP Regist. Meadowcraft Surg. Aylesbury Aug 1996 - July 1997; SHO Oxf. Region VTS.

TOOMEY, Mr Paul 31 Eastfield Road, Western Park, Leicester LE3 6FE Tel: 0116 285 4737 — MB BS 1983 Lond.; FRCS Eng. 1988; FRCS Ed. 1988. (Char. Cross) Research Fell. (Surg.) Leicester Roy. Infirm. Prev: Regist. (Surg.) W.m. Hosp. Lond.; SHO Rotat. (Surg.) Char. Cross Hosp. Lond.; SHO (Orthop. & Trauma) Roy. United Hosp. Bath.

TOOMEY, Peter John York District Hospital, Wiggington Road, York YO31 8HE Tel: 01904 631313 — MB BS 1983 Lond.; FFA RCSI 1989. Cons. Anaesth. York Health Servs. NHS Trust. Prev: Cons. Anaesth. Stoke Mandeville Hosp. Aylesbury; Sen. Regist. (Anaesth.) Yorks. RHA.

TOOMEY, Mr William Francis (retired) 23 Allander Drive, Torrance, Glasgow G64 4LA Tel: 01360 620410 — MB ChB 1946 Glas.; FRFPS Glas. 1949; FRCS Glas. 1962. Prev: Cons. Surg. Roy. Alexandra Hosp. Paisley.

TOOMS, Mr Douglas (retired) Saddlers Cottage, Chaddesley Corbett, Kidderminster DY10 4SD Tel: 01562 323 — MB BCh 1945 Wales; BSc, MB BCh Wales 1945; FRCS Eng. 1948. Prev: Cons. Surg. Mid-Worcs. Hosp. Gp.

TOON, Christiane Gertrud Erika 51 Gorsebank Road, Hale Barns, Altrincham WA15 0BB — MD 1962 Hamburg; State Exam. Med. Hamburg 1961; Dip. Anaesth. Hamburg 1969. (Hamburg) Assoc. Specialist (Anaesth.) Wythenshawe Hosp. Manch.

TOON, Peter Dennis 206 Queensbridge Road, London E8 3NB Tel: 020 7254 1101 Fax: 020 7923 1541; 137 Roding Road, London E5 0DR Tel: 020 8986 6733 Fax: 020 8986 9905 Email: petertoon@aol.com — MRCS Eng. LRCP Lond. 1977; MSc Oxf. 1983; BSc (1st cl. Hons.) Lond. 1974, MB BS 1977; MRCGP 1984; DCH RCP Lond. 1983; DPMSA (Distinc.) 1982; AKC 1974. (King's Coll. Hosp.) Hon. Lect. Human Scis. & Med. Ethics St. Bart. Lond.; Edr. RCGP Pub.ations. Socs: Grad. Mem. Brit. Psychol. Soc.; Balint Soc. Prev: Educat. Facilitator LIZEI Progr. N. Thames; Asst. GP; GP Adviser Lond. Implementation Gp.

TOON, Philip Gerald Mulberry House, Cox Lane, Rossett, Wrexham LL12 0BH — MB ChB 1974 Manch.; MRCOG 1982; T(OG) 1991.

TOONE, Brian Kenneth Department of Psychological Medicine, King's College Hospital, Camberwell, London SE5 Tel: 020 7346 3228 Fax: 020 7346 3885 Email: brian.toone@kcl.ac.uk; 4 Grove Park, Camberwell, London SE5 8LT Tel: 020 7733 3499 — MB BS Lond. 1962; MPhil Lond. 1973; FRCP Lond. 1988; MRCP (UK) 1967; FRCPsych 1988, M 1973. (St. Geo.) Cons. Psychiat. Maudsley & Bethlem Roy. Hosps. & King's Coll. Hosp. Lond. Socs: Brit. Neuropsychiat. Assn.; Brit. Assn. Psychopharmacol. Prev: Sen. Regist. & Regist. Maudsley & Bethlem Roy. Hosps. Lond; Lect. & Sen. Lect. Inst. Psychiat.

TOONE, Peter Charles St Clements Surgery, Tanner Street, Winchester SO23 8AD Tel: 01962 852211 Fax: 01962 856010 — MB BS 1970 Lond.; MRCS Eng. LRCP Lond. 1971; MRCGP 1981; DObst RCOG 1974; DCH Eng. 1973. (King's Coll. Hosp.)

TOONE

TOONE, Robin Philip Donovan Old Mill Surgery, Marlborough Road, Nuneaton CV11 5PQ Tel: 024 7638 2554 Fax: 024 7635 0047; 97 Milby Drive, Nuneaton CV11 6GD Tel: 01203 385771 — MRCS Eng. LRCP Lond. 1965; DObst RCOG 1967. (Guy's) Prev: Ho. Surg. Putney Hosp.; Cas. Off. Padd. Gen. Hosp.; Obst. Ho. Off. Bromley Hosp.

TOOP, Dorothy Margaret (retired) Auchochan House Flat 79, New Trows Road, Lesmahagow, Lanark ML11 0JS Tel: 01555 890035 Email: bdtoop@compuserve.com — MB ChB Ed. 1944; DObst RCOG 1967. Prev: Med. Off. Saiburi Christian Hosp. S. Thailand.

TOOP, Kenneth Monro The James Cook University Hospital, Marton Road, Middlesbrough TS4 3BW Tel: 01642 854857 Fax: 01642 854857 Email: toopkfscs@aol.com; 604 Yarm Road, Eaglescliffe, Stockton-on-Tees TS16 0DQ Tel: 01642 780780 — MB ChB 1972 Ed.; FRCOG 1995, M 1980. (Univ. Ed.) Cons. O & G S. The James Cook Univ. Hosp. Middlesbrough; Hon. Sen. Lect. (Obst. & Gyn.) Univ. Dundee. Socs: Exec. Comm. Mem. Christian Med. Fell.ship. Prev: Sen. Regist. Manch. & Oldham HAs; Regist. Aberd. Teachg. Hosps.; SHO W.. Gen. Hosp. Edin.

TOOP, Michael James Department of Pathology, Harrogate District Hospital, Lancaster Park Road, Harrogate HG2 7SX Tel: 01423 553056 Fax: 01423 553229 Email: miketoop@csi.com — MB 1979 Camb.; BChir 1978; MRCP (UK) 1983; MRCPath 1986; FRCPath 1996. (Cambridge) Cons. Chem. Path. Harrogate HA. Prev: Sen. Regist. (Chem. Path.) Birm. HA.

TOOP, Robert Leslie 5 The Elms, Ellington, Morpeth NE61 5LH Tel: 01670 860428 — MB BS 1970 Newc.; DIH Eng. 1980; DObst RCOG 1972. Med. Dir. Occupat. Health Med. Servs. Socs: Assoc. Fac. Occupat. Med. RCP Eng; Soc. Occupat. Med. Newc. Br.. Prev: Phys. Occupat. Health N. Eng. Indust. Health Serv. Newc.

TOOP, William James (retired) 23 Erskine Hill, Polmont, Falkirk FK2 0UH Tel: 01324 715873 — MB ChB Ed. 1938; DTM & H Ed. 1947. Prev: Med. Off. China Inland Mission Hosp. Dali, Yunnan, China.

TOOR, Mr Karamjit Singh 79a Scotts Road, Southall UB2 5DF Tel: 020 8574 0637 — MB BS 1966 Panjab; MB BS Panjab (India) 1966; FRCS Eng. 1975; DO Eng. 1970.

TOORAWA, David Ahmed Wolsey Road, Hemel Hempstead HP2 4SH Fax: 01442 244554; The Orchard, 152 St. Johns Road, Hemel Hempstead HP1 1NR Tel: 01442 254366 Fax: 01442 244554 — MB BS 1967 Lond.; MRCGP 1978; DObst RCOG 1969. (Univ. Coll. Hosp.) Socs: BMA. Prev: Ho. Surg. (Obst.) Vict. Matern. Hosp. Barnet SHO (Path.) Barnet Gen. Hosp.

TOOSEY, Joyce Brenda Metcalf (retired) Fairways, 8 Wealdhurst Park, Broadstairs CT10 2LD Tel: 0841 860166 — MB BS Lond. 1941; MRCS Eng. LRCP Lond. 1941; DPH Eng. 1943. Prev: MOH Blandford Boro. & RD, Wimborne & Cranborne RD & Wimborne UD &.

TOOSY, Ahmed Tahir Coombe Farm, Oaks Road, Croydon CR0 5HL — MB BS 1994 Lond.

TOOSY, Tahir Hafeez The Coppice, West Drive, Carshalton SM5 4EL Tel: 020 8642 2308 — MB BS 1967 Punjab; MB BS Punjab (Pakistan) 1967. (King Edwd. Med Coll. Lahore)

TOOT, Marc Old Harbourhouse, Quay St., Minehead TA24 5UJ — Artsexamen 1992 Amsterdam.

TOOTH, Barbara Park House Medical Centre, 18 Harvist Road, London NW6 6SE Tel: 020 8969 7711 Fax: 020 8969 8880; 37 Arlington Road, Camden, London NW1 7ES — MB BS 1963 Lond. (London Hospital Whitechapel) Socs: Roy. Soc. of Med.

TOOTH, David Roy Kiveton Park Primary Care Centre, Chapel Way, Kiveton Park, Sheffield S26 6QU Tel: 01909 770213 Fax: 01909 772793 — MB BChir Camb. 1989; MA (Hons.) Camb. 1989; MRCGP 1993; DFFP 1993; DCH RCP Lond. 1992.

TOOTH, Elisabeth Ann (retired) 29 Sunningdale Close, Handsworth Wood, Birmingham B20 1LH Tel: 0121 523 8392 — MB BS Lond. 1958; FRCOG 1979, M 1965; DObst RCOG 1960. Prev: Cons. Gyn. & Obst. Sandwell Dist. Gen. Hosp. W. Bromich.

TOOTH, Jacqueline Anne Owlthorpe Surgery, 52 Broadlands Avenue, Sheffield S20 6RL Tel: 0114 247 7852 Fax: 0114 248 3691; 53 Ribblesdale Drive, Regency Court, Ridgeway, Sheffield S12 3XE — MB ChB 1978 Sheff.; DRCOG 1980.

TOOTH, John Anthony (retired) 17 Chesham Road, Wilmslow SK9 6EZ Tel: 01625 582337 — MB ChB 1955 Birm.; MRCP Lond. 1968; FRCPath 1977, M 1965; Dip. Bact. Lond 1964. Cons. Bacteriol. United Manch. Hosps.; Hon. Lect. in Bact. Univ. Manch. Prev: Sen. Bacteriol. Pub. Health Laborat., Soton. Gen. Hosp.

TOOTH, Julie Suzanne 1 Birch Grove, Meir Heath, Stoke-on-Trent ST3 7JN — MB ChB 1991 Leeds.

TOOTHILL, Susan Valerie The Cedars Surgery, 26 Swanley Centre, Swanley BR8 7AH Tel: 01322 663111/663237 Fax: 01322 614867; 73 Pollyhaugh, Eynsford, Dartford DA4 0HE — MB BS 1980 Lond.

TOOVEY, Angela Joy 2 Goldington Road, Bedford MK40 3NG Tel: 01234 351341 Fax: 01234 341464 — MB ChB 1978 Manch.; MRCGP 1983; DCH RCP Lond. 1981; DRCOG 1980.

TOOVEY, Anthony Rupert Goldington Road Surgery, 2 Goldington Road, Bedford MK40 3NG Tel: 01234 351341 — MB ChB 1978 Manch.; MRCP (UK) 1981; MRCGP 1987; DRCOG 1986.

TOOZE, Reuben Matthew Dept of Histopathology, Adden Brookes Hospital, Box 235, Hills Rd, Cambridge CB2 2QQ Tel: 01223 217163 Email: tmt22@cam.ac.uk; 11 Milford St, Cambridge CB1 2LP — MB BS 1992 Lond.; PhD Lond. 1998. (St Barts.) Specialist Regist. Prev: Clin.Research Fell. Camb Univ.

TOOZS-HOBSON, Mr Philip Milton Brimingham Womens Hosp, Metchley Park, Edgbaston, Birmingham B15 2TG; Tel: 01364 824381 — MB BS 1989 Lond.; MFFP 1996; MRCOG 1994. (St Marys Hosp. Med. Sch.) Cons. O&G Brimingham Wom.'s Hosp. Birm. Socs: ICS. Prev: Research Regist. (Urodynamics) King's Coll. Hosp. Lond.; Regist. (O & G) Chelsea & W.m. Hosp. Lond.; SHO (A & E) St. Mary's Hosp. Lond.

TOPA, Giuseppe Nicola Francesco 7 Castle Street, Tunbridge Wells TN1 1XJ — State Exam Perugia 1989.

TOPHAM, Clare Ann Wild Harries, Hayes Lane, Slinford, Horsham RH13 7SL — MB BS 1967 Lond.; MRCS Eng. LRCP Lond. 1967; FRCR 1975; DMRT Eng. 1974. (Guy's) Cons. Radiotherap. & Oncol. St. Luke's Hosp. Guildford & Crawley. Socs: BMA. Prev: Regist. & Sen. Regist. (Radiother. & Oncol.) W.m. Hosp. Lond.

TOPHAM, Emma Jane Wild Harrys, Hayes La, Slinfold, Horsham RH13 7SL — BM BCh 1997 Oxf.

TOPHAM, Hugh William 76 Avenue Road, St Neots, Huntingdon PE19 1LH — MRCS Eng. LRCP Lond. 1946. (Guy's) Prev: Ho. Surg. Pembury Hosp.; Outpat. Off. Guy's Hosp.

TOPHAM, Mr John Harcourt (cons. rooms), Goring Hill Hospital, Bodiam Avenue, Goring-By-Sea, Worthing BN11 4PN Tel: 01903 506699 Fax: 01903 242348 — MRCS Eng. LRCP Lond. 1967; MB BS Lond. 1967; BDS 1963; FRCS Eng. 1972. (Guy's) Cons. ENT Surg. Roy. Sussex Co. Hosp. Brighton, Worthing Hosp. & Roy. Alexandra Childr. Hosp. Brighton. Socs: Brighton & Sussex M-C Soc.; Fell. Roy. Soc. Med. Prev: Regist. & Sen. Regist. (ENT) Lond. Hosp.; Ho. Surg. & Ho. Phys. Guy's Hosp. Lond.

TOPHAM, Katherine Mary BATLSK BFPO 10 — BM 1985 Soton.; DFFP 1993.

TOPHAM, Lawrence Garth, OStJ, Surg. Capt. RN Retd. (retired) Tilings, Holt Close, Wickham, Fareham PO17 5EY Tel: 01329 832072 — MB ChB 1937 Leeds; MD Leeds 1946; FRCP Ed. 1967, M 1957; MRCP Lond. 1969. Prev: Hon. Phys to HM the Qu./Prof. Med. Roy. Navy & RCP Lond.

TOPHAM, Liam Arthur Top Flat, 9 Sherwood Rise, Nottingham NG7 6JG — BM BS 1993 Nottm.

TOPHAM, Peter Stewart 10 St Agnes Way, Horeston Grange, Nuneaton CV11 6TN — MB ChB 1988 Birm.; ChB Birm. 1988.

TOPHAM, Simon Paul James Street Family Practice, 49 James Street, Louth LN11 0JN Tel: 01507 611122 Fax: 01507 610435; 132 Newmarket, Louth LN11 9EN Tel: 01507 610561 Email: simon.topham@virgin.net — MB BS 1987 Newc. (Newc.) GP Partner.

TOPHILL, Mr Paul Robert Department of Urology, Royal Hallamshire Hospital, Glossop Road, Sheffield S10 2JF Tel: 0114 271 1900 Fax: 0114 271 3680; 183 Ecclesall Road S., Sheffield S11 9PN Tel: 0114 235 1831 — MB ChB 1981 Leic.; MD Sheff. 1997; FRCS (Urol.) 1995; FRCS Eng. 1987. Cons. Urol. Surg. Roy. Hallamsh. Hosp. Sheff.

***TOPIWALA, Nimisha Prakash** 7A Station Road, London N21 3SB — MB BS 1998 Lond.; MB BS Lond 1998.

TOPLEY, Elizabeth (retired) 1 Wickens Place, High St, West Malling ME19 6NB Tel: 01732 849442 Email: daves.quakerdave@freeserve.co.uk — MB BS 1939 Lond.; MD

TORQUATI

Lond. 1952. Prev: Prof. Ibarapa Project Univ. Coll. Hosp. Ibadan, Nigeria.

TOPLEY, Elizabeth Mary Childhealth Service, Mansfield Community Hospital, Stockwellgate, Mansfield NG18 5QJ; 21 Greendale Ave, Edwinstone, Mansfield NG21 9NA Tel: 01623 785198 — MB ChB 1978 Sheff. Socs: MRCGP.

TOPLIS, Mr Philip John Dept. Obstetrics & Gynaecology, Frimley Park Hopital Trust, Camberley GU16 5UJ; Wyck Farmhouse, Wyck, Nr. Alton GU34 3AL — MB ChB 1973 Bristol; FRCS Ed. 1979; FRCS Glas. 1979; FRCOG 1993, M 1980. (Bristol University) Cons. O & G W. Surrey & NE Hants. HA. Socs: Fell. Roy. Soc. Med.; Brit. Soc. Colpos. & Cerv. Path.; Brit. Soc. Gyn. Endoscopy. Prev: Sen. Regist. John Radcliffe Hosp. Oxf.; Regist. (O & G) Guy's Hosp. & Char. Cross Hosp. Lond.; Resid. Qu. Charlottes & Chelsea Hosp. for Wom. Lond.

TOPLISS, Claire Joanne 51 Murvagh Close, Cheltenham GL53 7QX — MB BS 1993 Newc.

TOPORSKI, Katja Portsmouth NHS Trust, Queen Alexandra Hospital, Southwick Hill Rd, Coshak, Portsmouth PO6.3LU Tel: 01705 286000; 13 Chelsea Road, Southsea PO5 1NH Tel: 01705 755171 Email: andrewskate@easynet.co.uk — State Exam Med. Technical U Munich 1992; DCH 1999. Specialist Regist.(Anaest.). Prev: SHO. (Anaest.) 98-99; SHO. (Paediat.) 97-98; SHO. (Anaest.) 96-97.

TOPP, Dudleigh Oscar (retired) 21 Old Bincombe Lane, Sutton Poyntz, Weymouth DT3 6NB — MB BS 1949 Lond.; MFCM 1972; FRCPsych 1980, M 1971; DPM Eng. 1965; DMJ Soc. Apoth. Lond. 1962. Prev: Capt. R.A.M.C.

TOPP, Judith Mary Oak Hill Health Centre, Oak Hill Road, Surbiton KT6 6EN Tel: 020 8399 6622 Fax: 020 8390 4470; 6 King Charles Road, Surbiton KT5 8PY Tel: 020 8399 1004 — MB BS 1975 Lond.; MRCGP 1980; DRCOG 1978; DCH Eng. 1977. (St. Bart.) Prev: SHO (Obst.) N.wick Pk. Harrow; SHO (Paediat.) Qu. Mary's Hosp. Childr. Carshalton; Ho. Surg. St. Bart. Hosp. Lond.

TOPPER, Ruth P.J. Kaye and Partners, Northwick Surgery, 36 Northwick Park Road, Harrow HA1 2NU Tel: 020 8427 1661 Fax: 020 8864 2737 — MB ChB 1975 Manch.

TOPPING, Adam Partington 33 Broughton Way, Rickmansworth WD3 8GW — MB ChB 1992 Leic.

TOPPING, James Stirrat (retired) 64 Grange Paddock, Worlaby, Brigg DN20 0PD — MB ChB 1931 Glas. Prev: Ho. Phys. & Outdoor Ho. Surg. Glas. Roy. Infirm.

TOPPING, Joanne Liverpool Women's Hospital, Crown Street, Liverpool L8 7SS — MB ChB 1984 Liverp.

TOPPING, Miss Nicola Claire 6 Meadow Walk, Chapel Allerton, Leeds LS7 4RN — MB ChB 1992 Leeds; MB ChB (Distinc.) Psychiat. Leeds 1992; DRCOG 1994; MRCOPHTH 1999. Specialist Regist. Yorks. Ophth. Rotat. Prev: SHO (Ophth.) Leeds Gen. Infirm.; SHO (Ophth.) Birm. & Midl. Eye Centre.

TOPPING, Susan 114 Ashtons Green Drive, St Helens WA9 2AT — MB BCh 1980 Wales.

TOPPING, Walter Alan Lodge Health, 20 Lodge Manor, Coleraine BT52 1JX Tel: 028 7034 4494 Fax: 028 7032 1759 — MB BCh BAO 1975 Belf.; MRCGP 1979; DCH RCPSI 1978. GP Trainer.

TOPPLE, Nicola Anne (Lane) North Staffordshire Hospital, Newcastle Road, Stoke-on-Trent ST4 6QG — MB ChB 1993 Sheff.; FRCS 2001 (Royal College of Radiologists). Specialist Regist. Rotat. (Radiol.) N. Staffs. Socs: Roy. Coll. Radiol. Prev: SHO (Med.) Roy. Shrewsbury Hosp.

TORABI, Kouros Crownhill Surgery, 103 Crownhill Road, Plymouth PL5 3BN Tel: 01752 771713 — MD 1967 Tehran; MD 1967 Tehran.

TORBET, Mr Thomas Edgar (retired) 66 Netherblane, Blanefield, Glasgow G63 9JP — MB ChB 1953 Glas.; FRCS Ed. 1967; FRCOG 1973, M 1960, DObst 1957. Cons. O & G S.. Gen. Hosp. Glas. Prev: Sen. Regist. (O & G) Ayrsh. Centr. Hosp. Irvine.

TORBOHM, Ingo Karl-Heinz Bryn Teg, Gwalchmai, Holyhead LL65 4RB — State Exam Med 1990 Lubeck.

TORDOFF, Simon George The Old Forge, Welford Road, Naseby, Northampton NN6 6DF — MB ChB 1980 Cape Town.

TORE, Vidyadhar Baosingh House No. 19, Doctors Quarters, Old Church Hospital, Romford RM7 0BE — MB BS 1985 Bombay; FRCA Lond. 1994. Socs: Fell. Roy. Coll. Anaesth.

TORKINGTON, Albert Peter James Roseberry Topping, 1 Westgate Drive, Bridgnorth WV16 4QF — MB ChB 1969 Ed.

TORKINGTON, Ian Michael Graeme Sussex Private Clinic, The Green, St Leonards-on-Sea TN38 0SY Tel: 01424 439439; The Rock, Llanengan, Pwllheli LL53 7LG — MB ChB 1967 Ed.; FFA RCS Eng. 1973. (Ed.) Private GP; Med. Dir. Sussex Private Clinic. Prev: Resid. (Anaesth.) Roy. Vict. Hosp. Montreal, Canada; Regist. (Anaesth.) Roy. Infirm. Edin.

TORKINGTON, Jared Mill House, Michelham Priory, Upper Dicker, Hailsham BN27 3QN — MB BS 1991 Lond.

TORKINGTON, Mark John 23 Hill Street, Carnforth LA5 9DY — MB ChB 1987 Manch.; DCH RCP Lond. 1990. Trainee GP Lancs. VTS.

TORKINGTON, Roberta Marlene 1 Furzebank Park, Hythe, Southampton SO4 6HQ; 1 Shirley Avenue, Southampton SO15 5RP Tel: s. 773258 & 771356 — MB ChB 1976 Pretoria; BSc Pretoria 1971, MB ChB 1976; DRCOG 1981; Cert. JCC Lond. 1980. (Pretoria) Prev: Med. Off. Essex AHA.

TORLESSE, Ruth Mary Treverbyn, Main St., Stillington, York YO61 1LG Tel: 01347 810203 — MB ChB 1994 Ed. (Edinburgh)

TORLEY, Denis Francis 20 Queensborough Gardens, Glasgow G12 9PP — MB ChB 1959 Glas.; MRCPsych 1972; DPM Eng. 1965. (Glas.) Cons. Psychiat. Dykebar Hosp. Paisley. Prev: Regist. Psychiat. Stobhill Gen. Hosp. Glas.; Regist. Psychiat. Bellsdyke Hosp. Larbert; Sen. Regist. St. Geo. Hosp. Morpeth.

TORLEY, Donna Flat 3/1, 71 Ashley St., Glasgow G3 6HW — MB ChB 1998 Glas.

TORMEY, Vincent Joseph Dept of Immunology, Royal Free Hospital, Pond St, London NW3 2QG Tel: 020 7794 0500 — MB BCh BAO 1989 Dub.; MRCPath 2000; BA (Biochemistry) 1991; MRCPI 1992; PhD (Immunology) 1999. Cons. Immunol. Roy. Free Hosp. Lond.

TORNARI, Kyriacos Chrysostomou 32 Addington Drive, North Finchley, London N12 0PH Tel: 020 8445 7913 — MD 1970 Lille. (Fac. Libre de Med. Lille)

TORNEY, John James 1 Westland Avenue, Newcastle BT33 0BZ — MB BCh BAO 1993 Belf.

TORODE, Nigel Basil Park Lane Medical Centre, 82 Park Lane, Bedhampton, Havant PO9 3HN; Cambric Cottage, Woodmancote, Emsworth PO10 8RD Tel: 01243 373456 — BM 1980 Soton.; MRCGP 1984; DRCOG 1982. (Southampton)

TORODE, Stewart Arthur, OBE Barnston, Park Close, Fetcham, Leatherhead KT22 9BD — MB ChB 1966 Ed.; FRCP Ed. 1990; MRCP (UK) 1976; DPhysMed. Eng. 1971. (Ed.) Med. Dir. & Cons. Rheum. & Rehabil. Horder Centre Arthritis CrowBoro.; Cons. Rheumatologist at King Edwd. VIIth Hosp., Midhurst.; Cons. Rheumatologist at Epsom Day Surg. Unit, Epsom, Surrey. Socs: Brit. Soc. Rheum.; Brit. Assn. Rehabil. Med.; Brit. Assn. Sport & Med. Prev: Cons. Rheum & Rehabil. DSMRU RAF Headley Ct. Epsom; Cons. Adviser Rheum. & Rehabil. RAF.

TÖRÖK, Robert Zoltàn — MB BS 1995 Lond.; MRCS 2000 (Ed. A & E); FRCA 1998 (Primary) London; Dip. IMC RCS Ed. 1997. (Guys - UMDS) SpR, A&E Kings. Coll. Hosp. Socs: Ass. Mem. Brit. Ass. A&E Med.; Fac. of A & E Med.; Brit. Ass Immediate Care Doctor.

TOROK, Zoltan 37A Ladysmith, Gomeldon, Salisbury SP4 6LE — MB ChB 1966 Sheff.; PhD Lond. 1979; MSc Surrey 1968; MFOM RCP Lond. 1983. (Sheff.) Socs: Soc. Occupat. Med.; Soc. Clin. Neurophysiol. (EEG).

TOROSSIAN, Feirooz Sinbad Bedros Balham Health Centre, 120 Bedford Hill, London SW12 9HS Tel: 020 8673 1720 Fax: 020 8673 1549; 56 Windermere Avenue, London SW19 3ER — MB ChB 1980 Basrah; MRCGP 1994; MRCOG 1991.

TORPEY, Nicholas Peter Addenbrooks Dialysis Centre, Addenbrookes Hospital, Box 118, Hills Rd, Cambridge CB1 1QQ Tel: 01223 245151; 1 Delles ottage, Carmen St, Great Chesterford, Saffron Walden CB10 1NR Tel: 01799 531305 — MB BS 1994 Lond.; PhD Camb. 1991; MRCP (UK) 1997. (St Georges Hospital Medical School London) Research Fell. (Nephrol.) Anglia Region, Addenbrookes Hosp.

TORQUATI, Fabio Roberto Woodlea House Surgery, 1 Crantock Grove, Bournemouth BH8 0HS Tel: 01202 300903 Fax: 01202 304826; 27 Egerton Road, Bournemouth BH8 9AY — MB BS 1987 Lond.

TORR

TORR, Mrs Barbara 45 St Werburgh's Road, Chorlton-cum-Hardy, Manchester M21 0UN Tel: 0161 881 6560 — MB ChB 1951 Manch.; BDS 1946. (Manch.) Dent. Off. Pk. Hosp. Davyhulme. Prev: Asst. Lect. Dent. Sch. Manch. Univ.; Orthop. Ho. Surg. Manch. Roy. Infirm.; Demonst. Manch. Dent. Hosp.

TORR, James Bernard Doughty 45 St Weyburgh's Road, Chorlton-cum-Hardy, Manchester M21 0UN Tel: 0161 881 6560 — MD 1957 Manch.; MB ChB 1948, BDS 1969. (Manch.) Fell. Manch. Med. Soc. Prev: Lect. (Oral Surg.) Manch. Dent. Hosp.; Lect. in Anat. Manch. Univ.; Squadron Ldr. RAF Med. Br.

TORRANCE, Aileen Muriel 7 Fairlight Road, Hythe CT21 4AD Tel: 01303 265787 — MB ChB 1973 Ed.; DA Eng. 1977. Clin. Asst. (Anaesth.) William Harvey Hosp. Ashford Kent & St. Martin's Hosp. Canterbury Kent.

TORRANCE, Alison Meta Elizabeth Craiglockhart Surgery, 161 Colinton Road, Edinburgh EH14 1BE Tel: 0131 455 8494 Fax: 0131 444 0161 — MB ChB 1975 Dundee.

TORRANCE, Andrew Henderson (retired) 2 Ashburton Road, Hugglescote, Coalville, Leicester LE67 2HA Tel: 01530 832663 Email: andrew-torrance@supanet.com — BM BCh 1943 Oxf.; MA Oxf. 1943; FRCGP 1982, M 1956. Prev: Ho. Surg. Leicester Roy. Infirm.

TORRANCE, Caroline Jane Aberdare Hospital, Aberdare CF44 0RF — MB BS 1982 Lond.; Dip Palliat Med 2000 Cardiff; FRCS Ed. 1986; Dip. GU Med. Soc. Apoth. Lond. 1995; DRCOG 1989. Staff Grade (Palliat. Med.) N. Glam. NHS Trust. Prev: Clin. Asst. (Genitourin. Med.) Roy. Gwent Hosp. Newport.; Regist. (Radiol.) Manch. AHA; SHO (Gen. Surg.) N.ampton Gen. Hosp.

TORRANCE, Ian Leitch 23 Eliot Place, Blackheath, London SE3 0QL — MB ChB 1980 Dundee; MFOM RCP (UK) 1993; MRCGP 1986. (Dundee) Cons. Occupat. Phys.; Hon. Sen. Clin. Lect. (Occupat. Med.) Inst. Occupat. Health Univ. Birm. Socs: Soc. Occupat. Med.; Assoc. of Local Auth. Med. Advisers. Prev: Director of Occupational Health Roy. Hosp.s NHS Trust Lond.; Gp. Occupat. Health Adviser Nat. Grid Company Lond.; Med. Off. Brit. Coal Gateshead.

TORRANCE, Mr John Daly (retired) 6 St Thomas Road, Lytham St Annes FY8 1JL Tel: 01253 724302 — MB ChB 1959 Glas.; FRCS Ed. 1967. Prev: Cons. Orthop. Surg. Vict. Hosp. Blackpool.

TORRANCE, John Malcolm Castle Surgery, 5 Darwin Street, Castle, Northwich CW8 1BU Tel: 01606 74863 Fax: 01606 784847; 5 Darwin Street, Northwich CW8 1BU — MB ChB 1974 Manch.; MRCGP 1980; DRCOG 1978.

TORRANCE, Marion Elizabeth 3 Greenbank Crescent, Edinburgh EH10 5TE — MB ChB 1985 Manch.; MSc Lond. 1993; MRCP (UK) 1992. Cons. Community Paediat. China. Socs: RCPCH; BACCH. Prev: Cons. Comm. Paed. Nothd.; Sen. Regist. (Community Child Health) N.. & Yorks. Region; SCMO (Paediat.) Camden & Islington.

TORRANCE, Mary Heather (retired) 3 Greenbank Crescent, Edinburgh EH10 5TE Tel: 0131 447 3230 — MB ChB 1949 Ed.; MRCP Lond. 1953. Prev: SCMO (Community Med.) Lothian Health Bd.

TORRANCE, Thomas Charles Dover Health Centre, Maison Dieu Road, Dover CT16 1RH Tel: 01304 865544; 51 Crabble Lane, Dover CT17 0NY Tel: 01304 202525 — MB ChB 1970 Glas. (Glas.) Prev: GP Trainer Kirkmuirhill; Med. Regist. StoneHo. Hosp.; Jun. Ho. Off. Glas. Roy. Infirm.

TORRANCE, William Nisbet Spearhead Associates, Spearshill, Tayport DD6 9HT Tel: 01382 552248 — MB ChB 1963 St. And.; Dip. Soc. Med. Ed. 1972. Indep. Consultancy (Pub. Health Med.) Spearhead Assocs. Tayport; Hon. Sen. Lect. (Community & Occupat. Med.) Univ. Dundee. Socs: BMA & Scott. Soc. Med. Admin.s. Prev: Cons. Pub. Health Med. Tayside HB; Med. Admin. Ninewells Hosp. & Med. Sch. Dundee; Research Fell. (Community Med.) E.. RHB (Scotl.).

TORRENS, James Derek Longwater Lane Medical Centre, Longwater Lane, Old Costessey, Norwich NR8 5AH Tel: 01603 742021 Fax: 01603 740271 — MB BCh 1973 Belfast; MB BCh 1973 Belfast.

TORRENS, James Kirkpatrick Carragh House, Moneydig, Garvagh, Coleraine BT51 5LF — MB ChB 1989 Dundee; MRCP (UK) 1993; DTM & H Liverp. 1995. Specialist Regist. (Infec. Dis.s & Gen. Med.) Seacroft Hosp. Leeds. Prev: Regist. (Infec. Dis. & Trop. Med.) Seacroft Hosp. Leeds.

TORRENS, Rebecca Louise Lower Mill Cottage, Furnace Lane, Madeley, Crewe CW3 9EU — MB BS 1996 Newc.

TORRES, Maria Do Rosario Carvalho Bellevue Medical Centre, 26 Huntingdon Place, Edinburgh EH7 4AT — Lic Med Coimbra 1980.

TORRIE, Edwin Cecil Main Street, Cullybackey, Ballymena BT42 — MD 1946 Belf.; MB BCh BAO 1940, DPH 1949; MFCM 1972. (Qu. Univ. Belf.) JP; Dist. Admin. Med. Off. Antrim/Ballymena Health Dists. Prev: Div. Med. Off. Antrim Co. Health Comm.; Surg. Lt. RNVR; Med. Off. Musgrave & Clark Clinic, Belf.

TORRIE, Edwin Peter Hodgett X-Ray Department, Royal Berkshire Hospital, London Road, Reading RG1 5AN Tel: 01734 877930; Cranhull Cottage, The Old Orchard, Mill Lane, Calcot, Reading RG31 7RS Tel: 01734 417592 — MB BCh BAO 1973 Belf.; FRCR 1983; DMRD 1981. Cons. Radiol. Roy. Berks. Hosp. Reading.

TORRY, Michael John William Sutton Moors, 1 Overhill Road, Wilmslow SK9 2BE — BM BS 1996 Nottm.

TORRY, Rebecca Bermondsey and Lansdowne Medical Centre, The Surgery, Decima Street, London SE1 4QX Tel: 020 7407 0752 Fax: 020 7378 8209; St. George's Vicarage, 89 Westcombe Pk Road, London SE3 7RZ Tel: 020 8858 3006 — MB 1980 Camb.; BChir 1979; MRCGP 1983; DObst RCOG 1982. Gen. Pract. Princip.; Course Organiser, Guys & St. Thomas' GP Vocational Train. Scheme, Lond. SE1.

TOSE, Christine Barbara 13 Haddington Road, Beaumont Park, Whitley Bay NE25 9UP — MB BS 1970 Newc. (Newc.)

TOSE, John Melvin Whitley Bay Health Centre, Whitley Road, Whitley Bay NE25 2ND Tel: 0191 253 1113; 13 Ashfield Grove, Whitley Bay NE26 1RT — MB BS 1972 Newc.; MRCGP 1976.

TOSE, Jonathan Central Surgery, Stanhope Parade, Heal Gordon St, South Shields NE33 4JP — MB BS 1994 Newc.

TOSELAND, Michael Anthony Thatched Cottage, 20 Meadow Lane, Little Houghton, Northampton NN7 1AH Tel: 01604 891751 — MB ChB 1954 Birm.; MRCS Eng. LRCP Lond. 1954. (Birm.) Med. Adviser KAB seatings N.ampton. Prev: Ho. Surg. (O & G) & Ho. Phys. Solihull Hosp.

TOSELAND, Olga Rosemary Stacey House, Hardingstone, Northampton Tel: 01604 61382 — MB ChB 1954 Birm.; MRCS Eng. LRCP Lond. 1954; FFA RCS Eng. 1964; DA Eng. 1961. (Birm.) Cons. Anaesth. Kettering Gen. Hosp. Socs: BMA. Prev: Ho. Surg. (ENT) & Sen. Regist. Anaesth. Qu. Eliz. Hosp. Birm.; Sen. Regist. Anaesth. N. Staffs. Roy. Infirm. Stoke-on-Trent.

TOSH, Grahame Cameron Southend Hospital, Prittlewell Chase, Westcliff on Sea SS0 0RY Tel: 01702 221401 Fax: 01702 221413 Email: dr.tosh@hospital.southend.nhs.uk; Palliative Care Team Office, Basildon Hospital, Nethermayne, Basildon SS16 5NL Tel: 01268 53088 Fax: 01268 53088 — MB BS 1985 Lond.; FCAnaesth. 1990. Cons. Palliat. Med. S.end & Basildon Hosps. Prev: Cons. Palliat. Med. & Med. Dir. Fair Havens Hospice.

TOSH, Joseph Lupset Surgery, off Norbury Road, Wakefield WF2 8RE Tel: 01924 376828 Fax: 01924 201649; 109 Cumbrian Way, Lupset Park, Wakefield WF2 8LA — MB BCh BAO 1971 Dub.; MRCGP 1975; DObst RCOG 1974; DCH RCPS 1973.

TOSHNER, David 5 Douglas Avenue, Giffnock, Glasgow G46 6NX — MB ChB 1966 Glas. (Glas.) Prev: Regist. Dept. Mat. Med. & Therap. Stobhill Gen. Hosp. Glas.; Phys. i/c Asthma Rehabil. Inst. Arad, Israel; Cons. Allergist Hadassah Med. Sch. Jerusalem.

TOSHNIWAL, Mishrilal Hiralal 42 Burnside Gardens, Lodge Road, Walsall WS5 3LB — MB BS 1969 Poona.

TOSSON, Safwat Roushdy 9A Coniscliffe Road, Hartlepool TS26 0BS — MB ChB 1977 Ain Shams; MRCOG 1983; MObstG Liverp. 1984. Cons. O & G Hartlepool & Peterlee NHS Trust. Prev: Sen. Regist. Roy. Gwent Hosp.; Regist. Taunton, Liverp. & Arrowe Pk. Hosps.

TOSTEVIN, Miss Philippa Mary Jane St Georges Hospital, Blackshaw Road, Tooting, London SW17; Kingwood, Elmgrove Road, Cobham Tel: 01932 860345 Email: pippa_tostevin@lineare.net — MB BS 1991 Lond.; BSc Lond. 1986; FRCS Oto. Lond. 1996. p/t Specialist Regist. (Otolaryngol.) S. W. Thames. Prev: SHO (Paediat. Surg.) John Radcliffe Oxf.; SHO (OtoLaryngol.) Roy. Nat. ENT Hosp.; SHO (NeoSurg.) Arkinson Morley Hosp.

TOSZEGHI, Anthony de 56 Elsworthy Road, London NW3 3BU Tel: 020 7722 5208 Fax: 020 7586 5704 — MD 1943 Pecs.; MD Pecs 1943; LRCP LRCS Ed. LRFPS Glas. 1959. (Univs. Vienna & Pecs) Clin. Asst. Roy. Free Hosp. Lond. Socs: BMA. Prev: Cons. Clin. Haemat. & Med. Peterfy Hosp. Budapest.

TOTE, Subodh Prabhakar 3 Wilmington Gardens, Barking IG11 9TW — MB BS 1993 Lond.

TOTH, Mathias West Mount, 32 King Edward Avenue, Dartford DA1 2HZ Tel: 01322 220060 Fax: 01322 400428 Email: drmathiastoth@mops.in2home.co.uk — State Exam Med 1987 Hamburg; MD Hamburg 1991; MRCP (UK) 1997. Specialist Regist. Gen & Geriat. Med. Socs: Roy. Coll. Phys.; Brit. Geriat. Soc.

TOTHAM, April CNBS Midlands & South West, Southmead Road, Bristol BS10 5ND; Long Acre Cottage, Main St, Farrington Gurney, Bristol BS39 6UB — MB BS 1972 Lond.; DA Eng. 1979; DObst RCOG 1975. (Middlx.) Staff Phys. (Transfus.) NBS Midl. & SW. Prev: Clin. Asst. (Paediat. Oncol.) United Bristol Healthcare Trust; Clin. Med. Off. (Child Health) Bath Dist. HA; GP Rendcomb.

TOTHILL, Anne Ursula 80 Clifton Hill, London NW8 0JT — MD 1968 Lond.; MB BS 1959. (Roy. Free) Hon. Lect. Inst. O & G Lond.; Sen. Clin. Med. Off. (Obst. & Gyn.) Hammersmith Hosp. & Qu.; Charlotte's Hosp. for Wom. Lond. Prev: Lect. Clin. Pharmacol. Middlx. Hosp.; Asst. Lect. Pharmacol. Dept. Guy's Hosp. Med. Sch.; Research Fell. Pharmacol. Dept. Roy. Free Hosp. Med. Sch.

TOTHILL, Catherine Louise Westfield, Hognaston, Ashbourne DE6 1PU — MB BS 1992 Lond.

TOTHILL, Geoffrey 68 Grange Gardens, Pinner HA5 5QF Tel: 01850 953163 — MB BS 1988 Lond. SHO (Neurosurg.) Roy. Lond. Hosp. Trust. Prev: SHO (A & E) Lewisham Hosp. Lond.; SHO (Cardiothoracic Surg.) St. Thos. Hosp. Lond.; Ho. Off. (Gen. Med.) Gloucester Roy. Hosp.

TOTHILL, Sally Anne Ladywell Medical Centre (West), Ladywell Road, Edinburgh EH12 7TB Tel: 0131 334 3602 Fax: 0131 316 4816; 30 Craigmount Terrace, Edinburgh EH12 8BW — MB ChB 1982 Ed.; BSc (Med. Sci) 1979; MRCGP 1986; DRCOG 1985; LFHOM 1997. (Edinburgh) GP Trainer. Prev: SHO (Rehabil. Med.) Astley Ainslie Hosp. Edin.; SHO (A & E) Bangour Gen. Hosp. Broxburn; SHO (O & G) Vict. Hosp. Kirkcaldy.

TOTMAN, Marissa Bernadette 91 The Green, Epsom KT17 3JX — BM BCh 1997 Oxf.

TOTTEN, Eileen Sycamore House, Tile Barn, Woolton Hill, Newbury RG20 9UZ — MB ChB 1977 Glas.

TOTTEN, Joseph Wilson Sycamore House, Tile Barn, Woolton Hill, Newbury RG20 9UZ Tel: 01635 255584 Fax: 01635 255584 Email: wilson@totten.com — MB ChB 1977 Glas.; MFPM 1989; DPM Eng. 1984. Gp. R & D Dir. Shire Pharmaceut. plc Andover. Socs: Fac. Pharmaceut. Med.; Fell. Roy. Soc. Med. Prev: Vice-Pres. Clin. R & D Astra Charnwood LoughBoro.; Dir. of Developm. Fisons plc.

TOTTLE, Anthony John Tel: 01452 395558 Fax: 01452 394535 — MB BCh 1983 Wales; MRCP (UK) 1986; FRCR 1990. Cons. Radiol. Glos. Roy. Hosp. Prev: Sen. Regist. (Radiodiag.) SW RHA; Regist. (Radiodiag.) Bristol & W.. HA; SHO (Gastroenterol.) Frenchay Hosp. Bristol.

TOTTLE, John Alan Gothelney Cottage, Charlynch Lane, Charlynch, Bridgwater TA5 2PG Tel: 01278 652493 — MB BS 1950 Lond.; MRCS Eng. LRCP Lond. 1950; DPH Eng. 1956. (Char. Cross.) Prev: Cas. Off. Watford Peace Memor. Hosp.; Ho. Surg. Taunton & Som. Hosp.; Ho. Surg. (Obst.) Musgrave Pk. Hosp. Taunton.

TOTTLE, Sarah 26 North Hill, Fareham PO16 7HP Tel: 01329 513858 — MB ChB 1993 Birm.; DCH 1997; DRCOG 1998; MRCGP 1998. GP Regist. Drayton Surg. Drayton Hants. Prev: SHO (O & G) St Richard's Hosp. Chichester; SHO (Paediat.) St Richard's Hosp. Chichester; SHO (Orthop.) Qu. Alexandra Cosham.

TOTTS, Kaye Susan Sunderland Royal Hospital, Kayll Rd, Sunderland SR4 7TP Tel: 0191 565 6256; 252 Croham Valley Road, South Croydon CR2 7RD — MB BS 1988 Newc.; FRCS (A&E) Ed 1996. Specialist Regist. (A&E) Sunderland Roy. Infirm. Prev: SHO (Orthop.) Hexham; SHO (A & E) Sunderland & S. Shields Hosps.; SHO (Anaesth.)Aberd. Roy. Infirm.

TOU, Samson Iong Heng 1st Floor Flat 16 Craigie Street, Aberdeen AB25 1EL — MB ChB 1997 Aberd.

TOUBIA, Mrs Nahid Farid Rainbo, 59 Bravington Road, London W9 3AA Tel: 020 8968 5573 Fax: 020 8968 5573 Email: rainbouk@aol.com; 42 Milman Road, London NW6 6EG Email: ntoubia@aol.com — MB ChB 1974 Cairo; FRCS Eng. 1980; MSC. ECON. University of London, 1989. (QASR AL Aini- Eygpt) Pres. of Internat. Not-For-Profit-Organisation(Charity); Adjunct Prof. Clin. Pub. Health, Columbia Univ., Sch. of Pub. Health, New York.

TOUGH, Alison Margaret Baillieston Health Centre, 20 Muirside Road, Baillieston, Glasgow G69 7AD Tel: 0141 531 8040; Glencairn, 2 Heather Place, Lenzie, Kirkintilloch, Glasgow G66 4UJ — MB ChB 1977 Dundee; MRCGP 1981. Prev: Trainee GP S. Qu.sferry Health Centre; Community Paediat. Train. The Sch. of Community Paediat. Edin.

TOUGH, Harry Gordon 106 Church Way, Weston Favell, Northampton NN3 3BQ — MB ChB 1956 Aberd.; FRCPsych 1982, M 1972; DPM Eng. 1963. Cons. Psychiat. Mayfair Centre Community Ment. Health Kettering.

TOUGH, Sandra Livingstone 10 The Firs, Salters Road, Newcastle upon Tyne NE3 4PH — MB ChB 1980 Aberd.; MRCPsych 1985.

TOUN, Akumoere Yinkori 42 Whinfield Road, Claines, Worcester WR3 7HF — MB BS 1989 Lond.; MRCP (UK) 1992.

TOUNJER, Isfendiar Ali 48 Eburne Road, London N7 6AU — LMSSA 1960 Lond.

TOUQUET, Mr Robin, RD Accident and Emergency Department, St. Mary's Hospital, Praed St., London W2 1NY Tel: 020 7886 1200 Fax: 020 7886 6366 Email: robin.touquet@st-marys.nhs.uk — MB BS 1971 Lond.; FRCS Eng. 1979; FFAEM 1993; MRCGP 1976; T(S) 1991; DObst RCOG 1974; DCH Eng. 1973. (Westm.) Cons. A & E Med. St. Mary's Hosp. Lond.; Hon. Clin. Sen. Lect. Imperial Coll. Lond.; Examr. FFAEM; Mem. Edit. Bd. E.M.J.; Regional Adviser Med. Counc. on Alcohol. Socs: Brit. Assn. Accid. & Emerg. Med.; Med. Counc. on Alcohol; Inst. for Learning and Teachg. Prev: Sen. Regist. (A & E) St. Geo. & Mayday Hosps. Lond.; Regist. (Surg.) Univ. Coll. Hosp. Lond.; GP Faversham, Kent.

TOURISH, Paul Gerard 2 Mill Lane, Houghton Green, Warrington WA2 0SU — MB BCh BAO 1989 NUI.

TOURLE, Colin Alfred Brook Cottage, Mill Lane, Hellingly, Hailsham BN27 4HD — MB BS 1965 Lond.; MRCS Eng. LRCP Lond. 1965; DObst RCOG 1967. (King's Coll. Hosp.) Socs: BMA. Prev: Ho. Phys. King's Coll. Hosp. Lond.; Ho. Surg. Dulwich Hosp. Lond; Ho. Surg. (Obst.) Cuckfield Hosp. Sussex.

TOURRET, Lisa Jane Department of Trauma & Orthopaedics, University Hospital, Queen's Medical Centre, Nottingham NG7 2UH — MB ChB 1991 Sheff.

TOVEY, David Ian Herne Hill Group Practice, 74 Herne Hill, London SE24 9QP Tel: 020 7274 3314 Fax: 020 7738 6025 Email: david.tovey@gp-g85016.nhs.uk; 46 Dalmore Road, London SE21 8HB — MB ChB 1983 Bristol; FRCGP 2000; MRCGP 1989; DCH RCP Lond. 1987. (Bristol) Tutor (Gen. Pract.) King's Coll. Hosp. Lond. Prev: Trainee GP Wimbledon VTS; SHO (Paediat.) St. Marys Hosp. Lond.; Trainee GP/SHO GP Middlx. Hosp. Lond. VTS.

TOVEY, Mr Frank Ivor, OBE (retired) 5 Crossborough Hill, Basingstoke RG21 4AG Tel: 01256 461521 Fax: 01256 323696 — MB ChB (Hons.) Bristol 1944; ChM Liverp. 1962; FRCS Eng. 1947; MRCS Eng. LRCP Lond. 1944. Hon. Research Fell. (Surg.) Univ. Coll. Lond.; Asst. Edr. Trop. Doctor. Prev: Cons. Surg. Basingstoke & Dist. Hosp.

TOVEY, Gail Frances 7 Uplands Dr, Wolverhampton WV3 8AB — MB ChB 1997 Birm.

TOVEY, Geoffrey Harold, CBE (retired) Monks Retreat, Monkton Combe, Bath BA2 7EX — MB ChB 1940 Bristol; MD (Distinc.) Bristol 1944; MB ChB (Distinc. Pub. Health) 1940; FRCP Lond. 1974, M 1968; FRCPath 1964. Cons. Adviser Blood Transfus. DHSS; Hon. Cons. Blood Transfus. to Army. Prev: Dir. S.W Regional Blood Transfus. Centre, Bristol & UK Transpl.

TOVEY, John Ernest (retired) 17 Patricia Avenue, Worthing BN12 4NE Tel: 01903 505163 — MB ChB 1952 Bristol; MD Bristol 1960; FRCPath 1973, M 1964.

TOVEY, Lucas Alfred Derrick (retired) Old Charm Cottage, Old Scriven, Knaresborough HG5 9DY — MD 1957 Bristol; MB ChB 1950; FRCOG 1989; FRCPath 1973, M 1964. Prev: Cons. Haemat. & Path. Yorks. RHA.

TOVEY, Peter John (retired) 160 St.ly Road, Birmingham B23 7AH Tel: 0121 350 2323 Fax: 0121 382 0169 — MB ChB 1960 Birm.; MRCS Eng. LRCP Lond. 1960. Ho. Off. (Surg.) Dudley Rd. Hosp. Prev: Ho. Phys. Hallam Hosp. W. Bromwich.

TOVEY

TOVEY, Ronald Brian 58 Lye Green Road, Chesham HP5 3LS; The Stapleford Centre, 25a Eccleston St, Belgravia, London SW1W 9NP Tel: 020 7823 6840 Fax: 020 7730 3409 — MB BS 1983 Lond.; BSc Hons. Lond. 1979, MB BS 1983.

TOVEY, Stuart John (retired) 11 Corkran Road, Surbiton KT6 6PL — MB ChB 1969 Bristol; MRCP (UK) 1980; MRCGP 1981. Phys. i/c Genitourin. Med. Guy's Hosp. Lond. Prev: Sen. Regist. (Genitourin. Med.) Middlx. Hosp. Lond.

TOWELL, Anne (retired) The Firs, Florencecourt, Enniskillen BT92 1BZ Tel: 02866 348331 — MB BCh BAO 1940 Dub.; BA, MB BCh BAO Dub. 1940. Prev: Clin. Med. Off. Fermaragh.

TOWELL, John Douglas Middleway Surgery, Middleway, St. Blazey, Par PL24 2JL Tel: 01726 812019 Fax: 01726 816464; 39 Trevance Park, Tywardreath, Par PL24 2PY Tel: 01726 815959 — MB ChB 1969 Leeds; Cert. Counselling Exeter 1989.

TOWER, Julian Edmund Christopher (retired) Grassgarth, Natland, Kendal LA9 7QH — MB BChir 1953 Camb.; MRCGP 1964. Prev: Resid. Obst. Off. St. Thos. Hosp.

TOWER, Sophie Elisabeth The Home House, Stoke St Michael, Bath BA3 5JH — MB ChB 1998 Sheff.

TOWERS, Barbara Minnie (retired) Stonewalls, Old Park Lane, Bosham, Chichester PO18 8EZ Tel: 01243 573189 — MB BChir 1946 Camb.; MRCS Eng. LRCP Lond. 1946. Prev: Sessional Med. Off. W. Sussex AHA.

TOWERS, David George Cape Hill Medical Centre, Raglan Road, Smethwick B66 3NR Tel: 0121 558 0871 Fax: 0121 555 6125; 31 Wheatsheaf Road, Birmingham B16 0RZ — MB ChB 1973 Birm.; MRCGP 1977. (Birmingham) Prev: SHO (Psychiat.) All St.s Hosp. Birm.; Trainee GP Birm. VTS; Ho. Off. Dudley Rd. Hosp. Birm.

TOWERS, Elizabeth Andrea Burnside, Chelford Road, Prestbury, Macclesfield SK10 4AW — MB ChB 1970 Sheff.

TOWERS, Elizabeth Madge Whitley House Surgery, Moulsham Street, Chelmsford CM2 0JJ Tel: 01245 352194 Fax: 01245 344478 — MB BS 1982 Lond.

TOWERS, Mr John Francis, Cartwright Prize RCS Eng. 1971-75 52 Mount Ephraim Lane, Streatham, London SW16 1JD — MRCS Eng. LRCP Lond. 1967; MSc Lond. 1980, MDS 1982; FDS RCPS Glas. 1969; FFD RCSI 1969; LDS Liverp. 1961; FRCS Ed. 1985. (Liverp) Cons. Oral & Maxillo-facial Surg. St. Geo. Hosp. Lond. & Mayday Hosp. Croydon. Socs: Fell. Brit. Assn. Oral Surgs.; BMA. Prev: Sen. Lect. (Oral Surg.) Univ. Lond.; Sen. Regist. (Oral Surg.) St. Geo. Hosp. Gp.; Regist. (Oral Surg.) United Liverp. Hosps.

TOWERS, Jonathan Robert 7 Bossell Road, Buckfastleigh TQ11 0DE Tel: 01364 42534 Fax: 01364 644057 — MB ChB 1985 Sheff.; MRCGP 1992; DA 1990.

TOWERS, Judith Sarah 31 Bloomfield Road, Bath BA2 2AD; Oldland Surgery, 192 High St, Oldland Common, Bristol BS30 9QQ Tel: 0117 932 4444 Fax: 0117 932 4101 — MB BS 1988 Lond.; MRCGP 1992.

TOWERS, Malcolm Kinsey 93 Harley Street, London W1N 1DF Tel: 020 7935 9242 Fax: 020 7487 2831; 44 Dene Road, Northwood HA6 2DE Tel: 01923 821216 — MB BChir Camb. 1946; FRCP Lond. 1970; MRCP (UK) 1951. (Lond. Hosp.) Socs: Fell. Roy. Soc. Med.; Brit. Cardiac. Soc. Prev: Cardiol. Harefield Hosp.; Cons. Cardiometrics Hosps. For Dis. of Chest Lond.; 1st Asst. Inst. Cardiol.

TOWERS, Shona Hamilton (retired) 22 Stocks Lane, Chester CH3 5TF Tel: 01244 318528 — MB ChB 1956 Liverp.; MD Liverp. 1968, MB ChB 1956; FRCOG 1975. Prev: Consult. (O & G) Chester Health Dist.

TOWERS, Simon John Bridge Street Practice, 21 Bridge Street, Driffield YO25 6DB Tel: 01377 253441 Fax: 01377 241962; Tel: 01377 254763 — BM BCh 1975 Oxf.; M.Med sci 1999; MRCGP 1979; DRCOG 1979. Prev: Trainee GP Bristol VTS; Ho. Phys. King's Coll. Hosp. Lond.; Ho. Surg. FarnBoro. Hosp. Kent.

TOWERS, Stephen 3 Hall Court, Sutton in Craven, Keighley BD20 7NF — MB ChB Sheff. 1982; MD Camb. 1983.

TOWERS, Susan Marie The Ridge Medical Practice, 3 Paternoster Lane, Great Horton, Bradford BD7 3EE Tel: 01274 502905 Fax: 01274 522060 — MB ChB 1985 Manch.

TOWEY, Raymond Martin 8 White House Close, Solihull B91 1SL — MB ChB 1967 Manch.; FFA RCS Eng. 1972. Miss. Doctor, Tanzania. Prev: Cons. Anaesth. Guy's Hosp. Lond.

TOWIE, Hugh Gerald The Abbey Practice, The Family Health Centre, Stepgates, Chertsey KT16 8HZ Tel: 01932 561199 Fax: 01932 571842 — MB ChB 1977 Glas.; MRCGP 1984.

TOWLE, Natalie Deborah 24 St.John's Avenue, Churchdown, Gloucester GL3 2DD Tel: 01452 713036; 6 Beeches Road, Charlton Kings, Cheltenham GL53 8NQ Tel: 01242 260497 — MB BS 1991 Lond.; MRCGP Lond. 1996; DRCOG 1995; DFFP 1995; DGM RCP Lond. 1993. (University of London (University College & Middlesex)) Retainer Gen. Pract. Prev: GP Regist. Cheltenham; SHO (O & G) Worcester Roy. Infirm.; SHO (Oncol.) Cheltenham Gen. Hosp.

TOWLER, Adam Hilltop House, Bourton on the Hill, Moreton-in-Marsh GL56 9AL; 11 Holders Lane, Birmingham B13 8NL Tel: 0121 449 3803 Email: adam.towler@virgin.net — BM BCh 1992 Oxf.; BA Oxf. 1989, BM BCh 1992; MRCP. 1995. Staff Grade (Dermatol.) New Cross Hosp. Wolverhampton. Prev: SHO (Gen. Med.) St. Jas. Univ. Hosp. Leeds.

TOWLER, Gillian Margaret Whitehorse Vale Surgery, Whitehorse Vale, Barton Hills, Luton LU3 4AD Tel: 01582 490087; 8 Barton Avenue, Dunstable LU5 4DF Tel: 01582 662795 — MB ChB 1971 Bristol; DCH Eng. 1975; DObst RCOG 1973. (Bristol) Princip. in Gen. Pract. Socs: Assoc. Mem. RCGP.; BMA.

TOWLER, Gillian Mary Monkgate Health Centre, 35 Monkgate, York YO31 7PB Tel: 01904 342989; 22 Monkgate Cloisters, York YO31 7HY Tel: 01904 611399 — MB ChB 1990 Manch.; MRCGP 1996; DCH RCP Lond. 1995; DRCOG 1996. (Manch.) GP Princip. Monkgate Health Centre, York. Socs: York Med. Soc.

TOWLER, Mr Hamish Moray Andrew 149 Harley Street, London W1N 2DE Tel: 020 7935 4444 Fax: 0208 446 4854 Email: hmat@hmatowler.co.uk; Fax: 020 8446 4854 Email: hmat@hmatowler.co.uk — MB ChB 1979 Aberd.; BMedBiol Aberd. 1976; FRCS Ed. 1987; MRCP (UK) 1982; FRCOphth 1989; FRCP Ed 2000. (University of Aberdeen) Cons. Ophth. Whipps Cross Hosp. Lond. Prev: Lect. (Ophth.) Moorfields Eye Hosp. Lond.; Lect. (Ophth.) Univ. Aberd.; Sen. Regist. (Ophth.) E. Anglia RHA.

TOWLER, Joan Norma (retired) 7 Belmont Avenue, Baildon, Shipley BD17 5AJ Tel: 01274 592915 — MB ChB Leeds 1946, DPH 1953; MFCM 1972; DCH RCPS Glas. 1972. Prev: SMO Bradford DHA.

TOWLER, Mr Julian Max 3 Penrith Avenue, Dunstable LU6 3AN — BM BCh 1967 Oxf.; FRCS Eng. 1973. (St. Thos.) Cons. Urol. Surg. Luton & Dunstable Hosp. Prev: Sen. Regist. (Urol.) Aberd. Roy. Infirm.; SHO (Gen. Surg.) Cheltenham Gen. Hosp.; Regist. (Urol.) Newc. Gen. Hosp.

TOWLERTON, Glyn Richard Magill Dept. of Anaesth., Chelseaa & Westm. Hospital, Fuutam Road, London SW10 Tel: 020 8746 8026 — MB BS 1990 (Hons.) Lond.; BSc Lond. 1987; MRCP (UK) 1993; FRCA 1996. (St. Bartholomew's London) Anaesth. Cons. Director Pain Managem. Unit Chelsea & W.minister Lond. Socs: BMA; RCA; RCP.

TOWLSON, Katherine Louise Vale of Leven DGH, Alexandria G83 0UA Tel: 01389 603924; Hillend Cottage, Quarry Road, Fintry, Glasgow G63 0XD Tel: 01360 860576 Fax: 01360 860535 — MB BS 1986 Lond.; BA (Hons.) Camb. 1982, MA 1986; LMSSA Lond. 1985; MRCPsych 1990; DCCH RCP Ed. 1987. Cons. (Child & Adolesc. Psychiat.) Vale of Leven Dist. Gen. Hosp. Prev: Sen. Regist. (Child & Adolesc. Psychiat.) W. Scotl. Train. Scheme; Regist. (Psychiat.) Roy. Edin. Hosp.

TOWN, Valerie Joan Kings Road Surgery, 67 Kings Road, Harrogate HG1 5HJ Tel: 01423 875875 Fax: 01423 875885 — MB ChB 1983 Sheff.

TOWNELL, Mr Nicholas Howard Tayside University Hospitals Trust, Ninewells Hospital & Medical School, Dundee DD1 9SY; Rosebank, Hillside, Montrose DD10 9HZ — MB BS 1972 Lond.; FRCS Ed. 1993; FRCS Eng. 1977. Cons. Urol.; Clin. Director for Surg. and Oncol.; Apptd. Tutor (Minimally Invasive Surg.) RCS Edin; Hon. Sen. Lect. (Surg.) Univ. Dundee. Socs: Soc. Minimally Invasive Ther.; Brit. Assn. Urol. Surgs. Prev: Sen. Regist. (Gen. Surg. & Urol.) Roy. Free Hosp. Lond.

TOWNEND, Anne Mary The Health Centre, 20 Cleveland Square, Middlesbrough TS1 2NX Tel: 01642 245069 Fax: 01642 230388; 8 High Green, Great Ayton, Middlesbrough TS9 6BJ Tel: 01642 722695 — MB BS 1979 Newc.; MRCGP 1983.

TOWNEND, Mr Ian Ralph Department of Urology, Doncaster Royal Infirmary, Armthorpe Road, Doncaster DN2 5 Tel: 01302

TOWNSEND

366666 Fax: 01302 320098; 22 Partridge Flatt Road, Bessacarr, Doncaster DN4 6SD Tel: 01302 533293 — MB ChB 1973 Ed.; MS Soton. 1986; FRCS Eng. 1979; FRCS Ed. 1979. (Ed.) Cons. Urol. Doncaster Roy. Infirm. Socs: Fell. Roy. Soc. Med.; Brit. Assn. Urol. Surgs.; Brit. Soc. for EndoUrol. Prev: Pharmaceut. Phys. Rhone-Poulenc Rorer; Hon. Sen. Regist. & Research Fell. (Surg.) Soton. Univ.; Regist. (Gen. Surg. & Urol.) Hallamsh. Hosp. Sheff.

TOWNEND, Mr John Richard Leslie St. Helens House, 2 The Drive, Chichester PO19 5RE Tel: 01243 530411 Fax: 01243 530411 Email: jtownend@headandneck.co.uk; St. Helens House, 2 The Drive, Chichester PO19 5RE Tel: 01243 528291 — MB BS 1971 Lond.; BDS Lond. 1967; MRCS Eng. LRCP Lond. 1971; FDS RCS Eng. 1974, L 1966. (Oxf.) Cons. Oral & Maxillofacial Surg. Chichester, Worthing & Surrey Sussex Health Trusts; Hon. Cons. Maxillofacial Surg. King Edwd. VII Hosp. Midhurst; Hon. Clin. Tutor UMDS Lond. Socs: Fell. Brit. Assn. Oral & Maxillofacial Surg.; Eur. Acad. Facial Plast. Surg.; UK Regist. Expert Witnesses. Prev: Sen. Regist. (Oral Surg. & Plastic Surg.) Sheff. HA; Regist. (Oral Surg.) & SHO (Plastic Surg.) Oxf. HA.

TOWNEND, Jonathan Nicholas 47 Jacoby Place, Priory Road, Birmingham B5 7UN — MB ChB 1983 Birm.

TOWNEND, Michael Smithy Cottage, Millhouse, Hesket Newmarket, Wigton CA7 8HR Tel: 016974 78477 Fax: 016974 78477 Email: miketow@msn.com; Lorton Park Cottage, High Lorton, Cockermouth CA13 9UG Tel: 016974 78477 Fax: 016974 78477 Email: miketow@msn.com — Dip Travel Med Glasg. 1996; MB ChB (Hons.) Leeds 1962. (Leeds) Writer & Lect. on Travel Health, Travel Health Adviser; Hon. Clin. Teach., Univ. of Glas.; Tutor in travel Med., St Martins Coll., Lancaster; Medico-legal Examr. Socs: Internat. Soc. Mt.ain Med.; Internat. Soc. Travel Med.; Brit. Travel Health Assn.

TOWNEND, Richard Hugh Malcolm (retired) 22 Wingfield Road, Alfreton DE55 7AN — LRCPI & LM, LRSCI & LM 1957; LRCPI & LM, LRCSI & LM 1957. Prev: Ho. Surg., Ho. Phys. & Ho. Surg. (O & G) Vict. Hosp. Keighley.

TOWNEND, William James King 64 Errwood Road, Manchester M19 2QH — MB ChB 1992 Leeds.

TOWNER, Christine Hazle 56 Limpsfield Road, Sanderstead, South Croydon CR2 9EB Tel: 020 8657 3067 — MB BS 1955 Lond.; FRCP Ed. 1980 M 1964. (Westm.) Cons. Phys. Croydon Health Auth. Socs: BMA & Brit. Geriat Soc. Prev: SHO Geriat. Unit, W. Middlx. Hosp. Isleworth; Regist. Dept. Geriat. Med. United Camb. Hosps; Sen. Regist. Geriat. Unit, Brighton Gen. Hosp.

TOWNER, Helen Denise The New Aylesford Surgery, R. B. L. U., Aylesford, Maidstone Tel: 01622 882384 — MB ChB 1981 Bristol; MRCGP 1987; Cert. Family Plann. JCC 1985; DRCOG 1985. Trainee GP Maidstone. Prev: Cas. Off. W.. Regional Hosp. Pokhara Nepal; SHO (Paediat. & Med.) Maidstone Gen. Hosp.

TOWNLEY, Adam David 3 North Square, London NW11 7AA — MB ChB 1998 Manch.

TOWNLEY, Alison National Blood Service, Leeds Blood Centre, Bridle Path, Leeds LS15 7TW Tel: 0113 214 8600 Fax: 0113 214 8696 — MB ChB 1974 Sheff. Assoc. Specialist Nat. Blood Serv. Leeds.

TOWNLEY, Douglas William The Coach House, Ty Mawr Llan, Eglwysbach, Colwyn Bay LL28 5UD Tel: 01492 650698 — MB ChB 1943 Liverp.; MRCS Eng. LRCP Lond. 1943. (Liverp.)

TOWNLEY, Paul Andrew West End Medical Practice, 1 Heysham Road, Heysham, Morecambe LA3 1DA Tel: 01524 831931 Fax: 01524 832516; 379 Heysham Road, Morecambe LA3 2BP Tel: 01524 853509 Email: paul.townley@ukonline.co.uk — MB ChB 1980 Manch.; MRCGP 1984; DRCOG 1984.

TOWNLEY, Stephen Anthony 2 Spinney View, Liverpool L33 7XX Email: satownley@hotmail.com — MB BCh 1993 Wales; MRCP (UK) 1997; BSc (Hons) (Wales) 1990. (UWCM)

TOWNSEND, Adrian Philip The Surgery, New Street, Stockbridge SO20 6HG Tel: 01264 810524 Fax: 01264 810591 Email: adrian.townsend@gp-j82016.nhs.uk — MB ChB 1981 Manch.; BSc (Med. Sci.) St. And. 1978. Prev: SHO Rotat. Hastings AHA.

TOWNSEND, Alain Robert Michael Institute of Molecular Medicine, John Radcliffe Hospital, Hedington, Oxford OX3 9DU Tel: 01865 752328; 6 Polstead Road, Oxford OX2 6TN Tel: 01865 512714 — MB BS 1977 Lond.; MB BS (Distinc. Med.) Lond. 1977; PhD Lond. 1984; MRCP (UK) 1979. (St. Mary's)

TOWNSEND, Alan Swainson, MBE (retired) Wegberg, Cronk Drine, Union Mills, Douglas IM4 4NG Tel: 01624 851525 — MB BS Lond. 1956; MRCS Eng. LRCP Lond. 1956; FRCOG 1977, M 1964; DObst RCOG 1958. Prev: Cons. O & G I. of Man.

TOWNSEND, Angela Joy Woodpecker Cottage, Bailey End Lane, Ross-on-Wye HR9 5TR — MB BS 1986 Lond.; BSc Lond. 1983, MB BS 1986.

TOWNSEND, Mr Arthur Carlisle (retired) Slipper House, Emsworth PO10 8BS — MB BChir 1950 Camb.; FRCS Eng. 1959. Prev: Orthop. Surg. Kent & Sussex Hosp.

TOWNSEND, Mr Calver 114 Harley Street, London W1G 7JJ Tel: 020 7935 1565 Fax: 020 7224 1752 — MB BS 1967 Lond.; FRCS Eng. 1975; FRCOphth 1988; DO Eng. 1972. (Middlx.) Hon. Cons. Ophth. Surg. St. Mary's & W.. Eye Hosps. Lond. Socs: Fell. Roy. Soc. Med.; UK & Irel. Soc. Cataract & Implant Surgs.; BMA. Prev: Resid. Surg. Off. Moorfields Eye Hosp. (City Rd. Br.) Lond.; SHO W.. Eye Hosp. Lond.; Ho. Off. (Ophth. & Dermat.) Middlx. Hosp.

TOWNSEND, Carolyn Louise Meadow View, Dean La, Cookham, Maidenhead SL6 9AF — BM BCh 1997 Oxf.

TOWNSEND, Catherine Rose Silverwood, The Fairway, Weybridge KT13 0RZ Tel: 019323 47648 — MB BS 1959 Lond.; MRCS Eng. LRCP Lond. 1959; DO Eng. 1966; MRCOphth 1988. (Roy. Free) Clin. Asst. Roy. Free Hosp. Lond.; Clin. Asst. W.. Ophth. Hosp. Lond.; Clin. Asst. St. Peter's Hosp. Chertsey. Socs: BMA. Prev: Regist. Roy. Eye Hosp. Lond.; Sen. Surg. Off. Bath Hosp. Gp.; Ho. Surg. (Ophth.) Roy. Free Hosp.

TOWNSEND, Christopher John c/o Meadway, Carlton Lane, Wirral CH47 3DB — MB ChB 1991 Birm.; BSc Birm. 1991, MB ChB 1991. Short Term Overseas Program. Coordinator Tear Fund Teddington. Prev: Ho. Off. (Med.) Kidderminster; Ho. Off. (Surg.) Newcross & Wolverhampton.

TOWNSEND, Christopher Stephen Salop Road Medical Centre, Salop Road, Welshpool SY21 7ER Tel: 01938 553118 Fax: 01938 553071 — MB BS 1971 Newc.; MRCGP 1975.

TOWNSEND, David William Bute House, Grove Medical Centre, Wootton Grove, Sherborne DT9 4DL Tel: 01935 810900 Fax: 01935 810901; Sheeplands, Sheeplands Lane, Sherborne DT9 4BW Tel: 01935 815362 — MB BS 1973 Lond.; DRCOG 1979. (Middlx.) GP Sherborne; Clin. Asst. (Ophth.) Sherborne; Sch. D. Sherborne Sch. for Girls.

TOWNSEND, Mr Edward Richard Lambettis, Horn Hill, Rickmansworth Lane, Gerrards Cross SL9 0QU Tel: 01895 828580 — MB BS 1970 Lond.; FRCS Eng. 1976; MRCS Eng. LRCP Lond. 1970. Cons. Thoracic Surg. Harefield, Hillingdon, King Edwd. VII, Wexham Pk. & N.wick Pk. Hosps. Prev: Sen. Regist. (Cardiothoracic Surg.) St. Geo. & Soton Hosps.; Regist. (Cardiothoracic Surg.) Kings Coll. Hosp. & Brook Gen. Hosp. Lond.

TOWNSEND, Eric William John (retired) Culmer, 39 Fore St., Shaldon, Teignmouth TQ14 0EA Tel: 01626 873741 — MRCS Eng. LRCP Lond. 1940. Prev: Med. Off. Molesey Hosp.

TOWNSEND, Giles Edward 42 Bodley Road, New Malden KT3 5QE — MB BS 1995 Lond.

TOWNSEND, Helen Angus (retired) St. Edmunds Lodge, Park Road, Haslemere GU27 2NL — MB BS Adelaide 1949. Prev: Assoc. Med. Director, Revlon Health Care, E.bourne, E. Sussex.

TOWNSEND, Horace Robert Allen (retired) 9 St Blaize Court, Cirencester GL7 1JA Tel: 01285 885263 — MB BCh BAO 1952 NUI; FRCP Ed. 1974, M 1971. Prev: Cons. Clin. Neurophysiol. Nat. Hosp. Nerv. Dis. Qu. Sq. Lond.

TOWNSEND, Mr John Health Control Unit, Terminal 3, Heathrow Airport, Hounslow TW6 1NB Tel: 020 8745 7419 Fax: 020 8745 6181; 89E Victoria Drive, London SW19 6PT Tel: 020 8785 7675 — MB BS Lond. 1959; BSc (Hons.) (Physiol.) Lond. 1956; FRCS Ed. 1969; MRCS Eng. LRCP Lond. 1959; DObst RCOG 1962. (St. Bart.) Sen. Clin. Med. Off. Health Control Unit Heathrow Airport Lond.; Sen. Clin. Off. Health Control Unit Terminal 3 Heathrow Airport Lond. Prev: Med. Dir. ECHO Internat. Health Servs. Ltd.; Med. & Healthcare Cons. Tear Fund Ltd.; Hosp. Surg. & Supt. Christian Hosp. Manorom, Thailand.

TOWNSEND, John Anthony (retired) New Dover Road Surgery, 10 New Dover Road, Canterbury CT1 3AP Tel: 01227 462197 Fax: 01227 786041 — MRCS Eng. LRCP Lond. 1967; DObst RCOG 1970; DA Eng. 1970.

TOWNSEND

TOWNSEND, John Crispin The Shrubbery, 65A Perry Street, Northfleet, Gravesend DA11 8RD Tel: 01474 356661 Fax: 01474 534542 — MB ChB 1980 Sheff.; MRCPath 1987; DRCOG 1992. Prev: Trainee GP Lewisham VTS; Specialist (Chem. Path.) Woden Valley Hosp., Austral.

TOWNSEND, John Stafford The Harrowby Lane Surgery, Grantham NG31 9NS Tel: 01476 79494; 18 New Beacon Road, Grantham NG31 9JR — MB BS 1974 Lond.

TOWNSEND, Judith Margaret Redhill, 85 Wyke Road, Weymouth DT4 9QN — MB ChB 1977 Bristol; MRCPsych 1984.

TOWNSEND, Mr Julian Charles Francis (retired) 17 Townsend Drive, St Albans AL3 5RB Tel: 01727 862565 — MB BChir 1957 Camb.; FRCS Eng. 1964. Prev: Cons. Surg. St. Albans City Hosp.

TOWNSEND, Katharine Centurier 13 Great Eastern Street, Cambridge CB1 3AB — MB BS 1991 Lond.

TOWNSEND, Laura Zoe The Gate Cottage, Reading Road N., Fleet GU51 4AQ — MB BS 1998 Lond.

TOWNSEND, Mark Redhill, 85 Wyke Road, Weymouth DT4 9QN — MB ChB 1977 Bristol; DRCOG 1979.

TOWNSEND, Mary (retired) 31 Cromley Road, High Lane, Stockport SK6 8BU — MB BS 1944 Lond.; MRCP Lond. 1948; MFCM 1973; DCH Eng. 1946. Prev: SCM (Child Health) Stockport AHA.

TOWNSEND, Michael Stephen Arnold (retired) Earle House, 9 High St, Spalding PE11 1TW Tel: 01775 722020 Fax: 01775 714378 Email: msat@d-lweb.net — MB BChir 1965 Camb.; MA Camb. 1966; FRCGP 1988, M 1971; DObst RCOG 1967. Mem. Lincs. Local Med. Comm.; Med. Adviser to S. Holland Dist. Counc. Prev: GP Mem. Pigrim Hosp. Boston, Unit Managem. Bd.

TOWNSEND, Neal William Hathaway 29 Rutland Avenue, Freckleton, Preston PR4 1HL — MB ChB 1995 Manch.

TOWNSEND, Mr Paul Leslie Gordon The Old Malt House, High St., Iron Acton, Bristol BS37 9UQ — MB BS 1963 Lond.; BSc (Hons.) Lond. 1960, MB BS 1963; FRCS Eng. 1968; FRCS Canada 1972. (Univ. Coll. Hosp.) Cons. Plastic Surg. Frenchay Hosp. Bristol. Prev: Sen. Regist. (Plastic Surg.) Frenchay Hosp. Bristol; Regist. (Plastic Surg.) Odstock Hosp. Salisbury.

TOWNSEND, Peter 19 Crofton Drive, Baglan, Port Talbot SA12 8UL — MB BS 1989 Lond.

TOWNSEND, Mr Peter Thomas 28 Whitecroft, Horley RH6 9BZ Fax: 01293 822973 Email: peter@gynaesurgeon.com — MB BS 1975 Lond.; MRCS Eng. LRCP Lond. 1975; FRCOG 1992, M 1979. (Guys Hospital) Cons. O & G E. Surrey and Sussex NHS Trust.

TOWNSEND, Philip Simon The Health Centre, Gibson Lane, Kippax, Leeds LS25 7JN Tel: 0113 287 0870 Fax: 0113 232 0746 — MB ChB 1987 Liverp.

TOWNSEND, Raymond Francis (retired) Fairacre, The Byeway, West Wittering, Chichester PO20 8LJ Tel: 01243 514481 — MRCS Eng. LRCP Lond. 1936; MRCGP 1968. Prev: Consg. Med. Off. Henry Wiggin & Co. Hereford; Med. Regist. W.m.

TOWNSEND, Roger Maurice 8 Blenheim Gardens, Reading RG1 5QG — MB BS 1993 Lond.; BSc Lond. 1990, MB BS 1993.

TOWNSEND, Stephen John Bitterne Park Surgery, 28 Cobden Avenue, Bitterne Park, Southampton SO18 1BW Tel: 023 80585 655/6 Fax: 023 8055 5216 — MB BS 1976 Newc.; MRCGP 1989. Prev: Surg. Lt.Cdr. RN.

TOWNSHEND, David Nicholas 225 Osborne Road, Newcastle upon Tyne NE2 3LB — MB BS 1997 Newc.

TOWNSHEND, Jennifer Margaret Parkgate Health Centre, Park Place, Darlington DL1 5LW Tel: 01325 462762; West House, The Lendings, Startforth, Barnard Castle DL12 9AD — MB BS 1974 Newc.; MRCGP 1979.

TOWNSHEND, Neil William Norman Barn Close Surgery, 38-40 High Street, Broadway WR12 7DT Tel: 01386 853651 Fax: 01386 853982; Peel House, High St, Broadway WR12 7AJ Email: neil.townshend@boa.org.uk — MB BS 1980 Lond.; DRCOG 1983. Chief Med. Off. Internat. Luge Federat.; Chairm. Nat. Sports Med. Inst. UK. Prev: Mem. (Vice-Chairm.) Brit. Olympic Assn.

TOWNSLEY, Andrew Easterhouse Health Centre, 9 Auchinlea Road, Glasgow G34 9HQ Tel: 0141 531 8170 Fax: 0141 531 8110 — MB ChB 1988 Glas.

TOWNSLEY, Gerald Stewart York Road Surgery, York Road, Southwold IP18 6AN Tel: 01502 722326 Fax: 01502 724708; 47 High Street, Southwold IP18 6DJ Tel: 01502 723590 — MRCS Eng. LRCP Lond. 1969; Dip. IMC RCS Ed. 1989. (St. Thos.) Prev: SHO (Geriat.) W. Norwich Hosp.; SHO (O & G) Colchester Matern. Hosp.; SHO (Surg. & Cas.) Norf. & Norwich Hosp.

TOWNSLEY, Patricia Philippa 41 Brownside Road, Cambuslang, Glasgow G72 8NH — MB BCh BAO 1987 Belf.

TOWNSLEY, William London IRYO Centre, 234/236 Hendon Way, London NW4 3NE Tel: 020 8202 7272 Fax: 020 8202 6222; 12 Wymondham, Queensmead, St. Johns Wood Park, London NW8 6RD Tel: 020 7722 3866 Fax: 020 7722 3866 Email: drwtownsley@compuserve.com — MRCS Eng. LRCP Lond. 1943. (Middlx.) Med. Ref. Various Insur. Cos.; Cons. Lond. Info. Centre (Rash Dematol.). Socs: Brit. Med. Laser Assn. Prev: Ho. Surg. Qu. Alexandra Hosp. Portsmouth; Capt. RAMC.

TOWNSON, Peter John Hope Farm Medical Centre, Hope Farm Road, Great Sutton, South Wirral CH66 2WW Tel: 0151 357 3777 Fax: 0151 357 1444; Ravenswood, Mill Lane, Willaston, South Wirral CH64 1RW Tel: 0151 327 6324 — MB ChB 1979 Liverp.

TOWRISS, Mark Hamilton The Surgery, 31 Tunbridge Lane, Bottisham, Cambridge CB5 9DU Tel: 01223 811203 Fax: 01223 811853 — MB BS 1977 Newc.; MRCGP 1985; DCH RCP Lond. 1984. (Newcastle-upon-Tyne) Princip. GP Bottisham. Prev: Regist. (Med.) Dunedin Pub. Hosp., NZ; Ho. Phys. Newc. Gen. Hosp.; Ho. Surg. Shotley Bridge Hosp. Durh.

TOWSE, Margaret Susan (retired) 49 Polefield Road, Manchester M9 7EN — MB ChB 1975 Manch.; MSc Manch. 1981; MRCPsych 1979. Prev: p/t Cons. Psychiat. (Psychother.) N. Manch. Gen. Hosp.

TOWSON, Nigel Bernard Dene Towson and Partners, Juniper Road, Boreham, Chelmsford CM3 3DX Tel: 01245 467364 Fax: 01245 465584; The Surgery, Strutt Close, Hatfield Peverel, Chelmsford CM3 2HB Tel: 01245 380324 Fax: 01245 381488 — MB BS 1972 Lond.; MRCS Eng. LRCP Lond. 1972; FRCGP 1996, M 1980; DRCOG 1973. (Roy. Free) Lect. (Primary Care & Populat. Studies) Roy. Free Hosp. Sch. Med.; Course Organiser Chelmsford VTS. Socs: Chelmsford Med. Soc. Prev: Ho. Phys. (Gen. Med.) Luton & Dunstable Hosp.; Ho. Surg. (Gen. Surg. & Obst.) Roy. Free Hosp. Lond.

TOWUAGHANTSE, Mr Emmanuel Flat 20, Kent Court, North Acre, London NW9 5GF — MB BS 1978 Benin; B BS Benin 1978; FRCS Ed. 1985.

TOY, Alison Jane Mechie and Partners, 67 Owen Road, Lancaster LA1 2LG Tel: 01524 846999 Fax: 01524 845174 — MB BS 1983 Lond.; MRCGP 1988.

TOY, Elizabeth Winifred 55 Sylvan Road, Exeter EX4 6EY — MB BS 1993 Lond.; MRCP (UK) 1996. Regist. (Clin. Oncol.) Velindre Hosp. Cardiff. Prev: SHO (Med.) Roy. Devon & Exeter Hosp.

TOY, John Leslie Imperial Cancer Research Fund, 44 Lincoln's Inn Fields, London WC2A 3PX; Chalmadale, Troutstream Way, Loudwater, Rickmansworth WD3 4LB — MB ChB 1968 Leeds; PhD CNAA 1981; FRCP 1993; MRCP (UK) 1973; FFPM RCP (UK) 1994, M 1989. Med. Dir. at ICRF; Hon. Cons. Phys. Hammersmith Hosp. Lond. Socs: Roy. Soc. Med. (Ex Pres. Counc. Oncol. Sect.). Prev: Sen. Med. Off., Dept. of Health; Vice-Pres. (Clin. Investig.) SmithKline Beecham; Lect. & Hon. Sen. Regist. (Med.) Univ. Leeds & Leeds Gen. Infirm.

TOY, Matthew Jonathan Chalmadale, Troutstream Way, Loudwater, Rickmansworth WD3 4LB — MB ChB 1998 Leeds.

TOY, Rosemary Gade House Surgery, 99B Uxbridge Road, Rickmansworth WD3 7DJ Tel: 01923 775291 Fax: 01923 711790; Chalmadale, Troutstream Way, Rickmansworth WD3 4LB — MB ChB 1970 Leeds; DCH RCPS Glas. 1972; DFFP RCOG 1998.

TOYE, Rosemary Radiology Department, University Hospital Lewisham, Lewisham High St., London SE13 6LH Tel: 020 8333 3000 Ext: 6754 Email: rt@dr-toye.demon.co.uk — MB BS 1984 Lond.; MA Oxon. 1983; FRCR Eng. 1990; AKC 1984. (King's Coll. Hosp.) Cons. Univ. Hosp. Lewisham Lond.; Hon. Sen. Lect. UMDS Lond. Prev: Cons. Greenwich Dist. Hosp. Lond.; Lect. & Hon. Sen. Regist. (Radiol.) King's Coll. Sch. Med. & Dent. Lond.; Sen. Regist. (Diagn. Radiol.) King's Coll. Hosp. & St. Geo. Hosp. Lond.

TOYN, Caroline Elisabethe Department of Pathology, Dudley Road Hospital, Birmingham Tel: 0121 554 3801; 35 Eastfield Road, Westbury on Trym, Bristol BS9 4AE Tel: 0117 962 9479 — MB ChB 1985 Glas.; BSc (Hons) Glas. 1982, MB ChB 1985. Regist. (Path.) Dudley Rd. Hosp. Birm.

TOYN, Joanne Louise 10 Belvedere Drive, Dukinfield SK16 5NW — MB BS 1998 Lond.

TOYNBEE, Jean Constance Chapel Cottage, Ganthorpe, York YO60 6QD — BM BCh 1948 Oxf.; BM BCh Oxon. 1948. (Oxf.) Socs: BMA; York Med. Soc.

TOYNE, Anushya (Thanabalasingham) The Grantham Centre, Beckett House, Grantham Rd, London SW9 9OL Email: anushyatoyne@aol.com; 122 Harbut Road, London SW11 2RE Tel: 020 7228 7028 — MB BS 1991 Lond.; MRCGP 1998; DRCOG 1996. (Roy. Free Hosp. Lond.) GP Partner, The Grantham Centre, Beckett Ho., Grantham Rd, Stockwell, Lond. Prev: GP Regist. Lond.; SHO (Paediat.) Watford Gen. Hosp.; SHO Rotat. (O & G & Gen. Med.) Lister Hosp. Stevenage.

TOYNTON, Christopher John (retired) The Medical Specialist Group, Alexandra House, Les Frieteaux, St Martin's, Guernsey GY1 1XE — MB BS 1961 Lond.; DLO RCS Eng. 1985; DObst RCOG 1967. Surg. (ENT) P.ss Eliz. Hosp. Guernsey. Prev: SHO (Gyn. & Obst.) Buchanan Hosp. St. Leonards-on-Sea.

TOYNTON, Nicola Jane Yealm Medical Centre, Yealmpton, Plymouth PL8 2EA Tel: 01752 880567 Fax: 01752 880582 Email: ymc@epulse.net; Lower Marsh Farm, Landulph, Saltash PL12 6NG Tel: 01752 848041 — MB BS 1983 Lond.; MRCGP 1987; DCH RCP Lond. 1987; DRCOG 1986. (St. Thomas Hospital Medical School London University) GP Princip. Yealmpton. Prev: Trainee GP Tunbridge Wells VTS; Ho. Surg. (Gen. Surg. & ENT) St. Thos. Hosp. Lond.

TOYNTON, Mr Stephen Clement ENT Department, St. Thomas's Hospital, Lambeth Palace Road, London SE1 7EH Tel: 020 7928 9292; 35 The Mead, Beckenham BR3 5PF Tel: 020 8658 7985 — MB BS 1986 Lond.; FRCS (Otol.) Eng. 1991. Regist. (ENT) St. Thos. Hosp. Lond. Prev: SHO (ENT) St. Mary's Hosp. Lond.; SHO (A & E) St. Mary's Hosp. Lond.; SHO (Gen. Surg.) Qu. Mary's Hosp. Sidcup.

TOZER, Amanda Jane 266 Broadway N., Walsall WS1 2PT — MB BCh 1990 Wales.

TOZER, Rita Doreen Clarissa 7A Wendover Lodge, Church St., Welwyn AL6 9LR Tel: 01438 715989 — MB BS 1949 Lond.; MRCS Eng. LRCP Lond. 1949; DObst RCOG 1950. (Roy. Free) Prev: Sen. Med. Off. (Family Plann.) Barnet HA; GP Welwyn.

TOZER, Roger David Worthing Hospital, Lyndhurst Road, Worthing BN11 2DH Tel: 01903 205111 Fax: 01903 285101 Email: roger.tozer@wash-tr.sthames.nhs.uk — MB BS 1981 Lond.; FRCP (UK) 1986. Cons. Phys. (Med. for the Elderly) Worthing Hosp. Prev: Sen. Regist. St. Geo. Hosp. Lond.

TRACE, Jonathan Paul Ian Fallon and Partners, 1 Houghton Lane, Shevington, Wigan WN6 8ET Tel: 01257 253311 Fax: 01257 251081 — MB ChB 1976 Liverp.

TRACE, Thomas (retired) 2 Sutton Close, Folkestone CT19 5LL Tel: 277750 — MB ChB 1954 Liverp.; FFCM 1979, M 1974; DPH Cardiff 1969. DMO S.E. Kent Health Auth. Prev: DCP Lewisham Dist., Lambeth, & S.wark HA.

TRACEY, Colin Anthony The Orchard Surgery, Commercial Road, Dereham NR19 1AE Tel: 01362 692916 Fax: 01362 698347 — MB BS 1976 Lond.

TRACEY, Dennis Michael Department of Public Health Medicine, Highland Health Board, Beechwood Park, Inverness IV2 3HG Tel: 01463 717123 Fax: 01463 235189 Email: dennis@traceyhouse.freeserve.co.uk; 60 Crown Drive, Inverness IV2 3QG Tel: 01463 226486 — MB ChB 1976 Sheff.; MRCGP 1982; MFPHM 1989. Med Dir. Highland Primary Care NHS Trust.; Hon. Clin. Sen. Lect. (Pub. Health Med.) Univ. Aberd.; Hon. Lect. Centre for Internat. Health, Qu. Margt. Coll. Edin.; Cons. Pub. Health Med. & Med. Prescribing Adviser Highland HB. Socs: Internat. Union Against Tuberc. & Lung Dis. Prev: Tuberc. Advisor Min. Health Lesotho; Sen. Regist. (Community Med.) N. Derbysh. HA; Med. Off. St. Eliz. Hosp. Lusikisiki, Transkei.

TRACEY, Fergal 26 Inishowen Park, Portstewart BT55 7BQ — MB BCh BAO 1985 Belf.

TRACEY, Miriam Ellen 19 Ardmore Park, Finaghy, Belfast BT10 0JJ — MB ChB 1991 Dundee.

TRACEY, Noreen Geraldine Teresa 5 Hackett Villas, Omagh BT78 1LU; 73 Greystown Avenue, Belfast BT9 6UH — MB BCh BAO 1986 Belf.; MRCP (UK) 1989; FRCR 1993; FFR RCSI 1992. Cons. Radiol. Belf. City Hosp.

TRACEY, Susan Keppoch Road Surgery, Keppoch Road, Culloden, Inverness IV2 7LL Tel: 01463 793400 Fax: 01463 793060; 60 Crown Drive, Inverness IV2 3QG — MB ChB 1976 Sheff.; MRCGP 1994; DRCOG 1978. Prev: Med. Off. Transkei S. Afr.; GP SIDA Lesotho, Afr.; Asst. GP Sheff.

TRACEY, Turlough John Coleraine Health Centre, Castlerock Road, Coleraine BT51 3HP Tel: 028 7034 4834 Fax: 028 7035 8914 — MB BS 1990 Lond.

TRACEY, Vivien Vaile (retired) 1 Fountain Court, Ipswich Road, Norwich NR1 2QA Tel: 01603 625359 — BSc, MB BCh Wales 1944; FFCM 1976, M 1972; DPH Lond. 1961; DCH Eng. 1947. Specialist Community Med. N.ampton Dist. HA. Prev: Sen. Med. Off. N.ants. CC.

TRACY, Hilda Joan Dale End Road, Barnston, Wirral CH61 1DD — MB ChB 1957 Liverp.; PhD Liverp. 1965, MB ChB 1957. (Liverp.)

TRACY, Peter Michael 10 Beech Grove., Porthcawl CF36 5DP — MB BCh 1980 Wales.

TRAFFORD, Paul Jeremy Flat D, Shalstone Manor, Shalstone, Buckingham MK18 5LT — MB ChB 1983 Liverp.; BSc (Biochem.) Liverp. 1978, MB ChB 1983. (Liverpool) Socs: Liverp. Med. Inst. & Liverp. Soc. Anaesth.; Assn. Anaesth.

TRAFFORD, Penelope Anne Watling Medical Centre, 108 Watling Avenue, Burnt Oak, Edgware HA8 0NR Tel: 020 8906 1711 Fax: 020 8201 1283; 42 London Road, Stanmore HA7 4NU Tel: 020 8958 4237 — MB BS 1979 Lond.; MRCGP 1984. GP Princip.; Assoc. Dean, The Lond. Deanery.

TRAFFORD, Peter Alan (retired) Timsbury, off Portway, Wells BA5 2BB Tel: 01749 673254 — MB BS Lond. 1943; MRCS Eng. LRCP Lond. 1942; DPM Eng. 1972. Prev: Sen. Med. Off. HM Prison Med. Serv.

TRAFFORD, Peter Damian Occupational Health Unit, Jubilee House, Jubilee St., Blackburn BB1 1EP Tel: 01254 587883 Fax: 01253 589630 Email: damian.trafford@blackburn.gou.uk; 45 Dukes Brow, Blackburn BB2 6DH Tel: 01254 56056 Email: drafford@doctors.org.uk — MB BS 1974 Lond.; MSc Manch. 1996; MFOM RCP Lond. 1997; AFOM RCP Lond. 1993; DRCOG 1977. (Lond. Hosp. Med. Coll.) p/t Occupat.al Health Cons., Capita plc and Blackburn with Darwen Boro. Counc.; Sen. Med. Adviser Blackburn Boro. Counc. Socs: Assn. Local Auth. Med. Advisors; Soc. Occupat. Med. Prev: Director of Med. Servs., Company Health Ltd; Occupat. Phys. Rochdale Healthcare NHS Trust; GP Glos.

TRAGEN, David Robb Farm, Tuxford Road, Egmanton NG22 0HA; 5 Kilmalcolm Close, Prenton CH43 9QT Tel: 0151 652 4775, 07812 040509 Email: davetragen@hotmail.com — MB ChB 2000 Manchester. (Manchester) Sen. Ho. Off., Accid. + Emerg., Rochdale Infirm. Prev: PRHO Urol., Stepping Hill Hosp. Stockport; PRHO Orthop., Stepping Hill Hosp., Stockport; Gen. Med./Gastroenterol./Elderly Med., N. Manch. Gen. Hosp.

TRAGEN, Dawn Justine 44 Parkstone Avenue, Whitefield, Manchester M45 7QH — MB ChB 1994 Manch.; DRCOG 1997. (Manchester) GP Cheadle Hulme, Chesh. Prev: SHO (Med.) N. Manch. Gen. Hosp.; SHO (O & G) N. Manch. Gen. Hosp.; SHO (Paediat.) Booth Hall Childr.'s Hosp.

TRAGEN, Leslie 5 Kilmalcolm Close, Prenton, Prenton CH43 9QT Tel: 0151 652 4775 — MB ChB 1951 Liverp.; MRCGP 1965; DObst RCOG 1958. p/t Med. Advis. & Examr. Nestor Disabil. Anal. Socs: Liverp. Med. Inst.; Birkenhead & Wallasey Med. Socs. Prev: Dep. Police Surg. Merseyside Police; GP Wirral FPC; Capt. RAMC Jun. Anaesth. Specialist.

TRAHERNE, John Bernard 48 Brixton Water Lane, London SW2 Tel: 020 7274 1521 — MB BS 1958 Lond.; MRCS Eng. LRCP Lond. 1958. (King's Coll. Hosp.) Prev: ENT Clin. Asst. Lond. Hosp. & Roy. Nat. Throat, Nose & Ear Hosp.; Ho. Phys. Belgrave Hosp. Childr.

TRAILL, Charles Gordon The Surgery, Sydenham House, Mill Court, Ashford TN24 8DN Tel: 01233 645851 Fax: 01233 638281; Leighton House, Church Road, Kennington, Ashford TN24 9DQ — MB BS 1969 Lond.; MRCGP 1976; DObst RCOG 1971. Clin. Asst. (Dermat.) Kent & Canterbury Hosp.; CMO Paediatric Audiol. Ashford Kent.

TRAILL, Erica Ruth Bochruben House, Torness, Inverness IV2 6TZ — MB ChB 1985 Ed.

TRAILL, Lilias McAlpine (retired) Bellevue, 2 Pendreich Road, Bridge-of-Allan, Stirling FK9 4PZ — MB ChB 1944 Glas.; DPH

TRAILL

1967; MFCM 1972. Prev: Sen. Med. Off. (Community Med.) Forth Valley HB.

TRAILL, Zoe Christina 75 Old High Street, Headington, Oxford OX3 9HT — MB BS 1986 Lond.

TRAIN, Jean Dick (retired) Cathkin, 4 Nunholm Place, Dumfries DG1 1JR Tel: 01387 53033 — MB ChB 1951 Glas. Prev: SCMO Dumfries & Galloway Health Bd.

TRAIN, Jonathan James Andrew 30 Avenue Road, Doncaster DN2 4AQ Email: jon_train@compuserve.com — MB ChB 1983 Bristol; FRCA. 1990; MBA 1995. Cons.(Anaest.) Doncaster Roy Infirm. Doncaster. Socs: BMA & Assn. Anaesth. Prev: Sen. Regist. Rotat. (Anaesth.) Roy. Free Hosp. Lond.; Fell. Cardiothoracic Anaesth. Acad. Ziekenmuis Groningen, Netherlands.

TRAIN, Peter Holly Cottage, Wickham St Paul, Halstead CO9 2PS — MB BS 1952 Lond. (St. Bart.) Prev: Ho. Surg. & Ho. Phys. Essex Co. Hosp. Colchester.

TRAIN, Mr Thomas Scott Rutherford (retired) Cathkin, 4 Nunholm Place, Dumfries DG1 1JR Tel: 01387 253033 — MD Glas. 1959, MB ChB 1951; FRCS Glas. 1981; FRCOG 1970, M 1956. Prev: Cons. O & G Dumfries & Galloway Hosp. Gp.

TRAINER, Jean Forbes (retired) Westfield Bungalow, Kirkfieldbank, Lanark ML11 9UH Tel: 01555 661285 — MB ChB 1952 Ed. Prev: Cas. Off. & Ho. Off. (Orthop.) Law Hosp. Carluke.

TRAINER, Peter James Department of Endocrinology, Christie Hospital, Wilmslow Road, Manchester M20 4BX Tel: 0161 446 3664, 0161 446 3772 — MB ChB 1983 Ed.; MD 1997; FRCP 1998; BSc Ed. 1980; MRCP (UK) 1986. Cons. (Endocrinol.) Christie Hosp. Prev: Sen. Lect., Hon. Cons. (Endocrinol.) St. Bart. Hosp. Lond.

TRAN, Ann Dao c/o P & O Cruises (UK) Ltd., Richmond House, Terminus Terrace, Southampton SO14 3PN Tel: 02380 534200 Fax: 02380 227920; 75 Brockenhurst Avenue, Worcester Park KT4 7RH Tel: 020 8337 1250 — MB ChB 1990 Bristol; MRCGP 1995. Asst. Ship's Doctor P & O Cruises (UK) Ltd. Soton. Socs: BMA & Med. Defence Union. Prev: Trainee GP/SHO Exeter VTS.

TRAN, Anna Thi Huyen 24 The Glade, Coventry CV5 7BU — MB ChB 1998 Leic.

TRAN, Huong Nam Paul 42 Station Road, Bearsden, Glasgow G61 4AL — MB BCh BAO 1986 Belf.

TRAN, Minh Ngoc 8 Tasman Cl, Mickleover, Derby DE3 5LF — MB ChB 1997 Manch.

TRAN, Tan Loc 11 Lytton Road, Pinner HA5 4RH — MB BS 1978 Lond.

TRANMER, Christopher Kings Avenue Surgery, 23 Kings Avenue, Buckhurst Hill IG9 5LP Tel: 020 8504 0122 Fax: 020 8559 2984; 17 Queens Avenue, Woodford Green IG8 0JE Tel: 020 8505 5171 — MB BS Lond. 1967; MRCS Eng. LRCP Lond. 1967; MRCGP 1975; Dip. Primary Care Rheum. Bath Univ. 1998. (Roy. Free) Hosp. Pract. (Rheum. & Rehabil.) King Geo. Hosp. Ilford. Socs: BMA; Forest Med Soc; Ilford Med soc. Prev: Regist. (Gen. Med.) King Geo. Hosp. Ilford; SHO (O & G) Ilford Matern. Hosp.; SHO (Paediat.) Qu. Eliz. II Hosp. Welwyn Garden City.

TRANMER, Francoise Marie 17 Queens Avenue, Woodford Green IG8 0JE — MB BS 1997 Lond.

TRANMER, Louise Solange Wanstead Place Surgery, 45 Wanstead Place, Wanstead High Street, Wanstead, London E11 2SW Tel: 020 8989 2019 Fax: 020 8532 1124; 17 Queens Avenue, Woodford Green IG8 0JE Tel: 020 8505 5171 Fax: 020 8559 2812 Email: ctranmer@ndirect.co.uk — MB BS 1970 Lond.; MRCS Eng. LRCP Lond. 1969. (Roy. Free) Clin. Asst. in Colposcopy, Whipps Cross Univ. Hosp. Prev: Ho. Surg. King Geo. Hosp. Ilford; Ho. Phys. Barking Hosp.

TRANTER, Alan William (retired) 33 Stanley Avenue, Beckenham BR3 6PU Tel: 020 8658 8986 — MB BS 1951 Lond.; MB BS (Hons. Surg.) Lond. 1951; MRCS Eng. LRCP Lond. 1951; FFCM 1978, M 1972; DPH Eng. 1958, DCH 1954. Prev: Dist. Med. Off. Bromley AHA.

TRANTER, John Victor (retired) 37 Burland Avenue, Tettenhall, Wolverhampton WV6 9JJ Tel: 01902 753388 — MB ChB 1957 Birm.; MRCS Eng. LRCP Lond. 1958. Prev: Gen. Practioner Drs Tranter & Fowler Wolverhampton.

TRANTER, Julie Bletchingdon Road Surgery, Bletchingdon Road, Islip, Kidlington OX5 2TQ Tel: 01865 371666 Fax: 01865 842475 — BM BCh 1985 Oxf.; MRCGP 1989.

TRANTER, Liam Kevin Flat 4, 8 Cambridge Rd, Kingston upon Thames KT1 3JY — MB ChB 1997 Otago.

TRANTER, Richard Argoed, Pen y Cefn Road, Caerwys, Mold CH7 5BH — MB ChB 1994 Manch.

TRANTER, Richard Church Street Surgery, 27-28 Church St, Whitehaven CA28 7EB Tel: 01946 693660; 3 Round Close Park, Scilly Banks, Whitehaven CA28 8UH Tel: 01946 67276 — MB ChB 1987 Birm.; MRCGP 1991; DCH RCP Lond. 1990.

TRANTER, Mr Robert Martyn David Sussex Nuffield Hospital, Warren Road, Wooding Dean, Brighton BN2 6DX Tel: 01273 627032 Fax: 01273 627033 Email: rtranter@uk-consultants.co.uk; Foxdown, 50 Longhill Road, Ovingdean, Brighton BN2 7BE Tel: 01273 32455 Email: bren.bob@virgin.net — MB ChB 1974 Bristol; BDS Birm. 1967; FRCS Eng. 1979; FDS RCS Eng. 1972. Cons. Otolaryngol. Brighton & P.ss Roy. Hosp. Haywards Heath. Socs: Co. Chairm. HCSA; BMA; Brighton & Hove Med. Soc. (Sec.). Prev: Sen. Regist. Qu. Eliz. Hosp. Birm.; SHO (Oral Surg.) Plymouth Gen. Hosp.; SHO (Plastic Surg.) Frenchay Hosp. Bristol.

TRANTER, Miss Sheena Elizabeth 5 Grosvenor Road, Leamington Spa CV31 2NN — MB ChB 1991 Bristol; FRCS Eng. 1996. (Bristol) Specialist Regist. Rotat. (Gen. Surg.) SW.

TRAPIELLA, Beatriz 20 Melrose Close, Southsea PO4 8EZ — LMS 1992 Basque Provinces.

TRAPNELL, David Hallam (retired) Dumbles Cottage, Woodend Lane, Awre, Newnham GL14 1EP — BA (1st cl. Hons. Nat. Sc. Trip. Pt. 1) Camb 1949, MA 1953, MD 1963, MB BChir 1952; FRCP 1975, M 1957; FRCR 1975; FFR 1961; DMRD Eng. 1959. Prev: Cons. Radiol. W.m. Hosp.

TRAPNELL, Mr John Eliot (retired) Ropewind, Snails Lane, Blashford, Ringwood BH24 3PG — MB BChir 1954 Camb.; MD Camb. 1966, MA, MB BChir 1954; FRCS Eng. 1961. Hon. Cons. Surg. Roy. Bournemouth Hosp. Prev: Pres. Pancreatic Soc. Gt. Brit. & Irel. 1980.

TRAQUAIR, Katherine Elizabeth Corona (retired) Rothiemay House, Huntly AB54 7ND — MB ChB 1942 Ed. Prev: Surg. Regist. Hairmyres Hosp. E. Kilbride.

TRAQUAIR, Malcolm Ross Cairncraig House, 1 Hamilton Road, Mount Vernon, Glasgow G32 9QD Tel: 0141 778 5789 Fax: 0141 778 3488 Email: 999tra@compuserve.com — MB ChB 1978 Glas.; MPhil (Law & Ethics) Glas. 1992. Disabil. Med. Adviser BA Med. Servs. Scotl.; Chief Med. Off. RSAC (Motorsport) Ltd. Socs: Brit. Assn. Rally Doctors; GP Writers Assn. Prev: SHO (O & G) Stobhill Hosp. Glas.; SHO Glas. Inst. of Radiother.; Ho. Surg. & Ho. Phys. StoneHo. Hosp. Lanarksh.

TRAQUAIR, Mr Ramsay Nairn (retired) Rothiemay House, Huntly AB54 7ND Tel: 0146 681298 — MB ChB 1934 Ed.; BA Camb. (Nat. Sc. Trip. Pt. I) 1931; FRCS Ed. 1939. Prev: Orthop. Surg. Hairmyres Hosp. E. Kilbride.

TRASH, David Bellas 2300 Corporate Circle, Suite 100, Henderson NV 89074, USA Tel: 720 731 8224 Email: jjpatelmd@aol.com — MB BS 1965 Lond.; FRCP Lond. 1983; MRCP (UK) 1971; MRCS Eng. LRCP Lond. 1965. (Roy. Free) p/t Cons. Phys. Manor Hosp. Walsall.

TRASK, Colin William Lawson Southend Hospital, Prittlewell Chase, Westcliff on Sea SS0 0RY Tel: 01702 221223 Fax: 01702 221037; 17 Parkanaur Avenue, Thorpe Bay, Southend-on-Sea SS1 3HX — BM BCh 1974 Oxf.; MA, BM BCh Oxf. 1974; FRCR 1982. Cons. (Radiother. & Oncol.) S.end Hosp.; Hon. Sen. Lect. (Clin. Oncol.) Middlx. Hosp. Lond. Prev: Sen. Regist. (Radiother. & Oncol.) Univ. Coll. Hosp. Lond.

TRASK, Michael Darien 4 Dunham Rise, Altrincham WA14 2BB — MB ChB 1968 Manch.; FFA RCS Eng. 1975; DObst RCOG 1970. Cons. Anaesth. Salford AHA (T). Socs: Assn. Anaesths.

TRATHEN, Bruce Christopher The Old Plough, 7 The Street, Wallington, Baldock SG7 6SW — MB BS 1989 Lond.

TRATHEN, Duncan Paul 117 Green Dragon Lane, London N21 1HE; 36B Durley Road, London N16 5JS — MB BS 1994 Lond.

TRAUB, Anthony Ivor 6 Broomhill Park Central, Belfast BT9 5JD — MD 1980 Belf.; MD (Hons.) Belf. 1980, MB BCh BAO 1972; FRCOG 1989, M 1977. Cons. & Sen. Lect. Midw. & Gyn. Qu. Univ. Belf.

TRAUB, Michael Max 9 De Freville Avenue, Cambridge CB4 1HN — MB BS 1973 Lond.; MRCP (U.K.) 1976; MRCS Eng. LRCP Lond.

1973. Sen. Regist. (Neurol.) Lond. Hosp. Prev: SHO (Med.) King's Coll. Hosp. Lond.; SHO IC St. Thos. Hosp. Lond.

TRAUE, Denise Carolyn 9 Meadow Way, Potters Bar EN6 2NJ — MB BS 1996 Lond.

TRAVELL, Paul David Littlewick Medical Centre, 42 Nottingham Road, Ilkeston DE7 5PR Tel: 0115 932 5229 Fax: 0115 932 5413 — MB ChB 1983 Leic.; MRCGP 1988; DRCOG 1988. Prev: SHO (Ophth.) PeterBoro. Gen. Hosp.

TRAVELL, Rosemund Margaret 2/l, 17 Cleghorn St., Dundee DD2 2NQ — MB ChB 1998 Dund.; MB ChB Dund 1998.

TRAVENEN, Michael James Longshut Lane West Surgery, 24 Longshut Lane West, Stockport SK2 6SF Tel: 0161 480 2373 Fax: 0161 480 2660.

TRAVERS, Anne Frances South Humber Health Authority, Health Place, Wrawby Road, Brigg DN20 8GS Tel: 01652 659659; 27 Oakwell Mount, Leeds LS8 4AD — MB ChB 1977 Leeds; BSc (Hons.) Leeds 1974, MB ChB 1977; MRCP (UK) 1981; MPH 1994; MFPHM 1996. (Leeds) Cons. (Pub. Health Med.) S. Humber Health Auth. Socs: Soc. Social Med.; Brit. Geriat. Soc.; Assn. UK Pub. Health. Prev: Sen. Regist. (Geriat.s) Leeds Gen. Infirm.; Assoc. Research Fell. Univ. Coll. Lond.; Med. Off. St. Peter's Mission Hosp. Chisumbanje, Zimbabwe.

TRAVERS, Carolyn Victoria Ashley House, Church Lane, Hampsthwaite, Harrogate HG3 2HB — MB BCh 1982 Wales.

TRAVERS, Mr Eric Horsley (retired) 10 Martlets, West Chiltington, Pulborough RH20 2QD Tel: 01798 813127 — MB ChB 1936 Ed.; FRCS Eng. 1941; MRCS Eng. LRCP Lond. 1939. Prev: Cons. Surg. N. Teesside Hosp. Gp.

TRAVERS, James (retired) c/o Fisher, 28 Octavia Terrace, Greenock PA16 7SR — MB ChB 1935 Glas.

TRAVERS, John Francis Croftfoot Road Surgery, 30 Croftfoot Road, Glasgow G44 5JT Tel: 0141 634 0431 Fax: 0131 633 5284 — MB ChB 1979 Glas.

TRAVERS, Kathleen Mary 19 Finch Road, Greenock PA16 7DG — MB ChB 1982 Glas.

TRAVERS, Peter Rowlstone Covox Centre, The Old Mill, Tudor St., Exeter EX4 3BR Tel: 01392 430997; 38 Winchester Avenue, Exwick, Exeter EX4 2DJ Tel: 01392 277660 — MB BS 1942 Lond.; MRCS Eng. LRCP Lond. 1942; DPhysMed. Eng. 1954. (St. Thos.) Indep. Sports Med. & Rehabil. Cons. Covox Centre Exeter; Cons. in Physical and Sports Med., BRd.meadow Sports Centre, Devon. Prev: Convenor Med. Advis. Comm. Brit. Amateur Athletic Bd.; Lect. (Physiol. & Sports Med.) Sch. Educat. Univ. Exeter; Wing Cdr. (Ret) RAF Med. Br.

TRAVERS, Raymond Francis Rampton Hospital Authority, Retford DN22 0PD Tel: 01777 247759 Fax: 01777 247221 — MB BCh BAO 1984 NUI; LRCPI & LM, LRCSI & LM 1984; MRCPsych 1991. Cons.(Forens Psychait.) Rampton Hosp Auth.; Sen Lect.(Hon) Univ of Sheff. Socs: Liverp. Psychiat. Soc.; Brit. Neuropsychiat. Soc.; Linc Med Soc. Prev: Sen. Regist. (Forens. Psychiat.) Scott Clinic Merseyside.

TRAVERS, William John Elton South Forest Locality, Mental Health Centre, 21 Thorne Close, London E11 4HU Tel: 020 8535 6948 Fax: 020 8535 6822 — MB BS 1981 Newc.; MRCPsych. 1988; MRCGP 1985; DRCOG 1984. Cons. Psychiat. N. E. Lond. Ment. Health Trust, Lond. Prev: Sen. Regist. Rotat. (Psychiat.) St. Bart. Hosp. Lond.

TRAVILL, Christopher Michael Crowholt, George St., Woburn, Milton Keynes MK17 9PX — MB BS 1980 Lond.; MD Lond. 1994; MRCP (UK) 1983. Cons. Cardiol. Luton & Dunstable Hosp. & Harefield Hosp. Socs: Brit. Pacing & Electrophysiol. Gp; Brit. Cardiac Soc. Prev: Sen. Regist. Char. Cross & W.m. Med. Sch. Lond.; Regist. Profess. Unit of Therap. Char. Cross & W.m. Med. Sch. Lond.

TRAVIS, Alison 2 Newlands Road, Cockermouth CA13 0AH Tel: 01900 824084 — BM BS 1996 Nottm.; BMedSci Nottm. 1994. (Nottm.) SHO (Gen. Med.) York Dist. Hosp. Prev: Jun. Ho. (Gen. Surg. & Med.) Qu. Med. Centre. Nottm.

TRAVIS, Charles David Elms Surgery, 5 Derby Street, Ormskirk L39 2BJ Tel: 01695 571560 Fax: 01695 578300 — MB ChB Liverp. 1970; MRCGP 1977; DObst RCOG 1972.

TRAVIS, Michael John Institute of Psychiatry, De Crespigny Park, Camberwell, London SE5 8AF — MB BS 1990 Lond.; BSc (Hons.) Lond. 1987; MRCPsych 1994. (Guy's Hosp.) Lect. & Hon. Sen. Regist. Inst. Psychiat. Lond. Prev: Sen. Regist. (Psychiat.) St. Bart. &

Homerton Hosps. Lond.; Hon. Sen. Regist. (Psychiat.) Bethlem & Maudsley Hosps. Lond.

TRAVIS, Paul Polkyth Surgery, 14 Carlyon Road, St Austell PL25 4EG Tel: 01726 75555; 37 Cooperage Road, Trewoon, St Austell PL25 5SJ Tel: 01726 75871 Fax: 01726 75871 — MB 1984 Camb.; BChir 1983; BSc St. And. 1980.

TRAVIS, Peter James Grove Road Surgery, 3 Grove Road, Solihull B91 2AG Tel: 0121 705 1105 Fax: 0121 711 4098; Woodside, 232 Streetsbrook Road, Solihull B91 1HF Tel: 0121 705 7867 — MB ChB Manch. 1967; FRCGP 1987, M 1974; DObst RCOG 1969. (Manchester) Socs: BMA & Assur. Med. Soc. Prev: Ho. Off. (Surg., Med. & Obst.) Withington Hosp. Manch.

TRAVIS, Phyllida Jane 4 Lyncroft Gardens, London W13 9PU Tel: 020 8579 9000 — MB BS 1981 Lond.; Msc (Health Plann. & Financing) Lond. 1994; MA Oxf. 1981; MRCGP 1987; DRCOG 1987; DCH RCP Lond. 1986. Technical Off. WHO.

TRAVIS, Simon Piers Leigh Gastroenterology Unit, Derriford Hospital, Plymouth PL6 8DH Tel: 01752 792112 Fax: 01752 792240 Email: simon.travis@phnt.swest.nhs.uk — MB BS 1981 Lond.; DPhil Oxf. 1992; MRCP (UK) 1987; FRCP 1998. Cons. Phys. & Gastroenterol. Derriford Hosp. Plymouth. Prev: Sen. Regist. (Gastroenterol. & Gen. Med.) John Radcliffe Hosp. Oxf.; Jun. Research Fell. Linacre Coll. Oxf.; Regist. St. Thos. Hosp. Lond.

TRAVIS, Susan Elisabeth 291 Oldham Road, Rochdale OL16 5HX; 18 Spencer Lane, Bamford, Rochdale OL11 5PE Tel: 01706 369603 — MB ChB 1980 Manch.; BSc St. And. 1977; DRCOG 1983; DCH RCP Lond. 1982.

TRAWIN, Celestine Carol Lower Ground Floor, 70 Fentiman Road, London SW8 1LA — MB BCh 1993 Witwatersrand.

TRAYERS, Mary Margaret (retired) Ivy Lodge, Main Road, Wrangle, Boston PE22 9AD — MB BCh BAO 1947 NUI. Prev: GP Boston Lincs.

TRAYLING, Anthony Peter Allam Old School Surgery, Rectory Fields, Cranbrook TN17 3JB Tel: 01580 715729 Fax: 01580 715729; Dog Kennel Farm, Cranbrook TN17 2PT — MRCS Eng. LRCP Lond. 1962. (Guy's) Med. Off. Cranbrook Sch. & Dulwich Coll. Preparatory Sch.; Hon. Treas. The Europ. Union for Sch. & Univ. Health & Med. Socs: Kent Postgrad. Med. Soc. Prev: Ho. Surg. & Ho. Phys. Roy. Surrey Co. Hosp.; Resid. Obst. Off. Kent & Canterbury Hosp.

TRAYNER, Iris Aird McNeil 42 Rivermeads Avenue, Twickenham TW2 5JQ Tel: 020 8898 7144 — MB BS 1962 Lond.; MRCS Eng. LRCP Lond. 1961. (St. Mary's) Clin. Asst. Dept. Chem. Path. Hammersmith Hosp. Lond.; Research Fell. MRC Lipoprotein Team Hammersmith Hosp. Lond. Socs: Fell. Roy. Soc. Med.; Brit. Hyperlipidaemia Assn. Prev: Ho. Surg. St. Mary's Hosp. Padd.; Research Asst. Dept. Endocrinol. Hammersmith Hosp. Lond.; Regist. Dept. Chem. Path. Hammersmith Hosp. Lond.

TRAYNER, James Dixon Limeleigh Medical Group, 434 Narborough Road, Leicester LE3 2FS Tel: 0116 282 7070 Fax: 0116 289 3805; 4 Hathaway, Links Road, Kirby Muxloe, Leicester LE9 2BP Tel: 0116 239 3289 — MB ChB 1964 Glas.; DObst RCOG 1971. (Lond.) Socs: Leicester Med. Soc. Prev: Resid. in Obst. Robroyston Hosp. Glas.; Surg. Resid. Glas. Roy. Infirm.; Med. Resid. W. Dist. Hosp. Glas.

TRAYNER, Justin William Glenfield Surgery, 111 Station Road, Glenfield, Leicester LE3 8GS — MB ChB 1990 Leic. SHO (O & G) Sorrento Matern. Hosp. Moseley Birm. Prev: Ho. Off. (Gen. Surg.) Geo. Eliot Hosp. Nuneaton; Ho. Off. (Gen. Med.) Leicester Gen. Hosp.

TRAYNOR, Christine Patricia 137 Osbaldwick Lane, York YO10 3AY — MB ChB 1995 Leic.

TRAYNOR, David Bernard Pennells and Partners, Gosport Health Centre, Bury Road, Gosport PO12 3PN Tel: 023 9258 3344 Fax: 023 9260 2704 — MB ChB 1976 Manch.; MRCGP 1980; DRCOG 1980.

TRAYNOR, James Philip 582 Crow Road, Glasgow G13 1NP Tel: 0141 954 7823 Email: jamie@traynor94.freeserve.co.uk — MB ChB 1994 Aberd.; MRCP UK 1997. (Aberd.) SHO (Nephrol.) Stobhill Hosp. Glas. Prev: SHO (Neph. & Med.) Monklands Dgm Lanarks.

TREACHER, David Floyd Mead Ward, Intensive Care Unit, St. Thomas' Hospital, London SE1 7EH Tel: 020 7928 9292 Fax: 020 7922 8240 Email: david.treacher@gstt.sthames.nhs.uk; 23 Cole Park Road, Twickenham TW1 1HP Tel: 020 8892 0849 — MB BS

TREACY

1975 Lond.; BA (Hons.) Oxf. 1972; FRCP Lond. 1992; MRCP (UK) 1978. (St. Thos. Lond.) Cons. Phys. & Dir. of Intens. Care. Guy's & St. Thos. Hosp. NHS Trust Lond. Socs: BMA; Brit. Thorac. Soc.; Eur. Soc. Intens. Care.

TREACY, Finbarr Patrick (retired) 108 Monton Road, Eccles, Manchester M30 9HG — LRCPI & LM, LRSCI & LM 1950; LRCPI & LM, LRCSI & LM 1950.

TREACY, Patrick Joseph Knockaraven Garrison, Enniskillen BT74 4AE — MB BCh BAO 1986 NUI; LRCPSI 1986.

TREACY, Peter John Department of Surgical & Anaesthetic Sciences, Floor K, Royal Hallamshire Hospital, Sheffield S10 2JF Tel: 0114 282 1290 Fax: 0114 271 3791 — MB BS 1984 Adelaide; MD Adelaide 1994; FRACS 1994. Clin. Lect. (Gen. Surg.) Univ. Sheff.; Sen. Regist. Roy. Hallamsh. Hosp. Sheff. Prev: Sen. Regist. Roy. Adelaide Hosp., Austral.

TREADGOLD, Nicholas John Pollok Health Centre, 21 Cowglen Road, Glasgow G53 6EQ Tel: 0141 531 6860 Fax: 0141 531 6808; Tel: 0141 322232 — MB ChB 1985 Leeds.

TREADGOLD, Ursula Ann Anderby, Gore End, Newbury RG20 0PH — BM 1991 Soton.

TREADWELL, Elizabeth Anne 144 Henwick Road, Worcester WR2 5PB — MB ChB 1967 Birm.; DPM Eng. 1974. Clin. Asst. (Psychiat.) Worcester Roy. Infirm. (Newtown Br.). Prev: Clin. Asst. (Psychiat.) Powick Hosp.; Regist. (Psychiat.) Powick Hosp.; Ho. Surg. & Ho. Phys. Worcester Roy. Infirm.

TREAGUST, Janette Denise — MB BS 1988 Lond.; MFPHM 2000; BSc (Hons.) Lond. 1985; MRCGP 1992; DRCOG 1991. Sen. Regist. (Pub. Health Med.) Som. Avon Health Auth.

TREANOR, Orla Teresa 8 Greenan Road, Newry BT34 2PJ; 15 Cairnshill Park, Belfast BT8 6RG Tel: 01232 729 5918 — MB BCh BAO 1994 Belf.; DCH Dublin 1997; DRCOG Lond 1997; MRCOP 1998. Socs: DMA; MPS.

TREASADEN, Ian Henry Three Bridges Secure Unit, West London Mental Health NHS Trust, Uxbridge Road, Southall UB1 3EU — MB BS 1975 Lond.; MRCS Eng. LRCP Lond. 1975; MRCPsych 1979; ECFMG Cert 1975. (Lond. Hosp.) Cons. Forens. Psychiat. Three Bridges Secure Unit, Lond.; Hon. Sen. Lect. (Forens. Psychiat.) St. Mary's Hosp. Campus, Imperial Coll. Sch. of Med. Lond. Socs: BMA. Prev: Sen. Regist. (Forens. Psychiat.) Maudsley Hosp. Bethlem Roy. Hosp. & BRd.moor Special Hosp. Lond.; Research Fell. & Hon. Sen. Regist. (Forens. Psychiat.) Univ. Soton.

TREASURE, Janet Linda Institute of Psychiatry, De Crespigny Park, London SE5 8AF Tel: 020 7919 3180 Fax: 020 7919 3182 Email: j.treasure@iop.bpmf.ac.uk; 56 Talfourd Road, London SE15 5NY Tel: 020 7701 4955 Fax: 020 7701 8737 — MB BS 1978 Lond.; PhD Lond. 1975, BSc 1973; MRCP (UK) 1980; MRCS Eng. LRCP Lond. 1978; FRCPsych 1995, M 1984. (St. Thos.) Cons. Eating Disorder Unit Maudsley Hosp. Lond. Prev: Sen. Lect. Inst. Psychiat. Lond.; Regist. Maudsley Hosp.; SHO St. Helier Hosp.

TREASURE, Joanna Consultant Cellular Pathologist, Southport & Ormskirk NHS Trust, Southport District General Hospital, Southport PR8 6TN Tel: 01695 583651 — MB BS 1985 Lond.; MA Camb. 1986, BA 1982; MRCPath 1994. Cons. Cellular Path. S.port& Ormskirk NHS Trust. Socs: Assn. Clin. Path.; Internat. Acad. Path.; Brit. Soc. for Clin. Cytol. Prev: Cons. Cellular Path. Ormskirk & Dist. Gen. Hosp.; Clin. Lect. (Path.) & Hon. Sen. Regist. Univ. Manch.; Regist. (Histopath.) Soton. Gen. Hosp.

TREASURE, Paul William Royal Shrewsbury Hospital, Copthorne Road, Shrewsbury SY3 Tel: 01743 261000; The Wain House, Betton Strange, Shrewsbury SY5 6HZ Tel: 01743 344746 — MB BS 1992 Lond. SHO (Paediat.) Roy. Shrewsbury Hosp.

TREASURE, Richard Anthony Robert Plas Ffynnon Medical Centre, Middleton Road, Oswestry SY11 2RB Tel: 01691 655844 Fax: 01691 668030; Bryn Teg, Hengoed, Oswestry SY10 7EH Tel: 01691 653402 Fax: 01691 671864 — MB BS 1981 Lond.; MRCP (UK) 1984; MRCGP 1989. Prev: Trainee GP Brecon VTS; Regist. (Med.) Char. Cross Hosp. Lond.; SHO (Med.) W.m. Hosp. Lond.

TREASURE, Professor Tom Professor Cardiothoracic Surgery, Guy's and St. Thomas's, London SE1 9RT; 56 Talfourd Road, London SE15 5NY Tel: 020 7701 4955 Fax: 020 7701 8737 — MD Lond. 1982, MS 1978, MB BS 1970; FRCS Eng. 1975; MRCS Eng. LRCP Lond. 1970. (Guy's) Cons. Cardiothoracic Surg. Guy's Hiospital. Socs: Brit. Cardiac Soc. & Med. Research Soc.; Fell. Europ. Soc. Cardiol. Prev: Cons. Cardiothoracic Surg St Geo.'s Hosp.; Cons.

Cardiothoracic Surg. Middlx. & Univ. Coll. Hosps.; Sen. Regist. Lond. Chest & Brompton Hosp. Lond. & Ho. Surg. Thoracic Unit. Guy's Hosp. Lond.

TREASURE, Wilfrid Muirhouse Medical Group, 1 Muirhouse Avenue, Edinburgh EH4 4PL Tel: 0131 332 2201; 16/1 Broughton Road, Edinburgh EH7 4EB Tel: 0131 556 7650 — MB BS 1983 Lond.; MB BS Camb. 1983; MA Camb. 1977; MRCP (UK) 1985; MRCGP 1990; T(GP) 1991; DCH RCP Lond. 1991; DRCOG 1990; Cert. Family Plann. JCC 1990.

TREBBLE, Timothy Golden Broom, Broombarn Lane, Great Missenden HP16 9JD — MB BS 1991 Lond.

TREBLE, Mr Nicholas John Department of Orthopaedics, North Devon District Hospital, Raleigh Park, Barnstaple EX31 4JB Tel: 01271 322747; Muddiford House, Muddiford, Barnstaple EX31 4EZ Tel: 01271 850822 — MB ChB 1977 Liverpool; MChOrth. Liverp. 1985,; FRCS Eng. 1983; MRCS Eng. LRCP Lond. 1977. Cons. Orthop. Surg. S. W.. RHA. Socs: Fell. BOA; Brit. Soc. of Childr.'s Orthopaedic Surg.s; Brit. Assn. of Knee Surgs. Prev: Sen. Regist. Mersey RHA; Clin. Research Fell. Roy. Childr. Hosp., Melbourne.

*TREDGET, Andrews Douglas, Capt. RAMC 2 Scotney Close, Farnborough, Orpington BR6 7AB Tel: 0780 1257 909 — MB BS 1997 Lond.; BSc Lond. 1994.

TREDGET, Janet Mair Priory Medical Practice, 48 Bromham Road, Bedford MK40 2QD Tel: 01234 262040 Fax: 01234 219288 — MB ChB 1983 Sheff.; MRCGP 1987; DRCOG 1987.

TREDGETT, Michael William 1 Bagnall Cottages, Cinderhill Road, Nottingham NG6 8SD — MB ChB 1991 Ed.

TREDGOLD, Barnaby 13 Florence Road, Brighton BN1 6DL — MB BS 1996 Lond.

TREDGOLD, Christopher Francis Tel: 01273 688333 Fax: 01273 671128 — MB BChir 1967 Camb.; MRCS Eng. LRCP Lond. 1967; FRCGP 1993, M 1973; DObst RCOG 1969. (Univ. Coll. Hosp.)

TREE, Andrea Mary Hollies Surgery, Elbow Lane, Liverpool L37 4AF Tel: 01704 877600 Fax: 01704 833811 — MB ChB 1981 Liverp.; MRCGP 1990; DRCOG 1985. GP Formby. Prev: Trainee GP Formby VTS.

TREE, Annabelle Lucy 27 Ferring Lane, Ferring, Worthing BN12 6QT Tel: 01903 242152 — MB BS 1988 Lond. Trainee GP Woking VTS. Prev: SHO (Cas.) St. Peter's Hosp. Chertsey; Ho. Off. (Surg.) Heatherwood Hosp. Ascot; Ho. Off. (Med.) St. Cross Hosp. Rugby.

TREE, Deborah Anne 5 Lyndale Close, Leyland, Preston PR25 3DT — MB ChB 1983 Liverp.

TREE, John Rutherford 20 Kimbolton Avenue, Bedford MK40 3AA Tel: 01234 52112 — MRCS Eng. LRCP Lond. 1924; MB BS Lond. 1926; MD Lond. 1933. (Middlx.) Prev: SHMO Bedford Gen. Hosp.; Res. Med. Off. Q. Charlotte's Hosp.; Ho. Surg. Middlx. Hosp.

TREE-BOOKER, David Anselm Lupset Surgery, off Norbury Road, Wakefield WF2 8RE Tel: 01924 376828 Fax: 01924 201649 — MRCS Eng. LRCP Lond. 1978; Cert. FPA 1981.

TREFZER, Siegfried 3 Sandwell Crescent, London NW6 1PB — State Exam Med 1987 Berlin.

TREGASKES, Sarah Nadine 17 Ellsworth St, Bethnal Green, London E2 0AU — MB BS 1998 Lond.

TREGASKIS, Brian Francis Belford Hospital, Fort William PH33 6BS Tel: 01397 702481; St. Clement, Spean Bridge PH34 4EN Tel: 01397 712657 Email: tregaskis@compuserve.com — MB BS 1981 Lond.; FRCP Ed. 1995; MRCP (UK) 1984. (Middlx.) Cons. Phys. (Gen. Med. & Gastroenterol.) Belford Hosp. Fort William; Postgrad. Tutor 1994. Socs: Brit. Soc. Gastroenterol.; (Asst. Sec.) RCP Edin.; Nutrit. Soc. Prev: Sen. Regist. (Med.) Leicester; Regist. (Med.) Dundee & Roy. Cornw. Hosp. Truro; Mem. Soc. Apoth.

TREGASKIS, Moira St. Clement, Lodge Gardens, Spean Bridge PH34 4EN — MB ChB 1979 Ed.; BSc Ed. 1976; DRCOG 1982; Cert. Family Plann. JCC 1982. Doctors Highland Retainer Scheme. Prev: GP Truro; CMO Leics.; Trainee GP Bath VTS.

TREGEAR, Cecilia 144 Harley Street, London W1; 94 Ashley Road, Walton-on-Thames KT12 1HP — D Med y Cir Colombia 1977.

TREGENZA, Nicholas Jeremy Charles (retired) Bodriggy Health Centre, 60 Queens Way, Bodriggy, Hayle TR27 4PB Tel: 01736 753136 Fax: 01736 753467 — MB 1970 Camb.; BA Camb. 1966,

BChir 1969; MRCGP 1978; DCH Eng. 1972; DObst RCOG 1971. Prev: SHO (Paediat.) Poole Gen. Hosp.

TREGER, Aubrey 27 Langdale Court, Kingsway, Hove BN3 4HF — MB BCh 1971 Witwatersrand.

TREGILLUS, Eva Victoria (retired) Rockmount, Mill Hill Top, Reeth, Richmond DL11 6SQ Tel: 01748 884710 — MB ChB 1942 Liverp.; MD Liverp. 1946, MB ChB 1942. Prev: GP Darlington FPC.

TREGILLUS, John (retired) Rockmount, Mill Hill Top, Reeth, Richmond DL11 6SQ Tel: 01748 884710 — MB ChB 1943 Birmingham; MD Birm. 1951, MB ChB 1943; MRCS Eng. LRCP Lond. 1943; FRCPath 1963. Prev: Sen. Cons. Pathol. Memor. Hosp. Darlington.

TREHAN, Anubha 62 Carrwood, Halebarns, Altrincham WA15 0EP Tel: 0161 980 2428 — MB ChB 1995 Manch. (Manch.) SHO (Med.) Blackburn.

TREHAN, Mr Ashwini Kumar Department of Obstetrics, Dewsbury & District Hospital, Healds Road, Dewsbury WF13 4HS Tel: 01924 465105; Oxford House, 436 Oxford Road, Cleckheaton BD19 4LB Tel: 01274 870567 — MB BS 1978 Ranchi; FRCS Ed. 1986; MRCOG 1983; DRCOG 1985. Cons. O & G Dewsbury Health Care. Prev: Sen. Regist. (O & G) St. Thos. Hosp. Lond.

TREHAN, Vijay Kumar Brooks Bar Medical Centre, 162-164 Chorlton Road, Old Trafford, Manchester M16 7WW Tel: 0161 226 7777 Fax: 0161 232 9963; 62 Carrwood, Halebarns, Altrincham WA15 0EP Tel: 0161 980 2428 — MB BS 1969 Jammu & Kashmir. (Govt. Med. Coll. Srinagar) Med. Off. Lancs. Cricket Club. Prev: SHO (Orthop.) Roy. Cornw. Hosp. (City) Truro; SHO (Orthop.) Winford Orthop. Hosp.; SHO (A & E) W.on-super-Mare Gen. Hosp.

TREHARNE, Anne Elizabeth East & Gloucestershire NHS Trust, Child Health Services Department, County Offices, St Georges Road, Cheltenham GL50 3ES Tel: 01242 516235; Aballava, 18 Wincel Road, Winchcombe, Cheltenham GL54 5YE — MB ChB 1955 Manch. SCMO (Community Child Health) E. Glos. NHS Trust. Socs: Fac. Comm. Health; SW Paediat. Club. Prev: Clin. Med. Off. Cumbria & Carlisle; Sen. Med. Off. Manch.

TREHARNE, Christopher James Ty-Elli Group Practice, Ty Elli, Llanelli SA15 3BD Tel: 01554 772678 / 773747 Fax: 01554 774476 — MB BCh 1983 Wales. Clin. Asst. (Endoscopy) Dyfed.

TREHARNE, Eifion Ty Elli, Vauxhall, Llanelli SA15 Tel: 01554 772678; 19 Swiss Valley, Llanelli SA14 8BS Tel: 01554 774102 — MB ChB 1957 Leeds. (Leeds)

TREHARNE, Mr Gareth David 29 Burlington Road, Withington, Manchester M20 4QA — MB ChB 1992 Leic.; FRCS (Ed.) 1997. (Leic.) Specialist Regist.(Gen Surg.) Manc. Prev: Research Fell. Dept. Surg. Leic. Univ.

TREHARNE, Ian Alan Lloyd Turner Rise Consulting Rooms, 55 Turner Road, Colchester CO4 5JY Tel: 01206 752228 Fax: 01206 752223; 1 Les Bois, Layer De La Haye, Colchester CO2 0DT Tel: 01206 738258 — MB ChB 1972 Aberd.; FRCOG 1994, M 1978. Cons. O & G Essex Rivers Trust Colchester.

TREHARNE, Ian Raymond Willowbrook Health Centre, Cottingham Road, Corby NN17 2UR Tel: 01536 260303 Fax: 01536 406761; Dallington House, Kettering Road, Geddington, Kettering NN14 1AW Tel: 01536 742267 — BM BCh 1968 Oxf.; MA, BM BCh Oxf. 1968; MRCGP 1975; AFOM 1981; DIH 1981; DObst RCOG 1971.

TREHARNE, Miss Linda Jane Dallington House, 6 Kettering Road, Geddington, Kettering NN14 1AW — MB ChB 1994 Bristol; FRCS (Eng) 1998; BSc (Hons) Anat Sci. (Bris.) 1991.

TREHARNE, Philip Gordon 8 Tebourba Drive, Alverstoke, Gosport PO12 2NT Tel: 01705 503240 — MRCS Eng. LRCP Lond. 1947; MA, MB BChir Camb. 1947. (Camb. & St. Bart.) Prev: Ho. Surg. St. Bart. Hosp.; Sen. Ho. Surg. Woolwich Memor. Hosp.; Capt. RAMC.

TREHARNE JONES, Robert Walnut Lodge Surgery, Walnut Road, Chelston, Torquay TQ2 6HP Tel: 01803 605359 Fax: 01803 605772; The Mill Stone, 8 Oxlea Road, Wellswood, Torquay TQ1 2HF Tel: 01803 214864 Email: tjwizard@eclipse.co.uk — MRCS Eng. LRCP Lond. 1979; LMSSA Lond. 1978; Cert. Prescribed Equiv. Exp. JCPTGP 1985; Cert. Family Plann. JCC 1984. (St. Bart.) Princip. GP & Trainer Torquay; Med. Edr. Regatta Magazine; Managing Dir. UpFront Med. Communications; Managing Dir. Wizard Wheeze GP Computing Cons.; Marketing Dir. Sullivan Cuff Med. Computing; Med. Cons. AAH Meditel plc. Socs: GP Writers Assn.; Brit. Assn. Sport & Med.; Assoc. Mem. Med. Jl.ists Assn.

Prev: SHO (O & G) P.ss Roy. Hosp. Hull; SHO (Psychiat.) Roy. Cornw. Hosp. Truro; Demonst. (Human Morphol.) Nottm. Univ.

TREIP, Cecil Stanley (retired) 25 High Street, Waterbeach, Cambridge CB5 9JU — MB BS 1947 Lond.; MA Camb. 1962; PhD Lond. 1962, MD 1952; FRCPath 1973, M 1963. Univ. Lect. (Path.) Univ. Camb.; Hon. Cons. Neuropath. Addenbrooke's Hosp. Camb. Prev: Univ. Sen. Asst. Path. Addenbrooke's Hosp. Camb.

TRELEAVEN, Jennifer Gillian Royal Marsden Hospital, Downs Road, Sutton SM2 5PT Tel: 020 8661 3200 Fax: 020 8643 7958 — MD 1987 Camb.; BA (Psychol.) Leic. 1967; MA Camb. 1976, MD 1987, MB BChir 1974; FRCP Lond. 1993; MRCP (UK) 1977; FRCPath 1994, M 1982. Cons. Haemat. And Hon. Sen. Lect. Roy. Marsden Hosps.

TRELINSKI, Marek Jerzy Bridge Surgery, St. Peters Street, Stapenhill, Burton-on-Trent DE15 9AW Tel: 01283 563451 Fax: 01283 500896; Norwood Cottage, Hall Grounds, Rolleston-on-Dove, Burton-on-Trent DE13 9BS Tel: 01283 813816 — MB BS 1976 Lond.; BSc (Hons.) Lond. 1972; MRCS Eng. LRCP Lond. 1975; MRCGP 1981; DRCOG 1980; DCH Eng. 1979. (St. Mary's) Princip. (Gen. Pract.) Burton on Trent. Prev: Trainee GP Sidcup VTS; SHO (Gen. Med.) Ramsgate Wing, Thanet Dist. Hosp.; Ho. Phys. & Ho. Surg. St. Mary's Hosp. Lond.

TRELIVING, Linda Rose Allowai Centre, 1 Allowai Place, Dundee DD4 8UA — MB ChB 1981 Glas.; MRCPsych 1985. Cons. Psychiat. In Psychother., Psychother. Dept., Dundee. Prev: Cons. Psychiat. Roy. Dundee Liff Hosp. (Special Responsibil. for Psychother.).

TRELOAR, Adrian Joseph Room 19, Memorial Hospital, Shooters Hill, London SE18 Tel: 0208 312 6407 Fax: 0208 312 6527 — MB BS 1984 Lond.; BSc Lond. 1981, MB BS 1984; MRCP (UK) 1989; MRCPsych 1991; MRCGP 1989; DCH RCP Lond. 1988; DRCOG 1988. Cons. & Sen. Lect. (Psychiat. in old age) UMDS Guy's & Dxleas Trust. Kent. Socs: EAGP; IPA. Prev: Sen. Regist. (Psychiat.) Maudsley Hosp. Lond.; Regist. Rotat. (Psychiat.) Guy's Hosp. Lond.; GP Sandwell.

TRELOAR, Emma Jane Southmead Hospital, Westbury on Tryn, Bristol BS10 Tel: 0116 249 0490; 10 The Park, Portishead, Bristol BS20 7LT Tel: 0116 255 8669 — MB ChB 1997 Leic. (University of Leicester) SHO (O & G) Leicester Gen. Hosp.; SHO. (Neonate.) S.mead Hosp.; SHO. (Gyn.) Frenchay Hosp.; SHO. (Obs.) S.mead Hosp. Prev: PRHO (Oncol./Gen. Med.) Leicester Roy. Infirm.; PRHO (Gyn./Gen. Surg.) Leicester Roy. Infirm.

TREMAINE, Kenneth James Benefits Agency Medical Services, Government Buildings, Flowers Hill, Bristol BS4 5LA Tel: 0117 971 8311 Fax: 0117 971 8482; 18 Wiltshire Avenue, Yate, Bristol BS37 7UF — MB ChB 1976 Bristol. Med. Off. Benefits Agency. Socs: Brit. Med. Acupunct. Soc. Prev: GP Bristol.

TREMBALOWICZ, Franciszek Czeslaw (retired) 18 Firwood Close, Hampden Park, Eastbourne BN22 9QL Tel: 01323 504714 — Med. Dipl. Lwow 1937; DMRD Eng. 1958. Cons. Radiol. Pinderfields Gen. Hosp. Wakefield. Prev: Regist. Radiol. Dept. Roy. Infirm. Cardiff.

TREMBATH, Professor Richard Charles Leicester Genetics Centre, Leicester Royal Infirmary NHS Trust, Infirmary Square, Leicester LE1 5WW Tel: 0116 258 5736 Fax: 0116 258 6057 Email: rtrembat@hgmp.mrc.ac.uk — MB BS 1981 Lond.; BSc (Hons.) Lond. 1978; FRCP Lond. 1996; MRCP (UK) 1984. (Guy's) Prof. (Med. Genetics) Univ. of Leicester. Socs: Brit. Clin. Genetics Soc.; Amer. Soc. Human Genetics. Prev: Lect. (Med. Genetics.) ICH Lond.; SHO Brompton Hosp. & Lond. Chest Hosp.; Jun. Lect. (Med.) Guy's Hosp. Med. Sch. Lond.

TREML, Jonathan Mayday University Hospital, Croydon CR7 7YE Tel: 020 8401 3000; 128 Central Road, Morden SM4 5RL Tel: 020 8640 4456 Email: streml@hotmail.com — MB BS 1994 Lond.; BA (Hons.) Oxf. 1991; MRCP (UK) 1997. (Char. Cross & Westm.) Specialist Regist. (Gen. Med. & Geriat. Med.) Mayday Hosp. Prev: Specialist Regist. (Gen. Med. & Geriat. Med.) Crawley Hosp.; SHO (Gen. Med.) Qu. Mary's Univ. Hosp. Lond.

TREMLETT, Catherine Helen 41 Thorne House, Wilmslow Road, Fallowfield, Manchester M14 6DW — MB ChB 1991 Manch.; BSc (Hons.) St. And. 1988. SHO (Med. Microbiol.) Whiston Hosp. Prescot. Prev: Ho. Off. (Surg. & Med.) Withington Hosp. Manch.

TREMLETT, Joanne Catherine 49 London Road, Twyford, Reading RG10 9EJ — MB 1984 Camb.; MA Camb. 1985, MB

TREMLETT

1984, BChir 1983. Trainee Windsor VTS. Prev: Ho. Off. Addenbrookes Hosp. Camb. & Hinchinbrook Hosp. Huntingdon.

TREMLETT, John Edward (retired) 6 Hobs Meadow, Solihull B92 8PQ Tel: 0121 743 3511 — MB ChB 1946 Birm. Prev: Ho. Surg. Roy. Infirm. Huddersfield.

TREMLETT, Michael Richard 60 Langbaurgh Road, Hutton Rudby, Yarm TS15 0HL — BM 1982 Soton.; FRCA. 1990; DCH RCP Lond. 1986; DA (UK) 1985. Cons. Anaesth. S. Cleveland Hosp. Middlesbrough. Prev: Sen. Regist. (Anaesth.) Newc.; Regist. Rotat. (Anaesth.) Bristol; Vis. Asst. (Anaesth.) Johns Hopkins Hosp. Baltimore, MD, USA.

TREMLETT, Pauline Diane Ballington Manor, Wylye, Warminster BA12 0QF Tel: 01985 483 2345 — MB ChB 1968 Liverp. Prev: Clin. Asst. (Rheum.) W. Hill Hosp. Dartford.; SHO Renal Unit Roy. Devon & Exeter Hosp.; SHO (Obst.) City Hosp. Exeter.

TRENCH, Alistair John Merrylaw, Doune Road, Dunblane FK15 9AR Tel: 01786 823552 — MB ChB 1968 Ed.; FFA RCS Eng. 1973. (Ed.) Cons. Anaesth. Roy. Infirm. Stirling & Roy. Inform. Edin.; Regist. (Anaesth.) Bangour Gen. Hosp. Broxburn; Ho. Phys. Milesmark Hosp. Dunfermline. Socs: Soc. Anaesths. Gt. Brit. & Irel.

TRENCHARD, Peter John Clement (retired) 25 Park Road, Rushden NN10 0RW Tel: 01933 358009 — MB BS 1967 Lond.; MRCS Eng. LRCP Lond. 1967; MRCGP 1979; DObst RCOG 1969. Hon. Asst. Rockingham Forest NHS Trust. Prev: Lect. (Path.) Guy's Hosp. Med. Sch. Lond.

TREND, Patrick St John The Royal Surrey County Hospital, Guildford GU2 7XX — MB BS 1979 Lond.; PhD Lond. 1987, MB BS 1979; MA Oxf. 1980; FRCP 1997. (St. Thos.) Cons. Neurol. Roy. Surrey Co. Hosp. Guildford.

TREND, Ulla Doncaster Gate Hospital, Rotherham S65 1DW Tel: 01709 820000; Bole Hill Cottages, Norton, Sheffield S8 8QE — MB ChB 1977 Manch.; MSc Nottm. 1994; BSc St. And. 1974; MRCPsych 1989; DCH RCP Lond. 1983. Cons. Community Paediat. Rotherham Priority Health Trust.

TRENDELL-SMITH, Nigel Jeremy Department of Histopathology, Charing Cross Hospital, Fulham Palace Road, London W6 8RF Tel: 020 8846 1234; 27 North End Road, Yatton, Bristol BS49 4AW Tel: 01934 833565 — MB BS 1989 Lond.; BSc Lond. 1986; DRCPath Lond. 1994. Sen. Regist. (Histopath.) Char. Cross Hosp. Lond. Prev: Demonst. (Path.) Univ. Bristol.

TRENFIELD, John Dennis Stuart 5 Julian Close, Sneyd Park, Bristol BS9 1JX Tel: 0956 420794 — MB BS 1996 Lond. SHO (Surg.) Kingston Hosp.

TRENFIELD, Sarah Margaret Flat 34, Carrara Wharf, Ranelagh Gardens, Fulham, London SW6 3UJ — MB ChB Bristol 1995; BDS Bristol 1988; FDS RCS Eng. 1993; Primary FRCA 1997 - Roy. Coll. Anaesth. (University of Bristol) SHO Anaesth. St Mary's Hosp. Paddington Lond.; Specialist Regist. (Anaesth.) Imperial Sch. of Med.

TRENHOLM, Philip William Christie Hospital, 550 Wilmslow Road, Withington, Manchester M20 4BX Tel: 0161 446 3000 — MB ChB 1992 Manch.; MRCP (UK) 1997. (Manch.) Specialist Regist. (Clin. Oncol.) Chrisie Hosp. Manch.

TRENT, Michael Paul The Cobham Health Centre, 168 Portsmouth Road, Cobham KT11 1HT Tel: 01932 867231 Fax: 01932 866874 — MB BS 1980 Lond.

TRENT, Robert Sidney Woodside Medical Centre, Jardine Crescent, Coventry CV4 9PL Tel: 024 7669 4001 Fax: 024 7669 5639; 29 Turnlands Close, Walsgrave, Coventry CV2 2PT Tel: 024 76 611440 — MRCS Eng. LRCP Lond. 1976.

TRENT, Roger John Western Infirmary, Dumbarton Road, Glasgow G11 6NT Tel: 0141 211 2000; 214 Nithsdale Road, Glasgow G41 5HD Tel: 0141 427 5607 — BM Soton. 1985; MRCP (UK) 1989; DA (Roy Coll Anaesths) 1990; MD (Univ of Aberdeen) 1998. Research Fell. Cardiol. Aberd.

TRENT, Sally Louise 76 Comeragh Road, London W14 9HR — MB BS 1993 Lond.; BSc Lond. 1990; MRCP (UK) 1996.

TREPESS, John Neville Bognor Medical Practice, West Street, Bognor Regis PO21 1UT Tel: 01243 823864 Fax: 01243 623800 — BSc Lond. 1983, MB BS 1986; MRCGP 1990; DRCOG 1990; DCH RCP Lond. 1990. Prev: Trainee GP E.bourne VTS.

TREPTE, Nicola Jane Barbara 65 Selhurst Close, London SW19 6AY — MB BS 1988 Lond.

TRESADERN, Mr John Christopher The Royal Infirmary, Infirmary Road, Blackburn BB2 3LR Tel: 01254 263555 — BM BCh 1972 Oxf.; BA (Hons.) Oxf. 1969; ChM Manch. 1984; FRCS Eng. 1977. Cons. Gen. Surg. Blackburn Roy. Infirm.

TRESCOLI SERRANO, Carlos Tadeo Dept of Medicine, Nottingham City Hospital NHS Trust, Nottingham NG5 1PB; 47 Russell Drive, Wollaton, Nottingham NG8 2BA — LMS 1987 Valencia; MRCP (UK) 1992. Sen. Regist. Nott. City Hosp. NHS Trust.

TRESEDER, Andrew Stephen Department Geriatric Medicine, Morriston Hospital, Swansea SR6 6NL Tel: 01792 703384 — MB BCh 1974 Wales; FRCP (UK) 1980; DCH Eng. 1977. Cons. Phys. (Geriat. Med.) W. Glam. HA.

TRESIDDER, Andrew Philip Tavender Glanvill and Partners, Springmead Surgery, Summerfields Road, Chard TA20 2HB Tel: 01460 63380 Fax: 01460 66483 — MB BS 1983 Lond.; MRCGP 1988; DRCOG 1986. Socs: Brit. Holistic Med. Assn.; Brit. Assn. of Flower Essence Producers (Chairm.).

TRESIDDER, Ian Robert Southover Medical Practice, Bronshill Road, Torquay TQ1 3HD Tel: 01803 327100 Fax: 01803 316295; Aller View, 32 Decoy Road, Newton Abbot TQ12 1DY Tel: 01626 51028 — MB BS 1986 Lond.; BSc Lond. 1983, MB BS 1986; MRCP (UK) 1989; MRCGP 1991; DRCOG 1991. Clin. Asst. (Respirat. Med.) S. Devon Healthcare Torbay Hosp. Prev: SHO (A & E) Torbay Hosp. Torquay.

TRESIDDER, Jane Scott Boulton Clinic, Wyndham St., Alvaston, Derby DE24 0EP Tel: 01332 574823; 61 West End, Wirksworth, Derby DE4 4EG Tel: 01629 823953 — MB BS 1970 Lond.; FRCP Lond. 1995; MRCP (Paediat.) (UK) 1983; DCH Eng. 1978; DTM & H Liverp. 1973; DObst RCOG 1972. (St. Thos.) Cons. Community Paediat. S.. Derbysh. HA. Socs: Brit. Paediat. Assn. (Community Paediat. Gp.). Prev: Sen. Regist. (Community Paediat.) Dept. Child Health Nottm. HA; Regist. (Community Paediat.) Univ. Hosp. Nottm. HA; Regist. (Paediat.) Derbysh. Child. Hosp.

TRESIDDER, Nicholas John Hassengate Medical Centre, Southend Road, Stanford-le-Hope SS17 0PH Tel: 01375 673064 Fax: 01375 675196 — MB BS 1980 Lond.; MRCGP 1984; DRCOG 1983.

TRESILIAN, Kathleen Edith (retired) 19 Wyndham Street, Brighton BN2 1AF — MB BS 1927 Lond.; MRCS Eng., L.R.C.P. Lond. 1923. Prev: Clin. Asst. St. John's Skin Hosp. Leicester Sq. & Lond. Hosp.

TRESMAN, Robert Lewis 50 Oakfield Avenue, Hitchin SG4 9JD — MB BS 1981 Lond.; PhD Lond. 1971, BSc (Hons. Anat.) 1966, MB BS 1981; MRCPsych 1986. (Univ. Coll. Hosp.) Prev: Regist. (Psychiat.) Lond. Hosp.; Regist. (Psychiat.) Goodmayes Hosp. Ilford.

TRETHOWAN, Brian Anthony 1 Elm Court, Elm St., Belfast BT7 1DU — MB BCh 1998 Belf.

TRETHOWAN, William Nicholas Department of Occupational Medicine, Royal Shrewsbury Hospital, Mytton Oak Road, Shrewsbury SY3 8XQ Tel: 01743 231122; Shrubbery, Westbury, Shrewsbury SY5 9QX — MB BS 1974 Lond.; MRCP (UK) 1978; MRCS Eng. LRCP Lond. 1974; MFOM RCP Lond. 1987. Cons. Occupat. Med. Roy. Shrewsbury Hosp.

TREUB, Martin Jacobus Flat 19, Block 1, Friarsfield Nurses Home, Friars Road, Newport NP20 4EZ — Artsexamen 1993 Amsterdam.

TREVAIL, Philip Roy Pool Health Centre, Station Road, Pool, Redruth TR15 3DU Tel: 01209 717471 Fax: 01209 612160; Mayfield Whitehall, Scorrier, Redruth TR16 5BB — BM 1986 Soton.; MRCGP 1992; DFFP 1995; DRCOG 1990. (Soton.) Gen. Practitioner; Police Surg. Camborne; Clin. Asst. (Geriat.) Camborne - Redruth Community Hosp.; Med. Manager Assn. Cornw. Doctors on Call (Kernow Doc). Prev: Trainee GP/SHO Roy. Cornw. Hosp. Truro; SHO (A & E) Roy. Hants. Co. Hosp. Winchester.

TREVAN, Anthony Charles (retired) 27 Cheam Road, Ewell, Epsom KT17 1QX Tel: 020 8393 5445 Fax: 020 8393 5445 — MB BS Lond. 1951; MRCGP 1975; DCH Eng. 1954; DObst RCOG 1953.

TREVARTHEN, Franklyn David 10 Hertford Road, Digswell, Welwyn AL6 0EB Tel: 01438 714056 Fax: 01438 840617 Email: dtrevar934@aol.com; 10 Hertfod Road, Digswell, Welwyn AL6 0EB Tel: 01438 714056 Fax: 01438 840617 Email: dtrevar934@aol.com — MB BS 1960 Lond.; DObst RCOG 1962; DMJ (Clin.) Soc. Apoth. Lond. 1970; Cert Av Med MoD (Air) & CAA 1973; MFOM RCP Lond. 1983. (Univ. Coll. Hosp.) Med. Off. Lond. Luton Airport including N.A.T.S employees Med. Examr. CAA (UK), FAA (USA) and CAD (Hong Kong, China). Socs: Soc. Occupat. Med.; Internat. Soc.

Travel Med.; Roy. Aeronautical Soc. (Aviat. Sect.). Prev: Hon. Cons. Occupat. Health Luton & Dunstable Hosp. NHS Trust; Med. Off. Dunstable & Plant Med. Off. Luton Vauxhall Motors Ltd.; Med. Off. Avdel Ltd. & GKN Lincoln Electric Ltd. Welwyn Gdn. City.

TREVELYAN, Mary Harriet (retired) Sighthill Health Centre, Calder Road, Edinburgh EH11 4AU Tel: 0131 537 7030 Fax: 0131 537 7005 — MB BS 1963 Lond.; DObst RCOG 1967. Prev: Lect. (Social Med.) St. Thos. Hosp. Med. Sch. Lond.

TREVELYAN, Nicola Clare 56 Plymouth Place, Leamington Spa CV31 1HN; Email: nic.trevelyan@lineone.net — MB ChB 1994 Manch.; BSc St. And. 1991; MRCP 1998. (Manchester) Regist. (Paediat.) Walsgrave Hosp. Coventry.; SHO (Paediat.) N.ampton Gen. Hosp. Prev: Regist. (Paediat.) Auckland Healthcare Ltd., NZ; SHO (Paediat.) Liverp. Woms. Hosp. & Alder Hey Hosp.

TREVELYAN, Thomas Arnold Onion Patch, 8 The Spinney, Itchenor, Chichester PO20 7DF Tel: 01243 511038 Fax: 01243 512489 — MB BChir Camb. 1967; MRCGP 1973. (St. Thos.) Part time GP. Socs: BMA. Prev: GP Princip., Kensington 1970-1999.

TREVELYAN, Thomas Rhys Sconce, Llannefydd, Denbigh LL16 5EY — MB BChir 1973 Camb.; MRCPsych 1977.

TREVELYAN THOMAS, Mary Kate Middle Farm House, Long Crichel, Wimborne BH21 5JU — MB BS (Hons.) Surg. Lond. 1978; MA Camb. 1979; MRCGP 1983. (Westm.)

TREVETT, Andrew James Langaskill, Harray, Orkney KW17 2JT; 4 Park Quadrant, Kelvinbridge, Glasgow G3 6BS Tel: 0141 332 0205 — MB ChB 1987 Glas.; MA Camb. 1984; MRCP Glas. 1990; DTM & H Liverp. 1990. Wellcome Vis. Lect. (Med.) Univ. Papua New Guinea. Socs: Fell. Roy. Sch. Trop. Med. & Hyg.; PNG Med. Soc. Prev: SHO (Med.) Vict. Infirm. Glas.

TREVETT, Mr Michael Charles West Meadow, Bell Lane, Lower Broad Heath, Worcester WR2 6RR Tel: 01905 641038 — MB ChB 1982 Cape Town; FCS(SA) 1993; FRCS (E) 1996; M Med (Orthop.) Cape Town Univ. 1994. (Cape Town) Cons. Orthop.

TREVOR, Alison Jane Castlefields Health Centre, Chester Close, Castlefields, Runcorn WA7 2HY Tel: 01928 566671 Fax: 01928 581631 — MB BChir 1986 Camb.; MA Camb. 1987; DRCOG 1990. Clin. Med. Off. (Family Plann.) Chester & Halton Community NHS Trust. Prev: Trainee GP Warrington Dist. Gen. Hosp. VTS; SHO (A & E) Macclesfield Dist. Gen. Hosp.

TREVOR, Sally Parkfield Medical Centre, The Walk, Potters Bar EN6 1QH Tel: 01707 651234 Fax: 01707 660452; 58 Bradmore Way, Brookmans Park, Hatfield Heath, Hatfield AL9 7QX Tel: 01701 647133 — MB BS 1990 Lond.; BSc Lond.1987; MRCGP 1994; DRCOG 1994.

TREVOR-ROPER, Mr Patrick Dacre (retired) 3 Park Square W., London NW1 4LJ Tel: 020 7935 5052 Fax: 020 7935 5052 — MB BChir 1940 Camb.; MA Camb. 1940, MD 1959; FRCS Eng. 1947; MRCS Eng. LRCP Lond. 1940; Hon. FCOphth 1990; DOMS Eng. 1942. Cons. Ophth. Surg. W.m. Hosp., Moorfields Eye Hosp. & King Edwd. VII Hosp. Offs. Lond.; Cons. Edr. Maj. Probl. in Ophth.; Mem. Edit. Comm. Modern Med. & Annals Ophth. Prev: Edr. Eye 1949-87.

TREW, Mr David Richard West Kent Eye Centre, Farnborough Hospital, Farnborough, Orpington BR6 8ND Tel: 01689 814407 Fax: 01689 814410 — MB BS 1983 Lond.; MA Camb. 1980; FRCOphth 1993; FRCS Eng. 1988; DO RCS Eng. 1987. Cons. Ophth. Bromley Hosps. NHS Trust. Socs: S.. Ophth. Soc.; Fell. Roy. Soc. Med.

TREW, Geoffrey Howard Institute of Obstetrics & Gynaecology, Hammersmith Hospital, Du Cane Road, London W12 0NN Tel: 020 8383 2372 Fax: 020 8383 2371 Email: g.trewic@ic.ac.uk; Lodge Hill Farm, Haw Lane, Bledlow Ridge, High Wycombe HP14 4JQ — MB BS 1984 Lond.; MRCOG 1991. (St. Geos. Lond.) Cons. Gyn. Hammersmith Hosp. Lond.; Hon. Sen. Lect. Imperial Coll., Lond.. Socs: Brit. Fertil. Soc.; Amer. Soc. Reproduc. Med.; Brit. Soc. Gyn. Endoscopy. Prev: Sen. Regist. (O & G) Hammersmith Hosp. Lond.; Sen. Regist. & Lect. (O & G) Roy. Lond. Hosp.; Regist. (O & G) Guy's Hosp. Lond.

TREW, Judith Mary 10 Jock Inkson's Brae, Elgin IV30 1QE — MB ChB 1984 Glas.; MRCGP 1990; DCH Glas. 1988. Prev: Clin. Med. Off. Ayrsh. & Arran HB.; Staffgrade Community Paediat.

TREW, Julie Mildred 47 Landrock Road, London N8 9HR — MB BS 1977 Lond.

TREW, Robert James Oakcroft, 12 Grimwade Avenue, Croydon CR0 5DG Tel: 020 8684 219 — MB ChB 1962 Ed.; DObst RCOG 1969. (Ed.) Prev: SHO Accid. Luton & Dunstable Hosp. Luton; SHO (Med. & Surg.) Roy. Manch. Childr. Hosp.; SHO Christie Hosp. & Holt Radium Inst. Manch.

TREWBY, Catherine Scott Hurgill House, 24 Hurgill Road, Richmond DL10 4BL — MB BS 1973 Lond.; MRCP (UK) 1976; MRCGP 1980. Prev: SHO & Ho. Phys. St. Geo. Hosp. Lond.; Paediat. Regist. St. Peter's Hosp. Chertsey.

TREWBY, Peter Nicholas Memorial Hospital, Darlington DL3 6HX — MD 1980 Camb.; MB 1972, BChir 1971; FRCP Lond. 1986; MRCP (UK) 1973. Cons. Phys. Darlington Memor. Hosp. Socs: Fell. Roy. Soc. Med.; Brit. Soc. Gastroenterol. Prev: SHO Brompton Hosp. Lond.; Regist. King's Coll. Hosp. Lond.; Sen. Regist. (Med.) St. Mary's Hosp. Lond.

TREWEEKE, Paul Stewart Department Radiology, North Devon District Hospital, Barnstaple EX31 4JB Tel: 01271 322619; Witham, Bydown, Swimbridge, Barnstaple EX32 0QB Tel: 01271 830170 — MB BS 1979 Lond.; FRCR 1986. Cons. Radiol. N. Devon Dist. Hosp. Prev: Sen. Regist. (Radiol.) Char. Cross Hosp. Lond.; Regist. (Radiol.) St. Thos. Hosp. Lond.

TREWHELLA, Mrs Jean Dorothy (retired) The Old Rectory, Stansfield, Sudbury CO10 8LT — MB ChB 1955 Bristol. Prev: Assoc. Specialist St. Ebba's Hosp. Epsom.

TREWHELLA, Matthew John The Mill, Killerby, Darlington DL2 3UQ — MB BS 1981 Lond.; BA (Hons.) Oxf. 1977; FRCR 1987. Cons. Radiol. N. Tees Gen. Hosp. Stockton-on-Tees. Prev: Cons. (Radiol.) P.ss of Wales RAF Hosp. Ely; Hon. Clin. Asst. (Radiol.) Hosp. for Sick Childr. Gt. Ormond St. Lond.; Hon. Regist. (Radiol.) Middlx. Hosp. Lond.

TREWIN, Peter John Heselton Balance Street Practice, 36 Balance Street, Uttoxeter ST14 8JG Tel: 01889 562145 Fax: 01889 568164; Hill House, Denstone, Uttoxeter ST14 5HL Tel: 01889 590767 — MB BS 1983 Lond.; DCH RCP Lond. 1986; DRCOG 1986. (Char. Cross) Prev: Trainee GP Mid Sussex VTS; Cas. Off. Cuckfield Hosp.

TREWINNARD, Barry Francis White House Surgery, Weston Lane, Weston, Southampton SO19 9HJ Tel: 023 8044 9913 Fax: 023 8044 6617; The White House, Weston Lane, Woolston, Southampton SO19 9HJ Tel: 01703 449913 — MB ChB 1975 Manch.

TREWINNARD, Karen Rosemary 279 Upper Deacon Road, Bitterne, Southampton SO19 5JJ — BM 1979 Soton.; MFFP 1993; Cert. Family Plann. JCC 1982. Instruc. Doctor Family Plann. & Well Wom. Serv. Portsmouth; Med. Jl.ist Freelance Columnist Wom. Alive Magazine; Natural Family Plann. Teach. Catholic Marriage Advis. Counc. Socs: Affil. Mem. Med. Jl.ists Assn.; Assn. BRd.casting Doctors.

TREWINNARD, Philip James 1082 Huddersfield Road, Scouthead, Oldham OL4 4AG — MB ChB 1978 Manch.

TREZIES, Allister James Harris 41 Downs Hill, Beckenham BR3 5ET — MB BS 1991 Lond.

TREZISE, Catherine Anne 6 Mill Lane, Hoobrook, Kidderminster DY10 1XP; Ridge Hill, Brierley Hill Road, Stourbridge DY8 5ST — MB ChB 1986 Birm.; BSc (Hons.) Pharmacol. Birm. 1983, MB ChB 1986; DGM RCP Lond. 1992; MRCPsych 1997. SCMO W. Midl. Train. Scheme Learning Disabil. Psychiat. Prev: Clin. Med. Off. (Psychiat.) Burton Rd. Hosp. Dudley.; Specialist Regist. W. Midl. Train. Scheme Learning Disabil. Psychiat.

TRIAY, Charles Henry 109 St Georges Square Mews, London SW1V 3RZ; PO Box 207, San Pedro, Alcantara, Malaga 29670, Spain Tel: 34 5278 0540 Fax: 34 5278 6534 Email: triaymedic@mercuryin.es — MB BS 1982 Lond. Prev: SHO (Paediat. & A & E) St. Mary's Teach. Gp.

TRIBE, Elizabeth Mary (retired) 255 Canford Lane, Westbury on Trym, Bristol BS9 3PF — MB BS 1954 Lond.

TRIBE, Peter Humphrey, CStJ (retired) Stockbury, Normanston Drive, Oulton Broad, Lowestoft NR32 2PX Tel: 01502 573441 — MB BS 1948 Lond.; MRCS Eng. LRCP Lond. 1945. Prev: GP Anaesth. & Resid. Med. Off. LoW.oft & N. Suff. Hosp.

TRIBLEY, Anthony Richard Winchcombe Medical Practice, The Surgery, Abbey Terrace, Winchcombe, Cheltenham GL54 5LL Tel: 01242 602307 Fax: 01242 603689 — BM BCh 1989 Oxf.; MA Oxf. 1993, BA 1986; MRCGP 1994; DRCOG 1993; DCH RCP Lond. 1992. (Oxf.)

TRIBLEY

TRIBLEY, Kim Diane 14 Murray Close, Bishops Cleeve, Cheltenham GL52 8XE Tel: 01242 678630 — BM BCh 1989 Oxf.; MA Camb. 1993, BA 1986; MRCGP 1994; DRCOG 1993; DCH RCP Lond. 1992. Prev: Trainee GP Cheltenham.

TRIBUKAIT, Ulrich Flat 6, Exwick House, Royal Devon & Exeter Hospital (Heavitree), Gladstone Road, Exeter EX1 2ED — State Exam Med 1991 Freiburg.

TRICK, Kerith Lloyd Kinsey (retired) St. Andrew's Hospital, Northampton NN1 5DG Tel: 01604 29696 — MB BS 1960 Lond.; MRCS Eng. LRCP Lond. 1960; FRCPsych 1984, M 1972; DPM Eng. 1963. Vis. Cons. Psychiat. St. And. Hosp. N.ampton. Prev: Cons. Psychiat. St. And. Hosp. N.ampton & St. Crispin Hosp.

TRICKER, Mr John Antony Lessenden House, Rimpton, Yeovil BA22 8AB Tel: 01935 850922 Fax: 01935 822196 — MB BS 1966 Lond.; FRCS Eng. 1973; MRCS Eng. LRCP Lond. 1966. (St. Bart.) Cons. Orthop. & Traum. Surg. Yeovil Dist. Hosp. Socs: Fell. BOA. Prev: Clin. Lect. (Orthop. Surg.) Univ. Oxf.; Hon. Sen. Regist. Nuffield Orthop. Centre & John Radcliffe Hosp. Oxf.

TRICKETT, Alan Charles Henry (retired) Roe Beech, Beaulieu Road, Lyndhurst SO43 7DA Tel: 01703 282732 — MB ChB 1961 Ed.; MRCGP 1969; DObst RCOG 1963.

TRICKETT, Anthony Robert, MBE Bayview Surgery, Bayview, Longhope, Stromness KW16 3NY Tel: 01856 701209 Fax: 01856 701224; Glebelands, Longhope, Stromness KW16 3PA Tel: 01856 701460 — MRCS Eng. LRCP Lond. 1964; FRSH 1996. (Manch.) GP Is. of Hoy, Orkney; HMA Longhope Lifeboat (RNLI). Socs: Fell. Roy. Soc. Med.; Fell. Roy. Soc. Health. Prev: Asst. Lect. (Anat.) Univ. Manch.; SHO (Path., Surg. & Paediat.) Roy. Manch. Childr. Pendlebury.

TRICKETT, Jonathan Paul Roe Beech, Beaulieu Road, Lyndhurst SO43 7DA — MB BS 1994 Lond.

TRICKEY, Mr Edward Lorden (retired) 43 Beverley Gardens, Stanmore HA7 2AP Tel: 020 8863 6964 — MB BS 1944 Lond.; FRCS Eng. 1950; MRCS Eng. LRCP Lond. 1944. Prev: Cons. Orthopaedic Surg. Roy. Nat. Orthopaedic Hospitak Stanmore.

TRICKEY, Mr Nicholas Robert Allan 4 Albany Road, Windsor SL4 1HL Tel: 01753 866311 Fax: 01753 850817; 4 Priory Close, Sunningdale, Ascot SL5 9SE Tel: 01344 623687 Fax: 01344 872425 — MB BS 1962 Lond.; MB BS (Hons. Obst. & Gyn.) Lond. 1962; FRCS Eng. 1967; MRCS Eng. LRCP Lond. 1962; FRCOG 1983, M 1970. (St. Mary's) Prev: Cons. O & G Heatherwood Hosp. Ascot & King Edwd. VII Hosp. Windsor.; Sen. Regist. (O & G) Soton. Gen. Hosp. & St. Geo. Hosp. Lond.; Regist. (O & G) St. Mary's Hosp. Lond.

TRICKLEBANK, Barry The Swan Medical Centre, 4 Willard Road, Yardley, Birmingham B25 8AA Tel: 0121 706 0216 Fax: 0121 707 3105 — MB ChB 1986 Birm.

TRICKS, Charles David Wrington Vale Medical Group, Station Road, Wrington, Bristol BS40 5NG Tel: 01934 862532 Fax: 01934 863568; The Cottage, Ladymead Lane, Langford, Bristol BS40 5EF Tel: 01934 852652 Email: charles.tricks@dial.pipex.com — BM BCh 1978 Oxf.; BA 1975; MRCGP 1982; DRCOG 1980. (Oxford)

TRICKS, Norman Charles (retired) Templars, Stoford, Halse, Taunton TA4 3JJ Tel: 01823 433466 — MB ChB 1952 Bristol; MRCS Eng. LRCP Lond. 1951. Prev: Ho. Phys. & Cas. Off. Bristol Roy. Infirm.

TRIFFITT, David James Bramley House, Mill Orchard, E. Hanney, Wantage OX12 0JH Tel: 01235 868314; 74 Sunningwell Road, Oxford OX1 4SX Email: davetriff@hotmail.com — MB BS 1992 Lond.; MRCGP 1997; DRCOG 1997. (London Hospital Medical College) GP Clin. Asst. S. Oxf. Health Centre. Socs: MDU; BMA. Prev: GP Regist. Eyrisham, Oxon.; SHO (O & G) Leicester Gen. Hosp.; Med. Rep. Raleigh Internat. Expedition to Belize.

TRIFFITT, Mr Paul David School of Medicine, Glenfield General Hospital, Groby Road, Leicester LE3 9QP — MD 1991 Leic.; MA Oxf. 1982, BM BCh 1981; FRCS Eng. 1986. Sen. Regist. (Orthop. Surg.) Leic. Socs: Assoc. Mem. Brit. Orthop. Assn.; Brit. Orthop. Research Soc.

TRIGG, Cecilia Jane Department of Respiratory Medicine & Allergy, Guy's Hospital, St Thomas' St., London SE1 9RT Tel: 0207 955 4608 Fax: 0207 955 4608; Cage Farm Lodge, 68 The Ridgeway, Tonbridge TN10 4NN — MB BS 1983 Lond.; 1999 (CCST) Immunology; MD Lond. 1992; MRCP (UK) 1986. p/t Hon. Cons. Allergist, Guy's Hosp. Lond. Socs: Fell. Roy. Soc. Med.; Brit. Thorac. Soc. (Mem.); Brit. Soc. Allergy Cha Immunol. (Mem.). Prev: Sen. Regist. In Allergy, Guy's Hosp. Lond.; Research Fell. Dept. Respirat. Med. St. Bart. Hosp. Lond.; SHO & Regist. Rotat. Kings Coll. Hosp. Lond.

TRIGG, Hilary Anne Fairlands Avenue, Worplesdon, Guildford GU3 3NA Tel: 01483 594250 Fax: 01483 598767 Email: hat@doctors.org.uk; 39 Ashenden Road, Guildford GU2 7XE Tel: 01483 573339 — MB BS 1981 Lond.; MRCGP 1986; DRCOG 1985; DCH RCP Lond. 1984. (King's Coll.) Prev: Trainee GP Guildford VTS; Ho. Surg. Brook Gen. Hosp. Woolwich; Ho. Phys. Dulwich Hosp. King's Health Dist.

TRIGG, Kenneth Haddon (retired) Middle Fell, Rockshaw Road, Merstham, Redhill RH1 3BZ Tel: 01737 643313 — MB BS 1954 Lond.; FRCGP 1976, M 1965; DObst RCOG 1958. Prev: Provost S.W. Thames Fac. RCGP.

TRIGG, Sarah Louise 98 Upper Cliff Road, Gorleston, Great Yarmouth NR31 6AL — BM 1998 Soton.

TRIGG, Susan Elizabeth Ellis Clifton Surgery, 151-153 Newport Road, Roath, Cardiff CF24 1AG Tel: 029 2049 4539 Fax: 029 2049 4657 — MB BCh 1987 Wales; MRCGP 1992.

TRIGGS, Angharad Jane 99 King George V Dr N., Heath, Cardiff CF14 4EH — MB BCh 1998 Wales.

TRIGWELL, Peter John Department of Liaison Psychiatry, Leeds General Infirmary, Great George St., Leeds LS1 3EX Tel: 0113 392 5246 Fax: 0113 392 8389 Email: peter.trigwell@leedsth.nhs.uk — MB ChB 1989 Leeds; MMedSc Leeds 1994; MRCPsych 1993. (Leeds) Cons. Liaison Psychiat. And Psychosexual Leeds Gen. Infirm.; Hon. Sen. Clin. Lect. Univ. Leeds. Prev: Research Sen. Regist. (Psychiat.) St James' Univ. Hosp. Leeds; Sen. Regist. (Psychiat.) Leeds Gen. Infirm.; Sen. Regist. (Psychiat.) High Royds Hosp. Leeds.

TRIHIA, Helen 23A Craven Terrace, Lancaster Gate, London W2 3QH — Ptychio Iatrikes 1987 Athens.

TRIKAS, Athanasios Hammersmith Hospital, Department of Cardiology, Echocardiography Section, Du Cane Road, London W12 0NN — Ptychio Iatrikes 1984 Athens.

TRIKHA, Sanjay Paul 151 Heaton Road, Bradford BD9 4RZ — MB BS 1997 Lond.

TRILL, Andrea Susan 51 Grosvenor Park, London SE5 0NH — MB BS 1990 Lond.; BSc, MB BS (Hons.) Lond. 1990.

TRIMBLE, Mr David Keith George 6 Grenroe, Moira, Craigavon BT67 0DT Tel: 01846 613265 Email: keith.trimble@virgin.net — MB BCh BAO 1995 Belf.; FRCSI. 1999. SHO. (ENT Surg.) Antrim Area Hosp. N. Irel..

TRIMBLE, Freda Mary 155 Ballyskeagh Road, Drumbeg, Dunmurry, Belfast BT17 9LL — MB BCh BAO 1982 Belf.; MB BCh Belf. 1982.

TRIMBLE, Ian Michael Geoffrey Black and Partners, Sherwood Health Centre, Elmswood Gardens, Sherwood, Nottingham NG5 4AD Tel: 0115 960 7127 Fax: 0115 985 7899; 23 Tavistock Avenue, Mapperley Park, Nottingham NG3 5BD Tel: 0115 985 7401 — BM BS 1982 Nottm.; MPhil Nottm. 1980, BMedSci 1979; MRCGP 1988. GP Princip.; GP Adviser NHSE.

TRIMBLE, Karl Thomas 41 Boden Road, Birmingham B28 9DL — MB ChB 1993 Liverp.

TRIMBLE, Michael 41 Hampton Manor, Belfast BT7 3EL — MB ChB 1992 Dundee.

TRIMBLE, Professor Michael Robert Department of Clinical Neurology, Institute of Neurology, National Hospital, Queen Square, London WC1N 3BG Tel: 020 7837 3611 Fax: 020 7837 3611 Email: mtrimble@ion.ucl.ac.uk — MB ChB 1970 (Hons) Birm.; MD 1993; FRCP 1986 Lond.; MRCP 1972; BSc 1967 (1st Class Hons) Birm.; FRCPsych 1982; MPhil 1976 Lond; MRCPsych 1975. Prof. Inst. Neurol. Lond.; Cons. Nat. Hosp. Neurol. & Neurosurg. Dis. Qu. Sq. Lond. Socs: Fell. Amer. Psychiat. Assn.; Fell. Roy. Soc. Med.; Amer. Neurol. Assn.

TRIMBLE, Peter Henry Chester 19 Ormiston Park, Belfast BT4 3JT — MB BCh BAO 1985 Belf.

TRIMBLE, William George Clements Dunluce Health Centre, 1 Dunluce Avenue, Belfast BT9 7HR; 16 Cleaver Park, Malone Road, Belfast BT9 5HX — MB BCh BAO 1965 Dub.; FRCGP 1986, M 1971.

TRIMLETT, Richard Henry James Pen-y-Fai Nurseries, Pen-y-Fai, Bridgend CF31 4LX — MB BS 1992 Lond.

TRIVEDI

TRIMM, Ann Kathleen 128 Eccles Old Road, Salford M6 8QQ Tel: 0161 736 1972; 494 Liverpool Street, Salford M6 5QZ Tel: 0161 736 1972 — MRCS Eng. LRCP Lond. 1957; BSc (Anat.) Lond. 1954, MB BS (Hons. Med.) 1957. (Roy. Free) GP Salford; Clin. Asst. Hope Hosp. Salford. Prev: Ho. Phys. & Ho. Surg. Roy. Free Hosp.; Sen. Ho. Off. Stamford & Rutland Hosp.

TRIMMING, Helen Mary Dr Ayre & Partners, Hartlepool Health Centre, Victori Road, Hartlepool T26 8DB; 25 St Edmunds Green, Sedgefield TS21 3H7 — MB BChir 1994 Camb.; MRCGP 1999; DRCOG 1998; DFFP 1998. (Camb.) GP salaried, Hartlepool PCT; GP s/i Palliat. Care Hospice, Hartlepool. Prev: GP Regist. Cleveland VTS; Salaried GP, McKenzie Ho., Hartlepool; GP Regist., Sedgefield.

TRIMMINGS, Mr Nigel Peter Tel: 01962 854941 Fax: 01962 840959 — MB BS 1975 Lond.; FRCS Eng. 1980; MRCS Eng. LRCP Lond. 1975. (St. Mary's) Cons. Surg. Orthop. Roy. Hants. Co. Hosp. Winchester; Hon. Clin. Prof., St Geo.'s Univ., Grenada, W. Indes. Socs: Fell. BOA; Brit. Elbow & Shoulder Soc.; Roy. Soc. Med. - Mem. of Counc. Commail Orthopadiesetion. Prev: Sen. Regist. (Orthop.) Roy. Free & Windsor Gp.

TRINDER, Johanna Homefield, Wilkes Farm, Doynton, Bristol BS30 5TJ — MB BS 1990 Lond.; MRCOG 1995. (Charing Cross and Westminster) Research Regist. (O & G).

TRINDER, Thomas John 16 Manor Hill, Carnesure Manor, Killinchy Road, Comber, Newtownards BT23 5FN Tel: 01247 870422 — MB BCh BAO 1986 Belf.; MD Belf. 1995; FFA RCSI 1990. Cons. (Anaesth. & Intens. Care) Ulster Hosp. Belf.; Dir. Intens. Care. Socs: Assn. Anaesth.; Intens. Care Soc. Irel.; Soc. Critical Care Med. Prev: Chief Regist. (Intens. Care Unit) Roy. Adelaide Hosp., Australia; Research Fell. Regional Intens. Care Unit Roy. Hosps. Belf.

TRING, Frederick Charles (retired) Spring House Farm, Gowland Lane, Cloughton, Scarborough YO13 0DU Tel: 01723 870395 — MB ChB Sheff. 1967; PhD Sheff. 1982, MA 1972, MD 1973; LDS 1966; MRCGP 1976. Prev: Cons. Dermat. Bradford, Airedale & Wharfedale Hosps.

TRING, Ian Charles Department of Anaesthesia, Scarborough Hospital, Scalby Road, Scarborough YO12 6QL Tel: 01723 368111; Spring House Farm, Gowland Lane, Cloughton, Scarborough YO13 0DU Tel: 01723 870319 — MB BS 1981 Lond.; MRCS Eng. LRCP Lond. 1981; FFA RCSI 1985; FRCA 1997; DA Eng. 1983. (St. Bart.) Cons. Anaesth. ScarBoro. Hosp. Socs: Assn. Dent. Anaesth.; Assn. Anaesth.; Yorks. Soc. Anaesth. Prev: Sen. Regist. Rotat. (Anaesth.) Yorks. RHA.

TRING, Jonathan Patrick 28 Leicester Road, Uppingham, Oakham LE15 9SD — MB ChB 1989 Leeds; FFA RCSI 1996.

TRINGHAM, Jennifer Ruth 41 West End, West Haddon, Northampton NN6 7AY — MB ChB 1993 Birm.

TRINICK, Thomas Richard The Ulster Hospital, Belfast BT16 0RH Tel: 028 9048 4511 Fax: 028 9048 7131 Email: tom.trinick@ucht.n-i.nhs.uk; 3 Malone Meadows, Belfast BT9 5BG Tel: 028 9066 7803 Fax: 028 9066 7803 Email: Thomas.Trinick@btinternet.com — MB BCh BAO 1977 Belf.; BSc (Hons.) Belf. 1975, MD 1988; FRCP Ed. 1996; FRCP Lond. 1998; MRCP (UK) 1981; FRCPath 1995, M 1986; FRCPI 2000. (Qu. Univ Belf.) Cons. Chem. Path. and Phys. Ulster Hosp. Belf. And Chairm. of the Regional Med. Audit Comm., N.I.; Hon. Clin. Lect., Clin. Biochem.ry, Qu.s Univ. of Belf.; Lect. in BioMed. Sci.s, Univ. of Ulster; NI Regional Tutor in Clin. Biochem.ry. Socs: Hyperlip. Assn.; Irish Cardiac Soc.; Irish Angiology Soc. Prev: Sen. Regist. (Chem. Path.) Roy. Vict. Hosp. Belf.; Sen. Regist. Clin. Biochem.ry and Metab. Med. Roy. Vict. Infirm. Newc. upon Tyne.

TRIPATHI, Bharat Prasad Golf Course Road Surgery, 11 Golf Course Road, Livingston EH54 8QF — MB BS 1967 Punjab; MB BS Punjabi 1967. (Govt. Med. Coll. Patiala) GP Livingston.

TRIPATHI, Dharam Narain St Nicholas Health Centre, Saunder Bank, Burnley BB11 2EN Tel: 01282 422528 Fax: 01282 832834 — MB BS 1958 Lucknow; MB BS 1958 Lucknow.

TRIPATHI, Dharmendra Pati The Jersey Practice, Heston Health Centre, Cranford Lane, Hounslow TW5 9ER Tel: 020 8321 3434 Fax: 020 8321 3440 — MB BS 1968 Patna; DTD Patna 1971; DTCD Wales 1976. (Patna Med. Coll.) SHO Cefn Mably Hosp. Socs: Fell. Internat. Federat. Sports Med. Athens; Coll. Chest Phys. U.S.A.

TRIPATHI, Dhiraj 11 Golf Course Road, Livingston EH54 8QF — MB ChB 1994 Ed.

TRIPNEY, Robert Edmiston Scott Delapre Medical Centre, Gloucester Avenue, Northampton NN4 8QF Tel: 01604 761713; 17 Favell Way, Northampton NN3 3BZ Tel: 01604 403396 — MB ChB Ed. 1961; MRCP Lond. 1969; DCH Eng. 1965; DObst RCOG 1963. Hosp. Pract. (Electrocardiog.) N.ampton Gen. Hosp. Socs: BMA; CMF. Prev: Pres. N.ants. Med. Soc.

TRIPP, Joanna Claire Scott 20 Inverleith Gardens, Edinburgh EH3 5PS — MB BS 1987 Lond.

TRIPP, John Howard Department of Child Health, Royal Devon & Exeter Hospital (Wonford), Barrack Road, Exeter EX2 5DW Tel: 01392 403148 Fax: 01392 403158 Email: jhtripp@ex.ac.uk; Pixie Cottage, Alphington, Exeter EX2 8TD Tel: 01392 270392 — MB BS 1968 Lond.; BSc Lond. 1965, MD 1979; FRCP Lond. 1986; MRCP (UK) 1971; FRCPCH 1997. (Guy's) Sen. Lect. (Child Health) Univ. Exeter Postgrad. Med. Sch.; Cons. Paediat. Roy. Devon & Exeter Hosp. Exeter. Socs: Brit. Soc. Allergy & Clin. Immunol.; Fell. Coll. Paediat. & Child Health; Fell. RCP. Prev: Sen. Regist. Hosp. Sick Childr. Gt. Ormond St. Lond.; Research Fell. Inst. Child Health Lond.

TRIPP, Sarah Jane Carreg-y-Borth, Telford Road, Menai Bridge LL59 5DT — MB ChB 1991 Leeds.

TRIPPE, Helen Ruth West Surrey Health Authority, The Ridgewood Centre, Old Bisley Road, Camberley GU16 9QE Tel: 01276 671718; Summerfield, Park Road, Winchester SO22 6AA — BM 1985 Soton.; BA Birm. 1967; MFPHM RCP (UK) 1994. (Soton.) Cons. Pub. Health Med. W. Surrey Health Auth. Camberley Surrey. Prev: Sen. Regist. (Pub. Health Med.) Wessex Inst. Pub. Health Med. Winchester; Vis. Fell. Fac. Educat. Univ. Soton.; Regist. (Pub. Health Med.) Salisbury Dist. Health Auth.

TRISCOTT, Ann Patricia (retired) 11 Rutland Court, Queen's Drive, London W3 0HL Tel: 020 8992 0411 — MB ChB 1961 Birm.; FFA RCS Eng. 1969; DA Eng. 1964. Cons. Anaesth. Harefield Hosp. Middlx. Prev: Sen. Regist. Hammersmith Hosp.

TRISTRAM, Amanda Jane Renby Fold Farm Cottage, Mossy Lea Rd, Wrightington, Wigan WN6 9SA — MB ChB 1991 Sheff.; MRCOG. 1998. SHO (Obst & Gyn.) Manch. Prev: SHO (O & G) Sheff.

TRISTRAM, Stephen John The North Hampshire Hospital, Aldermaston Road, Basingstoke RG24 9NA Tel: 01256 313569; Walnut Tree House, 5 Paddock Fields, Old Basing, Basingstoke RG24 7DB Tel: 01256 28327 Email: drstristram@cs.com — MB ChB 1968 St. And.; DObst RCOG 1971. (St. And.) p/t Med. Off. Sun Life Financial of Cananda, Basingstoke, Hants.; Practicing rights: The Hants. Clinic, Basingstoke, Pk.side Hosp. Wimbledon, St. Anthony's Hosp. N. Cheam. Socs: BMA & Roy. Soc. Med.

TRITTON, Barbara Antoinette 62 Windsor Drive, Chelsfield, Orpington BR6 6HD Tel: 01689 852204; Quinneys, The Hillside, Pratts Bottom, Orpington BR6 7SD Tel: 01689 58257 — MB BS 1966 Lond.; MRCS Eng. LRCP Lond. 1965. (Westm.) Mem. Bromley LMC. Prev: Ho. Surg. W.m. Childr. Hosp.; Ho. Phys. FarnBoro. Hosp. Kent.

TRITTON, Denise Frances Tamarisk, 4 School Road, Finstock, Chipping Norton OX7 3BW — MB BS 1993 Lond.; MRCP (UK) 1997. (Charing Cross and Westminster) Specialist Regist. (Paediat.) Oxf. Rotat.

TRIVEDI, Alka Deepak Warrington Road Surgery, 429A Warrington Road, Abram, Wigan WN2 5XB Tel: 01942 866277 Fax: 01942 866198 — MB BS 1973 Indore.

TRIVEDI, Deepak (Surgery), 4-12 Westleigh Lane, Leigh WN7 5JE Tel: 01942 607627 Fax: 01942 261747; 21 Houghwood Grange, Ashton in Makefield, Wigan WN4 9LT Tel: 01942 722803 Fax: 01942 261747 — MB BS 1973 Indore.

TRIVEDI, Devyani Vipin Scarisbrick Practice, 13 Scarisbrick New Road, Southport PR8 6PX Tel: 01704 531114 Fax: 01704 533794; 13 Scarisbrick New Road, Southport PR8 6PX — MB BS 1966 Gujarat; MFFP 1993; DGO 1968. (B.J. Med. Coll. Ahmedabad) GP S.port; Sen. Clin. Med. Off. St. Helen's & Knowsley HA. Prev: Regist. (O & G) St. Helier Hosp. Carshalton.

TRIVEDI, Hemant Vishvanath Parker Drive Medical Centre, 122 Parker Drive, Leicester LE4 0JF Tel: 0116 235 3148; 16 All Saints Road, Thurcaston, Leicester LE7 7JD Tel: 0116 236 3076 Fax: 0116 236 3076 — MB BS 1966 Bombay. (Grant Med. Coll.) Socs: LMS; BMA; LMC. Prev: SHO (Obst.), SHO (Gyn.) & SHO (Surg.) Leicester Roy. Infirm.

TRIVEDI

TRIVEDI, Janakbala 6 Gaudi Walk, Rogerstone, Newport NP10 0AG — MB BS 1964 Calcutta; DObst RCOG 1972.

TRIVEDI, Jitendrakumar Shreeji Medical Centre, 22 Whitby Road, Slough SL1 3DQ Tel: 01753 527988 Fax: 01753 530269 — MB BS 1974 Baroda; MB BS 1974 Baroda.

TRIVEDI, Kiran Mayee Great Barr Group Practice, 912 Walsall Road, Great Barr, Birmingham B42 1TG Tel: 0121 357 1250 Fax: 0121 358 4857; 27 Athlone Road, Walsall WS5 3QU — MB BS 1961 Vikram; DObst RCOG 1971.

TRIVEDI, Kirit Girijashankar 8 Walnut Drive, Bishop's Stortford CM23 4JT — MB BS 1972 Gujarat.

TRIVEDI, Monica 27 Athlone Road, Walsall WS5 3QU — MB BS 1996 Lond.

TRIVEDI, Ravi Shanker 51 Stambourne Way, Upper Norwood, London SE19 2PY Tel: 020 8653 6865 — MB BS 1942 Lucknow; DTM & H Eng. 1955.

TRIVEDI, Sanjay Hemant 16 All Saints Road, Thurcaston, Leicester LE7 7JD — MB ChB 1997 Sheff.

TRIVEDI, Mr Satish Kumar 83 Woodstock Avenue, Golders Green, London NW11 9RH Tel: 020 8458 8288 Email: sat.sum@thefree.net; 83 Woodstock Avenue, Golders Green, London NW11 9RH — MB BS 1974 Jiwaji; FRCS Glas. 1984; FRCS Ed. 1983; DO RCS Eng. 1976. (G. R. Med. Coll. Gwalior (MP))

TRIVEDI, Sheilah 155 Covington Way, Norbury, London SW16 3AQ Tel: 020 8679 3379 Email: sheilahji@iname.com — MB BS 1990 Lond.; MRCGP 1995. (St. Geos. Med. Sch. Lond.) Socs: BMA & Med. Defence Union. Prev: Locum GP Trainee GP Berks.

TRIVEDI, Vipin Ambalal Scarisbrick Practice, 13 Scarisbrick New Road, Southport PR8 6PX Tel: 01704 531114 Fax: 01704 533794 — MB BS 1966 Gujarat; DA Gujarat 1968. (B.J. Med. Coll. Ahmedabad) Socs: Assoc. Mem. RCGP; Indian Soc. Anaesth.; BMA. Prev: Regist. (Anaesth.) Roy. Infirm. Aberd., Moorfields Eye Hosp. (City Rd. Br.) Lond. & City Hosp. Nottm.

TRIVEDI, Vishnuprasad Jagjivandas 49 Corfton Road, London W5 1AQ — MRCS Eng. LRCP Lond. 1978; LAH Dub. 1957; LCPS Bombay 1945.

TROJANOWSKI, Andrzej 26 Rowfant Road, London SW17 7AS Tel: 020 8673 6314 — Lekarz 1970 Warsaw; FFA RCSI 1984; DA S Afr. 1979. Specialist (Anaesth.) Tygerberg Hosp. S. Afr. Prev: Regist. (Anaesth.) Qu. Charlotte's Hosp. for Wom. Lond.

TROLLEN, Robert Michael Milton Medical Centre, 109 Egilsay Street, Glasgow G22 7JL Tel: 0141 772 1183 Fax: 0141 772 2331; 35 Winton Lane, Kelvinside, Glasgow G12 0QD Tel: 0141 357 5641 — MB ChB 1972 Glas. Mem. LMC. Socs: BMA.

TROLLOPE, Anne Alexander 3 Wellace Barn Cottages, Draycott, Moreton-in-Marsh GL56 9LG — MB ChB 1984 Liverp.; DRCOG 1990.

TROMANS, Anthony Matthew 13 Russell Street, Wilton, Salisbury SP2 0BG — MB ChB 1978 Manch.

TROMANS, Jonathan Paul Gwent Health Authority, Mamhilad House, Mamhilad Park Estate, Pontypool NP4 0YP Tel: 01495 765112; 31 Middlegate Court, Cowbridge CF71 7EF Tel: 01446 773485 — BM BCh 1976 Oxf.; BA (1st cl.) Oxf. 1972; MFPHM RCP (UK) 1993. (Oxford) Cons. Pub. Health Med., Gwent Health Auth. Pontypool. Prev: Sen. Med. Off., Nat. Assembly for Wales, Cardiff; Sen. Regist. (Pub. Health Med.) Health Promotion Auth. For Wales Cardiff; Princip. GP Cowes I. of Wight.

TROMANS, Philip Marcel Chesterfield Royal Hospital, Calow, Chesterfield S44 5BL Tel: 01246 277271 Email: philiptromans.cndrh-tr@trent.nhs.uk — MB ChB 1973 Liverp.; FRCOG 1992, M 1978. Cons. O & G Chesterfield & N. Derbysh. Roy. Hosp. Socs: N. Eng. Obst. & Gyn. Soc.; (Co. Chairm.) Derbysh. Hosp. Cons. & Specialists Assn. Prev: Lect. (O & G) Univ. Liverp.; Hon. Sen. Regist. Liverp. HA.

TROMPETAS, Alexander Selsdon Park Medical Practice, 95 Addington Road, South Croydon CR2 8LG Tel: 020 8657 0067 Fax: 020 8657 0037; Marlowes, Tandridge Road, Warlingham CR6 9LS Tel: 01883 627027 — Ptychio Iatrikes 1985 Ioannina; MBBS Ioannina Greece 1985; MRCGP 1990. (Med. Sch. Univ. Ioannina, Greece) Sen. Partner Selsdon Pk. Med. Pract.; Tutor (Gen. Pract.) Croydon; Chairm. Centr. Croydon PCG; Starnet Lead GP (S. Thames Region). Prev: Clin. Asst. (HIV) Croydon; Chairm. Centr. Croydon Commiss.ing Gp.

TROMPETER, Richard Simon Great Ormond Street Hospital for Children NHS Trust, London WC1 3JH Tel: 020 7813 8305 Fax: 020 7829 8841 Email: trompr@gosh.nhs.uk; 1 Holt Close, London N10 3HW — MB BS 1970 Lond.; FRCP Lond. 1989; MRCP (UK) 1973; MRCS Eng. LRCP Lond. 1970; FRCPCH 1997. (Guy's) Cons. Paediat. (Nephrol.) Hosp. for Childr. Gt. Ormond St. Lond.; Sen. Clin. Lectrurer; Inst. of Nephrol.; UCLH Lond. Socs: Internat. Soc. of Nephrol.; Internat. Soc. of Paeditrcs & Nephrol.; Brit. Transpl. Soc. Prev: Cons. Paediat. Roy. Free Hosp. & Med. Sch. Lond.; Lect. & Hon. Sen. Regist. (Paediat.) Guy's Hosp. Lond.; Research Fell. Inst. Child Health Lond. & Regist. Hosp Sick Childr. Gt. Ormond St.

TROMPETER, Sara 1 Holt Close, London N10 3HW Tel: 020 8444 8985 — MB ChB 1997 Bristol; BSc (Hons) Psychol. 1994. (Bristol) Paediat. SHO UCH Hosp., Lond. Socs: BMA. Prev: SHO ATE Kings Coll. Hosp., Windsor; Ho. Off. (Surg.) Whipps Cross Hosp. Lond.; Ho. Off. (Med.) Bristol Roy. Infirm.

TROOP, Anne Catherine Long Meadow, Shawes Drive, Anderton, Chorley PR6 9HR Tel: 01257 480604 — MB ChB 1980 Liverp.; FRCR 1986; DMRD Liverp. 1984. Cons. Radiol. Roy. Albert Edwd. Infirm. Wigan.

TROOP, Patricia Ann, CBE Dept of Health, Richmond House, 79 Whitehall, London SW1A 2NL Tel: 020 7210 5591 Fax: 020 7930 4636 Email: pat.troop@doh.gsi.gov.uk — MB ChB 1971 Manch.; MSc Manch. 1979; FFCM 1986, M 1980. Dep. Chief Med. Off., Dept. of Health; Vis. Prof. at the Lond. Sch. of Hyg. Prev: Regional Director of Pub. Health (E.ern Region, Formerly Anglia & Oxf., formerly E. Anglia Chief Camb. HA & Camb FHSA.

TRORY, Graham Howard Hartlepool Healthcentre, Victoria Road, Hartlepool TS26 8DB Tel: 01429 278139 Fax: 01429 864004 — MB ChB 1988 Dundee. Trainee GP Bangor VTS.

TROSS, Samantha Zoisa 23 Kitchener Road, Thornton Heath, Croydon CR7 8QN Email: zoisa1@aol.com — MB BS 1992 Lond.; FRCS Eng. 1997. SHO Rotat. (Surg.) Roy. Lond. Hosp.; Specialist Regist. (Orthop.) S.E Thames. Prev: SHO (Orthop. Surg.) Mayday Univ. Hosp. Thornton Heath.; SHO (A & E) St. Geo. Hosp. Trust; Demonst. (Anat.) Qu. Mary & W.field Coll. Lond.

TROSSER, Alan Highbury Grange Health Centre, Highbury Grange, London N5 2QB Tel: 020 7226 2462 — MB BS 1978 Lond.; BSc Lond. 1973; MRCP (UK) 1980. (Univ. Coll. Hosp.) Prev: Research Fell. & Hon. Regist. (Cardiac) King's Coll Hosp. Lond.

TROTMAN, Ivan Frank Tel: 020 8872 3872 Email: iftrotman@hotmail.com; 74 Moor Lane, Rickmansworth WD3 1LQ — MB BS 1971 Lond.; MD Lond. 1988; FRCP Lond. 1994; MRCP (UK) 1975. Cons. Phys. & Dir. (Palliat. Med.) Mt. Vernon Hosp. N.wood. Socs: Brit. Soc. Gastroenterol. & Assn. Palliat. Med. Prev: Sen. Regist. & Research Fell. Dept. Gastroenterol. Centr. Middlx. Hosp. Lond.; Sen. Regist. (Gen. Med. & Geriat.) United Oxf. Hosps.; Squadron Ldr. (Med. Specialist) RAF Med. Br.

TROTT, Leonard Inglis Bryn Elfed, Pontrhydyfen, Port Talbot SA12 9TN Tel: 01639 896244 — MB BCh 1957 Wales.

TROTT, Peter Alan Department of Cytopathology, Royal Marsden Hospital, Fulham Road, London SW3 6JJ Tel: 020 7352 8171; Flat 1, 20-21 Marylebone High St, London W1M 3PE Tel: 020 7224 4617 — MB BChir 1966 Camb.; MRCS Eng. LRCP Lond. 1959; FRCPath 1984, M 1972. (Guy's) Cons. Path. (Cytol.) Roy. Marsden Hosp. & Dir. Path. The Lond. Clinic Edr. Cytopath.; Cons. Cytopath. to Army. Socs: (Pres.) Brit. Soc. Clin. Cytol. Prev: Cons. Path. (Cytol.) St. Stephen's Hosp. Lond.; Research Fell. (Path.) St. Pauls Hosp. Lond.

TROTTER, Barbara Marion (retired) Half Acre, Southfields, Speldhurst, Tunbridge Wells TN3 0PD — MB ChB Liverp. 1947; DA Eng. 1953. Prev: Asst. Anaesth. Kingston Hosp. Gp.

TROTTER, Carol Agnes 11 Holmesland Lane, Botley, Southampton SO30 2EH — MB ChB 1973 Dundee; MRCPsych 1977. Cons. Psychiat. (Psychogeriat.) St. Jas. Hosp. Portsmouth. Mem. BMA.

TROTTER, Christopher 50 Browmere Drive, Croft, Warrington WA3 7HR — MB ChB 1979 Aberd.

TROTTER, Mr Geoffrey Alan 28 Buckingham Close, Petts Wood, Orpington BR5 1SA Tel: 01689 833441 Fax: 01622 723066 Email: gatrotter@msn.com — MB ChB 1975 Liverp.; MS Soton. 1986; FRCS Eng. 1980. Cons. Gen. Surg. Maidstone Hosp. Prev: Sen. Regist. (surg.) Guy's Hosp. Lond.; Regist. (Surg.) Basingstoke Dist. Hosp.; Regist. & Tutor (Surg.) Bristol Teach. Hosps.

TROTTER, Geoffrey Gerald Rushbottom Lane Surgery, 91 Rushbottom Lane, Benfleet SS7 4EA Tel: 01268 754311 — MB BS 1976 Lond.

TROTTER, John King (retired) Spindlewood, Tredrea Gdns, Perran-ar-Worthal, Truro TR3 7QG Tel: 01872 863468 — MRCS Eng. LRCP Lond. 1946; FFA RCS Eng. 1957; DA Eng. 1954. Prev: Cons. Anaesth. W. Cornw. Clin. Area.

***TROTTER, Matthew Ian** Sunset Cottage, Blackpond Lane, Lower Bourne, Farnham GU10 3NW — MB ChB 1995 Birm.

TROTTER, Penelope Anne Musgrove Park Hospital, Taunton TA1 5; Church Hill Cottage, Halse, Taunton TA4 3AB Tel: 01823 432815 — MB BS 1980 Lond.; MRCGP 1986; DCH RCP Lond. 1985; DRCOG 1985. (Lond. Hosp.) Staff Doctor Gyn. (Colposcopy & Family Plann.) Som. HA. Prev: Clin. Asst. (Colposcopy) Som. HA; Trainee GP N.umbrian VTS.

TROTTER, Philip Miles 92 Blenheim Place, Aberdeen AB25 2DY — MB ChB 1976 Aberd.; FRCPsych 1998; MRCPsych 1981. Cons. Psychiat. Roy. Cornhill Hosp. Aberd. Prev: Cons. Pscyhiat. Stratheden Hosp. Cupar & Kingseat Hosp. Newmachar; Lect. (Psychiat.) Univ. Dundee; Regist. Roy. Cornhill Hosp. Aberd.

TROTTER, Robin Fenwick Goodacre and Partners, Swadlincote Surgery, Darklands Road, Swadlincote DE11 0PP Tel: 01283 551717 Fax: 01283 211905; 4 Home Farm, Geary Lane, Bretby, Burton-on-Trent DE15 0QE Tel: 01283 702221 — MB ChB 1980 Birm.; MRCGP 1986. (Birm.) Prev: Trainee GP Measham; Ho. Phys. & SHO (Med.) Burton on Trent Gen. Hosp.

TROTTER, Simon Edward Dept of Histopathology, Birmingham Heartlands Hospital, Bordesley Green E., Birmingham B9 5SS Tel: 0121 685 5877 Fax: 0121 685 5898; 4 Elm Road, Windsor SL4 3ND Tel: 01753 869651 — MB BS 1980 Lond.; MRCPath 1992. (Lond. Hosp.) Cons.(Histopath & Cytopath.) Heartlands & Solihull NHS Trust. Socs: Fell. Roy. Soc. Med.; Internat. Acad. Path. (Brit. Div.). Prev: Sen. Regist. (Histopath.) Roy. Brompton & Nat. Heart & Lung Inst. Lond.

TROTTER, Simon Hony Links Medical Centre, 4 Hermitage Place, Edinburgh EH6 8BW Tel: 0131 554 1036 Fax: 0131 555 3995; 7 Stirling Road, Edinburgh EH5 3HZ — MB ChB 1975 Ed.; BA Camb. 1972; MRCGP 1982; DRCOG 1977.

TROTTER, Thomas Alan 12 Fairway Close, Brunton Park, Gosforth, Newcastle upon Tyne NE3 5AR Tel: 0191 236 4836 — MB BS 1950 Durh.

TROTTER, Timothy Nigel Anaesthetic Department, Glenfield General Hospital, Leicester — MB ChB 1981 Manch.; MB ChB (Hons.) Manch. 1981; BSc St. And. 1978; FCAnaesth 1989; MRCGP (Distinc.) 1985; DRCOG 1984. Cons. Anaesth. Glenfield Gen. Hosp. Prev: Lect. (Anaesth.) Univ. Leic.

TROUGHTON, Alison Mary Josephine Dobson, Gray and Troughton, The Health Centre, Tavanagh Avenue, Portadown, Craigavon BT62 3BU Tel: 028 3835 1393 — MB BCh BAO 1987 Belf.; MRCGP 1991; DRCOG 1992; DCH Dub. 1990; Dip. Ment. Health Belf. 1990. GP Partner Job share. Prev: Trainee GP Stranraer; SHO Craigavon Area Hosp.

TROUGHTON, Alvan Harold 45 Victoria Road, Cirencester GL7 1ES; Department of Radiology, Princess Margaret Hospital, Swindon SN1 4JU — MB ChB 1978 Bristol; FRCR 1989; MRCP (UK) 1983; FRCP 1998. Cons. (Radiol.) P.ss Margt. Hosp. Swindon.

TROUGHTON, Jean Mary (Surgery) 9 Godstow Road, London SE2 Tel: 020 8310 7066; (resid.) 145 Tile Kiln Lane, Bexley DA5 2BQ — LRCP LRCS 1949 Ed.; LRCP LRCS Ed. LRFPS Glas. 1949. Prev: Asst. Co. MOH S.E. Essex Area; Gyn. Ho. Surg. & Ho. Phys. Rush Green Hosp. Romford; Ho. Surg. Finchley Memor. Hosp.

TROUGHTON, Kimberley Elizabeth Vance 2 Lime Kiln Lane, Aghalee, Craigavon BT67 0EZ; 2 The Old Orchard, Lime Kiln Lane, Aghalee, Craigavon BT67 0EZ — MB BCh BAO 1990 Belf.; MRCP (UK) 1994; DCH Dub. 1993. Cons. Community Paediat., Antrim Area Hosp., Antrim, N.I.

TROUGHTON, Oliver Wylde Green, Carleton Road, Pontefract WF8 3NP — MB ChB 1951 Birm.; MRCP (UK) 1969; DCH Eng. 1964. Socs: BMA & Midl. Paediat. Soc. Prev: Paediat. Regist. Coventry Hosp. Gp.; Ho. Surg. & Ho. Phys. Selly Oak Hosp. Birm.; Paediat. Ho. Phys. Manor Hosp. Walsall.

TROUGHTON, Thomas William Eric The Health Centre, High Street, Catterick Village, Richmond DL10 7LD Tel: 01748 811475 Fax: 01748 818284; Oakleigh House, Brompton-on-Swale, Richmond DL10 7HN — MB BCh BAO 1980 Belf.; DRCOG 1982.

TROUGHTON, Timothy St John Tel: 020 7703 4550 Fax: 020 7703 1888 — MB BCh BAO 1992 Belf.; MRCGP 1996; DFFP 1997; DCH Dub. 1995; DRCOG 1995; DGM RCPS Glas. 1994. (Belf.)

TROUGHTON, Victoria Andrea Greenwich & Bexley Cottage Hospice, 185 Bostall Hill, Abbey Wood, London SE2 0QX Tel: 020 8312 2244 Fax: 020 8312 0202; 154 Wricklemarsh Road, Blackheath, London SE3 8DP — BM 1994 Soton.; DMH Belf. 1996.

TROUGHTON, William David Harold (Surgery) 9 Godstow Road, London SE2 Tel: 020 8310 7066; (resid.) 145 Tile Kiln Lane, Bexley DA5 2BQ — MB BCh BAO 1949 Dub.; DA Eng. 1966. (TC Dub.) Prev: Ho. Surg. Rush Green Hosp.; Anaesth. Regist. Harold Wood Hosp. & Lond. Hosp.

TROULI, Chariklia Flat 3, Brockley Hill House, Royal National Orthopaedic Hospital, Brockley Hill, Stanmore HA7 4LP — Ptychio Iatrikes 1986 Athens.

TROUNCE, Christopher Charles McIntosh, Trounce and Harvey, Health Centre, Orchard Way, Chillington, Kingsbridge TQ7 2LB Tel: 01548 580214 Fax: 01548 581080; Holset House, Holset, East Portlemouth, Salcombe TQ8 8PL — MB BS 1978 Lond.; MRCP (UK) 1982; MRCGP 1984.

TROUNCE, David Quartermaine (retired) 63 Madeira Park, Tunbridge Wells TN2 5SX Tel: 01892 529942 — MB BS Lond. 1944; MD Lond. 1950; FRCP Lond. 1973, M 1949; MRCS Eng. LRCP Lond. 1945; DCH Eng. 1949. Prev: Cons. Paediat. Harlow Hosp. Gp.

TROUNCE, John Quartermaine Royal Alexandra Hospital for Sick Children, Brighton BN1 3JN Tel: 01273 328145 Fax: 01273 736685 — MB BS 1976 Lond.; MD Leic. 1994; FRCP Lond. 1994; MRCP (UK) 1981; MRCS Eng. LRCP Lond. 1976; FRCPCH 1997; DCH RCP Lond. 1980. (Guy's) Cons. Paediat. Roy. Alexandra Hosp. for Sick Childr. Brighton. Socs: Neonat. Soc.; Paediat. Intens. Care Soc. Prev: Sen. Regist. (Paediat.) Qu. Med. Centre Nottm.; Regist. (Paediat.) Leics. Roy. Infirm.; SHO (Paediat.) Qu. Eliz. Hosp. Childr. Lond.

TROUNCE, Professor John Reginald Farnehill, Ightham, Sevenoaks TN15 9HE Tel: 01732 882556 — MB BS 1943 Lond.; MB BS (Hons. Med. & Path.) Lond. 1943; MD Lond. 1946; FRCP Lond. 1964, M 1944; MRCS Eng. LRCP Lond. 1943. (Guy's) Emerit. Prof. Clin. Pharm. & Emerit. Phys. Guy's Hosp. Lond. Socs: Pharm. Soc. & Assn. of Phys. Prev: Sen. Asst. & Sen. Regist. (Med.) Guy's Hosp. Lond.; Regist. (Med.) Nat. Heart Hosp. Lond.

TROUNCE, Nicholas David Heene and Goring Practice, 145 Heene Road, Worthing BN12 4PY Tel: 01903 235344 Fax: 01903 247099; 9 Landsdowne Court, Worthing BN11 5HD Tel: 01903 49889 — MB BChir 1976 Camb.; BA Camb. 1973; DRCOG 1981; DCH Eng. 1979. (Westm.) Princip. GP Worthing. Prev: SHO (Med.) St. Heliers Carshalton; SHO (Paediat.) St. Richards Hosp. Chichester; SHO (O & G) St. Richards Hosp. Chichester.

TROUNCE, Richard Fleming Lincoln Road Practice, 63 Lincoln Road, Peterborough PE1 2SF Tel: 01733 565511 Fax: 01733 569230 — MB BS 1983 Lond.; DCH RCP Lond. 1988.

TROUNSON, William Noy 42 Church End, Biddenham, Bedford MK40 4AR — MB BS 1977 Lond.; MRCP (UK) 1981.

TROUP, David Farquharson Arrochar Surgery, Kirkfield Place, Arrochar G83 7AE Tel: 01301 702531 Fax: 01301 702746; 35 George Street, Helensburgh G84 7EU Tel: 01436 674474 — MB ChB 1976 Aberd.; MRCGP 1980. Socs: Assoc. Mem. Fac. Homoeop.; Brit. Soc. Experim. & Clin. Hypn.; BASICS. Prev: GP Turriff; Trainee GP Aberd. VTS.

TROUP, Dorothy Iona (retired) 61 Woodside Drive, Forres IV36 2UF Tel: 01309 675724 — MB ChB 1949 Ed.; DObst RCOG 1954. Prev: Med. Adviser Dorothy Ho. Foundat. Bath.

TROUP, Douglas (retired) Group Practice Centre, Old Chester Road, Great Sutton, South Wirral — MB ChB 1951 Glas.; DObst RCOG 1955.

TROUP, Ian McCrae (retired) 3 Bonspiel Gardens, Camphill Road, Dundonald, Belfast DD5 2LH Tel: 01382 774907 Email: tktroup@aol.com — MB ChB St. And. 1943; DMedRehab Eng. 1976. Hon. Research Fell. Dept. Orthop. & Traum. Surg. Dundee Univ. Prev: Cons. Rehabil. Med. (Prosth.s & Orthotics) Dundee Limb Fitting Centre.

TROUP, John Duncan Gordon Kirkton House, Cairnie, Huntly AB54 4TR Tel: 01466 760207 Fax: 01466 760300 Email:

TROUTON

john.troup@kirkton-house.fsnet.co.uk — MRCS Eng. LRCP Lond. 1949; DSc Med. Lond. 1989, PhD 1968; FFOM (Hons.) RCP Lond. 1994, MFOM 1985. (St. Thos.) Hon. Sen. Research Fell. (Orthop. Surg.) Univ. Aberd. Socs: Fell. Ergonomics Soc. Prev: Cons. & Vis. Prof. Inst. Occupat. Health, Helsinki; Hon. Cons. Phys. Roy. Free Hosp. Lond.; Research Fell. Inst. Orthop. & Dir. Dawn Trust Unit for Spinal Research.

TROUTON, Thomas Graham Antrim Hospital, 45 Bush Road, Antrim BT41 2RL Tel: 028 944 24287 Fax: 028 944 24679 Email: tom.trouton@uh.n-i.nhs.uk; 74 Ballinderry Road, Lisburn BT28 2QS — MB BCh BAO 1983 Belf.; BSc (Hons.) Belf. 1980, MD 1989; FRCP Ed. 1996; MRCP (UK) 1986; FRCP Lond. 1997. Cons. Cardiol. Antrim Hosp.; Hon. Cons. Roy. Gp. Hosps. Belf. Socs: BMA; Coun. Mem. Irish Cardiac Soc.; Brit. Cardiac Soc. Prev: Clin. Research Fell. Cardiol. Mass. Gen. Hosp. & Harvard Med. Sch. Boston, USA; Sen. Regist. (Cardiol.) Roy. Vict. Hosp. Belf.; Research Fell. Roy. Vict. Hosp. Belf.

TROWBRIDGE, Michael David The Veterinary Surgery, Ralphs Ride, Bracknell RG12 9LG; 2 Kingfisher Drive, Barnstaple EX32 8QW — MB BS 1992 Lond.

TROWELL, Geoffrey Mark Highbridge Medical Centre, Pepperall Road, Highbridge TA9 3YA Tel: 01278 783220 Fax: 01278 795486; 5 Wallace Wells Road, Burnham-on-Sea TA8 1JP Tel: 01278 792581 Email: mark@trowell.prestel.co.uk — MB BS 1987 Lond.; MRCGP 1993; DRCOG 1991. (Char. Cross & Westm. Med. Sch.) Police Surg. Som.

TROWELL, Hugh Miles Sandown Medical Centre, Melville Street, Sandown PO36 8LD Tel: 01983 402464 Fax: 01983 405781 Email: hugh.trowell@gp-j84013.nhs.uk; Email: hugh@trowell.com — MB BS 1988 Lond.; MRCGP 1992; Cert. Family Plann. JCC 1992; T(G) 1992; DRCOG 1992, prize medal. (St. Thomas' Hospital, London) GP I. of Wight. Prev: Trainee GP I. of Wight VTS; SHO (Psychiat.) Newcroft Hosp. Newport, I. of Wight.

TROWELL, Jeremy Everard Pathology Laboratory, Ipswich Hospital NHS Trust, Heath Rd, Ipswich IP4 5PD Tel: 01473 703732 Email: trowellj@ijsk-tr.anglox.nks.uk — MB 1968 Camb.; BChir 1967; MRCPath 1974. (St. Bart.) Cons.Histopath, Ipswich Hosp. NHS Trust. Socs: Path. Soc.; Assn. of Clin. Pathologists. Prev: Ho. Surg. Roy. Berks. Hosp. Reading; Ho. Phys. Ronkswood Hosp. Worcester; Lect. Path. Univ. Birm.

TROWELL, Joan Mary John Radcliffe Hospital, Oxford OX3 9DU Tel: 01865 220944 Fax: 01865 751100 Email: joan.trowell@ndm.ox.ac.uk; Camp Corner Cottage, Old London Road, Milton Common, Thame OX9 2JR — MB BS 1964 Lond.; FRCP Lond. 1987, M 1967; MRCS Eng. LRCP Lond. 1964. (Roy. Free) Univ. Lect. & Hon. Cons. Phys. Nuffield Dept. Clin. Med. Univ. Oxf.; Apptd. to the Gen. Med. Counc. by Universities of Oxf. and Camb. Socs: Brit. Assn. for the Study of the Wives; Med. Wom.'s Federat., Past Pres. 1998-1999; Brit. Soc. of Gastroenterol. Prev: Regist. (Med.) Hammersmith Hosp. & Addenbrooke's Hosp. Camb.; Ho. Phys. Brompton Hosp. Lond.; Dep. Dir. Clin. Studies Oxf. Univ. Med. Sch.

TROWELL, Joanna Elizabeth 3 St Stephen's Close, Willerby, Hull HU10 6DG — MB BS 1996 Lond.

TROWELL, Judith Ann 45 Heath Drive, Potters Bar EN6 1EJ Tel: 01707 652205 — MB BS Lond. 1965; MRCS Eng. LRCP Lond. 1965; FRCPsych 1983, M 1976; DPM Eng. 1976; DCH Eng. 1969; M Br PA Soc. (Roy. Free) Cons. Psychiat. Child & Family Dept. Tavistock Clinic Lond.; Hon. Sen. Lect. Roy. Free Hosp. Sch. Med.; Vice Pres. Young Minds. Socs: Brit. Psychoanal. Soc.; Internat. Soc. for Preventaion of Child Abuse & Neglect.

TROWER, Christopher Simon Geoffrey, Squadron Ldr. RAF Med. Br. Retd. Poplar Grove Surgery, Meadow Way, Aylesbury HP20 1XB Tel: 01296 482554 Fax: 01296 398771; Hinderton, Maltmans Lane, Gerrards Cross SL9 8RP Tel: 01753 887044 Fax: 01753 891933 Email: 106103.2333@compuserve.com — MB BS 1974 Lond.; MRCS Eng. LRCP Lond. 1973; MRCGP 1979; DRCOG 1976. (St. Bart.) Princip. Partner Walton Gr. Surg. Aylesbury; Med. Adviser Bucks. HA; Bd. Mem./Clin. Governance Lead Aylesbury Vale PCG. Socs: BMA (Exec. Bucks. Div.); (Chairm.) Assn. Primary Care Med. Advisors; Vice-Chairm. Iain Rennie Hospice at Home. Prev: Chairm. Assn. of Primary Care Med. Advisers; GP Chalfont St. Peter; Sen. Med. Off. RAF Locking.

TROWER, Katharyne Jayne Longacre, 76 Preston Crowmarsh, Wallingford OX10 6SL — BM BS 1997 Nottm.

TROWER, Tyrone Paul Balidon Centre, Summerlands Hosp, Preston Rd, Yeovil BA20 2BX Tel: 01935 424511; Linden Lea, Ryme Road, Yetminster, Sherborne DT9 6JY — BM 1988 Soton.; MRCPsych 1993. Cons.(Child & Adoles Psychiat.) Som.. Prev: Regist. (Psychiat.) St. Jas. Hosp. Portsmouth & Knowle Hosp. Fareham; Regist. (Psychiat.) Roy. S. Hants. Hosp. Soton.; SHO (Psychiat.) Craylingwell Hosp. Chichester.

TROWLER, Eric Patrick Brookland House, 501 Crewe Road, Wistaston, Crewe CW2 6QP Tel: 01270 67250 — MB ChB 1959 Manch.

TROYACK, Anthony David East Barnet Health Centre, 149 East Barnet Road, Barnet EN4 8QZ Tel: 020 8440 7417 Fax: 020 8447 0126 — MB ChB 1968 Leeds; DObst RCOG 1970.

TRUCKLE, Simon Email: struckle@doctors.org.uk — MB BS 1996 Lond.; DRCOG 2000 Lond. (Royal London) GP Regist. Brighton. Prev: SHO Paediat., Brighton; SHO OBS & Gynae., Brighton; SHO Psychiat., Brighton.

TRUDGILL, Michael John Ashley, Squadron Ldr. RAF Med. Br. Station Medical Centre, RAF Linton on Ouse, York YO6 2AD Tel: 01347 848261; Ivy House, High St, Clophill, Bedford MK45 4BE Tel: 01525 860529 Fax: 01525 60529 Email: mike_trudge@classicmsn.com — MB BCh 1989 Wales; MRCGP 1996; DAvMed 1997; Dip. IMC 1995. (Wales) Sen. Med. Off. Flight Med. Off. GP/Aviat. Med. Linton on Ouse York. Socs: Roy. Aeronaut. Soc. Prev: Med. Off. RAF Leeming Med. Off. Ascension Is.

TRUDGILL, Nigel John 55 Penrhyn Road, Hunters Bar, Sheffield S11 8UL Tel: 0114 268 6877 — MB ChB 1988 Sheff.; MRCP (UK) 1991. Regist. (Gen. Med. & Gastroenterol.) Chesterfield & N. Derbysh. Roy Hosp. Prev: Regist. (Gen. Med. & Gastroenterol.) N.. Gen. Hosp. Sheff.; SHO (Cardiol., Med. & Renal Med.) N.. Gen. Hosp. Sheff.

TRUE, Rodney Charles (retired) 15 Southcrofts, Nantwich CW5 5SG Tel: 01270 610206 — MB ChB 1967 Leeds; MRCPsych 1972; DPM Eng. 1971. Cons. Psychiat. Mersey RHA. Prev: Sen. Regist. Birm. AHA (T).

TRUELOVE, Sidney Charles (retired) 14 Diamond Court, Banbury Road, Oxford OX2 7AA Tel: 01865 554749 — MB BChir 1938 Camb.; MD Camb. 1946; Hon. MD Madrid 1993; Hon. MD Crete 1989; Hon. MD Tübingen 1986; FRCP Lond. 1961, M 1947. Prev: Dir. (Clin. Studies) Univ. Oxf.

TRUEMAN, Angela Margaret City Hospital, Hucknall Road, Nottingham NG5 1PJ Tel: 0115 969 1169; Pear Tree Cottage, Padleys Lane, Burton Joyce, Nottingham NG14 5EB Tel: 0115 969 1169 — BSc Lond. 1964, MB BS 1967; FRCP Lond. 1987; MRCP (UK) 1971; MRCS Eng. LRCP Lond. 1967. (Roy. Free) Cons. Phys. (Geriat. Med.) City Hosp. Nottm.

TRUEMAN, Christopher John Ashby Turn Primary Care Centre, Ashby Link, Scunthorpe DN16 2UT — MB BCh 1985 Wales.

TRUEMAN, Freda Adelaide (retired) 12Llys Llewelyn, Meadow Farm, Llantwit fardre, Pontypridd CF38 2HQ Tel: 01446 732089 Fax: 01443 207889 Email: f.a.t@tesco.net — MB ChB Manch. 1951. Prev. Assoc. Specialist (Trauma & Orthop. Surg.) S. Glam. AHA (T).

TRUEMAN, Geoffrey Bruce 11 Hanover Drive, Chislehurst BR7 6TA — MB ChB 1987 Manch.; DRACOG 1990, M 1995. Regist. (O & G) Roy. Bournemouth Hosp.

TRUEMAN, Julie Anne 22 Merchants Quay, Salford Quays, Manchester Email: julie@man36.freeserve.co.uk; 22 Merchants Quay, Salford Quays, Manchester M5 2XR Tel: 0161 876 0121 Email: chaigh@globalnet.co.uk — MB ChB 1993 Leeds; MRCP (UK) 1997. (Leeds) Specialist Regist. (Paediat.) Roy. Manch. Childr. Hosp. Socs: Paediat. Research Soc.; Manch. Med Soc.

TRUEMAN, Mark David The Surgery, 2 Crescent Bakery, St. Georges Place, Cheltenham GL50 3PN Tel: 01242 226336 Fax: 01242 253587; Glenroy, 14 Church Road, St Marks, Cheltenham GL51 7AN Tel: 01242 227852 — BSc (Hons.) (Genetics) Lond. 1976, MB BS 1979; MFA RCS Eng. 1986; DCH RCP Lond. 1988; DA (UK) 1985; DRCOG 1982. (Univ. Coll. Hosp.) Prev: Regist. (Anaesth.) Cheltenham & Dist. HA.

TRUEMAN, Richard Simon Church Grange Health Centre, Bramblys Drive, Basingstoke RG21 8QN Tel: 01256 329021 Fax: 01256 817466; 27 Belvedere Gardens, Chineham, Basingstoke

RG24 8GB Tel: 01256 332654 — MB ChB 1987 Aberd.; MRCGP 1991. Socs: BMA.

TRUEMAN, Trevor The Willows, 6 Orchard Road, Malvern WR14 3DA Tel: 01684 573722 — MB ChB 1972 Birm.; BSc (Hons. Anat.) Birm. 1969; MD Birm. 1982; MRCP (UK) 1976. Socs: (Chairm.) Oromia Support Gp. (Human Rights & Pro-Democracy Organisat.).

TRUESDALE, Peter Jeffrey (retired) Trehill Cottage, Heathfield, Tavistock PL19 0LB Tel: 01822 810716 — MB ChB Leeds 1955; MFPHM 1989; MFCM 1974; FFOM RCP Lond. 1985, MFOM 1979; DIH Eng. 1970; DPH Lond. 1963. Prev: Hon. Phys. to HM the Qu.

TRUMAN, Kirstie Helen Cypher House, 8 Goose Island, Maritime Quarter, Swansea SA1 1UB — MB BCh 1997 Wales.

***TRUMAN, Lucy Ann** 4 Somermead Court, Maltsters Way, Lowestoft NR32 3PQ — BM 1994 Soton.; BSc (Biochem. Physiol.) Lond. 1990.

TRUMP, Dorothy Department of Medical Genetics, Box 134, Addenbrooke's Hospital NHS Trust, Hills Road, Cambridge CB2 2QQ Tel: 01223 216446 Email: dt207@cam.ac.uk; 28 George Street, Cambridge CB4 1AJ — BChir 1988 Camb.; BA Camb. 1985, MD 1996; MRCP (UK) 1991. (Univ. Camb. & Roy. Lond. Hosp.) Sen. Lect. & Hon. Cons. (Clin. Genetics) Addenbrooke's Hosp.. Prev: MRC Train. Fell. (Molecular Med.) RPMS Hammersmith Hosp. Lond.; Regist. (Med., Diabetes & Endocrinol.) N.wick Pk. Hosp.; SHO Rotat. (Med.) Guy's Hosp. Lond.

TRUMPER, Anne Louise 45 Moor Allerton Crescent, Leeds LS17 6SH — MB ChB 1986 Manch. SHO (Anaesth.) Trafford Gen. Hosp. Manch.

TRUMPER, Michele Josephine 1 Louisa Gardens, London E1 4NG — MB BS 1996 Lond.

TRUSCOTT, Douglas Ellis (retired) Twin View, Higher Carvossa, Ludgvan, Penzance TR20 8AJ — MB BS Lond. 1945; FRCR 1994; DMRD Eng 1951. Prev: Cons. Radiol. W. Cornw. Hosp.

TRUSCOTT, Janet Hilary 5 Kent Road, Bishopston, Bristol BS7 9DN — MB ChB 1971 Liverp.; MRCPsych 1977. Cons. Psychiat. S.mead Hosp. Bristol. Prev: Sen. Lect. (Ment. Health) Univ. Bristol; Sen. Regist. (Psychiat.) Bristol; Hon. Lect. (Ment. Health) Univ. Bristol.

TRUSSELL, Mr Richard Radford, OBE Whitmoor House, Ashill, Cullompton EX15 3NP Tel: 01884 840145 — MB ChB 1945 Birm.; ChM Birm. 1964, MB ChB 1945; FRCOG 1964, M 1951. Prof. Emerit. (O & G) Univ. Lond. at St. Geo. Hosp. Med. Sch. Socs: Fell. (Ex-Pres.) Assn. Surgs. E. Afr. & Fell. Roy. Soc. Med. Prev: Prof. (O & G) Makerere Univ. Kampala, Uganda.

TRUST, Patrick Martin Bank Street Surgery, 46-62 Bank Street, Alexandria G83 0LS Tel: 01389 752419 Fax: 01389 710521; Beaumaris, Church Avenue, Cardross, Dumbarton G82 5NS Tel: 01389 841387 — MB BS 1971 Lond.; FRCGP 1996, M 1982. Hosp. Pract. (Geriat.) Vale of Leven Hosp. & Dumbarton Jt. Hosp.; Chairm. Argyll & Clyde HB (Primary Care Audit Comm.). Prev: Assoc. Adviser (Gen. Pract). Dumbarton Dist. Univ. Glas.; Regist. MRC Blood Pressure Unit W.. Infirm. Glas.; SHO (Med.) Hammersmith Hosp. Lond.

TRUTER, Keith William Campbell Langley Corner, Ifield Green, Crawley RH11 0NF Tel: 01293 527114 Fax: 01293 553510; 9 Selbourne Close, Pound Hill, Crawley RH10 3SA Tel: 01293 885303 Email: keithtruter2@aol.com — BM BCh 1974 Oxf.; MA Oxf. 1975; MRCGP 1982; DRCOG 1982. Princip. Dr. Royds-Jones & Partners, Crawley. Socs: Roy. Coll. Gen. Practitioners. Prev: SHO (O & G) St. Richards Hosp. Chichester.; Trainee GP Crawley; SHO (Med.) Brit. Milit. Hosp. Hong Kong.

TRY, Jacqueline Louise Faversham Meadows, Mumfords Lane, Chalfont St Peter, Gerrards Cross SL9 8TQ — MB ChB 1987 Leic.

TRYE, Caroline Julia 59 Northumberland Road, Leamington Spa CV32 6HF — MB BCh 1991 Wales; MRCGP 1996; DCH RCP Lond. 1995; DRCOG 1995. (Univ. Wales Coll. Med.)

TRYTHALL, David Arthur Heaton 21 Lossie Drive, Iver SL0 0JR — MRCS Eng. LRCP Lond. 1946; MD Lond. 1950, MB BS 1946; MRCP (UK) 1949.

TRYTHALL, Janet Dr Gray's Hospital, Elgin IV30 1SN Tel: 01343 543131; Seaview, Covesea, Duffus, Elgin IV30 5QS Tel: 01343 814816 — MB BS 1971 Newc.; FFA RCS 1982; DObst RCOG 1973. (Univ. New. u. Tyne) Assoc. Specialist (Anaesth.) Doctor Gray's Hosp. Elgin. Prev: Trainee GP Blyth N.d. VTS; Regist.

(Anaesth.) Newc. AHA (T); Med. Off. Nchanga Consolidated Copper Mines (Broken Hill Div.) Kabwe, Zambia.

TRZCINSKI, Christopher John Markfield Surgery, The Green, Markfield LE67 9WU Tel: 01530 242313 Fax: 01530 245668; 13 Jonathan Close, Groby, Leicester LE6 0DM — BM 1984 Soton.; BM Soton 1984; MRCGP 1991; DRCOG 1988; DCH RCP Lond. 1987. Prev: Trainee GP Salisbury HA VTS.

TRZECIAK, Andrzej Wladyslaw The Health Centre, Chapel Street, Thirsk YO7 1LG Tel: 01845 523154 Fax: 01845 526213 — MB BS 1983 Lond.

TSAGURNIS, Ioannis 11 Welford Road, Sutton Coldfield B73 5DP — State Exam Med. Dusseldorf 1987.

TSAHALINA, Efthalia 75 Lewsey Road, Luton LU4 0EN — Ptychio latrikes 1991 Ioannina.

TSAI, Her Hsin Castle Hill Hospital, Castle Road, Cottingham HU16 5JQ; 260 Crow Road, Glasgow G11 7LA — MB ChB 1983 Aberd.; MB ChB. Aberd. 1983; MRCP (UK) 1986. Regist. (Med.) Grampian Health Bd.

TSAI-GOODMAN, Beverly Department of Paed. Cardiology, Ward 32, Royal Hospital for Sick Children, Upper Maudlin St., Bristol BS2 8DJ Tel: 0117 921 5411 — BM 1990 Soton.; MRCP (UK) 1994. SpR in Paediatric Cardiol.

TSAKONAS, Dionyssios Room 153 Nurses Home, Royal Orthopaedic Hospital, Woodlands, Northfield, Birmingham B31 2AP — Ptychio Iatrikes 1985 Athens.

TSAKOS, Elias Department of Obstetrics & Gynaecology, Sunderland Royal Hospital, Kayll Road, Sunderland SR4 7TP Tel: 0191 565 6256; 17B Eslington Terrace, Newcastle upon Tyne NE2 4RL Tel: 0191 281 4079 Email: elias.tsakos@newcastle.ac.uk — Ptychio Iatrikes 1991 Thessalonika; BSc CP 1997 (Brit. Soc. Cytol. & Cervical Path.); MRCOG 1994; DFFP 1993. Specialist Regist. (O & G) Sunderland Roy. Hosp. Prev: Specialist Regist. (O & G) Qu. Eliz. Hosp. Gateshead 1996-97; S. Cleveland Hosp. MiddlesBoro. 1995-96; SHO (Fertil.) Regulat. Research Centre for Reproduc. Med. Roy. Vict. Infirm. Newc. u. Tyne; Specialist Regist. Gateshead, Qu. Eliz. Hosp.

TSAM, Linda 19 Tangmere, Harrison St., London WC1H 8JG — MB BS 1992 Lond.; BSc (Hons.) Lond. 1989, MB BS 1992; MRCP (UK) 1997. (UCL)

TSAMIS, Michail Room 14, Floor 1, Parkstone House, Poole Hospital, 35 Parkstone Road, Poole BH15 2NG — State Exam 1993 Rome.

TSAN, Neville St. Mary's, Belvedere Lane, Goldsithney, Penzance TR20 9DH Tel: 01736 710741 — MRCS Eng. LRCP Lond. 1937. (St. Geo.)

TSANG, Bing 19A Tunstall Crescent, Leicester LE4 9DX — MB BS 1991 Lond.

TSANG, David Tze Kwan 44 Ethelbert Gardens, Gants Hill, Ilford IG2 6UN — MB BS 1994 Lond.

TSANG, Fiona Jane 2C Blenheim Road, London SW20 9BB — MB BS 1998 Lond.; MB BS Lond 1998.

TSANG, Mr Geoffrey Man Kwan 5 Blyth Close, Walton, Chesterfield S40 3LN — MB ChB 1987 Birm.; FRCS Ed. 1991.

TSANG, Hoo Fong 86 Market Street, Holyhead LL65 1UW — MB ChB 1997 Liverp.

TSANG, Hoo Kee 10 Old Post Road, Holyhead LL65 2RL — MB BCh 1997 Wales.

TSANG, Pierre Bridgeton Health Centre, 201 Abercromby Street, Glasgow G40 2DA Tel: 0141 531 6670 Fax: 0141 531 6505; 2 Muirhead Grove, Baillieston, Glasgow G69 7JT Tel: 0141 771 0003 Email: drpierre@tsang.freeserve.co.uk — MB ChB 1978 Glas. (Univ. Glas.)

TSANG, Roger Wah-Kwong 51 West Wynd, Newcastle upon Tyne NE12 6FP; 9A Kwong on Building, Wan Tau St, Tai Po, N.T., Hong Kong Tel: 656 3593 — MB ChB 1988 Glas.; MRCP (UK) 1991.

TSANG, Said Wan Mandy 85 Mote Hill, Hamilton ML3 6EA — MB ChB 1998 Glas.

TSANG, Mr Thomas Tat Ming Jenny Lind Children's Department, Norfolk & Norwich Hospital, Norwich NR1 3SR Tel: 01603 287171 Fax: 01603 287584 — MB BS 1982 Hong Kong; BSc (Hons.) Lond. 1977; FRCS Ed. 1987. Cons. Paediat. Surg. Norf. & Norwich Hosp. Socs: Fell. Roy. Coll. Surgs. Edin.; Brit. Assn. Paediat. Surg. Prev:

TSANG

Higher Surgic. Trainee (Paediat. Surg.) Qu. Med. Centre Univ. Hosp. Nottm.; Sen. Regist. (Paediat. Surg.) John Radcliffe Hosp. Oxf.; Regist. Roy. Manch. Childr. Hosp.

TSANG, Wai-Ming 55 Lamplighters Close, Hempstead, Gillingham ME7 3NZ — LRCP LRCS 1983 Ed.; LRCP LRCS Ed. LRCPS Glas. 1983. (Taiwan) Ho. Off. Stracathro Hosp. Brechin. Prev: Resid. Radiol. Dept. Nat. Taiwan Univ. Hosp. Taiwan.

TSANG, Woon Chau 11 The Thistles, Westlands, Newcastle ST5 2HL — MB BCh BAO 1991 Belf.; MB BCh Belf. 1991; FRCS (Ed.) 1997. (Queen's University Belfast)

TSANG, Woon Choy 28 Lambert Park, Dundonald, Belfast BT16 1LG — MB BCh BAO 1988 Belf.

TSANG, Woon Kam 28 Lambert Park, Dundonald, Belfast BT16 1LG Tel: 01232 489076 — MB ChB 1995 Sheff. (Univ. Sheff.) SHO (O & G) Sheff. Prev: (SHO) (O & G) Sheff.; SHO (A&E) Sheff.; SHO (Geuito-Urin. med.) Sheff.

TSANG WAN MEI, Mona Convent Garden Medical Centre, 47 Shorts Garden, London WC2 Tel: 020 7379 7209; 11 Abdale Road, London W12 7ER — MB BS 1971 Hong Kong.

TSANG WING KEUNG, Dr 144 Harley Street, London W1; 11 Abdale Road, London W12 7ER Tel: 020 8743 2031 — MB BS 1969 Hong Kong; FRCOG 1990, M 1975; DObst RCOG 1973. Prev: Cons. O & G Tung Wah Gp. Hosps. Hong Kong; SCMO Tower Hamlets HA.

TSANGARIDES, Mr Georgios Andreas County Hospital, Lincoln LN2 5QY, Egypt Tel: 01522 512512 — Ptychio Iatrikes 1969 Athens; FRCS Ed. 1991. Staff Grade Orthop. Co. Hosp. Lincoln LN2 5QY.

TSAO, Sabrina Siu-Ling 14 Melbourne House, 50 Kensington Place, London W8 7PW Tel: 020 7727 4885 Fax: 020 7727 4885 — MB BS 1993 Lond. SHO (Paediat.) Lewisham Hosp. Lond.

TSAVELLAS, Mr George 68 Ecclesbourne Gardens, London N13 5HZ — MB BS 1990 Lond.; FRCS Eng. 1996; FRCS Ed. 1996. Specialist Regist. (Gen. Surg.) Wessex Higher Surgic. Train. Scheme. Prev: SHO Rotat. (Surg.) Univ. Coll. & Middlx. Hosp. Lond.

TSE, Bonnie Si-Wang The Glebe Surgery, Monastery Lane, Storrington, Pulborough RH20 4LR Fax: 01903 740700 — MB BS 1979 Lond.; MRCGP 1987; DCH RCP Lond. 1981. (Lond.)

TSE, Chun-Kee Victor c/o Drive W. Richardson, 14 Avon, Hockley, Tamworth B77 5QA — MB BChir 1984 Camb.; PhD Lond. 1981.

TSE, David Tit Kin 53 Icknield Drive, Ilford IG2 6SE — MB BS 1978 Lond.

TSE, Mr Ho-Wah Middlesborough General Hospital, Ayresome Green Lane, Middlesbrough TS5 5AZ — MB BCh BAO 1985 NUI; FRCSI 1990.

TSE, Nan Yuin 7 Ulster Road, Margate CT9 5RZ — MB ChB 1996 Leeds.

TSE, Samson Chun Yiu Ashdyke, Wheatley Lane, Carlton-Le-Moorland, Lincoln LN5 9JA — MB ChB 1990 Glas.

TSE, Wai Yee Department of Nephrology, Queen Elizabeth Medical Centre, Edgbaston, Birmingham B15 2TH Tel: 0121 472 1311 Fax: 0121 627 2527 Email: w.y.tse.1@bham.ac.uk; 1 Nortune Close, Wychall Lane, King's Norton, Birmingham B38 8AJ Tel: 0121 459 8956 — MB ChB 1989 Leeds; BSc (Hons.) Leeds 1986, MB ChB (Hons.) 1989; MRCP (UK) 1992. Regist. Rotat. (Gen. Med. & Nephrol.) Qu. Eliz. Med. Centre Birm. Prev: SHO Rotat. (Med.) Newc.; Train. Fell. MRC.

TSE, Yin Ha Anissa 6 Farfield Grove, Beeston, Nottingham NG9 2PW — BM BS 1992 Nottm.

TSE SAK KWUN, Pin Cheong Waverley Avenue, 6 Waverley Avenue, Fleetwood FY7 8BN Tel: 01253 778448; 27 Princes Way, Fleetwood FY7 8PG Tel: 01253 875179 — MB ChB 1985 Manch.; MRCGP 1989; DCH RCP Lond. 1988; DRCOG 1987; BSc (Hons) St. And 1980. (St Andrews and Manchester)

TSEKOURAS, Anastasios Department of Plastic Surgery, Countess of Chester Hospital, Liverpool Road, Chester CH2 1BQ — Ptychio Iatrikes 1987 Athens. Regist. (Plastic Surg.) Countess of Chester Hosp.

TSELENTAKIS, Mr Georgis 11 Jasmine Close, Worcester WR5 3LU — Ptychio Iatrikes 1988 Thessalonika; FRCS Glas. 1994.

TSENG, Evelin Hing Ying Tanglewood, Hawthorne Road, Bickley, Bromley BR1 2HN Tel: 020 8295 0935 — MB BS 1975 Lond.; MRCP (UK) 1979; MRCS Eng. LRCP Lond. 1975; MSc Lond. 1995.

(Guy's) Cons. (Community Paediat.s) Ravenshourne NHS Trust Kent. Prev: Sen. Regist. (Optimum Health Servs.) Lond.

TSEUNG, Ka Wai Manor Farm Medical Centre, Manor Farm Road, Huyton, Liverpool L36 0UB Tel: 0151 480 1244 Fax: 0151 480 6047; 271 Menlove Avenue, Woolton, Liverpool L25 7SA — MB ChB 1980 Liverp.; BSc (Hons.) Liverp. 1976, MB ChB 1980. (Liverpool)

TSEUNG, Man Hong Tel: 0151 424 3986 Fax: 0151 424 1009 — MB ChB 1987 Liverp.; BSc (Hons) Liverp. 1984; MRCGP 1993; Cert. Family Plann. JCC 1991; DRCOG 1991. (Liverp.) GP Princip.; Clin. Lead in Palliat. Med. for Runcorn & Widnes PCG. Prev: Trainee GP Ormskirk Dist. Gen. Hosp.; SHO (Paediat.) Alder Hey Hosp. Liverp.; SHO (Cardiothoracic Med.) BRd.green Hosp. Liverp.

TSIAPRAS, Dimitrios 41 Aldbourne Road, London W12 0LW — Ptychio Iatrikes 1984 Athens.

TSINTIS, Panayiotis Andrea 14 Peterborough Drive, Lodge Moor, Sheffield S10 4JB — MB ChB 1983 Sheff.; MRCP (UK) 1987. Sen. Med. Off. Med. Control Agency DoH. Prev: Regist. (Med.) Glas. Roy. Infirm.; SHO (Gen. & Geriat. Med.) Nether Edge Hosp. Sheff.; SHO (A & E) Roy. Hallamsh. Hosp. Sheff.

TSO, Marie Teresa Bik Yan 28 Meadowbank, Watford WD19 4NP — MB ChB 1987 Glas.

TSOI, Kenney Cham Fai 99 Elmhurst Drive, Hornchurch RM11 1NZ — MB BS 1997 Lond.

TSOKODRYI, Casper 40 Somers Road, London E17 6RX — MB BS 1984 Lond.

TSOLAKIS, Marios Georgiou Flat 59, Viceroy Court, Wilmslow Road, Didsbury, Manchester M20 2RH Email: tsolakis@doctors.org.net — MB ChB 1990 Manch.; MRCGP 1995. (Univ. Manch.) Socs: BMA; Med. Protec. Soc. Prev: Trainee GP/SHO Univ. Liverp.

***TSUI, Janice Chung Sze** 50 Grosvenor Road, Petts Wood, Orpington BR5 1QU Tel: 01689 825528 Email: jcstsui@msn.com — BChir 1996 Camb.; MB Camb. 1997.

TSUI, Mr Steven Shi Lap Department of Cardiothoracic Surgery, Papworth Hospital, Papworth, Cambridge CB3 8RE Tel: 01480 364297 Fax: 01480 364332 — MB BChir 1988 Camb.; MA Camb. 1989, MD 1996; FRCS Eng. 1992; FRCS (Cth.) 1997. (Univ. Camb.) Cons. (Cardiothoracic Surg.) Papworth Hosp. Prev: Research Fell. Duke Univ. Med. Center, USA.

TUANO, Raquel 1 Cropton Way, Manor Fard, Hindley Green, Wigan WN2 4RT — MB ChB 1998 Leic.

TUBBS, Diana Barbara 48 Ridgmont Road, Seabridge, Newcastle ST5 3LB — MB BS 1970 Lond.; MRCS Eng. LRCP Lond. 1970; DCH Eng. 1974. (St. Bart.) Clin. Asst. (Cystic Fibrosis) Newc. Prev: SHO (Paediat.) Hammersmith Hosp. Lond.; Med. Off. (Paediat.) Wusasa Hosp. Zaria, Nigeria.

TUBBS, Hugh Robert Department of Clinical Infection, City General Hospital, Stoke-on-Trent ST4 6QG Tel: 01782 552298 Fax: 01782 711540 — MB BS 1970 Lond.; MB BS (Hons. Distinc. Therap. & Applied Pharmacol.) 1970; MSc (Distinc. & Frederick Murgatroyd Award) Lond. 1977; FRCP Lond. 1987, M 1973; MRCS Eng. LRCP Lond. 1970; DCH Eng. 1978. (St. Bart.) Cons. Phys. N. Staffs. Hosp. In Clin. Infec., Trop. Dis.s and Gen. Internal Med.; Sen. Lect. Sch. Postgrad. Med. Keele Univ.; Director of PostGrad. Educat., Div. of Med., N. Staffs Hosp. Socs: Fell. Roy. Soc. Med.; Roy. Soc. Trop. Med. & Hyg. Prev: Cons. Phys. & Lect. (Immunol.) Ahmadu Bello Univ. Hosp., Nigeria; Regist. Liver Unit King's Coll. Hosp. Lond.; MRC Fell. Lond. Sch. Hyg. & Trop. Med.

TUBBS, Mr Oswald Nigel Nuffield Hospital, 22 Somerset Road, Edgbaston, Birmingham B15 2QQ Tel: 0121 456 2000 Fax: 0121 452 2881; 41 Ellesboro Road, Harborne, Birmingham B17 8PU Tel: 0121 427 3272 Fax: 0121 428 4561 Email: nigel@tubbs.freeserve.co.uk — MRCS Eng. LRCP Lond. 1964; MB Camb. 1964, BChir 1963; FRCS Eng. 1970; FICS 1977; MA Camb. 1962. (St. Thos.) Cons. Surg. Univ. Hosp. and Roy. Orthopaedic Hosp. Birm.; Hon. Lect. Surg. Univ. Birm.; Edr. Injury Brit. Jl. Accid. Surg. Socs: Brit. Orthop. Assn.; Fell. Inst. of Sports Med.; Brit. Assn. for Surg. of Knee. Prev: Sen. Surg. Regist. Robt. Jones & Agnes Hunt Orthop. Hosp. OsW.ry; SHO (Thoracic Surg.) St. Thos. Hosp.; Ho. Surg. Nat. Hosp. Nerv. Dis. Qu. Sq.

TUBBS, Sophie Clare 34 Rocks Lane, London SW13 0DB — MB BS 1997 Lond.

TUCKER

TUBMAN, Terese Margaret 22 Churchtown Road, Gerrans, Portscatho, Truro TR2 5DZ.

TUBMAN, Thomas Richard John 46 Rugby Road, Belfast BT7 1PS — MB BCh BAO 1983 Belf.; BSc (Hons.) (Anat.) Belf. 1980, MD 1993, MB BCh BAO 1983; MRCP (UK) 1987. SHO (Med.) Waveney Hosp. Ballymena. Socs: Ulster Med. Soc.

TUBMEN, Henry, TD (retired) Front Street, Pelton, Chester-le-Street DH2 1DE Tel: 0191 370 0263 — MB BS 1951 Durh.

TUBOKU-METZGER, Adeyemi Frank, OBE Tel: 020 8648 2011; 136 Streatham Road, Mitcham CR4 2AE Tel: 020 8648 2011 — MRCS Eng. LRCP Lond. 1942; FRCP Glas. 1964, M 1962; Dip. Med. Acupunc. 1997; FRFPS Glas. 1953; DTM & H Liverp. 1950. (Univ. Coll., Lond. Hosp. & Liverp.) JP Sierra Leone; Cons. Phys. Sierra Leone. Socs: BMA; Brit. Med. Acupunct. Soc. Prev: Mem. WHO Advis. Expert Panel; Sen. Specialist Phys. MoH, Sierra Leone.

TUCK, Alison Wendy Barton Road, Tewkesbury GL20 5QQ — MB ChB 1981 Brist.; MFFP 1994; DRCOG 1985. SCMO/Instruc. Doctor (Family Plann.) Worcester.

TUCK, Barry Austin Avenue Road Surgery, 28A Avenue Road, Malvern WR14 3BG Tel: 01684 561333 Fax: 01684 893664; Lilac Cottage, Picken End, Hanley Swan, Worcester WR8 0DQ Tel: 01684 310528 — MB ChB 1981 Birm.; MRCGP 1985; DRCOG 1985.

TUCK, Christine Scott (retired) 9 Bootham Crescent, York YO30 7AJ Tel: 01904 623841 — MB BS 1963 Lond.; FRCS Ed. 1968; FRCOG 1986, M 1971. Prev: Cons. (O & G) York Health Dist.

TUCK, Edgar Allen Marshall (retired) 5 Monkswood, Silverstone, Towcester NN12 8TG Tel: 01327 857469 — MB BS 1954 Lond.; MRCS Eng. LRCP Lond. 1953.

TUCK, Gillian Wansford & King's Cliffe Practice, Old Hill Farm, Yarwell Road, Wansford, Peterborough PE8 6PL Tel: 01780 782342 Fax: 01780 783434; Drift End, First Drift, Wothorpe, Stamford PE9 3JL — MB ChB 1971 Manch.; DA Eng. 1973.

TUCK, Harry Angell (retired) Grange Cottage, Thorpe Lane, Cawood, Selby YO8 3SG Tel: 01757 268168 — MB BS 1937 Lond. Prev: Regional Med. Off. Regional Med. Serv. (E. Midl. Div.) DHSS.

TUCK, Jeremy John Hobart, Lt.-Col. Commanding Officer, 5 General Support Medical Regt., Fulwood Barracks, Preston PR2 8AA Tel: 01772 260500 — MB BS 1983 Lond.; MRCGP 1993; MSc (Public Health) Lond. (Lond. Hosp.) Specialist Regist. Pub. Health Med. Socs: Fell. Roy. Soc. of Med. Yeomen; Worshipful Soc. Apoth. Prev: Staff Off. (Med. Br.) Permanent Jt. HQ, N.wood.

TUCK, Jonathan Stephen Department of Radiology, Royal Bolton Hospital, Minerva Road, Bolton BL4 0JR — MB ChB 1980 Glas.; FRCS Glas. 1984; FRCR 1989. (Glas. Univ.) Cons. Radiol. Roy. Bolton Hosp. Socs: Brit. Soc. Interven. Radiol.; CIRSE. Prev: Sen. Regist. (Diagn. Radiol.) Manch. Roy. Infirm.; Vis. Asst. Prof. Radiol. Univ. Maryland Med. Systems Baltimore, USA; Sen. Regist. (Diagn. Radiol.) Christie Hosp. Manch.

TUCK, Michael Elmitt (retired) Channel View Surgery, 3 Courtenay Place, Teignmouth TQ14 8AY Tel: 01626 774656 — MB BChir 1959 Camb.; MA, MB Camb. 1959, BChir 1958; DObst RCOG 1960. Prev: Ho. Phys. & Ho. Off. Dept. O & G Middlx. Hosp. Lond.

TUCK, Simon Julian Drift End, First Drift, Wothorpe, Stamford PE9 3JL — MB ChB 1971 Manch.; FRCP Lond. 1995; MRCP (UK) 1975; DCH Eng. 1977. Cons. Paediat. P'boro. Dist. Hosp. Socs: Brit. Paediat. Assn.; Neonat. Soc. Prev: Sen. Regist. (Paediat.) Addenbrooke's Hosp. Camb.; Sen. Regist. (Paediat.) Norf. & Norwich Hosp.

TUCK, Stephen Paul 25 Chantry Way E., Swanland, North Ferriby HU14 3QF; 95 Townsgate, Silkstone, Barnsley S75 4SW — MB ChB 1993 Leeds; BSc. SHO Rotat. (Med.) The Roy. Hallamshire Hosp., Sheff. Socs: BMA. Prev: SHO (Neurol.) Pinderfield Wakefield; SHO Rotat. (Med.) Barnsley Dist. Gen. Hosp. S. Yorks.; Ho. Off. (Surg.) St. James Univ. Teachg. Hosp.

TUCK, Susan Catherine Channel View Surgery, 3 Courtenay Place, Teignmouth TQ14 8AY Tel: 01626 774656 — MB BS 1959 Lond. (Middlx.) Prev: Ho. Surg. Middlx. Hosp.; Ho. Phys. P.ss Alice Hosp. E.bourne.

TUCK, Susan Margaret Department Obst. & Gyn., Royal Free Hospital, Hampstead, London NW3 2QG Tel: 020 7794 0500 — MD 1984 Bristol; MB ChB 1974; MRCGP 1978; FRCOG 1992, M 1980, D 1977; DCH Eng. 1977. Cons. O & G Roy. Free Hosp. Lond. Socs: Fell. Roy. Soc. Med. Prev: Sen. Regist. John Radcliffe Hosp. Oxf.; Regist. King's Coll. Hosp. Lond.

TUCKER, Andrew John Kirkham Medical Practice, St. Alban's Road, Torquay TQ1 3SL Tel: 01803 323541 Fax: 01803 314311; Hill Park Farm, Lower Gabwell, Stokeinteignhead, Newton Abbot TQ12 4QR — MB BS 1979 Lond.; BSc (Hons.) Lond. 1975, MB BS 1979; MRCGP 1984; DRCOG 1981. (St. Bart.) Prev: SHO (O & G) St. Bart. Hosp. Lond.; SHO (Geriat. & Paediat.) Crawley Hosp.

TUCKER, Andrew John Westlands Medical Centre, 20B Westlands Grove, Porttchester, Fareham PO16 9AD Tel: 01705 377514 — BM 1990 Soton.; MRCGP 1994; DRCOG 1994. Trainee GP/SHO Portsmouth & SE Hants. VTS. Prev: Ho. Off. (Med.) St. Mary's Hosp. Portsmouth; Ho. Off. (Surg.) Poole Gen. Hosp.

TUCKER, Anna Katherine 37 Barkfield Lane, Liverpool L37 1LY — MB ChB Liverp. 1994; DRCOG 1996. Gen. Practitioner Neston Surg. Mellocu La. Neston S. Wirral. Prev: GP Regist. Manor Health Centre Liscard Wirral; GP Regist. Villa Med. Centre Prenton Wirral.

TUCKER, Mr Antony Gower Bradford Royal Infirmary, Duckworth Lane, Bradford BD9 6RJ Tel: 01274 364118 — MB ChB 1972 Sheff.; FRCS Eng. 1977. Cons. ENT Bradford Roy. Infirm. Prev: Sen. Regist. (ENT) Liverp. AHA (T); Regist. (ENT) Avon AHA (T); SHO (Plastic Surg.) Nottm. City Hosp.

TUCKER, Audrey Kathleen Princess Grace Hospital, Nottingham Place, London W1M 3FD Tel: 020 7486 1234 Fax: 020 7486 1084; 391 Lauderdale Tower, Barbican, London EC2Y 8NA Tel: 020 7628 0126 Fax: 020 7628 0126 — MB BS Lond. 1964; FFR 1970; DMRD Eng. 1967. (St. Bart.) Cons. Radiol. P.ss Grace Hosp. Lond. Socs: Fell. Roy. Soc. Med.; Fell. Med. Soc. Lond. Prev: Cons. Radiol. St. Bart. Hosp. Lond.; Sen. Regist. (Diag. Radiol.) Middlx. Hosp. Lond.; Ho. Surg. St. Bart. Hosp.

TUCKER, Barbara Rose 13 Letchworth Avenue, Chatham ME4 6NP — MB BS 1964 Lond. (Lond. Hosp.) Prev: Ho. Surg. & Ho. Phys. St. Bart. Hosp. Rochester.

TUCKER, Barry Flat D, Sealyham Staff Residences, Withybush Hospital, Haverfordwest SA61 2PZ — MB BCh 1992 Wales.

TUCKER, Danny Edward Rotherham General Hospital, Moorgate Rd, Rotherham S60 2UD Tel: 01709 820000; 518 Fulwood Road, Sheffield S10 3QD Email: dt.@dr.com — MB BS 1993 Lond.; MRCOG 1999. Specialist Regist. (O & G) Cen Sheff. Univ Hosp. Prev: SHO (O & G & Genitourin. Med.) City Hosp. Nottm.; Ho. Phys. Maidstone Gen. Hosp.; Ho. Surg. Kings Coll. Hosp. Lond.

TUCKER, David Stone (retired) 10 West Cliff, Southgate, Gower, Swansea SA3 2AN Tel: 01792 234737 Fax: 01792 234737 Email: dst@southgate71.fsnet.co.uk — MB BS 1958 Lond.; MRCS Eng. LRCP Lond. 1956; MRCGP 1973. Prev: Ho. Surg. Bolingbroke Hosp. Lond.

TUCKER, Dawn Louise 60 St Peters Road, West Mersea, Colchester CO5 8LN — MB BS 1996 Lond.

TUCKER, Graham Paul Nines and Partners, Shoreham Health Centre, Pond Road, Shoreham-by-Sea BN43 5US Tel: 01273 440550; Questa, 19 Heyshott Close, Lancing BN15 0QJ Tel: 01903 753595 — MB 1976 Camb.; BChir 1975; MRCGP 1980; DRCOG 1979; DCH Eng. 1978. Prev: Ho. Phys. OldCh. Hosp. Romford; Trainee GP Windsor VTS.

TUCKER, Helen Holme 3 Selby Close, Westlands, Newcastle ST5 3JB Tel: 01782 615168 Email: helenandjohn@3.selby.freeserve.co.uk — MB BS 1967 Lond.; MRCS Eng. LRCP Lond. 1967; MFFP 1993. (Roy. Free) SCMO (Community Gyn. & Family Plann.) N. Staffs. Hosp. Centre NHS Trust; Clin. Lect. (Postgrad. Med.) Univ. Keele. Socs: Brit. Menopause Soc.; Brit. Soc. Colpos. & Cerv. Path.

TUCKER, Howard Simon 3 Weaver Ct, Torquay TQ2 7RT — MB BCh 1997 Wales.

TUCKER, John Burnard (retired) Netherwayes, 1 Sidmouth Road, Honiton EX14 1BE Tel: 01404 42317 Fax: 01404 42317 Email: diabebli@eurobell.co.uk — MB ChB Bristol 1941.

TUCKER, Mr John Keith 77 Newmarket Road, Norwich NR2 2HW Tel: 01603 614016 Fax: 01603 766469 Email: ktucker77@aol.com; The Mill House, Mill Road, Barnham Broom, Norwich NR9 4DE Tel: 01603 759470 Fax: 01603 759580 Email: ktucker@aol.com — MB BS 1968 Lond.; FRCS Eng. 1973; MRCS Eng. LRCP Lond. 1968. (Char. Cross) Cons. Orthop. Surg. Norf. & Norwich Hosp. Socs: BMA; Hon. Sec. Brit. Hip Soc.; Brit. Orthop. Assn. Prev: Sen. Regist.

TUCKER

(Orthop.) St. Bart. Hosp. Lond.; Regist. (Surg.) Addenbrooke's Hosp. Camb.; Ho. Surg. Char. Cross Hosp. Lond.

TUCKER, John Shackleton St Luke's Hospital, Little Horton Lane, Bradford BD5 0NA Tel: 01274 365213; Spring Head, 436 Haworth Road, Allerton, Bradford BD15 9LL — MB ChB 1966 (Hons. Distinc. Med.) Leeds; BSc (cl. II Hons.) Leeds 1966; FRCP Lond. 1987; MRCP (UK) 1972. (Leeds) Cons. Phys. (Geriat. Med.) St. Luke's Hosp. Bradford. Socs: Brit. Geriat. Soc. Prev: Ho. Phys. Leeds Gen. Infirm.; Lect. (Med. & Geriat. Med.) Univ. Manch.

TUCKER, Kerry Elizabeth 3 Rosebery Av, Colchester CO1 2UJ — MB ChB 1997 Birm.

TUCKER, Kevan Paul 88 Glenlee Lane, Long Lee, Keighley BD21 5QY Tel: 01535 600488; 46 James Hall Gardens, Walmer, Deal CT14 7TA Tel: 01304 364077 — MB ChB 1987 Leeds. Trainee GP. Airdale VTS. Prev: Pre-Regist. Hse. Jobs (Med.) Roy. Halifax Infirm. & Leeds Gen. Infirm. (Surg. Urol.).

***TUCKER, Matthew Harold** 3 Green Lane, Purley CR8 3PP — MB ChB 1998 Birm.

TUCKER, Peter William, MBE, TD (retired) 31 Julians Acres, Berrow, Burnham-on-Sea TA8 2LX Tel: 01278 780526 — MB BChir Camb. 1950; DObst RCOG 1952; MRCGP 1960. Prev: Capt. RAMC.

TUCKER, Philippa Margaret Mill Road Surgery, 61 Mill Road, Mile End, Colchester CO4 5LE Tel: 01206 845900 Fax: 01206 844090 — MB BS 1980 Newc.

TUCKER, Phillip James (retired) Stonecross Surgery, 25 Street End Road, Chatham ME5 0AA — MB BS Lond. 1964. Prev: Ho. Off. (Surg.) Whipps Cross Hosp. Lond.

TUCKER, Roderick John Wolstanton Medical Centre, Palmerston Street, Newcastle ST5 8BN Tel: 01782 627488 Fax: 01782 662313; 3 Selby Close, Westlands, Newcastle ST5 3JB Tel: 01782 615168 — MB BS Lond. 1966; FRCGP 1986, M 1971; DFFP 1993. (Roy. Free) p/t Clin. Asst. (Diabetes) N. Staffs. Hosp. Centre Stoke-on-Trent. Socs: BMA; N. Staffs. Med. Inst. Prev: Ho. Surg. (ENT) Roy. Free Hosp. Lond.; Ho. Phys. N. Staffs. Roy. Infirm. Stoke-on-Trent.

TUCKER, Rosemary Jane Tudor Cottage, Fivehead, Taunton TA3 6PJ — MB BS 1990 Lond.; MRCGP 1995; MRCP (Paeds) 1998.

TUCKER, Sam Michael 152 Harley Street, London W1N 1HH Tel: 020 7935 1858 Fax: 020 7224 2574; 65 Uphill Road, Mill Hill, London NW7 4PT Tel: 020 8959 0500 Fax: 020 8959 0500 Email: sammtucker@aol.com — MB BCh Witwatersrand 1952; FRCP Lond. 1990; FRCP Ed. 1973, M 1961; FRCPCH 1997; DCH Eng. 1957. (Witwatersrand) Hon. Cons. Paediat. Hillingdon Hosp. & Mt. Vernon Hosp. N.wood; Hon. Dir. Research Hillingdon Hosp. & Brunel Univ.; Hon. Lect. (Paediat. & Cardiol.) Inst. Dis. of Chest Brompton Hosp. Lond; Assoc. Prof. Dept. Mech. Engin. Brunel Univ. W. Lond. Socs: Brit. Paediat. Assn. & Brit. Cardiac Soc.; Roy. Soc. Med. (Ex-Pres. Sect. Paediat.); Counc. Mem. Roy. Soc. Med. (Treas.). Prev: Sen. Regist. (Paediat.) St. Geo. Hosp. Lond.; Regist. (Paediat.) Middlx. Hosp. & Qu. Eliz. Hosp. Childr. Lond.

TUCKER, Sarah Catherine 3 Weaver Court, Torquay TQ2 7RT Tel: 01803 400564 — MB ChB 1992 Bristol; FRCS Lond. 1998. SHO (Surg.) Torbay Gen. Prev: SHO (Plastics) Morriston Swansea; SHO (Orthop.) Cardiff Roy. Infirm.; SHO (Gen. Surg.) Gwent.

TUCKER, Sian Elizabeth 32 Millers Meadow, Rainow, Macclesfield SK10 5UE — BM BS 1994 Nottm.

TUCKER, Simon Christopher Department of Dermatology, Hope Hospital, Stott Lane, Salford M6 8HD — MB ChB 1992 Birm.

TUCKER, Stephen Robert 12 St Michael, Norwich NR3 1EP — MB BS 1983 Lond.; MRCPsych 1991.

TUCKER, Mr Stewart Kenneth 34A Waterlow Road, London N19 5NH — MB BS 1988 Lond.; FRCS Eng. 1992. Regist. (Orthop.) Univ. Coll. & Middlx. Hosps. Prev: SHO (A & E) Univ. Coll. Hosp. Lond.; SHO (Orthop. & Gen. Surg.) Watford Gen. Hosp.

TUCKER, Susan Elizabeth 196 Redmayne Drive, Chelmsford CM2 9XE — MB BS 1989 Lond.

TUCKER, Mrs Valerie Alberta Elsie (retired) La Maison de Haut, Rue Des Messuriers, St Peters, Guernsey GY7 9SL Tel: 01481 65191 — MB BS Lond. 1953; DA Eng. 1955. Prev: Ho. Phys. & Resid. Anaesth. St. Thos. Hosp.

TUCKER, Vanessa Lynn 4 Arran Close, Cosham, Portsmouth PO6 3UD Tel: 02392 379510 — BM 1988 Soton.; MRCP (UK) 1992; FRCA 1997. Specialist Regist. (Anaesth.) Wessex Region. Prev: Regist. (Med.) St. Mary's Hosp. Portsmouth; SHO (Anaesth.) Soton. Univ. Hosps.; SHO (Anaesth. & Med.) Qu. Alexandra Hosp. Portsmouth.

TUCKER, William Frank Gordon Alexandra Hospital, Woodrow Drive, Redditch B98 7UB; 2 Inett Way, Manor Oaks, Droitwich WR9 0DN — MB BS 1976 Lond.; MRCP (UK) 1978; MRCS Eng. LRCP Lond. 1976; FRCP (Lond) 2000. (St. Geo.) Cons. Dermat. N. Worcs. Health Dist. Prev: Sen. Regist. & Tutor (Dermat.) Roy. Hallamsh. Hosp. Sheff.; Regist. (Dermat.) St. Mary's Hosp. Lond.

TUCKERMAN, James Gerard Seafield Medical Centre, Barhill Road, Buckie AB56 1FP Tel: 01542 835577 Fax: 01542 835092 — MB ChB 1976 Aberd.

TUCKEY, Jacqui Ellen Ella Gordon Unit, St Marys Hosp, Milton Rd, Portsmouth PO3 6; 12 Myers Close, Swanmore S032 2RN — MB ChB 1988 Bristol; MRCOG 1993. (Univ. Bristol) Specialist Regist. Comm Gyn. St Marys Hosp. Portsmouth. Prev: Regist. (O & G) Roy. Gwent Hosp. Newport; Specialist Regist.(Ob + Gyn.) N. Hants Hosp. Basingstoke; Clin. Ass.(Ob + Gyn.) Roy United Hosp. Bath.

TUCKEY, Jennifer Patricia Royal United Hospital, Bath BA1 3NG Tel: 01225 428331; Wier House, Lower Stoke, Limpley Stoke, Bath BA2 7FR Tel: 01225 723103 — MB ChB 1983 Bristol; FRCA 1989; DCH RCPS 1987. Cons. Anaesth., Roy. United Hosp. Bath. Socs: Obst. Anaesth. Assn.; Assn. Anaesth.; Clin. Soc. Bath. Prev: Staff Grade Anaesth. Bath; Regist. (Anaesth.) Plymouth & Portsmouth; SHO (Paediat.) Poole Bournemouth.

TUCKFIELD, Christopher John 37 Glisson Road, Cambridge CB1 2HA — MB BS 1984 Sydney.

TUCKLEY, Catharine Mary (retired) 17 Horwood Avenue, Derby DE23 6NX Tel: 01332 348423 — MB ChB 1962 Aberd.

TUCKLEY, Jonathan Marc 25 Links Road, Poole BH14 9QR — MB BS 1991 Lond.; BSc (Hons.) Lond. 1988, MB BS 1991. SHO (Anaesth.) Roy. Cornw. Hosp. Treliske Truro.

TUCKMAN, Emanuel (retired) 27 Downside Crescent, London NW3 2AN Tel: 020 7794 5725 — MD 1963 Lond.; MB BS 1944; DCH Eng. 1945, DTM & H 1947. Prev: Nuffield Trav. Fell. 1963.

TUCKWELL, Gareth David Burrswood Hospital, Groombridge, Tunbridge Wells TN3 9PY Tel: 01892 863637 Fax: 01892 862597 Email: gareth.tuckwell@burrswood.org.uk; 2 Sutherland Road, Tunbridge Wells TN1 1SE Tel: 01892 519318 Email: gareth@tuckwell-family.co.uk — MB BS 1971 Lond.; MRCS Eng. LRCP Lond. 1971; MRCGP 1977; DObst RCOG 1973; Dip. Palliat. Med. Wales 1992. (St. Bart.) Dir Macmillan Cancer Relief; Trustee of St Columba's Fell.sh. inter health. Socs: Fell. Roy. Soc. Med.; BMA; Assn. Palliat. Med. Prev: Ho. Phys. St. Bart. Hosp. Lond.; Ho. Surg. (O & G) Roy. Sussex Co. Hosp. Brighton; Med.Dir Burrswood Hosp.Tunbridge Wells.

TUCKWELL, Leonard Arthur Aysgarth, 132 Earnsdale Road, Darwen BB3 1JA — MB BS 1958 Sydney; MRCOG 1973; FRCOG 1985; DFFP 1999. (Sydney) InDepend. Cons. Gynaecologist Darwen Lancs; Clin. Med. Off. (Family Plann.) Bolton Hosp. NHS Trust. Prev: Cons. (O & G) Blackburn, Hyndburn & Ribble Valley HA; Lect. O & G Univ. Bristol.

TUCKWELL, Wendy Ann 80 Bank End Lane, Huddersfield HD5 8EN Tel: 01484 311034 — MB ChB 1969 Leeds; DObst RCOG 1974; MPH Leds 1999. Socs: BMA. Prev: GP Hull.

TUDBALL, Patricia 23 Tegfan, Pontyclun CF72 9BP — MB BCh 1986 Wales. Staff Grade (Gen. Psychiat.) Gwent Community Health Care Trust.

TUDBERRY, Rachel Alice 31 Percy Road, London N21 2JA — MB BS 1997 Lond.

TUDDENHAM, Alfred David, SBStJ (retired) 24 Seaway Avenue, Friars Cliff, Christchurch BH23 4EX Tel: 01425 275880 — MB BS 1953 Lond.; MRCS Eng. LRCP Lond. 1953; MRCGP 1971; Assoc. Fac. Occupat. Med. RCP Lond. 1979. Soton. Approved Med. Examr. Roy. Commercial Union & other insur. cos. Prev: Div. Med. Off. Brit. Rlys. S.. Region, Brit. Rail Maintenance Ltd., Brit. Sealink (UK) Ltd. Portsmouth Assoc. Brit. Ports.

TUDDENHAM, Professor Edward George Denley Haemostasis Research Group, MRC Clinical Sciences Centre, Imperial College School of Medicine, Hammersmith Hospital, Du Cane Road, London W12 0NN Tel: 020 8383 8235 Fax: 020 8383 8319 Email: edward.tuddenham@csc.ac.uk; 17 Bedford Road, Alexandra Park, London N22 7AU — MB BS Lond. 1968; MD Lond. 1985; FRCP Lond. 1987, M 1974; FRCPath 1987, M 1975; FRCP Ed 1997.

(Westm.) MRC Clin. Sci. Staff, Dir. Haemostasis Research Gp. Clin. Sci.s Centre Imperial Coll. Sch. Med. Lond.; Prof. Haemostais Imp. Coll. Sch. of Med. & Hon. Cons. Haemat. Hammersmith Hosp.Lond. Socs: World Federat. Haemophilia; Internat. Soc. Thrombosis & Hemostasis; (Comm. Mem.) Brit. Soc. Hemostasis & Thrombosis. Prev: Sen. Lect. (Haemat.) & Co-Dir. Haemophilia Centre Roy. Free Med. Lond.; Lect. (Haemat.) Welsh Nat. Sch. Med. Cardiff; Regist. (Path.) United Liverp. Hosps.

TUDDENHAM, Laurence Marcus Central Scotland Healthcare, Old Denny Road, Larbert FK5 4SD — MB ChB 1996 Ed. (Ed.) SHO (Psychiat.) Centr. Scotl. Healthcare NHS Trust.

TUDOR, Gareth Raymond 68 High Street, Abertridwr, Caerphilly CF83 4FD — MB BCh 1989 Wales; BSc (Hons.) Wales 1986, MB BCh 1989. SHO (Cardiothoracic Med.) Scully, Llandough & UHW Hosps. Cardiff. Prev: Ho. Off. (Surg.) Morriston Hosp. W. Glam.; Ho. Off. (Med.) UHW S. Glam.

TUDOR, Gary John 11 St John Street, Manchester M3 4DW — MB ChB 1976 Manch.

TUDOR, Gary Paul Top House, Seaview Crescent, Paignton TQ3 1JJ Tel: 01803 550058 — MB ChB 1990 Manch.; MSc Wales 1983. SHO (A & E) Roy. Devon & Exeter Hosp.

TUDOR, John (retired) Mortimer's Farm House, Foxton, Cambridge CB2 6RR Tel: 01223 870352 — MB BS Lond. 1957; MRCS Eng. LRCP Lond. 1957; FFR 1973; DMRD Eng. 1971; DObst RCOG 1960. Cons. (Diag. Radiol.) Addenbrookes Hosp. Camb. Prev: Sen. Regist. Dept. Radiodiag. Hammersmith Hosp. Lond.

TUDOR, Mr John Colin Winton House, Portsdown Hill Road, Portsmouth PO6 1BE Tel: 023 92 389044; 38 St. Edwards Road, Southsea PO5 3DJ Tel: 023 92 738123 Fax: 01705 793894 Email: 101340.234@compuserve.com — MA, MB Camb. 1967 BChir 1966; FRCS Eng. 1975; FRCS Ed. 1974; FRCOphth 1993; DO Eng. 1972. (St. Bart.) Cons. Ophth. Qu. Alexandra Hosp. Eye Unit Portsmouth. Socs: Amer. Acad. Ophth.,; BMA & Hosp. Cons. & Specialist Assn. (Co. Chairm. Hants.). Prev: Sen. Regist. Soton. Eye Hosp.; Regist. (Ophth.) Bristol Eye Hosp.

TUDOR, John Gowen The Church Street Practice, David Corbet House, 2 Callows Lane, Kidderminster DY10 2JG Tel: 01562 822051 Fax: 01562 827251; The Goddes farm House, The Greenway, Rock, Bewdley DY14 9SN Tel: 01299 832163 — MB ChB 1984 Birm.; BSc (Hons.) Birm. 1981.

TUDOR, Mary Maud (retired) 8 South Bourne Close, Selly Park Road, Selly Park, Birmingham B29 7LU Tel: 0121 471 4154 — MB BCh BAO 1942 NUI; Sch. Dent. Anaesth. Birm. Prev: Sen. Res. Anaesth. Qu. Eliz. Hosp. Birm.

TUDOR, Nerys Llwyd Trannon, 4 Bryn Eryl, Ruthin LL15 1DT Tel: 01824 23150 — MB BS 1963 Lond. (Roy. Free & Cardiff) Clin. Med. Off. Clwyd HA. Prev: Paediat. Ho. Off. E. Glam. Hosp. Ch. Village, Ho. Surg. Caerphilly; Dist. Miner's Hosp.

TUDOR, Mr Richard Gowen The Lodge, Great Alne, Alcester B49 6HR Tel: 01789 488225 Fax: 01789 488610 — MB ChB 1979 Birm.; BSc (Hons.) (Anat.) Birm. 1976, MD 1987; FRCS Eng. 1983; FRCS Ed. 1983. Cons. Surg. Alexandra Healthcare NHS Trust; Hon. Sen. Clin. Lect. (Surg.) Univ. Birm. Prev: Lect. (Surg.) Univ. Birm.; Research Fell. Gen. Hosp. Birm.; Ho. Surg. Profess. Unit Qu. Eliz. Hosp. Birm.

TUDOR, Virginia Sarah Northfield Health Centre, 15 St. Heliers Road, Northfield, Birmingham B31 1QT Tel: 0121 478 1850 Fax: 0121 476 0931 — MB ChB 1978 Birm.; DRCOG 1981.

TUDOR DE SILVA, Hewavasam Patuwata Badathuruge 14 Hawkwood, Maidstone ME16 0JQ — MB BS 1973 Sri Lanka.

TUDOR JONES, Rhiannedd 65 Cranbrook Street, Cardiff CF24 4AL — MB BCh 1994 Wales.

TUDOR-JONES, Thomas 50 Westport Avenue, Ridgewood Park, Mayals, Swansea SA3 5EQ Tel: 01792 402207 Fax: 01792 295952 — MB ChB Birm. 1959; DPH Wales 1971; DObst RCOG 1961. (Birm.) Dir. Occupat. Health Serv. Univ. Coll. Swansea; Clin. Asst. (Dermat.) Singleton Hosp. Swansea. Prev: MOH Port Talbot Municip. Boro.; SHO (Obst.) Mt. Pleasant Hosp. Swansea; Ho. Phys. & Surg. Swansea Gen. Hosp.

TUDOR MILES, Andrew Peter Tudor The Surgery, 35A High Street, Wimbledon, London SW19 5BY Tel: 020 8946 4820 Fax: 020 8944 9794; 77 Bolingbroke Grove, London SW11 6HB — MB BS 1966 Lond.; FRCGP 1991, M 1980. (St. Geo.) Med. Adviser Youngs Brewery; Hon. Med. Off. All Eng. Lawn Tennis Club; Hon.

Med. Off. Kings Coll. Sch. Wimbledon. Prev: Regist. (Med.) St. Thos. Gp. Hosps.; SHO Infec. Dis. Unit & SHO (Paediat.) St. Geo. Hosp. Tooting.

TUDOR-THOMAS, William Richard (retired) Old Orchard, Pardys Hill, Corfe Mullen, Wimborne BH21 3HW Tel: 01929 603940 Fax: 01202 603940 Email: a2wtt@aol.com — MB BS 1971 Lond.; DObst RCOG 1976. Vice-Chairm. Poole Hosp. NHS Trust; HMA, Dorset ME Support Gp. Prev: Sen. Partner, Swange Med. Pract.

TUDOR-WILLIAMS, Trevor Gareth Fax: 44 (0) 20 7886 6249 Email: g.tudor-williams@ic.ac.uk — MB BS 1977 Lond.; MRCP (UK) 1982. (St. Thos.) Sen. Lect. in Paediatric Infec. Dis.s. Imperial Coll.. Lond. Socs: Harveian Soc. Lond.

TUDWAY, Andrew John Christie 13 Wykeham Gate, Haddenham, Aylesbury HP17 8DF — MB 1970 Camb.; BA Camb. 1966, MB 1970, BChir 1969; FRCPath 1988, M 1976. Cons. (Histopath.) Stoke Mandeville Hosp. Aylesbury. Prev: Lect. Path. Univ. Bristol.

TUFAIL, Adnan 20 Orchard Castle, Cardiff CF14 9BA; Jules Stein Eye Institute, 100 Stein Plaza, UCLA, Los Angeles 90024, USA — MB BS 1989 Lond.; FRCOphth 1994. Fell. Ophth. Jules Stein Eye Inst. UCLA Los Angeles, USA. Prev: SHO Moorfields Eye Hosp.

TUFAIL, Samia Department of Medicine, Poole General Hospital, Poole BH15 2JB Tel: 01202 665511; 8 Lampeter Close, off Mount Hermon Road, Woking GU22 7TD Tel: 01483 756850 — MB BS 1983 Lahore, Pakistan; MRCP (UK) 1991. Career Regist. (Gen. Med.) Poole Gen. Hosp.

TUFFILL, Mr Sidney George (retired) 57 Fitzjames Avenue, Croydon CR0 5DN Tel: 020 8654 6333 — MB BS (Hons., Distinc. Forens. Med. & Pub. Health) Lond. 1942; FRCS Eng. 1947; MRCS Eng. LRCP Lond. 1942; LLB Lond.

TUFFIN, Mr James Robert Maxillofacial Unit, University Hospital of South Manchester, Withington, Manchester M20 2LR Tel: 0161 291 3006 Fax: 0161 291 4171 — BM 1983 Soton.; BDS Lond. 1974; FRCS Ed. 1989; FDS RCS Eng. 1978. (Univ. Soton.) Cons. Oral & Maxillofacial Surg. S. Manch. Univ. Hosps. Trust; Cons. Oral & Maxillofacial Surg. Stockport Hosps. Trust. Socs: Fell. Brit. Assn. Oral & Maxillofacial Surg.; BMA; Eur. Assn. Cranio-Maxillo. Surg. Prev: Sen. Regist. (Oral & Maxillofacial Surg.) NW RHA.

TUFFNELL, Derek John Yorkshire Clinic, Bradford Road, Bingley BD16 1TW — MB ChB 1983 Leeds; MRCOG 1988. Cons. O & G Bradford NHS Trust. Prev: Sen. Regist. (O & G) Yorks. RHA; Regist. (O & G) St. Jas. Hosp. Leeds.

TUFFREY, Catherine 27 Moor Croft Drive, Longwell Green, Bristol BS30 7DB — BM BS 1994 Nottm. SHO (Neonates) S.mead Hosp. Bristol. Socs: RCP; RCPCH. Prev: SHO Rotat. (Paediat.) Roy. United Hosp. Bath.

TUFFT, Nigel Richard 22 Parker Bowles Drive, Market Drayton TF9 3EU — MB ChB 1988 Bristol.

TUFNELL, Guinevere Child & Family Service, The Traumatic Stress Clinic, 73 Charlotte Street, London W1T 4PL Tel: 020 7530 3666 Fax: 020 7530 3677 — MB BS 1977 Lond.; FRCPsych 2001; MA Camb. 1967; MRCPsych 1981. (Royal Free) Cons. Child & Adolescent Psychiat., Camden & Islington NHS Trsut Lond. Socs: Roy. Coll. Psychiat.s. Prev: Cons. Psychiat.. Child & Adolescent Psychiat., Forest Healthcare Trust, Lond..

TUFT, Stephen John Moorfields Eye Hospital, 162 City Road, London EC1V 2PD Tel: 020 7253 3411 Fax: 020 7566 2019 Email: stuft@compuserve.com — MB BChir 1978 Camb.; MD Camb. 1992; MRCS Eng. LRCP Lond. 1977; FRCOphth 1990; FRACS 1983; FRACO 1983. (King's. Coll. Hosp.) Cons. Ophth. Moorfields Eye Hosp. Lond. Socs: BMA. Prev: Cons. Ophth. ChristCh., NZ; Lect. (Clin. Ophth.) Moorfields Eye Hosp. Lond.; Research Fell. Inst. Ophth. Lond.

TUGGEY, Justin Mark 22 Town Mills, West Mills, Newbury RG14 5HW — MB ChB 1994 Leeds.

TUINMAN, Cornelius Petrus Schepersmaat 2, 9405 TA Assen, Postbus 28000, 400 HH Assen, Netherlands; 24 Rubislaw Den N., Aberdeen AB15 4AN Tel: 01224 321100 — Artsexamen 1976 Rotterdam. Sen. Med. Adviser Shell. Exploration Aberd.

TUITE, Mr Jeremy Dennis Broomfield Hospital, Court Road, Chelmsford CM1 7ET Tel: 01245 514201 Fax: 01245 514644; 4 Culvert Close, Coggeshall, Colchester CO6 1PB — MB ChB 1975 Leeds; FRCS Eng. 1981. (Leeds) Cons. Orthop. Surg. Mid Essex

TUKE

Hosp. NHS Trust. Chelmsford. Socs: Brit. Orth. Assn.; Brit. Elbow & Shoulder Soc. Prev: Sen. Regist. Roy. Nat. Orthop. Hosp.

TUKE, John Underwood Bute House, Grove Medical Centre, Wootton Grove, Sherborne DT9 4DL Tel: 01935 812226 Fax: 01935 817055; Frampton Farm, Leigh, Sherborne DT9 6HJ — MB BS 1963 Lond.; MRCS Eng. LRCP Lond. 1963; DObst RCOG 1965.

TUKE, John Wilson Millside House, Mill Road, Buxhall, Stowmarket IP14 3DS Tel: 01449 737643 Fax: 01449 737512 Email: jw@tuke.keme.co.uk — MB BS Durh. 1956; MRCGP 1969; FRCPCH 1998; DCH RCPS Glas. 1968; MFPHM 2000. (Newcastle) InDepend. Cons. In Pub. Health Med. Socs: BMA. Prev: Cons. Pub. Health Med. Suff. HA; GP Morpeth.

TULHURST, Jennifer Elizabeth Dept. Pathology, Glasgow Royal Infirmary, 84 Caslte St, Glasgow G4 0SF; 5 Silverhills, Rosneath, Helensburgh G84 0EW Tel: 0121 685 4223 Fax: 0121 685 4041 — MB ChB 1992 Glas. Cons. Pathologist, Path., Glas. Roy. Infirm. Glas.

TULL, David 23 Lavender Road, Leicester LE3 1AL — MB ChB 1991 Leicester.

TULLBERG, Harriet Teresa Wynn Carnewater Practice, Dennison Road, Bodmin PL31 2LB Tel: 01208 72321 Fax: 01208 78478; Kingsberry, 38 Rhind St, Bodmin PL31 2EL Tel: 01208 76867 — MB ChB 1983 Bristol; MRCGP 1990; DRCOG 1986.

TULLETT, David Charles 33B Aldermans Hill, Hockley SS5 4RP — MB BChir 1988 Camb.; BA Camb. 1982, MB BChir 1988.

TULLETT, Mr William Melville Accident & Emergency Department, Western Infirmary, Dumbarton Road, Glasgow G11 6NT Tel: 0141 211 2651 Fax: 0141 339 3046 Email: william.tullett@carleol.co.uk; 47 Thomson Drive, Bearsden, Glasgow G61 3PA Tel: 0141 942 0686 — MB ChB 1978 Aberd.; FRCS Ed. 1987; MRCP (UK) 1981; FRCPS Glas. 1991; FFAEM 1994; Dip. Forens. Med. Glas 1989; Dip. Sports Med. 1997. Cons. (A & E & Intens. Ther.) W.. Infirm. Glas. Socs: Brit. Assn. Accid. & Emerg. Med.; ICS. Prev: Sen. Regist. (A & E) W.. Infirm. Glas.; Regist. (Med.) W.. Infirm. Glas.

TULLEY, Margaret Mary Brookside Surgery, Brookside Close, Gipsy Lane, Earley, Reading RG6 7HG — MB BS 1979 Lond.; MRCGP 1983; DCH RCP Lond. 1982; DRCOG 1982.

TULLEY, Paul Nicholas 10 Ennerdale Road, Formby, Liverpool L37 2EA Tel: 01704 877264 — MB BS 1993 Lond.; BSc (Biochem. & Immunol.) Lond. 1990, MB BS 1993. SHO (A & E) Char. Cross Hosp. Lond. Prev: Demonst. (Anat.) Char. Cross & W.m. Med. Sch. Lond.; Ho. Surg. Char. Cross Hosp. Lond.; Ho. Phys. W. Middlx. Hosp. Lond.

TULLO, Mr Andrew Brent Manchester Royal Eye Hospital, Oxford Road, Manchester M13 9WH Tel: 0161 276 5522 Fax: 0161 272 6618 Email: atullo@central.cmht.nwest.nhs.uk — MB ChB 1974 Bristol; MD Bristol 1982; FRCS Glas. 1983; FRCOphth 1992. (Univ. Bristol) Cons. Manch. Roy. Eye Hosp.; Hon. Sen. Lect. Univ. Manch.; Vis. Prof. UMIST. Socs: BMA; (Treas.) Europ. Eye Bank Assn. Prev: Wellcome Trust Research Fell. Univ. Bristol; Sen. Regist. Manch. Roy. Eye Hosp.

TULLOCH, Alexander David 158 Durham Road, London SW20 0DG — MB BS 1998 Lond.

TULLOCH, Alexander Kinnison (retired) 20 Jedburgh Road, Dundee DD2 1SR Tel: 01382 566447 — MB ChB 1941 St. And.; DOMS Eng. 1948. Prev: Cons. Ophth. Ninewells Hosp. Dundee, Roy. Infirm. Dundee, King's.

TULLOCH, Alistair John (retired) 36 Church Lane, Wendlebury, Bicester OX25 2PN Tel: 01869 243278 Fax: 01869 243278 — MD 1976 Aberd.; MB ChB 1950; FRCGP 1975, M 1959; DObst RCOG 1956. GP Research Off. Univ. Health Care Epidemiol. Univ. Oxf. Prev: Hon. Research Fell. Community Health Project Unit Clin. Epidemiol. Univ. Oxf.

TULLOCH, Barrie Charles Mews Close Health Centre, Mews Close, Ramsey, Huntingdon PE26 1BP Tel: 01487 812611 Fax: 01487 711801; 59 Main Street, Great Gidding, Huntingdon PE28 5NU Tel: 01832 293236 Fax: 01487 711801 Email: http:freespace/virgin.net/ramsey.hc/index.html — MB ChB 1963 Leeds. (Leeds) Prev: Ho. Phys. & Ho. Surg. St. Jas. Hosp. Leeds; Ho. Surg. (Obst.) St. Mary's Hosp. Leeds; Ho. Phys. (Paediat. & Dermat.) St. Jas. Hosp. Leeds.

TULLOCH, Mr Christopher John Low Carlbury, Piercebridge, Darlington DL2 3TP — MB ChB 1977 Liverp.; MCh Orthop. Liverp. 1984, MB ChB 1977; FRCS Eng. 1982; FRCS Ed. 1982. Cons. Orthop. Surg. N. Tees Gen. Hosp. Stockton-on-Tees. Socs: Fell. BOA. Prev: Sen. Regist. (Orthop.) Mersey RHA.

TULLOCH, David E (retired) 23 Ravelston Heights, Edinburgh EH4 3LX Tel: 0131 332 4404 — MB ChB 1951 Ed.

TULLOCH, Mr David Neill, Surg. Cdr. RN Retd. Department of Urology, Western General Hospital, Crewe Road, Edinburgh Tel: 0131 537 1582 Email: dnt@doctors.net — MB BS 1979 Lond.; FRCS Ed. 1986. (St Bartholomew's) Cons. Urol. W.ern Gen. Hosp. Edin. Socs: Brit. Assn. Urol. Surgs. Prev: Cons. Urol. RN Hosp. Haslar; Sen. Regist. (Urol.) Inst. Urol. & St. Bart. Hosp. Lond.

TULLOCH, James Stuart 8 North Parade, Bootham, York YO30 7AB — MB BS 1997 Newc.

TULLOCH, Janet Gillespie The Vicarage, 15 St John's Hill, Wimborne BH21 1BX Tel: 01202 883490 — MB ChB 1977 Dundee; DO RCS Eng. 1983. (Dundee) Staff Grade (Ophth.) Roy. Vict. Hosp. Bournemouth. Prev: Clin. Asst. (Ophth.) Newc. Gen. Hosp.; Regist. (Ophth.) Newc. Gen. Hosp.; SHO (Ophth.) Manch. Roy. Eye Hosp.

TULLOCH, John Alexander, MC (retired) Woodvale, Edzell, Brechin DD9 7TF Tel: 01356 648234 — MB ChB 1943 Ed.; MD Ed. 1950; FRCP Lond. 1974, M 1963; FRCP Ed. 1956, M 1948. Prev: Cons. Phys. Stracathro Hosp. Brechin.

TULLOCH, Lynda Joyce Craiglockhart Surgery, 161 Colinton Road, Edinburgh EH14 1BE Tel: 0131 455 8494 Fax: 0131 444 0161; 21-5 Russell Gardens, Edinburgh EH12 5PP Tel: 0131 538 7484 Email: ljt@doctors.org.uk — MB ChB 1983 Ed.; MRCGP 1987; DRCOG 1985. (Ed.)

TULLOCH, Pamela Mary Buchanan Marlborough Medical Practice, The Surgery, George Lane, Marlborough SN8 4BY Tel: 01672 512187 Fax: 01672 516809; Hillside, Granham Hill, Marlborough SN8 4DG — MB ChB 1979 Ed.; MRCGP 1984; DRCOG 1981. (Ed.)

TULLOH, Harold Peter (retired) 12 Fairhaven Road, Lytham St Annes FY8 1NN Tel: 01253 726123 — MB BS 1949 Durh.; FRCR 1975; FFR 1962; DMRD Liverp. 1959; DMRD Eng. 1959. Prev: Cons. Radiol. Blackpool & Fylde Gp. Hosps.

TULLOH, Robert Michael Rhys Department of Paediatric Cardiology, 11th Floor, Guy's Tower, Guy's Hospital, St Thomas St., London SE1 9RT Tel: 020 7955 4616 Fax: 020 7955 4614 Email: robert.tulloh@gstt.sthames.nhs.uk — BM BCh 1984 Oxf.; MA Oxf. 1985; MRCP (UK) 1987; MRCPCH 1996; FRCPCH 1997. (Oxford) Cons. Paediat. Cardiol. Guy's & St. Thomas's Hosp. Lond. Socs: Brit. Cardiac Soc.; Fell. Roy. Soc. Med. Prev: Sen. Regist. (Paediat. Cardiol.) Roy. Brompton Hosp. Lond.; Brit. Heart Foundat. Research Fell. Inst. Child Health; Regist. (Paediat. Cardiol.) Birm. Childr.'s Hosp. & Hosp. Sick Childr. Lond.

TULLY, Adrian Mark Vale of Leven Dist. Gen. Hospital, Alexandria G83 0UA Tel: 01389 754121 — MB ChB 1977 Dundee; FRCA 1984. Cons. Anaesth. Argyll & Clyde Acute Servs. NHS Trust; Hon. Sen. Clin. Lect. Fac. of Med. Glas. Univ.

TULLY, Beryl Angela (retired) 6 Falcondale Walk, Westbury-on-Trym, Bristol BS9 3JG — MB ChB 1962 Bristol. Prev: SCMO S.mead Health Serv. NHS Trust & United Bristol Hosp. Trust.

TULLY, Elizabeth Margaret Knox 5 Trafalgar Place, Bath Road, Devizes SN10 2AN — MB BCh BAO 1988 Belf.; MB BCh Belf. 1988; MRCGP 1992. Trainee GP Doncaster VTS. Prev: Jun. Ho. Off. Tyrone Co. Hosp. Omagh.

TULLY, Joanna Mary Institute of Child Health, 30 Guildford Street, London WC1N 1EH Tel: 0207 242 9789 Email: jotully2000@yahoo.com — MB BS 1993 Lond.; MRCP UK 1996. (St. Mary's) p/t Specialist Regist. (Paediat.) N. W. Thames Rotat.; Clin. Research Fell., Dept. Paediatric Epidemiol. & Biostatistics; Clin. Research Fell., Dept. Paedriatric Epidemiol. & Biostatics, Inst. of Child Health, Lond.

TULLY, Kathryn Nicola The Ross Practice, Keats House, Bush Fair, Harlow CM18 6LY Tel: 01279 692747 Fax: 01279 692737; 13 Hampton Gardens, Sawbridgeworth CM21 0AN — MB BS 1985 Lond.; MRCGP 1994; DRCOG 1990. (Lond. Hosp. Med. Coll. Univ. Lond.) Prev: Trainee GP Crawley VTS; SHO (O & G & Psychiat.) Crawley.

TULLY, Winifred Margaret Michal Whiteways, 17 Kennedy Road, Shrewsbury SY3 7AB — MRCS Eng. LRCP Lond. 1959; DCH

Eng. 1961. (Guy's) Prev: Med. Off. Family Plann Assn.; Med. Off. Brook Advisory Centre for Young People.

TULWA, Mr Nirmal 57 Castlefields, Rothwell, Leeds LS26 0GN — MB ChB 1985 Manch.; FRCS Ed. 1991; FRCS (Orth) 1999. (Manchester)

TUMA, Tuma Abdul-Karem Hartlepool General Hospital, Holdforth Road, Hartlepool TS24 9AH Tel: 01429 522826 Fax: 01429 863983 — MB ChB 1973 Mosul Iraq; MRCPsych 1982. (Mosul, IRAQ.) Cons. (Old Age Psychiat.).

TUMATH, David Edward Ferguson Cornwall Gardens Surgery, 77 Cornwall Gardens, Cliftonville, Margate CT9 2JF Tel: 01843 209300 — MB BCh BAO Belf. 1971. Hosp. Pract. (Diabetes) Qu. Eliz. the Qu. Mother Hosp. Margate. Socs: Fell. Roy. Soc. Med.; Christian Med. Fell.sh. Mem.; BMA Mem.

TUMMALA, Venkateswara Rao 4 Parkwood Avenue, Roundhay, Leeds LS8 1JW — MB BS 1972 Andhra. SCMO Barnsley Community & Priority Servs. Trust.

***TUMMAN, Jonathan James Wilfred** Department of Urology, Manchester Royal Infirmary, Oxford Road, Manchester M13 9WL Email: jtumman@yahoo.co.uk — MB ChB 1995 Manch.; 1999 MRCSED.

TUN, May Sanyu 56 Woodside, Wimbledon, London SW19 7AF — MB BS 1982 Lond.

TUN, Oo Mersey Regional Spinal Injuries Centre, Southport & Formby District General Hospital, Town Lane, Southport PR8 6PN — MB BS 1984 Med. Inst. (I) Rangoon.

TUN, Si Thu Vicarage Lane Surgery, 189 Vicarage Lane, Blackpool FY4 4NG Tel: 01253 838997 Fax: 01253 699375 — MB BS 1973 Med Inst (I) Rangoon; MB BS 1973 Med Inst (I) Rangoon.

TUN, Victor Whyteleafe Surgery, 19 Station Road, Whyteleafe CR3 0EP Tel: 01883 624181 Fax: 01883 622498; 3 Wheat Knoll, Kenley CR8 5JT Tel: 020 8645 0272 — MB BS 1980 Lond.; DRCOG 1983. (Guy's Hospital)

TUN MIN, Dr H2 Unit, Bolton General Hospital, Minerva Road, Farnworth, Bolton BL4 0JR Tel: 01204 390390; 9 Renfrew Drive, Beaumont Chase, Off Wigan Road, Bolton BL3 4XX — MB BS 1976 Mandalay; DO RCSI 1995. Clin. Asst. (Ophth.) Bolton Gen. Hosp. & Hope Hosp. Salford. Prev: SHO Jas. Paget Hosp. Gt. Yarmouth & Leighton Hosp. Crewe.

TUNBRIDGE, Anne Jacqueline Coppermill, Church Lane, Weston-on-the-Green, Bicester OX25 3QS Tel: 01869 350691 — MB ChB 1993 Birm.; DTM & H Liverp. 1995. (Birm.) SHO (Gen. Med.) Poole Hosp. Dorset. Prev: Med. Pract. Bethesda Hosp. Ubombo, Kwazulu/Natal S. Afr.; SHO (Paediat.) St. Peter's Hosp. Chertsey; SHO (A & E) N. Middlx. Hosp. Lond.

TUNBRIDGE, Felicity Katherine Edith (retired) Coppermill, Church Lane, Weston-on-the-Green, Bicester OX25 3QS Tel: 01869 350691 Fax: 01869 350691 — MB BS 1963 Lond.; AFOM Lond. 1982; DObst RCOG 1965; DA Eng. 1967. Prev: Staff Grade Phys. Diabetes Research Laborat. Radcliffe Infirm. Oxf.

TUNBRIDGE, Ronald David Gregg Department of Medicine, Manchester Royal Infirmary, Manchester M13 9WL Tel: 0161 276 4156 Fax: 0161 274 4833; 55 Manor Drive, Manchester M21 7QG Tel: 0161 448 9590 — MB BS Lond. 1968; MD Lond. 1982; FRCP Lond. 1984; MRCP (UK) 1970; MRCS Eng. LRCP Lond. 1968. (St. Mary's) Sen. Lect. (Med.) Univ. Manch.; Hon. Cons. Phys. & Hosp. Dean (Clin. Studies) Manch. Roy. Infirm. Socs: Brit. Hypertens. Soc. Prev: Lect. (Med.) St. Mary's Hosp. Med. Sch. Lond.; MRC Jun. Research Fell. St. Mary's Hosp. Steroid Unit Lond.

TUNBRIDGE, William Michael Gregg PGMDE, The Triangle, Roosevelt Drive, Headington, Oxford OX3 7XP Tel: 01865 740606 Fax: 01865 740 604 Email: pgdean@oxford-pgmde.co.uk — BChir 1964 Camb; MB 1965 Camb; MD 1977 Camb; MA 1965 Camb; 1965 MRCS Eng. LRCP Lond.; FRCP Lond. 1979, M 1968; DTM & H Liverp. 1967. (Univ. Coll. Hosp.) Dir. of Postgrad. Med. Educat. & Train. Univ. Oxf. & Postgrad. Dean (Oxf.); Hon. Cons. Phys. John Radcliffe Hosp. & Radcliffe Infirm. Oxf.; Prof.ial Fell. Wadham Coll. Oxf. 1994-. Socs: Soc. Endocrinol.; Thyroid Club (Ex-Pres.); Diabetes UK. Prev: Cons. Phys. Newc. Gen. Hosp.; Sen. Lect. (Med.) Univ. Newc.; Regist. (Med.) Hammersmith Hosp.

TUNE, George Sydney c/o X-Ray Department, Friarage Hospital, Northallerton DL6 1JG — MB ChB 1974 Manch.; PhD Bristol 1962, BA 1959; DMRD Eng. 1978. Cons. Radiol. Friarage Hosp. N.allerton, St. John of God Hosp. Prev: Sen. Regist. (Radiol.) Univ.

Hosp. S. Manch.; Ho. Surg. Manch. Roy. Infirm.; Ho. Phys. Vict. Hosp. Blackpool.

TUNG, Kean Tat Department of Radiology, Royal South Hampshire Hospital, Brintons Terrace, Southampton; Timber Leas, 10 Beechwood Crescent, Chandlers Ford, Eastleigh SO53 1PA — FRCP 1999; FRCP UK 1999; BM BCh Oxf. 1982; MRCP (UK) 1985; FRCR 1990; T(R) (CR) 1992. Cons. Radiol. Soton. Univ. Hosp. Trust.

TUNG, Mun-Yee Florence Road, London W5 3UA — MB BS 1996 Lond.

TUNGEKAR, Muhammad Fahim Muhammad Yousuf Department of Histopathology, St. Thomas Hospital, London SE1 7EH Tel: 020 7928 9292; 18 Woodville Road, Leytonstone, London E11 3BH — MB BS 1973 Bombay; MD 1975 Bombay; FRCPath 1991, M 1979. (Grant Medical College, Bombay) Sen. Lect. & Cons. Histopath. St. Thos. Hosp. Lond. Socs: Internat. Acad. Path. (Brit. Div.); Assn. Clin. Path.; Nat. Acad. of Med. Sci. (India). Prev: Assoc. Prof. & Cons. Histopath. Univ. Kuwait; Sen. Regist. (Histopath.) St. Geo. Hosp. Med. Sch. Lond.; Lect. Grant Med. Coll. Bombay.

TUNGLAND, Ole Petter The Central Sheffield University Hospitals, North Trent Medical Audiology, Royal Halamshire Hospital, Glossop Road, Sheffield S10 2JF Tel: 0114 271 1853 Fax: 0114 271 1855; 5 Balmoak Lane, Tapton, Chesterfield S41 0TH Tel: 01246 273218 — Cand Med 1973 Oslo; T(M) 1991. Cons. Audiol. Med. The Centr. Sheff. Univ. Hosps. Prev: Cons. Audiol. Med. Hosp. Sick Childr. Gt. Ormond St. Lond.; Cons. ENT & Audiol. Skövde Centre Hosp. Sweden & Vestfold Centre Hosp. Tønsberg, Norway; Sen. Cons. ENT Audiol. Ring Med. Centre Oslo, Norway.

TUNIO, Mr Ali Murad Department of Surgery, University College of London Medical School, 67-73 Riding House St., London W1P 7PN — MRCS Eng. LRCP Lond. 1987; FRCS Ed. 1991.

TUNIO, Fazal The Surgery, Elm Tree Medical Centre, Elm Tree Avenue, Stockton-on-Tees TS19 0UW Tel: 01642 603330 Fax: 01642 675656 — MB BS 1968 Sind. (Liaquat Med. Coll.) Prev: Cas. Med. Off. Middlesbrough Gen. Hosp.; Trainee GP Kingsbury Lond.

TUNKEL, Sarah Alisa 8 Corringham Court, Corringham Road, London NW11 7BY — MB BS 1989 Lond. (Univ. Coll. Lond.) Healthcare Consultancy, Deloitte & Touche Lond.; Research Fell. Fetal Med. Kings Coll. Hosp. Sch. of Med. Dent.

TUNN, Edward James Department of Rheumatology, Royal Liverpool Hospital, Liverpool — MD 1990 Glas.; BSc (Hons.) Glas. 1976, MD 1990, MB ChB 1978; MRCP (UK) 1981. Cons. Rheum. Roy. Liverp. Hosp.

TUNNADINE, Charles Henry John 6 Lewes Road, Ditchling, Hassocks BN6 8TT — MB BS 1981 Lond.

TUNNADINE, David Edward (retired) Europa House, West St., Bassett Road, Leighton Buzzard LU7 1DD Tel: 01525 851888 — BA, MB BChir Camb. 1953; DObst RCOG 1956; FRCGP 1983, MRCGP 1969. Prev: Res. Med. Off. Beckenham Matern. Hosp.

TUNNADINE, Lesley Prudence Dundas (cons. rooms), Flat 7, Wimpole House, 29 Wimpole St., London W1M 7AD Tel: 020 7636 9896; 6 Lewes Road, Ditchling, Hassocks BN6 8TT — MB BS 1953 Lond.; MFFP 1993; DObst RCOG 1956. (Guy's) Scientif. Dir. (Clin. & Train.) Inst. Psychosexual Med. Lond. Socs: Inst. Psychosexual Med. Prev: Regist. (O & G) Chichester Hosp. Gp.

TUNNEY, Patrick James 10 Willow Tree Court, Brooklands Road, Sale M33 3SE — MB BCh BAO 1984 NUI; MRCPI 1993.

TUNNICLIFF, Malcolm 1 Turn Furlong, Kingsthorpe, Northampton NN2 8BZ — MB BS 1997 Lond.

TUNNICLIFFE, William Stuart Inglemere, Moseley Road, Hallow, Worcester WR2 6NJ — MB BCh 1986 Witwatersrand; MSc (Epidemiol.) Lond. 1994; MRCP (UK) 1992. Research Regist. Chest Research Inst. E. Birm. Hosp.; Research Regist. Heartlands Research Inst. Birm.

TUNSTALL, Mair Anne 50 Springbourne, Frodsham, Warrington WA6 6QD — MB ChB 1991 Leeds.

TUNSTALL, Michael Eric Department of Environmental and Occupational Medicine, University Medical School, Foresterhill, Aberdeen AB25 2ZD Tel: 01224 681818 Ext: 52459 Fax: 01224 662990; 9 South Headlands Crescent, Newtonhill, Stonehaven AB39 3TT Tel: 01569 730228 Fax: 01569 731706 — MB BS Lond. 1952; MRCS Eng. LRCP Lond. 1952; FFA RCS Eng. 1959; DA Eng. 1956; DObst RCOG 1955. (Univ. Coll. Hosp.) Hon. Cons. Anaesth.

TUNSTALL

Aberd. Roy. Hosps. NHS Trust; Hon. Research Fell. (Environm. & Occupat. Med.) Univ. Aberd. Socs: (Ex-Pres.) Obst. Anaesth. Assn.; Scott. Soc. Anaesth.; Hon. Mem. Assn. Anaesth. Prev: Cons. Anaesth. Aberd. Hosps.; Jt. Sen. Regist. (Anaesth.) Portsmouth Hosp. Gp. & United Oxf. Hosps.; Regist. (Anaesth.) Middlx. Hosp.

TUNSTALL, Nigel Robert 131 Kinson Road, Bournemouth BH10 4DG — MB BS 1990 Lond.

TUNSTALL, Patricia June St. Helens & Knowsley Health Authority, Cowley Hill Lane, St Helens WA10 2AP Tel: 01744 33722; Brookside Cottage, 1 Fiveways, Springfield Lane, Eccleston, St Helens WA10 5EL Tel: 01744 26588 — MB ChB Liverp. 1966, MCommH 1975; MFCM 1986; MFPHM 1990; DObst RCOG 1968. Cons. Pub. Health Med. St. Helens & Knowsley HA. Prev: Regional SCM (Special Servs.) Mersey RHA; Cons. Pub. Health Med. Mersey RHA.

TUNSTALL, Shaun 10 Grenville Avenue, Preston PR5 4UA — MB ChB 1990 Leeds.

TUNSTALL, Susan Rebecca Macmillan Unit, Frenchay Hospital, Bristol — MB BS Newc. 1986. Cons. (Palliat. Med.) Frenchay Hosp. Bristol.

TUNSTALL PEDOE, Dan Sylvester 29 Meynell Crescent, London E9 7AS Tel: 020 8986 2762 — MB BChir 1965 Camb.; DPhil Oxf. 1970; MA 1965; FRCP Lond. 1979, M 1967. (St. Bart.) Sen. Lect. & Cons. (Med. & Cardiol.) St. Bart. & Homerton Hosps. Lond.; Med. Dir. Lond. Marathon. Socs: Life Vice-Pres. Brit. Assn. Sports & Med.; Roy. Soc. Med. (Pres. Sports Med. Sect.). Prev: Research Physiol. Cardiovasc. Research Inst. San Francisco, USA; Sen. Regist. Radcliffe Infirm. Oxf.; Ho. Phys. St. Bart. Hosp. Lond.

TUNSTALL-PEDOE, Professor Hugh David Cardiovascular Epidemiology Unit, Ninewells Hospital & Medical School, Dundee DD1 9SY Tel: 01382 644255 Fax: 01382 641095 — MB BChir 1965 Camb.; MB (Distinc. Surg., Gyn & Obst.) Camb. BChir 1965; MA Camb. 1965, BA (1st cl. Hons.) 1961, MD 1977; FRCP Ed. 1986; FRCP Lond. 1981, M 1967; FFPHM RCP (UK) 1981, M 1978. (Camb. & Guy's) Prof. & Dir. Cardiovasc. Epidemiol. Unit & Sen. Lect. (Med.) Ninewells Hosp. Univ. Dundee; Hon. Cons. Cardiol. & Pub. Health Med. Dundee Teachg. Hosps. NHS Trust. Socs: Fell. Europ. Soc. Cardiol.; Assn. Phys. Prev: Sen. Lect. (Epidemiol.) & Hon. Phys. St. Mary's Hosp. Med. Sch. Lond.; Lect. (Med.) Lond. Hosps.; Mem. Clin. Scientif. Staff. MRC Social Med. Unit.

TUNSTALL-PEDOE, Oliver Daniel 4 Hill Street, Broughty Ferry, Dundee DD5 2JL — BChir 1996 Camb.

TUPPEN, Jonathan James Avenue Road Surgery, 2 Avenue Road, Warley, Brentwood CM14 5EL Tel: 01277 212820 Fax: 01277 234169 Email: jonathan.tuppen@gp-f81023.nhs.uk; 42 Junction Road, Brentwood CM14 5JN Email: jtuppen@doctors.org.uk — MB ChB 1984 Manch.; MRCGP 1988; DRCOG 1987. Co. Chairm., Exec. Comm., Billericay Brentwood & Wickford PCT, Trust HQ. Prev: Regist. (Med. for Elderly) Qu. Mary's Hosp. Sidcup; Trainee GP Lond. VTS.

***TUPPEN, Nicola Michelle** 4 Luton Avenue, Broadstairs CT10 2DH — MB ChB 1995 Birm.

TUPPER, Annemarie Dora (retired) 97 Cambridge Road, West Wimbledon, London SW20 0PU Tel: 020 8946 5486 — MB BS Lond. 1952; DPhysMed. Eng. 1968; DObst RCOG 1955. Prev: Cons. Rehabil. Univ. Coll. Hosp. Lond.

TUPPER, Catherine Helen Atkinson Health Centre, Market St., Barrow-in-Furness LA14 2LR — BM BS 1983 Nottm.; BMedSci (Hons.) Nottm. 1981; MFFP 1993; MRCGP 1990. Cons. (Family Plann. & Reproductive Health Care). Prev: Head Family Plann. S. Cumbria.

TUPPER, David James Luepin Basingstoke District Hospital, Basingstoke RG24 9NA Tel: 01256 817718 — MB ChB 1973 Leeds; FRCP Lond. 1995; MRCP (UK) 1978. Cons. Geriat. Basingstoke Dist. Hosp. Socs: Internat. Soc. Quality Assur. Health Care. Prev: Sen. Regist. (Geriat. Med.) Soton. Gen. Hosp.; Regist. (Gen. Med.) Co. Hosp. Hereford; SHO (Gen. Med.) WillesBoro. Hosp. Ashford.

TUPPER, Nicholas Adrian 37 Wadbrough Road, Sheffield S11 8RF Email: drnat@globalnet.co.uk — MB ChB 1995 Sheff. (University of Sheffield) Med. SHO, Doncaster.

TUPPER, Ruth Carol Anne 6 Gill Croft, Stannington, Sheffield S6 6FQ — MB ChB 1997 Sheff. Socs: Med. Protec. Soc.; BMA.

Prev: Pre-Regist. Ho. Off. (Gen. Surg.); Pre-Regist. Ho. Off. (Gen. Med.).

TUPPER-CAREY, Darrell Alexander 13 The Avenue, Colchester CO3 3PA Tel: 01206 575517 — MB ChB 1987 Birm.; FCAnaesth. Cons. (Anaesth.) James Paget Hosp. Gt Yarmouth. Prev: SHO (Anaesth.) Birm. Hosp.; SHO (Med.) Russells Hall Hosp. Dudley W. Midl.; Ho. Off. Dudley Rd. Hosp. Birm. & WalsGr. Hosp. Coventry.

TURA, Jenny Elizabeth Heath Lane Surgery, Earl Shilton, Leicester LE9 7PB Tel: 01455 844431; 8 Browns Close, Sapcote, Leicester LE9 4FZ — MB ChB 1984 Leic. Prev: Trainee GP Leics. VTS; SHO (Psychiat.) Carlton Hayes Hosp.; SHO (A & E) Leicester Roy. Infirm.

TURBERFIELD, Laura Marion Temple Cowley Health Centre, Templar House, Temple Road, Oxford OX4 2HL Tel: 01865 777024 Fax: 01865 777548 — BM BCh 1987 Oxf.; BA Camb. 1984; DRCOG 1990. Prev: Trainee GP Kidlington Health Centre Oxon.; SHO (Gen. Med., O & G & Dermat.) Oxf. HA.

TURBERVILLE, Stephen Matthew 38 St Rualds Close, Wallingford OX10 0XE Tel: 01903 873739 — MB BS 1992 Lond. (St. Geo. Hosp. Med. Sch.) SHO (Psychiat.) Fair Mile Hosp. Cholsey. Prev: SHO (Paediat.) St. Mary's Hosp. Lond., Hillingdon Hosp. Uxbridge & S.lands Hosp. Shoreham-by-Sea; SHO (A & E) St. Helier Hosp. Carshalton.

TURBERVILLE SMITH, Rachel Jane 9 The Ridgeway, Upwey, Weymouth DT3 5QQ — MB BS 1992 Lond.

TURBERVILLE SMITH, Rupert John Frederick Place Surgery, 11 Frederick Place, Weymouth DT4 8HQ Tel: 01305 774411 Fax: 01305 760417 — MB BS 1992 Lond.

TURBIN, Diana Rose Abbeys Meads Medical Practice, Elstree Way, Swindon SN25 4YX — BSc Lond. 1981, MB BS 1984; MRCP (UK) 1987; DCH RCP Lond. 1987. (Univ. Coll. Hosp.) GP Swindon.

TURBITT, Deborah Ann 12 Cheverell House, Pritchards Road, London E2 9BN Tel: 020 7739 8971 — MB BS 1986 Lond.

TURCK, Walter Peter George 98-100 Market Street, Edenfield, Ramsbottom, Bury BL0 0JL Tel: 0170682 2435 — MB ChB 1963 St. And.; FRCP Ed. 1977, M 1968; FRCP Lond. 1980, M 1968. (St. And.) Cons. Phys. Bury Gen. Hosp. & Rossendale Gen. Hosp.; Postgrad. Clin. Tutor Univ. Manch. Prev: Cons. Phys. Alice Ho Miu Ling Nethersole Hosp.; Clin. Lect. Univ. Dept. Med. Hong Kong; Sen. Regist. (Med.) Manch. AHA (T).

TURCZANSKA, Ewa Hillside, Bodfari, Denbigh LL16 4DE — MB BS 1981 Lond.

TURFITT, Edward Neil Petroc Group Practice, The Surgery, St Columb Major, St Columb TR9 6AA Tel: 01637 880359 Fax: 01637 881482; Polwithen, St Columb TR9 6BA Tel: 01637 880511 — MB BS Lond. 1968; MRCS Eng. LRCP Lond. 1968; DObst RCOG 1974; Cert JCC Lond. 1978. (Guy's) Clin. Asst. (Colposcopy) Cornw.. Prev: Ho. Surg. & Ho. Phys. Beckenham Hosp.; Resid. Obst. Brit. Milit. Hosp. Munster; Maj. RAMC.

TURFITT, Mary Elizabeth The Perranporth Surgery, Perranporth TR6 0PS Tel: 01872 572255 — MB BS 1968 Lond.; MRCS Eng. LRCP Lond. 1968; Cert JCC Lond. 1978. (Guy's) Prev: Ho. Surg. Orpington Hosp.; Ho. Phys. St. Nicholas' Hosp. Plumstead.

TURFREY, Deborah Jane 30 Station Road, Bearsden, Glasgow G61 4AL — MB BS 1990 Lond.; FRCA 1995. (St. Mary's Hosp. Lond.) Specialist Regist. (Anaesth.) Glas. Prev: Research Fell. (Anaesth.) Glas. Univ.

TURFREY, Donna Marie Ferrers Cottage, Lullington Road, Edingale, Tamworth B79 9JA — MB BS 1994 Lond.

TURJANSKI, Nora Ruth 105 Fellows Road, London NW3 3JS — Medico 1983 Buenos Aires.

TURK, David Charles (retired) 36 Sefton Road, Fulwood, Sheffield S10 3TP — BM BCh 1948 Oxf.; DM Oxf. 1962, BM BCh 1948; MRCP Lond. 1950; FRCPath 1970, M 1963. Prev: Cons. Microbiol. Pub. Health Laborat. Sheff.

TURK, Edward Peter (retired) Sunny Meadow Farm, Long Buckby Wharf, Northampton NN6 7PP Tel: 01327 842574 — MB BChir 1974 Camb.; MRCPath 1982.

TURK, Gary Nicholas Antrim Health Centre, Station Road, Antrim BT41 4BS Tel: 028 9448 7812 Fax: 028 9446 4930 — MB BCh BAO 1982 Belf.; MRCGP 1987.

TURK, Jeremy St. Georges Hospital Medical School, Cranmer Terrace, London SW17 0RE Tel: 020 8725 2618 Fax: 020 8725 3592 Email: j.turk@sghms.ac.uk; 10 Rocombe Crescent, London SE23 3BL — MB BS 1982 Lond.; BSc (Hons.) Lond. 1979; MD

Lond. 1995; FRCPCH 1997, M 1996; MRCPsych 1986; DCH RCP Lond. 1984. (Middlx. Hosp. Med. Sch.) Sen. Lect. (Child & Adolesc. Psychiat.) St. Geo. Hosp. Med. Sch. Lond.; Hon. Cons. Child & Adolesc. Psychiat.; Pathfinder NHS Trust Lond. Socs: Soc. Study Behavioural Phenotypes; Assoc. Mem. Child Psychiat. Research Soc.; Brit. Assn. Behavioural & Cognitive Psychother. Prev: Wellcome Research Fell. (Psychiat.) Inst. Child Health Lond.; Sen. Regist. (Child Psychiat.) Hosp. for Sick Childr. Gt. Ormond St. Lond.; Regist. (Psychiat.) Bethlem & Maudsley Hosps. Lond.

TURK, Professor John Leslie Flat 21, Lulworth Court, 13 Cannon Hill, London N14 7DJ — DSc Lond. 1967, MD 1959, MB BS (Hnrs.) 1953; FRCS Eng. 1978; FRCP Lond. 1975, M 1970; MRCS Eng., LRCP Lond. 1953; FRCPath 1974, M 1963. (Guy's) Emert. Prof. Path. Univ. Lond. Socs: Path. Soc. & Brit. Soc. Immunol. Prev: Sir William Collins Prof. of Path. Roy. Coll. Surg. & Univ. Lond.; Reader in Immunol. Inst. Dermat. Lond.; Mem. Scientif. Staff, MRC, Nat. Inst. Med. Research.

TURK, Kenneth Arthur Deane (retired) The Old Cottage, Cooksmill Green, Chelmsford CM1 3SJ Tel: 01245 248522 Fax: 01245 248522 — MD (Path.) Lond. 1948, MB BS 1944; MRCS Eng. LRCP Lond. 1943; FRCPath 1967. Prev: Hon. Cons. Histopath. Unit ICRF Lond.

TURK, Theresa (retired) Flat 21, Lulworth Court, 13 Cannon Hill, London N14 7DJ — MB BS 1950 Lond.; MB BS (Hnrs Path.) Lond. 1950; MRCS Eng. LRCP Lond. 1950; DCH Eng. 1953. Prev: Paediat. Regist. W. Middlx. Hosp. Isleworth.

TURKIE, Peter Victor High Street Surgery, 15 High Street, Overton, Wrexham LL13 0ED Tel: 01978 710666 Fax: 01978 710494 (Call before faxing); Fairfield, 32 Salop Road, Overton-on-Dee, Wrexham LL13 0EH Tel: 01978 710595 — MB BS 1969 Lond.; MRCP (UK) 1974. (St. Geo.) GP; Med. Adviser N. Wales HA. Prev: Regist. (Med.) Liverp. RHB.

TURKINGTON, Douglas Newcastle City Health NHS Trust, Department of Psychiatry, Royal Victoria Infirmary, Newcastle upon Tyne NE1 4CP Tel: 0191 232 5131 Fax: 0191 227 5281; 5 Gerrard Close, Briere Dene, Whitley Bay NE26 4NS Tel: 0191 251 6343 Fax: 0191 223 2206 Email: dougturk@aol.com — MB ChB 1981 Glas.; MRCPsych 1986; FRCPsych 1998. Sen. Lect. (Liason Psychiat.) & Cons. Psychiat. at Roy. Vict. Infirm. Newc.-u-Tyne. Prev: Cons. Psychiat. St. Nicholas Hosp. Newc.; Sen. Regist. (Psychiat.) Roy. Hallamsh. Hosp. Sheff.; Sen. Regist. (Psychiat.) Bassetlaw Dist. Gen. Hosp. Worksop.

TURKINGTON, John Ronald Andrew Castle Practice, Carrickfergus Health Centre, Taylors Avenue, Carrickfergus BT38 7HT Tel: 028 9336 4193 Fax: 028 9331 5947 — MB BCh BAO 1996 Belf.

TURKINGTON, Peter Malcolm St James University Hospital, Bechett Street, Leeds LS9 7TF Tel: 0113 2066037; 72 Wynford Avenue, West Park, Leeds LS16 6JW — MB ChB 1993 Leeds; MRCP 1996. (Leeds university) Specialist Regist., Respiratury Med., Yorks. Socs: Brit. Thoracic Soc.; Europ. Respiratroy Soc.; Amer. Thoracic Soc.

TURLE, George Charles (retired) 5 Moorfield, Canterbury CT2 7AN Tel: 01227 65448 — MD 1952 Lond.; MB BS 1948; FRCPsych 1987, M 1972; DPM Eng. 1951. Prev: Cons. Psychiat. In-pat. Adolesc. Unit St. Augustines Hosp. Canterbury.

***TURLEY, Andrew Jones** 156 Blair Athol Road, Banner Cross, Sheffield S11 7GD Tel: 0114 268 5273; 7 Hill Close, Darlington Tel: 01325 461885 — MB ChB 1998 Sheff.; MB ChB Sheff 1998; BMedSci (Hons) 1995.

TURLEY, Isabel Mary Area F, X-Ray Department, Wythenshawe Hospital, Southmoor Road, Manchester M23 9LT — MB ChB 1976 Manch.; FRCR 1982; DMRD Eng. 1980. Cons. Radiol. Wythenshawe Hosp. Manch.

TURLEY, James Francis Woodlands Park Health Centre, Canterbury Way, Wideopen, Newcastle upon Tyne NE13 6JL Tel: 0191 236 2366 Fax: 0191 236 7619; 15 Albany Mews, Gosforth, Newcastle upon Tyne NE3 4JW Tel: 0191 284 0026 — MB BS 1966 Durham.

TURLEY, Jeanette Marie Windsor House Surgery, Corporation Street, Morley, Leeds LS27 9NB Tel: 0113 252 5223 Fax: 0113 238 1262 — MB ChB 1988 Sheff.

TURLEY, Joanne (T/R) 29 Dorchester Avenue, Glasgow G12 0EG — MB ChB 1995 Glas.

TURLEY, Simon Jack Summerlands Surgery, Starts Hill Road, Farnborough, Orpington BR6 7AR Tel: 01689 852165 Fax: 01689 854512; Parkshaw, New Road, Sundridge, Sevenoaks TN14 6AR Tel: 01959 562672 — MB BS 1977 Lond.; MRCS Eng. LRCP Lond. 1977. (Guy's)

TURLEY, Stephen Anthony The Avenues Medical Group, 27-29 Roseworth Avenue, Gosforth, Newcastle upon Tyne NE3 1NB Tel: 0191 285 8035; 12 Bloomsbury Court, Newcastle upon Tyne NE3 4LW — MB BCh BAO 1986 Belf.; MRCGP 1991; D.Occ.Med. RCP Lond. 1996; DRCOG 1989. Prev: Trainee GP N.umbria; SHO (O & G) Newc. Gen. Hosp.; Ho. Off. Belf. City Hosp.

TURNBERG, Daniel 5 Broadway Avenue, Cheadle SK8 1NN — MB ChB 1994 Leeds.

TURNBERG, Professor Sir Leslie Arnold, KBE Public Health Laboratory Service, 61 Colindale Avenue, London NW9 5DF Tel: 020 8200 1295; 5 Broadway Avenue, Cheadle SK8 1NN Tel: 0161 428 4237 — MB ChB Manch. 1957; MD Manch. 1966; FRCP Ed. 1993; FRCPI 1993; FRCP Lond. 1973, M 1961; FRCPS 1994; DSc Salford 1996; DSc Manch. 1998. (Manch.) Chairm. Bd. of Pub. Health Laborat. Serv. Lond.; Scientif. Adviser, Assn. Med. Research Charities; Pres. Med. Protec. Soc.; Pres. Med. Counc. on Alcoholism; Chairm. UK.Forum for Genetics & Insur. Socs: Brit. Soc. Gastroenterol.; Assn. of Phys. of GB & Irel.; Vice Pres. Acad. Med. Scis. Prev: Pres. Roy. Coll. Phys.; Prof. Med. Univ. Manch.; Sen. Lect. (Med.) Univ. Manch.

TURNBULL, Adam Lothian (retired) Pippins, North Warren, Aldeburgh IP15 5QF Tel: 01728 452888 Email: andjturnbull@doctors.org.uk — BM BCh 1947 Oxf.; DM Oxf. 1955, BM BCh 1947; FRCP Lond. 1969, M 1952. Prev: Phys. Lond. Hosp.

TURNBULL, Alastair John Tel: 01904 631313 — MD 1985 Lond.; BSc Lond. 1979, MB BS 1982; MRCP (UK) 1985; T(M) 1993; FRCP 1998. (St Thomas's Hospital London) Cons. Phys. & Gastroenterol. York. Dist. Hosp. Prev: Sen. Regist. (Gen. Med. & Gastroenterol.) Freeman Hosp. Newc. u Tyne; Research Fell. & Hon. Sen. Regist. Rayne Inst. St. Thos. Hosp. Lond.; Regist. (Med.) & Ho. Phys. St. Thos. Hosp. Lond.

TURNBULL, Alexander David Beech Hill Medical Practice, 278 Gidlow Lane, Wigan WN6 7PD Tel: 01942 821899 Fax: 01942 821752; 102 Whitley Crescent, Wigan WN1 2PU Email: alexdt.wigan@tinyonline.co.uk — MB ChB 1971 Glas.; MRCGP 1975; Dip. Med. Ethics Keele 1991. Socs: GP Writers Assn. Prev: Benefits Agency.

TURNBULL, Mr Andrew Robert Rathmullen House, 4A Combe Road, Bath BA2 5HX Tel: 01225 837484 — MB BS 1967 Lond.; MS Soton. 1977; FRCS Eng. 1972. (St. Thos.) Hons. Cons. Gen. & Vasc. Surg. Bath Roy. United Hosp. NHS Trust. Prev: Lect. & Hon. Sen. Regist. (Surg.) Surg. Div. Fac. Med. Soton. Univ.; Regist. (Surg.) Soton. Univ. Hosp.

TURNBULL, Anna Therese Mary Doctors Surgery, Half Moon Lane, Wigton CA7 9NQ Tel: 016973 42254 Fax: 016973 45464; The Ghyll, Carwath Bridge, Rosley, Wigton CA7 8AU — MB ChB 1981 Aberd.; MRCGP 1985; DRCOG 1985. GP Wigton.

TURNBULL, Anne 8 Lochview Road, Bearsden, Glasgow G61 1PP — MB ChB 1992 Glas. SHO (A & E) S.. Gen. Hosp. Glas.

TURNBULL, Anne Elizabeth Department of Radiology, Derby City General Hospital, Uttoxeter Road, Derby DE22 3NE Tel: 01332 340131; Springfield House, Moor Lane, Ockbrook, Derby DE72 3SA — BM BCh 1983 Oxf.; MA Oxf. 1985; FRCR 1990. Cons. Radiol. Derby City Hosp. & Derby Roy. Infirm. Prev: Sen. Regist. (Radiol.) Qu. Med. Centre Nottm.

TURNBULL, Catherine Mary Tollerton Surgery, 3-5 Hambleton View, Tollerton, York YO61 1QW Tel: 01347 838231 — MB BS 1982 Lond.; T(GP) 1991; DCH RCP Lond. 1988; DRCOG 1985. (St. Thos.) Asst. GP Tollerton York. Prev: Clin. Med. Off. (Paediat.) Newc. HA; SHO (Cas. & O & G) & Ho. Surg. St. Thos. Hosp. Lond.

TURNBULL, Christopher James Arrowe Park Hospital, Upton, Wirral CH49 5PE Tel: 0151 604 7064 Fax: 0151 604 7192 — MB BChir 1975 Camb.; MA Camb. 1971; FRCP Lond. 1993; MRCP (UK) 1977; MRCGP 1979; DCH Eng. 1979; DObst RCOG 1976. (Westm.) Cons. Phys. (Geriat. Med.) Arrowe Pk. Hosp. Upton. Socs: Brit. Geriat. Soc. (Train. Comm.); Pk.inson's Dis. Soc.; Brit. Diabetic Assn. Prev: Chairm. Mersey Specially Train. Comm.; Clin. Dir. (Med. for Elderly) Arrowe Pk. Hosp.; Sen. Regist. (Geriat.) Clatterbridge Hosp. Wirral.

TURNBULL

TURNBULL, Clare Ann 30 Selby Road, West Bridgford, Nottingham NG2 7BL — BM BCh 1997 Oxf.

TURNBULL, Colin Michael Main X-Ray Department, Western General Hospital, Crewe Road, Edinburgh EH4 2XU Tel: 0131 537 2042 Fax: 0131 537 1027; 31 Inveralmond Drive, Cramond, Edinburgh EH4 6JX Tel: 0131 312 6765 — MB ChB 1971 Ed.; BSc (Med. Sci.) Ed. 1969; FRCP Ed. 1988; MRCP (UK) 1974; FRCR 1978; DMRD Ed. 1976. Cons. Cardioradiol. W.. Gen. Hosp. Edin.; Hon. Sen. Lect. (Radiodiag.) Univ. Edin. Socs: Fell. Roy. Coll. Radiol. (Regional Postgrad. Adviser SE Scotl.); Fell. Roy. Coll. Phys.; BMA. Prev: Sen. Regist. & Regist. (Radiodiag.) Roy. Infirm. Edin.; SHO (Gen. Med.) E.. Gen. Hosp. Edin.

TURNBULL, David Hepburn (retired) 11 Tewkesbury Avenue, Marton, Middlesbrough TS7 8NB — MB BS Durh. 1942; MD Durh. 1953; MRCP Lond. 1948. Prev: Resid. Med. Off. Roy. Vict. Infirm. Newc. u. Tyne.

TURNBULL, David Keith 58 Penrhyn Road, Sheffield S11 8UN — BM 1989 Soton.

TURNBULL, Donald Malcolm Westwinds, Redburn Row, Chilton Moor, Houghton-le-Spring DH4 6PX — MB BS 1950 Durh. (Durh.) Prev: Ho. Phys. Dryburn Hosp. Durh.; Ho. Surg. Gyn. Roy. Vict. Infirm. Newc. upon Tyne.

TURNBULL, Douglass Matthew Department of Neurology, The Medical School, University of Newcastle upon Tyne, Framlington Place, Newcastle upon Tyne NE2 4HH Email: d.m.tunrbull@ncl.ac.uk — MB BS 1976 Newc.; PhD Newc. 1984, MD 1984; FRCP Lond. 1991; MRCP (UK) 1978. Prof. Neurol. Univ. Newc.; Hon. Cons. Neurol. Newc. AHA.

TURNBULL, Edith Barton 15 Carrick Drive, Coatbridge ML5 1JX — MB ChB 1948 Glas. (Glas.)

TURNBULL, Elizabeth Paterson Nicol 2 Blenheim Drive, Oxford OX2 8DG — MD 1954 Aberd.; MB ChB 1950.

TURNBULL, Gael Lundin (retired) 12 Strathearn Place, Edinburgh EH9 2AL — MD 1951 Pennsylvania USA; BA Camb. 1948; MCPS 1956; DA Eng. 1957. Prev: Hosp. Pract. (Anaesth.) Kidderminster & Dist. HA & S. Cumbria HA.

TURNBULL, George Anthony (retired) Hawthorn Bank, Silverdale, Carnforth LA5 0SQ Fax: 01524 702210 Email: georgeturnbull@compuserve.com — MB BS Durh. 1955; FRCOG 1978, M 1965. Cons. O & G N. Lancs. S. W.morland Hosp. Gp. Prev: Cons. O & G N. Lancs. S. W.morland Hosp. Gp.

TURNBULL, Georgina Helen Longwitton Hall, Longwitton, Morpeth NE61 4JJ — MB BS 1996 Lond.

TURNBULL, Gordon James, Wing Cdr. RAF Med. Br. Retd. Ticehurst House Hospital, Ticehurst, Wadhurst TN5 7HU Tel: 01580 200391 Fax: 01580 201006 Email: turnbullhq@fetohmail.com; The Brewery House, Broad Town, Swindon SN4 7RE Tel: 01793 731569 Fax: 01793 731569 — MB ChB 1973 Ed.; BSc (Med. Sci.) Ed. 1970; FRSA 1999; FRCPsych 1995, M 1982; FRCP Ed. 1995; MRCP (UK) 1979; FRGS 1977. (Edinburgh) Clin. Dir. Traum. Stress Managem. Centre Ticehurst Hse. Hosp. Wadhurst; Cons. Psychiat. Civil Aviat. Auth.; Hon. Sen. Lect. Psychiat.Univ.Kent. Prev: Cons. Psychiat. P.ss Alexandra Hosp. RAF Wroughton.

TURNBULL, Helen Elizabeth 4 Hollycross, Crazies Hill, Reading RG10 8QB — MB ChB 1998 Ed.

TURNBULL, Ian William X-Ray Department, Hope Hospital, Eccles, Salford Email: iwturnbull@medleg.freeserve.co.uk; 3 New Hall Avenue, Heald Green, Cheadle SK8 3LQ Tel: 0161 437 5924 — MB ChB 1971 Ed.; BSc Ed. 1968; FRCR 1978; DMRD Ed. 1975. Cons(Neuro.) Hope Hosp. Eccles, Salford, Manch.; Lect. Dept. Diagn. Radiol. Univ. Manch.; Vis. Prof. Univ. Hosp. Lond., Ontario, Canada. Socs: Fell. Roy. Soc. Med.; F. Ch.S; Brit. Soc. Neuroradiol. Prev: Sen. Regist. (Radiol.) Soton. Gen. Hosp.; SHO (Med. Renal Unit) & Regist. (Radiol.) Roy. Infirm. Edin.

TURNBULL, James Cameron 8 Wood Lane, Timperley, Altrincham WA15 7QB Email: 100531.406@compuserve.com — MB BS 1972 Lond.; BSc (Hons.) Lond. 1968; MRCS Eng. LRCP Lond. 1972. (Univ. Coll. Lond. & Univ. Coll. Hosp.) Socs: (Hon. Treas.) Sale Med. & Dent. Soc.; Trafford Oncol. Soc. Prev: GP Altrincham.

TURNBULL, Jane Claire South Durham Health Care NHS Trust, Archer Street Clinic, Darlington DL3 6LT Tel: 01325 465218; 12 Cleveland Terrace, Darlington DL3 7HA Tel: 01325 482279 — MB BS Newc. 1970; DCH RCP Lond. 1986. Staff Grade (Child Health) S. Durh. Health Care NHS Trust Darlington. Socs: N. Eng. Paediat. Assn. Prev: Clin. Med. Off. N.d. HA.

TURNBULL, Lesley Susan Department of Pathology, The Women's Hospital, Catharine St., Liverpool L8 7 Tel: 0151 709 1000; Stable Cottage, Gunley Hall, Marton, Welshpool SY21 8JL — MB ChB 1979 Ed.; BSc (Hons.) (Bact.) Ed. 1976, MB ChB 1979; MRCPath 1986. Cons. Cytol. Wom. Hosp. Liverp. & Roy. Liverp. Hosp.; Hon. Lect. Liverp. Med. Sch. Socs: BMA. Prev: Cons. Histopath. St. Geo. Hosp. Med. Sch. Lond.; Sen. Regist. (Histopath.) N. W.. RHA.

TURNBULL, Lindsay Wilson 30 Kaimes Road, Edinburgh EH12 6JT — MB ChB 1979 Ed.; BSc (Hons.) (Path.) Ed. 1976, MB ChB 1979. SHO (Gen. Med.) Roy. Infirm. Edin. Socs: BMA. Prev: Ho. Phys. & Ho. Surg. Roy. Infirm. Edin.

TURNBULL, Malcolm John Uxbridge Health Centre, George St., Uxbridge UB8 1UB Tel: 01895 231925 Fax: 01895 813190; The Corner Cottage, 45 Stratton Road, Beaconsfield HP9 1HR — BM BCh 1969 Oxf.; MA, BM BCh Oxf. 1969; DObst RCOG 1971.

TURNBULL, Margaret Helen Fleming (retired) 17 Orchard Drive, Bridgnorth WV16 4HY Tel: 01746 763080 — MB ChB Ed. 1945, DPH 1953. Prev: Asst. Co. Med. Off. & Sch. Med. Off. Salop CC.

TURNBULL, Mark King Street Surgery, 22A King Street, Hereford HR4 9DA Tel: 01432 272181 Fax: 01432 344725 — MB BS 1988 Lond.; MRCGP 1993; DCH RCP Lond. 1991; DRCOG 1991. Clin. Asst. (Cardiol.) Hereford Co. Hosp.

TURNBULL, Maureen Anne The Bungalow, Kilianan, Abriachan, Inverness IV3 8LA Email: mo_turnbull@yahoo.com — MB ChB 1993 Glas.; DRCOG Lond. 1997; DFFP Lond. 1997. Locum Gen. Practitioner & Locum Staff Grade A & E.

TURNBULL, Michael Robert Castlehead Medical Centre, Ambleside Road, Keswick CA12 4DB Tel: 017687 72025 Fax: 017687 73862; Fellbeck, Rogerfield, Keswick CA12 4BQ Tel: 017687 72442 — MB BS Durh. 1966. (Durh.)

TURNBULL, Nigel Bruce Hereward Medical Centre, Exeter Street, Bourne PE10 9NJ Tel: 01778 394188 Fax: 01778 393966 — MB ChB 1970 Sheff.; MRCGP 1975; DCH RCPS Glas. 1972.

TURNBULL, Penny Jo Top Flat S., 38 Thomson St., Aberdeen AB25 2QP — MB ChB 1997 Aberd.

TURNBULL, Peter Walpole Road Surgery, 12 Walpole Road, Bournemouth BH1 4HA Tel: 01202 395195 Fax: 01202 304293 — MB BCh 1978 Wales; BA Nat. Sc. Camb. 1975; MRCP (UK) 1981. GP Princip. Bournemouth. Prev: Regist. Cardiac. Dept. St. Thos. Hosp. Lond.; Regist. (Gen. Med.) Poole Gen. Hosp.; Ho. Phys. Med. Unit Univ. Hosp. Cardiff.

TURNBULL, Susan Mildred Department of Health, Wellington House, 133-155 Waterloo Road, London SE1 8UG Tel: 020 7972 4378 Fax: 020 7972 4559 Email: sturnbul@doh.gov.uk; 18 Pewley Way, Guildford GU1 3PY Tel: 01483 830822 Email: susan.turnbull@virgin.net — MB BS 1981 Newc.; MRCGP 1985. Sen. Med. Off. (Communicable Dis.s) Brit. Dept. of Health. Prev: Med. Adviser Driver & Vehicle Licensing Agency; GP Blaydon-on-Tyne; Trainee GP E. Cumbria VTS.

TURNBULL, Thomas Alan, Surg. Cdr. RN Retd. 34 Martlets Court, Queen St., Arundel BN18 9NZ Tel: 01903 883762 — MRCS Eng. LRCP Lond. 1936; DA Eng. 1944. (Guy's) Prev: Hon. Med. Adviser Merchant Navy & Airline Offs. Assn.; Sen. Specialist Urol. RN; Surg. Cdr. RN.

TURNBULL, Mr Timothy John (cons. rooms), 32 The Drive, Hove BN3 3JD Tel: 01273 820082 Fax: 01273 731137 — MB BS 1974 Lond.; FRCS Eng. 1978. Cons. Orthop. Surg. Roy. Sussex Co. Hosp. & Roy. Alexandra Hosp. Sick Childr. Brighton. Socs: Fell. BOA & Roy. Soc. Med.; Brit. Assn. for Surg. of Knee; Brit. Orthopaedic Foot Surg. Soc. Prev: Sen. Regist. (Orthop.) Roy. Lond. Hosp. & Roy. Nat. Orthop. Hosps. Lond.; Clin. Fell. Hosp. for Sick Childr., Toronto.

***TURNER, Agnes Jane** 13 Upper Malone Crescent, Upper Malone Rd, Belfast BT9 6PR Tel: 01232 201095 — MB BCh BAO 1996 Belf.

TURNER, Mr Alan Gordon Peterborough Hospitals NHS Trust, Edith Cavell Hospital, Bretton Gate, Peterborough PE3 9GZ Tel: 01733 875226 Fax: 01733 875639; Millstone, 48 Main St, Ailsworth, Peterborough PE5 7AF Tel: 01733 380666 Fax: 01733 380666 Email: alangturner@hotmail.com — MB BS Lond. 1968; BSc Lond. 1965; FRCS Eng. 1973; FRCS Ed. 1973; MRCS Eng. LRCP Lond. 1968. (Char. Cross London University) Cons. Urol. P'boro. & Stamford Hosps. & Med. Dir. P'boro. Hosp. NHS Trust. Socs: Fell.

Roy. Soc. Med.; Brit. Assn. Urol. Surgs.; Société Internat.e D'Urologie. Prev: Lect. (Urol. & Renal Transpl.) Char. Cross Hosp. Lond.; Lect. (Urol.) Inst. Cancer Research & Roy. Marsden Hosp. Lond.; Regist. (Urol.) Char. Cross Hosp. Lond.

TURNER, Alan Muir Wessex Nuffield Hospital, Winchester Road, Chandler's Ford, Eastleigh SO50 2DW Tel: 01703 260919; 4 Hiltingbury Road, Chandler's Ford, Eastleigh SO53 5SW Tel: 01703 253019 — MB BChir 1973 Camb.; MB Camb. 1973, BChir 1972; FRCP Lond. 1991; MRCP (UK) 1975. (Guy's) Cons. Neurol. Wessex Neurol. Centre Soton., Qu. Alexandra Hosp. & St. Mary's Hosp. Portsmouth. Prev: Regist. (Neurol.) Nat. Hosp. Nerv. Dis. Qu. Sq. Lond.; Regist. (Neuropsychiat.) St. Thos. Hosp. Lond.

TURNER, Alastair Ronald 12 Froghall Road, Aberdeen AB24 3JL — MB ChB 1997 Aberd.

TURNER, Albert (retired) 25 Station Lane, Mickle Trafford, Chester CH2 4EH Tel: 01244 301748 — MB ChB Liverp. 1954; MRCGP 1977. Prev: Ho. Phys. Sefton Gen. Hosp.

TURNER, Alison Jane 28 Jenner House, Restell Close, Vanbrugh Hill, London SE3 7UW — MB BS 1989 Lond.

TURNER, Alison Robertson Church Street Surgery, 30 Church Street, Dunoon PA23 8BG Tel: 01369 703482/702778 Fax: 01369 704502; Westgate, Toward, Dunoon PA23 7UA Tel: 01369 87251 — MB ChB 1970 Glas. (Glas.) Socs: BMA.

TURNER, Mr Alistair 35 Wrottesley Road, Tettenhall, Wolverhampton WV6 8SG — MB BCh 1973 Wales; BSc (Hons.) Wales 1970, MB BCh 1973; MChOrth Liverp. 1983; FRCS Eng. 1978; FRCS Ed. 1978. (Welsh National School Medicine) Cons. Orthop. Surg. Roy. Hosp. & New Cross Hosp. Wolverhampton. Socs: Fell. BOA; Brit. Soc. Childr. Orthop. Surg. Prev: Sen. Lect. (Orthop. Surg.) Univ. Liverp.; Regist. (Orthop. & Trauma) Nuffield Orthop. Centre Oxf.; Regist. Christie Hosp. & Holt Radium Inst. Manch.

TURNER, Mr Allan Roderick Queen Margaret Hospital, Dunfermline KY12 0SU Tel: 01383 623623 Fax: 01383 674004 Email: ailean2000@yahoo.com; 34 Couston Street, Dunfermline KY12 7QW — MB ChB 1965 Ed.; FRCS Eng. 1972; FRCS Ed. 1971. (Ed.) Cons. Gen. Vasc. Surg. Qu. Margt. Hosp. NHS Trust; Hon. Sen. Lect. Univ. Edin.; Examr. RCS Ed.; Regional Adviser to R. Coll. of Surg.s of Edin. Socs: BMA; Vasc. Soc. GB; Assn. Surg. Prev: Asst. Prof. Surg. Pahlavi Univ. Shiraz, Iran; Regist. (Surg.) Clatterbridge Hosp. Bebington, BRd.green Hosp. Liverp. & Glas. Roy. Infirm.

TURNER, Andrea Dept. Of Immunobiology, Kings College London, Guys Hospital, St Thomas Street, London SE1 3UL Email: andrea.turner@kcl.ac.uk; Tel: 01935 816831 Fax: 01935 816831 Email: celtique@clara.co.uk — MB BChir 1991 Camb.; MRCP (UK) 1994. p/t MRC Clin. Research Fell., ImmunoBiol. Dept. Guy's Hosp. Lond.

TURNER, Andrew Frere Lowesmoor Medical Centre, 93 Lowesmoor, Worcester WR1 2SA Tel: 01905 723441 Fax: 01905 724987; 288 Bath Road, Worcester WR5 3ET Tel: 01905 769153 — MB BS 1984 Lond.; DRCOG 1989. (Westminster Medical School) Socs: Primary Care Soc. Gastroenterol.

TURNER, Andrew James Leslie Public Health Laboratory, Institute of Pathology, Newcastle General Hospital, Westgate Road, Newcastle upon Tyne NE4 6BE Tel: 0191 273 8811 Fax: 0191 226 0365 Email: newaturn@north.phls.nhs.uk — MB ChB 1979 Manch.; FRCPath 1997; MRCPath 1989; Dip. Bact. Manch. 1985. (Manchester)

TURNER, Andrew Neil Renal Medicine (MRU, University of Edinburgh, Royal Infirmary, Lauriston Place, Edinburgh EH3 9YW Email: http://renux.dmed.ed.ac.uk/edren — BM BCh 1980 Oxf.; PhD Lond. 1992; MA Camb. 1981; FRCP Lond. 1996; FRCP Ed. 1997; MRCP (UK) 1984. Prof. Nephrol. Univ. Edin. Socs: Renal Assn.; Brit. Soc. Immunol.; Assn. Phys.s. Prev: Sen. Lect. & Hon. Cons. Med. & Therap. Univ. of Aberd.; Research Fell. Renal Unit Roy. Postgrad. Med. Sch. Lond.; Regist. (Med.) York Dist. Hosp.

TURNER, Angus William Mure Flat 6, 192 Bedford Hill, London SW12 9HL — MB BS 1986 Lond.

TURNER, Anita Jacqueline 42 Haddricks Mill Road, Newcastle upon Tyne NE3 1QL — MB BS 1990 Newc.

TURNER, Anne Curtis (retired) The Old Vicarage, Church Road, Combe Down, Bath BA2 5JJ Tel: 01225 833226 Fax: 01225 833226 — MB BS 1962 Lond.; MFFP 1993. Prev: SCMO (Family Plann.) Bath.

TURNER, Anne Marie 14 Brisbane Grove, Hartburn, Stockton-on-Tees TS18 5BW — BM BS 1997 Nottm.

TURNER, Anne Ruth 101 Rowland Way, Aylesbury HP19 7SP; 15 The Meadows, Whitchurch, Aylesbury HP22 4TL — MB BChir 1993 Camb.; MRCP (UK) 1995; DRCOG 1998; DCH 1998. (Cambridge and Charing Cross) VTS GP Trainee Stoke Mandeville Hosp. Bucks. Socs: BMA; Roy. Coll. Phys. Prev: SHO (Med.) Wexham Pk. Hosp. Slough; Regist. (Haemat.) John Radcliffe Hosp. Oxf.

TURNER, Anthony Ambrose Fiddler's Cottage, Longborough, Moreton-in-Marsh GL56 0QE Tel: 01451 831373 — MB BS 1948 Lond. (Guy's) Socs: Med. Anthroposophical Assn.; Assoc. Fac. Homoeop.

TURNER, Archibald (retired) 7A Larchlea S., Darras Hall, Ponteland, Newcastle upon Tyne NE20 9LW Tel: 01661 823068 — MB BS Durh. 1952. Prev: Clin. Med. Off. Gateshead HA.

TURNER, Arthur Francis (retired) Meadows Cottage, Radipole Village, Weymouth DT4 9RY Tel: 01305 782763 — MB BCh BAO 1934 Belf.; DPH Lond. 1937. Prev: Co. MOH Dorset.

TURNER, Barbara Anne 507 North Drive, Thornton-Cleveleys FY5 2HY — MB BS 1993 Lond.

TURNER, Benjamin Charles 3 Bridgelands, Copthorne, Crawley RH10 3QW Fax: 01342 719577; 3 Bridgelands, Copthorne, Crawley RH10 3QW Email: btu6960362@aol.com — MB BS 1992 Lond.; BSc Lond. 1989; MRCP (UK) 1995. (St. Bart. Hosp. Lond.) Specialist Regist. (Diabetes, Endocrinol. & Gen. Med.); Research Fell. Roy. Bournemouth Hosp. & St. Thos. Hosps. Lond. Socs: Diabetic Assn. Prev: Specialist Regist. (Diabetes, Endocrinol. & Gen. Med.) Qu. Alex. Hosp. Portsmouth; Specialist Regist. (Diabetes, Endocrinol. & Gen. Med.) P.ss Margt. Hosp. Swindon; SHO (Gen. Med.) Roy. Sussex Co. Hosp. Brighton.

TURNER, Benjamin Patrick Flat 1, Lenton Abbey, Derby Road, Beeston, Nottingham NG9 2SN — MB BS 1991 Lond.

TURNER, Beryl Rachel (retired) Sandalwood, 21 Courtyard Gardens, Wrotham, Sevenoaks TN15 7DS — MB ChB 1943 Liverp. Prev: Chest Phys. SE Thames HA.

TURNER, Beverley Anne Dronfield Health Centre, High St., Dronfield, Sheffield S18 1PY Tel: 01246 419040 Fax: 01246 291780; Green Gables, Valley Road, Barlow, Dronfield, Sheffield S18 7SN — MB ChB 1972 Leeds; MRCGP 1976.

TURNER, Caroline Mallorie Irwin St Martins Practice, 319 Chapeltown Road, Leeds LS7 3JT Tel: 0113 262 1013 Fax: 0113 237 4747 — BM 1980 Soton.; MRCGP 1989; DRCOG 1982.

TURNER, Carolyn Joan Old School Surgery, Church St., Seaford BN25 1HH Tel: 01323 890072; 25 Blatchington Hill, Seaford BN25 2AJ — MB BS 1987 Lond. (King's Coll. Sch. Med. & Dent.) Princip. GP Seaford. Prev: Princip. GP Crowthorne, Berks.; GP Princip. Newhaven.

TURNER, Charles Godfrey Bodidris, 10 Park Road W., Sutton-on-Sea, Mablethorpe LN12 2NQ Tel: 01507 442296 — MRCS Eng. LRCP Lond. 1959. (Leeds) Prev: Regist. (Anaesth.) Harrogate Gen. Hosp.; SHO (Obst.) ScarBoro. Gen. Hosp.; Ho. Surg. & Ho. Phys. Otley Gen. Hosp.

TURNER, Charlotte Flat 2, 10 Friars Walk, Exeter EX2 4AY — BM BCh 1988 Oxf.

TURNER, Christopher Top Flat, 60 Addison Gardens, London W14 0DP — BM BCh 1996 Oxf.

TURNER, Christopher Brian Hodson and Partners, Park Farm Medical Centre, Allestree, Derby DE22 2QN Tel: 01332 559402 Fax: 01332 541001; 39 Burley Lane, Quarndon, Derby DE22 5JR Tel: 01332 840138 — MB BS 1973 Lond.; MRCS Eng. LRCP Lond. 1973; MRCGP 1978; DCH Eng. 1978; DRCOG 1978. (Roy. Free) Prev: SHO A & E Dept. Lond. Hosp.; Ho. Surg. Roy. Free Hosp.; Ho. Phys. St. And. Hosp. Lond.

TURNER, Christopher Mitchell 10 Coden Terrace, Haymarket, Edinburgh EH11 2BJ — MB ChB 1992 Ed.

TURNER, Claire Louise Susan 72 Chiltern Drive, Surbiton KT5 8LW — MB ChB 1996 Birm.; ChB Birm. 1996. (Birmingham)

TURNER, Clare Elizabeth 16 Vandra Close, Malvern WR14 1EJ Tel: 01684 567209 — MB BCh 1998 Wales.

TURNER, Clare Louise Houghton Farmhouse, Ringmore, Kingsbridge TQ7 4HH — MB BS 1988 Lond.; DCH RCP Lond. 1991. Staff Grade Paediat. Derriford Hosp. Plymouth.

TURNER

TURNER, Colin The Health Centre, Elm Grove, Mengham, Hayling Island PO11 9AP Tel: 023 9246 6224 — MB ChB 1983 Bristol; MRCGP 1987; DRCOG 1987. GP Hayling Is. Hants.

TURNER, Colin Mure (retired) Podkin Farm, High Halden, Ashford TN26 3HS — MB ChB 1944 Glas.

TURNER, David Alexander Hatfield Road Surgery, 70 Hatfield Road, Ipswich IP3 9AF Tel: 01473 723373 — MB BS 1971 Lond.; MRCP (UK) 1974; MRCS Eng. LRCP Lond. 1971; DCH Eng. 1975. Hosp. Pract. (Gen. & Chest Med.) Ipswich Hosp.

TURNER, David Charles Turner, Hart, Appleton and Briggs, Woodsend Medical Centre, School Place, Corby NN18 0QP Tel: 01536 407006 Fax: 01536 401711; 16 Church Lane, Dingley, Market Harborough LE16 8PG Tel: 01858 535319 Fax: 01536 401711 Email: dcturner2@aol.com — MB BS 1969 Lond.; MRCGP 1985; Dip. Med. Educat. Dund 1994. (St. Geo.) GP Corby; Cons. Weetabix, Golden Wonder, Orchard Ho. Foods. Socs: Brit. Assn. Performing Arts Med.; BMA. Prev: Regist. (Path.) Roy. Hants. Co. Hosp. Winchester & St. Geo. Hosp. Lond.; Ho. Phys. Epsom Dist. Hosp.; Ho. Surg. St. Geo. Hosp. Lond.

TURNER, David John Gosford House, 3 Noel Road, Oulton Broad, Lowestoft NR32 3JS Tel: 01502 564263 Email: caritas@totalise.co.uk; 5 The Rushes, Bray on Thames, Berks SL6 1UW Email: caritas@totalise.co.uk — MB ChB 1960 Ed.; FFA RCS Eng. 1967; DA Eng. 1964. (Ed.) Cons. Anaesth. Jas. Paget Hosp. Gt. Yarmouth. Socs: BMA; E. Anglian Assn. Anaesth. Prev: Sen. Regist. (Anaesth.) Roy. Infirm. Edin.; Regist. (Anaesth.) Ipswich & E. Suff. Hosp.

TURNER, David John Pencester Surgery, 10/12 Pencester Road, Dover CT16 1BW Tel: 01304 240553 Fax: 01304 201773 — MB ChB 1978 Ed.

TURNER, David Patrick James 2 School Lane, Stanton-by-Dale, Ilkeston DE7 4QJ — MB ChB 1989 Leic.

TURNER, David Paul Ventnor Medical Centre, 3 Albert Street, Ventnor PO38 1EZ Tel: 01983 852787 Fax: 01983 855447; Fowlsdown Farm, Whiteley Bank, Ventnor PO38 3AF — MB ChB 1977 Birm.

TURNER, Professor David Robert Department of Histopathology, St George's Hospital, Blackshaw Road, London SW17 0QT Tel: 020 8725 5264 Fax: 020 8767 7984 — MB BS Lond. 1962; PhD Lond. 1969; MRCS Eng. LRCP Lond. 1962; FRCPath 1984, M 1972. (Guy's) Cons. Histopath. (Renal Dis.) St Geo.s Hosp. Lond.; Emerit. Prof. Path. Nottm. Univ.; Emerit. Cons. Histopath. Univ. Hosp. Nottm.; Mem. WHO Comm. cl.ificat. & Nomenclature of Renal Dis.; Advis. Edr. Internat. Dictionary of Med. & Biol.; Adviser Edr. Jl. Clin. Path. & Internat. Jl. Experim. Path; CPA Insp. Socs: BMA; Path. Soc.; Roy. Soc. Med. Prev: Vice-Dean Univ. Nottm. Med. Sch.; Cons. Histopath. MusGr. Pk. Hosp. Taunton; Reader & Prof. Histopath. Guys Hosp. Med. Sch. Lond.

TURNER, Deborah Celia Greenhill Health Centre, 482 Lupton Road, Sheffield S8 7NQ Tel: 0114 237 2961 — MB ChB 1978 Sheff.; DCCH RCP Ed. 1983; DRCOG 1980. Socs: BMA. Prev: SHO (Paediat.) Sheff. Childr. Hosp.; SHO (Gyn. & Obst.) Jessop Hosp. Wom. Sheff.

TURNER, Deborah Louise Derriford Hospital, Department Haematology, Plymouth PL6 8DH Tel: 01752 777111 — MB BS 1992 Lond.; MRCPath 2001; BSc (Hons.) 1989; MRCP (UK) 1996. (Royal Free)

TURNER, Delphine Ruth 35 Station Road, Felstead, Dunmow CM6 3HD — MB BS 1976 Lond.; MRCP 1979.

TURNER, Mr Derek Thomas Leslie Pilgrim Hospital, Sibsey Road, Boston PE21 9QS Tel: 01205 442096 Fax: 01205 442084 Email: derekturner@ulh.nhs.uk; 109 Spilsby Road, Boston PE21 9PE Tel: 01205 361913 — MB BS 1968 Lond.; MS Soton. 1981; FRCS Eng. 1973. (Guy's) Cons. Urol. Pilgrim Hosp. Boston; Clin. Director (Urol.) United Lincs. Hosps. Socs: BMA; Brit. Assn. Urol. Surgs. Prev: Lect. (Surg.) Soton. Univ.

TURNER, Diane 17 Oakfield Terrace, Tyllwyn, Ebbw Vale NP23 6AG — MB BCh 1987 Wales.

TURNER, Mr Douglas Patrick Breen (retired) 74 Leicester Road, Uppingham, Oakham LE15 9SD Fax: 01325 464914 — MRCS Eng. LRCP Lond. 1939; FRCS Eng. 1948. Prev: Cons. Gen. Surg. BRd.green Hosp. & Mill Rd. Matern Hosp. Liverp.

TURNER, Duncan 6 Traquair Park W., Edinburgh EH12 7AL — MB ChB 1997 Aberd.

TURNER, Edward Charles Shiregreen Medical Centre, 492 Bellhouse Road, Sheffield S5 0RG Tel: 0114 245 6123 Fax: 0114 257 0964 — MB ChB 1988 Sheff.; DRCOG 1992.

TURNER, Elaine Inglis Killin Medical Practice, Laggan Leigheas, Ballechroisk, Killin FK21 8TQ Tel: 01567 820213 Fax: 01567 820805 — MB ChB 1983 Ed.; BSc (Hons.) Ed. 1980; DRCOG 1987. Prev: Regist. (Clin. Biochem.) Roy. Infirm. Edin.; Research Regist. (O & G) Roy. Vict. Infirm. Newc. u. Tyne.

***TURNER, Emily** 26 Westlake Gardens, Worthing BN13 1LF Tel: 01903 264057 — MB ChB 1995 Leic.

TURNER, Mr Eric Anderson (retired) 19B School Road, Moseley, Birmingham B13 9ET Tel: 0121 449 8217 — MB ChB 1940 Glas.; FRCS Eng. 1949. Prev: Neurosurg. Qu. Eliz. Hosp. Birm.

TURNER, Erin Sinclair 25 All Saints Road, Kings Heath, Birmingham B14 7LL — MB ChB 1991 Birm.; ChB Birm. 1991.

TURNER, Ethel Barbara (retired) 4 Mortain Road, Rotherham S60 3BX Tel: 01709 370169 — MB ChB 1962 Sheff. Prev: Cons. Genitourin. Phys. Rotherham Dist. Gen. Hosp.

TURNER, George Craven (retired) 25 Timms Lane, Formby, Liverpool L37 7DW Tel: 0170 48 31323 — MB ChB 1947 Leeds; MD Leeds 1957, MB ChB 1947; FRCPath 1969, M 1963. Prev: Dir. Liverp. Regional Pub. Health Laborat.

TURNER, Mr George Stewart Manchester Royal Eye Hospital, Oxford Road, Manchester M13 9WH Tel: 0161 276 1234 — MB BS 1977 Lond.; FRCS Eng. 1984; MRCP (UK) 1982. (St. Geo.) Cons. Ophth. Manch. Roy. Eye Hosp. Socs: Assn. Research in Vision & Ophth. Prev: Cons. Ophth. Taunton & Som. Hosp.; Lect. (Clin. Ophth.) Inst. Ophth. Lond.; Resid. Surgic. Off. Moorfields Eye Hosp. Lond.

TURNER, Gerald McDonald Ambrose (retired) Dove Cottage, 2 Ragleth View, Ludlow Road, Little Stretton, Church Stretton SY6 6RF — MB ChB 1949 Ed.; FRCP Ed. 1971, M 1955. Prev: Cons. Phys. Dunoran Home (Guy's Hosp.) Bromley.

TURNER, Gillian 62 Sandymount Street, Belfast BT9 5DQ — MB BCh BAO 1990 Belf.

TURNER, Gillian Elrick Department of Haematology, Norfolk & Norwich Hospital, Norwich NR1 3SR Tel: 01603 286286 Fax: 01603 286918 Email: gill.turner@norfolk-norwich.thenhs.com — MB ChB 1981 Ed.; BSc (Hons.) Med. Sci. Ed. 1978, MD 1992, MB ChB 1981; FRCP (Edin) 2000; MRCPath 1993. (Ed.) Cons. Haematol. Norf. - Norwich NHS Trust, Norwich. Prev: Sen. Regist. (Haemat. & Blood Transfus.) N.. RHA.; Regist. (Haemat.) W.. Gen. Hosp. Edin.; Regist. (Med.) Roy. Infirm. Edin.

TURNER, Gillian Frances Lymington Infirmary, East Hill, Lymington SO41 9ZH Tel: 01590 676085; Arnewood Corner, Arnewood Bridge Road, Sway, Lymington SO41 6ER — MB BS 1981 Lond.; FRCP Lond. 1994; MRCP (UK) 1983; MRCS Eng. LRCP Lond. 1981. Cons. Phys. Geriat. Med. Soton. & Lymington. Socs: Brit. Geriat. Soc.; Hosp. Cons. & Spec. Assn. Prev: Sen. Regist. W. Midl.

TURNER, Gillian Margaret X-Ray Department, Derby City General Hospital, Uttoxeter, Derby DE22 3NE Tel: 01332 340131 Fax: 01332 625844; The Mount, Yeldersley, Ashbourne DE6 1LS — MB BS 1984 Lond.; BSc Lond. 1981; FRCR 1992. (Univ. Coll. Hosp. Med. Sch.) Cons. Radiol. Derby City Gen. Hosp. Prev: Sen. Regist. (Radiol.) Nottm. HA.

TURNER, Glynnis Ida Flat 5, St. Charles Hospital, Exmoor St., London W10 6DZ — MB BS 1991 Lond.

TURNER, Guy Allan, Surg. Cdr. RN Retd. Anaesthetic Department, Royal West Sussex Hospital, Spitalfield Lane, Chichester PO19 4SE Tel: 01243 788122 Fax: 01243 831600 Email: guyturner@rws-tr.sthames.nhs.uk; 72A West Gate, Chichester PO19 3HH Tel: 01243 783923 — MB BS 1975 Lond.; MRCS Eng. LRCP Lond. 1975; FFA RCS 1981. (Westminster) Cons. Anaesth. St. Richards Hosp. Chichester. Prev: Cons. Anaesth. Intens. Care Unit RN Hosp. Haslar Gosport.

TURNER, Gwendoline Department of Clinical Genetics, Ashley Wing, St James University Hospital, Leeds Tel: 0113 243 3144; 68 Duchy Road, Harrogate HG1 2EZ Tel: 01423 506772 — MB ChB 1967 Ed. (Ed.) ICRF Genetic Epidemiol. St. Jas. Hosp. Leeds; Dep. Clin. Genetics St. Jas. Hosp. Leeds.

TURNER, Harriet Jemima Holcroft, Common Lane, Lower Stretton, Warrington WA4 4PD — MB BS 1998 Newc.; MB BS Newc 1998.

TURNER, Helen Elizabeth 17 White Hart Close, Castle Square, Benson, Oxford OX10 6NX — MB BChir 1991 Camb.; MRCP (UK) 1993. Regist. Roy. Berks. Hosp. Reading. Prev: SHO St. Geo. Hosp., St. Thos. Hosp. & Hammersmith Hosp. Lond.

TURNER, Helen Mary (retired) Bodnant, Keighley Road, Colne BB8 7HL Tel: 01282 865615 — MRCS Eng. LRCP Lond. 1950; FRCPCH 1997; MFCM 1973; DPH Manch. 1966. Prev: SCMO Burnley HA.

TURNER, Hendrika Jacoba Doctors Residence, Royal Victoria Infirmary, Queen Victoria Road, Newcastle upon Tyne NE1 4LP — MB ChB 1986 Stellenbosch.

TURNER, Henry Richard 10 Armit Place, St Andrews KY16 8RE Tel: 01334 75198 — MB ChB 1945 St. And.; FFA RCS Eng. 1962, DA Eng. 1960. (St. Andrews)

TURNER, Hugh Dundonald Coxhoe Medical Practice, 1 Lansdowne Road, Cornforth Lane, Coxhoe, Durham DH6 4DH Tel: 0191 377 0340 Fax: 0191 377 0604; 15 Roast Calf Lane, Bishop Middleham, Durham DH7 9AT Email: mid.sedge@btinternet.com — MRCS Eng. LRCP Lond. 1989; MA Oxf. 1984, BA (Hons. Physiol.) 1980. Socs: Fell. Roy. Soc. Health; ARM Represen. N. Durh. Div. Prev: Trainee GP Cleveland VTS; SHO (Med.) S. Cleveland Hosp. & Roy. Shrewsbury Hosp.

TURNER, Ian Mark 50 Woodlands Park, Whalley, Clitheroe BB7 9UG — MB ChB 1997 Dundee.

TURNER, Ian Maxwell The Surgery, Sandy Lane, Brewood, Stafford ST19 9ES Tel: 01902 850206 Fax: 01902 851360 — MB ChB 1972 Liverp.; DRCOG 1977; DCH Eng. 1976.

TURNER, Jacqueline Susan South Parade Surgery, 1 South Parade, Penzance TR18 4DJ Tel: 01736 362082 Fax: 01736 332933 — MB BS 1968 Lond.; MRCS Eng. LRCP Lond. 1968.

TURNER, Mr James Andrew (retired) Carey House, Magham Down, Hailsham BN27 1PR Tel: 01323 844646 — MB BS 1947 Lond.; FRCS Eng. 1954.

TURNER, Jean (retired) Carey House, Magham Down, Hailsham BN27 1PR Tel: 01323 844646 — MB BS 1949 Lond.

TURNER, Mrs Jean McGiven Springburn Health Centre, 200 Springburn Way, Glasgow G21 1TR Tel: 0141 531 9691 Fax: 0141 531 6705; Beechwood, 1 Balmore Road, Milngavie, Glasgow G62 6ES — MB ChB 1965 Aberd.; DA Eng. 1970. (Aberd.) GP Glas. Prev: Regist. Anaesth. Aberd. Roy. Infirm.; Regist. Anaesth. S.. Gen. Hosp. Glas.

TURNER, Jennifer Jane Abbotsham Barton, Bideford EX39 5AP — MB BS 1990 Lond.

TURNER, Jeremy James Osborne Flat 8, No. 8 Frognal, London NW3 6AJ — MB BS 1993 Lond.; BSc Lond. 1990, MB BS 1993. SHO (Med.) Hammersmith Hosp. Lond.

TURNER, Joanna 12A Grey Point, Helen's Bay, Bangor BT19 1LE — MB BCh BAO 1992 Belf.

TURNER, Joanna Judith Bitterne Park Surgery, 28 Cobden Avenue, Southampton SO18 1BW Tel: 02380 585655 Fax: 02380 555215; Chase Grove, Waltham Chase, Southampton SO32 2LF Tel: 01489 891416 — MB ChB 1988 Bristol; MRCGP Lond. 1997; T(GP) 1996; DTM & H RCP Lond. 1993; MRCP (UK) 1992.

TURNER, Joanna Margaret 17 Summerhill Street, Newcastle upon Tyne NE4 6EJ — MB BS 1994 Newc.

TURNER, Joanna Patricia Rushall Medical Centre, 107 Lichfield Road, Rushall, Walsall WS4 1HB Tel: 01922 622212 Fax: 01922 637015 — MB BS 1986 Lond.; MRCGP 1992; DRCOG 1991; DCH RCP Lond. 1990.

TURNER, Joanne Louise South Merton Elderly Team, Springfield Hospital, Glenburnierd, Tooting, London SW17 — MB BS 1989 Lond.; MRCPsych 1994.

TURNER, John Consett Medical Centre, Station Yard, Consett DH8 5YA Tel: 01207 216116 Fax: 01207 216119; 9 Kempton Close, Derwent Braes, Shotley Bridge, Consett DH8 0UB Tel: 01207 501797 — MB BS 1980 Newc.; MRCGP 1984; DRCOG 1984. GP Consett.

TURNER, John Chatterton Shipley (retired) Miller's Cottage, Walkern Mill, Walkern, Stevenage SG2 7NP Tel: 01438 861250 — MRCS Eng. LRCP Lond. 1953; MA Camb. 1955, MB BChir 1954; DObst RCOG 1956.

TURNER, John Edward Tel: 01277 263033 Fax: 01277 771474 — BSc Lond. 1966, MB BS 1969; MRCS Eng. LRCP Lond. 1969; MFFP 1993; MRCGP 1975; Dip. Palliat. Med. Wales 1991; DObst RCOG 1972. (Univ. Coll. Hosp.) Clin. Asst. Renal Unit Kent & Canterbury Hosp. Prev: SHO (Med. & O & G) Cuckfield Hosp.; Ho. Surg. Ipswich & E. Suff. Hosp.

TURNER, John Ferens (retired) The Old Vicarage, Church Road, Combe Down, Bath BA2 5JJ Tel: 01225 833226 — MB BS 1962 Lond.; DObst RCOG 1967. Prev: Gen. Practitioner, Bath.

TURNER, John Halifax, SBStJ Magnolia House, 27 Carisbrooke Gardens, Knighton, Leicester LE2 3PR Tel: 0116 210 7740 Fax: 0116 210 7741 Email: jht3@le.ac.uk — MB BChir 1971 Camb.; MB Camb. 1972 BChir 1971; MA Camb. 1972. (Guy's) Clin. Lect. Dept. of Gen. Pract. & Primary Care Leicester Univ.; Teachg. Assoc. Drs Platts, Drucquer, Sharp, Shaw & Ward; Educat. Coord. Leics. GP. Salaried scheme. Socs: Leic. Med. Soc.; AUDGP; CMF. Prev: Ho. Surg. & Ho. Phys. (Gen. Med.) St. Nicholas Hosp. Plumstead.; Sen. Partner Gen. Pract. (Retd.) Leics.

TURNER, John Jeffrey Directorate of Medicine, University Hospital Aintree, Lower Lane, Liverpool L9 7AL Tel: 0151 529 2881 Fax: 0151 529 2420 Email: wendy.thompson@aaht.nwest.nhs.uk; Claddagh House, 20 Dowhills Road, Blundellsands, Liverpool L23 8SW — MB BS Lond. 1966; FRCP Lond. 1988; MRCP (UK) 1972; MRCS Eng. LRCP Lond. 1966. (St. Mary's) Cons. Phys. Univ. Hosp. Alm Tree Liverp. & Aintree Hosp. NHS Trust; Clin. Dir. & Head Med. Servs. Aintree Hosps.; Hon. Clin. Lect. Univ. Liverp. Socs: (Ex-Counc.) Brit. Geriat. Soc.; Liverp. Med. Inst. Prev: Sen. Regist. (Nuffield Dept. Med.) Radcliffe Infirm. Oxf.; Regist. (Med. & Endocrinol.) St. Vincent's Hosp. Dub.; Ho. Phys. (Med. Unit) St. Mary's Hosp. Lond.

TURNER, John Morris Department of Anaesthesia, Addenbrookes Hospital, Hills Road, Cambridge CB2 2QQ Tel: 01223 217434; 29 Church Street, Little Shelford, Cambridge CB2 5HG Tel: 01223 842344 — MB ChB 1965 Bristol; FFA RCS Eng. 1970. (Bristol) Cons. Anaesth. Camb. HA. Socs: BMA. Prev: Cons. Anaesth. Midl. Centre Neurosurg. & Neurol. Smethwick; Lect. (Anaesth.) Univ. Leeds; Sen. Regist. (Anaesth.) United Birm. Hosps.

TURNER, John Richard Timmis (retired) 32 Richmond village, St Josephs Park, Nantwich CW5 6TD Tel: 01270 625560 — MRCS Eng. LRCP Lond. 1936; MA Camb. 1943, BA 1933. JP. Prev: Ho. Surg., Ho. Phys. & Resid. Anaesth. St. Geo. Hosp.

TURNER, John Robert Bentley Glenturner, 3 Summer Meadow, The Uplands, Mill Hill Lane, Pontefract WF8 4HZ Tel: 01977 704762 Fax: 01977 704762 — MB ChB Leeds 1954; FRCP Lond. 1978, M 1960. Mem. Med. Appeals Tribunals. Socs: Assur. Med. Soc. Prev: Cons. Phys. Pontefract HA; Sen. Regist. (Med.) & Resid. Med. Off. Leeds Gen. Infirm.

TURNER, John Robinson (retired) Corner House, Cropton, Pickering YO18 8HH Tel: 01751 417586 — MRCS Eng. LRCP Lond. 1952. Prev: Surg. Cunard SS Company.

TURNER, John Scott Adult Intensive Care Unit, Royal Brompton National Heart & Lung Hospital, Sydney St., London SW3 6NP — MB ChB 1980 Cape Town; MMed. 1989; FCP(SA) 1988. Doverdale Fell. Roy. Brompton & Nat. Heart Hosp. Lond. Prev: Cons. Surg. ICU Groote Schuur Hosp. Cape Town S. Africa; Sen. Regist. (Respirat.) Groote Schuur Hosp. Cape Town, S. Africa.

TURNER, John Sydney (retired) 7 Crynfryn Buildings, Aberystwyth SY23 2BD Tel: 01970 612045 — MRCS Eng. LRCP Lond. 1947. Prev: Gen. Pract. Tregaron & Ceredigion.

TURNER, John Victor Cedar House Surgery, 14 Huntingdon Street, St. Neots, Huntingdon PE19 1BQ Tel: 01480 406677 Fax: 01480 475167; 28 Woodlands, St. Neots, Huntingdon PE19 1UE — MB BS 1968 Newc. (Newc.) Socs: BMA.

TURNER, Mr John William (retired) 15 Springkell Drive, Pollokshields, Glasgow G41 4EZ Email: m800jwt@aol.com — MB BS 1956 Lond.; FRCS Glas. 1974; FRCS Ed. 1962; MRCS Eng. LRCP Lond. 1956. Prev: Sen. Regist. Dept. Surg. Neurol. Roy. Infirm. Edin.

TURNER, Jonathan Andrew McMahon, RD Royal Bournemouth Hospital, Castle Lane E., Bournemouth BH7 7DW Tel: 01202 303626 Fax: 01202 704863 Email: jonathan.turner@rbch-tr.swest.nhs.uk — MB BS Lond. 1970; FRCP Lond. 1990; MRCP (UK) 1973. (Middlx. Hosp. Med. Sch.) Cons. Phys. E. Dorset Health Dist. Socs: Mem. of the Brit. Thoracic Soc. Exec. Comm. Prev: Lect. (Med.) Middlx. Hosp. Med. Sch. Lond.; Regist. (Med.) Centr. Middlx. Hosp. Lond.

TURNER, Joseph Edward 25 Westland Road, Knebworth SG3 6AS — MB BS 1992 Lond.

TURNER

TURNER, Joseph Greenwood 13 Promenade, Southport PR8 1QY Tel: 01704 536398 — MRCS Eng. LRCP Lond. 1950. (St. Mary's)

TURNER, Julian Geoffrey Litchdon Medical Centre, Landkey Road, Barnstaple EX32 9LL Tel: 01271 23443 Fax: 01271 25979; Higher Westaway, Newton Tracey, Barnstaple EX31 3PL Tel: 01271 858417 — MB BS 1969 Lond.; FRCGP 1988, M 1978; DFFP 1995; DCH Eng. 1977; DObst RCOG 1971. (Middlx.) Examr. RCGP. Socs: Fell. Roy. Soc. Med. Prev: Regist. (Med.) Chas. Gardner Hosp. Perth, W. Austral.; Regist. (Med.) Launceston Gen. Hosp. Tasmania, Austral.; SHO (O & G) N. Devon Dist. Hosp. Barnstaple.

TURNER, Julian Paul Marine Medical, Blyth Health Centre, Thoroton Street, Blyth NE24 1DX Tel: 01670 396520 Fax: 01670 396537; 12 Caseton Close, Whitley Bay NE25 9PL Tel: 0191 253 2912 — MB BS 1982 Newc. SHO (Gen. Med.) Freeman Hosp. Newc.

TURNER, Julie Annabel 83 Bushey Wood Road, Sheffield S17 3QD — MB ChB 1993 Manch. Specialist Regist., Med. Microbiol. Prev: SHO (Microbiol.) N.. Gen. Hosp. Sheff.

TURNER, Justin Andrew 2 Chapel Fold, Leeds LS6 3RG — MB ChB 1992 Leeds.

TURNER, Karina Louise The Charter Medical Centre, 88 Davigdor Road, Hove BN3 1RF Tel: 01273 738070/770555 Fax: 01273 220 0883 — MB ChB 1992 Manch.

TURNER, Kate Jane 46 Woodside Way, Short Heath, Willenhall WV12 5NH — MB ChB 1996 Ed.

TURNER, Katherine Jane Drumchapel Health Centre, 80-90 Kinfauns Drive, Glasgow G15 7TS Tel: 0141 211 6120 Fax: 0141 211 6128 — MB ChB 1977 Sheff.

TURNER, Kathryn Lesley Top Right Flat, 68 Randolph Road, Glasgow G11 7JL — MB ChB 1993 Dundee.

TURNER, Kevin James Punchetts, West Riding, Tewin Wood, Welwyn AL6 0PD — BM BCh 1993 Oxf.; FRCS Eng. 1997. SHO (Urol.) Ch.ill Hosp. Headington, Oxf. Prev: Demonst. (Anat.) Univ. Camb.

TURNER, Linda Margaret (Freeman) Middle House, Solefields Road, Sevenoaks TN13 1PJ — MB ChB 1991 Manch.; MRCP (UK) 1994; FRCR 1998. Cons. Radiologist, Bromley Hosps. NHS Trust, S. Lond.

TURNER, Lisa Maudsley Hospital, Denmark Hill, London SE5 8AZ Tel: 020 7703 6333 — MB ChB 1989 Bristol; BSc Bristol 1986, MB ChB 1989; MRCPsych 1994. Regist. (Psychiat.) Maudsley Hosp. Lond. Prev: SHO (Path.) S.mead Hosp. Bristol; Ho. Off. S.mead Hosp. Bristol; Ho. Off. W.on Gen. Hosp. W.on Super Mare.

TURNER, Lorraine Denise Pilgrim Hospital, Boston PE21 9QS; 5 Hazeldene Road, East Hamilton, Leicester LE5 1UA — MB ChB 1995 Birm.; BSc (1st cl Hons.) Physiology Birm. 1993; MBChB Birm. 1995; MRCP 1998. (Birmingham) Specialist Regist. (Respirat Med.) Pilgrim Hosp. Boston. Socs: Brit. Thoracic Soc..; BMA. Prev: SHO. IC. Hammersmith Hosp.; SHO Rotat. (Med.) Leicester.

TURNER, Lynda Anne North Tees and Hartlepool NHS Trust, North Tees Gen Hosp, Hardwick, Stockton-on-Tees TS19 8PE; 45 The Front, Middleton-One-Row, Darlington DL2 1AU — MB BS 1977 Newc.; MFFP.1993; MIPM. 1999. Clinician (Familiy Plann.) N Tees & Hartlepool NHS Trust.; Sen. Clin. Med. Off. (Family Plann.) Gateshead HA.

TURNER, Lynda Mary Beechvale, 11 Quarterlands Road, Drumbeg, Lisburn BT27 5TN — MB BCh BAO 1983 Dub.; DRCOG 1987.

TURNER, Marc Leighton John Hughes Bennett Laboratory, University of Edinburgh Dept of Oncology, Western General Medicine, Crewe Rd, Edinburgh EH4 2XU Tel: 0131 537 1575 Fax: 0131 537 3160 Email: marc.turner@ed.ac.uk; 27 Glengarry Crescent, Falkirk FK1 5UD Tel: 01324 630704 — MB ChB 1982 Manch.; FRCP (Ed) 1999; PhD Ed. 1996; MRCP (UK) 1987; MRCPath 1997. Sen. Lect. Univ. Edin.; Hon. Cons. Haemat. Lothian Univ. Hosps. Trust; Hon. Cons. Haemat. Scott. Nat. Blood Transfus. Serv.; Clin. Director, Edin. and SE Scotl. Blood Transfusion centre. Socs: Brit. Soc. For Haemat.; Brit. Blood Transfus. Soc.; Internat. Soc. for Experim. Haemat. Prev: Sen. Regist. (Transfus. Med.) Edin. & SE Scotl. Blood Transfus. Serv.; Clin. Research Fell. (Haemat.) Edin. Roy. Infirm.; Regist. (Haemat.) Edin. Roy. Infirm.

TURNER, Margaret Anne (retired) 17 Wyedale Crescent, Bakewell DE45 1BE — MB ChB Manch. 1953.

TURNER, Margaret Deborah Occupational Health Department, Centre for Occupational Health, 45 Bush Road, Antrim BT41 2RL Tel: 01849 424407 Fax: 01849 424402; 10 Windsor Heights, Old Glenarm Road, Larne BT40 1UL — MB BCh BAO 1985 Belf.; MRCGP 1990; DRCOG 1988; DCH Dub. 1987. (Qu. Univ. Belf.) Clin. Med. Off. (Occupat. Health) N. Health & Social Servs. Bd.; Forens. Med. Off. P.A.N.I. Socs: BMA; Assn. Police Surg.; Soc. Occupat. Med. Prev: Trainee GP Ballymena; SHO (Gen. Med.) Moyle Hosp. Larne; SHO (O & G) Route Hosp. Ballymoney.

TURNER, Mark Andrew Consultant Psychiatrist, Duchess Kent Psych Hospital, Horne Rd, Catterick Garrison DL9 4; 44 Milbourne Road, Bury BL9 6PX — MB ChB 1989 Liverp.; MRCP (UK) 1992; MRCPsych 1995; MSC 1998; MA 1993; Mphil 1999. Gen. Adult Psychiat. Prev: Lect. Forens. Psychiat., Inst. Psychiat., Lond.; Sen. Reg. NeuroPsychiat. St. Thomas's Hosp., Lond.

TURNER, Mark Anthony Benjamin 53 Lowther Cr, Leyland, Preston PR26 6QA — MB ChB 1997 Manch.

TURNER, Mark Augustine Timothy 8 Chiffon Way, Salford, Manchester M3 6AB Tel: 0161 834 6135 Email: m.turner@fs1.mci.man.ac.uk — MB ChB 1991 Manch.; MRCP (UK) 1994; DRCOG 1993. Research Fell. (Child Health) Univ. Manch.; Hon. Regist. Manch. Childr. Hosp.; Clin. Fell. Centr. Manch. NHS Trust.

TURNER, Mark Stephen Cardiology Department, South West Cardiothoracic Centre, Derriford Hospital, Plymouth PL6 8DH Tel: 01752 792661 Fax: 01752 792666; 5 Dalewood Rise, Laverstock, Salisbury SP1 1SE — MB ChB 1990 Bristol; MB ChB (Hons.) Bristol 1990; MRCP (UK) 1996. Specialist Regist. (Cardiol.)'. Prev: Regist. (Gen. Med. & Cardiol.) Derriford Hosp. Plymouth.

TURNER, Martin Robert Skyways Medical Centre, 2 Shelley Crescent, Hounslow TW5 9BJ Tel: 020 8569 5688 Fax: 020 8577 9952 — MB ChB 1977 Sheff. Prev: SHO (Psychiat.) Hillingdon Hosp. Middlx.; SHO (A & E) Ashford Hosp. Middlx.; SHO (Dermat. & Geriat.) Highlands Hosp. Lond.

TURNER, Martin St John Larkfield Centre,, Garngaber Avenue, Lenzie, Glasgow G66 3UG Tel: 0141 776 7100 Fax: 0141 776 7462 Email: martinturner@glacomen.scot.nhs.uk — MB BS 1984 Lond.; MPhil Ed. 1990; MA, BA (Hons.) Camb. 1981; MRCPsych 1989; T(Psych) 1994. (Roy. Free Hosp. Lond.) Cons. Psychiat. Stobhill Hosp. Glas.; Hon. Clin. Sen. Lect. (Psychol. Med.) Univ. Glas. Socs: Roy. Soc. Med.; Roy. Coll. Psychiat. Prev: Sen. Regist. (Psychiat.) W. Scotl. Train. Scheme Gtr. Glas. HB; Sen. Med. Research Fell. Roy. Edin. Hosp.; Regist. Roy. Edin. Hosp.

TURNER, Mary The Malt House, Cuddington, Aylesbury HP18 0AS — MB ChB 1960 Ed.; DObst RCOG 1962.

TURNER, Matthew Edward Clay 78 Northwood Road, Whitstable CT5 2EZ — MB BS 1993 Lond.; MRCP (UK) 1997. (St. Geo.)

TURNER, Matthew William Harding 5 Humberstone Road, Cambridge CB4 1JD — MB BChir 1992 Camb.

TURNER, Maurice John The Paddocks, 9 Boxwood Way, Warlingham CR6 9SB — MB 1955 Camb.; BChir 1954; FRCP Ed. 1979, M 1963; FRCR 1962; DMRD Eng. 1959. (Camb. & Bristol) Prev: Cons. Radiol. The Lond. Clinic, Lond. Hosp. Whitechapel & Torbay Hosp. Torquay.

TURNER, Maxwell Herman (retired) 59 Middlefield Lane, Hagley, Stourbridge DY9 0PY Tel: 01562 882228 — MB ChB 1947 Liverp.; MRCS Eng. LRCP Lond. 1947; MMSA Lond. 1956.

TURNER, Michael Arthur Scarborough Hospital, Scalby Road, Scarborough YO12 6QJ — MB ChB 1966 Ed.; FFA RACS 1979; FFA RCS Eng. 1971. (Ed.) Cons. Anaesth. ScarBoro. Hosp. Socs: Assn. Anaesths. & Obst. Anaesth. Assn. Prev: Cons. Anaesth. Dunedin Pub. Hosp. & Lect. (Anaesth.) Univ Otago Dunedin, NZ; Sen. Regist. Dundee Gen. Gp. Hosps.

TURNER, Michael John Dept. of Cellular Pathology, Wycombe Hospital, High Wycombe HP11 2TT Fax: 01494 425674 — MB BS 1973 Lond.; FRCPath 1990; MRCPath 1980. (Westm. & King's Coll.) Cons. Histopath. Wycombe Gen. Hosp. High Wycombe Bucks. Prev: Sen. Regist. (Histopath.) W.m. Med. Sch. Lond.; Sen. Regist. (Histopath.) St. Stephens Hosp. Lond.; SHO (Path.) W.m. Hosp. Lond.

TURNER, Michael Skinner 10 Harley Street, London W1G 9 PF Tel: 020 7467 8359 Fax: 020 7228 7495; The Lawn Tennis Assn., Queen's Club, London W14 9EG Tel: 020 7381 7071 Fax: 020

TURNER

7381 3001 Email: michael.turner@LTA.org.uk — MB BS Lond. 1970; MD Washington 1972; MRCS Eng. LRCP Lond. 1970. (St. Thos.) Chief Med. Adviser Jockey Club, Lawn Tennis Assn. Socs: Edr.ial Bd. Mem. of the Brit. Journal of sports Med.; Soc. for Tennis Med. & Sci. Prev: Dir. Med. Servs. Brit. Olympic Assn.; Chief Med. Adviser Texaco, BZW; Vickers, P & O, Hongkong & Shanghai Bank.

TURNER, Mr Murdo Alexander (retired) The Oaks, Glasson, Carlisle CA7 5DT — MB ChB Ed. 1956; FRCS Ed. 1959; FRCS Glas. 1974. Prev: Cardiothoracic Surg. Gt.er Glas. Health Bd. 1966-1993, Glas..

TURNER, Naomi (retired) 59 Middlefield Lane, Hagley, Stourbridge DY9 0PY Tel: 01562 882228 Email: naomi_turner@link.org — MRCS Eng. LRCP Lond. 1953; DCH Eng. 1957. Prev: Clin. Asst. (Paediat.) Corbett Hosp. Stourbridge & Wordsley Hosp.

TURNER, Naomi Margaret 65 Hazelwood Avenue, Newcastle upon Tyne NE2 3HU — MB BS 1997 Newc.

TURNER, Neal Andrew The Barn, Lilac Tree Farm, Bawtry Road, Hatfield Woodhouse, Doncaster DN7 6PH — MB ChB 1988 Leeds. Prev: Trainee GP Wakefield & Nottm. City Hosp.; SHO (O & G) Huddersfield Roy. Infirm.

TURNER, Neil 19 Ryecroft Avenue, Whitton, Twickenham TW2 6HH — MB BS 1980 Lond.; MRCGP 1984; DRCOG 1983.

TURNER, Neville Brindley 18 Appleton Drive, Whitmore, Newcastle ST5 5BT Tel: 01782 680540 Email: neville.turner@btinternet.com — MB ChB 1990 Ed.; DA Lond. 1994. (Univ. Ed. Med. Soc.) Staff Anaesth. N. Staff. Hosp.

TURNER, Nicholas Arden Medical Centre, Church Road, Tiptree, Colchester CO5 0HB Tel: 01621 816475 Fax: 01621 819902 — MB ChB 1984 Leic.; MRCGP 1990.

TURNER, Nicholas Charles 13 Belbroughton Road, Oxford OX2 6UZ — BM BCh 1997 Oxf.

TURNER, Mr Nicholas Owen 9 The Davids, Bournville Copse, Birmingham B31 2EX Tel: 0121 477 9455 Fax: 0121 476 6003 Email: nickclaireturner@aol.com — MB ChB 1983 Birm.; FRCS Eng. 1990. Cons. ENT Surg. Walsall Hosps. NHS Trust; Cons. ENT Surg. BUPA Hosp. Little Ashton; Mem ASFGB Med. Comm.; Hon Med Adviser to Englisth Sch.s swimming assoc. Socs: BMA & Med. Defence Union; Midl. Inst. Otol.; B. A. O.H. N S. Prev: Regist. (ENT) Russells Hall Hosp. Dudley, Qu. Eliz. Hosp., Dudley Rd. Hosp. Birm., Walsgrave Hosp. & Coventry & Warwick Hosp.

TURNER, Nicola Simone Calcot Medical Centre, Hampden Road, Chalfont St. Peter, Gerrards Cross SL9 9SA Tel: 01753 887311 Fax: 01753 890639 — BM 1992 Soton.; BSc (Hons.) Psychol. Soton. 1991; MRCGP 1996; DRCOG 1994. (Soton.)

TURNER, Norman Robert Balfour (retired) (Surgery), 304 Tollcross Road, Glasgow G31 4UR — LRCP LRCS 1943 Ed.; LRCP LRCS Ed. LRFPS Glas. 1943. Prev: Cas. & Exam. Surg. Colvilles Clyde Iron Works.

TURNER, Patricia Elizabeth May Staffordshire County Council, Occupational Health Unit, 15 Tipping St., Stafford ST16 2LN Tel: 01785 276280 Fax: 01785 224410; 51 Cocknage Road, Dresden, Stoke-on-Trent ST3 4AT Tel: 01782 312541 — MB BCh 1965 Wales; AFOM RCP Lond. 1991. (Cardiff) Co. Occupat. Health Phys. Staffs. CC. Socs: Fell. Roy. Soc. Med.; Soc. Occupat. Med. Prev: GP Stoke-on-Trent; Med. Off. Michelin Tyre Co. Stoke-on-Trent; Sen. Med. Off. Achimota Sch. Hosp. Ghana.

TURNER, Patricia Margaret The Corner Surgery, 180 Cambridge Road, Southport PR9 7LW Tel: 01704 505555 Fax: 01704 505818; 40 Coudray Road, Southport PR9 9PE — MB BS 1974 Lond. Prev: SHO (Cas. & Microbiol.) Roy. Lond. Hosp.

TURNER, Paul The Health Centre, Pond Road, Shoreham-by-Sea BN43 5US Tel: 01273 440550 Fax: 01273 462109; 291 Upper Shoreham Road, Shoreham-by-Sea BN43 5QA Tel: 01273 463755 — MB BS 1969 Lond.; MRCS Eng. LRCP Lond. 1969; DObst RCOG 1971. (St. Bart.) Prev: Ho. Phys. & Ho. Surg. Bury Gen. Hosp.; Ho. Off. (O & G) Fairfield Gen Hosp.

TURNER, Paul St. Peter's Hospital, Guildford Road, Chertsey KT16 0PZ Tel: 01932 872000; 3 Miller Road, Colliers Wood, London SW19 2DB Tel: 020 8540 7360 — MB BS 1996 Lond. (St. George's Hospital Medical School) SHO in Paediat. St. Peter's Hosp. Chertsey. Prev: SHO in A & E Med. N. Hants Hosp. Basingstoke; SHO in Paediat. N. Hants Hosp. Basingstoke; PRHO in Gen. Surg. Frimley Pk. Hosp. Frimley.

TURNER, Paul Christopher Thomas 39 Repton Road, West Bridgford, Nottingham NG2 7EP — MB BS 1985 Lond.

TURNER, Paul Jeremy Neuro X-Ray Department, Pinderfields NHS Hospital Trust, Aberford Road, Wakefield WF1 4; Smithy Cottage, Main Street, Newton Kyme, Tadcaster LS24 9LS — MB ChB 1985 Leeds; MRCP (UK) 1989; FRCR 1994. (Leeds) Cons. Vasc. Radiol. Pinderfields Hosps. NHS Trust Wakefield. Socs: Roy. Coll. Radiol.; Brit. Soc. of Interven.al Radiol.; CIRSE. Prev: Sen. Regist. (Radiol.) St. Jas. Univ. Hosp. Leeds, Leeds Gen. Infirm. & Bradford Roy. Infirm.

TURNER, Paul Robert Wilson The Karis Medical Centre, Waterworks Road, Edgbaston, Birmingham B16 9AL Tel: 0121 454 0661 Fax: 0121 454 9104 — MB ChB 1991 Birm.; ChB Birm. 1991.

TURNER, Paul Stephen Haverhill Road, Stapleford, Cambridge CB2 5BX Tel: 01223 842429 — MB BS 1983 Lond.; BSc (Med. Sci.) Lond. 1980, MB BS 1983. (St. Mary's) SHO (Trop. Dis.) Hosp. Trop. Dis. St. Pancras Lond. Prev: SHO (A & E) Dunfermline & W. Fife Hosp.; Ho. Off. (Orthop.) Dunfermline & W. Fife Hosp.; Ho. Off. Gen. Med. Hosp. St. Cross Rugby.

TURNER, Pauline Camusfearna, 81 Waggon Road, Brightons, Falkirk FK2 0EL — MB ChB 1998 Glas.

TURNER, Peter 20 High Mill Road, Hamsterley Mill, Rowlands Gill NE39 1HE — MB BS 1970 Newc.; BSc (Anat.) Newc. 1967, MB BS 1970; FRCP Lond. 1989; MRCP (U.K.) 1974. Cons. Phys. Qu. Eliz. Hosp. Gateshead.

TURNER, Peter Breen Holly Tree Cottage, Chapel Lane, Mowsley, Lutterworth LE17 6NX — MB BS 1976 Lond.; MRCPsych 1982. Cons. Gen. Psychiat. Leics. HA (T). Prev: Sen. Regist. (Psychiat.) Leics. HA; Regist. (Psychiat.) Notts. HA.

TURNER, Mr Peter John Droitwich Knee Clinic, St. Andrews Road, Droitwich WR9 8YX Tel: 01905 794858 Fax: 01905 621458 Email: turnerpj@aol.com; Owl Hill Farm, Dunhampton, Stourport-on-Severn DY13 9SS Tel: 01905 621053 Fax: 01905 795916 — MB ChB 1965 Cape Town; FCS(SA) Orth 1988 (Cape Town). (Univ. Cape Town) Cons. Knee Surg. Droitwich Knee Clinic; Knee Surg. & Arthroscopic (inc. Ligament Reconstruction) & Jt. RePl.m. Sports Med (Knee Related); Vis. Cons. Mater Hosp. Belf. Socs: BOA; BASK; ISAKOS. Prev: Cons. Orthop. Groote Schuur Hosp.; Cons. P.ss Alice Orthop. Hosp. Cape Town; Cons. Orthop. Surg. Wynberg Hosp. Cape Town, S. Afr.

TURNER, Peter Percival, OBE (retired) Kitwells Lodge, Green St., Shenley, Radlett WD7 9BD Tel: 020 8953 7229 — MB BS 1945 Lond.; MD Lond. 1950, MB BS 1945, DPH 1959; FRCP Lond. 1971, M 1953; DIH Eng. 1959. Prev: Cons. Phys. Edgware Gen. Hosp.

TURNER, Mr Philip Gartside Ryley Mount, 432 Buxton Road, Stockport SK2 7JQ Tel: 0161 483 9333 Fax: 0161 419 9913 — MB ChB 1978 Manch.; FRCS Eng. 1982; FRCS Ed. 1982. Cons. Orthop. Surg. Stockport HA. Prev: Sen. Regist. (Orthop.) Withington Hosp. Manch.

TURNER, Philip James Eardley and Partners, Biddulph Medical Centre, Well Street, Biddulph, Stoke-on-Trent ST8 6HD Tel: 01782 512822 Fax: 01782 510331 — BM BS 1987 Nottm.; BMedSci (Hon.) Nottm. 1985; MRCGP 1991; Dip. GU Med. Soc. Apoth. Lond. 1990; Cert. Family Plann. JCC 1990. (Nottingham) GP Princip. The Med. Centre, Biddulph Stoke on Trent; GP Research fell. N. Staffs. GP Research Network. Prev: Staff Grade (Genitourin. Med.) Countess of Chester NHS Trust; Regist. (Emerg.) Waikato Hosp., NZ; Trainee GP Doncaster VTS.

TURNER, Mr Philip John Stanwell Road Surgery, 95 Stanwell Road, Ashford TW15 3EA Tel: 01784 253565 Fax: 01784 244145; 28 Fordbridge Road, Ashford TW15 2SG Tel: 01784 44636 — MB ChB 1977 Sheff.; FRCS Ed. 1981; DRCOG 1984.

TURNER, Rachel 3 Bridgelands, Copthorne, Crawley RH10 3QW Email: btu6960362@aol.com — MB BS 1993 Lond.; BSc Lond. 1990; DRCOG 1995. (St. Bartholomew's Hospital London) GP. Prev: SHO (Psychiat.) Seymour Clinic Swindon; SHO (Cas.) Roy. Sussex Co. Hospial Brighton.; SHO (Elderly Care) Poole Gen. Hosp.

TURNER, Richard Duke 68 Duchy Road, Harrogate HG1 2EZ Tel: 01423 506772 — MB ChB 1967 Ed.; FFCM RCP (K) 1993, M 1985. (Ed.) Cons. Pub. Health Med. E. Riding HA. Prev: SCM (Informat. & Research) Yorks. RHA; Manager Health Policy Anal. Unit Yorks RHA.

TURNER

TURNER, Richard George North Hampshire Hospital (G. Floor), Allergy, Aldermaston Road, Basingstoke RG24 7NA Tel: 01256 314972 Fax: 01256 314796; Monk Sherborne House, Monk Sherborne, Basingstoke RG26 5HL Tel: 01256 329021 Fax: 01256 817466 — MB BS Lond. 1970; MRCP (U.K.) 1974; MRCS Eng. LRCP Lond. 1970. (Charing Cross Hospital, University of London) p/t Specialist Allergy Basingstoke Hosp.; Hon. Clin. Teach. Univ. Soton. Socs: Brit. Soc. of Allergy & Clin. Immunol.; Intern. Stress Managem. Assn.; Brit. Soc. Allergy & Environm. Med. Prev: Fell. Internal Med. Ochsner Med. Foundat. New Orleans, USA; Ho. Phys. Nat. Hosp. Nerv. Dis. Lond.; Regist. (Med.) Lambeth & St. Thos. Hosp. Lond.

TURNER, Richard John Duncan Macmillan House, Nottingham Healthcare (NHS) Trust, Dorchester Road, Nottingham NG3 6AA Tel: 01159 249924; Punch Bowl House, 111 Main St, Woodborough, Nottingham NG14 6DA Tel: 0115 965 2539 — MB ChB St. And. 1969; MD Dundee 1977; FRCPsych 1990, M 1974; DPM Eng. 1972. Cons. Psychiat. Nottm. Healthcare Trust, Univ. Hosp.; Med. Dir. Nottm. Healthcare Trust; Clin. Teach. Univ. Nottm. Med. Sch. Prev: Assoc. Postgrad. Dean Nottm. Med. Sch.; Lect. (Ment. Health) Bristol Univ.

TURNER, Richard John Department of Dermatology, Churchill, Old Road, Oxford OX3 7LS Tel: 01865 228258 Fax: 01865 228260 Email: jturner@bigfoot.com — MB BCh 1989 Wales; MRCP (UK) 1992. Cons. (Dermatol.) Ch.ill Hosp. Oxf. Lead Clinician/ Clin. Director; Hon. Sen. Clin. Lect. (Oxf.); Clin. Tutor (Trinity Coll.). Socs: Exec. Comm. Brit. Soc. of Dermat.; Brit. Assn. of Dermat.; Brit. Soc. Dermatologic Surg. Prev: Lect. (Dermat.) Univ. Wales Coll. Med. Cardiff.; Regist. (Gen. Med. & Endocrinol.) Caerphilly Miners Hosp. M. Glam.; Sen. Reg (Dermatol.) RVI.

TURNER, Richard John Newbold (retired) 125 Finchfield Lane, Wolverhampton WV3 8EY Tel: 01902 763108 — MB BChir Camb. 1963; MA Camb. 1964; FFA RCS Eng. 1967. Cons. Anaesth. The Roy. Wolverhampton NHS Trust. Prev: Sen. Regist. (Anaesth.) United Birm. Hosps.

TURNER, Robert Geoffrey 3 Bronrhin Court, Mountain Road, Caerphilly CF83 1HY — MB BCh 1993 Wales.

TURNER, Robert John The Topsham Surgery, The White House, Holman Way, Topsham, Exeter EX3 0EN Tel: 01392 874646 Fax: 01392 875261; Walnut Cottage, Oil Mill Lane, Clyst St Mary, Exeter EX5 1AH Tel: 01392 877262 — MB BS 1978 Newc.; MRCGP 1983; DA Eng. 1981.

TURNER, Robert William c/o 17 Launde Road, Oadby, Leicester LE2 4HH — MB ChB 1992 Sheff.

TURNER, Rodney Martin (retired) Flat 2, 59 Mount Ararat Road, Richmond TW10 6PL Tel: 0818 332 2167 — MB BS 1951 Durh.; FRCGP 1980, M 1960. Prev: Sen. Lect. (Gen. Pract.) United Dent. & Med. Sch. Lond.

TURNER, Ronald William (retired) 2 Connaught Close, Connaught Gardens, Clacton-on-Sea CO15 6HL Tel: 01255 422282 — MB ChB 1957 Leeds; MRCGP 1968; DLO Eng. 1963; DObst. RCOG 1962. Prev: Ho. Surg. (ENT) Leeds Gen. Infirm.

TURNER, Rosalie Jane 29 Rectory Road, Frampton, Cotterell, Bristol BS36 2BN — MB ChB 1986 Sheff.; MRCGP 1993.

TURNER, Rosemary Christine 5 Osmund Close, Worth, Crawley RH10 7RG Tel: 01293 884250 — MB BS 1983 Lond.; MRCP (UK) 1986; FRCP (UK) 1999. Cons. Palliat. Care Brighton. Prev: Sen. Regist. Roy. Marsden Hosp. Sutton; Regist. (Gen. Med. & Med. Oncol.) Guy's Hosp. Lond.

TURNER, Roy Sydney Leonard 16 Vicarage Road, Kidlington OX5 2EL — MA, BM BCh Oxf. 1957; LMSSA Lond. 1956. (Oxf.) Socs: Oxf. Med. Soc. Prev: Ho. Phys. Osler Hosp. Oxf.; Ho. Phys. & Paediat. Ho. Off. Roy. Berks. Hosp.

TURNER, Royston Campbell Beechvale, Drumbeg, Lisburn — LRCPI & LM, LRSCI & LM 1944; LRCPI & LM, LRCSI & LM 1944.

TURNER, Rupert Jonathan Clay 78 Northwood Road, Whitstable CT5 2EZ — MB ChB 1993 Birm.; MRCP 1997; DCH 1997. (Birm.)

TURNER, Ruth Vivien Thurnaby and Barwick Medical Group, Trenchard Avenue, Thurnaby TS15 0BZ Tel: 01642 762921 — MB BChir 1985 Camb.; DRCOG 1990. (Cambridge)

TURNER, Sandra Lynne Christie Hospital NHS Trust, Wilmslow Road, Withington, Manchester M20 4BX Tel: 0161 446 3000; 8 Windermere Close, Choleywood, Rickmansworth WD3 5LF — MB BS 1987 Sydney.

TURNER, Sarah Louise 20 Sefton Avenue, Heaton, Newcastle upon Tyne NE6 5QR — MB BS 1992 Newc.

TURNER, Scott David Theatre Royal Surgery, 27 Theatre Street, Dereham NR19 2EN Tel: 01362 852800 Fax: 01362 852819 — MB ChB 1988 Ed.; Dip. IMC RCS Ed. 1990.

TURNER, Sharon Ann 15 Warwick Road, Stafford ST17 4PD Tel: 01785 57674 — MB ChB 1986 Birm.; DRCOG 1988. SHO (Psychiat.) St. Geo. Hosp. Stafford. Socs: BMA. Prev: SHO/Trainee GP N. Staffs. Hosp. Centre Stoke-on-Trent VTS.

TURNER, Sheelagh Maria Cruddas Park Surgery, 178 Westmorland Road, Cruddas Park, Newcastle upon Tyne NE4 7JT — MB BS 1974 Newcastle; MB BS Newc. 1974. (Newcastle) GP Newc.

TURNER, Simon 88 Rockingham Road, Kettering NN16 9AD — MB ChB 1997 Dundee.

TURNER, Simon John Shipley Peartree Lane Surgery, 110 Peartree Lane, Welwyn Garden City AL7 3XW Tel: 01707 329292; 62 Peartree Lane, Welwyn Garden City AL7 3UH Tel: 01707 329292 — MB BS 1980 Lond. (Middlx.)

TURNER, Simon Julian 4 Twyford Close, Manchester M20 2YR — MB ChB 1993 Manch.

TURNER, Sophie Louise 2 Grange Road, Crawley Down, Crawley RH10 4JT Tel: 01342 716688 — MB ChB 1996 Liverp. SHO GP Train. Scheme.

***TURNER, Stacy Lee** Llanberis, Caernarfon LL55 4EL — MB ChB 1997 Liverp.; BSc (Hons. Cell Biol.) Liverp. 1994; MB ChB (Hons.) Liverp. 1997.

***TURNER, Stephen** Flat 7, 11 James Court, 493 Lawnmarket, Edinburgh EH1 2PB — MB ChB 1998 Ed.

TURNER, Stephen Denys The Health Centre, Thame OX9 Tel: 0184 421 2553 — MB 1959 Camb.; BChir 1958; FRCGP 1987; DObst RCOG 1961. (Camb. & St. Thos.)

TURNER, Stephen Lindsay 45 Blythswood Crescent, Largs KA30 8HX — MB ChB 1995 Glas.

TURNER, Mr Stephen Michael Department Orthopaedics, Coventry & Warwickshire Hospital, Stoney Stanton Road, Coventry CV1 4FH Tel: 024 76 224055; Earlsdon Consulting Rooms, 15 Palmerston Road, Earlsdon, Coventry CV5 6FH Tel: 024 76 678472 Fax: 01203 678818 — MB ChB 1978 Liverp.; ChM Liverp. 1993, MB ChB 1978; FRCS Ed. 1983. Cons. Orthop. Surg. Coventry HA. Socs: Fell. Brit. Orthop. Soc.; Brit. Soc. Surg. Hand. Prev: Sen. Regist. (Orthop. Surg.) NW RHA; Regist. (Orthop.) Guy's, Lewisham & Brighton Hosp.; Tutor (Orthop.) Univ. Manch.

TURNER, Stephen Richard Doctors Surgery, Newton Way, Baildon, Shipley BD17 5NH Tel: 01274 582506 Fax: 01274 532426; 9 Belmont Rise, Baildon, Shipley BD17 5AN Tel: 01274 587207 — MB ChB 1973 Ed.; DA Eng. 1978; DObst RCOG 1975; Cert JCC Lond. 1979. Prev: Ho. Off. (Surg.) Roy. Hosp. Sick Childr. Edin.; Ho. Off. (Med.) Bangour Gen. Hosp. Broxburn; Trainee Gen. Pract. Livingston Vocational Train. Scheme.

TURNER, Stuart William Tel: 020 7224 4285 Fax: 020 7224 4265 Email: stuart.turner@traumatic-stress.com — MB BChir 1977 Camb.; MD Camb. 1987, MA 1977; FRCP Lond. 1996; MRCP (UK) 1981; FRCPsych 1994, M 1981. (Univ. Camb. & Middlx.) p/t Cons. Psychiat. Traum. Stress Clinic, Nat. Referral Centre for PTSD; Trustee Redress; Dir. Research & Developm. N. Centr. Thames Community Research Consortium; Civil. Cons. Adviser (Trauma) to Director of Defence Psychiat. Socs: Fell. RSM; UK Trauma Gp. - Chair; Internat. Soc. Traum. Stress Studies - Sec. Prev: Campus Dean (Community Health Serv.) Univ. Coll. Lond. Med. Sch.; Med. Dir. Camden & Islington Community Trust; Sen. Lect. (Psychiat.) Univ. Coll. & Middlx. Sch. Med. Lond.

TURNER, Susan — MB ChB 1989 Manch.; PhD Med. Biophysics Manch. 1984; MSc Pharmacol. Manch. 1982, BSc Pharmacy 1980; MFOM 1997; Cert. Occupat. Med. 1997. (University Manchester) Accredit. Specialist in Occupat. Med. (MFOM/CCST); Cons. Occupat. Phys. Oldham NHS Trust. Socs: Roy. Pharmaceut. Soc.; Fac. Occupat. Med.; Soc. Occupat. Med. Prev: Lect. (Occupat. Med.) Univ. of Manch.

TURNER, Susan Eve Heather Grange, Hurst Road, Biddulph, Stoke-on-Trent ST8 7RU — MB ChB 1991 Leic.; MRCG P 1995; DFFP 1994; DRCOG 1994.

TURNER, Susan Louise 19 Gladstone Avenue, Chester CH1 4JX — MB ChB 1988 Leic.

TURNER, Susan Margaret 67 Greenville Drive, Low Moor, Bradford BD12 0PT — MB ChB 1994 Liverp.; MRCP(UK) Edin. 1997.

TURNER, Suzanne Dale Pitt Farm, Ancient Lane, Hatfield Woodhouse, Doncaster DN7 6PJ — MB ChB 1986 Sheff.; MRCGP 1990.

TURNER, Thelma Elisabeth 8 Watering Close, Lower Somersham, Ipswich IP8 4QG — MB ChB 1981 Leeds.

TURNER, Thomas Blake Mountsandel Surgery, 4 Mountsandel Road, Coleraine BT52 1JB Tel: 028 7034 2650 Fax: 028 7032 1000; 7 Forrest Park, Coleraine BT52 1JJ — MB BCh BAO 1972 Belf.; FRCGP 1994, M 1976; DCH RCPSI 1975; DObst RCOG 1975. Socs: BMA. Prev: SHO (Gen. Med. & Psychiat.) Craigavon Area Hosp.

TURNER, Thomas Liley Yorkhill NHS Trust, Glasgow G3 8WD Tel: 0141 201 0000; Highlands, Moor Rd, Strathbalne, Glasgow G63 9EY — MB ChB 1966 St. And.; MB ChB (Commend.) St. And. 1966; FRCP Ed. 1982; FRCP Glas. 1982; MRCP (U.K.) 1971; FRCPCH. Cons. (Paediat.) Qu. Mother's Hosp. & Roy. Hosp. Sick Childr. Glas.

TURNER, Trevor Howard Department of Psychological Medicine, St. Bartholomews Hospital, West Smithfield, London EC1A 7BE Tel: 020 7601 7946 Fax: 020 7601 7097 — MB BS 1976 Lond.; BA (Hons. Classics) Bristol; MD Lond. 1990; FRCPsych 1994, MRCPsych 1981. (St. Bartholomews) Cons. Psychiat. St. Bartholomews Hosp. & Homerton Hosp. Lond.; Clin. Director, E. Lond. and the City Ment. Health NHS Trust, Lond. Prev: Lect. Inst. Psychiat. Lond.; Lect. & Hon. Sen. Regist. St. Bartholomews Hosp. Lond.; Regist. Maudsley Hosp. Lond.

TURNER, Wayne Mark 74 Leander Avenue, Choppington NE62 5BD Tel: 01670 812443 — MB ChB 1993 Leic.

TURNER, William (retired) 1 Premiere Park, Ilkley LS29 9RQ — MB ChB (2nd cl. Hons.) Leeds 1950; LLB Lond. 1958; FFCM 1972; DPH Leeds (Distinc.) 1957. Prev: Regional Med. Off. Yorks. RHA.

TURNER, William David Watson Mark Street Surgery, 2 Mark St., Rochdale OL12 9BE Tel: 01706 48255 Fax: 01706 526640; 5 Tyrone Drive, Rochdale OL11 4BE Tel: 01706 368424 — MB ChB 1966 Glas. (Glas.) Socs: BMA. Prev: Ho. Phys. & Ho. Surg. & SHO O & G Birch Hill Hosp. Rochdale.

TURNER, William Dundonald (retired) 25 Ashfield Road, Leicester LE2 1LB Tel: 0116 270 8336 — MB ChB 1950 Sheff.; FFA RCS Eng. 1954; DA Eng. 1952. Anaesth. Leicester Hosp. Gps. Prev: Sen. Regist. (Anaesth.) United Sheff. Hosps.

TURNER, Mr William Henry Department of Urology, Princess Royal Hospital, Saltshouse Road, Hull HU8 9HE Tel: 01482 701151 Fax: 01482 676635 Email: l00322.1731@compuserve.com — BM BCh 1983 Oxf.; MD Camb 1997, MA 1984; FRCS (Urol.) 1997; FRCS Eng. 1987. (Camb. & Oxf.) Sen. Regist. (Urol.) P.ss Roy. Hosp. Hull. Socs: Internat. Continence Soc.; Assoc. Mem. BAUS; Jun. Mem. Europ. Assn. Urol. Prev: Resid. Urol. Inselspital Bern, Switz.; Research Fell Univ. Dept. Pharmacol. Oxf.; Regist. (Urol.) Ch.ill Hosp. Oxf.

TURNER, William James Russell Barrhead Health Centre, 201 Main St., Barrhead, Glasgow G78 1SA Tel: 0141 880 6161 Fax: 0141 881 5636; 11 Craigton Crescent, Greenfarm, Newton Mearns, Glasgow G77 6DN Email: 101777.632@compuserve — MB ChB 1980 Ed.; BSc Med. Sci. Ed. 1977, MB ChB 1980; DCH RCPS Glas. 1984; DRCOG 1982.

TURNER, William Joseph (retired) Peel House Medical Centre, Avenue Parade, Accrington BB5 6RD Tel: 01254 237231 Fax: 01254 389525 — MB ChB 1966 Liverp. Prev: SHO, Cas. Off., Ho. Surg. & Ho. Phys. Walton Hosp. Liverp.

TURNER, William Wilson 51 Cocknage Road, Dresden, Stoke-on-Trent ST3 4AT; Alma House, 89 Blurton Road, Blurton, Stoke-on-Trent ST3 2BS — MB BCh 1962 Wales. (Cardiff) Clin. Asst. (Psychiat.) St. Edwd. Hosp. N. Staffs. HA. Socs: Fell. Roy. Soc. Med. Prev: Sen. Med. Off. i/c Achimota Sch. Hosp., Ghana.

TURNER, Winston Murray Leslie (retired) Bodnant, Keighley Road, Colne BB8 7HL Tel: 01282 865615 Email: turner@helwyn38.freeserve.co.uk — MRCS Eng. LRCP Lond. 1938; MD Lond. 1945, MB BS (Hnrs.) 1938; FRCP Lond. 1971, M 1945; FRCPCH 1997; DCH Eng. 1949; DLO Eng. 1942. Prev: Cons. Paediatr. Burnley Health Dist.

TURNER, Yvonne Jane School Cottage, School Lane, Washington, Pulborough RH20 4AP — MB BS 1990 Lond.

TURNER-PARRY, Alison Joanne 10 Windmill Rise, Poppleton Road, York YO26 4TX — MB ChB 1998 Leeds.

TURNER-STOKES, Lynne Frances Regional Rehabilitation Unit, Northwick Park Hospital, Watford Road, Harrow HA1 3UJ Tel: 020 8869 2800 Fax: 020 8869 2803 Email: lynne.turner-stokes@dial.pipex.com; 55 Fitzroy Park, Highgate, London N6 6JA Tel: 020 8340 2464 Fax: 020 8340 2227 — MB BS 1979 Lond.; MA (Phys. Sci.) Oxf. 1983, BA 1976; DM Oxf. 1989; MRCP (UK) 1982. Cons. Rehabil. Med. Regional Rehabil. Unit. N.wick Pk. Hosp. Lond.; Hon. Assoc. Reader Brunel Univ. Socs: (Exec. Counc.) Brit. Soc. Rehabil. Med.; Brit. Soc. Rheum.; Soc. Research Rehabil. Prev: Sen. Regist. (Rheum. & Rehabil.) N.wick Pk. & Middlx. Hosp.; Research Regist. (Rheum.) Middlx. Hosp. Lond.; Regist. Rotat. (Gen. Med.) Univ. Coll. Hosp. Lond.

TURNER-WARWICK, Professor Dame Margaret Elizabeth Harvey, DBE Pynes House, Silver St, Thorverton, Exeter EX5 5LT Tel: 01392 861173 Fax: 01392 860940 — BM BCh 1950 Oxf.; FRCPS Glas. 1991; FRCP Ed. 1988; FRCR 1994; FRCPCH 1996; FRCPath 1992; FRCPC 1989; FRCA 1991; FRCGP 1990; FFPHM RCP (UK) 1990; FFOM RCP Lond. 1990; PhD Lond. 1961; FACP 1988; FRACP 1983; Hon. DSc Leics. 1998; MA, DM Oxf. 1956; Hon. DSc Camb. 1993, Oxf. 1992, Sussex 1992, Hull 1991; Hon. DSc Exeter 1990; Hon. DSc Lond. 1990; Hon. DSc New York 1985; FRCS Eng. 1993; FRCPSI 1992. Hon. Consg. Phys.; Emerit. Prof. Med. Lond. Univ.; Hon. Bencher Middle Temple; Fell. UCL 1991; Hon. Fell. LMH Oxf.; Hon. Fell. Girton Camb.; Hon. Fell. Imperial Coll. 1996; Hon. Fell. Green Coll. Oxf. Socs: Assn. Phys.; (Ex-Pres.) Brit. Thoracic Soc.; Fell. (Ex-Pres.) RCP Lond. Prev: Pres. Roy. Coll. Phys. Lond.; Prof. Thoracic Med. Cardiothoracic Inst.; Dean Cardiothoracic Inst.

TURNER-WARWICK, Mr Richard Trevor Pynes House, Thorverton, Exeter EX5 5LT Tel: 01392 860940 — BM BCh 1949 Oxf.; Hon. FRACS 1981; MA Oxf., BSc 1946; DM Oxf. 1957, MCh 1962; Hon. DSc New York 1987; FRCP Lond. 1980, M 1955; FRCS Eng. 1954; FRCOG 1990; FACS 1970; Hon. FACS 1997. Emerit. Cons. Surg. Middlx. Hosp., Inst. Urol. & Univ. Coll. Med. Sch. Lond.; Robt. Luff Foundat. Fell. Reconstruc. Urol.; Sen. Lect. Inst. Urol.; Emerit. Cons. Surg. Middlx. Hosp.; Cons. Urol. St. Peter's Hosp.; Hon. Cons. Urol. Surg. Roy. P. Alfred Hosp. Sydney. Socs: Fell. Urol. Soc. Austral.; Counc. RCS Eng. (Hunt. Prof. 1957 & 77); Assn. Surg. (Moynihan Prize 1958). Prev: Sen. Urol. Cons. K. Edwd. VII Hosp. Offs., Hosp. St. John & St. Eliz. & Roy. Nat. Orthop. Hosp. Lond.; Resid. Columbia Presbyt. Med. Center New York; Res. Surg. Off. St. Paul's Hosp.

TURNEY, John Harry Leeds General Infirmary, Great George St., Leeds LS1 3EX Tel: 0113 392 3757 Fax: 0113 392 6560 Email: jturney@ulth.northy.nhs.uk; 35 The Avenue, Roundhay, Leeds LS8 1JG Tel: 0113 266 5882 — MB BChir 1975 Camb.; MA Camb. 1974; FRCP Lond. 1990; MRCP (UK) 1978; T(M) 1991. (King's Coll. Hosp.) Cons. Phys. & Nephrol. Leeds Gen. Infirm.; Mem., Comm. of Safety of Devices. Socs: (Pres.) Brit. Renal Symp.; (Exec. Comm.) Renal Assn. Prev: Sen. Regist. Qu. Eliz. Hosp. Birm.

TURNEY, Mr Joseph Pett (retired) Fairwater, Dinham, Ludlow SY8 1EH Tel: 01584 874800 — MB BS 1941 Lond.; MB BS (Hnrs. Distinc. in Surg.) Lond. 1941; FRCS Eng. 1948; MRCS Eng. LRCP Lond. 1941. Prev: Maj. RAMC.

TURNEY, Theresa Mary Brown and Partners, 35 Saughton Crescent, Edinburgh EH12 5SS Tel: 0131 337 2166 Fax: 0131 313 5059; 5 Corrennie Gardens, Edinburgh EH10 6DG — MB BS 1981 Newc.; MRCGP 1986; DCCH RCP Ed. 1986; DRCOG 1985.

TURNHEIM, Erwin (retired) 28 Dovehouse Close, Whitfield, Manchester M45 7PE Tel: 0161 766 4050 — MB ChB 1947 Polish Sch. of Med.

TURNIDGE, Janet Mary Birch Terrace Surgery, 25A Birch Terrace, Hanley, Stoke-on-Trent ST1 3JN Tel: 01782 212436 — MB ChB 1989 Manch.; BSc St. And. 1986; MRCGP 1993; DCH RCP Lond. 1992; DRCOG 1991.

TURNILL, Adelaide 75 Ermine Street, Huntingdon PE29 3EZ Tel: 01480 453038 Fax: 01480 434104 — MB BCh BAO 1969 Belf. Gen. Practitioner; Hosp. practitioner Dept of Old age Psychiat., Hingtingbrooke Hosp., Huntingdon. Prev: Clin. Asst. (Psychgeriat.

TURNOCK

Med.) Dept. Ment. Health for the Elderly Hinchingbrooke Hosp Huntingdon.

TURNOCK, Karen 10 Princes Close, Bishops Waltham, Southampton SO32 1RL — MB ChB 1991 Leeds; BSc (Hons.) Leeds 1988; MRCP (UK) 1994. Regist. (Paediat.) St. Mary's Hosp. Portsmouth.

TURNOCK, Mr Richard Roulston Department Paediatric Surgery, Royal Liverpool Children's Hospital, Alder Hey, Liverpool L12 2AP Tel: 0151 252 5750 Fax: 0151 252 5362 — MB ChB 1977 Liverp.; FRCS (Paediat.) 1992; FRCS Ed. 1982. (Liverp.) Cons. Paediat. Surg. Roy. Liverp. Childr. Hosp.; Hon. Clin. Lect. Univ. Liverp.

TURNPENNY, Peter Douglas Department of Clinical Genetics, Royal Devon & Exeter Hospital (Wonford), Barrack Road, Exeter EX2 5DW Tel: 01392 403151 Fax: 01392 403151 Email: turnpenn@eurobell.co.uk — MB ChB 1977 Ed.; BSc Ed. 1974; MRCP (UK) 1986; FRCP 1998; FRCPCH 1997, M 1996; DCH RCP Lond. 1982; DRCOG 1980. (Edinburgh) Cons. Clin. Geneticist Roy. Devon & Exeter Healthcare NHS Trust; Lect. Univ. of Plymouth; Hon. Senoir Lect., Univ. of Exeter. Socs: Brit. Soc. of Human Genetics; Amer. Soc. Human Genetics. Prev: Head (Paediat.) The Nazareth Hosp. EMMS, Israel.

TURPIN, Claude Dunbar Hillcroft, Buckingham Road, Brackley NN13 7EL Tel: 01280 704340 — BA Dub. 1943, MB BCh BAO 1947; LM Rotunda Hosp. 1947. (TC Dub.)

TURPIN, David Frank 39 Mons Street, Hull HU5 3SZ — MB BS 1989 Lond.

TURPIN, Jean Alexandra (retired) Lingmoor, 160 Queen Alexandra Road, Sunderland SR3 1XL Tel: 0191 522 7489 Email: docturpin@aol.com — MB BS 1952 Durh.; DPH Newc. 1968; BA 1999. Prev: Sen. Med. Off. Health Dept. Sunderland Co. Boro.

TURPIN, John Steepwood, Milford Road, Newtown SY16 3HD Tel: 01686 626941 — BM BCh 1952 Oxf.; MA, BM BCh Oxon. 1952; DObst RCOG 1956; AFOM RCP Lond. 1979. (Oxf. & Univ. Coll. Hosp.) Clin. Asst. Montg. Co. Infirm. Newtown; Indust. Med. Off. BRD Co. Newtown. Socs: Soc. Occupat. Med. Prev: Ho. Phys. & Ho. Surg. Univ. Coll. Hosp. Lond.; Clin. Asst. Roy. Salop Infirm. Shrewsbury.

TURPIN, Margaret Jean (retired) 17 Bayswater, Marlborough SN8 1DX Email: margaret@turpin501freeserve.co.uk — MB BS 1954 Lond.; MRCGP 1971; DObst RCOG 1958. Prev: SHO (O & G) Rochford Gen. Hosp.

TURPIN, Marianne Christine Bears Den, 6 Albany Road, Woodhall Spa LN10 6TS Tel: 01526 353475 — MB ChB 1964 St. And. (St. And.) Asst. GP New Surg. Woodhall SPA. Socs: BMA. Prev: GP Saxilby; Clin. Asst. (Child Psychiat.) Lawn Hosp. Lincoln; Asst. MOH Lincoln.

TURPIN, Philip John Yardley Green Medical Centre, 75 Yardley Green Road, Bordesley Green, Birmingham B9 5PU Tel: 0121 773 3737; 1 Station Road, Hampton in Arden, Solihull B92 0BJ — BM BCh 1983 Oxf.; BA Oxf. 1980; MRCGP 1988; DCH RCP Lond. 1986. (Oxf.) Prev: SHO (Gen. Med.) Derby Roy. Infirm.; SHO (Paediat., Infec. Dis. & Geriat. Med.) E. Birm. Hosp.; SHO (O & G) Solihull Hosp.

TURRALL, (Phoebe) Ann c/o Anaesthetic Department, Queen Alexandra Hospital, Cosham, Portsmouth PO6 3LY Tel: 023 92 286279 Fax: 023 92 286681; 2 Brooklyn Drive, Waterlooville PO7 7SX Tel: 023 92 262502 — MB BChir 1965 Camb.; BA Camb. 1965; FFA RCS Eng. 1972; DA Eng. 1969. (Lond. Hosp.) Cons. Anaesth. Qu. Alexandra's Hosp. Portsmouth. Socs: Assn. Anaesth. Gt. Brit. & N. Irel.; BMA & Portsmouth Cons. & Specialists Assn. Prev: Sen. Regist. (Anaesth.) Salisbury & Hammersmith Hosp.; Regist. (Anaesth.) Univ. Coll. Hosp. Lond.; Regist. (Anaesth.) Balmain Hosp. Sydney, Austral.

TURRELL, Charlotte Mary Kont + Sussex Hosp, Mount Ephraim, Tunbridge Wells TN4 8AT; April Cottage, Westdown Lane, Burwash Common, Etchingham TN19 7JT Tel: 01435 883398 — MB BS 1998 Lond.; MB BS Lond 1998. HO. (Surg.) Kent + Sussex Hosp.

TURRILL, Jane Elizabeth 439 Beechdale Road, Aspley, Nottingham NG8 3LF; 1 Farndon Green, Woolaton Park, Nottingham NG8 1DU — MB ChB 1982 Sheff.

TURTLE, Alan Manson Richhill Clinic, 6 Greenview, Maynooth Road, Richhill, Armagh BT61 9PD; 46 Maynooth Road, Richhill, Armagh BT61 9RG — MB BCh BAO 1976 Belf.; DRCOG 1979.

TURTLE, Frances 164 Knockan Road, Rathkenny, Ballymena BT43 7LP; 12 Millburn Mews, Ballyclare BT39 9DP — MB ChB 1990 Ed.; MRCP. Gen. Med. Locum Med Off. Antrim. Prev: Staff Grade (Cardiol.) Ballymena.; Research Fell. (Cardiol.) Roy. Gp. of Hosps. Belf.

TURTLE, James Audley Westgate Bay Avenue Surgery, 60 Westgate Bay Avenue, Westgate-on-Sea CT8 8SN Tel: 01843 831335 Fax: 01843 835279 — MB BS 1973 Lond.; DRCOG 1978. (Middlx.)

TURTLE, James Brian (retired) Semaphore House, Semaphore Road, Birchington CT7 9JP Tel: 01843 41443 — MRCS Eng. LRCP Lond. 1948; DObst RCOG 1952. Prev: Clin. Asst. (Geriat.) Thanet Dist. Hosp. Ramsgate.

TURTLE, Mark Jonathan West Wales General Hospital, Carmarthen SA31 2AF Tel: 01267 235151 Fax: 01267 237662; Nant Y Grove, Llangynог, Carmarthen SA33 5DE Tel: 01267 211391 Email: mark.turtle@ukgateway.net — MB BS 1975 Lond.; MRCS Eng. LRCP Lond. 1975; FFA RCS 1981. (Guy's) Cons. Anaesth. W. Wales Gen. Hosp. Carmarthen. Socs: Assn. Anaesth. Gt. Brit. & Irel.; Internat. Assn. Study of Pain; Intens. Care Soc. Prev: Sen. Regist. Bristol & W.on HA; Regist. Salford HA.

TURTON, Catherine Louise Ash House, Main St., Barkston Ash, Tadcaster LS24 9PR — MB ChB 1994 Leeds.

TURTON, Charles William Gilmour Bankside, Ditchling Common, Burgess Hill RH15 0SJ Tel: 01444 233307 — MB BS 1970 MB BS Lond.; MD Lond. 1980; MRCP (U.K.) 1973; FRCP 1988. (King's Coll. Hosp.) Cons. Phys. (Respirat. Med.) Brighton Healthcare NHS Trust. Prev: Sen. Regist. (Med.) Brompton Hosp. Lond.; Sen. Regist. Roy. Free Hosp. Lond.; Regist. (Med.) St. Geo. Hosp. Lond.

TURTON, Edmund Philip Leo Ash House, Main St., Barkston Ash, Tadcaster LS24 9PR — MB ChB 1992 Leeds.

TURTON, Jane Llandough Hospital, Penlan Road, Penarth CF64 2XX Tel: 029 2071 5426, 029 2071 6957 — MB ChB 1987 Manch.; MSc Cardiff 1994; MRCGP 1995; DGM RCP Lond. 1993; DCH RCP Lond. 1992. p/t Clin. Asst. (Day Hosp. & Bone Reseach Unit) Llandough Hosp., Cardiff & Valo NHS Trust Penarth. Prev: Regist. (Gen. Pract.) Cardiff; SHO (c/o Elderly) Llandough Hosp.; SHO (Paediat. & Obst.) Univ. Hosp. of Wales.

TURVEY, Andrew John Bromley Hospitals NHS Trust, Cromwell Ave, Bromley BR2 9AJ Tel: 020 8289 700 Fax: 020 8289 7127 — MB BS 1988 Lond.; BSc (Hons.) Lond. 1985, MB BS 1988; FRCA 1994. (St. Bartholomew's Hospital Medical College) Cons.(Anaest.)Bromley Hosp. Kent. Socs: Assn. Anaesth.; Obst. Anaesth. Assn.; ICS. Prev: Specialist Regist. (Anaesth.) St. Mary's Hosp. Lond.; Regist. (Anaesth.) Roy. Marsden Hosp. Lond.

TURVEY, Joanne Sarah 51 Waverley Avenue, Twickenham TW2 6DQ — MB BS 1998 Lond.

TURVILL, James Lawrence 15 Pickwick Road, London SE21 7JN — MB ChB 1988 Manch.; MB ChB (Hons.) Manch. 1988; BSc (Med Sci) St. And. 1985; MRCP (UK) 1991. Research Fell. (Digestive Dis.) Research Centre Med. Coll. St. Bart. Hosp. Lond.

TURVILL, Jonathan William, Surg. Cdr. RN Cockenzie & Port Seton Health Centre, Avenue Road, Prestonpans EH32 0JU Tel: 01875 812998 Fax: 01875 814421; Email: jturv95446@aol.com — MB BCh 1977 Wales; MRCGP 1983; DRCOG 1984. (Welsh National School of Medicine) Occupat. Phys. BMI Healthcare. Prev: Princip. Med. Off. HMS Rooke, Gibraltar; Princip. Med. Off. RN SQ Cochrane; Sen. Med. Off. UKSU AfS., Naples.

TURVILL, Phyllis Tel: 020 7485 6104 Fax: 020 7485 5277; 9 Denning Road, London NW3 1ST Tel: 020 7794 6114 — MB BS 1966 Lond.; MRCS Eng. LRCP Lond. 1966; DMJ Soc. Apoth. Lond. 1978. (St. Bart.) Sen. Forens. Med. Examr. Metrop. Police; Med. Adviser Brit. Agencies for Adoption & Fostering. Socs: Assn. Police Surgs. Gt. Brit.; Med. Wom. Federat. Prev: Ho. Phys. & Ho. Surg. St. Margt.'s Hosp. Epping; Paediat. Ho. Phys. Whipps Cross Hosp. Lond.

TURVILL, Shelagh Bernadette 15 Pickwick Road, London SE21 7JN — MB BS 1992 Lond.; MB BS (Hons.) Lond. 1992. Specialist Regist. (Anaesth.) N. Thames Rotat. Socs: Freeman Worshipful Soc. Apoth. Lond. Prev: SHO (Anaesth.) St. Thomas Hosp. Lond.

TURVILLE, Sheila Anne Church Road Surgery, Church Road, Kyle IV40 8DD Tel: 01599 534257 Fax: 01599 534107 — MB ChB 1980 Aberd.; DRCOG 1986.

TUSON, Mr Julian Richard Donagh Department of Radiology, John Radcliffe Hospital, Oxford Tel: 01865 220825; 14 Coburg Wharf, Liverpool L3 4EB — MB BChir 1980 Camb.; BA Camb. 1976, MA, MChir 1991; FRCS Eng. 1985; FRCR 1995. Sen. Regist. (Radiol.) John Radcliffe Hosp. Oxf. Prev: Clin. Supervisor Sch. Clin Med. & Hon. Sen. Clin. Research Fell. (Surg.) Univ. Camb.; Regist. Rotat. (Surg.) Addenbrooke's Hosp. Camb. & St. Geo. Hosp. Lond.

TUSON, Mr Kenneth William Rhodes (cons. rooms), Nuffield Hospital, Kingswood Road, Tunbridge Wells TN2 4UL Tel: 01892 541346 Fax: 01892 515689 Email: k.tuson@nuffield-woc.freeserve.co.uk; Gyll cottage, Vale Road, South St., Mayfield TN20 4DB Tel: 01435 873216 — MB ChB Manch. 1966; FRCS Ed. 1971; FRCS Lon. 1998. (Manch.) Cons. Orthop. Surg. Tunbridge Wells Health Dist.; Cons. Surg. UMDS Med. Sch. Socs: Hosp. Cons. & Special. Assn. Vice Pres.; World Orthop. Concern (Chair); Fell. BOA. Prev: Sen. Regist. (Orthop.) King's Coll. Hosp. Lond.; Regist. Univ. Dept. Orthop. Manch. Roy. Infirm.; Asst. Resid. (Surg.) Vancouver Gen. Hosp., Canada.

TUT, Thomas Than 9 The Avenue, Mansfield NG18 4PN — MB BS 1975 Med. Inst. (I) Rangoon.

TUTHILL, David Paul 21 Weardale Gardens, Enfield EN2 0BA — MB BCh 1990 Wales.

TUTIN, Alan Frederick Merrow Park Surgery, Kingfisher Drive, Guildford GU4 7EP Tel: 01483 503331 Fax: 01483 303457; Woodstock, 6 Hillier Road, Guildford GU1 2JQ — MB BS 1974 Newc.; BSc.

TUTIN, Angela Myfanwy Merrow Park Surgery, Kingfisher Drive, Guildford GU4 7EP Tel: 01483 503331 Fax: 01483 303457; Woodstock, 6 Hillier Road, Guildford GU1 2JQ — MB BS 1973 Newc.; DObst RCOG 1975.

TUTT, Andrew Nicholas James Royal Marsden Hospital, Fulham Road, London SW3 6JJ Tel: 020 7352 8171 Email: andrewt@icr.ac.uk; 15 Allestree Road, London SW6 6AD — MB ChB 1990 Bristol; MRCP (UK) 1993; FRCR 1997. (Bristol Univ.) Hon. Specialist Regist. (Clin. Oncol.) Roy. Marsden Hosp. Lond.; Clin. Research Fell. Inst. Cancer Research. Prev: SHO (Gen. Med.) Hosp. Centre Stoke-on-Trent.

TUTTE, Kevin Philip Somers Town Health Centre, Blackfriars Close, Southsea PO5 4NJ Tel: 023 9285 1199 Fax: 023 9281 4626 — MB ChB 1980 Birm.; MRCGP 1985.

TUTTLE, Sheena Gilbert Road Medical Group, 39 Gilbert Road, Bucksburn, Aberdeen AB21 9AN Tel: 01224 712138 Fax: 01224 712239 — MB ChB 1965 Aberd.; MB ChB Aberd. 1965.; MD Aberd. 1971.

TUTTON, Elizabeth Vanda Mary Castleton Health Centre, 2 Elizabeth Street, Castleton, Rochdale OL11 3HY Tel: 01706 658905 Fax: 01706 343990; 5 Bowling Green Way, Bamford, Rochdale OL11 5QQ — MB ChB 1979 Manch.; DRCOG 1981.

TUTTON, Geoffrey Robert Cronehills Health Centre, West Bromwich B70 Tel: 0121 553 6277 — MB ChB 1970 Birm.; MRCGP 1978.

TUTTON, Mr Miles Kenneth 17 Blackfriars, Chester CH1 2NU Tel: 01244 342460 Fax: 01244 342460 — MB BS 1974 Lond.; BSc (Biochem., Hons.) Lond. 1970; FRCS Eng. (Ophth.) 1983; FRCS Eng. 1978; MRCS Eng. LRCP Lond. 1974; DO Eng. 1981. (Lond. Hosp.) Cons. Ophth. Countess of Chester Hosp. NHS Trust. Socs: Fell. Roy. Coll. Ophth.; Fell. Roy. Soc. Med.; Counc. Mem. UKISCRS. Prev: Sen. Regist. (Ophth.) Manch. Roy. Eye Hosp.; Regist. (Ophth.) Soton. Eye Hosp.; Clin. Asst. Moorfields Eye Hosp. Lond.

TUTTY, Christopher Leake (retired) 8 Hall Park, Berkhamsted HP4 2NU Tel: 01442 862150 — MB BS 1950 Lond.; DObst RCOG 1955. Prev: Ho. Surg. St. Thos. Hosp. Lond.

TUTTY, Michael Benjamin Department Obstetrics and Gynaecology, Derriford Hospital, Plymouth Tel: 01752 777111; 1 Speculation Cottage, Yealmpton, Plymouth PL8 2JS — BM BCh 1993 Oxf.; MRCP (UK) 1996. SHO (O & G) Derriford Hosp. Plymouth. Prev: SHO (Psychiat.) Glenbourne Unit Derriford Plymouth; SHO (ENT) Roy. Devon & Exeter Hosps.; SHO (Gen. Med.) Roy. Devon & Exeter Hosp.

TUXFORD, Ann Félicité (retired) 34 Styal Road, Wilmslow SK9 4AG — MB ChB 1957 St. And.; MD (Commend) Dundee 1969. Prev: Lect. (Bact. & Virol.) Univ. Manch.

TUXFORD, Keith (retired) 4 Royds Avenue, Accrington BB5 2LE Tel: 01254 236351 — MB ChB Manch. 1948; MRCS Eng. LRCP Lond. 1948. Prev: GP Accrington.

TWADDLE, John Lindsay Thomas 19 Hawarden Hill, Brook Road, London NW2 7BR — MB BS 1998 Lond.

TWADDLE, John Steven Abronhill Health Centre, Pine Road, Cumbernauld, Glasgow G67 3BE Tel: 01236 723223 Fax: 01236 781426 — MB ChB 1983 Ed.; BSc Ed. 1981; MFFP 1993; MRCGP 1989; DRCOG 1988. Socs: GP Asthma Gp.; Brit. Soc. Med. & Dent. Hypn. Prev: Coordinator (Family Plann.) Motherwell & Clydesdale Unit Lanarksh. HB; SHO (Psychiat.) Baynor Village Hosp. Broxburn; SHO (Obst.) William Smellie Mem. Hosp. Lanark.

TWADDLE, Shona Passfoot Cottage, Balmaha, Glasgow G63 0JQ — MB ChB 1993 Glas. Specialist Regist. (Chem Path/ Clin Biochem.) Nothingham City Hosp.

TWAIJ, Mohammed Hussain Abdul Rassol Ali East Surrey Hospital, Redhill RH1 5RH; 5 Mayfield Road, Sutton SM2 5DU — MB ChB 1976 Baghdad; DCH RCP Lond. 1983. Staff Paediat. E. Surrey Hosp. Redhill. Prev: Sen. Regist. (Paediat.) Stoke Mandeville Hosp.

TWAMLEY, Huw William James The Old Rectory, Wolvesnewton, Chepstow NP16 6NY — MB ChB 1996 Manch.

TWARDZICKI, Halina Maria Ludwika 51 Heath Park Road, Gidea Park, Romford RM2 5UL Tel: 01843 51978 — MB ChB 1963 Birm. (Birm.) Clin. Med. Off. (Community Med.) Havering Health Dist. Socs: BMA & Nat. Assn. Family Plann. Doctors. Prev: GP Havering; Med. Off. Dr. Barnardo's Barkingside.

TWEDDEL, Ann Cowan University Hospital of Wales, Department of Cardiology, Heath Park, Cardiff CF14 4XW Tel: 029 2074 7747 Fax: 029 2074 7484 — MB ChB 1972 Glas.; MD Glas. 1993. Dir. Nuclear Cardiol. Univ. Hosp. Wales Cardiff.

TWEDDELL, Alan Leonard Worcestershire Health Authority, Shrub Hill Road, Worcester WR4 9RW Tel: 01905 760000 — MB BS 1971 Queensland; MFPHM RCP (UK) 1990; MRCOG 1982; FFPHM RCP (UK) 1998. Cons. Pub. Health Med. Worcs. HA. Prev: Sen. Regist. (Community Med.) W. Midl. RHA; Regist. (O & G) Newc. HA.

TWEDDELL, Gillian Anne 36 Riverside Gardens, Busby, Glasgow G76 8EP — MB ChB 1988 Glas.; DRCOG 1992.

TWEDDELL, William Hillman 33 Rangeways, Kingswinford DY6 8PN — LRCPI & LM, LRSCI & LM 1958; LRCPI & LM, LRCSI & LM 1958. GP Kingswinford.

TWEDDLE, Deborah Anne Department of Child Health, Royal Victoria Infirmary, Queen Victoria Road, Newcastle upon Tyne NE1 4LP Tel: 0191 202 3033 Fax: 0191 202 3060 Email: d.a.tweddle@ncl.ac.uk; 25 Wolveleigh Terrace, Gosforth, Newcastle upon Tyne NE3 1UP Tel: 0191 213 2405 — MB ChB 1991 Manch.; MB ChB (Hons.) Manch. 1991; BSc (Hons.) Manch. 1988; MRCP (UK) 1994. (Manch.) Research Assoc. & Hon. Regist. (Paediat. Oncol.) Child Health Dept. & Cancer Research Unit Univ. Newc. u. Tyne. Socs: BMA; Brit. Paediat. Assn.; MDU. Prev: Clin. Fell. (Paediat. Oncol.) Leukaemia Research Fund; SHO (Paediat.) John Radcliffe Hosp. Oxf.; Sen. Supervisory Resid. Duke Paediat. Hosp. Durh., N. Carolina, USA.

TWEED, Carolyn Susan 459 Whirlowdale Road, Sheffield S11 9NG — MB ChB 1980 Sheff.; MRCGP 1984; FRCR 1992; DRCOG 1983.

TWEED, Charles Robert Carlton Hall, Carlton-on-Trent, Newark NG23 6NW Tel: 01636 821421 — MB BS 1991 Lond.

TWEED, Michael Jason Glenfield Hospital, Groby Road, Leicester LE3 9QP — MB ChB 1988 Leeds; MRCP (UK) 1994. Regist. (Integrated & Respirat. Med.) Glenfield Hosp. Leicester. Socs: Brit. Thorac. Soc.; Roy. Coll. Phys. Lond. Prev: Regist. (Gen. Med.) P'boro. Dist. Hosp. & Milton Keynes Gen. Hosp.

TWEEDALE, John Lindsay Great Shelford Health Centre, Ashen Green, Great Shelford, Cambridge CB2 5EY Tel: 01223 843661 Fax: 01223 844569; 4 Finch's Close, Stapleford, Cambridge CB2 5BL Tel: 01223 845651 — MB ChB 1980 Bristol; MRCGP 1985; DA (UK) 1987; DRCOG 1985.

TWEEDIE, David Gilbert Castle Hill, Lower Fulbrook, Warwick CV35 8AS Tel: 01926 624686 — MB BS 1962 Lond.; FFA RCS Eng. 1966. (Westm.) Cons. Anaesth. S. Warks. HA. Socs: Fell. Roy. Soc. Med. Prev: Sen. Regist. (Anaesth.) Liverp. RHB; Regist.

TWEEDIE

(Anaesth.) BRd.green Hosp. Liverp.; SHO (Anaesth.) W.m. Hosp. Lond.

TWEEDIE, Dawn Mary Finlayson Street Practice, 33 Finlayson Street, Fraserburgh AB43 9JW Tel: 01346 518088 Fax: 01346 510015 — MB ChB 1986 Dundee.

TWEEDIE, Ian Edward Department of Anaesthesia, University Hospital Aintree NHS Trust, Lower Lane, Liverpool L9 7AL Tel: 0151 529 5152 Fax: 0151 529 5155 — MB ChB 1981 Liverp.; FFA RCS Eng. 1987; DA (UK) 1987. (Liverpool) Cons. Anaesth. Univ. Hosp. Aintree NHS Trust Liverp.; Cons. Neuroanaesthetics The Walton Centre. Socs: Treas. of Liverp. Soc. of Anaestuetists; Chairm. of Assn. of Mersey ICU's. Prev: Vis. Asst. Prof. of Anesthesiol. Oregon Health Scs. Univ., USA.

TWEEDIE, Mr James Hamilton Stoke Mandeville Hospital NHS Trust, Mandeville Road, Aylesbury HP21 8AL Tel: 01296 316559 Fax: 01296 315296; Loosley House, Loosley Row, Princes Risborough HP27 0PF Tel: 01844 346819 — MB BS 1973 Lond.; MS Lond. 1984, BSc (Hons.) 1970; FRCS Eng. 1979; FRCS Ed. 1978. (St. Bart.) Cons. Surg. (Gen. Surg.) Stoke Mandeville Hosp. Aylesbury. Socs: Assn. Endoscopic Surgs.; Fell. Assn. of Coloproctol. GB & Irel.; Assn. Of Surg.s GB & Irel. Prev: Sen. Regist. (Gen. Surg.) Univ. Hosp. Nottm.; Research Fell. Univ. Missouri Colombia, USA; Sen. Regist. St. Mark's Hosp. for Dis. of Colon & Rectum Lond.

TWEEDIE, Roderick John The Deepings Practice, Godsey Lane, Market Deeping, Peterborough PE6 8DD Tel: 01778 579000 Fax: 01778 579009; 66 West End, Langtoft, Peterborough PE6 9LU Tel: 0140 24 345034 — MB ChB 1973 Glas.; MRCGP 1978; DObst RCOG 1975. (Univ. Glas.) Prev: Chairm. P'boro. GP Forum; Course Organiser P'boro. VTS; Trainee GP Dumfries VTS.

TWEEDIE-STODART, Nancy Marjorie 2 Balfour Place, St Andrews KY16 9RQ Tel: 01334 473223 — MB ChB Ed. 1950; DPM Eng. 1960. (Ed.) Affil. RCPsych. Prev: Cons. Child Psychiat. Preston Health Dist.; Cons. Psychiat. Roy. Cornhill Hosp. Aberd.; SHO Maudsley Hosp. Lond.

TWEEDLE, Mr David Ernest Frederick The Beeches Consulting Centre, Mill Lane, Cheadle SK8 2PY Tel: 0161 491 2908 Fax: 0161 428 1692; 5 Bramway, Bramhall, Stockport SK7 2AP Tel: 0161 440 0273 — MB ChB 1964 St. And.; ChM Dund 1974; FRCS Eng. 1988; FRCS Ed. 1969. (St. And.) Cons. Surg. Univ. Hosp. S. Manch. & The Christie Hosp. Manch.; Hon. Assoc. Lect. Univ. Manch. Socs: Brit. Soc. Gastroenterol.; Surgic. Research Soc.; Internat. Hepato-Pancreato-Biliary Assn. Prev: Sen. Lect. (Surg.) Univ. Manch.; Sen. Regist. (Surg.) Newc. Univ. Hosp. Gp.; Research Assoc. (Surg.) Peter Bent Brigham Hosp. Boston, USA.

TWEEDLE, Isabella Simpson 10 Brookdale Road, Bramhall, Stockport SK7 2NW Tel: 0161 440 0588 — MB ChB 1965 St. And.; DA Eng. 1968; DCP Sheff. 1993. (St. And.) SCMO (Child Health) N. Manch. Socs: Manch. Med. Soc.; BAACH. Prev: Clin. Med. Off. Manch. Hosp. & Community NHS Trust; Clin. Asst. (Anaesth.) Gateshead Health Dist.; SHO (Anaesth.) W. Cumbld. Hosp. Hensingham.

TWEEDLE, Mr James Richard 65 First Avenue, Netherlee, Glasgow G44 3UA — MB ChB 1989 Glas.; FRCS Ed. 1995.

TWEEDLIE, Iain Kinloch 260 Union Grove, Aberdeen AB10 6TR — MB ChB 1997 Aberd.

TWEEDY, Mark Hans 52 Queens Gardens, Bayswater, London W2 3AA — MB BS 1978 Lond.

TWEEDY, Peter Stuart (retired) 24 Carrwood Avenue, Bramhall, Stockport SK7 2PY Tel: 0161 439 3632 — MRCS Eng. LRCP Lond. 1942; MD Lond. 1952, MB BS 1942; FRCP Lond. 1973, M 1949. Prev: Cons. Geriatr. Stockport HA.

TWELVES, Christopher John CRC Department of Medical Oncology, Beatson Oncology Centre, Western Infirmary, Glasgow G11 6NT Tel: 0141 211 2000 — MB ChB 1980 Sheff.; MD Sheff. 1995; BMedSci. (Hons.) Sheff. 1977; MRCP (UK) 1984; FRCP 1997; MRCP (UK) 1984; FRCP Glas. 1998; FRCP Lond. 1998. (Sheffield) Sen. Lect. & Hon. Cons. (Med. Oncol.). Socs: Assn. Cancer Phys.; Amer. Soc. Clin. Oncol.; Eur. Soc. Med. Oncol. Prev: Lect. & Hon. Sen. Regist. (Med. Oncol.) Guy's Hosp.; ICRF Clin. Research Fell. Guy's Hosp. Lond.; Regist. (Med. Oncol.) Univ. Coll. Hosp. Lond.

TWELVES, Nigel Ponteland Medical Group, Thornhill Road, Ponteland, Newcastle upon Tyne NE20 9PZ Tel: 01661 825513 Fax: 01661 860755 — MB BS 1988 Newc.

TWENA, Diane Michelle Baronsmere Road Surgery, 39 Baronsmere Road, East Finchley, London N2 9QD Tel: 020 8883 1458 Fax: 020 883 8854; 62 Kingsley Way, London N2 0EW — MB ChB 1988 Manch.; BSc (Hons.) Manch. 1985; MRCGP 1993. SHO (Psychiat.) Chase Farm Hosp. Enfield NE Thames RHA.

TWENEY, Jessica Cornelia St Helier Bluebell Medical Centre, 356 Bluebell Road, Sheffield S5 6BS Tel: 0114 242 1406 Fax: 0114 261 8074; 11 Penrhyn Road, Hunters Bar, Sheffield S11 8UL Tel: 0114 266 6567 — MB ChB 1983 Bristol; BSc (Hons.) Bristol 1980; DRCOG 1989. Gen. Pract. Clin. Asst. (Elderly Psychiat.) Sheff. Prev: SHO (O & G) Nether Edge Hosp. Sheff.; Research Fell. & SHO (Chest Med.) Roy. Hallamsh. Hosp. Sheff.

TWENTYMAN, Llewelyn Ralph (retired) Willoughby, Dale Road, Forest Row RH18 5BP Tel: 01342 822151 — MB BChir 1943 Camb.; MRCS Eng. LRCP Lond. 1943; FFHom. 1959. Prev: Cons. Phys. Roy. Lond. Homoeop. Hosp.

TWENTYMAN, Orion Peter Department of Respiratory Medicine, Leicester House, Norfolk & Norwich Hospital, Norwich NR1 3SR Tel: 01603 289646 Fax: 01603 289640 — BM 1979 Soton.; PhD Soton. 1994; MRCP (UK) 1982. (Univ. Soton.) Cons. Phys. Norf. & Norwich Hosp. Socs: Brit. Thorac. Soc.; Amer. Thoracic Soc.; Eur. Respirat. Soc. Prev: Sen. Regist. (Respirat. & Gen. Med.) Papworth & Addenbrooke's Hosps. Camb.; MRC Investigator Univ. Soton.; Regist. (Med.) Manch. Roy. Infirm.

TWIDDY, Peter Jonathan McIntosh, Gourlay and Partners, 1 India Place, Edinburgh EH3 6EH Tel: 0131 225 9191 Fax: 0131 226 6549; 46 Hillpark Avenue, Edinburgh EH4 7AH — MB ChB 1985 Ed.; MRCGP 1993; DCCH RCP Ed. 1991.

TWIDELL, Sara Mary Beckingham Bridgford House, Horninghold, Market Harborough LE16 8DH Tel: 01858 555204 — MB ChB 1993 Ed.

TWIGG, Annette Isobel Watford Road Surgery, 16 Watford Road, Crick, Northampton NN6 7TT Tel: 01788 822203 Fax: 01788 824177 — BM BS 1984 Nottm.

TWIGG, Caroline Evelyn — MB ChB 1987 Leeds; MRCGP 1991; DCCH RCP Ed. 1993; DRCOG 1990. Socs: Nat. Assn. Non-Princip.s.

TWIGG, Jeremy Philip Dodwell 52 Hazelbank Terrace, Edinburgh EH11 1SL — MB BS 1992 Lond.

TWIGG, Lesley Judith Syston Health Centre, Melton Road, Syston, Leicester LE7 2EQ — MB ChB 1982 Leic.; MRCGP 1988. Prev: SHO (Med.) Leicester Roy. Infirm.

TWIGG, Simon Frank Guilsborough Surgery, High Street, Guilsborough, Northampton NN6 8PU Tel: 01604 740210/740142 Fax: 01604 740869; Witherford, 5 Foxhill Road, West Haddon, Northampton NN6 7BQ Tel: 01788 87762 — BMedSci (Hons.) Nottm. 1982, BM BS 1984; DCH RCP Lond. 1986.

TWIGG, Steven James 2 Clifton Park Road, Clifton, Bristol BS8 3HL Email: steve.twigg@lineone.net — MB BChir 1993 Camb.; BA (Hons.) Camb. 1990; MRCP UK 1997. (Camb.) SpR (Anaesth.) Bristol Roy. Infirm.

TWIGLEY, Alison Jane Luton & Dunstable Hospital Tel: 01227 766877 Fax: 01277 783191 — MB BS 1976 Lond.; MRCS Eng. LRCP Lond. 1976; FFA RCS Eng. 1980. (St. Mary's) Cons. Anaesth. Luton & Dunstable Hosp. Socs: Assn. Anaesth.; Assn. Of Obstetric Anaesth.; Brit. Orthopaedic anaesth. Assn. Prev: Sen. Regist. (Anaesth.) Hammersmith Roy. Postgrad. Hosp.; Regist. (Anaesth.) Char. Cross Hosp. Lond.; SHO (Anaesth.) Edgware Gen. Hosp. Lond.

TWINE, Martin Richard Bounds Green Group Practice, Gordon Road, Bounds Green, London N11 2PF Tel: 020 8889 1961; Home Farm Cottage, Ponsbourne Park, Newgate Street Villiage, Hertford SG13 8QT Tel: 01707 872377 Email: martintwine@csi.com — MB BS 1983 Lond.; BA (Physiol. Sc.) Oxf. 1980; MFHom 1994; MRCGP 1987; DGM RCP Lond. 1987; DRCOG 1986; DCH RCP Lond. 1986. (Univ. Coll. Hosp.) GP Tutor UCL. Prev: Trainee GP N.wick Pk. Hosp. VTS; Ho. Surg. Barnet Gen. Hosp.; Ho. Phys. N.ampton Gen. Hosp.

TWINEM, Gillian Shirin 10 Colvil Street, Belfast BT4 1PS — MB BCh BAO 1989 Belf.

TWINER, David Anthony Neil Lansdowne Surgery, Waiblingen Way, Devizes SN10 2BU Tel: 01380 722939 Fax: 01380 723790; Olive House, High St, Rowde, Devizes SN10 2ND — MB BS Lond. 1964; DA Eng. 1971; DObst RCOG 1971. (Westm.) Clin. Asst. Deviles Community Hosp. Socs: Clin. Soc. Bath & Med. Offs. Sch. Assn. Prev: Regist. (Anaesth.) Roy. Berks. Hosp. Reading; Ho. Surg. (Surg.) & Cas. Off. W.m. Hosp.; Anaesth. Devizes Hosps.

TWINHAM, Douglas John Beverley Road Surgery, 87 Beverley Road, Hessle HU13 9BR Tel: 01482 648552 Fax: 01482 642600; 2 The Paddock, Swanland, North Ferriby HU14 3QW Tel: 01482 633261 — MB ChB 1965 Leeds. Socs: Hull Med. Soc.

TWINING, Daniel Hugh (retired) Rivendell, Kingsale Road, Salcombe TQ8 8AS Tel: 01548 842757 — BM BCh Oxf. 1940.

TWINING, Peter Department of Radiology, Queens Medical Centre, Nottingham NG7 2UH Tel: 0115 970 1064 Fax: 0115 970 1064 Email: peter.twining@nottingham.ac.uk — MB BS 1979 Lond.; MRCS Eng. LRCP Lond. 1979; FRCR 1985. (Guys Hospital) Cons. Radiol.

TWISLETON-WYKEHAM-FIENNES, Mr Alberic George Department of Surgery, St George's Hospital Medical School, Cranmer Terrace, London SW17 0RE Tel: 020 8725 5584 Fax: 020 8725 3594; 19 Pendarves Road, London SW20 8TS Tel: 020 8946 0597 — MB BS 1976 Lond.; BSc (Hons.) Lond. 1973, MS 1987, MB BS 1976; FRCS Eng. 1981. (St. Bart.) Sen. Lect. & Hon. Cons. Surg. Dept. Surg. St. Geo. Hosp. Med. Sch. Lond.; AO Foundat. Vis. Prof. & Martin Allguwer Trauma Schol. 1990, Switz; ATLS Instruc. RCS Eng. 1989. Prev: Lect. & Hon. Sen. Regist. (Surg.) St. Geo. Hosp. Med. Sch. Lond.; Wellcome Clin. Research Fell. St. Geo. Hosp. Lond.; Ho. Surg. St. Bart. Hosp. Lond.

TWIST, Andrew Mark 457 Liverpool Road, Ainsdale, Southport PR8 3BN — MB ChB 1984 Liverp. SHO (Infec. Dis.) Fazakerley Hosp. Liverp. Prev: SHO (A & E) S.port Gen. Infirm.

TWIST, Donald Chisnall 42 Briestfield Road, Thornhill, Dewsbury WF12 0PW Tel: 01924 452202 — MB ChB 1950 Leeds. (Leeds) Prev: Ho. Phys. Ackton Hosp. Nr. Pontefract; Asst. Cas. Off. Pontefract. Gen. Infirm.; Capt. RAMC.

TWIST, John Stuart (retired) Rosskeen, Crich, Matlock Tel: 0177 385 2466 — MRCS Eng. LRCP Lond. 1942; MRCS Eng., LRCP Lond. 1942. Prev: Ho. Phys. St. Jas. Hosp. Leeds.

TWIST, Joyce Rosalie (retired) Maranatha, 22 Main Road, Littleton, Winchester SO22 6PS Tel: 01962 880475 Email: pat-twist@beeb.net — MB ChB 1945 Liverp.; DCH Eng. 1947; DObst RCOG 1948; LMCC 1950. Prev: Clin. Med. Off. Winchester & Mid Hants. Family Plann. Serv.

TWIST, William Andrew 353 Gathurst Road, Orrell, Wigan WN5 8QE — MB ChB 1988 Birm.; ChB Birm. 1988.

TWISTON DAVIES, Mr Ceri William The General Hospital, St Helier, Jersey JE1 3QS Tel: 01534 622483 Fax: 01534 21415; Le Hurel Farm, La Ruette Pinel, Mont Cochon, St Lawrence, Jersey JE3 1HF Tel: 01534 864072 Fax: 01534 862543 Email: twiston@itl.net — MB BS 1976 Lond.; FRCS Ed. 1981; MRCS Eng. LRCP Lond. 1976. (Middlx.) Cons. Orthop. Surg. States of Jersey. Socs: Fell. BOA; Liveryman Worshipful Soc. Apoth. Prev: Sen. Regist. Wessex Regional Orthop. Train. Scheme; Regist. (Gen. Surg. & Orthop.) Yeovil Dist. Hosp.; Cas. Off. (Surg.) & Demonst. (Anat.) Middlx. Hosp. Lond.

TWITCHEN, Michael John Unit of Medicine in Relation to Oral Disease, Floor 22, Guy's Tower, Guy's Hospital, London SE1 9RT Tel: 020 79555 2323; 27 Lime Grove, The Dell, Angmering, Littlehampton BN16 4HA — MB BS 1993 Lond.; BDS Lond. 1986; LMSSA Lond. 1993; FFD RCSI 1996; LDS RCS Eng. 1986. Lect. (Med. in Relation to Oral Dis.) Guy's Hosp. Lond. Prev: SHO (Med.) Worthing Hosp. Sussex.

TWITE, Mark David 24 Elm Grove, Garboldsham, Diss IP22 2RY Email: doc.mtwite@easynet.co.uk — MB BChir 1994 Camb.; MRCP (Paediat.) 1997. (Camb.)

TWITE, Simon Jonathan 42 Bridgemere Drive, Framwellgate Moor, Durham DH1 5FG Tel: 0191 386 2429 Email: sjtwite@compuserve.com — MB ChB 1996 Ed.; BSc. (Hons.) Med. Sci. Ed. 1995. (Edinburgh) SHO Med. Rotat. Dryburn Hosp. Co. Durh. Prev: PRHO (Surgic.) CrossHo. Hosp. Kilmarnock Scotl.; PRHO (Med.) Borders Gen. Hosp. Melrose Scotl.

TWIVY, Samuel Barstow Willow Cottage, 16 Moor End, Eaton Bray, Dunstable LU6 2HN Tel: 01525 220543 — MRCS Eng. LRCP Lond. 1951. (Lond. Hosp.)

TWOHEY, Linda Caroline Department of Anaesthetics, Kettering General Hospital NHS Trust, Rothwell Road, Kettering NN16 8UZ Tel: 01536 492746 — MB BS 1982 Lond.; MA Camb. 1983; FFARCS Eng. 1988. (Univ. Camb. & Fac. Clin. Scis. Univ. Coll. Lond.) Cons. Anaesth. Kettering Gen. Hosp. Prev: Sen. Regist. Rotat. (Anaesth.) N.ampton & Oxf.; Regist. (Anaesth.) Harefield Hosp. Middlx.; Regist. (Anaesth.) The Lond. Hosp.

TWOHIG, Michael McDermot Royal Sussex County Hospital, Eastern Road, Brighton BN2 5BE Tel: 01273 609060 Fax: 01273 609060 Email: mike.twohig@brighton-healthcare.nhs.uk — MB BChir 1975 Camb.; MA Camb. 1974; FFA RCS Eng. 1979. (Camb. & King's Coll. Hosp.) Cons. Anaesth. Brighton & Sussex Univ. Hosp. NHS Trust. Socs: Hon. Sec. SE Soc. Of Anaesth. Prev: Sen. Regist. (Anaesth. & Intens. Care) Kings Coll. Hosp. Lond.

TWOMEY, Alan Franics John 59 Castleton Avenue, Wembley Park, Wembley HA9 7QE — MB BS 1996 Lond.

TWOMEY, Brendan Peter 24 Flambard Road, Harrow HA1 2NA Tel: 020 8907 1887 — MB BCh BAO 1973 NUI; FRCR 1981; DObst RCPI 1975; DCH NUI 1975. (Univ. Coll. Dub.) Cons. (Radiol.) N.wick Pk. Hosp. Harrow. Prev: Intern Mater Miser. Hosp. Dub.; SHO (Med.) Our Lady of Lourdes Hosp. Drogheda; Ho. Off. (Obst.) Coombe Hosp. Dub.

TWOMEY, Catherine Ann Scartho Medical Centre, 26 Waltham Road, Grimsby DN33 2QA Tel: 01472 871747 Fax: 01472 276050; Fieldgate Lodge, Main Road, Ashby cum Fenby, Grimsby DN37 0QW Tel: 01472 828348 — MB BS 1986 Lond.; BSc Lond. 1983, MB BS 1986; MRCGP 1990. GP. Socs: Roy. Coll. Gen. Pract.

TWOMEY, James Aiden Department of Neurophysiology, Pinderfields General Hospital, Aberford Road, Wakefield WF1 4DG — MD 1986 NUI; MB BCh BAO 1973; FRCP Lond. 1994; MRCP (UK) 1977. Cons. Clin. Neurophysiol. Pinderfields Gen. Hosp. Wakefield. Prev: Sen. Regist. (Clin. Neurophysiol.) Leeds Gen. Infirm. & St. Jas. Hosp. Leeds; Regist. (Neurol.) Derbysh. Roy. Infirm.; SHO Rotat. Withington Hosp. Manch. & Christie Hosp. Manch.

TWOMEY, Jerome Christopher Medical Centre, Okehampton EX20 1AY Tel: 01837 52233; Elmfield House, Hatherleigh, Okehampton EX20 3JY — MB BChir 1958 Camb.; MA, MB Camb. 1958, BChir 1957; MRCOG 1967. (St. Mary's) Prev: Surg. Cdr. RN; Sen. Specialist (O & G) RN Hosp. Malta.

TWOMEY, John (retired) 7 Newcombe Close, Dunchurch, Rugby CV22 6ND Tel: 01788 810779 — MB BCh BAO 1948 NUI; FMCM 1984, M 1972; DPH Lond. 1963; DTM & H Eng. 1955. Prev: SCM. Coventry Health Dist.

TWOMEY, John Lawrence 3 Ealing Village, London W5 2LY — MB BCh BAO 1993 NUI.

TWOMEY, Mr John Matthew 4 Haines Hill, Taunton TA1 4HW — MB BS 1978 Lond.; BSc Lond. 1975; FRCS Eng. 1985; MRCP (UK) 1982; MRCS Eng. LRCP Lond. 1978. (Guy's) Cons. Ophth. Taunton.

TWOMEY, John Michael The Mary Potter Health Centre, Gregory Boulevard, Hyson Green, Nottingham NG7 5HY — MB BCh BAO 1955 NUI. (Cork)

TWOMEY, Michael James 57 The Common, Parbold, Wigan WN8 7EA — MB BCh BAO 1983 NUI.

TWOMEY, Michael Patrick Keiran Keepers Cottage, Barrock Park, Southwaite, Carlisle CA4 0JS Tel: 01697 473461 — MB BCh BAO NUI 1960; MRCPsych 1977; MRCOG 1969; DPM Eng. 1966. (Cork) Cons. Psychiat. Sedgefield Community Hosp. Cons. Psychiat. Socs: (Hon. Sec.) Soc. Clin. Psychiat.; Roy. Soc. Med. Prev: Cons. Psychiat. Garlands Hosp. Carlisle; Cons. O & G Mullingar Co. Hosp. & Letterkenny Gen. Hosp.; Regist. Dumfries & Galloway Roy. Infirm.

TWOMEY, Patrick Joseph 7 Culverhay, Wotton-under-Edge GL12 7LS Tel: 01453 844830 — MB BCh BAO 1980 NUI. Trainee GP Wotton-under-Edge.

TWOMEY, Paul Anthony Scartho Medical Centre, 26 Waltham Road, Grimsby DN33 2QA Tel: 01472 871747 Fax: 01472 276050; 239 Louth Road, Holton Le Clay, Grimsby DN36 5AE Tel: 01472 828348 — MB BS 1986 Lond.; MA Camb. 1986; MRCGP 1990; DGM RCP Lond. 1989. Socs: BMA. Prev: Trainee GP Grimsby VTS.

TWOMEY, Peter James Golden Chiddenbrook Surgery, Threshers, Crediton EX17 3JJ Tel: 01363 772227 Fax: 01363 775528; Higher Woolsgrove, Sandford, Crediton EX17 4PJ — MB BS 1984 Lond.; MRCGP 1991; DRCOG 1988; DCH RCP Lond. 1987. Prev: SHO (Paediat.) Kingston Hosp.; SHO (O & G) Centr. Middlx. Hosp.; SHO (A & E) Lewisham & Guy's Hosp.

TWORT, Antony Edward Peter (retired) Bryn Tor, Deanery Road, Godalming GU7 2PQ Tel: 01483 415823 — MB BS 1948 Lond.; MRCP Lond. 1958; MFCM 1972; DPH Lond. 1954. Prev: Dist. Community Phys. Winchester & Centr. Hants. Health Dist.

TWORT

TWORT, Charles Hamish Crampton Division of Medicine, GKT School of Medicine, St Thomas Hospital, London SE1 7EH Tel: 020 7928 9292 Fax: 020 7922 8305 — MB BChir 1976 Camb.; MA Camb. 1977, MD 1990; FRCP Lond. 1993; FRCP Ed. 1993; MRCP (UK) 1978. Sen. Lect. (Med.)and PostGrad. Dean GKT Sch. of Med. Lond.; Hon. Cons. Phys. and Director of PostGrad. Med. Educat. Guy's & St. Thos. Hosps. Trust Lond.

TWORT, Richard John 200 Ardgowan Road, London SE6 1XA Tel: 020 8698 9662 Fax: 020 8461 2457 Email: dickietwort@compuserve.com — MB BChir 1979 Camb.; MA Camb. 1976, MB BChir 1979; MRCGP 1984. Clin. Med. Off. Nat. Blood Auth. Prev: GP S. Lond.

TWYBLE, Thomas Stewart (retired) 94 Southchurch Boulevard, Southend-on-Sea SS2 4UZ Tel: 01702 465319 — LRCP LRCS Ed. LRFPS Glas. 1960. Prev: SHO Purdysburn Hosp. Belf.

TWYCROSS, Robert Geoffrey (retired) Sir Michael Sobell House, Churchill Hospital, Oxford OX3 7LJ Tel: 01865 225 891 Fax: 01865 741 867 — BM BCh Oxf. 1965; DM Oxf. 1977; FRCP Lond. 1980, M 1969; FRCR 1996. Emerit. Clin. Reader in Palliat. Med., Univ. Oxf; Director, World Health Organisation's Collaborative Centre for Palliat. Care; Accademic Dir., Oxf. Internat. Centre for Palliat. Care. Prev: Research Fell. St. Christopher's Hospice Lond.

TWYDELL, Helen Jane 34 Park Road, Southborough, Tunbridge Wells TN4 0NX Tel: 01892 542700 — MB BS 1998 Lond.; MB BS Lond 1998.

TWYMAN, Derek Gould (retired) 9 Queenswood House, Crane Bridge Road, Salisbury SP2 7TW — MB 1956 Camb.; BChir 1955; DObst RCOG 1962. Prev: Ho. Surg. & Ho. Phys. Memor. Hosp. Cirencester.

TWYMAN, Mr Roy Sean Epsom General Hospital, Epsom KT18 7EG Tel: 01372 735110 — MB BS 1982 Lond.; FRCS (Orth.) 1992; FRCS Eng. 1986. (Westm.) Cons. Orthop. Surg. Epsom Gen. Hosp. Prev: Sen. Regist. (Orthop.) Middlx. Hosp. & Roy. Nat. Orthop. Hosp. Lond.; Regist. (Orthop.) W.m. Hosp. Lond.

TWYMAN, Victor Ronald Holme Leys, Burmington, Shipston-on-Stour CV36 5AR Tel: 01608 664215 — MB BS 1954 Lond.; DObst RCOG 1960. (Char. Cross) Med. Disabil. Analyst. Prev: Princip. GP Newark Notts.; Cas. Off. Char. Cross Hosp.; Flight Lt. RAF Med. Br.

TYACK, Susan Rosalind Harrison Department, Radcliffe Infirmary, Woodstock Road, Oxford OX2 6HE; Walnut Cottage, Ebbs Lane, East Hanney, Wantage OX12 0HL — MB BS Lond. 1962. (Lond. Hosp.) Clin. Asst. (Genitourin. Med.) Radcliffe Infirm. NHS Trust, Aylesbury Vale NHS Trust.; Clin. Med. Off. (Family Plann.) Oxon. Community Health NHS Trust. Socs: Med. Soc. Study VD; Fac. Fam. Plann. & Reproduc. Health Care; BSSCP. Prev: Asst. GP Abingdon; Clin. Med. Off. (Community Health) Huddersfield HA; SCMO (Family Plann.) Oxon. HA.

TYAGI, Mr Ajai Kumar 94 Turnberry Road, Great Barr, Birmingham B42 2HU — MB BS 1988 Bombay; FRCS Ed. 1994.

TYAGI, Mr Dinesh Chandra 14 Farm Grove, Rugby CV22 5NQ Tel: 01788 71911 — MB BS 1962 Lucknow; BSc Agra 1957; FRCS Ed. 1979. (G.S.V.M. Med. Coll. Kanpur)

TYBULEWICZ, Aniela Teresa (retired) 31 Queen's Crescent, Newington, Edinburgh EH9 2BA Tel: 0131 667 7842 — MB BS 1990 Lond.; MRCP (UK) 1994. p/t Paediat. Specialist Regist. Roy. Hosp. for Sick Childr. Edin.

TYBULEWICZ, Suzanna Maria Eat Calder Medical Practice, 197 Main St, East Calder, Livingston EH53 0EW; 71 The Broadway, Walsall WS1 3EZ Tel: 01922 622144 Fax: 01922 622144 Email: normanyoung@excite.co.uk — MB BS 1989 Lond.; DRCOG 1993.

TYDEMAN, Graham Stephen John Barruchlaw Lodge, Brighouse, Bathgate EH48 3DW — MB BCh 1985 Wales; BSc Cardiff 1983.

TYE, Jennifer Christine 3 Woodgreen Croft, Oldbury, Warley B68 0DG Tel: 0121 422 2322 — MB BS 1991 Lond. Specialist Regist. (Anaesth.) Qu. Eliz. Hosp. Birm. Socs: BMA; Train. Mem. Assn. AnE.h. Prev: SHO (ITU) Walsgrave Hosp. Coventry; SHO (Anaesth.) New Cross Hosp. Wolverhampton & Stafford Dist. Gen. Hosp.

TYE, Tracy Elizabeth 4 Elm Grove Road, Whitchurch, Cardiff CF14 2BW — MB ChB 1986 Leic.

TYERMAN, Gillian Veronica Rotherham Road Medical Centre, 100 Rotherham Road, Barnsley S71 1UT Tel: 01226 282587 — MB ChB 1977 Sheff.; MRCGP 1981.

TYERMAN, Kay Sarah North View, Edmundbyers, Consett DH8 9NJ — MB BChir 1992 Camb.; MA Camb. 1993; MRCP (UK) 1995.

TYERMAN, Peter Frank Rotherham Road Medical Centre, 100 Rotherham Road, Barnsley S71 1UT Tel: 01226 282587 Fax: 01226 291900; Swaithe Villa, Low Swaithe, Worsbrough, Barnsley S70 3QF — MB ChB 1977 Sheff.; MRCGP 1981.

TYERS, Mr Anthony Gordon Salisbury District Hospital, Salisbury SP2 8BJ Tel: 01722 336262 Fax: 01722 322871; Huckleberry, Bouverie Close, Salisbury SP2 8DY Fax: 01722 339538 — MB BS 1970 Lond.; FRCS Ed. (Ophth.) 1980; FRCS Eng. 1975; MRCS Eng. LRCP Lond. 1970; FRCOphth 1989; DO Eng. 1977. (Char. Cross) Cons. Ophth. Surg. Salisbury Dist. Hosp. Socs: Fell. Roy. Soc. Med.; Comm. Mem. Europ. Soc. Ophth. Plastic & Reconstruc. Surg.; BMA. Prev: Sen. Regist. Middlx. Hosp. & Moorfields Eye Hosp. Lond.; Fell. Mass. Eye & Ear Infirm. Boston, USA; Resid. Surg. Off. Moorfields Eye Hosp. Lond.

TYERS, David John 12 Chandos Street, Netherfield, Nottingham NG3 3LG; 33 Hazel Grove, Mapperley, Nottingham NG3 6DQ Tel: 0115 926 7341 — MB ChB 1980 Leic.; MRCGP 1987; DRCOG 1987.

TYERS, Rachael Natalie Sian 38 Caerphilly Road, Bassaleg, Newport NP10 8LF — MB BCh 1995 Wales.

TYERS, Renee Constance Barbara New Hall Hospital, Salisbury SP5 4EY Tel: 01722 331021; Salisbury District Hospital, Salisbury SP2 8BJ Tel: 01722 336262 — Artsexamen 1980 Utrecht; MRCOphth 1989; DO Eng. 1985. Clin. Asst. (Ophth.) Salisbury Dist. Hosp. Socs: Fell. Roy. Soc. Med.; BMA. Prev: Clin. Asst. Moorfields Eye Hosp. Lond.; SHO (Ophth.) St. Bart. Hosp. Lond.; Resid. (Ophth.) Acad. Med. Centre Amsterdam.

TYLDEN, Elizabeth 322 South Lambeth Road, London SW8 1UQ Tel: 020 7720 6622 Fax: 020 7498 7248; St. Julians, Sevenoaks TN15 0RX Tel: 01732 458261 Fax: 01732 454005 — MB BChir 1943 Camb.; BA (Nat. Sc. Trip.) Camb. 1939 MA 1943; MRCS Eng. LRCP Lond. 1943; MRCPsych 1971. (Camb. & Lond. Sch. Med. Wom. and West Lond. Hosp.) Hon. Cons. Psychiat. Bromley Hosp.; Chairm. Lambeth Drugline; Pres. Stepping Stones Club. Socs: Roy. Soc. Med.; Marcé Soc.; Founder Mem. Expert Witness Inst. Prev: Hon. Research Fell. Acad. Dept. Psychiat. UCH & Middlx. Hosp.; Mem. DHSS Working Party on The Treatm. of Drug Addic.; Mem. Comm. on Health of Hosp. Staff.

***TYLDESLEY, David Barry** Anaesthetic Department, Ysbyty Gwynedd, Bangor LL57; Castellor, 19 Overlea Avenue, Deganwy, Llandudno Tel: 01492 83646 — MB BCh 1979 Wales.

TYLDESLEY, Roy Cooke (retired) 9 Woodland Court, Knoll Hill, Bristol BS9 1NR Tel: 0117 968 2399 — MB ChB 1951 Ed.; FRCGP 1980, M 1973. Prev: Phys. i/c BUPA Health Screening Bristol.

TYLDESLEY SMITH, Jeanette Thelma Ashbrooke (retired) Beaconsfield, Golf Road, Gourock PA19 1DQ Tel: 01475 633936 — MB ChB 1963 Glas.; BSc (Hons.) Glas. 1960; FRANZCP 1985, M 1974; DPM Ed. & Glas. 1968. Prev: Cons. Psychiat. Argyll & Clyde HB.

TYLEE, André Trevor Stonecot Surgery, 115 Epsom Road, Sutton SM3 9EY Tel: 020 8644 5187; 18 Lower Hill Road, Epsom KT19 8LT Tel: 01372 812157 — MB BS 1978 Lond.; MD Lond. 1994; MRCPsych 1996; FRCGP 1994, M 1984. (Guy's) Sen. Lect. (Sect. Epidemiol. & Primary Care) Inst. Psychiat. Lond.; Dir. RCGP Unit for Ment. Health Educat. Inst. Psychiat. Lond.; Hon. Sen. Lect. (Gen. Pract.) St. Geo. Hosp. Socs: Roy. Soc. Med.; Assn. Univ. Depts. Gen. Pract.; Med. Scientif. Network. Prev: Ment. Health Foundat. Research Fell.; SHO Nuffield Ho. Guys Hosp.; Ho. Phys. Guy's Hosp.

TYLER, Arthur Kenneth Fossicks, Sheet, Petersfield Tel: 01730 62494 — BM BCh 1942 Oxf.; BA (Hons.) 1939, BM BCh Oxon. 1942; DPhysMed Eng. 1947. (Oxf.) Hon. Cons. Phys. (Rheum. & Rehabil.) Portsmouth & S.E. Hants. Health Dist; Med. Dir. Qu. Alexandra Cerebral Palsy Day Unit. Socs: Fell. Roy. Soc. Med.; Med. Disabil. Soc. Prev: Asst. Med. Off. Dept. Physical Med. St. Thos. Hosp.; Regist. Roy. Nat. Hosp. Rheum. Dis. Bath; Regist. Dept. Physical Med. Hosp. Sick Childr. Gt. Ormond St.

TYLER, Christopher Kenneth Graburn County Hospital, Greetwell Road, Lincoln LN2 5QY Tel: 01522 512512 — MB BS 1980 Lond.; FFA RCS Eng. 1985. Dir. Intens. Care & Cons. Anaesth. Co. Hosp. Lincoln. Prev: Clin. Tutor Univ. Nottm.

TYLER, Clare Louise Wearne Cottage, Brookland Corner, Somerton Road, Langport TA10 9SN — MB BCh 1992 Wales.

TYLER, Geoffrey James Nevells Road Surgery, Letchworth SG6 4TS Tel: 01462 683051; 111 Norton Road, Letchworth SG6 1AG Tel: 686339 — MB ChB 1966 Leeds; DObst RCOG 1968. (Lond.) Socs: Primary Care Soc. in Rheum.; Local Med. Comm.; GP Writers Assn. Prev: Ho. Phys. St. James Univ. Hosp. Leeds; Ho. Surg. BromsGr. Gen. Hosp.; Ho. Off. (Obst.) Cuckfield Hosp.

TYLER, Geoffrey Norman Flat 12, Park Parade, Harrogate HG1 5NS Tel: 01423 67294 — LRCP LRCS 1942 Ed.; LRCP LRCS Ed. LRFPS Glas. 1942; DIH Eng. 1964. (Ed.)

TYLER, Jacqueline Ann 19 Baynes Close, St. Cleer, Liskeard PL14 5RT — MB BS 1981 Lond. (St. George's Hospital Medical School) Private GP Cornw. Prev: GP Harlow & Ware.

TYLER, Janet Barbara 31 Brooks Road, Wylde Green, Sutton Coldfield B72 1HP Tel: 0121 686 5869 — MB BS 1959 Lond.; MRCS Eng. LRCP Lond. 1959. (King's Coll. Hosp. Lond.) Med. Adviser to Adoption Panel Nch Midl.s. Socs: BMA; Fac. Family Plann. & Reproduc. Health Care. Prev: SCMO (Child Health and Family Plann.) N. Birm. Community Trust.

TYLER, Jean Elizabeth Bristol Disablement Services Centre, North Bristol NHS Trust, Westbury on Trym BS10 5NB; Mill Cottage, Kinver Grange, Ferney, Dursley GL11 5AB — MB ChB 1979 Bristol; MSc Lond. 1986; DA Lond. 1981. (Bristol Univ.) Prev: Dist. HIV Preven. Coordinator Pub. Health Med. Glos. Health; Sen. Regist. (Community Med.) NW Thames RHA; SHO (Geriat.) Guy's Hosp. Lond.

TYLER, John Edward The Surgery, Pound Close, Oldbury, Warley B68 8LZ Tel: 0121 552 1632 Fax: 0121 552 0848; 154 Lightwoods Hill, Smethwick B67 5ED Email: john.tyler@btinternet.com — MB ChB 1972 Birm.; MB ChB Birm. 1975; BSc (Hons., Med. Biochem.) Birm. 1972; DRCOG 1978. (Birm.) Med. Off. Lemförder UK, Darlaston & Birwelco Ltd. Socs: BMA. Prev: Trainee GP Kidderminster VTS; SHO Midl. Centre Neurosurg. & Neurol. Smethwick; Ho. Phys. Gen. Hosp. Birm.

TYLER, Lionel Edward, OStJ (retired) 2 Lower Prestwood Road, Wednesfield, Wolverhampton WV11 1JP Tel: 01902 735224 Email: lionel.tyler@talk21.com — MB ChB Birm. 1949; MD Birm. 1964; MRCS Eng. LRCP Lond. 1950; Hon. FRCGP 1974; FFOM RCP Lond. 1995, MFOM 1984. Prev: Chief Med. Off. GKN plc.

TYLER, Mark Andrew Jenner Health Centre, Turners Lane, Whittlesey, Peterborough PE7 1EJ Tel: 01733 203601 Fax: 01733 206210; Hamlet House, 2B High St, Benwick, March PE15 0XA Tel: 01354 677373 — MB ChB 1993 Manch.; DFFP.

TYLER, Mark John Cheam Family Practice, The Knoll, Parkside, Cheam, Sutton SM3 8BS Tel: 020 8770 2014 Fax: 020 8770 1864 — MB BS 1987 Lond.; MRCGP 1992; DCH RCP Lond. 1991. Prev: Trainee GP Henfield Health Centre; SHO (O & G) S.lands Hosp. Shoreham-by-Sea.

TYLER, Mr Michael Paul Howard 4 Eaton Gate, Northwood HA6 2NN — MB ChB 1988 Aberd.; FRCS Eng. 1992; ChM Aberd. 1998. Specialist Regist. (Plastic Surg.) Radcliffe Infirm. Oxf.

TYLER, Patricia Valerie St. Paul's Vicarage, Hawkstone Close, Newcastle ST5 1HT — MB ChB Manch. 1963.

TYLER, Philippa Anne Church Orchard, Church Lane, Kingston, Canterbury CT4 6HY — MB BS 1998 Lond.; BSc 1995. HO. (Surg / Orthop.) Whillington Hosp. Lond. Prev: Ho. Off. (Med.) N. Middlx. Hosp. Lond.

TYLER, Robert John The Health Centre, Water St., Port Talbot SA12 6HR Tel: 01639 891376 — MB BCh 1957 Wales.

TYLER, Roger Medhurst Woodnook Cottage, Woodnook Lane, Old Brampton, Chesterfield S42 7JF; Royal Hospital, Chesterfield S44 5BL Tel: 01246 277271 Fax: 01246 552620 — BM BCh 1972 Oxf.; MRCP (UK) 1976; DCH Eng. 1975. Cons. Paediat. Roy. Hosp. Chesterfield. Prev: Sen. Regist. (Paediat.) Qu. Mary's Hosp. Childr. Carshalton & St.; Geo. Hosp. Lond.; Regist. (Paediat.) Notts. AHA (T).

TYLER, Shantha Stephnie Arumaiammal Brimington Medical Centre, Foljambe Road, Brimington, Chesterfield S43 1DD Tel: 01246 220166 Fax: 01246 208221; 12 Rose Avenue, Calow, Chesterfield S44 5TH — MB BS 1973 Lond.; FP Certificate 1984; DCH Eng. 1975. (King's Coll. Hosp.) GP Princip.; Hon. Clin. Tutor Sheff. Med. Sch. Prev: Clin. Asst. (Psychogeriat.) N. Derbysh. HA; Trainee GP Nottm. VTS; SHO (Paediat.) Sydenham Childr. Hosp.

TYLER, Vera Jean (retired) Herons Lake, St. Giles-in-the-Wood, Torrington EX38 7HZ — MB ChB Liverp. 1957. Sen. Clin. Med. Off. N. Devon. Healthcare Trust. Prev: Med. Off. Milk Marketing Bd. Dartington Crystal & Savage Industs. Torrington.

TYLER, Xenia Margaret Department of Histopathology and Cytopathology, Norfolk and Norwich Hospital, Brunswick Road, Norwich NR1 3SR Tel: 01603 289897 Fax: 01603 286017; St Mary's House, 10 Crome Road, Norwich NR3 4RQ Tel: 01603 622158 — MB ChB 1984 Leic.; MRCPath 1991. Cons. Path. Norf. & Norwich Hosp. Socs: Assn. Clin. Pathol.; (Brit. Div.) Internat. Acad. Path. Prev: Cons. Path. Roy. Berks. Hosp. Reading; Sen. Regist. (Histopath.) N.ampton Gen. Hosp. & John Radcliffe Hosp. Oxf.; Regist. (Histopath.) Leicester Roy. Infirm. & Gen. Hosp.

TYM, Elizabeth Leigh 17 Humberstone Road, Cambridge CB4 1JD Tel: 01223 562610 Email: liz@liztym.freeserve.co.uk — MB ChB 1955 Sheff.; MA Camb. 1988; MRCS Eng. LRCP Lond. 1955; MRCPsych 1976; DPM Eng. 1975. Assoc. Lect. Camb. Univ; Cons. Psych. Rochford Hosps. S.end on Sea. Prev: Research Assoc. (Psychiat.) New Addenbrooke's Hosp. Camb.; Unit Med. Dir. N. Ryde Hosp. Sydney NSW, Austral.

TYMENS, Darren Craig 4 Lockerly Close, Lymington SO41 8ER — MB BChir 1993 Camb.

TYMMS, David James Royal Albert Edward Infirmary, Wigan Lane, Wigan WN1 2NN Tel: 01942 244000 — MB ChB 1975 Leeds; MD Leeds 1986; FRCP Lond. 1994. Cons. Phys. Roy. Albert Edwd. Infirm. Wigan. Prev: Sen. Regist. (Gen. Med., Diabetes & Endocrinol.) Bath & Soton.; Lect. (Med.) Gen. Infirm. Leeds; William Hewitt Research Fell. (Med.) Gen. Infirm. Leeds.

TYNAN, Michael John 5 Ravensdon Street, London SE11 4AQ — MD 1971 Lond.; MB BS 1958; FRCP Lond. 1983, M 1978. Joseph Levy Prof. Paediat. Cardiol. Guy's Hosp. Med. Sch. Lond.

TYNAN, Paul Francis King Street Surgery, 38 King Street, Lancaster LA1 1RE Tel: 01524 32294 Fax: 01524 848412 — MB BS 1984 Lond.

TYNE, Hilary Louise 25 Riversmead, Hoddesdon EN11 8DP — MB ChB 1998 Liverp.

TYRE, Nigel William Ferguson Mental Health Service for the Elderly, Hundens Lane, Darlington DL1 1 Tel: 01325 382639 — MB ChB 1976 Dundee.

TYRELL, Martin Scott (retired) Burwood, Burlings Lane, Knockholt, Sevenoaks TN14 7PF — MRCS Eng. LRCP Lond. 1956; MRCGP 1966; LDS RCS Eng. 1952; DObst RCOG 1958.

TYRER, Malcolm Dennis and Partners, The Medical Centre, Folly Lane, Bewsey, Warrington WA5 0LU Tel: 01925 417247 Fax: 01925 444319 Email: malcolm.tyrer@gp-n81056.nhs.uk; 26 Littlecote Gardens, Appleton, Warrington WA4 5DL Tel: 01925 601780 — MB ChB 1985 Leeds; MRCGP 1991; DFFP 1996; DCCH RCGP 1991; DRCOG 1990. (LEEDS) Princip., Gen. Pract., Folly La. MC, Warrington; UnderGrad. Tutor, Univ. of Liverp..; GP Trainer; Vocational Train. scheme organiser - Warrington. Prev: Maj. RAMC.

TYRER, Mervyn John Flat 15, Bracknell Gate, Frognal Lane, London NW3 7EA — MB BCh 1989 Witwatersrand.

TYRER, Professor Peter Julian Head of Department of Public Mental Health, Academic Department of Psychiatry, The Paterson Centre, 20 South Wharf Road, London W2 1PD Tel: 020 7886 1655 Fax: 020 7886 1994 — MB BChir 1966 Camb.; MD Camb. 1975, BA 1966; FRCP Lond. 1993; MRCP Lond. 1968; FFPHM RCP (UK) 1998; MFPHM RCP (UK) 1993; FRCPsych 1979, M 1973; DPM Eng. 1969. (St. Thos.) Prof. Community Psychiat. St. Mary's Hosp. Med. Sch. & Hon. Cons. Psychiat. NW Lond. Ment. Health NHS Trust. Prev: Cons. Psychiat. Notts. AHA (T); Sen. Lect. (Psychiat.) Univ. Soton.; Clin. Research Fell. MRC.

TYRER, Stephen Patrick Department of Psychiatry & Anaesthetics, Royal Victoria Infirmary, Newcastle upon Tyne NE1 4LP Tel: 0191 282 4412 Fax: 0191 282 0466 Email: s.p.tyrer@ncl.ac.uk; 3 Brandling Park, Newcastle upon Tyne NE2 4QA Tel: 0191 281 0886 Email: sptyrer@yahoo.com — MB BChir 1966 Camb.; MA Camb. 1982; LMCC 1978; FRCPsych 1987, M 1972; DPM Eng. 1969. (Camb. & Middlx.) Cons. Psychiat in Neurorehab Roy. Vict Infirm Necastle upon Tyne & Prudhoe Hosp., N.d; Chief Examr. Roy. Coll. of Psychiats. Lond.; Hon. Sen. Lect. Univ. Newc. Socs: Eur. Coll. Neuropsychopharm.; Roy. Soc. Med.; Fell. Canad. Coll. Neuropsychopharmacol. Prev: Vis. Prof. Dept. Psychiat. McMaster

TYRIE

Univ. Hamilton, Ontario, Canada; Sen. Lect. (Psychiat.) Univ. Newc.; Lect. (Psychiat.) Char. Cross Hosp. Lond.

TYRIE, Christine Mary Mental Health Unit, Royal Victoria Infirmary, Newcastle upon Tyne NE1 4LP Tel: 0191 282 5706 Fax: 0191 227 5281 — MB BS 1978 Newc.; MA Leeds 1993; MRCPsych 1983; DRCOG 1980. Cons. Psychiat. Roy. Vict. Infirm. Newc.; Private Pract.: Lindisfarne Suite, Nuffield Hosp., Clayton Rd., Newc. upon Tyne. Socs: BMA; MDU. Prev: Cons. Psychiat. Penrith Hosp.; Cons. Psychiat. Grimsby, S. Humberside; Cons. Psychiat. Tatchbury Mt. Hosp. Soton.

TYRRELL, Betty Moyra (retired) Ash Lodge, Dean Lane, Whiteparish, Salisbury SP5 2RN Tel: 01794 884352 — MB ChB 1949 Sheff. Prev: Clin. Med. Off. Wilts. AHA.

TYRRELL, Christopher Guy 6 The Armoury, London Road, Shrewsbury SY2 6PA Tel: 01743 235606 — MB ChB 1980 Manch.

TYRRELL, Christopher John Department of Radiotherapy & Oncology, Derriford Hospital, Plymouth PL6 8DH Tel: 01752 763995 Fax: 01752 763997; Gem Cottage, Grenofen, Tavistock PL19 9EP — MB ChB (Hons.) Bristol 1970; FRCP Lond. 1991; MRCP (UK) 1972; FRCR (Ther.) 1975. Cons. Clin. Oncol. Plymouth & Cornw. HA's; Hon. Sen. Lect. Univ. Plymouth Postgrad. Med. Sch. Prev: Lect. & Regist. (Radiother.) Roy. Marsden Hosp.; Ho. Phys. & Ho. Surg. Bristol Roy. Infirm.; Ho. Phys. Whittington Hosp. Lond.

TYRRELL, David Arthur John, CBE (retired) Ash Lodge, Dean Lane, Whiteparish, Salisbury SP5 2RN Tel: 01794 884352 Fax: 01794 884352 — MB ChB (Hons.) Sheff. 1948; FRS 1970; MD (Distinc.) Sheff. 1953; Hon. DSc Sheff. 1979; DM (Hon.) Soton. 1990; FRCP Lond. 1965, M 1949; FRCPath 1971, M 1964. Prev: Dir. Common Cold Unit Salisbury.

TYRRELL, Graham Robert Shere Surgery and Dispensary, Gomshall Lane, Shere, Guildford GU5 9DR Tel: 01486 202066 Fax: 01486 202761; Orchard Leigh, Combe Lane, Shere, Guildford GU5 9JD Tel: 01483 203332 — MB BS 1974 Lond.; DObst RCOG 1976. (St George's Medical School London)

TYRRELL, Jennifer Clare Children's Centre, Royal United Hospital, Bath BA1 3NG Tel: 01225 824217 Fax: 01225 824212 Email: jennifer.tyrrell@ruh-bath.swest.nhs.uk — MB BS 1977 Lond.; MA Oxf. 1978; DM Nottm. 1991; FRCP Lond. 1996; MRCP (UK) 1981; DCH Eng. 1980. (Westm.) Cons. Paediat. Roy. United Hosp. Bath. Socs: Roy. Coll. Paediat. & Child Health. Prev: Sen. Regist. (Paediat.) John Radcliffe Hosp. Oxf.

TYRRELL, Judith Mary Highfield, 1 Chalgrove Road, Sutton SM2 5JT Tel: 020 8643 3844 — MB BCh BAO 1973 Dub.; MRCP (UK) 1980; DCH NUI 1975; DObst RCOG 1975. Clin. Asst. St. Helier Hosp. Carshalton. Prev: Regist. (Med.) Harefield Hosp. Uxbridge; SHO (Med.) Basingstoke Dist. Hosp.; Ho. Phys. & Ho. Surg. Adelaide Hosp. Dub.

TYRRELL, Malcolm Franklin (retired) Broken Hill, Miles Lane, Cobham KT11 2EA Tel: 01932 862267 — MB BS 1961 Lond.; MRCS Eng. LRCP Lond. 1961; FRCA 1966; DA Eng. 1963. Prev: Cons. Anaesth. W.m. Hosp. Lond. & Qu. Mary's Univ. Hosp. Roehampton.

TYRRELL, Nicolette Marie St Andrews Medical Centre, 30 Russell Street, Eccles, Manchester M30 0NU Tel: 0161 707 5500 Fax: 0161 787 9159 — MB ChB 1982 Manch.; MRCGP 1986; DRCOG 1986. (Manch.) Single handed Gen. Practitioner. Prev: SHO (O & G) Hope Hosp. Salford.

TYRRELL, Philippa Jane Department of Geriatric Medicine, Hope Hospital, Eccles Old Road, Salford M6 8HD Tel: 0161 787 5586 Fax: 0161 787 5586 Email: ptyrrell@fs1.ho.man.ac.uk; 4 Fulshaw Avenue, Wilmslow SK9 5JA Tel: 01625 523711 — MB BS 1981 Lond.; MA Camb. 1982; MD Lond. 1992; MRCP (UK) 1985; FRCP 2000. Med. Dir. Stroke Servs. Hope Hosp. Salford. Prev: Sen. Regist. (c/o Elderly) Char. Cross Hosp. Lond.; Research Regist. MRC Cyclotron Unit Hammersmith Hosp. Lond.; Regist. (Med.) St. Mary's Hosp. Lond.

TYRRELL, Prudencia Norah Mary 12 Alloe Brook, Montford Bridge, Shrewsbury SY4 1DA — MB BCh BAO 1984 Dub.; MRCPI 1987; FRCR 1991. Cons. Radiol. Robt. Jones & Agnes Hunt Orthop. & Dist. Hosp. NHS Trust OsW.ry. Prev: Sen. Regist. (Radiol.) W. Midl.; Regist. (Radiol.) W. Midl.; Regist. (Med.) Meath Hosp. Dub.

TYRRELL, Richard Francis Eastney Health Centre, Highland Road, Southsea PO4 9HU Fax: 023 9273 4900 — MB BS 1979 Lond.; MRCS Eng. LRCP Lond. 1978. (Charing Cross) Hon. Lect. (Gen. Pract.) Univ. Soton.

TYRRELL, Simon Nicholas 4 Redland Drive, Kirk Ella, Hull HU10 7UZ — MD 1993 Leeds; MB ChB Manch. 1980; MRCOG 1985; T(OG) 1991. Cons. O & G Hull Matern. Hosp. Socs: N. Eng. Obst. & Gyn. Soc.; Brit. Med. Ultrasound Soc. Prev: Lect. & Regist. (O & G) St. Jas. Hosp. Leeds; SHO (O & G) Wythenshawe Hosp. Manch.

TYRYNIS-THOMAS, Sian Angharad Birchwood Surgery, North Walsham NR28 0BQ; Old Manor Farm House, The Hill, Swanton Abbott, Norwich NR10 5EA Tel: 01692 538224 Fax: 01692 538224 — MB BS 1987 Lond.

TYSOE, Julia Margaret c/o Major A.R. Tysoe RLC, 24 Reg RLC BFPO 39 — MB ChB 1992 Birm.

TYSON, Anthony John Burnside House, Beamish, Stanley DH9 0RR — MB BS 1977 Newc.; MRCGP 1981.

TYSON, Carol Joan Windsor Cottages, 62 The Street, Blundeston, Lowestoft NR32 5AQ — MB BS 1983 Lond.; DCH RCP Lond. 1993. Assoc. Specialist Jas. Paget Hosp. Gt. Yarmouth. Socs: BPA. Prev: Regist. (Paediat.) Stoke Mandeville Hosp. Aylesbury; Clin. Med. Off. (Paediat.) Lond.; Regist. (Paediat.) Dunedin Hosp., NZ.

TYSON, Claudine Margaret (retired) Otterford Mill, Otterford, Chard TA20 3QL — MB ChB 1957 Birm.; DObst RCOG 1959.

TYSON, Peggy Olive Mary (retired) Millbeck Place, Millbeck, Keswick CA12 4PS Tel: 017681 73278 — MRCS Eng. LRCP Lond. 1941; DCH Eng. 1944.

TYSON, Victor Claud Henry (retired) Highfield, Hill Lane, Hathersage, Hope Valley S32 1AY Tel: 01433 650232 — MB ChB Sheff. 1948. Prev: Adjudicating Med. Auth. DHSS Sheff. & Barnsley.

TYSZCZUK, Lidia Teresa 24B Broadlands Road, London N6 4AG Tel: 020 8341 4357 — MB BS 1989 Lond.; MRCP 1993. (Char. Cross & Westm. Med. Sch.)

TYTHERLEIGH, Mr Matthew Grosvenor 3 Jubilee Cottages, Cox Green Lane, Maidenhead SL6 3EX Tel: 01628 639691 Email: matthew.tytherleigh@medicalpages.net — MB BS 1992 Lond.; FRCS Eng. 1996. (St. Bart. Hosp. Lond.) Specialist Regist. (Gen. Surg.) Oxf. Deanery.

TYTHERLEIGH-STRONG, Graham Michael The Lantern House, Burgess Wood Road, Beaconsfield HP9 1EH — MB BS 1990 Lond.

TYTLER, Jennifer Ann 5 Devisdale Court, Altrincham WA14 2AU — MB ChB 1977 Birm.; FFA RCS Eng. 1983; DRCOG 1980; DCH 1980.

TZABAR, Yoav Haim Cumberland Infirmary, Newtown Rd, Carlisle CA2 7HY Tel: 01228 523444 — MB ChB 1984 Dundee; FRCA 1993; DA (UK) 1990. Cons.(Anaest.) Cumbld. Infirm. Carlisle. Prev: Sen. Regist. (Anaesth.) Univ. Wales Coll. Med. Cardiff; Med. Off. Brit. Antartic Survey; Regist. (Anaesth.) Aberd. Roy. Hosp.

TZIFA, Constantina Doctor's Residence, Wordsley Hospital, Stream Road, Stourbridge DY8 5QX — Ptychio Iatrikes 1991 Thessalonika.

TZOULIADIS, Vissarion (retired) 129A Hadham Road, Bishop's Stortford CM23 2QD Tel: 01279 656895 — Ptychio Iatrikes Athens 1953; DMRD Eng. 1960. Prev: Cons. Radiol. Herts. & Essex Gen. Hosp. Bishop's Stortford & P.ss Alexandra Hosp. Harlow.

U-KING-IM, Jean Marie Kim Sin Flat E, Ashtree House, 3 Claremont Road, Newcastle upon Tyne NE2 4AN — MB BS 1998 Newc.

UBEROI, Raman X-Ray Department, Gateshead NHS Trust, Queen Elizabeth Hospital, Sherrif Hill, Gateshead NE9 6SX — MB BChir 1985 Camb.; BMSc (Path.) Dunde1983; MRCP (UK) 1988; FRCR 1992. Cons. Radiol. Gateshead NHS Trust; Hon. Sen. Lect. Univ. Newc. Socs: Med. Protec. Soc. Prev: SHO (Med., Rheum. & Geriat.) Treliske Hosp. Truro; SHO (A & E) Roy. Vict. Infirm. Newc.; Ho. Off. (Med.) Addenbrooke's Hosp. Camb.

UBEROY, Vijayinder Kumar 30 Dorian Road, Hornchurch RM12 4AN — MB BS 1971 Poona; DTCD Delhi 1972. (Armed Forces Med. Coll. Poona) SHO Ipswich Hosp. (Foxhall Wing).

UBHAYAKAR, Gaurang Narayan 15 Elmes Drive, Southampton SO15 4PH; 15 Elmes Drive, Regents Park, Southampton SO15 4PH — BM 1988 Soton. SHO (Med.) Qu. Alexandra Hosp. Portsmouth.

UBHI, Baljinder Singh 95 Heworth Village, York YO31 1AN Email: drtim@compuserve.com — MB ChB 1992 Leeds; BSc (Hons.) 1987; MRCP 1997. (Leeds) Lect. (Paediat. Child Heath) St. Jas. Univ. Hosp. Leeds.

UBHI, Mr Charanjeit Singh University Hospital, Queen's Medical Centre, Nottingham NG7 2UH Tel: 0115 924 9924; 27 Melton Gardens, Edwalton, Nottingham NG12 4BJ — MB ChB 1977 Manch.; MD Manch. 1987; FRCS Eng. 1983; FRCS Ed. 1982. Cons. Gen. Surg. Univ. Hosp. Nottm. Socs: Brit. Assn. of Endocrine Surgs.; Assn. ooSurg.s of GB & NI. Prev: Lect. (Surg.) St. Jas. Hosp. Leeds; Tutor Dept. Surg. St. Jas. Hosp. Leeds; Regist. (Gen. Surg.) Univ. Hosp. Qu. Med. Centre Nottm.

UBHI, Satpaul Rectory Lodge, Church View, Patrington, Hull HU12 0SQ — MB ChB 1990 Sheff.; DRCOG 1993; DCH RCP Lond. 1992.

UBHI, Mr Sukhbir Singh Leicester Royal Infirmary, Infirmary Square, Leicester LE1 5WW Tel: 0116 254 1414 Fax: 0116 258 6083 Email: sukhbir.ubhl@uhl-tr.nhs.uk; 22 Old Charity Farm, Stoughton, Leicester LE2 2EX — MB ChB 1983 Leic.; MD Leic. 1994; FRCS Eng. 1989; FRCS Ed. 1988. (Leicester) Cons. Gen. Surg., Leicester Roy. Infirm., Leicester; Cons. Gen. Surg. Leicester Roy. Infirm. Prev: Research Fell. (Surg.) Univ. Leicester; Regist. (Surg.) Soton. & Salisbury.; Higher Surg. Trainee Leicester Hosps.

UBHI, Verjinderpal Singh 75 Westway, London SW20 9LT Tel: 020 8540 5553 — MB BS 1980 Lond.; MRCGP 1984; DRCOG 1984; DCH RCP Lond. 1983. (St. Bart.) Prev: Trainee GP St. Bart./Hackney Hosps. VTS; Ho. Surg. St. Bart. Hosp. Lond.; Ho. Phys. P. of Wales Hosp. Lond.

***UBOGU, Emamoke Eromedoghene** Email: e-ubogu@doctors.org.uk; Email: e-ubogu@doctors.org.uk — MB ChB 1998 Birm.; DRCOG 2001.

***UBOGU, Eroboghene Ekamereno** Imperial College of Science Technology, Wilson House, 38-76 Sussex Gardens, London W2 1UF — MB BS 1998 Lond.; MB BS Lond 1998.

UDAL, Michael Stannard Gosbury Hill Health Centre, Orchard Gardens, Chessington KT9 1AG Tel: 020 8397 2142 Fax: 020 8974 2717; 85 Common Road, Claygate, Esher KT10 0HU Tel: 01372 62329 — BM BCh 1968 Oxf.; MRCGP 1982; DCH Eng. 1971; DObst RCOG 1970; FRCGP 1996. (Oxford Univ/Kings Coll Lond) Prev: Ho. Off. (Med. Surg. & O & G) Kings Coll. Hosp. Lond.; Ho. Off. (Paediat.) FarnBoro. Hosp., Kent.

UDDIN, Farakh Javed 107 Grassington Road, Nottingham NG8 3PE — MB ChB 1998 Leeds; BSc (Hons) Leeds 1995.

UDDIN, Mr Jimmy Mohamed 59 Rowfant Road, London SW17 7AP — BChir 1991 Camb.; MA Camb. 1991, BChir 1991; FRCOphth 1995. (Cambridge University) Specialist Regist. E. Anglia, Norf. & Norwich Hosp. Socs: AAD (Amer. Acad. of Opthinology). Prev: SHO (Ophth. & Plastics) Gt. Ormond St. Hosp. Lond.

UDDIN, Kutub 21 Rampart Street, London E1 2LA — MB BS 1998 Lond.

UDDIN, Md Mashuk 73 Disraeli Road, London E7 9JU — MRCS Eng. LRCP Lond. 1993.

UDDIN, Shahana 37 Freemantle Road, Barkingside, Ilford IG6 2BD — MB BS 1996 Lond.

UDEJIOFO, Susan Frances 56 Louth Road, Sheffield S11 7AW; 484 Manchester Road, Sheffield S10 5PN — MB ChB 1987 Sheff.; MRCGP 1991.

UDEN, John Anthony Bampton Surgery, Landells, Bampton, Oxford OX18 2LJ — MB BS 1985 Lond.

UDEN, Stephen Central Research, Pfizer Ltd., Sandwich CT13 9NJ Tel: 01304 616161 Fax: 01304 618323; Maxwell House, 103 Old Dover Road, Canterbury CT1 3PG — MB BS 1982 Lond.; BSc (Hons.) Lond. 1979; MRCP (UK) 1985; MFPM RCP (UK) 1993. (St. Thos.) Dir. Pfizer Centr. Research. Socs: BMA. Prev: Research Regist. Manch. Roy. Infirm.; SHO (Gen. Med. & Haemat.) Qu. Mary's Hosp. Sidcup; SHO (Med.) Manch. Roy. Infirm.

UDENKWO, George 84 Millicent Fawcett Court, Pembury Road, London N17 6SX — MB BCh BAO 1964 NUI.

***UDENZE, Christopher Chukwuekelua** NDU Surgery, St Anns Health Centre, St Anns, Well Road, Nottingham NG3 3PX Tel: 0115 950 5455 Fax: 0155 958 8493 — MB BS 1986 Lond.

UDESHI, Umesh Laxmidas Kidderminster Hospital, Bewdley Road, Kidderminster DY11 6RJ Tel: 01562 823424 Fax: 01562 513014 — MB BCh 1979 Wales; FRCR 1986. Cons. Radiol. Worcs. Acute Hosps. NHS Trust. Socs: Brit. Inst. Radiol. & Brit. Med. Ultrasound Soc.; Brit. Soc. Interven. Radiol. Prev: Sen. Regist. & Regist. (Radiol.) W. Midl. RHA; SHO (Med.) Bridgend Gen. Hosp.

UDEZUE, Emmanuel Olisaebuka Saudi Arabian Oil Company, Medical Services Organisation, Aramco Box. 7490, Udhailiyah 31311, Saudi Arabia Tel: 00 966 3 577 8687 Fax: 00 966 3 577 2844 Email: manevans@hotmail.com, manevans@yahoo.com; 3A Winston Avenue, Branksome, Poole BH12 1PA Tel: 01202 718460 — MB BS 1973 Ibadan; MSc (Clin. Trop. Med.) Lond. 1982; MRCPI 1982, FRCPI 1998; FACTM 1982; DHMSA Soc. Apoth, Lond. 1978. (University of Ibadan Medical School, Nigeria) Head of Internal Med., Aramco Al Hasa Med. Center, Saudi Arabia. Socs: Fell. Roy. Soc. Trop. Med. & Hyg.; Fell. Fac. Hist. Med. & Pharmacy Soc. Apoth.; Brit. Diabetic Assn. Prev: Cons. Phys. Aramco Med. Serv.s, S. Arabia; Cons. Phys. & Lect. (Pharmacol. & Therap.) Univ. Nigeria & Teachg. Hosp. Enugh, Nigeria; Regist. (Med.) Roy. Lond. Hosp., Luton & Dunstable & St. Mary's Hosps. Luton.

UDO, Ededet Akpan 112 Jubilee Avenue, Romford RM7 9LT — MB BS 1981 Lagos; MRCOG 1990.

UDOEYOP, Mr Udoeyop Walter 24 Spring Shaw Road, Orpington BR5 2RH — MB BS Ibadan 1980; FRCS Ed. 1994.

UDOKANG, Mariel Jane Bournbrook Medical Practice, 480 Bristol Road, Selly Oak, Birmingham B29 6BD Tel: 0121 472 0129 — MB ChB 1974 Birm.; MRCP (UK) 1993; MRCGP 1978; T(GP) 1991.

UDUKU, Ngozi Ola-Adetokunbo New Surgery, 2 Morley Road, London SE13 6DQ Tel: 020 8297 7999 Fax: 020 8297 7880 — MB ChB 1984 Leic.; BSc (Hons.) Leic. 1982, MB ChB 1984; MRCGP 1994; DRCOG 1988. (Leicester) Med. Examr. Metrop. Police; GP Tutor Kings Coll. Sch. Med. & Dent. Socs: African & Caribbean Med. Soc.

UDWADIA, Zarir 20 Cranford Lodge, Victoria Drive, London SW19 6HH — MB BS 1985 Bombay; MRCP (UK) 1988.

UDWIN, Edgar Leon (retired) 45 Thornbury Court, 36 Chepstow Villas, London W11 2RE — MB BCh 1942 Witwatersrand; FRCPsych 1981; DPM Lond. 1951. Prev: Med. Dir. BRd.moor Hosp.

UEBERHORST, Anne Nevill Hall Hospital, Abergavenny NP7 7EG — State Exam Med. Bonn 1991.

UFF, Jeremy Stephen Department Clinical Pathology, Gloucester Royal Infirmary, Great Western Road, Gloucester GL1 3NN — MB BChir 1971 Camb.; MA, MB Camb. 1971, BChir 1970; MRCP (UK) 1972; MRCPath 1976. Cons. Gloucestershire Roy. Hosp. Gloucester. Prev: Sen. Lect. St. Geo. Hosp. Med. Sch. Lond.; Sen. Regist. (Histopath.) Hammersmith Hosp. Lond.; SHO (Med.) Lond. Hosp.

UFODIAMA, Bertram Enechukwu 20 Meadowcroft Road, Outwood, Wakefield WF1 3TA Tel: 01924 871975 — MB BS 1980 Nigeria; MRCP (UK) 1994. Staff Grade Paediat. Pinderfields Gen. Hosp. Wakefield. Socs: MRCPCH.

UGARGOL, Chandrashekar Prabhakar Prospect House Medical Centre, 84 Orrell Road, Orrell, Wigan WN5 8HA Tel: 01942 222321 Fax: 01942 620327 — MB BS 1966 Bombay.

UGBOMA, Ike Anthony Francis 24 Monarch Court, Lyttelton Road, London N2 0RA — MB BS 1996 Lond.

UGBOMA, Koyi James 3 Mount Drive, Wembley Park, Wembley HA9 9ED — BM BCh 1976 Nigeria; MSc (Clin. Nuclear Med.) Lond. 1985; LMSSA Lond. 1984.

UGGIAS, Barbara Flat7, Block 2, Residences, Stafford District General Hospital, Weston Road, Stafford ST16 3SA; 15 Lower Oxford Road, Newcastle ST5 0PB — State Exam 1989 Sassari.

UGLOW, Mr Michael George Queen Alexandra Hospital, Cosham, Portsmouth PO6 3LY Tel: 02392 286864 Fax: 02392 286570 Email: mgu@muglow.freeserve.co.uk; Gainsborough House, Winchester, Boorley Green, Southampton SO32 2DH Tel: 01489 788329 — MB BS 1989 Lond.; FRCS Eng. 1993; FRCS (Tr & Orth) 1998. (St Geo. Hosp. Lond.) Cons. Trauma & Orthopaedic Surg. Portsmouth; Ingham Fell., The New Childrs. Hosp. Sydney Australia. Socs: Brit. Orthopaedic Trainees Assoc., Pres.., 98/99; Brit. Orthopaedic Foot Surg. Soc.; Brit. Soc. Childr.'s Orthopaedic Surg. Prev: Regist. (Orthop.) Portsmouth; Regist. (Orthop.) Soton. Gen. Hosp.; Regist. (Orthop.) Basingstoke.

UGLOW, Paul Andrew 3 Bramhall Park Grove, Bramhall, Stockport SK7 3PS; 10 Galloway Drive, Kennington, Ashford TN25 4QQ — MB BS 1998 Lond.; MB BS Lond 1998.

***UGOCHUKWU, Uchechukwu Ogugua** 77A Stratford Road, London E13 0JN — LRCP LRCS LRCPS 1998 Ed., Glas.

UGOJI, Uchechi Ugochukwu 51 Brookfield Avenue, Loughborough LE11 3LN — MB ChB 1963 Glas.; FRCP Glas. 1992; FRCPC 1972; MRCP (UK) 1969.

UGWU

UGWU, Clement Nwokolo Halton General Hospital, Runcorn WA7 2DA Tel: 01928 714567 Fax: 01928 715666 — MD 1971 Kharkov; MD (Hons.) Kharkov Med. Inst. 1971; MRCPI 1979; MRCS Eng. LRCP Lond. 1975; FRCPI. (Kharkov Med. Inst.) Cons. Phys. (Geriat. Med.) Halton Health Dist. Prev: Sen. Regist. (Geriat. Med.) N. Tees Gen. Hosp. Stockton-on-Tees; Regist. (Med.) N. Lonsdale Hosp. Barrow-in-Furness; Ho. Off. (Gen. Surg.) Oldham & Dist. Gen. Hosp.

UGWUMADU, Augustine Nnamdi Department of Obstetrics & Gynaecology, St. Georges Hospital, Blackshaw Road, London SW17 0QT Tel: 020 86721255 Ext: 0506 Fax: 020 8725 0078 Email: augwumad@sghms.ac.uk; Flat 4, 4 Homefield Road, Wimbledon Village, London SW19 4QE Tel: 020 89460473 — MB BS 1986 Lagos; MRCOG 1994. (Univ. Lagos Coll. Med., Nigeria) Cons. Obst. & Gynaecoogist & Hon. Sen. :ecturer St. Geo.s Hosptial, Lond. Prev: Regist. (O & G) St Peter's Hosp. Chertsey; Regist. (O & G) St. Helier Hosp. Carshalton & Qu. Mary's Hosp. Roehampton; SNR. Regist. (O&G) St. Geo.s Hosp. 2000-2001.

UHAMA, Joseph Nnajiuba c/o Dr C Ezechukwu, 5 Cobland Road, London SE12 9SD — State DMS 1994 Pavia.

UHEBA, Mr Mokhtar Ali 35 Gilbert Road, Camberley GU16 7RD — MB BCh 1981 Al Fatah, Libya; FRCS Glas. 1990.

UHEGWU, Ndubuisi 28 Todds Walk, Andover Est., London N7 7RB — MB BS 1982 Nigeria.

UHR DELIA, John Anthony 8 Grove Lodge, 9-11 Hampstead Lane, London N6 4RT — MB BS 1997 Lond.

UINGS, Anne Elizabeth 9 Crich Circle, Littleover, Derby DE23 6DS Tel: 01332 46888 — MB ChB 1977 Sheff.

UITENBOSCH, Martin The Surgery, Denmark Street, Darlington DL3 0PD Tel: 01325 460731 Fax: 01325 362183 — Artsexamen 1987 Amsterdam. (Amsterdam) GP Darlington, Co. Durh.

UKACHI-LOIS, Justice Onyemuche 11 Swingate Close, Lordswood, Chatham ME5 8RH — MB BS 1986 Lond.

UKACHUKWU, Ijeoma 80 Tanfield Avenue, Neasden, London NW2 7RT Tel: 020 8452 9051 Email: five7foot@hotmail.com — MB BS 1994 Lond.; BSc, Hons, (Lond.) 1992; DRCOG 1996; DFFP 1998; MRCGP 1998 - RCGP. (St Mary's Paddington) GP Asst., Ealing Pk. Health Centre, Lond. Socs: BMA.

UKRA, Mr Hani Abdul Hameed Rashid 51 Friars Place Lane, London W3 7AQ Tel: 020 8248 9682 — MB ChB 1972 Baghdad; LRCP LRCS Ed. LRCPS Glas. 1985; FRCS Glas. 1983. (Univ. Baghdad) Prev: Cons. Orthop. & Trauma Surg. Al-Hammadi Hosp. Olaya, Riyadh, Saudi Arabia; Cons. Orthop. Salalah, Oman.

UL HAQ, Ikram 24 Player Green, Deer Park, Livingston EH54 8RZ; 9 Summerhill Garden, Leeds LS8 2EL Tel: 0113 22 56890 — MB BS 1984 Pubjab. Staff Grade, A&E, Leeds Gen. Infirm., Leeds. Socs: MDU.

ULAHANNAN, Thomas John Dept of Diabetes & Endocrinology, Radcliffe Infirmary, Oxford OX2 6HE Tel: 01865 224523 Fax: 01865 224652 Email: thomasu@radius.jr2.ox.ac.uk; 14 Hastoe Grange, Oxford OX3 7TF — MB ChB 1991 Leeds; BSc (Hons.) Med. Microbiol. Leeds 1988; MRCP (UK) 1994. Sen. Regist. (Diabetes & Endocrinol.) Radcliffe Infirm. Oxf. Socs: BMA; Soc. For Endocrinol.; BDA. Prev: Sen. Regist. (Gen. Med.) John Radcliffe Hosp. Oxf.; Regist. (Med.) Leicester Roy. Infirm. & Kettering Gen. Hosp.

ULLAH, Mr Aamer Saeed 2 Cutler Close, Marton-in-Cleveland, Middlesbrough TS7 8QD — MB BS 1993 Lond.; FRCS 1998. (Charing Cross & Westminster)

ULLAH, Habib 51 Sandbeds Road, Pellon, Halifax HX2 0QL Tel: 01422 330860; 18 Gatesgarth Crescent, Lindley, Huddersfield HD3 3LG Tel: 01484 460349 — MB ChB 1978 Bristol. (Bristol) Police Surg. Huddersfield (W. Yorks. Police). Socs: Roy. Coll. of Gen. Practitioners (Assoc.); Brit. Soc. for Heart Failure; Primary Care Cardiovasc. Soc.

ULLAH, Hadayat Patel and Partners, 4 Bedford Street, Bletchley, Milton Keynes MK2 2TX Tel: 01908 377101 Fax: 01908 645903 — MB ChB 1990 Glas.

ULLAH, Khan Mohmad Shafi 34 Marquis Road, London N4 3AP — MB BS 1963 Dacca.

ULLAH, Mahmood Iqbal 14 Galston Avenue, Newton Mearns, Glasgow G77 5SF — MB ChB 1972 Glas.; FRCP Glas. 1988; MRCP (UK) 1977; T(M) 1991; DCH RCPS Glas. 1976; DObst. RCOG 1974. Cons. Phys. Qu.s Pk. Clinic. Prev: Chairm. Med. Divis. Al Shaty Teachg. Hosp., Jeddah; Cons. Phys. Heathfield Hosp. Ayr; Lect. (Med.) Middlx. Hosp.

ULLAH, Mr Ramzan Mohammed 25 Hampton Manor, Belfast BT7 3EL — MB BCh BAO 1989 Belf.; FRCS Ed. 1993.

ULLAH, Saif 49 Cranleigh Gardens, Luton LU3 1LS — MB BS 1982 Karachi.

ULLAH, Mr Shakir 29 Broadlands, Shann Park, Keighley BD20 6HX — MB BS 1979 Peshawar; FRCS Ed. 1989.

ULLEGADDI, Ashok Fakirappa Royal Shrewsbury Hospital, Shelton, Shrewsbury SY3 8DN Tel: 01743 231122; 58 Primrose Drive, Sutton Park, Shrewsbury SY3 7TP — MB BS 1968 Mysore; DPM RCPSI 1987. (Kasturba Med. Coll. Manipal) Assoc. Specialist (Psychiat.) Shrops. HA.

ULLEGADDI, Rajesh 58 Primrose Drive, Shrewsbury SY3 7TP Tel: 01743 245826 — MB ChB 1994 Aberd. SHO (Gen. Med.) Walsgrave Hosp. Coventry.

ULLIOTT, Elaine Elizabeth Jane Huthwaite Health Centre, New Street, Huthwaite, Sutton-in-Ashfield NG17 2LR Tel: 01623 513147 Fax: 01623 515574; Homeston Farm, 10 Alfreton Road, Newton, Alfreton DE55 5TP — MB ChB 1980 Sheff.; CPDC 2001 Warwick; DRCOG 1983.

ULLYATT, Kim Joy O'Grady-Peyton International, Centre Ct., 1301 Stratford Road, Hall Green, Birmingham B28 9HH — MB ChB 1995 Orange Free State.

ULYATT, The Hon. Mrs Frances Margaret (retired) 8 Market Place, Tetbury GL8 8DA Tel: 01666 504009 — MB BS Lond. 1943; FFA RCS Eng. 1957; DA Eng. 1948. Prev: Cons. Anaesth. Croydon & Warlingham Hosp. Gp.

ULYETT, Ian Hartsholme, Main Road, Asby, Workington CA14 4RT — MB ChB 1977 Sheff.; FFA RCS Eng. 1982. Cons. (Anaesth.) W. Cumbld. Hosp. Socs: Assn. Anaesths. Prev: Sen. Regist. (Anaesth.) N. W.. RHA; Regist. (Anaesth.) Sheff. AHA; Regist. (Anaesth.) Oldham AHA.

UMACHANDRAN, Velaitham 10 Nightingale Way, London E6 5JR — MB BS 1976 Sri Lanka; MRCP (UK) 1983.

UMAPATHEE, P Bentley Health Centre, Askern Road, Bentley, Doncaster DN5 0JX Tel: 01302 874416 Fax: 01302 875820 — MRCS Eng. LRCP Puvanasundaram; MB BS 1975 Sri Lanka; MB BS 1975 Sri Lanka.

UMAPATHY, Arumugam Bath Road Surgery, 450 Bath Road, Cippenham, Slough SL1 6BB Tel: 01628 602564 Fax: 01628 660122 — MB BS 1972 Ceylon; MB BS 1972 Ceylon.

UMAPATHY, Kandasamy 82A Whitchurch Road, Heath, Cardiff CF14 3LX — MB BS 1986 Colombo, Sri Lanka; MRCP (UK) 1994.

UMAR, Mr Abdulqadir 31 Sneckyeat Court, Hensingham, Whitehaven CA28 8PG; 31 Sneckyeat Court, Hensingham, Whitehaven CA28 8PG — MB BS 1979 Ahmadu Bello, Nigeria; FRCS Ed. 1990. Specialist Regist., Roy. Vict. Infirm., Newc. Socs: Pancreatic Club; Affil. Mem. Assn. of Surgs. of GB & Ire; BMA. Prev: Specialist Regist. Freeman Hosp. Newc.; Specialist Regist. (Surg.) W. Cumbld. Hosp. Whitehaven; Regist. (Surg.) Wansbeck Hosp.

UMARIA, Nina 5A Wynford Road, London N1 9QN — MB BS 1992 Lond.

UMARJI, Shamim Ismail Mohamed 3 Osborne Road, Clifton, Bristol BS8 2HA — BM BCh 1996 Oxf. (Oxford) SHO, Surgic. Rothation, Bristol, Roy. Infirm. Socs: Oriel Coll. Med. Soc. Oxf. Prev: A & E, St Thomas's Hosp. Lond.

UMBRICH, Paul 4 Heron Way, Langton Road, Norton, Malton YO17 9AX — MB ChB 1991 Manch.

UMEBUANI, V C Edgworth Medical Centre, 354 Bolton Road, Turton, Bolton BL7 0DU Tel: 01204 852226 — MB ChB 1977 Nigeria; MB ChB 1977 Nigeria.

UMEH, Chukwuemeka Frederick 1 Perivale Drive, Strawberry Fields, Oldham OL8 2JJ — MB BS 1986 Nigeria; MB BS U. Nigeria 1986; MRCP (UK) 1993.

UMERAH, Francis Ngozi The Children's Centre, 70 Walker St., Hull HU3 2HE Tel: 01482 221261 Fax: 01482 617606; 737 Beverley Road, Hull HU6 7ES Tel: 01482 859652 — MB BS 1983 Lagos; MRCP (UK) 1995; DCH RCP Lond. 1995. Cons. Paediat. Hull & E. Riding Community Health NHS Trust Hull; Cons. Paediat., Hull Roy. Infirm., Anlaby Rd., Hull. Prev: Clin. Med. Off. (Child Health) Community & Priority Servs. NHS Trust Barnsley.

UMESH, Shivanna 15 Cormorant Avenue, Houston, Johnstone PA6 7LG Tel: 01505 613462 — MB BS 1974 Mysore; LRCP LRCS Ed. LRCPS Glas. 1983; DCCH RCP Ed. 1984; DCH RCPS Glas. 1983; DCH RCPSI 1980. SCMO (Hearing Impairment) Johnstone Health Centre; Med. Pract. Roy. Hosp. Sick Childr. Glas. Socs: Brit. Assn. Community Drs in Audiol. Prev: Clin. Med. Off. Linwood Health Centre Renfrewsh.

UMNUS, Lutz 18 Clarence Road, Warrington WA4 2PQ Fax: 01925 486965 — State Exam Med 1992 Rostock. GP Warrington. Socs: MDU.

UMOREN, Denis Mbong Ikpe Lodge, Linden Road, Yeovil BA20 2BH — MB BS 1979 Lagos; MRCOG 1988. (Coll. Of Med. Univ. of Lagos.) Assoc. Specialist, O & G, Yeovil Dist. Hosp., Yeovil, Som.. Socs: Brit. Soc. for Colposcopy & Cervical Path..

UMPLEBY, Mr Henry Clark Department Surgery, Royal United Hospital, Combe Park, Bath BA1 3NG Tel: 01225 824542 Fax: 01225 824542 — MB ChB 1975 Bristol; FRCS Eng. 1980; T(S) 1991. Cons. Gen. Surg. Roy. United Hosp. Bath. Socs: RCS (Eng.); Assn Surg.; Brit. Assn. Surg. Oncol. Prev: Wellcome Surgic. Research Fell. 1982; Lect. Univ. Soton. 1984-87.

UMPLEBY, Madeline Hilda Jane (retired) Flat 3, 37 Arundell Road, Weston Super Mare BS23 2QH Tel: 01934 412182 — MRCS Eng. LRCP Lond. 1921; DPH Eng. 1928.

UMRANI, W M The Surgery, 152 Plashet Road, Upton Park, London E13 0QT Tel: 020 8472 0473 Fax: 020 8471 2243 — LMSSA 1969 London; LMSSA 1969 London.

UNADKAT, M D Oak Lane Medical Centre, Oak Lane, Twickenham TW1 3PE Tel: 020 8894 1730 Fax: 020 8893 8667.

UNADKAT, M M Oak Lane Medical Centre, 6 Oak Lane, Twickenham TW1 3PA.

UNCLE, Kenneth Albert The Orchards Health Centre, Gascoigne Road, Barking IG11 7RS Tel: 020 8594 1311; 130 Upney Lane, Barking IG11 9LT Tel: 020 8594 4353 — MB BS 1982 Lond.; BSc (1st cl. Hons.) Birm. 1975. (Westminster Hospital Medical School)

UNCLES, David Roy Department of Anaesthesia, Worthing Hospital, Lyndhurst Road, Worthing BN11 2DH Tel: 01903 205111; Amballa, Golden Acre, East Preston, Littlehampton BN16 1QP Tel: 01903 786007 Fax: 01903 786007 — MB BS 1985 Lond.; FRCA 1992; FFA RCSI 1991. Prev: Asst. Prof. Health Scis. Centre Charlottesville Virginia, USA.; Sen. Regist. Nuffield Dept. Anaesth. Oxf.

UNDERHILL, Fiona Eastwood Road Medical Centre, London E18 Tel: 020 8530 4108; 28 Monkhams Avenue, Woodford Green IG8 0EY — MB BS 1982 Lond.; DRCOG 1984.

UNDERHILL, Gillian Susan Department of Virology, Public Health Laboratory, St. Mary's General Hospital, Milton Road, Portsmouth PO3 6AQ Tel: 0239 282 4652 Fax: 0239 282 4652 Email: gill.underhill@smail101.porthosp.swest.nhs.uk — MRCS Eng. LRCP Lond. 1978; BSc Lond. 1975, MB BS 1978; MRCPath 1985; FRCPath 1996. (St. Mary's) Cons. Virol. Pub. Health Laborat. St. Mary's Gen. Hosp. Portsmouth. Prev: Sen. Regist. (Virol.) St. Mary's Hosp. Lond.; Trainee Path. St. Mary's Hosp. Lond.; Ho. Off. (Surg.) Vict. Hosp. Blackpool.

UNDERHILL, Helen Clare 14 Foxgrove Avenue, Beckenham BR3 5BA — MB BS 1988 Lond.; MRCP (UK) 1991; DCH RCP Lond. 1991.

UNDERHILL, Helen Louise The Old Vicarage, Collingbourne Kingston, Marlborough SN8 3SE — BM 1997 Soton.

UNDERHILL, Simon Wrexham Maelor Hospital, Croesnewydd Road, Wrexham LL11 7TD Tel: 01978 291100; The Hermitage, Hindford, Oswestry SY11 4NP — MB ChB 1977 Leeds; FRCA 1983. Cons. Anaesth. Wrexham Maelor Hosp.

UNDERHILL, Mr Timothy John Mill Stream Cottage, Whatlington, Battle TN33 0ND — MB ChB 1980 Bristol; FRCS Ed. 1984. Cons. A & E Med. Hastings HA. Prev: Sen. Regist. (A & E Med.) Trent RHA.

UNDERHILL, Yvonne Margaret The Surgery, High Street, Heathfield TN21 8JD Tel: 01435 864999; Millstream Cottage, Whatlington, Battle TN33 0ND — MB BS 1981 Lond.; MRCP (UK) 1984. Gen. Practitioner. Prev: GP Nottm.; Trainee GP Salisbury VTS; SHO (O & G) Salisbury HA.

UNDERWOOD, Alan David The Health Centre, Manor Road, Beverley HU17 7BZ Tel: 01482 862733 Fax: 01482 864958 — MB ChB 1988 Ed.

UNDERWOOD, Betty Park Gate Surgery, 28 St. Helens Road, Ormskirk L39 4QR Tel: 01695 72561 Fax: 01695 571709; 25 Greetby Hill, Ormskirk L39 2DP — MB ChB 1961 Liverp.; DFFP 1993; DObst RCOG 1964.

UNDERWOOD, Caroline Jane Tel: 01768 245219 Fax: 01768 891052; Croft House, Lamonby, Penrith CA11 9SS — MB ChB 1976 Birm.; MRCGP 1981; DCH RCP Lond. 1982; DRCOG 1978; Cert JCC Lond. 1978. Prev: SHO (Paediat.) Qu.s Pk. Hosp. Blackburn; Ho. Phys. Ronkswood Br. Worcester Roy. Infirm.; Ho. Surg. Castle St. Br. Worcester Roy. Infirm.

UNDERWOOD, Carolyn Julie 1 Delapre Cr Road, Northampton NN4 8NG — MB BS 1998 Lond.

UNDERWOOD, Christine Lavinia Butterburn Clinic, Reid Square, Dundee DD3 6RP Tel: 01382 884163; 6 Mallaig Avenue, Dundee DD2 4TW Tel: 01382 643066 — MB ChB 1974 Dundee; MFHom ECP Lond. 1986; DObst RCOG 1976. (Dundee Univ.) Clin. Asst. Homoeop. Clinic Butterburn Clinic Dundee; Research Assoc. Dept of Med. Ninewells Hosp. & Med. Sch. Dundee.

UNDERWOOD, Elizabeth Marion Lucy Medical Centre, 12 East King Street, Helensburgh G84 7QL Tel: 01436 673366 Fax: 01436 679715; Helensburgh Medical Centre, 12 East King St, Helensburgh G84 7QL Tel: 01436 673366 — MB ChB 1987 Liverp.; MRCGP 1994; DFFP 1993; DRCOG 1992. (Liverp.) Prev: Trainee GP Alloa Health Centre.

UNDERWOOD, Felicity Susan Harriet 266 Wollaton Road, Beeston, Nottingham NG9 2PP — MB BS 1993 Lond.

UNDERWOOD, Gayle Henderson 41 Philips Street, Bainsford, Falkirk FK2 7JE — MB ChB 1986 Aberd.; DCH RCPS Glas. 1988. SHO (Palliat. Med.) Marie Curie Centre Glas.

UNDERWOOD, Ian Richard Claypath Medical Practice, 26 Gilesgate, Durham DH1 1QW Tel: 0191 333 2830 Fax: 0191 333 2836; 13 The Grove, North End, Durham City, Durham DH1 4LU Tel: 0191 386 3968 — MB ChB 1968 Aberd. GP Durh.; Clin. Asst. (Ophth.) Univ. Hosp. of N. Durh.

UNDERWOOD, Professor James Cressée Elphinstone Department of Pathology, University of Sheffield Medical School, Beech Hill Road, Sheffield S10 2RX Tel: 0114 271 2501 Fax: 0114 278 0059 Email: jceu@shef.ac.uk; 258 Fulwood Road, Sheffield S10 3BL Tel: 0114 266 9273 — MB BS 1965 Lond.; MD Lond. 1973; MRCS Eng. LRCP Lond. 1965; FRCPath 1972. (St. Bart.) Joseph Hunter Prof. Path. Univ. Sheff. Med. Sch.; Edr. Histopathol.; Hon. Cons. Centr. Sheff. Univ. Hosps. Socs: Path. Soc.; Internat. Acad. Path. Prev: Reader (Path.) Univ. Sheff. Med. Sch.; Regist. (Path.) St. Bart. Hosp. Lond.; MRC Fell. Chester Beatty Research Inst. Lond.

UNDERWOOD, Jeremy Robert Argyle House, 3 Lady Lawson St., Edinburgh EH3 0XY; 19 Main Street, Low Valley Field, Dunfermline KY12 8TF — MB ChB 1980 Leic.; MRCGP 1989; DRCOG 1988.

UNDERWOOD, Linda Ann 22 Deuchar Street, Newcastle upon Tyne NE2 1JX — MB BS 1993 Newc.

UNDERWOOD, Margaret Cramond Cestria Health Centre, Whitehill Way, Chester-le-Street DH2 3DJ Tel: 0191 388 7771 Fax: 0191 387 1803; 13 The Grove, North End, Durham DH1 4LU Tel: 0191 386 3968 — MB ChB Aberd. 1968; DObst RCOG 1971. (Univ. Aberd.) GP Chester-le-St..

UNDERWOOD, Mr Mark Anthony Brincliffe, 7 St Michael Drive, Helensburgh G84 7SF Tel: 01436 674381 Email: mauip@clinmed.gla.ac.uk — MB ChB 1987 Liverp.; MB ChB (Hons.) Liverp. 1987; MD Liverp. 1996; FRCS Ed. 1991; FRCS (Urol.) Ed. 1998. (Liverp.) Cons. Urol. Glas. Roy. Infirm. Prev: Career Regist. (Urol.) S.. Gen. Hosp. Glas.; Clin. Research Fell. Glas. Roy. Infirm.; Lect. (Urol.) Glas. Roy. Infirm.

UNDERWOOD, Martin Ralph Queen Mary College, University of London; 12 Orchard Rise, Longborough, Moreton-in-Marsh GL56 0RG — MB ChB 1978 Manch. Sen. Lect., Qu. Mary Coll., Univ. of Lond.

UNDERWOOD, Michael Cambridge House, 6 Tennyson Avenue, Chesterfield S40 4SW — MB ChB 1988 Liverp.; BSc Liverp. 1986; MRCGP 1995; T(GP) 1995; DCH RCP Lond. 1992; DRCOG 1991. (Liverp.)

UNDERWOOD, Paul Martyn 25 Lime Road, Oxford OX2 9EQ — MB ChB 1994 Leeds.

UNDERWOOD, Richard (retired) 25 Greetby Hill, Ormskirk L39 2DP Tel: 01695 576229 — MB ChB 1961 Liverp.

UNDERWOOD

UNDERWOOD, Stanley Albert (retired) 188 Mount Vale, York YO24 1DL Tel: 01904 626588 — MRCS Eng. LRCP Lond. 1929; BSc Lond. 1922, MB BS 1929; DIH Soc. Apoth. Lond. 1947. Assoc. Roy. Sch. Mines. Prev: Med. Off. Rowntree & Co., York.

UNDERWOOD, Professor Stephen Richard Royal Brompton Hospital, Sydney St., London SW3 6NP Tel: 020 7351 8811 Fax: 020 7351 8822 Email: r.underwood@ic.ac.uk; 2A Mount Ephraim Lane, Streatham, London SW16 1JG Tel: 020 8769 5631 — BM BCh 1977 Oxf.; MA Oxf. 1976; MD Lond. 1994; FRCP Lond. 1996; MRCP (UK) 1979; FRCR 1996. Prof. Cardiac Imaging Imperial Coll. Sch. Med. & Hon. Cons. Roy. Brompton Hosp. Lond.; Hon. Cons. Roy. Marsden Hosp. Lond.; Hon. Sen. Lect. UCL. Socs: Brit. Cardiac Soc.; Fell. Europ. Soc. Cardiol.- Co-Chair, Educat. Comm.; Brit. Nuclear Cardiol. Soc- Post Chairm. Prev: Hon. Sen. Regist. (Cardiol.) Middlx. Hosp.; Regist. (Gen. Med.) The Lond. Hosp.; SHO (Gen. Med.) The Radcliffe Infirm. Oxf.

UNDERWOOD, Susan Mary Anaesthetic Department, Bristol Royal Infirmary, Bristol BS2 8HW — MB ChB 1981 Bristol; FRCA 1986 Eng.; DA (UK) 1985. (Univ. Bristol) Cons. Anaesth. Bristol Roy. Infirm. Socs: Assoc. of Cardiothoracic Anaesth.s; Soc. Of Anaesth.s of the S. W. Region; Roy. Coll. of Anaesth.s. Prev: Sen. Regist. (Anaesth.) Roy. Lond. Hosp.

UNDERWOOD, Thomas James 22 North Road, Berkhamsted HP4 3DX Tel: 01442 864382 — MB ChB 1996 Liverp.; Dip Trop Med.& Hygiene - Liverp. 1997.

UNDERWOOD, Timothy James 6 Southampton Road, London NW5 4HX — MB BS 1998 Lond.

UNDERWOOD, Trevor A Chancellor House Surgery, 6 Shinfield Road, Reading RG2 7BW Tel: 0118 931 0006 Fax: 0118 975 7194 — MRCS Eng. LRCP Lond. 1978 London; MB BS; MRCS Eng. LRCP Lond. 1978 London.

UNDERWOOD-WHITNEY, Anthony John (retired) Old Vicarage Cottage, Sutton Maddock, Shifnal TF11 9NG Tel: 01952 730676 — MB BChir 1945 Camb.; BA Camb. 1942, MB BChir 1945. Prev: RAF VR Med. Br.

UNDRILL, Guy Marcus Barrow Hospital, Barrow Gurney, Bristol BS48 3SG Tel: 01275 392811 Email: guy.undrill@bris.ac.uk — MB ChB 1989 Bristol; MA Lancaster 1992; MRCPsych 1995. (Bristol) Specialist Regist. (Psychiat.) Bristol Rotat.

UNGAR, Alexander Moorthwaite Cottage, Wigton CA7 0LZ — BM BCh 1962 Oxf.

UNGAR, Stuart Charles The Ground Floor Consulting Suite, The Princess Grace Hospital, 42/52 Nottingham Place, London W1U 5NY Tel: 020 7580 6789 Fax: 020 7224 3836 Email: stuungar@aol.com; 49 Tottenham Street, London W1T 4RZ — MB BS Lond. 1968, Acad. Dip. Gen. Biochem. 1965; MRCP (UK) 1971; MRCS Eng. LRCP Lond. 1968. (Roy. Free) Med. Off. Nat. Transcommunications & Indep. Television Commiss.; Med. Dir. The Doctors Laborat. Socs: Fell. Roy. Soc. Med. & Med. Soc. Lond.; Counc.Mem.Indep.Doctors.Forum. Prev: Regist. Psychiat. Unit. St. Mary Abbots Hosp. Lond.; Regist. Qu. Charlotte's Hosp. Lond.; SHO (Respirat. Med.) Roy. Postgrad. Med. Sch. Lond.

UNGAR-SARGON, Julian Yehuda The Gainsborough Clinic, 80 Lambeth Road, London SE1 7PW Tel: 020 8346 7019 Fax: 020 8346 7019 Email: ungar@palm.net; Suite 17, Mayflower Lodge, Regents Park Road, London N3 Tel: 020 346 7019 — MB BS Lond. 1974; MA Brandeis 1992; MRCS Eng. LRCP Lond. 1974; MTS (Harvard) 1988; PhD (Brandeis Uni) 1999. (The Roy. Lond. Hosp. Med. Coll.) Indep Pract. Lond., Neurol.; Dir., E.M.G. Laborat. The GainsBoro. Clinic Lond.; Cons. The GainsBoro. Clinic. Lond. Socs: Amer. Acad. Neurol. (Bd. Eligible); Diplomate, Amer. Acad. Pain Managem. (Bd. Certified); Diplomate, Bd. of Clin. Electrodiagnostic Med. (Bd. Certified). Prev: Asst. Prof. Med. Coll. Pennsylvania, USA; Instruc. Harvard Med. Sch. Boston Mass., USA.; Med. Dir., Lifeline Med. Center, Indiana, USA.

UNGARO, Anna Rita Shakespeare Road Surgery, 17 Shakespeare Road, Bedford MK40 2DZ Tel: 01234 327337 — MB BS 1991 Lond.

UNIA, Catherine The Alec Turnbull Clinic, East Oxford Health Centre, Cowley Road, Oxford OX4 1XD Tel: 01865 486123 Fax: 01865 486125; 2 Chilswell Road, Oxford OX1 4PJ Tel: 01865 723445 — MB ChB 1975 Birm.; MFFP. Clin. Med. Off. (Community Med. & Family Plann.) Oxf.; Sen. Clin. Med. Off. Socs: Assoc. Mem. Inst. of Psychosexual Med.

UNITT, Esther 17 Curlew Wharf, Castle Marina, Nottingham NG7 1GU — BM BS 1995 Nottm.

UNITT, Helen Margaret 32 Brook Lane, Nanpantan, Loughborough LE11 3RA — MB ChB 1991 Leeds; BSc (1st cl. Hons. Biochem.) Leeds 1988; DCH RCP Lond. 1994; DFFP 1994; DRCOG 1993; MRCP (London) 1997. SHO (Paediat.) Leicester Roy. Infirm.; Long Term Locum GP LoughBoro. Prev: Trainee GP Derby VTS.

UNKLES, Roderick Dewar 9 Woodvale Avenue, Bearsden, Glasgow G61 2JS — MB ChB 1953 Glas.; FFA RCS Eng. 1961; DA Eng. 1959.

UNNI, Kolathur Variath Sreekantan 164 Lyon Park Avenue, Wembley HA0 4HG — MB BS 1974 Kerala; MRCPsych 1979.

UNNIKRISHNAN, Manghat 32 Hallfield, Ulverston LA12 9TA Tel: 01229 54780 — MB BS 1961 Madras; FRCP Glas. 1982, M 1966. (Stanley Med. Coll. Madras) Cons. Phys. in Geriat. Furness Gen. Hosp. Barrow-in-Furness. Socs: BMA; Assoc. Mem. Brit. Geriat. Soc. Prev: Ho. Phys. Pinderfields Gen. Hosp. Wakefield; Med. Regist. N. Lonsdale Hosp. Barrow-in-Furness; Asst. in Geriat. Doncaster Hosp. Gp.

UNNITHAN, Sujata Balagopalan Worthing Priority Care NHS Trust, Options Community Drug & Alcohol Team, 24 Grafton Road, Worthing BN11 1QP Tel: 01903 204539; 11 Woodside, Barnham, Bognor Regis PO22 0HZ — MB ChB 1985 Liverp.; MRCPsych 1990; Dip Stress Managem 1998. Cons. Alcohol & Drug Misuse Worthing Priority Care NHS Trust. Prev: Cons. Alcohol & Drug Misuse Kingston & Dist. Community NHS Trust; Med. Off. DoH (Communicable Dis. Br.); Sen. Regist. Maudsley Hosp. Lond.

UNSWORTH, Anthony (retired) 4 Upper Linney, Ludlow SY8 1EF Tel: 01584 877314 — MB ChB 1951 Liverp.; DObst RCOG 1955.

UNSWORTH, David Joseph Southmead Hospital, Bristol BS10 5ND Tel: 0117 959 5629 Email: joeunsworth@hotmail.com — MB BS 1987 Lond.; PhD (Immunol.) Lond. 1982, MB BS 1987; FRCP 1999; MRCPath 1993; MRCP (UK) 1991; BSc (Hons.) Biochem. Leeds 1977. Cons. Clin. Immunol. S.mead Hosp, Bristol. Prev: Sen. Regist. (Clin. Immunol.) Addenbrooke's Hosp. Camb.; SHO Rotat. (Med.) Hammersmith Hosp. Lond.

UNSWORTH, Francis James Swn-yr-Afon, Abercegir, Machynlleth SY20 8NR Tel: 01650 511821 — MB ChB 1955 Manch.

UNSWORTH, James Oak Tree Lane Centre, 91 Oak Tree Lane, Selly Oak, Birmingham B29 6JA Tel: 0121 627 8221 — MB ChB 1980 Sheff.; MRCP (UK) 1983; FRCP (UK) 1996. (Sheffield.) Cons. in Rehabil. Med., S.ern Birm. Community Health Trust.

UNSWORTH, Nicholas John 86 Vanbrugh Park, Blackheath, London SE3 7AL Tel: 020 8858 2588 — MB BChir 1978 Camb.; LMSSA Lond. 1977; FLEX Lic. (USA) 1986; LMCC 1983; CCFP 1985; MRCGP 1983. Socs: BMA (Exec. Mem. Blackheath & S. Lond. Div.); Canad. Med. Assn.; (Fac. Bd.) RCGP S. Lond. Prev: Indep. GP Toronto & Winnipeg; Lect. Univ. Toronto.

UNSWORTH, Philip Francis Department of Microbiology, Tameside General Hospital, Ashton-under-Lyne OL6 9RW Tel: 0161 331 6500 Fax: 0161 331 6496; 1 Pine Road, Didsbury, Manchester M20 6UY Tel: 0161 445 6480 — MB ChB 1971 Manch.; BSc (Hons) Manch. 1968, MB ChB 1971; FRCPath 1989, M 1977. Cons. Microbiol. Tameside & Glossop Trusts. Socs: Hosp. Infec. Soc. Assn. Clin. Paths. and Assoc. Med. Microbiologists. Prev: Sen. Microbiol. Centr. Pub. Health Laborat. Lond.; Lect (Microbiol.) St. Thos. Hosp. Med. Sch. Lond.; Asst. Lect. (Path.) Middlx. Hosp. Med. Sch. Lond.

UNTER, Charles Ernest Marcell Department of Paediatrics, The Maidstone Hospital, Hermitage Lane, Maidstone ME16 9NN Tel: 01622 224204 Fax: 01622 224495; Silver Fern, Church Road, Offham, West Malling ME19 5NY Tel: 01732 872800 — MB BS 1975 Lond.; MRCS Eng. LRCP Lond. 1975; FRACP 1986; DRCOG 1977. (Char. Cross) Cons. Paediat. Maidstone and Tunbridge wells NHS Trust, Maidstone Hosp., Maidstone; Med. Director Maidstone and Tunbridge Wells NHS Trust; Hon. Cons. Paediat., Kings Coll. Hosp., Lond. Socs: Fell. Roy. Coll. Paediat. & Child Health; Brit. Paediatric Respirat. Soc.; Brit. Med. Assn. Prev: Cons. Paediat. Taranaki Area HB, NZ; Sen. Regist. P. of Wales Childr. Hosp. Sydney, Austral.; Regist. (Paediat.) ChristCh. Hosp., NZ.

UNWIN, Mr Andrew John Phoenix House, 9 Nightingale Walk, Windsor SL4 3HS Tel: 01753 868622 Fax: 01753 868642 Email: unwinaj@aol.com — MB BS 1988 Lond.; FRCS 1995 (Orth); FRCS 1992; BSc 1985 (Hons.). Cons. Orthopaedic Surg. Windsor

Orthopaedic Clinic, Windsor; Clin. Lect. in Anat., Imperial Col. Lond. Socs: Edu. Sec., Rheum. Arth. Surg. Soc.; Brit. Ortho. Assn; Anat. Soc. Prev: Lect. (Anat.) Char. Cross & W.m. Med. Sch. Lond.; Registra Rotat. N. W. Thames; Cons. Orthop. Surg., Wrexham Pk. Hosp., Berks.

UNWIN, Arthur Benson (retired) 112 Cambridge Street, London SW1V 4QF Tel: 020 7235 2333 Fax: 020 7235 2333 — MB BChir 1941 Camb.; BA (Hons.) Camb. 1938, MA 1942; MRCS Eng. LRCP Lond. 1941. Prev: Ho. Phys. St. Jas. Hosp. Balham & St. Thos. Hosp.

UNWIN, David Edmund John The Surgery, Ravenghyll, Kirkoswald, Penrith CA10 1DQ Tel: 01768 898560 Fax: 01768 898905 — MB BChir 1976 Camb.; MA Camb. 1976; MRCGP 1983; DRCOG 1981; DCH Eng. 1980. (Univ. Coll. Hosp.) Prev: Ho. Phys. Whittington Hosp. Lond.; Ho. Surg. Addenbrooke's Hosp. Camb.

UNWIN, David John Shaw Bottom House, Colden, Hebden Bridge HX7 7HX — MB ChB 1982 Liverp.

UNWIN, Elizabeth Finola (retired) Lindow House, Londow Lane, Wilmslow SK9 5LH Tel: 01625 531149 — MB BCh BAO 1950 Belf.; DCH Eng. 1954. Prev: Res. Med. Off. Booth Hall Childr. Hosp. Manch.

UNWIN, Helen Margaret Beech Hill Medical Practice, 278 Gidlow Lane, Wigan WN6 7PD Tel: 01942 821899 Fax: 01942 821752 — MB BS Lond. 1985; MRCGP 1990; DRCOG 1988. GP Wigan.

UNWIN, Jonathan Rosebank Surgery, 153B Stroud Road, Gloucester GL1 5JQ Tel: 01452 522767 — MB BS 1981 Lond.; MRCGP 1986; DRCOG 1986. (St. Mary's Hosp.) Clin. Asst. (O & G & X-Ray) Glos.

UNWIN, Lesley Gladys Blantyre Health Centre, 64 Victoria Street, Blantyre, Glasgow G72 0BS Tel: 01698 826331 — MB ChB 1987 Glas.; MRCGP 1992.

UNWIN, Michael Richard Princess Road Surgery, 475 Princess Road, Withington, Manchester M20 1BH Tel: 0161 445 7805 Fax: 0161 448 2419; 118 Park Road, Timperley, Altrincham WA15 6TQ Tel: 0161 905 2046 — MB ChB 1985 Manch.; BSc St. And. 1982.

UNWIN, Nigel Christopher Department of Epidemiology & Public Health, University of Newcastle, Newcastle upon Tyne NE2 4HH; 60 Rothbury Terrace, Newcastle upon Tyne NE6 5XJ — BM BCh 1984 Oxf.

UNWIN, Paul William Borough Green Medical Practice, Quarry Hill Road, Borough Green, Sevenoaks TN15 8BE Tel: 01732 883161 Fax: 01732 886319; Wrotham Surgery, St. Mary's Road, Wrotham, Sevenoaks TN15 Tel: 01732 882009 — MB BS 1986 Lond.; MRCGP Lond. 1992; DCH RCP Lond. 1991; DRCOG 1989; DGM RCP Lond. 1989. Clin. Asst. (ENT) Sevenoaks.

UNWIN, Philip Roger Fax: 01491 411296; Harpsden Court Farm, Harpsden, Henley-on-Thames RG9 4AT Tel: 01491 578382 — MB BS 1982 Lond.; Dip Occ Med 2000; MRCGP 1988; DRCOG 1986. (St Mary's) GP Henley-on-Thames; Med. Off. Microsoft UK Reading. Socs: Soc Occ Med.

UNWIN, Professor Robert John Centre for Nephrology, Institute of Urology & Nephrology, Royal Free and University College, Medical School, Middlesex Hospital, London W1W 7EY Tel: 020 76799302 Fax: 020 7637 7006 Email: robert.unwin@ucl.ac.uk; Dellwood, 4 Uplands Close, Gerrards Cross SL9 7JH Tel: 01753 885654 — BM 1976 Soton.; BM (Hons.) Soton. 1976; PhD Lond. 1983; FRCP Lond. 1994; MRCP (UK) 1978. Hon. Cons. Phys. Univ. Coll. Lond. Hosp. Trust; Prof. (Nephrol. & Physiol.) 1997. Prev: Reader (Nephrol. & Physiol.) Univ. Coll. Lond. Med. Sch.; Hon. Cons. Phys. & Sen. Lect. (Renal Med. & Physiol.) Middlx. Hosp. Lond.; Sen. Lect. (Clin. Pharmacol.) Roy. Postgrad. Med. Sch. Hammersmith Hosp. Lond.

UNWIN, Rosamond Sylvia c/o LCCN, PO Box 21, Numan, Adamawa State, Nigeria; Camlarg, 8 Warwicks Bench Road, Guildford GU1 3TL — MB BS 1982 Lond.; LMSSA Lond. 1982; MRCGP 1990; DTM & H Liverp. 1991; DA (UK) 1984. (Univ. Coll. Hosp.) Primary Health Care Facilitator, NE Nigeria. Socs: Christ. Med. Fell.sh. Prev: Trainee GP N.allerton VTS.

UNWIN, Thomas Alasdair Edmund 4 Firbank Drive, Woking GU21 1QT; 4 Firbank Drive, Woking GU21 1QT — MB BS 1986 Lond.; BSc (Physiol.) Lond. 1981; MRCGP 1990; DTM & H Liverp. 1991. APOS Dept. for Internat. Developm. (DFID). Socs: Fell. Roy. Soc. Med.; Christ. Med. Fell.sh. Prev: Clin. Lect. TeleMed. Roy. Free

Hosp. Sch. Med.; Sen. Med. Off. LCCN Med. Progr. Nigeria; Trainee GP W. Cumbria VTS.

UNYOLO, Paul Michael 3 Castledykes Road, Dumfries DG1 4SN Tel: 01387 257716 — MB ChB 1984 Manch. Regist. (Gen. Surg.) Monklands & Bellshill NHS Trust. Prev: SHO (Orthop.) Dumfries & Galloway Acute & Matern. NHS Trust; SHO (Gen. Surg.) Cornw. & I. of Scilly HA.

UPADHYAY, Mr Ajay Kumar 20 The Glebe, Hawley, Blackwater, Camberley GU17 9BB Tel: 01276 600216 — MB BS 1980 Delhi; FRCS Glas. 1985; FRCS Ed. 1984. Regist. Surg. Crawley Hosp. Sussex. Socs: Fell. Roy. Soc. Med. Prev: Regist. (Surg. & Urol.) Rushgreen & OldCh. Hosp. Romford; SHO (Surg.) St. Mary's Hosp. Newport; SHO (Orthop.) Redhill Gen. Hosp.

UPADHYAY, Bipin Bhaishankar Fieldhead Hospital, Ouchthorpe Lane, Wakefield WF1 3SP Tel: 01924 327467 Fax: 01924 327461 — MB ChB 1977 Nairobi; MRCPsych 1987. (University of Nairobi Medical School) Cons. Psychiat. Learning Disabil. Serv.s Fieldhead Hosp. Wakefield. Socs: Assn. Child Psychol. & Psychiat.; Amer. Assn. Ment. Retardation; Europ. Assn. Ment. Health in Ment. Retardation. Prev: Cons. (Psychiat. & Gen. Psychiat.) Dewsbury Dist. Hosp.; Sen. Regist. (Psychiat.) Fieldhead Hosp. Wakefield; Sen. Regist. (Psychiat.) High Royds Hosp. Ilkley & Meanwood Pk. Hosp. Leeds.

UPADHYAY, Deepak Raj Staff Neonatologist, Special Care Baby Unit, North Manchester General Hospital, Manchester M8 5RB Fax: 0161 720 2982 Email: drupadhyay@aol.com; 92 Peninsula II, Kersal Way, Salford M7 3ST Tel: 0161 792 6953 — MB BS 1980 Rajasthan; MB BS Rajasthan, India 1980; MD (Paed.) 1986; MRCP (U/c) 1996; MRCP Ch 1996. (Judhpur India) Staff Neonatologist N. Manch. Gen. Hosp. Manch. Socs: Life Mem. Nepal Med. Assn.; Nepal Paediat. Soc.; MRCPCH. Prev: Paediat. Regist. Ipswich Hosp. Ipswich; Paediat. Regist. Qu. Mary's Hosp., Sidcup; Paediat. SHO Dernfard Hosp. Plymouth.

UPADHYAY, Mahendra Thapa and Partners, The Health Centre, Forge Road, Machynlleth SY20 8EQ Tel: 01654 702224 Fax: 01654 703688 — MB BS 1971 Gauhati; MB BS 1971 Gauhati.

UPADHYAY, Mr Ramesh Narasimhacharya 9 Mold Road Estate, Gwersyllt, Wrexham LL11 4AA Tel: 01978 753566 — MB BS 1967 Osmania; MS (ENT) Osmania 1973, MB BS 1967; DLO RCPSI 1983.

UPADHYAY, Sunil Kumar Department of Radiotherapy & Oncology, Princess Royal Hospital, Salthouse Road, Hull HU8 9HE Tel: 01482 701151 Fax: 01482 676570 Email: upadhyay@dial.pipex — MB BS 1975 Lucknow; MD (Radiother.) Delhi 1980, DMRT 1978. Assoc. Specialist Clin. Oncol .P.ss Roy. Hosp. Hull. Prev: Staff Radiat. Oncol. P.ss Roy. Hosp.

UPADHYAY, Vipul Amritlal c/o Mr. B. B. Konnur, 38 Sevington Road, Hendon, London NW4 3RX — MB BS 1986 Gujarat.

UPADHYAYA, Ajaya Kumar 16 Cavendish Gardens, West Didsbury, Manchester M20 1LA — MB BS 1977 Berhampur; MD Chandigarh 1983; MRCPsych 1986; DPM Bombay 1982.

UPADHYAYA, Geetha 29 Deighton Avenue, Sherburn in Elmet, Leeds LS25 6BR Tel: 01977 683715 Fax: 01274 223306 Email: info@kalasangam.demon.co.uk — MB BS 1972 Madras; MD Madras 1984; PhD Madras 1990. (Mdras University) Socs: Assn. Clin. Biochem.; BMA.

UPADHYAYA, Linda Mary 37 Osberton Place, Hunters Bar, Sheffield S11 8XL Tel: 0114 268 0429 — MB ChB 1984 Sheff.

UPADHYAYA, Rachna Rashmi 2 Lynn Close, Cyncoed, Cardiff CF23 6LG — MB BCh 1994 Wales.

UPCHURCH, Francis Charles Medeva Pharma Ltd., Regents Park, Kingston Road, Leatherhead KT22 7PQ Tel: 01372 364002 Fax: 01372 364155 Email: francisupchurch@evans41ccmail.compuserve.com — MB ChB 1977 Birm.; BSc Birm. 1972; MFPM RCP (UK) 1993; DRCOG 1981. Med. Dir., Europe, Medeva Pharma Ltd. Prev: Assoc. Med. Dir. Allen & Hanburys Glaxo; GP Penzance; Trainee GP Taunton VTS.

UPCHURCH, Susan Marlowe House, Marlowe Court, Basingstoke RG24 9DD Tel: 01256 328860 Fax: 01256 351911; 47 Regent Court, Herriard, Basingstoke RG21 4HP Tel: 01256 325433 — MB ChB 1969 Manch.; DObst RCOG 1971. (Manch.) Prev: SHO (Obst.) N. Herts. Hosp. Hitchin; Ho. Surg. W. Herts. Hosp. Hemel Hempstead; Ho. Phys. St. Helier Hosp. Carshalton.

UPILE, Tahwinder 11 Botany Avenue, Bradford BD2 1EU — MB ChB 1992 Manch.

UPJOHN

UPJOHN, Adam Carnegie (retired) 15 Ferry Path, Cambridge CB4 1HB — MRCS Eng. LRCP Lond. 1958.

UPJOHN, Clive Henry Critchett (retired) 4 Clark Place, Belford NE70 7LT Tel: 01668 213224 — MB BChir 1940 Camb.; MA, MD Camb. 1951, MB BChir 1940; FRCP Lond. 1972, M 1941; MRCS Eng. LRCP Lond. 1939; DCH Eng. 1948. Prev: Cons. Paediat. Bromley Health Dist.

UPJOHN, Gillian Margaret (retired) 15 Ferry Path, Cambridge CB4 1HB — MB ChB 1958 Sheff.; MRCGP 1977.

UPPAL, Gurjeet Singh White City Health Centre, Australia Road, Shepherds Bush, London W12 7PH Tel: 020 8749 4145 — BM 1986 Soton.; MRCGP 1992; DRCOG 1989; Cert. Family Plann. JCC 1988. Prev: SHO (O & G) W. Dorset Hosp. Dorchester; SHO (Orthop.) Weymouth & Dist. Hosp.; SHO (Paediat.) Brisbane, Austral.

UPPAL, Harmandeep Kaur Uppal Villa, Minster Drive, Minster on Sea, Sheerness ME12 2LA — MB BS 1996 Lond.

UPPAL, Harpreet Singh 16 Pinto Close, Birmingham B16 9EP — MB ChB 1994 Manch.

UPPAL, Manjinder Singh Flat 4, 28 Lennox Road S., Southsea PO5 2HU; 26 Park Lane, Slough SL3 7PF — BM 1989 Soton.; MRCGP 1993; DRCOG 1992.

UPPAL, Rajanpal Singh 38 Shirland Mews, London W9 3DY — MB BS 1993 Lond.

UPPAL, Mr Rakesh 149 Harley Street, London W1N 2DE Tel: 020 7935 6397 Fax: 020 7486 4578 — MB ChB 1981 Manch.; BSc (Med. Sci.) St. And. 1978; FRCS (CTh) 1996; FRCS Eng. 1988. Cons. Cardiothoracic Surg. Barts & Lond. Chest Hosps. Socs: BMA; Soc. Cardiothoracic Surgs. GB & Irel.

UPPAL, Sheila White City Health Centre, Australia Road, Shepherds Bush, London W12 7PH Tel: 020 8749 4145 — MB BS 1987 Lond.; BSc (Hons.) Lond. 1984; MRCGP 1992; DRCOG 1989; Cert. Family Plann. JCC 1989. Prev: SHO (Cas. & Orthop.) Poole Gen. Hosp.; SHO (O & G) Qu. Mary's Hosp. Lond.; SHO (Paediat.) Mater. Childr. Hosp. Brisbane, Austral.

UPPALA, Raju Gudaru 37 Bron y Nant, Croesnewydd Road, Wrexham LL13 7TZ — MB BS 1986 Shivaji, India.

UPPONI, Sara Suresh 128 Coventry Road, Nuneaton CV10 7AD — MB BS 1994 Lond.

UPPONI, Suresh Krishna 128 Coventry Road, Nuneaton CV10 7AD — MB BS 1956 Bombay. (Grant Med. Coll. Bombay)

UPRICHARD, Andrew Charles Geoffrey 2 Park Street, Hillsborough BT26 6AL — MD 1988 Ed.; MB ChB 1981; MRCP (UK) 1984. Research Fell. Dept. Therap. Belf. City Hosp.

UPRICHARD, William James Nicholas 84C College Place, London NW1 0DJ — MB BS 1996 Lond.; BSc 1993; MRCP (UK) 1999. (UCLMS) SHO (Med.) Hammersmith Hosp. Lond.

UPSDELL, Margaret Ann 85 Church Road, Woolton, Liverpool L25 6DB — MB ChB 1965 Liverp.; Dip. Ven. Liverp. 1986.

UPSDELL, Mr Stephen Mark Department of Urology, The Royal Infirmary, Lindley, Huddersfield HD3 3EA Tel: 01484 342802; Potter House Farm, Birdnest Lane, Cumberworth, Huddersfield HD8 8YF Tel: 01484 603187 — MD 1990 Lond.; MB BS 1979 Lond.; FRCS Eng. 1984; FRCS Ed. 1984. (Char. Cross) Cons. Urol. Huddersfield Roy. Infirm. Socs: Fell. Europ. Bd. Urol. Prev: Sen. Regist. (Urol.) Manch.; Research Regist. (Nuclear Med. & Urol.) Manch. Roy. Infirm.

UPSHALL, Robert Thomas Percy Whinfield Surgery, Whinbush Way, Darlington DL1 3RT Tel: 01325 481321 Fax: 01325 380116; 6 Fife Road, Darlington DL3 7SY Tel: 01325 462168 Fax: 01325 381106 Email: rtpu@aol.com — MB BS 1976 Lond.; BSc (Hons.) Lond. 1973; MRCS Eng. LRCP Lond. 1976; DRCOG 1980. (Univ. Coll. Hosp.) Med. Adviser Kvaerner Cleveland Bridge & Rexam Corrugated Ltd. Darlington; Clin. Asst. (Psychiat.) Durh. Priority Care NHS Trust; Med. Off. Hmyos Deerbolt, Barnard Castle. Socs: Brit. Soc. Med. & Dent. Hypn.; Soc. Occupat. Med. Prev: Trainee GP Redhill VTS; Ho. Phys. Basingstoke Dist. Hosp.; Ho. Surg. Qu. Alexandra Hosp. Portsmouth.

UPTHEGROVE, Rachel Anne 62 Coleshill Road, Curdworth, Sutton Coldfield B76 9HA — MB BS 1993 Lond.

UPTON, Alan Frazier (retired) 29 Barker Road, Sutton Coldfield B74 2NY Tel: 0121 354 1829 — MB ChB 1941 Birm.; Cert. Av Med. MoD (Air) & Civil; Aviat. Auth. 1976. Prev: Ho. Surg. Birm. Matern. Hosp.

UPTON, Christopher Ernest 4/6 Longfleet Road, Poole BH15 2HX Tel: 01202 676111 — MB BS 1955 Lond.; FRCGP 1982, M 1976; DObst RCOG 1958. (King's Coll. Hosp.) Jt. Course Organiser Dorset GP Train. Course. Prev: Med. Regist. Gen. Hosp. Poole; Obst. Ho. Off. Camb. Matern. Hosp.; Ho. Phys. Diabetic Dept. & Ho.; Surg. Urol. & Orthop. Depts. King's Coll. Hosp.

UPTON, Christopher John Jenny Lind Children's Department, Norfolk and Norwich University Hospital, Brunswick Road, Norwich NR4 7UY Tel: 01603 287544 Fax: 01603 287584 Email: chris.upton@norfolk-norwich.thenhs.com; Long Reach, 86 The St, Brundall, Norwich NR13 5LH Tel: 01603 717204 Email: chrisupton@bizonline.co.uk — MB ChB 1981 Bristol; MB ChB (Hons.) Bristol 1981; DM Nottm. 1994; MRCP (UK) 1984; DCH RCP Lond. 1984; FRCP 1997; FRCPCH 1997. (Bristol) Cons. Paediat. Norf. & Norwich Hosps.; Hon. Sen. Lect. Univ. of E. Anglia. Socs: Brit. Paediat. Respirat. Soc.; Brit. Assn of Perinatal Med.; Paediat. Research Soc. Prev: Sen. Regist. (Paediat.) Derby & Nottm.; Research Fell. Univ. Nottm.; Regist. Nottm. HA.

UPTON, Mr Julian John Mainwaring Somerset Nuffield Hospital, Staplegrove Elm, StapleGr., Taunton TA2 6AN Tel: 01823 286991 Fax: 01823 338951; Comeytrowe Lodge, Comeytrowe Lane, Taunton TA1 5JD Tel: 01823 283485 Fax: 01823 342168 — MB BChir 1962 Camb.; MB Camb. 1963, BChir 1962; FRCS Ed. 1972; FRCS Eng. 1969; MRCS Eng. LRCP Lond. 1962. (Guy's) Cons. ENT Surg. Som. AHA. Socs: BMA; S. W.. Laryngol. Assn.; (Ex-Pres.) W. Som. Med. Soc. Prev: Sen. Regist. (ENT) Yorks. RHA Train. Scheme; Regist. (ENT) Leeds Gen. Infirm.; Regist. (Gen. Surg.) Leeds Univ. Hosp.

UPTON, Karen Elizabeth 96 Grove Park, London SE5 8LE — MB BS 1982 Lond.

UPTON, Karina Mary Amwell Surgery, 27/29 Amwell Street, London EC1 1UN; 58 Springdale Road, London N16 9NX — BSc (1st cl. Hons.) Lond. 1984, MB BS 1988; MRCP (UK) 1991; MRCGP 1994; DRCOG 1993; DCH RCP Lond. 1992. Prev: Trainee GP Lond.; SHO (Med.) Hammersmith & Roy. Free Hosps. Lond.; SHO (Paediat.) St. Mary's Hosp. Lond.

UPTON, Margaret Isabel (retired) 202 Attenborough Lane, Attenborough, Beeston, Nottingham NG9 6AL Tel: 0115 925 4305 — MB BS 1953 Lond.; MRCS Eng. LRCP Lond. 1952. Prev: Asst. Sec. S.E. Eng. BMA.

UPTON, Mark Neil Woodlands Family medical centre, 106 Yarm lane, Stockton-on-tees TS18 1YE — MB BS 1987 Lond.; BSc Pharmacol. (1st cl. Hons.) Lond. 1982; MSc Epidemiol. Lond. 1995, MSc Human & Applied Physiol. 1985; MRCGP 1993; DFFP 1996; DRCOG 1991. (Lond.) p/t GP, woodlands family Med. centre; Cons. Sen. Lect. in Clin. Epidemiol., univ. of Bris. Prev: GP/Regist. N.allerton; SHO (Psychiat. & Med.) Friarage Hosp. N.allerton; SHO (Paediat., A & E & O & G) Cumbld. Infirm. Carlise.

UPTON, Mark William Martin 22 Sion Hill, Clifton, Bristol BS8 4AZ — MA Oxf. 1987, BM BCh 1985; DCH RCP Lond. 1987. SHO (Rotat.) Roy. Berks. Hosp. Reading.

UPTON, Neil The Gowerton Medical Centre, Mill Street, Gowerton, Swansea SA4 3ED Tel: 01792 872404 Fax: 01792 875170 — MB ChB 1969 Ed.

UPTON, Paul Martin The Old Vicarage, Church Road, Mabe, Penryn TR10 9JG — MB BS 1984 Lond.; MRCP (UK) 1987; FRCA 1990. Cons. Anaesth. & ITU Roy. Cornw. Hosps. Trust Truro; Clin. Sub Dean for Roy. Cornw. Hosps., The Peninsula Med. Sch. Socs: Assn. Anaesth.; SW Soc. Anaesth.; ASME. Prev: Sen. Regist. (Anaesth.) S. W.. RHA.; Regist. (Anaesth.) Oxf. RHA.; SHO (Med.) S. W.. RHA.

UPTON, Pauline Ann (retired) 38 Silverknowes Drive, Edinburgh EH4 5HH — MB BS 1966 Newc.; MSc Ed. 1986; FFPHM RCP (UK) 1996; MFCM 1988; DObst RCOG 1968. 6J Fair A Far, Edin. EH4 6QE Tel: 0131 336 3452. Prev: Sen. Regist. (Community Med.) Lothian HB.

UPTON, Peter Gaunt 59 Kimbolton Road, Higham Ferrers, Wellingborough NN10 8DU — MB BS 1977 Lond.; MA Camb. 1974, BA 1972.

UPTON, Susan Nancy Redlam Surgery, 62 Redlam, Blackburn BB2 1UW Tel: 01254 260051 Fax: 01254 691937; Bentham Road Health Centre, Mill Hill, Blackburn BB2 4PN Tel: 01254 209918 — MB BS 1976 Newc.; DCCH RCP Ed. 1986; MFFP 1997. Prev: Clin. Med. Off. Burnley Health Dist.

UPTON, William Stuart Avenue Road Surgery, 3 Avenue Road, Dorridge, Solihull B93 8LH Tel: 01564 776262 Fax: 01564 779599; 5 Warren Drive, Dorridge, Solihull B93 8JY — MB ChB 1972 Birm.; MRCGP 1983; DObst RCOG 1974.

UPWARD, James Walter 15 The Close, Royston SG8 7JT Tel: 01763 43327 — MB BS 1975 Lond.; MRCP (UK) 1978; MRCS Eng. LRCP Lond. 1975.

UQLAT, Luay Nayel Eid c/o Student Cage, Level 6, Ninewells Hospital, Dundee DD1 9SY — MB ChB 1992 Dundee.

URBANIAK, Dorota 762 Fulham Road, London SW6 5SH — MD 1985 Warsaw; LMSSA Lond. 1993. SHO (Gyn. & Obst.) Qu. Mary's Univ. Hosp. Lond.

URBANIAK, Professor Stanislaw Joseph Tel: 01224 685685 Fax: 01224 698899 Email: s.j.urbaniak@abdn.ac.uk; 14 Earlspark Crescent, Bieldside, Aberdeen AB15 9AY — MB ChB Ed. 1970; BSc (Hons. Biochem.) Ed. 1967, PhD 1978; FRCP Lond. 1990; FRCP Ed. 1982; MRCP (UK) 1972; FRCPath 1994, M 1985. (Ed.) Prof. of Transfus. Med., Acad. Transfus. Med. Unit, Dept. Med. & Therap. Abdn. Univ. Med. Sch.; Hon. Cons. Grampian Univeristy Hosp. Trust, Abdn.; Nat. Advis. In ImmunohaemOtol., Scot. Nat. Blood Transfus. Serv., Edin. Socs: Past Pres., Europ. Soc. Hemapheresis.; Brit. Soc. Haematol.; Brit. Blood Transfus. Soc. Prev: Dir. Aberd. & NE Scotl. Blood Transfus. Serv.; Sen. Regist. & Dep. Dir. Edin. & SE Scotl. Blood Transfus. Centre; MRC Jun. Research Fell. (Therap.) Roy. Infirm. Edin.

URCH, Catherine Elizabeth 2 Glendale House, Cardigan Road, Richmond TW10 6BW — BM 1991 Soton.; BSc (1st cl. Hons.) Soton. 1990; MRCP (UK) 1994. Wellcame Clin. Research Fell., Dept. Pharmacol., UCL Lond. Prev: Regist. (Palliat. Med.) Trinity Hospice; Sen. Regist. (Palliat. Med.) Trinity Hospice St. Thos. Hosp. Lond.

URE, David Stuart, MBE Department of Anaesthesia, Glasgow Royal Infirmary, Glasgow G4 0SF Tel: 0141 211 4621 Fax: 0141 211 4622 Email: david.ure@aol.com; 244 Crow Road, Glasgow G11 7LA Tel: 0141 337 3274 — MB ChB 1990 Aberd.; FRCA 1995. (Aberdeen) Specialist Regist. (Anaesth.) Glas. Roy. Infirm. Socs: BMA; Assn. Anaesth. Prev: Career Regist. (Anaesth.) Glas. Roy. Infirm.

UREK, Fatma Hepgul 18 Oman Court, Oman Avenue, London NW2 6AY Tel: 020 8450 3552 — Tip Doktoru 1968 Istanbul; MD Istanbul 1973; T(GP) 1991. (Istanbul) Locum GP in N.-W. Lond. Socs: Med. Defence Union. Prev: GP Princip., Lond.; GP Lond.; Regist. (Haemat.) S.end Gen. Hosp.

UREN, Neal Gordon Royal Infirmary, Lauriston Place, Edinburgh EH3 9YW Tel: 0131 536 2593 Fax: 0131 536 2021 Email: nealuren@hotmail.com — MB ChB 1984 Ed.; BSc (Hons.) Med. Sci. Ed. 1981, MD (Hons.) 1994; MRCP (UK) 1987. (Ed.) Cons. Cardiol. Roy. Infirm. Edin.; Working GP on Coronary Circ. - Europ. Soc. Cardiol. Socs: Fell. Europ. Soc. Cardiol.; Fell. Amer. Assn. Of Cardiol.; Fell. Amer. Coll.Cardiol. Prev: Sen. Regist. (Cardiol.) Glenfield Hosp. Leics.; Research Regist. & Regist. Hammersmith Hosp. Lond.; Sen. Interven. Fell. Stanford Univ. Hosp., Calif.

UREY, Michelle Roseanne 297 Ballynahinch Road, Lisburn BT27 5LX — MB BCh BAO 1993 Belf.

URICH, Henry 12 Moat Lodge, Harrow on the Hill, Harrow HA1 3LU Tel: 0208 422 6848 — MB ChB 1943 Polish Sch. Med.; MB ChB Polish Sch. of Med. 1943; MD Bristol 1958; FRCP Lond. 1973, M 1946; MRCS Eng. LRCP Lond. 1947; FRCPath 1972, M 1963. (Lwow & Polish Sch. Med. Ed.) Prof. Emerit. Neuropath. Univ. Lond.; Cons. Neuropathol. Lond. Hosp. Socs: Sen. Mem. Brit. Neuropath. Soc. & Assn. Brit. Neurols. Prev: Asst. Research Neuropathol. Frenchay Hosp. Bristol; Demonst. (Path.) Univ. Bristol; Resid. Path. Bristol Roy. Infirm.

URIDGE, Christopher Frank Ashlea, Cane Lane, Gr., Wantage OX12 0AA — MB BS 1983 Lond.

URIEL, Alison Jane Kings Cross Hospital, Clepington Road, Dundee DD3 8EA Tel: 01382 816116; Top Flat, 4 Baxter Park Terrace, Dundee DD4 6NL — MB BS 1987 Lond.; MRCP (UK) 1990; DTM & H Liverp. 1992. Regist. (Infec. Dis.) King's Cross Hosp. Dundee. Socs: Roy. Soc. Trop. Med. & Hyg. Prev: Regist. (Gen. Med.) Roy. Berks. Hosp. Reading; Regist. (Genitourin. Med.) Char. Cross Hosp. Lond.

URMILA-RAO, Naraharisetty Grosvenor Medical Centre, 62 Grosvenor Street, Stalybridge SK15 1RZ Tel: 0161 303 7250 Fax: 0161 303 8377 — MB BS 1967 Osmania; MB BS 1967 Osmania.

URMSTON, John Hewlett Brabazon (retired) Ranchlands, Landford Wood, Landford, Salisbury SP5 2ES Tel: 01794 390354 — MRCS Eng. LRCP Lond. 1947. Civil Aviat. Auth. Approved Examr. for Aircrew. Prev: Sen. Ho. Surg. St. Thos. Hosp.

URQUHART, Alexander (retired) Knapp Hill House, Bath Road, Wells BA5 3HT — MB ChB 1947 Glas.; DPM Eng. 1965. Prev: Cons. Psychiat. Mendip Hosp. Wells, Som.

URQUHART, Alexander Scott Ridley Medical Group, Blyth Health Centre, Blyth NE24 1DX Tel: 01670 354417 — MB BS 1951 Durh.; FRCGP 1977, M 1960.

URQUHART, Andrew Duncan 23 Notting Hill, Belfast BT9 5NS — BM BCh 1992 Oxf.; MA Oxf. 1995, BA 1989; MRCP (UK) 1995. (Oxford Univ.) Research Fell., Dept Geriat. Med, Qu.s Univ. of Belf. Prev: Regis. Gen. Med./Endocrinol., Belf City Hosp.; Regist. (Geriat. Med) Belf. City. Hosp.; SHO (Geriat. Med.) Roy. Vict. Hosp. Belf.

URQUHART, Anne The Surgery, Main Street, Bridge of Earn, Perth PH2 9PW Tel: 01738 812000 Fax: 01738 812333 — MB ChB 1976 Dundee; MRCGP 1981; DRCOG 1978.

URQUHART, Calum Keppoch Road Surgery, Keppoch Road, Culloden, Inverness IV2 7LL Tel: 01463 793400 Fax: 01463 793060 — MB ChB 1987 Ed.; MRCGP 1993. GP Culloden, Inverness.

URQUHART, Craig Stirling 69 Shelley Drive, Bothwell, Glasgow G71 8TA — MB ChB 1998 Glas.

URQUHART, Daniel Rennie Forth Park Maternity Hospital, Kirkcaldy KY2 5RA; 19 Whytehouse Avenue, Kirkcaldy KY1 1UW Tel: 01592 263239 — MD 1990 Aberd.; MB ChB 1981; MRCOG 1986. Cons. Forth Pk. Matern. Hosp. Kirkcaldy.

URQUHART, George Edwin Duthie (retired) 26A Dundee Road, West Ferry, Dundee DD5 1LX — MB ChB 1960 Ed.; FRCPath 1979, M 1967. Prev: Cons. Microbiol. (Virol.) Virus Unit Dept. Bact. Med. Sch. Ninewells Hosp. Dundee.

URQUHART, Graham Wylie Department of Clinical Radiology, Torbay Hospital, Lawes Bridge, Torquay TQ2 7AA Tel: 01803 614567; The Farm House, 4 Higher Alston Farm, Alston Lane, Churston Ferrers, Brixham TQ5 0HT Tel: 01803 842599 — MB BS 1973 Queensland; FRCR 1990; DMRD Eng. 1981. Cons. Diag. Radiol. Torbay Hosp. Torquay. Prev: Clin. Asst. (Diag. Radiol.) Torbay Hosp. Torquay; Sen. Regist. St. Mary's Hosp. Lond.

URQUHART, Mr Hector Maconochie (retired) Killiganoon, 20 Culduthel Road, Inverness IV2 4AJ Tel: 01463 233142 — MB ChB Ed. 1940; FRCS Ed. 1947.

URQUHART, James Frederick 112 Brighton Road, South Croydon CR2 6AD — MB BS 1954 Lond.

URQUHART, James Macconnell (retired) 35 Albany Terrace, Dundee DD3 6HS Tel: 01382 322928 — MB ChB Glas. 1941; FFPHM 1980, M 1972; DPH Eng. 1950. Prev: Dist. Med. Off. Dundee Health Dist.

URQUHART, John Cameron, Maj. RAMC Retd. Department of Anaesthetics, West Suffolk Hospital, Bury St Edmunds IP33 2QZ Tel: 01284 713000 Fax: 01284 701993; 15 Wentworth Close, Fornham St. Martin, Bury St Edmunds IP28 6XE — MB BS 1985 Lond.; FRCA 1993; DA (UK) 1989; Cert. Av. Med. 1990. (St. Thos. Hosp. Lond.) Cons. Anaesth. W. Suff. Hosp. Bury St. Edmunds. Socs: Assn. Anaesth. Prev: Sen. Regist. Rotat. (Anaesth.) E. Anglia; Hon. Regist. (Anaesth.) Qu. Charlottes & Chelsea Hosp. Lond.

URQUHART, Kenneth Roderick (retired) 18 Larch Road, Dumbreck, Glasgow G41 5DA Tel: 0141 427 1497 — MB ChB (Commend.) Glas. 1939. Prev: Asst. Chest Phys. S.W. Dist. Glas. & S.. Gen. Hosp. Glas.

URQUHART, Margaret McRobb (retired) 10 Atwater Court, Faversham Road, Lenham, Maidstone ME17 2PW — MB ChB 1946 Aberd. Prev: Sessional Clin. Med. Off. SE Thames HA.

URQUHART, Rachael 6 Swalcliffe Road, Tadmarton, Banbury OX15 5TE — MB ChB 1991 Liverp.; DFFP 1996; MRCGP 1996; DRCOG 1994. p/t GP (Locum); CMO in Family Plann. Prev: GP Partner Walton Health Centre, Walton-on-Thames, Surrey.

URQUHART, Ranald Pirie Macdonald (retired) 12 Langbourne Avenue, London N6 6AL Tel: 020 8348 3693 — MB ChB 1952 Ed.; FRCPsych 1986, M 1971; DPM Eng. 1958. Staff Mem. Brent Cons. Centre & Centre for Research into Adolesc Breakdown. Prev: Cons. Child Psychiat. Uxbridge & Hayes Child Guid. Clinics & Hillingdon Hosp.

URRUTY, Jean-Pierre The White House, High St., Conisborough, Doncaster DN6 9AF — MB ChB 1964 Leeds.

URRY

URRY, Pauline Althea (retired) 67 Heathcroft, Hampstead Way, London NW11 7HL Tel: 020 8731 9145 Email: paulinekahn@btconnect.com — MB ChB 1947 Cape Town. Prev: Cons. Neuropath. Whittington Hosp. Lond., Roy. Free Hosp. Lond. & Camden & Islington AHA (T).

URSELL, Christine Emily The University Health Centre, Southampton University, Highfield, Southampton SO17 1BJ Tel: 02380 557531; Storn, Pinelands Road, Chilworth, Southampton SO16 7HH — MB BS 1974 Newc.; DRCOG 1978; DCH Eng. 1977. Phys. Univ. Health Centre Soton. Univ. Prev: Trainee GP Yeovil VTS; SHO (Med.) Coppetts Wood Hosp. Lond.; Ho. Phys. Roy. Vict. Infirm. Newc.

URSELL, Mrs Kathleen Mary (retired) 25 Southfield Approach, Charlton Kings, Cheltenham GL53 9LN Tel: 01242 526883 — MB ChB 1943 Birm.; DCH Eng. 1948. Prev: Child Health Serv. Glos.

URSELL, Mr Paul Gerry Roy Harfitt Eye Unit, Sutton Hospital, Cotswold Road, Sutton SM2 5NF Tel: 0208 296 4288 Fax: 0208 770 3869 Email: paul@cataract-doctor.com — MB BS 1989 Lond.; MD 2000 lond; FRCOphth 1995. (St. Mary's Hosp. Med. Sch. Lond.) Cons. Ophthal. Epsom & St Hellier NHS Trust. Socs: FRCOphth; Assn. Res. in Vision & Ophth.; Green Coll. Oxf. Prev: IRIS Fund Research Fell. (Ophth.) St. Thos. Hosp. Lond.; Clin. Lect. Nuffield Dept. Ophth. Univ. Oxf.; Anterior segment Fellow, Lions Eye Institute, Perth Australia.

URSELL, Mr William William Harvey Hospital, Kennington Road, Willesborough, Ashford TN24 0LZ — MB BS 1960 Lond.; FRCS Eng. 1967; MRCS Eng. LRCP Lond. 1960; FRCOG 1982, M 1969. (St. Geo.) Cons. O & G William Harvey Hosp. Ashford, Roy. Vict. Hosp Folkestone, Buckland Hosp. Dover; Vict. Hosp. Deal & Kent & Canterbury Hosp.; Examr. Centr. Midw. Bd. Socs: Fell. Roy. Soc. Med. Prev: Sen. Regist. (O & G) King's Coll. Hosp. Lond.; Resid. Med. Off. Qu. Charlotte's Matern. Hosp. Lond.; SHO Hosp. Sick Childr. Gt. Ormond St. Lond.

URWIN, Gillian Department of Microbiology, Colchester General Hospital, Colchester CO4 5JL; Churchgate House, Rectory Hill, East Bergholt, Colchester CO7 6TG — MB BS 1986 Lond.; MSc Lond. 1991; MRCPath 1993. (St. Thos. Hosp. Med. Sch.) Cons. Microbiol. Essex Rivers Healthcare Trust Colchester. Prev: Sen. Regist. (Med. Microbiol.) SE Thames Region; Lect. (Med. Microbiol.) Lond. Hosp.

URWIN, Mr Graeme Henry Department of Urology, York District Hospital, Wigginton Road, York YO31 8HE Tel: 01904 453619 Fax: 01904 544437 — MD 1989 Sheff.; MB BS Lond. 1975; FRCS Eng. 1979; MRCS Eng. LRCP Lond. 1975. (St. Mary's) Cons. Urol. York Dist. Hosp. Prev: Sen. Regist. (Urol. Surg.) Roy. Hallamsh. Hosp. Sheff.; Wellcome Surgic. Research Fell. Univ. Sheff.; Regist. (Gen. & Urol Surg.) Roy. Hallamsh. Hosp. Sheff.

URWIN, Jacqueline Eleanor The Surgery, 20 Lee Road, Blackheath, London NW7 1LJ Tel: 020 8852 1235 Fax: 020 8297 2193; The Surgery, 20 Lee Road, Blackheath, London SE3 9RT — MB BS 1979 Lond.; MRCGP 1988; FFA RCS Eng. 1984.

URWIN, Keith (retired) Westbrook, Maer Road, Exmouth EX8 2DB Tel: 01395 265618 — MRCS Eng. LRCP Lond. 1960. Prev: GP Cwmbran Gwent.

URWIN, Olive Mary (retired) 2 Laxton Grove, Trentham, Stoke-on-Trent ST4 8LR Tel: 01782 641843 — MRCS Eng. LRCP Lond. 1962; MRCPsych 1977; DPM Eng. 1976; DA Eng. 1965. Prev: Cons. Child & Family Psychiat. N. Staffs. HA.

URWIN, Stephen Windhill Green Medical Centre, 2 Thackley Old Road, Shipley BD18 1QB Tel: 01274 584223 Fax: 01274 530182; Glenwood, Stubbings Road, Baildon, Shipley BD17 5DZ — MB ChB 1981 Leeds; MRCGP 1985; DRCOG 1984. GP Shipley.

URWIN, Susan Christine Peterborough General Hospital, Peterborough; 18 Highland Avenue, Norwich NR2 3NP — MB BS 1990 Lond.; BSc Basic Med. Scs. & Pharmacol. Lond. 1987; MRCP (UK) 1994; FRCA 1997. Specialist Regist. (Anaesth.) Norf. & PeterBoro. Hosp. Prev: Specialist Regist. - Norf. & Norwich Hosp.; SHO (Anaesth.) Addenbrooke's Hosp. Camb. & Lister Hosp. Stevenage; Regist. (Gen. Med.) P.ss Margt. Hosp. Swindon.

USBORNE, Caroline Margaret 54 Grange Cross Lane, Wirral CH48 8BQ Tel: 0151 625 5001 — MB ChB 1993 Liverp.; BSc Liverp. 1988. SHO (Cardiol. & Med.) Wirral. Prev: SHO (Gen. Med.) Roy. Liverp. Hosp.; Ho. Off. BRd.green Hosp.

USHA, Tindivandam Ramakrishnan 1 Clos Du Parcq, Richmond Road, St Helier, Jersey JE2 3GL — MB BS 1974 Madras.

USHA-RANI, V Upper Parliament Street Surgery, 334 Upper Parliament Street, Liverpool L8 3LD Tel: 0151 709 1263.

USHER, Alan Stanley Guy 14 Crabtree Drive, Norwood, Sheffield S5 7AZ — MB ChB 1986 Sheff.

USHER, Hans-Eric 48 Hampden Road, Brighton BN2 2TN — MB BS 1990 Lond.

USHER, James Richard Cumberland House, Jordangate, Macclesfield SK10 1EG Tel: 01625 428081 Fax: 01625 503128; Greenacres, 155 Langley Road, Langley, Macclesfield SK11 0DR Tel: 0126025 2038 Email: maccdoc@email.msn.com — MB ChB 1981 Birm.; MRCGP 1986; DRCOG 1985; DCH RCP Lond. 1985. (Birm.)

USHER, John Leonard 58 Victoria Road, Crosby, Liverpool L23 7XZ — MB BS 1998 Lond.

USHER, Stephen Mark 9 Tweenways, Chesham HP5 3LP — MB BCh 1995 Wales.

USHER-SOMERS, Nicholas Erdington Medical Centre, 103 Wood End Road, Erdington, Birmingham B24 8NT Tel: 0121 373 0085 Fax: 0121 386 1768 — MB ChB 1976 Birm.; MRCGP 1985; DRCOG 1982. Prev: SHO King Edwd. VII Hosp. Midhurst & Dudley Guest Hosp.; Ho. Surg. Gen. Hosp. Birm.

USHERWOOD, Martin McDougall Stoke Mandeville Hospital NHS Trust, Mandeville Road, Aylesbury HP21 8AL Tel: 01296 316550 Fax: 01296 316144; Hermit's Cottage, Dinton, Aylesbury HP17 8UP Tel: 01296 748129 Fax: 01296 747813 — MB BS Lond. 1967; MRCS Eng. LRCP Lond. 1967; MFFP 1993; FRCOG 1984, M 1972; DObst RCOG 1969. (Lond. Hosp.) Cons. O & G Stoke Mandeville Hosp. NHS Trust; Asst. Med. Dir. Aylesbury; Teach. (Obst. & Gyn.) Lond. Univ.; Chairm. Four Counties Colposcopy Gp.; Regional Adviser for RCOG Oxf. Region; Chairm. Oxf. Regional Gyn. Cancer Gp. Socs: Fell. Roy. Soc. Med.; Brit. Soc. Colpos. & Cerv. Path.; BMA. Prev: Sen. Regist. (O & G Unit) Lond. Hosp.; Resid. Surg. Off. Hosp. Wom. Soho Sq. Lond.; Resid. Med. Off. Qu. Charlotte's Matern. Hosp.

USISKIN, Sasha Isadora 17 Northmoor Road, Oxford OX2 6UW — MB BCh 1997 Wales.

USMAN, Farina 101 Shakespeare Avenue, Bath BA2 4RQ — BM 1991 Soton.

USMAN, Mr Tamoor Princess Royal Hospital, Apley Castle, Telford TF1 6TF — MB ChB 1989 Manch.; FRCS Ed (Gen. Surg.) 2000; BSc (Hons.) St. And. 1986; FRCS Ed. 1993. (St. And. & Manch.) Cons. Gen. & BrE. Surg. P.ss Roy. Hosp. Telford. Socs: BMA. Prev: Specialist Regist., Gen. Surg. Walsgvane Hsop. Coventry; SPR (Gen. Surg.) City Hosp. Birm.; Specialist Regist. (Gen. Surg.) Heartlands Hosp. Birm.

USMANI, Imran 21 Rectory Park Road, Sheldon, Birmingham B26 3LJ — BM BS 1996 Nottm.

USMANI, Mr Islam Ahmed 29A Sweetcroft Lane, Hillingdon, Uxbridge UB10 9LE Tel: 01252 863291 Fax: 01252 863288 — MB BS 1962 Lucknow; FRCS Ed. 1977. (K.G. Med. Coll. Lucknow) Sen. Med. Off. (Civil.) MoD S.E. Dist. Aldershot. Prev: Sen. Med. Off. (RAF); Surgic. Regist. Sefton Hosp. Liverp.; Surgic. Regist. Roy. Albert Edwd. Infirm.

USMANI, Mumtaz Parveen 29A Sweetcroft Lane, Hillingdon, Uxbridge UB10 9LE Tel: 020 7202 8304 Fax: 020 7202 8314 — MB BS 1962 Lucknow; DObst RCOG 1974. (King. Geo. Med. Coll. Lucknow) Sen. Med. Off. (Civil.) Camb. Milit. Hosp. Aldershot. Prev: Sen. Med. Off. (RAF) M.O.D.; Regist. (O & G) Wigan.

USMANI, Omar Sharif 48 Leinster Square, London W2 4PU — MB BS 1993 Lond.; MRCP (UK) 1996. (King's Coll. Sch. Med. & Dent. Lond.) Specialist Regist. (Thoracic Med.) Lond. Prev: SHO Rotat. (Med.) King's Coll. Hosp. Lond.

USSELMANN, Bernhard Michael Selly Oak Hospital, Birmingham B29; 5 Mayfield Close, Solihull B91 3FN Email: usselmann@doctors.org.uk — MB BChir 1991 Camb.; MRCP (UK) 1994. SpR (Gastroenterol. & Gen. Med.) Selly Oak Hosp. Birm. Prev: SpR (Hepat.) Qu. Eliz. Hosp. B'ham; Research Regist., Gastroenterol., Univ of Warwick, Coventry; SpR (Gastroentrology & Gen. Med.) Heartlands Hosp. B'ham.

USSHER, Christopher William James, LVO (retired) Stonecroft, Myrtle Road, Crowborough TN6 1EY Tel: 018926 654628 — MRCS Eng. LRCP Lond. 1947; FRCP Ed. 1981, M 1965. Prev: Exec. Med. Adviser Private Pats. Plan Tunbridge Wells.

USSHER, Jonathan Howard Parade Surgery, The Parade, Liskeard PL14 6AF Tel: 01579 342667 Fax: 01579 340650; Polgray, Tregay

Lane, Liskeard PL14 6RQ Tel: 01579 342960 — MB BS 1970 Lond.; MRCS Eng. LRCP Lond. 1971; MRCGP 1975; DRCOG 1977. (St. Bart.)

USTIANOWSKI, Andrew Peter Drusus de Sas University College London Hospitals, Grafton Way, London W1 — MB BS 1991 Lond.; MRCP (UK) 1994; DTM & H RCP Lond. 1995. Infec. Dis.s SpR, Univ. Coll. Lond. Prev: Regist. (Infec. Dis.) Harold Wood Hosp. Essex; Research Fell. & Hon. Lect. (Infec. Dis.s) Univ. Coll. Lond. Med. Sch.

USTIANOWSKI, Peter Andrew Westwood House, Betteshanger, Deal CT14 ONL Tel: 01304 614840 Email: peter_ustianowski@excite.co.uk; Westwood House, Betteshanger, Deal CT14 ONL Tel: 0130 461 4840 Email: ustianowski_peter@hotmail.com — MB BS 1965 Lond.; MRCS Eng. LRCP Lond. 1963; MFHom 1971; Cert. Family Plann. JCC 1970; DObst RCOG 1965. (Guy's) Cons. Phys. (Homoeop. Med. & Hypnother.) Betteshanger, Near Deal, Kent. Socs: Assur. Med. Soc.; Brit. Soc. Med. & Dent. Hypn.; Fell.Roy.Soc.Med. Prev: Fell. & Clin. Asst. (Med. & Dermat.) Roy. Lond. Homoeop. Hosp.; Resid. (O & G) Coventry Hosp. Gp.

USZYCKA, Barbara Stefania Aleksandra 15 The Greenway, Rayner's Lane, Pinner HA5 5DR — MB BS 1992 Lond.

UTHAYAKUMAR, Sundaralingam North Herts NHS Trust, Lister Hospital, Woodlands Clinic, Correys Mill Lane, Stevenage SG1 4AB Tel: 01438 781094 Fax: 01438 781545 — MB BS 1983 Ceylon; MRCS Eng. LRCP Lond. 1987; MRCOG 1993; MFFP 1994. Cons. Genito-Urin. Phys. Lister Hosp. Stevenage Herts.

UTIDJIAN, Haig Leon Dikran (retired) 3 The Spinney, Sudbury Hill Close, Wembley HAO 2QS Tel: 020 8904 3996 — MB BS 1954 Lond. Prev: GP Wembley.

UTIDJIAN, Margaret Rosemary Anahid Maternity Unit, Harold Wood Hospital, Gubbins Lane, Romford RM3 0BE Tel: 01708 345533; 20 Harrow Drive, Hornchurch RM11 1NU Tel: 01708 470694 — MB BS 1960 Lond.; MRCS Eng. LRCP Lond. 1960; FRCOG 1979, M 1966, DObst 1964. (Univ. Coll. Hosp.) Cons. O & G Havering Hosps. NHS Trust. Prev: Regist. (O & G) Hackney Hosp.; Lect. (O & G) Univ. Coll. Hosp. Med. Sch. Lond.; Specialist (O & G) Paphos Govt. Hosp., Cyprus.

UTTING, Helen Jessica Wakelin Anaesthetic Department, Basildon Hospital, Basildon SS16 5NL Tel: 01268 533911 Fax: 01268 593948; 185 Priests Lane, Shenfield, Brentwood CM15 8LF Tel: 01277 222204 Fax: 01277 222204 — MB BS Queensland 1964; FFA RCS Eng. 1969; FRCA. Cons. Anaesth. Basildon & Thurrock Gen. Hosps. Trust. Socs: Assn. Anaesth.; Roy. Soc. Med.; BMA. Prev: Sen. Regist. Manch. Region & Roy. Lond. Hosp.

UTTING, John Arthur Broomfield Hospital, Chelmsford CM1 7ET Tel: 01245 440761 — MB BS 1965 Western Australia; FRCP Lond. 1987, M 1969. (W. Austral.) Cons. Phys. Broomfield Hosp. Chelmsford. Socs: Fell. Roy. Soc. Med. Prev: Sen. Med. Regist. Baguley Hosp. Manch.

UTTING, Matthew Robert 84 Heyscroft Road, Manchester M20 4UZ — MB ChB 1997 Manch.

UTTING, Sarah Michele Water Lane Surgery, Brixton Water Lane, Brixton, London SW2 1QE — MB ChB 1991 Birm.; DRCOG 1994; MRCGP 1995. GP Princip., WaterLa. Surg., Brixton Water La., Lond. Prev: VTA, St Geo.s Hosp. Med. Sch.; Trainee/Regist. G,P Morden Hall Med. Centre.; SHO (O & G & Paediat.) St. Geo. Hosp. Lond.

UTTLEY, Mr David (retired) Burrellhill, Skirwith, Penrith CA10 1RL Tel: 01768 88669 — MB ChB 1958 Leeds; FRCS Ed. 1965; FRCS Glas. 1966. Neurosurg. St. Geo. Hosp. & SW Thames RHA; Vis. Surg. S.. (W.m.) Health Dist., St. Helier Hosp., Roy. Surrey Co. Hosp. Guildford, Roy. Marsden Hosp.; Hon. Sen. Lect. (Surg.) St. Geo. Hosp. Med. Sch.; Cons. Neurol. Surg. Wolfson Med. Rehabil. Centre. Prev: 1st Asst. Dept. Neurosurg. Nat. Hosp. Qu. Sq. Lond.

UTTLEY, Joanna Mary Clare 2 Clarendon Crescent, Edinburgh EH4 1PT Tel: 0131 332 6780 — MB ChB 1961 Glas.; DObst RCOG 1963; Dip Occ Med 1995. (Glas.) Prev: Lect. & Regist. (Path.) Univ. Edin.; Occupat. Phys. Roy. Infirm. Edin.

UTTLEY, William Richard 2 Clarendon Crescent, Edinburgh EH4 1PT Tel: 0131 332 6780 Email: billutt.comm.msn; Whakapapa Ski Field, Top of the Bruce, National Park North Island, New Zealand Tel: 00 64 07 892 3738 — MB ChB 1991 Ed.; MRCGP 1996; DRCOG 1994. (Ed.) Whakapapa Ski Doctor New Zealand. Prev: Whakapara Ski Doctor, NZ; GP Trainee Aberd.

UTTLEY, William Sutcliffe (retired) 2 Clarendon Crescent, Edinburgh EH4 Tel: 0131 332 6780 — MB ChB 1961 Ed.; FRCP Ed. 1976, M 1965; DCH Eng. 1964; DObst RCOG 1963. Prev: Ho. Phys. & Ho. Surg. Edin. Roy. Infirm.

UWECHUE, Mr Joseph Lawrence Emeka 7 Stonehill Road, East Sheen, London SW14 8RR Tel: 020 8876 4588 — Lekarz 1972 Krakow; Lekarz Krakow, Poland 1972; FRCS Ed. 1979; Dip Urol. . Lond. 1990. Cons. Surg. Milit. Hosp. Benin City, Nigeria. Prev: Sen. Regist. (Surg.) Univ. Benin Teach. Hosp. Benin City, Nigeria.

UZOCHUKWU, Boniface Chidi 8 Holt Way, Leeds LS16 7QP — MB BS 1977 Ibadan; MRCOG 1987. Regist. (O & G) Dewsbury Dist. Hosp. Prev: Regist. (O & G) Forth Pk. Hosp. Kirkcaldy; Acting Regist. (O & G) Worcester Roy. Infirm.; SHO (O & G) New Cross Hosp. Wolverhampton.

UZOIGWE, Augustine Onuoha Department of Anaesthetics, Pontefract General Infirmary, Pontefract WF8 1PL Tel: 01977 792361 — MB BS 1971 Ibadan; DA Eng. 1982.

UZOKA, Anthony Anene Eworitsemogha Grovemead Health Partnership, 67 Elliot Road, Hendon, London NW4 3EB Tel: 020 8203 4466 Fax: 020 8203 1682; No. 1 Jones Cottage, Barnet Road, Arkley, Barnet EN5 3LH Tel: 020 8441 8554 Fax: 020 8441 8554 Email: anthonyuzoka@lizto.demon.co.uk — MB BCh BAO 1992 NUI; DRCOG 1994; MRCGP 1997. (University College Dublin) GP Princip.

UZOKA, Kenneth Amechi Oritsetimeyin 30 Harcourt Road, London E15 3DU — MB BCh BAO 1990 NUI.

UZOKWE, Christopher Osita King Fahad Hospital, PO Box 204, Al Baha, Saudi Arabia Tel: 00 966 7 7254000; 192 Platt Lane, Whelley, Wigan WN1 3YA Tel: 01942 820284 — MB BS 1982 Lagos; MRCP (UK) 1991. Cons. Emerg. Med. King Fahad Hosp. Al Baha, Saudi Arabia. Prev: Regist. Trafford Gen. Hosp. Manch., Preston Roy. Infirm. & Manch. Roy. Infirm.

UZUN, Orhan Department of Paediatric Cardiology, E Floor, Leeds General Infirmary, Great George St., Leeds LS1 3EX — Tip Doktoru 1986 Istanbul.

VAAL, Michiel Franciscus Rothwell & Desborough Health Care Group, 35 High St., Desborough, Kettering NN14 2NB — Artsexamen 1989 Rotterdam.

VACHHANI, Maganlal Khimchand 103 Doris Road, Spark Hill, Birmingham B11 4ND — MB BS 1969 Gujarat. (M.P. Shah Med. Coll. Jamnagar) SHO (Urol.) Vict. Hosp. Burnley.

VADAS, Ralph Attila 1 Melina Court, Melina Place, London NW8 — MB BS 1977 Lond.; MRCS Eng. LRCP Lond. 1977.

VADASZ, Imre Silver Birches, Bower Lane, Shoreham, Sevenoaks TN15 6XT Tel: 01959 525562 — MB BS 1964 Lond.; FRCP Lond. 1982, M 1966; MRCS Eng. LRCP Lond. 1964. Cons. Phys. & Rheum. Dartford & Gravesham HA. Prev: Sen. Regist. Guys Hosp. Lond.; Clin. Tutor Dartford Brit. Post-Grad. Med. Federat.

VADGAMA, Bhumita 50 Manor Road, Thurmaston, Leicester LE4 8AG — MB ChB 1992 Leic.

VADGAMA, Professor Pankaj Maganlal Section of Clinical Biochemistry, University of Manchester, Hope Hospital, Salford M6 8HD Tel: 0161 787 4428 Fax: 0161 787 4429 — MB BS 1971 Newc.; PhD Newc. 1984, BSc (1st cl. Hons.) Chem. 1976; FRCPath 1988, M 1977; FRSC 1996; CChem 1996; Cphys FInstP. Prof. Clin. Biochem. & Hon. Cons. Chem. Path. Univ. Manch. Socs: Assn. Clin. Biochem. Prev: Hon. Cons. Chem. Path. Roy. Vict. Infirm. Newc.; Sen. Regist. Newc. Gen. Hosp.; MRC Train. Fell.

VADGAMA, Sanjay 70 Brampton Road, London NW9 9DD; 9 Cranleigh Gardens, Harrow HA3 0UP — MB BS 1996 Lond.

VADHER, Sapna 5 Roydale Close, Loughborough LE11 5UW — MB ChB 1998 Sheff.; MB ChB Sheff 1998.

VADNAI, Gabor 29 Rockcliffe, South Shields NE33 3JH — LMSSA 1971 Lond.; MD Szeged 1965; FFA RCS Eng. 1975; DA Eng. 1974. (Szeged) Staff Anaesth. Leiden Acad. Hosp. Leiden, Netherlands. Prev: Regist. (Anaesth.) Guy's Hosp. Lond.; SHO (Anaesth.) St. Thos. Hosp. Lond.; SHO (Anaesth.) Univ. Coll. Hosp. Lond.

VAFAIE, Kasra 27 Warneford Street, London E9 7NG — MB BS 1993 Lond.

VAFIDIS, Mr Jonathan Anthony 8 Albert Crescent, Penarth CF64 Tel: 01222 703702 — MB 1977 Camb.; MA Camb. 1976, MB 1977, BChir 1976; FRCS Eng. 1981. (Guy's) Cons. Neurosurg. Univ. Hosp. Wales. Socs: Soc. Brit. Neurol. Surg. Prev: Sen. Regist. & Regist. (Neurosurg.) Radcliffe Infirm. Oxf.

VAGGERS

VAGGERS, Stewart David 15 Coronation Avenue, Fishponds, Bristol BS16 3TS — MB ChB 1985 Leeds; BSc (Psychol.) Leeds 1982, MB ChB 1985; MRCPsych 1990. Prev: Regist. (Psychiat.) Glenside Hosp. Bristol.

VAGHADIA, Himat Department of Anaesthetics, Vancouver General Hospital, 855 West 12th Avenue, Vancouver BC V5Z 1M9, Canada Tel: 604 875 4575 Fax: 604 875 5209; 21 Crescent Drive S., Woodingdean, Brighton BN2 6RA Tel: 01273 306974 — MB BS 1979 Lond.; BSc (Special) Lond. 1976, MB BS 1979; FRCPC 1986; LMCC 1985; FFA RCS Eng. 1984. (St. Bart.) Head Div. (Ambulatory Anaesth.) Vancouver Gen. Hosp. Surgic. Day Care Centre; Cons. Staff Anaesth. Vancouver Gen. Hosp. & Assoc. Anaesth. Servs.; Asst. Prof. Anaesth. & Asst. Prof. Health Care & Epidemiol. Univ. Brit Columbia; Assoc. Staff (Anaesth.) P. Geo. Region Hosp., Richmond Gen. Hosp; Peace Arch Hosp., Mt. St. Josephs Hosp. & St. Vincent Hosp. Brit. Columbia. Socs: Canad. Anaesth. Soc. & Brit. Columbia Asnaesth. Assn. Prev: Regist. (Anaesth.) Roy. Free, Middlx., Qu. Charlotte's, Soho & E.man Dent. Hosps. Lond.; Clin. & Research Fell. (Anaesth.) Vancouver Gen. Hosp. & Univ. Brit. Columbia Canada; Resid. (Anaesth.) Vancouver Gen. Hosp., St. Paul's Hosp., Grace Matern. Hosp. & Brit. Columbia Childr. Hosp. Canada.

VAGHANI, Jethalal Tapubhai The Health Centre, High Street, Dodworth, Barnsley S75 3RF Tel: 01226 203881 — MB BS 1978 Saurasthra. (Saurasthra) GP Barnsley, S. Yorks.

VAGHELA, Harkishan Kanji Malabar Road Medical Centre, 60 Malabar Road, Leicester LE1 2PD Tel: 0116 251 8047; 26 Mount Pleasant, Oadby, Leicester LE2 4UA Tel: 0116 271 8381 — MB ChB 1981 Leic.; BSc (Hons.) Leic. 1979.

VAGHELA, Hersad Mohan 219 Chapter Road, London NW2 5LU — MB BS 1997 Lond.

VAGHELA, Naresh Narshi Loughborough University Medical Centre, Loughborough University of Technology, Loughborough LE11 3TU Tel: 01509 222061 — MB ChB 1985 Leic.; BSc Leic. 1983; DRCOG 1988. (Leicester) GP Princip. Med. Centre LoughBoro. Univ.; Hosp. Prat. Diabetes. Socs: BMA.

VAGHMARIA, Anil Orchard Surgery, Knypersley Road, Norton-in-the-Moors, Stoke-on-Trent ST6 8HY Tel: 01782 534241 Fax: 01782 541068 — MB ChB 1973 Birm.; MSc (Primary Med. Care) Keele 1992; DCH S. Afr. 1976. (Godfrey Huggins Med. Sch. Salisbury) Prev: Regist. (Paediat.) N. Staffs. Matern. Hosp.; SHO (Paediat.) Birm. Childr. Hosp.; SHO (Paediat.) Hammersmith Hosp. Lond.

VAHDATI-BOLOURI, Mitra 13 Woodside Grove, Henbury, Bristol BS10 7RF Tel: 0385 792115 — MB BS 1996 Lond.; BSc Lond. 1995. (Charing Cross and Westminster) Med. SHO Kent & Canterbury Hosps. Prev: Med. Ho. Off. Chelsea & W.minster Hosp.; Surg. PR Ho. Off. W. Middlx. Univ. Hosp.; Med. PR Ho. Off. Horton Gen. Hosp. Banbury.

VAHID ASSR, Mohammad Djamel Site 56, Bradford Heights, Carrickfergus BT38 9EB Tel: 01960 360829 Email: m.vahisassr@qub.ac.uk; 25 Red Fort Drive, Bradford heights, Carrickfergus BT38 9EB Tel: 01960 360829 Email: djamelvahidassr@hotmail.com — MB BCh BAO 1991 Belf.; MRCP (UK) 1994; MD Belf. 1997. (Queen's University Belfast) Specialist Regist. Socs: BGS.

VAHRMAN, Julius (retired) 16 Lytton Road, Pinner HA5 4RH — MB BS 1942 Lond.; MRCS Eng. LRCP Lond. 1936; FRCP Ed. 1977, M 1961.

VAID, Jaishi Tel: 01743 761242 Fax: 01743 761601 Email: jaishivaid@hotmail.com; The Oaks, 5 Blakebrook, Kidderminster DY11 6AP Tel: 01562 755119 — MB BS 1971 Osmania; FRCPCH 1997; MD (Paediat.) Osmania 1976; Dip. Community Paediat. Warwick 1983; DCH RCPS Glas. 1977. Cons., Community Paediat., Shrops.'s Community & Ment. Health NHS Trust. Shrewsbury,Shrops.. Socs: Kidderminster Med. Soc. Prev: SCMO (Child Health) Kidderminster Health Care NHS Trust & Kidderminster Gen. Hosp.; Regist. (Paediat.) Geo. Elliott Hosp. Nuneaton; Resid. Postgrad. Inst. Child Health Niloufer Hosp. Hyderabad.

VAID, Muhammad Ashraf Ebrahim 234 Arbroath Road, Dundee DD4 7SB — MB BS 1979 Karachi; MRCP (UK) 1989.

VAID, Sudha Clare Street Surgery, 6 Clare Street, Riverside, Cardiff CF11 6BB Tel: 029 2066 4450; 6 Clare Street, Riversdale, Cardiff CF11 6BB Tel: 029 2066 4450 — MB BS 1961 Punjab (India). Socs: Assoc. Mem. Fac. Hom. NHS Med. Pract.; Med. Protec. Soc.

VAID, Sundar Jaishi Alexander Road Surgery, 32 Alexander Road, Darlaston, Wednesbury WS10 9LJ Fax: 0121 526 2546; The Oaks, 5 Blakebrook, Kidderminster DY11 6AP — MB BS 1976 Madras; BSc (Chem.) Madras 1970; DA (UK) 1980. Socs: Fac. Fam. Plann. & Reproduc. Health Care. Prev: Trainee GP Wolverhampton.

***VAID, Vrunda** The Oaks, 5 Blakebrook, Kidderminster DY11 6AP Tel: 01562 755119; The Oaks, 5 Blakebrook, Kidderminster DY11 6AP Tel: 01562 755119 — MB ChB 1998 Manch.; MB ChB Manch 1998.

VAIDYA, Ashwinkumar Liladhar Ormskirk District & General Hospital, Wigan Road, Ormskirk L39 2AZ; 128 Wigan Road, Ormskirk L39 2BA — MB BS 1980 Bombay; FRCA 1993. Staff Grade (Anaesth.) Ormskirk Dist. & Gen. Hosp. Lancs. Socs: BMA.

VAIDYA, Mr Dinesh Vithal Department of Urology, Treliske Hospital, Treliske, Truro TR1 3LJ — MB BS 1986 Bombay; FRCS Ed. 1991.

VAIDYA, Gunvantrai Ambaram 140 Newdegate Road, Bedworth, Nuneaton CV12 8EP — MB BS 1947 Bombay. (Grant Med. Coll.) Clin. Med. Off. Nuneaton (N. Warks.) Health Dist.

VAIDYA, Kishor Shripad Chorley & S. Ribble DGH, Chorley PR7 1PP Tel: 01257 247187 Email: kishor.vaidya@tesco.net; 24 Osnaburgh Court, Dairsie, Cupar KY15 4SU Tel: 01334 870657 Email: kishor@vaidya1.freeserve.co.uk — MB BS 1985 Bombay; MRCP (UK) 1990. (Goa Med. Coll., India) Cons. Phys. Chorley & S. Ribble DGH. Socs: Caledonian Soc. Gastroenterol. Prev: Cons. Phys. Law Hosp. Carluke; Staff Grade Phys. (Gastroenterol.) Ninewells Hosp. & Med. Sch. Dundee; Regist. Rotat. (Geriat. & Gastroenterol.) Birm. Heartlands Hosp.

VAIDYA, Rajnikant Babubhai (retired) 18 Infield Park, Barrow-in-Furness LA13 9JL — MB BS 1954 Bombay; MRCOG 1967, DObst 1962. Prev: SHO (Gen. Surg.) Gen. Hosp. Burnley.

VAIDYA, Tribhubana Nanda (retired) Tel: 01246 260772 Email: tribhubanv@yahoo.co.uk — MB BS 1965 Patna. Prev: SHO (Neurosurg.) Middlesbrough Gen. Hosp.

VAIDYANATHAN, Subramanian Flat 3B, Y Block, District General Hospital, Town Lane, Kew, Southport PR8 6PN Tel: 01704 547471 Ext: 4408 — MB BS 1970 Madras; MCh - 1976 Postgraduate Institute of Medical Education and Research, Chandigash India; PhD - 1984 Postgraduate Institute of Medical Education and Research, Chandigash India. Trust Doctor Regional Spinal Injuries Centre, S.port. Socs: BMA; Inter. Med. Soc. Paraplegia; Liverp. Med. Inst. Prev: Vis. Prof. to the Univ. of Mass., Worcester, MA, USA.

VAILE, Charlotte Louise Brookhouse, Brookside, Stretton on Dunsmore, Rugby CV23 9LY Tel: 01203 543020 — MB ChB 1993 Sheff.; DRCOg 1997. GP Regist. Romsey Hants. Prev: SHO (O & G) York Dist. Hosp.; SHO Wellington Hosp., NZ; SHO (A & E) N.. Gen. Hosp. Sheff.

VAILE, Elizabeth City Medical Services Ltd., 17 St Helen's Place, London EC3A 6DE Tel: 020 7638 3001 — MB BS 1962 Lond.; MRCS Eng. LRCP Lond. 1962; DObst RCOG 1965; T(GP) 1991. (King's Coll. Hosp.) Med. Off. City Med. Servs. Ltd. Prev: Ho. Phys. King's Coll. Hosp. Lond.; Ho. Surg. S. Lond. Hosp. Wom.; Ho. Off. (Obst.) Roy. Vict. Hosp. Bournemouth.

VAILE, Howard Graham Occupational Health Department, Chelsea and Westminster Hospital, 369 Fulham Road, London SW10 9NH Tel: 0206 8746 8330 Fax: 020 8746 8331; 16 Crofton Avenue, Chiswick, London W4 3EW Tel: 0208742 8049 Email: hgv@bigfoot.com — MB BS 1962 Lond.; MRCS Eng. LRCP Lond. 1962; FFOM RCP Lond. 1990, M 1978; DIH Soc. Apoth. Lond. 1969; T(OM) 1991; FRCP Lond. 1999. (King's Coll. Hosp.) Cons. Occupat. Med. Socs: Soc. Occupat. Med.; BMA. Prev: Chief Med. Off. BBC Lond.; Med. Adviser IMI plc Birm.; Med. Adviser Commonw. Smelting Ltd. Avonmouth.

VAILE, Julian Charles 16 Sycamore Road, Bournville, Birmingham B30 2AD — MB ChB 1991 Birm.; ChB Birm. 1991; MRCP (UK) 1994. Regist. (Cardiol.) Qu. Eliz. Hosp. Birm.

VAILE, Michael Steel Berkeley West Kent Health Authority, Preston Hall, Maidstone ME20 7NJ Tel: 01622 710161 Fax: 01622 710980; 63 Joy Lane, Whitstable CT5 4DD — MB BS Lond. 1962; FFPHM RCP (UK) 1987; MRCGP 1976; DObst RCOG 1965; DA Eng. 1964; FRCP 1998. (St. Thos.) Dir. (Pub. Health Med.) W. Kent HA. Prev: GP; Resid. Anaesth. St. Thos. Hosp.

VAILLANT, Charles Harry Cavendish Medical Centre, 214 Park Road North, Birkenhead CH41 8BU Tel: 0151 652 1955; 88

VALENTINE

Shrewsbury Road, Birkenhead CH43 6TF — MB ChB 1978 Liverp.; PhD Liverp. 1971, BSc (Hons.) 1968; MRCS Eng. LRCP Lond. 1978; DRCOG 1983.

VAIRAVAN, Mr Manickam St. Mary's Hospital, Newport PO30 5TG Tel: 01983 524081; 120 Old Road, East Cowes PO32 6AX Tel: 01983 280558 — MB BS 1984 Madras; FRCS Ed. 1990; FRCS Glas. 1990. Staff Surg. St Mary's Hosp. Newport, I. of Wight. Socs: FICS 1995; Assn. Surg.; BMA. Prev: Regist. (Surg.) Neath Gen. Hosp., Mt. Vernon Hosp. Middlx. & Nevill Hall Hosp. Abergavenny.

VAISHNAV, Mr Avirat Aniruddh Paediatric Surgical Unit, Children's Hospital, Western Bank, Sheffield S10 2TH — MB BS 1977 Poona; MS Chandigarh 1980; FRCS Ed. 1984.

VAISHNAW, Akshay Krishnakant Department of Med., Addenbrooke's Hospital, Cambridge CB2 2QQ Tel: 01223 245151; 8 Belmont Avenue, Wembley HA0 4HN Tel: 020 8903 0922 — MB BCh 1986 Wales; BSc Wales 1983, MB BCh 1986; MRCP (UK) 1989. Regist. (Med.) Addenbrooke's Hosp. Camb. Prev: SHO (Neurol.) Nat. Hosp. Nerv. Dis. Lond.; SHO (Med.) Univ. Hosp. Wales.

VAIZEY, Ms Carolynne Jane The Middlesex Hospital, Mortimer Street, London W1T 3AA Tel: 020 7380 9454 Fax: 020 7380 9162 Email: carolynne.vaizey@uclh.org — MD University of London; MB ChB Cape Town; FCS (South Africa); FRCS (Gen.). (Cape Town) Cons. Colorectal Surg., The Middlx. Hosp.; Hon. Sen. Lect., Univ. Coll. Lond.; Sen. Research Fell., St Mark's Hosp. Socs: Assn. of Colorectal Surg.s, Roy. Soc. of Med.

VAIZEY, Mary Jane (retired) Drove House, Gipsey Bridge, Boston PE22 7DB Tel: 01205 280388 Fax: 01205 280388 Email: mjvaizey@doctors.org.uk — FRCPCH 1997; BM BCh Oxf. 1965; MA Oxf. 1965; FRCP Lond. 1989; MRCP (UK) 1970; DCH Eng. 1968. Prev: Cons. Paediat. Pilgrim Hosp. Boston.

VAJA, Kanji Harji (retired) Balsall Heath Health Centre, 43 Edward Road, Birmingham B5 7JE Tel: 0121 446 2500 Fax: 0121 440 5861 — MB BS 1963 Gujarat. Salaried G.P (PMS Pilot) Heart of Birm., PCG. Prev: G.P Sen. Partner-The Wand Med. Centre, Birm., W. Midl.s.

VAJA, Rakesh 44 Cross Road, Croydon CR0 6TA — MB ChB 1994 Leeds. SHO (Anaesth.) Mayday Univ. Hosp. Thornton Heath. Prev: SHO (A & E Med.) Colchester Gen. Hosp.; Ho. Off. (Surg.) Leicester Gen. Hosp.; Ho. Off. (Med.) Leeds Infirm.

VAJPEYI, Ravi — MB BS 1964 Lucknow. (G.S.V.M. Med. Coll. Kanpur) Prev: Med. Off. Family Plann. Clinics Boro. Lewisham.

VAJPEYI, Uma Shankar 13 Addiscombe Grove, Croydon CR0 5LR — MB BS 1964 Lucknow.

VAKHARIA, Bipin Ramaniklat Galleries Health Centre, Washington Centre, Washington NE38 7NQ Tel: 0191 416 1841 — MB BS 1972 Gujarat. (Gujarat) GP Washington, Tyne & Wear.

VAKIL, Anita 1 Cambridge Road, Owlsmoor, Sandhurst GU47 0UB Tel: 01344 777015 Fax: 01344 777226 — MB BS 1991 Lond.; DFFP 1996; MRCGP 1996; DCH RCP Lond. 1995; DRCOG 1995. (Charing Cross & Westminster) GP Princip.

VAKIL, Mary Alice Osborne (retired) 54 Bonser Road, Twickenham TW1 4RG Tel: 020 8892 8659 — MB BCh BAO 1949 Belf. Prev: SCMO (Child Health) Wandsworth Community Health.

VAKIL, Pervez Ardeshir Friars Walk, 29 Cedar Road, Farnborough GU14 7AU — MB BS 1957 Bombay; DObst RCOG 1970.

VAKIL, Sarosh Dhunjishaw (cons. rooms), 11 Moor Park Avenue, Preston PR1 6AN; Fiddlers Green, Walker Lane, Fulwood, Preston PR2 7AP — MB BS 1959 Lond.; FRCP Ed. 1980; FRCP Lond. 1979, M 1967.

VAKIS, Mr Stelios 117 More Close, St Pauls Court, London W14 9BW; 21 Hann Road, Rownhams, Southampton SO16 8LN — MB BS 1989 Lond.; FRCS Ed. 1994.

VALABHJI, Prassankumar (retired) The Paddock, 124A Heol Isaf, Radyr, Cardiff CF15 8EA — MB BCh 1960 Wales; FRCP Lond. 1981; MRCP (U.K.) 1964. Cons. Phys. E. Glam. Gen. Hosp. Prev: Med. Regist. Miners Treatm. Centre Llandough Hosp.

VALDEZ, Frederick Neville 8 Hillside View, Denton, Manchester M34 7EZ Tel: 0161 320 5419 — M.B., Ch.B. Manch. 1945.

VALE, John Allister City Hospital NHS Trust, Birmingham B18 7QH Tel: 0121 507 4123 Fax: 0121 507 5580 — MB BS 1968 Lond.; MD Lond. 1980; FRCP Glas. 1997; FRCP Ed. 1994; FRCP Lond. 1984; MRCP (UK) 1973; MRCS Eng. LRCP Lond. 1968; FFOM RCP Lond. 1992. (Guy's) Dir. Nat. Poisons Informat. Serv. & W. Midl. Poisons Unit & Cons. Clin. Pharmacol. City Hosp. NHS Trust; Examr. MRCP (UK) & AFOM; Sen. Clin. Lect. (Therap. & Clin. Toxicol Med.) Univ. Birm.; Chairm. MRCP (UK) Part 1 Exam. Bd. & Sec. MRCP (UK) Policy Comm. Socs: (Mem. Exec. Comm.) Brit. Toxicol. Soc.; Brit. Pharm. Soc.; Fell. Amer. Acad. Clin. Toxicol. 1988. Prev: Co-Dir. Centre for Chem. Incidents Birm.; Trustee Amer. Acad. Clin. Toxicol.; Pres. Europ. Assn. Poisons Centres & Clin. Toxicol.

VALE, Mrs Joyce Cecile (retired) Coppice, Rock Hill, Georgeham, Braunton EX33 1JP — MB BS 1959 Lond. Cytologist Guy's Hosp. Lond.

VALE, Mr Justin Alastair Department of Urology, St. Mary's Hospital, Praed St., London W2 1NY Tel: 020 8991 2389; Dalhousie, 30 Woodville Road, Ealing, London W5 2SF Tel: 020 8991 2389 — MB BS 1984 Lond.; BSc Lond. 1981, MS 1992; FRCS (Urol.) 1993; FRCS Eng. 1988. Cons. Urol. Surg. St. Mary's Hosp. Lond. Prev: Sen. Regist. (Urol.) St. Mary's Hosp. Lond.

VALE, Kathryn Elliott Old Orchard, Chapel Hill, Sedlescombe, Battle TN33 0QX — BM BCh 1974 Oxf.; MRCGP 1981; MRCPsych 1979; DRCOG 1977.

VALE, Philip Temple The Beeeches, School Lane, Bronington, Whitchurch SY13 3HN — MB BS 1960 Durh.; FFOM RCP Lond. 1990, MFOM 1978; DIH Soc. Apoth. Lond. 1972. Prev: Sen. Employm. Med. Adviser EMAS.

VALE, Raymond John Coppice, Rock Hill, Georgeham, Braunton EX33 1JP Tel: 01271 890684 — MB BS 1948 Lond.; FRCP Ed. 1969, M 1954; MRCS Eng. LRCP Lond. 1948; FFA RCS Eng. 1954; DA Eng. 1950. (Guy's) Emerit. Cons. Anaesth. Guy's Hosp. & Chelsea Hosp. for Wom. Lond. Socs: Assn. Anaesth.; Fell. Roy. Soc. Med. (Mem. Sect. Anaesth.). Prev: Res. Anaesth. Guy's Hosp. & Maxillo-Facial & Plastic Surg. Unit E.; Grinstead.

VALE, Simon Sebastian Harley House Surgery, 2 Irnham Road, Minehead TA24 5DL Tel: 01643 703441 Fax: 01643 704867; Tel: 01643 707911 Fax: 01984 656559 — MB BS 1988 Lond.; BSc Lond. 1979; MRCGP 1992. GP Harley Ho. Surg. Minehead; Hosp. Practioner Accdent and Emergncy Minehead; Clin. Asst. Som. Drugs Serv. Taunton. Socs: MRCGP.

VALEINIS, Mara 332 Oakwood Lane, Leeds LS8 3LF Tel: 0113 248 7407 — MRCS Eng. LRCP Lond. 1967.

VALENTE, Jane Elizabeth The Old Rectory, 1 Church St., Fen Ditton, Cambridge CB5 8SU Tel: 01223 292234 — MB BS 1987 Lond.; MRCP (UK) 1993. Paediat. Cons. Hinchingbrooke Hosp. Huntingdon. Prev: Sen. Regist. (Paediat.) Camb.

VALENTINE, Amor Adam (retired) 9 Towers Drive, Kirby Muxloe, Leicester LE9 2EW Tel: 0116 239 2234 — MB ChB 1940 St. And.; FRCPsych 1971; DPM Lond. 1951. Prev: Med. Supt. & Cons. Psychiat. Glenfrith Hosp. Leic.

VALENTINE, Mr Brian Harvey Kent Lodge Clinic, 6 Trinity Trees, Eastbourne BN21 3LD Tel: 01323 648357; The Paddock, 96 High St, Westham, Pevensey BN24 5LJ Tel: 01323 768070 — MB BS 1966 Lond.; FRCS Ed. 1975; MRCS Eng. LRCP Lond. 1966; FRCOG 1991, M 1975; DObst 1973. (Guy's) Cons. Adviser & Chairm. Asst. Conception Unit Esperance Private Hosp. E.bourne; Clin. Lect. UCH & Middlx. Med. Schs.; Cons. (Obst. & Gyn.) E.bourne Dist. Gen. Hosp. Socs: Brit. Soc. Colpos. & Cerv. Path.; Brit. Soc. Gyn. & Oncol. Prev: Sen. Regist. (O & G) Notts. AHA(T); Regist. (O & G) Nottm. City Hosp.; Maj. RAMC, SHO (Obst.) Louise Margt. Matern. Hosp. Aldershot.

VALENTINE, Christopher Brett Department of Genitdurinary Medicine, Ravenscraig Hospital, Inverkip Road, Greenock PA16 9HA Tel: 01475 656308 Email: chris.valentine@renver-pct.scot.nhs.uk — MB ChB 1986 Leeds; 2001 FRCP, (Lond); BSc Leeds 1983; MRCP (UK) 1990; DFFP 1995; Dip. GU Med. Soc. Apoth. Lond. 1994. (Leeds) Cons.Genito. Urin. Med. renver Primary Care NHS Trust. Socs: Soc. Study VD; Internat. AIDS Soc.; Brit. Soc. Colposc. & Cervic. Pathol. Prev: Lect. (Genitourin. Med.) Univ. Liverp.; Research Fell. MRC HIV Clin. Trials Centre (Clin. Epidemiol.) Roy. Brompton & Nat. Heart & Lung Inst. Lond.; Research Fell. (Clin. Immunol.) St. Mary's Hosp Lond.

VALENTINE, David Angus Filey Surgery, Station Avenue, Filey YO14 9AE Tel: 01723 515881 Fax: 01723 515197; The Low Barn, Hunmanby, Filey YO14 0JY Tel: 01723 890308 Fax: 01723 891309

VALENTINE

— MB ChB 1962 Leeds; MB ChB (Distinc.) Leeds 1964; BSc (1st cl. Hons. Physiol.) Leeds 1962. (Leeds)

VALENTINE, David Edward West Harwood Crofts, West Calder EH55 8LF — MB BCh BAO 1982 NUI.

VALENTINE, David Thomas Wigan Road Surgery, 246 Wigan Road, Bryn, Ashton-in-Makerfield, Wigan WN4 0AR Tel: 01942 727270 Fax: 01942 272197 — MB ChB Liverp. 1993. Assoc. Phys. Bolton.

VALENTINE, James Low Wood, Ben Rhydding, Ilkley LS29 8AZ Tel: 01943 609491 — MB ChB 1929 Glas.; DPM Lond. 1933; FRCPsych 1971. (Univ. Glas.) Socs: BMA; Fell. Roy. Coll. of Psychiat.s. Prev: Hon. Cons. Psychiat. Scalebor Pk. Burley-in-Wharfedale & Leeds Gen.; Phys. Supt. & Cons. Psychiat. Scalebor Pk. Burley-in-Wharfedale; Cons. Psychiat. Leeds Univ. Dept. Stud. Health.

VALENTINE, Jane Louise Linden Medical Centre, 9A Linden Avenue, Maidenhead SL6 6HD Tel: 01628 20846 Fax: 01628 789318 — MB ChB 1985 Manch.; DRCOG 1988. (Manchester) GP Maidenhead.

VALENTINE, John Carpenter Water Meadows, Harrold, Bedford MK43 7DE Tel: 01234 720383 Email: jackval@lineone.net — MB ChB (2nd cl. Hons.) Bristol 1941; FRCPath 1963. Prev: Cons. Morbid Anat. & Histopath. N. Beds. HA; Capt. IMS/IAMC; Lect. (Path.) Univ. Bristol.

VALENTINE, John Paul St Chads Surgery, Gullock Tyning, Midsomer Norton, Bath BA3 2UH Tel: 01761 413334 Fax: 01761 411176 — BM BCh 1972 Oxf.; MA Oxf. 1972, BSc 1970, BM BCh 1972; MRCGP 1977; DRCOG 1977; DCH Eng. 1975. Course Organiser Bath & Swindon VTS. Prev: Trainee GP Swindon-Cirencester VTS; Ho. Surg. Roy. United Hosp. Bath; Ho. Phys. Radcliffe Infirm. Oxf.

VALENTINE, Jonathan Michael James Department of Anaethetics, The Norfolk & Norwich Hospital, Brunswick Road, Norwich NR1 3SR Tel: 01603 287086 Fax: 01603 287886; The Church Apiary, 111 The St, Brooke, Norwich NR15 1JU Email: jon.valentine@virgin.net — MB ChB 1986 Leeds; MRCP (UK) 1989; FRCA 1992. Cons. Anaesth. & Pain Managem. Norf. & Norwich Hosp. Socs: Chairm., Anglian Pain Soc. Prev: Sen. Regist. (Anaesth.) Yorks. Region; Sen. Regist. Melbourne, Austral.; Regist. (Anaesth.) St. Jas. Univ. Hosp. Leeds.

VALENTINE, Laurence 28 Emlyn Road, London W12 9TD Tel: 020 8743 5287 — MB BS 1954 Lond. (Univ. Coll. Hosp.)

VALENTINE, Linda Church Plain Surgery, Loddon, Norwich NR14 6EX Tel: 01508 520222 — MB ChB 1987 Leeds; DRCOG 1991; DCH RCP Lond. 1991. GP Asst. Ch. Plain Surg. Loddon Norwich. Prev: GP Warrengate Surg. Wakefield; Trainee GP Wakefield VTS.

VALENTINE, Malcolm Jack Brimmond Medical Group, 106 Inverurie Road, Bucksburn, Aberdeen AB21 9AT Tel: 01224 713490 Fax: 01224 716317 Email: malcolm.valentine@brimmond.groupian.scot.nhs.uk; 104 Desswood Place, Aberdeen AB15 4DQ — MB ChB 1982 Aberd.; FRCGP 1997; MD 2001; MRCGP 1986; DRCOG 1985. Gen. Practitioner, Aberd.; Hon. Clin. Lect. (Gen. Pract.) Univ. Aberd.; Occupat. Phys. Schlumberger, Aberd.; Asst. Director of PostGrad. of Educat. Gp.ian. Socs: Nat. Assn. of GP Tutors- Vice Chairm. Prev: Hon. Clinician Hyperbaric Unit Grampian HB; Trainee GP NE Scotl. VTS.

VALENTINE, Mary Josephine New Court Surgery, Borough Fields Shopping Centre, Wootton Bassett, Swindon SN4 7AX Tel: 01793 852302 Fax: 01793 851119 — MB ChB 1980 Bristol; MRCP (UK) 1984; MRCGP 1987; DA (UK) 1986. GP Wootton Bassett; Hosp. Pract. (Endocrinol. & Gen. Med.) P.ss Margt. Hosp. Swindon.

VALENTINE, Mr Neil Wilson Stracathro Hospital, Brechin DD9 7QA Tel: 01356 647291 Fax: 01356 665101; 78 Lour Road, Forfar DD8 2AZ Tel: 01307 463427 Fax: 01307 467836 Email: nwvalentine@compuserve.com — MB ChB 1980 Glas.; FRCS Glas. 1984. Cons. Orthop. Surg. Stracathro Hosp. Brechin; Hon. Sen. Lect. Univ. Dundee. Socs: Fell. Brit. Scoliosis Soc.; Fell. BOA; Fell. Europ. Spine Soc. Prev: Sen. Regist. (Orthop.) OsW.ry & Stoke-on-Trent; Research Fell. (Spinal) Hartshill Orthop. Hosp. Stoke on Trent; Regist. (Orthop.) Vict. Infirm. & Glas. Roy. Infirm.

VALENTINE, Nicola Jane 121 Hale Drive, London NW7 3EJ — MB BS 1990 Lond.; BSc Lond. 1987; MRCGP 1994; DRCOG 1993. Asst. GP Lond. Prev: Trainee GP Lond.

VALENTINE, Mr Peter William Martin 121 Hale Drive, London NW7 3EJ — MB BS 1990 Lond.; FRCS Eng. 1995.

VALENTINE, Prudence (retired) 11 Stancomb Avenue, Ramsgate CT11 0EX Tel: 01843 592039 — MB BS 1952 Lond.; MRCS Eng. LRCP Lond. 1952; DObst RCOG 1955.

VALENTINE, Simon Hugh Charles Tel: 020 8997 4747 Fax: 020 8566 7422 — MB BS 1985 Lond.; Dip Sports Med 2001 Bath; MRCGP 1989.

VALENTINE, Wilfrid Henry, OBE, ERD (retired) The Arches, Albourne, Hassocks BN6 9DJ Tel: 01273 833294 — MA, MD Camb. 1942, MB BChir 1936; MRCS Eng. LRCP Lond. 1935. Prev: Regional Med. Off. DHSS.

VALENTINI, Patrizia 80 Plumstead Common Road, London SE18 3RD — Laurea 1995 Milan.

VALERIO, Mr David Grantham & District NHS Trust, 101 Manthorpe Road, Grantham NG31 8DG Tel: 01476 565232 Fax: 01476 590441; 138 Manthorpe Road, Grantham NG31 8DL Tel: 01476 571611 — MB ChB 1970 Sheff.; MS Sheff. 1982; FRCS Eng. 1975; FRCS Ed. 1975. Cons. Gen. Surg. Grantham & Kesteven Gen. Hosp. Prev: Sen. Regist. (Gen. Surg.) Aberd. Roy. Infirm.

VALERIO, Dorando (retired) 97 Prince of Wales Road, Sheffield S2 1EZ Tel: 0114 397124 — LRCS 1939 Ed.; L.R.C.P., L.R.C.S. Ed., L.R.F.P.S. Glas. 1939. Prev: Clin. Asst. Out-pats. S.. Gen. Hosp. Glas.

VALI, Ahmed Mohamed 689 Crompton Way, Bolton BL1 8TL — MB BChir 1980 Camb.; MA Camb. 1981; FRCR 1986. Sen. Regist. (Radiol.) NW Regional HA.

VALIANT, Kevin Anthony 4 Albert Street, Wheelton, Chorley PR6 8HF — MB ChB 1988 Leic.

VALLANCE, Barry Daniel Hairmyres Hospital, Eaglesham Road, East Kilbride, Glasgow G75 8RG Tel: 01355 585000 Fax: 01355 584473; Faraways, 5 Sandringham Avenue, Newton Mearns, Glasgow G77 5DU Tel: 0141 639 1962 Fax: 0141 639 6775 — MB ChB 1973 Glas.; FRCP Glas. 1987. (Glasgow University) Cons. Phys. & Cardiol. Hairmyres & StoneHo. Hosps. Lanarksh. Acute Hosps. NHS Trust. Socs: Brit. Cardiac Soc.; Scott. Soc. Phys.; Scott. Cardiac Soc. Prev: Lect., Sen. Regist. & Regist. (Med. Cardiol.) Glas. Roy. Infirm.; Hon. Research Regist. (Med.) S.. Gen. Hosp. Glas.

VALLANCE, Harry David Anaesthetic Department, North Manchester General Hospital, Delauneys Road, Crumpsall, Manchester M8 5RL Tel: 0161 795 4567 — MB ChB 1984 Leeds; FRCA 1993; DA (UK) 1987. Cons. (Anaesth.) N. Manch. Gen. Hosp. Socs: Assn. Anaesth.; Manch. Med. Soc.; Obst. Anaesth. Assn. Prev: Sen. Regist. (Anaesth.) Booth Hall Childr. Hosp. Manch.

VALLANCE, James Howard 12 Lumley Road, Durham DH1 5NP — MB ChB 1997 Ed.

VALLANCE, Kevin Andrew George Eliot Hospital NHS Trust, College St., Nuneaton CV10 7DJ Tel: 01203 351351 — MB ChB 1980 Birm.; FRCR 1986. Cons. Radiol. Geo. Eliot Hosp. NHS Trust Nuneaton. Prev: Sen. Regist. & Regist. (Radiol.) W. Midl. RHA; SHO (Cardiothoracic Surg.) Coventry HA.

VALLANCE, Norma Bryan 56 Russell Drive, Bearsden, Glasgow G61 3BB — MB ChB 1970 Glas.

VALLANCE, Patrick John Thompson 28 Bushnell Road, London SW17 8QP Tel: 020 8675 2267 — MB BS Lond. 1984; BSc Lond. 1981, MD 1990; MRCP (UK) 1987. Prof. & Hon. Cons. Clin. Pharmacol. Univ. Coll. Hosp. Lond. Prev: Sen. Lect. & Hon. Cons. Clin. Pharmacol. St. Geo. Hosp. Med. Sch. Lond.; Lect. (Clin. Pharmacol.) & Hon. Regist. (Med.) St. Geo. Hosp. Med. Sch. Lond.; Wellcome Clin. Fell.

VALLANCE, Mr Ramsay 56 Russell Drive, Bearsden, Glasgow G61 3BB — MB ChB 1969 Glas.; FRCS Glas. 1973; FRCR 1976; DMRD Eng. 1977. (Glas.) Cons. Radiol. Gartnavel Gen. Hosp. Glas.; Hon. Clin. Sen. Lect. (Radiol.), Univ. of Glas. Prev: Regist. (Diag. Radiol.) S.. Gen. Hosp. Glas.; Sen. Regist. (Diag. Radiol.) & Jun. Ho. Phys. W.. Infirm. Glas.

VALLANCE, Reuben Leon Brunswick Health Centre, Brunswick St., Hartfield Close, Chorlton on Medlock, Manchester M13 9YA Tel: 0161 273 4901; 4 Singleton Close, Salford M7 4NF — LRCP LRCS 1949 Ed.; LRCP LRCS Ed. LRFPS Glas. 1949; MRCGP 1976. (Anderson Coll. Glas.) Prev: Capt. RAMC; Ho. Phys. & Ho. Obstetr. Crumpsall Hosp. Manch.

VALLANCE, Tony Roger Leicester General Hospital, Gwendolen Road, Leicester LE4 5PW Tel: 0116 249 0490; 20 Gloucester

Crescent, Melton Mowbray LE13 0AQ Tel: 01664 64791 — MB BS 1972 Lond.; MRCP (UK) 1977; MRCS Eng. LRCP Lond. 1972. (Westm.) Cons. Phys. in Geriat. Med. Leicester Gen. Hosp.

VALLANCE-OWEN, Mr Andrew John BUPA, 15-19 Bloomsbury Way, London WC1A 2BA Tel: 020 7656 2037 Fax: 020 7656 2708 Email: vallanca@bupa.com; 13 Lancaster Avenue, Hadley Wood, Barnet EN4 0EP Tel: 020 8440 9503 Fax: 020 8364 8770 — MB ChB 1976 Birm.; MBA Open 1994; FRCS Ed. 1982. Gp. Med. Dir. BUPA Lond. Socs: Worshipful Soc. Apoth.; Roy. Soc. Med.; BMA. Prev: Med. Dir. BUPA Health Servs.; Under Sec. & Scott. Sec. BMA; Provin. Sec. N. of Eng. BMA.

VALLANCE-OWEN, John 10 Spinney Drive, Great Shelford, Cambridge CB2 5LY Tel: 01223 842767; 17 St. Matthews Lodge, Oakley Square, London NW1 1NB Tel: 020 7388 3644 — MB BChir Camb. 1946; MA Camb. 1946, BA (Hons.) 1943, MD 1951; FRCPI (Hon.) 1970; FRCP Lond. 1962, M 1946; FRCPath 1971. (Camb. & Lond. Hosp.) Vis. Prof. Imperial Coll. of Sc. Technol. & Med. Hammersmith Hosp. Lond.; Cons. Phys. Lond. Indep. Hosp. Socs: Assn. Phys.; Med. Res. Soc.; Roy. Soc. Med. Prev: Foundat. Prof. & Chairm. Dept. Med., Chinese Univ. Hong Kong; Prof. Med. Qu.'s Univ. Belf. & Cons. Phys. Roy. Vict. Hosp. Belf.; Reader (Med.) Univ. Newc. & Cons. Phys. Roy. Vict. Hosp. Newc.

VALLE, Anne McKay (retired) 1/4 Greenhill Court, Edinburgh EH9 1BF Tel: 0131 447 4286 — LRCP LRCS Ed., LRFPS Glas. 1950; FFCM 1984, M 1974; DObst RCOG 1955. Prev: SCM. Hull HA.

VALLE, Juan William Department of Medical Oncology, Christie Hospital NHS Trust, Manchester M20 4BX Tel: 0161 446 8106 Fax: 0161 446 3299 Email: juan.valle@christie-tr.nwest.nhs.uk — MB ChB 1989 Sheff.; MSc 2000 (Oncology) Univ. of Manch.; MRCPI 1994. Sen. Lect./ Hon. Cons. (Med. Oncol.) Christie Hosp. NHS Trust; Hon. Cons. (Med. Oncol.) N. Manch. Gen. Hosp. NHS Trust. Socs: BMA; ASCO; UKCCR. Prev: Specialist Regist. (Med. Oncol.) Christie Hosp. NHS Trust Manch.; Research Regist. (Med. Oncol.) Christie Hosp. NHS Trust Manch.; SHO (Gen. Med.) Walsgrave Hosp. Coventry.

VALLE ATELA, Virginia Madeira Health Centre, 1A Madeira Road, Poole BH14 9ET — LMS 1994 Basque Provinces.

VALLELY, Andrew John Brian 29 Earl Road, Northfleet, Gravesend DA11 7AE — MB BS 1990 Lond.; MRCP (UK) 1994; DTM & H RCP Lond. 1992. (Roy. Free Hosp. Sch. Med.) Dist. Med. Off. Rabaraba Dist. & Diocese of Dogura, Milne Bay Province, PNG.

VALLELY, Carolyn Teresa Joan Andress, Annaghmore, Portadown, Craigavon — LRCPI & LM, LRSCI & LM 1962; LRCPI & LM, LRCSI & LM 1962.

VALLELY, Stephen Ronald Department of Radiology, Belfast City Hospital, Lisburn Road, Belfast BT7 9AB Tel: 02890 263840 Fax: 02890 263790 Email: stephen.vallely@bch.n-i.nhs.uk; Email: svallely@doctors.org.uk — MB BCh BAO 1985 Belf.; MD Belf. 1993; FFR RCSI 1996; FRCR 1991. (Qu. Univ. Belf.) Cons. Radiol. Belf. City Hosp. Prev: Cons. Radiol. Ulster Hosp. Dundonald.

VALLET, Elspeth Anne Woodlands Surgery, 24 Woodlands, Meeting House Lane, Balsall Common, Coventry CV7 7FX Tel: 01676 532587 Fax: 01676 535154; 73 Old Station Road, Hampton in Arden, Solihull B92 0HA Tel: 01676 32213 — MB BS 1976 Lond.; MRCS Eng. LRCP Lond. 1976; DRCOG 1981. (Roy. Free) GP Balsall Comon.

VALLIS, Christopher John Department of Paediatric Anaesthesia, Royal Victoria Infirmary, Newcastle upon Tyne NE1 4LP Tel: 0191 232 5131 Fax: 0191 282 5376 Email: c.j.vallis@ncl.ac.uk — MB BS 1975 Lond.; BSc Lond. 1972, MB BS 1975; FRCPCH 1997; FRCA 1980; DCH Eng. 1981. (Univ. Coll. Hosp.) Cons. Paediat. Anaesth. Roy. Vict. Infirm. Newc. u. Tyne; Hon. Clin. Lect. Univ. Newc. Socs: Assn. Paediat. Anaesth. Prev: Sen. Regist. (Anaesth.) St. Thos. Hosp. & Hosp. for Sick Childr. Lond.

VALLIS, Katherine Anne 37 Beech Croft Road, Oxford OX2 7AY — MB BS 1981 Lond.; MRCP (UK) 1984; FRCR 1988. (St. Bart.) Prev: Clin. Research Fell. ICRF Molecular Pharmacol. Gp.; Sen. Regist. (Clin. Oncol.) Hammersmith Hosp. Lond.

VALLIS, Mr Martin Philip Tel: 01502 505100 Fax: 01502 505101 — MB BS 1979 Lond.; FRCS Glas. 1985; MRCGP 1988; DRCOG 1987. GP LoW.oft.; Hosp. Practitioner (ENT) Jas. Paget Hosp. Gorleston Norf.

VALLIS, Susan Carol Regent Road Surgery, 10/12 Regent Road, Lowestoft NR32 1PA Tel: 01502 565252; Ashley House, Borrow Road, Oulton Broad, Lowestoft NR32 3PW — BM BS 1986 Nottm.; BMedSci Nottm. 1984, BM BS 1986; BSc Birm. 1976. Prev: GP LoW.oft Retainer Scheme.

VALLON, Alan Geoffrey Crawley Hospital, West Green Drive, Crawley RH11 7DH Tel: 01293 527866 — MB ChB 1972 Manch.; FRCP Lond. 1994; MRCP (UK) 1976; T(M) 1991. Cons. Phys. With Responsibil. c/o Elderly Crawley & Horsham Hosps.; Dir. Of Med. Educat., Surrey & Sussex healthcare NHS Trust. Socs: Brit. Soc. Gastroenterol. & Brit. Geriat. Soc. Prev: Sen. Regist. (Med. & Geriat. Med.) Middlx. Hosp. Lond.; Regist. (Med. & Gastroenterol.) Middlx. Hosp. Lond.; SHO (Med. & Gastroenterol.) Manch. Roy. Infirm.

VALLOW, Peter Warneford (retired) 38 Ashbourne Avenue, Cleckheaton BD19 5JJ Tel: 01274 873585 — MB ChB 1951 Leeds. Prev: GP Heckmondwike, W. Yorks.

VALLOW, Mrs Rachel Betty (retired) 38 Ashbourne Avenue, Cleckheaton BD19 5JJ — MB ChB 1950 Leeds. Prev: Ho. Surg. (O & G) Leeds Gen. Infirm.

VALLS BALLESPI, Jordi 10 Harefield Close, Enfield EN2 8NQ — LMS 1989 Barcelona. SHO (Med.) S.end Hosp. Socs: Assn. Study Obesity. Prev: SHO (Geriat.) Rochford Hosp. S.end Healthcare NHS Trust; Ho. Off. (Med.) Peterboro. Dist. Hosp.

VALLURI, Parthasarathy The Medical Centre, 32 High Street, Rishton, Blackburn BB1 4LA Tel: 01254 884226 Fax: 01254 726190 — MB BS 1973 Madras; MB BS 1973 Madras.

VALMAN, Hyman Bernard 105 Bridge Lane, London NW11 0EU Tel: 020 8458 1951 Fax: 020 8458 1951 — MB BChir Camb. 1958; MA Camb. 1958, MD 1974; FRCP Lond. 1978, M 1967; DCH Eng. 1963; DObst RCOG 1963; FRCPCH 1996. (Camb. & Westm.) p/t Cons. Paediat. N.wick Pk. Hosp. Harrow; Archiv. Roy. Coll. of Paediat. and Child Health. Socs: Fell. Roy. Soc. Med. Prev: Sen. Regist. Hosp. Sick Childr. Gt. Ormond St. Lond.; Regist. (Paediat.) Qu. Eliz. Hosp. Childr. Hackney; Cas. Off. W.m. Hosp.

VALMIKI, Vidyasagar Halappa 2 Hall Drive, Oadby, Leicester LE2 4HE — MB BS 1978 Poona; LRCP LRCS Ed. LRCPS Glas. 1983.

VALORI, Roland Mark Glocestershire Royal Infirmary, Gt. Western Rd, Gloucester GL1 3NN Tel: 01452 394620 Fax: 01452 394892 Email: r.valori@step1.net; Tel: 01242 526657 — MB BS 1976; MD Lond. 1984; MRCP (UK) 1978; T(M) 1989; MSc 2000 (Oxon.). Cons. Phys. & Gastroenterol. Glos. Roy. Hosp.; Clin. Tutor. Prev: Cons. Phys., Univ. Coll. and Middlx. Hosps. 1989-93.

VALSALAN, Umadevi The Surgery, 122 Sutton Road, Erdington, Birmingham B23 5TJ Tel: 0121 373 0056 Fax: 0121 382 3212; 22 Sir Alfreds Way, Sutton Coldfield B76 1ES Tel: 0121 329 3076 — MB BS 1966 Mysore; MRCOG 1974, DObst 1970. (Kasturba Med. Coll. Mangalore) Prev: Regist. (Ment. Subnorm.) Chelmsley Hosp. Birm.; SHO (Gyn. & Obst.) Leicester Gen. Hosp.; Ho. Off. (Gen. Surg.) S. Middlx. Hosp. Isleworth.

VALSALAN, Velandy Coombil 22 Sir Alfreds Way, Sutton Coldfield B76 1ES Tel: 0121 329 3076 — MB BS 1961 Karnatak; BSc (Zool.) Madras 1955; DPM RCPSI 1972. (Kasturba Med. Coll. Mangalore) Cons. Psychiat. (Ment. Subn.) Chelmsley Hosp. Birm. Socs: Inst. Ment. Subn. Prev: Sen. Regist. Chelmsley Hosp. Birm.; Regist. Towers Hosp. Leicester & Cane Hill Hosp. Coulsdon.

VAMADEVA, Praba 1 Maes yr Ysgol, Peniel, Carmarthen SA32 7BT Tel: 01267 238615 — MB BS 1985 Peradeniya; MRCP (UK) 1991.

VAMADEVAN, Thampiah Long Lane Medical Centre, 19 Long Lane, Halesowen B62 9LL Tel: 0121 559 2044 Fax: 0121 602 0555 — MB BS 1970 Ceylon.

VAN 'T HOFF, Walter (retired) Granida, 9 East St., Hambledon, Waterlooville PO7 4RX Tel: 01705 632382 — MB BChir 1946 Camb.; MA Camb. 1948; FRCP Lond. 1971, M 1952. Prev: Cons. Phys. N. Staffs. Hosp. Centre Stoke-on-Trent.

VAN AMELSVOORT, Therese Aldegonda Maria Josephina Flat 32, Boss House, 2 Boss St., London SE1 2PS; 89 Statensingel, Gouda 2805 BG, Netherlands Tel: 00 31 1820 27983 — Artsexamen 1991 Rotterdam. SHO (Psychiat.) Bethlem & Maudsley NHS Trust Lond.

VAN AMERONGEN, Andre Jacques, DFC (retired) Grafton House, Blisworth, Northampton NN7 3BN Tel: 01604 858208 — MB BCh Witwatersrand 1950; FRCOG 1966, M 1958. Prev: Sen. Cons. (O & G) Govt. Rhodesia & Nyasaland.

VAN ARENTHALS

VAN ARENTHALS, Adriana Johanna Sandrina Kenwood, Main Road, Bosham, Chichester PO18 8PH Tel: 01243 572727 — Artsexamen 1990 Free U Amsterdam; Artsexamen Free Univ Amsterdam 1990; DCH RCP Lond. 1993.

VAN ASCH, Patti Fishponds Health Centre, Beechwood Road, Fishponds, Bristol BS16 3TD; The Sign of the Dolphin, Westerleigh, Bristol BS37 8QQ Tel: 01454 312122 — MB BS 1964 Lond.; MRCS Eng. LRCP Lond. 1964; DObst RCOG 1966. (St. Mary's) Prev: Ho. Surg. Addenbrooke's Hosp. Camb.; Regist. (Anaesth.) S.mead Hosp. Bristol.

VAN BEINUM, Michael Elias Department of Adolescent Psychiatry, Possilpark Health Centre, Denmark St., Glasgow G21 Tel: 0141 531 6107 — MB ChB 1983 Ed.; SAPP; MPhil Ed. 1991; BSc (Hons.) Sussex 1974; MRCPsych 1988. (Edinburgh) Cons. Adolesc. Psychiat. PossilPk. Health Centre Glas.; Hon. Sen. Lect. Univ. Glas. Socs: (Scott. Exec.) Roy. Coll. Psychiat. (Child & Adolesc. Sect.); Clin. Tutor, Roy. Coll. of Psychiat.s.

VAN BESOUW, Jean-Pierre William Gerard Dept. of Anaesthesia, St. George's Hospital, London SW17 0QT Tel: 020 8725 3317 Email: jpvb@gas.mailbox.co.uk; Tel: 020 8541 1992 Email: jpbv@cableinet.co.uk — MB BS 1981 Lond.; BSc (Hons.) Lond. 1978, MB BS 1981; FRCA 1985. (St. Barts.) Cons. Anaesth. St. Geo. Hosp. Lond.; Examr. Roy. Coll. of Anaesth. Socs: Assn. Cardiothoracic Anaesth.; Assn. Anaesth. Prev: Sen. Regist. (Anaesth.) St. Bart., Hosp. for Sick Childr. & Whipps Cross Hosps. Lond.; Regist. (Anaesth.) St. Geo. Hosp. Lond.; SHO Rotat. (Med. Intens. Ther. Unit & Anaesth.) Whittington Hosp. Lond.

VAN BOXEL, Pieter Jacobus Willem West Berkshire Priority Care Service, 3-5 Craven Road, Reading RG1 5LF — MB ChB 1972 Cape Town; MRCPsych. 1977; FRCP 1999 (Psych). Cons. (Child & Adolesc. Psychiat.) Family & Young Persons Unit Reading. Prev: Sen. Regist. (Child & Adolesc. Psychiat.) Guys Hosp. Lond.

VAN BUREN, Alison Elizabeth Town Gate Practice, Chepstow Community Hospital, Tempest Way, Chepstow NP16 5XP Tel: 01291 636444 Fax: 01291 636465; Sylvian Cottage, Glyn Road, Tintern Parva, Chepstow NP16 6TH Tel: 01291 689315 — MB ChB 1988 Bristol; MRCP (UK) 1992; DFFP 1995. Socs: BMA. Prev: Trainee GP Chepstow; SHO Rotat. (Gen. Med.) E. Birm. Hosp.; Family Pract. Residency Progr. Denver Colorado, USA.

VAN BUREN-SCHELE, Michael Northern Devon Healthcare, North Devon District Hospital, Raleigh Park, Barnstaple EX31 4JB Tel: 012713 22665 Fax: 012713 11523 — MB ChB 1982 Leic.; MRCPsych. 1988. (Leicester) Cons. Psychiat. N. Devon Healthcare Barnstaple. Gen. Adult Psychiat. & Psychiat. of old age. Prev: Sen. Regist. (Psychiat.) St. Bart. & Homerton Hosps. Lond.; Sen. Regist. (Psychiat.) Warley Hosp. Brentwood.

VAN BUUREN, Caspar Maurits Dieuwert The Close, Wingate TS28 5LS — Artsexamen 1986 Amsterdam.

VAN COOTEN, Sarah Eileen 49 Hawksfield Road, London SE23 2TN — MB BS 1991 Lond.; DRCOG 1994. (Univ. Coll. Lond.) Socs: MRCGP.

VAN DE MEULEBROUCKE, Bart St. John's Court, Block 116, Howden, Livingston EH54 6PP — MD 1989 Louvain.

VAN DE PETTE, John Edward William Frimley Park Hospital, Frimley, Camberley GU16 7UJ Tel: 01276 604153 Fax: 01276 604924; Tel: 01483 894884 — MB BS 1977 Lond.; BSc (Hons.) Lond. 1974; FRCP Lond. 1991; MRCS Eng. LRCP Lond. 1977; FRCPath 1994. (Guy's) Cons. Haemat. Frimley Pk. Hosp. & Farnham Hosp.; Hon. Cons., Roy. Surrey Co. Hosp.; Speciality Lead Haematologist, Partnership Path. Prev: Sen. Regist. St. Thos. Hosp. Lond.

VAN DE VELDE, Robert Ijntze 2 Harthill Avenue, Gildersome, Morley, Leeds LS27 7EY — Artsexamen 1992 Amsterdam.

VAN DE WALLE, Jeroen Godelieve Jozef 9 Twyford Mews, Pig Lane, Bishop's Stortford CM22 7PA — Artsexamen 1991 Rotterdam.

VAN DEN BENT, Paul Jacques Gordon and Partners, 1 North Street, Peterborough PE1 2RA Tel: 01733 312731 Fax: 01733 311447 — Artsexamen 1986 Rotterdam; MRCGP 1990. (Erasmus Univ. Rotterdam)

VAN DEN BERGHE, Rosalind Cathryn 12 Woodland Close, Marlow SL7 3LE Email: vandenb@compuserve.com — BM BS 1980 Nottm.; BMedSci 1978.

VAN DEN BERK, Joannes Catharine Leon Marie Grantham Health Centre, Beckett House, Grantham Road, London SW9 9DL — Artsexamen 1989 Nijmegen. GP Princip.

VAN DEN BOS, Alexander 179 Broadfield Road, Moss Side, Manchester M14 7JH — MB ChB 1998 Manch.

VAN DEN BOSCH, Cornelia Anne Department of Public Health, East London & City Health Authority, 81-91 Commercial road, London E1 1RD Tel: 020 8983 4345 Fax: 020 8981 4811 — MB BS 1968 Lond.; MSc Distinc. (Clin. Trop. Med.) Lond. 1984, MD 1994; MRCP (UK) 1978; MRCS Eng. LRCP Lond. 1968; DCH Eng. 1977; Cert JCC Lond. 1980. (St. Mary's) Lead Cons. Communicable Dis. Control City & Port of Lond. & Hackney Dept. Pub. Health. E. Lond. & City AHA; Hon. Lect. (Toxicol.) St. Bart. Med. Coll.; Hon. Sen. Lect. (Microbiol.) Roy. Lond. Med. Coll.; Hon. Cons. Paediat. Kamuzu Centr. Hosp. Lilongwe, Malawi. Socs: Fell. Roy. Soc. Trop. Med. & Hyg.; Brit. Paediat. Assn. Prev: Sen. Med. Off. DoH Lond.; Sen. Research Fell. (Virol.) Roy. Postgrad Med. Sch. & Hon. Cons. Hammersmith Hosp. Lond.; Sen. Lect. & Hons. Cons. Paediat. Dept. Trop Paediat. Liverp. Sch. Trop. Med.

VAN DEN BROEK, Adrianus Johannes Cornelis Maria 2 The Green, Somerleyton, Lowestoft NR32 5PX Tel: 01502 730513 Email: audbrock@usa.net — Artsexamen 1993 Leiden.

VAN DEN BROEK, Alyson Elizabeth Laburnum House, Hinders Lane, Gloucester GL19 3EZ Tel: 01452 830424 — BM BS 1990 Nottm.; MRCGP. (Nottm.) Socs: Brit. Assn. Sport & Med.; Fac. Fam. Plann. & Reproduc. Health.

VAN DEN BRUL, Karen Ann Health Centre, Bishops Close, Spennymoor DL16 6ED Tel: 01388 811455 Fax: 01388 812034 — MB BS 1982 Newc.; MRCGP 1986; DRCOG 1985. p/t Gen. Practitioner, Spennymoor, C.Durh. Prev: Clin. Asst. (Diabetes) Bishop Auckland Gen. Hosp.

VAN DEN BRUL, Peter John (retired) Haverigg, The Park, Drinkstone, Bury St Edmunds IP30 9ST Tel: 01359 270384 — MB BS Lond. 1952; FFA RCS Eng. 1968; DA Eng. 1959. Prev: Cons. Anaesth. Bury St. Edmunds Health Dist.

VAN DEN DWEY, Katia Sandwell Heath Care NHS Trust, Hallam St., West Bromwich B71 4HJ — MD 1991 Ghent.

VAN DEN HURK, Peter Johannes Department of Obstetrics & Gynaecology, 7th Floor, N. Wing, St Thomas' Hospital, Lambeth Palace Road, London SE1 7EH; 53 Celestial Gardens, Lewisham, London SE13 5RP Tel: 020 8297 9842 — Artsexamen 1992 Amsterdam; DRCOG - RCOG 1995. (Amsterdam) Specialist Regist. (O & G), St. Thomas' Hosp., Lond., SE1. Prev: Lewisham Hosp.; Stoke-on-Trent Hosp.

VAN DER AA, Nathalie Flat 209, 36 Shad Thames, London SE1 2YE Tel: 020 7357 8366 — MD 1993 Louvain.

VAN DER HAUWAERT, Nicolas The Medical Specialist Group, PO Box 113, Alexandra House, St Martin's, Guernsey GY1 3EX — MD 1988 Louvain.

VAN DER HEIDEN, Elik Reinier Johannes 21A Brookfield Road, Basement Flat, Hackney, London E9 5AH Tel: 020 8533 0521 — Artsexamen 1988 Utrecht; FRCA 1997. (Rijksuniversiteit - Utrecht - Netherlands) Specialist Regist. (Anaesth.) Roy. Lond. Hosp. Socs: RCA; Assoc. of AN. In Gt. Britain & Irel.; OAA.

VAN DER HEIJDEN, Ludovicus Petrus Johannes Heathcliffe, Main St., Palterton, Chesterfield S44 6UR — Artsexamen 1985 Nijmegen.

VAN DER KNAAP, Jill 9 Elmwood Avenue, London N13 4HG — MB BS 1967 Lond.; MRCPsych 1972; DPM Eng. 1971. (Lond. Hosp.) Prev: Clin. Asst. Eric Shepherd Unit Leavesden Hosp. Herts.; Sen. Regist. (Sub-N.) Harperbury Hosp. Radlett; Sen. Regist. (Child Psychiat.) St. Mary's Hosp. Lond. & Paddington Centre for Psychother.

VAN DER LEE, Aileen Janet The Surgery, Station Road, Bridge of Weir PA11 3LH Tel: 01505 612555 Fax: 01505 615032 — MB ChB 1983 Ed.

VAN DER LIJN, Ronald 93 Sandringham Road, Doncaster DN2 5JA — Artsexamen 1993 Utrecht.

VAN DER LINDEN, HARALD HARRY EMANUEL M Trent Vale Medical Practice, 876 London Road, Trent Vale, Stoke-on-Trent ST4 5NX Tel: 01782 746898 — Artsexamen 1989 Nijmegen; Artsexamen 1989 Nijmegen.

VAN DER MERWE, William Gerard Doctors Mess, Royal Cornwall Hospital, Truro TR1 3UP — MB ChB 1991 Cape Town.

VAN DER MEULEN, Jacobus Josephus Nicolaas Marie 14 Sunbury Road, Eton, Windsor SL4 6BA — Artsexamen 1995 Rotterdam.

VAN DER MOST, Renee Nathalie Primavera, Wheatsheaf Enclosure, Liphook GU30 7EJ — MB BS 1998 Lond.; PhD Cambridge 1993; BA (Hons) Camb 1989.

VAN DER OEST, Christina Hendrika Stepney Green Medical Practice, 45-47 Ben Jonson Road, London E1 4SA Tel: 020 7790 1059 Fax: 020 7702 7454; 47C Brick Lane, London E1 6PU Tel: 020 7247 1864 — MB ChB 1982 Otago; DCH Otago 1986; Dip. Obst. Otago 1985. (Otago, NZ) GP Lond.

VAN DER PLAS, Frank Peter Wish Valley Surgery, Talbot Road, Hawkhurst, Cranbrook TN18 4NB Tel: 01580 753211 Fax: 01580 754612 — Artsexamen 1990 Amsterdam.

VAN DER PUTT, Rohan Patrick 24 Kenwood Gardens, Ilford IG2 6YQ — MB BS 1992 Lond.

VAN DER SANDE, Maria Antonia Bernarda 48 Nansen Village, 21 Woodside Avenue, London N12 8RW — Artsexamen 1985 Free U Amsterdam; Artsexamen Free Univ Amsterdam 1985.

VAN DER STAR, Richard John Department of Clinical Neurophysiology, Wessex Neurological Centre, Southampton General Hospital, Southampton SO16 6YD Tel: 02380 796786 Fax: 02380 798557; 27 Satchell Lane, Hamble, Southampton SO31 4HF — BM 1980 Soton.; FRCP 2000 Lond. Cons. Clin. Neurophysiol. Wessex Neurol. Centre Soton. Gen. Hosp. Prev: Sen. Regist. (Clin. Neurophysiol.) Wessex Neurol. Centre; Regist. (Med.) Soton. Gen. Hosp. & Qu. Alexandra Hosp. Portsmouth.

VAN DER VOET, Johannes Cornelis Maria South Cleveland Hospital, Marton Road, Middlesbrough TS4 3BW Tel: 01642 850850 Fax: 01642 854940 — Artsexamen 1989 Amsterdam. (Univ. Amsterdam) Cons. Clin. Oncol. S. Cleveland Hosp. Middlesbrough; Specialist in Radiother. 1995. Prev: Sen. Regist. (Clin. Oncol.) Christie Hosp. Manch.

VAN DER VOORT, Judith Henriette 23 Pontcanna Street, Cardiff CF11 9HQ — Artsexamen 1988 Utrecht; MRCP (UK) 1993.

VAN DER WALT, Lona Basement Flat 1, 72 Denbigh St., London SW1V 2EX — MB ChB 1991 Stellenbosch.

VAN DER WATT, Michael John 48 Stratford Drive, High Wycombe HP10 0QH — MB ChB 1985 Cape Town.

VAN DER WEYDEN, Barendina Johanna (retired) The Hollies, 11 Albion Hill, Loughton IG10 4RA Tel: 020 8508 6540 Fax: 020 8508 6540 — MB BS 1963 Lond.; MRCS Eng. LRCP Lond. 1963; DObst RCOG 1966. Prev: Assoc. Specialist (Ultrasound & Echocardiogr.) & Hon. Clin. Asst. (Gen. Med.) Whipps Cross Hosp. Lond.

VAN DESSEL, Michael Gerard The Spinney Medical Centre, 23 Whittle Street, St Helens WA10 3EB Tel: 01744 758999 Fax: 01744 758322; Aisling, 16 Elm Grove, Eccleston Park, Prescot L34 2RX Tel: 0151 426 6501 — MB BCh BAO 1982 NUI; BSc NUI 1984. Socs: Liverp. Med. Inst.; St. Helens Med. Soc.

VAN DIEPEN, Hendrikus Reinder 6 Butler Gardens, Market Harborough LE16 9LY — Artsexamen 1988 Groningen.

VAN DOORN, Ms Catharina Adriana Maria Great Ormond Street Hospital for Children, Cardiac Wing, Great Ormond Street, London WC1N 3JH Tel: 0207 4059200 Fax: 0113 392 8056 — Artsexamen 1984 Utrecht; FRCS (CTh) 1997; FRCS Eng. 1991; FRCS Ed. 1990; MD Leeds 1998. (State Univ. Utrecht, Netherlands) Sen. Clin. Lect. in Cardiothoratic Surg. Prev: Sen. Regist. (Paediat. Cardiothoracic Surg.) Birm. Childr.'s Hosp.; Sen Reg. (Paediat. Cardilthoracic Surg.) Gt. Ormand St. Hosp.; Sen. Regist. (Cardiothoracic. Surg.) Leeds Gen. Infirm.

VAN DORP, Francoise Anne Oaks Cottage, Enton, Godalming GU8 5AG — BM BCh 1990 Oxf.

VAN DORP, Maria Hester Oaks Cottage, Enton Green, Godalming GU8 5AG Tel: 01483 416605 — Artsexamen 1963 Leiden. (Leiden) Assoc. Specialist (Geriat. Med.) NW Surrey HA.

VAN DUIJN, Niklaas The Grange Practice, Allerton Clinic, Wanstead Crescent, Allerton, Bradford BD15 7PA Tel: 01274 541696 — Artsexamen 1990 Groningen. (Groningen) GP Bradford, W. Yorks.

VAN DYK, Jasper Jacobus PO Box 888, Dereham NR20 5TR — MB ChB 1991 Stellenbosch.

VAN ESSEN, Janet Clark (retired) 6 Hatlex Hill, Hest Bank, Lancaster LA2 6ET Tel: 01524 822616 — MB ChB 1941 Ed. Prev: SCMO (Community Med.) Bromley HA.

VAN EVERY, Thomas Hugo 28 Chantry View Road, Guildford GU1 3XS — MB ChB 1995 Birm.; ChB Birm. 1995. SHO (O & G) Chelsea & W.minster Hosp.

VAN EYK, Josef Johannes Sarum Road Hospital, Sarum Road, Winchester SO22 5HA — MB ChB 1982 Stellenbosch.

VAN GEENE, Mr Peter Academic Department of Obstetrics & Gynaecology, Northern Road Hospital, Herries Road, Sheffield S5 7AU — MB BS 1981 Lond.; FRCS Ed. 1985; MRCOG 1991. (Char. Cross) Birthright Research Fell. (Gyn. Oncol.) Acad. Dept. O & G Dudley Rd. Hosp. Birm. Prev: Regist. (O & G) S.mead Hosp. Bristol; Regist. (Surg.) King Edwd. VII Hosp. Windsor.

VAN GELDEREN, David Stewart 25 Eastry Avenue, Bromley BR2 7PE — MB BCh 1990 Witwatersrand.

VAN GELDEREN-SWART, Adriana Geertje 23 Fulmar Drive, East Grinstead RH19 3XL — Artsexamen 1992 Amsterdam.

VAN GRIETHUIJSEN, Hendrik Jan Oakdale, Flag Lane, Little Neston, South Wirral CH64 9RS — Artsexamen 1987 Utrecht.

VAN GRUTTEN, Mary (retired) 88 Gove Hill Road, Tunbridge Wells TN1 1ST — MB BS Lond. 1950; MRCS Eng. LRCP Lond. 1950. Prev: Cons. Dermat. Dartford & Gravesham, & Medway Health Dists.

VAN HAGEN, Thomas Christopher 319 Muswell Hill Broadway, London N10 1BY — MB BS 1995 Lond.

VAN HAMEL, Jennifer Clare Margaret Princess Margaret Hospital, Okus Road, Swindon SN1 Tel: 01793 426389; The Old Rectory, 36 The Street, Hullavington, Chippenham SN14 6DU — MB BS 1987 Lond.; FRCA 1992. Cons. Anaesth. P.ss Margt. Hosp. Swindon.

VAN HASSELT, Gillian Louise Mary 6 Dunkeld Road, Bournemouth BH3 7EN Tel: 01202 291666 Fax: 01202 292039 Email: gillvh@netcomuk.co.uk — MB BCh 1976 Witwatersrand; FFA RCS Eng. 1982. Cons. Anaesth. Poole Gen. Hosp. Trust.

VAN HEEL, David Alexander 149 Avondale Road, Shipley BD18 4QZ — BM BCh 1993 Oxf.; MA Cantab. 1994; MRCP (UK) 1993. (Oxf.)

VAN HEYNINGEN, Charles Clinical Laboratories, University Hospital Aintree, Lower Lane, Liverpool L9 7AL Tel: 0151 529 3907 Fax: 0151 529 3310 Email: charles.van_heyningen@aht.nwest.nhs.uk; 3 Grosvenor Close, Southport PR8 2TJ — MB BS 1973 Lond.; BSc Biochem. Lond. 1970; FRCPath 1996, M 1983. Cons. Chem. Path. Aintree Hosps. (NHS) Trust & S.port & Ormskirk (NHS) Trust; Hon. Lect. (Clin. Chem.) Univ. Liverp. Socs: Assn. Clin. Biochem.; Brit. Hyperlipidaemia Assn.; Roy. Coll. Pathol. Prev: Sen. Regist. (Chem. Path.) W.m. Hosp. Lond. & Kingston Hosp. Surrey; Regist. (Chem. Path.) St. Geo. Hosp. Lond.

VAN HILLE, Mr Philip Thomas Department of Neurosurgery, General Infirmary at Leeds, Great George St., Leeds LS1 2EX Tel: 0113 392 6648 Fax: 0113 392 6315; Grange House, 203 Shay Lane, Walton, Wakefield WF2 6NW Tel: 01924 253686 — MB ChB 1972 Cape Town; FRCS Eng. 1980. Cons. Neurosurg. Gen. Infirm. Leeds. Prev: Cons. Sen. Regist. (Neurosurg.) Leeds W.. HA.

VAN HOOGSTRATEN, Johannes Wilhelmus Antonius Petrus Friarage Hospital, Northallerton DL6 1JG — Artsexamen 1989 Groningen.

VAN HORICK, Helen Health Risk Resources International Ltd., 4th Floor, 40 Lime St., London EC3M 5EA Tel: 020 7220 7890 Fax: 020 7220 7891 Email: hvanhorick@hrri.co.uk; Fieldfare House, Manor Farm Barns, Bradford Road, Atworth, Melksham SN12 8HZ — MB BS 1977 Lond. Dir. Informat. Socs: Assoc. Mem. RCGP; Assoc. Mem. RCGP; BAMM. Prev: Dir., Nat. Centre for Clin. Audit, BMA; Managing Cons. PricewaterHo.; Sen. Cons. Ernst & Young.

VAN IDDEKINGE, Basil Department of Obstetrics & Gynaecology, Hammersmith Hospital, Du Cane Road, London W12 0NN — MB BCh 1966 Witwatersrand; FCOG S. Afr. 1972; MRCOG 1973. (Witwatersrand) Sen. Lect. (O & G) Hammersmith Hosp. Lond. Prev: Cons. (O & G) Baragwanath Hosp. Johannesburg, S. Africa; Regist. (O & G) Hammersmith Hosp. Lond. & Johannesburg Gen.; Hosp., S. Africa.

VAN KEMPEN, Christopher Edward Meddygfa Newydd, Main Street, Goodwick SA64 0BN Tel: 01348 872802 Fax: 01348 874717 Email: chris@goodwicksurgery.co.uk; 1 & 2 Rhoslannog Cottages, Mathry, Haverfordwest SA62 5HG Tel: 01348 872802 Fax: 01348 874717 Email: chris@goodwicksurgery.co.uk — BM

VAN LANY

1983 Soton. Prev: SHO (A & E) Weymouth & Dist. Hosp.; SHO (Orthop.) Weymouth & Dist. Hosp.; Ho. Surg. Dorset Co. Hosp. Dorchester.

VAN LANY, Peggy 79 Barrowby Gate, Grantham NG31 8RA — MD 1996 Louvain. (K.U. Leuven) SHO (O & G) P'boro. Dist. Hosp.

VAN LENNEP, Toni Doreen 29 Burlington Avenue, Richmond TW9 4DF — MB ChB 1989 Cape Town.

VAN LEUVEN, Brenda Diana (retired) 23 Priory Mansions, 90 Drayton Gardens, London SW10 9RG Tel: 020 7373 5888 — MD 1953 Lond.; MB BS 1946; FRCP Lond. 1977, M 1952; FRCR 1975; FFR 1962; DMRD Eng. 1958. Prev: Cons. Radiol. St. Stephen's & St. Mary Abbot's Hosps. Lond.

VAN LIESHOUT, Theodorus Antonius 4/14A Turner Street, London E1 2AS — MB BS 1987 Queensland.

VAN LOO, Greet North Tees General Hospital, Hardwick, Stockton-on-Tees TS19 8PE — MD 1992 Louvain.

VAN LOO, Ulrike Doris Butlesdon House, Low Buston, Morpeth NE65 0XY — State Exam Med. Hannover 1989.

VAN LOO-PLOWMAN, Ingrid Helen Geraldine 139 Hemingford Road, Islington, London N1 1BZ Tel: 0207 607 5307 — Artsexamen 1992 Leiden.

VAN MAARSEVEEN, Petrus Leonardus Newland Health Centre, 187 Cottingham Road, Hull HU5 2EG Tel: 01482 492219 Fax: 01482 441418 — Artsexamen 1985 Nijmegen; DRCOG 1992. (Katholieke Univ. Nijmegen) GP Hull.

VAN MARLE, William 18 St Mary's Road, Harborne, Birmingham B17 0HA — MB ChB 1978 Birm.

VAN MIERT, Matthew Marinus 18 Layfield Road, Brunton Park, Newcastle upon Tyne NE3 5AA; 9 Saxon Road, Hoylake, Wirral CH47 3AE — MB BS 1984 Lond.; MA Camb. 1985; FRCA 1990. (St. George's London) Cons. Anesth. Wirral Trust.

VAN MOURIK, Indra Darmini Maria Liver Unit, Birmingham Children's Hospital, Steelhouse Lane, Birmingham B4 6NH Tel: 0121 333 8255 Fax: 0121 333 8251; 23 Shooters Close, Birmingham B5 7LN Tel: 0121 440 8517 Email: ivanmourik@lineone.net — Artsexamen 1988 Amsterdam; MRCPI 1995. (Univ. Amsterdam) Specialist Regist. (Paediat.) City Hosp. NHS Trust, Birm. Socs: MRCPCH. Prev: Clin. Research Fell. & Hon. Regist. Liver Unit Birm. Childr. Hosp.

VAN MOURIK, Willem Jacobus 8 Gallalaw Terrace, Newcastle upon Tyne NE3 1TD — Artsexamen 1986 Utrecht; MRCPsych 1995.

VAN MULDERS, Kathleen Rotherham District General Hospital, Moorgate Road, Oakwood, Rotherham S60 2UD — MD 1992 Louvain.

VAN NIEUWBURG, Margriet Adriana Cornelia 6 Northbourne Avenue, Morpeth NE61 1JG — MB BS 1991 Newc. Ho. Off. (Gen. Med.) S. Tyneside Dist. Gen. Hosp. Prev: Ho. Off. (Gen. Surg.) Dryburn Hosp. Co. Durh.

VAN NIMMEN, Bart Royal Devon & Exeter Hospital (Wonford), Barrack Road, Exeter EX2 5DW — MD 1992 Louvain.

VAN NUNEN, An Rehabilitation Research Unit, Southampton General Hospital, Tremona Road, Southampton SO16 6YD — MD 1992 Louvain.

VAN OLDENBORGH, Mr Hermanus Marius 12 Upper Wimpole Street, London W1G 6LW Tel: 020 7935 3289 — MB ChB 1965 Cape Town; FRCS Ed. 1972; FRCSI 1977; DO Eng. 1975. Socs: Ophth. Soc. UK & Mem. Oxf. Ophth. Congr. Prev: Sen. Regist. Moorfields Eye Hosp. Lond.

VAN OSS, Helen Georgina Park Lane Surgery, Park Lane, Woodstock OX20 1UD Tel: 01993 811452 — MB BS 1978 Lond.; MRCGP 1982; DRCOG 1982.

VAN PAESSCHEN, Wim Epilepsy Research Group, 33 Green Square, London WC1N 3BG — MD 1984 Antwerp.

VAN PELT, Howard John Ferdinand London Road South Surgery, 366 London Road South, Lowestoft NR33 0BQ Tel: 01502 573333 Fax: 01502 581590; 53 Walmer Road, Lowestoft NR33 7LE Tel: 01502 568625 — MRCS Eng. LRCP Lond. 1968; DObst RCOG 1971. (Leeds)

VAN REENEN, Samantha 12 Rothesay Court, Harleyford Road, London SE11 5SU — MB BCh 1997 Witwatersrand.

VAN RHIJN, Maarten Flat 3, Priscilla House, Sunbury Cross Centre, Sunbury-on-Thames TW16 7BG — Artsexamen 1986 Rotterdam.

VAN ROOYEN, Anita 98A High Street, Edgware HA8 7HF — MB ChB 1992 Stellenbosch.

VAN ROOYEN, Elise 45 Kipling Road, Cheltenham GL51 7DG — MB ChB 1980 Pretoria.

VAN ROSS, Ernest Rodney Edward Disablement Services Centre, Withington Hospital, Cavendish Road, Manchester M20 1LB Tel: 0161 613 7257 Fax: 0161 613 7201; 12 Butley Lane, Prestbury, Macclesfield SK10 4HU — MB BS 1973 Bangalore; MCh (Orth) Liverp. 1983; FRCS Eng. 1979; FRCP 2000 Lond. Cons. Rehabil. Med. Withington Hosp. & Manch. Roy. Infirm. Socs: (Sec.) Amputee Med. Rehabil. Soc. (Pres.); Brit. Soc. Rehabil. Med. (Exec. Comm).

VAN ROSS, Rosemary Theresa Goretti Park Green House, Sunderland Street, Macclesfield SK11 6HW Tel: 01625 429555; 12 Butley Lane, Prestbury SK10 4HU Tel: 01625 820956 — MB BCh BAO; DCH; DRCOG; MRCGP. (Cork, Ireland) p/t GP, Macclesfield.

VAN RYSSEN, John Stephen Michael William Peter The Seven Dials Medical Centre, 24 Montpelier Crescent, Brighton BN1 3JJ Tel: 01273 773089 Fax: 01273 207098 — MRCS Eng. LRCP Lond. 1969.

VAN RYSSEN, Maureen Ellen Philomena Dobbins, Castle Lane, Bramber, Steyning BN44 3FB Tel: 01903 879051 — MB BS 1965 Lond.; MRCS Eng. LRCP Lond. 1964; FFA RCS Eng. 1972. (Roy. Free) Cons. Anaesth. Worthing & S.lands Hosp. Trust. Prev: Sen. Regist. Dept. Anaesth. Guy's Hosp. Lond.; Regist. (Anaesth.) Auckland Hosp. Bd., NZ; Ho. Phys. & Ho. Surg. Roy. Vict. Hosp. Folkestone.

VAN SAENE, Hendrik Karel Firminus Department of Medical Microbiology, University of Liverpool, PO Box 147, Liverpool L69 3BX Tel: 0151 706 4399 Fax: 0151 706 5805 Email: h.c.kelly@liv.ac.uk; 321 The Colonnades, Albert Dock Village, Liverpool L3 4AB — MD 1973 Louvain; PhD Groningen 1982; FRCPath 1997, MRCPath 1987. Reader (Med. Microbiol.) Univ. Liverp.; Hon. Cons. Microbiol. Roy. Liverp. Childr. NHS Trust Alder Hey. Socs: Eur. Soc. Clin. Microbiol. & Infect. Dis.; Brit. Assn. Med. Microbiols.

VAN SCHAICK, Suzanna Hilary 9 King Edward Street, Oxford OX1 4JA Tel: 01865 242657 Fax: 01865 200983; 6 Bankside, Headington, Oxford OX3 8LT Tel: 01865 450702 Fax: 01865 450398 Email: 100537.613@compuserve.com — BM BCh 1976 Oxf.; BA Oxf. 1972; MRCP (UK) 1978.

VAN SCHAYK, Marjolein Scapa Medical Group, Health Centre, New Scapa Road, Kirkwall KW15 1BQ Tel: 01856 885445 Fax: 01856 873556.

VAN SEENUS, Theodora Edith Community Child Health, Birling Ward, Preston Hall, Maidstone ME20 7NY — Artsexamen 1971 Leiden; DCH RCP Lond. 1986. (Leiden, The Nethrlands) Clin. Med. Off. (Community Child Health) Maidstone.

VAN SOMEREN, Robert Niall Melville 13 The Close, London N14 6DP — MB ChB 1979 Ed.; MD Ed. 1988; MRCP (UK) 1985. Cons. Phys. Chase Farm Hosp. Enfield.

VAN SOMEREN, Vivienne Hazel Department of Child Health, Royal Free Hospital, Pond St., London NW3 2QG Tel: 020 7794 0500 Fax: 020 7830 2210 Email: vivienne.vansomeren@rfh.nthames.nhs.uk; 13 The Close, London N14 6DP Tel: 020 8882 7239 — MB ChB 1976 Ed.; MD Ed. 1985; MRCP (UK) 1979. Cons. Paediat. & Sen. Lect. (Child Health) Roy. Free Hosp. Lond. Socs: FRCPCh; FRCP Edin. Prev: Lect. (Paediat.) UMDS Guy's & St. Thos. Hosps. Lond.

VAN SPELDE, J Standish Medical Practice, Rodenhurst, Church Street, Standish, Wigan WN6 0JP Tel: 01257 421909 Fax: 01257 424259 — Artsexamen 1988 Nijmegen; Artsexamen 1988 Nijmegen.

VAN STADEN, Gavin Nicholas 167 Hamlin Lane, Exeter EX1 2SQ — MB BCh 1996 Witwatersrand.

VAN STEENIS, Dick (retired) 11 Lilac Close, Milford Haven SA73 1DF Tel: 01646 690550 Fax: 01646 690550 Email: vsteenis@pgen.net — MB BS 1959 Adelaide. Prev: Clin. Asst. (Oncol.) St. Richards Hosp. Chichester.

VAN STIGT, Elisabeth Saskia Langford Medical Practice, 9 Nightingale Place, Bicester OX26 6XX Tel: 01869 245665 — MB BS 1989 Lond.; MRCGP 1994; DFFP 1994. GP Princip.

VAN'T HOFF, Hugh Colin 45 Eldon Terrace, Windmill Hill, Bristol BS3 4PA Tel: 0117 949 4481 — MB BS 1985 Lond.; BSc (Hons.) Lond. 1982, MB BS 1985; MRCGP 1993; DTM & H Liverp. 1990.

VAN'T HOFF, William Gordon Great Ormond Street Hospital, Great Ormond St., London WC1N 3JH Tel: 020 7405 9200 Fax: 020 7829 8841 Email: w.vanthoff@ich.ucl.ac.uk — MB BS 1983 Lond.; BSc (1st cl. Hons.) Lond. 1980, MD 1994; MRCP (UK) 1986; FRCPH 1999. (Guy's) Cons. Paediat. Nephrol. Gt. Ormond St. Hosp. for Childr. NHS Trust. Prev: Lect. (Paediat. Nephrol.) Inst. Child Health Lond.; Lect. (Paediat.) Guy's Hosp. Lond.; Regist. (Paediat.) John Radcliffe Hosp. Oxf.

VAN TERHEYDEN, Kenneth Malcolm René The Health Centre, Melbourn Street, Royston SG8 7BS Tel: 01763 242981 Fax: 01763 249197 — MB BS 1977 Lond.; MRCS Eng. LRCP Lond. 1977. (Roy. Free)

VAN TERHEYDEN, Nicolas John Eskdale René 11 Oaklands, Westwood Drive, Ilkley LS29 9RE — MB BS 1986 Lond.

VAN TOOREN, Richard 25 Greville House, Kinnerton St., London SW1X 8EY — MB BS 1966 Lond.; MRCS Eng. LRCP Lond. 1966.

***VAN TWUYVER, Paulien** 20 Elie Avenue, Barnhill, Dundee DD5 3SF — MB ChB 1986 Dundee; FRCA 1992.

VAN VELSEN, Cleo Lorely John Howard Centre, 2 Crozier Terrace, Hackney, London E9 6AT Tel: 020 8919 8562 Fax: 020 8919 8421 — MB BS 1984 Lond.; MRCPsych 1989. (Kings Coll. Hosp. Lond.) Cons. Forens. Psychotherapist John Howard Centre Lond.; Hon. Cons. Psychotherapist Maudsley Hosp. Lond.; Hon. Cons. Psychotherapist Gt. Ormond St. Lond. Socs: Founder Mem. Internat. Assn. Forens. Psychother.; Assoc. Mem. Brit. Inst. Psychoanal. Prev: Cons. Psychother. Maudsley Hosp. Lond.; Sen. Regist. (Psychother.) Maudsley Hosp. Lond.; Exam. Doctor Med. Foundat. c/o Victims of Torture.

VAN VELZEN, Professor Dick Fetal & Infant Pathology, Department of Pathology, Royal Liverpool Children's Hospital Alder Hey, Eaton Road, Liverpool L12 2AP Tel: 0151 707 0414 — Artsexamen 1979 Free U Amsterdam; Artsexamen Free Univ Amsterdam 1979. Prof. Fetal & Infant Path. Univ. Liverp.; Head Dept. Fetal & Infant Path. (Histopath.) Roy. Liverp. Childr. Hosp. Alder Hey; Research Cons. CIBA-GEIGY Pharmaceut. Horsham & CIBA-GEIGY Forschungs Inst. Basle. Switz. Socs: Soc. Paediat. Path. USA & Paediat. Path. Soc. Europe (Comm.). Prev: Head Electron Microscopy Dept. & Head Dept. Paediat. Path. SSDZ Delft,The Netherlands.

VAN VOLLEVELDE, Martha Irene Pontefract General Infirmary, 92 Southgate, Pontefract WF8 1PN Tel: 01977 600600 — Artsexamen 1988 Free U Amsterdam; Artsexamen Free Univ Amsterdam 1988.

VAN WOERDEN, Hugo Cornelis Danestone Medical Centre, Fairview Street, Danestone, Aberdeen AB22 8ZP Tel: 01224 822866 Fax: 01224 707532 — MB ChB 1987 Aberd.; MRCGP 1991; DRCOG 1993; DGM RCP Lond. 1992. (Aberdeen) GP; Med. Screening, BUPA.

VAN WOERKOM, Arthur Ernest 304 Pickhurst Lane, West Wickham BR4 0HT — BChir 1978 Camb.

VAN WYK, Andre Louis Flat 8, 125 Hornsey Lane, London N6 5NH — MB ChB 1983 Cape Town.

VAN WYK, Gerrit Jacobus Anaestetics Deptartment, Maidstone Hospital, Hermitage Lane, Maidstone ME16 9NN Tel: 01622 29000; 20 Chapmill, St. Quentins Road, Capetown 8001, South Africa — MB ChB 1979 Stellenbosch; BSc Stellenbosch 1974; DA (UK) 1990.

VAN ZINDEREN BAKKER, Rindert Dirk St John's Hill Surgery, 39 St. John's Hill, Sevenoaks TN13 3NT Tel: 01732 747202 Fax: 01732 747218; 70 Bradbourne Road, Sevenoaks TN13 3QA Tel: 01732 464772 Email: rbakker@aol.com — MB ChB 1968 Pretoria; MFHom 1984. (Cape Town Pretoria)

VAN ZON, Geert Jan 15 Cherry Tree Avenue, Scarborough YO12 5DX — Artsexamen 1994 Groningen.

VAN ZWANENBERG, Timothy David Adelaide Medical Centre, Adelaide Terrace, Newcastle upon Tyne NE4 8BE; 8 Queens Road, Jesmond, Newcastle upon Tyne NE2 2PP — MRCS Eng. LRCP Lond. 1971; MB Camb. 1972, BChir 1971; MRCGP 1977; DRCOG 1973. Sen. Lect. Dept. Family & Community Med. Univ. Newc. upon Tyne. Prev: Med. Supt. Nonga Base Hosp. Rabaul, Papua New Guinea; Provin. Health Off. E. New Brit. Papua New Guinea.

VAN ZYL, Jacobus Eduard The Head and Neck Unit, The Royal Marsden Hospital, Fulham, London SW3 6JJ — MB ChB 1981 Stellenbosch.

VAN ZYL, Margaret Elizabeth Newlands, Cud Lane, Edge, Stroud GL6 6ND Tel: 01452 812773 — MB ChB 1955 Aberd.; MA Aberd. 1949, MB ChB 1955. (Aberd.)

VANAT, Mohamedhusein Rajbhai 65 Warrior Square, Southend-on-Sea SS1 2JJ Tel: 01702 467679 Fax: 01702 603207; 68 Wyatts Drive, Thorpe Bay, Southend-on-Sea SS1 3DE Tel: 01702 585912 — MB BS 1969 Gujarat. (B.J. Med. Coll. Ahmedabad)

VANAT, Tarala Mohamedhusein 68 Wyatts Drive, Thorpe Bay, Southend-on-Sea SS1 3DE Tel: 01702 585912 — MB BS 1969 Gujarat. (M.P. Shah Med. Coll. Jamnagar)

VANCE, Gillian Helen Sarah Southampton General Hospital, Tremona Road, Southampton SO16 6YD Tel: 02380 777222; 12 Lansdowne Park, Lisburn BT27 5DJ Tel: 01846 601858 — MB BChir 1993 Camb.; MRCP (UK) 1995. Clin. Research Fell. Soton. Gen. Hosp. Socs: BMA; MDU. Prev: SHO (Paediat. Cardiol.) Soton. Gen. Hosp.

VANCE, John Peden (retired) Traquair, Holmwood Avenue, Uddingston, Glasgow G71 7AJ Tel: 01698 813134 — MD Glas. 1975, MB ChB 1960; FRCP Glas. 1987; FFA RCS Eng. 1965; DObst RCOG 1962. Hon. Clin. Lect. (Anaesth.) Univ. Glas. Prev: Cons. Anaesth. Roy. Infirm. Glas.

VANDEBERGHE, Colette Rosine Elise Hanna Lodge, Hamm Court, Weybridge KT13 8YF — MD 1985 Liege.

VANDELDT, Adrian Patrick 14 Sandymount Drive, Wallasey CH45 0LL — MB ChB 1993 Liverp.

VANDEN DRIESEN, Manik Mary 80F Randolph Avenue, London W9 1BG Tel: 020 7289 6647 — MB BS 1990 West. Austral.; DFFP 1996. Clin. Asst. (Genitourin. Med.) Lond. Prev: SHO (Genitourin. Med.) St. Thos. & Guy's Hosps. Lond.; SHO (Geriat.) Univ. Coll. & Middlx. Hosps. Lond.; SHO (Oncol.) St. Mary's Hosp. Lond.

VANDENBERGHE, Elisabeth Anne Michelle Haematology Department Floor A, Royal Hallamshire Hospital, Glossop Road, Sheffield S10 2JA Email: evandenb@hamp.mrc.ac.uk; The Barn, 23 Millhouses Lane, Sheffield S7 2HA — MB BCh BAO 1983 NUI; PhD Leuven 1992; MRCPI 1985; MRCPath 1993. (Univ. Coll. Dub.) Cons. Haemat. Roy. Hallamsh. Hosp. & Sheff. Childr. Hosp.; Hon. Lect. Sheff. Univ. Socs: Brit. Soc. Haematol.; Eur. Haematol. Assn. (Mem. Eur. Bone Marrow Transpl. Gp.). Prev: Sen. Regist. Rotat. (Haemat.) Univ. Coll. Hosp. Middlx.; Research Fell. Haemat. Malig. Cytogenetics Catholic Univ. of Louvain, Belgium; Regist. (Haemat.) Mater Miser. Hosp. Dub.

VANDENBURG, Malcolm John Positive Under Pressare, 21F Devonshire Place, London W1G 6HZ Tel: 020 7935 0110 Fax: 020 7486 0505; 26 Christchurch Hill, Hampstead, London NW3 1LG Tel: 020 7435 9386 Fax: 020 7435 2672 — MB BS 1973 Lond.; BSc (Hons.) Lond. 1970; FRCP Lond. 1996; FFPM RCP (UK) 1994. (St. Bart.) Pharmaceut. Dir. & MD, Positive under Pressure; Clin. Advantage Phaemacutical Servs.; Dir. Positive Solutions. Help with Addic.. Socs: Med. Res. Soc.; Fell. Amer. Coll. Clin. Pharmacol.; Amer. Acad. Pharmacat. Phys. Prev: Pres. & CEO IBRD-Rostrum Global Ltd. Romford; Dir. Clin. Research Merck Sharpe & Dohme UK; Lect. (Med.) & Hon. Sen. Regist. Lond. Hosp.

VANDENDRIESEN, Nedra Marguerite Westminster Hospital, Magill Department of Anaesthesia, Dean Ryle St., London SW1P 2AP Tel: 020 8746 8000; 41 Leith Mansions, Grantully Road, Maida Vale, London W9 1LH Tel: 020 7286 2022 — MB BS 1987 Western Australia; DTM & H RCP Lond. 1989. SHO (Anaesth.) W.m. Hosp. Lond.

VANDENDRIESSCHE, Marianne Adrien Withelmina 4 Upper Wimpole Street, London W1G 6LF Tel: 020 7323 2830 Fax: 020 7224 2930 — MD 1978 Ghent; Dip. Surg. Spec Belgium 1984. (Ghent University Medical School Belgium) Cons. Vasc. Surg. Institut Moderne Ghent, Belgium; Private Pract. Lond.; Cons. Vasc. Surg. St Vincent's Hosp. Ghent, Belgium. Socs: Fell. Roy. Soc. Surg. Belgium; Fell. Roy. Belgium Soc. Vasc. Surg.; Benelux Soc. Phlebology. Prev: Surg. Asst. Hopital Hotel Dieu, Rouen; Surg. Asst Hopital Notre Dame de Bon Secours, Paris; Surg. Asst. Univ. Hosp., Antwerp.

VANDENWIJNGAERDEN, Stany 52 Abbey Road, Eastbourne BN20 8TD — MD 1989 Louvain.

VANDERPUIJE, John Abraham 6 Hedgerley Gardens, Greenford UB6 9NT — MB BS 1970 Lond.; MRCS Eng. LRCP Lond. 1970.

VANDERVELDE, Elise Mimi 25 Sinclair Grove, London NW11 9JH Tel: 020 8455 9190 — MB BS 1961 Durh.; Dip. Bact. Lond 1966. (Newc.) Prev: Sen. Microbiol. Pub. Health Laborat. Serv. Lond.; SHO

VANDERWERT

(Path.) Roy. Free Hosp. Lond.; Ho. Surg. & Ho. Phys. Roy. Vict. Infirm. Newc.

VANDERWERT, Russell Travis 2 Broomfield Road, Leeds LS6 3DE — MB ChB 1977 Leeds.

VANDYK, Edward (retired) PO Box 5569, Newbury RG20 8YY — MB BS 1970 Lond.; MRCS Eng. LRCP Lond. 1970; MRCGP 1980.

VANEZIS, Professor Peter Department of Forensic Medicines & Science, University of Glasgow, Glasgow G12 8QQ Tel: 0141 330 4573 Fax: 0141 330 4602; 17 Thornly Park Avenue, Paisley PA2 7SD — MB ChB 1972 Bristol; PhD Lond. 1990; MD Bristol 1985; FRCPath 1990, M 1978; DMJ (Path.) Soc. Apoth. Lond. 1976; FRCP (Glas) 1998, M 1996. (Univ. Bristol) Regius Prof. Forens. Med. & Sci. & Head Dept. Univ. Glas.; Hon. Cons. Forens. Med. to Army; Hon. Cons. Forens. Med. Gtr. Glas. HB, & Govt. RePub. Cyprus & Medico-Legal Inst Santiago, Chile. Socs: Fell. (Counc.) Brit. Assn. Forens. Med.; BMA; (Pres.) Brit. Acad. Forens. Scis. Prev: Reader & Head (Forens. Med. & Toxicol.) Char. Cross & W.m. Med. Sch. Lond.; Sen. Lect. (Forens. Med.) Lond. Hosp. Med. Coll.

VANG, Senga Katrine 170 Oldcroft Place, Aberdeen AB16 5UJ — MB ChB 1998 Aberd.; MB ChB Aberd 1998.

VANGIKAR, Madhusoodan Baburao (retired) 12 Summerfield Drive, Tyldesley, Manchester M29 7PQ Tel: 01942 894046 — MB BS Poona 1954.

VANGIKAR, Michael Milind 4 Wendover Close, Noctorum, Birkenhead CH43 9HU Tel: 0151 652 5974 — FRCA 1997; MB ChB Liverp. 1991. Specialist Regist. (Anaesth.) Mersey Deanery.

VANHEGAN, Gillian Margaret 79 Harley St, London W1G 8PZ Tel: 020 7486 1586 Fax: 020 7486 0397; Westbourne, 9 Alverstone Rd, London NW2 5JS Tel: 020 8459 2311 Fax: 020 7486 0397 Email: gillian.vanhegan@virgin.net — MB BS 1970 Lond.; MRCS Eng. LRCP Lond. 1970; DObst RCOG 1972; MFFP 1993. (St. Bartholomew's Hospital Medical School) Med. Dir. & Cons. In Med. Gyn. & Psychosexual Med., Lond. Brook Advisory Centres; Cons. Psycho-Sexual Med. BUPA Lond.; Cons. Psychosexual Med. Riverside H.A. Lond. Socs: Inst. Psychosexual Med. & Fac. Family Plann.; Fac. Fam. Plann. & Reproductive Healthc/o R.C.O.G.; Brit. Menopause Soc. Prev: Sessional Med. Off. Camden & Islington AHA (T); SHO (Obst. Unit) Roy. Free Hosp. Lond.; Ho. Phys. St. Bart. Hosp. Lond.

VANHEGAN, Mr John Andrew David (retired) 79 Harley Street, London W1N 1DE Tel: 020 7487 4278 Fax: 020 7486 0397 Email: john.vanhegan@virgin.net — MB BS 1970 Lond.; FRCS Eng. 1976; MRCS Eng. LRCP Lond. 1970; Cert. Higher Surgic. Train. RCS Eng. 1982. Cons. Orthop. Surg. Lond. Prev: Sen. Regist. (Orthop.) Hammersmith Hosp. Lond.

VANHEGAN, Robert Ian Princess Margaret Hospital, Okus Road, Swindon SN1 8AA Tel: 01793 426676 Fax: 01367 244037 Email: vanheganri@doctors.org.uk; The Firs, 83 London St, Faringdon SN7 8AA Tel: 01367 242368 Fax: 01367 244037 — BM BCh 1970 Oxf.; DPhil Oxf. 1969, MA 1968; FRCPath 1991, M 1979. (Oxford) Cons. Path. P.ss Margt. Hosp. Swindon. Socs: Expert Witness Inst.; Path. Soc; Assn of Clin. Pathol. Prev: Clin. Tutor (Path.) Univ. Oxf.; Lect. (Physiol.) Lady Margt. Hall.

VANHOUSE, Sheila Hazel Meadowside Family Health Centre, 30 Winchcombe Road, Solihull B92 8PJ Tel: 0121 743 2560/742 5666 Fax: 0121 743 4216; 8 Burgess Croft, Hampton Coppice, Solihull B92 0QJ — BM BS 1984 Nottm.; MRCGP 1989; DRCOG 1988. (Nottm.) GP Solihull.

VANIA, Abdul-Kader Arrazi Medical Centre, 1 Evington Lane, Leicester LE5 5PQ Tel: 0116 249 0000 Fax: 0116 249 0088 Email: vandoc27@yahoo.co.uk — MB ChB 1987 Leic.; DFFP 1995; MRCP (UK) 1990. Regist. (Thoracic Med. & Neurol.) Centr. Middlx. Hosp. Lond.; Clin. Asst. Dept. Endocrinol. LRI. Prev: SHO (Endocrinol., Neurol., Dermat. & Haemat.) Leic. Roy. Infirm.

VANIER, Therese Marie (retired) 12 Chestnut House, Barston Road, London SE27 9HD Tel: 020 8761 4670 — MB BChir 1953 Camb.; FRCP Lond. 1978, M 1959. Prev: Cons. Phys. St. Christopher's Hospice Lond.

VANITA, Dr 29 West End, Sherborne St John, Basingstoke RG24 9LE — MB BS 1970 Panjab.

VANKELECOM, Frieda Watford General Hospital, Vicarage Road, Watford WD18 0HB Tel: 01923 217415 — MD 1990 Louvain.

VANN, Adrian Michael 14 Ecton Lane, Sywell, Northampton NN6 0BA — MB ChB 1993 Liverp.

VANN, James Anthony St Thomas Court Surgery, St. Thomas Court, Church Street, Axminster EX13 5AG Tel: 01297 32126 Fax: 01297 35759 — MB BS 1978 Lond.; MA Oxf. 1972; DRCOG 1982.

VANNER, Anne Marie Narvik Ho., Princess Alexander Hosp., Addison House, Fourth Avenue, Harlow CM20 1DF; 21 Rowney Gardens, Sawbridgeworth CM21 0AT Tel: 01279 723431 Fax: 01279 724151 Email: andy-vanner@yahoo.co.uk — MB BCh 1967 Wales; MRCGP 1981; AFOM RCP Lond. 1993. (Cardiff) Occupat.al Health Phys.; Company Med. Off. Nortel Networks & Merck Sharpe & Dohme Harlow; Occupat. Health Phys. P.ss Alexandra Hosp. NHS Trust Harlow; Sen. Occupat. Health Adviser to Harlow Occupat. Health Serv.; Health & Safety Apptd. Doctor for Lead Asbestos & Ionising Radiat.; Occupat.al Health Phys, to N.I.B.S.C.; Sen. Clin. Fell. in OCI Med. Addenbrookes Hosp., Camb. Socs: BMA; Soc. Occupat. Med.; Assoc. Mem. Fac. Occupat. Med. Prev: Retd. G.P. Addison Ho. Harlow.

VANNER, Richard Guy Gloucestershire Royal NHS Trust, Great Western Road, Gloucester GL1 Tel: 01452 528555 — MB BS 1981 Lond.; FRCA 1986. Cons. Anaesth. Glos. Roy. NHS Trust.

VANNER, Tracey Frances Margaret Good Hope Hospital, Rectory Road, Sutton, Coldfield B75 7RR — MB BCh 1987 Wales; MRCOG 1993. Cons. Obst. & Gynaecologist, Good Hope Hosp. NHS Trust, Sutton, Coldfield. Socs: Brit. Fetal Matern. Med. Soc.; Birm. & Midl.s Obst. & Gyn. Soc.

VANNIASEGARAM, Mr Iyangaran The Willows, St. George's Hospital, 117 Suttons Lane, Hornchurch RM12 6RS Tel: 01708 465462 Fax: 01708 465158 Email: ivanniasegaram@compuserve.com — MB BS 1977 Sri Lanka; MSc (Med.) Lond. 1991; FRCS Ed. (Orl.) 1987; DLO RCS Eng. 1984. Cons. Audiological Med. BHB Community Health Care NHS Trust & Gt. Ormond Hosp. for Childr. NHS Trust. Socs: BMA; Brit. Assn. Audiol. Phys.; Internat. Assn. Phys. in Audiol. Prev: Sen. Regist. (Audiological Med.) Nat. Hosp. Neurol. & Neurosurg., Roy. Nat. Throat, Nose & Ear Hosp. & Gt. Ormond St. Hosp.; +Lond.

VANSTRAELEN, Michel 55 Castleton Road, Ilford IG3 9QW — MD 1986 Louvain.

VAQUAS, Shah Muhammad 1 Hillside, Welwyn Garden City AL7 4PZ — MB BS 1982 Karachi; MRCPI 1993.

VAQUAS, Shams 10 Canonsfield Road, Welwyn AL6 0QH — MB BS 1985 Karachi; FRCS Ed. 1990.

VARA, Roshni 120 Central Road, Worcester Park KT4 8HT — MB BS 1998 Lond.

VARADA REDDY, Peta Srinivasulureddy Department of Radiology, Medway Hospital, Windmill Road, Gillingham ME7 5NY — MB BS 1973 Sri Venkateswara; BSc Sri Venkateswara 1967, MB BS 1973; FRCR 1982; DMRD Eng. 1979; DMRD Madras 1976. (Kurnool Med. Coll.) Cons. Radiol. Medway Hosp. Prev: Cons. (Radiol.) St. John's Hosp. Livingston; Sen. Regist. Roy. Infirm. Edin.; Regist. (Radiol.) Roy. Infirm. Edin. & St. Peter's Hosp. Chertsey.

VARADARAJAN, Chathapurum Ramanathan 2 Daphene Gardens, Limavady Road, Waterside, Londonderry BT47 6LX Tel: 01504 44707 — MB BS 1969 Mysore; BSc Kerala 1962; FFA RCSI 1974. (Kasthurba Med. Coll. Mangalore) Cons. Anaesth. Altnagelvin Hosp. Lond.derry. Socs: Intractable Pain Soc. Gt. Brit. & Irel. Prev: Tutor & Regist. Dept. Anaesth. S. Belf. Gp. Hosps.; Cons. i/c Pain Relief Clin. Altnagelvin Hosp. Lond.derry.

VARADARAJAN, Mr Raghu Tudor Cottage, 63 Borrowcop Lane, Lichfield WS14 9LS Email: 106575.3377@compuserve.com — MB BS 1988 Madras; FRCS Ed. 1992. Regist. (HPB Surg.) St. Vincent's Hosp. Elm Pk. Dub. Prev: Regist. (Vasc. Surg.) Galway; Regist. (Gen. Surg.) P.ss Margt. Hosp. Swindon.

VARADARAJAN, Mr Sadagopan James Paget Hospital, Great Yarmouth NR31 6LA — MB BS 1975 Madras; MS (Gen. Surg.) Madras 1978, MB BS 1975; FRCS Ed. 1986. Specialist Regist., Dept. of Surg., James Paget Hosp. Gt. Yarmouth. Prev: Staff Surg. Qu. Eliz. Hosp. King's Lynn.

VARADHARAJAN, Subbaraman 14 New Heath Close, Wednesdfield, Wolverhampton WV11 1XX — MB BS 1988 Madras.

VARADI, Stefan 9 Penton Hall, Penton Hall Drive, Staines TW18 2HR Tel: 01784 456501 — MD Prague 1929; FRCPath 1964. (Charles Univ. Prague) Emerit. Haemat. N. Gen. Hosp. Sheff. Socs: Internat. Soc. Haematol.; Brit. Soc. Haematol.; Roy. Soc. Med.

Prev: Clin. Asst. Med. Clinic, Chas. Univ., Prague; Lt.-Col. Phys. i/c Milit. Hosp. Prague; Cons. Haemat. N.. Gen. Hosp. Sheff.

VARAGUNAM, Thambipillai 27 Edenvale Road, Mitcham CR4 2DP — MB BS 1955 Ceylon; MRCP (UK) 1961.

VARAH, Sri 22 Augusta Close, Grimsby DN34 4TQ — MB BS 1978 Sri Lanka.

VARATHARAJ, Jayaratnam 22 Allens Road, Enfield EN3 4PN — MB BS 1976 Sri Lanka; LRCP LRCS Ed. LRCPS Glas. 1985.

VARAWALLA, Nermeen Yunus 14 Ashworth Mansions, Elgin Avenue, London W9 1JL — MB BS 1985 Bombay; DPhil Oxf. 1992; MD Bombay 1988; MRCOG 1993. Sen. Regist. Rotat. (O & G) W. Midl. Prev: Regist. Rotat. Oxf.; Rhodes Research Fell. Univ. Oxf.; Lect. (O & G) Univ. Bombay.

VARCHEVKER, Jose Arturo 27 Dunstan Road, London NW11 8AG Tel: 020 8381 4555 Fax: 020 8381 4477 — Medico Buenos Aires 1968; Social Psych. Buenos Aires 1967. Assoc. Specialist (Psychiat.). Socs: Brit. Psychoanal. Soc.; Brit. Inst. Psychoanal.; Fell. Lond. Centre of Psychotherap. Prev: Clin. Asst. MarlBoro. Family Serv.; Cons. N.W. Thames RHA; Regist. Cassel Hosp. Richmond & Henderson Hosp. Sutton.

VARDE, Kishor Department of Obstetrics & Gynaecology, East Glamorgan General Hospital, Church Village, Pontypridd CF38 1AB — MB BS 1959 Durham.

VARDI, Glen Droitwich Knee Clinic, St Andrew's Road, Droitwich WR9 8YX Tel: 01905 794558 Fax: 01905 795916; 80A Southover, London N12 7HB — MB ChB 1984 Pretoria.

VARDILL, David Melbury, Broad Oak, Sturminster Newton DT10 2HG — MB BCh 1998 Wales.

VARDON, Valerie Mary Elderly Health Services, Queen Alexandra Hospital, Cosham, Portsmouth PO6 3LY Tel: 023 92 286 059; 12 Dornmere Lane, Waterlooville PO7 8QH Tel: 023 9226 3723 — MB BS 1972 Newc.; MRCP (UK) 1977. Assoc. Specialist (Elderly Health Serv.) Qu. Alexandra Hosp. Portsmouth. Prev: Sen. Community Med. Off. (c/o Elderly) Newc. HA; Sen. Regist. (Geriat.) Newc. Gen. Hosp.

VARDY, Dulcie Lucia Fieldway, West Strand, West Wittering, Chichester PO20 8AU — MB ChB 1956 Leeds; DPH Lond. 1963. (Leeds)

VARDY, Emma Rachael Louise Cunningham Pele House, Middle Road, Shilbottle, Alnwick NE66 2XS — MB ChB 1998 Sheff.; MB ChB Sheff 1998. Sho, (A & E) N.ern Gen. Hosp. Sheff.. Prev: HO, Rotat. N.ern Gen. Hosp.

VARDY, Jennifer Margaret 1/L 5 Peel Street, Glasgow G11 5LL — MB ChB 1994 Glas.

VARDY, Peter Ivan War Pensions Agency, Norcross, Blackpool FY5 3TA Tel: 01253 333134 — MB BS Lond. 1962; MRCGP 1971; DObst RCOG 1964; AKC 1962. (Westm.) Med. Adviser War Pens. Agency Blackpool. Prev: GP Runcorn; Ho. Surg. & Ho. Phys. St. Stephen's Hosp. Chelsea; Ho. Surg. (O & G) & Ho. Phys. (Paediat.) Chester City Hosp.

VARDY, Sarah Brigitte c/o Mr R Vardy, 4 Bracken Lane, Retford DN22 7EU — MB BS 1992 Lond.

VARDY, Mr Stephen James, Wing Cdr. RAF Med. Br. Retd. Ophthalmic Department, Peterborough District General Hospital, Thorpe Road, Peterborough PE3 6DA Tel: 01733 875730 Fax: 01733 874939 — MB ChB 1982 Birm.; FRCS Ed. 1990; FRCOphth 1993. (Birmingham) Cons. Ophth. PD Hosp.s Trust; Cons. Adviser (Ophth.) RAF; Cons. Ophth. MDHU P'boro. Socs: UK Soc. Cataract & Refractive Surg.; RCM. Prev: Cons. Ophth. RAF (H) Wroughton; Fell. Moorfields Eye Hosp. Lond.; Sen. Regist. The Eye Hosp. Soton.

VAREY, Nicolas Calvert Caduceus, Main St., Knedlington, Goole DN14 7EU Tel: 01430 430833 Fax: 01430 431178 Email: nick.varey@lineone.net — MB ChB St. And. 1965; FFPM 1994, M 1990. (St. And.) Med. Dir. Reckitt & Colman Ltd. Hull. Socs: Hull Med. Soc. Prev: Chairm. Roy. Hull Hosps. Trust; Specialist (Dermat.) Camb. Milit. Hosp. Aldershot; Ho. Surg. & Ho. Phys. Hull Roy. Infirm.

VARGHESE, Chirakal Mathai 47 Winterfield Drive, Bolton BL3 4TE — MB BS 1972 Kerala; MRCP 1 1985; DCH; DCCH Edin 1986; DTM & H Liverp. 1986; MSc Manchester, 1991. Cons., Community Pediatrician, in Audiol.

VARGHESE, David 12 Abbey Drive, Church Lane, London SW17 9PN — MB ChB 1995 Liverp.

VARGHESE, Gracy Usha Pramila Central Middlesex Hospital, Park Royal, London NW10 7NS Tel: 020 8965 5733; 12 Abbey Drive, Church Lane, London SW17 9PN Tel: 020 8767 9351 Fax: 020 8767 9351 Email: mobile 0585 686295 — MB BS 1972 Kerala; BSc Kerala 1965; MFFP 1993; MRCOG 1989; DRCOG 1983. (Trivandrum Med Coll Kerala India) Locum Cons. Obstet & Gyn. Socs: Brit. Menopause Soc.; BMJ; MRCOG. Prev: Cons. Obst. Gyn. P.ss Alexandra Hosp. Harlow Essex.

VARGHESE, Mr Jose Chacko Department of Radiology, Beaumont Hospital PO Box 1297, Beaumont Road, Dublin, Republic of Ireland; 236 Great West Road, Hounslow TW5 0BJ Tel: 020 8572 2634 — MB ChB 1985 Glas.; FRCS Ed. 1989; FRCR 1994. Sen. Regist. (Diagn. Radiol.) N. Staffs. Hosp. Trust.; Lect. (Diagn. Radiol.) Beaumont Hosp. Dub. Socs: BMA.

VARGHESE, Manalil Alexander High Street Medical Centre, 91/91A High St., Wrekenton, Gateshead NE9 7JR Tel: 0191 491 0666 — MB BS 1975 Kerala. GP Gateshead, Tyne & Wear.

VARGHESE, Mathew 69A Carrickfergus Road, Larne BT40 3JX Tel: 01574 270283 Email: varghese68@freeserve.co.uk — MB BS 1974 Nagpur; FRCP Lond. 1997; MRCP (UK) 1977. (Govt. Med. Coll. Nagpur) Cons. Phys. Moyle Hosp. Larne; Fell. Ulster Med. Soc. Socs: Brit. Geriat. Soc. Prev: Sen. Regist. (Geriat. Med.) Roy. Vict. Hosp. Belf.

VARGHESE, Mr Soonu West Cumberland Hospital, Hensingham, Whitehaven CA28 8JG Tel: 01946 693181 Email: svarghese@compuserve.com; Willowdene, Little Broughton, Cockermouth CA13 0YG Tel: 01900 824914 — MB BS 1973 Mysore; FRCS Ed. 1983; FCOphth 1989; DO RCS Eng. 1978. Cons. Ophth. W. Cumbld. Hosp. Whitehaven; Mem. Coll. Ophth.; Mem. (Internat. Mem.) Amer. Acad. Ophth. Socs: N. Eng. Ophth. Soc.; Eur. Soc. Colossal & Refractive Surg. Prev: Cons. & Sen. Regist. Al-Qassimi Hosp. Sharjah UAE; Regist. S.. Gen. Hosp. Glas.

VARIA, Haren Nitin Tel: 07968 824549 Email: haren@carrotmail.com; 1 Craigweil Close, Stanmore, London HA7 4TR Tel: 07968 824549 Email: haren@carrotmail.com — MB ChB 1997 Leicester. (University of Leicester) Specialist Regist., Diagnostic Radiol., N. Manch. Train. scheme. Prev: Sen. Ho. Off., Kettering Gen. Hosp., N.ants.

VARIAN, John Anthony 7B Follet Road, Toposham, Exeter EX3 0JP — MB BCh BAO 1979 NUI; MRCPsych 1985.

VARIEND, Sadick 94 Ashdell Road, Broomhill, Sheffield S10 3DB Tel: 0114 266 0404 — MD 1979 Cape Town; MB ChB 1965; FRCP Lond. 1990; MRCP (UK) 1972; FRCPath 1989, M 1977; DCH Eng. 1971. (Cape Town) Cons. Histopath. Sheff. Childr. Hosp.; Hon. Clin. Lect. (Path. & Paediat.) Univ. Sheff.

VARKER, Jonathon Andrew 376 St Helens Road, Bolton BL3 3RR Tel: 01204 62418; 11 Newstead Drive, Bolton BL3 3RE Tel: 01204 64123 — MB ChB Manch. 1989; MRCGP 1993.

VARKEY, Arun Thomas Roche House, 33 Eastfield Crescent, Laughton, Sheffield S25 1YT — MB BS 1981 Berhampur.

VARKEY, Sujatha Roche House, 33 Eastfield Crescent, Laughton, Sheffield S25 1YT — MB BS 1985 India; MRCP (UK) 1990.

VARKEY, Thoppil Antony Willenhall Medical Centre, Croft/Gomer Street, Willenhall WV13 2DR Tel: 01902 600833 Fax: 01902 609403; 76 Bilston Road, Willenhall WV13 2JL Tel: 01902 636840 — MB BS 1972 Mysore. (Kasturba Med. Coll. Mangalore) GP Willenhall. Prev: Regist. (Psychiat.) Worcester Roy. Infirm. (Newton Br.) & Towers Hosp. Leics.; Regist. (Psychiat.) Stallington Hosp. Stoke-on-Trent.

VARLEY, Bruce Quinton 5 Albion Mews, Thornhill Road, London N1 1JX Tel: 020 7607 5723 Fax: 020 7607 5723 — MRCS Eng. LRCP Lond. 1976; BSc (Physiol.) Lond. 1970, MB BS 1976; FFA RCS Eng. 1980. (St. Bart.) Cons. Anaesth. St. Bart. Hosp. Lond.; Cons. Anaesth. King Edwd. VII Hosp. for Offs. Lond. Socs: Fell. Roy. Soc. Med.; Assn. Anaesth. GB & Irel. & Harveian Soc. Lond. Prev: Cons. Anaesth. St. Marks Hosps. Lond.; Cons. Anaesth. & Hon. Lect. Groote Schuur Hosp. Univ. Cape Town.

VARLEY, Edith Mary (retired) 7 Melrose Crescent, Hale, Altrincham WA15 8NN Tel: 0161 980 6437 — BM BCh 1957 Oxf.; FFA RCS Eng. 1965; DA Eng. 1961. Prev: Cons. Anaesth. Wythenshawe Hosp. Manch.

VARLEY, Gordon Jesse (retired) 9 Sycamore Crescent, Macclesfield SK11 8LL Tel: 01625 425741 — MB ChB Birm. 1955. Prev: Ho. Phys. & Ho. Surg. (Obst.) Solihull Hosp.

VARLEY, Gordon Ward 23 Old North Road, Wansford, Peterborough PE8 6LB — MB ChB 1983 Leeds.

VARLEY

VARLEY, Rose Anne 25 Mitford Road, London N19 4HJ — MB BCh BAO 1975 NUI.

VARLEY, Ruth 41 Tower Street, Barnsley S70 1QS — MB ChB 1995 Leeds.

VARLEY, Simon Charles 129 Regent Road, Lostock, Bolton BL6 4DX — MB BS 1988 Lond.; FRCA 1993. Cons. (Anaesth.) Manch. Roy. Infirm.

VARLEY, Yvonne Worth 261 New hey Road, Huddersfield HD3 4GH Tel: 01484 648967 — BM 1977 Soton.; BSc Lond. 1966; DCH RCP Lond. 1984; DCCH RCP Ed. 1984; DFFP 1998; DOccMed 1998. Occupat.al Med. Private Provides. Socs: Soc. Occupat. Med.; Hudds. Med. Soc. (Pres. 1999-2000). Prev: Occupat.al Med. Adviser Univ. Huddersfield HD1 3DH; Princip. GP The Univ. Huddersfield HD1 3DH.

VARMA, Aarti 42 Alwen Avenue, Huddersfield HD2 2SJ — MB ChB 1992 Leeds. Prev: SHO (Orthop.) Castle Hill Hosp. Cottingham; SHO (Gen. Surg.) Castle Hill Hosp.

VARMA, Alakh Niranjan (retired) Rauceby Hospital, Sleaford NG34 8PP Tel: 01529 416048 Fax: 01529 488239 — MB BS 1956 Patna; BSc Patna 1949; MRCPsych 1972; DPM Eng. 1971; DPM Ed. 1971. Cons. Child Psychiat. S. Lincs. Health Dist. Prev: Sen. Med. Off. Min. of Health, Ghana.

VARMA, Aloke 9 Stone Street, Southsea PO5 3BN — MB ChB 1996 Manch.

VARMA, Bhola Nath 32 Brookfield Drive, Boothstown, Worsley, Manchester M28 1JY — MB BS 1954 Patna; TDD Wales 1958. (Patna) Socs: BMA. Fell. Amer. Coll. Chest Phys. Prev: Regist. Chest Dis. E. Birm. Hosp. Birm. & Birm. Chest Clinic, Manch.; Chest Clinic & Monsall Hosp Manch.

VARMA, Chetan 95 Montbelle Road, London SE9 3NY — MB BS 1992 Lond.; BSc Hons. Lond. 1989, MB BS 1992.

VARMA, Mr Jagmohan Singh Department of Surgery, The Medical School, The University, Newcastle upon Tyne NE2 4HH Tel: 0191 282 4384 Fax: 0191 282 0330 Email: j.s.varma@ncl.ac.uk; The West Wing, Netherton Hall, Nedderton Village, Bedlington NE22 6AS Tel: 01670 823185 Fax: 01670 821274 Email: j.s.varma@ncl.ac.uk — MB ChB 1977 Ed.; BSc (Hons.) Ed. 1974, MD 1988; FRCS Ed. 1982. (Ed.) Sen. Lect. & Hon. Cons. Surg. Med. Sch. Newc. u. Tyne; Vis. Lect. (Surg.) P. Wales Hosp, Chinese Univ. Hong Kong, 1988. Socs: Surgic. Research Soc. UK; Assn. Coloproctol.; Brit. Soc. Gastroenterol. Prev: Sen. Regist. (Gen. Surg.) Teachg. Hosp. Edin.; Wellcome Trust Surgic. Research Fell. Univ. Edin. Dept. Surg. & Urol. W.. Gen. Hosp. Edin.; SHO (Path.) Edin.

VARMA, Kailash Behari Colinton Road Surgery, 163 Colinton Road, Edinburgh EH14 1BE — MB BS 1962 Patna. (Patna) GP Edin.

VARMA, Mahendra Pratap Singh Erne Hospital, Enniskillen BT7 6AY Tel: 02866 324711 Fax: 02866 329655; Sionghasan, Bellanleck, Enniskillen BT92 2BA Tel: 02866 348770 — LRCPI & LM, LRSCI & LM 1969; PhD 1975; FRCP Lond. 1996; FRCP Glas. 1988; FRCPI 1984; MRCP (UK) 1977; FESC 1989; FCCP 1987. (RCSI) Cons. Phys. & Cardiol. Erne Hosp. Enniskillen. Socs: Irish Cardiac Soc.; Fell. Roy. Acad. Med. Dub.; Fell. Amer. Coll. Chest Phys.

VARMA, Meena Colinton Road Surgery, 163 Colinton Road, Edinburgh EH14 1BE; (Surgery), 30 Chesser Crescent, Edinburgh EH14 1SB Tel: 0131 443 2456 — MB BS 1966 Ranchi; DObst RCPI 1975. (Rajendra Med. Coll.)

VARMA, Munivenkatappa Ravindra 43 Fairholme Avenue, Eccleston Park, Prescot L34 2RN.

VARMA, Paula Nina Ty-Newydd Farmhouse, Sigingstone, Cowbridge CF71 7LP — MB BCh 1994 Wales; BSc Ed. 1989. SHO (Med.) Pontypridd.

VARMA, Mr Rajat Kumar 15 Sycamore Drive, Royal Hospital, Chesterfield S44 5DX Tel: 01246 277271 — MB BS 1984 Delhi; FRCS Ed. 1989.

VARMA, Rajesh Dept. of Obs & Gyn, Queens Medical Centre, Nottingham NG7 2UH — MB ChB 1995 Aberd. Specialist Regist., Dept. of Obs. & Gyn. Qu.s Med. Centre, Notts.

VARMA, Rajiv Linden Lea, Hillwood Grove, Hutton Mount, Brentwood CM13 2PD — MB BS 1980 Delhi; MRCOG 1987.

VARMA, Rashmi Bala 95 Montbelle Road, London SE9 3NY — MB BS 1993 Lond.

VARMA, Mr Ravi Medical Centre, 8 Rushton Street, London N1 5DR; 8 Rosemary Drive, Redbridge, Ilford IG4 5JD Tel: 020 8550 5593 — MB BS 1963 Bihar; MS 1966 Bihar. (Darbhanga Med. Coll.) Clin. Asst. Minor Injuries Unit St. Leonards Hosp. Lond. Socs: BMA. Prev: Clin. Asst. (Orthop. & A & E) Whipps Cross Hosp. Lond.; Regist. (Orthop.) Whipps Cross Hosp. Lond.

VARMA, Sandeep Fax: 0292 919596 Email: varma@doctors.org.uk — MB BCh 1993 Wales; BMedSc (Hons.) Path. Sci. Wales 1991; MRCP (UK) 1996. Specialist Regist. (Dermat.) Univ. Hosp. Wales. Socs: BMA; Brit. Soc. of Pediatric Dermat.; Brit. Assn. of Dermat.

VARMA, Sanjay 163 Colinton Road, Edinburgh EH14 1BE — MB ChB 1991 Ed.

VARMA, Mr Sanjay Kumar Leicester Royal Infirmary, Infirmary Square, Leicester LE1 5WW Tel: 0116 258 5851 Fax: 0116 258 5852; Email: plasticsurgeon@postmaster.co.uk — MB BS 1977 All India Inst. Med. Sciences; FRCS (Plast) Ed. 1992; FRCS Ed. 1981. (All India Inst. Med. Sci.) Cons. Plastic Surg. Leicester Roy. Infirm. Socs: Brit. Assn. Plastic Surg.; Brit. Assn. Aesthetic Plastic Surgs. Prev: Sen. Regist. (Plastic Surg.) Leeds & Bradford; Regist. (Plastic Surg.) Leicester.

VARMA, Mr Thelekat Raman Kerala The Walton Centre for Neurology and Neurosurgery, Fazakerley, Liverpool L9 7LJ — MB BS 1972 Bangalor; MB BS Bangalore 1972; FRCS Ed. 1979. (Bangalore Med. Coll.) Cons. Neurosurg. The Walton Centre for Neurol. & Neurosurg. Liverp. Prev: Cons. Neurosurg. Dundee Roy. Infirm.; Sen. Regist. (Neurosurg.) Univ. Hosp. Wales Cardiff; Regist. (Neurosurg.) Hallamsh. Hosp. Sheff. & Walton Hosp. Liverp.

VARNAM, Michael Adrian Windmill Practice, The Health Centre, Beaumont Street, Sneinton, Nottingham NG2 4PJ Tel: 0115 950 5426; 73 Stanton Road, Ilkeston DE7 5FW Tel: 0115 932 2639 — MFPHM 2000; FRIPHH 2001; DM Nottm. 1988; MB BS Lond. 1967; FRCGP 1980, M 1972; DObst RCOG 1969. (Lond. Hosp.) Mem. City Counc. Area Comm.; Vice Chairm. PEC Nottm. PCT, Non Exec. Bd. Health Developm. Agency. Prev: Assoc. Advisor Gp.; Chairm. RCGP Educat. Div.; Course Organiser VTS Nottm.

VARNAM, Robert Michael 73 Stanton Road, Ilkeston DE7 5FW — MB ChB 1995 Manch.

VARNAVA, Amanda Maria Deborah 53 Etchingham Park Road, London N3 2EB; 9 St Mark's Place, London W11 1NS — MB BS 1990 Lond.; BA Oxf. 1987; MRCP Lond. 1993. (Oxford and St Bartholomew's) Research Regist. (Cardiol.) St Geo.'s Hosp. Lond. Prev: Regist. (Cardiol.) Roy. Brompton & St Geo.'s Hosps. Lond.

VARNAVIDES, Christakis Kyriacos Dib Lane Practice, 112A Dib Lane, Leeds LS8 3AY Tel: 0113 295 4650 Fax: 0113 295 4663; 40 North Park Avenue, Leeds LS8 1EJ Tel: 0113 266 2132 Fax: 0113 266 2132 — MB ChB Leeds 1970; BSc (Hons.) Leeds 1967; FRCGP 1987, M 1977; Cert. Family Plann. JCC 1979; DObst RCOG 1972. (Leeds) Tutor (Gen. Pract.) Univ. Leeds; Examr. Roy. Coll. Gen. Pract.; Trainer (Gen. Pract.) Leeds AHA (T); Clin. Asst. (Dermat.) Leeds Gen. Infirm. Prev: Chairm. Yorks. Fac. RCGP; Regist. (Med. & Mineral Metab.) & Ho. Phys. Leeds Gen. Infirm.; SHO (Obst.) Leeds Matern. Hosp.

VARNEY, Angela Dawn The Thatched Cottage, Hill St., Calmore, Southampton SO40 2RX — MB ChB 1985 Liverp.; DRCOG 1990. GP Soton.

VARNEY, Mrs Patricia Ann (retired) Riverthatch, The Abbotsbrook, Bourne End SL8 5QU Tel: 01628 521077 — MRCS Eng. LRCP Lond. 1974; MFFP 1993; Dip. GU Med. Soc. Apoth. Lond. 1992. Prev: Clin. Asst. (Genitourin. Med.) Char. Cross Hosp. Lond. & Vict. Clinic for Sexual Health.

VARNEY, Paul Ronald Lilac Cottage, Buttons Lane, West Wellow, Romsey SO51 6BR — MB BCh 1971 Wales; MRCGP 1975; DObst RCOG 1974. Prev: Hon. Clin. Tutor Univ. Soton. Med. Sch.

VARNEY, Veronica Ann St Helier NHS Trust, Wrythe Lane, Carshalton SM5; 59 Meadow Walk, Epsom KT19 0AX — MB BS 1983 Lond.; MRCP (UK) 1987; MD; FRCP 2000. Regist. (Med., Clin. Allergy & Immunol.) Roy. Brompton Papworth Hosp.; Gen. med.; Resp. med.; Immunol. & allergy (CCST). Prev: Regist. & Research Regist. Roy. Brompton Hosp. Lond.; Regist. (Chest Med. & Intens. Care Med.) Papworth Hosp. & AddenbrookesHosp. Camb.

VARSANI, Gattotkutch Bhimji 7 Compton House, 4 Carlisle Road, Shirley, Southampton SO16 4BS — BM 1998 Soton.

VARSANYI, George 16 Stosmarsh House, Cowley Road, London SW9 6HH — MB ChB 1991 Otago.

VARSHNEY, Giriraj Kishore Rhys House Family Health Care, Rhys House, James St, Ebbw Vale NP23 6JG Tel: 01495 307407; 4 Panty-Fforest, New Town, Ebbw Vale NP23 5FR Tel: 01495 308821 — MB BS 1968 Lucknow; BSc Agra 1962; DTCD Wales 1995. (K.G. Med. Coll. Lucknow) Socs: Med. Protec.

VARSHNEY, Mahavir Prasad Worle Health Centre, 125 High St, Worle, Weston Super Mare BS22 6HB Tel: 01934 510510 Fax: 01934 522088; Riverbank Medical Centre, Walford Avenue, Worle, Weston Super Mare BS22 7YZ Tel: 01934 521133 Fax: 01934 522226 — LMSSA 1979 Lond.; BSc Aligarh 1964, MB BS 1969; DCH Dub. 1977; DTM & H Liverp. 1974. (J.N. Medical Coll., Aligarh, India)

VARTAN, Charles Philip Westbourne Medical Centre, Milburn Road, Bournemouth BH4 9HJ Tel: 01202 752550 Fax: 01202 769700; 18 Fairview Park, Overbury Rd, Poole BH14 9JZ Tel: 01202 741517 — MB BS Lond. 1966; MRCP (UK) 1970; MRCS Eng. LRCP Lond. 1966; FRCP 1999. (St. Bart.) Hosp. Pract. (Gastroenterol., Endoscopy. & Biliary Endoscopy) Bournemouth Gen. Hosp.

VARTIKOVSKI, Rolland Flat 40, 250 Camphill Avenue, Glasgow G41 3AS — Vrach 1968 Kishinev Medical Inst. USSR.

VARTY, Christopher Paul The Orchard Surgery, Penstone Park, Lancing BN15 9AG Tel: 01903 843333 Fax: 01903 843332; Tel: 01903 521329 — MB BS 1989 Lond.; DCH RCP Lond. 1994. (St. Geo. Lond.)

VARTY, Mr Kevin Department of Surgery, Addenbrookes NHS Trust, Box 201, Hills Road, Cambridge CB2 2QQ Tel: 01223 216992 Fax: 01223 216015 Email: kvarty@uk-home.co.uk — BM BCh 1985 Oxf.; BA (Hons.) Oxf. 1985, BM BCh Oxf. 1985; FRCS (Gen.) 1997; FRCS Eng. 1989; MD 1994. Cons. (Vasc. Surg.) Camb. Socs: Vasc. Surg. Soc. Prev: SHO (Gen. Surg.) Wonford Hosp. Exeter.; Regist. Nottm. Derby; Sen. Regist. Leics.

VARUGHESE, Mohini Anna 38 West Way, Shirley, Croydon CR0 8RB — MB BS 1998 Lond.

VARUGHESE, Punnackattu Scaria 16 Methuen Road, Edgware HA8 6EX — MB BS 1972 Kerala.

VARUGHESE, Reuben Thomas Jacob 116 Chesterfield Gardens, London N4 1LR — MB BS 1988 Lond.

VARVEL, David Adrian Brundall Medical Partnership, The Dales, Brundall, Norwich NR13 5RP Tel: 01603 712255 Fax: 01603 712156; 3 Brandon Court, Brundall, Norwich NR13 5NW Tel: 01603 712463 — MB BS 1967 Lond.; DObst RCOG 1971. (Univ. Coll. Hosp.) Socs: BMA. Prev: SHO (O & G) W. Suff. Gen. Hosp. Bury St. Edmunds; Ho. Phys. (Gen. Med.) & Ho. Surg. (Gen. Surg.) P.ss Margt. Hosp. Swindon.

VAS FALCAO, Custodio Mariano Gustavo Withybush General Hospital, Fishguard Road, Haverfordwest SA61 2PZ Tel: 01437 773189; Rushacre House, Redstone Road, Narberth SA67 7ES Tel: 01834 861322 — MB BS 1982 Bombay; MRCPCH 1996; DCH RCP Lond. 1985. Cons. Paediat. Withybush Gen. Hosp. HaverfordW.

VASA, Mr Sanjiv Arunchandra 12 Dorset Road, Altrincham WA14 4QN — MB BS 1973 Gujarat; MB BS Gujarat. 1973; FRCS Ed. 1979; FRCS Glas. 1979. (N.H.L. Municip. Med. Coll.) Cons. Plastic Surg. Ahmedabad, India.

VASANTH, Esther Chandrika Bag Lane Surgery, 32 Bag Lane, Atherton, Manchester M46 0EE Tel: 01942 896489 Fax: 01942 888793 — MB BS 1970 Bangalore; MB BS 1970 Bangalore.

VASANTHAKUMARI, Somasundaramurthy c/o Dr Meena Choksi, 20 Penrhos, Radyr, Cardiff CF15 8RJ — MB BS 1977 Madras; MRCOG 1988.

VASANTHI-SREENIVASAN, Pudiya 30 Green Pastures, Stockport SK4 3RA — MB BS 1974 Mysore; DObst RCPI 1983.

VASEY, David Whitby Group Practice, Spring Vale Medical Centre, Whitby YO21 1SD Tel: 01947 820888 Fax: 01947 603194 — MB ChB 1967 Liverp.; MA Camb. 1968; DObst RCOG 1969. (Camb. & Liverp.) Clin. Asst. (Ophth.) Whitby Hosp. Prev: Squadron Ldr. RAF Med. Br., Specialist O & G; SHO W. Suff. Gen. Hosp. Bury St. Edmunds; Ho. Off. S.port Gen. Infirm.

VASEY, David Peregrine Department of Obstetrics & Gynaecology, The Ipswich Hospital, Heath Road, Ipswich IP4 5PD; 15 Sandhurst Avenue, Ipswich IP3 8DU — MB BCh 1969 Wales; MB BCh 1969 Wales; FRCS (C) 1981; FRCOG 1988, M 1975. Cons. O & G The Ipswich Hosp. Prev: Specialist in O & G Univ. Alberta Hosp. Edmonton Alberta; Canada.

VASEY, Jean Margaret 104 Hayes Road, Bromley BR2 9AB Tel: 020 8460 5631 — MB BS 1963 Lond.; DO Eng. 1966. (St. Thos.) Assoc. Specialist Moorfields Eye Hosp. Lond. & Bromley Hosp. Prev: Cons. (Ophth.) Cane Hill Hosp. Coulsdon; Clin. Asst. Ophth. Dept. St. Geo. Hosp. Lond.; Med. Asst. W.. Ophth. Hosp. Lond.

VASEY, Joyce Lilly (retired) Fieldhurst Farm, Fieldhurst Road, Cornholme, Todmorden OL14 8JL Tel: 01706 814036 — MB BS 1950 Durh.

VASEY, Paul Austin Beatson Oncology Centre, Western Infirmary, Glasgow G11 6NT Tel: 0141 2112318 Fax: 0141 2111869 Email: pav1y@clinmed.gla.ac.uk; Tel: 0141 5700350 — MB ChB 1988 Dundee; MSc Glas. 1994; MD Dundee 1996; MRCP (UK) 1991. Sen. Lect. & Hon. Cons. (Med. Oncol.) Beatson Oncol. Centre, W.. Infirm. Glas. Socs: (Comm.) Assn. Cancer Phys. Prev: Lect. & Hon. Sen. Regist. (Med. Oncol.) Beatson Oncol. Centre W.. Infirm. Glas.; Research Fell. & Hon. Regist. (Med.) Beatson Oncol. Centre Glas.; SHO Rotat. (Gen. Med.) Stobhill Gen. Hosp. Glas.

VASEY, Ronald Owen Offerton Health Centre, 10 Offerton Lane, Offerton, Stockport SK2 5AR Tel: 0161 480 0324; 56 Higher Hill Gate, Stockport SK1 3PZ Tel: 0161 480 2352 Fax: 0161 480 3158 — LMSSA 1970 Lond.; MRCS Eng. LRCP Lond. 1972.

***VASEY, Sarah Elyse** 8 Winchester Drive, Exmouth EX8 5QA — MB ChB 1996 Birm.

VASFALCAO, Isabel Ignatius Rushacre House, Redstone Road, Narberth SA67 7ES Tel: 01834 861322 — MB BS 1982 Bombay. Assoc. Psychiat. Derwen NHS Trust Carmarthen.

VASHISHT, Sohan Lal Warrior Square Surgery, 61 Warrior Square, Southend-on-Sea SS1 2JJ Tel: 01702 618411 Fax: 01702 464163 — MB BS 1971 Gujarat.

VASHISHT, Sudha Rani 6 Beaufort Gardens, Ilford IG1 3DB Tel: 020 8544 4636 — MB BCh 1985 Wales; DRCOG 1989. SHO (Paediat.) Lond. Hosp. Prev: Trainee GP Chelmsford; SHO (O & G) Rush Green Hosp. Romford; SHO (Geriat.) Hillingdon Hosp. Uxbridge.

VASI, Surendrakumar Chhotubhai (retired) 51 Grassmoor Road, Birmingham B38 8BU — MB BS Bombay 1966. GP Birm.; Hosp. Pract. Selly Oak Hosp. (Varicose Veins Clinic) Birm. Prev: Ho. Surg. (Gen. Surg.) Manor Hosp. Walsall.

VASI, Varsha 26 Coventon Road, Aylesbury HP19 9JL — MB ChB 1998 Leeds.

VASISHTA, Sanjeev Tel: 01633 234234; Wyeland Villa, Homs Road, Ross-on-Wye HR9 7DG — MB BS 1982 Delhi; MRCP (UK) 1989. (Mavlana Azad Coll. Delhi) Specialist Regist. (Gen. & Geriat. Med.) Glan Hafren NHS Trust. Prev: Regist. (Gen. Med.) Herefordsh. HA.; SHO (Gen. Med.) Gravesend & N. Kent. Hosps.; SHO (Gen. & Geriat. Med.) Herts. & Essex Gen. Hosp.

VASKOVIC, Tania 61 Carlisle Place, London SW1P 1HZ — LRCP LRCS LRCPS 1998 Ed., Glas.; LRCP Ed LRCS Ed LRCPS Glas 1998.

VASS, Alexander Dimitri 14 Holt Drive, Kirby Muxloe, Leicester LE9 2EX — MB BS 1994 Lond.

VASS, Helena Sophie Brunswick House, 299 Glossop Road, Sheffield S10 2HL Tel: 0114 271 6890 — BM BS 1990 Nottm.; MRC Psych. Specialist Regist., Psychother.

VASS, Lesley Margaret 1 Delnies Park, Inverness IV2 4PA — MB ChB 1993 Aberd.

VASS, Neil Norroy The Surgery, 1 Binfield Road, London SW4 6TB Tel: 020 7622 1424 Fax: 020 7978 1436; Tel: 020 8874 6894 Fax: 020 8875 0473 — MB BS 1981 Lond.; MSc Lond. 1994; MRCGP 1997; DPD 1990; DRCOG 1985; DFFP 1997. (St Thos. Hosp. Lond.) Edit. Bd. Palliat. Care Today; Clin. Asst. Dermat. Sutton Hosp. Prev: Gen. Practitioner, Battersea, 1985-98; Trainee GP St. Thos. Hosp. VTS, 82-85.

VASSALL-ADAMS, Nicola Irene High Hedges, Brookthorpe, Gloucester GL4 0US Tel: 01452 813656 — MB BS 1967 Lond. (Middlx.) Assoc. Specialist (Psychiat./Psychother.) Glos. HA. Prev: Ho. Surg. Tilbury Hosp.; Ho. Phys. St. And. Hosp. Billericay; SHO (Psychiat.) Middlx. Hosp. Lond.

VASSALLO, Alison Ann The Lennard Surgery, 1-3 Lewis Rd, Bedminster Down, Bristol BS13 75D Tel: 0117 964 2211 Fax: 0117 987 3227 — MB BS 1991 Lond.; MRCGP 1995; DCH RCP Lond. 1996; DFFP 1994; DRCOG 1994. (St. Bart. Med. Coll.)

VASSALLO

VASSALLO, Catherine Maria The Haleacre Unit, Amersham General Hospital, Whielden Street, Amersham HP7 0JB Tel: 01494 724422 — MB.BS 1991 Lond.; MA Oxon 1994; MSc. London 1997; MRCPsych 1997. Rot. Specialist Regist., Oxf. Socs: MRCPsych. Prev: Regist. Rotat. (Psychiat.) Oxf.; SHO Rotat.(Psychiat.)UCL.

VASSALLO, Mr David John, Lt.-Col. RAMC Royal Hospital Haslar, Gosport PO12 2AA Tel: 02392 762118 Fax: 02392 762960 — MRCS Eng. LRCP Lond. 1981; FRCS Ed. 1985. Cons. Gen. Surg. Roy. Hosp. Haslar. Gosport; Hon. Sen. Lect., Leonard Chesh. Centre for Conflict Recovery, Univ. Coll., Lond. Socs: Haywood Club; Swinfen Charitable Trust; Roy. Soc. of Med. Prev: Cons. Gen. Surg. Duke of Connaught Unit, Musgrave Pk. Hosp. Belf.; Cons. Gen. Surg. Camb. Milit. Hosp. Aldershot; Sen. Regist. (Gen. Surg.) Camb. Milit. Hosp. Aldershot, St. Bart. Hosp. Lond. & St. Peter's Hosp. Chertsey.

VASSERMAN, David The Surgery, 66 Long Lane, London EC1A 9EJ Tel: 020 7600 9440 — MB ChB 1982 Manch.; MRCGP 1990; MRCPsych 1988.

VASSILAS, Christopher Alexander Department of Old Age Psychiatry, West Suffolk Hospital, Hardwick Lane, Bury St Edmunds IP33 2QZ Tel: 01284 763131 — MD 1994 Bristol; MPhil Ed. 1988; MB ChB Liverp. 1980. Socs: Roy. Coll. Psychiat. Prev: Lect. (Ment. Health) Univ. Bristol.

VASSILIADIS, Nikolaos Department of Forensic Medicine, Guy's Hospital, St Thomas St., London SE1 9RT — Ptychio Iatrikes 1974 Thessalonika.

VASSILIKOS, Panagiotis Human Diabetes & Metabolism Research Centre, Floor 4, William Leech Building, Department of Medicine, Medical School, Framlington Place, Newcastle upon Tyne NE2 4HH — Ptychio Iatrikes 1966 Athens.

VASSILIOU, George Steliou Hammersmith Hospital, Du Cane Road, London W12 0HS; 10 Goodrich House, Sewardstone Road, London E2 9JN Email: georger@lineone.net — MB BS 1994 Lond.; MB BS (Distinc.) Lond. 1994; BSc (1st cl. Hons.) Pharmacol. Lond. 1991; MRCP (UK) 1997. Specialist Regist. (Haemat.) N. Thames Deanery Centr. Middlx. Hosp., Hammersmith Hosp., Roy. Free Hosp., Gt. Ormond St. Hosp. for Sick Childr. Socs: Hellenic Med. Soc.; Regist. Train. RCPath.; Brit. Soc. Haematol. Prev: SHO (Haemat.) Addenbrooke's Hosp. Camb.

VASU, Vimal Whitecroft, Glynogwr, Blackmill, Bridgend CF35 6EL — MB BS 1998 Lond.

VASUDAVEN, Bhargawa King's Drive Surgery, 2 King's Drive, Gravesend DA12 5BG Tel: 01474 560717; 359 Singlewell Road, Gravesend DA11 7RL — MBBS Bombay 1976; FRCS Ed 1984. (Grant Medical College Bombay, India) Sector GP in local PCG (responsible for 34 GPs in 10 different Pract.s); GP Chairm. Local Community Hosp. Project. Prev: Chm Jt. Commiss.ing Gp. Dartford Dist.

VASUDEV, Kadaba Srinath Department of Pathology, Victoria Hospital, Blackpool FY3 8NR Tel: 01253 300000 Fax: 01253 303675; 10 Silverdale Road, Lytham St Annes FY8 3RE Tel: 01253 720747 Fax: 01253 720747 Email: vasudev@globalnet.co.uk — MB BS Bangalore 1967; FRCPath 1976. (Bangalore Med. Coll.) Cons. Histopath. Vict. Hosp. Blackpool. Socs: BMA (Sec. Blackpool & Fylde Div.); Overseas Doctors Assn.; Assn. Clin. Path. & Internat. Acad. Path. Prev: Postgrad. & Undergrad. Tutor Univ. Manch.

***VASUDEV, Naveen Srinath** 10 Silverdale Road, Lytham St Annes FY8 3RE — MB ChB 1998 Dund.; MB ChB Dund 1998; BMsc (Hons) 1995.

VASUDEVA, Arvind Kumar 89 Stuart Road, Wimbledon, London SW19 8DJ Tel: 020 8715 5066 — BM BCh 1987 Oxf.; MA Camb. 1988; MRCP (UK) 1992; MRCGP 1991; DCH RCP Lond. 1991; DRCOG 1990. Research Fell. (Cardiol.) St. Geo. Hosp. Med. Sch. Lond.

VASUDEVA KAMATH, Surathkal Scholes, Wigan WN1 3NH — MB BS 1974 Mysore; MB BS 1974 Mysore.

VASUDEVAN NAIR, Devakiamma Chandrasekharan Willenhall Health Centre, Field Street, Willenhall WV13 2NZ Fax: 01902 634448 — MB BS 1973 Kerala.

VATER, Mairlys Anaesthetic Department, Derby City General Hospital, Southern Derbyshire Acute Hospitals NHS Trust, Derby DE22 3NE Tel: 01332 340131 Fax: 01332 290559; The Grange, Packhorse Road, Melbourne, Derby DE73 1EG Tel: 01332 863653 — MB BCh 1975 Wales; FFA RCS Eng. 1980; DA Eng. 1978. (Wales) Cons. Anaesth. S.ern Derbysh. Acute NHS Trust.

VATERLAWS, Albert Lynwood 54 Tyn-y-Parc Road, Rhiwbina, Cardiff CF14 6BP — MB BCh 1964 Wales; MRCP (U.K.) 1971; DCMT . Lond. 1972.

VATHENEN, Arumugam Santhire Cardiorespiratory Department, Alexandra Hospital, Woodrow Drive, Redditch B98 7UB Tel: 01527 503030 Fax: 01527 512000 Email: santi@vathenen.com; Fax: 01789 766 835 Email: santi@vathenen.com — BM 1980 Soton.; DM Soton. 1989; MRCP (UK) 1983; T(M) 1992; FRCP (Lond) 1998. (Southampton) Cons. Phys. Respirat. & Gen. Med. Alexandra Hosp. Redditch. Socs: Brit. Thorac. Soc. & Amer. Thorac. Soc. Prev: Sen. Regist. (Respirat. & Gen. Med.) Killingbeck Hosp. Leeds; Research Fell. (Respirat. Med.) City Hosp. Nottm.; Regist. (Gen. Med.) Glenfield Hosp. Leicester.

VATISH, Manu 94 Clough Road, Rotherham S61 1RF Email: mvatish@doctors.org.uk — BChir 1994 Camb.; MBCamb. 1994; DPhil Oxon 1992; M.A. Oxon 1989. (Camb.) Specialist Regist., (O & G) Oxf. Rotat.; Clin. Lect. Warwick Univ. 1999. Prev: SHO Qu. Charlotte's Hosp. O & H; SHO John Radcliffe Hosp. O&H.

VATISH, Ravi Kumar Kirpal Medical Practice, Soho Health Centre, Louise Road, Handsworth, Birmingham B21 0RY Tel: 0121 554 0033 — MB ChB 1976 Sheffield; MB ChB 1976 Sheffield.

VATS, Archana 36 Castellain Mansions, Castellain Road, London W9 1HA — MB BChir 1992 Camb.; MA Camb. 1994. SHO Rotat. (Surg.) St. Mary's NHS Trust Lond.

VATSALA, Chandakacherla Narasimha c/o Drive B. Shah, 73 Lakeside Gardens, Merthyr Tydfil CF48 1EW — MB BS 1985 Sri Venkateswara.

VAUDREY, Barbara Wood Hall, Stoke Ash, Eye IP23 7ES — MB BS 1953 Lond.; LMSSA Lond. 1953. (St. Bart.)

VAUGHAN, Andrew Richard Sinclair Snaefell Surgery, Cushag Road, AnaghCoar, Douglas IM2 2SU Tel: 01624 676622 Fax: 01624 674515; 72 Ard Reayrt, Ramsey Road, Laxey IM4 7QU — MB ChB 1989 Dundee; 1998 (Hon. Fac. of Homeopothy); DFFP 1994; DRCOG 1994. Socs: BMA.

VAUGHAN, Antony Rathbone Bron Derw Surgery, Bron Derw, Garth Road, Bangor LL57 2RT Tel: 01248 370900 Fax: 01248 370652; Perfeddgoed Bach, Caerhun, Bangor LL57 4DS Tel: 01248 370350 — MB BS 1972 Lond.; MRCGP 1980; DObst RCOG 1974. (Lond. Hosp.) Med. Adviser N. Wales Health Auth. Prev: SHO Copthorne Hosp. Shrewsbury; Ho. Off. Neurosurg. Unit Lond. Hosp.; Resid. King Edwd. VII Memor. Hosp., Bermuda.

VAUGHAN, David Atkinson 29 Mile End Road, Norwich NR4 7QX Tel: 01603 443300 Fax: 01603 446012; Email: dvaughan@doctors.org.uk — MB BS 1979 Lond.; MRCGP 1984; DCH RCP Lond. 1983; DRCOG 1983.

VAUGHAN, David Hughes (retired) Mill Hill Cottage, 190 Woodford Road, Poynton, Stockport SK12 1EH — MB ChB 1950 Ed.; FFPHM 1989; FFCM 1977, M 1974; DPH Manch. 1958. Prev: Cons. Pub. Health Med. N. W.. RHA.

VAUGHAN, David John Adrian Northwick Park Hospital, Watford Road, Harrow HA1 3UJ Tel: 020 8869 3969 Fax: 020 8869 3975 — MB BS 1991 Lond.; FRCA 1996. (St Marys) Cons. Anaesth., N. W. Lond. NHS Trust, N.wick Pk. Hosp., Harrow. Socs: Anaesth. Res. Soc.; Obst. Anaesth. Assn.; Eur. Anaesthesiologists Assn. Prev: Regist. (Anaesth.) St. Mary's Hosp. Lond.; Lect. in Anaesth. and ITU, Imperial Coll., Lond.

VAUGHAN, Deborah Laura Jane Wentloog Road Health Centre, 98 Wentloog Road, Rumney, Cardiff CF3 8EA Tel: 029 2079 7746 Fax: 029 2079 0231 — MB BCh 1988 Wales.

VAUGHAN, Donna Athena Stranraer Health Centre, Edinburgh Road, Stranraer DG9 7HG — MB BCh BAO 1984 Belf.; DMH Belf. 1992. Med. Off. Ekwendeni Hosp., Malawi.

VAUGHAN, George Thomas Ormsacre, 41 Barnton Avenue, Edinburgh EH4 6JJ — MB ChB 1962 Ed.; FFR 1971; FRCR 1975.

VAUGHAN, Sir Gerard Folliott 28 Ponsonby Terrace, London SW1P 4QA Tel: 020 7821 6729 Fax: 020 7834 6694 — MB BS 1947 Lond.; FRCP Lond. 1966, M 1949; Hon. FRCS Lond. 1993; FRCPsych 1971; Acad. DPM 1953. (Guy's) Managing Edr. W.m. Publishing Ltd. Jl. Sci. in Parliament. Socs: (Ex-Pres.) Cons. Med. Soc. Prev: Cons. Emerit. Guy's Hosp. Lond.

VAUGHAN, Gerard Joseph Bewicke Health Centre, 51 Tynemouth Road, Wallsend NE28 0AD Tel: 0191 262 3036 Fax:

0191 295 1663 — MB BCh BAO 1980 NUI. GP Wallsend, Tyne & Wear.

VAUGHAN, Jenny Rosemary 238 Down Road, Portishead, Bristol BS20 8HU — BM BS 1992 Nottm.

VAUGHAN, John Anthony 9 The Lees, Malvern WR14 3HT. — MB BCh 1980 Wales; MRCPsych 1985. Cons. Psychiat. Worcester & DHA. Prev: Cons. Psychiat. Leics. HA.

VAUGHAN, John Martin Measham Medical Unit, High Street, Measham, Swadlincote DE12 7HR Tel: 01530 270667 Fax: 01530 271433; 39 Burton Road, Ashby-de-la-Zouch LE65 2LF Tel: 01530 412220 — MB ChB 1971 Liverp.; FRCGP 1987, M 1975; DObst RCOG 1973; DCH Eng. 1973.

VAUGHAN, Mr John Michael Martin c/o HE, Shell Centre, London SE1 7NA Tel: 020 7934 3770 Fax: 020 7934 7046 Email: j.m.m.vaughan@openmail2.cmo.spdc-lagos.simis.com; 28 Huntingdon Gardens, London W4 3HX Tel: 020 8742 3009 Fax: 020 8742 3009 — MB BChir 1973 Camb.; MA Camb. 1973; FRCS Eng. 1979; AFOM RCP Lond. 1996; Cert. Av. Med. 1991. (Camb. & St. Mary's) Chief Med. Off. Shell Petroleum Developm., Nigeria. Socs: Fell. Roy. Soc. Med.; Soc. Occupat. Med. Prev: Sen. Med. Adviser Shell UK; Surg. Shell Petroleum Developm. Company Lagos, Nigeria & Brunei; Sen. Med. Advisor. Shell Intern. Petroleum com.

VAUGHAN, Professor John Patrick Department of Public Health & Policy, London School of Hygiene & Tropical Medicine, Gower St., London WC1E 7HT Tel: 020 7636 8636 Fax: 020 7637 5391 — MB BS 1961 Lond.; MD Lond. 1978; FRCP Ed. 1982, M 1965; MRCS Eng. LRCP Lond. 1961; FFPHM RCP (UK) 1988, M 1974; DTPH Lond 1969; DCMT . Lond. 1964; DObst RCOG 1963. (Guy's) Prof. Health Care Epidemiol. Lond. Sch. Hyg. & Trop. Med.; Hon. Cons. Pub. Health Med. N. Thames RHA. Socs: Fell. Roy. Soc. Trop. Med. & Hyg. Prev: Sen. Lect. (Trop. Epidemiol.) Lond. Sch. Hyg. & Trop. Med.; Sen. Lect. Community Health (Epidemiol.) Univ. Nottm.; Sen. Lect. (Community Med.) Univ. Dar es Salaam, Tanzania.

VAUGHAN, Joseph (retired) 5 Clumber Road, Sheffield S10 3LE Tel: 0114 230 1736 — MD 1942 Czechoslovakia. Prev: Ho. Surg. Lister Hosp. Hitchin.

VAUGHAN, Kevin Francis The Smethwick Medical Centre, Regent Street, Smethwick, Warley B66 3BQ Tel: 0121 558 0105 Fax: 0121 555 7206; 104 Wentworth Road, Harborne, Birmingham B17 9SY Tel: 0121 427 6420 — MB 1972 Camb.; MB BChir Camb. 1972; MA Camb. 1972; MRCGP 1988; DA (UK) 1976; DObst RCOG 1973. Prev: Med. Supt. Kisiizi Hosp, Uganda.

VAUGHAN, Mark Owen Avenue Villa Surgery, Brynmor Road, Llanelli SA15 2TJ Tel: 01554 774401 Fax: 01554 775229 — MB BCh 1979 Wales; MRCGP (Distinc.) 1983; FRCGP 1997. (University of Wales College of Medicine) Chair. Carmarthenshire Local Health Gp.; Chair Carmarthenshire health and social care partnership Bd. Prev: PostGrad. Organiser, P. Philip Hosp., LLa.lli.

VAUGHAN, Matthew Mountfort 5 Manby Road, Malvern WR14 3BD Email: matthewmvaughan@yahoo.com — MB ChB 1991 Sheff.; MMedSc, Keele 1998; FRCR, 1997. Fell. in Radiol., Carnell Univ. Med. Center, New York Presbyt. Hosp. Cornell. Prev: SR, Radiol., John Radcliffe Hosp. Oxf..

VAUGHAN, Merrell Sandra Thame Health Centre, East Street, Thame OX9 3JZ Tel: 01844 261066 — MB BS 1991 Lond.

VAUGHAN, Michael Crofton Health Centre, Slack Lane, Crofton, Wakefield WF4 1HJ Tel: 01924 862612 — MB ChB 1970 Manch.; BSc Manch. 1967, MB ChB 1970; MRCP (U.K.) 1973. (Manch.) Prev: SHO Med. Univ. Hosp. of S. Manch.

VAUGHAN, Mrs Naomi Victoria MASU St Marys Hospital, Norfolk Place, London W2 Tel: 020 7886 6666 Email: n.v.vaughan@ic.ac.uk; 28A Lime Grove, London W12 8EA Tel: 020 7749 9812 — MB BS 1991 Lond.; FRCS Eng. 1997. Research Fell. (Gen. Surg.) Acad.

VAUGHAN, Nicholas John Ashton Royal Sussex County Hospital, Eastern Road, Brighton BN2 5BE Tel: 01273 696955 Fax: 01273 676345 Email: nvaughan@mistral.co.uk; The Hundred, Brighton Road, Woodmancote, Henfield BN5 9RT — MB BChir 1975 Camb.; MB BCh Camb. 1975; MA Camb. 1975; MD Camb. 1985; FRCP Lond. 1991; MRCP (UK) 1977. Cons. Phys. & Clin. Dir. (Med.) Roy. Sussex Co. Hosp. Brighton & Hove Gen. Hosp.; Hon. Sen. Lect. KCL. Socs: Brit. Diabetic Assn.; Eur. Assn. for Study Diabetes. Prev: Sen. Regist. (Med.) St. Geo. Hosp. Lond.; Regist. (Med.) Middlx. Hosp. Lond.; SHO Hammersmith Hosp. Lond.

VAUGHAN, Pamela Kathleen 1 Stormont Villas, Massey Avenue, Belfast BT4 2JT — MB BCh BAO 1975 Belf.

VAUGHAN, Paul Howard The Medical Centre, Station Road, Haydock, St Helens WA11 0JN Tel: 01744 734419 Fax: 01744 454875; 3 Pike House Road, Eccleston, St Helens WA10 5JZ Tel: 01744 755258 — MB ChB 1971 Liverp. (Liverp.) GP Princip.

VAUGHAN, Philip Joseph The Surgery, Bridge St., Polesworth, Tamworth B78 1DT Tel: 01827 330269; The Magnolias, Curlew Close, Warton, Tamworth B79 0HL Tel: 01827 892893 — MRCS Eng. LRCP Lond. 1964. (Leeds) Socs: BMA. Prev: Ho. Surg. & Ho. Phys. Clayton Hosp. Wakefield; SHO Obst. Doncaster Roy. Infirm.; RAF Med. Br.

VAUGHAN, Ralph Stephens 17 Ash Tree Close, Radyr, Cardiff CF15 8RX — MB BS 1966 Lond.; FFA RCS Eng. 1970; DA Eng. 1968. (Middlx.) Cons. Anaesth. Univ. Hosp. Wales & Hon. Clin. Teach. Univ. Wales Coll; Med. Cardiff. Socs: Assn. Anaesths. Prev: Ho. Phys. Middlx. Hosp. Lond.; Ho. Surg. St. And. Hosp. Billericay; Lect. Anaesth. Welsh Nat. Sch. Med. Cardiff.

VAUGHAN, Robert Kings Cross Surgery, 199 King Cross Road, Halifax HX1 3LW Tel: 01422 330612 Fax: 01422 323740 — MB ChB 1989 Leeds.

VAUGHAN, Mr Roger Norfolk & Norwich Hospital, Brunswick Road, Norwich NR9 5BP Tel: 01603 286395 — MB ChB 1974 Leeds; BSc (Hons.) Leeds 1971, MB ChB 1974; FRCS Eng. 1979. Cons. Cardiothoracic Surg. E. Anglia RHA. Prev: Sen. Regist. (Cardiothoracic Surg.) S. Manch. Health Dist.; SHO (A & E) Frenchay Hosp. Bristol; Demonst. Anat. Leeds Univ.

VAUGHAN, Roger John (retired) 43 Kings Road, Emsworth PO10 7HW Tel: 01243 375638 — MB BChir 1953 Camb.; MA Camb. 1953; MRCGP 1973. GP Horndean. Prev: Ho. Phys. Lister Hosp. Hitchin.

VAUGHAN, Simon Timothy Andrew 14 Tintagell Close, Feniscowles, Blackburn BB2 5JN Tel: 01254 200962 Email: s.vaughan@virgin.net — MB ChB 1989 Manch.; BSc (Hons.) Manch. 1986; MRCP (Ed.) 1993; FRCA 1997. (Victoria University of Manchester) Specialist Regist. (Anaesth.) N. W. Region. Prev: Specialist Regist. (Anaesth.) Hope Hosp. Salford; SHO (Anaesth. & A & E) Roy. Preston Hosp.; SHO (Gen. Med.) Blackburn Roy. Infirm. & Qu. Pk. Hosp. Blackburn.

VAUGHAN, Susan Jacqueline Trinity Street Surgery, 1 Trinity Street, Norwich NR2 2BG Tel: 01603 624844 Fax: 01603 766829; Hatherley Farm House, Mill Road, Little Melton, Norwich NR9 3NZ Tel: 01603 810581 — MB 1971 Camb.; BChir 1970; MRCP (UK) 1978; DCH Eng. 1974; DObst RCOG 1972. (St. Mary's)

VAUGHAN-DAVIES, Sophie Louise 3 Chestnut Drive, Egham Hill, Egham TW20 0BJ — MB BS 1998 Lond.

VAUGHAN HUDSON, Gillian Rose (retired) Owls Hatch Cottage, Seale, Farnham GU10 1JD Tel: 01252 782456 — MB BS Lond. 1961; FRCP 1997. Trustee of Lymphoma Research Trust & Lymphoma Assn. Prev: Dir. of BNLI.

VAUGHAN-HUGHES, Richard Gareth (retired) 32 Heath Farm Road, Codsall, Wolverhampton WV8 1HT Tel: 01902 842818 — MB ChB 1959 Liverp. Prev: Regist. (Paediat.) St. Catherine's Hosp. Birkenhead.

VAUGHAN-JACKSON, Mr Oliver James, VRD (retired) 25 Barton Farm, Cerne Abbas, Dorchester DT2 7LF — BM BCh 1932 Oxf.; FRCS Eng. 1936; MRCS Eng. LRCP Lond. 1932; Hon. DSc Memor. Univ. Newfld. 1973. Prev: Cons. Orthop. Surg. Lond. Hosp.

VAUGHAN-JONES, Neal Dalton Square Surgery, 8 Dalton Square, Lancaster LA1 1PP Tel: 01524 842200 — MB ChB 1985 Birm.; MRCP (UK) 1988; MRCGP 1992; T(GP) 1992; DRCOG 1990. Prev: SHO Rotat. (Med.) Preston; Trainee GP Keighley & Addingham.

VAUGHAN-LANE, Mr Timothy Hinchingbrooke Hospital, Hinchingbrooke Park, Huntingdon PE29 6NT Tel: 01480 416416; Elms Farm, 111 Great North Road, Eaton Socon, St Neots, Huntingdon PE19 8EL Tel: 01480 477475 — MB ChB 1971 Birm.; FRCS Eng. 1977. Cons. Orthop. Hinchingbrooke Hosp. Huntingdon. Socs: Fell. BOA. Prev: Cons. Orthop. Surg. RAF; Sen. Regist. (Orthop.) Addenbrooke's Hosp. Camb.; Sen. Regist. (Orthop.) Newmarket Gen. Hosp.

VAUGHAN-SMITH, Stephen Uxbridge Health Centre, George St., Uxbridge UB8 1UB Tel: 01895 231925 Fax: 01895 813190; Brickfield Cottage, Knighton Way Lane, New Denham, Uxbridge UB9 4EQ Tel: 01895 273517 — MB BS 1983 Lond.; PhD Birm.

VAUGHAN WILLIAMS

1971, MSc 1968; BSc Nottm. 1967; DRCOG 1987. (St. Marys London) Clin. Asst. (A & E) Wexham Pk. Hosp. Slough.; Sect. 12 Approved Doctor, Ment. Health Act. Socs: Brit. Assn. Immed. Care Schemes.

VAUGHAN WILLIAMS, Catherine Ann (retired) Starting Haw, Low St, Austwick, Lancaster LA2 8BN Tel: 015242 51714 Fax: 015242 51714 Email: c.a.v-w@ntlworld.com — MB ChB 1979 Liverp.; MB ChB Liverp. 1970; MD Liverp. 1981; FRCOG 1993, M 1976. Prev: Cons. O & G Dumfries & Galloway HB.

VAUGHAN WILLIAMS, Professor Edward Miles 153 Woodstock Road, Oxford OX2 7NA Tel: 01865 515839 Fax: 01865 515839 Email: edward.vaughanwilliams@hertford.ox.ac.uk — DSc Oxf. 1961, BSc 1946, DM 1953, BM BCh 1947; FRCP Lond. 1984, M 1979. (Oxf.) Socs: Hon. Fell. Doctor Honoris Causa, Paris 1982 & Amer. Coll. Clin.; Emerit. Fell. Hertford Coll. Oxf.; Pharmacol., Physiol. & Cardiac Socs. Prev: Creasy Vis. Prof. Clin. Pharmacol. Chicago Med. Sch. 1990; Fell. Rockefeller Foundat. 1951.; Schorstein Research Fell. Univ. Oxf. 1950.

VAUGHTON, Mr Keith Chivers Swansea NHS Trust, Morriston Hospital, Swansea SA6 6NL Tel: 01792 703591 Fax: 01792 796438 Email: keith.vaughton@swansea-tr.wales.nhs.uk — BM BCh 1971 Oxf.; MA Oxf. 1971; FRCS Eng. 1976; DObst RCOG 1973. (Oxford University) Cons. Urol. Surg.Swansea NHS Trust; Regional speciality Adviser for Wales to the Roy. Coll. of Surg.s; Regional Adviser to Brit. Assn. of Urological Surg.s; Honarary Sen. Lect. to Univ. of Wales Coll. of Med. Socs: Brit. Assn. Urol. Surg.; Chairm., Welsh Urological socuiety; Internat. Urol. Soc.

VAUSE, Michael Harold 90 Bloom Street, Edgeley, Stockport SK3 9LH Tel: 0161 480 2726 — MB ChB 1956 Manch. Prev: Ho. Surg. Bolton Roy. Infirm.; Ho. Phys. Birch Hill Hosp. Rochdale; Asst. Res. Surg. Off. Stockport Infirm.

VAUSE, Sarah Helen St. Mary's Hospital, Hathersage Road, Manchester M13 0JH Tel: 0161 276 6426 — MB ChB 1987 Manch.; MD 1997; MRCOG 1993. Cons. in Feto material Med., St. Mary's Hosp., Manch.

VAUTREY, Richard Mark Meanwood Group Practice, 548 Meanwood Road, Leeds LS6 4JN Tel: 0113 295 1737 Fax: 0113 295 1736 — MB ChB 1988 Manch.; MRCGP 1994; DRCOG 1991; DCH RCP Lond. 1991.

VAUX, Alison Silvretta, 23 Went Hill Close, Ackworth, Pontefract WF7 7LP Tel: 01977 704962 — MB BS 1962 Lond.; MRCS Eng. LRCP Lond. 1962; DObst RCOG 1966. (St. Bart.) Sen. Community Med. Off.(Family Plann.) Wakefield & Pontefract Community NHS Trust. Socs: BMA; Fac. Family Plann. Prev: Child Welf. Med. Off. & Family Plann. Med. Off. Wakefield; SHO (Gen. Med.) Ronkswood Hosp. Worcester; Ho. Phys. (Paediat.) Roy. Alexandra Hosp. Brighton.

VAUX, David John Talbutt Lincoln College, Oxford OX1 3DR — BM BCh 1984 Oxf.; MA, DPhil. Oxf. 1982. Lect. (Experim. Path.) Univ. Oxf.

VAUX, Richard Hugh Cutcliffe The Surgery, Yeoman Lane, Bearsted, Maidstone ME14 4DS Tel: 01622 37326; Greenhill House, Otham, Maidstone ME15 8RR Tel: 01622 861245 — MB BChir 1960 Camb.; MA Camb. 1961; DObst RCOG 1964; DCH Eng. 1963. (Guy's)

VAVASOUR, Simon Mark Andrew Paston Surgery, 9-11 Park Lane, North Walsham NR28 0BQ Tel: 01692 403015 Fax: 01692 500619 Email: simon.vavasour@gp.d82066.nhs.uk; 5 Mile End Road, Norwich NR4 7QY Tel: 01603 457961 Email: simon.vavasour@ukgateway.net — MB BS 1991 Lond.; MRCGP 1996. (Char. Cross & Westm.) PCG Bd. Mem., N. Norf.

VAVRECKA, Milan John Frank The Surgeries, Grafton Road, Canvey Island SS8 7BT Tel: 01268 682277; 16B Grafton Road, Canvey Island SS8 7BT Tel: 01268 692280 — MUDr 1953 Prague; LMSSA Lond. 1975.

VAZ, Francis Guilherme South Warwickshire Hospital, Lakin Road, Warwick CV34 5BW Tel: 01926 495321 Fax: 01926 482609 — MB BS Bangalor; FRCP Lond. 1996, M (UK) 1981; FRCP 2000 Edin. Cons. Phys. Warwick Hosp.; Clin. Dir. Socs: Brit. Geriat. Soc. Prev: Sen. Regist. N.: RHA; Research Regist. (Brit. Foundat. Age Research) Cardiff Roy. Infirm.; Med. Regist. Edgware Gen. Hosp. Middlx.

VAZ, Mr Francis Melvin 46 Norwood Park Road, London SE27 9UA — MB BS 1994 Lond.; BSc (Hons.) Lond. 1991; FRCS 1998; FRCS (Oto) 1999.

VAZ, Olive Kathleen 11A Eton Place, Eton College Road, London NW3 2BT Tel: 020 7722 3242 — MB BS 1956 Calcutta; DCH Lond. 1964. (Nilratan Sarkar Med. Coll.)

VAZ PATO, Maria Department of Clinical Neurophysiology, The National Hospital for Neurology & Neurosurgery, Queen Square, London WC1N 3BG — Lic Med Coimbra 1988.

VAZE, Bhaskar Chintaman Waterloo Road Surgery, 279 Waterloo Road, Cobridge, Stoke-on-Trent ST6 3HR Tel: 01782 279915 — MB BS 1963 Nagpur.

VAZE, Nirmala Ramesh Weston super Mare General Hospital, Grange Road, Weston Super Mare BS23 4TQ — MB BS 1971 Ranchi.

VAZIR, Muhummmad Hasan Althagelvin Hospital, Londonderry BT47 6SB Tel: 02871 345171 Ext: 4175 Fax: 02871 611259 Email: hasan@vazir.u-net.com; 8 Clarenence Avenue, Londonderry BT48 7NH — MB BS 1979 Karachi; MRCPath 1991; T(Path) 1991; FRCP 2000 (Path). (Dow Med. Coll. & Civil Hosp., Karachi) Cons. Histopath./Cytopath. Altivagelvin Hosp. Socs: BMA; ACP; Roy. Soc. Med. Prev: Cons. Path. Antrim Hosp.; Cons. Path. & Head Path. Shaukat Khanum Memor. Cancer Hosp., Lahore, Pakistan; Higher Specialist Trainer Progr. Univ. Coll. Hosp. Galway & St Vincents Hosp. Dub.

VAZIRI, Katherine 45 Milner Drive, Whitton, Twickenham TW2 7PH — MB ChB 1995 Manch.

VAZIRI, Mr Manoocher Accident & Emergency Department, Prince Philip Hospital, Bryngwyn Mawr, Dafen, Llanelli SA14 8QF; 16 King George Court, Derwen Fawr, Swansea SA2 8AR — MD 1962 Tehran; FRCS Ed. 1969; LMSSA Lond. 1968. (Tehran) Cons. A & E P. Philip Hosp. LLa.lli. Socs: Brit. Assn. Accid. & Emerg. Med.; BMA. Prev: Cons. Surg. Nat. Iranian Oil Co. Hosp., Abadan; Regist. (Surg.) Mansfield Gp. Hosps.; SHO St. Helier Hosp. Carshalton.

VEAL, Christopher Trevor 3 Oak Vale, Bosillion Lane, Grampound, Truro TR2 4QY Tel: 01726 882220 — MB BS 1972 Newc.; FFPHM RCP 2000 (UK); MFPHM RCP (UK) 1993; MPH Leeds 1992; MRCGP 1976. (Newcastle upon Tyne) Med. Dir. & Cons. (Pub. Health Med.) Calderdale & Kirklees Health Auth.. Cons. in Pub. Health Med. Cornw. and the Isles of Scilly Health Auth.

VEAL, Hilary Linda Plain, Ash Hall Lane, Soyland, Ripponden, Sowerby Bridge HX6 4NU — MB BS 1972 Newc.

VEALE, David Mikael William de Coverly The Priory Hospital North London, The Bourne, Southgate, London N14 6RA Tel: 020 8882 8191 Fax: 020 8447 8138 Email: david@veale.co.uk; Tel: 020 8444 3522 — MB BS 1982 Lond.; MPhil Lond. 1989, BSc 1979, MD 1995; MRCPsych 1987. (Roy. Free) Cons. Psychiat., The Priory Hosp. N. Lond., Lond.; Hon. Cons. Psychiat. Enfield Community Care Trust Lond.; Hon. Sen. Lect. Univ. Dept. Psychiat. Roy. Free Hosp. And Univ. Coll. Med. Sch. Socs: (Ex Treas.) Brit. Assn. Behavioural & Congnitive Psychotherapies; Ex Chairm. Obsessive Action. Prev: Lect. (Behavioural Psychother.) Inst. Psychiat. Lond.; Sen. Regist. (Psychiat.) Maudsley Hosp. Lond.; Regist. (Psychiat.) Roy. Free Hosp. Lond.

VEALE, Douglas James Rheumatology, Leeds General Infirmary, George St, Leeds LS1 3RX Tel: 0113 292 3956 Fax: 0113 292 3804 Email: rrrdjv@leeds.ac.uk — MB BCh BAO 1984 NUI; LRCPSI 1984; MRCPI 1988; MD 1992, National University of Ireland. (Royal College of Surgeons in Ireland) Sen. Lect./ Cons., Univ. of Leeds. Socs: Brit. Sociery of Rheum.; Amer. Coll. of Rheum.; Irish Soc. of Rheumatol.

VEALE, Michael Henry Dumergue (retired) Hantone House, Meysey Hampton, Cirencester GL7 5JR — MRCS Eng. LRCP Lond. 1944; BA, MB BChir Camb. 1947. Prev: Temp. Surg. Lt. RNVR.

VEALE, Michael Joseph Jessop Medical Practice, 24 Pennine Avenue, Riddings, Alfreton DE55 4AE Tel: 01773 602707 Fax: 01773 513502 — MB BCh 1979 Wales.

VEALE, Philippa Rosemary 20 Hall Farm Court, Main St., Stanton-by-Dale, Ilkeston DE7 4QH — MB BS 1994 Lond.

VEALE, William Frederick de Coverly, TD (retired) 64 Wilbury Road, Hove BN3 3PY Tel: 01273 734635 Fax: 01273 734635 — BM BCh 1933 Oxf.; MA Oxf. 1981, BA (Hons.) 1930. Prev: Ho. Surg. & Res. Obst. Off. Bristol Roy. Infirm.

VEALL, Guy Richard Quentin 34 Ranmoor Road, Ranmoor, Sheffield S10 3HG — MB BS 1986 Lond.; FRCA. 1992.

VEALL, Roger Martin (retired) 1 Plant's Close, East Wellow, Romsey SO51 6AW Tel: 01794 22192 — MRCS Eng. LRCP Lond. 1965; MPhil Lond. 1970, MB BS 1965; MRCP Lond. 1967; MRCPsych 1972. Prev: Cons. (Ment. Handicap) Tatchbury Mt. Hosp.Calmore.

VEASEY, Duncan Andrew Rectory Farm, East Chaldon Road, Winfrith Newburgh, Dorchester DT2 8DJ Tel: 01305 852457 — MB BS 1977 Lond.; BSc (Biochem.) Lond. 1975; LMSSA Lond. 1977; MRCPsych 1983; DPM 1982. (St. Bart.) Private Pract. Medico-Legal Cons. Socs: Liveryman Worshipful Soc. Apoth.; Founder Mem. Soc. Expert Witnesses; Foundat. Mem. Expert Witness Inst. Prev: Cons. Psychiat. Avalon NHS Trust Yeovil; Cons. (Psychiat.) W. Dorset Ment. Health NHS Trust; Med. Dir. Huntercombe Manor Maidenhead.

VEASEY, Keith Alan Rose Cottage, 14 Nichols St., Desborough, Kettering NN14 2QU Tel: 01536 710061 — MB ChB 1981 Leic.; BA (Hons.) Stirling 1976.

VECHT, Mr Joshua Andrew — MBBS; MRCS 2001 Eng. (Royal Free Hosp. Univ. of London)

VECHT, Romeo Jacques The Wellington Hospital, Circus Road, London NW8 9JG Tel: 020 7328 4105 Fax: 020 7328 0463 Email: r.vecht@virgin.net; 118 Maida Vale, London W9 1PT Tel: 020 7328 4105 Fax: 020 7328 0463 — MB ChB 1962 Bristol; FRCP Lond. 1991; MRCP (UK) 1973; FESC 1994; FACC 1983. Cons. Cardiol. Wellington Hosp. Lond.; Cons. Cardiol. Harley St. Clinic, Lond.; Cons. Cardiol. Heart Hosp., Lond.; Cons. Cardiol.Roy. Brompton Hosp., Lond. Socs: Brit. Cardiac Soc.; FACC; Roy. Soc. Med. Internatl. Andreas Gruentzig Soc. Prev: Hon. Cons. Cardiol. Acad. Surg. & Cardiovasc. Units St. Mary's Hosp. Lond.; Sen. Regist. (Cardiol.) St. Mary's Hosp. Lond.; Regist. (Cardiol.) Groote Schuur Hosp. Cape Town.

VEDAVATHY, Kanara Krishnan 199 College Road, Crosby, Liverpool L23 3AX Tel: 0151 931 5972 — MB BS 1974 Kerala; MRCOG 1991.

VEDI, Krishan Kumar 7 Pexwood, Chadderton, Oldham OL1 2TS Tel: 0161 624 3302 — MB ChB 1966 Sheff.; FRCP Lond. 1988; MRCP (UK) 1971. (Sheff.) Cons. Phys. (Gen. Med., Diabetes & Endocrinol.) Roy. Oldham Hosp. Prev: Regist. (Neurol.) Roy. Hosp. Sheff. (Fulwood Annexe); Sen. Regist. (Gen. Med., Neurol. & Nephrol.) Withington Hosp. Manch.; Sen. Regist. (Gen. Med., Diabetes & Endocrinol.) Manch. Roy. Infirm.

VEDI, Mr Vikas 5 Shelley Crescent, Hounslow TW5 9BQ Email: v.vedi@redinet.freeserve.co.uk — MB BS 1989 Lond.; MB BS Lond. 1992; BSc (Hons.) Biochem. & Immunol. Lond. 1989; FRCS Eng 1997. (Univ. Coll. and Middlx. Hosp. Med. Sch.) Specialist Regist. (Orthop.) S. W. Thames Region. Socs: BOTA; BMA; Asso. Mem. Brit. Orthopaedic Assoc. Prev: Football Assn. Research Fell. (Orthop. & IMR) St. Mary's Hosp. Lond.; SHO Rotat. (Surg.) St. Peters NHS Trust Chertsey; SHO (Orthop.) Soton. Gen. Hosp.

VEDPATHAK, Vinit Sheshnath Department of Anaesthetics, Glan Clwyd Hospital, Rhyl LL18 5UJ — MB BS 1983 Bombay.

VEEDER, Arthur Saul, OStJ 56 Montagu Avenue, Gosforth, Newcastle upon Tyne NE3 4JN Tel: 0191 285 8484 — MRCS Eng. LRCP Lond. 1941, DMJ; FRSA. (Manchester) Police Surg. Newc. Socs: Brit. Acad. Forens. Sci.; BMA; (Counc.) Assn. Police Surgs. Prev: Ho. Surg. (Neurol.) Winwick E.M.S. Hosp. Warrington; Cas. Off. & Ho. Phys. Burton-on-Trent Gen. Infirm.; Capt. RAMC.

VEENHUIZEN, Paul Gerrit The Manor Clinic, 31 Manor Road, Folkestone CT20 2SE Tel: 01303 851146 Fax: 01303 220914; Email: paveenhuizen@aol.com — Artsexamen 1989 Utrecht. p/t GP.

VEENHUIZEN, Philippa Anne Manor Road Surgery, 31 Manor Road, Folkestone CT20 2SE Tel: 01303 851122 Fax: 01303 220914; 2 Cliff Road, Folkestone CT20 2JD — MB ChB 1982 Leeds; MRCGP 1991; DTM & H Liverp. 1993; DRCOG 1991; DCH RCP Glas. 1990.

VEERABANGSA, Mohamed 124 Buckswood Drive, Gossops Green, Crawley RH11 8JG Tel: 01293 535615 & profess. 527866 — MB BS 1968 Ceylon; MRCPsych 1978; DPM Eng. 1977. (Peradeniya) Cons. Psychiat. (Ment. Illness) with s/i in Psychogeriat. Crawley Hosp. & Horsham Hosp. Socs: BMA. Prev: Sen. Regist. (Adult Psychiat.) Acad. Dept. Univ. Leicester; (W.cotes Hosp.) &

Leicester Roy. Infirm.; Sen. Regist. PsychoGeriat. Assessm. Unit Leicester Gen. Hosp.

VEERAMANI, Ramasamy Broadmoor Hospital, Crowthorne RG45 7EG Tel: 01344 773111; 74A New Wokingham Road, Crowthorne RG45 6JP — MB BS Madras 1970; DPM Univ Madras, 1977; B.Clin Psych. Lond 1992. Assoc. Specialist in Forens. Psychiat. BRd.moor Hosp. Crowthorpe Berks. Socs: Affil. The Roy. Coll. of Psychiat.s Lond.; BMA.

VEERAVAHU, Ratneswary Mathura, 14 Barford Close, Westbrook, Warrington WA5 8TL — MB BS 1969 Ceylon. (Univ. Ceylon, Colombo) Clin. Med. Off. St. Helens & Knowsley Community Health Trust; Clin. Med. Off. (Occupat. Health) St. Helen's & Knowsley Hosps. Trust. Prev: Clin. Med. Off. S. Birm. HA; Clin. Med. Off. W. Birm. Auth.

VEERAYYA, Y Hirwaun, Aberdare CF44 9SP.

VEGA, Eileen Joyce 9 Auden Close, Lincoln LN2 4BS Tel: 01552 22126 — MB ChB 1958 Liverp.; DLO Eng. 1967. GP Lincoln.

VEGA ESCAMILLA, Ignacio 66 Hazel Drive, Woodley, Reading RG5 3SA — LMS 1991 Oviedo.

VEIDENHEIMER, Malcolm Charles Health Care International, Beardmore St., Clydebank G81 4HX Tel: 0141 951 5660 Fax: 0141 951 5744 — L 1957 Newfoundland Med. Bd.; MD CM Qu. Univ. Canada 1954; FRCSC 1961. Vice-Chairm. Surg. & Chief Div. Gen. Surg. Health Care Internat. Scotl. Prev: Ex-Chairm. Sect. Colon & Rectal Surg. Lahey Clinic Foundat. Burlington, Mass, USA; Lect. (Surg.) Harvard Med. Sch. Boston, Mass., USA.

VEIGA, Maria Arminda Caeiro Killingbeck Hospital, York Road, Leeds LS14 6UH — Lic Med 1991 Lisbon; Lic Med. Lisbon 1991.

VEIRAS, Maria Bernadette 121 All Souls Avenue, Willesden, London NW10 3AT — MB BS 1996 Lond.

VEITCH, Andrew McCulloch 15 Kitchener Road, East Finchley, London N2 8AS — MB BS 1988 Lond.; BSc (Hons.) Physiol. Lond. 1984, MB BS 1988; MRCP (UK) 1991. Research Fell. (Gastroenterol.) St. Bart. Hosp. Lond. Prev: Regist. (Gastroenterol.) Roy. Lond. Hosp., St. Bart. Hosp. & Homerton Hosp. Lond.

VEITCH, Mr Derek Young 3 Pinecrest Drive, Bieldside, Aberdeen AB15 9FJ — MB ChB 1978 Ed.; FRCS Eng. 1988; FRCS Ed. (Otolaryngol.) 1985; FRCS Ed. 1983. Cons. ENT Grampian HA Aberd. Prev: Sen. Regist. Rotat. (ENT) Leicester & Nottm.; Regist. (ENT) Roy. Nat. Throat, Nose & Ear Hosp. Lond.

VEITCH, Donald 19 Stokesley Road, Marton, Middlesbrough TS7 8DT — MB BS 1949 Durh.; LM Dub. 1955.

VEITCH, Elizabeth Mary Helen Kelso Road Health Centre, Kelso Road, Coldstream TD12 4LG Tel: 01890 882711 Fax: 01890 883547; Monument Cottage, Coldstream TD12 4AT — MB BS 1979 Lond.; MRCGP 1991. (Roy. Free)

VEITCH, Graeme Reston (retired) May Trees, 12 Davenham Avenue, Northwood HA6 3HN Tel: 01923 822361 — MB ChB Glas. 1951; FFA RCS Eng. 1970; DA Eng. 1963; DObst RCOG 1956. Prev: Cons. Anaesth. Mt. Vernon Hosp. N.wood Middlx.

VEITCH, Ian Henry Mitford (retired) 200 Brooklands Road, Sale, Manchester M33 3PB — MB BChir 1954 Camb.; FFCM 1977, M 1974; DObst RCOG 1960. Prev: Area Med. Off. Salford AHA (T).

VEITCH, John William Beech House Group Practice, Beech House, 54 Main Street, Egremont CA22 2DB Tel: 01946 814488 Fax: 01946 820372; Beech House Medical Group, St. Bridgets Lane, Egremont CA22 2B Tel: 01946 820692 Fax: 01946 820372 — MB ChB 1965 Ed.; FRCGP 1988, M 1975. (Ed.) Asst. Med. Off. BNFL Sellafield; Div. Police Surg. Whitehaven; Med. Off. Cumbria Rubgy Union. Socs: (Ex-Sec.) W. Cumbld. Med. Soc.; Ex. Provost Cumbria Fac. of RCGP. Prev: Regist. (Anaesth.) W. Cumbld. Hosp. Hensingham; SHO (Anaesth.) E.. Gen. Hosp. Edin. & Leith Hosp. Edin.

VEITCH, Tanya Muirhead Medical Centre, Muirhead, Dundee DD2 5NH Tel: 01382 580264 Fax: 01382 581199; 1 Norwood Crescent, Dundee DD2 1PD — MB ChB 1984 Dundee; DRCOG 1987.

VEITCH, Yvonne Pinfold Medical Practice, The Health Centre, Pinfold Gate, Loughborough LE11 1DQ Tel: 01509 263753 Fax: 01509 264124 — MB BS 1972 Newc.; BSc (Hons.) Physiol. Newc. 1969, MB BS 1972; MRCGP 1991; DFFP 1993. GP LoughBoro.; Clin. Asst. (Genito-urin. Med.) Leic.

VEJDANI, Kiomars Surrey Oaklands NHS Trust, Kingsfield Centre, Philanthropic Road, Redhill RH1 4DP Tel: 01737 288288 Fax:

VEKES

01737 288289; 19 Hunters Chase, South Godstone, Godstone RH9 8HR Tel: 01342 893056 — MD Tehran 1964; MRCPsych 1973; DPM Eng. 1973. (Tehran) Cons. (Psychiat.) Learning Disabil. Kingsfield Centre Redhill.

VEKES, Katalin Cherry Lodge, 29 Byerley Way, Crabbet Park, Crawley RH10 7YU Tel: 01293 884733 — MRCS Eng. LRCP Lond. 1981; MD Semmelwis, Hungary 1965; DCH Lond. 1983. SCMO (Community Child Health) Wandsworth HA. Socs: BMA & Brit. Paediat. Assn.

VELAMAIL, Vetrivel Morthen Road Surgery, 2 Morthen Road, Wickersley, Rotherham S66 1EU Tel: 01709 549711; 3 First Lane, Wickersley, Rotherham S66 1DU — MB ChB 1986 Sheff.

VELAMATI, Mohan Das Medway Hospital, Gillingham ME7 5NY Tel: 01634 46111 — MB BS 1971 Osmania; FFR RCSI 1979; DMRD Eng. 1978. (Gandhi Med. Coll.) Cons. Radiol. Medway Hosp. Gillingham. Prev: Sen. Regist. (Radiol.) Leeds AHA (T); Regist. (Radiol.) Aberd. Roy. Infirm.

VELANGI, Laxmikant Govind Civic Centre Place, Shildon Tel: 01388 772408; The Orchard, 55 Dene Hall Drive, Bishop Auckland DL14 6UF — MB BS 1962 Karnatak. (Kasturba Med. Coll. Mangalore) Socs: BMA. Prev: SHO Surg. Dryburn Hosp. Durh.; SHO Obst. Bensham Hosp. Gateshead; SHO Orthop. Co. Hosp. Durh.

VELANGI, Mark Rajan Haematology Department, Royal Victoria Infirmary, Newcastle upon Tyne Tel: 0191 232 5131; 41 Larkspur Terrace, Jesmond, Newcastle upon Tyne NE2 2DT — MB ChB 1991 Ed.; MRCP (UK) 1996. Specialist Regist. (Haemat.) Newc. Prev: SHO (Med.) New Cross Hosp. Wolverhampton.

VELANGI, Shireen Sarita Department of Dermatology, Sunderland Royal Hospital, Kayll Road, Sunderland SR2 7TP Tel: 0191 569 9004 Fax: 0191 569 9201 — MB ChB 1991 Ed.; MRCP (UK) 1995. Cons. Dermatol. N. Durh. NHS Trust. Socs: Roy. Coll. of Phys.s; Brit. Assn. of Dermatol.s; Internat. Soc. for the Study of Vulvo-Vaginal Dis.s.

VELASCO ALBENDEA, Jose Manuel Scunthorpe General Hospital, Cliff Gardens, Scunthorpe DN15 7BH Tel: 01724 282282; 21 Wentdale Road, Pontefract WF8 3RG — LMS 1993 Granada. (Granada Univ., Spain) SHO (O & G) Scunthorpe Gen. Hosp. Prev: SHO (O & G) Doncaster R.I.; SHO (Oncol.) Cookridge Hosp. Leeds; SHO (O & G) Hull Roy. Hosp.

VELAUDAPILLAI, Chitra Priyadharshini Brindhavan, Stow Road, Sturton by Stow, Lincoln LN1 2BZ — MB BS 1977 Sri Lanka; LRCP LRCS Ed. LRCPS Glas. 1984; FRCS Ed. 1988; FRCOphth 1992. Regist. (Ophth.) Co. Hosp. Lincoln; Ophth. Med. Practitioner; Indep. and self employed.

VELAZQUEZ GUERRA, Maria Dolores 15 Lynton Mansions, McAuley Close, London SE1 7BW — LMS 1992 U Autonoma Madrid.

VELDTMAN, Gruschen Rodney Department Paediatric Cardiology, Leeds General Infirmary, Great George St., Leeds LS1 3EX Tel: 0113 243 2799 Email: gveldtma@ulth.northy.nhs.uk; 2 Crofthouse Grove, Morley, Leeds LS27 8PA Tel: 0113 253 3461 — MB ChB 1991 Cape Town; MRCP(UK) 1995; Dip. Obst. 1992. Specialist Regist. (Paediat. Cardiol.) Leeds Gen. Infirm.; Fell. Adult Congen. Cardiol.; for 1999 & 2000, Toronto Canada. Socs: BPEG; BPCA. Prev: SHO (Gen. Paediat.) Roy. Hosp. for Sick Childr., Yorkill Glas.

VELDTMAN, Ursula Margarete 5C Orchard Court, The Royal National Orthopaedic Hospital, Brockley Hill, Stanmore HA7 4LP — State Exam Med 1990 Gottingen.

VELINENI, Mr Venkat Eswarlu Alexandra Hospital, Woodrow Drive, Redditch B98 7UB Tel: 01527 503030 Fax: 01527 512002 Email: v.velini@hotmail.com; Tel: 01527 579509 — MB BS 1973 Banaras Hindu; FRCS Ed. 1983. (Institute of Medical Sciences) Cons. Surg. - ColoProctol., Worcs. Acute Hosp.s NHS Trust.

VELKES, Valerie Liebe 20 Wilton Row, London SW1X 7NS — MB ChB 1959 Cape Town.

VELLA, Emmanuel Joseph (retired) Pathology Laboratory, Lakin Road, Warwick CV34 5BJ Tel: 01926 491801 — MB ChB 1974 Birm.; BSc Birm. 1971, MB ChB 1974; FRCPath. 1993, M 1981. Cons. Histopath. Warwick Hosp. Prev: Sen. Regist. (Histopath.) St. Thos. Hosp. Lond. & St. Mary's Hosp. Portsmouth.

VELLA, Ivan Flat 10, 21/22 Lilley Road, Liverpool L7 OLP — MRCS Eng. LRCP Lond. 1983.

VELLA, Mark Anthony William Harvey Hospital, Ashford TN24 0LZ Tel: 01233 633331; Highfield Lodge, St Monica's Rd, Kingsdown, Deal CT14 8AZ Tel: 01304 362399 — MRCS Eng. LRCP Lond. 1979; MPhil Lond. 1985; MRCP (UK) 1982; FRCP (UK) 1998. (Guy's) Gen. Med. (Diabetes & Hyderlipidaemia). Prev: Sen. Regist. Guy's Hosp. Lond.; Regist. (Med.) Whittington Hosp. Lond.; Regist. (Med.) Univ. Coll. Hosp. Lond.

VELLA, Ray The Surgery, 14 Manor Road, Beckenham BR3 5LE Tel: 020 8650 0957 Fax: 020 8663 6070; 21 Aldersmead Road, Beckenham BR3 1NA Tel: 020 8778 2859 Email: ray.vella@btinternet.com — MRCS Eng. LRCP Lond. 1981; MRCGP 1986. (Guy's)

VELLA, Victoria Mary Patricia Simmonds Accident & Emergency Department, Ronkswood Branch, Worcester Royal Infirmary, Worcester Tel: 01905 763333; Yew Tree Cottage, Adams Hill, Clent, Stourbridge DY9 9PS Tel: 01562 885435 — MB BCh 1986 Wales. Clin. Asst. (A & E) Selly Oak Hosp. Birm.; Sen. Trust Grade (A & E).

VELLA BONELLO, Louise Martha 37 Flood Street, London SW3 5ST — MRCS Eng. LRCP Lond. 1978; FFA RCS Eng. 1982. Cons. Anaesth. Roy. Free Hosp. Lond. Prev: Vis. Asst. Prof. Anaesth. & ITU John Hopkins Hosp. Baltimore; Lect. & Sen. Regist. St. Thos. Hosp.; Regist. Guy's Hosp. Lond.

VELLACOTT, Clive Walter Orchard Acre, 25 Oaks Lane, Postwick, Norwich NR13 5HD Tel: 01603 433432 — MB BS Lond. 1968; MRCS Eng. LRCP Lond. 1968; FRCA 1972. (Lond. Hosp.) Prev: Sen. Regist. (Anaesth.) Roy. Vict. Infirm. Newc.; Regist. (Anaesth.) Roy. Infirm. Edin.

VELLACOTT, Ian Diarmid The Croft, Middle St., Dunston, Lincoln LN4 2EW — MB BCh 1977 Wales; FRCOG 1996, M 1983. Cons. O & G Lincoln Co. Hosp.; Clin. Teach., Univ. of Nottm. Prev: Lect. & Sen. Regist. (O & G) Roy. Free Hosp. Lond.; Regist. (O & G) Middlx. Hosp. & Woms. Hosp. Soho Sq. Lond.; Research Regist. (O & G) St. Thos. Hosp. Lond.

VELLACOTT, Mr Keith David Royal Gwent Hospital, Cardiff Road, Newport NP20 2UB Tel: 01633 234112 Fax: 01633 234252; Glasllwch House, 4 Glasllwch Crescent, Newport NP20 3SE Tel: 01633 252303 Fax: 01633 223127 Email: k.d.vellacott@btinternet.com — MB BS 1972 Lond.; DM Nottm. 1981; FRCS Eng. 1977; MRCS Eng. LRCP Lond. 1972; DCH Eng. 1975. (Lond. Hosp.) Cons. Surg. Roy. Gwent Hosp. Newport; Hon. Sen. Lect. Univ. Wales Coll Med. Socs: Assn. Surg.; Assn. Coloproctol. Prev: Sen. Regist. (Surg.) Bristol & W.on HA; Wellcome Research Fell. Nottm. Univ. Regist. Cheltenham Gen. Hosp.; SHO United Bristol. Hosps.

VELLACOTT, Michael Nelson Plas y Bryn Surgery, Chapel Street, Wrexham LL13 7DE Tel: 01978 351308 Fax: 01978 312324; Cottsmoor House, Ruthin Road, Wrexham LL11 3BP Tel: 01978 354260 — MB BS 1972 Lond.; MRCS Eng. LRCP Lond. 1970; AFOM RCP Lond. 1988. Fact. Doctor Tetra Pak, Pouvair Ltd; Apptd. Doctor under Lonising Radiat. Regulator 1985, Pirelli Cables Ltd (Wrexham & Prescott), Rescam Image Products, Hoyalens Ltd.

VELLACOTT, William Noel (retired) Long Cottage, Stonebarrow Lane, Charmouth, Bridport DT6 6RA Tel: 01297 560381 — MRCS Eng. LRCP Lond. 1950; LMSSA Lond. 1939; MA Camb. 1940; FRCA 1965; FFA RCS Eng. 1954; DA Eng. 1946. Prev: Cons. Anaesth. Worcester Roy. Infirm.

VELLANI, Zarina Iqbal Ramzan (retired) 138 Bawnmore Road, Rugby CV22 6JT Tel: 01788 813869 — MB BS 1959 Lond.; MRCS Eng. LRCP Lond. 1959; MFCM RCP (UK) 1985; DObst RCOG 1961. Prev: Dir. Pub. Health Harrow HA.

VELLENOWETH, Sarah Margaret The Almshouse Surgery, Trinity Medical Centre, Thornhill Street, Wakefield WF1 1PG Tel: 01924 327150 Fax: 01924 327165; 16 Bottom Boat Road, Bottom Boat, Stanley, Wakefield WF3 4AY Tel: 01924 820486 Email: 113045.2124@compuserve.com — MB ChB 1989 Leeds; MRCGP 1995; DFFP 1993; DRCOG 1992. (Leeds) Princip. GP. Prev: Trainee GP Wakefield VTS.

VELLODI, Ashok Metabolic Unit, Great Ormond St. Hospital for Children NHS Trust, Great Ormond St., London WC1N 3JH Tel: 020 7405 9200 Fax: 020 7813 8597 Email: ashok.vellodi@gosh-tr.nthames.nhs.uk; 55 Georges Wood Road, Brookmans Park, Hatfield AL9 7BX — MB BS 1976 Poona; MD (Paediat.) All India Inst. Med. Scs. 1979; FRCP 1995, MRCP 1982; FRCPCH 1997. Cons. Paediat. & Hon. Sen. Lect. Metab. Unit Gt. Ormond St. Hosp. Childr. NHS Trust. Prev: Sen. Regist. (Paediat.) St. Thos. Hosp.

Lond.; Lect. (Child Health) W.m. Childr. Hosp. Lond.; Regist. Alder Hey Childr. Hosp. Liverp.

VELLODI, Chandrika Barnet General Hospital, Wellhouse Lane, Barnet EN5 3DJ Tel: 020 8440 5111; 55 Georges Wood Road, Brookmans Park, Hatfield AL9 7BX — MB BS 1978 Lond.; MRCP (UK) 1982. (St. Bart.) Cons. Phys. (Geriat. Med.) Barnet Gen. Hosp. Socs: Brit. Geriat. Soc. Prev: Sen. Regist. (Geriat. & Med.), Roy. Liverp. Hosp.; Regist. (Med.) Walton Hosp. Liverp.

VELMURUGIAH, Mr Velupillai 18 Hafod Cwnin, Carmarthen SA31 2AU — MB BS 1982 Sri Lanka; FRCS Eng. 1993; DLO RCS Eng. 1991. Regist. (ENT Surg.) Kings Mill Hosp. Sutton in Ashfield.

VELTKAMP, Ulrich Axel Flat 6, Block 1, Glan Clwyd Hospital, Rhuddlan Road, Bodelwyddan, Rhyl LL18 5UJ — State Exam Med 1992 Cologne.

VELUPILLAI, Suntheralingam 113 Balaam Street, London E13 8AF Tel: 020 8472 1238 Fax: 020 8470 1739; 39 Knighton Road, London E7 0EE — MB BS 1962 Ceylon. (Ceylon) Socs: BMA; Roy. Soc. Med. Prev: Regist. (Venereol.) St. Bart. Hosp. Lond. & Homerton Gr. Clinics E. Hosp. Lond.; SHO (Venereol.) St. Bart. Hosp. Lond. & P. of Wales Hosp. Lond.

VELUSAMI, Othimalaigounder Gaer Medical Centre, 71 Gaer Road, Newport NP20 3GX Tel: 01633 840827 — MB BS 1974 Madras; BSc 1967; DA (UK) 1982. (Madras University) GP A & E Gen. Surg., Psychiat. Anaesth. & O & G; Police Surg.; Examg. Med. Practitioner EMP for DLA. Socs: LMC.

VENABLES, Andrew John The Elms Resource Centre, Odsal Clinic, Odsal Road, Bradford BD6 1PR — MB BS 1979 Newc.; 1989 M.Med. Sci. (Clin. Psych.); MRCGP 1985; MRCPsych 1988.

VENABLES, Mr Christopher Wilfred Freeman Hospital, High Heaton, Newcastle upon Tyne NE7 7DN Tel: 0191 284 3111; 57 Hackwood Park, Hexham NE46 1AZ Tel: 01434 608277 Fax: 01434 608277 Email: chris.venab@argonet.co.uk — MB BS Lond. 1958; MS Lond. 1970; FRCS Eng. 1961; MRCS Eng. LRCP Lond. 1958. (Westm.) Emerit. Cons. Surg. (Gastroenterol.) Freeman Hosp. Newc. Socs: Fell. Roy. Soc. Med.; NE Surgic. Soc.; Brit. Soc. Gastroenterol. Prev: Hon. Lect. & Sen. Lect. (Surg.) Univ. Newc.; Research Fell. Mt. Sinai Hosp. New York, USA; Cons. in Surgic. Gastroenterol. Freeman Hosp.: Newc.

VENABLES, Elizabeth Mary Charing Cross Hospital, Earling, Hammersmith & Fulham Mental Health Trust, Fulham Place Road, London W6 8RF Tel: 020 8846 1509 Fax: 020 8846 1133; Flat 2, 131 Hammersmith Grove, London W6 0NJ Tel: 020 8563 7106 Email: bessievenables@yahoo.com — MB BS 1992 Adelaide; MRCPsych Dec. 1999. Specialist Regist., Pychogeriats.

VENABLES, Graham Stuart Royal Hallamshire Hospital, Sheffield S10 2JF Tel: 0114 2712197 Fax: 0114 271 2441 Email: graham.venables@sth.nhs.uk — BM BCh 1973 Oxf.; BA 1970 (MA) Camb; DM Oxf. 1984; FRCP Lond. 1991; FRCP Ed. 1989; MRCP (UK) 1976; Dip. Phil & Health Care Swansea; FRCOPhth 1999. (Camb. & Oxf.) Cons. Neurol.Sheff. Teachg. hosp. NHS Trust; Clin. Director Neurosci.s, Sheff. Teachg. Hosp. Socs: Europ. Stroke Counc. Prev: Sen. Lect. (Med. Neurol.) Dept. Neurosci. Univ. Edin.; 1st Asst. (Neurol.) Univ. Newc.; Assoc. Post Dean Sheff. Med. Sch.

***VENABLES, Joanne Margaret** 59 The Breaches, Easton in Gordano, Bristol BS20 0LY — MB ChB 1996 Birm.

VENABLES, Katherine Margaret Department of Occupational & Environmental Medicine, Imperial College School of Medicine, National Heart & Lung Institute, Dovehouse St., London SW3 6LR Tel: 020 7351 8328 Fax: 020 7351 8336 Email: k.venables@ic.ac.uk; 32 Franconia Road, Clapham, London SW4 9ND Tel: 020 7720 2481 — MB BS 1973 Lond.; BSc Lond. 1970, MD 1987, MSc (Distinc.) Occupat. Med. 1980; FRCP Lond. 1994; MRCP (UK) 1977; MFPHM RCP (UK) 1996; MFOM RCP Lond. 1988, FFOM 1993; MSc 1995. (St. Bart.) Univ. Lect.Iniv.Oxf; Hon. Cons. Pub. Health Kensington, Chelsea & W.m. HA; Sen. Lect. Imperial Coll. Sch. Med. Nat. Heart & Lung Inst. Lond. & Hon. Cons. Phys. Brompton Hosp. Lond. Socs: Chairm. Sci. Comm. Epidemiol.; Internat.Commiss. Occupat.Health; Res. Comm. Brit. Thoracic Soc. Prev: Lect. Lond. Sch. Hyg. & Trop. Med.; Lect. Cardiothoracic Inst. Lond.; Regist. St. Geo. Hosp. & St. Thos. Hosp. Lond.

VENABLES, Malcolm Crown Street Surgery, 17 Crown Street, Swinton, Rotherham S64 8LY Tel: 01709 583862; Brookside, Manor Lane, Adwick-upon-Dearne, Mexborough S64 0NN Tel: 01709 583677 — MB ChB 1982 Sheff. (Sheff.) Socs: MRCGP.

VENABLES, Martin Geoffrey Malcolm Hillside Farm, Ireton Wood, Idridgehay, Belper DE56 2SD Tel: 01335 70532 — BM BCh 1948 Oxf. Prev: Ho. Surg. ENT Dept. Roy. Hosp. Sheff.; Ho. Phys. Roy. Infirm. Sheff.

VENABLES, Michael Thomas CAMHS, Horsham Hospital, Hurst Road, Horsham RH12 2DR Tel: 01403 227014 — MRCS Eng. LRCP Lond. 1980; BA Oxf. 1973; MRCPsych 1984. (Middlesex Hosp.) Cons. Child & Adolesc. Psychiat. SurAd NHS Trust, Horsham Hosp. Socs: Assn. Child Psychol. & Psychiat.

VENABLES, Paul Andrew 11A Pheasant Walk, Littlemore, Oxford OX4 4XX — BM 1998 Soton.

VENABLES, Peter (retired) 29 The Avenue, Andover SP10 3EP — MB BChir Camb. 1944; MRCP Lond. 1945; MRCS Eng. LRCP Lond. 1944. Prev: Cas. Med. Off. & Med. Regist. Middlx. Hosp.

VENABLES, Peter (retired) 13 Lyon Avenue, New Milton BH25 6AP — MB BS 1951 Lond.; MRCGP 1966. Prev: Jun. Surg. Specialist RAMC.

VENABLES, Thomas Leopold The Surgery, 2A St. Wilfrids Square, Calverton, Nottingham NG14 6FP Tel: 0115 965 2294 Fax: 0115 965 5898; Salterford House, Calverton, Nottingham NG14 6NZ Tel: 0115 965 5316 Fax: 0115 965 5627 — MB BChir 1965 Camb.; MB Camb. 1965, BChir 1964; MA CAmb. 1965; FRCP 1997; FRCGP 1980, M 1972. (Camb. & Westm.) Socs: (Pres.) Nottm. M-C Soc.; Osler Club Lond.; Nottm. Medico-Legal Soc. Prev: Upjohn Trav. Fell.; Med. Specialist RAF.; Lect. (Gen. Pract.) Nottm. Univ. Med. Sch.

VENESS, Alan Maurice City Hospital NHS Trust, Dudley Road, Birmingham B18 7QH Tel: 0121 554 3801 Email: alan.veness@cityhos/bham.wmids.nhs.uk; 43 Pilkington Avenue, Sutton Coldfield B72 1LA Email: alanv@care4free.net — MB ChB Birm. 1964; FRCA Eng. 1970. (Birmingham) Cons. Anaesth. City Hosp. NHS Trust Birm. Socs: Assn. Anaesth.; Obst. Anaesth. Assn. & Midl. Soc. Anaesth. Prev: Sen. Regist. (Anaesth.) St. Geo. Hosp. Lond. & Hosp. Sick Childr. Gt. Ormond St.

VENETO, Bruno The Thatches, Crossing Road, Palgrave, Diss IP22 1AW Tel: 01379 643314 — State DMS 1989 Padua. Prev: SHO (Cas., Gen. Surg. & Orthop.) Hammersmith Hosp. Lond.; Demonst. (Anat.) St. Geo. Hosp. Med. Sch. Lond.; Cas. Off. St. Helier Hosp. Carshalton.

VENISON, Tania Dawn 11 Holt Close, Elstree, Borehamwood WD6 3QH Tel: 020 8953 9359; 12 Buick House, Tidworth Road, Bow, London E3 4WX Tel: 020 8953 9359 — MB BS 1996 Lond. (Royal London Hospital Medical College) SHO (Gen. Med.). Prev: SHO (Oncol.); Ho. Off. (Gen. Surg.); Ho. Off. (Gen. Med.).

VENKAT, Kandasami Ramaswamy Eastgate, Gillott Road, Edgbaston, Birmingham B16 0EU Tel: 0121 454 1712; Srisai, 40 Selwyn Road, Edgbaston, Birmingham B16 0SN Tel: 0121 454 4721 — MB BS 1964 Madras; Diabetes & ITS Managem. 2000 Warwick; Diploma in Acupunc. 1996 UK; MRCGP 1974. (Madural Med. Coll.) Socs: BMA; FRSM 1998. Prev: Regist. (A & E) Vict. Hosp. Blackpool; SHO (Cas. & Gen. Surg.) St. Jas. Hosp. Tredegar; Asst. Med. Off. (Surg.) S.. Rly. HQ Hosp. Mysore.

VENKAT-RAMAN, Gopalakrishnan Renal Unit, St Mary's Hospital, Portsmouth PO3 6AD Tel: 023 92 866115 Fax: 023 92 866108; Tel: 023 92 388025 Email: annapurna@clara.net — MB BS 1974 Poona; MD Delhi 1978; FRCP Lond. 1992; MRCP (UK) 1980; MNAMS (India) 1979. Cons. Nephrol. Wessex Regional Renal & Transpl. Unit; Sen. Lect. Univ. Soton.; Cons. Phys. St. Mary's Hosp. Portsmouth; Hon Cons Nephrol S.ampton Gen Hosp; Hon Cons Nephrol P.ss Eliz. Hosp Guernsey. Socs: Internat. Soc. Nephrol.; Renal Assn.; Brit. Hypertens. Soc. Prev: Lect. (Med.) Univ. Soton.; Regist. (Med.) Sunderland Roy. Infirm.; Sen. Resid. (Med.) Safdarjang Hosp. New Delhi.

VENKAT RAMAN, Mr Narayanaswamy Department of Fetomaternal Medicine, Maternity Day Care Unit, St Mary's Hospital, Praed St., London W2 1NY Tel: 020 7886 6691 Fax: 020 7886 2169 Email: venkar@bizonline.co.uk; House 5, Kershaw Close, Langton Gate, 118 North St, Hornchurch RM11 1SW Tel: 01708 459276 — MB BS 1980 Osmania; MD Osmania 1985; Dip Nat Bd Examin (NBE), New Delhi,1986; MRCOG 1992; Cert. Adv Ultrasound RCOG/RCR Lond. 1997. (Osmania Med. Coll., Hyderabad, India) Staff Grade Specialist Feto-Matern. Med. Dept. of

VENKATA RAMA SASTRY

Obst. St Mary's Hosp. Lond. Socs: BMA; Fell. Roy. Soc. Med. Lond. Prev: Regist. O & G, The Jessop Hosp. Hosp. For Wom., Sheff.. UK; Regist. O & G, the Doncester Roy. Infirm. & Montagu Hosp. NHS Trust, Doncester, S.Yorks. UK.

VENKATA RAMA SASTRY, Kolluri c/o Professor A. D. Medelow, Department of Neurosurgery, Newcastle General Hospital, Westgate Road, Newcastle upon Tyne NE4 6BE — MB BS 1969 Sri Venkateswara.

VENKATA RAO, Mr Kesani 9 Alliance Close, Wembley HAO 2NG Tel: 020 8903 0647 — MB BS 1973 Andhara India; FRCSI 1985.

VENKATACHALAM, Dhanvanti Narayan Hollybank Surgery, 31 London Road, Sittingbourne ME10 1NQ Tel: 01795 472534/425439 Fax: 01795 473886; Almond Lodge, 46 Almond Grove, Hempstead, Gillingham ME7 3SE Tel: 01634 234365 — MB BS 1981 Mysore; DObst RCPI 1987. GP Princip. Sittingbourne Kent.

VENKATARAMAN, Geetha Department of Obstetrics & Gynaecology, West Middlesex University Hospital, Twickenham Road, Isleworth TW7 6AF Tel: 020 8565 5435 Fax: 020 8565 5973; 53 The Beeches, 200 Lampton Road, Hounslow TW3 4DF Tel: 020 8577 9007 — MB BS 1975 Madras; MD Madras 1985; MRCOG 1993. Clin. Asst. (O & G) W. Middlx. Univ. Hosp.

VENKATARAMAN, Marakatham c/o Mrs H. Faulkner, Personnel Department, Maternity Unit, Walsgrave Hospital NHS Trust, Clifford Bridge Road, Coventry CV2 2DX — MB BS 1983 Madras; MRCP (UK) 1989.

VENKATARAMANAN, Mr Palgudi Ramaswamy Flat 710, Block 7 Friars Field, Royal Gwent Hospital, Newport NP20 4EZ; 3 Townsend Close, Woodloes Park, Warwick CV34 5TT Tel: 01926 497620 — MB BS 1978 Madurai; FRCS Ed. 1987. Regist. (Orthop.) Roy. Gwent Hosp. Newport. Prev: Regist. (Orthop.) Furness Gen. Hosp. Barrow in Furness.

VENKATARATNAM BABU, Kari 95 Park Way, Crawley RH10 3BS — MB BS 1973 Sri Venateswara.

VENKATASUBBA RAO, Sonti Shanti, Woodhart Lane, Eccleston, Chorley PR7 5TB Tel: 01257 452281 — MB BS 1953 Madras. (Madras) Sessional Med. Off. DSS. Prev: Ho. Off. Stoke-on-Trent Hosp. Gp.; SHO Bolton Hosp. Gp.; JHMO Roy. Hosp. Wolverhampton.

VENKATESAN, Mr Dhamaraikulam 24 Landseer Close, Liberty Avenue, Hamilton Gardens, London SW20 2UT — MB BS 1970 Bangalor; MB BS Bangalore 1970; FRCS Ed. 1976. (Bangalore Med. Coll.) Regist. (Gen. Surg.) Horton Gen. Hosp. Banbury. Prev: SHO (Thoracic Surg.) St. Helier Hosp. Carshalton; Rotating SHO (Surg.) Taunton & Som. Hosp. (MusGr. Pk. Br.); SHO (Gen. Surg. & Cas.) Dreadnought Seamen's Hosp. Greenwich.

VENKATESAN, Pradhib Bimingham Heartlands Hospital, Birmingham B9 5SS Tel: 0121 766 6611; 11 Mossdale Road, Nottingham NG5 3GX — MB BChir 1984 Camb.; PhD Nottm. 1996; MRCP (UK) 1986; DTM & H RCP Lond. 1994. (Univ. Camb.) Clin. Lect. (Infec.) Univ. Birm. Prev: Wellcome Research Fell. (Microbial Dis.) Univ. Nottm.; Regist. (Med.) City Hosp. Nottm.; SHO (Cardiol.) Hammersmith Hosp. Lond.

VENKATESH, Maya Nayak 12 Shetland Drive, Glendale Estate, Nuneaton CV10 7LA — MB BS 1988 Mangalore; FRCS Ed. 1993.

VENKATESH, Udupa Rajagopal St Lukes Hospital, Department of Paediatrics, Little Horton Lane, Bradford BD6 1RG — MB BS 1983 Madras; MRCPI 1991.

VENKATESH, Mr Viswanathan AG1, Leicester Royal Infirmary, Staff Residences, Walnut St., Leicester LE2 7GJ — MB BS 1981 Madras; FRCS Ed. 1990.

VENKATESHAM, Guduguntla Chiswick Health Centre, Fishers Lane, London W4 1RX Tel: 020 8321 3551 Fax: 020 8321 3556 — MB BS 1974 Osmania; MFFP 1993. CMO (Family Plann.) & Instruc. Dr. Socs: Overseas Doctors Assn. (Ex-Treas. NW Thames Div.); (Ex-Treas.) Osmania Med. Grad.s Assn.; Fund Raising Sec. SHRI Venkatesware (Balaji) Temple of UK.

VENKATESWARAN, Mahadevan North Staffordshire Royal Infirmary, Princes Road, Hartshill, Stoke-on-Trent ST4 7LN — MB BS 1956 Malaya; FRCR 1975; FFR 1974; DMRD Eng. 1974.

VENKATESWARLU, Vasantham District General Hospital, Town Lane, Kew, Southport PR8 6NJ; 10 Wennington Road, Southport PR9 7EU — MB BS 1971 Sri Venkateswara; DA Eng. 1976. (Kurnool Med. Coll.) Clin. Med. Off. (Anaesth.) Dist. Gen. Hosp. S.port. Prev: Regist. (Anaesth.) Gem. Hosp. Jersey.

VENKATRAMAN, T B Bawtry Road Surgery, 171 Bawtry Road, Brinsworth, Rotherham S60 5ND Tel: 01709 828806 — MB BS 1975 Delhi; MB BS 1975 Delhi.

VENKITESWARAN, Nemmara Thiruvenkitanathan Parkgate Medical Centre, Netherfield Lane, Parkgate, Rotherham S62 6AW Tel: 01709 514500 Fax: 01709 514490 — MB BS Bangalore 1967.

VENKITESWARAN, Ramachandran (retired) 2A Bradpole Road, Strouden Park, Bournemouth BH8 9NX Tel: 01202 532253 — MB BS Karnatak 1964; MRCGP 1975; DRCOG 1974; DCH RCP Lond. 1971.

VENN, Carl Stuart Abertillery Health Centre, Abertillery; 15 Alma Street, Brynmawr NP23 4DZ — MB ChB 1983 Bristol; BSc Bristol 1980, MB ChB 1983; MRCGP 1990; DRCOG 1988.

VENN, Mr Graham Erskine Suite 305, Emblem House, London Bridge Hospital, 27 Tooley St., London SE1 2PR Tel: 020 7378 6566 Fax: 020 7378 8156 Email: graham@gvenn.demon.co.uk; Flat 106, The Listed Building, 350 Highway, London E1w 3HU Tel: 020 77902257 Fax: 020 7378 Ext: 8156 — MB BS 1977 Lond.; FETCS 1998; MS Lond. 1991; FICS Chicago 1990; FRCS Eng. 1982; FRCS Ed. 1981. Cons. Cardiothoracic Surg. Guy's & St. Thos. Hosp.; Hon. Cons. Cardiac Surg. to Brit. Army; Hon. Sen. Lect. Univ. Lond. Socs: Brit. Cardiac Soc.; Roy. Soc. Med.Past Pres. of cardiothuracic Sect.; Eur. Assn. Cardiothoracic Surg. Prev: Sen. Regist. (Cardiothoracic Surg.) Middlx., Hammersmith & Harefield Hosps. Lond.

VENN, Michael George Pierre, OBE, Air Commodore RAF Med. Retd. 51 Willoughby Drive, Empingham, Oakham LE15 8PY Tel: 01780 460602 Fax: 01780 460602 — MB BS 1955 Lond.; FFOM RCP Lond. 1994, MFOM 1980; DAvMed Eng. 1968; MRAeS 1976. (Middlx.) Indep. Cons. Aviat. & Occupat. Med.; Aviat. Med. Gp. Roy. Aeronautical Soc. Socs: Fell. Aerospace Med. Assn.; Soc. Occupat. Med. Prev: Dep. Head. Med. Servs. John Lewis Partnership plc Lond.; Commandant RAF Centr. Med. Estab. RAF Kelvin Hse. Lond.; Aerospace Med. Staff. Off. Brit. Defence Staff Washington, USA.

VENN, Paul Hex (retired) Milber Down, 7 Selwyn Road, Eastbourne BN21 2LD — MRCS Eng. LRCP Lond. 1948; FFA RCS Eng. 1954; DA Eng. 1953. Prev: Cons. Anaesth. E.bourne Dist. Gen. Hosp.

VENN, Peter John Clare House, Lewes Road, East Grinstead RH19 3SY — MB BS 1979 Lond.; FFA RCS Eng. 1984. Cons. Anaesth. Qu. Vict. Hosp. E. Grinstead; Examr. Roy. Coll. Anaesth. Socs: Fell. Roy. Soc. Med.; Assn. Anaesth.; Plastic Surg. & Burns Anaesth. Assn. Prev: Sen. Regist. Nuffield Dept. Anaesth. Oxf, RHA; Lect. (Anaesth.) Nat. Hosp. Nerv. Dis. Qu. Sq. Lond.; Regist. (Anaesth.) Char. Cross Hosp. Lond.

VENN, Philippa Mary Cleveland Clinic, 12 Cleveland Road, St Helier, Jersey JE1 4HD Tel: 01534 722381/734121 — BM 1989 Soton.; MRCP (UK) 1992; MRCGP 1994. GP Jersey Chanel. Prev: Trainee GP Chelmsford; SHO (O & G) St. Johns Hosp. Chelmsford; SHO (Gen. Med.) Qu. Eliz. Hosp. Birm.

VENN, Richard Mark 7 New Road, Forest Green, Dorking RH5 5SA — MB BS 1987 Lond.

VENN, Mr Robin John (retired) 32 Whiting Street, Bury St Edmunds IP33 1NP Tel: 01284 755093 Email: robin.venn@virgin.net — MB BS Lond. 1951; FRCOG 1973, M 1960; MMSA 1963. Prev: Cons. O. & G Bury St. Edmunds.

VENN, Sarah Joanna The Bridge Centre, Foundry Bridge, Abertillery NP13 1BQ Tel: 01495 322682 Fax: 01495 322686; 15 Alma Street, Brynmawr NP23 4DZ Tel: 01495 313541 — MB ChB Bristol 1983; MRCGP 1989; DGM RCP Lond. 1986; DCH RCP 1995. (Bristol) GP & Specialist Regist. (Pub.h Health) Gwent. Prev: Volunteer Action Health S. India; GP Princip.; Staff Grade (Community Paediat.).

VENN, Mrs Suzanne Nicola St Richard's Hospital, Chichester PO19 4SE — MB BS 1987 Lond.; MS 1996; FRCS 1999 (Urol); FRCS Eng. 1992. p/t Cons. Urological Surg., St Richard's Hosp., Chichester; Sen. Lect. Inst. of Urol., UCLH.

VENN-TRELOAR, Josephine Mary Community Child Health Services, Memorial Hospital, Shooters Hill, Woolwich, London SE18 3RZ — MB BS 1984 Lond.; MRCGP 1988; DRCOG 1987; AKC 1984. Clin. Med. Off. (Child Health) Greenwich Healthcare NHS Trust. Prev: GP Asst. Vanburgh Hill Health Centre; GP Retainer Scheme Ingleton Ave. Surg. Welling.

VENNAM, Mr Ramesh Babu 3 Maes Celyn, Wrexham LL13 7QG — MB BS 1979 Nagarjuna India; FRCS Glas. 1989. Regist. (Gen. Surg.) Blackburn Roy. Infirm.

VENNER, Elizabeth Anne Tredale Cottage, Tregunna, St Breock, Wadebridge PL27 7HX Tel: 01208 813114 — MB BS 1992 Lond.; BSc (Hons.) Lond. 1989; MRCP (UK) 1995.

VENNER, Mr Robert Martin Whincorft, 288 Glasgow Road, Waterfoot, Eaglesham, Glasgow G76 0EW — MB ChB 1968 Birm.; FRCS Ed. 1975.

VENNING, Geoffrey Richard 14 Lucas Road, High Wycombe HP13 6QG Tel: 01494 526543 Fax: 01494 463318; Malastreges, Cuzance, par Martel Lot 46600, France Tel: 00 33 65 327536 Fax: 00 33 65 327536 — BM BCh 1944 Oxf.; FRCP Lond. 1973, M 1949. (Oxf.) Dir. Pharmaceut. Research Serv. Ltd.; Vis. Lect. Sheff. Univ. Med. Sch. Socs: Founder Fell. Fac. Pharmaceut. Med.; Fell. Roy. Soc. Med.; Airborne Med. Soc. Prev: Vice-Pres. Janssen Pharmaceutica N.V. Belgium, & Dir. of Research & Developm. UK; Sen. Med. Off. Med. Div. DHSS; Sen. Regist. (Med.) Univ. Dept. Med. Manch. Roy. Infirm. & Manch. RHB.

VENNING, Helen Elizabeth Paediatric Rheumatology Clinic, Department of Child Health, University Hospital, Nottingham NG7 2UH Tel: 0115 924 9924 Ext: 43442 Fax: 0115 849 3313 Email: helenvenning@gmc.demon.co.uk — BM BS 1977 Nottm.; BMedSci Nottm. 1975; FRCP Lond. 1994; MRCP (UK) 1981; FRCPCH 1997. (Nottm.) Cons. Paediat. Rheum. Univ. Hosp. Nottm. Prev: Cons. Paediat. (Rheum. & Community) Nottm. Community Unit.

***VENNING, Jane Wentworth** 9 Gresham Road, Oxted RH8 0BS Tel: 01883 713761; 2 Giebe Street, St. Clements, Oxford OX4 1SQ Tel: 01865 245409 — MB ChB 1995 Birm.

VENNING, Mary Ruth (retired) 14 Lucas Road, High Wycombe HP13 6QG Tel: 01494 526543 — BM BCh 1944 Oxf.; CPH Wales 1951. Prev: SCMO Bucks. CC.

VENNING, Michael Charles Teaching Unit 6, University Hospital of South Manchester, Nell Lane, Didsbury, Manchester M20 2LR Tel: 0161 291 3667 Fax: 0161 291 3670 Email: mike.venning@smuht.nwest.nhs.uk; 12 Kingston Road, Didsbury, Manchester M20 2RZ Tel: 0161 445 7238 — BM BCh 1979 Oxf.; PhD Cornell 1976; BA Oxf. 1969, BM BCh 1979; MRCP (UK) 1981; FRCP (UK) 1996. (Oxford) Cons. Renal & Gen. Phys. Univ. Hosp. S. Manch.; Hon. Lect. Univ. Manch. Med. Sch.; Roy. Coll. Tutor, Smith Manch. Univ. Hosp. Socs: Renal Assn.; Internat. Soc. Nephrol.; Internat. Soc. Peritoneal Dialysis. Prev: Lect. (Med.) Univ. Newc.; Research Regist. Hammersmith Hosp. Lond.; Sen. Ho. Off. Brompton Hosp.

VENNING, Molly Anne (retired) 4 Buckstone Close, London SE23 3QT Email: molvenning@cw.com.net — MB BS 1974 Lond.; MRCPsych 1985. Prev: Sen. Regist. (Psychother.) Bethlem Roy. & Maudsley Hosps.

VENNING, Stephanie Louise The Wheatcroft, Weasenham, King's Lynn PE32 2SW — MB BS 1998 Newc.

VENNING, Vanessa Ann Churchill Hospital, Headington, Oxford OX3 7LJ Fax: 01865 228232; 22 Ormond Road, Wantage OX12 8EG Tel: 01235 764133 — BM BCh 1978 Oxf.; BA Oxf. 1975, DM 1994; MRCP (UK) 1980; FRCP 1997. (Oxford) Cons. Dermat.Ch.ill Hosp. Oxf. Prev: Sen. Regist. (Dermat.) Slade Hosp. Oxf.; Cons. Dermat., N. Hants. Hosp.s.

VENTER, Jan Adriaan 1 Mouliniux Park Gardens, Tunbridge Wells TN4 8DL — MB ChB 1989 Pretoria.

VENTERS, Angus Dougall 3 The Avenue, Leeds LS15 8JN — MB ChB 1983 Glas.

VENTERS, Brian Parkgrove Terrace Surgery, 22B Parkgrove Terrace, Edinburgh EH4 7NX Tel: 0131 312 6600 Fax: 0131 312 7798; 4 East Barnton Gardens, Edinburgh EH4 6AR Tel: 0131 336 3553 — MB ChB 1975 Ed.; BSc (Med. Sci.) Ed. 1972. (Ed.) Prev: Ho. Off. (Orthop. Surg.) Roy. Infirm. Edin.; Ho. Off. (Respirat. Unit) N.. Gen. Hosp. Edin.; Clin. Asst. Beechmont Hosp. Edin.

VENTERS, Gregor Lachlan Pentland Medical Centre, 44 Pentland View, Currie EH14 5QB Tel: 0131 449 2142 Fax: 0131 451 5855 — MB ChB 1984 Ed.

VENTERS, Nicholas David 48 Brantwood Road, Bradford BD9 6QA — MB ChB 1998 Liverp.

VENTHAM, Peter Anthony Anaesthetics Department, Poole Hospital Trust, Longfleet Road, Poole BH15 2JB Tel: 01202 665511 Fax: 01202 442672; The Old Barn, Millhams St, Christchurch BH23 1DN Tel: 01202 484307 — BM 1976 Soton.; BSc (Hons.) Biochem. Wales 1969; FFA RCS Eng. 1984. Cons. Anaesth. Dorset HA. Socs: Assn. Anaesth. & Pain Soc. Prev: Sen. Regist. (Anaesth.) Roy. Free & N.wick Pk. Hosps.

VENTON, Tamsin Jayne Riverside Surgery, Albion St., Shaldon, Teignmouth TQ14 0DF Tel: 01626 873331 Fax: 01626 772107; Glendevon Medical Centre, 3 Carlton Place, Teignmouth TQ14 8AB Tel: 01626 770955 Fax: 01626 772107 — MB BS 1988 Lond.; MRCGP 1993; DFFP 1994. Prev: Trainee GP Torbay HA VTS.

VENTRESCA, Giampietro 15 Steele Road, London W4 5AB Tel: 020 8987 8810 — State DMS 1983 Milan; MD Milan 1988; MSc Aberd. 1991; MFPM RCP (UK) 1996. Socs: Scott. Soc. Experim. Med.; Brit. Pharm. Soc. (Clin. Sect.).

VENTRESS, Michael Andrew 76 Moorside Crescent, Fishburn, Stockton-on-Tees TS21 4DH — MB ChB 1993 Liverp.

VENTRY, Lorna Margaret Health Centre, 103 Paisley Road, Renfrew PA4 8LL Tel: 0141 886 2012; 20 Strathmore Avenue, Paisley PA1 3DT Tel: 0141 810 4275 — MB ChB 1979 Glas.; DRCOG 1981.

VENUGOPAL, Janardanan Bransholme South Health Centre, Goodhart Road, Bransholme, Hull HU7 4DW Tel: 01482 831257; 61 The Dales, Cottingham HU16 5JS — MB BS 1968 Kerala. (Trivandrum Med. Coll.) Prev: Regist. (Psychiat.) Walsgrave Hosp. Coventry; SHO (Geriat.) Alexandra Hosp. Barnstaple; SHO (Geriat.) De Lancey Hosp. Cheltenham.

VENUGOPAL, Ramaswamysetty Esk Road Medical Centre, 12 Esk Road, London E13 8LJ Tel: 020 7474 9002 Fax: 020 7473 1917.

VENUGOPAL, Sriramashetty, OBE (retired) Aston Health Centre, 175 Trinity Road, Aston, Birmingham B6 6JA Tel: 0121 328 3597 Fax: 0121 327 1674 — MB BS 1960 Osmania; MFPHM (RCP) 1998; FRSH 1997; DMRD Madras 1965; FRCGP 1997, M 1990; FRIPHH 1988. Mem. Local Med. Comm. & Dist. Med. Comm.; Nat. Pres. Brit. Minority Ethnic Health Professional Assn. (BMEHPA). Prev: Hosp. Pract. (Psychiat.) All St.s Hosp. Birm.

VENUS, Matthew Robert 43A Settles Street, London E1 1JN — MB BS 1997 Lond.

VERBER, Ian Graham North Tees General Hospital, Stockton-on-Tees TS19 8PE Tel: 01642 617617 Fax: 01642 624940 Email: i.g.verber@ncl.ac.uk; Old School House, Bentley Wynd, Yarm TS15 9BS Tel: 01642 788992 — MB BCh 1974 Wales; FRCP Lond. 1995; MRCP (UK) 1980; FRCPCH 1997; DCH Eng. 1977. Cons. Paediat. N. Tees Health Trust; Clin. Lect. Univ. Newc. Socs: BMA; Brit. Assn. Perinatal Med.; N. Eng. Paediatric Soc. (Sec.). Prev: Lect. (Child Health) St. Geo. Hosp. Med. Sch. Lond.; Research Fell. Roy. Manch. Childr. Hosp.; Ho. Off. Hosp. Sick Childr. Lond.

VERBORG, Stefan Andreas Department of Postgraduate Medicine, Thornburrow Drive, Stoke-on-Trent ST4 7QB; 87 Aberporth Road, Llandaff, Cardiff CF14 2PQ — State Exam Med 1986 Dusseldorf; FRCPS Glas. 1993.

VERBOV, Professor Julian Lionel 31 Rodney Street, Liverpool L1 9EH Email: verbov@madasafish.com; 38 Montclair Drive, Liverpool L18 0HB Tel: 0151 722 0074 Email: hverbov@cs.com — FLS 2001; MB ChB Liverp. 1959; MD Liverp. 1971; FRCP Lond. 1978, M 1965; MRCS Eng. LRCP Lond. 1959; FIBiol 1985, M 1979, C 1979; FRCPCH 1991. (Liverp.) Hon. Prof. Dermat. Univ. Liverp.; JP; Cons. Paediat. (Dermat.) Roy. Liverp. Childr. Hosp. NHS Trust Alder Hey; Cons. Fingerprint Soc. Socs: Fell. Roy. Soc. Med.; Fell. Zoolog. Soc. Lond.; Past-Exec. Mem. Brit. Assn. Dermat. Prev: Edr. Brit. Jl. Dermat.; Cons. Dermat. I. of Man; Sen. Regist. (Dermat.) St. Bart. Hosp. Lond.

VERCOE, Michael George Skinner 20 Allington Mead, Exeter EX4 5AP Tel: 01392 56479 — MB BS 1950 Lond.; MRCS Eng. LRCP Lond. 1950; DObst RCOG 1954. (St. Bart.)

VERCOE, Stephen Ide Lane Surgery, Ide Lane, Alphinton, Exeter EX2 8UP Tel: 01392 439868 Fax: 01392 493513; Hillpark, Christow, Exeter EX6 7NP — MB BS 1983 Lond.; MA Camb. 1984; MRCGP 1987; DRCOG 1986; Cert. Family Plann. JCC 1986. (Camb. & Univ. Coll. Hosp.) Socs: BMA. Prev: Trainee GP Exeter VTS; Ho. Phys. Whittington Hosp. Lond.; Ho. Surg. N.ampton Gen. Hosp.

VERCOE-ROGERS, John Patrick 9 Brookvale, Broughshane, Ballymena BT43 7JQ — MB BCh BAO 1991 NUI.

VERDIN, Stuart Michael Edge Grove School, Aldenham, Radlett — MB BS 1991 Lond.; DA (UK) 1995. Clin. Research Fell. Roy. Free Hosp.

VERDON, Jonathon Hendley Cranleigh Health Centre, 18 High Street, Cranleigh GU6 8AE Tel: 01483 273951 Fax: 01483 275755 — MB BS 1974 Lond.; MRCS Eng. LRCP Lond. 1974; DRCOG 1978. Prev: GP Trainee Brighton VTS; SHO (Anaesth.) Hammersmith Hosp.; Ho. Surg. Roy. Free Hosp. Lond.

VERDON, Patricia Elizabeth (retired) Haroldston, 27 Park Crescent, Emsworth PO10 7NT Tel: 01243 372514 — MB BS Lond. 1946. Prev: Clin. Asst. (Path.) Portsmouth Dist. Hosps.

VERE, Duncan Wright 14 Broadfield Way, Buckhurst Hill IG9 5AG — MB BS (Hons.) Lond. 1952; MD Lond. 1964; FRCP Lond. 1968, M 1954; Hon FFPM RCP (UK) 1994. (Lond. Hosp.) Emerit. Prof. of Therap. Lond. Univ. Socs: Brit. Pharm. Soc. Prev; Cons. Phys. Lond. Hosp.; Med. Off. RAF Inst. Aviat. Med. FarnBoro.; 1st Asst. & Ho. Phys. Med. Unit Lond. Hosp.

VERE-HODGE, Mr Nicholas (retired) Watersmead, Donhead Saint Mary, Shaftesbury SP7 9DP Tel: 01747 728 — MB BChir 1938 Camb.; FRCS Eng. 1940; MRCS Eng. LRCP Lond. 1938. Prev: Hon. Cons. Orthop. Surg. E. Dorset Health Dist.

VEREL, Agnes Cobden Miller (retired) 7 Warren Rise, Coal Aston, Dronfield S18 2EB — MB ChB Aberd. 1947. Prev: Co. Med. Off. Union Carbide UK Ltd., Carbon Products Div. Sheff.

VEREL, David (retired) 1 Mussons Close, Corby Glen, Grantham NG33 4NY Tel: 01476 550083 — MB BChir Camb. 1943; MD Camb. 1948; FRCP Lond. 1967, M 1945. Prev: Regional Cardiol. Trent.

VERGANI, Professor Diego Institute of Hepatology, RFUCMS, 69-75 Chenies Mews, London WC1E 6HX Tel: 020 7388 2116 Fax: 020 7380 0405 Email: d.vergani@ucl.ac.uk; 14 Crab Hill, Beckenham BR3 5HE Tel: 020 8658 6003 Fax: 020 8658 6211 Email: diego@vergani.demon.co.uk — MD 1971 Milan; PhD Lond. 1990; State Exam Milan 1972; Dip. Clin. Immunol. Milan 1979; Dip. Internal Med. Milan 1976. (Milan) Prof. & Hon. Cons. (Immunol.) Univ. Coll. Lond. Med. Sch. Socs: Fell. Roy. Coll. Path. Prev: Prof. & Hon. Cons. (Immunol.) King's Coll. Sch. Med. & Dent. Lond.

VERGANO, James Bruno (retired) 3 Beltane Drive, Wimbledon, London SW19 5JR Tel: 020 8946 3189 — MB BChir 1952 Camb.; BA (Nat. Sc. Trip.) Camb. 1948, MA 1951, MB Bchir 1952; LMSSA Lond. 1951; FRCGP 1979, M 1962. Prev: GP Kensington Lond.

VERGHESE, Anthony Richard Sundon Medical Centre, 142-144 Sundon Park Road, Sundon Park, Luton LU3 3AH Tel: 01582 571130 Fax: 01582 564452 — MB ChB 1978 Leeds; MRCGP 1987; DRCOG 1985.

VERGHESE, Chandy Intensive Care Unit, Royal Berkshire Hospital, Reading RG1 5AN Tel: 01734 875111; 6 The Mount, Reading RG1 5HL Tel: 01734 310234 — MB BS 1974 Madras; FFA RCS Eng. 1982; DA (UK) 1978. Cons. Anaesth. (Intens. Care) Roy. Berks. Hosp. & Battle Hosp. Reading. Socs: Intens. Care Soc.; Assn. Anaesth.; Founder Mem. Soc. Airway Managem. Prev: Sen. Lect. & Hon. Cons. Lond. Hosp. Med. Coll. & Newham HA; Lect. & Hon. Sen. Regist. (Anaesth.) The Lond. Hosp. Whitechapel; Lect. & Hon. Sen. Regist. Whipps Cross Hosp. Lond.

VERGHESE, Gigi Sara Carnarvon Road Surgery, 7 Carnarvon Road, Southend-on-Sea SS2 6LR Tel: 01702 466340 Fax: 01702 603179 — MB BS 1977 Kerala; MD Dermat. Calicut 1981; MB BS Univ. Kerala 1977; DTM & H 1986.

VERGHESE, Kaliyilil Luke Grove Road Surgery, 59-63 Grove Road, Eastbourne BN21 4TX Tel: 01323 720606 Fax: 01323 412331 — MRCS Eng. LRCP Lond. 1974.

VERGHESE, Rachel 27 Mill Road, Cambridge CB1 2AB — MB BS 1981 Kerala; MRCOU UK 1993.

VERGIS, Mercy Elizabeth 29 Desborough Road, Hitchin SG4 0NN — MB ChB 1992 Bristol; MRCP (UK) 1996.

VERGNAUD, Stephanie 15 Buchanan Gardens, London NW10 5AD — MD 1988 Paris; MRCPsych 1994.

VERHEUL, Meindert Roger 8 Lavenda Close, Hempsted, Gillingham ME7 3TB — MB BS 1984 Lond.; DCH RCP Lond. 1989; DRCOG 1988. GP Chatham Kent.

VERIKIOU, Katherine 18 Canterbury House, Royal St., London SE1 7LN — Ptychio Iatrikes 1988 Athens.

VERINDER, Mr David George Reginald West Cumberland Hospital, Hensingham, Whitehaven CA28 8JG Tel: 01946 693181 Fax: 01946 523532; Sanderson House, Summerhill, Sandwith, Whitehaven CA28 9UP Tel: 01946 690429 — MB ChB Sheff. 1968; FRCS Eng. 1973; MRCS Eng. LRCP Lond. 1968. (Sheff.) p/t Cons. Orthop. Surg. W. Cumbria Health Care NHS Trust W. Cumbld. Hosp. Whitehaven. Prev: Cons. Orthop. Surg. Bassetlaw HA; Cons. Orthop. Surg. Worksop & Retford Health Dists.; Sen. Regist. Rotat. (Orthop.) Sheff. AHA (T).

VERITY, Christopher Michael The Child Development Centre, Addenbrooke's Hospital, Hills Road, Cambridge CB2 2QQ Tel: 01223 216662 Fax: 01223 242171; The White Cottage, 67 High St, Grantchester, Cambridge CB3 9NF Tel: 01223 840227 — BM BCh Oxf. 1970; MA Oxf. 1972; FRCP Lond. 1990; MRCP (UK) 1974; FRCPCH 1997; DCH RCP Lond. 1978. (St. Thos.) Cons. Paediat. Neurol. Addenbrooke's Hosp. Camb.; Assoc. Lect. Med. Sch. Univ. Camb. Socs: Brit. Paediat. Neurol. Assn.; Assn. Brit. Neurol.; Internat. League Against Epilepsy, Brit. Br. Prev: Lect. (Child Health) Bristol Roy. Hosp. Sick Childr.; Fell. (Paediat. Neurol.) Univ. Brit. Columbia, Vancouver Canada; Ho. Phys. Hosp. Sick Childr. Gt. Ormond St. Lond.

VERITY, David Harding Birmingham & Midland Eye Hospital, Church St., Birmingham B3 2NS Tel: 0121 236 4911 Fax: 0121 233 9213; 10 Duffield Road, Walton on the Hill, Tadworth KT20 7UQ Tel: 01737 814242 Fax: 01737 814242 — BM BCh 1991 Oxf.; BA (Hons.) Physiol. Oxf. 1989. SHO (Ophth.) Birm. Eye Hosp. Socs: Christ. Med. Fell.sh.; Soc. Apoth.; ARVO. Prev: SHO (Ophth.) St. John Ophth. Hosp. Jerusalem; SHO (Ophth.) Salisbury Dist. Hosp.; SHO (Neurosurg.) Soton.

VERITY, Donald Wrathall, TD (retired) Blea Busk, Nr. Askrigg, Leyburn DL8 3JD Tel: 01969 650742 — MRCS Eng. LRCP Lond. 1950.

VERITY, Henry John, TD Heathcote Medical Centre, Heathcote, Tadworth KT20 5TH Tel: 01737 360202 Fax: 01737 370119 Email: john.henry@gp-h8l070.nhs.uk; 10 Duffield Road, Walton-on-The-Hill, Tadworth KT20 7UQ Tel: 01737 814242 Fax: 01737 279555 Email: hjverity@doctors.org.uk — MB BChir Camb. 1965; LMSSA Lond. 1964. (Trinity Coll. Camb. & St. Thos.) Prev: Surg. Lt. RN; Supt. St. Michaels Miss. Hosp. Kuruman, S. Afr.; Sen. Med. Off. Fogo Cott. Hosp. Newfld.

VERITY, Jennifer Catherine Terry The Castle Practice, Health Centre, Central Street, Ludgershall, Andover SP11 9RA Tel: 01264 790356 Fax: 01264 791256; 12 Lambourne Way, Thruxton, Andover SP11 8NE — MB BS 1971 Lond.; MRCS Eng. LRCP Lond. 1971; MFFP 1994; Cert. FPA 1975; DObst RCOG 1974. (St. Bart.) GP Ludgershall; Clin. Asst. i n Psychiat. at Andover CMHT. Prev: Ho. Off. (Obst.) St. Bart. Hosp. Lond.; Ho. Surg. N. Middlx. Hosp. Lond.; Ho. Phys. St. Leonard's Hosp. Lond.

VERITY, Lisa Jane 39 Midge Hall Drive, Rochdale OL11 4AX — MB ChB 1993 Leic.

VERITY, Richard Henry Edenfield Road Surgery, Cutgate Shopping Precinct, Edenfield Road, Rochdale OL11 5AQ Tel: 01706 344044 Fax: 01706 526882; 39 Midge Hall Drive, Bamford, Rochdale OL11 4AX Tel: 01706 31942 — MB BS 1969 Lond.; DObst RCOG 1971. (Roy. Free)

VERITY, Robert Gavin 137 Sheffield Road, Woodhouse, Sheffield S13 7ER — MB ChB 1998 Sheff.

VERITY, Tara 33 Manor Road, Caddington, Luton LU1 4EE — MB BChir 1991 Camb.; MRCGP 1995; DRCOG 1994; DCH RCP Lond. 1993. Socs: BMA; Christ. Med. Fell.sh. Prev: Trainee GP/SHO Whittington Hosp. Lond. VTS.

VERJEE, Salim Abdulmahmed Kassam Suleman Coplow, Main Road, Fyfield, Abingdon OX13 5LN Tel: 01865 390716 — MB ChB 1969 East Africa; MRCGP 1975. (Makerere Univ. Coll.) Clin. Asst. (Blood Transfus.) John Radcliffe Hosp. Oxf. Prev: SHO (Path.) Bristol Roy. Infirm.; SHO (Paediat.) Newc. Gen. Hosp.; SHO (Med.) Ashington Hosp.

VERMA, Ajit Kumar The Childrens Centre, Lowestoft Road, Gorleston, Great Yarmouth NR31 6SQ; 12 Wyngates, Blofield, Norwich NR13 4JG Tel: 01603 716509 — MB BS 1974 Patna; MRCPI 1983; DCH RCPS Glas. 1981; FRCPCH (UK) 1997; FRCP (L) 1999. Cons. Paediat. (Community Paediat.) Childr. Centre Gt. Yarmouth. Socs: Brit. Paediat. Assn.; BMA; Brit. Assn. Comm. Child Health.

VERMA, Amar Nath The Surgery, 302 Vicarage Road, King's Heath, Birmingham B14 7NH Tel: 0121 444 5959 Fax: 0121 441 4050 — MB BS 1972 Bihar. (DMC Darbhanga, Bihar, India)

VERMA, Amarjit Newhall Street Surgery, 14-16 Newhall Street, Cannock WS11 1AB Tel: 01543 506511 Fax: 01543 462356 — MB BS 1972 Punjabi. Socs: Cannock Med. Soc.

VERMA, Arpana 100 Moorcroft Road, Moseley, Birmingham B13 8LU — MB ChB 1995 Manch.

VERMA, Ashwin St. Helier Hospital, Wrythe Lane, Carshalton SM5 1AA — MB BChir 1989 Camb.; BA Camb. 1986, MB BChir 1989; MRCP (UK) 1992. Regist. (Gastroenterol.) St. Helier Hosp. Carshalton. Prev: SHO Rotat. (Med.) St. Geo. Hosp. Lond.; Ho. Surg. Profess. Unit Guy's Hosp. Lond.; Ho. Phys. N.wick Pk. Hosp.

VERMA, Dev Kumar 119 Old Park Ave, Enfield EN2 6PP — MB BS 1997 Lond.

VERMA, Hira Lal Verma, Meir Health Centre, Saracen's Way, Meir, Stoke-on-Trent ST3 7DS Tel: 01782 319321; 4 Pine Tree Drive, Stoke-on-Trent ST11 9HF Tel: 01782 397856 — MB BS 1966 Bihar.

VERMA, Mahipal Singh Hartley Road Medical Centre, 91 Hartley Road, Radford, Nottingham NG7 3AQ Tel: 0115 942 2622 Fax: 0115 924 9150; 3 Dormy Close, Bramcote, Nottingham NG9 3DE Tel: 0115 925 7007 Fax: 0115 925 7007 — MB BS 1967 Lucknow; MS (Orthop.) Kanpur 1970; DObst RCOG 1974; Dip. Orthop. Lucknow 1968. (G.S.V.M. Med. Coll. Kanpur) Clin. Asst. (Rheum.) Univ. Hosp. Nottm. Socs: Overseas Doctors Assn. Prev: Med. Off. Dept. of Sch. Health; Demonst. (Orthop.) Med. Coll. Meerut, India; Resid. SHO (Orthop. & Cas.) Qu. Eliz. Hosp. Gateshead.

VERMA, Narinder Kumar c/o Little Plumstead Hospital, Hospital Road, Little Plumstead, Norwich NR13 5EW; 6 Blofield Road, Brundall, Norwich NR13 5NN — MB BS 1974 Punjab; MRCPsych 1982; T(Psych) 1991; DPM Lond. 1979. (Govt. Med. Coll. Patiala) Cons. Psychiat. Little Plumstead Hosp. Norwich.

VERMA, Neelam The Crown Wood Medical Centre, 4A Crown Row, Bracknell RG12 0TH Tel: 01344 310310 Fax: 01344 310300; Poney's Close Surgery, Broad Lane, Bracknell RG12 9BY Tel: 01344 424070 — MB BS 1967 Jammu & Kashmir. (Med. Coll. Srinagar) Socs: Windsor & Dist. Med. Soc.

VERMA, Raman Kumar 4 Pinetree Drive, Blythe Bridge, Stoke-on-Trent ST11 9HF — MB BS 1993 Lond. (St. Geo. Hosp. Med. Sch.) SHO (Intens. Care) Addenbrooke's Hosp. Camb. Socs: Train. Mem. Assn. Anaesth. Prev: SHO Rotat. (Anaesth.) N.wick Pk., St. Mark's Hosps. Middlx. & Mt. Vernon Hosp. N.wood, Middlx.; Ho. Off. (Surg.) Walsgrave NHS Trust; Ho. Off. (Med.) N. Staffs. NHS Trust.

VERMA, Ranjeet Gorleston Medical Centre, Stuart Close, Gorleston-on-Sea, Great Yarmouth NR31 7BU Tel: 01493 650490 — MB BS 1979 Patna; MB BS 1979 Patna.

VERMA, Ranjit Derby City General Hospital, Uttoxeter Road, Derby DE22 3NE Tel: 01332 625549 Fax: 01332 625583; Oak Lodge, 43 Farley Road, Derby DE23 6BW Tel: 01332 603585 Fax: 01332 295128 Email: ranjit@verma.family.com — MB ChB 1975 Manch.; FRCA Eng. 1980; DA Eng. 1978. (Manch.) Cons. Anaesth. S.ern Derbysh. Acute NHS Trust. Socs: Derby Med. Soc.; Assn. Anaesth.; Obst. Anaesth. Assn. (ex. Comm. Mem. & Treas.). Prev: Sen. Regist. (Anaesth.) Nottm. HA; Regist. & SHO (Anaesth.) Liverp. HA.

VERMA, Ratan Kumar 4 Pine Tree Drive, Blythe Bridge, Stoke-on-Trent ST11 9HF — MB BS 1991 Lond.; BSc (Hons.) Physiol. Lond. 1988; MRCP (UK) 1995. Regist. (Radiol.) Leicester Roy. Infirm. Prev: Regist. (Med.) Neath Gen. Hosp.; SHO (Med.) Univ. Hosp. Wales, Cardiff Roy. Infirm. & Llandough Hosps. Cardiff; Ho. Surg. W.m. Hosp.

VERMA, Rinku 6 Blofield Road, Brundall, Norwich NR13 5NN — MB BS 1998 Lond.

VERMA, S K Cornerways Medical Centre, 27 Woolfall Heath Avenue, Huyton, Liverpool L36 3TH Tel: 0151 489 4444 Fax: 0151 489 0528.

VERMA, Santosh Kumar The Surgery, 192 Charles Road, Small Heath, Birmingham B10 9AB Tel: 0121 772 0398 Fax: 0121 772 4268 — MB BS 1973 Ranchi; MB BS 1973 Ranchi.

VERMA, Sapna 32 Emerson Road, Birmingham B17 9LT — MB ChB 1994 Birm.; ChB Birm. 1994; MRCP 1998.

VERMA, Sarla Rampton Hospital, Retford DN22 0RD Tel: 0177 247722 Fax: 01777 247737; Greenacres, 2 Green Fields Lane, Folkingham, Sleaford NG34 0SH — MB BS 1972 Punjab; BSc Punjab 1966; MRCPsych 1978; DPM Eng. 1975. (Medical College Rohtak, Punjab University, India) Cons. Forens. Psychiat. Rampton Hosp. Retford; Clin. Audit Co-Ordinator Rampton Hosp.

VERMA, Mrs Savitri (retired) 7 Charlotte Grove, Beeston, Nottingham NG9 3HU — MB BS 1942 Punjab.

VERMA, Seema 53 Gayton Road, London NW3 1TU — MB BS 1987 Lond.; FRCOphth 1993. Regist. (Ophth.) St. Mary's Hosp. Lond.; SHO (Ophth.) St. Thos. Hosp. & S.end Gen. Hosp.

VERMA, Sonia Sujata Samantha 18 Lyndhurst Court, Albert Rd, Stoneygate, Leicester — MB ChB 1997 Bristol.

VERMA, Sonu Geetanjali 34 Green Street, Fallowfield, Manchester M14 6TJ — MB ChB 1996 Manch.

VERMA, Sunil Regional Secure Unit, St. Bernards Hospital, Uxbridge Road, Southall UB1 3EU — MB BS 1983 Ranchi; MRCPsych 1994.

VERMA, Surendra Pratap Singh 57 Wyld Way, Wembley HA9 6PT — MB BS 1964 Vikram.

VERMA, Upender Kumar 17 The Crescent, Ilford IG2 6JF — MB BS 1985 Lond. (Guy's) Trainee GP Chingford. Prev: SHO (Psychiat.) Claybury Hosp. Woodford Bridge; SHO (Acute Med. for Elderly & A & E) Whipps Cross Hosp. Lond.

VERMAAK, Zoe Alberta Gwent Community Health, Oakfield House, Llanfrechfa Grange, Cwmbran NP44 8YN Tel: 01633 623497 Fax: 01633 623508 — MB ChB 1971 Cape Town; MSc Louisianna 1994; Dip. Pub Health 1980; Dip. Trop Med. & Hyg 1979; Dip. Child Health 1978. Cons. Paediat.Gwent Community Health Wales; Postgrad. Lect. (Community Health) Cardiff Univ. Socs: Fell. Roy. Soc. Trop. Med. & Hyg.; Fell. RCP & CH; Fell. Roy. Inst. Pub. Health. Prev: Dep. Dir. Pub. Health I. of Man; Sen. Med. Off. Cape Div. Counc.; Sen. Med. Off. CMR Infec. Dis. Hosp., Johannesburg.

VERMEIRE, Claudine Nutford House, Room 195, University of London, Brown St., London W1H 5UL — MD 1984 Louvain.

VERMEULEN, Jan Willem Broadmoor Hospital, Crowthorne RG45 7EG Tel: 01344 773111 Fax: 01344 773327 — MB ChB 1968 Cape Town; BA (Hons.) Univ. S. Afr. 1976, BSc (Hons.) 1985; MRCPsych 1979; DPM Eng. 1979. Cons. Forens. Psychiat. BRd.moor Hosp. Crowthorne. Prev: Cons. Forens. Psychiat. HM Prison Norwich; Hon. Lect. (Forens. Psychiat.) Univ. Zimbabwe; Cons. Psychiat. (Forens. Psychiat.) Min. Health, Zimbabwe.

VERNE, Julia Elvira Caroline Wanda 7 Boileau Road, Ealing, London W5 3AL — MB BS 1986 Lond.

VERNER, Ian Robert (retired) Crompton Cottage, Stoner Hill Road, Froxfield, Petersfield GU32 1DY Tel: 01730 263247 — MB ChB Ed. 1949; FFA RCS Eng. 1956; DA Eng. 1954. Prev: Cons. Anaesth. Middlx. Hosp. Lond. & St. Bart. Hosp. Lond.

VERNEY, Geoffrey Ivan 87 Barton Road, Cambridge CB3 9LL Tel: 01223 352526 — MB BChir 1952 Camb.; MA Camb. 1959, MB BChir 1952; FRCR 1975; FFR 1963; DMRD Eng. 1959. (Camb. & St. Bart.) Cons. (Diag. Radiol.) Addenbrooke's Hosp. Camb. & Papworth Hosp. Socs: BMA & Roy. Soc. Med. Prev: Maj. RAMC (TAVR) Cons. Radiol.; Squadron Ldr. RAF Med. Br.; Sen. Regist. (Diag. Radiol.) Roy. Vict. Infirm. Newc. upon Tyne &.

VERNHAM, Guy Anthony Department of ENT, Victoria Infirmary, Langside, Glasgow G42 9TY Tel: 0141 649 4545; 33 Queensberry Avenue, Clarkston, Glasgow G76 7DU Tel: 0141 571 8827 — BM 1981 Soton.; FRCS (Otol.) Ed. 1990; Cert. Specialist Train. (Otolaryngol) Europe 1994. Staff Grade (OtoLaryngol.) Vict. Infirm. Glas.

VERNON, Anthony Richard Wallingford Medical Practice, Reading Road, Wallingford OX10 9DU Tel: 01491 835577 Fax: 01491 824034; Mill Lodge, Reading Road, Cholsey, Wallingford OX10 9HG Tel: 01491 651355 — MB BS 1978 Lond.; MRCGP 1989; DRCOG 1984. (St. Mary's)

VERNON, Clare Christine Department of Clinical Oncology, Hammersmith Hospital, Du Cane Road, London W12 0NN Tel: 020 8740 3177 Fax: 020 8743 8766; 18 Brookfield Avenue, Ealing, London W5 1LA Tel: 020 8997 1786 — MB BChir 1977 Camb.; MA Camb. 1977; FRCR 1983. Cons. Radiother. & Oncol. Hammersmith Hosp. Lond.; Vis. Prof. Radiat. & Oncol. Qu. Mary Hosp. Univ. Hong Kong; Sec. Radiother. Club. Socs: (Pres.) Europ. Soc. Hyperthermic Oncol.; (Counc.) Roy. Soc. Radiol. Prev: Sen. Lect. (Hyperthermia) MRC Hammersmith Hosp. Lond.; Sen. Regist.

VERNON

(Radiother.) Middlx. Hosp. Lond. & Mt. Vernon Hosp. N.wood; Regist. (Radiother.) Middlx. & Roy. Free Hosps. Lond.

VERNON, David Russell Henderson Medical Directorate, Victoria Infirmary, Langside, Glasgow G42 9TY Tel: 0141 201 6000 Fax: 0141 201 5206; 73 Woodside Drive, Waterfoot, Eaglesham, Glasgow G76 0HD — MB BS Lond. 1967; FRCP Glas. 1987; MRCP (UK) 1972; MRCS Eng. LRCP Lond. 1967; FRCP Lond. 1998. (Guy's) Cons. Phys. Vict. Infirm. Glas. Socs: Brit. Soc. Allergy & Clin. Immunol.; Brit. & Scott. Thoracic Socs.; Eur. Respirat. Soc. Prev: Sen. Regist. (Respirat. & Gen. Med.) Gtr. Glas. HB; Regist. (Med.) Glas. Roy. Infirm. & Raigmore Hosp. Inverness.

VERNON, Fiona Hyslop Health Centre, Thornhill DG3 5AA Tel: 01848 330208 Fax: 01848 330223; Cairnview, Waulkmill Park, Carronbridge, Thornhill DG3 5BA — MB ChB 1982 Glas.; DRCOG 1984. GP Thornhill Dumfriessh. Prev: GP Dumfries & Galloway VTS.; GP Cumnock.

VERNON, Gordon Richard Peter Aufrere 25 Lennox Gardens, Knightsbridge, London SW1X 0DE Tel: 020 7589 3103 — MRCS Eng. LRCP Lond. 1952. (St. Mary's) Surg. Lt. RNVR. Mem. BMA. Prev: Ho. Surg. Epsom Dist. Hosp.; Res. Med. Off. Stafford Gen. Infirm.

VERNON, Jane Evelyn The Old Court House Surgery, Throwley Way, Sutton SM1 4A Tel: 020 8643 8866 — MB BS 1979 Lond.; DRCOG 1981. (Univ. Coll. Hosp.)

VERNON, Jane Melanie 24 Woodside Road, Downend, Bristol BS16 2SL Tel: 0117 956 5510 — BM 1985 Soton.; FRCA 1995; MRCGP 1990; DRCOG 1989. (Southampton) Cons. Anaesth. Nottm. City Hosp. Prev: Specialist Regist. (Anaesth.) Nottm.; Trainee GP Torbay Hosp. VTS; SHO (Anaesth.) Roy. Devon & Exeter Hosp.

VERNON, Jennifer Alexandra 5 Alfred Salter House, Longfield Estate, Fort Road, London SE1 5PS Tel: 020 7231 7801 — MB BChir 1978 Camb.; MA, MB Camb. 1978, BChir 1977. (St. Geo.)

VERNON, John David Sidney (retired) Crugmawr Cottage, Pemparc, Cardigan SA43 1RE Tel: 01239 613649 — MB BChir Camb. 1954; BA Camb. 1950. Prev: Assoc. Specialist Spinal Unit Stoke Mandeville Hosp. Aylesbury.

VERNON, John Gervase John Tasker House Surgery, 56 New Street, Great Dunmow, Dunmow CM6 1BH Tel: 01371 872121 Fax: 01371 873793; Martingales, Causeway End Road, Felsted, Dunmow CM6 3LU Tel: 01371 820481 — MB BS 1977 Lond.; MB BS Lond. Lond. 1977; BA Camb. 1974; MRCP (UK) (Paediat.) 1984; FRCGP 1995, M 1985; DCH RCP Lond. 1979; DRCOG 1979. (Univ. Coll. Hosp.) Prev: Clin. Asst. (Diabetes) Herts & Essex Hosp. Bishop's Stortford.

VERNON, John Martin Nottingham City Hospital, Hucknall Road, Nottingham NG5 1PB Tel: 0115 969 1169; 9 Holme Close, Woodborough, Nottingham NG14 6EX — BM BS 1985 Nottm.; FRCA 1991. Cons. Anaesth. Nottm. City Hosp. Socs: MRCAnaesth.; Assn. Anaesth. Prev: Sen. Regist. (Anaesth.) Nottm.; Anaesth. Research Fell. Emory Univ. Atlanta, USA.

VERNON, John Parry Hawkhill Medical Centre, Hawkhill, Dundee DD1 5LA Tel: 01382 669589 Fax: 01382 645526; 31 The Logan, Liff, Dundee DD2 5PJ Tel: 01382 580176 — MB ChB 1977 Dundee; MRCGP 1982.

VERNON, John Paxton (retired) Tinshill Lane Surgery, 8 Tinshill Lane, Leeds LS16 7AP Tel: 0113 267 3462 Fax: 0113 230 0402 — MB ChB 1964 Leeds.

VERNON, Kevin Grant Flat 3, 76 Castle Road, Southsea PO5 3AZ Tel: 01705 871812 — BM 1994 Soton. SHO (A & E) Poole Gen. Hosp. Prev: SHO (O & G) & Ho. Off. (Med.) St. Mary's Hosp. Portsmouth; Ho. Off. (Surg.) Qu. Alexandra's Hosp. Portsmouth.

VERNON, Margaret Mathews Hawkhill Medical Centre, Hawkhill, Dundee DD1 5LA Tel: 01382 669589 Fax: 01382 645526; 31 The Logan, Liff, Dundee DD2 5PJ Tel: 01382 580176 — MB ChB 1978 Dundee.

VERNON, Michael Seymour Chasefield, Braiswick, Colchester CO4 5BQ Tel: 01206 853318 — MB BS Lond. 1966; MRCS Eng. LRCP Lond. 1965; FFA RCS Eng. 1970. (Guy's) Cons. Anaesth. Essex Rivers Healthcare Trust, Colchester. Socs: Assn. Anaesths. Prev: Cons. Anaesth. NE Essex DHA; Sen. Regist. (Anaesth.), Ho. Surg. & Ho. Phys. Guy's Hosp. Lond.; Regist. (Anaesth.) Ipswich & E. Suff. Hosp.

VERNON, Peter Heygate (retired) 66 Collington Avenue, Bexhill-on-Sea TN39 3RA Tel: 01424 216112 — MRCS Eng. LRCP Lond. 1945; MFOM RCP Lond. 1981; DPH Lond. 1950. Prev: Sen. Med. Off. SE Region Brit. Gas Corp.

VERNON, Peter Leslie Humphrey (retired) 21 Moorfield, St. Stephens, Canterbury CT2 7AN Tel: 01227 450192 — MB BS Lond. 1960; MRCS Eng. LRCP Lond. 1960; DObst RCOG 1963. Med. Mem. Tribunal Serv. Prev: Obst. Ho. Surg. & Ho. Phys. Buckland Hosp. Dover.

VERNON, Phillip Raymund Acumedic, 101-105 Camden High Street, London NW1 7JN Tel: 020 7388 6704 Fax: 020 7387 8081; Tel: 020 8352 2983 — MRCS Eng. LRCP Lond. 1977; Cert Prescribed Equival Exp JCPTGP 1981; Dip. Med. Acupunc. 1998; DCM Beijing 1998. (Sheff.) Specialist in Chinese Med. (Acupunc. and Chinese Herbal Med.) Lond.; Specialist in Chinese Med. Acumedic Foundat. Lond.; Asst. GP to Dr. Ko, Lond.; Specialist in Chinese Med., ChristCh. Hall Surg., Crough End, Lond. Socs: Brit. Med. Acupunct. Soc.; Chinese Med. Inst. and Register (Lond.). Prev: Indep. Acupunc. Liverp.; GP Gold Coast Qu.sland, Austral.; Specialist in Acupunc. Dept. Neurol. Walton Hosp. Liverp.

VERNON, Stephen Andrew Department of Ophthalmology, University Hospital, Nottingham NG7 2UH Tel: 0115 924 9924; Little Orchard, 66 Main St, Woodborough, Nottingham NG14 6EA — MB ChB 1978 Bristol; DM Nottm. 1994; FRCS Eng. 1982; FRCOphth 1988; DO Eng. 1982. Cons. Ophth. Univ. Hosp. Nottm. Socs: Eur. Glaucoma Soc.; Midl. Ophth. Soc. (Pres. 2000 -2001); UK & Eire Glaucoma Soc. (Counc. Mem.). Prev: Sen. Regist. Oxf. Eye Hosp.; Regist. Bristol Eye Hosp.; Ho. Phys. Profess. Med. Unit Bristol Roy. Infirm.

VERNON-PARRY, James, RD Breck House, Carlton Forest, Worksop S81 0TR Tel: 01909 730560 — MB ChB 1951 Manch.; FRCOG 1974, M 1961, DObst 1957; D. Orth 1948; MMSA Lond. 1962; Cert Av Med MoD (Air) & CAA; Aviat Auth. 1974. (Manch.) Sen. Cons. O & G Bassetlaw DHA; Hon. Clin. Lect. (Obst. & Gyn.) Univ. Sheff.; Examr. RCOG & Univ. Sheff.; Authorised Med. Examr. Bd. of Trade & Civil Aviat. Auth. Socs: Fell. Ulster Obst. & Gyn. Soc.; Fell. N. Eng. Obst. & Gyn. Soc. (ex Hon. Gen. Sec.); Fell. Brit. Coll. Optom. Prev: Sen. Regist. O & G S. Belf. Hosp. Gp. & Hon. Sen. Tutor (O & G) Qu.s's Univ. Belf.; Res. Obst. Surg. St. Mary's Hosps. Manch. & Tutor (O & G) Vict.Univ. Manch.; Jun. Off. (Obst.) Qu. Charlotte's Matern. Hosp. Lond.

VERNON-PARRY, Kathleen Claire (retired) Breck House, Carlton Forest, Worksop S81 0TR Tel: 01909 730560 — MB ChB 1953 Manch.; DA Eng. 1957. Prev: Assoc. Specialist in Anaesth. Worksop & Retford Hosp. Gp.

VERNON-ROBERTS, Mark (retired) Widegate Cottage, Widegate, Swansea SA3 2AB Tel: 01792 232126 — MB BS 1968 Lond.; DObst RCOG 1970.

VERNON-SMITH, Jillian Wendy Seven Posts Surgery, Prestbury Road, Prestbury, Cheltenham GL52 3DD Tel: 01242 244103 — MB BS 1990 Lond. (GUYS Hosp.)

VEROW, Peter Graham Occupational Health Unit, 30 Hallam Close, Hallam St., West Bromwich B71 4HU Tel: 0121 607 3417 Fax: 0121 607 3420 Email: peter.verow@swellhot.wmids.nhs.uk; 54 Sandhills Lane, Barnt Green, Birmingham B45 8NX Tel: 0121 445 1181 Email: petelsport@aol.co — MB BS 1977 Lond.; MRCS Eng. LRCP Lond. 1976; MFOM RCP Lond. 1990, AFOM 1987; Dip. Sports Med. Lond 1983; Cert. Family Plann. JCC 1981; DA Eng. 1980; FFOM 1997. (St. Mary's) Cons. Occupat. Health Phys. Sandwell HA; Hon. Sen. Lect. Birm. Univ. Socs: Soc. Occupat. Med.; (Chairm.) Assn. NHS Occupat. Phys. Prev: Occupat. Phys. Rover Gp. Ltd. Birm.

VEROW, Peter William The Old Rectory, Bugthorpe, York YO41 1QG Tel: 01759 368444 Fax: 01759 364444 — MB BCh 1966 Wales; FRCR 1974; DMRD Eng. 1971; Lic. Roy. Inst. Chem. 1971. (Cardiff) Socs: Brit. Soc. Skeletal Radiol. Prev: Cons. Radiol. Dist. Gen. Hosp. York.; Sen. Regist. (Radiol.) Univ. Hosp. of Wales Cardiff. Lect. (Diag.Radiol.) Welsh Nat. Sch. Med.; SHO Dept. Cardiol. Sully Hosp.

VERPAELE, Alexis Department of Plastic Surgery, West Norwich Hospital, Norwich NR2 3TU — MD 1988 Ghent.

VERRICO, Joseph Anthony Alexander (retired) 26 Glenville Avenue, Giffnock, Glasgow G46 7AH — MB ChB 1944 Glas.

VERRIER JONES, Edward Roger (retired) Greenfields, Newport Road, St Mellons, Cardiff CF3 5TW Tel: 029 2036 1941 — MB 1962 Camb.; Hon. FRCPCH 2001; MA Camb. 1967, BA 1958, MB

1962, BChir 1961; FRCP Lond. 1979, M 1968; FRCP Ed. 1978, M 1967; DCH Eng. 1965. Prev: Cons. Paediatr. Llandough Hosp. NHS Trust.

VERRIER JONES, Kate KRUF Children's Kidney Centre for Wales, University Hospital of Wales, Heath Park, Cardiff CF14 4XN Tel: 029 2074 4919 Fax: 029 2074 4822 Email: verrier-jones@cf.ac.uk — MB BCh 1969 Wales; FRCP Lond. 1987; MRCP (UK) 1972; FRCPCH 1997. (Welsh National School Of Medicine) Laura Ashley Reader, Paediat. Nephrol. Dept. of Child Health Univ. of Wales Coll. of Med. Socs: Brit. Assn. Paediat. Nephrol. & Europ. Soc. Paediat.; Nephrol. Sec. Gen.; Internat. Paediatric Nephol. Assn., Ass. Sec. 1997-2000. Prev: Cons. Paediat. Nephrol. Cardiff Roy. Infirm; Sen. Regist. (Paediat. Nephrol.) Cardiff Roy. Infirm.; Regist. Hammersmith Hosp. Lond. & Soton. Gen. Hosp.

VERRILL, Mark William Royal Marsden Hospital, Fulham Road, London SW3 6JJ Tel: 020 7352 8171 Fax: 020 7352 5441 Email: markv@icr.ac.uk; 23 The Crescent, Belmont, Sutton SM2 6BP Tel: 020 8643 3507 — MB BChir 1989 Camb.; MA Camb. 1990, BA 1986; MRCP (UK) 1993. Sen. Regist. (Med. Oncol.) Roy. Marsden Hosp. Lond. Socs: Amer. Soc. Clin. Oncol.; Assn. Cancer Phys.; Brit. Assn. Cancer Research. Prev: Clin. Research Fell. CRC Centre Cancer Therap. Inst. Cancer Research Sutton.

VERRILL, Peter John Alde Reach, Saxmundham Rd, Aldeburgh IP15 5PD Tel: 01728 454177 — MB BS 1953 Lond.; FFA RCS Eng. 1959; DA Eng. 1957. (Univ. Coll. Hosp.) Emerit. Cons. UCL Hosps. Socs: Fell. Univ. Coll. Lond. Prev: Cons. Anaesth. Univ. Coll. Hosp.; Fell. Anesthesiol. Mayo Clinic Rochester, USA; Dean Fac. Clin. Scis. Univ. Coll. Lond.

VERRILL, Richard Peter Framfield House Surgery, 42 St. Johns Street, Woodbridge IP12 1ED Tel: 01394 382157; Little Red House, Hasketon, Woodbridge IP13 6JA — MB BS 1981 Lond.; MRCGP 1986; DRCOG 1986.

VERRINDER, Christian John Langworthy Kate's Cottage, 128 Botley Road, Chesham HP5 1XN — BM BS 1996 Nottm.

VERSO, Nancy Elizabeth 19 Brindley Quays, Braunston, Daventry NN11 7AN — MB ChB 1998 Liverp.

VERSTRATEN, Leendert Department of Orthopaedic Surgery, Mayday University Hospital, London Road, Croydon CR7 7YE Tel: 020 8684 6999 — Artsexamen 1988 Rotterdam. SHO (Orthop.) Mayday Univ. Hosp. Thornton Heath. Prev: SHO (Gen. Surg.) Soton. Gen. Hosp.; SHO (Orthop. Surg.) Lord Mayor Treloar Hosp. Alton; SHO (A & E) Soton. Gen. Hosp.

VERSTREKEN, Patrick 15 Morcroft Road, Huyton, Liverpool L36 8BG — MD 1991 Ghent.

VESELY, Mr Martin Jacob John 103 Lincoln Park, Amersham HP7 9HF — BM BCh 1991 Oxf.; MA Camb. 1992; FRCS Eng. 1995.

VESEY, Jennifer Springfield Surgery, Park Road, Bingley BD16 4LR Tel: 01274 567991 Fax: 01274 566865; 5 Pennygate, Spring Lane, Eldwick, Bingley BD16 3BN Email: jennifer@vesey50.freeserve.co.uk — MB ChB 1972 Birm.; MRCP (UK) 1975; DObst RCOG 1974. GP Princip. Prev: Regist. (Paediat.) Auckland Hosp. Bd. N.Z.; SHO (Neonat. Paediat.) John Radcliffe Hosp. Oxf.

VESEY, Richard John Springfield Surgery, Park Road, Bingley BD16 4LR Tel: 01274 567991 Fax: 01274 566865 — MB ChB 1972 Birm.; MRCGP 1979. G.P Princip.; Trainer Airedale Vocational Train. Scheme. Prev: Anaesth. Regist. Auckland Hosp. Bd. New Zealand; Res. Med. Off. Warwick Gen. Hosp.

VESEY, Mr Sean Gerard Tara Hall, 54 Westbourne Road, Birkdale, Southport PR8 2JB — MB BCh BAO 1979 NUI; FRCS 2001 (Eng.); FEBU 1992; FRCSI 1983. Cons. Urol. S.port & Ormskirk Hosps. Socs: Fell. Roy. Soc. Med.

VESSELINOVA-JENKINS, Chrisso Kolevo 118 Harley Street, London W1N 1AG Tel: 020 7935 5635 Fax: 020 7487 5595; 24 Albany Road, Blackwood NP12 1DZ Tel: 01495 224725 Fax: 01495 228330 — State Exam. Med. Pavlov Higher Inst. Med. Plovdiv 1956. Med. Dir. Nikolai Sleep Monitoring Clinic St Luke's Hosp. Lond. Socs: Fell. Roy. Soc. Med. Prev: Asst. Prof. Dept. Epidemiol. Med. Acad. Sofia, Bulgaria; Clin. Asst. P.H.L.S. Cardiff; Mem. Roy. Coll. Pediat. Child Health.

VESSEY, Professor Martin Paterson, CBE Division of Public Health & Primary Health Care, Institute of Health Sciences, Old Road, Oxford OX3 7LF Tel: 01865 227030 Fax: 01865 226993 Email: martin.vessey@dphpc.ox.ac.uk; 8 Warnborough Road, Oxford OX2 6HZ Tel: 01865 552698 — MB BS 1959 Lond.; MB BS (Hons. Applied Pharmacol. & Therap.) Lond. 1959; FFFP 1994; MA Oxf. 1974; MD Lond. 1971; FRCP Lond. 1987; FRCP Ed. 1979, M 1978; FRCOG 1989; FRCGP 1983; FFPHM 1974; FRS 1991. (Univ. Coll. Hosp.) p/t Prof. Pub. Health Univ. Oxf.; Fell. St. Cross Coll. Oxf. Socs: BMA; Brit. BrE. Gp.; Internat. Epidemiol. Assn. Prev: Lect. Dept. Regius Prof. Med. Radcliffe Infirm. Oxf.; Mem. Scientif. Staff, MRC Statistical Research Unit; Ho. Off. Barnet Gen. Hosp.

VESSEY, Stephen John Rupert Clinical Pharmacology, Glaxowellcome R & D, Greenford Road, Greenford UB6 0HE Tel: 020 8966 3036 Email: rv51037@glaxowellcome.co.uk; 15B Gaisford Street, Kentish Town, London NW5 2EB Tel: 020 7267 0808 — BM BCh 1989 Oxf.; MA Oxf. 1991, D Phil 1997, BM BCh 1989; MRCP (UK) 1992. (Oxf.) Clin. Research Phys. Glaxowellcome R & D, UK.

VESSEY, William Clifford Remillo, Orford Road, Binbrook, Market Rasen LN8 6DU — MB ChB 1998 Ed.

VESTEY, James Patrick Department of Dermatology, Raigmore Hospital, Perth Road, Inverness IV2 3UJ Tel: 01463 704000 — BM 1978 Soton.; DM Soton. 1990; FRCP Ed. 1996; MRCP (UK) 1982; T(M) 1991. (Soton.) Cons. Dermat. Raigmore Hosp. Prev: Cons. Dermat. Roy. Hull Hosps.; Lect. (Dermat.) Roy. Infirm. Edin.

VESTEY, Miss Sarah Brunhilde Longcourt Cottage, Randwick, Stroud GL6 6HJ Tel: 01453 757770 — MB BS 1990 Lond.; FRCS. (UCL) BrE. Fell. Regis. Chelterham Gen. Hosp. Socs: FRCS.

VETHANAYAGAM, Seemampillai 1 The Lindens, Church Road, Copthorne, Crawley RH10 3RD — MB BS 1971 Ceylon; T(OG) 1994.

VETHANAYAGAM, Stephen Vetharatnam St. Annes Centre, 729 The Ridge, St Leonards-on-Sea TN37 7PT Tel: 01424 754889 Fax: 01424 754130 — MB BS 1974 Colombo. Assoc. Specialist (Psychogeriat.) Hastings & Rother NHS Trust. Socs: Fell. RSM; Internat. PsychoGeriat. Assoc. Prev: Staff Grade Psychiat. (Psychogeriat.) Hastings & Rother NHS Trust.; Regist. (Forens. Psychiat.) Hellingly Hosp. Hailsham.

VETPILLAI, Mr Muruguppillai 52 North Way, London NW9 0RB — MB BS 1970 Ceylon; FRCS Eng. 1980; FRCS Ed. 1978. Staff Grade Surg. (A & E) Watford Gen. Hosp. Prev: Sen. Lect. (Surg.) Univ. Jaffna, Sri Lanka.

VETPILLAI, Soranambigai 52 North Way, London NW9 0RB — MB BS 1970 Ceylon; DPath Eng. 1980. Staff Grade (Haemat.) N. Lond. Blood Transfus. Serv. Edgware. Prev: Lect. (Microbiol.) Univ. Jaffna, Sri Lanka.

VETTER, Norman John Donan Dêg, 31 Heol Isaf, Radyr, Cardiff CF15 8AG — MB ChB 1967 Ed.; MD Ed. 1976; MFCM 1977; Dip. Community. Med. Ed. 1975. (Ed.) Sen. Lect. (Pub. Health Med.) Dept. Epidemiol. & Community Med. Univ. Wales. Socs: Brit. Geriat. Soc. & Cardiff Med. Soc. Prev: Dir. Research Team for c/o Elderly Welsh Nat. Sch. Med. Cardiff; Fell. (Community Med.) Edin. Univ.; Research Fell. Lipids in Cardiol. & Mobile Intens. Care.

VETTIANKAL, Giby George 4 School Road, Newry BT34 5QA — MB BCh BAO 1994 Belf.

VETTRAINO, Mark Damian 51 Brendan Road, Nottingham NG8 1HX — MB ChB 1990 Ed.

VEVERS, Geoffrey William Gwynne The Health Centre, Thatcham, Newbury RG18 3HD Tel: 01635 867171 Fax: 01635 876395 Email: geoffrey.vevers@gp-k81073.nhs.uk — MB BS 1977 Lond.; DOCC MED 1999; MRCS Eng. LRCP Lond. 1976. (Guy's) Socs: Roy. Soc. of Med. Prev: SHO (Neurol. & Dermat.) Guy's Hosp. Lond.

VEVERS, Jeremy Jock Moatfield Surgery, St. Michaels Road, East Grinstead RH19 3GW Tel: 01342 327555 Fax: 01342 316240; The Hollies, East Hill Lane, Copthorne, Crawley RH10 3JA Tel: 01342 716238 Email: jeremy@vevers.demon.co.uk — MB BS 1974 Lond.; DA Eng. 1979; DCH Eng. 1978; DRCOG 1977. (St. Bart.)

VEYS, Charles Arthur, OBE (retired) 11 Pearce's Orchard, Henley-on-Thames RG9 2LF Tel: 01491 579557 — MB ChB Liverp. 1956; MD Liverp. 1973; FFOM RCP Lond. 1979; Cert. Occupat. Hyg. 1969; DIH Soc. Apoth. Lond. 1963; DPH 1962; MBIOH 1997. Med. Expert Witness Consultancy. Prev: Chief Med. Off. Michelin Tyre plc Stoke-on-Trent.

VEYS, Paul Anthony Great Ormond Street, Hospital for Children NHS Trust, London WC1N 3JH Tel: 020 7813 8335 Fax: 020 7813 8552; 13 Eyot Gardens, London W6 9TN Tel: 020 8748 6729 —

VEYSEY

MB BS 1983 Lond.; MRCP (UK) 1986; MRCPath 1991. (St. Barts. Hosp.) Cons. Paediat. (Bone Marrow Transpl.) Gt. Ormond St. Hosp. for Childr. NHS Trust.

VEYSEY, Martin John 5 Raymere Gardens, London SE18 2LB — MB BS 1991 Lond.; MRCP (UK) 1994. Specialist Regist., Greenwich, Hosp. Prev: Research Fell. (Gastroenterol.) Guy's Hosp. Lond.; SHO Rotat. (Med.) P.ss of Wales Hosp. Bridgend.

VEYSEY, Sian Louise 1 Newland Street, Rugby CV22 7BJ Tel: 01788 536616 — MB BS 1993 Lond. (St. Geos. Hosp.)

VEYSI, Veysi Tuna Department of Anatomy, University of Leeds, Leeds LS1; 113 Belmont Avenue, Cockfosters, Barnet EN4 9JS Tel: 020 8449 1493 — MB ChB 1993 Leeds; BSc Leeds 1992, MB ChB 1993. Demonst. (Anat.) Univ. Leeds.

VHADRA, Elizabeth Mary Tall Pines, Haytor, Newton Abbot TQ13 9XY Tel: 01364 661274 Email: vhadra@easynet.co.uk — MB BS 1994 Lond.; BSc (Hons.) Anthropol. Lond. 1991; DRCOG 1997; DCH 1996; MRCGP 1998; DFFP 1999. (St. Bart. Hosp. Med. Coll. Lond.) Locum. Prev: GP Regist. Heavitree, H. C. Exeter; SHO (Psychiat.) Wonford Hse. Hosp. Exeter; SHO (O & G) Whittington Hosp. Lond.

VHADRA, Mr Ranjan Kumar Hey Barn Farm, Glossop Road, Little Hayfield SK22 2NR Tel: 01663 749477 — MB BS 1992 Lond.; FRCS Eng 1997. (St Bartholomews) Specialist Regist. in Trauma Orthop., N. W. Rotat. Socs: FRCS - Roy. Coll. at Surg.s at Eng. (Fell.); BOA - Brit. Orthopaedic Assn. (Assoc. Mem.).

VIAGAPPAN, Gnanamani Martin Microbiology Laboratory, University Hoispital, Lewisham, London SE13 6LH — MB BS 1983 Lond.; MSc Lond. 1994; MRCPath 1994. Cons. (microbiologist) Univ. Hosp. Lewisham. Prev: Regist. (Microbiol.) Whittington Hosp. Lond.; Sen. Regist. (Microbiol.) St. Geo. Hosp. Lond.

VIALE, Jean Paul Nuffield Department of Anaesthetics, University of Oxford, Radcliffe Infirmary, Oxford OX2 6HE — MD 1976 Lyons.

VIALE, Nicholas John Tel: 01603 421834 — MB BS 1984 Lond.; MRCPsych 1994. Cons. In Geriat. Psychiat. Prev: Trainee GP Twickenham Lond.; Sen. Regist. (Psychiat.) Roy. Free & Assoc. Hosps. Lond.

VIAN, Andrew Stanley The Sidings, Dicks La, Westhead, Ormskirk L40 6JA — MB BCh 1997 Wales.

VIAPREE, Mr Roger Oliver 78 Ridgeview Road, London N20 0HL — MB ChB 1974 Glas.; FRCS Ed. 1985; DLO RCS Eng. 1982. SHO (Plastic Surg.) Manor Hosp. Nuneaton. Prev: SHO (ENT) St. Margt. Hosp. Epping & Bedford Gen. Hosp.; SHO (ENT) & (Gen. Surg.) Luton & Dunstable Hosp. Luton.

VIBERTI, Professor Giancarlo Francesco Unit for Metabolic Medicine, 5th Floor Thomas Guy House, GKT School of Medicine, KCL Guy's Hospital, London SE1 9RT Tel: 020 7020 7955 Fax: 020 7020 7955 Email: giancarlo.viberti@kcl.ac.uk — MD Milan 1969, State DMS 1975; FRCP Lond. 1990; MRCP (UK) 1985; Dip. Endocrinol. Turin 1971. (Univ. Turin) Prof. Diabetes & Metab. Med., Head Unit Metab. Med. & Cons. Phys. GKT Sch. of Med. King's Coll. Lond. Socs: Internat. Soc. Nephrol.; Eur. Soc. Study Diabetes.

VIBHUTI, Ravi Churchill Clinic, 94 Churchill Avenue, Chatham ME5 0DL Tel: 01634 842397 — MB BS 1974 Karnatak; T(GP) 1991. Vasectomy Surg. & Family Plann. Cons. Socs: Sec. BMA Dartford Gravesend & Medway Div.; Conserv. Med. Soc.

VICARAGE, Philip Harrison Meopham Medical Centre, Wrotham Road, Meopham, Gravesend DA13 0AH Tel: 01474 814811/814068 Fax: 01474 814699; The Tiles, Wrotham Road, Culverstone Meopham, Gravesend DA13 0RE Tel: 01732 822653 — MB ChB 1979 Manch.; BSc St. And. 1976. Sen. Partner Gen. Pract. Meopham, Kent; Occupat. Phys. Socs: Fell. Roy. Soc. Med.; Kent Local Med. Comm. Prev: Palliat. Care Phys.; Clin. Asst. (Haemat.).

VICARIO RUIZ, Francisco 29A Harvey Road, Boscombe, Bournemouth BH5 2AE — LMS 1982 Cordoba; SpR, GMC, European Specialist Medical Qualifications Order 1995.

VICARY, David John The Health Centre, Castleton Way, Eye IP23 7DD Tel: 01379 870689; Park Farm, Brome, Eye IP23 8AH Tel: 01379 870550 Email: david@vicary.softnet.co.uk — MB BChir 1973 Camb.; FRCP 1997; MRCP (UK) 1975; DCH Eng. 1974; DObst RCOG 1974. (Cambridge and Kings College Hospital London) GP; Chairm. Standing Comm. of GPs RCP. Prev: Ho. Phys. Nottm. Gen. Hosp.; Ho. Surg. & Ho. Off. (Obst.) King's Coll. Hosp. Lond.; Chairm. Suff. LMC.

VICARY, Frederick Robin Highgate Hospital, 17 View Road, London N6 4DJ Tel: 020 8341 6989 Fax: 020 8348 7205 Email: robin@flossy.demon.co — MB BS 1969 Lond.; FRCP Lond. 1984; MRCP (UK) 1971. (Westm.) Cons. Phys. (Gen. Med. & Gastroenterol.) Whittington Hosp. Lond. Prev: Sen. Regist. W.m. Hosp. Lond.; Med. Off. Salvation Army Hosp. Chikankata, Zambia; Regist. (Med.) Univ. Coll. Hosp. Lond.

VICCA, Anthony Francis Microbiology Department, Diana Princess of Wales Hospital, Scartho Road, Grimsby DN33 2BA Tel: 01472 874111 Email: tony.vicca@nelincs-tr.trent.nhs.uk — MB ChB 1987 Aberd.; MRCPath 1996, D 1992. Const. Microbiol., Diana P.ss of Wales Hosp. Grimsby. Prev: Sen. Regist. (Microbiol.) Leics. Path. Serv.; Reg. (Microbiol.) Centr. MicroBiol. Labs Edin.

VICE, Patricia Ann Royal Preston hospital, Sharoe Green Lane, Fulwood, Preston PR2 9HT Tel: 01772 710811 Fax: 01772 712944; 35 Dukes Meadow, Ingol, Preston PR2 7AS Tel: 01772 731931 Email: vicepa@websurf.co.uk — MB ChB 1969 Leeds; BSc Leeds 1966; MRCP (UK) 1972; FCRP Lond. 1989. Cons. Phys. Roy. Preston Hosp. s/i Endocrinol. & Diabetes.

VICK, John Alexander Stewart (retired) The Pines, 7 Wymondley Close, Hitchin SG4 9PW Tel: 01462 432904 Fax: 01462 459591 Email: john.vick@virgin.net — MB BS Lond. 1960; MRCS Eng. LRCP Lond. 1960; MRCGP 1971; DObst RCOG 1963. Hon. Hosp. Pract. (Paediat.) Lister Hosp. Prev: GP Hitchin.

VICKERS, Alison Ruth Gill Street Health Centre, 11 Gill Street, London E14 8HQ Tel: 020 7515 2211 — MB BS 1990 Lond.; MSc 1999 Public Health London School Hygiene and Tropical Medicine; BSc Lond. 1987; DROG 1994; MRCGP 1995; Dip (Primary Care Therapeutics) 1997. (Charing Cross & Westminster) GP Princip. (3/4 Time).

VICKERS, Andrew Philip Humble Bee Nest, Littedale Road, Quernmore, Lancaster LA2 9EP — MB BS 1977 Lond.; FFA RCS Eng. 1982; MRCS Eng. LRCP Lond. 1977. (St. Thomas') Cons. (Anaesth.) Morcambe Bay Acute Hosps. Trust. Socs: Counc. Mem. The Pain Soc.

VICKERS, Anthony Adrian (retired) Highfield, Brook Bank, Broadwas-on-Teme, Worcester WR6 5NE Tel: 01886 821471 — MB BS 1942 Lond.; ADMR 1944; FRCR 1975; FFR 1950. Prev: Cons. Radiol. Worcester Roy. Infirm.

VICKERS, Beatrice Ann Josephine 32 Graceland Gardens, London SW16 2ST — MB BS 1991 Lond.

VICKERS, Professor Christopher Francis Howard Bronallt, Dyffryn Ardudwy LL44 2BE Tel: 01341 247784 — MB ChB Manch. 1950; MD Manch. 1960; FRCP Lond. 1971, M 1958; FRCP Ed. 1970, M 1956. Emerit. Cons. Dermat. Roy. Liverp. Hosp. BRd. Green Gen. Hosp. & Roy. Liverp Childr. Hosp. (Alder Hey Br); Emerit. Prof. (Dermat.) Univ. Liverp. Socs: (Ex-Pres.) N. Eng. Dermat. Soc.; Hon. Mem. Brit. Soc. Paediat. Dermat.; Hon. Mem. Amer. Soc. Dermat. Prev: Prof. Dermat. Univ. Liverp.; Cons. Dermat. Roy. Liverp., Newsham Gen. & Alder Hey Childr. Hosps. Liverp.; Assoc. Prof. W.. Reserve Univ. Cleveland, USA.

VICKERS, David Michael Stockport NHS Trust, The Path Lab., Poplar Grove, Stockport SK2 7JE Tel: 0161 419 5607; Booth Farm Cottage, Kinder Road, Hayfield, High Peak SK22 2LJ Tel: 01663 746009 — MB ChB Liverp. 1967; FRCPath 1976. Cons. Histopath. Stepping Hill Hosp. Stockport. Prev: Sen. Regist. (Histopath.) N. W.. RHA; Regist. (Path.) Whiston Hosp.; SHO (Path.) & Ho. Off. BRd.green Hosp. Liverp.

VICKERS, David William Community Child Health, Ida Darwin, Fulbourn, Cambridge CB1 5EE Tel: 01223 884160 Fax: 01223 884161 Email: david.vickers@lifespan-tr.anglox.nhs.uk; The Mill, Abriwgton Pigotts SG8 0SA Tel: 01763 853424 Email: dwvickers@doctors.org.uk — BM BCh 1982 Oxf.; FRCPCH 1997; MA Oxf. 1983; MRCP (UK) 1986. (Oxf.) Cons. Community Paediat. S. Cambs.; Hon. Cons. Paediat. Addenbrooke's Hosp. NHS Trust; Assoc.s Univ. Lect., Univ. of Cambs.

VICKERS, Gareth Andrew 4 Kenilworth Close, Wistaston, Crewe CW2 6SN — MB ChB 1992 Manch.

VICKERS, James Roderick 38 Brook Street, Benson, Wallingford OX10 6LH Tel: 01491 833583; Neb Corner, Neb Lane, Oxted RH8 9JN Tel: 01883 713741 — MB BS 1988 Lond.; MRCGP 1994; DRCOG 1994. Socs: Med. Protec. Soc.

VICKERS, Jean Elizabeth Wigan & Bolton Health Authority, Bryan House, 61 Standishgate, Wigan WN1 1AH Tel: 01942 772868; 46

Albert Road W., Bolton BL1 5HG Tel: 01204 840367 — MB BS 1972 Lond.; MFPHM RCP (UK) 1992; MRCGP 1984. (Univ. Coll. Hosp.) Cons. Pub. Health Med. Wigan & Bolton HA. Prev: Med. Dir. Coll. Health Serv. Bloomsbury HA; Ho. Phys. & Ho. Surg. St. Chas. Hosp. Lond.

VICKERS, John Cedric Earnswood Medical Centre, 92 Victoria Street, Crewe CW1 2JR Tel: 01270 257255 Fax: 01270 501943; Moss Side, 126 Main Road, Wybunbury, Nantwich CW5 7LS — MB ChB 1972 Liverp.; MRCGP 1977; DObst RCOG 1975.

VICKERS, Mr Jonathan Hayward 70 Chesterfield Road, St Andrews, Bristol BS6 5DP Tel: 0117 924 3356 Email: atonks@bmj.com — MB ChB 1986 Bristol; BSc (Hons.) Bristol 1983; FRCS Eng. 1991; FRCS Gen. Surg. 1998. Specialist Regist. (Surg.) Univ. Bristol.

VICKERS, Julie Patricia Castleside Farm, Tattenhall Lane, Beeston, Tarporley CW6 9UA — MB ChB 1997 Dundee.

VICKERS, Kenneth Whitley Road Medical Centre, 1 Whitley Road, Collyhurst, Manchester M40 7QH Tel: 0161 205 4407 Fax: 0161 203 5269 — MB ChB 1984 Manch.; MRCGP 1988; DCH RCP Lond. 1987; DRCOG 1987. Med. Ref. for UK Sports Diving Med. Comm.

VICKERS, Lewis Edward 8 Almond Drive, East Kilbride, Glasgow G74 2HX Tel: 0141 222898 Email: lewvickers@aol.com — MB ChB 1990 Glas.; MRCP 1994. Specialist Regist. (Cardiol. & Gen. Med.) W. Scotl.. Prev: research fell. (Cardiol.), Glas. Roy. Infirm.; SHO (Cardiol.) Glas. Roy. Infirm.; SHO (Gen. Med.) The Ayr Hosp.

VICKERS, Mark Adrian Rothley, 3 Gowanbrae Road, Bieldside, Aberdeen AB15 9AQ Email: m.a.vickers@abdn.ac.uk — BM BCh 1983 Oxf.; BA Camb. 1980; DM Oxf. 1992; MRCP (UK) 1986; MRCPath 1995. Sen. Lect. (Haemat.) Aberd. Univ. Prev: Sen. Regist. (Haemat.) Roy. Berks. Hosp. Reading & John Radcliffe Hosp. Oxf.; Regist. (Haemat.) Hammersmith Hosp. Lond.; MRC Train. Fell. John Radcliffe Hosp. Oxf.

VICKERS, Martin John Bridge Road Surgery, 66-88 Bridge Road, Litherland, Liverpool L21 6PH Tel: 0151 949 0249 Fax: 0151 928 2008 — BM BCh 1985 Oxf.; MA Oxf. 1990, BA 1982; DGM RCP Lond. 1989. Mem. Sefton LMC; Mem. Bootle and Cataerland, Primary Care Trust. Prev: GP Auckland NZ; Trainee GP Cumbria.

VICKERS, Professor Michael Douglas Allen, OBE (retired) North Pines, 113 Cyncoed Road, Cardiff CF23 6AD Tel: 02920 753698 Fax: 02920763865 Email: md.vickers@virgin.net — MB BS Lond. 1955; MRCS Eng. LRCP Lond. 1955; FFA RCS Eng. 1959; Hon. FFA RACS 1976; DA Eng. 1957. Emerit. Prof. Anaesth. Univ. of Wales Coll. Med. Cardiff. Prev: Pres. World Federat. of Anaesthesiologists.

VICKERS, Phillip James High Street Surgery, High Street, Pewsey SN9 5AQ Tel: 01672 563511 Fax: 01672 563004; Mead House, Milton Lilbourne, Pewsey SN9 5LJ Tel: 01672 562358 Email: pjvickers@lineone.net — MB BS 1971 Lond.; MRCS Eng. LRCP Lond. 1971; DObst RCOG 1976. (Westm.) Mem. Wilts. LMC. Prev: Regist. (Microbiol. & Immunol.) W.m. Hosp. Lond.; SHO (A & E) Qu. Mary's Hosp. Roehampton; Ho. Surg. Profess. Unit. W.m. Hosp. Lond.

VICKERS, Rachel Jane Eldon Cottage, Scounslow Green, Uttoxeter ST14 8RE — MB ChB 1987 Bristol; FRCA 1993. Sen. Regist. (Anaesth.) Midls. RHA. Prev: Regist. (Anaesth.) Leicester Roy. Infirm.

VICKERS, Mr Roger Henry 149 Harley Street, London W1G 6BN Tel: 020 7935 4444 Fax: 020 7935 5742; 11 Edenhurst Avenue, London SW6 3PD Tel: 020 7736 1065 — BM BCh 1970 Oxf.; MA Oxf. 1970; FRCS Eng. 1975. (St. Thos.) Orthop. Surg. to HM The Qu.; Cons. Orthop. Surg. St. Geo. Hosp. & K. Edwd. VII Hosp. for Offs. Lond.; Civil. Cons. Orthop. Surg. to the Army. Socs: Apptd. Mem. Counc. Med. Defence Union; Non-Exec. Director Med. Sickness Soc. Prev: Sen. Regist. (Orthop.) Char. Cross Hosp. Lond.; Regist. (Surg.) Watford Gen. Hosp.; SHO (Orthop.) Rowley Bristow Orthop. Hosp. Pyrford.

VICKERS, Miss Sarah Frances Sussex Eye Hospital, Eastern Road, Brighton BN2 5BF Tel: 01273 606126 Fax: 01273 69 36 74 — MB BS 1976 Lond.; FRCS Eng. 1983; FRCOphtn. (St. Thos.) Cons. Ophth. Sussex Eye Hosp. Brighton & Hurstwood Pk. Hosp. Haywards Heath. Socs: FEU. Roy. Con. Ophlnalmdogist; Fell., Roy. Coll. of Ophth.s; Amer. Acad. Ophth. Prev: Resid. Surg. Off. Moorfields Eye Hosp. Lond.; Strabismus Fell. Moorfield Eye Hosp.

VICKERS, Terence 3 Bolsover Close, Manor Gardens, Long Hanborough, Oxford OX8 8RH — MB ChB 1960 Leeds.

VICKERS, William John, CMG (retired) 174 Ashby Road, Burton-on-Trent DE15 0LG — MRCS Eng. LRCP Lond. 1922; DPH Camb. 1924, DTM & H 1930; C St J; Barrister at Law Inner Temple 1938. Prev: DMS Singapore.

***VICKERSTAFF, Helen Jane** 5 Aldermoor Avenue, Storrington, Pulborough RH20 4PT Tel: 01903 743346; 5 Aldermoor Avenue, Storrington, Pulborough RH20 4PT Tel: 01903 743346 — MB BS 1998 Lond.; MB BS Lond 1998; BSc Lond 1995.

VICKERSTAFF, Kirsten Moraich 1 Ferrars Court, Huntingdon PE29 3BU — BA (Hons.) Camb. 1987, MB BChir 1991; DRCOG 1994; DCH RCP Lond. 1993.

VICKERY, Christopher The Surgery, Hillsgarth, Baltasound, Unst, Shetland ZE2 9DY — MB ChB 1983 Leeds; BSc Leeds 1981, MB ChB 1983.

VICKERY, Christopher James 31 Kings Avenue, Bishopston, Bristol BS7 8JL Tel: 0117 944 5870 — MB ChB 1988 Bristol; BSc (Biol.) Lond. 1982; FRCS Eng. 1992. Rotat. Surg. Regist. SW Surg. Rotat. Prev: Regist. (Surg.) Derriford Plymouth; Regist. (Surg.) Frenchay.

VICKERY, Mr Christopher Michael (retired) Trevean, Kenwyn Church Road, Truro TR1 3DR Tel: 01872 273398 Email: cmv@treveantruro.freeserve.co.uk — MB BS Lond. 1953; FRCS Eng. 1959. Prev: Cons. Surg. W. Cornw. Clin. Area.

VICKERY, Mr Craig William 10 Linden House, Barkley's Hill, Stapleton, Bristol BS16 1FB Tel: 0117 965 3192 Email: craig.w.vickery@bristol.ac.uk — BM BCh 1993 Oxf.; MA Cantab 1994; FRCS Eng. 1997. (Oxf.) Clin. Research Fell. Bristol Roy. Infirm. Socs: Surgs. in Train.; Eur. Org. Research & Treatm. of Cancer. Prev: SHO (Gen. Surg.) Frenchay Hosp. Bristol; SHO (Neurosurg.) Frenchay Hosp. Bristol; SHO (Orthop.) Frenchay Hosp. Bristol.

VICKERY, Heather Felicity Ann (retired) Glebe Cottage, Church Lane, Baylham, Ipswich IP6 8JS — MB BS 1953 Lond.; MRCS Eng. LRCP Lond. 1954; DPM Eng. 1967. Prev: Med. Off. (Psychol. Med.) Middlx. Hosp. Lond.

VICKERY, Ian Malcolm Newman Oral Surgery Clinic, 35 Lower Redland Road, Redland, Bristol BS6 6TB Tel: 0117 946 6188 Fax: 0117 946 6177 Email: ivickery@aol.com — MRCS Eng. LRCP Lond. 1967; MB ChB Bristol 1967, BDS 1958; FDS RCS Eng. 1970, L 1958. (Bristol) Cons. Oral Surg. Newman Oral Surg. Clinic Bristol. Socs: Brit. Assn. Oral & Maxillo-Facial Surgs.; Brit. Assn. OGL & Maxillo. Surgs. Prev: Cons. Oral Surg. S.mead HA; Sen. Regist. United Bristol Hosps.; Specialist RAF Hosp. Changi, Singapore.

VICKERY, Kenneth, OStJ 18 Ravens Croft, Mount Road, Eastbourne BN20 7HX Tel: 01323 724315 — MB BS Lond. 1943; MD Lond. 1947; MRCS Eng. LRCP Lond. 1941; FFPHM RCP (UK) 1975; DPH Eng. 1947. (St. Bart.) Prev: Med. Ref. E.bourne Crematorium; Hon. Cons. Pub. Health E.bourne; MOH Co. Boro. E.bourne.

VICKERY, Michael Hadden (retired) 5 Westgrove, Fordingbridge SP6 1LS Tel: 01425 652492 — MB BS 1950 Lond.; MRCS Eng. LRCP Lond. 1950; DObst RCOG 1954.

VICKERY, Sheena Helen Elizabeth — MB BS 1982 Lond.; DRCOG 1986. (Guy's) Prev: Princip. Gen. Pract., Banks Surg., 272 Wimborne Rd., Bournemouth, BH3 7AT; GP Trainee Ealing Hosp. VTS.

VICTOR-BEZA, Miriam The Surgery, 84 Ingleton Avenue, Welling DA16 2JZ Tel: 020 8303 1655 Fax: 020 8298 9228 — FRIPHH (London); Medic 1961 Bucharest; Medic 1961 Bucharest. CMO, Child Health. Socs: Mem. Fac. of Child Health; Fell. Inst. of Hyg. and Pub. Health; Mem. Griffith Developm. Assessm. Gp.

VICTORIA, Bernadette Anne 9 Teesdale Close, Lincoln LN6 0XW Tel: 01522 471853 — MB BS 1982 Rajasthan; FRCA 1994.

VICTORY, Jason George Grinham Northwick Park Hospital, Watford Row, Harrow HA1 3UJ — BM BCh 1991 Oxf.

VIDGEON, Steven David 41 Great Thrift, Petts Wood, Orpington BR5 1NE — MB BS 1998 Lond.

VIDHANI, Kim Sleepy Hollow, Halloughton, Southwell NG25 0QP Tel: 01636 814147; 13 Arlington Drive, Mapperley Park, Nottingham NG3 5EN Tel: 0115 960 2091 — MB ChB 1990 Leeds. Specialist Regist. (Anaesth.) Nottm. Socs: Intens. Care Soc.; Assn.

VIDHYADHARAN

Anaesth. & BMA. Prev: SHO (Anaesth.) Nottm.; SHO (Cardiol.) N.ern en. Hosp. Sheff.; SHO (Renal Med.) N.ern Gen. Hosp. Sheff.

VIDHYADHARAN, Anitha 15 Bartle Avenue, London E6 3AJ — MB BS 1993 Lond.

VIDYASAGAR, Halevoor Nagabhushan St. Georges Hospital, Corporation St., Stafford ST16 3AG Tel: 01785 57888 — MB BS 1979 Bangalor; MB BS Bangalore 1979; MRCPsych 1987. Cons. Psychiat. (special responsibil. Forens. Psychiat.) St. Geo. Hosp. Stafford.

VIDYAVATHI, Manthravadi 5 Broadhalgh, Rochdale OL11 5LX — MB BS 1981 Andhra; MRCP (UK) 1990.

VIEGAS, Marisa 36 Queen's Gate Place Mews, London SW7 5BQ Tel: 020 7589 6473 Fax: 020 7589 7176 — MB BS 1980 Lond.; MRCP (UK) 1983.

VIEL, Maurizio 15 Harley Street, London W1N 1DA; Flat 2, 27 Hyde Park Gardens, London W2 2LZ — State DMS 1984 Milan.

VIEL, Roberto 15 Harley Street, London W1N 1DA Tel: 020 7636 4272 Fax: 020 7436 1677; Flat 11, 28 Hyde Park Gardens, London W2 2NB Tel: 020 7724 9269 — State Exam 1984 Milan. Socs: Brit. Assn. Cosmetic Surg.; Amer. Acad. Cosmetic Surg.; Società Italiana Di Chirurgia Estetica.

VIETEN, Daniela 107 Coombe Lane W., Kingston upon Thames KT2 7HE Email: dvieten@hotmail.com — MB BCh 1997 Wales.

VIEWEG, Reinout 181 Laburnum Grove, Portsmouth PO2 0HE — BM BS 1988 Nottm.; DRCOG 1991.

VIG, Stella 84 Tewkesbury Street, Cardiff CF24 4QT — MB BCh 1991 Wales; BSc (Hons.) Wales 1988; FRCS Eng. 1995; FRCS Ed. 1995. Calman Specialist Regist. Rotat. (Gen. Surg.) Llandough Hosp. Cardiff.

VIGANO, Paola Clelia 12 Falkland Avenue, London N3 1QR — MB BS 1994 Lond.

VIGARS, Susan Patricia 16 Cortayne Road, London SW6 3QA — MB BS 1994 Lond.

VIGGERS, Jennifer Mary Garden House, Swanmore Road, Droxford, Southampton SO32 3PT — MB BS 1967 Lond.; MRCS Eng. LRCP Lond. 1967; DA Eng. 1970. (St. Thos.) Phys. Early Diag. Unit Roy. Marsden Hosp, Lond. Prev: SHO (Anaesth.) & Ho. Phys. Kingston Hosp.; Ho. Surg. Qu. Alexandra Hosp. Portsmouth.

VIGUSHIN, David Michael Department of Cancer Medicine, 6th Floor MRC Cyclotron Building, Imperial College of Science, Technology & Medicine, Hammersmith Hospital Campus, DU Lane Rd, London W12 0NN — PhD 1995 University of London; MB BCh 1986; MRCP Eng. LRCP 1990 Royal College of Physicians of London; PhD 1995 (Thesis entitled In Vitro & In Vivo Studies of C-Re) University of London. (University of the Witwatersrand) Sen. Lect. in Cancer Med., Imperial Coll. of Sci., Technol. & Med., Lond.; Hon. Cons. in Med. Oncol. Hammersmith Hosps. NHS Trust, Lond. Socs: Mem. of Brit. Med. Assn.; Mem. of Assn. of Cancer Phys.s; Active Mem. of Amer. Assn. for Cancer Research. Prev: Clin. Lect. (Hon. Sen. Regist.) Med. Oncol., Imperial Coll. of Sci., Technol. & Med., Hammersmith Hosps. NHS Trust Lond.; Research Fell. (Hon. Regist.) Immunol. Med., Roy. Postgrad. Med. Sch. & Hammersmith Hosp., Lond.; Sen. Ho. Off. in Gen. Med. Geo. Eliot Hosp. Nuneaton.

VIIRA, David John 59 Pangfield Park, Coventry CV5 9NN — MB BS 1993 Lond.

VIIRA, Judith Ann 85 New Road, Croxley Green, Rickmansworth WD3 3EN — MB BS 1991 Lond.

VIJAN, Sureshkumar Gangavishen 45 Oaklands Avenue, Littleover, Derby DE23 7QH Tel: 01332 775526 — MB BS 1979 Bombay; MRCPI 1987.

VIJAYA, Vipran 42 Shakespeare Crescent, London E12 6LN — MB ChB 1994 Liverp.

VIJAYA BHASKAR, Pothapragada 13 Bryn Rhhedyn, Pontypridd CF37 3DP — MB BS 1974 Andhra.

VIJAYA GANESH, Thulasiraman 4 Bonrek Close, Hainault, Ilford IG6 2QL — MB BS 1988 Madurai-Kamaraj, India.

VIJAYA KUMAR, Marithammanahally Nanjundiah Ground Floor Flat, 69 Swanmore Road, Ryde PO33 2TG — MB BS 1979 Bangalor; MB BS Bangalore 1979; MRCPI 1985.

VIJAYADURAI, Pavaladurai Department of Immunology, * *, Sharoe Green Lane N, Fulwood, Preston PR2 9HT Tel: 01772 710131 Fax: 01772 710130; 14 Chevasse Walk, Liverpool L25 5HJ Tel: 0151 428 4020 — MB BS 1982 Colombo; MRCP (UK) 1990; DRCPath 1993; MRCPath 1997. Cons. (Immunol.), Roy. Preston Hosp. Preston & Hope Hosp. Salford, Manch. Socs: Brit. Soc. Immunol.; BMA; MRCPath. Prev: Sen. Regist. (Immunol.) Roy. Liverp. Univ. Hosp.; Regist. & SHO (Immunol.) Qu. Med. Centre Nottm.; Regist. Stepping Hill Hosp. Manch. & Halifax Gen. Hosp.

VIJAYAKULASINGAM, Vijayaluxumidevi 36 Stanstead Manor, St James Road, Sutton SM1 2AZ — MB BS 1983 Colombo, Sri Lanka; FRCA 1992.

VIJAYAKUMAR, Kodali 15 Speedwell Crescent, Scunthorpe DN15 8UP — MB BS 1973 Andhra.

VIJAYAKUMAR, Marimuthu 4 Stonefield, Six Acres, London N4 3PG — LRCP LRCS Ed. LRCPS Glas. 1994.

VIJAYAKUMAR, Matada Nanjundaradhya 11 Alnwick House, Marton Road, Middlesbrough TS4 3SP — MB BS 1974 Mysore.

VIJAYAKUMAR, Narayanaswami Leicester General Hospital NHS Trust, Gwendolen Road, Leicester LE5 4PW — MB BS 1981 Madras.

VIJAYAKUMAR, P Hirwaun Health Centre, Hirwaun, Aberdare CF44 9NS Tel: 01685 811999 Fax: 01685 814145.

VIJAYAKUMAR, Shanmugam 395 Rochdale Old Road, Bury BL9 7TB — MB BS 1979 Bangalore.

VIJAYAKUMAR, Swaminathan 19B Staff Residenc, Royal Inverclyde Hospital, Larkfield Road, Greenock PA16 0XN — MB BS 1986 Madras.

VIJAYAN, Kesava Pillai Royal National Orthopaedic Hospital, Stanmore HA7 4LP Tel: 020 8954 2300 — MB BS 1983 Madurai Kamaraj; MSc Orthop. Lond. 1989. Regist. (Orthop.) Roy. Nat. Orthop. Hosp. Stanmore.

VIJAYANATHAN, Sanjay 2 Irvine Avenue, Harrow HA3 8QE — MB BS 1991 Lond.

VIJAYARAGHAVAN, Shanti Newham General Hospital, Glen Road, Plaistow, London E13 8SL Tel: 020 7476 4000 Fax: 020 7368 8002; 202 East End Road, London N2 0PZ Tel: 020 8883 1214 Email: vshanti@bt.com — MB BS 1986 Bombay; MPhil Lond. 1995; MD Bombay 1988; MRCP (UK) 1991. (Grant Med. Coll. Bombay) Cons. Phys. (Diabetes & Endocrinol.) Newham Gen. Hosp.; Hon. Sen. Lect. (Med.) Roy. Lond. & St. Bart. Sch. Med. & Dent. Lond. Prev: Lect. (Med.) Roy. Lond. & St. Bart. Sch. Med. & Dent. Lond.

VIJAYARAGHAVAN, Srinivasan 4 Westfield Road, Bishop Auckland DL14 6AE — MB BS 1975 Madurai Kamaraj Univ.; FRCA 1993.

VIJAYARATNAM, Deena Dayalan 147 Helmsley Road, Newcastle upon Tyne NE2 1RE — MB BS 1998 Newc.

VIJAYASIMHULU, Gorjala Thirumala Scunthorpe General Hospital, Scunthorpe DN15 7BH Tel: 01724 282282; Sai Nivas, Grayingham Road, Kirton in Lindsey, Gainsborough DN21 4EL Tel: 01652 640158 — MB BS 1971 Sri Venkateswara; FRCR 1979; DMRD Madras 1974. (Kurnool Med. Coll.) Cons. Radiol. Scunthorpe & Goole Hosps. Prev: Cons. Radiol. Shotley Bridge Gen. Hosp.; Cons. Radiol. Dryburn Hosp. Durh.; Sen. Regist. Newc. Teach. Gp. Hosps.

VIJAYKUMAR, Mr Annaswami Royal Infirmary, Bolton Road, Blackburn BB2 3LR Tel: 01254 294000 Fax: 01254 294050; Logan House, Main Road, Eastburn, Keighley BD20 7SJ Tel: 01535 633356 Fax: 01535 633356 Email: annaswami.vijaykumar@binternet.com — MB BS 1972 Madras; FRCS Ed. 1989; FRCOphth 1990; DO RCPSI 1976. (Madras Medical College) Cons. Ophth. Blackburn, Hyndburn & Ribble Valley Healthcare NHS Trust & Burnley Health Care NHS Trust. Socs: N. Eng. Ophthalmol. Soc.; UK & Irel. Soc. Cataract & Reactivre Surg.; Internat. Mem. Amer. Acad. Opth. Prev: Assoc. Specialist (Ophth.) Huddersfield NHS Trust; Regist. (Ophth.) Newc. Gen. Hosp., Hull Roy. Infirm. & Huddersfield Roy. Infirm.; SHO (Ophth.) Newc. Gen. Hosp.

VIJAYKUMAR, Usha Bradford NHS Trust, St. Luke's Hospital, Little Horton Lane, Bradford BD5 0NA Tel: 01274 734744; Logan House, Main Road, Eastburn, Keighley BD20 7SJ — MB BS 1973 Madras. (Madras Med. Coll.) Clin. Med. Off. (Child Health & Family Plann.) Bradford HA. Socs: Fac. Community Health; Soc. Pub. Health. Prev: SHO (Geriat. Med.) Castle Hill Hosp. Cottingham; SHO (Gen. Med.) Qu. Eliz. Hosp. Gateshead; Ho. Off. (Gen. Med.) Dunston Hill Hosp. Gateshead.

VIJEYASINGAM, Mr Rajasingham 58 Cholmley Gardens, Fortune Green Road, Hampstead, London NW6 1AJ — MB BS 1984 Lond.; FRCS Eng. 1990; FRCS Ed. 1989.

VIJH, Meena 188 Creynolds Lane, Solihull B90 4ES — MB BS 1985 Himachal Pradesh; MRCP (UK) 1995.

VIJH, Mr Vikram 54 Paxford Road, Wembley HA0 3RQ — MB BS 1988 Lond.; FRCS Eng. 1992; FRCS Ed. 1992. Regist. (Plastic Surg.) Pan Thames. Socs: Fell. Roy. Soc. Med.; BMA. Prev: Regist. Plastic Surg. St Andrews, Billcieay; Research Regist. (Plastic Surg.) Mt. Vernon Hosp. N.wood.

VILAPLANA CANNON, John Paul 30 Mossywood Place, Cumbernauld, Glasgow G68 9DS — LMS 1991 U Autonoma Barcelona.

VILARINO-VARELA, Maria Jose 10B Antill Road, London E3 5BP — MB BS 1993 Lond.

VILCHES MORAGA, Arturo Doctors Residence, Burnley Hospital, Casterton Avenue, Burnley BB10 2PQ Tel: 01282 425071; 38 Healdwood Drive, Burnley BB12 0EA — LMS 1993 U Complutense Madrid; MRCP part 1, October 1997. SHO (Gen. Med. & MFE) Roy. Preston. Socs: BMA; MDU. Prev: SHO & Ho. Off. (Gen. Med.) Burnley Gen. Hosp.; SHO (Gen. Med.) Roy. Preston Hosp.

VILE, John Mark Warneford Hospital, Oxford OX3 7JX; 13 Lee Close, Kidlington OX5 2XZ — BM 1988 Soton.; BA Oxf. 1984. Regist. (Psychiat.) Oxf. RHA.

VILE, Kathryn Sarah Marjorie East Street Medical Centre, East Street, Okehampton EX20 1AY Tel: 01837 52233; Middle Gooseford, Whiddon Down, Okehampton EX20 2QH Tel: 01647 231210 Fax: 01647 231210 — MB ChB 1985 Bristol; MRCGP 1989; Cert. Family Plann. JCC 1989. (Bristol) Prev: Trainee GP Exeter HA VTS; Ho. Surg. Torbay Hosp. Torquay; Ho. Phys. Ham Green Hosp. S.mead.

VILLAFANE CASANTE, Mr Oscar Canniesburn Hospital, Department of Plastic Surgery, Glasgow G61 1QL Tel: 0141 211 5600 Fax: 0141 211 5652; Irunlarrea 13A, Atico 9A, Pamplona, Navarra ES-31008, Spain Tel: 00 34 48 263457 Email: ovillafane@hotmail.com — LMS 1990 Navarre; FRCS Glas. 1998. (Navarra) SHO III Acting Regist. (Plastic Surg.) Canniesburn Hosp. Socs: BMA; MDU. Prev: SHO (Plastic Surg.) Bradford Roy. Infirm.; SHO (Plastic Surg.) Kingston Gen. Hosp. Hull.

VILLAGE, Anne Lesley 64 Hillside Road, Beeston, Nottingham NG9 3AY — MB ChB 1976 Sheff.; MFPP 1993. (Sheff.) Prev: GP Sefton Retainer Scheme.

VILLAGRAN MORENO, Jose Maria 9 Dalegarth, Hurst Park Avenue, Cambridge CB4 2AG Tel: 01223 322745 — LMS 1983 Cadiz.

VILLAQUIRAN URIBE, Jaime Alberto 40 Beaumont Terrace S., Gosforth, Newcastle upon Tyne NE3 1AS — Medico y Cirujano 1982 Univ. del Valle; Medico y Cirujan Univ. del Valle 1982.

VILLAR, B Louise Bell The Vineyard, Wind Mill Hill, Saffron Walden CB10 1RR Tel: 01799 516200 Fax: 01799 516799 — MB ChB 1974 Aberd.; MRCP (UK) 1982; MRCGP 1984; DRCOG 1978.

VILLAR, Monica Tracey Anne Poole Hospital NHS Trust, Longfleet Road, Poole BH15 2JB Tel: 01202 665511 Fax: 01202 442993 — MB BS 1983 Lond.; MA Camb. 1984; DM Soton 1997; MRCP (UK) 1986; FRCP 1998. (New Hall, Camb. Univ. & King's Coll. Hosp. Med. Sch.) p/t Cons. Phys. (Med. for Elderly) Poole Hosp. NHS Trust. Socs: Brit. Geriat. Soc. Prev: Sen. Regist. (Gen. Med. & Geriat.) Roy. Bournemouth Gen. Hosp. & S. Hants. Hosp. Soton.

VILLAR, Mr Richard Neville Cambridge Hip & Knee Unit, BUPA Cambridge Lea Hospital, 30 New Road, Impington, Cambridge CB4 9EL Tel: 01223 235888 Fax: 01223 235884 Email: rvillar@uk-consultants.co.uk — MB BS 1977 Lond.; MA Camb. 1997; BSc (Anat.) Lond. 1974; MS Soton. 1987; FRCS Eng. 1982. (St. Thos. Hosp. Lond.) p/t Cons. Orthop. Addenbrooke's Hosp. Camb.; Assoc. Lect. Univ. Camb. Socs: Fell. BOA; Eur. Hip Soc.; Eur. Soc. Knee Surg. & Arthroscopy. Prev: Sen. Regist. (Orthop.) Addenbrooke's Hosp. Camb.; Regist. (Orthop.) Soton. Gen. Hosp.; Capt. RAMC.

VILLATORO LOPEZ, Eduardo Antonio 54 York Street, Bedford MK40 3RJ — LMS 1992 Cordoba.

VILLENEAU, Alexandre Georges (retired) Mutton's Farm, Ashington RH20 3AJ Tel: 01903 892640 — MB BS Lond. 1952. Prev: Ho. Phys. St. Geo. Hosp. Lond. & Atkinson Morley's Hosp. Lond.

VILLIERS, Charles Russell (retired) 16 Bath Road, Reading RG1 6NS — MB BChir 1963 Camb.; MA Camb. 1987, BA 1960, MB BChir 1963; FRCR 1975; FFR 1972; DMRD Eng. 1969. Prev: Cons. Radiol. Roy. Berks. Hosp. Reading.

VILLIERS, Christopher Tile House Surgery, 33 Shenfield Road, Brentwood CM15 8AQ Tel: 01277 227711 Fax: 01277 200649; 104 Chelmsford Road, Shenfield, Brentwood CM15 8RL Tel: 01277 227219 Email: chris.villiers@virgin.net — MB BS 1988 Lond.; MA Oxf. 1989; MRCGP 1993; DRCOG 1991; DGM RCP Lond. 1991. (London) GP Princip.; Bd. Mem. Brentwood PCG. Socs: (Sec.) Brentwood Dist. Med. Soc. Prev: GP/Regist. Harold Hill, Romford; SHO (O & G, Med. & Rheum.) Harold Wood Hosp. Romford.

VILLIERS, Gertrude Isobel Lamb Bell Cottage, 29 Dean St., Brewood, Stafford ST19 9BU Tel: 01902 850905 — LLB Wolverhampton University 1980; MB BCh BAO Dub. 1952. (Univ. Coll. Dub.) SCMO Mid Staffs. HA. Prev: Anaesth. Wolverhampton AHA.; Sen. Med. Off. Matern. & Child Welf. Derbysh. CC; Ho. Surg. (Orthop.) Vict. Infirm. Glas.

VILLIERS, James Dermott 18 Four Ashes Road, Brewood, Stafford ST19 9HX Tel: 01902 850619 Fax: 01902 850619 — MB ChB 1948 Manch.; MRCS Eng. LRCP Lond. 1948; DA (UK) 1960. Emerit. Cons. Anaesth. St. Geo. Hosp. New Vict., Austral. Socs: Austral. Med. Assn. & Austral. Soc. Anaesth. Prev: Vis. Anaesth. Roy. Melbourne & Alfred Hosps. Melbourne, Austral.; Surg. Capt. Roy. Austral. Naval Reserve.

VIMALACHANDRAN, Chandrakumar Dale 306 Wood Lane, Heskin, Chorley PR7 5NT — MB ChB 1997 Liverp.

VINALL, Mr Paul Stuart Clarendon Wing, General Infirmary at Leeds, Belmont Grove, Leeds LS2 9NS Tel: 0113 392 2657 Fax: 0113 392 6531; 6 Adel Pasture, Leeds LS16 8HU Tel: 0113 261 1612 — MB BS 1969 Lond.; FRCOG 1988, M 1975. (Univ. Coll. Hosp.) Cons. O & G Leeds Gen. Infirm.; Sen. Clin. Lect. (Obst. & Gyn.) Univ. Leeds. Prev: Lect. (O & G) Univ. Leeds; Regist. Birm. Matern. Hosp. & Birm. & Midl. Hosp. Wom.; Research Asst. Univ. Coll. Hosp. Med. Sch. Lond.

VINAYAGAMOORTHY, Chelliah 371 Watford Road, St Albans AL2 3DD — MB BS 1966 Ceylon; MRCP (UK) 1975. (Ceylon) Sen. Regist. (Haemat.) Qu. Eliz. Hosp. Birm.

VINAYAGAMOORTHY, Murugesu (Surgery), The Green, Swanwick, Derby DE73 1HJ Tel: 01773 605018 — LRCP LRCS Ed. LRCPS Glas. 1978.

VINAYAGAMOORTHY, Pushpam Medical Centre, 2 Birchwood Lane, South Normanton, Derby DE65 3D Tel: 01773 862907; Birindavanam, Leavale, Broadmeadows, South Normaton, Alfreton DE55 3NA Tel: 01773 863291 — LRCP LRCS 1978 Ed.; LRCP LRCS Ed. LRCPS Glas. 1978.

VINAYAGUM, Sandra Rita 62 Hamilton Road, Golders Green, London NW11 9EJ — MB ChB 1985 Manch.

VINAYAK, Mr Bippon Chander 190 Goodman Park, Slough SL2 5NL — MB BS 1986 Lond.; FRCS Eng. 1992; FRCS Ed. 1990. Clin. Lect. & Hon. Sen. Regist. (Otolaryngol.) Univ. Oxf. Prev: Regist. (ENT) Oxf.; Regist. & SHO (ENT) St. Mary's Hosp. Lond.

VINAYAK, Inder Paul Victoria Medical Centre, 12-28 Glen Street, Hebburn NE31 1NU Tel: 0191 483 2106 Fax: 0191 428 5270 — MB BS 1964 Panjab. (Panjab) GP Hebburn, Tyne & Wear.

VINAYAK, Veena Victoria Medical Centre, 12-28 Glen Street, Hebburn NE31 1NU Tel: 0191 483 2106 Fax: 0191 428 5270 — MB BS 1974 Rajasthan. (Rajasthan) GP Hebburn, Tyne & Wear.

*****VINAYAKA-MOORTHY, Vidhiya** 65 Revell Road, Kingston upon Thames KT1 3SL — MB BS 1997 Lond.; BSc Lond. 1994.

VINCE, Mr Alastair Stuart Department of Orthopaedics, Northampton General Hospital, Cliftonville, Northampton NN1 5BD Tel: 01604 544467 — MB ChB 1986 Birm.; FRCS Glas. 1992; FRCS (Orth) 1998. (Birmingham) Cons. Orthopaedic & Trauma Surg. N.ampton Gen. Hosp. N.ampton. Socs: RSM - Counc. Orthopaedic Sect.; Bir. Hip. Soc. Prev: Regist. (Orthop.) Addenbrooke's Hosp. Camb.

VINCE, Frank Peter — MB 1963 Camb.; BChir 1962; FRCP Lond. 1979, M 1966. (Lond. Hosp.) p/t Cons. Phys. Coventry Gp. Hosps.; Chief Med. Off. Axa Sun Life Insur. Co. Socs: Fell. Roy. Soc. Med.; Fell. Assur. Med. Soc.; Soc. Endocrinol. Prev: Lect. (Endocrinol.) Lond. Hosp.; Regist. Addenbrooke's Hosp. Camb.; Ho. Off. Lond. Hosp.

VINCE

VINCE, Jonathan Department of Forensic Psychiatry, Shaftesbury Clinic, Springfield Hospital, Glenburnie Road, London SW17 7DJ Tel: 020 8682 0033 Fax: 020 8682 3450 Email: jvince@swlstg-tr.nhs.uk — MB BS 1986 Lond.; 1997 Dip FMH; BSc (Hons.) Lond. 1983; MRCPsych 1991. (Univ. Coll. Lond.) Cons. Forens. Psychiat. & Hon. Sen. Lect., S. W. Lond. & St. Geo. NHS Trust. & St Geo.'s Hosp. Med. Sch.

VINCENT, Alexandra Joy 36 Lansdowne Road, Purley CR8 2PA — BM 1997 Soton. SHO Rotat., E. Surrey, Hosp. Redhill.

VINCENT, Andrew Patrick Les Saisons Surgery, 20 David Place, St Helier, Jersey JE2 4TD Tel: 01534 720314 Fax: 01534 733205; La Meadowbank, Rue de la Vallee, St Mary, Jersey JE3 3DL Tel: 01534 484490 Email: andy@localdial.com — BM 1987 Soton.; MRCGP 1992.

VINCENT, Professor Angela Carmen Institute of Molecular Medicine, John Radcliffe Hospital, Oxford OX3 9DU Tel: 01865 222323 Fax: 01865 222402; Taverners, Woodeaton, Oxford OX3 9TH Tel: 01865 59636 — MB BS 1966 Lond.; MSc (Biochem.) Lond. 1969; MRCS Eng. LRCP Lond. 1966; MRCPath 1991; FRCPath 1997. (Westm.) Univ. Lect. (Clin. Neuroimmunol.) Univ. Oxf.; Hon. Cons. Immunol. John Radcliffe Hosp. Oxf.; Prof. Neuroimmunol. Univ. Oxf. Socs: Assn. Brit. Neurol.; Brit. Soc. Immunol. Prev: Reader (Neurol.) Inst. Molecular Med. John Radcliffe Hosp. Oxf.; Univ. Research Lect. Inst. Molecular Med. John Radcliffe Hosp. Oxf.; Research Assoc. Roy. Free Hosp. Lond.

VINCENT, Angus 24A Eslington Terrace, Newcastle upon Tyne NE2 4RL Tel: 0191 212 0621 Fax: 0191 212 0621 Email: lwirz@compuserve.com — MB ChB 1994 Glas. Specialist Regist. Rotat. (Anaesth.) N.en Region.; SHO Rotat. (Anaesth. & Gen. Med.) Wansbeck Hosp. Ashington & Freeman Hosps. Newc. Socs: BMA; Intens. Care Soc.; Assn. of Anaesth. GB & Irel.

VINCENT, Antonia Louise Taverners, Woodeaton, Oxford OX3 9TH — MB BS 1993 Lond.

VINCENT, Christian Mervyn Abiodun 25 Wyatt Park Road, London SW2 3TN — MRCS Eng. LRCP Lond. 1969.

VINCENT, Doris Susan Downfield Medical Practice, 325 Strathmartine Road, Dundee DD3 8NE Tel: 01382 812111 Fax: 01382 858315; 1 Station Brae, Newport-on-Tay DD6 8DQ Tel: 01382 543156 — MB ChB St. And. 1968; MRCGP 1979; FRCGP 1998.

VINCENT, Elizabeth Clare The Doctors House, Victoria Road, Marlow SL7 1DN Tel: 01628 484666 Fax: 01628 891206; 9 Claremont Road, Marlow SL7 1BH — BM BS 1980 Nottm.

VINCENT, Emma Jane Old Mint Cottage, Horse Fair Lane, Cricklade, Swindon SN6 6BN — MB ChB 1997 Birm.

VINCENT, Harry Raymond (retired) The Nook, Long Horsley, Morpeth NE65 8UP — MRCS Eng. LRCP Lond. 1943. Prev: Dep. Med. Supt. Perth & Dist. Hosp. Gp.

VINCENT, James Christian 11 Garden Lane, Southsea PO5 3DP — BM 1986 Soton.; MRCP (UK) 1991; FRCA 1994; DA (UK) 1990. Cons. Anaesth. Portsmouth Hosp. NHS Trust.

VINCENT, John Alistair London Fields Medical Centre, 38-44 Broadway Market, London E8 4QJ Tel: 020 7254 2883 — MB BS 1986 Lond.; MRCGP 1992.

VINCENT, John Anthony West Timperley Medical Centre, 21 Dawson Road, Altrincham WA14 5PF Tel: 0161 929 1515 Fax: 0161 941 6500; 9 Charter Close, Sale M33 5YG Tel: 0161 969 6861 — MB ChB 1986 Leeds; DRCOG 1992. Prev: Sen. Med. Off. RAF Newton; Trainee GP/SHO RAF (H) Wroughton VTS; Jun. Med. Off. RAF Lyneham.

VINCENT, Mark Aidan (retired) The Orchard, 6B High St, Henlow SG16 6BS Tel: 01462 814460 Fax: 01462 814460 Email: di.vincent@btinternet.com — BM BCh 1978 Oxf.; BMM BCh Oxf. 1978; MA Oxf. 1980, BA (Hons.) 1975; FRCGP 1995, M 1983; DRCOG 1980.

VINCENT, Michael Edwin 43 Tinsley Road, London E1 3DA — MB BS 1981 Lond.; MRCGP St. Bart 1987; DRCOG 1986; DCH RCP Lond. 1985; DGM RCP Lond. 1985. Prev: GP Esher, Surrey.

VINCENT, Michael Leonard Briardene, Wylam Wood Road, Wylam NE41 8HX — MB ChB 1994 Manch.

VINCENT, Nicholas Robert John The Writtle Surgery, 16A Lordship Road, Writtle, Chelmsford CM1 3EH Tel: 01245 421205 Fax: 01245 422094; 18 Little Meadow, Writtle, Chelmsford CM1 3LG Tel: 01245 421523 — MB BS 1982 Lond.; DRCOG 1986. Clin. Asst. (Colposcopy) St. Johns Hosp. Chelmsford. Socs: BMA; Christ. Med. Fell.sh. Prev: Trainee GP E.bourne VTS; Ho. Phys. BromsGr. & Redditch Hosp.; Ho. Surg. Ipswich Hosp.

VINCENT, Noel Aidan — MB ChB 1944 Sheff.; DA Eng. 1954. Emerit. Cons. Anaesth. Rotherham Dist. Gen. Hosp. Rotherham & Montagu Hosp. MexBoro. Socs: BMA (Ex-Chairm. Rotherham Br.).

VINCENT, Paul William Birtley Medical Group Practice, Birtley Medical Group, Durham Road, Birtley, Chester-le-Street DH3 2QT Tel: 0191 410 3421 Fax: 0191 410 9672 — MB BS 1982 Lond.; MRCGP 1986; D.Occ.Med. RCP Lond. 1995; DA (UK) 1989; DCCH RCP Ed. 1987; DRCOG 1986. (King's College London) Socs: Christian Med. Fell.sh.

VINCENT, Philippa Jane Stockbridge Surgery, New St., Stockbridge SO20 6HG; 78 Stockbridge Road, Winchester SO22 6RL — MB BS 1996 Lond.; BSc Hons (Psychol.) 1993; DCH, RCP Lond. 1998; DROG, RCOG 1998; DFFP RCOG 1998. (Univ. Coll. Lond.) GP Regist., VTS Winchester.

VINCENT, Professor Richard Cardiac Department, Royal Sussex County Hospital, Eastern Road, Brighton BN2 5BE Tel: 01273 696955 Fax: 01273 684554; 53 Hill Drive, Hove BN3 6QL Tel: 01273 558714 Fax: 01273 298644 Email: r.vincent@sussx.ac.uk — MB BS Lond. 1970; BSc (Pharmacol.) Lond. 1967, MD 1984; FRCP Lond. 1985; MRCP (UK) 1973; MRCS Eng. LRCP Lond. 1970. (King's Coll. Hosp.) Cons. Cardiol. Roy. Sussex Co. Hosp. Brighton; Hon. Cons. Cardiol. KCH Lond.; Prof. Med. Sci. Sussex Univ.; Head Med. Univ. Brighton; prof. Med., Univ. Brighton. Socs: Brit. Cardiac Soc.; Roy. Soc. Med.; Exec. Mem., Resusc. Counc. (UK). Prev: Lect. Univ. Sussex Falmer; Sen. Regist. (Gen. Med.) Roy. Sussex Co. Hosp. Brighton & King's Coll. Hosp. Lond.

***VINCENT, Simon Mark** Leicester royal Infirmary, Infirmary Close, Leicester LE1 5WP Tel: 0116 354 1414; Wits End, Welford Road, South Kilworth, Lutterworth LE17 6DY Tel: 01858 575343 — MB ChB 1997 Leic.

VINCENT, Stephen Hereward, Surg. Cdr. RN Retd. Tel: 02380 796749 Fax: 02380 796816; Hawthorns, East End, Lymington SO41 5SY Tel: 01590 626370 Fax: 01590 626491 Email: steve@hawthorns3.demon.co.uk — MB BS 1970 Lond.; MA Camb. 1970; MRCS Eng. LRCP Lond. 1970; FRCGP 1997; MRCGP 1979; DCH Eng. 1978. (St. Thos.) Assoc. Adviser (Gen. Pract.) Soton. & SW Hants. Health Dist; Cons. Adviser in Gen. Pract. to Med. Director Gen. (Naval). Socs: BMA; ASME; Roy. Naval Med. Club. Prev: Course Organiser Soton. Day Release Course.

VINCENT-BROWN, Amanda Meredith Barclay 6 Pine Grove Mews, Pine Grove, Weybridge KT13 9BD — MRCS Eng. LRCP Lond. 1976.

VINCENT-KEMP, Ruth (retired) Dunwood Hall, Longsdon, Leek ST9 9AR Tel: 01538 385071 — MRCS Eng. LRCP Lond. 1947; DCH Eng. 1953. Prev: Clin. Asst. (Paediat.) N. Staffs. Gp. Hosps.

VINCENT-SMITH, Lisa Mayling 37 Roslea Drive, Dennistoun, Glasgow G31 2QR — MB ChB 1997 Glas.

VINCENTI, Gareth Edward Paul The Harrogate Clinic, 23 Ripon Road, Harrogate HG1 2JL Tel: 01609 778730 Fax: 01609 778730 — MB BS 1981 Newc.; MRCPsych 1988; FRCPsych 2000. Cons. Psych. in Private Pract.; Director Postgrad. Educat., Harrogate Clinic; Force Psychiat., Gtr. Manch. Police. Socs: Marcé Soc.; Seasonal Affective Disorder Assn.; Roy. Soc. Med. Prev: Cons. Psychiat. N.allerton Health Serv. NHS Trust; Dir. Postgrad. Educat. N.allerton; Vis. Cons. Psychiat., N.allerton Remand Centre.

VINCHENZO, A Stanley Road Surgery, 204 Stanley Road, Bootle L20 3EW Tel: 0151 922 5719.

VINCINI, Cornelio 21 Bridge Street, Driffield YO25 6DB — MB BS 1980 Lond.; MRCGP 1984; DRCOG 1984.

VINDEN, Sybil Rosemary (retired) Heathfield House, Cale Green, Stockport SK2 6RA — MB ChB 1961 Cape Town. p/t Clin. Asst. (Psychiat. & Rehabil.) Stockport. Prev: GPVTS.

VINDLA, Mona Sherrington Park Medical Practice, 402 Mansfield Rd, Sherwood, Nottingham NG5 2EJ Fax: 0115 985853; Camelot, 8 Tromode Close, Douglas IM2 5PE Tel: 01623 452900, 01624 662644 — MB BS 1988 Lond.; Docc Med 2001; MRCGP 1992; DRCOG 1991. GP Princip. Nottm.; Health Adviser for health at work, providing Occupat.al health advice. Socs: Soc. of Occupat.al Med. Prev: Trainee GP Gt. Yarmouth & Waveney VTS; Ho. Phys. Orsett Hosp.; Ho. Surg. Whipps Cross Hosp. Lond.

VINDLA, Srinivas Department of Obs & Gyn, Queens Medical Centre, Nottingham NG7 2UH; 30 Black Scotch Lane, Mansfield NG18 4JX — MB BS 1989 Lond.; BSc (Hons.) Zool. Lond. 1986. Specialist Regist., Dept. of Obs.& Gyn. Qu.s Med. Centre, Notts. Prev: SHO (O & G) Nottm.; SHO (O & G) Jas. Paget Hosp. Gt. Yarmouth.

VINDLACHERUVU, Madhavi Flat 15, Lyndhurst, London Road, Leicester LE2 2AP — BChir 1995 Camb. Ho. Off. (Gen. Surg.) Ipswich Hosp. Prev: Ho. Off. (Gen. Med.) Qu. Eliz. Hosp. King's Lynn.

VINDLACHERUVU, Mr Raghu Ram 47 Grosvenor Avenue, Jesmond, Newcastle upon Tyne NE2 2NP Tel: 0191 281 7328 — MB BChir 1994 Camb.; MA Camb. 1995; FRCS Lond. 1997. Specialist Regist. in Neurosurg., Newc. Gen. Hosp., W.gate Rd., Newc. Prev: Sen. Ho. Off. (Gen. Surg.) Chase Farm Hosp. Enfield Lond.; SHO (Gen. Surg.) Roy. Free Hosp. Lond.; Sen. Ho. Off. (Neurosurg.) Atkinson Morley's Hosp. Lond.

VINE, Alison Mary Immunology Department, ICSM St Mary's, Norfolk Place, London W2 1PG Tel: 020 7594 3731 Fax: 020 7402 0653 Email: a.vine@ic.ac.uk — MB BS 1990 Lond.; DPhil Oxon. 1996. (Char. Cross and Westm. Med. Sch.) Wellcome Postdoctoral Fell.; Speciality: Immunogenetics of HTLV-I Infect.; Immunol. Dept. I.C.S.M. at St. Mary's Lond. Prev: Wellcome Clin. Train. Fell. Dep. Human Anat. Oxf.

VINE, David John West Wirral Group Practice, 33 Thingwall Road, Irby, Wirral CH61 3UE Tel: 0151 648 1846 Fax: 0151 648 0362; 7 Pond View Close, Heswall, Wirral CH60 1YH Tel: 01513426231 Fax: 0151342 6231 Email: drdavevine@aol.com — MB ChB 1974 Liverp.; MRCGP 1978; DCH RCPS Glas. 1978; DObst RCOG 1976. Socs: BMA; Christian Med. Fell.ship.

VINE, Joseph (retired) Vine House, Vicarage Hill, Loxwood, Billingshurst RH14 0RQ Tel: 01403 752547 — MB ChB 1927 Manch.

VINE, Pauline Rosemary Anaesthetic Department, Bromley Hospital, Cromwell Avenue, Bromley BR2 9AJ — MB BS 1977 Lond.; BSc (1st cl. Hons.) Lond. 1974, MB BS 1977; MRCP (UK) 1980; FFA RCS Eng. 1982. (Univ. Coll. Hosp.) Cons. Anaesth. Bromley Hosps Trust.

VINE, Richard John c/o Ballyclare Health Centre, George Avenue, Ballyclare BT39 9HL — MB BCh BAO 1977 Belf.; DRCOG 1980.

VINE, Roland Stephen (retired) Shola, Fielden Road, Crowborough TN6 1TR Tel: 01892 661381 — MRCS Eng. LRCP Lond. 1934; FRCPath 1964. Prev: Chief Inspec. Cruelty to Animals Act, Home Office.

VINE, Sydney Maudsley (retired) 2 Woolven Close, Parkstone, Poole BH14 0QT Tel: 01202 730330 — MB BChir 1947 Camb.; BA Camb. 1940, MA, MB BChir 1947; FRCP Lond. 1974, M 1952; MRCS Eng. LRCP Lond. 1943. Mem. Med. Counc. on Alcoholism. Prev: Phys. i/c Dept. Geriat. Med. Reading Area Hosps.

VINEN, Catherine Susanna Department of Renal Medicine, St. George's Hospital, Medical School, Cranmer Terrace, London SW17 — BChir 1990 Camb.; MRCP 1994. Clin. Res. Fell. Dept. of Renal Med. St. Geo.'s Hosp. Med. Sch.

VINER, Anthony Sidney (retired) Castle Cottage, Creech Heathfield, Taunton TA3 5EH Tel: 01823 443905 — MRCS Eng. LRCP Lond. 1952. Prev: Med. Off. DHSS.

VINER, Clare Rachel 4 Florence Road, Southsea PO5 2NE — MB ChB 1997 Leeds.

VINER, Michael Anthony The Oaklands Practice, Yateley Medical Centre, Oaklands, Yateley GU46 7LS Tel: 01252 872333 — MB BS 1975 Lond.; MA Camb. 1976; MRCS Eng. LRCP Lond. 1975; DRCOG 1979; Cert JCC Lond. 1979. (Camb. & St. Mary's) Prev: SHO (O & G), (A & E) & (Paediat.) Berks. AHA.

VINES, Benjamin Homfray 17 Chivenor Grove, Kingston upon Thames KT2 5GE — BM 1998 Soton.

VINES, Jill Rachel Long Street Practice, 51 Long Street, Cerne Abbas, Dorchester DT2 7JG Tel: 01300 341666 Fax: 01300 341090; Frome Farrow, 7B Dorchester Road, Frampton, Dorchester DT2 9NB — MB BS 1975 Lond.; MFHom 1998; MRCGP 1981; DRCOG 1977; LRCP 1975 Lond.; MRCS Eng. GP; Homeop. Clinic. Prev: GP Dorchester & Falmouth.

VINESTOCK, Morris David Section of Forensic Psychiatry, St. Georges Hospital Medical School, Jenner Wing, Cranmer Terrace, London SW17 0RE Tel: 020 8725 5567 Fax: 020 8725 2475 — MB ChB 1979 Ed.; MRCPsych 1992. Lect. (Forens. Psychiat.) St. Geo. Hosp. Med. Sch. Univ. Lond.

VINEY, Deirdre Bradley Cote Cottage, Cote, Bampton, Oxford OX18 2EG — MB BCh BAO 1957 Dub.; BA Dub. 1955, MB BCh BAO 1957; DA Eng. 1961. (T.C. Dub.)

VINEY, Mark Trevor Balmoral Surgery, 1 Victoria Road, Deal CT14 7AU Tel: 01304 369880 — MB BS 1989 Lond.; MRCGP 1993; DFFP 1993; Cert. Prescribed Equiv. Exp. JCPTGP 1993; DRCOG 1992; Cert. Family Plann. JCC 1991; AKC Lond. 1989. GP Trainer; Clin Assist. Vict. Hosp. Deal. Prev: Trainee GP Tunbridge Wells HA VTS.

VINEY, Michael James (retired) 59 Thorogate, Rawmarsh, Rotherham S62 7HN — MB ChB 1955 Manch. Prev: Ho. Surg. Crumpsall Hosp. Manch. & Burton-on-Trent Infirm.

VINEY, Paul Leonard 75 Wiltshire Road, Salisbury SP2 8HT — MB BS 1996 Lond.

VINEY, Rebecca Margaret Morris Globe Town Surgery, 82-86 Roman Road, London E2 0PG; 84 Cloudesley Road, London N1 0EB — MB BS 1986 Lond.; Dip OCC MED 1997. (St. Bart. Hosp.) GP Tutor & Course Organiser GP Non-Princip. & Asst. GP, Globe Town Surg. Socs: Soc. Occupat. Med.; BMA. Prev: Princip. GP Jubilee St. Pract. Lond.

***VINEY, Richard Philip Charles** 11 Don Close, Edgbaston, Birmingham B15 3PN — MB ChB 1995 Birm.

VINIKER, Mr David Alan Private Office, c/o Holly House Hospital, High Road, Buckhurst Hill IG9 5HX Tel: 020 8504 6886 Fax: 020 8504 6678; Tel: 020 8504 6886 Fax: 020 8504 6678 — MB BS 1971 Lond.; MD Lond. 1983; FRCOG 1995, M 1976. (Univ. Coll. Hosp.) Cons. O & G Whipps Cross Hosp.; Hon. Sen. Lect. Univ of Lond. Socs: Amer. Soc. Reproduc. Med.; Brit. Fertil. Soc.; Brit. Menopause Soc. Prev: Sen. Regist. (O & G) Leicester Roy. Infirm.; Research Sen. Regist. (O & G) Univ. Coll. Hosp. Lond.; Regist. (O & G) Lond. Hosp.

VINING, David 141 Wigton Lane, Alwoodley, Leeds LS17 8SH — MB ChB 1941 Leeds. (Leeds) Prev: Police Surg.; Div. Surg. St. John Ambul. Brig.; Res. Med. Off. Gen. Hosp. Rotherham.

VINING, Roy MacDona Herringfleet, Heath Pond, St. Olaves, Great Yarmouth NR31 9HL Tel: 01493 488385 Fax: 01493 488385 — MB BS 1953 Lond. (St. Mary's)

VINITHARATNE, Indra Clydesdale Close, Ramleaze, Swindon SN5 5YE — MB BS 1967 Ceylon; Cert. Family Plann. JCC 1981.

VINITHARATNE, Juwundara Kankanamalage Padmasiri Department of Anaesthetics, Aldermaston Road, Basingstoke RG24 9NA; 55 Linden Avenue, Old Basing, Basingstoke RG24 7HS Tel: 01256 473651 — MB BS 1967 Ceylon. Staff Grade (Anaesth.) N. Hants. Hosp. Basingstoke. Socs: BMA.

VINNICOMBE, Mr John Hindon House, Havant Road, Emsworth PO10 7JE Tel: 01243 372528 — MB BChir 1956 Camb.; MChir Camb. 1966, MA 1956; FRCS Eng. 1958. (St. Thos.) Cons. Urol. Surg. Portsmouth Hosp. Gp.; Clin. Teach. Soton. Univ. Med. Sch.; Cons. Urol. Surg. King Edwd. VII Hosp. Midhurst. Prev: Sen. Surg. Regist. & Sen. Cas. Off. St. Thos. Hosp. Lond.; Research Fell. Stanford Univ. Med. Center, Calif., USA; Hon. Sec. & Treas. Brit. Assn. Urol. Surgs.

VINNICOMBE, Sarah Jane Department of Radiology, St Bartholomew's Hospital, West Smithfield, London EC1A 7BE; Flat 2, 16 Lorn Road, Stockwell, London SW9 0AD — MB BS 1984 Lond.; BSc (Hons.) Lond. 1981; MRCP (UK) 1987; FRCR 1993. (St. Thos.) Cons. Diagn. Radiol. St. Bart. Hosp. Lond. Prev: Sen. Regist. & Regist. (Diagn. Radiol.) St. Geo. Hosp. Lond.; Regist. (Med.) Univ. Coll. Hosp. Lond.

VINOD KUMAR, Indu 7 Crowden Walk, Pogmoor, Barnsley S75 2LU — MB BS 1978 Osmania.

VINOD KUMAR, Mr Puzhankara Ambalavattah Department of Plastic Surgery, Whiston Hospital, Prescot L35 5DR Tel: 0151 430 1401 Fax: 0151 430 1855; 1 The Gables, Eccleston Park, Prescot L34 2TH Tel: 0151 431 1553 Email: vinodkumar@email.msn.com — MB BS Poona 1970; MS Chandigarh 1975, MCh 1979, MNAMS 1979; FRACS 1992. Cons. Plastic Surg. Whiston Hosp. Socs: Plastic Surg. Soc. & Brit. Assn. Plastic Surgs.; Roy. Austral. Coll. Surgs.; Brit. Assn. Aesthetic Plastic Surgs. Prev: Cons. Plastic Surg. Pinderfields Gen. Hosp. Wakefield; Sen Research Fell. St. Vincents Hosp. Melbourne, Austral.; Assoc. Prof. Jipmer Pondicherry.

VINSON, Marianne Claire Argyll & Clyde Health Board, Ross House, Hawkhead Road, Paisley PA2 7BN Tel: 0141 842 7230 Email: marianne.vinson@achb.scot.nhs.uk; 9 Novar Drive, Glasgow G12 9PX Email: marianvin@aol.com — MB ChB 1987 Birm.; MFPHM RCP (UK) 1995. Cons. Pub. Health Med. Argyll & Clyde HB. Prev: Sen. Regist. (Pub. Health Med.) Oxf. RHA.

VINSON, Paul Selby The Surgery, 50 The Glade, Furnace Green, Crawley RH10 6JN Tel: 01293 612741; 5 River Mead, Crawley RH11 0NS — MB BS Lond. 1991; MRCGP 1995; DRCOG 1995. (Univ. Coll. Med. Sch.) GP Princip. Prev: Trainee GP Crawley VTS; Ho. Off. (Surg.) Stoke-on-Trent; Ho. Off. (Med.) Warwick.

VINT, David Geoffrey Dyson (retired) Riverside Farm, Wooton Courtenay, Minehead TA24 8RE — MB BChir 1952 Camb.; MA, MB BChir Camb. 1952. Prev: Surg. Lt. RNVR.

VIOLARIS, Nicodemis Stavrou 16 Dale View Close, Barnston, Wirral CH61 1DU — MB BS 1982 Lond.

VIOLET, John Albert 43 Holmefield Court, Belsize Grove, London NW3 4TT Tel: 020 7483 4309 — MB BS 1993 Lond.; BSc (Hons.) Lond. 1991; MRCP 1997. (Royal Free Hospital) Specialist Regist. (Oncol.) Pan-Thames Rotat. Scheme (E. Wing). Prev: SHO (Oncol.) St Bart. Hosp. Lond.; SHO (Renal Med.) Lister Hosp. Stevenage.

VIPOND, Amanda Jane 15 Queen's Down, Creech St Michael, Taunton TA3 5QY — BM 1990 Soton.; MRCP (UK) 1995. SHO (Anaesth.) Exeter.

VIPOND, Mr Mark Neil Gloucestershire Royal Hospital, Gloucester GL1 3NN Tel: 01452 394675 Fax: 01452 394813 — MB BS 1983 Lond.; MS Lond. 1991; FRCS Ed. 1987; FRCS Eng. 1987. Cons. Gen. Surg. Glos. Roy. Hosp. Socs: Assn. Surg.; Surgic. Research Soc.; Brit. Soc. Gastroenterol. Prev: Sen. Regist. (Gen. Surg.) Bristol Roy. Infirm.; Lect. (Surg.) Univ. Bristol.

VIPULENDRAN, Sureka 30 Greenhill Crescent, Merlins Bridge, Haverfordwest SA61 1LK Tel: 01437 760622 — MB BS 1980 Sri Lanka.

VIPULENDRAN, Velupillai Department of Child Health and Paediatrics, Withybush General Hospital, Fishguard Road, Haverfordwest SA62 2PZ Tel: 01437 773848 Fax: 01437 773848 Email: v.vipulendran@virgin.net; Redhill House, Camrose, Haverfordwest SA62 6HU Tel: 01437 764668 — MB BS 1974 Peredeniya; FRCP (UK) & FRCPCH; Dip. Community Paediat. Nottm. 1989; Cert. Community Paediat. Warwick 1988. Cons. Community Paediat. Pembrokesh. NHS Trust. Prev: Regist. (Community Paediat.) Nottm. HA; Med. Off. (Clin.) Centr. Birm. HA; Regist. (Neonat. & Gen. Paediat.) Selly Oak Hosp. & Sorrento Matern. Hosp. Birm.

VIRAPEN, Matthew Peter The Country Medical Centre, 122 Ballinlea Road, Armoy, Ballymoney BT53 8TY Tel: 028 2075 1266 Fax: 028 2075 1122; 58 Boyland Road, Ballymoney BT53 8LJ — MRCS Eng. LRCP Lond. 1970.

VIRCHIS, Andres Eliseo Dept. of Haematology, Barnet Hospital, Wellhouse Lane, Barnet EN5 3DN Tel: 020 8216 4383 Fax: 020 8216 4837 Email: andres.virchis@barnet-chase-tr.nhs.uk — MB BS 1988 Lond.; BSc Lond. 1985; MRCP (UK) 1991; DRCPath 1995; MRCPath 1999. (Univ. Coll. Lond.) Cons. Haemat. Barnet Hosp, Herts.; Hon. Cons. Haemat. Univ. Coll. Lond. Hosps. Lond. Socs: BMA; Brit. Soc. Haematol.; Amer. Soc. Haemat. Prev: Sen. Regist. (Haemat.) Roy. Free Hosp.; Sen. Regist. (Haemat.) Hillingdon Hosp.; Regist. (Haemat.) Hammersmith Hosp. & N.wick Pk. Hosp.

VIRDEE, B S Kiran Virdee Medical Centre, Sultan Road, Lordswood, Chatham ME5 8TJ Tel: 01634 669221 Email: bhagwant.virdee@gp-g82664.nhs.uk; 79 Kenilworth Road, Coventry CV4 7AF Tel: 02476 418195 — MBBS. (Seth G.S Medical College) Gen. Practitioner, Chatham, kent.

VIRDEE, Manjit Singh 39 Tenby Road, Moseley, Birmingham B13 9LX — MB ChB 1983 Leic.

VIRDEE, Munmohan Singh 529 Hurst Road, Bexley DA5 3JS — MB BS 1994 Lond.; BSc Hons. 1991; MRCP Uk 1997. (UMDS of GUY's & St Thomas') BHF Jun. Research Fell., Dept. of Cardiol. St Geo.'s Hosp. Lond.

VIRDEE, Tejinder Singh Bacon Lane Surgery, 11 Bacon Lane, Edgware HA8 5AT Tel: 020 8952 7876; 128 Pinner Hill Road, Pinner HA5 3SH — MB ChB 1979 Manch. Clin. Med. Off. (Paediat. Home Care) St. Mary's Hosp. Lond. Prev: Regist. (Paediat.) Whipps Cross Hosp. Lond.; SHO (Cardiol.) Hosp. Sick Childr. Gt. Ormond St. Lond.

VIRDEN, Joy Collins The Surgery, Bower Mount, The Square, Yalding, Maidstone ME18 6HB Tel: 01622 814373 Fax: 01622 814549; The Court Lodge, Yalding, Maidstone ME18 6HX Tel: 01622 814509 Fax: 01622 814962 Email: joyvirden@aol.com — MB BChir 1971 Camb.; MA Camb. 1972; DObst RCOG 1973.

VIRDI, Deshminder Singh Central Hill Practice, 60 Central Hill, London SE19 1DT Tel: 0208 670 7117 — MB BS 1994 Lond. (St. Geos. Hosp. Med. Sch.)

VIRDI, Rajiv Pritpal Singh Montague Health Centre, Oakenhurst Road, Blackburn BB2 1PP Tel: 01254 268416 Fax: 01254 268450; 2 Gib Lane, Livesey, Blackburn BB2 5BP Tel: 01254 209049 Email: virdi@easynet.co.uk — MB BS 1974 Poona. Clin. Assit. (Endoscopy) Blackburn. Socs: Fell. Roy. Soc. Med.

VIRGO, Fiona Emma Pettetts Farm House, East Green, Great Bradley, Newmarket CB8 9LU — MB BS 1997 Lond.

VIRGO, Morag Anne c/o D. Small, 26 Mansionhouse Road, Edinburgh EH9 2JD — MB ChB 1984 Glas.; MRCGP 1988; T(G) 1991.

VIRJEE, James Pesi Directorate of Clinical Radiology, Bristol Royal Infirmary, Bristol BS2 8HW Tel: 0117 928 2729 — MB ChB 1970 Bristol; FRCR 1976. (Bristol) Cons. Radiol. United Bristol Healthcare Trust.

VIRJEE, Shareen 157 Kyverdale Road, Stoke Newington, London N16 6PS Tel: 020 8806 3786 — MB ChB 1993 Ed.; MRCP Ed. 1996. (Edinburgh) Specialist Regist. Rotat. (Diabetes & Endocrinol.) N. W. Thames; Specialist Regist. St Mary's Hosp. Socs: MRCP; Brit. Endocrine Societies; Diabetes UK. Prev: Specialist Regist. Rotat. Watford Gen. Hosp.; Specialist Regist. Rotat. Hemel Hempstead & Chelsea & W.minster Hosps.; Specialist Regist. Rotat. Chelsea & W.minster Hosps.

VIRJI, Abbas Abdulhussein Nasser St Giles Surgery, 40 St. Giles Road, London SE5 7RF Tel: 020 7252 5936; 40 Winterbrook Road, Herne Hill, London SE24 9JA Tel: 020 7737 3352 Fax: 020 7642 5946 Email: abby@globalnet.co.uk — MB ChB 1969 Liverp.; MSc Lond. 1990; MRCGP 1974. (Liverp.) LMC. Prev: GP Tutor St. Thos. Dist.; Clin. Asst. (Rheum.) King's Healthcare.

VIRR, Mr Andrew Jonathan 10 Margret Road, Headington, Oxford OX3 8NG Email: virr@btinternet.com — 1995 MBBchir, Camb; 2000 MSC Birmingham; 1999 MRCS; MA Camb. 1997; BA (Hons.) Camb. 1993. (Univ. Camb. & Addenbrooke's Hosp.) p/t SPR, (A&E) Oxf. Deanery. Socs: BMA; FAEM; BAEM. Prev: SHO (Orthop.) Nuffield Orthop. Centre Oxf.; SHO (Urol.) Ch.ill Hosp. Oxf.; SHO (A & E) John Radcliffe Hosp. Oxf.

VIS-NATHAN, Sreeni The Medical Centre, Wear St., Jarrow NE32 3JN Tel: 0191 428 0606 Fax: 0191 427 6159 — MB BS 1974 Kerala.

VISAVADIA, Bhavin Gordhan 94 Marlborough Road, London N22 8NN — MB BS 1998 Lond.

VISHU (VISHWANATH), Mudigere Channaveerappa Western Isles Hospital, Stornoway, Isle of Lewis HS1 2AF Tel: 01851 704704 Fax: 01851 706240; 20 Braighe Road, Stornoway, Isle of Lewis Tel: 01851 702762 — MB BS 1974 Mysore; MD; MRCP. Cons. Phys. (Cardiol.). Socs: Brit. Cardiac Soc.; BMA; Brit. Soc. Heart Failure.

VISHWABHAN, Mr Satya Prakash 103 Porlock Avenue, Weeping Cross, Stafford ST17 0HT — MB BS 1969 Lucknow; FRCS Glas. 1987.

VISHWANATH, Luna Sharmila 22 Swallowdale, Wolverhampton WV6 8DT — MB BS 1983 Dacca; FRCS Ed. 1991.

VISHWANATH, Mandagere Ramamurthy 10 Windermere Avenue, Eastern Green, Coventry CV5 7GP — MB BS 1987 Mysore.

VISHWANATH, Mr Mayasandra Subramanyam 22 Swallowdale, Wolverhampton WV6 8DT — MB BS 1979 Bangalore; FRCS Ed. 1987.

VISHWESHWAR RAO, Hadigal Venkat Raj 530 West Street, Crewe CW2 8SG Tel: 01270 257467 — MD 1977 Osmania; MD (Gen. Med.) Osmania 1977, MB BS 1973.

VISHWESHWAR RAO, Mr Vunnam Tyrone County Hospital, Omagh BT79 0AP Tel: 01662 45211 — MS Andhra 1966; MB BS Nagpur 1962; FRCS Glas. 1981; FRCS Ed. 1981. Assoc. Specialist Tyrone Co. Hosp. Omagh. Socs: BMA.

VISICK, James Hedley (retired) Sherbrooke, Chandler Road, Stoke Holy Cross, Norwich NR14 8RQ Tel: 01508 494474 — MB BS Lond. 1961; FRCR 1975; FFR 1969; DMRD Eng. 1967. Prev: Cons. Radiol. Norf. & Norwich Hosp.

VISICK, Julia 134 Millstream Way, Leegomery, Telford TF1 6QT — MB ChB 1996 Birm.

VISICK, Robert Hedley (retired) 3 Lloyd Close, Heslington, York YO10 5EU Tel: 01904 411138 — MB BS 1957 Lond.; DCH Eng. 1964; DObst RCOG 1962. Prev: SHO (Child Health) St. Bart. Hosp. Lond.

VISRAM, Anil Rustamali 5 Cylers Thicket, Welwyn AL6 9RS — MB BCh 1986 Wales; BSc (Hons.) Wales 1983, MB BCh 1986.

VISSER, Michael James Dixton Surgery, Dixton Road, Monmouth NP25 3PL Tel: 01600 712152 Fax: 01600 772634 — MB BS 1989 Lond.; BSc Lond. 1986, MB BS 1989. GP Partnership, 3/4 Time. Prev: SHO (Anaesth.) Gloucester Roy. Hosp.

VISUVANATHAN, Shikandhini Department of Microbiology, Herts & Essex Hospital, Haymeads Lane, Bishop's Stortford CM23 5JH Tel: 01279 827138 Fax: 01279 656075 — MD 1992 Lond.; MSc Lond. 1991, MD 1992, MB BS 1983; MRCPath 1992; FRCP 2001 (Path). (The Middlesex Hospital Medicla School) Cons. Microbiol. P.ss Alexandra Hosp. Harlow. Socs: BMA; Hosp. Infec. Soc.; Assn. Med. Microbiologists. Prev: Sen. Regist. (Microbiol.) Univ. Coll. Hosp. Lond.

VISUVARATNAM, Mailoo St. Albans City Hospital, Normandy Road, St Albans AL3 5PN Tel: 01727 866122; 24 New Greens Avenue, St Albans AL3 6HS Tel: 01727 862697 — MD 1958 Ceylon; FRCP Ed. 1982; FRCP Lond. 1981. Assoc. Specialist (Geriat.) St. Albans City Hosp. Prev: Cons. Phys. Gen. Hosp. Kandy, Sri Lanka.

VISUVARATNAM, Thanalakshumi Community Health Services, Mentmore, Church Crescent, St Albans AL3 5JB Tel: 01727 830130; 24 New Greens Avenue, St Albans AL3 6HS Tel: 01727 862697 — MB BS 1961 Ceylon; DTPH 1973. Clin. Med. Off. NW Herts. HA. Socs: Fac. Comm. Health. Prev: Med. Off. (Matern. & Child Health) Kandy, Sri Lanka.

VISVA NATHAN, Sivapragasam Gosbury Hill Health Centre, Orchard Gardens, Chessington KT9 1AG Tel: 020 8397 2142 Fax: 020 8974 2717; Halton House, 22 Pelhams Walk, Esher KT10 8QD — MB ChB 1964 Glas.; FRCP Glas. 1989; MRCP (UK) 1970; MRCGP 1980. (Glas.) Clin. Asst. (Thoracic & Gen. Med.) Kingston Hosp. Kingston u. Thames; Med. Off. Surbiton Gen. Hosp.

VISVANATHAN, Mr Ramanathan 9 Tranmere Court, Langley Park Road, Sutton SM2 5HE — BM BCh 1975 Nigeria; BM BCh Univ. Nigeria 1975; FRCSI 1980; FRCS Eng. 1980; FRCS Ed. 1980. Prev: Research Fell. (Surg.) Univ. Manch. & Hope Hosp. Salford; Research Fell. (Surg.) Harvard Med. Sch. Beth Israel Hosp. Boston, USA; Cons. Surg. Univ. Teachg. Hosp., Maiduguri, Nigeria & Univ. Hosp. Kelantan,Malaysia.

VISVANATHAN, Shyamala Padmini 32 The Drive, Rickmansworth WD3 4EB — MRCS Eng. LRCP Lond. 1978. SHO (Anaesth.) Wexham Pk. Hosp. Prev: SHO (Anaesth.) Hull Roy. Infirm.; Ho. Off. (Surg.) Hull Roy. Infirm.; Ho. Off. (Med.) Law Hosp.

VISWALINGAM, Niramala Devi Moorfields Eye Hospital, City Road, London EC1V 2PD Tel: 020 8946 6407; 2 Peek Crescent, Wimbledon, London SW19 5ER — MB BS 1967 Madras; DO RCS Eng. 1970. (Christ. Med. Coll. Vellore) Assoc. Specialist Moorfields Eye Hosp. Lond.; Clin. Research Assoc. Inst. Ophth. Socs: Fac. Ophth.; Fell. Roy. Soc. Med. Prev: Regist. & SHO Kings Coll. Hosp. Lond.

VISWAN, Anjiparampil Kumaran Warwick Hospital, Lakin Road, Warwick CV34 5BW Tel: 01926 495321 Fax: 01926 403715 — MB BS 1965 Kerala; FRCP Ed. 1992; FRCP Lond. 1988; MRCP (UK) 1975; DCH RCPS Glas. 1970. (Trivandrum Med. Coll.) Cons. Phys. S. Warks. Gen. Hosps. NHS Trust. Socs: BMA. Prev: Sen. Regist. (Geriat. Med.) E. Birm. Hosp.

VISWANATH, Immaneni King George Hospital, Goodmayes, Ilford IG3 8YB Tel: 020 8983 8000; 45 Viking Way, Brentwood CM15 9HY Tel: 01277 219963 — MB BS 1968 Banaras Hindu; MB BS Banaras, Hindu 1968; MD Banaras Hindu 1973; MRCP (UK) 1980. Assoc. Specialist (Med. & Gastroenterol.) King Geo. Hosp. Ilford. Prev: Sen. Regist. (Med.) Armed Forces Hosp. Riyadh, Saudi Arabia; Regist. (Med. & Gastroenterol.) Dudley Hosp.; Regist. (Med. & Geriat.) Buckland Hosp. Dover.

VISWANATH, Mantha 3 Hospital Crescent, Harold Wood Hospital, Romford RM3 0BE — MB BS 1983 Sambalpur; MRCPI 1990.

VISWANATHAN, Ananth Chitur Flat 72, Elm Quay Court, 30 Nine Elms Lane, London SW8 5DF Tel: 020 7498 2217 Fax: 020 7498 2217 Email: a.viswanathan@ucl.ac.uk — MB BS 1989 Lond.; BSc (Hons.) Lond. 1986; FRCOphth 1994. Specialist Regist. Rotat. (Ophth.) N. Thames. Prev: Internat. Glaucoma Assn. Research Fell. Inst. Ophth. Lond.; SHO (Ophth.) St. Thos. Hosp. Lond.

VISWANATHAN, Manickam The Surgery, 20 Kendal Parade, Silver Street, Edmonton, London N18 1ND Tel: 020 8803 0020; 2 Crowland Gardens, Southgate, London N14 6AP — MB BS 1968 Ceylon. (Ceylon)

VISWANATHAN, Mary Jayanthi 124 Hamilton Place, Aberdeen AB15 5BB — MB BS 1984 Madras; MRCOG 1995.

VISWANATHAN, Palamiswamy Urology Department, Pontefract General Infimary, Friarwood Lane, Pontefract WF8 1PL — MB BS 1971 Madras.

VISWAPATHI, Kandula Upper Flat, 32 Nutley Lane, Reigate RH2 9HS — MRCS Eng. LRCP Lond. 1987; MB BS Bangalore 1978.

VISWESVARAIAH, M The Clinic, Barbers Avenue, Rawmarsh, Rotherham S62 6AE Tel: 01709 522831 — MB BS 1974 Madras; MB BS 1974 Madras.

VITAL, Marcos Freddy Dean Cross Surgery, 21 Radford Park Road, Plymstock, Plymouth PL9 9DL Tel: 01752 404743 — MRCS Eng. LRCP Lond. 1971; DObst RCOG 1973. GP Princip. Plymouth; Sen. Med. Off. No. 3 MHU RAF St. Mawgan at Rank of Sqad.; Ldr. RAF St. Mawgan Cornw.; Med. Adviser Tecalemit Plymouth, Gleason Work Ltd. Plymouth; Med. Adviser Becton Dickinson Ltd. Plymouth; Med. Adviser Gleason Works Ltd.; Adjudicating Med. Practitioner BAMS; Examr. Norwegian Med. Directorate. Socs: Plymouth Med. Soc. (Sec. Exchange with France); BMA (Sec. Plymouth Br.). Prev: Civil. Med. Pract. & Sen. Med. Off. RAF Mt.batten Plymouth.

VITES, Charles Montague 3 The Sycamores, Beaufort Avenue, Brooklands, Sale M33 3WH Tel: 0161 969 7161 — MB ChB 1940 Leeds. (Leeds)

VITES, Jillian 56 Belsize Road, London NW6 4TG Tel: 020 7372 6845 — MB ChB 1973 Manch.; MRCPsych 1977. Clin. Asst., Adolesc. Dept. Tourstoch Clinic. Socs: Assoc. Mem. Inst. Psychoanal., RCPsych.

VITES, N P Naylor Street Surgery, 4 Naylor Street, Manchester M40 7JH Tel: 0161 205 3177 — MB ChB 1978 Manchester; MB ChB 1978 Manchester.

VITHANA, Tilaka Alderney Hospital, Poole BH12 4NB Tel: 01202 735537 Fax: 01202 730657; 63A Cynthia Road, Parkstone, Poole BH12 3JE Tel: 01202 380643 — MB BS 1967 Ceylon. (Colombo) Assoc. Specialist (Ment. Illness) Alderney Hosp. Poole. Socs: Affil. Roy. Coll. Psychiat. Prev: Clin. Asst. (Psychogeriat.) Alderney Hosp. Poole; Regist. (Psychiat.) Herrison Hosp. Dorchester.

VITHAYATHIL, Kurian Joseph Genitourinary Clinic Leatherhead Hospital, Polar Road, Leatherhead KT22 8SD Tel: 01372 362845 Fax: 01372 378498 — MB BS 1979 Poona; MRCP (UK) 1985. Cons. Phys. (Geniturin. Med.) Leatherhead Hosp. Socs: BMA; Med. Soc. Study VD. Prev: Sen. Regist. (Geniturin. Med.) Soton. Univ. NHS Trust; Regist. Geniturin. Med. Roy. Berks. Hosp. Reading.

VITHLANI, Mr Kishor Popatlal Netherley Health Centre, Middlemass Hey, Liverpool L27 7AF Tel: 0151 498 4054 Fax: 0151 487 5767 — MB BS 1979 Baroda; FRCS Ed. 1987; MRCS Eng. LRCP Lond. 1987.

VITTLE, June Emily Pwllderi, 13 Rock House Est., Letterston, Haverfordwest SA62 5SQ Tel: 01348 451 — MB BCh 1957 Wales. (Cardiff) Med. Asst. (Geriat.) Withybush Gen. Hosp. HaverfordW.. Assoc. Mem. Socs: Brit. Geriat. Soc. Prev: Regist. Psychiat. Cefn Coed Hosp. Swansea; Ho. Surg., Ho. Phys. (Paediat.) & SHO Thoracic Surg. Unit Morriston; Hosp.

VITTY, Frederick Peeter Meldrum, Vitty and Pfeiffer, 40-42 Kingsway, Waterloo, Liverpool L22 4RQ Tel: 0151 928 2415 Fax: 0151 928 3775; Oakley, 4 Abbotsford Road, Blundellsands, Liverpool L23 6UX — MB 1980 Camb.; BChir 1979. (Camb. & St. Geo.) Prev: Ho. Off. (Surg.) Ashford Gen. Hosp. Middlx.; Ho. Off. (Med.) St.Geo. Hosp. Lond.; Trainee GP Chester VTS.

VIVA, Mr Charles Middlesbrough General Hospital, Ayresome Green Lane, Middlesbrough TS5 5AZ Tel: 01642 850850 Fax: 01642 854136 — MB BS 1961 Punjab; FRCS Eng. 1969; FRCS Ed. 1968; T(S) 1991. Sen. Cons. Plastic, Aesthetic & Hand Surg. Middlesbrough Gen. Hosp.; DL.

VIVE, Jeremy Utaman c/o X-Ray Department, Crawley Hospital, West Green Drive, Crawley RH11 7DH Tel: 01293 527866 — MB

VIVEASH

BS 1982 Lond.; BSc (Hons.) Lond. 1979, MB BS 1982; FRCR 1990; T(R) (CR) 1991. (St. Thos.) Cons. Radiol. Mid Downs HA. Prev: Sen. Regist. Rotat. (Diag. Radiol.) Leicester Roy. Infirm.; Regist. Rotat. (Radiol.) Qu. Med. Centre Nottm.; SHO Rotat. (Gen. Med.) City Hosp. Nottm.

VIVEASH, Dawn Maria Thistledown, Jordans Lane, Willingdon, Eastbourne BN22 0LL — MB BS 1983 Lond.; BPharm. (Hons.) Lond. 1977, MB BS 1983; MRCP (UK) 1986. Med. Adviser Upjohn Ltd. Crawley. Prev: SHO (Med.) Soton. Gen. Hosp.; Ho. Surg. Edgware Gen. Hosp.; Ho. Phys. Univ. Coll. Hosp. Lond.

VIVEKANANDA, Chatchithanantham 16 The Causeway, Sutton SM2 5RS — MB BS 1976 Sri Lanka; LRCP LRCS Ed. LRCPS Glas. 1985; DGM RCP Lond. 1985. Trainee GP Purley. Prev: SHO (Geriat. Med.) St. Helier Hosp. Carshalton & Sutton Hosp.; SHO (A & E) N. Middlx. Hosp. Lond.; SHO (Dermat.) Grimsby Dist. Gen. Hosp.

VIVEKANANDAMURTY, Kadiyala 36 Braithwaite Road, Lowton, Warrington WA3 2AY Tel: 01942 718221 — MB BS 1975 Andhra.

VIVEKANANTHAN, Malarvizhi 188 Ashbourne Road, Mitcham CR4 2DQ — MB BS 1993 Lond.

VIVIAN, Mr Anthony James Primrose House, 48A Primrose Hill Road, London NW3 3AA Tel: 020 7483 2459 — MB BS 1984 Lond.; FRCS Eng. 1989; FCOphth. 1989. Sen. Regist. (Ophth.) Moorfields Eye Hosp. Lond. Socs: Med. Protec. Soc. Prev: Regist. Soton. Eye Hosp.; Fell. Paediat. Ophth. Gt. Ormond St. Lond.

VIVIAN, Charles Trevarthen Benedict, Squadron Ldr. RAF Med. Br. Retd. 4 St Peters Road, Cirencester GL7 1RG Email: ctbvivian@aol.com — MB BS 1988 Lond.; MRCGP 1994; DFFP 1996; Dip CPC 1996. (St. Thos. Hosp. Lond.) Occupat. Med. Socs: Christ. Med. Fell.sh.; Soc. Occup. Med. Prev: Princip. GP; GP RAF Mt. Pleasant, Falkland Is.s & RAF High Wycombe; Trainee GP RAF Gutersloh VTS.

VIVIAN, Patrick Cyril (retired) Pumney, Drayton Road, Sutton Courteney, Abingdon OX14 4AJ Tel: 01235 848205 — MB BChir 1953 Camb.; MA Camb. 1958, MB BChir 1953; DObst RCOG 1958. Prev: GP Abingdon.

VIVIAN, Peter Graham (retired) 21 Southern Lane, Barton-on-Sea, New Milton BH25 7JA — MB ChB 1952 Liverp.

VIVIAN-AB-EWART, Vivian Raymond 9 Erw Goch, Waunfawr, Aberystwyth SY23 3AZ Tel: 01970 623336 — LMSSA 1952 Lond.; DA Eng. 1957. (Guy's Hosp. Lond.) Socs: Med. Defence Union; BMA. Prev: GP Kent FPC; Cons. Anaesth. Wellington Hosp. New Zealand; Sen. Specialist Anaesth. Belize City Hosp. Belize.

VIVIERS, Louis Flat 2, Clare Court, 54 Clarendon Road, London W11 2HJ — MB ChB 1988 Stellenbosch.

VIVORI, Elena (retired) 7 Dudlow Grange, Green Lane, Liverpool L18 2EP — MD 1958 Genoa; LRCP LRCS Ed. LRCPS Glas. 1966; DA Eng. 1969; FFA RCS Eng. 1972. Prev: Cons. Paediat. Anaesth. Alderhey Childr.'s Hosp., Liverp.

VIZE, Mr Charles Edward 1 Mornington Villas, Manningham, Bradford BD8 7HB Tel: 01274 546861 Fax: 01274 487705; Cotswold, 18 Southfield Road, Burley-in-Wharfedale, Ilkley LS29 7PA Tel: 01943 863198 — BSc (Hons.) NUI 1969, MB BCh BAO 1967; FRCS Ed. 1973. Cons. ENT Surg. Bradford Roy. Infirm. Prev: Lect. (Otorhinolaryng.) Univ. Liverp. & ENT Infirm. Liverp.; SHO & Regist. ENT Infirm. Liverp.

VIZE, Christine Mary Avon and Western Wiltshire Mental Health Partnership Trust, Green Lane Hospital, Devizes SN10 5DS Tel: 01380 731200 Fax: 01380 731308 Email: christine.vize@awp.nhs.uk; Fax: 01380 830385 — MB BChir 1986 Camb.; MA Camb. 1987; MRCPsych 1990. p/t Cons. Gen. Adult Psychiat. & Dep. Med. Director, Avon & Wilts. Partnership. Prev: Lect. & Hon. Sen. Regist. St. Mary's Hosp. Med. Sch. Lond.; Hon. Regist. (Psychiat.) Addenbrooke's Hosp Camb.; Regist. (Psychiat.) Fulbourn Hosp. Camb.

VIZE, Mr Colin John 3 St Chads Grove, Headingley, Leeds LS6 3PN Email: vize@cwnet.com — MB BS 1993 Newc.; FRCPath. Coll of Ophchalmology, 1998. (Newc. Upon Tyne) Specialist Regist. (Ophth.), Yorks., Deanery. Prev: SHO (Ophth.) St James Univ. Hosp. Leeds; SHO (Ophth.) Sunderland Eye Infirm.; SHO (Neurosurg.) Regional Neurosci. Centre Newc. Gen. Hosp.

VIZZA, Enrico Royal Free Hospital, Department of Obstetrics & Gynaecology, Minimally Invasive Therapy Unit, Pond St., London NW3 2QG — State DMS 1994 Rome.

VLACHOU, Paraskevi 35 Oliver Court, London Rd, Leicester LE2 2PQ — MB ChB 1997 Leic.

VLACHTSIS, Helen 22 Heycroft, Gibbet Hill, Coventry CV4 7HE Tel: 024 76 414463; Flat 1, 1 Gillbrook Road, Didsbury, Manchester M20 6WH Tel: 0161 448 7246 — MB ChB 1995 Manch.; BSc (Hons) Physiol. Manch. 1992. (Manchester) SHO (Anaesth.) Roy. Oldham Hosp. Socs: Fell. Manch. Med. Soc.; MRCAnaesth.; BMA. Prev: SHO (Chest Med./Cardiol.) Wythenshawe Hosp.; Ho. Off. (Surg.) MRI; Ho. Off. (Med.) Hope Hosp. Salford.

VLASTO, Mr Philip (retired) Little Ham, The Common, Child Okeford, Blandford Forum DT11 8QY Tel: 01258 861359 — BM BCh 1943 Oxf.; FRCS Eng. 1979. Prev: Mem. Med. & Survival Comm. & Med. Ref. RNLI.

VLIES, Margaret Joan Hillcrest Medical Centre, Holt Road, Wrexham LL13 8RG; 3 Croeshowell Court, Croeshowell Hill, Rossett, Wrexham LL12 0AA Tel: 01244 571307 — MB BS Lond. 1975; MRCS Eng. LRCP Lond. 1975; MRCGP 1981; DRCOG 1979. (Guy's) Asst. GP Wrexham. Prev: Trainee GP Carshalton VTS.

VLIES, Mr Philip Robin 3 Croeshowell Court, Croeshowell Hill, Rossett, Wrexham LL12 0AA Tel: 01244 571307 — MB BChir 1971 Camb.; MA, MB Camb. BChir 1971; FRCS Ed. 1977; FRCOG 1989, M 1976. (Camb. & St. Mary's) Cons. O & G Wrexham Maelor Hosp. NHS Trust. Prev: Lect. & Sen. Regist. (O & G) Middlx. Hosp. Lond.; Sen. Regist. Nat. Wom.'s Hosp. Auckland, New Zealand; Resid. Med. Off. Qu. Charlotte's Hosp. Lond.

VLISSIDES, Dimitrios Nikolaos 239 School Road, Sheffield S10 1GN Tel: 0114 266 4110 — Ptychio Iatrikes 1972 Athens; PhD Sheff. 1976. (Athens Med. Sch.) Lect. Dept. Psychiat. Univ. Sheff. & Roy. Hallamshire Hosp. Socs: Roy. Coll. Psychiat. (Mem. Collegiate Trainees' Comm. & Represen. Coll. Educat. Comm.). Prev: Sen. Regist. Fulbourn Hosp.; Clin. Research Asst. Univ. Sheff.

VO, Van Toan 38A Stamford Road, Birmingham B20 3PJ — MB BS 1995 Lond.

VODDEN, Ms Julie Jane Tel: 01823 333444 — MB ChB 1986 Bristol; 1999 (FRCS Ed.); MRCGP 1992; DRCOG 1991; DA (UK) 1988. Staff Grade (Ophth.) MusGr. Pk. Hosp. Taunton. Socs: Roy. Coll. Ophth.

VODDEN, Vera Marjorie (retired) 20 Beverley Road, Leamington Spa CV32 6PJ — LRCP LRCS 1951 Ed.; LRCP LRCS Ed. LRFPS Glas. 1951; DO Eng. 1957. Prev: Assoc. Specialist (Ophth.) W. Midl. RHA.

VOETEN, F Danetre Medical Practice, The Health Centre, London Road, Daventry NN11 4EJ Tel: 01327 703333 Fax: 01327 311221 — Artsexamen 1991 Nijmegen; DRCOG 1995. (Univ. Katholieke Nijmegen)

VOGEL, Louis (retired) 25 Sandringham House, Windsor Way, London W14 0UD Tel: 020 7603 5581 Email: louis.vogel@which.net — MB BS 1945 Lond.; FRCPath 1976, M 1964; DCP Lond 1950. Prev: Cons. Path. Newham HA & Roy. Lond. Hosp.

VOGEL, Markus Werner Flat 1, 13 Essendine Road, London W9 2LT — State Exam Med 1993 Frankfurt.

VOGEL, Mary Louise William Harvey Hospital, Kennington Road, Ashford TN24 0LZ — MB ChB 1981 Bristol; MRCPsych 1986. Cons. Psychiat. S. Kent Community Healthcare Trust. Prev: Sen. Regist. E. Anglian RHA; Regist. & SHO Barrow Hosp. Bristol.

VOGEL, Melanie 286A The Broadway, London NW9 6AE — State Exam Med 1994 Berlin.

VOGELZANG, Sophia Antonia Mitchell and Partners, New Chapel Surgery, High Street, Long Crendon, Aylesbury HP18 9AF Tel: 01844 208228 Fax: 01844 201906 — MB BChir 1992 Camb. Trainee GP/SHO Stoke Mandeville Hosp. Prev: Ho. Off. St. Thos. & Roy. Sussex Co. Hosps.; Ho. Off. (Oncol. & Radiother.) N.ampton Gen. Hosp.

VOGLER, Eleanor Jillian Arnott (retired) 40 The Avenue, Rounday, Leeds LS8 1JG Tel: 0113 266 1885 Fax: 0113 237 0678 Email: jon@vogler.demon.co.uk — MA Peace Studies Bradford 1994; MB ChB Bristol 1961; MRCPsych 1972; DPM Eng. 1965. Prev: Cons. Psychiat. Rehabil. Lynfield Mt. Hosp.

VOGT, Julie 71 Rodenhurst Road, London SW4 8AF — MB BS 1991 Lond. (St. Thomas' Hospital London) Specialist Regist. (Paediat.) Barnet Gen. Hosp.

VOGT, Stephen 9 Dudley Road, Grantham NG31 9AA Tel: 01476 579650 — MB BChir 1978 Camb.; BChir 1977; MA Camb. 1978; FRCOG 1998. (St. Mary's) Cons. O & G Grantham & Dist. Gen.

Hosp. Lincs. Prev: Regist. (O & G) W.m. & Kingston Hosps.; SHO (Gyn.) Samarit. Hosp. Lond.; SHO (Perinatol.) & Ho. Surg. St. Mary's Hosp. Lond.

VOGT MANDUCA, Ursula Western Eye Hospital, London NW1 Tel: 020 7402 4211; 148 Harley Street, London W1N 1AH Tel: 020 7935 1207 Fax: 020 7224 1528 — State Exam Med 1978 Dusseldorf; MD Ophth. Dusseldorf 1980. (Univ. Dusseldorf) Assoc. Specialist W.. Eye Hosp. Lond.; Dir. Contact Lens Clinic W.. Eye Hosp.; Aviat. Ophth. Civil Aviat. Auth.; Med. Ophth. & Contact Lens Pract. Harley St.; Ophth. Med. Pract. Med. Eye Centres. Socs: (Ex-Hon. Sec.) Med. Contact Lens. Assn.; Brit. Contact. Lens Assn.; Eur. Contact Lens Soc. Ophth. Prev: Clin. Asst. W.. Ophth. Hosp. Lond.; Clin. Asst. Moorfields Eye Hosp.; Resid. Asst. Univ. Clinic Dusseldorf, Germany.

VOGWELL, Paul Charles 37 Rosemount Close, Oxton, Birkenhead CH43 2LR — MB BS 1988 Lond.; BSc Lond. 1985, MB BS 1988. Regtl. Med. Off. Roy. Army Med. Corps.

VOHRA, Akbar Department of Anaesthesia, Manchester Royal Infirmary, Oxford Road, Manchester M13 9WL Tel: 0161 276 4552 Fax: 0161 276 8027 Email: avorha@compuserve.com; Squirrels Chase, Lea Bank Close, Macclesfield SK11 8PU — MB ChB 1983 Manch.; FCAnaesth 1989; DA (UK) 1985. (Manchester) Cons. Anaesth.(Cardiac Anaesth. and Intens. Care) Manch. Roy. Infirm. Socs: Assn. Anaesth. Gt. Brit. & Irel. & Anaesth. Research Soc.; Assn. of Cardiothoracic Anaesth.s; Soc. of Critical Care Med. Prev: Sen. Regist. (Anaesth.) NW RHA; Regist. Rotat. (Anaesth.) Wigan Hosp. & Manch. Roy. Infirm.; SHO (Neonat. Med.) St. Mary's Hosp. Manch.

VOHRA, Ameet Oak Lodge, Lee Chapel Lane, Basildon SS16 5NX — MB BS 1993 Lond.

VOHRA, Anjna Devi c/o P. Vohra, 115 Arundel Drive, Harrow HA2 8PW Tel: 020 8864 1343 — MB BS 1943 Punjab. (Lady Hardinge Med. Coll. New Delhi)

VOHRA, Jatinder Paul Singh 7 Edlington Drive, Nottingham NG8 2TD — MB ChB 1993 Sheff.

VOHRA, Shashi Sussex Wald & Downs NHS Trust, Martyn Long Centre, 78 Crawley Road, Horsham RH12 4HN Tel: 01403 266966 Fax: 01403 272140; 2 Wells Close, Horsham RH12 1US Tel: 01403 265296 — MB BS 1965 Delhi; DFFP 1993; Cert. JCC Lond. 1977; DObst RCOG 1970; DGO Delhi 1968. (Lady Hardinge Med. Coll.) Staff Grade (Learning Disabil.) Martyn Long Centre Horsham. Prev: SHO (Obst.) Bushey Matern. Hosp. & City of Lond. Matern. Hosp.; Med. Off. Birm. Family Plann. Assn.

VOHRA, Shiv Lal Worthing Priority Care NHS Trust, 1 St George's Road, Worthing BN11 2DS Tel: 01903 843354 Fax: 01903 843351; 2 Wells Close, Horsham RH12 1US Tel: 01403 265296 — MB BS 1964 Delhi; DPM Eng. 1969. (Maulana Azad Med. Coll.) Cons. Psychiat. (Learning Disabil.) Worthing Priority Care NHS Trust. Prev: Sen. Regist. (Psychiat.) Chelmsley Hosp. Birm. & Child Guid. Centre Coventry; Regist. (Psychiat.) Centr. Middlx. Hosp. Lond.; Med. Off. (Psychiat.) Maulana Azad Med. Coll. & Assoc. Hosps. New Delhi, India.

VOHRA, Suleman 5 Roundwood Avenue, Reedleu, Burnley BB10 2LH — MB BS 1962 Karachi.

VOHRA, Sumeet Abbey Lane Surgery, 23 Abbey Lane, Sheffield S8 0BJ Tel: 0114 274 5360 Fax: 0114 274 9580 — MB BS 1990 Lond.; MBBS Lond. 1992; MRCGP 1992. (Charing Cross & Westminster) GP Princip.; Dir. Sheff. GP Co-op. Socs: Sheff. Medicolegal Soc.

VOHRAH, Anil Raj Walsgrove Hospital, Clifford Bridge Road, Coventry — MB BS 1986 Lond.; MRCP (UK) 1989; FRCR 1994. Cons. Walsgrave Hosp. NHS Trust.

VOHRAH, Ram Chand The Surgeries, Lombard Street, Newark NG24 1XG Tel: 01636 702363 Fax: 01636 613037; 25 Greet Lily Mill, Station Road, Southwell NG25 0ET — MB BS 1986 Lond.; MRCGP 1994. (Westm.)

VOICE, Allan Flaxmead House, Chesterfield Road, Tibshelf, Derby — MB BS 1974 Lond.; MRCS Eng. LRCP Lond. 1974; FFA RCS Eng. 1981. (St. Mary's) Cons. Centr. Notts. HA.

VOICE, Elizabeth Andrea 24 Balmoral Close, Lichfield WS14 9SP — MB ChB 1988 Leeds; MRCGP 1992; DCCH Warwick 1996. Staff Grade (Community Paediat.) SE Staffs. Prev: Locum GP Lichfield; SHO (Palliat. Med.) Derbysh. Roy. Infirm.; Trainee GP W.gate Pract. Lichfield.

VOICE, Sally-Anne Mathers Townhead Surgery, Townhead, Murray Lane, Montrose DD10 8LE Tel: 01674 76161 Fax: 01674 673151; St. Clement's, 97 Glamis Road, Forfar DD8 1DR Tel: 01307 467002 — MB ChB 1992 Dundee; DFFP 1995; DRCOG 1995. Partner, Townhead Surg. Montrose. Socs: BMA; MDU; MSS.

VOIGHT, Mary Wentworth House, Bexton Lane, Knutsford WA16 9AE Tel: 01565 632846 — MB ChB Liverp. 1962. (Liverp.) Sen. Med. Off. DSS. Prev: Med. & Health Off. Govt. Hong Kong.

VOISEY, Miss Sarah Carolyn 16 Port Lane, Hursley, Winchester SO21 2JS Tel: 01962 775447 — BM 1993 Soton.; FRCS 1998. SHO Anaesth. St Richards Hosp. Chichestr. Socs: BMA. Prev: Regist. Paediat. Surg., Soton., Gen. Hosp.; SHO Intens. Care, Qu. Alexandra Hosp. Portsmouth; SHO (Gen. Surg.) N. Hants. Hosp. Basingstoke, Poole Hosp, Dorset & Qu. Alexandra Hosp. Portsmouth.

VOKE, Jennifer Mary Haematology Department, Queen Elizabeth II Hospital, Welwyn Garden City AL7 4HQ Tel: 01707 365209; 16 Hollybushn Lane, Harpenden AL5 4AT Tel: 01582 460739 — FRCPath; MB BS Lond. 1968; MRCS Eng. LRCP Lond. 1968; MRCPath 1975. (Univ. Coll. Hosp.) p/t Cons. Haemat. E. Herts. NHS Trust Welwyn Garden City; Cons. Haemat. Luton & Dunstable Hosp. NHS Trust, Beds. Prev: Sen. Regist. (Haemat.) Roy. Free Hosp. Lond.; Regist. (Haemat.) Univ. Coll. Hosp. Lond.; Leukaemia Research Fell. Hosp. Sick Childr. Gt. Ormond St. Lond.

VOKINS, Amanda Jane Tel: 01273 556317; 2 West End Avenue, Brundall, Norwich NR13 5RF Tel: 01603 715966 — MB BS 1989 Lond.; MRCGP 1995; DRCOG 1992; DCH RCP Lond. 1991. (Middlx. Hosp.) Salaried Gen. Practitioner Norwich.

VOKINS, Colin Guy The Surgery, 42 Upper Rock Gardens, Brighton BN2 1QF Tel: 01273 600103 Fax: 01273 620100 — MB BS Lond. 1966; DObst RCOG 1969. (St. Thos.)

VOLANS, Mr Andrew Philip Accident & Emergency Department, Scarborough Hospital, Woodlands Drive, Scarborough YO12 6QL Email: volansa@mail.scarney.northy.nhs.uk; Chestnut Cottage, Bridge Close, Burniston, Scarborough YO13 0HS — MB ChB 1983 Leeds; BSc (Hons.) Leeds 1978; FRCS Ed. 1988; FFAEM 1996; DA (UK) 1986. (Leeds) Cons. (A & E) ScarBoro. Hosp. Socs: BMA & Fac. Accid. & Emerg. Med.; Roy. Coll. Surg. Edin. Prev: Sen. Regist. (A & E) Roy. Hallamsh. Hosp. Sheff.; Regist. (Neurosurg.) Maudsley Hosp. Lond.; Regist. (Orthop.) & SHO Rotat. Airedale HA.

VOLANS, Glyn Noel — MB BS Newc. 1968; BSc (Hons. Physiol.) Durham. 1965; MD Newc. 1975; FRCP Lond. 1984; MRCP (UK) 1972. Dir. Med. Toxicology Unit & Cons. Phys. Guy's & St. Thomas' Hosp. Trust; Hon. Sen. Lect. UMDS. Socs: Fell. Roy. Soc. Med.; Brit. Toxicol. Soc.; Brit. Pharmacol. Soc. Prev: SHO Artific. Kidney Unit & Gen. Med. Roy. Vict. Infirm. Newc.; Regist. (Gen. Med.) Newc. Gen. Hosp.; Research Fell. Clin. Pharmacol. & Migraine Clinic St. Bart. Hosp.

VOLIKAS, Ingrid 22 Marrowells, Weybridge KT13 9RN — MB BS 1993 Lond.

VOLK, Heather Margaret Jean Jaguar Cars halewood, Halewood, Liverpool L24 Tel: 0151 443 4320; 46 Heyes Lane, Alderley Edge SK9 7JY Tel: 0151 485 6320 — MB BS 1976 Lond.; MRCS Eng. LRCP Lond. 1976; MFOM RCP Lond. 1994, AFOM 1987; MRCGP 1982. (Guy's) p/t Sen. Med. Off. Jaguar Cars Ltd.; Med. Adviser John Lewis Partnership. Socs: Soc. Occupat. Med.

VOLKERS, Mr Robert Charles 29 Hans Place, London SW1X 0JY Tel: 020 7584 7435 Fax: 020 7225 2816; Penleigh Mill, Dilton Marsh, Westbury Tel: 01373 822142 — MB BS 1967 Lond.; FRCS Eng. 1973; MRCS Eng. LRCP Lond. 1967. (St. Bart.) Prev: Regist. Plastic Surg. Frenchay Hosp. Bristol.

VOLLMER, Juliane Princess Royal Hospital, Salthouse Road, Hull HU8 9HE; 27 West End, Walkington, Beverley HU17 8SX — State Exam Med 1992 Essen; State Exam Med Essex 1992.

VOLLUM, Dorothy Isabella (retired) Flat 1, 15 St Germans Place, London SE3 0NN Tel: 020 8858 3741 — MB BS 1960 Lond.; FRCP Lond. 1979, M 1965; DCH Eng. 1964; AMQ 1966. Prev: Cons. Dermat. Lewisham Hosp.

VOLMINK, James Andrew Wolfson College, Linton Road, Oxford OX2 6UD — MB ChB 1982 Cape Town.

VOLPE, Nicola 50 Castle Road, Mount Sorrel, Loughborough LE12 7EU — State Exam 1980 Rome.

VON ARX, Mr Derek Peter Luton and Dunstable Hospital, Lewsey Road, Luton LU4 0DZ Tel: 01582 491122; Westwood House, 19 Highfields, Bedford MK45 5GN Tel: 01525 714039 Email:

VON ARX

derekvonarx@66sisters.freeserve.co.uk — MB BS 1993 Lond.; FRCS (OMFS) 2000; BDS Lond. 1978; FRCS Ed. 1997; FDS RCS Ed. 1984. (Kings Coll. Lond.) Cons. (Oral & Maxillofacial Surg.) Luton and Dunstable Hosp.; Cons. (Oral & Maxillofacial Surg.) The Lister Hosp., Stevenage. Socs: Jun. Fell. Brit. Assn. Oral & Maxillofacial Surg.; BMA. Prev: Specialist Regist. (Oral & Maxillofacial Surg.) Kent and Canterbury Hosp., Guy's Hosp. Lond., St. Geo.s Hosp., Lond.

VON ARX, Otto Albert 17 East Grove Road, Exeter EX2 4LX — MB ChB 1993 Stellenbosch.

VON BACKSTROM, Andre George 20 Lackford Road, Coulsdon CR5 3TA Tel: 01737 552785 Fax: 01737 556945 Email: avonb@aol.com; 20 Lackford Road, Coulsdon CR5 3TA Tel: 01737 552785 Fax: 01737 556945 Email: avonb@aol.com — MB ChB 1988 Pretoria. (University of Pretoria) Sedationist in NHS Dent. Pract.s, Socs: Social Coordinator for S.O.C.S. (Soc. for Conscious Sedation); SAAD (Soc. for Advancem. of Anaesth. in Dent.); ADA (Assn. of Dent. Anaesthestists). Prev: Hon. Clin. Asst. Anaesthetic Dept. Roy. Berks. Hosp. Reading.

VON BERGEN, Julian Edward (retired) Hatch Green Lodge, Hatch Beauchamp, Taunton TA3 6TN Tel: 01823 480884 — BM BCh 1949 Oxf.; BM BCh Oxon. 1949. Prev: Capt. RAMC.

VON BERGEN, Mrs Sheila (retired) Hatch Green Lodge, Hatch Beauchamp, Taunton TA3 6TN Tel: 01823 480884 — BM BCh 1949 Oxf.; BM BCh Oxon. 1949.

VON BIEL, Thomas Arnim 11 Newling Way, High Salvington, Worthing BN13 3DG — MB ChB 1986 Otago.

VON BREMEN, Beate Christiane Doctors Accommodation, Alder Hey Children's Hospital, Eaton Road, West Derby, Liverpool L12 2AP Tel: 0151 228 4811 — State Exam Med. Hamburg 1988. SHO (Paediat.) Alder Hey Hosp. Liverp. Socs: BMA. Prev: SHO (Paediat.) Sunderland Dist. Gen. Hosp.; Trainee GP Elgin, Scotl.

VON EICHSTORFF, Peter Daniel George East Oxford Health Centre, Manzil Way, Cowley Road, Cowley, Oxford OX4 1XD Tel: 01865 242109; 60 Bagley Wood Road, Kennington, Oxford OX1 5LY — MB ChB 1988 Dundee; MA (Hons.) Dundee 1982. Socs: Roy. Coll. Gen. Pract.; BMA. Prev: Ships Med. Off. Actaeon Shipping.

VON FRAGSTEIN, Martin Franz Frederick Prestwood House Surgery, 74 Midway Road, Midway, Swadlincote DE11 7PG Tel: 01283 212375 Fax: 01283 551923 — BM BS 1984 Nottm.; MMedSci Nottm. 1998; T(GP) 1991; MRCGP 1988; DGM RCP Lond. 1987; BMedSci Nottm. 1982. Lect. (Gen. Pract.) Univ. Nottm.; Hon. Sec. Nottm. Guild Catholic Doctors.

VON FRAUNHOFER, Michael Anthony Heald Green Health Centre, Finney Lane, Heald Green, Stockport SK7 3JD Tel: 0161 436 8384 Fax: 0161 493 9268 Email: mike@vonf.freeserve.co.uk — MB ChB 1990 Manch.; MRCGP 1994; D.Occ.Med. RCP Lond. 1996; T(GP) 1994. Occupat. Health Phys. Tameside Gen. Hosp.; Med. Off. St Anne's Hospice; Med. Off. Francis Ho. Socs: Fac. Occupat. Med.

VON FRAUNHOFER, Nicola Anne Merton Child & Family Service, Cricket Green Polyclinic, Birches Close, Cricket Green, Mitcham CR4 4LQ Tel: 020 8770 8828 Fax: 020 8770 8848 — MB ChB Bristol 1988; MRCPsych 1993. (Bristol) Cons. (Child & Adolesc. Psychiat.) Merton Child Guid. Clinic. Prev: St. Geo. Hosp. Train. Schemes (Psychiat./Child & Adolesc. Psychiat.).

VON GOETZ, Therese Campbell Bolling Chesterhill, Newport-on-Tay DD6 8QY — MB ChB 1987 Dundee; BA Oxf. 1984; FRCS Eng. 1993. Research S. Thames Deaner. Socs: BMA (Jun. Doctor Comm.); Med. Wom. Federat.; Guild Catholic Doctors. Prev: Regist. (Neurosurg.) Atkinson Morley's Hosp.; SHO (Gen. Surg.) Basingstoke Dist. Hosp.; SHO (Gen. Surg.) Roy. Berks. Hosp. Reading.

VON KAISENBERG, Constantin Sylvius Leopold Research Centre for Foetal Medicine, Kings College Hospital, Denmark Hill, London SE5 9RS — State Exam Med 1990 Heidelberg.

VON ONCIUL, Julia 64A Fitzgeorge Avenue, London W14 0SW — State Exam Med. Dusseldorf 1989.

VON SCHREIBER, Simon Krishna 42 Queen Victoria Road, Sheffield S17 4HT — MB BS 1992 Lond.

VONAU, Barbara Ursula Chelsea & Westminster Hospital, St. Stephen's Centre, 369 Fulham Road, London SW10 9NH Tel: 020 8846 6183 Fax: 020 8846 7582; Cabbage Cottage, 14 Blackheath Rise, London SE13 7PN Tel: 020 8852 4044 — State Exam Med 1991 Erlangen; MD Erlangen 1992; MRCOG 1997; Dip Genitoaurin Med.1999. (Friedrick Alexander Univ., Erlangen) Specialist Train.

Regist. GUM/HIV Char. Cross & Chelsea & W.m. Hosp. Socs: BMA; MSSVD. Prev: Research Regist. (Genitourin. Med.) Chelsea & W.m. Hosp. Lond.; SHO (O & G) Qu. Charlotte's Hosp. Lond.; SHO (O & G) Heatherwood Hosp. Ascot & Luton & Dunstable Hosp.

VOOGHT, Mary Winifred (retired) Guilton Ash, Tile Barn, Woolton Hill, Newbury RG20 9UX — M.B., B.S. Durh. 1940. Prev: Ho. Surg. Gyn. Dept. & Res. Anaesth. Roy. Vict. Infirm. Newc.

VORA, Ajay Jaikishore Department of Paediatric Haematology, Sheffield Children's Hospital, Sheffield S10 2TH Tel: 0114 271 7358 Fax: 0114 276 2289 Email: a.j.vora@sheffield.ac.uk — MB BS 1985 Bombay; MRCPath 1991; MRCP (UK) 1989; MD Bombay 1986. Cons. Paediat. Haemat. Sheff. Childr. Hosp.; Hon. Lect. Univ. Sheff. Prev: Sen. Regist. Haemat. Sheff.; Regist. Haemat. Leicester.

VORA, Ajaykumar The Medical Centre, 34 Victoria Road, Barnetby DN38 6JR Tel: 01652 688203 Fax: 01652 680841 — MB ChB 1983 Manch.; MRCGP 1987; DRCOG 1987. GP Barnetby. Prev: Trainee GP Bury VTS; Ho. Off. (Med.) Bury HA; Ho. Off. (Surg.) Oldham HA.

VORA, Ashok Kumar West Heath Surgery, 196 West Heath Road, Northfield, Birmingham B31 3HB Tel: 0121 476 1135 Fax: 0121 476 1138; 94 Rednal Road, Kings Norton, Birmingham B38 8DU Tel: 0121 459 2431 — MB BS 1977 Lond.; DRCOG 1982. (St. Mary's) Prev: Trainee GP Birm. VTS; SHO (A & E) Hillingdon Hosp. Uxbridge; SHO (Paediat., Geriat. & O & G) VTS Selly Oak Hosp. Birm.

VORA, Jitendu Popatlal Dept. of Diabetes & Endocrinology, Royal Liverpool University Hospitals, Liverpool L7 8XP Tel: 0151 706 3470 Fax: 0151 706 5877 Email: jiten.vora@rlbuh-tr.nwest.nhs.uk — BChir 1978 Camb.; MB 1978 Camb.; FRCP 1996; MD 1991. (Univ of Cambridge) Cons. (Diabetes & Endocrinol.) Roy. Liverp. Univ. Hosp.; Hon. Sen. Lect. (Med.) Univ. Liverp. Socs: Fell., Roy. Coll. of Med.; Mem. Diabetes UK; Mem. Soc. of Endocrinol.

VORA, Mahendra Shamji 18 Elgin Avenue, Kenton, Harrow HA3 8QL Tel: 020 8909 2579 — MB BS 1970 Bombay. Socs: Defence Union.

VORSTER, DeWet Stockstrom Erme House MT Gould Hospital, Plymouth PL4 7QD Tel: 01752 268011; Santa Maria, Wrangaton, South Brent TQ10 9HJ Tel: 01364 3286 — MB ChB 1953 Cape Town; FRCPsych 1988, M 1971; DPM Eng. 1959; DPsych McGill 1959. Cons. Child & Adolesc. Psychiat. MT Gould Hosp. Plymouth CHRN (SW). Socs: Assn. Child Psychol. & Psychiat. Chairm. SW Br. & Amer Psychiat Assn. Prev: Cons. Psychiat. Johannesburg Gen. Hosp., Tara Hosp. & Johannesburg; Child Guid. Clinic S. Afr.; Cons. Child & Adolesc. Psychiat. Staines & Godalming Child Guid.

VORSTER, Mr Mark Andrew Regal Chambers, Bancroft, Hitchin SG5 1LL Tel: 01438 812494 Fax: 01438 816497 — MB BS 1982 Lond.; BSc Lond. 1979; FRCS Eng. 1990; MRCGP 1993; DRCOG 1989. (Westminster) GP; Clin. Asst. (Colonscopy) Lister Hosp. Stevenage. Prev: Trainee GP Ivybridge VTS; Regist. (Surg.) Groote Schuur Hosp. Cape Town, S. Afr.; SHO (O & G) Freedom Fields Hosp. Plymouth.

VORSTER, Timothy Neill 53 Muschamp Road, London SE15 4EG — MB BS 1990 Lond.

VOS, Adrian Lawrence 39 Hargrave Road, London N19 5SH — MB BS 1996 Lond.

VOS, Helen Patricia (retired) 46 Main Street, Escrick, York YO19 6LA — MB BChir 1984 Camb.; MA Camb. 198; MRCGP 1988; DRCOG 1988; DCH RCP Lond. 1987; Cert. Family Plann. JCC 1987. Prev: Trainee GP Oxf.

VOSE, Helen Clare Bishop Auckland General Hospital, Cockton Hill Road, Bishop Auckland DL14 6AD — MB BS 1998 Newc.

VOSE, Mark Anthony Frome Medical Practice, Health Centre, Park Road, Frome BA11 1EZ Tel: 01373 301300 Fax: 01373 301313; Innox Hill Cottage, 35 Innox Hill, Frome BA11 2LN Tel: 01373 467993 Email: mark@voses.freeserve.co.uk — MB BS 1986 Lond.; MRCGP 1990; DRCOG 1989.

VOSE, Mark Joseph 52 Elmsfield Avenue, Rochdale OL11 5XN — MB ChB 1996 Manch.

VOSS, Harold James, ERD (retired) Walnut Cottage, 10 Corby Road, Cottingham, Market Harborough LE16 8XH Tel: 01536 771787 — MRCS Eng. LRCP Lond. 1939; MPhil Leic. 1987, BA 1981; FRCPath 1963. Cons. Path. Kettering & Dist. Hosp. Gp. Prev: Asst. Path. Withington Hosp. Manch.

VOSS, Kerstin Lucia 59 Northumberland Street, Edinburgh EH3 6JQ Tel: 0131 556 5992 — MB ChB 1993 Dundee.

VOSS, Miranda Dean Lodge, Iron Acton, Bristol BS20 7JA — MB ChB 1987 Aberd.

VOSS, Simon Nicholas Southampton & SW Hampshire Health Commission, Oakley Road, Southampton SO16 4GX Tel: 02380 725400 Fax: 02380 725457; 1A Abbotts Way, Highfield, Southampton SO17 1QU Tel: 02380 725400 — MB BS 1981 Lond.; BSc (Pharmacol.) Lond. 1978, MB BS (Hons.) 1981; MFPHM RCP (UK) 1992; MRCGP 1986; DRCOG 1987; Cert. Family Plann. JCC 1984. Med. Adviser (Primary Care) & Cons. Pub. Health Med. Soton. & SW Hants. Health Commiss. & Hants. FHSA. Prev: Med. Off. Chas. Johnson Memor. Hosp. Nqutu, Zululand; GP Stroud.

VOSS, Susan Barbara c/o Dr B. D. Sharpe, Magill Department of Anaesthesia, Chelsea & Westminster Hospital, 369 Fulham Road, London SW10 9NH — MB BS 1986 Sydney.

VOTRUBA, Marcela Department of Molecular Genetics, Institute of Opthalmology, Bath St., London EC1V 9EL Tel: 020 7608 6806 Fax: 020 7608 6863 Email: mvotruba@hgmp.mrc.ac.uk; 74 Trinity Road, Wimbledon, London SW19 8QZ Tel: 020 8542 0483 — BM BCh 1987 Oxf.; BA Oxf. 1984; MA 1987; FRCOphth 1992. (University of Oxford Medical School) Wellcome Research Fell. Inst. Ophth. & Hon. Regist. Moorfields Eye Hosp. Lond. Socs: Fell. Roy. Soc. Med. Lond.; Assn. for Research in Vision & Ophth.; Brit. Soc. of Human Genetics. Prev: Regist. (Ophth.) Bristol Eye Hosp.; SHO (Ophth.) St. Geo. Hosp. & Roy. Lond. Hosp.; SHO (Neurosurg.) St. Bart. Hosp. Lond.

VOUGAS, Vassilios Liver Transplant Surgery Department, Kings College Hospital, Denmark Hill, London SE5 9RS — Ptychio latrikes 1982 Athens. Sen. Regist. (Liver Transpl. Surg.) King's Coll. Hosp. Lond.

VOUSDEN, James Ernest Health Centre, New Street, Beaumaris LL58 8EL Tel: 01248 810818 Fax: 01248 811589; Hafod Wen, Llanddona, Beaumaris LL58 8UU Tel: 01248 811566 — MB BCh 1984 Wales. (Welsh Nat. Sch. Med.) Clin. Asst. (Oncol.) Llandudno Gen. Hosp. Gwynedd. Socs: Roy. Coll. Gen. Practs.

VOWDEN, Mr Peter Bradford NHS Hospital Trust, Bradford Royal Infirmary, Duckworth Lane, Bradford BD9 6RJ Tel: 01274 364466 Fax: 01274 364807 Email: peter.vowden@bradfordhospitals.nhs.uk; Broxholme, 13 Staveley Road, Nab Wood, Shipley BD18 4HD Tel: 01274 585043 Fax: 01274 825367 Email: peter.vowden@blueyonder.co.uk — MD 1984 Leeds; MB ChB 1976; FRCS Eng. 1980. (Leeds) Cons. Surg. Vasc. & Gen. Surg. Bradford Roy. Infirm.; Head of Serv. Surg. Socs: Vasc. Soc. of GB and Irel.; Surg. Research Soc.; Eur. Vasc. Soc.

VOWLES, Hilary Anne John Denmark Unit, Prestwich Hospital, New Bury Road, Manchester M25 3BL Tel: 0161 772 3400 Fax: 0161 798 5853; 34 Egerton Street, Prestwich, Manchester M25 1FQ Tel: 0161 798 7180 — MB BS 1986 Lond. Staff Grade Psychiat. John Denmark Unit Prestwich Hosp. Manch. Prev: Regist. (Psychiat.) Borders Health Auth.

VOWLES, Julie Elizabeth Flat 11, The Grange, 114 Avenue Road, Acton, London W3 8QL Tel: 020 8993 3702; 3 The Pastures, Llanyravon, Cwmbran NP44 8SR Tel: 01633 482765 — MB BS 1991 Lond.; BSc (Hons.) Lond. 1988; MRCP (UK) 1994. Specialist Regist. (Geriat. & Gen. Med.) Univ. Coll. & St Pancras Hosp. Lond. Prev: Regist. (Geriat. & Gen. Med.) N.wick Pk. Hosp. Harrow; Regist. (Geriat. & Gen. Med.) Centr. Middlx. Hosp. NHS Trust.

VOWLES, Mr Keith Douglas John (retired) Honeyway, Dunsford, Exeter EX6 7AX Tel: 01392 811503 — MB ChB (Gold Medal) Bristol 1946; FRCS Eng. 1953. Prev: Cons. Surg. Roy. Devon & Exeter Hosp.

VOWLES, Mary (retired) Honeyway, Dunsford, Exeter EX6 7AX Tel: 01392 811503 — MB ChB Bristol 1947; DCH Eng. 1951. Prev: Assoc. Specialist (Genetic Counselling) Paediat. Dept. Roy. Devon & Exeter Hosp.

VOWLES, Richard Henry First Floor Flat, 39 Handforth Road, London SW9 0LL — MB BS 1989 Lond.

VOWLES, Rosalind Elizabeth 12 Englewood Road, London SW12 9NZ — MB ChB 1993 Birm.; ChB Birm. 1993; FRCS Eng. 1997.

VOWLES, Stuart Cooper Lemon Street Surgery, 18 Lemon Street, Truro TR1 2LZ Tel: 01872 73133 Fax: 01872 260900 — MB BCh 1974 Wales; FRCGP 1995, M 1981; DCH Eng. 1979. Socs: BMA.

Prev: SHO (Psychiat.) St. Lawrence's Hosp. Bodmin; SHO (Paediat.) Roy. Cornw. Hosp. (City & Treliske) Truro.

VOYCE, Christine Eirwen (retired) The Health Centre, High St., Redbourn, St Albans AL3 7LZ — MB BS 1986 Lond.; MRCGP 1990; Dip. Family Plann. JCC 1990; DCH RCP Lond. 1988. Clin. Asst. (A & E) Luton & Dunstable Hosp. NHS Trust; Clin. Med. Off. (Family Plann. & Reproductive Health Care) S. Beds. Community Health Care Trust. Prev: GP Welwyn Garden City & Hatfield.

VOYCE, Margaret Elizabeth Brighton General Hospital, Elm Grove, Brighton BN2 3EW Tel: 01273 696955; Fivestones, Little Black Hill, Lindfield, Haywards Heath RH16 2HE — MB BS 1977 Lond.; Dip. Scientif. Basis Dermat. (Merit) 1993; DRCOG 1980. (King's Coll. Hosp.) Assoc. Specialist (Dermat.) Brighton Health Care Trust; Assoc. Specialist Mid Downs. Socs: Brit. Assn. Dermat. Prev: GP Haywards Heath.

VOYCE, Michael Albert (retired) Chyvogue Cottage, Perranwell Station, Truro TR3 7JX — MB ChB 1959 Bristol; 1959 MB ChB Bristol; 1968 MD Bristol; 1989 FRCP Lond.; 1976 FRCP Ed.; M 1963; 1962 DCH Eng.; FRCP 1997 CH. Cons. Paediat. & Med. Dir. Roy. Cornw. Hosp. Trust. Prev: Lect. (Child Health) Univ. Bristol.

VOYSEY, Joanna Rachel 7 Cedar Close, Horsham RH12 2BN — BM BS 1986 Nottm.

VOYSEY, Margaret Mary (retired) 9 Reading Street Road, St. Peters, Broadstairs CT10 3EA Tel: 01843 863019 — MB BS 1954 Lond.; FFA RCS Eng. 1961; DA Eng. 1956. Prev: Unit Gen. Manager Canterbury & Thanet HA.

VRAHIMIS, Nicos 12 Curie Crost, Leegomery, Telford TF1 4DD — MB ChB 1985 Orange Free State.

VRANAKIS, Konstantinos Flat 8, 17 Inverness Terrace, London W2 6JE — Ptychio latrikes 1977 Athens.

VRANJKOVIC, Vera 256 Guardwell Cr., Edinburgh EH17 7SL — MB BS 1996 Lond. (Univ. Coll. Lond.) SHO (A & E) Vict. Hosp. Kirkcaldy. Prev: Ho. Off. (Gen. Med.) Taunton-MusGr. Hosp.; Ho. Off. (Gen. Surg.) Cheltenham Gen. Hosp.

VRANJKOVIC, Vlade 12 Shadwell Road, Bristol BS7 8EP — MB ChB 1994 Aberd.

VREEDE, Eric 61A Quinton Street, London SW18 3QR Tel: 020 8767 2896 Email: ericvreede@compuserve.com — Artsexamen 1983 Amsterdam; FFA RCSI 1994. (University of Amsterdam) Prev: Regist. Rotat. (Anaesth.) St. Geo. Hosp. Lond.; Sen. Regist. (Anaesth.) Roy. Brompton Hosp.; Sen. Regist. Rotat. (Anaesth.) Chelsea & W.minster Hosp.

VRIES, Leonardus Adrianus Gerardus 16 Broadmeadow Lane, Stratford-upon-Avon CV37 9FD — Artsexamen 1990 Maastricht.

VRIONIDES, Yianis 14 Ronneby Close, Oatlands Chase, Weybridge KT13 9SB Tel: 01932 248484 — Ptychio latrikes 1968 Athens; MRCP (UK) 1974. (Univ. Athens) Cons. Phys. Hillingdon Hosp. Uxbridge.

VROEGOP, Paul Gilles 142 Wellesley Road, London W4 3AP — MB ChB 1995 Auckland.

VU, Thai Quoc 50 Bankfield Avenue, Lonasight, Manchester M13 0ZP — MB BS 1998 Lond.

VUCEVIC, Michael Dept. Anaesthetics, D Floor, Jubilee Wing, Leeds General Infirmary LS1 3BX — MB ChB 1980 Birm.; FFA RCS Eng. 1987. Cons. Anaesthetics & Intens. Care, Leeds Gen. Infirm. Prev: Hon. Cons. & Sen. Lect. (Anaesth.) Univ. Leeds.; Sen. Regist. Rotat. (Anaesth.) Leeds RHA; Regist. (Anaesth.) Centr. & N. Birm. HAs.

VUCEVIC, Ranko 9 St Mildreds Road, Chelmsford CM2 9PU — MB BS 1995 Lond.

VUJANIC, Gordan Department of Pathology, University of Wales College of Medicine, Heath Park, Cardiff CF14 4XN Tel: 029 2074 2706 Fax: 029 2074 4276 — PhD Belgrade, Yugoslavia 1989, DS (Path.) 1983, MD 1978.

VULLIAMY, Christopher Benjamin Brecon War Memorial Hospital, Brecon LD3 7NS Tel: 01874 622443 Fax: 01874 610233; Lower Gaer Farm House, Tretower, Crickhowell NP8 1SB Tel: 01874 730859 — MB BS 1972 Lond.; FRCP Lond. 1996; MRCP (UK) 1977; MRCS Eng. LRCP Lond. 1970; FRCPCH 1997, M 1996; T(M)(Paediat.) 1991; DCH Eng. 1974; DA Eng. 1973; DObst RCOG 1973. (Guy's) Cons. Paediat. (Community) Powys Health Care NHS Trust; Cons. Paediat. Nevill Hall & Dist. Trust. Socs: Welsh Paediat. Soc.; Brit. Assn. Community Child Health. Prev: Sen. Regist.

VULLIAMY

(Paediat.) Bristol Childr. Hosp. & S.mead Hosp.; Sen. Regist. (Paediat.) Exeter Hosp.; Regist. (Paediat.) S.mead Hosp. Bristol.

VULLIAMY, David Gibb (retired) The Old School House, Lower Bockhampton, Dorchester DT2 8PZ — 1941 MRCS Eng. LRCP Lond.; 1942 MB BChir; 1952 MD Camb.; 1970 FRCP Lond., M 1949; 1997 FRCPCH (Hon); 1948 DCH Eng. Prev: Cons. Paediatr. W. Dorset Hosps.

VULPE, Anna-Maria 11 Birch House, Lingwood Close, Southampton SO16 7GH — BM 1983 Soton.

VUYYURU, Sivakumari Rao and Vuyyuru, Group Practice Centre, Howard Street, Glossop SK13 7DE Tel: 01457 854321 — MB BS 1971 Andhra; MB BS Andhra, India 1971.

VYAS, Aashish 63 Hatch Road, London SW16 4PW — MB ChB 1990 Manch.

VYAS, Bhupendra Shambhuprasad Ware Road Surgery, 59 Ware Road, Hoddesdon EN11 9AB Tel: 01992 463363 Fax: 01992 471108; 15 Barclay Close, Hertford Heath, Hertford SG13 7RW — MB BS 1967 Poona; DPM Eng. 1972. (B.J. Med. Coll. Poona)

VYAS, Deborah Ruth Shirley Health Centre, Grove Road, Shirley, Southampton SO15 3 Tel: 02380 783611 — BM 1986 Soton.; MRCGP 1993; DRCOG 1988. Prev: SHO Soton. & SW Hants. HA VTS.

VYAS, Dharmendra Kantilal Ballards Lane Surgery, 209 Ballards Lane, London N3 1LY Tel: 020 8346 0726 — MB BS 1970 Saurashtra; MB BS 1970 Saurashtra.

VYAS, H D Melbourne Road Health Centre, 63 Melbourne Road, Leicester LE2 0GU Tel: 0116 254 5301 — MB BS 1964 Baroda; MB BS 1964 Baroda.

VYAS, Harish Gunvantrai Department of Child Health, Queens Medical Centre, University Hospital, Nottingham NG7 2UH Tel: 0115 924 9924 Email: harish.vyas@mail.gmcuh-tr.trent.nhs.uk — MB BS 1975 Lond.; DM Nottm. 1986; FRCP Lond. 1996; MRCP (UK) 1978; FRCPCH 1997. Cons. Paediat. (Intens. Care & Respirat. Med.) Qu. Med. Centre Nottm. Socs: Amer. Thoracic Soc.; Paediat. Intens. Care Soc.; Soc. Critical Care Med. Prev: Research Fell. (Child Health) Univ. Nottm.

VYAS, Mr Janardan Kantilal Basildon Hospital, Basildon SS16 5NL Tel: 01268 533911; 165 Waldegrave, Kingswood, Basildon SS16 5EJ Tel: 01268 533763 — MB BS 1972 Saurashtra; MSc (Orthop.) Lond. 1985; FRCS Glas. 1983. (Shri M.P. Shah Med. Coll. Jamnagar) Assoc. Orthop. Surg. Basildon Hosp.; Hon. Lect. Lond. Sch. Osteop. Socs: BMA; Overseas Doctors Assn.; Brit. Orthop. Assn. Prev: Regist. (Orthop.) Basildon Hosp., OldCh. Hosp. Romford & Qu. Eliz. II Hosp. Welwyn Gdn. City.

VYAS, Julian Ramesh Department of Child Health, University of Leicester, Leicester LE1 7RH Email: jrv2@le.ac.uk; 28 Old Road, Walgrave, Northampton NN6 9QW Tel: 01604 781683 — MB BS 1988 Lond.; MRCP (UK) 1993. (Guy's Hosp. Med. Sch. Univ. Lond.) Clin. Lect. & Hon. Regist. (Child Health) Univ. Leicester & Leicester Roy. Infirm. Socs: Roy. Coll. Paediat. & Child Health. Prev: Regist. N.ampton Gen. Hosp.; SHO Rotat. (Paediat.) Birm. Childr. Hosp.; SHO (Med.) Jas. Paget Hosp. Gt. Yarmouth.

VYAS, Jyotsana Belmont Health Centre, 516 Kenton Lane, Kenton, Harrow HA3 7LT Tel: 0208 427 1213; 29 Broadhurst Avenue, Edgware HA8 8TP — BM. (Southampton Univ.) GP - Harrow.

VYAS, Kshama Hemant Old Station Road Surgery, 157 Old Station Road, Hayes UB3 4NA Tel: 020 8573 2037 Fax: 020 8813 7552 — MB BS 1975 Delhi; DRCOG 1982. (New Delhi, India) Socs: Med. Protec. Soc.

VYAS, Paresh Paresh Vyas, Institute of Molecular Medicine, John Radcliffe Hospital, Oxford OX3 9DU Tel: 01865 222392 Fax: 01865 222500 — BM BCh 1986 Oxf.; MRCP (UK) 1989. (Oxford) Wellcome Sen. Clin. Fell., Inst. Molecular Med. Dept. of Haemat. John Radcliffe Hosp. Oxf.; Wellcome Sen. Clin. Fell. Childrs. Hosp. Harvard Med. Sch. Boston, MA, USA. Prev: Sen. Regis. (Heanatology), Roy. Free. Hosp.; MRC Train. Fell. Inst. Molecular Med. John Radcliffe Hosp. Oxf.; SHO (Gen. Med./Haemat.) Univ. Coll. Hosp.

VYAS, Rashmikant Bhogilal Gallowhill Surgery, 4-6 Gallowhill, Larkhall ML9 1EX Tel: 01698 884082 Fax: 01698 889211 — MB BS 1972 Calcutta. Clin. Asst. (A & E) Lanarksh. Socs: Med. Defence Union.

VYAS, Samir Kumar Salisbury District Hospital, Odstock Road, Salisbury SP2 8BJ Tel: 01722 336262 Fax: 01722 332606; Clearbury Lodge, Nunton Lane, Nunton, Salisbury SP5 4HZ — BM Soton. 1986; DM 1997; MRCP (UK) 1989. Cons. Phys. & Gastroenterol. Salisbury Dist. Hosp. Socs: BMA; Brit. Assn. Studies Liver; Pancreatic Soc. Prev: Sen. Regist. (Gen. Med. & Gastroenterol.) Soton. Gen. Hosp.; Brit. Dig. Foundat. Research Train. Fell. & Hon. Regist. Soton. Gen. Hosp.; Regist. (Med.) Soton. Gen. Hosp.

VYAS, Mr Sanjay Kumar Southhampton Hospital, Westbury-on-Trym, Bristol BS10 5NB; Vynes House, Lodge Lane, Nailsea, Bristol BS48 2BA — MB BS 1985 Lond.; MD Lond. 1992; MRCOG 1991. Cons. O & G S.mead Hosp. Bristol. Prev: Sen. Regist. (O & G) St. Michael's Hosp. Bristol; Research Fell. (O & G) King's Coll. Hosp. Lond.

VYAS, Sunil 60 Abbey Avenue, Wembley HA0 1LL — MB ChB 1992 Glas.

VYRAMUTHU, Navaratnam 282 Cassiobury Drive, Watford WD17 3AP — MUDr 1972 Prague; FFR RCPI 1986.

VYRNWY-JONES, Peter, Maj. RAMC 5 Stoke Farthing Courtyard, Broadchalke, Salisbury SP5 5ED — MSc Occupat. Med. Lond. 1983, BSc (Hons.) 1973, MB BS 1975; MFOM RCP Lond. 1985, AFOM 1981; DAvMed RCP Lond. 1980. Cons. in Aviat. Med. (Army) attached USAARL Alabama, USA. Socs: Soc. Occupat. Med.; Roy. Aeronaut. Soc. Prev: Cons. Aviat. Med. (Army) RAF Inst. Aviat. Med.; Specialist Aviat. Med. (Army) BAOR.

VYSE, Timothy James Rheumatology Department, ICSM, Hammersmith Campus, London W12 0NN Tel: 020 8383 2339 Email: t.vyse@ic.ac.uk — MA Camb. 1982; MB BS Lond. 1985; MRCP (UK) 1989; PhD 1994. Wellcome Trust Sen. Fell. Imperial Coll., Lond. Prev: Fulbright research fell.; Nat. Jewish Center for Immunol., Denver, USA.

VYSE-PEACOCK, Alicca 232 Queens Promenade, Blackpool FY2 9HA — MB ChB 1991 Manch.

VYVYAN, Henry Arthur Luke Department of Anaesthetics, St George's Hospital, Blackshaw Road, London SW17 0QT Tel: 020 8672 1255 — MB BS 1985 Lond.; FRCA 1990. Sen. Regist. (Anaesth.) St. Geo. Hosp. Lond. Prev: Sen. Regist. (Anaesth.) Roy. P. Alfred Hosp. Sidney, Austral.

VYVYAN, Mary Louise 19 Prebend Mansions, Chiswick High Road, London W4 2LU — MB BS 1991 Lond.

WAAS, Moderage Joseph Heron Bernard The Surgery, Sturton Road, North Leverton, Retford DN22 0AB Tel: 01427 880223 Fax: 01427 880927; Hillcrest, Gainsborough Road, Saundby, Retford DN22 0AB Tel: 01427 848816 — MB ChB 1974 Sheff.; FRCOG 1998; MFFP 1993; MRCOG 1982, DRCOG 1980. Princip. GP N. Leverton Notts.

WACE, Jocelyn Richard Department of Anaesthetics, Queen Alexandra Hospital, Portsmouth PO6 3LY Tel: 023 92 286279 Fax: 023 92 286681 — BM BCh 1986 Oxf.; MA Camb. 1986, BA 1983; FRCA 1992. Cons. (Anaesth.) Portsmouth.

WACE, Malini Rookery Medical Centre, Rookery House, Newmarket CB8 8NW Tel: 01638 665711 Fax: 01638 561280; Boyarin Lodge, Bury Road, Newmarket CB8 7BT Tel: 01638 664848 — MB 1984 Camb.; MA Camb. 1985, MB 1984, BChir 1983; MRCGP 1988; DRCOG 1986. Prev: GP Camb.

WACE, Rupert Orlando Orchard House Surgery, Fred Archer Way, Newmarket CB8 8NU Tel: 01638 663322 Fax: 01638 561921 — MA Camb. 1985, MB 1984, BChir 1983; MRCGP 1988; DCH RCP Lond. 1987; DRCOG 1987. Prev: Trainee GP Newmarket VTS; SHO (Paediat.) Heath Rd. Hosp. Ipswich.

WACHSMUTH, Christian Werner 3 Maypole Mews, Barwick in Elmet, Leeds LS15 4PE — MB BS 1990 Lond.

WACHSMUTH, Rachel Caroline 3 Maypole Mews, Barwick in Elmet, Leeds LS15 4PE; St. James Hospital, Beckett St, Leeds LS9 7TF Tel: 0113 206 4575 — BChir 1992 Camb.; MRCP 1996. (Univ. Camb. & Addenbrooke's) Specialist Regist. (Dermat.) St. James & Leeds Gen. Infirm. Prev: SHO (Gen. Med.) St. Jas. Univ. Hosp. Leeds.

WACHTEL, Sean Lawrence 42 Hullmead, Shamley Green, Guildford GU5 0UG — MB ChB 1994 Leic.; DTM & H Liverpool; DFFP; BSc Leic. 1991; MRCP (UK) Ed. 1997. GP Regist. Gillingham Dorset.

WACKS, Harvey 24 Danesway, Prestwich, Manchester M25 0FS — MB ChB 1959 Manch.; BSc Manch. 1954, MB ChB 1959; FRCPath. 1982, M 1969. (Manch.) Cons. Pathol. Sunderland Hosp.

Gp. Prev: Regist. Path. Withington Hosp. Manch. & Roy. Lancaster Infirm.; Regist. Surg. Vict. Hosp. Blackpool.

WACLAWSKI, Eugene Raphael Renfrewshire & Inverclyde Primary Care NHS Trust, Occupational Health Service, The Hollybush, Dykebar Hospital, Grahamston Road, Paisley PA3 7AD Tel: 0141 884 9080 Fax: 0141 884 9061 Email: ewaclaws@renfrewshire-tr.scot.nhs.uk; 1 Novar Drive, Hyndland, Glasgow G12 9PX Email: ewaclaws@ewem.net — MD 1990 Glas.; MB ChB 1981; FRCP Glas. 1994; MRCP (UK) 1984; MFOM RCP Lond. 1990; FFOM 1995. Cons. Occupat. Phys. & Dir. Occupat. Health Renfrewsh. Healthcare NHS Trust; Hon. Clin. Sen. Lect. Univ. Glas. Socs: Soc. Occupat. Med.; Brit. Occupat. Hyg. Soc. Prev: Cons. Occupat. Phys. Inst. Occupat. Med. Ltd. Edin.

WACOGNE, Ian David 30 Green Street, Milton Malsor, Northampton NN7 3AT Email: 100623.1321@compuserve.com — BM BCh 1993 Oxf.; BA (Hons.) Oxf. 1990; MRCP (UK) 1996. (Oxf.) SHO (Paediat.) Birm. Childr. Hosp. Prev: SHO (Paediat.) N.ampton Gen. Hosp.; Ho. Off. (Gen. Med.) John Radcliffe Hosp. Oxf.; Ho. Off. (Gen. Surg.) Derriford Hosp. Plymouth.

WADA, Ibrahim Bourn Hall Clinic, Bourn, Cambridge CB3 7TR — MB BS 1980 Ahmadu Bello Nigeria; MB BS Ahmadu Bello, Nigeria 1980; MRCOG 1988. Socs: Brit. Fertil. Soc. Prev: Cons. Gyn. Bourn Hall Clinic Camb.; Clin. Fell. Regional IVF Unit St. Mary;'s Hosp. Manch.

WADAMS, Stephen John Frederick 68 Browning Avenue, Bournemouth BH5 1NW — MB BS 1996 Lond.

WADD, Nicholas James 25 Rossett Beck, Harrogate HG2 9NT — MB BS 1990 Newc.

WADDELL, Andrew Michael Park Surgery, 278 Stratford Road, Shirley, Solihull B90 3AF Tel: 0121 241 1700 Fax: 0121 241 1821; 35 Manor Road, Solihull B91 2BL — MB ChB 1984 Birm.

WADDELL, Mr Angus Neil 7 Longfield Road, Bishopston, Bristol BS7 9AG Email: anguswaddell@compuserve.com — MB BS 1990 Lond.; FRCS Eng. 1994.

WADDELL, Christine Agnes Pathology Department, Birmingham Women's Hospital, Edgbaston, Birmingham B15 2TG Tel: 0121 627 2723 Fax: 0121 627 2624 Email: christine.waddell@bham-womens.thenhs.com; 29 Elmdon Road, Selly Park, Birmingham B29 7LF Tel: 0121 472 7668 — MB ChB 1970 Sheff.; MSc (Clin. Cytopath.) Lond. 1993; DObst RCOG 1972. (Sheff.) Assoc. Specialist (Cytopath.) Birm. Wom. Hosp. Socs: Internat. Acad. Cytol.; Internet. Acad; Assn. Clin. Path. Prev: Regist. (Path.) Sheff. AHA (T).

WADDELL, David Laird No 1 Manse Court, Kirk Wynd, Blairgowrie PH10 6HN Tel: 01250 5143 — MB ChB 1938 Glas. (Glas.) Prev: Gp. Med. Off. Brit. Rlys. (Manch.); Regist. (Ophth.) Leicester Roy. Infirm.; Capt. RAMC.

WADDELL, Fiona Margaret Corbridge House, Corbridge-on-Tyne, Corbridge NE45 5LE Tel: 01434 633012 — MB BS 1957 Durh. (Newc.) Clin. Asst. Orthop. Surg. Hexham Gen. Hosp.; Assoc. Specialist Blood Transfus. Centre Newc. Prev: Ho. Off. Roy. Vict. Infirm. Newc.; SHO & Ho. Off. P.ss Mary Matern. Hosp. Newc.

WADDELL, Mr Gordon Alex Bryce The Glasgow Nuffield Hospital, Glasgow G12 0PJ — MB ChB 1967 Glas.; DSc Glas. 1992, BSc (Hons.) Physiol. 1964; MD Glas. 1976; FRCS Glas. 1983; FRCS Ed. 1971. (Glas.) Cons. Surg. (Orthop.) Glas. Nuffield Hosp.; Hon. Prof. Rheum. Univ. Manch. 1996; Hon. Prof. Orthop. Univ. Glas. 1992.

WADDELL, James, OBE (retired) Glengarry, 2 Cottesmore Gdns, Hale Barns, Altrincham WA15 8TS Tel: 0161 904 9050 — LRCP LRCS 1945 Ed.; LRCP LRCS Ed. LRFPS Glas. 1945; MFOM RCP Lond. 1981; MRCGP 1957. Prev: Cons. Med. Advis. to Kellogg Co. (GB) Ltd.

WADDELL, James Alexander Rooks Nest, Somerford Road, Cirencester GL7 1TX Tel: 01285 651079 — MB ChB 1956 Ed.; FRCP Ed. 1970, M 1960; FRCP Lond. 1974, M 1963. Prev: Cons. Phys. P.ss Margt. Hosp. Swindon & Cirencester Hosp.; Sen. Regist. Med. W.m. Hosp. Gp.; Brit. Postgrad. Med. Federat. Trav. Fell.

WADDELL, James Lindsay (retired) 11 Station Avenue, Haddington EH41 4EG Tel: 01620 823322 — MB ChB 1960 Ed.; FRCP Ed. 1990, M 1967; MRCPsych 1971; DPM RCPS Glas. 1963. Prev: Phys. Supt. Hermanflat Hosp. Haddington.

WADDELL, Joanne Elisabeth 35 Manor Road, Solihull B91 2BL — MB ChB 1985 Birm. Med. Off. DSS Midl. S. Region Birm.; Asst. GP.

WADDELL, John Michael Northumberland Community Health, The Health Centre, Civic Precinct, Forum Way, Cramlington NE23 6QN Tel: 01670 713021 Fax: 01670 735880 — MB ChB 1981 Birm.; BSc Birm. 1978; MRCGP 1988; DCH RCP Lond. 1987; DRCOG 1984. (Birmingham) GP Cramlington, N.d.; Clin. Asst. (Urol.).

WADDELL, Michael Osborne, MC (retired) North Side, Wall, Hexham NE46 4DU Tel: 01434 681904 — MB BS 1952 Durh.; MD Vermont 1967.

WADDELL, Myra McInnes Buckingham Terrace Surgery, 31 Buckingham Terrace, Glasgow G12 8ED Tel: 0141 221 6210 Fax: 0141 211 6232 — MB ChB 1975 Glas.; MRCP (UK) 1979; MRCGP 1983; DRCOG 1977.

WADDELL, Nicholas John Hamilton 20 Alderbrook Road, Solihull B91 1NN — MB ChB 1983 Birm.

WADDELL, Nicola Margaret Russell The Palatine Centre, 63/65 Palatine Road, Manchester M20 3LJ Tel: 0161 434 3555; 38 Kings Road, Wilmslow SK9 5PZ — MB BS 1987 Lond.; MA Oxf. 1984; DRCOG 1990; DCH RCP Lond. 1990. Clin. Med. Off. (Family Plann. & Reproduc. Health Care) Palatine Centre Manch. Prev: Trainee GP N.ants.; SHO (Paediat.) N.ampton Gen. Hosp.

WADDELL, Turner Raith (retired) Fairways, Andover Down, Andover SP11 6LJ — MRCS Eng. LRCP Lond. 1944. Prev: Med. Off. Enham-Alamein Village Settlem.

WADDELOW, Mrs Janet (retired) 30 Fearnville Mount, Leeds LS8 3DL Tel: 0113 265 3909 — MB ChB 1951 Leeds; FRCOG 1989, M 1961, DObst 1954. Prev: Clin. Asst. (O & G) St. Jas. Univ. Hosp. Leeds.

WADDINGHAM, Rosemary Morland Surgery, 40 New Road, Tadley RG26 3AN Tel: 01189 816661 Fax: 01189 817533; Blandford Hithe, Brimpton, Reading RG7 4TD Tel: 0118 971 3332 Fax: 0118 971 3332 — MB ChB 1977 Leeds; MRCGP 1994; DRCOG 1981; Family Plann. JCC Cert. 1981. (Leeds) GP Princip.

WADDINGHAM, Susanna Elizabeth Roundham Wing, St James Hospital, Beckett St., Leeds LS6 4SF — MB BS 1993 Lond. SHO Psychiat. Leeds CMHT.

WADDINGTON, Christopher Ware Road Surgery, 59 Ware Road, Hoddesdon EN11 9AB Tel: 01992 463363 Fax: 01992 471108 — MB BS 1980 Lond.; BA (Oxf.) 1977; DRCOG 1984.

WADDINGTON, Derek (retired) 53 Southway Lane, Plymouth PL6 7DL Tel: 01752 773926 — MB ChB Sheff. 1951.

WADDINGTON, Duncan Calderdale & Huddersfield, NHS Trust, St. Lukes Hospital, Blackmoorfoot Road, Crosland Moor, Huddersfield HD4 5RQ Tel: 01484 343588 — MB BS Newc. 1986; MMedSc (Leeds) 1994. Cons. (Psychiat.) Calderdale & Huddersfield NHS Trust,Huddersfield. Socs: Roy. Coll. Psychiat. Prev: Sen. Regist. Manch. Train. Scheme (Psychiat.); Regist. W. Yorks. Train. Scheme (Pschiatry); Regist. Newc. Train. Scheme (Psychiat.).

WADDINGTON, Gerald Eugene Stoneham Lane Surgery, 6 Stoneham Lane, Swaythling, Southampton SO16 2AB Tel: 023 8055 5776 Fax: 023 8039 9723; GP Practice Addren., 6 Stoneham Lane, Swaythline, Southampton SO16 2AB Tel: 02380 555116 Fax: 023 803 99723 — MB ChB 1972 Bristol; MRCGP 1978. (Bristol) Med. Adviser Cunard Steamship Ltd.; Surg. Lt.-Cdr. RNR.

WADDINGTON, Michael Hugh Guy (retired) Stonecott, 18 Chappell Road, Hoylandswaine, Sheffield S36 7JD — MB ChB 1951 Leeds.

WADDINGTON, Richard John 37 Langton Court, Ponteland, Newcastle upon Tyne NE20 9AT — MB BS 1994 Lond.; BA Oxf. 1991. (Univ. Coll. Lond. Med. Sch.) SHO (Anaesth.) Roy. Free Hosp. Lond.

WADDINGTON, Mr Richard Turner Golden Cross, Cawthorne, Barnsley S75 4HR — MB ChB 1963 Sheff.; FRCS Eng. 1970; FRCS Ed. 1969. (Sheff.) Cons. Surg. (Gen. Surg.) Barnsley Dist. Gen. Hosp. Socs: Sheff. Med. Soc. Prev: Flight Lt. RAF Med. Br., Med. Off. P.ss Mary's RAF Hosp. Halton; Sen. Regist. (Gen. Surg.) Roy. Hosp. Sheff.

WADDINGTON, Sara Jane The Surgery, 233A Brook Lane, Sarisbury Green, Southampton SO31 7DQ; Oak Tree House, Wangfield Lane, Curdridge, Southampton SO32 2DA — MB BS 1980 Lond.; BSc. (Hons.) Pharmacol. Lond. 1973; MRCGP 1984; DRCOG 1982.

WADDLE, Kristin Division of Medical & Molecular Genetics, Guy's Hospital, 8th Floor Guy's Tower, St Thomas St., London SE1 9RT Tel: 020 7955 4648 Fax: 020 7955 4644 Email:

WADDY

k.waddle@umds.ac.uk; Flat C, Napier Hall, Hide Place, London SW1P 4NJ — State Exam Med 1992 Mainz; MRCP UK 1996. (Johannes Gutenberg University Mainz, Germany) Specialist Regist. (Clin. Genetics) Guy's Hosp. Lond. Socs: Brit. Soc. Human Genetics.

WADDY, Donald Campbell (retired) 9 Ladygrove Paddock, Drayton Road, Abingdon OX14 5HT Tel: 01235 535336 — MB ChB Sheff. 1933. Prev: Cons. Chest Phys. W. Midl. RHA.

WADDY, Elizabeth Mary Bridge Surgery, St. Peters Street, Stapenhill, Burton-on-Trent DE15 9AW Tel: 01283 563451 Fax: 01283 500896; 45 Tower Road, Burton-on-Trent DE15 0NH Tel: 01283 547322 — BM BS 1977 Nottm.; MRCGP 1982; DRCOG 1981; DCH RCP Lond. 1981. (Nottm.) Prev: SHO Burton-on-Trent VTS; SHO (Rheum.) Middlx. Hosp.; Ho. Off. (Med.) Nottm. Gen. Hosp. & (Surg.) Hillingdon Hosp. Uxbridge.

WADDY, Ethel Hunter (retired) 2 Pine Court, Little Brington, Northampton NN7 4EZ Tel: 01604 770255 — MB ChB Sheff. 1930. Prev: Anaesth. Manfield Orthop. Hosp.

WADDY, George William (retired) The Old Hall, Pitsford Road, Moulton, Northampton NN3 7SS Tel: 01604 405757 — MB BS 1952 Lond.; MRCS Eng. LRCP Lond. 1952. Prev: Mem. N.ants. Local Med. Servs. Comm. & BMA.

WADDY, Rosemary Stacy, OStJ Medical and Industrial Services Ltd, 23 St Leonards Road, Eastbourne BN21 3PX Tel: 01323 724889 Fax: 01323 721161 Email: rosemaryw@access24.com; 4 Evelyn Way, Stoke D'Abernon, Cobham KT11 2SJ Tel: 01932 864458 Fax: 01932 864458 — MB BS 1970 Newc.; MFOM RCP Lond. 1985, AFOM 1981; DAvMed 1994; DIH Eng. 1981; DObst RCOG 1973; DA Eng. 1973; Cert. Av. Med. 1989. (Newc. u. Tyne) Cons. Occupat.al health, Med. and Indust. Serv.s ltd; Area Surg. St. John Ambul. Socs: Soc. Occupat. Med. Prev: Sen. Med. Off. Brit. Airways; SMO John Lewis Partnership; Med. Off. Ascension Is.

WADE, Abdel Aziz Hussien Coventry & Warwickshire Hospital, Stoney Stanton Road, Coventry CV1 4FH Tel: 024 76 844163/4 Fax: 024 76 844168; 1 Tintagel Grove, Kenilworth CV8 2PG Tel: 01926 512862 — MB BCh 1965 Cairo; MRCOG 1975. Cons. Genitourin. Med. Coventry & Warks. Hosp.; Hon. Sen. Lect. Birm. Med. Sch. Socs: (Pres.) Midl. Soc. Genitourin. Med. Prev: Sen. Regist. (Genitourin. Med.) Manch. Roy. Infirm.; Lect. (Gyn. & Obst.) Benghazi Univ., Libya; Regist. (O & G) Mid-Staffs. HA.

WADE, Alan Grierson Clydebank Health Centre, Kilbowie Road, Clydebank G81 2TQ Tel: 0141 531 6410 Fax: 0141 531 6413; Cintra, 15 Edgehill Road, Bearsden, Glasgow G61 3AB Tel: 0141 942 3589 Fax: 0141 951 1931 Email: alan@edgehill.deomon.co.uk — MB ChB 1969 Glas.; FRCA Eng. 1973. (Glas.) Dir. Community Pharmacol. Serv. Ltd. Glas.; Chairm. Gen. Pract. Research Clydebank.

WADE, Alan Hugh (retired) 41 Uplands Avenue, High Solington, Worthing BN13 3AE Tel: 01903 267760 — MB ChB 1953 Aberd.

WADE, Andrew 9 Royal Garth, Beverley HU17 8NL — MB ChB 1971 Leeds; T(Psych) 1991.

WADE, Andrew Orlando 2 Edwin Road, Didcot OX11 8LF — MB BS 1994 Lond.; BSc (Biochem.) Lond. 1991. (Charing Cross & Westm.)

WADE, Catherine Bernadette Court Yard Surgery, John Evans House, 28 Court Yard, London SE9 5QA Tel: 020 8850 1300 Fax: 020 8294 2378; Reeves House, The St, Horton Kirby, Dartford DA4 9BY Tel: 01322 860225 — MB BS 1980 Lond.; DRCOG 1983. (Guy's Hospital)

WADE, Charlotte Gillian Bradburn Winglock House, 40 Seymour Road, Newton Abbot TQ12 2PU — MB BS 1998 Lond.; MB BS Lond 1998.

WADE, Christine Annette Warre House, Bishops Lydegard, Taunton TA4 3LH — MB BS 1964 Lond.

WADE, Courtenay Chirgwin, TD (retired) c/o The Royal Bank of Scotland, 38 Park St., Croydon CR9 1YS — MB ChB St. And. 1956, DPH 1963. Hon. Cons. Phys. (Community Med.) Char. Cross Hosp. Lond. Prev: Dist. Community Phys. S. Hammersmith Health Dist. (T).

WADE, David Charles County Surgery, 202-204 Abington Avenue, Northampton NN1 4QA Tel: 01604 32918 Fax: 01604 601578 — MB ChB 1987 Leic.; BSc (Hons) Med. Sci. Leic. 1984; DRCOG 1991. (Leicester) Clin. Asst. (Epilepsy) N.ampton.

WADE, Professor Derick Treharne Rivermead Rehabilitation Centre, Abingdon Road, Oxford OX1 4XD Tel: 01865 240321 Fax: 01865 200185 Email: derick.wade@dial.pipex.com; 28 Polstead Road, Oxford OX2 6TN Tel: 01865 556031 Email: derick.wade@dial.pipex.com — MB BChir 1974 Camb.; MA Camb. 1974, MD 1985; FRCP Lond. 1994; MRCP (UK) 1976. (St. Thos.) Cons. Neurol. Rivermead Hosp. Oxf.; Edr. Clin. Rehabil. Socs: (Counc.) Soc. Research in Rehabil.; Brit. Assn. Neurol.; Brit. Soc. Rehabil. Med. Prev: Regist. (Clin. Neurophysiol.) Nat. Hosp. Nerv. Dis. Lond.; Regist. (Neurol.) & SHO (Neurosurg.) Frenchay Hosp. Bristol.

WADE, Elizabeth Clare 55 Withdean Crescent, Brighton BN1 6WG — MB BS 1996 Lond.; BA (Hons.) Brighton 1988. (St. Bart.) SHO (Psychiat.) Homerton Hosp. Lond.; Staff Grade A & E Roy. Lond. Hosp; SHO Paediat Roy. Alexandra. Hosp. Brighton; SHO A & E Rotat. Roy. Sussex Co. Hosp. Brighton. Prev: SHO (A & E) Roy. Lond. Hosp.

WADE, Frazer Alan 149 (2F2) Buccleuch Street, Edinburgh EH8 9NE — MB ChB 1994 Ed.

WADE, Isobel Renwick 112 Leylands Lane, Heaton, Bradford BD9 5QU — MB ChB Glas. 1969; Dip. Palliat. Med. Wales 1993; DA Eng. 1971. (Glas.) Assoc. Specialist Palliat. Med. Manorlands Hospice. Oxenhope. W. Yorks. Socs: Assoc. of Palliat. Med.; BMA. Prev: Clin. Asst. (Anaesth.) Bradford AHA; Regist. Soton. Univ. Hosps.; Regist. & SHO (Anaesth.) Portsmouth Gp. Hosps.

WADE, Jane Rosanne (retired) 55 Withdean Crescent, Brighton BN1 6WG Tel: 01273 556711 — MB BChir 1962 Camb.; DPH Liverp. 1965. Prev: Cons. Community Paediat. S. Downs Health NHS Trust.

WADE, Jeremy James Dulwich Public Health Laboratory & Medical Microbiology, King's College School of Medicine & Dentistry, King's College Hospital, Denmark Hill, London SE5 9RS Tel: 020 7346 3033 Fax: 020 7346 3404 Email: jeremywade@kcl.ac.uk — MB BS 1983 Lond.; MD Lond. 1997; MSc Lond. 1990; MRCPath 1993. (Univ. Lond.) Cons. & Hon. Sen. Lect. (Med. Microbiol.) Dulwich Pub. Health Laborat. & Med. Microbiol. King's Coll. Sch. Med. & Dent. Socs: Hosp. Infec. Soc.; Brit. Soc. Antimicrob. Chemother.; Path. Soc. Prev: Lect. & Hon. Sen. Regist. (Med. Microbiol.) King's Coll. Sch. Med. & Dent. Lond.

WADE, Mr John David Throckenholt, Cranes Lane, Kingston, Cambridge CB3 7NJ Tel: 01233 262275 — MB BChir 1939 Camb.; MA, MB BChir Camb. 1939; FRCS Ed. 1959; FRCS Eng. 1941; MRCS Eng., LRCP Lond. 1938. (Camb. & Univ. Coll. Hosp.) Socs: Assn. Thoracic Surgs. Gt. Brit. & Assn. Surgs. Gt. Brit. Prev: Cons. Thoracic Surg. Roy. Infirm. Edin.; Dorothy Temple Cross Fell.; Clin. & Research Fell. Mass. Gen. Hosp.

WADE, John Kennington (retired) Manor Cottage, Potterhanworth, Lincoln LN4 2DN Tel: 01522 791288 — MB BS 1962 Lond.; MRCS Eng. LRCP Lond. 1962. Prev: Hosp. Pract. (ENT) Co. Hosp. Lincoln.

WADE, John Philip Huddart Hammersmith Hospitals Trust, Charing Cross Hospital, Fulham Palace Road, London W6 8RF Tel: 020 8846 1303 Fax: 020 8846 7487 Email: jwade@hhnt.org; 11 Gardnor Road, Hampstead, London NW3 1HA Tel: 020 7431 2900 — MD 1982 Camb.; MB 1975, BChir 1974, BA 1971; FRCP Lond. 1991; MRCP (UK) 1976. Cons. Neurol. Char. Cross Hosp. Lond. & Wexham Pk. Hosp. Slough. Prev: Sen. Regist. (Neurol.) Nat. Hosps. Nerv. Dis. & St. Bart. Hosp. Lond.; Fell.sh. Ontario Heart & Stroke Foundat. Univ. Hosp. Lond. Ontario.

WADE, Kim 37 Station Road, Skelmanthorpe, Huddersfield HD8 9AU — BM BS 1992 Nottm.

WADE, Malcolm John Windy Ridge, 112 Leylands Road, Bradford BD9 5QU Tel: 01274 499703 — MB BS 1968 Lond.; MRCS Eng. LRCP Lond. 1968; FFA RCS Eng. 1973; DA Eng. 1971; DObst RCOG 1970. (Lond. Hosp.) Cons. Anaesth. Bradford Roy. Infirm. Socs: Fell. Roy. Soc. Med.; Assn. Anaesths. Prev: Sen. Regist. Rotat. Soton. & W.m. Hosps.; Regist. (Anaesth.) Portsmouth Hosp. Gp.; Obst. Off. St. Mary's Matern. Hosp. Portsmouth.

WADE, Mary Ward Pickering (retired) 22 Hill Top Avenue, Cheadle Hulme, Cheadle SK8 7HY Tel: 0161 485 2228 — MB ChB 1943 Manch.; MRCS Eng. LRCP Lond. 1943.

WADE, Nigel Ross Jubilee Surgery, Barrys Meadow, High St Titchfield, Fareham PO14 4EH Tel: 01329 844220 Fax: 01329 841484 — MB ChB 1987 Birm.; MRCGP 1991; DRCOG 1991.

WADE, Professor Owen Lyndon, CBE (retired) c/o The Medical School, University of Birmingham, Birmingham B15 2TJ Tel: 0121 472 1301 — MB BChir 1945 Camb.; MD Camb. 1951, MA 1945;

WADSWORTH

Hon. MD Belf. 1989; FRCP Lond. 1964, M 1948; Hon. FRCPI 1970; MRCS Eng. LRCP Lond. 1945; Hon. FFPM RCP Lond. 1989. Trustee (Ex-Chairm.) Arthur Thomson Charitable Trust Univ. Birm.; Mem. (Ex-Chairm.) Formulary Comm. for Brit. Nat. Formulary; Mem. Med. Commiss. & Chairm. Comm. Review Med. Prev: Dean Fac. of Med. Univ. Birm. 1978-1984.

WADE, Mr Peter John Fraser Oak House, Eastwood Business Village, Binley Business Park, Binley, Coventry CV3 2UB Tel: 024 7656 1900 Fax: 024 7656 1901; Sedgemere, Fernhill Lane, Fen End, Kenilworth CV8 1NU Tel: 01676 532114 Fax: 01676 535448 Email: peterwade@sedgemere.freeserve.co.uk — MB BS 1971 Lond.; FRCS Eng. 1976; LMCC 1974. (St. Thos.) Cons. Orthop. & Hand Surg. Clinic. Dir. Trauma & Orthop. Coventry; Clin. Dir. Trauma Univ. Coventry & Warwicks. NHS Trust; Counc. Mem., Brit. Soc. of Surg. for the hand. Socs: Coun. Mem. Brit. Orthopaedic Assoc.; Coun. Mem. Brit. Soc. Surg. of Hand; Coun. Mem. BMA. Prev: Clin. Tutor Coventry & Warks. Hosp.; Sen. Regist. (Orthop. S. E. Thames Rha; Sen. Research Regist. (Orthop.) St. Thomas Hosp. Lond.

WADE, Richard Geoffrey Huddart Albany Surgery, Albany Street, Newton Abbot TQ12 2TX Tel: 01626 334411 Fax: 01626 335663; Wingelock House, 40 Seymour Road, Newton Abbot TQ12 2PU Tel: 01626 54459 — MB ChB 1971 Manch.; FRCGP 1999; MRCGP 1979; DObst RCOG 1973. NHS Direct Advis. Prev: Sen. Ho. Phys. (Paediat.) Roy. Manch. Childr. Hosp.; Ho. Phys. & Ho. Surg. Manch. Roy. Infirm.

WADE, Robin Moorlands Surgery, 139 Willow Road, Darlington DL3 9JP Tel: 01325 469168; 26 Linden Avenue, Darlington DL3 8PP — MB ChB 1976 Sheff.; DRCOG 1982.

WADE, Roger Hedley 350 Telegraph Road, Heswall, Wirral CH60 6RW — MB ChB 1992 Liverp.; FRCS Ed. 1996. Specialist Regist. (Orthop.).

WADE, Rosemary Verity St. Nicholas Hospice, Macmillan Way, Hardwick Heath, Bury St Edmunds IP33 2QY — MB BS 1985 Lond.; MRCGP 1994. (Middlx. Hosp.) p/t Sp. Regist. (Palliat. Med.), St. Nicholas Hospice, Bury St. Edmunds.

WADE, Rowena Juliet Rowan House, Crooks Lane, Studley B80 7QX — MB BS 1996 Lond.

WADE, Sally Jane 26 Linden Avenue, Darlington DL3 8PP — MB BS 1980 Newc.; MRCGP 1984.

WADE, Simon Elizabeth Street Medical Centre, 9 Elizabeth Street, Corby NN17 1SJ Tel: 01536 202507 Fax: 01536 206099; 18 Brunswick Gardens, Corby NN18 9ER Tel: 01536 746067 — MB BS 1986 Lond.; MRCGP 1990; DRCOG 1990; DCH RCP Lond. 1989. (Kings College School of Medicine and Dentistry) GP Princip. Socs: BMA; Med. Protec. Soc.

WADE, Siobhan Michelle 60 North Circular Road, Belfast BT15 5FE — MB BCh 1998 Belf.

WADE, Thomas Henry Hanbury 54 Harley Street, London W1N 1AD Tel: 020 7580 7558 — MB BChir 1949 Camb.; MA MB BChir Camb. 1949. (Univ. Coll. Hosp.) Med. Adviser To Embassy of RePub. of Congo; Med. Represen. in Lond. For Abu Dhabi. Socs: BMA. Prev: Surg. Regist. Qu. Mary's Hosp. Childr. Carshalton; Asst. Lect. Anat. Univ. Coll. Cardiff; Clin. Asst. St. John's Hosp. Dis. of Skin Lond.

WADE-EVANS, Elizabeth Marion (retired) Ebenezer House, Orcop, Hereford HR2 8SD — MB BS 1950 Lond.

WADE-EVANS, Tom (retired) Ebenezer House, Orcop, Hereford HR2 8SD — MRCS Eng. LRCP Lond. 1948; BSc Wales 1945; MD Lond. 1961, MB BS 1951; FRCPath 1977, M 1965. Cons. Pathol. Birm. Wom. Hosps.; Hon. Cons. Path. Centr. Birm. HA. Prev: Ho. Phys. & Ho. Surg. O & G Depts. W.m. Hosp.

WADE-EVANS, Victoria Jane Ebenezer House, Orcop, Hereford HR2 8SD — MB BS 1981 Lond.

WADE-THOMAS, Rodney Bridge House Surgery, 30 Taunton Road, Bridgwater TA6 3LS Tel: 01278 423190 Fax: 01278 445357 — LRCPI & LM, LRSCI & LM 1970. Prev: Ex.Sen. GO Princip. Bridge Ho. Surg., Bridgwater.

WADE-WEST, Susan Charis Bishops Waltham Surgery, Lower Lane, Bishops Waltham, Southampton SO32 1GR Tel: 01489 892288 Fax: 01489 894402; The Surgery, Lower Lane, Bishops Waltham, Southampton SO32 1GR Tel: 01489 892288 Fax: 01489 894402 — MB BS 1977 (Hons.) Lond.; MRCP (UK) 1983; DRCOG 1982. (Roy. Free) GP Bishops Waltham. Prev: Research Regist.

(Paediat.) Soton. Gen. Hosp.; SHO (Med. & O & G) Soton. Gen. Hosp.

WADE WEST, Thomas (retired) Wayside, Kew Lane, Old Bursledon, Southampton SO31 8DG Tel: 02380 403136 Fax: 023 8040 3136 — MB BS Lond. 1953; MRCS Eng. LRCP Lond. 1949; DObst RCOG 1953. Prev: Ho. Phys. (Obst.) St. Thos. Hosp.

***WADEHRA, Vineet** Flat 1, 2 Marchmont Road, Edinburgh EH9 1HZ; 34 Hadrian Court, Darras Hall, Newcastle upon Tyne NE20 9JU Email: vineetur@bigfoot.com — MB ChB 1998 Ed.; MB ChB Ed 1998; BSc (Med Sci) Ed 1995.

WADERA, Satish Prakash 478 Landseer Road, Ipswich IP3 9LU Tel: 01473 274494 Fax: 01473 727742 Email: michele.abson@gp-d83614.nhs.uk — DA 1970 (Lond.); MBBS 1966. (Darbhanga Med. Coll., Darbhanga (Bihak), India) Gen. Med. Practitioner, Ipswich.

WADEY, Juan Antonio Estevez 27 Arnold Road, Bromley Cross, Bolton BL7 9HL — MB BS 1990 Lond.

WADEY, Lee Paul Flat 3, 106 Drakefield Road, London SW17 8RR — MB BS 1989 Lond.

WADGAONKAR, Pushkar Surendra Flat 76, Grosvenor Towers, Broadway, Belfast BT12 6HG — MB BS 1989 Bombay; MRCP (UK) 1995.

WADGE, Dennis Allen (retired) Wellspring Lodge, Wellspring Road, Southrepps, Norwich NR11 8XA Tel: 01263 833603 — MB BS 1955 Lond. Prev: Ho Surg. Redhill Co. Hosp.

WADGE, Ernest John, OStJ (retired) Rowanwood, Bell Lane, Lower Broadheath, Worcester WR2 6RR — MB ChB 1944 Birm. Prev: Ho. Surg. Gen. Hosp. Birm.

WADGE, Valerie Anne Jesmond Clinic, 48 Osborne Road, Jesmond, Newcastle upon Tyne NE2 2AL Tel: 0191 281 4060 Fax: 0191 281 0231; 80 Moor Road N., Gosforth, Newcastle upon Tyne NE3 1AB Tel: 0191 213 2362 — MB BS 1978 Newc.; MRCGP 1982; Cert. JCC Lond. 1980; DFFP 1997. (Newcastle Upon Tyne) Tutor (Gen. Pract.) Newc. u. Tyne; Gen. Practitioner.

WADGE, Winifred Joan (retired) 28 Church Street, Great Missenden HP16 0AZ Tel: 01240 64943 — MB BS 1936 Lond.; MA Camb. 1930; FRCS Eng. 1939; MRCS Eng. LRCP Lond. 1934. Prev: Surg. ENT Dept. Univ. Coll. Hosp.

WADHWA, Harish Kumar The Surgery, 191 Barrows Lane, Yardley, Birmingham B26 1QS Tel: 0121 783 2719 — MB BS 1971 Delhi.

WADHWA, Pradeep 5 St Michael's Road, London NW2 6XD — MB BS 1979 Lond.; MRCGP 1983; DRCOG 1982; DCH RCP Lond. 1982.

WADHWA, Vivek Kumar 241 Ainsworth Road, Bury BL8 2SQ — MB ChB 1998 Manch.

WADHWANI, Gulab Harjasram 1C Western Road, Sutton SM1 2SX — MB BS 1965 Bombay.

WADLEY, Mr John Patrick University Department Neurosurgery, Institute of Neurology, Queen Square, London WC1N 3BG Tel: 020 7837 3611 Email: j.wadley@ion.ucl.ac.uk; Flat 501, The Beaux Arts Building, Manor Gardens, London N7 6JX Tel: 020 7272 0621 — MB ChB 1989 Liverp.; FRCS Ed. 1994. Clin. Lect./Research Fell. (Neurosurg.) Inst. Neurol. Lond. Socs: Assoc. Mem. Soc. Brit. Neurol. Surgs.; Fell. Roy. Soc. Med.; Brit. Stereotactic and Image Guided Neurosurg. Gp. Prev: Regist. (Neurosurg.) Char. Cross Hosp. Lond.; Regist. (Neurosurg.) Roy. Free Hosp. Lond.; Demonst. (Anat.) Univ. Liverp. Sch. of Med.

WADLEY, Martin Stuart c/o 2 Wimsland Crt., Holcot, Northampton NN6 9SA — MB ChB 1990 Sheff.

WADMAN, Simon Mark The Surgery, High Street, Heathfield TN21 8JD Tel: 01435 864999/862192 Fax: 01435 867449; Albury Cottage, Hadlow Down, Uckfield TN22 4HS — MB BS 1982 Lond.

WADROP, Thomas Anthony Middle House, 2 Box Drive, Nunthorpe, Middlesbrough TS7 0RH Tel: 01642 324679 Fax: 01642 317339 — MB ChB 1967 Ed.; MRCGP 1980; DMJ 1995. (Ed.) GP; Princip. Police Surg. Cleveland. Socs: Assn. Police Surg.; RSM. Prev: Gen. Pract. Coveby Newham, Cleveland.

***WADSLEY, Jonathan Charles** 15 Onley Street, Norwich NR2 2EA Tel: 01603 766522 — BChir 1995 Camb.; MB BChir Camb. 1996; MA Camb. 1997.

WADSWORTH, Arthur Mayow (retired) 35 Glyn Garth Court, Menai Bridge LL59 5PB Tel: 01248 715269 — MB ChB 1938 Birm.; MRCS Eng. LRCP Lond. 1938. JP.

WADSWORTH

WADSWORTH, Bridget Ann Littlegates, Hinton St George TA17 8SN — MB BS 1977 Lond.

WADSWORTH, David John 94 Main Street, Cononley, Keighley BD20 8NR — MB ChB 1960 Leeds.

WADSWORTH, Francis Morrison Edmund The Lodge, Icomb, Cheltenham GL54 1JB — MB BS 1990 Lond.

WADSWORTH, George Reginald (retired) Beech House, Barrule Park, Ramsey IM8 2BR Tel: 01624 815471 — MB ChB 1940 Liverp.; MD Liverp. 1952. Prev: Prof. Physiol. Univ. Singapore.

WADSWORTH, Julian Ashley 16-18 Foster Lane, Hebden Bridge HX7 8HF — MB ChB 1994 Leeds.

WADSWORTH, Mark Ronald The Surgery, 28 Holes Lane, Woolston, Warrington WA1 4NE Tel: 01925 653218 Fax: 01925 244767 — MB ChB 1984 Manch.; DCH RCP Lond. 1986; DRCOG 1988; Cert. Family Plann. JCC 1987. GP Warrington.

WADSWORTH, Mr Paul Vincent (retired) 61 Dyke Road Avenue, Hove BN3 6DA Tel: 01273 507074 — MA Oxf. 1948, BM BCh 1944; FRCS Eng. 1951; DObst RCOG 1949. Prev: Cons. ENT Surg. Roy. Sussex Co., Sussex Throat & Ear, Roy. Alexandra Childr., Haywards Heath & Cuckfield Hosps. & Chailey Heritage.

WADSWORTH, Richard Department of Anaesthesia, Manchester Royal Infirmary, Oxford Road, Manchester M13 9WL Tel: 0161 276 4033 Fax: 0161 273 6211; Harley Bank South, Victoria Road, Todmorden OL14 5LD Email: richardw@appleonline.net — MB BChir 1986 Camb.; BSc St. And. 1983; FRCA 1992. (Univ. Camb.) Cons. Anaesth. Manch. Roy. Infirm. Socs: Assn. Anaesth.; Manch. Med. Soc.; BMA. Prev: Sen. Regist.(Anaesth.), Regist. & SHO NW RHA.

WADSWORTH, Susan Jennifer 162A Westbourne Grove, London W11 2RW — MB BS 1990 Lond.; MRCP (UK) 1993.

WADSWORTH, Susan Margaret Lakeside Surgery, Cottingham Road, Corby NN17 2UR Tel: 01536 204154; Riverbanks, Caldecott, Market Harborough LE16 8RU — FRCGP 1999; MA Oxf. 1986, BM BCh 1984; MRCGP 1988; DRCOG 1987.

WADSWORTH, Mr Thomas Gordon 152 Harley Street, London W1N 1HH Tel: 020 7723 5785 Fax: 020 7629 8210; Apartment 7, 7 Curzon Street, Mayfair, London W1J 5HG — LMSSA 1953 Lond.; MChOrth Liverp. 1962; LLM 1994; FRCS Eng. 1962; FRCS Ed. 1962; MRCS Eng. LRCP Lond. 1954; FACS 1972; FICS 1971; Dip. Amer. Bd. Orthop. Surg. 1974. (Liverp. Cardiff & Ed.) Cons. Orthop. & Hand Surg. Roy. Hosps. Trust, St Bartholomews & The Roy. Lond. Hosps. RTD. Socs: Sen. Fell. BOA; (Ex-Counc.) Brit. Soc. for Surg. of Hand; Founder Mem. Brit. Elbow & Shoulder Soc. (Ex-Mem. Comm.). Prev: Cons. Emerit. Orthop. & Hand Surg. Homerton Hosp.(RTD); Examr. (Gen. Surg. & Path.) RCS Ed.(Formerly); Examr. The United Examg. Bd.(Formerly).

WADSWORTH, Timothy Mayow The Church Street Practice, David Corbet House, 2 Callows Lane, Kidderminster DY10 2JG Tel: 01562 822051 Fax: 01562 827251; Comely Bank, Lowe Lane, Wolverley, Kidderminster DY11 5QP Tel: 01562 850210 — MB ChB 1970 Birm.; BSc Ed. 1964; MRCGP 1979. (Birm) Clin. Asst. Kidderminster Hosp.

WADUD, Rubina c/o Mr Raquibuddin Ahmed, 40 Queen Elizabeth's Walk, Wallington SM6 8JF — MB BS 1984 Dacca.

WADZISZ, Faustyna Jowita 10 Dorchester Court, Wray Common Road, Reigate RH2 0UD — MB BCh BAO 1955 NUI; DPM Eng. 1963. Assoc. Specialist (Psychiat.) Epsom Dist. Hosp. Socs: BMA.

WAGENAAR, Natasja Medacs Locum Agency, High Street House, Newmarket St., Skipton BD23 2HU — Artsexamen 1994 Free U Amsterdam; Artsexamen Free Univ Amsterdam 1994.

WAGG, Adrian Stuart Department of Geriatric Medicine, University College Hospital, 25 Grafton Way, London WC1E 6AU Tel: 020 7380 9910 Fax: 020 7380 9652 Email: a.wagg@ucl.ac.uk; 13 Selwyn Road, Bow, London E3 5EA Tel: 020 8981 7909 — FRCP 2001; MB BS Lond. 1988; MRCP (UK) 1991. (Lond. Hosp. Med. Coll.) p/t Sen. Lect. (Med.) Univ. Coll. Lond.; Hon. Cons. Camden & Islington Community Health Serv. NHS Trust; Cons. Phys. & Geriatician Univ. Coll. Lond. Hosp.; Clin. Director, Med. and Emerg. Serv.s UCLH. Socs: Brit. Geriat. Soc. & Amer. Geriat. Soc.; Internat. Continence Soc. Prev: Sen. Regist. Camden & Islington Health Serv. NHS Trust; Sen. Regist. N.wick Pk. Hosp.; Regist. (Med.) Roy. Lond. Hosp.

WAGG, Audrey (retired) Treeton House, Redesmouth Road, Bellingham, Hexham NE48 2EH Tel: 01434 220358 — MB BS 1950 Durh. Prev: Deptm. Med. Off. Durh. HA.

WAGG, Michael George (retired) Treeton House, Redesmouth Road, Bellingham, Hexham NE48 2EH Tel: 01434 220358 — MB ChB 1950 St. And.; FFA RCS Eng. 1962; DA Eng. 1959. Prev: Cons. Anaesth. Sunderland Hosp. Gp.

WAGGET, Mr John Royal Victoria Infirmary, Newcastle upon Tyne NE1 4LP Tel: 0191 232 5131 — MB BS 1961 Durh.; FRCS Eng. 1966. (Durh.) Cons. Paediat. Surg. Newc. AHA (T). Socs: Brit. Assn. Paediat. Surg. Prev: Chief Resid. (Paediat. Surg.) Childr. Hosp. Philadelphia, USA; Regist. (Paediat. Surg.) Babies Hosp. Newc.

WAGHORN, Alison Jane Royal Liverpool University hospital Trust, Prencot St., Liverpool L7 8XP — MB ChB 1986 Birm.; FRCS Eng. 1992; FRCS Ed. 1990; MD 1999; FRCS Gen Ssurg 1999. Cons. Endocrine & BrE.. Surg. Roy. Liverp. Univ. Trust. Prev: Anat. Demonstr. Univ. Coll. Lond.; SHO Rotat.Kent & Cantebury Hosp.; Regist. Rotat. NW Thames.

WAGHORN, David Anthony Green Trees, 75 Hollies Avenue, West Byfleet KT14 6AN — MB BS 1987 Lond.

WAGHORN, David John Department of Microbiology, Wycombe Hospital, Queen Alexandra Road, High Wycombe HP11 2TT Tel: 01494 425246 Fax: 01494 425090; 40 Kinghorn Park, Maidenhead SL6 7TX — MB BS 1980 Lond.; MSc 1988 Lond.; FRCPath 1996, M 1989; DRCOG 1983. (Char. Cross) Cons. Microbiol. Wycombe Gen. Hosp. High Wycombe. Socs: Assn. Med. Microbiol.; Hosp. Infec. Soc.; Roy. Soc. Med. Prev: Lect. & Hon. Sen. Regist. (Microbiol.) St. Thos. Hosp. Lond.

WAGHORNE, Nigel Julian Prince Philip Hospital, Dafen, Llanelli SA14 8QF Tel: 01554 756567; Towy Cottage, Ferryside SA17 5ST — MB BCh 1992 Wales. Staff Grade Doctor, A & E, P. Philip Hosp., LLa.lli. Carmasthenshire.

WAGLE, Sudhir Ghanashyam Maldon Road Surgery, 39 Maldon Road, Danbury, Chelmsford CM3 4QL Tel: 01245 225868 Fax: 01245 224253; 6 Mill Lane, Danbury, Chelmsford CM3 4LF — MB BS 1974 Bombay. Socs: BMA; MDU. Prev: SHO (Gen. Med. & Cardiol.) Rush Green Hosp. Romford.

WAGMAN, Mr Harvey St Marys Hospital, Praed St., London W2 Tel: 020 7886 6666 Ext: 1061; 13 Eleanor Crescent, Mill Hill, London NW7 1AH Tel: 020 8959 0821 Fax: 020 8959 1161 — MB BS Lond. 1960; FRCS Ed. 1968; MRCS Eng. LRCP Lond. 1960; FRCOG 1981, M 1968. (Lond. Hosp.) Cons. O & G Sen. Lect. St Mary's Hosp. Lond. W2; Examr. RCOG; Regional Assessor Matern. Mortality. Socs: Fell. Roy. Soc. Med.; Brit. Soc. Colpos.; Brit. Assn. Day Surg. Prev: Sen. Regist., Regist., Resid. Accouch. & Resid. Anaesth. Lond. Hosp.

WAGMAN, Lyndon Lane End Medical Group, 25 Edgwarebury lane, Edgware HA8 8LJ Tel: 020 8958 4233 Fax: 020 8905 4657 — MB BS 1989 Lond.; BSc Lond. 1986; MRCGP 1993; DRCOG 1992. Mem. W. Barnet PCG; GP Regist. Trainer. Prev: Clin. Asst. (Oncol.) Roy. Free Hosp. Lond.; Trainee GP Edgware VTS.

WAGNER, Alan John Woodlands Medical Centre, Woodland Road, Didcot OX11 0BB Tel: 01235 511355 Fax: 01235 512808 — MB BS 1966 Lond.; DAvMed Eng. 1970. (Middlx.) Prev: Ho. Off. Middlx. Hosp. Lond.

WAGNER, Catharine Helen — MB ChB 1974 Liverp.; MRCGP 1978; DRCOG 1976. (Liverpool) Socs: Roy. Coll. Gen. Pract.

WAGNER, H Rising Brook Surgery, Merrey Road, Stafford ST17 9LY Tel: 01785 251134 Fax: 01785 222441 — MB ChB 1985 Cape Town; MB ChB 1985 Cape Town.

WAGNER, Margaret Marian Fennell (retired) Basement Flat, 10 Frederick Place, Weymouth DT4 8HQ — MB BS 1948 Lond.; MRCS Eng. LRCP Lond. 1947; FRCPath 1975, M 1964. Prev: Scientist MRC Pneumoconiosis Unit.

WAGNER, Nicholas Alan Giles Department of Mental Health for Older People, Stonebow Unit, The County Hospital, Union Walk, Hereford HR1 2ER Tel: 01432 355444 — FRCPsych 2000; MB BS Lond. 1970; MRCS Eng. LRCP Lond. 1969; MRCPsych 1975; DPM Eng. 1974. (St. Bart.) Cons. Psychiat. Hereford; Second Opinion Apptd. Doctor Ment. Health Act Commiss.; Med. Mem. Ment. Health Review Tribunal. Prev: Cons. Psychiat. W. Middlx. Univ. Hosp.; Hon. Sen. Lect. (Psychiat.) Char. Cross & W.m. Med. Sch. Lond.; Cons. Ment. Health Older People Herefordsh. Primary Care NHS Trust.

WAGNER, Peter Robinson (retired) Spindrift, 39 Duport Bay, St Austell PL26 6AQ Tel: 01726 63167 — MB BS 1948 Lond.; MD Lond. 1967; MRCS Eng. LRCP Lond. 1948; DObst RCOG 1966. Prev: Cons. Aviat. Med. ASP EC Systems Ltd. Yeovil.

WAGNER, Robert Michael Cheviot Way Health Centre, Cheviot Way, Bourtreehill South, Irvine KA11 1JU Tel: 01294 211993 Fax: 01294 218461; 78 Kilnford Drive, Dundonald, Kilmarnock KA2 9ET Tel: 01563 851126 — MB ChB 1970 Bristol; DObst RCOG 1974. (Bristol) Prev: Med. Off. Grenfell Assn. Labrador & Newfld.; SHO (Anaesth.) Roy. Devon & Exeter Hosp.; Med. Off. Parbatti S. Himalayan Expedit.

WAGNER, Simon David 3 Elmfield Road, London N2 8EB — MB BS 1984 Lond.

WAGSTAFF, Alison 13 Cleveden Gardens, Kelvinside, Glasgow G12 0PU — BM BS 1979 Nottm.; FFA RCS Eng. 1985. Cons. Inst. Neurol. Sc. Glas. Prev: Sen. Regist. N.. RHA.

WAGSTAFF, Anthony Edward 1 Rayleigh Close, Newton Road, Cambridge CB2 2AZ Tel: 01223 357175 — MB BChir 1952 Camb.; MA, MB BChir Camb. 1952; MFOM RCP Lond. 1978; DAvMed Eng. 1971; DIH Soc. Apoth. Lond. 1964. (Westm.) Indep. Cons. Occupat. Health Phys. Camb. Socs: Internat. Acad. Aviat. & Space Med.; Fell. Roy. Soc. Med.; Soc. Occupat. Med. Prev: Sen. Med. Off. Civil Aviat. Auth.; Squadron Ldr. RAF Med. Br.; Chief Med. Off. Gulf Air Bahrain.

WAGSTAFF, Dorothea Primrose (retired) 7 Saxon Place, Lower Buckland Road, Lymington SO41 9EZ Tel: 01590 671975 — MB BChir Camb. 1949; BA Camb. 1946; MA Camb. 1998. Prev: Jun. Hosp. Med. Off. N. Lond. Blood Transfus. Centre.

WAGSTAFF, Elizabeth (retired) Willowbank House, Wear View, Durham DH1 1LW Tel: 0191 386 9367 — MB BS Durh. 1943; MRCOG 1949. Prev: Sen. Regist. St. Mary's Hosps. Manch.

WAGSTAFF, Joan (retired) 55 McKernan Court, 89 High St., Sandhurst GU47 8HH Tel: 01252 875791 — MB BS 1939 Lond.; MRCS Eng. LRCP Lond. 1938. Prev: Ho. Phys. Univ. Coll. Hosp.

WAGSTAFF, John Kenneth (retired) Willowbank House, Wear View, Durham DH1 1LW Tel: 0191 386 9367 — MD Camb. 1953, MB BChir 1942; FRCP Lond. 1970, M 1948; MRCS Eng. LRCP Lond. 1942. Prev: Clin. Tutor Sussex Postgrad. Med. Centre.

WAGSTAFF, Miles Harvey 36 Christopher Close, Norwich NR1 2PQ — MB BChir 1993 Camb.

WAGSTAFF, Peter John 104 Castlecroft Road, Wolverhampton WV3 8LU; St Michael's House, 1 Lower St., Tettenhall, Wolverhampton WV6 9AA — MB ChB 1986 Birm.; DCM 1989. (Birmingham) Princip. Gen. Pract. Prev: SHO (Paediat.) Worcester Roy. Infirm.; SHO Rotat. (Surg.) Worcester Roy. Infirm.; SHO (A & E) Wolverhampton Hosp.

WAGSTAFF, Rebecca Jane Croftlands, Castle Carrock, Brampton CA8 9LT Tel: 01228 70409 Email: rebecca.wagstaff@ncha.nhs.uk — MB ChB 1985 Liverp.; MSc Newc. 1991; MFPHM 1992. Cons. in Pub. Health Med., Dept Pub. Health Med., N. Cumbria Health Auth., Carlisle, Cumbria. Prev: Sen.Regist. (Pub. Health Med.) N.. RHA.

WAGSTAFF, Thomas Ian Newcastle upon Tyne Hospitals NHS Trust, Freeman Hospital, Queen Victoria Road, Newcastle upon Tyne NE1 4LP Tel: 0191 232 5131 Fax: 0191 227 5173; 9 King John's Court, Darras Hall, Ponteland, Newcastle upon Tyne NE20 9AR Tel: 01661 823329 — MB BS 1965 Lond.; BSc (Special. Anat.) Lond. 1962, MD 1979; MRCS Eng. LRCP Lond. 1965; FRCOG 1983, M 1970. (Univ. Coll. Hosp.) Cons. Emerit., Freeman Hosp., Newc. upon Tyne. Socs: Scientif. Fell. Zool. Soc. Lond.; Blair Bell Res. Soc.; Worshipful Soc. Apoth. Prev: Cons. O & G & Clin. Dir. Roy. Vict. Infirm. Newc. u. Tyne; Regist. (O & G) Luton & Dunstable Hosp.; Lect. & Sen. Regist. (Obst. Unit) & Ho. Surg. & Ho. Phys. Univ. Coll. Hosp. Lond.

WAGSTAFF, William (retired) 8 Longacre Road, Dronfield, Sheffield S18 1UQ — MB ChB Manch. 1957; FRCP Lond. 1990; FRCP Ed. 1988; FRCPath 1980, M 1968; DTM & H Eng. 1960. Prev: Dir. Regional Transfus. Centre Sheff.

WAGSTYL, Jan Wendel St James's Practice, 138 Croydon Road, Beckenham BR3 4DG Tel: 020 8650 0568 Fax: 020 8650 4172; 138 Croydon Road, Beckenham BR3 — MB ChB 1983 Birm.; MRCGP 1987; DCH 1986; DRCOG 1986. Princip GP Birm.

WAGSTYL, Sabina 8 Vicarage Road, Harborne, Birmingham B17 0SP — MB BCh BAO 1954 NUI. (Galway) Asst. MOH Pub. Health Dept. Birm. Prev: Ho. Phys. & Ho. Surg. Roy. Infirm. Huddersfield; Ho. Phys. Paediat. City Gen. Hosp. Stoke-on-Trent; SHO Cas. Selly Oak Hosp. Birm.

WAH, Tze Min 44 Sudbury Heights Avenue, Greenford UB6 0LX — MB ChB 1995 Leeds.

WAHAB, Mr Mohammed Adel Parkwood Health Centre, Long Catlis Road, Parkwood, Gillingham ME8 9PR — MB BCh 1971 Alexandria; FRCS Glas. 1979.

WAHAB, Mumtaz Abdul Lister Hospital, Coreys Mill Lane, Stevenage SG1 4AB Tel: 01438 314333; 1 Bassetts Close, Farnborough, Orpington BR6 7AQ — MB BS 1981 Osmania; MB BS Osmania Univ. India 1981; MRCS Eng. LRCP Lond. 1988; DRCOG 1993. Staff Grade Doctor (O & G) Lister Hosp. Stevenage.

WAHBA, Mr Hany Fahmy St Marks Medical Centre, 24 Wrottesley Road, Plumstead, London SE18 3EP Tel: 020 8854 7685 Fax: 020 8317 3098; 28 Beechwood Rise, Chislehurst BR7 6TJ Tel: 020 8468 7897 Email: nany.wahba@btinternet.com — MB BCh 1978 Cairo; FRCS Ed. 1985; MRCS Eng. LRCP Lond. 1979. (Cairo) Clin. Asst. (Gen. Surg.) Greenwich Health Care Trust. Prev: SHO (Gen. Surg.) Roy. Liverp. Hosp.; SHO Rotat. (Surg.) Univ. Hosp. Wales & Cardiff Roy. Infirm.; SHO (Orthop. Surg.) P'boro. HA.

WAHBA, Nabil Youssef 16 Kings Avenue, Eastbourne BN21 2PF Tel: 01323 24026 — MB ChB 1970 Alexandria; Dip Counsel CSCT 1998; Dip Psychother BHR 1989. Private Counsellor & Psychotherapist. Socs: Accred. Mem. Med. & Den. Soc.Hypn.; Retd. Mem. Assn. Anaesth. Prev: Staff Grade in Pyschiatry, Ticehurst; Assoc. Specialist in Anaesth., Dist. Gen. Hosp., E.bourne.

WAHBY, Cesar Cesai Tawfiq 16 Chervilles, Maidstone ME16 9JE — MB ChB 1955 Baghdad; LMSSA Lond. 1961; DPM Eng. 1965. (Baghdad) Med. Asst. Long Gr. Hosp. Epsom. Socs: Roy. Med.-Psych. Assn. Prev: Ho. Surg. Hammersmith Hosp. & Roy. Marsden Hosp. Chelsea; Cas. Off. W. Lond. Hosp.

WAHEDNA, Irfan Barnsley District General Hosptial, Gawber Road, Barnsley S75 2EP — MB BS 1983 Karachi; MRCP (UK) 1988; FRCP 1999. Cons. Phys. Barnsley Dist. Gen. Hosp. Prev: Sen. Regist. Univ. Coll. Hosp. Lond.; Research Fell. (Respirat.) City Hosp. Nottm.; Regist. (Respirat. Gen. Med.) Lodge Moor Hosp. Sheff.

WAHEED, Abdul Pontllanfraith Health Centre, Off Blackwood Road, Pontllanfraith, Blackwood NP12 2YU Tel: 01495 227131 Fax: 01495 220361 — MB BS 1978 Peshawar, Pakistan; MRCS Eng. LRCP Lond. 1984.

WAHEED, Muhammad 30 Woodstock Close, Upton, Macclesfield SK10 3DZ — MB BS 1965 Punjab.

WAHEED, Nosheen 30 Woodstock Close, Macclesfield SK10 3DZ — MB ChB 1992 Manch.

WAHEED, Mrs Waheeda Fields House, Fields Park Avenue, Newport NP18 2JS Tel: 01633 211703 — MB BS 1959 Punjab; MB BS Punjab (Pakistan) 1959; MRCPsych 1972; DPM Eng. 1969. (King. Edwd. Med. Coll. Lahore) Cons. Psychiat. St. Cadoc's Hosp. Caerleon. Prev: SHO (Cas.) St. Peter's Hosp. Chertsey & King's Lynn Gen. Hosp.; Res. Med. Off. Vict. Hosp. Woking.

WAI, Angela Sin-Yi 58 Bancroft Avenue, London N2 0AS — MB ChB 1982 Dundee; DA Eng. 1985. Regist. (Anaesth.) Roy. Free Hosp. Lond. Prev: Regist. (Anaesth.) S.end HA.

WAIGHT, Catherine Teresa Trinity Hospice, 30 Clapham Common, Northside, London SW4 0RN; 17 St Georges Court, Garden Row, London SE1 6HD — BM BS 1987 Nottm.; MRCGP 1992.

WAIN, Eileen Anne (retired) Brander Lodge, Tripp Lane, Linton, Wetherby LS22 4HX Tel: 01937 581157 — MB ChB 1960 Glas.; FFPHM RCP (UK) 1991; DPH Leeds 1978; DObst RCOG 1963. Prev: Dir. Pub. Health Leeds HA.

WAIN, Emma Charlotte Elizabeth 19 Sandfield Road, Headington, Oxford OX3 7RN — MB BS 1996 Lond.

WAIN, Mark Owen The Surgery, Bull Yard, Simson Street, Spilsby PE23 5JE Tel: 01790 752555 Fax: 01790 754457 — MB BS 1978 Lond.; BSc 1975 Lond.; BSc Lond. 1975; FRCS Ed. 1983; MRCGP 1987.

WAIN, Michael Louis Whitstable Health Centre, Harbour Street, Whitstable CT5 1BZ Tel: 01277 263033 Fax: 01277 771474; Little Hall Farm, Alcroft Grange, Tyler Hill, Canterbury CT2 9NN Tel: 01227 463824 — MB BChir 1973 Camb.; MA Camb. 1974, BA (Hons.) 1969, MB BChir 1973; MRCP (UK) 1975. (St. Mary's)

WAIN

WAIN, Sarah Helen 87 St Cyrus Road, Colchester CO4 4LR — MB ChB 1998 Birm.

WAIND, Arthur Philip Booth, DSC (retired) 14 Woodland Road, Ulverston LA12 0DX Tel: 01229 583086 — MRCS Eng. LRCP Lond. 1938; MD Leeds 1946, MB ChB 1938; FRCP Lond. 1969, M 1947. Prev: Cons. Phys. S.W. Cumbria Health Dist.

WAIND, Catherine Mary (retired) 14 Woodland Road, Ulverston LA12 0DX Tel: 01229 583086 — MB ChB 1947 Leeds. Prev: Sen. Med. Off. Family Plann. SW Cumbria.

WAINE, Colin, OBE Sunderland Health Authority, Durham Road, Sunderland SR3 4AF Tel: 0191 565 6256 Fax: 0191 528 3455; 42 Etherley Lane, Bishop Auckland DL14 7QZ Tel: 01388 604429 — MB BS 1959 Durh.; MB BS (2nd cl. Hons.) Durh. 1959; FRCGP 1976, M (Distinc.) 1968; FRCPath 1992. (King's Coll. Univ. Durh.) Dir. Health Progr. & Primary Care Developm. Sunderland HA. Socs: (Ex-Chairm.) Roy. Coll. Gen. Pract.; Assoc. Mem. BPA; N. Eng. Med. Soc. Prev: Hosp. Pract. (Paediat.) Bishop Auckland Gen. Hosp.; Chairm. Clin. & Research Div. RCGP; Cons. & Brit. Delegate to Europ. Health Comm. Primary Care & Preven. Gp.

WAINE, Julie Marie 3 Sycamore Cottages, Frimley Road, Camberley GU15 2RA — BM 1994 Soton.

WAINFORD, Claire Michele 18 The Gardens, London SE22 9QE — MB BS 1988 Lond.; BSc Anat. Lond. 1985, MB BS 1988.

WAINHOUSE, Catherine Louise Flat 1, 41 Achillies Road, London NW6 1DZ — MB ChB 1991 Leic.

WAINSCOAT, James Stephen 14 Woodlands Close, Headington, Oxford OX3 7RY Tel: 01865 220330 Fax: 01865 221778 Email: jsw2@pinnacle.ox.ac.uk — MB ChB 1972 Liverp.; MSc (Immunol.) Birm. 1975; FRCP Lond. 1991; MRCP (UK) 1976; FRCPath 1992, M 1980. Cons. Haemat. John Radcliffe Hosp. Oxf.; Hon Director CRF Molecular Haemat. Prev: MRC Clin. Sc. Nuffield Dept. Clin. Med. Oxf.; Sen. Regist. (Haemat.) John Radcliffe Hosp. Oxf.

WAINSCOTT, Gillian Rose Darville 39 Croftdown Road, Harborne, Birmingham B17 8RE Tel: 0121 427 4466 Fax: 0121 427 4466 — MB ChB 1968 Bristol; MRCPsych 1992; DCH RCP Lond. 1972. (Bristol) Cons. Psychiat. Qu. Eliz. Psychiat. Hosp. Birm. Prev: SHO (Paediat.) Hammersmith Hosp. Lond.; SHO (Paediat.) Brompton Hosp. Lond.; SHO (Med.) Bristol Roy. Infirm.

WAINSTEAD, Harold (Surgery), 1 Highdown Avenue, Worthing BN13 1PU Tel: 01903 65656; 17 Romney Court, Winchelsea Gardens, Worthing BN11 5EU — MRCS Eng. LRCP Lond. 1946 Lond.; BA, MB BChir Camb. 1949; MRCS Eng. 1945 LRCP Lond. 1946. (Camb. & St. Geo.) Prev: Res. Med. Off. Roy. Vict. Hosp. Folkestone; Ho. Surg. St. Geo. Hosp.; Squadron Ldr. RAF.

WAINWRIGHT, Alexandra Jeannette Rosalind Rothschild House Surgery, Chapel Street, Tring HP23 6PU Tel: 01442 822468 Fax: 01442 825889; 14 Hillside, Cheddington, Leighton Buzzard LU7 0SP — BM 1983 Soton.; MRCGP 1987. GP Tring. Prev: Trainee GP Lincoln VTS.

WAINWRIGHT, Mr Andrew Morris Nuffield Orthopaedic Centre, Oxford OX3 9DU Tel: 01865 741155 — FRCS 2000 (Tr & Orth); MB ChB Leic. 1990; BSc (Hons.) Leic. 1987; FRCS Eng. 1994. (Leicester University) Specialist Regist. (Trauma & Orthop.) Nuffield Orthopaedic Centre, Oxf. Socs: Girdlestone Orthopaedic Soc.; Brit. Orthopaedic Trainees Assoc.; Brit. Orthopaedic Assoc. Prev: SHO (Plastic Surg.) Exeter; SHO (Orthop. & Gen. Surg.) Bristol.

WAINWRIGHT, Andrew Tristan Staff and Partners, Queensway Medical Centre, Olympic Way, Wellingborough NN8 3EP Tel: 01933 678767 Fax: 01933 676657; 4 The Paddocks, Orlingbury, Kettering NN14 1JU — MB ChB 1983 Manch.; DRCOG 1986.

WAINWRIGHT, Anthony Christopher Shackleton Department Anaesthetics, The General Hospital, Tremona Road, Southampton SO16 6YD Tel: 02380796135 Fax: 02380794348; Ashton Cottage, Kewlake Lane, Cadnam, Southampton SO40 2NS Tel: 02380812642 Fax: 02380812642 Email: c.wainwright@virgin.net — MB BS 1967 Lond.; FRCA 1971. (St. Thos.) Cons. Anaesth. Soton. Univ. Hosps. NHS Trust. Socs: Assn. Anaesth.; BMA; RSM. Prev: Lect. Univ. Bristol; Sen. Regist. Univ. Hosp. of Wales Cardiff.

WAINWRIGHT, Anthony John Neuadd Felin, Talgarth, Brecon LD3 — MB ChB 1953 Birm.

WAINWRIGHT, Christian Thomas New House, College Rd, Denstone, Uttoxeter ST14 5HR — MB ChB 1997 Leic.

WAINWRIGHT, Christopher John Mount Pleasant Farm, Chalvington, Hailsham BN27 3TB — MB ChB 1987 Sheff.

WAINWRIGHT, Christopher John-Paul 21 Ratcliffe Road, Haydon Bridge, Hexham NE47 6ER — BM BS 1994 Nottm.; BMedSci (Hons.) Nottm. 1990. Research Fell.Qu. Eliz. Hosp. Prev: SHO (Orthop.) Tyneside; SHO (A&E) S. Tyneside; Ho. Off. (Med.) Freeman Hosp. Newc.

WAINWRIGHT, David Theodore Neaudd Felin, Talgarth, Brecon LD3 0BN — MB ChB 1984 Birm.

WAINWRIGHT, Mr Denys (retired) 101 Swains Lane, Highgate Village, London N6 6PJ Tel: 020 8340 2131 — MB ChB 1932 Liverp.; MCh Orth. Liverp. 1934, MB ChB 1932; FRCS Eng. 1971; FRCS Ed. 1937; Hon. DSc Keele 1975. Cons. Orthop. Surg. Robt. Jones & Agnes Hunt Orthop. Hosp. OsW.ry. Prev: Cons. Orthop. Surg. N. Staffs. Hosp. Centre.

WAINWRIGHT, Elizabeth Ann Carron Hill, 221 Wallasey Road, Wallasey CH44 2AD; 11 Gainsborough Road, Southport PR8 2EY Tel: 01704 565782 — MB ChB 1985 Liverp.; MRCGP 1989; DRCOG 1988. GP S.port. Prev: Trainee GP/SHO Liverp. VTS.; Ho. Off. Roy. Liverp. Hosp.

WAINWRIGHT, Geoffrey Anson Oakengates Medical Practice, Limes Walk, Oakengates, Telford TF2 6JJ Tel: 01952 620077 Fax: 01952 620209 — MB BS 1968 Newc.; DTM & H Liverp. 1972. (Newc.) Socs: BMA. Prev: Jun. Ho. Off. (Med.) Dryburn Hosp. Durh.; SHO (Paediat.) Bishop Auckland Gen. Hosp.; Med. Off. Brit. Solomon Is.s Protec.

WAINWRIGHT, James Russell Health Centre, Pen y Bont, The Roe, St Asaph LL17 0LU Tel: 01745 583208 Fax: 01745 583748 — MB ChB 1990 Liverp.; BSc (Hons.) Med. Cell Biol. Liverp. 1987; MRCGP 1994.

WAINWRIGHT, Jennifer Rose 126 King George V Drive N., Heath, Cardiff CF14 4EL — MB ChB 1990 Sheff. Higher Professional Train. Fell. (Gen. Pract.) Univ. Glas. Socs: RCGP; MDDUS.

WAINWRIGHT, John, OBE 8 Windsor Court, Warren Drive, Deganwy, Conwy LL31 9TN Tel: 01492 583259 Email: jwainwright@enterprise.net — MB BS 1950 Lond.; MRCS Eng. LRCP Lond. 1950. (St. Bart.) Prev: Act. Squadron Ldr. RAF Med. Br.

WAINWRIGHT, Nicholas James Department of Dermatology, Monklands Hospital, Monkscourt Avenue, Airdrie ML6 0JS Tel: 01236 746162 Fax: 01236 746239 Email: nwainwright@laht.scot.nhs.uk — MB BS 1986 Lond.; MA Oxon. 1977; MRCP (UK) 1990; FRCP (Edin) 2000. (Univ. Coll. & Middlx. Hosp.) Cons. Dermat. Monklands & Belshill Hosps. Trust Airdrie; Hon. Clin. Sen. Lect. Univ. Glas. Socs: Brit. Assn. Dermat.; PhotoMed. Soc. Prev: Sen. Regist. (Dermat.) Ninewells Hosp. Dundee; Regist. (Dermat.) Ninewells Hosp. Dundee; Regist. (Gen. Med. & Endocrinol.) Leeds Gen. Infirm.

WAINWRIGHT, Paul Arthur Noel (retired) Four Winds, 5 Springpool, Winstanley, Wigan WN3 6DE Tel: 01942 222554 — MB ChB 1948 St. And. Prev: Flight Lt. RAF Med. Br.

WAINWRIGHT, Raymond James Department of Cardiology, King's College Hospital, Denmark Hill, London SE5 9RS — MD Lond. 1982, MB BS 1971; FRCP Lond. 1993; MRCP (UK) 1973; MRCS Eng. LRCP Lond. 1971. (Guy's) Cons. Cardiol. King's Coll. Hosp. Lond. Prev: Cons. Cardiol. Brook Gen. Hosp. Lond.; Sen. Regist. Dept. Cardiol. Guy's Hosp. Lond.

WAINWRIGHT, Robert Iain Gellybank House, Kinross KY13 0LE — MB BChir 1990 Camb.

WAINWRIGHT, Shelagh Joan 101 Swains Lane, Highgate Village, London N6 6PJ Tel: 020 8340 2131 — MB ChB Cape Town 1931. (Cape Town) Prev: Ho. Phys. Fleming Hosp. Newc.; Res. Med. Off. Alder Hey Childr. Hosp. Liverp.; Ho. Surg. St. Mary's Hosp. Manch.

WAISE, Ahmed Ali Mohammad Friarage Hospital, Northallerton DL6 1JG Tel: 01609 779911 Fax: 01609 764632 Email: a.waise@northallerton.onyxnet.co.uk — MB ChB 1973 Baghdad; FRCP Lond. 1999; FRCPath 1998; MRCPath 1989; LRCP LRCS Ed. LRCPS Glas. 1983; MRCP (UK) 1982. Cons. Chem. Path.endocrinologist Friarage Hosp. N.allerton. Prev: Sen. Regist. & Regist. (Chem. Path.) N. W.. RHA; SHO (Gen. Med.) Roy. Infirm. Blackburn; SHO (Gen. Med.) Yarmook Hosp., Baghdad.

WAIT, Christopher Martin Little Croft, Duns Tew, Bicester OX25 6JR — MB BCh 1981 Oxf.; MA, MB BCh Oxf. 1981; FFA RCS Eng. 1986. Cons. Anaesth. Horton Hosp. Banbury Oxon. HA. Prev: Research Regist. & Sen. Regist. (Anaesth.) Nuffield Hosp. Oxf.

WAIT, Hilary Jane 132 Grand Drive, London SW20 9EA; 22 Mossville Gardens, Morden SM4 4DG — MB BS 1983 Lond.; DCH RCP Lond. 1988; DRCOG 1987; DA (UK) 1986. Prev: Trainee GP Lond.; SHO (Neonates) All St.s Hosp. Chatham; SHO (Paediat.) Maidstone Hosp.

WAITE, Alasdair 39 Nunholme Road, Dumfries DG1 1JW — MB ChB 1994 Aberd.

WAITE, Alison 45 Coach Road, Guiseley, Leeds LS20 8AY — MB ChB 1995 Manch.

WAITE, Anthony John 9 Kenwood Road, Shrewsbury SY3 8AH — LMSSA 1993 Lond.

WAITE, Christopher Grenfell 54 Tarrant Street, Arundel BN18 9DN — MRCS Eng. LRCP Lond. 1973.

WAITE, Christopher John 30 Bristol Avenue, Saltburn-by-the-Sea TS12 1BW — MB BCh 1994 Wales.

WAITE, David William (retired) 63 Chazey Road, Caversham, Reading RG4 7DU Tel: 0118 947 5606 — MB ChB 1963 Manch.; FRCR 1975; FFR 1973; DMRD Eng. 1971; DA Eng. 1967; DObst RCOG 1965.

WAITE, Frank Thomas John (retired) Waite, McFadden and Brown, 35 George Street, Dumfries DG1 1EA Tel: 01387 53724 Fax: 01387 259780 — MB ChB Ed. 1966; MRCP (UK) 1972; FRCP Ed 1999.

WAITE, Heather Claire Sunnybrook House, Llangoed, Beaumaris LL58 8NY — BM BS 1995 Nottm.

WAITE, Ian 12 Sedgefield Road, Radcliffe, Manchester M26 1YE; 31 Conningsby Close, Bromley Rise, Bromley Cross, Bolton BL7 9NY — MB ChB 1990 Manch.; FRCA 1995. (Manch.) Cons. Anaesth. Pain Managem.Roy.Bolton.Hosp.Bolton.

WAITE, Ian Joseph (retired) 35 Belmont Avenue, Baildon, Shipley BD17 5AJ Tel: 01274 586884 — MB ChB Sheff. 1952; DObst RCOG 1953. Prev: Regist. Childr. Hosp. Bradford.

WAITE, Jonathan Flat 6, Arundel House, Nottingham NG7 1BS — MB ChB 1976 Ed.; BSc (Hons.) (Pharmacol.) Ed. 1973, MB ChB 1976; MRCPsych 1980. Cons. Psychiat. Dept. Health c/o Elderly Qu. Med. Centre Nottm. Socs: Fell. Roy. Med. Soc. Edin.

WAITE, Jonathan Chapman 152 Revelstoke Road, London SW18 5PA — MB BS 1994 Lond.

WAITE, Kathrin Elizabeth Ashford Hospital, London Road, Ashford TW15 1AA; 31 Severn Drive, Hinchley Wood, Esher KT10 0AJ — MB 1981 Camb.; MA Camb. 1981, MB 1981, BChir 1980. Cons. Anaesth. Ashford Hosp. Middlx. Socs: Assn. Anaesth. Gt. Brit. & Irel.; Pain Soc. Prev: Sen. Regist. (Anaesth.) Hammersmith Hosp. Lond.; Regist. (Anaesth.) St. Peters Hosp. Chertsey.

WAITE, Malcolm Austin 8 Hintlesham Avenue, Edgbaston, Birmingham B15 2PH Tel: 0121 454 4401 — MB ChB 1964 Leeds; MD Leeds 1973; FRCP Lond. 1984; MRCP Lond. 1969. Cons. Phys. Selly Oak Hosp. Birm. Socs: Internat. Hypertens. Soc.; Eur. Hypertens. Soc.; Brit. Hypertens. Soc. Prev: Cons. Phys. & Lect. (Med.) Qu. Eliz. Hosp. Birm.; Clin. Scientist MRC Blood Pressure Research Unit W.. Infirm. Glas.

WAITE, Norma Rosemary 7 Belmont Road, Southampton SO17 2GD Tel: 02380 585858 — BM 1983 Soton.; DRCOG 1986.

WAITER, Michael Robert David Glaxo Wellcome plc, Greenford Road, Greenford UB6 0HE Tel: 020 8422 3434 — MB BS 1984 Lond.; BSc (Hons.) Pharmacol. 1980; AFPM RCP Lond. 1996; Dip. Pharm. Med. RCP (UK) 1995; DA (UK) 1991. (St. Bart.) Director Neurol. and Psychiat. Clin. Developm. Glaxo Wellcome plc. Prev: Europ. Director (Anaesth./Analgesia Clin. Research) Glaxo Wellcome plc.

WAITT, Dora Joy 15 Richmond Road, Thornton Heath, Croydon CR7 7QE — MB BS 1992 Lond.

WAITT, Roger Henry Francis Falstead House, The Street, HamSt., Ashford TN26 2HG Tel: 01233 732206 — MB BS 1963 Lond.; LMSSA Lond. 1961; DMRD Eng. 1968; DObst RCOG 1963.

WAIWAIKU, Kokulo Nyanpee Kents Hill Road Family Doctors, 411 Kents Hill Road North, Benfleet SS7 4AD Tel: 01268 753591 Fax: 01268 794585; 277 Hart Road, Thundersilly, Benfleet SS7 3UW Tel: 0116 875 5591 Email: el2zorzer@aol.com — MD 1980 Univ. Liberia; BSc Liberia 1973; DCCH Ed 1988; DTM & H Liverp 1989; MSc London 1990. (R M Doeliotti, Liberia) GP Princip. Socs: BMA.

WAJED, Mohammed Ali 220 Sandridge Road, St Albans AL1 4AL Tel: 01727 835505 Fax: 01727 835505 Email: mohammedwajed@hotmail.com — MB BS 1963 Dacca; FRCP Lond. 1991; MRCP (UK) 1973; MRCS Eng. LRCP Lond. 1974; DPhysMed Eng. 1969. (Chittagong Med. Coll.) Cons. Rheum. & Rehabil. Hemel Hempstead Gen. Hosp., St. Albans City Hosp. & Garston Manor Med. Rehabil. Centre. Socs: Hosp. Cons. & Spec. Assn.; Brit. Soc. Rheum. & Mem. BMA. Prev: Sen. Regist. Norf. & Norwich Hosp.; Sen. Regist. (Rheum.) Lond. Hosp.; Regist. (Rheum.) King's Coll. Hosp. Lond.

WAJED, Mr Shahjehan Ali Dept. of Surgery, Royal Free Hospital, Pond Street, London NW3 2QG Email: s.wajed@ifc.ucl.ac.uk; 70 Blake Road, London N11 2AM Fax: 079 7071 8037 Email: swajed@hotmail.com — BM BCh 1992 Oxf.; BA Camb. 1989, MA 1993; FRCS Eng. 1996. (Oxf.) Specialist Regist. Rotat. (Gen. Surg.) N. Thames; Lect. in Surg., Roy. Free and VCL Med. Sch. Prev: Research Fell. 1999-2000; Dept. of Surg., Univ. of S.. Calif., Los Angeles, USA.

WAJID, Abdul 81 Havering Gardens, Chadwell Heath, Romford RM6 5BH Tel: 020 8590 4479 — MB BS 1962 Punjab; MB BS Punjab (Pakistan) 1962; DCH RCPS Glas. 1965. (Nishtar Med. Coll. Multan) SCMO Redbridge HCT.

WAJID, Mohammad Abdul c/o 3 Woburn Grove, Hartlepool TS25 1HD — MB BS 1989 Punjab.

WAKANKAR, Hemant Madhukar Department of Orthopaedics, Kent and Sussex Hospital, Mount Ephraim, Tunbridge Wells TN4 8AT Tel: 01892 526111; Flat 1, Derwent House, Barnet EN5 3HD Tel: 020 8440 3949 Email: hemantw@aol.com — MB BS 1988 Bombay; MS (Orth) Bombay 1990; DNB (Orth) New Delhi 1991; FRCS Glas. 1995; MChOrth Liverp. 1996; FRCS (Orth) 1997. (Bombay, India) Jt. Revision Fell. (Orthop.) Kent & Sussex Hosp. Tunbridge Wells & Horder Centre for Arthritis CrowBoro.

***WAKATSUKI, Mai** Hylands, harvest Hill, Bourne End SL8 5JJ Tel: 01628 525760 Email: m_wakatsuki@hotmail.com — BM BS 1998 Nottm.; BM BS Nottm 1998; BMedSci 1996.

WAKE, Angela Margaret The Surgery, 2 Church Lane, Merton Park, London SW19 3NY Tel: 020 8542 1174 Fax: 020 8544 1583 — MB BS 1979 Lond.; BSc. (Biochem.) Lond. 1976. (Lond. Hosp.)

WAKE, Anne Marian Royal Gwent Hospital, Cardiff Road, Newport NP20 2UB Tel: 01633 234321; 35 Bryn Glas, Thornhill, Cardiff CF14 9AA Tel: 01222 615322 — MB BCh 1977 Wales; FRCR 1983. (Welsh National School Medicine) Cons. Radiol. Glan Hafren NHS Trust Newport. Socs: Roy. Coll. Radiol. & Brit. Inst. Radiol.; BMA. Prev: Cons. Radiol. P. Chas. Hosp. Merthyr Tydfil; Sen. Regist. (Radiol.) Univ. Hosp. Wales Cardiff.

WAKE, Carie Ann 2 Acorn Place, Basildon SS16 6RJ — MB BS 1997 Lond.

WAKE, Colin Reginald Manor House, Cross Lane, Holcombe, Bury CO8 5HR — MB ChB 1970 Manch.; MRCOG 1977. Cons. (O & G) Fairfield Gen. Hosp. Bury.

WAKE, Deborah Jane 4 Park Place, Lunanhead, Forfar DD8 3NA — MB ChB 1998 Ed.

WAKE, Mr Mark 1 Dartmouth Avenue, Pattingham, Wolverhampton WV6 7DP — MB ChB 1983 Birm.; FRCS Eng. 1989; FRCS Ed. 1988.

WAKE, Martyn Charles The Surgery, 2 Church Lane, Merton Park, London SW19 3NY Tel: 020 8542 1174 Fax: 020 8544 1583 — MB BS 1979 Lond.; BSc (Anat.) Lond. 1976, MB BS 1979; DRCOG 1982. (Guy's)

WAKE, Michael John Clayton Department of Maxillofacial Surgery, Queen Elizabeth Hospital, Queen Elizabeth Med. Centre, Edgbaston, Birmingham B15 2TH Tel: 0121 627 2303 Fax: 0121 627 2302; The Lodge, 30A Frederick Road, Edgbaston, Birmingham B15 1JN Tel: 0121 455 7654 Fax: 0121 455 8705 Email: mjcwake@compuserve.com — MB ChB Birm. 1969; BDS Birm. 1962; FDS RCS Eng. 1972; FRCS(Edin) 2000. (Birmingham) Cons. Oral & Maxillofacial Surg. Univ. Hosp. Birm. NHS Trust & Birm. Childr. Hosp. NHS Trust; Cons. Craniofacial Surg. Birm. Childr. Hosp. NHS Trust; Hon. Sen. Clin. Lect. Univ. Birm.; Director W. Midl.s Cleft and/or Palate Serv. Socs: Fell. Brit. Assn. Oral & Maxillofacial Surg. Pres. 1999; Inst. Accid. Surg.; Europ. Soc. for cranofacial Surg. Prev: Sen. Regist. (Oral Surg.) St. Thos. Hosp. Lond.; Lect. (Oral Surg.) Roy. Dent. Hosp. Lond.; Hon. Edr. Brit. Jl. Oral & Maxillofacial Surg.

WAKE

WAKE, Pamela Judith Knarsdale House, Roseworth Crescent, Newcastle upon Tyne NE3 1NR — BM BS 1993 Nottm.

WAKE, Mr Philip Nicholas 5 Ashbourne Avenue, Blundellsands, Liverpool L23 8TX — MB ChB 1969 Liverp.; FRCS Eng. 1974; DCH Eng. 1973. Cons. (Vasc. & Gen. Surg.) Mersey RHA.

WAKE, Suzanne Louise 5 Ashbourne Avenue, Liverpool L23 8TX — BM BS 1994 Nottm.

WAKEEL, Riadh Adil Petrous King George Hospital, Barley Lane, Goodmayes, Ilford IG3 8YB Tel: 020 8970 8064 Fax: 020 8970 8124; 17 Chigwell Park Drive, Chigwell IG7 5BD Tel: 020 8500 6424 Fax: 020 8281 9904 — MB ChB Baghdad 1969; FRCP Ed. 1997; MRCP (UK) 1985; MRCPI 1985; Dip. Dermat. Lond. 1977; FRCP Lond. 1998. (Baghdad University) Cons. Dermat. King Geo. Hosp. Ilford Essex. Socs: Brit. Assn. Dermat.; Fell. Roy. Soc. Med.; Amer. Acad. of Dermat. Prev: Sen. Regist. & Hon Lecturer (Dermat.) Aberd. Roy. Infirm.; Regist. (Dermat.) Stobhill Gen. Hosp. Glas.; Regist. (Med.) Orpington Hosp.

WAKEFIELD, Mr Andrew Jeremy 43 Taylor Avenue, Kew Gardens, Richmond TW9 4EB — MB BS 1981 Lond.; FRCS Eng. 1985. (St. Mary's) Hon. Sen. Lect. Roy. Free Hosp. Sch. Med. Lond.

WAKEFIELD, Catharine Jane 12 Victoria Road S., Southsea PO5 2BZ Tel: 01705 823857; 16 Burbidge Grove, Southsea PO4 9RR Tel: 01705 831989 — MB BS 1979 Lond.; DRCOG 1982.

WAKEFIELD, Mr Christian Hamilton University of Edinburgh, Department of Surgery, Royal Infirmary of Edinburgh, Lauriston Place, Edinburgh EH3 9YN Tel: 0131 536 3819 Fax: 0131 228 2661; 12 Bangholm Bower Avenue, Edinburgh EH5 3NS Tel: 0131 552 2790 Email: cwake@netmatters.co.uk — MD 1998 Lond.; MB BS Lond. 1989; BSc Lond. 1988; FRCS Ed. 1996. Lect. (Surg.) Edin. Socs: Surgic. Research Soc. (Patey Prize). Prev: SHO (Surg.) Roy. Infirm. Edin.; Research Fell. (Surg.) Acad. Surg. Unit St. Mary's Hosp. Lond.

WAKEFIELD, Christopher John Wakefield and Partners, Lever Chambers Centre for Health, 1st Floor, Ashburner Street, Bolton BL1 15Q Tel: 01204 360030/31 Fax: 01204 360033; The Lindens, 235 Greenmount Lane, Bolton BL1 5JB Tel: 01204 492957 — MB ChB 1971 Manch.; DObst RCOG 1974.

WAKEFIELD, Deborah Ann The White Rose Surgery, Exchange Street, South Elmsall, Pontefract WF9 2RD Tel: 01977 642412 Fax: 01977 641290 — MB ChB 1986 Leeds.

WAKEFIELD, Graham Stanley (retired) Dale Cottage, Charlcombe Lane, Bath BA1 8DR Tel: 01225 312248 Fax: 01225 312248 — MB BS 1953 Lond.; FRCP Lond. 1971, M 1955. Prev: Cons. Neurol. Roy. United Hosp. Bath.

WAKEFIELD, Marion Ann Sue Nicholls centre, Manu House, Bierton Road, Aylesbury HP20 1EG Tel: 01296 489951 — MB BS 1969 Lond.; FRCP Lond. 1994; MRCP (UK) 1975; FRCPCH 1997, M 1996; DCH Eng. 1972. (Lond. Hosp.) Cons. Paediat. Manor Ho. Hosp. Aylesbury. Socs: Fell. Roy. Soc. Med. Prev: Sen. Regist. (Paediat.) Aylesbury Health Dist. & Pk. Hosp. Childr. Oxf.; Regist. (Paediat.) Stoke Mandeville Hosp. Aylesbury; SHO (Paediat.) Aylesbury Health Dist.

WAKEFIELD, Mavis (retired) 5 The Grange, Chorleywood Close, Rickmansworth WD3 4EG — MB ChB 1951 Birm.; MRCP Ed. 1955. Prev: SCMO (Community Health Servs.) Hillingdon HA.

WAKEFIELD, Peter Clive Whitehorse Vale Surgery, Whitehorse Vale, Barton Hills, Luton LU3 4AD Tel: 01582 490087 — MB BS 1967 Lond.; MRCS Eng. LRCP Lond. 1967.

WAKEFIELD, Richard John 61 The Mount, Selby YO8 9BD — BM 1991 Soton. (Soton. Med. Sch.) Research Fell. in Rheumat. Leeds Gen. Infirm.

WAKEFIELD, Ruth Margaret Fairfield General Hospital, Rochdale Old Rd, Bury BL9 7TD — MB ChB 1989 Sheff.; MRCP (UK) 1994; MRCPCH 1997. (Sheffield) Cons. (Paediat.) Fairfield Gen. Hosp. Lancs. Socs: Mem. of the Roy. Coll. of Paediat. And Child Health. Prev: Regist. Rotat. (Paediat.) St. Jas. Univ. Hosp. Leeds, Bradford Roy. Infirm. & St Luke's Bradford.; Specialist Regist. (Paediat.) St. Jas. Univ. Hosp., Leeds.

WAKEFIELD, Mr Simon Eyles 15 Bristol Road, Sheffield S11 8RL — MB BS 1987 Lond.; BSc (Hons.) Chem. Surrey 1982; FRCS Eng. 1991. Lect. (Gen. Surg.) Trent RHA. Prev: Regist. (Gen. Surg.) Oxon. RHA.

WAKEFIELD, Susan Margaret Stockwell Lodge Medical Centre, Rosedale Way, Cheshunt, Waltham Cross EN7 6HL Tel: 01992 624408 Fax: 01992 626206; 61 Tolmers Road, Cuffley, Potters Bar EN6 4JG — MB BS 1976 Lond.; BSc (Hons.) Lond. 1973; MRCP (UK) 1979. (St. Thos.) Prev: Regist. (Gen. Path.) & SHO (Gen. Med.) FarnBoro. Hosp., Kent.

WAKEFIELD, Valerie Ann Barnsley District General Hospital, Barnsley S75 2EP; Ringwood Cottage, Rails Road, Rivelin, Sheffield S6 6GF — MB ChB 1977 Sheff.; MRCP (UK) 1982. Cons. Phys. i/c c/o Elderly.

WAKEFORD, Neil Anthony Andrew Neatenden Farm, New England Lane, Sedlescombe, Battle TN33 0RP — MB ChB 1992 Manch.

WAKEFORD, Timothy David Carpalla Villa, Carpalla, Foxhole, St Austell PL26 7TY — MB BS 1998 Lond.

WAKEHAM, Craig Timothy Long Street Practice, 51 Long Street, Cerne Abbas, Dorchester DT2 7JG Tel: 01300 341666 Fax: 01300 341090; Five Bells House, Piddletrenthide, Dorchester DT2 7QX Tel: 01300 348690 — BM BS 1984 Nottm.; BMedSci. Nottm. 1982; MRCGP 1989; DRCOG 1988. (Nottm.) Princip. GP Clin. Asst. (Diabetes) Dorchester.

WAKEHAM, Niklas Rufus 49 Chetwynd Road, London NW5 1BX — MB BS 1996 Lond.

WAKEHAM, Patricia Forster 6 Stenders Court, Mitcheldean GL17 0HX — MB ChB 1962 Manch.

WAKELEY, Mr Charles John Old Bittern Barn, West Harptree, Bristol BS40 6HQ — MB BS 1983 Lond.; BSc Lond. 1980; FRCS Eng. 1987; FRCS Ed. 1987; FRCR 1991. Cons. Radiol. Bristol Roy. Infirm. Socs: BMA; RCR; BSSR. Prev: Sen. Regist. (Radiol.) Bristol Roy. Infirm.; SHO (Gen. Surg.) Mayday Hosp. Thornton Heath; SHO (A & E) Char. Cross Hosp. Lond.

WAKELEY, Sir John Cecil Nicholson, CStJ (retired) Mickle Lodge, Mickle, Trafford, Chester CH2 4EB Tel: 01244 300316 — MB BS 1950 Lond.; FRCS Eng. 1955; MRCS Eng. LRCP Lond. 1950; FACS 1973. Prev: Sen. Regist. (Surg.) King's Coll. Hosp. Lond. & Roy. Postgrad. Med. Sch. Hammersmith Hosp.

WAKELEY, Richard Michael (retired) Coves Cottage, High St, St Peters, Broadstairs CT10 2TH Tel: 01843 869478 — MB BS Lond. 1957.

WAKELIN, James Herbert Sydney (retired) Hollybanks, Old Peterston Road, Groes Faen, Pontyclun CF72 8NU Tel: 029 2089 1790 — MB BCh 1948 Wales; BSc Wales 1945, MB BCh 1948; MRCGP 1989; DObst RCOG 1950. Prev: Ho. Phys. & Ho. Surg. O & G E. Glam. Hosp. Pontypridd.

WAKELIN, Sarah Helen Dept of Dermatology, St Marys Hospital, Praed St., London W2 1NY Tel: 020 7886 1194 Fax: 020 7886 1134 Email: sarahwakelin@st-marys.nhs.uk; Tel: 01923 835973 Fax: 01923 835973 — MB BS 1988 Lond.; BSc (Hons.) Pharmacol. Lond. 1985; MRCP (UK) 1991. (Kings College London) Cons. Derm. St Marys. Hosp; Hon. Sen. Lect. Imperial Coll. of Sci., Technol. and Med. Socs: BMA; Brit. Assn. Dermat.; Europ. Soc. of contact dermatitis. Prev: Sen. Regist. (Dermat.) St. John's Inst. St. Thos. Hosp. Lond.; Sen. Regist. (Dermat.) Amersham Hosp. Bucks.; Regist. (Dermat.) Roy. Berks. Hosp. Reading.

WAKELING, Anthony 59 Bishopsthorpe Road, London SE26 4PA Tel: 020 8778 6994 — MB ChB 1961 Birm.; PhD Birm. 1966, BSc 1958, MB ChB 1961; FRCPsych. 1979, M 1972; DPM Lond. 1968. (Birm.) Prof. Psychiat. Roy. Free Hosp. Sch. Med. Lond.; Hon. Cons. (Psychiat.) Roy. Free Hosp. & Friern Hosp. Lond. Prev: Sen. Lect. Psychiat. Roy. Free Hosp. Sch. Med. Lond.; Sen. Regist. Psychiat. Maudsley Hosp. Lond.

WAKELING, Emma Louise Institute of Child Health, London WC1N Email: e.wakeling@rpms.ac.uk; 80 Bradmore Park Road, London W6 0DT — MB BS 1992 Lond.; BA Oxf. 1989. Hon. Research Regist. Inst. of Child Health Lond. Prev: SHO (Paediat.) Gt. Ormond St. Hosp. Lond.

WAKELING, Howard Grenville 15 Emmett Road, Rownhams, Southampton SO16 8JB — MB BS 1988 Lond.; BSc Lond. 1985, MB BS 1988; MRCP (UK) 1993; FRCA 1994. (Middlx. Hosp. Med. Sch. Lond.) Specialist Regist. Wessex Rotat. Prev: Rotat. Regist. Basingstoke & Soton.; Vis. Assoc. in Anaesth. Duke Univ. Med. Center N. Carolina; SHO (Anaesth.) Roy. United Hosp. Bath & S.mead Hosp. Bristol.

WAKELING, John Amaziah 148 Wenallt Road, Cardiff CF14 6TQ — MB BCh 1994 Wales.

WALDEN

WAKELING, Marilen 59 Bishopsthorpe Road, London SE26 4PA Tel: 020 8778 6994 — MB ChB 1961 Birm.; DPM Eng. 1965. (Birm.) Community Med. Off. Lewisham & Guy's Health Dists.; Sen. Clin. Med. Off. (Family Plann.) Optimum Health Servs.; Family Plann. Instruct. Doctor. Socs: Foundat. Mem. Fac. Community Health; NAFPD. Prev: Regist. (Child Psychiat.) King's Coll. Hosp. Lond.; Regist. All St.s' Hosp. Birm.; Ho. Phys. Midl. Nerv. Hosp. Birm.

WAKELING, Zoe Claire 40 Dunholme Road, Newcastle upon Tyne NE4 6XE — MB BS 1998 Newc.

WAKELY, Catherine 15 Acacia Grove, London SE21 8ER — BM BS 1994 Nottm.

WAKELY, Mr David Mark Good Shepherd Hospital, PO Box 2, Siteki, Swaziland — MB BS 1992 Lond.; Dip IMC (RCS Ed) 2000; FFAEM 2001; BSc (Hons.) Lond. 1989; FRCS Eng. 1996. (Char. Cross & Westm. Hosp. Lond.) Head of Surg. and Emerg. Serv.s, Good Shepherd Hosp. Siteki, Swaziland. Socs: Brit. Assn. Accid. & Emerg. Med.; Fac. Accid. & Emerg. Med. Prev: Specialist Regist. (A & E) P.ss Margt. Hosp. Swindon; Regist. (A & E) Qu. Mary's Univ. Hosp. Lond.; SHO (Cardiothoracic Surg.) Roy. Brompton Hosp. Lond.

WAKELY, Denis 3 Westbourne Crescent, Whitchurch, Cardiff CF14 2BL — MRCS Eng. LRCP Lond. 1951.

WAKELY, Isabel Kate Elizabeth 3 Westbourne Crescent, Whitchurch, Cardiff CF14 2BL Tel: 029 206 6281 — MB ChB 1953 Bristol; DObst RCOG 1956.

WAKELY, James Nicholas 7 St George's Close, Great Bromley, Colchester CO7 7HZ — MRCS Eng. LRCP Lond. 1980; MA (Theol.) Camb. 1977, MB BChir 1983; DFFP 1993. Clin. Asst. (Psychiat.) Clacton Hosp.; Dep. Police Surg. Chelmsford. Prev: SHO (O & G) Rush Green Hosp. Romford; SHO (Cas. & Orthop.) Herts & Essex Hosp. Bishops Stortford; SHO (Psychiat.) P.ss Alexandra Hosp. Harlow.

WAKELY, John Henry (retired) Redcroft, Meols Drive, Hoylake, Wirral CH47 4AQ Tel: 0151 632 1777 — LRCP LRCS 1941 Ed.; LRCP LRCS Ed. LRFPS Glas. 1941; FFA RCS Eng. 1954; DA Eng. 1948. Prev: Cons. Anaesth. Liverp. AHA (T) & St. Helens & Knowsley AHA.

WAKELY, Suzanne Louise Hempstead House, Hempstead Road, Uckfield TN22 1DU — BM 1997 Soton.

WAKEMAN, Anne Juanita 42 Marsh Lane, Penkridge, Stafford ST19 5BP — MB ChB 1988 Birm.; ChB Birm. 1988; BSc (Hons.) Pharmacy Aston; DRCOG 1991. SHO (A & E) Dudley Rd. Hosp. Birm.; Princip. (Gen. Pract.) Wolverhampton. Prev: Princip. GP Frankley Health Centre Birm.; GP Trainee Frankley Health Centre; SHO (Psychiat.) Barnsley Hall Hosp.

WAKEMAN, Mr Robert Basildon Hospital, Nethermayne, Basildon SS16 5NL Tel: 01268 593742 — MB BS 1981 Lond.; FRCS Eng. 1986; FCS(SA) Orth. 1992; T(S) 1994. Cons. Orthop. Basildon Hosp. Prev: Regist. Rotat. (Orthop.) Roy. Free Hosp. Lond.

WAKERLEY, Mark Brice Flat 2, Penleys Court, Penleys Grove St., York YO31 7RW — MB BS 1992 Lond.

WAKERLEY, Rebecca Louise 6 Peacocks Close, Stokesley, Middlesbrough TS9 5QD Tel: 01642 713231 — MB BS 1996 Newc.

WAKES MILLER, Clive Hugh Moss Cottage, The Green, Thornham, Hunstanton PE36 6NIT Tel: 01485 512525 Email: wmclive@aol.com — MB BS 1962 Lond.; MRCS Eng. LRCP Lond. 1962; AFOM RCP Lond. 1982; MRCGP 1970; Cert. Av. Med. 1970. (Guy's) p/t Med. Examr. Benefits Norf. Prev: GP Sutton on Sea Lincs.; GP Shefford Beds.; Regist. (Paediat.) Jenny Lind Hosp. Norwich.

WAKLEY, Edward John (retired) c/o Weston Super Mare General Hospital, Grange Road, Uphill, Weston Super Mare BS23 4TQ — MB ChB 1964 Bristol; MD Bristol 1978; FRCP Lond. 1984; MRCP (UK) 1970; DObst RCOG 1967. Cons. Phys. (Cardiol.) W.on Area Health Trust. Prev: Sen. Regist. Plymouth Health Dist. & Bristol Health Dist. (T).

WAKLEY, Gillian Margaret Kidsgrove Medical Centre, Mount Road, Kidsgrove, Stoke-on-Trent ST7 4AY Tel: 01782 784221 Fax: 01782 781703; 80 Sneyd Avenue, Newcastle ST5 2PY Tel: 01782 624447 Fax: 01782 624447 — MB ChB Bristol 1965; MFFP 1994. Sen. Clin. Lect. (Primary Care) Keele Univ. 1997. Socs: Inst. Psychosexual Med.

WAKTARE, Johan Esbjorn Patrik 103 Canbury Avenue, Kingston upon Thames KT2 6JR Tel: 020 8286 8021 Email: jwaktare@sghms.ac.uk — MB ChB 1989 Manch.; MRCP 1993. Clin. Research Regist. (Cardiol. Scis.) St. Geos. Hosp. Med. Sch.

WALAPU, Myanga Fumbanani Macdonald Department of Public Health Medicine, St. Davids Hospital, PO Box 13, Carmarthen SA31 3YH Tel: 01267 234501 Fax: 01267 223337 — MB ChB 1978 Manch.; MSc Manch. 1985; MFCM RCP (UK) 1986; DRCOG 1980. Cons. Pub. Health Med. Dyfed, Powys HA.

WALAWENDER, Andrzej Josef c/o JAT, PO Box 367, Twickenham TW2 7TU Tel: 020 8898 7429 Fax: 020 8894 4335 Email: jatco@compuserve.com — MB BS 1985 Lond.

WALAYAT, Muhammed Department of Cardiology, Royal Hospital for Sick Children, Edinburgh EH9 1LF Tel: 0131 667 1991; 6/2 Dalrymple Crescent, Edinburgh EH9 2NU — MB BS 1985 Pakistan; MRCP (UK) 1991.

WALBAUM, David William Flat 3/3, 1 Woodlands Drive, Glasgow G4 9EQ — MB ChB 1993 Glas.; MRCP (UK) 1996. (Glas.)

WALBAUM, Mr Philip Raby (retired) 10 Ravelston Heights, Ravelston House Park, Edinburgh EH4 3LX — MB ChB 1944 Ed.; MB ChB (Hnrs.) Ed. 1944; FRCS Ed. 1948. Prev: Cons. Cardiothoracic Surg. Lothian HB.

WALBRIDGE, David Gerrard Department of Psychiatry, Royal South Hants Hospital, Graham Road, Southampton SO14 0YG Tel: 02380 634288 — MB ChB 1981 Bristol; BSc Bristol 1978, MD 1993; MRCPsych 1986. Cons. Psychiat. Roy. S. Hants. Hosp. Soton.; Hon. Clin. Teach. Univ. Soton. Prev: Sen. Regist. (Psychiat.) Warneford Hosp. Oxf.; Regist. & SHO (Psychiat.) Barrow Hosp. Bristol; SHO (Gen. Med.) Dist. Gen. Hosp. Gorleston.

WALBROOK, Emma Elizabeth 71 Earlswood Road, Redhill RH1 6HJ — MB BS 1997 Lond.

WALBURN, Michael Brian Department of Anaethesia, Bristol Royal Infirmary, Marlborough Street, Bristol BS2 8HW — MB ChB 1990 Bristol.

WALBY, Mr Anthony Peter 41 Derryvolgie Avenue, Belfast BT9 6FP — MB BCh BAO 1974 Belf.; MB BCh Belf. 1974; FRCS Ed. 1979. Cons. Otorhinolaryng. Roy. Vict. Hosp., Roy. Belf. Hosp. for Sick Childr. & City Hosp. Belf.

WALBY, Ceri Woodlands Surgery, Woodlands Terrace, Caerau, Maesteg CF34 0SR Tel: 01656 734203; 7 Pen-y-Wain Road, Cardiff CF24 4GB — MB BCh 1989 Wales; MRCP (UK) 1992; MRCGP 1996. (Univ. Wales Coll. Med.)

WALCOT, Nicholas Ralph Henry 26 Watts Lane, Teddington TW11 8HQ — MB BS 1993 Lond.

WALCZAK, Mr Jonathan Peter Beauchamp 6 Chichester Drive, Sevenoaks TN13 2NR Email: jongenu@aol.com — MB BS 1987 Lond.; BSc (Biochem.) Lond. 1984; FRCS Eng. 1992; FRCS (Orth.) 1998. (UMDS) Cons. Trauma. Orthop. Surg. Bromley Hosp. NHS Trust; Treas. to S. E. Thames higher Train. Progr. in Orthopaedic Surg. Socs: BOTA; Assoc. Mem. BOA.

WALCZAK, Paul Martin 45 Queens Road, Liverpool L23 5TP — LMSSA 1976 Lond.

WALD, David Samuel St Charles Hospital, Exmoor St., London W10 6DZ — MB BS 1993 Lond.

WALD, Professor Nicholas John Dept of Environm. & Preven. Med. Wolfson Institute, Barts & Queen Mary Lond. School, of Med. & Dent., Charterhouse Square, London EC1M 6BQ Tel: 020 78826269 Fax: 020 78826270 Email: n.j.wald@qmul.ac.uk; 9 Park Crescent Mews E., London W1N 5HB Tel: 020 76362721 — 2000 Cbiol FiBiol; MB BS Lond. 1967; DSc (Med.) Lond. 1987; FRCP Lond. 1986; FRCOG 1992; FPHM RCP Lond. 1982; F Med Sci 1998. (Univ. Coll. Hosp.) Prof. Environm. & Preven. Med. & Hon. Cons. (Chairm.) Wolfson Inst. Barts. & The Lond.Qu. Mary Sch. Med. & Dent.; Edr. Jl. Med. Screening; Chairm., Wolfson Inst. of Preventative Med. Socs: Assn. Phys. Prev: Dep. Dir. ICRF Cancer Epidemiol. & Clin. Trials Unit Univ. Oxf.; Mem. Scientif. Staff Med. Research Counc. N.wick Pk. Hosp.; Regist. (Med.) Univ. Coll. Hosp. Lond.

WALDEK, Stephen Renal Unit, Hope Hospital, Salford M6 8HD Tel: 0161 789 7373 Fax: 0161 787 5775 Email: steve@ren.srht.nwest.nhs.uk; 31 Harboro Road, Sale M33 5AN Tel: 0161 973 6275 Email: walkeks@compuserve.com — MB BCh 1971 Wales; FRCP Lond. 1990; MRCP (UK) 1974. Cons. Nephrol. Salford, DHA; Med. Dir. Prev: Sen. Regist. (Nephrol.) Sheff. AHA (T).

WALDEN, Amanda 1 Howe Close, Mudeford, Christchurch BH23 3JA — MB ChB 1983 Liverp.; Cert. Family Plann. JCC 1986.

WALDEN

Retainer Scheme in Gen. Pract. Bournemouth. Prev: SHO (O & G) Poole Gen. Hosp.; Community Med. Off. E. Dorset HA; Trainee GP Boscombe VTS.

WALDEN, Andrew Peter Flat B, 165 Battersea Rise, London SW11 1HP — MB BS 1994 Lond.

WALDEN, Anne Fiona Doreen 49 Barcombe Heights, Preston, Paignton TQ3 1PU — MB BS 1985 Lond.; DRCOG 1989. Prev: Trainee GP CMH VTS.

WALDEN, Faye The Medical Centre, 143 Rookwood Avenue, Leeds LS9 0NL; 6 Wigton Grove, Leeds LS17 7DZ — MB ChB Leeds 1962. (Leeds)

WALDEN, Henry 444 Oakwood Lane, Leeds LS8 3LG — MRCS Eng. LRCP Lond. 1926. (Leeds)

WALDEN, Neil Patrick Michael Marazion Surgery, Gwallon Lane, Marazion TR17 0HW; Elm Cottage, Relubbus, Penzance TR20 9EP Tel: 01736 763417 — MB BS 1982 Lond.

WALDEN, Peter Alexander Mennie (cons. rooms), 47 Hugh St., London SW1V 1QJ Tel: 020 7828 0913 Fax: 020 7233 7616; 85 Rusthall Avenue, Chiswick, London W4 1BN Tel: 020 8994 4363 — MB BS 1964 Lond.; BAcC 1980; MRCP (UK) 1970; MRCS Eng. LRCP Lond. 1963; DObst RCOG 1966. (St. Geo.) Socs: Fell. Roy. Soc. Med.; BMA.

WALDEN, Richard John (retired) Bossall, 126 Bluehouse Lane, Limpsfield, Oxted RH8 0AR Tel: 01883 712952 Fax: 01883 712952 — MB BS 1963 Lond.; MD Lond. 1989; MRCS Eng. LRCP Lond. 1963; Dip. Pharm. Med. RCP (UK) 1976. Prev: Clin. Asst. (Endocrinol.) Middlx. Hosp. Lond.

WALDEN, Susan Jane, Maj. RAMC 85 Rusthall Avenue, London W4 1BN Tel: 020 8994 4363 — MB BS 1991 Lond.; DRCOG 1995; DCCH 1995; MRCGP 1998. (King's Coll.)

WALDEN, Tracey Anne 8 Hartnell Court, Albert Road, Corfe Mullen, Wimborne BH21 3TY — MB BS 1992 Lond. (St. Bart.) Med. Off. Joseph Weld Hospice Dorchester (p/t). Prev: Princip. (Gen. Pract.) The Pk. Surg. Yeovil.

WALDENBERG-NAMROW, Caroline 39 Winding Way, Leeds LS17 7RG — MB ChB 1995 Manch.; BA Hons. Oxf. 1993.

WALDER, Andrew David Anaesthetic Department, North Devon District Hospital, Raleigh Park, Barnstaple EX31 4JB — MB BS 1986 Lond.; MRCP (UK) 1991; FRCA 1992. Clin. Dir. (Intens. Care) N. Devon Dist. Hosp.

WALDER, Professor Dennis Neville 21 Osbaldeston Gardens, Gosforth, Newcastle upon Tyne NE3 4JE Tel: 0191 285 2327 — MB ChB 1940 Bristol; MD Bristol 1947, ChM 1965; FRCS Eng. 1954; FRCS Ed. 1954; MFOM RCP Lond. 1980. (Bristol) Emerit. Prof. Surg. Sc. Univ. Newc.; Hon. Cons. Surg. Roy. Vict. Infirm. Newc. Prev: Chairm. MRC Decompression Sickness Panel; Hunt Prof. RCS Eng. 1965.

WALDER, Geoffrey Peter Lilliput Surgery, Elms Avenue, Lindisfarne, Poole BH14 8EE — MB BS 1974 (per GMC) Newcastle. GP; Clin. Asst. in Opthalmology.

WALDES, Mr Rodney Maxwell Greenford Avenue Medical Centre, 322 Greenford Avenue, London W7 3AH Tel: 020 8578 1880; 96 Church Road, Hanwell, London W7 3BE Tel: 020 8567 3665 Fax: 020 8567 3665 — MB ChB 1970 Manch.; FRCS Eng. 1977. (Manch.) Prev: Regist. (Radiodiag.) Hammersmith Hosp. Lond.; Regist. (Surg.) Hammersmith Hosp. Lond.; Regist. (Surg.) King Edwd. Memor. Hosp. Ealing.

WALDIE, Mr Wilfrid (retired) Moorcroft, Old Whisky Road, Auchterhouse, Dundee DD3 0RD Tel: 01382 320232 — MB ChB 1947 Glas.; FRCS Ed. 1960. Cons. Orthop. Surg. Dundee Roy. Infirm.; Hon. Sen. Lect. in Orthop. Surg. Univ. Dundee. Prev: Sen. Orthop. Regist. Bridge of Earn Hosp. Perth.

WALDIN, Ian Ernest Gwynne High Green Surgery, 16 High Green, Gainford, Darlington DL2 3DL Tel: 01325 730204 — MB BS 1979 Lond.; LMSSA Lond. 1977; MRCGP 1985; DRCOG 1983; DCH RCP Lond. 1983. (St. Bart.)

WALDMAN, Adam Daniel Bernard Department of Diagnostic Radiology, Middlesex Hospital, London W1N 8AA Tel: 020 7323 6772 Email: adam@medphys.ucl.ac.uk; 3 Davenant Road, London N19 3NW — MB BChir 1993 Camb.; PhD Bristol 1985; BSc (Hons.) Lancaster 1981; MA Camb. 1994; MRCP (UK) 1995. Specialist Regist. (Diagnostic Radio.) UCL Hosps. Prev: SHO (Med.) Whittington & Hammersmith Hosps.; Ho. Off. (Surg.) W. Suff. Hosp.; Ho. Off. (Med.) Addenbrooke's Hosp. Camb.

WALDMAN, Brian Lewin (retired) Edgehill, Ogdens N., Fordingbridge SP6 2QD Tel: 01425 653660 — MB BS 1960 Lond.; FRCGP 1981, M 1973; DObst RCOG 1964. Prev: Ho. Phys. & Ho. Surg. Roy. W. Sussex Hosp. Chichester.

WALDMAN, Ernest Isidor 16 Dorrington Road, Sale M33 5EB — MB ChB 1951 Liverp.

WALDMAN, Jack (retired) 62A Warren Drive, Wallasey CH45 0JT Tel: 0151 639 7091 — MRCS Eng. LRCP Lond. 1943; MRCGP 1963.

WALDMAN, Louise Jane Stamford Hill Group Practice, 2 Egerton Road, Stamford Hill, London N16 6UA Tel: 020 8800 1000 Fax: 020 8880 2402; 3 Davenant Road, London N19 3NW — MB ChB 1987 Bristol; MRCGP 1999; DFFP 1995; DGM RCP Lond. 1991. (Bristol) p/t GP Stamford Hill Lond. Prev: Staff Grade (Community Paediat.) City & E. Lond.; GP/Regist. Stamford Hill Gp. Pract. Lond.

WALDMAN, Nicola Sarah The Merton Surgery, 156-8 Merton High Street, London SW19 1AZ Tel: 020 8540 1109 Fax: 020 8543 3353; 3B Norman Road, South Wimbledon, London SW19 1BW Email: doc-holliday@saqnet.co.uk — MB BS 1990 Lond.; MRCGP 1996; DFFP 1996; DRCOG 1995; T(GP) 1996. (St. Mary's Hospital) GP Princip. Merton Surg. Lond.

WALDMAN, Steven Joseph Ailsa Craig Medical Group, 270 Dickenson Road, Longsight, Manchester M13 0YL Tel: 0161 224 5555 Fax: 0161 248 9112; 61 Linksway, Gatley, Cheadle SK8 4LA Tel: 0161 491 2910 — MB ChB 1972 Liverp.; MRCGP 1976; Cert FPA 1976; DObst RCOG 1975. GP Trainer. Prev: SHO (Paediat.) W. Middlx. Hosp. Isleworth; SHO (Med.) Hadassah Hosp. Jerusalem, Israel; SHO (O & G) St. Mary's Hosp. Lond.

WALDMANN, Carl Samuel, Squadron Ldr. RAF Med. Br. Retd. Intensive Care Unit, Royal Berkshire Hospital, Reading RG1 5AN Tel: 01189 877249 Fax: 01189 877250; 2 Dewe Lane, Burghfield, Reading RG30 3SU Tel: 01189 576381 Fax: 01189 877250 Email: cswald@aol.com — MB BChir 1976 Camb.; MA, MB Camb. 1976, BChir 1975; Europ. Dip. Intens Care Med. 1993; FFA RCS Eng. 1980; DA Eng. 1978. (Cambridge University and The London Hospital) Cons. Anaesth. & Dir. Intens. Care Units Roy. Berks. & Battle Hosps. Reading; Div. Director, Clin. support Serv. at Roy. Bertsabattle NHS Trust. Socs: Intens. Care Soc.; Counc. of IC Soc.; Assn. Anaesth. Prev: Lect. Lond. Hosp. Med. Sch.; Sen. Regist. (Anaesth.) Gt. Ormond St. Hosp. Lond.; Sen. Regist. Lond. Hosp. Whitechapel.

WALDOCK, Mr Andrew Torbay Hospital, Lawes Bridge, Torquay TQ2 7AA Tel: 01803 614567; 56 Barkleys Hill, Stapleton, Bristol BS16 1AD Tel: 0117 958 6477 Email: awaldcock@hotmail.com — BM BS 1989 Nottm.; BMedSci Nottm. 1987; FRCOphth 1994. (Nottm.) Specialist Regist. (Ophth.)Bristol Hosp. Prev: Specialist Regist. (Ophth.) Roy. Devon & Exeter Hosp.; Research Regist. (Ophth.) Bristol Eye Hosp.; Specialist Regist. Orpth. Torbay Hosp.

WALDOCK, Fiona Joy Victoria Medical Centre, 7 Victoria Crescent West, Barnsley S75 2AE Tel: 01226 282758 Fax: 01226 729800; 44 Granville Street, Barnsley S75 2TQ Tel: 01226 203798 Email: waldoc@global.net.uk — MB ChB 1983 Leic.; MRCGP 1988; DRCOG 1987. (Leicester) GP; Med. Off. St. Peter's Hospice Barnsley; Clin. Asst. St. Peter's Hospice Barnsley. Prev: Trainee GP Leicester VTS.

WALDON, Richard David Rowcroft Medical Centre, Rowcroft Retreat, Stroud GL5 3BE Tel: 01453 764471 Fax: 01453 755247; Woodlands, South Woodchester, Stroud GL5 5EQ Tel: 01453 872158 — MB BS 1986 Lond.; BSc Lond. 1981; DCH RCP Lond. 1990. Prev: SHO & Clin. Med. Off. (Paediat.) Epsom Dist. Gen. Hosp. Surrey; SHO (A & E) St. Stephens Hosp. Lond.; SHO (Gen. Med.) Epsom Dist. Gen. Hosp. Surrey.

WALDRAM, Mr Michael Andrew 5 Silverhills, Rosneath, Helensburgh G84 0EW Tel: 0121 685 4223 Fax: 0121 685 4041 — MB BS 1977 Lond.; FRCS Ed. (Orth.) 1987; FRCS Ed. 1982. Cons. Orthop. & Hand Surg. Roy. Orthop. Hosp. Birm. & Selly Oak Hosp. Birm. Socs: Brit. Orthop. Assn.; Brit. Soc. Surg. Hand. Prev: Christine Kleinert Hand Fell.sh. Louisville, Kentucky.; Sen. Regist. Roy. Orthop. Hosp. Birm.; Regist. (Surg.) Basingstoke Dist. Hosp.

WALDRON, Alexandra Catherine Houston 26 Graham Park Road, Gosforth, Newcastle upon Tyne NE3 4BH — MB ChB 1995 Sheff.

WALDRON, Brian Alan Long Acre Lodge, Flatts Lane, Calverton, Nottingham NG14 6JZ Tel: 0115 965 3283 — MB BS 1960 Lond.;

MRCS Eng. LRCP Lond. 1960; FFA RCS Eng. 1971; DA Eng. 1964; DObst RCOG 1963; MRCGP 1968. (St. Mary's) Cons. Anaesth. Nottm. City Hosp. & Univ. Hosp. Nottm.; Clin. Teach. Univ. Nottm. Socs: Obst. Anaesth. Assn. & Intractable Pain Soc. Prev: Sen. Regist. (Anaesth.) & Research Fell. (Anaesth.) Univ. Hosp. Wales Cardiff; Regist. (Physical Med.) Whittington Hosp. Lond.

WALDRON, Bryan Le Gros (retired) 51 Dunraven Drive, Derriford, Plymouth PL6 6AT Tel: 01752 792691 — MB BChir 1957 Camb.; BA, MB Camb. 1958, BChir 1957; FFA RCS Eng. 1961; DA Eng. 1959. Cons. Anaesth. Plymouth Health Dist.

WALDRON, Felicity Mary The Surgery, Church Lane, Bishopthorpe, York YO60 6PS Tel: 01904 630918 — MB ChB 1976 Dundee.

WALDRON, Gerard John Mark Northern Health & Social Services Board, County Hall, Galgorm Road, Ballymena BT42 1QB Tel: 01266 662207 Email: gerry.waldron@nhssb.ni.nhs.uk; 35 Sourhill, Ballymena BT42 2LG Tel: 01266 40606 Fax: 01266 48488 — MB BCh BAO 1981 NUI; MFPHM 1995. (Galway) Cons. (Publ. Health Med.) N. Health & Socl Servs. Bd. Prev: Cons. Solihull HA; Sen. Regist. Dumfries & Galloway HB; Regist. & Sen. Regist. Croydon HA.

WALDRON, Gillian 31 Maidstone Road, Bounds Green, London N11 2TR Tel: 020 8888 4253 — MB ChB 1971 Birm.; MRCPsych 1975. Cons. Psychiat. Gr.lands Priory Hosp. Lond. Prev: Cons. Psychiat. Tower Hamlets HA; Lect. (Psychiat.) Lond. Hosp.

WALDRON, Harry Arthur 31 Maidstone Road, London N11 2TR — MD 1977 Birm.; PhD Birm. 1975, MD 1977, MB ChB 1971; FRCP Lond. 1993; MRCP (UK) 1977; FFOM RCP Lond. 1980, M 1978; DHMSA Lond. 1974. Cons. Phys. St. Mary's Hosp. Lond.; Research Fell. Inst. Archeology UCL; Edr. Brit. Jl. Indust. Med. Socs: Soc. Occupat. Med.; Fell. Roy. Soc. Med. Prev: Sen. Lect. (Occupat. Med.) Lond.; Ho. Surg. & Ho. Phys. Gen. Hosp. Birm.

WALDRON, Jean Winifred (retired) 12 Park Road, Fowey PL23 1ED — MB ChB 1954 Leeds; DCH Eng. 1963; MA 1996; M Th 1998.

WALDRON, Mr John ENT Department, Royal United Hospital, Bath BA1 3NG; 66 Murhill, Limpley Stoke, Bath BA2 7FQ — MB BS 1981 Lond.; FRCS (Otol.) Eng. 1986. Cons. ENT Surg. Roy. United Hosp. Bath.

WALDRON, John Pius 19 Pembridge Crescent, London W11 3DX — MB BCh BAO 1978 NUI; MRCPI 1980.

WALDRON, Martin Nigel Schering-Plough Ltd, Schering-Plough House, Shire Park, Welwyn Garden City AL7 1TW Tel: 01707 363780 Fax: 01707 363690; 24 Westlecote Gardens, Luton LU2 7DR — MB BS 1980 Lond. Med. Marketing Manager Schering-Plough Ltd. Prev: Sen. Med. Adviser Hoechst Roussel Ltd.; GP Luton; Ho. Surg. Roy. Free Hosp. Lond.

WALDRON, Mary Department of Child Health, Southampton General Hospital, Tremona Road, Southampton SO16 6YD Tel: 02380 798809 — MB BCh BAO 1980 NUI; MRCPI 1987. (Galway) Cons. Paediat. Nephrol. Soton. Univ. Hosp. Socs: Internat. Paediat. Nephrol. Assn.; Brit. Assn. Paediat. Nephrol.

WALDRON, Michael Jeremy Fowey Health Centre, Rawlings Lane, Fowey PL23 1DT Tel: 01726 832451; Cedron House, 32 Tower Park, Fowey PL23 1JD Tel: 01726 833209 — BSc Wales 1978, MB BCh 1983; MRCGP 1988; DCH RCP Lond. 1986.

WALDRON, Michael John Caldbeck and Partners, Hurst Close, Gossops Green, Crawley RH11 8TY Tel: 01293 527138 Fax: 01293 522571 — MB BS 1987 Lond.; DRCOG 1991. Prev: Trainee GP E.bourne VTS; SHO (Gen. Med.) St. Marys Hosp. E.bourne; Ho. Off. (Gen. Surg.) E.bourne Dist. Gen. Hosp.

WALDRON, Murray Neil Houston 26 Graham Park Road, Gosforth, Newcastle upon Tyne NE3 4BH — BM BCh 1992 Oxf.

WALDRON, Richard William The Surgery, 102 Preston Road, Weymouth DT3 6BB Tel: 01305 832203; The Spinney, 97 Wyke Road, Weymouth DT4 9QS — MB BS 1980 Lond.; MBA 1999 Bournemouth; DRCOG 1985.

WALDRON, Susan May Graeme Medical Centre, 1 Western Avenue, Falkirk FK2 7HR Tel: 01324 624437 Fax: 01324 633737; 15 Panbrae, Boiness, Edinburgh EH51 0EJ Tel: 01506 824836 Email: suenick1@aol.com — MB ChB 1989 Manch.; BSc (Med. Sci.) St. And. 1986; MRCGP 1993; DCCH RCP Ed. 1994; DRCOG 1992. GP. Prev: Trainee (Community Paediat.) Sighthill Health Centre

Edin.; Chief Med. Off. VRO Rajahmundry Andhra, Pradesh, India; SHO (A & E) Falkirk Roy. Infirm.

WALDRUM, Christopher Ian Greengate Medical Centre, 1 Greengate Lane, Birstall, Leicester LE4 3JF Tel: 0116 267 7901 — MB ChB 1989 Leic.

WALE, Laurence William 15 Pearman Street, London SE1 7RB — MB BS 1983 Lond.

WALE, Martin Charles Johnson CDSC (Trent), Public Health Laboratory, Queens Medical Centre, Nottingham NG7 2UH Tel: 0115 970 9048 Fax: 0115 970 9019 Email: mwale@phls.nhs.uk — BM BS 1980 Nottm.; BMedSci (Hons.) Nottm. 1978; MRCPath 1990; Dip. Bact. Manch. 1988; FRCPath 1998. (Nottm.) Cons. Regional Epidemiol. CDSC (Trent) Nottm.; Hon. Cons. Microbiol. PHLS Trent. Prev: Cons. Microbiol. & Communicable Dis. Control Soton.; Sen. Regist. Pub. Health Laborat. City Hosp. Nottm. & Hon. Regist. Pub. Health Laborat. Portsmouth; Med. Off. 40 Commando R.M.

WALE, Peter Frederick (retired) 202 Attenborough Lane, Beeston, Nottingham NG9 6AL Tel: 0115 9254 305 — MB BS 1955 Lond.; MRCS Eng. LRCP Lond. 1955; FFR 1967; DMRT Eng. 1960. Cons. Radiother. Derbysh. Roy. Infirm. & Nottm. Gen. Hosp. Prev: Cons. Radiotherap. Romford Hosp. Gp.

WALES, Alan Christopher Bergamot House, 37 Long Meadows, Burley-in-Wharfedale, Ilkley LS29 7RY Tel: 01943 865139 — MB ChB 1965 Leeds; MRCGP 1980; DObst RCOG 1971. (Leeds) p/t Specialist (Disabil. Med.) W. Yorks. Prev: Med. Adviser Teach.'s Pension Scheme; Med. Adviser Benefits Agency Med. Servs.; GP Penistone & Stannington Sheff.

WALES, Andrew Thomas Peggs La Cottage, Queniborough, Leicester LE7 3DF — MB BS 1998 Lond.

WALES, Deborah Anne Finch Mill Farm, Miles Lane, Appley Bridge, Wigan WN6 9JA Tel: 01257 252316 — MB ChB 1986 Leeds; MRCP (UK) 1993; FRCA 1994. Specialist Regist. (Respir. Med.) Wythenshave Hosp. Manch. Socs: Brit. Thorac. Soc. Prev: Regist. (Respir. Med.) Roy. Lancast. Infirm.; Regist. (Resp. Med.) Hope Hosp. Salford.

WALES, Elisabeth Lucy Hall Garth, Kingsley Road, Frodsham, Warrington WA6 6BB — MB ChB 1993 Bristol.

WALES, Elizabeth 9 The Woodlands, Esher KT10 8DD — MB BS 1949 Durh.; LMSSA Lond. 1947; MFCM 1975; DCH Eng. 1959; DPH Leeds 1961; DObst RCOG 1963. (Durh.) Prev: Sen. Med. Off. DHSS.

WALES, Emma Kathryn Hallgarth, Kingsley Road, Frodsham, Warrington WA6 6BB — MB BS 1994 Newc.

WALES, Ian Frederick Hall Lisburn Health Centre, Linenhall Street, Lisburn BT28 1LU; 33 Windsor Hill, Carnreagh, Hillsborough BT26 6RL Tel: 01846 683443 — MB BCh BAO 1982 Belf.; MRCGP 1988; DRCOG 1986; DCH Dub. 1986.

WALES, Jeremy Kenneth Harvard c/o University Department of Paediatrics, Sheffield Children's Hospital, Western Bank, Sheffield S10 2TH Tel: 0114 271 7508 Fax: 0114 275 5364 Email: j.k.wales@sheffield.ac.uk — BM BCh 1979 Oxf.; MRCP; MA Oxf. 1980, DM 1990; FRCP Lond. 1994; FRCPCH 1997. Sen. Lect. (Paediat. Endocrinol.) & Hon. Cons. Paediat. Univ. Sheff. Socs: Eur. Soc. Paediat. Endocrinol.; Brit. Soc. Paediat. Endocrinol. Prev: Lect. (Paediat.) Sheff. Univ.; Regist. (Paediat.) Soton. & Basingstoke.

WALES, Joanne Elizabeth Jane Macclesfield District General Hospital, Victoria Road, Macclesfield SK10 3BL Tel: 01625 421000; 7 Moorlands Close, Tytherington, Macclesfield SK10 2TL Tel: 01625 428528 — MB ChB 1986 Liverp.; DA (UK) 1989. Clin. Asst. (Anaesth.) Macclesfield Dist. Gen. Hosp.

WALES, John Kenneth Academic Unit of Medicine, Martin Wing, The General Infirmary, Leeds LS1 3EX Tel: 0113 392 3470 Fax: 0113 242 3811; School House, Acaster-Selby, Appleton Roebuck, York YO23 7BP Tel: 01904 744220 — MB ChB Leeds 1960; MD Leeds 1965; FRCP Lond. 1979; M 1968. (Leeds) Sen. Lect. Univ. Leeds & Hon. Cons. Phys. Leeds Teach. Hosps. NHS Trust. Socs: Chairm. Assn. Brit. Clin. Diabetologists; Diabetes UK - Mem.; Assn. Study Obesity - Mem. Prev: Asst. Prof. Med. Geo. Washington Sch. Med. Washington, DC; MRC Jun. Research Fell. (Pharmacol.) Univ. Leeds.; Prof. Chairm. Dept. Med. FM HS UAE Univ. United Arab Emerates.

WALES, John Michael Glenfield General Hospital, Groby Road, Leicester LE3 9QP Tel: 0116 287 1471 Fax: 0116 255 6841; Peggs

WALES

Lane Cottage, Pegg Lane, Queniborough, Leicester LE7 3DF Tel: 0116 260 5726 — MB BChir 1966 Camb.; BChir 1965; FRCP Lond. 1981; MRCP (UK) 1970. (St.Bart.) Cons. Phys. (Gen. & Chest Med.) Glenfield Gen. Hosp. Leicester; Assoc. Med. Director, UHL Trust (Univ. Hosps. Leicester NHS Trust). Socs: BMA & Brit. Thoracic Soc. Prev: Sen. Regist. (Med.) Soton. Gp. Hosps.; SHO Warwick Hosp.

WALES, Nicholas Michael 40 Parkholme Road, London E8 3AG — MB BS 1991 Lond.

WALES, Raymond Mitchell Dumbarton Health Centre, Station Road, Dumbarton G82 1PW Tel: 01389 602655 Fax: 01389 602622 — MB ChB 1970 Glas.

WALES, Richard Michael Department of Psychiatry, St. Andrews Hospital, Yarmouth Road, Norwich NR7 0EW Tel: 01603 31122; 132 South Hill Road, Thorpe, Norwich NR7 0LR — MB ChB 1982 Aberd. SHO (Forens. Psychiat.) Norwich HA. Prev: SHO (Radiother. & Oncol.) Norwich HA; Regist. (Chest, Gen. & Geriat. Med.) W. Essex HA.

WALESBY, Mr Robin Kingsley 88 Harley Street, London W1N 1AE Tel: 020 7486 4617; Fleur House, 7 The Drive, Coombe Hill, Kingston upon Thames KT2 7NY Tel: 020 8942 6368 Fax: 020 8949 6835 — MRCS Eng. LRCP Lond. 1970; MSc Lond. 1972, MB BS 1970; FRCS Eng. 1975. (Roy. Free) Sen. Lect. & Cons. Cardiothoracic Surg. Roy. Free & Univ. Colllege Hosp. Med. Sch. Socs: Soc. Cardiothorac. Surg. GB & Irel.; Eur. Soc. Cardiothorac. Surg. Prev: Cons. Cardiothoracic Surg. Lond. Chest Hosp. Roy. Free Hosp. & S.end Health Auth.; Sen. Regist. (Cardiothoracex Surg.) Roy. Postgrad. Med. Sch. Lond. Hosp. Sick Childr. Lond. & Middlx. & Harefield Hosps. Lond.

WALEWSKA, Renata Janina Flat 35, Shore Court, Shore Lane, Sheffield S10 3BW — MB ChB 1993 Sheff.

WALFORD, Claire Susan Northwood Health Centre, Neal Close, Northwood HA6 1TQ Tel: 01923 820844; Heathbourne Lodge, Heathbourne Road, Bushey, Watford WD23 1PA Tel: 020 8950 0344 Fax: 020 8950 0344 — MB BS 1975 Lond.; MRCGP 1987; DCH Eng. 1977. (Univ. Coll. Hosp.) Cons. Grade Specialist (Primary Care) A & E Dept. UCL Hosps Trust. Socs: BMA; Nat. Assn. Fundholding Pract. Prev: SHO (A & E) Univ. Coll. Hosp. Lond.; Trainee GP Harrow Weald Middlx.; Regist. (Paediat.) N.wick Pk. Hosp.

WALFORD, David Henry Howard 15 Shore Road, Little Bispham, Thornton-Cleveleys FY5 1PF — MB BChir 1948 Camb.; MA, MB BChir Camb. 1948. (Camb. & St. Thos.) Prev: Ho. Phys. Grimsby & Dist. Hosp.

WALFORD, Diana Marion Public Health Laboratory Service, 61 Colindale Avenue, London NW9 5DF Tel: 020 8200 1295 Fax: 020 8358 3242 — MB ChB Liverp. 1968; MSc (Epidemiol.) Lond. 1987; BSc (1st cl. Hons) Liverp. 1965, MD 1976; FRCP Lond. 1990; MRCP (UK) 1972; FRCPath 1986, M 1974; FFPHM RCP (UK) 1995, M 1989. Dir. Pub. Health Laborat. Serv. Lond. Socs: Founder Mem. Brit. Blood Transfus. Soc.; Hon. Life Mem. Brit. Assn. Med. Managers. Prev: Dep. Chief Med. Off. DoH; Dir. NHS Managem. Exec.; Hon. Cons. (Haemat.) Centr. Middlx. Hosp.

WALFORD, Frank Roy (retired) 15 Grove Road, Chichester PO19 2AR Tel: 01243 533947 — MB ChB Birm. 1958; FRCPath 1980, M 1967. Prev: Cons. St. Wilfrids Hospice Chichester.

WALFORD, Geraldine Ann 65 Princetown Road, Bangor BT20 3TD — MB BS 1976 Lond.

WALFORD, Harriet Katherine The Barn, Eastrop, Stratfield Mortimer, Reading RG7 3NR Tel: 01189 331635 Mobile: 0780 123 3966 Email: harrietw@lineone.net — MB ChB 1986 Bristol; BA (Hons.) Brighton 1997; MRCGP 1991. p/t Locum GP & Asst. GP.

WALFORD, Linda Jane Leeds Psychotherapy Training Institute, 2A Weetwood Lane, Leeds LS16 5LS Tel: 0113 278 9953 — MB ChB 1980 Leeds; MRCPsych 1985. Dir. (Clin. Train.) Leeds Psychother. Train. Inst.

WALFORD, Miss Mary Elizabeth (retired) Sibford, Church Hill, Marnhull, Sturminster Newton DT10 1PU Tel: 01258 820201 — MB ChB 1948 St. And.; FRCS Eng. 1956. Prev: Cons. Orthop. Surg. Portsmouth Gp. Hosps.

WALFORD, Norman Quentin 10 Queen Quay, Welshback, Bristol BS1 4SL — MB 1977 Camb.; BChir 1976; MRCPath 1987. Sen. Lect. (Histopath.) Univ. Amsterdam. Prev: Lect. (Histopath.) Inst.

Child Health; Regist. (Histopath.) Hammersmith Hosp.; Ho. Off. Liver Unit King's Coll. Hosp.

WALFORD, Rita (retired) Flat 42, The Four Tubs, Little Bushey Lane, Bushey Heath, Watford WD23 4SJ Tel: 020 8950 6950 — MB ChB 1938 Birm. Prev: RAF Med. Br. 1942-45.

WALFORD, Sally Anne 24 Victoria Place, Stirling FK8 2QT — MB ChB 1985 Sheff.

WALFORD, Simon Diabetes Centre, Royal Wolverhampton Hospital NHS Trust, New Cross Hospital, Wolverhampton WV10 0QP Tel: 01902 643007 Fax: 01902 643173 — MB BChir 1975 Camb.; MA 1975 Camb.; MD 1984 Camb.; FRCP Lond. 1992; MRCP (UK) 1976. Cons. Phys. Roy. Wolverhampton Hosps. NHS Trust.; Clin. Sub-Dean, Univ. of Birm. Sch. of Med. Prev: Med. Director, Roy. Wolverhampton Hosps. NHS Trust; 1st Asst. (Med. Endocrinol.) Med. Sch. Univ. Newc.; Regist. & Novo Research Fell. (Med.) Univ. Hosp. Nottm.

WALGAMA, Suduweli Kondage Lettis 80 Countisbury Avenue, Bush Hill Park, Enfield EN1 2NN Tel: 020 8360 5179 — MB BS 1968 Ceylon; MRCP (UK) 1978; MRCS Eng. LRCP Lond. 1980; DCH Eng. 1979. (Ceylon) Clin. Med. Off. Enfield & Haringey AHA. Prev: SHO (Paediat., Gen. Med. & Geriat. Med.) St. Margt's Hosp. Epping.; SHO (Geriat. Med.) St. Geo. Hosp. HornCh..

WALI, Gitanath Druids Heath Surgery, 27 Pound Road, Druids Heath, Birmingham B14 5SB Tel: 0121 430 5461 — MB BS 1974 Mysore; MB BS 1974 Mysore.

WALI, Mr Jaweed Accident & Emergency Department, Coleraine Hospital, Coleraine BT52 1JA Tel: 01265 44177; 12 Castlewood Avenue, Coleraine BT52 1JR Tel: 01265 53746 — MB BS 1977 Karnatak; FRCS Ed. 1985; FRCS Glas. 1985; FFAEM. Assoc. Specialist (A & E) Coleraine Hosp.

WALI, Jonathan David 27 Putnoe Lane, Bedford MK41 9AD Tel: 01234 267652 — MB BS 1990 Lond. Prev: Trainee GP Bedford Gen. Hosp.

WALI, Ravindar Kumar 2/2, 48 St Andrews Square, Glasgow G1 5PP — MB BS 1976 Kashmir; MRCP (UK) 1991.

WALIA, Sandeep 774 Great West Road, Isleworth TW7 5NA — MB BS 1988 Lond.

WALIMBE, Sharadini Station Road Surgery, 269 Station Road, Sykehead, Shotts ML7 4AQ Tel: 01501 823490; 6 Camstradden Drive W., Bearsden, Glasgow G61 4AJ — MB BS 1966 Poona; LRCP LRCS Ed. LRCPSI Glas. 1972; MRCOG 1972.

WALINCK, Jean Margaret (retired) The Latch, 9 Marine Parade, North Berwick EH39 4LD Tel: 01620 2760 Fax: 01620 892760 — MB ChB 1954 Ed.; MRCGP 1965; DObst RCOG 1956.

WALJI, Mohamed-Taki Ismail Walji, Balsall Heath Health Centre, 43 Edward Road, Balsall Heath, Birmingham B12 9JP Tel: 0121 446 2500 Fax: 0121 440 5861 — MB BS 1977 Lond.; MRCS Eng. LRCP Lond. 1977; MRCGP Lond. 1982.

WALJI, Shahenaz Farouk Oakleigh, 24 Tring Avenue, Ealing Common, London W5 3QA — MB BS 1977 Lond.; MRCP (UK) 1981. (Roy. Free)

WALK, David Alexander Email: david.walk@which.net — MB BS Lond. 1957; MRCP Lond. 1961; FRCPsych 1978, M 1971; DPM Eng. 1965. (Roy. Free) Emerit. Hon. Cons. Child Psychiat. Pathfinder NHS Trust. Prev: Cons. Child Psychiat. St. Geo. Hosp. Lond.; Hon. Sen. Lect. St. Geo. Hosp. Med. Sch.; Cons. Child Psychiat. Qu. Mary's Hosp. Childr. Carshalton.

WALKDEN, Diana Whitehouse Farm, Preston on the Hill, Warrington WA4 4LW Tel: 01928 714337 — MB ChB 1960 Liverp.; MB ChB (Hnrs.) Liverp. 1960; MRCS Eng. LRCP Lond. 1960. (Liverp.) Clin. Asst. Dept. A & E W. Chesh. Hosp. Socs: Liverp. Med. Inst.; Chester & N. Wales Med. Soc. Prev: Hon. Phys. & Hon. Surg. Roy. S.ern Hosp. Liverp.

WALKDEN, Mr John Alexander Denis Whitehouse Farm, Preston on the Hill, Warrington — MRCS Eng. LRCP Lond. 1957; MB ChB Liverp. 1957, MChOrth 1967; FRCS Eng. 1965. (Liverp.) Cons. Orthop. Surg. W. Chesh. & Centr. Wirral Hosps. Mem. Liverp.; Med. Inst. & Chester & N. Wales Med. Soc. Prev: Sen. Orthop. Regist. United Liverp. Hosps. & Liverp. RHB; Orthop. Regist. & Surg. Regist. Profess. Unit BRd.green Hosp.; Liverp.

WALKDEN, Leon 1 Parkside, Hampton Hill, Hampton TW12 1NU Tel: 020 8943 3673 — MRCS Eng. LRCP Lond. 1946. (St. Geo.) Clin. Asst. W. Middlx. Univ. Hosp. & Hillingdon Hosp. Uxbridge. Socs: Sec. Brit. Assn. Traumatol. in Sport. Prev: Asst. Venereol. W.

Middlx. Hosp. Isleworth, Hillingdon Hosp. & Centr.; Middlx. Hosp. Acton; Clin. Asst. Paediat. Dept. W. Middlx. Hosp.

WALKDEN, Susan Bridget X-Ray Department, Poole Hospital NHS Trust, Longfleet Road, Poole BH15 2JB Tel: 01202 665511; 39 Birchwood Road, Parkstone, Poole BH14 9NW Tel: 01202 747287 Email: sbwhnon.demon.co.uk — MB BChir Camb. 1969; MA Camb. 1969; FFR 1974; DMRD Eng. 1972. (Camb. & St. Thos.) Cons. Radiol. Wessex RHA. Socs: Fell. Roy. Soc. Med.; Fell. Roy. Soc. Radiol.; Brit. Inst. Radiol.

WALKDEN, Valerie Mary Department of Dermatology, Wexham Park Hospital, Slough SL2 4HL Tel: 01753 633108 Fax: 01753 633762; 2 Burlington Road, Burnham, Slough SL1 7BQ Email: valavwalkden.freeserve.co.uk — MB BS 1974 Lond.; FRCP 1999; MRCP (UK) 1977; MRCS Eng. LRCP Lond. 1974; BSc (Hons.) Lond. 1971. (Roy Free Lond.) p/t Cons. Demat. Wexham Pk. Hosp. Socs: Fell. Roy. Soc. Med.; Fell. St. John's Hosp. Dermat. Soc.; Brit. Assn. Dermat. Prev: Sen. Regist. (Dermat.) Amersham Gen. Hosp. Bucks.; Clin. Research Asst. Wycombe Gen. Hosp. High Wycombe; Regist. (Dermat.) Roy. Berks. Hosp. Reading.

WALKDEN, Walter James (retired) Arisaig, Water Lane, Eyam, Hope Valley S32 5RG — MB ChB Birm. 1944; FRCP Lond. 1973, M 1950. Prev: Cons. Phys. Sandwell HA.

WALKER, Abigail Helen Towerhurst, The Av, Collingham, Wetherby LS22 5BU — MB ChB 1997 Ed.

WALKER, Adrian Bernard Department of Endocrinology and Diabetes, Ward 60, Nines Block, City General Hospital, Stoke-on-Trent ST4 6QG — BM BCh 1988 Oxf.; MA Oxf. 1989; MRCP (UK) 1992; DM Oxf. 2000. (Oxford) Cons. Phys. (Diabetes & Endocrinol.) N. Staffs. Hosp. Prev: Sen. Regist. (Gen. Med., Diabetes & Endocrinol.) Liverp.; Research Fell. (Diabetes) Univ. Liverp.; Regist. (Gen. Med., Diabetes & Endocrinol.) Roy. Liverp. Univ. Hosp.

WALKER, Adrian Kerr Yates Beaver's Lodge, Penpol, Devoran, Truro TR3 6NP Tel: 01872 864994 — MB BS Lond. 1968; MRCS Eng. LRCP Lond. 1968; FFA RCS Eng. 1974; DObst RCOG 1972; DA Eng. 1970. (Guy's) Cons. Anaesth. Roy. Cornw. Hosps. Trust. Prev: Sen. Regist. Addenbrooke's Hosp. Camb.; Med. Off. Brit. Solomon Is.s; Med. Dir. Roy. Cornw.. Hosp. Trust.

WALKER, Adrian Mark Public Health Laboratory, Ysbyty Gwynedd, Bangor LL57 2PW Tel: 01248 384367 Fax: 01248 370163 Email: mark.walker@phls.wales.nhs.uk; Tyn Lon, Pentraeth LL75 8YH Tel: 07899 910061 Email: mark@toya.demon.co.uk — MB 1974 Camb.; MA Camb. 1974; MA, MB; MRCPath. 1982. (Middlx.) Cons. Microbiol. & Dir. Bangor PHL. Socs: FRCPath.; BMA; PHMEG. Prev: Cons. Communicable Dis. Control Gwynedd Health Auth.; Cons. Microbiol. Preston, Chorley & S. Ribble Health Dists.; Sen. Regist. (Microbiol.) Addenbrooke's Hosp. Camb.

WALKER, Aileen Elizabeth WS Atkins Healthcare, Clifton House, Clifton Place, Glasgow G3 7YY Tel: 0141 332 7030; 21 Blacklands Place, Lenzie, Kirkintilloch, Glasgow G66 5NJ Tel: 0141 776 0592 — MB ChB 1977 Glas.; MFPHM RCP (UK) 1988; MPH Leeds 1984; MHSM 1990. Cons. Med. Planner WS Atkins Healthcare Glas. Prev: Cons. Pub. Health Med. Scott. CSA; Regist. (Psychiat.) N. Canterbury Hosp. Bd. ChristCh., NZ; Trav. Sec. Christian Med. Fell.sh.

WALKER, Alan 61 Amber Heights, Ripley DE5 3SP Tel: 01773 44067; 28 Hands Road, Heanor DE75 7HA — MB ChB 1978 Glas.; MRCP (UK) 1982.

WALKER, Alan Eastfield Group Practice, 1 Eastway, Eastfield, Scarborough YO11 3LS Tel: 01723 582297 Fax: 01723 582528; May Dene, Beech Lane, West Ayton, Scarborough YO13 9JG Tel: 01723 862320 — MB ChB 1974 Leeds; BSc (Hons.) (Anat.) Leeds 1971; DRCOG Lond. 1981; DCH RCPS Glas. 1979. Prev: Lect. (Anat.) Univ. Leeds Med. Sch.

WALKER, Alan George (retired) 10 Mapleleaf Close, Selsdon, South Croydon CR2 8BD Tel: 020 8657 0911 — MB ChB 1945 Manch.; BSc Manch. 1942, MB ChB 1945. Prev: GP S. Croydon, Chesh. & Manch.

WALKER, Mr Alasdair James, Surg. Cdr. RN Department of Surgery, Derriford Hospital, Plymouth PL6 8DH Tel: 01752 763776 Fax: 01752 769724 Email: alasdair.walker@phnt.swest.nhs.uk — MB ChB 1979 Glas.; FRCS Glas. 1985; T(S) 1991. (Glas.) Cons. Gen. & Vasc. Surg. Derriford Hosp. Plymouth & RN. Socs: Fell. Roy. Soc. Med.; Vasc. Surg. Soc.; Brit. Assn. of Med. Managers. Prev: Hon. Sen. Regist. (Vasc. Surg.) Roy. Infirm. Edin.; Sen. Specialist

(Surg.) RN Hosp. Plymouth & Haslar; Squad. Med. Off. HMS Plymouth.

WALKER, Alexander Gordon Rosedale Surgery, Ashburnham Way, Carlton NR33 8LG Tel: 01502 505100; The Red House, North Cliff, Kessingland, Lowestoft NR33 7RA Tel: 01502 740397 — MB ChB 1978 Manch.; D.Occ Med. RCP Lond. 1995; DRCOG 1981. p/t Med. Adviser Birds Eye Walls Ltd.; G.P. Tutor, LoW.oft. Prev: Trainee GP Norwich VTS.

WALKER, Alexander Kirkland (retired) 23 Handley Cross, Manor Wood, Medomsley, Consett DH8 6TZ Tel: 01207 563227 — MB ChB 1955 Glas.; AFOM 1981; MRCGP 1975; DIH Soc. Apoth. Lond. 1972; DObst RCOG 1959. Occupat. Health Phys. Co. Health Ltd. Tyne & Wear.

WALKER, Alexander Percy (retired) Bentfield, Maryborough Road, Prestwick KA9 1SW Tel: 01292 477876 Fax: 01292 678893 — MB ChB Glas. 1939; MRCGP 1965; DObst RCOG 1947. Dep. Lt. Ayr & Arran. Prev: Adj. Med. Off. DHSS.

WALKER, Alexander Peter 11 Kirkburn Drive, Strathblane, Glasgow G63 9EE — MB ChB 1952 Glas.; MRCGP 1968; DObst RCOG 1957.

WALKER, Alison 29 Meadowburn, Bishopbriggs, Glasgow G64 3HA — MB ChB 1991 Dundee; FDS RCS Eng. 1992.

WALKER, Alison C/o, A & E Department, Leeds General Infirmary, Gt. George St., Leeds LS1 3EX — BChir 1995 Camb.; 1998 Dip IMC RCS Edin.; MBBS Camb. 1995; BA (Med. Sci.) Camb. 1992; BDS Ed. 1987; FDS RCS Eng. 1992; FRCS Eng. 1998. (Cambridge) A & E SPR Yorks. Region. Prev: Regist. (Oral & Maxillofacial Surg.) Pinderfields Hosp. Wakefield.

WALKER, Alison Edith Little Kroft, Petham, Canterbury CT4 5RE — MB BS 1986 Lond.; BA Camb 1983; MRCP (UK) 1990.

WALKER, Amanda Balmacaan Road Surgery, Balmacaan Road, Drumnadrochit, Inverness IV63 6UR Tel: 01456 450577 Fax: 01456 450799 — MB ChB 1986 Ed.; MRCGP 1991; DRCOG 1988.

WALKER, Amanda Elizabeth Top Flat, 5 Ferdinand St., London NW1 8ES — MB BS 1992 Lond.; BA (Hons.) Oxf. 1989. Specialist Regist. Radiol. The Middlx./UCH Hosp. Lond.

WALKER, Amy 28 Eastheath Avenue, Wokingham RG41 2PJ — MB ChB 1998 Leeds.

WALKER, Andrew Allan (retired) Ladyacre Cottage, Old Park Lane, Farnham GU10 5AA — MB ChB 1956 Ed.

WALKER, Andrew Douglas William Schaw House, Stair, Mauchline KA5 5JA Tel: 01292 591213 — MB ChB 1978 Ed.; MSc Ed. 1984, BSc 1975; MFCM 1989. Chief. Admin. Med. Off. & Dir. Health Plann. & Pub. Health Ayrsh. & Arran HB. Prev: Cons. Pub. Health Fife HB.

WALKER, Angela Hoyland Health Centre, 2 Duke St., Hoyland, Barnsley S74 9QS Tel: 01226 742915 Fax: 01226 745585; 6 Towngate, Thurlstone, Sheffield S36 9RH — MB ChB 1982 Leeds.

WALKER, Angela 5 Osborne Road, Buckhurst Hill IG9 5RR — MB ChB 1991 Liverp.

WALKER, Angela Margaret 4 Copse View Cottages, Redenham, Andover SP11 9AT — MB BS 1970 Lond.; MRCP (UK) 1976; MRCS Eng. LRCP Lond. 1970; DCH Eng. 1973; DObst RCOG 1973. (Guy's) Socs: BMA.

WALKER, Ann Elizabeth Norwood Road Surgery, 70 Norwood road, Southall UB2 4EY Tel: 020 8574 4454 — MB ChB 1986 Bristol; DRCOG 1991; DCH RCP Lond. 1989. (Univ. Bristol) GP S.all. Prev: Clin. Asst. (Community Paediat.) W. Lond. Healthcare; Trainee GP Greenford Middlx.

WALKER, Ann Mary 12 Shire Oak Road, Leeds LS6 2DE — MB ChB 1973 Glas.

WALKER, Anna Krystyna Springfield House, Burnt House Lane, Preesall, Poulton-le-Fylde FY6 0PQ — MB ChB 1985 Glas.; MRCGP 1989.

WALKER, Anne Catherine Pinhoe Surgery, Pinn Lane, Exeter EX1 3SY Tel: 01392 469666 Fax: 01392 464178; Egremont, Red Cross, Silverton, Exeter EX5 4DE Tel: 01392 860641 — MB ChB 1968 St. And. (St. And.) Prev: SHO (Anaesth.) United Birm. Hosps.; Ho. Off. King's Cross Hosp. Dundee; Ho. Surg. Selly Oak Hosp. Birm.

WALKER, Anne Elizabeth Stockett Lane Surgery, 3 Stockett Lane, Coxheath, Maidstone ME17 4PS Fax: 01622 741987; Tel: 01580 720586 — MB BS 1980 Lond.; MRCGP 1985; Cert. Family Plann. JCC 1984; DRCOG 1984; DCH RCP Lond. 1983. p/t Gen. Pract.

WALKER

WALKER, Anne Exley (retired) 39 Rectory Drive, Wingerworth, Chesterfield S42 6RU Tel: 01246 277021 — MB ChB Sheff. 1958; MD Sheff. 1965; FRCP Ed. 1975, M 1966. Prev: Cons. Dermat. Roy. Hosp. Chesterfield & United Sheff. Hosps.

WALKER, Anne Muriel Zuill 10 Royal Terrace, Glasgow G3 7NT — MB ChB 1963 Glas.; DObst. RCOG 1965; Dip. Ven. Soc. Apoth. Lond. 1975. Clin. Asst. (Genitourin. Med.) Glas. Roy. Infirm. Prev: Dir. Health Commiss. NSW Sexually Transm. Dis. Clinic Sydney, Austral.

WALKER, Annette 47 Harperley Gardens, Stanley DH9 8RZ; 24b Tasman St, Nelson, New Zealand Tel: NZ (03)545 6167 Fax: NZ (03)545 9007 — MB ChB 1992 Leeds. GP Locum.

WALKER, Anthea Noel The Hollies, West Felton, Oswestry SY11 4JU — MB BS 1972 Lond.; FRCS Eng. 1979.

WALKER, Mr Anthony Paul Laughton Hall, Laughton, Gainsborough DN21 3PP Tel: 01427 628688 — MB ChB 1973 Leeds; FRCS Eng. 1978. Cons. Orthop. Surg. Scunthorpe Gen. Hosp. Socs: Fell. BOA. Prev: Sen. Regist. (Orthop.) Yorks. RHA.

WALKER, Antony Hayden 34 Newbould Lane, Sheffield S10 2PL — MB ChB 1994 Sheff.

WALKER, Archibald Brian Kilsyth Medical Partnership, Kilsyth Health Centre, Burngreen Park, Kilsyth, Glasgow G65 0HU Tel: 01236 822081 Fax: 01236 826231; Rosamar, Allanfauld Road, Kilsyth, Glasgow G65 9DE — MB ChB 1973 Glas.; MD Glas. 1990; Dip. Sports Med. Scott. Roy. Med. Coll. Hon. Sen. Lect. Glas. Univ. Socs: Brit. Assn. Sports Med.; Amer. Counc. Sports Med.

WALKER, Arthur Alexander (retired) Sarnia, Hernes Nest, Bewdley DY12 Tel: 01299 402363 — MB BS 1953 Durh.

WALKER, Audrey Mai 10 Oak Lane, Wilmslow SK9 6AA — MB ChB 1956 Sheff.

WALKER, Ava e80B Denton Road, London N8 9NT — MB BS 1979 Lond.

WALKER, Barrie Dr B Walker and Partners, Health Centre, Gosforth Road, Seascale CA20 1PN Tel: 01946 728101; Lyndale, Gosforth Road, Seascale CA20 1HA Tel: 0194 67 28551 Email: barriewalker2@arcinter.net — MB BChir 1972 Camb.; MA Camb. 1971; FRCGP 1991, M 1978; DObst RCOG 1974. (Middlx.) Med. Off. DERAProof & Experim. Estab. Eskmeals; Chairm. Cumbria Primary Care Effectiveness Gp.; Mem. N.ern & Yorks. Regional Cancer Working Gp.; Mem. & Clin. Governance Lead W. Cumbria PCG. Prev: Trainee GP Guildford VTS; Ho. Surg. (Surg.) Middlx. Hosp. Lond.; Ho. Phys. Kettering Gen. Hosp.

WALKER, Barry Egerton St. James's University Hospital, Leeds LS9 7TF — MD 1971 Leeds; MB ChB 1961; FRCP Lond. 1979, M 1966. (Leeds) Cons. Phys. & Lect. Med. St. Jas. Hosp. Leeds. Socs: BMA & Brit. Soc. Gastroenterol. Prev: SHO Chapel Allerton Hosp. Leeds; Ho. Off. (Gen. Surg.) Leeds Gen. Infirm.; Ho. Off. (Gen. Med.) Bradford Roy. Infirm.

WALKER, Bernard Hugh The Surgery, Grasmere Drive, High Bentham, Lancaster LA2 7JP Tel: 01524 261202 Fax: 01524 262222905 — MB ChB 1968 Manch. (Manch.) Prev: Res. Clin. Pathol. Manch. Roy. Infirm. Ho. Surg. Ancoats Hosp. Manch.; Ho. Phys. Crumpsall Hosp. Manch.

WALKER, Beverley Jane Summerley House, Ellwood Road, Beaconsfield HP9 1EN Tel: 01494 670942 Fax: 01494 670698 — MB BS 1978 Lond.; MRCP (UK) 1981; AKC. (King's Coll. Hosp.) Socs: BDA. Prev: Lect. (Nephrol.) Inst. Urol.

WALKER, Brian Follett 5 The Crescent, Whitley Bay NE26 2JG — MB ChB 1979 Dundee.

WALKER, Professor Brian Robert University of Edinburgh, Endocrinology Unit, Medical Sciences Department, Western General Hospital, Edinburgh EH4 2XU Tel: 0131 537 1736 Fax: 0131 537 1012 Email: b.walker@ed.ac.uk — MB ChB 1986 Ed.; BSc Ed. 1984, MD 1993; MRCP (UK) 1989. Sen. Research Fell. Brit. Heart Foundat. & Prof. of Endocrinol. Univ. Edin. W. Gen. Hosp.; Hon. Cons. Phys. W. Gen. Hosp. Socs: (Sec.) Caledonian Soc. Endocrinol. Prev: MRC Train. Fell. Univ. (Med.) W.. Gen. Hosp. Edin.

WALKER, Brian William McWhirter (retired) 1 Wood Drive, St. Mellion, Saltash PL12 6UR Tel: 01579 351240 Email: brimarg@ukgateway.net — MB ChB Glas. 1960; DObst RCOG 1965.

WALKER, Bryan Alexander The Consultation Suite, Lourdes Hospital, Liverpool L18 1HQ Tel: 0151 733 7123 Fax: 0151 735 0446 — MD 1969 Liverp.; FRCP Lond. 1974, M 1965; MB ChB 1956. Cons. Phys. Lourdes Hosp. Liverp.; Cons. Med. Off. Roy. Sun Alliance Ltd; Cons. Med. Off. Roy. Liver Assur. Socs: Assn. Phys.; Fell. Assur. Med. Soc.; Fell. Roy. Soc. Med. Prev: Cons. Phys. Roy. Liverp. Univ. Hosp. & BRd.green Hosp.; Lect. Liverp. Univ.

WALKER, Carol Louise Market Street Health Group, 52 Market St., East Ham, London E6 2RA Tel: 020 8472 0202; 24 Lyal Road, Bow, London E3 5QG Tel: 020 8980 3836 — MB BS 1994 Lond.; MA Camb. 1995; DRCOG 1996. GP Regist. Market St. Health Centre, E.ham Lond. Prev: SHO (Psychiat.) E.ham Memor. Hosp.; SHO (Paediat.) Newham Gen. Hosp.; SHO (O & G) Newham Gen. Hosp.

WALKER, Carolyn Anne Crompton Health Centre, High Street, Shaw, Oldham OL2 8ST Tel: 01706 842511 Fax: 01706 290751; 1 Alkrington Green, Middleton, Manchester M24 1ED — MB ChB 1990 Leeds; MRCGP 1995; DCCH RCP Ed. 1993. (Univ. Leeds)

WALKER, Catherine Elizabeth 17 Standmoor Road, Whitefield, Manchester M45 7PJ Tel: 0161 766 7795 — MB ChB 1995 Birm. (Univ. Birm.) SHO (Anaesth.) Russells Hall Hosp. Dudley. Prev: SHO (A & E) The Roy. Perth Hosp. Perth, W.ern Australia; SHO (Paediat.) Qu. Pk. Hosp. Blackburn.

WALKER, Charles Herbert (retired) Maple Down, 28 ndellsands Road E., Blundellsands, Liverpool L23 8SQ — MD Aberd. 1958, MB ChB 1951. Prev: Ho. Off. Aberd. Roy. Infirm.

WALKER, Charles Victor Stuart Cavendish Medical Centre, 214 Park Road North, Birkenhead CH41 8BU Tel: 0151 652 1955 — MB ChB 1982 Liverp.

WALKER, Christine Ann 2/L 23 Havelock Street, Glasgow G11 5JF Tel: 0141 334 3209 — MB ChB 1994 Glas.; DRCOG Lond. 1997.

WALKER, Christine Anne Northampton General Hospital NHS Trust, Cliftonville, Northampton NN1 5BD Tel: 01604 544538 Fax: 01604 545988; The Walnuts, Church St, Blakesley, Towcester NN12 8RA Tel: 01327 860747 — BM BCh 1983 Oxf.; BA (Hons. Physiol. Sci.) Oxf. 1980; MRCP (UK) 1990; DCH RCP Lond. 1987; DRCOG 1986. (Oxford) Cons. (Paediat.) N.ampton Gen. Hosp. Socs: Fell. RCPCH. Prev: Sen. Regist. (Paediat.) N.ampton Gen. Hosp.; Sen. Regist. (Paediat.) Roy. Hosp. Sick Childr. Edin.; Research Fell. (Child Life & Health) Univ. Edin.

WALKER, Christopher Prestwood Road West Surgery, 81 Prestwood Road West, Wednesfield, Wolverhampton WV11 1HT Tel: 01902 721021 Fax: 01902 306225; Latymer, Links Avenue, Tettenhall, Wolverhampton WV6 9QF Tel: 01902 751197 — MB 1974 Camb.; BChir 1973; FRCGP 1994, M 1978. (St. Mary's) Postgrad. Tutor S. Staffs Med. Centre. Prev: SHO (Cas.) & Ho. Surg. St. Mary's (Harrow Rd. Br.) Hosp. Lond.; Ho. Phys. Qu. Eliz. II Hosp. Welwyn Gdn. City.

WALKER, Christopher Allan 8 Ratcliffe Drive, Huncote, Leicester LE9 3BA — MB ChB 1971 Manch.; BSc (Hons. Physiol.) Manch. 1968, MB ChB 1971; MRCPsych 1975; DPM Eng. 1975. Cons. Psychiat. Towers Hosp. Leicester. Prev: Lect. (Psychiat.) Univ. Leicester; Regist. & Sen. Regist. Univ. Hosp. S. Manch.

WALKER, Mr Christopher Charles Email: chris.walker@meht.nhs.uk; 154 Hanging Hill Lane, Hutton, Brentwood CM13 2HG — MB BS 1968 Newc.; FRCS Eng. 1974. (Newcastle Upon Tyne) Cons. Plastic Surg. St Andrews Centre for Plastic Surg. and Burns, Broomfield Hosp., Chelmsford; Cons. Plastic Surg. Whipps Cross Hosp. Lond.; Hon. Cons. Plastic Surg. Roy. Lond. Hosp.; Hon Sen. Lect. St Barts Med. Coll.; Med. Director, Mid Essex Hosps. Trust. Socs: Fell. Roy. Soc. Med.; Brit. Ass. Plastic Surg. Hon Treas. & Coun. Mem.; Brit. burn ass Counc. Mem. Prev: Sen. Regist. (Plastic Surg.) Univ. Hosp. S. Manch., Christie Hosp. & Booth Hall Childr. Hosp. Manch.; Regist. (Plastic Surg.) Mt. Vernon Hosp. & Univ. Coll. Hosp. Lond.; Regist. MRC Burns Research.

WALKER, Christopher Darnton (retired) 9 Brit View Road, West Bay, Bridport DT6 4HY Tel: 01308 456267 Email: win.walker@talk21.com — MB BChir Camb. 1962; MRCS Eng. LRCP Lond. 1961. Prev: Med. Ref. Eltham Crematorium.

WALKER, Christopher Francis Victoria Surgery, 5 Victoria Road, Holyhead LL65 1UD; Yeovil, The Mountain, Holyhead LL65 1YW Tel: 01407 764791 — MB ChB 1973 Birm.; MRCGP 1980; DA (UK) 1980; DRCOG 1979.

WALKER, Christopher James Park Health Centre, 190 Duke Street, Sheffield S2 5QQ Tel: 0114 272 7768; 57 Meersbrook Road, Sheffield S8 9HU — MRCS Eng. LRCP Lond. 1979.

WALKER, Mr Christopher John Maidstone Hospital, Hermitage Lane, Barming, Maidstone ME16 9QQ Tel: 01622 729000 Ext: 4209; Chittenden House, Lovehurst Lane, Staplehurst, Tonbridge TN12 0EX Tel: 01580 891989 Fax: 01580 891989 Email: boneswalki@aol.com — MB BS 1966 Lond.; FRCS Eng. 1973; MRCS Eng. LRCP Lond. 1966. (St. Mary's) Cons. Orthop. Surg. The Maidstone Hosp. Socs: Brit. Orthopaedic foot Surg. Soc. Prev: Sen. Orthop. Regist. St. Mary's Hosp. Lond., Battle Hosp. Reading & Roy. Nat. Orthop. Hosp. Lond.; Surg. Regist. (Profess. Unit) St. Mary's Hosp. Lond.

WALKER, Christopher Peter Ravenscroft Department of Anaesthesia and intensive care, Royal Brompton and Harefield NHS Trust, Harefield, Uxbridge UB9 6JH — MB BS 1990 Lond.; FRCA 1996; CCST 1999. (University of London - Royal Free Hospital) Cons. in Cardiothoriac Anaesth. and Intens. care, Harefield Hosp. Socs: FRCAnaesth.; BMA; Assn. Anaesths. Prev: Spr Locum Cons., Roy. Brompton and Harefield Hosp.s; Vis. Sen. Regist., Univ. of Natal, Durban; Spr Hammersmith and Roy. Marsden Hosp.s.

WALKER, Mr Christopher Richard Department of Orthopaedic Surgery, Royal Liverpool University Hospital, Prescot St., Liverpool L7 8XP Tel: 0151 706 3440 Fax: 0151 706 2440; Tel: 0151 709 5967 Fax: 0151 707 0609 — MRCS Eng. LRCP Lond. 1981; MCh (Orth.) Liverp. 1990; FRCS (Orth.) 1994; FRCS Eng 1988; FRCS Ed 1986. (Liverpool) Cons. Trauma & Orthop. Surg. Roy. Liverp. Univ. Hosp. Socs: Fell. BOA; Brit. Orthop. Foot Surg. Soc. Prev: Lect. (Orthop. & Accid. Surg.) Roy. Liverp. Univ. Hosp.; Regist. (Orthop.) Mersey RHA; Research Fell. Thackary Clin. Univ. Liverp.

WALKER, Clive Reece Weybridge Health Centre, 22 Church Street, Weybridge KT13 8DW Tel: 01932 853366 Fax: 01932 844902; 18 Mayfield Road, Weybridge KT13 8XD Tel: 01932 851100 — MB BS Lond. 1968; MRCP (U.K.) 1972; FRCP 1998. (St Georges Hosp Lond) GP & Hosp. Pract. Thoracic Med. Prev: Regist. (Med.) & Resid. Med. Off. St. Geo. Hosp. Lond.; Clinician MRC Laborats., The Gambia.; Asst. Div. Med. Off. Weybridge.

WALKER, Mr Colin Burleigh Springbank House, School Lane, Boldre, Lymington SO41 5QE Tel: 01590 673718 — MB BChir 1949 Camb.; MA Camb. 1958, MB BChir 1949; FRCS Eng. 1958. (St. Thos.) Socs: FCOphth. Prev: Emerit. Cons. Ophth. Surg. Soton. Univ. Hosp. Gp.; Sen. Regist. (Ophth.) St. Thos. Hosp. Lond.; Chief Clin. Asst. & Sen. Res. Off. Moorfields Eye Hosp. City Rd.

WALKER, Colin Cecil Russell (retired) Inglewood, Place Road, Melksham SN12 6JN Tel: 01225 707044 — MB ChB 1948 Ed. Prev: Ho. Phys. Edin. Roy. Infirm.

WALKER, Colin Dieppe (retired) Cranwill Dene, Cricket Hill Lane, Yateley GU46 6BQ Tel: 0125 870788 — MB BS 1959 Lond. Prev: Ho. Surg. & Res. Obst. Asst. W.m. Hosp. Lond.

WALKER, Colin Heriot MacDonald (retired) 61 Dalkeith Road, Dundee DD4 7JJ Tel: 01382 454323 — MB ChB 1946 Ed.; MD Ed. 1952; FRCP Ed. 1963, M 1950; FACC 1963; Hon. FRCPCH 1996; DCH Eng. 1951. Hon. Reader (Child Health) Univ. Dundee. Prev: Cons. Paediat. Tayside HB.

WALKER, Colin Peter 41 The Delph, Lower Earley, Reading RG6 3AN — MB BS 1981 Lond.; MRCP (UK) 1986. Regist. (Gen. Med.) Roy. Berks. Hosp. Reading. Prev: SHO (Gen. Med.) St. Helier Hosp. Carshalton; SHO (A & E) St. Bart. Hosp. Lond.

WALKER, Mr Colin Robert Connell Flat 4/3 Canada Court, 63 Miller St., Glasgow G1 1EB Tel: 0141 221 2554 — MB ChB 1987 Manch.; FRCPS Glas. 1992; FRCS Ed. 1992. SHO (Orthop.) Vic. Infirm. Glas.

WALKER, David Airdrie Health Centre, Monkscourt Avenue, Airdrie ML6 0JU Tel: 01236 766446 Fax: 01236 766513; 18 Arthur Avenue, Airdrie ML6 9EZ Tel: 01236 762198 — MB ChB 1986 Glas.; BSc Strathclyde 1981; DFM Glas. 1993. Dep. Police Surg. Socs: Assn. Police Surg.; BMA.

WALKER, David Andrew Oldfield Road, Honley, Huddersfield HD9 6NL Tel: 01484 664934 Email: dawalker@doctors.org.uk — MD 1979 Liverp.; MB ChB 1971; MRCP (U.K.) 1974; FRCP 1990. Cons. Phys. (Geriat. Med.) St. Luke's Hosp., Huddersfield Roy. Infirm. & Mill Hill Hosp. Socs: BMA & Brit. Geriat. Soc. Prev: Sen. Regist. (Geriat.) Barnes Hosp. Cheadle & Manch. Roy. Infirm.; Lect. Med. Unit Manch. Roy. Infirm.; Research Fell. Depts. Med. & Med. Biochem. Univ. Hosp. Wales, Cardiff.

WALKER, David Austin Department of Child Health, University Hospital, Nottingham NG7 2UH Tel: 0115 924 9924 Fax: 0115 970 9382 Email: david.walker@nottingham.ac.uk; 92 Parkside, Wollaton, Nottingham NG8 2NN Tel: 0115 928 2635 — BM BS 1977 Nottm.; BMedSci Nottm. 1975; FRCP Lond. 1996; Fell. Roy. Coll. Paediat. & Child Health. Sen. Lect. (Paediat. Oncol.) Univ. Hosp. Nottm.; Cons. Paediat. Oncol. Socs: UK Childh. Cancer Study Gp. (Chairm. Brain Tumour Comm.); FRCPCh.; Fell. RCP. Prev: Research Fell. Roy. Childr. Hosp. Melbourne, Austral.; Clin. Fell. Leukaemia Research Fund Hosp. for Sick Childr. Gt. Ormond St. Lond.

WALKER, David Douglas 12 Essex Brae, Edinburgh EH4 6LN — MB ChB 1959 Ed.; DPH 1962; FFOM RCP Lond. 1994, M 1978; MFCM 1974; DIH Dund 1970. Cons. Ocxcupat. Health Phys. Edin. Socs: Fell. Roy. Soc. Med.; Soc. Occupat. Med. Prev: Med. Adviser Brit. Gas. (Scotl.); Med. Off. Inst. Occupat. Med. Nat. Coal Bd.; Maj. RAMC.

WALKER, Mr David Ian Beechwood Consulting Rooms, The Highfield Hospital, Manchester Road, Rochdale OL11 4LZ Tel: 01706 766608 Fax: 01706 766602; Lynton, 49a Church walks, Llandudno, Conwy LL30 2HL Tel: 01492 874152 Fax: 01492 873738 Email: davidiwalker@aol.com — MB ChB 1965 Manch.; FRCS Ed. 1970. (Manch.) Cons. Orthop. Surg. Rochdale Health Serv. Trust. Prev: Sen. Regist. (Orthop. Surg.) Manch. AHA (T); Regist. (Orthop.) Wrightington Hosp. Appley Bridge; Lect. (Physiol.) Univ. Manch.

WALKER, David James Caldy Cottage, 189 Saughall Road, Blacon, Chester CH1 5HG — MB ChB 1995 Manch. SHO (Orthop.) Surg. Chester Hosp.; Anat. Demonst. Univ. Liverp; Ho. Off. (Surg.) Hope Hosp. Manch.; Ho. Off. (Med.) Nobles Hosp. I. of Man.

***WALKER, David John** 36 Tapton Mount Close, Sheffield S10 5DJ — MB ChB 1994 Birm.

WALKER, David John 29 Bemersyde Drive, Jesmond, Newcastle upon Tyne NE2 2HL — MD 1986 Newc.; MA Camb 1978, BA 1974; MB BS 1977; MRCP UK 1980; FRCP Uk 1993. Cons. Rheum. Newc. & Tyneside HA.

WALKER, David John Macclesfield District General Hospital, Victoria Road, Macclesfield SK10 3BL Tel: 01625 421000 — MB ChB 1970 Liverp.; FRCP Lond. 1991; MRCP (UK) 1975. Cons. Phys. Macclesfield Dist. Gen. Hosp. Socs: Liverp. Med. Inst. & Brit. Geriat. Soc.; BMA. Prev: Sen. Regist. (Geriat.) Newsham Gen. Hosp. Liverp. & David Lewis N.. Hosp. Liverp.; Regist. (Med.) Liverp. AHA (T).

WALKER, David John 25 Flatwoods Road, Claverton Down, Bath BA2 7AQ Tel: 01225 834308 Email: walker@doctorsnet.co.uk — MB ChB 1985 Birm.; MD Warwick 1994; MRCOG 1990. (Birm.) Cons. O & G Roy. United Hosp. Bath. Prev: Sen. Regist. Rotat. (O & G) W. Midl. RHA.; Research Regist. (O & G) Univ. Warwick; Regist. Rotat. (Obst.) W. Midl. RHA.

WALKER, David Martin Tel: 01225 461262 Fax: 01225 310738 Email: david.walker@gp-l81655.nhs.uk — BM BS 1975 Nottm.; MRCGP 1980; DRCOG 1978. Prev: Trainee GP/SHO Char. Cross Hosp. Lond. VTS; Asst. Lect. (Human Morphol.) Nottm. Univ. Med. Sch.; Cas. Off. Nottm. Gen. Hosp.

WALKER, David Michael Department of Cardiology, Conquest Hospital, The Ridge, St Leonards-on-Sea TN37 7RD Tel: 01424 755255 Ext: 6319 Email: david.walker@fsmail.net; Greystones, 11 Grange Road, Hastings TN34 2RL Tel: 01424 752054 — MB BChir 1985 Camb.; MA Camb. 1986, MD 1995; MRCP (UK) 1988. (Camb. & St. Thos) Cons. Cardiol. Conquest Hosp. Hastings; Cons. Cardiol. KCH Lond.; Cons. Cardiol. Roy. Sussex Co. Hosp. Brighton. Socs: Brit. Cardiac Soc.; Cardiac Interven. Soc.; Soc. Heart Failure. Prev: Sen. Regist. (Cardiol.) St. Mary's Hosp. & Hammersmith Hosp. Lond.; Regist. (Cardiol.) Soton. Gen. Hosp.; Clin. Lect. (Cardiol.) Univ. Coll. Hosp. Lond.

WALKER, David Ralph 13B St Thomas Street, Newcastle upon Tyne NE1 4LE Tel: 0191 261 5927 — MB BS 1987 Newc.; MSc Newc. 1994, BMedSc 1986, MB BS 1987; MRCP (UK) 1991; MFPHM RCP (UK) 1994. Sen. Regist. (Pub. Health Med.) Centres for Dis. Control & Prevent. Atlanta, USA.

WALKER, Deborah Mary The Hawthorns, Burleigh Lane, Ascot SL5 8PF — MB BS 1978 Lond.; MRCS Eng. LRCP Lond. 1978; DCH Eng. 1981; MRCGP 1982 DRCOG 1982. (Roy. Free) p/t Non Princip., Gen. Pract., Ascot; Clin. Asst. Antenatal Clinic, King Edwd. VII Hosp., Windsor.

WALKER, Deirdre Susan 26 Grenville Drive, Cambuslang, Glasgow G72 8DS — MB ChB 1993 Ed.

WALKER

WALKER, Dennis (retired) 27 Avenue Road, Doncaster DN2 4AE Tel: 01302 342181 — MB ChB 1951 Leeds. Prev: Ho. Surg. (Orthop.) St. Jas. Hosp. Leeds.

WALKER, Derek Lindsay (retired) Ludloes, Gloucester St., Painswick, Stroud GL6 6QR Tel: 01452 813253 — MRCS Eng. LRCP Lond. 1948; MD Lond. 1958, MB BS 1949; FRCPsych 1971; DPM Eng. 1954. Hon. Cons. Dept. Applied Neurophysiol. Gloucester Roy. Hosp. Prev: Cons. Psychiat. & Phys. Supt. Horton Rd. & Coney Hill Hosps.

WALKER, Desmond (retired) Wellfield House, Sunderland Bridge Vill., Croxdale, Durham DH6 5HB — MB BS 1952 Durh. Prev: G.P Durh. City.

WALKER, Dorothy Elizabeth Blackhall Medical Centre, 51 Hillhouse Road, Edinburgh EH4 3TH Tel: 0131 332 7696 Fax: 0131 315 2884; 110 Craigcrook Road, Edinburgh EH4 3PN — MB ChB 1980 Aberd.; MRCGP 1984; DRCOG 1984.

WALKER, Dorothy May 7 Hightown, Collieston, Ellon AB41 8RS — MB ChB 1955 Aberd. Prev: Sen. Med. Off. W. Suff. CC.

WALKER, Douglas Arthur Jack 65 Grove Road, Millhouses, Sheffield S7 2GY — BM BCh 1980 Oxf.; DPhil Oxf. 1986, MA, BM BCh 1980; FFA RCS Eng. 1986. Sen. Regist. (Anaesth.) Roy. Hallamsh. & N. Gen. Hosps. Sheff. Prev: Lect. Anaesth. Univ. Sheff.

WALKER, Douglas Ewen (retired) 51 Belgrave Road, Corstorphine, Edinburgh EH12 6NH Tel: 0131 334 4583 — MB ChB 1943 Aberd.; DPH Aberd. 1948. Prev: Sen. Med. Off. Scott. Home & Health Dept.

WALKER, Douglas Robert Castlegait Surgery, 32 Castle Street, Montrose DD10 8AG Tel: 01674 672554 Fax: 01674 675025; 10 Morven Avenue, Montrose DD10 9DL — MB ChB 1984 Dundee.

WALKER, Mr Duncan Roy 15 North Grange Mount, Headingley, Leeds LS6 2BY — MB ChB 1968 Glas.; FRCS Ed. 1972. Cons. (Cardiothoracic Surg.) Regional Cardiothoracic Centre Killingbeck Hosp. Leeds & Dept. Cardiothoracic Surg. Leeds Gen. Infirm; Killingbeck Hosp. Leeds & Dept. Cardiothoracic Surg. Leeds Gen. Infirm. Socs: Thoracic & Cardiovasc. Surg. Soc. Prev: Regist. (Cardiothoracic Surg.) Brompton Hosp. Lond.; Research Fell. Dept. Cardiac Surg. Univ. Alabama Birm., USA; Sen. Regist. Hosp. Sick Childr. Gt. Ormond St. Lond.

WALKER, Edward Corrie 4-6 Kirkgate, Hanging Heaton, Batley WF17 6DA Email: ed@limeland.down.co.uk — MB ChB 1986 Sheff.; FRCA 1991; DA (UK) 1989. Staff Doctor (A & E) Dewsbury Health Care Trust.

WALKER, Mr Edward Milnes Milton Keynes General NHS Trust, Saxon St., Eaglestone, Milton Keynes MK6 5LD Tel: 01908 243075 Fax: 01908 243075; Model Farm, 4 Brook End, North Crawley, Newport Pagnell MK16 9HH Tel: 01234 391781 — MB BS 1969 Lond.; FRCS Eng. 1974; MRCS Eng. LRCP Lond. 1969. (Middlx.) Cons. Urol. Milton Keynes Hosp. Socs: Assoc. Mem. BAUS. Prev: Sen. Regist. (Gen. Surg.) Nottm. Gen. Hosp.; Regist. (Surg.) W.m. Hosp. Lond. & N.ampton Gen. Hosp.

WALKER, Elizabeth Harriet 11 Blackthorn Road, Kenilworth CV8 2DS; 11 Blackthorn Road, Kenilworth CV8 2DS — MB BS 1994 Lond.; DCH 1998. (KCSMD London) GP Regist. Winchester.

WALKER, Elizabeth Helen 1 Hampton Mews, Stockport SK3 8SY Tel: 0161 487 3986 — MB BS 1996 Lond.; BSc Hons. St. George's Hosp Med. Sch.1993. (St. Georges Hospital Medical School) SHO Psychiat. Stepping Hill hospistal Stockport (p/t).

WALKER, Elizabeth Helen May 10 Curle Avenue, Lincoln LN2 4AN Tel: 01552 530777 — MB BChir 1953 Camb.; MA, MB BChir Camb. 1953; DCH Eng. 1955; FRCOG 1978, M 1965. (Univ. Coll. Hosp.) Emerit. Cons. Lincoln Gp. Hosps. Socs: N. Eng. Obst. & Gyn. Soc.; Wom. Gyn. Vis. Club. Prev: Lect. (O & G) Roy. Free Hosp. Lond.; Regist. (O & G) Newc. Gen. Hosp.; Med. Off. St. Luke's Hosp. Chabua, India.

WALKER, Elizabeth Jane 6 Bromyard Avenue, Sutton Coldfield B76 1RQ — MB ChB 1994 Birm.; ChB Birm. 1994.

WALKER, Emma Jane (Surgery), 82 Little Road, London SW6 1TN; 21 Gastein Road, London W6 8LT — MB BS 1991 Lond.; DRCOG 1995.

WALKER, Emma Katherine Lucy BBC TV, White City, 201 Wood Lane, London W12 7TS Tel: 020 8752 6349 Email: emma.walker@bbc.co.uk — MB ChB 1987 Ed.; BM ChB Ed. 1987; BSc (Hons. Path.) Ed. 1985. Producer BBC TV. Prev: Ho. Off. W.. Gen. Hosp. Edin.

WALKER, Eric Department of Pathology, Crosshouse Hospital, Kilmarnock KA2 0BE Email: eric.walker@aaaht.scot.nhs.uk — MB ChB 1986 Aberd.; PhD Aberd. 1979, BSc (Hons.) 1975; MRCPath 1994. Cons. Path. CrossHo. Hosp. Kilmarnock. Prev: Sen. Regist., Regist. & SHO (Path.) Roy. Infirm. Glas.

WALKER, Evelyn Claire Eskbridge Medical Centre, 8A Bridge Street, Musselburgh EH21 6AG Tel: 0131 665 6821; 'Kirklands', Main St, Gullane EH31 2AL Tel: 01620 842879 Fax: 01620 842879 — MB ChB 1986 Ed.; MRCGP 2000; MA 1986 Cantab; DRCOG 1988; MA Cantab 1986; DRCOG 1988; DRCOG 1988. (Cambridge & Edinburgh) GP Retainer,; Represen. on Lotian Med. Comm. Socs: MDDUS; BMA. Prev: Trainee GP at Eskbridge Med. Centre; SHO (Med. Paediat.) Roy. Hosp. Sick Childr. Edin.; SHO (O & G) Simpsons Mem. Matern. Hosp. Edin.

WALKER, Ewa Maria 17 Oakhill Avenue, London NW3 7RD Tel: 020 7431 3436 Fax: 020 7431 3436 — Lekarz 1972 Poland. Indep. Psychother. Pract. Lond. Prev: SHO (Clin. Path. & Haemat.) St. Geo. Hosp. Lond.; Sen. Research Fell & Hon. Regist. BMT Unit Roy. Free Hosp. Lond.; Pharmaceut. Phys. Wellcome Foundat.

WALKER, Ewen Macaulay — MD 1990 Aberd.; MB ChB (Commend.) 1977; MRCOG 1982; FRCOG 1997. Cons. O & G Ayrsh. Centr. Hosp. Irvine. Socs: Brit. Gynaecol. Cancer Soc.; Brit. Soc. Colposcopy and Cervical Cytol. Prev: Research Fell. Addenbrooke's Hosp. Camb.; Regist. Edin. Roy. Infirm. & Simpson Memor. Matern. Hosp.; Lect. (O & G) Ninewells Hosp. Dundee.

WALKER, Fiona Amberley, Romsey Road, Cadnam, Southampton SO40 2NN — BM 1992 Soton.

WALKER, Fiona Christine 104 Ormonde Crescent, Netherlee, Glasgow G44 3SW — MB ChB 1989 Ed.; MRCGP 1996. (Univ. Ed.) Clin. Asst. (Palliat. Med.) Cedar Hse. Kirkcaldy. Prev: GP Regist. Edin.

WALKER, Folliott Charles Edward Johnson and Partners, Langley House, 27 West Street, Chichester PO19 1RW Tel: 01243 782266/782955 Fax: 01243 779188; Fletchers, Lockgate Road, Sidlesham Common, Chichester PO20 7QH Tel: 01243 641968 Fax: 01243 641968 — MB BS 1982 Lond.; BSc Hons. (Anat.) Lond. 1979; MRCGP 1986; DRCOG 1985. (St. Thos.) Prev: Trainee GP Basingstoke VTS; Ho Phys. Worthing Hosp. Lond.; Ho. Surg. St. Geo. Hosp. Lond.

WALKER, Professor Frederick Department of Pathology, University Medical Buildings, Foresterhill, Aberdeen AB25 2ZD Tel: 01224 681818 Fax: 01224 663002 Email: f.walker@abdn.ac.uk — MB ChB 1958 Glas.; MB ChB (Commend.) Glas. 1958; PhD Glas. 1966, MD (Hons. & Bellahouston Medal) 1971; FRCPath 1978, M 1966. (Univ. Glas.) Regius Prof. Path. Univ. Aberd.; Hon. Cons. Aberd. Roy. Hosps. NHS Trust. Socs: Chairm. & Gen. Sec. Path. Soc. GB & Irel.; Scott. Soc. Experim. Med. Prev: Foundat. Prof. Path. Univ. Leicester; Sen. Lect. (Path.) Univ. Aberd.; Lect. (Path.) Univ. Glas.

WALKER, Frederick Hughes Clifftops, 7 Sea Gate View, Sewerby, Bridlington YO15 1ET Tel: 01262 602223 — MB BS 1950 Lond.; MRCS Eng. LRCP Lond. 1950. (Guy's)

WALKER, Gail Allison The Surgery, 62 Windsor Drive, Orpington BR6 6HD Tel: 01689 852204 Fax: 01689 857122; Treetops, 39 Oxenden Wood Road, Orpington BR6 6HP — MB BS 1979 Lond.; MRCGP 1984.

WALKER, Garry William 2 Meilke Cutstraw, Cutstraw Road, Stewarton, Kilmarnock KA3 5HU — MB ChB 1989 Glas.

WALKER, Geoffrey (retired) 27 Wollaton Hall Drive, Nottingham NG8 1AF Tel: 0115 916 0736 — MB BS 1950 Lond.; MSc Lond. 1970, BSc 1947; Hon. DSc CNAA 1991; FRCP Lond. 1983, M 1952; FRCPath 1977, M 1965. Prev: Cons. Chem. Path. Univ. Hosp. Nottm.

WALKER, Mr Geoffrey Fleetwood (retired) 9D The Grove, Highgate Vill., London N6 6JU Tel: 020 8340 2313 Fax: 020 8340 2313 Email: geoffrey.walker@bigfoot.com — MB BS 1951 Lond.; FRCS Eng. 1958; FRCS Ed. 1958. Volun. Developing Country orthapaedic Teachg., Worl Orthapedic Concern (UK) in Africa and S.E. Asia. Prev: Prof. Univ. Addis Ababa.

WALKER, Geoffrey Robert 52 Inglethorpe Square, Fulham, London SW6 6NT Tel: 020 7610 3354 — MB BS 1995 Lond.; BSc (Hons.) Westm. 1988, MB BS Lond. 1995. (Char. Cross & Westm.) SHO (Anaesth.) St Peters Hosp. Chertsey. Socs: Train. Mem. Assn.

WALKER

AnE.h. Prev: SHO (Anaesth.) Roy. Surrey, Hosp. Guilford; SHO (Acc. & Emerg.) Qu. Mary's Hosp. Koethampton.

WALKER, George Dymond Oldfield Surgery, 45 Upper Oldfield Park, Bath BA2 3HT Tel: 01225 421137 Fax: 01225 337808; Bracelands, Stoneage Lane, Tunley, Bath BA2 0DS Tel: 01761 472094 — MB BChir 1961 Camb.; MB Camb. 1961, BChir, 1960; MRCGP 1977; DObst RCOG 1962; Cert JCC Lond. 1976. (Lond. Hosp.) Apptd. Lead Off. Bath. Socs: Soc. Occupat. Med. & Internat. Health Eval. Assn. Prev: Ho. Surg. Lond. Hosp.; Ho. Phys. Roy. United Hosp. Bath .

WALKER, George Peter (retired) Kent House, 18 Redhills Road, Arnside, Carnforth LA5 0AU Tel: 01524 762156 Fax: 01524 762156 Email: peterwalker@doctors.org.uk — MB ChB 1954 Manch.; FRCOG 1975, M 1961, DObst 1957. Prev: Cons. O & G Roy. Liverp. & Mill Rd. Matern. Hosp. Liverp.

WALKER, George Richard Leyburn Medical Practice, The Nurseries, Leyburn DL8 5AU Tel: 01969 622391 Fax: 01969 624446; Manor Barn, Harmby, Leyburn DL8 5PD — MB ChB 1969 Manch.

WALKER, Giles Austen 59 Clarendon Rise, London SE13 5EX — MB BS 1994 Lond.

WALKER, Gordon McPherson The Surgery, Station Rd, Yarmouth PO41 0QP — MB ChB 1984 Sheff.; MRCGP Lond. 1988; DCH RCP Lond. 1987. GP Yarmouth. Prev: GP Freshwater.

WALKER, Gordon Trevor 57 Newfield Lane, Dore, Sheffield S17 3DD; 98 Bents Road, Sheffield S11 9RL — MB ChB 1965 Sheff. (Sheff.) SHO (Gen. Surg.) Derby City Hosp. Socs: Counc. BMA. Prev: SHO (Orthop.) Roy. Infirm. Sheff.

WALKER, Graeme Alexander (3F1) 15 Livingstone Place, Marchmont, Edinburgh EH9 1PB — MB ChB 1996 Ed.

WALKER, Graham Duncan 3 West Hayes, Lymington SO41 3RL — MB BS 1982 Lond.; MRCP (UK) 1985; FRCR 1991. Sen. Regist. (Diag. Radiol.) Wessex Train. Sch. Prev: Regist. (Gen. Med.) Guy's Hosp. Lond.; SHO (Rotat.) Gen. Med. E. Dorset HA.

WALKER, Graham John Northampton General Hospital NHS Trust, Cliftonville, Northampton NN1 5BD — MB ChB 1985 Dundee; MBA Heriat-Watt Univ. 1995; FFA RCSI 1991; FCAnaesth 1991; DRCOG 1989; DA (UK) 1988. Cons. Anaesth. N.ampton Gen. Hosp. Prev: Sen. Regist. (Anaesth.) Roy. Infirm. Edin.; Regist. Rotat. (Anaesth.) Edin. Lothian HB; SHO (Anaesth. & O & G) Chester HA.

WALKER, Gregor Murray 2 Lorn Place, Kirkintilloch, Glasgow G66 3NS — MB ChB 1994 Manch.

WALKER, Heather Ann Cameron c/o Anaesthetic Department, North Manchester General Hospital, Delaunays Road, Crumpsall, Manchester M8 5RB — MB ChB 1972 Ed.; BSc (Med. Sci.) Ed. 1969, MB ChB 1972; FFA RCS Eng. 1981; FFA RCSI 1981; DA Eng. 1975; DObst RCOG 1974. Cons. (Anaesth.) N. Manch. Gen. Hosp. Prev: Sen. Regist. (Anaesth.) Sheff. AHA; Regist. (Anaesth.) Derbysh. Roy. Infirm. Derby; Regist. (Anaesth.) Newc. AHA.

WALKER, Heather Jane 35 Addison Road, Hove BN3 1TQ — MB ChB 1994 Liverp.

***WALKER, Helen Joanne** Avon Croft, High Hawsker, Whitby YO22 4LH — MB ChB 1998 Liverp.; MB ChB Liverp 1998.

WALKER, Herbert Alan Stephens (retired) Ferndale, 10 Newbridge Crescent, Wolverhampton WV6 0LN Tel: 01902 753316 — MB BS 1953 Durh. Prev: Asst. Resid. Med. Off. & Ho. Phys. (Childr.) Roy. Vict. Infirm. Newc.

WALKER, Iain William Caythorpe Surgery, 52-56 High Street, Caythorpe, Grantham NG32 3DN Tel: 01400 272215 Fax: 01400 273608; 9 Health Farm Close, Sudbrook, Grantham NG32 3SP Tel: 01400 230172 — BM BCh 1989 Oxf.; MA Camb. 1990; MRCGP 1994; DRCOG 1993; Cert. Family Plann. JCC 1992; DCH RCP Lond. 1991. GP. Socs: Christ. Med. Fell.sh.; BMA. Prev: Trainee GP/SHO Nottm. VTS; Trainee GP/SHO Macclesfield Dist. Gen. Hosp. VTS; Ho. Off. (Surg.) Roy. United Hosp. Bath.

WALKER, Isabeau Alexandra Great Ormond Street Hospital, Great Ormond Street, London WC1 3JH — MB BChir 1984 Camb.; FRCA 1990. Cons. Paediat. Anaesth. Gt. Ormond St. Hosp. NHS Trust Lond.

WALKER, Isobel Deda Dept of Haematology, Glasgow Royal Infirmary, Glasgow G4 0SF Tel: 0141 552 5692 Fax: 0141 211 4919; 44 North Grange Road, Bearsden, Glasgow G61 3AF — MD Glas. 1983, MB ChB 1967; FRCP Ed. 1986; FRCPath 1984, M 1974. (Glas.) Cons. Haemat. Glas. Roy. Infirm. & Hon. Clin. Sen.

Lect. Univ. Glas.; Chairm. Steering Comm. UK NEQAS Blood Coagulation. Socs: Brit. Soc. Haematol. (Ex-Pres.); Chairm. Brit. Comm. Standards in Haematol.; Internat. Soc. Thrombosis & Haemostasis. Prev: Sen. Regist., Regist. & SHO (Haemat.) Glas. Roy. Infirm.

WALKER, Jack (retired) Lincoln Road, Leasingham, Sleaford NG34 8JS Tel: 01529 302644 — MB ChB 1953 Birm.; BSc (Hons.) Birm. 1950; MRCGP 1973; DObst RCOG 1955; DA Eng. 1955. Prev: Clin. Asst. (Anaesth.) Boston Hosp. Gp.

WALKER, Jacqueline 1 Witham Close, Chandler's Ford, Eastleigh SO53 4TJ — BM 1994 Soton. SHO (Gen. Med.) Yeovil Dist. Hosp. Prev: SHO (Gen. Med.) E. Surrey Hosp.; SHO (Gen. Med.) Salisbury Dist. Hosp.

WALKER, Jacqueline Rosemary Coldstone House, Shipton Road, Ascott-u-Wychwood, Chipping Norton OX7 6AG Tel: 01993 832708 Fax: 01993 832823; Coldstone House, Shipton Road, Ascott-u-Wychwood, Chipping Norton OX7 6AG Tel: 01993 832708 Fax: 01993 832823 — MRCS Eng. LRCP Lond. 1976; MSc Lond. 1981, MB BS 1976; FRCPath. 1982. (Westm.) p/t Hon. Clin. Asst. Prev: Cons. Communicable Dis. Control N.W. Surrey HA.; Cons. Virol. Pub. Health Laborat. Epsom; Asst. Microbiol. Pub. Health Laborat. New Addenbrookes Hosp. Camb.

WALKER, James 40 Sevenoaks Avenue, Heaton Moor, Stockport SK4 4AW Tel: 0161 432 7316 — MB ChB 1938 Aberd. (Aberd.)

WALKER, James, DFC (retired) 23 Bellevale Avenue, Ayr KA7 2RP Tel: 01292 267184 — MB ChB St. And. 1951; FRCGP 1981, M 1971.

WALKER, James 23 St Johns Road, Ballygowan Road, Hillsborough BT26 6ED — MB BCh BAO 1977 Belf.; FRCR 1984; DMRD RCP Lond. 1982. Cons. Radiol. Craigavon Area Hosp. Socs: Ulster Radiol. Soc. Prev: Sen. Regist. & Regist. (Radiol.) Belf. City Hosp. & Roy. Vict. Hosp.

WALKER, James Alexander Grasmere, Rowhorne Road, Nadderwater, Exeter EX4 2JE Tel: 01392 211895 — MB BS Lond. 1949; MRCGP 1963. (Char. Cross) Prev: Ho. Surg. Char. Cross Hosp.; Ho. Phys. Bridge of Earn Hosp.; Med. Off. RAF.

WALKER, James Campbell 10 Liberton Drive, Edinburgh EH16 6NN — MB ChB 1946 St. And.; DPH 1963. (St. And.) Socs: BMA. Prev: Ho. Surg. Stracathro Hosp. Brechin; Asst. MOH Dundee Corp.; Dep. MOH & Dep. Princip. Sch. Med. Off. Co. Boro. Hartlepool.

WALKER, James David Department of Diabetes, Royal Infirmary of Edinburgh, Edinburgh EH3 9YW Tel: 0131 536 2071 Fax: 0131 536 2075; 13 Denham Green Place, Edinburgh EH5 3PA Tel: 0131 551 1306 Email: jdwalker@cwcum.net — MB BS 1982 Lond.; BSc (Hons.) Lond. 1979, MD 1994; MRCP (UK) 1985; FRCP FRCP (Edin) 1999. (Middlx.) Cons. Phys. (Gen. Med. & Diabetes) Roy. Infirm. Edin. Socs: Brit. Diabetic Assn.; Amer. Diabetic Assn.; Eur. Assn. for Study Diabetes. Prev: Sen. Regist. (Gen. Med., Endocrinol. & Diabetes) St. Bart. Hosp. Lond.; Regist. & SHO (Med. Rotat.) Lond. Hosp.

WALKER, Mr James Downie Lynton House, Parkside View, Leeds LS6 4NS — MB ChB 1956 Leeds; FRCS Ed. 1968.

WALKER, Professor James Johnston Department of Obstetrics & Gynaecology, St. James's University Hospital, Leeds LS9 7TF Tel: 0113 206 5872 Fax: 0113 234 3450 Email: msjjjw@leeds.ac.uk; 12 Shire Oak Road, Headingley, Leeds LS6 2DE Tel: 0113 278 9599 Fax: 0113 234 3450 — MD 1992 Glas.; MB ChB 1976; MRCP (UK) 1981; FRCP Glas. 1991; MRCOG 1981; FRCOG. Prof. O & G Univ. Leeds St. Jas. Univ. Hosp. Socs: Blair Bell Res. Soc.; FRCP (Ed. & Glas.); Fell. Roy. Coll. Obst. & Gyn. Prev: Reader, Sen. Lect. & Lect. (O & G) Glas. Uiv.

WALKER, Mr James Montserrat (retired) 33 Chestnut Avenue, Southborough, Tunbridge Wells TN4 0BT Tel: 01892 535546 Email: jimwalker@btinternet.com — MB BCh BAO Belf. 1957; FRCS Ed. 1964; FRCS Eng. 1964; FFAEM 1993; DTM & H Liverp. 1967. Prev: Cons. i/c Emerg. & Accid. Kent & Sussex Hosp. Tunbridge Wells.

WALKER, James Stewart (retired) Strathmore, 15 Dundas Crescent, Kirkwall KW15 1JQ — MB ChB 1962 St. And.; DObst RCOG 1972; DA Eng. 1967.

WALKER, James William Berkshire Independent Hospital, Wensley Road, Coley Park, Reading RG1 6UZ Tel: 01189 560056; Kendrick House, 96 Kendrick Road, Reading RG1 5DW Tel: 01189 872191 Fax: 01189 756705 — MB BS Lond. 1958; MRCGP 1967; DObst

WALKER

RCOG 1959. (Char. Cross) Chief Med. Adviser S.. Electric & Indep. Pract. Clin. Hypn. & Behaviour Ther.; Authorised Med. Examr. Civil Aviat. Auth.; Med. Adviser, John Lewis Ptnsp.Med. Adviser, hewlett Packard. Socs: Fell. Roy. Soc. Med.; Accred. Mem. Soc. Med. & Dent. Hypn.; Soc. Occupat. Med. Prev: Cons. Phys. (Occupat. Health) St. Mary's Hosp. Newport, I. of Wight; Med. Off. RAF.

WALKER, James William Simon Alison Lea Medical Centre, Calderwood, East Kilbride, Glasgow G74 3BE Tel: 01355 233981 Fax: 01355 261689 Email: simmon.walker@alisonlea.ianpot.scot.nhs.uk; 69 East Kilbride Road, Busby, Glasgow G76 8HX Tel: 0141 644 5582 — MB ChB Glas. 1969; FRCGP 1994, M 1976; DObst RCOG 1971. (Glas.) Drs Walker, & Partners, Alison Lea Med. Centre, E. Kilbrike. Socs: (Ex-Pres.) E. Kilbride Med. Soc.; Glas. Midl. & W.. Med. Assn. (Ex-Pres.). Prev: SHO (Med.) Stobhill Hosp. Glas.; Ho. Off. Glas. Roy. Matern. Hosp. & Roy. Hosp. Sick Childr. Glas.; Sen. Clin. Tutor, Dept. of Gen. Pract. Univ. Glasg.

WALKER, Jan Andrew Bernard Lumsden Department of Clinical Biochemistry, Wexham Park Hospital, Slough SL2 4HL Tel: 01753 633448 Fax: 01753 633448 Email: ian.walker@hwph_tr.nhs.uk — MB ChB 1987 Bristol; MD Soton. 1997; MA Camb. 1985; MRCPath 1997. (Bristol) Cons. Chem. Path. Heatherwood & Wexham Pk. Hosps. Slough. Socs: Assn. Clin. Biochem.; Brit. Hyperlip .Assn. Prev: Sen. Regist. (Biochem.ry) St. Mary's Hosp. Lond.; Reg. Biochem.ry, S.ampton Gen Hosp.; SHO (Gen. Med.) Roy. Gwent Hosp.

WALKER, Jane US Department, Simpson Memorial Maternity Pavillion, Royal Infirmary of Edinburgh, Lauriston Place, Edinburgh EH3 9YW Tel: 0131 536 2935 Fax: 0131 536 2933; 1 Cluny Place, Edinburgh EH10 4RH Tel: 0131 452 8254 — MB ChB 1986 Ed.; BSc Ed. 1984; MRCP (UK) 1989; FRCR 1992; DMRD Ed. 1991. (Ed.) p/t Cons. Radiol. Simpson Memor. Matern. Pavilion Edin.

WALKER, Janet (retired) Ladyacre Cottage, Old Park Lane, Farnham GU10 5AA Tel: 01252 712107 — MB ChB 1955 Sheff.

WALKER, Janet Elizabeth Aldborough Forge, Boroughbridge, York YO51 9HG — MB BS 1994 Newc.

WALKER, Janet Margaret 10E Cross Lane, Lisburn BT28 2TH — MB BCh BAO 1986 Belf.; MFHom 1992; MRCGP 1991; D.Occ.Med. RCP Lond. 1996. (Qu. Univ. Belf.) Prev: GP Asst., Templemore Ave. HC Belf.; Trainee GP Newtownabbey; SHO (O & G) Mid-Ulster Hosp.

WALKER, Jason Michael 16 Crown Terrace, Dowanhill, Glasgow G12 9ES — MB ChB 1994 Glas.

WALKER, Jean Barbara 24 Sivermere Park, Shifnal TF11 9BN — MB ChB 1982 Leeds.

WALKER, Jeanne Elizabeth (retired) 228 Upper Batley Low Lane, Batley WF17 0JF Tel: 01924 444365 — MB ChB 1948 Leeds. Prev: Ho. Phys. & Asst. Cas. Off. Leeds Pub. Disp. & Hosp.

WALKER, Jeffery Miles (retired) Porchfield House, Mickleton, Chipping Campden GL55 6RZ Tel: 01386 438872 — MB ChB Birm. 1950; FRCP Lond. 1975, M 1960; FRCP Ed. 1971, M 1957; MRCS Eng. LRCP Lond. 1950. Prev: Cons. Phys. Salford HA.

WALKER, Jennifer Louise 50 Dorling Drive, Epsom KT17 3BH — BM BS 1996 Nottm.

WALKER, Jennifer Mary (retired) Rectory Farmhouse, Englishcombe, Bath BA2 9DU Tel: 01225 425073 Email: jennie@barnhire.com — MB Camb. 1961, BChir 1960. Prev: Med. Adviser W.. Nat. Adoption Soc. Bath.

WALKER, Jennifer Susan Department of Anaesthetics, L & IDGH, Glengallen Road, Oban PA34 4HH Tel: 01631 567500; Foothills, Ganavan, Oban PA34 5TU Tel: 01631 562827 Email: jennifer.walker2@virgin.net — MB ChB 1988 Ed.; BSc (Hons.) St. And. 1985; FRCA 1994; DA (UK) 1991. Cons. Anaesth. Lorn & Is.s Dist. Gen. Hosp. Oban. Socs: Pain Soc.; ESRA; Scott. Anaesth. Soc. Prev: Sen. Regist. (Anaesth.) S.ern Gen. Hosp., Glas.; Career Regist. Rotat. (Anaesth.) W.. Infirm. Glas.; SHO (Anaesth.) Law Hosp. Carluke & Glas. Roy. Infirm.

WALKER, Jenny Paediatric Surgical Unit, Sheffield Childrens Hospital, Western Bank, Sheffield S10 2TH Tel: 0114 271 7000 Fax: 0114 276 8419; Converted Garage, Carlton, Leyburn DL8 4AY Tel: 01969 640676 — MB ChB 1974 Leeds; ChM Leeds 1986; FRCS Eng. 1983; FRCS Ed. 1982. Cons. Paediat. Surg. Sheff. Childr. Hosp. Sheff. Prev: Sen. Regist. (Paediat. Surg.) Alder Hey Hosp. Liverp.; Research Regist. (Urol.) City Hosp. Nottm.; Gen. Med. Off. State Brunei.

WALKER, Jeremy David Saunders Church Street Medical Centre, 11B Church Street, Eastwood, Nottingham NG16 3BP Tel: 01773 712065 Fax: 01773 534295; 38 Central Avenue, Hucknall, Nottingham NG15 7JH Tel: 0115 955 0623 — BM BS 1988 Nottm.; BMedSci 1986; MRCGP 1993; T(GP) 1993. (Nottingham) GP Princip. Prev: Trainee GP/SHO N. Notts. VTS; Ho. Off. (Surg.) Derbysh. Roy. Infirm.; Ho. Off. (Med.) City Hosp. Nottm.

WALKER, Joan Lyall (retired) 4 Moorway, Tranmere Park, Guiseley, Leeds LS20 8LB Tel: 01943 875324 — MB ChB 1948 Glas. Prev: Gen. Practitioner Bradford.

WALKER, Joanna Margaret Department of Paediatrics, St. Marys Hospital, Milton Road, Portsmouth PO3 6AD Tel: 023 92 866100 Fax: 023 92 866101 Email: joanna.walker@smail01.porthosp.swest.nhs.uk — MB BS 1982 Lond.; BA York 1977; MRCP (UK) 1985. (Roy. Free) Cons. Paediat. Portsmouth Hosps. NHS Trust. Socs: Brit. Soc. Paediative Endocrinol. & Diabetes; Brit. Diabetic Assn.; United Kingdom Childr.s Cancer Study Gp. (Assoc. Mem.). Prev: Clin. Lect. (Paediat.) Camb. Univ.; Clin. Research Fell. Soton. Univ.; SHO Profess. Med. Unit Hosp. Sick Childr. Lond.

WALKER, Joanna Margaret 24 Kingsway, Scarborough YO12 6SG — MB ChB 1993 Ed.; BSc (Hons.) Newc. 1988.

WALKER, Joanna Margaret 14 Hightree Drive, Henbury, Macclesfield SK11 9PD — MB ChB 1998 Dund.

WALKER, Joanna Victoria 30 Carnarvon Road, Redland, Bristol BS6 7DS — MB BS 1998 Lond.

WALKER, John Brian (retired) Quay House, Portscatho, Truro TR2 5HF Tel: 01872 580456 — BM BCh Oxf. 1947. Prev: Capt. RAMC, Jun. Ophth. Specialist.

WALKER, John Douglas c/o Mr J.P.D. Walker, 71 Granville St., Woodville, Swadlincote DE11 7JQ — MB BCh 1956 Witwatersrand; FRCOG 1983, M 1964.

WALKER, John Edward Stuart Grebe House, 27 Westgate, Hornsea HU18 1BP Tel: 01964 533430 — MRCS Eng. LRCP Lond. 1963; DObst RCOG 1965. (Leeds) Socs: Brit. Assn. Sport & Med. Prev: SHO (Dermat.) Gen. Infirm. Leeds; Ho. Off. (Gen. Med. & Surg.) St. Jas. Hosp. Leeds; Ho. Off. St. Luke's Matern. Hosp. Bradford.

WALKER, John Geoffrey (retired) 42 Highgate High Street, London N6 5JG Tel: 020 8348 7955 — MD 1971 Lond.; MB BS (Hons.) 1958; FRCP Lond. 1974, M 1960. Hon. Cons. Phys.Gastroenterolsit St. Mary's Hosp. Lond. Prev: Hon. Cons. Phys.Gastroenterolsit St. Mary's Hosp. Lond.

WALKER, Professor John Hilton Low Luddick House, Woolsington, Newcastle upon Tyne NE13 8DE Tel: 0191 286 0551 — MD Durh. 1959. MB BS 1954; FFCM 1976, M 1972; FRCGP 1977, M 1972; DPH Newc. 1964; Hon. FRCPCH 1996. Emerit. Prof. Univ. Newc. Prev: Prof. & Head, Dept. Family & Community Med. Univ. Newc.; Chairm. Exam. Bd. Roy. Coll. Gen. Pract.; Mem. Soc. Social Med. & Brit. Paediat. Assn.

WALKER, John Yuill (retired) 47 Victoria Park Road, Exeter EX2 4NU Tel: 01392 496401 — MB ChB 1931 Ed. Prev: Ho. Phys. Edin. Roy. Infirm. & Leith Gen. Hosp.

WALKER, Jonathan 4 Chatsworth Close, Wistaston, Crewe CW2 6SW — MB ChB 1993 Liverp.; BSc (Hons.) Physiol. Liverp. 1990; MRCP (UK) 1996; DTM & H Liverp. 1997. SHO Anaesth. Roy. Liverp. Univ. Hosp. Liverp. Prev: SHO (Gen. Med.) Aintree Hosps. Liverp.

WALKER, Josephine Merrien Georgian House, 81 Carolgate, Retford DN22 6EH Tel: 01777 709543 Fax: 01777 709004; Welham Hall, Welham, Retford DN22 0SF Tel: 01777 701252 Fax: 01771 701252 — MB ChB 1977 Sheff. Indep. GP (Herbal Med., Acupunture, Complementary Therapies); Med. Adviser for EMP (UK) Ltd Aaron Assocs. Prev: Partner Drs Smith, Brown, Crooks & Walker Retford; Clin. Asst. GU Med. Dept. Bassetlaw Hosp.

WALKER, Julie Amanda 95 Towwgate, Silkstone, Barnsley S75 4SW — MB ChB 1993 Leeds.

WALKER, June Abercrombie 27 Finch Lane, Bushey, Watford WD23 3AJ — MRCS Eng. LRCP Lond. 1962; FFA RCS Eng. 1979; DA Eng. 1975. (Univ. Aberd. & Roy. Free) Prev: Cons. Anaesth. Watford Gen. Hosp.; Sen. Regist. N. Middlx. & Roy. Free Hosps. Lond.

WALKER

WALKER, Mrs June Margaret (retired) 20 Woolsington Park S., Newcastle upon Tyne NE13 8BJ — MB BS Durh. 1950. Clin. Med. Off. Newc. HA.

WALKER, Justin Robert Andrew 7 Sudbury.Drive, Lostock, Bolton BL6 4PP — MB ChB 1993 Ed.

WALKER, Katherine Justice Ormiston East, Brittains La, Sevenoaks TN13 2NF — MB ChB 1997 Bristol.

WALKER, Kathleen Rutledge Vinniehill, Gatehouse of Fleet, Castle Douglas DG7 2EQ — MB ChB 1949 Manch. (Manch.)

WALKER, Keith Sinclair 43 Station Road, Scalby, Scarborough YO13 0QA Email: keithwalker@tesco.net — MB ChB 1963 Glas.; FRCGP 1985, M 1976. (Glas.) Retd. G.P. Partner; Locum G.P., ScarBoro. area. Socs: Fell. of Roy. Coll. of Gen. Practitioners. Prev: Hosp. Pract. Diabetic Clinic ScarBoro. Hosp.; Regist. (Med.) Aberd. Gen. Hosp. Gp.; Asst. Resid. (Path.) Boston City Hosp., USA.

WALKER, Mr Kenneth Alexander Abbeylands, Abbots Drive, Virginia Water GU25 4SE Tel: 01344 843758 — MB BS 1960 Lond.; FRCS Eng. 1972; MRCS Eng. LRCP Lond. 1960. (St. Bart.) Emerit. Cons. Surg. (Trauma & Orthop.) Ashford.(Middlx.) Hosp.; Med. Cons. RAC Motor Sport Assoc. & RAC Med. Panel; Chairm.. Motor Sport assoc. Med. Panel. Socs: Fell. BOA; Brit. Assn. Surg. Knee; Internat. Soc. Arthroscopy, Knee Surg. & Orthop. Sports Med. Prev: Chief Asst. (Orthop.) St. Thos. Hosp. Lond.; Asst. Prof. Orthop. Surg. Albert Einstein Med. Coll. New York; Regist. (Orthop.) W.m. Hosp. Lond.

WALKER, Kenneth Grant University Department of Surgery, Western Infirmary, Glasgow G11 6NT Tel: 0141 211 2163 Fax: 0141 334 1826; 108 Norse Road, Glasgow G14 9EQ — MB ChB 1989 Aberd. Clin. Research Fell. Univ. Glas. Socs: Brit. Transpl. Soc. Prev: SHO (Paediat.) Roy. Hosp. Sick Childr. Glas.; SHO (A & E) W.. Infirm. Glas.; SHO (Surg.) W.. Infirm. Glas.

WALKER, Kenneth Peter, OBE, TD Executive Medical Centre, 24 Chatsworth Road, Croydon CR0 1HA Tel: 020 8688 3430 Fax: 020 8688 4150; Shalcombe Manor, Shalcombe, Yarmouth, Isle of Wight PO41 0UF Tel: 01983 531551 — LMSSA Lond. 1954; AFOM RCP Lond. 1978. (Guy's) Dir. Exec. Med. & Occupat. Health Centre Croydon; Med. Adviser to Schumberger, W.. Geophyical, Halliburton, Brown & Roots, Kverner & Balfour Beatty Overseas, W.S. Atkins & RAC; Col. RAMC TA. Socs: Soc. Occupat. Med.; Airbourne Med. Soc. Prev: Chief Med. Off. Nestles Gp.; Ho. Phys. & Ho. Surg. (Obst.) Redhill Co. Hosp.

WALKER, Kevin John Grianon, Dunbar Lane, Duffus, Elgin IV30 5QN — MB ChB 1998 Ed.

WALKER, Mr Lawrence Urology Department, Monklands District General Hospital, Monkscourt Avenue, Airdrie ML6 0JS Tel: 01236 712281; 14 Westbourne Crescent, Bearsden, Glasgow G61 4HD Tel: 0141 942 6462 Fax: 0141 942 2854 Email: lawniew87@hotmail.com — MB ChB 1997 Glas.; MD Glas. 1992; FRCS Eng. 1984; FRCS Glas. 1982; FRCS Glas. (Urol.) 1998. (Glasgow) Cons. Urol. Monklands Hosp. Prev: Sen. Regist. (Urol.) W. of Scotl. Rotat.

WALKER, Leighton James 23 Maybush Road, Wakefield WF1 5AZ — MB ChB 1996 Ed.

WALKER, Leonard (retired) 25 Moor Lane, E. Ayton, Scarborough YO13 9EW — MRCS Eng. LRCP Lond. 1954; DA Eng. 1956. Prev: Cons. Anaesth. S. Trafford Hosps. Gp.

WALKER, Lewis Ardach Health Centre, Highfield Road, Buckie AB5 1JE Tel: 01542 831555 Fax: 01542 835799 Email: lewis.walker@ardach.grampion.scot.nhs.uk — MB ChB 1981 Aberd.; FRCP 1999 Glasg.; MRCP (UK) 1984; DRCOG 1988.

WALKER, Linda Jean Elizabeth Mid-Ulster Hospital, Magherafelt BT45 5EX — MD 1986 Belf.; MB BCh BAO 1977; MRCP (UK) 1980. Cons. Phys. & Geriat. Mid-Ulster Hosp. Magherafelt.

WALKER, Mair Bron Wylfa, Llangunnor Road, Carmarthen SA31 2PB Tel: 01267 236516 — MB BCh 1959 Wales; DCH Eng. 1972. (Cardiff) Socs: Assoc. Mem. BPA; Fac. Comm. Health; FRCPCh. Prev: SCMO Carmarthen/Dinefwr Health Unit; Med. Off. Family Plann. Assn. Clinics; Asst. Med. Off. Pub. Health W. Glam. Div.

WALKER, Margaret (retired) 27 The Avenue Road, Doncaster DN2 4AE Tel: 01302 342181 — MB ChB 1951 Leeds.

WALKER, Margaret Helen 36 Kilmardinny Gate, Bearsden, Glasgow G61 3ND — MB ChB 1951 Glas. Med. Bd. Pract. DSS. Prev: Med. Ho. Off. & Ho. Off. O & G Stobhill Hosp.

WALKER, Margaret Julia Bute Lodge, 182 Petersham Road, Richmond TW10 7AD — MB BS 1991 Lond.

WALKER, Margaret Mary 4 Chalfonts, York YO24 1EX — MB ChB 1952 Liverp. (Liverp.)

WALKER, Margaret Mary 4 Glenpark Avenue, Giffnock, Glasgow G46 7JF Tel: 0141 638 3928 — MB ChB 1968 Glas.; MRCPsych 1975; DObst RCOG 1970. (Glasgow) p/t Cons. Psychiat. Pk.head Hosp. Glas. Prev: Sen. Regist. (Psychiat.) Gtr. Glas. HB; Regist. (Psychiat.) S.. Gen. Hosp. Glas.; SHO (Gen. Med.) Glas. Roy. Infirm.

WALKER, Marion Winifred 9 Swallow Craig, Dalgety Bay, Dunfermline KY11 9YR Tel: 01383 824278; Department of Radiology, Queen Margaret Hospital, Whitefield Road, Dunfermline KY12 Tel: 01383 623623 Fax: 01383 627072 — LRCPI & LM, LRCSI & LM 1969; FFR RCSI 1979; DMRD Eng. 1976. (RCSI) Cons. Radiol. Fife HB Qu. Margt. Hosp. Dunfermline. Prev: Cons. Radiol. Hairmyres Hosp. E. Kilbride; Sen. Regist. & Regist. (Radiol.) Vict. Infirm. Glas.& Roy. Infirm. Glas.

WALKER, Marjorie Mary Department of Histopath., St Mary's Hospital, Praed St., London W2 1NY Email: mm.walker@ic.ac.uk — BM BS 1976 Nottm.; MRCPath 1984; FRCPath 1996. Sen. Lect. & Hon. Cons. St. Mary's Hosp. Lond.

WALKER, Mark Department of Medicine, School of Clinical Medical Sciences, Floor 4, William Leech Building, Medical School, Framlington Place, Newcastle upon Tyne NE2 4HH Tel: 0191 222 7019 Email: mark.walker@ncl.ac.uk — MB BS 1983 Newc.; MD Newc. 1992, BMedSci (1st cl. Hons.) 1980, MB BS 1983; FRCP 1997. Sen. Lect. & Hon. Cons. (Diabetes) Sch. Clin. Med. Scis. New. u. Tyne. Prev: Regist. (Med.) Roy. Hallamsh. Hosp. Sheff.

***WALKER, Mark Adam** 9 Swallow Craig, Dalgety Bay, Dunfermline KY11 9YR — MB ChB 1997 Ed.

WALKER, Mark Andrew Kilve Cottage, Maddocks Slade, Knoll, Burnham-on-Sea TA8 2AN Tel: 01278 788209 — MB ChB 1966 Bristol; FFA RCS Eng. 1975; DA Eng. 1972; DObst RCOG 1970. (Bristol)

WALKER, Mark Christopher Michael Lytham Road Surgery, 352 Lytham Road, Blackpool FY4 1DW Tel: 01253 402546 Fax: 01253 349637 — MB ChB 1986 Dundee; MRCGP 1991.

WALKER, Marten James The Group Practice, Health Centre, Springfield Road, Stornoway HS1 2PS Tel: 01851 703145 Fax: 01851 706138; Ingleside, 75 Newvalley, Laxdale, Stornoway HS1 — MB ChB 1984 Aberd.; MRCGP 1989; Cert Family Plann. JCC 1989; DRCOG 1988; DCH RCP Lond. 1987. Prev: Trainee GP Aboyne; SHO (O & G) Highland HB; SHO (Paediat.) Soton. & SW Hants. HA.

WALKER, Martin Bernard Department of Anaesthetics, Derriford Hospital, Plymouth PL6 8DH Tel: 01752 792691 Fax: 01752 763287 Email: martin.walker@phnt.swest.nhs.uk; Didham Farm, Buckland Monachorum, Yelverton PL20 7NW Tel: 01822 854474 — MB BS 1984 Lond.; FRCA 1989. Cons. Anaesth. Derriford Hosp. Plymouth. Prev: Sen. Regist. (Anaesth.) Oxf. RHA; Regist. (Anaesth.) St. Bart. Hosp. Lond.; Asst. Prof. Univ. Texas.

WALKER, Martin Joseph Ryhope Health Centre, Black Road, Sunderland SR2 0RY Tel: 0191 521 0210 Fax: 0191 521 4235; 85 Ryhope Road, Sunderland SR2 7SZ — MB ChB 1978 Dundee.

WALKER, Martine Anne The Firs, Fulbourn Hospital, Cambridge CB1 5EF — MB BS 1987 Sydney.

WALKER, Mary Alice 3 Baylie Street, Stourbridge DY8 1AZ Tel: 01384 379530 — MB BS 1974 Lond.; MA Camb. 1973; DCH Eng. 1976. (St. Mary's)

WALKER, Mary Frances Laurel Bank Surgery, 216B Kirkstall Lane, Leeds LS6 3DS Tel: 0113 230 7474 Fax: 0113 230 2475; 6 Welburn Avenue, Leeds LS16 5HJ Tel: 0113 274 7661 — MB ChB 1968 Glas.; MRCP (UK) 1972; DCH 1972; MFFPRHC. (Glasgow)

WALKER, Mary Patricia c/o The North Brink Practice, 7 North Brink, Wisbech PE13 1JR — MB BCh BAO 1987 NUI; LRCPSI 1987.

WALKER, Matthew Charles 37 Littleton Street, London SW18 3SZ — MB BChir 1990 Camb.; BA Camb. 1986; MRCP (UK) 1992.

WALKER, Matthew Craig Middleton and Partners, Sele Gate Surgery, Hencotes, Hexham NE46 2EG Tel: 01434 602237 Fax: 01434 609496 — MB ChB 1989 Leeds; MRCGP 1993; DRCOG 1992.

***WALKER, Michael** 24 Peterborough Close, Worcester WR5 1PW — MB ChB 1995 Birm.; BSc (Hons.) Pharmacol. Birm. 1992.

WALKER

WALKER, Mr Michael Alexander West Cumberland Hospital, Hingsingham, Whitehaven CA28 8JG Tel: 01946 693181; How Garth, Pardshaw, Cockermouth CA13 0SP — MD 1989 Ed.; MB ChB 1978; FRCS Ed. 1983. Cons. Gen. & Vasc. Surg W. Cumbld. Hosp. Whitehaven.

WALKER, Michael Campbell The Surgery, 16 Windsor Road, Chobham, Woking GU24 8NA Tel: 01276 857117; Changan, Sendmarsh Road, Ripley, Woking GU23 6JN Tel: 01483 225987 — MB ChB 1990 Bristol; MRCGP 1996. GP Partner Surrey. Socs: MDU. Prev: SHO (O & G) Frimley Pk. Hosp.; SHO (A & E) Frimley Pk. Hosp.

WALKER, Professor Michael Grant Department of Vascular Surgery, Manchester Royal Infirmary, Oxford Road, Manchester M13 9WL Tel: 0161 276 4525 Fax: 0161 276 8014 Email: mgwalker@fsi.cmht.nwest.nhs.uk; Manor Lodge, Mill Lane, Cheadle SK8 2NT Tel: 0161 428 0291 Fax: 0161 428 6202 — MB ChB Aberd. 1964; ChM Aberd. 1976; FRCS Ed. 1970. Prof. Vas. Surg. Manch. Roy. Infirm. Prev: Cons. Vasc. Surg. Manch. Roy. Infirm.; Sen. Regist. (Surg.) Edin. Roy. Infirm.; Research Fell. (Vasc. Surg.), Ho. Surg. & Ho. Phys. Aberd. Roy. Infirm.

WALKER, Michael Peter (retired) Oak Tree House, 39 Oak Lodge Tye, White Hart Lane, Springfield, Chelmsford CM1 6GY Tel: 01245 466683 — MB ChB 1949 Bristol. Prev: GP Chelmsford.

WALKER, Neal William 6 Pines Close, Lurgan, Craigavon BT66 7PF — MB BCh BAO 1993 Belfast; DRCOG 1996; DGM RCPS Glas. 1995. (Belfast) Socs: Roy. Coll. of Gen. Practitioners.

WALKER, Neil Alexander (retired) — MB BS 1970 Lond. Prev: Regist. (Paediat.) St. Lukes Hosp. Guildford.

WALKER, Neil Patrick John Department of Dermatology, Churchill Hospital, Headington, Oxford OX3 7LJ Tel: 01865 228237 Fax: 01865 228260; The Old Pottery, Coldstone House, Shipton Road, Ascott-u-Wychwood, Chipping Norton OX7 6AG Tel: 01993 832812 Fax: 01993 832832 Email: neilpjwalker@dialpipex.com — MB BS 1975 Lond.; BSc Lond. 1972; FRCP Lond. 1993; MRCP (UK) 1978; MRCS Eng. LRCP Lond. 1975. (Westm.) Hon. Cons. Dermat. Ch.ill Hosp. Oxf. Socs: Brit. Assn. Dermat.; Brit. Soc. Dermat. Surg.; (Comm.) Eur. Soc. Micrographic Surg. Prev: Sen. Lect. St. John's Inst. Dermat. St. Thos. Hosp. Lond.; Sen. Regist. (Dermat.) Addenbrooke's Hosp. Camb.; Fell. Micrographic Surg. & Cutan. Oncol. Cleveland Clinic Ohio, USA.

WALKER, Nicholas Allen 11 Dochdwy Road, Llandough, Penarth CF64 2PB — MB BCh 1970 Wales; MRCGP 1980. GP Cardiff.

WALKER, Nicholas David Fairfield Cottage, Macrae Road, Yateley GU46 6NQ — BM 1989 Soton.; DA (UK) 1993; DRCOG 1992.

WALKER, Nicholas Lawrence 142 Main Street, Barton Under Needwood, Burton-on-Trent DE13 8AB — MB ChB 1981 Birm.; MRCP (UK) 1985. Med. Off. Occupat. Health Serv. Nottm. Prev: Sen. Med. Off. GKN plc; Asst. Works Med. Off. Assoc. Octel Co. Ellesmere Port; SHO (Gen. Med.) Warneford Hosp. Leamington Spa.

WALKER, Nicholas Paul Ravenscraig Hospital, Inverkip Road, Greenock PA16 9HA Tel: 01475 633777 Ext: 5121, 01475 656147 Email: nick.walker@renver-pct.scot.nhs.uk — MB ChB 1989 Auckland; 1986 BHB Auckland; MRCPsych 1995. (Univ. Auckland, New Zealand) Sen. Regist. (Gen. Psychiat.) & Clin. Lect. (Ment. Health) Roy. Cornhill Hosp. & Univ. Aberd. - Cons. (Gen. & Rehabil. Psychiat.) & Clin. Senical Sen. Lect. (Psychol. Med.) Revenscraig Hosp. & Univ. of Glas. Socs: Roy. Coll. of Psychiat.s, Lond. Prev: Sen. Regist. & Clin. Regist., Roy. Cornhill Hosp. & Univ. of Aberd., Aberd. 1996-1999.

WALKER, Nigel George Grange Lea, 23 Hollingwood Lane, Bradford BD7 2RE Tel: 01274 571437 Fax: 01274 571437 — MB BS 1978 Lond. (London) GP Bradford, W. Yorks.

WALKER, Norman Anthony (retired) 13 Brookside, Cambridge CB2 1JE Tel: 01223 351625 — MB BS 1947 Lond.; MRCS Eng. LRCP Lond. 1947. Prev: Ho. Phys. & Ho. Surg. Lond. Hosp.

WALKER, Norman Jan Piet, OBE Salisbury Medical Centre, 474 Antrim Road, Belfast BT15 5GF Tel: 028 9077 7905 — MB BCh BAO 1972 Belf.; MRCGP 1980. (Queen's University Belfast) GP Trainer Belf.; JP. Socs: Fell. Ulster Med. Soc.; Irish Coll. of Gen. Pract.

WALKER, Patrick George Tel: 020 7224 3054; 65 Cranley Gardens, Muswell Hill, London N10 3AB — MD 1984 Lond.; MB BS 1973; FRCOG 1992, M 1980; T(OG) 1986. Cons. Gyn. Roy. Free Hosp. Lond.; Sen. Regist. (Obst. & Gyn.) Univ. Coll. Hosp. Lond. Socs: Vice Pres. Of Brit. Soc. Of Colposcopy & Cerv. Path.; Assis. Treas. Int. Fed. For Cervical Path. & Colposcopy. Prev: Florence & William Blair Bell Memor. Research Fell. RCOG.

WALKER, Paul Crawford Independent Public Health, PO Box 48, Westbury on Trym, Bristol BS9 1HT Tel: 0117 968 2205 Fax: 0117 968 2205 Email: paul@crawfordwalker.freeserve.co.uk; 8 Church Avenue, Sneyd Park, Bristol BS9 1LD Tel: 0117 968 2205 Fax: 0117 968 2205 — MB BChir 1966 Camb.; MA Camb. 1991; FFCM 1980; Dip. Soc. Med. Ed. 1971. (Cambridge) Sen. Partner Indep. Pub. Health Bristol; Vis. Fell. Univ. W. Eng.; Partner, Health Creation Partnership Bristol. Socs: Bristol M-C Soc.; BMA; Brit. Soc. Rehabil. Med. Prev: Sen. Lect. Univ. Wales Coll. Med. Cardiff; Dir. (Pub. Health) Norwich HA; Regional Med. Off. NE Thames RHA.

WALKER, Paul Phillip Department of Respiratory Medicine, University Hospital Aintree, Lower Lane, Liverpool L9 7AL; 38 Chandag Road, Keynsham, Bristol BS31 1NR — BM BS 1992 Nottm.; BMedSci (Hons.) Nottm. 1990; MRCP (UK) 1995. (Nottm.) Specialist Regist. (Respirat. Med.), Merseyside Region.

WALKER, Paul Reginald 334 Canford Lane, Bristol BS9 3PW Tel: 0117 924 8809 — MRCS Eng. LRCP Lond. 1973; MD Lond. 1986, MB BS 1973; MRCP (UK) 1975. Cons. Phys. S.mead Hosp. Bristol. Socs: Med. Research Soc. & Brit. Cardiac Soc. Prev: Sen. Regist. Bristol Roy. Infirm.; Regist. Roy. Free Hosp. Lond.

WALKER, Paul Thomas 16 South Avenue, Chichester Park, Belfast BT15 5DW — MB ChB 1994 Dundee.

WALKER, Peter Alan 99 Stamfordham Road, Fenham, Newcastle upon Tyne NE5 3JN — MB ChB 1983 Leeds.

WALKER, Peter Elton The Portland Hospital, 234 Gt Portland Street, London W1W 5QT Tel: 020 7390 8312 Fax: 020 7390 8311; Lyndhurst, 31 Steeple Road, Southminster CM0 7BD Tel: 01621 773701 Fax: 01621 773601 — MB BChir 1961 Camb.; MA Camb. 1962; FRCP Lond. 1986, M 1967; MRCS Eng. LRCP Lond. 1960; FRCPCH 1996; DCH Eng. 1963. (St. Thos.) Cons. Portland Hosp. Wom. & Child Lond. Socs: Brit. Paediat. Assn. Prev: Cons. Frimley Pk. Hosp. Surrey; Hon. Phys. Leicester Roy. Infirm.; Hon. Surg. Addenbrooke's Hosp. Camb.

WALKER, Peter Irvine Tod 36 Kilmardinny Gate, Bearsden, Glasgow G61 3ND — MB ChB 1951 Glas. Med. Ref. Scott. Home & Health Dept. Prev: Regional Med. Off. Scott. Home & Health Dept.

WALKER, Peter John Robert Doctors Surgery, West Lane, Shap, Penrith CA10 3LT Tel: 01931 716230 Fax: 01931 716231; Rayside Cottage, Rayside, Shap, Penrith CA10 3ND Tel: 01931 713372 — MB ChB 1981 Manch.; BSc (Med. Sci.) St. And. 1978. Socs: Brit. Med. Acupunc. Soc.

WALKER, Mr Philip Martin 22 Mossdale Avenue, Bolton BL1 5YA Tel: 01204 483122 Email: p.m.walker@btinternet — MB ChB 1992 Manch.; FRCS Ed. 1997. Regist. (Gen. Surg.) Bury Gen. Hosp. Bury. Socs: Manch. Med. Soc. Prev: SHO (Gen. Surg.) Birch Hill Hosp. Rochdale; SHO (Ear, Nose & Throat) Fairfield Hosp. Bury.

WALKER, Philippa Jane Ferndale, 10 Newbridge Crescent, Wolverhampton WV6 0LN — MB ChB 1993 Birm.

WALKER, Philippa May Riverside Medical Practice, Roushill, Shrewsbury SY1 1PQ Tel: 01743 352371 Fax: 01743 340269 — MB ChB 1980 Manch.; MRCGP 1987; DRCOG 1983.

WALKER, Phillip Edward Court House, 42 Beaconsfield Road, Woolton, Liverpool L25 6EL — MB ChB 1970 Liverp.

WALKER, Phillip Roy (retired) Dunbelly Barn, Orlingbury Road, Isham, Kettering NN14 1HW Tel: 01536 726282 — BM BCh 1951 Oxf.; MA Oxf. 1949.

WALKER, Phyllis Jane Learning Disabilities Service, Carseview Avenue, Medipark, Dundee DD2 1HN Tel: 01382 878711 — MB ChB 1980 Aberd.; MRCPsych 1987; DRCOG 1984. (Univ. Aberd.) Cons. Psychiat. Roy. Dundee Liff Hosp. Prev: Sen. Regist. (Psychiat.) Roy. Dundee Liff Hosp.

WALKER, Raymond Grant Drymen Road Surgery, 96 Drymen Road, Bearsden, Glasgow G61 2SY Tel: 0141 942 9494 Fax: 0141 931 5496; 52 North Grange Road, Bearsden, Glasgow G61 3AF Email: camtarn@hotmail.com — MB ChB 1979 Glas. (Glas. Univ.)

WALKER, Richard Charles Michael Waterloo House Surgery, Waterloo House, 42-44 Wellington Street, Millom LA18 4DE Tel: 01229 772123 — MB ChB 1990 Birm.; MRCGP 1993; DRCOG 1993.

WALKER, Richard Irving The Manor Street Surgery, Manor Street, Berkhamsted HP4 2DL Tel: 01442 875935; 72 Greenway, Berkhamsted HP4 3LF Tel: 01442 875614 — MB BS 1980 Lond.; MRCGP 1986.

WALKER, Richard Mark Health Centre, Village Road, Llanfairfechan LL33 0NH Tel: 01248 680021 Fax: 01248 681711; Glanffrwd, Fernbrook Rd, Penmaenmawr LL34 6DE — MB ChB 1985 Manch.; MRCGP 1989; DRCOG 1988.

WALKER, Richard Stephen 48 Hanbury Road, Dorridge, Solihull B93 8DN — MB BS 1982 Newc.; FFA RCS Eng. 1988. Sen. Regist. W. Midl. Anaesth. Rotat. Train. Scheme. Prev: Post Fell.sh. Regist. (Anaesth.) Coventry; Regist. (Anaesth.) Qu. Med. Centre Nottm.; SHO (Anaesth.) Roy. Vict. Infirm. Newc.

WALKER, Richard William North Tyneside Healthcare NHS Trust, North Tyneside General Hospital, Rake Lane, North Shields NE29 8NH Tel: 0191 273 2709 Fax: 0191 293 2709 Email: r.w.walter@ncl.ac.uk — MB BS 1982 Newc.; FRCP 1999; FRACP 1991; DTM & H Liverp. 1989; MRCP (UK) 1985; FRCP Edin 2000. Cons. Phys. (Gen. Med. & Geriat.) N. Tyneside Gen. Hosp. Socs: Fell. Roy. Soc. Trop. Med. & Hyg.; Brit. Geriat. Soc.; African Gerontol. Soc. Prev: Research Assoc. Tanzanian Adult Morbidity & Mortality Project; Sen. Regist. Rotat. (Med. & Geriat.) N.. Region; Sen. Regist. (Med.) Roy. Vict. Hosp. Banjul, The Gambia.

WALKER, Rita Cecily (retired) Foxgloves, 134 Eastmoor Park, Harpenden AL5 1BP — MB BS Lond. 1958; BSc Lond. 1954; FRCP Lond. 1984; MRCP (UK) 1970; MRCS Eng. LRCP Lond. 1958; DCH Eng. 1961. Prev: Cons. Geriat. Med. OldCh. Hosp. Romford & St. Geo. Hosp. HornCh..

WALKER, Robert Yew Tree Cottage Surgery, 15 Leyton Road, Harpenden AL5 2HX Tel: 01582 712126 Fax: 01582 462414; Pine Needles, 12 Roundwood Park, Harpenden AL5 3AB Tel: 01582 768720 — MB BCh 1978 Wales; MRCGP 1984; DRCOG 1983. GP Trainer.

WALKER, Robert Alan 175 Lugtrout Lane, Solihull B91 2RU — MB ChB 1987 Birm.

WALKER, Robert Alistair 25 Slievenamaddy Avenue, Newcastle BT33 0DT — MB BCh BAO 1994 Belf.

WALKER, Robert Bernard William (retired) Blackford Grange, Flat 22, 39 Blackford Avenue, Edinburgh EH9 3HN Tel: 0131 667 0578 Email: rw@hebrides.u-net.com — MB ChB 1937 Ed. Prev: Med. Off. DGM Hosp. Livingstonia, Malawi.

WALKER, Robert Douglas Clifton House S., 8 Moor Road, Clifton, Workington CA14 1TS Tel: 01900 603762 — MB ChB 1971 Liverp.; FRCP Ed. 1997; MRCP (UK) 1974; MRCS Eng. LRCP Lond. 1971; MICGP 1987; FRCGP 1992, M 1977. Dir. Primary Care N. Cumbria HA; Examr. Irish Coll. Gen. Pract. Prev: GP Workington, Cumbria; Ho Off. Profess. Med. & Surg. Units & Regist. (Med.) BRd.green Hosp. Liverp.

WALKER, Mr Robert Glyndwr 62 Kilburn Road, York Y010 4DE Tel: 01904 631468 — MB BS 1989 Lond.; MRCOG 1995. (Royal Free Hospital School of Medicine) Specialist Regist. (O & G), Yorks. region; Locum Cons. (O & G), Friarage Hosp., N.allerton. Prev: Regist. (O & G) Inverclyde Roy. Hosp. Greenock; SHO (O & G) Glas. Roy. Infirm. & Glas. Roy. Matern. Hosp.; SHO (O & G) Vict. Infirm. & Rutherglen Matern. Hosp.

WALKER, Robert James Cornerstone Surgery, 469 Chorley Old Road, Bolton BL1 6AH Tel: 01204 495426 Fax: 01204 497423; 22 Carlton Road, Bolton BL1 5HU Tel: 01204 491360 — MB ChB 1977 Manch.; BSc (Med. Sci.) St. And. 1974.

WALKER, Robert Sibbald Rominar, Erskine Road, Whitecraigs, Glasgow G46 6TH Tel: 0141 639 4808 Email: roberthswalker@dial.pipex.com — MB BS 1945 Lond.; MD Lond. 1949; FRCP Ed. 1972, M 1949; FRCP Glas. 1967, M 1962; LRCP LRCS Ed. LRFPS Glas. 1944. (Anderson Coll. Glas.) Cons. Phys. Glas. Socs: Scott. Soc. Phys.; Scott. Cardiac Soc. Prev: Cons. Phys. Law Hosp. Carluke; Capt. RAMC; Sen. Regist. (Med.) Roy. Infirm. Glas.

WALKER, Mr Robert Toby The Fitzwilliam Hospital, South Bretton, Peterborough PE3 9AQ Tel: 01733 874000; Holly House, High St, Morcott, Oakham LE15 9DN Tel: 01572 747429 — MB BS 1974 Lond.; MS Lond. 1988; FRCS Eng. 1979. (St. Geo.) Cons. Gen. & Vasc. Surg. P'boro. Dist. Hosp., Stamford & Rutland Hosp. Prev: Sen. Regist. (Vasc. Surg.) P.ss Alexandra Hosp. Qu.sland, Austral.; Regist. & Sen. Regist. Rotat. St. Geo. Hosp. Lond.; Research Regist. St. Jas. Hosp. Balham.

WALKER, Robert William Mundell Royal Manchester Children's Hospital, Pendlebury, Manchester M27 4HA Tel: 0161 794 4696; 73 Church Road, Urmston, Manchester M41 9EJ — MB ChB 1984 Glas.; FRCA. 1989; DCH RCPS Glas. 1986. Cons. Paediatric Anaesth., RMCH. Socs: BMA; AAGBI; Assoc. of Paed. Anaesth.s. Prev: Regist. (Anaesth.) Trafford Gen. Hosp. & Hope Hosp. Salford; Regist. (Anaesth.) W.mead Hosp. Sydney, Austral.; Sen. Regist. (Anaesth.) N.W. RHA.

WALKER, Robin Jeremy Gastrointestinal Unit, University Hospital Aintree, Lower Lane, Liverpool CH47 7AL Tel: 0151 529 4420 Fax: 0151 529 4896; Briar Lea, Acres Road, Meols, Wirral CH47 9SQ Tel: 0151 632 1107 — MB ChB 1965 Liverp.; MB ChB (Hons.) Liverp. 1965; BSc (Hons.) Liverp. 1962; FRCP Lond. 1980, M 1968. (Liverp.) Cons. Phys. & Dir. Gastroenterol. Univ. Hosp. Aintree. Prev: Regist. (Gastrointestinal) & Lect. (Med.) W.. Gen. Hosp. Edin.; Lect., Hon. Sen. Regist. & MRC Fell. Liver Unit King's Coll. Hosp. Lond.

WALKER, Rodney William Hearn The Royal London Hospital, Whitechapel, London E1 1BB Tel: 020 7377 7359 — BM BCh 1975 Oxf.; BA 1972,MA Camb. 1976; MRCP (UK) 1977; PhD Lond. 1986; FRCP Lond. 1993. (Oxf.) Cons. Neurol. Barts and the Lond. NHS trust. Prev: Sen. Regist. (Neurol.) Nat. Hosp. for Nerv. Dis. & St. Bart. Hosp. Lond.; Regist. (Neurol.) Nat. Hosp. for Nerv. Dis. Lond.; Ho. Phys. Radcliffe Infirm. Oxf.

WALKER, Mr Roger Michael Haydn Department of Urology, Epsom & St Helier NHS Trust, Epsom Hospital, Dorking Road, Epsom KT18 7EG Tel: 01372 735106 Fax: 01372 735159 Email: rmhwalker@baus.org.uk; 52 Inglethorpe Street, Fulham, London SW6 6NT Tel: 0207 610 3354 Email: rmhwalker@baus.org.uk — MB BS 1989 Lond.; FRCS Eng. 1993; FEBU 2001; FRCS FRCS (urol) 1999. (Charing Cross & Westminster Med School) Cons.Surg. (Urol.) Epsom & St Helier NHS Trust, Epsom & St Helier Hosp. Surrey. Socs: Fell. Roy. Coll. Surgs.; Fell. Roy. Soc. Med.; Full Mem. BAUS. Prev: Regist. (Urol.) Char. Cross Hosp. Lond.; Regist. (Urol.) Hammersmith Hosp.; Regist (Urol.) N.wiccк Pk. Hosp.

WALKER, Ronald James Friockheim Health Centre, Westgate, Friockheim, Arbroath DD11 4TX Tel: 01241 828444 Fax: 01241 828565; Three Trees, Redford, Carmyllie, Arbroath DD11 2RD Tel: 01241 860347 Fax: 01241 860347 — MB ChB 1977 Dundee; MRCGP Ed. 1984. GP Friockheim Health Centre; Civil. Med. Off. Roy. Marines Condor.

WALKER, Rosalie Anne Betts Avenue Medical Centre, 2 Betts Avenue, Benwell, Newcastle upon Tyne NE15 6TD Tel: 0191 274 2767/2842 Fax: 0191 274 0244 — MB BS 1983 Lond.; BSc Lond. 1980, MB BS 1983; MRCGP 1987; DRCOG 1987. Trainee GP N.umbria VTS; SHO (Dermat.) Roy. Vict. Infirm. Newc. Prev: SHO (Psychiat.) St. Geo. Hosp. Morpeth.; SHO (Cas.) Hexham Gen. Hosp.; SHO (O & G) S. Shields Gen. Hosp.

WALKER, Rosemary Ann Breast Cancer Research Unit, Clinical Sciences, Glenfield Hospital, Grosy Road, Leicester LE3 9QP Email: raw14@ie.ac.uk — MB ChB 1971 Birm.; MD Birm. 1980; FRCPath 1989, M 1977. Reader (Path.) Univ. Leicester. Prev: Lect. (Path.) Univ. Birm.; Regist. (Path.) Warwick Hosp.; SHO (Clin. Path.) United Birm. Hosps.

WALKER, Ross Thomas Alan, Maj. RAMC Osnabruck Garrison Group Practice BFPO 36 Tel: 00 49 541960 5423; 36 Elwyndene Road, March PE15 9BL Tel: (01354) 52302 — MB BS Lond. 1982; MRCGP 1989; DTM & H Liverp. 1986; DRCOG 1988. Sen. Med. Off. Osnebruck Garrison Gp. Pract. Socs: BMA & Med. Protec. Soc. Prev: Sen. Med. Off. Herford Garrison BFPO 15; RMO 16th 5th Qu. Roy. Lancers & 2nd 2nd Gurkha Rifles.

WALKER, Roy Oliver Dunkeld, 119 Worcester Lane, Pedmore, Stourbridge DY9 0SJ Tel: 01562 886542 — MB ChB Birm. 1956; DObst RCOG 1960. (Birm.) Chairm. Med. Bd. Prev: GP Stourbridge; Squadron Ldr. RAF Med. Br.; Resid. Med. Off. Childr. Hosp. Birm.

WALKER, Mr Russell William Nevill Hall Hospital, Abergavenny Tel: 01873 732732; Bannut Tree, Garway Hill, Hereford HR2 8RT Tel: 01981 580019 — MB BS 1987 Lond.; FRCS Eng. 1992; FRCS (Trauma & Orthop)1999. (St. George's Hospital Medical School) Cons., Nevill Hill Hosp., Abergavenny. Socs: Brit. Trauma Soc.; BOA; BMA. Prev: Regist. (Orthop.) St. Geo. Hosp. Lond.; Ho. Phys. K. Edwd. VII Hosp. Midhurst; Ho. Surg. St. Geo.'s Hosp. Lond.

WALKER

WALKER, Ruth Elizabeth White Lodge Medical Practice, 68 Silver Street, Enfield EN1 3EW Tel: 020 8363 4156 Fax: 020 8364 6295 — MB ChB 1966 St. And.

WALKER, Sally Elizabeth Rose, Spink, Smith and Walker, Spring Terrace Health Centre, Spring Terrace, North Shields NE29 0HQ Tel: 0191 296 1588 Fax: 0191 296 2901; 28 Beverley Terrace, North Shields NE30 4NU — MB BS 1991 Newc. GP.

WALKER, Samantha Anne 6 Bromyard Avenue, Sutton Coldfield B76 1RQ — MB ChB 1994 Birm.; ChB Birm. 1994.

WALKER, Sara Child & Family Consultation Service, Mount Gould Hospital, Mount Gould Road, Plymouth PL4 7QD Tel: 01752 272351 Fax: 01752 516271 — MB BCh 1976 Wales; MRCPsych 1992. Cons. Child & Adolesc. Psychiat. Plymouth Acute Hosps. Trust.

WALKER, Sarah Belle Chapel Cottage, Hamstead Marshall, Newbury RG20 0HP — MB ChB 1991 Aberd.

WALKER, Sarah Catherine Betty (retired) St. Angelas, 5 Litfield Place, Clifton, Bristol BS8 3LU Tel: 0117 973 5525 — MB BS 1937 Lond.; MD Lond. 1945; MRCS Eng. LRCP Lond. 1933; DPH Lond. 1937. Prev: Ho. Phys. Roy. Free Hosp. & S. Lond. Hosp. Wom.

WALKER, Sarah Louise 51 Chantry Road, Moseley, Birmingham B13 8DN — MB ChB 1979 Manch.; FRCR 1985.

WALKER, Shona Ann Department old age Psychiatry, Clerkseat, Royal Cornhill Hospital, Aberdeen Tel: 01224 681818 Ext: 57285; 29 Osborne Place, Aberdeen AB25 2BX Tel: 01224 641582 — MB ChB 1986 Aberd.; MRCGP 1990; MRCPsych 1992. Sen. Regist. (Psychiat.) Aberd. Prev: Regist. & SHO (Psychiat.) Aberd.; Trainee GP Skene VTS.

WALKER, Sian Rebecca The Old Gaol, Temple St., Brill, Aylesbury HP18 9SX Tel: 01844 238762; Bristol-Myers Squibb Pharmaceuticals Ltd, 141-149 Staines Road, Hounslow TW3 3JA Tel: 020 8754 3632 Fax: 020 8572 7348 Email: sian.walker@bms.com — MB ChB 1984 Leeds; MRCGP 1988; DRCOG 1990; Cert. Family Plann. JCC 1988; Dip. Pharm. Med 1998 (RCP). (Leeds) Sen. Cardiovasc. Med. Adviser. Prev: Med. Advisor WYETH; GP Castle Hedingham Essex; Trainee GP Tidworth.

WALKER, Mr Simon 3 Chedworth Drive, Old Hall Gardens, Baguley, Manchester M23 1LW Tel: 0161 945 8300 Email: simon-walker@msn.com — MB ChB 1993 Sheff.; FRCOphth 1998. (Sheff.) Specialist Regist. Rotat. (Ophth.) Manch. Roy. Eye Hosp. Socs: Med. Protec. Soc. Prev: SHO Rotat. (Ophth.) W. Glas. Tennent Inst. Glas.; Hon. Off. Roy. Hallamsh. Hosp. Sheff.; Sen. Health Off. (A & E) Doncaster Roy. Infirm.

WALKER, Simon Charles 42 River Court, Upper Ground, London SE1 9PE — MB BS 1989 Lond.

WALKER, Simon Wyndham Department of Clinical Biochemistry, The Royal Infirmary, Edinburgh EH3 9YW Tel: 0131 536 2700; Simla Lodge, Letham Drive, Haddington EH41 4EQ — MB BS 1977 Lond.; BA (1st cl. Hons.) Oxf. 1972, MA 1975, DM 1989. (Middlx.) Sen. Lect. (Clin. Biochem.) Univ. Edin. & Hon. Cons. Lothian HB. Prev: Lect. (Clin. Biochem.) Univ. Edin. & Hon. Sen. Regist. Lothian Health Bd.; Wellcome Research Fell. (Human Metab. & Clin. Biochem.) Univ. Sheff.; Lect. (Path.) Univ. Leicester.

WALKER, Stephanie 15 Craigboy Road, Donaghadee BT21 0LP — MB ChB 1998 belf.; MB ChB belf 1998.

WALKER, Stephen Eric Nene Valley Medical Centre, Clayton, Orton Goldhay, Peterborough PE2 5GP Tel: 01733 366600 Fax: 01733 370711 — MB BS 1986 Lond.

WALKER, Stephen Lloyd c/o 80 Parkside, Wollaton, Nottingham NG8 2NN — MB ChB 1991 Bristol.

WALKER, Stuart Anthony 43 Corbiehill Place, Edinburgh EH4 5AX — MB ChB 1967 Ed. (Ed.) Socs: BMA. Prev: Cas. Off. Leith Hosp. Edin.

WALKER, Stuart Keith Flat 2, Cedar House, Elmbank, Barnet Road, Barnet EN5 3HD — MB BCh 1990 Wales; MRCP (UK) 1993.

WALKER, Mr Stuart Robert 8 Trefoil Close, Hamilton, Leicester LE5 1TF; 12 Lindisfarne Drive, Loughborough LE11 4FX Tel: 01509 844155 Email: stuart.walker@virgin.net — MB BS 1990 Lond.; FRCS Eng. 1994. Regist. (Surg.) Leics.

WALKER, Susan 112 West Street, Huddersfield HD3 3JX Fax: 01484 461113 Email: dr.suewalker@virgin.net — MB BS 1983 Newc.; MRCGP 1988; DFFP 1994; DRCOG 1987. (Newcastle upon Tyne) Prev: Med. Off. St. Francis Hosp. Zambia, Afr.; GP Hartlepool; Med. Off. Raleigh Fitkin Memor. Hosp. Manzini Swaziland, (Afr.).

WALKER, Susan Hilda 76 Chadwick Street, Belfast BT9 7FD — MB BCh BAO 1990 Belf.; MRCGP 1994; DRCOG 1993; DGM RCP Lond. 1992.

WALKER, Susan Jane Box Surgery, London Road, Box, Corsham SN13 8NA Tel: 01225 742361; 8 Queens Parade, Bath BA2 2NJ Tel: 01225 424460 Fax: 01225 310738 — MB BS 1979 Lond.; MRCS Eng. LRCP Lond. 1979; MFHom 1994; MRCGP 1986; DCH RCP Lond. 1983. (Char. Cross) Socs: Inst. Psychosexual Med.

WALKER, Susan Mary 35 Daleside, Greetland, Halifax HX4 8QD — MB ChB 1995 Sheff.

WALKER, Suzanne Claire Worcester Royal Infirmary NHS Trust, Newtown Road, Worcester WR5 Tel: 01905 763333; 24 Peterborough Close, Worcester WR5 1PW Tel: 01905 767374 Email: suzywalker@lepe.freeserve.co.uk — MB ChB 1995 Birm.; BSc (Hons.) Biochem. Birm. 1992. (Birm.) SHO (VTS) Wors. Roy. Infirm. Prev: SHO (Med.) Good Hope Hosp. NHS Trust Sutton Coldfield; Ho. Off. (Med.) Good Hope Hosp. NHS Trust Sutton Coldfield; Ho. Off. (Surg.) City Hosp. NHS Trust Birm.

WALKER, Tara 389 Upper Shoreham Road, Shoreham-by-Sea BN43 5NF; 271 Hadley Highstone, Hadley Green, Barnet EN5 4PU — MB BS 1993 Lond.; 2001 MRCPath Lond. Locum Cons. Histopath., Qu. Alexander Hosp., Cosham, W. Sussex. Socs: RSM - Young Fell. Represen. within Path. Comm.; BMA. Prev: Specialist Regist. (Histopath.) Roy. Free Hosp. Hampstead.

WALKER, Thomas Hamilton 10 Golf Course Road, Knightsridge W., Livingston EH54 8QF Tel: 01506 38833 — LRCP LRCS 1949 Ed.; LRCP LRCS Ed. LRFPS Glas. 1949. Socs: Airborne Med. Soc. Prev: Ho. Surg. Bangour Gen. Hosp.; O & G Ho. Off. Simpson Matern. Pavil. & Roy. Infirm. Edin.; Lt. RAMC.

WALKER, Thomas Milnes 38 Redlands Road, Reading RG1 5HD — MB BS 1968 Lond.; FRCR 1976; DMRD Eng. 1975. (Middlx.) Cons. Radiol. Roy. Berks. Hosp. Reading. Prev: Regist. (Radiol.) Bristol Roy. Infirm.; Lect. (Radiol.) Univ. W. Indies Kingston, Jamaica.

WALKER, Timothy Jonathan Dept. of Anaesthesia, Queen Elizabeth II Hospital, Howlands, Welwyn Garden City AL7 4HQ Tel: 01707 365445 Fax: 01707 365446 Email: tim.walker@qeii.enherts-tr.nhs.uk; 60 Uplands Road, Hornsey Vale, London N8 9NJ Fax: 020 8347 9574 — MB BS 1988 Lond.; FRCA. (Middlesex UCH) Cons. Anaesth. Qu. Eliz. II Hosp. Welwyn Garden City herts.

WALKER, Timothy Richard Wolfe Park Road Surgery, 3 Park Road, Shepton Mallet BA4 5BP Tel: 01749 342350 Fax: 01749 346845 — MB ChB 1977 Dundee. Med. Off. H.M. Prison Cornhill Shepton Mallet. Prev: Trainee GP Basingstoke VTS; Ho. Surg. Basingstoke Dist. Hosp.; Ho. Phys. Perth Roy. Infirm.

WALKER, Timothy Samuel John 179 Hillhall Road, Lisburn BT27 5JA — MB BCh BAO 1987 Belf.

WALKER, Valerie Chemical Pathology, Level D, South Block, Southampton General Hospital, Tremona Road, Southampton SO16 6YD Tel: 02380 796419 Fax: 02380 796 4339 Email: valerie.walker@suht.swest.nhs.uk — MB ChB Liverp. 1969; MD 1976; BSc (Hons.) Liverp. 1966; FRCPath 1989, M 1977; FRCPCH. Cons. Chem. Path. Soton. Gen. Hosp.; Hon. Clin. Sen. Lect. (Human Genetics) Fac. Med. Univ. Soton.; Head of Trace Element Unit, Soton.Gen.Hosp.; Cons. (Chem. Path.) BUPA Chalybeate Hosp., Soton. Socs: Soc. Study of inborn errors in Metab.; Mem. Brit. inherited Metab. Dis. Gp.; Mem. Assn. Clin. Biochem.s. Prev: Sen. Lect. (Clin. Biochem.) Fac. Med. Univ. Soton.; Hon. Cons. Chem. Path. Soton. Gen. Hosp.

WALKER, Mr Victor Gordon Stonelands, Binstead Road, Ryde PO33 3NJ Tel: 01983 563980 — MB BS 1942 Melbourne; FRCS Eng. 1948. (Melb.) DL. Prev: Cons. Surg. I. of Wight Gp. Hosps.; Vis. Surg. H.M. Prisons, Pk.hurst & Camp Hill.; Mem. Ct. Examrs. RCS Eng.

WALKER, William Clark (retired) Saddlers Barn, 6 Chantry Court, Ripley, Harrogate HG3 3AD Tel: 01423 771026 — MB ChB 1950 Ed.; MD Ed. 1966; FRCP Lond. 1976, M 1963; FRCP Ed. 1971, M 1956. Prev: Cons. Phys. Pinderfields Gen. Hosp. Wakefield.

WALKER, William Easton 6 Fenny Lane, Meldreth, Royston SG8 6NN — MB ChB 1968 Glas.

WALKER, William Edward Broadmeadow Health Centre, Keynell Covert, Kings Norton, Birmingham B30 3QT Tel: 0121 458 1340 — MB BS 1981 Lond.; MRCGP 1985; DCH RCP Lond. 1984; DRCOG

WALL

1983; Cert. Family Plann. JCC 1983. (Char. Cross) Prev: GP Hendon.

WALKER, Mr William Farquhar 438 Blackness Road, Dundee DD2 1TQ Tel: 01382 668179 — MB ChB 1948 St. And.; MB ChB (Commend.) St. And. 1948; FRSE 1973; DSc St. And. 1975, ChM 1958; FRCS Eng. 1954; FRCS Ed. 1953; FIBiol. 1988. Emerit. Prof. Vasc. Surg. Univ. Dundee. Socs: (Ex-Pres.) Assn. Surgs.; (Ex-Pres.) Assn. Vasc. Surgs. GB & Irel. Prev: Cons. Surg. Ninewells Hosp. Dundee; Hon. Prof. Vasc. Surg. Univ. Dundee; Sen. Lect. (Surg.) Univ. St. And.

WALKER, William Henry Andrew Cherryvalley Health Centre, Kings Square, Belfast BT5 7AR — MB BCh BAO 1985 Belf.; MRCGP 1989; DCH Dub. 1989; DRCOG 1988. Prev: SHO (Paediat., O & G & Med.) Ulster Hosp. Dundonald.

WALKER, William Izett (retired) 10 Ediscum Garth, Bishop Auckland DL14 6UH Tel: 01388 603143 — MD 1941 Glas.; MB ChB 1930; MRad Liverp. 1948; DMRD Eng. 1948. Prev: Radiol. Gen. Hosp. Bishop Auckland & Memor. Hosp. Darlington.

WALKER, William Lumsden, SBStJ (retired) 6 Kellaway Crescent, Westbury-on-Trym, Bristol BS9 4TE Tel: 0117 942 4197 — MB ChB Aberd. 1941; MD Aberd. 1963; FRCPsych 1971; DPM Roy. Med. Psych. Assn. 1953; DPH 1947. Prev: Cons. Child & Adolesc. Psychiat. Roy. Hosp. Sick Childr. Bristol, & S.mead Hosp.

WALKER, William Marshall (retired) 36 Dalziel Drive, Glasgow G41 4HX Tel: 0141 427 0666 Email: w.h.walker@talk21.com — MB ChB 1950 Glas.

WALKER, Mr William Martin (retired) Round Hill Lodge, Little Alne, Solihull B95 6HP Tel: 01564 793363 — MB ChB 1943 St. And.; BSc St. And. 1943; FRCS Eng. 1950; DOMS Eng. 1947. Prev: Surg. Birm. & Midl. Eye Hosp.

WALKER, Mr William Stanley 9 Shandon Road, Shandon, Edinburgh EH11 1QG — MB BChir 1977 Camb.; MA, Camb. 1978, MB BChir 1977; FRCS Eng. 1982; FRCS Ed. 1981. Cons. Cardiothoracic Surg. Lothian Health Bd. Edin.

WALKER, Wilson David HM Prison, Southall St., Manchester M60 9AH Tel: 0161 834 8626 Fax: 0161 833 1864; 6 Goatscliffe Cottages, Main Road, Grindleford, Hope Valley S32 2HG Tel: 01433 631674 — MB ChB 1983 Birm.; MRCPsych 1989; Dip. Addic. Behaviour Lond. 1992; Dip. Prison Med. (RCGP/RCP, London/RC Psych) Birm.1998. Sen. Med. Off. Clin. Dir. HMP Manch. Prev: Med. Off. HM Y.O.I. Glen Parva Leic.; Regist. (Psychiat.) Co. Hosp. Lincoln; Regist. (Psychiat.) Nottm. Rotat. Train. Scheme.

WALKER, Woodruff John Thornton Copse, South Munstead, Godalming GU8 4AB Tel: 0148 632324 — MB BS 1970 Lond.; FRCR 1978. (Middlx.) Cons. Radiol. Roy. Surrey Co. Hosp. Guildford. Prev: Regist. & Cons. Radiol. Groote-Schuur Hosp. Capte Town. S. Africa.

***WALKER, Yvonne Julie** 35 Caotrop Place, Stirling FK7 7XS Fax: 01786 480074 — MB ChB 1997 Aberd.

WALKER, Zoe Anne Manor Lodge, Middle St., Kilham, Driffield YO25 4RL — MB BS 1997 Newc.

WALKER, Zuzana St Margaret's Hospital, The Plain, Epping CM16 6TN Tel: 01279 827488 Fax: 01992 571089 Email: z.walker@ucl.ac.uk — MD 1983 Charles Univ. Prague; MRCS Eng. LRCP Lond. 1987; MRCPsych 1992; DGM RCP Lond. 1989. Sen. Lect. (Old Age Psychiat.) Univ. Coll. Lond. Prev: Lect. (Old Age Psychiat.) Univ. Coll. Lond.; Research Fell. (Psychiat.) Univ. Coll. Lond.; Regist. Rotat. (Psychiat.) N. Lond. Train. Scheme.

WALKER-BAKER, Lee 139 Malefant Street, Cardiff CF24 4QF — MB BCh 1995 Wales.

WALKER-BONE, Karen Elizabeth MRC Environmental Epidemiology Unit, Southern General Hospital, Tremona Road, Southampton SO16 6YD — BM 1991; MRCP 1995. (Soton.) Specialist Regist. Rheum; ARC Clin. Research. Fell. Socs: BMA; BSR.

WALKER-BRASH, Mr Robert Munro Thorburn (retired) Dene Cottage, 6 Ramley Road, Pennington, Lymington SO41 8GQ Tel: 01590 672215 — BM BCh Oxf. 1944; MA Oxf. 1945; FRCS Eng. 1950. Surg. Orpington & Sevenoaks Hosps. Prev: Sen. Regist. & Ho. Surg. St. Bart. Hosp. Lond.

WALKER-DATE, Susan Elizabeth Adeline Road Surgery, 4 Adeline Road, Boscombe, Bournemouth BH5 1EF Tel: 01202 309421 Fax: 01202 304893 — MB BS 1989 Lond. Prev: Trainee GP Hatfield; SHO (O & G, Med. & Med. for Elderly) Qu. Eliz. II Hosp. Welwyn Gdn. City; Ho. Off. Frimley Pk. Hosp.

WALKER-KINNEAR, Malcolm Henry Royal Edinburgh Hospital, Morningside Park, Edinburgh EH10 5HF Tel: 0131 537 6000; 7 Lasswade Court, 32 School Green, Lasswade EH18 1NB Email: mhwk@aol.com — MB ChB 1990 Aberd.; MRCPsych 1995. (Aberd.) Specialist Regist. (Psychiat.) Lothian HB. Socs: Roy. Coll. Psychiat.; Internat. Assn. Cognitive Psychother. Prev: Regist. (Psychiat.) Lothian HB; SHO (Psychiat.) Lothian & Grampian HBs.

WALKER-LOVE, May Pettigrew Tel: 01236 731738; Leebank, 8 Garngaber Avenue, Lenzie, Glasgow G66 4LJ Tel: 0141 776 1623 — MB ChB 1975 Glas.; MRCGP 1980; DA Eng. 1980; DCH RCPS Glas. 1977; DRCOG 1977. (Glas.) GP Lanarksh. Socs: Lanarksh. LMC; BASICS; Brit. Menopause Soc. Prev: GP Kirkintilloch; Clin. Asst. (Geriat.) Stobhill Hosp. Glas.; Clin. Asst. (Anaesth.) Paisley.

WALKER-SMITH, Professor John Angus University Department Paediatric Gastroenterology, Royal Free Hospital, London NW3 2QG Tel: 020 7830 2779 Fax: 020 7830 2146; 16 Monkham's Drive, Woodford Green IG8 0LQ Tel: 020 8505 7756 Fax: 020 8505 7756 — MB BS 1960 Sydney; MD Sydney 1971; FRCP Lond. 1977, M 1964; FRACP 1972, M 1965; FRCP Ed. 1978, M 1963; FRCPCH 1997. (Sydney) Emerit. Prof. Paediat. Gastroenterol Univ of Lond. Socs: (Sec.) Europ. Soc. Pediat. Gastroenterol. (ESPGHAN); Brit. Soc. Gastroenterol.; Brit. Soc. Paediat. Gastroenterol. & Nutrit. Prev: Research Fell. Kinderklinik Zurich, Switz.; Staff Phys. (Gastroenterol.) Roy. Alexandra Hosp. Childr. Sydney, Austral.; Prof. Paediat. Gastroenterol. Med. Coll. St Bartholomew Hosp. Lond.

WALKINGTON, Robert Paul Emmanuel Northgate Medical Practice, 1 Northgate, Canterbury CT1 1WL Tel: 01227 463570 Fax: 01227 786147 — MB ChB 1990 Birm.; MRCGP 1994; DRCOG 1993. (Birm) GP; Clin.Asst.GU.Med.

WALKINSHAW, Stephen Andrew Liverpool Womens Hospital, Crown St., Liverpool L8 7SS Tel: 0151 708 9988; 43 Menlove Avenue, Liverpool L18 2EH — MB ChB 1978 Glas.; BSc (Hons.) (1st cl. Genetics) Glas. 1975, MD, 1990; MRCOG 1983. Cons. Fetal Med. Liverp.; Hon. Lect. Univ. Liverp. Prev: RCOG Train. Fell. (Fetal Med.) Newc.

WALKLEY, Jullien Hardie Caton Ladybarn Group Practice, 177 Mauldeth Road, Fallowfield, Manchester M14 6SG Tel: 0161 224 2873 Fax: 0161 225 3276; 34 Errwood Road, Manchester M19 2PH Tel: 0161 286 2574 — MB ChB 1984 Manch.

***WALL, Alison Deborah** 16 The Oaklands, Rugeley WS15 2SD — MB ChB 1994 Leic.

WALL, Anthony Robert James The Health Centre, Hermitage Road, St John's, Woking GU21 1TD Tel: 01483 723451 Fax: 01483 751879; Four Walls, Hook Hill Lane, Hook Heath, Woking GU22 0PT Tel: 01487 763150 Fax: 01483 724510 Email: afourwalls@aol.com — MB BS 1974 Lond.; MRCS Eng. LRCP Lond. 1973; DCH Eng. 1977. (St. Bart.) GP; Team Med. Attendant Bisley Football Club & Woking Athletic Club; Dir. Clin. Trials Research Unit. Socs: BSMA Guildford Med. Soc.; Brit. Assn. Sports Med. Prev: Regist. (Paediat.) N.. Gen. Hosp. Sheff.; Regist. (Med. & Paediat.) Barnet Gen. Hosp.; SHO (Paediat.) Edgware Gen. Hosp. Lond.

WALL, Catherine Elizabeth York Road Group Practice, York Road, Ellesmere Port CH65 0DB — MB BS 1987 Lond.; MRCGP 1992; DA (UK) 1993; DCH RCP Lond. 1992; DRCOG 1991. G.P. Princip.

WALL, Christina Mary Whitby Group Practice, 114 Chester Road, Whitby, Ellesmere Port, South Wirral CH65 6TG Tel: 0151 355 6151 Fax: 0151 355 6843; 9 Field Hey Lane, Willaston, Neston, South Wirral CH64 1TG Tel: 0151 327 4187 — MB BS 1981 Newc.; DFFP 1998; DRCOG 1983. (Newcastle upon Tyne)

WALL, David Anthony Kearsley Medical Centre, Jackson St., Kearsley, Bolton BL4 8EP Tel: 01204 73164 — MB ChB 1981 Manch. Socs: Assoc. Mem. Roy. Coll. Gen. Pract.; Bolton & Dist. Med. Soc.

WALL, David William Ley Mill Surgery, 228 Lichfield Road, Sutton Coldfield B74 2UE Tel: 0121 308 0359 Fax: 0121 323 2682; 150 Lichfield Road, Four Oaks, Sutton Coldfield B74 2TF — MB ChB 1970 Birm.; FRCP 1997 London; FRCGP 1986 London; Mmed 1998 Dundee; MRCP (U.K.) 1972; MRCGP 1976. p/t Dep. regional postGrad. dean (W.Midl.s Deanery) Birm. Prev: Regist. (Med.) Qu. Eliz. Hosp. Birm.; SHO (Med.) Univ. Rhodesia.

WALL, Ian Francis Gordon and Partners, The Redwell Medical Centre, 1 Turner Road, Wellingborough NN8 4UT Tel: 01933 400777 Fax: 01933 671959 Email: ian.wall@gp-k83011.nhs.uk —

WALL

MB ChB 1977 Birm.; MRCGP 1982; DMJ(Clin) Soc. Apoth. Lond. 1994; D.Occ.Med. RCP Lond. 1994; T(GP) 1991. Princip. Police Surg. N.ants. Police. Prev: Lect. (Anat.) Univ. Birm.; Ho. Phys. Selly Oak Hosp. Birm.; Ho. Surg. Gen. Hosp. Birm.

WALL, Ian John 39 Wilsden Way, Lyne Paddock, Kidlington OX5 1TN — MB BS 1985 Lond.

WALL, Jerome Patrick 29 Carrick Road, Ayr KA7 2RD — MB ChB 1958 Glas.; DPA 1968; FFCM 1981, M 1974; DPH Lond. 1964. (Glas.) Chief Admin. Med. Off. Ayrsh. & Arran HB. Socs: BMA. Prev: Gp. Med. Supt. S. Lanarksh. Gp. Hosps. & Motherwell, Hamilton & Dist. Gp. Hosps.; Asst. Co. Med. Off. Health Warw. CC.

WALL, John Anthony (retired) 96 Merton Mansions, Bushey Road, London SW20 8DG Tel: 020 8540 9956 — MB BS 1959 Lond.; MRCS Eng. LRCP Lond. 1959; DObst RCOG 1963. Prev: Chief Exec. Med. Defence Union.

WALL, Leslie Errol (retired) 23 Maida Avenue, London W2 1SR — MB ChB 1949 Birm.; MRCGP 1970; DObst RCOG 1962. Prev: Outpat. Off. Roy. Throat, Nose & Ear Hosp.

WALL, Lucy Rosalind Imperial Cancer Research Fund, Medical Oncology Unit, Department of Clinical Oncology, Western General Hospital, Crewe Road, Edinburgh EH4 2XU Email: walll@icrf.icnet.uk — MB BS 1990 Lond.; MRCP (UK) 1994. Translational Fell.

WALL, Lyndon Trevor Occupational Medical Consultancy, 52 Greenhill, Blackwell, Bromsgrove B60 1BL Tel: 0121 445 5251 Fax: 0121 445 6228 Email: lyndonpaula.omc@virgin.net — MSc (Occupat. Med.) Lond. 1980; LMSSA Lond. 1969; MRCGP 1975; DObst RCOG 1973; FFOM RCP Lond. 1994, MFOM 1987, AFOM 1981. (Leeds) Indep. Occupat. Phys. Socs: Soc. Occupat. Med.; Nat. Back Pain Assn. Prev: Chief Med. Adviser Minerva Health Managem. Redditch; Sen. Med. Off. RAF Med. Br.; Sen. Employm. Med. Adviser.

WALL, Martyn Turner Station Approach, Frinton-on-Sea CO13 9JT Tel: 01255 850101 Fax: 01255 851004 — MB BS 1978 Lond.

WALL, Michael Keith South Staffordshire Health Authority, Mellor House, Corporation St., Stafford ST16 3SR Tel: 01785 252233 Fax: 01785 221131; The Beeches, 121 Walsall Road, Lichfield WS13 8AD Tel: 01543 258750 — MRCS Eng. LRCP Lond. 1975; MA Camb. 1974; FFPHM RCP (UK) 1996; MFCM 1986. Dir. Pub. Health & Strategy Policy S. Staffs. HA. Prev: Dir. Pub. Health & Plann. M. Staffs. HA; Cons. Pub. Health Med. SE Staffs. HA; Sen. Regist. (Community Med.) W. Midl. RHA.

WALL, Michele 11 Beaver Close, Lexden, Colchester CO3 5DZ — MB ChB 1993 Leic.

WALL, Owen Richard 32 Park Villa Court, Roundhay, Leeds LS8 1EB — MB ChB 1998 Leeds.

WALL, Patrick Gerard Communicable Disease Surveillance Centre, 61 Colindale Avenue, London NW9 5EQ; 11 Bittern Court, Eagle Drive, London NW9 5BD — MB BCh BAO 1986 NUI; MSc (Infec. Dis.) Lond. 1992; LRCPSI 1986; MFPHM RCP (UK) 1994; MVB NUI 1979; MRCVS 1979; Dip. Internal. Health. RCSI 1990. Cons. Pub. Health Laborat. Servs. Communicable Dis. Surveillance CentreLond. Prev: Sen. Regist. (Pub. Health Laborat. Servs.) Communicable Dis. Surveillance Centre Lond.; Med. Off. Kabanga Hosp. Kigoma Tanzania; Regist. (Pub. Health Med.) Wessex RHA.

WALL, Robert Anthony Sutton Community Mental Health Team, Patrick House, 5 Maney Corner, Birmingham Road, Birmingham B72 1QL Tel: 0121 685 6703 Fax: 0121 321 2695; Culm Davy, 2 Devonshire Road, Handsworth Wood, Birmingham B20 2PQ Tel: 0121 240 6801 Email: rawall@hotmail.com — MB ChB 1974 Birm.; MRCPsych 1979. Cons. Psychiat. N.ern Birm. Ment. Health (NHS) Trust. Prev: Chairm. Div. of Psychiat. N. Birm. HA; Chairm. Med. Advisery Comm. N.ern Birm. Ment. Health Trust.

WALL, Robert Arthur 79 Westwood Drive, Little Chalfont, Amersham HP6 6RR Tel: 01494 5370 — MB BS 1971 Lond.; MSc (Med. Microbiol.) Lond. 1979, MB BS 1971; MRCP (UK) 1973; MRCPath 1982. (Lond. Hosp.) Cons. Microbiol. Clin. Research Centre & N.wick Pk. Hosp. Harrow. Prev: Microbiol. MRC Laborat. Fajara, The Gambia; Sen. Regist. (Microbiol.) Univ. Coll. Hosp. Lond.; MRC Train. Fell. Dept. Microbiol. Lond. Sch. Hyg. & Trop. Med.

WALL, Tracey Jane Morriston Hospital, Morriston, Swansea SA6 6NL Tel: 01792 703280 — MB BCh 1988 Wales; FRCA 1996. (University Hospital Wales) Cons. Anaesth. Moriston Hosp., Swansea. Prev: Specialist Regist. (Anaesth.) Welsh Sch. of Anaesth.

WALL, William Henry Jeremy Radiology Department, Royal Lancaster Infirmary, Ashton Road, Carnforth LA1 4RP; 23a Lindeth Road, Silverdale, Carnforth LA5 0TT Tel: 01524 701083 — MB BS Lond. 1965; FRCR 1980; DMRD Eng. 1978; DObst RCOG 1969. (Lond. Hosp.) Cons. Radiol. Roy. Lancaster & W.morland Gen. Infirm. Hosp.

WALLACE, Agnes Dunlop Stromvar, 2 Kirkton Road, Dumbarton G82 4AS Tel: 01389 61655 — MB ChB 1973 Glas.

WALLACE, Alan Douglas Department of Radiology, Royal Alexandra Hospital NHS Trust, Corsebar Road, Paisley PA2 Tel: 0141 580 4335 — MB ChB 1987 Glas.; MRCP (UK) 1991; FRCR 1996. (Univ. Glas.) Cons. (Radiol.) Roy. Alexandra Hosp. NHS Trust Paisley; Clin. Director, Diagnostics Directorate, RAH NHS Trust, Corsebar Rd, Paisley; Cons. Radiologist, Ross Hall Hosp., Crookston Rd, Glas. Socs: Roy. M-C Soc. Glas.; Scott. Radiol. Soc. Prev: Sen. Regist. (Diagnostic Radiol.) Glas. Roy. Infirm.; Regist. (Diagnostic Radiol.) Glas. Roy. Infirm.; Regist. (Med.) Univ. W.. Infirm. Glas.

WALLACE, Alan Stewart (retired) Harmony House, 2 Harnham Road, Salisbury SP2 8JG Tel: 01722 334347 — MRCS Eng. LRCP Lond. 1944; DObst RCOG 1948; DMJ (Clin.) Soc. Apoth. Lond. 1969. Prev: Div. Police Surg. Wilts Constab.

WALLACE, Alan Stewart Grangewood Surgery, Chester Road, Shiney Row, Houghton-le-Spring DH4 4RB Tel: 0191 385 2898; 31 Breamish Drive, Rickleton, Washington NE38 9HS Tel: 0191 415 3419 Email: awallace40@aol.net — MB ChB 1982 Manch.; MB ChB (Hons.) Manch. 1982; BSc (Med. Sci.) St. And. 1979; MRCGP 1986. (Manchester) GP Princip. Prev: Trainee GP Edin.; SHO (Paediat. & Med.) Roy. Albert Edwd. Infirm. Wigan; SHO (O & G) Billinge Hosp. Wigan.

WALLACE, Alison Rowena Bartongate Surgery, 115 Barton Street, Gloucester GL1 4HR Tel: 01452 422944 Fax: 01452 387871; The Bage, Vowchurch, Hereford HR2 ORL Tel: 01981 550666 — MB BS 1987 Lond.; MRCGP 1993; DRCOG 1991. (Univ. Coll. Lond./Middlx. Lond.)

WALLACE, Ann Christine Margaret 19 Moreton Road, Bosham, Chichester PO18 8LL — MB BS 1979 Lond.; BSc (Hons.) Lond. 1976, MSc (Distinc.) 1989, MB BS 1979; DCH RCP Lond. 1986. Cons. Paediat. Community Child Health Chichester.

WALLACE, Ann Kathleen Poole Farm, Poole Lane, Woolacombe EX34 7AP Tel: 01271 870817 — MB BS 1974 Lond.; MRCS Eng. LRCP Lond. 1974; DCH Eng. 1976; DRCOG 1977. (Roy. Free) Community Med. Off. (Paediat.) N. Devon Healthcare Trust.

WALLACE, Anne Maree Lothian Health, 148 Pleasance, Edinburgh EH8 9RS Tel: 0131 536 9148 Fax: 0131 536 9164; 33 Malleny Millgate, Balerno, Edinburgh EH14 7AY — MB ChB 1978 Aberd.; MSc Ed. 1983; MFCM 1985. Cons. (Pub. Health Med.) Lothian Health Bd. Socs: Fell. Fac. Pub. Health Med.

WALLACE, Mr Antony Francis, TD Mill Green Cottage, Mill Green, Ingatestone CM4 0HX Tel: 01277 353133 — MB BS (Hons. Surg., Hyg. & Forens. Med.) Lond. 1950; FRCS Eng. 1955; DHMSA 1982. (Univ. Coll. Hosp.) Hon. Cons. (Plastic Surg.) RAF; Emerit. Cons. (Plastic Surg.) to The Army & RN. Socs: Hon. Mem. Brit. Assn. Plastic Surg.; Milit. Surg. Soc. Prev: Cons. Plastic Surg. St. Bart. Hosp. Lond., Regional Plastic Surg. Centre Billericay K. Edwd. VII Hosp. for Offs. Lond.

WALLACE, Archibald Duncan Lilybank House, Campbeltown PA28 Tel: 01586 52658 & profess. 52105 — MB ChB 1948 Glas. (Glas.) GP Campeltown. Prev: Unit Med. Off. Kintyre Unit Argyll & Clyde Health Bd.; Ho. Surg. & Asst. Cas. Surg. Glas. W.. Infirm.

WALLACE, Betty Eileen (retired) Capons Farm, Cowfold, Horsham RH13 8DE Tel: 01403 864386 — MB BCh BAO 1952 Dub.; MA, MD Dub. 1960; FRCPath 1969. Prev: Consult. (Microbiol.) Sussex Co. Hosp. Brighton.

WALLACE, Brian Anthony The Evelyn Hospital, Trumpington Road, Cambridge CB2 2AF Tel: 01223 303336 Fax: 01223 316068; Keffords, Barley, Royston SG8 8LB Tel: 01763 848287 — MB BS 1961 Lond.; MRCS Eng. LRCP Lond. 1960; DObst RCOG 1961. (Lond. Hosp.) Aviat. Med. Examr. Civil Aviat. Auth. (UK) & Federat. Aviat. Auth. (USA). Prev: Sen. Med. Off. Govt. Uganda; GP Royston, Herts.

WALLACE, Brian Bernard (retired) 12 Holly Grove, Lisvane, Cardiff CF14 0UJ Tel: 029 2075 3447 — MB BS 1961 Lond.;

FRCGP 1978, M 1969; DObst RCOG 1963. Prev: Sen. Lect. (Gen. Pract.) Univ. Wales Coll. Med.

WALLACE, Catherine Jane 14 Mortonhall Park Loan, Edinburgh EH17 8SN — MB ChB 1998 Aberd.

WALLACE, Catherine Lucy Mary 219 Boroughbridge Road, York YO26 6AY — MB ChB 1997 Liverp.

WALLACE, Colin Andrew Fishponds Health Centre, Beechwood Road, Fishponds, Bristol BS16 3TD Tel: 0117 965 6281 — MB ChB 1975 Glas.

WALLACE, Mr Colin Ernest Cromwell Hospital, Cromwell Road, London SW5 0TU Tel: 020 7460 5700 Fax: 020 7460 5555 — MB BS 1963 Sydney; FRCS Ed. ENT 1970; T(S) 1991. (Sydney Australia) Cons. ENT Surg. Cromwell Hosp. Lond. Socs: BMA; RSM; MDU.

WALLACE, Daphne Rowena Duckworth (retired) The Vicarage, Skipton Road, Earby, Barnoldswick, Barnoldswick BB18 6JL — MB ChB St. And. 1965; FRCPsych 1994. M 1976; Dip. Psychother. Liverp. 1990; DPM Newc. 1972. Cons. Psychiat. of Old Age Leeds Community & Ment. Health Trust. Prev: Cons. Psychiat. of Old Age Leeds Community & Ment. Health Trust.

***WALLACE, Mr David Hamilton** 35 Dunscore Brae, Hamilton ML3 9DH — MB ChB 1987 Ed.; FRCS Glas. 1992.

WALLACE, David Ian Ross St Brannocks Road Medical Centre, St. Brannocks Road, Ilfracombe EX34 8EG Tel: 01271 863840; Poole Farm, Poole Lane, Woolacombe EX34 7AP Tel: 01271 870817 — MB BS 1975 Lond.; MRCGP 1990; DRCOG 1979. (Roy. Free)

WALLACE, David John Muirhead Medical Centre, Muirhead, Dundee DD2 5NH Tel: 01382 580264 Fax: 01382 581199; 34 Forest Park Place, Right Ground Floor Flat, Dundee DD1 5NT Tel: 01382 227687 Email: dwall94080@aol.com — MB ChB 1976 Dundee; MRCGP 1982; DRCOG 1980. Prison Med. Off.

WALLACE, Mr David Michael Alexander 7 Hermitage Road, Edgbaston, Birmingham B15 3UP — MB BS 1970 Lond.; FRCS Eng. 1976. Cons. Urol. Qu. Eliz. Hosp. Birm.

WALLACE, Donald (retired) The Surgery, 237 St Mary's Lane, Upminster RM14 3BX Tel: 01402 226626 — MB BS 1951 Lond.; MRCS Eng. LRCP Lond. 1951. Prev: GP Upminster.

WALLACE, Donald Angus 33 Burghley Street, Bourne PE10 9NS — BM BCh 1986 Oxf.

WALLACE, Donald Greer The Surgery, Erskine View, Old Kilpatrick, Glasgow G60 5JG Tel: 01389 874281 Fax: 01389 890919; 25 Morven Road, Gartconnell, Bearsden, Glasgow G61 3BY Tel: 0141 942 3546 — MB ChB 1971 Glas.; MRCGP 1976; DObst RCOG 1973. (Glasgow) Gen. Practitioner in Old Kilpatrick & Clydebank; Med. Off. c/o the Elderly Blawarthill Hosp. Glas. Prev: SHO (O & G) Vale of Leven Hosp. Alexandria; Ho. Off. (Gen. Surg. & Med.) Roy. Alexandra Infirm. Paisley.

WALLACE, Eda Jacqueline Queens House, Flat 2,7, Queens Hospital, Queens Road, Croydon CR9 2PQ — MB BS 1989 West Indies.

WALLACE, Edgar (retired) Sunningdale, 19 Ashley Road, Taunton TA1 5BS Tel: 01823 284165 — MB ChB Bristol 1955; MRCS Eng. LRCP Lond. 1955; MMSA Lond. 1962; FRCOG 1985, M 1974, DObst 1957. Asst. O & G MusGr. Pk. Hosp. Taunton. Prev: Cas. & Orthop. Ho. Surg. & Ho. Phys. Bristol. Roy. Infirm.

WALLACE, Edwin Lindsay Markinch Medical Centre, 19 High Street, Markinch, Glenrothes KY7 6ER Tel: 01592 610640 Fax: 01592 612089 — MB ChB 1978 Aberdeen; MB ChB Aberd. 1978. (Aberdeen) GP Glenrothes, Fife.

WALLACE, Elisabeth Caroline Hall Farm, Coney Weston, Bury St Edmunds IP31 1HG — MB BS 1976 Lond.; DCH Eng. 1980; DRCOG 1978. (St. Mary's)

WALLACE, Elizabeth Ann Hay Gowanpark, Sandyhill Road, Banff AB45 1BE Tel: 01261 22443 — MB ChB 1965 Aberd.; DPH Glas. 1970; CIH Dund 1983. (Aberd.) Socs: Soc. Occupat. Med.; BMA. Prev: Asst. Co. MOH Banffsh.; SHO (Geriat.) Ashludie Hosp. Dundee; Ho. Off. Craig Dunain Hosp. Inverness.

WALLACE, Elsie Lilian Mary 31 Grayscroft Road, London SW16 5UP Tel: 020 8764 2060 — LRCP 1954 Irel.; LRCPI & LM, LRCSI & LM 1954; MFPHM 1989; MFCM 1972; MFOM RCPI 1980; MFOM RCP Lond. 1978; DPH Eng. 1967; Specialist Accredit. (Occupat. Med.) RCP Lond. 1978. (RCSI) Socs: Soc. Occupat. Med. Prev: Sen. Employm. Med. Adviser EMAS; PMO Lond. Boro. Ealing; Sen. Med. Off. & Med. Off. Lond. Boro. S.wark.;'Effects of n-Butyl Glycidyl Ether Exposure'.

WALLACE, Elsie Noel Kate 45 Fort Picklecombe, Maker, Torpoint PL10 1JB — MB BS 1939 Lond.; MRCS Eng. LRCP Lond. 1939; DMRT Eng. 1953. (Univ. Coll. Hosp.)

WALLACE, Euan David Vine Cottage, East Harting, Petersfield GU31 5NQ Tel: 01730 825265 Email: euanjiu@onctel.net.uk — MB 1965 Camb.; MA Camb. 1966, BChir 1964; MRCP U.K. 1969; DObst RCOG 1972. (Camb. & St. Thos.) Assoc. Specialist, Macmillan Unit, King Edwd. VII Hosp. Maidhurst, W.Sussex GU29 OBL; Hosp. Pract., Med. Outpats., Petersfield Hosp. Petersfield, Hants.; Clin. Assist., Dermat., St. Mary's Hosp. Portsmouth. Socs: Liveryman Worshipful Soc. Apoth. Lond.; BMA. Prev: GP Tutor & Regist. (Med.) Qu. Alexander Hosp. Cosham; Cas. Off. & Ho. Surg. Eye Dept. St. Thos. Hosp. Lond.

WALLACE, Ewan Donaldson Great Western Road Medical Group, 327 Great Western Road, Aberdeen AB10 6LT Tel: 01224 571318 Fax: 01224 573865; 14 Carnegie Crescent, Aberdeen AB15 4AE — MB ChB 1983 Aberd.; MRCGP 1987; DRCOG 1987. GP Aberd.

WALLACE, Ewan Duncan 1A Aucharn, Sunnypark, Kinross KY13 8BX — MB ChB 1997 Glas.

WALLACE, Fiona 45 Stanley Street, Southsea PO5 2DS — MB BS 1992 Lond.

WALLACE, Gillian Margaret Fleming 24 Corrennie Gardens, Edinburgh EH10 6DB — MB ChB 1993 Ed.

WALLACE, Hilda Rockcliffe (retired) East Leake Hall, East Leake, Loughborough LE12 6LQ — MB ChB 1922 Ed. Prev: Lect. in Health Educat. Leic.

WALLACE, Iain Wilson Thornliebank Health Centre, 20 Kennishead Road, Thornliebank, Glasgow G46 8NY Tel: 0141 531 6979 Fax: 0141 531 6910 — MB ChB 1984 Glas.; BSc (Hons.) Glas. 1981, MB ChB 1984; MRCGP 1989; DRCOG 1987. Prev: Ho. Phys. & Ho. Surg. W. Infirm Glas.

WALLACE, Ian Muiredge Surgery, Buckhaven, Leven KY8 1HJ Tel: 01592 3299 — MB ChB 1959 St. And. (St. And.) Prev: Ho. Phys. & Sen. Ho. Off. Cas. Dept. Dundee Roy. Infirm.; Ho. Off. (O & G) Maryfield Hosp. Dundee.

WALLACE, Ian Robert (retired) 3 Saxon Close, Exning, Newmarket CB8 7NS Tel: 01638 577331 — MB BCh BAO Belf. 1954; FRCGP 1986, M 1968; DCH Eng. 1957.

WALLACE, Ian Watson (retired) 7A Greenhill Road, Farnham GU9 8JN Tel: 01252 726090 — MB Camb. 1960, BChir 1959; DObst RCOG 1961; DCH Eng. 1961. Prev: GP Farnham.

WALLACE, Mr Ian William John, OStJ BUPA Murrayfield Hospital, Corstorphine Road, Edinburgh EH12 6UD Tel: 01506 419666 Fax: 01506 460386; Rivaldsgreen House, Friarsbrae, Linlithgow EH49 6BG Tel: 01506 845700 Fax: 01506 845100 — MB ChB 1964 Ed.; BSc Ed. 1962; FRCS Ed. 1968. (Ed.) Cons. Surg. & Urol. St. John's Hosp. Howden; Dir. (Clin. Servs.) W. Lothian NHS Trust. Socs: Assoc. Mem. BAUS. Prev: Cons. Surg. Bangour Gen. Hosp. Broxburn; Lect. (Clin. Surg.) Univ. Edin.; Regist. Rotat. (Surg.) Lothian HB.

WALLACE, Ingrid Maria 29 Bassett Road, Leighton Buzzard LU7 1AR Tel: 01525 373111 Fax: 01525 853767; 4 Fortescue Drive, Shenley Church Road, Milton Keynes MK5 6BJ Tel: 01908 504339 Fax: 01908 504339 Email: drswallace@aol.com — MB BS 1989 Lond.; MRCGP 1993; DCH RCP Lond. 1992; DRCOG 1991. Course Organiser, Aylesbury.

WALLACE, James Department of Oral Surgery, St. John's Hospital, Howden Road W., Livingston EH54 6PP Tel: 01506 419666; Blochairn, 2 March Pines, Edinburgh EH4 3PF Tel: 0131 539 2223 — MB ChB 1969 Glas.; BDS 1960; FDS RCS Ed. 1987; FDS RCS Eng. 1973. Cons. Oral. Surg. St. John's Hosp. Livingston.; Hon. Sen. Lect. Univ. Edin. Prev: Sen. Lect. (Oral Surg.) Univ. Edin.; Sen. Regist. (Dent.) St. Bart. Hosp. Lond.; Regist. (Oral Surg.) Canniesburn Hosp.

WALLACE, James Gordon (retired) 2 Eastwood House, 2 Greetwell Road, Lincoln LN2 4AQ Tel: 01522 530654 — BM BCh 1950 Oxf.; MA Oxf. 1950; FRCPath 1977, M 1966; Dip. Bact. Lond 1960; DCP Lond 1956. Prev: Cons. Bacteriol. & Dir. Pub. Health Laborat. Lincoln.

WALLACE, Mr James Randall Law Hospital NHS Trust, Carluke ML8 5ER Tel: 01698 361100; 5 Brierybank Avenue, Lanark ML11 9AN Tel: 01555 663490 — MB ChB 1966 Glas.; FRCS Eng. 1971; FRCS Glas. 1970. (Glas.) Cons. Surg. Law Hosp. NHS Trust Carluke.

WALLACE

WALLACE, James Richard Chapman (retired) Penwood, The Avenue, Ross-on-Wye HR9 5AW — LMSSA 1950 Lond.

WALLACE, James Thomas 40 Hadham Road, Bishop's Stortford CM23 2QT Tel: 01279 654053 — MB BS 1949 Lond.; MRCS Eng. LRCP Lond. 1949; Cert. Av Med. MoD (Air) & CAA 1973. (Lond. Hosp.) Apptd. Examr. Min. of Civil Aviat. & Federal Aviat. Admin. USA. Prev: Med. Off. Stansted Airport; Apptd. Med. Inspec. Commonw. Immigrants & Aliens; Ho. Surg. & Res. Anaesth. Roy. Berks. Hosp. Reading.

WALLACE, Jan Barbara Beatson Oncology Centre, Western Infirmary, Dumbarton Road, Glasgow Tel: 0141 211 2000; 90 Kessington Road, Bearsden, Glasgow G61 2QB Tel: 0141 563193 — MB ChB 1991 Leic.; MRCP (UK) 1994; MSc (Oncol.) Glas. 1996; FRCR 1998. (Leicester) Specialist Regist. (Clin. Oncol.) BeatsonOncol.Centre Glas.

WALLACE, Jennifer Anne 8 Riverside, Craigends, Houston, Johnstone PA6 7DL — MB BS 1967 Lond.; MRCS Eng. LRCP Lond. 1967; FFA RCS Eng. 1973; DA Eng. 1970.

WALLACE, Mrs Jessie Stewart (retired) 94 Finnart Street, Greenock PA16 8HL Tel: 01475 725013 — MB ChB 1961 Glas. Clin. Med. Off. Gtr. Glas. HB. Prev: clin med off GGNB.

WALLACE, Mr John 209 Findhorn, Forres IV36 3YS — MB ChB 1963 Ed.; FRCS Ed. 1970; FCOphth 1989. Hon. Sen. Lect. Univ. Aberd.; Cons. Ophth. Grampian Health Bd. Prev: Sen. Regist. Dept. Ophth. W.. Infirm. Glas.; Research Fell. MRC Epidemiol. Research Unit Cardiff; Ho. Off. Metab. Unit W.. Gen. Infirm. Edin.

WALLACE, John Alastair Kennedy 120 South Street, Armadale, Bathgate EH48 3JU — MB ChB 1942 Ed.; DPH 1958; DIH Soc. Apoth. Lond. 1968. (Ed.) Prev: Maj. RAMC.

WALLACE, John Alexander Beech Lodge, 9 Enagh Road, Ballymoney BT53 7PN Tel: 012656 65591 — MB BCh BAO 1969 Belf.; FRCOG 1988, M 1974. Cons. (O & G) Robinson Memor. & Route Hosps. Ballymoney & Coleraine Hosp. Prev: Jun. Cons. (O & G) King Edwd. VIII Hosp. Durban, S. Africa.

WALLACE, Julia Dawn Woodside Medical Group A, 80 Western Road, Woodside, Aberdeen AB24 4SU Tel: 01224 492631 Fax: 01224 276173; 14 Carnegie Crescent, Aberdeen AB15 4AE Tel: 01224 324696 — MB ChB 1983 Aberd.; MRCGP 1988; DRCOG 1987. Prev: Regist. (A & E) Grampian HB.

WALLACE, Katherine Ann Gunn 8 Riverside, Houston, Johnstone PA6 7DL — MB ChB 1996 Ed.

WALLACE, Kenneth Robert 41 Church Pavement, Swine Gate, Grantham NG31 6RL Tel: 01476 560360 Email: kennethwallace@compuserve.com — MB BChir Camb. 1948; BA Camb. 1948; MFHom 1970; Dip. Bact. Lond 1953. (Camb. & Guy's) Prev: Ho. Surg. S. Hosp. Dartford; RAF Med. Br.; Sen. Bacteriol. Pub. Health Laborat. Serv.

WALLACE, Kim Deidre 6 Victoria Gardens, Marlow Road, High Wycombe HP11 1SY Tel: 01494 558022 Fax: 01494 511113 — MB BS 1983 Lond.; MRCGP 1987; DRCOG 1986; DCH RCP Lond. 1985. (St Marys) Clin. Asst. Gen. Surg. Prev: GP High Wycombe; Trainee GP Banbury VTS.

WALLACE, Lorinda Bronheulog, Pendine, Carmarthen SA33 4PA — MB ChB 1946 Manch.

WALLACE, Margaret 9 Rochford Way, Bishopstone, Seaford BN25 2TA — MB ChB 1954 Glas.; DCH RFPS Glas. 1958. (Glas.) Prev: Paediat. Regist. E. Riding Hosp. Gp. & Newc. Hosp. Gp.

WALLACE, Margaret Anne Florence 81 Sweep Road, Cookstown BT80 8JT — MB BCh BAO 1965 Belf. Cas. Off. S. Tyrone Hosp. Dungannon. Prev: SHO (Ophth.) Roy. Vict. Hosp. Belf.; Ho. Off. (O & G) & (Paediat.) Ulster Hosp. Dundonald.

WALLACE, Marina Helen 10 Naylor Road, London N20 0HN — MB BS 1990 Lond.; FRCS Eng. 1994.

WALLACE, Mark Jonathan Gosford Hill Medical Centre, 167 Oxford Road, Kidlington OX5 2NS Tel: 01865 374242 Fax: 01865 377826 — MB BS 1991 Lond.; BSc (Hons.) Lond. 1988; MRCGP 1995; DCH RCP Lond. 1994; DRCOG 1993. GP Princip. Gosford Hill Med. Centre Oxf. Prev: GP Regist. Lond. Acad. Trainee Scheme.

WALLACE, Mary Clark 18 The Walnuts, Branksome Road, Norwich NR4 6SR Tel: 01603 56005 — MB ChB 1947 Glas. (Univ. Glas.) Prev: Ho. Surg. Sorrento Matern. Hosp. Birm.; Ho. Phys. Alder Hey Childr. Hosp. Liverp. & Leicester Gen. Hosp.

WALLACE, Maureen Elizabeth Hamilton Willenhall Oak Medical Centre, 70 Remembrance Road, Coventry CV3 3DP Tel: 024 7663 9909 Fax: 024 7630 5312 — MB BCh BAO 1976 Belf.; MRCGP 1980; ECFMG Cert. 19769.

WALLACE, Mr Maurice 128 Clarence Road, Windsor SL4 5AT Tel: 01753 867915 Fax: 01753 867910 — MB ChB 1959 Glas.; FRCS Eng. 1966. (Glas.) Cons. ENT Surg. Wexham Pk. Hosp. Slough, King Edwd. VII Hosp. Windsor & Maidenhead Hosp. Socs: Fell. Roy. Soc. Med.; Hosp. Cons. & Spec. Assn. Prev: Sen. Regist. (ENT) Roy. Free Hosp. Lond.; Sen. Regist. Roy. Nat. Throat, Nose & Ear Hosp.; Regist. (ENT) Glas.

WALLACE, Michael Andrew (3F3), 26 Springvalley Ter, Edinburgh EH10 4PY — MB ChB 1997 Ed.

WALLACE, Mr Murray Evelyn Queen's Hospital, Burton Hospital NHS Trust, Burton-on-Trent DE13 0RB Tel: 01283 566333 — MB BCh 1982 Witwatersrand; FCS(SA) Orth 1991; T(S) 1992. Cons. Orthop. Surg. Burton Hosp. NHS Trust; Hon. Clin. Sen. Lect. (Orthop.) Keele Univ. Stoke-on-Trent. Socs: Fell. BOA; BMA. Prev: Sen. Regist. Musgrave Pk. Hosp. Belf.

***WALLACE, Nicola Suzanne** 174 Bridge Street, Portadown, Craigavon BT63 5AS — MB BCh BAO 1994 Belf.; BSc 1992; FRCA 1999.

WALLACE, Norah Eileen (retired) 20 Randolph Avenue, London W9 1BL — MRCS Eng. LRCP Lond. 1935. Prev: Asst. Sch. Med. Off. Surrey.

WALLACE, Norman Walker Whin Park Medical Centre, 6 Saughton Road, Edinburgh EH11 3RA Tel: 0131 455 7999 Fax: 0131 455 8800 — MB ChB 1976 Ed.; BSc (Med. Sci.) Ed. 1973; MRCGP 1981. (Ed.) Premises Adviser Lothian - Primar Care Unit. Prev: Trainee (Paediat.) & SHO (Geriat.) Lothian HB; Obst. EMMS Hosp. Nazareth, Israel.

WALLACE, Olga Nanette Meadowbank, Warren Close, Payhembury, Honiton EX14 3NA — MB BS 1976 Lond.; MRCS Eng. LRCP Lond. 1976.

WALLACE, Paul Anthony Castle Practice, 2 Hawthorne Road, Castle Bromwich, Birmingham B36 0HH Tel: 0121 747 2422 Fax: 0121 749 1196; 8 Wilkinson Croft, Birmingham B8 2RE — MB BCh BAO 1984 NUI.

WALLACE, Peter Gunn MacRae 8 Riverside, Craigends, Houston, Johnstone PA6 7DL — MB ChB 1968 Glas.; FFA RCS Eng. 1973; DObst RCOG 1970. Cons. Anaesth. W.. Infirm. Glas.

WALLACE, Richard Barnes Towcester Medical Centre, Link Way, Towcester NN12 6HH Tel: 01327 359339 Fax: 01327 358944 — MB ChB 1972 Bristol; MRCGP 1977.

WALLACE, Richard Brian Northern Ireland Civil Service, Occupational Health Service, Lincoln Building, 27-45 Great Victoria St., Belfast BT2 7AD Tel: 01232 251548 — MB BCh BAO 1980 Dub.; BA Dub. 1980; MFOM RCPI 1997, LFOM 1995; MICGP 1987; DRCOG 1983. (Trinity Coll. Dub.) Occupat. Health Phys. (Occupat. Health) N. Irel. Civil Serv. Belf. Socs: Soc. Occupat. Med. Prev: GP BrookeBoro.; Univ. Phys. Univ. Ulster Coleraine; Indust. Med. Off. Harland & Wolff plc Belf.

WALLACE, Mr Richard Gilmore Hanna 8 My Ladys Mile, Holywood BT18 9EW Tel: 01232 425298 Fax: 01232 425298; 8 My Ladys Mile, Holywood BT18 9EW Tel: 01231 425298 Fax: 01231 425298 — MD 1987 Belf.; MCh (Orth.) Liverp. 1984; MB BCh BAO 1975; FRCS Ed. 1982. Cons. Orthor. Surg. Musgrave Pk. Hosp. Belf. & Ulster Hosp. Dundonald. Prev: Sen. Regist. (Orthop. Surg.) Musgrave Pk. Belf.

WALLACE, Richard James Callon (retired) Rutherglen Health Centre, 130 Stonelaw Road, Rutherglen, Glasgow G73 2PQ Tel: 0141 531 6030 Fax: 0141 531 6031 — MB ChB Ed. 1963; DObst RCOG 1965. Princip. GP Glas. Prev: Maj. RAMC.

WALLACE, Robert Hamilton 84 Linkside Avenue, Oxford OX2 8JB — MB ChB 1986 Auckland.

WALLACE, Robert John 21 Malone Hill Park, Belfast BT9 6RE — MB BCh BAO 1966 Belf.; MRCOG 1972.

WALLACE, Ronald Macdonald Oldmeldrum Medical Centre, The Meadows, Oldmeldrum, Inverurie AB51 0BF Tel: 01651 872239 Fax: 01651 872968 Email: ron.wallace@oldmeldrum.grampian.scot.nhs.uk; 27 Westbank Park, Oldmeldrum, Inverurie AB51 0DG Tel: 01651 872861 Email: r.wallace@connect-2.co.uk — MB ChB 1978 Aberd.; FRCGP 1997, M 1982. Teach. Fell. (Gen. Pract.) Univ. Aberd.

WALLACE, Rosemary Margaret 39 Pemberley Avenue, Bedford MK40 2LE — MB ChB 1974 Glas.; MRCOG 1980, DObst. 1976.

WALLACE, Sally 6 Gledhow Avenue, Leeds LS8 1NU — MB ChB 1992 Sheff.; MRCGP 1996.

WALLACE, Sheila Jean Little Ton, Llanvapley, Abergavenny NP7 8SN Tel: 01600 780457 — MB BS Lond. 1958; FRCP Ed. 1978, M 1965; FRCPCH 1997; DObst RCOG 1960. (Univ. Coll. Hosp.) Socs: (Bd. Mem.) Internat. Child Neurol. Assn. (Vice-Pres.); (Ex-Treas.) Brit. Paediat. Neurol. Assn. Prev: Hon. Lect. (Child Health) Univ. Edin.

WALLACE, Simon Andrew 11 Golden Square, London W1F 9JB Tel: 020 766 6377 Fax: 020 7664 6372 Email: swallace@worldcare.co.uk; 46 Eaton Place, Brighton BN2 1EG Tel: 01273 695671 — MB BS 1984 Lond.; MFPHM RCP (UK) 1992; DRCOG 1988. (Char. Cross Hosp.) Med. Cons. World Care UK. Socs: BMA; Roy. Soc. Med. Prev: Locum Cons. (Pub. Health Med.) Fife HB; Trainee GP/SHO (Paediat., O & G, A & E & Orthop.) Brighton HA; Trainee Progr. (Pub. Health Med. S.Thames Region (E.).

WALLACE, Siobhan Lodge Health, 20 Lodge Manor, Coleraine BT52 1JX Tel: 028 7034 4494 Fax: 028 7032 1759; 86 Coolyvenny Road, Coleraine BT51 3SF — MB ChB 1992 Dundee; MRCGP 1996; DFFP 1995; DRCOG 1994. (Dundee) GP. Socs: (Comm.) N.. Irel. Family Plann. Assn.; RCGP; NI Female GP Assn. Prev: GP/Regist. Coleraine.

WALLACE, Susan 32 Duchywood, Heights Lane, Bradford BD9 6DZ — MB ChB 1994 Ed.

***WALLACE, Suzanne Vera Frances** High Trees, Foxwood Lane, Woodborough, Nottingham NG14 6ED; 5 Royal Standard House, Standard Hill, Nottingham NG1 6FX — BM BCh 1997 Oxf.

WALLACE, Tara Mary Radcliffe Infirmary, Woodstock Road, Oxford OX2 6HE Tel: 01865 311188; 55 Islip Road, Oxford OX2 7SP — MB BS 1991 Lond.; MRCP (UK) 1995. (Char. Cross & Westm.) Specialist Regist. (Diabetes & Endocrinol.) Radcliffe Infirm. Oxf. Socs: Brit. Diabetic Assn.; Brit. Endocrine Soc. Prev: Regist. (Diabetes, Endocrinol. & Med.) Roy. Berks. Hosp. Reading; SHO (Gen. Med.) S.mead Hosp. Bristol.

WALLACE, Thomas John 53 Palinwood Road, Delph, Oldham OL3 5UW Tel: 01457 874416 — MB ChB 1958 Ed.; FRCP Ed. 1978, M 1964. (Ed.) Cons. Phys. Oldham Health Auth. Socs: Fell. Manch. Med. Soc.; Oldham Med. Soc. Prev: Research Med. Off. Myocardial Infarction Research Unit Scott Hosp.; Plymouth; Regist. (Med.) E.. Gen. Hosp. Edin.

WALLACE, Victoria Ann 4 Bowes Lyon Place, Lytham St Annes FY8 3UE — MB BS 1997 Lond.

WALLACE, Wendy June Queenhill Medical Practice, 31 Queenhill Road, South Croydon CR2 8DU Tel: 020 8651 1141 Fax: 020 8651 5011; 15 Searchwood Road, Warlingham CR6 9BB Tel: 0188 362 5749 — MB BS 1973 Lond.; MRCS Eng. LRCP Lond. 1973; DA S. Afr. 1976. (Roy. Free) Prev: Regist. (Anaesth.) Johannesburg Gen. Hosp. Univ. Witwatersrand.

WALLACE, William Andrew Hamilton Department of Pathology, Northern General Hospital, Herries Road, Sheffield S5 7AU — MB ChB 1986 (Hons.) Ed.; PhD Ed. 1995; BSc (Hons.) Ed. 1984; MRCP (UK) 1989; MRCPath 1997, D 1996. (Edinburgh) Cons. (Histopath.) N.ern Gen. Hosp. NHS Trust Sheff. Prev: Sen. Regist. (Path.) Roy. Infirm. Edin. NHS Trust; Postgrad. Research Fell. Edin. Univ. Fac. Med.; Regist. (Path.) Edin. Univ. Med. Sch.

WALLACE, Professor William Angus Division of Orthopaedic & Accident Surgery, University Hospital, Queens Medical Centre, Nottingham NG7 2UH Tel: 0115 970 9407 Fax: 0115 942 3656 Email: angus.wallace@nottingham.ac.uk; High Trees, Foxwood Lane, Woodborough, Nottingham NG14 6ED Tel: 0115 965 2372 Fax: 0115 965 4638 Email: angus.wallace@virgin.net — MB ChB 1972 St. And.; FRCS (Orthop.) Ed. 1985; FRCS Ed. 1977; FRCS Eng. 1997. Prof. Orthop. & Accid. Surg. Univ. Nottm.; Hon. Cons. Orthop. Surg. Qu. Med. Centre; Nottm. & City Hosp. Nottm.; Hon. Cons. Surg. Portland Traing. Coll. Socs: Vice-Pres. RCS Edin.; Chairm. Nat. Sports Med. Inst.; Vice-Pres. Brit. Elbow & Sholder Soc. Prev: Sen. Lect. (Orthop. Surg.) Univ. Manch. & Cons. Orthop. Surg. Hope; Hosp. Salford; Lect. (Orthop. Surg.) Univ. Nottm.; MRC Research Fell. (Orthop.).

WALLACE, William David 174 Bridge Street, Portadown, Craigavon BT63 5AS — MB BCh 1998 Belf.

WALLACE, William Forbes Pentland Medical Centre, 44 Pentland View, Currie EH14 5QB Tel: 0131 449 2142 Fax: 0131 451 5855; 11 Cherry Tree Park, Balerno EH14 5AQ Tel: 0131 449 2951 — MB ChB 1970 Glas.; MRCGP 1974; DObst RCOG 1972. (Glasgow) GP Princip.; GP Trainer. Socs: Ed. Clin. Club; BMA; RCGP.

WALLACE, Professor William Frederick Matthew Dept of Physiology, Medical Biology Centre, 97 Lisburn Road, Belfast BT9 7BL Tel: 01232 335796 Fax: 01232 235483 — MB BCh BAO 1961 Belf.; BSc (Physiol.) (1st cl. Hons.) Belf. 1958, MD 1966; FRCP Lond. 1981, M 1966; FRCA 1991. Prof. Applied Physiol. Qu. Univ. Belf.; Cons. Physiol. Belf. City Hosp.; Examr., RCS Ed, CARCSI. Socs: Fell. Roy. Acad. Med. Irel.; Physiol. Soc.; Med. Res. Soc. Prev: Regist. N. Irel. Hosps. Auth.; Vis. Prof. Physiol. Univ. Jos, Nigeria.

WALLACE, William Hamilton 4 Belmont Avenue, Uddingston, Glasgow G71 7AX Tel: 01698 2652 — MB ChB 1957 Ed. (Ed.) Prev: Orthop. Regist. Kilmarnock Infirm.; Med. Off. Ballochmyle Hosp. Mauchline; Surg. Ho. Off. Kilmarnock Infirm.

WALLACE, William Hamish Beith Royal Hospital for Sick Children, Sciennes Road, Edinburgh EH9 1LF Tel: 0131 536 0426 Fax: 0131 536 0430 Email: hamish.wallace@luht.scot.nhs.uk — MB BS 1980 Lond.; FRCPCH 1997; MD 1992 Lond.; FRCP 1994 Ed; MRCP 1985 Uk; FRCPCH 1997. (St. Geo. Hosp. Med. Sch. Lond.) Cons. Paediat. Oncol. Roy. Hosp. Sick Childr. Edin.; Sen. Lect. (Child Life & Health) Univ. Edin. Socs: Eur. Soc. Paediat. Endocrinol.; Soc. Internat. Oncol. Paediat. Prev: Sen. Regist. (Paediat.) Hosps. for Sick Childr. Gt. Ormond St. Lond.; Research Fell. (Paediat. Endocrinol.) Christie Hosp. & Radium Inst. Manch.; Regist. (Paediat.) Roy. Hosp. for Sick Childr. Edin.

WALLACE, William Herschel Scott (retired) 403 Malden Road, Worcester Park KT4 7NU Tel: 020 8337 1594 — MRCS Eng. LRCP Lond. 1928; MD (State Med.) Lond. 1932, MB BS 1930; DPH Eng. 1930. Prev: PMO GLC.

WALLACE, William Morton Murray (retired) Rosalynn, Brodick KA27 8DP Tel: 01770 302306 — MB ChB 1951 Glas.

WALLACE, William Shaw (retired) Flat 2, Ascot House, Third Avenue, Hove BN3 2PD Tel: 01273 778 7114 — MB ChB 1942 Glas.; MRCGP 1955. Prev: Ho. Phys. Glas. Roy. Infirm.

WALLACE, Wilson Macaulay, OStJ, Lt.-Col. RAMC Retd. 16 College Court, Royal Hospital, Chelsea, London SW3 4SR — MB BCh BAO Belf. 1964; FRCP Lond. 1998 M 1972. Ranald Martin Medal (Trop. Med.) & 2nd Montefiore Prize (Milit. Surg.) RAM Coll. Millbank; Cons. Phys. Roy. Hosp. Chelsea. Prev: Sen. Med. Off. RAF Innsworth; Cons. Phys. Brit. Milit. Hosp. Hong Kong; Cons. Phys. RAF Hosp. Wroughton & Qu. Eliz. Milit. Hosp. Woolwich.

WALLACE-JONES, Dudley Richard (retired) Little Garth, Wood Lane, Parkgate, Neston, South Wirral CH64 6QX Tel: 0151 336 4160 — MA Camb. 1948, BA 1944, MB BChir 1946; FRCR 1983; DMR Liverp. 1951; DMRD Lond.1951. Prev: Cons. Radiol. Walton & Fazakerley Hosp. Liverp.

WALLACH, Abraham Leisor 41 Beehive Lane, Ilford IG1 3RQ Tel: 020 8554 7905 — MD 1936 Nancy; MRCGP 1960; DObst RCOG 1949.

WALLAGE, Sarah Dugald Baird Centre, Aberdeen Roy.Infirm, Goresterhill, Aberdeen AB25 2ZN — MB BS 1991 Lond.; MRCOG 1997. Clin. Research. Fell. Gyn. Dugald Baird Centre Aberd. Prev: Specialist Regist. Rotat. Oug W. Mids.

WALLAM, Timothy David Field House Surgery, Victoria Road, Bridlington YO15 2AT Tel: 01262 673362; The Forge, Middle St, Rudston, Driffield YO25 4UF Tel: 01262 420711 — BM BS 1983 Nottm.; BMedSci (Hons.) Nottm. 1981, BM BS 1983; MRCGP 1987; DGM RCP Lond. 1986, DRCOG 1987. Prev: Ho. Off. (Med. & Surg.) Furness Gen. Hosp. Barrow-in-Furness; Trainee GP Notts. VTS.

WALLAT, Wolfgang Curran and Partners, Manor Health Centre, 86 Clapham Manor Street, London SW4 6EB Tel: 020 7411 6866 Fax: 020 7411 6857 Email: wolfgang.wallat@gp-g85708.nhs.uk; 211 Restons Crescent, Eltham, London SE9 2JZ — State Exam Med 1986 Hannover; MD Hannover 1988; MRCGP 1995. GP Princip.; Formulary Comm. Mem., Guy's & St. Thomas' NHS Trust; Med.s Managem. Comm. Mem., N. Lamberth PCG.

WALLAT-VAGO, Susan Beatrice 40 Lake Road, London SW19 7EX — MB ChB 1985 Leic.

WALLBANK, Gail Rosemary Plas Newydd, Carno, Caersws SY17 5JR Tel: 01686 420212 — MB ChB 1971 Birm.; DRCOG 1978. Prev: GP Newtown Pwys 2. GP Surgeries Newtown, Powys; Clin. Med. Off. (Community Health) Powys HA.; Med. Off. Family Plann. Clinics. Powys HA.

WALLBANK

WALLBANK, Ian William 240 Minster Court, Liverpool L7 3QH — MB ChB 1989 Liverp.

WALLBANK, Nicola Jane 6 Walleys Drive, Newcastle ST5 0NG; The Tyles, 41 Montagu Road, Datchet, Slough SL3 9DT — MB BChir 1992 Camb.; MA Camb. 1994; MRCGP 1997; DRCOG 1995; DCH RCP Lond. 1994. (Fitzwilliam Coll. Camb.) GP. Prev: GP Trainee Watford VTS.

WALLBANK, William Alistair Covenant House, Cider Mill Lane, Chipping Campden GL55 6HU — MB BS 1961 Lond.; MRCS Eng. LRCP Lond. 1961; FFA RCS Eng. 1966. (Guy's) Cons. Anaesth. Univ. Hosp. of S. Manch.

WALLBRIDGE, Christopher Martyn 304 Dobbin Hill, Sheffield S11 7JG — MB ChB 1977 Sheff.; MRCPsych. 1982. Cons. Psychiat. Sheff. HA; Hon. Clin. Lect. Univ. Sheff. Prev: Lect. Psychiat. Univ. Sheff.; Regist. (Psychiat.) Sheff. HA.

WALLBRIDGE, David Ross Royal Shrewsbury Hospital, Mytton Sar Road, Shrewsbury SY3 8DN Tel: 01743 261000 — MB ChB 1984 Birm.; MRCP (UK) 1987; MD 1996. Cons. Phys. & Cardiol. Prev: Regist. (Cardiol.) Glas. Roy. Infirm.

WALLEN, Gerald Desmond Patrick (retired) Wonford House Hospital, Dryden Road, Exeter EX2 5AF Tel: 01392 403624 Fax: 01392 403477 — MB ChB 1957 Birm.; MRCS Eng. LRCP Lond. 1957; FRCPsych 1984, M 1971; DPM Eng. 1966; DObst RCOG 1963. Cons. Psychiat. Exeter HA. Prev: Lect. (Psychiat.) Univ. Sheff.

WALLER, Aruna 92 Dobcroft Road, Sheffield S7 2LS — MRCS Eng. LRCP Lond. 1974. (Univ. Rhodesia)

WALLER, Christine Margaret 56 Percy Road, Ore, Hastings TN35 5AR — MB BS 1985 Melbourne.

WALLER, Christopher John 90 Hazelhurst Road, Worsley, Manchester M28 2SP — MB ChB 1995 Bristol.

WALLER, Deborah Jane Beaumont Street Surgery, 19 Beaumont Street, Oxford OX1 2NA Tel: 01865 240501 Fax: 01865 240503; Dean Court House, 89 Eynsham Road, Botley, Oxford OX2 9BY Tel: 01865 862017 — MB BChir 1985 Camb.; MRCGP 1990; DCH RCP Lond. 1987. Socs: BMA. Prev: Clin. Lect. Wellcome Trust; Trainee GP Oxf. VTS.

WALLER, Dennis H 153 Monks Road, Lincoln LN2 5JJ — MB BS 1956 Bombay. (Grant Med. Coll.)

WALLER, Deryk Pierre Edmund 3A Shrewsbury Road, Oxton, Wirral — MB ChB 1989 Sheff.; MRCGP 1998.

WALLER, Dilys Claire Elizabeth The Surgery, Cockfield, Bishop Auckland DL13 5AF Tel: 01388 718202 Fax: 01388 710600; Burn Farm, Willington, Crook DL15 0HZ Tel: 01388 747484 — MB BS 1985 Newc.; MRCP (UK) 1988; MRCGP 1990; DCH RCP Lond. 1989. (Newc.)

WALLER, Idris Stanley Hereford House, Staindrop, Darlington DL2 3LQ; (Surgery), Woodview, Cockfield, Bishop Auckland DL13 5AF — MRCS Eng. LRCP Lond. 1949; MA, MB BChir Camb. 1949; DObst RCOG 1952. (Camb. & Univ. Coll. Hosp.) Prev: Med. Off. Glaxo Operats. UK Barnard Castle.

WALLER, James Otway DeWarrenne (retired) 3 Ironlatch Close, St Leonards-on-Sea TN38 9JQ Tel: 01424 429117 — MB BS 1963 Lond.; MRCP Lond. 1965; MRCS Eng. LRCP Lond. 1963. Prev: Gen. Practitioner.

WALLER, Joanne Marie The Surgeries, Lombard St., Newark NG24 1XG Tel: 01636 702363; 4 Behay Gardens, Staythorpe, Newark NG23 5RL — MB ChB 1992 Leeds; MRCGP 1997; DCH 1997; DRCOG 1996. (Leeds) GP. Prev: GP Regist. Bridge St. Med. Pract. Otley; SHO (Paediat.) Airedale Gen. Hosp.; GP Regist. Grange Pk. Surg. Burley in Wharfdale.

WALLER, John Gamble, Col. late RAMC Retd. 20 Hartfield Road, Bexhill-on-Sea TN39 3EA Tel: 01424 843806 — MB ChB 1945 Ed.; FRCGP 1980, M 1965; DObst RCOG 1971; DCH RCP Lond. 1968; DTM & H RCP Lond. 1964. (Edin.) Prev: Phys. Roy. Commiss. Jubail Project, Saudi Arabia; GP Oldham.

WALLER, Jonathan Francis 37 Church Hill, Epping CM16 4RA Tel: 01992 576649 — MB BS 1972 Lond.; BSc (Anat., 1st cl. Hons.) Lond. 1969, MD 1982; FRCP Lond. 1992; MRCP (UK) 1975. Cons. Phys. P.ss Alexandra Hosp. NHS Trust Harlow. Prev: Sen. Regist. (Gen. & Respirat. Med.) Roy. Free & Brompton Hosps.; Research Fell. Lung Func. Unit Brompton Hosps.; Regist. (Gen. Respirat. Med.) Lond. Hosp.

***WALLER, Julian Ronald Lee** 46 Hill Street, Burton-on-Trent DE15 9LA — MB ChB 1998 Birm.

WALLER, Julie Alison 46 St Cadoc Road, Heath, Cardiff CF14 4NE — MB BCh 1979 Wales; MRCGP 1983; DCH RCP Lond. 1992; DRCOG 1982.

WALLER, Kathleen Grace Ealing Hospital, Uxbridge Road, Southall UB1 3HW Tel: 020 8574 2444; 34 Sunnyside Road, Ealing, London W5 5HU Tel: 020 8567 8195 — BM BCh 1988 Oxf.; BA (2nd cl. Hons. Physiol.) Oxf. 1985; MRCOG 1993; DM 1997. Sen. Regist.Obyst.Gyn.Ealing Hosp. Prev: Regist. (O & G) Watford Gen. Hosp. & Hammersmith Hosp.; Research Fell. (O & G) Univ. Wales Coll. Med. Cardiff; Sen. Regist. (O & G) Hammersmith Hosp.

WALLER, Mark Gorsey Lane Surgery, 93 Gorsey Lane, Ford, Liverpool L21 0DF Tel: 0151 928 7757 Fax: 0151 928 9125; 5 Glebe End, Sefton Village, Liverpool L29 6YB Tel: 0151 531 8829 — MB ChB 1982 Liverp.; DRCOG 1985. Med. Off. Liverp. Football Club. Prev: Clin. Asst. (A & E) Alder Hey Chldr. Hosp. Liverp.; SHO (Paediat.) Roy. Liverp. Chldr. Hosp.; SHO (O & G) Fazakerley Hosp. Liverp.

WALLER, Patrick Charles 15 Tamella Road, Botley, Southampton SO30 2NY Tel: 01489 784846 Fax: 01489 784846 Email: patrick.waller@btinternet.com — MB ChB 1980 Sheff.; MD Sheff. 1989, BMedSci. 1977; FRCP Ed. 1993; MRCP (UK) 1983; FFPM RCP (UK) 1995; MPH Glas. 1988. Specialist (Pharmacovigilance) Med. Control Agency DoH Lond.; Vis. Prof. (Pharmacological Scis.) Univ. of Newc.-upon-Tyne. Socs: Brit. Hypertens. Soc.; Brit. Pharm. Soc.; Internat. Soc. Pharmacoepidemiol. Prev: Sen. Research Fell. Drug Safety Research Unit Soton.; Research Fell. Glas. Blood Pressure Clinic; Research Regist. (Cardiovasc. Dis.) Roy. Hallamsh. Hosp. Sheff.

WALLER, Robin Eric West child and family therapy team, Centenary house, 55 Albert Terrace Rd, Sheffield S6 3BR Tel: 0114 226 2034 — MB ChB 1972 Birm.; MRCPsych 1984. Cons. Child & Adolesc. Psychiat. Sheff. HA. Prev: Sen. Regist. (Child & Adolesc. Psychiat.) Leics. HA.

WALLER, Rosalind Wye Surgery, 67 Oxenturn Road, Wye, Ashford TN25 5AY Tel: 01233 812414/812419 Fax: 01233 813236; Burnthouse Farm, Station Road, Chartham, Canterbury CT4 7HU — MB BS 1981 Lond.; BSc Bristol (Chem. Phys.) 1975; DCH RCP Lond. 1984. (Middlx.) GP Ashford Kent. Prev: SHO Qu. Eliz. Hosp. for Childr. Lond.; SHO (Neonat.) John Radcliffe Hosp. Oxf.; SHO (Paediat.) N.wick Pk. Hosp. Harrow.

WALLER, Sally Louise Nettleham Medical Practice, 14 Lodge Lane, Nettleham, Lincoln LN2 2RS Tel: 01522 751717 Fax: 01522 754474 — MB BS 1989 Newc.; MRCGP 1994; DFFP 1994. Prev: Trainee GP Lincoln.

WALLER, Simon Charles 25 Thorncombe Road, London SE22 8PX — MB BS 1996 Lond. Socs: MRCPCH.

WALLER, Stella Mary Queen Elizabeth II Hospital, Essendon Ward, Howlands, Welwyn Garden City AL7 4HQ; 2 High Ash Road, Wheathampstead, St Albans AL4 8DY Tel: 01582 832465 Email: stella@aewaller.co.uk — MB BS 1978 Newc.; DO Eng. 1982. Assoc. Specialist. Socs: MRCOphth. Prev: Regist. (Ophth.) Luton & Dunstable Hosp.

WALLER, Thomas Arthur Naunton PO Box 92, Woodbridge IP12 4QJ Fax: 01473 736550; Novocastria, Sandy Lane, Waldringfield, Woodbridge IP12 4QY Tel: 01473 736224 — MB BS 1970 Lond.; MRCS Eng. LRCP Lond. 1970; Dip. Biochem. Lond 1967; DRCOG 1972. Prev: Ho. Surg. (Cardio-Thoracic Surg.) St. Bart. Hosp. Lond.; Ho. Surg. (O & G) King's Coll. Hosp. Lond.; SHO (Gen. & Neonat. Paediat.) St. Stephens Hosp. Lond.

WALLER, Timothy John (retired) The Surgery, Madams Paddock, Chew Magna, Bristol BS40 8PP Tel: 01275 332420 Fax: 01275 333860 — MB BS 1967 Lond.; MRCS Eng. LRCP Lond. 1967. Prev: SHO (O & G) Yeovil Matern. Hosp.

WALLERS, Kenneth John Department of Radiology, Monklands District General Hospital, Monkscourt Avenue, Airdrie ML6 0JS Tel: 01236 748748 Fax: 01236 746223 — MB ChB 1976 Dundee; FRCR 1984; DMRD Eng. 1980. Cons. Radiol. Monklands Dist. Gen. Hosp. Airdrie.

WALLEY, Betty Margaret (retired) Yew Tree House, Harris Lane, Abbots Leigh, Bristol BS8 3RZ Tel: 01275 372520 — MB BS 1948 Lond.; DPH Bristol 1963; DCH Eng. 1966. Prev: SCMO (Child Psychiat.) Avon AHA.

WALLEY, Denis Raymond Flat 3, 2 Selborne Road, Hove BN3 3AG — MB BCh BAO 1987 NUI.

WALLEY, John Deric 10 Ashwood Villas, Leeds LS6 2EJ — MB BS 1977 Newc.; MRCGP 1982; MFPHM RCP (UK) 1991; MCommH Liverp. Sch. Trop. Med. 1987; DTM & H Liverp. 1982; DRCOG 1979. Sen. Lect. (Internat. Pub. Health) Nuffield Inst. for Health Univ. Leeds & Hon. Cons. Pub. Health Leeds HA.

WALLEY, Kenneth (retired) 8 Valencia Road, Liverpool L15 8LL — MB ChB 1951 Liverp.; MFOM RCP Lond. 1978.

WALLEY, Margaret Ruth (retired) Dowles Croft, Greenacres Lane, Bewdley DY12 2RE Tel: 01299 400250 — MB ChB 1950 Manch.; MB ChB Manch. 1950 DPM Durh. 1955; MRCPsych 1971. Prev: Cons. Psychiat. Durh. CC.

WALLEY, Professor Thomas Joseph Department Pharmacology & Therapeutics, University of Liverpool, PO Box 147, Liverpool L69 3BX — MD 1990 NUI; MB BCh BAO 1980; FRCPI 1993, M 1982; FRCP (Lond.) 1995; MRCP (UK) 1984. Prof. Clin. Pharmacol. Univ. Liverp.; Hon. Cons. Phys. & Clin. Pharmacol. Roy. Liverp. Hosp.; Hon. Cons. Clin. Pharmacol. Mersey RHA. Socs: Assn. Phys. Prev: Sen. Lect. (Pharmacol. & Therap.) Univ. Liverp.; Lect. (Pharmacol. & Therap.) Univ. Liverp.

WALLICE, Malcolm Robert Bruce (retired) 2 Oaklands Avenue, Rhosnesni, Wrexham LL13 9EW Tel: 01978 364506 — MB ChB 1954 Liverp.; DObst RCOG 1956.

WALLICE, Patrick Donald Bruce (retired) 7 Willow Drive, Wrea Green, Preston PR4 2NT — MB ChB 1955 Liverp.; AFOM RCP Lond. 1982; DObst RCOG 1957. Prev: SCMO (Occupat. Health) Preston DHA.

WALLING, Alice Elisabeth Health Centre, Church St., Houghton-le-Spring DH4 4DN; 142 Gilesgate, Durham DH1 1QQ Tel: 0191 384 6076 — MB BS 1984 Newc.; MRCGP 1988.

WALLING, Martyn Ronald Parkside Surgery, Tawney Street, Boston PE21 6PF Tel: 01205 365881 Fax: 01205 357583; Belmont, 23 Sibsey Road, Boston PE21 9QY — MB ChB 1976 Sheff.; FRCGP 1994, M 1980; MFFP 1994; DRCOG 1980. Clin. Asst. (Obst. Ultrasound) Family Plann. Clinic Ment. Handicap Unit; Edit. Bd. Brit. Jl. Sexual Med. Prev: Vis. Fell. Internat. Med. Mass. Gen. Hosp. Boston, USA; Trainee GP Boston, Lincs. VTS; Ho. Surg. Roy. Hosp. Sheff.

WALLING, Miranda Rebecca 21 Dungarvan Drive, Pontprennau, Cardiff CF23 8PY Tel: 01222 735640 — MB ChB 1997 Bristol; DRCOG 1999.

WALLINGTON, David Michael AON occupational health, 2 Circus Place, London EC2M 5RS Tel: 020 7628 0523 — MB BCh 1976 Wales; FFOM RCP Lond. 1995, MFOM 1987; DIH Lond. 1983; DA Eng. 1981. Director Clin. Occupat.al Med. AON Occupat.al Health. Socs: Soc. Occupat. Med.; (Chairm.) Lond. GRP; Counc. SOM. Prev: Dir. of Occupat. Health Metropoliton Police Serv.; Chief Occupat. & Sen. Occupat. Health Phys. Wellcome Foundat. Ltd. Dartford Kent; Med. Off. & Sen. Med. Off. Rolls-Royce plc Derbysh.

WALLINGTON, Margaret 126 Chosen Way, Hucclecote, Gloucester GL3 3BZ — MB BCh 1974 Wales; MRCOG 1979; DObst. RCOG 1976.

WALLINGTON, St Clair Hamilton Archer (retired) The Rectory, Langtree, Torrington Tel: 0180 55 273 — MB ChB 1927 Birm.

WALLINGTON, Timothy Baden Amesbury House, Gloucester Road, Almondsbury, Bristol BS32 4AA Tel: 01454 614192 Email: ac113@beeb.net — MB BChir 1970 Camb.; BA (1st cl.) Camb. 1967; FRCP Lond. 1988; FRCPath 1995. (Camb.) Cons. Immunol. Nat. Blood Serv. Bristol & S.mead Hosp. Bristol. Prev: Sen. Regist. (Immunol.) Nottm. City Hosp.; Regist. (Med.) S.mead Hosp. Bristol; MRC Jun. Research Fell. S.mead Hosp. Bristol.

WALLIS, Andrew James Greenlanes, Ullenhall, Solihull B95 5NF — MB BS 1991 Lond.

WALLIS, Charles Burne Department of Anaesthetics, Western General Hospital, Edinburgh EH4 2XG Tel: 0131 537 1000; 20 Seton Place, Edinburgh EH9 2JT — MB ChB 1984 Ed.; FRCA. 1992; DRCOG 1986. Cons. Anaesth. Socs: Scott. Intens. Care Soc. & NE Scott. Soc. Anaesth. Prev: Sen. Regist. Ninewells Hosp. Dundee; SHO (Anaesth.) W.. Gen. Hosp. Edin.

WALLIS, Christopher Julian The Health Centre, Charlton Road, Andover SP10 3LD Tel: 01264 350270 Fax: 01264 336701 — MB ChB Bristol 1975; MRCGP 1982; DCH Eng. 1981; DRCOG 1980.

WALLIS, Clive Bernard Crown Street Surgery, 17 Crown Street, Swinton, Rotherham S64 8LY Tel: 01709 583862 — MB ChB 1980 Sheff. Prev: Trainee GP Burnley VTS.

WALLIS, Daniel Nathan Accident & Emergency Department, St. Thomas' Hospital, Lambeth Palace Road, London SE1 7EH — MB BS 1981 Lond.; MRCP (UK) 1986; MRCGP 1988; DCH RCP Lond. 1989; DRCOG 1986. cons. (A & E Med.) Guy's & St. Thomas' Hosp. Trust.

WALLIS, David Elliot (retired) 1 Overlea Road, London E5 9BG — MB ChB 1949 Birm.; MRCS Eng. LRCP Lond. 1949.

WALLIS, Diane Elizabeth Ley Hill Surgery, 228 Lichfield Road, Sutton Coldfield B74 2UE; 2 Pages Close, Sutton Coldfield B75 7TA Tel: 0121 308 0359 — MB ChB Dundee 1983; MRCGP 1988. (Dundee) Asst. GP.

WALLIS, Elspeth Gordon The New Surgery, The Nap, Kings Langley WD4 8ET Tel: 01923 261035 Fax: 01923 269629; Woodlands, Gorelands Lane, Chalfont St Giles HP8 4HQ Tel: 0124 072723 — MB BS 1972 Lond.; MRCP (UK) 1978; DCH Eng. 1974. (Middlx.) Prev: Regist. Radiother. Middlx. Hosp. Lond.; Regist. (Med. Oncol.) St. Bart. & Hackney Hosps.; Regist. (Med. & Paediat.) St. And. Hosp. Bow.

WALLIS, Erica Joy Room L100 Floor L, Ryal Hallamshire Hospital, Glossup Rd, Sheffield S10 2JF Email: e.j.wallis@sheffield.ac.uk — MB ChB 1992 Sheff. (Sheffield) Research Asst. (Clin. Pharmacol. & Ther.) Univ. Sheff.

WALLIS, Ethel Marjorie (retired) 38 Solent Way, Alverstoke, Gosport PO12 2NS — MB ChB 1948 Ed.; DPH Eng. 1957; DObst RCOG 1951. Prev: SCMO (Child Health) Portsmouth & SE Hants. HA.

WALLIS, Geoffrey Garfit Casa Rohan, Longwood Hall, Bingley BD16 2RX Tel: 01274 568072 Fax: 01274 568072; Harrogate Clinic, 23 Ripon Road, Harrogate HG1 2JL Tel: 01423 500599 Fax: 01423 531074 — MB BS Lond. 1942; MD Lond. 1966; MRCS Eng. LRCP Lond. 1941; FRCPsych 1971; DPM Eng. 1955; CCST 1996. (Univ. Coll. Hosp.) Cons. Psychiat. Harrogate Clinic. Socs: Fell. Roy. Soc. Med.; Leeds & W. Riding Medico-Legal Soc.; Soc. Clin. Psychiat. Prev: Cons. Psychiat. High Royds Hosp. Menston; Hon. Lect. Univ. Leeds; Adviser (Psychiat.) Med. Dir. Gen. (Naval).

WALLIS, Graham Ian 44 Hambleton Grove, Knaresborough HG5 0DB — BM BS 1997 Nottm.

WALLIS, Helen 27 Hampermill Lane, Oxhey, Watford WD19 4NS — MB ChB 1984 Leeds.

WALLIS, Helen Louise 27 Sunny Bank Road, Liverpool L16 7PN — MB ChB 1992 (Hons.) Birm.; MRCP (UK) 1995. Specialist Regist. Rotat. (Cardiol.) Wessex.

WALLIS, James Fintan Edward Mary Aberdeen Royal Infirmary, Foresterhill, Aberdeen AB25 2ZN Tel: 01224 681818 Email: f.wallis@abdn.ac.uk; The Lodge, Tornadee Hospital, Milltimber AB13 0HW Tel: 01224 869845 — MB BCh BAO 1987 NUI; MRCPI 1990; FRCR 1994; FFR RCSI 1994. (Univ. Coll. Dub. Irel.) Sen. Lect. (MRI) Hon. Cons. Aberd. Roy. Infirm. Prev: Sen. Regist. (Diagnostic Imaging) Aberd. Roy. Infirm.; Regist. (Radiol.) St. Jas. Hosp. Dub.

WALLIS, Mr John Department of Cardiothoracic Surgery, South Cleveland Hospital, Middlesbrough TS4 3BW Tel: 01642 850850; 64 Langbaurgh Road, Hutton Rudby, Yarm TS15 0HL — MB BS Lond. 1973; BSc (1st cl. Hons.) Lond. 1970; FRCS Eng. 1980; MRCP (UK) 1977; MRCS Eng. LRCP Lond. 1973; DA Eng. 1975. Cons. Cardiothoracic Surg. S. Cleveland Hosp. Middlesbrough. Prev: Research Fell. (Cardiothoracic Surg.) Univ. Alabama, Birm., Alabama, USA.

WALLIS, John Harold Skirbeck House, 140 Spilsby Road, Boston PE21 9PE Tel: 01205 2320 — MB BS 1946 Lond. (Lond. Hosp.) Prev: Ho. Phys. & Ho. Surg. Lond. Hosp.

WALLIS, Jonathan Peter 50 Elmfield Road, Gosforth, Newcastle upon Tyne NE3 4BB — MB BS 1979 Lond.; MRCPath 1989. Cons. Haemat. Freeman Hosp. Newc. u. Tyne.

WALLIS, Malcolm Montgomery (retired) 32 Strand Court, Topsham, Exeter EX3 0AZ — MB ChB 1934 Liverp. Prev: Ho. Phys. & Res. Anaesth. Roy. S.. Hosp. Liverp.

WALLIS, Michael St Johns Street Surgery, 16 St. Johns Street, Kempston, Bedford MK42 8EP Tel: 01234 851323 Fax: 01234 843293 — MRCS Eng. LRCP Lond. 1972.

WALLIS, Michael Graham Staines Health Centre, Knowle Green, Staines TW18 1XD Tel: 01784 883620 Fax: 01784 441244; Walnut Tree House, 11 Lammas Close, Staines TW18 4XT — MRCS Eng. LRCP Lond. 1973. (St. Mary's) Socs: Brit. Med. Acupunc. Soc.

WALLIS

WALLIS, Michael Owen Wallis and Partners, The Health Centre, 5 Stanmore Road, Stevenage SG1 3QA Tel: 01438 313223 Fax: 01438 749734 — MB BS 1977 Lond.; MRCS Eng. LRCP Lond. 1976.

WALLIS, Nicola Trudle Syngenta Central Toxicology Laboratory, Alderley Park, Macclesfield SK10 47G Tel: 01625 510927 Fax: 01625 517911 Email: nicola.wallis@syngenta.com — MB ChB 1987 Birm.; MRCPath 1987; BSc 1984 ((Hons) Anat.); Dip Pharm 2000. (Birmingham) Head of Path. Prev: Sen. Regist. (Histopath.) N.. W.. RHA.; Regist. (Histopath.) N.. W.. RHA; SHO (Path.) Centr. Birm. HA.

WALLIS, Patricia Gwendoline (retired) 44 Blackheath Park, London SE3 9SJ Tel: 020 8852 7110 Fax: 020 8852 7110 Email: pat-wallis@doctors.org.uk — MB BS 1953 Lond.; FRCP Lond. 1974, M 1958; FRCPCH 1997; DCH Eng. 1955; DObst RCOG 1955. Hon. Cons. Paediat. Lewisham Childr. Hosp. Prev: Cons. Paediat. Childr. Hosp. Sydenham & Lewisham Hosp.

WALLIS, Peter (retired) Abdy Cottage, The Green, Whiston, Rotherham S60 4JD — MRCS Eng. LRCP Lond. 1952.

WALLIS, Peter Barnham Medical Centre, 134 Barnham Road, Barnham, Bognor Regis PO22 0EH Tel: 01243 555829 Fax: 01243 554218 — MB BS 1965 Lond.; MRCS Eng. LRCP Lond. 1965. (King's Coll. Hosp.) Socs: BMA. Prev: SHO (Path.) & Ho. Surg. (ENT Surg.) King's Coll. Hosp. Lond.; Ho. Phys. Dulwich Hosp.

WALLIS, Peter John Walker Department Geriatric Medicine, Boldesley Green East, Birmingham Heartlands Hospital, Yardley Green Road, Birmingham B9 5SS Tel: 0121 424 0769 Fax: 0121 753 0653 Email: wallisp@heartsol.wmids.nhs.uk; 38 Alderbrook Road, Solihull B91 1NN Tel: 0121 711 4078 Email: peterwallis@compuserve.com — MB BS 1977 Lond.; MB BS (Hons.) Lond. 1977; BSc Lond. 1974; FRCP Lond. 1995; MRCP (UK) 1979. (St. Mary's) Cons. Phys. (Geriat. Med.) Birm. Heartlands Hosp.; Hon. Sen. Clin. Lect. Univ. Birm. Prev: Sen. Regist. (Gen. & Geriat. Med.) W. Midl. Train. Scheme; Regist. (Med.) W.m. Hosp. Lond.; Research Fell. The Lond. Hosp. Whitechapel.

WALLIS, Rachel Louise 49 Little Brook Road, Sale M33 4WG — MB ChB 1991 Sheff.

WALLIS, Ruth Mary 42 Stockwell Green, London SW9 9HX — BM 1980 Soton.

WALLIS, Sheila Mary Dingley Child Development Centre, Battle Hospital, Oxford Road, Reading RG30 1AG Tel: 0118 963 6213 Fax: 0118 963 6209; 31 Heron Island, Caversham, Reading RG4 8DQ Tel: 0118 948 4976 — MB ChB 1969 Manch.; FRCP Lond. 1994; MRCP (UK) 1974; FRCPCH 1997; DCH Eng. 1972. Cons. Paediat. (Developm. Paediat.) Roy. Berks. & Battle Hosps. Reading. Socs: Neonat. Soc.; Brit. Paediat. Neurol. Assn.; Eur. Acad. Childh. Disabil. Prev: Sen. Regist. (Paediat.) Roy. Berks. Hosp. Reading & Wolfson Centre Inst. Child Health Lond.; Research Fell. (Paediat.) Qu. Charlotte's Hosp. Wom. Lond.

WALLIS, Simon Charles Chorley & South Ribble District General Hospital, Preston Road, Chorley; 33 Southport Road, Chorley PR7 1LF — MB BChir 1975 Camb.; FRCP 1993; MRCP (UK) 1978. (Camb./Birm.) Cons. Phys. (Diabetes & Endocrinol.) Chorley & S. Ribble Dist. Gen. Hosp. Prev: Sen. Lect & Hon. Cons. Endocrinol. & Metab. Roy. Postgrad. Med. Sch. Hammersmith Hosp. Lond.; Clin. Sci. MRC Clin. Research Centre Harrow; MRC Research Fell. Recombinant DNA Technol. St. Marys & St. Bart. Lond.

WALLIS, Mr Simon William John H2 Ophthalmic Unit, Royal Bolton Hospital, Minerva Road, Farnworth, Bolton BL4 0JR Tel: 01204 390519 Fax: 01204 390554; 93 Waterslea Drive, Bolton BL1 5FA — MB ChB 1980 Manch.; FRCS Ed. 1988; FCOphth. 1989; DO RCS Eng. 1986. Cons. Ophth. Bolton Hosps. Prev: Sen. Regist. Manch. Roy. Eye Hosp.

WALLIS, Timothy David Nettleham Medical Practice, 14 Lodge Lane, Nettleham, Lincoln LN2 2RS Tel: 01522 751717; Kerio, Chestnut Close, Sudbrooke, Lincoln LN2 2RD Tel: 01522 751211 Email: timwalkerio@aol.com — MB ChB 1965 Ed. (Ed.) Med. Practitioner Lincoln; HM Dep. Coroner Lincoln Dist. Prev: Clin. Asst. (Dermat.) Lincoln Co. Hosp.; Med. Off. Kapsowar Hosp. Kenya; Sen. Health Off. (Surg.) Mildmay Mission Hosp. Lond.

WALLIS, William Richard James 6A Mildford Place, London W1P 9HH — MB Camb. 1987, BChir 1986; LMSSA Lond. 1986; MRCP Lond. 1990; PhD Lond. 1997. (St Thomas') Regist. Cardiol. St. Barts. Socs: Brit. Cardiac Soc.; Roy. Coll. Phys.; BCIS.

WALLMAN, Paul Daniel 41 Cassandra Court, Asgard Drive, Salford M5 4TW — MB ChB 1992 Manch.

WALLOND, Julia Clare 4 Newcombe Street, Exeter EX1 2TG — MB ChB 1998 Bristol.

WALLS, Mr Andrew David Finlay Uplands, 83 Edinburgh Road, Dumfries DG1 1JX Tel: 01387 252830 Fax: 01387 241741 — MB BS 1967 Lond.; FRCS Ed. 1986; FRCS Eng. 1973. (St. Thos.) Cons. Surg. Dumfries & Galloway Acute & Matern. NHS Trust; Dir. Postgrad. Med. Educat. Dumfries & Galloway HB; Clin. Sen. Lect. Univ. Aberd.; Hon. Sen. Lect. Univ. Glas. Socs: Brit. Soc. Gastroenterol.; BMA; Chairm. LREC. Prev: Sen. Regist. (Surg.) W.. Gen. Hosp. Edin.; Ho. Surg. St. Thos. Hosp. Lond.; Lect. (Anat.) King's Coll. Lond.

WALLS, Anne Teresa Rose 37 Glenmaquill Road, Magherafelt BT45 5EW — MB BCh BAO 1992 NUI.

WALLS, Dorothy Brown (retired) Hesslewood, The Orchard, Kitty Frisk House, Hexham NE46 1UN — MB BS 1949 Durh. Prev: Ho. Surg. & Ho. Phys. (Gyn. & Obst.) Roy. Vict. Infirm. Newc.

WALLS, Mr Eldred Wright 19 Dean Park Crescent, Edinburgh EH4 1PH Tel: 0131 332 7164 — MB ChB 1934 Glas.; MB ChB (Hons.) Glas. 1934; FRSE; BSc Glas. 1931, MD (Hons.) 1947; FRCS Ed. 1981; FRCS Eng. 1976. (Univ. Glas.) Emerit. Prof. Anat. Univ. Lond.; Hon. Cons. Anat. St. Mark's Hosp. Lond. Socs: (Ex-Pres.) Anat. Soc.; (Pres.) Assn. Blind Chartered Physiother. Prev: Dean Middlx. Hosp. Med. Sch.; Lect. (Anat.) Univ. Edin.; Sen. Lect. (Anat.) Univ. Wales.

WALLS, Elizabeth Cairns (retired) 40 Lake Avenue, Walsall WS5 3PA Tel: 01922 649749 — MB BCh BAO Belf. 1946.

WALLS, Fionnuala Bernadette 29 High Street, Draperstown, Magherafelt BT45 7AB Tel: 01648 28201 — MB BCh BAO 1977 NUI; DRCOG 1981. GP Draperstown.

WALLS, Hugh Emmet Christopher (retired) 40 Lake Avenue, Walsall WS5 3PA Tel: 01922 649749 — MB BCh BAO NUI 1943.

WALLS, Janet 57 Brampton Avenue, Macclesfield SK10 3RH — MB ChB 1986 Liverp.

WALLS, Jessie Vivien Mary 19 Dean Park Crescent, Edinburgh EH4 1PH Tel: 0131 332 7164 — MB ChB 1934 Glas.; DPH Glas. 1936. (Glas.)

WALLS, John Bradshaw 53 Church Road, Altofts, Wakefield WF3 4HR — MB ChB 1968 Leeds; BSc (Anat.) Leeds 1965, MB ChB 1968; DMRD Eng. 1977. (Leeds) Cons. Radiol. Pinderfields Gen. Hosp. Wakefield.

WALLS, Joseph Alan 50 Garston Old Road, Grassendale, Liverpool L19 9AG Tel: 0151 427 0467 Email: joewalls@mcmail.com; Tynemouth, North Shields NE30 2QF Tel: 0191 258 5408 — MB ChB 1996 Liverp. BST Merseyside Rotat. Arrowe Pk. Hosp. Wirral Merseyside.

WALLS, Marguerite Joan Church View House, Church Lane, Adel, Leeds LS16 8DG Tel: 0113 261 3882 — MB ChB 1947 Leeds. (Leeds) Prev: Clin. Med. Off. Leeds E. & W.. HA; Ho. Surg. (Obst.) St. Jas. Hosp. Leeds; Ho. Phys. Dewsbury Gen. Infirm.

WALLS, Maurice Youll 52 Woolsington Gardens, Woolsington, Newcastle upon Tyne NE13 8AR Tel: 0191 286 9999 — MB BS 1955 Durh.; MFPHM 1989; MFCM 1974; DPH Newc. 1966. Assoc. Specialist Nat. Blood Transfus. Serv.; Mem. N.. Regional Med. Comm.; Mem. N.. Regional Manpower Comm. Socs: N.. Region Assoc. Specialist Gp. Prev: Sen. Med. Off. (Community Med.) Newc. AHA; GP Newbiggin-by-the-Sea; Ho. Off. Shotley Bridge Hosp.

WALLS, Ngaire Jean Chaldon Road Surgery, Chaldon Road, Caterham CR3 5PG Tel: 01883 345466 Fax: 01883 330942; Wood End, 80 Welcomes Road, Kenley CR8 5HE Tel: 020 8660 0770 — MB BS 1975 Lond.; MRCS Eng. LRCP Lond. 1975; DRCOG 1977. (St. Mary's)

***WALLS, Nicholas Ian** James Paget Hospital, Great Yarmouth NR31 6AL — MB ChB 1996 Ed.

WALLS, Sally The Fold, Hickling Lane, Kinoulton, Nottingham NG12 3ED — MB BS 1993 Newc.

WALLS, Timothy John Department of Neurology, Newcastle General Hospital, Westgate Road, Newcastle upon Tyne NE4 6BE Tel: 0191 273 8811 Fax: 0191 272 4823 Email: t.j.walls@ncl.ac.uk; 18 Adeline Gardens, Gosforth, Newcastle upon Tyne NE3 4JQ Tel: 0191 285 8281 — MB BS 1977 Newc.; MB BS (Hons.) Newc. 1977; MD Newc. 1988, BMedSci (Hons.) 1974; FRCP Lond. 1994; MRCP (UK) 1979. Cons. Neurol. Newc. Gen. Hosp. Prev: Sen.

Regist. (Neurol.) Newc. Gen. Hosp.; Research Assoc. (Neurol.) Univ. Newc.; Research Fell. & Fulbright Schol. Mayo Clinic Rochester, USA.

WALLS, William Alexander Hesslewood, The Orchard, Kitty Frisk House, Hexham NE46 1UN Tel: 01434 607400 — MB BS 1951 Durh.

WALLS, William David Clayton Hospital, Northgate, Wakefield WF1 3JS Tel: 01924 214141; 98 Ouzlewell Green, Loft House, Wakefield WF3 3QW Tel: 0113 282 1376 — MB ChB 1960 Leeds; MD (Distinc.) Leeds 1969; FRCP Lond. 1979, M 1965. Cons. Phys. Pinderfields & Clayton Hosps. Wakefield. Socs: Brit. Soc. Gastroenterol.; Brit. Soc. Med. & Dent. Hypn. Prev: Sen. Regist. (Gen. Med.) Leeds RHB; Research Asst. (Med.) Univ. Leeds.

WALLS, William Kenneth Johnstone Church View House, Church View, Adel, Leeds LS16 8DG Tel: 0113 261 3882 — MB ChB 1940 Leeds; MRCS Eng. LRCP Lond. 1941. (Leeds) Hon. Lect. (Anat.) & Life Fell. Univ. Leeds. Socs: Anat. Soc.& BMA. Prev: Sen. Lect. (Anat.) Univ. Leeds; Instruc. Doctor (Family Plann.) Leeds AHA; Regist. (Surg. & Neurosurg.) Leeds Gen. Infirm.

WALLWORK, Mr John Department of Cardiothoracic Surgery, Papworth Hospital, Papworth Everard, Cambridge CB3 8RE Tel: 01480 364418 Fax: 01480 831281 Email: jenny.ainsworth@papworth-tr.anglox.nhs.uk; 3 Latham Road, Cambridge CB2 2EG Tel: 01223 352827 — MB ChB 1970 Edin.; BSc (Hons.) Ed. 1967; FRCS (ad eund.) 1992; FRCS Ed. 1974; FRCP Edin 2000. (Edinburgh) Cons. Cardiothoracic Surg. Papworth Hosp. Camb.; Med. Dir. 1997; Dir. Transpl. Serv.; Assoc. Lect. Univ. Camb. Socs: Internat. Soc. Heart & Lung Transpl.; Internat. Transpl. Soc.; (Counc.) Europ. Soc. for Organ Transpl. Prev: Chief Resid. Cardiovasc. Surg. & Cardiac Transpl. Stanford Univ. Med. Sch., USA; Sen. Regist. (Cardiothoracic Surg.) St. Bart. Hosp. Lond.

WALLWORK, Lynne Louise Parkville, 2 Deemount Terrace, Ferryhill, Aberdeen AB11 7RX Tel: 01224 580909 Fax: 01224 580909 — MB ChB 1997 Aberd.; MBchB 1997; BSc Med. Sci 1995. (Aberdeen) GP VTS SHO.

WALLWORK, Michael Anthony Fieldhead Surgery, Leymoor Road, Golcar, Huddersfield HD7 4QQ Tel: 01484 460298 Fax: 01484 460296; Spinney Court, 3A Thorpe Lane, Almondbury, Huddersfield HD5 8TA Tel: 01484 304486 — MB ChB 1987 Leeds; MRCGP 1992; DRCOG 1991. GP Huddersf. Socs: BMA; Brit. Med. Acupunct. Soc.

WALLWORTH, Roy Allen Peel House Medical Centre, Avenue Parade, Accrington BB5 6RD Tel: 01254 237231 Fax: 01254 389525; 58 Woodfield Avenue, Accrington BB5 2PJ — MB BS 1981 Lond.; MRCGP 1985; DRCOG 1985.

WALMSLEY, Annabel Michaela 6 Windlesham Park, Woodlands Lane, Windlesham GU20 6AT — MB BS 1996 Lond.

WALMSLEY, Anona Elizabeth Lisburn Health Centre, Linenhall Street, Lisburn BT28 1LU Tel: 02892 603333 Fax: 02892 501503; Green Acres, 202 Belsize Road, Lisburn BT27 4DT Tel: 01846 670725 Fax: 01846 661119 — MB BCh BAO 1974 Belf.; DRCOG 1976; MRCGP 1979. (Queens University Belfast)

WALMSLEY, Anthony John Department of Anaesthetics, Eastbourne DGH, Kings Drive, Eastbourne BN21 2NA Tel: 01323 417400; 3 Macmillian Drive, Eastbourne BN21 1SU Tel: 01323 643736 — MB BS 1978 Lond.; FFA RCS Eng. 1982. Cons. Anaesth. E.bourne DHA.

WALMSLEY, Mr Byron Henry Baddeley House, Woodend, Wickham, Fareham PO17 6LB Tel: 01329 832811 — MB ChB 1974 Dundee; BSc St. And. 1971; FRCS Eng. 1980. Cons. Urol. St. Mary's Hosp. Portsmouth. Prev: Sen. Regist. (Urol.) St. Mary's Hosp. Portsmouth; Sen. Regist. Inst. Urol. Lond.

WALMSLEY, David Royal Lancaster Infirmary, Ashton Road, Lancaster LA1 4RP Tel: 01524 65944 Fax: 01524 846346 Email: david.walmsley@l.bay-tr.nwest.nhs.uk — MB ChB 1981 Birm.; FRCP 1999; MD Birm. 1991; MRCP (UK) 1984; BSc Birm. 1978. (Birmingham) Cons. Phys. (Diabetes & Endocrinol.) Morecambe Bay Hosps. NHS Trust.

WALMSLEY, David Antony (retired) Willow House, School Lane, Great Leighs, Chelmsford CM3 1NL — MB BS Lond. 1954; FFA RCS Eng. 1957; DA Eng. 1956. Prev: Cons. Anaesth. Mid Essex Hosps. Trust.

WALMSLEY, Felicity Jane 15 Riselaw Crescent, Edinburgh EH10 6HN — MB ChB 1974 Ed.; MRCGP 1983.

WALMSLEY, Gerald Luke 22 Limehill Road, Tunbridge Wells TN1 1LL Tel: 01892 515344 — MB ChB 1973 Leeds.

WALMSLEY, James Marcus 25 Julian Road, West Bridgford, Nottingham NG2 5AJ — MB BS 1992 Newc.

WALMSLEY, Katharine Mary Flat 6, Harmont House, 20 Harley St., London W1G 9PH Tel: 020 7580 1442 Fax: 020 7580 0494; 29 Patshull Road, London NW5 2JX Tel: 020 7485 5179 — MB ChB 1971 Bristol; MB ChB (Hons.) Bristol 1971; FRCR 1977; DMRD Eng. 1976. Cons. Radiol. Univ. Coll. Lond. Hosps. & King Edwd. VII Hosp. for Offs. Lond. Prev: Sen. Regist. (Radiodiag.) Middlx. Hosp. Lond.

WALMSLEY, Paul Nigel Hudson 92 Kentmere Drive, Cherry Tree, Blackburn BB2 5HF — MB ChB 1980 Birm.

***WALMSLEY, Phillip Jonathan** 36 Lucerne Street, Sefton Park, Liverpool L17 8XT Email: pjwalmsley@liverpool.ac.uk; Shireburn House, 236 Garstang Road, Fulwood, Preston PR2 9QB Tel: 01772 718785 — MB ChB 1995 Manch.

WALMSLEY, Richard Anthony (retired) Rose Farm, Chester Road, Helsby, Warrington WA6 0AN Tel: 01928 725261 Email: van.walms@btinternet.com — MB ChB Liverp. 1956. Prev: Hosp. Pract. (Geriat.) Warrington Gen. Hosp.

WALMSLEY, Russell Stuart 28 Kidderminster Road, West Hagley, Stourbridge DY9 0QD — MB ChB 1986 Bristol; MD 2000 Bristol; MRCP (UK) 1991. Phys./Gastroenterologist; N. Shore Hosp., Auckland, New Zealand. Socs: Brit. Soc. of Gastroenterol.; New Zealand Soc. of Gastroenterol.; Roy. Coll. of Phys. of Lond. Prev: Research Fell. (Gastroenterol.) Roy. Free Hosp. Med. Sch. Lond.; Regist. (Gastroenterol. & Gen. Med.) Gen. Hosp. & Qu. Eliz. Hosps. Birm.

WALMSLEY, Sarah Ruth 91 Peffermill Road, Edinburgh EH16 5UX — MB ChB 1997 Ed.

WALMSLEY, Terry Ann Tonge Moor Health Centre, Thicketford Road, Bolton BL2 2LW Tel: 01204 365449; 6 The Walled Gardens, Shaw Hill, Whittle-le-Woods, Chorley PR6 7PD — MB ChB 1971 Manch.; DObst RCOG 1973.

WALMSLEY, Thomas Osborn Clinic, Fareham PO16 7ES Tel: 01329 288331 Fax: 01329 825519 — MB ChB 1970 Dundee; FRCPsych 1997; MRCPsych 1974. Cons. Psychiat. Portsmouth Healthcare NHS Trust; Clin. Teach. Soton. Univ. Socs: Fell. Roy. Soc. of Med. Prev: Cons. Psychiat. Roy. Edin. Hosp.; Hon. Sen. Lect. (Psychiat.) Univ. Edin.

WALPOLE, Gerard Anthony Mary Operations Div., Maydown Works, PO Box 15, Londonderry BT47 1TU — MB BCh BAO 1980 NUI; AFOM RCP Lond. 1989; MRCGP 1984; DIH Lond. 1989.

WALPOLE, Rachel Helen 48 Macdowall Road, Edinburgh EH9 3EG; Department of Anaesthetics, Royal Infirmary of Edinburgh, Lauriston Place, Edinburgh EH3 9YW — MB ChB 1991 Ed.; FRCA Lond. 1996. (Edinburgh) Specialist Regist. (Anaesth.) SE Scotl. Sch. Anaesth. Prev: SHO (Anaesth.) SE Scotl. Train. Scheme & Wansbeck Gen. Hosp. N.d.

WALPORT, Professor Mark Jeremy Division of Medicine, ICSM, Hammersmith Campus, Du Cane Road, London W12 0NN Tel: 020 8383 3299 Fax: 020 8383 2024 Email: m.walport@ic.ac.uk — MB BChir 1977 Camb.; PhD Camb. 1986, MA 1981; FRCP Lond. 1990; FRCPath 1997, M 1991; F Med Sci 1998. Prof.Imperial.Coll.Sch.Med./Chair.Div.Med;Hon.Cons.Hammersmith Hosp.; Regist. Acad. Med. Sci. Socs: (Counc.) Brit. Soc. Rheum. Prev: Prof. Med. Roy. Postgrad. Med. Sch. & Hon. Cons. Hammersmith Hosp. Lond.; MRC Train. Fell. MRC Mechanisms in Tumour Immunity Unit Camb.

WALPORT, Samuel (retired) 16 Grange Gardens, Pinner HA5 5QE Tel: 020 8868 3951 — LRCP LRCS Ed. LRFPS Glas. 1944. Prev: Capt. RAMC.

WALSH, Miss Aideen Kathleen Mary Room MO13, North Staffordshire Hospital - City General, Newcastle Road, Stoke-on-Trent ST4 6QG Tel: 01782 552176 — MB BCh BAO 1984 NUI; BSc NUI 1986; MD Leicester 1994; FRCS Ed. 1989; FRCS Eng. 1989; LRCPI & LM, LRCSI & LM 1984. (RCSI) Cons. Gen. & Vasc. Surg. N. Staffs. Hosp. Stoke-on-Trent; Hon. Clin. Sen. Lect. (Surg.) Keele Univ. Prev: Higher Surgic. Trainee W. Midl. RHA; Research Fell. (Surg.) Univ. Leicester.

***WALSH, Alison Barbara** 24 Rokeby Crescent, Strathaven ML10 6EG — MB ChB 1998 Glas.; MB ChB Glas 1998.

WALSH

WALSH, Anthony Romney House Surgery, 39-41 Long Street, Tetbury GL8 8AA Tel: 01666 502303 Fax: 01666 504549 — MB ChB 1970 Manch.; DObst RCOG 1972.

WALSH, Anthony Copleston 57 Frithwood Crescent, Kents Hill, Milton Keynes MK7 6HQ Tel: 01908 696838 Fax: 01908 677457 Email: anthony@walsh.powernet.co.uk — MB BS 1976 Lond.; BA Oxf. 1970; MRCGP 1981; DCH Eng. 1979. Prev: GP Princip. Stirchley Health Centre Telford; GP Princip. Walnut Tree Health Centre Milton Keynes.

WALSH, Mr Anthony Richard 44 Carpenter Road, Birmingham B15 2JJ — MB BChir 1977 Camb.; FRCS Eng. 1981.

WALSH, Bartholomew Department of Public Health Medicine, Kingston & Richmond Health Authority, 17 Upper Brighton Road, Surbiton KT6 6LH Tel: 020 8390 1111 Fax: 020 8390 5028; 26 Grove Road, Barnes, London SW13 0HH Tel: 020 8876 6358 — MB BCh BAO 1981 NUI; BA Lond. 1988; MSc Pub. Health Lond. 1995; MRCPath 1990; Dip. Hist. Med. Soc. Apoth. Lond. 1992; Dip. Clin. Microbiol. Lond 1989. Cons. Communicable Dis. Control Surrey. Prev: Sen. Regist. (Microbiol.) Wycombe Gen. Hosp. & John Radcliffe Hosp. Oxf.; Regist. N. Middlx. Hosp. Lond.; SHO St. Mary's Hosp. Lond.

WALSH, Beth Flat 1, 20 Ruthven St., Glasgow G12 9BT — MB ChB 1997 Glas.

WALSH, Catherine Mary S3, Box 175, Addenbrooke's Hospital, Cambridge CB2 2QQ — MB BCh BAO 1984 NUI; MRCPsych. 1988. Cons. Psychiat. Addenbrooke's Hosp. Camb.

WALSH, Christopher John Lytham Eastgate Surgery, 31B York Place, Knaresborough HG5 0AD Tel: 01423 867451 Fax: 01423 860446 — MB ChB 1985 Leeds; MRCGP 1989; DRCOG 1988.

WALSH, Mr Ciaran Joseph Wirral Hospital NHS Trust, Arrowe Park, Arrowe Park Road, Upton, Wirral CH49 5PE Tel: 0151 604 7052 Fax: 0151 604 1760 Email: ciaran.walsh@ccmail.wirralh-tr.nwest.nhs.uk — MB BCh BAO 1984 NUI; LRCPSI 1984; BSc Mch FRCSI (Gen). Cons. Colorectal & Gen. Surg. Socs: BAPEN; ASCRS; Assn. of Colopractol.

WALSH, Colum 126 Edge Lane Drive, Liverpool L13 4AF — MB BS 1992 Newc.

WALSH, David Andrew Rheumatology Unit, City Hospital, Hucknall Road, Nottingham NG5 1PB Tel: 0115 969 1169 Ext: 46376 Email: david.walsh@nottingham.ac.uk; Department Rheumatololology, Kings Mill Centre, Mansfield Road, Sutton-in-Ashfield NG17 4JL Tel: 01623 22515 Ext: 3656 Fax: 01623 672348 — MB BS 1985 Lond.; PhD Lond. 1994; MA Camb. 1986; MRCP (UK) 1988. Sen. Lect. & Hon. Cons. Nottm. Univ.

WALSH, David Anthony Priory Medical Group, Cornlands Road, Acomb, York YO24 3WX Tel: 01904 781423 Fax: 01904 784886 — MB BS 1971 Lond.

WALSH, David Brian (retired) Information Systems Department, Perth & Kinross Healthcare NHS Trust, Perth PH1 1NX Tel: 01738 623311 Fax: 01738 473244 — MB ChB 1965 Manch.; MRCPath 1972. Project Doctor - IHIS Project. Prev: Cons. Dundee Teachg. Hosps. NHS Trust.

WALSH, David Ian Plantation House Medical Centre, 2-6 Austin Friars, London EC2N 2HE Tel: 020 7929 2733 Fax: 020 7628 6002 — MB BS 1985 Lond. (Roy. Free Hosp. Lond.) Indep. GP Lond. Socs: Roy. Soc. Occupat. Md. Prev: SHO (Paediat.) Brook Gen. Hosp; SHO (Anaesth.) St. Mary's Hosp. Lond.; SHO (O & G) Fairfield Hosp. Sydney, Austral.

WALSH, David Michael 36A Methley Street, London SE11 4AJ — MB BS 1993 Lond.

WALSH, Deirdre Ann 16 Swilly Park, Portstewart BT55 7FL — MB BCh BAO 1983 NUI.

WALSH, Dermot Simon Lawrence Hill Health Centre, Hassell Drive, Bristol BS2 0AN Tel: 0117 955 5241 Fax: 0117 941 1162; 42 Colthurst Drive, Hanham, Bristol BS15 3SG — MB BCh BAO 1981 NUI; MRCGP 1986; DObst RCPI 1984; DCH NUI 1983. (Nat. Univ. of Irel.) Prev: SHO (Psychiat.) St. Vincent's Hosp. Dub.

WALSH, Eamonn John Mercheford House Surgery, Mercheford House, Elwyn Road, March PE15 9BT Tel: 01354 656841 Fax: 01354 660788 — MB BS 1980 Lond.; MRCGP 1985; DRCOG 1985.

WALSH, Edward John Sandway, Thornton Gate, Thornton-Cleveleys FY5 1JN Tel: 01253 852704 — MRCS Eng. LRCP Lond. 1957; MFCM 1974; DPH Liverp. 1963. (Liverp.) Sen. Med. Off. DHSS. Prev: Dep. MOH Blackpool Co. Boro.

WALSH, Edward Michael 7 Richmond PArk Road, Clifton, Bristol BS8 3AS — MRCS Eng. LRCP Lond. 1971; MB BS Lond. 1971; BSc Lond. 1967; FFA RCS Eng. 1976. (St. Bart.) Cons. (Anaesth.) S.mead Hosp. Bristol. Prev: Sen. Regist. (Anaesth.) Bristol Health Dist. (T); Cons. (Anaesth.) Oman Armed Forces; Lect. (Anaesth.) Lond. Hosp. Med. Coll.

WALSH, Eleanor Susan Torwold, 23 Ledcameroch Crescent, Bearsden, Glasgow G61 4AD — MB BCh BAO 1972 Dub.; BA Dub. 1970; FFA RCSI 1976; DA RCPSI 1974. Cons. (Anaesth.) Stobhill Hosp., Glas. Prev: Cons. (Anaesth.) Centr. Middx Hosp., Lond.; Sen. Regist. (Anaesth.) Hammersmith Hosp. Lond.

WALSH, Elizabeth Anna Maria 24 Warriner Gardens, London SW11 4EB — MB BCh BAO 1991 NUI; MRCGP 1995; DRCOG 1994.

WALSH, Elizabeth Mary 11 Clapham Mansions, Nightingale Lane, London SW4 9AQ — MB BCh BAO 1989 NUI; LRCPSI 1989.

WALSH, Elizabeth Maureen Fowberry House, The Green, Longfizamlington NE65 8AQ — MB BS 1975 Newc.; MRCGP 1981; DA Eng. 1980.

WALSH, Ewart Geoffrey Biomedical Sciences, University New Buildings, Edinburgh EH8 9AG; 64 Liberton Drive, Edinburgh EH16 6NW Tel: 0131 664 3046 Email: g.walsh@holyrood.ed.ac.uk — BM BCh Oxf. 1947; FRSE 1959; BA (1st cl. Hons.) Oxf. 1943, MA, BSc 1947; MD Harvard 1947; FRCP Ed. 1968, M 1966; FRCP Lond. 1967, M 1950; DTM & H Liverp. 1948. Hon. Specialist (Neurophysiol.) Roy. Hosp. Sick Childr. Edin.; Hon. Fell. Dept. Physiol. Univ. Edin.; Vis. Prof. Univ. of Centr. Eng. Socs: Physiol. Soc. Prev: Reader (Physiol.) Univ. Edin.; Asst. Nuffield Dept. Clin. Med. Oxf.; WHO Vis. Prof. Baroda Med. Coll., India.

WALSH, Geoffrey Parkin (retired) 26 Gorse Road, Blackburn BB2 6LZ Tel: 01254 59195 — MB ChB 1954 St. And.; DObst RCOG 1955. Prev: Ho. Phys. Blackburn Roy. Infirm.

WALSH, Gillian Dianne Sutton Park Surgery, 34 Chester Road North, Sutton Coldfield B73 6SP Tel: 0121 353 2586 Fax: 0121 353 5289; 31 Marlpit Lane, Four Oaks, Sutton Coldfield B75 5PH — MB ChB 1984 Birm.; BSc (Hons.) Birm. 1981; MRCGP 1989; DRCOG 1988. Prev: Trainee GP Sutton Coldfield VTS; SHO (O & G) Solihull Hosp.; SHO (Paediat.) Sandwell Dist. Gen. Hosp. Bromwich.

WALSH, Graham 3 Sunny Bank, Leeds LS8 4EB — MB BS 1998 Lond.

WALSH, Graham John Armada Surgery, 28 Oxford Place, Western Approach, Plymouth PL1 5AJ Tel: 01752 665805 Fax: 01752 220056 — MB ChB 1969 Bristol; D.Occ.Med.; DFFP; DObst RCOG 1972. (Bristol) Gen. Practitioner - Plymouth; Occupat.al Health Pract. - Plymouth; Medico-Legal Reporting, Plymouth; Vasectomy Serv., Plymouth. Socs: Plymouth Med. Soc.; Soc. Occupat. Med.; Plymouth Med. Centre Club. Prev: Accid. and Emerg. Dept., Plymouth; Family Plann. Clinic, Plymouth.

WALSH, Helen Margaret (Earnshaw) 3 Rydal Gardens, West Bridgford, Nottingham NG2 6JR — MB ChB 1988 Sheff.; MRCGP 1993; DRCOG 1991. p/t GP Asst.

WALSH, Mr Henry Patrick John Lourde Hospital, Greenbank Road, Liverpool L18 1H — MB ChB 1978 Manch.; MChOrth Liverp. 1985; FRCS Eng. 1982. Cons. Orthop. Surg. Alder Hey Childr. Hosp. & Fazakerley Hosp. Liverp. Socs: Brit. Orthop. Assn; Foot & Ankle Soc.; Brit. Soc. Childr. Orthop. Surg. Prev: Sen. Lect. & Hon. Cons. (Orthop. & Accid. Surg.) Univ. Liverp.; Clin. Lect. & Hon. Sen. Regist. (Orthop. & Accid. Surg.) Univ. Liverp.; Regist. (Orthop.) Roy. Liverp. Hosp. & Alder Hey Childr. Hosp.

WALSH, Hilary Margaret The Doctors House, Victoria Road, Marlow SL7 1DN Tel: 01628 484666 Fax: 01628 891206; Jonquils, Frieth Road, Marlow SL7 2JQ Tel: 01628 486887 — MB ChB 1971 Liverp.; DObst RCOG 1973.

WALSH, Ian 49 St Pauls Close, Farington Moss, Preston PR26 6RT — MB ChB 1998 Glas.

WALSH, Mr Ian Kinsella 3 Palace Gardens, Chichester Park, Belfast BT15 5DT — MB BCh BAO 1987 Belf.; FRCPS Glas. 1991; FRCSI 1991; FRCS Urol 1998. (Queens University of Belfast) Specialist Regist. (Urol.) Belf. City Hosp. Socs: Irish Radiat. Research Soc.; Assn. Surg. Train.; Brit. Assn. Urol. Surgs. Prev: Clin. Research Fell. & SHO (Urol.) Belf. City Hosp.; Regist. (Surg.) Coleraine Hosp.

WALSH

WALSH, Jacinta Marie 20 St Paul's Close, Adlington, Chorley PR6 9RS — MB BCh 1993 Wales.

WALSH, Jacqueline Anne Flat 2, 37 Lingfield Road, Wimbledon Village, London SW19 4PZ Tel: 020 8946 8964 — MB BS 1987 Lond.; MRCP (UK) 1991; MRCGP 1994; DCH RCP Lond. 1990; DRCOG Lond. 1993. (St. Bart.) GP Lond. Prev: SHO (O & G) Guy's Hosp. Lond.; SHO (Paediat.) Whipps Cross Hosp. Lond.; SHO (Cas.) Guy's Hosp. Lond.

WALSH, James (retired) 53 Stockton Lane, York YO31 1BP Tel: 01904 424407 — MB BCh BAO NUI 1943.

WALSH, James Bernard, OStJ 14 Ashley Park, Armagh BT60 1EU Tel: 028 3752 8332; 14 Ashley Park, Armagh BT60 1EU Tel: 028 3762 8332 — MB BCh BAO 1956 Belf.; FRCPI 1986, M 1965; MRCPsych 1971; DPM RCPSI 1962. Private Pract. with some locum Appts. Socs: BMA; R.Col. Psychiat.s. Prev: Cons. Psychiat. S.. Health & Social Servs. Bd.; Cons. Psychiat. Tyrone & Fermanagh Hosp. Omagh; Sen. Regist. Purdysburn Hosp.

WALSH, James Michael Meade, RD, SBStJ Westcourt, 12 The Street, Rustington, Littlehampton BN16 3NX Tel: 01903 784311 Fax: 01903 850907; The Laurels, Ash Lane, Rustington, Littlehampton BN16 3BT Tel: 01903 773771 Fax: 01903 850907 — MB BS 1967 Lond.; MRCS Eng. LRCP Lond. 1967; DObst RCOG 1970. (Lond. Hosp.) Med. Off. Littlehampton Hosp. & Zachary Merton Community Hosp. Rustington; Surg. Capt. RNR; Dep. Co. Surg. St. John Ambul. Brig. Sussex. Socs: Fell. Roy. Soc. Med.; Assn. Police Surg.; BMA. Prev: Dir. Med. Reserves RNR; Regist. RN Matern. Unit Malta; Chairm. Social Servs. W. Sussex CC & Sussex Police Auth.

WALSH, James Sarto John 15 Broomyknowe, Edinburgh EH14 1JZ — LRCPI & LM, LRSCI & LM 1977; LRCPI & LM, LRCSI & LM 1977; FRCR 1987; FFR RCSI 1986.

WALSH, James Thomas 57 Station Road, Mickleover, Derby DE3 5GJ — MRCS Eng. LRCP Lond. 1969.

WALSH, Janet Elizabeth Richmond House, Grosvenor Road, Wrexham LL11 1BT Tel: 01978 350050 Fax: 01978 261243 — MB BS 1986 Lond.; MRCPsych. Cons.. (Child & Adolesc. Psychiat.)Wrexham N.Wales.

WALSH, Janette Pickerton Cottage, The Village, Burton, South Wirral CH64 5TF — MB ChB 1978 Liverp.; FFR RCSI 1985; DMRD 1982. Cons. Radiol. Arrowe Pk. Hosp. Wirral.

WALSH, Jennifer Susan 8 Roseacre Cl, Hornchurch RM11 3NJ — MB ChB 1997 Sheff. SHO Med. Roy. Hallamshire Hosp. Sheff.

WALSH, Joanna Elizabeth Royal Alexandra Hospital, Corse bar Road, Paisley PA2 9PN Tel: 0141 580 4454 Fax: 0141 580 4207 Email: jo.walsh@rah.scot.nhs.uk; Wellbank House, Campsie Glen, Glasgow G66 7AR — MB ChB 1989 Aberd.; MRCP (UK) 1993. (Aberd.) Cons. Puediat. + Puediat. Rheum. Roy. alexendra Hosp. and intrclyke Roy. Hosp.; Clin. Lect. Univ. of Glas. Socs: Brit. Paediat. Rheum. Gp; RCPCh.; BMA. Prev: Specialist Regist. Paediat. (Rheum.) Gt. Ormond St. Hosp. Lond.; Specialist Regist. Paediat. (Rheum.) Birm. Childr.'s Hosp.; Regist. PICU Roy. Hosp. Sick Childr., Glas.

WALSH, Joanna Ismay 104 Howard Drive, Letchworth SG6 2DG — BM 1993 Soton.; MRCGP 2000 UK; MRCP (paeds.) Lond. 1997. GP Locum Bristol.

WALSH, Joanne The Health Centre, Back Hills, Botesdale, Diss IP22 4WG Tel: 01379 898295 — MB ChB 1992 Manch.; DFFP; BSc St. And. 1989. Asst GP Botesdale Health Centre Botlesdale Diss (P/T).

WALSH, John Christopher St. Stephen's Centre, 369 Fulham Road, London SW10 9TH Tel: 020 8746 8000 — MB BS 1989 Lond.; MRCP (UK) 1994. Sen. Regist. (HIV & Genitourin. Med.) Chelsea & W.m. Hosp. Lond.

WALSH, Mr John Kingsley Princes Margaret Hospital, Osborne Road, Windsor SL4 3SJ Tel: 01753 841716 Fax: 01753 859407 Email: walsh@windsor91.fsnet.co.uk; 62 Kings Road, Windsor SL4 2AH Tel: 01753 840603 Email: walsh@windsor91.fsnet.co.uk — MB ChB (Otago) 1962; FRCS (Ed) 1970; FRACS (Orth) 1971. (University of Otago) Private Medico-Legal Cons., P.ss Margt. Hosp., Windsor, SL4 3SJ; Medico-Legal Cons., 10 Harley St., Lond. W1G 3. Prev: Cons. Orhthopaedic Surg., Ashford Hosp. Middlx.

WALSH, John Paul Rosyth Surgery, 195 Queensferry Road, Rosyth, Dunfermline KY11 2LQ — MB BCh BAO 1990 Dub.

WALSH, John Terence 3 Rydal Gardens, West Bridgford, Nottingham NG2 6JR — MB ChB 1989 Sheff.; BMedSci. (Hons.) Sheff. 1988; MRCP (UK) 1992. Cons. Cardiol. Qu.s Med. Centre. Notts. Socs: Brit. Cardiac Soc.; Brit. Soc. Heart Failure; Brit. Soc. Echocardiography. Prev: Research Fell. (Cardiol.) Qu. Med. Centre Nottm.; SHO (Gen. Med.) Roy. Hallamsh. Hosp. Sheff.; SHO (Gen. Med.) Qu. Med. Centre Nottm.

WALSH, Joseph Michael Greenfield House, 169 Kirk Road, Wishaw ML2 7BZ Tel: 01698 375544 Email: j.m.walsh@btinternet.com — MB ChB 1958 Glas. (Glas.) Med. Mem. Indep. Tribunal Servs. Prev: GP Princip. Health Centre Wishaw; Regist. (Surg.) Law Hosp. Carluke; Regtl. Med. Off. Gurkha Engineers Malaya.

WALSH, Josephine Lynne Canute Surgery, 66A Portsmouth Road, Woolston, Southampton SO19 9AL Tel: 023 8043 6277 Fax: 023 8039 9751 — MB BCh 1974 Dublin; MB BCh Dub. 1974. (Dublin) GP Soton.

WALSH, Joyce Bench Mark Barn, Elswick Lodge, Mellor, Blackburn BB2 7EX — MB ChB 1958 Ed.

WALSH, Kevin John Hinchingbrooke Hospital, Huntingdon PE29 6NT Tel: 01480 416416 Fax: 01480 416490; Orchard House, Bury Road, Ramsey, Huntingdon PE26 1NA Tel: 01487 815981 — BM BCh 1979 Oxf.; MA Camb. 1980; DM Soton. 1992; FRCP Lond. 1998. (Oxf.) Cons. Phys. Hinchingbrooke Healthcare NHS Trust Huntingdon. Socs: Brit. Geriat. Soc. Prev: Sen. Regist. (Geriat.) W. Midl. Regional Train. Scheme; Research Regist. MRC Soton.; Lect. (Rehabil.) Univ. of Soton.

WALSH, Lesley Jane 77 Wyatt Road, Sutton Coldfield B75 7NH Tel: 0121 378 4127 — MB ChB 1987 Bristol; BA Open 1983; MRCP (UK) 1990. Regist. Rotat. (Gen. Med.) City Hosp. Nottm. Prev: SHO Rotat. (Gen. Med.) N. Birm. Gen. Hosp.; Ho. Off. (Geriat. Med.) Derbysh. Roy. Infirm.

WALSH, Mrs Margaret Litchfield Chingford Health Centre, 109 York Road, Chingford, London E4 8LF Tel: 020 8529 8655; 34 The Avenue, Loughton IG10 4PX Tel: 020 8508 6598 — MB ChB 1965 Sheff. SCMO Waltham Forest HA.

WALSH, Marie Therese Josephine 8 McLean Drive, Priorslee Grange, Priorslee, Telford TF2 9RT — MB BCh BAO 1980 NUI; FRCR 1986; DCH RCPSI 1981. Cons. Radiol. P.ss Roy. Hosp. Telford.

WALSH, Mark 121 Albert Drive, Sheerwater, Woking GU21 5QY — MB BS 1996 Lond.

WALSH, Martin Paul Seffield Occupational Health Service, Northern General Hospital, Herries Road, Sheffield S5 7AU Tel: 0114 271 4161 Fax: 0114 244 4470; 26 Stainmore Avenue, Sothall, Sheffield S20 2GN Tel: 0114 247 3845 — MRCS Eng. LRCP Lond. 1971; MSc (Occupat. Med.) Lond. 1975; DFFP 1996; 1998 DEBHC Oxf.; DIH Eng. 1976; DObst RCOG 1974. p/t Occupat.al Phys., Sheff. Occupat.al Health Serv., N:. Gen. Hosp., Sheff.; Occupat.al Phys., BMI Health Servs. Leeds. Socs: Soc. of Occupat.al Med.; Assn. of NHS Occupat.al Health Phys.s. Prev: Trainee GP Neath VTS; Mem. Scientif. Staff MRC & DHSS Epidemiol. & Med. Care Unit N.wick Pk. Hosp. Harrow.; Gen. Practitioner, Birley Health Centre, Sheff. 1976-2000.

WALSH, Mary Clare Wentloog Road Health Centre, 98 Wentloog Road, Rumney, Cardiff CF3 8EA Tel: 029 2079 7746 Fax: 029 2079 0231; Daintree Surgery, 98 Wentloog Road, Rumney, Cardiff CF3 8EU Tel: 029 2079 7746 — MB BCh 1985 Wales; DCH RCP Lond. 1988; DRCOG 1988. (University of Wales College of Wales) GP Princip.

WALSH, Mary Madeleine Theresa Women's Secure Services, Annesley House Hospital, Mansfield Rd, Annesley, Nottingham NG15 0AR Tel: 01623 727901 Fax: 01623 727927 — BM BS 1978 Nottm.; MA Psychoanalytical Studies, Uni. Of E. London & Tavistock Clinic; BMedSci Nottm. 1976; MRCPsych 1989; MRCGP 1982; DCH RCP Lond. 1984. Cons. Forens. Psychiat. Wom.'s Secure Servs. Nottm. Prev: Cons. Forens. Psychiat. Rampton Hosp. 1995-2001 Retford, Nottm.; Sen. Regist. Rotat. (Psychiat.) Nottm. Train. Scheme.

WALSH, Matthew Joseph 17 Meadow Court, Allerton, Bradford BD15 9JZ — MB ChB 1987 Leeds.

WALSH, Maureen Yvonne 30 Ravenhill Court, Belfast BT6 8FS — MB BCh BAO 1978 Belf.

WALSH

WALSH, Melanie Frances 17 Stockwood Close, Blackburn BB2 7QW — MB BCh BAO 1991 Belf.

WALSH, Mr Michael Edward The Mid-Yorkshire Nuffield Hospital, Outwood Lane, Horsforth, Leeds LS18 4HP Tel: 0113 258 8756 Fax: 0113 225 3823 Email: mikewalsh@in2000.net; The Close, 7 Wetherby Road, Leeds LS8 1JU Tel: 0113 273 3453 — MB ChB 1978 Ed.; MPhil Stathclyde 1989; FRCS (Orth.) Ed. 1992; FRCS Ed. 1984. Cons. Orthopaedic Surg. (inDepend.). Socs: Brit. Orthop. Assn. & Brit. Elbow & Shoulder Soc.; Brit. Soc. Surg. Hand. Prev: Cons. Orthopaedic Surg. (inDepend.).

WALSH, Mr Michael Stephen Department of Surgery, The Royal London Hospital, London E1 1BB Tel: 020 7377 7723 Fax: 020 7377 7044; 193A Blackstock Road, Highbury, London N5 2LL Tel: 020 7690 8802 Fax: 020 7690 8802 — MB BS 1984 Lond.; BSc Lond. 1981; MS Lond. 1996; FRCS Eng. 1988; FRCS 1997. (St. Mary's) Cons. Gen. Trauma Vasc. Surg. Roy. Lond. Hosp. Socs: Vasc. Surg. Soc.; Assn. Surg.; Brit. Trauma Soc. Prev: Sen. Regist. (Vasc. Surg.) Univ. Coll. Hosp. Lond.; Sen. Regist. (Gen. Surg.) S.end Gen. Hosp.; Cons. (Gen. & Vasc. Surg.) Whipps Cross Hosp. Lond.

WALSH, Nigel Dennis The Old Coach House, High Street, Chipping Campden GL55 6HB Tel: 01386 849288 — MRCS Eng. LRCP Lond. 1952 Lond.; MRCGP 1970; FFM RCP 1989 UK. (St. Geo.) Cons. pharmaceutical Phys.; The Med. expert partnership. Socs: Fell. Roy. Soc. Med.; Brit. Assn. Pharmaceut. Phys. Prev: Med. Dir. Warner Lambert Internat.; Hon. Med. Off. Dorrigo Hosp., Austral.; Resid. Obst. Asst. St. Geo. Hosp. Lond.

WALSH, Patrick Francis 96 Brisbane Road, Largs KA30 8NN — MB ChB 1981 Glas.; BSc Glas. (Immunol.) 1978, MB ChB 1981; FRCR 1987. Cons. Radiol. Inverclyde Roy. Hosp. Greenock. Prev: Regist/Sen. Regist. (Radiol.) Gtr. Glas. HB.; SHO (A & E/Orthop.) Hairmyres Hosp. E. Kilbride.

WALSH, Patrick Joseph Finton Millbrook, Little Malvern, Malvern WR14 4JP Tel: 01684 575554 — MB BS 1947 Lond.; DPM 1955 Eng.; MRCPsych 1971; MRCPsych 1971; DPM Eng. 1955. (Guy's) Socs: Fell. Roy. Soc. Med.; BMA. Prev: Cons. Psychiat. S. Worcs. Hosp. Grp.; Asst. Psychiat. St. Bernard's Hosp. S.all; Sen. Regist. (Psychiat.) Warlingham Pk. Hosp.

WALSH, Patrick Martin (retired) 56 Main Street, Newcastle BT33 0AE Tel: 013967 23221 — MB BCh BAO Belf. 1953.

WALSH, Patrick Michael John 411 Allenby Road, Southall UB1 2HG — BM BCh 1964 Oxf.; DPM Eng. 1967.

WALSH, Mr Patrick Vaughan Raigmore Hospital, Inverness IV2 3UJ Tel: 01463 704000 Fax: 01463 711322; Mid Feabuie, Culloden Moor, Inverness IV2 5EQ Tel: 01463 792534 — MB BS 1971 Lond.; MS 1983 Lond.; FRCS Glas. 1993; FRCS Eng. 1977. (Lond. Hosp.) Cons. Surg. Raigmore Hosp. Inverness. Socs: Fell. Roy. Soc. Med.; BASO. Prev: Sen. Regist. (Surg.) Gtr. Glas. HB; Research Fell. (Surg.) Univ. Liverp.; Regist. (Surg.) Chester Roy. Infirm.

WALSH, Peter Alexander 12 Sykes Close, Greenfield, Oldham OL3 7PT — MB ChB 1991 Leeds.

WALSH, Peter Roderick Steppes Mill House, Bodenham Moor, Hereford HR1 3HS — MRCS Eng. LRCP Lond. 1942; MRCP Lond. 1952. (Middlx.)

WALSH, Raymond Staveleigh Medical Centre, King Street, Stalybridge SK15 2AE Tel: 0161 304 8009 Fax: 0161 303 7207; Fairhaven, 20 Werneth Road, Woodley, Stockport SK6 1HW — MB ChB 1972 Manch.; DObst RCOG 1975.

WALSH, Redmond Clapham Family Practice, 51 Clapham High Street, London SW4 7TL Tel: 020 7622 4455 Fax: 020 7622 4466; 13 Brookwood Rise, Artane, Dublin 5, Republic of Ireland — MB BCh BAO 1983 NUI; LRCPI & LM LRCSI & LM 1983.

WALSH, Richard Joseph 5 Kingsley Crescent, Long Eaton, Nottingham NG10 3DA Tel: 0160 76 62370 — MB BS 1973 Lond.; MRCS Eng. LRCP Lond. 1973. (Guy's)

WALSH, Richard Nicholas 45 Dapdune Court, Woodbridge Road, Guildford GU1 4RU — MB ChB 1989 Birm.

WALSH, Mr Rory McConn Department Ear, Nose & Throat, Guy's Hospital, St Thomas St., London SE1 9RT; Flat 4, House 2, The Paragon, London SE3 0NX Tel: 020 8852 7505 — MB BCh BAO 1987 Dub.; FRCS Eng. 1993. Regist. (ENT) Guy's & Lewisham Hosps. Lond. Prev: SHO (ENT) Lewisham Hosp. Lond.; SHO (Gen. Surg.) Hammersmith Hosp. Lond.; Demonst. (Anat.) Trinity Coll. Dub.

WALSH, Ruth Clare Orchard House, 12A Station Road, Studley B80 7HS — MB BS 1998 Lond.

WALSH, Sarah Jane 13 York Street, Norwich NR2 2AN Tel: 01603 623461 — MB ChB 1992 Birm.; FRCA 1998. Specialist Regist. Anglia Deanery. Socs: Birm. Med. Res. Expeditionary Soc.; Intens. Care Soc. Prev: SHO (Anaesth.) Burton on Trent; SHO (ITU) Roy. Lond. Hosp.; SHO (Anaesth.) Birm. Heartlands Hosp.f.

WALSH, Sean Perry 13 Hartley Avenue, Highfield, Southampton SO17 3QY — BM 1990 Soton. Specialist Regist. (Orthop.) Wessex. Prev: SHO (Gen. Surg.) W. Suff. Hosp. Bury St. Edmunds.

WALSH, Simon James 1 Lagan Villas, Dromore BT25 1LN — MB BCh 1997 Belf.

WALSH, Simon James Meade The Laurels, 44 Ash Lane, Rustington, Littlehampton BN16 3BT — MB BS 1994 Lond.; MRCP(UK) 1999. (The London Hospital Medical College) SHO (Med.) P.ss Alexandra Hosp. Harlow. Prev: SHO Orthop., Whipps Cross Hosp., Lond.; SHO Elderly Med., Whipps Cross Hosp., Lond.; SHO Paediaric A&E, Qu. Eliz. Hosp., Lond.

WALSH, Simon Roy The Surgery, 2 Heathcote Street, Newcastle ST5 7EB Tel: 01782 561057 Fax: 01782 563907; Maple House, Church Road, Aston Juxta Mondrum, Nantwich CW5 6DR Tel: 01270 627868 — MB ChB 1979 Manch.; Cert. FPA 1981.

WALSH, Siobhan Maire Michelle 17 Kirkton Road, Kirktonhill, Dumbarton G82 4AS Tel: 01389 62193 — MB ChB 1983 Glas.; DCCH RCP Ed. 1988; DRCOG 1987.

WALSH, Siobhan Mary 1 Shelley Court, Cheadle Hulme, Cheadle SK8 6JH — MB BCh BAO 1992 NUI.

WALSH, Stephanie 12 Church Lane, Nether Poppleton, York YO26 6LB — MB ChB 1985 Leeds; MRCGP 1989. (Univ. Leeds) Clin. Asst. (Palliat. Med.) St. Leonards Hospice York.

WALSH, Susan Jane Maple House, Church Road, Aston Juxta Mondrum, Nantwich CW5 6DR Tel: 01270 627868 — MB ChB 1981 Manch.; MFFP 1994; DRCOG 1983; Cert. FPA 1985; Dip. Genito Urinary Med & Venerol 1999. SCMO (Family Plann.) Chesh. Community Healthcare Trust Nantwich; Clin.Asst.Genito-Urin. med.Roy.Liverp.Univ.Hosp.

WALSH, Terence John 19 Burrell Close, Prenton, Birkenhead CH42 8QE Tel: 0151 608 8353 — MRCS Eng. LRCP Lond. 1954.

WALSH, Mr Timothy Hays Roud Cottage, Roud, Ventnor PO38 3LH Tel: 01983 840675 — MB BS 1970 Lond.; MS Lond. 1984; BSc Physiol. 1966; FRCS Eng. 1975. (Univ. Coll. Hosp. Lond.) Cons. Surg. Wessex RHA Isle of Wight; Clin. Tutor I. of Wight; Mem. Ct. Examrs. RCS Eng. Prev: Regist. (Surg.) Addenbrooke's Hosp. Camb.; Sen. Regist. (Surg.) Lond. Hosp.; Resid. Surg. Off. St. Mark's Hosp. Lond.

WALSH, Timothy Simon Royal Infirmary of Edinburgh, Lauriston Place, Edinburgh EH3 9YW Tel: 0131 536 1000 Email: tim@walsh.sol.co.uk — MB ChB 1988 Ed.; MD (Edinburgh) 1999; BSc (Hons.) Ed. 1986; MRCP (UK) 1991; FRCA 1994. (Edin.) Cons. Anaesth. IC RIE Edin; Hon. Sen. Lect. RIE. Socs: Intens. Care Soc.; Scott. Intens. Care Soc.; BMA.

WALSH, William John St. Andrews at Harrow, Bowden House Clinic, London Road, Harrow-on-the-Hill, Harrow HA1 3JL Tel: 020 8966 7000 Fax: 020 8864 6092 — MB BS 1968 Queensland; MRCPsych 1987; FRANZCP 1986. (Univ. Queensland, Austral.) Cons. Psychiat., Bowden Ho. Clinic, Harrow. Prev: Cons. Psychiat. Aylesbury Vale Healthcare; Cons. Psychiat. Watford Gen. Hosp.; Indep. Cons. Psychiat. Brisbane, Austral.

WALSH, Mr William Kevin Plouer Hill House, Causey Hill, Hexham NE46 2DL — MB BS 1968 Newc.; FRCS Eng. 1973. Orthop. Surg. Gen. Hosp. Hexham. Prev: Sen. Regist. Birm. Accid. Hosp.; Sen. Regist. (Orthop.) & Regist. (Orthop.) Robt. Jones & Agnes Hunt Hosp. OsW.ry.

WALSH, William Roger Lane End, Glen Auldyn, Lezayre, Ramsey IM7 2AD Tel: 01624 812213 — MB BChir 1948 Camb.; MA Camb. 1948. (Guy's & Camb.)

WALSH-WARING, Mr Gerald Patrick (retired) Corace House, Broad St., East Isley, Newbury RG20 7LW — MB BS 1958 Lond.; FRCS Eng. 1964; DLO Eng. 1962. Hon. Cons. ENT Surg. Hammersmith Hosp. Lond.; Cons. i/c Jt. St. Mary's & Hammersmith Hosps. Head & Neck Oncol. Serv.; Examr. for Fell.sh. Otolaryngol. RCS Eng. Prev: Sen. Regist. (ENT) St. Mary's Hosp. Lond.

WALSHAM, Anna Clare The Old Hall, 1 High St., Billingborough, Sleaford NG34 0QA — MB ChB 1997 Manch.

WALTER

WALSHAW, Carol Anne Oakworth Health Centre, 3 Lidget Mill, Oakworth, Keighley BD22 7HY Tel: 01535 643306 Fax: 01535 645832 — MB ChB 1974 Liverp.

WALSHAW, Colin Francis Radiology Dept, Victoria Hospital, Blackpool FY3 8NR Tel: 01253 306912 Fax: 01253 306960 — MB ChB 1984 Manch.; MSc Manch. 1991, MB ChB 1984; MRCP (UK) 1987; FRCR 1994. Cons. Radiol. Vict. Hosp. Blackpool. Prev: Sen.Reg.Radiol.Univ.Hosp.Wales.Cardiff.

WALSHAW, Martin John 12 Moreton Road, Upton, Wirral CH49 6LL — MB ChB 1978 Liverp.

WALSHAW, Mr Nigel William David (retired) 10A Busley Way, Christchurch BH23 2HF Tel: 01202 475032 Email: nwalshaq@eurobell.co.uk — MRCS Eng. LRCP Lond. 1965; MA (Double 1st cl. Hons.) Camb. 1962, MB 1966; BChir 1965; FRCS Eng. 1971; LMSSA Lond. 1965; DO Eng. 1969. Prev: Cons. Ophth. Surg. Roy. Gwent Hosp. Newport.

WALSHAW, Russell John The Surgery, Manlake Avenue, Winterton, Scunthorpe DN15 9TA Tel: 01724 732202 Fax: 01724 734992 — MB ChB 1966 Sheff.; MRCGP 1971. (Sheff.) Med. Sec. N. Lincs. & E. Yorks. LMC; Mem. Gen. Med. Servs. Comm. Socs: BMA. Prev: SHO (Obst.) Nether Edge Hosp. Sheff.; Ho. Surg. Sheff. Roy. Hosp.; Ho. Off. (Med.) Sheff. Roy. Infirm.

WALSHE, Adrian Dominic Flat 24, Elmwood Court, Pershore Road, Birmingham B5 7PD — MB BS 1985 Newc.

WALSHE, David Kevin 31 Cambridge Road, Linthorpe, Middlesbrough TS5 5NG Tel: 01642 88662 — MB BCh BAO 1943 Dub.; BA, MB BCh BAO Dub. 1943. (TC Dub.) Police Surg. Co. Boro. Middlesbrough; Med. Off. Remand Home Middlesbrough. Socs: Assn. Med. Internat. de Notre Dame de Lourdes. Prev: Ho. Surg. Ho. Phys. & Res. Surg. Off. N. Ormesby Hosp. Middlesbrough.

WALSHE, Elaine Teresa 45 Ashwood Avenue, Bridge of Don, Aberdeen AB22 8XH — MB BCh BAO 1985 NUI.

WALSHE, Ethna Ann (retired) Glencroft, 213 Wythenshawe Road, Manchester M23 9DB Tel: 0161 998 3511 — MB ChB 1952 Glas.; DA Eng. 1956. Prev: Ho. Off. Redlands Hosp. Wom. Glas. & Stockton & Thornaby Hosp.

WALSHE, Geraldine Miriam 7 Minley Close, Cove, Farnborough GU14 9RT — MB BCh BAO 1955 NUI.

WALSHE, John Psychotherapy Department, 1 Hospital Road, Colchester CO3 3HJ Tel: 01206 769798 — LRCPI & LM, LRCSI & LM 1970; MRCPsych 1976. Cons. Psychotherapist W.E.E. Ment. Health NHS Trust & M.D.E. Community Ment. Health Trust; Med. Dir. of W.E.E. M.H. Trust; Hon. Fell. Essex Univ. 1989. Socs: Inst. Gp. Anal.

WALSHE, John Michael Department Neurology, Middlesex Hospital, London W1N 8AA Tel: 020 7636 8333 Ext: 4873; Broom Lodge, 58 High Street, Hemingford Grey, Huntingdon PE28 9BN Tel: 01480 462487 — MB BChir Camb. 1945; MD (hon. causa) Uppsala 1994; MA Camb. 1945, ScD 1965; FRCP Lond. 1964, M 1949. (Univ. Coll. Hosp.) Hon. Sen. Lect. (Med.) UCL & (Neurol.) Middlx. Hosp. Lond. Socs: Assn. Phys. Prev: Bilton Pollard Trav. Fell. Boston City Hosp.; Reader (Metab. Dis.) Univ. Camb.; Hon. Cons. Phys. Addenbrooke's Hosp. Camb.

WALSHE, Kieran Gerard Church View Surgery, 14 Church View, Dundrum, Newcastle BT33 0NA; 8 Castle View, Castle Hill, Dundrum, Newcastle BT33 0NA Tel: 013967 51757 Email: kwalshe@talk21.com — MB BCH BAO NUI 1977; MD NUI 1985; MRCGP 1986; MICGP 1986. (Univ. Coll. Cork) Assoc. Specialist (Diabetes) Lagan Valley Hosp. Lisburn; Eli Lilly Research Fell. (Metab. Unit) Roy. Vict. Hosp. Belf. Socs: Brit. Diabetic Assn.; Eur. Assn. Study Diabetes. Prev: Regist. (Med. & Endrocrinol.) Roy. Vict. Hosp. Belf.; Eli Lilly Research Fell.; Intern & SHO Limerick Regional Hosp.

WALSHE, Margaret Mary (retired) 9 Church End., Haddenham, Aylesbury HP17 8AH Tel: 01844 291731 — MB BS 1956 Lond.; FRCP Lond. 1976, M 1962; MRCS Eng. LRCP Lond. 1956; DObst RCOG 1958. Prev: Cons. Dermat. Aylesbury, Milton Keynes & Wycombe HAs.

WALSHE, Mary Bridget Anne 40 Spratt Hall Road, London E11 2RQ — MB BCh BAO 1978 Dub.; MB BCh Dub. 1978.

WALSHE, Peadar Bernard Marybrook Medical Centre, Berkeley GL13 9BL Tel: 01453 810228 Fax: 01453 511778 — MB BCh BAO 1981 Dub. (Dub.) Socs: BMA (Counc. Mem. Glos. Br.).

WALSHE-BRENNAN, Kieran Stanislaus Apartment 9 Moygannon Court, Warrenpoint, Newry BT34 3JW Tel: 016937 52530; c/o Sir Patrick McKenna, 19 Barrule Park, Ramsey Tel: 01624 812071 — MSc Belf. 1949, MB BCh BAO 1957; MFCM 1974; MRCPsych 1971; DPM Dub. 1965; DPH Belf. 1961. Socs: Fell. Roy. Soc. Health; Fell. Roy. Inst. Pub. Health & Hyg.; FRSS. Prev: Clin. Lect. Sheff. Univ. 1966-1971; Cons. Psychiat. Mersey RHA, Roy. Hallamsh. Hosp. Sheff. & Yorkton & Melville Hosps. Canada.; Lect. Keele Univ. 1975-1982 and Examr.

WALSMA, P Whitefields Surgery, Hunsbury Hill Road, Camp Hill, Northampton NN4 9UW Tel: 01604 760171 Fax: 01604 708528 — Artsexamen 1976 Groningen; Artsexamen 1976 Groningen.

WALSTER, Verity Margaret Joanna St. Andrew's Cottage, Foston on the Wolds, Driffield YO25 8BN — MB ChB 1991 Glas.; MRCGP 1995; DFFP 1994. GP Asst. Old Fire Station Pract. Beverley; Sessional Med. Off. (Reproductive & Sexual Health) E. Yorks. Community Healthcare Trust.

WALSWORTH-BELL, Joanna Pierce South Staffordshire Health Authority, Mellor House, Corporation St., Stafford ST16 3SR Tel: 01785 52233; Junction House, Fradley Junction, Alrewas, Burton-on-Trent DE13 7DN Tel: 01283 791457 — MB BS 1971 Lond.; MSc (Social Med.) Lond. 1978; MRCS Eng. LRCP Lond. 1971; MFPHM Eng. 1981; DCH Eng. 1975; MSSc Manchester 1992. (St. Bart.) Cons. Pub. Health Med. S. Staffs. HA. Socs: Fell. Fac. Pub. Health Med. Prev: Regional Specialist Pub. Health Med. NW RHA; Sen. Regist. (Community Med.) St. Thos. Hosp. Lond.; Regist. (Community Med.) Hants. AHA (T).

WALT, Helen J Yardley Green Medical Centre, 73 Yardley Green Road, Bordesley Green, Birmingham B9 5PU Tel: 0121 773 3838 Fax: 0121 506 2005; 48 Westfield Road, Edgbaston, Birmingham B15 3QG Tel: 0121 455 0043 — MB BS 1978 Lond. (Westm.)

WALT, Robert Peter Birmingham Heartlands Hospital, Bordesley Green E., Birmingham B9 5ST; 48 Westfield Road, Edgbaston, Birmingham B15 3QG — MB ChB Brim. 1976; MD Birm. 1986; FRCP Lond. 1992; MRCP (UK) 1978. Cons. Phys. (Gastroenterol.) Birm. Heartlands Hosp. Prev: Sen. Lect. & Hon. Cons. Dept. Med. Qu. Eliz. Hosp. Birm.; Lect. & Hon. Sen. Regist. (Therap.) Univ. Hosp. Nottm.; Regist. Acad. Dept. Med. Roy. Free Hosp. Lond.

WALTER, Christine Marian 79 Penland Road, Haywards Heath RH16 1PJ — MB BS 1972 Lond.; DCH RCP Lond. 1976; DObst. RCOG 1973. Clin. Med. Off. (Child Health.) Mid. Downs HA.

WALTER, Christopher John Stephen (retired) 56 Herbert Street, Cambridge CB4 1AQ — MB BS 1960 Lond.; FRCPsych 1987, M 1971; DPM Eng. 1965. Prev: Cons. Psychiat. P.ss Alexandra Hosp. Harlow & Herts. & Essex Gen. Hosp. Bishop's Stortford.

WALTER, Mr Darren Paul 4 Alexandra Grove, Pudsey LS28 8QG Email: 106070.3001@compuserve.com — MB ChB 1989 Manch.; FRCS Ed. 1993; Dip. Immediate Med. Care RCSurg. Ed. 1998. Specialist Regist. (Emerg. Med.) Yorks. Region. Socs: Brit. Assn. Immed. Care Schemes. Prev: HEMS Regist. Roy. Lond. Hosp.; Med. Off. Cave Rescue Organisation.

WALTER, Elizabeth Jane Flat 4, Chesterfield House, Westbourne Place, Clifton, Bristol BS8 1RX — MB BS 1982 Lond.; BSc (Intercalated Psychol.) Lond. 1978; MRCPsych 1993; MRCGP 1987; DRCOG 1987; DCH RCP Lond. 1985. Regist. (Psychiat.) Barrow Hosp. Bristol.

WALTER, Fiona Mary Mutlow Hill, Wendens Ambo, Saffron Walden CB11 4JL; Mutow Hall, Wendens Ambo, Saffron Walden CB11 4JL Tel: 01799 540440 Email: fmw22@medschl.cam.ac.uk — MB BChir 1983 Camb.; MSC Lond. 2000; MA Camb. 1982; FRCGP 1995, M 1987; DRCOG 1985; DCH RCP Lond. 1984. (St. Thos.) Research Fell., GP & Care research unit, Univ. of Camb.; GP. Asst.. Dr Stephens and Partners, Camb.

WALTER, Hazel Pamela Steeple View, 3 Yarkhill Barns HR1 3TD Tel: 01432 890320 Fax: 01432 890360 Email: hazelwalter@compuserve.com — MB BS Lond. 1968; MRCS Eng. LRCP Lond. 1968; MRCGP 1980; DFFP 1994; DMJ(Clin) Soc. Apoth. Lond. 1994; DObst RCOG 1970. (Middlx.) Forens. Phys. W. Mercia. Socs: Roy. Soc. Med. (Counc. Clin. Forens. Med. Sect.); Assn. Police Surg.; Brit. Assn. Forens. Servs. Prev: Clin. Asst. (Genitourin. Med.) Ambrose King Centre, The Roy. Lond. Hosp.; Clin. Asst. (Genitourin Med.) St. Anne's Hosp., Sexual Health Centre Lond.; GP Trainer Palmers Green Lond.

WALTER

WALTER, Ian McNeil 63 Thanet Road, Bexley DA5 1AP — MRCS Eng. LRCP Lond. 1947. (Lond. Hosp.)

WALTER, James Andrew The Health Centre, Stokenchurch, High Wycombe HP14 3TG Tel: 01494 483633 Fax: 01494 483690; Luke House, Water End, High Wycombe HP14 3XH — MRCS Eng. LRCP Lond. 1970; DCH Eng. 1973. (St. Mary's) Prev: Trainee Gen. Pract. Cirencester Vocational Train. Scheme; Med. Off. Tarawa, Kiribati.

WALTER, Joanna Clare 27 Vicarage Gardens, Scunthorpe DN15 7BA — MB BChir 1989 Camb.

WALTER, John Hugh Tel: 0161 727 2137 Fax: 0161 727 2137 Email: john@jhwalter.demon.co.uk; The Cottage, 15 Blantyre Road, Swinton, Manchester M27 5ER — MB BS 1978 Lond.; MSc Lond. 1987, MD 1990; FRCP Lond. 1996; MRCP (UK) 1984; FRCPCH Lond. 1997; DCH RCP Lond. 1983. (St. Mary's) Cons. Paediat. (Inherited Metab. Dis.) Roy. Manch. Childr. Hosp. Socs: Chair of Coun. of Soc. for the study of inborn errors of Metab.; Brit. inherited Metab. Dis. gp. Prev: Lect. (Child Health) Univ. Bristol; Clin. Research Fell. Inst. Child Health Lond.

WALTER, Julian Patrick Wharton Lindfield Medical Centre, High Street, Lindfield, Haywards Heath RH16 2HX Tel: 01444 457666 — MB 1972 Camb.; BChir 1971 Camb.; DObst 1973. GP Blackburn. Prev: GP Bethnal Green Med. Mission ('77-'88); GP Trainer E. Lond. VTS. ('80-'88); GP Balcombe & Handcroass, Haywards Health ('88-'00).

WALTER, Kenneth Herbert (retired) 4 Harwood Gardens, Burfield Road, Old Windsor, Windsor SL4 2LJ Tel: 01753 864474 — MRCS Eng. LRCP Lond. 1939. Prev: Area Surg. St. John Ambul. Brig.

WALTER, Lilian Starr (retired) 2 Searle Road, Farnham GU9 8LJ — MB BS 1950 Lond.; DObst RCOG 1953.

WALTER, Margaret Valerie Church Farm House, Ripple, Deal CT14 8JL Tel: 01304 372113 — MB BS Lond. 1958; MRCS Eng. LRCP Lond. 1959; DO Eng. 1966. (Lond. Hosp.) Clin. Asst. (Ophth.) Kent & Canterbury Hosp. Prev: Clin. Asst. Ophth. Roy. Vict. Hosp. Folkestone & Vict. Hosp. Deal; Gyn. & Obst. Ho. Off. & Ho. Surg. Roy. Vict. Hosp. Folkestone.

WALTER, Michael The Surgery, 1 Arlington Road, Eastbourne BN21 1DH Tel: 01323 727531 Fax: 01323 417085; 16 Compton Drive, Eastbourne BN20 8BU — MB BS 1965 Lond.; FRCGP 1988, M 1975; MRCS Eng. LRCP Lond. 1965; DObst RCOG 1968. (Guy's) Prev: SHO (Paediat.) St. Luke's Hosp. Guildford; Ho. Surg. & Ho. Phys. Roy. Surrey Co. Hosp.

WALTER, Nigel Richard The Surgery, 24 Albert Road, Bexhill-on-Sea TN40 1DG Tel: 01424 730456/734430 Fax: 01424 225615; 23 Little Twitten, Cooden, Bexhill-on-Sea TN39 4SS Tel: 01424 843394 — MB BS 1981 Lond.; MRCGP 1986; DRCOG 1986.

WALTER, Norah (retired) 4 Sunbury Avenue, East Sheen, London SW14 8RA — MB BCh BAO 1943 Belf.; MFCM 1974; DCH Eng. 1947. Prev: Princip. Med. Off. Richmond, Twickenham & Roehampton HA.

WALTER, Mr Pelham Howard Hurstwood Park Hospital, Haywards Heath RH16 7SJ Tel: 01444 441881 Fax: 01444 417995 — MB BS 1969 Lond.; BSc Lond. 1966, MB BS 1969; FRCS Eng. 1975. (Lond. Hosp.) Cons. (Neurosurg.) Hurstwood Pk. Hosp., Haywards Heath. Socs: BMA. Prev: Sen. Regist. (Neurosurg.) Lond. Hosp. Whitechapel; Regist. (Neurosurg.) Brook Hosp. Lond.; Regist. (Neurosurg.).

WALTER, Rachel Mary 21 Weston Lea, West Horsley, Leatherhead KT24 6LG — MB ChB 1989 Sheff.; MRCGP 1994; DRCOG 1994.

WALTER, Robert David Ellaslea, 29 Castle Douglas Road, Dumfries DG2 7PA Email: rob.walter@virgin.net — MB ChB 1994 Leic.; MRCGP 1998. GP Reg Dunscore.

WALTER, Shaun Julian 12 Bury Street, Norwich NR2 2DN — MB ChB 1988 Sheff.

WALTER, Stephen 24 Farrington Crescent, Hampton Park, Lincoln LN6 0YG Tel: 01522 688166; 40 High Street, Studley B80 7HL — MB ChB 1982 Birm.; MRCGP 1986; DRCOG 1985; DCH RCP Lond. 1985. Prev: Trainee GP Lincs. VTS.

WALTER, Timothy Neil St Johns Road Surgery, 10 St. Johns Road, Newbury RG14 7LX Tel: 01635 40160 — MB BS 1985 Lond.; MRCGP 1990.

WALTERS, Alexander Demetrius West End Road Surgery, 62 West End Road, Bitterne, Southampton SO18 6TG Tel: 023 8044 9162 Fax: 023 8039 9742 — MB BS 1986 Lond.

WALTERS, Alun James (retired) Roseland, Poltimore, Exeter — MRCS Eng. LRCP Lond. 1949; BDS Lond. 1943; LDS RCS Eng. 1942. Prev: Dent. Surg. W. Eng. Sch. For Partially Sighted, Exeter.

WALTERS, Anita Sian c/o 44 Landor Avenue, Killay, Swansea SA2 7BP — MB ChB 1992 Bristol; BSc (Physiol.) Bristol 1988.

WALTERS, Anna Ellen 24 Prenton Hall Road, Birkenhead CH43 0RA — BM BCh 1990 Oxf.; BA (Hons.) Oxf. 1987; FRCS Ed. 1994. Specialist Regist. (Plastic Surg.)Norf. & Norwich Univ. Hosp. Prev: SHO (Plastic) Qu. Mary's Univ. Hosp. Lond.; SHO (Gen. Surg. & A & E) Hammersmith Hosp. Lond.; SPR Plastics Addenbrookes.

WALTERS, Anne Marisia Wessex Renal Unit, St. Mary's Hospital, Milton Road, Portsmouth PO3 6AD; 18 Park Crescent, Emsworth PO10 7NT — MB ChB 1982 Glas.; MD Glas. 1994; FRCS Eng. 1986; FRCS Ed. 1986; FRCS Glas. 1986. Cons. Gen. & Transpl. Surg. Portsmouth Hosps. NHS Trust. Prev: Lect. (Surg.) Univ. Camb.; Career Regist. W. Yorks.; Research Fell. (Gastroenterol.) Mayo Clinic Mayo Grad. Sch. Med. Mi., USA.

WALTERS, Antony Mayford House Surgery, Boroughbridge Road, Northallerton DL7 8AW Tel: 01609 772105 Fax: 01609 778553; 25 South Parade, Northallerton DL7 8SG Email: antony.walters@btinternet.com — MB ChB 1983 Liverp.; Dip. In Travel Medicine Glasgow 1999; Dip. Health Econ. Aberd 1990. (Liverp.) Princip. Gen. Pract., N.allerton, N. Yorks; Mem. N. Yorks. LMC. Socs: Internat. Soc. Travel Med. Prev: Team Doctor for Ford World Rally Team (2000); GP Ceduna, S. Australia (1988-1989); SHO (A & E) N. Manch. Gen. Hosp. (1984).

WALTERS, Audrey Marguerite Bedgrove Surgery, Brentwood Way, Aylesbury HP21 7TL Tel: 01296 330330 Fax: 01296 399179; 18 Coombe Avenue, Wendover, Aylesbury HP22 6BX Tel: 01296 623230 — MB BS 1982 Lond.; MRCGP 1986; DRCOG 1985. (St. Mary's)

WALTERS, Brian Tennant (retired) 43 Bennett Drive, Hove BN3 6US — LRCP LRCS Ed. LRFPS Glas. 1949. Prev: Resid. Med. Off. Profess. Orthop. Unit Roy. Infirm. Edin.

WALTERS, Carolyn Clare 15 Barnard Road, Leigh on Sea SS9 3PH — BM 1994 Soton.; DRCOG 1998; DFFP 1998. (Southampton) Salaried Rotating Gen. Practitioner, C/o S. Essex Health Auth. Arcadia Ho., The Drive, Brentwood. Prev: SHO (O & G) S.end Hosp.; GP Regist., N. St. Med. Care Rainsford; SHO Paediat. S.end Hosps.

WALTERS, Catherine Charlotte (retired) 4 Parsonage Close, Stratford-Sub-Castle, Salisbury SP1 3LP — MB ChB Bristol 1949.

WALTERS, Catrin Mallt Child Development Centre, Ormskirk District General Hospital, Wigan Road, Ormskirk L39 2JW Tel: 01695 598959 Fax: 01695 583028; 49 Menlove Avenue, Cauderstones, Liverpool L18 2EH — MB ChB 1977 Liverp.; DRCOG 1979; DCH 1983; MRCP (UK) 1992. (Liverpool) Cons. Community Paediat. W. Lancs. NhS Trust Ormskirk; Med. Off. (Paediat. A & E) Alderhey Hosp. Socs: MRCPCH.

WALTERS, Constance (retired) 89 Regent Road, Leicester LE1 6YG Tel: 0116 256 4141 — MB BCh 1924 Wales; BSc Wales 1921, MB BCh 1924. Prev: Asst. Ophth. Leicester Roy. Infirm. & Sch. Clinics Leicester Co.

WALTERS, Professor Dafydd Vaughan Department of Child Health, St. George's Hospital Medical School, Cranmer Terrace, London SW17 0RE Tel: 020 8725 5973 Fax: 020 8725 2858 Email: dwalters@sghms.ac.uk — MB BS 1971 Lond.; BSc (Physiol.) Lond. 1968; FRCP Lond. 1988, M 1974; FRCPCH 1997. (Univ. Coll. Lond.) Prof. Child Health St. Geo. Hosp. Med. Sch. Lond. Socs: Eur. Soc. Paed. Res.; Sec. Assoc. Clin. Profs. Paediat.; Dep. Chairm. of Exec. Comm.. Physiol. Soc. Prev: Reader & Hon. Cons. Paediat. Univ. Coll. Lond.; MRC Trav. Fell. CVRI Univ. Calif. Med. Centre San Francisco, USA.

WALTERS, Daniel Desmond Dept. of Paediatrics, Bronglais General Hospital, Aberystwyth SY23 1ER Tel: 019 7062 3131 Fax: 019 7063 — MB BCh 1966 Wales; MSc Lond. 1975; FRCP Lond. 1996; MRCP (UK) 1973; FRCPCH 1997; DCH Eng. 1969. Cons. Paediat. Bronglais Gen. Hosp. Aberystwyth. Prev: Sen. Regist. (Paediat.) Oxf. RHA; Regist. W.m. Hosp. Lond.; Research Asst. Middlx. Hosp. Lond.

WALTERS, David Paul Flanders Field, Brook St, Fovant, Salisbury SP3 5JB Tel: 01722 714896 Email: david.walters1@virgin.net — LMSSA 1981 Lond.; MD Lond. 1992, MB BS 1982; MRCP (UK) 1986; FRCP 1997. Cons. Phys. Salisbury Dis. Hosp. Socs: Brit.

Diabetic Assn. (Med. & Scientif. Sect.); Brit. Geriat. Soc. Prev: Sen. Regist. (Gen. & Geriat. Med.) Oxf.; BDA Research Fell. Poole Gen. Hosp.; Regist. Rotat. (Med.) Soton. & Salisbury.

WALTERS, Elizabeth Anne Child & Family Consultation Service, The Royal London Hospital, Whitechapel, London E1 1BB Tel: 020 7377 7390 Fax: 020 7247 3699; 39 Willow Road, Hampstead, London NW3 1TN — MB ChB 1972 Glas.; MRCPsych 1984. Cons. Child Psychiat.The Roy. Lond. Hosp. Whitechapel. Prev: Cons. Child Psychiat. Pk. Hosp. for Childr. Oxf.

WALTERS, Ewan Glyndwr ICN Pharmaceuticals, Mallard House, Peregrine Business Park, Gomm Road, High Wycombe HP13 7DL Tel: 01494 444555 Fax: 01494 473398; 1A Juniper Drive, High Wycombe HP12 3LT — MB ChB 1979 Bristol; BSc Bristol 1979. Med. Dir. ICN Pharmaceut. High Wycombe. Prev: Regist. (Med. Biochem.) Univ. Hosp. Wales Cardiff.

WALTERS, Frances Judith Vale Pleasant, Silverdale, Newcastle ST5 6PS — MB BS 1983 London; MB BS 1983 London.

WALTERS, Mrs Frances Mary The Medical Centre, 377 Stamfordham Road, Westerhope, Newcastle upon Tyne NE5 2LH Tel: 0191 286 9178 Fax: 0191 271 1086; Lane End House, Main St, Corbridge NE45 5LE Tel: 0143 463 2281 — MB ChB 1965 Glas. (Glas.) Br. Med. Off. N.d. Red Cross; Chairm. New. LMC. Socs: BMA & Brit. Med. Pilots Assn. Prev: Regtl. Med. Off. 101 Fd. Regt. RA(V); Ho. Surg. Good Hope Hosp. Sutton Coldfield; Ho. Phys. Newc. Gen. Hosp.

WALTERS, Francis James Hamilton (retired) Meadow View Cottage, Whitcombe Manor, Whitcombe, Dorchester DT2 8NY Tel: 01305 250430 — MB BS Lond. 1941; MD Lond. 1948; FRCP Lond. 1973, M 1947; MRCS Eng. LRCP Lond. 1941. Prev: Chest Phys. St. Peter's Hosp. Chertsey.

WALTERS, Francis James MacDonald Anaesthetic Department, Frenchay Hospital, Bristol BS16 1LE Tel: 0117 970 2020 Fax: 0117 957 4414 Email: frank.walters@north-bristol.swest.nhs.uk; Parson's Well, Littleton-on-Severn, Bristol BS35 1NR Tel: 01454 412531 Fax: 0870 162 3992 Email: frank_walters@compuserve.com — MB BChir Camb. 1970; MA Camb. 1971; FFA RCS Eng. 1974. (Univ. Coll. Hosp.) Cons. Anaesth. Frenchay Hosp. Bristol. Socs: Assn. Anaesth.; (Past Pres.) Plastic Surg. & Burns Anaesth.; Europ. Acad. Anasthesia - Senator. Prev: Lect. (Anaesth.) Univ. Soton.; Clin. Fell. (Anaesth.) Hosp. Sick Childr. Toronto, Canada; Ho. Surg. Univ. Coll. Hosp. Lond.

WALTERS, Gavin St. James Hospital, Beckett St., Leeds LS9 7 Tel: 0113 243 3144; 53 High Street, Crofton, Wakefield WF4 1NG — MB ChB 1990 Leeds; MRCP (UK) 1993; FRCOphth 1996. SHO (Ophth.) St. Jas. Hosp. Leeds. Prev: SHO (Renal Med.) St. Jas. Hosp. Leeds; SHO Rotat. (Med.) Killingbeck Hosp. Leeds; Ho. Off. (Surg.) Huddersfield Roy. Infirm.

WALTERS, Gerald Ernest (retired) Pine Trees, Forest Road, Grantown-on-Spey PH26 3JL — MB 1949 Calcutta. Prev: Med. Off. Brit. Honduras.

WALTERS, Giles Desmond 34 Trent Road, Nottingham NG2 4FH Email: gilesw@rivernet.com.au — MB ChB 1990 Ed.; BA Camb. 1987; MRCP (UK) 1993. Specialist Regist. (Renal Med.) Leic. Gen. Hosp. Prev: Regist. Rotat. (Renal) Leicester Gen. Hosp.; SHO Rotat. (Gen. Med.) Lothian.; SHO (Gen. Med.) Falkirk & Dist. Roy. Infirm.

WALTERS, Glyn (retired) Rockhurst, Burwash, Etchingham TN19 7HW Tel: 01435 882525 — MB BS 1949 Lond.; MRCGP 1961; MRCS Eng. LRCP Lond. 1949. Prev: Ho. Surg. Lond. Hosp.

WALTERS, Glyndwr (retired) 4 Parsonage Close, Stratford-Sub-Castle, Salisbury SP1 3LP — MD Bristol 1958, MB ChB 1949; FRCP Lond. 1971, M 1952; FRCPath 1970, M 1963. Prev: Cons. Chem. Pathol. Bristol Roy. Infirm.

WALTERS, Helen Mary Queenswood Surgery, 223 London Road, Waterlooville PO8 8DA Tel: 01705 263491 Email: helen.walters@gw.nm-ha.sweet.nhs.uk; Rivendell, Hill House Hill, Liphook GU30 7PX Tel: 01428 751969 Email: charles.walters@which.net — MB ChB 1989 Leic.; DRCOG 1993; Dip Health Managem Keele 1996. (Leicester University) GP Waterlooville; Primary Care Med. Adviser N. & Mid Hants HA; PCG Bd. Mem.

WALTERS, Huw Llewellyn 34 Alleyn Road, Dulwich, London SE21 8AL — MB BCh 1966 Wales; FRCR 1978; DMRD Eng. 1975.

WALTERS, James Howard Parsons Well, The Village, Littleton-upon-Severn, Bristol BS35 1NR — MB BS 1998 Lond.

WALTERS, Joanne Tel: 01482 667108 Fax: 01482 665090 — MB ChB 1988 Sheff.; MRCP (UK) 1992; MRCGP 1995. (Sheffield) Clin. Med. Off. (Family Plann.) E. Yorks. Prev: Clin. Asst. Diabetes/Endocrinol.

WALTERS, John Christopher 4 The Old School, Whiteshill, Stroud GL6 6AB — MB ChB Ed. 1965; DO Eng. 1974.

WALTERS, John Duncan, OStJ, Surg. Capt. RN Retd. (retired) Two Ways, 30 St John's Road, Cosham, Portsmouth PO6 2DR Tel: 01705 376599 — MB BS 1951 Lond.; DPH 1959; MFOM RCP Lond. 1979; MFCM 1974; DIH Soc. Apoth. Lond. 1956. Prev: Cons. Pub. Health Med. St. Mary's Hosp. Portsmouth.

WALTERS, John Nicholas Whitfield, 26 Station Approach, Shepperton TW17 8AL Tel: 01932 231003 Email: nickwalters@medix-uk.com — MB BCh 1978 Wales; MSc 1997; MLCOM 1997; MRCGP 1987; DRCOG 1983; DA (UK) 1981; Dip Musculoskel Med. 1997. (Welsh Nat. Sch. Med.) Civil. Med. Practitioner Defence Med. Servs. Train. Centre Aldershot; Private Pract. Osteop. & Orthop. Med. Socs: Fell. Roy. Soc. Med.; BMA. Prev: Squadron Ldr. RAF Med. Br.; Ships Surg. P & O Steam Navigation Co.; Surg. Lt. Cdr. RN.

WALTERS, Katherine Rachel Dept of Primary Care Sciences, Royal Free & University College London Medical School, Archway Campus Holborn Union Building Highgate Hill, London N19 5NF Email: k.walters@ucl.ac.uk — BM BS 1992 Nottm.; BMedSci (Hons.) Nottm. 1990; DRCOG 1996; DFFP 1996; DCH RCP Lond. 1995; MRCGP 1997. (Nottm.) Clin. Lect. Primary Care UCL; GP Asst. Lond. Socs: Mem. BMA; Fell.Roy.Soc.Med. Prev: Reg.Lond.Academ.Train.Scheme.

WALTERS, Mark Ian 24 Hayward Close, Walkington, Beverley HU17 8YB — MB ChB 1988 Sheff.; MRCP (UK) 1992.

WALTERS, Martin David Stewart St. Mary's Hospital, South Wharf Road, London W2 1BL — MB BChir 1977 Camb.; MRCP (UK) 1982. Sen. Lect. St. Mary's Hosp. Med. Sch. & Hon. Cons. Paediat. St. Mary'sHosp. Lond.

WALTERS, Mary Elizabeth (retired) 2 Dollar Street, Cirencester GL7 2AJ Tel: 01285 2953 — MRCS Eng. LRCP Lond. 1948; BSc Lond. 1942; LLCO 1968. Prev: Clin. Asst. (Physical Med.) P.ss Margt. Hosp. Swindon.

WALTERS, Matthew Robertson 98 Southbrae Drive, Glasgow G13 1TZ — MB ChB 1994 Glas.

***WALTERS, Melanie Jane** 91 Jacoby Place, Priory Road, Edgbaston, Birmingham B5 7UW — MB ChB 1998 Birm.

WALTERS, Melvyn Terence Department of Rheumatology, Latilla Building, Royal Sussex County Hospital, Eastern Road, Brighton BN2 5BE Tel: 01273 696955 Ext: 4630 Fax: 01273 673466; Hundred Steddle Barn, Brighton Road, Woodmancote, Henfield BN5 9RT — MB ChB 1975 Manch.; DM Soton. 1989; FRCP Lond. 1993; MRCP (UK) 1979; DCH RCP Lond. 1981. (Manchester) Cons. Rheum. Roy. Sussex Co. Hosp. Brighton.

WALTERS, Morgan De Parys Medical Centre, 23 De Parys Avenue, Bedford MK40 2TX Tel: 01234 350022 Fax: 01234 213402 — MB BCh 1986 Wales.

WALTERS, Nigel Stewart Helmsley Medical Centre, Carlton Road, Helmsley, York YO62 5HD Tel: 01439 770288 Fax: 01439 771169 Email: nigel.walters@gp-b82068.nhs.uk; 4 Flatts Lane, Wombleton, York YO62 7RU Tel: 01751 431827 — MB BS 1971 Lond.; BSc (Hons. Pharmacol.) Lond. 1968; DObst RCOG 1975.

WALTERS, Pamela Mary Bethel Villa, Llannon, Llanelli SA14 8JW — MB BCh 1993 Wales.

WALTERS, Patricia Elizabeth Forge Road Surgery, Forge Road, Southsea, Wrexham LL11 5RR Tel: 01978 758311 Fax: 01978 752351 — MB ChB 1978 Manch. GP Wrexham.

WALTERS, Patricia Lynne Lane End House, Main St., Corbridge NE45 5LE — MB ChB 1995 Glas.

WALTERS, Peter John 16 Chaldon Green, Basingstoke RG24 8YS Tel: 01256 471979 — MB BS 1985 Lond.; DCH RCP Lond. 1991; DRCOG 1991.

WALTERS, Philip John Waterloo House Surgery, Waterloo House, 42-44 Wellington Street, Millom LA18 4DE Tel: 01229 772123; Wood House, The Hill, Millom LA18 5HG — MB ChB 1983 Liverp. Prev: SHO (Radiother. & Geriat.) Cumbld. Infirm. Carlisle.

WALTERS, Richard Bryn 6 Netherfield Road, Somersall, Chesterfield S40 3LS Tel: 01246 568518 — MB BS 1992 Lond.; MRCGP 1996; Cert. Prescribed Equiv. Exp. JCPTGP 1996; DFFP

WALTERS

1996; DRCOG 1994. (St. Geo. Hosp. Med. Sch.) Prev: Trainee GP N. Gwent VTS.

WALTERS, Richard Jon Llewellyn 18 Frensham Walk, Farnham Common, Slough SL2 3QG Tel: 01753 646380 — MB BS 1993 Lond.; MRCP (Lond.) 1996; BSc Lond. 1992. Research Regist. Dept. Neurol. St Mary's Lond. Prev: SHO (Med.) St. Mary's Lond.

WALTERS, Richard Lewis General Hospital, Rothwell Road, Kettering NN16 8UZ; Cartref, Grafton Underwood, Kettering NN14 3AA — MB BS 1965 Lond.; FRCP Lond. 1971. Cons. Phys. (Geriat. & Gen. Med.) Kettering Health Dist.

WALTERS, Mr Robert Frederick Cardiff Eye Unit, University Hospital of Wales, Cardiff CF4 1XW Tel: 029 2074 3862 — MB BS 1982 Lond.; BSc (Hons.) Aberd. 1971; DO RCS Eng. 1986; FRCS Eng. 1986; FRCOphth 1988. (Roy. Free Hosp. Sch. Med.) Cons. Ophth. Univ. Hosp. Wales Cardiff. Socs: BMA; Roy. Soc. Med. Prev: Sen. Regist. (Ophth.) Soton & Portsmouth HAs; Sen. Regist. Moorfields Eye Hosp. Lond.

WALTERS, Roger Daniel 6A Netherby Drive, Pollokshields, Glasgow G41 5JA — MB BS 1990 Lond.

WALTERS, Roger Owen Child Health Loddon NHS Trust, North Hampshire Hospital, Aldermaston Road, Basingstoke RG24 9NA Tel: 01256 314798 Fax: 01256 314796; 2 Vyne Meadow, Sherborne St. John, Basingstoke RG24 9PZ Tel: 01256 850457 Fax: 01256 850457 Email: roger.walters@argonet.co.uk — MB BS 1963 Lond.; FRCP Lond. 1987; MRCP (UK) 1975; DTM & H Eng. 1971; FRCPCH; DCH Eng. 1970. (St. Thos.) Cons. Paediat. & Med. Dir. Loddon NHS Trust. Socs: BMA. Prev: Cons. Paediat. Camb. Milit. Hosp. Aldershot; Cons. Paediat. Brit. Milit. Hosp., Hong Kong.

WALTERS, Sarah Department of Public Health & Epidemiology, Medical School, University of Birmingham, Birmingham B15 2TT Tel: 0121 414 6760 Fax: 0121 414 7788 Email: s.walters@bham.ac.uk — MB BS 1985 Lond.; BSc (Hons.) Surrey 1980; MRCP (UK) 1988; MFPHM RCP (UK) 1992; FRCP (UK) 1999; FFPHM (UK) 1999. (St. George's Hosp. Med.Sch.) Sen. Lect. (Pub. Health & Epidemiol.) Univ. Birm. Med. Sch. Socs: Brit. Thorac. Soc. Prev: Lect. (Pub. Health Med.) Univ. Birm. Med. Sch.; Trainee (Pub. Health Med.) W. Midl. RHA; Regist. (Chest Med.) E. Birm. Hosp.

WALTERS, Sarah Elizabeth 14 Green Leys, St Ives, Huntingdon PE27 6SB — BChir 1996 Camb.

WALTERS, Simone Melinda Bridewell Cottage, Christchurch, Coleford GL16 7NR — MB BCh 1991 Wales.

WALTERS, Susan Jayne 34 Alleyn Road, Dulwich, London SE21 8AL — MB BCh 1966 Wales.

WALTERS, Miss Tena Kerry Hotham House, 14 Hotham Close, Swanley BR8 7UX Tel: 01322 662165 Fax: 01322 614116; Tel: 020 8308 3253 Fax: 020 8308 3228 — MB BS 1983 Lond.; MS Lond. 1994; FRCS Eng. 1987. (St. Barth.) Cons. (Gen. Surg./BrE.)/Lead Clinician Qu. Mary's Sidcup. Socs: RSM; Assn. Surg.; BASO. Prev: SHO Rotat. (Surg.) Kent & Canterbury Hosp; Sen. Regist. (Gen. Surg.) Welsh Train. Scheme; Lect. (Gen. Surg.) Profess. Unit Med. Coll. St. Bart. Hosp. Lond.

WALTERS, Trevor James (retired) 7 Ffrwd Vale, Neath SA10 7BA — MRCS Eng. LRCP Lond. 1935; MRCS Eng., LRCP Lond. 1935.

WALTERS, Walter Duncan Alloa Health Centre, Marshill, Alloa FK10 1AQ Tel: 01259 212088 Fax: 01259 724788; 18 Kellie Place, Alloa FK10 2DW Tel: 01259 215186 — MB ChB 1968 Glas. Socs: BMA. Prev: Ho. Off. (Surg.) Ballochmyle Hosp.; Ho. Off. (Med.) Roy. Alexandria Infirm.

WALTERSON, Laurence Imlach (retired) Craiglea, Biggar ML12 6RE Tel: 01899 221542 — MB ChB 1957 Aberd.

WALTHAM, Matthew 169 Kennington Road, London SE11 6SF — BChir 1994 Camb.

***WALTHER, Axel** Accident & Emergency Department, Addenbrooke's Hospital, Cambridge CB2 2QQ Tel: 01223 245151; Gluckstrasse 11, Hanau 63452, Germany — BM BCh 1997 Oxf.; MA (Hons.) Camb. 1994.

WALTHEW, Richard Ian 13 Priory Road, Wilmslow SK9 5PS — MB BCh 1992 Wales; BSc (Hons) Wales 1989; MRCGP 1996. (Univ. Wales Coll. Med. Cardiff)

WALTON, Alexander Munro Medical Centre, West Elloe Avenue, Spalding PE11 2BY Tel: 01775 725530 Fax: 01775 766168; Stonegate Lodge, Love Lane, Spalding PE11 2PE Tel: 01775 724759 Fax: 01775 766168 — MB BS Durh. 1965; MRCGP 1975. (Newc.) Police Surg. Spalding; Med. Off. Johnson Hosp. Spalding; Clin. Asst. Welland Hosp. Spalding. Prev: SHO, Ho. Phys. & Ho. Surg., Newc. Gen. Hosp.; Demonst. (Anat.) Edin. Univ.

WALTON, Anna Marie 17 Rees Drive, Coventry CV3 6QF — BM 1995 Soton. SHO Rotat. (Gen. Med.) P.ss Margt. Hosp. Swindon. Prev: RMO (Emerg. Med.) Fremantle Hosp., Australia.

WALTON, Anthony William James 18 Glebe Drive, Rayleigh SS6 9HJ — MB BCh 1973 Witwatersrand; T(GP) 1991.

WALTON, Bryan 9 Loom Lane, Radlett WD7 8AA Tel: 01923 853923 Fax: 01923 853570; 9 Loom Lane, Radlett WD7 8AA Tel: 01923 853923 Fax: 01923 853570 — MB BS Lond. 1966; FFA RCS Eng. 1970. (Lond. Hosp.) Hon. Cons. Anaesth. & Intens. Care Roy. Lond. Hosp. Trust.; Adviser. Anaesth/Intens. care P.ss Grace Hosp. Prev: Cons. Anaesth. Roy. Lond. Hosp.

WALTON, Caroline Elizabeth Richmond Medical Centre, 462 Richmond Road, Sheffield S13 8NA Tel: 0114 239 9291 Fax: 0114 253 0737; 256 Dobcroft Road, Ecclesall, Sheffield S11 9LJ Tel: 0114 262 1851 — MB ChB 1982 Sheff.; MRCGP 1986.

WALTON, Catherine Elizabeth 23 Regent Street, Kettering NN16 8QG — MB BS 1986 Lond.

WALTON, Christopher 23 Ferriby High Road, North Ferriby HU14 3LD — MB BS 1974 Newc.; FRCP Lond. 1993; MRCP (UK) 1977. Cons. Phys. (Gen. Med., Diabetes & Endocrinol.) Hull Roy. Infirm. Socs: Brit. Diabetic Assn. Prev: Sen. Regist. (Med.) Hull & Leeds Rotat. Hull Roy. Infirm. & Leeds Gen. Infirm.; Tutor (Med.) Manch. Roy. Infirm.; Regist. (Med. & Diabetes) St. Jas. Univ. Hosp. Leeds.

WALTON, Christopher James Fulwell Medical Centre, Ebdon Lane, off Dene Lane, Sunderland SR6 8DZ Tel: 0191 548 3635 — MB ChB 1980 Birm.

WALTON, David Alan Parkgate Health Centre, Park Place, Darlington DL1 5LW Tel: 01325 462396; 242 Carmel Road N., Darlington DL3 9TG — MB BS 1960 Durh. (Durh.) Socs: BMA. Prev: Squadron Ldr. RAF Med. Br.; SHO & Ho. Surg. (O & G) Newc. Gen. Hosp.

WALTON, David John O'Colmain and Partners, Fearnhead Cross Medical Centre, 25 Fearnhead Cross, Fearnhead, Warrington WA2 0HD Tel: 01925 847000 Fax: 01925 818650; The Cottage, Bellhouse Lane, Grappenhall, Warrington WA4 2SG — BSc (Hons.) Manch. 1981, MB ChB 1984; MRCGP 1989; DRCOG 1987; DCH RCP Lond. 1986. Prev: Trainee GP; SHO (Cas.) Hope Hosp.; SHO (Psychiat.) Bridgewater Hosp.

WALTON, Donald Arthur Douglas Hopwood House, The Vineyard, Lees Road, Oldham OL4 1JN Tel: 0161 633 2988 Fax: 0161 678 6266; The Hawthorns, 154 Turf Pit Lane, Moorside, Oldham OL4 2NE — MB ChB Manch. 1973.

WALTON, Dorothy Patricia Mayday Hospital, Thornton Heath, Croydon CR7 7YE Tel: 020 8401 3000; 3 Hoadly Road, Streatham, London SW16 1AE Tel: 020 8769 1791 — MB BS Lond. 1968; MRCS Eng. LRCP Lond. 1968; FFA RCS Eng. 1974. (Char. Cross) Cons. Anaesth. Mayday Hosp. Thornton Heath. Prev: Regist. (Anaesth.) W.m. Hosp. Lond.; SHO (Anaesth.) St. Geo. Hosp. Lond. & St. Jas. Hosp. Lond.

WALTON, Douglas Ashley Hugh (retired) Sunnybank, Quarry Lane, Allithwaite, Grange-over-Sands LA11 7QJ Tel: 0153 95 32188 — MB 1941 Calcutta; DMRD Eng. 1950. Prev: Cons. Radiol. Rochdale HA.

WALTON, Eileen Elizabeth Ty Mawr Gwyn, Flemingston, Barry CF62 4QJ Tel: 01446 750410 — MB BS 1957 Durh.

WALTON, Ernest Ward, TD (retired) 32 The Green, Norton, Stockton-on-Tees TS20 1DX Tel: 01642 554653 — MD 1957 Durh.; MB BS 1949; FRCPath 1972, M 1963. JP. Prev: Chairm. Exec. Med. Dir., Cleveland Med. Laborat. Ltd.

WALTON, Gail Margaret Littlewick Medical Centre, 42 Nottingham Road, Ilkeston DE7 5PR Tel: 0115 932 5229 Fax: 0115 932 5413; 44 Church Lane, Cossall, Nottingham NG16 2RW — MB ChB 1983 Bristol; MRCGP 1988; DRCOG 1987. Trainee GP Heanor VTS, Derbysh. Prev: SHO (Paediat. & O & G) S. Derbysh. HA.

WALTON, Gary Michael Appleby, 93 Knutsford Road, Row of Trees, Alderley Edge SK9 7SH Fax: 01625 584014 — MB ChB 1995 Manch.; MSc Manch. 1994; MDS Manch. 1989; BDS Manch. 1984; FRCS Eng. 1997; FDS RCS Ed. 1989. Lect./Specialist Regist. Oral & Maxillofacial Surg. Univ. Manch. Socs: BMA; Assn. Oral & Maxillofacial Surgs.; Internat. Assn. Oral & Maxillofacial Surgs. Prev:

SHO (Gen. Surg.) Wythenshawe Hosp. Manch.; SHO Orthop. Wythenshawe Hosp. Manch.; Lect. & Hon. Regist. (Oral & Maxillofacial Surg.) Univ. Manch.

WALTON, Heather Ann Stewart The Allport Surgery, Treetops Primary Healthcare Centre, Bridle Road, Bromborough, Wirral CH62 6AR Tel: 0151 328 5630 — MB ChB 1992 Liverp.; DRCOG 1996 Birm. GP; GP The Allport Surg., Treetops Primary Healthcare Centre, Bridle Rd., BromBoro., Wirral. Prev: SHO (Paediat.) Chester; GP/Regist. Neston; SHO (O & G) Wirral.

WALTON, Heather Frances 16 Thorpe Place, Tattershall LN4 9NT Tel: 01526 345956; Tel: 01526 345956 — MB BS 1989 Lond.; MRCGP 1995; DRCOG 1994; DFFP 1994; DCH RCP Lond. 1993.

WALTON, Professor Henry John 38 Blacket Place, Edinburgh EH9 1RL Tel: 0131 667 7811 Fax: 0131 662 0337 — MB ChB 1946 Cape Town; PhD Ed. 1966; MD (Hons.) Tucuman 1992; MD (Hons.) Lisbon 1990; MD (Hons.) Uppsala 1984; MD Cape Town 1954; FRCP Ed. 1968, M 1966; FRCPsych 1971; DPM Lond. 1956. (Cape Town) Prof. Emerit. Psychiat. & Internat. Med. Educat. Univ. Edin.; Edr. Med. Educat. Socs: (Ex-Pres.) Assn. Med. Educat. Europe; (Ex-Pres.) World Federat. Med. Educat. Prev: Prof. Dept. Psychiat. Univ. Edin.; Sen. Regist. Maudsley Hosp. Lond.; Sen. Research Fell. (Psychiat.) Coll. Phys. & Surg. Columbia Univ. NY, USA.

WALTON, Ian James 14 Horseley Heath, Tipton DY4 7QU Tel: 0121 557 2027 Email: ianwalton@btinternet.com — MB BS 1980 Lond.; MRCGP 1986. Hosp. Practitioner in Psychiat., Dudley Relief Clinic; Chair. Tipton Care Organisation PMS Project.

WALTON, Ian Thomas Hallgarth Surgery, Cheapside, Shildon DL4 2HP Tel: 01388 772362 Fax: 01388 774150; Hall Farm, Mordon, Nr. Sedgefield, Stockton-on-Tees TS21 2EY Tel: 01740 623753 — MB ChB 1979 Dundee.

WALTON, Ivan George Department of Medicine of Elderly, Charing Cross Hospital, Fulham Palace Road, London W6 8RF Tel: 020 8846 1564 Fax: 020 8846 1307; 31 Grafton Square, London SW4 0DB — BM BCh 1968 Oxf.; MA Oxf. 1968; FRCP Lond. 1995; MRCP (UK) 1974; DObst RCOG 1976. (Oxf.) Cons. Geriat. Char. Cross Hosp. Lond. Socs: Brit. Geriat. Soc. Prev: GP Teignmouth, Devon.

WALTON, James Hartley 20 Sinah Lane, Hayling Island PO11 0EY — MB BS 1968 Lond.; MRCS Eng. LRCP Lond. 1967; DA Eng. 1979.

WALTON, Jane Catherine 10 Wolds Drive, Farnborough, Orpington BR6 8NS — MB BS 1992 Lond.; BSc (Hons.) Lond. 1991. (St. Mary's Hospital Paddington) Specialist Regist. St. Geo.'s Rotat.

WALTON, Jennifer Margaret 110 Monton Road, Eccles, Manchester M30 9HG — MB ChB 1979 Manch.; DRCOG 1982.

WALTON, Jill Deirdre National Blood Service East Anglia Centre, Long Road, Cambridge CB2 2PT Tel: 01223 548000; Raggles, Noons Folly, Newmarket Road, Royston SG8 7NG Tel: 01763 244616 Email: jdh@raggles.fsnet.co.uk — MB BCh 1965 Witwatersrand; FFA RCS Eng. 1971. (Witwatersrand) Med. Off. Nat. Blood Trans. Serv.

WALTON, John Alexander Walton and Partners, West Street Surgery, 12 West Street, Chipping Norton OX7 5AA Tel: 01608 642529 Fax: 01608 645066; New England, Hastings Hill, Churchill, Chipping Norton OX7 6NA Tel: 01608 658249 Email: jwchippy@aol.com — MB ChB 1975 Cape Town; MRCGP 1982; DRCOG 1981; frcgp 1999. (Cape Town) GP Trainer Chipping Norton; PGC Bd. Mem. N. Ox. & S. N.ants. PCG. Socs: BMA; RCGP. Prev: SHO (GP Linked) Horton Gen. Hosp. Banbury; Med. Supt. St. Matthews Gen. Hosp. Ciskei S. Afr.; SHO (Paediat.) Red Cross Childr. Hosp. Cape Town.

WALTON, John Leaver Leicester Terrace Health Care Centre, 8 Leicester Terrace, Northampton NN2 6AL Tel: 01604 33682 Fax: 01604 233408 — BM BCh 1972 Oxf.; MA, MSc; FRCGP 1997; MRCGP 1977. Prev: SHO N.ampton Gen. Hosp.; Ho. Off. Radcliffe Infirm. Oxf.

WALTON, Lord John Nicholas, TD (retired) 13 Norham Gardens, Oxford OX2 6PS Tel: 01865 512492 Fax: 01865 512495 — MB BS (1st cl. Hons.) Durh. 1945; Hon. FRCP Ed. 1981; Hon. FRCPath 1993; Hon. FRCPsych 1993; Hon. DCL Newc. 1988; Hon. FRCPC 1984; Hon. FACP 1980; Laurea Hon. Causa Genea 1992; Hon. Dr. de l'Univ. Aix-Marseille 1975; DSc Newc. 1972; MD Durh. 1952; Hon. DSc Oxf. Brookes 1994; Hon. DSc Hull 1988; Hon. DSc Leic.

1980; Hon. DSc Leeds 1979; Hon. MD Sheff. 1987; FRCP Lond. 1963, M 1950. Hon. Fell. (Ex-Warden) Green Coll. Oxf. Prev: Pres. Gen. Med. Counc. 1982-89.

WALTON, Jonathan James 34 Newbould Lane, Sheffield S10 2PL — MB ChB 1994 Sheff.

WALTON, Kenneth Robert 7 Leighton Avenue, Pinner HA5 3BW — MB BS 1976 Lond.; MA Camb. 1973; MRCP (UK) 1979.

WALTON, Professor Kenneth Walter William Henry 7 Selly Close, Selly Park, Birmingham B29 7JG Tel: 0121 471 5223 Email: kwaltonb29@hotmail.com — MRCS Eng. LRCP Lond. 1942; PhD Birm. 1954, DSc 1976; MD Lond. 1949, MB BS 1942; FRCPath 1965. (Univ. Coll. Hosp.) Emerit. Prof. Birm. Univ.; Hon. Cons. Birm. AHA (T). Socs: Fell. Roy. Soc. Med.; Path. Soc. Prev: Asst. Pathol. Dept. Morbid Anat. Univ. Coll. Hosp. Med. Sch.; Maj. RAMC, Specialist in Path. Army Path. Serv.

WALTON, Krystyna Floyd Unit for Neurological Rehabilitation, Birch Hill Hospital, Rochdale OL12 9QB Tel: 01706 754240 Fax: 01706 754241 Email: krystyna.walton@exchange.rhc-tr.nwest.nhs.uk — MB ChB 1977 Liverp.; FRCP Lond. 1995; MRCP (UK) 1980; Europ. Dip. Phys. Med. & Rehab. 1995. Cons. Rehabil. Med. Rochdale healthcare NHS Trust; Cons. Rehabil. Med. Highbank Brain Injury Unit, Bury; hon cons in rehab, Salford Roy. Hosp.s NHS Trust. Prev: Sen. Regist. (Rheum. & Rehabil.) NW RHA; Regist. (Neurol.) N. Manch. Gen. Hosp.

WALTON, Linda Margaret 3 Beechwood Terrace, Newport-on-Tay DD6 8JG Tel: 01382 543194 — MB ChB 1974 Liverp.; FFA RCS Eng. 1979. Assoc. Specialist (Anaesth.) Ninewells Hosp. Dundee.

WALTON, Lynda Jane 32 Marton Drive, Wolviston Court, Billingham TS22 5BA Tel: 01642 553770 — BM BS 1996 Nottm.; BMedSci Nottm. 1994. (Nottm.) SHO Paediat. Nottm. Prev: Resid. Med. Off. Qu. Eliz. II Hosp. Brisbane Australia.

WALTON, Margaret Jean 22 Chapel Street, Milborne St Andrew, Blandford Forum DT11 0JP — MRCS Eng. LRCP Lond. 1957; DCH Eng. 1964. Assoc. Specialist (Paediat.) Dorchester & W. Dorset Hosp. Gp. Prev: Res. Med. Off. Odstock Hosp. Salisbury; Paediat. Regist. Bournemouth & E. Dorset Hosp. Gp.

WALTON, Mark Ronald Yorkshire Street, 80 Yorkshire Street, Burnley BB11 3BT Tel: 01282 420141 Fax: 01282 832477 — MB ChB 1983 Leic.

WALTON, Mary Ellen 46 King Georges Road, Pilgrims Hatch, Brentwood CM15 9LD — MB BS 1984 Lond. (Char. Cross) Clin. Med. Off. (Child Health) Mid Essex HA.

***WALTON, Melanie Jane** 239 Hubert Road, Selly Oak, Birmingham B29 6ES — MB ChB 1995 Birm.

WALTON, Michael Robert High House, West Harsley, Northallerton DL6 2DR — MB BS 1969 Lond.; FFA RCS Eng. 1975. Cons. Anaesth. Friarage Hosp. N.allerton. Prev: Anaesth. Regist. Radcliffe Infirm. Oxf.; Sen. Regist. Addenbrooke's Hosp. Camb. & Norf. & Norwich Hosp.

WALTON, Neil Patrick 4 Tower Close, Horsham RH13 7AF — MB BS 1993 Lond.

WALTON, Nicolas 20 Bridgebank Road, Smithybridge, Littleborough OL15 8QU — MB ChB 1988 Leic.

WALTON, Nina Kylie Dorothy — MB ChB 1995 Leic. SPR Anaesth.

WALTON, Paul Robert The Surgery, Cross Road, Sacriston, Durham DH7 6LJ Tel: 0191 371 0232; Ford House, Ford Road, Lanchester, Durham DH7 0SH Tel: 01207 521345 — MB ChB 1977 Manch.; BSc St. And. 1974.

WALTON, Peter Kenneth Henry Playhatch Farmhouse, Foxhill Lane, Playhatch, Reading RG4 9QT — MB BChir 1982 Camb.; MA Camb. 1985; MBA Lond. 1988. Managing Dir. Dendrite Clin. Systems Ltd. Lond. Prev: Sen. Managem. Cons. Internat. Hosps. Gp.; Resid. (O & G) Nat. Guard King Khalid Hosp. Jeddah.

WALTON, Rebecca Sarah High House Farm, West Harsley, Northallerton DL6 2DR — BM BS 1994 Nottm.

WALTON, Richard Stuart Castlecroft Road Surgery, 104 Castlecroft Road, Castlecroft, Wolverhampton WV3 8LU Tel: 01902 761629 Fax: 01902 765660 — MB ChB 1969 Birm.

WALTON, Robert Douglas 56 St Johns Crescent, Clowne, Chesterfield S43 4EB — MB ChB 1977 Manch.

WALTON, Robert John Grove Medical Practice, Shirley Health Centre, Grove Road, Shirley, Southampton SO15 3UA Tel: 023 8078 3611 Fax: 023 8078 3156; 21 Holly Hill, Southampton SO16 7ES

WALTON

Tel: 02380 769847 — MB BS 1968 Lond.; DPhil Oxf. 1979; BSc (Physiol.) Lond. 1965; MRCP (UK) 1972; MRCGP 1985. (King's Coll. Hosp.) Prev: Lect. Univ. Soton.; Fell. Research Univ. Oxf.; Regist. (Med.) Radcliffe Infirm. Oxf.

WALTON, Robert Thompson Bury Knowle Health Centre, 207 London Road, Headington, Oxford OX3 9JA Tel: 01865 761651 Fax: 01865 768559; 24 Staunton Road, Headington, Oxford OX3 7TW — MB BS 1983 Lond.; FRCP 2001; FRCGP 2000; BSc Lond. 1980; MRCP (UK) 1986; MRCGP 1987; DCH RCP Lond. 1986. (St. Geo.) Hon. Sen. Clin. Lect. Socs: Med. Protec. Soc. Prev: SHO (O & G) Ashford Hosp. Middlx.; SHO (Gen. Med.) St. Geo. Hosp. Lond.; Clin. Asst. (Gastroenterol.) Wycombe Gen. Hosp.

WALTON, Sharon Marie 166 Kirkham Road, Freckleton, Preston PR4 1HU — MB BS 1994 Newc.

WALTON, Simon Anthony 157 Chewton Street, New Eastwood, Nottingham NG16 3JR — MB BS 1992 Newc.

WALTON, Simon Murray Walpole House, Cambridge Road, Stansted CM24 8TA Email: s.walty@aol.com — MB BS 1994 Lond.

WALTON, Stephen 14 Whiteadder Way, Isle of Dogs, London E14 9UR — MD 1978 Manch.; MB ChB 1973; MRCP (U.K.) 1976. Cons. Cardiol. Aberd. Roy. Infirm.

WALTON, Stephen Frederick Stockwell Road Surgery, 21 Stockwell Road, Knaresborough HG5 0JY Tel: 01423 867433 Fax: 01423 869633 — BSc (Hons.) (Med. Biochem. Studies) Birm. 1976, MB ChB 1979; MRCGP 1983; DRCOG 1982; DCH RCP Lond. 1982. Prev: Trainee GP Harrogate; SHO Selly Oak Hosp. Birm.

***WALTON, Stephen Robert** Finlow Hill Cottage, Finlow Hill Lane, Over Alderley, Macclesfield SK10 4UG — MB ChB 1995 Sheff.

WALTON, Stuart Michael Department of Obstetrics & Gynaecology, North Tees Health NHS Trust, Stockton-on-Tees TS19 8PE Tel: 01642 617617 Fax: 01642 624203; The Downs, The Spital, Yarm TS15 9EU Tel: 01642 783898 — MB BS 1968 Newc.; MFFP 1993; FRCOG 1985, M 1973. Cons. O & G N. Tees Gen. Hosp. Stockton-on-Tees; Regional Coll. Adviser. Socs: Fac. Fam. Plann. & Reproduc. Health Care (Mem. Train. & Educat. Comm., Convenor for MCQs, Part I MFFP & Chairm. High Specialist Train. Sub-Comm.). Prev: Sen. Lect. (O & G) Wellington Clin. Sch. Med. Wellington, NZ; Lect. (O & G) Univ. Nairobi, Kenya.

WALTON, Susan Elizabeth The Surgery, Cross Road, Sacriston, Durham DH7 6LJ Tel: 0191 371 0232; Ford House, Ford Road, Lanchester, Durham DH7 0SH Tel: 0191 521345 — MB ChB 1979 Manch.; BSc (Med. Sci.) St. And. 1976.

WALTON, Susan Elizabeth Community Health Office, Nuffield Health Centre, Welch Way, Witney OX28 6JQ Tel: 01993 776920; Minster Cottage, Church St, Charlbury, Oxford OX7 3PR Tel: 01608 811096 — MB ChB 1963 Bristol; Dip. Community Paediat. Warwick 1983. (Bristol) Sen. Med. Off. (Child Health & Family Plann.) Oxf. Radcliffe Hosp. NHS Trust. Socs: Brit. Paediat. Assn.; Foundat. Mem. Fac. Community Health; Fac. Family Plann. & Reproduc. Health Care. Prev: Hon. SHO (Paediat.) Radcliffe Infirm. Oxf.; Clin. Med. Off. Harrow Health Dist.; Asst. Sch. Med. Off. Salop CC.

WALTON, Suzanne Joy South Essex Health Authority, Arcadia House, The Drive, Warley, Brentwood CM13 3BE Email: suzanne.walton@sessex-ha.nthames.nhsuk — MB BS 1994 Lond.; MSc 2001 London; BSc 1991 London; MRCPH 1999. (UCMSM) Prev: SpR Paediat. St John's Hosp. Chelmsford; SHO Gt. Ormond St. Hosp.; SHO (Paediat.) P.ss Alexandra Hosp. Harlow Essex.

WALTON, Thomas James 5 Sandfield Close, Scunthorpe DN17 2XE Email: tjwalton@doctors.org.uk — BM BS 1998 Nottm.

WALTON, Thomas James Hartley Department Rheumatology, Dulwich Hospital, East Dulwich Grove, London SE22 8PT Tel: 020 7737 4000; 20 Sinah Lane, Hayling Island PO11 0EY — MB BS 1992 Lond.; MRCP. (Royal Free) SPR Rheum. and Gen. Med.

WALTON, Wendy Jane Marden Medical Practice, 25 Sutton Road, Shrewsbury SY2 6DL Tel: 01743 241313; Holm House, Station Road, Pontesbury, Shrewsbury SY5 0QY Tel: 01743 792714 Email: wendy-jane@doctors.org.uk — MB BS 1982 Lond.; MRCGP 1987; DRCOG 1985; DA Eng. 1984. p/t GP.

WALTON-SMITH, Peter Russell (retired) 6 The Birches Close, North Baddesley, Southampton SO52 9HL Tel: 01703 733089 — MB BChir Camb. 1958; MA Camb. 1958; DObst RCOG 1959. Prev: GP Soton.

WALUUBE, David Daniel Falijala William Harvey Hospital, East Kent Hospitals NHS Trust, Kennington Road, Ashford TN24 0LZ Tel: 01233 633331 Ext: 86041 Fax: 01233 616043; 6 Pennine Way, Downswood, Maidstone ME15 8YG — MB ChB 1970 Makerere; DA 1985 UK; 2002 MRCA.

WALWYN, Jane Louise 51 Clovelly Avenue, Grainger Park, Newcastle upon Tyne NE4 8SE Tel: 0191 272 0889 — MB BS 1990 Newc.; MRCGP 1994; DRCOG 1993. Trainee GP N.umbria VTS.

WALZMAN, Michael George Elliot Hospital NHS Trust, College St., Nuneaton CV10 7DJ — MB 1974 Dub.; MD 1985 Dub.; MB BCh BAO 1974; MRCOG 1979; FRCOG 1995. (Trinity College, Dublin) Clin. tutor Geo. Eliot Hosp Nuneaton.

WAMBEEK, Nicholas Dominic 24 Chestnut Road, Horley RH6 8PF Tel: 01293 786704 — MB BS 1985 West. Australia.

WAMUO, Ihuoma Alozua 50 Cheviot Gardens, London NW2 1QE — MB BS 1988 Ibadan; MRCP (UK) 1994.

WAN, Mr Andrew Chung Ting Flat 79, Consort Rise House, Buckingham Palace Road, London SW1W 9TB — MB BCh BAO 1991 NUI; FRCSI 1996; LRCP &S I 1991. Specialist Regist. N.W. Thames; Research Fell. Socs: Roy. Soc. of Med. - Fell.

***WAN, Ka-Ming Bettina** 13 Eleanor Close, Rotherhithe, London SE16 6PA Tel: 020 7237 2174 Email: bwan@mcmail.com — MB BS 1996 Lond.

WAN, Sidney Kam Hung Ystrad Wrallt, Nantgaredig, Carmarthen SA32 7LG — MB BCh 1979 Wales; MRCP (UK) 1982; FRCR 1989.

WAN HO HEE, Horatio Tameside General Hospital, Ashton-under-Lyne OL6 9RW Tel: 0161 331 5151 Fax: 0161 331 5222; 2nd Floor, 16 Nicholas Street, Manchester M1 2TR Tel: 0161 228 2548 — MSc (Clin. Pharmacol.) Manch. 1977; MB BS Hong Kong 1969; FRCP Lond. 1992; MRCP (UK) 1975. (Hong Kong) Cons. Phys. Geriat. Med. Tameside Gen. Hosp. Ashton-under-Lyne. Socs: BMA. Prev: Lect. & Hon. Sen. Regist. (Geriat. Med.) Univ. Manch.; Med. Off. (Gen. Med.) Nethersole Hosp. Hong Kong; Regist. (Med.) S.E. Kent Health Dist.

WAN HUSSEIN, Husswan Yasmin 74 Humphrey Road, Manchester M16 9DF; 16 Monton Avenue, Eccles, Manchester M30 9HS — MB ChB 1997 Manch.

WANAS, Taha Mahmoud Department Genitourinary Medicine, New Cross Hospital, Wednesfield Road, Wolverhampton WV10 0QP Tel: 01902 644835 Fax: 01902 644830; 61 Sabrina Road, Wightwick, Wolverhampton WV6 8BP Tel: 01902 380424 Fax: 01902 762203 — MB BCh Cairo 1964; DS Cairo 1967; MFFP 1995; FRCOG 1991, M 1976. (Univ. Cairo) Cons. Phys. (Genitourin. Med.) Newcross Hosp. Wolverhampton & Hon. Sen. Clin. Lect. Univ. Birm. Med. Sch.; Cons. Phys. (Genitourin Med.) Sir Robt. Peel Tamworth Staffs. Socs: Med. Soc. Study VD; Counc. Brit. Erectile DysFunc. Soc.; Pres. Midl. Soc. Genitourin. Med. Prev: Sen. Regist. (Genitourin. Med.) N.. RHA; Regist. (O & G) Bradford & Worthing HAs.

WAND, Mr Jonathan Sinclair Consultant Orthopaedic Surgeon, Cotswold Nuffield Hospital, Talbot Road, Cheltenham GL51 6QA Tel: 01242 273245 Fax: 01242 250031 Email: jon.wand@virgin.uk; Evington Lodge, Coombe Hill, Gloucester GL19 4AS Tel: 01242 680504 — MB BS 1977 Lond.; BSc Lond. 1974, MB BS 1977; FRCS Eng. 1983. Cons. Orthop. Surg. E. Glos. NHS Trust Cheltenham. Socs: Fell. BOA. Prev: Sen. Regist. (Orthop.) W.m. & Univ. Coll. Hosp. Lond.; MRC Train. Fell. (Bone Dis. Research Gp.) N.wick Pk. Hosp. Middlx.; Lect. (Anat.) St. Bart. Med. Coll. Hosp. Lond.

WAND, Laurence Geoffrey Rowland, TD (retired) The Homestead, 19 Gidea Close, Gidea Park, Romford RM2 5NP Tel: 01708 745268 — MB BChir Camb. 1947; MA Camb. 1947; MRCS Eng. LRCP Lond. 1946; FRCGP 1992, M 1967. Prev: Col. late RAMC (V).

WAND, Penelope Jane Marie Curie Centre, Caterham, Harestone Drive, Caterham CR3 6YQ Tel: 01883 832600 Fax: 01883 832633; Glebe House, Big Common Lane, Bletchingly, Redhill RH1 4QE Tel: 01883 744571 Fax: 01883 341992 Email: jwand@mariecurie.org — MB BS 1972 Lond.; FRCP Lond. 1995; MRCP (UK) 1977; FRCR 1987. Cons. Palliat. Med. & Med. Dir. Marie Curie Centre Caterham.; Hon. Cons. E. Surrey Healthcare Trust. Prev: Sen. Regist. Roy. Marsden Hosp.; Regist. (Med.) St. Luke's Hosp. Guildford.

WANDER, Adam Paul Ampthill Square Medical Centre, 217 Eversholt St., London NW1 1DR Tel: 020 7387 0420 Fax: 020 7387 6161 — MB ChB 1992 Ed.; BSc 1990; MRCGP 1997; DRCOG 1996; DFFP 1996. (Edin) GP; GP Tutor. Socs: MPS.

WANDER, Mr Georges Charles Andrew Bishops Place Surgery, 1 Bishops Place, Paignton TQ3 3DZ Tel: 01803 559421 Fax: 01803 663381 — MB BChir 1979 Camb.; FRCS Glas. 1985. Prev: Regist. (Gen. Surg.) Torbay Hosp.; SHO (O & G) W. Suff. Hosp. Bury St. Edmunds.

***WANDLESS, Anna Louise** 23 Moorend Crescent, Leckhampton, Cheltenham GL53 0EJ — BM BCh 1998 Oxf.; BM BCh Oxf 1998.

WANDLESS, Gillian Mary Brookfield, Church Lane, East Norton, Leicester LE7 9XA Tel: 0116 259 8300 Email: wandless@btinternet.com — MB BS 1967 Lond.; MRCS Eng. LRCP Lond. 1967; MFFP 1993; DObst RCOG 1969. (Roy. Free) p/t Cons. Family Plann. & Reproduc. Health Care Leics. and Rutland Healthcare(NHS)trust. Prev: SCMO Fosse Health NHS Trust Leics.; Clin. Asst. (Genitourin. Med.) Leicester Roy. Infirm. Trust; Sessional Med. Off. Univ. Leicester Stud. Health Serv.

WANDLESS, Irene 19 Meldon Way, High Shincliffe, Durham DH1 2PZ — MD 1981 Newc.; MB BS 1972; MRCP (U.K.) 1975.

WANDLESS, John Godfrey Brookfield, Church Lane, East Norton, Leicester LE7 9XA — BSc (Hons. Physiol.) Lond. 1965, MB BS 1968; MRCS Eng. LRCP Lond. 1968; FFA RCS Eng. 1973. (Roy. Free) Cons. Anaesth. Leicester Roy. Infirm. & Leicester Gen. Hosp. Prev: Sen. Regist. (Anaesth.) Lond. Chest Hosp. & Middlx. Hosp. Lond.; Regist. (Anaesth.) Hosp. Sick Childr. Gt. Ormond St. Lond.

WANDLESS, Roger John c/o Mrs A. M. Wandless, 25 Parkside Avenue, Cockermouth CA13 0DR — MB ChB 1989 Birm.; MRCP (UK) 1993.

WANDLESS, Stephen 5 Gosmore Road, Hitchin SG4 9AN — MB BS 1977 Lond. (The Lond. Hosp. Whitechapel)

WANENDEYA, Nina Yayeri Hinchingbrooke Hospital, Hinchingbrooke Park, Huntingdon PE29 6NT; 9 thorpe meadows, Peterborough PE3 6GA — MB ChB 1990 Aberd.; FRCS Eng. 1996; FRCS Ed. 1996. Specialist Regist. (Gen. Surg.) Anglia Region; Regist. Surg. PeterBoro. Dist. Hosp. Socs: Affil. Fell. Assn. Surg. GB & Irel. Prev: SHO (Gen. Surg.) Lister Hosp. Stevenage; Regist. (Surg.) Hinchingbrooke Hosp. Huntingdon.

WANG, Gordon Ka Pun Yateley Health Centre, Yateley GU46 7LS; 63 Willowmead Close, Woking GU21 3DN — MB BS 1988 Lond.

WANG, Ian (retired) 12 Croftbank Avenue, Bothwell, Glasgow G71 8RT Tel: 01698 852249 — MB ChB 1944 Ed.; FRCP Ed. 1963, M 1946; FRCP Glas. 1972, M 1969. Prev: Cons. Phys. Vict. Infirm. Glas.

WANG, Jayson Ee Hur Apartment 291, Metro Central Heights, 119 Newington Causeway, London SE1 6DB — MB ChB 1995 Aberd.

WANG, Mr Man Kin 25 Rothamsted Avenue, Harpenden AL5 2DN Tel: 01582 762233 — MB 1963 Camb.; BChir 1962; FRCOphth 1994; FRCS Eng. 1969; DO Eng. 1967. (Camb. & Univ. Coll. Hosp.) Cons. Ophth. Luton & Dunstable Hosp. & Mid Herts Hosp. Gp. Socs: Assn. Eye Research & Oxf. Ophth. Congr. Prev: Sen. Regist. & Lect. Univ. Dept. Manch. Roy. Eye Hosp.; Research Asst. (Chem. Path.) Univ. Coll. Hosp. Med. Sch. Lond.; SHO Eye Dept. Univ. Coll. Hosp. Lond.

WANG, Mou Yee Ellen 1 Debden Close, Royal Park Gate, Kingston upon Thames KT2 5GD — MB BCh 1986 Wales; FRCS (Ophth.) Ed. 1998.

WANG, Rong Zeng Chinese Medical Centre, 150 Station Road, Finchley Central, London N3 2SG Tel: 020 8343 4393 — MD Kweiyang, China 1950. Socs: Chinese Med. Assn.; BMA. Prev: Dir. Surgic. Dept. Chui Yang Lin Hosp. Peking, China; Clin. Asst. (Urol.) Dept. Hammersmith Hosp. Lond.; Regist. Wessex Regional Transpl. Unit St. Mary's Hosp. Portsmouth.

WANG, Stephen Tao-Sing c/o Mr & Mrs M Wang, 5 Fairmead Walk, Waterlooville PO8 9AL — MB BS 1992 Lond.

WANG, Timothy Wai-Ming Department of Clinical Biochemistry, Frimley Park Hospital, Portsmouth Road, Frimley, Camberley GU16 7UJ Tel: 01276 604118 Fax: 01276 604924 Email: tim.wang@fph-tr.nhs.uk — MB ChB 1983 Sheff.; PhD Open Univ. 1996; MRCPath 1998. (Sheffield) Cons. Clin. Biochem.ry. Frimley Pk. Hosp. Surrey and Roy. Surrey Co. Hosp.; Sen. Lect. Metab. Endocrine, Nutrit.al Med. Univ, Surrey.

WANG EE JEN, Mr Wilson Flat 6, Gloucester House, Worcester Place, Oxford OX1 2SB — MB BS 1988 Lond.; FRCS Glas. 1995. Girdlestone Memor. Schol.. Nuffield Dept. Orthop. Surg. Univ. Oxf.

WANGER, Karen Marie 127 City Road, Chester Green, Derby DE1 3RR — MB ChB 1992 Birm.

WANI, Ali Mohmad 21 Medeswell, Orton Malborne, Peterborough PE2 5PA — MB BS 1967 Jammu & Kashmir.

WANI, Mushtaq Ahmad Morriston Hospital NHS Trust, Morriston, Swansea SA6 6NL Tel: 01792 703246 — MB BS 1974 Jammu & Kashmir; MRCP (UK) 1986; MRCP(I) 1987. (Govt. Med. Coll. Srinagar Kashmir) Cons. Phys. (Gen. & Geriat. Med.) Morriston Hosp. Swansea. Prev: Sen. Regist. Chelsea & W.m. Hosp. Lond.; Regist. (Gen. Med.) Jas. Paget Hosp. Yarmouth; SHO (Gen. Med.) Chase Farm Hosp. Enfield & Llandudno Gen. Hosp.

WANI, Mustaq Ahmad South Hornchurch Clinic, Southend Road, Rainham RM13 7XR Tel: 01708 557601 Fax: 01708 555945 — MB BS 1973 Jammu & Kashmir; MB BS 1973 Jammu & Kashmir.

WANIGARATNE, Dayananda Sirisena HM Prison Woodhill, Tattenhoe St., Milton Keynes MK4 4DA Tel: 01908 501999 Fax: 01908 505417 — MB BS Ceylon 1969; DPM Eng. 1980. Sen. Med. Off., Head of Health Care Home Off. (Prison Med. Serv.). Socs: Civil Serv. Med. Gp Comm. 1998/99. Prev: Sen. Med. Off. HMP Pentonville & Holloway; Med. Off. Durh. Prison; Regional Med. Off. (Malariol.) Matara, Sri Lanka.

WANKE, Miriam Eva Andrea 16 West Park Road, Smethwick, Smethwick B67 7JJ — State Exam Med 1990 Mainz.

WANKLYN, Peter David Kimbolton 5 Prospect Place, Horsforth, Leeds LS18 4BW — MB ChB 1987 Birm.; MB ChB (Hons.) Birm. 1987; MRCP (UK) 1990. (Birm.) Cons. Geriat. Leeds Gen. Infirm. Gt. Geo. St. Leeds. Socs: BMA & Brit. Geriat. Soc. Prev: SR Elderly Med. St. James Leeds; SR Med. St. James Leeds; SR Med. LGI, Leeds.

WANKOWSKA, Heather Claire Department of Sexual Health, Clinic 11, Ipswich Hospital NHS Trust, Heath Road, Ipswich IP4 2EH Tel: 01473 703264 Fax: 01473 703263; Combs Hall, Combs, Stowmarket IP14 2EH Tel: 01449 676859 — MB BS 1974 Lond.; MRCGP 1978; DFFP 1995; Dip. Ven. Soc. Apoth. Lond. 1986. (Univ. Coll. Hosp.) Hon. Cons. (Sexual Health) Ipswich Hosp. Socs: BMA; MSSVD; AGUM. Prev: Clin. Asst. (Genitourin. Med.) E. & W. Suff. AHA's; Trainee GP Ipswich VTS; Ho. Off. (Med. & Surg.) Warneford Hosp. Leamington Spa.

WANKOWSKI, Adam Franciszek Combs Ford Surgery, Combs Lane, Stowmarket IP14 2SY Tel: 01449 678333 Fax: 01449 614535; Combs Hall, Combs, Stowmarket IP14 2EH — MB BS 1974 Lond.; MRCGP 1978.

WANNAN, Gary John Cotswold House, Sutton Hospital, Sutton SM2 5NF Tel: 020 8296 4456 — MB ChB 1991 Ed.; BSc (Med. Sci.) Ed. 1989; MRCGP 1995; DCH Glas. 1994; MRC Psych 1998. (Edin) Specialist Regist. Child Psychiat.St Geo.s Hosp Lond.

WANSA, Mr Simon 138 The Water Gardens, London W2 2DE — MB BCh BAO 1984 NUI; FRCS Ed. 1991; LRCPI & LM, LRCSI & LM 1984.

WANSBROUGH-JONES, Mark Harding St. Georges Hospital Medical School, Cranmer Terrace, London SW17 0RE Tel: 020 8725 5828 Fax: 020 8725 3487 Email: wansbrou@sghms.ac.uk; 7 Highview Road, London SE19 3SS Tel: 020 8653 7968 — MB BS 1969 Lond.; MSc (Immunol.) Lond. 1976, MB BS 1969; FRCP Lond. 1987, MRCP (UK) 1972. (St. Thos.) Cons. & Sen. Lect. (Infec. Dis.) St. Geo. Hosp. Lond. Prev: Regist. (Med.) Hammersmith Hosp. Lond.; Lect. Liver Unit King's Coll. Hosp. Lond.

WANT, Ernest (retired) 1 The Pines, Cow Lane, Bramcote, Nottingham NG9 3BB — MB ChB 1936 Bristol. Prev: Ho. Phys. Roy. Gwent Hosp. Newport.

WANTMAN, Adam Craig 27 Shenley Hill, Radlett WD7 7AU — MB BS 1993 Lond.

WAPSHAW, Mr Henry (retired) 5 Whittingehame Drive, Glasgow G12 0XS Tel: 0141 339 7705 — MD 1947 Glas.; ChM 1954, MB ChB 1933; FRCS Glas. 1962; FRCS Ed. 1940.

WAPSHAW, Jean Angus 5 Whittingehame Drive, Glasgow G12 0XS Tel: 0141 339 7705 — MB ChB 1942 Glas.; MB ChB (Commend.) Glas. 1942. Assoc. Specialist Med. Computing, Glas. Blood Pressure Clinic. Prev: Med. Asst. Blood Pressure Clinic Glas.;

WARAICH

Asst. Biochem. Dept. Univ. Glas.; Ho. Phys. Roy. Infirm. Glas. & Hosp. Sick Childr. Glas.

WARAICH, Manprit Kaur 117 Southend Road, Stanford-le-Hope SS17 7AA — MB BS 1991 Lond.

WARAICH, Mohammed Khalid 234 St Saviours Road, Leicester LE5 3SH — MB ChB 1998 Leic.; MB ChB Leic. 1998.

WARBEY, Victoria 26 Belsize Square, London NW3 4HU Tel: 020 7794 0194 Email: vikki@warbey.demon.co.uk — MB BS 1996 Lond.; MA 1997. (Camb.) Med. SHO Rotat. at Hillingdon & Harefield Hosp.

WARBRICK-SMITH, David Warbrick-Smith and Partners, The Moat House Surgery, Beech Close, Warboys, Huntingdon PE28 2RQ Tel: 01487 822230 Fax: 01487 823721 Email: moat@wardoc.demon.co.uk; 4 Meadow Close, Hemingford Grey, Huntingdon PE28 9DN Tel: 01480 493648 Email: moat@wardoc.demon.co.uk — MB BS 1972 Lond.; DObst RCOG 1976; DA Eng. 1978. (Middlx.)

WARBURTON, Anne Louise Red Lion Surgery, 86 Hednesford Road, Cannock WS11 2LB Tel: 01543 502391; Cranmore, Longden Common Lane, Longden, Shrewsbury SY5 8AQ Tel: 01743 718513 — MB ChB 1985 Manch.; BSc Manch. 1982; MRCGP 1990; DFFP 1995; DRCOG 1990; Cert. Family Plann. JCC 1989. Socs: St. Paul; BMA. Prev: Asst. GP Worthen, Shrops. & Long Stratton; GP Princip. Newport, Shrops.

WARBURTON, Carol Jill 2 Lavender Close, Rugby CV23 0XB — MB ChB 1993 Birm.; MRCGP 1998. (Univ. Birm.) GP Princip. p/t, Rugby.

WARBURTON, Christopher James Aintree Chest Centre, University Hospital Aintree, Lower Lane, Liverpool L9 7AL Tel: 0151 525 5980 Fax: 0151 529 2847; The Hollies, 62 Chorley Road, Hilldale, Parbold, Wigan WN8 7AS Tel: 01257 462662 — MB ChB 1987 Manch.; FRCP 2001 (Lond.); MD Manch. 1996; MRCP (UK) 1990; AFOM RCP Lond. 1993. (Manch.) Cons. Phys. (Respirat. & Gen. Med.) Univ. Hosp. Aintree Liverp.; Clin. Lect. Univ. Liverp.; Hon. Fell. Univ. Salford. Socs: Brit. Thorac. Soc. Prev: Sen. Regist. (Thoracic Med.) Fazakerley Hosp. Liverp.; Sen. Regist. (Thoracic Med.) Freeman Hosp. Newc. u. Tyne.

WARBURTON, David John Robert Lutterworth Health Centre, Gilmorton Road, Lutterworth LE17 4EB Tel: 01455 553531; Wychwood, Dunton Lane, Ashby Parva, Lutterworth LE17 5HX Tel: 01455 209633 — MB ChB 1963 Manch.; MRCS Eng. LRCP Lond. 1963; DObst RCOG 1965. (Manch.)

WARBURTON, Elizabeth Anne Box 83 Neuroscience, Addenbrokes Hospital, Cambridge CB2 2HB Tel: 01223 217844 Email: eaw23@medschl.cam.ac.uk; 26 High Street, Bottesford, Scunthorpe DN17 2RE Tel: 01724 868372 — MB BS 1987 Lond.; DM 1998 Oxf.; MA 1986 Oxf.; BA Oxf. 1984; MRCP (UK) 1990. Cons. In Stroke Med. Addenbrookes Camb.; PPP Mid Career Award 2000-2002. Socs: Brit. Assn. of Stroke Phys.s. Prev: Regist. (Med.) Epsom & Char. Cross Hosp. Lond.; SHO Rotat. (Med.) N.wick Pk. Hosp. Harrow.; Research Regist. Char. Cross & Hammersmith Hosp. Lond.

WARBURTON, Ian Richard Ovoca, 460 Didsbury Road, Heaton Mersey, Stockport SK4 3RT Tel: 0161 432 2032 Fax: 0161 947 9689 — MB ChB 1979 Manch.; MRCGP 1983.

WARBURTON, Michael Charles 112 Stanford Avenue, Brighton BN1 6FE — MB BS 1982 Lond.; MBA 1999 Imperial College; MRCGP 1990; DRCOG 1987. Clin. Director, Modernisation Team, Brighton Healthcare; Dir. Mid Sussex Out of Hours CoOperat.; Med. Off. Brighton Rugby Club. Prev: Chairm. Mid Sussex PCG; Chairm. Prof. Exec. Mid Sussex PCT.

WARBURTON, Richard Croft Cottage, Hollins Lane, Forton, Preston PR3 0AB — MB BS 1964 Lond. Aviat. Med. Specialist Brit. Aerospace Warton.

WARBURTON, Richard Alistair The Health Centre, Rydal Road, Ambleside LA22 9BP Tel: 015394 32693; Croft Cottage, Hollins Lane, Forton, Preston PR3 0AB — MB BS 1990 Newc.

WARBURTON, Thomas Harold Martin (retired) 5 Bavant Road, Brighton BN1 6RD Tel: 01273 552294 Email: mrwarbur94@aol.com — MB BS (Hnrs.) Lond. 1953; MRCS Eng. LRCP Lond. 1953; DObst RCOG 1955. Prev: GP Peacehaven.

WARD, Adam Anthony Department of Musculosketal Medicine, Royal London Homoeopathic Hospital, Great Ormond Street, London WC1N 3HR Tel: 020 7837 8833 Fax: 020 7833 7229; 41 Frankfield Rise, Tunbridge Wells TN2 5LF Tel: 01892 525799 — MB BS 1972 Lond.; Dip. Med. Ac.; MSc Lond. 1978; MRCGP 1982; Dip. Orth. Med. Paris 1983; MFHom 1984. (Westm.) Clin. director & Cons. Phys. Orthopaedic & Musculosketal Med.Roy. Lond. Homoeoп. Hosp.; Examr. for Diploma in Musculosketal Med. Soc. of Apoth. of Lond. Socs: (Counc.) Brit. Inst. Musculosketal Med.; Brit. Med. Acupunct. Soc.; Fell. Fac. Homoeoр. Lond. Prev: Phys. (Orthop. Med.) Hotel Dieu, Paris, France; Lect. & Hon. Sen. Regist. (Epidemiol.) W.m. Hosp. Med. Sch. Lond.; Edr. BRd.way.

WARD, Adrian Denis The Surgery, Lorne Street, Lochgilphead PA31 8LU Tel: 01546 602921 Fax: 01546 606735 — MB ChB 1984 Leeds. GP Lochgilphead, Argyll. Prev: SHO (A & E) Huddersfield Roy. Infirm.; SHO (Chest Med.) Pontefract Gen. Hosp.; SHO (Anaesth.) Airedale Gen. Hosp. Keighley.

WARD, Adrian Lawrence Alloa Health Centre, Marshill, Alloa FK10 1AQ Tel: 01259 212088 Fax: 01259 724788 — MB ChB 1990 Aberd.; BMedBiol. (Hons.) Aberd. 1990; MRCGP 1994; DCH RCP Lond. 1993; DRCOG 1993; DFFP 1993; Cert. Family Plann. JCC 1992. (Aberd.) GP Alloa; Med. Off. United Glass Alloa; Fact. Med. Off. Weir Pumps Alloa. Socs: Roy. Coll. Gen. Pract.; BMA.

WARD, Alan Blakey 21 Wadsworth Park, Branthwaite, Workington CA14 4SR — MB BS 1942 Durh.; FFA RCS Eng. 1954; DA Eng. 1950. (Univ. Durh.) Socs: Assn. Anaesths. Prev: Cons. Anaesth. W. Cumbld. Gp. Hosps.

WARD, Alan Edward 41 Parklands Drive, North Ferriby HU14 3EY — MB ChB Ed. 1964; BSc (Hons.) Ed. 1961; FFPM RCP (UK) 1993. (Ed.)

WARD, Alan Geoffrey The Surgery, Marlpits Road, Honiton EX14 2 NY Tel: 01404 41141 Fax: 01404 46621; 10 Glen Farm Crescent, Honiton EX14 2GX Tel: 01404 549487 Email: agward@ntlworld.com — MB ChB 1981 Leic.; MRCGP 1986; Cert. Family Plann. JCC 1985; DRCOG 1985; DCH RCP Lond. 1985. (Leicester) Socs: Devon & Exeter Med. Soc. Prev: Trainee GP Plymouth VTS.

WARD, Alan Robert Godfrey Watford Road Surgery, 16 Watford Road, Crick, Northampton NN6 7TT Tel: 01788 822203 Fax: 01788 824177 — MRCS Eng. LRCP Lond. 1970. (St. Mary's) Prev: Ho. Surg. Gulson Hosp. Coventry; Ho. Phys. & Regist. (Cas.) St. Cross Hosp. Rugby.

WARD, Alastair Hugh Ernespie, Longdogs Lane, Ottery St Mary EX11 1HX Tel: 01404 812621 — MB BS 1987 Lond.; MRCP (UK) 1991; MRCGP 1995; DRCOG 1994; DCH RCP Lond. 1994; DTM & H 1998. (Guy's Hosp. Med. Sch. Lond.) Med. Co-Ordinator Farah, Afghanistan. Prev: Med. Off. i/c Muthale Miss. Hosp., Kenya; Trainee GP Poole VTS; Regist. (Gen. & Renal Med.) Roy. Sussex Co. Hosp. Brighton.

WARD, Alexandra Monica Vivienne Bacon House, Greatworth, Banbury OX17 2DX — MB BS 1992 Lond.; MRCP (UK) 1995.

WARD, Alison Mary 49A Canynge Road, Clifton, Bristol BS8 3LH — BMed 1992 Newc., NSW.

WARD, Allan Edward Abbey Health Centre, East Abbey Street, Arbroath DD11 1EN Tel: 01241 872692; 15 Monkbarns Drive, Arbroath DD11 2DS — MB ChB 1980 Dundee; MRCP (UK) 1983; MRCGP 1986; DRCOG 1985.

WARD, Andrea Susan Wadlerslade Surgery, Walderslade, 194 King Street, Hoyland, Barnsley S74 9LL Tel: 01226 743221 Fax: 01226 741100; 5 Paterson Croft, Stocksbridge, Sheffield S36 1JP — MB ChB 1989 Sheff.; MRCGP 1993; DFFP 1994; DCH RCP Lond. 1991. Socs: Christ. Med. Fell.sh.

WARD, Andrew South Wigston Health Centre, 80 Blaby Road, South Wigston, Leicester LE18 4SE Tel: 0116 210 0486; 16 Brookhouse Avenue, Leicester LE2 0JE Tel: 0116 210 0486 — MB ChB 1992 Leic.; DRCOG. (Leicester) GP Princip.

WARD, Andrew James Markham House, 140 Wyke Road, Weymouth DT4 9QR — MB BS 1998 Lond.

WARD, Angela Claire Elizabeth 35 Foads Lane, Ramsgate CT12 5JP — MB BS 1985 Lond.

WARD, Ann Maureen (retired) Cherwell, Meadway, Berkhamsted HP4 2PN Tel: 01442 864968 — MB BS Lond. 1957; DObst RCOG 1958. Prev: Ho. Off. (Obst.) Kingsbury Matern. Hosp. Lond.

WARD, Anne Josephine Mary 24 Ashleigh Road, Anerley, London SE20 7YW Tel: 020 8778 7005 — MB BCh BAO 1986 Dub.; MB BCh Dub. 1986; MD 1994; MRCPI 1988; MRCPSYCH 1993. Cons. (Psychother.) Maudsley Hosp. Lond.

WARD, Mr Anthony The Marlborough Surgery, George Lane, Marlborough SN8 4BY — MB ChB 1969 Bristol; FRCS Eng. 1974; FRACS 1975.

WARD, Anthony Barrington, Maj. RAMC Retd. North Staffordshire Rehabilitation Centre, The Haywood, High Lane, Burslem, Stoke-on-Trent ST6 7AG Tel: 01782 835721 Fax: 01782 838721 Email: abward@msn.com; Bearstone Farm, Bearstone, Market Drayton TF9 4HG Tel: 01630 647135 Fax: 01630 647135 Email: abwand@msn.com — MB ChB 1975 Dundee; BSc St. And. 1972; FRCP Lond. 1994; FRCP Ed. 1992; MRCP (UK) 1981. Cons. & Sen. Lect. (Rehabil. Med.) N. Staffs. Hosp. Stoke-on-Trent; Sen. Lect. Postgrad. Med. Sch. Univ. Keele. Socs: (Pres.) Brit. Soc. Rehabil. Med; Brit. Soc. Rheum.; (Pres.) Europ. Bd. Phys. Med. & Rehabil. Prev: Cons. Rheum. & Rehabil. Qu. Eliz. Milit. Hosp. Lond.; Sen. Regist. (Rheum.) St. Thos. Hosp. Lond.; Regtl. Med. Off. 50th Missile Regt. RA.

WARD, Mr Anthony Joseph Department of Orthopaedic Surgery, Frenchay Hospital, Frenchay Park Road, Bristol BS16 1LE Tel: 0117 970 1212 Fax: 0117 957 2335; Fax: 0117 962 9776 Email: ajwardorth@aol.com — BM BS 1981 Nottm.; BMedSci. (Hons.) Nottm. 1979; FRCS Eng. 1986. (Nottingham University) Cons. Orthop. Surg. Frenchay Hosp. Bristol. Socs: Brit. Orthop. Assn.; Brit. Trauma Soc.; Brit. Hip Soc. Prev: Sen. Regist. (Orthop. Surg.) Bristol & Plymouth S. W.. RHA.

WARD, Anthony Milford Department of Immunology, PO Box 894, Sheffield S5 7YT Tel: 0114 271 5552 Fax: 0114 261 9893 Email: amw@immqas.org.uk; 19 Kerwin Drive, Dore, Sheffield S17 3DG Tel: 0114 236 6996 — MB BChir Camb. 1966; MA Camb. 1966; MRCS Eng. LRCP Lond. 1963; FRCPath 1982, M 1970. (St. Bart.) Hon. Cons. Clin. Immunol. Sheff. HA; Reader (Immunol.) Acad. Div. Med. Univ. Sheff.; Dir. Supraregional Specific Protein Ref. Unit.; Cons. Clin. Immunol. Rotherham DGH NHS Trust; Cons. Clin. Immunol. Doncaster & MexBoro. NHS Trust. Socs: Assn. Clin. Pathols. & Brit. Soc. Immunol.; Amer. Assoc. Clin. Chem. Prev: Lect. (Path.) Sheff. Univ.; Regist. (Clin. Path.) United Sheff. Hosps.; Resid. (Clin. Path.) St. Geo. Hosp. Lond.

WARD, Arthur John (retired) Hawthorne, Owler Park Road, Ilkley LS29 0BG — BSc (Hons. Physics) Durh. 1943; MB ChB Leeds 1952; FFR 1958; DMRT Eng. 1955. Sen. Clin. Lect. Univ. Leeds; Cons. Radiother, Leeds AHA (T). Prev: Regist. Radiother. Centre Leeds.

WARD, Barbara 9 Arno Vale Road, Woodthorpe, Nottingham NG5 4JH Tel: 0115 926 7552 — MB BS 1946 Lond.; DCH Eng. 1958; DA Eng. 1954. (Lond. Sch. Med. Wom.) Sen. Med. Off. (Community Med.) Nottm. AHA (T). Socs: BMA. Prev: Res. Anaesth. Roy. Free Hosp. & Luton & Dunstable Hosp.; Ho. Phys. Roy. Hosp. Richmond.

WARD, Barbara-Anne St Saviours Surgery, Merick Road, Malvern Link, Malvern WR14 1DD Tel: 01684 572323 Fax: 01684 891067 — MB BS 1981 Lond.; DRCOG 1983.

WARD, Barnaby James Essex Lodge, 85 Chaveney Road, Quorn, Loughborough LE12 8AB — BChir 1995 Camb.

WARD, Benjamin Charles Henry (retired) 12 Bickerton Road, Headington, Oxford OX3 7LS Tel: 01865 761859 — MRCS Eng. LRCP Lond. 1944; DMR Lond 1946. Prev: Radiol. Qu. Mary's Hosp. Childr. & St. Helier's Hosp. Carshalton.

WARD, Brian Hermitage Green Lodge, Hermitage Green Lane, Winwick, Warrington WA2 8SJ Tel: 01925 26164 — MB ChB 1950 Manch.; FRCPsych 1972; DPM Leeds 1958. (Manch.) Cons. Psychiat. Winwick Hosp. Warrington. Socs: BMA. Prev: Med. Supt. Winwick Hosp.; Asst. Sen. Med. Off. Leeds RHB; Area Psychiat. RAMC.

WARD, Carol Patricia Royal South Hampshire Hospital, Brinton Terrace, off St Mary's Road, Southampton Tel: 02380 634288; 7 Dale Close, Littleton, Winchester SO22 6RA Tel: 01962 883185 — MB BS 1980 Lond.; MRCP (UK) 1983; MRCGP 1986; DRCOG 1985. (Middlx.) Staff Grade Radiother. & Oncol. Roy. S. Hants. Hosp. Prev: GP Asst. Stockbridge; Trainee GP Lechlade; SHO (Gen. Med. & A & E) P.ss Margt. Hosp. Swindon.

WARD, Caroline Sandra Nutt Radiology Department, Kingston Hospital NHS Department, Galsworthy Road, Kingston upon Thames KT2 7QB Tel: 020 8546 7711; 2 Coombe Rise, Kingston upon Thames KT2 7EX Tel: 020 8942 0222 — MB BCh BAO 1977 Dub.; FRCPI 1992; MRCPI 1980; FRCR 1985; DMRD RCR 1984; DCH Univ. Coll. Dub. 1981. (Trinity Coll. Dub.) Cons. Radiol. Kingston Hosp. Kingston u. Thames. Socs: Roy. Coll. Radiol.; Brit. Inst. of Radiol.; Roy. Coll. Phys.s of Irel. Prev: Cons. Radiol. Ashford Hosp. Middlx.; Sen. Regist. (Radiol.) St. Geo. Hosp. Lond.

WARD, Catherine Joyce 61 Hallam Grange Road, Sheffield S10 4BL — MB ChB 1980 Sheff.; DCH RCP Lond. 1987.

WARD, Catherine Sarah Flat 4, 13 Lavender Gardens, Battersea, London SW11 1DH Tel: 020 7350 2722 — MB BS 1994 Lond.; MRCGP 2001; BSc 1991 (Hons.) Lond.; DRCOG 1999; MRCP 1999. GP Assoc., SLOVTS, Lond.

WARD, Catherine Theresa 80 Old Street, Hill Head, Fareham PO14 3HN — MB BS 1997 Lond.

WARD, Cecilia Caroline Grange Park, Moy, Dungannon BT71 7EQ Tel: 018687 84238 Fax: 01868 784238 — MB BCh BAO Belf. 1957; DCH RCP Lond. 1961; MFFP 1993. SCMO (Family Plann.) Craigavon Area Hosp. & S. Tyrone Hosp.; Assoc. Specialist (Paediat.) S. Tyrone Hosp.; Occupat. Health Phys. S. Tyrone Hosp. & St. Lukes Hosp. Armagh. Socs: Ulster Med. Soc.; (Ex-Chairm.) N. Irel. Family Plann. Doctors Assn.; Brit. Menopause Soc. Prev: SHO Roy. Belf. Hosp. for Sick Childr. & Roy. Vict. Hosp. Belf.; Ho. Off. Roy. Vict. Hosp. Belf.

WARD, Chandan 30 Ewell Downs Road, Ewell, Epsom KT17 3BW — MB ChB 1966 Aberd. (Aberd.) Prev: Research Off. (Ophth.) Amsterdam Univ.

WARD, Christine Joan Garden Flat, 33 Cathcart Road, London SW10 — MB BS 1982 Lond.

WARD, Christopher Regional Cardiac Centre, Wythenshawe Hospital, Southmoor Road, Manchester M23 9LT Tel: 0161 946 2390; 72 Manchester Road, Wilmslow SK9 2JY Tel: 01625 523378 — MD 1975 Dundee; MB ChB St. And. 1964; FRCP Lond. 1993; FRCP Ed. 1982; MRCP (UK) 1969. (St. And.) Cardiol. Wythenshawe Hosp. Manch.

WARD, Christopher Albert The Clayton Medical Centre, Wellington Street, Clayton le Moors, Accrington BB5 5HU Tel: 01254 383131 Fax: 01254 392261 — MB ChB 1974 Dundee; BSc St. And. 1971. Clin. Asst. (Cardio.) DHA Represent.

WARD, Christopher Charles Brockwell Centre, Brockwell Centre, Northumbrian Road, Cramlington NE23 1XZ Tel: 01670 392700 Fax: 01670 392701; 17 Yarmouth Drive, Westwood Grange, Cramlington NE23 1TL Tel: 01670 732211 Email: chrisward@brockmed.freeserve.co.uk — MB BS 1978 Newc.

WARD, Professor Christopher David University of Nottingham, Rehabilitation Research Unit, Derby City General Hospital, Uttoxeter Road, Derby DE22 3NE Tel: 01332 625680 Fax: 01332 625681 Email: c.d.ward@nottingham.ac.uk; 82 Edward Road, West Bridgford, Nottingham NG2 5GB Tel: 0115 981 2238 — MD 1983 Camb.; MB BChir 1977; FRCP (1992). Head Div. of Rehabil. & Ageing Univ. of Nottm.; Hon. Cons. (Rehabil. Med. & Neurol.) S. Derbsh. Hosps. NHS Trust. Socs: Brit. Soc. Rehab. Med.; Assn. Brit. Neurols.; Fell. Roy. Soc. Med. Prev: Prof. (Rehabil. Med.) Univ. Nottm.; Sen. Lect. Univ. Dept. Rehabil. & Cons. Neurol. Soton Gen. Hosp.; Clin. Lect. Dept. Neurol. Oxf. Univ.

WARD, Christopher John The Surgery, 54 Thorne Road, Doncaster DN1 2JP Tel: 01302 361222 — MB ChB 1982 Leeds.

WARD, Christopher Lane Charles 67 Coronation Road, Bristol BS3 1AS Tel: 0117 966 9724 — MB BS 1967 Lond.; MA Oxf. 1961; MRCP (UK) 1970; DCH Eng. 1975; DTM & H Liverp. 1975. (Middlx.) Hosp. Pract. Roy. Hosp. for Sick Childr. Bristol. Prev: Cas. Med. Off. Middlx. Hosp. Lond.; Regist. W. Middlx. Hosp. Isleworth.

WARD, Mr Christopher Margrave 15 Cumberland Road, Kew, Richmond TW9 3HJ Tel: 020 8948 4990 Fax: 020 8332 7770 — MB BS Lond. 1966; MA Lond. 1992, BSc 1962; FRCS Eng. 1972; MRCS Eng. LRCP Lond. 1965. (Lond. Hosp.) Hon. Cons. Plastic & Reconstrvc. Surg. Char. Cross Hosp. & W. Middlx. Hosp. Socs: Brit. Assn. Plastic Surgs.; Brit. Soc. Surg. Hand.; Acad. of Experts. Prev: Cons. (Plastic Surg.) Char. Cross Hosp.; Peter Buckler Vis. Prof. Univ. Washington Sch. of Med. 1998; Sen. Regist. (Plastic Surg.) Hammersmith Hosp. Lond.

WARD, Christopher Raymond 66 Woodlea, Middlesbrough TS8 0TX — BM BS 1985 Nottm.

WARD, Crispian Stanley (retired) 41 Southlands Drive, Huddersfield HD2 2LT Tel: 01484 429090 Fax: 01484 429090 — MB BS 1949 Lond.; FFA RCS Eng. 1956; DA Eng. 1956. Hon. Cons. Anaesth. Huddersfield Hosp. Prev: Regist. (Anaesth.) United Liverp. Hosps. & Croydon Hosp. Gp.

WARD

WARD, Cyril (retired) Corner Bungalow, 1 Rugby Lane, Stretton-on-Dunsmore, Rugby CV23 9JH Tel: 02476 542772 — LRCP LRCS 1952 Ed.; LRCP LRCS Ed. LRFPS Glas. 1952; FFA RCS Eng. 1960; DA Eng. 1957. Cons. Anaesth. Coventry Gp. Hosps. Prev: Anaesth. Regist. Hexham Gen. Hosp.

WARD, Daniela Antonia 71 Dan-y-Bryn Avenue, Radyr, Cardiff CF15 8DQ — MB ChB 1990 Ed.; MRCGP 1994. Clin. Asst. Addic. Unit WhitCh. Hosp. Cardiff. Prev: SHO (A & E) Wrexham Maelor NHS Hosp.; SHO (Psychiat.) Roy. Cornhill Hosp. Aberd.; SHO (Med. & Paediat.) Ninewells Hosp. Dundee.

WARD, David Anthony 3 Greenfield road, Newcastle upon Tyne NE3 5TN Tel: 0191 219 5023 Fax: 0191 219 5022 — MB ChB 1987 Sheff.; MRCPsych 1995. Cons. Adolesc. Psychiat.

WARD, Mr David Anthony Department of Orthopaedics, Kingston Hospital, Galsworthy Road, Kingston upon Thames KT2 7QB Tel: 020 8546 7711 Fax: 020 8355 2982 Email: david.ward@kh-tr.sthames.nhs.uk; Weylands, Pyrford Road, West Byfleet KT14 6QY Tel: 01932 348282 Fax: 01932 336676 — MB BS 1985 Lond.; FRCS (Orth.) 1994; FRCS Eng. 1989; FRCS Ed. 1989. Cons. Orthop. & Trauma Kingston Hosp. Kingston-upon-Thames. Socs: Fell. BOA; Roy. Soc. Med.; Brit. Trauma Soc. Prev: Cons. Orthop. & Trauma Qu. Mary's Univ. Hosp. Lond.; Sen. Regist. (Orthop.) Char. Cross Hosp. Lond.; Regist. Rotat. (Orthop.) St. Geo. Hosp. Lond.

WARD, David Arthur 6 St Wilfrids Road, Bessacarr, Doncaster DN4 6AA — MB ChB 1978 Manch.; MRCP Lond. 1980; FRCR 1985. Cons. Radiol. Doncaster Roy. Infirm. Prev: Regist. (Radiol.) Gen. Infirm. & St. Jas. Hosp. Leeds; Regist. (Gen. Med.) Doncaster Roy. Infirm.

WARD, Mr David Christopher The Friarage Hospital, Northallerton DL6 1JG — MB BS 1973 Bangalore; ChM Leeds 1989; FRCS Ed. 1977; LRCP LRCS Ed. LRCPS Glas. 1979. Cons. Surg. N.allerton HA. Socs: Assn. Surg.; Assn. Coloproctol.; Assn. Upper G.I. Surg. Prev: Lect. (Surg.) Univ. Leeds & Hon. Sen. Regist. Leeds W.. HA.

WARD, David Ernest 50 Wimpole Street, London W1M 7DG Tel: 020 7935 3747 Fax: 020 7224 3451 Email: d.ward@heart.org.uk — MRCS Eng. LRCP Lond. 1971; MD Lond. 1981, BSc (Physiol.) 1968, MB BS 1971; FRCP Lond. 1989; MRCP (UK) 1973. (Guy's) Cons. Cardiol. St. Geo. Hosp. Lond. Socs: Fell. Amer. Coll. Cardio.; Brit. Cardiac Soc. Prev: Sen. Regist. (Cardiol.) Brompton Hosp. Lond.; Regist. (Cardiol.) St. Bart. Hosp. Lond.; Regist. (Med.) Char. Cross Hosp. Lond.

WARD, David Gareth 30 Bennett Park, London SE3 9RB — MB ChB 1998 Liverp.

WARD, David George The Surgery, Marlpits Road, Honiton EX14 2DD Tel: 01404 41141 Fax: 01404 46621 — MB BS 1983 Lond.; BSc Lond. 1980; MRCGP 1987; DRCOG 1988. (St. Geo.) Prev: Trainee GP VTS Univ. Exeter; Ho. Off. (Med.) St. Geo. Hosp. Lond.; Ho. Off. (Surg.) Derriford Hosp. Plymouth.

WARD, David James — MB ChB 1979 Dundee; MRCGP 1989; BSc (Hons.) Dund 1974. Prev: Surg. Cdr. Rn.

WARD, Mr David Joseph Department of Plastic Surgery, Leicester Royal Infirmary, Leicester LE1 5WW Tel: 0116 258 5786 Fax: 0116 258 6082; Sauvey Castle Farm, Withcote, Oakham LE15 8DJ Tel: 01664 454870 Fax: 01664 454880 Email: plastic.surgeon@virgin.net — MB BS 1976 Lond.; FRCS Eng. 1980; T(S) 1991. (King's Coll. Hosp.) p/t Cons. (Plastic Surg.) Leicester Roy. Infirm.; Professional Conduct Comm., Gen. Med. Counc. (Apptd. Mem.); Examr. Intercollegiate Bd. Plastic Surg.; Clin. Teach. Univ. Leic. Sch. Med. Socs: Brit. Assn. Plastic Surg.; Brit. Assn. Aesthetic Plastic Surgs.; Brit. Burns Assn. Prev: Mem. Ct. Examrs. RCS Eng.; Sen. Regist. (Plastic Surg.) Qu. Vict. Hosp. E. Grinstead; Regist. (Plastic Surg.) St. Geo. & Qu. Mary's Hosps. Lond.

WARD, David Michael The Surgery, 29 Chesterfield Drive, Ipswich IP1 6DW Tel: 01473 741349 — MB ChB 1984 Bristol; BA (Hons.) Oxf. 1981; MB ChB (Hons.) Bristol 1984; MRCGP 1989; T(GP) 1991; DRCOG Lond. 1988; DCH RCP Lond. 1987.

WARD, Mr David Michael, OBE, KStJ (retired) The Hermitage, Ringmore, Shaldon, Teignmouth TQ14 0ET Tel: 01626 873392 Email: sonmikward@btinternet.com — MB ChB 1955 Birm.; FRCS Eng. 1965; FCOphth 1989; DO Eng. 1962; DObst RCOG 1959. Prev: Cons. Ophth. Torbay Hosp. Torquay.

WARD, David Ralph Compton Health Centre, Compton, Ashbourne DE6 1GN Tel: 01335 300588; Lower Brook Barn, Snelston, Ashbourne DE6 2GP — MB ChB 1987 Birm.; DRCOG 1991; DFFP 1997. GP Princip. Derbysh.

WARD, David William Wisteria Cottage, 76 Sunnyhill Road, Streatham, London SW16 2UL — MB BS 1988 New South Wales.

WARD, Deborah Louise 53 Blackstock Road, Sheffield S14 1AB — MB ChB 1992 Leic.

WARD, Debra Levenshulme Health Centre, Dunstable Street, Manchester M19 3BX Tel: 0161 225 4033 Fax: 0161 248 8020 — MB ChB 1985 Manch.; MRCGP 1989; DRCOG 1989.

WARD, Denis Allan (retired) Kirkvale, Lea, Matlock DE4 5JP Tel: 01629 534604 — MB ChB 1949 Leeds; LDS Leeds, BChD 1941. Prev: GP Crich, Dethick, Lea, & Holloway.

WARD, Derek James Birmingham Heartlands Hospital, Bordesley Green E., Birmingham B9 5SS; 22 Charterhouse Drive, Hillfied, Solihull B91 3FH — MB ChB 1993 Bristol; BSc (Hons.) Bristol 1990; MRCP (UK) 1996. Research Fell. Chest Research Inst. Birm. Heartlands Hosp.

WARD, Dermot Joseph 4 Jubilee Terrace, Chichester PO19 1XL Tel: 01243 778716 — LRCPI & LM, LRCSI & LM 1961; FRCPI 1972, M 1965; FRCPsych 1984, M 1971; DPM Eng. 1965. p/t Indep. Cons. Psychiat., Chichester; Med. Mem., Ment. health review tribunal, Surbiton, Surrey; Second opinion advisory Phys. Ment. health act commision, Nottm. Socs: Fell. Roy. Soc. Med.; BMA; Exec. Mem.Soc. of Clin. Psychiat.s. Prev: Cons. Psychiat. St David's Hosp. Carmathern & Graylingwell Hosp. Chichester; Cons. Psychiat. & Clin. Dir. St. Loman's Hosp. Dub.; Sen. Regist. (Psychiat.) Roundway Hosp. Devizes.

WARD, Derrick Edward Whitchurch Road Medical Centre, 210-212 Whitchurch Road, Heath, Cardiff CF14 3NB Tel: 029 2062 1282 Fax: 029 2052 0210; 41 Caegwyn Road, Whitchurch, Cardiff CF14 1TB — MB BCh 1973 Wales; MRCGP 1979; DRCOG 1978; Cert JCC Lond. 1978. (Cardiff) Clin. Asst. (Genitourin. Med.) Cardiff Roy. Infirm.; Clin. Tutor, Coll. Med., Univ. of Wales. Prev: Surg. Lt. RN; Ho. Surg. Accid. Unit Cardiff Roy. Infirm.; Ho. Phys. Llandough Hosp. Penarth.

WARD, Dorothy May Blair 6 Ballantrae, Stewartfield, East Kilbride, Glasgow G74 4TZ Tel: 0141 248881 Fax: 0141248886 Email: dbegg@epulse.net — MB ChB Glas. 1950; MRCGP 1994. (Glas.) Med. Mem. Disabil. Appeals Tribunal W. of Scotl.; Med. Assessor Indep. Tribunal Serv. W. of Scotl. Socs: Fell. BMA; Fell. Roy. Soc. Med.; Med. Wom. Internat. Assn. Prev: GP Glas.; Hosp. Pract. (Geriat.) Cowglen Hosp. Glas.; Ho. Off. (Med.) Thoracic Surg. Unit, Woodend Hosp. Aberd.

WARD, Duncan Brand Grosvenor House Surgery, Grosvenor House, Warwick Square, Carlisle CA1 1LB Tel: 01228 536561 Fax: 01228 515786 — MB ChB 1979 Manch.; MRCGP 1984; DRCOG 1983. Prev: SHO (O & G) Univ. Hosp. S. Manch.; SHO (Paediat.) St. Mary's Hosp. Manch.; SHO (Paediat.) Roy. Hosp. Sick Childr. Glas.

WARD, Edward (retired) Badger's Earth, Little Missenden, Amersham HP7 0RD — MB BCh BAO 1951 Dub.; FFCM 1983, M 1974; DPH Liverp. 1964. Prev: Dir. Pub. Health Wycombe HA.

WARD, Eileen Gillian Marloes, 23 Avenue Road, Dorridge, Solihull B93 8LD Tel: 01564 772032 — MB ChB 1964 Birm.; MRCOphth 1989; DO Eng. 1980. (Birm.)

WARD, Eileen Mary Claire Talbot, Ward, Seery and Ahmad, Gardenia Surgery, 2A Gardenia Avenue, Luton LU3 2NS Tel: 01582 572612 Fax: 01582 494553 — MB BCh BAO 1976 NUI; DRCOG 1980; MRCGP 1980; DCH Eng. 1979. (Univ. Coll. Galway, Eire) Socs: BMA. Prev: Duty Dep. Police Surg. (S. Bed.).

WARD, Elizabeth Sheffield 4 Patten Road, London SW18 3RH Tel: 020 8874 4938 Fax: 020 8874 4938 — MB BS 1967 Lond.; MBAcC 1995; MBAcA 1992; LicAc 1992. (Middlx.) Med. Off. Family Plann. Clinics Lond.; Clin. Asst. (Dermat.) Hillingdon & Hounslow AHA. Prev: SHO (Paediat.) Mayday Hosp. Croydon; Ho. Phys. N. Middlx. Hosp. Lond.; Ho. Surg. Harefield Hosp.

WARD, Eric Townhead Surgeries, Settle BD24 9JA Tel: 01729 822611 Fax: 01729 892916; Warrendale House, 2 Townhead Avenue, Settle BD24 9RQ Tel: 01729 823341 — MB ChB 1970 Manch.; MRCGP 1976; DObst RCOG 1972. (Manch.) Prev: Trainee GP Airedale VTS; SHO (O & G) Withington Hosp. Manch.; Ho. Surg. Manch. Roy. Infirm.

WARD, Francis Gosman (retired) 37 High Street, Datchet, Slough SL3 9EQ — MB ChB 1959 St. And.; FCCP (USA) 1989; MFOM RCP

Lond. 1981; T(OM) 1992. Prev: Sen. Med. Adviser Benefits Agency Med. Servs. DSS.

WARD, Gemma Clare Central Clinic, Childrens Centre, Durham Road, Sunderland; 5 Thornhill Terrace, Sunderland SR2 7JL — MB BS 1983 Newc.; MSc (Community Paediat.) 1990; DCCH RCP Ed. 1987. Assoc. Specialist (Community Child Health) Childr.'s Centre Sunderland. Socs: Reg. Rep. BACDA; BACCH; RCPCH. Prev: SHO (Haemat.) Roy. Infirm. Sunderland.; SHO (Psychiat.) Cherry Knowle Hosp. Sunderland.

WARD, Geoffrey David 10 Mellish Road, Walsall WS4 2ED Tel: 01922 627726 Fax: 01922 646852 — MB BS Lond. 1964; MRCS Eng. LRCP Lond. 1964; FRCOG 1982, M 1969. (Univ. Coll. Hosp.) Cons. O & G Walsall Hosps. NHS Trust. Socs: Fell. Birm. & Midl. Obst. & Gyn. Soc.; N. Irel., N. Eng. & Scott. Obst. & Gyn. Soc.; Gyn. Travellers Club. Prev: Sen. Regist. (O & G) Jessop Hosp. Wom. Sheff.

WARD, George Priestley (retired) 15 Wenthill Close, Ackworth, Pontefract WF7 7LP Tel: 01977 600370 — MB ChB 1952 Leeds; FRCGP 1981, M 1965; DA Eng. 1970. Prev: Hosp. Pract. (Anaesth.) Pontefract Gen. Infirm.

WARD, Gerald Lipson, DSC, VRD (retired) Kelso, 14 Stoughton Lane, Stoughton, Leicester LE2 2FH Tel: 0116 271 3104 — MB BChir 1935 Camb.; MA Camb. 1935; MRCS Eng. LRCP Lond. 1933; FRCGP 1978, M 1953. Prev: Ho. Surg. St. Geo. Hosp. Lond.

WARD, Graham Gordon (retired) Ernespie, Longdogs Lane, Ottery St Mary EX11 1HX Tel: 01404 812621 Fax: 01404 812621 Email: graham_ward@talk21.com — MB BS 1960 Lond.; MRCS Eng. LRCP Lond. 1959; MRCGP 1968; DObst RCOG 1961. Chairm. Ottery St. Mary Hosp. League of Friends. Prev: Ho. Surg. (Orthop.) Guy's Hosp. Lond.

WARD, Graham Russell Kennedy Way Surgery, Kennedy Way, Yate, Bristol BS37 4AA Tel: 01454 313849 Fax: 01454 329039 — MB BCh 1983 Wales. GP Yate. Prev: SHO (Rotat.) (Gen. Med.) Walsgrave Hosp. Coventry; Ho. Off. (Gen. Med.) Roy. Gwent Hosp. Newport; Ho. Off. (Surg.) Univ. Coll. Hosp. Cardiff.

WARD, Mr Harry Charles Tel: 020 8333 3000 Fax: 020 8690 1963 — MB BS 1975 Lond.; MS Lond. 1992; FRCS Eng. 1979. Cons. Paediat. Surg. Uni. Hosp. Lewisham & Guy's & St. Thos. NHS Trust. Prev: Sen. Regist. (Paediat. Surg.) Hosp. Sick Childr. Lond.; Regist. (Paediat. Surg.) Qu. Eliz. Hosp. Sick Childr. Lond.; Research Fell. Acad. (Surg.) St. Mary's Hosp. Lond.

WARD, Helen Department of Epidemiology & Public Health, Imperial College School of Medicine, London W2 1PG Tel: 020 7594 3805 Fax: 020 7402 2150 Email: h.ward@ic.ac.uk — MB ChB 1981 Sheff.; MSc (Epidemiol. Distinc.) Lond. 1993; MFPHM RCP (UK) 1993; FFPHM RCP (UK) 1999. Sen. Lect. (Pub. Health Med.) Imperial Coll. Sch. Med. St. Mary's Hosp. Lond.; Hon. Cons. Pub. Health Med. N. Thames RHA; Hon. Cons. Epidemiol. St. Mary's Hosp. Trust Lond. Socs: Soc. Study VD. Prev: Sen. Regist. (Pub. Health Med.) NW Thames RHA; Research Fell. (Epidemiol.) & Research Regist. (Genitourin. Med.) St. Mary's Hosp. Med. Sch. Lond.

WARD, Helen Emily Middleton Lodge Surgery, New Ollerton, Newark NG22 9SZ Tel: 01623 860668 Fax: 01623 836073 — BM BS 1980 Nottm.; MRCGP 1985; DRCOG 1985.

WARD, Helen Louise 3 Steeple Court, Coventry Road, London E1 5QZ — MB BS 1992 Lond.

WARD, Helen Mary Walls General Practice, Walls General Practice, Walls, Shetland ZE2 9PF Tel: 01595 809352; Anderville Walls 2EZ 9PF — MB ChB 1986 Sheff.; BSc Zool. Sheff. 1979; BMedSci Sheff. 1985; MRCGP 1996.

WARD, Hester Janet Teresa Lothian Health Board, 148 Pleasance, Edinburgh EH8 9RS Tel: 0131 536 9000; 7 Wardie Crescent, Trinity, Edinburgh EH5 1AF Tel: 0131 552 0519 — MB BS 1987 Lond.; MSc (Pub. Health Med.) Lond. 1993, BSc (Hons.) Biochem. 1984; MRCP (UK) 1991; MFPHM RCP (UK) 1995. (Char. Cross & Westm.) Cons. (Pub. Health Med.) Lothian HB - on secondment to the Nat. CJD Surveillance Unit, Edin. Prev: Sen. Regist. (Pub. Health Med.) Lothian HB; Regist. (Pub. Health Med.) SE HA & SE Thames RHA; SHO (Med.) Char. Cross Hosp. Lond.

WARD, Ian James Spokes and Partners, Phoenix Family Care, 35 Park Road, Coventry CV1 2LE Tel: 024 7622 7234 Fax: 024 7663 4816; 29 Coopers Walk, Bubbenhall, Coventry CV8 3JB — MB ChB 1980 Leeds; DRCOG 1984.

WARD, Ian Roger 196 Foundry Lane, Southampton SO15 3LE — BM 1995 Soton.

WARD, Ida Joyce (retired) Kirkvale, Lea, Matlock DE4 5JP Tel: 01629 534604 — MB ChB 1949 Leeds; MRCS Eng. LRCP Lond. 1949; Cert Family Plann. RCOG, RCGP & Family Plann; Assn. 1976. Prev: GP Crich, Dethick, Lea & Holloway.

WARD, Iris Violet Irene (retired) 19 Knowle Village, Budleigh Salterton EX9 6AL Tel: 01395 442404 — MB BS 1925 Lond.; MB BS (Hons.) Lond. 1925; MD Lond. 1930; DCH Eng. 1950. Prev: Asst. Paediat. Research Unit Exeter City Hosp.

WARD, Jacqueline Anne 29 Coopers Walk, Bubbenhall, Coventry CV8 3JB — MB ChB 1980 Leeds; MRCGP 1984; D.Occ.Med. RCP Lond. 1995; DFFP 1995; DRCOG 1983.

WARD, James (retired) Eildon, Murrell Hill, Grange-over-Sands LA11 7HN Tel: 015395 34425 — MB ChB 1945 Liverp.; DCP Lond 1952; DPath Eng. 1957; FRCPath 1975, M 1963. Prev: Cons. Clin. Pathol. Scott. Borders Hosp. Gp.

WARD, James Christopher Rodney Flat 5 Collingwood House, 10 Collingwood Ter, Newcastle upon Tyne NE2 2JP — MB BS 1997 Newc.

WARD, James Peter 79 Albert Road, Gourock PA19 1NJ — MB ChB 1987 Glas.

WARD, James Robin 1 Farnham Lane, Ferrensby, Knaresborough HG5 9JG — MB ChB 1965 Sheff.; DObst RCOG 1967. Prev: GP Richmond; Clin. Asst. (O & G & Radiol.) Darlington Memor. Hosp.; Ho. Obst. Off., Ho. Phys. & Ho. Surg. Maelor Gen. Hosp. Wrexham.

WARD, Jane Department of Physiology, UMDS, St. Thomas Campus, Lambeth Palace Road, London SE1 7EH Tel: 020 7928 9292 Fax: 020 7928 0729 Email: jane.ward@umds.ac.uk; 2 Newstead Avenue, Orpington BR6 9RL Tel: 01689 872987 — MB ChB 1977 Manch.; PhD Lond. 1988; BSc Manch. 1974, MB ChB 1977. Sen. Lect. (Physiol.) UMDS Guy's & St. Thos. Hosp. Lond.

WARD, Janet Amelia The Surgery, Marlpits Road, Honiton EX14 2DD Tel: 01404 41141 Fax: 01404 46621 — MB BS 1981 Lond.; MRCGP 1987; T(GP) 1991.

WARD, Jean Lomax (retired) 27 Elms Drive, Bare, Morecambe LA4 6DG Tel: 01524 410657 — MB ChB 1955 Leeds; MRCGP 1968; DObst RCOG 1957. Prev: GP Morecambe Health Centre.

WARD, Jean Paula Rock Hall, Nidd, Harrogate HG3 3BB Tel: 01423 770077 — MB BS 1949 Lond.; MRCS Eng. LRCP Lond. 1948; DA Eng. 1954; DObst RCOG 1950. (Roy. Free) Anaesth. Harrogate & Ripon Hosp. Gp. Socs: BMA & Yorks. Soc. Anaesths. Prev: Gyn. & Obst. Ho. Surg. Roy. Free Hosp.; O & G Regist. Padd. Hosp.; SHO (Anaesth.) Addenbrooke's Hosp. Camb.

WARD, Jenifer Ann (retired) The Coach House, 1A Meadows Close, Portishead, Bristol BS20 8BU — MB ChB 1968 Birm. Prev: Sen. Med. Off. DHSS.

WARD, Mr Jeremy Bruce Department of Surgery, Royal Liverpool University Hospital, University of Liverpool, Liverpool L69 3BX Tel: 0151 706 4170; 16 Addingham Road, Liverpool L18 2EW Tel: 0151 475 0846 — MB ChB Ed. 1989; FRCS Ed. 1993. Lect. Dept. Surg. Roy. Liverp. Univ. Hosp. Socs: Pancreatic Soc. Prev: Specialist Regist. (Gen. Surg.) Warrington Hosp.; Research Fell. (Surg. & Physiol.) Univ. of Liverp.; SHO (Surg.) Warrington.

WARD, John Dale (retired) Royal Hallamshire Hospital, Glossop Road, Sheffield S10 2JF Tel: 0114 271 2938 Fax: 0114 271 3708 — MB BS Lond. 1961; BSc Lond. 1958, MD 1971; FRCP Lond. 1976, M 1965. Cons. Phys. Roy. Hallamsh. Hosp. Sheff.; Prof. Diabetic Med. Univ. Sheff. Prev: Sen. Regist. Lond. Hosp.

WARD, John Edward Hendon Anaesthetic Department, Queen Medical Centre, Nottingham NG7 2UH Tel: 0115 924 9924; Email: jehwood@ntlworld.com — BM BS 1986 Nottm.; FRCA 1994; CCST 1998. (Nottingham) Cons. (Anaesth.) Sheff. Socs: Vasc. Anaesth. Soc.; Brit. Soc. of orthopaedic Anaesth.s (ord-Mem.); ass of Anaesth.s of GB & I (ord-Mem.). Prev: Research Regist. (Anaesth.) Nottm. & Derby; Regist. Rotat. (Anaesth.) Nottm. & Mansfield; Regist. (A & E) Cairns Qu.sland, Austral.

WARD, John Kingsley 2 Meadway, Westcliff on Sea SS0 8PJ Tel: 01702 710810 — MB BS 1960 Durh.; FRCOG 1980, M 1967, DObst 1962. Cons. O & G S.end-on-Sea Hosp. Gp. Socs: BMA. Prev: Ho. Phys. (Med.) Roy. Vict. Infirm. Newc.; SHO (Surg.) & Regist. (O & G) Newc. Gen. Hosp.

WARD

WARD, John Luzzi Campbell (retired) 22B Duchy Road, Harrogate HG1 2ER Tel: 01423 560299 — M.B., Ch.B. Leeds 1941. Prev: Ho. Phys. Leeds Gen. Infirm.

WARD, Mr John Peter Esperance House, Esperance Private Hospital, 1 Hartington Place, Eastbourne BN21 3BG Tel: 01323 410717 Fax: 01323 730313; Clematis Cottages, Boreham Lane, Boreham St., Nr. Herstmonceux,, Hailsham BN27 4SL Tel: 01323 832186 — MB BS Lond. 1962; MS Lond. 1974; FRCS Eng. 1967; MRCS Eng. LRCP Lond. 1962; T(S) 1991; Specialist Accredit. (Urol.) RCS Eng. 1974. (St. Mary's) p/t Hon. Cons. Urol. E.bourne NHS Trust; Cons. Urol. Esperance Private Hosp. E.bourne; Hon. Sen. Clin. Lect. Inst. Urol. Univ. Coll. Univ. Lond.; Examr. MD. Univ. Mansoura, Egypt; Examr. Inst. Urol. Univ. Lond.; Exam. FRCS (Part B) RCS in Irel. 1996/7. Socs: Fell. Roy. Soc. Med. (Ex-Counc. Mem. Sect. Urol.); Brit. Assn. Urol. Surgs.; (Ex-Pres.) Euro. Intra-Renal Surg. Soc. Prev: Sen. Regist. (Urol) St. Bart. Hosp. Lond.; Resid. Surg. Off. St. Peter's, St. Paul's, St. Philip's Hosps. & Inst.Urol. Lond.; Research Fell. (Surg.) Univ. Colorado Med. Centre Denver, USA.

WARD, John Philip Quarrier Woodgate Valley Practice, 61 Stevens Avenue, Woodgate Valley, Birmingham B32 3SD Tel: 0121 427 6174 Fax: 0121 428 4146; 15 Park Hill Road, Harborne, Birmingham B17 9SJ Tel: 0121 427 3169 — MB ChB 1983 Birm. Clin. Asst. Roy. Orthop. Hosp. Birm. Socs: Birm. Med. Inst.

WARD, John Richard Appletree Medical Practice, 47a Town Street, Duffield, Belper DE56 4GG Tel: 01332 841219 — MB ChB 1978 Dundee.

WARD, John William 8 Lanes Avenue, Northfleet, Gravesend DA11 7HR Tel: 01474 59633 — MB BS 1975 Lond.; FRCR 1983.

WARD, John William 85 Chaveney Road, Quorndon, Loughborough LE12 8AB Tel: 01509 412862 — MB ChB 1968 Sheff.; BPharm Nottm. 1961; FRCP Lond. 1988; MRCP (UK) 1972. (Sheff.) Cons. Clin. Pharmacol. Glenfield Gen. Hosp. Leicester; Prof. Clin. Pharmacy Univ. Nottm. Socs: Brit. Pharm. Soc.; Brit. Thorac. Soc. Prev: Lect. (Pharmacol. & Therap.) Univ. Sheff.

WARD, John William Keith Winton, Thame Lane, Culham, Abingdon OX14 3DS Tel: 01235 525364 Fax: 01235 525364 — MB ChB 1972 St. And.; FRCGP 1995, M 1976; DFFP 1993; Cert. JCC Lond. 1976; DObst RCOG 1974. Trainer (Gen. Pract.) Oxf. RHA. Socs: Pres. Osler Club Lond.; BMA; Fell. Med. Soc. Lond. Prev: SHO (Infec. Dis.) King's Cross Hosp. Dundee.

WARD, Jonathan Francis Campbell Coach House, Duchy Rd, Harrogate HG1 2ER Tel: 01423 560299 — MB BS 1971 Lond.

WARD, Karen Louise 12 Poplar Place, Gosforth, Newcastle upon Tyne NE3 1DR — MB BS 1990 Newc.; MRCOG 1996; DFFP 1994.

WARD, Katherine Alexandra Greyroofs, 30 Stanstead Road, Caterham CR3 6AA — MB BS 1998 Lond.

WARD, Katherine Nora Department of Virology, University College London Medical School, Windeyer institute for medical sciences, 46 Cleveland St., London W1T 4JF Tel: 020 7679 9137 Fax: 020 7580 5896 Email: k.n.ward@ucl.ac.uk — MB BChir 1983 Camb.; PhD Lond. 1973, BSc 1969; MA Camb. 1990; FRCPath 1998, MRCPath 1989. (Camb.) Cons. & Hon. Sen. Lect. Univ. Coll. Lond. Hosps. Trust & Univ. Coll. Lond. Med. Sch. Socs: Soc. Gen. Microbiol.; Eur. Soc. Clin. Virol.; Internat. Soc. Antiviral Research. Prev: Sen. Lect. & Hon. Cons. Imperial Coll. Sch. of Med. & Hammersmith Hosp.; Clin. Lect. (Path.) Univ. Camb.; Hon. Sen. Regist. (Virol.) Addenbrooke's Hosp. Camb. & Hon. Asst. Med. Microbiol. Pub. Health Laborat. Camb.

WARD, Kathleen Anne Mid Staffordshire General Hospitals NHS Trust, Weston Road, Stafford ST16 3SA Tel: 01543 576038 Fax: 01543 576034 — MB BCh BAO 1987 Belf.; MRCP (UK) 1990; MD 1993. (Queens university of Belfast) Cons. Derm. Cannock Chase Hosp. Staffs. Socs: Brit. Ass of Dermatol.s; Roy. Coll. Phys.s; Roy. Soc. Med.

WARD, Kathryn Frances 43 Keslake Road, London NW6 6DH — MB BS 1986 Lond.

WARD, Kathryn Louise 13 Chatsworth Avenue, Southwell NG25 0AE — MB BS 1992 Lond.

WARD, Kathryn Patricia Airedale General Hospital, Skipton Road, Steeton, Keighley BD20 6TD Tel: 01535 652511 Fax: 01535 651209; Glenaire, Green Lane, Glusburn, Keighley BD20 8RU Tel: 01535 632146 — MB ChB 1975 Birm.; FRCP Lond. 1994; MRCP (UK) 1979; FRCPCH 1997; DCH Eng. 1978. Cons. Paediat. & Neonatol. Airedale Gen. Hosp.; Designated Dr for Child Protec. N. Yorks. HA. Socs: Brit. Paediat. Assn. & Nutrit. Soc.; Brit. Soc. Paediat. Gastroenterol. Prev: Cons. Paediat. Airedale Gen. Hosp.; Sen. Regist. (Paediat.) Roy. Aberd. Childr. Hosp.; Research Regist. Grampian HB.

WARD, Kaye Churchgate Surgery, 119 Manchester Road, Denton, Manchester M34 3RA Tel: 0161 336 2114 Fax: 0161 320 7045 — MB ChB 1989 Manch.; MRCGP 1993.

WARD, Kevin Jason 37 Hardy Barn, Shipley, Heanor DE75 7LY — MB BS 1994 Lond.; MRCGP 1997. Specialist Regist. in Palliat. Med., St. James Univ. Hosp., Leeds. Prev: SHO Palliat. Med., St. Gemmas Hospice, Leeds.

WARD, Kevin John 5 Elmton Lane, Eythorne, Dover CT15 4AR Email: kevin.ward@connect2.co.uk — MB BS 1991 Lond.; BSc Lond. 1988, MB BS 1991; MRCP 1994. (Kings Coll.Sch.Med.Dentist.Lond)

WARD, Kirsty Louise 16 Brookhouse Avenue, Leicester LE2 0JE — MB ChB 1992 Leic.

WARD, Lesley Monica Moir Medical Centre, Regent St., Long Eaton, Nottingham NG10 1QQ Tel: 0115 973 5820 Fax: 0115 946 0197; 20 Bostocks Lane, Risley, Derby DE72 3SX Tel: 0115 917 9738 — MB ChB 1979 Sheff. (Sheffield)

WARD, Lindsay Stuart Stirchley Medical Practice, Stirchley Health Centre, Stirchley, Telford TF3 1FB Tel: 01952 660444 Fax: 01952 415139 — BM 1978 Soton.; BM (Hons.) Soton. 1978.

WARD, Lisabeth Lee Taylor and Partners, Shirehampton Health Centre, Pembroke Road, Shirehampton, Bristol BS11 9SB Tel: 0117 916 2233 Fax: 0117 930 8246 — MB BS 1984 Lond.; DCH RCP Lond. 1989.

WARD, Lucy 4 Patten Road, London SW18 3RH — MB BS 1996 Lond.

WARD, Lucy Elizabeth Community Team, 3rd Floor, Shieldfield Health Centre, 4 Clarence Walk, Newcastle upon Tyne NE2 1AL Tel: 0191 232 2766 Email: l.e.ward@ncl.ac.uk — MB ChB 1983 Manch.; MRCGP 1990. Staff Grade (Social Paediat.) Community Team, Newc. u. Tyne; Lect. Dept. Primary Health Care, Newc.

WARD, Malcolm Gordon Bulling Lane Surgery, Bulling Lane, Crich, Matlock DE4 5DX Tel: 01773 852966 Fax: 01773 853919; Hilltop Cottage, Parkhead, Matlock DE4 5GY Tel: 01773 852737 — MB ChB 1977 Leeds; MRCGP 1981.

WARD, Malcolm Robert 60 Polwarth Street, 1st Floor Right Side, Glasgow G12 9TL — MB ChB 1985 Otago.

WARD, Mark Alistair Auckland Medical Group, 54 Cockton Hill Road, Bishop Auckland DL14 6BB Tel: 01388 602728 — MB BS 1982 Lond.

WARD, Mark Robert (retired) Norvic Clinic, Thorpe, Norwich NR7 0SS — MB ChB 1984 Birm. Cons. Forens. Psychiat. Norwich.

WARD, Martyn Lester 24 St James Road, Wokingham RG40 4RT Tel: 01734 732955 — MB BS 1978 Lond.; FCAnaesth. 1990. Head of Project Developm. Sandoz Pharmaceut. Frimley; Clin. Asst. (Anaesth.) Frimley Pk. Hosp. Surrey.

WARD, Mr Martyn Wootton, OBE, Group Capt. RAF Med. Br. Retd. (retired) The Ridgway Hospital, Moormead Road, Wroughton, Swindon SN4 9DD Tel: 01793 814848 Fax: 01793 814852 Email: martyn@jill02.freeserve.co.uk — MB BS Lond. 1964; FRCS Ed. 1974. Locum Cons. (Orthop. Surg.) P.ss Marg. Hosp. Swindon. Prev: Hon. Sen. Regist. Harlow Wood Orthop. Hosp. Mansfield.

WARD, Mary 55 Gallacher Avenue, Forrest Walk, Paisley PA2 9HE — MB BCh BAO 1986 NUI.

WARD, Mary McLelland 3 Spire Heights, Gilstead Lane, Gilstead, Bingley BD16 3LN Tel: 01274 566066 — MB ChB Glas. 1951; FRCPsych 1993, M 1972; Dip. Psychother. Leeds 1976; DPM Eng. 1970; DObst RCOG 1953. (Glas.) Hon. Cons. Child Psychiat. Bradford HA. Socs: Assn. Family Ther.; Assn. Child Psychol. & Psychiat. Prev: Cons. Child Psychiat. Bradford HA; Cons. Psychiat. Stud. Health Univ. Bradford; Sen. Regist. (Child & Adolesc. Psychiat.) St. Jas. Hosp. Leeds.

WARD, Matthew Margrave 15 Cumberland Road, Richmond TW9 3HJ — MB ChB 1997 Bristol.

WARD, Maurice Alfred George (retired) Kelvin, 8 Penenden Heath Road, Maidstone ME14 2DA Tel: 01622 752760 — MB ChB Birm. 1937; DPH Eng. 1941. Prev: Hyg. Specialist RAMC.

WARD, Michael (retired) 13 The Quarries, Swindon SN1 4EX Tel: 01793 536030 — MB BS 1958 Durh.; FRCGP 1981, M 1974.

WARD, Michael 1 Knapp Rise, Haslingfield, Cambridge CB3 7LQ — MB BS 1994 Lond.

WARD, Michael Conor 2 Coombe Rise, Kingston upon Thames KT2 7EX — MB BCh BAO 1979 NUI; MD NUI 1987; LRCPI & LM, LRCSI & LM 1979; MRCP (UK) 1982. Cons. Phys. & Sen. Lect. Geriat. St. Helier Hosp. Carshalton & St. Geo. Hosp. Med. Sch. Lond. Prev: Sen. Regist. (Geriat. Med.) St. Geo. Hosp. Lond.

WARD, Michael Elliott Nuffield Department of Anaesthetics, Oxford Radcliffe NHS Trust, Oxford OX3 9DU Tel: 01865 221587 Fax: 01865 220027 Email: michael.ward@nda.ox.ac.uk — MB BS Lond. 1969; MRCS Eng. LRCP Lond. 1969; FFA RCS Eng. 1973. (King's Coll. Hosp.) Cons. Anaesth. Nuffield Dept. Anaesth. John Radcliffe Hosp. Oxf.; Med. Dir. Oxon. Ambul. Serv.; Mem. Jt.Roy. Coll. & Ambul. Liaison Comm.; Company Sec. Resus. Counc. Trading Co. Prev: Sen. Regist. (Anaesth.) Qu. Vict. Hosp. E. Grinstead; Lect. (Anaesth.) King's Coll. Hosp. Lond.; Ho. Surg. & Regist. (Anaesth.) King's Coll. Hosp. Lond.

WARD, Michael James 86 Glenshan Road, Londonderry BT47 3SF — MB BCh BAO 1994 Belf.

WARD, Michael Jonathan King's Mill Hospital, Mansfield Road, Sutton-in-Ashfield NG17 4JL Tel: 01623 22515 — MB ChB 1976 Dundee; MB ChB (Hons.) Dundee 1976; DM Nottm. 1983; FRCP Lond. 1994; MRCP (UK) 1978. Cons. Phys. Mansfield.; Clin. Tutor Univ. Nottm. Socs: Brit. Thorac. Soc.; Amer. Thoracic Soc.

WARD, Michael Joseph 361 Methilhaven Road, Methil, Leven KY8 3HR Tel: 01333 426913 Fax: 01333 422300; Tel: 01333 423107 — MB ChB 1978 Ed.; LMCC Vancouver 1981. (Edin.) GP Clin. Asst. (Geriat.) Randolph Wemyss Hosp. Buckhaven. Prev: GP Clin. Asst. (Anaesth.) Randolph Wemyss Hosp. Buckhaven; GP Clin. Asst. (Cas.) Vict. Hosp. Kirkcaldy.

WARD, Michael Kingsley 11 Wilson Gardens, Newcastle upon Tyne NE3 4JA — MB BS (2nd Cl. Hons.) Newc. 1969; FRCP Lond. 1984; MRCP (U.K.) 1972. Cons. Nephrol. Roy. Vict. Infirm. Newc. upon Tyne; Sen. Lect. Med. Univ. Newc. Prev: Lect. in Med. Univ. Newc.; Hon. Sen. Regist. Dept. Med. Roy. Vict. Infirm. Newc. upon Tyne; Regist. Dept. Med. Hammersmith Hosp. Lond.

WARD, Mr Michael Phelps, CBE Pheasant Hill, Lurgashall, Petworth GU28 9EP — MB BChir 1949 Camb.; MA Camb. 1962, BA 1946, MD 1968; FRCS Eng. 1955; MRCS Eng. LRCP Lond. 1949. (Camb. & Lond. Hosp.) Emerit. Cons. Surg. St. And. Hosp. Bow & Newham Dist. Gen. Hosp.; Hon. Lect. (Surg.) Lond. Hosp. Med. Coll. Socs: Fell. Roy. Soc. Med. & Assn. Surgs.; Master Soc. Apoth. 1993-4. Prev: Asst. Resid. Roy. Vict. Hosp. Montreal, Canada; Regist. (Thoracic & Gen. Surg.) & Sen. Regist. (Gen. Surg.) Lond. Hosp.

WARD, Michael Thomas (retired) Great Crabthorn, 80 Old St, Hill Head, Fareham PO14 3HN Tel: 01329 662581 Fax: 01329 662581 — MB BS 1958 Lond.; MRCS Eng. LRCP Lond. 1958; DObst RCOG 1960; MRCGP 1996. Prev: Assoc. Dir. Postgrad. Gen. Pract. Educat. Wessex.

WARD, Mr Michael William Noel Chase Farm Hospital, The Ridgeway, Enfield EN2 8JL Tel: 020 8366 6600; 51 Lanchester Road, Highgate, London N6 4SX — BM BCh 1972 Oxf.; MA Oxf. 1972, MCh 1985, BM BCh 1972; FRCS Eng. 1978. (Univ. Coll. Hosp.) Cons. Surg. Chase Farm & Highlands Hosp. Enfield.

WARD, Morag Christine Lochee Health Centre, 1 Marshall St., Dundee DD2 3BR Tel: 01382 611283 — MB ChB 1984 Dundee. (Dundee) GP Dundee.

WARD, Nicholas Alexander Lawton Bampton Surgery, Landells, Bampton OX18 2LJ Tel: 01993 850257; 9 Bushey Row, Bampton OX18 2JX Tel: 01993 851226 — MB BChir 1989 Camb.; MA Camb. 1989; MRCGP 1992; DCH RCP Lond. 1991; DRCOG 1991. Socs: BMA.

WARD, Nicholas Charles Grange Medical Centre, West Cliff Road, Ramsgate CT11 9LJ Tel: 01843 595051 Fax: 01843 591999 — MB BS 1986 Lond.; DRCOG 1989.

WARD, Nicholas John Towcester Medical Centre, Link Way, Towcester NN12 6HH Tel: 01327 359953 Fax: 01327 358929 — MB BS 1986 Lond.; MRCGP 1991; DRCOG 1989. Prev: Trainee GP N.ampton VTS.

WARD, Nicholas Mark Carnwarth Health Centre, 7 Biggar Road, Carnwath, Lanark ML11 8HJ Tel: 01555 840214 — MB ChB 1988 Ed. SHO (Cas.) Hull Roy. Infirm. Prev: SHO (A & E) Perth Roy. Infirm.

WARD, Nicholas Steven Institute of Neurology & National Hospital for Neurology & Neurosurgery, London WC1N Email: n.ward@fil.ion.ucl.ac.uk — MB BS 1989 Lond.; BSc Lond. 1986; MRCP (UK) 1994. Clin. Fell. in Stroke Med. Inst. of Neurol. & Nat. Hosp. Neurol. & Neurosurg., Lond. Prev: Specialist Regist. (Neurol.) Roy. Lond. Hosp.; SHO Nat. Hosp. Neurol. & Neurosurg. Lond.; Specialist Regist. (Neurol.) Nat. Hosp. Neurol. & Neurosurg.

WARD, Nicolas Wyndham University Hospital of Wales, Heath Park, Cardiff CF14 4WZ; 10 Groveland Road, Birchgrove, Cardiff CF14 4QX — MB ChB 1990 Birm.; ChB Birm. 1990. Specialist Regist. (Histopath.) Univ. Hosp. Wales. Prev: Lect. (Anat.) Birm. Univ. Med. Sch.

WARD, Nicole Low Heulah Cottage, Dunsley, Whitby YO21 3TL — MB ChB 1997 Manch.

WARD, Professor Owen Conor Maurice Kennedy research centre for Emeritus staff, University College, Dublin H, Republic of Ireland; 18 Thamespoint, Teddington TW11 9PP Tel: 020 8977 0153 Fax: 020 8977 0153 — MB BCh BAO 1947 NUI; MB BCh BAO (Hons.) NUI 1947; MD (Paediat.) NUI 1951; FRCP Lond. 1995; FRCP Glas. 1983; FRCPI 1959, M 1952; FRCPCH (Hon.) 1997; DCH NUI 1949; DCH RCPSI 1948. (Univ. Coll. Dub.) Emerit. Prof. Paediat. Univ. Coll. Dub.; Adviser Emerit. Down Syndrome Assn. of Irel; Hon. Cons. Paediat., Kingston Hosp. NHS Trust. Socs: Eur. Assn. Paediat. Cardiols.; Fell. Roy. Soc. Med.; Scientif. Counc. Europ. Down Syndrome Assn. (Brussels). Prev: Cons. Paediat. Our Lady's Hosp. Sick Childr. Crumlin; Sen. Regist. (Child Health) Univ. Liverp.; Ho. Phys. Mater Miser. Hosp. Dub.

WARD, Pamela Mary Hunter's Close, Low Hawsker, Whitby YO22 4LE — MB ChB 1996 Ed.

WARD, Patricia Ann St Mary's Hospital, Praed Street, London NW2 1NY; 2 Angel Cottages, Milespit Hill, Mill Hill, London NW7 1RD — MB BS 1988 Lond.; FRCS Ed. 1993; MRCP (UK) 1991; FFAEM 1997. (Univ. coll. and Middlx. Sch. of Med.) Cons. (A & E Med.) St. Mary's Hosp. Praed St. Lond. Socs: Fell. Fac. A&E Med.; Brit. Assn. Accid. & Emerg. Med. Prev: Regist. (A & E) St. Mary's Hosp. Lond.; Regist. Helicopter Emerg. Med. Serv. Chems. Roy. Lond. Hosp. Lond.; Specialist Regist. A & E Whipps Cross Hosp. Lond.

WARD, Patrick Gerald (retired) Dunturk, Castlewellan BT31 9PF Tel: 013967 78461 — MB BCh BAO 1961 Belf. Prev: Med. Off. Holywell Hosp. Antrim.

WARD, Patrick James 17 Third Avenue, Chelmsford CM1 4EX — MB BS 1992 Lond.

WARD, Patrick Joshua, MBE (Surgery) Wakefield House, Bessbrook, Newry BT35 7DA Tel: 028 3083 0400; Broomhill, 16 Goragh Road, Newry BT35 6PZ Tel: 028 3026 3470 — LRCPI & LM, LRSCI & LM 1954; MRCGP 1968; AFOM RCP Lond. 1983; DPH Belf. 1956. (Roy. Coll. Surgs. Dub. & Qu. Univ. Belf.) Occupat. Health; Staff Med. Officer Daisy Hill Hosp. Newry; JP; Dep. Lt. Co. Armagh; Med. Adviser Norbrook Laborat. Lts Newry. Socs: Fell. BMA. Prev: Chairm. Local Med. Comm. (S.. Area); Hon. Treas. G.M.S.C. (N. Irel.); SHO Ulster Hosp. Childr. & Wom. Belf.

WARD, Paul John Whitby Group Practice, Spring Vale Medical Centre, Whitby YO21 1SD Tel: 01947 820888; Brook Cottage, Raw, Whitby YO22 4PP — MB ChB 1971 Leeds; DObst RCOG 1973. Prev: Ho. Off. Bradford Roy. Infirm.; SHO (Obst.) Profess. Unit. Leeds Matern. Hosp.; SHO (Paediat.) Alder Hey Hosp. Liverp.

WARD, Paul Stanley Department of Child Health, Derriford Hospital, Brest Road, Plymouth PL6 8DH Tel: 01752 763454 Fax: 01752 763467 Email: paul.ward@phnt.swest.nhs.uk; 5 Raynham Road, Stoke, Plymouth PL3 4EU Tel: 01752 561744 Email: wardps@lineone.net — MB ChB 1977 Bristol; BSc (Med. Microbiol.) Bristol 1974; FRCP Lond. 1995; FRCPCH 1997, M 1996; DCH Eng. 1979. (Bristol) Cons. Paediat. Derriford Hosp. Plymouth. Socs: Brit. Soc. Paediat. Endocrinol. & Diabetes; Assoc. Mem. UK Childr. Cancer Study Gp. Prev: Sen. Regist. (Paediat.) Addenbrooke's Hosp. Camb.; Sen. Regist. (Paediat.) Norf. & Norwich Hosp.; Research Fell. & Regist. (Paediat.) Bristol Roy. Hosp. for Sick Childr.

WARD, Penelope 13 Damask Close, West End, Woking GU24 9PD — MB BS 1978 Lond.; MRCOG 1987. Clin. Research Asst. St. Mary's Hosp. Med. Sch. Lond.

WARD, Peter James Kharbhih 56 St Peters Avenue, Cleethorpes DN35 — MB BS 1964 Gauhati.

WARD

WARD, Peter James Macready (retired) The King's House, 29 Keppel St., Dunston, Gateshead NE11 9AR Tel: 0191 460 7404 — MB BChir 1966 Camb.; MA Camb. 1968; DCH Eng. 1968. Prev: Co-Founding Dir. Emmaus Christian Healing Trust Gateshead.

WARD, Peter John 5 Firwood Stables, Bolton BL2 3AQ — MB ChB 1989 Bristol.

WARD, Peter John (retired) Red Cow Byre, Watling St., Kensworth, Dunstable LU6 3QT Tel: 01582 840527 — MB BS Lond. 1960. Prev: GP St. Albans.

WARD, Mr Peter John Hurstwood Park Neurological Centre, Princess Royal Hospital, Lewes Road, Haywards Heath RH17 7SJ Tel: 01444 441881 Fax: 01444 417995 Email: peter.ward@mid-sussex.sthames.nhs.uk; 31 Silverdale Road, Burgess Hill RH15 0ED Tel: 01444 242511 Fax: 01444 242511 Email: peterjward@doctors.org.uk — MB BS Lond. 1971; BSc Lond. 1968; FRCS Eng. 1977. (Middlx.) Cons. Neurosurg. Mid Downs HA. Socs: BMA (Sec. Mid Downs Div.); Mem. Soc. Brit. Neurol. Surgs. Prev: Sen. Regist. (Neurosurg.) St. Bart. Hosp. Lond.; Regist. Inst. Neurol. Sci. Glas. & Nat. Hosp. Qu. Sq. Lond.; Ho. Phys. & Ho. Surg. Middlx. Hosp. Lond.

WARD, Peter John (retired) Pinfold Surgery, Station Road, Owston Ferry, Doncaster DN9 1AW Tel: 01427 728443 Fax: 01427 728558 — MB BS 1958 Lond. Prev: Clin. Asst. (Psychiat.) Scunthorpe Gen. Hosp.

WARD, Peter Michael Charing Cross Hospital, Fulham Palace Road, London W6 8RF Tel: 020 8846 1234 — MB BS 1986 Lond.; BSc (Physiol.) Lond. 1979; FRCA 1990. Cons. Anaesth. Char. Cross Hosp. Lond.

WARD, Peter Roger (retired) 260 Broomhill Road, Aberdeen AB10 7LP Tel: 01224 313804 — MB ChB 1951 Manch.; DMRD Eng. 1957; FRCR 1975; FFR 1961. Prev: Cons. Radiol. Roy. Infirm. Aberd.

***WARD, Phillip John** British Military Hospital, Rinteln BFPO 29 — LRCP 1979 Lond.

WARD, Rachel Ann The Health Centre, Worcester Street, Stourport-on-Severn DY13 8EH Tel: 01299 827141 Fax: 01299 879074; Eardiston View, Menith Wood WR6 6UD — MB ChB 1986 Liverp.; BSc Pharmacol. Liverp. 1981. (Liverpool) Prev: SHO (Paediat.) Good Hope Hosp. Sutton Coldfield.

WARD, Rachel Ann Moorlands Medical Centre, Dyson House, Regent St., Leek ST13 6LU Tel: 01538 399008; Lower Brook Barn, Virgins Alley Lane, Snelston, Derby DE6 2GP — MB ChB 1987 Birm. Prev: Community Paediat. N. Staffs. HA GPVTS.

WARD, Richard Humphry Thomas (retired) University College Hospital, 25 Grafton Way, London WC1E 6AU Tel: 020 7383 7916 Fax: 020 7380 9816 — MB BChir Camb. 1963; MA Camb. 1964; MRCS Eng. LRCP Lond. 1962; FRCOG 1981, M 1968; DObst RCOG 1964. Cons. & Sen. Lect. (O & G) Univ. Coll. Hosp. Lond. Prev: Lect. Univ. Coll. Hosp. Med. Sch. Lond.

WARD, Richard Leonard (retired) Clouds Hill, Mellor, Blackburn BB2 7HA Tel: 0125 481 2404 — MD Lond. 1950, MB BS 1943; FRCP Lond. 1970, M 1948; MRCS Eng. LRCP Lond. 1942. Prev: Cons. Phys. Blackburn Health Dist.

WARD, Richard William George Lower Loady Farm, Highweek, Newton Abbot TQ12 2AS Tel: 01626 208020 — MB ChB 1975 Birm. (Birmingham)

WARD, Robert Derek Markham House, 140 Wyke Road, Wyke Regis, Weymouth DT4 9QR — MB BS 1971 Lond.; MRCS Eng. LRCP Lond. 1971; DObst RCOG 1975. (Guy's) Prev: SHO (O & G) & SHO (Paediat.) Salisbury Gen. Hosp. (Odstock; Br.); SHO (A & E) Hillingdon Hosp. Uxbridge.

WARD, Mr Robert Douglas 5 West Road, Kingston upon Thames KT2 7HA Tel: 020 8942 8884 Email: drrobertward@hotmail.com — MB BS Lond. 1994; FRCS (Eng.) 1998. (St Georges Hosp) Ho. Off. (Gen. Surg.) Ashford Hosp. Middlx. Prev: Ho. Off. (Gastroenterol. & Gen. Med.) St. Richards Hosp. Chichester.; Ho. Off. (Gen. Surg.) Ashford Hosp. Middlx.; SHO A & E Worthing Hosp. W. Sussex.

WARD, Robert John The Surgery, 50 The Glade, Furnace Green, Crawley RH10 6JN Tel: 01293 612741 — BM BS 1986 Nottm.; BM BS Nottm.1986.

WARD, Roger Sidney Dale End Farm, Clifton-on-Teme, Worcester WR6 6DS — MB ChB 1965 Birm.; FFR 1971; DMRD Eng. 1969. (Birm.) Cons. Radiol. & Nuclear Phys. Worcester Roy. Infirm. Prev: Sen. Regist. (Radiol.) United Birm. Hosps.

WARD, Ronald Wilfred The Surgery, Snainton, Scarborough YO13 9AP Tel: 01723 859302 — MB BS 1972 Lond.; BSc (Hons.) (Biochem.) Lond. 1969, MB BS 1972; MRCGP 1978. (St. Thos.)

WARD, Rosalind Frances 5 Rivers Edge, Charlton Marshall, Blandford Forum DT11 9PJ — MB ChB 1997 Glas.

WARD, Rosalind Mary 10 Mellish Road, Walsall WS4 2ED — MB BS 1964 Lond.; MRCS Eng. LRCP Lond. 1964; FFA RCS Eng. 1984; DA Eng. 1969. (Univ. Coll. Hosp.) Cons. Anaesth. E. Birm. Hosp. Socs: Assn. Anaesth. of GB & Irel.; Med. Wom. Federat. Prev: Sen. Regist. (Anaesth.) W. Midl. RHA.; Jun. Resid. (Anaesth.) Univ. Coll. Hosp. Lond.

WARD, Roselle Paulette Stephanie 33 Killeaton Crescent, Derriaghy, Belfast BT17 9HB — MB BCh BAO 1993 Belf.

WARD, Rosemary Virginia Hurst (retired) 5 Rosemont Road, Richmond TW10 6QN — MB BS 1959 Lond.; MRCS Eng. LRCP Lond. 1959. Prev: GP Richmond.

WARD, Ruth The Health Centre, 20 Duncan Street, Greenock PA15 4LY Tel: 01475 724477; 107 Finnart Street, Greenock PA16 8HN — MB ChB 1978 Glas.; DRCOG 1980. GP Greenock Health Centre.; Clin. Asst. Palliat. Care Ardgowan Hospice, Greenock.

WARD, Sarah Louise 71 Chandos Ave, London N20 9EG — MB BS 1993 Lond.

WARD, Mr Sean Edward Charles Clifford Dental Hospital, Wellesley Road, Sheffield S10 2SZ Tel: 0114 271 7810 — MB ChB 1982 Liverp.; BDS Liverp. 1972; FRCS Ed. 1988; FFD RCSI 1985. Cons. Oral & Maxillofacial Surg. Sheff. HA; Cons. Maxillofacial Surg. AMI Thornbury Hosp. & Claremont Hosp. Sheff. Socs: Fell. Brit. Assn. Oral & Maxillofacial Surg.; BMA; Brit. Assn. Head & Neck Oncol. Prev: Sen. Regist. (Oral & Maxillofacial Surg.) Trent RHA.

WARD, Sheelagh Margaret Area Community Child Health Department, Stirling Royal Infirmary, Stirling FK8 2AU Tel: 01786 434000; 7 Manse Crescent, Stirling FK7 9AJ Tel: 01786 464321 — MB ChB Glas. 1969. (Glas.) Staff Grade (Community Paediat.) Forth Valley Primary Care NHS Trust. Prev: Clin. Med. Off. Forth Valley HB; Ho. Off. (Med.) Falkirk & Dist. Roy. Infirm.; Ho. Off. (Surg.) Stirling Roy. Infirm.

WARD, Shelley Jane 2 Ringstead Way, Aylesbury HP21 7ND — BChir 1988 Camb.

WARD, Simon Charles Department of Radiology, St. Mary's Hospital, Milton Road, Portsmouth PO3 6AD Tel: 023 92 866173 — MB BS 1984 Lond.; BSc (Hons.) Lond. 1981; MRCP (UK) 1987; FRCR 1991; T(R) (CR) 1992. Cons. (Radiol.) Portsmouth Hosps. NHS Trust.

WARD, Simon Jeremy Health Centre, St. John Street, Mansfield NG18 1RH Tel: 01623 622541 Fax: 01623 423821; New Manor Farm Barn, Greaves Lane, Edingley, Newark NG22 8BJ Tel: 01623 882809 — MB ChB 1985 Birm.; DFFP 1993; DRCOG 1989. Clin. Tutor (Gen. Pract.) Nottm. Socs: BMA; Mansfield Med. Soc. Prev: SHO (Med.) Staffs. Gen. Infirm.; SHO (Paediat. & O & G) Stafford Dist. Gen. Hosp.

WARD, Simon Jonathan 6 Cambridge Close, Sale, Manchester M33 4JY — MB ChB 1989 Ed.

WARD, Simon Joseph 32 Dovercourt Road, London SE228ST — MB BS 1986 Lond.; MA Camb. (1983); MPhil Camb. 1997; MSc (Paediat.) Lond. 1996; FRCS Ed. 1994; MRCP (UK) 1991. (King's College) Cons. Paediatric A + E, King Geo. Hosp. Ilford. Socs: Assoc. Study Med. Ed. Prev: Hon. Regist. (Paediat., A & E) Alder Hey Childr. Hosp. Liverp.; Hon. Regist. (Paediat., Intens. Care) Gt. Ormond St. Childr. Hosp.; Resp. Fell. Gt.Ormond St. Child. Hosp.

WARD, Simon Michael 18 Birkett Drive, Bolton BL1 7DE — MB BS 1994 Lond.

WARD, Stephanie Department of Child Health, Tickhill Road Hospital, Tickhill Road, Balby, Doncaster DN4 8QL Tel: 01302 796246 Fax: 01302 796377; 31 Scaftworth Close, Bessacarr, Doncaster DN4 7RH — MB ChB 1974 Sheff.; MMSc Leeds Univ. 1997; MRCPCH; MFFP. (Sheff.) Assoc. Specialist (Paediat.)/Community Child Health Doncaster Roy. & Maitagu Hosp. Trust Doncaster; Clin. Med. Off.; Doncaster Healthcare Trust; Family Plann.

WARD, Stephen 7 August House, 17 Palmeira Avenue, Westcliff on Sea SS0 7RP — MB ChB 1974 Manch.; FFA RCS Eng 1979. Cons. Anaesth. N.E. Thames RHA.

WARDALE

WARD, Stephen Exmouth Health Centre, Claremont Grove, Exmouth EX8 2JF Tel: 01395 273001 Fax: 01395 273771; Caledon, Westbourne Terrace, Budleigh Salterton EX9 Tel: 01395 446276 — MB ChB 1980 Liverp.; MRCP (UK) 1983; MRCGP 1987; DRCOG 1987. Trainer GP Pract.

WARD, Stephen Christopher 45 Stretton Road, Great Glen, Leicester LE8 9GN — MB BS 1996 Lond.

WARD, Stephen George Lilac Cottage, 6 Low St., Brotherton, Knottingley WF11 9HQ — MB ChB 1979 Leeds.

WARD, Stephen Patrick 30 Whyke Road, Chichester PO19 2HW; Flat 8 Jenner House, Restell Close, London SE3 7UW — MB BS 1990 Lond.

WARD, Stephen Thomas Sandy Lane Surgery, Sandy Lane, Leyland, Preston PR25 2EB Tel: 01772 909915 Fax: 01772 909911 — MB ChB 1978 Liverp.

WARD, Stuart Andrew Porteous Fryern and Millers Dale Partnership, Fryern Surgery, Oakmount Road, Chandlers Ford, Eastleigh SO53 2LH Tel: 023 8027 3252/3458 Fax: 023 8027 3459 — BM 1986 Soton.; DRCOG 1989. Prev: Trainee GP Portsmouth VTS.

WARD, Susan Clare Southwold, Wilmslow Road, Woodford, Stockport SK7 1RH Tel: 0161 439 4001; AEA International, 38 Russell St, Causeway Bay, Hong Kong Tel: 00 852 2528 9900 Fax: 00 852 2528 9933 Email: drsueward@hotmail.com — MB BS 1991 Lond.; DCH RCP Lond. 1993; MRCGP 1995; DRCOG 1995. GP; Hon. Lect. (Gen. Pract.). Socs: BMA & MPS. Prev: GP Discovery Bay Med. Centre, Hong Kong; Lect. Gen. Pract. Roy. Free Sch. of Med.

WARD, Miss Susan Jennie Kings Mill Hospital, Sutton-in-Ashfield NG17 4JT; High Barn, 160 Edwards Lane, Sherwood, Nottingham NG5 3HZ — BM BS 1980 Nottm.; BMedSci Nottm. 1978; DM Nottm. 1995; FRCS Ed. 1986; MRCOG 1989; DM 1995. (Nottm.) Cons. (O & G) Kings Mill Hosp.; Sec. Med. Woms. Federat. E. Midl.s; Dist. Tutor (Obst. & Gyn.) Mansfield. Socs: Fell. Birm. Midl. Obst. & Gyn. Soc. Prev: Sen. Regist. Nottm. Hosps.; Regist. (O & G) Leicester Gen. Hosp.; Regist. (Urol.) & SHO (O & G) Univ. Hosp. Nottm.

WARD, Susan Margaret Haematology Department, Queen Mary's Sidcup NHS Trust, Frognal Avenue, Sidcup DA14 6LT Tel: 020 8308 3023 Fax: 020 8308 3153 — MB BS 1977 Lond.; BSc (Med. Sci.) Lond. 1974; MRCP (UK) 1981; MRCPath 1988; FRCPath 1997; FRCP 1999. (St. Mary's) p/t Cons. Haematologist Qu. Mary's Sidcup NHS Trust.

WARD, Susan Mary Eborall and Partners, Fountain Medical Centre, Sherwood Avenue, Newark NG24 1QH Tel: 01636 704378/9 Fax: 01636 610875 — MB ChB 1974 Liverp.; DRCOG 1976.

WARD, Talbert (retired) 77 Emm Lane, Heaton, Bradford BD9 4JH Tel: 01274 482405 — MB BS Durh. 1948; MRCGP 1960; Dip. Psychother. Leeds 1978. Prev: Sen. Med. Off. Stud. Health Serv. Bradford Univ.

WARD, Thomas County Practice, Barking Road, Needham Market, Ipswich IP6 8EZ Tel: 01449 720666 Fax: 01449 720030 — MB ChB 1966 Glas.; DCH RCPS Glas. 1969. (Glas.) Prev: Regist. (Gen. Med.) Dept. Mat. Med. Glas. Univ.; Ho. Off. (Paediat.) & Ho. Phys. Stobhill Gen. Hosp. Glas.

WARD, Thomas Arthur Brook Cottage, Raw, Robin Hoods Bay, Whitby YO22 4PP — MB BS 1996 Lond.

WARD, Thomas William 155 Newton Drive, Blackpool FY3 8LZ Tel: 01253 392814 Fax: 01253 300261; 111 Newton Drive, Blackpool FY3 8LZ Fax: 01253 300261 — MB ChB 1977 Sheff.; FRCGP 1996, M 1982; DRCOG 1981; DCH Eng. 1979; DFFP 1996. (Sheff.) Fell. Higher Profess. Train. N. W. (E.) Region; Hon. Sen. Lect. Lanc. Postgrad. Sch. Med. Health. Prev: Course Organiser (Gen. Pract.) Blackpool VTS.; Clin. Asst. (Dermat.) Vict. Hosp. Blackpool.

WARD, Timothy Staveleigh Medical Centre, King Street, Stalybridge SK15 2AE Tel: 0161 304 8009 Fax: 0161 303 7207; 314 Stockport Road, Marple, Stockport SK6 6ET — MB BS 1978 Newc.; MRCGP 1982; DRCOG 1980.

WARD, Timothy Mark Gordon French Weir Health Centre, French Weir Avenue, Taunton TA1 1NW Tel: 01823 331381 Fax: 01823 323689 — MB BS 1990 Lond.; BSc Lond. 1987; MRCGP 1995; DFFP 1995.

WARD, Timothy Peter 80 Old Street, Fareham PO14 3HN — MB BS 1993 Lond.; BSc Psychol. Lond. 1992, MB BS 1993.

WARD, Tracey Jane Conquest Hospital, The Ridge, St Leonards-on-Sea TN37 7RD Tel: 01424 755255 — MB BS 1984 (Hons.) Lond.; MRCP (UK) 1992; MSc Community Paediatrics 1997; MRCGP 1988 (Distinction); FRCPCH 1997; DCH RCP Lond. 1990; DRCOG 1987. Cons. Community Paediat. Hastings & Rother NHS Trust. Prev: Sen. Regist. (Communtiy Paediat.) Optimum Health Care Lewisham & S.wark; Regist. (Community Paediat.) Guy's & Lewisham Hosps.; Trainee GP Ipswich VTS.

WARD, Miss Victoria Mary Margaretha 1 Hamilton House, 8 Victory Place, Quayside, London E14 8BQ Email: vmmw@aol.com — MB ChB 1993 Leic.; FRCSI 1997; 1998 FRCS (Oto). Specialist Regist. in OtoLaryngol., Guy's & St Thomas Trust, Lond.

WARD, Wendy Ann (Surgery), 1 Kew Gdns. Road, Richmond TW9 3HN Tel: 020 8940 1048 Fax: 020 8332 7644; 15 Cumberland Road, Richmond TW9 3HJ Tel: 020 8940 4252 Fax: 020 8332 7770 — MB ChB Bristol 1970; MSc Lond. 1996; MRCGP 1980; DRCOG 1978; DCH Eng. 1973. (Bristol University)

WARD, William (retired) 47 Marlow Road, Gainsborough DN21 1YG Tel: 01427 613873 — MB BCh BAO 1949 NUI; DPH (2nd Cl. Hons.) 1954. Prev: MoH GainsBoro. UD & RD & Isle of Axholme RD.

WARD, William Christopher (retired) 19 Harperley, Astley Village, Chorley PR7 1XB Tel: 01257 271808 Email: billward@bigward.net — MB ChB 1980 Manch.; BSc (Hons.) Manch. 1977, MB ChB 1980. Prev: SHO (Geriat.) Bolton Gen. Hosp.

WARD, William Daniel 52 Wimpole Road, Colchester CO1 2DL Tel: 01206 794794 Fax: 01206 790403; 113 Prettygate Road, Colchester CO3 4DZ Tel: 01206 572705 — MB ChB 1963 Glas. (Glas.) Ex-Chairm. Essex LMC. Socs: Chairm. NE Essex Doctors Emerg. Serv. (BASICS). Prev: Ho. Surg. & Ho. Phys. Glas. Roy. Infirm.; Ho. Surg. (Obst.) Bushey Matern. Hosp.

WARD, William Duncan 67 The Avenue, Richmond TW9 2AH — MB BS 1994 Lond.

WARD-BOOTH, Ronald Patrick Brook Hill Surgery, 30 Brook Hill, Little Waltham, Chelmsford CM3 3LL Tel: 01245 360253 Fax: 01245 361343; Markhams Cottage, Pleshey, Chelmsford CM3 1HY Tel: 973 37 298 — MB BS 1974 Lond.; BDS Birm. 1967.

WARD-BOOTH, Stephen Marshall Cottage, Foston Lane, Peatling Magna, Leicester LE8 5UH — MB ChB 1997 Leic.

WARD-CAMPBELL, Gordon James 12 Rosset Green Lane, Harrogate HG2 — BM BS 1994 Nottm.

WARD-MCQUAID, John Michael Cherry Garth, 16 Humberston Avenue, Humberston, Grimsby DN36 4SJ — LRCPI & LM, LRSCI & LM 1969; LRCPI & LM, LRCSI & LM 1969; FFA RCS Eng. 1978. Cons. Anaesth. Grimsby Dist. Gen. Hosp.

WARD PLATT, Martin Peter Ward 35, Royal Victoria Infirmary, Queen Victoria Road, Newcastle upon Tyne NE1 4LP Tel: 0191 282 5197 Fax: 0191 282 5038 Email: m.p.ward-platt@ncl.ac.uk; Email: m.p.ward-platt@ncl.ac.uk — MB ChB 1979 Bristol; MD Bristol 1989; FRCP Lond. 1994; MRCP (UK) 1983; FRCPCH 1998; FRCP Edin 2000. (Bristol) Cons. Paediat. Sen. Lect. (Child Health) Roy. Vict. Infirm. Newc. u. Tyne; Hon. Cons. Paediat., N.umbria Healthcare NHS Trust. Socs: Brit. Assn. Perinatal Med.; Soc. Reproduc. & Infant Psychol.; Internat. Assn. Study of Pain. Prev: Cons. Paediat. Clin. Sub-Dir. for Neonat. Servs. P.ss Mary Matern. Hosp. Newc.; Sen. Regist. (Neonat.) Newc. HA; Fell. (Neonat.) Monash Med. Centre, Melbourne.

WARD PLATT, Patricia (retired) Greengates Cottage, Astley Burf, Stourport-on-Severn DY13 0SD Tel: 01299 879638 — BM BCh Oxf. 1947; DCH Eng. 1949. Prev: Stud. Health Phys. (Stud. Health Serv.) Liverp. Univ.

WARDALE, Derek Corner House, Hedgerley, Slough SL2 3XL Tel: 01753 642730; 87 Farnham Lane, Farnham Royal, Slough SL2 2AT Tel: 01753 525964 — MB BS 1953 Lond.; MRCS Eng. LRCP Lond. 1953; DObst RCOG 1955. (W. Lond.) Socs: BMA. Prev: SHO Dept. Dermat. & Obst. Ho. Off. W. Middlx. Hosp. Isleworth; Ho. Surg. Roy. N.. Hosp. Lond.

WARDALE, Janette Gibb Fender Way Health Centre, Fender Way, Birkenhead CH43 9QS Tel: 0151 677 9103 Fax: 0151 604 0392; 7 Barker Road, Irby, Wirral CH61 3XH Tel: 0151 648 5325 — MB ChB 1970 Glas.; Cert. Family Pract. JCC 1976. Prev: Regist. (Path.)

WARDALL

United Liverp. Hosps.; Ho. Off. (Med.) S.. Gen. Hosp. Glas.; Ho. Off. (Surg.) Vict. Infirm. Glas.

WARDALL, Gordon James 11 Beechwood, Linlithgow EH49 6SD — MB ChB 1984 Ed.; FRCA 1989; T(Anaesth.) 1993. Cons. Anaesth. Falkirk & Dist. Roy. Infirm. Prev: Sen. Regist. (Anaesth.) Roy. Infirm. Edin.

WARDALL, Andrea Flynn Top Floor Right, 102 Queensborough Gardens, Glasgow G12 9RU — MB ChB 1991 Ed.

WARDALL, Anthony Michael John Tel: 01243 815514 Fax: 01622 723601 — MB BChir 1987 Camb.; MA Camb. 1981; MRCPsych 1991. Cons. (Child & Adolesc. Psychiat.) Invicta Community NHS Trust. Prev: Sen.Regist. (Child & Adolesc. Psychiat.) St. Geo. Hosp. Lond.; Cons (C&A psychiat) Instit ch Trust.

WARDELL-YERBURGH, John Gerald Oswald (retired) 6 Old Northwick Lane, Worcester WR3 7LY Tel: 01905 452518 Email: northwick6@aol.com — MB BChir 1949 Camb.; MA, MB BChir Camb. 1949; MRCPsych 1972; DPM Eng. 1954. Prev: Cons. Psychiat. John Connolly Hosp. Rednal.

WARDELL-YERBURGH, Sheena Jane 1 The Park, Kingscote, Tetbury GL8 8XY — MB BCh 1987 Wales. Prev: GP Nailsworth Retainer Scheme.

WARDELL-YERBURGH, Tom Charles May Lane Surgery, Dursley GL11 4JN Tel: 01453 540540 Fax: 01453 540570 — MB BCh Wales 1987. Prev: Trainee GP Cheltenham; SHO (Dermat.) Glas. Roy. Hosp.; SHO (A & E) Glos. Roy. Infirm.

WARDEN, David John Collington Surgery, 23 Terminus Road, Bexhill-on-Sea TN39 3LR Tel: 01424 217465/216675 Fax: 01424 216675; 8 Meads Road, Bexhill-on-Sea TN39 4SY — MB BS 1985 Lond.; MA Camb. 1989, BA 1982. (Lond. Hosp.) Clin. Asst. (Rheumat.) Conquest Hosp. Hastings.

WARDEN, Kenneth Henry (retired) 9 Varndean Gardens, Brighton BN1 6WJ Tel: 01273 884175 — MB BS Lond. 1954; MRCS Eng. LRCP Lond. 1958; LMCC 1972; MRCGP 1965; DObst RCOG 1958.

WARDEN, Matthew Giles Top Flat, 347A New King's Road, London SW6 4RJ Tel: 020 7731 3435 — MB BS 1995 Lond. (UMDS Guy's & St. Thos. Lond.) SHO (Psychiat.) St. Bart. Hosp. Lond.

WARDEN, Rachel Edna Copelands, 31 Well Lane, Stock, Ingatestone CM4 9LZ Tel: 01277 840650 — MRCS Eng. LRCP Lond. 1955; MB Camb. 1956, BChir 1955; DTM & H Antwerp 1958; DObst RCOG 1962. (Camb. & Lond. Hosp.)

WARDHAUGH, Allan Doyle The Lodge, Talygarn, Pontyclun CF72 9JT — MB ChB 1989 Ed.

WARDHAUGH, Emma Jane 42 Cecil Street, Glasgow G12 8RJ — MB ChB 1997 Glas.

WARDILL, Lesley Forster 9 May Fields, Sindlesham, Wokingham RG41 5BY Tel: 0118 978 3495 Email: lesley.wardill@virgin.net — MB ChB Liverp. 1957; MRCPsych 1982; DPM Eng. 1973; DCH Eng. 1960. (Liverpool University) Indep. Pract. Wokingham. Socs: Roy. Coll. Psychiats. Prev: Assoc. Specialist (Psychiat.) Wokingham Ment. Health Servs. & Eldon Day Hosp. Reading; Clin. Asst. (Psychiat.) Warneford Hosp. Oxf.

WARDLAW, Mr Douglas 10 Monearn Gardens, Milltimber, Milltimber AB13 0EA Tel: 01274 732386 — MB ChB 1969 Ed.; FRCS Ed. 1974. Sen. Regist. (Orthop. Surg.) Aberd. Roy. Infirm. Socs: Assoc. Mem. Brit. Orthop. Assn. Prev: Regist. (Orthop. Surg.) Aberd. Roy. Infirm.

WARDLAW, Joanna Marguerite Department of Clinical Neurosciences, Western General Hospital, Crewe Road, Edinburgh EH4 2XU Tel: 0131 343 6639 Fax: 0131 332 5150 Email: jmw@skull.dcn.ed.ac.uk — MB ChB 1982 Ed.; BSc (Hons.) Physiol. Ed. 1979, MB ChB (Hons.) 1982; MRCP (UK) 1986; FRCR 1988; DMRD 1987; MD 1994. Reader (Neuroradiol.) Univ. Edin.; Hon. Cons. Neuroradiol. W.. Gen. Hosp. NHS Trust Edin. Prev: Cons. Neuroradiol. S.. Gen. Hosp. NHS Trust Glas.

WARDLAW, Mark Mitchell Stirrat Stockland Green Health Centre, 192 Reservoir Road, Erdington, Birmingham B23 6DJ Tel: 0121 373 5405 Fax: 0121 386 4909 — MB ChB 1982 Dundee; BMSc (1st cl. Hons.) Dund 1979, MB ChB 1982. Prev: SHO (Obst.) Manygates Matern. Hosp. Wakefield; SHO (Paediat.) Roy. Manch. Childr Hosp. Pendlebury; SHO (Gyn.) Burnley Gen. Hosp.

WARDLE, Albert Dennis (retired) 165 Moor Green Lane, Moseley, Birmingham B13 8NT Tel: 0121 449 0700 — MB ChB 1953 Birm. Prev: GP Birm.

WARDLE, Andrew Roger 77 Meadow Bank, Penperlleni, Pontypool NP4 0AY — BM BCh 1989 Oxf.

WARDLE, David Phillip Anthony c/o Doctors' Mess, Musgrove Park Hospital, Taunton Tel: 01823 284468; 23 Lon Cedwyn, Sketty, Swansea SA2 0TH Tel: 01792 201728 — MB ChB 1995 Manch.; BSc (Hons.) St. And. 1992. (St. And. & Manch.) SHO (Surg.) MusGr. Pk. Hosp. Taunton. Prev: Ho. Off. (Renal) Manch. Roy. Infirm.; Ho. Off. (Gen. Surg. & Orthop.) MusGr. Pk. Hosp. Taunton.

WARDLE, Edwin Nigel 81 Gloucester Avenue, Grimsby DN34 5BU — MB BChir Camb. 1959; MD Camb. 1975; MRCP (UK) 1964. Socs: Med. Res. Soc.; Internat. Soc. Nephrol.; Eur. Renal Assn.

WARDLE, John Kenneth Pathology Department, Noble's Isle of Man Hospital, Douglas IM1 4QA Tel: 01624 642350 Fax: 01624 642180 Email: wardle@mcb.net; Cooyrt Vane, Ballamodha, Ballasalla IM9 3AY Tel: 01624 824316 Fax: 01624 827068 — MB BS 1975 Lond.; FRCPath 1994, M 1982. Cons. Path. Noble's IOM Hosp. Douglas; Dir. I. of Man Blood Transfus. Serv. Socs: Brit. Soc. Antimicrob. Chemother.; Assn. Clin. Path. Prev: Cons. Microbiol. Wolverhampton Pub. Health Laborat.; Asst. Lect. (Path.) St. Thos. Hosp. Med. Sch. Lond.; Sen. Regist. (Microbiol.) Newc. Gen. Hosp.

WARDLE, Judith Cecilia Rosanne (retired) Fourwinds, 49a Union St., Hamilton ML3 6NA Tel: 01698 424926 — MB BS 1956 Lond.; MMedSci. (Nottm.) 1981; MRCS Eng. LRCP Lond. 1958; MFPHM 1989; DObst RCOG 1958. Prev: Cons. Pub. Health Med. Lanarksh. HB.

WARDLE, Nicholas Stuart 7 Chester Gardens, Morden SM4 6QL Email: nic@nwardle.freeserve.co.uk — MB BS 1998 Lond.; MB BS Lond 1998. (St George's Hospital Medical School)

WARDLE, Mr Peter Gordon Women's Health Services, The Cotswold Centre, Southmead Hospital, Bristol BS10 5NB Tel: 0117 959 5171; Roseacre, 15 Clevedon Road, Flax Bourton, Bristol BS48 1NQ Tel: 01275 463228 Fax: 01275 463925 Email: peter@flaxb.freeserve.co.uk — MB ChB Bristol 1975; MD Bristol 1988; FRCS Eng. 1982; FRCOG 1996, M 1983. (Bristol) Cons. O & G Wom.'s Health Servs. Bristol. Socs: (Hon. Sec.) Brit. Fertil. Soc.; BMA. Prev: Cons. & Sen. Lect. O & G Univ. Bristol; Dep. Dir. Univ. Bristol Centre for Reproductive Med.; RCOG Fell. (Reproduc. Med.) Univ. Bristol.

WARDLE, Robert Stanley (retired) Highfield, 23 Knoll Park, St Clement, Truro TR1 1FF Tel: 01872 242560 — MB BChir 1954 Camb.; MA Camb. 1955, MB BChir 1954; DObst RCOG 1958. Prev: Gen. Pract., Chard, Som.

WARDLE, Rosalind Mary Holsworthy Health Centre, Western Road, Holsworthy EX22 6DH Tel: 01409 253692 Fax: 01409 254184 — MB ChB 1985 Bristol; MRCGP 1989; Cert. Family Plann. JCC 1989; DCH RCP Lond. 1988; Dip. Ther. 1997. (Bristol) Gen. Practitioners Holsworthy. Prev: Trainee GP Plymouth VTS; SHO (O & G) Solihull Hosp.; SHO (Dermat.) Plymouth.

WARDLE, Stephen Paul Neonatal unit, Liverpool Women's Hospital, Crown St, Liverpool L8 7SS Tel: 0141 708 9988 Fax: 0151 702 4082; Ivy Bank, Alvanley Drive, Helsby, Warrington WA6 9QE Tel: 01928 723450 Email: s.p.wardle@liverpool.ac.uk — MB ChB 1990 Liverp.; MRCP (UK) 1993; MRCPCH; MD Liverpool, 1999. (Liverpool) Lect. in Nionatal Med., Univ. of Liverp. Prev: Research Regist. Liverp. Wom. Hosp.; Regist. Rotat. (Paediat.) NW Region; SHO Rotat. (Paediat.) Mersey Region.

WARDLE, Terence David Sunnycroft, Clayhanger Lane, Mere, Knutsford WA16 6QG — BM BS 1984 Nottm.; BM BS (Hons.) Nottm. 1984; DM Nottm. 1992, BMedSci (Hons.) 1982; MRCP (UK) 1987. Lect. (Med.) Hope Hosp. Manch. Prev: Research Fell. Univ. Dept. Med. Hope Hosp. Manch.; Regist. Rotat. (Med.) N. Staffs. Med. Centre Stoke-on-Trent; SHO Rotat. (Med.) N. Staffs. Med. Centre Stoke-on-Trent.

WARDLE, William Christopher (retired) 16 Mathesons Gardens, Morpeth NE61 1ET — MB BS 1921 Durh.

WARDLEY, Andrew Michael Department of Medical Oncology, Greenlea Oncology Unit, Huddersfield Royal Infirmary, Huddersfield HD3 3EA Tel: 01484 482150 Fax: 01484 482187 Email: awardley@hrioncology.demon.co.uk; Ash Tree Cottage, 72 The Village, Thrustonland, Huddersfield HD4 6XX Tel: 01484 666171 — MB ChB 1989 Manch.; MRCP (UK) 1993. Specialist Regist. Med. Oncol. Leeds Rotat. Socs: Roy. Coll. Phys.; Assn. Cancer Phys. Prev: Research Regist. (Med. Oncol.) Christie Hosp. Manch.; Clin. Lect. (Hon. Regist.) Manch. Univ. in Med. Oncol.

WARDLEY, James Raymond 21 Broomfield Drive, Alderholt, Fordingbridge SP6 3HY — MD Manch. 1942, MB ChB 1935; MRCS Eng. LRCP Lond. 1935. (Manch.) Socs: Fell. Manch. Med. Soc. Prev: Ho. Surg. Roy. Infirm. Manch.; Phys. Lake Hosp. Ashton-under-Lyne; Med. Specialist, Maj. R.A.M.C.

WARDMAN, Andrew George Leigh Infirmary, The Avenue, Leigh WN7 1HS Tel: 01942 672333; 54 Albert Road W., Heaton, Bolton BL1 5HG — MB ChB Ed. 1976; MD Ed. 1986; FRCP Lond. 1995; MRCP (UK) 1980. Cons. Phys. Wigan & Leigh Health Servs. Trust. Prev: Sen. Regist. (Med.) Leeds & Bradford.

WARDMAN, Derek Graham — MB ChB 1981 Leeds; FFPHM RCP (UK) 1995; MFCM 1988; MPH Leeds 1986. Dir. Of Pub. Health, Calderdale & Kirklees H.A; 5 River Pk., Honley, Holmfirth HD9 6PS.

WARDMAN, Lyn Elizabeth Heaton Medical Centre, 2 Lucy St., Bolton BL1 5PU Tel: 01204 843677 Fax: 01204 495485; 54 Albert Road W., Heaton, Bolton BL1 5HG — MB ChB 1980 Leeds; MRCGP 1985.

WARDROP, Alan G Monk Street Health Centre, 74 Monk Street, Aberdare CF44 7PA Tel: 01685 875906 Fax: 01685 875906.

WARDROP, Charles Alexander James Broom Hill, 111 Viewlands Road W., Perth PH1 1EH Tel: 01738 638588 — MB ChB 1962 St. And.; FRCP Ed. 1982, M 1968; FRCPath 1982, M 1970. (St. And.) Hon. Cons. Haematol. Socs: Eur. Soc. Paediat. Research; UK Neonat. Soc. Prev: Lect. (Haemat.) Univ. Glas.; Ho. Phys. Dundee Roy. Infirm.; Ho. Surg. Maryfield Hosp. Dundee.

WARDROP, Nicola 11 Vere Road, Kirkmuirhill, Lanark ML11 9RS — MB ChB 1998 Ed.

WARDROP, Mr Peter John Charles Department of ENT, Crosshouse Hospital, Kilmarnock KA2 0BE Tel: 01563 577326 Fax: 01563 577974 — MB BCh 1988 Wales; FRCS Ed. 1994; FRCS Eng. 1992; FRCS (Orl.) Ed. 1998. (Wales) Cons. ENT Ayrsh. & Arran NHS Trust CrossHo. Hosp. Kilmarnock. Socs: ORS; BAOHNS - Brit. Assn. Otolaryngologists - Head Neck Surg.s; BCIG - Brit. Cochlear Implant Gp. Prev: Regist. (ENT) City Hosp. Edin.; SHO (Surg.) Qu. Med. Centre Nottm.; SHO (Plastics) St. Luke's Bradford.

WARDROPE, Mr James Accident & Emergency Department, Northern General Hospital, Herries Road, Sheffield S5 7AU Tel: 0114 243 4343 Fax: 0114 261 1897 — MB ChB 1978 Ed.; FRCS Eng. 1983; FRCS Ed. 1982; FRCS (A&E) Ed. 1986; FFAEM 1993. p/t Cons. A & E Med. N. Gen. Hosp. Sheff. Socs: Brit. Assn. Accid. & Emerg. Med. (Chairm. Acad. Sub. Comm.); Fell. Fac. A&E Med. (Treas.). Prev: Sen. Regist. (A & E) Roy. Hallamsh. Hosp. Sheff.; Research Regist. Univ. Leeds; Regist. Rotat. (Surg.) Leeds Gen. Infirm.

WARDROPPER, Alison Grace Dryburn Hospital, North Road, Durham DH1 5TW Fax: 0191 384 9879; 19 The Drive, Gosforth, Newcastle upon Tyne NE3 4AH Tel: 0191 284 5406 — BM BS 1986 Nottm.; MRCP (UK) 1989. Cons. in Genitourin. Med.,Dryburn and Bishop Auckland Hosp.; Honourary Cons. Phys., Newc. Gen. Hosp. Socs: MSSUD; AGUM; RCP(Lond.).

WARE, Anthony Wicks 1 Westgarth Gardens, Bury St Edmunds IP33 3LB Tel: 01284 754253 — MRCS Eng. LRCP Lond. 1955.

WARE, Mr Charles Francis Wakefield Old Manse, 147 Ballynahinch Road, Hillsborough BT26 6BD — MB BCh BAO 1958 Belf.; FRCSI 1974; FRCS Ed. 1965; FRCOphth 1991; DO RCS Eng. 1966. Assoc. Specialist EHSSB/SHSSB N. Irel. Prev: Sen. Regist. Eye & Ear Clinic Belf.

WARE, Christopher John Grattan (retired) 6 The Green, Cuddesdon, Oxford OX44 9JZ — MB BS 1978 Lond.; MRCPsych 1989; MRCGP 1985; DRCOG 1985. Prev: Sen. Regist. (Psychiat.) Warneford Hosp. Oxf.

WARE, Claire-Louise 22 Gnoll Cr, Neath SA11 3TF — BM 1997 Soton.

WARE, Clive Charles Newark Road Surgery, 501 Newark Road, South Hykeham, Lincoln LN6 8RT Tel: 01522 537944 Fax: 01522 510932 — MB ChB 1985 Liverp.; MBA Leeds 1994; FRCGP 1997, M 1989; T(GP) 1991; DRCOG 1989; DGM RCP Lond. 1988; DCH RCP Lond. 1988. (Liverp.)

WARE, Mr Colin Clement Tree Tops, 247 Thorpe Hall Avenue, Thorpe Bay, Southend-on-Sea SS1 3SG Tel: 01702 86797 — MB BS 1962 Lond.; BSc Lond. 1954, MB BS (Hons.) 1962; FRCS Eng. 1965. (Westm.) Cons. Surg. S.end-on-Sea Gp. Hosps. Socs: Fell. Roy. Soc. Med.; Fell. Assn. Surg. Prev: Sen. Surg. Regist. W.m.

Hosp.; Lect. in Surg. St. Thos. Hosp. Lond. Ho. Surg. St. Jas. Hosp. Balham.

WARE, Delyth Ann Pencoed and Llanharan Medical Centres, Heol-yr-Onnen, Pencoed, Bridgend CF35 5PF Tel: 01656 860270 Fax: 01656 861228; 6 Parklands, Corntown, Bridgend CF35 5BE Tel: 01656 662948 — MB BS 1977 Lond.; BSc (Biochem.) Lond. 1974; MRCS Eng. LRCP Lond. 1977; MRCGP 1991; DCH Eng. 1979. (Guy's)

WARE, Mr Howard Elliott 134 Harley Street, London W1 Tel: 020 7935 0482; St. Bartholomew's Hospital, West Smithfield, London EC1A 7BE Tel: 020 7601 8888 — MB BS 1980 Lond.; FRCS (Orth.) 1992; FRCS Eng. 1986; FRCS Ed. 1985. Cons. Orthop. Surg. St. Bart. Hosp. Lond. Socs: BMA, Brit. Orthop. Assn. & Brit. Hip Soc.

WARE, Mrs Jean Marian (retired) 4 Bearcroft Gardens, Mickleton, Chipping Campden GL55 6TY Tel: 01368 438988 — MB BS 1957 Lond. Family Plann. Med. Off. & Sessional Sch. Med. Off. S.end Health Dist. Prev: Clin. Med. Off. Lond. Boro. Havering.

WARE, Mr John Walter (retired) 152 Harley Street, London W1N 1HH Tel: 020 7935 8868 Email: john.ware@coonnectfree.co.uk — MB ChB Bristol 1953; FRCS Ed. 1970. Prev: Cons. Traum. & Orthop. Surg.

WARE, Lynda Maria Morland House Surgery, 2 London Road, Wheatley, Oxford OX33 1YJ Tel: 01865 872448 Fax: 01865 874158; 6 The Green, Cuddesdon, Oxford OX44 9JZ Email: lyndaware@aol.com — MB BChir 1978 Camb.; MA Camb. 1978; MRCGP 1983; DRCOG 1980. (Westm.) GP Wheatley, Oxf.; Clin. Tutor (Gen. Pract.) Univ. Oxf. Socs: Brit. Menopause Soc.

WARE, Robert John 1B Reddons Road, Beckenham BR3 1LY — MB BS 1972 Lond.; FFA RCS Eng. 1976. (King's Coll. Hosp.) SHO (Anaesth.) King's Coll. Hosp. Lond.

WARE, Ronald William (retired) Flat 2, The Willows, 83 Vincent Square, London SW1P 2PF Tel: 020 7828 2686 — MRCS Eng. LRCP Lond. 1952; DA Eng. 1969; DIH Soc. Apoth. Lond. 1961; DObst RCOG 1958; DLO Eng. 1956. Prev: Med. Dir. Mobil Saudi Arabia Inc.

WARE, Stephen John 74 Norsey Road, Billericay CM11 1AT Tel: 01277 58659 — MB BS 1967 Lond.; MRCP (UK) 1970; DCH Eng. 1969. (St. Thos.) Cons. Paediat. Basildon & S.end Health Dists.

WAREHAM, Conrad Arthur 6 Peterborough Drive, Sheffield S10 4JB — BM 1984 Soton.

WAREHAM, David William Harold Wood Hospital, Gubbins Lane, Harold Wood, Romford RM3 0BE; Flat 7, Lagonda House, 20 Tidworth Road, London E3 4XS Tel: 020 8980 1784 — MB BS 1994 Lond. (Lond. Hosp. Med. Coll.) SHO (Gen. Med.) Harold Wood Hosp. Prev: SHO (A & E & c/o Elderly) Whipps Cross Hosp. Lond.; Ho. Off. (Gen. Med.) Roy. Lond. Hosp.

WAREHAM, Karen Patricia 7 Kipling Close, Yateley GU46 6YA — MB ChB 1995 Bristol; MRCP 1998. SHO. Med.derriford.Hosp. Plymouth.

WAREHAM, Nicholas John Institute of Public Health, University of Cambridge, Forvie Site, Robinson Way, Cambridge CB2 2SR Tel: 01223 330300 Fax: 01223 330330 Email: njw1004@medschl.cam.ac.uk; 4 Kingfisher Close, Bourn, Cambridge CB3 7TJ — MB BS 1986 Lond.; PhD Camb. 1997; MSc Pub. Health Med. Lond. 1991; MRCP (UK) 1990; MFPHM RCP (UK) 1992. MRC Clinician Scientist Fell. Inst. (Pub. Health) Camb.; Hon. Cons. Pub. Health Med Camb. & Huntingdon Health Commiss. Prev: Sen. Regist. (Epidemiol. & Pub. Health Med.) Inst. Pub. Health Camb.; Harkness Fell. Harvard Sch. Pub. Health.

WAREHAM, Valerie Ann 5 The Grange, North Beach Road, Balmedie, Aberdeen AB23 8XG — MB ChB 1987 Aberd.

WAREING, Christopher Robert c/o Mr A D Wareing, RAC Symes & Co Solicitors, 4-6 Robert St., Scunthorpe DN15 6NG — MB BChir 1977 Camb.

WAREING, Mr Michael John ENT Department, Guys Hospital, London SE1 9RT Tel: 020 7955 5000 Email: michaelwareing@clara.net; 39 Culverden Avenue, Tunbridge Wells TN4 9RE — MB BS 1988 Lond.; BSc Lond. 1985; FRCS (Otol.) Eng. 1993; FRCS Eng. 1992; FRCS 1998. (St. Bart. Hosp. Med. Coll.) Specialist Regist. Rotat. (Otolarygol. Head & Neck Surg.) S. Thames (E.); Neurotological Fell. Addenbrookes Hosp.Camb. Socs: BMA; Brit. Assn. Otol. Head & Neck Surg. Prev: TWJ Fell. (Otol.) Univ. Calif.,

WARENIUS

San Francisco; SHO (ENT) Addenbrooke's Hosp. Camb.; SHO (Gen. Surg.) E. Surrey Hosp. Redhill.

WARENIUS, Hilmar Meek University of Liverpool, Oncology Research Unit, Department of Medicine, The Duncan Building, Daulby St., Liverpool L69 3GA Tel: 0151 706 4530 Fax: 0151 706 5802 Email: warenius@liverpool.ac.uk; 14 Delavor Road, Heswall, Wirral CH60 4RN Tel: 0151 342 3034 — MB BChir Camb. 1969; PhD Camb. 1980, MA 1970; FRCP Lond. 1987; MRCP (UK) 1971; MRCS Eng. LRCP Lond. 1968; FRCR 1975; DMRT 1973. (Camb. & Middlx.) Prof. & Dir. Oncol. Research Univ. of Liverp.; Hon. Prof, Guangxi Med. Univ., China. Socs: Brit. Oncol. Assn.; Eur. Soc. Therap. Radiol. & Oncol.; Brit. Assn. Cancer Research. Prev: Vis. Prof. & Hon. Cons. Clin. Oncol. Hammersmith Hosp. Lond.; Hon. Coordinator MRC Fast Neutron Studies Clatterbridge Hosp. Merseyside; Cons. Radiotherap. & Oncol. Newc. Gen. Hosp.

WARES, Alastair Neil Pendyffryn Medical Group, Ffordd Pendyffryn, Prestatyn LL19 9DH Tel: 01745 886444 Fax: 01745 889831; 6 The Circle, Prestatyn LL19 9EU — MB ChB 1979 Liverp.; M.Phil. (Medical Law) Glasgow 2001; MPhil 2001 Glasgow. Howes, Jessup, Wares, Serven, Williams, Phillips, Campbell, Popat & Morrison.

WARFIELD, Adrian Thomas Department of Cellular Pathology (Histopathology), The Medical School, Vincent Drive, Birmingham B15 2TT Tel: 0121 414 4012, 0121 414 4016 Fax: 0121 414 4019 — MB ChB 1986 Birm.; MRCPath 1994. Cons. Histopath. Univ. Hosps. NHS Trust; Hon. Sen. Clin. Lect. (Path.) Univ. of Birm.; Cons. Histopath. Birm. Heartlands Hosptial. Socs: Brit. Soc. Clin. Cytopath.; Assn. Clin. Path.; Path. Soc. Prev: Sen. Regist. (Histopath.) N. Staffs. Hosp. Centre & Birm. Heartlands Hosp.

WARIN, Andrew Peter The Royal Devon & Exeter Hospital (Wonford), Barrack Road, Exeter EX2 5DW Tel: 01392 402250 Fax: 01392 402210; The Gables, Priory Close, East Budleigh, Budleigh Salterton EX9 7EZ Email: andrew.warin@lineone.net — MB BS Lond. 1967; FRCP Lond. 1983; MRCP (UK) 1970; MRCS Eng. LRCP Lond. 1967. (Guy's) Cons. Dermat. Roy. Devon & Exeter Hosp. Exeter. Socs: Fell. Roy. Soc. Med. (Dermat. Sect.); Brit. Assn. Dermat.; Amer. Acad. of Dermat. Prev: Cons. Dermat. St. John's Hosp. Dis. Skin Lond.; Sen. Lect. Inst. Dermat. Lond.; Assoc. Prof. Dermat. Pahlavi Univ. Med. Sch., Iran.

WARIN, Judith Mary Psychotherapy Department, Wonford House Hospital, Dryden Road, Exeter EX2 5AF Tel: 01392 403446; Maranatha, Rewe, Exeter EX5 4EU — MB BS 1968 Lond.; BSc (Biochem.) Lond. 1965. (Guy's) Clin. Asst. (Psychother.) Wonford Hse. Hosp. Exeter. Prev: Clin. Asst. (Psychother. & Radiother.) Wonford Hosp. Exeter; Clin. Asst. Renal Unit Roy. Devon & Exeter Hosp. (Wonford); SCMO Lewisham Health Dist.

WARIN, William Arthur Southmead Health Centre, Ullswater Road, Bristol BS10 6DF Tel: 0117 950 7150 Fax: 0117 959 1110; 3 Burlington Road, Bristol BS6 6TJ — MB ChB 1979 Birm.; MRCGP 1986; DRCOG 1984. Prev: Trainee GP S.mead Bristol.

WARING, Angela Bell Bellevue, 35 Limefield, Gilmerton, Edinburgh EH17 8PF — MB ChB 1996 Ed.; MB ChB (Hons.) Ed. 1996; BSc (Hons.) Ed. 1994; MRCP (UK) 1999; MRCPCH 1999. (Univ. Ed.) Clin. Res. Fell. (Paediat. Oncol.). Socs: MRCPCH. Prev: Paediat. SHO Rotat., SE Scotl.

WARING, Eileen (retired) 25 The Glen, Worthing BN13 2AD Tel: 01903 691027 — MRCS Eng. LRCP Lond. 1956. Prev: SCMO Worthing.

WARING, Howard Linton Ingersley Unit, Macclesfield District Hospital, Macclesfield SK10 3BL Tel: 01625 663722 Fax: 01625 663107 — MB ChB 1973 Ed.; MD Lond. 1988; MD Aberd. 1988; MRCPsych. 1978. Cons. Psychiat. E. Chesh. Trust Macclesfield. Socs: Roy. Coll. Psychiat.

WARING, Ian Stuart Tudor Lodge Health Centre, 3 Nithsdale Road, Weston Super Mare BS23 4JP Tel: 01934 622665 Fax: 01934 644332 — MB ChB 1965 Bristol.

WARING, James Rodney War Memorial Health Centre, Crickhowell NP8 1AG Tel: 01873 810255 Fax: 01873 811949 — MB BS 1959 Durh.; DObst RCOG 1966. (Durh.) Med. Off. Brecon Mt.ain Rescue Team. Prev: Ho. Surg. & Ho. Phys. Roy. Vict. Infirm. Newc.; RMO 2 Para.

WARING, John Richard Northgate Surgery, Northgate, Pontefract WF8 1NF Tel: 01977 703635 Fax: 01977 702562; Arncliffe, 110 Carleton Road, Pontefract WF8 3NQ Tel: 01977 600941 Email: johnwaring@breathe.com — MRCS Eng. LRCP Lond. 1969. (Manch.) Chairm. Wakefield LMC.

WARING, Mr Michael Room 656C, Skipton House, 80 London Road, Elephant & Castle, London SE1 6LH Tel: 020 7972 5120 Fax: 020 7972 5134; Hawk House, Church Lane, E. Haddon, Northampton NN6 8DB Tel: 01604 770369 — MB BChir 1972 Camb.; BA (Hons.) Open 1988; MA Camb. 1972; MRCS Eng. LRCP Lond. 1971; FRCS Eng. 1978. Sen. Med. Off. DoH Elephant & Castle.

WARING, Nicholas Anthony (retired) 14 Shaws Park, Hexham NE46 3BJ Tel: 01434 607452 — MRCS Eng. LRCP Lond. 1955; MA Camb. 1973. Prev: Regional Med. Off. DHSS.

WARING, Nicholas John Gillies and Overbridge Medical Partnership, Brighton Hill, Sullivan Road, Basingstoke RG22 4EH Tel: 01256 479747; Spinney Cottage, North Waltham Road, Oakley, Basingstoke RG23 7EA Tel: 01256 780397 Email: nick@spinneyco.freeserve.co.uk — MB BCh 1971 Wales; MRCS Eng. LRCP Lond. 1972; FRCGP 1987, M 1975; DObst RCOG 1973. (Welsh Nat. Sch. Med.) Socs: Worshipful Soc. Apoth. Lond.; Wessex Res. Netw. Prev: SHO (Paediat.) & Ho. Surg. Univ. Hosp. of Wales Cardiff; Ho. Phys. Roy. S. Hants. Hosp. Soton.

WARING, William Brian (retired) Durnford Medical Centre, 113 Long St., Middleton, Manchester M24 6DL Tel: 0161 643 2011 — MB ChB 1956 Manch. Prev: Ho. Surg. Manch. Roy. Infirm.

WARING, William Stephen Bellevue, 35 Limefield, Gilmerton, Edinburgh EH17 8PF Tel: 0131 664 9950 — MB BCh BAO 1995 Belf.; BMedSci (Hons.) Belf. 1993; MRCP (UK) 1998 Queens University Belf. Clin. Lect. (Clin. Pharmacol. & Med.) Univ. of Edin.; Hon. Specialist Regist. (Gen. Med. & Clin. Pharmacol.). Prev: SHO Rotat. (Med.) S. E. Scotl.

WARINTON, Andrew David Rakaia Lodge, Langford Place, Lower Langford, Bristol BS40 5BP — BChir 1988 Camb.

WARK, Kathryn Jessie London Chest Hospital, Royal Hospitals NHS Trust, Bonner Road, London E2 9JX Tel: 020 8980 4433 — MB BS 1973 Queensland; FFA RCS Lond. 1980. (Univ. Queensland) Cons. Anaesth. (Cardiothoracic Anaesth.) Lond. Chest & St. Bart. Hosps. Roy. Hosps. NHS Trust. Socs: Anaesth. Res. Soc.; Assn. Cardiothoracic Anaesth. Prev: Cons. Anaesth. Guy's Hosp. Lond.; Sen. Regist. Lond. Hosp.

WARKE, Timothy Royal Victoria Hospital, Grosvenor Road, Belfast BT12 6BA Tel: 01232 240503; 38 Haddington Hill, Derriaghy Road, Lisburn BT28 3AU Tel: 01846 601216 — MB BCh BAO 1995 Belf. (Qu. Univ. Belf.) SHO Rotat. (Med.) Roy. Vict. Hosp. Belf. Prev: Ho. Off. Roy. Vict. Hosp. Belf.

WARLAND, Jane Christine Grey Walls, Smith Hill, Bishopsteignton, Teignmouth TQ14 9QT Tel: 01626 773565; The Annexe, Woodgate Farm, Cliffords Mesne, Newent GL18 1JU Tel: 01531 822875 — MB ChB 1995 Leeds; BSc Leeds 1992. (Leeds) SHOA & E)Roy.Shrewsbury Hosp. Socs: BMA; MDU.

WARLEY, Anthony Robert Holmes Salisbury District Hospital, Salisbury SP2 8BJ Tel: 01722 336262 — MB BS 1978 Lond.; MD Lond. 1988; MRCP (UK) 1981; FRCP 1998. (Westm.) Cons. Phys. Gen. & Respirat. Med. Salisbury Dist. Hosp. Prev: Sen. Regist. (Med.) Frenchay Hosp. & Bristol Roy. Infirm.; Research Fell. Ch.ill Hosp. Oxf.; SHO MusGr. Hosp. Taunton.

WARLEY, Mogamat Arashat (retired) 69 Rosebery Road, Muswell Hill, London N10 2LE Tel: 020 8444 2937 — MD 1963 Cape Town; BA Cape Town 1946, MD 1963, MB ChB 1946; FRCPCH 1997, DCH Eng. 1954. Prev: Cons. Paediat. Brook Gen. & Greenwich Dist. Hosps. Lond.

WARLOW, Allan Llewellyn (retired) The Old Cottage, L'Ancresse, Vale, Guernsey GY3 5 — MRCS Eng. LRCP Lond. 1947.

WARLOW, Andrea Linda 4 Hayston Avenue, Hakin, Milford Haven SA73 3EB — MB BCh 1979 Wales; DCH RCP Lond. 1983.

WARLOW, Professor Charles Picton Department of Clinical Neurosciences, Western General Hospitals, Crewe Road, Edinburgh EH4 2XU Tel: 0131 537 2082 Fax: 0131 332 7886 Email: cpw@skull.dcn.ed.ac.uk — MD 1975 Camb.; BA 1965 Camb.; 1998 FMEDSci; MB BChir 1968 Camb.; FRCP Glas. 1993; FRCP Ed. 1987; FRCP Lond. 1983; MRCP (UK) 1970. (Camb.) Prof. Med. Neurol. Univ. Edin.; Hon. Cons. Neurol. Socs: Fell. Acad. Med. Sci. (1998); Brit. Assn. Stroke Phys. (Pres. Elect); Assn. Brit. Neurol. (Pres. 2001-3) & Amer. Neurol. Assn. Prev: Clin. Reader (Neurol.)

Univ. Oxf.; Lect. (Med.) Aberd. Univ.; Regist. & Sen. Regist. (Neurol.) Nat. Hosps. Nerv. Dis. Lond.

WARLOW, Colin Norman, Surg. Cdr. RN Retd. 27 Bellair Road, Havant PO9 2RG Tel: 023 9247 5447 Fax: 023 9247 5447 — MB BCh BAO NUI 1960; MRCGP 1974; Dip. GU Med. Soc. Apoth Lond. 1989; DTM & H Eng. 1967. (Univ. Coll. Dub.) Med. Off. (Genitourin.) HMS Nelson Portsmouth; Adviser (Genitourin. Med.) MDG(N). Socs: Med. Soc. Study VD; Assn. Genitourin. Med.; Soc. of Study of Sexually Transm. Dis.s of Irel. Prev: PMO HMS Sultan, Mercury & Fearless.

WARLOW, Jennifer Jane University of Bradford Health Centre, Laneisteridge Lane, Bradford BD5 0NH Tel: 01274 234979 Fax: 01274 235940 — MB ChB 1985 Leeds; DCCH 1993; DRCOG 1988. (Leeds)

WARLOW, Mr Peter Frederick Maurice 16 The Crescent, Brixton, Plymouth PL8 2AP Tel: 01752 880946 — MB BS Lond. 1950; FRCS Ed. 1961.

WARLOW, Steven Rosemary Medical Centre, 2 Rosemary Gardens, Parkstone, Poole BH12 3HF Tel: 01202 741300; 9 Overbury Road, Parkstone, Poole BH14 9JL Tel: 01202 743495 — MB BS 1979 Lond.; MA Camb. 1979; MRCS Eng. LRCP Lond. 1979; MRCGP 1983; DRCOG 1981. (Westm.)

WARLTIER, Betty Rosemary (retired) 19 Woodhall Avenue, Pinner HA5 3DY Tel: 020 8866 3985 — MB BChir 1952 Camb.; MA Camb. 1952; MRCS Eng. LRCP Lond. 1952; FFA RCS Eng. 1955; DObst RCOG 1957; DA Eng. 1954. Cons. Anaesth. Mt. Vernon Hosp. N.wood. Prev: Sen. Regist. (Anaesth.) Char. Cross Hosp.

WARMAN, Linda Helen 19 Park Drive, London NW11 7SN — MB ChB 1972 Manch.; DObst RCOG 1975.

WARMINGER, Max Bracondale, Norwich NR1 2AE — MB ChB 1976 Liverp.; MRCS Eng. LRCP Lond. 1976; DA Eng. 1979.

WARNAKULASURIYA, Kasturiaraachige M R D S (Surgery), 12 North St., Winlaton, Blaydon-on-Tyne NE21 6BX Tel: 0191 414 8874; Dalry, Elm Bank Road, Wylam NE41 8HS Tel: 01661 853139 — MB BS 1962 Ceylon.

WARNE, Roger William Department Geriatric Medicine, Royal Perth Hospital, Wellington St., Perth 6000, Australia Tel: 00 619 2242099 Fax: 00 619 2243339 Email: rogewarn@rph.health.wa-gov.au; 35 Elm Tree Park, Yealmpton, Plymouth PL8 2ED Tel: 01752 880457 — MB BS 1971 Lond.; MMed Melbourne 1984; FRCP Ed. 1994; FRACP 1979; MRCP (UK) 1975; MRCS Eng. LRCP Lond. 1971. (FRCP Lond 1997) Phys. Bentley Health Serv. Aged Care Servs. Perth, Austral.; Assoc. Prof. Sch. Pub. Health. Curtin Univ of Tech. Australia. Socs: State Comm. Austral. Assn. Gerontol.; Aus. Soc. Geriat.. Med; Brit.Geriat.s Soc. Prev: Phys. (Geriat. Med.) Roy. Perth Hosp. W. Austral.; Convenor Teach. Geriat. Med. Gp. & Federal Represen. Teach. & Research Austral. Geriat. Soc. W.. Austral. Div.; Sen. Specialist Phys. (Geriat. Med.) Heidelberg Repatriation Hosp.

WARNE, Stephanie Anastasia 5 Summerhill, Prehen Park, Londonderry BT47 2PL Tel: 01504 347902 Email: warnesa@cardiff.ac.uk — MB BCh 1995 Wales. (Univ. Wales Coll. Med.) SHO (Gen. Surg.) E. Glam. Hosp.; SHO (Paediat. Surg.) Gt. Ormond St Childr. Hosp. Lond. Socs: MDU; Wom. in Surg. Train. Prev: SHO (Cardiothoracic Surg.) Univ. Hosp. of Wales Cardiff; SHO (Orthop.) E. Glam. Hosp. Pontypridd; SHO (Gen. Surg.) Univ. Hosp. Wales Cardiff.

WARNELL, Ian Haydn Department of Anaesthesia, Newcastle General Hospital, Newcastle upon Tyne NE6 4BE Tel: 0191 273 8811 — MB BS 1977 Lond.; MRCP (UK) 1981; FFA RCS Eng. 1983. Cons. Anaesth. Newc. Gen. Hosp.

WARNER, Adrian Anthony Little Acre, Ufford Road, Bainton, Stamford PE9 3BB — MB 1967 Camb.; BChir 1966; FFR 1974; DMRD Eng. 1972; Cert Amer. Bd. Radiol. 1975. (Middlx.) Cons. Radiol. Hinchingbrooke Hosp. Huntingdon. Prev: Sen. Cons. Radiol. Nat. Guard K. Khalid Hosp., Saudi Arabia; Teach. (Radiol.) Univ. Camb. & Univ. Leicester; Cons. Radiol. P'boro. Dist. Hosp.

WARNER, Andrew Philip 54 Lemon Street, Truro TR1 2PE; 16 Shepherds Hill, Southam, Leamington Spa CV47 1GD Tel: 01926 811023 Email: asqwif@bt.internet — MB BS 1995 Lond. (St. Georges Hospital) GP Regist. Kineton Surg. Socs: GP VTS Warwick Hosp.

WARNER, Barry Graham 2 Liquorstane, Falkland, Cupar KY15 7DQ; 8 Silver meadows, barton, Richmond DL10 6SL — MB ChB 1997 Dundee. SHO Surgic. Rotat. Darlington Memor. Hosp.

WARNER, Cedric Martin Woodlands Health Centre, Allington Road, Paddock Wood, Tonbridge TN12 6AR Tel: 01892 833331; Pimms Place, Peckham Bush, Tonbridge TN12 5LL Tel: 01622 871736 — MB ChB 1963 Birm.; MRCGP 1969; DObst RCOG 1966. (Birm.) Med. Off. Child Welf. Clinic Kent CC; Trainer GP SE Thames RHA. Socs: BMA. Prev: Mem. Dist. Managem. Team Tunbridge Wells DHA; Clin. Asst. (Rheum.) Homoeop. Hosp. Tunbridge Wells; SHO (Trauma) Kidderminster Gen. Hosp.

WARNER, Charles Whitlow, MC (retired) 4 Calder Park Court, Calderstones Road, Liverpool L18 3HZ Tel: 0151 724 3148 — MB ChB 1933 Liverp.; FRCGP 1975, M 1957. Prev: GP Woolton.

WARNER, Christopher Arlington c/o Dr Charles Greenidge, Swift Place, East Kilbride, Glasgow G75 8RT; c/o Mr. & Mrs. Gladstone Pollard, Joystone, Pine Gardens, St. Micheal, Barbados — MB BS 1977 W. Indies.

WARNER, Christopher Eric James Osmaston Road Medical Centre, 212 Osmaston Road, Derby DE23 8JX Tel: 01332 346433 Fax: 01332 345854 — BM BS 1989 Nottm.; BMedSci Nottm. 1987; MRCGP 1993.

WARNER, Darren Paul 2 Church View, Burley Lane, Menston, Ilkley LS29 6EX — MB ChB 1991 Leeds.

WARNER, Diana Lewen The Surgery, 43 Nevil Road, Bishopston, Bristol BS7 9EG Tel: 0117 924 5630 Fax: 0117 924 5630 — MB BS 1982 Lond. Prev: Trainee GP E. Glam. Gen. Hosp. VTS.

WARNER, Edward Maurice (retired) 204 Hall Green Road, West Bromwich B71 2DX Tel: 0121 588 2456 — MB ChB 1948 Birm.

WARNER, Graham Terrance Anthony Tel: 01702 221225 Fax: 01702 221249 — MB BS 1988 Lond.; BSc (Hons.) Lond. 1985; MD (Lond.) 1997; MRCP (UK) 1992. (Middlesex Hospital) Cons. Neurol., S.end Hosp. Socs: BMA; MDU; Assoc. Brit. Neurols. Prev: Specialist Regist. (Neurol.) Wessex Neuro Centre Soton. Gen. Hosp.; Research Regist. (Neurol.) Roy. Lond. Hosp.; Regist. (Cardiol. & Med.) Roy. Sussex Co. Hosp.

WARNER, Gregory Nightingale Surgery, Greatwell Drive, Cupernham Lane, Romsey SO51 7QN Tel: 01794 517878 Fax: 01794 514236; 27 Raglan Close, Chandlers Ford, Eastleigh SO53 4NH Tel: 01703 255551 — MB BS 1985 Lond.; MA Camb. 1986; MRCGP 1989; DCH RCP Lond. 1987; DRCOG 1987. (King's Coll. Hosp.)

WARNER, James (retired) 30 Jury Park, South Molton EX36 4DW — MB ChB Birm. 1953; MRCPsych 1971. Prev: Med. Dir. & Cons. (Child Psychiat.) Child Guid. Serv. Coventry.

WARNER, Mr James Garth Royal Bolton Hospital, Minerva Road, Farnworth, Bolton BL4 0JR Tel: 01204 390374 Fax: 01204 390344 — MB ChB 1987 Manch.; BSc St. And. 1984; FRCS Eng. 1991; FRCS (Tr & Orth.) 1997 Intercoll Spec Bd. (St. And. & Manch.) Cons. Orthopaedic and Trauma Surg., Roy. Bolton Hosp. Prev: Sen. Regist. (Orthop. Surg.) Hope Hosp. Salford; Sir Harry Platt Research Fell. (Orthop.) & Hon. Sen. Regist. (Orthop. Surg.) Univ. Manch.; Regist. (Orthop.) Stockport Infirm.

WARNER, James Robert The Surgery, Park Lane, Stubbington, Fareham PO14 2JP Tel: 01329 664231 Fax: 01329 664958; 15 Sumar Close, Stubbington, Fareham PO14 2EH — MB ChB 1976 Manch.; BSc (Med. Sci.) St. And. 1973; DRCOG 1984. Hosp. Pract. (Endoscopy) RH Haslar Gosport; Chairm. Portsmouth & SE Hants. LMC; Hon. Lect. Soton. Med. Sch. Prev: Surg. Lt. Cdr. RN; Sen. Med. Off. HM S/m Resolution (Port).

WARNER, Jennifer Anne Anaesthetic Department, City Hospital, Hucknall Road, Nottingham NG5 1PB — MB BS 1978 Lond.; FFA RCS Eng. 1982. (St. Mary's) Cons. Anaesth. City Hosp. Nottm.; Elective Pathway, Clin. Lead; Clin. Lead Book Admissions; Dep. Nat. Clin. Lead Booked Admissions. Prev: Clin. Director, Theatres and Anaesth.

WARNER, Professor John Oliver Allergy Inflammation Siencies Child Health, MP 803, Lev. G Centre Block, Southampton General Hospital, Tremona Road, Southampton SO16 6YD Tel: 02380 796160 Fax: 02380 796378 Email: jow@soton.ac.uk; Compass Copse, 48 Wilderness Heights, West End, Southampton SO18 3PS Tel: 02380 470600 — F Med Sci 1999; FAARAI 2001; MD Sheff. 1979; MB ChB Sheff. 1968; FRCP Lond. 1986; MRCP (UK) 1972; FRCPCH 1997; DCH Eng. 1970. (Sheff.) Prof. Child Health Univ.

WARNER

Soton.; Edr.-in-Chief Paediat. Allergy & Immunol. Socs: (Ex-Sec.) Brit. Soc. Allergy & Clin. Immunol.; Eur. Respirat. Soc. (Ex-Head Paediat. Assembly 1993-97).; Amer. Thoracic Soc. Prev: Reader (Paediat.) Nat. Heart & Lung Inst. Lond. Univ.; Hon. Cons. Paediat. Brompton Hosp. & St. Mary's Hosp. Lond.; Sen. Regist., Research Fell. & Hon. Sen. Regist. Hosp. for Sick Childr. Gt. Ormond. St. Lond.

WARNER, Justin Tobias 15 Mafeking Road, Penylan, Cardiff CF23 5DQ Tel: 029 2048 7047 — MB BCh 1989 Wales; BSc (Biochem.) 1984; MRCP (UK) 1992. Regist. (Paediat.) Llandough NHS Trust Hosp. Cardiff.

WARNER, Karen Lesley Worden Medical Centre, West Paddock, Leyland, Preston PR5 1HW Tel: 01772 423555 Fax: 01772 623878; The Old School House, Withington Lane, Heskin, Chorley PR7 5LU — MB ChB 1987 Manch.; MRCGP 1991; DRCOG 1992. (Manchester) Prev: Trainee GP Preston VTS; SHO (Paediat. & Psychiat.) Roy. Preston Hosp. Lancs.

WARNER, Katharine Jane Nightingale Surgery, Greatwell Drive, Cupernham Lane, Romsey SO51 7QN Tel: 01794 517878 Fax: 01794 514236; 27 Raglan Close, Chandlers Ford, Eastleigh SO53 4NH Tel: 01703 255551 — MB BS 1983 Lond.; MA Camb. 1984; MRCGP 1988; DRCOG 1986. (King's Coll. Hosp.) Hon. Clin. Tutor Soton. Univ. Prev: Clin. Med. Off. (Child Health) Soton.

WARNER, Malcolm David Faringdon Health Centre, Coxwell Road, Faringdon SN7 7ED Tel: 01367 242388 Fax: 01367 243394; Astley House, Market Place, Faringdon SN7 7HU Tel: 01367 240049 Email: malcolmwarner@compuserve.com — MB BS 1973 Lond.; DCH Eng. 1976. (Lond. Hosp.)

WARNER, Michael Weston The Cottage, Royston Road, Wendens Ambo, Saffron Walden CB11 4JX — MB ChB 1995 Manch.

WARNER, Nicholas James St. Cadoc's Hospital, Lodge Road, Caerleon, Newport NP18 3XQ Tel: 01633 436842 Email: nick.warner@gwent.wales.nhs.uk — MB ChB 1981 Birm.; MRCPsych 1985. Cons. Psychiat. Old Age Gwent HA. Prev: Sen. Regist. (Psychiat.) Worcester Roy. Infirm.; Regist. (Psychiat.) WhitCh. Hosp. Cardiff; SHO/Regist. (Psychiat.) St. Crispin Hosp. N.ampton.

WARNER, Nicola Jane 2 Church View, Burley Lane, Menston, Ilkley LS29 6EX — MB ChB 1991 Leeds.

WARNER, Nicola Jane Department Clinical Oncology, Churchill Hospital, Old Road, Headington, Oxford OX25 4RT Tel: 01865 225262 Fax: 01865 225264; Orchard House, Orchard Lane, Uppes Heyfard, Oxford OX25 5LD — BM 1985 Soton.; MRCP (UK) 1988; FRCR 1995. p/t Cons. Clin. Oncol. Ch.ill Hosp. Oxf. Prev: Regist. Fell. W.mead Hosp. Sydney, Australia; Regist. (Radiother. & Oncol.) Ch.ill Hosp. Oxf.

WARNER, Rachel Wynne Community Health Sheffield NHS Trust, Argyll House, 9 Williamson Road, Sheffield S11 9AR Tel: 0114 271 8656 Fax: 0114 271 6643 — MB BS 1985 Lond.; MSc (Psychiat.) Manch. 1994; MA Oxf. 1986; MRCPsych 1992; MRCGP 1989. Cons. Psychiat. Community Health Sheff.

WARNER, Richard Graham The Surgery, Kingstone, Church Road Lyde, Hereford HR2 9EY Tel: 01981 250215 Fax: 01981 251171; The Coach House, Lower Faton, Eaton Bishop, Hereford HR2 9QE — BM BCh 1985 Oxf.; MA Oxf. 1987; MRCGP 1995; DCH RCP Lond. 1988.

WARNER, Richard John Crox Barn, Main St., Tur Langton, Leicester LE8 0PJ — MB BS 1985 Lond.

WARNER, Rodney Harry Lewen Practice A, Hinckley Health Centre, 27 Hill Street, Hinckley LE10 1DS; The Courtyard, Higham Lane, Stoke Folding CV13 6EX Tel: 07771 983249 — MB BS 1979 Lond.; BSc Lond. 1976; MRCGP 1984; DRCOG 1983. (Middlx.) Clin. Asst. (Orthop.) Leicester.

WARNER, Stephen Terence The Health Centre, Doctor Lane, Mirfield WF14 8DU Tel: 01924 495721 Fax: 01924 480605 — MB ChB 1978 Leeds; LicAc. 1992. Indep. Acupunc. W. Yorks. Socs: Hudds. Med. Soc.

WARNER, Sven Nicholas Banks Health Centre, Newgate Street, Worksop S80 1HP Tel: 01909 500266 Fax: 01909 478014; Brook House, Netherthorpe, Worksop S80 3JG Tel: 01909 483066 — MB ChB 1981 Sheff.; MRCGP 1985; DRCOG 1984. Med. Off. Welbeck Coll. Worksop; Mem. N. Notts. N.Notts LMC. Prev: Trainee GP Kiveton Pk. Health Centre Sheff.; SHO (Paediat. & O & G) Bassetlaw Dist. Hosp. Worksop; SHO (A & E) Roy. Hallamsh. Hosp. Sheff.

WARNER, Thomas Treharne Department Clinical Neurosciences, Royal Free Hospital School of Medicine, Rowland Hill St., London NW3 2PF Tel: 020 7794 0500 Fax: 020 7431 1577 Email: thom63@mailhost.rfhsm.ac.uk — BM BCh 1987 Oxf.; MRCP (UK) 1990; PhD Lond. 1997. Sen. Lect. (Neurol.) Hon. Cons. Neurol. Roy. Free Hosp. Sch. of Med. Liste Hosp. Stennage Nat. Hosp. for Neurol. & Neurosurg. Lond. Prev: Lect. (Neurogenetics) Inst. Neurol. Lond.

WARNER, Zyta Lidia (retired) Villa D'Este, 248 East Lane, North Wembley, Wembley HA0 3LQ — MB BCh BAO 1956 NUI. Prev: GP Harrow.

WARNER-SMITH, John Duff Wallis and Partners, The Health Centre, 5 Stanmore Road, Stevenage SG1 3QA Tel: 01438 313223 Fax: 01438 749734 — BM BS 1975 Nottm.

WARNES, Gordon David Caskgate Street Surgery, 3 Caskgate Street, Gainsborough DN21 2DJ Tel: 01427 612501 Fax: 01427 615459 — MB ChB 1984 Leeds; MRCGP 1988; DCH RCP Lond. 1987.

WARNES, Professor Thomas Walter University Department of Gastroenterology, Manchester Royal Infirmary, Manchester M13 9WL Tel: 0161 276 4316 Fax: 0161 276 8779; Cotswold, 66 Moss Road, Alderley Edge SK9 7JB Tel: 01625 584310 — MB ChB Manch. 1962; MD Manch. 1975; FRCP 1980, M 1967. (Manch.) Cons. Phys. (Gastroenterol.) Manch. Roy. Infirm.; Hon. Lect. (Med.) Manch. Univ.; Vis. Pofessor, Dept. Biomolecular Sci., Univ. Manch. Inst. Sci. & Technol., July 1999. Socs: Brit. Soc. Gastroenterol.; Assn. Phys.; Internat. Assn. Study of Liver. Prev: Sen. Regist. & Regist. (Med.) Univ. Coll. Hosp. Lond.; Tutor (Med.) Univ. Manch.

WARNKE, Neville Alan 3 Augusta Avenue, Northampton NN4 0XP — MB ChB 1991 Liverp.

WARNOCK, Ann Margaret Mary Quayside Medical Practice, 82-84 Strand Road, Londonderry BT48 7NN Tel: 028 7126 2790 Fax: 028 7137 3729 — MB BCh BAO 1983 Belf.

WARNOCK, Mr David Samuel 2 Deramore Crescent, Moira, Craigavon BT67 0SQ Tel: 01846 619293 — MB BCh BAO 1991 Belf.; MB BCh Belf. 1991; FRCS Ed. 1995. SHO (Surg.) Roy. Vict. Hosp. Belf. Socs: Ulster Med. Soc.

WARNOCK, Doreen Graine (retired) 32 Parklands Way, Hartlepool TS26 0AP Tel: 01429 266437 — MB ChB 1940 Ed.; DObst RCOG 1949; DPH Ed. 1943. Prev: Dept. Med. Off. City Aberd.

WARNOCK, Jessie Helen (retired) Ardmore, 8 Regent Place, West Ferry, Dundee DD5 1AT Tel: 01382 730299 — MB BCh BAO 1945 Belf.

WARNOCK, John Mathers Turnbull (retired) Kishmul, Burnside Road, Fettercairn, Laurencekirk AB30 1XX Tel: 01561 340366 — MB ChB 1953 Glas. Prev: Ho. Off. (Surg & Med.) Hairmyres Hosp. E. Kilbride.

WARNOCK, Monica Mary Stoke Gifford Medical Centre, Ratcliffe Drive, Stoke Gifford BS34 8UE Tel: 0117 979 9430 — MB BCh BAO 1989 Belf.; DGM 1991; DRCOG 1992; DCH 1996; MRCGP 1993. (QUB) GP; Clin. Asst. Palliat. med. St Peters Hosp. Bristol.

WARNOCK, Niall Geoffrey York District Hospital, Wigginton Road, York YO31 8HE Tel: 01904 453856 Fax: 01904 454718 — MB ChB 1983 Leeds; MRCP (UK) 1986; FRCR 1990; T(R) (CR) 1992. Cons. Radiol. York Dist. Hosp. Prev: Asst. Prof. (Radiol.) Univ. Iowa.

WARNOCK, Peter James Scottish Airports Ltd., St. Andrews Drive, Glasgow Airport, Paisley PA3 2SW; 60 Highburgh Road, Dowanhill, Glasgow G12 9EJ — MB ChB 1978 Ed.; BSc (Hons. Path.) Ed. 1975, MB ChB 1978; AFOM RCP Lond. 1988; MRCGP 1984. (Ed.) Occupat. Phys. Scott. Airports Ltd. Prev: Occupat. Phys. Lond. Regional Transport; Med. Off. HMS Revenge; Regist. (Ophth.) Roy. Infirm. Edin.

WARNOCK, Sheila Mary 14 Avon Grove, Edinburgh EH4 6RF — MB BCh BAO 1980 Belf.

WARNOCK, William Alexander 215 Spring Grove Road, Isleworth TW7 4AF Tel: 020 8560 7750 Fax: 020 8232 8927 — MB BCh BAO 1964 Belf. (Qu. Univ. Belf.)

WARR, Carolyn Anne 14 Church Lane, Cliftonwood, Bristol BS8 4TR Tel: 0117 921 3117 — MB ChB 1993 Bristol; MRCP Lond. 1997. (Bristol) SHO (Anaesth.) Gloucester Roy. Hosp. Prev: SHO Rotat. (Renal Med./ITU/Anaesth.); SHO (Endocrine, Gen. Med. Neurol.) Frenchay Hosp. Bristol.

WARR, Edward Ernest 24 Leoplod Road, Bristol BS6 — MB ChB 1963 Bristol.

WARR, Oenone Carol Clanricarde Surgery, Clanricarde Road, Tunbridge Wells TN1 4PJ — MB BS 1980 Lond.; MRCGP 1985; DRCOG 1985. (St. Thos.) GP Tunbridge Wells Retainer Scheme; Clin. Asst. (Rheum.) Kent & Sussex Hosp. Trust Tunbridge Wells. Prev: GP Lond.; SHO (Med.) The Amer. Hosp. Paris; SHO (Med.) St. Peter's Hosp. Chertsey.

WARR, Mr Robert Philip 14 Church Lane, Clifton, Bristol BS8 4TR Tel: 0117 921 3117 — BM 1989 Soton.; FRCS Eng. 1995. Research Regist. (Plastic Surg.) Frenchay Hosp. Bristol. Prev: SHO Rotat. (Surg.) Frenchay Hosp. Bristol.

WARRACK, Alexander John Noel, MBE (retired) 2 Southbourne Court, Drury Lane, Dore, Sheffield S17 3GG Tel: 0114 236 3156 — MRCS Eng. LRCP Lond. 1937; MD Path. Lond. 1948, MB BS 1937; FRCPath 1963; DTM & H Eng. 1947. Prev: Cons. (Histopath.) N.. Gen. Hosp. Sheff.

WARRACK, John Hyslop (retired) 37 Arlington Road, Littleover, Derby DE23 6NZ — MB ChB 1947 Aberd.

WARRAN, Patricia Chanterlands Avenue Surgery, 149-153 Chanterlands Avenue, Hull HU5 3TJ Tel: 01482 343614; 101 Ferriby High Road, North Ferriby HU14 3LA — MB ChB 1974 Manch.; MRCGP 1991; FFA RCS Eng. 1979.

WARRANDER, Anna (retired) 4 Clark Place, Belford NE70 7LT Tel: 01668 213224 — MB BS 1959 Lond.; MRCS Eng. LRCP Lond. 1959. Clin. Med. Off. N.d. HA. Prev: Clin. Med. Off. Bromley HA.

WARRE, John Henry Devonshire House Surgery, Essington, North Tawton EX20 2EX Tel: 01837 82204 Fax: 01837 82459 — MB ChB 1971 Birm.; DObst RCOG 1974. (Birm.) Socs: BMA; BASICS. Prev: GP Tomintoul.

WARRELL, Professor David Alan The Centre for Tropical Medicine, (University of Oxford), John Radcliffe Hospital, Headington, Oxford OX3 9DU Tel: 01865 220968 Fax: 01865 220984 Email: david.warrell@ndm.ox.ac.uk; 4 Larkin's Lane, Old Headington, Oxford OX3 9DW — F Med Sci; BM BCh Oxf. 1964; MA Oxf 1964, DSc 1990, DM 1970; FRCP Lond. 1977, M 1966; MRCS Eng. LRCP Lond. 1965; FRCP Ed 1998. (Oxf & St. Thos.) Prof. Trop. Med. & Infec. Dis. & Founding Dir. Centre Trop. Med. (Emerit.) Univ. Oxf.; Cons. Malaria, Snake Bite & Rabies WHO; Hon. Cons. Phys. Oxon. HA; Hon. Cons. Malaria to the Army; Hon. Clin. Dir. Alistair Reid Venom Research Unit Liverp. Sch. Trop. Med.; Hon. Med. Adviser Roy. Geograph. Soc.; Pro Bono Med. Panel, Foreign & Commonw. Office. Socs: Pres. Internat. Federat. Trop. Med.; Assn. Phys.; Pres. Roy. Soc. Trop. Med. & Hyg. Prev: Founding Dir. Wellcome-Mahidol Univ. Oxf. Trop. Med. Research Bangkok, Thailand; Lect. & Hon. Cons. Phys. Roy. Postgrad. Med. Sch. Lond.; Sen. Lect. & Cons. Phys. Ahmadu Bello Univ. Hosp. Zaria, Nigeria.

WARRELL, David Watson (retired) Beudy Ychain, Llanfaglan, Caernarfon LL54 5RA Tel: 01286 672710 — MB ChB 1953 Sheff.; MD Sheff. 1964; MRCS Eng. LRCP Lond. 1953; FRCOG 1970. Prev: Urol. Gyn. Centr. Manch. Hosps. Trust.

WARRELL, Mary Jean 4 Larkins Lane, Old Headington, Oxford OX3 9DW Tel: 01865 220968 Fax: 01865 760683 — MB BS 1971 Lond.; MRCP (UK) 1974; FRCPath 1990, M 1978. (St. Mary's) Prev: Wellcome Research Fell. Sir William Dunn Sch. Path. Oxf.; Cons. Fac. Trop. Med. Mahidol Univ. Bangkok, Thailand; Sen. Regist. (Clin. Virol.) Ch.ill Hosp. Oxf.

WARRELL, Richard John Department of Health Care of the Elderly, Derriford Hospital, Derriford Road, Plymouth PL6 8DH — MB ChB 1975 Liverp.; MRCP (UK) 1979. Cons. Phys. in c/o Elderly Plymouth Primary Care Trust. Prev: Sen. Regist. (Geriat. Med.) Wessex RHA.

WARREN, A Peter Medical Services, Sutherland House, 29-37 Brighton Road, Sutton SM2 5AN Tel: 020 8652 6000 Fax: 020 8652 6160; 21 Glengall Road, London SE15 6NJ Tel: 020 7237 2180 Fax: 020 7237 2180 Email: apwarren@apwarren.com — MB ChB 1968 St. And.; DDAM 2000 (Faculty of Occupational Medicine); MRCGP 1987. Med. Adviser Med. Servs. Lond.; Hon. Med. Adviser Roy. Philharmonic Orchestra. Socs: Assn. Med. Advisers to Brit. Orchestras; Brit. Assn. Performing Arts Med.; Assur. Med. Soc. Prev: Clin. Asst. (Dermat.) Kings Coll. Hosp. Lond.; Clin. Asst. (Radiotherap.) Norf. & Norwich Hosp.; GP Norwich & Lond.

WARREN, Alan John MRC Laboratory of Molecular Biology, Hills Road, Cambridge CB2 2QH Tel: 01223 202937 Fax: 01223 417178 Email: ajw@mrc-lmb.cam.ac.uk — MB ChB 1986 Glas.; PhD Camb. 1995; BSc Glas. 1983; MRCP (UK) 1989; MRCPath 1997. (University of Glasgow) MRC Sen. Clin. Fell.; MRC Sen. Clin. Fell. Laborat. Molecular Biol. Camb. Socs: Brit. Soc. of Haemat.; Amer. Soc. of Haemat. Prev: MRC Clin. Scientist & Hon. Sen. Regist. Camb.; MRC Train. Fell. LMB Camb.

WARREN, Angela Elizabeth The Forest Group Practice, The Surgery, Bury Road, Brandon IP27 0BU Tel: 01842 813353 Fax: 01842 815221; Hartley Place, Nursery Lane, Hockwold, Thetford IP26 4ND Tel: 01842 828824 — MRCS Eng. LRCP Lond. 1975; BSc (Hons.) (Pharm.) Lond. 1972, MB BS 1975; DCH Eng. 1980; DRCOG 1977; Cert JCC Lond. 1977. (Guy's Hosp.)

WARREN, Anna Kristin 1A Witherington Road, London N5 1PN Tel: 020 7607 2524 — MB BS 1991 Lond.; BSc (Hons.) Lond. 1988; MRCP (UK) 1994. Lect. & Hon. Sen. Regist. (c/o Elderly) Qu. Mary & W.field Coll. & Roy. Lond. Hosps. Lond. Prev: Regist. (Gen. Med. & c/o Elderly) Bromley Hosp. Kent.

WARREN, Anne Yvonne Department of Histopathology, Peterborough District Hospital, Thorpe Road, Peterborough PE3 6DA Tel: 01733 874648 Fax: 01733 874971 — MB BS 1987 Lond.; MSc (Clin. Cytopath.) Lond. 1996; MRCPath 1995. Cons. Histopath. P'boro. Dist. Hosp. Prev: Sen. Regist. (Histopath.) P'boro. Dist. Hosp.; Hon. Regist. (Histopath.) St. Bart. Hosp. Lond.; Ho. Off. (Surg.) Univ. Coll. & Middlx. Hosps. Lond.

WARREN, Anthony John Cygnet Hospital Ealing, 23 Lorfton Road, Ealing W5 2HT Tel: 0208 991 6699 Fax: 0208 991 0440 Email: cygnetdoc@aol.com — MB BS 1972 Lond.; 1993 Tpsych; BSc Lond. 1969; MRCPsych 1977. (Middlx.) Cons. Pyshchiatrist; Vis. Cons. Psychiat., Bowden Ho. Clinic, Harrow. Socs: Mem. BMA; Fell. RSM; Mem. RCPsych. Prev: Regist. (Psychiat.) St. Geo. Hosp. Med. Sch. & Atkinson Morley's; Sen. Regist. (Psychiat.) St. Geo. Hosp. Med. Sch.; Cons. Psychiat., Hillingdon Hosp.

WARREN, Antony Richard Lensfield Medical Practice, 48 Lensfield Road, Cambridge CB2 1EH Tel: 01223 352779 Fax: 01223 566930 — BM BCh 1978 Oxf.; MA Oxf. 1980, BA (Hons.) 1975; MRCGP 1982; DRCOG 1980. Socs: BMA; Anglo-French Med. Soc. Prev: Trainee GP Rookery Med. Centre Newmarket; SHO (Geriat.) Chesterton Hosp. Camb.; SHO (Obst.) John Radcliffe Hosp. Oxf.

WARREN, Bryan Frederick Department of Cellular Pathology, John Radcliffe Hospital, Headington, Oxford OX3 9DU Tel: 01865 220510 Fax: 01865 220574 — MB ChB 1981 Liverp. Cons. Path. John Radcliffe Hosp. Oxf. Socs: Assn. Clin. Path. (Scientif. Meetings Sec.); Assn. Coloproctol.; Brit. Soc. Gastroenterol. (Hon. Sec. Path.) Mem. IBA Comm. Prev: Lect. (Path.) Bristol Univ.

WARREN, Carol Ann Department of Genito Urinary Medicine, Nottingham City Hospital Trust, Hucknall Road, Nottingham NG5 1PB Tel: 01159 627746; 15 Bradshaw Drive, Holbrook, Belper DE56 0SZ — MB ChB 1967 Manch.; MRCOG 1980; DObst RCOG 1969. (Manch.) Staff Phys. (Genitourin. Med.) Nottm. City Hosp. Socs: Med. Soc. Study VD; Soc. Colposcopy & Cervical Path. Prev: Sen. Regist. (Genitourin. Med.) Nottm. Gen. Hosp. & Leicester Roy. Infirm; Regist. (Genitourin. Med.) Nottm. Gen. Hosp.; Regist. (O & G) Newc. Gen. Hosp.

WARREN, Caroline Jane 35 Kingsway, London SW14 7HL — MB BS 1985 Lond.; MRCGP 1995.

WARREN, Charles Buchanan Moncur (retired) Bings Hall, Chelmsford Road, Felsted, Dunmow CM6 3EP Tel: 01371 820262 — MRCS Eng. LRCP Lond. 1932; BA Camb., FRCP Lond. 1967, M 1946; DCH Eng. 1938. Hon. Cons. Paediatr. Chelmsford & Colchester Hosp. Gps. Prev: Chief Asst. & Ho. Phys. Childr. Dept. St. Bart. Hosp.

WARREN, Christine Anne Penarth Health Centre, Stanwell Road, Penarth CF64 3XE Tel: 029 2070 0911; 6 Thorn Grove, Penarth CF64 5BZ — MB BCh 1984 Wales; MRCGP 1991; DCH RCP Lond. 1988; Dip. Therap. Wales 1995. (Welsh National School of Medicine) Med. Adviser Bro Taf HA.

WARREN, Christopher William Department of Histopathology, Royal Hallamshire Hospital, Sheffield S10 2JF Tel: 0114 271 2811 Fax: 0114 271 2200 Email: chris.warren@csuh-tr.trent.nhs.uk; 333 Crimicar Lane, Sheffield S10 4EN Tel: 0114 263 0994 Email: chrisww@compuserve.com — MB ChB 1988 Sheff.; MB ChB (Hons.) Sheff. 1988; PhD Sheff. 1987; BMedSci (1st cl. Hons.) Sheff. 1983; MRCPath 1996. Cons. Histopath./Cytopathol. Cent. Sheff.

WARREN

Univ. Hosp. NHS Trust. Prev: Sen. Regist. & Regist. Rotat. (Histopath.) Leeds (N.. & Yorks: RHA); SHO Rotat. (Histopath.) Sheff. HA; Ho. Off. N.. Gen. & Roy. Hallamsh. Hosps. Sheff.

WARREN, Clive Edwin John Stuart House Surgery, 20 Main Ridge West, Boston PE21 6SS Tel: 01205 362173 Fax: 01205 365710 — MB BS 1980 Lond.; MA (1st Cl.) (Camb.) 1981; MRCGP (Distinc.) 1984; DRCOG 1983. (Westm.) Prev: Trainee GP Pilgrim Hosp. Boston VTS; Ho. Surg. W. Suff. Hosp. Bury St. Edmunds; Ho. Phys. W.m. Hosp.

WARREN, Edward St leger Jubilee Avenue Surgery, 24 Jubilee Avenue, Whitton, Twickenham TW2 6JB Tel: 020 8893 8464 Fax: 020 8893 3954 — MB ChB 1974 Witwatersrand. (Witwatersrand) Accredit. Trainer (Gen. Pract.) Twickenham.

WARREN, Elisabeth 64 Mountway, Waverton, Chester CH3 7QF Tel: 01244 332091 — State Exam Med 1978 Cologne; MD Cologne 1979; DCCH RCP Ed. 1991. Community Paediat. & SCMO Chesh. Community Health Care Trust Nantwich. Prev: Clin. Med. Off. Wirral HA; SHO (Paediat.) Städet Krankenhaus Leverkusen, W. Germany.

WARREN, Elizabeth Jane Callington Health Centre, Haye Road, Callington PL17; Prospect Farm, Latchley, Gunnislake PL18 9AX — MB ChB 1978 Birm. Prev: Regist. (Anaesth.) Plymouth Gen. Hosp.; SHO (Anaesth.) N. Staffs. Hosp. Centre Stoke-on-Trent.

WARREN, Fiona Margaret The Group Practice Surgery, Chester Road, Whitby, Ellesmere Port, South Wirral CH65 6TG Tel: 0151 355 6153 Fax: 0151 355 6843 — MB ChB 1984 Liverp.; MRCGP 1989; DRCOG 1988. (Liverpool) Prev: SHO (A & E) & Ho. Off. Walton Hosp. Liverp.; Trainee GP Chester VTS.

WARREN, George Albert Ramsden Keystone, 47 Firle Road, Eastbourne BN22 8EE Tel: 01323 29492 — LRCPI & LM, LRSCI & LM 1932; LRCPI & LM, LRCSI & LM 1932. (RCSI)

WARREN, Grace Chandrani Mental Health Unit, Rotherham District General Hospital, Moorgate, Rotherham S60 2UD Tel: 01709 820000 — MB ChB 1984 Sheff.; MRCPsych 1991. Cons. (en. Adult Psychiat.) Rotherham Priority Health NHS Trust; Hon. Clin. Lect., Univ. of Sheff. Socs: Roy. Coll. Psychiat.; BMA. Prev: Lect. Univ. Dept. Psychiat. Sheff.; Research Regist. (Psychiat.) Univ. Sheff.; Regist. (Psychiat.) Sheff. HA.

WARREN, Jill St. Michaels Hospice, Hornbeam Park Avenue, Harrogate HG2 8QL — MB BS 1984 Newc.; MRCGP 1988; Dip. Palliat. Med. Wales 1994; DGM RCP Lond. 1988. Med. Dir. St. Michaels Hospice Harrogate. Prev: Med. Dir. St. And. Hospice Grimsby.

WARREN, Joan Elizabeth (retired) 69 Marlborough Road, Worthing BN12 4HD Tel: 01903 246342 — MB ChB MB ChB St. And. 1952; DPH Eng. 1970. Prev: SCMO W. Sussex AHA.

WARREN, John (retired) The Cottage, Palmers Lane, Aylsham, Norwich NR11 6JA Tel: 01263 733013 — MRCS Eng. LRCP Lond. 1949.

WARREN, John Bowen D41 Odhams Walk, London WC2H 9SB — MB BS 1977 Lond.; MD Lond. 1983; FRCP Lond. 1994; MRCP (UK) 1979. (Guy's) Med. Cons. Med. Control. Agency Lond.; Hon. Sen. Lect. (Clin. Pharmacol.) St. Thos. Hosp. Lond. Socs: Brit. Pharmacol. Soc.; Amer. Heart Assn.; Brit. MicroCirc. Soc. Prev: Sen. Lect. & Hon. Cons. Nat. Heart & Lung Inst. Lond.; Sen. Regist. (Clin. Pharmacol.) Hammersmith Hosp. Lond.

WARREN, John Lewis (retired) 17 Oldfield Drive, Stone ST15 8XZ — MB BS 1947 Lond.; MRCGP 1973; DObst RCOG 1949. Prev: Obst. Regist. Bromley Hosp.

WARREN, John Nettleton (retired) La Casetta, Elm Grove, Barnham, Bognor Regis PO22 0H — MB BChir 1935 Camb.; MA Camb. 1935, MB BChir 1935; MRCS Eng. LRCP Lond. 1930, DPM 1933.

WARREN, John Pelham Princess Alexandra Hospital, Harlow CM20 1QX Tel: 01279 444455; 3 Watlington Road, Old Harlow, Harlow CM17 0DX Tel: 01279 419704 Fax: 01279 429771 — MB BChir 1967 Camb.; MB Camb. 1967, BChir 1966; FRCP Lond. 1987; MRCP (UK) 1970; DCH Eng. 1968. (Camb.) Cons. Phys. P.ss Alexandra Hosp. Harlow. Prev: Sen. Regist. (Med.) King's Coll. Hosp. Lond.; Ho. Phys. Lond. Hosp.

WARREN, Jonathan Sidney Nightingale Road Surgery, 1 Nightingale Road, London N9 8AJ Tel: 020 8804 3333 Fax: 020 8805 7776; 122A Wood Street, Barnet EN5 4DA — MB BS 1974 Lond.; BSc (Hons.) (Pharmacol.) Lond. 1971; MRCGP 1981; DFFP

1993. (St. Geo.) Sen. Partner GP Edmonton; Clin Asst. (Ment. Handicap) Chase Farm Hosp. Enfield. Socs: Brit. Soc. Med. & Dent. Hypn. Prev: Clin. Asst. (Paediat.) N. Middlx. Hosp. Lond.; Clin. Asst. (Obst.) Whittington Hosp. Lond.; Cas. Off. & Ho. Off. (Surg.) St. Geo. Hosp. Tooting.

WARREN, Joseph Brian Nursery House, Forest Road, Ascot SL5 8QU Tel: 01344 885300 — MA Camb. 1958, MB 1964, BChir 1963; MRCS Eng. LRCP Lond. 1958; FFA RCS Eng. 1971; DObst RCOG 1961. (St. Mary's) Private Anaesth. Pract. Prev: Cons. Heatherwood-Waxham Pk. Hosps. Trust; Sen. Regist. Char. Cross Hosp. Gp.; Regist. Groote Schuur Hosp. Cape Town, S. Afr.

WARREN, Kathleen Maud 75 Laleham Road, Staines TW18 2EA — MB ChB 1934 Glas. (Univ. Glas.)

WARREN, Lynn Margaret 164 Hazelwood Lane, London N13 5HJ — MB BS 1996 Lond.

WARREN, Martin John X-Ray Department, Luton & Dunstable NHS Trust, Lewsey Road, Luton LU4 0DZ Tel: 01582 491122 Fax: 01582 497418 — MB BS 1978 Lond.; BSc Lond. 1975; MRCP (UK) 1982; FRCR 1987. (St. Thos.) Cons. Radiol. Luton & Dunstable NHS Trust.

WARREN, Mary Ethel St Helier Hospital, Wrythe Lane, Carshalton SM5 1AA Tel: 020 8296 3032 Fax: 020 8296 3013; 29 Send Barns Lane, Send, Woking GU23 7BS — BM BCh 1975 Oxf.; MSc Nuclear Med. Lond. 1995; FRCR 1991; BA 1969; BMCH 1973; Cert. Adv Study Health Managem 1999. (Oxf. & St. Bart.) Cons. Radiol. St. Helier Hosp. Carshalton. Socs: BMA; BNMS; Fell. Roy. Coll. Radiols. Prev: Sen. Regist. (Radiol.) St. Geo. Hosp. Lond.; Regist. (Radiol.) Frimley Pk. Hosp. & St. Geo. Hosp. Lond.

WARREN, Matthew David 14 Henley Road, Ipswich IP1 3SL — MB BS 1994 Newc.

WARREN, Michael Donald 2 Bridge Down, Bridge, Canterbury CT4 5AZ Tel: 01227 830233; 2 Bridge Down, Bridge, Canterbury CT4 5AZ Tel: 01227 830233 — MB BS Lond. 1946; MD Lond. 1952; FRCP Lond. 1975, M 1969; FFCM RCP (UK) 1972; DIH Eng. 1952; DPH (Distinc.) Lond. 1952; FFPHM 2000. (Guy's) Emerit. Prof. Social Med. Univ. Kent. Socs: Fell. Roy. Soc. Med.; Hon. Mem. Soc. Social Med. Prev: Prof. & Dir. Health Servs. Research Unit Univ. Kent; Prof. Community Health Lond. Sch. Hyg. & Trop. Med.; Acad. Regist. Fac. Community Med.

WARREN, Michael Robert Stoneleigh Surgery, Police Square, Milnthorpe LA7 7PW Tel: 015395 63307; Cairnsmore, Dugg Hill, Heversham, Milnthorpe LA7 7EF Tel: 0153 95 63536 — MB ChB 1967 Leeds; MB ChB (Hons.) Leeds 1967. Prev: Ho. Surg. Profess. Surgic. Unit & Cas. Off. Gen. Infirm. Leeds; Ho. Phys. Chapel Allerton Hosp. Leeds.

WARREN, Mr Nicholas Paul Accident & Emergency Department, Northwick Park Hospital, Watford Road, Harrow HA1 3UJ — MB BS 1976 Lond.; MA Oxf. 1977; FRCS Eng. 1982; FRCS Ed. 1982. Career Regist. (Surg.) N.W. Thames RHA. Prev: SHO (Accid. Dept.) Lond. Hosp.

WARREN, Nigel Raymond Oak Tree Clinic, Redding Way, Knaphill, Woking GU21 2QS Tel: 01483 488 7490 Fax: 01483 474096; 29 Send Barns Lane, Send, Woking GU23 7BS — MRCS Eng. LRCP Lond. 1977; BA Oxf. 1959; Dip. Addic. Behaviour Lond. 1991. (St. Bart.) Hon. Cons. Forens. Psychiat. Socs: BMA. Prev: Sen. Med. Off. HM YOI & Remand Centre Feltham Middlx.; Regist. (Forens. & Gen. Psychiat.) Brookwood Hosp. Knaphill; Regist. (Psychiat. inc. Ment. Health) Rubery Hill Hosp. S. Birm.

WARREN, Patrick David 107 Neasden Lane, London NW10 2UH — MRCS Eng. LRCP Lond. 1948. (Lond. Hosp.) Socs: BMA & Assn. Police Surgs. Gt. Brit. Prev: Ho. Surg. Surgic. Unit & Ho. Surg. Dept. Neurosurg. Lond. Hosp.

WARREN, Paul Anthony Surrey Hampshire Borders NHS Trust, Bridge Centre, Basingstoke RG21 7PJ Tel: 01256 316303 Fax: 01256 316356 — BM 1980 Soton.; MRCPsych 1985. Surrey Hamshire Borders NHS Trust. Prev: Sen. Regist. (Psychiat.) Basingstoke Dist. Hosp.; Sen. Regist (Psychiat.) Roy. S. Hants Hosp. Soton.; Sen. Regist (Psychiat.) Wessex Regional Secure Unit.

WARREN, Paul David South Lambeth Road Practice, 1 Selway House, 272 South Lambeth Road, London SW8 1UL Tel: 020 7622 1923 Fax: 020 7498 5530 — MB BS 1985 Lond.

WARREN, Mr Paul James Orthopaedic Department, Level 5, Northwick Park Hospital, Watford Road, Harrow HA1 3UW; 9 Claremont Road, Marlow SL7 1BH — MB BS 1981 Lond.; BSc

Lond. 1978; MS Lond. 1994; FRCS (Orth.) 1994; FRCS Eng. 1985. (Lond. Hosp.) Cons. Orthop. Surg. N.wick Pk. Hosp. Harrow. Prev: Sen. Regist. (Orthop.) Middlx. & Roy. Nat. Orthop. Hosps.; Research Fell. (Orthop.) Roy. Nat. Orthop. Hosp. Stanmore; Regist. (Orthop.) Roy. Free Hosp. Lond. & Windsor Gp. Hosps.

WARREN, Peter Michael Ty'r Dderwen, Cwrt Henri, Dryslwyn, Carmarthen SA32 8RX Tel: 01558 668039 — MB ChB 1972 St. And.; MRCP (UK) 1976.

WARREN, Mr Richard Anthony 152 Harley Street, London W1G 7LH Tel: 020 7935 3834 Fax: 020 7224 2574 Email: doctor.warren@virgin.net — MD Sheff. 1988; MB ChB Liverp. 1976; FRCS Ed. 1981; FFAEM 1993; FICS 1989. (Liverp.) Cons. Surg. Indep. & Medico Legal Pract. Lond. Clinic. Socs: Medico-Legal Soc.; Brit. Soc. Trauma; Brit. Inst. Musculosketal Med. Prev: Clin. Tutor & Sen. Examr. (Surg.) Univ. Lond.; Cons. Surg. W.m. & St. Stephens Hosp. Lond.

WARREN, Richard Charles Norfolk and Norwich Hospital, Brunswick Road, Norwich Tel: 01603 286286 Fax: 01603 286781; 14 Christchurch Road, Norwich NR2 2AE Tel: 01603 454173 Fax: 01603 454173 — MB BS 1977 Lond.; FRCOG 1996, M 1983; DCH RCP Lond. 1980; DRCOG 1979. (King's Coll. Hosp.) Cons. O & G Norf. & Norwich Hosp.; Regional Adviser (Obst. & Gyn.) E. Anglia; Counc. RCOG; Counc. RCOG Med. workforce Advisery Comm. Socs: Chairm. RCOG Med. Workforce Advisory Comm. Prev: Research Fell. & Clin. Sen. Regist. King's Coll. Hosp. Lond.; regional Adviser (obs+Gyn) E. Anglia.

WARREN, Roderic Ellis Public Health Laboratory, Royal Shrewsbury Hospital, Shrewsbury SY3 8XQ Tel: 01743 261163 Fax: 01743 261292 Email: rwarren@mids.phls.nhs.uk; Email: roderic.warren@btinternet.com — MB BChir 1971 Camb.; MA Camb. 1971; FRCPath 1988, M 1977. p/t Gp. Dir. PHLS Midl.; Hon. Sen. Lect. (Infec. Dis.) Univ. Birm.; Director, Shrewsbury & Telford PHL. Socs: Brit. Soc. Antimicrob. Chemother. Counc.; Hosp. Infec. Soc. Prev: Cons. Microbiol. Addenbrooke's Hosp. Camb.; Sen. Regist. Camb. Health Dist. (T); Clin. Lect. (Microbiol.) W.m. Med. Sch.

WARREN, Roderick Edward 11 St Swithuns Ter, Lewes BN7 1UJ — MB ChB 1997 Ed.

WARREN, Rosemary Jane Sandways Cottage, Bourton, Gillingham SP8 5BQ — MB BS 1970 Lond. (Middlx.) Prev: Ho. Surg. Wembley Hosp.; Ho. Phys. S. Lond. Hosp. Wom. & Childr.

WARREN, Ruth Mary Leigh Addenbrooke's Hospital, Cambridge CB2 2QQ Tel: 01223 217627 Fax: 01223 217886 Email: rmlw2@cam.ac.uk; 3 Watlington Road, Old Harlow, Harlow CM17 0DX Tel: 01279 419704 Fax: 01279 429771 — MB BChir 1967 Camb.; MA Camb. 1967, MD 1995; FRCP Lond. 1991; MRCP (UK) 1971; FRCR 1976; DCH Eng. 1969. (Camb. & Lond. Hosp.) Cons. Radiol. Addenbrooke's Hosp. Camb. Prev: Med. Dir. & Cons. Radiol. P.ss Alexandra Hosp. NHS Trust; Sen. Regist. (Radiol.) King's Coll. Hosp. Lond.; Ho. Phys. & Ho. Surg. Lond. Hosp.

WARREN, Simon John Paul 5 Fairoak Close, Kenley CR8 5LJ Tel: 020 8668 3940 — MB BS 1993 Lond.; MA Camb. 1986. SHO (Histopath.) Guys Hosp. Lond. Prev: Ho. Off. (Med.) St. Thos. Hosp.; Ho. Off. (Surg.) E.bourne Dist. Gen. Hosp.

WARREN, Simon Stuart Derby City General Hospital, Uttoxeter Road, Derby DE22 3NE Tel: 01332 340131; 1 The Granary, Aldridge, Walsall WS9 8NY — BM BS 1996 Nottm.; BMedSci Nottm. 1994. SHO (Gen. Med.) Derby City Hosp. Prev: SHO (A & E) Barnet; SHO (Cardiol.) Warwick.

WARREN, Stella Avis Frida (retired) 16 Ashdown Road, Portishead, Bristol BS20 8DP Tel: 0117 984 9081 — MB ChB Bristol 1957.

WARREN, Mr Stephen John Barnet & Chase Farm NHS Trust, Chase Farm Hospital, The Ridgeway, Enfield EN2 Tel: 0208 967 5981 Fax: 0208 370 9043; Pavilion, Roundhurst, Haslemere GU27 3BN Tel: 0208 967 5981 Fax: 0208 370 9043 — MB BS 1986 Lond.; FRCS (Gen. Surg.) 1999; MS Lond. 2000; BSc Hons Lond. 1983; FRCS (Ed.) 1991. (London Hospital Medical College) Cons. Gen. Surg. with an interest in ColoProctol. & Laparoscopic Surg. Socs: Assn. of Coloproctol.; Assn. of Endoscopic Surg.s; Assn. of Surg.s of GB & Irel. Prev: Lect. (Surg.), Roy. Lond. Hosp.; Specialist Regist. Univ. Coll. Hosp. & Middlx. Hosp.; Specialist Regist. Colchester Gen. Hosp.

WARREN, Stephen John Hyde Park Surgery, 2 Hyde Park Road, Mutley, Plymouth PL3 4RJ Tel: 01752 224437 Fax: 01752 217029; 33 Widey Lane, Crownhill, Plymouth PL6 5JS Tel: 01752 771991 Email: sjwarren@globalnet.co.uk — MB ChB 1977 Manch.; MRCGP 1981; DCH RCP Lond. 1987.

WARREN, Stephen John CAMHS, Lennard Lodge, 3 Lennard Road, Croydon CR0 2UL Tel: 020 8700 8800 Fax: 020 8700 8809 — MB BS 1985 Lond.; MRCPsych 1990; DCH RCP Lond. 1987. (Guy's Hosp.) Cons. Child & Adolesc. Psychiat. Croydon CAMHS; Hon. Cons. Psychiat. Roy. Marsden Hosp. Lond. Socs: ACPP. Prev: Sen. Regist. (Child & Adolesc. Psychiat.) St. Geo. Hosp. Lond.; Regist. (Psychiat.) Leeds HA.

WARREN, Stephen Willis Old Station Surgery, 39 Brecon Road, Abergavenny NP7 5UH Tel: 01873 859000 Fax: 01873 850163 — MB BS 1978 Lond. (St. Mary's) Prev: Ho. Phys. King Edwd. VIII Hosp. Windsor; Ho. Surg. St. Mary's Hosp. Lond.

WARREN, Susan West Wales General Hospital, Glangwili, Carmarthen SA31 2AF Tel: 01267 235151; Ty'r Dderwen, Cwrt Henri, Dryslwyn, Carmarthen SA32 8RX Tel: 01558 668039 — MB ChB 1972 Dundee; FRCPCH 1997; MRCGP 1979; DCH Eng. 1974. Cons. Paediat. (Community Child Health) Carmarthen & Dist. NHS Trust.

WARREN, Susan Jacqueline 9 Westcroft Park, Broadstone BH18 8LX — BM 1988 Soton.

WARREN, Vanessa Jean 79 Westbourne Road, West Kirby, Wirral CH48 4DH — MB ChB 1992 Liverp.

WARREN, Virginia Jane BUPA, BUPA House, 15 Bloomsbury Way, London WC1A 2BA Tel: 020 7656 2049 Fax: 020 7656 2708 Email: warrenv@bupa.com — MB BChir 1981 Camb.; MA Oxf. 1985, BA (Hons.) 1978; MD Camb. 1987; MFPHM RCP (UK) 1993; DHMSA 1981; FFPHM RCP (UK) 2000. Cons. Pub. Health Med. BUPA. Socs: (Treas.) Camb. Med. Grad.s Club. Prev: Sen. Regist. (Pub. Health Med.) Fac. Pub. Health Med. & E. Anglia RHA; Research Fell. (Gastroenterol.) Addenbrooke's Hosp. Camb.

WARREN, William Edward Burncross Surgery, 1 Bevan Way, Chapeltown, Sheffield S35 1RN Tel: 0114 246 6052 Fax: 0114 245 0276 — MB ChB 1977 Sheff.; MRCGP 1981; DRCOG 1979.

WARREN-BROWNE, Caroline Yelverton The Willow Surgery, Coronation Road, Downend, Bristol BS16 5DH Tel: 0117 970 9500 — MB ChB 1979 Bristol; MRCGP 1984.

WARREN-BROWNE, Muriel G (retired) The School House, Elsted, Midhurst GU29 0JY Tel: 01730 825297 — MB ChB Ed. 1946. Prev: Clin. Asst. (Dermat. & Rheum.) St. Richard's Hosp. Chichester.

WARRENDER, Thomas Stuart Mercheford House Surgery, Mercheford House, Elwyn Road, March PE15 9BT Tel: 01354 656841 Fax: 01354 660788; 8 Regent Avenue, Manchester PE15 8LN Tel: 0161 54928 — MB ChB 1971 Ed.; BSc (Med. Sci.) Ed. 1968, MB ChB 1971; DObst RCOG 1973. Prev: SHO (O & G) Simpson Memor. Matern. Pavil. Roy. Infirm. Edin.; Surg. Ho. Off. Roodlands Hosp. Haddington.

WARRENDER, Tracey 29 Overhill Gardens, Bridge of Don, Aberdeen AB22 8QR — MB ChB 1998 Aberd.

WARRENS, Anthony Nigel Imperial College School of Medicine, Renal Unit, Hammersmith Hospital, Du Cane Road, London W12 0NN Tel: 020 8383 3152 Fax: 020 8383 2002 Email: a.warrens@rpms.ac.uk — BM BCh 1984 Oxf.; PhD Lond. 1996; BSc Glas. 1981; MRCP (UK) 1987. (Oxf.) Sen. Lect. & Hon. Cons. Phys. Renal Unit & Dept. Immunol. Imperial Coll. Sch. of Med. Hammersmith Hosp. Lond. Socs: Renal Assn.; Collegiate Mem. RCP Lond.; Brit. Transpl. Soc. Prev: MRC Clinician Scientist & Hon. Sen. Regist. Hammersmith Hosp. Lond.; Regist. (Med.) Hammersmith & Ashford Middlx. Hosp.; SHO (Med.) Hammersmith & Brompton Hosps. & Nat. Hosp. Nerv. Dis. Lond.

WARRICK, Mr Charles Kay, CBE (retired) 5 The Fellside, Kenton, Newcastle upon Tyne NE3 4LJ Tel: 0191 285 5328 Email: charles@warrick.freeserve.co.uk — MB BS 1940 Lond.; FRCP Lond. 1973, M 1966; FRCS Ed. 1946; MRCS Eng. LRCP Lond. 1939; FRCR 1975; FFR 1953; DMR Lond 1941. Prev: Radiol. i/c Roy. Vict. Infirm. & Clin. Lect. Radiol. & Lect. Radiol.

WARRICK, John Walmsley (retired) Old Stables, Osmington, Weymouth DT3 6ET Tel: 01305 832113 — MRCS Eng. LRCP Lond. 1938; FFA RCS Eng. 1954; DA Eng. 1944. Prev: Cons. Anaesth. W. Dorset Gp. Hosps.

WARRICK

WARRICK, Michael John Sewell Spa Road Surgery, Spa Road East, Llandrindod Wells LD1 5ES Tel: 01597 824291 / 842292 Fax: 01597 824503 — MB ChB 1977 Birm.; MRCGP 1981; DRCOG 1980.

WARRICK, Stephanie Margaret Spa Road Surgery, Spa Road East, Llandrindod Wells LD1 5ES Tel: 01597 824291 / 842292 Fax: 01597 824503 — BSc (Hons.) Birm. 1973, MB ChB 1977; MRCGP 1993; DCH RCP Lond. 1992; DRCOG 1989.

WARRILOW, William Henry Edwin 6 Thornden Court, Thornden Lane, Rolvenden, Cranbrook TN17 4PS — MB ChB 1987 Cape Town.

WARRINER, Richenda Miriam (retired) Scorton, Lime Tree Close, E. Preston, Littlehampton BN16 1JA Tel: 01903 770707 — MB BS 1956 Lond.; LMSSA Lond. 1956; DObst RCOG 1959. Prev: Obst. Ho. Surg. Hillingdon Hosp.

WARRINER, Sara Elizabeth Beech House, Wentworth Court, Harlington, Dunstable LU5 6HZ Tel: 01525 872266 Email: warriners@aol.com; 26 Ashcroft Road, Luton LU2 9AU Tel: 01582 722555 — MB BS 1980 Lond. (Roy. Free Hosp.) Prev: SHO Roy. Nat. Throat, Nose & Ear Hosp.; Cas. Off. Lond. Hosp. Whitechapel; Ho. Off. Roy. Free Hosp. Lond.

WARRINER, Stephen James Rose Cottage, Main St., Bonby, Brigg DN20 0PL; 3B Maloane Terrace, Jesmond, Newcastle upon Tyne NE2 3AN — MB ChB 1992 Birm.; MRCPCH 1991. (Birm)

WARRINGTON, Bernadette Mary Veronica Health Centre, Rodney Road, Walton-on-Thames KT12 3LB Tel: 01932 228999 Fax: 01932 225586; 3 Sidney Road, Walton-on-Thames KT12 2NB — MB BS 1961 Lond. (Middlx.)

WARRINGTON, Mr George BUPA Gatwick Park Hospital, Povey Cross Road, Horley RH6 0BB Tel: 01293 785511 Fax: 01293 823367 — MD 1971 Malta; FRCS Eng. 1978. (Malta) Cons. ENT Surg. Crawley & Horsham Hosps. & New E. Surrey, Caterham & Oxted Hosps. Socs: Brit. Assn. Otol. Head & Neck Surg. Prev: Sen. Regist. Roy. Nat. Throat, Nose & Ear Hosp. Lond.; Sen. Regist. (ENT) St. Geo. Hosp. Lond.; Demonst. (Anat.) Univ. Leeds.

WARRINGTON, Jane Susan St helena Hospice, Barncroft Close, Eastwood Drive., Colchester CO4 4SF Tel: 01206 845566 Fax: 01206 842445 Email: ehall@sthelenahospice.org.uk — MB ChB 1978 Birm.; MRCPsych 1983. Cons. Psychiat. Leicester Gen. Hosp. Prev: Lect. Psychiat. Ment. Subnorm. Univ. Leic.; Hon. Sen. Regist. Leic. HA.

WARRINGTON, Jill Royal Cornhill Hospital, Cornhill Road, Aberdeen AB25 2ZH Tel: 01224 663131 — MB ChB 1987 Aberd.; MRCPsych 1991. Cons. (Psychiat. of Old Age) Roy. Cornhill Hosp.

WARRINGTON, John Richard 22 Deuchar Street, Newcastle upon Tyne NE2 1JX — MB BS 1996 Newc.

WARRINGTON, Nigel John Netherton Health Centre, Halesowen Road, Dudley DY2 9PU Tel: 01384 254935 Fax: 01384 242468 — MB ChB 1980 Birm.; MRCGP 1985. (Birmingham)

WARRINGTON, Rachel 59 Pettingale Road, Croesyceiliog, Cwmbran NP44 2NZ — MB BS 1998 Lond.

WARRINGTON, Robert The Health Centre, Rodney Road, Walton-on-Thames KT12 3LB Tel: 01932 228999 — MB BChir 1960 Camb.; BA Camb. 1960; DObst RCOG 1963. (Middlx.)

WARRINGTON, Shirley Royal Victoria Infirmary, Queen Victoria Road, Newcastle upon Tyne NE1 4LP Tel: 0191 232 5131; 2 Beechfield Road, Gosforth, Newcastle upon Tyne NE3 4DR Tel: 0191 285 6310 — MB BS 1986 Newc.; MRCP Ed. 1993; MRCGP 1991; DCH RCP Lond. 1990; DRCOG 1989; MRCPCH 1997. Regist. (Paediat.) Newc. Socs: N. Eng. Paediatric Soc. Prev: Regist. (Paediat.)Sunderland; Regist. (Paediat.) N.umberland; Regist. (Peadiat.) Gateshead.

WARRINGTON, Stephen 196 Harbour Lane, Milnrow, Rochdale OL16 4EL — MB ChB 1989 Manch. SHO Rotat. (Psychiat.) Salford Ment. Health Servs. Prestwich Hosp. Train Scheme.

WARRINGTON, Steven John Hammersmith Medicines Research Ltd., Central Middlesex Hospital, Acton Lane, London NW10 7NS Tel: 020 8961 4130 Fax: 020 8961 8665 Email: swarrinton@hmr-pharmacology.co.uk — MB BChir 1972 Camb.; MA Camb. 1972, MD 1984; FRCP Lond. 1991; FRCP Ed. 1990; MRCP (UK) 1974; FFPM RCP (UK) 1991. (St. Bart.) Med. Dir. Hammersmith Med. Research Ltd.; Hon. Lect. (Clin. Pharmacol.) St. Bart. Hosp. Lond. Socs: Brit. Pharm. Soc. Prev: Research Regist. (Cardiol. & Clin.

Pharmacol.) St. Bart. Hosp. Lond.; Lect. (Clin. Pharmacol.) St. Bart. Hosp. Med. Coll. Lond.; Resid. Med. Off. Nat. Heart Hosp. Lond.

WARRIS, Kauser Jabeen 114 New Road E4 9SY Tel: 020 8524 8124; 71 Empress Avenue, Woodford Green IG8 9DZ Tel: 020 8505 6392 — MB BS 1984 Punjab; MRCGP 1999; DRCOG 1997. GP Redbridge and Waltham Forest HA.

WARSAP, Alan John, QHP, OStJ, Brigadier late RAMC Retd. Llaneth House, St. Margarets, Vowchurch, Hereford HR2 0RF — BM BCh 1965 Oxf.; MA Oxf. 1965; FRCGP 1982, M 1973. (Oxf.) Med. Mem.The Appeals Serv.; Civil. Med. Pract. (Gen. Pract.) MoD. Socs: Fell. Med. Soc. Lond.; BMA. Prev: Dir. Army Gen. Pract.; Sen. Lect. (Gen. Pract.) RAMC; SMO Roy. Milit. Acad. Sandhurst.

WARSHOW, Usama Majid Mbarak 33 Sturdee House, Shipton St., London E2 7SA — MB BS 1998 Lond.

WARSOP, Andrew David 16 High Meadow, Tollerton, Nottingham NG12 4DZ — MB ChB 1989 Manch.

WARTAN, Sonia Wahan Anaesthetic Department, Epsom & St Helier NHS Trust, St Helier Hospital, Wrythe Lane, Carshalton SM5 1AA Tel: 020 8296 2444 — MB ChB 1981 Baghdad; MB ChB Baghdad Iraq 1981; FFA RCS Eng 1993. Cons. Anaesth. Pain. Managem. Epsom. St Helier. NHS Trust. Socs: Internat. Assn. Study of Pain; Pain. Soc; Assn. Anaesth. Prev: Sen.Reg.anaesth.Guys Hosp.; Research.Fell.Chronic Pain.Managem.Guys.Hosp.

WARTNABY, Helen Tamarisk, 12 Kingsham Avenue, Chichester PO19 2AN — MB BS 1988 Lond.; MRCGP 1994.

WARTNABY, Kathleen Mary (retired) 11 Greenhurst Lane, Hurst Green, Oxted RH8 0LD Tel: 01883 714461 — MD Lond. 1965, MB BS 1955; MRCP Lond. 1958; MRCPsych 1972; DPM Eng. 1966. Prev: Cons. Psychiat. Netherne Hosp. Coulsdon, Redhill Gen. Hosp. & Oxted Hosps.

WARWICK, Adrian Paul Wordsley Hospital, Department of Obstetrics & Gynaecology, Stream Road, Wordsley, Stourbridge DY8 5QX Tel: 01384 456111; The Leys, The Shortyard, Wolverley, Kidderminster DY11 5XF — MB ChB 1984 Liverp.; MRCOG 1990. Cons. O & G Dudley Gp. Hosps. NHS Trust. Socs: Brit. Soc. Colpos. & Cerv. Path.; Brit. Gyn. Cancer Soc. Prev: Sen. Regist. City Hosp. & Birm. & Midl. Hosp. Wom.; Research Fell. N: Staffs. Matern. Hosp; Regist. Rotat. (O & G) W. Midl., Stoke-on-Trent, Stafford & Shrewsbury.

WARWICK, Mr David John Southampton University Hospital, Tremona Road, Southampton SO16 6YD Tel: 02380 796248 Fax: 02380 794414; Tel: 02380 794414 Email: djwarwick@compuserve.com — BM 1986 Soton.; MD Bristol 1995; FRCS (Orth.) 1996; FRCS Eng. 1990; Dip. IMC RCS Ed. 1989. (Soton.) p/t Cons. Hand Surg. Soton. Univ. Hosps. NHS Trust Soton. Socs: Fell. BOA; Brit. Soc. Surg. Hand. Prev: Fell. (Hand Surg.) Roy. N. Shore Hosp. Sydney Australia; Lect. (Orthop.) Univ. Bristol & Sen. Regist. S & W RHA; Career Regist. (Orthop.) S. W.. RHA.

WARWICK, Frederick (retired) — MB BChir 1959 Camb.; FFR 1970; DCH Eng. 1964, DMRD 1966. Prev: Cons. Radiol. Manch. Roy. Infirm.

WARWICK, Graham Lawrie Department of Nephrology, Leicester General Hospital, Glendolen Road, Leicester LE2 2FL Tel: 0116 258 8038 Email: gwarwick@eving.igh_tr_trert.nhs.uk; Stoctone House, 19A Gaulby Lane, Stoughton, Leicester LE2 2FL Email: graham_warwick1@excite.co.uk — MB ChB 1981 Glas.; MD Glas. 1991; FRCP Lond. 1997; MRCP (UK) 1984. Cons. Nephrol. Leicester Gen. Hosp. Prev: Sen. Regist. (Nephrol. & Gen. Med.) Roy. Infirm. Glas.; Hon. Regist. & Lect. Renal Unit & Inst. Biochem. Roy. Infirm. Glas.; Regist. (Gen. Med. & Nephrol.) Glas. Roy. Infirm.

WARWICK, Helen Marie Levitts Surgery, Levitts Road, Bugbrooke, Northampton NN7 3QN Tel: 01604 830348 Fax: 01604 832785; 42 Pound Lane, Bugbrooke, Northampton NN7 3RH — BM BS 1989 Nottm.; BMedSci 1987 Nottm.; MRCGP 1994 Lond.; DCH 1992 Glas.; DRCOG 1991 Lond. (Nottm.) GP Princip. Socs: BMA; MDU. Prev: SHO (Cas.) N.ampton Gen. Hosp.; SHO GP Trainee N.ants.; SHO Palliat. Med. Cynthia Spencer Hospice N.ants.

WARWICK, Hilary Margaret Clare Department of General Psychiatry, St. George's Hospital Medical School, Cranmer Terrace, London SW17 0RE Tel: 020 8725 5543 — MB ChB 1980 Leeds; MMedSci (Clin. Psychiat.) Leeds 1985, MB ChB 1980; MRCPsych 1984. Sen. Lect. (Psychiat.) St. Geo.'s Hosp. Sch. Lond. Prev: Sen. Regist. Maudsley Hosp. Lond.

WARWICK, Jeremy Swain Fell Cottage Surgery, 123 Kells Lane, Low Fell, Gateshead NE9 5XY Tel: 0191 487 2656 — MB BS 1988 Newc.

WARWICK, John Richard Broughton House Surgery, 20 New Way, Batley WF17 5QT Tel: 01924 420244 Fax: 01924 422490; The Old Manse, 33 Caledonia Road, Batley WF17 5NS Tel: 01924 420234 Email: john@warwi.freeserve.co.uk — MB ChB 1985 Manch.; FRCGP 1998; T(GP) 1991; MRCGP 1989; BSc (Med. Sci.) St. And. 1982, BSc (Astron./Physics) 1979. (St Andrews & Manchester) GP Partner & Princip.; Bd. Mem. & Clin. Governance Lead PCG.

WARWICK, Jonathan Paul Nuffield Department of Anesthetics, Radcliffe Infirmary, Woodstock Road, Oxford OX2 6HE Tel: 01865 224774; 30 Cotswold Close, Minster Lovell, Witney OX29 0SX Tel: 01993 779121 — MB ChB 1987 Birm.; FRCA 1993; DA (UK) 1990. Cons. (Anaesth.) Radcliffe Infirm. Oxf. Socs: Hon. Sec. Assn Burn & Reconstruc. Anaesth. Prev: Sen. Regist. (Anaesth.) John Radcliffe Hosp. Oxf.; Sen. Regist. (Anaesth.) Milton Keynes Gen. Hosp. NHS Trust; Regist. (Anaesth.) P.ss Mary Hosp. RAF Akrotiri.

WARWICK, Lily Anne (retired) Newbattle Group Practice, Mayfield, Dalkeith EH22 — MB ChB 1965 Ed.

WARWICK, Malcolm Stewart (retired) Cannons, Croftswood, Ilfracombe EX34 — MB ChB 1955 Birm.; MRCS Eng. LRCP Lond. 1955; DPH Ed. 1957; DObst RCOG 1960. Med. Staff Ilfracombe & Dist. Cott. Hosp.; Police Surg.; Local Treasury Med. Off. Prev: Ho. Phys. & Ho. Surg. Qu. Eliz. Hosp. Birm.

WARWICK, Michael McDonald 7 Redford Loan, Colinton, Edinburgh EH13 0AY — MB ChB 1992 Aberd.; MPhil Ed. 1999. SHO (Psychiat.), Roy. Edin. Hosp. Socs: MRCPsych.

WARWICK, Nicholas Graham 23 High Tree Drive, Earley, Reading RG6 1EU — MB BS 1986 Lond. (CXHMS)

WARWICK, Ralph Roderick Gardner Tel: 0131 663 1051 Fax: 0131 654 0665; (home) Fala House, 55 Eskbank Road, Dalkeith EH22 3BU — MB ChB 1966 Ed.; BSc (Hons. Bact.) Ed. 1964; MRCP (U.K.) 1970; MRCGP 1977.

WARWICK, Rowena Jane Dorley Cottage, 66 Churchway, Haddenham, Aylesbury HP17 8HA — MB BS 1988 Lond.; BSc (Hons.) Lond. 1985, MB BS 1988; MRCP (UK) 1991. Sen. Regist. (Radiol.) Roy. Free Hosp. Lond.

WARWICK, Ruth Marilyn North London Blood Transfusion Centre, Colindale Avenue, Edgeware, London NW9 5BG — MB ChB 1973 Bristol; FRCP 1997; FRCPath 1992, M 1980; MRCP (UK) 1977. Lead Cons., tissue Serv.s, Nat. chronological. Prev: Lead Cons. tissue and stem cell donor care, Lond. and S. E. Nat. Blood Serv.; Sen. Regist. (Haemat.) Roy. Free Hosp. Lond.; Cons. Haemat. Qu. Charlottes Hosp. Wom. Lond., RPGMS.

WARWICK, Wilfred James Greer (retired) Plas Gwyn, 257 Penn Road, Wolverhampton WV4 5SF Tel: 01902 341361 — MB BCh BAO 1937 Dub.

WARWICK-BROWN, Janet Margaret Denmead Health Centre, Hambledon Road, Denmead, Waterlooville PO7 6NR Tel: 023 9225 7112 Fax: 023 9225 7113; 7 Brent Court, Emsworth PO10 7JA Tel: 01243 371502 — MB BS 1980 Lond.; BSc (Hons.) Lond. 1977; MRCOG 1988; DRCOG 1984. (St. Bart.) Hosp. Pract. Dept. Obst. & Gyn. St. Mary's Hosp. Portsmouth. Prev: Regist. (O & G) St. Mary's Hosp. Portsmouth.

WARWICK-BROWN, Mr Nigel Peter ENT Department, Southend Hospital, Prittlewell Chase, Westcliff on Sea SS0 0RY Tel: 01702 435555 Fax: 01702 221300; Tel: 01702 557959 Fax: 01702 551924 Email: warwickbrowns@tinyworld.co.uk — MB BS 1978 Lond.; FRCS Eng. 1985; FRCSI 1984. (Lond. Hosp.) Cons. Surg. (ENT) S.end Hosp. Socs: Fell. Roy. Soc. Med. Prev: Sen. Regist. (ENT) Radcliffe Infirm. Oxf. & Roy. Berks. Hosp. Reading; Regist. (ENT) Char. Cross Hosp. Lond.; SHO (ENT) Roy. Nat. Throat, Nose & Ear Hosp. Lond.

WARWICK-BROWN, Robert (retired) 47 Colts Bay, Craigweil, Bognor Regis PO21 4EH Tel: 01243 262457 — MB BChir Camb. 1948; MA Camb. 1948; AFOM RCP Lond. 1981. Prev: Ho. Surg. Thoracic Unit & Lect. (Anat.) St. Bart. Hosp.

WARWICKER, Peter Maciej The Grove Medical Centre, Church Road, Egham TW20 9QJ Tel: 01784 433159 Fax: 01784 477208; 50 Simons Walk, Finglefield Green, Egham TW20 9SQ Tel: 01784 430090 — MB BS 1987 Lond.; MRCGP (Distinc.) 1991; DRCOG 1991.

WASAN, Balvinder Singh 28 Charlbert Court, Charlbert St., London NW8 7BX Tel: 020 7722 9865 — MB BS 1994 Lond.; BSc Lond. 1991. SHO (Med.) Hammersmith Hosp. Lond. Prev: SHO (Med.) Hillingdon & Harefield Hosps. Middlx.

WASAN, Harpreet Singh 16 Chesterfield Road, Chiswick, London W4 3HG Tel: 020 8 987 8807 Fax: 020 8383 4758 Email: wasan@icof.icnet.uk; 6/E Haven Court, 128 Leighton Road, Hong Kong Tel: 00 852 5771386 Fax: 00 852 5597550 — MB BS 1986 Lond.; MB BS (Hons.) Lond. 1986; MRCP (UK) 1990. Med. Research Counc. Train. Fell. Imperial Cancer Research Fund Lond.; Hon. Sen. Regist. (Med. Oncol.) Hammersmith Hosp. Roy. Postgrad. Med. Sch. Prev: Regist. Rotat. (Gen. Med.) Univ. Coll. Hosp., Middlx., Whittington., Lond. Chest Hosps.; SHO Rotat. (Gen. Med.) St. Geo. Hosp. Lond.; SHO (Med.) St. Mary's Hosp. Lond.

WASAN, Prabhjote Kaur 16 Chesterfield Road, Chiswick, London W4 3HG Tel: 020 8987 8807 — MB BS 1991 Lond. Trainee GP/SHO Ealing Hosp. Lond VTS.

WASAWO, Steven Peter 37 Hawksworth Road, Horsforth, Leeds LS18 4JP — MB ChB 1993 Leeds.

WASCHK, Gisbert 92 Dalberg Road, London SW2 1AW Tel: 020 7737 7318 — State Exam Med. Cologne 1989.

WASFI, Fawzi Mahmood 392 Fulham Palace Road, London SW6 6HU — MRCS Eng. LRCP Lond. 1979.

WASHBROOK, Reginald Alfred Hryhoruk, TD 219 Lichfield Road, Rushall, Walsall WS4 1EA Tel: 01922 640384 — MB ChB 1956 St. And.; MSc McGill 1967; FRCPsych 1992, M 1971; DPM Eng. 1962; DPM Lond. 1960. Maj. RAMC (V). Socs: Internat. Soc. Criminols. & Brit. Counc. Alcoholism. Prev: Research Fell. (Foren. Psychiat.) Univ. McGill, Canada; Ho. Surg. Derbysh. Childr. Hosp. Derby; Ho. Phys. Dundee Roy. Infirm.

WASHINGTON, Avril Joan Dept. Paediatrics & Child Health, Homerton Hospital NHS Trust, Homerton Row, London E9 6SR Tel: 020 8510 7876 Fax: 020 8510 7171 — MB BS 1984 Lond.; MRCP (UK) 1990. (Kings College Hospital) Consltant Paediat., Dept. Paediat. & Child health, Homerton Hosp., Hackney, Lond. Socs: Brit. Med. Assn.s; Roy. Coll. Paediat. & Child Health; Med. Interview Teachg. Assn. Prev: Sen. Regist. (Paediat.) Roy. Free Hosp. Lond.; Regist. (Paediat. A & E) Qu. Eliz. Hosp. Childr. Lond. (P/T); Regist. Rotat. (Paediat.) Roy. Lond. Hosp.

WASHINGTON, James Stephen (retired) 8 Elliott Avenue, Frenchay, Bristol BS16 1PB Tel: 0117 956 7846 — MB ChB Leeds 1948; DIH Eng. 1962. Prev: Med. Adviser Hepworth Minerals & Chems. Ltd.

WASHINGTON, Mark Ian Neston Surgery, Mellock Lane, Little Neston, South Wirral CH64 4BN Tel: 0151 336 3951 Fax: 0151 353 0173; 96 The Priory, Neston, South Wirral CH64 3ST — MB ChB 1989 Liverp.; DRCOG 1994; DCH RCP Lond. 1992. GP, Neston Surg., Neston.

WASHINGTON, Robert John Mackenzie Womack, Elbury Lane, Churston Ferrers, Brixham TQ5 Tel: 01803 842117 — MB ChB Birm. 1961; DObst RCOG 1963. (Birm.) Asst. Surg. (Orthop. & Trauma) Torbay Hosp. Torquay. Socs: BMA. Prev: Ho. Surg. & Ho. Phys. Gen. Hosp. Birm.; Obst. Ho. Off. Dudley Rd. Hosp. Birm.; Cas. Surg. Regist. Gen. Hosp. Birm.

***WASHINGTON, Stephen James** 45 Back Lane, Longton, Preston PR4 5BE — MB ChB 1998 Birm.; ChB Birm. 1998.

WASHINGTON, Suzanne Elizabeth Jayne 33 Fulmer Road, Sheffield S11 8UF Tel: 0114 266 0442; 244 Shear Brow, Blackburn BB1 8DS Tel: 01254 698501 — MB ChB 1994 Sheff. SHO (A & E) Chesterfield & N. Derbys. Roy. Hosp. NHS Trust. Prev: Ho. Off. (Gen., Renal & Cardiothoracic Surg.) N.. Gen. Hosp. Sheff.; Ho. Off. (Gen. Med. & Dermat.) Chesterfield Hosp. Derbysh.

WASILEWSKI, Anna Wanda Waverly Cottage, Exelby, Bedale DL8 2HB — MB ChB 1992 Liverp.

WASIM, M Glyn Ebwy Surgery, James Street, Ebbw Vale NP23 6JG Tel: 01495 302716 Fax: 01495 305166 — MB BS 1974 Patna; MB BS 1974 Patna.

WASON, Anne-Marie Bradford Hospitals NHS Trust, X-ray Department, Duckworth Lane, Bradford BD9 6RJ Tel: 01274 364543 — BM BS 1986 Nottm.; BMedSci Nottm. 1983; MRCP (UK) 1989; FRCR 1993. Cons. Radiol.

WASPE, Sharon Rose 29 Atherstone Close, Oadby, Leicester LE2 4SP Tel: 0116 2711 059 — MB ChB 1998 Leic. (Leicester) Pre-Registration Ho. Off. in Gen. Med., Pilgrim Hosp., Boston, Lincs.

WASS

Prev: Pre-Regist. Ho. Off. in Gneral Surg., Kettering Gen. Hosp., Kettering, N.amptonshire.

WASS, Mr Alastair Roland Accident & Emergency Department, Pinderfields General Hospital, Aberford Road, Wakefield WF1 4DG Tel: 01924 201688 Fax: 01924 814864; Barn Moor, 1 Hungate Close, Dame Lane, Saxton, Tadcaster LS24 9TP Tel: 01937 557151 — MB BS 1987 Lond.; FRCS Eng. 1992; FFAEM 1997.

WASS, Professor John Andrew Hall Department of Endocrinology, Radcliffe Infirmary, Woodstock Road, Oxford OX2 6HE Tel: 01865 224765 Fax: 01865 224617 Email: john.wass@anglox.nhs.uk; West Wing, Kirtlington Park, Kirtlington, Kidlington OX5 3JN Tel: 01869 350375 — MB BS 1971 Lond.; MD Lond. 1980; FRCP Lond. 1986; MRCP (UK) 1973; MRCS Eng. LRCP Lond. 1971; MA Oxford 1995. (Guy's) Cons. Phys. (Endocrinol. & Metab.) Radcliffe Infirm. & Nuffield Orthop. Centre Oxf.; Prof. Endocrinol. Univ. Oxf. Socs: Amer. Endocrinol. Soc.; Soc. Endocrinol.; Assoc. Phys. Prev: Prof. Clin. Endocrinol. St. Bart. Hosp. Med. Sch. Lond.; Regist. Guy's Hosp. Lond. & King's Coll. Hosp. Lond.

WASS, Valerie Jean Lambeth Walk Group Practice, 5 Lambeth Walk, London SE11 6SP Tel: 020 7735 4412 Fax: 020 7820 1888 — MB BS 1972 Lond.; BSc Lond. 1969; MRCP Lond. 1982; MRCS Eng. LRCP Lond. 1972; FRCGP 1995; DCH Eng. 1974. (Guy's) Sen. Lect. (Primary Health Care Med. Educat.) UMDS Lond. Prev: Regist. (Med.) Guy's Hosp. Lond.

WASSEF, Mouneer Abd-Elshahid Treloar Haemophilia Centre, Holybourne, Alton GU34 4EN Tel: 01420 88415; 6 Marshal Close, The Butts, Alton GU34 1RA — MB BCh 1962 Ain Shams. (Cairo) SCMO Treloar Haemophilia Centre Alton & Basingstoke Dist. Hosp. Prev: Regist. (Haemat.) St. Mary's Hosp. Lond.; Regist. (Haemat.) N. Middlx. Hosp. Lond.; Regist. (Haemat. & Histopath.) Birch Hill Hosp. Rochdale.

WASSERBERG, Mr Jonathan Department of Neurosurgery, Queen Elizabeth Hospital, Birmingham; 19 Chestnut Close, Streetly, Sutton Coldfield B74 3EF Tel: 0121 580 9642 — MB BChir Camb. 1985; BSc (Hons.) Leic. 1983; FRCS Eng. 1990. (Camb.) Sen. Lect. & Hon. Cons. Neurosurg. Qu. Eliz. Hosp. Birm. Socs: Assoc. Mem. Soc. Brit. Neurol. Surgs. Prev: Regist. (Neurosurg.) S. Gen. Hosp. Glas. & Hull Roy. Infirm.; Sen. Regist. (Neurosurg.) S. Gen. Hosp. Glas.

WASSIF, Wassif Samuel 9 Giles House, 158/160 Westbourne Grove, London W11 2RJ Tel: 020 7727 7835 Fax: 020 7221 7824 — MB ChB 1980 Assiut; MB ChB Assiut Egypt 1980; MSc Lond. 1993. Sen. Regist. (Clin. Biochem.) King's Coll. Hosp. Lond. Prev: Regist. King's Coll. Hosp. Lond.; SHO Leicester Roy. Infirm.

WASSMER, Evangeline Birmingham Children's Hospital Neurology Dept, Steelhouse Lane, Birmingham B4 6NH; Flat 7, 22 Carpenter Road, Edgbaston, Birmingham B15 2JN — Artsexamen 1994 Amsterdam; DCH 1996; MRCP 1996. Specialist Regist. (Paediat. Neurol.). Socs: RCPaed.

WASSON, Ciaran Whiterock Health Clinic, 6 Whiterock Grove, Belfast BT12 7RQ Tel: 028 9032 3153 Fax: 028 9061 9431; 181 Upper Lisburn Road, Belfast BT10 0LJ Tel: 01232 619431 — MB BCh BAO 1981 Belf.; DFFP 1993. (Qus. Belf.) Socs: Fell. Ulster Med. Soc.; Assoc. Mem. Irish Otolaryngol. Soc.

WASSON, Colin Michael Alexander 14 Styal Road, Wilmslow SK9 4AE Email: colin.wasson@virgin.net — MB ChB 1992 Manch. Specialist Regist. (Anaesth.).

WASSON, Jane Fulton McIlwaine The Health Centre, 20 Cleveland Square, Middlesbrough TS1 2NX Tel: 01642 245069 Fax: 01642 230388; 8 Morton Carr Lane, Nunthorpe, Middlesbrough TS7 0JU Tel: 01642 316112 — MB ChB 1975 Bristol; Cert. Family Plann. JCC 1979.

WASSON, Lorraine Frances 91 Linn Road, Larne BT40 2BA — MB BCh BAO 1993 Belf.

WASSON, Sharon Jane 14 Styal Road, Wilmslow SK9 4AE — MB ChB 1992 Manch.

WASTELL, Professor Christopher Chelsea Westminster Hospital, Surgical Unit, Fulham Road, London SW10 9NH Tel: 020 8746 8463 Fax: 020 8746 8282 Email: c.wastell@cxwms.ac.uk; 7 Manor Way, Beckenham BR3 3LH Tel: 020 8650 5882 Fax: 020 8650 5882 Email: cwastell@globalnet.co.uk — MB BS Lond. 1957; MS Lond. 1966; FRCS Eng. 1960; MRCS Eng. LRCP Lond. 1957. (Guy's) Emerit. Prof. & Hon. Cons. Gen. & Gastroenterol. Surg. Chelsea W.m. Hosp., Imperial Coll. of Med. Lond.; Hon. Cons. Surg. Roy.

Hosp. Chelsea & Roy. Brompton Hosp. Lond. Socs: Hellenic Soc. Experim. Med.; Hunt. Soc. (Ex-Pres.); Roy. Soc. Med. Prev: Lect. (Surg.) W.m. Med. Sch. Lond.; Regist. (Surg.) W.m. Hosp. Lond.; C. & H. J. Gaisman Research Fell. (Surg.) Mt. Sinai Hosp., NY.

WASTELL, Hilary Janet Department of clinical biochemistry, Freeman Hospital, High Heaton, Newcastle upon Tyne NE7 7BN Tel: 0191 223 1094 Fax: 0191 223 1292 Email: hilary.wastell@tfh.nuth.notrhy.nhs.uk — MB BS 1981 Newc.; MSc Newc. 1977; BSc (Hons.) Leeds 1972; MRCPath 1988. p/t Cons. Chem. Path. Freeman Hosp., Newc. Upon Tyne. Socs: Assn. Clin. Biochem.; Ass. Clin. Path. Prev: Sen. Regist. (Chem. Path.) Newc. Gen. Hosp.; Ho. Phys. & Surg. Roy. Vict. Infirm. Newc.

WASTI, Sabahat Asim Odstock Hospital, Salisbury General Hospital, Salisbury SP2 8BJ — MB BS 1982 Pershawar.

WASTIE, Jonathan Charles 37B Preston Park Avenue, Brighton BN1 6HG — MB BS 1992 Lond.; BSc (Hons.) Lond. 1986, MB BS 1992; Dip GUM 1998. (Charing Cross/Westminster) Clin. Asst. GUM/HIV; CMO Community HIV. Socs: BHIVA.

WASTIE, Martin Lovat Radiology Department, University Hospital, Nottingham NG7 2UH Tel: 0115 970 9197 — MB 1965 Camb.; BChir 1964; FRCP Lond. 1992; FRCR 1975; FFR 1973; DMRD Eng. 1970. (Camb. & Guy's)

WASTY, Mr Syed Wajahat Hussain 1 Foxhome Close, Willow Grove, Chislehurst BR7 5XT — MB BS 1981 Karachi; FRCS Glas. 1986.

WASU, P S The Surgery, 275A Kings Road, South Harrow, Harrow HA2 9LG Tel: 020 8866 0920 Fax: 020 8426 1104 — MB BS 1974 Banaras Hindu; MB BS 1974 Banaras Hindu.

WAT, Cynthia Kam Yin Roche Pharmaceuticals, 40 Broadwater Road, Welwyn Garden City AL7 3AY; 54 Cumberland Terrace, London NW1 4HJ — MB BS 1992 Lond.; MRCP (UK).

WAT, Dennis Shu-Chang 1st Floor Flat, 77 Cowbridge Road, Canton, Cardiff CF11 9AF — MB BCh 1998 Wales.

WATCHMAN, Isaac Godfrey (retired) 50 Rockbourne Avenue, Liverpool L25 4TL — MB BCh BAO Belf. 1943.

WATERER, Rachel Mary Arbury Medical Centre, Cambridge Drive, Stockingford, Nuneaton CV10 8LW Tel: 024 7638 8555 Fax: 024 7635 2396; Arbury Medical Centre, Cambridge Drive, Nuneaton CV10 8LW Tel: 01203 388555 — BM BS 1985 Nottm.; MRCGP 1990; DRCOG 1988. (Nottm.) GP Princip. Prev: GP Beverley.

WATERER, Suzanne Cathryn Brunton Place Surgery, 9 Brunton Place, Edinburgh EH7 5EG Tel: 0131 557 5545 — MB ChB 1982 Dundee; MRCGP 1986; DFFP 1994; DRCOG 1986.

WATERFALL, Joan Margaret (retired) 15 Remus Gate, Brackley NN13 7HY Tel: 01280 702812 — MB ChB Manch. 1946; DA Eng. 1953. Cons. Anaesth. P. Chas. Hosp. Merthyr & Cynon Valley Gp. Prev: Staff Asst. (Anaesth.) Mayo Clinic, USA.

WATERFALL, Mr Nicholas Brian 97 Bromham Road, Bedford MK40 4BS — MB BS 1969 Lond.; FRCS Eng. 1975. (St. Bart.) Cons. Surg. Bedford Gen. Hosp. Socs: Fell. Roy. Soc. Med.; Brit. Assn. Urol. Surg. Prev: Sen. Regist. (Surg.) Char. Cross Hosp. Lond.; Regist. (Surg.) Bedford Gen. Hosp.; Ho. Off. St. Bart. Hosp. Lond.

WATERFIELD, Mr Andrew Hamilton Princes Wing, Queen Elizabeth II Hospital, Welwyn Garden City AL7 4HQ Tel: 01707 365265 Fax: 01707 365244; Dairy Cottage, Lamer Lane, Wheathampstead, St Albans AL4 8RG Tel: 01582 831261 Fax: 01582 831262 Email: 618ahw@globalnet.co.uk — MB BS Lond. 1978; FRCS Ed. 1983; FRCS Eng. 1984 (St. Mary's) Cons. Surg. Orthop. & Trauma Qu. Eliz. II Hosp. Welwyn Gdn. City. Socs: Fell. BOA; BMA. Prev: Sen. Regist. & Regist. (Orthop.) Lond. Hosp. Whitechapel; Sen. Regist. (Orthop.) Roy. Nat. Orthop. Hosp. Stanmore; Chief Resid. (Orthop.) Mass. Gen. Hosp. & Clin. Fell. Harvard Med. Sch. Boston, USA.

WATERFIELD, Nicholas Peter 64 Shaftsbury Way, Twickenham TW2 5RP — MB BS 1982 Lond.

WATERFIELD, Peter Hepburn (retired) Tregarne House, Mawnan Smith, Falmouth TR11 5JP — MB BS 1960 Lond.; MRCS Eng. LRCP Lond. 1958; DObst RCOG 1960. Prev: Ho. Phys. St. Helen's Hosp. Hastings.

WATERHOUSE, Angela Marie High Street Surgery, Cumberland House, 8 High Street, Stone ST15 8AP Tel: 01785 813538 Fax: 01785 812208; 4 The Crescent, Stone ST15 8JN — MB ChB 1990 Birm.; ChB Birm. 1990; MRCGP 1994; DCH RCP Lond. 1993. (Birm.) GP Partner.

WATERHOUSE, Clive Yare Valley Medical Practice, 202 Thorpe Road, Norwich NR1 1TJ Tel: 01603 437559 Fax: 01603 701773 — MB ChB 1983 Leeds; MRCGP 1989.

WATERHOUSE, David Graham Cornishway Medical Centre, 37 Cornishway, Woodhouse Park, Manchester M22 0LY Tel: 0161 437 1467 Fax: 0161 493 9043; 9 Turnberry Drive, Wilmslow SK9 2QW — MB BChir 1979 Camb.; MA, MB Camb. 1979, BChir 1978; DRCOG 1982.

WATERHOUSE, Elizabeth Aileen (retired) Clare Farm, Dullingham, Newmarket CB8 9UJ Tel: 01638 507267 Fax: 01638 507267 — MB BS 1952 Durh. Prev: Sessional Med. Off. Region. Blood Transfus. Serv. Camb.

WATERHOUSE, Esther Tremaine 54 Grand Avenue, London N10 3BP — BM BS 1991 Nottm. Sen. Regist., Palliat. Med., Leicester.

WATERHOUSE, John Crichton Royal Hospital, Dumfries DG1 4TG Tel: 01387 244000 Fax: 01387 257735 — MB ChB 1976 Dundee; MD Dundee 1986; MMedSci Leeds 1983; MRCPsych 1983. Cons. Psychiat. Crichton Roy. Hosp. Dumfries.

WATERHOUSE, Mr Norman 55 Harley Street, London W1N 1DD Tel: 020 7636 4073 Fax: 020 7636 6417 Email: wtrhouse@globalnet.co.uk — MB ChB 1978 Birm.; FRCS Ed. 1982; FRCS Eng. 1982; FRCS (Plast Surg.) 1988. Cons. Plastic & Reconstruc. Surg. Chelsea & W.minster Hosp. Socs: Roy. Soc. Med. (Ex-Pres. Plastic Surg. Sect.). Prev: Sen. Regist. (Plastic & Reconstruc. Surg.) Mt. Vernon & W. Middlx. Hosps.; Craniofacial Fell. S. Austral. Craniofacial Unit Adelaide Childr. Hosp., Austral.; Vis. Prof. in cranofacial Surg. Qater 1998.

WATERHOUSE, Paul White's Farm, Sampford, Arundel, Wellington TA21 9QN — MB BS 1990 Lond.

WATERHOUSE, Thomas Dennis (retired) Whites Farm, Sampford Arundel, Wellington TA21 9QN Tel: 01823 672435 Fax: 01823 673142 Email: c.waterhouse@viergin.net — MB ChB 1961 Bristol; FFA RCS Eng. 1970; DA Eng. 1967; DObst RCOG 1967. Cons. Anaesth. S. Som. Clin. Area. Prev: Lect. Nuffield Dept. Anaesth. Radcliffe Infirm. Oxf.

WATERLOW, Professor John Conrad, CMG (retired) 15 Hillgate Street, London W8 7SP Tel: 020 7727 7456 — MB BChir 1942 Camb.; FRS 1982; ScD Camb. 1966, MD 1948; Hon. DSc Reading 1983; Hon. DSc W. Indies 1978; FRCP Lond. 1969. Prev: Dir. MRC Trop. Metab. Research Unit Univ. W. Indies.

WATERLOW, John Kenneth (retired) 1 Springfield Road, Hinckley LE10 1AN Tel: 01455 446483 — MB BS 1945 Lond. Prev: GP Hinckley.

WATERMAN, Charles Edward (retired) 19 Marley Avenue, New Milton BH25 5LQ Tel: 01425 614816 — MB BS 1947 Lond.; MRCS Eng. LRCP Lond. 1940. Prev: Ho. Phys. & Ho. Surg. Lond. Hosp.

WATERMAN, David 24 Cowdray Court, Kingston Park, Newcastle upon Tyne NE3 2UA — MB BS 1995 Newc.

WATERMAN, Mark Rupert 7 Sandown Park, Belfast BT5 6HD — MB BCh BAO 1980 Belf.

WATERMAN, Susan Vivien 18 Elm Park Court, Elm Park Road, Pinner HA5 3LJ — MB BS 1987 Lond.

WATERMEYER, Sean Rawson, Flight Lt. RAF Med. Br. 112 Heathwood Road, Cardiff CF14 4BQ — MB BS 1990 Wales; BSc (Hons.) Wales 1985; MRCGP 1995; DRCOG 1995. Prev: Trainee GP BFPO 25.

WATERS, Mr Alan Addenbrooke's Hospital, Hills Road, Cambridge CB2 2QQ Tel: 01223 216676; Minglepen, Mingle Lane, Great Shelford, Cambridge CB2 5BG Tel: 01223 844160 Fax: 012230 842241 Email: alanwaters@sosi.net — MB ChB 1971 Ed.; MChir Camb. 1985, MA 1983; BSc (Med. Sci. Biochem.) (Hons.) Ed. 1968; FRCS Eng. 1976; FRCS Ed. 1975. Cons. Neurosurg. Addenbrooke's Hosp. Camb. Socs: Soc. Brit. Neurol. Surgs. Prev: Lect. (Neurosurg.) Univ. Camb.; Sen. Regist. (Neurosurg.) Addenbrooke's Hosp. Camb.; Regist. (Surg. & Neurosurg.) Edin. Roy. Infirm.

WATERS, Professor Alan Harold Department of Haematology, St. Bartholomew's Hospital, London EC1A 7BE Tel: 020 7601 8202; 16 Woodville Gardens, Ealing, London W5 2LQ Tel: 020 8997 6822 — MB BS (Hons.) Queensland 1958; PhD Lond. 1963; FRCP Lond. 1984; MRCP (UK) 1977; FRACP 1975, M 1972; FRCPath 1976, M 1963; FRCPA 1971, M 1965. (Queensld.) Emerit. Prof. Haemat. Qu. Mary & W.field Coll. Lond.; Hon. Cons. Haemat. St. Bart. Hosp. Socs: (Ex-Counc.) Brit. Blood Transfus. Soc.; (Ex-Pres.) Brit. Soc. Haematol.; (Ex-Counc. Path Sect.) Roy. Soc. Med. Prev: Hon. Cons. Haemat. St. Bart. Hosp.; Lect. & Hon. Sen. Regist. (Haemat.) Roy. Postgrad. Med. Sch. & Hammersmith Hosp. Lond.; Haematol. St. Vincent's Hosp. Melbourne, Austral.

WATERS, Alice May 21 Ingham Drive, Coldean, Brighton BN1 9GL Tel: 01273 66893 — MB BS 1939 Madras; DGO 1940; DObst RCOG 1948. Prev: Asst. Surg. Govt. Gen. Hosp. Madras; Graded Surg. & Gyn. IAMC; Specialist Trainee O & G W. Middlx. Hosp. Isleworth.

WATERS, Andrew Derek The Health Centre, Gibson Lane, Kippax, Leeds LS25 7JN Tel: 0113 287 0870 Fax: 0113 232 0746 — BM BS 1983 Nottm.

WATERS, Anthony Kevin 10 Chapel Close, Helmsley, York YO62 5BE Tel: 01439 771474 Email: akwaters@btinternet.com — MA, MB Camb. 1969, BChir 1968; FRCP Lond. 1986, M 1972. (Camb. & St. Mary's) Cons. Phys. Wharfedale Gen. Hosp. Otley; Clin. Lect. Univ. Leeds. Prev: Sen. Regist. Leeds AHA; Governors' Research Fell. & Med. Regist. Char. Cross Hosp. Lond.

WATERS, Arthur Gwyn Glenconna, Loughor, Swansea Tel: 01792 2055 — MRCS Eng. LRCP Lond. 1936. (Cardiff & Lond. Hosp.)

WATERS, Brian Westbrook, Castle St., Rhuddlan, Rhyl LL18 5AB — MB ChB 1973 Liverp.; MRCP (UK) 1978; FFA RCS Eng. 1984; DA Eng. 1982; DObst RCOG 1975.

WATERS, Brian Harry Tudor 4 Shelley Close, Abingdon OX14 1PP — MB BS 1991 Lond.

WATERS, Catherine Miriam 4 Shelley Close, Abingdon OX14 1PP — MB BS 1989 Lond.

WATERS, Claire Elizabeth Mount Vernon Hospital, Rickmansworth Road, Northwood HA6 2RN — MB ChB 1992 Sheff.; MRCP (UK) 1995.

WATERS, Colin George (retired) Spinneys, Saunton, Braunton EX33 1LG Tel: 01271 812032 — MB BChir 1957 Camb.; BA (1st cl. Hons.) Camb. 1953; MRCGP 1969; DA Eng. 1959; DObst RCOG 1958. Prev: Gen. Practitioner, Caen Health Centre,Braunton, N Devon.

WATERS, Deborah Jane Tel: 01495 752444 Fax: 01495 767820 — MB BS Lond. 1985; BSc Lond. 1983; MRCGP 1990; Cert. Family Plann. JCC 1989; DRCOG 1989; DCH RCP Lond. 1987. (Char. Cross Hosp. Med. Sch.) p/t Gen. Practitioner. Prev: GP Barry; Trainee GP Ealing Hosp. S.all VTS; Staff Grade (Community Paediat.) Glan Hafren NHS Trust.

WATERS, Mr Eric Albert Heath Cottage, Clarendon Road, Alderbury, Salisbury SP5 3AT Tel: 01722 710069; Salisbury Health Care NHS Trust, Salisbury District Hospital, Salisbury SP2 8BJ Tel: 01722 336262 Fax: 01722 331529 Email: evican@globalnet.co.uk — BSc Leeds 1965, MB ChB 1968; FRCS Ed. 1984; FRCS Eng. 1974; FFAEM 1996. Cons. in A & E Salisbury Dist. Hosp.; Med. Dir. Salisbury Health Care.

WATERS, Fiona Helen Drings Close Surgery, 1 Drings Close, Over, Cambridge CB4 5NZ Tel: 01954 231550 Fax: 01954 231573; Minglepen, 20 Mingle Lane, Great Shelford, Cambridge CB2 5BG Tel: 01223 844160 — MB ChB 1974 Ed.; DObst RCOG 1976. Prev: GP Swavesey.

WATERS, Fiona Mary 147 Ruxley Lane, Epsom KT19 9EX — MB ChB 1992 Manch.

WATERS, Fiona Sarah Highlands, Old Lane, Stanningfield, Bury St Edmunds IP29 4SA — MB BS 1997 Lond.

WATERS, Harry 28 Castlenau, London SW13 9RU Tel: 020 8748 5512 — LM 1925 Rotunda; BA, MB BCh BAO Dub. 1925. (T.C. Dub.) Lect. & Examr. Brit. Red Cross Soc.; Examr. in 1st Aid ILEA; Hon. Med. Off. Amateur Boxing Assn. Eng. Socs: Hunt. Soc. & W. Lond. M-C Soc. Prev: Med. Off. i/c W.. Hosp. Mobile Unit; Surg. Clin. Asst. W. Lond. Hosp. Hammersmith; Capt. RAMC.

WATERS, Harry Jason Asian Leadership InStreet, Phuket 8300, Thailand; 12 Convent Gardens, Findon, Worthing BN14 0RZ — MB BS 1995 Lond.; BSc Lond. 1992. (St. Mary's) Med. Dir. Asian Ldr.ship Inst. Thailand.

WATERS, Harry Richard Carna, 12 Covent Gardens, Findon, Worthing BN14 0RZ — MB BS 1964 Lond.; MRCS Eng. LRCP Lond. 1964; FFA RCS Eng. 1968; DObst RCOG 1967; DA Eng. 1966. (St. Mary's) Cons. Anaesth. Worthing, S.lands & Dist. Gp. Hosps. Socs: Assn. Anaesths. Prev: Sen. Regist. St. Thos. Hosp. Lond.

WATERS, Helen Maria 25 Cranmore Avenue, Belfast BT9 6JH — MB BS 1996 Lond.

WATERS

WATERS, Henry John Village Medical Centre, 400-404 Linthorpe Road, Middlesbrough TS5 6HF Tel: 01642 851234 Fax: 01642 820821; 45 Byemoor Avenue, Great Ayton, Middlesbrough TS9 6JP Tel: 01642 724291 — MB BS 1973 Newc.; MRCGP 1977; DCH RCPS Glas. 1976. Clin. Asst. (Rheum.) S. Cleveland Hosp. Middlesbrough & N.; Tees Gen. Hosp. Stockton-on-Tees.

WATERS, Hilary Mary Eastdene, The Folly, Ditcheat, Shepton Mallet BA4 6QS — MB BS 1978 Lond.

WATERS, Ieuan Rhys 9 Heol Yr Onnen, Pencoed, Bridgend CF35 5PF — MB ChB 1989 Leeds.

WATERS, Ifan Richard (retired) 15 Abbey House, Cirencester GL7 2QU — MRCS Eng. LRCP Lond. 1943. Prev: SCMO Wilts. HA. RAF Med. Br.

WATERS, Jennifer Kate 39 Stow Road, Stow-cum-Quy, Cambridge CB5 9AD — MB BS 1998 Lond.

WATERS, John (retired) 18 Bryony Road, Weoley Hill, Birmingham B29 4BU — MB ChB 1954 Birm.; MRCS Eng. LRCP Lond. 1954; MRCGP 1969; DObst RCOG 1962; DPH Eng. 1958. Prev: GP Birm.

WATERS, John Mortimer Dr J M Beck and Partners, 21 Beaufort Road, Southbourne, Bournemouth BH6 5AJ Tel: 01202 433081 Fax: 01202 430527; 58 Sopers Lane, Christchurch BH23 1JF Email: jwaters@tcp.co.uk — MB BS 1976 Lond.; MRCS Eng. LRCP Lond. 1976; MRCGP 1984. (St. Geo.) GP Princip.; Hosp. Pract. Cardiac Dept. Roy. Bournemouth Hosp. Prev: Trainee GP Bournemouth VTS; Ho. Surg. St. Geo. Hosp. Tooting; Ho. Phys. Mayday Hosp. Croydon.

WATERS, Mr John Stephen (retired) The Coach House, Ufford Place, Lower Ufford, Woodbridge IP13 6DP — MB BS Lond. 1957; MS Lond. 1972; FRCS Eng. 1962. Prev: Cons. Surg. Singleton & Morriston Hosps. Swansea.

WATERS, Justin St Clair 33A Ballingdon Road, London SW11 6AJ — MB BS 1993 Lond.

WATERS, Mr Kenneth John 78 Harley Street, London W1N 1AE Tel: 020 7255 1308 Fax: 020 7580 4238 — MB BS Newc. 1969; FRCS Eng. 1975; DObst RCOG 1971. Indep. Cons. Gen. & Vasc. Surg. Lond. Socs: Vasc. Surg. Soc.; Brit. Assn. Day Surg.

WATERS, Margaret Joan 4 Ferndown, Claremont Road, Surbiton KT6 4RY Tel: 020 8390 2310 — MB BS 1940 Lond.; MRCS Eng. LRCP Lond. 1937; DPH Ed. 1940.

WATERS, Margaret Ronaldson (retired) c/o Royal Bank of Scotland, Piccadilly Branch, Haymarket, London SW1Y 4SE — MB ChB 1924 Ed.; DMRE Camb. 1925. Prev: Radiol. Gen. Hosp. Stroud.

WATERS, Maria Bernadette 6 Crescent Drive, Petts Wood, Orpington BR5 1BD — MB BS 1993 Lond.

WATERS, Marion Rosemary Westbrook, Castle St., Rhuddlan, Rhyl LL18 5AB — MB ChB 1975 Manch.; FRCS Eng. 1980.

WATERS, Mark Richard Cantilupe Surgery, 49-51 St. Owen Street, Hereford HR1 2JB Tel: 01432 268031 Fax: 01432 352584; 9 Clive Street, Hereford HR1 2SB Tel: 01432 267116 — BM 1987 Soton.; MRCGP 1991; DRCOG 1990. (Southampton) GP Tutor Herefordshire; GP Trainer. Prev: Trainee GP/SHO Hereford Co. Hosp. VTS; Ho. Phys. Addenbrookes Hosp. Camb.; Ho. Surg. United Norwich Hosp.

WATERS, Michael Alan Turton 6 Golding Avenue, Marlborough SN8 1TH — MB BS 1951 Lond.; FRCP Ed. 1971, M 1957; MRCS Eng. LRCP Lond. 1951; FRCPsych 1972, M 1971; DPM Eng. 1954. (Char. Cross) Prev: Cons. Psychiat. Swindon Health Dist.

WATERS, Michael Francis Ray, OBE Hospital for Tropical Diseases, 4 St Pancras Way, London NW1 0PE Tel: 020 7387 4411 Fax: 020 7383 0041; 3 Regents Close, Radlett WD7 7DB Tel: 01923 854292 — MB BChir 1952 Camb.; MA Camb. 1960, BA (1st Cl. Hons.) 1949; FRCP Lond. 1974, M 1958; FRCPath 1978, M 1973. (Camb. & Univ. Coll. Hosp.) Mem. MRC Extern. Sci. Staff, Dept. Bact. Sch. Path. & Hon. Cons. Bact. Middlx. Hosp. Med. Sch. Lond.; Cons. Leprol. Hosp. Trop. Dis. Lond. Socs: Fell. Roy. Soc. Trop. Med. & Hyg.; (Ex-Pres.) Assn. Phys. Malaysia. Prev: Dir. Leprosy Research Unit Nat. Leprosy Control Centre Sungei Buloh, Malaysia; Regist. (Med.) Univ. Coll. Hosp. Lond.; Capt. RAMC.

WATERS, Patrick Tylers Croft, Hawkers Lane, Nash Pitch, Fownhope, Hereford HR1 4PS — MRCS Eng. LRCP Lond. 1940; MRCS Eng., LRCP Lond. 1940.

WATERS, Robert Christopher Sea Moor View, Bittaford, Ivybridge PL21 0EF — MB ChB 1960 St. And.; MRCPsych 1971; DPM Eng. 1964. Cons. Psychiat. Plymouth Health Dist. Socs: BMA. Prev: Sen. Regist. & Psychiat. Regist. Warneford Hosp. Oxf.; Cons. Psychiat. (Ment. Handicap) Hull Health Dist.

WATERS, Ruth Anne Plastic Surgery & Burns Unit, Sellyoak Hospital, Raddlebarn Road, Birmingham B29 6JD Tel: 0121 627 8905 Fax: 0121 627 8782; 3 Church View Farm, Osgathorpe, Loughborough LE12 9SY — BM 1983 Soton.; FRCS (Plast) 1996; FRCS Eng. 1988. Cons. Plastic Surg. Univ. Hosp. NHS Trust Birm. Socs: Brit. Microsurgic. Soc. Prev: Hand Surg. Fell. Pulvertaft Hand Centre Derbysh. Roy. Infirm.; Sen. Regist. (Plastic Surg.) W. Midl.; Regist. (Plastic Surg.) W. Norwich Hosp.

WATERS, Ryan John 3 Florence Road, Fleet GU52 6LF — MB BS 1998 Lond.

WATERS, Simon Howard 5 Highview Road, London W13 0HA — BM 1998 Soton.

WATERS, Stephen David 42 Longfields, Ongar CM5 9BZ — MB BS 1992 Lond.; MRCP (UK) 1998; Bsc (hons) Sociology applied to medicine 1989. (London Hospital Medical College) Specialist Regist. in Gen. (internal) Med. & Geriat.s, W. Midl.s Rotat. Socs: W Midl.s Inst. Ageing & Health; Brit. Geriat. Soc.; BMA. Prev: SHO (Med. Rotat.) Colchester Gen. Hosp.; SHO (A+E) S.end Hosp.; HO (Surg.) Roy. Lond. Hosp.

WATERS, Stephen James Medical and Industrial Services Ltd, 23 St Leonard's Road, Eastbourne BN21 3UT Tel: 01323 724889 Fax: 01323 721161; 29 Chichester Drive E., Saltdean, Brighton BN2 8LD Tel: 01273 883689 Email: swaters@gpiag_asthma.org — MB ChB 1982 Liverp.; T(GP) 1991; DCCH RCGP 1986; DRCOG 1985; Dip. Occ. Med. Roy. Coll. Phys. 1998. (Liverp.) Occupat. Phys. MIS Ltd E.bourne; Comp.Med.Advis. Socs: Soc. Occupat. Med.; Christ. Med. Fell.sh.; Fell. Roy. Soc. Med. Prev: GP Peacehaven; SHO (Community Child Health) Edin.; SHO (O & G, Psychiat., A & E) Liverp.

WATERS, Stuart Scott St James Surgery, Harold Street, Dover CT16 1SF Tel: 01304 225559 Fax: 01304 213070 — MB ChB 1977 Manch. Prev: SHO (Gen. Med.) Manch. Roy. Infirm.; SHO (Chest Med.) Blackpool Vict. Infirm.

WATERS, Sylvia Doris Muriel 34 Les Venelles, Alderney Tel: 0148 182 2534 — MRCS Eng. LRCP Lond. 1946; MSc Lond. 1931. (Roy. Free) Med. Off. Comm. on Safety Of Meds. Socs: BMA. Prev: Cons. Phys. (Rheumat. & Rehabil. Med.) Lond. Jewish Hosp.; Regist. (Rheumat. & Rehabil. Med.) St. Thos. Hosp.; Med. Off. Phys. Dept. Moorfields Eye Hosp.

WATERS, Thomas Cyril Swallowfield, Wheelers Lane, Linton, Maidstone ME17 4BN — MB ChB 1957 Bristol; MRCPsych 1971; DPM Eng. 1963. (Bristol) Cons. Psychiat. Maidstone Child Guid. Serv., Maidstone Hosp. Socs: BMA. Prev: Sen. Regist. Child Psychiat. Bristol Childr. Hosp. & Child & Family; Guid. Serv. Bristol & Tutor in Ment. Health Univ. Bristol; Regist. (Psychiat.) Littlemore Hosp. Oxf. & St. Crispin Hosp. Duston.

WATERS, Professor William Estlin Orchards, Broxmore Park, Sherfield English, Romsey SO51 6FT Tel: 01794 884254 — MB BS Lond. 1958; FFPHM RCP (UK) 1989; FFCM 1976, M 1974; DIH St. And. 1965. (St. Bart.) Emerit. Prof. Community Med. Univ. Soton. Prev: Sen. Lect., Reader & Prof. (Clin. Epidemiol. & Community Med.) Soton. Univ.; on Staff MRC Epidemiol. Unit (S. Wales) Cardiff; Sec. Internat. Epidemiol. Assn.

WATERS, William Harvey (retired) 15 Green Lane, Liverpool L13 7DY Tel: 0151 228 9101 — MRCS Eng. LRCP Lond. 1953.

WATERS, William Hotchkis Richmond, MBE, KStJ (retired) Ash Hill Lodge, Hatfield, Doncaster DN7 6JG Tel: 01302 350567 — MB ChB 1952 Glas.; FRCGP 1977. Prev: GP Doncaster.

WATERSON, Imogen Margaret West Norfolk P.C.T., St. James, Extons Road, King's Lynn PE30 5NU Tel: 01553 816368 Fax: 01553 761104 Email: imogen.waterson@westnorfolk.pct-nhs.uk; The Old Rectory, Saxthorpe, Norwich NR11 7BJ Tel: 01263 587610 — MB BChir 1973 Camb.; MA Camb. 1974; MRCP (UK) 1978; T(M)(Paediat.) 1992; DObst RCOG 1976; FRCP 1997; FRCPCH 1997. (Cambridge and St. Bartholomew's Hospital) Cons. Comm. Paediat. W. Norf. PCT, Kings Lynn; Trainer Assn. for Research in Infant & Child Developm. Socs: Brit. Assn. of Community Child Health (BACCH). Prev: SCMO (Comm. Paediat.) Norwich HA; Regist. (Paediat. & Gen. Med.) Shrewsbury.

WATERSON, Peter Graham Springfield Medical Practice, 9 Springfield Road, Bishopbriggs, Glasgow G64 1PJ Tel: 0141 772 4744 Fax: 0141 772 3035; 67 Stirling Drive, Bishopbriggs, Glasgow G64 3PG Tel: 0141 772 4642 — BM BCh 1962 Oxf.; DObst 1966.

WATERSTON, Anthony John Ross Community Paediatric Department, Newcastle General Hospital, Newcastle upon Tyne NE4 6BE Tel: 0191 273 8811 Ext: 23362 Fax: 0191 219 5072 Email: a.j.r.waterston@ncl.ac.uk; 20 Burdon Terrace, Jesmond, Newcastle upon Tyne NE2 3AE Tel: 0191 281 6752 Email: a.j.r.waterston@acl.ac.uk — MB ChB St. And. 1968; MD Dundee 1990; FRCP Lond. 1993; MRCP (UK) 1976; MRCPCH 1996; DObst RCOG 1971; DCH RCP Lond. 1971; FRCPCH 1997. (St. And. & Dundee) Cons. Community Paediat. Newc. Gen. Hosp.; Hon. Sen. Lect., Univ. of Newc. Socs: (Pres.) N. Eng. Paediat. Soc.; FRCPCh. Prev: Convenor Brit. Assn. Community Child Health; Clin. Research Fell. & Hon. Cons. Paediat. Univ. Dundee; Cons. & Lect. (Child Health) Univ. Zimbabwe, Harare.

WATERSTON, Ashita Marie The Royal Marsden Hospital, Downs Road, Sutton SM2 5PT Tel: 020 8642 6011; 46 Jacksons Lane, Highgate, London N6 5SX Tel: 020 8348 1336 — MB ChB 1993 Glas.; BSc Glas. 1990; MRCP (UK) 1996. SHO (Med. Oncol.) Roy. Marsden Hosp. Lond. Prev: SHO (Med.) Monklands Dist. Gen. Hosp. Airdrie.

WATERSTON, Elizabeth Cartington Terrace Medical Group, 1 Cartington Terrace, Heaton, Newcastle upon Tyne NE6 5RS Tel: 0191 265 5755 Fax: 0192 276 2921; 20 Burdon Terrace, Jesmond, Newcastle upon Tyne NE2 3AE Tel: 0191 281 6752 — MB ChB 1968 St. And.; MRCGP 1986; Dip FPA. 1971. Socs: Med. Wom. Federat.; BMA. Prev: Trainee GP Dundee VTS; Med. Off. (Geriat.) Parirenyetwa Hosp. Harare Zimbabwe; Regist. (Geriat.) Roy. Vict. Hosp. Dundee.

WATERSTON, Paul Fyfe Main Street Surgery, 31 Main Street, Lochwinnoch PA12 4AH Tel: 01505 842200 Fax: 01505 843144; 31 Main Street, Lochwinnoch PA12 4AH Tel: 01505 842200 — MB ChB 1975 Glas. GP Lochwinnoch, Renfrewsh.

WATERSTONE, John Justin Department of Obstetrics & Gynaecology, Kings College Hospital, Denmark Hill, London SE5 8RX; 90 Highlands Heath, Portsmouth Road, Putney, London SW15 3TY Tel: 020 8785 7887 — MB BCh BAO 1982 Dub.; BSc Dub. 1976; MRCOG 1988; DCH RCPSI Dub. 1984. Research Regist. (O & G) Kings Coll. Med. Sch., Kings Coll. Hosp. Lond.

WATERSTONE, Mark Peter Malcolm Department of Public Health, UMDS, Capital House, 42 Linton St., London SE1 3QD Tel: 020 8299 3480 Email: m.waterstone@umds.ac.uk; 79c Overhill Road, London SE1 3QD Tel: 020 7955 4945 — MB BS 1990 Lond.; MRCOG 1996. Specialist Regist. S. E. Thames & Research Fell. UMDS Guy's & St Thomas Hosp. Lond. Socs: Fell. RSM.

WATERWORTH, Alison Margaret The Grange Medical Centre, Dacre Banks, Harrogate HG3 4DX Tel: 01423 780436 Fax: 01423 781416 Email: alison.waterworth@gp-b82004.nhs.uk — MB BS 1973 Newc.; DObst RCOG 1976. (Newcastle)

WATERWORTH, Alison Sarah St. James's Hospital, Leeds; 46 George Street, Saltaire, Shipley BD18 4PT — BM BCh 1997 Oxf.; MA Oxf. 1999. (Oxf.) Trainee (Gen. Surg.(. Prev: Anat. Demonst., Leeds Univ.; SHO (A&E), Bradford Roy. Infirm.

WATERWORTH, Mr Paul David 7 Perowne Street, Cambridge CB1 2AY — MB ChB 1988 Ed.; FRCS Ed. 1992.

WATERWORTH, Susan Mary Hunter House, Redworth, Newton Aycliffe DL5 6NW — MB BS 1973 Newc.

WATERWORTH, Mr Thomas Alan, OStJ, RD, QHS 7 Moultrie Road, Rugby CV21 3BD Tel: 01788 573593 Fax: 01788 551416 — MB BS 1965 Lond.; FRCS Eng. 1970; MRCS Eng. LRCP Lond. 1965. (St. Geo.) Cons. Surg. Hosp. Walsgrave Hosp. Coventry. Prev: Sen. Regist. United Birm. Hosps.

WATFORD, Norman Charles Trevor (retired) Martlets, East Wittering, Chichester PO20 8DU Tel: 01243 670110 — MB BS Lond. 1945; MRCP Lond. 1950. Prev: Ho. Surg. & Ho. Phys. Pembury Hosp.

WATHEN, Christopher George Department of Medicine, Wycombe Hospital, High Wycombe HP11 2TT Tel: 01494 425006 — MB ChB 1979 Ed.; MB ChB (Hons.) Ed. 1979; BSc (1st cl. Hons.) Ed. 1976, MD 1988; FRCP Lond. 1996; FRCP Ed. 1995; MRCP (UK) 1982; DRCOG 1981; LM Dub. 1980. (Ed.) Cons. Phys. Oxf. Region; Cons. Phys. Stoke Mandeville Bucks. Socs: Amer. Thoracic Soc. Prev: Sen. Regist. (Gen. Respirat. Med.) City Hosp., Roy. Infirm. Edin. & N.. Gen. Hosp.; Lect. (Med.) Univ. Edin.

WATHEN, David John The Surgeries, Lombard Street, Newark NG24 1XG Tel: 01636 702363 Fax: 01636 613037; 4 Speight Close, Winthorpe, Newark NG24 2PF — MB ChB 1984 Birm.; MRCGP 1989; DCH RCP Lond. 1991; DRCOG 1988. Socs: BMA.

WATHEN, Susan Jane Oakwood House, Derby Road, Haslemere GU27 1BS — MB BS 1987 Lond.; MRCGP 1992; DRCOG 1991. GP Retainer. Socs: BMA. Prev: Asst. GP The Surg. Burlington La., Lond.

WATKEYS, Jane Elizabeth Mary Crowndale Health Centre, Crowndale Road, London NW1 1BD Tel: 020 7530 3039 Fax: 020 7530 3044; Flat 14, Prusom's Island, Wapping High St, Wapping, London E1W 3NH Tel: 020 7481 4340 Fax: 020 7481 4340 — MSc Lond. (Community Med.) 1981; MB BCh Wales 1968; FFPHM RCP (UK) 1994; DCH RCP Lond. 1970; FRCPCH 1997. Cons. Community Paediat. Camden & Islington NHS Trust. Prev: SCM (Child Health) & Cons. Community Paediat. S.Glam. HA.; SCMO Camberwell HA.; Regist. (Paediat.) Nevill Hall Hosp. Abergavenny.

WATKIN, Andrew Ross Amman Valley Medical Practice, Meddyga'r Waun Surgery, Graig Road, Ammanford SA18 1EG Tel: 01269 822231 — MB ChB 1984 Birm.

WATKIN, Bernard Curtis 62 Wimpole Street, London W1M 7DE Tel: 020 7486 8684 Fax: 020 7935 8269 — MB BS 1962 Lond.; DPhysMed Eng. 1966. (St. Bart.) Scientif. Adviser (Orthop.) ICI Ltd.; Cons. IMG (Internat. Managem. Gp.). Socs: Brit. Assn. Manip. Med. & Soc. Orthop. Med. Prev: Hon. Clin. Asst. (Rheum.) St. Stephen's Hosp. Lond.; Regist. Arthur Stanley Inst. Rheum. Middlx. Hosp. Lond.; Regist. (Physical Med.) St. Thos. Hosp. Lond.

WATKIN, Mr David Francis Lloyd (retired) The Gables, 8 Knighton Rise, Oadby, Leicester LE2 2RE Tel: 0116 270 5855 — MB BChir Camb. 1959; MA Camb. 1960, MChir Camb. 1965; FRCS Eng. 1962. Prev: Clin. Sub-Dean Univ. Leicester Sch. Med.

WATKIN, Elisabeth Marian Radiology Department, Leicester General Hospital, Gwendolen Road, Leicester LE5 4PW Tel: 0116 249 0490 Fax: 0116 258 4525; The Gables, 8 Knighton Rise, Oadby, Leicester LE2 2RE Tel: 0116 270 5855 — MB BS Lond. 1960; MRCS Eng. LRCP Lond. 1960; FRCR 1975; FFR 1973; DMRD Eng. 1970. (Westm.) Cons. Radiol. Leicester Gen. Hosp. Socs: Brit. Inst. Radiol.; Brit. Soc. Interven. Radiol.; Brit. Nuclear Med. Soc. Prev: Sen. Regist. (Diag. Radiol.) Leics. AHA (T); Regist. (Diag. Radiol.) N.. Gen. Hosp. Sheff.; Ho. Phys. & Ho. Surg. St. Stephen's Hosp. Lond.

WATKIN, Elizabeth Jane 29 Thornbeck Avenue, Hightown, Liverpool L38 9EX — MB ChB 1987 Liverp.

WATKIN, Frances Marguerite 49 Stroma Road, Allerton, Liverpool L18 9SN — MB ChB 1996 Liverp.

WATKIN, Mr Gwyn Thomas Ysbyty Gwynedd, Bangor LL57 2PW Tel: 01248 352994; Pant y Ddolen, Halfway Bridge, Bangor LL57 4AD Tel: 01248 352994 — MB BS 1974 Lond.; MS Lond. 1987, MB BS 1974; FRCS Eng. 1978. (Middlx.) Cons. Gen. & Vasc. Surg. Gwynedd HA. Socs: Fell. Roy. Soc. Med.; Vasc. Surg. Soc. Prev: Sen. Regist. (Surg.) Bloomsbury Vasc. Unit Middlx. Hosp. Lond.

WATKIN, Hywel Beech House Surgery, Beech House, 69 Vale Street, Denbigh LL16 3AY Tel: 01745 812863 Fax: 01745 816574 — MB BS 1978 Lond.; M.Sc. (Musculoskelet. & Osteop. Med.) Lond. 1997; BSc (Hons.) Phys. Med. Lond. 1975, MB BS 1978; MRCGP 1982; MLCOM 1997; Dip M-S Med. SA 1997; DCH Eng. 1981; DRCOG 1980. (Guy's) Socs: Accred. Mem. Brit. Med. Acupunc. Soc.; Brit. Inst. Musculoskel. Med.

WATKIN, Iestyn Morgan (retired) Y Tygwyn, Brynhendre, Waunfawr, Aberystwyth SY23 3BW Tel: 01970 623315 — MB BCh 1943 Wales; PhD Lond. 1951; BSc Wales 1940, MSc 1946; FFPHM RCP (UK) 1991; FFCM RCP (UK) 1972; DPH 1948. Univ. Extern. Examr. (for Higher Degrees) Blood Gp. Anthropol. Prev: Co. Med. Off. of Health Cardigansh.

WATKIN, Janet Byron House Surgery, 30 Byron Road, Gillingham ME7 5QH Tel: 01634 576347 Fax: 01634 570159 — MB ChB 1980 Sheff.

WATKIN, John Ernest 68 Harley Street, London W1N 1AE Tel: 020 7935 3980 Fax: 020 7636 6262; Great Yard, Whitedown, Wootton St. Lawrence, Basingstoke RG23 8PF Tel: 01256 850678 — BSc, MB BCh Wales 1952. (Cardiff) Prev: Phys. E. India Clinic Calcutta, India; Maj. RAMC RARO.

WATKIN, John Ivan The Surgery, Highfield Road, North Thoresby, Grimsby DN36 5RT Tel: 01472 840202; The Maltings, Station Road, North Thoresby, Grimsby DN36 5QS Tel: 01472 840202 — MB ChB 1959 Sheff. (Sheff.) Prev: Clin. Asst. (Anaesth.) Grimsby Gp.

WATKIN

Hosps.; Regist. Anaesth. United Sheff. Hosps.; Ho. Surg. Sheff. Roy. Infirm.

WATKIN, Lucy Ann Chase Farm Hospital, 127 The Ridgeway, Enfield EN2 8JL — MB BS 1998 Lond.

WATKIN, Nicholas Andrew 15 St Mary's Road, Oxford OX4 1PX — BM BCh 1989 Oxf.

WATKIN, Peter Morton Homestead Cottage, 1 Occupation Lane, Shooters Hill, London SE18 3JH — MB BS 1972 Lond.; MSc Manch. 1988; MRCS Eng. LRCP Lond. 1972; DCH Eng. 1977. Sen. Med. Off. (Audiol.) Redbridge & Waltham Forest HA; Head of Audiol. Serv. Redbridge & Waltham Forest HA. Socs: Fac. Comm. Health. Prev: Sen. Med. Off. (Clin.) Redbridge HA.

***WATKIN, Richard** 81 Dan-y-Bryn Avenue, Radyr, Cardiff CF15 8DQ — MB ChB 1998 Birm.

WATKIN, Ross Rickard Orchard Cottage, Rectory Road, Mugswell, Coulsdon CR5 3SY Tel: 01737 557564 Email: rosswatkin@yahoo.co.uk — MB BS Lond. 1957; MRCS Eng. LRCP Lond. 1957; FFA RCS Eng. 1964; DA Eng. 1961; DObst RCOG 1960. (Guy's) Emerit. Cons. Anaesth. Guy's Hosp. Lond. Socs: Assn. Anaesth. Prev: Chairm. SE Thames RHA Anaesth. Specialty Sub-Comm.

WATKIN, Sara Louise Neonatal Intensive Care Unit, Nottingham City Hospital, Hucknall Road, Nottingham NG5 1PB Tel: 0115 969 1169 Fax: 0115 962 7926 Email: swatkin@ncht.trent.nhs.uk; Hillside House, Church View, Osgathorpe, Longbrough LE12 9XE Tel: 01530 222 828 — MB ChB 1986 Manch.; FRCPCH 1997 UK; MD Keele 1996; MRCP (UK) 1989. (Manch.) Cons. Neonatologist Nottm. City Hosp. Socs: BMA; Brit. Assn. Perinatal Med.; FRCPCh. Prev: Lect. & Hon. Sen. Regist. (Child Health) Qu. Med. Centre Nottm.; Research Regist. (Paediat.) Acad. Dept. Paediat. Univ. Keele; Regist. (Paediat.) Nottm. City Hosp.

WATKIN, Simon Wilfred Department of Respiratory Medicine, Leicester House, Norfolk & Norwich Hospital, Norwich NR1 3SR Tel: 01603 289644 Fax: 01603 289640; 26 Badgers Brook Road, Drayton, Norwich NR8 6EY Tel: 01603 262047 — MB ChB 1983 Liverp.; BSc (Hons.) (Physiol.) Liverp. 1980, MD 1994; FRCP 1999. Cons. Respirat., HIV & Gen. Med. Norf. & Norwich Hosp. Trust. Socs: Brit. Thorac. Soc.; Norwich M-C Soc. Prev: Sen. Regist. (Respirat. & Gen. Med.) Roy. Liverp. Univ. Hosp.; Regist. (Respirat. Med.) Glas. Roy. Infirm.; CRC Clin. Research Fell. (Radiati. Oncol.) Clatterbridge Hosp.

WATKIN JONES, Andrew St James's University Hospital, Leeds LS9 7TF Tel: 0113 243 3144; 9 Woodlea Court, Woodlea Village, Meanwood Park, Leeds LS6 4SL Email: andy.watkin.jones@lineone.com — MB ChB 1997 Leeds. Basic Surgic. Train. Rotat., St Jas. Univ. Hosp.

WATKINS, Alan Douglas 32 Kelburn Close, Chandlers Ford, Eastleigh SO53 2PU — MB BS 1986 Lond.

WATKINS, Alistair James Hadleigh House Medical Centre, 20 Kirkway, Broadstone BH18 8EE Tel: 01202 692268 Fax: 01202 658954 — MB BS 1989 Lond.; MRCGP 1995.

WATKINS, Armond Vincent 37 Addison Road, London W14 — MB BS 1960 Lond.

WATKINS, Beverley Joy Whittington Road Surgery, 9 Whittington Road, Norton, Stourbridge DY8 3DB Tel: 01384 393120 Fax: 01384 353636 — MB ChB 1983 Birm.; MRCGP 1987; DRCOG 1986; DCH RCP Lond. 1986. Prev: Trainee GP Dudley VTS.

WATKINS, Christopher John The Surgery, 15 West Town Road, Backwell, Bristol BS48 3HA Tel: 0117 462026 Fax: 0117 795609; 2 The Green, West Town, Backwell, Bristol BS48 3BG Tel: 01275 464239 — MRCS Eng. LRCP Lond. 1967; PhD Lond. 1980, MB BS 1967; FRCGP 1983, M 1971; DObst RCOG 1970; DA Eng. 1969. (St. Bart.) Cons. Sen. Lect. Gen. Pract. Bristol Univ. Socs: BMA; AUDGP; Bristol M-C Soc. Prev: Reader Gen. Pract. United Med. & Dent. Sch. Lond.

WATKINS, Daphne Louisa (retired) — MB 1967 Camb.; MA Camb. 1976, MB 1967, BChir 1966.

WATKINS, David 100 Newmarket Road, Norwich NR2 2LB — MB BS 1952 Lond.; MRCS Eng. LRCP Lond. 1952. (St. Bart.) Hosp. Pract. (Chest) Norwich Health Dist.; Clin. Asst. (Continuing Care) Priscila Bacon Lodge Norwich.

WATKINS, David Ainsley (retired) — MRCS Eng. LRCP Lond. 1945. Prev: Ho. Phys. Swansea & Morriston Hosps.

WATKINS, David Charles 32 Ormiston Crescent, Knock, Belfast BT4 3TQ; 10 Barkers Lane, Sale M33 6RG — MB ChB 1991 Ed.; Dip SEM (GB &I) 2000; MRCP Ed. 1996; MRCPCH 1996. Specialist Regist. (Paed.) Booth Hall Childr.'s Hosp, Man.

WATKINS, David Jeremy 3 Abney Court Drive, Bourne End SL8 5DL — MB BS 1996 Lond.

WATKINS, David John The Portland Practice, St Paul's Medical Centre, 121 Swindon Road, Cheltenham GL50 4DP Tel: 01242 707792; The Surgery, Glebe Farm Court Road, Hatherley, Cheltenham GL51 3EB Tel: 01242 863333 — MB 1969 Camb.; BChir 1968; DObst RCOG 1973.

WATKINS, David Mansell (retired) Chestnuts, Lettons Way, Dinas Powys CF64 4BY — MB BCh 1946 Wales; BSc Wales 1943, MB BCh 1946; DA RCPSI 1949. Mem. Advis. Comm. Borderlined Subst.s. Prev: GP Anaesth. P. of Wales Orthop. Hosp. Rhydlafar.

WATKINS, David William 76 Corporation Road, Newport NP19 0AX — MB BCh 1954 Wales.

WATKINS, Dorothy Caroline (retired) 51 Llwyn-Y-Grant Road, Penylan, Cardiff CF23 9HL Tel: 029 2047 1550 — MRCS Eng. LRCP Lond. 1961; MFFP 1993. Prev: SCMO Gwent HA.

WATKINS, Eileen Dorothy (retired) Glaslyn, Riverside, Tiddington Road, Stratford-upon-Avon CV37 7BD Tel: 01789 298085 Fax: 01789 298085 Email: revdocmw@waitrose.com — MB ChB Leeds 1959.

WATKINS, Eileen Gertrude (retired) Glyn Heulog, Usk NP15 1HY — MB BCh BAO 1952 NUI; MFCM 1974; DPH (Hons.) NUI 1955. Med. Off. DSS. Prev: Dep. Med. Off. Health & Dep. Sch. Med. Off. Rhondda Glam.

WATKINS, Elizabeth Judith 19 Grosvenor Mount, Leeds LS6 2DX Tel: 0113 278 7019 — MB ChB 1980 Liverp.; FRCA 1998; MRCGP 1984; DCH RCP Lond. 1982; DRCOG 1982. Anaesth. Specialist Regist. Prev: Indep. Med. Adviser Calderdale FHSA.

WATKINS, Eric Paul Holmes Kent Elms Health Centre, Rayleigh Road, Leigh-on-Sea SS9 5UU; 24 Kings Road, Westcliff on Sea SS0 8LL — MB BS 1980 Lond.; MRCS Eng. LRCP Lond. 1979.

WATKINS, Professor Eric Sidney Department of Neurosurgery, The Princes Grace Hospital, 42-52 Nottingham Place, London W1M 3FD Tel: 020 7486 1234 Fax: 020 7232 0525; Belmont House, Lennel Road, Coldstream TD12 4ET Tel: 01890 882411 Fax: 01890 882007 — BSc (Hons. Physiol.) Liverp. 1949, MD 1956, MB ChB 1952; FRCS Ed. 1969. (Liverp.) Prof. Emerit. Neurosurg. Lond. Hosp. Med. Coll. & Hon. Cons. Neurosurg. Lond. Indep. Hosp. Socs: Soc. Brit. Neurosurgs. & Amer. Acad. Neurosurgs. Prev: Prof. Neurosurg. State Univ. New York Syracuse, USA; Clin. Neurosurgic. Research Asst. Middlx. Hosp. Lond.

WATKINS, Gareth David Coquet Medical Group, Amble Health Centre, Percy Drive, Amble, Morpeth NE65 0HD Tel: 01665 710481 Fax: 01665 713031; 6 Lingfield Close, Warkworth, Morpeth NE65 0YN — MB BS 1985 Newc.; MRCGP 1989; DRCOG 1989. (Newcastle)

WATKINS, Gina Olwen 2 Dollis Road, Finchley, London N3 1RG — MB BS 1987 Lond.; BSc Lond. 1984, MB BS 1987. Trainee GP Broomfield Hosp. Chelmsford VTS. Prev: Ho. Phys. Chase Farm Hosp. Enfield; Ho. Surg. Univ. Coll. Hosp. Lond.

WATKINS, Guy David 42 High Street, Melbourn, Royston SG8 6DZ — MB BS 1987 Lond.; MRCGP 1991.

WATKINS, Professor Hugh Christian Cardiovascular Medicine, University of Oxford, John Radcliffe Hospital, Oxford OX3 9DU Tel: 01865 220257 Fax: 01865 768844 Email: hugh.watkins@cardiov.ox.ac.uk — MB BS 1984 Lond.; PhD Lond. 1995, BSc 1981, MD 1995; FRCP 1997, M 1987. (St. Bartholomew's) Field Marshal Alexander Prof. Cardiovasc. Med. Univ. Oxf.; Hon. Cons. Cardiol. & Med. John Radcliffe Hosp. Oxf.; Prof.ial Fell. Exeter Coll. Oxf. Socs: Assn. Phys. Prev: Asst. Prof. Med. Harvard Med. Sch. Boston & Assoc. Phys. Brigham & Wom. Hosp. Boston, USA.

WATKINS, Janet Child Development Centre, 151 Locksway Road, Southsea PO4 8LD Tel: 01705 894410; 59 Western Way, Gosport PO12 2NF Tel: 01705 521054 — MB 1978 Camb.; BChir 1977; MRCP (UK) 1989; DRCOG 1982; DCH Eng. 1979. Specialist Regist. (Community Child Heath) Portsmouth. Prev: Staff Grade (Community Child Health) Soton.; Community Paediat. RAF Hosp. Wegberg; Clin Med. Off. (Child Health) P'boro. HA.

WATKINS

WATKINS, Jean Margaret Winton Health Centre, 31 Alma Road, Winton, Bournemouth BH9 1BP Tel: 01202 519311; 25 Copse Road, Burley, Ringwood BH24 4EG Tel: 01425 403224 Fax: 01425 402088 Email: jeanwatkins@compuserve.com — MB BS 1955 Lond.; MRCS Eng. LRCP Lond. 1955; MRCGP 1976; DCH Eng. 1958; DObst RCOG 1957. (Roy. Free) Community Med. Off. (Family Plann.) Dorset HA. Prev: GP The Alma Partnership, Bournemouth; GP Lakeside Health Centre Thamesmead; Sen. Lect. (Gen. Pract.) Guy's & St. Thos. United Med. & Dent. Sch. Lond.

WATKINS, Joanne Department of Psychiatry, Hellesdon Hospital, Drayton Road, Norwich NR6 5BE — MB ChB 1995 Leic. (Leic.) SHO Rotat. (Psychiat.) Norwich Ment. Health Trust. Prev: SHO Rotat. (Med.) Leicester Hosps.; Ho. Surg. (Gen. Surg. & Gyn.) Leic. Gen. Hosp.; Ho. Phys. (Ge. Med./Rheum.) Leic. Roy. Infirm.

WATKINS, John Ceri-Nant, 3 Cefn Buchan Close, Llangwm, Usk NP15 1HW; 38 Cotswold Way, Newport NP19 9DL Tel: 01633 270934 — MB BCh 1981 Wales; BSc Wales 1975, MB BCh 1981; MRCGP 1985. 2nd Prize Nat. Syntex Award 1985.

WATKINS, John Department of Cardiology, St. Mary's General Hospital, Milton Road, Portsmouth PO3 6AD Tel: 023 92 866065 Fax: 023 92 866067; 18 Cousins Grove, Southsea PO4 9RP Tel: 02392 739151 Fax: 01705 739151 Email: jwat18@aol.com — MRCS Eng. LRCP Lond. 1973; MB BS Lond. 1973, BSc 1970; FRCP Lond. 1990; MRCP (UK) 1976. (St. Bart.) Clin. Dir. for Med. Socs: Brit. Cardiac Soc.; Brit. Pacing & Electrophysiol. Gp. Prev: Cons. Phys. (Cardiol.) Portsmouth & S.E. Hants. HA; Sen. Regist. Cardiol. John Radcliffe Hosp. Oxf.; Harkness Fell. (Cardiovasc. Pharmacol.) Univ. Calif., San Diego.

WATKINS, John Benjamin (retired) 51 Llwyn-Y-Grant Road, Penylan, Cardiff CF23 9HL Tel: 029 2047 1550 — MB BS 1961 Lond.; MFOM RCP Lond. 1982. Prev: Sen. Med. Off. Brit. Steel Corp. Llanwern Gp. Newport.

WATKINS, John Frederick Ty Mynydd, Llanwenarth, Abergavenny NP7 7LA Tel: 01873 854492 — MB BChir 1949 Camb.; MA Oxf. 1960; MA Camb. 1960, MD 1961, BA, MB BChir 1949; Dip. Bact. Lond 1956. (Camb. & Middlx.) Emerit. Prof. Med. Microbiol. Welsh Nat. Sch. Med. Cardiff. Prev: Reader (Experim. Path.) Oxf. Univ.; Eleanor Roosevelt Cancer Research Fell. Salk Inst. La Jolla, USA.

WATKINS, John Stirling (retired) — MB BS Newc. 1966; FRCP Lond. 1985; MRCP (UK) 1970. Prev: SHO (Neurol.) Newc. Gen. Hosp.

WATKINS, Karen 18 Park Street, Bladon, Woodstock OX20 1RW — MB ChB 1993 Leic. Clin. Research Fell. Univ. of Liverp. Prev: SHO (O & G) Leicester Gen. Hosp.

WATKINS, Kevin Paul Wadebridge Health Centre, Wadebridge PL27 7BS Tel: 01208 2222 — MB BS 1981 Lond.

WATKINS, Mr Laurence Dale Institute of Neurology, Queen Square, London WC1N 3BG Tel: 020 7837 3611 Fax: 020 7837 2458; 13 Wigan Road, Westhead, Ormskirk L40 6HY — MB 1984 Camb.; BChir 1983; MA Camb. 1984; FRCS Eng. 1989. Clin. Lect. (Neurol. Surg.) Inst. Neurol. Lond. Prev: Regist. (Surg. Neurol.) Nat. Hosp. for Neurol. & Neurosurg. Lond.; Regist. (Neurosurg.) Hosp. for Sick Childr. Gt. Ormond St. Lond.

WATKINS, Linda Marion c/o Miss C Wiltshire, Arrowe Park Hospital, Arrowe Park Road, Wirral CH49 5PE — MB ChB 1998 Liverp.

WATKINS, Mr Mark John Guy Royal Hospital Haslar, Gosport PO12 2AA Tel: 02392 762118 Fax: 02392 762960; 59 Western Way, Gosport PO12 2NF — MB 1978 Camb.; BChir 1977; FRCS Ed. 1983. Cons. Gen. Surg. Roy. Hosp. Haslar.

WATKINS, Mary Dare Bush House, Oakleigh Park Avenue, Chislehurst BR7 5PB Tel: 020 8467 6999 — MB BS 1950 Lond.; MRCP Lond. 1954; MRCS Eng. LRCP Lond. 1950. (Roy. Free) Prev: Sen. Regist. Willesden Chest Clinic; Med. Regist. St. Stephen's Hosp. Chelsea; Ho. Phys. Roy. Free Hosp. Lond.

WATKINS, Mary Elana Station Road Surgery, 99 Station Road, Redhill RH1 1EB Tel: 01737 761201 Fax: 01737 780510; 15 The Fairways, Somerset Road, Redhill RH1 6LP Tel: 01737 243882 — MB BS 1970 Lond.; MRCS Eng. LRCP Lond. 1970; DObst RCOG 1974. (St. Mary's)

WATKINS, Mary Elizabeth Community Health Office, Ambulance Head Quarters, Ascots Lane, Stanstead Road, Welwyn Garden City AL7 4HL Tel: 01707 365229 Fax: 01707 365329; 81 Valley Road, Welwyn Garden City AL8 7DR Tel: 01707 338159 — MB BS 1967 Lond. (St. Geo.) SCMO Welwyn Gdn. City. Socs: Assoc. Mem. Coll. Paediat. Prev: Med. Off. Mzuzu Health Centre, Malawi; Med. Off. Mbabane Govt. Hosp., Swaziland.

WATKINS, Meredith Wynne (retired) Hafodwenog, Wellfield Place, Glynneath, Neath SA11 5EP — MB ChB 1960 Ed.; DObst RCOG 1962. Prev: Ho. Surg., Ho. Phys. & SHO (O & G) Caerphilly Dist. Miner's Hosp.

WATKINS, Merryl Dilys Ada Roundwood Surgery, Wood St., Mansfield NG18 1QQ — MB BS 1992 Lond.; BSc 1989; DCh 1994; DRCOG 1995; MRCGP 1998. GP. Prev: Ho. Phys. Harold Wood Hosp. Essex; Ho. Surg. P.ss Alexandra Hosp. Harlow.; Trainee GP Mansfield VTS.

WATKINS, Monica Eileen (retired) 38 Eversley Park Road, Winchmore Hill, London N21 1JS Tel: 020 8882 8986 — MB BS 1951 Lond.; MRCS Eng. LRCP Lond. 1951; MFPHM 1989; MFCM 1972. Prev: Specialist Community Med. (Social Servs.) Enfield & Haringey AHA.

WATKINS, Nicholas Andrew North Hey, Mill St., Chagford, Newton Abbot TQ13 8AW — MB BS 1991 Lond.

WATKINS, Nigel Ross c/o 14 Bristol Terrace, Bargoed CF81 8RF; 12 Maelog Close, Pontyclun CF72 9AF — MB BCh 1984 Wales.

WATKINS, Olga 24 Tulipan Crescent, Callender FK17 8AR Tel: 01877 330587 Email: doug780@adl.com — MB ChB 1976 Glas.; Dip. Pract. Dermat. Wales 1995; DRCOG 1978. Clin. Asst. (Dermat.) Stirling Roy. Infirm.

WATKINS, Oswald Heath, MC (retired) Tymperleys, Crossway Green, Chepstow NP16 5LX Tel: 01291 623181 — MB BChir 1952 Camb.; MA Camb. 1952, MB BChir 1952; DObst RCOG 1956. Prev: Ho. Surg. St. Thos. Hosp. Lond. & Sorrento Matern. Hosp. Birm.

WATKINS, Peter Frank Anthony (retired) Weir Mill, Drewsteignton, Exeter EX6 6QA Tel: 01647 24223 — MRCS Eng. LRCP Lond. 1943; DObst RCOG 1949, Prev: Clin. Asst. Dermat. P.ss Margt. Hosp. Swindon & Roy. Devon &.

WATKINS, Peter Holmes (retired) The Old Barn, The Street, Pakenham, Bury St Edmunds IP31 2JX — BM BCh 1950 Oxf.; MA Oxf. 1953, BA 1947. Prev: Regist. (Med.) Horsefield Hosp. Middx.

WATKINS, Peter John (retired) King's Diabetes Centre, King's College Hospital, Denmark Hill, London SE5 9RS Tel: 020 7346 3241 Fax: 020 7346 3407 Email: peter.watkins1@virgin.net — MB BChir 1962 Camb.; MB Camb. 1962, BChir 1961; MD Camb. 1968; FRCP Lond. 1975, M 1965. Hon Cons. (Gen. Med. & Diabetes) King's Coll. Hosp. Lond.; Edr. Jl. RCP Lond. 1998. Prev: Vis. Prof. Amsterdam Med. Centre 1985.

WATKINS, Rhona 9G Hughenden Gardens, Glasgow G12 9XW — MB ChB 1977 Glas.; MD Glas. 1987; FRCPath 1996, M 1983; Dip. Forens. Med. Glas 1995. Cons. W. Scotl. Blood Transfus. Serv.; Hon. Clin. Sen. Lect. Glas.

WATKINS, Rhys Mervyn Heathville Road Surgery, 5 Heathville Road, Gloucester GL1 3DP Tel: 01452 528299 Fax: 01452 522959; Villa Vinaria, 95 London Road, Gloucester GL1 3HH — MB BS 1979 Lond.; MRCGP 1984; DRCOG 1983. Clin. Asst. (ENT) Glos. Roy. Hosp.; Police Surg. Glos. Constab.

WATKINS, Roger Dexter (retired) 3 Kathleen Park, Helensburgh G84 8TH — MB ChB 1968 Aberd.; MRCGP 1977. Prev: Ho. Surg. (Orthop.), Ho. Off. (Paediat.) & Ho. Off. (O & G).

WATKINS, Mr Roger Malcolm Derriford Hospital, Derriford Road, Plymouth PL6 8DH Tel: 01752 792108 Fax: 01752 517562; Bay Tree House, The Crescent, Crapstone, Yelverton PL20 7PS Tel: 01822 852504 — MB BChir 1976 Camb.; MA Oxf. 1983, MChir 1986; MA Camb. 1977; FRCS Eng. 1980. (Camb. & Westm.) Cons. Surg. Derriford Hosp. Plymouth. Socs: Brit. Assn. Surg. Oncol.; Assn. Surg.Gt. Brit. & N. Ire.; BrE. speciality Grp of BASO. Prev: Sen. Regist. (Surg.) Roy. Marsden Hosp. & W.m. Hosp. Lond.; Clin. Lect. (Surg.) Nuffield Dept. of Surg. John Radcliffe Hosp. Oxf.; Demonst. (Anat.) Univ. Camb.

WATKINS, Ronald Peter Sycamore, 33A Aylesbury Road, Wing, Leighton Buzzard LU7 0PD Tel: 01296 682556 Fax: 01296 682556 — MB ChB Liverp. 1949; Cert. JCC Lond. 1980; DObst RCOG 1969.

WATKINS, Rosemary Anne 264 Rotton Park Road, Edgbaston, Birmingham B16 0LU Tel: 0121 429 2683; 12 Jasmin Croft, Kings Heath, Birmingham B14 5AX — MB ChB 1972 Birm.; DObst RCOG 1974. (Birmingham) Asst. GP. p/t, Dr IS Marok, Birm.

WATKINS

WATKINS, Russell Julian Department of Ophthalmology, West Norwich Hospital, Bowthorpe Road, Norwich NR2 3TU Tel: 01603 286286 Fax: 01603 288261 Email: r.j.watkins@anglia.ac.uk — MB ChB 1997 Leic.; PhD Brad. 1991; BSc (Hons) Bradford. 1985; MCOptom 1986. (Leic.) Clin. Asst. (Ophth.), W. Norwich Hosp. (PT); Sen. Lect. Anglia Polytechnic Univ. Prev: SHO (Ophth.) W. Norwich Hosp.; Ho. Off. (Med. & Surg.) Leic. Hosps.

WATKINS, Ruth Primrose Felicity ICSM St Mary's Department of Microbiology, Wright Fleming Institute, Norfolk Place, London W2 1PZ Tel: 020 7886 1557 Email: r.watkins@ic.ac.uk; 11 Elborough Street, Southfields, London SW18 5DP Tel: 020 8874 2297 — MB BS 1973 Lond.; MSc Lond. 1984, BSc (Hons.) 1970, MB BS 1973; MRCP (UK) 1977; MRCPath 1986. (St. Bart.) Sen. Lect. & Hon. Cons. Virol. Imperial Coll. Sci. Technol. & Med. & St.Mary's Hosp. Lond. Prev: Cons. & Sen. Research Fell. (Virol.) Hammersmith Hosp. Lond.; Sen. Regist. (Virol.) St. Geo. Hosp. Lond.; Regist. Med. Microbiol. Lond. Hosp.

WATKINS, Ryan Charles 18 Southridge Rise, Crowborough TN6 1LG — BM BS 1992 Nottm.; MRCP UK 1996.

WATKINS, Sally Louise 3 Rushall Close, Walsall WS4 2HQ Tel: 01922 620583 — MB ChB 1997 Birm. SHO (Paediat.) Wolverhampton. Prev: HO. Off. (Surg.) Good Hope Hosp. Sutton Coldfield; Ho. Off. (Med.) Walsall Manor Hosp. Walsall.

WATKINS, Sarah Catherine 18 Cousins Grove, Southsea PO4 9RP — MB BS 1998 Lond.

WATKINS, Sarah Elizabeth 7A High St. Mews, Leighton Buzzard LU7 1EA Tel: 01525 379769 Fax: 01525 377298; 1 Copper Beech Way, Leighton Buzzard LU7 3BD Tel: 01525 372524 — MB BS 1969 Lond.; MRCGP 1983; DObst RCOG 1972. (St. Mary's) Med. Acupunc.; Police Surg. Beds. Socs: AFME Lond.

WATKINS, Sid 19 Boxley House, Pembury Est., Hackney, London E5 8LG — MB BS 1983 Lond.

WATKINS, Sidney Maurice Kynoch (retired) 8 Airlie Court, Gleneagles Village, Auchterarder PH3 1SA — MB ChB Aberd. 1937. Prev: Ho. Surg. Roy. Hosp. Chesterfield.

WATKINS, Simon David 26 Hillside Crescent, Harrow HA2 0QX — BM 1993 Soton.

WATKINS, Stanley Albert South Burden Farm, Broadbury, Okehampton EX20 4LF Tel: 01837 87316 — MB BS 1953 Lond. (Westm.) Prev: Regist. Colindale Hosp.; Sen. Ho. Off. Lond. Chest Hosp. (Country Br.) & W. Lond. Hosp.

WATKINS, Stephen James David Bartley Green Health Centre, Romsley Road, Bartley Green, Birmingham B32 3PR Tel: 0121 477 4300 — MB BS 1988 Lond.

WATKINS, Stephen John Stockport Health Authority, Springwood House, Hazel Grove, Stockport SK7 5BY Tel: 0161 419 5467 Fax: 0161 482 4740 Email: stephen.watkins@stockport-ha.nwest.nhs.uk; 1 Parklands, Shaw, Oldham OL2 8LW Tel: 01706 846017 — MB ChB 1974 Manch.; MSc (Community Med.) Manch. 1982, BSc (Hons.) (Pharmacol.) 1971; FFPHM RCP (UK) 1993, M 1984. Dir. Pub. Health Stockport HA; Med. Adviser MSF Health & Safety Off.; Chairm. Transport & Health Study Gp.; Hon. Lect. Univ. Manch.; Co-Chairm. Unemploym., Economics & Health Study Gp. Socs: BMA (Past Chairm. Comm. Pub. Health Med. & Community Health); Manch. Med. Soc.; (Past Pres.) Med. Practs. Union. Prev: SCM Oldham HA; Regist. (Med.) W. Pk. Hosp. Macclesfield; SHO (Geriat.) Wythenshawe Hosp. Manch.

WATKINS, Stephen John Owen Carnewater Practice, Dennison Road, Bodmin PL31 2LB Tel: 01208 72321 Fax: 01208 78478 — Dip. Ther. (Cardiff) 998; MB BS Lond. 1970; FRCGP 1993, M 1980; DCH Eng. 1973; DObst RCOG 1972. (Middlx.) VTS Course organiser Cornw. Prev: Research Fell. (Primary Health Care & Gen. Pract.) Postgrad. Med. Sch. Univ. Plymouth; VTS Course organiser Cornw.; Univ. Clin. Tutor (Gen. Pract.) Cornw.

***WATKINS, Stuart Craig** 5 Ebberston Road E., Rhos-on-Sea, Colwyn Bay LL28 4DP Tel: 01492 547889 Fax: 01492 534834 Email: stuartwatkins@hotmail.com — MB ChB 1995 Birm.; ChB Birm. 1995.

WATKINS, Susan Mary Marchfield House, Church Road, Marlow SL7 3RZ; 2 Clipper View, Edgbaston, Birmingham B16 9DJ Tel: 0121 455 7829 Fax: 0121 454 8627 — MB BS 1990 Lond.; Dip. Anaesth. Roy. Coll. Anaesth. 1994. (Royal Free Hospital School of Medicine) Specialist Regist. (Anaesth.) Coventry Sch. of Anaesth. Socs: Assn. Anaesth.; MRCAnaesth.

WATKINS, Susan Patricia (retired) 9 Manor Drive, Bathford, Bath BA1 7TY Tel: 01225 858726 — MB ChB 1959 Birm.; DObst RCOG 1961. Prev: GP N.ants.

WATKINS, Sylvia Madeleine Stoneleigh, 13 Priory Way, Hitchin SG4 9BJ Tel: 01462 451775 — BM BCh 1961 Oxf.; MA Oxf. 1961, DM 1973, BM BCh 1961; FRCP Lond. 1980, M 1964. (Oxf. & St. Bart.) Cons. Phys. & Med. Oncol. Lister Hosp. Stevenage. Socs: BMA; Assn. Cancer Phys. Prev: Sen. Regist. (Med.) Roy. Free Hosp. Lond.; Regist. Univ. Nervenklinik, Heidelberg, Germany; Ho. Phys. St. Bart. Hosp. Lond.

WATKINS, Thomas Irvin (retired) 41 Springfield Road, Ulverston LA12 0EJ Tel: 01229 582913 — MB ChB 1938 Leeds; MRCGP 1976.

WATKINS, Timothy The Old Vicarage, Spilsby Road, Horncastle LN9 6AL Tel: 01507 522477 Fax: 01507 522997; Langton Hill Farm, Langton Hill, Horncastle LN9 5JP — MB ChB 1983 Sheff.; MRCGP 1987; Dip. IMC RCS Ed. 1991. Socs: Lincs. LMC; Brit. Assn. Immediate Care Nat. Educat. Comm.

WATKINS, Tudno Gareth Lewis e31 Cae Rex, Llanblethian, Cowbridge CF71 7JS — MB BCh 1971 Wales; FFA RCS Eng. 1975.

WATKINS, Watcyn Richard 2nd Floor, Hayes House, Cardiff Tel: 029 2038 3626; Glyn Heulog, Usk NP15 1HY Tel: 0129 167 2024 — LRCPI & LM, LRSCI & LM 1956; LRCPI & LM, LRCSI & LM 1956; MFOM RCP Lond. 1980; DO RCPSI 1968; DRCOG 1962; DObst RCOG 1961. Sen. Med. Off. Wales & SW Eng. Civil Serv. Occupat. Health Serv. Socs: BMA; Assoc. Fell. Roy. Soc. Med. Prev: Asst. Sen. Med. Off. Welsh Hosp. Bd.; Med. Supt. Esso Standard.

WATKINSON, Mr Anthony Francis Consultant Radiologist, c/o X-Ray Department, Royal Free Hospital, Pond St., Hampstead, London NW3 2QG Tel: 020 7830 2170 Fax: 020 7830 2969 Email: anthony.watkinson@rfh.nthames.nhs.uk; Cornerways, South View Road, Pinner Hill, Pinner HA5 3YB Tel: 020 866 6359 Email: melosborne@compuserve.com — MB BS 1984 Lond.; MSc Oxf. 1979; FRCS Eng. 1988; FRCR 1991. (Roy. Free Hosp. Lond.) Cons. & Hon. Sen. Lect. (Radiol.) Roy. Free Hosp. Lond. Socs: BMA; Brit. Soc. Interven. Radiol.; Soc. Cardiovasc. & Interven. Radiol. Prev: Lect. (Interven. Radiol.) UMDS Guy's Hosp. Lond.; Fell. (Interven. Radiol.) Vancouver Gen. Hosp., Canada; Regist. (Radiol.) Bristol Roy. Infirm.

WATKINSON, Duncan James 77 Romsey Road, Winchester SO22 5DL — MB BS 1992 Newc.

WATKINSON, Geoffrey (cons. rooms), Nuffield McAlpin Clinic, Beaconsfield Road, Glasgow G12 0PJ Tel: 0141 334 9441; Glasgow Nuffield Hospital, Beaconsfield Road, Glasgow G12 0PJ — MRCS Eng. LRCP Lond. 1943; MD Lond. 1945, MB BS 1943; FRCP Glas. 1971, M 1969; FRCP Lond. 1962, M 1944. (St. Bart.) Examr. RCPS Glas. Socs: (Ex-Pres.) Brit. Soc. Gastroenterol.; (Ex-Pres. & Ex-Sec.Gen.) Organisat. Mondial de Gastroenterol. Prev: Hon. Lect. (Med.) & Internal Examr. Univ. Glas.; Cons. Phys. & Gastroenterol. W.. Infirm., Gartnavel Gen. & S.. Gen. Hosps. Glas.; Cons. Phys. York Hosp. Gp.

WATKINSON, Hilary Leith Bonnyrigg Health Centre, High Street, Bonnyrigg EH19 2DA Tel: 0131 663 7272; 54 Grange Loan, Edinburgh EH9 2EP Tel: 0131 667 6360 — MB ChB 1971 Ed.; DA Eng. 1976; DObst RCOG 1973. Med. Asst. (Anaesth.) Lauriston Dent. Centre Edin.

WATKINSON, Mr John Carmel ENT Department, Queen Elizabeth Hospital, Vincent Drive, Edgbaston, Birmingham B15 2TH Tel: 0121 627 2295 Fax: 0121 627 2291; 34 Wellington Road, Edgbaston, Birmingham B15 2ES Tel: 0121 440 1981 Fax: 0121 440 1981 — MB BS 1979 Lond.; MS Lond. 1990, MSc (Nuclear Med.) 1987; FRCS (Orl.) Eng. 1986; FRCS Ed. 1984; FRCS Glas. 1984; FICS 1991; DLO RCS Eng. 1986. (Roy. Free) Cons. Otolaryngol. Qu. Eliz. Hosp. Birm. Socs: Fell. Roy. Soc. Med.; Brit. Nuclear Med. Soc.; BMA. Prev: Sen. Regist. (Otolaryngol.) Guy's Hosp. Lond.; Sen. Regist. (Head & Neck & Plastics) Roy. Marsden Hosp. Lond.; SHO (Otolaryngol.) Roy. Free Hosp. Lond.

WATKINSON, Leonard Neal Ghyll House, Kirkland, Frizington CA26 3XY — BM BS 1983 Nottm.

WATKINSON, Margaret Carroll (retired) Grove Gables, 12 Hampton Grove, Meysey Hampton, Cirencester GL7 5JN Tel: 01285 851661 — MB BS Durh. 1949. Prev: Vis. Psychiat. Bristol & W.on HA.

WATSON

WATKINSON, Michael Neonatal Unit, Birmingham Heartlands Hospital, Bordesley Green E., Birmingham B9 5ST Tel: 0121 424 2719 Fax: 0121 424 2718 — MB BChir 1973 Camb.; FRCPCH 1997; FRCP Lond. 1992; MRCP (UK) 1975. Cons. Paediat. Birm. Heartlands Hosp. Prev: Sen. Regist. (Paediat) St. Geo. Hosp. Lond.; Research Paediat. MRC Dunn Nutrit. Unit Keneba, The Gambia; Regist (Paediat.) Roy. Vict. Infirm. Newc. u. Tyne.

WATKINSON, Peter James The Old Bungalow, 887 Whittingham Lane, Goosnargh, Preston PR3 2AU — MRCS Eng. LRCP Lond. 1968.

WATKINSON, Peter James 17 Warwick Street, Crookes, Sheffield S10 1LX — MB ChB 1993 Sheff.

WATKINSON, Peter Martin New Court Surgery, 39 Boulevard, Weston Super Mare BS23 1PF Tel: 01934 624242 Fax: 01934 642608; The Beeches, 11 Woodland Road, Weston Super Mare BS23 4HF Tel: 01934 417734 — MB ChB 1971 Manch.; DObst RCOG 1975. Prev: Clin. Asst. (ENT) W.on Gen. Hosp.; SHO (Obst.) S.mead Hosp. Bristol; SHO (Gyn.) Ham Green Hosp. Pill.

WATKINSON, Sally Ann Pheasey The Surgery, Woodland View, West Rainton, Durham DH7 6RQ Tel: 0191 584 3809; 11 Rosemount, Plawsworth Road, Durham DH1 5GA — MB BS 1987 Newc.; MRCGP 1991. (Newcastle-u-Tyne) Part. Gen. Pract. W. Rainton, Durh. Prev: Trainee GP Newc. u. Tyne.

WATKINSON, Sally Jane 30 Deerlands Road, Chesterfield S40 4DF — MB BS 1997 Lond.; BSc 1994.

WATKINSON, Susan Elizabeth 2 Torridon Close, Sinfin, Derby DE24 9LJ — MB ChB 1977 Leeds; FFA RCSI 1984.

WATKINSON, William Michael Forbes (retired) Pinehill Surgery, Pinehill Road, Bordon GU35 0BS Tel: 01420 472113 — MB BS 1973 Lond.; MRCS Eng. LRCP Lond. 1973. Prev: Sen. Med. Off., Bordon Garrison, Bordon, Hants.

WATKISS, Jonathan Bruce Flat 22, The Lab Building, 177 Rosebery Ave, London EC1R 4TN — MB BS 1989 Lond.; MRCGP 1993; T(G) 1993; DRCOG 1992; FRCA 1998. Specialist Regist. (Anaesth.) Centr. N. Lond. Rotat. UCH/Roy. Free. Prev: Repatriation Med. SHO Anaesth. Barts/Roy. Lond.; Psychiat. SHO St Chas. Hosp. Lond.

WATLING, Mark Ian Lewis 2 Ash Cottages, 20 Oxted Green, Milford, Godalming GU8 5DA — MB ChB 1981 Birm.; MRCGP 1986; AFPM RCP Lond. 1995; Dip. Pharm. Med. RCP (UK) 1994; Dip. Sports Med. Lond. 1988; DRCOG 1987. Socs: Roy. Soc. Med.; Brit. Assn. Sport & Med.; Brit. Assn. Pharm. Phys.

WATMOUGH, David Dept. of Gastroenterol., Queens Hospital, Belvedere Road, Burton-on-Trent DE13 0RB Tel: 01283 566333 — MB ChB 1986 Sheff.; BMedSci Sheff. 1986, MB ChB 1986; FRACP 1997. (Sheffield) Cons.(Gen. Med. & Gastroenterol.) Qu.s Hosp. Burton upon Trent, Staffs. Socs: Gastroenterolog. Soc. Australia & W.Midl.s Phys. Assoc. Prev: Advanced Trainee (Gastroenterol.) Sir Chas. Gardiner Hosp. Perth, Australia; Regist. (Gen. Med.) Roy. Perth Hosp., Australia; Regist. Univ. Dept. Med. Roy. Perth Hosp. W.. Austral.

WATMOUGH, Gerald Ian Market Street Health Centre, Market Street, Ullapool IV26 2XE Tel: 01854 612015/612595 Fax: 01854 613025; 47 Forest View Road, Loughton IG10 4DY — MRCS Eng. LRCP Lond. 1973; BSc Lond. 1969, MB BS 1972. (St. Bart.) Prev: Regist. (Paediat.) Raigmore Hosp. Inverness; Regist. (Paediat.) & Regist. (Anaesth.) Palmerston N. Hosp., N.Z.

WATMOUGH, Patrick John 18 Millfield Road, Chorley PR7 1RE — MB ChB 1996 Dundee.

WATNEY, Duncan Martyn (retired) Larchwood, 15 Lower Saronbury, Crowborough TN6 1EB — MB BChir 1955 Camb.; MRCGP 1967; DObst RCOG 1957. Prev: GP CrowBoro.

WATNEY, Patsy Jeanne Moncaster (retired) Waterton, The Wad, West Wittering, Chichester PO20 8AH Tel: 01243 513592 — MB BChir 1956 Camb.; MA Camb. 1956, MD 1972; FRCOG 1979, M 1964. Prev: Cons. O & G Sandwell Dist. Gen. Hosp. W. Bromwich.

WATRAS, Gregory Jan Maharishi Ayur Ved Health Centre, 3 Rowan Road, Ashurst, Skelmersdale WN8 6UQ Tel: 01695 51008; Evergreens, Allendale Drive, St. Ishmaels, Haverfordwest SA62 3TP Tel: 01646 636330 — MB ChB 1973 Sheff. Med. Dir. Maharishi Ayur-Ved Health Centre Skelmersdale. Prev: GP Milford Haven.

WATRASIEWICZ, Krystyna Ewa 30 Drayton Hill, London W13 0JF — MRCS Eng. LRCP Lond. 1961.

WATRELOT, Antoine Medicare Français, 3 Harrington Gardens, London SW7 4JJ Tel: (20) 7370 4999; Cres, Clinique Saint Maurice, 85 Bis Cours Albert Thomas, Lyon 69003, France Tel: 00 33 78 531750 Fax: 00 33 72 360773 Email: watrelot@wanadoo.fr — MD 1978 Grenoble; DGO Grenoble 1979. Cons. IVF Clinic, Lyon. Socs: Amer. Assn. Gyn. Laparoscopists.; (Pres.) Infertil. Centre of Lyons, France; IVF French Soc. Prev: Regist. & Head of Clinic. Grenoble Hosp., France; Sen. Regist. Hosp. St. Joseph, Lyon, France.

WATSHAM, Christine Mary Priscilla Chaldon, 26 Hauxton Road, Little Shelford, Cambridge CB2 5HJ Tel: 01223 842638 — MB BS 1963 Lond.; MRCS Eng. LRCP Lond. 1963; FFA RCS Eng. 1968; DA Eng. 1965; DObst RCOG 1965. (Roy. Free) Cons. Anaesth. Bourn Hall Clinic Camb. Socs: Assn. Dent. Anaesth. & Brit. Soc. Med. & Dent. Hypn. Prev: Cons. Anaesth. Newmarket Gen. Hosp.

WATSON, Agnes Teak The Old Barn, King St., Bishop's Stortford CM23 2NB — MB ChB 1990 Leeds; FRCA 1997. Locum Cons., Anaesthetics, St. Andrews, Broomfield Hosp., Chelmsford. Prev: Regist. (Anaesth.) The Roy. Hosp. Lond. Sch. of Anaesth.; Regist. (Anaesth.) Qu.'s Med. Centre Nottm.

WATSON, Alan 286 Cottingham Road, Hull HU6 8QA — MB BS 1979 Newc.; MRCOG 1986. Assoc Spec Obst & Gyn Roy Hull Hosp. Prev: Staff Grade Roy Hull Hosp.

WATSON, Alan Rees Children & Young People's Kidney Unit, City Hospital, Hucknall Road, Nottingham NG5 1PB Tel: 0115 962 7961 Fax: 0115 962 7759 Email: watpaed@aol.com; 78 Lambourne Drive, Wollarton, Nottingham NG8 1GR — MB ChB 1973 Ed.; FRCP Ed. 1988; MRCP (UK) 1976; FRCPCH 1997. (Edinburgh) Cons. Paediat. Nephrol. City Hosp. Nottm.; Special Sen. Lect., Sch. of Human Developm., Univ. of Nottm. Socs: Chairm., Ethics of Clin. Pract.,; Convenor Europ. Paediatric Pertoneal Working Gp. Prev: Staff Nephrol. Hosp. Sick Childr. Toronto, Canada; Lect. (Child Health) Univ. Manch.; Regist. Paediat. Durban, S. Africa.

WATSON, Alan Spence (retired) Beggars Bush House, 55 Ravensheugh Road, Levenhall, Musselburgh EH21 7SZ Tel: 0131 665 4537 — MB ChB 1950 Ed.; MRCGP 1968. Chairm. Panel on Ethics. Inveresk Research Internat., Elphinstone Research Centre, Tranent, Scotl. Prev: GP Musselburgh.

WATSON, Alastair John Mackenzie Department of Medicine, University of Liverpool, Daulby St., Liverpool L69 3GA Tel: 0151 706 4074 Fax: 0151 706 5802 Email: alastair.watson@liv.ac.uk; 7 Ridgebourne Close, Warrington WA5 9YB Tel: 01925 574207 — MB BS 1980 Lond.; MD Camb. 1989; MRCP (UK) 1983; FRCP 1999. (St. Thomas' London) Prof. (Med.) Univ. Liverp.; Hon. Cons. Phys. Roy. Liverp. Univ. Socs: Brit. Soc. Gastroenterol.; Amer. Gastroenterol. Assn. Prev: Sen. Lect. (Med.) Univ. Manch.; Research Fell. (Gastroenterol.) John Hopkins Hosp., Baltimore, USA; Research Regist. St. Bart. Hosp. Lond.

WATSON, Alexander Davidson West Gate Health Centre, Charleston Drive, Dundee DD2 4AD Tel: 01382 632771 Fax: 01382 633839; 5 West Park Gardens, Dundee DD2 1NY Tel: 01382 667321 — MB ChB 1973 Dundee; MRCGP 1977; DObst RCOG 1975; FRCGP 1999. (Dundee) Princip. in Gen. Pract. W.gate Health Centre Chas.ton Dr., Dundee; Clin. Asst. Hypertens. Unit Ninewells Hosp. Dundee. Socs: Brit. Hypertens. Soc.; Scott. Thoracic Soc. Prev: Clin. Asst. Chest Unit Kings Cross Hosp. Dundee.

WATSON, Alexander Stewart 12 Abbey Park, Auchterarder PH3 1EN — MB ChB 1949 Glas.

***WATSON, Alexander William** Steep, Hook Hill, South Croydon CR2 0LB — MB ChB 1998 Leeds; BSc (UCL) 1997.

WATSON, Alison Jane 3 Bowtrees, Ashbrooke Range, Sunderland SR2 7TL Tel: 0191 510 9395 — MB ChB 1979 Dundee; MBA Durh. 1995; MFPHM 1990. Prev: Cons. Pub. Health Med. Sunderland HA.

WATSON, Alison Margaret Parkside Family Practice, Green Road Surgery, 224 Wokingham Road, Reading RG6 1JT Tel: 0118 966 3366 Fax: 0118 926 3269; Copperstones, Little Lane, Upper Bucklebury, Reading RG7 6QX Tel: 01635 871871 — MB BS Lond. 1969; MRCS Eng. LRCP Lond. 1969; FRCGP 1996, M 1975; DObst RCOG 1971. (Westm.) Course Organiser Reading VTS. Prev: GP Thatcham Health Centre Berks.

WATSON, Alison Mary Thornley Street Surgery, 40 Thornley Street, Wolverhampton WV1 1JP Tel: 01902 26843 Fax: 01902 688500; 40 Thornley Street, Wolverhampton WV1 1JP — MB ChB 1982 Birm.

WATSON

WATSON, Allan John Stewart Field House Surgery, Victoria Road, Bridlington YO15 2AT Tel: 01262 623362; Chantry Cottage, West St, Flamborough, Bridlington YO15 1PH Tel: 01262 850501 — MB ChB 1963 Ed.; DObst RCOG 1966.

WATSON, Mr Allan Philip The Eye Unit, Southport General Infirmary, Scarisbrick New Road, Southport PR8 6PH Tel: 01704 703457; 11 Belgrave Road, Southport PR8 2DZ — MB BCh BAO 1980 NUI; DO RCS Eng. 1983; FRCS Ed. 1984; FRCOphth 1989. Cons. Ophth. Surg. S.port & Ormskirk NHS Trust. Socs: United Kingdom and Irel. Soc. of Cataract and Refractive Surg.s; Europ. Soc. of Cataract and Refractive Surg.s.

WATSON, Andrew Brailsford Arbury Road Surgery, 114 Arbury Road, Cambridge CB4 2JG Tel: 01223 364433 Fax: 01223 315728; 17 Nursery Walk, Cambridge CB4 3PR Tel: 01223 323269 — MB BS 1983 Lond.; MRCGP 1989; DRCOG 1987; DGM RCP Lond. 1986. SHO (O & G) Newmarket Gen. Hosp. Socs: RCGP; Primary Care Theum. Soc. Prev: SHO (A & E) Hinchingbrooke Hosp. Huntingdon.; Ho. Phys. Hartlepool Gen. Hosp.; Ho. Surg. Roy. Free Hosp. Lond.

WATSON, Andrew Henry Paediatric Department, St. Mary's Hospital, Newport PO30 5TG Tel: 01983 534343 Fax: 01983 534597; Tel: 01983 563042 Fax: 01983 812123 — MB BS 1974 Lond.; FRCP Lond. 1992; MRCP (UK) 1977; MRCS Eng. LRCP Lond. 1974; DCH Eng. 1976; FRCPCH 1997. (St. Geo.) Cons. Paediat. I. of Wight. Prev: Lect. & Hon. Sen. Regist. (Paediat.) St. Bart., Lond. Hosp. & Qu. Eliz. Hosp. Lond.; Regist. (Paediat.) Qu. Charlotte's Matern. Hosp. Lond.

WATSON, Andrew John Sowerby Department of Obstetrics and Gynaecology, Tameside General Hospital, Fountain St., Ashton-under-Lyne OL6 9RW — MB ChB 1986 Leeds; MRCOG 1991. Cons. in O & G; Hon. Clin. Lect. Obst. & Gyn. Manch. Univ. Socs: Brit. Soc. Colpos. & Cerv. Path.; Brit. Fertil. Soc.; Internat. Continence Soc. (UK).

WATSON, Andrew Norman 5 Alderson Road, Harrogate HG2 8AS Tel: 01423 67810 — MB ChB 1954 Leeds; FFA RCS Eng. 1968; DA Eng. 1965; DObst RCOG 1958. (Leeds) Cons. Anaesth. Leeds Gen. Infirm. Prev: Regist. Anaesth. Dept. Hull 'A' Hosp. Gp.; Sen. Med. Off. Esso Petroleum Co. Ltd.; Med. Off. BP Petroleum Co.

WATSON, Angela Station Road Surgery, 2 Station Road, Prestwick KA9 1AQ Tel: 01292 671444 Fax: 01292 678023; 3 Southpark Avenue, Prestwick KA9 1PY Tel: 01292 474042 — MB ChB 1970 Glas.; MRCGP 1975; DObst RCOG 1972. Clin. Asst. (Haemat.) Ayr Hosp. Prev: Trainee GP N. Ayrsh. VTS.

WATSON, Mr Angus James Mackintosh No. 10, Sillerton House, 16 Albyn Terrace, Aberdeen AB10 1YP Tel: 01224 644929 Email: a.j.watson@abdn.ac.uk; No. 10, Sillerton House, 16 Albyn Terrace, Aberdeen AB10 1YP Tel: 01224 644929 Email: anguswatson@compuserve.com — MB ChB 1991 Manch.; BSc (Med. Sci.) St. And. 1988; FRCS Ed. 1995. (St. And. & Manch.) Regist. (Gen. Surg.) Higher Surgic. Train. Scheme Grampian Region; Research Fell. (Surg.) Aberd. Univ. Prev: SHO Rotat. (Surg.) Hope Hosp. Salford; SHO (A & E) & Demonst. (Anat.) Roy. Hallamsh. Hosp. Sheff.

WATSON, Ann Department of Haematology, Stoke Mandeville Hospital, Aylesbury HP21 8AL Tel: 01296 84111; Gorwell Cottage, Gorwell, Watlington OX49 5JB Tel: 01491 613840 — MB BS 1975 Lond.; BSc (Physiol.) Lond. 1972; MRCP (UK) 1978; MRCPath 1985. Cons. Haemat. Stoke Mandeville Hosp. Aylesbury. Prev: Sen. Regist. (Haemat.) Roy. Berks. Hosp. Reading; Regist. (Haemat.) Glas. Roy. Infirm.

WATSON, Anna Catherine 24 Kent Gardens, Ealing, London W13 8BU Tel: 020 8998 3283 — MB ChB 1989 Bristol; FRCA 1995. Regist. (Anaesth.) St. Mary's Hosp. Lond. Prev: SHO (Anaesth.) St. Bart. Hosp. Lond.

WATSON, Anne (retired) Luther Street Medical Centre, Luther St., Oxford OX2 9HE Tel: 01865 862995 — MRCS Eng. LRCP Lond. 1964; MA, BM BCh Oxf. 1964; DFFP 1993. GP; Trustee Parent-Infant Project. Prev: Clin. Asst. (Paediat.) Stoke Mandeville Hosp. Aylesbury.

WATSON, Anne McIntyre Maryfield Medical Centre, 9 Morgan Street, Dundee DD4 6QE Tel: 01382 462292 Fax: 01382 461052; 320 Blackness Road, Dundee DD2 1SD Tel: 01382 566429 — MB ChB 1982 Dundee; MRCGP 1986; DRCOG 1984. Clin. Asst. (Palliat. Med.) Roxburghe Hse. Dundee.

WATSON, Annette Barbara Joiner's Cottage, Linton-on-Ouse, York YO30 2AS — MB ChB 1986 Leeds.

WATSON, Anthony 19 Beamish Way, Winslow, Buckingham MK18 3EU Tel: 01296 4235 — MB BS 1979 Lond.; FRCGP 2001; MRCGP 1983; DRCOG 1981.

WATSON, Anthony The Cobham Health Centre, 168 Portsmouth Road, Cobham KT11 1HT Tel: 01932 867231 Fax: 01932 866874; 1 Randolph Close, Stoke D'Abernon, Cobham KT11 2SW Tel: 01932 862966 — MB BS 1971 Lond.; Dip. Pharm. Med. RCP 1981.

WATSON, Professor Anthony Level 2, Consulting Rooms, Princess Grace Hospital, 42-52 Nottingham Place, London W1U 5NY; 25 St. Edmund'sCt., St. Edmund's Terrace, London NW8 7QL Tel: 020 7586 846 Fax: 020 7586 956 — MB ChB 1965 Manch.; MD Manch. 1975; FRCS Ed. 1988; FRCS Eng. 1970; FRACS 1990. (Manch.) Vis. Prof. Surg. Roy. Free Hosp. Sch. Med. Lond. Socs: Counc. Mem. Brit. Soc. Gastroenterol.; Assn. Surg.; Counc.Mem. Assoc. Upper Gastrointestinal Surg. GB & Irel. Prev: Prof. Surg. Univ. Sydney; Cons. Surg. Roy. Lancaster Infirm.; Sen. Regist. (Surg.) Univ. Hosp. Wales.

WATSON, Anthony James Magali, Hook Road, Ampfield, Romsey SO51 9DB — MB BS 1949 Durh.; DA Eng. 1971; DCH Eng. 1951. (Newc.) Hosp. Pract. (Anaesth.) Roy. Co. Hosp. Winchester. Prev: Regist. (Med.) & Ho. Phys. Childr. Dept. & Cardiovasc. Dept. Gen. Hosp. Newc.

WATSON, Anthony John (retired) Bewley Cottage, Ismays Road, Ightham, Sevenoaks TN15 9BE Tel: 01732 885337 — MA, MB Camb. 1957, BChir 1956; DObst RCOG 1960. Prev: Hosp. Pract. (ENT) Weald Kent Trust.

WATSON, Anthony Thayne (retired) 6 Princess Royal Close, Lincoln LN2 5RX Tel: 01522 523007 — MB ChB Ed. 1948; MRCGP 1965; DObst RCOG 1951. Prev: Resid. Ho. Off. (Obst.) City Gen. Hosp. Sheff.

WATSON, Mr Antony Charles Harington (retired) St. Helens, Waverley Road, Melrose TD6 9AA Tel: 01896 822082 Fax: 01896 822082 Email: awatson@scottishborders.com — MB ChB Ed. 1960; FRCS Ed. 1964. Non-Exec. Dir. Borders Gen. Hosp.; Hon. Cons. Plastic Surg. Roy. Hosp. for Sick Childr. Edin.; Vice-Chairm. Med. Research Working Party, Healing Foundat. Prev: Cons. Plastic Surg. Lothian HB.

WATSON, Arthur Barrie (retired) 83 Buckingham Road, Shoreham-by-Sea BN43 5UD — MB BS 1954 Lond.; DObst RCOG 1960.

WATSON, Arthur Vincent Reid, MBE (retired) The Rowans, Craigour Road, Torphins, Banchory AB31 4HE Tel: 01339 882140 — MB ChB 1958 Aberd.; MRCGP 1971; DObst RCOG 1961. Prev: Ho. Phys. Roy. Aberd. Hosp. Sick Childr.

WATSON, Barbara (retired) 8 Culver Road, Winchester SO23 9JF — MB ChB 1950 Ed. Prev: Clin. Asst. in Psychiat. at the Dept. of Psychiatry. Roy. S. Hants Hosp. S.ampton.

WATSON, Beverley Jill 16 Gains Lane, Great Gidding, Huntingdon PE28 5NL — MB BS 1986 Lond.; FRCA 1993. (Univ. Coll. Lond.) Cons. Anaesth. Qu. Eliz. Hosp. Kings Lynn.

WATSON, Brian (retired) Callow Stocking, Knighton on Teme, Tenbury Wells WR15 8NA Tel: 01584 781667 — MB ChB 1953 Birm. Prev: GP Handsworth Birm.

WATSON, Brian Granville 12 Westfield Avenue, Gosforth, Newcastle upon Tyne NE3 4YH Tel: 0191 285553 — MB BS 1965 Durh.; FFA RCS Eng. 1969. Cons. Anaesth. Regional Cardiothoracic Surg. Centre Freeman Hosp. Newc. Socs: Hon. Sec. N. Eng. Soc. Anaesth. Prev: Sen. Regist. (Anaesth.) Newc.; Sen. Med. Off. (Anaesth.) Baragwanath Hosp. Johannesburg; Regist. (Anaesth.) Alder Hey Childr. Hosp. Liverp.

WATSON, Mr Carl Memorial Hospital, Darlington DL3 6HX; Ingle Nook, 46 Cleveland Avenue, Darlington DL3 7HG — MB ChB 1981 Leeds; FRCS Ed. 1986. Cons. ENT Surg. Memor. Hosp. Darlington. Prev: Sen. Regist. (Otolaryngol.) Gen. Infirm. Leeds.

WATSON, Carole Anne Grove House Practice, St. Pauls Health Centre, High St, Runcorn WA7 1AB Tel: 01928 566561 Fax: 01928 590212; 23 Sylvan Close, Selsdon, South Croydon CR2 8DS — MB BS 1990 Lond.; MRCGP 1994; DFFP 1994; DRCOG 1993; DCH RCP Lond. 1992.

WATSON, Caroline Elizabeth 20 West Ferryfield, Edinburgh EH5 2PU — MB ChB 1987 Ed.; MRCGP 1991; T(GP) 1991. Med.

Asst. Inveresk Clin. Research Ltd. Edin. Prev: Trainee GP Lothian VTS.

WATSON, Caroline Iylah Jane 3 Knole Way, Sevenoaks TN13 3RS — MB BChir 1994 Camb.

WATSON, Caroline Jane The Medical Centre, The Meadows, Old Meldrum, Inverurie AB51 0BF Tel: 01651 872239; St Peters Brae, Peterwell Road, Fyvie, Turriff AB53 8RF — MB ChB 1986 Aberd.

WATSON, Catherine Julie 204 London Road, Chippenham SN15 3BG — MB ChB 1993 Bristol.

WATSON, Ceri Susan 38 Newport View, Heading Ley, Leeds LS6 3BX — MB ChB 1994 Leeds.

WATSON, Christine Anne 118 Waterloo Road, Haslington, Crewe CW1 5TA Tel: 01270 581269 — MB ChB 1984 Ed.

WATSON, Christine Mary (retired) 36 Alleyn Road, West Dulwich, London SE21 8AL Tel: 020 8670 0444 Fax: 020 8670 0562 Email: jimw@casab.demon.co.uk — MB BS Lond. 1961; MD Lond. 1973; MRCS Eng. LRCP Lond. 1961; MFFP 1993; DCH Eng. 1963; DObst RCOG 1963. Prev: Cons. Family Plann. & Reproduc. Healthcare Optimum Health Servs. Lond.

WATSON, Christopher Anthony The Health Centre, University of Sussex, Falmer, Brighton BN1 9RW Tel: 01273 249049 Fax: 01273 249040; 36 Chichester Drive E., Saltdean, Brighton BN2 8LB Fax: 01273 297218 — MB BS 1981 Lond.; DRCOG 1983. (St. Mary's) Prev: SHO (Orthop. & Trauma & O & G) Roy. Sussex Co. Hosp. Brighton; SHO (Paediat. Surg.) Roy. Alexandra Childr. Hosp. Brighton.

WATSON, Christopher Greenhowe 50 The Oval, Harrogate HG2 9BA — MB ChB Sheff. 1955. (Sheff.) Prev: SHO City Gen. Hosp. Sheff.; Ho. Phys. Childr. Hosp. Sheff.; Ho. Surg. (Orthop.) Roy. Hosp. Sheff.

WATSON, Mr Christopher John Edward Oxford Transplant Centre, Churchill Hospital, Headington, Oxford OX3 7LJ Tel: 01865 225357 Email: chris.watson@nds.ox.ac.uk; Kite House, 3 Rowland Close, Wolvercote, Oxford OX2 8PW — MB BChir 1984 Camb.; FRCS (Gen.) 1995; MA Camb. 1985, BA (Hons.) 1981, MD 1994; FRCS Eng. 1988. (Camb.) Cons. (Transpl. Surg.) Ch.ill Hosp. Oxf. Prev: Sen. Regist. (Transpl.) Addenbrookes Camb.; Sen. Regist. (Gen. & Vasc. Surg.) John Radcliffe Hosp. Oxf.; Regist. (Gen. Surg.) Addenbrooke's Hosp. Camb.

WATSON, Christopher Neville (retired) The Moat House, Moor Lane, Keswick, Leeds LS17 9ET Tel: 01937 573344 — BM BCh 1950 Oxf.; MA, BM BCh Oxon. 1950. Prev: Ho. Surg. Thoracic Unit, Guy's Hosp.

WATSON, Claire Green Lane Hospital, Devizes SN10 5DS Tel: 01380 731200 Fax: 01380 731308; 4 Stapleford Close, Chippenham SN15 3FZ Email: 106232.1216@compuserve.com — MB ChB 1974 Manch.; MRCPsych 1985. Cons. Psychiat. of Old Age Green La. Hosp. Devizes. Prev: Cons. Psychiat. of Old Age Roundway Hosp. Devizes; Sen. Regist. (Psychiat. Old Age) St. Martin's Hosp. Bath & Torbay Hosp.; Regist. (Gen. Psychiat.) St. John's Hosp. Bucks.

WATSON, Colin (retired) 8 Church View, Narborough, Leicester LE9 5GY Tel: 0116 286 5916 — MB ChB 1954 Leeds; FRCGP 1972, M 1961; DObst RCOG 1956. Prev: Hon. Lect. (Obst. in Gen. Pract.) Univ. Leeds.

WATSON, Courtney O'Neill 42 Pullman Court, Streatham Hill, London SW2 4ST — MB BS 1991 West Indies.

WATSON, Craig Fyvie Health Group, Health Centre, 27 Parnassus Gardens, Fyvie, Turriff AB53 8QD Tel: 01651 872239 Fax: 01651 872968; St Peters Brae, Peterwell Road, Fyvie, Turriff AB53 8RD Tel: 01651 891430 — MB ChB 1984 Ed.; MRCGP 1989; DRCOG 1988.

WATSON, Cyril Colin East Crest, Red Lane, Colne BB8 7JR — MB BS 1965 Lond.; MRCP Lond. 1968; MRCS Eng. LRCP Lond. 1965. (Roy. Free) Cons. Phys. Burnley Gp. Hosps. Prev: Sen. Med. Regist. Derby Roy. Infirm.; Med. Regist. Nottm. Gen. Hosp.; Regist. (Cardiol.) Groby Rd. Hosp. Leicester.

WATSON, Dale Gary Flat 3, 74 Northumberland Road, Manchester M16 9PP — MB ChB 1996 Liverp.

WATSON, Danie-Marie Kim 150 Ruskin Park House, Champion Hill, London SE5 8TL — MB BS 1994 Lond.

WATSON, Daphne Alice Sutton (retired) Wrightington Hospital, Hall Lane, Appley Bridge, Wigan WN6 9EP Tel: 01257 256244 — MB BChir 1967 Camb.; BA Camb. 1963; FFA RCSI 1973. Cons. Anaesth. Wrightington Hosp. for Jt. Dis. Prev: Cons. Anaesth. W. Lancs. NHS Trust.

WATSON, David (retired) Flat 15, The Courtyard, Block 1, Auchlochan House, Lesmahagow, Lanark ML11 0JS Tel: 01555 895618 — MB ChB 1936 Glas.

WATSON, David Email: d.watson@ed.ac.uk — MB ChB 1983 Ed.; BSc (Med. Sci.) Ed. 1980; FFA RCS Eng. 1988; DA (UK) 1986. (Ed. Univ.) Cons. Anaesth. Roy. Infirm Edin. Socs: Scott. Soc. Anaesth. & Edin. & E. Scotl. Soc. Anaesth.; Scott. Intens. Care Soc.

WATSON, David Adams Brae Terrace Surgery, Brae Terrace, Munlochy IV8 8NG Tel: 01463 811200 Fax: 01463 811383; Tulach Ard, Munlochy IV8 8ND Tel: 01463 811430 — MB ChB 1971 Aberd. Prev: GP Arrochar; GP Glenrothes; SHO (O & G) Raigmore Hosp. Inverness.

WATSON, David Andrew 21 Oldfield Road, Sale M33 2AP — MB ChB 1989 Manch. Regist. Rotat. (Anaesth.) Manch.

WATSON, Mr David Anthony (retired) Darbys House, High St., Chipping Campden GL55 6AL Tel: 01386 841164 Email: davidwatson32@hotmail.com — MB BS 1946 Lond.; FRCS Eng. 1955; MRCS Eng. LRCP Lond. 1945. Hon. Cons. Adviser Nat. Heart Research Fund. Prev: Cons. Cardiothoracic Surg. Gen. Infirm. & Killingbeck Hosp. Leeds.

WATSON, David Bruce Friarwood Surgery, Carleton Glen, Pontefract WF8 1SU Tel: 01977 703235 Fax: 01977 600527 — MB ChB 1985 Leeds. Prev: SHO (Gen. Med.) Pontefract Gen. Infirm.; Ho. Off. (Gen. Med.) Pontefract Gen. Infirm.; Ho. Off. (Gen. Surg.) Harrogate Dist. & Gen. Hosps.

WATSON, David George Agar 3 Loris Road, Hammersmith, London W6 7QA — MB BS 1967 Sydney; MRCP (UK) 1970; DCH RCP Lond. 1971.

WATSON, David Graham Central Surgery, Sussex Road, Gorleston-on-Sea, Great Yarmouth NR31 6QB Tel: 01493 414141 Fax: 01493 656253; Central Surgery, Sussex Road, Gorleston, Great Yarmouth NR31 6QB Tel: 01493 414141 Fax: 01493 656253 Email: watson@omsimedical.demon.co.uk — MB BS 1971 Lond.; AFOM RCP Lond. 1981; DObst RCOG 1973. (St. Thos.)

WATSON, David Howard Victoria Surgery, Victoria Street, Bury St Edmunds IP33 3BD Tel: 01284 725550 Fax: 01284 725551 — MB BS 1966 Lond.; MRCS Eng. LRCP Lond. 1965. (Char. Cross) Prev: Regist. (Med.) W. Herts. Hosp. Hemel Hempstead; SHO (Anaesth.) Lincoln Co. Hosp.; SHO (Obst.) Hull Matern. Hosp.

WATSON, David James 71 New Edinburgh Road, Uddingston, Glasgow G71 6AB — MB ChB 1991 Manch.

WATSON, David Kay 20 Chester Road, Wrexham LL11 2SA — MB BS 1972 Newc.; MRCPath 1980. Cons. Haemat. Maelor Gen. Hosp. Wrexham. Prev: Sen. Regist. (Haemat.) Gen. Infirm. Leeds; Regist. (Path.) Huddersfield Roy. Infirm.; SHO (Path.) Soton. Gen. Hosp.

WATSON, David Lister (retired) St. Mildred's, North St., Milverton, Taunton TA4 1LG Tel: 01823 400447 — MB ChB Manch. 1948; FRCGP 1983, M 1975. Prev: Sen. Ho. Off. & Ho. Phys. Manch. Roy. Infirm.

WATSON, David Lyndon Hyde Park Surgery, 3 Woodsley Road, Leeds LS6 1SG Tel: 0113 295 1235 Fax: 0113 295 1220 — MB ChB 1987 Leeds.

WATSON, Mr David Malcolm, TD 115A Harley Street, London W1G 6AR Tel: 020 7935 8922 Fax: 020 7486 0211; 11 Meadway Close, Hampstead Garden Suburb, London NW11 7BA Tel: 020 8455 2507 — MB BS 1957 Lond.; FRCS Eng. 1963; FRCOphth 1989. (St. Thos.) Emerit. Cons. Guy's & St Thos. Hosp. Lond.; Ophth. Surg. King Edwd. VII Hosp. Lond.; Ophth. Surg. Hosp. St. John & Eliz. Lond. Socs: Fell. Roy. Soc. Med.; Fell. Ophth. Soc. UK. Prev: Cons. Ophth. Surg. Guy's Hosp. Lond.; Chief Clin. Asst. Detachm. Unit Moorfields Eye Hosp. (High Holborn) Lond.; Ho. Surg. & Chief Asst. Eye Dept. St. Thos. Hosp. Lond.

WATSON, David Michael 1 Dunelm Street, South Shields NE33 3JT — MB ChB 1986 Leeds.

WATSON, David Norman Severn House Surgery, 96 Albert Road, Stechford, Birmingham B33 8AG Tel: 0121 783 2893 Fax: 0121 785 0914; 28 Old Church Road, Water Orton, Birmingham B46 1NJ Email: dnwatson@lineone.net — MB ChB 1980 Ed.; BSc (Med. Sci.) Ed. 1977. (Ed.) Prev: GP Warks.; Community Child Health Off. Warks.

WATSON

WATSON, Mr David Patrick Hubert Emergency Department, Royal United Hospitals, Bath BA1 3NG Tel: 01225 824002 Fax: 01225 825636 Email: david.watson@ruh-bath.swest.nhs.uk — MB BCh BAO 1982 NUI; FRCSI 1987; FFAEM 1994. Cons. A & E Bath Roy. United Hosps. Prev: Cons. A & E Guy's Hosp. Lond.; Sen. Lect. (A & E) Guy's Hosp. & Lewisham Hosp.

WATSON, David Paul Bartram Hamilton Medical Group, 4 Queens Road, Aberdeen AB15 4ZT Tel: 01224 622345 Fax: 01224 627426; 13 Salisbury Terrace, Aberdeen AB10 6QG Tel: 01224 572796 — MB ChB 1984 Aberd.; AFOM RCP Lond. 1995; MRCGP 1988; DRCOG 1987. Occupat. Phys. Aberd. Socs: Brit. Assn. Sport & Med.; Soc. Occupat. Med. Prev: Trainee GP Aberd. VTS; Regist. (A & E) Aberd. Roy. Infirm.; SHO (A & E) Roy. Aberd. Childr. Hosp.

WATSON, Mr David Selby 27 Sunbury Avenue, West Jesmond, Newcastle upon Tyne NE2 3HD — MB ChB 1991 Ed.; FRCS Ed. 1996. Research Fell. (Surg.) Univ. Newc. u. Tyne.

WATSON, Deborah Shan Boughay Chelwood, Chelynch, Shepton Mallet BA4 4PZ Tel: 01749 880257 — MB BS 1991 Lond.; FRCA 1995. Reg.Anaesth.Auck.Hosp. Prev: SHO (Paediat.) Luton & Dunstable Hosp.; SHO (A & E) Salisbury Dist. Hosp.; SHO (Anaesth.) Bath Roy. United Hosp. NHS Trust.

WATSON, Miss Deirdre Clare Torbitt Thoracic Surgical Unit, Norfolk & Norwich Hospital, Brunswick Road, Norwich NR1 3SR Tel: 01603 286395 Fax: 01603 287882 — MB BS 1971 Lond.; FRCS Ed. 1975; FRCS Eng. 1975; MRCS Eng. LRCP Lond. 1971. (Guy's) Cons. Thoracic Surg. Norf. & Norwich Hosp. Socs: Soc. Cardiothoracic Surgs. GB & Irel.; Coun. Mem. Europ. Assn. for Cardiothoracic Surg. Prev: Cons. Thoracic Surg. Birm. Heartlands & Childr. Hosps.

WATSON, Mr Desmond John North Riding Infirmary, Newport Rd, Middlesbrough TS1 5JE Tel: 01642 850850 Fax: 01642 854070; 6 Ferguson Way, Redmarshall, Stockton-on-Tees TS21 1FB Tel: 01742 631031 — BM BCh 1980 Oxf.; MA Oxf. 1988; FRCS (Otol.) Eng. 1986. Cons. Otolaryngolist S. Tees Acute Hosp.s HNS Trust. Prev: Cons. Otolaryngol. W. Suff. HA.; Regist. Sen. Regist. (Otolaryng.) Bristol & Bath Hosps.; SHO (Otolarnyg.) Roy. Nat. Throat Nose & Ear Hosp. Lond.

WATSON, Diana Louise Top Floor Middle, 9 South East Circus Place, Edinburgh EH3 4TJ — MB ChB 1994 Ed.

WATSON, Diane 11 Gartmore Close, Paisley PA1 3NG — MB ChB 1983 Glas.

WATSON, Diane The Portland Road Practice, 16 Portland Road, London W11 4LA Tel: 020 7727 7711 Fax: 020 7226 6755; 17 Bloemfontein Road, London W12 7BH Tel: 020 8740 0765 — MB BS 1983 Lond.; BA Camb. 1980; MRCGP 1996; DRCOG 1986. Cement Tutor Imperial Coll. & GP Princip. Lond. Prev: Ho. Surg. Guy's Hosp. Lond.; Ho. Phys. Lewisham Hosp. Lond.

WATSON, Doreen 7 Four Acres Drive, Kilmaurs, Kilmarnock KA3 2ND — MB ChB 1991 Glas.

WATSON, Dorothy Betty Dougal Corsenside, Cooden Close, Bexhill-on-Sea TN39 4TQ Tel: 0142 433014 — MB BS 1948 Lond.; MRCS Eng. LRCP Lond. 1942. (Roy. Free) Prev: Ho. Surg. Roy. Free Hosp. Lond.; Capt. RAMC.

WATSON, Duncan MacDonald West Cumberland Hospital, Whitehaven CA28 8JG; Weston Lodge, 2 Brigham Road, Cockermouth CA13 0AX — MB BS 1976 Newc.; FFARCS 1982. Cons. (Anaesth.) W. Cumbld. Hosp. Whitehaven.

WATSON, Duncan McKenzie Ivy House, High St, Walton, Lutterworth LE17 5RG — MB ChB 1981 Leic.; FFA RCSI 1988. Cons. Anaesth. Intens. Care Walsgrave Hosp. Trust Coventry. Prev: Sen. Regist. (Anaesth.) Sheff.

WATSON, Edward Norton (retired) 42 Chester Close South., Regent's Park, London NW1 4JG Tel: 020 7486 6965 — MRCS Eng. LRCP Lond. 1944; MFOM RCP Lond. 1979. Prev: Chief Med. Off. Gen. Counc. Brit. Shipping & Merchant Navy Estab.

WATSON, Elizabeth Anne St Ronans Health Centre, Buchan Place, Innerleithen EH44 6QE Tel: 01896 830203 Fax: 01896 831202; Rowanburn, 146 Galashiels Road, Stow, Galashiels TD1 2RA Tel: 01578 730269 — MB ChB 1985 Bristol; MRCGP 1990; DRCOG 1990; DCH RCP Lond. 1987. (Bristol) Partner GP St Ronan's Health Centre Innerleithen; Clin. Asst. Dingleton Hosp., Melrose. Prev: Med. Off. St. And. Nursing Home Drygrange; Trainee GP Earlston; SHO (O & G) Roy. Infirm. Edin.

WATSON, Elizabeth Anne 286 Cottingham Road, Hull HU6 8QA — MB BS 1980 Newc. Asst. EM.

WATSON, Elizabeth Thompson 111 Needless Road, Perth PH2 0LB — MB ChB 1939 St. And. (St. And.)

WATSON, Emma Jane 13 Grasleigh Way, Allerton, Bradford BD15 9AN — MB ChB 1993 Ed.

WATSON, Mr Eric Alan John 166 Dawlish Road, Selly Oak, Birmingham B29 7AR Tel: 0121 471 3617 Email: eaj.watson@virgin.net — MB ChB 1991 Birm.; MRCOG 1998. Cons. Obst. & Gynaecologist, Wordsley Hosp., Dudley Gp. of Hosps. HNS Trust.

WATSON, Eric Reed (retired) 27 Kilnford Drive, Dundonald, Kilmarnock KA2 9EU Tel: 01563 851458 — MB ChB Leeds 1950; BSc Leeds 1947; FFR 1964; DMRT Eng. 1957. Prev: Cons. Radiotherap. W.. Infirm. Glas.

WATSON, Fiona Elizabeth Community Drug Problem Service, 22-24 Spittal St., Edinburgh EH3 9DU Tel: 0131 537 8345 Fax: 0131 537 8350 Email: fiona@mainsload.freeserve.co.uk; 22 Baberton Mains Loan, Edinburgh EH14 3EP — MB ChB 1982 Dundee; MRCPsych 1989; MRCGP 1987. Cons. Psychiat. Drug Dependency Lothian Primary Care Trust.

WATSON, Fiona Jane 219 Bellenden Road, London SE15 4DG Tel: 020 7277 6389 — MB BS 1992 Newc.; DFFP 1997. Socs: BMA.

WATSON, Fiona Lorraine 5 Magheralave Park N., Lisburn BT28 3NL — MB BCh 1998 Belf.

WATSON, Forbes Gordon 17 Kirkintilloch Road, Kirkintilloch, Glasgow G66 4RN — MB ChB 1989 Glas.

WATSON, Frederick James The Wooden Bungalow Medical Practice, Victoria St., Wrappy, Market Rasen LN8 5PF Tel: 01673 858880; Hilltop, Hameringham, Horncastle LN9 6PG Tel: 0165 888245 — MB BCh BAO 1978 Belf.

WATSON, Garron Maxwell Holmedene, Armthorpe, Doncaster DN3 3AB Tel: 01302 831200 — MB ChB 1950 Manch. Prev: SHO (O & G) Whitehaven Gen. Hosp.; SHO Cas., Gen. & Orthop. Surg. Gen. Hosp. Middlesbrough.

WATSON, Gavin Moffat The Surgery, 15 King Street, Paisley PA1 2PR Tel: 0141 889 3144 Fax: 0141 889 7134 — MB ChB 1967 Glas.; MRCGP 1972; DObst RCOG 1969. Prev: Trainee Gen. Pract. Glas. Vocational Train. Scheme.

WATSON, Geoffrey Wilfred 42 Huckley Way, Bradley Stoke, Bristol BS32 8AR Tel: 0117 969 2893 — MB BS 1989 Lond.; DA (UK) 1992. SHO Rotat. (Gen. Med.) Frenchay Hosp. Bristol. Prev: SHO (Anaesth., Trauma & Orthop.) P.ss Margt. Hosp. Swindon.

WATSON, George Craig Shepperton Health Centre, Shepperton Court Drive, Laleham Road, Shepperton TW17 8EJ Tel: 01932 245289 — MB BS 1952 Lond. (Lond. Hosp.) Prev: Ho. Surg. Poplar Hosp.; Res. Anaesth. Lond. Hosp.; Sen. Ho. Phys. Nottm. Childr. Hosp.

WATSON, George Dickson 1 Corbelly Hill, Dumfries DG2 7SQ — MB ChB 1973 Glas.; FRCR 1981; DMRD Eng. 1978.

WATSON, Mr George Stanley (retired) 5 Nevile Park, Tunbridge Wells TN4 8NW — MB ChB 1944 Ed.; FRCS Ed. 1953.

WATSON, Georgina Mary 18 Ravelston Dykes, Edinburgh EH4 3ED Tel: 0131 332 2798 — MB ChB 1975 Glas.; DRCOG 1977; Cert. Family Plann. JCC 1977. Prev: GP Glas & Bristol.

WATSON, Gerald Howard Vincent Strabane Health Centre, Upper Main Street, Strabane BT82 8AS Tel: 028 7138 4118; 8 Coach Road, Baronscourt, Newtownstewart, Omagh BT78 4BF Tel: 016626 61980 — MB BCh BAO 1976 Dub.; MRCGP 1983; DRCOG 1978. (T.C. Dub.) Socs: Assoc. Mem. BMA.

WATSON, Mr Gerald Stewart 8 Cunning Park Drive, Doonfoot, Ayr KA7 4DT Tel: 01292 441989 — MB ChB 1966 Ed.; FRCS Ed. 1970. (Ed.) Cons. Urol. Ayr Hosp. Prev: Sen. Regist. (Urol.) Roy. Infirm. Edin.; Regist. Rotat. (Surg.) S. Lothian Health Dist.; Regist. (Surg.) Vict. Hosp. Kirkcaldy.

WATSON, Gillian Carol 73 Morven Road, Bearsden, Glasgow G61 3BY Tel: 0141 942 6724 — MB ChB 1997 Glas. (Glasgow Univ.) SHO (A&E), Blackburn Roy. Infirm. Prev: SHO (Paediat.), CrossHo. Hosp.; Jun. Ho. Off. (Surg.), Hairmyre Hosp.; Jun. Ho. Off. (Med.), Ayr Hosp.

WATSON, Gillian Marie Therese 8 Barnsbury Terrace, London N1 1JH — MB BS 1992 Lond.

WATSON

WATSON, Graham Charles Maryfield Medical Centre, 9 Morgan Street, Dundee DD4 6QE Tel: 01382 462292 Fax: 01382 461052; 320 Blackness Road, Dundee DD2 1SD — MB ChB 1981 Dundee. Socs: Roy. Coll. Gen. Pract.

WATSON, Graham David Almsford House Surgery, 1 Almsford House, Beckfield Lane, Acomb, York YO26 5PA Tel: 01904 799000 Fax: 01904 789407; 73 Foxwood Lane, Alcomb, York YO24 3LQ Tel: 01904 781616 Fax: 01904 789723 — MB ChB 1969 Leeds; DObst RCOG 1971.

WATSON, Mr Graham Michael Eastbourne District General Hospital, King's Drive, Hill, Eastbourne BN21 2UD Tel: 01323 417400 Fax: 01323 414954; Wannock Place, Jevington Road, Wannock, Polegate BN26 5NT Tel: 01323 487786 — MB BChir 1976 Camb.; MD Camb. 1989; FRCS (Urol.) 1988; FRCS Eng. 1979. Cons. (Urol.) E.bourne Dist. Gen. Hosp. Prev: Sen. Regist. St. Peter's Hosp. Lond.; Sen. Lect. St. Peter's Hosp. Lond.; Cons. (Urol.) Whittington Hosp. Lond.

WATSON, Mr Harold Bernard (retired) 7 Riverside Drive, Solihull B91 3HH — MB ChB 1940 Birm.; FRCS Glas. 1950; MRCS Eng. LRCP Lond. 1940; FRCOG 1966, M 1952, DObst 1941. Hon. Sen. Clin. Lect. Univ. Birm.; Lect. & Examr. Centr. Midw. Bd. Prev: Regist. (O & G) United Birm. Hosps.

WATSON, Harold Kirk (retired) 30 Queensberry House, Friars Lane, Richmond TW9 1NU Tel: 020 8948 1190 — MB ChB 1948 Sheff. Prev: Med. Dir. Dome/Hollister-Stier.

WATSON, Mr Harold Preston (retired) 3 High Orchard, St. Clement's Road, St Helier, Jersey JE2 4PH — MB ChB 1938 St. And.; FRCS Ed. 1947. Prev: Surg. Colonial Hosp. Port of Spain Trinidad.

WATSON, Heather Kay 7 Humbie Road, Eaglesham, Glasgow G76 0LX — MB ChB 1998 Ed.

WATSON, Helen Deborah 106 Colne Road, Earby, Colne BB18 6XS — MB ChB 1987 Leeds.

WATSON, Helen Jennifer Lutterworth Road Medical Centre, 58 Lutterworth Road, Blaby, Leicester LE8 4DN Tel: 0116 247 7828 — MB ChB 1980 Leic. (Leicester) Prev: SHO (Obst.) Leeds Gen. Infirm.; SHO (Gen. Med./Chest Dis.) Groby Rd. Hosp. Leics.

WATSON, Helen Mairi Stewart Northumberland Health Authority, Morley Croft, Loansdean, Morpeth NE61 2DL Tel: 01670 394400 Fax: 01670 394501; 11 Park Drive, Deuchar Park, Morpeth NE61 2SY Tel: 01670 513583 — MB ChB 1974 Aberd.; MSc Dub. 1981; FFPHM 1994. Cons., Pub. Health Med., N.d. HA.

WATSON, Helen Mary 11 Brookfield, Mawdesley, Ormskirk L40 2QJ — BM BCh 1990 Oxf.; DRCOG 1994; DCH RCP Lond. 1993. Prev: Trainee GP N.umbria VTS; SHO (Gen. Med.) S. Cleveland Hosp. Middlesbrough; SHO (Paediat.) Roy. Vict. Infirm. Newc.

WATSON, Helen Rosemary Lower Farm, Mabberley, Pontesbury, Shrewsbury SY5 0TP — MB BChir 1982 Camb.; BSc (Hons.) St. And. 1978; FRCR 1989. Cons. Diag. Radiol. Roy. Shrewsbury Hosp. Prev: Sen. Regist. (Diag. Radiol.) Nottm. HA.

WATSON, Helen Susan 233 Bellenden Road, London SE15 4DQ — MB BS 1990 Lond.; MRCOG 1996. Specialist Regist. (O & G) Maidstone Hosp. Maidstone, Kent. Prev: Specialist Regist. (O & G) St Thos. & Guys Hosps.; Specialist Regist. (O & G) Pembury Hosp., Kent.

WATSON, Henry George Department of Haematology, Aberdeen Royal Infirmary, Aberdeen AB25 2ZN Tel: 01224 681818 Fax: 01224 840714 Email: henry.watson@arh.grampian.scot.nhs.uk — MB ChB 1983 Aberd.; MD 1997; FRCP Ed 1997; MRCP (UK) 1988; MRCPath 1994. (Univ. Aberd.) Cons. Haemat. Aberd. Roy. Infirm. Prev: Sen. Regist. (Haemat.) Roy. Infirm. Edin.; Lect. (Haemat.) Univ. Edin.; Regist. (Haemat.) W. Midl. HA.

WATSON, Howard (retired) 8 Woodthorpe Lane, Sandal, Wakefield WF2 6JH — MB ChB Leeds 1956; DObst RCOG 1958. Prev: Ho. Phys. (Obst.) & Ho. Surg. Halifax Gen. Hosp.

WATSON, Howard Peter National Britiania occupational division, Britannia house, Caerphilly CF83 3GG Email: howard_watson@natbrit.com; Linden House, 4 Woodland Close, St. Arvans, Chepstow NP16 6EF — MB ChB 1980 Leeds; MRCGP 1988; AFOM RCP Lond. 1993. (Leeds) Occupat. Phys. and Med. director, Nat. Britannia Occupat. Health Div. Prev: Med. Off. Brit. Steel plc Llanwern Works; Med. Off. Brit. Rail; Occupat.al Phys. BUPA Occupat.al health.

WATSON, Hugh Philipson 2 Burghley Road, Wimbledon, London SW19 5BH Tel: 020 8946 1245 — MB BS 1953 Lond.; MRCS Eng. LRCP Lond. 1953; MRCGP 1961. (St. Mary's) Socs: Fell. Roy. Soc. Med. Prev: Regional Med. Off. Ranks Hovis McDougall Ltd.; Clin. Asst. Wilson Hosp. Mitcham; Ho. Surg. (ENT) St. Mary's Hosp. Lond.

WATSON, Hugh Stewart Kelso (retired) 45 Grange Road, Cheddleton, Leek ST13 7NP Tel: 01538 360210 — MB ChB 1951 Ed. Prev: GP Leek.

WATSON, Iain Hart The Gardeners Cottage, Grenofen Manor, Grenofen, Tavistock PL19 9ES Tel: 01822 616186 — MB ChB 1948 Ed.; MRCGP 1956; DObst RCOG 1954. (Ed.)

WATSON, Ian Alastair Ross, Col. late RAMC Retd. (retired) 16 Mill Rise, Mill Lane, Bourton, Gillingham SP8 5DH Tel: 01747 841387 Email: alastair.watson@btinternet.com — MB BS 1952 Durh.; MRCGP 1976; DTM & H Eng. 1969. Prev: Ho. Phys. (Orthop.) & Ho. Surg. (ENT) Roy. Vict. Infirm. Newc.

WATSON, Ian Douglas 63-83 Hylton Road, Sunderland SR4 7AF Tel: 0191 567 9179 Fax: 0191 514 7452 — MB ChB Dundee 1979; MRCGP 1983; DRCOG 1981. GP; Bd. Mem. Sunderland S. PCG.

WATSON, Ian Norman O'Colmain and Partners, Fearnhead Cross Medical Centre, 25 Fearnhead Cross, Fearnhead, Warrington WA2 0HD Tel: 01925 847000 Fax: 01925 818650; Longford Street Surgery, Longford St, Warrington WA2 7QZ — MB ChB 1982 Liverp.

WATSON, Ian Peter Michael Saddleworth Medical Practice, The Clinic, Smithy Lane, Uppermill, Oldham OL3 6AH Tel: 01457 872228 Fax: 01457 876520 — MB ChB 1992 Leic.; MRCGP 1997.

WATSON, Isabel Frances Well Close Square Surgery, Well Close Square, Berwick-upon-Tweed TD15 1LL Tel: 01289 356920 Fax: 01289 356939 — MB BS 1976 Newc.; MRCGP 1980. GP Berwick upon Tweed. Prev: GP Asst. Durh. Univ. Health Centre; Clin. Med. Off. Sch. Health Serv. Morpeth.

WATSON, Ivan Robert George 17 Edenvale Park, Omagh BT78 5EB — MB BCh BAO 1992 Belf.

WATSON, James Bernard 86 Wateringpool Lane, Lostock Hall, Preston PR5 5UA — MB BS 1993 Lond.

WATSON, James David Intensive Care Department, Homerton Hospital NHS Trust, Homerton Row, London E9 6SR Tel: 020 8510 7303 Fax: 020 8510 7668 Email: watson@dwatson.demon.co.uk; 80 Inverine Road, Charlton, London SE7 7NL — MB BS 1977 Lond.; BSc Lond. 1974, MB BS 1977; FRCA 1982. (St. Bart.) Cons. & Sen. Lect. (Anaesth. & Intens. Care Med.)Barts and The Lond. NHS Trust Lond. Prev: Sen. Regist. (Anaesth.) Soton. & Poole Gen. Hosps.; Research Regist. (Anaesth. & ITU) St. Bart. Hosp. Lond.; Regist. (Anaesth.) Nat. Heart Hosp.

WATSON, Mr James Davidson Department of Plastic Surgery, St John Hospital, Livingston EH54 6PP Tel: 01506 419666 Fax: 01506 460592; 18 Ravelston Dykes, Edinburgh EH4 3ED Tel: 0131 332 2798 — MB ChB 1975 Glas.; MB ChB (Commend.) Glas. 1975; FRCS Ed. 1990; FRCS Glas. (Plast) 1987; FRCS Glas. 1979. (Glasgow University) Cons. Plastic Surg. St. John's Hosp. W. Lothian NHS Trust; Hon. Cons. in Burns & Plastic Surg. Brit. Army; Hon. Sen. Lect. in Surg., The Univ. of Edin. Prev: Sen. Regist. (Plastic Surg.) Frenchay Hosp. Bristol; Regist. (Plastic Surg.) Canniesburn Hosp. Glas.; Regist. (Surg.) W. Scotl. Surgic. Train. Scheme.

WATSON, James Derek (retired) 14D Adelaide Park, Belfast BT9 6FX Tel: 02890 682152 — MB BCh BAO 1942 Belf. Prev: Sen. Med. Off. DHSS.

WATSON, James Ingram The Taymount Surgery, 1 Taymount Terrace, Perth PH1 1NU Tel: 01738 627117 Fax: 01738 444713; 4 Hatton Mews, Perth PH2 7DR Tel: 01738 625069 — MB ChB 1963 Glas.; DObst RCOG 1965. (Glas) Med Adviser Highland distillers Perth.

WATSON, Professor James Patrick Division of Psychiatry, Guy's King College & St Thomas' School of Medicine, London SE1 9RT Tel: 020 7955 4247 Fax: 020 7955 2976; 36 Alleyn Road, Dulwich, London SE21 8AL Tel: 020 8670 0444 Fax: 020 8670 0562 — MB BChir Camb. 1960; MD Camb. 1974; FRCP Lond. 1978, M 1964; FRCPsych 1977, M 1971; Acad. DPM Univ. Lond. 1967; DCH Eng. 1963. (King's Coll. Hosp.) Emerit. Prof. of Psychiat. GKT, King's Coll. Lond. Prev: Sen. Lect. & Cons. Psychiat. St. Geo. Hosp. Med. Sch. Lond.; Sen. Regist. Bethlem Roy. & Maudsley Hosps. Lond.

WATSON

WATSON, James Victor Little Hilden, London Road, Tonbridge TN10 3DD — MB BS 1964 Lond.; DMRT Eng. 1969.

WATSON, Jane Christine East Street Surgery, 6-7 East Street, Ware SG12 9HJ Tel: 01920 468777 Fax: 01920 484892; 2 Musleigh Manor, Widbury Gardens, Ware SG12 7AT Tel: 01920 469637 — MB BS Lond. 1983; DRCOG 1987; Cert. Family Plann. JCC 1987. Prev: Trainee GP Luton & Dunstable VTS; Ho. Phys. Luton & Dunstable Hosp.; Ho. Surg. Roy. Free Hosp.

WATSON, Jennifer Margaret Beaumaris, Church Avenue, Cardross, Dumbarton G82 5NS Tel: 01389 841387 — MB BS 1971 Lond.; MFFP 1993. (St. Mary's Hosp. Lond.) Clin. Asst. (Colposcopy) W.. Infirm. Glas. & Vale of Leven Alexandria; Instruc. Doctor Glas. Family Plann. Assn. Prev: SHO (Obst. & Anaesth.) & Ho. Phys. St. Mary's Hosp. Lond.

WATSON, Jennifer May Lennox and Partners, 9 Alloway Place, Ayr KA7 2AA Tel: 01292 611835 Fax: 01292 284982; 8 Cunning Park Drive, Doonfoot, Ayr KA7 4DT Tel: 01292 441989 — MB ChB Ed. 1966; Cert. Prescribed Equiv. Exp. JCPTGP 1981; Cert. FPA 1971. (Ed.) Prev: Trainee GP Ayr VTS; Regist. SE Scotl. Blood Transfus. Serv.; Ho. Off. (O & G) W.. Gen. Hosp. Edin.

WATSON, Jeremy Neil Bewley Cottage, Ismays Road, Ightham, Sevenoaks TN15 9BE — MB BS 1985 Lond.; MRCGP 1990; DRCOG 1990.

WATSON, Joanna (Dennis) The Surgery, Mount Avenue, Shenfield, Brentwood CM13 2NL Tel: 01277 224612 Fax: 01277 201218; 14 Surman Crescent, Hutton, Brentwood CM13 2PP — MB BS 1981 Lond.; DRCOG 1984.

***WATSON, Joanne** 24 Spring Close, Lutterworth LE17 4DD — MB ChB 1998 Birm.

WATSON, Joanne Marie Royal Bournemouth Hospital, Castle Lane E., Bournemouth BH7 7DW; 87 Elliot Rise, Hedge End, Southampton SO30 2RW — MB BS 1991 Lond.; BSc Lond. 1988; MRCP (UK) 1994. (UMDS (St. Thomas.)) Specialist Regist. Prev: Regist. Rotat. (Med.) Wessex; SHO Rotat. (Med.) Soton. Univ. Hosps.

WATSON, John (retired) Rhone Hill, Dungannon — MB BCh BAO 1941 Belf.; FRCOG 1963, M 1949. Prev: Cons. Obstetr. & Gynaecol. S. Tyrone Hosp. Dungannon.

WATSON, Mr John (retired) Iddons, Henleys Down, Catsfield, Battle TN33 9BN Tel: 01424 830226 Email: john.watson@iddons.demon.co.uk — MB BChir 1939 Camb.; MA Camb. 1939; FRCS Ed. 1947; FRCS Eng. (ad eund.) 1963; MRCS Eng. LRCP Lond. 1938. Hon. Cons. Plastic Surg. Qu. Vict. Hosp. E. Grinstead. Prev: Cons. Plastic Surg. Roy. Lond. Hosp. & King Edwd. VII Hosp. for Offs.

WATSON, John Essex House, Station Road, Barnes, London SW13 0LW Tel: 020 8876 9882 Fax: 020 8876 1033 — MB BS 1966 Lond.; FRACGP 1974; DRCOG 1977. Med. Contributor Telemed Surrey; Co. Doctor ICL Windsor. Socs: BMA; Assoc. Mem. Roy. Soc. Med. Prev: Clin. Asst. (Obst.) Kingston Hosp.; SHO (O & G) Enfield Hosp.; Ho. Surg. & Ho. Phys. Hillingdon Hosp.

WATSON, Mr John Arthur Standish Pilgrim Hospital, Sibsey Road, Boston PE21 9QS; Tytton Hall, Wyberton, Boston PE21 7HT Tel: 01205 310305 — MB BS 1980 Lond.; FRCS Ed. 1986. Cons. Orthop. Surg. Pilgrim Hosp. Boston.

WATSON, Professor John David Northern H & SS Board, County Hall, Galgorm Road, Ballymena BT42 1QB Tel: 01266 662208 — LM 1972 Rotunda; BA Dub. 1969, MB BCh BAO 1971; MFCM 1977; DObst RCOG 1973; FFPHM 1990; FFCM 1986; Dip. Soc Med. Ed. 1974; FRCP 1999. Dir. of Pub. Health NHSSB Ballymena.; Vis. Prof.Pub.Health Univ.Ulster. Prev: Asst. Chief Admin. Med. Off. EHSSB Belf.; Clin. Clerk Rotunda Hosp. Dub.; Ho. Off. Roy. Matern. Hosp. Belf.

WATSON, John Ernest Keogh and Keenleside, Beech House Surgery, 1 Ash Tree Road, Knaresborough HG5 0UB Tel: 01423 542564 — MB BCh BAO 1945 Belf. (Belf.) Treasury Med. Off.

WATSON, John Martin PHLS Communicable Disease Surveillance Centre, 61 Colindale Avenue, London NW9 5EQ Tel: 020 8200 6868 Fax: 020 8200 7868 Email: jwatson@phls.org.uk — MB BS 1979 Lond.; MSc Lond. 1984; FRCP Lond. 1995; MRCP (UK) 1982; FFPHM RCP (UK) 1995; MFPHM RCP (UK) 1989. (Med. Coll. St. Bart. Hosp. Lond.) Cons. Clin. Epidemiol. & Head Respirat. Div. I. Div. PHLS Communicable Dis. Surveillance Centre Lond.; Hon. Sen. Lect. (Infec. & Trop. Dis.) Lond. Sch. Hyg. & Trop. Med. Socs: Jt.

Tuberc. Comm. Brit. Thoracic Soc.; Internat. Union Against Tuberc. & Lung Dis.; Europ. Sci. Working Gp Influenza. Prev: Hon. Sen. Lect. Nat. Heart & Lung Inst. Roy. Brompton & Nat. Heart Hosp. Lond.

WATSON, John Maxwell Wellclose Square, Berwick-upon-Tweed TD15 1LL Tel: 01289 306634; Windyridge, Scremerston, Berwick-upon-Tweed TD15 2RJ Tel: 01289 305201 — MB ChB 1977 Aberd.; MRCP Ed. 1984.

WATSON, John Palmer (retired) Mpprend, Farnhill, Keighley — MB ChB 1938 Leeds; DObst RCOG 1940; MRCGP 1969. Prev: Ho. Surg. Hosp. Wom. Leeds & Leeds Matern. Hosp.

WATSON, John Paul Leeds General Infirmary, Great George St., Leeds LS1 3EX Tel: 0113 243 2799 Fax: 0113 392 6316 — MB 1984 Camb.; BA Camb. 1981, MB 1984, BChir 1983; MRCP (UK) 1987; DTM & H RCP Lond. 1989. (Camb.) Cons. Phys.; Hon. Sen. Lect. Univ. of Leeds; Respirat. Med., Leeds Teachg. Hosp. NHS Trust Leeds. Socs: Christ. Med. Fell.sh.; Brit. Thorac. Soc.; Europ. Respirat. Soc. Prev: Sen. Regist. Leeds Gen. Infirm./Killingbeck Hosp.; Research Fell. Worcester Roy. Infirm.; Phys. Tansen Hosp. United Mission Nepal.

WATSON, John Smyly (retired) 28 Thornton Hill, Wimbledon, London SW19 4HS Tel: 020 8946 5276 — MRCS Eng. LRCP Lond. 1943; MD Lond. 1950, MB BS 1943; MRCP Lond. 1949. Prev: Cons. Phys. (Geriat.) St. Geo. & Bolingbroke Hosps. Lond.

WATSON, Mr John Trevor (retired) 60 The Paddock, Busby, Glasgow G76 8SL — MB ChB Glas. 1961; FRCS Ed. 1966. Cons. Orthop. Surg. Hairmyres Hosp. E. Kilbride. Prev: Resid. in Path. Boston City Hosp., U.S.A.

WATSON, John Ulric The Surgery, Fairfield Medical Centre, Lower Road, Great Bookham, Leatherhead KT23 4DP Tel: 01372 452755; The Flint House, 36 Middle Farm Place, Effingham, Leatherhead KT24 5LA Tel: 01372 454787 — MB BS 1962 Lond.; DA Eng. 1966; DObst RCOG 1964. (St. Bart.) Vice-Chairm. Surrey FHSA; Chairm. Surrey LMC. Socs: BMA; BMAS. Prev: SHO (O & G) Redhill Gen. Hosp.; Ho. Surg. & Ho. Phys. Whipps Cross Hosp.; Ho. Surg. (O & G) St. Bart. Hosp.

WATSON, Jonathan Mark Grosvenor Medical Centre, Grosvenor Street, Crewe CW1 3HB Tel: 01270 256348 Fax: 01270 250786; 118 Waterloo Road, Haslington, Crewe CW1 5TA Tel: 01270 581269 — MB ChB 1984 Ed.; MRCGP 1989.

WATSON, Jonathan Peter 4 Fairville Close, Cramlington NE23 3GJ — BM BCh 1989 Oxf.; MA Camb. 1990, BA 1986; MRCP (UK) 1992. Regist. (Gastroenterol.) N. Shields. Prev: Traine Fell. Med. Research Counc.

WATSON, Joyce Macdonald (retired) 16 Montague Street, Broughty Ferry, Dundee DD5 2RD — MB ChB 1960 St. And.; FRCP Ed. 1981, M 1966; DObst RCOG 1964. Prev: Cons. Phys. (Geriat. & Gen. Med.) Durh. Gp. Hosps.

WATSON, Joyce Manners Hilltop, 2 Manor Road, Hartlepool TS26 0EH Tel: 01429 272717 — MB BS 1950 Durh.; DObst RCOG 1952. (Newc.) Prev: Ho. Phys. Middlesbrough Gen. Hosp.; Ho. Surg. (Obst.) Sorrento & Lordswood Matern. Hosps. Birm.; Ho. Surg. (Gyn.) Wom. Hosp. Birm.

WATSON, Joyce Margaret — MB ChB 1986 Glas.; DFFP 1999; T(GP) 1993; DRCOG 1992. (Glasgow) GP Non-Princip.

WATSON, Karen Alicia Robin Hood Surgery, 1493 Stratford Rd, Hall Green, Birmingham B28 9HT — MB ChB 1989 Liverp.; DA (UK) 1995; DFFP 1995. GP Birm. Prev: GP/Regist. Chessington; SHO (O & G) Epsom Hosp. Surrey; SHO (Paediat. & Anaesth.) Kingston Hosp.

WATSON, Keith John K12 Medical Centre, HMS Nelson, Queen St., Portsmouth PO1 3HH — MB ChB 1982 Birm.; BSc Birm. 1979, MB ChB 1982. Civil. Med. Pract. Med. Centre HMS Nelson Portsmouth.

WATSON, Kenneth Charles 15 Succoth Place, Edinburgh EH12 6BJ — MD 1955 Aberd.; MB ChB 1947; FRCP Ed. 1981, M 1972; FCPath 1968, M 1964. (Aberd.) Cons. Microbiol. W.. Gen. Hosp. Edin. Prev: Prof. Microbiol. Univ. Natal, S. Afr.; Asst. Dept. Bact. Univ. Aberd.

WATSON, Kenneth Melvyn The Manor House, Twigworth, Gloucester GL2 9PW; (Surgery), 16 Cheltenham Road, Gloucester GL2 0LS Tel: 01452 35959 — MB BS 1966 Lond.; MRCS Eng. LRCP Lond. 1967; DObst RCOG 1968. (King's Coll. Hosp.) Prev: SHO King's Coll. Hosp. Lond.; Med. Off. Nkana Hosp. Kitwe, Zambia; Med. Off. Aberd. Hosp. New Glas., Nova Scotia, Canada.

WATSON, Kevin John Cohen and Partners, West Lodge Surgery, New Street, Farsley, Pudsey LS28 5DL Tel: 0113 257 0295 Fax: 0113 236 2509; The Barn, Holt Lane, Adel, Leeds LS16 7NN Tel: 0113 267 5733 — MB ChB 1969 Leeds; DA Eng. 1974; DObst RCOG 1973.

WATSON, Laura Jane Radiology Department, West Suffolk Hospital, Hardwick Lane, Bury St Edmunds IP33 2QZ Tel: 01284 713376 — BM BCh 1981 Oxf.; MA Oxf. 1982; FRCR 1987. (Oxford) p/t Cons. Radiol. W. Suff. Hosps. NHS Trust. Socs: Brit. Inst. Radiol.; Brit. Med. Ultrasound Soc. Prev: Sen. Regist. (Diag. Radiol.) & Frenchay Hosp. Bristol & John Radcliffe Hosp. Oxf.

WATSON, Lawrence Joseph Castlegate Surgery, Castle Street, Hertford SG14 1HH Tel: 01992 589928; 6 Park Road, Hertford SG13 7LF — MB BS Lond. 1973; DObst RCOG 1976.

WATSON, Leila Margaret (retired) 2 House o' Hill Brae, Edinburgh EH4 5DQ Tel: 0131 336 3750 — MB ChB Ed. 1947; MFCM 1972; DPH Ed. 1957. Prev: Community Med. Specialist Health Educat. Div. Common Servs. Agency.

WATSON, Lesley Jean 1 Jesmond Court, Newton Aycliffe DL5 7HU — MB ChB 1992 Leeds.

WATSON, Lilla (retired) 4 Edgerton Road, Leeds LS16 5JD — MB BS 1957 Durh. Ref. Regional Med. Serv. Prev: GP Leeds.

WATSON, Linda Ann 127 York Road, (Chadwick House), Hartlepool TS26 9ND Tel: 01429 234646; 5 The Green, Elwick Village, Hartlepool TS27 3ED — MB BS 1987 Lond.

WATSON, Louise 43 Westlands Avenue, Slough SL1 6AH — MB BCh 1991 Wales.

WATSON, Lyal Clifton Albert (retired) 18 Hadley Heights, Hadley Road, Barnet EN5 5QH Tel: 020 8447 1825 — MB BS Sydney 1950; FRCP Lond. 1975, M 1969; FRACP 1965, M 1953. Prev: Cons. & Hon. Cons. Phys. Univ. Coll. Hosp. Lond.

WATSON, Malcolm John Wester Ballochearn Farm, Balfron, Glasgow G63 0QE Tel: 0141 860357 — MB ChB 1995 Glas. (Glasgow) SHO A&E Roy.Alex.Hosp. Paisley. Socs: Full Mem. MRCP Glas. Coll. Prev: SHO (Med.) S.ern Gen. Hosp. Glas.; SHO (A & E) Glas. Roy. Infirm. & W.ern Infirm. Glas.

WATSON, Mando 1 Hillgate Place, London W8 7SL — MB BChir 1987 Camb.; MA Camb. 1987; MRCP (UK) 1992. Cons. Paediat., St Marys Hosp., Lond. Prev: Locum paediatric Cons., W. Middlx. Univ. Hosp.; Sen. Regist. (Paediat.) Chelsea & W.m. Hosp. Lond.; Regist. (Paediat.) St. Geo. Hosp. Lond.

WATSON, Mr Mark Alexander Norfolk and Norwich Health Care Trust, Brunswick Road, Norwich NR1 3SR Email: mark@norwichflexi.demon.co.uk; 13 Chapel Lane, Thorpe St. Andrew, Norwich NR7 0EX Tel: 01603 702452 — MB BS 1991 Lond.; BSc (Hons) Lond. 1988; FRCS Eng. 1995. (St. Thomas's Hospital)

WATSON, Mark Benjamin St Thomas Health Centre, Cowick Street, St. Thomas, Exeter EX4 1HJ Tel: 01392 676677 Fax: 01392 676677 — MB ChB 1989 Bristol; MRCGP 1994; DRCOG 1994. Prev: Trainee GP Exeter VTS.

WATSON, Mark Edward James Cassio Surgery, 62-68 Merton Road, Watford WD18 0WL Tel: 01923 226011 Fax: 01923 817342 — MB BS 1982 Lond.; DRCOG 1985. (Char. Cross) Med. Mem. Herts. FHSA. Socs: Fell. Roy. Soc. Med.; W Herts. & Watford Med. Soc. Prev: SHO (O & G) Char. Cross & W. Lond. Hosp.; SHO (A & E & Orthop.) Watford Gen. Hosp.; Ho. Surg. Char. Cross Hosp. Lond.

WATSON, Mr Mark Gordon Donacaster Royal Infirmary, Armthorpe Road, Doncaster DN2 5LT Tel: 01302 366666; South View, Dame Lane, Misson, Doncaster DN10 6EB Tel: 01302 719179 Email: mark.watson@which.net — MB ChB Birm. 1981; FRCS (Orl.) Eng. 1986; T(S) 1991. Cons. ENT Surg. Doncaster Roy. Infirm. & Montagu Hosp. MexBoro., Bassetlaw Dist. Gen. Hosp.; Clin. Dir. (Special Surg.) Doncaster Roy. Infirm. Socs: Otolaryngol. Research Soc. & Brit. Voice Assn. Prev: Sen. Regist. (Otolaryngol.) Freeman Hosp. Newc. & Sunderland Gen. Hosp.; Regist. (Otolaryngol.) Birm. HAs; Cas. Off. & SHO (Otolaryngol.) Dudley Rd. Hosp. Birm.

WATSON, Mark Robert Llwynbedw Medical Centre, 82/86 Caerphilly Road, Birchgrove, Cardiff CF14 4AG Tel: 029 2052 1222 Fax: 029 2052 2873 — MB BCh 1983 Wales.

WATSON, Martha Huie (retired) 24 Hills Road, Strathaven ML10 6LQ Tel: 01357 521054 — MB ChB 1944 Glas. Prev: Cons. Phys. (Geriat.) Lanarksh. HB.

WATSON, Martin William 7 Humbie Road, Eaglesham, Glasgow G76 0LX — MB ChB 1995 Glas.

WATSON, Mary (retired) 21 Tretawn Gardens, London NW7 4NP — MB ChB 1933 Ed. Prev: Princip. Med. Off. Lond. Boro. Barnet. Ho. Surg. Vict. Infirm. Glas.

WATSON, Mary, SJM (retired) 9 Penn Lea Road, Bath BA1 3RF Tel: 01225 421754 — MB ChB 1935 New Zealand; FFA RCS Eng. 1954; DA Eng. 1947. Prev: Cons. Anaesth. Roy. United & St. Martin's Hosps. Bath & Bath & Wessex Orthop Hosp.

WATSON, Mary Aitken 57 Gartmore Road, Paisley PA1 3NG Tel: 0141 889 5880 — MB ChB 1967 Glas.; FRCP Glas. 1988; MRCP (UK) 1971; DObst RCOG 1969. (Glas.) Assoc. Specialist Renal Unit W.. Infirm. Glas.

WATSON, Mary Eileen Campbell Trumpington Street Medical Practice, 56 Trumpington Street, Cambridge CB2 1RG Tel: 01223 361611 Fax: 01223 356837; 40 Plumian Way, Balsham, Cambridge CB1 6EG Tel: 01223 290905 — MB BChir 1988 Camb.; MB BChir Camb. 1989; MA Camb. 1989, BA Med. Sci 1985; MRCGP 1995; DRCOG 1992; DCH RCP Lond. 1991. (Camb.) Prev: GP Rawdon, Leeds.

WATSON, Maureen Rachel Homefirst Community Health & Social Services Trust, Holywell Hospital, 60 Steeple Road, Antrim BT41 2RJ Tel: 02894 413191 Fax: 02894 413190 — MB BCh BAO 1976 Belf.; MA Belf. 1997; MRCPsych 1981; FRCPsych. Cons. Psychiat. Holywell Hosp. Antrim; Head of Ment. Health Serv.s.

WATSON, Maxwell Sheldrake 79 Northland Village, Dungannon BT71 6JN; 79 Northland Village, Dungannon BT71 6JN Tel: 0186 87 23501 — MB ChB 1985 Ed.; MRCGP 1989; DCH RCSI 1988; DRCOG 1988. GP Dungannon. Socs: RCGP; BMA.

WATSON, Melville Stuart Queens Road Medical Group, 6 Queens Road, Aberdeen Tel: 01224 681818 Fax: 01224 662994 Email: m.s.watson@abdn.ac.uk — MB ChB 1988 Aberd.; MSc Aberd. 1995; MRCGP 1992; T(GP) 1992. (Aberd.) Gen. Practitioner.

WATSON, Michael (retired) Cherry Orchard, 50 Buxton Road, Weymouth DT4 9PN Tel: 01305 773885 — MB BS Lond. 1961; MRCS Eng. LRCP Lond. 1961; MRCGP 1974; DObst RCOG 1963.

WATSON, Michael County Practice, Barking Road, Needham Market, Ipswich IP6 8EZ Tel: 01449 720666 Fax: 01449 720030 — MB BS 1971 Newc.; DObst RCOG 1973. Prev: SHO (Paediat.) Univ. Hosp. W. Indies, Jamaica; SHO (Obst.) St. Mary's Hosp. Kettering.

WATSON, Michael David (retired) Estoril, 9 The Old Bath Road, Sonning, Reading RG4 6SZ Tel: 01189 693764 — MB BS Lond. 1962; DTM & H Liverp. 1997. GP Reading. Prev: Med. Off. Jamaica.

WATSON, Mr Michael Ellis Department of Urology, Royal Preston Hospital, Sharoe Green Lane, Fulwood, Preston PR2 9HT Tel: 01772 710483 Fax: 01772 710946 — PhD Glas. 1975, MB ChB 1968; FRCS Glas. 1975. (Glasgow University) Cons. (Urol.) Roy. Preston Hosp. Socs: Brit. Assn. Urologic. Surgs.; BMA. Prev: Sen. Regist. (Urol.) Roy. Hallamshire Hosp. Sheff.; Regist. (Urol.) Roy. Infirm. Glas.; Regist. (Surg.) Roy. Infirm. Glas.

WATSON, Michael James (retired) Lawrence Hill Health Centre, Hassell Drive, Bristol BS2 0AN Tel: 0117 955 5241 Fax: 0117 941 1162 — MB ChB 1956 Bristol; MRCS Eng. LRCP Lond. 1956. Prev: SHO (Gen. Surg.) Frenchay Hosp. Bristol.

WATSON, Michael Leonard Royal Infirmary, Edinburgh EH3 9YJ — MD 1986 Ed.; BSc (Hons.) Ed. 1970, MD 1986, MB ChB 1973; FRCP Ed. 1986. (Edinburgh) Cons. Phys. Roy. Infirm. Edin.; Chief Med. Off. Scott. Provident Insur. co.; Chief Med. Off. N.ern lightHo. Bd. Socs: Dean Roy. Coll. Phys. Edin.

WATSON, Mr Michael Selby Suite 306, Emblem House, London Bridge Hospital, Tooley St., London SE1 2PN Tel: 020 7403 5858 Fax: 020 7357 8192 — MB BChir 1967 Camb.; MB BChir (Distinc.) Camb. 1967; MA Camb. 1967; FRCS Eng. 1971; MRCP (UK) 1970; MRCS Eng. LRCP Lond. 1966. (Westm.) Cons. Orthop. Surg. Guy's Hosp. Lond. Socs: Fell. BOA; (Ex-Pres.) Europ. Soc. Surg. of Shoulder & Elbow; Corresp. Mem. Amer. Soc. of Shoulder & Elbow Surg. Prev: Lect. Inst. Orthop. Lond.; Regist. W.m. Hosp. Lond.

WATSON, Michael William Pasteur Mérieux MSD Ltd., Mallards Reach, Bridge Avenue, Maidenhead SL6 1QP Tel: 01628 587632 Fax: 01628 671722 Email: miwatson@pmmsd.com; 123 Stormont Road, London SW11 5EJ Tel: 020 7223 5958 — MB ChB 1988 Birm.; MRCP (UK) 1992; Dip. Pharm. Med. RCP (UK) 1995. (Birm.) Med. Dir. Pasteur Mérieux MSD Ltd. UK. Socs: Brit. Assn.

WATSON

Pharmaceut. Phys.; Roy. Soc. Med. Prev: Clin. Project Scientist Takeda Euro R & D Centre GmbH; Med. Adviser Bristol-Meyers Squibb Pharmaceut. Ltd.; Regist. Rotat. (Gastroenterol.) Barking Hosp.

WATSON, Michael William St Isan Road Surgery, 46 St. Isan Road, Heath, Cardiff CF14 4UR Tel: 029 2062 7518 Fax: 029 2052 2886; 12 Mill Close, Lisvane, Cardiff CF14 0XQ Tel: 029 2076 3354 Fax: 029 2076 4777 — MB ChB 1964 Bristol; DCCH RCP Ed. RCGP & FCM 1983; DMJ (Clin.) Soc. Apoth. Lond. 1971. (Bristol) Socs: Cardiff Med. Soc. Prev: Clin. Asst. (Psychiat.) Bristol Roy. Infirm.; Ho. Surg. Bristol Roy. Infirm.; Ho. Phys. Bristol Roy. Hosp. Sick Childr.

WATSON, Neale Ramsay The Hillingdon Hospital, Pield Heath Road, Uxbridge UB8 3NN Tel: 01865 279445 Fax: 01865 279444 Email: nrwatson@denham.demon.co.uk; Antiquities, Village Road, Denham Village, Uxbridge UB9 5BE Tel: 01865 834635 — MB BS 1983 Lond.; MRCOG 1992. (Roy. Free Hosp.) Cons. O & G Hillingdon Hosp. Uxbridge. Socs: Fell. Roy. Soc. Med. (Obst. & Gyn. Sect.). Prev: Regist. (O & G) King's Coll. Hosp. Lond.; Lect. (O & G) John Radcliffe Hosp. Oxf.

WATSON, Nicholas Alan Eastbourne District General Hospital, Eastbourne BN21 2UD Tel: 01323 417400; 15 The Grove, Patton, Eastbourne BN20 9DA — MB BS 1984 Lond.; FRCA Eng. 1988. Cons. Anaesth. E.bourne Dist. Gen. Hosp. Socs: Assn. Anaesth.; Intens. Care Soc. Prev: Sen. Regist. (Anaesth.) St. Mary's Hosp. Lond.; Regist. (Anaesth.) St. Mary's Hosp. Lond.; SHO (Anaesth.) E.bourne Dist. Gen. Hosp.

WATSON, Nicholas Andrew 30A Wimpole St, London W1G 8YA Tel: 07000 781687; Melmore, 10 Golf Road, Stanton-on-the-Wolds, Keyworth, Nottingham NG12 5BH Tel: 0160 773603 — BM BS Nottm. 1975; MRCGP 1979; Cert. JCC Lond. 1980; DCH Eng. 1979. Pres. Soc. Orthop. Med. Socs: Fell. (Pres.) Soc. Orthop. Med.; Brit. Inst. Orthop. Med. & Roy. Soc. Med. Prev: Treas. Inst. Orthop. Med.; Chairm. Soc. Orthop. Med.

WATSON, Nicholas Timothy Bryce 8 Corberry Avenue, Dumfries DG2 7QQ Email: brycewatson@compuserve — MB ChB 1972 St. And.; FFA RCS Eng. 1977; DObst RCOG 1974. Cons. Anaesth. Dumfries & Galloway Health Bd.

WATSON, Mr Nicolas James James Paget Hospital, Lowestoft Road, Great Yarmouth NR31 6LA Tel: 01493 452452; Bracken Hill, Priory Road, St. Olaves, Great Yarmouth NR31 9HQ — BM 1984 Soton.; FRCS Eng. 1988; FRCOphth 1988. Cons. Ophth. Jas. Paget Hosp. Gt. Yarmouth. Prev: Sen. Regist. & Regist. (Ophth.) Aberd. Roy. Infirm.

WATSON, Nigel Frank Arnewood Practice, Milton Medical Centre, Avenue Road, New Milton BH25 5JP Tel: 01425 620393 Fax: 01425 624219; 8 Albert Road, New Milton BH25 6SP Tel: 01425 621130 Fax: 01425 621130 Email: nfwat@aol.com — MB BS 1982 Lond.; MRCGP 1987; Cert. Family Plann. JCC 1986; DRCOG 1986; DCH RCP Lond. 1985. (Westm.) GP Princip. New Milton; Chairm. LMC Soton. & SW Hants.; GPC Wessex Regional Represen.; Bd. Mem. PCG. Prev: Trainee GP Rugby VTS; SHO Roy. Nat. Orthop. Hosp. Lond.; SHO (A & E) Univ. Coll. Hosp. Lond.

WATSON, Norma 5 Craiglockhart Loan, Edinburgh EH14 1HU — MB ChB 1979 Ed.; MRCGP 1983.

WATSON, Norman Philip (retired) Sandford St Martin, Sandford St Martin, Chipping Norton OX7 7AG — MB ChB 1945 Liverp. Prev: Regist. (Med.) Roy. Infirm. Liverp.

WATSON, Norval 628 Fulwood Road, Sheffield S10 3QJ Tel: 0114 230 5102 — MB ChB Glas. 1946; DPH Glas. 1953. (Glas.) Emerit. Cons. Spinal Injuries Unit Lodge Moor Hosp. Sheff. Socs: Internat. Soc. Paraplegia. Prev: Dep. Phys. Supt. Lodge Moor Hosp. Sheff.; Regist. (Infec. Dis.) Ruchill Hosp. Glas.; Surg. Lt. RN.

WATSON, Patricia Mary School Clinic, Morley St., Brighton BN2 2RA Tel: 01273 693600; 4 Court Ord Road, Rottingdean, Brighton BN2 7FD — MB BS 1973 Newc.

WATSON, Paul Anthony Windrush Health Centre, Welch Way, Witney OX28 6JS Tel: 01993 702911 Fax: 01993 700931 — BM BCh 1983 Oxf.; MA Camb. 1984; MRCGP 1987; DCH RCP Lond. 1986; DRCOG 1985. (Oxford, Cambridge) GP Princip. Windrush Health Centre Witney. Prev: Trainee GP Windsor VTS.; Ho. Phys. Horton Gen. Hosp. Banbury; Ho. Surg. Profess. Unit John Radcliffe Hosp. Oxf.

WATSON, Paul Stephen Cambridge and Huntingdon Health Authority, Fulbourn Hospital, Fulbourn, Cambridge CB1 5EF Tel: 01223 475038; 40 Plumian Way, Balsham, Cambridge CB1 6EG Tel: 01223 290905 — MB BChir 1988 Camb.; MA Camb. 1989; MFPHM RCP (UK) 1992; MPH Leeds 1992; DCH RCP Lond. 1990. (Univ. Camb. Clin. Sch.) Dir. of Acute Servs. Camb. & Hunt. HA. Prev: Cons. Pub. Health Med. Wakefield HA.

WATSON, Penelope Ann Wester Hailes Health Centre, 7 Murrayburn Gate, Edinburgh EH14 2SS Tel: 0131 537 7300 Fax: 0131 537 7337; 37 Fernielaw Avenue, Edinburgh EH13 0EF Tel: 0131 441 5827 Fax: 0131 441 6253 Email: mckee@cableinet.co.uk — MB ChB 1972 Ed.; MFFP 1993; MRCGP 1984; DObst RCOG 1974; M.Sc (Public Helath), Edin., 1999. (Ed.) Community Med. Off. (Family Plann.) Lothian HB; GP Mem. of S.W. Edin., LHCC for Clinic Effectiveness. Socs: BMA; Scott. Family Plann. Med. Soc.; GP Writers Assn. Prev: SHO Simpson Memor. Matern. Pavil. Ed.; Ho. Off. Roy. Infirm. Ed.; GP Locality Coordinator S. W. Edin. at Lothian Health.

WATSON, Peter (retired) Apartment 16, Martello Place, Golf Road, Felixstowe IP11 7NB Tel: 01394 276919 — MB ChB 1955 Liverp. JP. Prev: Sen. Med. Off. DHSS Centr. Office Norcross, Blackpool.

WATSON, Peter Greystones, 2 Main St., Newtown Linford, Leicester LE6 0AD — MB ChB 1958 Manch.; MRCGP 1971; DObst RCOG 1961. (Manch.) Prev: Ho. Surg. Profess. Unit Manch. Roy. Infirm.; Ho. Phys. & Sen. Ho. Off. (Paediat.) Pk. Hosp. Davyhulme.

WATSON, Peter Andrew Farr Links Medical Practice, 144A King Street, Aberdeen AB24 5BD Tel: 01224 644463 Fax: 01224 630231; 33 Duthie Terrace, Aberdeen AB10 7PP Tel: 01224 313156 — MB ChB 1984 Aberd.; MRCGP 1988; DRCOG 1987. (Aberdeen) Clin. Sen. Lect. (Gen. Pract.) Aberd. Univ.; GP Facilitator (Commun. Care). Prev: Trainee GP Aberd. VTS; SHO (Gen. Psychiat.) Roy. Cornhill. Hosp. Aberd.

WATSON, Peter George Department of Genitourinary Medicine, Newcastle General Hospital, Westgate Road, Newcastle upon Tyne NE4 6BE Tel: 0191 256 3257 Fax: 0191 256 3256 Email: peter.watson@ncht.north.nhs.uk — MB ChB 1979 Ed.; BSc (Med. Sci.) (Hons.) Ed. 1976; MRCP (UK) 1982; DMRD Ed. 1984. (Univ. Ed.) Cons. Genitourin. Med. Newc. City Health NHS Trust & N.umbria Health Care NHS Trust; Clin. Lect. Infec. Dis.s & Trop. Med. Univ. Newc. u. Tyne. Socs: (Sec.) Assn. Genitourin. Med.; Med. Soc. Study of VD; Soc. Study Sexually Transm. Dis. Irel. Prev: Sen. Regist. (Genitourin. Med.) Glas. Roy. Infirm.; Regist. (Radiol.) Roy. Infirm. Edin.

WATSON, Mr Peter Gordon 17 Adams Road, Cambridge CB3 9AD Tel: 01223 353789 Fax: 01223 460910 Email: peter.g.watson@btinternet.com — MB BChir 1957 Camb.; MA Camb. 1957; FRCS Eng. 1963; MRCS Eng. LRCP Lond. 1956; FRCOphth 1988; DO Eng. 1960. (Univ. Coll. Hosp.) Hon. Cons. Ophth. Surg. Moorfields Eye Hosp. Lond. & Addenbrooke's Hosp. Camb; Chairm. Educat. Internat. Counc. Ophth.; Boerhaave Prof., Univ. of Leiden, The Netherlands. Socs: Hon. FRCOpth. Prev: Sen. Lect. Inst. Ophth. & Moorfields Eye Hosp.; Sen. Resid. Ophth. Moorfields Eye Hosp.; Ho. Surg. & Ho. Phys. Univ. Coll. Hosp. Lond.

WATSON, Peter James Tanfield View Surgery, Scott Street, Stanley DH9 8AD Tel: 01207 232384; The Cardinals, Queens Road, Blackhill, Consett DH8 0BL Tel: 01207 509428 — BM BS Nottm. 1978; BMedSci Nottm. 1976; MRCGP 1984. (Nottm.)

WATSON, Mr Peter Sherratt (retired) 8 Stratton Place, Shop Lane, Wells-next-the-Sea NR23 1JR — MB BS 1948 Lond.; FRCOG 1968, M 1954; FRCS Eng. 1957; MRCS Eng. LRCP Lond. 1949. Prev: Cons. Obstetr. & Gynaecol. Qu. Eliz. II Hosp. Welwyn Gdn. City.

WATSON, Mr Philip Charles (retired) 2 Station New Road, Brundall, Norwich NR13 5PQ Tel: 01603 712137 — MB BS 1942 Lond.; FRCS Eng. 1946; MRCS Eng. LRCP Lond. 1941. Cons. Surg. Pilgrim Hosp. Boston. Prev: Surg. Tutor & Chief Asst. St. Bart. Hosp.

WATSON, Philip Hugh SmithKline Beecham Pharmaceuticals, New Frontiers Science Park, Third Avenue, Harlow CM19 5AW Tel: 01279 644156 Fax: 01279 644707 — MB BS 1986 Lond.; MRCP (UK) 1990; Dip. Pharm. Med. RCP (UK) 1993. Dir. & Clin. Investig. SmithKline Beecham Pharmaceut. Harlow. Prev: Clin. Research Phys. Wellcome Foundat. Beckenham; SHO Rotat. (Med.) St. Mary's Hosp. & Roy. Brompton Hosp. Lond.

WATSON, Philippa Jane Quartly Department of Anaesthetics, Wycombe General Hospital, High Wycombe HP11 2TT Tel: 01494

WATSON

425260; Forge House, Coleshill, Amersham HP7 0LR Tel: 01494726736 — MB ChB 1973 Dundee; FFA RCS Eng. 1978. Cons. Anaesth. Wycombe Gen. Hosp.

WATSON, Rachel 58 Barons Mead, Southampton SO16 9TD — BM 1993 Soton.

WATSON, Rachel Halliwell Surgery, Lindfield Drive, Bolton BL1 3RG Tel: 01204 23642; 23 Third Street, Bolton BL1 7NN — BM BS 1988 Nottm.; MRCGP 1994; DFFP 1994.

WATSON, Reginald Hubert Glendyne, Haygrove Road, Bridgwater TA6 7HZ — MB BCh BAO 1938 NUI; DPH Leeds 1942. Med. Off. Health Bridgwater.

WATSON, Richard James Craigallian Avenue Surgery, 11 Craigallian Avenue, Cambuslang, Glasgow G72 8RW Tel: 0141 641 3129 — MB ChB 1983 Glas.; MRCGP 1989; DRCOG 1990; DCH RCP Lond. 1989. GP Cambuslang Glas. Prev: GP Belén Nicaragua.

WATSON, Richard Marshall Manor House Surgery, Providence Place, Bridlington YO15 2QW Tel: 01262 602661 Fax: 01262 400891 — MB BS 1975 Lond.

WATSON, Richard Scott Hawthorne Cottage, 56 Ridge St., Stourbridge DY8 4QF — MB BS 1983 Lond.

WATSON, Robert Alistair Mackay Sighthill Health Centre, 380 Calder Road, Edinburgh EH11 4AU Tel: 0131 537 7060; 1 Loaning Crescent, Peebles EH45 9JR — MB ChB 1976 Ed.; MRCP (UK) 1984; MRCGP 1986; DTCH Liverp. 1982. (Edinburgh)

WATSON, Robert Anthony 16 Coplow Avenue, Tean, Stoke-on-Trent ST10 4JQ — MB ChB 1993 Leeds.

WATSON, Robert Daniel Steadman Tel: 0121 507 4239 Fax: 0121 507 5650; 4 Richmond Hill Gardens, Edgbaston, Birmingham B15 3RW — MD 1981 Birm.; BSc Birm. 1970, MB ChB 1973; FRCP Lond. 1989; MRCP (UK) 1976. Cons. Cardiol. City Hosp. Dudley Rd. Birm.; Hon. Sen. Lect. Univ. Birm. Socs: Brit. Cardiac Soc.; Brit. Hypertens. Soc.; Brit. Cardiovasc. Interven. Soc. Prev: Cons. Cardiol. Dudley Rd. Hosp. Birm.; Lect. Dept. Med. Univ. Birm.; SHO (Med.) Llandough Hosp. Penarth.

WATSON, Robert Doré St Marys Road Surgery, St. Marys Road, Newbury RG14 1EQ Tel: 01635 31444 Fax: 01635 551316 — MB BS 1973 Lond.; MRCGP 1978.

WATSON, Robert George Peter Grandview, 21 Ballymenoch Road, Holywood BT18 0HH Tel: 01232 426486 — MB BCh BAO 1977 Belf.; BSc (Hons.) Physiol. Belf. 1974, MD 1985, MB BCh BAO 1977; MRCP (UK) 1981. Sen. Lect. & Cons. Phys. Med. Qu. Univ. Belf. & Roy. Vict. Hosp. Belf. Prev: Sen. Regist. (Internal Med.) EHSSB.

WATSON, Robert Graham Dunblane Medical Practice, Well Place, Dunblane FK15 9BQ Tel: 01786 822595 Fax: 01786 825298 — MB ChB 1983 Ed.; DRCOG 1985; Cert. Family Plann. JCC 1985.

WATSON, Mr Robert John Four Trees, 159 Ribchester Road, Clayton Le Dale, Blackburn BB1 9EE Tel: 01254 245879 — MB BS 1977 Newc.; ChM Manch. 1987; FRCS Eng. 1981. Cons. Surg. Blackburn Roy. Infirm.

WATSON, Robin Joseph Derby Road Practice, 52 Derby Road, Ipswich IP3 8DN Tel: 01473 728121 Fax: 01473 718810; Tarnside Road, Witnesham, Ipswich IP6 9EH — BSc (1st cl. Hons.) Belf. 1973, MB BCh 1976; MRCGP 1982; DRCOG 1982.

WATSON, Ronald Innes Courtyard Surgery, The Courtyard, London Road, Horsham RH12 1AT Tel: 01403 253100 Fax: 01403 267480 — MB BS 1975 Lond.; DRCOG 1978. (Middlx.) Prev: Resid. Med. Off. St. Margt.'s Hosp. Wom. Sydney & Mater Miser.; Childr. Hosp. Brisbane Australia; Resid. (Med.) Toronto E. Gen. Hosp. Canada.

WATSON, Sally Jane Collfryn, Bethesda Bach, Caernarfon LL54 5SH — MB ChB 1997 Manch.

WATSON, Sandra Jane Surrey Hampshire Borders NHS Trust, Farnham Road Hospital, Farnham Road, Guildford GU2 7LX Tel: 01483 443535 — MB BS 1978 Lond.; MRCS Eng. LRCP Lond. 1978; MRCPsych 1986; Cert. Family Plann. JCC 1980. Cons. Psychiat. Surrey Hants. Borders NHS Trust Guildford.

WATSON, Miss Sandra Jayne Homerton Hospital, Homerton Row, London E9 6SR; Tel: 020 7481 9829 — MB BS 1994 Lond.; DRCOG 1997; MRCOG 1999. p/t Specialist Regist. (O & G) Homerton Hosp. Prev: Specialist Regist. (O & G) Whipps Cross Hosp.; Specialist Regist. (O & G) Newham Hosp.

WATSON, Sarah Anne Mangrove Hall Farm Cottage, Mangrove Green, Cockernhoe, Luton LU2 8QE — MB ChB 1988 Cape Town.

WATSON, Sarah Lucie Sweet Apple Cottage, Martin, Fordingbridge SP6 3LF Tel: 01725 519281 — MB BS 1988 Lond.; FRCOphth 1994. SHO (Ophth.) King Edwd. VII Hosp. Windsor. Prev: SHO (Ophth.) King's Coll., St. Bart. & Gt. Ormond St. Hosps. Lond.

WATSON, Sarah Margaret The Health Centre, Goodly Date, Windermere LA23 2EG Tel: 015394 45159 Fax: 015394 46029; 5 LangriggeCt., Langrigge Drive, Bowness-on-Windermere, Windermere LA23 3AJ Tel: 015394 45558 — BM BCh 1977 Oxf.; MA Camb. 1977; MRCP (UK) 1980; MRCGP 1981.

***WATSON, Simon Dominic John** Flat 4, 19-21Parkfield Road, Bradford BD8 7AA — MB BS 1988 Newc.

WATSON, Simon James Montalto Medical Centre, 2 Dromore Rd, Ballynahinch BT24 8AH Tel: 01622 741919; 11 Lancet Lane, Maidstone ME15 9RX — MB ChB BAO 1988 Belf.; DFFP 1995 Belfast; MRCGP 1993; DCH RCPI 1994; DRCOG 1992; DMH Belf. 1991. Dep. Forens. Med. Off.. Belf.

WATSON, Simon James William 59 Willowtree Avenue, Gilesgate Moor, Durham DH1 1EA Email: simon.watson@doctors.org.uk — MB ChB 1996 Liverp.; MB ChB (Commendation) Liverp. 1996; BClinSci. (1st cl. Hons.) Liverp. 1995; MRCP UK Feb 1999. (Liverp.) SHO (Gen. Med.) Qu.'s Med. Centre Univ. Hosp. Nottm. Prev: Ho. Phys. & Surg. Roy. Liverp. Hosp.

WATSON, Simon Paul 34 Millfield Gardens, Nether Poppleton, York YO26 6NZ — MB ChB 1989 Leeds; DCH RCP Lond. 1994; DRCOG 1992.

WATSON, Simon Peter Atter The Surgery, Worcester Road, Great Witley, Worcester WR6 6HR Tel: 01299 896370 Fax: 01299 896873 — MB BS 1982 Nottm.; MRCGP 1987; DRCOG 1985.

WATSON, Stanley Valentine John (retired) 4 Edgerton Road, Leeds LS16 5JD — MB BS 1954 Durh. Prev: Ref. Div. Med. Serv.

WATSON, Stephen David Royal Albert Edward Infirmary, Wigan Lane, Wigan WN1 2NN Tel: 01942 244000; 1 Amber Grove, Westhoughton, Bolton BL5 3LE Tel: 01942 811707 — MB ChB 1985 Manch.; BSc Manch. 1982; MRCP (UK) 1990; FRCR 1996. Cons. Radiol. Wigan & Leigh NHS Trust.

WATSON, Stephen John Lincoln Road Practice, 63 Lincoln Road, Peterborough PE1 2SF Tel: 01733 565511 Fax: 01733 569230 — MB ChB 1982 Dundee; BSc (Hons.) Dund 1978, MB ChB 1982; MRCGP 1986; DRCOG 1984. Socs: BMA. Prev: Trainee GP Angus VTS; Jun. Med. Ho. Off. King's Cross Hosp. Dundee; Jun. Surg. Ho. Off. Ninewells Hosp. Dundee.

WATSON, Mr Stewart Fernleigh Consulting Centre, 77 Alderley Road, Wilmslow SK9 1PA Tel: 01625 536488 Fax: 01625 548348 — MB Camb. 1971, BChir 1970; FRCS Eng. 1974; MRCP (UK) 1972. (Univ. Coll. Hosp.) Cons. Plastic & Hand Surg. Wythenshaw Hosp., Manch. &Pendelbury Childr. Hosp. & Hope Hosp. Socs: BSSH; BAPS; BAAPS. Prev: Cons. Plastic Surg. St. Lawrence Hosp. Plastic & Reconstrcu. Surg. Centre Chepstow; Sen. Regist. (Plastic Surg.) Withington Hosp. Manch.

WATSON, Stuart Department of Psychiatry, Leazes Wing, RUI, Newcastle upon Tyne Email: stuart.watson@ncl.ac.uk — MB BS 1992 Newc.; MRCPsych 1997. (Nescastle) Regist. (Psychiat.) N.ern Regional Rotat. Prev: SHO Rotat. (Psychiat.) N.d.

WATSON, Stuart Brown — MB ChB 1984 Aberd.

WATSON, Susan Clare Stockwell Lodge Medical Centre, Rosedale Way, Cheshunt, Waltham Cross EN7 6HL Tel: 01992 624408 Fax: 01992 626206 — MB BS 1978 Lond.; DRCOG 1981. (Roy. Free)

WATSON, Susan Victoria Worth Hall Paddock, Turners Hill Road, Worth, Crawley RH10 4PE Tel: 01293 883962 — MB BS 1984 Lond.; BSc (Intercalated) Lond. 1981; DRCOG 1988; Cert. Family Plann. JCC 1988.

WATSON, Tara Elizabeth 49 Wilton Crescent, Southampton SO15 2QG — BM Soton l984; MRCGP 1988; DCH RCP Lond. 1987. GP Soton Retainer Scheme. Socs: BMA. Prev: Trainee GP Hants.

WATSON, Terence Mark Maes-y-Coed Doctors Surgery, Maes-y-Coed, Glandwr Park, Builth Wells LD2 3DZ Tel: 01982 552207 Fax: 01982 553826; 8 North Road, Builth Wells LD2 3BU Tel: 01982 552337 — MB BS 1970 Lond.; DObst RCOG 1975. Chairm. & Powys Commiss.ing Gp. Socs: Powys BMA (Vice Chairm.). Prev: Ho. Surg. & Ho. Phys. King's Lynn Dist. Hosp.; Med. Off. Brit. Solomon Is.s.

WATSON

WATSON, Theresa Olivia Tara, Great Edstone, York YO62 6PB Tel: 017514 32036 — MB ChB Birm. 1960; BA 1998. Prev: Med. Off. WHO Smallpox Progr. Bangladesh.

WATSON, Timothy Mark Furze Cottage, Cheriton Bishop, Exeter EX6 6HF — BM BS 1994 Nottm.

WATSON, Timothy Peter Flat 1, 52 West End Lane, West Hampstead, London NW6 2NE — MB BS 1997 Lond.

WATSON, Timothy Richard The Surgery, Village Hall, Worthen, Shrewsbury SY5 9HT Tel: 01743 891401 Fax: 01743 891668; Plox Cottage, Brockton, Worthen, Shrewsbury SY5 9HU — MB ChB 1967 Liverp.

WATSON, Tracey Elizabeth 14 Park View Avenue, Burley Park, Leeds LS4 2LH — MB ChB 1992 Leeds; MRCP Glasgow 1999. (Leeds)

WATSON, Veronica Frances 27 Well Orchard, Bamberbridge, Preston PR5 8HJ — MB ChB 1989 Glas.

WATSON, Wendy Anne 14 Granville Place, Aberdeen AB10 6NZ — MB ChB 1995 Aberd.

WATSON, William Forbes Beech House Surgery, 1 Ash Tree Road, Knaresborough HG5 0UB Tel: 01423 542564 — MB BCh BAO 1975 Belf.; DRCOG 1977.

WATSON, William Frederick (retired) The Rose Garden, Oldlands Hall, Herons Ghyll, Uckfield TN22 3DA Tel: 01825 712369 Fax: 01825 712224 — LRCP LRCS Ed. LRCPS Glas. 1948.

WATSON, William Howison Haematology Department, Monklands District General Hospital, Airdrie ML6 0JS Tel: 01236 712099, 01236 748748 Fax: 01236 746129 Email: william.watson@laht.scot.nhs.uk; Hundalee, Larch Avenue, Lenzie, Glasgow G66 4HX Tel: 0141 777 6405 — MB ChB (Commend.) Glas. 1968; BSc (Hons. Physiol.) Glas. 1966; FRCP Glas. 1987; MRCP (UK) 1975; FRCPath 1987, M 1975. (Glasgow) Cons. Haemat. Monklands Gen. Hosp. Airdrie; Hon. Clin. Sen. Lect. Univ. Glas. Prev: Lect. (Haemat.) Univ. Dept. Haemat. Glas. W. Infirm.

WATSON, William Humphreys, MC (retired) 17 St John's Hill, Shrewsbury SY1 1JJ Tel: 01743 231387 — MB BS Lond. 1950; MRCS Eng. LRCP Lond. 1950; MRCGP 1967; DObst RCOG 1952. Prev: Res. Obstetr. . Guy's Hosp.

WATSON, William Rowell (retired) The Little Manor House, 9 Manor Close, Tunbridge Wells TN4 8YB Tel: 01892 528261 — MRCS Eng. LRCP Lond. 1941; FFA RCS Eng. 1954; DA Eng. 1944. Hon. Cons. Anaesth. E.bourne Health Dists.

WATSON, Winifred (retired) Melrose, Stapleton, Presteigne LD8 2LR Tel: 01544 267330 Fax: 01544 267330 — MB ChB Leeds 1954.

WATSON, Winifred Mary Bertha (retired) 17 St John's Hill, Shrewsbury SY1 1JJ — MB ChB Aberd. 1947.

WATSON, Yolanda Maria Rita 5 West Park Gardens, Dundee DD2 1NY — MB ChB 1973 Ed.; BSc (Med. Sci.) Ed. 1970, MB ChB 1973. (Ed.) Clin. Asst. & Psychogeriat. Day Hosp., Ashludie Hosp. Monifieth.

WATSON-HOPKINSON, William Ian (retired) 12 Highclere Drive, Camberley GU15 1JY Tel: 01276 502222 — MB BS 1958 Lond.; BSc (Anat.) Lond. 1955, MB BS 1958; MFOM RCP Lond. 1982. Prev: Centre for Human Sci. Defence Research Agency FarnBoro. Hants.

WATSON-JONES, Alan (retired) Gardener's Cottage, Airds Bay, Taynuilt PA35 1JR Tel: 01866 822356 — MB ChB 1942 Birm. Prev: Ho. Phys. Qu. Eliz. Hosp. Birm.

WATSON-JONES, Deborah Lindsay 12 Walden Lodge Close, Devizes SN10 5BU — BM BCh 1988 Oxf.; MSc (Communicable Dis. Epidemiol.) Lond. 1995; BA (Hons.) Zool. Oxf. 1982; MRCP (UK) 1992. Research Fell. Lond. Sch. Hyg. & Trop. Med. Lond. Socs: BMA; Study Soc. VD; Roy. Soc. Trop. Med. & Hyg.

WATSON-JONES, Esther Margaret Christine 2 The Steadings, Clifton, Morpeth NE61 6AH — MB ChB 1968 Cape Town.

WATT, Alan 74 St David's Way, Watford Farm, Caerphilly CF83 1EZ — MB ChB 1986 Aberd. Regist. (Geriat. Med.) Llandough Hosp. Cardiff. Prev: Regist. (Geriat. Med.) Caerphilly Miners Dist. Hosp.; SHO (A & E) N. Tees Gen. Hosp. Stockton-on-Tees; Ho. Off. (Med.) New Cross Hosp. Wolverhampton.

WATT, Alan Douglas Waddesdon Surgery, Goss Avenue, Waddesdon, Aylesbury HP18 0LY Tel: 01296 658585 Fax: 01296 658467; 2 Manor Gardens, Main St, Grendon Underwood, Aylesbury HP18 0UT — MB BS 1980 Lond.; MRCGP 1985; DRCOG 1983. (Charing Cross) Gen. Med. Practitioner, Aylesbury, Bucks.

WATT, Alastair James 32 Bradley Street, Wotton-under-Edge GL12 7AR — MB BS 1996 Lond.

WATT, Alastair James McCurrach Worcester Street Surgery, 24 Worcester Street, Stourbridge DY8 1AW Tel: 01384 371616; 24 Worcester Street, Stourbridge DY8 1AW Tel: 01384 371616 — MRCS Eng. LRCP Lond. 1971; BSc (Biochem.) Lond. 1968, MB BS 1971; MRCGP 1979; DRCOG 1977. (Roy. Free) Assoc. RCPath. Lond.; Mem. Primary Health Care, Specialist Gp. Brit. Computer Soc. Prev: SHO (Paediat.) Wordsley Hosp. nr Stourbridge; Regist. (Path.) Bristol Roy. Infirm.; SHO (Psychiat.) Burton Rd. Hosp. Dudley.

WATT, Alexander 83 Moss Lane, Hesketh Bank, Preston PR4 6AA — MB ChB Ed. 1952; MFOM RCP Lond. 1978; DPH Ed. 1959; DIH Lond. 1961. Socs: Soc. Occupat. Med. Prev: Sen. Specialist (Occupat. Med.) ARAMCO Dhahran, Saudi Arabia; HM Med. Insp. Factories; Dep. MoH Lagos, Nigeria.

WATT, Alexander John (retired) 32 Spoutwells Drive, Scone, Perth PH2 6RR Tel: 01738 551548 — MB ChB 1956 Aberd. Prev: Authorised Med. Examr. Civil Aviat. Auth.

WATT, Alison Margaret (retired) Tarrywood, Whitchurch, Tavistock PL19 9LE Tel: 01822 612304 Fax: 01822 612304 — MB BS (Hons.) Lond. 1955; FRCOG 1989, M 1960, DObst 1957. Prev: Assoc. Specialist (Colposcopy) Derriford Hosp. Plymouth.

WATT, Andrew Graeme Tower House, Stewarton, Kilmarnock KA3 5JH Email: 100743.3514@compuserve.com; Tower House, Strwarton, Kilmarnock KA3 5JH Email: wattsupdoc@mac.com — MB ChB 1983 Glas.; BSc (Hons.) Glas. 1979; MRCP (UK) 1989; DTM & H Liverp. 1990. (Glas.) Specialist Regist. (Gen. & Geriat. Med.) Glas. Prev: Med. Off. Lady Willingdon Hosp. Manali, India; Dept. of Med. for Elderly Vict. Infirm. Glas.

WATT, Andrew H Medicines Assessment Research Unit, Medical School, Foresterhill, Aberdeen AB25 2ZD Tel: 01224 404923 Fax: 01224 840559 — MB ChB 1977 Aberd.; BA Open 1989; MD (Hons.) Aberd. 1987, BMedBiol (Commend.) 1974; FRCP Ed. 1990; MRCP (UK) 1981; FFPM RCP (UK) 1991, M 1989; Dip. Pharm. Med. RCP 1989. Dir. Med. Assessm. Research Unit Univ. Aberd.; Sen. Lect. (Clin. Pharmacol.) Univ. Aberd.; Hon. Cons. Aberd. Roy. Hosps. NHS Trust; Edr. Pharmaceut. Med. Socs: Brit. Pharm. Soc. & Internat. Soc. Pharmacoepidemiol. Prev: Sen. Med. Off. Scott. Home & Health Dept. Edin.; Clin. Research Off. (Pharmacol. & Therap.) Univ. Wales Coll. Med. Cardiff; Regist. (Cardiol.) Univ. Hosp. of Wales Cardiff.

WATT, Andrew James Bruce Dept. Of Diagnostic Imaging & Clinical Physics, The Royal Hospital for Sick Children, Dalnair Street, Yorkhill, Glasgow G3 8SF Tel: 0141 201 0100 Fax: 0141 201 0098 — MB ChB 1990 Glas.; MRCP Glas. 1993; FRCR 1997. Cons. Paediatric Radiologist, Roy. Hosp. for Sick Childr., Glas. Socs: Roy. Coll. Phys. & Surgs. Glas.; Fell. Roy. Coll. Radiols.

WATT, Andrew Niall Finlayson Street Practice, 33 Finlayson Street, Fraserburgh AB43 9JW Tel: 01346 518088 Fax: 01346 510015 — MB ChB 1986 Aberd.; MRCGP 1992.

WATT, Anne Mure Strathbogie Cottage, Cormistone, Biggar ML12 6NS Tel: 0189 93 236 — MB ChB 1939 Ed.; Dip. Soc. Med. 1970.

WATT, Archibald David Glasgow Occupational Health, Glasgow Royal Infirmary, Wishart Street, Glasgow G31 3HT Tel: 0141 211 0427 Email: david.watt@northglasgow.scot.nhs.uk; 15 Newtyle Road, Paisley PA1 3JU Tel: 0141 882 1078 Fax: 0141 882 1078 Email: d.watt@watt90.freeserve.co.uk — MB ChB 1973 Dundee; FRCP, RCP (Glas) 1999; FFOM RCP Lond. 1993, M 1984, A 1983; MRCGP 1979; DRCOG 1977; DCH RCPS Glas. 1976; FRCP Glas 1999. Cons. Occupat. Med. Gtr. Glas. HB.; Hon. Sen. Lect. (Pub. Health) Univ. Glas.; Chairm. Scot-Gp. Soc. Socs: Epilepsy Assn. Scotl. Prev: Med. Off. The Post Office Glas.; Employm. Med. Adviser HSE Glas.; Train. Progr. Dir. In Occupat.al Med. W. of Scotl. PostGrad. Med Educ. Bd.

WATT, Barry Huntly Health Centre, Jubilee Hospital, Bleachfield Street, Huntly AB54 8EX Tel: 01466 792116 Fax: 01466 794699 — MB ChB 1989 Aberd.; MRCGP 1993. GP. Prev: SHO (Orthop. & Cas.) Borders Gen. Hosp. Melrose.; Trainee GP Peebles.

WATT, Brian (retired) Mycobacteria Laboratory, City Hospital, Edinburgh EH10 5SB Tel: 0131 536 6357 Fax: 0131 536 6152 — MB ChB 1965 Ed.; MD Ed. 1972; FRCP Ed. 1993; FRCPath. 1984.

Dir. Scott. Mycobact. Ref. Laborat.; Cons. Bacteriol. City Hosp. Edin.; Pat. Servs. Dir. Med. Microbiol. Servs. Lothain Univ. Hosp. NHS Trust; Hon. Sen. Lect. (Bact.) Univ. Edin. Prev: Cons. Microbiol. W.. Gen. Hosp. Edin.

WATT, Carolyn Susan Butterwick Hospice, Middlefiedl Rd, Stockton-upon-tees TS19 8XN Tel: 0191 565 6256 Fax: 0191 569 9253; 45 Ashfield Park, Whickham NE16 4SQ — MB ChB 1982 Glas.; MRCGP 1986; Dip. Palliat. Med. Wales 1997; DRCOG 1984. Palliat. Care Phys., Butterwick Hospice, Stockton-upon-Tees. Socs: Assn. Palliat. Med.; BMA; Palliat. Care Forum. Prev: Clin. Asst. Palliat. Med. St. John's Hospice Slyne Lancaster; GP Irvine; SPR Palliat. Med., N.. Deanery.

WATT, Constance Maria Elisabeth 12 Fulton Place, Dalrymple, Ayr KA6 6QB — MB ChB 1980 Aberd.; DA Eng. 1984.

WATT, Cynthia Mary 50 Stockport Road, Marple, Stockport SK6 6AB Tel: 0161 426 0299 Fax: 0161 427 8112; 34 Townscliffe Lane, Mellor, Stockport SK6 5AP — MB ChB 1979 Manch.; DRCOG 1981. (Manch.)

WATT, Mr David Anthony Landon 40 Cromwell Street, Walkley, Sheffield S6 3RN — MB ChB 1991 Sheff.; FRCS Ed. 1996. (Sheff.) Research Fell. (Plastic Surg.) Univ. Bradford.

WATT, David Campbell (retired) 75 Wykeham Way, Haddenham, Aylesbury HP17 8BU Tel: 01844 291966 — MB ChB Glas. 1943; BSc Glas. 1940, MD 1951; FRCPsych 1972; DPM Eng. 1948. Prev: Maudsley, St. John's Hosp. Stone.

WATT, David Erickson Tollgate Health Centre, 220 Tollgate Road, London E6 5JS Tel: 0207 445 7700 Fax: 0207 445 7715 Email: david.watt@pg-f84093.nhs.uk; 70 Cadogan Terrace, London E9 5HP Tel: 020 8986 3420 Fax: 020 8986 3420 — MB ChB 1983 Sheff.; BMedSci Sheff. 1980. Socs: (Hon. Sec.) Balint Soc. Prev: Trainee GP Birm. & Lond. VTS.

WATT, David Sproul Langaller, Pilcorn St., Wedmore BS28 4AP — MB ChB 1944 Glas. (Glas.)

WATT, Douglas Arthur Lawrence (retired) Sruthan House, Lochaline, Morvern, Oban PA34 5XT Tel: 01967 421632 — MB ChB 1956 Glas.; FRCP Lond. 1975, M 1961; FRCP Glas. 1972; FRCP Ed. 1974, M 1962; FRFPS Glas. 1959; DObst RCOG 1958. Prev: Sen. Regist. (Med.) Stobhill Gen. Hosp. Glas.

WATT, Douglas Burns Stewart (retired) 53 Christian Fields, Norbury, London SW16 3JU Tel: 020 8764 8450 — LRCP LRCS 1949 Ed.; LRCP LRCS Ed., LRFPS Glas. 1949.

WATT, Elizabeth 91 Locksley Park, Belfast BT10 0AT Tel: 01232 626858 — MB BCh BAO 1992 Belf.; DCH RCPS Glas. 1998. Staff Grade Paediat.Ulster Hosp.

WATT, Elizabeth Margaret Department of Reproductive Medicine, St. Michaels Hospital, Southwell St., Bristol BS2 8EG Tel: 01179 285767 Fax: 01179 285792; Felwood House, Stanshalls Lane, Felton, Bristol BS40 9UQ Tel: 01275 472519 — MB BS Lond. 1966; MFFP 1994; DObst RCOG 1968. (Roy. Free) SCMO (Reproduc. Med.) United Bristol Healthcare Trust; Sen. Clin. Med. Off. S.mead & Som. HAs; Research Assoc. UK Family Plann. Research Network Univ. Exeter; Sen. Clin. Med. Off. Brook Advis. Centre Bristol; Specialist Asst. Dept. Reproduct. Med. St. Michaels Hosp. Bristol. Socs: Eur. Soc. Human Reproduc. & Embryol.; Brit. Fertil. Soc.; Brit. Menopause Soc. Prev: Ho. Surg. (Obst.) Whittington Hosp.; Ho. Surg. Roy. Free Hosp.

WATT, Fiona Elizabeth 20 Morland Avenue, Leicester LE2 2PE — MB BS 1998 Newc.

WATT, Florence Anne Glenside Hospital, Blackberry Hill, Stapleton, Bristol BS16 1ED — MB ChB 1983 Ed.; MRCPsych 1990; DRCOG 1985. Regist. (Psychiat.) Train Scheme Glenside Hosp. Bristol. Prev: SHO (Psychiat.) Torbay Hosp. Train. Sch. Torquay; GP Plymouth; Trainee GP Dumfries & Galloway VTS.

WATT, Frances Joan 7 Moorland Park, Gayton, Wirral CH60 8QJ — BM BCh 1996 Oxf. (Oxford) SHO Rotat. (Gen. Med.) P.ss Margt. Hosp. Swindon.

WATT, Frances Katherine Fishponds Health Centre, Beechwood Road, Fishponds, Bristol BS16 3TD Tel: 0117 908 2365 Fax: 0117 908 2377; 17 Fordington Dairy, Athelstan Road, Dorchester DT1 1FD — MB BS 1989 Lond.; MRCGP; DRCOG; DFFP. (St Bart.'s)

WATT, Gavin Michael Cluness Fadlydyke, Muad, Peterhead AB42 5RY — MB ChB 1990 Aberd.

WATT, Gordon Lorimer (retired) Rosebank, 30 Main St., Alford AB33 8PX Tel: 0197 55 62172 — MB ChB 1949 Aberd. Prev: GP Aberd.sh.

WATT, Professor Graham Charles Murray Department General Practice, University of Glasgow, 4 Lancaster Crescent, Glasgow G12 0RR Tel: 0141 211 1682 Fax: 0141 576 2010 Email: g.c.m.watt@clinmed.gla.ac.uk; 15 Banavie Road, Glasgow G11 5AW Tel: 0141 576 2010 — MB ChB Aberd. 1976; MD Aberd. 1990, BMedBiol (Path) 1973; FRCP Glas. 1990; MRCP (UK) 1979; FFPHM RCP (UK) 1994; MFCM 1987; MRCGP 1986; FRCGP 1999; F.Med.Sci 2000. Prof. Gen. Pract. & Head of Dept.; Attached Worker MRC Pub. Health & Social Serv.s Unit. Univ. Glas. Prev: Sen. Lect. (Pub. Health) Univ. Glas.; Sen. Med. Off. Scott. Home & Health Dept. Edin.; Head Glas. Monica Project Centre.

WATT, Graham Cheyne (retired) 1A Old Priory Road, Easton-in-Gordano, Bristol BS20 0PB Tel: 01275 372214 — MB ChB 1937 Ed.; DTM Liverp. 1938.

WATT, Graham John 6 Meadow Bank, Stockport SK4 2HL — MB ChB 1991 Manch.

WATT, Gregor 37 Kirkhill Road, Edinburgh EH16 5DE Tel: 0131 662 9912 — MB ChB 1992 Ed.; BSc (Hons.) Med. Sci. Ed. 1991; DCCH RCP Ed. 1995; MRCGP 1997. Paediat. Regist. (Gen. Pract.). Prev: Regist. (A & E) Melbourne, Austral.; SHO (O & G) Roy. Infirm. Edin.; SHO (Paediat.) Roy. Hosp. Sick Childr. Edin.

WATT, Helen Patricia 19 Haughgate Close, Woodbridge IP12 1LQ Tel: 01394 384078 — MB ChB St. And. 1952. Prev: Sen. Med. Off. (Ment. Health) Doncaster Co. Boro.; Cas. Off. & Ho. Surg. (ENT) Putney Hosp.

WATT, Iain Department of Clinical Radiology, Bristol Royal Infirmary, United Bristol Healthcare NHS Trust, Bristol BS2 8HW Tel: 0117 928 2729 Fax: 0117 928 3267 Email: iain.watt@nbnt.swest.nhs.uh; 8 Parrys Grove, Stoke Bishop, Bristol BS9 1TT Tel: 0117 968 7101 Email: iain.watt@netgates.co.uk — MB BS Lond. 1966; FRCP Lond. 1996; MRCP (UK) 1970; FRCR 1975; FFR 1974; DMRD Eng. 1972; DObst RCOG 1968. (Lond. Hosp.) Cons. Radiol. United Bristol Healthcare NHS Trust. Socs: Fell. BOA; Brit. Soc. Rheum.; Pres. Europ. Soc. Skeletal Radiol. Prev: Sen. Regist. (Diag. Radiol.) Bristol Health Dist. (T); Regist. (Med.) P. of Wales's Gen. Hosp. Lond.; Ho. Phys. (Med.) St. Ann's Gen. Hosp. Lond.

WATT, Mr Iain Inverclyde Royal Hospital, Larkfield Road, Greenock PA16 0XN Tel: 01475 37103 — MB ChB 1976; MD 1987 Aberd.; FRCS Glas. 1982. Cons. Gen. Surg. Inverclyde Roy. Hosp. Greenock. Socs: Fell. Roy. Coll. Phys.s & Surveyor of Glas.; Assn. of Surg. Gt. Britain & Irel.

WATT, Ian Alexander Kennaway 34 Townscliffe Lane, Marple Bridge, Stockport SK6 5AP — MB ChB 1991 Manch.

WATT, Ian Douglas Edwards and Partners, Wargrave House, 23 St. Owen Street, Hereford HR1 2JB Tel: 01432 272285 Fax: 01432 344059; The Pines, 52 Southbank Road, Hereford HR1 2TL Tel: 01432 272904 — MB BS 1972 Lond.; DA Eng. 1977; DObst RCOG 1975. (Lond. Hosp.) GP Trainer Hereford VTS.

WATT, Professor Ian Scot Department of Health Studies, University of York, York YO10 5DD Tel: 01904 434 104 Email: isw1@york.ac.uk; 50 Frenchgate, Richmond DL10 7AG Tel: 01748 850 913 — MB ChB 1981 Manch.; MPH 1991 Leeds; MFPHM 1993 RCP, UK; FFPHM 1999 RCP, UK. (St Andrew's & Manchester Univ.) Prof. (Primary & Community Care) Univ. of York; Hon. Cons. Pub. Health Med.; GP Princip. (Job Share). Prev: Sen. Regist. (Pub. Health Med.) Yorks. RHA; GP Lancs.; Vis. Lect. (Pub. Health Med.) Univ. Leeds.

WATT, Sir James, KBE, Surg. Vice-Admiral (retired) 7 Cambisgate, Church Road, Wimbledon, London SW19 5AL Tel: 020 8947 0146 — MB BS Durh. 1938; MD Newc. 1972; MS Durh. 1949; FRCP Lond. 1975; FRCS Eng. 1955; FICS 1963; Hon. DCh Newc. 1978; Hon. FRCS Ed. 1976. Prev: Med. Dir.-Gen. Navy.

WATT, James Affleck Gilroy (retired) 3 Middleton Drive, Helensburgh G84 7BE — MB ChB Ed. 1958; MD Ed. 1970; FRCP Ed. 1977, M 1963; FRCPsych 1985, M 1973; DPM Eng. 1966. Prev: Cons. Psychiat. Gartnavel Roy. Hosp. Glas.

WATT, James Currie 28 Kinpurnie Road, Ralston, Paisley PA1 3HH — MB ChB 1969 Aberd.

WATT

WATT, James Miller 36 Westfield Road, Edgbaston, Birmingham B15 3QG — MB ChB 1970 Birm.; FFA RCSI 1974; DObst RCOG 1972; DA Eng. 1973. Cons. (Anaesth.) Centr. Birm. Health Dist. (T).

WATT, Jean Barbara Meole Cottage, Mill Road, Meole Brace, Shrewsbury SY3 9JT — MB ChB 1972 Birm.; FRCPCH 1997; FRCP Lond. 1994; MRCP (UK) 1975. Cons. Paediat. Cross Ho.s Shrewsbury & Roy. Shrewsbury Hosp. Socs: Brit. Paediat. Assn. Prev: Sen. Regist. St. Mary's Hosp. Lond.; Regist. (Paediat.) Hosp. Sick Childr. Gt. Ormond St.

WATT, Joanne Rachel 77 Rosebery Crescent, Jesmond, Newcastle upon Tyne NE2 1EX Tel: 0191 281 6598 — MB BS 1997 Newc. (Newcastle upon Tyne) GP VTS.

WATT, John A Hillwood Cottage, Newbridge EH28 8LU — MB ChB 1941 Ed.; BA Oxf. 1936; MRO 1990; MLCOM 1989. (Oxf. & Ed.) Socs: Brit. Inst. Musculoskel. Med.; BOA; NBPA. Prev: Lect. (Physiol.) Univ. Edin.; Resid. Phys. Roy. N.. Infirm. Inverness; Surg. Lt. RNVR, Specialist Anaesth.

WATT, John Newton Queensway Medical Centre, Doctors Surgery, Queensway, Poulton-le-Fylde FY6 7ST Tel: 01253 890219 Fax: 01253 894222 — MB ChB 1985 Manch.; MRCGP 1989; DRCOG 1988. Prev: Trainee GP Stockport Chesh. VTS.

WATT, John Valentine 17 Dukehaugh, Peebles EH45 9DN — MB ChB 1953 Aberd. (Aberd.) Prev: Ho. Off. Stracathro Hosp.; Ho. Off. Dr. Gray's Hosp. Elgin.

WATT, John William Heddle Southport & Ormskirk Acute Hospital Trust, Town Lane, Southport PR8 6PN Tel: 01704 547471 Fax: 01704 543156 Email: john.watt@mail.soh-tr.nwest.nhs.uk; 26 Yew Tree Road, Ormskirk L39 1NU Tel: 01695 578843 Email: johnwhwatt@mauriceg.demon.co.uk — MD 1981 Liverp.; MD Liverpool 1973; FFA RCS Eng. 1977. (MB ChB Liverpool 1973) Cons. Anaesth. S.port & Ormskirk Acute Hosp. Trust.

WATT, Jonathan William Glendinning Salford Royal Hospitals NHS Trust, Hope Hospital, Stott Lane, Salford M6 8HD Tel: 0161 789 7373 Email: jwatt@fs1.ho.man.ac.uk; 5 Warwick Drive, Hale, Altrincham WA15 9EA Tel: 0161 928 6717 Email: jon@watt.u-net.com — MB BS Lond. 1985; FRCA. 1992. Cons. Pain Managem. & Anaesth., Salford Roy. Hosp. Socs: Assn. Anaesth.

WATT, Joyce Mary (retired) 26 Guildford Drive, Chandlers Ford, Eastleigh SO53 3PT — MB BS Lond. 1957. Prev: SHO Chest Clinic Plaistow Hosp. Lond.

WATT, Karen Patricia 23 Forbes Road, Edinburgh EH10 4EG — MB ChB 1996 Ed.

WATT, Linda Janet Leverndale Hospital, 510 Crookston Road, Glasgow G53 7TU — MB ChB 1978 Aberd.; FRCPsych 1999; MRCPsych 1983. Med. Servs. Manager & Cons. Psychiat. Glas.

WATT, Lisbeth Lynda 34 Craignish Avenue, Norbury, London SW16 4RN — MB ChB 1978 Bristol; FRCS Eng. 1985; DO RCS Eng. 1982. Assoc. Specialist Ophth. Qu. Mary's Hosp. Sidcup.

WATT, Lucinda Mary Johnstone 8 Broomhill Court, Londonderry BT47 6WP — MB BCh BAO 1984 Belf.; MRCGP 1989; DCH Dub. 1988; DRCOG 1988. Staff Grade c/o the Elderley Altnagelvin Area Hosp. Lond.derry. Socs: MRCGP. Prev: GP Retainer Scheme, Crumlin Co. Antrim; SHO (Psychiat.) Holywell Hosp. Antrim; Trainee GP. Co. Antrim N. Irel. VTS.

WATT, Margaret Jean Terrago Lodge, 46 West St., Easton-on-the-Hill, Stamford PE9 3LS Tel: 01780 765562; Terrago Lodge, 46 West St., Easton-on-the-Hill, Stamford PE9 3LS — MB BS 1959 Lond.; FFA RCS Eng. 1965; DA Eng. 1961; DObst RCOG 1961. (Lond. Hosp.) Hon. Cons. Anaesth. S.end-on-Sea Hosps. Socs: Assn. Anaesths. Prev: Cons. Anaesth. S.end-on-Sea Hosp. Gp.; Sen. Regist. (Anaesth.) Lond. Hosp. & Gen. Hosp. S.end; Regist. (Anaesth.) Lond. Hosp. & Poplar Hosp.

WATT, Mark James 18 Great Western Place, Aberdeen AB10 6QL — MB ChB 1998 Aberd.

WATT, Michael Ward 21, Royal Victoria Hospital, Grosvenor Road, Belfast BT12 6BA Tel: 01232 894921 Fax: 01232 235258 Email: michael.watt@rght.n-i.nhs.uk; 20 Ashvale Drive, Hillsborough BT26 6DN Tel: 01846 689552 — MB BCh BAO 1985 Belf.; BSc (Hons.) Physiol. Belf. 1982; MRCP (UK) 1988. Cons. Neurol. Roy. Vict. Hosp. Belf. Prev: Sen. Regist. & Regist. (Neurol.) Roy. Vict. Hosp. Belf.

WATT, Monika Martha Department Environemntal & Occupational Medicine, Foresterhill, Aberdeen AB25 2ZD Tel: 01224 681818 Ext: 52459; Quartains, Drumoak, Banchory AB31 5EP Tel: 01330 811636 — MB ChB 1976 Leeds; MSc Aberd. 1993; MFOM RCP Lond. 1996. (Leeds) Force med. Advis. Grampian Police.

WATT, Natalie Ann Centre For Respiratory Research, University College London, Rayne Institute, 5 University Street, London WC1E 6JJ Tel: 020 7679 6976, 0207 790 6418 Fax: 020 7679 6973 Email: a.reinhard@ucl.ac.uk, natwatt@fsmail.net — MB BS 1988 Lond.; FRCA 1995. Socs: Assn. Anaesth.; Obst. Anaesth. Assn.; Difficult Airway Soc. Prev: SpR St. Thomas & Guy's NHS Trust; Regist. PICU Sydney, Australia.

WATT, Nicola 11 Kilmaurs Drive, Giffnock, Glasgow G46 6ET — MB ChB 1993 Glas.

WATT, Nicola Karen Bury Farm House, Church La, Broxbourne EN10 7QF — MB ChB 1997 Sheff.

WATT, Mr Nigel Alan Roderick Departmentof Orthopaedic Surgery, University South Carolina, Two Richland Medical Park Suite 404, Columbia SC 29203, USA Tel: 00 1 803 7656812; 128 Broadwater Street W., Worthing BN14 9DJ Tel: 01903 36888 — MB BChir 1978 Camb.; MA Camb. 1979, MB BChir 1978; FRCS Ed. 1984; FRCS Eng. 1984; FRCS Ed. (Orth.) 1989. (King's Coll. Hosp.) Sen. Regist. (Orthop. Surg.) Guy's & St. Thomas Hosp. Higher Train. Rotat.. Prev: Regist. (Orthop. Surg.) P.ss Margt. Rose Orthop. Hosp. Edin.; Surgic. Regist. Addenbrookes Hosp. Camb.; Cas. Off. ChristCh. Pub. Hosp. New Zealand.

WATT, Penelope Ann Four Winds, 10 Andover Road N., Winchester Tel: 01962 880050 — MB BS 1960 Lond.; MRCS Eng. LRCP Lond. 1960.

WATT, Peter Arbuthnot (retired) Tarrywood, Whitchurch, Tavistock PL19 9LE — MA, MB BChir Camb. 1952; MRCP Lond. 1960; MRCS Eng. LRCP Lond. 1952; FRCGP 1991; DObst RCOG 1956. Prev: Ho. Phys. Ho. Surg. & Resid. Accouch. Lond. Hosp.

WATT, Peter John Four Winds, 10 Andover Road N., Winchester Tel: 01962 880050 — MB BS 1960 Lond.; MD Lond 1969; MB BS 1960; MRCP Lond. 1962; MRCS Eng. LRCP Lond. 1960. Prof. of Microbiol. Soton. Univ.; Cons. Microbiol. Wessex RHB. Socs: Roy. Soc. Med. & Soc. Gen. Microbiol. Prev: Sen. Regist. Bacteriol. Hammersmith Hosp. Lond.; Sen. Lect. Bacteriol. St. Mary's Hosp. Med. Sch. Lond.

WATT, Robert MacKay, OBE (retired) 4 Youlston Close, Shirwell, Barnstaple EX31 4JW — MB ChB 1966 PhD Ed. 1972, BSc Ed1963, MB ChBEd 1966; Dip. Community. Med. Ed. 1976. Prev: Home Off. Chief Insp. Animals (Scientif. Procedures) Act 1986.

WATT, Roger William Royal Bolton Hospital, Minerva Road, Farnworth, Bolton BL4 0JR Tel: 01204 390546 Fax: 01204 390657 Email: sandra.isherwood@bolton-tr.nwest.nhs.uk; The Squirrels, 105 The Hall Coppice, Egerton, Bolton BL7 9UF — MB BS Lond. 1968; FRCP Lond. 1990; MRCP (UK) 1975; DCH Eng. 1970; FRCPCH 1997. (St. Bart.) Cons. Paediat. Bolton Hosps. NHS Trust. Prev: Sen. Regist. (Paediat.) Wigan & Roy. Manch. Childr. Hosp.; Tutor (Paediat.) Univ. Manch.; Regist. (Paediat.) St. Geo. Hosp. Lond.

WATT, Ruby Margaret Julie Elmbank Group, Foresterhill Health Centre, Westburn Road, Aberdeen AB25 2AY Tel: 01224 696949 Fax: 01224 691650 Email: ruby.watt@elmbank.grampian.scot.nhs.uk — MB ChB 1980 Aberd.; BMedBiol Aberd. 1978; FRCGP 1994, M 1987; DRCOG 1989. (Aberdeen) Examr. MRCGP.

WATT, Sheila Margaret Raigmore Hospital, Inverness IV2 3UJ; 9 Paton Street, Inverness IV2 4SN — MB ChB 1990 Aberd.; DCCH Edin 1996. GP Regist. Ardersier Med. Pract.; Staff Grade Community Paediat. Inverness. Socs: BMA.

WATT, Simon Geoffrey 126 Deepdale Drive, Rainhill, Prescot L35 4QJ — MB ChB 1998 Liverp.

WATT, Sioban Elizabeth 50 Frenchgate, Richmond DL10 7AG Tel: 01748 850913 — MB ChB 1981 Manch.; DCP Sheff. 1992; DRCOG 1984. Prev: SCMO Hull HA.

WATT, Stephanie Jane Department Anaesthetics, Barnet General Hospital, Wellhouse Lane, Barnet EN5 3DJ; 60 Kenterne Drive, Barnet EN5 2NN — MB BS 1985 Lond.; FRCA 1996. Cons. Anaesth. Barnet Gen. Hosp.

WATT, Stephen James Quartains, Drumoak, Banchory AB31 5EP Tel: 01330 811636 — MB BS 1973 Lond.; FRCP Ed. 1990; MRCP (UK) 1977; MRCS Eng. LRCP Lond. 1973; AFOM RCP Lond. 1988. (St. Bart.) Sen. Lect. Dept. Environm. & Occupat. Med. Univ. Aberd. Prev: Lect. (Med.) Univ. Aberd.; Res. Fell. (Cardiovasc. Studies & Med.) Gen. Infirm. Leeds; Ho. Off. (Orthop.) St. Bart. Hosp. Lond.

WATT, Stephen John 21 Cumberland Street, South East Lane, Edinburgh EH3 6RU — MB ChB 1998 Ed.

WATT, Thomas Arthur (retired) 3 Southern Avenue, Rutherglen, Glasgow G73 4JN Tel: 0141 634 8737 — MB ChB 1943 Glas.; MRCGP 1956.

WATT, Tracey Craven dept. Of Anaesthetics, Royal Oldham Hospital, Oldham OL1 2JH — MB ChB 1983 Manch.; FRCA 1990; FCAnaesth. 1990.

***WATT, Victoria Beatrice** Olive House, Black Lane, Loxley, Sheffield S6 6SE Tel: 0114 234 3082 — MB ChB 1998 Sheff.; MB ChB Sheff 1998.

WATT, William Alexander (retired) Cheriths Brook, Charlton Drive, Charlton Kings, Cheltenham GL53 8ES Tel: 01242 515642 — MB ChB 1946 Aberd.; MRCGP 1953. Prev: Ho. Surg. Beckenham Hosp. & Aberd. Matern. Hosp.

WATT, William Morison Grosvenor Road Surgery, 17 Grosvenor Road, Paignton TQ4 5AZ Tel: 01803 559308 Fax: 01803_ 526702; Bardwell, Hookhills Road, Paignton TQ4 7NH — MB BS 1972 Lond.; MSc (Health Care) Exeter 1991; ASSOCIPD 1998; MRCGP 1977. (St. Mary's) Assoc. Adviser S. W.. RHA; Lect. Univ. Exeter. Socs: BMA. Prev: PGEA Coordinator S. W.. RHA; Clin. Tutor (Gen. Pract.) S. W.. RHA.

WATT-SMITH, Jane Ann Anaesthetic Department, Queen Alexandra Hospital, Cosham, Portsmouth PO6 3LY Tel: 023 92 379451; Rose Cottage, Prinsted Lane, Prinstead, Emsworth PO10 8HT Tel: 01243 379584 — MB BS 1971 Lond.; FFA RCS Eng. 1976. Cons. Anaesth. Qu. Alexandra Hosp. Portsmouth.

WATT SMITH, Stephen Richard maxillofacial Unit, John Radcliffe Hospital, Oxford OX3 9DU Tel: 01865 221400 Fax: 01865 22043 Email: steve.watt-smith@clinical-medicine.ox.ac.uk — MB BS 1982 Lond.; MD Lond 1994. (UCL Lond) Cons. Maxillofacial. Surg. John Radcliffe Hosp. Oxf; Hon. Clin. Sen. Lect. Nuffield. Dept. Surg. Univ. Oxf.

WATT-SMYRK, Charles William c/o 2 Keswick Close, Cringleford, Norwich NR4 6UW — MB BS 1976 Lond. GP Maidenhead.

WATTERS, Mr Anthony Thomas dept of Orthopaedics, Bradford Royal Infirmary, Duckworth Lane, Bradford BD9 6RJ Tel: 01274 364552 — MB ChB 1977 Glas.; FRCS Ed. 1984. Cons. Orthop. Trauma Bradford Roy. Infirm. Socs: BOA.

WATTERS, Barbara (retired) Langside, Bassenthwaite, Keswick CA12 4QH Tel: 0159 681471 — MB BS 1948 Lond.; MRCS Eng. LRCP Lond. 1947; DCH Eng. 1957.

WATTERS, Bernard Vincent Benbree, 67 Carrive Road, Forkhill, Newry BT35 9TE — MB BCh BAO 1992 Belf.

WATTERS, Elizabeth Ann The Orchards, Toft Road, Knutsford WA16 9EB Tel: 01565 632104 — MRCS Eng. LRCP Lond. 1960.

WATTERS, Fionnuala Mary (retired) 41 Ashley Park, Newry Road, Armagh BT60 1EU Tel: 01861 523656 — LRCPI & LM, LRCSI & LM 1961; FFCM 1984, M 1975; DPH Belf. 1970. Examg. Med. Practitioner DHSS. Prev: Cons. in Pub. Health Med., SHSSB Armagh HQ.

WATTERS, Mr Gavin William Roger — BM BCh 1987 Oxf.; FRCS (ORL) 1997; FRCS Eng. 1991. Cons in otoLaryngol. head & neck surg. Prev: Sen Regist Qu. Alexander Hosp Portsmouth; Sen. Regist. (Otolaryngol.) St Marys/Roy. Marsden Hosps. Lond.

WATTERS, James 109 Hodges Street, Wigan WN6 7JE Tel: 01942 493676 — MB ChB 1976 Ed.; MRCPsych 1985; DCH RCP Lond.1981. Clin. Med. Off. (Community Paediat.) Wigan.

WATTERS, Janet Patricia Donegall Road Surgery, 293 Donegall Road, Belfast BT12 5NB Tel: 028 9032 3973; 21 Beechlands, Belfast BT9 5HU — MB BCh BAO 1983 Belf.; MRCGP 1989; DCH Dub. 1988; DRCOG 1988; DGM RCP Lond. 1986. (Queens University Belfast) Socs: Ulster Med. Soc. Prev: Trainee GP HillsBoro.; SHO (Paediat. & Infec. Dis.) Belf. City Hosp.

WATTERS, Joan Katherine Bridge House, Main St., Weeton, Leeds LS17 0AY — MB ChB 1965 Sheff.; FRCR 1975; FFR 1972; DMRD Eng. 1970. Cons. Radiol. Leeds Gen. Infirm. Prev: Ho. Phys. Roy. Hosp. Sheff.; Regist. (Radiol.) United Sheff. Hosps.; Sen. Regist. (Radiol.) Nottm. Univ. Gp. Hosps.

WATTERS, John Gerald Houghton Health Centre, Church Street, Houghton-le-Spring DH4 4DN Tel: 0191 584 2154 — MB BS 1975 Newc. GP Hebburn, Tyne & Wear.

WATTERS, Julie Stirling Trust Hospital, Stirling Tel: 01786 434000; 28 Hawthorn Road, Prestonpans EH32 9QF — MB ChB 1986 Ed.; DA (UK) 1989. SHO (Anaesth.) Stirling Trust Hosp. Prev: SHO (A & E) Roy. Edin. Infirm.; SHO (A & E) Roy. Hosp. Sick Childr. Glas.

WATTERS, Kenneth John 27 Cheyne Row, London SW3 5HW — MB BCh BAO 1974 Dub. (Dublin University) VP Clin. Research Europe Covance; Clin. Asst. (Diabetes) Ealing Hosp. Trust. Prev: Dir. Med. Safety & Regulatory Affairs SmithKline Beecham Consumer Healthcare.

WATTERS, Malcolm Peter Raitt Warenne House, Great Coxwell, Faringdon SN7 7NB Email: malandemma@msn.com — MB BChir 1989 Camb.; MRCP (UK) 1992; FRCA 1995. Cons. Anaaesthesia/ITU, P.ss Margt. Hosp., Swindon. Prev: Regist. SW Region Anaesth. Train. Scheme.

WATTERS, Margaret Mary 19 Blanchland Drive, Sunderland SR5 1PT — LRCP LRCS 1941 Ed.; LRCP LRCS Ed. LRFPS Glas. 1941. (Anderson & St. Mungo's Colls. Glas.)

WATTERS, Norah Patricia (retired) Caladh Ur, Braes, Ullapool IV26 2SZ Tel: 01854 612098 — MB ChB Aberd. 1951; DA Eng. 1957; DObst RCOG 1954.

WATTERS, Oonagh Frances 29 Robin Hood Lane, Kingston Vale, London SW15 3PU — MB ChB 1976 Dundee.

WATTERS, Patrick Thomas 10 The Grove, Radlett WD7 7NF Tel: 01923 855434 & profess. 081 954 5641 — MB BCh BAO 1954 NUI; FFA RCS Eng. 1971; DA Eng. 1956. (Univ. Coll. Dub.) Cons. Anaesth. Edgware Gen. Hosp. & Colindale Hosp.; Hon. Cons. Anaesth. Hosp. St John's & St Eliz. Lond. Socs: Assn. Anaesths. Prev: Wing Cdr. RAF Med. Br. Cons. Anaesth.; Anaesth. Regist. Roy. Nat. Orthop. Hosp. Stanmore; Hon. Research Fell. Dept. Anaesths. RCS Lond.

WATTERS, Rachel Maryann Maruia, 18 Drews Park, Knotty Grove, Beaconsfield HP9 2TT Tel: 01494 681593 — MB ChB 1985 Otago.

WATTERS, Sean Robert Watercress Medical Group, Mansfield Park Surgery, 5A Mansfield Park, Lymington Bottom Road, Medstead, Alton GU34 5PZ Tel: 01420 562922 Fax: 01420 562923 — MB BS 1984 Lond.; MRCGP 1990; DRCOG 1990; FFA RCS Eng. 1988. (St. Thos.) Socs: BMA. Prev: Trainee GP Poole VTS; Regist. (Anaesth.) Char. Cross & Hillingdon Hosps.

WATTERSON, Brian Robert Saintfield Health Centre, Fairview, Saintfield, Ballynahinch BT24 7AD Tel: 028 9751 0575 Fax: 028 9751 1895; 11 Linden Close, Saintfield, Ballynahinch BT24 7BH Tel: 01238 519040 — MB BCh BAO 1968 Belf.; MRCGP 1973; DObst RCOG 1972. (Belf.) Prev: Hosp. Pract. (Geriat.) Ards & Bangor Hosps.

WATTERSON, Gillian Annette Flat 186C, Worcester Royal Infirmary, Newton Road, Worcester WR5 1JB — MB BCh BAO 1994 Belf.; MRCPH 1997; MRCP. SHO (Paediat.) Leicester Roy. Infirm.; Specialist Regist. (Paediat.). Socs: RCP; RCPaed. Prev: Ho. Off. Roy. Vict. Hosp. Belf.; SHO Paediat. Rotat., Leicester Roy. Infirm.

WATTIE, Mr James Alistair (retired) 'Belmont', Botcheston Road, Newtown Unthank, Newtown LE9 9Fb — MB ChB 1960 Aberd.; FRCS Eng. 1967; DMRD Ed. 1969. Cons. Radiol. Leicester Hosps. Gp. Prev: Lect. Anat. Univ. Aberd.

WATTIE, Joanna Mackenzie (retired) — MB ChB 1966 Aberd.; FFOM RCP Lond. 1995, MFOM 1987; Spec. Accredit. Occupat. Med. JCHMT 1988. Prev: Sen. Employm. Med. Adviser EMAS Health & Safety Exec. Leicester.

WATTIE, John Nicholson (retired) Spindles Ridge, Old Farm Copse, West Wellow, Romsey SO51 6RJ Tel: 01794 322534 — MB ChB 1947 Aberd.; FRCP Ed. 1980, M 1958; DObst RCOG 1953; DCH Eng. 1952. Prev: GP Romsey.

WATTIE, Moira Louise 5E Burston Road, London SW15 6AR — MB BS 1993 Lond.; DA (UK) 1995. N. W. Thames Deanery Curr.ly at Ealing Hosp. NHS Trust. Prev: SHO (Anaesth.) Char. Cross Hosp. Lond.; SHO (Geriat.) Univ. Coll. Lond. Hosps.

WATTIS, Professor John Philip St. Luke's Hospital, Blackmoorfoot Road, Huddersfield HD4 5RQ Tel: 01484 343451 Email: john.wattis@cht.nhs.uk; Tel: 01977 695939 Email: johnwattis@aol.com — MB ChB 1972 Liverp.; FRCPsych 1991, M 1978; DPM Eng. 1978. Cons. Psychiat. Huddersfield NHS Trust; Vis. Prof. of Old Age Psychiat., Huddersfield Univ. Prev: Med. Director, Leeds Community & Ment. Health NHS Trust; Sen. Lect. (Psychiat.) Univ. Leeds Sch. Clin. Med.; Sen. Lect. & Cons. Psychiat. of Old Age Newsam Centre Seacroft Hosp. Leeds.

WATTON

WATTON, Desmond 303 Hagley Road, Pedmore, Stourbridge DY9 0RJ — MB ChB 1952 Birm.

WATTON, Eric The Surgery, 24 Broadwater Road, Worthing BN14 8AB Tel: 01903 231701; Pine Tree Cottage, 60 Poulters Lane, Worthing BN14 7TA — MB BS 1963 Lond.; MRCS Eng. LRCP Lond. 1963; DObst RCOG 1965. (King's Coll. Hosp.) Prev: Ho. Phys. & Ho. Surg. Dulwich Hosp.; Ho. Off. (Paediat.) Bristol Roy. Hosp. Sick Childr.

WATTON, Mary Joyce (retired) Southwood, Church Road, Purley CR8 3QQ Tel: 020 8660 3235 — MB ChB Leeds 1951.

WATTON, Richard John Whitehouse Surgery, 189 Prince of Wales Road, Sheffield S2 1FA Tel: 0114 239 7229 Fax: 0114 253 1650 — MB ChB 1981 Sheff.; MRCGP 1985; DRCOG 1985; DCH RCP Lond. 1984.

WATTON, Robert William (retired) Southwood, Church Road, Purley CR8 3QQ Tel: 020 8660 3235 — MB BS Lond. 1954; AFOM RCP Lond. 1982; FFPHM 1987; FFCM 1983, M 1972; DPH Eng. 1957, DIH 1963; DCH RCP Lond. 1958. Prev: Sen. Med. Off. DHSS.

WATTS, Andrew Charles Sarum House Surgery, 3 St. Ethelbert Street, Hereford HR1 2NS Tel: 01432 265422 Fax: 01432 358440 — MB BS 1985 Lond.

WATTS, Andrew John 36 Banbury Road, Kidlington OX5 2BU Tel: 01865 372656; 27 Salisbury Road, Crookes, Sheffield S10 1WA Tel: 0114 266 0487 — MB ChB 1994 Sheff. GP Locum. Prev: GP/Regist. Barnsley Dist. Gen. Hosp. VTS; SHO (Gen. Med.) Barnsley Dist. Gen.; SHO (O & G) Barnsley Dist. Gen.

WATTS, Andrew Mark Honor Oak Health Centre, 20-21 Turnham Road, London SE4 2HH Tel: 020 7639 9797; Seasons, 40 Madeira Avenue, Bromley BR1 4AY Email: 100523.1623@compuserve.com — MB BS 1989 Lond.; BSc (Hons.) Nursing CNAA 1983; MRCGP 1993; DFFP 1993; DCH RCP Lond. 1992. (Roy. Free Hosp. Sch. Med.) GP S. Lond. Homeless Team; RCGP/RCN/DoH Educat. Fell.sh. (Jt. Research Post Promoting Interprofessional Train. Between GP Regist & Community Nurses); Health Quality Serv.-Surveyor (King's Fund). Socs: (Bd.) Interprofessional Educat.

WATTS, Andrew Rodney 15 Druid Woods, Avon Way, Bristol BS9 1SX — MB ChB 1992 Sheff.

WATTS, Anne Brown 16 Calumet, Reynolds Road, Beaconsfield HP9 2LZ Tel: 01494 677700 — MB ChB 1946 Glas. Prev: Clin. Asst. Dermat. Wycombe Gen. Hosp.; Ho. Surg. Roy. Infirm. Glas.; Ho. Surg. (Obst.) Dudley Rd. Hosp. Birm.

WATTS, Anthony James Caythorpe Surgery, 52-56 High Street, Caythorpe, Grantham NG32 3DN Tel: 01400 272215 Fax: 01400 273608; Ivy House, Dycote Lane, Welbourn, Lincoln LN5 0NJ — MB ChB 1984 Leic.; MRCGP 1988; DRCOG 1987.

WATTS, Arthur Stanley (retired) The Frith, Mortimer, Reading RG7 2JL Tel: 01734 332487 — BSc (Hons. Physiol.) Lond. 1937, MD 1947, MB BS; MRCP Lond. 1943; MRCS Eng. LRCP Lond. 1940. Prev: Med. Regist. W.m. Hosp.

WATTS, Beverley Louise 18 Litchford Road, Ashley, New Milton BH25 5BQ Tel: 01425 621375; 15 Alresford Road, Winchester SO23 0HG Tel: 01962 870875 — MB BS 1993 Lond.; BSc (Hons.) Lond. 1990; MRCP (Lond.) 1995. (UMDS (Guy's)) Specialist Regist. (A & E Med.) Wessex Region. Socs: Roy. Coll. Phys. (Lond.); Brit. Assn. Accid. & Emerg. Med.; Fac. for Accid. & Emerg.

WATTS, Christopher Waterloo Surgery, 617 Wakefield Road, Waterloo, Huddersfield HD5 9XP Tel: 01484 531461 — MB ChB 1978 Manch.

WATTS, Christopher Cameron William 71 Christchurch Road, London SW14 7AT — MB BS 1998 Lond.

WATTS, Christopher John Barking and Havering Health Authority, Directorate of Public Health, The Clockhouse East St., Barking IG11 8EY Tel: 020 8532 6362 Fax: 020 8532 6354 Email: bhha@globalnet.co.uk; 15 Cromwell Avenue, Highgate, London N6 5HN Tel: 020 8245 4135 Fax: 020 8245 4135 — MB BS 1971 Sydney; MSc (Soc. Med.) Lond. 1980; BSc (Med.) Sydney 1968; FFPHM RCP (UK) 1993; MFCM 1981; DTM & H Sydney 1978; FFPHM RCP (Austral.) 1991; FRCP (UK) 1998. (Sydney) Dir. Pub. Health Barking & Havering HA. Socs: Assn. Directors of Pub. Health. Prev: Dir. Med. Serv. (Austral.); Specialist (Community Med.) Barking Havering & Brentwood HA; Sen. Regist. (Community Med.) City & E. Lond. AHA.

WATTS, Colin 58 Chiltern Road, Sheffield S6 4QX — MB BS 1991 Newc.

WATTS, Darren Paul 17 Brockridge Lane, Frampton, Cotterell, Bristol BS36 2HU — MB BS 1993 Lond.

WATTS, Darryl Russell Blackberry Hill Hospital, Manor Road, Bristol BS16 2EW — MB ChB 1984 Bristol; MSc Bristol 1992, MB ChB 1984; MRCPsych. 1989. Cons. Gen. Psychiat. Blackberry Hill Hosp. Bristol.

WATTS, David Anthony 8 Annandale Street, Edinburgh EH7 4AN — MB ChB 1992 Ed.; MRCP 1998. SHO (Gen. Med.) Stirling Roy. Infirm. Stirling.

WATTS, Derrett James North Staffordshire Combined Healthcare Trust, City General Hospital, Stoke-on-Trent ST4 1NF Tel: 01782 715444; 4 Meriden Road, Clayton, Newcastle ST5 4HE Tel: 01782 611516 — MB BCh 1987 Wales; DRCOG 1992; MRCPsych 1997. (University of Wales) Specialist Regist. Rotat. (Psychiat.) W. Midl. Socs: Christian Med. Fell.sh.; BMA. Prev: Regist. Rotat. (Psychiat.) N. Staffs. Combined Healthcare Stoke-on-Trent; GP Stoke-on-Trent; Trainee GP/SHO N. Staffs. HA VTS.

WATTS, Edward Thomas Spinney View, Tebworth Road, Wingfield, Leighton Buzzard LU7 9QH — MB ChB 1973 Birm.

***WATTS, Emma Jayne** 68 Cargill Road, Earlsfield, London SW18 3DZ Tel: 020 8874 6157 — MB BS 1998 Lond.; MB BS Lond 1998.

WATTS, Eric James Department Haematology, Basildon Hospital, Basildon SS16 5NL; Cherry Cottage, 11 Parkway, Shenfield, Brentwood CM15 8LH — MB ChB 1971 Glas.; DM Soton 1988; FRCP Glas. 1995; MRCP (UK) 1978; FRCPath 1996, M 1984. Cons. Haemat. Basildon & Thurrock HA. Prev: Sen. Regist. (Haemat.) Soton. Hosp. & Portsmouth Hosp.; Regist. (Haemat.) Hammersmith Hosp.

WATTS, Erica Caroline 104 Chatto Road, Torquay TQ1 4HY — BM Soton. 1982; DCH RCPS Glas. 1985. GPTorquay; CA Oncol.; BA Doctor. Prev: Trainee GP Dawlish VTS; SHO (O & G & Paediat.) Plymouth HA; SHO (Cas.) Torbay HA.

WATTS, Mr George Thomas 4 Amesbury Road, Moseley, Birmingham B13 8LD Tel: 0121 449 2242 — ChM Birm. 1959, MB ChB 1944; FRCS Eng. 1950. (Birm.) Cons. Surg. United Birm. Hosps. Socs: Assn. Surg. & Moynihan Chir. Club. Prev: Lect. in Surg. Univ. Birm.; Res. Surg. Off. Qu. Eliz. Hosp. Birm.; Research & Clin. Fell. (Surg.) Mass. Gen. Hosp. Boston.

WATTS, Graham Vincent The Health Centre, Cakeham Road, East Wittering, Chichester PO20 8BH Tel: 01243 673434 Fax: 01243 672563 — BM 1977 Soton.

WATTS, Helen Rose Benefits Agency Medical Services, Govt Buildings, Flowers Hill, Bristol BS4 Tel: 0117 971 8311 — MB BS 1971 Sydney. Med. Adviser BAMS, Bristol. Socs: Roy. Inst. Pub. Health & Hyg. Prev: Acting SCMO E. Wilts. Health Care.

WATTS, James Christopher Anaestetic Department, Burnley General Hospital, Casterton Avenue, Burnley BB10 2P Tel: 01282 425071 — MB ChB 1989 Manch.; BSc (Med. Sci.) St. And. 1986; FRCA 1995. (St. And. & Manch.) Cons. Anaesth. Burnley Gen. Hosp. Socs: Intens. Care Soc.; Assn. Anaesth.; Difficult Airway Soc. Prev: Sen. Regist. (Anaesth.) P.ss Roy. Hosp. Telford; Sen. Regist. Roy. Shrewsbury Hosp.; Sen. Regist. (Anaesth.) Stoke on Trent.

WATTS, Mrs Jennifer Anne Royal Hampshire County Hospital, Romsey Road, Winchester SO22 5DG Tel: 01962 863535 Fax: 01962 824429; Hollybank cottage, Row Hill, Bramshaw, Lyndhurst SO43 7JE Tel: 02380 812432 Fax: 02380 811371 — MB 1972 Camb.; BChir 1971; FRCS Eng. 1981; FRCOphth 1988; DO Eng. 1974. Cons. Ophth. Roy. Hants. Co. Hosp. Winchester. Prev: Sen. Regist. (Ophth.) Roy. Vict. Hosp. Bournemouth.

WATTS, Jillian Patricia Tottington Health Centre, 16 Market Street, Tottington, Bury BL8 4AD — MB ChB 1987 Liverp.; MRCGP 1993; DFFP 1996; DRCOG 1991. (Liverp.) GP Princip. Tottington Health Centre Bury Lancs. Socs: BMA. Prev: GP Bury Retainer Scheme; Asst. (Chest Med.) Bury Gen. Hosp.

WATTS, Joanna Prudence 7 Little St. Johns Street, Woodbridge, Ipswich IP12 1EE Tel: 01394 382046; 7 North Close, Ipswich IP4 2TL Tel: 01473 254080 — BM BCh 1977 Oxf.; MA Camb. 1979, BA 1974; MRCGP 1981; DRCOG 1979. (Oxf.) p/t GP Partner Ipswich. Prev: SHO (Accid. Serv.) Radcliffe Infirm. Oxf.; SHO (Rheum.) Battle Hosp. Reading; SHO (Obst.) John Radcliffe Hosp. Oxf.

WATTS, Mr John Aubrey Ewart (retired) Four Winds, Dartford Road, Horton Kirby, Dartford DA4 9JE Tel: 01322 863256 — MB

BS 1940 Lond.; FRCS Ed. 1942; MRCS Eng. LRCP Lond. 1940. Prev: Cons. Surg. Dartford Dist. Hosp.

WATTS, Professor John Cadman, OBE, MC, Col. late RAMC (retired) 1 Athenrye Court, Cumberland Street, Woodbridge IP12 4AP Tel: 01394 382618 — MB BS Lond. 1938; FRCS Eng. 1949; MRCS Eng. LRCP Lond. 1936. Prev: Cons. Orthop. Surg. Bedford Gen. Hosp.

WATTS, John David Dundonald Medical Practice, 9 Main Street, Dundonald, Kilmarnock KA2 9HF Tel: 01563 850496 Fax: 01563 850426; 24 Main Street, Dundonald, Kilmarnock KA2 9HE Tel: 01563 850496 Fax: 01563 851349 — MB ChB 1963 Glas.; MRCGP 1996. Chief Exec. Ayrsh. Doctors on Call; Sec. Ayrsh. & Arran LMC. Socs: BMA. Prev: Capt. RAMC; Ho. Off. Aberystwyth Gen. Hosp.

WATTS, John Ffrancon Worcester Royal Infirmary, Ronkswood Branch, Newtown road, Worcester WR5 1HN; Stonehall farmhouse, Stonebow Road, Drakes Broughton, Worcester WR10 2AT — MD 1985 Wales; MB BCh 1975 Wales; FRCOG 1993, M 1981. (Welsh Nat. Sch. Med.) Cons. O&G Worcester acute Hosp. NHS trust. Prev: Cons. O & G City Hosp. NHS Trust Birm.

WATTS, John Stephen 13 The Broadway, Summersdale, Chichester PO19 4QR — MB BCh 1995 Wales.

WATTS, Julie Denise Anaesthetic Department, Royal Free Hospital, Pond St., London NW3 2QG; 89 Chetwynd Road, London NW5 1DA — MB BS 1978 Monash; FRCA 1992. Cons. Anaesth. & Hon. Sen. Lect. Roy. Free Hosp. Socs: Roy. Soc. Med.; MRCAnaesth.

WATTS, Kathleen Alison (retired) — MB BS 1976 Newc.; FRCS Ed. 1981; FFAEM 1993. Prev: Cons. A & E City Hosp. NHS Trust Birm.

WATTS, Kathryn Anne 2 Nottingham Street, Cardiff CF5 1JP — MB BCh 1977 Wales.

WATTS, Keith Charles 23 Charleville Road, London W14 9JJ — MB BS 1993 Lond.

WATTS, Malcolm Richard Fernside, 9 North Road, Ormesby St.Margaret, Great Yarmouth NR29 3SA Tel: 01493 730537 — MB ChB 1974 Bristol; MRCGP 1979.

WATTS, Margaret Ishbel 19 Upper Bayble Point, Isle of Lewis HS2 0QG — MB BS 1979 Lond.; MRCS Eng. LRCP Lond. 1979; MRCGP 1985.

WATTS, Marjorie Emily The Maze, Boars Head, Crowborough TN6 3HE Tel: 01892 652407 — MB BS 1953 Lond.; MFCM 1972; DPH Eng. 1959; DObst RCOG 1955. (Char. Cross) Dist. Med. Off. Greenwich HA. Socs: BMA. Prev: Dep. MOH Lond. Boro. Greenwich; Dep. MOH Metrop. Boro. Camberwell, Med. Off. LCC; Ho. Surg. Char. Cross Hosp. Lond.

WATTS, Mr Mark Thomas Arrowe Park Hospital, Upton, Wirral CH49 5PE Tel: 0151 604 7047 — MB ChB 1981 Birm.; FRCS Eng. 1986; FRCOphth. 1988; DO RCS Eng. 1986. (Birmingham) Cons. Ophth. Arrowe Pk. Hosp. Wirral.; Hon. Sen. Lect. Roy. Liverp. Univ. Hosp.; Hon. Assoc. Clin. Prof. Univ. of Ohio; hon ass clin prof Geo. washington Univ. Prev: Sen. Regist. Roy. Hallamsh. Hosp. Sheff.; Fell. Moorfields Eye Hosp. Lond.; Regist. Birm. & Midl. Eye Hosp.

WATTS, Martin 14 Trenchard Avenue, Stafford ST16 3QB — MB ChB 1988 Leeds.

WATTS, Martin Alan Waterloo Surgery, 191 Devonport Road, Stoke, Plymouth PL1 5RN Tel: 01752 563147 Fax: 01752 563304; Glencoe, 1 Glencoe Villas, Clearbrook, Yelverton PL20 6JB Tel: 01822 852400 — MB BS Lond. 1979; DRCOG 1982.

WATTS, Michael Barrett Randolph Medical Centre, 4 Green Lane, Datchet, Slough SL3 9EX Tel: 01753 541268 Fax: 01753 582324 — MB BS 1985 Lond.; MRCGP 1989. Prev: Ho. Phys. Char. Cross Hosp. Lond.; Ho. Surg. W. Herts. Hosp.; Trainee GP Edware Gen. Hosp. VTS.

WATTS, Michael Robin (retired) The Surgery, St. Mary St., Thornbury, Bristol BS35 2AT Tel: 01454 413691 — MB ChB Bristol 1961; DObst RCOG 1963. Police Surg. Prev: SHO (Obst.), Ho. Surg. & Ho. Phys. S.mead Hosp. Bristol.

WATTS, Michael Roland 32 Woodlands Road, Bexleyheath DA7 4AE — BM BS 1990 Flinders.

WATTS, Michelle Christina Foreside of Cairn, Eskhill, Forfar DD8 3TQ — MB ChB 1991 Aberd.

WATTS, Neera Public Health Sevices, Le Bas Centre, St Saviours Road, St Helier, Jersey JE1 4HR Tel: 01534 89933 — MB BS 1979 Mysore; MRCS Eng. LRCP Lond. 1981. Clin. Med.Off.

WATTS, Nita 23 Woodfall Avenue, Barnet EN5 2EZ — MB BS 1976 Lond.

WATTS, Paul Michael 12A Flodden Road, London SE5 9LH — MB BS 1990 Lond.; BSc (Hons.) Lond. 1987, MB BS 1990; MRCP Lond. 1993.

WATTS, Peter (retired) 3 Myrtle Cottages, St Mary's TR21 0JG Tel: 01720 422146 — MRCS Eng. LRCP Lond. 1939; DMRD Eng. 1946. Prev: Sen. Radiol. Roy. Devon & Exeter Hosp.

WATTS, Philip Edward 8 Burton St, Marnhull, Sturminster Newton DT10 1PP Tel: 01258 820483 Fax: 01258 821350; 35 Church Street, Sturminster Newton DT10 1DB Tel: 01258 473545 — MB BS 1967 Lond.; MRCS Eng. LRCP Lond. 1967; Dobst RCOG 1969; MRCS Eng. LRCP Lond. 1967; DObst RCOG 1969. (St. Mary's) Gen. Practitioner. Socs: Roy. Soc. of Med. Prev: Police Surg. Sturminster Newton & Sherborne; SHO (O & G) Qu. Eliz. II Hosp. Welwyn Garden City; Ho. Phys. Harold Wood Hosp.

WATTS, Richard Arthur Department of Rheumatology, Ipswich Hospital NHS Trust, Ipswich IP4 5PD Tel: 01473 702362 Fax: 01473 702039 Email: rwatts@ipsh-tr.anglox.nhs.uk; Bury Hill House, Woodbridge IP12 1JD Tel: 01394 382422 Email: richard.watts2@btinternet.com — BM BCh 1982 Oxf; BM BCh Oxf. 1982; MA Oxf. 1982, DM 1991; MRCP (UK) 1985; MRCS Eng. LRCP Lond. 1981; FRCP Lond. 1999. (Oxf.) Cons. Rheum. Ipswich Hosp.; Hon. Sen. Lect. Sch. Health. Univ.E. Anglia. Socs: Fell. Amer. Coll. Rheum.; Brit. Soc. Rheum.; Brit. Soc. Immunol. Prev: Sen. Regist. (Rheum.) Norf. & Norwich Hosp.; Sen. Regist. (Rheum.) Addenbrooke's Hosp. Camb.; Research Fell. Bloomsbury Rheum. Unit Lond.

WATTS, Richard William Ernest The Consulting Rooms, Wellington Hospital, Wellington Place, London NW8 9LE Tel: 020 7586 5959 Ext: 2572 Fax: 020 7483 0297 Email: info@wellingtonchc.demon.co.uk; 14 Holly Lodge Gardens, Highgate, London N6 6AA Tel: 020 8340 7725 — MB BS (Hons.) Lond. 1945; PhD Lond. 1953, MD 1960; DSc Lond. 1973; FRCP Lond. 1967, M 1949; CChem 1975; FRSC 1971. (St. Bart.) Cons. Phys. (Gen. Med., Endocrinol., Metab. Dis. & Renal Dis.) Wellington Hosp., Harley St. Clinic. Hosp. of St. John & Eliz.; Hon. Cons. Phys. Hammersmith Hosp.; Vis. Prof. Div. Med. Imperial Coll. of Sci., Technol. & Med. Hammersmith Hosp. Socs: Emerit. Mem. Biochem. Soc.; Assn. Phys. & Med. Research Soc. (Hon. Life Mem.); Examr. (rep Lond.) 76/92. Prev: Head Div. Inherited Metab. Dis. Asst. Dir. (Clin.) & Cons. Phys. MRC Clin. Research Centre & N.wick Pk. Hosp. Harrow; Hon. Cons. Phys. St. Bart. Hosp. Lond. & Reader Human Metab. Univ. Lond.; Vis. Sci. Nat. Inst. Health Bethesda, USA.

WATTS, Roger (retired) Wilmercroft, Wilmerhatch Lane, Epsom KT18 7EQ Tel: 0137 272 0835 — MB BS Lond. 1953. Prev: Ho. Surg. Guy's Hosp. Lond.

WATTS, Ronald Williams (retired) Moor Cottage, Advie, Grantown-on-Spey PH26 3LP Tel: 01807 510241 — MB BChir 1937 Lond.; MB BChir. Camb 1937; MRCS Eng. LRCP Lond. 1937. Prev: Ho. Phys. & Cas. Off. St. Thos. Hosp. Lond.

WATTS, Shelagh Rosemarie (retired) Anglers Reach, 42 Hampton Park Road, Hereford HR1 1TH Tel: 01432 266430 — MB BS 1953 Lond.; MRCS Eng. LRCP Lond. 1953; FRCA Eng. 1958; DA Eng. 1955.

WATTS, Simon George Thomas Avenue Road Surgery, 3 Avenue Road, Dorridge, Solihull B93 8LH Tel: 01564 776262 Fax: 01564 779599; 374 Station Road, Dorridge, Solihull B93 8ES — MB ChB 1983 Birm.

WATTS, Simon James 5 Edwards Lane, Sherwood, Nottingham NG5 3AA — MB BCh 1989 Witwatersrand.

WATTS, Stephen James George Clare Surgery, Swan Drive, New Road, Chatteris PE16 6EX Tel: 01354 695888 Fax: 01354 695415 — MB BS 1979 Lond.; 1987 JCPTGP; 1993 Dip FP RCOG; Cert. Family Plann. JCC 1986. (St. Marys) Gen. Practitioner, Geo. Clare Surg., Chatterls; Police Surg., Centr. Div., Camks Constab.; Prison Med. Off. Socs: Mem. Roy. Soc. Med. Prev: SHO (Paediat. Surg.) Hosp. Sick Childr. Lond.; Ho. Phys. St. Mary's Hosp. Lond. W9.

WATTS, Stephen John The Surgery, 8 Shenfield Road, Brentwood CM15 8AB Tel: 01277 218393 Fax: 01277 201017; 19 Middleton Road, Shenfield, Brentwood CM15 8DL — MB BS 1973 Lond.; BSc Lond. 1970; MRCGP 1981. (St. Geo.)

WATTS, Terence Christopher 40 March Court, Warwick Drive, London SW15 6LE Tel: 0191 789 8678; 10 Warwick Road, Earls

WATTS

Court, London SW5 9U Tel: 020 7373 0901 — MB ChB 1977 Cape Town; MRCPsych 1987. Indep. Psychiat. Lond.

WATTS, Toni Ivy House, Dycote Lane, Welbourn, Lincoln LN5 0NJ — MB ChB 1984 Leic.; MRCGP 1988; DRCOG 1987. GP Lincoln.

WATTS, Uma 95 Hartfield Avenue, Elstree WD6 3JJ Tel: 0208 953 7337 — MB BS 1955 Agra.

WATTS, Vikram Kumar Priory Hospital N. London, The Bourne, Southgate, London N14 6RA Tel: 020 8882 8191 Fax: 020 8447 8138 — MB BS 1981 Lond.; BSc (Hons.) Lond. 1977; MRCPsych 1989. (St. Mary's) Staff Cons.; Hon. Sen. Lect. Roy. Free Hosp. Lond. Socs: MRCPsych. Prev: Sen. Regist. (Psychiat.) Maudsley Hosp. Lond.; Regist. (Psychiat.) St. Geo. Hosp. Lond.

WATTS, Yvonne Health Centre, St. Williams Way, Thorpe, Norwich NR7 0AJ Tel: 01603 701010 Fax: 01603 701211; 52 Catton Grove Road, Norwich NR3 3NW Tel: 01603 414177 — BM BS 1979 Nottm.; DRCOG 1981.

WATTS-RUSSELL, Julian Victor André Biggin Hall, Benefield, Peterborough PE8 5AB Tel: 01832 205350 Fax: 01832 205350 Email: j.watts.russell@farmline.com — MB ChB 1966 Birm.; MRCP (UK) 1970; FFA RCS Eng. 1972; DA W. Indies 1968. (Birm.) Socs: BMA. Prev: Regtl. Med. Off. Coldstream Guards; Anaesth. Specialist RAMC; Regist. (Med.) St. Mary's Hosp. Lond.

WATTS-TOBIN, Mary Elizabeth Ann Blake 68 Rydal Road, Lancaster LA1 3HA — MA, MB Camb. 1966, BChir 1965; MRCS Eng. LRCP Lond. 1965; MRCPsych 1977; FRCPsych 1997; DPM Eng. 1976. (Univ. Coll. Hosp.) Cons. Psychiat. Lancaster Moor Hosp.

WATTSFORD, Richard Haddon (retired) 40 Eastern Way, Ponteland, Newcastle upon Tyne NE20 9PF Tel: 01661 871749 — MB BS Durh. 1951; MRCGP 1966. Prev: Ho. Phys. & Ho. Surg. Roy. Vict. Infirm. Newc.

WATURA, Jill Christine 13 Yr Efail, Treoes, Bridgend CF35 5EG Tel: 01656 655469 — MB BCh 1986 Wales; Cert. Family Plann. JCC 1992; T(GP) 1991. Staff Grade (Community Child Health) Bridgend. Socs: Fam. Plann. Assn. Prev: Trainee GP/SHO Wales VTS; Ho. Off. (O & G) Swansea.

WATURA, Roland Department of Radiology, University of Wales College of Medicine, Cardiff CF14 4XN Tel: 01656 655469; 13 Yr Efail, Treoes, Bridgend CF35 5EG Tel: 029 2074 3028 Fax: 01222 743029 — MB BCh 1986 Wales; MRCP (UK) 1990; FRCR 1994. Prev: Sen. Regist. (Radiol.) & Lect. (Diagn. Radiol.) Univ. Hosp. Wales Cardiff.

WATWOOD, Kenneth Bethel, Wildwood Drive, Stafford ST17 4PY — MB ChB 1961 Birm.; MRCS Eng. LRCP Lond. 1961. (Birm.) Socs: BMA. Prev: Sen. Ho. Surg. (Obst & Gyn.) Groundslow Hosp. Tittensor; Ho. Surg. & Ho. Phys. Staffs. Gen. Infirm.

WAUCHOB, David William (retired) 4 Highfields, Heswall, Wirral CH60 7TF Tel: 0151 342 6858 — MB BCh BAO 1941 Belf.; FFCM RCP (UK) 1979, M 1972; DPH Belf. 1948. Prev: MOH & Princip. Sch. Med. Off. Blackpool Co. Boro.

WAUCHOB, Todd Duncan Liverpool Women's Hospital NHS Trust, Department Anaesthesia, Crown St., Liverpool L8 7SS Tel: 0151 708 9988 — MB ChB 1978 Leeds; FFARCS Eng. 1983; DRCOG 1984. Cons. Anaesth. Liverp. HA. Socs: Obst. Anaesth. Assn.; Assn. Anaesths.; BMA. Prev: Sen. Regist. (Anaesth.) Trent RHA; Regist. (Anaesth.) Sheff. HA Trent Region; SHO (Anaesth.) York Dist. Gen. Hosp.

WAUDBY, Hectorina 35 Grigor Drive, Inverness IV2 4LS — MB ChB 1951 Aberd. Prev: Med. Off. Overseas Staff Leprosy Mission; Relieving Doctor Hayling Chau Leprosarium, Hong Kong; Med. Off. Itu Leprosy Colony, Nigeria.

WAUGH, Eleanor Margaret Woodside of Allanton, Auldgirth, Dumfries DG2 0SA Tel: 01387 74230 — MB ChB 1934 Glas. (Univ. Glas.) Prev: Disp. Ho. Surg. Roy. Hosp. Sick Childr. Glas.; Asst. Med. Off. Murray Roy. Perth & Severalls Hosp. Colchester.

WAUGH, Janet Gordon Stewart (retired) 2 Mill Lane, Wadenhoe, Peterborough PE8 5XD — MB BS Lond. 1946; MRCS Eng. LRCP Lond. 1946; Cert JCC Lond. 1967.

WAUGH, Jason Jonathon Scott 57 Ridge Road, London N8 9LJ — MB BS 1989 Lond.; BSc (Hons.) Lond. 1986; DA (UK) 1992. SHO (Obst.) Univ. Coll. Hosp. Lond.

WAUGH, Martin Fenham Hall Surgery, Fenham Hall Drive, Fenham, Newcastle upon Tyne NE4 9XD — MB BS 1980 Newcastle; MB BS Newc. 1980. (Newcastle) GP Newc.

WAUGH, Michael Anthony General Infirmary, Leeds LS1 3EX Tel: 0113 392 6762; Wellfield House, 151 Roker Lane, Pudsey LS28 9ND — MB BS 1966 Lond.; FRCP Lond. 1995; FRCPI 1994, M 1993; FACSHP 1997; Dip. Ven. Soc. Apoth. Lond. 1974; DHMSA Lond. 1970. (Char. Cross) Cons. Phys. (Genitourin Med.) Gen. Infirm. Leeds; Sen. Clin. Lect. (Genitourin. Med.) Univ. Leeds; Dep. Edr. Internat. Jl. STD & AIDS. Socs: Founding Mem. Europ. Acad. Dermat. Venerol.; Internat. Union against Sexually Transm. Infecs. (Past Pres.); Med. Soc. for Study of Venereal Dis.s (Past Pres.). Prev: Sen. Regist. Genitourin. Med. Char. Cross Hosp. Lond; SHO Dermat. St. Johns Hosp. Dis. Skin Lond.

WAUGH, Norman Robert Mailpoint 728, Boldrewood, University of Southampton, Southampton SO16 8AJ — MB ChB 1972 Ed.; FRCP Ed. 1995; FRCP Glas. 1992; MRCP (UK) 1979; FFPHM RCP (UK) 1994; MPH Dundee 1986; MFCM 1986; DA Eng. 1974. Sen. Lect. in Pub. health and health Technol. Assessm., Univ. of S.ampton. Prev: Regist. (Med.) Dumfries & Galloway Roy. Infirm.; SHO (Anaesth.) E.. Gen. Hosp. Edin.; Ho. Phys. Chalmers Hosp. Edin.

WAUGH, Peter John Coultershaw Farm House, Petworth GU28 0JE Email: 100334.475@compuserve.com — MB BCh BAO 1978 NUI; MA Dub. 1984; LRCPI & LM, LRCSI & LM 1978; MFOM RCP Lond. 1994, AFOM 1985; DAvMed RCP Lond. 1982. Socs: BMA.

WAUGH, Peter Nicolson 23 Ganstead Lane, Bilton, Hull HU11 4AS Tel: 01482 811307 — MB ChB 1948 Glas. (Univ. Glas.) Prev: Med Adv. To D.V.L.A. - Hull & Dist.; Gen Med. Pract. - E. Hull; Regist. (Med.) E. Riding & Hull 'A' Hosp. Gps.

WAUGH, Robert Edward Michael Market Street Health Group, 52 Market Street, East Ham, London E6 2RA Tel: 020 8548 2200 Fax: 020 8548 2288 — BM 1978 Soton.; MRCGP 1983.

WAUGH, Sheila Margaret Lang Flat 15, 208 Old Dumbarton Road, Glasgow G3 8QB — MB ChB 1995 Glas.

WAUGH, Walter Norman (retired) 34 St Baldreds Road, North Berwick EH39 4PY Tel: 01620 892454 — MB ChB 1956 St. And.; MRCGP 1968; DObst RCOG 1961.

WAWMAN, Denise Margaret Irene Chevallier South Court Surgery, 11 Warden Road, Minehead TA24 5DS Tel: 01643 706767 Fax: 01643 706601 — MB ChB 1990 Leic.; MRCGP 1994. Prev: GP Wolverhampton; Trainee GP Wolverhampton; SHO Rotat. (Med.) New Cross Hosp. Wolverhampton.

WAWMAN, Ronald John (retired) Stable Cottage, Lewdown, Okehampton EX20 4DQ — MB ChB Sheff. 1957; FRCPsych 1980, M 1971; DPM Eng. 1962. Prev: PMO DHSS.

WAXMAN, Professor Jonathan Hugh Department of Oncology, Royal Postgraduate Medical School, Hammersmith Hospital, Du Cane Road, London W12 0NN Tel: 020 8383 4651 Fax: 020 8383 4653 — MD 1986 Lond.; BSc (Hons.) Lond. 1972, MD 1986, MB BS 1975; FRCP Lond. 1990; MRCP (UK) 1978. Prof. & Hon. Cons. Roy. Postgrad. Med. Sch. Imperial Coll. Hosp. Lond.; Chairm. of the Proslzlz cancer charity. Socs: Assn. Phys.; Amer. Soc. Clin. Oncol. Prev: Sen. Regist. (Oncol.) St. Bart. Hosp. Lond.; Regist. (Med.) St. Mary's Hosp. Lond.; SHO Lond. Chest Hosp.

WAY, Adam Christian 16 Kenmore Court, 26 Acol Road, London NW6 3AG Email: adamcway@hotmail.com — MB ChB 1998 Sheff. (Sheffield) SHO Gen. Surgic., N.wick Pk. & St. Marys Hosp., Watford Rd., Harrow. Prev: Orthop., N.wick Pk. Hosp., Harrow; A & E, N.wick Pk. Hosp., Harrow; Orthop., Roy. Nat. Orthopaedic Hosp. (RNOH).

WAY, Mr Bernard Gordon Barnsley D & H, Gawber Road, Barnsley S75 2; 1 The Paddock, Woolley, Wakefield WF4 2LZ Tel: 01226 384641 — MB BS Lond. 1963; FRCS Ed. 1972. (Middlx.) Cons. Urol. Surg. Barnsley HA. Socs: Brit. Assn. Urol. Surgs. Prev: Regist. (Surg.) Roy. Hosp. Wolverhampton; Surg. Regist. Crewe Memor. Hosp.; Regist. (Urol. Surg.) Newc. Univ. Hosps.

WAY, Bernard Philip James The Surgery, School Hill House, 33 High Street, Lewes BN7 2LU — MB ChB 1974 Birm.; MRCP (UK) 1978. Princip. in Gen. Pract., E. Sussex Health Auth., Maddison, Heath, Lamb, Way Swaine, E. Sussex; Hosp. Practioner Cardiac Dept. Roy. Sussex Co. Hosp. Brighton. Prev: Regist. (Cardiol.) Guy's Hosp. Lond.; SHO (Cardiol.) Lond. Chest Hosp.; SHO (Med.) Qu. Alexandra Hosp. & Wessex Regional Renal Unit Portsmouth.

WAY, Beryl Joy Broughton House Surgery, Redenhall Road, Harleston IP20 9AY Tel: 01379 852213; Beech Tree Cottage,

Walpole, Halesworth IP19 9AU — MRCS Eng. LRCP Lond. 1973. (Guy's) Prev: Regist. (Psychiat.) Maudsley Hosp. Lond.; SHO (Psychiat.) FarnBoro. Hosp. Kent; Ho. Surg. Guy's Hosp. Lond.

WAY, Carolyn Frances Broadway Green Farm, Petham, Canterbury CT4 5RX Tel: 01227 700283; Homestead, Blackhill Road, Wellow, Romsey SO51 6AQ Tel: 01794 322493 — MB BS 1993 Lond.; BSc Lond. 1990. (King's Coll. Lond.) SHO (Anaesth.) Soton. Gen. Hosp. Prev: SHO (c/o Elderly) E.bourne; SHO (A & E) Brighton; Ho. Off. (Surg.) Lond.

WAY, Geoffrey Leslie, OStJ (retired) Court Cottage, Milford, Godalming GU8 5HJ Tel: 01483 424548 — MRCS Eng. LRCP Lond. 1938; FFA RCS Eng. 1953; DA Eng. 1946. Prev: Cons. Anaesth. Guildford & Godalming Gp. Hosps. & King Edwd. VII Hosp. Midhurst.

WAY, Hedwig Marianne Martha (retired) 10 Bushmead Road, Luton LU2 7EU Tel: 01582 728037 — LRCP LRCS 1952 Ed.; LRCP LRCS Ed. LRFPS Glas. 1952. Prev: Asst. GP Luton.

WAY, Marion Crosbie (retired) 5 Foxes Row, Brancepeth, Durham DH7 8DH — BM BCh 1946 Oxf.; MA, BM BCh Oxf. 1946; FRCPsych. 1980, M 1973; DPM Eng. 1970; DTM & H Liverp. 1949; DCH Eng. 1949. Mem. Ment. Health Commiss. Prev: Cons. Psychiat. Earls Ho. Hosp. Durh.

***WAY, Mark Gregory** 59 Holmfield Avenue, Stoneygate, Leicester LE2 2BG Tel: 0116 2700 433 — MB ChB 1998 Leic.; MB ChB Leic 1998.

WAY, Melanie Bentley Village Surgery, Bentley, Farnham GU10 5LP Tel: 01420 22106; Stonecroft, 8 Pottery Lane, Wrecclesham, Farnham GU10 4QG Tel: 01252 716327 — MB BS 1986 Lond.; MRCGP 1990. Socs: BMA. Prev: Retainer Farnham Health Centre; Trainee GP Medway VTS.

WAYCOTT, John Angus, OStJ. (retired) Howgill, The Green, Ripley, Woking GU23 6AJ — MB BChir Camb. 1945; MRCP Lond. 1950; DCH Eng. 1949. Barrister-at-Law, Middle Temple.

WAYDENFELD, Stefan William (retired) 1 Tenterden Close, London NW4 1TJ Tel: 020 8203 5254 Email: waydenfeld@cs.com — LRCPI & LM, LRSCI & LM 1953; LRCPI & LM, LRCSI & LM 1953; MRCGP 1963. Prev: GP Lond.

WAYGOOD, Alistair Roy 1 Grove Park Terrace, London W4 3QG — MRCS Eng. LRCP Lond. 1970; MB BS Lond. 1970.

WAYMAN, Mr John 7 Bernard Close, Rackheath, Norwich NR13 6QS — MB BS 1991 Newc.; FRCS Eng. 1995.

WAYMAN, Matthew James Calver 15 Northcliffe Avenue, Nottingham NG3 6DA — MB ChB 1992 Leeds.

WAYMONT, Mr Brian Department of Urology, New Cross Hospital, Wolverhampton WV10 0QP Tel: 01902 307999 Fax: 01902 642872 — MB ChB Birm. 1980; MD Birm 1993; FRCS (Urol.) 1995; FRCS Ed. 1985. (Birm.) Cons. Urol. New Cross Hosp. Wolverhampton NHS Trust. Prev: Sen. Regist. (Urol.) Mersey RHA; Regist. (Urol.) Selly Oak Hosp. Birm.; Research Regist. (Urol.) Qu. Eliz. Hosp. Birm.

WAYNE, Adrian Nicholas Brondesbury Medical Centre, 279 Kilburn High Road, London NW6 7JQ Tel: 020 7624 9853 Fax: 020 7372 3660 — MB BS 1981 Lond.; BSc (Hons.) (Biochem.) Lond. 1978; MRCGP 1985; DRCOG 1985; DCH RCP Lond. 1984. (Univ. Coll. Hosp.) Socs: BMA. Prev: Trainee GP St. Bart. Hosp. VTS; Ho. Surg. Univ. Coll. Hosp. Lond.; Ho. Phys. St. Bart. Hosp. Lond.

WAYNE, Christopher John 9 Northwick Terrace, London NW8 8JE — MB ChB 1989 Birm.

WAYNE, David Johnson (retired) 39 Warkworth Street, Cambridge CB1 1EG Tel: 01223 352505 Fax: 01223 462508 Email: drdwayne@aol.com — BM BCh Oxf. 1958; MA Oxf. 1958; FRCP Lond. 1979, M 1963; FRCP Ed. 1976, M 1963. Prev: Cons. Phys. (Gen. Med. & Geriat. & Diabetes & Endocrinol.) Jas. Paget, Healthcare, NHS Trust Gt. Yarmouth.

WAYNE, Harold Leslie 93 Copeland Drive, Parkstone, Poole BH14 8NP — MB ChB 1948 Manch. (Manch.)

WAYNE, Norman Douglas 38 Oakdene Park, Finchley, London N3 1EU Tel: 020 8349 1160 Fax: 020 8349 1160 — MRCS Eng. LRCP Lond. 1941; DIH Eng. 1955; CPH 1954. (Middlx.) Med. Ref. Zurich, Permanent & Other Assur. Cos.; Chairm. & Mem. Med. Bd. Min. of Social Security. Socs: Assoc. Fac. Occupat. Med. RCP Lond; Soc. Occupat. Med.; Assur. Med. Soc. Prev: Cas. Surg. Off. Roy. Berks. Hosp. Reading; Postgrad. (Med.) St. Mary Islington Hosp. Highgate; Capt. RAMC 1942-1946.

WAYTE, Christopher No 18 Surgery, 18 Upper Oldfield Park, Bath BA2 3JZ Tel: 01225 427402 — MB ChB 1980 Bristol; BSc (Biochem.) Bristol 1977; MRCGP 1987; DRCOG 1985. G.P. Princip.; Clin. Asst., BrE. Unit, Roy. United Hosp., Bath.

WAYTE, Donald Malcolm, Lt.-Col. RAMC Pathology Department, Gwynedd General Hospital, Bangor LL57 2PW Tel: 01248 384261 Fax: 01248 355130; Rattlebone House, 18 Coed y Castell, Penybryn Road, Bangor LL57 1PH Tel: 01248 351785 — MB BS 1957 Birm.; MB ChB Birm. 1957; MD Birm. 1969; MRCS Eng. LRCP Lond. 1957; FRCPath 1979, M 1967; DTM & H Eng. 1959, DPath 1964. (Birm.) Cons. Path. Dist. Gen. Hosp. Bangor; Home Office Path. NW Forens. Sc. Laborat. Chorley. Socs: BMA; BAFM; IAP. Prev: Lt.-Col. RAMC, Pathol. AFIP Walter Reed Army Med. Center Washington, USA; Reader Path. Roy. Army Med. Coll. Millbank, Lond.; Ho. Phys. Qu. Eliz. Hosp. Birm.

WAYTE, Jeffrey Alan 11 Mortens Wood, Amersham HP7 9EQ — MB BS 1983 Adelaide.

WEADICK, Paul Richard Stanhope Surgery, Stanhope Road, Waltham Cross EN8 7DJ Tel: 01992 635300 Fax: 01992 624292 — MB ChB 1983 Liverp.

WEALE, Mr Adrian Elliott Department of Orthopaedics, Bristol Royal Infirmary, Marlborough St., Bristol BS2 8HW Tel: 0117 230000 Fax: 0117 928 2659; 7 Stoke Park Road, Stoke Bishop, Bristol BS9 1LE Tel: 0117 968 7957 Fax: 0117 928 2659 Email: ae.weale@virgin.net — MB BS 1986 Lond.; MS 2001 Lond.; FRCS Eng. 1991; FRCS (Orth.) 1996; FRCS Edin 2000. (St. Mary's) Cons. Orthop. Surg. Bristol Roy. Infirm.; Hon. Sen. Clin. Lect. Univ. Brist.; Hon. Cons. S.mead Hosp. Bristol. Prev: Biomet research fell. Univ. of Oxf.; Sen. Regist. (Orthop. & Traum. Surg.) Bristol Roy. Infirm.; Regist. (Orthop. & Traum. Surg.) Bristol Roy. Infirm.

WEALE, Andrew Robert 560 Warwick Road, Solihull B91 1AD — BM BS 1996 Nottm.

WEAR, Alan Nicholas Tel: 02380 840044 Fax: 02380 207554 — MB BS 1980 Lond.; BSc (Biomed. Sci.) Lond. 1977; MRCPsych 1989; MRCGP 1985; DRCOG 1984. (Roy. Free) Cons. Psychiat. Marchwood Priory Hosp.; Clin. Teach. Soton. Med. Sch. Socs: Assoc. Mem. Gp. Analytic Soc. Prev: Cons. St. James Hosp. Portsmouth; Sen. Regist. Wessex Regional Rotat. Portsmouth; Squibb Research Fell. Oxf. Univ.

WEAR, Ian Joseph Duke Street Surgery, 4 Duke Street, Barrow-in-Furness LA14 1LF Tel: 01229 820068 Fax: 01229 813840; The White Rose, 13 Walnut Hill, Holebeck, Barrow-in-Furness LA13 0JX Tel: 01229 839174 Fax: 01229 839174 Email: ianw@globalnet.co.uk — MB BS 1989 Newc.; DRCOG 1993.

WEARDEN, David John Northfield & Mastrick Medical Practice, Quarry Road, Aberdeen AB16 5UW; 23 Cromar Gardens, Kingswells, Aberdeen AB15 8TF — MB ChB 1985 Aberd.

WEARE, Roy Alan Central Surgery, Bell Street, Sawbridgeworth CM21 9AQ Tel: 01279 723172; 9 Clipped Hedge, Hatfield Heath, Bishop's Stortford CM22 7EG Tel: 01279 730227 — MB BChir 1975 Camb.; MRCP (UK) 1981. (Middlesex Hospital London) Prev: Regist. (Renal Med.) The Roy. Infirm. Edin.; Regist. (Med.) Chelmsford & Essex Hosps.; SHO (Cardiol.) Harefield Hosp. Middlx.

WEARING, Elizabeth Ann 38 Dukes Wood, Crowthorne RG45 6NF Tel: 01344 775653; 38 Dukes Wood, Crowthorne RG45 6NF Tel: 01344 775653 — MB BS 1970 Newc.; DA Eng. 1972; HFFP RCOG. Lead Clinician Family Plann. Surrey/Hants. Borders Trust; Clin. Asst. (Anaesth. St.Peter's Hosp. Chertsey. Prev: Regist. (Anaesth.) St. Peters Hosp. Chertsey; Hon. Surg. & Hon. Phys. P.ss Alexandra Hosp. Harlow.

WEARMOUTH, Elizabeth Margaret Department of Child Health, Eastbourne District General Hospital, Kings Drive, Eastbourne BN21 2UD Tel: 01323 417400 Fax: 01323 413751 Email: maggie.wearmouth@ed-tr.sthames.nhs.uk — MB ChB 1980 Leeds; MRCP (UK) 1985; FRCPCH 1997; MRCGP 1985; DCH RCP Lond. 1983; Cert. Family Plann. JCC 1985. Cons. in Child Health & Paediat.; Paediat. Adviser, James Ho. Hospice in the Community Ashwood Nursing Ho., Burwash E. Sussex. Socs: BMA; Brit. Assn. Perinatal Med.; Sec. S. Thames Paediat. Soc. Prev: Sen. Regist. (Paediat. & Community Child Health) Basingstoke & Soton.; Research Fell. (Paediat. Neurol.) Soton Gen. Hosp.; Regist. (Paediat.) Poole Gen. Hosp.

WEARN, Andrew Mark The Laurie Pike Health Centre, 95 Birchfield Road, Handsworth, Birmingham B19 1LH Tel: 0121 554

WEARN

0621 Fax: 0121 554 6163; 922 Bristol Road, Sellyoak, Birmingham B29 6NB — MB ChB 1990 Birm.; MRCGP 1995; DFFP 1995; M.Med.Sci. Birm. 1998. (Birm.) Lect. (Gen. Pract.) Birm. Socs: BMA; AUDGP; CMF.

WEARN, John Leonard (retired) — MB BS 1960 Lond.; MRCS Eng. LRCP Lond. 1960; FRCGP 1988; DObst RCOG 1963.

WEARNE, Iain Michael James 10 Highbury Crescent, London N5 1RN — MB ChB 1991 Birm.; ChB Birm. 1991.

WEARNE, John Penrose Great Sutton Medical Centre, Old Chester Road, Great Sutton, Ellesmere Port CH66 3PB Tel: 0151 339 3126 Fax: 0151 339 9225; 6 Dibbins Green, Wirral CH63 0QF Tel: 0151 334 7640 Fax: 0151 343 0313 Email: jwearne@compuserve.com — MB ChB 1982 Liverp.; FRCGP 1996, M 1986; DRCOG 1985. (Liverp.) Clin. Asst. (Ophth.) Arrowe Pk. Hosp. Birkenhead.

WEARNE, Simon 41 Boscathnoe Way, Heamoor, Penzance TR18 3JS; 33 Khaha Road, Tooting, London SW17 0EN Tel: 020 8082 1059 — MB BS 1998 Lond.; MA(Oxon.) 1992. (St Georges)

WEARNE, Susan Marion South Bank Medical Centre, 175 Bishopthorpe Road, York YO23 1PD; 3 Longwood Link, York YO30 4UG Email: susan.w.tim.h@dial.pipex.com — BM Soton. 1987; MRCGP 1991; DFFP 1994; DRCOG 1992; DCH RCP Lond. 1990. (Southampton) Hon. Sen. Clin. Lect. Leeds Univ. Prev: Trainee GP Kettering Dist. Gen. Hosp.; Ho. Off. Roy. S. Hants. Hosp.

WEARS, Robert Solihull Hospital, Lode Lane, Solihull B91 2JL Tel: 0121 711 4455 Fax: 0121 711 5057; 55 Links Drive, Solihull B91 2DJ — MB ChB 1986 Manch.; MSc Lond. 1994; MRCP (UK) 1990; FRCP Lond. 1998. (Manch.) Cons. Phys. Gen. Med. (interest c/o elderly) Solihull Hosp.; Hon. Sen. Clin. Lect. Socs: Brit. Geriat. Soc.; W. Midl. Inst. of Ageing and Health; Midl. Gastroenterol. Soc. Prev: Sen. Regist. (Gen. & Geriat. Med.) W. Midl. Regional Train. Scheme; Regist. Rotat. (Gen. & Geriat. Med.) N. & E. Birm.

WEATHERALL, Sir David John New Centre Weatherall Inst. of Molecular Medicine, University of Oxford, John Radcliffe Hospital, Headington, Oxford OX3 9DS Tel: 01865 222360 Fax: 01865 222501 Email: liz.rose@imm.ox.ac.uk; 8 Cumnor Rise Road, Cumnor Hill, Oxford OX2 9HD — Hon. FRCPCH 1996; Hon. DSc Mahidol, Uni. Thailand, 1999; Hon. DSc Exeter, 1999; Hon. DSc McGill, 1999; Dec. Of Humane Letters, Johns Hopkins Univ. 1998; MB ChB (Hons.) Liverp. 1956; Hon. DSc Ed. 1989; Hon. DSc Manch 1988, South Bank Univ. 1995; Hon. MD Nottm. 1993; Hon. MD Sheff. 1989; Hon. MD Leeds 1988; FRCP Ed. 1983; FRCP Lond. 1969, M 1958; FRCPath 1978, M 1969; Hon. FACP 1991; Hon. Imperial Coll. 1990; FRS 1977; Hon. FRCOG 1988; Hon. FRACP 1986; MA Oxf. 1974; MD Liverp. 1962 FRCP FRCP Ed.; Hon. MD Leeds 1988, Hon. LLD Bristol 1994, Liverp. 1991; Hon. DSc Lond. 1993, Oxf. Brookes Univ. 1995; Hon. DSc Keele 1993; Hon. DSc Aberd. 1991; Hon. DSc Leic. 1991. Emerit. Regius Prof. Med. Univ. Oxf.; Hon. Dir. MRC Molecular Haemat. Unit; Hon. Cons. Phys. Oxon. HA; Stud. Christ Ch. Oxf.; Emerit. Hon. Dir., Inst. for Molecular Med. Univ. Oxf. Socs: Assn. Phys.; Brit. Soc. Haematol.; Hon. Mem. Assn. Amer. Phys. Prev: Prof. Haemat. Univ. Liverp.; Nuffield Prof. Clin. Med. Univ. Oxf.

WEATHERALL, Josephine Alice Coreen (retired) Willows, Charlbury, Oxford OX7 3PX Tel: 01608 810200 — BSc 1944, MB ChB Ed. 1945; FFCM 1980, M 1973. Prev: Cons. Epidemiol. to EEC Concerted Action - EUROCAT.

WEATHERALL, Miles (retired) Willows, Charlbury, Oxford OX7 3PX — DSc Oxf. 1966, DM 1952, BM BCh 1943. Prev: Dir. (Estab.) Wellcome Research Laborats. Beckenham.

WEATHERBY, Emma Dale 186 Grove Lane, Cheadle Hulme, Cheadle SK8 7NH — MB ChB 1992 Bristol.

WEATHERBY, Stuart John 4 The Avenue, Alsager, Stoke-on-Trent ST7 2AN — MB ChB 1993 Bristol.

WEATHERHEAD, Anne Elizabeth (retired) Newton Park, 59 Brechin Road, Kirriemuir DD8 4DE — MB ChB 1960 Ed.; MRCPsych 1983. Prev: Med. Off. Ment. Welf. Commiss. for Scotl.

***WEATHERHEAD, Martin Paul** Southwick Health Centre, The Green, Southwick, Sunderland SR5 2LT Tel: 0191 548 6550 Fax: 0191 548 0867 — MB BS 1988 Newc.

WEATHERHEAD, Susan Margaret Central Milton Keynes Medical, 1 North Sixth Street, Central Milton Keynes, Milton Keynes MK9 2NR Tel: 01908 605775 Fax: 01908 676752; 1 Abraham Close, Willen Park, Milton Keynes MK15 9JA Email:

sksandt@aol.com — MB BS 1982 Lond.; BA Oxf. 1979; MRCGP 1986; DCH RCP Lond. 1987; DRCOG 1984.

WEATHERILL, Barbara Ann Fforestfach Medical Centre, 118 Ravenhill Road, Fforestfach, Swansea SA5 5AA Tel: 01792 581666 Fax: 01792 585332; Sheraton House, Gowerton Road, Three Crosses, Swansea SA4 3PX Tel: 01792 872001 Fax: 01792 872001 — BM 1978 Soton.; MRCP (UK) 1981; MRCGP 1987; DRCOG 1980. Prev: Trainee GP Bedford VTS; Clin. Asst. (Haemat.) & Regist. (Gen. Med.) Bedford Gen. Hosp.

WEATHERILL, David 17 Blaidwood Drive, Durham DH1 3TD — MB ChB 1973 Leeds; PhD Leeds 1982, BSc (Hons.) 1970; FFA RCS Eng. 1977. (Leeds) Cons. Anaesth. Dryburn Hosp. Durh.

WEATHERILL, Mr John Randolph Springbank House, Menston Old Lane, Menston, Ilkley LS29 7QQ — MB BS 1961 Lond.; FRCS Eng. 1967; DO Eng. 1964. Cons. Ophth. Bradford Roy. Infirm.; Hon. Vis. Prof. Ophth. Sci. Bradford Univ. Socs: Ophth. Soc. UK. Prev: Sen. Regist. Bristol Eye Hosp.

WEATHERILL, Julia 20 Meadows Lane, Darton, Barnsley S75 5PF — MB ChB 1996 Ed.

WEATHERILL, Walter Frederick 12 St Martin's Court, Lairgate, Beverley HU17 8JB — MRCS Eng. LRCP Lond. 1948; MRCGP 1966. (Leeds)

WEATHERLEY, Anne Ash Surgery, Chilton Gardens, Ash, Canterbury CT3 2HA Tel: 01304 812227; Longbrook, Church Hill, Elmstone, Preston, Canterbury CT3 1HL — MB ChB 1979 Leeds; MRCGP 1984; DRCOG 1983; DCH RCP Lond. 1983.

WEATHERLEY, Mr Christopher Roy 1 The Quadrant, Wonford Road, Exeter EX2 4LE Tel: 01392 272951 Fax: 01392 421662 — MD 1980 Liverp.; MB ChB 1968; FRCS (Orthop.) Ed. 1984; FRCS Eng. 1974; FRCS Ed. 1973. (Liverp.) Cons. Spinal Surg. P.ss Eliz. Orthop. Centre & Roy. Devon & Exeter Hosp. (Wonford).

WEATHERLEY, Pauline Logan 54 Grasmere Road, Muswell Hill, London N10 2DJ — MB ChB 1972 Aberd.; DO RCS Eng. 1990.

WEATHERLEY, Rachel Ellen 16 Moorhouse Cl, Chester CH2 2HU — MB ChB 1997 Leeds.

WEATHERSTONE, Jane Murray 135 Seatonville Road, Monkseaton, Whitley Bay NE25 9EG — MB ChB 1986 Sheff.

WEATHERSTONE, Robert MacKenzie 23 Chigwell Rise, Chigwell IG7 6AQ Tel: 020 8500 3280; Havering Hospitals Trust, Oldchurch Hospital, Romford RM7 0BE Tel: 01708 746090 — MB BChir 1971 Camb.; MA, MB Camb. 1971, BChir 1970; FRCP Lond. 1989; MRCP (UK) 1974. Cons. Phys. Havering Hosps. Trust.

WEATHERUP, Alan Salisbury Road Surgery, 98 Salisbury Road, Barry CF62 7LN Tel: 01446 720049 Fax: 01446 733691; 52 Picton Road, Rhoose, Barry CF62 3HU — MB BCh 1983 Wales; MRCGP 1988. CME Tutor Vale Glam. Socs: BMA; Barry Med. Soc.; Cardiff Med. Soc.

WEATHERUP, Claire Helen Pershore Health Centre, Priest Lane, Pershore DY11 5PA — MB ChB 1988 Birm.; MRCGP 1993. (Birmingham)

WEATHERUP, James (retired) 38 Malone Hill Park, Malone Road, Belfast BT9 6RE — MB BCh BAO Belf. 1954; DObst RCOG 1956.

WEATHERUP, John 1 Hoadly Road, London SW16 1AE — MB BCh BAO 1947 Belf.

WEAVER, Andrew Yew Tree Lodge, Poulton Royd Drive, Bebington, Wirral CH63 4LD — MB BS 1985 Lond.; MRCP (UK) 1989; FRCR 1993; MD Univ. Lond. 1997. (Westm.) Cons. (Clin. Oncol.) Oxf.

WEAVER, Andrew Bernard Child & Adolescent Mental Health Service, Macclesfield DGH, Victoria road, Macclesfield SK10 33L Tel: 01625 663772 — MB ChB Manch. 1984; MRCPsych 1988. (Manchester) Cons. Child & Adolesc. Psychiat. E. Chesh. NHS Trust Macclesfield; Clin. Lect. Univ. Liverp. Socs: ACPP. Prev: Sen. Regist. (Child & Adolesc. Psychiat.) Manch.; Regist. Rotat. (Psychiat.) N. Manch.

WEAVER, Andrew John Winch Lane Surgery, Winch Lane, Haverfordwest SA61 1RN Tel: 01437 762333 Fax: 01437 766912 — MB ChB 1972 Bristol; MRCGP 1978; Dip. Ther. Wales 1995; DObst RCOG 1974. Prev: SHO (O & G & Paediat.) W. Wales Gen. Hosp. Carmarthen; Ho. Surg. St. Martin's Hosp. Bath.

WEAVER, Ann Lynette Bartlett Winch Lane Surgery, Winch Lane, Haverfordwest SA61 1RN Tel: 01437 762333 Fax: 01437 766912; Redlands, 10 Merlins Hill, Haverfordwest SA61 1PQ — MB ChB 1972 Bristol; MRCGP 1978; Dip. Ther. Wales 1995. Prev: SHO

(O & G) W. Wales Gen. Hosp. Carmarthen; Ho. Surg. MusGr. Pk. Hosp. Taunton; Ho. Phys. Roy. United Hosp. Bath.

WEAVER, Miss Anne Elizabeth 4 Hazell Park, Amersham HP7 9AB Tel: 01494 729470 Email: aeweaver@bigfoot.com — BM BS 1995 Nottm.; Dip IMC 2000 (RCS Ed.); BMedSci Nottm. 1993; MRCS Eng. 1998. (Nottingham) Specialist Regist. (A&E Med.), Merseyside Rot.

WEAVER, Anthony David Odiham Health Centre, Deer Park View, Odiham, Hook RG29 1JY; Butterwood, The St, North Warnborough, Hook RG29 1BG Tel: 01256 703132 Fax: 01256 703508 — BM BCh 1974 Oxf.; MA Oxf. 1975; DCH Eng. 1977. (Univ. Coll. Hosp.) Socs: Assoc. Mem. Brit. Med. Acupunc. Soc.; Soc. Occupat. Med.

***WEAVER, Christine Beverley** 4 Hazell Park, Amersham HP7 9AB — MB ChB 1998 Birm.

WEAVER, Corinna Mary (retired) 15 Queenwood, Cyncoed, Cardiff CF23 9LE — MB BCh Wales 1959; FRCP Ed. 1981, M 1968; DCH Eng. 1961; DObst RCOG 1962; FRCPCH 1994. Prev: Cons. Paediat. Univ. Hosp. of Wales Cardiff.

WEAVER, Mr Edward John Martin (retired) The Lone Pine, Matching Green, Harlow CM17 0QB Tel: 01279 731295 — MRCS Eng. LRCP Lond. 1945; MA, MB BChir Camb. 1945; FRCS Eng. 1948. Hon. Cardio-Thoracic Surg. Lond. Hosp. Prev: Surg. (Thoracic) Roy. Masonic Hosp. Lond.

WEAVER, Hamilton Melville (retired) Croftcroy, Manse Road, Killin FK21 8UY Tel: 01567 820567 — MB ChB 1940 Ed. Prev: GP P'boro.

WEAVER, Helen 41 Bolton Road E., Wirral CH62 4RU — MB ChB 1994 Dundee; DRCOG 1996.

WEAVER, Helen Paula Bicester Health Centre, Bicester OX26 6AT; 3 Ventfield Close, Horton-cum-Studley, Oxford OX33 1AN Tel: 01865 351013 — MB ChB 1988 Bristol; MRCGP 1995; DRCOG 1993; DA (UK) 1991. (Bristol) Asst. GP Oxon. Prev: SHO (A & E) Stockport Infirm.; Trainee GP Burton Rd. Family Pract. Manch. & Bridge St. Surg. W. Yorks.

WEAVER, John Andrew 37 Adelaide Park, Belfast BT9 6FY Tel: 01232 668789 — MD 1954 Belf.; MB BCh BAO 1950; FRCP Lond. 1970, M 1954. Cons. Phys. Roy. Vict. Hosp. Belf.; Capt. RAMC, TA, Med. Off. N. Irish Horse. Prev: Med. Research Counc. Trav. Fell. in Med. (Eli Lilly Fell.) Endocrine; Dept. Johns Hopkins Hosp. Baltimore; Med. Regist. Roy. Vict. Hosp. Belf.

WEAVER, Mr John Patrick Acton (retired) 229 Strathmartine Road, Dundee DD3 8QQ Tel: 01382 889383 Fax: 01382 889383 — BM BCh Oxf. 1954; MA Oxf. 1950; BA (1st cl. Hons. Animal Physiol.) 1950; BSc 1952; DM MCh 1968; FRCS Eng. 1961; FRCS Ed. 1960. Prev: Cons. Urol. Roy. Dundee Infirm. & Hon. Sen. Lect. (Surg.) Univ. Dundee.

WEAVER, Jolanta Urszula St Annes Cottage, Church Chare, Whickham, Newcastle upon Tyne NE16 4SH Tel: 0191 488 2745 Fax: 0191 491394 Email: wju.weaver@virgin.net — MRCS Eng. LRCP Lond. 1984; PhD Lond. 1993; MRCP (UK) 1987. (Lond. Hosp. Coll.) Sen. Regist. (Diabetes, Endocrinol. & Gen. Med.) Freeman Hosp. Newc. u. Tyne; Sen. Lect. (Diabetes Med.) Qu. Eliz. Hosp.; Dept. of Med. Univ. of Newc. Socs: Med. Res. Soc.; Soc. Endocrinol.; Brit. Diabetic Assn. Prev: Sen. Regist. (Diabetes, Endocrinol. & Gen. Med.) Roy. Vict. Infirm. Newc. & Middlesbrough Gen. Hosp.; Lect. (Endocrinol.) Roy. Hosp. Lond.

WEAVER, Judith Barbara 75 Hamilton Avenue, Harbourne, Birmingham B17 8AS — MB BS 1966 Lond.; MD Lond 1978, MB BS 1966; FRCS Ed. 1973; MRCS Eng. LRCP Lond. 1966; FRCOG 1986, M 1973. (Univ. Coll. Hosp.) Cons. Obst. Birm. Matern. Hosp. Prev: Lect. Dept. O & G Welsh Nat. Sch. Med. Cardiff; Regist. (O & G) United Birm. Hosps.; SHO Gyn. Univ. Coll. Hosp. Lond.

WEAVER, Kevin Nicholas John Happy House Surgery, Durham Road, Sunderland SR3 4BY Tel: 0191 528 2222; 15 Roker Park Terrace, Sunderland SR6 9LY — MB ChB 1982 Manch.

WEAVER, Professor Lawrence Trevelyan Department of Child Health, Yorkhill Hospitals, Dalnair St., Glasgow G3 8SJ Tel: 0141 201 0236 Fax: 0141 201 0837 — MB BChir 1973 Camb.; MA Camb. 1973, MD 1986, BA 1970; FRCP Lond. 1994; FRCP Glas. 1994; MRCP (UK) 1979; MRCS Eng. LRCP Lond. 1973; DCH Eng. 1979; DRCOG 1977; FRCPCH 1998. (St. Thos.) Prof. Child Health Univ. Glas.; Hon. Cons. Paediat. Yorkhill Hosps. Glas. Socs: Counc. Europ. Soc. Paediat. Gastroenterol. Nutrit.; Nutrit. Soc.; Brit. Soc. Gastroenterol. Prev: Mem. Scientif. Staff MRC Dunn Nutrit. Unit.

Camb.; MRC Research Fell. Dunn Nutrit. Unit Camb.; Fulbright Travel Schol. Harvard Univ. Med. Sch.

WEAVER, Mark Gordon Department of Psychological Medicine, William Harvey House, St Bartholumew's Hsopital, London EC1A 7BE; 67 Stanmore Road, Edgbaston, Birmingham B16 9SU — MB BS 1984 Lond.; MRCpsych 1990. (King's College Hospital, London) Cons. Psychiat. St Bartholumew's Hosp. Prev: Sen. Regist., St Bartholumew's Hosp., Rotat.

WEAVER, Michael Kenneth 47 Elsdon Road, Gosforth, Newcastle upon Tyne NE3 1HY; 47 Elsdon Road, Gosforth, Newcastle upon Tyne NE3 1HY — MB BS 1983 Newc.

WEAVER, Nicola Frances Parkway Medical Centre, 2 Frenton Close, Chapel House Estate, Newcastle upon Tyne NE5 1EH Tel: 0191 267 1313 Fax: 0191 229 0630 — MB BS 1987 Lond.; BA Camb. 1984; MRCP (UK) 1991.

WEAVER, Mr Paul Cassford Queen Alexandra Hospital, Cosham, Portsmouth PO6 3LY Tel: 023 92 379451 Fax: 023 92 214162 Email: paulweaver@qmailol.porthosp.swest.nhs.uk; 9 Sarum Close, Sarum Road, Winchester SO22 5LY Tel: 01962 863081 Fax: 01962 863081 Email: paulweave01@hotmail.com — MB BS Lond. 1960; MD Lond. 1970; FRCS Ed. 1967; FRCS Eng. 1967; MRCS Eng. LRCP Lond. 1960. (St. Bart.) p/t Cons. Surg., Oncol. & Upper Gastrointestinal Portsmouth Hosps. NHS Trust; Clin. Teach. & Examr. Surg. Wessex Med. Sch. Univ. Soton; Sen. Lect. Med. Educat. Socs: Fell. Brit. Assn. Surg. Oncol.; Fell. Assoc. Surgs. GB & Irel.; (Past Pres.) Wessex Surgs. Prev: Sen. Regist. (Surg.) W.m. Hosp. Lond. & Clin. Asst. St. Marks Hosp.; Regist. (Surg.) St. Bart. Hosp. Lond.; Ho. Off. (Gen. Surg. & Orthop.) Unit St. Bart. Hosp. Lond.

WEAVER, Mr Ralph Michael Hexham General Hospital, Hexham NE46 1QJ — BSc (Anat.) Lond. 1967, MB BS 1970; FRCS Eng. 1976. Cons. Gen. Surg. N.d. HA.; Med. Dir. Hexham Gen. Hosp. Prev: Sen. Surg. Regist. W. Midl. Regional Train. Scheme; Ho. Phys. Univ. Coll. Hosp. Lond.

WEAVER, Richard David Talbot Medical Centre, 63 Kinson Road, Bournemouth BH10 4BX Tel: 01202 523059 Fax: 01202 533239; 17 Eleanor Drive, Bear Wood, Bournemouth BH11 9PB Tel: 01202 573248 Fax: 01202 573248 — MB BCh BAO 1978 Belf.; MRCGP 1986; DRCOG 1981. (Qu. Univ. Belf.) GP; Assoc. Dir. Postgrad. GP Educat. (Dorset). Prev: Course Organiser Dorset VTS; Chairm. E. Dorset Non-Fundholders Gp.; Tutor (Gen. Pract.) Bournemouth & ChristCh.

WEAVER, Sean Anthony 4 Burford Road, East Harnham, Salisbury SP2 8AN Email: s.a.weaver@bath.ac.uk — BM BCh 1993 Oxf.; MRCP 1996. (Oxf.) Research Fell.(Gastroenterol. & Gen. Med.).

WEAVER, Simon Richard 7 Westville Road, Cardiff CF23 5DE — MB BCh 1997 Wales.

WEAVERS, Barbara Janet St Michaels Hospice, Bartestree, Hereford HR1 4HA Tel: 01432 851000; The Villa Farm, Pendock, Staunton, Gloucester GL19 3PG — MB BCh 1977 Wales. Med. Off. St. Michaels Hospice Hereford.

WEAVIND, Glenn Peter 16 Taw Drive, Chandlers Ford, Eastleigh SO53 4SL — BM 1980 Soton.; MRCPath. 1989.

WEAVING, Hester Claudia (retired) Rose Cottage, Station Road, Armathwaite, Carlisle CA4 9PL — MB BCh BAO 1949 Belf.; MRCPsych 1972; DPM RCPSI 1952. Psychiat. Eden Valley Hospice Carluke. Prev: Cons. Psychiat. Durh. Health Dist. & Co. Hosp. Durh.

WEAVING, Jennifer Elizabeth — MB ChB 1982 Manch.; BSc (Med. Sci.) St. And. 1979; DRCOG 1985. Regist. In O&G, Carlisie. Prev: Trainee GP E. Cumbria VTS; Ho. Off. (Med./Surg.) Rochdale HA.

WEAVING, Peter Geoffrey Brampton Medical Practice, 4 Market Place, Brampton CA8 1NL Tel: 016977 2551 Fax: 016977 41944; Castellane House, Great Corby, Carlisle CA4 8NQ Tel: 0169 772551 — BM BS 1981 Nottm.; BMedSci. Nottm. 1979, BM BS 1981; MRCGP 1986; DRCOG 1985. Prev: Trainee GP/SHO Brampton Cumbria; SHO (Gen. & Geriat. Med.) Birch Hill Hosp. Rochdale; Ho. Off. (Gen. Med.) Bury Gen. Hosp.

WEBB, Adele Frances 143 Woodstock Avenue, Glasgow G41 3SE — MB BS 1991 New South Wales.

WEBB, Adrian Leslie 400 Bald Hill Road, Warwick RI 02886, USA; 3 Midhurst Close, Chilwell, Nottingham NG9 5FQ — MB BS 1980 Lond.; MRCPsych 1984. Staff Psychiat. Harvard Community Health Plan of New Eng. Warwick, R hode. Is., USA; Clin. Asst.

WEBB

Prof. Brown Univ. Providence Rhode Is. USA. Socs: Amer. Psychiat. Assn.; Roy. Coll. Psychiat. Prev: Med. Director E. Bay Ment. Health Center Inc. Barrington Rhode Is., USA; Staff Psychiat., Psychiat. Specialists Inc. Pawtucket Rhode Is., USA.

WEBB, Alan Edward Royal Hospital for Sick Children, Yorkhill, Glasgow G3 8SJ Tel: 0141 201 0000; 186 Nithsdale Road, Pollokshields, Glasgow G41 5EU Tel: 0141 433 2590 Email: acwebb@globalnet.co.uk — MB ChB 1989 Ed.; MRCP Ed. 1994. Specialist Regist. (Paediat.). Prev: Sen. (Paediat.) Nazareth Hosp. Nazareth 16100 Israel; Supervisory SHO Roy. Aberd. Childr.s Hosp.

WEBB, Alan Terence 37 Millhouse Woods Lane, Cottingham HU16 4HA Tel: 01482 876176 — MB BS 1986 Lond.; MD Lond. 1995; MRCP (UK) 1990. Regist. (Nephrol. & Gen. Med.) Univ. Hosp. S. Manch. Socs: BMA. Prev: Research Fell. & Hon. Regist. Char. Cross Hosp. Lond.; Regist. (Gen. Med. & Nephrol.) P.ss Roy. Hosp. Hull; Regist. (Thoracic Med.) Castle Hill Hosp.

WEBB, Alexandra Joan St. Wilfrid's Hospice, Grosvenor Road, Chichester PO19 2FP Tel: 01243 775302 Fax: 01243 538171 — MB ChB 1979 Ed.; FFA RCSI 1987. Cons. Palliat. Med. St Wilfrid's Hospice Chichester.; Hon. Cons.(Palliat. Med.) St. Richard's Hosp. & Sussex, Weald & Down NHS Trusts Chichester. Prev: Sen. Regist. (Palliat. Med.) St. Columba's Hospice Edin.; Sen. Regist. McMillan Fell. Chronic Pain & Palliat. Med. Bradford & Leeds HAs.

WEBB, Alison Dora (retired) Fernleigh, 4 Church Park, Newton Ferrers, Plymouth PL8 1AJ Tel: 01752 873033 — BM BCh Oxf. 1949; MRCS Eng. LRCP Lond. 1948; DPM Eng. 1972. Prev: Sen. Regist. (Child Psychiat.) Nuffield Child Psychiat.

WEBB, Andrew Arthur Charlton 3 Gwynne Park Avenue, Woodford Green IG8 8AB — MB BS 1992 Lond.

WEBB, Andrew James 31 Westbourne Close, Salisbury SP1 2RU Tel: 0411 305772; Top flat, 40 Oakhill Road, London SW15 2QR Tel: 020 8874 6397 — MB BS 1994 Lond.; BSc (Hons.) Lond. 1991; MRCP Irel. 1998. (Charing Cross and Westminster) Specialist Regist. (Clin. Pharmacol. & Gen. Med.) Roy. Lond. Hosps, NHS Trust. Prev: SHO Rotat. (Med.) Brighton.

WEBB, Andrew John Elderly Care Unit, Dorset County Hospital, Williams Avenue, Dorchester DT1 2JY Tel: 01305 251150 Fax: 01305 254155 — MB BS 1975 Newc.; MRCP (UK) 1979. Cons. Phys. c/o Elderly W. Dorset HA. Socs: Brit. Geriat. Soc.

WEBB, Andrew Michael Department of Anaesthesia, Lincoln County Hospital, Greetwell Road, Lincoln LN2 5QY Tel: 01522 512512 — MB ChB 1986 Leic.; FRCA 1995. Cons. Anaesth., Lincoln Co. Hosp. Socs: Pain Soc.

WEBB, Andrew Roy University College London Hospitals, Department of Intensive Care, Middlesex Hospital, Mortimer St., London W1T 3AA Tel: 020 7380 9008 Fax: 020 7636 3264 Email: a.webb@academic.uclh.nthames.nhs.uk — MB BCh 1981 Wales; MD Wales 1993; FRCP Lond. 1997; MRCP (UK) 1984. (Univ. Wales) Clin. Dir. Intens. Care & Cardiac Servs. & Cons. Phys. Univ. Coll. Lond. Hosps. Socs: Fell. Roy. Soc. Med.; Eur. Soc. Intens. Care Med.; Intens. Care Soc. Prev: Cons. Phys. (ITU) Bloomsbury & Islington HA; Clin. Research Fell. & Lect. (Med.) St. Geo. Hosp. Med. Sch.; Regist. (Med.) S & W Glam. HA.

WEBB, Andrew Russell 11 Gilders, Sawbridgeworth CM21 0EE — MB BS 1990 Lond.; BSc Lond. 1986; MRCP (UK) 1994. Research Fell. & Hon. Regist. Roy. Marsden Hosp. Prev: SHO Rotat. (Med.) Chase Farm.

WEBB, Anne Margaret Caroline Central Abacus, 40/46 Dale Street, Liverpool L2 5SF Tel: 0151 284 2500 Fax: 0151293 2005 — MB ChB 1981 Sheff.; MFFP 1993; MRCOG 1988; MRCGP 1985; DRCOG 1983. Cons. Family Plann & Reproduc. Health Care N. Mersey Community NHS Trust; Regional Adviser (Mersey) Fac. of Family Plann. & Reproductive Health Care RCOG. Socs: Bd. Mem. Fac. Family Plann & Reproduc. Health Care RCOG; (Bd. Mem.) Europ. Soc. Contracep. Prev: SCMO (Family Plann.) Centr. Manch. & S. Manch.; WHO Research Fell. Manch. Univ.

WEBB, Mr Anthony John (cons. rooms), 7 Percival Road, Clifton, Bristol BS8 3LE Tel: 01179 738349 Fax: 01179 733809; Grange Park House, 10 Grange Park, Westbury-on-Trym, Bristol BS9 4BP Tel: 01179 629320 — MB ChB Bristol 1953; ChM Bristol 1974; FRCS Eng. 1959. (Bristol) Sen. Research Fell. Univ. Bristol; Sen. Clin. Lect. (Surg.) Univ. Bristol 1990. Socs: Brit. Soc. Clin. Cytol.; Brit. Assn. Endocrine Surgs. (Ex-Pres.); Brit M-C Soc. (Ex-Pres.). Prev: Cons. Surg. Bristol Roy. Infirm.; Sen. Regist. (Surg.) Qu. Eliz. Hosp. Birm.; Regist. (Surg.) Frenchay Hosp. Bristol.

WEBB, Professor Anthony Kevin 50 Swann Lane, Cheadle Hulme, Cheadle SK8 7HU Email: theswebbs@hotmail.com — MB BS 1972 Lond.; FRCP Lond. 1990. Prof. of Thoriac Med.. Wythenshawe Hosp. Prev: Cons. Phys. N. Manch. Gen. Hosp. & Monsall Hosp.; Sen. Regist. (Chest Med.) Wythenshawe Hosp. Manch.; Regist. (Med.) Whipps Cross Hosp. & Lond. Hosp.

WEBB, Antony Roger The Surgery, High Street, Cheslyn Hay, Walsall WS6 7AB Tel: 01922 701280 — MRCS Eng. LRCP Lond. 1975.

WEBB, Brendan Joseph Ampleforth Abbey, York YO62 4EN Tel: 01439 766810 Fax: 01439 766724 — MA Camb. 1945; MRCS Eng. LRCP Lond. 1943. (Camb. & St. Bart.) Prev: Surg. Lt. RNVR; Ho. Surg. St. Bart. Hosp.

WEBB, Brian Wykeham (retired) Nigella, West Monkton, Taunton TA2 8QT Tel: 01823 412442 — MB BS Lond. 1946; MD Lond. 1952; FRCP Lond. 1970, M 1953; MRCS Eng. LRCP Lond. 1945; FRCPCH 1997; DCH Eng. 1951. Cons. Paediat. W. Som. Health Dist. Prev: Vis. WHO Prof. Paediat. & Child Health Univ. Khartoum.

WEBB, Carol Louise Ilkeston Health Centre, South Street, Ilkeston DE7 5PZ Tel: 0115 932 2933 Email: drswebb@btconnect.com; 19 Maxwell Street, Breaston, Derby DE72 3AH Tel: 01332 872680 — BM BS 1987 Nottm.; DRCOG 1991.

WEBB, Carole Ann Queens Hospital Burton, Belvedere Road, Burton-on-Trent DE13 0RB Tel: 01283 566333; The Ridgeway, 46A Main St, Repton, Derby DE65 6FB Tel: 01283 704873 — MB ChB 1984 Sheff.; FRCA 1991. (Sheff.) Cons. Anaesth. & Intens. Care Qu. Hosp. Burton-on-Trent. Prev: Sen. Regist. (Anaesth.) Midl. Train. Scheme; Regist. Rotat. (Anaesth.) Stoke-on-Trent.

WEBB, Cecil Hugh The Royal Hospitals NHS Trust, Grosvenor Road, Belfast BT12 6BA Tel: 02890 240503 Fax: 02890 311416 — MB BCh BAO 1985 Belf.; BDS Belf. 1971; FRCPath 1991, M 1979; FFPath RCPI 1990. Cons. Clin. Bact. Roy. Hosps. NHS Trust. Prev: Sen. Lect. & Cons. Oral Med. & Path. Sch. Dent. Sci. Univ. Dub.; Lect. (Microbiol. & Immunobiol.) Qu. Univ. Belf.

WEBB, Christopher David Tel: 01748 811475 Fax: 01748 818284; Prospect House, Harmby, Leyburn DL8 5PE Tel: 01969 623199 — MB ChB 1993 Leeds; MRCGP 1997; DFFP 1997; DRCOG 1996. (Leeds) GP Princip. Catterick Village Health Centre. Prev: Harrogate VTS.

WEBB, Christopher James 5 Lawson Close, Woolston, Warrington WA1 4EG — MB ChB 1994 Liverp. SHO (ENT) Arrowe Pk. Hosp. Wirral Merseyside. Prev: SHO (Orthop.) Bury & Fairfield Hosp.; SHO (Ear, Nose & Throat) Roy. Liverp. Hosp.; SHO (Ear, Nose & Throat) N. Manch. Gen. Hosp.

WEBB, Christopher Lewis Wakely (retired) Rose Cottage, Sandford Orcas, Sherborne DT9 4RP Tel: 01963 220362 — MB BS 1960 Lond.; MRCS Eng. LRCP Lond. 1960; DObst RCOG 1962; DA Eng. 1964. Prev: SCMO Port & Environm. Health Soton. & SW Hants. HA (T).

WEBB, Clyde Bernard Park Street Practice, Park Street, Ripon HG4 2BE Tel: 01765 692366 Fax: 01765 606440 — MB BS 1979 Lond.; MRCGP 1983; Dip. Occ. Med. 1995; DRCOG 1983. (Roy. Free Hosp. Sch. Med.) Socs: SOM.

WEBB, David Brynley Picton House, Llanblethian, Cowbridge CF71 7JF Tel: 01656 752752 — MB BChir 1973 Camb.; MA Camb. 1972, MD 1986; FRCP 1996. Cons. Phys. (Gen. Med.) P.ss of Wales Hosp. Bridgend. Socs: Sec. Dist. Gen. Nephrologists Soc. Prev: Lect. (Renal Med.) Cardiff Roy. Infirm.

WEBB, Professor David John Clinical Pharmacology Unit & Research Centre, University Department of Medicine, Western General Hospital, Edinburgh EH4 2XU Tel: 0131 537 2003 Fax: 0131 537 2003 Email: d.j.webb@ed.ac.uk; 26 Inverleith Gardens, Edinburgh EH3 5PS Tel: 0131 552 4518 Fax: 0131 552 4518 — MB BS 1977 Lond.; F Med. Sci. 1999; MD Lond. 1990; FRCP Lond. 1994; FRCP Ed. 1992; MRCP (UK) 1980; FFPM RCP (UK) 1993. (Lond. Hosp.) Christison Prof. Therap. & Clin. Pharmacol. Univ. Edin. & Hon. Cons. Phys. W.ern Gen. Hosp. Edin.; Chairm. Univ. Dept. Med. W. Gen. Hosp. Edin.; Ldr. Centre for Research in Cardiovasc. Biol.; Dir. Clin. Research Centre W.ern Gen. Hosp. Edin.; Chairm. Lothian Area Drug & Therap. Comm. Socs: Brit. Hypertens. Soc.; Internat. Soc. Hypertens.; Brit. Pharm. Soc. (Sec. Clin. Sect.). Prev: Sen. Lect. (Med.) Univ. Edin.; Lect. (Clin. Pharmacol.) & Hon. Sen.

Regist. (Med.) St. Geo. Hosp. Lond.; Clin. Scientist MRC Blood Pressure Unit W.ern Infirm. Glas..

WEBB, David Kenneth Humphries Department of Haematology, Great Ormond St. Children's Hospital, Great Ormond St., London WC1N 3JH Tel: 020 7829 8831 Fax: 020 7813 8410; Hognore Farm, Pilgrims Way, Wrotham, Sevenoaks TN15 7NN — MB BS 1978 Lond.; MD Lond. 1990; MRCP (UK) 1981; MRCPath 1990; FRCP (UK) 1995; MRCPCH 1996. (Guy's Hospital London) Cons. (Paediat. Haemat.).

WEBB, David Robert 41 Upland Road, Selly Park, Birmingham B29 7JS — MB ChB 1997 Aberd.

WEBB, Diana Margaret (retired) St. Giles Hospice, Fisherwick Lane, Whittington, Lichfield WS14 9LH Tel: 01283 711989 Email: diana.webb@st-giles-hospice.org.uk — MB BS 1984 Newc.; BA Camb. 1981; MRCGP 1989; DRCOG 1988. Cons. Palliat. Med. St Giles Hospice Lichfield Staffs; Cons. Palliat. Med. Good Hope Hosp. Sutton Coldfield; Cons. Palliat. Med. Mid Staffs Acute Trust Stafford; Cons. Palliat. Med. Katherine Hse. Hospice Stafford.

WEBB, Donald Albert (retired) 1 Waterdale Close, Westbury-on-Trym, Bristol BS9 4QN Tel: 0117 962 2061 — MB ChB Sheff. 1956. Prev: Assoc. Specialist Blood Transfus. Centre S.mead Hosp. Bristol.

WEBB, Elizabeth (retired) — MB ChB 1965 Cape Town; BSc Cape Town 1958; MRCPsych 1976; DPM Eng. 1971. Prev: Cons. Child & Adolesc. Psychiat. Walthamstow Lond.

WEBB, Elizabeth Mary Grove House Surgery, 18 Wilton Road, Salisbury SP2 7EE; Island Cottage, West Harnham, Salisbury SP2 8EU Tel: 01722 334537 — MB BS 1966 Lond.; MRCS Eng. LRCP Lond. 1966; MRCGP 1979; DCH Eng. 1971; DObst RCOG 1968. (St. Bart.)

WEBB, Elspeth Valmai Jocelyn Department Child Health, University of Wales College of Medicine, Cardiff CF14 4XN Tel: 029 2037 2451 Fax: 029 2074 3359 — MB BS 1978 Lond.; FRCP 1996; MRCP (UK) 1983; FRCPCH 1997; DCH RCP Lond. 1981; DTM & H RCP Lond. 1980. (St Geos. Hosp. Lond.) Hon. Cons. Paediat. Community Child Health Cardiff Community Health Care Trust; Sen. Lect. Child Health Univ. of Wales Coll. Med. Socs: Brit. Assn. of Community Child Health; Roy. Soc. Trop. Med. & Hyg.; Welsh Paediat. Soc. Prev: Lect. (Community & Child Health) Qu. Med. Centre Nottm.; Regist. (Paediat.) St. David's & Llandough Hosps. Cardiff; GP Trainee Isle of Skye VTS.

WEBB, Emma Jane Students Health Service, 25 Belgrave Road, Clifton, Bristol BS8 2AA Tel: 0117 973 7716; 1 Broadleys Avenue, Henleaze, Bristol BS9 4LY Tel: 0117 962 4800 Email: ejwebb@doctors.org.uk — MB ChB 1994 Bristol; DFFP 1999; DRCOG 1998. p/t GP, Univ. of Bristol, Bristol. Prev: GP Regist.; GP Locum, Bristol.

WEBB, Eric John Central Milton Keynes Medical, 1 North Sixth Street, Central Milton Keynes, Milton Keynes MK9 2NR Tel: 01908 605775 Fax: 01908 676752; Tel: 01908 311981 Email: drericwebb@clara.co.uk — MB BChir 1976 Camb.; MA Camb. 1976; DCH Eng. 1979. (Camb. & Char. Cross) Partner Centr. Milton Keynes Med. Gp.; Company Sec. MKDOC Ltd; Vasectomist - Marie Stoper. Socs: BMA; Medico-Legal Soc.; RSM. Prev: Trainee GP E. Som. (Yeovil) VTS; Ho. Surg. Addenbrooke's Hosp. Camb.; Ho. Phys. Norf. & Norwich Hosp.

WEBB, Frances Maxine Urmston Group Practice, 154 Church Road, Urmston, Manchester M41 9DL Tel: 0161 755 9870; 2A Broadoak Park Road, Monton, Eccles, Manchester M30 9LQ Tel: 0161 787 8235 — MB ChB 1983 Manch.; MRCGP 1988; DCH RCP Lond. 1985. (Manch.) Prev: SHO (O & G) St. Mary's Hosp. Manch.; SHO (Paediat.) Booth Hall Childr. Hosp. Manch.; SHO (A & E) Hope Hosp. Salford.

WEBB, Francis William Stanley, RD (retired) Glebe House, Church Lane, Baylham, Ipswich IP6 8JS Tel: 01473 830337 Fax: 01473 832854 Email: webb.baylham@themutual.net — MB 1961 Camb.; BChir 1960; FRCP Lond. 1984, M 1966; DObst RCOG 1964. Cons. Rheum. Ipswich Hosp. Prev: Regist. Rheum. Middlx. Hosp.

WEBB, Frank Ewart (retired) 29 Augustus Road, Edgbaston, Birmingham B15 3PQ Tel: 0121 455 9440 — MB ChB 1946 Birm.; MRCS Eng. LRCP Lond. 1946. Prev: GP Birm.

WEBB, Professor Hubert Eustace (retired) 12 Elm Grove, London SW19 4HE Tel: 020 8946 1808 Fax: 0191 947 2407 — DSc Med. Lond. 1990; MA Oxf. 1948, DM 1961, BM BCh 1951; FRCP Lond.

1969, M 1954; FRCPath 1988. Cons. Phys. Dept. Neurol. & Prof. Neurovirol. St. Thos. Hosp. Lond.; Dir. (Neurovirol.) Unit Rayne Inst. Prev: Temp. Staff Mem. Rockefeller Foundat.

WEBB, Hugh Basil Graham (retired) Mistlemead, North Tawton EX20 2HB Tel: 01837 82603 — MRCS Eng. LRCP Lond. 1950; DObst RCOG 1953. Prev: Med. Off. N.. Provinces, Nigeria.

WEBB, Jacqueline Susan 265 Welford Road, Leicester LE2 6BJ; 7 Serlby Lane, Harthill, Sheffield S26 7YD — MB ChB 1998 Leic.

WEBB, Janet Elizabeth Tel: 0161 972 9999 — MB ChB 1980 Sheff.; MRCGP 1994; DCCH 1993; DRCOG 1992. (Sheff.)

WEBB, Janet Lois Cheltenham Road Surgery, 16 Cheltenham Road, Gloucester GL2 0LS Tel: 01452 522575 Fax: 01452 304321; Longford Lodge, 109 Tewkesbury Road, Longford, Gloucester GL2 9BN — BM 1980 Soton.; MRCP (UK) 1984; MRCGP 1987.

WEBB, Mr Jason Crispin John 10 Grange Park, Westbury-on-Trym, Bristol BS9 4BP; Flat 4, All Saints Court, All Saints Road, Clifton, Bristol BS8 2JE — MB ChB 1994 Bristol; MB ChB (Hons.) Bristol 1994; BSc (Hons.) Cell & Molecular Path. Bristol 1991; FRCS Eng. Sen. SHO Orthop., S.mead Hosp., Bristol. Prev: SHO Rotat. (Surg.) Roy. Surrey Co. Hosp.; SHO Roy. Nat. Orthepaedic Hosp., Stanmore, Middlx.; SHO (A&E Med.) Bristol Roy. Infirm.

WEBB, Jennifer Neale Rushall House, Rushall Lane, Lytchett Matravers, Poole BH16 6AJ — MB ChB Bristol 1982; MRCGP 1986; DCCH RCP Lond. 1987; DRCOG 1984. Family Plann. Poole. Prev: GP Retainer Scheme Nottm. & Edin.

WEBB, Joan Dorothy (retired) Rose Gardens, 15 Eynsham Road, Oxford OX2 9BS Tel: 01865 863851 — MB BS 1946 Lond.; MRCS Eng. LRCP Lond. 1945; MRCP Lond. 1947. Prev: Clin. Asst. (Path.) King's Mill Hosp. Sutton-in-Ashfield.

WEBB, Joanna Heathcote Medical Centre, Heathcote, Tadworth KT20 5TH Tel: 01737 360202; 17 Tower Road, Tadworth KT20 5QY — MB BS Lond. 1968; MRCS Eng. LRCP Lond. 1968; MRCGP 1983. (St. Thos.) Prev: Ho. Surg. Sutton Gen. Hosp.; Ho. Phys. St. Thos. Hosp. Lond.

WEBB, Mr John Beverley 64 Norton Road, Letchworth SG6 1AE Tel: 01462 675628 Email: bevwebb@virginnet.co.uk — MRCS Eng. LRCP Lond. 1969; FRCS Eng. 1974; FRCOG 1993, M 1980. (St. Mary's) Cons. O & G Lister Hosp. Stevenage. Prev: Sen. Regist. (O & G) Hammersmith Hosp. Lond. & N.wick Pk. Hosp. Middlx.; GP/Surg. Austral. Inland Med. Serv.; Regist. (O & G) Roy. Free Hosp. & City of Lond. Matern. Hosp.

WEBB, John Francis, MC, Col. late RAMC Retd. (retired) 38 Westover Road, Fleet GU51 3DB Tel: 01252 613080 — MB BS Durh. 1940; MD Durh. 1956; FRCP Ed. 1972, M 1966. Prev: Phys. i/c MoD Sprue Research Team Hong Kong.

WEBB, John Gilbert Health Centre, Pwllheli Road, Criccieth LL52 0RR Tel: 01766 523451 Fax: 01766 523453; Erw Las, Penaber, Criccieth LL52 0ES Tel: 01766 522715 — MB BCh 1975 Wales.

WEBB, Mr John Kenneth Harold The Old Rectory, Saxelby, Melton Mowbray LE14 3PA — MB BS 1966 Lond.; FRCS Eng. 1971. Cons. Notts. HA & Harlow Wood Orthop. Hosp. & Univ. Hosp. Prev: Sen. Regist. (Rotat.) Robt. Jones & Agnes Hunt Orthop. Hosp.; OsW.ry; Fell. Rancho Las Amigos Hosp. Downey USA.

WEBB, Professor John Kingdon Guy, OBE Fernleigh, 4 Church Park, Newton Ferrers, Plymouth PL8 1AJ Tel: 01752 873033 — BM BCh Oxf. 1942; MA Oxf. 1947; FRCP Lond. 1967, M 1950. (Oxf.) Emerit. Prof. Child Health Univ. Newc.; Hon. Cons. Paediat. Roy. Vict. Infirm. Newc. Socs: FRCPCh; Hon. Fell. Indian Acad. Paediat. Prev: James Spence Prof. Child Health Univ. Newc.; Prof. of Paediat. & Dir. Christian Med. Coll. & Hosp. Vellore, India.

WEBB, John Neville 56 St Albans Road, Edinburgh EH9 2LX Tel: 0131 667 2637 — MB BChir 1960 Camb.; MD Camb. 1969, MA, MB 1960, BChir 1959; FRCP Ed. 1974, M 1964; DObst RCOG 1961. (Camb. & St. Thos.) Socs: Path. Soc.

WEBB, Mr Jonathan Mark 40 Berkeley Road, Bristol BS6 7PL — MB ChB 1987 Bristol; FRCS Eng. 1991.

WEBB, Jonathan Roy 49 Court Lane, London SE21 7DP Tel: 020 8693 3237 — MB BS 1968 Lond.; FRCP Lond. 1987; MRCP (U.K.) 1973. Cons. Phys. (s/i Respirat. Dis.) Brook Hosp. & Greenwich Dist. Hosp. Lond. Prev: Lect. & Hon. Sen. Regist. Guy's Hosp. Lond.

WEBB, Judith Ann Westwood Diagnostic Radiology Department, St. Bartholomews Hospital, London EC1A 7BE Tel: 020 7601 8329 Fax: 020 7601 8323; 3 Sellers Hall Close, Finchley, London N3 1JL

WEBB

Tel: 020 8346 2705 — MB BS 1967 Lond.; MD Lond. 1983, BSc (1st cl. Hons.) Physiol.) 1964; FRCP Lond. 1991; MRCP (UK) 1971; FRCR 1976; DMRD Eng. 1973. (St. Bart.) Cons. Diagn. Radiol. St. Bart. Hosp. Lond. Socs: FRSM; Soc. Uroradiol.; Euro. Soc. Uriradiol. (Past Pres). Prev: Sen. Regist. (Diagn. Radiol.) & Jun. Regist. (Med.) St. Bart. Hosp. Lond.; Instruc. (Diagn. Radiol.) Univ. Cal. San. Diego, USA.

WEBB, Mr Julian Francis Waldron St. Thomas Hospital, Lambeth Palace Road, London SE1 7EH; 14 Chatterton Road, Highbury, London N4 2DZ — MB BS 1987 Lond.; FRCS Ed. 1994.

WEBB, Kenneth Rhys Hughes and Partners, 15 Dereham Road, Mattishall, Dereham NR20 3QA Tel: 01362 850227 Fax: 01362 858466; Southfield House, Common Road, East Tuddenham, Dereham NR20 3NF Tel: 01362 880216 — MB BS 1975 Lond.

WEBB, Kevin Iain Flat G, Alexandra Court, 10A Alexandra Road, Weymouth DT4 7QH — MB ChB 1995 Cape Town.

WEBB, Mr Lennox Andrew Burnside Cottage, Kirk Road, Houston, Johnstone PA6 7HN — MB ChB 1987 Dundee; FRCS Ed. 1992; FRCOphth 1993, M 1990. (Dundee) Cons. Roy. Alexandra Hosp. Paisley Scotl.; Hon. Sen. Clin. Lect. Glas. Caledonian Univ. Glas. Socs: BMA. Prev: Orbit Oculoplastic & Anterior Segment Fell. Eye Care Centre Univ. Brit. Columbia, Canada; Sen. Regist. Tennent Inst. Ophth. Glas.

WEBB, Lesley Ann 26 Brisbane Grove, Hartburn, Stockton-on-Tees TS18 5BW — MB ChB 1978 Dundee; MRCP (UK) 1985. Regist. (Radiol.) Roy. Vict. Infirm. Newc. upon Tyne. Prev: SHO (Dermat.) Carter Bequest Hosp. Middlesbrough; SHO (Chest Med.) Poole Hosp. Middlesbrough; SHO (Gen. Med.) Hartlepool Gen. Hosp.

WEBB, Lindsay Joy Adshall Road Medical Practice, 97 Adshall Road, (off Councillor Lane), Cheadle SK8 2JN; 50 Swann Lane, Cheadle Hulme, Cheadle SK8 7HU — MB BS 1972 Lond.; MD Lond. 1981; MRCP (UK) 1974. (Middlx. Hosp.) Prev: CMO Centr. Manch.; MRC Research. Fell. Roy. Free Hosp. Lond.

WEBB, Lynda Jane 28A Ongar Road, Fulham, London SW6 1SJ — MB BS 1989 Lond.

WEBB, Margaret Corte (retired) 6 Christchurch Road, Norwich NR2 2AD Tel: 01603 51254 — MRCS Eng. LRCP Lond. 1936.

WEBB, Margaret Elizabeth Department of Child & Family Psychiatry, Southmead Hospital, Westbury On Trym, Bristol Tel: 0117 959 5800; 15 Ravens Cross Road, Long Ashton, Bristol BS41 9EA — MB BS 1961 Lond.

WEBB, Mark Robert 43 Cutsdean Close, Bishops Cleeve, Cheltenham GL52 8UT — MB BCh 1992 Witwatersrand.

WEBB, Michael Alfred Healey, KStJ 48 Offington Avenue, Worthing BN14 9PJ Tel: 01903 260095 Fax: 01903 690934 — MRCS Eng. LRCP Lond. 1961; FFOM RCP Lond. 1996, M 1980; DIH Soc. Apoth. Lond. 1978. (King's Coll. Hosp.) Cons. Occupat. Health W. Sussex.; Dep. Chief Cdr., St John Ambul. Socs: Soc. Occupat. Med. & Mem. BMA. Prev: Sen. Med. Adviser SE Area Post Off.; Med. Adviser Commonw. Smelting Ltd Avonmouth; Employm. Med. Adviser EMAS.

WEBB, Michael Stephen Carroll Department of Paediatrics, Gloucestershire Royal Hospital, Great Western Road, Gloucester GL1 3NN Tel: 01452 395122 Fax: 01452 395115 Email: mike.webb@connectfree.co.uk; Longford Lodge, Tewkesbury Road, Longford, Gloucester GL2 9BN Tel: 01452 730450 — MB ChB 1976 Bristol; FRCP Lond. 1995; FRCPCH 1998; FRCP 1998. Cons. Paediat. Glos. Roy. Hosp.; Paediatric Train. Progr. Director, S. W. Deanery; RCPCH Regional Adviser (Elect), S. W. Prev: Sen. Regist. (Paediat.) Soton. & Portsmouth HAs; Clin. Research Fell. Dept. Child Health Univ. Hosp. Nottm.; SHO (Paediat.) Roy. Hosp. Sick Childr. Gt. Ormond St. Lond.

WEBB, Michelle Claire The Renal Unit, Guy's & St Thomas' Hospital Trust, St Thomas St., London SE1 9RT — BChir 1988 Camb.; MA Camb. 1989, BChir 1988; MRCP (UK) 1991; MD (Camb.) 1997. Sen. Regist. Renal Med.

WEBB, Nicholas John Alexander Department pf Nephrology, Royal Manchester Children's Hospital, Pendlebury, Manchester M27 4HA Tel: 0161 727 2435 Fax: 0161 727 2630 Email: n.webb@lycosmail.com — BM BS 1986 Nottm.; BMedSci Nottm. 1984, BM BS 1986; FRCPCH 1997; DM Nottm. 1998; FRCP 1999. Cons. Paediat. Nephrol. Roy. Manch. Childr. Hosp. Manch. Socs: Brit. Assn. Paediat. Nephrol.; Internat. Paediat. Nephrol. Assn. Prev: Sen. Regist. (Paediat. Nephrol.) Roy. Manch. Childr. Hosp.; Clin.

Fell. (Paediat. Nephrol.) Hosp. for Sick Childr. Toronto; Regist. (Paediat.) Roy. Childr. Hosp. Melbourne.

WEBB, Peta Sedgley Seaton and Colyton Medical Practice, Seaton Health Centre, 148 Harepath Road, Seaton EX12 2DU Tel: 01297 20877 Fax: 01297 23031; Broadstone Farm House, Walditch, Bridport DT6 4LQ Tel: 01308 425665 — MB ChB 1984 Leic.; BSc (Hons.) Lond. 1979; DRCOG 1991. (Leicester)

WEBB, Peter The Health Centre, Station Road, Haydock, St Helens WA11 0JN Tel: 01744 34419 — MB ChB 1967 Liverp.; DObst RCOG 1969. Clin. Asst. (Rheum.) Whiston Hosp. Prescot.

WEBB, Mr Peter John The Old Farm, Gully Lane, Luppitt, Honiton EX14 4RZ Tel: 01404 891701 — MB BS 1969 Lond.; BSc 1965 Lond.; FRCS Eng. 1974; MRCS Eng. LRCP Lond. 1969. (Univ. Coll. Hosp.) Cons. Spinal Surg. MusGr. Pk. Hosp. Taunton. Prev: Cons. Orthop. Surg. Roy. Nat. Orthop. Hosp. Stanmore; Hon. Cons. Orthop. Surg. Italian Hosp. Lond.; Cons. Orthop. Surg. Hosp. Sick Childr. Lond.

WEBB, Mr Peter John Woodcut House, 238 Maidstone Road, Chatham ME4 6JN Tel: 01634 844755 Fax: 01634 844755 Email: 101671.3342@compuserve.com — MB BS 1972 Lond.; MS Lond. 1985; FRCS Eng. 1977. Cons. Surg. Medway NHS Trust. Socs: BMA; Assn. Surg.; Assn. Coloproctol. Prev: Sen. Regist. (Surgic.) King's Coll. Hosp. Lond.; Research Fell. Thrombosis Unit King's Coll. Hosp. Lond.; Ho. Surg. Profess. Unit Middlx. Hosp. Lond.

WEBB, Philip Guy Skellern and Partners, Bridport Medical Centre, North Allington, Bridport DT6 5DU Tel: 01308 421109 Fax: 01308 420869; Broadstone Farm House, Walditch, Bridport DT6 4LQ Tel: 01308 425665 — MB ChB 1980 Birm.; MRCP (UK) 1984. (Birm.)

WEBB, Rachel Delyth 25 Park Street, Denbigh LL16 3DE — MB ChB 1992 Liverp.

WEBB, Ralph James 27 Harford Drive, Watford WD17 3DQ — MB BS 1981 Lond.

WEBB, Ray Talbot, Wing Cdr. RAF Med. Br. Retd. Trinity Surgery, Norwich Road, Wisbech PE13 3UZ Tel: 01945 476999 Fax: 01945 476900 — BM 1978 Soton.; MRCGP 1983; DAvMed FOM RCP Lond. 1988; DRCOG 1983. Prev: Adviser (Gen. Pract.) RAF.; Ho. Surg. & Ho. Phys. Weymouth & Dist. Hosp.

WEBB, Rosemarie Felicity The Surgery, High Street, Epworth, Doncaster DN9 1EP Tel: 01427 872232 Fax: 01427 874944; 1 Mill Lane, Westwoodside, Doncaster DN9 2AF Tel: 01427 752193 — MB ChB Ed. 1971; FRCGP 1995, M 1975; DObst RCOG 1974; MFFP 1994. (Edinburgh) GP Princip.; Trainer GP Doncaster VTS. Prev: Trainee GP Doncaster VTS; Ho. Phys. & Ho. Surg. Hull Roy. Infirm.

WEBB, Samuel Wilson 26 Deramore Park S., Malone Road, Belfast BT9 5JY Tel: 01232 666543 — MB BCh BAO 1966 Belf.; BSc (Hons. Anat.) Belf. 1963, MB 1974, MB BCh BAO 1966; MD Belf. 1974; MRCP (UK) 1970. Cons. Cardiol. Roy. Vict. Hosp. Belf.

WEBB, Sarah Elizabeth 3 Abbey Street, Bath BA1 1NN Tel: 01225 462548 Email: drsarawebb@onetel.net.uk — MB BS 1970 Lond.; MRCGP 1979; DCH RCP Lond. 1974; DObst RCOG 1973.

WEBB, Sheila Joy Bradford HA, New Mill, Victoria Road, Saltaire, Shipley BD18 3LD Tel: 01274 366007; Trevethick, Cragg Drive, Ilkley LS29 8BE Tel: 01943 603227 — MB ChB 1974 Sheff.; Dip Ther 2001 Newc.; MFPHM RCP (UK) 1991; MPH Leeds 1988; MRCGP 1978; DRCOG 1977; FFPHM 1998. Cons. Pub. Health Med. Bradford HA. Prev: GP Bradford Univ. & Birkenhead; Sen. Regist. (Pub. Health Med.) Yorks RHA.

WEBB, Spencer Edwin 10 Upgrove Manor Way, Chessington Gardens, London SW2 2QX — MB BS 1996 Lond.

WEBB, Steven Anthony Rochford Flat 9, Bishopsbourne, 134-136 Westbourne Terrace, London W2 6QB Email: s.a.webb@ic.ac.uk — MB BS 1988 Western Australia; FRACP 1995. Research Fell. Molecular Infec. Dis. Unit Dept. Paediat. St. Mary's Hosp. Med. Sch. Lond.

WEBB, Stuart Charles St Charles Hospital, Exmoor St., London W10 6DZ Tel: 020 8962 4126 Fax: 020 8962 4131; 43 Granville Road, Barnet EN5 4DS — MB BS 1974 Lond.; BSc (Physiol.) Lond. 1971, MB BS 1974; MRCP (UK) 1978; MD Lond. 1985; FRCP (Eng.) 1992. (Univ. Coll. Hosp.) Cons. Phys. St Mary's Hosp. Lond. Socs: Brit. Cardiac Soc.; Brit. Pacing & Electrophysiol. Gp. Prev: Sen. Regist. (c/o the Elderly) Hammersmith Hosp. Lond.; Regist. (Cardiol.) Nat. Heart Hosp. Lond.; Regist. (Med.) Roy. Free Hosp. Lond.

WEBB, Timothy Birkett Nonesuch, 25 Park St., Denbigh LL16 3DE Tel: 01745 583910 Email: tim.webb@cd_tr.wales.nhs.uk; 25 Park Street, Denbigh LL16 3DE — MB BCh 1967 Wales; FFA RCS Eng. 1972; DA Eng. 1969. (Cardiff) Cons. Anaesth. Glan Clwyd Hosp.Conway and Denbighsh. NHS Trust. Socs: Assn. Dent. Anaesth.; Pain Soc.; Age Anaesth. Assn. Mem.ship sec & Treas. Prev: Sen. Regist. (Anaesth.) Singleton Hosp. Swansea & Univ. Hosp. Wales Cardiff; SHO (Orthop. & Trauma) Morriston Hosp. Swansea; SHO (O & G) Mt. Pleasant Hosp.

WEBB, Timothy Ewart Department of Psychiatry, West Suffolk Hospital, Hardwick Lane, Bury St Edmunds IP33 2QZ Tel: 01284 713590 Fax: 01284 713694 — MB ChB 1977 Birm.; FRCPsych 2001; MRCPsych 1983. Cons. Adult Psychiat. Local Health Partnerships NHS Trust; Director of Clin. Strategy, Local Health Partnership NHS Trust. Prev: Cons. Psychiat. Plymouth HA.

WEBB, Timothy Richard 7 Erasmus Way, Lichfield WS13 7AW — MB ChB 1997 Birm. Ho. Off. Roy. Shrewsbury Hosp. Shrewsbury.

WEBB, Walter Frederick (retired) 72 Privett Road, Alverstoke, Gosport PO12 3SX — MB BS 1959 Lond. Prev: Ho. Surg. & Ho. Phys. Char. Cross Hosp. Lond.

WEBB, Warwick Jeremy Stephen Tudor Lodge, 26 Mill Lane, Fordham, Ely CB7 5NQ Tel: 01638 721410; Orchard House, Newmarket CB8 5HS Tel: 01638 662292 — MB BS 1983 Lond.; BSc Lond. 1980, MB BS 1983; MRCP (UK) 1986; MRCGP 1989; DRCOG 1988. Prev: Regist. (Med.) Addenbrooke's Hosp. Camb.; SHO (Med.) N.wick Pk. Hosp. Harrow; Ho. Off. (Med.) Roy. Free Hosp. Lond.

WEBB, William Bert (retired) Underwood, Portskwitt, Newport NP26 5UL Tel: 01291 420267 — MB BChir 1947 Camb. Med. Off. Chepstow & Dist. Hosp.; Police Surg. Prev: Res. Med. Off. Surbiton Gen. Hosp.

WEBB, William Murcott William Harvey Hospital, Willesborough, Ashford TN24 0LZ Tel: 01233 633331; Ashley House, Swan Lane, Sellindge, Ashford TN25 6EB — MB ChB 1975 Birm.; BSc (Physiol.) Birm. 1972; FRCR 1985; DMRD Eng. 1984. Cons. Radiologist, E. Kent Hosps. NHS Trust. Prev: Sen. Regist. & Regist. (Radiol.) Hull Roy. Infirm.; SHO Rotat. (Gen. Surg. & Orthop.) Chelmsford.

WEBB-PEPLOE, Katharine Mary Royal Brompton Hospital, Sydney St., London SW3 6NP Tel: 020 7352 8121; 29 Fentiman Road, London SW8 1LD — MB BChir 1988 Camb.; BA Camb. 1985; MRCP (UK) 1991. Prev: Research Regist. (Cardiol.) Roy. Brompton Hosp. & Nat. Heart & Lung Inst. Lond.

WEBB-PEPLOE, Michael Murray, OBE The consulting rooms, York house, 199 Westminster Bridge Road, London SE1 7UT Fax: 020 7922 8301 Email: m.webb-peploe@doctors.org.uk; 27 Torrington Road, Claygate, Esher KT10 0SA Tel: 01372 464879 — MB 1961 Camb.; BChir 1960; FRCP Lond. 1976, M 1963. (Camb. & St. Thos.) Emerit. Cons. Cardiol., Guys and St Thomas NHS Trust. Socs: Brit. Cardiac Soc.; Ass of Phys.s of Gt. Britain & Irel. Prev: Cons. Phys. Dept. Cardiol. St. Thos. Hosp. Lond; Research Assoc. Mayo Clinic Rochester, Minn., USA; Hon civil Cons. Cardiol. to the Army.

WEBB-WILSON, Gavin John Rood Lane Medical Centre, 10 Rood Lane, London EC3M 8BN Tel: 020 7283 4027 Fax: 020 7626 2184; Ash Tree House, Horton Kirby, Dartford DA4 9BY Tel: 01322 863349 — MA, MB Camb. 1970, BChir 1969; MRCOG 1978. (St. Thos.) Examr. Various Shipping & Insur. Companies & Banks City of Lond. Socs: Fell. Assur. Med. Soc.; Med. Soc. Lond. Prev: Sen. Regist. (O & G) Nat. Wom. Hosp. Auckland, NZ; Regist. (O & G) St. Thos. Hosp. Lond.; Sen. Research Resid. Dept. Infertil. McGill Univ. Montreal.

WEBBER, Adam Paul 11 Grenfell Gardens, Harrow HA3 0QZ — MB ChB 1995 Bristol.

WEBBER, Andrew Mark Misbourne Practice, St. Giles Surgery, Townfield Lane, Chalfont St Giles HP8 4QG Tel: 01494 874006 Fax: 01494 875455; 27 Kings Road, Chalfont St Giles HP8 4HS Tel: 01494 873117 — MB BS 1983 Lond.; BSc Lond. 1980. (Middlx.) Prev: Trainee GP High Wycombe VTS; Ho. Phys. Qu. Eliz. II Hosp. Welwyn Garden City; Ho. Surg. Wycombe Gen. Hosp. High Wycombe.

WEBBER, Ian Trevor Aufrichtig 79A Belsize Park Gardens, London NW3 4JP — MB ChB 1978 Cape Town; MSc Epidemiol. Lond. 1983.

WEBBER, Jane Elizabeth 1 Staplake Rise, Starcross, Exeter EX6 8SJ — MB BS 1992 Lond.; MB BS (Hons.) Lond. 1992. (St. Geo. Hosp. Med. Sch. Lond.) SHO (Cardiothoracic Surg.) St. Geo. Hosp. Lond. Prev: Demonst. (Anat.) St. Geo. Hosp. Lond.; SHO (Orthop. Surg.) E. Surrey Hosp. Redhill; SHO (Neurosurg.) St. Bart. Hosp. Lond.

WEBBER, Jonathan Clinical nutrition unit, C floor south block, Queens medical centre, Nottingham NG7 2UH Fax: 0121 507 4988 Email: jonathon.webber@nottingham.ac.uk; 99 Park Hill Road, Harborne, Birmingham B17 9HH — BM BCh 1987 Oxf.; MA Camb. 1988; DM Nottm. 1994; MRCP (UK) 1990. Sen. Lect. in Clin. Nutrit. and Metab., Uni of Nottm.; Hon Cons. universsity Hosp. Nottm. Socs: Brit. Diabetic Assn.; Nutrit. Soc.; Ass for the study of obesity. Prev: Sen. Regist. (Diabetes & Gen. Med.) City Hosp. Birm.; Sen. Regist. Selly Oak Hosp. Birm.; Regist. (Diabetes & Gen. Med.) Heartlands Hosp. Birm.

WEBBER, Lawrence Martin Grand Drive Surgery, 132 Grand Drive, London SW20 9EA Tel: 020 8542 5555 Fax: 020 8542 6969 — MB BS Lond. 1961; MRCS Eng. LRCP Lond. 1960; DObst RCOG 1962. (Westm.) GP. Prev: Clin. Asst. Chest Clinic Kingston Hosp.; Med. Off. Nchanga Copper Mines Chingola, Zambia; Regist. (Med.) Qu. Mary's Hosp. Stratford.

WEBBER, Mr Mark Clifford Benjamin Withington Hospital, Nell Lane, West Didsbury, Manchester M20 2LR; 14 Beccles Road, Brooklands, Sale M33 3RP — MB ChB 1988 Manch.; BSc St. And. 1986; FRCS Ed. 1992. SHO (Gen. Surg.) Trafford Gen. Hosp. Prev: SHO (Orthop. & Gen. BrE. Surg.) Withington Hosp. Manch.

WEBBER, Michael Nottingham City Hospital, Hucknall Road, Nottingham NG5 1PB — MB BS 1967 Lond.

WEBBER, Michael George (retired) 21 Thornhill Close, Old Amersham, Amersham HP7 0EW Tel: 01494 431071 — MB BS 1951 Lond.; MRCGP 1965. Prev: Ho. Surg. Mt. Vernon Hosp. N.wood & Wembley Hosp.

WEBBER, Mr Peter Adrian ENT Department, Queen Elizabeth Hospital, King's Lynn PE30 4ET Tel: 01553 613724 Fax: 01553 613700 Email: peter.webber@klshosp.anglox.nhs.uk — MB BS 1977 Lond.; MAE 1997; FRCS (Orl.) Ed. 1984. Cons. ENT Surg. Qu. Eliz. Hosp., Kings Lynn; ENT Cons. Norf. and Norwich Univ. Hosp. NHS Trust.

WEBBER, Richard James, Surg. Lt. RN Hewitt Croft, Threshfield, Skipton BD23 5HB Tel: 01756 753473 — MB BS 1994 Lond. Med. Off. HMS Vigilant. Socs: BMA; MDU. Prev: Med. Off. HMS Vanguard, HMS Neptune & HMS Collingwood.

WEBBER, Roger Hugh London School of Hygiene & Tropical Medicine, Keppel St., London WC1E 7HT Tel: 020 7927 2438 Fax: 020 7580 9075 Email: r.webber@lshtm.ac.uk; Kiln Cottage, 45 North Lane, Buriton, Petersfield GU31 5RS Tel: 01730 266564 — MB BS 1967 Lond.; MSc Lond. 1980, MD 1976; MRCS Eng. LRCP Lond. 1967; DTPH Lond. 1973; DTM & H Liverp. 1969; DObst RCOG 1969. (Roy. Free) Sen. Lect. Lond. Sch. Hyg. & Trop. Med.; Cons. & Hon. Sen. Lect. (Trop. Med.) UCL Hosps. Socs: Fell. Roy. Soc. Trop. Med. & Hyg. Prev: Med. Co-ordinator & Community Health Specialist UK/Tanzania Health Project Mbeya Tanzania; Chief Med. Off. (Communicable Dis.) Solomon Is.

WEBBER, Mrs Sally Margaret Royal United Hospital, Bath BA1 3NG — MB BS 1983 Lond.; MRCP (UK) 1987; DO RCS Eng. 1989; FCOphth 1989. Cons. Ophth., Roy. United Hosp. Bath. Prev: Regist. (Ophth.) Roy. Hosp. Reading; Regist. K. Edwd. VII Hosp. Windsor; SHO & Regist. Rotat. Oxf. Eye Hosp.

WEBBER, Stephen John 280 Crookesmoor Road, Sheffield S10 1BE — MB ChB 1993 Sheff.

WEBBERLEY, Michael John Worcester Royal Infirmary, Ronkswood Branch, Newtown Road, Worcester WR5 1HN Tel: 01905 703333; Fort Royal House, 37 Fort Royal Hill, Worcester WR5 1BT — MB ChB 1982 Dundee; FRCP 2000 UK; MD Dundee 1991; MRCP (UK) 1985. Cons. Phys. (Gastroenterol.) Worcester Roy. Infirm. NHS Trust. Socs: BSG. Prev: Sen. Regist. (Med. & Gastroenterol.) Qu. Eliz. Hosp. Birm.

WEBBORN, Anthony David John Department of Sports Medicine, London Hospital Medical College, Royal London Hospital, Bancroft Road, London E1 4DG Tel: 020 7377 7839 Fax: 020 8983 6500; Esperance Private Hospital, Hartington Place, Eastbourne BN21 3BG Tel: 01323 410717 Fax: 01323 730313 — MB BS 1979 Lond.; MSc (Sports Med.) Lond. 1996; MRCGP 1985; Dip. Sports Med.

WEBBORN

(Distinc.) Lond. 1993. Clin. Research Fell. (Sports Med.) Lond. Hosp. Med. Coll. Socs: Amer. Coll. Sports Med.; E.bourne Med. Soc.; Brit. Assn. Sport & Med. Prev: Med. Off RAF; GP Polegate.

WEBBORN, David John Arthur Street Surgery, 47 Arthur Street, Brierfield, Nelson BB9 5RZ Tel: 01282 614599 — MB ChB 1982 Bristol; MRCGP 1986; DRCOG 1986. Course Organiser Burnley & Blackburn. Socs: BMA.

WEBER, Andrzej Marek 89 Southfield Road, Chiswick, London W4 1BB Tel: 020 8994 3099 Fax: 020 8747 8968; 14 North Avenue, Ealing, London W13 8AP Tel: 020 8997 2650 Fax: 020 8981 8020 Email: webers@keystone.demon.co.uk — MB BS 1981 Lond.; DRCOG 1984. (Roy. Free) Assoc. Specialist Ealing Hosp. Prev: Clin. Asst. Ealing Hosp.

WEBER, Beatrix Elisabeth Ocean's End Annexe, Rose Hill, Marazion TR17 0HB — State Exam Med. Munich 1988.

WEBER, Joelle 33 Cranbourne Gardens, London NW11 0HS — MB BS 1997 Lond.

WEBER, John Christian Peter (retired) The Ridings, Woodfield Lane, Brookmans Park, Hatfield AL9 6JJ Tel: 01707 650859 — MD Lond. 1949, MB BS 1944. Med. Cons. Pharmaceut. Indust. Lond. Prev: Sen. Med. Off. DHSS (Meds. Div.) Lond.

WEBER, Professor Jonathan Norden Jefferiss Research Laboratories, 4th Floor Wright - Institute, Imperial College School of Medicine, London W2 1PG Tel: 020 7594 3901 Fax: 020 7594 3906 Email: j.weber@ic.ac.uk; 50 St. Paul's Road, Islington, London N1 2QW — MB BChir 1979 Camb.; MA Camb. 1979; FRCP 1993, M (UK) 1983; FRCPath 1997. (Cambridge) Prof. (Genitourin. Med.) & Communicable Dis. Imperial St. Mary's Hosp. Coll. Sch. of Med. Lond.; Hon. Cons. (Phys.) St. Mary's Hosp. Socs: Brit. Infec. Soc.; MSSVD Counc. Prev: Sen. Lect. & Hon. Cons. (Phys.) Infec. Dis. Unit Roy. Postgrad. Med. Sch. Hammersmith Hosp. Lond.; Lect. Div. Cell & Molecular Biol. Chester Beatty Laboratories Inst. Cancer Research Lond.; Wellcome Research Fell. St. Mary's Hosp. Med. Sch. Lond.

WEBER, Jorg Stephan Andreas 74 Victoria Road, Saltaire, Shipley BD18 3JS — State Exam Med 1994 Berlin.

WEBER, Maurice Emile (retired) 310 Pickhurst Lane, West Wickham BR4 0HT Tel: 020 8460 0234 — MRCS Eng. LRCP Lond. 1942. Prev: Clin. Asst. Bromley Hosp.

WEBER, Stephan Flat 4, Greentrees, 6 Lansdowne, Worthing BN11 4NA — State Exam Med 1991 Berlin.

WEBLEY, Michael The Limes, 10 Churchway, Haddenham, Aylesbury HP17 8AA Tel: 01844 291356 — MB BS 1967 Lond.; FRCP Lond. 1986; MRCP (UK) 1970; MRCS Eng. LRCP Lond. 1967. (Westm.) Cons. Rheum. Oxf. Regional Rheum. Dis. Research Centre Stoke Mandeville Hosp. Aylesbury. Socs: FRSM; Brit. Soc. Rheum. Prev: Sen. Regist. W.m. Hosp. & St. Stephens Hosp. Lond.; Resid. Med. Off. Brompton Hosp. Lond.

WEBSDALE, Bruce Henry c/o Medcall, Phillip House, 8 Ravenswood Road, London SW12 9PJ — MB BS 1983 Lond.

WEBSTER, Abigail Louise 18 Briarwood, Wilmslow Park, Wilmslow SK9 2DH — MB ChB 1989 Liverp.

WEBSTER, Alan Rimmington (retired) 28 Castlegate, Helmsley, York YO62 5AB — MB ChB Leeds 1948; DObst RCOG 1949. Prev: Ho. Phys. Roy. Infirm. Bradford.

WEBSTER, Alison Glaxo Wellcome Research & Development, Greenford Road, Greenford UB6 0HE; 34 Hazlewell Road, London SW15 6LR — MB BS 1982 Lond.; BSc Lond. 1979, MD 1994; MRCPath 1989.

WEBSTER, Amanda Jennifer 13 Shitterton, Bere Regis, Wareham BH20 7HU; 12 Shepherds Way, West Lulworth, Wareham BH20 5SL — MB BS 1985 Lond.; FRCA. 1991. Anaesth. E. Dorset HA.

WEBSTER, Andrew c/o Sushee Webster, 28A Queen St., Stirling FK8 1HN — MB ChB 1997 Glas.

WEBSTER, Andrew Patrick Stone Home, Alton, Stoke-on-Trent ST10 4AG — MB ChB 1998 Liverp.

WEBSTER, Andrew Royston 406 Winchester Road, Southampton SO16 7DH — BM BCh 1987 Oxf.; FCOphth. 1991.

WEBSTER, Ann Margaret 3 Laurel Bank, Hamilton ML3 8EP — MB ChB 1990 Manch.

WEBSTER, Anna Louise Beinn Toaig, The Ross, Comrie, Crieff PH6 2JU — MB ChB 1998 Manch.

WEBSTER, Anthony David Bonython MRC Immunodeficiency Research Group, Royal Free Hospital School of Medicine, Department Clinical Immunology, Rowland Hill St., London NW3 2PF Tel: 020 7830 2141 Fax: 020 7830 2224 — MB BChir 1965 Camb.; MA Camb. 1968, BA 1961, MD 1993; FRCP Lond. 1981; FRCPath 1996. (St. Mary's) Sen. Lect. & Head MRC ImmunoDefic. Clinic Lond.; Hon. Cons. Clin. Immunol. Roy. Free Hosp. Med. Sch. Lond. Socs: Brit. Soc. Immunol. & Assn. Phys. Prev: Hon. Cons. Immunol. Clin. Research Centre N.wick Pk. Hosp. Harrow.

WEBSTER, Antony Peter 52 Highfield Road, Cheadle Hulme, Cheadle SK8 6EP — MB ChB 1992 Birm.

WEBSTER, Caroline Clair Infirmary Drive Medical Group, Consulting Rooms, Infirmary Drive, Alnwick NE66 2NR Tel: 01665 602388 Fax: 01665 604712 — MB BS 1987 Newc.

WEBSTER, Claire Diana Beausite, Beacon Road, Upper Wyche, Malvern WR14 4EH Tel: 01684 567568 Fax: 01684 567568 — MB ChB 1987 Manch.

WEBSTER, David Woolton House Medical Centre, 4b Woolton Street, Woolton, Liverpool LL5 5JA; Aisburth Hall Cottage, Grassendale, Liverpool L19 9EA — MB ChB 1989 Liverp.; MRCP (UK) 1992; MRCGP 1995. Assoc. Phys. NW Primary Care Initiative / GP Princip.; Liverp. Univ. Med. Sch. Socs: Liverp. Med. Inst.; Christian Med. Fell.ship. Prev: SHO (O & G) Liverp. Wom. Hosp. Trust; Assoc. Phys. N W Primary Care Initiative.

WEBSTER, David Anthony The Surgery, School Lane, Upton-upon-Severn, Worcester WR8 0LF Tel: 01684 592696 Fax: 01684 593122; The Grange, Hill End, Upton-on-Severn, Worcester WR8 0RN Tel: 01684 833239 — MB BS 1964 Lond.; MRCGP 1979; DTM & H Eng. 1971; DObst RCOG 1967. (St. Thos.) Socs: BMA. Prev: Med. Off. i/c Amudat Hosp., Uganda; MOH Marsabit Dist., Kenya.

WEBSTER, Mr David John Tatchell University of Wales, College of Medicine, Heath Park, Cardiff CF4 4XM Tel: 029 2074 2020 Fax: 029 2074 3199; Sunnycroft, 25 St. Edeyms Road, Cyncoed, Cardiff CF23 6TB Tel: 029 2075 7117 — MD Bristol 1986, MB ChB 1967; FRCS Eng. 1972. Sen. Lect. (Surg.) Univ. Wales Coll. Med. Cardiff; Hon. Cons. Surg. S. Glam. HA. Prev: Regist. Rotat. (Surg.) Univ. Hosp. Wales Cardiff; Lect. (Surg.) Welsh Nat. Sch. Med. Cardiff; Research Fell. Ohio State Univ. Columbus, USA.

WEBSTER, Deborah Jane Vesper Hawk Farm, Smarden, Ashford TN27 8PU — MB ChB 1997 Birm.

WEBSTER, Diana 36 Craignabo Road, Peterhead AB42 2YE; 31 Fairview Parade, Aberdeen AB22 8ZX Tel: 01224 706592 — MB ChB 1997 Aberd.; BSc Med Sci Aberd. 1995. (Aberdeen)

WEBSTER, Diana Christina Shirley — MB ChB 1977 Leeds; MPH Leeds 1982; MRCGP 1981; MFCM 1988; DRCOG 1980.

WEBSTER, Donald Drummond 7 Croft Hills, Stokesley, Middlesbrough TS9 5NW Tel: 01642 710088 — MB BS Durh. 1945; FRCPsych 1976, M 1971; DPM 1950. (Newc.) Prev: Cons. Psychiat. S. Tees Health Auth.

WEBSTER, Elizabeth 7 Croft Hills, Stokesley, Middlesbrough TS9 5NW Tel: 01642 710088 — M.B., B.S. Durh. 1945. (Newc. upon Tyne) Prev: Med. Off. Cherry Knowle E.M.S. Hosp. Sunderland; Asst. MOH (Matern. & Child Welf.) Middlesbrough.

WEBSTER, Elizabeth Ann Webster and Hanna, Newbury Park Health Centre, 40 Perrymans Farm Road, Ilford IG2 7LE Tel: 020 8518 2414 Fax: 020 8518 3194 — MB ChB 1970 Aberd.; MRCGP 1975.

WEBSTER, Eric Marshall The Health Centre, Osborn Road, Fareham PO16 7ER Tel: 01329 823456 Fax: 01329 285772; Bay Tree Cottage, 18 Church Road, Locks Heath, Southampton SO31 6LU — MB ChB 1979 Aberd.; MB ChB Aberdeen 1979; D. Clin. Hyp London 1998-.

WEBSTER, Fiona Barbara Vesper Hawk Farm, Smarden, Ashford TN27 8PU — MB BS 1970 Lond.; MRCS Eng. LRCP Lond. 1970.

WEBSTER, Frances 2 Glebelands Avenue, South Woodford, London E18 2AB Tel: 020 8989 6272; 46 Malmesbury Road, London E18 2NN — BM BS 1985 Nottm.; MRCGP 1990. Trainee GP/SHO Chase Farm Hosp. Enfield. Prev: Ho. Off. (Med.) St. Geo. Hosp. Lincoln; Ho. Off. (Surg.) N. Middlx. Hosp. Lond.

WEBSTER, Frederick Lawrence (retired) 25 Hanbury Road, Clifton, Bristol BS8 2EP Tel: 0117 973 8041 — MB ChB Bristol 1959; DA Eng. 1962; DObst RCOG 1963.

WEBSTER, George John Mitchell 47 North Road, London N6 4BE — MB BS 1991 Lond.; BSc (Hons.) Lond. 1988; MRCP

Lond. 1994. Regist. (Gasteroenterol.) Whittington Hosp. Lond. Prev: SHO (Cardiol.) Roy. Brompton Nat. Heart & Lung Hosp. Lond.; SHO (Neurol.) Hammersmith Hosp. Lond.

WEBSTER, George Waddell (retired) 15 Northcliffe Gardens, Broadstairs CT10 3AL — MB ChB Aberd. 1953; MRCGP 1965.

WEBSTER, Gillian Kelso The Mission Practice, 208 Cambridge Heath Road, London E2 9LS Tel: 020 8983 7300 Fax: 020 8983 6800; 67 Ellesmere Road, London E3 5QU — MB ChB 1970 Liverp.; MRCP (UK) 1974; MRCGP 1983; DTM & H Liverp. 1979; DObst. RCOG 1972. Gen. Practitioner Mission Pract. Lond.; Clin. Asst., Dermat. Dept. St Andrews Hosp., Bow Lond. E3. Prev: Med. Off. Magila Hosp. Tanga Region, Tanzania, E. Afr.; Dep. Sen. Med. Off. Nixon Memor. Methodist Hosp. Segbwema, Sierra Leone, W. Afr.

WEBSTER, Grace Alexandra Mary (retired) 9 Cleveland Court, Kent Avenue, London W13 8BJ Tel: 020 8998 5112 — MB ChB 1947 Aberd.; MFCM 1973; DPH Lond. 1960; DObst RCOG 1951. Prev: Specialist Community Med. Hounslow & Spelthorne DHA.

WEBSTER, Graham David Woodeside Health Centre, Barr Street, Glasgow G20 7LR Tel: 0141 531 9570 Fax: 0141 531 9572; 9 Kingsborough Gardens, Glasgow G12 9NH — MB ChB 1978 Aberd.

WEBSTER, Mr Guy Michael Dept. of Urology, Worcester Royal Infirmary, Newtown Rd, Worcester WR5 — MB ChB 1988 Birm.; FRCS 1997; FRCS Ed. 1992. Cons. Urol. N. Worcs. Acute NHS Trust. Socs: Brit. Assn. of Urological Surg.s.

WEBSTER, Helen Louise — MB ChB 1995 Dundee. (Dundee) GP Retainee, Rotherham. Prev: GP Retainee, Cambs.; GP Regist., Halifax, W.Yorks.

WEBSTER, James 6 Newburgh Drive, Middleton Park, Bridge of Don, Aberdeen AB22 8SR — MB ChB 1969 Aberd.

WEBSTER, James Bruce Lindsay (retired) 17 The Gorseway, St. Georges Road, Hayling Island PO11 0DR Tel: 023 9246 4103 Fax: 01705 464103 Email: bruce@linweb.fsnet.co.uk — MB BChir 1964 Camb. Prev: GP Hayling Is.

WEBSTER, Janet Patricia 21 Lloyd Street, Mareeba QLD 4880, Australia Email: janetross@bigfoot.com — MB ChB 1988 Leeds; 2000 Grad. Dip. Of Rural Gen. Pract., Australia; FACR 1999 RM; FRACGP 1999. (Leeds Univ. Med. Sch.) Sen. Med.Off. Mareeba Hosp. Socs: Fell. RACGP; Fell. ACRRM; Mem. Of far N. Old Rural Div. Of GP. Prev: GP Regist. Rockhampton, Qu.sland, Australia; GP Regist. Airlie Beach Qu.sland, Australia; Princip. Ho. Off., Mackay Base Hosp., Qu.sland, Australia.

WEBSTER, Jennifer Ann Ward 30, Stirling Royal Infirmary, Livilands Gate, Stirling FK8 2AU Tel: 01786 434000 — MB ChB 1977 Dundee; MRCPsych 1983. Cons. Psychiat. Stirling Roy. Infirm. Prev: Cons. Psychiat. Hartwood Hosp. Shotts & Hairmyres Hosp. E. Kilbride; Sen. Regist. (Psychother.) Roy. Edin. Hosp.

WEBSTER, Joanne 247 Newbold Road, Chesterfield S41 7AQ — MB BS 1998 Newc.

WEBSTER, John Aberdeen Royal Infirmary, Aberdeen AB25 2ZN Tel: 01224 553718 Fax: 01224 553081 Email: j.webster@arh.grampian.scot.nhs.uk; Arisaig, Old Skene Road, Kingswells, Aberdeen AB15 8TA Tel: 01224 743828 — MB ChB 1973 Aberd.; MD Aberd. 1981; FRCP Ed. 1988; MRCP (UK) 1975. Grampian Univ. Hosp.s trust, Aberd. Socs: Brit. Hypertens. Soc. & Brit. Pharmacol. Soc. Prev: Sen. Lect. (Med. & Therap.) Univ. Aberd.; MRC Fell. Roy. Postgrad. Med. Sch. Lond.; Cons. Phys. Aberd. Roy Hosps. NHS Trust.

WEBSTER, John Webster and Twomey, Rainford Health Centre, Higher Lane, Rainford, St Helens WA11 8AZ Tel: 01744 882855 Fax: 01744 886559 — MB ChB 1974 Liverp.; DRCOG 1977.

WEBSTER, John Corner Cottage, The Avenue, Calverton, Nottingham NG14 6FH — MB ChB 1960 Liverp.; FRCOG 1989, M 1978.

WEBSTER, John Charles Thompson Lynfield Mount Hospital, Heights Lane, Bradford BD9 6DP Tel: 01274 494194 — MB BChir 1975 Camb.; MMedSci Leeds 1984; MA, MB Camb. 1975, BChir 1974; MRCPsych 1983. (Camb. Univ.) Cons. Psychiat. Lynfield Mt. Hosp. Bradford. Prev: Tutor (Psychiat.) Univ. Leeds; Sen. Regist. (Psychiat.) St. Jas. Hosp. Leeds.

WEBSTER, Mr John Herbert Harker (retired) Greenwood, 15 Westbourne Crescent, Southampton SO17 1EA Tel: 0236 055 7614 — MRCS Eng. LRCP Lond. 1953; MA Camb. 1955, MChir 1963,

MB BChir 1954; FRCS Eng. 1960. Prev: Cons. Surg. Soton. Univ. Hosps. Trust.

WEBSTER, Mr John Jeffrey 12 High Street, Uppermill, Oldham OL3 6HX — MB BS 1988 Lond.; FRCS Eng. 1992.

WEBSTER, John Louis (retired) 285 Beverley Road, Kirkella, Hull HU10 7AQ Tel: 01482 652692 — MB ChB Birm. 1955; FRCA 1963; DObst RCOG 1960. Prev: Cons. (Anaesth.) Hull & E. Yorks. HA.

WEBSTER, Jonathan Department of Diabetes & Endocrinology, Northern General Hospital, Herries Road, Sheffield S5 7AU Tel: 0114 226 6926 Fax: 0114 226 6924; 21 Cortworth Road, Ecclesall, Sheffield S11 9LN Tel: 0114 235 1637 — MB BS 1983 Lond.; MA Camb. 1985, MD 1993; MRCP (UK) 1986; FRCP FRCP (London) 2000. (Westminster Medical School London, Clare College Cambridge) Cons. Phys. & Endocrinol. N. Gen. & Roy. Hallamsh. Hosps. Sheff. Socs: Soc. Endocrinol.; Eur. Neuroendocrine Assn. Prev: Lect. (Med. & Endocrinol.) Univ. Wales Coll. Med. Cardiff; Research Fell (Med.) Cedars-Sinai Med. Center UCLA Sch. Med. Los Angeles Calif., USA; MRC Train. Fell. Neuroendocrine Sect. (Med.) Univ Wales Coll of Med. Cardiff.

WEBSTER, Julie Anne Sleaford Medical Group, Riverside Surgery, 47 Boston Road, Sleaford NG34 7HD Tel: 01529 303301 Fax: 01529 415401; Belvoir Lodge, 71 Woolsthorpe Road, Woolsthorpe-by-Colsterworth, Grantham NG33 5NT Tel: 01476 860875 — MB BS 1982 Lond. (Guys Hospital) Prev: Trainee GP Pilgrim Hosp. Boston VTS.

WEBSTER, Karen 4 Old Clare Road, Tandragee, Craigavon BT62 2EX — MB BCh BAO 1991 Belf.

WEBSTER, Karyn Flat D, 2 Fraser St., Aberdeen AB25 3XS Tel: 01224 636153 — MB ChB 1994 Aberd. Trainee GP/SHO Aberd. VTS. Prev: Ho. Off. Aberd. Roy. Infirm.

WEBSTER, Mr Keith Department Maxillofacial surgery, University hospital Birmingham, Edgbaston, Birmingham B15 2DT Tel: 0121 706 1587 Email: kwebster@bigfoot.com; 7 Kineton Green Road, Solihull B92 7DY — MB BS 1991 Lond.; BDS Liverp. 1983; FRCS Eng. 1993; FDS RCS Eng. 1990; FRCS 1997; MMEDSCI Birm 1999. (Guy's) Cons. menofacial Surg., Univ. Hosp. Birm. NHS Trust; Cons. menofacial Surg. Heartland and Solihull NHS Trust; Hon Sen. Lect. Birm. Dent. Sch. Prev: Sen. Regist. (Oral & Maxillofacial Surg.) Roy. Hosp. Wolverhampton; Regist. (Oral Surg.) N. Staffs. NHS Trust; SHO (Surg.) St. Helier NHS Trust.

***WEBSTER, Laura Helen** 16 Inchcape Road, Broughty Ferry, Dundee DD5 2LL — MB ChB 1998 Dund.; MB ChB Dund 1998.

WEBSTER, Louise Katherine c/o J C Webster, The Dennen, 59 Wilden Road, Renhold, Bedford MK41 0LY; Adel Manor Cottage, off Long Causeway, Adel, Leeds LS16 8EX — MB ChB 1993 Leic.; FRCA 2001 Lond. p/t Specialist Regist. Anaesth. N/W Yorks.

WEBSTER, Lynne Department of Psychiatry, Manchester Royal Infirmary, Oxford Road, Manchester M13 9WL Tel: 0161 276 5365 Fax: 0161 276 5444 — MB ChB Manch. 1977; BSc (Psychol.) Manch. 1974, MSc 1984; FRCPsych 1996, M 1983. Cons. Psychiat. i/c Psychosexual Med. Manch. Roy. Infirm.; Hon. Lect. (Psychiat. & Obst. & Gyn.) Univ. Manch. Socs: Accred. Mem. Brit. Assn. Sexual & Marital Ther.; Manch. Medico-Legal Soc.; Fell. Roy. Soc. Med. Prev: Sen. Regist. (Psychiat.) Univ. Hosp. S. Manch.

WEBSTER, Malcolm Long Lane Medical Centre, Long Lane, Liverpool L9 6DQ Tel: 0151 530 1009 — MB ChB 1960 Liverp.; DObst RCOG 1963.

WEBSTER, Mark Frenchwood Avenue Surgery, 49 Frenchwood Avenue, Preston PR1 4ND Tel: 01772 254173 — MRCS Eng. LRCP Lond. 1982. (Liverp.)

WEBSTER, Martin Howard Glenside Practice, Castle Bytham Surgery, 12b High Street, Castle Bytham, Grantham NG33 4RZ Tel: 01780 410205 Fax: 01780 410817 — MB ChB 1979 Dundee; MRCGP 1987; DA Eng. 1982. Prev: Med. Off. RAF.

WEBSTER, Mr Martyn Hector Cochrane Regional Plastic and Reconstructive Surgery Unit, Canniesburn Hospital, Bearsden, Glasgow G61 1QL Tel: 0141 211 5697 Fax: 0141 211 5652 Email: martynw@globalnet.co.uk; Trinity Chambers, 18 Woodside Terrace, Glasgow G3 7XH Tel: 0141 332 0035 Fax: 0141 332 0037 — MB ChB Glas. 1963; FRCS RCPS Glas. 1972.

WEBSTER, Mary Augusta 6 Forest Lawns, 124 Streetly Lane, Sutton Coldfield B74 4TD Tel: 0121 353 2654 Fax: 0121 353 2654 — MB ChB Birm. 1949; MRCS Eng. LRCP Lond. 1949; DObst

WEBSTER

RCOG 1950. (Birm.) Cytol. & Menopause Councillor W. Midl.; Med. Examr. DSS - NDA Med. Servs. Socs: Brit. Cytol. Soc.; Brit. Menopause Soc. Prev: Clin. Asst. Burton-on-Trent Gen. Hosp.; SCMO SE Staffs. HA; Med. Off. Selfridge Ltd. Lond.

WEBSTER, Mary Rosamund Lendal House, 91 Marton Road, Bridlington YO16 7PX Tel: 01262 672907 — MB BS 1938 Lond.; MRCS Eng. LRCP Lond. 1935; FRCOG 1974, M 1942; DPH Leeds 1939. (Roy. Free Hosp. Lond.) Socs: N. Eng. O & G Soc. & BMA. Prev: Res. Obst. Off. St. Mary's Hosp. Manch.

WEBSTER, Michael Harvey Taunton & Somerset Hospital, Musgrove Park, Taunton TA1 5DA Tel: 01823 333444 Fax: 01823 342635 — MB ChB 1972 Bristol; FRCP Lond. 1995; FRCPCH 1997; DCH Eng. 1974. Cons. Paediat., Taunton and Som. Hosp.; Cons. Paediat. Metab. Med., N. Bristol NHS Trust. Prev: Sen. Regist. (Paediat.) Birm. HA (T).

WEBSTER, Nigel Charles Harding Newcroft Surgery, Mill Street, Rocester, Uttoxeter ST14 5JX Tel: 01889 590208 Fax: 01889 590196 — MB ChB 1969 St. And.; DCH Eng. 1972.

WEBSTER, Professor Nigel Robert Wickerinn Farmhouse, Banchory AB31 5QX — MB ChB 1977 Leeds; PhD Leeds 1985, BSc (Hons.) (Pharmacol.) 1974; FRCP Ed. 1996; FFA RCS Eng. 1981.

WEBSTER, Nola Jean White Lodge Practices, 21 Grosvenor Street, St Helier, Jersey JE1 4HA Tel: 01534 23892 Fax: 01534 601955; 6 Vic Q Farm Close, Grouville JE3 9FL — MB ChB 1965 Birm.; BSc Birm. 1962. (Birm.) GP Jersey. Socs: BMA. Prev: GP Birm.; Research Fell. (Pharmacol.) Birm. Med. Sch.; Ho. Phys. & Ho. Surg. E. Birm. Hosp.

WEBSTER, Patricia Alice Charlotte (retired) 285 Beverley Road, Kirkella, Hull HU10 7AQ Tel: 01482 652692 — MB BS Lond. 1955; DObst RCOG 1958; FRCPCH 1997. Prev: Clin. Asst. (Paediat.) Hull HA.

WEBSTER, Patricia Anne The Surgery, Manlake Avenue, Winterton, Scunthorpe DN15 9TA Tel: 01724 732202 Fax: 01724 734992; 8 North Street, Roxby, Scunthorpe DN15 9QN Tel: 01724 732461 — MB ChB 1982 Sheff.; MRCGP 1987; DRCOG 1986. (Sheff.) Prev: Trainee GP Scunthorpe HA VTS.

WEBSTER, Penelope Kate Farfield Group Practice, St. Andrew's Surgeries, West Lane, Keighley BD21 2LD Tel: 01535 607333 Fax: 01535 611818; Allendale, 5 Manor Drive, Harrogate HG2 0HR — MB ChB 1983 Leeds; MRCGP 1988; DRCOG 1987; DCH RCP Lond. 1986. (Leeds.) GP p/t. Prev: Trainee GP Airedale VTS; Ho. Off. Seacroft Hosp. Leeds; Ho. Off. St. Lukes Hosp. Bradford.

WEBSTER, Peter Mark Maudsley Hospital, Denmark Hill, London SE5 8AZ — MB BChir 1993 Camb.; MA Camb. 1992. (Camb. & Roy. Lond.) Specialist Regist. (Psychiat.) Maudsley Hosp. Lond. Socs: Med. Defence Union. Prev: Specialist Regist., Maudsley; SHO (Psychiat.) Maudsley Hosp. Lond.

WEBSTER, Philip Powell Manselton Surgery, Elgin Street, Manselton, Swansea SA5 8QQ Tel: 01792 653643 / 642459 Fax: 01792 645257; 41 De-La-Beche Road, Sketty, Swansea SA2 9AR Tel: 01792 280425 — MB BS 1975 Lond.; DRCOG 1977. (St. Geo. Hosp. Med. Sch.) Socs: MDU; BMA.

WEBSTER, Premila Nalini Division Of Public Health, Institute of Health Science, University of Oxford, Old Road, Headington, Oxford OX3 7LF Tel: 01865 226735 Email: premila.webster@dphpc.ox.ac.uk — MB BS 1978 Madras; DA Madras 1982; DA 1987; MSc Lond. 1993; MFPHM 1998. (Christian Medical College) Director of Educat. & Train. in Pub. Health/ Cons./ Hon. SNR, Lect., Inst. of H.Sci.s, Univ. Oxf. Socs: Counc. Mem. of the Sect. of Epidemiol. & Pub. Health, The Roy. Soc. of Med., UK. Prev: Cons. WHO Health Cities Project Europ. Office, Copenhagen.

WEBSTER, Priscilla Jacqueline Russell 7 Wood Lane, Iver SL0 0LQ — MRCS Eng. LRCP Lond. 1981; BSc Lond. 1978, MB BS 1981. (St. Bart.) Regist. (Path.) St. Bart. Hosp. Lond. Prev: SHO (Path.) St. Bart. Hosp. Lond.; Ho. Surg. St. Bart. Hosp. Lond.; Ho. Phys. Whipp's Cross Hosp. Lond.

WEBSTER, Rachel Claire 45 Dene Bank, Bradshaw, Bolton BL2 3EA — MB ChB 1994 Liverp.

WEBSTER, Rae Elizabeth Department of Anaesthetics, Northampton General Hospital NHS Trust, Cliftonville, Northampton NN1 5BD Tel: 01604 545671 Fax: 01604 545672 Email: sleepngh@demon.co.uk — MB ChB 1979 Aberd.; FFA RCS Eng. 1985; MBA (Open) 1997. Cons. Anaesth. & Intens. Care N.ampton Gen. Hosp. NHS Trust. Prev: Cons. Anaesth. & Intens Care. Dundee Teachg. Hosps. Trust; Clin. Fell. (Critical Care) Toronto Hosp. (W.. Div.) Toronto, Ontario.

WEBSTER, Reginald Christopher, TD 24 Lynwood Court, Middleton Road, Manchester M8 4JX — MB BCh BAO 1928 NUI; BSc NUI 1927, MD 1933, MB BCh BAO (1st Hons.) 1928; DPH Manch. 1938; DCH Eng. 1947; LM Coombe 1932. (Cork & Manch.) Med. Asst. Calderstones Hosp. Whalley; Corps. Surg. St. John Ambul. Brig. Socs: FRSH. Prev: Div. MOH Lancs. CC & Co. Dist.; Col. late RAMC; Div. MOH & Sch. Med. Off. W. Riding CC.

WEBSTER, Richard Hugh Longlevens Surgery, 19b Church Road, Longlevens, Gloucester GL2 0AJ Tel: 01452 522695 Fax: 01452 525547; Longlevens Surgery, 19b Church Road, Longlevens, Gloucester GL2 0AJ Tel: 01452 522695 — MB BChir 1988 Camb.; MA Camb. 1989; MRCGP 1993. (Cambridge and King's College London) Prev: Trainee GP Cheltenham & Gloucester VTS; SHO (Med.) Univ. Hosp. of Wales Cardiff.

WEBSTER, Richard William (Surgery), 4 Londesborough Road, Market Weighton, York YO43 3AY; Totterdownhill Farm, Nunburnholme, York YO42 1QA — MB BS 1973 Newc.; MRCGP 1977.

WEBSTER, Robert Anthony 1 Christina Street, Harrogate HG1 2DF — MB ChB 1993 Leeds.

WEBSTER, Robert Edward, Squadron Ldr. RAF Med. Br. Retd. National Blood Service, Trent Centre, Longley Lane, Sheffield S5 7JN Tel: 0114 203 4813 Fax: 0114 203 4811 — MB BS 1982 Lond.; MRCPath 1992. (St. Geo. Hosp. Med. Sch.) Cons. Haemat. Nat. Blood Serv. Sheff. Prev: Cons. Haemat. RAF Inst. Path. & Trop. Med. Aylesbury; SHO (Path.) Roy. Liverp. Hosp. Liverp.; Ho. Phys. (Gen. & Geriat. Med.) St. Jas. Hosp. Lond.

WEBSTER, Robert William Johan 150 Claremont, Alloa FK10 2EG Tel: 01259 212088 — MB ChB 1964 Ed.; DRCOG 1971.

WEBSTER, Sally Elizabeth Marshall Cottage, Great Peatling Lodge, Foston Lane, Peatling Magna, Leicester LE8 5UH — MB ChB 1997 Leic.

WEBSTER, Sara Wallace Aigburth Hall Cottage, 1A Aigburth Hall Avenue, Liverpool L19 9EA — MB ChB 1992 Liverp. Prev: SHO (Dermat.) Roy. Liverp. Univ. Hosp.

***WEBSTER, Sarah Carolyn** 29 Bond Street, Stirchley, Birmingham B30 2LB — MB ChB 1998 Birm.

WEBSTER, Sharon Lesley 5A Brookfield Road, Hycule Cote GL3 Tel: 01452 617298 — MB BCh Wales 1989; MRCGP 1995; DRCOG 1993. (Univ. Wales Coll. Med.) p/t Asst. GP Gloucester & Gen. Pract. Gloucester. Prev: SHO (Psychiat.) St. Geo. Hosp. Stafford; SHO (ENT) Roy. Hosp. Wolverhampton.

WEBSTER, Stephen George Philip Ferry Corner, Water St., Old Chesterton, Cambridge CB4 1NZ Tel: 01223 359037 — MRCS Eng. LRCP Lond. 1964; MA Camb.; MD Lond. 1973, MB BS 1964; FRCP Lond. 1988. (Lond. Hosp.) Private Med. Practitioner; Assoc. Lect. (Med.) Univ. Camb; The Appeals Serv., GMC. Socs: Brit. Geriat. Soc.; Brit. Soc. Res. on Ageing. Prev: Sen. Regist. (Gen. & Geriat. Med.) United Oxf. Hosps.; Research Regist. & Regist. (Med.) Univ. Hosp. S. Manch.

WEBSTER, Stephen James Crossley Practice, 16 Henley Road, Coventry CV2 1LP Tel: 024 7668 9435 Fax: 024 7666 7127 — MB BS 1967 Durh.; MRCP (U.K.) 1972. (Newc.)

WEBSTER, Timothy Michael, Wing Cdr. RAF Med. Br. Regional Medical Centre, RAF College, Cranwell, Sleaford NG34 8HB Tel: 01400 261201 Ext: 7375 Fax: 01400 261201; 5 Brauncewell Road, Cranwell, Sleaford NG34 8RN — MB BS 1983 Lond.; MRCGP 1988; DAvMed. 1995 (RCP); DFFP 1993; DRCOG 1987. (Roy. Free) Sen. Med. Off. RAF Coll. Cranwell. Prev: Hon. Regist. (A & E) Addenbrooke's Hosp. Camb; SHO (O & G) Leic. Roy. Infirm.; Ho. Surg. (Acad. Depts. Surg. & O & G) Roy. Free Hosp. Lond.

WEBSTER, Victoria Jayne 25 St Edeyrn's Road, Cardiff CF23 6TB Email: v.j.webster@sheffield.ac.uk — MB ChB 1992 Sheff.; FRCA 1997. (Sheffield)

WEBSTER, Victoria Louisa Dept. Anaesthesia, Queen's Medical Centre, University Hospital, Nottingham NG7 2UH — MB BS 1993 Lond.; FRCA 1999 Lond.; DA (UK) 1996. (King's Coll. Lond.) p/t Specialist Regist. (Anaesth.) Qu. Med. Centre Nottm. Prev: SHO (Anaesth.) Qu. Med. Centre Nottm.; SHO (Anaesth.) W. Dorset Gen. Hosp.; SHO (A & E) Weymouth Hosp. Dorset.

WEBSTER, Vincent George The Stone House, Alton, Stoke-on-Trent ST10 4AG Tel: 01538 702210 Fax: 01538 703500 — LRCPI & LM, LRSCI & LM 1971; LRCPI & LM, LRCSI & LM 1971.

WEBSTER-HARRISON, Philip John Jackson and Partners, Port View Surgery, Higher Port View, Saltash PL12 4BU Tel: 01752 847131 Fax: 01752 847124 — MB BS 1984 London; MB BS 1984 London.

WEBSTER-SMITH, Claudia Suzanne Brockham Court Farm, Brockham Green, Brockham, Betchworth RH3 7JS — MB ChB 1998 Manch.

WEDATILAKE, Gigurawa Gamage David 41 North Close, Kettering NN15 7L8 — MB BS 1968 Ceylon.

WEDDELL, Craig Robert Esso Petroleum UK Limited, Occupational Health, Fawley refinery, Southampton SO45 1TX Tel: 01703 896190 Fax: 01703 896234 — MB BS 1991 Lond.; AFOM 2000; DRCOG 1995; MRCGP 1996. Med. Off. (Occupat. Health) Esso Petroleum UK Ltd. Socs: Mem. Roy. Coll. of Gen. Practitioners; Mem. of the Soc. of Occupat.al Med.

WEDDELL, David John The Surgery, 2048 Bristol Road, Rubery, Birmingham B45 9JL Tel: 0121 457 7966 — MB ChB 1976 Birm.

WEDDELL, Jean Mary (retired) 8 Denny Crescent, London SE11 4UY Tel: 020 7735 9303 — MD 1972 Lond.; MB BS 1953; FFCM 1977, M 1972; FRCP Lond. 1999. Prev: Sen. Lect. Dept. Community Med. St. Thos. Hosp. Lond.

WEDDERBURN, Mr Andrew Weir 22 Church Street, Romsey SO51 8BU — MB BS 1990 Lond.; FRCS Eng. 1994. Sen. SHO (Gen. Surg.) Roy. S. Hants. Hosp.; Demonst. UMDS. Prev: SHO (A & E) Worthing Hosp.; Ho. Phys. St. Peter's Hosp. Chertsey; Ho. Surg. St. Thos. Hosp. Lond.

WEDDERBURN, Clare 22 Church Street, Romsey SO51 8BU Tel: 01794 512852 Email: weds1@aol.com — MB BS 1993 Lond.; DCH 1997; DA (UK) 1995; MRCGP 1998. (UMDS) GP Retainer Scheme. Prev: GP Regist. Blackfield Health Centre Soton.; SHO (O & G) Roy. Hampsh. Co. Hosp. Winchester; SHO (Paediat.) St. Richard's Hosp. Chichester.

WEDDERBURN, John Pyle (retired) 11 Kingfisher Court, Tyler St., Stratford-upon-Avon CV37 6GF Tel: 01789 67776 — MB BS Durh. 1944. Prev: GP Wolverhampton & Hypnother.

WEDDERBURN, Lucy Rachel Imperial Cancer Research Fund, Lincoln's Inn Fields, London WC2A 3PX; 83 Listria Park, London N16 5SP — MB BS 1986 Lond.; BA (Hons.) Camb. 1982; MRCP (UK) 1989. Clin. Research Fell. Imperial Cancer Research Fund Lond. Socs: Brit. Soc. Immunol. & Brit. Soc. Rheum. Prev: Regist. (Med.) The Roy. Lond. Hosp.; SHO Roy. Marsden Hosp.; SHO The Lond. Chest Hosp.

WEDDERBURN, Stephen Rubislaw Place Medical Group, 7 Rubislaw Place, Aberdeen AB10 1QB Tel: 01224 641968 Fax: 01224 645738; 19 Rubislaw Park Crescent, Aberdeen AB15 8BT Tel: 01224 318306 Fax: 01224 326771 — MB ChB 1979 Aberd.; MRCGP 1983; DRCOG 1984; Cert. Family Plann. JCC 1983. (Aberd. Univ.) p/t Primary Care Dermatol. Kincardine Community Hosp. Stonehaven; Hosp. Practitioner, Woolmanhill Hosp., Aberd. Infirm.; Asst. Club Doctor Aberd. Football Club. Socs: Garioch Med. Soc.; Med. Chai Soc.; Primary Care Dermatol. Soc.

WEDDERSPOON, Andrew David 4 Heathwood Walk, Bexley DA5 2BP — MB BS 1961 Lond.; MRCS Eng. LRCP Lond. 1961. (Lond. Hosp.) Prev: Ho. Surg. Poplar Hosp.; Ho. Phys. St. And. Hosp. Bow.

WEDELES, Elinor Holmes 5 Sharples Hall Street, London NW1 8YL Tel: 020 7722 4450 — MRCS Eng. LRCP Lond. 1942. (W. Lond.) Indep. Pract. (Psychoanal.) Lond. Socs: Brit. Psychoanal. Soc.

WEDGBROW, Cheryl Stephanie 1 Western Drive, Hanslope, Milton Keynes MK19 7LA Tel: 01908 510230; 7 Croft Lane, Roade, Northampton NN7 2QZ — MB BS 1991 Lond.; BSc (Hons.) Lond. 1988; MRCGP 1995; DRCOG 1994. Clin. Asst. Family Plann. Prev: Trainee GP N.ampton Gen. Hosp.; SHO (A & E) Horton Gen. Hosp. Banbury; Ho. Off. (Surg.) Qu. Mary's Univ. Hosp. Lond.

WEDGWOOD, Mr Dennis Leveson Royal Shrewsbury Hospital, Copthorne, Mytton Oak Road, Shrewsbury SY3 8BR Tel: 01743 261151 Fax: 01743 261366 — MB BS 1970 Lond.; BDS Lond. 1960; FRCS Ed. 1985; FDS RCS Eng. 1966; FRCD (C) 1978. (Westminster) Cons. Oral & Maxillofacial Surg. Roy. Shrewsbury Hosp., Robt. Jones & Agnes Hunt Orthop. Hosp. OsW.ry & P.ss Roy. Hosp. Telford. Socs: Fell. Brit. Assn. Oral & Maxillofacial Surg.; BMA. Prev: Chief Dent. Serv. Health Sci. Centre Winnipeg Manitoba, Canada; Prof. & Chairm. Oral & Maxillofacial Surg. Univ. Manitoba; Cons. Oral & Maxillofacial Surg. St. Boniface Hosp. Winnipeg.

***WEDGWOOD, Frances** 14 Raeburn Street, London SW2 5QU — MB BS 1994 Lond.; MA Hons. Camb. 1991.

WEDGWOOD, Ivan Marston (retired) Beechwood, 25 Main St., Copmanthorpe, York YO23 3ST Tel: 01904 707660 — MRCS Eng. LRCP Lond. 1949. Prev: Ho. Surg. & Sen. Res. Anaesth. Off. Gen. Infirm. Leeds.

WEDGWOOD, John, CBE 156 Ashley Gardens, Thirleby Road, London SW1P 1HW Tel: 020 7828 8319 — MA Camb. 1948, MD 1954, MB BChir 1948; FRCP Lond. 1968, M 1949; MRCS Eng. LRCP Lond. 1943. (Camb. & Guy's) Chairm. RSAS Age Care; Vice-Pres. Roy. Hosp. for Neurodisabil. Lond. Socs: FRSM; Liveryman Soc. Apoth.; BMA. Prev: Cons. Phys. Geriat. Middlx. Hosp. Lond.; Dir. Med. & Research Servs. Roy. Home & Hosp. Putney Lond.; Sen. Med. Regist. Cardiol. Dept. St. Bart. Hosp. Lond.

WEDGWOOD, John Philip The Green Surgery, The Green, Church Lane, Brailsford, Ashbourne DE6 3BX Tel: 01335 360328 Fax: 01335 361095; Nether Cropper Farm, Back Lane, Sutton on The Hill, Derby DE6 5JL Tel: 0128 373 4631 — MB ChB 1983 Leeds; MRCGP 1987; DRCOG 1986. Prev: Trainee GP Derby VTS; Ho. Phys. (Gen. Med.) Roy. Halifax Infirm.; Ho. Surg. (Orthop./Gen. Surg.) St. Jas. Univ. Hosp. Leeds.

WEDGWOOD, Jonathan James 25 Main Street, Copmanthorpe, York YO23 3ST — MB BCh BAO 1988 NUI; LRCPSI 1988; FRCA 1994; DA (UK) 1992. Regist. (Anaesth.) Roy. Infirm. Edin.; Cons. (Anaesth.) W.. Gen. Hosp. Edin. Prev: SHO (Anaesth.) Roy. Infirm. Edin.

WEDGWOOD, Kevin Roy 302 Beverley Road, Anlaby, Hull HU10 7BG — MB ChB 1978 Leeds; BSc (Hons.) (Biochem.) Leeds 1975, MB ChB 1978. Research Regist. Univ. Dept. Surg. Univ. Missouri Columbia USA. Prev: SHO/Regist. Surg. Rotat. St. Jas. Hosp. Leeds.

WEDLEY, John Raymond Suite 304, Emblem House, London Bridge Hospital, 27 Tooley St., London SE1 2NP Tel: 020 7403 3876; 16 Glamorgan Road, Hampton Wick, Kingston upon Thames KT1 4HP — MB ChB 1968 Liverp.; FFA RCS Eng. 1974; DA Eng. 1971. Cons. Anaesth. & Pain Managem. Guy's & St Thomas' NHS Trust Lond. Prev: Sen. Lect. (Anaesth.) Guy's Hosp. Lond.

WEDLOCK, Karen 61 Woodhead Green, Hamilton ML3 8TJ — MB ChB 1998 Glas.

WEDZICHA, Professor Jadwiga Anna Academic Respiratory Medicine, Dominion House, St Batholomew's Hospital, London EC1A 7BE Tel: 020 8983 2219 Fax: 020 8983 2279 Email: j.a.wedzicha@qmul.ac.uk — MB BS 1978 Lond.; BA Oxf. 1975; MD Lond. 1985; FRCP Lond. 1994; MRCP (UK) 1980. (St. Bart.) Prof. (Respirat. Med.) St. Bart.'s & Roy. Lond. Sch. Med. Dent.; Hon.Con.Phys Bart and the Lond. Trust. Socs: Eur. Respirat. Soc.; Brit. Thorac. Soc.; Amer. Thoracic Soc. Prev: Sen. Regist. (Thoracic Med.) Lond. Hosp.; Regist. Lond. Chest Hosp.; SHO Brompton Hosp. Lond.

WEE, Alexander Andre Boon Liang 9 Arlington, London N12 7JR — MB BS 1993 Lond.

WEE, Bee Leng Countess Mountbatten House, Moorgreen Hospital, Botley Road, West End, Southampton SO30 3JB Tel: 02380 477414 Fax: 02380 473501 — MB BCh BAO 1988 Dub.; MRCGP 2001; MICGP 1992; Dip. Palliat. Med. Wales 1994; DObst RCOG 1991; DCH RCP Lond. 1990. (Trinity Coll. Dub.) Cons. Palliat. Med. Countess Mt.batten Hse. Soton.; Sen. Lect. Palliat. Med. Soton. Uni. Socs: Roy. Coll. Gen. Pract.; Assn. Palliat. Med. Prev: Med. Off. i/c Bradbury Hospice Hong Kong; Trainee GP Dub. VTS.

WEE, Christine Eng Lin 67 Elmcroft Crescent, North Harrow, Harrow HA2 6HL — MB BS 1996 Lond.

WEE, Michael Yoong Kan Department of Anaesthesia, Poole Hospital NHS Trust, Longfleet Road, Poole BH15 2JB Tel: 01202 665511 Fax: 01202 42672; Goldthorn, 31 Queens Park South Drive, Queens Park, Bournemouth BH8 9BH — MB ChB 1978 Dundee; MB ChB Dundee 1982; BSc (1st cl. Hons. Biochem.) Dund 1978; FFA RCS Eng. 1986. (University of Dundee) Lead Cons. - Obst. Poole Hosp.; Hon. Sec., obstretics Anaesth.s ass. Socs: Assn. Anaesth.; Wessex Obst. Anaesth.; Hon. Sec. Obst. Anaesth. Assn. Prev: Sen. Regist. (Anaesth.) Brit. Roy. Infirm. & Roy. Cornw. Hosp.

Truro; Sen. Regist. (Anaesth.) Gentofte Hosp. Copenhagen, Denmark.

WEE, Sian-Choong Bushmills Medical Centre, 6 Priestland Road, Bushmills BT57 8QP Tel: 028 2073 1233 Fax: 028 2073 2810; The Old Quarry, 35 Craigaboney Road, Bushmills BT57 8XD — MB BCh BAO 1975 Belf.; MRCOG 1982, D 1978. (Belf.)

WEEDEN, Amanda Claire 47 New Street, Chagford, Newton Abbot TQ13 8BB — MB ChB 1994 Birm.; ChB Birm. 1994. SHO (Anaesth.) The Dudley Gp. of Hosps. NHS Trust Dudley W. Midl. Socs: MRCAnaesth.; BMA. Prev: SHO (A & E) Birm. Heartlands Hosp.

WEEDEN, Mr David Francis Norman Southampton General Hospital, Tremona Road, Southampton SO16 6YD Tel: 02380 796239 Fax: 02380 796277 Email: davidweeden@suht.swest.nhs.uk; Field House, Greenfield Close, Hedge End, Southampton SO30 4DN Tel: 02380404850 Fax: 02380404850 — MB BS Lond. 1972; FRCS (Cardiothor) Ed. 1985; FRCS Eng. 1977; MRCS Eng. LRCP Lond. 1972. (Roy. Free) Cons. Thoracic Surg. Wessex Cardiothoracic Centre Soton. Socs: Fell. Soc. Thoracic & Cardiac Surgs. Prev: Sen. Regist. & Regist. (Cardiothoracic) N.. Gen. Hosp. Sheff.; Resid. Surg. Off. Brompton Hosp. Lond.

WEEDER, Raymond George Greenbank House, 24 Greenbank Road, Tunstall, Stoke-on-Trent ST6 7EY Tel: 01782 814177 — MB ChB 1958 Ed. (Edin.) Prev: Sen. Med. Off. 224 Field Ambul. RAMC (V); Regist. (Med.) E. Cumbld. Hosp. Gp.; Regist. (Respirat. Dis.) Stoke-on-Trent Hosp. Gp.

WEEKENBORG, Marie-Anne Tanglewood, Trinity, Brechin DD9 7PS — Artsexamen 1986 Amsterdam. (Amsterdam)

WEEKES, Andrew John 24 Kerswill Road, Exeter EX4 1NY — BM BS 1991 Nottm.

WEEKES, Clare Alison Old Station Surgery, 39 Brecon Road, Abergavenny NP7 5UH Tel: 01873 859000 Fax: 01873 850163; 64 Chapel Road, Abergavenny NP7 7DS — MB BS 1983 Lond.; MRCGP 1987; DCH RCP Lond. 1986; DRCOG 1985.

WEEKES, Richard Duncan McCallum Tait and Partners, 68 Pipeland Road, St Andrews KY16 8JZ Tel: 01334 476840 Fax: 01334 472295; Loaning Hill, Kilmany, Cupar KY15 4PT Tel: 01382 330696 Email: weekes@msn.com — MB ChB Aberd. 1990; Dip IMC RCS Ed. 1996; MRCGP Roy. Coll. of GP's 1997; DFFP 1998. (Aberdeen) Partner in Gen. Pract.; Hon. Lect. at St. And. Univ. Socs: Roy. Coll. Gen. Pract.; BMA; Brit. Assn. of Immed. Care Schemes. Prev: Regtl. Med. Off. Roy. Green Jackets & Coldstream Guards.

WEEKS, Andrew David Scunthorpe General Hospital, Cliff Gardens, Scunthorpe DN15 7BH Tel: 01724 282282 Email: aweeks@surfaid.org; 20 Norwood Avenue, Scunthorpe DN15 7AR Tel: 01724 870392 Email: aweeks@doctors.org.uk — MB ChB 1989 Sheff.; DCH RCP Lond. 1992; MRCOG Lond. 1996. (Sheffield Univ.) Specialist Regist. (O & G),Jessop Hosp.Wom..Sheff. Prev: Research Regist., St Jas. Hosp., Leeds; SHO (O & G) Jessop Hosp., Sheff.; SHO (O & G) N.. Gen. Hosp. Sheff.

WEEKS, Ann Kathleen Ellesmere Medical Centre, Stockport Road, Cheadle Heath, Stockport SK3 0RQ Tel: 0161 428 6729 — MB ChB 1990 Liverp.; MRCGP 1994; DCH RCP Lond. 1992; DRCOG 1992. (Liverp.) GP Stockport Retainer Scheme.

WEEKS, David Cecil, Brigadier late RAMC Retd. 42A Church Road, Fleet GU51 4NB Tel: 01252 687205 Fax: 01252 687205 Email: david.weeks@dtn.ntl.com — MB ChB Bristol. 1957; FFPHM 1988, M 1973; DTM & H Eng. 1967. Prev: Sec. Gen. Counc. & Regist. of Osteopaths.; Hosp. Dir. K. Khalid Hosp., Jeddah; Commanding Off. Qu. Eliz. Milit. Hosp. Lond.

WEEKS, Ian Robert Bradley Shaw Health Centre, Crookesbroom Lane, Hatfield, Doncaster DN7 6JN; The Hawthorns, Churchill Avenue, Hatfield, Doncaster DN7 6LU Tel: 01302 350264 — MB ChB 1980 Aberd.; MRCGP 1984; DRCOG 1984.

WEEKS, Jennifer Hilary 78 St Margaret's Street, Rochester ME1 3BJ Tel: 01634 841072 — MB BS 1981 Lond. (Lond. Hosp.) BrE. Phys. Maidstone & Tunbridge Wells; BrE. Phys. Medway Towns. Prev: SHO (O & G) The Lond. Hosp.; SHO (Gen. Med.) Centr. Middlx. Hosp. Lond. & Roy. Cornw. Hosp. Truro.

WEEKS, Kenneth Frederick (retired) 2 Buckland Heights, Buckland Road, Newton Abbot TQ12 4DF — MB BS 1948 Lond.; FRCPsych 1974, M 1971; DPM Eng. 1952. Prev: Cons. Psychiat. Plymouth Clin. Area.

WEEKS, Marjorie Alice Mayview, Headcorn, Ashford TN27 9TD — MB BS 1963 Lond. (St. Thos.)

WEEKS, Mark Loring 10 St James Road, Chichester PO19 4HU — MB BS 1984 Lond. Trainee GP S.bourne Med. Centre. Prev: Regist. (Anaesth.) Whipps Cross Hosp. Manch.; SHO (Paediat.) S.land Hosp. Shoreham by Sea; SHO (A & E) The Lond. Hosp.

WEEKS, Michael Charles (Surgery), 205 Shard End Crescent, Shard End, Birmingham B34 7RE Tel: 0121 747 8291 Fax: 0121 749 5497; 78 Elmdon Lane, Marston Green, Birmingham B37 7EG Tel: 0121 779 2778 — MB ChB 1961 Birm.; DCH Eng. 1964. Prev: Ho. Phys. & Ho. Surg. Hallam Hosp. W. Bromwich; Ho. Phys. Birm. Childr. Hosp.

WEEKS, Nicola Jane 109 Barkham Ride, Finchampstead, Wokingham RG40 4EP — MB BCh 1998 Wales.

WEEKS, Paul Anthony 10 Johnson Street, Lemington, Newcastle upon Tyne NE15 8DL — MB BS 1977 Newc.

WEEKS, Peter Julien Harrodale, Grainbeck Lane, Killinghall, Harrogate HG3 2AA — MB ChB 1994 Liverp.

WEEKS, Philippe Harold 9 Upper Brighton Road, Surbiton KT6 6LQ — MB BS 1993 Lond.

WEEKS, Rachel Mary Brookside Group Practice, Brookside Close, Gipsy Lane, Earley, Reading RG6 7HG — MB ChB 1983 Ed.; MRCGP 1987; T(GP) 1991; DRCOG 1986; DCCH RCGP & FCM 1988.

WEEKS, Reginald Frank Istana, 8 Gospond Road, Barnham, Bognor Regis PO22 0EU Tel: 01243 552917 Fax: 01243 552917 Email: regweeks@supanet.com — MB ChB Bristol 1958. Socs: Fell. Fac. Accid. & Emerg. Med.; Brit. Assn. Accid. & Emerg. Med. Prev: Emerit. Cons. A & E St. Richards Hosp. Roy. W. Sussex Trust (RTO); Accid. & Admissions Off. Roy. W. Sussex Hosp. (St. Richard's); Ho. Phys. Roy. Sussex Co. Hosp. Brighton.

WEEKS, Robert Anthony 1 The Whitehouse, Mardy, Abergavenny NP7 6LB — MB BCh 1989 Wales.

WEEKS, Robert Victor Mill Road Surgery, Mill Road, Market Rasen LN8 3BP Tel: 01673 843556 Fax: 01673 844388; Walnut Cottage, Church St, Middle Rasen, Market Rasen LN8 3TR Tel: 01673 842474 — MB BS 1986 Lond.; MRCGP 1992; DRCOG 1993. Prev: Maj. RAMC.

WEEKS, Roger Lewis Weeks and Rana, 2 Deanhill Road, London SW14 7DF Tel: 020 8876 2424 Fax: 020 8876 3249; 9 Upper Brighton Road, Surbiton KT6 6LQ Tel: 020 8390 0910 Fax: 020 8390 9273 — MB BS 1969 Lond.; MRCS Eng. LRCP Lond. 1964; DObst RCOG 1971. (Char. Cross) Chairm. Safescript Ltd. Prev: Med. Author Cons. to NHS Centre for Coding & cl.ification; Gen. Med. Off. (for Min. of Overseas Developm.) Thakhek, Laos; Lect. (Anat.) King's Coll. Lond.

WEEKS, Victoria Christina 86 Barn Hill, Wembley Park, Wembley HA9 9LQ — MB BS 1980 Lond.; BSc. Lond. 1977.

WEEKS, William Thomas Shaftesbury Avenue, 119 Shaftesbury Avenue, Southend-on-Sea SS1 3AN Tel: 01702 582687 Fax: 01702 589143 — MB BS 1976 Lond.

WEEPLE, Joan Anne East Wing, Esk Medical Centre, Ladywell Way, Musselburgh EH21 6AA Tel: 0131 665 2267 Fax: 0131 653 2348; 19 Lauder Road, Edinburgh EH9 2JG Tel: 0131 668 1150 — MB ChB 1970 Glas. (Glas.) Prev: GP Glas. & N.olt; Ho. Phys. & Ho. Surg. N.wick Pk. Hosp. Harrow.

WEERA, Chitra Ranjan Waranakula 7 Millwell Crescent, Chigwell IG7 5HX Tel: 020 8500 6235 — MRCS Eng. LRCP Lond. 1959. (Middlx.)

WEERACKODY, Roshan Priantha 10 Balmoral Avenue, Glenmavis, Airdrie ML6 0PY — MB ChB 1998 Aberd.

WEERAKKODY, Chitra Sarojini 46 Caerphilly Close, Rhiwderin, Newport NP10 8RF Tel: 01633 894312 — MB BS 1974 Sri Lanka; MRCS Eng. LRCP Lond. 1991; DGM RCP Lond. 1993; DTCD Wales 1983.

WEERAKONE, Ratna Susantha 30 Cadshaw Close, Blackburn BB1 8RN Tel: 01254 65077 — MB BS 1951 Ceylon; DPH Ed. 1965. (Ceylon) Sen. Med. Off. (Adult Health & Social Servs.) Blackburn Health Dist. Prev: Med. Off. Antifilariasis Campaign, Ceylon; MOH Matara, Ceylon & Moratuwa, Ceylon.

WEERAKOON, Bernard Stanley, Capt. RAMC Scarisbrick Centre, Ormskirk District General Hospital, Ormskirk L39 2AZ Tel: 01695 577111; 1 Fulford Park House, Main St, Fulford, York YO10 4PQ — MB BS 1959 Ceylon; MRCPsych 1983; DPM RCPSI 1982.

(Ceylon) Cons. Psychiat. Ormskirk Dist. Gen. Hosp. Socs: Roy. Soc. Health; Ceylon Med. Assn.

WEERAMANTHRI, Sunil Piyaratne (retired) 20 The Willows, Glinton, Peterborough PE6 7NE Tel: 01733 253717 — MD Moscow Peoples Friendship Univ. 1966; PhD (Alternative Med.) Sri Lanka 1986; LMSSA Lond. 1979; MACF DAC Sri Lanka 1984. GP Princip. Orton Malborne. Prev: Regist. (O & G) Muhimtrili Hosp. Dar-es-Salaam, Tanzania.

WEERAMANTHRI, Tara Bernice Camberwell Child & Adolescent Service, Lister Health Centre, 25 Commercial Way, London SE15 6DP Tel: 020 7701 7371 Fax: 020 7701 8697 — MB BS 1978 Lond.; MRCPsych 1985. Cons. (Child. & Adolesc. Psychiat.) S. Lond. & Mandsley NHS Trust, Lond. Prev: Cons. (Child & Adolesc. Psychiat.) Newham HA Lond.

WEERASINGHE, Mr Bodipaksa Piyasiri 43 Torrington Drive, Harrow HA2 8ND — MB BS 1968 Ceylon; FRCS Eng. 1983; DLO RCS Eng. 1980. Assoc. Specialist (ENT Surg.) Conquest Hosp. St. Leonards on Sea. Prev: Clin. Asst. Hastings Roy. E. Sussex Hosp.; Regist. (ENT) E.bourne Gen. Hosp.; Cons. Anuradhapura Gen. Hosp.

WEERASINGHE, Mr Buddhadasa Dharmawansa 91 St Andrew's Road, South Church, Bishop Auckland DL14 6RY Tel: 01388 604338 — MB BS 1955 Ceylon; FRCS Eng. 1964; FRCS Ed. 1963. (Colombo Med. Sch.) Cons. Orthop. Surg. SW Durh. Health Dist.; Emerit. Cons. Orthop. Surg. SW Durh. Health Dist. Socs: Sen. Fell. BOA; BMA. Prev: Regist. (Surg.) Gen. Hosp. Colombo, Ceylon; Regist. (Orthop.) Harlow Wood Orthop. Hosp. Mansfield; Clin. Asst. (Orthop. & Limb Surg.) Roy. Vict. Infirm. Newc. u. Tyne.

WEERASINGHE, Padma Malini 2 Mulgrave Road, Harrow HA1 3UF Tel: 020 8864 4933 — MB BS 1968 Ceylon; FFA RCS Eng. 1980; FFA RCSI 1980; DA Eng. 1976. (Ceylon) Assoc. Specialist (Anaesth.) Ealing Hosp. S.all. Socs: Assn. Anaesth. Prev: Regist. (Anaesth.) S. Lond. Hosp. Wom.; SHO (Anaesth.) St. Margt. Hosp. Epping & Lister Hosp. Stevenage.

WEERASINGHE, Somaratna 52A Middleton Lane, Middleton St George, Darlington DL2 1AL — MB BS 1966 Ceylon; FRCPsych 1992, M 1976; DPM Eng. 1974. (Ceylon) Cons. Psychiat. Darlington Memor. Hosp.

WEERASINGHE, Yamuna Ninethrie 289B Alexandra Avenue, Harrow HA2 9DX — BM Soton. 1993; MRCP UK 1998. (Univ. Soton.) Specialist Regist. (Paediat.), Lond. Socs: Med. Defence Union; BMA. Prev: SHO (Paediat.) Gt. Ormond St. Hosp. Lond.; SHO (Neonat.) Hammersmith Hosp. Lond.

WEETCH, Gordon Andrews Department of Anaesthesia, Hairmyres Hospital, E. Kilbride, Glasgow G75 8RG Tel: 0141 20292; 41 Buchanan Drive, Rutherglen, Glasgow G73 3PF Tel: 0141 647 3225 — MB ChB 1973 Glas.; FFA RCS Eng. 1978. Cons. Anaesth. Hairmyres Hosp. E. Kilbride. Socs: BMA & Scott. Soc. Anaesth. Prev: Regist. (Anaesth.) Glas. Roy. Infirm.

WEETCH, Walter John 49 St Germains, Drymen Road, Bearsden, Glasgow G61 2RS Tel: 0141 942 2899 — MB ChB 1935 Glas. (Univ. Glas.) Socs: BMA. Prev: Ho. Phys. Roy. Infirm. Glas.; Ho. Surg. Kilmarnock Infirm.; Res. Med. Off. Isolat. Hosp. Romford.

WEETMAN, Professor Anthony Peter Clinical Sciences Centre, Northern General Hospital, Sheffield S5 7AU Tel: 0114 243 4343 Fax: 0114 256 0458 Email: contact@a-weetman.demon.co.uk — MB BS 1977 Newc.; DSc Newc. 1993, MD 1983; FRCP Lond. 1990; MRCP (UK) 1979. Prof. Med. Univ. Sheff. & Hon. Cons. Phys. N.. Gen. Hosp. Sheff.; Sir Arthur Hall Prof. Med. Univ. Sheff. Socs: Assn. Phys. & Europ. Thyroid Assn.; Fell., Acad. of Med. Sci.s. Prev: Lect. Univ. Camb.; Wellcome Sen. Research Fell. (Clin. Sc.) Univ. Camb.; MRC Trav. Fell. NIH Washington DC, USA.

WEETMAN, Jacqueline Patricia 9 William Street, Manchester M20 6RQ — MB ChB 1990 Manch.

WEETMAN, Myrna Gray Central Avenue Health Centre, Central Avenue, Ardrossan KA22 7DX Tel: 01294 463838 Fax: 01294 462798; 27 Caldwell Road, West Kilbride KA23 9LF Tel: 01294 823871 — MB ChB 1966 Sheff. (Sheff.) Socs: BMA.

WEGGELAAR, Jan Sevrien 19 St Mary Abbots Terrace, London W14 8NX — Artsexamen 1984 Nijmegen.

WEGNER, Matthias-Peter Paediatric Department, Poole Hospital NHS Trust, Longfleet Road, Poole BH15 2JB — State Exam Med 1991 Hamburg. SHO (Paediat.) Poole Hosp. NHS Trust. Prev: SHO (Paediat.) Glos. Roy. Hosp.

WEGSTAPEL, Mr Hendrik 10 Mayfield Road, Bromley BR1 2HD — Artsexamen 1984 Groningen; FRCS Ed. 1990.

WEHNER, Helen Elizabeth Hartcliffe Health Centre, Hareclive Road, Hartcliffe, Bristol BS13 0JP Tel: 0117 9645588/9647925 Fax: 0117 964 9055; 70 Church Road, Horfield, Bristol BS7 8SE Tel: 0117 942 0998 Email: rickhelen@dial.pipex.com — MB BS 1983 Lond.; MRCGP 1989; DCH RCP Lond. 1987; MPH Wales 1998. (Roy. Free Hosp. Sch. Med.) Lect. (Pub. Health Med.) Univ. Bristol; Hon. Specialist Regist. (Pub. Health Med.) Avon HA. Prev: Med. Off. St. Martin Hosp. Oshikuku, Namibia; GP Warminster.

WEHNER, Mary Elizabeth (retired) 7 Church Road, Thorpeness, Leiston IP16 4PJ Tel: 01728 453215 — MB BChir 1943 Camb.; MRCS Eng. LRCP Lond. 1941; DCH Eng. 1946. Prev: Clin. Med. Off. SW Herts. Health Dist.

WEI, Chun Wilson 173A Lanark Road, London W9 1NX — MB BCh BAO 1979 NUI; LRCPI & LM, LRCSI & LM 1979; DCH Dub. 1982.

WEI, Terence Chiu Man University Department Clinical Neurology, Institute of Neurology, Queen Square, London WC1N 3BG; 52 Eton Hall, Eton College Road, London NW3 2DR — MB 1987 Camb.; MA Camb. 1988, MB 1987, BChir 1986; MRCP (UK) 1990. Prev: Research Fell. Univ. Bristol & Inst. Neurol. Lond.; Regist. (Med.) Qu. Eliz. II Hosp. Welwyn Gdn. City; SHO (Neurosurg.) & Regist. (Neurol.) OldCh. Hosp. Romford.

WEI, Mr William Ignace 9A Woodbury Court, 137 Pokfulam Road, Hong Kong, Hong Kong; 173A Lanark Road, Maida Vale, London W9 1NX Tel: 020 7328 2619 — MB BS 1974 Hong Kong; FRCS Ed. (Orl.) 1978; FRCS Ed. (Gen.) 1978; DLO RCS Eng. 1984.

WEICH, Scott Richard University Department of Psychiatry, Royal Free Hospital School of Medicine, Rowland Hill St., London NW3 2PF Tel: 020 7794 0500 Email: scott@rfhsm.ac.uk — MB BS 1987 Lond.; MSc Lond. 1995; MA Camb. 1988; MRCPsych 1991. Sen. Lect. (Psychiat.) Roy. Free Hosp. Sch. Med. Lond.; Hon. Cons. Psychiat. Roy. Free Hosp. MHS Trust Lond. Prev: Clin. Research & Lect. Inst. of Psychiat. Lond.; Regist. Bethlem Roy. & Maudsley Hosp. Lond.

WEIDMANN, Sarah Jane Coach House Surgery, 12 Park Avenue, Watford WD18 7LX Tel: 01923 223178 Fax: 01923 816464 — MB BS 1980 Lond.; MRCGP 1985; DRCOG 1983. Course Organiser Watford VTS.

WEIGHELL, Robert David Friends Road Surgery, 49 Friends Road, Croydon CR0 1ED Tel: 020 8688 0532 Fax: 020 8688 2165; Greenacres, Woodhurst Lane, Oxted RH8 9ED — MB BS 1982 Lond.; DCH RCP Lond. 1985. (Guy's) Clin. Asst. Diabetic Clinic Mayday Hosp. Croydon; Clin. Asst. Rheum. Clinic Croydon Gen. Hosp. Prev: Trainee GP Pontefract VTS.; Ho. Phys. Mayday Hosp. Thornton Heath; Ho. Surg. Orpington Hosp.

WEIGHILL, Mr Francis James (cons. rooms), 15 St John St., Manchester M3 4DG Tel: 0161 834 7373 Fax: 0161 834 9294; The Firs,, Norley Road, Kingsley, Warrington WA6 6LS Tel: 01928 788190 — MB ChB 1964 Liverp.; MChOrth Liverp. 1971; FRCS Eng. 1970; FRCS Ed. 1969. (Liverp.) Cons. Orthop. Surg. Withington Hosp. & Wythenshawe Hosp. Manch.; Vis. Surg. Duchess of York Hosp. Babies Manch. Socs: Fell. BOA; BMA. Prev: Sen. Regist. (Orthop.) Liverp. Roy. Infirm.; Regist. (Surg.) Leith Hosp. Edin.; Clin. Research Fell. Hosp. Sick Childr. Toronto, Canada.

WEIGHILL, Gillian Elizabeth The Martlets Hospice, Wayfield Avenue, Hove BN3 7LW Tel: 01273 273400 Fax: 01273 273401; 67 Wayland Avenue, Brighton BN1 5JL Tel: 01273 882527 — MB BChir 1978 Camb.; MB BChir Camb. 1977; MA Camb. 1978; MRCGP 1982; Dip. Palliat. Med. Wales 1991; DCH Eng. 1980. Assoc. Specialist (Palliat. Med.) Martlets Hospice & Community Palliat. Care Team Brighton.

WEIGHILL, Mr John Stephen Sussex Throat & Ear Department, Royal Sussex County Hospital, Eastern Road, Brighton BN2 5BE Tel: 01273 69955 Fax: 01273 602730; 67 Wayland Avenue, Brighton BN1 5JL Tel: 01273 882527 — MB BS 1977 Lond.; FRCS (Orl.) Eng. 1982. (Westm.) Cons. ENT Surg. Brighton Health Care Roy. Sussex Co. Hosp., Roy. Alexandra Childr. Hosp. & Worthing HA. Socs: Roy. Soc. Med. (Sects. Otol. & Laryngol.); Brit. Assn. Otol. Prev: Sen. Regist. Manch. Roy. Infirm.; Interne D'Etranger Gustave Roussy Hosp., Paris.

WEIGHILL

WEIGHILL, Patricia Ann 21 Burton Avenue, Timperley, Altrincham WA15 6AQ Tel: 0161 969 1764 — MB ChB 1982 Liverp. SHO (O & G) Whiston Hosp. Merseyside.

***WEIGHTMAN, Helen Mary** 214B Loughborough Road, West Bridgford, Nottingham NG2 7EE — MB ChB 1996 Birm.

WEIGHTMAN, Nigel Challoner Microbiology Department, Friarage Hospital, Northallerton DL6 1JG — MB BS 1981 Lond.; FRCPath 1997; MRCPath 1988. Cons. Microbiol. Friarage Hosp. N.allerton. Prev: Sen. Regist. (Microbiol.) Pub. Health Laborat. Preston & Manch.; Regist. (Microbiol.) Bristol Roy. Infirm.

WEIGHTMAN, William Munro 27 Bangor Street, Roath Park, Cardiff CF24 3LQ — MB ChB 1980 Bristol; FFA RACS 1988.

WEIL, Dolores Maria The Surgery, Gaywood House, North St, Bedminster, Bristol BS3 3AZ Tel: 0117 966 1412 Fax: 0117 953 1250; 40 Caledonia Place, Bristol BS8 4DN Tel: 0117 973 5958 — BM BS 1983 Nottm.; MRCGP 1989.

WEIL, Eva 23 The Vale, Chelsea, London SW3 6AG Tel: 020 7352 2948 — MB BCh BAO 1949 Dub. (T.C. Dub.) Prev: Ho. Phys. Burnley Gen. Hosp. & Hope Hosp. Salford.

WEIL, John Gerard Northern Birmingham Health Care Purchasing Consortium, 1 Vernon Road, Edgbaston, Birmingham B16 9S; 9 Second Avenue, Selly Park, Birmingham B29 7HD Tel: 0121 414 0002 — MD 1983 Louvain; MRCP (UK) 1986. Sen. Regist. (Pub. Health Med.) W. Midl. RHA. Prev: Wellcome Research Fell. Univ. Birm.

WEILER-MITHOFF, Mrs Eva Maria Department of Plastic Surgery, Canniesburn Hospital, Switchback Road, Bearsden, Glasgow G61 1QL Tel: 0141 811 5798 Fax: 0141 211 5652 Email: weimit@msn.com — State Exam Med 1984 Marburg; FRCS (Plast) 1996; FRCS Ed. 1992. (Marburg/Germany) Cons. (Plastic Surg.) Canniesburn Hosp. Glas. Socs: BMA; BAPS. Prev: Sen. Regist. (Plastic Surg.) Canniesburn Hosp. Glas.; Regist. (Plastic Surg.) Frenchay Hosp. Bristol.

WEINBREN, Henrietta 36 Canonbury Square, Islington, London N1 2AN — MB BS 1986 Lond.; DRCOG 1991; DCH RCP Lond. 1991; MRCGP 1998. GP Asst. Lond.

WEINBREN, Herschell Kenneth 1 Kithurst Close, East Preston, Littlehampton BN16 2TQ — MB BCh 1946 Witwatersrand; BSc Witwatersrand 1942; MD 1957. (Witwatersrand) Prof. Experim. Path. Roy. Postgrad. Med. Sch. Lond. Prev: Reader in Experim. Path. Lond. Hosp. Med. Coll.; Prof. Path. Univ. Nottm.; Prof. Histopath. Roy. Postgrad. Med. Sch. Lond.

WEINBREN, Ian (retired) 18 Balmoral Road, St Annes, Lytham St Annes FY8 1ER Tel: 01253 720597 — MB BChir 1952 Camb.; FRCP Lond. 1974, M 1959. Prev: Cons. Phys. Blackpool & Fylde Hosp. Gp.

WEINBREN, Jeremy Hillingdon Hospital, Pield Heath Road, Uxbridge UB8 3NN Email: jeremy@weinbren.globalnet.co.uk — MB BS 1984 Lond.; FRCA 1994; DA (UK) 1989.

WEINBREN, Michael Jan 3 Westbury Park, Bristol BS6 7JB — MB BS 1980 Lond.

WEINBRENN, Gerald Hyman Department Radiology, Edgware General Hospital, Edgware HA8 0AD Tel: 020 8732 6720; Beechwood, 26A Rosecroft Avenue, London NW3 7QB — MB BCh 1957 Witwatersrand; MSc (Nuclear Med.) Lond. 1976; DMRD 1961. Cons. Radiol. Edgware Gen. Hosp. Prev: Sen. Regist. (Radiol.) W.m., Brompton & St. Stephens Hosps. Lond.

WEINER, Christopher Andrew 3 Lynton Park Road, Cheadle Hulme, Cheadle SK8 6JA — MB ChB 1993 Birm.

WEINER, Mr Graeme Martin The Lair, 2 Foxhill Barns, Foxhill Lane, Alvechurch, Birmingham B48 7BY — MB ChB 1988 Birm.; FRCS Eng. 1993. (Birm.) Specialist Regist. Rotat. (Otorhinolaryngol.) W. Midl. Socs: Assoc. Mem. Midl. Inst. Otol.; Otorhinological Res. Soc. Prev: SHO (Otolaryngol. & Head & Neck Surg.) Birm. Heartlands Hosp.; SHO (Neurosurg.) Midl. Centre for Neurosurg. & Neurol.; SHO (Otolaryngol.) Dudley Rd. Hosp. Birm.

WEINER, Michael Westernlea, 131 Denton Road, Andenshaw, Manchester M34 5BE — MB ChB 1967. (Liverpool) Medico-Legal Expert Witness; Fact. Doctor. Prev: GP.

WEINER, Nathan (retired) 85 Livingstone Road, Gillingham ME7 2EJ Tel: 0956 605515 — MB ChB Glas. 1947.

WEINGARTEN, Noëmi Joan Torrington Park Health Centre, 16 Torrington Park, North Finchley, London N12 9SS Tel: 020 8445 7622/4127; 3 Clorane Gardens, London NW3 7PR — MB BS 1975 Lond.; DCH Eng. 1979; DRCOG 1978. (Guy's)

WEINHARDT, Anne Barbara Department of Medical Microbiology, Glasgow Royal Infirmary, Castle St., Glasgow G4 0SF — MB ChB 1985 Leic.

WEINIGER, Carolyn Fiona Flat 2, 95 Sunny Gardens, London NW4 1SH — MB ChB 1992 Manch.

WEINKOVE, Cyril 14 Moor End Avenue, Salford M7 3NX — MB ChB 1963 Cape Town.

WEINREB, Irene Rachel Imperial College Health Centre, Southside, Watt;s Way, London SW7 1LU Tel: 020 7584 6301 Fax: 020 7594 9390; 63 Finsbury Park Road, London N4 2JY Tel: 020 7226 3441 Fax: 020 7594 9390 — MB BS 1976 Lond.; MRCS Eng. LRCP Lond. 1976; DRCOG 1979. (Roy. Free) GP Imperial Coll. Univ. Lond.; Chairperson Brit. Assoc. of Health Serv. in Higher Educat.; Dir. Clin. Studies Imperial Coll. Lond.

WEINSTEIN, Andrew Felix Chase Farm Hospital, Enfield EN2 8JL Tel: 020 8366 6600 — MB BChir 1978 Camb.; MA Camb. 1979, BA 1975, MB BChir 1978; FRCP 1997; MRCP (UK) 1983. Cons. Phys. Geriat. Med. Chase Farm Hosp. Prev: Sen. Regist. (Geriat. Med.) W.m. & Char. Cross Hosps.

WEINSTEIN, Charles Battle Hospital, Oxford Road, Reading RG30 1AG — MB BChir 1980 Camb.; MA Camb. 1981, BA 1978, MB BChir 1980; MSc (Computer Sc.) Birm. 1985; FRCP 1997, MRCP (UK) 1984.

WEINSTEIN, Vivian Felix 22 Northumberland Road, Leamington Spa CV32 6HA Tel: 01926 424062 Fax: 01926 889135 — MB BCh 1953 Witwatersrand; FRCP Lond. 1977, M 1957. Prev: Cons. Phys. S. Warks. Health Dist.

WEINSTOCK, Harold Steven Whitley Road Medical Centre, 1 Whitley Road, Collyhurst, Manchester M40 7QH Tel: 0161 205 4407 Fax: 0161 203 5269; 4 Pinfold Lane, Whitefield, Manchester M45 7JS — MB ChB 1975 Manch. (Manch.) Clin. Asst. (Gastroenterol.) N. Manch. Gen. Hosp.; Tutor (Gen. Pract.) Univ. Manch.; Bd. Mem. S. Manch. PCG; Med. Dir. Out of Hours CoOperat.

WEINSTOCK, Norman Graham 20 Acris Street, London SW18 2QP Tel: 020 8874 9423 — MB BCh 1967 Wales; MRCP (UK) 1972; DPM Eng. 1972; MFPHM 1989. Prev: Regist. (Cardiol.) Char. Cross Hosp. Lond.; Regist. (Psychiat.) Char. Cross Hosp. Lond.; SHO (Med.) St. Francis Hosp. Lond.

WEINSTOCK, Samuel The Health Centre, 1A Fountayne Road, London N16 7EA Tel: 020 8806 3311; 29 Nottingham Place, London W1U 5LW Tel: 020 7935 7674 — MRCS Eng. LRCP Lond. 1936. (Lond. Hosp.)

WEIR, Adam 50 Tavistock Drive, Mapperley Park, Nottingham NG3 5DW — MB BS 1998 Newc. SHO A&E Dryburn Hosp., Durh.

WEIR, Alan Duncan Kirriemuir Health Centre, Tannage Brae, Kirriemuir DD8 4DL Tel: 01575 573333 Fax: 01575 574230; Appin, 51 Brechin Road, Kirriemuir DD8 4DE — MB ChB 1980 Dundee.

WEIR, Mr Alastair McLean 22 Moriston Drive, Livingston EH54 9HT — MB ChB 1980 Ed.; BSc (Hons.) Ed. 1977, MB ChB 1980; FRCS Ed. 1985; MRCGP 1991; DMedRehab RCP Lond. 1992. Sen. Regist. (Rehabil. Med.) Astley Ainslie Hosp. Edin. Socs: Scott. Soc. Rehabil. (Comm. Mem.); Brit. Soc. Rehabil. Med.

WEIR, Alistair William Goold (retired) Rose Cottage, Kippen, Stirling FK8 3DT Tel: 01786 870493 — MB ChB Glas. 1950; FRCOG 1971, M 1958. Prev: Cons. O & G Stirling Roy. Infirm.

WEIR, Andrew Ian 16 The Oaks, Killearn, Glasgow G63 9SF Tel: 0141 550779 Fax: 0141 201 2519 Email: andrew@neurophysglas.org — MB ChB 1975 Glas.; MSc Glas. 1977, BSc (Hons.) 1971, MB ChB 1975; FRCP Glas. 1988; MRCP (UK) 1978. Cons. Clin. (Neurophysiol.) Inst. Neurol. Sc. S. Gen. Hosp. Glas.; Hon. Sen. Lect. (Neurol.) Univ. of Glas. Prev: Sen. Clin. Reasearch Fell. (Wellcome Trust) Inst. Neurol. Sc. S.; Gen. Hosp. Glas.

WEIR, Andrew Peter Department of Anatomy & Human Genetics, South Parks Road, Oxford OX1 3QX — MB BS 1994 Lond.; BA Camb. 1988; MBBS Lond. 1994; MRCP 1997. (Lond. Hosp.)

WEIR, Andrew Wickham The Shaftesbury Practice, Abbey View Medical Centre, Salisbury Road, Shaftesbury SP7 8DH Tel: 01747 856700 Fax: 01747 856701; Pensbury Close, Shaftesbury SP7 8QJ Tel: 01747 852437 — MB BS 1971 Lond.; MRCS Eng. LRCP Lond. 1971; DA Eng. 1975; DObst RCOG 1973. (St. Bart.) Med. Off. Guys

WEIR

Marsh Youth Custody Centre; Med. Off. W.m. Memor. Hosp. Shaftesbury. Socs: BMA. Prev: Clin. Asst. (Anaesth.) Salisbury Gen. Hosp.; SHO (Obst. & Anaesth.) Roy. Cornw. Hosp. Treliske; Ho. Surg. St. Bart. Hosp. Lond.

WEIR, Basil (retired) 64 Doddington Road, Swallowbeck, Lincoln LN6 7EU — MB ChB 1956 St. And. Prev: SHO (Paediat.) St. Geo. Hosp. Lincoln.

WEIR, Cameron John University Department of Anaesthesia, Ninewells Hospital and Medical School, Dundee DD1 9SY Tel: 01382 660111 Email: cweir@pnsi.dundee.ac.uk; 43 Bay Road, Wormit, Newport-on-Tay DD6 8LW — MB ChB 1993 Glas.; BSc 1988; FRCA 1997. (Glasgow Univ.) Research Fell./Specialist Regist. Socs: Scott. Soc. Anaesth.; Anaesth. Res. Soc.; Assn. of Anaesth.

WEIR, Clifford Ronald 10 Waterston Way, Lochwinnoch, Renfrewshire PA12 4EQ — MB ChB 1992 Glas.; MD 2001 Glasgow; BSc (Hons.) Glas. 1989; FRCOphth 1996. Tennent Inst. of Ophth., Gartnavel Gen. Hosp. Glas. Prev: Specialist Regist. Glas.; SHO Ophth., Glas.

WEIR, Mr Colin Derek Craigavon area hospital, 68 Lurgan Road, Portadown, Craigavon BT67 0QP Email: cdweir@dial.pipex.com; 36 Langtry Lodge, Moira, Craigavon BT67 0GT Tel: 02892 619638 Email: cdweir@dial.pipex.com — MB BCh BAO 1984 Belf.; FRCS Ed. 1988. (Queens university, Belfast) Cons. Gen. & Vasc. Surg. Craigavon Area Hosp. Portadown; Honourary Clin. Lect. in Surg., Qu.s Univ., Belf. Socs: Nutrit. Soc.; Vasc. Surg. Soc. GB & Irel.; Eur. Soc. Vasc. Surg. Prev: Sen. Regist. Vasc. Surgic. Units Roy. Vict. & Belf. City Hosp.

WEIR, David Cuthbertson Chest Unit, North Manchester General Hospital, Manchester M8 5RB Tel: 0161 720 2077 Fax: 0161 720 2048 Email: deweir@unpuserve.com; 10 Holmefield, Sale M33 3AN — MB ChB 1981 Ed.; BA Oxf. 1978; MRCP (UK) 1984; FRCP Lond 1996; MD Edin. 1995. (Edinburgh) Cons. Phys. in Gen. Med. with an interest in Respirat. Med., N. Manch. Gen. Hspital, Manch.; Hon. Clin. Lect., Univ. of Manch. Med. Sch.; Clin. Dir. Chest Directorate; Chairm. Clin. Audit Commitee. Socs: Eur. Respirat. Soc.; Inst. Health Serv. Manch. Prev: Research Fell. E. Birm. Hosp. & Solihull Hosps.

WEIR, Mr David John Freeman Hospital, Freeman Road, Newcastle upon Tyne NE7 7DN Tel: 0191 284 3111 Fax: 0191 223 1238 — MB ChB 1985 Dundee; FRCS (Orth.) 1995; FRCS Eng. 1990. Cons. Orthop. Surg. Freeman Hosp. Newc. u. Tyne. Socs: Fell. BOA. Prev: Sen. Regist. (Knee Fell.) Freeman Hosp. Newc.; Regist. Rotat. (Orthop.) N.. RHA; Regist. Rotat. (Surg.) Newc. u. Tyne.

WEIR, Desmond Alexander (retired) 9 Greystone Road, Antrim BT41 1HD Tel: 01849 463001 — MB BCh BAO 1942 Belf.; DPH 1948.

WEIR, Desmond Atholl Duncan (retired) Twillick, Boscastle PL35 0AB Tel: 01840 250504 — MB BS 1954 Lond. Prev: Med. Regist. Dorset Co. Hosp. Dorchester.

WEIR, Diarmid James Grant Sutherland House, 209 Mayburn Avenue, Loanhead EH20 9ER Tel: 0131 440 0149 — MB ChB 1986 Manch.; BSc St. And. 1983; DFFP 1994; DCH RCP Lond. 1993. Socs: BMA. Prev: SHO (A & E) Warrington Dist. Gen. Hosp.; SHO (Gen. Med.) Walton & Fazakerley Hosps. Liverp.; SHO (Cardiol.) BRd.green Hosp. Liverp.

WEIR, Donald Mackay 36 Drummond Place, Edinburgh EH3 6PW Tel: 0131 556 7646 Email: dmweir@ed.ac.uk — MB ChB 1955 Ed.; MD (Hons.) Ed. 1962; FRCP Ed. 1981, M 1976. (Ed.) Prof. Immunol. Dept. Med. Microbiol. Univ. Edin. Med. Sch.; Hon. Cons. Lothian HB; Hon. Fell. (Med. Microbiol.) Edin. Med. Sch. Socs: Brit. Soc. Immunol.; Eur. Inflammation Soc. Prev: Arthritis & Rheum. Counc. Research Fell. MRC Rheum. Research Unit Taplow.

WEIR, Fiona Jean Trevor Mann Baby Unit, Royal Sussex County Hospital, Eastern Road, Brighton BN2 5BE — MB BS 1982 Lond.; MRCP (UK) 1986. (King's Coll. Hosp. Lond.) Cons. Neonat. Roy. Sussex Co. Hosp.

WEIR, George James Stewart, Col. late RAMC British Military Hospital, Hong Kong BFPO 1 — MB ChB 1965 Glas. (Glas.) Prev: Cdr. Med. 4th Armoured Div.; Med. Adviser AFN., Oslo; CO 3 Armoured Field Ambul.

WEIR, Gordon Boundary House Surgery, Boundary House, Mount Lane, Bracknell RG12 9PG Tel: 01344 483900 Fax: 01344 862203 — MB ChB 1984 Glas.; MRCGP 1988; DRCOG 1986. (University of Glasgow) Prev: SHO Ayrsh. & Arran HB VTS; HO. Off. (Med. & Surg.) CrossHo. Hosp. Kilmarnock.

WEIR, Graeme 60 Whitless Court, Ardrossan KA22 7PB — MB ChB 1998 Ed.; MB ChB Ed 1998.

WEIR, Iain Kirkland Ivry House - Child, Adolescent & Family Consultation Service, 23 Henley Road, Ipswich IP1 3TF Tel: 01473 214811 Fax: 01473 280809; Bramblewood, Leeks Hill, Melton, Woodbridge IP12 1LW Tel: 01394 385909 Fax: 01394 382992 Email: weirwizard@aol.com — MB BS 1968 Lond.; MRCS Eng. LRCP Lond. 1968; MRCPsych 1975. (Guy's) Cons. Psychiat., Priv. Prac.; Cons. Psychiat. Ivy Ho. Child, Adolesc. & Fam. Consult. Serv. Local Health Partn. NHS Trust, Ipswich. Prev: Med. Dir. E. Suff.. Local Health Serv. NHS Trust; Clin. Dir. Child & Family Psychiat. E. Suff. Local Health Servs. NHS Trust; Cons. Child Psychiat. Guy's Hosp. & Lewisham Child & Family Psychiat. Clinic.

WEIR, Mr Ian George Cameron The Old Manse, Station Road, Friockheim, Arbroath DD11 4SE — MB ChB 1979 Glas.; FRCS Ed. 1986.

WEIR, Ivan Richard Joseph Park Avenue Medical Centre, 9 Park Avenue, Stirling FK8 2QR Tel: 01786 473529; 10 Batter Flatts Gardens, Stirling FK7 9JU Tel: 01786 465630 — MB BCh BAO 1983 Belf.; BSc (Hons. Biochem.) Belf. 1981; MRCGP 1987; DRCOG 1986; DCH RCPSI 1986. (Qu. Univ. Belf.)

WEIR, Jack, MC (retired) Marchfield, Port Glasgow Road, Kilmacolm PA13 4SG — MB ChB 1939 Glas.

WEIR, James Barclay De Vere The Surgery, 3 Glasgow Road, Paisley PA1 3QS Tel: 0141 889 2604 Fax: 0141 887 9039 — MB ChB 1975 Glas.; MRCGP 1980; DCH RCP Lond. 1978; DRCOG 1977. (Glas.) GP Paisley, Renfrewsh.

WEIR, James Simon Leslie The School House, Mews Lane, Winchester, Winchester SO22 4PS — MB BS 1997 Lond.

WEIR, James Thomson (retired) Rhana, 13 Hunters Grove, Hunters Quay, Dunoon PA23 8LQ — LRCP LRCS 1944 Ed.; LRCP LRCS Ed. LRFPS Glas. 1944; DTM & H Liverp. 1959. Sen. Med. Off. (Occupat. Health) Surrey CC Kingston upon Thames. Prev: Chief Med. Off. Kuwait Oil Co. K.S.C Ahmadi, Kuwait.

WEIR, Professor Jamie September Cottage, Skene, Westhill AB32 6UX — MB BS 1968 Lond.; FRCP Ed. 1985; MRCP (UK) 1972; FRCR 1975; DMRD Eng. 1973; FRANZCR 1998. Cons. Radiol. Grampian HB; Clin. Prof. Radiol. Univ. Aberd.

WEIR, Jane Jackson The Old Rectory Surgery, 18 Castle Street, Saffron Walden CB10 1BP Tel: 01799 522327 Fax: 01799 525436; 30 Saxon Way, Saffron Walden CB11 4EG — MB BChir 1982 Camb.; BSc St. And. 1979; MRCGP 1986; DRCOG 1986.

WEIR, Jennifer Mary 50 Killead Road, Aldergrove, Crumlin BT29 4EN — BM BCh 1992 Oxf.

WEIR, John, Surg. Lt.-Cdr. RN Retd. (retired) 21 The Glebe, Crail, Anstruther KY10 3UJ Tel: 01333 450752 — MB ChB 1938 Glas. Prev: Med. Off. DHSS.

WEIR, John Alexander Bonnybridge Health Centre, Larbert Road, Bonnybridge FK4 1ED Tel: 01324 812315 Fax: 01324 814696 — MB ChB 1977 Manch.; BSc St. And. 1974; DO RCS Eng. 1984. Prev: Regist. (Ophth.) W.m. Hosp. Lond.; SHO (Neurol.) Middlx. Hosp. Lond.; Ho. Off. Manch. Roy. Infirm.

WEIR, John Anthony David Marfleet Group Practice, 350 Preston Road, Hull HU9 5HH Tel: 01482 701834 — MB ChB 1985 Leeds.

WEIR, John Cumming Rankine Firwood, 44 Glasgow Road, Muirkirk, Cumnock KA18 3RN Tel: 0129 06 448 — MB ChB 1940 Glas. (Univ. Glas.) Prev: Ho. Phys. Roy. Alexandra Infirm. Paisley; Ho. Off. Mearnskirk EMS Hosp.; Capt. RAMC.

WEIR, John Gordon 34E The Limes, Linden Gardens, London W2 4ET Tel: 020 7727 1315 — MB ChB Aberd. 1952; MA Aberd. 1945, MD 1964; FRCPsych 1977, M 1971; DPM Eng. 1960. (Aberd.) Prev: Cons. Psychiat. St. Mary's Hosp. Lond. & Mildmay Mission Hosp.; Cons. Psychotherapist St. Bernard's Hosp. S.all.

WEIR, John Philip Dumbarton Road Surgery, 1398 Dumbarton Road, Glasgow G14 9DS Tel: 0141 959 1520 Fax: 0141 959 8463 — MB ChB 1971 Glas.; Dip Forens. Med. 1988.

WEIR, June Marie Prouteaux Cloverlea, 24 Clonevin Park, Lisburn BT28 3BL Tel: 01846 673531 — MB BCh BAO 1954 Belf. Assoc. Specialist (ENT) Roy. Vict. Hosp. Belf. Prev: JHMO (ENT) Daisy Hill Hosp. Newry.

WEIR, Mr Justin Neil Macdonald 115 Pembroke Road, Bristol BS8 3EU — MB BS 1992 Lond.; BSc (Hons.) Lond. 1989; FRCS

WEIR

Eng. 1996. (Char. Cross & Westm. Hosps.) Demonst. Path., Bristol Roy. Infirm. Socs: Liveryman Worshipful Soc. Apoth. Prev: research fell., Unvi. Depl Otorhinolaryng. Bristol.

WEIR, Karla Amanda Jane Bracken Ridge, Heath Ride, Finchampstead, Wokingham RG40 3QN — MB ChB 1984 Glas.; MRCGP 1988; DCH RCPS Glas. 1987. GP Crowthorne Berks. Prev: Clin. Med. Off. Soton. HA; Trainee GP Ayr.

WEIR, Karoline Mary Elmwood Medical Centre, 7 Burlington Road, Buxton SK17 9AY Tel: 01298 23019 — MB ChB 1984 Liverp.; FRCGP 1996, MRCGP 1988. (Liverp.) GP; Cas. Off. Prev: Trainee GP (O & G/Dermat./Ophth./ENT) Hinchinbrooke Hosp. Huntingdon VTS; RMO 1 Roy. Scots. Werl W. Germany; Trainee GP Celle Med. Centre, W. Germany VTS.

WEIR, Margaret Jean Castle of Fiddes, Stonehaven AB39 2XX Tel: 0156 94 213; 14 Cowley Street, London SW1P 3LZ Tel: 020 7799 3269 — MB BS 1969 Lond.; MRCP (UK) 1974; FRCP 1999. (Middx) Cons. Genitourin. Med./HIV Barnet NHS Trust Roy. Free NHS Trust; Hon. Sen. Lect. Roy. Free Hosp. Sch. Med. Socs: Assn. Genitourin. Med.; Med. Soc. Study VD. Prev: Sen. Med. Off. DoH; Sen. Regist. (Genitourin. Med.) Gtr. Glas. HB; Regist. (Dermat.) King's Coll. Hosp. Lond.

WEIR, Mark James Stewart Medical Centre, Gordon Barracks BFPO 31 — MB ChB 1988 Glas.

WEIR, Michael William 2 Fulshaw Hall Cottage, Harefield Drive, Wilmslow SK9 1NJ — MB ChB 1980 Birm.; MFCM 1987. Dir. Crosthwaite Trust. Prev: Cons. Pub. Health Med. Wirral DHA; Dir. (Community Med.) & Head Quality Assur. Wirral HA.

WEIR, Mr Neil Francis (cons. rooms) 2 West Road, Guildford GU1 2AU Tel: 01483 569719 Fax: 01483 306380 Email: jlo@pipex.com; Greensand Cottage, Seale, Farnham GU10 1HP Tel: 01252 783265 — MB BS 1965 Lond.; FRCS Eng. 1971; MRCS Eng. LRCP Lond. 1965. (Westm.) Cons. Surg. (ENT) Roy. Surrey Co. Hosp. Guildford; Hon. Cons. Otol. Atkinson Morley's Hosp. Lond.; Edr. Jl. Laryngol. & Otol. Socs: Fell. Roy. Soc. Med. (Ex Hon. Edr., Mem. Counc.) Pres.; Sec. Otol. And Hist. of Med.; Past Chairm. Livery Comm. Worshipful Soc. of Apoth. Prev: Sen. Regist. (ENT) Roy. Free Hosp. Lond.; Regist. (ENT) St. Thos. Hosp. Lond.; Ho. Surg. (ENT & Ophth.) W.m. Hosp. Lond.

WEIR, Nicholas Ulrick 17 Quillings Way, Borrowash, Derby DE72 3YA — MB ChB 1991 Sheff.; MRCP (UK) 1994. SHO (Neurol.) W.. Gen. Hosp. Edin.

WEIR, Patricia Margaret Department of Anaesthetics, Royal Bristol Hospital for Sick Children, St Michael Hill, Bristol BS2 8BJ Tel: 0117 921 5411 — MB ChB 1980 Glas.; FFA RCS Eng. 1987. Cons. Anaesth. United Bristol Healthcare Trust.

WEIR, Paul Edens 11 Demesne Grove, Holywood BT18 9NQ Tel: 028 9042 6887 Email: paul.weir@mater.n-i.nhs.uk — MB BCh BAO 1971 Belf.; MD Belf. 1978; FRCOG 1990, M 1977, DObst 1973. (Queens university of Belfast) Cons. O & G Mater Hosp. Trust; Train. Progr. Dir. (Obst. & Gyn.) N.ern Irel. Prev: Post Grad. Tutor Matern. Hosp. Trust; Chair. Med. Staff Matern. Hosp. Trust.

***WEIR, Philip Ashley** Seven Oaks Farm, Artabrackagh Road, Portadown, Craigavon BT62 4HB Tel: 02838 354 164 Email: philipaweir@hotmail.com — MB BCh BAO 1998 Belfast.

WEIR, Mr Robert Desmond Belgrave Medical Centre, 22 Asline Road, Sheffield S2 4UJ Tel: 0114 255 1184 — BM BS 1977 Nottm.; FRCS Ed. 1983.

WEIR, Robert Edward Peter 31 Lauderdale Drive, Petersham, Richmond TW10 7BS — MB BS 1996 Lond.

WEIR, Robert John Stuart (retired) Timbers, 248 London Road, Withdean, Brighton BN1 6YA Tel: 01273 552743 — MB BCh BAO Dub. 1946; BA Dub. 1946. Prev: Capt. RAMC.

WEIR, Robert Muir Liddell (retired) 70 Pettycur Road, Kinghorn, Burntisland KY3 9RW Tel: 01592 890410 — MD 1954 Glas.; MB ChB 1945.

WEIR, Ronald John Glasgow Nuffield Hospital, Beaconsfield Road, Glasgow G12 0PJ Tel: 0141 334 9441 Fax: 0141 339 1150 Email: ron@weir01.fsnet.co.uk; White Lodge, 21a Thorn Road, Bearsden, Glasgow G61 4BS Tel: 0141 943 1367 — MB ChB Glas. 1960; MD Glas. 1973; FRCP Glas. 1976, M 1965. Cons. Phys. Socs: Assn. Phys.; Internat. Soc. Hypertens. Prev: Cons. Phys., W. Glas. Hosp. Univ. NHS Trust.

WEIR, Rosemary Radiology Department, Hairmyers Hospital, East Kilbride, Glasgow G41 4NL Tel: 0141 20292; 27 Fotheringay Road, Pollokshields, Glasgow G41 4NL Tel: 0141 423 6370 — MB ChB 1969 Ed.; BSc (Med. Sc.) 1966; FRCR 1976; DMRD Eng. 1974. Cons. Radiol. Hairmyres Hosp. E. Kilbride.

WEIR, Roy Deans, OBE (retired) Creagan Gorm, Inverneil, Lochgilphead PA30 8ES Tel: 01546 606368 — MB ChB 1950 Aberd.; MD Aberd. 1962, DPH 1955; FRCP Lond. 1989; FRCP Ed. 1979, M 1970; FFCM 1972. Prev: Prof. of Social Med. Univ. Aberd.

WEIR, Susanne Marlow and Partners, The Surgery, Bell Lane, Minchinhampton, Stroud GL6 9JF Tel: 01453 883793 Fax: 01453 731670 — MB ChB 1986 Sheff.

WEIR, Mr William Ian Liverpool Cardiothoracic Centre, Broadgreen Hospital, Thomas Drive, Liverpool L14 3LB Tel: 0151 228 1616; 216 The Colonnades, Albert Dock, Liverpool L3 4AB Tel: 0151 709 8890 — MB BChir 1975 Camb.; MA, MB Camb. 1975, BChir 1974; FRCS Ed. (Cth.) 1987; FRCS Eng. 1982. (Camb. & Lond. Hosp.) Cons. Cardiothoracic Surg. Cardiothoracic Centre Liverp. Socs: Liverp. Med. Inst.; Soc. Cardiothor. Surg. Gt. Brit. & Irel. Prev: Sen. Regist. (Cardiothoracic Surg.) Lond. Hosp.; Fell. (Surg.) W.mead Hosp. Sydney, NSW; Regist. (Surg.) Nat. Heart & Chest Hosps. Lond.

WEIR, William Malcolm Windmill Cottage, Whipsnade, Dunstable LU6 2LL Tel: 01582 873425 Fax: 01582 873309 — MB BS 1956 Lond.; MRCS Eng. LRCP Lond. 1957; DObst RCOG 1962. (Middlx.) HM Coroner for Essex. Prev: Ho. Surg. & Ho. Phys. (Paediat.) Middlx. Hosp.; GP Beds.

WEIR, William Roderic Cameron 43 Lancaster Avenue, Hadley Wood, Barnet EN4 0ER — MB ChB 1972 Dundee; FRCP Lond. 1993, Ed. 1997; MRCP (UK) 1975. Cons. Phys. Roy. Free Hosp. & Coppetts Wood Hosp. Lond.; Hon. Sen. Lect. (Infec. Dis.) Roy. Free Hosp. Lond.; Hon. Sen. Lect. (Clin. Trop. Med.) Lond. Sch. Hyg. & Trop. Med. Socs: Fell. Roy. Soc. Trop. Med. & Hyg. Prev: Sen. Regist. (Med.) Roy. Free Hosp. Lond.; Sen. Regist. (Med.) Ahmadu Bello Univ. Teachg. Hosp. Zaria, Nigeria; Ho. Phys. Dundee Roy. Infirm.

WEIR, Winifred Isabella The Surgery, 15 King Street, Paisley PA1 2PR Tel: 0141 889 3144 Fax: 0141 889 7134; Mogarth, 62 Amochrie Road, Paisley PA2 0AH — MB ChB 1981 Glas.; MRCGP 1985; DCH RCPS Glas. 1985; DRCOG 1984.

WEIS, Ute Flat 10 Connaught House, Queen Alexandra Hospital, Southwick Hill Road, Cosham, Portsmouth PO6 3LY — State Exam Med 1993 Berlin.

WEISER, Richard Morriston Hospital, Ysbyty Treforys, Morriston, Swansea SA6 6NL Tel: 01792 702125 Fax: 01792 703249 — MB BCh 1964 Wales; FRCP Eng. 1983; MRCP (UK) 1971. (Welsh Coll. Med.) Cons. Neurol. Morriston Hosp. NHS Trust Swansea; Hon. Sen. Lect. Univ. Coll. Swansea. Socs: Assn. Brit. Neurol.; Med. Res. Soc. Prev: Sen. Regist. (Clin. Neurol. & Neurophysiol.) Regional Neurol. Centre Newc.; Regist. (Gen. Med.) Soton Gen. Hosp.; Eaton Research Fell. (Renal Dis.) Cardiff Roy. Infirm.

WEISL, Mr Hanus (retired) Glamorgan House, BUPA Hospital, Croescadarn Road, Pentwyn, Cardiff CF23 8XL Tel: 029 2073 6011 — MB ChB 1948 Manch.; MD (Commend.) Manch. 1953; MChOrth Liverp. 1958; FRCS Eng. 1957. Prev: Cons. Orthop. & Trauma Surg. S. Glam. AHA.

WEISS, Anna Maria North Wall Farm, Tideford Cross, Saltash PL12 5JY — State Exam Med 1987 Wurzburg; State Exam Med. Wurzburg 1987.

WEISS, Paul David Mitcheldean Surgery, Brook Street, Mitcheldean GL17 0AU Tel: 01594 542270 Fax: 01594 544897 — MB ChB 1993 Leeds; DCH 1997; DFFP 1996; MRCGP 1998. (Leeds) GP; Clin. Asst. in Endoscopy and Flexible Sigmoidoscopy at Dilke Hosp.

WEISSBERG, Alison Petersfield Medical Practice, Dr Farrant & Partners, 25 Mill Road, Cambridge CB1 2AB Tel: 01223 350647 Fax: 01223 576096; 116 Shelford Road, Trumpington, Cambridge CB2 2NF — MB ChB 1976 Birm.

WEISSBERG, Professor Peter Leslie Addenbroooke's Hospital, Cambridge CB2 2QQ Tel: 01223 331504 Fax: 01223 331505 Email: sgd21@medschl.cam.ac.uk — MB ChB 1976 Birm.; MD Birm. 1985; FRCP Lond. 1992; FRCP Ed 1996; MRCP (UK) 1978; F Med Sci 1999. Hon. Cons. Cardiol. Addenbrooke's Hosp. Cambs. & Papworth Hosp. Camb.; BHF Prof. (Cardiovasc. Med.) Univ. Camb. Addenbrooke's Hosp. Socs: Assn. Phys.; Brit. Cardiac Soc.; Brit.

Atherosclerosis Soc. (Chairm.). Prev: Lect. (Cardiovasc. Med.) Univ. Birm.; MRC Research Fell. Baker Inst. Melbourne, Austral.

WEISSEN, Pamela Rose Kinorth Medical Centre, 26 Abbotswell Crescent, Aberdeen AB12 5JW Tel: 01224 876000 Fax: 01224 899182; 4 Braeside Terrace, Aberdeen AB15 7TT Tel: 01224 321924 — MB ChB 1990 Aberd.; MRCGP 1994. Prev: Trainee GP/SHO (Psychiat.) Grampian HB VTS.

WEISSENHORN, Guenter Ignaz Department of Anaesthetics, Sandwell General Hospital, Lyndon, West Bromwich B71 4HJ — State Exam Med 1990 Heidelberg.

WEISZ, Gabriela Maria 25 Park Avenue, London NW2 5AN — State Exam Med. Dusseldorf 1985.

WEISZ, Michael Tibor 3 The Paddocks, Carlby, Stamford PE9 4NH — MB ChB 1983 Birm.; FCAnaesth 1990. Cons. Anaesth. P'boro. NHS Trust.

WEITHAUS, Norbert Freeman Hospital, High Heaton, Newcastle upon Tyne NE7 7DN — State Exam Med 1992 Erlangen.

WEITHERS, Mr Edghar Christopher North Middlesex Hospital, Sterling Way, Edmonton, London N18 1QX Tel: 020 8887 2000; 30 Courtland Avenue, Norbury, London SW16 3BE Tel: 020 8764 3362 — MRCS Eng. LRCP Lond. 1981; State Exam. Med. Heidleberg 1972; FRCS Ed. 1979.

WELARE-SMITH, Jayne Michele Spring Terrace Health Centre, Spring Terrace, North Shields NE28 0HQ Tel: 0191 296 1588; 5 Seaburn Grove, Seaton Sluice, Whitley Bay NE26 4HG Tel: 0191 237 0402 — MB BS 1991 Newc.; MRCGP 1996, DRCOG 1993. Princip. GP N. Shields.

WELBOURN, Mr Charles Richard Burkewood Musgrove Park Hospital, Taunton TA1 5DA; 94 Princess Victoria Street, Clifton, Bristol BS8 4DB — MB BS 1983 Lond.; MD Lond. 1991; FRCS Ed. & Glas. 1988; FRCS (Gen) Ed. 1995; FRCS 1997. (University College London) Cons. Surg. MusGr. Pk. Hosp. Taunton. Prev: Sen. Regist. S. W. Region; Sen. Regist. Bristol Roy. Infirm.; Research Fell. Harvard Med. Sch.

WELBOURN, Esther (retired) 4 Amhurst Court, Grange Road, Cambridge CB3 9BH Tel: 01223 350574 — MB ChB Aberd. 1936; MA Camb. 1963; MD (Commend.) Aberd. 1939; DCH Eng. 1940. Prev: Fell. Lect. & Dir. of Studies in Med. & Vet. Med. & Vice-Pres. New Hall Camb.

WELBOURN, Hebe Flower (retired) Elsie Brigg's House, 38 Church Road, Westbury on Trym, Bristol BS9 3EQ Tel: 0117 950 7242 — MB ChB 1944 Birm.; MD Birm. 1953; DCH Eng. 1952. Prev: SCMO Frenchay HA.

WELBOURN, Professor Richard Burkewood 2 The Beeches, Tilehurst, Reading RG31 6RQ Tel: 01189 429258 — MB BChir Camb. 1942; MA Camb., BA 1940, MD 1953; Hon. DSc Belf. 1985; Hon. MD Karolinska 1974; FRCS Eng. 1948. (Camb. & Liverp.) Emerit. Prof. Surg. Endocrinol. Univ. Lond. Socs: Hon. Fell. Amer. Surg. Assn.; Fell. W. Afr. Coll. Surgs. 1974; Fell. Internat. Surg. Soc. (Prize & Medal 1995). Prev: Vis. Schol. Univ. Calif., Los Angeles; Prof. Surg. & Dir. Dept. Surg. Roy. Postgrad. Med. Sch. & Hammersmith Hosp. Lond.; Prof. Surgic. Sc. Qu. Univ. Belf.

WELBOURNE, Arthur Sydney (retired) The Limes, Great Massingham, King's Lynn PE32 2JQ Tel: 01485 520422 — BM BCh 1949 Oxf.; BA, BM BCh Oxon. 1949. Prev: Ho. Phys. (Paediat.) Radcliffe Infirm. Oxf.

WELBOURNE, Jill (retired) Burnaby House, 14 Greenway Road, Redland, Bristol BS6 6SG Tel: 0117 973 0183 Fax: 0117 923 9527 Email: jill@wellbournes.freeserve.co.uk — BM BCh 1963 Oxf. Specialist Med. Advis. Althea Pk. Hse. Stroud. Prev: Clin. Asst. (Psychiat.) Profess. Unit Glenside Hosp. Bristol.

WELBURY, Janet The Childrens Centre, Durham Road, Sunderland SR3 4AF Tel: 0191 565 6256 Fax: 0191 569 9938; 42 East Avenue, Benton, Newcastle upon Tyne NE12 9PH Tel: 0191 292 2415 Email: janet.welbury@ncl.ac.uk, jwelbury@hotmail.com — MB ChB 1975 Sheff.; FRCPCH; MRCP (UK) (Paediat.) 1983; DRCOG 1977. Cons. Community Paediat. Childr. Centre Sunderland; Med. adviser to Barnards N. E., Newc. Upon Tyne.

WELBURY, Robert Richard Dental Hospital, Richardson Road, Newcastle upon Tyne NE2 4AZ Tel: 0191 232 5131 Fax: 0191 222 6137; 27 Swarland Avenue, Benton, Newcastle upon Tyne NE7 7TE Tel: 0191 266 3572 — MB BS 1984 Newc.; BDS 1978; PhD Newc. 1989, MB BS 1984; FDS RCS Eng. 1986. (Newcastle upon Tyne) Regional Cons. Paediat. Dent. Surg. Newc. u. Tyne; Hon. Sen. Lect. Newc. Univ.

WELBY, Sharon Bianca 1 Stone Cottage, Bell Vale Road, Gateacre, Liverpool L25 2QB Tel: 0151 428 9224 — BM BS 1985 Nottm.; MRCP (UK) 1988. Regist. (Haemat.) BRd.green Hosp. & Roy. Liverp. Hosp. Prev: SHO (Infect. Dis.) Fazakerley Hosp.; Regist. Rotat. (Med.) N.. Gen. Hosp. Sheff.

WELCH, Mr Andrew Robert ENT Department, Freeman Hospital, High Heaton, Newcastle upon Tyne NE7 7DN Tel: 0191 284 3111 Fax: 0191 223 1246 Email: andrewwelch@tfh.nuth.northy.nhs.uk; 12 Wilson Gardens, Gosforth, Newcastle upon Tyne NE3 4JA Tel: 0191 285 6514 Fax: 0191 285 5271 — MB BS 1976 Newc.; FRCS Eng. 1981. (Newcastle-upon-Tyne) Cons. Otolaryngol. Freeman Hosp. Newc u. Tyne; Hon. Clin. Lect. (Otolaryngol.) Univ. Newc. Prev: Sen. Regist. Roy. Vict. Infirm. Newc.; Regist. Leicester Roy. Infirm.

WELCH, Caroline Beatrice 1 Hoggarth Close, Petersfield GU31 4YY — MB BS 1984 Lond.

WELCH, Catherine Jane Cherry Croft, Grange Park, Swanland, North Ferriby HU14 3NA — MB ChB 1998 Manch.; MB ChB Manch 1998.

WELCH, Mr Christopher Charles Wayside Cottage, Stifford Clays Road, Orsett, Grays RM16 3LX Tel: 01375 892006 — MB ChB 1973 Manch.; FRCS Ed. 1981; FRCOG 1991, M 1979; DObst 1975. Cons. O & G Basildon & Thurrock HA. Prev: Lect. Dept. O & G Univ. Nottm.

WELCH, Christopher Ross Duchess of Westminster Wing, Arrowe Park Hospital, Upton, Wirral CH49 5PE Tel: 0151 604 7158 Fax: 0151 604 1552 Email: ross.welch@ccmail.wirralh-tr.nwest.nhs.uk; Fieldway, 17 Hillside Road, Heswall, Wirral CH60 0BJ — MB BS 1981 Lond.; FRCOG 2001; MD Lond. 1994; MRCOG 1989; DA (UK) 1985. (King's College Hospital Medical School) Cons. O & G Arrowe Pk. Hosp. Wirral. Socs: Internat. Fetal Med. & Surg. Soc.; Pres. Internat. Fetal Med. and Surg. Soc. (1998-99); Brit. Matern. Fetal Med. Soc. Prev: Lect. (Fetal Med.) Birm. Matern. Hosp.; Sen. Regist. (Fetal Med.) Liverp. Matern. Hosp.; Research Fell. (Fetal Med.) RPMS Inst. & O & G Qu. Charlotte's Hosp. Lond.

WELCH, Clive Gordon Kirby and Partners, Charlton Group Medical Practice, Charlton Street, Oakengates, Telford TF2 6DA Tel: 01952 620138 Fax: 01952 615282 — MRCS Eng. LRCP Lond. 1962; DA Eng. 1966.

WELCH, Coral Irmgard (retired) 27 The Glebe, Sudbury CO10 9SN — MB BS 1951 Lond.; MB BS (Hons.) Lond. 1951; DCH Eng. 1956. Prev: GP Colchester.

WELCH, David Macpherson (retired) 16 Kedleston Drive, Cringleford, Norwich NR4 6XN Tel: 01603 454996 — MB BS 1962 Lond.; MRCS Eng. LRCP Lond. 1961; DObst RCOG 1964. Chairm. Norf. & Norwich Benevolent Med. Soc.

WELCH, Dilys Mary The Rookery, Scotland Lane, Horforth, Leeds LS18 5HP Tel: 0113 22049 — MB ChB 1955 Sheff. Princip. Gen. Pract. Leeds. Prev: Med. Regist. Gen. Hosp. S. Shields.

WELCH, Emma Felicity Jane Spinaway, The Droveway, St Margaret's Bay, Dover CT15 6DE — MB ChB 1994 Bristol.

WELCH, Flora Mary Barnard Castle Surgery, Victoria Road, Barnard Castle DL12 8HT Tel: 01833 690707 — MB ChB 1981 Aberd.; MRCGP 1985; DRCOG 1984. Prev: Ho. Off. (Med.) Aberd. Roy. Infirm.; Ho. Off. (Surg.) Darlington Memor. Hosp.; Trainee GP N.allerton VTS.

WELCH, Geoffrey Philip Freshfield Surgery, 61 Gores Lane, Formby, Liverpool L37 3NU Tel: 01704 879430 Fax: 01704 833883; Amazonas, Sandy Lane, Hightown, Liverpool L38 3RP Tel: 0151 929 3216 — MB ChB 1980 Liverp.; DRCOG Lond. 1984; Cert. Family Plann. JCC 1984; DFFP (Rcog) 1998. (Liverpool) Cons. in Primary Care S.port & Formby Community NHS Trust; Clin. Asst. (Orthop. Surg.) S.port & Formby Dist. Gen. Hosp.; Med. Off. St. Joseph's Childr. Hosp. Formby.; Med. Assessor Independant Tribunal Serv.; Clin. ass Cardiol. S.port DGH. Prev: Princip GP. Liverp.

WELCH, George Hunter Department of Surgery, S. Glasgow Uni. Hospital NHS Trust, Govan Rd, Glasgow G51 4TF Tel: 0141 201 2731; Castlehill, 202 Nithsdale Road, Pollokshields, Glasgow G41 5EU Tel: 0141 422 1505 — MB ChB 1977 Glas.; MD Glas. 1987; FRCS Glas. 1981. (Univ. Glas.) Cons. Surg. (Vasc. Surg.) S. Glas. Uni. Hosp. NHS Trust; Hon. Sen. Lect., Dept. of Surg. Uni. Of Glas.; Bd. of Examr.s, Roy. Coll. Of Phys. And Surg. Glas. Socs:

WELCH

Vasc. Surgic. Soc. GB & Irel.; Assn. Surg. Of GB & Irel.; Amer. Coll. Of Angiology. Prev: Cons. Surg. (Gen. & Vasc. Surg.) S. Ayrsh. Hosp. NHS Trust; Sen. Regist. (Gen. Surg.) Gtr. Glas. HB; Regist. (Peripheral Vasc. Surg.) Glas. Roy. Infirm.

WELCH, Mr George Somerville, OBE, TD (retired) 63 Culduthel Road, Inverness IV2 4HQ — MB BS 1959 Lond.; FRCS Ed. 1988; FRCS Eng. 1963; MRCS Eng. LRCP Lond. 1959. Prev: Cons. Orthop. Surg. Highland HB.

WELCH, Mr Ian McLay Royal Hallamshire Hospital, Sheffield S10 2JF Tel: 0114 276 6222 — MB ChB 1991 (Hons.) Sheff.; FRCS 2000 (Gen. Surg./Upper GI); PhD Sheff. 1988, BSc (Hons.) 1983; FRCS Eng. 1995; FRCS Ed. 1995. Specialist Regist. Surg. N. Trent.

WELCH, Jan Mary Department of Sexual Health, King's College Hospital, Denmark Hill, London SE5 9RS Tel: 020 7346 3852 Fax: 020 7346 3486 — MB BS 1980 Lond.; BSc Lond. 1977; FRCP Lond. 1995. (St. Thos.) Cons. Genitourin. Med. King's Coll. Hosp. Lond.; Dir. Postgrad. Med. Ed. Kings Coll. Hosp.; PostGrad. Dean GKT Sch. of Med., Denmmark Hill Campus; Clin. Director of the Haven (King's Sexual Assault Referral Centre). Socs: Med. Soc. Study VD. Prev: Sen. Regist. (Genitourin. Med.) St. Thos. Hosp. Lond.; Sen. Regist. (Clin. Virol.) St. Thos. Hosp. Lond.; Regist. (Med. & Infec. Dis.) Hither Green Hosp. Lond.

WELCH, Jennifer Christine Dept. of Haematology, Sheffield Children's hospital, Western Bank, Sheffield S10 2TH Fax: 0114 271 7477 Email: jenny.welch@sch.nhs.uk — BM BS 1987 Nottm.; MRCPath 2001; BMedSci Nottm. 1985; MRCP (UK) 1991; Dip RCPath 1999. (Nottm.) p/t Cons. Paediatric Haematologist, Sheff. Childr.'s Hosp. Socs: Roy. Coll. of Paediat. & Child Health; Brit. Soc. Haematol.; UKCCSG. Prev: Regist. (Haemat.) N.Trent Train. Scheme; Leukaemia Research Fund Regist. (Paediat. Haemat. & Oncol.) Childr. Hosp. Sheff.; Regist. (Paediat.) Trent Regional Train. Scheme.

WELCH, John Philip Lane (retired) 10 Maison Dieu, Richmond DL10 7AU — MB ChB 1955 St. And. Prev: Ho. Phys. Harrogate & Dist. Gen. Hosp.

WELCH, Judith Anne 1 St Georges Road, Hightown, Liverpool L38 3RY — MB ChB 1978 Liverp.; MRCP Ed. 1981; DRCOG 1985.

WELCH, Kate Antonia Commercial Road Surgery, 75 Commercial Road, Leeds LS5 3AT Tel: 0113 275 2780; 18 Stanhope Avenue, Horsforth, Leeds LS18 5AR — MB BS 1984 Lond.; DRCOG 1988. Clin. Asst. (Dermat.) Leeds Gen. Infirm. Prev: SHO (Dermat.) York Dist. Hosp.

WELCH, Lesley Jayne Strensall Medical Centre, Southfields Road, Strensall, York YO32 5UA Tel: 01904 490532; 72 Greenshaw Drive, Haxby, York YO32 3DG — MB ChB 1983 Liverp.; MRCGP 1991; DRCOG 1987; Cert. Family Plann. JCC 1987. Prev: Trainee GP Henleaze Bristol VTS; SHO (O & G & Psych.) Doncaster Roy. Infirm.; Cas. Off. Doncaster Roy. Infirm.

WELCH, Mark 23 Talbot Grove, Roundhay, Leeds LS8 1AB — MB ChB 1984 Leeds. SHO (Cardiothoracic Surg.) Killingbeck Hosp. Leeds. Prev: SHO (ENT Surg.) Seacroft Hosp. Leeds; SHO (A & E) Leeds Gen. Infirm.; Ho. Off. (Gen. Surg. & Urol.) Leeds Gen. Infirm.

WELCH, Michael Thomas Christopher The Health Centre, Commercial Road, Skelmanthorpe, Huddersfield HD8 9DA Tel: 01484 862239; Denby Dale Surgery, 313 Wakefield Road, Denby Dale, Huddersfield HD8 8RX Tel: 01484 862239 — BM 1982 Soton. (Soton.) Prev: Clin. Asst. (Anaesth.) Dewsbury Gen. Hosp.; Trainee GP Failsworth VTS; SHO (Anaesth., O & G & A & E) Oldham HA.

WELCH, Mr Neil Thomas Nottingham City Hospital, Nottingham NG5 1PB Tel: 0115 9691169 — MB BS 1984 Lond.; BSc Lond. 1981; MS Lond. 1995; FRCS (Gen.) 1997; FRCS Ed. 1988. (Lond. Hosp. Med. Coll.) Cons. (Gen. Surg.) Nottm.. City hosp. Socs: BMA. Prev: Sen. Regist. (Gen. Surg.) Liverp. Hosp., NSW, Austral.; Sen. Regist. (Gen. Surg.) W. Midl. RHA; Research Fell. (Surg.) St. Joseph Hosp. Omaha, Nebraska, USA.

WELCH, Nigel Charles Cunningham Tel: 01384 459966 Fax: 01384 459885 — MB BCh 1973 Wales. (Welsh Nat. Sch. Med.)

WELCH, Nina Mary Waterfield House Surgery, 186 Henwood Green Road, Pembury, Tunbridge Wells TN2 4LR Tel: 01892 825488; 7 Heskett Park, Pembury, Tunbridge Wells TN2 4JF — MB BS 1989 Lond. (St George's London) Prev: Trainee GP & Ho. Surg. Frimley Pk. Hosp.; Ho. Phys. St. Geo. Hosp. Lond.

WELCH, Richard Arthur, CStJ Concept 2000, 250 Farnborough Road, Farnborough GU14 7LU Tel: 01252 528324 Fax: 01252 528325 Email: richard.welch@postoffice.co.uk; Toscanna, Soldridge Road, Medstead, Alton GU34 5JF Tel: 01420562228 Fax: 01252 528325 — MB ChB Glas. 1969; MSc (Occupat. Med.) Lond. 1985; FFOM RCP Lond. 1991, M 1985; MRCGP 1980; DIH Lond. 1984; DObst RCOG 1971; ECFMG Cert 1969. (Glas.) Chief Med. Adviser Post Office. Socs: FRSM (Pres. Occupat. Med. Sect.); Soc. Occupat. Med. (Ex. Comm. Mem.); BMA (Ex-Comm. Mem. Occupat. Health Sect.). Prev: Med. Off. Talbot Ltd. Linwood; GP The Health Centre, Linwood; Regist. (Psychiat.) Stobhill Hosp. Glas.

WELCH, Robert Brian Commercial Road Surgery, 75 Commercial Road, Leeds LS5 3AT Tel: 0113 275 2780 — MB BS 1953 Durh. (Durh.) Prev: Ho. Phys. & Ho. Surg. Roy. Vict. Infirm. Newc.; Ho. Off. Gyn. & Obst. Dept. Matern. Hosp. Sunderland; RAF.

WELCH, Robert Gordon (retired) Hartdale, Queensberry Avenue, Hartlepool TS26 9NW Tel: 01429 274397 — MD Lond. 1951, MB BS 1945; FRCP Lond. 1973, M 1950. Prev: Cons. Paediat. Hartlepool, N. & S. Tees Dist. HAs.

WELCH, Robert James Royal Shrewsbury Hospital, Mytton Oak Road, Shrewsbury SY3 8XQ Tel: 01743 261000 Fax: 01743 261444 Email: bob.welch@mail.rsh-tr.wmids.nhs.uk; Wychwood, Bicton Lane, Bicton, Shrewsbury SY3 8EU Tel: 01743 850081 Email: wychwood.bicton@lineone.net — MB ChB Manch. 1978; BSc Hons. Manch. 1976; MRCP (UK) 1982. Cons. Neonat. Roy. Shrewsbury Hosp. Prev: Sen. Regist. (Neonat. Paediat.) P.ss Mary Matern. Hosp. Newc.; Fell. (Neonat.) Univ. Alberta Hosps., Canada.

WELCH, Ronald Frank (retired) 20 Langton Avenue, Whetstone, London N20 9DB — MRCS Eng. LRCP Lond. 1940; MD Lond. 1946, MB BS 1940; FRCPath 1963. Hon. Cons. Path. Barnet Gen. Hosp. Prev: Cons. Pathol. Barnet & Finchley Health Dists.

WELCH, Rosemary Ann Beighton Health Centre, Queens Road, Beighton, Sheffield S20 1BJ Tel: 0114 269 5061 — MB BS 1984 Lond.; MRCGP 1989; DCH RCP Lond. 1990; DRCOG 1989. Prev: SHO (Community/ Gen. Paediat.) Sheff. HA; GP Trainee Eckington Derbysh.

WELCH, Sarah Louise Marina House, Addiction Resource Centre, 63-65 Denmark Hill, London SE5 Tel: 020 7703 6333 Fax: 020 7740 5730 Email: sphaslw@iop.bpmf.ac.uk; Addiction Research Unit, 4 Windsor Walk, London SE5 8LF Tel: 020 7703 6333 Fax: 020 7701 8454 — BM BCh 1988 Oxf.; MA (Camb.) 1988; DPhil Oxf. 1994; MRCPsych 1994. (Cambridge & Oxford) Cons. Psychiat. in the Addic.s; Hon. Sen. Lect. Inst. Psychiat.1998. Prev: Clin. Lect. in the Addic.s, Addic. Research Unit, Inst. Psychiat. & Hon. Sen. Regist. Bethlem & Maudsley NHS Trust; Regist. & SHO (Psychiat.) Maudsley Hosp. Lond.; Research SHO (Psychiat.) Univ. Oxf.

WELCH, Steven Brian 4 Porchester House, Philpot St., London E1 2JF — MB BS 1993 Lond.

WELCH, Mr Theodore Phillips 56 School Lane, Toft, Cambridge CB3 7RE Tel: 01223 263371 Fax: 01223 263371 — MB BS 1958 Lond.; FRCS Eng. 1964; MRCS Eng. LRCP Lond. 1958. (Univ. Coll. Hosp.) Prev: Cons. i/c A & E Dept. N.wick Pk. Hosp. Harrow; Regist. (Surg.) Roy. N.. Hosp. Lond. & Barnet Gen. Hosp.; Lect. (Surg.) Chiangmai Univ., Thailand.

WELCHER, Eileen Mary (retired) Middle Coombe Farm, Huish Champflower, Taunton TA4 2HG Tel: 01984 624683 Email: ewelcher@talk21.com — MB BS 1947 Lond.; FFA RCS Eng. 1963; DA Eng. 1957. Prev: Cons. Anaesth. Torbay Hosp. Gp.

WELCHEW, Edward Amin 201 Tom Lane, Fulwood, Sheffield S10 3PH — MB ChB 1974 Bristol; FFA RCS Eng. 1979. Cons. Anaesth. Sheff. HA; Hon. Clin. Lect. Univ. Sheff.; Vis. Lect. Sheff. Polytechnic. Socs: Anaesth. Research Soc. Prev: Lect. (Anaesth.) Univ. Sheff.

WELCHEW, Kathleen Lois 201 Tom Lane, Fulwood, Sheffield S10 3PH — MB ChB 1974 Bristol; MRCGP 1978; DRCOG 1977.

WELCHMAN, Charlotte Louise Sundial House, Altrincham Road, Styal, Wilmslow SK9 4JE — MB BS 1998 Newc.; MB BS Newc 1998.

WELDING, Ian Joseph The Elms, Crank Road, Billinge, Wigan WN5 7EX — MB ChB 1987 Manch.

WELDING, Robert Nigel 11 Polstead Road, Oxford OX2 6TW — MB BS 1990 Lond.

WELDON, Aileen Margaret 7 Lansdowne Square, Tunbridge Wells TN1 2NF — MB ChB 1987 Leeds.

WELDON, Brian Dominic 11 Drake Close, Aughton, Ormskirk L39 5QL — MB ChB 1974 Liverp.

WELDON, David Philip 26 Hill Crest Drive, Beverley HU17 7JL — MB BS 1997 Newc.

WELDON, Henry John (retired) 5 Downhills Drive, Liverpool L23 8SU Tel: 0151 924 3958 — MB BCh BAO 1945 NUI; LM Rotunda 1946; FFA RCS Eng. 1954; DA Eng. 1951. Prev: Cons. Anaesth. Liverp. HA.

WELDON, Jennifer Ruth 17 Devonshire Place, Jesmond, Newcastle upon Tyne NE2 2NB — MB BS 1998 Newc.; MB BS Newc 1998.

WELDON, Michael John Stoke Mandeville Hospital, Mandeville Road, Aylesbury HP21 8AL Tel: 01296 315000; 19 Dovecote, Haddenham, Aylesbury HP17 8BP Tel: 01844 299049 Email: mike@weldon.freeserve.co.uk — MB ChB 1986 Leeds; BSc (Hons.) Leeds 1983; MD 1997; MRCP (UK) 1989. (Leeds) Cons. Phys. & Gastroenterol. Stoke Mandeville Hosp. Bucks. Socs: Brit. Inflammation Research Assn.; Brit. Soc. Gastroenterol. Prev: Sen. Regist. St. Geo. Hosp. Lond.; Research Regist. (Gastroenterol.) St. Geo. Hosp. Med. Sch. Lond.; Regist. (Med.) N.. Gen. Hosp. Sheff.

WELDON, Oliver George William 4 The Cloisters, Newcastle upon Tyne NE7 7LS Tel: 0191 284 2057 — MB BS 1973 Lond.; MRCS Eng. LRCP Lond. 1973; FRCA 1978. (St. Bart.) Cons. Anaesth. Freeman Hosp. Newc. Socs: Assn. Anaesth.; BMA. Prev: Sen. Regist. (Anaesth.) SW RHA; SHO (Anaesth.) St. Bart. Hosp. Lond.; Ho. Phys. Roy. Sussex Co. Hosp. Brighton.

WELDON, Rachel Henriette Small Isles Medical Practice, Isle of Eigg PH42 4RL Tel: 01687 482427 Fax: 01687 482422 Email: rachelweldon@cs.com — Artsexamen 1987 Utrect.

WELEMINSKY, Antonin (retired) 45 Evesham Road, Middleton, Manchester M24 1QL — MD 1933 Prague. Prev: Asst. Chest Phys. Pontefract.

WELFARE, Mark Richard 5 Seaburn Grove, Seaton Sluice, Whitley Bay NE26 4HG Tel: 0191 237 0402 Fax: 0191 257 0606 Email: m.r.welfare@ncl.ac.uk; North Tyneside General Hospital, Rake Lane, North Shields NE30 8NH Tel: 0191 259 6660 — BM 1987 Soton.; MRCP (UK) 1989; MD 1998. Sen. Lect.Gastroent. Socs: Brit. Soc. Gastroenterol.; Molecular Epidemiol. Gp. Prev: Regist. Freeman Hosp. Newc.

WELFORD, James Richard Francis Girlington Road Surgery, 252 Girlington Road, Bradford BD8 9PB Tel: 01274 491448/9 Fax: 01274 483362 — MB ChB 1989 Leeds. (Leeds) GP Partner; Clin. Asst. (Gastroenterol.) W. Yorks.

WELFORD, Roy Audus Glastonbury Health Centre, 1 Wells Road, Glastonbury BA6 9DD Tel: 01458 834100 Fax: 01458 834371 — BM 1978 Soton.; MFHom RCP Lond. 1987; DRCOG 1982.

WELHAM, Geoffrey Martyn Oakdale, 3 Oakwood Lane, Leeds LS8 2PZ — MB ChB 1964 Leeds; MRCGP 1981; DA Eng. 1969.

WELHAM, Judith Renal unit, Wrexham Maelor Hospital, Croesnewydd Road, Wrexham LL13 7TD Tel: 01978 291100 — MB BCh 1986 Wales; MRCP (UK) 1989. Assoc. Specialist (Renal/Diabetes) Wrexham Maelor Hosp. Prev: Staff Grade Phys. (Renal Med.) Wrexham Maelor Hosp.; Regist. (Renal) Univ. Hosp. S. Manch.

WELHAM, Katie Louise Newnham College, Cambridge CB3 9DF — BChir 1996 Camb.

WELHAM, Mr Richard Alexander Norton, ED 72 Berkeley Avenue, Reading RG1 6HY Tel: 01189 584711 Fax: 01189 588110 — MB ChB 1959 Leeds; FRCS Eng. 1967; DO Eng. 1965. (Leeds) Cons. Ophth. Surg. Roy. Berks. Hosp. Reading. Socs: Reading Path. Soc.; Ophth. Soc. UK; Europ. Soc. Ophth. Plastic & Reconstruc. Surgs. Prev: Cons. Ophth. Surg. Moorfields Eye Hosp. Lond.; Pres. Reading Path.Soc.; Treas. Europ. Soc. Opth. Plastic & Reconstruct. Surg.

WELI, Mr Gamini Seneviratne ENT Department, Queen Elizabeth Hospital, Gayton Road, King's Lynn PE30 4ET Tel: 01553 766266; Snowdrop Hill, Glosthorpe Manor, Ashwicken, King's Lynn PE32 1NB Tel: 01553 630027 — MB BS 1971 Ceylon; FRCS Ed. 1983. (Peradeniya) Assoc. Specialist (ENT) Qu. Eliz. Hosp., Kings Lynn Norf. Prev: Cons. ENT Surg. Galle, Sri Lanka; Regist. (ENT) Roy. United Hosp. Bath; Regist. (ENT) Maelor Hosp. Wrexham.

WELI, Tajana Dilini Snowdrop Hill, Glosthorpe Manor, Ashwicken, King's Lynn PE32 1NB — MB ChB 1998 Manch.

WELLAND, Hilary Ann 23 The Paddocks, Hempstead, Gillingham ME7 3NG — MB BS 1994 Lond.

WELLBELOVE, Pamela Anne 2 Forester Road, Southgate, Crawley RH10 6EQ Tel: 01293 522231 — MB BS 1962 Lond.; MRCS Eng. LRCP Lond. 1962; DFFP 1993; DObst RCOG 1964. (Westm.) Socs: BMA.

WELLDON, Estela Valentina 121 Harley Street, London W1N 1DH Tel: 020 7935 9076; Portman Clinic, 8 Fitzjohns Avenue, London NW3 5NA Fax: 020 7447 3748 — Medico Univ. Nacional de Cuyo 1962; DSc (Hon) Oxf. Brookes 1997; FRCPsych 1987, M 1973. Cons. Psychother. & Clin. Tutor Portman Clinic Lond.; Dir. 1st. Dip. Course & Hon. Sen. Lect. (Forens. Psychother.) UCL; Mem. Bd. Dirs. Internat. Assn. Gp. Psychother.; Hon. Sen. Lect. UCL 1995. Socs: Internat. Assn. Forens. Psychother. (Pres.); BMA; Med. Protec. Soc. Prev: Postgrad. Fell. Menninger Sch. Psychiat. Topeka, USA.

WELLEN, Tamsyn 40 Hilda Wharf, Aylesbury HP20 1RJ — MB BCh 1997 Witwatersrand.

WELLER, Claire Susan 12 Ashtree Cl, Newcastle upon Tyne NE4 6ST — MB BS 1997 Newc.

WELLER, David Paul Department of Public Health Medicine & Epidemiology, University of Nottingham, Queens Medical Centre, Nottingham NG7 2UH Tel: 0115 970 9306 Fax: 0115 970 9316 — MB BS 1983 Adelaide; FRACGP 1989; FAFPHM 1992.

WELLER, Evelyn Mary Homecroft Surgery, Voguebeloth, Illogan, Redruth TR16 4ET Fax: 01209 843707 — MB BS 1974 Lond.

WELLER, Gillian de Mowbray Leigh (retired) 7 Cousins Grove, Southsea PO4 9RP Tel: 023 9273 2958 — MB BS 1957 Lond. Prev: Hosp. Pract. (Geriat.) St. Mary's Hosp. Portsmouth.

WELLER, Ian Vincent Derrick 63 Grimsdyke Road, Pinner HA5 4PP — MB BS 1974 Lond.; BSc (1st cl. Hons.) Physiol. Lond. 1971, MD 1983; MRCP (UK) 1977. (St. Bart.) Wellcome Trust Sen. Lect. Infec. Dis.; Hon. Cons. Acad. Dept. Genitourin. Med. Middlx. Hosp. Med. Sch. Lond. Socs: Med. Soc. Study of VD; Brit. Assn. Study of Liver. Prev: Regist. (Med.) St. Mary's Hosp. Paddington, Lond.; MRC Train. Fell. Roy. Free Hosp. Lond.; Lect. Acad. Dept. Genitourin. Med. Middlx. Hosp. Med. Sch. Lond.

WELLER, Jennifer Margaret Moorside, Charles Lane, Old Glossop, Glossop SK13 7SF — MB BChir 1963 Camb.; FRCR 1971; DMRD Eng. 1967. Cons. Radiol. N.E. Manch. Gp. Hosps.

WELLER, Professor Malcolm Philip Isadore 30 Arkwright Road, London NW3 6BH Tel: 020 7794 5804 Fax: 020 7431 1589 Email: malcolmweller@hotmail.com — MB BS 1972 Newc.; MA (Experim. Psychol.) Camb. 1959; FRCPsych 1987, M 1975; FBPsS 1986, AF 1980, M 1956; C.Pysch. (Newcastle upon Tyne) Emerit. Cons. Psychiat. St. Ann's Hosp. Lond.; Hon. Prof. Middlx. Univ.; Hon. Med. Adviser Nat. Scitzo. Fell.sh. JAMI etc; Extern. Examr. Manch. & Singapore Univs.; Chairm. N. Thames Regional Psychiat. Comm.; Edr-in-Chief Bailliers Clin. Psychiat. Series. Socs: FRSM; Standing Comm. Assn. Univ. Teach.s of Psychiat.; Founder Mem. Brit. Assn. Psychopharmacol. Prev: Vis. Fell. Fitzwilliam Coll. Camb.; Extern. Examr. Manch. & Singapore Univs.; Vice-Chairm. NE Thames Regional Comm. Hosp. Med. Servs.

WELLER, Matthew David 170 Dawlish Road, Selly Oak, Birmingham B29 7AR Tel: 0121 689 5573 Email: matt@well.force9.co.uk — MB ChB 1997 Birm. (Birm.) SHO Orthop. & Trauma Worcester Hosp.

WELLER, Michael Arthur, OBE, KStJ (retired) Aldboro' Lodge, Park St., Thaxted, Dunmow CM6 2ND Tel: 01371 830780 — MB BS Lond. 1949; MRCS Eng. LRCP Lond. 1948; FRCGP 1970. Prev: Hon. Nat. Chairm. (Support Gps.) Research into Ageing Lond.

WELLER, Peter Herbert Dept. of Respiratory Medicine, Birmingham Children's Hospital, Steelhouse Lane, Birmingham B4 6NH Tel: 0121 333 8202 Fax: 0121 333 8201 Email: pweller@bhamchildrens.wmids.nhs.uk — MB BChir Camb. 1969; MA Camb. 1970; FRCP Lond. 1986; MRCP (UK) 1973; FRPCH 1997. (St. Thos.) Cons. Paediat. Chest Phys. Birm. Childr.s Hosp. and City Hosp.; Hon. Clin. Sen. Lect. Univ. Birm. Prev: Research Fell. & Sen. Regist. Hosp. Sick Childr. Gt. Ormond St. Lond.

WELLER, Mr Peter Jeremy Oral Maxillofacial Surgery Department, Southend Hospital Trust, Prittlewell Chase, Westcliff on Sea SS0 0RY Tel: 01702 221014; Bay Lodge, 501 Victoria Avenue, Prittlewell, Southend-on-Sea SS2 6NL Tel: 01702 352442 Fax: 01702 352442 — MB BS 1983 Lond.; BDS 1973; FDS RCPS Glas. 1985; FRCS Ed. 1988. (Char. Cross Hosp.) p/t Cons. Oral Surg. S.end Hosp. Trust, Basildon & Thurrock Hosps. Trust. Socs: Fell. Brit. Assn. Oral & Maxillofacial Surg.; Hosp. Cons. & Spec. Assn.; BMA. Prev: Sen.

WELLER

Regist. (Oral. & Maxillofacial Surg.) W.m. Hosp. Lond.; Sen. Regist. (Oral Surg.) Guy's Hosp.; Regist. (Oral Surg.) St. Barts. Hosp.

WELLER, Richard John Greenhill Eastfield House Surgery, 6 St. Johns Road, Newbury RG14 7LW Tel: 01635 41495 Fax: 01635 522751; 8 Buckingham Road, Newbury RG14 6DJ Tel: 01635 40739 — MB ChB 1969 Leeds; DA Eng. 1973; DObst RCOG 1971. (Leeds)

WELLER, Richard Paul John Beresford University Department of Dermatology, Lauriston Building, Lauriston Place, Edinburgh EH3 9YW Email: r.weller@ed.ac.uk — MB BS 1987 Lond.; MD 2000 London; MRCP (UK) 1990. (St. Thos. Hosp.) Sen. Lect. (Dermat.) univ of Edinb. Socs: Brit. Assn. Dermatol.; Brit. Soc. Investig. Dermat.; Eur. Soc. Dermat. Rese. Prev: Regist. (Dermat.) Aberd. Roy. Infirm.; SHO (Dermat.) St. Thos. Hosp.; Regist. (Med.) Cairns Base Hosp. Qu.sland, Austral.

WELLER, Robin Moray, TD 2 Miles Road, Clifton, Bristol BS8 2JN — MB BS 1966 Lond.; MRCS Eng. LRCP Lond. 1965; FFA RCS Eng. 1970; DA Eng. 1968. (St. Bart.) Cons. Anaesth. Frenchay Hosp. Bristol. Socs: Past Pres. Bristol Medico-Legal Soc.; Pres. Soc. of Anaesth.s of S. W. Region; Past Pres. Cossham Med. Soc. Prev: Sen. Regist. (Anaesth.) Frenchay Hosp. Bristol & United Bristol Hosps.; Vis. Asst. Prof. Dept. Anaesth. Univ. Virginia Med. Center.

WELLER, Professor Roy Oliver Department Pathology (Neuropathology), Mail Point 813, Southampton General Hospital, Southampton SO16 6YD Tel: 02380 796669 Fax: 02380 796603 Email: row@soton.ac.uk; Qazvin, 22 Abbey Hill Road, Winchester SO23 7AT Tel: 01962 867465 — MB BS Lond. 1962; PhD Lond. 1967, BSc (Anat. Hons.) 1959, MD 1971; MRCS Eng. LRCP Lond. 1961; FRCPath 1982, M 1970. (Guy's) Prof. & Cons. Neuropath. Fac. of Med. Soton. Univ. & Soton. Univ. Hosps. NHS Trust; Regional Adviser in Path.. Pres. of the Brit. NeuroPath. Soc.; vice Pres. of the Internat. Soc. of Neuropath. Socs: Path. Soc.; Neuropath. Soc.; Assn. of Brit. NeUrol.s. Prev: Sen. Lect. & Cons. Neuropath. Guy's & Maudsley Hosps. Lond.; Vis. Prof. Singapore, 1984, 1994 & 1998, Zurich 1988, Zimbabwe 1991; NIH Fell. (Neuropath.) Albert Einstein Coll. Med. New York, USA.

WELLER, Stanley Douglas Victor (retired) 18 Gerrard Buildings, Pulteney Mews, Bath BA2 4DQ Tel: 01224 420020 — MB BS Lond. 1941; MD Lond. 1947; FRCP Lond. 1969, M 1947; MRCS Eng. LRCP Lond. 1941; DCH Eng. 1948; FRCP & CH 1998. Prev: Prof. of Child Health Makerere Univ. Coll. Kampala, Uganda.

WELLER, Stephan The Petersgate Medical Centre, 99 Amersall Road, Scawthorpe, Doncaster DN5 9PQ Tel: 01302 390490 — State Exam Med 1988 Bonn; Med. Doctorate Bonn 1990; MRCGP 1995; DFFP 1995. (Bonn, Germany)

WELLER, Timothy Mark Atticus Department of Medical Microbiology, City Hospital NHS Trust, Dudley Road, Birmingham B18 7QH — MB ChB 1988 Birm.; ChB Birm. 1988; MD Uni. Birm. 1999; MRCPath 1997. Cons. Microbiologist - City Hosp. Birm.

WELLESLEY, Amanda Jane 8 Michaels Close, London SE13 5BP — MB ChB 1985 Leeds; FRCS Ed. 1991.

WELLESLEY, Diana Gay Wessex Clinical Genetics Service, Princess Anne Hospital, Southampton SO16 5YA Tel: 02380 221716 Fax: 02380 794346 Email: dgw@soton.ac.uk; Abbotts Lodge, Fairfield Road, Shawford, Winchester SO21 2DA Tel: 01962 712409 Fax: 01962 712049 — BM 1977 Soton. (Southampton) p/t Assoc. Specialist (Clin. Genetics) P.ss Anne Hosp. Soton., Head of Prenatal Genetics, PAH, Soton. Socs: BMA; BINOCAR; Internat. Soc. Gen. Diag. Prev: Asst. (Genetics) P.ss Margt. Hosp. Perth, W. Austral.; Med. Off. Auth. for Intellectual Handicap, Perth, W. Austral.; Fell. Clin. Genetics Univ. S.. Calif., USA.

WELLESLEY, Hugo Arthur Lawrence 15 Stonehill Road, London SW14 8RR — MB ChB 1998 Bristol.

WELLINGHAM, Charles Bernard The Orchard, Sandy Lane, Waldringfield, Woodbridge IP12 4QY — MB BS 1976 Lond.; MRCGP 1981; DRCOG 1981; DCH Eng. 1980.

WELLINGS, Dean 9 Hickleton, Doncaster DN5 7BA — MB ChB 1992 Dundee.

WELLINGS, Michael John 300 Fencepiece Road, Ilford IG6 2TA Tel: 020 8500 0066 Fax: 020 8559 8670; 4 The Green, Woodford Green IG8 0NF Tel: 020 8504 0407 — MB BS 1968 Lond.; MRCGP 1979; DObst RCOG 1970. (St. Mary's) Clin. Asst. Surg. Forest Hosp. Buckhurst Hill. Socs: Brit. Soc. Allergy & Clin. Immunol.

WELLINGS, Paul (retired) Cley House, The Fairstead, Cley-next-the-sea, Holt NR25 7RJ Tel: 01263 741210 — MB BChir 1953 Camb.; BA Camb. 1950; DCH Eng. 1959; DObst RCOG 1958. Prev: SHO (Med.) Booth Hall Childr. Hosp. Manch.

WELLINGS, Mr Richard Matthew Walsgrave Hospital NHS Trust, Coventry — MB ChB 1982 Birm.; FRCR 1990; FRCS Ed. 1986. Cons. Radiol. Walsgrave Hosp. NHS Trust Coventry. Prev: Sen. Regist. (Radiol.) W. Midl. RHA; Regist. (Radiol.) W. Midl. Region.

WELLINGTON, Catherine Mary Sheet Street Surgery, 21 Sheet Street, Windsor SL4 1BZ Tel: 01753 860334 Fax: 01753 833696 — MB BS 1992 Lond.; BSc Lond. 1989; MRCGP 19986; DRCOG. (Middlesex Hospital University College London) GP.

WELLINGTON, Mr Peter Ernest Quarr Hill House, Quarr Hill, Ryde PO33 4EH Tel: 01983 811538 Fax: 01983 564286 — MB BCh BAO 1973 Dub.; FRCSI 1979. (TC Dub.) Cons. A & E St. Mary's Hosp. Newport, I. of Wight. Prev: Regist. (Orthop.) Meath Hosp. Dub., Wycombe Gen. Hosp. High Wycombe & Glas. Roy. Infirm.

WELLS, Mr Alan David 42 Exeter Gardens, Stamford PE9 2RN — MB BS 1974 Lond.; MS Lond. 1985, MB BS 1974; FRCS Eng. 1979. Cons. Gen. Surg. P'boro. Dist. Hosp. Prev: Sen. Regist. St. Thos. Hosp. Lond.; Regist. (Surg.) King's Coll. Hosp. Lond.; Research Fell. State Univ. New York, Buffalo USA.

WELLS, Alastair James The Moat House Surgery, Worsted Green, Merstham, Redhill RH1 3PN Tel: 01737 642207 Fax: 01737 642209 — MB BS 1983 Lond.; MRCGP 1987; DRCOG 1985. (Roy. Free) Socs: Assur. Med. Soc. Prev: SHO Croydon VTS; Ho. Surg. Roy. Free Hosp. Lond.; Ho. Phys. Barnet Gen. Hosp.

WELLS, Albert Logan 71 Pennard Road, Southgate, Swansea SA3 2AJ Tel: 01792 233315 — MB BCh BAO 1945 Belf.; MD Belf. 1951; MRCPI 1952; DCP Lond 1948; FRCPath 1966, M 1964. (Qu. Univ. Belf.) Prev: Cons. Path. LLa.lli Hosp. & Min. of Home Affairs N. Irel.; Princip. Regist. (Clin. Path.) Roy. Vict. Hosp. Belf.; Path. MRC Pneumoconiosis Research Unit, Cardiff.

WELLS, Alec Anthony 101 Montpelier Road, Brighton BN1 2LQ Tel: 01273 777807 Fax: 01273 777807; Braefield House, Southwell NG25 0PX Tel: 01636 813491 — MB ChB 1964 Sheff. (Sheff.) Private GP. Prev: Cas. Off. Roy. Hosp. Sheff.; Ho. Phys. Profess. Unit Childr. Hosp. Sheff.; SHO O & G Scarsdale Hosp. Chesterfield.

WELLS, Alison Elizabeth Burnt Oak, Heath Drive, Walton-on-the-Hill, Tadworth KT20 7QQ Tel: 01737 812788 — MB BS 1985 Lond.; DRCOG 1989.

WELLS, Andrew David Gair Cottage, Lochgair, Lochgilphead PA31 8SD — MB ChB 1984 Aberd.

WELLS, Angus William Flat 2, 1 Grosvenor Villas, Grosvenor Road, Newcastle upon Tyne NE2 2RU — MB ChB 1990 Ed.

WELLS, Anthony Lethbridge 5 London Road, Beccles NR34 9TZ Tel: 01502 712024 — MB BChir 1949 Camb.; BA, MB BChir Camb. 1949; DLO Eng. 1951; DObst RCOG 1953. (St. Bart.) Prev: Ho. Phys. St. Bart. Hosp.; Ho. Surg. Obst. Dept. Radcliffe Infirm. Oxf.; Capt. RAMC.

WELLS, Brian John Tel: 07000 935571 Fax: 07000 935572 Email: jrbrianwells@aol.com; Pendle House, Manor Farm, Elkstone, Cheltenham GL53 9PD Tel: 01242 870143 — MB BChir 1974 Camb.; MA Camb. 1973, BA 1970; FRCPsych 1996, M 1984. (Camb. & Middlx. Hosp.) Med. Director Riverside Ment. Health Trust. Socs: BMA; Soc. Study of Addic. Prev: Sen. Regist. Bethlem Roy. & Maudsley Hosps.; Cons. Psychait. & Lead Clin. Subst. Misuse Serv. Riverside Ment. Health Trust.

WELLS, Catherine Anne 6 Masefield Road, Stratford-upon-Avon CV37 7JT — BM 1997 Soton.

WELLS, Christine Anne Corney Place Medical Group, The Health Centre, Bridge Lane, Penrith CA11 8HW Tel: 01768 245226 Fax: 01786 245229; 10 Vestaneum, Crosby-on-Eden, Carlisle CA6 4PN Tel: 01228 573180 Email: wellsmustc@aol.com — MB BS 1994 Lond.; MB BS London 1994; PhD (Arts) London 1984; Dip Family Plann 1998 FFPA; MRCGP Royal College GPs 1998. (St. Bart. Hosp. Lond.) Clin. Med.off.Wellwoman, Family Plann & youth Serv.Dumfries & Galloway. Socs: FRSM; RCGPs; BMA. Prev: GP.

WELLS, Christopher William 16 Queens Avenue, Sunderland SR6 8DL — MB BS 1997 Newc.

WELLS, Clive Alan Department of Histopathology, St. Bartholomews Hospital, London EC1A 7BE — MB 1978 Camb.; BChir 1977; MRCPath 1986. Cons. Path. St. Bart. Hosp. Lond.;

Regional Co-ordinator BrE. Screening Path. N.E. Thames RHA Region. Socs: RCPath. Advis. Gp. on BrE. Cancer Screening.

WELLS, David Poulett (retired) Hilperton House, Hilperton, Trowbridge BA14 7RJ Tel: 01225 753845 — BM BCh 1958 Oxf.; FRCGP 1988, M 1973; DObst RCOG 1961.

WELLS, David Thomas, OStJ BUPA OH, Room 23, Wyvern House, Railway Terrace, Derby DE1 2RY Tel: 01332 714000 Fax: 01332 714601 Email: welssda@bupa.com; 14 Spenbeck Drive, Allestree, Derby DE22 2UH — MRCS Eng. LRCP Lond. 1971; DIH Eng. 1980; MFOM RCP Lond. 1983. (Sheffield) Cons. Occupat. Phys. (BUPA OH) Derby. Socs: Soc. Occupat. Med. Prev: Sen. Med. Off. Brit. Railways Bd. Derby; Regist. (A & E Med.) & SHO (Hand Surg.) Derbysh. Roy. Infirm.

WELLS, Derek Geoffrey (retired) Bron Teigl, Cwm Teigl, Llan Ffestiniog, Blaenau Ffestiniog LL41 4RF — MB BS 1947 Lond. Prev: Ho. Phys. & Res. Obst. Asst. W.m. Hosp.

WELLS, Derek Geoffrey Ty-Fry Cottage, Cliff Road, Hythe CT21 5XL Tel: 01303 266469 Email: d.g.wells@btinternet.com — MB BS Lond. 1961; FRCPath 1984, M 1972; Dip. Biochem. Chelsea Coll. Sci. & Technol. 1970. (Roy. Free) Cons. Haemat. E. Rent health trust. Prev: Sen. Regist. (Clin. Path.) Roy. Marsden Hosp. Lond.; Regist. (Chem. Path.) W.m. Hosp. Lond.; Res. Pathol. Nat. Hosp. Qu. Sq. Lond.

WELLS, Duncan Lewis 241 Tubbenden La S., Orpington BR6 7DW — MB BS 1997 Lond.

WELLS, Fanny (retired) Logan Cottage, 74 Gloucester Road, London SW7 4QW Tel: 020 7584 8281 — MD 1935 Bari.

WELLS, Mr Francis Charles — MB BS 1975 Lond.; MA Cantab. 1996; MS Lond. 1985, BSc (Hons.) 1972; FRCS Eng. 1980; MRCS Eng. LRCP Lond. 1975. (Char. Cross) Cons. Cardiothoracic Surg. Papworth Hosp. Camb.; Assoc. Lect. Univ. Camb. Socs: Fell. Roy. Soc. Med.; Brit. Thorac. Soc.; Cardiac Soc. Prev: Sen. Research Fell. (Cardiac Surg.) Univ. Alabama, USA; Sen. Regist. (Cardiothoracic Surg.) Brompton. Hosp. Lond.; Regist. (Surg.) Addenbrooke's Hosp. Camb.

WELLS, Francis Owen Old Hadleigh, London Road, Capel St Mary, Ipswich IP9 2JJ Tel: 01473 730101 Fax: 01473 730102 Email: fow5851@aol.com — MB BS 1960 Lond.; FRCP (London) 1999; FFPM (Distinc.) RCP (UK) 1995; FRCP Ed 1998. (Lond. Hosp.) p/t Cons. Pharmaceut. Phys. Medico-Legal Investig.s, Non-Exec. Director. Socs: Fell. BMA; Soc. Pharmaceut. Med. (Vice Chairm.); Fell. Roy. Soc. of Med. Prev: Dir. Div. Med. Sci. & Technol. Assn. Brit. Pharmaceut. Industry; Under-Sec. BMA; GP Ipswich.

WELLS, Francis Raymund (retired) The Magnolia Star, 8 Ballard Close, Poole BH15 1UH Tel: 01202 687359 Email: raymundw@hds.co.uk — BM BCh 1951 Oxf. Prev: Brain Bank Co-ordinator & Pk.inson's Dis. Soc. Research Fell. Inst. Neurol. Lond.

WELLS, Gareth Edward 59 Daniel Hill Street, Sheffield S6 3JH — MB ChB 1998 Sheff.

WELLS, Geoffrey George (retired) Norsewood, Broomheath, Woodbridge IP12 4DL Tel: 01394 386375 — MB ChB 1945 Ed.; AFOM RCP Lond. 1980. Employm. Med. Adviser EMAS; Clin. Asst. (Orthop.) Ipswich Hosp. Prev: Ho. Surg. Wingfield Morris Orthop. Hosp.

WELLS, Gillian Ruth Uppingham Road Medical Centre, 190 Uppingham Road, Leicester LE5 0QG Tel: 0116 276 6605; 3 Snowden's End, Wigston, Leicester LE18 1LG — MB ChB 1987 Leic.; MRCGP 1992; DRCOG 1991. (Leic.) Princip. GP Leic. Prev: Trainee GP Leicester VTS.

WELLS, Grahame John The Harrow Health Care Centre, 84-88 Pinner Road, North Harrow, Harrow HA1 4HZ; 4 Upper Lattimore Road, St Albans AL1 3TU Tel: 01727 830330 — MB BS 1979 Lond.

WELLS, Irving Pascoe Eydon Lodge, Yelverton PL20 6AS — MB BS 1972 Lond.; FRCP Lond. 1994; MRCS Eng. LRCP Lond. 1973; FRCR 1978. Cons. Radiol. Plymouth Gen. Hosp. Socs: Brit. Soc. Intervent. Radiol. (Mem. Counc.); Eur. Soc. Uroradiol. Prev: Sen. Regist. (Diag. Radiol.) King's Coll. Hosp. Lond.

WELLS, Jane Christine 73 Southfield Road, Oxford OX4 1NY — MB ChB 1982 Liverp.

WELLS, Jason Mark 18 Firtree Avenue, Countesthorpe, Leicester LE8 5TH — MB ChB 1993 Sheff.

WELLS, Jean Mary Staines Health Group, Staines Health Centre, Staines TW18 1XO — MB ChB 1967 Leeds.

WELLS, Jennifer Margaret, OBE, Col. L/RAMC Medical Branch, Hq 2 Div., Craigighall & Queensferry, W. Lothian EH30 9TN — MB ChB 1976 Glas.; FRCGP 2000; MSc (Gen. Pract.) Lond. 1995; MRCGP 1987; DRCOG 1982. Cdr. Med., HQ 2 Div.; Course Organiser Defence Med. Servs. GP Educat. Prev: Serv. Gen. Pract.

WELLS, Joan Catherine 173 Ashley Gardens, Emery Hill St., London SW1P 1PD Tel: 020 7828 0985 Fax: 020 7931 7635 — MB BS 1948 Lond.; MD Lond. 1950; MRCP Lond. 1950; MRCS Eng. LRCP Lond. 1948; MRCPsych 1972; DPM Eng. 1966; DCH Eng. 1955. (Roy. Free) Socs: FRSM. Prev: Cons. Psychiat. Qu. Mary's Hosp. Childr. & Merton HA; Sen. Regist. Maudsley Hosp. Lond.

WELLS, John Christopher Durant 45A Rodney Street, Liverpool L1 9EW Tel: 0151 708 9344 Fax: 0151 707 0609; Apt 311, The Colonnades, Albert Dock, Liverpool L3 4AB Tel: 0151 709 8180 Fax: 0151 707 0609 Email: cxwells@aol.com — MB ChB Liverp. 1970; MRCS Eng. LRCP Lond. 1970; LMCC 1974; FFA RCS Eng. 1978; FRCA Eng 1978. (Liverp.) Specialist (relief of Chronic Pain) Liverp.; Dir. Pain Relief (Research) Foundat.; Hon. Cons. (Pain Relief) Liverp. Marie Curie Home; Hon. Cons. (Pain Relief) Clatterbridge Centre for Oncol. Socs: Hon. Asst. Sec., Pain Soc. GB & Irel.; Chairm. Scient. Comm. Pain Soc. GB & Irel.; Hon. Sec. World Soc. Pain Clinicians. Prev: Dir. Centre for Pain Relief, Walton Hosp.; Hon. Sen. Lect. Univ. of Liverp.

WELLS, John Kirkwood Gillman Department of Anaesthetics, North Hampshire Hospital, Aldermaston Road, Basingstoke RG24 9NA — MB BS 1971 Lond.; FFA RCS Eng. 1979; DA Eng. 1974. (Westm.) Cons. Anaesth. Basingstoke & N. Hants. HA. Socs: Intens. Care Soc. Prev: Sen. Regist. Char. Cross Hosp. Med. Sch.; Regist. Brompton Hosp. Lond.

WELLS, John Michael Weston (retired) 7 Ringstead Road, Heacham, King's Lynn PE31 7JA Tel: 01485 70219 — MRCS Eng. LRCP Lond. 1940; DMRD Eng. 1947. Prev: Cons. Radiol. W. Norf. & King's Lynn Gen. Hosp.

WELLS, Jonathan Joseph Hillview Medical Centre, 60 Bromsgrove Road, Redditch B97 4RN Tel: 01527 66511; 43 Sandhills Road, Barnt Green, Birmingham B45 8NP Tel: 0121 445 1291 — MB BS 1987 Lond.; MRCP (UK) 1990; MRCGP 1993; T(GP) 1993; DRCOG 1992. Prev: Trainee GP Measham Med. Unit; Regist. (Gen. Med.) Leicester Roy. Infirm.; SHO (O & G) Leicester Gen. Hosp.

WELLS, Julie Alison 70 Mount Road, Canterbury CT1 1YF — MB BS 1996 Lond.

WELLS, Keith Marple Cottage Surgery, 50 Church Street, Marple, Stockport SK6 6BW Tel: 0161 426 0011 Fax: 0161 427 8160; 29 Hollins Lane, Marple Bridge, Stockport SK6 5BD Tel: 0161 449 8326 — MB ChB 1971 Manch.; MRCGP 1976; DObst RCOG 1974; DCH RCPS Glas. 1973. (Manchester) Prev: SHO (O & G) Withington Hosp.; SHO (Paediat.) & SHO (Med.) Stepping Hill Hosp. Stockport.

WELLS, Laurence Gregory Warwickshire Health Authority, Westgate House, Market St., Warwick CV34 4DE Tel: 01926 493491 Fax: 01926 495074 Email: greg.wells@warwick-ha.wmids.nhs.uk — MB ChB 1971 Cape Town; FFPHM RCP (UK) 1995. Dir. Pub. Health Warks. HA. Prev: SCM S. Warks. HA; Med. Off. & Med. Sup. Chas. Johnson Memor. Hosp., Zululand; Med. Off. German Inst. Med. Mission Tuebingen, W. Germany.

WELLS, Louise Claire Minton Altwood Close, Maidenhead SL6 4PP — MB BS 1993 Lond.

WELLS, Mark Philip Paul 14 Leechcroft Road, Wallington SM6 7JF — MB BS 1994 Lond.

WELLS, Martin David Cliftonville Road Surgery, 61 Cliftonville Road, Belfast BT14 6JN Tel: 028 9074 7361; 18 Piney Hills, Malone, Belfast BT9 5NR Fax: 01232 662622 — MB BCh BAO Belf. 1985; MRCGP 1991; DCH RCP Glas. 1989; DMH RCP Lond. 1989; DRCOG 1988; Cert. Family Plann. JCC 1988. (Qu. Univ. Belf.)

WELLS, Mary Beverley The Surgery, 160 Streetly Road, Erdington, Birmingham B23 7BD Tel: 0121 350 2323 Fax: 0121 382 0169; Forge Farm House, Forge Lane, Footherley, Lichfield WS14 0HU — MB ChB 1971 Birm.

WELLS, Mrs Meher Derek (retired) Ty-Fry Cottage, Cliff Road, Hythe CT21 5XL Tel: 01303 266469 — MB BS 1960 Osmania; MD Univ. Lond. 1990; FRCS Eng. 1970; FRCSI 1968. Research Fell. (Path.) Inst. Otol. & Laryngol. Lond.; Regist. Teach. Univ. Lond. Prev: Regist. Hosp. Sick Childr. Gt. Ormond St. Lond.

WELLS, Professor Michael Department of Pathology, University of Sheffield Medical School, Beech Hill Road, Sheffield S10 2RX Tel:

WELLS

0114 271 2397 Fax: 0114 278 0059 Email: m.wells@sheffield.ac.uk; 57 Ranmoor Crescent, Sheffield S10 3GW Tel: 0114 230 8260 Email: mike@mikewell.demon.co.uk — MB ChB 1976 Manch.; BSc (Hons.) Manch. 1974, MD 1986; FRCPath 1995, M 1983. Hon. Cons. Path. Univ. Hosps. Centr. Sheff.; Prof. Gyn. Path. Univ. Sheff. Socs: Brit. Gyn. Cancer Soc.; (Meeting Sec.) Path Soc. GB & Irel.; Internat. Acad. Path. (Ex-Hon. Sec. Brit. Div.). Prev: Prof. Gyn. Path. Univ. Leeds; Sen. Lect. Univ. Leeds; Lect. (Path.) Univ. Bristol.

WELLS, Michelle Lesley Launceston Medical Centre, Landlake Road, Launceston PL15 9HH Tel: 01566 772131 Fax: 01566 772223 — BM BS 1989 Nottm.; BMedSci (Hons.) Nottm. 1986. (Nottm.)

WELLS, Nigel John Nether Leazes, Beech Hill, Hexham NE46 3AG — MB ChB 1997 Dundee.

WELLS, Paula Department of Radiotherapy & Oncology, St Bartholomews Hospital, West Smithfield, London EC1A 7BE — MB BS 1986 Lond.; MRCP (UK) 1989; FRCR 1994. (St Bartholomews Hospital London) Cons. Clin Oncologist St Bartholomews Hosp Lond.. Prev: Sen. Regis. Clin. Oncol. Roy. Marsden Hosp. Lond.; Hon. Sen. Regist. & Research Sen. Regist. MRC Cyclotron Unit Hammersmith.

WELLS, Peter George (retired) High Trees, Dark Lane, Henbury, Macclesfield SK11 9PE Tel: 01625 420872 — MB ChB 1954 Sheff.; FRANZCP 1983, M 1981; FRCPsych 1979, M 1971; T(Psychiat.) 1991; DPM Eng. 1965; DObst RCOG 1956; DCH Eng. 1956. Lect. Univ. Manch. & Univ. Liverp.; Adviser to Visyon. Prev: Cons. Psychiat. (Adolesc. Servs.) Mersey & N. W. RHAs.

WELLS, Philip Andrew Eurdon Street Surgery, Ashton-under-Lyne OL6 6PR Tel: 0161 330 5104 — MB ChB 1983 Leeds; MRCGP 1991; DGM RCP Lond. 1989.

WELLS, Richard David 39 Regent Street, West End, Stoke-on-Trent ST4 5HQ — MB ChB 1995 Dundee.

WELLS, Richard Douglas William The Castle Practice, Health Centre, Central Street, Ludgershall, Andover SP11 9RA Tel: 01264 790356 Fax: 01264 791256; 28 St. James Street, Ludgershall, Andover SP11 9QF Tel: 01264 790398 — MB BS 1973 Lond.; BSc Lond. 1970; DObst RCOG 1976. (St. Bart.) GP Represen. Wilts LMC. Socs: Salisbury Med. Soc. Prev: Trainee GP Exeter VTS; Sen. Resid. Med. Off. (Obst.) Health Commiss. NSW, Austral.; Ho. Phys. St. Bart. Hosp. Lond.

WELLS, Robert Arthur Company Health Ltd., 335 Red Bank Road, Bispham Village Chambers, Bispham Village, Blackpool FY2 0HJ Tel: 01253 590555 Fax: 01253 590555; 43 Everest Drive, Bispham, Blackpool FY2 9DH — MB ChB 1978 Manch.; BSc. (Hons.) Manch. 1976; MBA Ed. 1995; MRCGP 1982; D.Occ.Med. RCO Lond. 1995. Managing Dir. Co. Health Ltd.; Occupat. Phys.; Apptd. Doctor (Health & Safety Exec.) for Lead, Asbestos, Compressed Air Surveillance & Ionising Radiat; Trainer (Gen. Pract.) Blackpool VTS; Med. Adviser P & O CMW Laboratories Kerry Foods. Socs: Soc. Occupat. Med. Prev: Med. Advisor to Tower & Winter Gdns. Blackpool; Med. Off. RAMC GSM (N. Irel.).

WELLS, Robert Cameron Rayford House, School Road, Hove BN3 5HX — MB BCh 1977 Wales.

WELLS, Roger Augustus Elm House Surgery, 29 Beckenham Road, Beckenham BR3 4PR Tel: 020 8650 0173; 154 Bromley Road, Beckenham BR3 6PG — MB BS 1978 Lond.; BSc (Hons.) Lond. 1975; MRCGP 1986; DRCOG 1983. (St. Mary's) Socs: Christian Med. Fell.sh. Prev: Trainee GP St. Peters Hosp. Chertsey.

***WELLS, Roger Noel** Prioryfield House, 20 Canon St., Taunton TA1 1SW Tel: 01823 323363 Fax: 01823 271072; Argyle House, New Buildings Lane, Gandy St, Exeter EX4 3LS Tel: 01392 213899 — MB BS 1971 Lond.; BSc (Hons.) Lond. 1967.

WELLS, Ruth Blackbrook Surgery, Lisieux Way, Taunton TA1 2LB Tel: 01823 259444 Fax: 01823 322715; The Cottage, Goosenford, Cheddon Fitzpaine, Taunton TA2 8LH — MB BS 1979 Lond.; MFFP 1992; MRCGP 1983; DRCOG 1981; DCH Eng. 1981. SCMO (Family Plann.) Som. HA.

WELLS, Sarah Louise Armitage 58 Byron Street, Hale, Altrincham WA14 2EL; 35 Weldale Drive, Stoney Gate, Leicester LE2 2AR Tel: 0116 270 9862 — MB ChB 1994 Liverp.; DRCOG 1996; DFFP 1996. (Liverp.) SHO Palliat. Med.Nottm. City Hosp. Prev: SHO (Paediat.) Arrowe Pk. Hosp. Wirral; GP Regist. Bunbury Med. Pract.; SHO Psych.Rugby Hosp.

WELLS, Simon Kingsley X-Ray Department, Musgrove Park Hospital, Taunton TA1 5DA; The Manor Lodge, Rectory Road, Norton Fitzwarren, Taunton TA2 6SE — MB BS 1976 Lond.; BA Oxf. 1973; FRCR 1983. (Middlx.) Cons. Radiol. Taunton & Som. Hosp. Taunton. Prev: Sen. Regist. (Radiol.) Soton. Gen. Hosp.; SHO (Med.) Nevill Hall Hosp. Abergavenny; SHO (Orthop.) Yeovil Dist. Hosp.

WELLS, Stephen Department of Histopathology, Royal Bolton Hospital, Minerva Road, Farnworth, Bolton BL4 0JR Tel: 01204 390534 Fax: 01204 390946; 6 Oaker Avenue, Didsbury, Manchester M20 2XH — MB ChB 1975 Manch.; FRCPath. 1993, M 1981. (Manchester) Cons. Histopath. Roy. Bolton Hosp. Prev: Sen. Regist. (Histopath.) Hope Hosp., Salford, Wythenshawe Hosp. Manch. & Univ. Manch.

WELLS, Mr Stuart Charles Somerset Nuffield Hospital, Stapelgrove Elm, Taunton TA2 6AN Tel: 01823 286991 Fax: 01823 250610; Town Farm House, North Curry, Taunton TA3 6LX Tel: 01823 490904 Fax: 01823 490904 — MB BS 1972 Lond.; FRCS Eng. 1979; MRCS Eng. LRCP Lond. 1972. Cons. & ENT Surg. Taunton & Som. Hosps. (MusGr. Pk. Br.) Taunton.

WELLS, Susan Margaret West Kirby Health Centre, The Concourse, Grange Road, Wirral CH48 4HZ Tel: 0151 625 9171 Fax: 0151 625 9499; 11 Bertram Drive, Meols, Wirral CH47 0LG Tel: 0151 632 0539 Fax: 0151 632 6424 — MB BChir 1983 Camb.; MA Oxf. 1989, BA 1980; FRCGP 1993, M 1987; DRCOG 1986. (Cambridge) GP Princip.; Clin. Asst. (Diabetes). Prev: Trainee GP Rotat. Chester VTS; Ho. Surg. Addenbrooke's Hosp. Camb.; Ho. Phys. Arrowe Pk. Hosp. Wirral.

WELLS, Timothy Alastair 7 Barbrook Close, Tilehurst, Reading RG31 6RT — MB BS 1996 Lond.

WELLS, Wilfrid Denys Edward Forge Farm House, Forge Lane, Footherley, Lichfield WS14 0HU — MB ChB 1974 Birm.; BSc (Hons.) Wales 1969. Hon. Sen. Lect. (Gen. Pract.) Univ. Birm. & (Pharmacy Policy & Pract.) Univ. Keele. Socs: (Sec.) W. Midl. Assn. Fundholding Practs.; Drug Utilization Res. Gp. UK. Prev: Postgrad. GP Tutor Walsall Manor Hosp.; Regist. (Med.) Dudley Rd. Hosp. Birm.; Regist. (Haemat.) E. Birm. Hosp.

WELLSTEED, Anthony John (retired) 18 New Close Road, Shipley BD18 4AU Tel: 01274 587558 — MB BS 1958 Lond.; FRCP Lond. 1982, M 1965. Prev: Cons. Infec. Dis. Bradford Roy. Infirm.

WELLSTOOD, Frederick Guy 10 Wood Street, Stratford-upon-Avon CV37 6JE Tel: 01789 293094 — MB ChB 1940 Birm. (Birm.) Prev: Ho. Surg. Gen. Hosp. Birm.; Capt. RAMC.

WELLSTOOD-EASON, Malcolm John Howard Queens Hospital, Belvedere Road, Burton-on-Trent DE13 0RB Tel: 01283 566333; The Old Forge, 7 Main St, Ravenstone, Coalville LE67 2AS — MB ChB 1968 Liverp.; MRCS Eng. LRCP Lond. 1969; FFA RCS Eng. 1977. Cons. Qus. Hosp. Burton on Trent. Prev: Cons. Leics. AHA (T).

WELLSTOOD-EASON, Susan Penelope Brandon Mental Health Unit, Leicester LE5 4PW; 53 Stamford Road, Oakham LE15 6HZ — MRCS Eng. LRCP Lond. 1970; MRCPsych 1982. Cons. Psychiat. Leicester Ment. Health Serv. Prev: Clin. Lect. (Psychiat.) Univ. Leic.; Regist. (Psychiat.) Leics. AHA (T); Med. Dir. Leicester Ment. Health Serv. NHS TrustMed. Dir. Leicester Ment. Health Serv. NHS Trust.

WELLUPPILLAI, Sivanesh 25 Richmond Terrace, Aberdeen AB25 2RQ — MB ChB 1992 Aberd.

WELLWOOD, Mr James McKinney 134 Harley Street, London W1N 3AH Tel: 020 7487 4212 Fax: 020 7486 1042; 50 Clifton Hill, St. Johns Wood, London NW8 0QG Tel: 020 7625 5697 — MB BChir Camb. 1966; MChir Camb. 1978, MA 1966; FRCS Eng. 1970. (Camb. & St. Thos.) Cons. Surg. Whipps Cross Hosp. Lond.; Clin. Dir. (Surg.) Forest Healthcare Trust; Hon. Sen. Lect. St. Bart. Hosp. Med. Sch. Lond. Socs: FRSM; Brit. Soc. Gastroenterol.; Assn. Endoscopic Surgs. Prev: Chief Asst. St. Bart. Hosp. Lond.; Hon. Sen. Regist. (Research) & Regist. (Surg.) St. Thos. Hosp. Lond.

WELLWOOD, Marion Rachel Three New Horizons Court, Brentford TW8 9EP Tel: 020 8975 2094 Fax: 020 8975 2499 Email: marion.r.wellwood@sb.com; 5 Hazell Park, Amersham HP7 9AB — MB ChB 1978 Ed.; BSc Ed. 1975, MB ChB 1978; FRCPC 1984; FRCP Toronto 1984. (Edinburgh University Medical School) Vice Pres. & Dir. Med. Communication SmithKline Beecham Pharmaceut.

WELPLY, Mr Gilman Adrian Chinnery Parkside Hospital, 53 Parkside, Wimbledon, London SW19 5NX Tel: 020 8947 8852 Fax:

01446 760730; White Gate Lodge, St. Nicholas, Cardiff CF5 6SJ Tel: 01446 760730 Fax: 01446 760730 Email: gwelply@doctors.org.uk — MB BS 1964 Lond.; FRCS Eng. 1968; MRCS Eng. LRCP Lond. 1964; FRCOG 1987, M 1971; T(OG) 1991. (St. Geo.) Prev: Cons. O & G St. Helier Hosp. Carshalton; Sen. Regist. (O & G) St. Geo. Hosp. Lond. & Soton. Gen. Hosp.; Regist. (O & G) St. Geo. Hosp. Lond.

WELSBY, Ann (retired) — LRCPI & LM, LRSCI & LM 1972; DObst RCOG 1975. Prev: GP E. Cumbria FPC.

WELSBY, Ian James 12 Belitha Villas, London N1 1PD — MB BS 1990 Lond.

WELSBY, Philip Douglas Infectious Disease Unit, Western General Hospital, Edinburgh EH4 2XU Tel: 0131 537 1000 Email: p.welsby@ed.ac.uk — MB BS Lond. 1970; FRCP Ed. 1984; MRCP (U.K.) 1973; MRCS Eng. LRCP Lond. 1970. (Roy. Free) Cons. Phys. in Communicable Dis. City Hosp. Edin. Prev: Sen. Regist. (Infec. Dis.) Roy. Free Hosp. Lond.; Med. Regist. S. Grampian Health Dist.; Med. Regist. St. Peter's Hosp. Chertsey.

WELSBY, Susan Mary 1708 Lanier Place, Washington DC NW20009, USA; 296 Singlewell Road, Gravesend DA11 7RF Tel: 01474 534648 — MB ChB 1978 Manch.; MPH USA 1992; DTM & H Liverp. 1985. Internat. Cons. Washington DC, USA. Prev: Med. Off. Health Governm. Barbados.

WELSH, Bernard Mark 53 Bromley Road, Beckenham BR3 5PA — MB ChB 1987 Aberd.; MA (Psychol.) St. And. 1982; MRCGP 1992; DTM & H Liverp. 1992.

WELSH, Professor Christopher Lawrence Medical School, Beach Hill Road, Sheffield S10 2RX Tel: 0114 271 2668 Fax: 0114 271 3959 Email: c.l.welsh@sheffield.ac.uk; 38 Clarendon Road, Sheffield S10 3TR Tel: 0114 230 5782 Fax: 0114 230 5782 — MB BChir 1973 Camb.; MA Camb. 1973, MChir 1986; FRCS Eng. 1977. Postgrad. Med. Dean Univ. Sheff.; Regional Postgrad. Dean NHSE Trent. Prev: Cons. Vasc. Surg. N.. Gen. Hosp. Sheff.; Clin. Dean Univ. Sheff.; Lect. & Sen. Regist. Surg. Profess. Unit St. Bart. Hosp. Lond.

WELSH, Colin David Eaton Road Surgery, 276 Eaton Road, West Derby, Liverpool L12 2AW Tel: 0151 228 3768 Fax: 0151 — MB ChB 1986 Liverp.; DRCOG 1992.

WELSH, Colin John Percy Huddersfield Royal Infirmary, Acre St., Lindley, Huddersfield HD3 3EA — MB ChB 1987 Glas.; MRCP (UK) 1990; BSc (Hons) Glas. 1985. Cons. Gen. Med. & Cardiol. Huddersfield Roy. Infirm. Prev: Regist. (Cardiol.) Leeds Gen. Infirm.; SHO Rotat. (Med.) Newc. u. Tyne.

WELSH, David William (retired) Williams Loke Health Centre, Williams Loke, St. Williams Way, Norwich NR7 0AJ Tel: 01603 33898 — MB ChB 1958 Ed. Prev: Hosp. Pract. (Diabetics) Norf. & Norwich Hosp.

WELSH, Miss Fenella Kate Sally Beechwood House, Offham, Lewes BN7 3QQ — MB BChir 1993 Camb.; FRCS 1997. (Camb. & St. Mary's Lond.)

WELSH, Geoffrey Hugh Student Health Centre, 42 Old Elvet, Durham DH1 3JF Tel: 0191 386 5081; Viewlands, Percy Terrace, Nevilles Cross, Durham DH1 4DY Tel: 0191 384 9824 — MB BS 1987 Newc.; MRCGP 1991. Prev: GP Coxhoe, Durh.

WELSH, Harry (retired) Drumhella, Mainsforth, Ferryhill DL17 9AA Tel: 01740 652159 — MB ChB 1956 Leeds.

WELSH, Janet Leila Graingerville Family Planning Clinic, 4 Graingerville North, Westgate Road, Newcastle upon Tyne NE4 6UJ Tel: 0191 219 5239; 73 Dunsgreen, Ponteland, Newcastle upon Tyne NE20 9EJ Tel: 01661 820358 Fax: 01661 820358 — MB BS 1980 Newc.; BA (Hons.) York 1974; MFFP 1994; MRCGP 1985; DRCOG 1984; DCH RCP Lond. 1983. Sen. Med. Off. Contracep. & Sexual Health Serv. Newc. City Health NHS Trust. Socs: Assoc. Mem. Inst. Psychosexual Med; BMA; Brit. Menopause Soc. Prev: Head Clin. Serv. (Family Plann. & Well Wom.) Newc. City Health NHS Trust; Lead Clinician (Audit) N.. Region & Heads Serv. Gp. (Community Family Plann.) Newc. u. Tyne; GP Wylam.

WELSH, Professor John Mill Cottage, Whitewreath Farm, Longmorn, Elgin IV30 8SL — MB ChB 1975 Dundee; BSc Dund 1971; FRCP Ed. 1992; FRCP Glas. 1992; MRCP (UK) 1979. Prof. Palliat. Med. Glas. Univ.

WELSH, Kennedy Robert 30 Princess Drive, Kirby Muxloe, Leicester LE9 2DJ — MB BS 1980 Lond.

WELSH, Lawrence 28 Handly Cross, Manor Woods, Medomsly, Consett DH8 6TZ — MB BS 1984 Lond.; BSc (Immunol.) Lond. 1981, MB BS 1984.

WELSH, Liz 24 Effingham Road, Bristol BS6 5BJ Tel: 0117 923 2469 — MB BS Lond. 1966; MSc Exeter 1990; MFHom RCP Lond. 1986; FFA RCS Eng. 1972; DObst RCOG 1968. (St. Bart.) Prev: Specialist Regist. Pub. Health; Trainee GP Honiton Devon; Cons. Anaesth. Ipswich Hosp.

WELSH, Mary Annette The Lennard Surgery, 1-3 Lewis Road, Bishopsworth, Bristol BS13 7JD Tel: 0117 964 0900 Fax: 0117 987 3227; 83 Sommerville Road, St. Andrews, Bristol BS7 9AE — MB ChB 1978 Bristol; MRCOG 1985; MRCGP 1983. (Bristol) Hosp. Pract. (Obst.) Bristol Matern. Hosp. & (Gyn.) St. Michael's Hosp Bristol; Course Organiser for Bristol GP Vocational Train. Scheme (2 sessions/week).

WELSH, Mary Catherine 54 Ridge End Villas, Headingley, Leeds LS6 2DA — MB ChB 1968 Leeds; Dip. Psychother. Leeds 1983; DPM Leeds 1972. (Leeds) Clin. Asst. Child & Family Serv. Airedale NHS Trust. Prev: Regist. (Psychiat.) Profess. Dept. Psychiat. Leeds Gen. Infirm.; Regist. (Child & Adolesc. Psychiat.) Highlands Adolesc. Unit; Regist. (Adult Psychiat.) Scalebor Pk. Hosp. Burley-in-Wharfedale.

WELSH, Peter Bryan (retired) Carabey House, Newbury Road, Lambourn, Hungerford RG17 7LL Tel: 01488 71914 Email: welsh.carabey@pop3.hiway.co.uk — MB ChB 1967 Birm. Prev: GP Argyll.

WELSH, Peter John Bodmin Road Health Centre, Bodmin Road, Ashton on Mersey, Sale M33 5JH Tel: 0161 962 4625 Fax: 0161 905 3317; Fern Bank, 34 South Grove, Brooklands, Sale M33 3AU Tel: 0161 962 6925 — MB ChB 1972 Manch.

WELSH, Roger Randal (retired) Montagu Farm, North St., Winkfield, Windsor SL4 4SY Tel: 01344 882716 — MB BS 1956 Lond.; MRACGP 1984; Cert. Av. Med. 1978. Prev: Med. Dir. HRH P.ss Christian's Hosp. Windsor.

WELSH, Sheila Lennox Holly Bush, Dykebar Hospital, Grahamston Road, Paisley PA2 7DE Tel: 0141 8845122 Fax: 0141 8848825 Email: Shelia.Welsh@renver-pct.scot.nhs.uk — MB ChB 1968 Glas.; MFFP 1993; DA Eng. 1971; DObst RCOG 1970. (Glasgow) Sen. Med. Off. (Family Plann. & Reproductive Health) Renfrewsh. & Inverclyde Primary Care NHS Trust. Socs: BMA; Brit. Menopause Soc.; Scott. Family Plann. Med. Soc. Prev: Regist. (Anaesth.) W.. Infirm. Glas.; Ho. Off. (Obst.) Qu. Mother's Hosp. Glas.; SCMO Glas. Family Plann. Clinic.

WELSH, Susan Frances North East Essex Mental Health NHS Trust, Boxted Road, Colchester CO4 5HG — MB ChB 1985 Glas.; MRCPsych 1999. Specialist Regist. Old Age Psychiat.

WELSH, Susan Hope 72 Quarry Avenue, Bebington, Wirral CH63 3HF Tel: 0151 645 6227 — MB ChB 1976 Glas. Clin. Asst. (Dermat.) Chester Roy. Infirm. Wirral Hosp. Trust; Staff Grade (Dermat.) Wirrall Hosp. Trust. Prev: GP Bebington; SHO (Dermat.) Clatterbridge Hosp. Wirral; Trainee GP Tayside VTS.

WELTON, Edward John (retired) Tre-Llydiart, Chirbury Road, Montgomery SY15 6QP Tel: 01686 668313 — MB ChB 1963 Liverp.; DObst RCOG 1965. Prev: GP Montgomery.

WELTON, Elizabeth Ann Tre-Llydiart, Chirbury Road, Montgomery SY15 6QP Tel: 01686 668313 Email: welton@dial.pipex.com — MB ChB 1964 Liverp.; DObst RCOG 1966. (Liverp.) Locum Gen. Practitioner. Prev: Clin. Asst. (Paediat. Orthop.) Roy. Shrewsbury Hosps.; Ho. Phys. & Ho. Surg. Liverp. Roy. Infirm.; Ho. Off. Mill Rd. Matern. Hosp. Liverp.

WELTON, Mark David Michael Trent Vale Medical Practice, 876 London Road, Trent Vale, Stoke-on-Trent ST4 5NX Tel: 01782 746898; 11 Sheridan Way, Stone ST15 8XG Email: markwelton@aol.com — MB ChB 1990 Birm.; MRCGP 1995. (Birmingham) Socs: (Pres.) Stoke Young Princips. Gp. Prev: Trainee GP N. Staffs. VTS.

WELTON, Robert (retired) Egerton House, Lees Road, Mossley, Ashton-under-Lyne OL5 0PQ Tel: 0145 783 3606 — MB ChB 1952 Manch.; FRCGP 1989, M 1976.

WELTON, Trudy The Red House, 26 Keswick Road, Cringleford, Norwich NR4 6UG — MB BS 1976 Lond.; MA Oxf. 1977. Prev: Med. Advisor Norf. FHSA; GP Norwich; Ho. Surg. St. Bart. Hosp. Lond.

WELZENBACH

WELZENBACH, Britta Juliana 60 Holly Hill, Bassett, Southampton SO16 7EW — State Exam Med 1992 Wurzburg.

WEMBRIDGE, Kevin Richard 26 Dover Road, Hunter's Bar, Sheffield S11 8RH — MB ChB 1993 Sheff.; FRCS Eng. 1999. SSHO (Orthop.) Barnsley Dist. Gen. Socs: MDU; MSS; BMA.

WEMYSS-GORMAN, Peter Bradley (retired) Lyndhurst, Hickman's Lane, Lindfield, Haywards Heath RH16 2PX Tel: 01444 483835 — MB BChir 1962 Camb.; MB Camb. 1962, BChir 1961; MA CAmb. 1962; MRCS Eng. LRCP Lond. 1961; FFA RCS Eng. 1968. Cons. Pain Managem. P.ss Roy. Hosp. Haywards Heath; Anaesth. Mid-Sussex NHS Trust. Prev: Sen. Regist. (Anaesth.) Roy. Vict. Infirm. Newc.

WEMYSS-HOLDEN, Mr Guy David Department of Urology, Blackburn Royal Infirmary, Blackburn BB2 3LR Tel: 01254 263555; Four Acres, Shire Lane, Hurst Green, Clitheroe BB7 9QR Tel: 01254 826744 — MB BS 1982 Nottm.; MD Nottm. 1993; FRCS (Urol.) 1994; FRCS Ed. 1987. Cons. Urol. Blackburn Roy. Infirm. Prev: Sen. Regist. (Urol.) NW Region Manch.

WEMYSS-HOLDEN, Simon Andrew Garden House, Back St., Ilmington, Shipston-on-Stour CV36 4LJ — BM BS 1988 Nottm.

WENDELBORN, Kurt Jon 36 Curie Court C11, Queens Medical Centre, Nottingham NG7 2UH Tel: 01623 22515 — MB ChB 1989 Auckland. Regist. (Psychiat.) Qu. Med. Centre Nottm. Socs: Inceptor Roy. Coll. Psychiat. Prev: SHO (Psychiat.) Winwick Hosp. Warrington.

WENDON, Julia Alexis Institute of Liver Studies, Kings College Hospital, Bessemer Road, London SE5 9PJ Tel: 020 7346 3252 Email: julia.wendon@kcl.ac.uk; 74 Talfourd Road, London SE15 5NZ — MB ChB 1982 Dundee; FRCP Lond. 1996. Sen. Lect. Inst. Liver Studies Kings Coll. Hosp. Lond.

WENGER, Margaret Beaton The Coach House, Standon, Stafford ST21 6RN Tel: 0178 270 791296 — MB ChB 1936 Birm.; DA Eng. 1938. (Birm.) Socs: BMA. Prev: Anaesth. Law Junction EMS Hosp. Carluke; Sen. Res. Anaesth. Leicester Roy. Infirm.; Res. Anaesth. Qu.'s Hosp. Birm.

WENGER, Mr Reginald Julien James (retired) Essex Nuffield Hospital, Brentwood CM15 8EN Tel: 01277 365134 Fax: 01277 365134 — MB BS 1968 Lond.; FRCS Eng. 1973; MRCS Eng. LRCP Lond. 1968; DObst RCOG 1970. Cons. Orthop. Surg. Prev: Sen. Regist. (Orthop.) King's Coll. Hosp. Lond.

WENGRAF, Carol Lindsay 47 St John's Park, London SE3 7JW Tel: 020 8858 4598 — MB BS 1962 Lond.; FRCS Eng. 1967; MRCS Eng. LRCP Lond. 1962. (Guy's) Cons. ENT Surg. Greenwich, Lewisham & Woolwich Hosp. Gps. Prev: Sen. Regist. ENT Dept. Guy's Hosp. Lond.; SHO ENT Dept. W.m. Hosp.

WENGROWE, Nolan Elliot Golders Hill Health Centre, Hillside, 151 North End Road, London NW11 7HX Tel: 020 8455 6886 Fax: 020 8201 9225; 13 Grey Close, London NW11 6QG Tel: 020 8455 9290 — MB ChB 1978 Cape Town; MRCGP 1984. Prev: SHO (Neonat.) Whittington Hosp. Lond.; SHO (Paediat.) N.wick Pk. Hosp. Harrow & Brompton Hosp. Lond.

WENHAM, Geoffrey Andrew Department of Anaesthetics, University hospital of Wales, Heath Park, Cardiff CF14 4XW Tel: 02920 743255; 7 Melin Dwr, Draethen, Newport NP10 8GL — MB BCh 1975 Wales; FFA RCS Eng. 1979. (Welsh Nat. Sch. Med.) Cons. Anaesth. Univ. Hosp. Wales.

***WENHAM, John Timothy** 4 Church Walk, Charlton Kings, Cheltenham GL53 8BJ — MB ChB 1998 Manch.; MB ChB Manch 1998.

WENHAM, Josephine Anne 6 Laburnum Mews, Stonehouse GL10 2PW — MB ChB 1998 Sheff.; MB ChB Sheff 1998.

WENHAM, Mr Peter William 31 Sutton Passeys Crescent, Wollaton Park, Nottingham NG8 1BX Tel: 0115 970 2481 — MB BChir 1973 Camb.; MD Camb. 1985; FRCS Eng. 1978. (St. Thos.) Cons. Gen. Vasc. Surg. Nottm. Univ. Hosp. & Nottm. City Hosp. Socs: Vasc. Soc. GB & Irel. Prev: Sen. Lect. Nottm. Univ.; Sen. Regist. Nottm. HA.

WENHAM, Timothy Nigel 8 Ramsey Road, Sheffield S10 1LR — MB ChB 1998 Sheff.

WENHAM, Vivienne Caroline 2 Fl 1 Leamington Place, Edinburgh EH10 4JR — MB ChB 1998 Ed.; MB ChB Ed 1998.

WENLEY, Mary Ruth The Surgery, 19 Amwell Street, Hoddesdon EN11 8TU Tel: 01992 464147 Fax: 01992 708698; 108 High Street, Roydon, Harlow CM19 5EE — MB BS 1983 Lond.; MRCGP 1987; DCH RCP Lond. 1987. Prev: Trainee GP W. Essex VTS.

WENLEY, William Gilson (retired) The Nether House, Brundall, Norwich NR13 5PA — MB BChir 1951 Camb.; FRCP Ed. 1975, M 1960; DPhysMed Eng. 1958; DObst RCOG 1953. Cons. Phys. (Rheum. & Rehabil.) Norwich Health Dist. Prev: Sen. Regist. (Phys. Med. & Rheum.) Ho. Surg. & Ho. Phys. Lond. Hosp.

WENSLEY, Richard Thomas 15 Cherington Road, Cheadle SK8 1LN — MB ChB 1963 Liverp.; MRCP (U.K.) 1973; FRCPath. 1982, M 1970. Cons. Haemat. Manch. Roy. Infirm. & Manch. Regional Blood Transfus. Centre. Prev: Sen. Regist. (Haemat.) Bristol Roy. Infirm.

WENSLEY, Susan Katherine Bristol Royal Infirmary, Marlborough St., Bristol BS2 8HW; 1 Fernbank Road, Redland, Bristol BS6 6QA Tel: 0117 907 1948 — MB ChB 1988 Bristol; MRCP (UK) 1992. Staff Grade (Geriat. Med.). Socs: Brit. Geriat. Soc.; Brit. Soc. of Gerontology. Prev: Regist. (Geriat. Med.) Brist. Roy. Infirm.; SHO Rotat. (Gen. Med.) Gloucester HA.

WENSTONE, Richard 12th Floor, Department of Anaesthesia & Intensive Care, Royal Liverpool University Hospital, Liverpool L7 8XP Tel: 0151 706 3191 Fax: 0151 706 5646 Email: wenstone@liverpool.ac.uk — MB ChB 1983 Manch.; FFA RCS Eng. 1988; DA (UK) 1985. Cons. Anaesth. & IC Roy. Liverp. Univ. Hosp. & Clin. Dir. IC; Hon. Clin. Lect. Univ. Liverp. Socs: Soc. Critical Care Med. & Intens. Care Soc.; Eur. Soc. Intens. Care Med. Prev: Sen. Regist. (Anaesth.) Mersey RHA; Fell. Critical Care Univ. Toronto; Regist. (Anaesth.) Liverp., St. Helens & Knowsley HA.

WENT, Emma Louise 4 Crown Point Drive, Bixley, Norwich NR14 8RR — MB BS 1993 Lond.

WENT, Janice 106 Upland Drive, Derriford, Plymouth PL6 6BG Tel: 01752 779786 — MB BCh BAO 1963 Dub.; MSc Birm. 1968; FRCPath 1984, M 1970; MCB 1971. Cons. Chem. Path. Dept. Clin. Chem. Derriford Hosp. Prev: Sen. Regist. Clin. Chem. Guy's Hosp. Lond.; Regist. (Chem. Path.) Birm. RHB.

WENTEL, James Douglas 38 Mountway, Waverton, Chester CH3 7QF; Plot 8, The Village Green, Hadnall, Shrewsbury SY4 — BM BS 1995 Nottm.

WENTWORTH, John Macquarie c/o Peterhouse, Cambridge CB2 1RD — MB BS 1994 Queensland.

WENZERUL, Alison Mary The Alderney Community Hospital, Ringwood Road, Parkstowe, Poole BH23 7JN — MB ChB 1977 Leeds; MRCPsych 1982; MRCPsych 1982. SPR Gen. Adult Psychiat. The Alderney Community Hosp., Pk.stowe, Poole. Socs: Roy. Coll. of Psychiatrisits; BMA. Prev: SPR Perinatal Psychiat., Old Manor Hosp., Salisbury; SPR Gen. Adult Psychiat., DOP, Soton.

WEPPNER, Gregory John The Dene, Goddards Green BN6 9LE — MB BS 1980 Queensland; LLM 1995 Univ. Of Wales, Col., Cardiff; 1995 LLM (Master of Laws Degree) Univ. of Wales, Coll. of Cardiff; MPhil Ed. 1992; MRCPsych. 1986. Cons. Forens. Psychiat., The Dene, Goddards Green. Prev: Sen. Regist. (Psychiat.) WhitCh. Hosp. Cardiff.

WERB, Mr Abraham (retired) 9 Oak Lodge Close, Dennis Lane, Stanmore HA7 4QB Tel: 020 8954 1588 — MB ChB 1945 Cape Town; FRCS Eng. 1970; FRCOphth 1989; DOMS Dub. 1956; DO Eng. 1956. Prev: Corneoplastic Unit Qu. Vict. Hosp. E. Grinstead.

WERCHOLA, Larysa Oksana (Surgery), 205 Russell Drive, Wollaton, Nottingham NG8 2BD Tel: 0115 928 3201 Fax: 0115 985 4981; Health Centre, 97 Derby Road, Stapleford, Nottingham NG9 7AT Tel: 0115 939 6111 Fax: 0115 970 9241 — MB BS 1982 Nottm.; MRCGP 1986; DObst 1985.

WERNEKE, Ursula Maudsley Hospital, Denmark Hill, London SE5 8AZ; Flat 5, 38 Wickham Road, London SE4 1NZ Tel: 020 7703 6333 Fax: 020 8691 8261 Email: uwerneke@usa.net — State Exam Med 1989 Dusseldorf; State Exam Med. Dusseldorf 1989; MD Dusseldorf 1990; Msc Lond. 1994; MRCPsych Lond. 1998. Specialist Regist. Maudsley Hosp. Socs: BMA; Roy. Coll. Psychiatr.; RSM. Prev: Cons. Researcher Lond. Health Economics Consortium Lond. Sch. Hyg. & Trop. Med. Lond.; Co-ordinator German Mammography Screening Office; SHO, Maudsley.

WERNER, David John Siegmar Fforestfach Medical Centre, 118 Ravenhill Road, Fforestfach, Swansea SA5 5AA Tel: 01792 581666 Fax: 01792 585332; 10 Rhyd y Defaid Drive, Sketty, Swansea SA2 8AH Tel: 01792 454404 Fax: 01792 585332 Email: d.werner@net.ntl.com — MB BS 1986 Lond.; BSc Lond. 1983, MB BS 1986; MRCGP 1990. (Univ. Coll. Lond.) GP Trainer Swansea Bay VTS.

WERNHAM, Catherine Mary Batheaston Medical Centre, Batheaston Medical Centre, Coalpit Road, Batheaston, Bath BA1 7NP Tel: 01225 858686 Fax: 01225 852521 — MB ChB 1993 Birm.; MA Camb. 1993, BA 1989; DRCOG 1995; DFFP 1995; MRCGP 1997. GP Partner.

WERNICK, Simon Paul Cosham Health Centre, Vectis Way, Portsmouth PO6 3AW Tel: 023 9238 1117 Fax: 0223 9221 4266; Knudge Cottage, Wickham Common, Wickham, Fareham PO17 6JQ Tel: 023 92 833373 — MB ChB 1976 Bristol; MRCGP 1980; DA (UK) 1981. GP Tutor Portsmouth.

WERNO, Anja Maria 31 Eltisley Avenue, Newnham, Cambridge CB3 9JG — State Exam Med 1993 Saarland.

WERREN, Josephine Patricia (retired) Tithe Barn House, Church Lane, Abridge, Romford RM4 1AD Tel: 01992 814626 — MB BS Lond. 1950; MRCS Eng. LRCP Lond. 1950; DObst RCOG 1954; DCH Eng. 1953. Med. Adviser Waltham Forest Housing Action Trust. Prev: GP Buckhurst Hill Essex.

***WERRETT, Gavin Charles** 36 Longmead, Merrow, Guildford GU1 2HW — MB ChB 1995 Bristol; MRCP.

WERRING, David John 76 Churchfield Road, Poole BH15 2QP — MB BS 1992 Lond.

WERRY, Carol Ann 26 Fleet Avenue, Upminster RM14 1PY — MB BS 1977 Lond. (St. Geo.)

WERRY, Diana Mary (retired) 7 Almond Close, Old Basing, Basingstoke RG24 7DW — MB BS 1962 Lond.; MRCS Eng. LRCP Lond. 1962; DMRD Eng. 1969; DObst RCOG 1965. Prev: Cons. Radiol. N. Hants. Hosp. NHS Trust & Bronglais Hosp. Aberystwyth.

WERTH, Fiona 46 Queen's Avenue, Muswell Hill, London N10 3BJ Tel: 020 8883 1846; 24 Calvert Road, Barnet EN5 4HJ Tel: 020 8447 0818 — MB BS 1986 Lond.

WESBY, Roger David St Bernard's Hospital, Uxbridge Road, Southall UB1 3HW — MB ChB 1978 Sheff.; MRCPsych. 1991; DRCOG 1988; DCH RCP Lond. 1986.

WESLEY, Helen Mary Mallott Oxleas, Oxleas NHS Trust, Pinewood Bexley Hospital, Old Bexley's Lane, Bexley DA5 2BF Tel: 01322 526282 Fax: 01322 556531; Spark Haw, Froghole, Crockham Hill, Edenbridge TN8 6TD Tel: 01732 866242 Fax: 01732 867707 — MB ChB Sheff. 1969; MRCP (UK) 1975; DCH Eng. 1971. (Sheff.) Cons. Community Paediat. Oxleas NHS Trust Bexley. Prev: Cons. Community Paediat. Ravensbourne NHS Trust Bromley; SCMO (Child Health) Mid. Surrey HA; Sen. Regist. (Paediat.) E. Berks. Health Dist.

WESS, Jennifer Mary Leasowe House, Northwood, Ellesmere SY12 0LU — MB ChB 1986 Liverp.; MRCGP 1992. (Liverp.)

WESSELL, Helen Naomi 12 Linton Grove, Leeds LS17 8PS — MB BS 1978 Sydney.

WESSELS, Helen Mary Annette Hewson 574 Daws Heath Road, Hadleigh, Benfleet SS7 2NL — MB BCh BAO 1955 NUI.

WESSELY, Simon Charles 103 Denmark Hill, Camberwell, London SE5 8AZ Tel: 020 7848 5130 Fax: 020 7848 5129 Email: s.wessely@icp.kcl.ac.uk — MD Oxf. 1993, MSc 1989, MA, BA, BM BCh 1981; FRCP 1997, FRCPsych; FMed Sa. (Psychiat.) SKT Sch. of Med. & Inst. Psychiat.; Prof. (Psychol. Med.) King's Coll. Sch. of Med. & Inst. of Psychiat. Socs: Fell. Acad. Med. Sci.s. Prev: Sen. Regist. Bethlem & Maudsley Hosps. Lond. & Nat. Hosp. Lond.; SHO (Med.) Freeman Hosp. Newc.

WESSELY, Tessa Louise Fyfield House, Fyfield, Andover SP11 8EP — MB BS 1984 Lond.

WESSON, Colin Martin (retired) Wellspring, Old Rydon Lane, Exeter EX2 7JZ Tel: 01392 873015 — MB BS 1964 Lond.; BDS (Hons.) 1958; LDS RCS 1958; FDS RCS Eng. 1968; MRCS Eng. LRCP Lond. 1964. Cons. Oral & Maxillofacial Surg. Qu. Eliz. II Hosp. Welwyn Garden City. Prev: Sen. Regist. (Dent.) King's Coll. Hosp. & Qu. Vict. Hosp. E. Grinstead.

WESSON, Ian McMillan 59 Addiscombe Road, Croydon CR0 6SD Tel: 020 8688 6290 Fax: 020 8686 5818; Haling Croft, 61 St. Augustine's Avenue, South Croydon CR2 6JB Tel: 020 8686 1173 — MB BS 1962 Lond.; AKC. (St. Geo.) Socs: Croydon Med. Soc. & BMA. Prev: Ho. Phys., Res. Obst. Asst. & Sen. Cas. Off. St. Geo. Hosp. Lond.

WESSON, Michael Lloyd Hesketh Centre, 51-55 Albert Road, Southport PR9 0LT Tel: 01704 530940 — MB ChB 1987 Liverp. Cons. Psychiat. S.port & Formby Community (NHS) Trust.

WEST, Mr Alaiyi Frederick Flat 2, 20 Eskdale Terrace, Jesmond, Newcastle upon Tyne NE2 4DN Fax: 0191 222 8514 Email: a.f.west@ncl.ac.uk — BM BS 1992 Nottm.; BMedSci 1990; FRCS. Research.Reg.Urol.Dept ofSurg.Univ.Newc. Prev: Demonst. (Anat.) Sheff. Univ.; Cas. Off. Wansbewck Hosp. N.d.

WEST, Alexander Glynn Orchard House, Eastling, Faversham ME13 0AZ — MB BS 1994 Lond.

WEST, Alison Margaret Queen Margaret Hospital, Dunfermline KY12 0SU Tel: 01383 623623 — MB ChB 1977 Ed.; MPhil 2001 Glas.; MPhil 1986 Ed.; MSc Informat. Sc. City 1980; MRCPsych 1983. (Edinburgh University) Cons. Psychiat. Fife Primary care NHS Trust; Psychiat. Perth Prison Sessional. Prev: Psychiat. Perth prison sessional.

WEST, Mr Andrew 1 White Cottages, Easby, Middlesbrough TS9 6JG Tel: 01642 724232 Email: 106373.1357@compuserve.com — MB BS 1976 Lond.; FRCS Eng. 1981; MRCS Eng. LRCP Lond. 1976; FFAEM 1993. (Guy's) Cons. A & E Med. Darlington Memor. Hosp. Socs: Brit. Assn. Emerg. Med. & BMA.

WEST, Andrew Fleming Park Hospital, Old Road, Headington, Oxford OX3 7LQ Tel: 01865 226213 — BM BCh 1985 Oxf.; BA Camb. 1981; MRCPsych 1995. Sen. Regist. (Child & Adolesc. Psychiat.) Post Hosp. for childr. Oxf. Socs: Assn. Child Psychol. & Psychiat.; Child & Adolesc. Gp.work Assn. Prev: Sen. Regist. (Child & Adolesc. Psychiat.) Berks. Addolesc. Unit Wokingham; Sen. Regist. (Child & Adolesc. Psychiat.) Berks. Child & Adolesc. Ment. Health Serv. Reading; Regist. (Psychiat. Learning Disabil. & Child & Adolesc. Psychiat.) Oxf.

WEST, Andrew John Stoneybridge Farm, Latcham, Wedmore BS28 4SB — MB BS 1970 Lond.; MRCS Eng. LRCP Lond. 1970.

WEST, Anne Prior The Manse, Old Walls, Llanrhidin, Gower, Swansea SA3 1HB — BM 1983 Soton.; MSc Lond. 1976, BSc 1975; MRCGP 1987; DCH RCP Lond. 1986; DRCOG 1985. Prev: Trainee GP Soton VTS.

WEST, Barbara Anne Kathleen Drumchapel Health Centre, 80-90 Kinfauns Drive, Glasgow G15 7TS Tel: 0141 211 6100 Fax: 0141 211 6104; 139 Canniesburn Road, Bearsden, Glasgow G61 1HB — MB ChB 1972 Ed.; FRCS Ed. 1977; MRCGP 1986.

WEST, Betty (retired) The Sett, 50 Eastfield Crescent, Badger Hill, York YO10 5JB Tel: 01904 412015 — BSc (Physiol.) Lond. 1949; MB ChB Manch. 1954. Prev: GP Chilwell.

WEST, Brian 271 Nantwich Road, Crewe CW2 6PF — MB ChB 1993 Sheff.

WEST, Charles Archibald Easthope Road Health Centre, Easthope Road, Church Stretton SY6 6BL Tel: 01694 722127 Fax: 01694 724604; Gorswen, Sandford Avenue, Church Stretton SY6 7AB Tel: 01694 722674 — MB ChB 1973 Birm. Prev: Unit Gen. Manager Shropsh. HA; Ho. Surg. Gen. Hosp. Birm.; Ho. Phys. Copthorne Hosp. Shrewsbury.

WEST, Mr Charles George Hook Woodstock, Junction Road, Deane, Bolton BL3 4NE — MB BChir 1970 Camb.; MA Camb. 1970; FRCS Eng. 1974. (Univ. Camb. & Guy's Hosp. Lond.) Cons. Neurol. Surg. Hope Hosp. Salford & Roy. Manch. Childr. Hosp.; Hon. Lect. (Neurosurg.) Univ. Manch. Socs: Fell. Coll. Surg. Hong Kong. Prev: Vis. Prof. Neurosurg. Chinese Univ. Hong Kong; Sen. Regist. (Neurosurg.) Roy. Vict. Hosp. Belf.

WEST, Christian Alexande 58 Seven Star Road, Solihull B91 2BY — MB ChB 1998 Leeds.

WEST, Christine Parry 29 Polton Road, Loanhead EH20 9BU — MD 1989 Ed.; MB ChB 1973; FRCOG 1993, M 1979; DCH Eng. 1976. Cons. O & G Edin. Roy. Infirm. & Simpson Memor. Matern. Pavil. Edin.; Sen. Lect. Univ. Edin. Prev: Sen. Regist. (O & G) Simpson Memor. Matern. Pavil. & Roy. Infirm. Edin.; SHO (Paediat. Surg.) Roy. Hosp. Sick Childr. Edin.

WEST, Clive Henry Dartford East Health Centre, Pilgrims Way, Dartford DA1 1QY Tel: 01322 274211 Fax: 01322 284329; Fiacre, Ash Road, Ash, Sevenoaks TN15 7HJ — MRCS Eng. LRCP Lond. 1967; MB BS Rangoon 1963; DObst RCOG 1969. Prev: Squadron Ldr. RAF Med. Br., Sen. Med. Off. Regional Med. Centre RAF; Halton & Med. Centre RAF Episkopi, Cyprus.

WEST, Colin Andrew Clifton Road Surgery, 95 Clifton Road, Rugby CV21 3QQ Tel: 01788 578800/568810 Fax: 01788 541063 — MB ChB 1977 Birm.; MA Oxf. 1982, BA 1968; MRCGP 1982; DRCOG 1981. (Birm.) GP Princip.; Clin. Asst. Rehabil. Med. Roy. Leamingston Sps Rehabil. Hosp.; Police Surg., Warks. Police. Socs:

WEST

Rugby & Dist. Med. Soc. Prev: SHO (Paediat. & Obst. & Gyn) Brit. Milit. Hosp. Rinteln, BFPO 29.

WEST, Colin John The Surgery, Woolton Hill, Newbury RG20 6NJ Tel: 01635 253324 — MB BS 1978 Lond.; MRCGP 1984; DCH RCP Lond. 1984; DRCOG 1982. Prev: Asst. Lect. Bland Sutton Inst. Middlx. Hosp. Lond.

WEST, David John Ashley Farmhouse, School Lane, Ashley, Market Drayton TF9 4LF Tel: 0163 087 2540 — MB ChB 1979 Leeds; FRCR 1986; DMRD 1985. Cons. Radiol. City Gen. Hosp. & N. Staffs. Roy. Infirm. Stoke on Trent. Prev: Lect. (Radiol. Sci.) United Med. & Dent. Schs. Guy's & St. Thos. Hosps. Lond.; Sen. Regist. N. Staffs. Roy. Infirm. Stoke-on-Trent.

WEST, David Martin (retired) — MB ChB 1975 Liverp.; FFA RCS Eng. 1979. Prev: Cons. Anaesth. & IC W. Lancs. DHA.

WEST, David Reuben White Rose Cottage, Swettenham, Congleton CW12 2LE — MB BS 1991 Lond.

WEST, Deborah Rosemary Sarah Gorswen, Sandford Avenue, Church Stretton SY6 7AB Tel: 01694 722674 — MB ChB 1973 Birm. Prev: Ho. Surg. Qu. Eliz. Hosp. Birm.; Ho. Phys. City Gen. Hosp. Stoke-on-Trent; Trainee Gen. Pract. Shrewsbury Vocational Train. Scheme.

WEST, Donald James 32 Fen Road, Milton, Cambridge CB4 6AD Tel: 01223 860308 Email: fad72@dial.pipex.com — MB ChB 1947 Liverp.; PhD Camb. 1967, Litt D 1979; MD Liverp. 1958; FRCPsych 1986, M 1971; DPM Lond. 1952. Emerit. Prof. Clin. Criminology Univ. Camb.; Emerit. Fell. Darwin Coll. Camb. Socs: World Psychiat. Assn.; Brit. Soc. Criminol. Prev: Ment. Health Act Commiss.er; Hon. Cons. Camb. Psychiat. Serv.; Sen. Regist. Forens. Unit Maudsley Hosp. Lond.

WEST, Dorothy Rutt House, Ivybridge PL21 0DQ Tel: 01752 892792 Fax: 01752 896547 — MRCS Eng. LRCP Lond. 1958; MFHom 1979. (Univ. Coll. Hosp.) Indep. Pract. (Homoeop. Med.) Devon. Prev: Ho. Surg. N. Middlx. Hosp. Edmonton; Ho. Phys. Co. Hosp. Hereford.

WEST, Elizabeth Alexandra The Old Rectory, Church St., Barkston, Grantham NG32 2NB — MB ChB 1998 Liverp.

WEST, Elizabeth Anne Ticehurst Clinic, 14-18 New Church Road, Hove BN3 4FH Tel: 01273 747464 Fax: 01273 727321; Redleaf, 22 Steep Lane, Findon, Worthing BN14 0UE Tel: 01903 874140 Fax: 01903 877585 — MB BS 1984 Lond. Staff Grade (Psychiat.) Ticehurst Clinic Hove. Prev: Clin. Asst. (Psychiat.) Brighton HA.

WEST, George Francis, OBE (retired) 8 Hayes Court, Sunnyside, Wimbledon, London SW19 4SH Tel: 020 8946 9409 — MB BCh BAO 1930 Dub.; BA, MB BCh BAO Dub. 1930; DTM & H 1931. JP. Prev: Med. Off. & Health Off. Kuala Lumpur.

WEST, George Philip (retired) Mentley, Clare Drive, Farnham Common, Slough SL2 3LL Tel: 01753 643810 — MB BS Lond. 1944; MRCS Eng. LRCP Lond. 1943. Prev: Cas. Phys. St. Mary's Hosp.

WEST, Gerard Patrick Woodside Health Centre, Barr Street, Glasgow G20 7LR Tel: 0141 531 9521 Fax: 0141 531 9545 — MB ChB 1981 Glas.; MRCGP 1988; Dip. Pract. Dermat. 1991; DRCOG 1983.

WEST, Gladys Mary Lesley (retired) Whipley Manor, Guildford Road, Normandy, Guildford GU3 2BE Tel: 01483 235198 — MRCS Eng. LRCP Lond. 1955. Prev: Asst. Psychiat. Abraham Cowley Unit St. Peters Hosp. Chertsey.

WEST, Hilary Department of General Practice, 5 Lambeth Walk, London SE11 6SP — MB BS 1998 Lond.

WEST, Mr James Department of Ophthalmology, The Royal Hallamshire Hospital, Glossop Road, Sheffield S10 2JF — MB BChir 1985 Camb.; MA 1987; FRCS Glas. 1989; FRCOphth 1989; DO Glas. 1988. Cons. Ophth. Roy. Hallamshire Hosp. Sheff.

WEST, Janet Rae 181 Monks Walk, Buntingford SG9 9DU Tel: 01763 273460 Email: jrwest@tinyonline.co.uk — MB ChB 1982 Dundee; Dip. IMC RCS Ed. 1995; DRCOG 1997. GP Regist. Royston Herts. Socs: BMA; Fac. Pre-Hosp. Care.

WEST, Joe 9 Fourth Avenue, Havant PO9 2QU — BM BS 1995 Nottm.

WEST, John Nicholas Wayne Q Floor, Royal Hallamshire Hospital, Glossop Road, Sheffield S10 2JF Tel: 0114 271 2935 — MB BS 1981 Lond.; MD Lond. 1992; MRCP (UK) 1984; FRCP 1999. (St.Thos. Hosp. Lond.) Cons. Cardiol. & Phys. Centr. Sheff. Univ. Hosp. Trust. Socs: Brit. Hypertens. Soc. & Brit. Cardiac Soc. Prev: Lect. (Cardiol.) Qu. Eliz. Hosp. Birm.; Regist. (Med.) Qu. Eliz. Hosp. Birm.; Ho. Phys. St. Thos. Hosp. Lond.

WEST, John Ronald Crook West, Gillies and Steeden, 7 Stanhope Mews West, London SW7 5RB Tel: 020 7835 0400 Fax: 020 7835 0979; 9 Ullswater Road, Barnes, London SW13 9PL Tel: 020 8748 1912 — MB BChir 1970 Camb.; MB Camb. 1970, BChir 1969; MA Camb. 1970; MRCS Eng. LRCP Lond. 1969; MRCGP 1974. (Camb. & St. Bart.)

WEST, Jonathan Alan, Registrar/SHO 100 Clapham Common Westside, London SW4 9AZ — MB BS 1993 Lond.; MRC Psych Part 1 1998. SHO Psychiat. Haudsley Hosp.

WEST, Jonathan David Peter 40 Bath Road, Banbury OX16 0TP Tel: 01295 255895 — MB BS 1995 Lond.; BA Camb 1992; MA Cambridge 1998. (Trinity Hall, Cambridge/ London Hospital Medical School) Banbury Gen. Pract., VTS.

WEST, Mr Jonathan Haden Royal Devon & Exeter Hospital, Exeter EX1 2ED Tel: 01392 411611; Riverview, Trews Weir Reach, Exeter EX2 4EG — MB BS 1978 Lond.; MA Camb. 1979; FRCS Eng. 1983; MRCOG 1985. Cons. Gyn. Roy. Devon & Exeter Hosp. Prev: Sen. Regist. Oxf. RHA.

WEST, Jonathan Joly McLaren (retired) 41 Five Mile Drive, Oxford OX2 8HT — MB BChir 1958 Camb.; BA Camb. 1954, MA 1958; DObst RCOG 1959. Prev: GP, Thatcham HC. Berks.

WEST, Mrs Judith Ann Opthalmology Department, The Royal Hallamshire Hospital, Glossop Road, Sheffield S10 2JF — MB BChir 1989 Camb.; MA Camb. 1990; FRCOphth 1994, M 1993.

WEST, Judith Vivienne Tel: 0116 255 6742 Fax: 0116 255 3850 — MB ChB 1983 Birm.; MD 1997; MRCP (UK) 1987; MD 1997. (Birm.) Cons. Paediat. Leics. & Rutland Healthcare Trust. Prev: Lect. (Child Health) Univ. Leicester; Fell. (Paediat. Thoracic Med.) Roy. Childr. Hosp. Melbourne, Vict., Austral.; Clin. Research Fell. Inst. Child Health & Hon. Lect. Univ. Birm.

WEST, Kerry Louise 72 Avon Crescent, Stratford-upon-Avon CV37 7EZ — MB BS 1991 Lond.

WEST, Kevin John The Corner, 1 Prestwold Lane, Hoton, Loughborough LE12 5SH — MB BS 1979 Lond.; FFA RCS Eng. 1984.

WEST, Kevin Paul Department of Histopathology, Leicester Royal Infirmary, Leicester LE1 5WW — MB ChB 1981 Leic.; FRCPath 1998; MRCPath 1987. Cons. Histopath. Univ. Hosps. of Leicester NHS Trust. Prev: Sen. Lect. (Path.) Univ. Leicester & Hon. Cons. Histopath Leics. HA.

WEST, Letitia Rozanne (retired) Nethercourt Lodge, Nethercourt Hill, Ramsgate CT11 0RZ Tel: 01843 586704 — MB ChB St. And. 1957; MRCPsych 1973; DPM Eng. 1966. Prev: Cons. Psychiat. St. Augustine's Hosp. Chartham Down.

WEST, Lydia Beatrice — MB ChB 1976 Leeds; MRCGP 1981; DFFP 1994; DRCOG 1980.

WEST, Margaret (retired) Walnut Tree Farm House, Main Road, Ashbocking, Ipswich IP6 9JX Tel: 01473 890623 — MB ChB Manch. 1960; DPH Manch. 1968; DCH Eng. 1964.

WEST, Martyn Richard John 72 Avon Crescent, Stratford-upon-Avon CV37 7EZ — MB BS 1989 Lond.

WEST, Mary Frances (retired) Fir Tree Cottage, The Common, Chipperfield, Kings Langley WD4 9BU Tel: 01923 260688 — MB BS Lond. 1950; FFA RCS Eng. 1960; DA Eng. 1956. Prev: Cons. Anaesth. Watford & Hemel Hempstead Gen. Hosps.

WEST, Nicholas Cowie 'Pasture Gate', Ennerdale Bridge, Cleator CA23 3AR — MB 1978 Camb.; BChir 1977; MRCP (UK) 1980; MRCPath 1984. Cons. Haemat. W. Cumbld. Hosp. Whitehaven.

WEST, Nicholas Edward John 58 Kenwood Drive, Shrewsbury SY3 8SY — MB BChir 1993 Camb.

***WEST, Noreen Stephanie** 37 Beechwood Road, Kings Heath, Birmingham B14 4AB — MB ChB 1991 Birm.

WEST, Pamela Gillian Riverview, 2 Trews Weir Reach, Exeter EX2 4EG Tel: 01392 79610 — MB BS 1976 Lond.; MRCS Eng. LRCP Lond. 1976. Private Asst. Nuffield Hosp. Exeter. Prev: Trainee GP Lond. (St. Thos.) VTS; Ho. Surg. (ENT) St. Thos. Hosp. Lond.; Ho. Phys. Kingston Hosp.

WEST, Pamela Karen Anne Central Dales Practice, Hawes DL8 3DR Tel: 01969 667200 Fax: 01969 667149 — MB ChB 1983 Leeds; MRCGP 1987; DRCOG 1987. GP Hawes N. Yorks. Prev: GP Wyke, Bradford.; GP Byfield, Normants.

WEST, Penelope Susan 12 Vicarage Gardens, Netheravon, Salisbury SP4 9RW — MB BS 1986 Lond.; BSc Lond. 1983, MB BS 1986; DA (UK) 1989. SHO (Spinal Injuries) Duke of Cornw. Spinal Treatm. Centre Odstock Hosp. Salisbury. Prev: SHO (Anaesth.) P.ss Margt. Hosp. Swindon Wilts; SHO (Anaesth.) William Harvey Hosp. WillesBoro.; Ho. Phys. Char. Cross Hosp. Lond.

WEST, Peter (retired) 27 Tilehouse Road, Guildford GU4 8AP Tel: 01483 566026 Email: peterwst@aol.com — MB BS 1944 Lond.; BM BCh Oxf. 1944; DCH RCP Lond. 1950; DPH Eng. 1949. Prev: Ho. Surg. Radcliffe Infirm. Oxf. & Hosp. Sick Childr. Gt. Ormond St.

WEST, Mr Peter Duncan Buller Queen Alexandra Hospital, Cosham, Portsmouth PO6 3LY Tel: 023 92 379451; Two School Cottages, School Lane, Bosham, Chichester PO18 8NY Tel: 01243 574175 — BM BCh 1979 Oxf.; MSc Manch. 1990; MA Oxf. 1980; FRCS Eng. 1985. Cons. Audiol. Med. Qu. Alexandra Hosp. Portsmouth & St. Richard's Hosp. Chichester.

WEST, Peter Guy Fortescue (retired) Halshayne Manor Farm, Wilmington, Honiton EX14 9JS Tel: 01404 831571 Email: pgfw@btinternet.com — MB BChir Camb. 1965; MRCPsych 1972; DPM Eng. 1970. Prev: Cons. Psychiat. Old Age Scalebor Pk. Hosp. Burley-in-Wharfedale.

WEST, Rebecca 22 Renault Drive, Broadstone BH18 8HW; 8 Sheepfold Avenue, Rushington, Littlehampton BN16 3SQ — MB BS 1994 Lond.; DFFP 1997. (Char. Cross and Westm. Med. Sch.) SHO (O & G) St. Richards Hosp. Chichester. Socs: MDU.

WEST, Richard Clive The Surgery, Harborough Road N., Northampton NN2 8LL Tel: 01604 845144 — MB ChB 1963 Ed. (Ed.)

WEST, Richard James Queen Elizabeth Hospital, Birmingham B15 7UZ Tel: 0121 972 1311; 23 Oxford Road, Birmingham B13 9EH Tel: 0121 449 6700 — MB ChB 1967 Ed.; FRCR 1977; FFR 1973; DMRD Eng. 1971. (Ed.) Cons. Radiol. Qu. Eliz. Hosp. Birm.; Hon. Sen. Lect. Birm. Univ. Socs: Sec. Brit. Soc. Interven.al Radiol. Prev: Sen. Regist. Dudley Rd. Hosp. & United Birm. Hosps.; Regist. (Radiodiag.) United Birm. Hosps.

WEST, Professor Richard John (retired) 4 Old Vicarage Place, Apsley Road, Bristol BS8 2TD Tel: 0117 973 8311 — MB BS Lond. 1962; MD Lond. 1975; FRCP Lond. 1979; MRCP (UK) 1967; FRCPCH 1997; DCH RCP Lond. 1969; DObst RCOG 1964. Med. Postgrad. Dean S. W.. Region & Hon. Prof. Med. Postgrad. Studies Univ. Bristol; Hon. Cons. Frenchay Hosp. Bristol; Hon. Cons. Paediat. United Bristol Healthcare Trust; Gen. Sec. Inst. Med. Ethics Lond. Prev: Dean, Sen. Lect. & Cons. Paediat. St. Geo. Hosp. & Med. Sch. Lond.

WEST, Richard John Woolpit Health Centre, Heath Road, Woolpit, Bury St Edmunds IP30 9QU Tel: 01359 240298 Fax: 01359 241975 Email: richard.west@gp-d83055.nhs.uk; The Foothills, Church Rd, Tostock IP30 9PA Email: richard@west25.freeserve.co.uk — MB ChB 1993 Manch.; MRCGP 1997 RCGS Lond.; DGM RCP Lond. 1996; DCH RCP Lond. 1995. (Manch.) GP Princip. Socs: Vice Chairm., Suff. Local Med. Comm. Prev: SHO (Geriat., O & G, Paediat. & A & E) W. Suff. Hosp.; GP Reg.

WEST, Roger John (retired) 12 Redwing Road, Kempshott, Basingstoke RG22 5UP Email: rogerwest@doctors.org.uk — MB BS 1965 Lond.; MSc Manch. 1974; MRCS Eng. LRCP Lond. 1965; FFCM 1980, M 1974; MRCGP 1972; DObst RCOG 1968. Prev: Dist. Med. Off. W. Suff. HA.

WEST, Ruth Margaret (retired) 32 Mercian Court, Park Place, Cheltenham GL50 2RA Tel: 01242 577182 — MB ChB Birm. 1940; DPH Eng. 1948; DObst RCOG 1942. Prev: Sen. Med. Off. Surrey AHA.

WEST, Sheila Leslie Department of Anaesthesia, Cheltenham General Hospital, Sandford Park Road, Cheltenham GL53 7AN Tel: 01242 222222 Fax: 01242 273405 Email: sheila.west@egnhst.org.uk — MB BS 1976 Lond.; MRCS Eng. LRCP Lond. 1975; FFA RCS Eng. 1981; DRCOG 1979. (Guy's Hospital Medical School) p/t Cons. Anaesth. E. Glos. NHS Trust.

WEST, Shirley Anne 4 Dilwyn Gardens, Bridgend CF31 3NT Tel: 01656 63930 — MB ChB 1972 Manch. (Manch.) Clin. Asst. P.ss of Wales Hosp. Bridgend. Socs: Assn. Anaesths. Prev: Regist. (Anaesth.) Univ. Hosp. Wales Cardiff.

WEST, Siaron Mair Ty Bryn Surgery, The Bryn, Trethomas, Newport CF83 8GL Tel: 02920 868011; Tel: 02920 498942 — MB BCh 1994 Wales; DRCOG 1999; MRCGP 2001. (univ.Wales) p/t GP Retainer Ty Bryn Surg. Trethomas Newport. Socs: Christ. Med. Fell.sh. Prev: SHO Paediat E. Glam..NHS.Trust; SHO O & G.E. Glam.. NHS. Trust; GP. Regist.

WEST, Simon Christopher 30 Topaz Street, Cardiff CF24 1PH — MB BCh 1991 Wales. SHO (Urol.) Cardiff Roy. Infirm.

WEST, Siobhan Louise 23 Avon Road, Hale, Altrincham WA15 0LB — MB ChB 1993 Bristol. Specialist Regist. Paediat. N. W. Region Rotat.

WEST, Stephen Edmund Corinthian Surgery, St Paul's Medical Centre, 121 Swindon Road, Cheltenham GL50 4DP Tel: 01242 707777 Fax: 01242 707776; Painters Cottage, Elkstone, Cheltenham GL53 9PV — MB BS 1976 Lond.; MRCS Eng. LRCP Lond. 1976; MRCGP 1983; MRCOG 1982. (Guys Hospital) Clin. Asst. (Colposcopy) Cheltenham.

WEST, Susan Elizabeth The Ridgeway Surgery, 1 Mount Echo Avenue, London E4 7JX Tel: 020 8529 2233 Fax: 020 8529 4484; Tailours, High Road, Chigwell IG7 6DL Tel: 020 8500 0293 Fax: 020 8500 1696 — MB BS 1978 Lond.; BSc Lond. 1973; DMJ (Clin.) Soc. Apoth. Lond. 1992; DRCOG 1980. (Middlx.)

WEST, Susan Helen Cossham Memorial Hospital, Lodge Road, Kingswood, Bristol BS15 1LF Tel: 0117 975 8054; 66 Woodstock Road, Redland, Bristol BS6 7ER — MB BS 1979 Newc.; MRCPsych 1988. Cons. Psychiat. Old Age Cossham Memor. Hosp. Bristol.

WEST, Suzanne Catheryn The Health Centre, Queensway, Billingham TS23 2LA Tel: 01642 552700/552151 Fax: 01642 532908 — MB ChB 1995 Leic.

WEST, Terence Edward Timothy 58 Kenwood Drive, Shrewsbury SY3 8SY Tel: 01743 233697 Fax: 01952 242218 — MB BChir 1964 Camb.; MD Camb. 1976, MA 1964; FRCP Lond. 1981, M 1967. (St. Mary's) Cons. Phys. P.ss Roy. Hosp. Telford & Roy. Shrewsbury Hosp. Socs: Soc. Endocrin.; Brit. Hyperlip. Assn. Prev: Lect. (Med.) St. Thos. Hosp. Med. Sch. Lond.; Regist. (Med.) Middlx. Hosp. Lond.; Ho. Phys. Med. Unit St. Mary's Hosp. Lond.

WEST, Thomas Stephens, OBE (retired) 30 Pineheath Road, High Kelling, Holt NR25 6QF — MB BS Lond. 1957.

WEST, Timothy Peter The Surgeries, Lombard Street, Newark NG24 1XG Tel: 01636 702363 Fax: 01636 613037; 61 Milner Street, Newark NG24 4AA Tel: 01636 679751 — MB ChB 1969 Liverp.; DPM Eng 1978; DObst RCOG 1971. (Liverp.) Prev: Regist. (Psychiat.) Roundway Hosp. Devizes; Ho. Phys. BRd.green Hosp. Liverp.

WEST-JONES, Jennifer Susan 12 Lytham Road, Leicester LE2 1YD — MB ChB 1998 Leic.

WESTABY, Catherine Alexandra Marie 5 Lawn Crescent, Richmond TW9 3NR — MB BS 1978 Lond.; BSc (Psychol.) Durh. 1973; MRCS Eng. LRCP Lond. 1978; DRCOG 1980.

WESTABY, David Flat 2, 20 Campden Hill Square, London W8 7JY — MB 1976 Camb.; BChir 1975; FRCP Lond. 1991; MRCP (UK) 1978. Cons. Phys. & Gastroenterol. Char. Cross Hosp. & Chelsea & W.m. Hosp. Lond. Socs: Internat. Assn. Study Liver & Europ. Assn. Study Liver. Prev: Cons. Phys. & Sen. Lect. Liver Unit King's Coll. Hosp. & Med. Sch. Lond.

WESTABY, Mr Stephen Oxford Heart Centre, John Radcliffe Hospital, Headley Way, Headington, Oxford OX3 9DU Tel: 01865 220268 Fax: 01865 220269 — MB BS 1972 Lond.; FRCS Eng. 1978. Sen. Cons. Cardiac Surg. John Radcliffe Hosp. Oxf..

WESTALL, Glen Philip 144 Melbourne Grove, London SE22 8SA — MB BS 1993 Lond.

WESTALL, William Graham Crwys Road Surgery, 151 Crwys Road, Cathays, Cardiff CF24 4XT Tel: 029 2039 6987 Fax: 029 2064 0523 — MB ChB Bristol 1962; DPH Bristol 1974; DObst RCOG 1965. Prev: Employm. Med. Adviser EMAS; SHO (Med.) E. Glam. Hosp. Pontypridd.

WESTAWAY, Christine Elizabeth The John Kelso Practice, Ball Haye Road, Leek ST13 6 — MB ChB 1985 Leic.

***WESTBROOK, Anthony Paul** Derbyshire Royal Infirmary, London Road, Derby — BM BS 1994 Nottm.

WESTBROOK, Freddie Kingshill Farm, Wishaw ML2 9PJ — MB ChB 1978 Manch.; BSc St. And. 1975; MRCGP 1982. Med. Quality Manager -sema Med. Servs.

WESTBROOK, Jonathan Leslie 26 Stanway Close, Witney, Oxford OX28 5GA — MB BS 1984 Lond.; MRCP (UK) 1987; FCAnaesth 1991. Cons. Anaesth. Oxf. Radcliffe Trust. Socs: Obst. Anaesth.

WESTBROOK

Assn. Prev: Sen. Regist. & Regist. (Anaesth.) John Radcliffe Hosp. Oxf.; SHO & Regist. (Gen. Med.) P.ss Margt. Hosp. Swindon.

WESTBROOK, Mark Andrew The Shrubbery, 65A Perry Street, Northfleet, Gravesend DA11 8RD Tel: 01474 356661 Fax: 01474 534542 — MB BS 1990 Lond.

WESTBROOK, Patricia Maud 19 Titchfield Road, Troon KA10 6AN — MB ChB Glas. 1961. (Glas.) Indep. GP & Hypnother. Troon; Cons. Lifestyle, AMI Ross Hall Hosp. Glas. Prev: Sen. Med. Off. (Family Plann.) Glas.; Ho. Surg. Roy. Samarit. Hosp. Glas.; Sch. Med. Off. Glas. Corp.

WESTBROOK, Shobha Jean Dartford East Health Centre, Pilgrims Way, Dartford DA1 1QY Tel: 01322 274211 Fax: 01322 284329 — MB BS 1989 Lond.

WESTBURY, Charlotte Beth Flat 7, 5 Onslow Square, London SW7 3NJ Tel: 020 7589 6652 Email: charlotte@westbury5.freeserve.co.uk — MB ChB 1994 Ed.; BSc (Hons.) (Med. Sci.) Ed. 1991; MRCP 1997. (Univ. Ed.) p/t Specialist Regist. (Clin. Oncol.), The Roy. Marsden NHS Trust, Lond. Socs: FRSM.

WESTBURY, Professor Gerald, OBE Apartment 4, 7 Cambridge Gate, London NW1 4JX — MB BS (Hons.) Lond. 1949; FRCP Lond. 1976, M 1951; FRCS Eng. 1952; Hon. FRCS Ed. 1993. (Westm.) Emerit. Prof. Surg. Univ. Lond. & Inst. Cancer Research. Socs: FRSM. Prev: Hon. Cons. Surg. Roy. Marsden Hosp.; Cons. Surg. W.m. Hosp. Lond.; Ho. Surg. & Sen. Regist. (Surg.) W.m. Hosp.

WESTBURY, Harry (retired) 2A Brickwall Lane, Ruislip HA4 8JX Tel: 01895 673137 — MB BS 1956 Lond.; MRCP Lond. 1961; MRCS Eng. LRCP Lond. 1956; FRCR 1975; FFR 1967; DMRD Eng. 1963. Cons. Radiol. Harefield & Mt. Vernon Hosps. Prev: Sen. Regist. (X-Ray) Soton. Gen. Hosp. & St. Mary's Hosp. Lond.

WESTCAR, Paul David Chapel Row Surgery, The Avenue, Bucklebury, Reading RG7 6NS Tel: 01189 713252 Fax: 01189 714161; Hidden Cottage, Rotten Row, Tutts Clump, Bradfield, Reading RG7 6LQ — MB BChir 1984 Camb.; MA Camb. 1985; MRCGP 1989; DRCOG 1989. (Cambridge & Westminster) Sch. Med. Adviser Bradfield Coll. Bradfield, Berks. Socs: (Ex-Sec.) Newbury Med. Soc. Prev: Trainee GP W. Suff. VTS.

WESTCOTT, Edward Daniel Anders 11 Roberts Lane, Chalfont St Peter, Gerrards Cross SL9 0QR — MB BS 1996 Lond.

WESTCOTT, Godfrey Francis BM Box 7894, London WC1N 3XX — MB BS 1952 Lond.

WESTCOTT, Mark Christopher 22 Fabian Road, London SW6 7TZ Tel: 020 7386 7803 — MB BS 1989 Lond.; FRCOphth 1993. (St. Thos. Hosp. Med. Sch.) Specialist Regist. N. Thames Rotat.; Research Fell. at The Inst. of Ophth. & Moorfields Eye Hosp. Prev: SHO W.. Eye Hosp. Lond.

WESTCOTT, Richard Howson East Street Surgery, East Street, South Molton EX36 3BU Tel: 01769 573811; 4 Paradise Lawn, South Molton EX36 3DJ Tel: 01769 572225 Email: rwestcott@cix.co.uk — BM BCh 1973 Oxf.; MA Oxf. 1973; FRCGP 1994, M 1977; DRCOG 1977; DCH Eng. 1976. Lect. 1997; Fell. Inst. Gen. Pract. Univ. Exeter; Assoc. Adviser Univ. Bristol; GP Trainer Devon. Prev: Trainee GP Exeter VTS; Ho. Phys. Radcliffe Infirm. Oxf.; Ho. Surg. Roy. United Hosp. Bath.

WESTCOTT, Tessa (retired) Pendle, Ledborough Wood, Beaconsfield HP9 2DJ Tel: 01494 674796 — MB BS 1960 Lond.; MRCS Eng. LRCP Lond. 1960. Prev: Assoc. Specialist (Gen. Med.) Wycombe Gen. Hosp. High Wycombe.

WESTENSEE, Wilma Alma Road Surgery, 68 Alma Road, Portswood, Southampton SO14 6UX Tel: 023 8067 2666 Fax: 023 8055 0972; Denny Cottage, Denny Lodge, Lyndhurst SO43 7FZ — MB ChB 1979 Stellenbosch. Prev: Trainee GP Bournemouth VTS; SHO (O & G, Rheum. & Rehabil.) Soton. Gen. Hosp.

WESTERDUIN, Frank Paul 64 Lauderdale Gardens, Hyndland, Glasgow G12 9QW Tel: 0141 339 0040 — MB ChB 1989 Dundee; FRCS Ed. 1995; DA (UK) 1993; MRCP (UK) 1996. Specialist Regist. (A & E) Glas. Roy. Infirm. Glas. Socs: Brit. Assn. Accid. & Emerg. Med.; FAEM; BASICS.

WESTERHOLM, Ronald 9 Northway Court, Bishopston, Swansea SA3 3JZ — MB BS 1965 Lond.; FRCPsych 1993; DPM Eng. 1970; DObst RCOG 1967. (Univ. Coll. Hosp.) Cons. Psychiat. Cefn Coed Hosp. Swansea.

WESTERMAN, R Millfield Surgery, Millfield Lane, Easingwold, York YO61 3JR Tel: 01347 821557 — MB BCh 1977 Wales; MB BCh 1977 Wales.

WESTERMANN, Willem Barend Pangbourne Medical Practice, The Boat House Surgery, Whitchurch Road, Pangbourne, Reading RG8 7DP Tel: 0118 984 2234 Fax: 0118 984 3022; Juniper House, Beckfords, Upper Basildon, Reading RG8 8PB Tel: 01491 671400 — MB BChir 1972 Camb.; BA Camb. 1968, MA, MB 1972, BChir 1971. (Camb.)

WESTERN, Hannah Ruth 22B Templars Avenue, London NW11 0NY — MB BS 1996 Lond.

WESTERN, Jane Margaret Beck House, 3 West Parade Road, Scarborough YO12 5ED Tel: 01723 352522; Manor Farmhouse, Old Ham Lane, Little Canford, Wimborne BU21 7LP — MB BS 1982 Lond.; Postgraduate Diploma in Clinical Psychiatry Leeds 2000; MRCGP 1986; DRCOG 1986. (St Mary's Hosp. Lond.) Staff Grade Child and Adolesc. Pschiatry Dept., ScarBoro.

WESTERN, Nicholas Vernon Blair Stockwell Lodge Medical Centre, Rosedale Way, Cheshunt, Waltham Cross EN7 6HL Tel: 01992 624408 Fax: 01992 626206; 8 Little Brook Road, Roydon, Harlow CM19 5LR Tel: 01279 792896 — MB BS 1987 Lond.; BA (Physiol. Sci.) Oxf. 1983.

WESTERN, Philip John The Lodge House, Parkfields, Arden Drive, Solihull B93 8LL — MB ChB 1993 Leic.

WESTFIELD, Millicent Bridget Falkirk Royal Infirmary, Falkirk Tel: 01324 24000; Ashgrove, 7 Learmonth St, Falkirk FK1 5AG Tel: 01324 21232 — MB ChB 1955 St. And. (St. And.) Assoc. Specialist (Geriat. Med.) Falkirk Roy. Infirm.

WESTGARTH, David Station Medical Group, Gatacre Street, Blyth NE24 1HD Tel: 01670 396540 Fax: 01670 396517; 20 Esher Gardens, Sandringham Park, Blyth NE24 3RR Tel: 01670 354642 — MB ChB 1972 Liverp.; MRCP (U.K.) 1975; MRCGP 1978. GP Blyth. Prev: Med. Regist. David Lewis N.. Hosp. Liverp.; SHO (Gen. Med.) Whiston Hosp.; Ho. Surg. & Ho. Phys. BRd.green Hosp. Liverp.

WESTGARTH, Sarah Elizabeth 43 Hillsden Road, Beaumont Park, Whitley Bay NE25 9XF — MB ChB 1998 Sheff.; MB ChB Sheff 1998.

WESTGARTH, Thomas John Nelson Health Centre, Cecil Street, North Shields NE29 0DZ Tel: 0191 257 1204/4001 Fax: 0191 258 7191 — MB BS 1969 Newcastle; MB BS Newc. 1969. (Newcastle) GP N. Shields Tyne & Wear.

WESTGARTH, Trevor (retired) Dingli, 5 Pinewood Close, Ashton Road, Lancaster LA2 0AD Tel: 01524 68338 — MB BS 1957 Durh.; DCP Lond 1963. Prev: Regist. N. Lancs. & S. W.mld. Gp. Path. Dept. & Roy. Postgrad. Med.

WESTGATE, Robert 5 Marina Avenue, Redcar TS10 5AD — MB BS 1993 Newc.

WESTHEAD, John Neil Irish Street, 17 Irish Street, Whitehaven CA28 7BU Tel: 01946 693412 Fax: 01946 592046; 25 The Crofts, St Bees CA27 0BH Tel: 01946 822674 — MB ChB 1970 Ed.; MD Ed. 1983; MRCGP 1977; MRCPsych 1975; DPM Eng. 1974. (Ed.)

WESTHEAD, Matthew James Knowle House Surgery, 4 Meavy Way, Crownhill, Plymouth PL5 3JB Tel: 01752 771895 — MB 1966 Camb.; BChir 1965; DObst RCOG 1967. (Camb. & St. Thos.)

WESTLAKE, Anthony Charles 15 Ascot Close, Eastbourne BN20 7HL Tel: 01323 644584 Fax: 01323 644584 — MB ChB 1972 Liverp.; AFOM RCP Lond. 1982; DA Eng. 1977. (Liverp.) Company Med. Adviser Med. & Indust. Servs. Ltd. E.bourne. Socs: Roy. Soc. Med.; Soc. Occupat Med.; BMA. Prev: Regional Med. Off. Brit. Rlys. Bd. Euston; Regist. (Anaesth.) Plymouth Gen. Hosp.; SHO (Anaesth.) IC Derbysh. Roy. Infirm.

WESTLAKE, Athene Sally Anaesthetic Department, St George's Hospital, Tooting, London SW17 0QT Tel: 020 8672 1255; 46 Seymour Walk, London SW10 9NF Tel: 020 7352 6768 — MB ChB 1989 Bristol; FRCA 1994. (Bristol Univ.) Specialist Regist. (Anaesth.) St Geos. Hosp. Socs: BMA & Assn. Anaesth. Prev: Specialist Regist. (Anaesth.) Qu. Mary's Univ. Hosp. Lond.; Specialist Regist. (Anaesth.) Roy. Brompton Hosp. Lond.; Regist. St Geo's Hosp. Lond.

WESTLAKE, Daphne Margaret Bath Road Surgery, 10 Bath Road, Slough SL1 3SA Tel: 01753 522627 Fax: 01753 554031; The Sloop, Beech Waye, Gerrards Cross SL9 8BL Tel: 01753 887127 — MB BS 1961 Lond.; MRCS Eng. LRCP Lond. 1961. (Lond. Hosp.)

WESTON

WESTLAKE, Helen Elizabeth 49 Earls Court Road, Penylan, Cardiff CF23 9DE — MB BCh 1991 Wales; BSc (Hons.) Biochem. Wales 1986. Trainee GP Cardiff VTS.

WESTLAKE, John David Penylan Road Surgery, 100 Penylan Road, Cardiff CF2 5HY Tel: 029 2046 1100 Fax: 029 2045 1623 — MB BCh 1988 Wales; MRCGP 1993; DRCOG 1991; DCH RCP Lond. 1991; T(GP) 1992. Prev: Trainee GP/SHO (Paediat. & O & G) Nevill Hall Hosp. Abergavenny; Ho. Off. (Gen. Med., Thoracic Med. & Gen. Surg.) Llandough Hosp.

WESTLAKE-GUY, Carol Howat Moston Lodge Children's Centre, Countess of Chester Health Park, Chester CH2 1UL Tel: 01244 364802; 13 The Spinney, Gayton, Wirral CH60 3SU Tel: 0151 342 4540 — MRCS Eng. LRCP Lond. 1961. SCMO (Community Child Health) Chester.

WESTMAN, Alison Jane Three Bridges Regional Secure unit, Ealing, Hammersmith & Fulham NHS Trust, Uxbridge Road, Southall UB1 3EU Tel: 020 8354 8200 Fax: 020 8967 5477; 1 Appletree Grove, Cumberland Drive, Redbourn, St Albans AL3 7PG — MB ChB 1983 Manch.; MRCPsych 1991; DRCOG 1986. (Manch.) Cons. Child Psychiat. Ealing Hammersmith & Fulham NHS Trust. Prev: Sen. Regist. (Child & Adolesc. Psychiat.) NW Lond. RHA.

WESTMERLAND, Simon Peter 2 Aston Gardens, Glossop SK13 8PJ — MB ChB 1993 Sheff.

WESTMORE, Mr Graham Anthony Camperduin, Littlemoor Lane, Sibsey, Boston PE22 0TU Tel: 01205 750912 Fax: 01205 311442 — MB BS 1970 Lond.; FRCS Eng. 1976. (Univ. Lond., St. Geo. Hosp. Lond.) Cons. ENT & Head & Neck Surg. Pilgrim Hosp. Boston. Socs: Fell. Roy. Soc. Med.; Brit. Skull Base Soc.; Eur. Skull Base Soc. Prev: Cons. ENT Surg. Milton Keynes Hosp.; Sen. Regist. (ENT) St. Geo. Hosp. Lond.

WESTMORELAND, Diana Department of Medical Microbiology, and Public Health Laboratory, University Hospital of Wales, Cardiff CF4 4XW Tel: 029 2074 2178 Fax: 029 2074 5341 — BM BCh 1984 Oxf.; DPhil Oxf. 1974; MA Camb. 1971; MSc Birm. 1972; FRCPath. Cons. Virol. Pub. Health Laborat. Serv. Cardiff.; Dep. Laborat. Dir. PHLS Wales, Cardiff. Prev: Asst. Microbiol. Pub. Health Laborat. Serv. Bristol.

WESTON, Adrian Hugh Spencer Llanfyllin Medical Centre, High Street, Llanfyllin SY22 5DG Tel: 01691 648054 Fax: 01691 648165; Tyn Llan, Llanfechain SY22 6UJ — MB BS 1979 Lond.; MRCGP 1987; DRCOG 1985.

WESTON, Alasdair Neil Rubislaw Terrace Surgery, 23 Rubislaw Terrace, Aberdeen AB10 1XE Tel: 01224 643665 Fax: 01224 625197 — MB ChB 1975 Aberd.

WESTON, Anne Louise Chapeloak Practice, 347 Oakwood Lane, Leeds LS8 3HA Tel: 0113 240 9999 Fax: 0113 235 9233; 48 North Park Avenue, Roundhay, Leeds LS8 1EY — MB ChB 1984 Bristol; MRCGP 1989; DCH RCP Lond. 1988; DRCOG 1987. GP Leeds. Prev: Partner in Gen. Pract. Bristol; GP Bristol; Trainee GP Nailsea VTS.

WESTON, Charles Elborough 63B Middle Lane, Crouch End, London N8 8PE Tel: 020 8347 9678 — MB BS 1988 Lond.; MRCP (UK) 1993; USMLE (I, II, III) 1996. (Roy. Free Hosp.) Specialist Regist. (Nephrol.and Gen. Med.) St. Helier Hosp.Carlshalton, Surrey. Socs: Renal Assn. Prev: Specialist Regist. (Nephrol.) St. Geo. Hosp. Lond.; Nephrol. Fell. TuLa. Univ. Med. Center Dept. Internal Med. Sect. Nephrol. New Orleans, USA; Regist. (Renal) King's Coll. Hosp. Lond.

WESTON, Christopher Graham Solihull Hospital, Lode Lane, Solihull B91 2JL Tel: 0121 424 5330 — MB ChB 1976 Birm.; FFA RCS Eng. 1981. Cons. (Anaesth.) Birm. Heartlands & Solihull Hosp. NHS Trust. Prev: Sen. Regist. (Anaesth.) W. Midl. RHA; Regist. (Anaesth.) Coventry AHA.

WESTON, Clive Frank Mantell Department of Cardiology, Singleton Hospital, Sketty, Swansea SA2 8QA Tel: 01792 205666 Fax: 01792 285354 — MB BCh 1981 Wales; MRCP (UK) 1984; FRCP 1999. (Wales) Cons. Cardiol. Singleton Hosp. Swansea; Hon. Sen. Lect., Univ. Wales Coll. of Med.; Dep. Director Swansea Clin. Sch. Socs: Brit. Cardiac Soc.; Resusc. Counc. Prev: Sen. Lect. (Cardiol.) Univ. Leeds; Lect. (Cardiol. Epidemiol.) Univ. Wales Coll. Med.; Regist. (Cardiol.) Univ. Hosp. Wales.

WESTON, David Andrew The Atherstone Surgery, 1 Ratcliffe Road, Atherstone CV9 1EU Tel: 01827 713664 Fax: 01827 713666; Schoonder Cottage, 1 Church Lane, Ratcliffe Culey, Atherstone CV9 3PA — MB ChB 1982 Leic. Socs: The Brit. Med. Acupunc. Soc.

WESTON, Mr David Manfred The Loddon Vale Practice, Hurricane Way, Woodley, Reading RG5 4UX Tel: 0118 969 0160 Fax: 0118 969 9103 Email: loddonvale@compuserve.com; Barn House, Tanners Lane, Chalkhouse Green, Reading RG4 9AB Tel: 0118 972 1878 Fax: 0118 972 2685 — MB BS 1966 Lond.; FRCS Eng. 1971; MRCS Eng. LRCP Lond. 1966. (Char. Cross) p/t Hosp. Pract. (Surg.) Roy. Berks. Hosp. Reading; Surg. Marie Stopes Clinic.

WESTON, Diane Helen 14 Aldridge Court, Baldock SG7 5TA — MB BS 1963 Lond.; MRCS Eng. LRCP Lond. 1963; MRCPsych 1973; DPM Eng. 1966. (Roy. Free) Cons. Child & Adolesc. Psychiat. Child & Family Guid. Clinic, Lister Hosp., Stevenage. Prev: Ho. Surg. & Paediat. Ho. Phys. St. Albans City Hosp.; Sen. Regist.; Dept. Childr. & Parents Tavistock Clinic Lond.

WESTON, Jane Crawley Hospital, West Green Drive, Crawley RH11 7DH Tel: 01293 600300 Fax: 01293 600404; Tel: 01293 889124 Email: jane@westonhoward.freeserve.co.uk — BM BCh 1988 Oxf.; MA Oxf. 1986, DPhil 1986; MRCPath 1994. (Oxf.) Cons. Histopath. & Cytopath. Crawley Hosp. Socs: BMA; Path. Soc.; Brit. Soc. Clin. Cytol. Prev: Sen. Regist. (Histopath.) Hammersmith Hosp. Lond.; Sen. Regist. & Regist. N.wick Pk. Hosp. Harrow.

WESTON, Jeremy Clive The Village Medical Centre, Market Square, Peel Street, Littleborough OL15 8AQ; 61/63 Littleclegg Road, Smithy Bridge, Littleborough OL15 0EF Tel: 01706 375835 — MB ChB 1977 Manch.; BSc (Med. Sci.) St. And. 1974. GP Princip. LittleBoro. Socs: Small Pract. Assn.

WESTON, John Arthur Barton The Abbey Practice, The Family Health Centre, Stepgates, Chertsey KT16 8HZ Tel: 01932 565655 Fax: 01932 501842; Chestnuts, Blackdown Avenue, Woking GU22 8QG — MB 1962 Camb.; BChir 1961; FRCGP 1979, M 1971; DCH Eng. 1966; DObst RCOG 1965. (St. Thos.) GP Princip.; GP Tutor St. Peter's Hosp. Chertsey. Socs: BMA. Prev: GP Trainee Course Organiser SW Thames RHA.

WESTON, John George (retired) Parks View, Glassonby, Penrith CA10 1DU — MB BS 1927 Lond.; MRCS Eng. LRCP Lond. 1926. Prev: Ho. Surg. (Genitourin. & Orthop.) & Resid. (Obst.) Guy's Hosp. Lond.

WESTON, John Lawrence (retired) Fyfield, Oldbury, Bridgnorth WV16 5EE Tel: 01746 765515 — MB ChB 1938 Birm. Prev: Cons. Surg. Manor Hosp. Walsall & Walsall Gen. Hosp.

WESTON, Judith Clare 164A Bellingham Road, London SE6 1EJ — MB ChB 1993 Liverp.

WESTON, Mark Elson (retired) Victoria House, Bluntisham Road, Needingworth, St Ives PE27 4TA Tel: 01480 466793 Fax: 01480 466739 — MRCS Eng. LRCP Lond. 1962; BA Oxf. 1959; DObst RCOG 1964. Prev: Ho. Phys. (Paediat.) St. Mary's Hosp. Lond.

WESTON, Michael Dennis 24 Plytree, Thorpe Bay, Southend-on-Sea SS1 3RA — MB BS 1980 Lond.; FCAnaesth 1990.

WESTON, Michael John Ultrasound Department, St James's University Hospital, Beckett St., Leeds LS9 7TF Tel: 0113 206 4330 Email: micheal.weston@gw.sjsuh.notrhy.nhs.uk; 48 North Park Avenue, Roundhay, Leeds LS8 1EY — MB ChB 1984 Bristol; MRCP (UK) 1987; T(R) (CR) 1992; FRCR 1990. Cons. Radiol. St. Jas. Univ. Hosp. Leeds; Hon. Sen. Clin. Lect. Univ. of Leeds. Socs: Brit. Inst. Radiol.; Brit. Med. Ultrasound Soc. Prev: Sen. Regist. (Radiodiag.) S. W.. RHA.; Regist. (Radiodiag.) Bristol Roy. Infirm.

WESTON, Michael John 148 Harley Street, London W1N 1AH Tel: 020 7487 5020 Fax: 020 7224 1528; Brambles, Elm Green Lane, Danbury, Chelmsford CM3 4DR Tel: 01245 226445 — MA, MB Camb. 1970, MD 1978, BChir 1969; FRCP Lond. 1982, M 1971. (Camb. & St. Thos.) Cons. Phys. Gen. Med. Broomfield Hosp. Chelmsford; Hon. Cons. Nephrol. KCH Lond. Socs: Renal Assn.; Med. Res. Soc. Prev: Cons. Phys. Gen. & Renal Med. King's Coll. Hosp. Lond.; Lect. (Med.) & Hon. Sen. Regist. King's Coll. Hosp. Lond.; Regist. (Med.) Roy. Sussex Co. Hosp. Brighton.

WESTON, Mr Neil Craig 7 Long Meadow, Gayton, Wirral CH60 8QQ Tel: 0151 342 4590 — MB BChir 1983 Camb.; BA (Phys. Sci.) Oxf. 1980; FRCS Eng. 1989. Regist. (Gen. Surg.) Whipps Cross Hosp. Lond. Prev: SHO (Urol.) Addenbrookes Hosp. Camb.; SHO (Gen. Surg.) Hinchingbrooke Hosp. Huntingdon.

WESTON, Penelope Mary East Barnet Health Centre, 149 East Barnet Road, Barnet EN4 8QZ Tel: 020 8440 7417 Fax: 020 8447 0126 — BSc (Food & Managem. Sc.) Lond. 1976, MB BS 1982;

WESTON

MRCGP 1986; DCH RCP Lond. 1986; DRCOG 1984. (Guy's) GP Princip. E. Barnet Health Centre.

WESTON, Peter (retired) 17 Cissbury Road, Worthing BN14 9LD — MB BChir 1958 Camb.; MA, MB Camb. 1958, BChir 1957; DObst RCOG 1963. Prev: GP Worthing.

WESTON, Mr Peter Alexander Murray (retired) Old Rectory, Church Town, Sebergham, Carlisle CA5 7HS Tel: 01697 476263 — MB BS 1951 Lond.; FRCS Eng. 1952; MRCS Eng. LRCP Lond. 1947; LMCC 1953. Prev: Cons. Surg. S. Regions Health Project, Mbeya, Tanzania.

WESTON, Peter Godfrey Woodhouse (retired) Wednesday Cottage, Main St., Buchlyvie, Stirling FK8 3LR Tel: 01360 850408 — MB ChB 1949 Ed. Cons. Hypnother. Edin. Prev: GP Edin.

WESTON, Philip John 68 Evington Drive, Leicester LE5 5PD — MB ChB 1987 Leic.

WESTON, Philip John High Pastures, 138 Liverpool Road North, Liverpool L31 2HW Tel: 0151 531 9420 Fax: 0151 527 2377 — MB ChB 1989 Liverp.; DCH RCP Lond. 1995; DRCOG 1995. Prev: Trainee GP S.port Dist. Gen. Hosp. VTS; SHO (Orthop.) Whiston Hosp.; SHO (Gen. Surg.) S.port Hosp.

WESTON, Mr Philip Mark Tempest Pinderfields Hospital, Aberford Road, Wakefield WF1 4DG Tel: 01924 201688 Fax: 01924 212921 — MB BCh 1980 Wales; MCh Wales 1989; FRCS (Urol.) 1991; FRCS Ed. 1984. (Welsh National School of Medicine) Cons. Urol. Surg. Pinderfields Hosp.; Roy. Coll. of Surg.s Tutor, Area Coordinator, Wakefield Div., Yorks. Sch. of Surg.. Socs: Med. Res. Soc.; EORTC GU Gp.; Brit. Assn. Urological Surg.s. Prev: Cons. Urol. Surg. Clayton Hosp. Wakefield; Sen. Regist. (Urol.) W. Midl. RHA; Regist. (Urol.) Cardiff Roy. Infirm. & Univ. Hosp. Wales.

WESTON, Sandra Jane 8 Clarence Street, Richmond TW9 2SA — MB BS 1989 Lond.; BSc Lond. 1986, MB BS 1989; DFFP 1993.

WESTON, Sian Nerys c/o Cefn Coed Hospital, Heol Waunarlwydd, Cockett, Swansea SA2 0GH Tel: 01792 561155 — MB BCh 1995 Wales. (Univ. Wales Coll. Med.) SHOold Age Psychiat. Cefn Coed Hosp. Swansea; SHO (Psychiat.) Cefn Coed Hosp. Swansea. Socs: Inceptor Roy. Coll. Psychiat. Prev: SHO (Child Psychiat.) Trehafod Unit Cefn Coed Hosp. Swansea; SHO (Adult Psychiat.) Cefn Coed Hosp. Swansea; SHO (Psychiat.) St. Jas. Univ. Hosp. Leeds.

WESTON, Theodore Paul Birbeck Medical Group, Penrith Health Centre, Bridge Lane, Penrith CA11 8HW Tel: 01768 245200 Fax: 01768 245295; The College, Tirrill, Penrith CA10 2JE Tel: 01768 245389 Email: mtweston@enterprise.net — MB BS 1982 Lond.; MRCGP 1990; DRCOG 1986. (Char. Cross) Prev: Trainee. GP N.ampton VTS; SHO (Dermat. & A & E) N.ampton HA.

WESTON, Trevor Edmund Thomas Robert Street Surgery, 89D Robert Street, London NW1 3QT Tel: 020 7387 4576 — MD 1962 Lond.; MB BS 1951; MRCGP 1958. (St. Bart.) Butterworth Gold Medal Coll. GP 1959; Cons. Venereol. Roy. Surrey Co. Hosp., Woking Vict. Hosp. & Frimley Pk. Hosp; Med. Off. Daily Telegraph Benev. Fund; Cons. Med. Edr. Family Doctor Pub.ats. Socs: BMA (Chairm. St. Pancras Div.); Airborne Med. Soc. Prev: Regist. Guy's Hosp. Lond.; Sen. Regist . St. Thos. Hosp.; Clin. Asst. St. Bart. Hosp. Lond.

WESTON, Vivienne Clare Department of Microbiology & PHL, University Hospital, Queens Medical Centre, Nottingham NG7 2UH — MB BS 1987 Lond.; MSc (Clin. Microbiol.) Lond. 1995; MRCP (UK) 1990; MRCPath 1998. (Roy. Free) Cons. (Microbiol) Qu. Med. Centre Nottm. Socs: RCPath; HIS; AMM. Prev: Sen. Regist. (Microbiol.) Qu. Med. Centre Nottm.; Regist. (Microbiol.) Leicester Roy. Infirm.; SHO (Renal Med.) Dulwich Hosp. Lond.

WESTON-BAKER, Elizabeth Jane Pamflete House, Holbeton, Plymouth PL8 1JR — MB BS Lond. 1977; MRCP (UK) 1979; MRCS Eng. LRCP Lond. 1977; MRCGP 1983. (Guy's)

WESTON-BURT, Paul Michael Woodlands Surgery, Tilgate Way, Tilgate, Crawley RH10 5BS Tel: 01293 525204 Fax: 01293 514778 — MB BChir 1966 Camb.; MA, MB Camb. 1966, BChir.1965; MRCS Eng. LRCP Lond. 1965; DObst RCOG 1968; DA Eng. 1968. (St. Bart.)

WESTON-DAVIES, Mr Wynne Hurst, TD Evolutec Ltd., The Magdalen Centre, Oxford Science Park, Oxford OX4 4GA Tel: 01865 784070 Fax: 01865 399991 Email: wwd@evolutec.co.uk — MB BS 1967 Lond.; FRCS Eng. 1972; MRCS Eng. LRCP Lond. 1967. (St. Mary's) Med. & Developm. Director, Evolutel Ltd., Oxf. Socs: FRCM.

Prev: Med. Dir. Cutis Clin. Research Ltd.; Europ. Med. Dir. Bristol Myers Squibb Convatec; Asst. Dir.y Clin. Research Squibb Europe.

WESTON SMITH, Paul Andrew Littlewick Medical Centre, 42 Nottingham Road, Ilkeston DE7 5PR Tel: 0115 932 5229 Fax: 0115 932 5413 — MB ChB 1973 Birm.; DRCOG 1978. Univ. Tutor (Gen. Pract.) Nottm. Med. Sch.; Chairm. Ilkeston Hosp. Med. Comm.; Exec. Mem. Erework, PCT. Socs: BMA; Derbysh. LMC. Prev: Trainee GP Cardiff (Welsh Nat. Sch. Med.) VTS.

WESTON-SMITH, Penelope Sara Brackenhill, 6 Bingham Avenue, Lilliput, Poole BH14 8NE — MB ChB 1987 Bristol; BSc (Hons.) Pharmacol. Bristol 1984; FRCA. 1992; DA (UK) 1990. Hosp retainer (Anaesthetics) Poole & Bournemouth Hosps. Socs: Assoc. Anaesth.; MRCAnaesth. Prev: Sen. Regist. (Anaesth.) Poole, Bournemouth & Soton. Hosps.; Regist. Rotat. (Anaesth) Bristol & Roy. Cornw. Hosps; SHO (Anaesth.) Bristol Roy. Infirm.

WESTON UNDERWOOD, Mr John Tel: 01580 240333; The Old Mill, Tregoose, Newquay TR8 4NE Email: jwu@millstreet.demon.co.uk — MB BS 1968 Lond.; BSc Lond. 1965; FRCS Eng. 1974; MRCS Eng. LRCP Lond. 1968. (St. Geo.) Cons. Surg. Benenden Hosp. Cranbrook. Prev: Surg. 1st Asst. St. Geo. Hosp. Lond.; Regist. (Surg.) St. Jas. Hosp. Lond.

WESTON UNDERWOOD, Rosemary Ann (retired) Hampton, Hawkhurst Road, Kenley CR8 5DL Tel: 020 8660 7706 — MB BS 1967 Lond.; MRCS Eng. LRCP Lond. 1967; DCH Eng. 1970; DObst RCOG 1969.

WESTPHAL-BURDON, Silke Ursula Tel: 0191 477 2169; Steadings Home Farm, Bridle path, Newcastle upon Tyne NE3 5EU — State Exam Med 1988 Berlin; MD 1990 Berlin; MRCGP 1996. (Berlin, Germany) p/t GP. Prev: GP Partner, 1 Cartington Tce Med. Gp., Heaton Newc. upon Tyne, NE6 5RS.

WESTROP, Richard John Tel: 01482 343671 Fax: 01482 448839 — MB ChB 1978 Dundee. GP Hull. Socs: Soc. Med. & Dent. Hypn.

WESTWATER, Jason John Flat 2/4 Parsonage Square, Collegelands, Glasgow G4 0TA — MB ChB 1995 Glas.

WESTWELL, Sarah Louise 104A Sherbrooke Road, London SW6 7QN — MB ChB 1995 Bristol.

WESTWICK, Rachel Jane 20 Brookway, London SE3 9BJ — MB ChB 1996 Liverp.

WESTWOOD, Mr Christopher Anthony The Laurels, Church Lane, Fotherby, Louth LN11 0UH — MB ChB 1968 Bristol; FRCS Eng. 1974. (Bristol) Cons. (Gen. Surg. & Urol.) Grimsby & Louth Health Dist. Prev: Sen. Regist. Leics. HA (T) & St. Peters Hosp. Lond.; SHO (Gen. Surg.) Frenchay Hosp. Bristol.

WESTWOOD, Christopher Norman Plympton Health Centre, Mudge Way, Plympton, Plymouth PL7 1AD Tel: 01752 346634; Old Treby Farm, Yealmpton, Plymouth PL8 2LJ Tel: 01752 880409 — MB BS 1970 Lond.; MRCS Eng. LRCP Lond. 1970; DObst RCOG 1973. (Char. Cross) Prev: Ho. Phys. & Ho. Surg. Char. Cross Hosp.; SHO (Obst.) & Cas. Off. Plymouth Health Dist.

WESTWOOD, Colin Timperley Health Centre, 169 Grove Lane, Timperley, Altrincham WA15 6PH Tel: 0161 980 3751 Fax: 0161 904 9678 — MB ChB 1973 Manch.; MRCGP 1981; DObst RCOG 1976; DCH Eng. 1976.

WESTWOOD, Dawn Lesley East Wing, Esk Medical Centre, Musselburgh EH21 6A Tel: 0131 665 2267; Eskwood, Lasswade EH18 1EJ — MB ChB 1989 Ed. Trainee GP Musselburgh.

WESTWOOD, Gavin Ralph Peel House Medical Centre, Avenue Parade, Accrington BB5 6RD Tel: 01254 237231 Fax: 01254 389525; Brooklands, 110 Hollins Lane, Accrington BB5 2JS — MB ChB 1985 Manch.; MRCGP 1989. Prev: Trainee GP Blackburn VTS.

WESTWOOD, Louisa Katherine Martagon, Rimes Close, Kingston Bagpuize, Abingdon OX13 5AL — BM BS 1994 Nottm.

WESTWOOD, Mark Anthony The Village Green Surgery, The Green, Wallsend NE28 6BB Tel: 0191 295 8500 Fax: 0191 295 8519 — MB ChB 1984 Leic. GP Wallsend, Tyne & Wear SHO (Med. Rotat.) Freeman Hosp. Newc. Prev: Ho. Off. (Med. & Surg.) Leicester Roy. Infirm.

WESTWOOD, Paul Arthur Newcombes Surgery, Newcombes, Crediton EX17 2AR Tel: 01363 772263 Fax: 01363 775906; Weirholme, Half Moon, Newton, St Cyres, Exeter EX5 5AB Tel: 01392 851414 Fax: 01392 851414 — MB ChB Liverp. 1967; MRCPsych 1976; MRCGP 1981; DPM Eng. 1971. (Liverp.) Prev: SHO W. Chesh. Psychiat. Hosp. Chester; Ho. Phys. Walton Hosp. Liverp.; Ho. Surg. BRd.green Hosp. Liverp.

WESTWOOD, Paul Richard Bodfeddyg, 102 High St., Glynneath, Neath SA11 5AL Tel: 01639 720311 Fax: 01639 727579; Pwll Dylluan, Penderyn, Aberdare CF44 9QA — MB BCh 1982 Wales; MRCGP 1991; DRCOG 1987; DFFP 1996. (Welsh National School of Medicine) GP Princip. Prev: RN Med. Off.

WESTWOOD, Suzanne Louise 6 Moorlands Park, Cuddington, Northwich CW8 2LY — BM BCh 1998 Oxf.

WESTWOOD, Tina Louise The Surgery, Wharf Road, Gnosall, Stafford ST20 0DB — MB ChB 1990 Dundee.

WESTWOOD, William Don 50 Belle Vue Road, Shrewsbury SY3 7LP — MB ChB 1986 Aberd.

WESTWOOD, William John Abbott (retired) 4 Church Lane, Lyddington, Oakham LE15 9LN Tel: 01572 822299 — BSc (Hons.) Birm. 1959, MB ChB (Hons.) 1962; DObst RCOG 1968; Cert. Family Plann. JCC 1976. Indep. Non-Princip. GP. Prev: GP Princip. Corby.

WESTWORTH, Betty Patricia (retired) 24 Virginia Beeches, Callow Hill, Virginia Water GU25 4LT Tel: 01344 843953 — MB ChB St. And. 1956; FFCM 1987; DPH Lond. 1967; DObst RCOG 1957. Prev: Specialist in Community Med. (Social Servs./Child Health) S.W. Surrey HA.

WETHERALL, Mr Anthony Philip Kidderminster General Hospital, Bewdley Road, Kidderminster DY11 6RJ — MB ChB 1978 Manch.; FRCS Eng. 1984; FRCS Ed. 1983. Cons. Gen. Surg. Kidderminster Gen. Hosp. Socs: Assn. Coloproctol. Prev: Cons. Gen. Surg. Roy. Air Force Med. Br.

WETHERALL, Linda Michelle 5 Farnham Park, Bangor BT20 3SR — MB ChB 1998 Manch.

WETHERALL, Michael Richard Brydges Department of Histopathology, Sunderland Royal Hospital, Kayll Road, Sunderland SR4 7TP Tel: 0191 565 6256 Fax: 0191 569 9230; 32 Oaklands, Gosforth, Newcastle upon Tyne NE3 4YP Tel: 0191 284 5932 — MB BS 1979 Newc.; MA Camb. 1975; MRCPath 1989. Cons. Histopath. Sunderland Roy. Hosp. Prev: Sen. Regist. (Histopath.) Roy. Vict. Infirm. Newc.; Demonst. (Path.) Roy. Vict. Infirm. Newc.

WETHERED, Oliver James Courtney Warley, Links Road, Winchester SO22 5HP Tel: 01962 852962 Fax: 01962 855410 Email: oliver@wethered.clara.net — MA Oxf. 1964; MB BS Lond. 1969; MRCP (U.K.) 1975; FRCR 1980; DMRD Eng. 1977; FRCR 1980; FRCP 1999. (Char. Cross) Cons. Diag. Radiol. Roy. Hants. Co. Hosp. Winchester. Prev: Sen. Regist. (Diag. Radiol.) St. Geo. Hosp. Lond.; Regist. (Radiol.) Guy's Hosp. Lond.; Regist (Med.) W. Middlx. Hosp. Lond.

WETHERELL, Mr Geoffrey Alfred (retired) Bank House, Shotwick Lane, Woodbank, Chester CH1 6HY Tel: 01244 880498 — MB ChB 1943 Liverp.; MChOrth 1953; FRCS Eng. 1952. Prev: Cons. Orthop. Surg. Clatterbridge Gen. Hosp.

WETHERELL, Heather Caroline The Health Centre, Viewley Centre, Hemlington, Middlesbrough TS8 9JQ Tel: 01642 590500 Fax: 01642 591721; Grangecroft, Kirkby Lane, Great Broughton, Middlesbrough TS9 7HG Email: wetherell@mcmail.com — BM BS 1988 Nottm.; BMedSci Nottm. 1986; MRCGP 1993; DRCOG 1992. Clin. Asst. (Anaesth.) Friarage Hosp. N.allerton. Prev: Trainee GP N.allerton VTS; SHO (Anaesth.) Friarage Hosp. N.allerton.

WETHERELL, Owen Charles (retired) Eden House, Old Malton, Malton YO17 6RT Tel: 01653 693243 — MB BChir Camb. 1962; MA Camb. 1962; MRCS Eng. LRCP Lond. 1961; DObst RCOG 1964. Prev: SHO (Paediat.) York Co. Hosp.

WETHERELL, Mr Roderick Grant Kent & Canterbury Hospital, Ethelbert Road, Canterbury CT1 3NG; Waylands, Town Hill, Bridge, Canterbury CT4 5AH — MB ChB 1978 Birm.; MD Birm. 1992; FRCS Ed. 1984. (Birm.) Cons. Orthop. Surg. Kent & Canterbury Hosp. Prev: Sen. Regist. (Orthop.) SE. Thames RHA; Research Fell. (Orthop.) Rayne Inst. St. Thos. Hosp. Lond.

WETHERELL, Simon Charles Queen Square Surgery, 2 Queen Square, Lancaster LA1 1RP Tel: 01524 843333 Fax: 01524 847550; Moorgate Barn, Littledale Road, Brookhouse, Lancaster LA2 9PH Tel: 01524 771363 — BM BCh 1985 Oxf.; MA 2000 Lancs. Uni; MRCGP 1989; DRCOG 1989.

WETHERILL, Diana Mary Lynwood, 16 Oxford Road, Dewsbury WF13 4JT Tel: 01924 465889 Fax: 01924 519434 — MB ChB Leeds 1965; MMedSc Leeds 1985; DMJ (Clin.) Soc. Apoth. Lond. 1991. (Leeds) Police Surg. W. Yorks. Socs: FRSM (Pres. Sect. Clin. Forens. And Legal Med.); BMA; Assn. Police Surg. Prev: GP,

Cleckheaton, W. Yorks; Med. Off. Fox's Biscuits Batley; Ho. Off. St. Jas. Hosp. Leeds.

WETHERILL, John Homer (retired) Lynwood, 16 Oxford Road, Dewsbury WF13 4JT Tel: 01924 465889 Fax: 01924 519434 — MB ChB (Hons.) Leeds 1959; FRCP Lond. 1981, M 1965. Prev: Cons. Phys. Dewsbury Health Care NHS Trust.

WETHERILL, Mr Martin Harry Shalstone Hill Farm, Shalstone, Buckingham MK18 5NB — MB BS 1973 Lond.; FRCS Ed. 1980; MRCS Eng. LRCP Lond. 1973. Cons. Orthop. Surg. Qu. Eliz. Milit. Hosp. Lond. Prev: Hon. Sen. Regist. Nuffield Orthop. Centre Oxf.; Hon. Sen. Regist. Orthop. Dept. Hosp. for Sick Childr. Gt. Ormond St.; Lond.

WETHERLY, James Marshall Rennie (retired) 41 Great Southern Road, Aberdeen AB11 7XY Tel: 01224 585141 — MB ChB 1951 Aberd.

WETSON, Ronald Ernest Steyning Health Centre, Tanyard Lane, Steyning BN44 3RJ Tel: 01903 843400 Fax: 01903 812981 — MB ChB 1974 Birm.; BSc (Hons.) (Biol. Scs.) Birm. 1969; MRCGP 1978; DCH Eng. 1977; DRCOG 1976.

WETTON, Charles William Neve 3 Rosedew Road, Hammersmith, London W6 9ET Tel: 020 8748 2867 — MB BS 1987 Lond.; MRCP (UK) 1990; FRCR 1994. Sen. Regist. St. Mary's Hosp. Lond. Prev: SHO W.m., St. Stephens, Roy. Marsden, Roy. Brompton & Nat. Heart Hosps.

WEXLER, Mr David Mark 54 Kingsmere Park, London NW9 8PL Tel: 020 8205 3912 — MB BS 1989 Lond.; FRCS Glas. 1994. (St. Bart. Univ. Lond.) Specialist Regist. Rotat. (Orthop.) N. Thames (W.). Prev: SHO (A & E) S.end Gen. Hosp.; Demonst. (Anat.) Roy. Free Hosp. Lond.

WEXLER, Sarah Anne Flat 2 Hartley House, 37 Belvedere, Lansdown Road, Bath BA1 5HR Tel: 01225 446707 Email: sarah@sboxwex.demon.co.uk — MB BS Lond. 1989; MRCP Lond. 1995; MRCPath. Part I 1997. (St. Bartholomews Hospital Medical School) Specialist Regist. Haemat. S.mead Hosp. Bristol.

WEY, Emmanuel Quintela 19 Norton Road, Leyton, London E10 7LQ Email: don-manny@hotmail.com — MB BS 1998 Lond. (St Georges) Paediat.SHO FarnBoro. Hosp. Prev: Ho. Off. Gen.med St Geo.s Hosp.Lond.

WEYELL, Richard Stanley Charles Hicks Centre, 75 Ermine Street, Huntingdon PE29 3EZ Tel: 01480 453038 Fax: 01480 434104; Kirk View, 39 Post St, Godmanchester, Huntingdon PE29 2AQ — MB BS 1985 Lond.; MRCGP 1991; DCH RCP Lond. 1990.

WEYHAM, Christopher John 19 Arlington Court, Stourbridge DY8 1NN — MB ChB 1998 Dund.

WEYMAN, Christine 14 Windsor Road, Finchley, London N3 3SS Tel: 020 8 349 1096; 1624 NW 12th Street, Gainesville FL 32609, USA Tel: 904 374882 — MB BS 1982 Lond.; PhD Lond. 1977; BSc NSW 1973. Fell. (Paediat. Haemat. & Oncol.) Univ. of Florida.

WEYMES, Cameron, TD (retired) Mill Cottage, Mill Hall, Eaglesham, Glasgow G76 0PD Tel: 0135 532506 — MSc Strathclyde 1969; MD Ed. 1963, MB ChB 1947; FRCP Glas. 1971, M 1967; FFCM 1972; DPH Glas. 1955. Prev: Hon. Surg. To H.M. the Qu..

WEYNDLING, Jadwiga Magdalena (retired) Eastleigh, Stoke St Michael, Bath BA3 5JT Tel: 01749 840859 — MB ChB 1953 Ed. Prev: Princip. GP Gorebridge Gp. Pract. Midlothian.

WHALE, Christopher Ian 9 Folder Lane, Sprotbrough, Doncaster DN5 7PD Tel: 01302 850107 Email: chriswhale@hotmail.com — MB ChB 1996 Liverp. Jun. Ho. Off. Mackay Base Hosp. Qu.sland, Australia. Prev: Ho. Off. Arrowe Pk. Hosp. Wirral.

WHALE, Kathleen (retired) 30 Burlington Road, Altrincham WA14 1HR — MB ChB 1955 Manch.; BA (Hons.) Manch. 1995; FRCPath 1988, M 1977; Dip. Bact. Manch. 1975; B Phil Manch. 1998. Prev: Cons. Med. Microbiol. Manch. AHA (T) (N. Dist.).

WHALE, Rowland 98 Cambridge Road, Great Shelford, Cambridge CB2 5JS Tel: 01223 842845 — MB BS 1977 Lond.; MSc (Gerontol.) Lond. 1990, MB BS 1977; MRCP (UK) 1980. Cons. Phys. Redbridge Heath Trust. Prev: Clin. Tutor Univ. Camb.

WHALE, Sally Ann The Surgery, Woden Road, Wolverhampton WV10 0BD; Email: sallywhale@doctors.org.uk — MB ChB 1985 Birm.; DRCOG 1988. (Birm.) GP; Black Country VTS Course Organiser; W'ton N.E. PCG Bd. Mem. Prev: Trainee GP Walsall & S. Birm. VTS.

WHALE

WHALE, William Richard South Downs NHS Trust, Brighton General Hospital, Brighton Tel: 01273 696011 Email: s.whale@bton.ac.uk; 14 Portland Mansions, 134-1336 Marine Parade, Brighton BN2 1DF — MB BS 1990 Lond. (St. Geo.) Cons. Psychiat., S. Downs NHS Trust, Brighton; Sen. Lect. Pyschiatry Univ. of Brighton, Brighton. Socs: MRCPsych. Prev: Sen. Regist. (Psychiat.) Haleacre Unit. Amersham; Sen. Regist. & Regist. (Psychiat.) Warneford Hosp. Oxf.; Clin. Research Fell., Univ. of Oxf.

WHALEN, Steven Howard Wessex Road Surgery, Wessex Road, Parkstone, Poole BH14 8BQ Tel: 01202 734924 Fax: 01202 738957; 14 Wynford Road, Poole BH14 8PG Tel: 01202 740119 — MB ChB 1975 Bristol; DA Eng. 1978. (Bristol)

WHALEN, Susan Mary 7 Penncroft, 456 Penn Road, Wolverhampton WV4 4HP — MB ChB 1987 Ed.

WHALEY, Anne Patricia sir Humphrey Davy Dept Anaesthesia, Bristol Royal Infirmary, Bristol BS2 8HW Tel: 01179 282163 — MB BS 1986 Lond.; MA (Med. Sci.) Camb. 1986; FRCA (UK) 1994, MRCP 1989. Cons. Anaesth. IC Bristol roy. Infirm. Socs: Train. Mem. Assn. Anaesth. Prev: Spr Anaesth. S. W. Rotat.; Cons. (ITU and Anaesth.) Bristol Roy. Infirm.; Sen. Regist. (ICU) Roy. Shove & Roy. Alexandra Child. Hosp. Sydney.

WHALEY, Katherine Elizabeth 52 Alma Road, Carshalton SM5 2PF — MB ChB 1995 Leic.

WHALEY, Professor Keith Immunology Department, Leicester Royal Infirmary, Infirmary Square, Leicester LE1 5WW Tel: 0116 258 6702 Fax: 0116 258 6704 — MB BS Glas. 1966; PhD Glas. 1973; MD Newc. 1972; FRCP 1983, M 1968; FRCPath 1986, M 1974. Prof. Immunol. Univ. Leicester; Hon. Cons. Immunol. Leic. Roy. Infirm. Socs: Brit. & Amer. Soc. Immunol.; Brit. Soc. Rheum. Prev: Vis. Prof. Strathelyde Univ. Glas.; Vis. Prof. Al-Azher Univ. Cairo.

WHALLETT, Andrew John The Guest Hospital, Dudley Group of Hospitals, Tipton Rd, Dudley D41 4SE; The Coach House, Holy Cross Green, Stourbridge DY9 0HG — MB ChB 1991 Birm.; MB ChB (Hons.) Birm. 1991; BSc (Hons.) Birm. 1988; MRCP (UK) 1995. Cons. Rheumatologist. Socs: Brit. Soc. for Rheum.; UK BEHGETS Forum. Prev: SHO (Med.) City Hosp. Birm.; SHO (Med.) Kidderminster Gen. Hosp.; Ho. Off. (Med.) Dudley Rd. Hosp. Birm.

WHALLETT, Diana Joan Thornbury Health Centre, Eastland Road, Thornbury, Bristol BS35 1DP Tel: 01454 412599 Fax: 01454 41911; Fairfield House, 58 Castle St, Thornbury, Bristol BS35 1HG Tel: 01454 412346 — MB ChB Birm. 1963; MFFP 1993; DObst RCOG 1965; Cert. Contracep. & Family Plann. RCOG & RCGP 1974; Instruc. Cert. 1976; Cert. Family Plann. JCC 1966. GP; Sen. Clin. Med. Off. Family Plann. Clinic N. Bristol NHS Trust. Prev: Ho. Phys. Qu. Eliz. Hosp. Birm.; Ho. Surg. (Obst.) Hallam Hosp. W. Bromwich.

WHALLETT, Miss Elizabeth Jane 58 Castle Street, Thornbury, Bristol BS35 1HG — MB ChB 1991 Birm.; FRCS Ed. 1997. (Birm.) SHO (Plastic Surg. & Burns.) N.ern Gen. Hosp. Sheff. Socs: Med. Protec. Soc.; Surgic. Soc. Prev: SHO (Plastic Surg.) N. Staffs. Hosp., SHO (Plastic Surg.) Morriston Hosp. Swansea; SHO (Plastic Surg.) Sandwell Healthcare NHS Trust; SHO (Thoracic Surg.) Birm. Heartlands Hosp.

WHALLETT, Michael John (retired) Fairfield House, 58 Castle St, Thornbury, Bristol BS35 1HG Tel: 01454 412346 — MB ChB Birm. 1962; DObst RCOG 1964. Prev: Med. Off. Thornbury Hosp.

WHALLEY, Francis Edward Rutherford House, Langley Park, Durham DH7 9XD Tel: 0191 373 1386 Fax: 0191 373 4288 — MB BS 1976 London; MB BS Lond. 1976. (London) GP Brandon, Co Durh.

WHALLEY, Frederick Lawrence (retired) Range House, Salterns Road, Lee-on-the-Solent PO13 9NL — MB BChir 1952 Camb.; MA Camb. 1952; MRCS Eng. LRCP Lond. 1953; DObst RCOG 1956; MRCGP 1965. Prev: Mem. Hants. LMC.

WHALLEY, James Thomas 3 Merton Place, Birkenhead CH43 4XD — MB ChB 1989 Dundee.

WHALLEY, John 22 Meadowcroft, Church Park N., Euxton, Chorley PR7 6BU Tel: 01257 276373 — MB ChB 1970 Leeds.

WHALLEY, John Andrew 22 Meadowcroft, Euxton, Chorley PR7 6BU — MB ChB 1995 Manch.

WHALLEY, Judith 23 Cloisters Road, Letchworth SG6 3JR Tel: 01462 686818; N. Herts NHS Trust, Health Centre, Bedford Road, Hitchin SG5 1HF Tel: 01438 314333 Ext: 3249 — MB ChB Sheff. 1967; DObst RCOG 1971; DCH RCPS Glas. 1969. (Sheff.) SCHO

Community Child Health. Socs: BMA; RCPCH. Prev: Ho. Phys. & Ho. Surg. Roy. Infirm. Sheff.

WHALLEY, Professor Lawrence Jeffrey Department of Mental Health, University Medical Buildings, Foresterhill, Aberdeen AB25 2ZD Tel: 01224 681818 Fax: 01224 663145; 16 Albert Terrace, Edinburgh EH10 5EA — MB BS Newc. 1969; MD Newc. 1976; FRCPsych 1990, M 1974; DPM Edin. 1973. Prof. Ment. Health Univ. Aberd.; Hon. Cons. Psychiat. Grampian HB. Socs: BMA; Soc. for Neurosci. Prev: Sen. Lect. (Psychiat.) Univ. Edin.; Sen. Clin. Sc. MRC Brain Metab. Unit Roy. Edin. Hosp.; Sen. Regist. (Psychiat.) Lothian HB.

WHALLEY, Mary Jane 85 Hamilton Road, Reading RG1 5RB — MB BS 1974 Lond.; MRCPsych 1978. Cons. Psychiat. Oxf. RHA. Prev: Sen. Regist. (Psychiat.) Littlemore Hosp. Oxf.; Ho. Off. Addenbrookes Hosp. Camb.

WHALLEY, Simon Adam Greenend, Coach Road, Ashover, Chesterfield S45 0JN — BM BS 1990 Nottm.; BMedSci Nottm. 1988; MRCP (UK) 1993.

WHAMOND, William Nelson, DFC Bishop's Barn, Cross Roads, Keighley BD22 9AQ Tel: 01535 642297 — MRCS Eng. LRCP Lond. 1950. (Guy's)

WHAPHAM, Miss Eileen Mary (retired) Flat 4, Burgesmede House, 2 Folly Lane, Petersfield GU31 4BH — MB BS 1932 Lond.; MB BS (Hons. Surg.) 1932; MD Lond. 1938; FRCS Eng. 1941; FRCOG 1954, M 1939. Hon. Cons. O & G S.end-on-Sea Hosp. Gp. Prev: Cons. Gyn. Mildmay Miss. Hosp. Bethnal Green.

WHARAM, Paul Christopher 79 Kerrs Way, Wroughton, Swindon SN4 9EG — BM 1984 Soton.; MRCGP 1991.

WHARFE, Simon Michael Webster The Coach House Surgery, 27 Canterbury Road, Herne Bay CT6 5DQ Tel: 01227 374040 Fax: 01227 741544 — MB BS 1974 Newc.; MRCGP 1978; DRCOG 1976. Local Med. Off Civil Serv. Dept. Med. Advisory Serv. Prev: Clin. Research Phys. Pfizer Cent. Research; Trainee GP Newc. VTS; Ho. Off. (Paediat. & Gen. Med.) Newc. Gen. Hosp.

WHARIN, Fiona Jane 60 Headlands, Kettering NN15 6DG — MB BS 1972 Lond.; MRCP (UK) 1996, L. 1972; MRCS Eng.; MRCPCH 1997; DCH RCP Lond. 1992; DRCOG 1977. Staff Grade Pract. Community Paediat.

WHARIN, Paul Douglas Headlands Surgery, 20 Headlands, Kettering NN15 7HP Tel: 01536 518886 Fax: 01536 415385; 60 Headlands, Kettering NN15 6DG — MB BChir 1972 Camb.; MA, MB Camb. 1972, BChir 1971; DObst RCOG 1975.

WHARRAM, Jonathan The Surgery, 14 Queenstown Road, Battersea, London SW8 3RX Tel: 020 7622 9295 Fax: 020 7498 5206 — MB BS 1981 Lond.; MRCGP 1985; Cert. Family Plann. JCC 1986; DCH RCP Lond. 1984; DRCOG 1983. Prev: GP Surrey.

WHARTON, Amanda Jane Nuffield Road, Chesterton, Cambridge CB4 1GL Tel: 01223 423424; Email: amandajane@doctors.org.uk — BSc Bristol 1975; Ph D Lond. 1985; MB BChir 1995 Camb. p/t Gen. Practitioner, Camb.; Camb. United Football Club Doctor, Camb.

WHARTON, Arthur Basil (retired) 9 Castle Court, Cleveland Way, Helmsley, York YO62 5AZ Tel: 01439 770937 — MB ChB 1948 Leeds. Prev: GP Selby N. Yorks.

WHARTON, Professor Brian Arthur MRC Childhood Nutrition Research Centre, Institute of Child Health, Guilford St., London WC1N 1EH Tel: 020 7905 2143 Fax: 020 7831 9903 Email: bwharton@ich.ucl.ac.uk; Old Rectory, Belbroughton, Stourbridge DY9 9TF Tel: 01562 730243 Fax: 01562 730243 Email: brianawharton@telinco.co.uk — MB ChB (Distinc. Social Med., Paediat. & Child Health) Birm. 1960; DSc Birm. 1994, MD (Hons.) 1968; MBA Warwick 1990; FRCP Glas. 1991; FRCP Lond. 1979, M 1965; FRCP Ed. 1974, M 1965; FRCPCH 1997; DCH Eng. 1962. (Birm.) Hon. Prof. Univ. Coll. Lond. Inst. of Child Health Lond. Socs: Nutrit. Soc. (UK, USA); Soc. for Paediat. Research (Europe and USA); Worshipful Soc. Apoth. Prev: Dir. Gen. Brit. Nutrit. Foundat. Lond.; Prof. Human Nutrit. Univ. Glas.; Cons. Paediat. Sorrento Matern. & Selly Oak Hosps. Birm.

WHARTON, Brian Kenneth, Wing Cdr. Lady Braye Consulting Suite, St. Andrews Hospital, Billing Road, Northampton NN1 5DG Tel: 01604 616000 Fax: 01604 232325; 3 Hall Close, Harpole, Northampton NN7 4DY — MRCS Eng. LRCP Lond. 1952; FRCPsych 1983, M 1971; DPM Eng. 1960. (Lond. Hosp.) p/t Vis. Cons. Psychiat. St. And. Hosp. Socs: Expert Witnesses.Soc. Prev: Cons.

Psychiat. St. Crispin Hosp. N.ampton; Wing Cdr. RAF Med. Br., Advis. Neuro-Psychiat. RAF Germany.

WHARTON, Christopher Frederick Percy The Medical Unit, Farnborough Hospital, Orpington BR6 8ND Tel: 01689 814098; 24-26 High Street, Chipstead, Sevenoaks TN13 2RP Tel: 01732 452906 Fax: 01732 452906 — BM BCh 1964 Oxf.; DM Oxf. 1972, MA 1964; FRCP Lond. 1980, M 1969; MRCS Eng. LRCP Lond. 1963. (Oxf. & Guy's Hosp. Lond.) p/t Cons. Phys. Bromley Acute Hosps. Trust. Socs: Brit. & Europ. Cardiac Soc. Prev: Sen. Regist., Regist. (Med. & Cardiol.), Ho. Surg. & Ho. Phys. Guy's Hosp. Lond.

WHARTON, Elen Oak Street Surgery, Oak Street, Cwmbran NP44 3LT Tel: 01633 866719 Fax: 01633 838208 — MB BCh 1981 Wales; MRCGP (Distinc.) 1987.

WHARTON, Elizabeth Valerie 60A Main Street, Donaghcloney, Craigavon BT66 7LR Tel: 01762 881225; 24 Ballymacormick Road, Dromore BT25 1QR Tel: 01846 692030 — MB BCh BAO 1969 Belf.

WHARTON, Iain Philip 10 Old Village Road, Little Weighton, Cottingham HU20 3US — MB BS 1997 Newc.

WHARTON, John Graham Burntwood Health Centre, Hudson Drive, Burntwood, Walsall WS7 0EN Tel: 01543 670162; 22 Footherley Road, Shenstone, Lichfield WS14 0NJ Tel: 01543 480890 — MB ChB 1977 Liverp.; BSc (1st cl. Hons.) Chem. Nottm. 1971; MRCP (UK) 1979; MRCGP 1985. (Liverp.) Prev: Research Stud. (Chem.) Univ. Camb; Regist. (Med.) John Radcliffe Hosp. Oxf.

WHARTON, Lucy Helen St. Michael's Cottage, Black Bull Lane, Fulwood, Preston PR2 9YB; 25 Marlborough Road, London W4 4EU — MB BS 1993 Lond.

WHARTON, Mr Malcolm Robert 5 Moor Park Avenue, Preston PR1 6AS Tel: 01772 555640 Fax: 01772 555640; St Michaels Cottage, Black Bull Lane, Fulwood, Preston PR2 9YB Tel: 01772 719202 — MB ChB Manch. 1962; MChOrth Liverp. 1972; FRCS Ed. 1969; DObst RCOG 1964. (Manch.) Cons. Orthop. Surg. Preston Health Dist. Socs: Fell. Manch. Med. Soc. & Brit. Orthop. Assn. Prev: Sen. Regist. (Orthop.) Manch. RHB; Regist. (Orthop.) Roy. S.. Hosp. Liverp.; SHO (Surg.) Manch. Roy. Infirm.

WHARTON, Paul John 3 Norbury Crescent, Littleover, Derby DE23 7QT — MB ChB 1995 Manch.

WHARTON, Richard Lloyd Newbridge Surgery, 129 Newbridge Hill, Bath BA1 3PT Tel: 01225 425807 Fax: 01225 447776; Hamswell Farm, Hamswell, Bath BA1 9DG Tel: 01225 891234 Fax: 01225 892334 Email: rlwharton@msn.com — MB ChB 1976 Bristol; MRCGP 1984; DRCOG 1978. Lect. (Gen. Pract.) Sch. of Postgrad. Med.; Tutor (Gen. Pract.) Bath Univ. Prev: Assoc. Tutor (Gen. Pract.) Bath.

WHARTON, Mr Richard Quartermaine 3 Hall Close, Harpole, Northampton NN7 4DY — MB BS 1991 Lond.; FRCS Eng. 1996. (United Med. & Dent. Schs.) Specialist Regist., The Roy. Marsden Hosp., Fulham Rd, Lond. - Chelsea & W.minster Rotat. Socs: Assoc. of Surg.s inTrain. Prev: Research Fell. (Gen. Surg.) Chelsea & W.m. Gen. Hosp. Lond.

WHARTON, Simon Peter 43 Milton Road, Sheffield S7 1HP — MB BS 1992 Lond.

WHARTON, Stephen Barrie Neuropathology Laboratory, University of Edinburgh, Western General Hospital, Crewe Road, Edinburgh EH4 2XU Tel: 0131 537 1975 Email: s.wharton@ed.ac.uk — MB BS 1988 Lond.; MSc Camb. 1995; BSc (Hons.) Lond. 1985; MRCPath 1997. (Charing Cross and Westminster London) Sen. Lect. & Hon. Cons. Neuropath. W.ern Gen. Hosp. Edin. Socs: Brit. Neuropath. Soc. Prev: Sen. Regist. (Neuropath.) Addenbrooke's Hosp. Camb.; Hon. Regist. (Histopath.) Addenbrooke's Hosp. Camb.; SHO (Histopath.) Addenbrooke's Hosp. Camb.

WHATLEY, Roger John (retired) 496A Semington Road, Melksham SN12 6DX Tel: 01225 702436 — MB ChB 1960 Bristol; MRCGP 1968; DObst RCOG 1962; DCH Eng. 1962.

WHATLEY, Sheila Ann (retired) 496A Semington Road, Melksham SN12 6DX Tel: 01225 702436 — MB ChB 1960 Bristol.

WHATLING, Paul James Faculty of Medical Informantics, Royal College of Surgeons of Edinburgh, Nicolson Street, Edinburgh EH8 9DW Tel: 0131 527 3412 Fax: 0131 527 1746 Email: paul.whatling@rcsed.ac.uk; Tel: 07979 750203 Fax: 0870 130 4817 Email: paul.whatling@rcsed.ac.uk — MB BCh 1990 Wales; FRCS Ed. 1995. (Wales) Dir. Fac. of Med. Informantics, Roy. Coll. of Surg.s of Edin. Socs: Brit. Med. Informantics Soc. Prev: Specialist Regist. (Gen. Surg.) Roy. Berks. Hosp. Reading; Regist. (Gen. Surg.) Wexham Pk. Hosp. Slough; Research Regist. (Vasc. Surg.) Univ. Hosp. Birm. & Univ. Birm.

WHATMORE, Peter Banks (retired) 101 Fairfield Park, Ayr KA7 2AU Tel: 01292 269603 — MRCS Eng. LRCP Lond. 1957; MB BS Lond. 1957, LLB 1951, DPM 1961; FRCPsych 1979, M 1970. Cons. Psychiat. i/c Admin. Douglas Inch Centre Glas. & Scott Home & Health Dept. (Prisons Div.). Prev: Cons. Psychiat. Murray Roy. Hosp. Perth.

WHATMORE, Mr William John The Barn, Vicarage Road, Stoneleigh, Coventry CV8 3DH Tel: 024 76 41470 — MB ChB 1961 Ed.; FRCS Ed. 1965. (Ed.) Cons. Neurosurg. Coventry AHA & S. Warks. Health Dist. Socs: Soc. Brit. Neurol. Surgs. Prev: Sen. Regist. (Neurosurg.) Edin. Roy. Infirm.

WHATMOUGH, Philip Michael Ash Vale Health Centre, Wharf Road, Ash Vale, Aldershot GU12 5BA Tel: 01252 317551; 136 Shawfield Road, Ash, Aldershot GU12 6SG — MB BS 1982 Lond.; BSc Lond. 1979; MRCGP 1992; DRCOG 1992. (King's Coll. Hosp.) Prev: SHO (Neonat. Intens. Care & Paediat.) St. Mary's Hosp. I. of Wight; Trainee GP Niton Ventnor I. of Wight; SHO (Gen. Med.) St. Mary's Hosp. Newport I. of Wight.

WHEAL, John Derek Launceston Medical Centre, Landlake Road, Launceston PL15 9HH Tel: 01566 772131 Fax: 01566 772223; Sheers Barton, Lawhitton, Launceston PL15 9NJ — MB BChir 1971 Camb.; MA Camb. 1972, MB BChir 1971; DCH Eng. 1976; DObst RCOG 1974. (Guy's)

WHEAR, Mr Nicholas Michael Russells Hall Hospital, Dudley DY1 2HQ Tel: 01384 244169 Fax: 01384 244169; Lyttelton Croft, St. Kenelms Road, Romsey, Halesowen B62 0NE Email: nwhear@hotmail.com — MB BS 1986 Lond.; BDS (Hons.) Lond. 1978, MB BS (Hons.) 1986; LDS RCS 1979; FRCS Ed. 1989; FDS RCS Eng. 1989. Cons. Maxillofacial Surg. Dudley & Wolverhampton NHS Trust. Socs: Fell. Brit. Assn. Oral & Maxillofacial Surg.; Brit. Microsurgic. Soc. Prev: Sen. Regist. (Maxillofacial Surg.) St. Thos. Hosp.; Sen. Regist. St. Richards Hosp. Chichester; Regist. Kings & St. Geo. Hosp. Lond.

WHEATCROFT, David John County Health Centre, Nevells Road, Letchworth SG6 4TS Tel: 01462 684334 Fax: 01462 484876; The Coach House, Mill Lane, Stotfold, Hitchin SG5 4NU — MB ChB 1970 St. And. Letchworth Hosp.; Police Surg. Stevenage Div.; Research Asst. UK Prospective Diabetes Study; Clin. Asst. Diabetic Clinic Lister Hosp. Stevenage. Socs: BMA. Prev: SHO (Obst.) Barrnurs Home N.ampton Gen. Hosp.; Ho. Phys. Gloucester Roy. Hosp.; Ho. Surg. Maryfield Hosp. Dundee.

WHEATCROFT, John Dixon (retired) Heather Cottage, 36 Canford Cliffs Avenue, Parkstone, Poole BH14 9QN Tel: 01202 708185 — MRCS Eng. LRCP Lond. 1949. Prev: GP Partner Pk.stone.

WHEATCROFT, Mary Susan The Town House, 123-125 Green Lane, Derby DE1 1RZ — MB BChir 1985 Camb.; BA Oxf. 1983; BSc Soton 1980; MRCPsych 1991. Cons. Child & Adolesc. Psychiat. S. Derbysh., Ment. Health Trust.

WHEATCROFT, Stephen Bentley 6 Lambourne Drive, Nottingham NG8 1GR Tel: 0115 928 5901 — MB ChB 1994 Birm.; BSc (Hons.) Birm. 1991.

WHEATE, Harold Wilson, OBE (retired) 50 Avenue Road, Sutton SM2 6JB — MB BS 1941 Lond.; MRCS Eng. LRCP Lond. 1940. Prev: Dir. of Train. All Africa Leprosy & Rehabil. Train. Centre Addis Ababa.

WHEATER, Andrew William 15 Milner Avenue, Bury BL9 6NG Tel: 0161 705 2850 Email: bill.wheater@zen.co.uk — MB BS 1981 Newc.; BSc (Med. Sci.) St. And. 1978; MSc (Comp Sci.) Manch. 1995; MRCOG 1989. Cons. Gyn. Merseyside Clinic Liverp.

WHEATER, Mary Queen Elizabeth Hospital, Gayton Road, King's Lynn PE30 4ET; Crow Trees, Setch Road, Blackborough End, King's Lynn PE32 1SL — MB BChir 1988 Camb.; PhD Camb. 1970; MRCP (UK) 1992; FRCPCH 1997. (Cambridge) Cons. Paediat. Qu. Eliz. Hosp. King's Lynn. Socs: Brit. Paediat. Neurol. Assn.; Fell. Coll. Paediat. & Child Health; Brit. Assn. Perinatal Med. Prev: Sen. Regist. Rotat. Addenbrooke's Hosp. Camb. & Norf. & Norwich Hosp.

WHEATER, Matthew James Abbots Gate, Abbotsbrook, Bourne End SL8 5QS — BM 1998 Soton.

WHEATER, Rebecca Anne 19 Moness Crescent, Aberfeldy PH15 2DL — MB ChB 1992 Manch.

WHEATLEY

WHEATLEY, Alexander Hugh 36 Elm Road, Hale, Altrincham WA15 9QP — MB ChB 1991 Birm.; ChB Birm. 1991; FRCS 1996; FRCS 1995. Specialist Regist. (ENT) Manch.

WHEATLEY, Anna Marie Kingswood Health Centre, Alma Road, Kingswood, Bristol BS15 4EJ Tel: 0117 961 1774 Fax: 0117 947 8969 — MB ChB 1984 Bristol. Prev: Trainee GP Brighton HA VTS.

WHEATLEY, Mr Brian Eastfield House, Bellerby, Leyburn DL8 5QP — MB BS 1962 Durh.; FRCS Ed. 1967. Dir. Research & Developm. Environm. Contaminants Med. Serv. Br. Dept. Nat. Health & Welf. Ottawa, Canada. Socs: Internat. Leprosy Assn. & BMA. Prev: Asst. Dep. Minister Health Servs. Developm. Dept. Health & Human Resources Yukon Govt., Canada; Assoc. Dir. Gen. Operat. Med. Servs. Br. Dept. Nat. Health & Welf., Canada; Dir. Environm. Contaminants Program, Med. Servs. Br. Dept. Nat. Health & Welf. Canada.

WHEATLEY, Charles Henry 18 Cedar Heights, Petersham, Richmond TW10 7AE — MB ChB 1946 Ed. (Ed.)

WHEATLEY, Christopher John Leyburn Medical Practice, The Nurseries, Leyburn DL8 5AU Tel: 01969 622391 Fax: 01969 624446 — MB BS 1965 Durh.; MFFP 1994; MRCOG 1970. Trainer (Gen. Pract.) Leyburn. Prev: GP (Surg. Obst.) Frobisher Bay Gen. Hosp. Baffin Is., Canada; Regist. Leeds Matern. Hosp.; SHO Jessop Hosp. Wom. Sheff.

WHEATLEY, David Christopher Ipswich Hospital, Heath Road, Ipswich IP4 5PD Tel: 01743 712233; Hollymead, Bradford Road, Winsley, Bradford-on-Avon BA15 2HN — MB BS 1987 Lond.

WHEATLEY, Professor David John Department of Cardiac Surgery, Glasgow Royal Infirmary, 10 Alexandra Parade, Glasgow G31 2ER Tel: 0141 304 4730 Fax: 0141 552 0987 Email: d.j.wheatley@clinmed.gla.ac.uk; 13 Lochend Drive, Bearsden, Glasgow G61 1ED Tel: 0141 942 1381 — MD 1979 Cape Town; ChM 1976, MB ChB 1964; FRCS Ed. 1969. (Cape Town) Prof. Cardiac Surg. Univ. Glas. Socs: Eur. Assn. Cardiothoracic Surg.; (Vice-Pres.) Soc. Cardiothoracic Surgs. GB & Irel. Prev: Sen. Lect. & Hon. Cons. Cardiac Surg. Univ. Edin.

WHEATLEY, David Pearse Department of Psychological Medicine, Royal Masonic Hospital, Ravenscourt Park, London W6 0TN Tel: 020 8740 9000 Fax: 020 8741 8290; 69 Broughton Avenue, Richmond TW10 7UL Tel: 020 8948 3659 Fax: 020 8948 3659 — MB BChir 1945 Camb.; MA Camb. 1945, MD 1951; MRCS Eng. LRCP Lond. 1945; FRCPsych 1982, M 1976. (Camb. & Guy's) Cons. Psychiat. Roy. Masonic Hosp. Lond.; Head GP Research Gp. & Psychopharmacol. Research Gp.; Vis. Sci. (Psychiat.) Univ. S. Florida Tampa, USA; Med. Cons. Feighurer Research Inst. San Diego & Lond. Socs: Hon. Mem. Brit. Assn. Psychopharmacol.; (Ex-Pres.) Internat. Soc. Investig. Stress. Prev: Hon. Med. Assoc. Maudsley Hosp. Lond. i/c Stress Clinic; Edr. Stress Med.; Mem. New Clin. Drug Eval. Unit Nat. Inst. Ment. Health, USA.

WHEATLEY, Donald Stewart Prospect House Surgery, Prospect House, King Street, Aspatria, Carlisle CA7 3AH Tel: 016973 20224 Fax: 016973 23624 — MB 1971 Cambridge; BChir 1970. (Cambridge) GP Carlisle.

WHEATLEY, Duncan Angus 10 Colley Rise, Lyddington, Oakham LE15 9LL — MB BS 1992 Lond.

WHEATLEY, Elizabeth Ann Picu, King's College Hospital, Denmark Hill, London SE5 9LS; 24 Philbeach Gardens, Earls Court, London SW5 9DY — MB BS 1984 Lond.; FRCA 1993; DA (UK) 1990. (St. Marys) Cons. Anaesth. and Intens. Care. Prev: Sen. Regist. Gt. Ormond St. Lond.

WHEATLEY, Emma Catherine Royal Bolton Hospital, Minerva Road, Farnworth, Bolton BL4 0JR Tel: 01204 390762 Fax: 01204 390640 — MB ChB 1988 Leeds; MB ChB (Hons.) Leeds 1988; FRCA 1994; DA (UK) 1991. Cons. (Anaesth. & IC) Bolton. Socs: Med. Protec. Soc.; Intens. Care Soc.

WHEATLEY, Graham, Maj. RAMC The Officers' Mess, Wavell Barracks BFPO 45 — BM BS 1986 Nottm.; BMedSci Nottm. 1984, BM BS 1986. Regt.. Med. Off. 1 Qu. Lancs. Regt.

WHEATLEY, Ian Michael Hereward Group Practice, Hereward Medical Centre, Exeter St., Bourne PE10 9NJ Tel: 01778 393399 — MB ChB 1990 Leic.; 2000 (Dip. Primary Care Rheumat.) Bath; MRCGP 1994; DCH RCP Lond. 1994. (Univ. Leicester) Socs: Primary Care Rheum. Soc.; Brit. Med. Acupunture Soc.

WHEATLEY, Kathleen Anne Wheatley and Macdonald, 163 Birmingham Road, Allesley Village, Coventry CV5 9BD Tel: 024 7640 3250 Fax: 024 7640 5009 — MB ChB 1976 Birm.; BSc (Hons.) (Anat.) Birm. 1973, MB ChB 1976; MRCGP 1984.

WHEATLEY, Mr Kevin Edward 30 Wilsford Green, Oak Hill Drive, Edgbaston, Birmingham B15 3UG Email: kevin@wheat.demon.co.uk — MB BS 1979 Newc.; MD Newc. 1993; FRCS Eng. 1985; FRCS Ed. 1984. Cons. Surg. (Gen. Surg.) Sandwell Gen. Hosp. Prev: Career Regist. W. Midl.

WHEATLEY, Margaret Valley View, Canada Lane, Caistor, Lincoln LN7 6RN — MB ChB 1963 Sheff. Clin. Med. Off. Scunthorpe HA.

WHEATLEY, Pamela Margaret (retired) The Health Centre, Viewley Hill Centre, Hemlington, Middlesbrough TS8 9JQ Tel: 01642 590500 — MB ChB 1972 Sheff.; MRCGP 1987; MRCPsych 1978. p/t Clin. Asst. (Palliat. Care) Butterwick Hosp. Stockton; Regist. (Psychiat.) St. Luke's Hosp. Middlesbrough. Prev: SHO (Psychiat.) Hartlepool Gen. Hosp.

WHEATLEY, Peter Kenneth (retired) Southwold, The Plains, Wetheral, Carlisle CA4 8LA Tel: 01228 560610 — MB BS 1953 Lond. Prev: Clin. Asst. Whitehaven Hosp.

WHEATLEY, Richard John Old Station Surgery, 39 Brecon Road, Abergavenny NP7 5UH Tel: 01873 859000 Fax: 01873 850163 — MB ChB 1984 Bristol; MRCGP 1988; DRCOG 1986. GP Abergavenny. Prev: Trainee GP Avon VTS.

WHEATLEY, Robert Central School Clinic, 158 Whitegate Drive, Blackpool FY3 9HG — MB BS 1986 Newc.; MRCP (UK) 1990; MRCPCH 1996. Cons. Community Paediat. Centr. Sch. Clinic Blackpool. Socs: Brit. Assn. Community Child Health. Prev: Sen. Regist. (Community Child Health) Trent RHA, Derby & Leicester; Regist. (Paediat.) Stoke-on-Trent.

WHEATLEY, Robin The Surgery, Front Street, Pelton, Chester-le-Street DH2 1DE Tel: 0191 382 6703 Fax: 0191 382 6715; 26 Harthope Close, Rickleton Village, Washington NE38 9DZ Tel: 0191 417 7503 Email: rob@harthorpe.freeserve.co.uk — MB BS 1983 Newc.; MRCGP 1987. (Newc. u. Tyne)

WHEATLEY, Sally-Anne 48 Spoutwells Drive, Scone, Perth PH2 6SB — MB ChB 1983 Ed.

WHEATLEY, Susan Ruth 16 Mayfair Gardens, Boston PE21 9NZ — MB ChB 1986 Ed.; MRCGP 1991. (Edinburgh) Prev: GP Lincs.; SHO (ENT & Ophth.) Pilgrim Hosp. Boston; Trainee GP Boston.

WHEATLEY, Mr Timothy John 182 Knighton Church Road, Leicester LE2 3JL — MB ChB 1989 Leeds; FRCS Ed. 1993.

WHEATLEY, Trevor Princess Royal Hospital, Lewes Road, Haywards Heath RH16 4EX Tel: 01444 441885 Email: twheatla@mid-sussex.sthames.nhs.uic; Mote Croft, Church Lane, Horsted Keynes, Haywards Heath RH17 7AY Tel: 01825 790467 Email: trevw@pavilion.co.uk — MB BChir 1974 Camb.; MA Camb. 1974, MD 1988; FRCP Lond. 1994; MRCP (UK) 1976; MD Camb. 1988. Cons. Phys. P.ss Roy. Hosp. W. Sussex; Vis. Lect. (Biochem.) Univ. Sussex. Socs: Brit. Diabetic Assn.; Amer. Endocrine Soc.; N. Amer. Menopause Soc. Prev: Clin. Lect. (Med.) Camb. Univ.; Hon. Sen. Regist. Addenbrooke's Hosp. Camb.; Regist. (Med.) Addenbrooke's Hosp. Camb.

***WHEATLEY, Victoria Jane** 25 Woodleigh Avenue, Birmingham B17 0NW — MB ChB 1997 Birm.

WHEATLEY PRICE, Michael (retired) Manor Lodge, Chew Magna, Bristol BS40 8QE Tel: 01275 332488 — BM BCh 1958 Oxf.; MA Oxf. 1957, BM BCh 1958; Dip. Ven. Soc. Apoth. Lond. 1976. Prev: Cons. Genitourin. Med. Avon AHA (T).

WHEATLEY PRICE, Nicola The Hedges Medical Centre, Eyres Monsell, Pasley Road, Leicester LE2 9BU Tel: 0116 225 1277 Fax: 0116 225 1477 — MB ChB 1992 Leic.; DRCOG 1995. (Leic.) p/t GP Leic.

WHEATLY, Rachel Sarah Wythenshawe Hospital, Manchester M23 9LT Tel: 0161 998 7070 Fax: 0161 946 2603; 58 Hazel Road, Altrincham WA14 1JL Tel: 0161 928 8612 — MB ChB 1982 Manch.; FCAnaesth. 1990; DA (UK) 1986. Cons. Anaesth. S. Manch. Univ. Hosps. NHS Trust. Prev: Sen. Regist. & Regist. (Anaesth.) NW RHA; SHO (Anaesth.) Chester HA.

WHEATSTONE, Sarah Elizabeth Ellesmere Lodge, St James Rd, Malvern WR14 2TS — MB ChB 1997 Bristol.

WHEBLE, Andrew Marcus North Devon District Hospital, Raleigh Park, Barnstaple EX31 4JB Tel: 01271 22577/22786; Halsinger Farm, Halsinger, Braunton EX33 2NL Tel: 01271 814504 Fax: 01271 816139 — MB BS 1972 Lond.; MRCOG 1982; FRCOG 1996. (Kings College Hospital Medical School) Cons. O & G N.

Devon Dist. Hosp. Barnstaple. Prev: Sen. Regist. (O & G) N. W.. RHA; Lect. Qu. Charlotte's Hosp. & Chelsea Hosp. for Wom.; Research Regist. John Radcliffe Hosp. Oxf.

WHEBLE, Suzanne Margaret Avicenna, High Street, Hopton, Diss IP22 2QX Tel: 01953 681303 Fax: 01953 681305; Northern House, Fakenham Magna, Thetford IP24 2QX Tel: 01359 268398 — MB BS 1975 Lond. (King's Coll. Hosp.) Prev: GP Knutsford Chesh.; Trainee GP S. Manch. VTS; SHO (Chest & Gen. Med.) Barrowmore Hosp. Gt. Barrow.

WHEBLE, Mr Victor Henry, SBStJ (retired) Spindrift, 4 Higher Ham, Georgeham, Braunton EX33 1JN Tel: 01271 890826 Fax: 01271 891066 Email: victor@vhwheble.freeserve.co.uk — BM BCh 1944 Oxf.; MA Oxf. 1945, BA 1941, BM BCh 1944; FRCS Ed. 1947; DTM & H Antwerp 1947. Prev: Vis. Research Fell. Wniv. UMIST.

WHEELAN, Lorna (retired) 71 Cottenham Park Road, London SW20 0DR Tel: 020 8946 6663 — MD 1954 Aberd.; MB ChB 1948; FRCPsych 1973; DPM Lond. 1953. Prev: Cons. King's Coll. Hosp.

WHEELANS, John Craig 11 Ladylands Terrace, Selkirk TD7 4BB — MB ChB 1998 Glas.

WHEELDIN, William Chorley Road Surgery, 65 Chorley Road, Swinton, Manchester M27 4AF Tel: 0161 794 6287 Fax: 0161 728 3415 — MB ChB 1989 Manch.; MRCGP 1993.

WHEELDON, Mr Francis Tasker (retired) St. Maurice House, 101 Fore St., Plympton St Maurice, Plymouth PL7 1ND — MB BS 1942 Lond.; FRCS Eng. 1947; MRCS Eng. LRCP Lond. 1941. Prev: Cons. Orthop. Surg. Plymouth Health Dist.

WHEELDON, Katy 83 Marlborough Avenue, Broomhill, Glasgow G11 7BT — MB ChB 1998 Glas.

WHEELDON, Nigel Mark South Yorkshire Cardiothoracic Unit, Northern General Hospital, Herries Road, Sheffield S5 7AU Tel: 0114 243 4343 Fax: 0114 261 0350 — MB ChB 1986 Manch.; MD Manch. 1993; MRCP (UK) 1989. Cons. (Cardiol.) S. Yorks. Cardiothoracic Unit Sheff. Socs: Brit. Cardiac. Soc.; Brit. Cardiovasc. Interven. Soc.; Brit. Soc. Echocardiography. Prev: Sen. Regist. (Cardiol.) Cardiothoracic Unit N.. Gen. Hosp. Sheff.; Sen. Regist. & Lect. (Cardiovasc. Med.) Ninewells Hosp. & Med. Sch. Dundee; Research Regist. (Cardiovasc. Med.) Ninewells Hosp. Dundee.

WHEELDON, Peter Tasker (retired) Forge Cottage, Main Road, Swalcliffe, Banbury OX15 5EH Tel: 01295 780747 — MB BS 1970 Lond.; MRCS Eng. LRCP Lond. 1970; DObst RCOG 1974. Prev: GP Lond.

WHEELDON, Roger St Annes Group Practice, 161 Station Road, Herne Bay CT6 5NF Tel: 01227 742226 Fax: 01227 741439 — MB ChB 1968 Sheff.; DCH Eng. 1970. (Sheff.) GP Herne Bay. Prev: Regist. (Paediat.) Sheff. Childr. Hosp.

WHEELDON, Timothy Julian 31 Seymour Street, Dundee DD2 1HA — MB ChB 1990 Aberd. Regist. (Psychiat.) Roy. Cornhill Hosp. Aberd.

WHEELDON, Veronica Catherine 83 Marlborough Avenue, Broomhill, Glasgow G11 7BT Tel: 0141 339 7099 — MB ChB 1972 Glas. (Glas.) Clin. Med. Off. E. Dist. Gtr. Glas. HB.

WHEELER, Alison West View Surgery, 9 Park Rd, Veynsham, Bristol BS31 1BX Tel: 0117 986 3063 Fax: 0117 986 5061 — MB BS 1979 Newc.; MRCGP 1983; DRCOG 1982. p/t GP Princip.

WHEELER, Alyson Jane John Radcliffe Hospital, Headington, Oxford OX3 9DJ; 42 Churchward Close, Grove, Oxford — MB BCh 1992 Wales.

WHEELER, Anne Karen The Surgery, Miller Way, Wainscott, Rochester ME2 4LP Tel: 01634 717450; 11 Margetts Place, Lower Upnor, Rochester ME2 4XF — BM BS 1985 Nottm.; DFFP 1998; MRCGP 1996; Cert. Prescribed Equiv. Exp. JCPTGP 1989; DRCOG 1989. GP Princip.

WHEELER, Anthony John 69 Blackboy Lane, London N15 3AP — MB BS 1994 Lond.; BSc (Physiol.) Lond. 1979, MB BS 1994; MRCP UK 1997. (UCL) SHO (Paediat.) Roy. Free Hosp. Lond.

WHEELER, Daniel Wren 130 Victor Road, Penge, London SE20 7JT — BM BCh 1994 Oxf.; MA Oxf. 1991; MRCP (Lond.) 1997. (Oxf.) SHO (Anaesth.) Greenwich Hosp. Lond. Socs: MDU. Prev: SHO (Gen. Med.) Poole Hosp.; SHO (Elderly Care) Poole Hosp.; SHO (A & E) John Radcliffe Hosp. Oxf.

WHEELER, David Collins Centre for Nephrology, Royal Free+University College, Medical School, Uni. Coll. Lond. Royal Free Campus, Rowland Hill Street, London NW3 2PF Tel: 020 7830 2930 Fax: 020 79830 2125 Email: d.wheeler@rfc.ucl.ac.uk — MB ChB 1980 Birm.; FRCP 1999; MD Birm. 1991; MRCP (UK) 1984. Sen. Lect. in Nephrol., Roy. Free Hosp., Lond..; Hon. Cons. Nephrologist Roy. Free Hosp. Lond.. Prev: Lect. (Med.) Univ. Wales Cardiff; MRC Trav. Fell. Boston, USA; MRC Train. Fell. Roy. Free Hosp. Lond.

WHEELER, David John Holmcroft Surgery, Holmcroft Road, Stafford ST16 1JG Tel: 01785 242172; 17 Burton Manor Road, Stafford ST17 9QJ — MB ChB 1968 Ed.; DObst RCOG 1972. GP; Clin. Asst. (Thoracic Med.) Staffs. Gen. Hosp. Stafford. Prev: SHO (O & G) Groundslow Hosp. Tittensor; SHO Med. Renal Unit Roy. Infirm. Edin.; Ho. Phys. Roy. Infirm. Edin.

WHEELER, David Michael Gallions Reach Health Centre, Thamesmead, London SE28 8BE Tel: 020 8333 5000; 3 Gregor Mews, Langton Way, London SE3 7JX — BSc Lond. 1974, MB BS 1979; MRCP (UK) 1983; MRCGP 1987; DCH RCP Lond. 1981; AKC. Course Organiser Greenwich VTS. Prev: Lect. (Gen. Pract.) UMDS Guy's & St. Thos. Hosps. Lond.

WHEELER, David Victor (retired) Highbridge House, High Bridge, Dalston, Carlisle CA5 7DR Tel: 016974 76086 Email: doc.wheeler@tesco.net — MB BS 1967 Lond. Prev: Principlee Gen. Pract., Dalston Carlisle.

WHEELER, Helen Louise 3 Church Street, Hay-on-Wye, Hereford HR3 5DQ — MB BS 1994 Lond.

WHEELER, Mr James Malcolm Donald Dept. Of Surgery, Northampton General Hospital, Northampton; 42 Churchward Close, Grove, Wantage OX12 0QZ — MB BCh 1992 Wales; MD 2000 Wales; FRCS Eng. 1996. (Univ. Wales Coll. Med.)

WHEELER, Jeremy Stuart The Symons Medical Centre, 25 All Saints Avenue, Maidenhead SL6 6EL Tel: 01628 626131 Fax: 01628 410051; The Coppice, Green Lane, Littlewick Green, Maidenhead SL6 3RH — MB BS 1981 Lond.; MRCS Eng. LRCP Lond. 1981; MRCGP 1985; DCH RCP Lond. 1985; DRCOG 1984. (Char. Cross) Clin. Asst. (Paediat.) St. Marks Hosp. Maidenhead; Clin. Med. Off. Bramerton Ment. Handicap Resid. Homes. Socs: Windsor Med. Soc. Prev: Trainee GP Richmond VTS; SHO (Paediat., O & G & Accid.) Centr. Middlx. Hosp. Lond.

WHEELER, Mr John Howard 8 Little Brownings, Sydenham Rise, London SE23 3XJ Tel: 020 8699 1802 — MB BS 1963 Lond.; FRCS Eng. 1970; FRCS Ed. 1967; LMCC 1985. (Char. Cross) Cons. Gen. Surg. P.. Rupert. Reg. Hosp. B.C., Canada. Socs: BMA. Prev: Cons. Gen. Surg. G.R. Baker Hosp. Quesnel B.C., Canada; Cons. Gen. Surg. St. Nicholas Hosp. Lond.; Regist. (Surg.) Gen. Hosp. Nottm. & Char. Cross Hosp. Lond.

WHEELER, Julian Guy Sarum House Surgery, 3 St. Ethelbert Street, Hereford HR1 2NS Tel: 01432 265422 Fax: 01432 358440; Walnut House, Priors Frome, Mordiford, Hereford HR1 4EH — MB BS 1968 Lond.; MRCS Eng. LRCP Lond. 1968; DObst RCOG 1970. (Guy's)

WHEELER, Kate Anne Hero Department of Paediatrics, Oxford Radcliffe Hospital, Headley Way, Oxford OX3 9DU Tel: 01865 741166 Fax: 01865 221083 Email: kate.wheeler@paediatrics.oxford.ac.uk; 6 Donnington Square, Newbury RG14 1PJ Tel: 01635 38310 — MB BS 1976 Lond.; MRCP (UK) 1980; MRCGP 1987; DCH Eng. 1979; DRCOG 1978. p/t Cons. Paediat. (Paediat. Oncol.) Oxf. Radcliffe Hosp. Prev: Sen. Regist. (Paediat.) John Radcliffe Hosp. Oxf.; Leukaemia Research Fell. & Hon. Sen. Regist. (Oncol. & Haemat.) Hosp. Sick Childr. Lond.

WHEELER, Kenneth Mons (retired) Fulford, Tredegar NP22 4LP Tel: 01495 722592 — BSc Wales 1937, MB BCh (Distinc. Surg. & Pub; Health) 1940. Clin. Asst. The Gen. & St. Jas. Hosps. Tredegar. Prev: Med. Off. i/c Geriat. & Isolat. Units Ashvale Hse. Tredegar.

WHEELER, Kevin Iain 47 Dedmere Road, Marlow SL7 1PE — MB ChB 1995 Dundee; BMSc Dund 1993; DRCOG 1998. (Univ. Dundee) SNO Paeds/Neonates. Shrewsbary. Aug 1999.

WHEELER, Professor Malcolm Hubert Aldbourne House, Cottrell Drive, Bonvilston, Cardiff CF5 6TY Tel: 01446 781126 Fax: 01446 781127 Email: m.h.wheeler@btinternet.com — MB BCh Wales 1965; MD Wales 1973; FRCS Eng. 1970. p/t Prof. & Cons. Surg. Univ. Hosp. Wales & Roy. Infirm. Cardiff. Socs: (Sec. & Treas.) Internat. Assn. Endocrine Surgs.; (Ex-Pres.) Brit. Assn. Endocrine

WHEELER

Surgs.; Pres. Elect:- Internat. Assn. Eudowine Surg. Prev: Sen. Lect. & Cons. Surg. Welsh Nat. Sch. Med. & Llandough Hosp. Penarth.

WHEELER, Michael Thomas Kennington Fairwater Health Centre, Plasmawr Road, Fairwater, Cardiff CF5 3JT Tel: 029 2056 6291 Fax: 029 2057 8870; 35 Windsor Road, Radyr, Cardiff CF15 8BQ Tel: 029 2084 2936 — MD 1985 Wales; MB BCh 1966; FRCGP 1987, M 1972; DObst RCOG 1968. Prev: Ho. Surg. & Obst. Ho. Surg. Cardiff Roy. Infirm.; Ho. Phys. St. David's Hosp. Cardiff.

WHEELER, Murray Stuart 17 Burton Manor Road, Stafford ST17 9QJ — BM 1993 Soton.; MRCP 1996. Specialist. Reg. Paediat.Hull. Roy. Infirm.

WHEELER, Patrick Clive Gage c/o The William Harvey Hospital, Ashford TN24 0LZ — BM BCh 1968 Oxf.; DM Oxf. 1977, MA, BM BCh 1968; FRCP Lond. 1987; MRCP (UK) 1971. (St. Thos.) Cons. Phys. & Gastroenterol. SE kent Health Dist. Socs: Brit. Soc. Gastroenterol.; BMA. Prev: Cons. Phys. SE Kent Health Dist.; Regist. (Med.) St. Thos. Hosp. Lond.; Lect. & Sen. Regist. King's Coll. Hosp. Med. Sch.

WHEELER, Patrick Crane 286 Victoria Park Road, Leicester LE2 1XE Email: wheeler_patrick@hotmail.com — MB ChB 1998 Leic.

WHEELER, Peter John 82 Sloane Street, London SW1X 9PA Tel: 020 7245 9333 Fax: 020 7245 9232; 4 Chester Row, London SW1 9JH Tel: 0207 730 4727 — MB BS 1975 Lond.; BSc (1st cl. Hons. Neurobiol.) Lond. 1971; MRCP (UK) 1978; MRCS Eng. LRCP Lond. 1975; MRCGP 1981; DRCOG 1980. (Guy's & King's Coll. Hosp.) Apoth. to HRH The P. of Wales; Vis. Med. Off. King Edwd. VII Hosp. for Offs. Lond. Socs: Worshipful Soc. Apoth. Prev: Regist. (Med.) King's Coll. Hosp. Lond.

WHEELER, Richard Alexander Edward Aldbourne House, Cottrell Drive, Bonvilston, Cardiff CF5 6TY Tel: 01446 781126 Email: raew58@hotmail.com — MB ChB 1997 Birm. (Birmingham) SHO (Gen. Med.), Sutton Coldfield. Socs: BMA; MDU. Prev: Ho. Off. (Renal Med.) Qu. Eliz. Hosp. Edgbaston Birm.

WHEELER, Richard Handley (retired) Kingsclere, 14 Beacon Road, Ditchling, Hassocks BN6 8UL Tel: 01273 843173 — MB BChir 1942 Camb.; FRCP Lond. 1972, M 1948; FRCPsych 1972; DPM Lond. 1950. Prev: Cons. Psychiat. St. Francis Hosp. Haywards Heath.

WHEELER, Mr Robert Alec Consultant Paediatric Surgeon, Southampton General Hospital, Tremona Road, Southampton SO16 6YD Tel: 02380 794144 Email: robert.wheele@suht.nhs.uk; Haisborough House, Furzey Lane, Brockenhurst SO42 7WB Tel: 01590 612266 — MB BS 1982 Lond.; FRCPCH 2000; MS Soton. 1991; FRCS 1988. (Char. Cross Hosp. Lond.) Cons. Paediat. Surg. Wessex Regional Centre; Surg. Cdr. RNR; Medico - Legal Adviser, Roy. Navy. Socs: Brit. Assn. Paediat. Surg.; Medico-Legal Soc.; UK CCSG. Prev: Sen. Regist. & Resid. Asst. Surg. & (Paediat. Surg.) Gt. Ormond St. Lond.; Regist. (Paediat. Surg.) Soton. Gen. Hosp.

WHEELER, Roger John Martonside Medical Centre, 1a Martonside Way, Middlesbrough TS4 3BY Tel: 01642 812266 Fax: 01642 828722; 5 Muirfield, Nunthorpe, Middlesbrough TS7 0JN Tel: 01642 300546 — BM BS 1981 Nottm.; BMedSci Nottm. 1979; MRCGP 1985; Dip. Ther. Newc. 1995; DRCOG 1985. Prev: GP Princip. N. Ormesby Middlesbrough; GP Trainee Bassetlaw VTS.

WHEELER, Terence Keith (retired) Church Farm., Great Eversden, Cambridge CB3 7HU Tel: 01223 264264 Fax: 01223 264264 — MB BS 1961 Lond.; MRCS Eng. LRCP Lond. 1961; FRCR 1975; FFR (Rohan Williams Medal) 1970; DMRT Eng. 1968. Cons. Clin. Oncol. Addenbrooke's (NHS) Trust Camb. Univ. Teachg. Hosps. Trust Oxf. Anglia RHA. Prev: Sen. Asst. Radiother. Univ. Camb.

WHEELER, Timothy 5 Park Lane, Twyford, Winchester SO21 1QT — BM BCh 1968 Oxf.; DM Oxf. 1979; MRCS Eng. LRCP Lond. 1967; MRCOG 1974. (St. Bart.) Sen. Lect. Dept. Human ReProduc. Soton. Univ. Fell. Roy. Soc. Socs: Blair Bell Research Soc.

WHEELER, Valerie Ann Coles Lane Health Centre, Coles Lane, Linton, Cambridge CB1 6JS Tel: 01223 891456 Fax: 01223 890033; 2 Martins Lane, Linton, Cambridge CB1 6NG Tel: 01223 891774 — MB ChB 1984 Dundee; DRCOG 1987.

WHEELER, Victor Warren 6 Wickham Gardens, Wolverhampton WV11 1SQ — MB BS 1987 W. Indies.

WHEELER, William Frederick (retired) Toogoolawah, Partridge Lane, Newdigate, Dorking RH5 5EE Tel: 01293 862468 Fax: 01293 862169 Email: williamwheeel@aol.com — MRCS Eng. LRCP Lond. 1949. Prev: Asst. Chest Phys. (Thoracic Med.) Lond. Chest Hosp.

WHEELEY, Martin St George 3M Health Care Ltd, Morley St., Loughborough LE11 1EP Tel: 01509 613367 Fax: 01509 613030 Email: mwheeley@mm.com; Farthings Barn, Doctors Lane, Breedon on the Hill, Derby DE73 1AQ Tel: 01332 865476 — MB BChir 1973 Camb.; MA Camb. 1973; MRCS Eng. LRCP Lond. 1972; FFPM RCP (UK) 1992; Dip. Pharm. Med. RCP (UK) 1980. (Camb. & Guy's) Dir. of Pharmacovigilance, Europe. Socs: BMA. Prev: Dir. of Europ. Pharmacovigila. Wyeth-Ayerst, UK; Dir. Investig.al Drug Safety Bristol-Myers Squibb Brussels, Belgium; GP P'boro.

WHEELEY, Susan Marian NbC Community NHS Trust, Community Administration Offices, Yardley Hospital Site, Yardley Green Road, Birmingham B9 5PX — MB BS 1979 Lond.; MSc Lond. 1992, BA 1971; DCH RCP Lond. 1984.

WHEELWRIGHT, Mr Eugene Frederick 2 Camstradden Drive E., Bearsden, Glasgow G61 4AH Tel: 0141 943 1236 Fax: 0141 557 0468 — MB BS 1980 Lond.; BSc (Pathol.) Lond. 1977; FRCS Eng. 1984. (King's Coll. Hosp.) Cons. Orthop. Surg. Glas. Roy. Infirm. & Stobhill Gen. Hosp. Glas. Prev: Sen. Regist. (Orthop.) P.ss Margt. Rose Orthop. Hosp. & Roy. Infirm. Edin.; Regist. (Surg.) Roy. Hallamsh. Hosp. Sheff.; SHO (Orthop.) Roy. Nat. Orthop. Hosp. Stanmore.

WHEILDON, Margaret Hilda Epsom and St Helier NHS Trust, St Helier Hospital, Wrythe Lane, Carshalton SM5 1AA Tel: 020 8296 2000 Fax: 020 8296 2962 Email: mwheildon@sthelier.sghms.ac.uk; Bourton, Blundel Lane, Stoke D'Abernon, Cobham KT11 2SE Tel: 01932 868000 Email: mwheilden@aol.com — MB BS Lond. 1966; MRCS Eng. LRCP Lond. 1966; DObst RCOG 1968; DA Eng. 1970; FRCA Eng. 1979. (King's Coll. Hosp.) Macmillan Cons. Palliat. Med. Epsom & St. Helier NHS Trust. Prev: Med. Dir. St. Raphael's Hospice Cheam; SHO (Anaesth.) & Ho. Surg. (A & E) King's Coll. Hosp.; Ho. Phys. (Paediat.) Belgrave Hosp. Childr.

WHELAN, Alan Patrick The Old Stables, Woolston, North Cadbury, Yeovil BA22 7BL — MB BS 1991 Lond.; BSc Lond. 1988; MRCP (UK) 1994. Regist. (Cardiol.) Freemantle Hosp. Austral. Prev: Regist. (Emerg. & Gen. Med.) Freemantle Hosp., Austral.; SHO Rotat. (Med.) Roy. Sussex Co. Hosp.

WHELAN, Diana Elizabeth Oakbridge, Three Oaks, Hastings TN35 4NG Tel: 01424 752577 — MB BS 1939 Lond.; MRCS Eng. LRCP Lond. 1939.

WHELAN, Edmund 5 Stoneycroft Close, Liverpool L13 0AT Tel: 0151 228 6558 — MB ChB 1981 Liverp.; MA (Med. Ethics) Keele 1993; FFA RCS Eng. 1985. Cons. Anaesth. St. Helens & Knowsley HA. Prev: Sen. Regist. (Anaesth.) Mersey RHA; Research Fell. (Anaesth.) Vanderbilt Univ. Nashville, USA.

WHELAN, Jeremy Simon Department of Medical Oncology, The Middlesex Hospital, Mortimer St., London W1T 3AA Email: j.whelan@ucl.ac.uk; 43 Hillfield Park, Muswell Hill, London N10 3QU — MB BS Lond. 1984; MD Lond. 1993; MRCP (UK) 1988. Cons. Med. Oncol. Middlx. Hosp. Lond.

WHELAN, Joan Allan (retired) 49 North Castle Street, St Andrews KY16 9RG Tel: 01334 477734 — MB ChB 1948 St. And.; FFA RCS Eng. 1974; DObst RCOG 1950; DA Eng. 1955. Prev: Cons. Anaesth. Dr. Grays Hosp. Elgin.

WHELAN, Katherine Manor Farm House, East Carlton, Yeadon, Leeds LS19 7BG Tel: 0113 250 4987 — MB BS 1971 Lond. (Univ. Coll. Hosp.)

WHELAN, Laura Majella 11 Primate's Manor, Armagh BT60 2LP — MB BCh BAO NUI 1980.

WHELAN, Michael Joseph 116 St Micheal's Road, Crosby, Liverpool L23 7UW — MB BCh 1992 Wales.

WHELAN, Niall (retired) Arrochar, Meadow Lane, North Cockerington, Louth LN11 7ER — MRCS Eng. LRCP Lond. 1951. Clin. Asst. Alfred Morris Head Injury Rehabil. Unit MusGr. Pk. Hosp. Taunton. Prev: Police Surg. Leics. Constab.

WHELAN, Nicholas Hugh Danes Dyke Surgery, 463A Scalby Road, Newby, Scarborough YO12 6UB Tel: 01723 375343 Fax: 01723 501582; Top House, Newlands Road, Cloughton, Scarborough YO13 0AR — MB ChB 1984 Sheff.; MRCGP (Distinc.) 1992; Dip. Ther. (Distinc.) Newc. 1996; DRCOG 1988.

WHELAN, Mr Peter Manor Farm House, East Carlton, Yeadon, Leeds LS19 7BG — MB BS 1971 Lond.; MS Lond. 1981, MB BS 1971; FRCS Eng. 1975. Cons. Urol. St. Jas. Univ. Hosp. Leeds. Prev:

Sen. Regist. (Urol.) Leeds & Bradford; Wellcome Surgic. Research Fell. Nuffield Dept. Surg. Oxf.; John Marshall Fell. in Surg. Path. Univ. Coll. Hosp. Med. Sch. Lond.

WHELAN, Rachel Mary 31 Beehive Hill, Birmingham Rd, Kenilworth CV8 1BY — MB ChB 1997 Bristol.

WHELAN, Ranger Michael (retired) Shamiana, 62 Ferndale Road, Burgess Hill RH15 0HG — MB ChB 1951 Liverp.; MRCS Eng. LRCP Lond. 1951; FFA RCS Eng. 1957; DA Eng. 1957. Prev: Cons. Anaesth. Mid-Sussex Hosp. Gp.

WHELAN, Robert James, Maj. RAMC 4 Stanley Crescent, Prescot L34 3LP — MB ChB 1972 Liverp.; BSc (Hons.) (Physiol.) Liverp. 1969, MB ChB 1972. Maj. 1st Bn. The Roy. Welsh Fusiliers Dyfed.

WHELAN, Roxana Josephine Hamilton Coombe Orchard, 5 Aveley Lane, Farnham GU9 8PN Tel: 01252 723802; 23 Carlyle Road, West Bridgford, Nottingham NG2 7NQ Tel: 0115 981 1568 Email: roxana@globalnet.co.uk — BM BS 1995 Nottm.; BMedSci Nottm. 1993. (Nottm.) GP Regist. Nottm. Prev: SHO (Integrated Med.) Lincoln; SHO (A & E) Doncaster; Ho. Off. (Med.) Lincoln & Ho. Off. (Surg.) Banbury.

WHELAN, Timothy Ranger, Maj. RAMC Retd. Pyle Street Health Centre, The Dower House, 27 Pyle Street, Newport PO30 1JW Tel: 01983 523525 — MB BChir 1981 Camb.; MA Camb. 1982; MRCGP 1993; Cert. Family Plann. JCC 1993; DGM RCP Lond. 1992; DLO RCS Eng. 1990. (St. Thos.) GP Princip. Newport Isle of Wight. Socs: Airborne Med. Soc. Prev: Trainee GP I. of Wight HA; Specialist (ENT Surg.) RAMC.

WHELDON, David Bryant 74 Kimbolton Road, Bedford MK40 2NZ — MB ChB 1973 Bristol.

WHELDON, Geoffrey Robert Ridge Garth, Briggswath, Whitby YO21 1RT Tel: 01947 810045 — MB BS 1945 Durh. (Newc. upon Tyne) Prev: Hon. Phys. to H.M. the Qu.; PMO RN Sick Quarters HMS Nelson Portsmouth; Surg. Capt. RN.

WHELDON, Miss Harriet Seraphine 15 Western Lane, London SW12 8JS — MB BS 1993 Lond.; FRCS Lond. 1998. (St. Georges) SHO (Surg.) Watford & Mt. Vernon.

WHELDON, Philippa Mary 70 Stanley Road, Cambridge CB5 8LB — MB BS 1983 Lond.; MSc Surrey 1977; BA Oxf. 1976. (St. Thomas)

WHELEHAN, Irene Maria 105 Banner Cross Road, Sheffield S11 9HQ Tel: 0114 236 3537 — MB BS 1990 Lond.; BSc Lond. 1987; FRCOphth 1994. Regist. (Ophth.) Roy. Hallamsh. Hosp. Sheff. Prev: SHO Moorfields Eye Hosp. Lond.

WHELEHAN, Joseph Mary (retired) Hillworth Lodge, Devizes SN10 5ET — LRCPI & LM, LRSCI & LM 1947; LRCPI & LM, LRCSI & LM 1947. Prev: Clin. Asst. Roundway Hosp. Devizes.

WHERE, Julie Leonie 109 Milner Road, Wirral CH60 5RX — MB ChB 1992 Liverp.

WHETHAM, Jennifer Margaret School House, Ashmore, Salisbury SP5 5AA — BM BS 1997 Nottm.

WHETSTONE, Sarah Church Street Partnership, 30A Church Street, Bishop's Stortford CM23 2LY Tel: 01279 657636 Fax: 01279 505464 — MB BS 1983 Lond.

WHEWELL, John, OBE 5 Cortland Road, Nunthorpe, Middlesbrough TS7 0JX Tel: 01642 315429 — MB ChB 1942 Manch.; BSc, MB ChB Manch. 1942; FRCGP 1971; DObst RCOG 1957. (Manch.) Prev: Vis. Prof. Dept. Family Pract. Univs. Arizona & Iowa U.S.A.; Ho. Surg. Blackburn Roy. Infirm.; Res. Med. Off. Townleys Hosp. Bolton.

WHEWELL, Peter John Regional Department of Psychotherapy, Claremont House, Off Framlington Place, Newcastle upon Tyne NE2 4AA Tel: 0191 282 4542, 0191 282 4547 — BM BCh 1971 Oxf.; FRCPsych 1991, M 1978; MRCGP 1976; DCH RCPS Glas. 1976; DObst RCOG 1974. Cons. Psychother. Newc. City Health Trust, Newc. u. Tyne. Socs: Scott. Assoc. of Psychoanal. Psychother.; Director N. of Eng. Assn. for Train. in Psychoanaly. Psychother.; Assoc. Mem. Brit. PsychoAnalyt. Soc. Prev: Cons. (Psychother.) N.. Region Dryden Rd. Hosp. Gateshead; Ho. Off. (Med.) Bolingbroke Hosp. Lond.

WHEYWELL, Roger Owls Lodge, Forton, Andover SP11 6NU — MB ChB 1967 Sheff.; FFPM RCP (UK) 1995. Dir. of Research & Developm. Bayer plc, Pharmaceut. Div. Socs: FRSM; Brit. Assn. Pharmaceut. Phys.

WHIBLEY, Hannah Kathrine 222 Brookside Avenue, Coventry CV5 8AD; The Cottage, Astley Burf, Stourport-on-Severn DY13 0RX

Tel: 01299 826191 — MB BS 1987 Lond.; FRCA 1995. (St Georges.Hosp.Lond) Cons. Anaesth.

WHICHELLO, Karen Jane The Nook, Withyham Road, Groombridge, Tunbridge Wells TN3 9QP Tel: 01892 863326; Glenandred Lodge, Corseley Road, Groombridge, Tunbridge Wells TN3 9PN Tel: 01892 863699 — MB BS 1988 Lond.; MRCGP 1993; DRCOG 1991. (UMDS Guy's) GP Asst. Groombridge, E Sussex. Prev: Trainee GP Cuckfield VTS; SHO (ENT) Kent & Sussex Hosp. Tunbridge Wells; Ho. Phys. Guy's Hosp. Lond.

WHICHER, Professor John Templeman Rush House, Deighton, York YO19 6HQ Tel: 01904 728237 Fax: 01904 728522 Email: jwhicher@compuserve.com — MB BChir 1970 Camb.; MSc Lond. 1977; MA Camb. 1970; FRCPath 1990, M 1977. (Westm.) Indep. Cons. Laborat. Med. Socs: Assn. Clin. Biochems. Prev: Prof. Molecular Path. Experim. Cancer Research Univ. Leeds; Prof. Chem. Path. Univ. Leeds Cons. Chem. Path. Gen. Infirm. Leeds; Cons. Chem. Path. St. Jas. Univ. Hosp. Leeds.

WHILE, Mr Adrian Christopher Anthony Adzor House, Wellington, Hereford HR4 8AP — MB 1975 Camb.; BChir 1974; FRCS Ed. 1982; FRCOphth 1992. Cons. Surg. (Ophth.) Vict. Eye Hosp. Hereford. Prev: Fell. in Vitreoretinal Surg. & Oculoplastic Surg. Moorfields Eye Hosp.; Lond.; Resid. Surgic. Off. Moorfields Eye Hosp. Lond.

WHILE, Janet Anne Newtons Surgery, The Health Centre, Heath Road, Haywards Heath RH16 3BB Tel: 01444 412280 Fax: 01444 416943 — MB BCh 1980 Wales; MFFP 1995; MRCGP 1992; DRCOG 1983. (Welsh Nat. Sch. Med.)

WHILE, Robin Symington Armstrong Jubilee Field Surgery, Yation Keynell, Chippenham SN14 7EJ Tel: 01249 782204; The Old School, Burton, Chippenham SN14 7NZ Tel: 01249 782959 Fax: 01249 783110 Email: robin.while@gp-j83603.nhs.uk — MB BS 1972 Lond.; MRCS Eng. LRCP Lond. 1972; LMCC 1977; FRCEP 2000; DObst RCOG 1975; Cert. Family Plann. JCC 1975. (St. Bart.) Occupat. Health Adviser Hygrade Foods Ltd. & Wavin Bldg. Products; Sen. Lect. Dept. Gen. Pract. Postgrad. Sch. Med. Univ. Bath; Assoc. Adviser (Gen. Pract.) Bath & Swindon; Team Doctor, Bath Rugby PLC. Socs: Disp. Doctors Assn.; Bath Clin. Soc. Prev: SHO (Obst.) Roy. Berks. Hosp. Reading; SHO (Psychiat.) St. Bart. Hosp. Psychiat. Unit Lond.; SHO (Paediat.) Hillingdon Hosp. Uxbridge.

WHILLIER, David Edward Woodlands Health Centre, Allington Road, Paddock Wood, Tonbridge TN12 6AR Tel: 01892 833331 Fax: 01892 838269; Email: david.whillier@virgin.net — MB BChir 1969 Camb.; MA Camb. 1967; MSc Lond. 1988; FRCGP 1993, M 1975; DObst RCOG 1972. (Camb. & St. Thomas) GP Princip. Drs Warner, D. Whillier, Anderson, Cheales, Potterton & V. Whillier, Paddock Wood, Kent; Examr. RCGP.; Clin. Goverance Lead & Bd. Mem. Kent Weald PCG. Socs: Counc. Represen. SE Thames Fac. RCGP. Prev: Asst. Dean (CME) S. Thames (E.); Chairm. Twerps Locality Commiss.ing Gp.; Course Organiser Tunbridge Wells VTS.

WHILLIS, David Radiotherapy Department, Raigmore Hospital, Inverness IV2 3UJ — MB BS 1978 Lond.; MRCP (UK) 1983; FRCR 1988. Cons. Radiother. & Oncol. Highland HB.

WHILLIS, Joanna Elisabeth Helens Lodge, Inshes, Inverness IV2 5BG — MB ChB 1980 Sheff.; BMedSci Sheff. 1978, MB ChB 1980; DRCOG 1986; DA Eng. 1984.

WHIMSTER, Jean Helen 15 Johnsburn Haugh, Balerno, Edinburgh EH14 7ND — MB ChB 1969 Glas.

WHINCUP, Graham Hastings District General Hospital, Hastings Tel: 01424 720444; Homestall, The St, Sedlescombe, Battle TN33 0QD Tel: 01424 870495 Fax: 01424 758068 Email: graham@grahamw.cablenet.co.uk — MB ChB 1975 Bristol; MD Sheff. 1987; FRCP Lond. 1981. Cons. Paediat. Hastings HA. Socs: (Pres.) BMA; Chair LNC. Prev: Sen. Regist. (Paediat.) St. Mary's Hosp. Lond. & N.wick Pk. Hosp. Harrow.

WHINCUP, Harry Hynes British Telecom, Camelford House, 87 Albert Embankment, London SE1 7TP — MB ChB 1947 Liverp.; MB ChB (Hnrs.) Liverp. 1947; MFOM RCP Lond. 1978. (Liverp.) Med. Off. BT Lond.; Accredit. Specialist Occupat. Med. Socs: Soc. Occupat. Med. Prev: Regional Med. Off. Brit. Telecom NW; Vis. Worker MRC Unit Research into Occupat. Aspects of Ageing Univ. Liverp.; Area Med. Off. Brit. Rlys.

WHINCUP, Peter Hynes Department of Public Health Sciences, St. George's Hospital Medical School, London SW17 0RE Email:

WHINN

p.whincup@sghms.ac.uk — MB BChir 1981 Camb.; PhD (Epidemiol.) Lond. 1991; FRCP 1997; MRCP (UK) 1983; FFPHM 1997; MFPHM 1993. Prof. St. Geo.'s Hosp. Med. Sch. Socs: Brit. Cardiac Soc.; Brit. Hypertens. Soc. Prev: Reader (Epidemiol.) Roy. Free Hosp. Sch. Med. Lond.; Brit. Heart Foundat. Research Fell. Roy. Free Hosp. Sch. Med. Lond.; Regist. (Med.) Ipswich Hosps.

*WHINN, Olivia Hannah 16 The Chesters, Newcastle upon Tyne NE5 1AF — MB ChB 1998 Birm.

WHINNEY, Mr David John Dickens 14 Osier Crescent, Muswell Hill, London N10 1QU Tel: 020 8442 2549 — MB BS 1989 Lond.; FRCS Eng. 1994.

WHIPP, Elisabeth Clare 25A Alma Road, Bristol BS8 2BZ — BM BCh 1972 Oxf.; MA Oxf. 1981; FRCR 1978. Cons. (Radiother. & Oncol.) Bristol Roy. Infirm. Prev: Sen. Regist. (Radiother. & Oncol.) Hammersmith Hosp. Lond.

WHIPP, Rev. Margaret Jane Hartlepool and District Hospice, 13 Hutton Avenue, Hartlepool TS26 9PW Tel: 01429 282100; Westlands, 12 St Charles Road, Tudhoe Village, Spennymoor DL16 6JY Tel: 01388 811461 Email: margaretwhipp@msn.com — MB ChB 1979 Sheff.; BA Oxf. 1976; MRCP (UK) 1982; FRCR 1986; FRCP 1988. Cons. (Palliat. Med.) Hartlepool Dist. Hospice; Med. Dir. Hartlepool & Dist. Hospice. Prev: Regist. (Med. Rotat.) Roy. Hallamshire Hosp. Sheff.; Cons. (Clin. Oncol.) W.on Pk. Hosp. Sheff.

WHIPPLE, Sarah Jane Bridget 21 Hampden Road, Wantage OX12 7DP Tel: 01235 770079; 21 Hampden Road, Wantage OX12 7DP Tel: 01235 770079 — MRCS Eng. LRCP Lond. 1980; Dip Family Plann. 1984. Locum GP in single handed Pract. Drayton Oxf.shire; Lately half term locum for 6/12 at Long Farlay Surg., Abirjda Cars, Matern. leave, Applying for partnership Curr.ly. Socs: BMA. Prev: Clin. Med. Off. (Community Child Health) W. Berks. Health Serv.; Resid. MO Camden Dist. NSW, Austral.; Clin. Asst. Chorleywood Elm Pract. Herts.

*WHISHAW, Evelyn Mary Watson Mead, Meadrow, Godalming GU7 3BZ Tel: 01483 415026 — LMSSA 1960 Lond.

*WHISKER, Lisa Jane 20 Windmill Drive, Croxley Green, Rickmansworth WD3 3FD — MB ChB 1998 Birm.

WHISKER, Richard Barrington 42 Shepherds Croft, Portland DT5 1DJ; 42 Shepherds Croft, Portland DT5 1DJ — MB ChB 1980 Leeds. (Leeds) Assoc. Specialist Anaesth., W. Dorset Hosps.

WHISKER, William Barrington Pennine Lodge, Old Lane, Sowerby Bridge HX6 4PA — MB ChB 1957 Bristol; DPH 1962; MFCM 1972. (Bristol) Cons. Community Phys. Oldham AHA & Proper Off. Oldham Metrop. DC. Prev: MOH Dewsbury Co. Boro.

WHISTLER, David Mark The Mote Medical Practice, St Saviours Road, Maidstone ME15 9FL Tel: 01622 756888 Fax: 01622 672573; Home Ville, Mill Bank, Headlorn, Ashford TN27 9RD Tel: 01622 891592 Email: markwhistler@compuserv.com — MB ChB 1979 Cape Town; MRCGP 1986. (UCT)

WHISTON, Rhona Jayne 115 Stock Lane, Wybunbury, Nantwich CW5 7HE — MB ChB 1993 Liverp.

WHISTON, Mr Richard John University Hospital of Wales, Heath Park, Cardiff CF14 4WZ Tel: 02920 743576 Email: whistonry@cf.ac.uk; 18 Heol-y-Felin, Rhiwbina, Cardiff CF14 6NB Tel: 02920 522991 — BM BS 1986 Nottm.; BMedSci 1984 Nottm.; DM 1995 Nottm.; FRCS 1991 Eng. (University of Nottingham) Cons. Gen. & Vasc. Surg. Univ. Hosp. Wales Cardiff. Prev: Regist. (Gen. Surg.) Univ. Hosp. Wales Cardiff.; SHO (A & E) Derbysh. Roy. Infirm.; SHO (Gen. Surg.) Nottm.

WHITAKER, Andrew Spencer Whitaker and Partners, 53 Bridge Street, Brigg DN20 8NS Tel: 01652 657779 Fax: 01652 659440; Tout Pres, Little Lane, Wrawby, Brigg DN20 8RW Tel: 01652 657908 — MB ChB 1980 Manch.; MRCGP 1984; DRCOG 1983. Prev: Trainee GP Cumbria VTS; Ho. Phys. & Ho. Surg. Roy. Lancaster Infirm.

WHITAKER, Anthony John 123 Skegby Lane, Mansfield NG19 6PF — MRCS Eng. LRCP Lond. 1973; FRCA 1978. (Leeds) Cons. Anaesth. i/c Intens. Care Kings Mill Hosp. Mansfield. Socs: Assn. Anaesths. & BMA; Intens. Care Soc.

WHITAKER, Mr Bernard Langdon (retired) Urquhart House, 71 High St., Buntingford SG9 9AE Tel: 01763 271293 — MB BS 1949 Lond.; MS Lond. 1971; FRCS Eng. 1957; MRCS Eng. LRCP Lond. 1949. Prev: Cons. Surg. Co. Hosp. Hertford & Qu. Eliz. II Hosp. Welwyn Gdn. City.

WHITAKER, Brian Carrstones, Halifax Road, Ripponden, Sowerby Bridge HX6 4AH Tel: 01422 822444 — MB ChB 1957 Leeds; DObst RCOG 1965. Med. Off. Overgate Hospice Elland. Socs: MRCGP; Fell. BMA. Prev: GP W. Yorks.; Ho. Surg. Leeds Gen. Infirm.; Ho. Phys. & Ho. Off. (Obst.) Halifax Gen. Hosp.

WHITAKER, David Kenneth 22 Pine Road, Manchester M20 6UZ Tel: 0161 445 8474 — BM BS 1975 Nottm.; BMedSci (Hons.) Nottm. 1973, BM BS 1975; FFA RCS Eng. 1980. Cons. (Anaesth.) Manch. Roy. Infirm. Socs: Manch. Med. Soc.; FRSM. Prev: Sen. Regist. (Anaesth.) Roy. Perth Hosp. W.. Australia; Regist. (Anaesth.) Wythenshawe Hosp. Manch.; Ho. Phys. Univ. Dept. Therap.

WHITAKER, Donald Callum Home Farmhouse, 36 The Street, Puttenham, Guildford GU3 1AR — MB ChB 1993 Ed.; FRCS (Ed.) 1997. (Edinburgh) Res. Fell., Cardiothoracic Surg., Middlx. Hosp., Lond.

WHITAKER, Geoffrey Brian (retired) 25 Exeforde Avenue, Ashford TW15 2EF Tel: 01784 254408 — MB BS Lond. 1949; DObst RCOG 1951. Prev: Obst. Ho. Surg. New End Hosp. Hampstead.

WHITAKER, George Robert Bruce (retired) White Edge, The Bent, Curbar, Calver, Sheffield S32 3YD — MB ChB 1947 Sheff.

WHITAKER, Graham 14 St Fagans Drive, St. Fagans, Cardiff CF5 6EF — MB BS 1992 Lond.

WHITAKER, Helen Jane Eccleston Health Centre, 20 Doctors Lane, Eccleston, Chorley PR7 5RA Tel: 01257 451221 Fax: 01257 450911 — MB ChB 1988 Leic.

WHITAKER, Mr Ian Alexander University Department of Orthopaedics, Clinical Science Building, St James Hospital, Beckett St., Leeds LS9 7TF — MB BS 1981 Lond.; FRCS 1985. (Char. Cross) Tutor (Orthop. Surg.) St. Jas. Univ. Hosp. Leeds. Socs: Assoc. Brit. Orthop. Assn. Prev: Rotat. Surg. Regist. Leeds E. HA; MRC Research Fell.

WHITAKER, Ian Michael 25 Fossway, York YO31 8SF — MB ChB 1972 Aberd.; BMedBiol 1969; MRCPsych 1977. Assoc. Fac. Homoeop.

WHITAKER, James Alexander John Milford Crossroads Surgery, Church Rd, Godalming GU8 5QR Tel: 01483 414461 Email: hamish.whitaker@gp-h81031.nhs.uk; East Overton, Brook, Godalming GU8 5UH — MB BS 1981 Lond.; MA Camb. 1981; MRCGP 1987. (Lond. Hosp.) GP Milford.; GP Tutor Guildford; GP Trainer Guildford, Chairm. W. Surrey PC Clin. Audit Grp. Prev: Trainee GP Epsom Dist. Hosp. VTS.

WHITAKER, Joan Winfield 35 Mayfair Gardens, Woodford Green IG8 9AB Tel: 020 8504 0819 — LRCP LRCS 1952 Ed.; LRCP LRCS Ed. LRFPS Glas. 1952; DObst RCOG 1957; Asst. MOH Waltham Forest. Prev: O & G Regist. Coventry & Warw. Hosp.; Ho. Surg. Simpson Memor. Pavil. Roy. Infirm. Edin.

WHITAKER, John Joseph Harrogate District Hospital, Lancaster Park Road, Harrogate HG2 7SX Tel: 01423 885959 Fax: 01423 881139 Email: john.whitaker@hhc-tr.northy.nhs.uk — MB ChB 1979 Ed.; FRCP 1996 London; MRCP (UK) 1982. Cons. Geriat. Med. Harrogate Healthcare NHS Trust.

WHITAKER, Jonathan Faraday (retired) Home Farmhouse, Puttenham, Guildford GU3 1AR Tel: 01483 810632 — MB BS Lond. 1957; DObst RCOG 1963. Prev: Ho. Surg. Roy. N.. Hosp.

WHITAKER, Juliet Mary Pump House, 27 Pump Hill, Loughton IG10 1RU — MB BChir 1992 Camb.

WHITAKER, Margaret Rosevear (retired) 21 Dene Park, Didsbury, Manchester M20 2GF — MB ChB 1949 Manch. Prev: Med. Off. Regional Blood Transfus. Serv. Manch.

WHITAKER, Mark John Didsbury Medical Centre, 645 Wilmslow Road, Didsbury, Manchester M20 6BA Tel: 0161 445 1957 Fax: 0161 434 9931; 13 Pine Road, Didsbury, Manchester M20 6UY — MB ChB 1982 Manch.; BSc (Hons.) Manch. 1976. Hosp. Practitioner, Gastroenterol.

WHITAKER, Nicola Harriet Georgina Yew Tree Cottage, Greys Green, Rotherfield Greys, Henley-on-Thames RG9 4QQ — MB BChir 1977 Camb.; MRCP (UK) 1979; MRCGP 1981. Clin. Asst. (Neurol. Rehabil.) Oxf. Prev: GP Oxf.; Sen. Regist. (Pub. Health Med.) Oxf.

WHITAKER, Nicola Tracey Hall Floor Flat, 28 West Park, Bristol BS8 2LT — MB ChB 1985 Bristol.

WHITAKER, Philip John 27 Beaumont Street, Oxford OX1 2NR Tel: 01865 311500 Fax: 01865 311720 Email: phil.whitaker@k-84049.nhs.uk — BM BS 1990 Nottm.; MA Univ. E. Anglia 1996;

MRCGP 1995; DFFP 1995. (Nottm.) GP Princip. Oxf.; Forens. Med. Examr., Thames Valley Police, Oxf.

WHITAKER, Mr Robert Henry (retired) 21 High Street, Great Shelford, Cambridge CB2 5EH Tel: 01223 843636 Fax: 01223 843636 — MB BChir 1964 Camb.; MA Camb. 1964, MD 1986, MChir 1967; FRCS Eng. 1967. Asst. Clin. Anatomist Univ. Camb. Prev: Hon. Sen. Lect. Inst. Urol. Lond.

WHITAKER, Roger X-Ray Department, Derbyshire Royal Infirmary, Derby — MB ChB 1952 Manch.; FFR 1961; DMRD Eng. 1959; Cons. Radiol Derby Hosp. Gp.

WHITAKER, Sarah Patricia East Overton, Brook, Godalming GU8 5UH — MB BS 1980 Lond.

WHITAKER, Simon Charles Department of Radiology, University Hospital, Nottingham NG7 2UH Tel: 0115 924 9924 Email: simon.whitake@nottingham.ac.uk; The Hazels, Pk Avenue, Plumtree Park, Nottingham NG12 5LU Tel: 0115 937 2775 — MB BChir 1983 Camb.; MA, MB Camb. 1983, BChir 1982; MRCP (UK) 1985; FRCR 1989. (Camb. & Middlx.) Cons. Radiol. Univ. Hosp. Nottm. Prev: Sen. Regist. (Radiol.) Univ. Hosp. Nottm.; SHO (Neurol.) The Brook Hosp. Lond.; SHO (Med.) Roy. Sussex Co. Hosp. Brighton.

WHITAKER, Stephen Gerard Locks Road Surgery, 51 Locks Road, Locks Heath, Southampton SO31 7ZL Tel: 01489 583777 Fax: 01489 571374 Email: stephen.whitaker@gp-j82023.nhs.uk; 83 Raley Road, Locks Heath, Southampton SO31 6PB Tel: 01489 601272 Fax: 01489 601744 Email: sgwhit@ntlworld.com — MB ChB 1975 Ed.; BSc Ed. 1972. (Ed.) Socs: BMA. Prev: Trainee GP Dudley & Stourbridge VTS; Ho. Off. (Gen. Med.) Bangour Gen. Hosp. Broxburn; Ho. Off. (Gen. Surg.) Greenock Roy. Infirm.

WHITAKER, Stephen John 24 The Crescent, Belmont, Sutton SM2 6BJ — BM 1981 Soton.; MRCP (UK) 1985; FRCR 1989.

WHITAKER, Tom (retired) 21 Dene Park, Didsbury, Manchester M20 2GF Tel: 0161 445 2560 — LLB Lond. 1965; MB ChB Manch. 1949. Prev: GP Manch.

WHITAKER, Valerie Suzanne Whitaker and Partners, 53 Bridge Street, Brigg DN20 8NS Tel: 01652 657779 Fax: 01652 659440; Blueberry House, 1 Maltkiln Lane, Brigg DN20 0RC — MB ChB 1980 Manch.; Member Institute of Psychosexual Medecine 1991; BSc St. And. 1977; MRCGP 1984; DRCOG 1982. Socs: Inst. Psychosexual Med. Prev: GP Kirton Lindsey; Trainee GP E. Cumbrian VTS; Ho. Surg. Salford Roy. Hosp.

WHITAKER, William Stoke House, Bar Lane, Wakefield WF1 4AD Tel: 01924 372374 — MB ChB (Hons.) Leeds 1943; BSc (Hons.) Leeds 1941, MD 1946; FRCP Lond. 1963, M 1948. (Leeds) Emerit. Cons. Phys. Leeds Gen. Infirm. Socs: Assn. Phys. & Irel. & Cardiac Soc. Prev: Sen. Clin. Lect. (Med.) Univ. Leeds; Cons. Cardiol. United Leeds Hosps.; Cons. Phys. Leeds RHB.

WHITBREAD, Lynette Forge Cottage, Middle St., Burton, Lincoln LN1 2RG — MB ChB 1969 Manch. Prev: Clin. Asst. Cas. Kent & Sussex Hosp. Tunbridge Wells; Cas. Off. Char. Cross Hosp. Lond.; SHO Kent & Sussex Hosp. Tunbridge Wells.

WHITBREAD, Rhoderick Peter Wragby Surgery, Old Grammar School Way, Wragby, Market Rasen LN8 5DA Tel: 01673 858206 Fax: 01673 857622; 13 Minster Road, Lincoln LN2 1PW Email: rhodw@aol.com — MB BS 1976 Lond.; FRCGP 1994. (King's College Hosp.) Princip. in GP; Adviser in BP Lincs.

WHITBREAD, Mr Timothy, Wing Cdr. Department of Surgery, Royal hospital Haslar, Haslar Road, Gosport PO12 2AA Tel: 02392 584255 Fax: 02392 762960 Email: timowhit@dsca.gov.uk — MB BS 1982 Lond.; FRCS Eng. 1990; FRCS Gen 1998. (Guys hospital) Cons. In Gen. And Vasc. Surg., Roy. Hosp. Halsar, Gosport, Hants..; Cons. Vasc. Surg., Qu. Alexandra Hosp.; Roy. Coll. Surgic. tutor.

***WHITBY, Anh Van** 20 Padstow Road, Enfield EN2 8BU — MB BS 1994 Lond.

WHITBY, Mr David Jonathan Wythenshawe Hospital, Southmoor Road, Manchester M23 9LT Tel: 0161 291 6383 Fax: 0161 291 4077 — MB BS 1979 Lond.; FRCS Eng. 1983; MRCS Eng. LRCP Lond. 1979; T(S) 1992. (Char. Cross) Cons. Plastic Surg. Univ. Hosp. S. Manch. Socs: Brit. Assn. of Plastic Surg.s (BAPS); Brit. Assn. of Aesthetic Plastic Surg.s (BAAPS); Craniofacial Soc. of Gt. Britain & Irel. (- Hon. Edit. Represen.). Prev: Sen. Regist. (Plastic Surg.) St. Jas. Univ. Hosp. Leeds; Regist. (Plastic Surg.) Univ. Hosp. S. Manch.; Smith & Nephew Research Fell. Univ. Calif., San Francisco 1990-91.

WHITBY, Elizabeth Barbara Scarborough Hospital, Scarborough YO12 6QL — MB BS 1975 Lond.; FRCS Eng. 1982. Cons. ENT ScarBoro. Dist. Gen. Hosp.

WHITBY, James Douglas (retired) 127 Warkton Lane, Barton Seagrave, Kettering NN15 5AP — MRCS Eng. LRCP Lond. 1943; MA Camb. 1950, MB BChir 1947; FFA RCS Eng. 1954; DA Eng. 1949. Prev: Anaesth. Gen. Hosp. Newc.

WHITBY, Margaret Evelyn The Green Practice, Waterside Health Centre, Beaulieu Road, Hythe SO45 4WX Tel: 023 8084 5955 Fax: 023 8020 1292; Homefield, Fritham, Lyndhurst SO43 7HL Tel: 02380 812132 — MB ChB 1983 Sheff.; MRCGP 1989; D.Occ.Med. RCP Lond. 1996. (Sheff.)

WHITBY, Peter James 1 Becontree Road, Liverpool L12 2BD — MB ChB 1997 Sheff.

WHITBY, Rachel Margaret Freens Ley, Busy Hill, Sutton St Nicholas, Hereford HR1 3AY — MB ChB 1979 Birm.

WHITBY, Robin James Linden Medical Group, Linden Medical Centre, Linden Avenue, Kettering NN15 7NX Tel: 01536 512104 Fax: 01536 415930; 3 Broom Way, Kettering NN15 7RB Tel: 01536 516043 — MB BS 1975 Lond.; DRCOG 1977. (Roy. Lond. Hosp. Med. Coll.) GP Kettering. Socs: Kettering & Dist. Ethical Comm. Prev: Trainee GP Hemel Hempstead; SHO Rotat. (Surg.) Norf. & Norwich Hosp.; SHO (A & E) Harold Wood Hosp.

WHITBY, Ruth (Alexander) St. George's Medical Centre, 7 Sunningfields Road, London NW4 Tel: 0208 202 6232; 991 Finchley Road, London NW11 7HB Tel: 0208 455 6710 Email: jben@whitby30.freeserve.co.uk — Japanese Medical Licence 1994; BSc (1st. Co. Hons.) Lond. 1986, MB BS 1989 1989 Lond.; DRCOG 1993. (King's College, London) G.P. at St. Geo.'s Med. Centre, Lond. NW4; Well Woman Clinic at Hillside Med. Centre, 151 N. End Rd., Lond. NW1. Prev: SHO (Paediat.) St. Mary's Hosp. Lond.; GP in Tokyo, Japan 1994-97; GP in Lond.; as above.

WHITBY, Sydney 37 Ravenscourt, Thornton Hall, Glasgow G74 5AZ Tel: 0141 644 5800 — LRCP LRCS 1951 Ed.; LRCP LRCS Ed. LRFPS Glas. 1951. (Anderson Coll. Med., Glas.) Socs: BMA. Prev: Ho. Surg. Roy. Sussex Co. Hosp.

WHITBY, Thomas Edgar (retired) Tyddyn-y-Traeth, Broad Beach Road, Rhosneigr LL64 Tel: 01407 810392 — MB ChB 1936 Liverp.; MRCS Eng. LRCP Lond. 1938.

WHITBY, William Stephen Hollybank, Stone St., Stanford North, Ashford TN25 6DF Tel: 01303 813304 — MB BS Lond. 1978; MRCGP 1983; DRCOG 1980.

WHITBY-SMITH, Brett James Ash Vale Health Centre, Wharf Road, Ash Vale GU12 5BA Tel: 01252 317551 Fax: 01252 338194 Email: brett.whitby-smith@gp-h81013.nhs.uk; Copse End, Glaziers Lane, Normandy, Guildford GU3 2EB — MB BS 1978 Lond.; MRCS Eng. LRCP Lond. 1978; MRCGP 1983; DRCOG 1981. (Roy. Free)

WHITCHER, David Martin The Tollerton Surgery, 5-7 Hambleton View, Tollerton, York YO612EW Tel: 01347 838231 Fax: 01347 838699 — MB ChB 1971 St. And. Prev: Regist. (Med.) York Dist. Hosp.; SHO (Med.) Soton. Univ. Hosps.

WHITCHER, Harold Wray, OBE, TD 5 Broadlands, Farnborough GU14 7ER; 5 Broadlands, Farnborough GU14 7ER — MB ChB 1939 Ed.; MA Oxf. 1954. (Univ. Ed.) Socs: Fell. Roy. Soc. of Med.

WHITCOMBE, Elizabeth Marion 44 Regent's Park Road, London NW1 7SX Tel: 020 7586 2436 — MB ChB 1981 Otago; PhD Lond. 1967; MA Oxf. 1962; MA New Zealand 1960.

WHITCROFT, Ian Andrew 38 Sheerwater Close, Padgate, Warrington WA1 3JE — MRCS Eng. LRCP Lond. 1979; MD Washington DC 1984; MD Liverp. 1986, MB ChB 1979; MRCP (UK) 1982; T(M) 1995; Cert. Family Plann. JCC 1986. Reader (Dermat.) Univ. Brit. Columbia, Canada. Prev: Att. Phys. (Internal Med.) Pierce Co. Health Dept. Tachma Wash. USA; Att. Phys. (Internal Med. & Emerg.) Wentworth Douglas Hosp. Dover NH, USA.

WHITCROFT, Sovra Isabella Jan Department of Obstetrics & Gynaecology, Royal Surrey County Hospital, Egerton Road, Guildford GU2 7XX Tel: 01483 571122 — MB ChB 1981 Liverp.; MRCOG 1989. Cons. O & G Roy. Surrey Co. Hosp. Guildford. Prev: Sen. Regist. (O & G) John Radcliffe Hosp. Oxf.; Regist. & SHO (O & G) S.mead Hosp. Bristol; SHO (O & G) Gen. & Matern. Hosps. Bristol.

WHITE, Adam Buchanan (retired) Norton Holt, Lanes End, East End, Hook Norton, Banbury OX15 5LG Tel: 01608 737789 — MRCS Eng. LRCP Lond. 1937; MD Manch. 1950, MB ChB 1937, DPH 1939. Prev: Sen. Cons. Chest Phys. Sunderland AHA.

WHITE

WHITE, Adrian Roger Postgraduate Medical School, University of Exeter, 25 Victoria Park Road, Exeter EX2 4NT Tel: 01392 424839 Fax: 01392 424989 Email: a.r.white@exeter.ac.uk; 11 Essa Road, Saltash PL12 4ED Tel: 01752 843462 — BM BCh 1972 Oxf.; MA Oxf. 1972; DObst RCOG 1975. Research Fell. (Complementary Med.) Postgrad. Med. Sch. Univ. Exeter. Socs: Brit. Med. Acupunct. Soc.

WHITE, Aideen St Claire 44 Westwood Road, Beverley HU17 8EJ — MB BCh BAO 1979 Dub.

WHITE, Aileen 77 Bonaly Rise, Colinton, Edinburgh EH13 0QU — MB ChB 1978 Aberd.; FRCS Ed. 1984; FRCS Glas. 1983.

WHITE, Alan Anthony James Fullarton Street Surgery, 24 Fullarton Street, Ayr KA7 1UB Tel: 01292 264260 Fax: 01292 283284; 8 Pattle Place, Alloway, Ayr KA7 4PS Tel: 01292 441402 — MB ChB 1983 Glas.; MRCGP 1987; DObst 1985. GP Ayr. Prev: SHO (Dermat.) Glas. Roy. Infirm.; Trainee GP/SHO Monklands Dist. Hosp. VTS; Ho. Off. Glas. Roy. Infirm.

WHITE, Albert Edward (retired) 69 Park Parade, Whitley Bay NE26 1DU Tel: 01632 252 3135 — MB BS 1945 Durh. Prev: Ho. Surg. G.B. Hunter Memor. Hosp. Wallsendon-Tyne & Profess. Surg. Unit, Roy. Vict. Infirm. Newc.

WHITE, Alexander 5 Balgair Road, Glasgow G63 0PP — LRCP LRCS 1950 Ed.; LRCP LRCS Ed. LRFPS Glas. 1950. (St. Mungo's Coll. & Univ. Glas.) Regist. Roy. Vict. Disp. Edin. Socs: BMA. Prev: Res. Med. Off. Honey La. Hosp. Waltham Abbey; Ho. Surg. Roy. Infirm. Glas.; Res. Asst. Phys. Belvidere Infec. Dis. Hosp. Glas.

WHITE, Alfred Charles Queen Elizabeth Psychiatric Hospital, Edgbaston, Birmingham B15 2QZ Tel: 0121 678 2014 Fax: 0121 678 2208 Email: alfredwhite@compuserve.com — MB BS 1970 Lond.; MD Lond. 1981; MRCS Eng. LRCP Lond. 1970; FRCPsych 1991, M 1974; DPM Eng. 1973. p/t Cons. Psychiat. (Liaison Psychiat.) Qu. Eliz. Psychiat. Hosp. Birm.; Hon. Sen. Lect. (Psychiat.) Univ. Birm. Socs: Medico legal Soc.; Birm. Med. Inst.

WHITE, Andrew James The Shieling, Upper Guildown, Guildford GU2 5EZ — MB BS 1988 Lond.; BSc (Hons.) Lond. 1985, MB BS 1988. Prev: Ho. Surg. Gloucester Roy. Hosp.; Ho. Phys. Edgware Gen. Hosp.

WHITE, Andrew John Crofton Health Centre, Slack Lane, Crofton, Wakefield WF4 1HJ Tel: 01924 862612 Fax: 01924 865519 — MB ChB 1975 Dundee. Prev: Trainee GP Salisbury VTS; SHO (Gen. Med. & Geriat.) N.gate Hosp. Gt. Yarmouth.

WHITE, Andrew John 51 Clogher Road, Lisburn BT27 5PQ — BChir 1995 Camb.

WHITE, Andrew Mark The New Surgery, Coychurch Road, Pencoed, Bridgend CF35 5LP Tel: 01656 860343 Fax: 01656 864451; Plot 63, Woodstock Gardens, Pencoed, Bridgend CF35 6ST — MB BCh 1984 Wales.

WHITE, Andrew Peter Anaesthetic Department, Milton Keynes Hospital, Eaglestone, Milton Keynes MK6 5LJ Tel: 01908 660033 Fax: 01908 660033 — MB BS 1980 Lond.; FFA RCS Eng. 1987. (Charing Cross) Cons. Anaesth. Milton Keynes Hosp. Prev: Sen. Regist. Rotat. (Anaesth.) Oxf.; Regist. (Anaesth.) St. Bart. Hosp. Lond.

WHITE, Andrew Steven Truman Department Geriatric Medicine, Christchurch Hospital, Christchurch BH23 2JX Tel: 01202 486361 — MB BS 1980 Lond.; MRCP (UK) 1984. Sen. Regist. (Geriat. Med.) Soton. & E. Dorset HA. Socs: Brit. Geriat. Soc. & BMA. Prev: Med. Regist. Jersey; Research Regist. Poisons Unit Guy's Hosp. Lond.

WHITE, Andrew William Ware Road Surgery, 77 Ware Road, Hertford SG13 7EE Tel: 01992 587961; 120 London Road, Ware SG12 9LY — MB BS 1983 Lond.; MRCGP 1988; DRCOG 1991.

WHITE, Angela The Cripps Health Centre, University Park, Nottingham NG7 2QW Tel: 0115 950 1654 Fax: 0115 948 0347; 35 Prestwood Drive, Aspley, Nottingham NG8 3LY — MB ChB 1969 Birm.; BA (Hons.) Open 1992. Phys. Univ. Health Serv. Nottm.

WHITE, Angela 16 Milton Avenue, Bath BA2 4QZ — MB ChB 1995 Bristol.

WHITE, Ann Bernadette Erne Health Centre, Erne Hospital, Cornagrade Road, Enniskillen BT74 6AY Tel: 028 6632 7192 Fax: 028 6632 8686 — MB BCh BAO 1984 NUI.

WHITE, Ann Catherine 2 Glebe Street, St Clements, Oxford OX4 1DQ; Appartment 12A, 929 Massachusetts Avenue, Cambridge MA02139, USA Email: anncwhite@partners.co — BM BCh 1996 Oxf. (Oxf.) Residency (Program in Paediats.) Massachussetts Gen. Hosp. Boston, USA. Socs: Amer. Acad. Paediat. Prev: Hse Off. (Med.) John Radcliffe, Oxf.; Hse Off. (Surg.) Torbay Hosp. Torquay.

WHITE, Anne Jean The Surgery, 3 Heyward Road, Southsea PO4 0DY Tel: 023 9273 7373; 72 Parkstone Avenue, Southsea PO4 0QZ Tel: 01705 731122 — MB ChB 1972 Manch.; FRCGP 1997; DObst RCOG 1974. GP Tutor. Prev: SHO (Paediat.) & SHO (O & G) St. Mary's Hosp. Portsmouth; SHO (Med.) Roy. Portsmouth Hosp.

WHITE, Anthony Buckingham Terrace Surgery, 31 Buckingham Terrace, Glasgow G12 8ED Tel: 0141 221 6210 Fax: 0141 211 6232; 5 Arnwood Drive, Glasgow G12 0XY Tel: 0141 357 1921 — MB ChB 1966 Aberd.

WHITE, Professor Anthony (retired) ENT Department, Royal United Hospital NHS Trust, Combe Park, Bath BA1 3NG Tel: 01225 824556 Fax: 01225 825466 — MB BS 1962 Lond.; PhD Bath 1993; FRCS Eng. 1970; MRCS Eng. LRCP Lond. 1965; T(S) 1991. Cons. ENT Surg. Roy. United Hosp. Bath; Vis. Prof. Sch. Mangem. Univ. Bournemouth 1996. Prev: Sen. Regist. Bristol United Hosps.

WHITE, Anthony David Department of Medicine for the Elderly, Wrexham Maelor Hospital, Croesnewydd Road, Wrexham LL13 7TD; Ty r Pinwydd, Wesley Road, Bwlchgwyn, Wrexham LL11 5UY — MD 1991 Camb.; MB 1975, BChir 1974; FRCP (Lond.) 1996; FRCP (Ed.) 1995; MRCP (UK) 1985. Cons. Phys. Med. for Elderly Wrexham Maelor Hosp. Wrexham. Socs: Brit. Geriat. Soc. Prev: R.I.D.E. Research Fell. & Hon. Sen. Regist. (Geriat. Med.) Univ. Hosp. Wales Cardiff; Regist. (Gen. Med.) Lister Hosp. Stevenage; Regist. (Geriat. Med.) Qu. Hosp. Croydon.

WHITE, Anthony George 152 Harley Street, London W1N 1HH Tel: 020 7935 8868 Fax: 020 7224 2574 — MB ChB 1959 Bristol; FRCP Lond. 1980, M 1966; DPhysMed Eng. 1971. Cons. Rheum. Roy. Free Hosp. & Whittington Hosp. Lond.; Hon. Med. Dir. N. Lond. Sch. Physiother. & Hon. Sen. Lect. (Clin. Med.) Clin. Sc. UCL. Socs: FRSM; Brit. Soc. Rheum. Prev: Sen. Regist. Roy. Free Hosp. Lond.

WHITE, Anthony John Simon Rookery Medical Centre, Rookery House, Newmarket CB8 8NW Tel: 01638 665711 Fax: 01638 561280; Wayside, Fordham Road, Newmarket CB8 7AQ Email: ajsw2@medschl.ac.uk — MB BChir 1972 Camb.; MA Camb. 1972; MRCP (UK) 1974; MRCGP (Distinc.) 1980; DCH Eng. 1973; FRCGP 1987. (Camb.) Approved Clin. Teach. & Trainer Camb. Univ. Med. Sch; Asst. Dir. (Gen. Pract.) Univ. Camb. Clin. Med. Sch. Prev: Clin. Asst. (Paediat.) Newmarket.

WHITE, Mr Barrie David Department of Neurosurgery, University Hospital, Queen's Medical Centre, Nottingham NG7 2UH Tel: 0115 970 9925 Fax: 0115 970 9104 — MB BS 1982 Lond.; BSc (Hons.) Pharmacol. CNAA 1977; FRCS (SN) 1994; FRCS Lond. 1987; MRCP (UK) 1986. (King's Coll.) Cons. Neurosurg. Univ. Hosp. Qu. Med. Centre Nottm. Prev: Sen. Regist. & Regist. (Neurosurg.) Univ. Hosp. Qu. Med. Centre Nottm.; Regist. (Neurosurg.) Nat. Hosp. Nerv. Dis. Lond.; SHO (Surg. & Med.) Roy. United Hosp. Bath.

WHITE, Brian John 32 Cooldarragh Park, Belfast BT14 6TH — BM BS 1996 Nottm.

WHITE, Bronwen Myfanwy Dykes Hall Medical Centre, 156 Dykes Hall Road, Sheffield S6 4GQ Tel: 0114 232 3236; 138 Brooklands Crescent, Sheffield S10 4GG — MB ChB 1973 Ed.; MRCGP 1977; DObst RCOG 1976.

WHITE, Caroline Claire 46 The Avenue, Ingol, Preston PR2 7AY — BM BS 1998 Nottm.

WHITE, Catharine Peta Department of Child Health, Singleton Hospital, Swansea SA2 8QA Tel: 01792 285047 Fax: 01792 285244; 45 Eaton Crescent, Uplands, Swansea SA1 4QL — MB BS 1980 Lond.; FRCP 1999; FRCPCH 1997; MRCP (UK) 1984. (Guy's Hosp. Lond.) Cons. Paediat. s/i Paediat. Neurol. Swansea NHS Trust; Hon. Lect. (Child Health) Univ. of Wales Coll. of Med. Prev: Sen. Regist. (Paediat. Neurol.) Liverp. Childr. Hosp.

WHITE, Catherine Anne Woodlands, Hampton Lane, Brook, Ashford TN25 5PN Tel: 01233 813615 — MB BS 1993 Lond.; MRCP, UK. Staff Grade HaemOtol.

WHITE, Catherine Elizabeth Princess Road Surgery, 475 Princess Road, Withington, Manchester M20 1BH Tel: 0161 445 7805 Fax: 0161 448 2419 — MB ChB 1987 Manch.

WHITE, Catherine Mary (retired) — MB ChB 1951 Glas.; MRCP Lond. 1966; DTM & H Liverp. 1988; DCH Eng. 1958; FRCPCH. Prev: Cons. Paediat., Stockport & Macclesfield Dist. Hosp.s.

WHITE, Catherine Sylvia Northenden Health Centre, 489 Palatine Road, Northenden, Manchester M22 4DH Tel: 0161 998 3206 Fax: 0161 945 9173; 24 Atwood Road, Didsbury, Manchester M20 6TD Email: cathswhite@hotmail.com — MB ChB 1988 Liverp.; DMJ 1998; DRCOG; MRCGP 1994; DCH RCP Lond. 1991. Forens. Phys. Manch.

WHITE, Chester, MBE, TD Darwin College, Cambridge CB3 9EU Tel: 01223 335660 Fax: 01223 335667; Grafton House, 22 Grafton St, Cambridge CB1 1DS Tel: 01223 356174 — PhD 1974, MA Camb. 1969; MSc Oxf. 1982; BA 1956, BSc, MA 1959, BM BCh Oxf. 1960. (Oxf. & St. Mary's) Sessional Med. Off. Nat. Blood Transfus. Serv. E. Anglian Blood Transfus. Centre & Univ. Camb. Div. Transfus. Med.; Fell. Darwin Coll. Camb.; Med. Off. The Welding Inst.; Med. Off. Camb. Cons.s Ltd. Socs: FRSM; Harveian Soc.; BMA. Prev: Sen. Regist. (Path.) P'boro. Hosp.; Head Dept. Clin. Research Huntingdon Research Centre; Sen. Asst. Research (Med.) Univ. Camb.

WHITE, Christine Rosemary c/o Department of Childs Health, Pendragon House, Treliske Hospital, Truro TR1 3XQ — BChir 1971 Camb.; MA, MB.

WHITE, Christopher de Boismaison Flat 2, 31 Albert Square, Dundee DD1 1DJ — MRCS Eng. LRCP Lond. 1970; MD Lond. 1977, MB BS 1970; MRCP (UK) 1972; MRCPsych 1977. Sen. Lect. (Psychiat.) Univ. Dundee. Prev: Sen. Research Fell. (Psychiat.) Univ. Camb.

WHITE, Christopher James Tel: 01633 258545 Fax: 01633 258564; 1, The Paddocks, Lodge Hill, Caerleon, Newport NP18 3BZ — MB BCh 1976 Wales; MRCGP 1980; DRCOG 1979. Sen. partner GP Princip.

WHITE, Christopher Paul The Surgery, Sydenham House, Mill Court, Ashford TN24 8DN Tel: 01233 645851 Fax: 01233 638281; (Surgery), Sydenham House, Church Road, Ashford TN24 8DN — MB BS 1970 Lond.

WHITE, Claire 8 Coolshinney Park, Magherafelt BT45 5JG — MB BCh 1998 Belf.

WHITE, Clement John (retired) 9 Church Side, Farnsfield, Newark NG22 8ET Tel: 01623 883152 — MB BS 1953 Lond.; FFA RCS Eng. 1963; DA Eng. 1959. Prev: Cons. Anaesth. Mansfield & Dist. Gen. Hosp. Harlow Wood Orthop. Hosp. & King's Mill Hosp. Sutton-in-Ashfield.

WHITE, Mr Clive Meldon 32 Hall Drive, Bramhope, Leeds LS16 9JE — MS Lond. 1983, MB BS 1970; FRCS Eng. 1975. Cons. Gen. Surg. Dewsbury Dist. Hosp.

WHITE, Colin 35 Newington Road, Middlesbrough TS4 3EF — MB BS 1992 Newc.

WHITE, Colin Pontefract General Infirmary, Pontefract WF8 1PL Tel: 01977 606250 Email: colin.white@panp-tr.notrhy.nhs.uk; 43 Newgate, Pontefract WF8 1NG Tel: 01977 795074 Email: whitedrc@aol.com — MB ChB 1969 St. And.; BSc (Biochem. & Physiol.) (1st cl. Hons.) St. And. 1966; FRCP Lond. 1990; FRCP Glas. 1984; MRCP (UK) 1972. Gen. Med. Diabetes & Endocrinol. Socs: BMA; Brit. Diabetic Assn. (Med. & Scientif. Sect.). Prev: Sen. Regist. (Med.) Manch. Roy. Infirm.; Lect. (Metab. Med.) Manch. Roy. Infirm.; Regist. (Med.) Glas. Roy. Infirm.

WHITE, Colin John Halton Hospital, Hospital Way, Runcorn WA7 2DA Tel: 01928 714567 — MB ChB 1990 Liverp.; MRCPsych 1994. Cons. Psych.Halton.Hosp.

WHITE, Conor Vincent Health Centre, Great James Street, Londonderry BT48 7DH Tel: 028 7137 8522 — MB BCh BAO 1980 Belf.; DRCOG 1983.

WHITE, Conrad North Durham Health Care NHS Trust, Department GU Medicine, University Hospital of North Durham, Durham DH1 5TW Tel: 0191 333 2660 Fax: 0191 333 6901 Email: c.white@ndhcnt.northy.nhs.uk — MB ChB 1980 Ed.; MRCOG 1986; Dip. GUM Soc. Apoth. Lond. 1989. (Edinburgh) Cons. Genitourin. Med. Durh. & Bishop Auckland. Socs: MSSUD (Mem. of Counc. 99/02); AGUM. Prev: Sen. Regist. (Genitourin. Med.) Cardiff; Regist. (O & G) Ninewells Hosp. Dundee & Bangour Gen. Hosp. Broxburn.

WHITE, Craig Alisdair Summerpole, Brilley, Whitney-on-Wye, Hereford HR3 6JH — MB BS 1998 Lond.

WHITE, Craig Steven (retired) Aston Clinton Surgery, 136 London Road, Aston Clinton, Aylesbury HP22 5LB Tel: 01296 630241 Fax: 01296 630033 — MB BS 1990 Lond.; MRCGP 1995; DRCOG 1994.

WHITE, Damian Frederick Augustus 11 St Annes Close, Lincoln LN2 5RB — MB BCh 1991 Witwatersrand.

WHITE, Daniel Paul Department of Psychological Medicine, St. Bartholomew's Hospital, London EC1A Tel: 020 8510 8606 Fax: 020 8510 8716 — MB BS 1984 Lond.; MRCPsych 1993; DA (UK) 1989. Cons. (Emerg. & Adult Psychiat.) St. Bart. & Homerton Hosps. Lond.; Clin. Tutor St Bart. SHO Rotat. Psychiat. Prev: Sen. Regist. Rotat. (Adult Psychiat) St. Bart. Hosp. Lond.

WHITE, Daphne Winifred 27 The Green, Dunmurry, Belfast BT17 0QA — MB BCh BAO 1970 Belf.; MRCP (UK) 1974.

WHITE, David Anthony Mulberry House, Castleford, Normanton & District Hospital, Lumley Street, Hightown, Castleford WF10 5LT Tel: 01977 605526 Fax: 01977 605501 — MB ChB 1992 Liverp.; 2001 CCST; 1999 Post Grad. Dip. Cog.Ther. Durham; BSc (Hons.) 1989; MRCPsych 1997; M Med Sci 1999. Specialist Regist. Child & Adolesc. Psychiat. Socs: Roy. Coll. Psychiats.; ACPP; BMA.

WHITE, David Anthony 19 Chestnut Grove, Harrogate HG1 4HS — MB ChB 1994 Leeds.

WHITE, David George Newpark Surgery, Talbot Green, Pontyclun CF72 8AJ Tel: 01443 228922 Fax: 01443 228319 — MB BCh 1980 Wales; MRCGP 1985; DRCOG 1984. GP Talbot Green.

WHITE, David Harper Norton Medical Centre, Billingham Road, Norton, Stockton-on-Tees TS20 2UZ Tel: 01642 360111 Fax: 01642 558672; The Grove, Coal Lane, Wolviston, Billingham TS22 5LW Tel: 01740 644764 — MB BS 1980 Lond.; MRCGP 1986; DRCOG 1983. (St. Mary's)

WHITE, David John Rosehill Surgery, 189 Manchester Road, Burnley BB11 4HP Tel: 01282 428200 Fax: 01282 838492; Kiddrow Lane Health Centre, Kiddrow Lane, Burnley — MB ChB 1988 Manch.; MA Oxf. 1989; MFFP 1995; MRCGP 1992. (Oxford & Manchester) Princip. Gen. Pract.; PCG Bd. Mem. & Clin. Governance Lead (Caldicott Guardian); Bd. Mem. Deputising Serv.; Mem. Instruc. Doctor GP Clin. Trial Panel Fac. of Family Plann.; BRd.casting Doctor BBC Radio Lancs. Socs: BRd.casting Doctors; BMA; Soc. Occupat. Med.

WHITE, David John, MBE (retired) Placketts, High St., Adderbury, Banbury OX17 3LS Tel: 01295 812679 — MB BS 1959 Lond.; DObst RCOG 1962.

WHITE, David John Hawthorn House, Heartlands Hospital, Birmingham B9 5SS Tel: 0121 753 0399 — MB ChB 1983 Sheff.; FRCP 1997. Cons. Genitourin: Med. Birm. Heartlands Hosp.; Hon. Sen. Clin. Lect. Univ. Birm. Socs: Med. Soc. Study VD; Brit. Soc. Study Vulval Dis.

WHITE, David John Kalson 412 Whirlowdale Road, Sheffield S11 9NL Tel: 0114 236 8466 — MB BS 1963 Newc.; FFA RCSI 1968; FFA RCS Eng. 1969. (Newc.) Cons. Anaesth. N. Gen. Hosp. Sheff.

WHITE, Mr David Robert Dryburn Hospital, North Road, Durham DH1 5TW — MB BS 1977 Lond.; BA Camb. 1974; FRCS Ed. 1983; FRCOG 1984. (St. Mary's) Cons. O & G N. Durh. Acute Hosps. Prev: Sen. Regist. (O & G) Mersey RHA; Regist. (O & G) Aberd. Matern. Hosp. & St. Davids Hosp. Bangor.

WHITE, David William 9 Tower Road S., Wirral CH60 7SY — MB ChB 1988 Liverp.; FRCR 1994.

WHITE, Davinia Marion 57 Dartmouth Road, Willesden, London NW2 4EP — MB ChB 1979 Otago; FRACP 1987.

WHITE, Dawn Helen Brookside Health Centre, Brookside Road, Freshwater PO40 9DT Tel: 01983 753433 Fax: 01983 753662 — MB BS 1987 Lond.; DRCOG 1994. GP. Socs: Diplomate RCOG. Prev: Trainee GP/SHO Harold Wood Hosp. Romford VTS; Ho. Off. (Gen. Med.) Char. Cross Hosp. Lond.; Ho. Off. (Gen. Surg.) Hemel Hempstead Hosp.

WHITE, Deborah St Pauls Surgery, Orams Mount, Winchester SO22 5DD Tel: 01962 853599; Tel: 0061 893415654 — MB BCh 1993 Wales; MRCGP 2000. GP St Pauls Surg. Winchester.

WHITE, Denis Michael Drummond (retired) Dolbeau, 1 Wall Park Road, Brixham TQ5 9UE — MD 1970 Bristol; MB ChB 1960; FRCPsych 1984, M 1971; DPM Eng. 1963. Prev: Cons. Psychiat. Dept. Ment. Health of Elderly Hereford HA.

WHITE

WHITE, Denis Simpson Hill Medical Group, The Hill, 192 Kingsway, Dunmurry, Belfast BT17 9AL Tel: 028 9061 8211 Fax: 028 9060 3911; Cosy Lodge, 23 Church Avenue, Dunmurry, Belfast BT17 9RS Tel: 01232 610540 — MB BCh BAO 1968 Belf.; FRCGP 1986, M 1972; DCH RCPSI 1970; DObst RCOG 1970; MICGP. (Belf.) Socs: Ulster. Med. Soc; Provost NI Fac.RCGP; Lagan Valley GP Assn. (Ex-Chairm.). Prev: Ho. Off. Roy. Vict. Hosp. Belf. Roy. Matern. Hosp. Belf. & Roy. Belf.; Hosp. Sick Childr.

WHITE, Denise Mary Haematology Department, Royal United Hospital, Coombe Park, Bath BA1 3NG Tel: 01225 428331; 11 Westbroke Gardens, Romsey SO51 7RQ Tel: 01794 523822 — BM 1982 Soton.; DM Soton. 1995; MRCP (UK) 1985; MRCPath 1992. Sen. Regist. (Haemat.) Bath HA. Socs: Brit. Soc. Haematol.; Assn. Clin. Path. Prev: Hon. Regist. Leukaemia Research Fund Clin. Train. Fell.sh.

WHITE, Derek Alexander British Telecommunications plc, BT Centre (pp A167), 81 Newgate St., London EC1A 7AJ Tel: 020 7356 4816 Fax: 020 7356 6047 Email: whited@btcentre.agw.bt.co.uk — MB ChB 1966 Ed.; BSc (Hons.) (Pharmacol.) Ed 1964; MRCGP 1972; FFOM RCP Lond. 1992, MFOM 1982, AFOM 1980; DIH Soc. Apoth. Lond. 1977. (Ed.) Chief Med. Off. BT plc. Socs: FRSM; Soc. Occupat. Med. Prev: Med. Off. E. Scottl. Occupat. Health Serv.; Med. Off. Cape Industries Ltd.; GP Stirling.

WHITE, Diana Elizabeth Medical Centre, Cambridge Avenue, Bottesford, Scunthorpe DN16 3LG Tel: 01724 842415 Fax: 01724 271437; 70 West Common Gardens, Old Brumby, Scunthorpe DN17 1EH Tel: 01724 863481 — MB BS 1975 Newc.; DRCOG 1980.

WHITE, Diana Gillian Department of Pathology, East Glamorgan NHS Trust, Pontypridd CF38 1AB Tel: 01443 218218 Fax: 01443 216040; Court Lea, Camerton Hill, Camerton, Bath BA2 0PS Tel: 01761 470782 — MSc (Med. Microbiol.) Lond. 1976; MB ChB Birm. 1967; FRCPath 1989, M 1977. (Birmingham) Cons. Microbiologist E. Glam. Gen. Hosp. Mid Glam. Socs: Assn. Clin. Path. & Brit. Soc. Antimicrobiol. Chemother.; Assn. Med. Microbiologists. Prev: Cons. Microbiol. & Dir. Pub. Health Laborat. Roy. United Hosp. Bath; Squadron Ldr. RAF Med. Br. Med. Off. (Path.) RAF Hosp. Cosford.

WHITE, Donald James, Group Capt. RAF Med. Br. Retd. (retired) 12 Collingwood Crescent, Broughty Ferry, Dundee DD5 2SX Tel: 01382 477452 — MB BS Madras 1947; FRCOG 1982, M 1969; DObst 1950. Prev: Cons. O & G RAF Hosp. Ely and Cons. Adviser (O & G) RAF.

WHITE, Donna Ann 33 St Patrick's Way, Wigan WN1 3EJ — MB ChB 1993 Manch.

WHITE, Dorothy Gertrude 3 Fairholme Gardens, York Road, Farnham GU9 8JB Tel: 01252 737904 — MB BCh BAO 1968 Belf.; FFA RCSI 1973. (Qu. Univ. Belf.) Cons. (Anaesth.) Frimley Pk. Hosp. Prev: Sen. Regist. (Anaesth.) Roy. Vict. Hosp. Belf. & Craigavon Area Hosp.

WHITE, Dragana (retired) Watergore, 142 Busbridge Lane, Godalming GU7 1QJ Tel: 01483 421012 — MD 1953 Belgrade; LRCP LRCS Ed. LRFPS Glas. 1959. Prev: Assoc. Specialist Milford Hosp. Godalming.

WHITE, Eileen (retired) Shere, 66 Parklands Road, Chichester PO19 3DU Tel: 01243 782055 — MB BCh BAO 1961 NUI. Prev: Assoc. Specialist (Anaesth.) Roy. W. Sussex Hosp.

WHITE, Elizabeth Antonia Crouch Oak Family Practice, 45 Station Road, Addlestone, Weybridge Tel: 01932 840123; Stonehill Lodge, Stonehill Road, Ottershaw, Chertsey KT16 0EW Tel: 01932 875155 Fax: 01932 875303 — MB ChB 1972 Manch.; MRCP (U.K.) 1974; MRCGP 1986; DObst RCOG 1975. (Manchester) Prev: Ho. Surg. & Ho. Phys. Withington Hosp. Manch.

WHITE, Elizabeth McCallum 4 Tremough Barton Cottages, Mabe, Penryn TR10 9EZ Email: drlizwhite@btopenworld.com; 4 Tremough Barton Cottages, Mabe, Penryn TR10 9EZ Email: drlizwhite@btopenworld.com — MB ChB 1962 Ed.; MD Ed. 1973; FFPHM RCP (UK) 1989, M 1974; DCH Eng. 1967; DPH Lond. 1964. Indep. Cons.; Cons. Communiable DisCl. Control, Cornw. & Ios HA. Socs: FRSM. Prev: Cons. AIDS Task Force Europ. Community with Jamaican Nat. AIDS Control Progr.; Sen. Clin. Lect. (Internat. Community Health) Liverp. Sch. Trop. Med.

WHITE, Emert 6A Frankland Crescent, Lower Parkstone, Poole BH14 9PX — MB ChB 1987 Birm. SHO (A & E) Warwick Hosp., S. Warks. HA.

WHITE, Eric George 6 Nab Wood, Shipley BD18 4HX — MB BS 1976 Newc.; MRCP (UK) 1980.

WHITE, Fiona Jane 5 Cross Lanes, Mockbeggar, Ringwood BH24 3NQ — BM BS 1993 Nottm.

WHITE, Fionuala Ann High Street Medical Group Practice, 29 High Street, Draperstown, Magherafelt BT45 7AB Tel: 028 7962 8201 Fax: 028 7962 7523 — MB BCh BAO 1982 NUI.

WHITE, Frances Elizabeth Dept Radiology, Royal Liverpool Hospital, Prescot St., Liverpool L7 8XP Tel: 0151 706 2000; Pine Ridge, Dawstone Road, Heswall, Wirral CH60 0BT — MB BS 1972 Lond.; FRCP (U.K.) 1996; FRCR 1979; DMRD Eng. 1978. (St. Bart) Cons. Radiol. Roy. Liverp. Univ. Hosp. Trust; Med. Director Roy. Liverp. Univ. Hosp.st Trust; Quality Assur. Radiologist NHS BSP N. W. Region. Prev: Cons. Radiol. Freeman Rd. & Newc. Gen. Hosps.; Cons. Radiol. St. Bart. Hosp. Lond.

WHITE, Frances Mary 7 Marlborough Avenue, Bromsgrove B60 2PG Tel: 01527 72975 — MB ChB 1949 Leeds; DObst RCOG 1951. (Leeds) JP; Med. Off. Dept. Surg. BromsGr. Gen. Hosp. Socs: Counc. BMA (Centr. Comm. Hosp. Med. Servs.).

WHITE, Francis James 1 St Germains, Bearsden, Glasgow G61 2RS — MB ChB 1989 Glas.

WHITE, Gary John 19 Burgh Road, Prestwick KA9 1QU — MB ChB 1986 Glas.

WHITE, Gavin James 30 Southcroft Road, London SW17 9TR Tel: 020 8353 12893417 — MB BCh BAO 1992 Dub. SHO (Surg.) St. Geo. Hosp. Lond. Prev: Cas. Off. Lagan Valley Hosp. Lisburn; Anat. Demonstr. Trinity Coll. Dub.; Ho. Off. (Surg.) Meath Hosp. Dub.

WHITE, Genie Yasmin The Surgery, Parkwood Drive, Warners End, Hemel Hempstead HP1 2LD Tel: 01442 250117 Fax: 01442 256185; Mentmore Views, Buckland Village, Aylesbury HP1 2LD — MB BS 1992 Lond.; DRCOG 1995; MRCGP 1996. GP Princip.

WHITE, George Baird 1 Sandleigh, Hoole, Chester CH2 3QN — MB ChB 1968 Aberd.

WHITE, George Malcolm James South Ryehill, Nunthorpe Village, Middlesbrough TS7 0NR Tel: 01642 316040 — MB ChB 1952 St. And.; FFA RCS Eng. 1959. (St. And.) Indep. Cons. Anaesth. Cleveland. Socs: N. Eng. Soc. Anaesth. (Ex-Pres.); Roy. Soc. Med. Prev: Anaesth. Specialist RAF Hosp. Halton; Regist. (Anaesth.) Radcliffe Infirm. Oxf.; Cons. Anaesth. Newc. RHB.

WHITE, George Philip Sunnyside Surgery, 4 Sunnyside Road, Clevedon BS21 7TA Tel: 01275 873588 Fax: 01275 875218; 32 St. Matthews Road, Cotham, Bristol BS6 5TU Tel: 0117 909 3177 — MB ChB 1979 Bristol; MRCGP 1984; DRCOG 1983. GP Avon HA.

WHITE, Gillian Mary 13 Princes Road, London SW19 8RQ — MB BS 1990 Lond.

WHITE, Gillian Patricia Windermere Health Centre, Goodley Dale, Windermere LA23 2EG Tel: 015394 42496; Lowthwaite Farm House, St. Johns in the Vale, Keswick CA12 4TS — MB BS 1985 Newc.; MRCGP 1989; DRCOG 1987. Prev: Trainee GP Carlisle VTS.

WHITE, Gordon Bentley Bruce (retired) 5 Meadway, Upton, Wirral CH49 6JG Tel: 0151 677 4573 — MRCS Eng. LRCP Lond. 1946; Dip. Bact. Lond 1950; DObst RCOG 1959. Prev: Cons. Microbiol. PHLS Liverp.

WHITE, Graham Lingholme Health Centre, Atherton St., St Helens WA10 2HT Tel: 01744 22612 Fax: 01744 454493; Dial House, Higher Lane, Rainford, St Helens Tel: 01744 882734 — MB ChB 1959 Manch.; DObst. RCOG 1962. (Manch.) Hosp. Pract. Rainhill Hosp. Socs: BMA & Vasectomy Advancem. Soc. Gt. Brit.

WHITE, H. John (retired) Himley Cottage, School Road, Himley, Dudley DY3 4LG Tel: 01902 893082 — MB ChB 1950 Birm.; DObst. RCOG 1954. JP. Prev: Chairm. Dudley Family Pract. Comm. 1973-87.

WHITE, Harry Vere (retired) 14 Millfield Gardens, Hexham NE46 3EG — LMSSA 1949 Lond.; BA Camb. 1942; MRCPsych 1972; DPM Eng. 1966. Prev: Sen. Med. Off. HM Prison Maidstone.

WHITE, Mr Harvey 149 Harley Street, London W1G 6DE Tel: 020 7935 4444 Fax: 020 7616 7633; 7 Arlington Square, Islington, London N1 7DS Tel: 020 7226 4628 — BM BCh 1961 Oxf.; MCh Oxf. 1970, DM 1967, MA 1961; FRCS Eng. 1970; MRCS Eng. LRCP Lond. 1962. (St. Bart.) Cons. Surg. Roy. Marsden Hosp. Lond. & King Edwd. VII Hosp. Offs. Lond. Socs: Med. Soc. Lond. (Pres.);

Hon. Mem. Edr. Roy. Soc. Med. 1990.; Chairm. Roy. Soc. Of Med. Press. Prev: SHO Hosp. Sick Childr. Gt. Ormond St. Lond.; Ho. Surg. Surgic. Unit & Sen. Regist. (Surg.) St. Bart. Hosp. Lond.

WHITE, Hazel Lorraine 58 Grimshaw Lane, Bollington, Macclesfield SK10 5LY — MB BChir 1993 Camb.

WHITE, Helen Dorothy 32 New La, Penwortham, Preston PR1 9JJ — MB ChB 1997 Liverp.

WHITE, Henry Gordon Budbrooke Medical Centre, Slade Hill, Hampton Magne, Warwick CV35 8SA Tel: 01926 403800 Fax: 01926 403855 — MB BS 1982 Lond.; BA 1979 Camb.; MRCGP 1987; DCH 1984 Lond.; DRCOG 1986 Lond. (St. Mary's Hosp.) GP.

WHITE, Henry Maxwell (retired) 7 Marlborough Avenue, Bromsgrove B60 2PG Tel: 01527 872975 — MB ChB Leeds 1947; MRCS Eng. LRCP Lond. 1947; MRCGP 1964; DObst RCOG 1951. Prev: Mem. Bd. Sc. & Educat. (BMA). 1976-1988.

WHITE, Hilary Anne Department of Accident and Emergency, Royal Sussex County Hospital, Eastern Road, Brighton BN2 5BE — MB BS 1998 Lond.; MB BS Lond 1998.

WHITE, Hugh Southmead Hospital, Southmead Road, Westbury-on-Trym, Bristol BS10 5NB Tel: 0117 959 5623; Old Garden House, Honey Hall Lane, Congresbury, Bristol BS49 5JX Tel: 01934 852230 — MB ChB 1975 Ed.; BSc (Physiol.) Ed. 1972; FRCPath 1983; DMJ Path) Soc. Apoth. Lond. 1993. (Ed.) Cons. Histopath. S.mead Hosp. Bristol; Home Office Path. Avon & Som. Hants, Wilts. Socs: Brit. Assn. Forens. Med. Prev: Sen. Regist. (Path.) Edin. Univ.

WHITE, Iain Harvey Laich Medical Practice, Clifton Road, Lossiemouth IV31 6DJ Tel: 01343 812277 Fax: 01343 812396; Traighean, Station Court, Burghead, Elgin IV30 — BSc (Med. Sci.) Ed. 1972, MB ChB 1975; MRCGP 1980; DCH RCP Lond. 1985; DRCOG 1978.

WHITE, Ian Leslie 23 Cross Lane, Frimley Green, Camberley GU16 6LP — MB BS 1991 Lond. (King's Coll. Sch. Med. & Dent. Lond.) Regist. Rotat. (Anaesth.) Hammersmith Hosp. Lond. Socs: BMA; Assn. Anaesth.

WHITE, Ian Richard 152 Harley Street, London W1G 7LH Tel: 020 7935 3834 Fax: 020 7620 0890 — MRCS Eng. LRCP Lond. 1976; MB BS Lond. 1976; BSc Lond. 1973; FRCP Lond. 1993; MRCP (UK) 1978; Cchem.FRCS 2001; DIH Lond. 1983; 2000 FFOM. (Guy's) Cons. Dermat. St. John's Inst. Dermat. St. Thos. Hosp. Lond.; Chairm. Scientif. Comm. for Cosmetic & Non- Food Prodicts. DG Sanco Europ. Commiss.; Mem. Scientif. Steering Comm. Europ. Commiss.; Advis. Comm. Borderline Subst.s Dept. of Health. (Chairm.). Socs: Europ. Soc. Contact Dermat.; Europ. Environm. & Contact Dermatitis research Gp.. Prev: Cons. & Sen. Regist. (Dermat.) St. John's Hosp. Dis. Skin Lond.; Regist. (Dermat.) Guy's Hosp. Lond.; Hon. Sen. Lect. (Dermat) UNDS.

WHITE, Ian Russell 9 Blinkbonny Avenue, Edinburgh EH4 3HT — MB ChB 1994 Aberd.

WHITE, Jacqueline Rosemary Phillips (retired) 55 Cumberland Street, Woodbridge IP12 4AQ — BM BCh Oxf. 1959; MA Oxf. 1959. Prev: SCMO Dorset HA.

WHITE, Mr James Robertson Angus (retired) Trevear, The Saltings, Lelant, St Ives TR26 3DL — MB ChB 1936 St. And.; FRCS Ed. 1939. Prev: Cons. Surg. W. Cornw. Hosp. Penzance & St. Michael's Hosp. Hayle.

WHITE, Jane Caroline Gilbert Road Medical Group, 39 Gilbert Road, Bucksburn, Aberdeen AB21 9AN Tel: 01224 712138 Fax: 01224 712239 — MB ChB 1988 Aberd.; MRCGP 1992; DRCOG 1994; DFFP 1994; DCCH RCP Ed. 1993. (Univ. Aberd.) Prev: SHO (A & E) Stirling Roy. Infirm. & Raigmore Hosp. Inverness; SHO (Community Psychiat.) Dingleton Hosp. Melrose.

WHITE, Jane Crossman Bartestree House, Bartestree, Hereford HR1 4DT — MB ChB 1952 Birm.; DObst RCOG 1954. (Birm.) Sen. Community Med. Off. (Family Plann.) HFDS Community Health NHS Trust. Prev: Ho. Phys. Childr. Hosp. Birm.; Ho. Surg. Marston Green Matern. Hosp.

WHITE, Janet Beryl Deliverance Church Medical Services, PO Box 1544, Mbale, Uganda; c/o Mr & Mrs V. Coles, 205 Farmers Close, Witney OX28 1NS Tel: 01993 772469 Fax: 01993 776073 Email: vernon.coles@btinternet.com — MB BS 1975 Lond.; BSc (Hons.) (Psychol.) Lond. 1972; MRCGP 1980; DRCOG 1979; DA Eng. 1978. (St Mary's London) Dep. Director Med. Serv. Deliverance Ch. Uganda. Prev: Doctor i/c King's Med. Centre, Nakuru, Kenya; GP Witney.

WHITE, Janet Fiona Church House, Condover, Shrewsbury SY5 7AA — BM 1987 Soton.; MRCPsych 1993.

WHITE, Janet Mary (retired) 39 Sunnyfield, Mill Hill, London NW7 4RD Tel: 020 8959 6348 — MB BS 1952 Lond.; DCH Eng. 1955.

WHITE, Janine Patricia Tyle House, Llanmaes, Llantwit Major CF61 2XZ — MB BCh 1974 Wales; MD Wales 1988; FRCP Lond. 1994; MRCP (UK) 1977. Cons. Phys. E. Glam. Gen. Hosp. Prev: Lect. (Tuberc. & Chest Dis.) Wales; Hon. Sen. Regist. (Med.) Llandough & Sully Hosps.; Research Fell. (Thoracic Med.) Guy's Hosp. Lond.

WHITE, Jason Noble 33 Mitchell Grove, East Kilbride, Glasgow G74 1QZ — MB ChB 1994 Glas.

WHITE, Jean Alexandra Finaghy Health Centre, 13-25 Finaghy Road South, Belfast BT10 0BX Tel: 028 9020 4444 — MB BCh BAO 1970 Belf.; MRCGP 1985. Socs: RCGP; Ulster Med. Soc. Prev: Ho. Off. Roy. Vict. Hosp. Belf.; SHO Roy. Matern. Hosp. Belf.

WHITE, Jean Haddow (retired) 107 Marine Avenue, Whitley Bay NE26 3LW Tel: 0191 253 4710 — MB BS 1945 Durh. Prev: GP Whitley Bay.

WHITE, Jeffery David 8 Aldwych Close, Nuthall, Nottingham NG16 1QH — MB ChB 1992 Dundee; MRCP UK July 1997. Specialist Regist. (Med. Oncol.) Nottm. City Hosp. NHS Trust.

WHITE, Jennifer Margaret Roxburgh House, Locharbriggs, Dumfries DG1 1RY — MB ChB 1991 Glas.

WHITE, Jessica Frances 23 Agate Road, London W6 0AJ — MB BChir 1994 Camb.

WHITE, Jill Barbara General Hospital, Northampton NN1 5BD Tel: 01604 34700; Beechwood, 1 Abington Park Crescent, Northampton NN3 3AD Tel: 01604 39253 — MB BS 1974 Lond.; FFA RCS Eng. 1982. (St. Mary's) Cons. Anaesth. N.ampton Dist. HA.

WHITE, Jill Christine (retired) Applegarth, Legg Lane, Wimborne BH21 1LQ Tel: 01202 883933 — MB BS 1948 Lond.; MRCS Eng. LRCP Lond. 1947; DPH Leeds 1959; DCH Eng. 1950. Prev: SCMO Dorset HA.

WHITE, Joanne Sally Orchard Surgery, Christchurch Medical Centre, Purewell Cross Road, Christchurch BH23 5ET Tel: 01202 481902 Fax: 01202 486887 — MB BS 1986 Lond.; MRCGP 1993.

WHITE, Mr John 328 Kelvindale Road, Glasgow G12 0NL — MB ChB 1946 Glas.; FRCS Glas. 1970; FRCS Ed. 1952. (Univ. Glas.) Cons. Emerit. Roy. Infirm. Glas.

WHITE, John Bell 51 Clogher Road, Lisburn BT27 5PQ — MB BCh BAO 1970 Belf.; FRCGP 1989, M 1974; DObst RCOG 1972; DCH RCPSI 1972. Prev: Ho. Off. Roy. Vict. Hosp. Belf.; Ho. Off. Roy. Belf. Hosp. Sick Childr.; Ho. Off. Roy. Matern. Hosp. Belf.

WHITE, John Charles 202 Psalter Lane, Sheffield S11 8UT Tel: 0114 268 5471 — MB ChB 1990 Sheff.; MRCP (UK) Ed. 1994; MRCGP 1995; Post Grad. Dip. Law Nottingham Law Sch.; Dip. Legal Practice. Trainee Solicitor. Socs: MDU; BMA; Roy. Coll. Phys. Ed.

WHITE, John Christopher (retired) Health Centre, Ponteland, Newcastle upon Tyne NE16 4PD — MB BS 1955 Durh. Prev: Ho. Phys. & Ho. Surg. Bishop Auckland Gen. Hosp.

WHITE, John Cosby Seal House, 34 Pottery Lane, London W11 4LZ — MB ChB 1940 Birm.; MRCS Eng. LRCP Lond. 1940. (Birm.) Sen. Lect. (Haemat.) Postgrad. Med. Sch. Lond.; Hon. Cons. Haemat. Hammersmith Hosp. Socs: Path. Soc. & Biochem. Soc. Prev: Ho. Surg. Birm. Gen. Hosp.; Asst. Lect. (Path.) Univ. Birm.; Asst. Path. Birm. United Hosp.

WHITE, John Ernest Stephen Respiratory Medicine, York District Hospital, Wigginton Road, York YO31 8HE Tel: 01904 453481 Fax: 01904 454747 Email: jwhitesurf@aol.com — BM BS 1985 Nottm.; BMedSci Nottm. 1983, BM BS 1985; MRCP (UK) 1988. Cons. Phys. Prev: Sen. Regist. (Respirat. Med.) Freeman Hosp. Newc.; Regist. (Chest. Med.) Freeman Hosp. Newc.; Regist. (Med.) Hexham Gen. Hosp.

WHITE, John Horder, Wing Cdr. RAF Med. Br. 6 Falkirk Road, Wroughton, Swindon SN4 9DU Tel: 01793 812821 — MB BS 1952 Lond.; MRCS Eng. LRCP Lond. 1952. (St. Mary's) Prev: Gp. Capt. RAF.

WHITE, John Howard 27 Southill Road, Poole BH12 3AW — MB ChB 1957 Leeds.

WHITE, John Hunter McNeil (retired) 10 Elvin Close, Lincoln LN2 1SP Tel: 01522 534336 — MB BS Lond. 1949; MRCS Eng.

WHITE

LRCP Lond. 1948. Prev: Assoc. Specialist (Psychiat.) Scunthorpe Gen., Grimsby Dist. Gen. Hosp., Lawn Hosp. & St. John's Hosp. Lincoln.

WHITE, John Jackson Barnard Castle Surgery, Victoria Road, Barnard Castle DL12 8HT Tel: 01833 690707 — MB BS 1975 Newc.; MRCGP 1979; DRCOG 1978.

WHITE, Jonathan Atherley 44 Napier Street, Burton-on-Trent DE14 3LN Tel: 01283 511958; Sandon, Heath Road, Bradfield, Manningtree CO11 2HX — BM BS 1982 Nottm. Prev: SHO (Psychiat.) Walsgrave Hosp. Coventry; SHO (Geriat.) N.ampton Gen. Hosp.; SHO (Gen. Orthop./A & E) Burton Dist. Hosp.

WHITE, Jonathan Celt Barton Health Centre, Short Lane, Barton-under-Needwood, Burton-on-Trent DE13 8LB Tel: 01283 712207 Fax: 01283 712116 — MB BS 1987 Lond.; MRCGP 1992; DRCOG 1991.

WHITE, Jonathan Charles North Devon District Hospital, Barnstaple EX31 4JB Tel: 01271 22577; Tremethick, Trevance, Wadebridge PL27 7QF — MB ChB 1991 Bristol; BSc (Hons.) Lond. 1982; MRCGP 1995.

WHITE, Mr Jonathan David Flat 4, Edward Court, Birmingham Road, Walsall WS1 2RF Tel: 01922 29959 — MB ChB 1990 Birm.; ChB Birm. 1990; FRCS Ed. 1996.

WHITE, Jonathan Francis Middleton Penn Manor Medical Centre, Manor Road, Penn, Wolverhampton WV4 5PY Tel: 01902 331166 Fax: 01902 575078; 39 St. Philip's Avenue, Penn, Wolverhampton WV3 7DU — MB ChB 1978 Birm.

WHITE, Mr Jonathan Samuel 3 Rhanbuoy Close, Carrickfergus BT38 8FF Email: jandp@easynet.co.uk — MB BCh BAO 1993 Belf.; BMedSci (Hons) 1991; FRCSI 1997.

WHITE, Julian Peter 186 Crofton Road, Orpington BR6 8JG; 186 Crofton Road, Orpington BR6 8JG Tel: 01689 54617 — MB BS 1981 Newc.; MRCPsych 1986. Clin. Asst. (Psychogeriat.) Qu. Mary's Hosp. Sidcup. Prev: Med. Off. HM Youth Custody Centre Rochester; Regist. & SHO (Psychiat.) Maidstone HA.

***WHITE, Julie Anne** 5 Downside, Gosport PO13 0JS Tel: 01329 513519 — MB ChB 1998 Leic.; MB ChB Leic 1998.

WHITE, Julie Susan 19 Stockdale Avenue, Redcar TS10 5EF — MB BS 1992 Newc.

WHITE, Kalasyam Kochayyappan The Surgery, Low Moor Road, Kirkby-in-Ashfield, Nottingham NG17 7BG Tel: 01623 759447; La Vista, Coxmoor Road, Sutton-in-Ashfield NG17 5LF Tel: 01623 552612 — MB BS 1964 Karnatak.

WHITE, Karen Jane Folkestone Community Mental Health Centre, 2-4 Radnor Park Avenue, Folkestone CT19 5BW Tel: 01303 222424 Fax: 01303 222444 — MB ChB 1982 Leeds; MRCPsych 1987. Cons. Community Psychiat. E. Kent Community Trust. Prev: Med. Dir. S. Kent Community Trust; Cons. & Sen. Lect. Community Psychiat. W. Lambeth Community Care Trust UMDS Lond.; Lect. (Community Psychiat.) UMDS Guys & St. Thomas Hosp. Lond.

WHITE, Kathleen Denise Department of neurology, Ninewells Hospital, Dundee Tel: 01382 660111 — MB ChB 1987 Dundee; BMSc (Hons) Path. Sci's. (Human Genetics) 1984; MRCP (UK) 1991. Locum Cons. Neurol. Ninewells Hosp.s Dundee. Prev: part time Sen. Regist. (neurol) Manch. Roy. Infirm.; seb Regist. (neuro) Vict. Infirm., Newc. Upon Tyne; Regissst (neura) Notrh RHA.

WHITE, Kevin 50 Long Lane, Aughton, Ormskirk L39 5AT — MB ChB 1961 Liverp.; MRCPsych 1971.

WHITE, Lesley Jane 3 Ravelston Park, Edinburgh EH4 3DX — MB ChB 1995 Aberd.

WHITE, Lilian Freda 18 Beach Road, Tynemouth, North Shields NE30 2NS Tel: 0191 258 7505 — MB BS 1954 Durh.; DPH Newc. 1968. (Newc.) Clin. Asst. Ashington Hosp.; Asst. Med. Off. Wallsend Municip. Boro. Prev: Ho. Phys. & Ho. Surg. Roy. Vict. Infirm. Newc.

WHITE, Lisa Antonia Marion 14 Leathwaite Road, London SW11 1XQ — BM BS 1993 Nottm.

WHITE, Liza Rebecca 41 Jenny Burton Way, Hucknall, Nottingham NG15 7QS — MB ChB 1995 Manch.; BSc Open 1995. SHO (Gen. Med.) Nottm. City Hosp.

WHITE, Lorraine Andrea 21 Badger Wood Walk, Badger Hill, York YO10 5HN — MB BS 1993 Newc.

WHITE, Lucy Anne Whiteleaf, Crawley, Winchester SO21 2QD — MB BCh 1988 Oxf.; MA Camb. 1985; MRCP (UK) 1992; FRCA 1995. Regist. (Anaesth.) Soton. Gen. Hosp. Prev: Regist. (Anaesth.) Portsmouth Hosps. Trust; SHO (Anaesth.) Soton. Gen. Hosp.; SHO (Gen. Med.) Basingstoke Dist. Hosp. & Soton. Gen. Hosp.

WHITE, Madeline Patricia Royal Hospital for Sick Children, Yorkhill NHS Trust, Glasgow G15 6PX — MB ChB 1973 Dundee; FRCPCH 1998; FRCP Glas. 1994; MRCP (UK) 1980; FRCPCL 1998. Cons. Paediat. Gtr. Glas. HB.

WHITE, Mr Malcolm Edward Eales (retired) 1 Manor Farmhouse, Vicarage Road, Stoneleigh, Coventry CV8 3DH Tel: 01203 410014 — MB BChir 1947 Camb.; FRCS Eng. 1953. Prev: Cons. Surg. Walsgrave Hosp. Coventry.

WHITE, Malcolm Gordon (retired) 35 Knowle Lane, Sheffield S11 9SL Tel: 0114 236 3577 — MB ChB 1959 Sheff.

WHITE, Malcolm Terence The Surgery, 18 Fouracre Road, Bristol BS16 6PG Tel: 0117 970 2033; 47 Church Road, Yate, Bristol BS37 5BH Tel: 01454 312155 — MB ChB 1956 Bristol; DObst RCOG 1958. (Bristol)

WHITE, Margaret M S Brookfield Surgery, Whitbarrow Road, Lymm WA13 9DB Tel: 01925 756969 Fax: 01925 756173 — MB ChB 1979 Manchester; MB ChB 1979 Manchester.

WHITE, Margaret Rose Mary (retired) Avondale, Pencader SA39 9AS — MB BCh 1957 Wales; BSc, MB BCh Wales 1957; DPM Eng. 1976. Prev: SCMO Gwent AHA.

WHITE, Margaret Stather 22 Upfield, Croydon CR0 5DQ Tel: 020 8654 1411 — MB ChB 1943 Sheff.; DObst RCOG 1948. (Sheff.) Prev: Asst. MOH Boro. Croydon; Ho. Surg. Infirm. Sheff.; Obst. Med. Off. St. Jas. Hosp. Balham.

WHITE, Marion Isobel Aberdeen Royal Hospitals NHS Trust, Foresterhill, Aberdeen AB25 2ZN Tel: 01224 681818 Fax: 01224 840555 — MB ChB 1972 Aberd.; BA Open 1988; FRCP Glas. 1986; MRCP (UK) 1974. Cons. Dermat. Aberd. Roy. Hosp. NHS Trust; Hon. Sen. Lect. Aberd. Univ. Prev: Research Fell. Inst. Dermat. Lond.

WHITE, Mark Andrew 16 Glenside Drive, Wilmslow SK9 1EH — MB ChB 1990 Manch.; MRCP (UK) 1994; FRCA 1996; DA (UK) 1995; AFPM 1998. (Manch.) Pharmaceut. Phys. Chesh.

WHITE, Mark Jonathan 15 Main Street, Thorner, Leeds LS14 3DX — MB ChB 1994 Leeds.

WHITE, Mark Thomas 15 Cole Crescent, Aughton, Ormskirk L39 5AJ — MB ChB 1994 Manch.

WHITE, Martin Newlands, 122 Derwen Fawr Road, Derwen Fawr, Swansea SA2 8DP Tel: 01792 203248; St. David's House, 1 Uplands Terrace, Uplands, Swansea SA2 0GU Tel: 01792 472922 — MB BCh 1975 Wales; FRCR 1982. (Cardiff) Cons. Radiol. Swansea NHS Trust Singleton Hosp. Prev: Sen. Regist. (Radiol.) Univ. Hosp. Wales Cardiff.

WHITE, Martin James Reeve Department of Epidemiology & Public Health, The Medical School, University of Newcastle upon Tyne, Newcastle upon Tyne NE2 4HH Tel: 0191 222 6275 Fax: 0191 222 8211 Email: martin.white@ncl.ac.uk — MB ChB 1983 Birm.; MSc 1989 Newc; MFPHM 1991 RCP, UK; FFPHM 1997 RCP, UK. (Birm.) Sen. Lect. & Cons. Pub. Health Med. Univ. Newc. u Tyne. Socs: Soc. Social Med.; BMA; Internat. Union Health Promotion & Educat. Prev: Lect. (Pub. Health Med.) & Hon. Sen. Regist. N.. RHA.

WHITE, Martin John 160 Greenacres, Wetheral, Carlisle CA4 8LU Tel: 01228 561397; 160 Greenacres, Wetheral, Carlisle CA4 8LU Tel: 01228 561397 Email: martin@thewhites.demon.co.uk — MB BS 1983 Newc.; FRCA 1989. Cons. Anaesth. Carlisle Hosps.; Lead clinician Intens. care unit, Cumbld. Infirm., Carlisle; Clin. Director-Anaesthetics, theatres and Intens. care, Cumbld. Infirm., Carlisle. Prev: Sen. Regist. (Anaesth.) N.. RHA.; Regist. S. Glam. HA.

WHITE, Mary Radiology Dept, Kingston University Hospital, Galsworthy Rd, Kingston upon Thames KT2 7QB Tel: 020 8546 7711; 19 Hollytree Close, London SW19 6EA Tel: 020 8789 4264 Email: mary53fran@asol.com — MB BCh BAO 1976 NUI; MRCPI 1979; FRCR 1983; DCH 1978. Cons. (Radiol.) Kingston Univ. Hosp. NHS Trust Kingston on Thames.

WHITE, Mary-Ellen The Ridings, Southlands Hospital, Shoreham-by-Sea Tel: 01273 455622 — MB BS 1991 Lond.; MRCPsych 1995.

WHITE, Mary Evelyn 52 King's Road, Richmond TW10 6EP — MB BCh BAO 1979 NUI; DRCOG 1985; DCH RCSI 1984.

WHITE, Mary Hester Roberta 30 Rhee Lance, Culcrow, Aghadowey, Coleraine BT51 4BF — MB ChB 1991 Sheff.

WHITE, Matthew 8E Hayton Road, Aberdeen AB24 2QR — MB ChB 1993 Aberd.

WHITE, Maurice 17 Jeffreys Street, London NW1 9PS Tel: 020 7267 1444 — BA, MB BCh BAO Dub. 1956, DPM 1960. (T.C. Dub.) Socs: Brit. Psychoanal. Soc.

WHITE, Michael Joseph Stakes Lodge Surgery, 3A Lavender Road, Waterlooville PO7 8NS Tel: 023 9225 4581 Fax: 023 9235 8867 — MB BS 1981 Lond.; MRCGP 1985; DRCOG 1985; DCH RCP Lond. 1984. (Lond. Hosp.) GP Princip. Drs. Boyle White Bateman King Burton. Prev: Trainee GP S. Gwent VTS.

WHITE, Michelle Claire 59 Links Road, Epsom KT17 3PP Tel: 01372 741183 — MB ChB 1994 Bristol; DCH RCP Lond. 1996. (Univ. Bristol) SHO (Anaesth.) Bristol. Socs: BMA; Assn. Anaesth.; Train. Mem RCA. Prev: SHO (Paediat. & Neonat. Med.) Taunton & Som. Hosp.; SHO (A & E Med.) Frenchay Hosp. Bristol.

WHITE, Mr Morven Allen 34 Coachmans Way, Hillsborough BT26 6HQ — MB ChB 1969 Ed.; BSc Ed. 1966, MB ChB 1969; FRCS Ed. 1976; AFOM Med. RCP Lond. 1979. (Ed.) Dir. Aberd. Indust. Doctors. Socs: Brit. Assn. Manip. Med.; Brit. Med. Acupunct. Soc.; Assoc. Mem. Fac. Homoeop.

WHITE, Neil Morgan Lloyd The Mumbles Medical Practice, 10 West Cross Avenue, Norton, Mumbles, Swansea SA3 5UA Tel: 01792 403010 Fax: 01792 401934 — MB BCh 1984 Wales; RCGP; MRCGP 1990.

WHITE, Nicholas The Chase, Glebe Lane, Burnham Overy Staithe, King's Lynn PE31 8JQ — MB ChB 1998 Manch.

WHITE, Nicholas Charles 74 Grange Road, Dudley DY1 2AW — MB ChB 1982 Birm.

WHITE, Professor Nicholas John Faculty of Tropical Medicine, Mahidol University, 420/6 Rajvithi Road, Bangkok 10400, Thailand Tel: 0066 2 460832 Fax: 0066 246 7795; Nuffield Department of Clinical Medicine, John Radcliffe Hospital, Headington, Oxford OX3 9DU Tel: 01865 220970 Fax: 01865 220984 — MRCS Eng. LRCP Lond. 1974; MD Lond. 1984, MB BS 1974; MRCP (UK) 1976; MA Oxf. 1986; FRCP 1989; DSc (Med.) Lond. 1995. Director Wellcome Mahidol Univ. Oxf. Trop. Med. Research Prog.

WHITE, Nicholas Kevin, Squadron Ldr. RAF Med. Br. 15 Main Street, Little Thetford, Ely CB6 3HA Tel: 01353 648303 — MB ChB 1983 Dundee; BSc (Hons.) Dund 1979; MRCGP 1989; DAvMed FOM RCP Lond. 1994; DRCOG 1985. Dep. Sen. Med. Off. RAF Akrotiri, Cyprus.

WHITE, Nicholas Peter 12 Brackenway, Formby, Liverpool L37 7HG — MB BS 1993 Newc.

WHITE, Nicola Janine Health Centre, Anstey Road, Alton GU34 2QX; Goldings, Worldham Hill, East Worldham, Alton GU34 3AT — MB BS 1981 Lond.; DRCOG 1985; MRCGP 1985; MRCGP 1985; DRCOG 1985.

WHITE, Nigel Antony 63 Kingfisher Close, Bedford MK41 7JR — MB BS 1989 Lond.

WHITE, Norman Victor 25 Springvale Avenue, Park Hall, Walsall WS5 3QB Tel: 01922 23210 — MB ChB 1954 Birm. (Birm.) Prev: Anaesth. SHO & Regist. Roy. Infirm. Stoke-on-trent; Ho. Phys. & Ho. Surg. Dist. Hosp. W. Bromwich.

WHITE, Mrs Pamela (retired) 13 Barntongate Avenue, Edinburgh EH4 8BQ Tel: 0131 339 7530 — MB ChB 1950 Ed.

WHITE, Pamela Jean (retired) 4 Rectory Close, Lower Heswall, Wirral CH60 4TB — MRCS Eng. LRCP Lond. 1960. Prev: SCMO Liverp. HA.

WHITE, Pamela Olive (retired) 12 Hill Lane, Hartley, Plymouth PL3 5QX — BA Open 1987; MB BS Lond. 1964; FFA RCS Eng. 1970; DA Eng. 1967. Prev: Sen. Regist. (Anaesth.) Birm. Hosps.

WHITE, Patricia Clare West Kirby Health Centre, Grange Road, Wirral CH48 4HZ Tel: 0151 625 9171 Fax: 0151 625 9171 — MB ChB 1988 Liverp.

WHITE, Patricia Mary Bury Knowle Health Centre, London Rd, Headington OX3 9JA Tel: 01865 761651 Email: pat.white@gp-k84009.nhs.uk; Little Cranford, Moulsford, Wallingford OX10 9HU — MB BS 1976 Lond.; MRCS Eng. LRCP Lond. 1976; DRCOG 1979; MRCGP 1982. Socs: Reading Path. Soc.

WHITE, Patrick Thomas Crown Dale Medical Centre, 61 Crown Dale, London SE19 3NY Tel: 020 8670 2414 Fax: 020 8670 0277 — MB BCh BAO 1976 NUI; MRCP (UK) 1979; FRCGP 1995, M 1980. (Univ. Coll. Dub.) Sen. Lect. (Gen. Pract.) Guy's King's Sch. Med. Socs: BMA. Prev: Lect. (Gen. Pract.) King's Coll. Sch. Med. &

Dent. Lond.; Research Fell. (Gen. Pract.) St. Geo. Hosp. Med. Sch. Lond.; Trainee GP Bangour VTS.

WHITE, Mr Paul Stephen The Directorate of Otolaryngology, Level 5, Ninewells Hospital & Medical School, Dundee DD1 9SY Tel: 01382 660111 Fax: 01382 632816 Email: paulw@dth.scot.nhs.uk; Brackenbrae, Emma Terrace, Blairgowrie PH10 6JA — MB ChB 1982 Otago; FRCS Ed. 1995; FRACS 1990; T(S) 1991. Cons. Otolaryngol. Ninewells Hosp. Dundee & Perth Roy. Infirm.; MATTUS Tutor (Otolaryngol.); Hon. Sen. Lect. Univ. Dundee; Cliincal Ldr. for ENT Serv.s,Tayside Univ. Hosp. NHS Trust. Socs: Brit. Assn. Otol.; NZ Soc. Otolaryngol. & Head & Neck Surg.; Scott. Otolaryngol. Soc. (Counc. Mem.). Prev: Cons. Otolaryngol. Lanarksh. HB; Sen. Regist. Glas. Roy. Infirm. & ChristCh. Hosp., NZ.

WHITE, Peter Denton St. Bartholomew's Hospital, Department of Psychological Medicine, London EC1A 7BE Tel: 020 7601 8108 Fax: 020 7601 7969 Email: p.d.white@qmul.ac.uk — MB BS 1977 Lond.; BSc (Hons.) Lond. 1974, MD 1993; FRCP Lond. 1995; MRCP (UK) 1981; FRCPsych 1995, M 1983. (St. Bart.) Sen. Lect. & Hon. Cons. Psychol. Med. St. Bart. & Roy. Lond. Med. & Dent. Sch. Lond. Socs: Internat. Coll. Psychosomatic Med.; Amer. Psychosomatic Assn. Prev: Lect. (Psychol. Med.) St. Bart. Hosp. Lond.; Ment. Health Foundat. Fell. St. Bart. Hosp. Lond.; Regist. Maudsley & Bethlem Roy. Hosp.

WHITE, Peter Gardner West End Medical Practice, 21 Chester Street, Edinburgh EH3 7RF Tel: 0131 225 5220 Fax: 0131 226 1910; 84 Craigcrook Road, Edinburgh EH4 3PN Tel: 0131 336 5505 — MB ChB 1970 Ed.; BSc (Hons.) Ed. 1967; MRCP (UK) 1974. (Ed.) Prev: Regist. Roy. Infirm. Edin.; SHO W.. Gen. Hosp. Edin.

WHITE, Peter James Nightingale Surgery, Great well Drive, Cupernham Lane, Romsey SO51 7QN Tel: 01794 517878 Fax: 01794 514236 Email: peterwhite@nightingalesurgery.com; Wealden, Chapel Lane, Timsbury, Romsey SO51 0NW Tel: 01794 367742 Email: peterwhite3@virgin.net — MB ChB 1974 Dundee; BSc (Med. Sci.) St. And. 1971; MRCGP 1979; FRCGP 1998. GP Tutor Soton.; Chairm. Steering Gp. Wessex Research Network. Socs: Nat. Assn. GP Tutors; RCGP.

WHITE, Peter Malcolm Castlehead Medical Centre, Ambleside Road, Keswick CA12 4DB Tel: 01768 772025 Fax: 01768 773862; Lowthwaite Farm House, St. Johns in the Vale, Keswick CA12 4TS — MB BS 1984 Lond.; BSc (Hons.) Lond. 1981; MRCGP 1988; DRCOG 1987.

WHITE, Peter Noel Graham Sleaford Medical Group, Riverside Surgery, 47 Boston Road, Sleaford NG34 7HD Tel: 01529 303301 Fax: 01529 415401; Spring House, Leasingham, Sleaford NG34 — MB BS 1965 Lond.; MRCS Eng. LRCP Lond. 1965; DObst RCOG 1967. (Univ. Coll. Hosp.) Clin. Asst. Clin. Immunol. Allergy Clinic Lincoln. Prev: Ho. Surg. W.m. Childr. Hosp.; Ho. Phys. Qu. Mary's Hosp. Roehampton; SHO Obst. Unit City Hosp. Nottm.

WHITE, Peter Reginald 90 Darnley Road, Gravesend DA11 0SW — MB BS 1973 Lond.; DRCOG 1982.

WHITE, Philip Graham Radiology Department, Morriston Hospital, Morriston, Swansea SA6 6NL Tel: 01792 703664 Fax: 01792 703674; 1 Little Highway Mews, Pennard Road, Southgate, Swansea SA3 2AD — MB BS 1984 Lond.; BSc Lond. 1981; MRCP (UK) 1987; FRCR 1991; T(R) (CR) 1993. Cons. Radiol. Morriston Hosp. Swansea; Cons. Radiol. Neath Gen. Hosp. Prev: Clin. Fell. (Radiol.) McMaster Univ. Camb.; Sen. Regist. & Regist. (Radiol.) S. Glam. Health Auth.

WHITE, Philip Michael 41 Harker Park, Carlisle CA6 4HS — MB ChB 1990 Liverp.; BSc (1st cl. Hons.) Liverp. 1988, MB ChB 1990. SHO (Med.) Roy. Liverp. Univ. Hosp.

WHITE, Philip Thomas 29 Blyth Hill Lane, London SE6 4UN — MB BCh 1987 Wales.

WHITE, Philip Wayman Felinheli Terrace Surgery, 1 Felinheli Terrace, Felinheli, Port Dinorwic LL56 4JF Tel: 01248 670423 Fax: 01248 670966; (Surgery), Coronation Road, Menai Bridge LL59 5BD Tel: 01248 712210 Fax: 01248 715829 — MB ChB 1976 Manch. Clin. Asst. (ENT) N. W. Wales Trust. Socs: BMA (Sec. N. W. Wales Div.).

WHITE, Philippa Jane Princess Anne Hospital, Coxford Road, Southampton SO16 5YA Tel: 02380 796041 — MB BS 1975 Lond.; MRCOG 1980, D 1978; FRCOG 1995. Cons. Obst. P.ss Anne Hosp. Soton.

WHITE

WHITE, Philippa Mary Bruce PHLS East, Directorate Office, Institute of Food Research, Norwich Research Park, Colney Lane, Norwich NR4 7UA Tel: 01603 506900 Fax: 01603 501188 Email: pwhite@phls.co.uk; 1 Carnation Cottage, 103 Dereham Road, Mattishall, Dereham NR20 3NU Tel: 01362 858494 — MB BS 1977 Lond.; MSc Lond. 1982, BSc (Hons.) 1974; MRCPath 1984; FRCPath 1995; MBA 1999. (Univ. Coll. Hosp.) Gp. Dir. PHLS E.; Cons. Microbiol. (Virol.) Pub. Health Laborat. Norwich; Hon. Lect. Univ. E. Anglia. Prev: Dir. Pub. Health Laborat. Norwich; Assoc. Specialist Virus Refer. Laborat. Lond.; Sen. Regist. Pub. Health Laborat. Coventry.

WHITE, Phoebe Margaret (retired) 15a South Street, Totnes TQ9 5DZ Tel: 01803 864007 — MB ChB 1949 Ed.; DCH Eng. 1953. Prev: SCMO Torbay.

WHITE, Priscilla Mary (retired) Hillside, Guineaford, Marwood, Barnstaple EX31 4EA Tel: 01271 371603 — MB 1965 Camb.; BChir 1964; MRCPsych 1976; DPM Eng. 1975; DCH Eng. 1967. Prev: Cons. Psychiat. & Adolesc. N. Devon Health Care Trust.

WHITE, Rachel Jane Crofton Surgery, 109a Crofton Rd, Orpington BR6 8HX Tel: 01689 822266 Fax: 01689 891790; 74 Towncourt Crescent, Lee, Pettswood BR5 1PJ — MB BS 1988 Lond.

WHITE, Ralph William 18 Loxley View Road, Sheffield S10 1QZ — MB ChB 1992 Sheff.

WHITE, Raymond George 59 Aberfoyle Crescent, Londonderry BT48 7PG Tel: 01504 63627 — MB BCh BAO 1976 Belf.; MRCOG 1981, D 1978. (Belf.) Regist. (O & G) Craigavon Area Hosp. Prev: Sen. Regist. (O & G) Centr. Hosp. Harare Zimbabwe; Regist. (O & G) Altnagelvin Hosp. Lond.derry; Research Fell. Roy. Vict. Hosp. Belf.

WHITE, Raymund John Auchinairn Road Surgery, 101 Auchinairn Road, Bishopbriggs, Glasgow G64 1NF Tel: 0141 772 1808 Fax: 0141 762 1274 — MB ChB 1984 Glas. SHO (Dermat.) Stobhill Hosp. Glas. Prev: SHO (Otolaryngol.) Stobhill Hosp. Glas.; SHO (Gen. Surg.) Monklands Dist. Gen. Hosp. Airdrie.

WHITE, Professor Richard Henry Reeve The Rye, 12 Cherry Hill Road, Barnt Green, Birmingham B45 8LJ Tel: 0121 445 4886 — MB BChir Camb. 1950; MA Camb. 1948; MD Birm. 1969; FRCP Lond. 1972, M 1954; MRCS Eng. LRCP Lond. 1950; DCH Eng. 1952; FRCPCH (Hon.) 1997. (Guy's) Emerit. Prof. Paediat. Nephrol. Univ. Birm. Socs: Hon. Life Mem. Brit. Assn. Paediat. Nephrol. (Pres. 1991-94); Hon. Life Mem. (Ex-Counc.lor) Europ. Soc. Paediat. Nephrol.; Hon. Life Mem. (Ex-Mem. Exec. Comm.) Renal Assn. Prev: Cons. Paediat. & Nephrol. Childr. Hosp. Birm.; Sen. Lect. & 1st Asst. (Paediat. & Child Health) Univ Birm.; Asst. to Dir. (Paediat.) Guy's Hosp. Lond.

WHITE, Richard Ian 23 St Johns Mansions, Clapton Square, London E5 8HT — MB BS 1978 Lond.; MRCPsych 1985.

WHITE, Richard Patrick Department of Neurology, St Mary's Hosp, Praed St, London W2 Tel: 0207 886 6666; Email: white.richard@ntlworld.com — MB ChB 1992 Leeds; MD 1999 Lond.; BSc (Hons.) Leeds 1989; MRCP (UK) 1995. (Leeds University) Specialist Regist. (Neurol.) St. Mary's Hosp., Lond.; Research Fell. And Hon. Regist., St Geo.'s Hosp., Lond. Prev: Specialist Regist. (Neurol.) Chelsea and W.minster Hosp., Lond.; Specialist Regist. (Neurol.) Nat. Hosp. For Neurol. and Neurosurg., Qu. Sq., Lond.; Research Fell. Dept. of Acad. Neurosci.s Kings Coll. Hosp.

WHITE, Robert John 30 Kingsdown Road, Northfield, Birmingham B31 1AH — MB ChB 1978 Birm.; MRCGP 1985. Trainee GP W. Cumbld. Hosp. Whitehaven VTS. Prev: Med. Regist. (Chest Dis.) Jersey Gen. Hosp.; SHO (Med.) Treliske Hosp. Truro; SHO (Med.) Tehidy Hosp. Camborne.

WHITE, Roderick John Stranraer Health Centre, Edinburgh Road, Stranraer DG9 7HG Tel: 01776 706566; Egmont, Larg Road, Stranraer DG9 — MB ChB 1976 Glas.; MRCGP 1981; DRCOG 1980. (Glas.)

WHITE, Roger George 101 Longdown Lane S., Epsom KT17 4JJ Tel: 01372 721001 — MB BS 1958 Lond.; DObst RCOG 1961. (St. Bart.) Ex Med. Off. Epsom Coll.; Sen. Med. Off. to United Racecourses Ltd. Prev: Ho. Phys., Research Asst. & GP Clin. Asst. St. Bart. Hosp. Lond.

WHITE, Roger James Crosshouse Hospital, Kilmarnock KA2 0BE Tel: 01563 521133; 4 Macrae Drive, Prestwick KA9 1NY Tel: 01292 479752 Email: roger1402@aol.com — MB ChB 1975 Dundee; FRCA 1980. Cons. Anaesth. CrossHo. Hosp. Kilmarnock.

WHITE, Roger James (cons. rooms), Litfield House, Clifton, Bristol BS8 3LS Tel: 0117 973 1323 Fax: 0117 973 3303; 4 Church Avenue, Stoke Bishop, Bristol BS9 1LD Tel: 0117 968 4207 Email: roger.white4@virgin.net — MA Camb. 1964, MD 1971, MB 1964, BChir 1963; FRCP Lond. 1980, M 1967. (Camb. & St. Bart.) Sen. Lect. Med. Bristol Univ.; Cons. Phys. Frenchay Hosp. Bristol. Prev: Research Asst. Cardiac Dept. St. Bart. Hosp.; Jun. Med. Regist. St. Bart. Hosp.; Sen. Med. Regist. St. Bart. Hosp. Lond.

WHITE, Roger William Barker (retired) 227 Park Road, Hartlepool TS26 9NG Tel: 01429 269395 — MA, MB Camb. 1961, BChir 1960; FRCP Lond. 1979, M 1965. Prev: Cons. Gen. Phys. Cardiol. Hartlepool Gen. Hosp.

WHITE, Roma Shareen (retired) 4 Frances Street, Chesham HP5 3EQ Tel: 01494 784568 — MB BS 1961 Lond.; MRCS Eng. LRCP Lond. 1961; DObst RCOG 1963. Prev: SCMO Camden & Islington Community Trust.

WHITE, Ronald Bertie William (retired) Beech Hill, Flore, Northampton NN7 4LL Tel: 01327 340377 — MB ChB 1959 Sheff.; BA Open 1990. Prev: GP Flore, N.ampton.

WHITE, Ronald James 19 Tyler Road, Limavady BT49 0DP — MB BCh BAO 1986 Belf.

WHITE, Rupert John Edward Trerose, Point Green, Devoran, Truro TR3 6NH — MB BS 1992 Lond.

WHITE, Ruth Elizabeth Bevis 51 Britannia Square, Worcester WR1 3HP — BM BCh 1983 Oxf.; MPhil Lond. 1990; MA Camb. 1983; MRCPsych 1988. Cons. Psychiat. Worcester Roy. Infirm. NHS Trust. Prev: Lect. (Psychiat.) St. Geo. Hosp. Lond.

WHITE, Ruth Margaret 4 Warton Terrace, Newcastle upon Tyne NE6 5LR — MB BS 1984 Newc.

WHITE, Ruth Robina Manor Farm House, 96 High St., Yelvertoft, Northampton NN6 6LQ — MB ChB 1983 Aberd.

WHITE, Sally Jane 350 Upper Richmond Road, London SW15 6TL Tel: 020 8788 0686; 94 Dora Road, London SW19 7HJ Tel: 020 8944 1387 Fax: 020 8946 1799 Email: mark.t@lineone.net — MB BS 1984 Lond.; MRCGP 1991. (Westm.) Prev: Trainee GP/SHO Rotat. Qu. Marys Hosp. Roehampton VTS.

WHITE, Samantha Irene 2 Meadowcroft Rise, Bierley, Bradford BD4 6EP — MB ChB 1993 Sheff.

WHITE, Sandra Katherine 4 High Ash Road, Wheathampstead, St Albans AL4 8DY Email: sandrawhite@doctors.org.uk — MB BS 1996 Lond.; BSc Lond. 1995. (St. Georges University of London)

WHITE, Sarah Ann Bents Green Surgery, 98 Bents Road, Sheffield S11 9RL Tel: 0114 236 0641 Fax: 0114 262 1069; Bents Green Surgery, 98 Bents Road, Sheffield S11 9RL Tel: 0114 236 0641 — MB ChB 1989 Sheff.; MRCGP Ed. 1994; DRCOG 1992; DFFP 1996. (Sheffield) GP; Family Plann. Doctor. Prev: Mem. BMA; Mem. RCGP; Mem. MPS.

WHITE, Sarah Caroline Louise Inver Cottage, Dunreggan, Moniaive, Thornhill DG3 4HQ Tel: 01848 200716 — MB ChB 1995 Birm.; ChB Birm. 1995. SHO Med. Dumfries & Galloway Roy.Infirm. Socs: BMA; MDU. Prev: SHO (A & E) Roy. Darwin Hosp. Australia; SHO (O & G) Roy. Darwin Hosp. Australia; SHO (Psychiat.) Crichton Roy. Hosp. Dumfries.

WHITE, Sean Anthony 119 Harley St, London W1G 6AN — MB BS 1988 Lond.; FRCA 1994. (The London Hospital Medical College) Cons. St Bartholomews Hosp. Smithfield, Lond. Socs: Assn. Anaesth.; Pain. Soc; IASP. Prev: Regist. (Anaesth.) Roy. Lond. Hosp. Trust.

WHITE, Sheelagh Mary (retired) 1 Cathedral Square, Fortrose IV10 8TB — MB ChB 1964 Ed.; FFA RCS Eng. 1970; DObst RCOG 1966. Prev: anaesthetics Cons., Inverness.

WHITE, Sheelagh McKie 7 Miller Street, Hamilton ML3 7EW — MB ChB 1977 Glas.

WHITE, Mr Stephen Howard Robert Jones & Agnes Hunt Orthop. & District Hospital NHS Trust, Oswestry SY10 7AG Tel: 01691 404000 Fax: 01691 404052; 84 Upper Road, Shrewsbury SY3 9JP Tel: 01743 232171 — BM BS 1980 Nottm.; DM Nottm. 1993, BMedSci 1978; FRCS Eng. 1984. Cons. Orthop. Surg. Robt. Jones & Agnes Hunt Orthop. & Dist. Hosp. OsW.ry & Roy. Shrewsbury Hosp. NHS Trust. Socs: Brit. Assn. Surg. Knee. Prev: Sen. Regist. (Traum. & Orthop. Surg.) Oxf.

WHITE, Stephen Innes Coniston, 25 Tower Road N., Wirral CH60 6RS — MB ChB 1977 Manch.; MD Manch. 1990; FRCP Lond. 1996; MRCP (UK) 1981; DRCOG 1979. Cons. Dermat. Wirral

Hosp. Prev: Clin. Lect. (Dermat.) Univ. Glas. & Hon. Sen. Regist. W.. Infirm. Glas.; Regist. (Dermat.) Roy. Vict. Infirm. Newc.; Ho. Phys. N. Manch. Gen. Hosp.

WHITE, Stephen Robert Broadway Surgery, 2 Broadway, Fulwood, Preston PR2 9TH Tel: 01772 717261 Fax: 01772 787652 — MB ChB 1986 Manch.

WHITE, Stephen Thomas Royal Victoria Hospital, Grosvenor Road, Belfast BT12 6BA — MB ChB 1983 Liverp.; MB ChB (Hons.) Liverp. 1983; FRCOphth 1994.

WHITE, Mr Steven Alan Department of Surgery, Leicester General Hospital, Gwendolen Road, Leicester LE5 4PW Tel: 0116 258 8080 Fax: 0116 249 0064 Email: steve.white@dial.pipex.com; 6 Aber Road, Stoneygate, Leicester LE2 2BA — MB ChB 1992 Leic.; MD 1998; FRCS 1998. (Leics) Lect.Surg. Univ. Leics; Hon. Specialist Regist. S. Trent. Train. Scheme Gen. Surg. Socs: Brit. Transpl..Soc; Pancreatic. Soc; Assoc.Surg. Prev: Hon. SHO (Surg.) Leicester Roy. Infirm.; Clin. Research Fell. (Surg.) Univ. Leics.; Transpl..Fell.Univ.Leics.

WHITE, Steven Robert Department of Clinical Neurophysiology, Great Ormond Street Hospital for Children, London WC1N 3JH Tel: 020 7405 9200 — MB BChir 1978 Camb.; FRCP 2000; BA (Psychol. & Phil.) Oxf. 1969, MA 1973, DPhil 1976; BA Camb. 1976; MRCPsych 1983. (Camb.) Cons. Neurophysiol. Gt. Ormond St. Hosp. For Childr. & St Mary's Hosp. Lond. Socs: Fell. Roy. Soc. Trop. Med. & Hyg.; Brit. Psychol. Soc.; Ass of Brit. neUrol.s. Prev: Cons. Neurophysiol., Barts & The Lond. Hosp.; Cons. Neurophysiol. Middlx. Hosp. & Whittington Hosp. Lond.; Sen. Regist. (Clin. Neurophysiol.) Gen. Infirm. & St. Jas. Univ. Hosp. Leeds.

WHITE, Stuart Malcolm 63 Wilmington Way, Brighton BN1 8JG — MB BS 1994 Lond.

WHITE, Susan 141 Brigstock Road, Thornton Heath, Croydon CR7 7JN Tel: 020 8684 1128; 94 Pollards Hill N., Norbury, London SW16 4NZ Tel: 020 8679 8267 — MB BS Newc. 1977; MRCGP 1982; DCH RCP Lond. 1982; DRCOG 1981. (Newcastle) GP Princip.; Clin. Asst. Cardiol. Mayday Hosp. Thornton Health; GP Tutor Kings Coll. Med. Sch.

WHITE, Susan Veronica c/o Dept. of Geriatric Medicine, University Hospital, Wales, Cardiff CF4 4XW Tel: 029 2074 3142 — MB BCh BAO 1989 NUI; MRCPI 1992; DTM & H Liverp. 1995. SpR Geriat., Roy. Gwent Hosp., Newport. Socs: Brit. Geriat. Soc.

WHITE, Thomas State Hospital, Carstairs Junction, Lanark ML11 8RP Tel: 01555 840293 Fax: 01555 840112 Email: tomw@tsh.scot.nhs.uk; 33 Main St, Symington, Biggar ML12 6XP, 01899 308235 — MB ChB 1983 Ed.; BSc (Hons.) Ed. 1980; MRCPsych 1988; Dip. Forens. Med. Glas 1995. (Edinburgh) Cons. Forens. Psychiat. State Hosp. Prev: Cons. Psychiat. Forth Valley HB; Sen. Regist. (Gen. Adult Psychiat.) Gtr. Glas. HB.

WHITE, Thomas George Edward 22 Upfield, Croydon CR0 5DQ Tel: 020 8654 1411 — MD 1953 Belf.; MB BCh BAO 1941; MRCOG 1947; MRCGP 1958. (Qu. Univ. Belf.) Socs: BMA; FRSM. Prev: Sen. Regist. Mayday Hosp. Croydon; Ho. Surg. Jessop Hosp. Wom. Sheff.; Maj. RAMC.

WHITE, Thomas John Clarence Avenue Surgery, 14 Clarence Avenue, Northampton NN2 6NZ Tel: 01604 718464 Fax: 01604 721589; 15 Park Avenue S., Northampton NN3 3AA Tel: 01604 633898 — MB BChir 1977 Camb.; MA, MB Camb. 1977, BChir 1976; MRCGP 1981; DCH Eng. 1980; DRCOG 1979. (Queens' Coll. Camb. & St. Bart. Lond.) Socs: BMA; N.ampton Med. Assn. Prev: Ho. Off. (Surg. & Med.) & SHO (Paediat. & O & G) N.ampton; Gen. Hosp.

WHITE, Thomas Milnes Fisher Medical Centre, Millfields, Coach Street, Skipton BD23 1EU; Westville, 17 West Bank Road, Skipton BD23 1QT Tel: 01756 700887 — MB BS 1983 Lond.; MA Oxf. 1980; MRCGP 1987; DRCOG 1986; DCH RCP Lond. 1986. Prev: Trainee GP Reading VTS; Med. Off. Matlala Hosp. Lebowa, S. Afr.

WHITE, Timothy Clarke Fairfield Surgery, Station Road, Flookburgh, Grange-over-Sands LA11 7SY Tel: 015395 58307 Fax: 015395 58442; Pendlehurst, Ulverston LA12 7HD — MB BChir 1976 Camb.; MA Camb. 1972; MRCP (UK) 1982; MPH Leeds 1992; MRCGP 1983; DRCOG 1978; DTM & H RCP Lond. 1984. Prev: Dir. Health Servs. Guadalcanal Province Sololom Is., Pacific Ocean.

***WHITE, Timothy Joseph** The Old Rectory, Macosquin, Coleraine BT51 4PN Tel: 01265 52640 — MB ChB 1997 Sheff.; MRCS Part 1.

WHITE, Timothy Oliver 264 School Road, Crookes, Sheffield S10 1GP — MB ChB 1995 Sheff.

WHITE, Trevor Guidepost Health Centre, North Parade, Guidepost, Choppington NE62 5RA Tel: 01670 822071 Fax: 01670 531068 — MB BS 1978 Newc.; DAvMed FOM RCP Lond. 1985. GP Choppington, N.d.; Home Office Head of Med. Servs.; Civil Aviat. Auth. Med. Examr. Prev: GP Newc.

WHITE, Valerie Leonora (retired) Beech Hill, Flore, Northampton NN7 4LL Tel: 01327 340377 — MB ChB 1956 Sheff. Prev: GP Flore, N.ampton.

WHITE, Veronica Lilian Coral 33 The Hooks, Henfield BN5 9UY — MB BS 1991 Lond.; BSc (Pharmacol. & Basic Med. Sci.) Lond. 1988; MRCP (UK) 1995. Regist. Rotat. S.end, Roy. Lond. & Lond. Chest. Hosps. Socs: Brit. Thorac. Soc.; FRSM; BMA. Prev: SHO Rotat. (Med.) Roy. Lond. Hosp.; Ho. Phys. OldCh. Hosp. Romford; Ho. Surg. Broomfield Hosp. Chelmsford.

WHITE, Wallace (retired) The Hill House, Holt Road, Letheringsett, Holt NR25 7YB Tel: 01263 713300 — MB BS 1954 Lond.; DObst RCOG 1961. Prev: Regist. & Ho. Off. (Dermat.) Lond. Hosp.

WHITE, William David Little Snakemoor, Sleepers Hill, Winchester SO22 4NA Tel: 01962 855888 — MB BS 1972 Lond.; FFA RCS Eng. 1977. (St. Geo.) Cons. Anaesth. Roy. Hants. Co. Hosp. Winchester. Socs: BMA; CCSC; Assn Anaesth. Prev: Sen. Regist. (Anaesth.) W.m. Hosp. & Soton. Gen. Hosp.; Regist. (Anaesth.) Bristol Roy. Infirm.; Ho. Surg. & Ho. Phys. Torbay Hosp.

WHITE, William Douglas 1 Willow Avenue, Barnes, London SW13 0LT Tel: 020 8876 0268 — MB BS 1952 Lond. Cons. Pathol. Ilford Gp. Laborat. Barking Hosp. Prev: Lect. in Bact. St. Geo. Hosp. Med. Sch. Lond.; Regist. (Path.) St. Geo. Hosp. Lond.; Regist. (Path.) Gp. Laborat. St. Mary Abbott's Hosp. Lond.

WHITE, William Francis (retired) 4 Rectory Close, Lower Heswall, Wirral CH60 4TB Tel: 0151 342 8102 Fax: 0151 384 4398 Email: wwhite3310@aol.com — MB ChB Manch. 1956; FRCA Eng. 1965.

WHITE, William Frederick Department of Clinical Oncology, St Luke's Cancer Centre, Royal Surrey County Hospital, Guildford GU2 7XX Tel: 01483 406767 Fax: 01483 406827 Email: billwhite@uk_consultants.co.uk; The Shieling, Upper Guilddown Road, Guildford GU2 4EZ Tel: 01483 39924 Fax: 01483 34191 — MB BS 1960 Lond.; MRCS Eng. LRCP Lond. 1960; FRCR 1975; FFR 1965; DMRT Eng. 1963. (Westm.) Cons. Radiother. &Oncol.St. Luke's Hosp.Guildford; Hon. Cons. Roy. King Edwd. VII Hosp. Midhurst; Cons. St.Pete's Hosp. Socs: Brit. Inst. Radiol.; Brit. Nuclear Med. Soc. Prev: Cons. W.minster Hosp. Lond.; Sen. Regist. W.minster Hosp.

WHITE, William Graham Meadowbank Health Centre, 3 Salmon Inn Road, Polmont, Falkirk FK2 0XF Tel: 01324 715540 Fax: 01324 716723; 1 Alexandra Park, Lenzie, Glasgow G66 5BH — MB ChB 1985 Glas.; MRCGP 1990.

WHITE, William Joseph (retired) Sherwin House, Hillfarrance, Taunton TA4 1AP Tel: 01823 461306 — MB BS 1951 Lond.; MRCS Eng. LRCP Lond. 1951. Prev: Med. Off. Roy. Ordnance Explosives Div. Bridgwater.

WHITE, Mr William Leslie Rous Surgery, Rous Road, Newmarket CB8 8DH Tel: 01638 662018; Blantyre, 11 Rous Road, Newmarket CB8 8DH Tel: 01638 662033 — MB ChB 1959 Ed.; FDS RCS Eng. 1954; FRCS Ed. 1968. (Ed.) Prev: Ho. Surg. Roy. Hosp. Sick Childr. Edin.; Regist. Gen. Surg. Newc. Gen. Hosp.

WHITE, Winston Timothy, OBE (retired) Wassledine, 4 Campton Road, Gravenhurst, Bedford MK45 4JB — MB BS Lond. 1951. Chairm. Luton & S. Beds. Hospice. Prev: Res. Ho. Off. Childr. Annexe & Res. Cas. Off. Luton & Dunstable Hosp.

WHITE-JONES, Robert Howel (retired) 38 Central Avenue, Eccleston Park, Prescot L34 2QP Tel: 0151 426 6885 — MB ChB Liverp. 1938; MD Liverp. 1948; FRCP Lond. 1972, M 1948; DCH Eng. 1947; DObst. RCOG 1940. Prev: Cons. Paediat. St. Helens & Whiston Hosps.

WHITEAR, John Robert 13 Holland Dwellings, Newton St., London WC2B 5ES — MB BS 1992 Lond.

WHITEAR, Shah-naz 13 Holland Dwellings, Newton St., London WC2B 5ES — MB BS 1992 Lond.

WHITEAR, Mr William Patrick Department of Diagnostic Imaging, Ipswich Hospital, Heath Road, Ipswich IP4 5PD Tel: 01473 712233 Fax: 01473 270655; 37 Tuddenham Road, Ipswich IP4 2SN Tel: 01473 213362 Email: patrick.whitear@dial.pipex.com — MB

WHITECROSS

BS 1975 Lond.; FRCS Eng. 1980; FRCR 1986. (St. Mary's) Cons. Radiol. Ipswich Hosp. Suff. Socs: BMA; Ipswich & Dist. Clin. Soc.; Brit. Inst. Radiol. Prev: Sen. Regist. (Radiol.) Univ. Coll. Hosp. Lond.; Regist. (Radiol.) St. Mary's Hosp. Lond.; Regist. Rotat. (Surg.) Manch. Roy. Infirm.

WHITECROSS, Susan Elizabeth Shiona Radiology Department, Royal Oldham Hospital, Oldham OL1 2JH Tel: 0161 627 8943 Fax: 0161 627 8948 Email: shiona.whitecross@oldham-tv.nwest.nhs.uk; Four Lanes End, 5 Pike Law Road, Golcar, Huddersfield HD7 4NL — MB ChB 1978 Glas.; FRCR 1984; DRCOG 1980. (Glasgow) Cons. Radiol. Oldham HA.; Clin. Dir. Dept. of Radiol. Oldham NHS Trust.

WHITEFIELD, Mr George Aaron 9A Belleisle Avenue, Uddington, Glasgow G71 7AP — LRCP LRCS 1948 Ed.; FRCS Ed. 1958; LRCP LRCS Ed. LRFPS Glas. 1948.

WHITEFIELD, Laurence Abraham Queen Mary's Hospital Sidcup, Sidcup DA14 6LT Tel: 020 8302 2678; 9 Priory Terrace, London NW6 4DG Tel: 020 7624 8042 Fax: 020 7624 8042 — MB BS 1989 Lond.; FRCOphth 1993. (Char. Cross & Westm.) Cons. Ophth., Qu. Mary's Hos. Sidcup. Prev: Regist. Rotat. (Ophth.) Roy. Free Hosp., Whittington Hosp. & Whipps Cross Hosp. Lond.; SHO (Ophth.) Univ. Coll. Lond. Hosp. & Qu. Eliz. II Hosp. Welwyn Gdn. City; Ho. Off. (Surg.) Char. Cross Hosp. Lond.

WHITEFIELD, Timothy David (retired) 8 Cock Pit Close, North Stainley, Ripon HG4 3HT Tel: 01765 635442 — MB BCh 1969 Wales; MRCGP 1977; AFOM RCP Lond. 1980. Medico-Legal Cons. & Publisher. Prev: GP Leeds.

WHITEFORD, David Mitchell — MB BChir 1958; MA 1977 Camb.; 1961 DCH; 1960 DObst RCOG. (Cambridge & St George's Hosp. London) Princip. in Gen. Pract., Walthamstow, Lond., E17. Socs: Walthamstow Med. Soc. (Pres.) '98-'99; Ex-Sec. Walthamstow Med. Soc.

WHITEFORD, Linda June 46 Elm Grove, Norton, Bromsgrove B61 0EJ Tel: 01527 875841 — BM. BCh Oxf. 1994; BA Oxf. 1991; DCH (RCP) 1997. (Oxford) GP Regist. Nottm.

WHITEFORD, Margo Lorraine Duncan Guthrie Institute of Medical Genetics, Yorkhill NHS Trust, Glasgow G3 8SJ Tel: 0141 201 0365 Fax: 0141 357 4277 Email: margo.whiteford@yorkhill.scot.nhs.uk; 27 Turnhill Avenue, Erskine PA8 7DL — MB ChB 1985 Dundee; BSc (Pharmacol.) Dund 1980, MB ChB 1985; MRCP (UK) 1990. Cons. Clin. Geneticist. Prev: Sen. Regist. (Med. Genetics) Roy. Hosp. for Sick Childr. Glas.

WHITEHALL, Adrian Leslie Village Surgery, 233 Village Street, Derby DE23 8DD Tel: 01332 766762 Fax: 01332 272084; Hilltop, 18 Church Lane, Darley Abbey, Derby DE22 1EW — MB ChB 1976 Leeds; MRCGP 1980; DRCOG 1978. Prev: Trainee Gen. Pract. Derby Vocational Train. Scheme; Ho. Surg. & Ho. Phys. York Dist. Hosp.; SHO (O & G) Fulford Matern. Hosp. York.

WHITEHEAD, Anita Lilian Histopathology Department Box 235, Addenbrooke's Hospital, Hills rd, Cambridge CB2 2QQ Tel: 01223 217163 Fax: 01223 216980 Email: alw37@cam.ac.uk — MB BS 1978 Lond.; BSc Bristol 1972; MRCPath 1987; FRCPath 1997. p/t Cons. In Paediat + Perinatal Path., Addenbrookes Hosp. Camb. Prev: Cons. Histopath. Hinchingbrooke Hosp. Huntingdon.

WHITEHEAD, Ann Penelope 19 Tring Avenue, Ealing, London W5 3QA Tel: 020 8992 1940 Fax: 020 8896 2922 — MB BS 1959 Lond.; MRCS Eng. LRCP Lond. 1959; MFFP 1993. (Guy's) Prev: SHO (Surg.) Dorking Gen. Hosp.; Asst. Hon. Surg. Cas. Off. & Hon. Phys. (Childr.s) Guy's Hosp. Lond.

WHITEHEAD, Anthony Martin Pfizer Ltd., Sandwich CT13 9NJ Tel: 01304 645122 Fax: 01304 656221 Email: whitetis@pfizer.com; 8 De Havillands, Bekerbourne, Canterbury CT4 5BW — MB ChB 1979 Liverp.; MFPM RCP (UK) 1991; Dip. Pharm. Med. RCP (UK) 1986; DRCOG 1983. Med. Dir. Pfizer Ltd. Sandwich, Kent. Prev: Med. Dir. Duphar Laborat. Ltd. Soton.; Trainee GP Basingstoke; SHO (A & E, Psychiat., Med., O & G) Basingstoke Dist.Hosp.

WHITEHEAD, Bruce Foster Cardiothoracic Unit, Great Ormond Street Hospital, for Children NHS Trust, London WC1N 3JH Tel: 020 7405 9200 Fax: 020 7813 8440 Email: bruce.whitehead@gosh-tr.nthames.nhs.uk; 27 Windsor Road, Wanstead, London E11 3QU — MB BS 1979 New South Wales; FRCP Lond. 1996; MRCP (UK) 1986; FRCP 1996; FRCPCH 1997. (NSW,Aust.) Cons. Transpl. Phys. (Paediat. Cardiothoracic Transpl.) Gt. Ormond St. Hosp. Childr. Lond. Socs: Int. Soc. Heart & Lung Transpl..; ERS; Transpl. Soc. Prev: Clin. Research Fell. Stanford Univ. Med. Centre Stanford, Calif., USA.

WHITEHEAD, Claire Loraine 7 Rogers Ruff, Northwood HA6 2FD — MB ChB 1993 Sheff.; BMedSci Sheff. 1992; MRCP (UK) 1997.

WHITEHEAD, Clare Elizabeth (retired) Dormans, Abbey Park, Burghfield Common, Reading RG7 3HQ — MB BChir 1959 Camb.; MA Camb. 1960; MRCP (UK) 1974. Prev: Cons. Phys. Rehabil. Battle Hosp. Reading.

WHITEHEAD, David Mark The Glebe Surgery, Monastery Lane, Storrington, Pulborough RH20 4LR Tel: 01903 742942 Fax: 01903 740700; Hartswood House, Water Lane, Storrington, Pulborough RH20 3LY — MB BS 1980 Lond.; MRCGP 1985; DRCOG 1983.

WHITEHEAD, Diane Yvonne Assumpta (retired) Wolsey Lodge, 1 St Mary's Road, Long Ditton, Surbiton KT6 5EU Tel: 020 8398 6286 — MB BS 1962 Lond.; MRCS Eng. LRCP Lond. 1962; DObst RCOG 1964.

WHITEHEAD, Edna Marion Department Paediatrics & Child & Adolescent Psychiatry, Chaucer Unit, Northwick Park Hospital, Watford Road, Harrow HA1 3UJ Tel: 020 8869 2640; 34 Elstree Road, Bushey Heath, Watford WD23 4GL Tel: 020 8950 9262 — MB BCh Wales 1959; MRCPCH 1996; DA Eng. 1966; DCH Eng. 1965; Dip. FPA. 1964; DObst RCOG 1961. Assoc. Specialist (Community Paediat.) N.wick Pk. Hosp. Harrow. Socs: BMA; Brit. Assn. Community Child Health; Med. Wom.s. Federat. Prev: Med. Off. Lond. Boro. Islington; Ho. Phys. Whipps Cross Hosp. Lond.; Ho. Phys. & Ho. Surg. Cardiff Roy. Infirm.

WHITEHEAD, Mr Edward Department of Otolaryngology & Head and Neck Surgery, Hull Royal Infirmary, Hull HU3 2JZ — MB ChB 1961 Ed.; FRCS Ed. 1967; FRCS (C) 1969. Prev: Active Staff Wellesley Hosp. Toronto, Canada; Asst. Prof. Univ. Toronto; Cons. ENT Surg. Doncaster Roy. Infirm.

WHITEHEAD, Elizabeth Monica Ealing Hospital NHS Trust, Uxbridge Road, Southall UB1 3HW Tel: 020 8574 2444 Fax: 020 8967 5630 Email: whitehead@ealingas.demon.co.uk; Orford House, Chiswick Mall, Chiswick, London W4 2PS Tel: 020 8994 0671 — MB BS 1983 Lond.; BSc Lond. 1980; FRCA 1987. (King's Coll. Hosp.) Cons. Anaesth. Ealing Hosp. Lond. Socs: Roy. Soc. Med.; Assn. Anaesth.; Fell. Roy. Coll. Anaesth.s. Prev: Sen. Regist. (Anaesth.) Middlx. Hosp. Lond.

WHITEHEAD, Esme Mary 2 Printshop Road, Lylehill, Templepatrick, Ballyclare BT39 0HZ Tel: 028 9443 3351 — MB ChB 1976 (Hons) Manch.; BSc Hons. (Med. Biochem.) Manch. 1973, MD 1986; MRCP (UK) 1978; DCH RCPS Glas. 1983; FRCP (Lond) 1997. Cons. Rheum. N. Bd. N. Irel. Prev: Sen. Regist. (Rheum.) Roy. Vict. Hosp. Belf.; Sen. Regist. (Pharmacol.) Belf. City Hosp.; Research Regist. (Endocrinol.) Christie Hosp. Manch.

WHITEHEAD, Evelyn Julie Hale Place, 29 Hale St., East Peckham, Tonbridge TN12 5HL Tel: 01622 871816 — MB ChB 1979 Manch.; DCH RCP Lond. 1983; DRCOG 1982.

WHITEHEAD, Gail Ann 67 Appledore Avenue, Bexleyheath DA7 6QJ — MB BCh 1994 Wales. (Univ. of Wales Coll. of Med.) Sen. SHO (Paediatr.) Blackpool Vict. Hosp. Prev: SHO (Paediatr.) Booth Hall Childr. Hosp. Manch.; SHO (Community Paediat.) N. Durh. NHS Trust; SHO (Neonat. Med.) St. Mary's Hosp. for Wom. & Childr. Manch.

WHITEHEAD, Helen Marie Downe Hospital, Pound Lane, Downpatrick BT30 Tel: 01396 613311; 2 Laurel Heights, Downpatrick BT30 6LH — MD 1990 Belf.; MB BCh BAO 1982; MRCP (UK) 1985; FRCP (Ed.) 1996; FRCP (Lond.) 1998. (Queen's University Belfast) Cons. Phys. Internal Med. & Diabetes Down & Lisburn Community Trust. Socs: Diabetes UK; Roy. Coll.e Phys.s (Lond.); Roy. Coll. Phys.s (Edin.).

WHITEHEAD, Iain Philip 41 Sandcliffe Road, Midway, Swadlincote DE11 7PQ — BM BS 1985 Nottm.

WHITEHEAD, John Anthony 2 BeaconCt., Greenways, Ovingdon, Brighton BN2 7AY Tel: 01273 303306; 2 BeaconCt., Greenways, Ovingdon, Brighton BN2 7AY Tel: 01273 303306 Email: j.a.whitehead@amserve.net — MB BS Lond. 1954; FRCPsych 1981, M 1971; DPM Eng. 1962. (Lond. Hosp.) Hon. Cons. Psychiat. S. Downs Health NHS Trust. Socs: Brit. Geriat. Soc.; Brighton & Sussex M-C Soc. Prev: Cons. Psychiat. S. Downs Health NHS Trust; Dep. Med. Dir. Prestwich Hosp. Manch.; Asst. Psychiat. Severalls Hosp. Colchester.

WHITEHEAD, John Ernest Michael (retired) Ashleigh Cottage, The St, Frampton on Severn, Gloucester GL2 7ED — MB BChir 1945 Camb.; MA Camb. 1946; MRCS Eng. LRCP Lond. 1944; FRCPath 1970; Dip. Bact. Lond 1953. Prev: Dir. Pub. Health Laborat. Serv. & Cons. Adviser (Microbiol.) DHSS.

WHITEHEAD, John Peter (retired) Yarde House, Combe Florey, Taunton TA4 3JB — MRCS Eng. LRCP Lond. 1943; FRCPath. 1967, M 1964. Prev: Cons. Histopath. Basilden/Thurrock Dist.

WHITEHEAD, John Peter Stockwell (retired) 40 Marton Gate, Bridlington YO16 6YD — MRCS Eng. LRCP Lond. 1943; FRCPath 1970, M 1964. Prev: Cons. Pathol. ScarBoro. Hosp.

WHITEHEAD, John Richard Edmund Barton Surgery, Barton Terrace, Dawlish EX7 9QH Tel: 01626 888877 Fax: 01626 888360 — BSc (1st cl. Hons. Psychol.) Bristol 1971; MB ChB 1977; MRCGP 1984. (Bristol) Hosp. Pract. (A & E) Roy. Devon & Exeter Hosp.; Force Med. Off. Devon & Cornw. Constab.; Hon. Research Fell. Dept. Police Studies Univ. Exeter. Socs: Soc. Occupat. Med. Prev: Trainee GP Univ. Exeter Postgrad. Med. Sch.; SHO (Anaesth.) Roy. Devon & Exeter Hosp. & Ho. Surg. Frenchay Hosp. Bristol; Ho. Phys. Roy. Devon & Exeter Hosp.

WHITEHEAD, Mr John Stanley Weston (retired) Ridgeway, Vicarage Lane, Burton-in-Kendal, Carnforth LA6 1NW — MB BChir 1947 Camb.; MA, MChir Camb. 1954, MB BChir 1947; FRCS Eng. 1951. Hon. Cons. Surg. Roy. Lanc. Infirm. Prev: Sen. Surg. Regist. Dudley Rd. Hosp. Birm. & United Oxf. Hosps.

WHITEHEAD, Judith Patricia Basildon Hospital, Basildon SS16 5NL Tel: 01268 533911 Fax: 01268 593948 — MB ChB 1981 Manch.; FFA RCS Eng. 1986. Cons. Anaesth. Basildon Hosp. Prev: Sen. Regist. Roy. Lond. Hosp.

WHITEHEAD, Kenneth Peter (retired) Mayfield Cottage, Depmore Lane, Kingsley, Warrington WA6 6UD Tel: 01928 88472 — MRCS Eng. LRCP Lond. 1942. Prev: Cas. Off. St. Mary's Hosp. Lond.

WHITEHEAD, Malcolm Ian Department of Obst. & Gyn., King's College Hospital, Denmark Hill, London SE5 8RX Tel: 020 7733 0224 Fax: 020 7737 6717; 28 Parthenia Road, Fulham, London SW6 4BE Tel: Ex. Dir. — MB BS 1970 Lond.; MRCS Eng. LRCP Lond. 1970; FRCOG 1989, M 1977, DObst 1973. (Roy. Free) Cons. O & G Kings Coll. Hosp. Lond. Socs: Internat. Menopause Soc. (Ex-Pres.); Brit. Menopause Soc. (Ex-Chairm.). Prev: Lect. (O & G) Kings Coll. Hosp. Lond.; Regist. Inst. O & G Qu. Charlotte's Hosp. & Chelsea Hosp. Wom.

WHITEHEAD, Mark William Herberts Lidge, Bishopston, Swansea SA3 3DW — MB BS 1984 Lond.; MRCP (UK) 1989.

WHITEHEAD, Mary Anne Brigstock Medical Centre, 141 Brigstock Road, Thornton Heath CR7 7JN Tel: 020 8684 1128 Fax: 020 8689 3647 — MB BS 1973 Lond.; BSc (Hons.) (Physiol.) Lond. 1970; MRCGP 1977; DRCOG 1976. p/t Clin. Asst. Diabetic Dept. St. Geo. Hosp. Tooting.

WHITEHEAD, Mary Barbara (retired) 7 Rogers Ruff, Northwood HA6 2FD Tel: 01923 829314 — MB ChB 1961 Liverp.; BSc (Hons. Physiol.) Liverp. 1956; DObst RCOG 1963. Prev: Lect. (Path.) Univ. Liverp.

WHITEHEAD, Michael James Department of Anaesthesia, Swansea NHS Trust, Singleton Hospital, Swansea SA2 8QA Tel: 01792 285427 Fax: 01792 208647; 19 Dysgwylfa, Sketty, Swansea SA2 9BG — MB ChB 1972 Bristol; FFA RCS Eng. 1976. Cons. Anaesth. Swansea NHS Trust; Clin. Dir. Theatre Servs. Swansea NHS Trust.

WHITEHEAD, Miranda Nialla (retired) Cleeves, Godshill Wood, Fordingbridge SP6 2LR Tel: 01425 652188 Email: mirandawhitehead@bentinck-cleeves.demon.co.uk — MB BS 1973 Lond.; MRCS Eng. LRCP Lond. 1973. Prev: GP Salisbury.

WHITEHEAD, Nicholas Francis Frome Medical Practice, Health Centre, Park Road, Frome BA11 1EZ Tel: 01373 301300 Fax: 01373 301313; 2 Raby Place, Bathwick Hill, Bath BA2 4EH — MB BS 1974 Lond.; MRCS Eng. LRCP Lond. 1974; MRCGP 1978. (Roy. Free) Bd. Mem. Mendip PCG & Lead Clin. Governance.

WHITEHEAD, Paul Timothy Sunderland District General Hospital, Kayll Road, Sunderland SR4 7TP Tel: 0191 565 6256; 4 Landscape Terrace, Greenside, Ryton NE40 4RX Tel: 0191 413 8453 — MB BS 1987 Newc.; BMedSc Newc. 1984; MRCP (UK) 1990; MPH Nottm. 1996; DTM & H Liverp. 1993. Specialist Regist. (Paediat.) N. & Yorks. RHA. Prev: Regist. (Pub. Health Med.) Trent RHA & Nottm.

HA; Regist. (Paediat.) Newc. u. Tyne; Dist. Med. Off. Bulolo, Papua New Guinea.

WHITEHEAD, Peter 190 King Street, Cottingham HU16 5QJ Tel: 01482 847250 — MB ChB 1964 Leeds. (Leeds) Prev: Dir. Hull Emerg. Call Serv.; Jun. Receiv. Room Off. Leeds Gen. Infirm.; Ho. Surg. Hull Roy. Infirm.

WHITEHEAD, Peter Norman St John's Avenue Surgery, 24 St. John's Avenue, Churchdown, Gloucester GL3 2DB Tel: 01452 713036 Fax: 01452 714726; Pegmore, Church Lane, Priors Norton, Gloucester GL2 9LS Tel: 01452 730352 — MB BS 1977 Lond.; MSc (Sports Med.) Nottm. 1995; MRCS Eng. LRCP Lond. 1977; DA Eng. 1982; DRCOG 1980. (Guy's) Socs: Med. Equestrian Assn. (Chairm.); FRSM. (Counc. Mem. Sect. Sports Med.).

WHITEHEAD, Peter Sinclair Fisher Medical Centre, Millfields, Skipton BD23 1EU Tel: 01756 799622 Fax: 01756 796194 — MB ChB 1981 Ed.; MA Camb. 1974; MRCGP 1985; DRCOG 1984.

WHITEHEAD, Peter Thomas 19 Tring Avenue, Ealing, London W5 3QA Tel: 020 8992 1940 Fax: 020 8896 2922 — MB BS 1959 Lond.; MRCS Eng. LRCP Lond. 1959. (Guy's) Prev: Ho. Surg. Cas. Off. & Ho. Phys. Guy's Hosp.

WHITEHEAD, Philip Jennings The Surgery, 1 Church Road, Mitcham CR4 3YU Tel: 020 8648 2579 Fax: 020 8640 4013 — MB BS 1970 Lond.; DObst RCOG 1972; DCH Eng. 1973. (St. Geo.) Tutor Div. Gen. Pract. St. Geo. Hosp. Med. Sch.; Apptd. Doctor EMAS Lead; Mem. Merton, Sutton & Wandsworth LMC. Prev: SHO (Obst.) St. Geo. Hosp. Lond.; SHO (Paediat.) Sydenham Childr. Hosp.

WHITEHEAD, Philip John Department of Pathology, Frenchay Hospital, Bristol BS16 1LE Tel: 0117 970 1212 Fax: 0117 957 1866 Email: philipwhitehead@north-bristol.swest.nhs.uk — MB ChB 1963 Bristol; FRCPath 1982, M 1970. Cons. Haemat. N. Bristol NHS Trust. Prev: Cons. Path. W. Cumbld. Hosp. Gp.; Sen. Regist. S. W.. Regional Tranfus. Centre Bristol; Regist. (Path.) United Sheff. Hosps.

WHITEHEAD, Robert Henry Brandwood Sean Yew Tree Cottage, 4 Butts Ash, Fawley Road, Hythe, Southampton SO4 — BM 1980 Soton. SHO (Anaesth.) W. Dorset Weymouth HA. Socs: Nat. Inst. Med. Herbalist.

WHITEHEAD, Simon Henry Department of Medicine, Level 5, Addenbrooke's Hospital, Hills Road, Cambridge CB2 2QQ Tel: 01223 336143; 47 Blackthorn Close, Woodhead Drive, Cambridge CB4 1FZ — MSc (Med. Immunol.) Lond. 1990, BSc (Hons.) 1985, MB BS 1987. Hon. Regist. (Med.) Addenbrooke's Hosp. Camb. Prev: Regist. & SHO (Immunol.) King's Coll. Hosp. Lond.; Ho. Off. (Gen. Med.) Lond. Hosp.; Ho. Surg. Rush Green & OldCh. Hosps. Romford.

WHITEHEAD, Stephanie Ann 28 The Crossways, Otley LS21 2AR Tel: 01943 466517 — MB ChB Leeds 1996; PhD. Microbiology 1988; BSc (Hons.) 1983. GP Regist.; SHO Paediat. Airedale W. Yorks.

WHITEHEAD, Stephen Mark 39 Sunny Hill, Milford, Derby DE56 0QR — MB ChB 1975 Leeds; MFPHM 1988; DTM & H Liverp. 1982; DRCOG 1977. Cons. Pub. Health Med. S.. Derbysh. HA. Prev: Med. Off. Maua Methodist Hosp. Kenya.

WHITEHEAD, Mr Stephen Michael 34 Tower Road W., St Leonards-on-Sea TN38 0RG Tel: 01424 718059 — MB BChir 1973 Camb.; MA 1973 Camb.; MChir 1986; FRCS Eng. 1977. Cons. Surg., Conquest Hosp. Hastings & Rother NHS Trust. Socs: Fell.of Assoc. of Surg. Of G.B. & Irel.; Vasc. Surg. Soc. GB & Irel.; Europ. Soc. Of Vasc. Surg. Prev: Sen. Regist. (Surg.) St. Thos. Hosp. Lond.; Regist. (Surg.) Kent & Canterbury Hosp.; Ho. Surg. St. Thos. Hosp. Lond.

WHITEHEAD, Susan Rm6206 Tomlinson House, Norcross, Thornton-Cleveleys FY5 3WP Tel: 01253 333231 Fax: 01253 330437; Wharmton House, 46 Oldham Road, Grasscroft, Oldham OL4 4HL — MB BS 1973 Lond.; MB BS (Hons.) Lond. 1973. (Univ. Coll. Hosp.) Med. Off. War Pens. Agency Norcross, Blackpool. Prev: GP Failsworth; Ho. Phys. & Ho. Surg. Crumpsall Hosp. Manch.

WHITEHEAD, Susan Carol Elborough Street Surgery, 81-83 Elborough Street, Southfields, London SW18 5DS Tel: 020 8874 7113 Fax: 020 8874 3682 — MB BS 1971 Lond.; MRCGP 1976; DObst RCOG 1974.

WHITEHEAD, Thomas Crosby The Close, Farnborough, Banbury OX17 1DZ — MB BS 1990 Lond.

WHITEHEAD

WHITEHEAD, Timothy Robin Stuart Waterman 19 The Waterside, Hellesdon, Norwich NR6 5QN Tel: 01603 417099; The Health Centre, Adelaide St, Norwich NR6 4JL Tel: 01603 625015 Fax: 01603 766820 — MRCS Eng. LRCP Lond. 1974. (Westm.)

WHITEHEAD, Vjera Brangjolica (retired) 18 Vineyard Road, London SW19 7JH — LAH Dub. 1965.

WHITEHEAD, William Harold Minfor Surgery, Park Road, Barmouth LL42 1PL Tel: 01341 280521 Fax: 01341 280912 — BM BCh 1980 Oxf.; MA, BM BCh Oxf. 1980; MRCGP 1986. Course Organiser Gwynedd VTS.

WHITEHORN, Melanie White House Surgery, Weston Lane, Weston, Southampton SO19 9HJ Tel: 023 8044 9913 Fax: 023 8044 6617 — BM Soton. 1981; MRCGP 1985; DCH RCP Lond. 1985; DRCOG 1983.

WHITEHORN, Rachel Mary — MB ChB 1988 Sheff.; BA (Med. Sci.) Camb. 1985; MRCGP 1992; DRCOG 1992. Prev: Clin. Asst. (Gen. Pract.) MosBoro. Health Centre Sheff.; SHO (O & G) Doncaster Roy. Infirm.; SHO (Paediat.) Barnsley Dist. Gen. Hosp.

WHITEHORN, Sharon Elizabeth 60 Knowlys Road, Heysham, Morecambe LA3 2PG — MB BCh 1982 Wales; DCH RCP Lond. 1988. Med. Adviser Benefits Agency Lancs.; Clin. Asst. (Genitourin. Med.) Lancs.; Med. Adviser Company Health Bispham Lancs. Prev: Staff Grade (Community Paediat.) Lancaster HA.

WHITEHOUSE, Alison Jayne 24 Chesford Crescent, Warwick CV34 5PR — MB ChB 1995 Leeds.

WHITEHOUSE, Andrew Beckwith George Eliot Hospital, College St., Nuneaton CV10 7DJ Tel: 01203 865255 Fax: 01203 865279; 16 Coleshill Road, Atherstone CV9 1BW Tel: 01827 717755 Email: abwhitehouse@compuserve.com — MB BChir 1974 Camb.; MA Camb. 1990; FRCP Lond. 1993; MRCP (UK) 1976. Cons. Phys. Geo. Eliot Hosp. Nuneaton; Assoc. Postgrad. Dean (Gen. Professional Train.) W. Midl.s Region; Teach. Clin. Med. Leicester Univ. Med. Sch. Socs: Nat. Assn. Clin. Tutors (Counc.); Brit. Geriat. Soc. Prev: Sen. Regist. Roy. Devon & Exeter Hosp.; Med. Off. Chas. Johnson Mem. Hosp. Nqutu, Kwazulu; SHO (Gen. Med.) Hillingdon Hosp. Uxbridge.

WHITEHOUSE, Andrew Michael Psychiatric Out Patients Department, B Floor, South Block, Queens Medical Centre, Nottingham NG7 2UH Tel: 0115 924 9924 — BM 1981 Soton.; MA Camb. 1989; MPhil Ed. 1985; MRCPsych 1985. Cons. Psychiat. Qu.s Med. centre Nottm. Socs: Brit. Med. Ass; Nottm.shire Medicolegal Soc. Prev: Clin. Lect. (Psychiat.) Addenbrookes Hosp. Camb.; Regist. (Psychiat.) Roy. Edin. Hosp.; Cons.(psychiat) bradgate Ment. health unit,Leics.

WHITEHOUSE, Anthony Richard Polkyth Surgery, 14 Carlyon Road, St Austell PL25 4EG Tel: 01726 75555; 4 Crinnis Wood Avenue, Carlyon Bay, St Austell PL25 3QD Tel: 01726 814415 — MB BS 1975 Lond.; MRCS Eng. LRCP Lond. 1975. (St. Bart.) GP Princip.; Local Med. Off. for Civil Serv.; Dist. Med. Off. Brit. Red Cross; Med. Adviser St. Austell Brewery; Med. Off. Roach Foods Ltd.; Examr. Med. Pract. DSS.

WHITEHOUSE, Professor Carl Raymond University of Manchester Medical School, Rusholme Health Centre, Walmer St., Manchester M14 5NP Tel: 0161 256 3015 Fax: 0161 256 1070 Email: carl.whitehouse@man.ac.uk; 12 St Brannocks Road, Chorlton-cum-Hardy, Manchester M21 0UP Tel: 0161 881 0343 — MB Camb. 1964, BChir 1963; MA Camb. 1964; FRCGP 1987, M 1969; DCH Eng. 1969; DObst RCOG 1965. (Camb. & St. Geo.) Prof. Teach. Med. in Community Univ. Manch. Socs: FRSM; BMA. Prev: SHO (Paediat.) Dorset Co. Hosp. Dorchester; Ho. Surg. St. Geo. Hosp. Lond.; Med. Off. Zambia Flying Doctor Serv.

WHITEHOUSE, Caroline Cheviot Road Surgery, 1 Cheviot Road, Millbrook, Southampton SO16 4AH Tel: 02380 773174 Fax: 02380 702748 — MB ChB 1987 Bristol.

WHITEHOUSE, David Haigh Health Centre, Redcar TS10 1SR Tel: 01642 475157; The Old Vicarage, Kirkleatham Village, Redcar TS10 5NN Tel: 01642 477716 — MB ChB 1954 Leeds. Prev: Cas. Off. Bradford Roy. Infirm.; Ho. Phys. St. Luke's Hosp. Bradford; Med. Off. RAMC (Nat. Serv.).

WHITEHOUSE, David Roger 4 Lakeside, Little Aston Hall, Sutton Coldfield B74 3BJ — MB ChB 1954 Birm.; MRCS Eng. LRCP Lond. 1954; DObst RCOG 1959.

WHITEHOUSE, Professor Graham Hugh Department of Medical Imaging, University of Liverpool, PO Box 147, Liverpool L69 3BX Tel: 0151 794 5755 Fax: 0151 794 5766; 9 Belmont Road, West Kirby, Wirral CH48 5EY Tel: 0151 625 6933 — MB BS 1965 Lond.; MB BS (Hons.) Lond. 1965; FRCP Lond. 1983, M 1967; MRCS Eng. LRCP Lond. 1965; FRCR 1975; FFR 1971; DMRD Eng. 1969. (Westm.) Prof. Diagn. Radiol. Univ. Liverp.; Hon. Cons. Radiol. Roy. Liverp. Univ. Hosp. & Wom. Hosp.; Edr. Brit. Jl. Radiol. Socs: Roy. Soc. Med. (Vice-Pres. Radiol. Sect.); (Counc.) Brit. Inst. Radiol.; Radiol. Soc. N. Amer. Prev: Sen. Lect. (Radiodiagn.) Univ. Liverp.; Sen. Regist. (Radiol.) United Bristol Hosps.

WHITEHOUSE, Joanna Louise — MB ChB 1992 Birm.; MRCP (UK) 1995. Regist. (Respirat. Med.) St. Thos. Hosp. Lond.

WHITEHOUSE, Professor Julian Michael Arthur Imperial College School of Medicine, The Reynold's Building, St Dunstan's Road, London W6 8RP Tel: 020 8846 7241 Fax: 020 8846 7222 — MB BChir Camb. 1967; MA Camb. 1967, MD 1975; FRCP Ed. 1994; FRCP Lond. 1979; MRCP (UK) 1970; MRCS Eng. LRCP Lond. 1966; FRCR 1992. (St. Bart.) Vice-Princip. Imperial Coll. Sch. Med.; Chairm. Counc. Paterson Research Inst., Christie Hosp. Manch. Socs: FRSM; Eur. Soc. Med. Oncol. (Past Vice Pres.); (Ex-Chairm.) Assn. Cancer Phys. Prev: Prof. Med. Oncol. Univ. Soton.; Cons. Phys. Soton. Univ. Hosps. (past vice pres.); Dir, CRC Wessex Regional Med. Oncol. Unit.

WHITEHOUSE, Nicola Jayne 35 Grange Road, Tettenhall, Wolverhampton WV6 8RE — MB ChB 1989 Sheff.

WHITEHOUSE, Nigel John 1 Mevagissey House, Royal Cornwall Hospital (Treliske), Truro TR1 3LJ; 20 Gwel Trencrom, Hayle TR27 6PJ — MB BS 1989 Lond.

WHITEHOUSE, Pauline Amanda Oak Villa, Engleton Lane, Brewood, Stafford ST19 9DZ — MB BS 1996 Lond.

WHITEHOUSE, Richard John 20 Brandy Hole Lane, Chichester PO19 4RY — MB BS 1992 Lond.

WHITEHOUSE, Richard William Department of Clinical Radiology, Manchester Royal Infirmary, Oxford Road, Manchester M13 9WL Tel: 0161 276 1234 Fax: 0161 276 4141 Email: rwhiteho@central.cmht.nwest.nhs.uk — MD 1993 Manch.; BSc (Hons.) 1978, MB ChB 1981; T(R)(CR) 1991. Cons. Radiol. Centr. Manch. HA; Hon. Clin. Lect. (Diag. Radiol.) Univ. Manch. Socs: Fell. Roy. Coll. Radiol.

WHITEHOUSE, Susan Janina Main house, Hollymoorway, Northfield, Birmingham B31 5HE Tel: 0121 678 3630 — MB ChB 1986 Birm.; MRCPsych 1992; MmedSci 1998. Locum Cons. Psychotherapist Main Ho. Therapeutic Community. Prev: Regist. Rotat. (Psychiat.) Birm.; Sen. Regist. Rotat. W. Mid. (Psychother.).

WHITEHOUSE, Tony — MB BS 1992 Lond.; BSc Lond. 1989. Specialist Regist. (Anaesth.) N. Thames (Centr.) Sch. of Anaesth.

WHITEHOUSE, William Patrick Audiffred Academic Child Health, E Floor / East Block, Queen's Medical Centre, Nottingham NG6 2UH Tel: 0115 924 9924 Fax: 0115 970 9382 — MB BS 1981 Lond.; FRCPCH 1997; BSc Lond. 1978; DCH Lond. 1983; FRCP 1997, MRCP (UK) 1986. (Lond. Hosp.) Sen. Lect. In Paediat. Neurol., Univ. of Nottm.; Hon. Cons. Paediat. Neurol. Qu.'s Med. Centre, Nottm. Socs: Brit. Paediat. Neurol. Assn. Counc. Mem.; Internat. League Against Epilepsy; Internat. Headache Soc. Prev: Cons. Paediat. Neurol. Childr. Hosp. Birm.; Sen. Regist. (Paediat. Neurol.) Childr. Hosp. Birm.; Research Fell. & Hon. Sen. Regist. (Paediat. Neurol.) Univ. Lond.

WHITEHURST, Antje Maria Florence Road Surgery, 26 Florence Road, Ealing W5 3TX — MB BS 1991 Lond.; MRCGP 1996. (St Mary's Hosp. Med. Sch. Lond.) Princip. in Gen. Pract. Socs: Roy. Coll. of Gen. Practitioners.

***WHITEHURST, Jane Andrea Claire** Royal Hallamshire Hospital, Glossop Road, Sheffield S10 2JF Tel: 0114 271 1900; 23 Longfield Road, Sheffield S10 1QW Tel: 0114 266 6078 — MB ChB 1997 Sheff.

WHITEHURST, Louise Mary (Brennan) Belgrave Medical Centre, 22 Asline Road, Sheffield S2 4UJ Tel: 0114 255 1184; Tel: 0114 236 7416 — MB ChB 1986 Sheff.; MRCGP 1990. (Sheffield University) GP. Prev: Trainee GP Oxf. VTS.

WHITEHURST, Philip Anaesthetics Department, Russells Hall Hospital, Dudley DY1 2HQ — MB ChB 1976 Aberd.; FFA RCS Eng. 1980. Cons. Anaesth. Dudley Gp. Hosps. Trust. Prev: Sen. Regist. (Anaesth.) Yorks. RHA; Regist. (Anaesth.) Univ. Coll. Hosp. Lond.

WHITELAW, Alan Stewart 9 Ambleside, East Kilbride, Glasgow G75 8TX — MB ChB 1998 Glas.

WHITELAW, Professor Andrew George Lindsay Neonatal Intensive Care Unit, Southmead Hospital, Southmead Road, Westbury-on-Trym, Bristol BS10 5NB Tel: 0117 959 5325 Fax: 0117 959 5324 Email: andrew.whitelaw@bristol.ac.uk — MB BChir 1971; MD 1978 Camb.; FRCP Lond. 1988; MRCP (UK) 1973; FRCPCH 1997. (Cambridge & St. Marys) Prof. of Neonat. Med., Univ. of Bristol; Cons. neonatologist, N. Bristol and United Bristol NHS Trusts. Socs: Neonat. Soc.; Roy. Coll. Paediat. and child health; Europ. Soc. for paediatric research. Prev: Cons. Neonatol. Hammersmith Hosp. Lond.; Neonat. Fell. Hosp. Sick Childr. Toronto, Canada; Ho. Phys. Hosp. Sick Childr. Gt. Ormond St. Lond.

WHITELAW, Catherine Anne Meadowbank Health Centre, 3 Salmon Inn Road, Falkirk FK2 OXF Tel: 01324 715446 Fax: 01324 717986 — MB ChB 1977 Glas.

WHITELAW, Donald Crawford 32 Lidgett Hill, Roundhay, Leeds LS8 1PE — MB ChB 1985 Ed.; MRCP (UK) 1989. SHO (A & E) Taunton & Som. Hosp. Taunton. Prev: Ho. Phys. Derriford Hosp. Plymouth; Ho. Off. Dept. Surgic. Neurol. W.. Gen. Hosp. Edin.

WHITELAW, Mr Douglas Edward Dunsland, Kintore, Aberdeen Tel: 01467 32339; Greenmyre, Oldmeldrum, Inverurie AB51 0DP — MB ChB 1990 Ed.; FRCS Ed. 1994. SHO (A & E Med.) Roy. Hosp. Sick Childr. Edin.

WHITELAW, Eileen Mary (retired) Laverock, 87 The Fairway, Aldwick Bay, Bognor Regis PO21 4EX — MB BS Lond. 1950.

WHITELAW, Elizabeth Anne Woodbridge Hill Surgery, 1 Deerbarn Road, Guildford GU2 8YB Tel: 01483 562230 Fax: 01483 452442 — BM 1992 Soton.; MRCGP 1996. (Soton.) Prev: Trainee GP Reading VTS.

WHITELAW, Fiona Margaret Elderslie House, Strathaven ML10 6PA — MB ChB 1990 Bristol; DTM & H RCP Lond. 1993. SHO (Paediat.) Barnsley Dist. Gen. Hosp. Prev: SHO (Infec. Dis. & Trop. Med.) Coppetts Wood Hosp. Lond.

WHITELAW, Joan Meadowside, Brooke, Oakham LE15 8DE — MB BS Lond. 1964; MRCS Eng. LRCP Lond. 1963; DCH RCPSI 1980; DObst RCOG 1974; DA Eng. 1972. (St. Thos.) Med. Off. (Anaesth.) & Clin. Med. Off. (Community Med.) Leics. HA. Prev: SHO (Paediat.) & Ho. Off. (O & G) St. Luke's Hosp. Bradford; SHO (Anaesth.) York 'A' Gp. Hosps.

WHITELAW, John Deryk Atkinson (retired) Laverock, 87 The Fairway, Aldwick Bay, Bognor Regis PO21 4EX — MB BS Lond. 1944; MRCS Eng. LRCP Lond. 1944. Prev: Sen. Med. Off. Home Office.

WHITELAW, Robert (retired) 36 Holmhead, Kilbirnie KA25 6BS Tel: 01505 683264 — MB ChB 1944 Glas.; MFOM RCP Lond. 1978; DPH (Commend.) St. And. 1948; DIH Eng. 1953; DIH Soc. Apoth. Lond. 1953; Specialist Accredit. (Occupat. Med.) 1978. Prev: HM Med. Insp. Facts.

WHITELAW, Mr Stuart Charles 75 Hillfoot Drive, Bearsden, Glasgow G61 3QG — MB ChB 1981 Glas.; FRCS Glas. 1988; FRCS Ed. 1987.

WHITELEY, Alan Mark 20 Sefton Drive, Mapperly Park, Nottingham NG3 5ER Tel: 0115 960 6514 Fax: 0115 960 6514 — MB BChir 1972 Camb.; MA, MB Camb. 1972, BChir 1971; FRCP 1988. (Camb. & St. Bart.) Cons. Neurol. Nottm. & Mansfield Hosps. Prev: Sen. Regist. (Neurol.) St. Bart. Hosp. & Nat. Hosp. Qu. Sq. Lond.; Regist. Lond. Hosp.; SHO Centr. Middlx. Hosp. Lond.

WHITELEY, Andrew Michael The medical Centre, Badgers Crescent, Shipston-on-Stour CV36 4BQ Tel: 01608 661845 Fax: 08700 553555 Email: andrew.whiteley@tmcc4.warwick-ha.wmids.nhs.uk — MB BS 1993 Lond. (St. Bart. Hosp. Lond.)

WHITELEY, Elizabeth Anne (retired) Heatherdale, 6 Harrowby Lane, Grantham NG31 9HX Tel: 01476 564379 — MB ChB 1954 Sheff.; MFCM 1972. Specialist Community Med. Community Servs. & Local Auth. Liaison S. Lincs. HA. Prev: Dep. Co. MOH & Dep. Princip. Sch. Med. Off. Parts of Kesteven, Lincs.

WHITELEY, Gillian Louise 57 Garstang Road W., Poulton-le-Fylde FY6 8AA — MB ChB 1984 Leeds.

WHITELEY, Mr Graham Stuart Wynward Ysbyty Gwynedd, Penrhosgarnedd, Bangor LL57 2PW Tel: 01248 384777 Fax: 01248 384777 — MB BS 1980 Lond.; MS Lond. 1990, MB BS 1980; FRCS Eng. 1985. (Royal Free Hospital School of Medicine) Cons. Surg. Gastroenterol. & Laparoscopic Surg. Ysbyty Gwynedd & Llandudno Gen. Hosp. Socs: Assn. Surg.; Brit. Soc. Gastroenterol.; Assn. Coloproctol. Prev: Lect. (Surg.) Centr. Manch. Hosps.; Lect. (Surg.) Univ. Hosp. S. Manch. & Christie Hosp.; Lect. (Surg.) Hope Hosp. Salford.

WHITELEY, Jane Holly House, Sunderland, Cockermouth CA13 9SS — MB BS 1957 Lond. (Roy. Free)

WHITELEY, Joan E. (retired) 43 Cunliffe Close, Banbury Road, Oxford OX2 7BJ Tel: 01865 553200 — MB BChir 1945 Camb.; PhD Camb. 1950. Prev: Asst. Dir. Research (Veterin. Clin. Med.) Sch. of Veterin. Med. Univ. Camb.

WHITELEY, Joanne Tracey Lordswood House, 54 Lordswood Road, Harborne, Birmingham B17 9DB Tel: 0121 426 2030 Fax: 0121 428 2658 — MB BS 1990 Lond.

WHITELEY, John David 44 Armstrong Road, Egham TW20 0RW — MB BS 1989 Lond.

WHITELEY, John Maxwell Flat 5, Summerfield Court, Edge Lane, Chorlton-Cum-Hardy, Manchester M21 9JN — MB ChB 1965 Manch.

WHITELEY, John Stuart The Wheelwrights Cottage, Wheelers Lane, Brockham, Betchworth RH3 7LA Tel: 0173 784 3446 Fax: 0173 784 3634 Email: stuart.whiteley@virgin.net — MB ChB Leeds 1950; FRCP Ed. 1970, M 1961; FRCPsych 1982, M 1972; DPM Eng. 1954. (Leeds) p/t Indep. Cons. Psychother. Surrey. Socs: FRSM; Gp. Analyt. Soc.; Int. Assn. Gp. Psychother. Prev: Cons. Psychiat. & Med. Dir. Henderson Hosp. Sutton; Cons. Psychiat. Warlingham Pk. Hosp.; Chief Asst. (Psychol. Med.) W.m. Hosp. Lond.

WHITELEY, Judith Chaelan, Irthington, Carlisle CA6 4NJ — MB ChB 1997 Dundee.

WHITELEY, Mr Mark Steven Department of Vascular Surgery, Royal Surrey County Hospital, Egerton Road, Guildford GU2 7XX Tel: 01483 571122 — MB BS 1986 Lond.; FRCS (Gen.) 1996; FRCS Ed. 1991; FRCS Eng. 1991; MS Bath 1998. (St. Bart.) Cons. Vasc. Surg. Roy. Surrey Co. Hosp.; Vis. Sen. Fell. Vasc. Surg. Univ. of Surrey. Socs: Vasc. Surgic. Soc.; Assn. Surg.; Eur. Soc. Vasc. Surg. Prev: Clin. Lect. (Surg.) & Hon. Sen. Regist. Univ. Oxf. Nuffield Dept. Surg. John Radcliffe Hosp. Oxf; Mem. Rouleaux Club (Vasc. Surgic. Trainee) Sec. 1994-1997; Lect. (Surg.) Univ. Bath & Roy. United Hosp. Bath.

WHITELEY, Michael Charles William Viewfield Medical Centre, 3 Viewfield Place, Stirling FK8 1NJ Tel: 01786 472028 Fax: 01786 463388 — MB BCh BAO 1983 Belf.; MRCGP 1987; DRCOG 1985.

WHITELEY, Patricia Gideon Medical Centre, 10 Chapel Lane, Arnold, Nottingham NG5 7DR Tel: 0115 920 7988; Varenna, 70 Nottingham Road, Lowdham, Nottingham NG14 7AP — MB ChB 1970 Leeds. Socs: Assoc. Mem. RCGP.

WHITELEY, Richard Whiteley and Partners, 4 Market Place, Billesdon, Leicester LE7 9AJ Tel: 0116 259 6206 Fax: 0116 259 6388 — MB ChB 1965 Manch.

WHITELEY, Simon Marcus Paediatric intensive care unit, St James University Hospital, Beckett Street, Leeds LS9 7TF Tel: 0113 243 3144 Fax: 0113 392 2645 Email: simonw@ulth.northy.nhs.uk; Tel: 01423 523036 — MB BS 1986 Lond.; FRCA 1992. Cons. (Paediat. Anaesth. & Paediat. IC) Gen. Infirm. Leeds.

WHITELEY, William Nichol Midway, Chapel Hill, Truro TR1 3BP — BM BCh 1997 Oxf.

WHITELOCK, David Ernest 52 High Street, Yelling, Huntingdon PE19 6SD — MB BS 1996 Lond.

WHITELOCKE, Mr Rodger Alexander Frederick 152 Harley Street, London W1G 7LH Tel: 020 7935 3834 Fax: 020 7224 2574; 19 Elvaston Place, London SW7 5QF Tel: 020 7584 9871 — MB BS 1968 Lond.; PhD Lond. 1975; FRCS Eng. 1976; MRCS Eng. LRCP Lond. 1968; FRCOphth 1989. (St. Bart.) Cons. Ophth. Surg. St. Bart. Hosp. & Roy. Marsden Hosp. Lond.; Lead Clin. (Ophth) Bart's & The Lond. NHS Trust; Teach. (Ophth.) Univ. Lond. Socs: Fell. Roy. Soc. Med.; Assn. Eye Research; Brit. Microcirculat. Soc. Prev: Hon. Vis. Prof. Visual Sci. City Univ. Lond.; Sen. Regist. & Sen. Resid. Surg. Off. Moorfields Eye Hosp. (City Rd. Br.) Lond.; Research Asst. Inst. Ophth. Univ. Lond.

WHITEMAN, Helen Ruth Adelaide Medical Centre, Adelaide Terrace, Benwell, Newcastle upon Tyne NE4 8BE Tel: 0191 219 5599 Fax: 0191 219 5596 — MB BS 1990 Newc. GP Newc.

WHITEMAN, Ingrid Ann 31 Meadow Drive, Prestbury, Macclesfield SK10 4EY — MB ChB 1986 Manch.; MRCGP 1990; T(GP) 1991.

WHITEMAN, Julia Ruth Postgraduate Medical Centre, West Middlesex University Hospital, Twickenham Road, Isleworth Tel: 020

WHITEMAN

8565 5406; 51 Wick Road, Teddington TW11 9DN Email: julia.whiteman@btinternet.com — MB BS 1981 Lond.; MRCGP 1985; DRCOG 1985; MA Univ. Westminster 1998. GP Tutor W. Middlx. Hosp. & Hammersmith Hosp. Prev: GP Sen. Partner Twickenham.

WHITEMAN, Paul Donald Whiteladies, Cross Lane, Brancaster, King's Lynn PE31 8AE — MB BS 1967 Lond.; MSc Lond. 1971, MD 1976; MRCS Eng. LRCP Lond. 1967. (Westm.) Prev: Dept. Head (Bioanalyt. Sci.s) Wellcome Foundat. Beckenham; Sen. Med. Off. (Nutrit.) DoH Lond.; Lect. (Paediat. Chem. Path.) Hosp. Sick Childr. Lond.

WHITEMAN, Sarah Jane Hilltops Medical Centre, Kensington Drive, Great Holm, Milton Keynes MK8 9HN Tel: 01908 568446 Fax: 01908 265028; 12 Oxfield Park Drive, Old Stratford MK7 8QB Tel: 01908 566967 Email: sarah.whiteman@btinternet.com — MB BS 1986 Lond.; 2001 DMJ (Clin); MRCGP 1990; Dip. IMC RCS Ed. 1994; DCH RCP Lond. 1993; DRCOG 1992; FRCGP 1998. (Roy. Free) Assoc. Adviser in GP Educat., PGMDE, Oxf. - Gen. Practitioner, Hilltops Med. Centre, Milton Keynes; Adviser, Nat. Clin. Assessm. Auth., Lond.; Exec. Director, Mkdoc, Milton Keynes; Police Surg., Beds, N.ants & Thames Valley. Socs: Assn. of Police Surg.s; Roy. Coll. of Gen. Practitioners- Thames Valley Fac. Bd. Mem. Prev: SSC RAF 1986-93.; GP Trainer & Course Organiser, Milton Keynes VTS; Clin. Asst., A & E , Stoke Mandeville.

WHITEMAN, Sheila Mary (retired) Holyhead Surgery, 1 Chester St., Coundon, Coventry CV1 4DH — MB ChB 1956 Sheff.

WHITEN, Christopher John 45 Ernest Gardens, London W4 3QU — MB BS 1996 Lond.

WHITENBURGH, Martin John 38 Sandfield Road, Liverpool L25 3PE — MB ChB 1991 Liverp.

WHITEOAK, Karen Lynne Wallace Tattenhall Medical Practice, High St., Tattenhall, Chester CH3 9PX; Huntington Hall, Aldford Road, Chester CH3 6EA — MB ChB 1983 Manch.; BSc (Med. Sci.) St. And. 1980.

WHITEOAK, Richard, Col. late RAMC The Royal Hospital, Haslar, Gosport PO12 2AA Tel: 02392 584255 Fax: 02392 762150 Email: richwhit@dsca.gov.uk; Tel: 02392 877039 — MB BChir 1977 Camb.; MB Camb. 1978, BChir 1977; MA Camb. 1978; FRCP Lond. 1995; MRCP (UK) 1981. (St. Thos.) Cons. Phys. P.ss Mary's Hosp. RAF Akrotiri BFPO 57. Socs: Brit. Soc. Gastroenterol.; BMA. Prev: Sen. Specialist (Med.) Qu. Eliz. Milt. Hosp. Woolwich; Cons. Phys TMPH AKROTRI BFPO57; Cons. Phys. BMH Rinteln BFPO 29.

WHITER, Alexandra Jane 10 Grange Avenue, London N20 8AD — BM BCh 1996 Oxf.

WHITER, Gaynor Lesley 10 Grange Avenue, Totteridge Village, London N20 8AD — MB BChir 1990 Camb.; DRCOG 1991. SHO (Anaesth.) MusGr. Pk. Hosp. Taunton. Prev: SHO (SCBU) Brighton; SHO (O & G) Brighton.

WHITER, Stephanie Anne Louise 43 Esmonde Road, Helston TR13 8BX — MB ChB 1990 Birm.; ChB Birm. 1990.

WHITESIDE, Anthony Health Centre, London St., Fleetwood FY7 6HD Tel: 01253 874486 & 0253 873312 — MB ChB 1966 Liverp.; MRCS Eng. LRCP Lond. 1966; DObst RCOG 1970. (Liverp.) Prev: SHO Med. Vict. Hosp. Blackpool; Cas. Off. Whlston Hosp. Prescot; Ho. Surg. David Lewis N.. Hosp. Liverp.

WHITESIDE, Bernard Godfrey Hanham Surgery, 33 Whittucks Road, Hanham, Bristol BS15 3HY Tel: 0117 967 5201 Fax: 0117 947 7749; 46 Barry Road, Oldland Common, Bristol BS30 6QY Tel: 0117 932 8831 — MB BS 1975 Lond.; MRCS Eng. LRCP Lond. 1974; MRCGP 1979; DRCOG 1978. (Guy's) Chairm. Assn. Fundholders Gp.; Mem. Avon LMC. Prev: Trainee GP Lond. (Brook Gen. Hosp.) VTS; Ho. Off. Orpington Hosp.

WHITESIDE, Catherine Elaine 6 Lawside Terrace, Dundee DD3 6EA — MB ChB 1998 Dund.

WHITESIDE, Christine Lesley 23 Alexandra Drive, Liverpool L17 8TB — MB ChB 1982 Liverp.

WHITESIDE, John Donald Northwood, Chestnut Avenue, Chichester PO19 4QE Tel: 01243 527614 — MB BCh BAO Dub. 1939; BA Dub. 1937, MD 1941; FRCP Lond. 1974, M 1968; FRCPI 1960, M 1941. (T.C. Dub.) Emerit. Cons. Phys. of Cardiol. St Richards Hosp. Chichester & King Edwd. VII Midhurst. Socs: Wessex Phys. Club; Brit. Cardiac Soc. Prev: Emerit. Cons. Phys. Chichester Health Dist.; Cons. Phys. King Edwd. VII Hosp. Midhurst; Med. Specialist RAFVR.

WHITESIDE, Jonathan Brian 6 Lawside Terrace, Dundee DD3 6EA — MB ChB 1994 Glas.

WHITESIDE, Mary Lorraine Whiteabbey Health Centre, 95 Doagh Road, Newtownabbey BT37 9QN Tel: 028 9086 4341 Fax: 028 9086 0443 — MB BCh BAO 1979 Belf.

WHITESIDE, Mr Michael Charles Richmond Antrim Area Hospital, 45 Bush Road, Antrim BT41 2RL; 1 The Orcuard, Circular Road, Belfast — MB BCh BAO 1986 Belf.; FRCSI 1990; MD 1997 Belf. Cons. Surg.

WHITESIDE, Michael William 7 Meadway, Bromborough, Wirral — MB BS 1970 Lond.; MRCS Eng. LRCP Lond. 1970; DCH RCPS Glas. 1974.

WHITESIDE, Olivia Bedford House, 82 Cornwall Road, Harrogate HG1 2NE — MB BS 1998 Lond.

WHITESIDE, Ralph Stephen 165 Cundy Street, Walkley, Sheffield S6 2WP — MB ChB 1989 Sheff.

WHITESIDE, Richard John 3 The Grange, Cairnburn Road, Belfast BT4 2PH — MB BCh BAO 1989 Belf.

WHITESIDE, Professor Thomas Charles Douay, MBE, Group Capt. RAF Med. Br. Retd. High Bank, Tighnabruaich PA21 2EB Tel: 00 33 66 827527, 01700 811600 — MB BCh 1945 Glas; Chartered Psychologist; PhD (Hawthorne Prize) Glas. 1955; MRCP Lond. 1971; FRAeS 1971. (University of Glasgow) Indep. Cons. Environm. Relations; Hon. Lect. (Aviat. Med.) Univ. Glas. Socs: Brit. Psychol. Soc.; Internat. Acad. Aviat. Med.; Soc. Of Experim. Psychol. Prev: Whittington Prof. Aviat. Med.; OC RAF Aviat. Med. Train. Centre N. Luffenham; Sen. RAF Cons. Advisor in Physiol.

WHITESIDE, William Noel, CStJ (Surgery) 10 Blyth Road, Bromley BR1 3RH Tel: 020 8460 7182; The House-on-the-Wall, Watts Lane, Chislehurst BR7 5PJ Tel: 020 8467 0958 — MB BCh BAO 1934 Dub.; BA, MB BCh BAO Dub. 1934. (T.C. Dub.) Dist. Surg. St. John Ambul. Brig. (Reserve); Hon. Vice-Pres. S.E. Sect. Lond. Br. Brit. Red Cross Soc. Socs: BMA & Harv. Soc. Prev: Wing Cdr. RAF Med. Br.

WHITESON, Adrian Leon, OBE 58A Wimpole Street, London W1M 7DE Tel: 020 7935 3351 Fax: 020 7487 2504; Pender Lodge, 6 Oakleigh Park N., London N20 9AR Tel: 020 8445 9365 — MB BS 1959 Lond.; MB BS (Hons. Therap. & Pharm.) Lond. 1959; MRCS Eng. LRCP Lond. 1959. (St. Geo.) Indep. GP Lond. & Chief Med. Off. Brit. Boxing Bd. Control; Chief Med. Off. Providence Capitol & Liberty Life Assur. Companies; Sen. Med. Examr. Scott. Widows, Abbey Life & Other Insur. Companies; Chief Med. Adviser Trafalgar Hse. Gp.; Chairm. Med. Commiss. World Boxing Counc. Prev: Clin. Asst. Diabetic Clinic St. Bart. Hosp. Lond.; Ho. Off. (Med.) & Cas. Off. St. Geo. Hosp. Lond.

WHITESON, Stephen Daniel 166 Kingsway, Gatley, Cheadle SK8 4NT — BM BS 1986 Nottm.

WHITEWAY, Alastair John Dept.haematology, Royal Free Hospital, Pond St., London NW3 2QG Tel: 020 7794 0500 Email: whiteway@rfhsm.ac.uk — MB BS 1991 Lond.; BSc 1985; MRCP 1995; Dip RCPath 1997. (Roy.Free.Hosp)

WHITEWAY, Miss Janet Elizabeth Department of Urology, South Cleveland Hospital, Middlesbrough TS4 3BW Fax: 01642 854/08; 10 Cornfield Road, Middlesbrough TS5 5QL Email: janetwhiteway@btinternet.com — BM BCh 1974 Oxf.; MCh Oxf. 1985, BM BCh 1974; FRCS Eng. 1979. (Oxf. & St. Thos.) Cons. Urol. S. Cleveland Hosp. Middlesbrough; Adviser in Urol., Chief Med. Off./N.C.E.P.O.D. Socs: Roy. Soc. Med. (Mem. Counc. Sect. Urol.) Brit. Assn. Urol. Surgs.; Epicurist N. Eng. Surg. Soc. Amer. Urol. Assoc. Prev: Sen. Regist. Freeman Hosp. Newc.; Regist. St Peter's Hosp. Lond.; Research Fell. St. Mark's Hosp. Lond.

WHITEWOOD, Colin Noel 18 Remburn Gardens, Lakin Road, Warwick CV34 5BW — MB BS 1991 Western Australia.

WHITEWOOD, Felicity Jane 18 Remburn Gardens, Lakin Road, Warwick CV34 5BW — MB BS 1991 Western Australia.

WHITEWRIGHT, John Rae 126 Crossbrook Street, Cheshunt, Waltham Cross EN8 8JY Tel: 01992 22908 & 24284; 97 Flamstead End Road, Cheshunt, Waltham Cross EN8 0JB — MB ChB 1966 Ed. (Ed.) Prev: Regist. (Med.) Preston Roy. Infirm.; SHO (O & G) Bolton Dist. Gen. Hosp.; SHO (Med.) Sharoe Green Hosp. Preston.

WHITFIELD, Andrea Marie 4 The Steeple, Caldy, Wirral CH48 1QE — MB ChB 1987 Bristol.

WHITFIELD, Andrew John The Surgery, All Saints House, 39 All Saints Road, Lightwater GU18 5SQ Tel: 01276 472248 Fax: 01276

473873; 18 Walkers Ridge, Camberley GU15 2DF — MB ChB 1985 Sheff. Med. Adviser BOC Gp. Surrey.

WHITFIELD, Ann (retired) 3 West Castle Road, Edinburgh EH10 5AT — MB BS 1959 Lond.; MRCS Eng. LRCP Lond. 1959; FFA RCS Eng. 1965; DA Eng. 1961. Prev: Cons. Anaesth. Edin. Roy. Infirm.

WHITFIELD, Mr Bernard Charles Stuart 7 Woodland Road, Kilner Park, Ulverston LA12 0DX Tel: 01229 582333 Fax: 01229 580934 — MB ChB 1976 Leeds; BSc (Hons.) (Med. Microbiol.) Leeds 1976; FRCS (Otol.) Ed. 1990; FRCS (Gen. Surg.) Ed. 1983; FCS Otol. S Afr 1987. Cons. Otorhinolaryng. Furness Gen. Hosp. Trust Barrow-in-Furness & W.morland Gen. Hosp. Trust Kendal. Socs: Brit. Assn. Otol.; N. Eng. ENT Soc.; Roy. Soc. Med. Prev: Clin. Lect. (Otolaryngol.) & Sen. Regist. Radcliffe Infirm. Oxf.; Clin. Lect. (Otolaryngol.) & Cons. Univ. Cape Town, SA.

WHITFIELD, Betty Elaine The Copse, Bannerdown Road, Baheaston, Bath BA1 7PL Tel: 01225 858855 — MB ChB Liverp. 1950; DObst RCOG 1951. (Liverp.)

WHITFIELD, Catherine Tracy The Old Post Office, Byton, Presteigne LD8 2HS — MB BS 1980 Lond.

WHITFIELD, Professor Charles Richard (retired) 7 Grange Road, Bearsden, Glasgow G61 3PL Tel: 0141 942 5585 — MB BCh BAO 1950 Belf.; MD Belf. 1965; FRCP Glas. 1981, M 1978; FRCOG 1969, M 1959. Prev: Regius Prof. Midw. Univ. Glas.

WHITFIELD, Christopher Digby 2 Glebelands Avenue, South Woodford, London E18 2AD Tel: 020 8989 6272 Fax: 020 8518 8753; 35 High View Road, London E18 2HL Tel: 020 8989 3816 — MB BCh BAO 1955 Dub.

WHITFIELD, Claire Anne 9 Calderstones Road, Liverpool L18 6HR — MB ChB 1986 Liverp.

WHITFIELD, Elizabeth Mary Derwent Clinic, Shotley Bridge General Hospital, Consett DH8 0NB — MB ChB 1985 Glas.; MRCPsych 1990. Cons. Psychiat. of Old Age Shotley Bridge Hosp. Co. Durh.

WHITFIELD, Estelle 22 Millfield Road, North Walsham NR28 0EB — MB ChB 1998 Leeds.

WHITFIELD, Frances Paston Surgery, 9-11 Park Lane, North Walsham NR28 0BQ Tel: 01692 403015 Fax: 01692 500619; Bradmoor Farm, North Walsham NR28 6BX — MB ChB 1973 Sheff.; FRCA Eng. 1978. (Sheffield) GP Tutor. Prev: Regist. (Anaesth.) Sheff. AHA (T).

WHITFIELD, George Thompson (retired) Cawood Croft, 471 Scalby Road, Newby, Scarborough YO12 6UA Tel: 01723 364847 — MB ChB Birm. 1957; MRCS Eng: LRCP Lond. 1957; FFA RCS Eng. 1969; DA Eng. 1962. Prev: Cons. Anaesth. ScarBoro. E. Yorks. Health Dists.

WHITFIELD, Gillian Anne Flat 3, 18 Smoke Lane, Reigate RH2 7HJ — MB BS 1998 Lond.; MB BS Lond 1998; MA CANTAB 1992.

WHITFIELD, Grace Patricia The Surgery, 11-13 Charlton Road, Blackheath, London SE3 7HB Tel: 020 8858 2632 Fax: 020 8293 9286; 7 Woolacombe Road, London SE3 8QJ Tel: 020 8856 3677 — MB ChB 1967 Sheff. (Sheff.) Socs: BMA.

WHITFIELD, Mr Hugh Newbold 43 Wimpole Street, London W1G 8AE Tel: 020 7935 3095 Fax: 020 7935 3147 Email: hughwhitfield@urologylondon.fsnet.co.uk; Cokes Green, Cokes Lane, Chalfont St Giles HP8 4TA Tel: 01494 762571 Fax: 01494 765389 — MB BChir 1969 Camb.; MA Camb. 1969, MChir 1978; FRCS Eng. 1973; MRCS Eng. LRCP Lond. 1968. (Camb. & St. Bart.) Cons. Urol., Battle Hosp, Reading; Edr. Brit. Jl. Urol. Internat.; Hon. Cons. Urol Gt. Ormond St. for sick Childr.; Hon. Cons. To the army. Socs: Brit. Assn. Urol. Surgs.; BMA; Roy. Soc. Med. Prev: Hunt. Prof. RCS Eng.; Chief Asst. (Urol.) St. Bart. Hosp. Lond.; Cons. Urol.Centr. Middlx.Hosp.Lond.

WHITFIELD, Juliette Jane The Burwell Surgery, Newmarket Road, Burwell, Cambridge CB5 0AE Tel: 01638 741234 Fax: 01638 743948; Lowfields, Lower End, Swaffham Prior, Cambridge CB5 0HT — BM 1987 Soton.; MRCGP 1992; DRCOG 1990. (Soton.)

WHITFIELD, Kathleen Mary (retired) 35 High View Road, South Woodford, London E18 2HL — MB BCh BAO 1955 Dub.; DA Eng. 1958.

WHITFIELD, Kevin John 16 Northumberland Gardens, Newcastle upon Tyne NE5 1PT Tel: 0191 267 4763 — MB BS 1994 Newc.; BMedSc Newc. 1993.

WHITFIELD, Mary Jeffery (retired) 29 Thorburn Road, New Ferry, Wirral CH62 1EN Tel: 0151 645 1860 — MRCS Eng. LRCP Lond. 1948. Prev: Resid. Asst. Med. Off. Walton Hosp. Liverp.

WHITFIELD, Michael John (retired) Whiteladies Health Centre, Whatley Road, Clifton, Bristol BS8 2PU Tel: 0117 973 1201 Fax: 0117 946 7031 — MB BChir 1963 Camb.; MA, MB Camb. 1963, BChir 1962; MRCS Eng. LRCP Lond. 1962; FRCGP 1980, M 1969; DPH Bristol 1969; DCH Eng. 1965; DObst RCOG 1964. Prev: Sen.Lect.Univ.Bristol.

WHITFIELD, Mr Patrick John 17 Harley Street, London W1N 1DA Tel: 020 7580 6283; 3 Coombe Neville, Warren Road, Kingston upon Thames KT2 7HW Tel: 020 8949 4344 — MB BS Lond. 1958; FRCS Eng. 1963; MRCS Eng. LRCP Lond. 1958. (St. Geo.) Cons. Plastic Surg. W.m. Hosp. Lond., Qu. Mary's Hosp. Rosehampton &SW Thames RHA; Cons. Plastic Surg. Roy. Lond. Hosp. Trust, Lond. E1. Socs: Fell. Roy. Soc. Med. (Pres. Plastic Surg. Sect.); Brit. Assn. Plastic Surg.; (Ex-Hon. Sec.) Brit. Assn. Aesthetic Plastic Surgs. Prev: Cons. Plastic Surg. W.m. Hosp. Lond., Qu. Mary's Hosp. Roehampton & SW Thames RHA; Resid. Asst. (Obst.) & Ho. Surg. (Gyn.) St. Geo. Hosp. Lond.; Sen. Regist. (Plastic Surg.) Burns & Oral Surg. Centre Qu. Mary's Hosp. Roehampton.

WHITFIELD, Paul Hudson 41 Nursery Road, Elstob Farm Est., Sunderland SR3 1NT — MB BS 1991 Newc.; BDS Dundee 1983.

WHITFIELD, Paul Nicholas Kings Corner Surgery, Kings Road, Ascot SL5 0AE Tel: 01344 623181 Fax: 01344 875129 — MB BS 1981 Lond.; BSc (Hons.) Physiol. Lond. 1978, MB BS 1981; MRCGP 1986; DRCOG 1984.

WHITFIELD, Mr Peter Cyril Tel: 01224 553453 — BM (Distinc.) 1999 Soton.; FRCS Eng. 1992; PhD Soton. 1998. Cons., Clin. Sen. Lect. Neurol. Surg. Grampain Univ. Hosps. Trust, Aberd. Socs: Soc. Brit. Neurosurg. Surg.; Fell. Roy. Coll. Surg.s (Eng.). Prev: Specialist Regist. (Neurol. Surg.) Addenbrooke's Hosp. Camb.; Med. Research Counc. Clin. Train. Fell. & Hon. Sen. Regist. (Neurosurg.) Addenbrooke's Hosp. Camb.; Regist. (Neurosurg.) Addenbrooke's Hosp. Camb.

WHITFIELD, Richard George Sarel, DSC (retired) 36 York Road, Walmer, Deal CT14 7EA — MRCS Eng. LRCP Lond. 1939; BA Oxf.

WHITFIELD, Roseanne Louise 3 Coombe Neville, Warren Road, Kingston upon Thames KT2 7HW Tel: 020 8949 4344 — MB BS 1993 Lond.; MFHom 1996; DRCOG 1997; MRCGP 1998. (St George's Hospital) GP Non-Princip.; Homeop. Phys.

WHITFIELD, Ruth Jeanne Chest Clinic, Mayday University Hospital, London Road, Croydon CR7 7YE Tel: 020 8401 3138 Fax: 020 8401 3460 Email: ruth.whitfield@mhc-tr.staines.nhs.uk; Oak House, Mount Gardens, London SE26 4NG Tel: 020 8291 2683 — MB BChir Camb. 1970; MA Camb. 1970; MRCP (UK) 1973; FRCP 1998. (Westm.) Assoc. Specialist (Thoracic Med.) Croydon Chest Clinic Mayday Hosp.; Assoc. Specialist (Diabetes) KCH Lond.; Med. Adviser Indep. Adopt. Serv. Lond. Prev: Regist. (Diabetes) Kings Coll. Hosp. Lond.; Regist. & SHO (Chest & Gen. Med.) Mayday Hosp. Croydon & Warlingham Pk. Gp. Hosps.

WHITFIELD, Stephen James Claypath Medical Practice, 26 Gilesgate, Durham DH1 1QW Tel: 0191 333 2830 Fax: 0191 333 2836 — MB ChB 1987 Aberd.

WHITFORD, David Leonard West Farm Avenue Surgery, 381 West Farm Avenue, Longbenton, Newcastle upon Tyne NE12 8UT Tel: 0191 266 1728 Fax: 0191 270 1488; 79 Jesmond Park W., Newcastle upon Tyne NE7 7BY Tel: 0191 281 1127 — MB BS 1982 Newc.; MA Camb. 1983; MRCGP 1986; DRCOG 1985. GP Newc. upon Tyne. Prev: Trainee GP N.umbria VTS.

WHITFORD, John Herbert William (retired) The Anchorage, 43 Meols Drive, Hoylake, Wirral CH47 4AF Tel: 0151 632 3608 — MB ChB 1962 Liverp.; FFA RCS Eng. 1969; DObst RCOG 1965. Prev: Cons. Anaesth. Wirral Hosp. Trust.

WHITFORD, Mrs Philippa 53 Ottoline Drive, Troon KA10 7AN — MB ChB 1982 Glas.; MD Glas. 1991; FRCS Glas. 1986. Cons. Surg. CrossHo. Hosp. Kilmarnock. Prev: Sen. Regist. (Gen. Surg.) Aberd. Roy. Infirm.; Cons. Gen. Surg. Ahli Arab Hosp., Gaza Strip; Regist. (Gen. Surg.) Inverclyde Roy. Hosp.

WHITHAM, Graham Tweedie Braidcraft Medical Centre, 200 Braidcraft Road, Glasgow G53 5QD Tel: 0141 882 3396 Fax: 0141

WHITHAM

883 3224; 4 Braehead Glebe, Stewarton, Kilmarnock KA3 5HG — MB ChB 1979 Dundee; MRCGP 1986.

WHITHAM, Sarah Elisabeth 40 Dagmar Road, Tivoli, Cheltenham GL50 2UG Tel: 01242 573480 — MB ChB 1994 Bristol. (Bristol)

WHITING, Professor Brian Faculty of Medicine, University of Glasgow, Glasgow G12 8QQ Tel: 0141 330 4249 Fax: 0141 330 5440 Email: dean@clinmed.gla.ac.ukk; 2 Milner Road, Jordanhill, Glasgow G13 1QL Tel: 0141 959 2324 Fax: 0141 959 2324 — MB ChB 1964 Glas.; MD Glas. 1976; FRCP Glas 1979; MRCP (UK) 1970; FFPM (Distinc.) RCP UK 1989; FRCP Ed. 1996. (Glas.) Dean (Fac. Med.) Univ. Glas.; Titular Prof. Clin. Pharmacol. Med. & Therap. & Dean (Fac. Med.) Univ. Glas.; Cons. Phys. Med. & Therap. W.. Infirm. Socs: Assn. Phys.; Brit. Pharm. Soc.; Found. Fell. Acad. Med. Sci. Prev: Reader & Sen. Lect. (Mat. Med.) Univ. Glas.; Cons. Phys. Univ. Med. Unit Stobhill Hosp. Glas.; Sen. Regist. (Med. & Clin. Pharmacol.) Univ. Med. Unit Stohill Hosp. Glas.

WHITING, Brian Hall Health Care Centre, 46 Longport, Canterbury CT1 1PJ Tel: 01227 762244 Fax: 01227 451124 — MB ChB 1970 Glas.; MRCGP 1976; DObst RCOG 1972; Cert JCC Lond. 1978. Prev: SHO (Obst.) Falkirk Roy. Infirm.; esid. (Med.) & Resid. (Surg.) Stirling Roy. Infirm.; Squadron Ldr. RAF Med. Br. & Lt. Col. RAMC.

WHITING, Frances Elizabeth (retired) Swan Acre, All Saints Lane, Sutton Courtenay, Abingdon OX14 4AG Tel: 01235 848701 — MB BS 1970 Lond.; MRCS Eng. LRCP Lond. 1970; DObst RCOG 1972. Clin. Med. Off. Oxf. HA. Prev: Ho. Phys. Luton & Dunstable Hosp.

WHITING, John Lee 14 Meadow Hill Road, Kings Norton, Birmingham B38 8DD — MB ChB 1990 Manch.

WHITING, John Michael Sturge (retired) 27 Spindlewood, Elloughton, Brough HU15 1LL Tel: 01482 669486 — MB BS 1941 Lond.; FRCGP 1980; DA Eng. 1958. Prev: Sen. Hosp. Med. Off. (Anaesth.) Beverley Dist. Hosps.

WHITING, Karen Alice Sunderland Royal Hospital, Kayll Road, Sunderland SR4 7TP Tel: 0191 565 6256; 1A Hillcrest, Durham DH1 1RB Email: karen.whiting@which.net — MB ChB 1984 Manch.; MB ChB (Hons.) Manch. 1984; MRCP (UK) 1990; FRCPCH 1997; MSc Warwick 1998. (Manchester) Cons. Paediat. (Neurodisabil.) Sunderland Roy. Hosp. Sunderland; Hon. Lect. Child Health Univ. of Newc. Socs: Brit. Paediat. Neurol. Assn. - Neurodisabil., Rep. on Exec. Counc.; Brit. Assn. Community Child Health - Neurodisabil. Rep. on CSAC; Child Developm. & Disabil. Gp. Roy. Coll. Paediat. & Child Health. Prev: Cons. Paediat. specialising in NeuroDisabil. E. Berks. Community NHS Trust & Coventry Healthcare NHS Trust; Cons. Paediat. specialising in Neurodisabil. N. Tees Gen. Hosp. Stockton-on-Tees.

WHITING, Martin Ross Collegiate Medical Centre, Brideoak St., Manchester M8 0AT Tel: 0161 205 4364; 23 Dales Lane, Whitefield, Manchester M45 7JN — MB ChB 1983 Manch.; MRCGP 1987.

WHITING, Norman Richard (retired) 28 Henderson Close, Lichfield WS14 9YN — MRCS Eng. LRCP Lond. 1960; BSc (Hons. Physiol.) Birm. 1957, MB ChB 1960; DObst RCOG 1963. Prev: Ho. Phys. & Ho. Surg. N. Ormesby Hosp. Middlesbrough.

WHITING, Paul Charles 223 Walkley Road, Walkley, Sheffield S6 2XN — MB ChB 1997 Sheff.

WHITING, Simon Langton Trevithick Surgery, Basset Road, Camborne TR14 8TT Tel: 01209 716721 Fax: 01209 612488; 21 Trelawney Road, Falmouth TR11 3LT Tel: 01326 317817 Email: simonwhiting@dial.pipex.com — MB BChir 1978 Camb.; MA, MB Camb. 1979, BChir 1978; BA (OU) 1995; MRCGP 1983; DRCOG 1982. (Camb. & Westm.) Clin. Asst. (A & E) Treliske Hosp. Truro. Prev: GP Burton-on-Trent; Trainee GP Derby VTS.

WHITING, Stephen William Shifnal Medical Practice, Shrewsbury Road, Shifnal TF11 8AJ Tel: 01952 460414 Fax: 01952 463192; Fernleigh, 25 Victoria Road, Shifnal TF11 8AE Tel: 01952 461640 — MB BS 1973 Lond.; MRCS Eng. LRCP Lond. 1972; MRCGP 1980; DObst RCOG 1975. Prev: Ho. Surg. Redhill Gen. Hosp.; Ho. Phys. Metrop. Hosp. Lond.

WHITLA, Denis Robin Auchenard, Brodick KA27 8A — MB BCh BAO 1961 Belf.; MRCP (UK) 1970; DCH; DTM & H. Med. Off. Health Ascension; Sen. Med. Off. Ascension Is. Servs.

WHITLEY, Alan John (retired) Endoscopy Unit, Seacroft Hospital, Leeds LS14 Tel: 0113 264 8164 — MRCS Eng. LRCP Lond. 1958; DTM & H Liverp. 1960. Hosp. Pract. Seacroft Hosp. Leeds.

WHITLEY, Ian 21 Beechdale, Thwaite St., Cottingham, Hull — MB ChB 1983 Leeds.

WHITLEY, Ian Graeme Leesbrook Surgery, Mellor Street, Lees, Oldham OL4 3DG Tel: 0161 621 4800 Fax: 0161 628 6717; 10 Treetops Close, Dobcross, Oldham OL3 5AS Tel: 01457 872522 — MB ChB 1988 Manch.; MRCGP 1992.

WHITLEY, John Manners The Old Stables, Rowden Abbey Farm, Bromyard HR7 4LS Tel: 01885 483066 Fax: 01885 483066 Email: johnwhitley@oldstables.dsbusiness.co.uk — MB BS 1967 Lond.; MRCS Eng. LRCP Lond. 1967. Lucum Cons. Anaesth. Worcester.

WHITLEY, Linsey Louise Fairways, 8 Morlais, Conwy Marina, Conwy LL32 8GJ — MB BS 1998 Lond.

WHITLEY, Michael William St Triduanas Medical Practice, 54 Moira Park, Edinburgh EH7 6RU Tel: 0131 657 3341 Fax: 0131 669 6055; 4 CrookstonCt., Crookston Road, Inveresk, Musselburgh EH21 7TR — MB ChB 1970 Aberd.; MRCGP 1977; DObst RCOG 1972.

WHITLEY, Simon Peter 11 Newlands Road, Newcastle upon Tyne NE2 3NT — MB BS 1997 Newc.; BOS Newc. 1990; FOS RCPS Glas. 1994. Basic Surgic. Trainee, N.ern region.

WHITLEY, Siobhan St Pauls Vicarage, Watling Avenue, Liverpool L21 9NU — MB BS 1998 Lond.

WHITLEY, Teresa Bridget Heath 300A Burdett Road, London E14 7DQ; Apartment 23, 5559 Hobart St, Pittsburgh PA 15217, USA — MB BChir 1989 Camb.; MRCP (UK) 1993.

WHITLINGUM, Gabriel Lawrence 4 Seelig Avenue, London NW9 7BB — MB BS 1996 Lond.

WHITLOCK, Jennifer Anne 70 Cudham Lane N., Cudham, Sevenoaks TN14 7RA — MRCS Eng. LRCP Lond. 1959.

WHITLOCK, Mr Michael Roy 51 Ickenham Road, Ruislip HA4 7BZ Tel: 01895 674888 Email: whitlock@emergencies.fsnet.co.uk — MB BCh BAO 1975 Dub.; BA Dub. 1975; FFAEM 1995; FRCSI 1981; MD Birmingham 2000. (Dublin University) Cons. A & E Barnet Hosp.; Clin. Dir. (A & E) WellHo. Trust Barnet, Edgware Hosps. Socs: FRSM; BMA. Prev: Sen. Regist. (A & E) E. Birm. Hosp.; Regist. (A & E) Wexham Pk. Hosp. Slough.

WHITLOCK, Nicholas James 53 High Street, Gosberton, Spalding PE11 4NW Tel: 01775 840140 — MB BS 1994 Lond. (Univ. Coll. & Middlx. Sch. Med.)

WHITLOCK, Paul Richard 42 Lucerne Road, Highbury, London N5 1TZ — MB BS 1994 Lond.; BSc (Hons.) Biochem. Liverp. 1989. (Univ. Coll. Lond. Med. Sch.) SHO (Orthop. Surg.) Addenbrooke's Hosp. Camb. Prev: SHO (A & E) Univ. Coll. Hosp. Lond.; SHO (Cardiothoracic Surg.) Roy. Brompton Hosp. Lond.

WHITLOW, Barry John 40 Milton Avenue, Sutton SM1 3QB — MB BS 1992 Lond.

WHITLOW, Christine Michele 40 Milton Avenue, Sutton SM1 3QB — MB BS 1992 Lond.

WHITLOW, William Michael Boultham Park Medical Practice, Boultham Park Road, Lincoln LN6 7SS Tel: 01522 874444 Fax: 01522 874466 — MB BS 1981 Lond.; MRCGP 1985; DRCOG 1984; DA (UK) 1987. (St. George Hospital Medical School)

WHITMARSH, Karen Ann Room 007, Doctors Residence, Cookridge Hospital, Cookridge, Leeds LS16 6QB — MB BS 1993 Lond. SHO (Oncol.and Radiother.) Cookridge Hosp. Prev: SHO Rotat. (Med.) Roy. Berks. & Battle Hosps.; SHO (Gen. Surg.) Wycombe Gen. Hosp.

WHITMARSH, Simon Patrick Flat 2, 55 Woodlands Road, Isleworth TW7 6JT — MB ChB 1987 Manch.; MRCP (UK) 1996; T(GP) 1993; DFFP 1993; DRCOG 1992. (Manch.) SHO (Paediat.) Kingston Hosp. Prev: SHO (Paediat.) St. Jas. Hosp. Leeds.; SHO (Neonatol.) Leeds Gen. Infirm.

WHITMARSH, Thomas Edward Glasgow Homoeopathic Hospital, 1053 Great Western Road, Glasgow G12 0XP Tel: 0141 211 1600 Fax: 0141 211 1631 — MB BS 1984 Lond.; BA Camb. 1981; FRCP London 2001; FFHom 1999. Cons. Phys. (Homoeop.) Glas. Homoeop. Hosp. Prev: Research Fell. (Neurosci.) Char. Cross & W.m. Med. Sch. Lond.; Sen. Regist. (Med. & Homoeop.) W.. Infirm. Glas.; Regist. (Gen. Med.) W.. Gen. Hosp. Edin.

WHITMARSH, Vincent Barrie Hunters Hill, Turners Hill Road, East Grinstead RH19 9LA Tel: 01342 328448 Fax: 01342 328448 Email: 106225.3610@compuserve.com — MB BS Lond. 1966; MRCS Eng. LRCP Lond. 1966; FFPM RCP (UK) 1990. (King's Coll. Hosp.) Cons. Pharmaceut. Phys. Sussex. Socs: FRSM. Prev: Dir. & Vice-Pres. Clin.

Safety & Pharmacoeconomics SmithKlein Beecham; Dir. Product Surveillance & Informat. Beecham Pharmaceut.; Med. Dir. (UK) Fisons Pharmaceut.

WHITMEY, Robert James 6 Stubbington Way, Fair Oak, Eastleigh SO50 7LR — MB ChB 1975 Ed.

WHITMORE, Alan Victor MRC Laboratory for Molecular Cell Biology, University College London, Gower St., London WC1E 6BT Tel: 020 7380 7016 Fax: 020 7380 7805 Email: a.whitmore@ucl.ac.uk; 33 Stangate, Royal St, London SE1 7EQ — BM BCh 1996 Oxf.; BM BCh Clin. Med. Oxf. 1996; PhD Visual Neurosci. Univ. Lond. Queen Mary Coll. 1987; BSc Hons. Biol. Sci. with Computing Univ. Lond. Westfield Coll. 1984. (Univ. Oxford Clin. Med. & St. Johns Coll.) MRC Clin. Research Fell. MRC Laborat. for Molecular Cell Biol. Univ. Coll. Lond.; Vis. Research Fell. Dept. of Visual Sci. Inst. of Ophth. Lond. Prev: SHO Dept. of Ophthmalogy St. Thomas' Hosp. Lond.; SHO Dept. of Ophthmalogy W. Suff. Hosp. Bury St. Edmunds.

WHITMORE, Alec Charles (retired) 29 Davies Avenue, Leeds LS8 1JZ Tel: 0113 266 3158 Email: alecwhitmore@hotmail.com — MB BS 1956 Lond.; MRCS Eng. LRCP Lond. 1956. Indep. GP Leeds.

WHITMORE, Bethany Lucille Accident and Emergency Dept, St Thomas's Hospital, Lambeth Palace Road, London SE1 7EH Tel: 020 7928 9292 Email: bethany.whitmore@gsst.sthames.nhs.uk; 33 Stangate, Royal St, London SE1 7EQ — MB BS 1994 Lond.; BSc (Hons.) Med. Chem. Lond. 1989; AFRCS ED (A&E) 1998. (Univ. Coll. & Middlx. Hosp. Sch. Med. Lond.) Registr. (A&E). Prev: SHO (Neurosurg.) Radcliffe Infirm. Oxf.; SHO (Gen. Med. & Haematol), W. Suff. Hosp.; SHO (A&E), John Radcliffe Hosp.

WHITMORE, David Noel Haematology Department, Queen Mary's Hospital Trust, Sidcup DA14 6LT; 36 Parkhurst Road, Bexley DA5 1AR Tel: 01322 527471 — MB BChir 1955 Lond.; MB BChir Camb. 1955; MA Camb. 1955; FRCP Lond. 1979, M 1958; MRCS Eng. LRCP Lond. 1954; FRCPath 1976, M 1964. (Camb. & Guy's) Clin. Asst. (Haemat.) Qu. Mary's Hosp. Trust Sidcup. Prev: Cons. Path. Lewisham Hosp. Lond.

WHITMORE, Ian Richard Spring Gardens Health Centre, Providence Street, Worcester WR1 2BS Tel: 01905 681781 Fax: 01905 681766; 1 The Orchards, Hatfield Lane, Hatfield, Worcester WR5 2PY Tel: 01905 820872 — BM BCh 1974 Oxf.

WHITMORE, Ian Vincent Laundry Cottage, Laundry Lane, Nazeing, Waltham Abbey EN9 2DY Tel: 01992 899206 Fax: 01992 899207 Email: iwhitmore@argonet.co.uk — MB BS 1968 Lond.; MD Lond. 1980; MRCS Eng. LRCP Lond. 1968. (Guy's Hosp.) Prof. (Anat.) Stanford Univ. Med. Sch. Calif. USA (Sept-Dec each year). Socs: FRSM; Fell. Brit. Assoc. Clin. Anat.; Anat. Soc. Prev: Lect. (Anat.) Manch. Univ.; Sen. Lect. (Topograph. Anat.) Qu. Mary & W.field Coll.

WHITMORE, Jane Margaret Whiston Health Centre, Old Colliery Rd, Whiston, Liverpool L35 3SX Tel: 0151 292 3585 Fax: 0151 426 8546; 30 Windy Harbour Road, Birkdale, Southport PR8 3DU Tel: 01704 572360 — MB BS 1981 Lond.; DipVen (Liverpool) 1996; Mem. Inst. Of Psychosexual Med. 1993; MFFP 1993. Cons. in family Plann. & reproductive health, St Helens & Knowsley Community NHS Trust.

***WHITMORE, Jennifer Jane** 9 Hogarth Road, Shottery, Stratford-upon-Avon CV37 9YU — MB ChB 1996 Birm.

WHITMORE, John Ludlow, MBE (retired) Brooklands, Freshwater PO40 9EW Tel: 01983 752421 — MRCS Eng. LRCP Lond. 1946. Prev: Med. Advisor to Dir. of Nuclear Trials Aldermaston & Pacific.

WHITMORE, Thomas Kingsley (retired) 2 Reddings, Welwyn Garden City AL8 7LA Tel: 01707 325995 — MRCS Eng. LRCP Lond. 1944; DCH Eng. 1946. Prev: Research Paediat. (Community Paediat. Research) W.m. Childr. Hosp. Lond.

WHITNALL, Mr Mark 57 Russell Avenue, Wollaton, Nottingham NG8 2BN Tel: 0115 928 2802 — MB ChB 1994 Bristol; BDS (Hons.) Cardiff 1987; FDS RCS Eng. 1992; FRCS Eng. 1998. Staff Surg. SHO (Maxillofacial) Lincoln. Socs: Brit. Assn. Oral & Maxillofacial Surgs. Prev: SHO (ENT) Suff.

WHITNEY, Dorothy June (retired) Gables, Courtmead Road, Cuckfield, Haywards Heath RH17 5LP Tel: 01444 417829 — MB BS 1953 Lond.; FRCS Eng. 1961; MRCS Eng. LRCP Lond. 1953; FRCOG 1974, M 1958, DObst 1955. Prev: Cons. (O & G) RN Hosp. Gibraltar.

WHITNEY, John Deryck Wallace (retired) 11 Wellfield Road, Alrewas, Burton-on-Trent DE13 7HB Tel: 01283 792303 — MB BS 1954 Lond.; MRCS Eng. LRCP Lond. 1955; FRCGP 1978, M 1961; MFOM RCP Lond. 1983, AFOM 1980; Accredit. Occupat. Med. RCP Lond. 1983; DIH Eng. 1982. Prev: Occupat. Phys. Birm. City Counc.

WHITNEY, Peter George 79 Hunters Road, Spital Tongues, Newcastle upon Tyne NE2 4ND — MB BS 1998 Newc.

WHITNEY, Roger William X-Ray Department, Broomfield Hospital, Court Road, Broomfield, Chelmsford CM1 7ET Tel: 01245 514527 Fax: 01245 514979; Appletree Cottage, Hartford End, Chelmsford CM3 1LE — MB BCh BAO 1980 Dub. Cons. Radiol. Broomfield Hosp. Chelmsford. Prev: Sen. Regist. (Radiol.) N. Staffs. Roy. Infirm. Stoke-on-Trent.

WHITROW, William (retired) 17A Culduthel Road, Inverness IV2 4AG Tel: 01463 242065 — MB BS 1957 Lond.; MRCS Eng. LRCP Lond. 1957; FRCPath 1982, M 1970; DCP Lond 1966. Prev: Med. Dir. N. Scotl. Blood Transfus. Serv.

WHITSON, Ann 26 Norfolk Road, Lytham, Lytham St Annes FY8 4JG — MB ChB 1977 Manch.

WHITTAKER, Alison Jean 70 South Borough Road, Victoria Park, London E9 7EE Tel: 020 8985 8939 — BChir 1990 Camb.; MB BChir Camb. 1990; MRCP UK 1993. Specialist Regist. (Respirat. Med.) N. E. Thames. Socs: Brit. Thorac. Soc.

WHITTAKER, Andrew Rainbow Medical Centre, 333 Robins Lane, St Helens WA9 3PN Tel: 01744 811211; 41 Forest Grove, Eccleston Park, Prescot L34 2RY — MB ChB 1977 Liverp.; DRCOG 1979.

WHITTAKER, Anne Margaret The Surgery, Denmark Street, Darlington DL3 0PD Tel: 01325 460731 Fax: 01325 362183; 3 Ashcroft Road, Darlington DL3 8PD Tel: 01325 468988 — MB BS 1974 Newc.; MRCGP 1978; DRCOG 1978. Clin. Asst. (Gen. Surg.) Friarage Hosp. N.allerton. Prev: GP Yarm; Trainee GP E. Cumbria VTS; Ho. Phys. & Ho. Surg. Cumbld. Infirm. Carlisle.

WHITTAKER, Bryony Eleanor 8 Lavant Road, Chichester PO19 4RH Tel: 01243 527264 Fax: 01243 530607; 7 Oldwick Meadows, Lavant, Chichester PO18 0BE — MB BS 1975 Lond.; MRCS Eng. LRCP Lond. 1975; DRCOG 1977. (Westm.) p/t Principle Gen. Pract. Chichester. Prev: SHO (Paediat.) & SHO (O & G) Roy. W. Sussex Hosp. St. Richard's Br.) Chichester; Ho. Surg. W.m. Hosp. Lond.

WHITTAKER, Caroline Anne Department of Dermatology, Amersham Hospital, Whielden St., Amersham HP7 0JD Tel: 01494 734600 Fax: 01494 734620; Roughacre, Chalfont Lane, Chorleywood, Rickmansworth WD3 5PP — MB BS 1984 Newc.; MRCGP 1988; Dip. Pract. Dermat. Wales 1996; DRCOG 1989; Cert. Family Plann. JCC 1989. Clin. Asst. (Dermat.) Amersham Hosp. Prev: Regist. (Dermat.) Aberd. Roy. Infirm.; Clin. Lect. Aberd.; GP Retainer Elms Surg. Chorleywood.

WHITTAKER, Christine Margaret Hollyoaks Medical Centre, 229 Station Road, Wythall, Birmingham B47 6ET Tel: 01564 823182 Fax: 01564 824127; Chapel Green Farm, Chapel Lane, Wythall, Birmingham B47 6JX — MB ChB 1971 Birm. Clin. Asst. Oncol. Solihull Hosp.

WHITTAKER, David John Dormans Cross E., Hollow Lane, Dormansland, Lingfield RH7 6NU Tel: 01342 833449 Fax: 01342 836649 Email: jd.whitworth@virgin.net — MB BCh 1983 Wales; Dip. Sports Med. Lond 1991; DA (UK) 1986. Specialist Anaesth. (Dent.) Poggo Anaesth. Gp. Prev: Chief Resid. King Edwd. VII Memor. Hosp. Bermuda; Dir. Diving Med. Serv. Cor-Brit. Diving Internat. Corfu.

WHITTAKER, Ian David Station Road Surgery, 74 Station Road, West Wickham BR4 0PU Tel: 020 8777 8245; 45 Steeple Heights, Biggin Hill, Westerham TN16 3UN — MB BS 1983 Lond. Prev: SHO (Paediat. & O & G) Shrodells Hosp. Watford; Ho. Phys. & Ho. Surg. Hartlepool Gen. Hosp.

WHITTAKER, James Anthony Cornerways, Woolfall Health Avenue, Huyton, Liverpool L36 3TH Tel: 0151 489 4444 — MB ChB 1960 Liverp. (Liverp.)

WHITTAKER, Jane 44 Churchwood Road, Manchester M20 6TY — MB ChB 1990 Manch.

WHITTAKER, John Alan Department of Haematology, University Hospital of Wales, Cardiff CF4 4XN Tel: 029 2074 7747 Fax: 029 2074 5084 — MB ChB 1962 Liverp.; MD (Samuels Prize) Liverp. 1970; FRCP Lond. 1980, M 1967; FRCPath 1985, M 1985. Reader (Haemat.) Univ. Wales Coll. of Med.; Cons. Haemat. Univ. Hosp. of

WHITTAKER

Wales Cardiff. Socs: Brit. Soc. Haematol.; Internat. Soc. Haematol.; Pres. Welsh Bone Marrow Transpl. Research Fund. Prev: Sen. Regist. (Med.) & SHO (Phys.) United Liverp. Hosps.; Fell. (Med.) Johns Hopkins Hosp. Baltimore, USA.

WHITTAKER, John Stuart (retired) 147 Grove Lane, Cheadle Hulme, Cheadle SK8 7NG Tel: 0161 440 0168 — MB ChB 1957 Manch.; BSc (Hons. Anat.) Manch. 1954; FRCPath 1978, M 1965. Prev: Cons. Histopath. Wythenshawe Hosp. Manch.

WHITTAKER, Mr Jonathan David Accident and Emergency Department, Royal Preston Hospital, Sharoe Green Lane N., Fulwood, Preston PR2 9HT Tel: 01772 710303 Fax: 01772 716955; 11 Barnstaple Way, Cottam, Preston PR4 0LY Tel: 01772 732139 — MB ChB 1987 Manch.; FFAEM 1998; FRCS Ed. 1993. Cons. (A & E Med.) Roy. Preston Hosp. Socs: Brit. Assn. Accid. & Emerg. Med.; Fell. Fac. Accid. & Emerg. Med. Prev: Sen. Regist. (A & E Med.) Roy. Preston Hosp.

WHITTAKER, Julie Anne Teresa Patterdale Lodge Medical Centre, Legh Street, Newton-le-Willows WA12 9NA Tel: 01925 227111 Fax: 01925 290605 — MB ChB 1981 Manch.

WHITTAKER, Karen Burnley Wood Medical Centre, 50 Parliament St., Burnley BB11 3JX Tel: 01282 425521 Fax: 01282 832556; 8 Queens Road, Burnley BB10 1XX Tel: 01282 428391 — MB ChB 1988 Manch. Princip. in Gen. Pract. Prev: Trainee GP/SHO Burnley Gen. Hosp.

WHITTAKER, Karl Ward 11 Caswell Lane, Portbury, Bristol BS20 7UF — MB ChB 1992 Birm.

WHITTAKER, Leslie Robert, OBE (retired) 56 Bollo Road, Chiswick, London W4 5LT Tel: 0208 995 5552 — MRCS Eng. LRCP Lond. 1945; FRCR 1964; DMRD 1955; DCH RCP Lond. 1949. Prev: Prof. Radiol. Fac. Med. Univ. Nairobi.

WHITTAKER, Mr Malcolm George Memorial Hospital, Hollyhurst Road, Darlington DL3 6HX Tel: 01325 380100 — MB ChB 1962 Leeds; FRCS Ed. 1968; FRCS Eng. 1968. Sen. Cons. Surg. Darlington & N.allerton HA's. Socs: Fell. Soc. Internat. Chir.; Roy. Soc. Med. (Vice Pres. Sect. Surg.); Assn. Coloproctol. Prev: Lect. (Surg.) & Sen. Regist. Surgic. Unit Univ. Coll. Hosp. Lond.; Regist. (Surg.) Gen. Infirm. Leeds.

WHITTAKER, Margaret Wardrop (retired) The Old Barn, Matthew Lane, Bradley, Keighley BD20 9DF Tel: 01535 633494 — MRCS Eng. LRCP Lond. 1945. Prev: Ho. Surg. & Ho. Phys. Wigan Infirm.

WHITTAKER, Mr Mark (retired) Hawthorn House, Ladderbanks Lane, Baildon, Shipley BD17 6RX Tel: 01274 583033 — MB BS 1965 Lond.; FRCS Eng. 1971; MRCS Eng. LRCP Lond. 1965. Cons. Surg. Bradford AHA.; Clin. Tutor (Bradford) Univ. Leeds; Hon. Lect. Surg. Univ. Leeds. Prev: Ho. Surg. St. Bart. Hosp.

WHITTAKER, Mark Adrian, Surg. Cdr. RN Department of Pathology, Royal Hospital Haslar, Gosport PO12 2AA Tel: 023 92 584255 Ext: 2816 Fax: 023 92 762549 Email: markwhit@dsca.gov.uk; 15 Mansvid Avenue, East Cosham, Portsmouth PO6 2LX Tel: 023 92 786703 Email: mark@whitbags.com — BM 1991 Soton.; MRCPath 2001. (Soton. Univ. Hosps. Med. Sch.) Cons., Histopath., Roy. Hosp. Haslar, Gosport, Hants.; Hon. Cons., Histopath., Qu. Alexandra Hosp., Cosham, Portsmouth, PO6 3LX. Socs: Train. Mem. Assn. Clin. Path.; Brit. Div. Internat. Acad. of Path. Prev: SpR (Histopath), Soton. Gen. Hosp., Soton.; SHO (Histopath.) RN Hosp. Haslar Gosport; Med. Off. HMS Liverp. BFPO 327, HMS Dolphin Gosport & Inst. Naval Med. (Diving Med.) Gosport.

WHITTAKER, Mark David Penfold, Houndscroft, Redborough, Stroud GL5 5DF — BM BS 1987 Nottm.

WHITTAKER, Martin Anthony Khetland, Moorend Lane, Slimbridge, Gloucester GL2 7DG — MB ChB 1993 Leic.

***WHITTAKER, Nuala Ann** 26 Crossland Road, Chorlton, Manchester M21 9DG — MB ChB 1995 Birm.; DRGOG.

WHITTAKER, Peter John Donald 8 Lavant Road, Chichester PO19 4RH Tel: 01243 527264 Fax: 01243 530607; 7 Oldwick Meadows, Lavant, Chichester PO18 0BE — MB BChir 1976 Camb.; MA Camb. 1982, BA 1972, MB 1976, BChir 1975; MRCGP 1980; DCH Eng. 1977 DRCOG 1978. (Camb. & Westm.) GP Chichester. Socs: BMA. Prev: SHO (Paediat.) & SHO (Med.) Roy. W. Sussex Hosp. (St. Richard's Br.) Chichester; Ho. Phys. W.m. Hosp. Lond.

WHITTAKER, Roger Graham 33 Hest Bank Lane, Hest Bank, Lancaster LA2 6DB — BChir 1994 Camb.

WHITTAKER, Russell Neil Lakeside Surgery, Cottingham Road, Corby NN17 2UR — MB BS 1981 Lond.; FRCEP 1999; MRCS Eng. LRCP Lond. 1981; MRCGP 1985; DRCOG 1984.

WHITTAKER, Sean Jowett Royal Free Hospital, Pond St., London NW3 2QG Tel: 020 7830 2376 Fax: 020 7830 2247 — MB ChB 1981 Manch.; MD Manch. 1994; MRCP (UK) 1984; FRCP (Lond.) 1998. (Manchester) Cons. Dermat. & Hon. Sen. Lect. Roy. Free Hosp. Lond.; Cons.Dermat and Sen. Lect. St. Johns Inst. of Dermat. St Thos. Hosp. Socs: Europ. org for research and Treatm. of cancer; Roy.Soc.Med; Brit.Soc.Dermat. Prev: Sen. Regist. St. John's Dermat. Centre St. Thos. Hosp. Lond.; Research Fell. (Molecular Genetics) RPMS Hammersmith Hosp. Lond.

WHITTAKER, Simon Mark 1 Maes Cadwgan, Creigiau, Cardiff CF15 9TQ — MB BCh 1997 Wales.

WHITTAKER, Stanley James 4 Leyfield Road, Sheffield S17 3EE — MB ChB 1984 Manch.; MRCOG 1995; MRCGP 1988; DRCOG 1990. Specialist Regist. (O & G) Sheff. Prev: Regist. (O & G) Jessop Hosp. Wom. Sheff.

WHITTAKER, Wendy Elizabeth Abernethy House, 70 Silver Street, Enfield EN1 3EP Tel: 020 8366 1314 Fax: 020 8364 4176 — MB BS 1977 Lond.; MRCS Eng. LRCP Lond. 1977.

WHITTAKER, William Ainsworth Highlands, Hadrian Way, Sandiway, Northwich CW8 2JR Tel: 01606 883396 — MB ChB 1951 Manch.

WHITTAKER, William McClure (retired) The Old Barn, Matthew Lane, Bradley, Keighley BD20 9DF Tel: 01535 633494 — MB ChB 1945 Manch. Prev: Ho. Phys., Ho. Surg. & Obst. Off. Withington Hosp. W. Didsbury.

WHITTALL, Geoffrey William (retired) 2 Troy Court, Kensington High St., London W8 7RD Tel: 020 7937 8260 — MB BCh 1934 Camb.; MRCS Eng. LRCP Lond. 1930.

WHITTAM, Mr David Elliott 37 Queens Road, Kingston upon Thames KT2 7SL Tel: 020 8549 4209 Fax: 020 8944 8059 — MB BS 1964 Lond.; FRCS Eng. 1968; MRCS Eng. LRCP Lond. 1964. (St. Geo.) Cons. ENT Surg. St. Geo. Hosp. Lond. & Atkinson Morley's Hosp. Wimbledon; Hon. Cons. ENT Surg. Roy. Marsden Hosp. Sutton. Socs: Brit. Assn. Otol.; Assn. Head & Neck Oncol. Prev: Sen. Regist. (ENT) St. Geo. Hosp. Lond.; Lect. (Anat. Med.) Sch. King's Coll. Univ. Lond.; Regist. (Neurosurg.) Atkinson Morley's Hosp. Lond.

WHITTAM, Lindsay Rosanne Kings College Hospital, Denmark Hill, London SE5; First Floor Flat, 70 Comeragh Road, London W14 9HR — MB BS 1990 Lond.; MRCP (UK) 1992. Specialist Regist. (Dermat.) Kings Coll. Hosp.

WHITTARD, Brian Ralph (retired) 5 Woodleigh Park, Shaldon, Teignmouth TQ14 0BE Tel: 01626 873304 — MB BS Lond. 1953; MRCS Eng. LRCP Lond. 1951; FFA RCS Eng. 1960. Prev: Cons. Anaesth. Torbay Hosp.

WHITTARD, Shirley Frances (retired) 5 Woodleigh Park, Shaldon, Teignmouth TQ14 0BE Tel: 01626 873304 — MB BS Lond. 1953; MRCS Eng. LRCP Lond. 1953; FFA RCS Eng. 1957. Prev: Assoc. Specialist (Anaesth.) Torbay Health Dist.

WHITTEN, Camilla Rose King Edward VII Hospital, Midhurst GU29 0BL; 5 Chanctonbury Way, Southgate W., Crawley RH11 8TE Tel: 01293 407572 — MB BS 1996 Lond. (Charing Cross and Westminster Medical School) SHO (Surg.) King Edwd. VII Midhurst; SHO (Surg.) St. Richards Hosp. Chichester. Prev: SHO (A & E) Salisbury Dist. Hosp.; SHO (Orthop.) E. Surrey Hosp. Redhill; Ho. Off. (Med.) St Richards Chichester.

WHITTEN, Lewis (retired) 11 Sandwick Court, Cyncoed Road, Cardiff CF23 6SS Tel: 01222 762572 — MB ChB 1927 Ed. Hon. Surg. St. John Ambul. Assn. Prev: Ho. Surg. & Ho. Phys. Vict. Hosp. Blackpool.

WHITTEN, Mark Peter 86 Cyncoed Road, Cyncoed, Cardiff CF23 5SH — MB BCh 1966 Wales; FFA RCS Eng. 1970. Cons. Anaesth. Univ. Hosp. Wales Cardiff.

WHITTEN, Sara Melissa 5 Chanctonbury Way, Crawley RH11 8TE — MB BS 1993 Lond.

WHITTER, Agnes Elizabeth (retired) 199 Queen's Road, Aberdeen AB15 8DB Tel: 01224 318627 — MB ChB 1951 Aberd.; DPH Ed. 1959; DObst RCOG 1957. Prev: Assoc. Specialist Dept. Clin. Oncol. Grampian Health Bd.

WHITTERIDGE, Sidney Morgan, VRD Inverlael, Loch Broom, Garve IV23 2PJ Tel: 0185 485262 — MRCS Eng. LRCP Lond. 1934.

(Guy's) Socs: Roy. Med.-Psych. Assn. Prev: Surg. Cdr. RNVR Neuro-Psychiat. Specialist; Mem. Psychiat. Advis. Comm. N.E. Metrop. RHB; Sen. Asst. Guy's Hosp. York Clinic.

WHITTET, Mr Heikki Bruce ENT Department, Singleton Hospital, Sketty Lane, Swansea SA2 8QA Tel: 01792 205666 Fax: 01792 208647 Email: heikki.whittet@swansea_tr.wales.nhs.uk — MB BS 1980 Lond.; FRCS 1986. (King's Coll. Hosp.) Cons. ENT Singleton Hosp. Swansea. Socs: Fell. Roy. Soc. Med.; Assoc. Mem. Brit. Assn. Otolaryngol. Prev: Sen. Regist. (ENT) Radcliffe Infirm. Oxf.; Regist. (ENT) Roy. Nat. Throat Nose & Ear Hosp. Lond.; SHO (ENT) Hosp. Sick Childr. Gt. Ormond St.

WHITTET, Martin Matthew, OBE (retired) — MB ChB Glas. 1942; FRCP Ed. 1960, M 1946; FRFPS Glas. 1945; FRCP Glas. 1964, M 1962; FRCPsych 1971; DPM Lond. 1944. JP. Inverness. Prev: Phys. Supt. Craig Dunain Hosp. & Cons. Psychiat. Highland HB & Hon. Sen. Clin. Lect. (Ment. Health) Univ. Aberd.

WHITTET, Sally Elizabeth The Surgery, 1 Binfield Road, London SW4 6TB Tel: 020 7622 1424 Fax: 020 7978 1436; 76 Whateley Road, London SE22 9DD Tel: 020 693 6482 — MB BS 1976 Lond.; MRCGP 1982.

WHITTICASE, James Edward 52 Bennett Road, Sutton Coldfield B74 4TH — MB BS 1997 Lond.

WHITTINGHAM, Christopher George Nattrass 20 Hampton Road, Twickenham TW2 5QB Tel: 020 8898 3245 — MB BS 1974 Lond. (Lond. Hosp.)

WHITTINGHAM, David Beck (retired) Antron Lodge, Sithney, Helston TR13 0RJ Tel: 01326 573375 — MB BS 1963 Lond.; MRCS Eng. LRCP Lond. 1963; FFA RCS Eng. 1967. Cons. Anaesth. St Michael's Hosp. Hayle Cornw. Prev: Cons. Anaesth. Cornw. & Isle of Scilly Hosp. Trust.

WHITTINGHAM, David Ivor (retired) Cotmandene, 41 Port Hill Road, Shrewsbury SY3 8RN Tel: 01743 235708 Email: david.whittingham@tesco.net — MB ChB 1962 Ed.; DObst RCOG 1965. Med. Mem. Disabil. Appeals Tribunal. Prev: Gen. Practitioner Shrewsbury (Retd.).

WHITTINGHAM, Edward Beck (retired) Runkerry, Foxfields, West Chiltington, Pulborough RH20 2JQ — M.B., Ch.B. Liverp. 1929; F.R.C.S. Eng. 1934; D.P.H. Liverp. 1931. Prev: Surg. Consult. OldCh. Hosp. Romford.

WHITTINGHAM, Fiona Gayle High House, Sandford, West Felton, Oswestry SY11 4EX Tel: 01691 610433 Fax: 01691 610433 — MB BCh 1988 Wales; BSc Wales 1985; MRCGP 1993; DRCOG 1992; DCH RCP Lond. 1991. GP Shrops. Retainer Scheme; Clin. Asst. in Dermat., Wrexham Maelor Hosp.; Clin. Doctor, Sexual Health Servs., Shrops. Community & Ment. Health Trust, Cross Ho.s, Shrewsbury. Prev: Trainee GP Shrewsbury; SHO (Accid & Emerg., O & G, Paediat. & Psychiat.) Roy. Shrewsbury Hosp.

WHITTINGHAM, Harold Warrender, OStJ, Group Capt. RAF Med. Br. Retd. 6 Oak Ash Green, Wilton, Salisbury SP2 0RR Tel: 01722 744539 — MB BChir 1939 Camb.; MA Camb. 1940; MRCS Eng. LRCP Lond. 1939; DTM & H Eng. 1959. (Camb. & Middlx.) Prev: PMO Brit. Forces Gulf; Command Med. Specialist Middle E. Air Force; Ho. Phys. Middlx. Hosp.

WHITTINGHAM, Margaret Anne (retired) Beech Cottage, 20 Abbot's Ride, Farnham GU9 8HY — MB BS 1947 Durh.; MRCGP 1968. Prev: Ho. Phys. Newc. Gen. Hosp.

WHITTINGHAM, Vincent Mark Fax: 01246 297277 Email: mark.whittingham@chcsnd-tr.trent.nhs.uk; Email: mark.whittingham@doctors.org.uk — MB ChB 1984 Liverp.; MRCPsych 1990. Cons(Psychiat. of Old Age) N. Derbysh.

WHITTINGHAM, William (retired) Eversley Centre, Hook RG27 0NJ Tel: 01256 732678 — MB BS 1949 Lond.; MRCS Eng. LRCP Lond. 1949; DObst RCOG 1958.

WHITTINGHAM, Winifred Prudence Cotmandene, 41 Port Hill Road, Shrewsbury SY3 8RN Tel: 01743 235708 — MB ChB 1962 Ed. (Ed.)

WHITTINGTON, Alan MacRae (retired) Beech Croft, 27 Locks Ride, Ascot SL5 8RA Tel: 01344 883758 — MRCS Eng. LRCP Lond. 1946. Prev: Emerg. Commiss. RAF.

WHITTINGTON, David Antony The Mission Practice, 208 Cambridge Heath Road, London E2 9LS Tel: 020 8983 7300 Fax: 020 8983 6800; 12 St. Johns Church Road, Hackney, London E9 6EJ Tel: 020 8986 9453 — MB ChB 1983 Birm.; MRCGP 1988; DRCOG 1986; DCH RCP Lond. 1985. Prev: SHO (A & E) Roy. Free Hosp. Lond.; SHO (O & G) Solihull Hosp.; SHO (Paediat.) Sandwell Dist. Gen. Hosp. W. Bromwich.

WHITTINGTON, John MacRae Mitchell and Partners, New Chapel Surgery, High Street, Long Crendon, Aylesbury HP18 9AF Tel: 01844 208228 Fax: 01844 201906; Manor Farm, Wotton Underwood, Aylesbury HP18 0SB Tel: 01844 237551 — MB BS 1976 Lond.; MRCGP 1981; DRCOG 1981.

WHITTINGTON, John Richard Twyford Manor, Twyford, Buckingham MK18 4EL Tel: 01296 730225 Fax: 01296 738893 Email: john@mediscience.co.uk — MB BS 1973 Lond.; MSc (Applied Statistics) Sheff. 1994; BSc (Physiol.) Lond. 1970; MRCP (UK) 1978; MRCS Eng. LRCP Lond. 1973; MFPM RCP (UK) 1989. (Westm.) Med. Dir. MediSci. Servs. Buckingham. Socs: Grad. Statistician Roy. Statistical Soc.; Brit. Assn. Pharmaceut. Phys. Prev: Hon. Sen. Research Assoc. (Cardiol.) N.wick Pk. Hosp.; Dir. Clin. Pharmacol. Advisory Servs. (Clin. & Gen.) Lond.

WHITTINGTON, Marc James 3 Langholme Close, Winstanley, Wigan WN3 6TT — MB ChB 1991 Manch.

WHITTINGTON, Richard Michael Coroner's Court, Newton St., Birmingham B4 6NE Tel: 0121 303 3228 Fax: 0121 233 4841; 3 Moreton Road, Oxford OX2 7AX Tel: 01865 556869 — LLD (Hon.) B'Ham 1997; DSc (Hon.) Aston 1991; MA Oxf. 1957, BM BCh Oxf. 1955; MRCGP 1975; DMJ(Clin) Soc. Apoth. Lond. 1972; DCH Eng. 1958; DObst RCOG 1957. (Oxf. & King's Coll. Hosp.) HM Coroner Birm. & Solihull; Hon. Teachg. Fell. Birm. Univ. Med. Sch. Socs: FRSM; Coroners Soc. Eng. & Wales. Prev: Pres. Coroners Soc. Eng. & Wales.; Pres. Birm. Med. Legal Soc.; Pres. Midl. Med. Soc.

WHITTINGTON, Timothy John 34 Knuston Spinney, Irchester, Wellingborough NN29 7ES — MB ChB 1990 Liverp.

WHITTLE, Adam Timothy Flat 1, 17 Granville Terrace, Edinburgh EH10 4PQ — MB BS 1989 Lond.; BA Oxf. 1986; MRCP (UK) 1993. Regist. (Respirat. Med.) Roy. Infirm. Edin. Prev: SHO (Med.) Leeds Gen. Infirm.

WHITTLE, Andrew David Kelso Avenue Health Centre, Kelso Avenue, Thornton-Cleveleys FY5 3LF Tel: 01253 853992 Fax: 01253 822649 — MB ChB 1982 Liverp.; MRCGP 1988; DRCOG 1986; DCH RCP Lond. 1985. GP Blackpool. Prev: Trainee GP Grimsby Dist. Gen. Hosp. VTS.

WHITTLE, David James Tadcaster Medical Centre, Crab Garth, Tadcaster LS24 8HD Tel: 01937 530082 Fax: 01937 530192 — BM BS 1983 Nottm.; BMedSci Nottm. 1981; MRCGP 1990; DRCOG Lond. 1988; DGM RCP Lond. 1989; DFFP 1996. Clin. Asst. (Rheum.) York Dist. Hosp. Socs: Primary Care Rheum. Soc.; Brit. Soc. Med. & Dent. Hypn. Prev: Trainee GP Chesh.

WHITTLE, Eileen Brookfields Health Centre, Seymour Street, Cambridge CB1 3DQ Tel: 01223 723160 Fax: 01223 723089; 10 Downham's Lane, Milton Road, Cambridge CB4 1XT — MB BS 1971 Lond.; MRCS Eng. LRCP Lond. 1971; DObst RCOG 1974. (Char. Cross) Clin. Asst. (Geriat.) Brookfields Hosp. Camb. Prev: SHO (Dermat.) Nottm. Gen. Hosp.; SHO (Paediat.) Addenbrooke's Hosp. Camb.; Ho. Surg. (Obst.) St. Bart. Hosp. Lond.

WHITTLE, Elizabeth Jane Upper Aultvaich, Beauly IV4 7AN — MB ChB 1977 Manch.; MRCGP 1981; DRCOG 1979.

WHITTLE, Elizabeth Ruth Anaesthetic Office, North Devon District Hospital, Raleigh Park, Barnstaple EX31 4JB Tel: 01271 22577; Southlands, Park Lane, Barnstaple EX32 9AL — MB ChB 1979 Bristol; FFA RCS Eng. 1984; DRCOG 1981. Devon Dist. Hosp. Barnstaple.

WHITTLE, Francis David (retired) Deanscourt, St Andrews KY16 9QT — MB BS 1956 Lond.; MA St. Andrew 2000.

WHITTLE, Professor Ian Roger, Maj. RAMC Retd. Department of Clinical Neurosciences, Western General Hospital, Crewe Road, Edinburgh EH4 2XU Tel: 0131 537 2103 Fax: 0131 537 2561 Email: irw@skull.din.ed.ac.uk — MB BS 1978 Adelaide; PhD Ed. 1990; MD Adelaide 1987; FRCS (Surg. Neurol.) Ed. 1985; FRACS 1985; FRCPE 1999. Cons. Neurosurg. W.. Gen. Hosp. Edin. & Roy. Infirm. Edin.; Forbes Prof. Surgic. Neurol. Univ. Ed. Socs: Soc. Brit. Neurol. Surgs.; Eur. Soc. Sterotactic & Func.al Neurosurg. Prev: Regist. (Neurosurg.) Roy. P. Alfred & Roy. Alexander Hosp. for Childr. Sydney, Austral.; SHO (Surg.) Roy. Adelaide Hosp., Austral.

WHITTLE, Jocelyn Kay 1 Bessybrook Close, Lostock, Bolton BL6 4EA Tel: 01204 846796 — MB ChB 1997 Manch.; BSc St. And. 1994. SHO O & G Billinge Hosp. Wigan. Prev: SHO A & E

WHITTLE

Roy.Albert.Inf.Wigan; Ho. Off. (Gen. Med.) Roy. Albert Edwd. Infirm. Wigan; Ho. Off. Gen Surg. Lancaster.

WHITTLE, Jonathan Roydon Spencer Princess Alexandra Eye Pavilion, Chalmers St., Edinburgh EH3 9 Tel: 0131 536 1000; 40A Buckingham Terrace, Edinburgh EH4 3AP Tel: 0131 315 4756 Fax: 0131 315 4756 — MB ChB 1985 Ed.; BSc (Hons.) Physiol. 1983; FRCS Ed. 1991; FRCOphth 1991; DORCS Eng. 1990. (Edin.) Head Acc. & Emerg. & Primary Care; Head of Serv., Electrodiagnostic Clinic Process Alexandra Eye Pavilion, Edin. Socs: Med. Protec. Soc. & Internat. Soc. Clin. Electrophysiol. of Vision. Prev: Regist. (Ophth) P.ss Alexandra Eye Pavilion Edin.; Regist. (Ophth) Vict. Hosp. Kirkaldy; SHO (Ophth) Sussex Eye Hosp. Brighton.

WHITTLE, Kenneth George Sunset Gardens Surgery, Sunset Gardens, Porthleven, Helston TR13 9BT Tel: 01326 562204; Tregonning Hill House, Ashton, Helston TR13 9TB Tel: 01736 762205 — MB BCh 1967 Wales; DObst RCOG 1971. Socs: BMA; W Penwith Med. Soc. Prev: SHO (Cardiothoracic Surg.) Sully Hosp.; SHO (Paediat.) United Cardiff Hosps.; SHO (Obst.) Yeovil Gen. Hosp.

WHITTLE, Professor Martin John Department of Fetal Medicine, Birmingham Maternity Hospital, Birmingham B15 2TT Tel: 0121 627 2775 Fax: 0121 415 4837 Email: m.j.whittle@bham.ac.uk; 5 Emerson Road, Birmingham B17 9LT Tel: 0121 684 3988 Fax: 0121 684 3988 — MD 1980 Manch.; MB ChB 1972; MB ChB 1972; FRCP Glas. 1988, M 1985; FRCOG 1988, M 1977; T(OG) 1991. (Manchester) Prof. Fetal Med. Univ. Birm.; Head Acad. Dept. of Obst. & Gyn. Prev: Cons. O & G Gt. Glas. HB; SHO (O & G) St. Mary's Hosp. Manch.; Ho. Phys. & Ho. Surg. Manch. Roy. Infirm.

WHITTLE, Monica Anne 50A Mornington Terrace, London NW1 7RT Tel: 020 7387 5330 — MB BS 1988 Lond.; MRCP (UK) 1992; FRCR 1995. (Guy's Hosp. Med. Sch.) Sen. Regist. (Diagn. Radiol.) Hammersmith Hosp. Lond. Prev: Regist. (Diagn. Radiol.) Hammersmith Hosp. Lond.; SHO (Gen. Med.) Qu. Marys Hosp. Sidcup; SHO (Cardiol.) Brook Gen. Hosp. Lond.

WHITTLE, Mr Richard John Miller (retired) Tamarisk, Howards Thicket, Duke's Wood, Gerrards Cross SL9 7NX — MB BS 1947 Lond.; FRCS Eng. 1953; MRCS Eng. LRCP Lond. 1951; FFR 1960; DMRT Eng. 1955. Prev: Dir. Radiother. Dept. St. Bart. Hosp. Lond.

WHITTLE, Roger Anthony Sean The Surgery, Corse, Staunton, Gloucester GL19 3RB Tel: 01452 840228 Fax: 01452 840072 — MB BS 1993 Lond.; DRCOG 1997; DFFP 1997; DGM RCP 1996; DCH RCP 1995; MRCGP 1998. (Kings Coll. Lond.) Prev: GP Regist. Cheltenham; SHO Rotat. Gloucs VTS.

WHITTLE, Trudy Lynn Foster 10 Grimond Lane, Dundee DD3 9UA — MB ChB 1997 Dundee.

WHITTLES, Susan Eleanor Rendcomb Surgery, Rendcomb, Cirencester GL7 7EY Tel: 01285 831257 — BM 1982 Soton.; MRCGP 1986; DCH RCP Lond. 1985. (Soton.) Prev: Trainee GP Cirencester VTS.

WHITTLESEY, Roger William Clare House Practice, Clare House Surgery, Newport Street, Tiverton EX16 6NJ Tel: 01884 252337 Fax: 01884 254401 — MRCS Eng. LRCP Lond. 1967; DObst RCOG 1972; DA Eng. 1971. Hosp. Pract. (Anaesth.) & Clin. Asst. (Ophth.) Tiverton Hosp. Devon.

WHITTLESTONE, Mr Timothy Harry 1 Grampian Close, Doncaster DN5 8JF — BM BCh 1992 Oxf.; MD (Bristol) 2001; MA Camb. 1993; FRCS Eng. 1996. (Oxf.) Specialist Regist. Urol. Bristol Roy. Infirm.; Hunt. Prof.ship RCS Eng.

WHITTON, Andrew Dean Charles Mechie and Partners, 67 Owen Road, Lancaster LA1 2LG Tel: 01524 846999 Fax: 01524 845174 — MB ChB 1981 Dundee; MRCGP 1986; DRCOG 1984.

WHITTON, Ingrid Hall Tel: 01132 381051 — MB ChB 1985 Glas.; MRCPsych 1990. (Glasgow) Cons. Psychiat. St. Jas. Univ. Hosp. Leeds.

WHITTON, Lesley Anne (retired) 21 Meadow Road, Watchfield, Swindon SN6 8SF Tel: 01793 784452 Email: al_box@lineone.net — MB ChB 1987 Dundee; MRCGP 1991; DCCH RCP Ed. 1994; DRCOG 1990. Prev: Clin. Med. Off. (Child Health) Preston HA.

WHITTON, Michael William Charles Hicks Centre, 75 Ermine Street, Huntingdon PE29 3EZ Tel: 01480 453038 Fax: 01480 434104 — MB ChB 1976 Leeds; Dip. Occ. Med. 1997; DRCOG 1982; AFOM 1998. (Leeds) Occupat.al Health Phys. Socs: Soc. Occupat. Med.

WHITTON, Tessa Louise 12 The Maltings, Fairlawn Road, Bristol BS6 5BB — BM 1989 Soton.; DTM & H Liverp. 1993; DA (UK) 1992. SHO (Paediat.) Roy. United Hosp. Trust Bath.

WHITTON, Theresa Jayne 156 Old Montague Street, London E1 5NA — MB BS 1997 Lond.

WHITTON, Tinku 18 Renters Avenue, London NW4 3RB Tel: 020 8202 9963 Fax: 020 8202 9963 — MB BS 1991 Lond.; MRCP 1997.

WHITTY, Bryan Lawrence Broomhill Practice, 41 Broomhill Drive, Glasgow G11 7AD Tel: 0141 339 3626 Fax: 0141 334 2399; 126 Cleveden Road, Glasgow G12 0JT Tel: 0141 334 9857 — MB ChB 1964 Glas.; DA Eng. 1968; DObst RCOG 1967. Tutor Glas. Univ.; Apptd. Doctor (Lead Regulats.). Prev: Med. Off. Nazareth Hosp., Israel; SHO (Anaesth.) W.. Infirm. Glas.; Med. Off. Christian Hosp. Chandraghona, Bangladesh.

WHITTY, Christopher John MacRae Email: c.whitty@lshtm.ac.uk — BM BCh 1991 Oxf.; MSc Lond. 1996; MA Oxf. 1991; MRCP (UK) 1995; DTM & H RCP Lond. 1996. Sen. Lect. Lond. Sch. Hyg. & Trop. Med.; Hon. Cons. Phys. Hosp. Trop. Dis Lond. & UCLH; Hon. Cons., Hosp. Trop. Dis. Lond. & UCLH. Prev: Sen. Regist., Guy's & St. Thomas's Hosp.s, Lond.; Sen. Regist. St. Geo.'s Hosp. Lond.; Clin. Lect. & Med. Spec. Coll. of Med.,Malawi Africa.

WHITTY, Hamlyn Peter Brian (retired) Dewhurst, Wadhurst TN5 6QB — MB BS 1962 Lond.; MRCS Eng. LRCP Lond. 1944; DO Eng. 1951. Prev: Sen. Hosp. Med. Off. & Assoc. Specialist Moorfields Eye Hosp. (City Rd. Br.) Lond.

WHITTY, Margaret Mary (retired) 3 Cavendish Court, Hobson Road, Oxford OX2 7JU Tel: 01865 557916 — MB BS 1939 Lond.; MRCS Eng. LRCP Lond. 1939. Med. Off. Oxf. FPA. Prev: Asst. Med. Off. Chest Clinic, United Oxf. Hosps.

WHITTY, Paula Michelle Newcastle, North Tyneside & Northumberland Mental Health NHS Trust, 1st Floor, Milvain Building, Westgate Rd, Newcastle upon Tyne NE6 4BE Tel: 0191 256 3881 Fax: 0191 273 2340 Email: paula.whitty@ncht.nonhy.nhs.uk — MB ChB 1985 Leeds; MSc (Distinc.) Lond. 1990; MFPHM RCP (UK) 1992; DA (UK) 1988; MD 2000 (Leeds). (University of Leeds)

WHITTY, Richard Terence 84 Davenport Avenue, Hessle HU13 0RW — BM BCh 1968 Oxf.; FFA RCS Eng. 1972; DA Eng. 1971. (Lond. Hosp. & Oxf.) Cons. Anaesth. Hull Roy. Infirm. Prev: Sen. Regist. Dept. Anaesth. Lond. Hosp.; Regist. Anaesth. Nat. Heart Hosp. Lond.; SHO Dept. Anaesth. St. Mary's Hosp. Lond.

WHITWELL, Duncan John 105 Western Avenue, Woodley, Reading RG5 3BL — BM BS 1993 Nottm.

WHITWELL, Elizabeth Anne (retired) 152 Bath Road, Banbury OX16 0TT Tel: 01295 266243 — MB BS Lond. 1962; MRCS Eng. LRCP Lond. 1962; DObst RCOG 1965; MFCH 1989. Prev: Staff grade Med. Off. community health.

WHITWELL, Francis David Southmead Hospital, Bristol BS10 5NB Tel: 0117 959 5898; 2 Goldney Avenue, Clifton, Bristol BS8 4RA Tel: 0117 974 1438 — MB BS 1968 Lond.; BA Oxf. 1970; 1995 FRC Psych.; MRCPsych 1975. (St. Thos.) Cons Psychiat. S.mead Hosps. Bristol; Hon. Sen. Clin. Lect. (Pyschiatry), Univ. Bristol. Prev: Lect. (Ment. Health) Univ. Bristol; Regist. (Psychiat.) Warneford Hosp. Oxf.; SHO (Neurol. & Rheum.) Lambeth Hosp. Lond.

WHITWELL, George Steven Little Cherith, Manor La, Gerrards Cross SL9 7NJ Tel: 01753 884394 — MB ChB 1997 Leic. SHO (A&E) Leicester Roy. Infirm. Socs: BMA; MPS. Prev: PRHO Gen. Med. Leic. Gen. Hosp.; PRHO Gen. Surg.Colology LR1.

WHITWELL, Joan Rosemary Liberton Hospital, Lasswade Road, Edinburgh EH16 6UB Tel: 0131 536 7828 Fax: 0131 536 7896; 5 Royal Circus, Edinburgh EH3 6TL Tel: 0131 225 1574 — MB ChB 1978 Ed.; PhD (Med. Physics) Leeds 1973; BSc (Mathematical Physics) Sussex 1968; MRCP (UK) 1983. (Ed.) Cons. Geriat. Med. Liberton Hosp. Edin. Socs: Brit. Geriat. Soc. Prev: Sen. Regist. (Geriat. Med.) Roy. Vict. Hosp. Edin.; Research Regist. (Clin. Pharmacol.) Roy. Infirm. Edin.; Med. Physicist Leeds Gen. Infirm.

WHITWELL, Mr John Bagatelle, Burton Road, Branskome Park, Bournemouth BH1 6DU Tel: 01202 765678 — MB BS 1946 Lond.; MS Lond. 1959, MB BS 1946; FRCS Eng. 1954; FCOphth 1988; DO Eng. 1951. (Char. Cross) Socs: FRSM; Ophth. Soc. Prev: Cons. Ophth. Surg. E. Dorset Health Dist.; Sen. Regist. Lond. Hosp. & Moorfields Eye Hosp.; Master Oxf. Ophth. Congr..

WHYTE

WHITWELL, Kerrie Ann 83 Westfield Avenue N., Saltdean, Brighton BN2 8HS — MB ChB 1992 Dundee; FRCS. Specialist Regist. Train. A&E N.Thames E.

WHITWHAM, Marian (retired) Beckstones, Askham, Penrith CA10 2PG Tel: 01931 712499 — MB ChB 1960 Manch. Prev: Ho. Surg. & Ho. Phys. Roy. S. Hants. Hosp. Soton.

WHITWORTH, Alan (retired) Westbrae, 89 West St, Reigate RH2 9DA Tel: 01737 249888 — MB BChir Camb. 1959; MA Camb. 1965; DObst RCOG 1961. Prev: Princip. GP Reigate.

WHITWORTH, Alan Graham North Swindon Practice, Home Ground Surgery, Thames Avenue, Haydon Wick, Swindon SN25 1QQ Tel: 01793 705777 — MB BS 1985 Lond.; LF Hom Faculty of Homeopathy 2001; Dip Occ Med 1988 Birmingham; PhD Manch. 1984. (St. Mary's Lond.) GP Princip., Swindon; Clin. Asst. Dermat. P.s Margt. Hosp. Swindon. Prev: GP Princip. S.sea Hants; Clin. Pharmacol. Hoechst UK Ltd.

WHITWORTH, Caroline Elizabeth Department of Renal Medicine, Edinburgh Royal Infirmary NHS Trust, Lauriston Place, Edinburgh EH3 9YW Tel: 0131 536 2339 Fax: 0131 536 1541 — MB ChB 1988 Ed.; BSc (Hons.) Pharmacol. Ed. 1985, MD 1995; MRCP (UK) 1991; FRCP (Edin) 2000. Cons. (Renal Med.); Hon. Clin. Sen. Lect. Dept. of Clin. & Surgic. Scis. Fac. of Med. Univ. of Edin. Socs: Renal Assn.; Brit. Transpl. Soc. Prev: Lect. & Hon. Sen. Regist. (Nephrol. & Hypertens.) Univ. Leicester; Lect. & Hon. Regist. (Renal Med.) Edin. Roy. Infirm.; Research Fell. Centre for Genome Research Ed.

WHITWORTH, Christopher Martin Pengarth Road Surgery, Pengarth Road, St Agnes TR5 0TN Tel: 01872 553881 Fax: 01872 553885; 34 Vicarage Road, St Agnes TR5 0TF Tel: 01872 553130 — MB BS 1988 Lond.; BSc Lond. 1985, MB BS 1988; MRCGP 1992. (St. Mary's) GP St. Agnes.

WHITWORTH, Diana Mary Sighthill Health Centre, 380 Calder Road, Edinburgh EH11 4AU Tel: 0131 537 7320 Fax: 0131 537 7005; 103 Gilmore Place, Edinburgh EH3 9PP — MB ChB 1987 Ed.; MA Oxf. 1989; MRCGP 1991; DRCOG 1990.

WHITWORTH, Fiona Kathryn 36 Elms Drive, Marston, Oxford OX3 0NJ — BM BCh 1994 Oxf.

WHITWORTH, Mr George Robert Sydenham Green Health Centre, 26 Holmshaw Close, London SE26 4TH Tel: 020 8778 3358; 26 Perry Rise, Forest Hill, London SE23 2QL Tel: 020 8291 3416 — MB ChB 1972 Alexandria; FRCS Eng. 1982; MRCS Eng. LRCP Lond. 1979. (Alexandria) Prev: Regist. (Orthop. Surg.) Lewisham Hosp.; SHO (Gen. Surg.) Ipswich Gen. Hosp.; SHO (Orthop. Surg.) Crawley Gen. Hosp.

WHITWORTH, Helen Elizabeth Edenfield RSU, Prestwich Hospital, Bury New Road, Manchester M25 3BL; c/o 49 Overton Lane, Hammerwich, Walsall WS7 0LQ — MB ChB 1990 Liverp.; MRCPsych 1995. (Liverp.) Specialist Regist. (Psychiat.) Manch.

WHITWORTH, Henry, MBE (retired) 34 Vicarage Road, St Agnes TR5 0TF Tel: 01872 552239 — MB BS 1943 Lond. Prev: Sen. Res. Med. Off. Duchess of York Hosp. Babies Manch.

WHITWORTH, James Alexander Grover 23 Ingham Road, London NW6 1DG — MB ChB 1979 Liverp.; MD Liverp. 1993; MRCP (UK) 1983. Sen. Lect. (Trop. Dis. Control) Lond. Sch. Hyg. & Trop. Med. Prev: MRC Clin. Epidemiol. Liverp.

WHITWORTH, Julia Caroline Helmford House Surgery, 283 High Street, London Colney, St Albans AL2 1EL Tel: 01727 823245; 23 Juniper Gardens, Shenley, Radlett WD7 9LA — MB BS 1981 Lond.; MRCGP 1986. (Roy. Free) Prev: GP Lochmaddy, I. of N. Uist; SHO (Paediat. & Gen. Med.) Maidstone Gen. Hosp.; Ho. Off. (Gen. Surg. & Orthop.) Qu. Eliz. Hosp. & King's Lynn Hosp.

WHITWORTH, Magda Whitworth, 234 Baring Road, London SE12 0UL Tel: 020 8851 5212; 26 Perry Rise, Forest Hill, London SE23 2QL Tel: 020 8291 3416 — MB ChB 1972 Alexandria; LMSSA Lond. 1978. (Alexandria) Princip. Gen. Pract. Socs: BMA.

WHITWORTH, Nina Helen Mount Pleasant Medical Centre, Ditherington Road, Shrewsbury SY1 4DQ Tel: 01743 235111; 18 Upper Road, Shrewsbury SY3 9JD — MB BS 1991 Lond.

WHOLEY, Vivienne Gay Dept. of GU Medicine, Solway Suite, Cumberland Infirmary, Carlisle CA2 7HY Tel: 01228 814814 — MB BS 1991 Newc.; Dip. GU Med. Soc. Apoth. Lond. 1995. (Newcastle Upon Tyne) Staff Grade (Genitourin. Med.). Socs: Soc. Study VD; Assoc. GU Med. Prev: Regist. (Genitourin. Med.) Newc. & Sunderland Gen. Hosps.; SHO (Genitourin. Med.) King's Coll. Hosp. Lond. & Newc. & Sunderland Gen. Hosps.; SHO Rotat. (Med.) Tyneside Dist. Hosp. S. Shields.

WHONE, Alan Lane 31 Mangotsfield Road, Mangotsfield, Bristol BS16 9JJ — MB ChB 1994 Birm.; ChB Birm. 1994; MRCP Lond. 1998. (Birmingham University Hospital) Research Fell.(Neurol.) Hammersmith Hosp., Lond. Socs: BMA. Prev: SHO (Neurol.) Kings Coll. Hosp. Lond.; SHO (Psychiat.) Maudsley Hosp. Lond.; SHO Rotat. (Gen. Med.) The Roy. Shrewsbury Hosp.

WHOOLEY, David John 82 College Road, London SE21 7LY — MB BCh BAO 1990 NUI.

WHORWELL, Peter James South Downs Cottage, South Downs Road, Bowdon, Altrincham WA14 3DS; Withington Hospital, Manchester M20 2LR Tel: 0161 291 3826 Fax: 0161 434 5194 — BSc (Hons.) Lond. 1970, MD 1979, MB BS 1969; FRCP Lond. 1988; MRCP (UK) 1972; MRCS Eng. LRCP Lond. 1969. (Guy's) Cons. Phys. & Sen. Lect. (Med.) Univ. Hosp. S. Manch.

WHOWELL, William Brian (retired) Charnwood House, Charnwood Road, Shepshed, Loughborough LE12 9NP Tel: 01509 503343 — MB BS 1946 Lond.; MRCS Eng. LRCP Lond. 1945; FRCGP 1972, M 1966. Prev: Mem. (Chairm. Conf.) (Chairm. Med. Pract. Comm.) Local Med. Comm.

WHY, Howard John Francis Queen's Hospital Burton, Belevedere Road, Burton-on-Trent DE13 0RB Tel: 01283 566333 Ext: 5541; Email: h_why@hotmail.com — MB ChB 1983 Leeds; MRCP (UK) 1988; FRCP 2000. (Leeds) Cons. Cardiol. Qu. Hosp. Burton-on-Trent; Hon. Cons. Cardiol. Glenfield Hosp. Leicester. Socs: Brit. Soc. Echocardiogr.; Brit. Cardiac Soc. Prev: Research Fell. & Hon. Regist. (Cardiol.) King's Coll. Hosp. Lond.; Regist. (Med.) Basildon & Orsett Hosp. Grays.

WHYATT, Nicholas David Rowden Surgery, Rowden Hill, Chippenham SN15 2SB Tel: 01249 444343 Fax: 01249 446797; Rose Cottage, Bowden Hill, Lacock, Chippenham SN15 2PW Tel: 01249 730516 — MB BS 1963 Lond.; MRCS Eng. LRCP Lond. 1963; DObst RCOG 1965. (St. Bart.) Med. Off. St. And. Hosp. Chippenham. Socs: BMA. Prev: Ho. Phys. Nuffield Dept. Med. Radcliffe Infirm. Oxf.; Ho. Surg. Metrop. Hosp. Lond.; Ho. Surg. (O & G) St. Mary Abbot's Hosp. Kens.

WHYBREW, Katherine Joanna 19 Beaumont Street Surgery, Oxford SE11 5TN — BChir 1996 Camb.

WHYBROW, Andrea Rapleys, Bashurst Hill, Horsham RH13 7PE — BM BS 1998 Nottm.

WHYBROW, Tracey Rebecca 23 Hobleythick Lane, Westcliff on Sea SS0 0RP — MB BS 1997 Lond.; BSc 1994. (St Barts Lond) SHO Med. Soton. Gen Hosp. Soton.

WHYLER, David Keith Kinmel Bay Medical Centre, The Square, Kinmel Bay, Rhyl LL18 5AU Tel: 01745 353965 Fax: 01745 356407 — MB ChB 1984 Ed.; DFFP 1993; Cert. Family Plann. JCC 1989. (Edinburgh) GP Rhyl; Clin. Med. Off. in Family Plann., Conwy and Denbighsh. Trust. Socs: Fell. (Ex-Pres.) Roy. Med. Soc. Edin. Prev: Trainee GP Clwyd FPC; Regist. Glan Clwyd Hosp. Bodelwyddan; Ho. Phys. & Ho. Surg. Roy. Infirm. Edin.

WHYMAN, Catherine Elizabeth 8 Whinmoor Gardens, Wellington Hill, Leeds LS14 1AF — MB BS 1998 Lond.

WHYMAN, Mr Mark Roy Cheltenham General Hospital, Department of Surgery, Sandford Road, Cheltenham GL53 7AN — MB BS 1984 Lond.; MS Lond. 1992; FRCS Eng. 1988. Cons. Gen. & Vasc. Surg. Cheltenham Gen. Hosp. Socs: Assn. Surg.; Vasc. Surg. Soc.; Eur. Soc. Vasc. Surg. Prev: Sen. Regist. S. W. Region; Regist. & Research Fell. Edin. Roy. Infirm.

WHYMARK, Andrew David 8 Cottesmore Drive, Loughborough LE11 2RL — MB ChB 1995 Sheff.

WHYMENT, William Henry (retired) 5 Allardyce Crescent, Aberlour AB38 9PQ Tel: 0134 05 746 — MB ChB 1939 St. And.

WHYTE, Mr Andrew Stanley (retired) The Glebe, Saline, Dunfermline KY12 9UT — MB ChB 1969 Glas.; FRCS Glas. 1974. Assoc. Specialist (Microbiol.) Fife Area Laborat. Vict. Hosp. Kirkaldy. Prev: Cons. Surg. Dunfermline & W. Fife Hosp.

WHYTE, Augustine Patrick 21 Fitzwalter Road, Colchester CO3 3SY — MB BCh BAO 1943 Dub.; MRCPsych 1974; DPM Eng. 1972. Cons. Psychiat. Severalls Hosp. Colchester.

WHYTE, Betty Isobel Croft-An-Righ, Elm Avenue, Lenzie, Kirkintilloch, Glasgow G66 4HJ Tel: 0141 776 2366 — MB ChB 1947 St. And. (St. And.) Prev: Ho. Surg. Matern. Dept. & Ear, Nose & Throat Ho. Surg. Roy. Infirm.; Dundee.

WHYTE

WHYTE, Christopher Robert Humerstone Grange Clinic, Turmaston Lane, Leicester LE5 0TA Tel: 0116 225 6430 Fax: 0116 225 6432; Humberstone Manor, 608 Gipsy Lane, Leicester LE5 0TB Tel: 0116 276 8725 — MB ChB 1968 Leeds; MRCPsych 1974; Dip. Psychother. Leeds 1976; DPM Leeds 1971. Cons. Psychother. Leicester.

WHYTE, Mr David Kirk 84 Balnakyle Road, Lochardil, Inverness IV2 4DJ Email: dkwhyte@aol.com — MD 1971 Dundee; MB ChB St. And. 1963; FRCS Ed. 1968; FCOphth 1989; DO Eng. 1965. (St. And.) Cons. Ophth. Surg. Highland HB; Hon. Sen. Lect. (Ophth.) Univ. Aberd. Socs: Highland Med. Soc.; Scot. Ophth. Club. Prev: Anat. Demonst. Qu.'s Coll. Univ. St. And.; Regist. Ophth. & Sen. Regist. Ophth. Dundee Roy. Infirm.

WHYTE, George Cordner (retired) 10 The Boarlands, Port Eynon, Eynon, Swansea SA3 1NX Tel: 01792 391252 — LRCPI & LM, LRCSI & LM 1941. Prev: Med. Off. Pneumoconiosis Med. Panels DHSS.

WHYTE, Hugh Primary Care Directorate, St. Andrew's House, Edinburgh EH1 3DG Tel: 0131 244 2054 Fax: 0131 244 2326 Email: ugh.whyte@scotland.gov.uk; 24 Garvock Hill, Dunfermline KY12 7UU Tel: 01383 732235 — MB ChB 1979 Ed.; MRCGP 1983; DRCOG 1981; FRCGP 1998. (Edinburgh) Sen. Med. Off. Managem. Exec. Scott. Office Health Dept.; Hon. Lect. Univ. Dundee. Prev: Med. Adviser (Primary Care) Tayside Health Bd.; Gen. Med. Practitioner.

WHYTE, Ian David King Street Surgery, King Street, Whalley, Blackburn BB7 9SL Tel: 01254 823273 Fax: 01254 824891; Longsight House, Longsight Road, Langho, Blackburn BB6 8AD Tel: 01254 245261 — MB ChB 1979 Liverp.; MRCGP 1989; DRCOG 1982.

WHYTE, Mr Ian Ferguson 32 Crown Drive, Inverness IV2 3QG — MB ChB 1981 Dundee; BMSc Dund 1978; FRCS Ed. 1990; FRCOphth 1990; MRCGP 1986; DO RCS Dub. 1988; DRCOG 1985. Ons. Ophth. Raigmore NHS Trust Inverness; Hon. Sen. Lect. Univ. Aberd. Socs: Brit. & Irish Assn. of Vitreoretinal Surgs. Prev: Sen. Regist. (Ophth.) Ninewells Teachg. Hosp. & Med. Sch. Univ. Dundee; Specialist Sen. Regist. (Vitreoretinal Surg.) Moorfields Eye Hosp. Lond.

WHYTE, Jennifer Anne 41 Gordon Road, Harborne, Birmingham B17 9HA — MB BCh BAO 1988 NUI.

WHYTE, Judith Carol (retired) Humberstone Manor, 608 Gipsy Lane, Leicester LE5 0TB — MB ChB 1968 Leeds; MRCPsych 1977; DPM Leeds 1973. Prev: Cons. Child Psychiat. S. Derbysh. HA.

WHYTE, Karen Flat 1/20 Ruthven Street, Glasgow G12 9BT — MB ChB 1997 Glas.

WHYTE, Kenneth Frank 99 East Kilbride Road, Busby, Glasgow G76 8JE — MD 1990 Glas.; MB ChB 1977; FRCP Glas. 1993; MRCP (UK) 1981.

WHYTE, Louis 325 Eaglesham Road, East Kilbride, Glasgow G75 8RW — M.B., Ch.B. Glas. 1946. (Univ. Glas.)

WHYTE, Martin Brunel Crispin, Belyars Lane, St Ives TR26 2DA — MB BS 1998 Lond.

WHYTE, Professor Moira Katherine Brigid Section of Respiratory Medicine, Division of Molecular & Genetic Medicine, Royal Hampshire Hospital, Sheffield S10 2JF Tel: 0114 271 2475 Fax: 0114 273 7623 Email: m.k.whyte@sheffield.ac.uk — MB BS 1984 Lond.; BSc (1st cl. Hons.) Lond. 1981; PhD Lond. 1994; MRCP (UK) 1987; FRCP 1998. (St. Bartholomew's Hospital Medical College) Prof. Respirat. Med. & Hon: Cons. Phys. Univ. Sheff. & Roy. Hallamsh. Hosp. Sheff. Prev: Wellcome Advanced Fell. & Hon. Cons. Gen. & Respirat. Med. Univ. Hosp. Nottm.; Sen. Regist. (Respirat. & Gen. Med.) Hammersmith Hosp. Lond.; MRC Train. Fell. (Cell Biol.) Roy. Postgrad. Med. Sch. Lond.

WHYTE, Morag Duncan Ritchie 2 Barony Court, Ardrossan KA22 8DZ — MB ChB 1991 Ed.

WHYTE, Nicholas John Dixon 40 Wabingham Road, London E5 8NF — MA, MB Camb. 1972, BChir 1971. (St. Bart.) Prev: Ho. Phys. & SHO Qu. Eliz. Hosp. Childr. Lond.; Med. Regist. N. Middlx. Hosp. Lond.

WHYTE, Robert (retired) 3 Fitzroy Place, Glasgow G3 7RH Tel: 0141 248 5451 Fax: 0141 248 5451 — MB ChB 1966 St. And.; FRCPsych 1985, M 1972; DPM Ed. & Glas. 1970. Cons. Psychother. Pk.head Hosp. Glas.; Hon. Clin. Sen. Lect. in (Psychol. Med.) Univ. Glas. 1991-. Prev: Sen. Regist. Roy. Dundee Liff Hosp.

WHYTE, Ross Boyd 10 Calder Avenue, Troon KA10 7JT — MB ChB 1998 Glas.

WHYTE, Sean Paul 26 Ashdown Road, Chandlers Ford, Eastleigh SO53 5QW — BM BCh 1996 Oxf.; MA Cantab) 1993. (Oxford) SHO (Psychiat.) Oxf.shire Ment. Healthcare NHS Trust Oxf.

WHYTE, Simon David 110 Priors Grange, High Pittington, Durham DH6 1DB — MB BS 1994 Newc. Clin. Research Fell. (Neonat. IC) S. Cleveland Hosp. Middlesbrough. Prev: SHO (Anaesth.) S. Cleveland Hosp. Middlesbrough; SHO (Anaesth.) Dryburn Hosp. Co. Durh.; SHO (Paediat. & Neonat.) Sunderland Dist. Gen. Hosp.

WHYTE, Stewart James Woodeside Health Centre, Barr Street, Glasgow G20 7LR Tel: 0141 531 9570 Fax: 0141 531 9572 — MB ChB 1980 Glas.; DRCOG 1981. (Glasgow)

WHYTE, Susan Frances Waverley, 70 East Kilbride Road, Busby, Glasgow G76 8HU — MB ChB 1969 St. And.; MRCPsych 1973; DPM Ed. & Glas. 1972; FRCPsych 1988; FRCP Ed 1998. Cons. Psychiat. Leverndale Hosp.; Educat.al Co-ordinator Gt.er Glas. Comm. NHS Trust. Prev: Regist. Roy. Dundee Liff Hosp.; Lect. in Psychiat. Univ. Dundee.

WHYTE, Ursula Mary (retired) 10 The Boarlands, Port Eynon, Swansea SA3 1NX Tel: 01792 391252 — MB BS Lond. 1949; MRCS Eng. LRCP Lond. 1949. Prev: Ho. Surg. Roy. Free Hosp. Lond.

WHYTE, William Giffen Rigislea, Neilston, Glasgow G78 3NY — MB ChB 1945 Glas.; FRCP Glas. 1967; FRFPS Glas. 1950. (Univ. Glas.) Sen. Regist. (Med.) Roy. Infirm. Glas. Prev: Capt. RAMC; Ho. Phys. Glas. Roy. Infirm.

WHYTE-VENABLES, David Henry Tangley Medical Centre, 10 Tangley Park Road, Hampton TW12 3YH Tel: 020 8979 5056; Lansdowne, Priory Road, Hampton TW12 2PB Tel: 020 8979 5150 — MB 1959 Camb.; BChir 1958. (St. Geo.) Prev: Ho. Surg. Gyn. Dept. & Res. Obst. Asst. Kersley Hosp. Coventry; Ho. Phys. & Ho. Surg. Epsom Dist. Hosp.

WHYTE-VENABLES, Francis Thellusson (retired) Church House, Pulborough RH20 1EG Tel: 01798 873713 — MB BS 1957 Lond. Prev: Ho. Surg. (O & G) Soton. Gen. Hosp.

WHYTE-VENABLES, Michaela Brixton Hill Group Practice, 22 Raleigh Gardens, London SW2 1AE Tel: 020 8674 6376 Fax: 020 8671 0283 — MB BS 1991 Lond.; MRCGP 1996; DRCOG 1995; DFFP 1995. (Roy. Free Med. Sch. Lond.) Hon. Research Fell. at Kings Coll. Hosp. Sch. of Med. & Dent. Prev: Trainee GP/SHO St. Thos. Hosp. Lond. VTS.

WHYTOCK, Patricia Hillfarrance House, Hillfarrance, Taunton TA4 1AW — MB ChB 1966 Birm.

WICKENDEN, David Hubert Hattersley Group Practice, Hattersley Road East, Hyde SK14 3EH Tel: 0161 368 4161 Fax: 0161 351 1989; 59 Dale Road, Marple, Stockport SK6 6NF Tel: 0161 427 2298 — MB BS 1961 Lond.; MRCS Eng. LRCP Lond. 1961; DA Eng. 1967; DObst RCOG 1964. (Lond. Hosp.)

WICKENDEN, Gillian Hope Pringle Head, Pringle Bank, Warton, Carnforth LA5 9PW — MB ChB 1991 Manch.; BA (Hons.) Manch. 1984. SHO (O & G). Prev: SHO (Anaesth.) Roy. Lancaster Infirm.; SHO (Paediat.) Roy. Lancaster Infirm.

WICKENDEN, Peter Douglas, Brigadier late RAMC Retd. Labwick Psychological Assessments Ltd., 111A Connaught Road, Fleet GU51 3QX Tel: 01252 616236 Fax: 01252 810127; Whitehill Lodge, Portsmouth Road, Ripley, Woking GU23 6EW Tel: 01483 225282 — MB 1954 Camb.; BChir 1953; FRCPsych. 1981, M 1971; DPM Eng. 1966; DObst RCOG 1959. (Camb. & Univ. Coll. Hosp.) Dir. Labwick Psychol. Assessm. Ltd.; Cons. Psychiat. Dept. of Community Psychiat. Duchess of Kent Barracks Aldershot. Socs: FRCPsych.; BMA. Prev: Cons. Psychiat. Brit. Milit. Hosp. Rinteln, BAOR; Cons. Psychiat. Camb. Milit. Hosp. Aldershot & Qu. Eliz. Milit. Hosp. Lond.; Cons. Psychiat. MRS Tidworth Delhi Barracks Tidworth Wilts.

WICKENS, Claire Louise 50 Gloucester Road, Dartford DA1 3DJ — MB ChB 1997 Dundee.

WICKENS, Lissa Catharine 79 High Street, Orwell, Royston SG8 5QN — MB BS 1997 Lond.

WICKERT, Alison Jean St George Health Centre, Bellevue Road, St. George, Bristol BS5 7PH Tel: 0117 961 2161 Fax: 0117 961 8761; 91 Kennington Avenue, Bishopston, Bristol BS7 9EX — MB ChB 1980 Bristol; BSc Bristol 1972; MRCGP 1984; DRCOG 1983.

WICKES, Alan Douglas Ashmore, 3 Miller St., Hamilton ML3 7EW Tel: 01698 425087 — MB ChB 1969 Glas.; FFA RCSI 1977. Chief of Anaesth. & Dir. (Intens. Care) King Faisal Milit. Hosp.; Khamis Mushyat, Saudi Arabia.

WICKHAM, Elizabeth Anne Medical Input, PO Box 246, Canterbury CT4 5YY Tel: 01227 700697 Fax: 01227 700697 Email: medical.input@dial.pipex.com; Earley House, Petham, Canterbury CT4 5RY Tel: 01227 700434 — MB BS 1965 Lond.; MRCS Eng. LRCP Lond. 1965. (Roy. Free) Indep. Pharm. Phys. Med. Input Canterbury. Socs: Fell. Fac. Pharmaceut. Phys.; FRSM. Prev: Sen. Med. Adviser Pfizer Ltd. Sandwich.

WICKHAM, Harvey Eugene Henry De La Vega 3A Hatherley Lane, Cheltenham GL51 6PN — MB BS 1994 Lond.

WICKHAM, Mr Henry (retired) The Oaks, 70 Victoria Road, Fulwood, Preston PR2 8NJ Tel: 01772 718197 — MB ChB 1945 Liverp.; FRCS Eng. 1961. Prev: Cons. ENT Surg. Roy. Preston Hosp. & Chorley & Dist. Hosp.

WICKHAM, Louisa Jane 15 Trafalgar Gate, Brighton Marina Village, Brighton BN2 5UY — MB BS 1996 Lond.

WICKHAM, Mr Martin Henry Department Otolaryngology, Barnsley District General Hospital NHS Trust, Gawber Road, Barnsley S75 2EP Tel: 01226 777756 Fax: 01226 202859; 8 The Croft, West Bretton, Wakefield WF4 4LH — MB ChB 1977 Manch.; FRCS Ed.DRL 1985. Cons. Otorhinolaryngol., Barnsley Gen. Hosp. NHS trust.

WICKHAM, Michael, CStJ (retired) Hirsel Cottage, Town Yetholm, Kelso TD5 8RG Tel: 01573 420355 — MB ChB 1941 Birm. Prev: Co. Surg. St. John Ambul. Worcs. & Hereford.

WICKHAM, Timothy Andrew 34 Winifred Lane, Aughton, Ormskirk L39 5DJ — MB BS 1993 Lond.

WICKINS, Michael Charles Townsend House, 49 Harepath Road, Seaton EX12 2RY Tel: 01297 20616 Fax: 01297 20810; Kimaric, Elm Farm Lane, Colyford, Colyton EX24 6QS — MB BS 1973 Lond.; BSc (Hons.) (Physiol.) Lond. 1969; MRCGP 1979. (Univ. Coll. Hosp.)

WICKRAMARATHNA, Lansakara Senanayake 9 Salisbury Avenue, St Albans AL1 4UB — MB BS 1967 Ceylon.

WICKRAMASEKERA, Mr Dhammika c/o Mr. S. J. Onions, No. 93 Llandaff Drive, Prestatyn LL19 8TU Tel: 01745 854894; No 9/1 Rajagiriya Road, Rajagiriya, Kotte, Sri Lanka — MB BS 1984 Colombo; FRCS Ed. 1992; LMSSA Lond. 1994; LRCP 1994; LRCPS 1994. Regist. (Surg.) Huddersfield Roy. Infirm. Prev: Regist. (Surg.) Ysbyty Gwynedd Hosp. Bangor.

WICKRAMASINGHE, Kalutara Muhandiramge Susil Sumathi 14 Meadow Close, London Colney, St Albans AL2 1RQ — MB BS 1958 Ceylon.

WICKRAMASINGHE, Lathika Skin Department, Oldchurch Hospital, Waterloo Road, Romford RM7 Tel: 01708 756090 Ext: 3473; Serendip, 20 Newlands Close, Hutton, Brentwood CM13 2SD Tel: 01277 200371 Fax: 01277 202414 — MB BS 1977 Sri Lanka. Staff Dermat. Old Ch. Hosp. Romford & Harold Wood Hosp. Essex. Prev: Regist. (Dermat.) Roy. Lond. & Whipps Cross Hosps. Lond.; Clin. Asst. (Gen. Med.) Barking Hosp. Essex; Regist. (Dermat.) Sunderland Roy. Infirm.

WICKRAMASINGHE, Liyanagae Sarath Piyatissa Harold Wood Hospital, Gubbins Lane, Harold Wood, Romford RM3 0BE Tel: 01708 708257 Fax: 01708 708283; Serendip, 20 Newlands Close, Hutton, Brentwood CM13 2SD Tel: 01277 200371 — MB BS 1971 Ceylon; FRCP Lond. 1991; MRCP (UK) 1980; DGM RCP Lond. 1985. Cons. Phys. (Med. for Elderly) Harold Wood Hosp. Romford & High Wood Hosp. Brentwood. Prev: Sen. Regist. (Geriat. & Gen. Med.) Sunderland Hosp.; Regist. (Gen. Med.) Burnley Gen. Hosp.

WICKRAMASINGHE, Sudatta Gunamangala Maithri 130A Wood Street, Chelmsford CM2 8BL — MB ChB 1996 Aberd.

WICKRAMASINGHE, Sunitha Nimal 32 Braywick Road, Maidenhead SL6 1DA Tel: 01628 21665 — MB BS 1964 Ceylon; ScD Camb. 1985, PhD 1968; FRCP Lond. 1991; MRCP (UK) 1987; FRCPath 1986, M 1975. Prof. Haemat. St. Mary's Hosp. Med. Sch. Lond.; Hon. Cons. Haemat. St. Mary's Hosp. Lond. Prev: Lect., Sen. Lect. & Reader (Haemat.) St. Mary's Hosp. Med. Sch. Lond.

WICKRAMASURIYA, Boosabaduge Pujitha Nalin 16 Blackfen Road, Sidcup DA15 8SN — MB BS 1994 Lond.

WICKRAMASURIYA, James Prasanna Flat 6, 52 Queens Gardens, London W2 3AA — MB BS 1990 Sydney.

WICKREMA, Felix Rajah De Silva 10 Moorlea Avenue, Dringhouses, York YO24 2PA Tel: 01904 702145 — MB BS 1965 Ceylon; DRCOG 1981. (Ceylon) Assoc. Specialist York Dist. Hosp.

WICKREMARATCHI, Mirdhu Mirmalani 34 Abbots Way, Bristol BS9 4SW — MB BCh 1997 Wales.

WICKREMASINGHE, Amal Sarah Leeds General Infirmary, Great George St., Leeds LS1 3EX Tel: 0113 243 2799 — MB ChB 1998 Leeds. SHO (O & G), Leeds Gen. Infirm., Leeds.

WICKREMASINGHE, Melissa Irene Yasmin 20 Greenleafe Drive, Ilford IG6 1LL — MB BS 1990 Lond.

WICKREMASINGHE, Sanjeewa Sudarshan Flat 21, Highgate Heights, 77 Shepherds Hill, London N6 5RF — MB BS 1996 Lond.

WICKREMASINGHE, Sarathchandra Piyasiri Newbury Group Practice, Newbury Park Health Centre, 40 Perrymans Farm Road, Barkingside, Ilford IG2 7LE Tel: 020 8554 3944 Fax: 020 8518 5911; 20 Greenleafe Drive, Barkingside, Ilford IG6 1LL Tel: 020 8550 3598 — MRCS Eng. LRCP Lond. 1959; MRCP Lond. 1967. (Univ. Coll. Lond. & W. Lond.) Rudolph Kohnstamm Prize (Med.) W. Lond. Hosp. Med. Sch. 1959. Prev: Ho. Phys. Ashford Hosp., Middlx.; SHO (Path.) Paddington Gen. Hosp.; Med. Regist. Wanstead Hosp.

WICKREMASINGHE, Sushila Malkanthi Newbury Group Practice, Newbury Park Health Centre, 40 Perrymans Farm Road, Barkingside, Ilford IG2 7LE Tel: 020 8554 3944 Fax: 020 8518 5911 — MB BS 1958 Ceylon; MRCP Lond. 1964. (Ceylon) Prev: Ho. Phys. Ashford Hosp., Middlx.; Med. Regist. Wanstead Hosp. Lond. & Connaught Hosp. Lond.

WICKREMESINGHE, Mr Sunanda Srilal Grantham Health Centre, Grantham Road, London SW9 9DL; 148 Burbage Road, Dulwich Village, London SE21 7AG — MB BS 1967 Ceylon; FRCS Eng. 1972. (Ceylon) Surg. & Endoscopy Mayday Univ. Hosp. Croydon. Prev: SHO (Surg.) St. Jas. Hosp. Balham; SHO (Orthop.) Rowley Bristow Orthop. Hosp. Pyrford & St. Peter's Hosp. Chertsey; SHO (Surg.) Hammersmith Hosp.

WICKS, Anthony Christopher Bateman 26 High Street, Kibworth Beauchamp, Leicester LE8 0HQ Tel: 0116 279 3562 — MB BCh BAO 1964 Dub.; MD Birm. 1973; FRCP Lond 1982, M 1969. (TC Dub.) Cons. Phys. Gastroenterol. Leicester Gen. Hosp.; Regional Coll. Adviser, Roy. Coll. of Phys.s, S. Trent. Socs: BMA & Brit. Soc. Gastroenterol. Prev: Sen. Lect. (Med.) Univ. Rhodesia, Salisbury.

WICKS, Malcolm MacKenzie (retired) — MB BS 1960 Lond.; MRCS Eng. LRCP Lond. 1960; MRCGP 1977; DObst RCOG 1963. Prev: SHO (O & G) Dorking Gen. Hosp.

WICKS, Margaret Helen Lister House Surgery, Lister House, 53 Harrington Street, Pear Tree, Derby DE23 8PF Tel: 01332 271212 Fax: 01332 271939 — BM BS 1983 Nottm.; MRCGP 1987. Prev: Trainee GP Derby VTS.

***WICKS, Neil Simon** 5 Truro Close, Lichfield WS13 7SR — MB ChB 1998 Birm.

WICKS, Rachel Caldew House Cottage, Dalston, Carlisle CA5 7LL — MB ChB 1992 Birm.

WICKS, Robert MacKenzie Flat 2, 1 Handforth Road, London SW9 0LS — MB BS 1984 Lond.

WICKSTEAD, David Harold The Corner Surgery, 99 Coldharbour Lane, London SE5 9NS Tel: 020 7274 4507 Fax: 020 7733 6545 — MB ChB 1988 Liverp.; DFFP 1996; DTM & H 1993; MSc (Health Care Ethics) 1992; T(GP) 1992. (Liverpool) GP Princip. Lond. Prev: Trainee GP Whiston & St. Helens VTS.

WICKSTEAD, Mr Michael Norfolk and Norwich Health Care Trust, Brunswick Road, Norwich NR1 3SR Tel: 01603 289718 Fax: 01603 288946 — MRCS Eng. LRCP Lond. 1978; MA Camb. 1978, MB BChir 1979; FRCS (Orl.) Eng. 1983. (Camb. & St. Thos.) Cons. ENT Surg. Norf. & Norwich Health Care Trust. Prev: Sen. Regist. (ENT Surg.) St. Thos. Hosp. Lond. & Hosp. for Sick Childr. Lond.

WICTOME, Jeffrey Southlea Surgery, 276 Lower Farnham, Aldershot GU11 3RB Tel: 01252 344868 Fax: 01252 342596; Brook House, Holbrook Close, Weybourne, Farnham GU9 9HS — MB ChB 1971 Liverp.; MRCGP 1976; DRCOG 1977.

WIDAA, Abdel Rahman Bolton General Hospital, Minerva Road, Farnworth, Bolton BL4 0JR Tel: 01204 22444; Bolton General Hospital, Minerva Road, Farnworth, Bolton BL4 0JR — MB BCh 1970 Ain Shams; DLO Eng. 1979. Clin. Asst. (ENT Surg. & Anaesth.) Bolton HA. Prev: Regist. (ENT Surg. & Anaesth.) Bolton HA.

WIDD, Sarah Elizabeth Kent paediatric audiology service, Cobtree and Prestonhall Hospital, Maidstone; 5 The Gube, Egerton, Ashford

WIDDAS

TN27 9DH Tel: 01233 756460 — MB BS 1972 Lond.; MSO 2000. (Kings college hospital) Clin. ass pred Audiol.; adjudicating Med off for benefits agency. Prev: Sen. Clin. Med. Off. (Child Health Community) SE Kent HA.

WIDDAS, Wilfred Faraday 16 Linden Grove, Great Linford, Milton Keynes MK14 5HF Tel: 01908 678993 Fax: 01908 678993 — MB BS Durh. 1938; PhD Lond. 1953, DSc 1958, BSc 1947. (Durh.) Emerit. Prof. Physiol. Univ. Lond., Roy. Holloway & Univ. Lond. Socs: FRSM; Hon. Mem. Physiol. Soc. Prev: Head Physiol. Bedford Coll.; Reader (Physiol.) King's Coll. Lond.; Sen. Lect. (Physiol.) St. Mary's Hosp. Med. Sch.

WIDDERS, Jane Ashby Turn Primary Care Centre, Ashby Link, Scunthorpe DN16 2UT Tel: 01724 842051 Fax: 01724 280346 — BM BS 1988 Nottm.; MRCGP 1995. GP Ashby Turn Surg. N. Lincs.

WIDDICOMBE, Professor John Guy Sherrington School of Physiology, United Medical Dental School, St Thomas' Hospital, Lambeth Palace Road, London SE1 7EH Tel: 020 7928 9292 Fax: 020 7028 0729 — BM BCh 1949 Oxf.; DPhil Oxf. 1953, MA 1950, BA 1946, DM 1967; FRCP Lond. 1977, M 1974. (Oxf. & St. Bart.) Emerit. Prof. Physiol. UMDS St. Thos. Hosp. Lond. Socs: Physiol. Soc.; Pharmacol. Soc. Prev: Emerit. Prof. Physiol. St. Geo. Hosp. Med. Sch. Tooting; Fell. Qu. Coll. Oxf., Nuffield Inst. Med. Research Oxf.; Sen. Lect. (Physiol.) St. Bart. Hosp. Lond.

WIDDICOMBE, Neil James 89 King Richard Drive, Bearswood, Bournemouth BH11 9UE — MB BS 1988 Lond.

WIDDISON, Mr Adam Lewis Department of Surgery, Royal Cornwall Hospital, Treliske, Truro TR1 3ST Tel: 01872 74242 Email: adam.widdison@relit.swest.nhs — MB BCh 1984 Oxf.; 2001 I.L.T.; MA Oxf. 1985, DM 1991; FRCS Eng. 1988. (Oxford Univ.) Cons. Surg. Roy. Cornw. Hosp.; Hunt. Prof. 1995; Educat.al Supervision. Socs: BMA; HCSA; RCS. Prev: Demonst. (Anat.) & Prospector Univ. Camb.

WIDDOWSON, David Jeremy 2 Bryn Avenue, Old Colwyn, Colwyn Bay LL29 8AL — MB BS 1980 Lond.; MA (Cambs.) 1977; DMRD Liverp. 1984; FRCR Lond. 1986. Cons. Radiol. Glan Clwyd Hosp. Bodelwyddan.

WIDDOWSON, Eric Julian St Chads Surgery, Gullock Tyning, Midsomer Norton, Bath BA3 2UH Tel: 01761 413334 Fax: 01761 411176; Manor Farm House, The Green, Farmborough, Bath BA2 0BA — MB BS 1986 Lond.; BSc (Hons.) Manch. 1980; LMSSA Lond. 1985; MRCGP 1990; DRCOG 1990; DCH RCP Lond. 1989. (Univ. Coll. Hosp.) Socs: Brit. Assn. Sport & Med. Prev: Trainee GP/SHO (Paediat. & O & G) Roy. United Hosp. Bath VTS; Trainee GP/SHO (Gen. Med. & Geriat.) Jersey Gen. Hosp. VTS.

WIDDOWSON, Fiona Jean Myra Hoppersford Farm, Pimlico, Brackley NN13 5TN — MB ChB 1995 Bristol; BSc Brighton 1989. (Bristol) SHO (A & E) Bedford Hosp. Prev: Ho. Off. (Surg.) MusGr. Pk. Hosp. Taunton; Ho. Off. (Med.) Roy. Cornw. Hosp. Treliske.

WIDDOWSON, Judith 1F1 5 Spittal Street, Edinburgh EH3 9DY — MB ChB 1998 Ed.

WIDDOWSON, Sally Melinda Barrington Medical Centre, 14-18 Athelstan St., Christchurch, New Zealand Tel: 00 64 3323069 Fax: 00 64 3328562; c/o Brow Head, Under Loughrigg, Ambleside LA22 9SB — MB ChB 1986 Sheff.; MRCGP 1995; DRCOG 1993.

WIDDRINGTON, Ian Harry South Hylton Surgery, 3-5 Cambria Street, South Hylton, Sunderland SR4 0LT Tel: 0191 534 7386 — MB ChB 1977 Leeds; MRCGP 1983; DRCOG 1982.

WIDE, Jonathan Martin Dept. of Radiology, Whiston Hospital, Prescot; 8 Whitbarrow Road, Lymm WA13 9AE — MB BChir 1989 Camb.; MA Camb. 1990, BA 1986; MRCP (UK) 1992; DMRD Liverp. 1995; FRCR 1996. Cons. (Radiol.) Whiston Hosp. Merseyside. Prev: Regist. (Radiodiagn.) Arrowe Pk. Hosp. Wirral; Regist. Roy. Liverp. Univ. Hosp.; SHO (Phys. & Renal Med.) Roy. Free Hosp. Lond.

WIDGINGTON, Nicola Jane The Simpson Health Centre, 70 Gregories Road, Beaconsfield HP9 1PS Tel: 01494 671571 Fax: 01494 680219; 21 Burkes Road, Beaconsfield HP9 1PB Tel: 01494 681235 — MB BS Lond. 1984; MRCGP 1988; DRCOG 1988; DCH RCP Lond. 1988.

WIDJAJA, Adji Widajat c/o Dr R. Turner, Oxford University, Diabetes Research Laboratories, Radcliffe Infirmary, Woodstock Road, Oxford OX2 6HE — State Exam Med 1991 Hanover.

WIECEK, Maryan Ryszard McNulty and Partners, Torkard Hill Medical Centre, Farleys Lane, Shieldfield, Nottingham NG15 6DY Tel: 0115 963 3676 Fax: 0115 968 1957; 188 Papplewick Lane, Hucknall, Nottingham NG15 8EH — BM BS 1977 Nottm.; MRCP (UK) 1981. Clin. Asst. (Dermat.) Kings Mill Hosp. Mansfield.

WIEJAK, Antoni Peter Atkinson Health Centre, Market Street, Barrow-in-Furness LA14 2LR Tel: 01229 822205 Fax: 01229 832938; Rampside Hall, Rampside, Barrow-in-Furness LA13 0PX — MB ChB 1979 Manch.; MRCGP 1983; DRCOG 1982. Dir. Furness Emerg. Doctor Servs.; Med. Off. Barrow Lifeboat.

WIELAND, Satu Sinikka Lillian 33 Hichisson Road, London SE15 3AN — State Exam Med. Hamburg 1988.

WIELD, Cathryn Emily 432 Winchester Road, Southampton SO16 7DH — MB BS 1983 Lond.; MB BS Lond. 1993; BSc (Hons.) Lond. 1980.

WIELD, Thelma Dorothy (retired) 9 LangtonsCt., Alresford SO24 9UE Tel: 01962 732696 — LRCP LRCS Ed. LRFPS Glas. 1952; FFCM 1987, MFCM 1982. Prev: Cons. Pub. Health Med. Croyon DHA.

WIELEZYNSKI, Maurycy (retired) 7 Bryn Meadows, Newtown SY16 2DS — LMS 1960 Madrid; LAH Dub. 1965; DObst RCOG 1966.

WIELINK, R C A Diana Chulmleigh Health Centre, Three Crossways, Chulmleigh EX18 7AA Tel: 01769 580269 Fax: 01769 581131 — Artsexamen 1988 Utrecht; Artsexamen 1988 Utrecht.

WIELOGÓRSKI, Andrzej Krzysztof 5 Park Drive, London W3 8ND — MB BS 1974 Lond.; FFA RCS Eng. 1980. Cons. Cardiothoracic Anaesth. St. Thos. Hosp. Lond. Guy's & St. Thos. Hosp. Trust. Prev: Cons. Cardiothoracic Anaesth. Cardiothoracic Unit Brook Gen. Hosp. Lond.

WIENER, Andrew Julian Child & Family Consultation and Therapy Centre, Marlowes Health Centre, The Marlowes, Hemel Hempstead HP1 1HE Tel: 01442 251132 Fax: 01442 218310 Email: andy.wiener@whch-tr.nthames.nhs.uk — MB ChB 1983 Ed.; MPhil 1996; MA RCA 1986; MRCPsych 1993. (Ed.) Cons. (Child & Adolesc. Psychiat.) Child & Family Clinic Hemel Hempstead. Prev: Sen. Regist. (Child & Adolesc. Psychiat.) Tavistock Clinic. Lond.; Regist. & SHO Maudsley Hosp. Lond.

WIENER, Jarmila Department of Obstetrics & Gynaecology, Royal Gwent Hospital, Newport NP20 2UB Tel: 01633 234234 Fax: 01633 656111; 9 Cwrt Cefn, Lisvane, Cardiff CF14 0US Tel: 02920 759076 — MB BCh 1971 Wales; DPhil Swansea 1993; FRCOG 1995, M 1976, D 1973; MFFP 1993; RCOG/RCR Advanced Train. Obst. Ultrasound 1993. Cons. O & G Roy. Gwent Hosp. Newport. Socs: (Treas.) Treas. Welsh Obst. & Gyn. Soc.; Internat. Soc. Ultrasound in Obst. & Gyn.; Brit. Med ultrasound Soc. Prev: Sen. Regist. (O & G) Univ. Hosp. Wales Cardiff & W. Glam. HA; Assoc. Specialist (O & G) Roy. Gwent Hosp. Newport.

WIER, John 83 Nelson Road, Rayleigh SS6 8HQ — BM 1983 Soton.

WIERSEMA, Ubbo Frank 100G Richmond Hill, Richmond TW10 6RJ — MB BS 1991 Newc.

WIERZBICKI, Anthony Stanislaw St Thomas Hospital, Lambeth Palace Road, London SE1 7EH Tel: 020 7928 9292 Fax: 020 7928 4226 Email: anthonywierzbicki@kcl.ac.uk; 6E Bedford Towers, Cavendish Place, Brighton BN1 2JG Tel: 01273 724378 — BM BCh 1986 Oxf.; MA Camb. 1987, BA 1983; DPhil Oxf. 1993. (Oxf.) Sen. Lect. & Hon. Cons. Chem. Path. UMDS of Guy's & St Thos. Lond. Socs: Amer. Soc. Human Genetics; Amer. Soc. Hypertens.; Internat. Atherosclerosis Soc. Prev: Lect. & Hon. Sen. Regist. (Chem. Path.) Char. Cross & W.m. Med. Sch.; Regist. (Med. Biochem.) Univ. Hosp. Cardiff; MRC Research Fell. (Neurosci.s) Inst. Molecular Med. Oxf.

WIERZBICKI, Wladyslaw (retired) 7 Circle Court, Harrowdene Road, Wembley HA0 2JP Tel: 020 8902 0689 — MD 1947 Bologna. Prev: Dent. Off. 11th Gen. Hosp. PRC Lla.rch Panna Camp nr. Wrexham.

WIESAND, Michael 23 Chestnut Close, Stourbridge DY8 3JL — State Exam Med. Erlangen 1990.

WIESELBERG, Hugh Michael Royal National paediatric Hospital, Brockley Hill, Stanmore HA7 4LP Tel: 020 8954 2300 Fax: 020 8420 4566; 8 Broughton Avenue, London N3 3ER Tel: 01923 249244 Email: 113110.1275@compuserve.com — MB BChir 1970 Camb.; MA Camb. 1975, BA 1966; MRCP (UK) 1975; MRCS Eng. LRCP Lond. 1969; MRCPsych 1976; DCH Eng. 1973. (Camb. & St. Geo.) Cons. Child & Adolesc. Psychiat. Roy. Nat. Orthop. Hosp. Stanmore; Hon. Sen. Clin. Lect. Univ. Coll. & Middlesx Sch. Med.

Lond. Prev: Regist. Bethlem Roy. & Maudsley Hosp. Lond.; Lect. Child Psychiat. Inst. Psychiat. Lond.; Cons. Middlx. & Univ. Coll. Hosps. Lond.

WIESEMANN, Peter 23 Blackstock Close, Headington, Oxford OX3 7JR Tel: 01865 771686 — State Exam Med 1993 Munich; DCH Lond. 1997. (University of Munich)

WIESENDANGER, Peter Hans 51 Church Street, Theale, Reading RG7 5BX Tel: 01734 302513 — MRCS Eng. LRCP Lond. 1953; MA Oxf. 1954, BM BCh 1953; DObst RCOG 1956. (King's Coll. Hosp.) Socs: Reading Path. Soc. Prev: Ho. Surg. & Cas. Off. King's Coll. Hosp.; O & G Regist. Roy. Berks. Hosp. Reading.

WIESSLER, Regine Erika Flat 4, 62 Kings Rd, Richmond TW10 6EP Tel: 020 8332 6306 or 07977 911 984 Email: r.wiessler@gn.apc.org — MB ChB 1990 Cape Town; MSc Lond. 1995; BSc (Br. Col.) 1984; DTM & H Lond. 1995; DRCOG 1998; LMCC(Canada) 1994. (Cape Town) GP. Socs: BMA.

WIGDAHL, James Douglas (retired) High Orchard, Chequers Lane, North Runcton, King's Lynn PE33 0QN Tel: 01553 840352 — BM BCh 1953 Oxf.; MA, BM BCh Oxf. 1953; MRCGP 1966; DObst RCOG 1957.

WIGFIELD, Arthur Salmon (retired) 35 Sandford Road, Mapperley, Nottingham NG3 6AL — MB BChir 1946 Camb.; MA, MD Camb. 1950, MB BChir 1946; MRCS Eng. LRCP Lond. 1936. Hon. Cons. Venereol. Newc HA (T). Prev: Cons. Venereol. Newc. Gen. Hosp.

WIGFIELD, Crispin Campbell 31 Ravenswood Road, Bristol BS6 6BW — MB ChB 1993 Birm.

WIGFIELD, Mary (retired) 22 Tamarack Close, Eastbourne BN22 0TR Tel: 01323 506075 — MB BS 1953 Lond.; MRCS Eng. LRCP Lond. 1953; MFFP 1993; DObst RCOG 1955. Sessional SCMO (Family Plann. & Psychosexual Med.) E.bourne & Co. Healthcare NHS Trust. Prev: Sen. Clin. Off. (Family Plann.) E.bourne Health Dist.

WIGFIELD, Miles Fraser Windrush Cottage, Itlay, Daglingworth, Cirencester GL7 7HZ — MB BS 1973 Lond.; DRCOG 1982; DCH Eng. 1976.

WIGFIELD, Ruth Elizabeth Department of Child Health, North Hampshire Hospital, Aldermaston Road, Basingstoke RG24 9NA Tel: 01256 313688 Fax: 01265 314796 Email: ruth.wigfield@bas.swest.nhs.uk; The Hornbeams, Dever Close, Micheldever, Winchester SO21 3SR Tel: 01962 774817 Fax: 01962 774817 Email: ruthwigfield@doctors.org.uk — BM 1982 Soton.; MRCP (UK) 1987; MRCPCH. (Soton.) p/t Cons. (Paediatr.), N. Hants. Hosp., Basingstoke. Socs: BAPM. Prev: Sen. Regist. (Paediat.) Soton. Univ. Hosps.; Research Fell. Inst. Child Health Bristol Univ.; Lect. & Hon. Regist. (Child Health & Neonat.) Bristol Univ.

WIGFIELD, Walter James (retired) 29 Glendale Avenue, Eastbourne BN21 1UT Tel: 01323 645161 — MB BChir 1950 Camb.; MFCM 1974; MFPHM 1989; DPH Eng. 1955. Hon. Cons. Community Med. E.bourne HA. Prev: SCM (Social Servs.) E. Sussex AHA & Coventry AHA.

WIGFULL, James Robert 58 Abbotsford Street, Flat 5, Dundee DD2 1DA — MB ChB 1993 Dundee.

WIGGAM, Malcolm Ivan Department of Health for the elderly, Royal Victoria Hospital, Grosvenor Road, Belfast BT12 6BA Tel: 028 9024 0503 Email: ivan.biggun@royalhospitals.n-i.nhs.uk — MB BCh BAO 1990 Belf.; MB BCh BAO (Hons.) Belf. 1990, MD 1997; MRCP (UK) 1993. (Belfast) Cons. Phys., Med. for the elderly, Roy. Vict. Hosp Belf. Socs: Brit. Diabetes Assn.; Irish Endocrine Soc.; Brit. Geriat. Soc. Prev: Clin.Train. Fell. Stroke Med. W.ern Gen. Hosp. Edinb.; Research Fell. Metab. Unit Roy. Vict. Hosp. Belf.; Sen. Regist. (Geriat/Gen. (Internal) Med. N.Irel.

*****WIGGANS, Stephen Mark** 17 Kirkstone Avenue, Cherry Tree, Blackburn BB2 5HJ — MB ChB 1996 Birm.

WIGGIN, Timothy Roger Greenwich Community Palliative Care Team, 185 Bostal Hill, Abbeywood, London SE18 4LP Tel: 020 8312 1166 Fax: 020 8312 2266; No. 1 MitreCt., Picardy Road, Belvedere DA17 5QP — MB BS 1987 Lond.; BSc Lond. 1983; MRCGP 1991.

WIGGINS, Betsy Linda 11 St Martins, Castle Bytham, Grantham NG33 4RH Tel: 01780 410433 — BM BCh 1974 Oxf.; MRCP (UK) 1977; MRCGP 1981; DCH Eng. 1978. Clin. Med. Off. S. Lincs.

WIGGINS, Mr Brian Christopher (retired) Rookery Medical Centre, Rookery House, Newmarket CB8 8NW Tel: 01638 665711 Fax: 01638 561280 — BM BCh 1967 Oxf.; FRCS Ed. 1972.

WIGGINS, Gillian Holt (retired) Keren, Kiln Lane, Winkfield, Windsor SL4 2DU Tel: 01344 884008 — MB ChB 1956 Birm. Prev: Assoc. Specialist Hillingdon Hosp. Uxbridge.

WIGGINS, Jacqueline Claire 63 Newlands Road, Skelton Green, Saltburn-by-the-Sea TS12 2DP — MB ChB 1998 Liverp.

WIGGINS, John Wexham Park Hospital, Wexham, Slough SL2 4HL Tel: 01753 634464 Fax: 01753 634464; Standen, Longbottom Lane, Seer Green, Beaconsfield HP9 2UL Tel: 01494 676571 — MD 1985 Birm.; MB ChB Birm. 1976; MRCP (UK) 1979; FRCP 1997. Cons. Phys. Wexham Pk. Hosp. Slough. Socs: Brit. Thorac. Soc.; Amer. Thoracic Soc.; Eur. Respirat. Soc. Prev: Sen. Regist. (Gen. & Thoracic Med.) Brompton & W.m. Hosps. Lond.; Regist. (Gen. & Thoracic Med.) E. Birm. Hosp.; Sheldon Research Fell. W. Midl. RHA.

WIGGINS, Lisa Joyce 24 Woodland Way, London N21 3QA — MB ChB 1994 Liverp.

WIGGINS, Miriam Rose Birmingham Childrens Hospital, Ladywood, Birmingham B4 6; 24 Alexander Close, Bognor Regis PO21 4PL — MB ChB 1993 Birm. SHO (Paediat.) Birm. Childr. Hosp.

WIGGINS, Peter Sidney Castlemilk Health Centre, 71 Dougrie Drive, Glasgow G45 9AW Tel: 0141 531 8585 Fax: 0141 531 8596; 26 Braidpark Drive, Giffnock, Glasgow G46 6NB Tel: 0141 637 8281 — MB ChB 1979 Glas.; MFHom RCP Lond. 1993; MRCGP 1983; DRCOG 1981. Prev: Trainee GP Glas. VTS.

WIGGINS, Robert James Pathology Department, Hemel Hempstead General Hospital, Hillfield Road, Hemel Hempstead HP2 4AD Tel: 01442 213141 Fax: 01442 60253 — MB ChB 1981 Dundee; MSc Lond. 1988; BMSc (Hons.) Dund 1978; MRCPath 1990; FRCPath 1998. Cons. MicroBiol. St Albans & Hemel Hempstead NHS Trust. Socs: FRSM; Assn. Clin. Paths.; Hosp. Infec. Soc. Prev: Sen. Regist. Whipps Cross Hosp. & St. Bart. Hosp. Lond.; Clin. Research Asst. St. Bart. Hosp. Med. Coll. Lond.; Regist. & SHO St. Bart. Hosp. Lond.

WIGGINS, William John Lutterworth Health Centre, Gilmorton Road, Lutterworth LE17 4EB Tel: 01455 553531; Swinford House, Swinford, Lutterworth LE17 6BJ Tel: 01788 860607 — MB BS Lond. 1968; MRCS Eng. LRCP Lond. 1968; DCH Eng. 1971; DObst RCOG 1970. (Guy's) Med. Adviser, Merck UK.; Med. Adviser, Blaby Dist. Counc.. Prev: Paediat. Canad. Forces Europe, Lahr, W. Germany.

WIGGLESWORTH, David Fearnley Bridge Street Practice, 21 Bridge Street, Driffield YO25 6DB Tel: 01377 253441 — MB ChB 1967 Leeds. Chairm.PEC Yorks. Wolds & Coast, Primary Care Trust. Socs: BMA (Ex-Pres.) E. Yorks. Div. Prev: Ho. Phys. & Ho. Surg. Chapel Allerton Hosp. Leeds; SHO Hull Roy. Infirm.

WIGGLESWORTH, Professor Jonathan Semple (retired) Wason House, Upper High St, Castle Cary BA7 7AT Tel: 01963 350360 Fax: 01963 359001 — MB BChir Camb. 1960; MD Camb. 1964; FRCPCH 1997; FRCPath 1977, M 1965. Prev: Beit Memor. Fell. Graham Research Dept. & Graham Schol. in Path., Graham Research Dept. Univ. Coll. Hosp. Med. Sch.

WIGGLESWORTH, Mark David Flat 3, 29 Grosenvor Place, Jesmond, Newcastle upon Tyne NE2 2RD — MB BS 1993 Newc.; DRCOG 1997; Dip. IMC RCS Ed. 1996; MRCGP 1998. (Newc.) SHO A&E Sunderland. Roy. Infirm. Prev: GP/Regist. & SHO (O & G) Carlisle.

WIGGLESWORTH, Pauline Birches, Treeton, Goole — MB ChB 1942 Leeds; DCH Eng. 1944. (Leeds)

WIGGLESWORTH, Robert, Lt.-Col. RAMC Tresillian House, Cranford Saint John, Kettering NN14 4AL Tel: 01536 330280 — MB BS Lond. 1940; FRCP Lond. 1969, M 1948; DCH Eng. 1950; FRCPCH 1997. (St. Bart.) Cons. Paediat. Shaftesbury Soc. Hinwick Hall Sch. WellingBoro., Roy. Nat. Inst. Blind Rushton Hall Sch. Kettering; Hon. Tutor (Paediat.) Guy's Hosp. Med. Sch. Lond. Socs: FRSM; (Counc.) Nat. Assn. Matern. & Child Welf. (Vice-Chairm. & Chairm. Educat. Comm.); N. N.ants. CPRE (Chairm.). Prev: Tutor & Sen. Regist. (Paediat.) Radcliffe Infirm. Oxf.; Med. Chief Asst. St. Bart. Hosp.; Lt.-Col. RAMC, Med. Specialist, DADMS 14th Army & ADMS ALFSEA & SEAC.

WIGHT, Ailsa Lockerbie Department of Health, Skipton House, 80 London Road, London SE1 6LH; 88 Shakespeare Road, London W3 6SN — MB BS 1981 Lond.; MSc Lond. 1987, MB BS 1981; FRCPath 1997. (Middlx.) Sen. Med. Off. DoH Lond. Prev: Sen.

Regist. (Med. Microbiol.) St. Mary's Hosp. Paddington Lond.; Asst. Lect. (Path.) Middlx. Hosp. Sch. Path. Univ. Lond.; Cas. Off. Univ. Coll. Hosp.

WIGHT, Alexander Muirhead 16-17 South Crescent, Ardrossan KA22 8EB Tel: 01294 463011 Fax: 01294 462790; Tamdhu, 11 Law Brae, West Kilbride KA23 9DD — MB ChB 1965 Glas. (Glas.)

WIGHT, Catherine Odessa 11 Vedonis Park, Hucknall, Nottingham NG15 6EW — MB ChB 1993 Aberd.

WIGHT, David John 48 Greenhill Road, Alveston, Bristol BS35 3NA — MB ChB 1990 Manch.

WIGHT, Derek George Douglas Department of Histopathology, Addenbrooke's Hospital, Cambridge CB2 2QQ Tel: 01223 217168 Fax: 01223 216980; Rustat House, 32 Rustat Road, Cambridge CB1 3QT Tel: 01223 248087 Fax: 01223 248087 — MB BChir 1963 Camb.; MA Camb. 1970, BA 1960, MB BChir 1963; FRCPath 1982, M 1970. (Camb. & St. Thos.) Cons. Pathol. Addenbrookes Hosp. Camb.; Assoc. Lect. (Path.) Univ. Camb; Fell. & Dir. of Studies in Path. & Clin. Med. St. John's Coll. Camb. Socs: Path. Soc.; Brit. Soc. Gastroenterol. Prev: Cas. Off. St. Thos. Hosp. Lond.; Lect. (Path.) St. Thos. Hosp. Med. Sch. & St. Geo. Hosp. Med. Sch. Lond.

WIGHT, Gillian Ruth Roulston Cottage, Sutton-under-Whitestone-Cliffe, Thirsk YO7 2PS Tel: 01845 597329 — MB BChir 1972 Camb.; MA Camb. 1972; Cert. Family Plann. JCC 1974; DCH Eng. 1973; DObst RCOG 1973. (Univ. Camb. & Middlx. Hosp. Med. Sch.) SCMO (Family Plann. & Sexual Health) York & N.allerton HAs. Socs: MFFP; York Med. Soc.; Assoc. Inst. Psychosexual Med. Prev: SHO (Paediat. & Anaesth.) & Ho. Off. (O' & G) Hillingdon Hosp. Uxbridge.

WIGHT, Henry Stephen Christian (retired) 2 St Roman's Avenue, Duffield, Derby DE6 4HG — MRCS Eng. LRCP Lond. 1943.

WIGHT, Jane Alison Sunnymead, 53 Birkenhead Road, Meols, Wirral CH47 5AF Tel: 0151 632 6660 Fax: 0151 632 5073 — MB BS 1987 Lond.; MRCGP 1991; T(GP) 1992; DFFP 1993; DRCOG 1991. GP. Prev: Trainee GP/SHO (O & G) Glos. Roy. Hosp. Gloucester & Cheltenham VTS; SHO (A & E) Cheltenham Gen. Hosp.; SHO (ENT) Roy. United Hosp. Bath.

WIGHT, Jeremy Peter Wakefield Health Authority, White Rose House, West Parade, Wakefield WF1 1LT Tel: 01924 213033 Fax: 01924 814401 Email: jeremy.wight@gw.wakeha.northy.nhs.uk — MB BChir 1982 Camb.; MB Bchir Camb 1982; MD Sheff. 1992; MRCP (UK) 1985; MFPHM RCP (UK) 1996. Dep. Director of Pub. Health; Sen. Lect., SCHARR, Sheff. Uni. Sheff. Prev: Sen. Regist. (Pub. Health Med.) Trent RHA; Regist. (Renal Unit) N.. Gen. Hosp. Sheff.

WIGHT, Katharine Clare Glenfield, Woodfarm Road, Malvern Wells, Malvern WR14 4PN — MB BCh 1995 Wales.

WIGHT, Nicholas James Derek 32 Rustat Road, Cambridge CB1 3QT Tel: 01223 248087 — MB 1991 Camb.; BChir 1990. Ho. Phys. Addenbrooke's Hosp. Cambs.

WIGHT, Mr Richard Graham North Riding Infirmary, Newport Road, Middlesbrough TS1 5JE Tel: 01642 854023 Fax: 01642 854064 — MB BS 1980 Newc.; FRCS (Otol.) Eng. 1987; FRCS (Otol.) Ed. 1985. Cons. ENT Surg. N. Riding Infirm. Middlesbrough. Socs: Ord. Mem. Sect. of Larryngol. Roy. Soc. Med. Prev: Sen. Regist. (ENT) St. Mary's Hosp. Lond. & Roy. Marsden Hosp.

WIGHT, Rosalind Marie 25 Durham Road, Edinburgh EH13 0LD Tel: 0131 669 3633 — MB ChB 1988 Dundee; T(GP) 1992. p/t GP Princip. (at Durh. Rd. Med. Gp.). Prev: Princip. Med. Off., Managing Hosp., S. Africa; GP Cons. Edin. Homeless Pract.

WIGHT, Vivien Laing Trevaylor Road Health Centre, Trevaylor Road, Falmouth TR11 2LH Tel: 01326 317317; Lamorna, Golladowr, Penhallow, Truro TR4 9LY Tel: 01872 573365 — MB ChB 1975 Dundee. Gen. Practitioner; Doctor for Cornw. Brook; Community Hosp. Doctor, Falmouth Hosp., Falmouth.

WIGHT, William John Rustat House, 32 Rustat Road, Cambridge CB1 3QT — MB BS 1993 Newc.

WIGHTMAN, Archibald Ewart (retired) Cockburn House, 48 William St., Helensburgh G84 8XX — MB ChB Ed. 1958.

WIGHTMAN, Arthur James Alexander Consulting Rooms, Murrayfield Hospital, 122 Corstorphine Road, Edinburgh EH12 6UD Tel: 0131 316 2524/2590 Fax: 0131 334 7338; 19 Greenhill Gardens, Edinburgh EH10 4BL Tel: 0131 447 5507 — MB BS 1967 Lond.; FRCR 1975; FFR 1974; DMRD Eng. 1972. (St. Mary's) Cons. Radiol. Roy. Infirm. Of Edin. Edin.; Hon.Sen. Lect. Univ. of Edin.; Cons. Radiol. Med. Reception Station (Army) Edin. Socs: Soc.

Apoth.; Scott. Radiol Soc. Prev: Sen. Regist. (Radiodiagn.) Roy. Infirm. Edin.; Regist. (Diagn. Radiol.) King's Coll. Hosp. Lond.; Regist. (Diagn. Radiol.) Hammersmith Hosp. Lond.

WIGHTMAN, Douglas Howe of Fife Medical Practice, 27 Commercial Road, Ladybank, Cupar KY15 7JS Tel: 01337 830765 Fax: 01337 831658 — MB ChB 1971 Ed.

WIGHTMAN, Sheila (retired) 16 Brandy Hole Lane, Chichester PO19 4RY Tel: 01243 527125 — MB ChB 1953 Manch.; DObst RCOG 1955. Prev: Assoc. Specialist (Psychogeriat.) Grayling Well Hosp. Chichester.

WIGHTMAN, Susan Jane Sharda, New Park Road, Cranleigh GU6 7HL — MB ChB 1986 Liverp.; MRCGP 1990.

WIGHTON, Christopher James 444 West Wycombe Road, High Wycombe HP12 4AH — MB ChB 1998 Leic.

WIGHTON-BENN, Wendy Helen (retired) Department of Biomedical Science, University of Sheffield, Western Bank, Sheffield S10 2TN Tel: 0114 282 4691 Fax: 0114 276 5413 — MB ChB 1985 Ed.; MRCPsych 1990; MD MD with Dist (Edin) 2000. Clin. Train. Fell. Med. Research Counc. Prev: Clin. Train. Fell. Med. Researchh Counc.

WIGLEY, Anne (retired) 90 Macklin Street, Derby DE1 1JX Tel: 01332 340381 — MB BS 1957 Lond.; MRCS Eng. LRCP Lond. 1957; FRCGP 1992; DObst RCOG 1960. Prev: Ho. Surg. (Gyn.) & Ho. Phys. (Diabetic) King's Coll. Hosp. Lond.

WIGLEY, Antonia Mary 132 Pencisely Road, Cardiff CF5 1DR Tel: 029 2056 4469 — MB BCh 1969 Wales.

WIGLEY, Elizabeth Janet Millennium Medical Centre, 121 Weoley Castle Road, Weoley Castle, Birmingham B29 5QD Tel: 0121 427 5201 Fax: 0121 427 5052; 36 Gleneagles Drive, Blackwell, Bromsgrove B60 1BD — MB ChB 1986 Birm. Prev: Trainee GP N.field Birm. VTS.

WIGMORE, John Sydenham (retired) 6 Laurel Drive, Burntwood, Walsall WS7 9BL Tel: 01543 682288 — MB ChB 1944 Birm. Prev: Ho. Surg. (Gyn. & Obst.) Roy. Berks. Hosp. Reading.

WIGMORE, Nicholas Paul Grosvenor House Surgery, Warwick Square, Carlisle CA1 1LB Tel: 01228 536561 — MB ChB 1984 Liverp.

WIGMORE, Mr Stephen John University Department of Surgery, Royal Infirmary of Edinburgh, 1 Lauriston Place, Edinburgh EH3 9YW Tel: 0131 536 3830 Fax: 0131 228 2661; 4 Magdala Mews, Edinburgh EH12 5BX — MB BS 1989 Lond.; BSc (1st. cl. Hons.) Lond. 1986; FRCS Ed. 1993. Research Fell. (Surg.) Roy. Infirm. Edin. Prev: SHO (A & E) & Demonst. (Anat.) Roy. Free Hosp. Lond.; SHO (Surg.) Roy. Infirm. Edin.; SHO (Surg.) St. John's Hosp. Livingston.

***WIGMORE, Timothy James** 16 Tyndale Court, Wesferry Road, Isle of Dogs, London E14 3TQ; 84 Westville Road, Shepherds Bush, London W12 9BD Tel: 020 8740 8146 — BM BCh 1994 Oxf.; BA Camb. 1991; FRCA 1999.

WIGNAKUMAR, Mr Velupillai 56 Twyford Road, West Harrow, Harrow HA2 0SL — MRCS Eng. LRCP Lond. 1988; FRCS Eng. 1991; FRCS Ed. 1991; LRCP LRCS Ed. LRCPS Glas. 1986.

WIGNALL, Brian Kay 86 Harley Street, London W1G 7HP Tel: 020 7935 5811 Fax: 020 7637 7202; 7 Falcon Lodge, Oak Hill Park, London NW3 7LD — MB ChB Manch. 1958; MRCP (UK) 1970; FRCR 1975; FFR 1973; DMRD Eng. 1971; DIH Eng. 1963. Cons. Radiol. Char. Cross. Hosp. Lond. Socs: Roy. Soc. Med.; Med. Soc. Lond. Prev: Cons. Radiol. St. Geo. Hosp. Lond.

WIGNALL, Deborah Christine Lowther Medical Centre, 1 Castle Meadows, Whitehaven CA28 7RG Tel: 01946 692241 Fax: 01946 590617; 2 Springfield Mansion, Bigrigg, Egremont CA22 2UT — MB ChB 1986 Sheff.; MRCGP 1991. GP Princip. Lowther Med. Centre Cumbria. Prev: Trainee GP W. Cumbria Scheme; Ho. Surg. & Ho. Phys. Nobles Hosp. Isle of Man.

WIGNALL, John Byron William Lytham Road Surgery, 2 Lytham Road, Fulwood, Preston PR2 8JB Tel: 01772 716033 Fax: 01772 715445 — MB ChB 1976 Manch.; BSc St. And. 1973.

WIGNALL, John Rossall Nicholas Beechcroft, 2 Lynwith Court, Carlton, Goole DN14 9SB — MB ChB 1973 Leeds.

WIGNALL, Oliver James West Suffolk Hospital, Hardwick Lane, Bury St Edmunds IP33 2QZ — MB BS 1998 Lond.

WIGNARAJAH, Nandani Department of Anaesthetics, North Tees General Hospital, Hardwick, Stockton-on-Tees TS19 8PE Tel: 01642 617617; 33 Crooks Barn Lane, Norton, Stockton-on-Tees TS20 1LR

Tel: 01642 554512 — MB BS 1970 Ceylon; DA Eng. 1978; FFA RCS Eng. 1980. (Peradeniya) Cons. Anaesth. (long term locum) N. Tees Gen. Hosp. Socs: Obst. Anaesth. Assn. Prev: Clin. Asst. (Anaesth.) N. Tees Gen. Hosp.; Regist. (Anaesth.) N. Tees Gen. Hosp., Yeovil Dist. Hosp. & Dryburn Hosp. Durh.; SHO (Anaesth.) Shotley Bridge Gen. Hosp. Consett.

WIGNELL, Debra Joan Windrush Surgery, 21 West Bar Street, Banbury OX16 9SA Tel: 01295 251491 — MB ChB 1986 Liverp.; MRCGP 1990; DCH RCP Lond. 1992; DRCOG 1989. Trainee GP Blackpool VTS; Community Med. Off. (Child Health) Stratford-upon-Avon.

WIGZELL, Francis Weir (retired) Flat 1, 24 Hepburn Gardens, St Andrews KY16 9DE Tel: 01334 475925 Email: frankwigzell@talk21.com — MB ChB St. And. 1948; MD St. And. 1958; FRCP Ed. 1971, M 1959. Prev: Cons. Geriat. Med. W. Dorset HA.

WIJAYAKOON, Amitha Punchikumari 51 Goodmayes Avenue, Goodmayes, Ilford IG3 8TN Tel: 020 8597 3740 — MB BS 1967 Ceylon; DO RCS Eng. 1977. Clin. Asst. (Ophth.) Lond. Hosp. Whitechapel & Moorfields Eye Hosp. Lond. Socs: Coll. Ophth. Prev: SHO (Ophth.) Edgware Gen. Hosp.

WIJAYARATNA, Lilamani Olivia 4 South Gardens, Wembley HA9 9PG — MB BS 1975 Sri Lanka; LMSSA Lond. 1992.

WIJAYARATNE, Wijayaratne Mudiyanselage TQP 14 Savannah Close, Kempston, Bedford MK42 8SH — MB BS 1975 Sri Lanka; MRCS Eng. LRCP Lond. 1987.

WIJAYASINGHE, Mr Garumuni Emerson De Silva 9 Coombe Lane W., Kingston upon Thames KT2 7EW — MB BS 1957 Ceylon; FRCS Eng. 1979; DO Eng. 1963; Dip. Amer. Bd. Ophth. 1980. (Ceylon) Assoc. Specialist Moorfields Eye Hosp. Lond. Prev: Eye Surg. Govt. Gen. Hosps. Badulla, Anuradhapura & Ratnapura, Sri Lanka.

WIJAYATILAKE, Dhuleep Sanjay 6 Mount Drive, Wembley Park, Wembley HA9 9ED Tel: 020 8357 9209 Email: sanjay@dircon.co.uk — MB BS 1996 Lond.; BSc (Neurosci.) 1995. (Charing Cross & Westminster Hospital) SHO (Anaesth.) Middlx. Hosp. Prev: SHO (Neurosurg., Neuro-IC & A & E).

WIJAYATILAKE, Narada The Surgery, 2 Falconwood Road, Welling DA16 3AF Tel: 020 7385 5728; 6 Mount Drive, Wembley HA9 9ED Tel: 020 8930 2323 — MB BS Ceylon 1966. (Colombo) Med. Off. Benefit Agency.

WIJAYAWARDENA, M A S S Halse Road Health Centre, Halse Road, Brackley NN13 6EJ Tel: 01280 703460 Fax: 01280 703460; Werney Lodge, 57A Manor Road, Brackley NN13 6ED Tel: 01280 700467 — MB BS 1967 Ceylon; MRCOG 1981; DObst RCOG 1975. (Univ. Ceylon)

WIJAYAWARDHANA, Primrose Orpington Hospital, Orpington BR6 9JU Tel: 01689 27050; 18 Goddington Chase, Orpington BR6 9EA — MB BS 1967 Ceylon; MRCP (UK) 1973; DGM RCP Lond. 1990; DCH RCP Lond. 1972. Research Regist. Orpington Hosp. Kent. Prev: Regist. St. Thos. Hosp. Lond.

WIJAYAWARDHANA, Upulranjan Dewamitta Grantham & District Hospital, Manthorpe Road, Grantham NG31 8DG Tel: 01476 565232 Fax: 01476 593512; Tel: 01476 594934 — MB BS Ceylon 1964; MD Ceylon 1967; FRCP Lond. 1984, M 1968; FACC 1985. Cons. Phys. Cardiol. Grantham & Dist. Hosp. Grantham. Socs: (Vice-Pres.) Asian Pacific Soc. Cardiol.; Brit. Cardiac Soc. Prev: Sen. Cardiol. Gen. Hosp. Colombo, Sri Lanka.; Clin. Dir. Integrated Med.

WIJAYAWICKRAMA, Asoka 3 Libbards Gate, Solihull B91 3XQ — MB BS 1998 Lond.

WIJAYSINGHE, Druseela The Surgery, 96 Sirdar Road, London W11 4EG Tel: 020 7727 9238 Fax: 020 7460 7305 — MB BS 1971 Bombay; MB BS 1971 Bombay.

WIJEKOON, Janananda Banda The Surgery, 872 Green Lane, Dagenham RM8 1BX Tel: 020 8599 7151 Fax: 020 8983 8784 — MB BS 1968 Ceylon.

WIJENDRA, Mr Somil Devendra Pallawela and Partners, Belmont Health Centre, 516 Kenton Lane, Kenton, Harrow HA3 7LT Tel: 020 8863 6863 Fax: 020 8863 9815; 56 Vernon Drive, Stanmore HA7 2BT Tel: 020 8427 1664 — MB BS 1974 Sri Lanka; FRCS Eng. 1987; FRCS Ed. 1987; MRCS Eng. LRCP Lond. 1986. (Fac. Med. Univ. Ceylon Peradeniya, Sri Lanka) Forens. Med. Examr. Middlx. Prev: Regist. (Orthop.) Memor. Hosp. Darlington.

WIJERATNE, Jayantha Jayasiri Belmont Health Centre, 516 Kenton Lane, Kenton, Harrow HA3 7LT Tel: 020 8863 6863 Fax: 020 8424 0542 — MBBS 1974 Univ. Of Sri Lanka; MRCP (UK) 1982; RCP & RCS London; LRCP, MRCS 1982; MD (Univ. Of Sri Lanka) 1983. Gen. Practitioner - Sen. Partner in Gp. Pract., Harrow Middx.; Police Surg. (Forens. Med. Examr.) Metrop. Police. Socs: Roy. Coll. of Phys.s, Lond.; Roy. Coll. of Surg.s, Lond.; BMA.

WIJERATNE, Renuka Kumari 21 Whitsand Road, Manchester M22 4ZA — MB ChB 1998 Manch.

WIJERATNE, Wijith Kumara 28 Blockley Road, Wembley HA0 3LR — BM 1995 Soton.

WIJESINGHE, Dona Priyalatha (retired) c/o 192 Winchmore Hill Road, London N21 1QR — MB BS 1954 Ceylon; FRCP Ed. 1983, M 1960; DCP Lond 1960; DPath Eng. 1959; DTM & H Eng. 1959. Prev: Cons. Histopath. Huddersfield.

WIJESINGHE, Lasantha Dinesh 42 Broughton Way, York YO10 3BG — MB BChir 1990 Camb. (Camb.) Research Fell (Vasc. Surg.) St. Jas. Univ. Hosp. Leeds. Prev: Regist. (Vasc. Surg.) St. Jas. Univ. Hosp. Leeds; Regist. (Gen. Surg.) York Dist. Hosp.; RSO Addenbrooke's Hosp. Camb.

WIJESUNDERA, Rohan Lalith Medical Residence, Walsgrave Hospital, Clifford Bridge Road, Coventry CV2 2DX — BM 1992 Soton. SHO (A & E) Centr. Middlx. Hosp. Lond. Socs: BMA & Med. Def. Union. Prev: SHO (Orthop.) Roy. Bournemouth Hosp.; Ho. Off. (Surg.) Basingstoke Dist. Hosp.; Ho. Off. (Med.) Roy. Bournemouth Hosp.

WIJESURENDRA, Chula Shrilal Stour Clinic, Kent & Canterbury Hospitals NHS Trust, Ethelbert Road, Canterbury CT1 3NG Tel: 01227 783120 Fax: 01227 783074 Email: chula.wijeswend@kch-tr.sthames.nhs.uk; 43 Ethelbert Road, Canterbury CT1 3NF Tel: 01227 783120 Fax: 01227 783074 Email: 100775.3422@compuserve.com — MB BS 1976 Sri Lanka; MRCP (UK) 1982; FRCP 1998. Cons. Genitourin. Med. Stour Clinic Kent & Canterbury NHS Trust & Qu. Eliz. The Qu. Mother Hosp.; Cons. Genitourin. Med. Sittingbourne Memor. Hosp. Socs: BMA; MSSVD; AGUM. Prev: Sen. Regist. (Genitourin. Med.) Cardiff Roy. Infirm.

WIJESURENDRA, Indrani Tilaka Department of Anaesthetics, Kent & Canterbury Hospital, Canterbury CT1 3NF Tel: 01227 766877; 43 Ethelbert Road, Canterbury CT1 3NF Tel: 01227 462287 — MB BS 1971 Ceylon; FFA RCS Eng. 1980. (Ceylon) Prev: Regist. (Anaesth.) Rushgreen Hosp. Romford; Regist. Moorfields Eye Hosp., Roy. Nat. Orthop. Hosp., Roy. Nat. ENT Hosp. & Whittington Hosp. Lond.

WIJESURIYA, Nilukshi Champika 33 Stanbury Court, 99 Haverstock Hill, London NW3 4RR — MB BS 1998 Lond.

WIJETHILLEKE, Mr Gigurawa Gamage Khemananda Medical Unit, 1 Croston Road, Lostock Hall, Preston PR5 5RS Tel: 01772 620160 — MB BS 1970 Ceylon; FRCS Eng. 1980. Princip. Gen. Pract., Medicare Unit, Lostock Hall, Preston; Clin. Assit. Haemat. Roy. Preston Hosp.

WIJETILLEKA, Ahangama Baduge Sunil Ananda Central Middlesex Hospital, Action Lane, Park Royal, London NW7 0NS Tel: 020 8949 3632; 332 Malden Road, New Malden KT3 6AU Tel: 020 8965 5733 — MB BS 1975 Sri Lanka; FFA RCSI 1984. Cons. Anaesth. Centr. Middlx. Hosp. Lond.

WIJETUNGE, Anil 13 Prout Grove, London NW10 1PU — MB BS 1988 Lond.

WIJETUNGE, Mr Don Bandula 51 New Caledonian Wharf, 6 Odessa St., London SE16 7TN Tel: 020 7394 9499 — MB BS 1967 Ceylon; FRCS Ed. 1976. (Ceylon) Cons. Surg. (A & E) St. Geo. Hosp. & Med. Sch. Lond. Prev: Regist. Profess. Surgic. Unit Univ. Camb.; 1st Asst. Dept. Surg. St. Geo. Hosp. Lond.

WIJETUNGE, Ukwattege Herbert Redley 55 Abbots Park, London Road, St Albans AL1 1TP — MB BS 1968 Nagpur; Dip. Acupunc. Sri Lanka Acupunc. Assn. 1977; Cert. Acupuncture. Sri Lanka Acupunc. Foundat. 1977.

WIJEWARDENA, Hattotuwa Chandrapala St. Ebbas Hospital, Hook Road, Epsom KT19 8QJ Tel: 01372 722212 — MB BS 1970 Ceylon; MRCPsych 1981; DPM Eng. 1980. (Peradeniya Med. Sch. Ceylon) Cons. Psychiat. Manor Hosp. Epsom. Prev: Sen. Regist. Cell Barnes Hosp. St. Albans; Regist. (Psychiat.) Walsgrave Hosp. Coventry; Regist. (Psychiat.) Dist. Hosp. Basingstoke.

WIJEWARDENE, Mr Primus Anura Sandwell General Hospital, West Bromwich B71 4HJ — MB BS 1980 Peradeniya; FRCS Glas.

WIJEYEKOON

1988; Dip. Urol. Lond 1991. Regist. (Surg. & Urol.) Bangor Dist. Gen. Hosp. Prev: Regist. (Surg.) Llandudno Gen. Hosp.

WIJEYEKOON, Sanjaya Prabhath 15 Rhodesia Road, London E11 4DF — MB BS 1996 Lond.; MA Camb. 1997. SHO Surg. Rotat. Whipps Crom Hosp. Lond.

WIJEYESEKERA, Kamani Geshan 2 Palatine Mansions, 126 Palatine Road, West Didsbury, Manchester M20 3ZA — MB BCh 1989 Wales; MRCP (UK) 1994; MRCGP 1999. (Univ. Wales Coll. Med.)

WIJNBERG, Andrew William Alberic The Surgery, 65 New Road, Rubery, Birmingham B45 9JT Tel: 0121 453 3591 Fax: 0121 457 7217 — MB ChB 1981 Cape Town; MB ChB 1981 Cape Town.

WIJNBERG, John Paul 65 Albany Road, Walton-on-Thames KT12 5QG — MB ChB 1988 Pretoria.

WIKNER, Gavin Walford (retired) Linfords, Staithe Road, Repps with Bastwick, Great Yarmouth NR29 5JU Tel: 01692 670444 — MB BS 1943 Durh. Prev: Ho. Surg. Roy. Vict. Infirm. Newc.

WIKNER, Robert Anthony Potterells Medical Centre, Station Road, North Mymms, Hatfield AL9 7SN Tel: 01707 273338 Fax: 01707 263564; Agape, 11 Morven Close, Potters Bar EN6 5HE Tel: 01707 657767 — MRCS Eng. LRCP Lond. 1975; MB BS Lond. 1975; BSc (Physiol.) Lond. 1970; MRCGP 1979; DRCOG 1978. (Royal Free Hospital)

WILBERFORCE, Barbara Doreen (retired) 11 Hawkins Close, Perry, Huntingdon PE28 0DQ Tel: 01480 811112 — MB ChB 1943 Birm.; MRCS Eng. LRCP Lond. 1943. Prev: Wing Cdr. RAF Med. Br.

WILBOURN, Gary 6 Cobnar Drive, Dunston Estate, Newbold, Chesterfield S41 8DD — BM 1995 Soton.

WILBRAHAM, Darren George 215B Tooting High Street, London SW17 0SZ — MB BS 1996 Lond.

WILBRAHAM, Kim 190 Maldon Road, Colchester CO3 3AZ — MB ChB 1989 Liverp.

WILBUSH, Joel c/o Barclays Bank, 207-215 Glossop Road, Sheffield S10 2GX — MB ChB 1943 Sheff.; DPhil Oxf. 1980; Dip. Ethnol. Oxf. 1972; FRCOG 1984, M 1950. (Sheff.) Adjunct Prof. Univ. Alberta, Edmonton AB, Canada. Socs: Fell. Roy. Soc. Med.; Founder Mem. Internat. Menopause Soc. Prev: Regist. (O & G) N. Middlx. Hosp.; Regist. (Gyn.) Co. Hosp. Lincoln; Capt. RAMC.

WILCOCK, Andrew Hayward House, Nottingham City Hospital, Hucknall Road, Nottingham NG5 1PB — MB ChB 1987 Birm.; MRCP (UK) 1991; DM Nottm. 1998. Sen. Lect. (Oncol. & Palliat. Med.) Nottm. City Hosp. Prev: Sen. Regist. (Palliat. Med.) Oxf. Radcliffe NHS Trust; Research Fell. (Respirat. & Palliat. Med.) Nottm. City Hosp.

WILCOCK, Anthony Charles, Wing Cdr. RAF Med. Br. Command Medical Officer, HQ PTC, RAF Innsworth, Gloucester GL3 1EZ Tel: 01452 712612 Ext: 5841; 2 Nicolson Close, Innsworth, Gloucester GL3 1DN Tel: 01452 855028 Email: charlie.wilcock@talk21.com — MB ChB 1983 Bristol; AFOM RCP Lond. 1994; MRCGP 1988; DFFP 1993; DAvMed FOM RCP Lond. 1991; DRCOG 1989; MSc 1997 Aberdeen; MFOM 1998. Command. Med. off. Occupat. Health, HQ personnel and Train. command, RAF Innswotth, Gloucester. Socs: Soc. Occupat. Med.

WILCOCK, Christian Jeremy Friends Road Surgery, 49 Friends Road, Croydon CR0 1ED Tel: 020 8688 0532 Fax: 020 8688 2165 — MB BS 1983 Lond.; BSc Lond. 1980. GP Croydon.

WILCOCK, David John 14 George Road, West Bridgford, Nottingham NG2 7PU Tel: 0115 987 2565; University Department of Radiology, Leicester Royal Infirmary, Leicester LE1 5WW Tel: 0116 258 6719 — MB BChir 1984 Camb.; MA (Hons.) Camb. 1981; MRCP (UK) 1988; FRCR 1992. Sen. Lect. (Diag. Radiol.) Leicester Roy. Infirm. Prev: Lect. Univ. Nottm.

WILCOCK, David John Pendlebury Health Centre, The Lowry Medical Centre, 659 Bolton Road, Pendlebury, Manchester M27 8HP Tel: 0161 793 8686 Fax: 0161 727 8011; Didsbury House, 13 Ellesmere Road, Ellesmere Park, Eccles, Manchester M30 9JY — MB ChB 1980 Dundee; MRCGP 1987.

WILCOCK, Florence Mary 6 Southfields Road, London SW18 1QN — BM BCh 1993 Oxf.; BA (Hons.) Physiol. Sci. Oxf. 1990; DFFP 1996. Specialist Regist. (O & G) NE Thames Region. Prev: SHO (Obst.) Whittington Hosp. Lond.; SHO (Paediat. Surg.) Gt. Ormond St. Hosp. Lond.; SHO (Gyn. & Neonat.) St. Mary's Hosp. NHS Trust.

WILCOCK, Jane Pendlebury Health Centre, The Lowry Medical Centre, 659 Bolton Road, Pendlebury, Manchester M27 8HP Tel: 0161 793 8686 Fax: 0161 727 8011; Didsbury House, 13 Ellesmere Road, Ellesmere Park, Eccles, Manchester M30 9JY — MB ChB 1983 Manch.; BSc (Hons.) 1980; MRCGP 1987; DRCOG 1988; DFFP 1997. (Manchester) GP & GP Trainer.

WILCOCK, Jonathan Michael Warbrick-Smith and Partners, The Moat House Surgery, Beech Close, Warboys, Huntingdon PE28 2RQ Tel: 01487 822230 Fax: 01487 823721 — MB ChB 1992 Leic.; MRCGP 1996. GP Princip.

WILCOCK, Michael Alan Threshold Day Hospital, 2 Dudhope Terrace, Dundee DD3 6HG Tel: 01382 322026 — MB ChB 1978 Dundee. (Dundee) Staff (Psychiat.) Tayside Primary Healthcare NHS Trust Dundee. Prev: Regist. (Psychiat.) Ravenscraig Hosp. Greenock.

WILCOCKSON, Alastair Quentin Medical Centre, Whale Island, Portsmouth PO2 8ER Tel: 02392 547137 Fax: 02392 547138 — MB ChB 1986 Sheff.; Dip. Sports Med. Lond. 1996. (Sheff.) GP Med. Centre Whale Is. Portsmouth; Sports Med. Specialist. Prev: SMO HQ Garrison, Brunei; Regtl. MO 1 A & SH; SHO BMH Rinteln.

WILCOX, Adrian Hervey Dept. of Chemical Pathology, St. Hellier Hospital, Carshalton SM5 1AA Tel: 020 8296 2661 Fax: 020 8641 2633 Email: hwilcox@sthelier.sghms.ac.uk; 63 Devon Road, Cheam, Sutton SM2 7PE Tel: 020 8642 2582 — MB 1974 Camb.; MSc Lond. 1985; MA Camb. 1978, MB 1974, BChir 1973; MRCP(I) 1982; MRCPath 1986; FRCPath 1996. Cons. Chem. Path. St. Helier Hosp. Carshalton; Hon. Sen. Lect. St. Geo. Hosp. Med. Sch. Lond. Socs: Assoc of Clin. Biochem.ry; Soc. For Study of Inborn Error of Metab.; Brit. Diabetic Assoc. Prev: Sen. Regist. (Chem. Path.) St. Geo. Hosp. Lond.

WILCOX, Alison Department of Pathology, Royal Infirmary, 84 Castle St., Glasgow G4; 1 Colonsay Drive, Newton Mearns, Glasgow G77 6TY — MB ChB 1977 Glas. Clin. Asst. (Cytol.) Roy. Infirm. Glas.; Med. Off. W. Scotl. Blood Transfus. Serv.

WILCOX, Anne-Marie Carmel 105 First Avenue, Gillingham ME7 2LF — MB ChB 1998 Leic.

WILCOX, Bryan (retired) Pine End, Upper Cwmbran Road, Cwmbran NP44 5SN Tel: 01633 483606 — MB BCh 1956 Wales. Prev: GP Cwmbran.

WILCOX, Christine 11 Northfield Road, Kings Norton, Birmingham B30 1JD Tel: 0121 458 1597 — MB ChB 1974 Birm.; Dip. Community Paediat. Warwick 1987. Clin. Med. Off. (Community Health Servs.) Birm. S. Health Dist.

WILCOX, Douglas Ewing Duncan Guthrie Institute of Medical Genetics, Royal Hospital for Sick Children, Yorkhill, Glasgow G3 8SJ Tel: 0141 201 0365 Fax: 0141 357 4277 Email: d.e.wilcox@clinmed.gla.ac.uk; 1 Colonsay Drive, Newton Mearns, Glasgow G77 6TY — MB ChB 1979 Glas.; BSc (Hons.) Glas. 1976; FRCP Glas. 1996; MRCP (UK) 1982. (Univ. Glas.) Sen. Lect. & Hon. Cons. Roy. Hosp. Sick Childr. Glas. Prev: Lect. (Med. Genetics) & Clin. Research Asst. Duncan Guthrie Inst. Med. Genetics Univ. Glas.; SHO (Med.) W.. Infirm. Glas.

WILCOX, Duncan Thomas Flat 21, Defoe House, Barbican, London EC2Y 8DN — MB BS 1987 Lond.

WILCOX, Fiona Jane Globetown Surgery, 82-86 Roman Road, London E2 0PG Tel: 020 8980 3023 Fax: 020 8983 4627; 80 Bonner Road, Bethanl Green, London E2 9JU Tel: 020 8981 6074 — MB BS 1986 Lond.; BSc Lond. 1983, MB BS 1986; MRCGP 1990; DRCOG 1990; DCH RCP Lond. 1989. (St. Barths. Hosp. Med. Sch.)

WILCOX, Frank Leonard Blackpool Victoria Hospital NHS Trust, Whinney Heys Road, Blackpool FY3 8NR Tel: 01253 300000 Fax: 01253 303651; Fax: 01253 302346 Email: frank@wilcoxfl.freeserve.co.uk — MB ChB Manch. 1977; BSc St. And. 1974; MD Manch. 1983; FRCOG 1995, M 1982; DRCOG 1979. (Manch. & St. And.) Cons. O & G Blackpool Vict. NHS Trust. Prev: Lect. St. Mary's Hosp. Manch.

WILCOX, Gregory Eugene Harold Road Surgery, 164 Harold Road, Hastings TN35 5NH Tel: 01424 720878/437962 Fax: 01424 719525; 24 Branksome Road, St Leonards-on-Sea TN38 0UA — MB BS 1981 Lond.; MRCGP 1986; DRCOG 1985. Exec. Chairm., Hastings And St Leonards PCT Hastings. Socs: Vice Chairm.. Nat. Assn. Of Primary Care.

WILCOX, Jodie 1 End Hall Road, Tettenhall Wood, Wolverhampton WV6 8HA — MB BCh 1998 Wales.

WILCOX, Kay Elizabeth The Medical Centre, 32 London Road, Sittingbourne ME10 1ND Tel: 01795 472109/472100 — MB BS

1984 Lond.; MRCGP 1992. Prev: SHO (O & G) All St.s Hosp. Chatham; SHO (Geriat. Med.) Kent & Canterbury Hosp.; SHO (Surg.) Qu. Eliz. Milit. Hosp. Lond.

WILCOX, Mark Anthony Pembury Hospital, Pembury, Tunbridge Wells TN2 4QS Tel: 01892 823535 Ext: 3181; Comptons, Down Lane, Frant, Tunbridge Wells TN3 9HP — MB ChB 1983 Bristol; DM Nottm. 1993; MRCOG 1989. Cons. O & G Pembury Hosp. Tunbridge Wells. Socs: Hong Kong Coll. Obst. & Gyn. Prev: Sen. Regist. (O & G) Qu. Med. Centre Nottm.; Vis. Lect. Chinese Univ., Hong Kong; Research Fell. (O & G) City Hosp. Nottm.

WILCOX, Mark Harvey Department of Microbiology, University of Leeds & Leeds General Infirmary, Leeds LS2 9JT Tel: 0113 233 5595 Fax: 0113 233 5649 Email: markwi@pathology.leeds.ac.uk — BM BS 1986 Nottm.; BM BS (Hons.) Nottm. 1986; DM Nottm. 1990, BMedSci (Hons.) 1984; MRCPath (Microbiol.) 1992. Sen. Lect. (Med. Microbiol.) Univ. Leeds & Hon. Cons. Leeds Gen. Infirm. Socs: Brit. Soc. Antimicrob. Chemother.; Sec. Hosp. Infec. Soc. Prev: Cons. Microbiol. Addenbrooke's Hosp. Camb. (PHLS); Clin. Lect. (Med. Microbiol.) Univ. Sheff. Med. Sch.; Clin. Research Fell. (Microbiol.) Univ. & City Hosps. Nottm.

WILCOX, Richard Gordon 89 Reservoir Road, Selly Oak, Birmingham B29 6SU — MB ChB 1997 Birm.

WILCOX, Richard Merlyn Laurence Wychall Lane Surgery, 11 Wychall Lane, Kings Norton, Birmingham B38 8TE Tel: 0121 628 2345 Fax: 0121 628 8282; 11 Northfield Road, Kings Norton, Birmingham B30 1JD Tel: 0121 458 1597 — MB ChB 1973 Birm.; MRCGP 1985. (Birm.)

WILCOX, Professor Robert George Department of Cardiovascular Medicine, University Hospital, Nottingham NG7 2UH Tel: 0115 970 9343 Fax: 0115 970 9384; 33 Trent View Gardens, Radcliffe on Trent, Nottingham NG12 1AY Tel: 0115 933 3165 — MB BS Lond. 1970; BSc (Hons.) Lond. 1967; DM Nottm. 1985; FRCP Lond. 1987; MRCP (UK) 1973. (London Hospital Medical College) Prof. Cardiovasc. Med. & Hon. Cons. (Med.) Dept. Med. Univ. Hosp. Nottm. Socs: Brit. Cardiac Soc.; Brit. Hypertens. Soc.; Assn. Phys. Prev: Reader & Sen. Lect. (Med.) Univ. Hosp. Nottm.; Lect. (Med.) Univ. Hosp. Nottm.; SHO (Med.) & Ho. Phys. & Ho. Surg. Lond. Hosp.

WILCOX, Tumini 162A High Road, London N2 9AS — LRCPI & LM, LRSCI & LM 1964; LRCPI & LM, LRCSI & LM 1964.

WILCZYNSKI, Peter Joseph George Lakeside Surgery, Cottingham Road, Corby NN17 2UR Tel: 01536 204154 Fax: 01536 748286; Wisteria Cottage, 36 High St, Stanion, Kettering NN14 1DF Tel: 01536 204004 Fax: 01536 204004 Email: wilczynski@msn.com — MB BS 1980 Lond.; MRCS Eng. LRCP Lond. 1980; DRCOG 1982. (St. Bart.) Chairm. CoOperat.; Police Surg. N.ampton Police.

WILD, Adrian Graham Three Villages Medical Practice, Audnam Lodge, Wordsley, Stourbridge DY8 4AL Tel: 01384 395054 Fax: 01384 390969; 80 Bridgnorth Road, Wollaston, Stourbridge DY8 3PA Tel: 01384 395352 — BM 1982 Soton.

WILD, Alan Frederick Houldsworth Medical Centre, 1 Rowsley Grove, Stockport SK5 7AY Tel: 0161 442 3322 Fax: 0161 442 2594; 23 Douglas Road, Hazel Grove, Stockport SK7 4JG Tel: 0161 456 9080 — MB ChB 1974 Manch.; DRCOG 1978. (Manch.) Socs: Assoc. Mem. Manch. Med. Soc. Prev: SHO (Med.) Bury Gen. Hosp; SHO (O & G) Oldham Gen. Hosp.; SHO (Anaesth.) Vict. Hosp. Blackpool.

WILD, Alfred Augustine — MB ChB Ed. 1948; FRCR 1975; FFR 1961; DMRD Ed. 1954; Cert Av Med MoD (Air) & CAA; Aviat. Auth. 1979. Socs: Brit. Inst. Radiol.; Roy. Coll. Radiol. Prev: Cons. Radiol. ScarBoro. Health Dist.; Sen. Regist. Edin. N.. Hosps. Gp.; Capt. RAMC.

WILD, Anne-Marie Castlefields Health Centre, Chester Close, Castlefields, Runcorn WA7 2HY Tel: 01928 566671 Fax: 01928 581631; 20 Hilltop Road, Stockton Heath, Warrington WA4 2ED Tel: 01925 67500 — MB BCh 1977 Wales; MRCGP 1987; DRCOG 1990.

WILD, David (retired) 16 Brandy Hole Lane, Chichester PO19 4RY Tel: 01243 527125 Email: david.wild2@btinternet.com — MB ChB 1953 Manch.; FFCM 1977, M 1974; DPH Liverp. 1958; DObst RCOG 1957. Prev: Dir. Pub. Health Med. SW Thames RHA.

WILD, David Andrew Hebden Bridge Health Centre, Hangingroyd Lane, Hebden Bridge HX7 6AG Tel: 01422 842333 Fax: 01422 842404; Chapel House Farm, Grey Stone Lane, Todmorden OL14 8RN — MB ChB 1977 Leeds; MRCGP Lond. 1981; DRCOG 1979.

WILD, Dominik Joyce Green Hospital, Joyce Green Lane, Dartford DA1 5PL — State Exam Med 1992 Berlin.

WILD, Ian Christopher St. John's Health Centre, Oak Lane, Twickenham TW1 3PA Tel: 020 8892 8996 — MB BS 1970 Lond.

WILD, Kathryn Airlie Dr Forbes and Partners, East Calder Medical Practice, 147 Main Street, East Calder, Livingston EH53 0EW Tel: 01506 882882 Fax: 01506 883630; 14 Craigmount Terrace, Corstorphine, Edinburgh EH12 8BW Tel: 0131 339 2517 Email: wild7cc@aol.com — MB ChB 1987 Dundee; MRCGP 1993; DCCH RCP Ed. 1993. p/t GP.

WILD, Michael Richard 11 Runswick Drive, Nottingham NG8 1JE — BM BS 1991 Nottm.

WILD, Nicholas James 179 Warton Terrace, Newcastle upon Tyne NE6 5DX — MB BS 1992 Newc.

WILD, Nicholas John Rolyan House, 20 Hill Top Road, Stockton Heath, Warrington WA4 2ED — MB BCh 1977 Wales; MRCP (UK) 1982; DCH Eng. 1978. Cons. Paediat. Warrington Dist. Gen. Hosp.; Clin. Tutor Univ. Liverp.

WILD, Nicola Jane 45 Hartledon Road, Birmingham B17 0AA — MB ChB 1997 Birm.

WILD, Rebecca 29 Seed Hill Terrace, Steeton, Keighley BD20 6QE — MB ChB 1987 Leeds.

WILD, Richard Norman Phairson Medical Ltd., 602 The Chambers, Chelsea Harbour, London SW10 0XF Tel: 020 7349 3100; Farmside, Bullbaiters Lane, Hyde Heath, Amersham HP6 5RS — MB ChB 1969 Leeds; MRCP (UK) 1973, FRCP (Ed.) 1995; DPM RCP Lond. Ed. & Glas. 1979; DCH Eng. 1972; FFPM 1992, M 1989. Med. Dir. Phairson Med. Ltd. Socs: Fell. Roy. Soc. Med. Prev: Lect. (Child Health) Univ. of Soton.; Regist. (Paediat.) Roy. Liverp. Childr. Hosp.

WILD, Roger Essery (retired) The Lodge, 16 Gwydrin Road, Calderstones, Liverpool L18 3HA Tel: 0151 722 9264 — MB ChB 1955 Liverp.; FFR 1970; DMRD 1966; DObst RCOG 1960; DCH Eng. 1960. Cons. Radiol. Warrington & Winwick NHS Trust.

WILD, Sarah Helen Health Care Research Unit, Leve B, South Academic Block, Southampton General Hospital, Southampton SO16 67D Tel: 02380 794774 — MB BChir 1987 Camb.; MFPHM 2000; 2000 PLD; MSc Lond. 1995, BSc 1984; MRCP (UK) 1989; MRCGP 1992; DRCOG 1991. Specialist Regist. (Pub. Health Med.) Univ. Of S.ampton. Prev: Wellcome Clin. Research Fell. Lond. Sch. Hyg. & Trop. Med.; Posdoctoral Fell. Stanford Univ., Calif.; Trainee GP Camb.

WILD, Simon Mark 8 Percheron Way, Droitwich WR9 7RF — MB BCh 1998 Wales.

WILD, Stephen Mark 28 Leadhall Lane, Harrogate HG2 9NE — MB ChB 1997 Leeds; MSc Liverp. 1984, BSc (Hons.) 1992. (Leeds)

WILD, Stephen Roger 32 Alnwickhill Road, Liberton, Edinburgh EH16 6LN — MB ChB 1967 Ed.; FRCP Ed. 1988; FRCR 1975.

WILD, Steven Peter Lower Gornal Health Centre, Bull Street, Gornal Wood, Dudley DY3 2NQ Tel: 01384 459621 Fax: 01384 359495 — MB ChB 1986 Manch.; DCH RCP Lond. 1991. Socs: Assn. Res. Infant & Child Developm. Prev: Regist. (Paediat.) Alexandra Hosp. Redditch; SHO (O & G) Birm. Woms. Hosp.; SHO (Paediat.) Birm. Childr. Hosp.

WILDBORE, Patricia Moira Hazelwood Group Practice, 27 Parkfield Road, Coleshill, Birmingham B46 3LD Tel: 01675 463165 Fax: 01675 466253; The Flower Patch, Shawbury Lane, Shustoke B46 2LA — MB ChB 1988 Birm.; DCH RCP Lond. 1992. p/t GP.

WILDBORE, Roger David Burnham Medical Centre, Love Lane, Burnham-on-Sea TA8 1EU Tel: 01278 795445 Fax: 01278 793024; 2 Brightstowe Road, Burnham-on-Sea TA8 2HW Tel: 01278 792110 — MB BChir 1963 Camb.; MA, MB Camb. 1963, BChir 1962; DObst RCOG 1964; DA Eng. 1965. (Camb. & Birm.)

WILDE, Mr Adam David Royal Cornwall Hospital, Truro TR1 3JW Tel: 020 8225 0000; Mount Rose, Wheal Anna, Goonhavern, Truro TR4 9NW Tel: 01872 540567 Email: adamwilde@cochlear.freeserve.co.uk — MB ChB 1987 Leeds; FRCS (Eng) 1992; FRCS (Orl) 1997. Cons. ENT Surg.

WILDE, Arthur Harold (retired) 24 Woodside Drive, Shrewsbury SY3 9BW — MB ChB 1952 Liverp.; DPH 1955; FFCM RCP (UK) 1984, MFCM 1972. Prev: Specialist Community Med. (Environm. Health) Shrops. HA.

WILDE

WILDE, Mr Godfrey Philip John Radcliffe Hospital, Headington, Oxford OX3 9DU Tel: 01865 221177 Fax: 01865 221231; 30 Dorchester Close, Headington, Oxford OX3 8SS Tel: 01865 308938 Fax: 01865 308938 Email: phil.wilde@ooec.ox.ac.uk — MB ChB 1980 Leeds; FRCS Eng. 1985. Cons. Trauma & Orthop. Surg. John Radcliffe Hosp. Oxf.. Socs: Fell. Roy. Soc. Med. & BOA; Brit. Trauma Soc. Prev: Cons. Orthop. Surg. Lister Hosp. Stevenage; Fell. (Arthroscopic Surg.) Toronto, Canada; Sen. Regist. (Orthop.) Nottm. Hosps.

WILDE, James Maxwell 4 Pierrepont Place, Bath BA1 1JX — MB BS 1993 Lond.

WILDE, James Piers 2 Malyon Court Close, Thundersley, Benfleet SS7 1TX — MB BS 1993 Lond.

WILDE, Jane Crooks 53 Ballycoan Road, Purdysburn, Belfast BT8 8LL — MB BCh BAO 1973 Belf.; MSc (Soc. Med.) Lond. 1977; MFCM 1980.

WILDE, Mr Jeremy Andrew 11 Glenmore Road, Salisbury SP1 3HF Tel: 01722 333191 — MB BChir 1974 Camb.; MA, MB BChir Camb. 1974; FRCS Eng. 1978; MRCOG 1983; FRCOG 1996. Cons. (O & G) Salisbury Dist. Hosp. Prev: Sen. Regist. Rotat. (O & G) Qu. Charlotte's Hosp. Lond.; Rotat. Regist. (O & G) St. Thos. Hosp. Lond. & Pembury Hosp.; Resid. Surgic. Off. (Gyn.) Chelsea Hosp. for Wom. Lond.

WILDE, Jonathan Thornton Department of Haematology, Queen Elizabeth Hospital, Queen Elizabeth Medical Centre, Edgbaston, Birmingham B15 2TH Tel: 0121 472 1311 — MB BChir 1980 Camb.; MD Camb. 1989; FRCPath 1999; FRCP 1997; MRCPath 1991; MRCP (UK) 1984; MA, MB Camb. 1980, BChir 1979. (Guy's) Cons. Haemat. Qu. Eliz. Hosp. Birm.

WILDE, Julia Margaret Homewood, 1 Barlow Fold Road, Romiley, Stockport SK6 4LH — MB ChB Manch. 1969; DCCH. SCMO Community Child Health.

WILDE, Margaret Helen 13 Wyndham Crescent, Bridgend CF31 3DW Tel: 01656 653292 — MB ChB Aberd. 1948. Prev: Asst. Med. Off. Swansea; Ho. Surg. (Gyn.) Aberd. Roy. Infirm.; Med. Off. Parc Hosp. Bridgend.

WILDE, Neil Theodore 31 Grange Road, Bramhall, Stockport SK7 3BD — MB ChB 1995 Manch.; BSc Lond. 1992.

WILDE, Robert Peter Havelock Department of Clinical Radiology, Bristol Royal Infirmary, Marlborough St., Bristol BS2 8HW Tel: 0117 928 2672 Fax: 0117 928 3267 — BM BCh 1974 Oxf.; BSc (1st cl. Hons. Anat.) Liverp. 1970; MRCP (UK) 1977; FRCR 1980. Cons. Radiol. United Bristol Healthcare Trust. Socs: Brit. Cardiac Soc.; Brit. Soc. Echocardiogr.; Brit. Cardiovasc. Interven. Soc. Prev: Clin. Dir. Cardiac Servs. United Bristol Healthcare Trust; Fell. (Cardiovasc. Radiol.) Green La. Hosp., Auckland, NZ; Sen. Regist. (Radiol.) Bristol Roy. Infirm.

WILDE, Simon Marcus 2A Storer Road, Loughborough LE11 5EQ — BM BS 1988 Nottm.; BMedSci Nottm. 1986; MRCGP 1993; DRCOG 1992; DCH RCP Lond. 1991. Prev: Clin. Asst. (Oncol.) Leics.; Trainee GP Lancaster VTS.

WILDE, Stephen Marek Julius Jozefowicz Marsh, Kennedy, Phipps, Chapman and Wilde, Netherfield Medical Practice, 2A Forester Street, Netherfield, Nottingham NG4 2NJ Tel: 0115 940 3775 Fax: 0115 961 4069 — MB BS 1985 Newc.; MRCGP 1989.

WILDE, Susan 65 Rossall Grange Lane, Fleetwood FY7 8AA Email: wilde_sue@hotmail.com — MB ChB 1998 Manch.

WILDEN, Julie 47 Glenavon Road, Ipswich IP4 5QD — BM BS 1995 Nottm.

WILDEN, Simon Derek Taylor and Partners, The Surgery, Hexton Road, Barton-le-Clay, Bedford MK45 4TA Tel: 01582 528701 Fax: 01582 528714 — MB BS 1990 Lond.; MA 1991 Oxon.; MRCGP 1994; DRCOG 1992; Cert. Family Plann. JCC 1992. (Pembroke College Oxford and St Mary's Hospital London) Socs: BMA; MRCGP. Prev: Trainee GP Bedford VTS.

WILDER-SMITH, Oliver Hamilton Gottwaldt 6C Sunnyside, Liverpool L8 3JD — MB ChB 1980 Liverp.

WILDERSPIN, Michael Piers Medical Department, Firth Rixson Forgings Ltd., Dale Road North, Darley Dale, Matlock DE4 2JB Tel: 01629 733621 Fax: 01629 734273; The Dell, 23 Clifton Road, Matlock Bath, Matlock DE4 3PW Tel: 01629 583190 Fax: 01629 583190 Email: mpw@mwawil.softnet.co.uk — MB BS 1959 Lond.; MRCS Eng. LRCP Lond. 1958; AFOM RCP Lond. 1983; FRCGP 1981, M 1968; DFFP 1994; Cert Family Plann 1976. (Guy's) Company Med. Adviser Firth Rixson plc & P.P. Payne Ltd. Socs: Soc. Occupat. Med.; BMA; FRSM. Prev: Employ. Med. Advis. EMAS; Ho. Surg. (Orthop.) Guy's & New Cross Hosps.; Ho. Phys. (Experim. Med.) & Resid. Clin. Path. Guy's Hosp.

WILDGOOSE, Alastair David Dryland Surgery, 1 Field Street, Kettering NN16 8JZ Tel: 01536 518951 Fax: 01536 486200 — MB BS 1974 Newc.; AFOM RCP Lond. 1993; MRCGP 1978.

WILDGOOSE, Charlotte Dorothy Sighthill Health Centre, 380 Calder Road, Edinburgh EH11 4AU Tel: 0131 453 5335 — MB ChB 1977 Glas.; DRCOG 1979.

WILDGOOSE, Joanna Linn Endsleigh House, Clampitt Road, Ipplepen, Newton Abbot TQ12 5RJ — MB ChB 1982 Sheff. Clin. Asst. Psychiat.

WILDGOOSE, Keith 19 Hindburn Close, Doncaster DN4 7RW — MB ChB 1980 Leeds; MRCPsych 1987. Cons. Old Age Psychiat. Doncaster Healthcare Trust.

WILDGOOSE, Nicholas William Endsleigh House, Clampitt Road, Ipplepen, Newton Abbot TQ12 5RJ — MB ChB 1980 Sheff.; MRCP (UK) 1984.

WILDIG, Catherine Elisabeth Fax: 01274 365010 — MB ChB 1989 Birm.; FRCPCH 2001; MRCP (UK) 1992; MRCPCH 1996; Mmedsc 1999 Leeds. (Birm.) p/t Cons. Paediat. (NeuroDisabil.) Child Developm. Centre, St. Luke's Hosp. Bradford. Prev: Sen. Regist. Community Paediat. St. James' Univ. Hosp. Leeds; Sen. Regist. (Community Paediat.) Pinderfields Hosp. Wakefield; Regist. (Paediat. Vict. Hosp. Blackpool & Roy. Manch. Childr.'s Hosp.

WILDIN, Miss Clare Joanne 2 Cedar Cottages, Rolleston Road, Skeffington, Leicester LE7 9YD Tel: 0116 259 6430 — MB ChB 1991 Leic.; FRCS Ed. 1995. Specialist Regist. (Orthop. Surg.) Leicester. Prev: SHO Rotat. (Surg.) Leicester; Demonst. (Anat.) Univ. Birm.

WILDIN, Helen Marie Runwell Hospital, The Chase, Wickford SS11 7QE — MB ChB 1989 Sheff. SHO (Psychiat.) S.end Community Care Trust.

WILDING, Graeme 13 Branksome Drive, Shipley BD18 4BB — MB BS 1997 Lond.

WILDING, Huw Ioan Coach and Horses Surgery, The Car Park, St. Clears, Carmarthen SA33 4AA Tel: 01994 230379 Fax: 01994 231449; Green Acres, Laugharne, Carmarthen SA33 4QU Tel: 01994 427520 — MB BS 1974 Lond.; MRCS Eng. LRCP Lond. 1974. (Westm.) Prev: Ho. Phys. Qu. Mary's Hosp. Roehampton; Ho. Surg. W.m. Hosp. Lond.

WILDING, John Paul Howard Clinical Sciences Centre, University Hospital Aintree, Longmoor Lane, Liverpool L9 7AL Tel: 0151 529 5885 Fax: 0151 529 5888 Email: j.p.h.wilding@liverpool.ac.uk — BM 1985 Soton.; DM Soton. 1994; MRCP (UK) 1988. (Soton.) Sen. Lect. (Diabetes, Endocrinol. & Gen. Med.) & Hon. Cons. Phys. Univ. Hosp. Aintree. Liverp. Socs: Brit. Diabetic Assn.; Assn. for Study Obesity; Eur. Assn. Study Diabetes. Prev: Sen. Regist. & MRC Train. Fell. (Med.) Hammersmith Hosp. Lond.; Regist. (Med.) Ealing & Hammersmith Hosp. Lond.

WILDING, Paul John 5 Upper Bradshaw, Slaithwaite, Huddersfield HD7 5UZ — MB ChB 1988 Leeds; MRCP (UK) 1991. SHO (A & E) Leeds Gen. Infirm. Prev: SHO (Chest Med.) Killingbeck Hosp. Leeds.

WILDING, Mr Robert Peter (retired) Maple Tree House, 68A Sedbergh Road, Kendal LA9 6BE — MB BChir 1959 Camb.; MA Camb. 1959; FRCS Eng. 1967. Prev: Cons. Gen. Surg. Orpington Hosp.

WILDMAN, Gillian Mary Florey Unit, Royal Berks Hospital, London Road, Reading RG1 5AN Tel: 0118 987 7213; 2 Bluecoat Walk, Harmans Water, Bracknell RG12 9NP — MB BCh 1979 Wales. Staff Grade Genito Urin. Med. Roy. Berks. Hosp. Reading.

WILDMAN, Martin James 14 Stoneycroft Close, Horwich, Bolton BL6 6AW — MB ChB 1989 Birm.; BSc (Hons.) Physiol. Birm. 1986, MB ChB 1989; MRCP (UK) 1993; DTM & H Liverp. 1993.

WILDMAN, Martyn Andrew 10 New Road, Shenley, Radlett WD7 9EA — MB BS 1997 Lond.; BSc Pharm 1994. (UCL) A & E SHO Barnet Gen. Hosp. Socs: BASICS.

WILDMAN, Simone Marianne Chantel Garden Flat, 10 Ongar Road, London SW6 1RJ — MB BS 1991 Queensland.

WILDMORE, Joan Christine High Stonecroft House, Newbrough, Hexham NE47 5AY — MB BS 1972 Newc. Clin. Med. Off. N.d. AHA.

WILDSMITH, Professor John Anthony Winston University Department of Anaesthesia, Ninewells Hospital & Medical School, Dundee DD1 9SY Tel: 01382 632427 Fax: 01382 644914 Email: j.a.w.wildsmith@dundee.ac.uk; 6 Castleroy Road, Dundee DD5 2LQ Tel: 01382 732451 Fax: 01382 732451 — MB ChB Ed. 1969; MD Ed. 1982; FRCP Ed. 1996 (by election); FFA RCS Eng. 1973. (Ed.) Prof. Anaesth. Univ. Dundee; Hon. Cons. Anaesth.Tayside univ hosp NHS trust. Dundee. Socs: Acad. Europ. Acad. of Anaesthesiol.; Edit. Bd. Brit. Jl. Anaesth.; Elec. Mem. Counc. Roy. Coll. Anaesths. Prev: Vis. Lect. Brigham & Wom. Hosp. Harvard Med. Sch. Boston, USA; Lect. (Dent. Anaesth.) Univ. Edin.; Cons. Anaesth. & Clin. Dir. Roy. Infirm. Edin.

WILDSMITH, Patricia Helen Mather Avenue Practice, 584 Mather Avenue, Liverpool L19 4UG Tel: 0151 427 6239 Fax: 0151 427 8876 — MB ChB 1990 Liverp.

WILDY, Guy Stephen Ivy House Surgery, 27 The Parade, St Helier, Jersey JE2 3QQ Tel: 01534 728777 Fax: 01534 728977 — MB ChB 1979 Bristol; MRCP (UK) 1983; MRCGP 1985; DRCOG 1984.

WILE, David Bowyer 97 Burtons Road, Hampton Hill, Hampton TW12 1DL — MB BCh 1978 Wales; MSc Clin. Biochem. Lond. 1993. Staff Grade Chem. Path. Aintree Hosps. NHS Trust. Socs: Brit. Soc. Human Genetics; Brit. Hyperlipid. Assn.; Assn. Clin. Biochem. Prev: Regist. (Chem. Path.) Roy. Postgrad. Med. Sch. Lond.; Clin. Research Fell. Roy. Postgrad. Med. Sch. Hammersmith Hosp. Lond.

WILES, Professor Charles Mark Department of Medicine (Neurol.), University of Wales Coll. of Med., Heath Park, Cardiff CF14 4XN Tel: 029 2074 3798 Fax: 029 2074 4166 — MB BS 1972 Lond.; BSc Lond. 1969, PhD 1980, MB BS 1972; FRCP Lond. 1987; MRCP (UK) 1975. (St. Thos.) Prof. Neurol. & Hon. Cons. Univ. Wales Coll. Med. Cardiff. Prev: Cons. Phys. Neurol. Nat. Hosp. For Nerv. Dis. Lond., Maida Vale & St. Thos. Hosps. Lond.; Sen. Regist. (Neurol.) Nat. Hosp. for Nerv. Dis. Qu. Sq. Lond. & St. Mary's Hosp. Lond.; Regist. (Neurol.) Nat. Hosp. Nerv. Dis. Qu. Sq. Lond.

WILES, Ian Derek The Surgery, 35 Great Pulteney Street, Bath BA2 4BY Tel: 01225 464187 Fax: 01225 485305 — BM BCh 1984 Oxf.; MA Camb. 1985 BM BCh 1984; MRCP (UK) 1987; MRCGP 1988; DCH RCP Lond. 1987; DRCOG 1986.

WILES, John Bromley Hospitals NHS Trust, Farnborough Hospital, Farnborough Common, Orpington BR6 8ND Tel: 01689 814336; 418 Footscray Road, New Eltham, London SE9 3TU Tel: 0208 859 6512 Fax: 020 8328 7101 Email: johnwiles@doctors.org.uk — MB ChB 1972 Leeds; Diploma in Teach. Educat. for Med. and Dent. 2001; Cert. JCC Lond. 1978; DObst RCOG 1974; Cert. Teaching S. Th. PGMDE 1997; MRCP 2000. (Univ. Leeds) Cons. Palliat. Med. Bromley Hosp. NHS Trust; Hon. Cons. Palliat. Med. King's Healthcare NHS Trust Lond.; Hon Cons Palliat. Med., St Christophers Hospice, Lond.; Med. Director, S. Bromley Hosp., Orpington. Socs: BMA; Fell. Roy. Soc. Med.; Assn. Palliat. Med. Prev: Med. Direct. St. Catherine's Hospice, Crawley; Med. Direct. St. Joseph's Hospice Lond.; Dir. & Chairm. Teesside Hospice Care Foundat. Middlesbrough.

WILES, John Richard 57 Brooklet Road, Heswall, Wirral CH60 1UJ — MB BS 1978 Lond.; FRCA 1984. (St. Geo.) Cons. Walton Centre for Neurol. & Neurosurg. NHS Trust Liverp. Prev: Cons. Anaesth. & Pain Relief Walton Hosp. Liverp.

WILES, Philip Graham North Manchester General Hospital, Crumpsall, Manchester M8 5RB Tel: 0161 795 4567; Elm Bank, Garth Road, Marple, Stockport SK6 6PB — MD 1985 Manch.; BSc (Hons.) St. And. 1973; MB ChB 1976; MRCP (UK) 1980. Cons. Phys. N. Manch. Gen. Hosp. Socs: Brit. Diabetic Assn. (Mem. Med. & Scientif. Sect.); Med. Research Soc. Prev: Lect. & Hon. Sen. Regist. (Med.) Gen. Infirm. Leeds; Research Fell. (Diabetes) King's Coll. Hosp. Lond.; SHO (Med.) Manch. Roy. Infirm., N. Manch. Gen. & Altrincham Gen. Hosps.

WILEY, David James (retired) 74 Pembroke Road, Clifton, Bristol BS8 3EG Tel: 0117 973 7962 — MB BCh BAO 1959 Belf.; LAH Dub. 1959. Prev: Ho. Phys. & Ho. Surg. Belf. City Hosp.

WILEY, Paul Francis Wiley, Sinclair and Kettell, The Surgery, Pound Piece, Maiden Newton, Dorchester DT2 0DB Tel: 01300 320206 Fax: 01300 320399 — MB BS 1974 Newc.; MRCP (UK) 1977; MRCGP 1980. Prev: Regist. (Paediat.) Roy. United Hosp. Bath; SHO (Paediat.) Newc. Gen. Hosp.; Ho. Surg. (Profess. Surg. Unit) Roy. Vict. Infirm. Newc.

WILEY, Yvonne Victoria 1st Floor, 74 Pembroke Road, Clifton, Bristol BS8 3EG — MB BCh BAO Belf. 1958; FRCPsych 1984, M 1972; DPM Eng. 1970. Cons. Psychiat. (Ment. Handicap) Stoke Pk. Hosp. Bristol. Prev: Sen. Lect. Dept. Ment. Health Univ. Bristol; Cons. Psychiat. (Ment. Handicap) Stoke Pk. Hosp. Bristol.; Sen. Regist. Stoke Pk. Hosp. Bristol.

WILFIN, Andrew Henry 10 Whirlowdale Cl, Sheffield S11 9NQ; 154 Beaufort Park, Beaufort Drive, London NW11 6DA Tel: 020 8905 5658 Email: andrew@wilfin.free-online.co.uk — MB ChB 1997 Manch. Psych. SHO St mary's Rotat. Ealing Hosp.

WILFORD, Jane Mary 241 Wilton Street, Glasgow G20 6DE Tel: 0141 946 4332 Fax: 0141 3305018 Email: jw49a@clinmed.gla.ac.uk — MRCS Eng. LRCP Lond. 1991; DTM & H RCP Lond. 1993; MRCGP 1996; AFOM 1998. (University College, Middlesex School of Medicine, London University) Specialist. Occupat. Med. Salus; Lect. Occupat. Health Dept. Pub. Health Univ. Glas. Socs: Soc. Occupat. Med.

WILFORD, Nicholas John 46 Brancepeth View, Brandon, Durham DH7 8TT Tel: 0191 378 4152 — MB BS 1993 Newc.; BMedSc (Hons.) Newc. 1990; DGM 1996; MRCGP 1997. (Newcastle upon Tyne) GP. Socs: Brit. Assn. Sport & Med.

WILFORD, Peter John The Mote Medical Practice, St Saviours Road, Maidstone ME15 9FL Tel: 01622 756888 Fax: 01622 672573 — MB BS 1981 Lond.; MRCGP 1986; DRCOG 1985; DCH RCP Lond. 1983.

WILKEN, Mr Bertie James, MBE Fockerby Hall, Garthorpe, Scunthorpe DN17 4SA Tel: 01724 798323 Email: wilkinbjw@aol.com — MD 1967 Ed.; MB ChB 1958; FRCP Ed. 1974, M 1963; FRCS Eng. 1962; FRCS Ed. 1961. (Ed.) Hon. Cons. Surg., Acad. Surgic. Unit, Uni. Of Hull. Socs: Brit. Soc. Gastroenterol.; Assn. Coloproctol. Prev: Surg. Specialist Centr. Hosp. Honiara, Solomon Is.; Cons. & Sen. Lect. (Surg.) Wessex RHA; Ho. Surg., Ho. Phys. & Cas. Off. Roy. Infirm. Edin.

WILKEN, Eric Howard (retired) 21 Leadhall Road, Harrogate HG2 9PE Tel: 01423 871329 — MB BS 1945 Durh. Prev: Ho. Phys. Gen. Hosp. Newc.

WILKERSON, John Noel Victoria Medical Centre, 7 Victoria Crescent West, Barnsley S75 2AE Tel: 01226 282758 Fax: 01226 729800; 1 Whinmoor Drive, Silkstone, Barnsley S75 4NR Tel: 01226 791164 — MB 1974 Camb.; BA Camb. 1970, MB 1974, BChir 1973; FFA RCS 1980; DObst. RCOG 1975; Brit. Med. Acupuncture Soc. Dip. 1998. GP Princip.; Clin. Asst. (Palliat. Care) St Peter's Hospice Barnsley. Socs: Accred. Mem. BMAS.

WILKES, Anna 7 Ashley Close, Hendon, London NW4 1PH — MB BS 1947 Durh.; DPH 1954. (Newc.-On-Tyne) Clin. Med. Off. Brent HA. Prev: Asst. Co. Med. Off. Herts. CC; Asst. Med. Off. Middlx. CC, E. Ham, Durh. Co.

WILKES, Deborah Ann — MB ChB 1986 Leic.; MRCGP 1991; DRCOG 1991.

WILKES, Dennis 93 Witherford Croft, Solihull B91 1UA — MB ChB 1978 Liverp.; MRCGP 1983.

WILKES, Professor Eric, MBE, OBE Curbar View Farm, Calver, Hope Valley S32 3XR Tel: 01433 631291 — MB BChir 1952 Camb.; MA Camb. 1952; Hon. MD Sheff. 1986; FRCP Lond. 1974, M 1954; FRCPsych 1980, M 1975; FRCGP 1973; DObst RCOG 1955. (St. Thos.) Socs: Fell. Roy. Soc. Med.; Sheff. M-C Soc. Prev: Cons. Emerit. Trent Region Palliat. & Continuing Care Centre; Hon. Vice-Pres. Nat. Counc. for Hospice & Specialist Palliat. Care Servs.; Co-Pres. St Luke's Hospice Sheff.

WILKES, Graeme Prospect House Medical Group, Prospect House, Prospect Place, Newcastle upon Tyne NE4 6QD Tel: 0191 273 4201 Fax: 0191 273 0129 — MB BS 1984 Newc.; MRCP (UK) 1990; MRCGP 1993. Regist. (Cardiol.) GreenLa. Hosp. Auckland, NZ. Prev: Regist. (Med.) Auckland Hosp. NZ.

WILKES, Heather Frances Briton Ferry Health Centre, Hunter Street, Briton Ferry, Neath SA11 5SF Tel: 01639 812270 Fax: 01639 813019; 15 The Paddocks, Tonna, Neath SA11 3FD — MB ChB 1989 Bristol; MRCGP 1993.

WILKES, Jeannette Marie 32 Burton Road, Withington, Manchester M20 3EB Tel: 0161 445 5907 Fax: 0161 448 0466 — MB ChB 1985 Manch.; MRCGP 1989; DRCOG 1988; DCH RCPS Glas. 1987.

WILKES

WILKES, Judith Alison The Stanegate, Great Whittington, Newcastle upon Tyne NE19 2HA — MB BS 1981 Newc.; FFA RCS 1988. Cons. Anaesth. Newc. Gen. Hosp.

WILKES, Mark Peter Department of Anaesthesia and Intensive Care, Queen Elizabeth Hospital, Edgbaston, Birmingham Tel: 0121 472 1311; 91 Greenfield Road, Harborne, Birmingham B17 0EH Tel: 0121 426 2386 Fax: 0121 605 2009 Email: mark.wilkes@btinternet.com — MB ChB 1984 Birm.; FRCA 1991. (Birmingham) Cons. Anaesth. Qu. Eliz. Hosp. Birm.

WILKES, Michael Charles Thomas Worcestershire HA, Isaac Maddox House, Shrub Hill Road, Worcester WR4 9RW Tel: 01905 760019 Fax: 01905 28672 — MB BS 1959 Lond.; MRCS Eng. LRCP Lond. 1958; FFCM 1986, M 1973; DPH Lond. 1967; DObst RCOG 1960. (Univ. Coll. Hosp.) Cons. Pub. Health Med. Worcs. HA. Prev: DPH Kidderminster HA; Dep. MOH Bath Co. Boro.; Surg. Lt. RN.

WILKES, Muriel Mary (retired) 21 College Hill, Sutton Coldfield B73 6HA Tel: 0121 355 2191 — MB BS 1944 Lond.; MRCS Eng. LRCP Lond. 1944; DA Eng. 1947. Prev: Resid. Anaesth. Birm. United Hosps. & Roy. W. Sussex Hosp. Chichester.

WILKES, Nicholas c/o Doctors Residence, Royal National Orthopaedic Hospital, Brockley Hill, Stanmore HA7 4LP — State Exam Med 1986 Hamburg.

WILKES, Nicholas Andrew John (retired) Hay and Kilner Solicitors, Merchant House, 30 Cloth Market, Newcastle upon Tyne NE1 1EE — MB BS 1983 Lond.; MA (Legal Studies) Newc. 1995; MFPP 1993; MRCOG 1989. Solicitor Newc. u. Tyne. Prev: Regist. (O & G) P.ss Mary Matern. Hosp. & Roy. Vict. Infirm. Newc.

WILKES, Nicholas Paul Fisher 14 Stack House, West Hill, Oxted RH8 9JA — MB BS 1979 Lond.

WILKES, Peter Richard Balmacaan Road Surgery, Balmacaan Road, Drumnadrochit, Inverness IV63 6UR Tel: 01456 450577 Fax: 01456 450799; Balnacraig, Drumnadrochit, Inverness IV63 6UX — MB ChB 1983 Glas.; PhD Glas. 1980; MPhil Reading 1976; BSc AKC Lond. 1973; MRCGP 1987; DCH RCPS Glas. 1986; DRCOG 1985. GP Culloden, Inverness.

WILKES, Robert Geoffrey 27B Warren Drive, Wallasey CH45 0JW Tel: 0151 639 6559 Fax: 0151 702 4006 — MB ChB 1966 Birm.; FFA RCS Eng. 1972. Clin. Dir. (Intens. Care) Roy. Liverp. Univ. Trust Hosp.

WILKES, Scott Coquet Medical Group, Amble Health Centre, Percy Drive, Amble, Morpeth NE65 0HD Tel: 01665 710481 Fax: 01665 713031 — MB ChB 1990 Leeds; MRCGP 1994; DRCOG 1993; DFFP 1993. Prev: Trainee GP Morpeth & Durh.; SHO (Psychiat.) Sunderland.

WILKEY, Anthony Donald 63 Stonerwood Avenue, Hall Green, Birmingham B28 0AX — MB ChB 1980 Birm.; FFA RCS Eng. 1985. Cons. Anaesth. Birm. Matern. & Qu. Eliz. Hosps. Birm. Prev: Sen. Regist. (Anaesth.) Midl. Anaesth. Train. Sch.; Vis. Asst. Prof. Univ. Texas Med. Br. Galveston.

WILKEY, Brian Reginald (retired) 42 Tunwells Lane, Great Shelford, Cambridge CB2 5LJ Tel: 01223 843061 — BM BCh 1958 Oxf.; FFA RCS Eng. 1964; DA Eng. 1962. Cons. Anaesth. Addenbrooke's Hosp. Camb.; Assoc. Lect. Univ. Camb. Prev: Sen. Regist. (Anaesth.) Univ. Coll. Hosp. Lond.

WILKIE, Alexandra Wightman Quartercormick, Downpatrick BT30 — MB BCh BAO 1955 Belf.; MFCM 1977.

WILKIE, Professor Andrew Oliver Mungo Institute of Molecular Medicine, The John Radcliffe, Oxford OX3 9DS Tel: 01865 222619 Fax: 01865 222500 — BM BCh 1983 Oxf.; MA Oxf. 1992, DM 1992; MA Camb. 1984, BA 1980; MRCP (UK) 1986; DCH RCP Lond. 1987; FRCP Lond. 1998. Wellcome Sen. Research Fell. (Clin. Sci.) Inst. Molecular Med. Oxf; Hon. Cons. Clin. Genetics. Ch.ill Hosp. Oxf. & Oxf. Craniofacial Unit Radcliffe Infirm; Prof. of Genetics, Univ. of Oxf. Prev: Sen. Regist. (Clin. Genetics) Univ. Hosp. Wales; Dysmorphol. Fell. (Paediat. Genetics) Inst. Child Health Lond.; MRC Train. Fell. MRC Molecular Haemat. Unit Oxf.

WILKIE, Clare Elizabeth Brixton Hill Group Practice, 22 Raleigh Gardens, London SW2 1AE Tel: 020 8674 6376 Fax: 020 8671 0283 — MB BS 1984 Lond.; BA Camb. 1976; MRCGP 1989; DRCOG 1987. Prev: Trainee GP St. Thos. Lond. VTS.

WILKIE, David John Port Glasgow Health Centre, 2-4 Bay Street, Port Glasgow PA14 5ED Tel: 01475 74532; 26 Douglas Avenue, Langbank, Port Glasgow PA14 6PE — MB ChB 1980 Glas.; MRCGP 1984; DRCOG 1983.

WILKIE, Douglas John Kenneth Rose Cottage, Lower Sandy Down Lane, Boldre, Lymington SO41 8PP — MRCS Eng. LRCP Lond. 1945; DOMS Eng. 1950.

WILKIE, Irene Abercromby (retired) — MB ChB 1959 Aberd. Prev: Med. Off. Bd. of World Mission Ch. of Scotl. Edin.

WILKIE, Jill Nicola 116 Bellingdon Road, Chesham HP5 2HF Tel: 01494 792962 Email: jillwilkie@hotmail.com — MB BS 1991 Lond.; FRCR 2000; BSc (1st. cl. Hons.) Pharm. 1988; MRCP (UK) 1994. p/t Regist. (Radiol.) Roy. Lond. Trust. Socs: BMA; Roy. Coll. Phys.; Roy. Coll. Radiol. Prev: SHO Rotat. (Med.) Roy. Lond. Trust.; Ho. Off. (Gen. Med.) Chase Farm Hosp.; Ho. Off. (Gen. Surg. & Urol.) Edgware Gen. Hosp.

WILKIE, Mr John Leonard (retired) Room 6, Abbeyfield Home, Danby Lodge, Ashcroft Road, Darlington DL3 8PD — MB ChB 1929 Ed.; FRCS Ed. 1932. Prev: Ophth. Surg. Darlington Memor. Hosp. & Newc. Eye Hosp.

WILKIE, John Richard Fowey House, 108 Berrybrook Meadow, Exminster, Exeter EX6 8UA — MB BS 1966 Lond.; MSc (Social Med.) Lond. 1973; DMRT Eng. 1971. (Lond. Hosp.) Staff Psychiat. Regional Secure Unit.Langdon Hosp. Dawlish. Socs: BMA; Affil. Roy. Coll. Psychiat.; Worshipful Soc. Apoth. Prev: Staff Psychiat. Cornw. & I. of Scilly HA; Regist. (Psychiat.) Exeter HA; Community Phys. Som. & Waltham Forest HAs.

WILKIE, Lesley McIntosh Ross House, Hawkhead Road, Paisley PA2 7BN Tel: 0141 842 7213 Fax: 0141 848 0165 — MB ChB 1975 Glas.; MSc Community Med. Manch. 1988; MFCM 1989; FFPHM RCP (UK) 1996, M 1989. (Glas.) Dir. Pub. Health Argyll & Clyde HB. Prev: Cons. Pub. Health Med. Argyll & Clyde HB; Sen. Regist. (Community Med.) NW RHA.

WILKIE, Martin Erskine The Sheffield Kidney Institute, Northern General Hospital NHS Trust, Herries Road, Sheffield S5 7AU Tel: 0114 243 4343 Fax: 0114 256 2514 Email: m.wilkie@sheffield.ac.uk — MB ChB 1984 Manch.; BSc St. And. 1981; MD Manch. 1994; MRCP (UK) 1987; FRCP(Lond) 1999. (St. And. & Manch.) Cons. Renal Phys. Sheff. Kidney Inst. Socs: Brit. Transpl. Soc.; Renal Assn.; Eur. Dialysis & Transpl.Assn. Prev: Sen. Regist. (Nephrol.) Sheff. Kidney Inst; Research Fell. (Nephrol.) Lond. Hosp.; Regist. (Nephrol.) Univ. Hosp. S. Manch.

WILKIE, Mary (retired) 2 Northgate, Lincoln LN2 1QS Tel: 01522 523231 — MB ChB 1956 Sheff.; DCH Eng. 1958. Prev: Ho. Phys. Roy. Hosp. Sheff. & Sheff. Childr. Hosp.

WILKIE, Michael John 24 Leggart Terrace, Aberdeen AB12 5UB Tel: 01224 873589 — MB ChB 1995 Aberd.

WILKIE, Pippa 24 Bramwith Road, Sheffield S11 7EZ — MB ChB 1990 Sheff.

WILKIE, Rosalie Anne 37 Meadowview Drive, Inchture, Perth PH14 9RQ — MB ChB 1977 Ed.; MRCP (UK) 1980.

WILKIE, Stewart Christopher 1/76 Kennishead Avenue, Thornliebank, Glasgow G46 8RT — MB ChB 1995 Glas.

WILKIE, Stuart The Surgery, Hemming Way, Chaddesley Corbett, Kidderminster DY10 4SF Tel: 01562 777239 Fax: 01562 777196; Ashcroft, Quarry Bank, Hartlebury, Kidderminster DY11 7TE — MB ChB 1987 Birm.; ChB Birm. 1987; DGM RCP Lond. 1992; DRCOG 1991; DCH RCP Lond. 1990.

WILKIE, Veronica Mary Myrtle Cottage, Quarry Bank, Hartlebury, Kidderminster DY11 7TE — MB ChB 1987 Birm.; MRCGP 1992; Dip. Occ. Med. 1996; DRCOG 1991; DCH 1990; DGM RCP Lond. 1989. (Birm.) Socs: Droitwich Med. Soc.

WILKIE, William Joseph Strone Place Surgery, Strone Place, Strone, Dunoon PA23 8RR Tel: 01369 840279 Fax: 01369 840664 Email: dministrator@gp84716-ac-hb-scot.nhs.uk; Tandiwe, Shore Road, Strone, Dunoon PA23 8TB Tel: 01369 840556 — MB ChB 1968 Glas. GP & Clin. Asst. Geriat. Unit & Day Hosp. Dunoon & Dist. Gen. Hosp. Argyll. Socs: Founder Mem. Cowal Med. Soc.

WILKIESON, Carol Anne Royal Alexandra Hospital, Paisley PA2 9PN — MB ChB 1983 Glas.; MRCP (UK) 1986; FRCP Glas. 1997. Cons. Phys. Med for Elderly Roy. Alexandra Hosp. Paisley. Socs: Brit. Geriat. Soc. Prev: Sen. Regist. (Geriat. Med.) Vict. Geriat. Univ. Glas.; Sen. Regist. (Med.) Gartnavel Gen. Hosp. Glas. & Stobhill Hosp.; Sen. Regist. (Geriat. Med.) S. Gen. Hosp. Glas.

WILKIN, David John Whiteley 55 St Stephens Road, Ealing, London W13 8JA — MB BS 1970 Lond.; MRCOG 1976.

WILKINS

WILKIN, John Marmaduke (retired) 28 Scarthoe Road, Grimsby DN33 2AD Tel: 01472 77543 — MB BChir 1939 Camb. Prev: Ho. Phys. St. Mary's Hosp.

WILKIN, Lucy Margaret (retired) 2 The Mews, Newton Park, Newton Solney, Burton-on-Trent DE15 0SU Tel: 01283 702168 — MB BCh BAO Belf. 1945. Community Med. Off. S.E. Staffs. HA.

WILKIN, Peter Michael Rowan 43 Charnmouth Court, St Albans AL1 4SJ — MB ChB 1976 Aberd.; DRCOG 1980.

WILKIN, Professor Terence James University of Plymouth, Department Medicine, Buckland House, Drake Circus, Plymouth PL4 8AA Tel: 01752 232925 Fax: 01752 232925 Email: t.wilkin@plymouth.ac.uk; Tel: 01822 855117 Fax: 01822 855117 — MD 1978 Dundee; MD (Commend.) Dundee 1978; MB ChB St. And. 1969; FRCP Lond. 1988; MRCP (UK) 1972; FRCP (Ed) 1999. Prof. Med. Univ. Plymouth; Hon. Cons. Phys. SW Region. Socs: Assn. Phys. & Roy. Soc. Med.; Diabetes UK; Amer. Diabetes Ass. Prev: Reader (Med. Endocrinol.) Univ. Soton.; Wellcome Sen. Lect. (Endocrinol.) Univ. Soton.; Lect. (Therap.) Univ. Dundee.

WILKIN, William Mitchel (retired) 2 The Mews, Newton Park, Newton Solney, Burton-on-Trent DE15 0SU Tel: 01283 702168 — MB BCh BAO 1945 Belf. Prev: Ho. Surg. Belf. City Hosp. & Jubilee Matern. Hosp. Belf.

WILKINS, Alastair MRC Cambridge Centre for Brain Repair, Forvie Site, Cambridge CB2 2PY Tel: 01223 231168 — MB BChir 1994 Camb.; MA (Hons.) Camb. 1995; MRCP (UK) 1996. (Camb.) Research.Reg./Hon.Clin.fell.Addenbrookes Hosp.Camb. Socs: Assn. Brit. Neurol.; BMA. Prev: Specialist Regist. (Neurol.) Norf. & Norwich Hosp.; SHO Nat. Hosp. Neurol.; SHO Rotat. (Med.) Sheff.

***WILKINS, Alexandre** 14 Kinnaird Av, Bromley BR1 4HG — MB ChB 1997 Birm.

WILKINS, Andrew Norman John 7 Abbey Meadow, Lelant, St Ives TR26 3LL Tel: 01736 756427; 9 Holmesland lane, Botley, Southampton SO32 1BY Tel: 01489 787901 Email: awilkins@clara.co.uk — MB ChB 1986 Manch.; DA 1989; FRCA 1994. (Manchester) Cons. Anaesth., S.ampton Gen. Hosp.

WILKINS, Angela Cameron Anaesthetic Department, Queen Alexandra Hospital, Cosham, Portsmouth Tel: 02392 286279 Fax: 02392 286681 Email: wilkins@qmail01.portosp.swest.nhs.uk; 9 Holmesland Lane, Botley, Southampton SO30 2EH Tel: 01489 787901 Email: awilkins@clara.co.uk — MB BS 1987 Adelaide; FRCA 1995. p/t Cons. in Anaesth., Portsmouth Hosps. NHS Trust, Portsmouth. Socs: Obstetric Anaesth.s Assn.

WILKINS, Mrs Anne Hazel 35 Fernside Road, Bournemouth BH9 2LB Tel: 01202 525471 — MB ChB 1998 Ed.; MB ChB Ed 1998. Prev: PRHO Gen surg Borders Gen Hosp.Melrose; PRHO Resp med.Roy.Infir.Edin.

WILKINS, Anthony John The Cardinal Clinic, Oakley Green Road, Windsor SL4 5UL Tel: 01753 869755 Fax: 01753 842852 Email: psyco@gppfs.clemon.co.uk; 14 Devonshire Place, London W1N 1PB Tel: 020 7935 0640 Fax: 020 7224 6256 — BSc Lond. 1975; MRCPsych 1983. (Roy. Free) Cons. Psychiat.heatherwood Hosp. Lond Rd, Ascot, Berks. SL5 8AA; Lect. (Forens. Psychiat.) Univ. Lond.

WILKINS, Bernard (retired) 52 Devonshire Court, New Hall Road, Salford M7 4JT — M.B., Ch.B. Manch. 1944.

WILKINS, Bridget Sally Pathology Department, Level E South Block, Southampton General Hospital, Tremona Road, Southampton SO16 6YD Tel: 02380 794946 Fax: 02380 796603 — MB BChir Camb. 1983; MRCPath 1990; DM Soton. 1992; PhD Soton. 1996; FRCPath 1999. (London and Cambridge) Sen. Lect. (Path.) Soton. Univ.; Honourary Cons. Histopath., S.ampton Univ. Socs: Europ. Ass for haematoPath.; Brit. lymphoma pathologists gp.; Path. Soc. Prev: Clin. Research Fell. (Path.) Soton. Univ.; Lect. (Path.) Soton. Univ.; Regist. (Path.) Leeds Gen. Infirm.

WILKINS, Carolyn Anne 22 Devonshire Place, London W1 Tel: 020 7935 9366; The Coach House, 71 West Drive, Harrow HA3 6TX Tel: 020 8954 5175 — MB ChB 1968 Birm.; DObst RCOG 1970. (Birm.) Specialist (Psychosexual Med.) Lond. Socs: Inst. Psychosexual Med. Prev: Research Fell. (Epidemiol.) Yale Univ., USA; Resid. (O & G) Univ. Miami, USA.

WILKINS, Christopher Jason 127 New Street, Andover SP10 1DR — BM BCh 1992 Oxf.

WILKINS, Christopher John The Oaks, 15 Barlaston Old Road, Trentham, Stoke-on-Trent ST4 8HD Email: cwilkins4@compuserve.com — MB ChB 1981 Bristol; FFA RCS Eng. 1987. Cons. Anaesth. N. Staffs. HA.; RCA Coll. Tutor. Prev: Sen. Regist. (Anaesth.) Yorks. RHA; Lect. (Anaesth.) Univ. Leic.

WILKINS, Clare Elizabeth — MB ChB 1992 Bristol; MRCP 1996. p/t Specialist Regist. (Paediat.) St. Mary's Hosp. Manch. Socs: BMA. Prev: Specialist Regist. (Paediat.) Addenbrooke's Hosp. Camb.; Specialist Resist. (Paediat.) Roy. Manch. Childr.'s Hosp.; Specialist Regist. (Paediat.) Ipswich Hosp. Ipswich.

WILKINS, Daniel Christian 14 Belcombe Place, Bradford-on-Avon BA15 1NA — MB ChB 1995 Bristol.

WILKINS, David Gordon (retired) Central Farm, Little-upon-Severn, Bristol BS35 1NR Tel: 01454 412233 Fax: 01454 281529 Email: dgwilkins@compuserve.com — MA, MB Camb. 1962, BChir 1961; DObst RCOG 1963; DA Eng. 1964; FFA RCS Eng. 1969. Prev: Cons. Anaesth. Bristol Healthcare trust.

WILKINS, Mr Denis Charles Nuffield Hospital, Plymouth PL6 8BG — MB ChB Liverp. 1966; MD Liverp. 1974; FRCS Eng. 1973. Cons. Gen. , Vasc. and endocrinological Surg.; Sen. Lect., Plymouth Postgrad. Med. Sch.; Examr., Intercollegiate Bd. of Surg., UK and Irel.; Chairm., Med. Staff Comm., Derriford Hosp., Plymouth; Chairm. Ct. of Examr.s Roy. Coll. of Surg.s of Eng.; Non exec director Brit. Antarctic survey Med. unit; Chair., SAC in Gen. Surg. , GB + Irel.; Surgic. Tutor, Roy. Coll. of Surg.s of Eng. Socs: Brit. Soc. Endocrine Surgs.; Mem. Vasc. Surg. Soc. GB & Irel.; Mem. Brit. Transpl. Soc. Prev: Past Chairm. regional Train. com in Gen. Surg., SW region; Sen. Regist. (Surg.) Addenbrooke's Hosp. Camb.; Med. Off. Brit. Antarctic Survey 1969.

WILKINS, Denise Elizabeth Maria Proctor and Partners, Doctors Surgery, 42 Heaton Road, Heaton, Newcastle upon Tyne NE6 1SE Tel: 0191 265 5911 Fax: 0191 265 6974; 14 Elmfield Road, Gosforth, Newcastle upon Tyne NE3 4AY Tel: 0191 285 6228 — MB ChB 1977 Dundee; MRCGP 1981; DRCOG 1979; Cert. JCC Lond. 1979.

WILKINS, Derek Charles, CBE Yew Tree Cottage, Webbs Green, Soberton, Southampton SO32 3PY Tel: 01489 877715; Yew Tree Cottage, Webbs Green, Soberton, Southampton SO32 2PY Tel: 01489 877715 — MB BS 1952 Lond.; MRCS Eng. LRCP Lond. 1952; DObst RCOG 1955. (Guy's) Brig. late RAMC(V); Civil. Med. Pract. MoD (Army). Prev: Ho. Phys., Asst. Ho. Surg. & Resid. (Obst.) Guy's Hosp.

WILKINS, Derrin Felicity 4 Sunnyside Cottages, Aldermaston Road, Basingstoke RG24 9LA — MB BS 1989 Lond.

WILKINS, Edmund Lygon North Manchester General Hospital, Delaunay's Road, Crumpsall, Manchester M8 6RL Tel: 0161 720 2733 Fax: 0161 720 2732 — MB BS 1977 Lond.; MRCP (UK) 1980; MRCPath 1987; FRCP Lond. 1996; FRCPath 1997; Dip. Bact. Manch. 1985; DTM & H Liverp. 1978. (Middlx.) Cons. Phys. Infec. Dis. N. Manch. Gen. Hosp. Socs: Brit. Soc. Study of Infec. Prev: Sen. Regist. (Infec. Dis.) N.wick Pk. Hosp. Middlx.; Sen. Regist. (Med. Microbiol.) Pub. Health Laborat. Portsmouth; Regist. (Med. Microbiol.) Pub. Health Laborat. Liverp.

WILKINS, Elizabeth Ann Llwyn Brwydrau Surgery, 3 Frederick Place, Llansamlet, Swansea SA7 9RY Tel: 01792 771465 — MB BS 1983 Lond.; MRCGP 1988.

WILKINS, Evelyn Margaret (retired) 78 Armorial Road, Styvechale, Coventry CV3 6GJ Tel: 024 76 414675 — MB ChB 1941 Birm.; MB ChB (Hons.) Birm. 1941. Prev: Sen. Med. Off. Coventry AHA (Child Health).

WILKINS, Geoffrey Selwyn Flat 1, Merlewood, 17 Langham Road, Bowdon, Altrincham WA14 2HT; Ordsall Health Centre, Salford M5 3PP Tel: 0161 877 0564 — MB ChB Manch. 1963; DObst RCOG 1965.

WILKINS, Helen Margaret 460 Didsbury Road, Heaton Mersey, Stockport SK4 3BT — BM 1979 Soton.; MRCGP 1983; DRCOG 1982. p/t Gen. Practitioner.

WILKINS, Helen Mary Redwynde, 4 North Close, Bromborough, Wirral CH62 2BU Tel: 0151 334 5206 — MB ChB 1982 Liverp. SCMO Wom. Serv. Wirral Community Healthcare NHS Trust. Socs: Accred. Mem. Brit. Assn. Sexual & Marital Ther. Prev: Trainee GP Ellesmere Port; SHO Arrowe Pk. Hosp. Upton; Ho. Off. Clatterbridge Hosp. Bebington.

WILKINS, Hubert Andrew 40 Overstrand Mansions, Prince of Wales Drive, Battersea Park, London SW11 4EZ — MB BChir 1964

WILKINS

Camb.; MA, MB BChir Camb. 1964; DTM & H Eng. 1968; DObst 1967.

WILKINS, Ingrid Anne 103 Bromham Road, Bedford MK40 4BS; 253 Queen Edith's Way, Cambridge CB1 8NJ — MB BS 1994 Lond.; BSc Lond. 1993; Dip. ATLS RCS Eng. 1995; ALS 1996; PALS 1997. (St. Bart. Hosp. Med. Sch.) SHO (Anaesth.) Camb. Prev: SHO (Neonates.) Homerton Lond.; SHO Rotat. (Anaesth.) Nottm.; SHO (A & E) N.. Gen. Hosp. Sheff.

WILKINS, Joanne Southcroft, 7 Clinton Road, Penarth CF64 3JB — BM BCh 1985 Oxf.; MA; MRCGP 1989; DRCOG 1987. p/t GP Retainee. Prev: Princip. in Gen. Pract., WhiteHo. Surg., Chipping Norton, Oxon.

WILKINS, Mr John Latreille (retired) City Hospital, Hucknall Road, Nottingham NG5 1P — MB 1961 Camb.; FRCS Eng. 1965; DObst RCOG 1962. Prev: Cons. Gen. Surg. Nottm. City Hosp.

WILKINS, John Leonard (retired) Flat 28, High Trees, Carew Road, Eastbourne BN21 2JB Tel: 01323 730865 — MB BS Lond. 1951; FRCP Ed. 1977, M 1960; MRCS Eng. LRCP Lond. 1951; DCH Eng. 1959; FRCPCH 1997. Prev: Sen. Research Assoc. Dept. Child Health Univ. Newc.

WILKINS, Lisa Katherine Coldharbour, Sand Down Lane, Newton St Cyres, Exeter EX5 5DF — BM 1992 Soton.; MRCP. Staff Grade Palliat. Med. St Annes Hosp Salford. Prev: SHO (Haemat.) Univ. Hosp. Wales Cardiff; SHO (Med.) Roy. Devon & Exeter Hosp.; S. SHO (Med.) Roy. Gwent Hosp. Newport.

WILKINS, Margaret Caroline Village Surgery, Gillett Road, Poole BH12 5BF Tel: 01202 525252 Fax: 01202 533956 — MB ChB 1967 Bristol; DObst RCOG 1969. (Bristol) Princip. In Gen. Pract. Village Surg. Poole; Clin. Asst. BrE. Clinic Roy. Bournemouth Hosp. Prev: Med. Off. Family Plann. Clinic Potters Bar; SHO (Obst.) City Matern. Hosp. Carlisle; Med. Off. Maseno Hosp., Kenya.

WILKINS, Margaret Freda West Wales General Hospital, Carmarthen SA31 2AF Tel: 01267 227616; 39 Llythrid Avenue, Uplands, Swansea SA2 0JJ Tel: 01792 297544 — MB ChB 1974 Bristol; BSc Bristol 1971; FRCR 1984. Cons. Clin. Oncol. W. Wales Gen. Hosp. Carmarthen. Prev: Staff Grade (Radiother.) Singleton Hosp. Swansea; Sen. Regist. (Radiother.) Velindre Hosp. Cardiff.

WILKINS, Margaret Janet Elizabeth Department of Pathology, Bedford Hospital, Kempston Road, Bedford MK42 9DJ Tel: 01234 792094 Fax: 01234 795886 Email: margaret.wilkins@bedhos.anglox.nhs.uk; Yew Trees, Windmill Hill, Hitchin SG4 9RT Tel: 01462 432457 — MB BS 1984 Lond.; MSc Lond. 1986; MRCPath 1992; FRCPath 2000. (Roy. Free) Cons. Histopath. & Cytopath., Bedford Hosp. Bedford. Prev: Sen. Regist. (Histopath.) St. Mary's Hosp. Lond.; Regist. (Histopath.) Hammersmith Hosp. Lond.; SHO/Regist. (Histopath.) Roy. Free Hosp. Lond.

WILKINS, Marie 7 Badgers Walk, Traps Lane, New Malden KT3 4RX — MB BCh 1984 Wales.

WILKINS, Mark Richard Institute of Ophthalmology, Bath St., London EC1V 9EL Tel: 020 7608 6942 Fax: 020 7608 6887 Email: m.wilkins@ucl.ac.uk; Flat 2, 98 Greencroft Gardens, London NW6 3PH Email: mwilkins@easynet.co.uk — MB BS 1990 Lond.; BA (Physiol. Sci.) Oxf. 1987; FRCOphth 1994. Research Fell. Inst. Ophth. Lond.; Research Regist. Moorfields Eye Hosp. Lond. Prev: SHO (Ophth.) King's Coll. Hosp., St. Geo. Hosp. & Frimley Pk. Hosp. Lond.

WILKINS, Martin Russell 4 Wakefield Crescent, Stoke Poges, Slough SL2 4BL — MB ChB 1979 Birm.

WILKINS, Matthew Latreille Department of Anaesthesia, West Suffolk Hospital, Bury St Edmunds IP33 2QZ Tel: 01284 713000 Fax: 01284 701993; Goverton Hill, Goverton, Bleasby, Nottingham NG14 7FN Tel: 01636 830266 — MB BS 1993 Newc. SHO (Anaesth.) W. Suff. Hosp. Bury St. Edmunds. Socs: BMA. Prev: SHO (A & E) Qu. Med. Centre Nottm.; SHO (Renal Transpl. & Med.) Roy. Vict. Infirm. Newc.

WILKINS, Mr Michael Hugh Queen Elizabeth II Hospital, Welwyn Garden City AL7 4HQ Tel: 01707 328111 — MB BS 1969 Lond.; FRCS Ed. 1976; FRCOG 1993, M 1975. (Middlx.) Cons. O & G Qu. Eliz. II Hosp. Welwyn Garden City & Hertford Co. Hosp. Socs: Brit. Soc. Colpos. & Cerv. Path.; BMA. Prev: Sen. Regist. (O & G) Whittington Hosp. & Univ. Coll. Hosp. Lond.; Regist. (O & G) Middlx. Hosp. Lond.; Resid. Med. & Surg. Off. Qu. Charlotte's Hosp. for Wom. Lond.

WILKINS, Peter Hendy The Surgery, 13 Fallodon Way, Henleaze, Bristol BS9 4HT Tel: 0117 962 0652 Fax: 0117 962 0839; 41 Bellevue Crescent, Clifton, Bristol BS8 4TF — MB ChB 1972 Bristol; DObst RCOG 1975. Clin. Asst. (Psycho Geriats.).

WILKINS, Peter Rigby 7 Badgers Walk, Traps Lane, New Malden KT3 4RX — MB BCh 1980 Wales.

WILKINS, Philip 78A New Dover Road, Canterbury CT1 3EQ — BChir 1990 Camb.

WILKINS, Philip Samuel Weston (retired) April Cottage, Prinsted Lane, Prinsted, Emsworth PO10 8HR Tel: 01243 377074 — MB ChB Birm. 1949; FRCP Lond. 1974, M 1960; DCH Eng. 1954. Cons. Phys. (Geriat.) Portsmouth & SE Hants. Health Dist.

WILKINS, Richard Anthony Cleveland House, 16 Spital Terrace, Gainsborough DN21 2HF Tel: 01427 613158 Fax: 01427 616644; 66 Willingham Road, Knaith Park, Gainsborough DN21 5ET Tel: 01427 810293 — MB ChB 1987 Dundee; MRCGP 1993. (Dundee)

WILKINS, Robert Anthony Wellington Hospital, Wellington Place, London NW8 9LE Tel: 020 7483 5078; The Coach House, 71 West Drive, Harrow HA3 6TX Tel: 020 8954 5175 — MB ChB 1964 Birm.; BSc Birm. 1961; FFR 1969; DMRD Eng. 1967. (Birm.) p/t Director of Radiol., Wellington Hosp. Prev: Cons. Radiol. N.wick Pk. Hosp. Harrow.

WILKINS, Sidney William (retired) Annedd Wen, Ruthin Road, Denbigh LL16 4RA Tel: 01745 812420 — MB ChB 1950 Birm.; MRCS Eng. LRCP Lond. 1949. Prev: Clin. Asst. (Psychiat.) N. Wales Hosp. Denbigh.

WILKINS, William Edward The Elms, Pen-y-Fai, Bridgend CF31 4LS — MB BCh 1972 Wales; MRCP (U.K.) 1976.

WILKINSON, Agnes Hallimond 54 Stokes Court, Diploma Avenue, East Finchley, London N2 8NX Tel: 020 8883 3680 — MB ChB Birm. 1939; MRCP Lond. 1942; FRCPsych 1985, M 1971. (Birm.) Profess. Mem. Soc. Analyt. Psychol. Socs: Gp. Analyt. Soc. Prev: Chairm. Med. Sect. Brit. Psychol. Soc.; Psychiat. Adviser Lond. Sch. of Economics; Phys. i/c Studs. Health Serv. Univ. Bristol.

WILKINSON, Alan Edward (retired) 22 Kingsend, Ruislip HA4 7DA Tel: 01895 635829 — MB BS Lond. 1951; MRCS Eng. LRCP Lond. 1939; FRCPath 1968. Prev: Director VD Refer. Laborat., The Lond. Hosp.

WILKINSON, Mr Alan James Belfast City Hospital, Lisburn Road, Belfast BT9 7AB Tel: 01232 263792; 16 Malone View Road, Belfast BT9 5PH Tel: 01232 616115 — MB BCh BAO 1973 Belf.; MD Belf. 1984; FRCS Ed. 1978. Cons. Surg. Belf. City Hosp. Prev: Cons. Surg. Roy. Vict. Hosp. Belf.; Sen. Surg. Tutor & Sen. Regist. Dept. Surg. Roy. Vict. Hosp. Belf.; Sen. Regist. Roy. Vict. Hosp. Belf.

WILKINSON, Mr Alan Royce Hull HU10 7TL Tel: 01482 653289; Springfield House Rise Road, Skirlaugh HU 11 5BH — MB ChB 1967 Sheff.; FRCS 1973 Eng.; FRCS Eng. 1973. (Sheff.) Cons. Surg. Hull Roy. Infirm.; Clin. Director, Critical Care. Socs: Ct. of Examrs. RCS Eng.; (Venous Forum) Vasc. Soc. Prev: Lect. (Surg.) Qu. Eliz. Hosp. Birm.; Regist. (Surg.) Gen. Infirm. Leeds; Ho. Surg. Roy. Infirm. Sheff.

WILKINSON, Alison Joan P.C.E.A. Chogoria Hospital, PO Box 35, Chogoria, Kenya; 70 Craigleith Hill Gardens, Edinburgh EH4 2JH — MB ChB 1976 Ed.; MRCOG 1991; DRCOG 1979. Specialist Obst. & Gyn. Pcea Chogoria Hosp. Kenya. Prev: Regist. (Obst. & Gyn.) Stirling Roy. Infirm.; SHO (Obst. & Gyn.) Furness Gen. Hosp. Barrow-in-Furness; SHO Regist. (Obst.) Nazareth Hosp. Israel.

WILKINSON, Alistair Thomas Great Western Road Medical Group, 327 Great Western Road, Aberdeen AB10 6LT Tel: 01224 571318 Fax: 01224 573865; 58 Cairnlee Avenue E., Cults, Aberdeen AB15 9NH — MB ChB 1975 Aberd.; FRCGP 194; MRCGP 1979.

WILKINSON, Mr Alwyn (retired) 26 Selkirk Avenue, Oldham OL8 4DQ Tel: 0161 624 9029 — MB ChB 1949 Manch.; FRCS Eng. 1961. Prev: Cons. Orthop. & Traum. Surg. Oldham Hosp.

WILKINSON, Andrea Janet Orchards Medical Centre, 10 Leigh Road, Boothstown, Worsley, Manchester M28 1CX; 65 Border Brook Lane, Worsley, Manchester M28. 1XJ — MB ChB 1990 Manch.; BSc (Hons.) Manch. 1987; MRCOG 1995; MRCOG 1997. (Manchester) GP Princip. Prev: Regist. NW Region; Clin. Research Fell.

WILKINSON, Andrew Cameron Howitt c/o Dr Martin Prior, 3 Rooke Way, London SE10 0JB — MB ChB 1947 New Zealand; FRACP 1973, M 1956.

WILKINSON

WILKINSON, Andrew John 93 Christchurch Street, Ipswich IP4 2DD Tel: 01473 212842 — MB BS 1966 Lond.; MRCGP 1978. (Lond. Hosp.) Prev: SHO (Med.) Ipswich & E. Suff. Hosp.; SHO (Clin. Pathol.) Lond. Hosp.; Phys. Whipps Cross Hosp.

WILKINSON, Andrew Mark Charles Andrews Clinic, West End, Redruth TR15 2SF Tel: 01209 881810 Fax: 01209 881816 Email: amwilkinson@yahoo.com — MB BS 1984 Newc.; MRCPsych 1988. Cons. Psychiat. of Old Age Cornw. Healthcare Trust. Prev: Cons. Psychiat. of Age Wirral Hosp. Trust; Sen. Regist. (Psychiat.) Mersey RHA; Regist. (Psychiat.) N. Yorks. GP VTS.

WILKINSON, Andrew Peter Descarrieres Castle Douglas Medical Group, Castle Douglas Health Centre, Academy Street, Castle Douglas DG7 1EE; Lochbank, Castle Douglas DG7 1TH Tel: 01556 503413 — MB ChB Ed. 1969; BSc (Med. Sci.) Ed. 1966; DObst RCOG 1972. (Edinbrgh) Brit. Med. Off. Brit. Red Cross Soc. Socs: BMA. Prev: Mem. & Vice-Chaim. Dumfries & Galloway HB; Mem. & Chairm. Dumfries & Galloway L.C.; Mem. SGMSC.

WILKINSON, Andrew Richard Broadshields Health Centre, Broadshields Way, Carterton OX18 1JA Tel: 01993 844567 Fax: 01993 841551; Northford House, Langford, Lechade GL7 3LW Tel: 01367 860508, 01623 795926 Email: andrewwilkinson@oxfordmedicolegal.com — MB BS 1974 Lond.; BSc Lond. 1970; MRCS Eng. LRCP Lond. 1974; MRCGP 1978; DMJ (Clin.) 1997; DFFP 1996; DRCOG 1979. (Lond. Hosp.) Tutor (Gen. Pract.) Univ. Oxf.; Police Surg. Thames Valley Police & Wilts. Constab.; Div. Surg. St. John Ambul. Socs: Oxf. Medico legal Soc. Prev: SHO (Paediat. & O & G) John Radcliffe Hosp. Oxf.; SHO (Med.) Warwick Hosp.

WILKINSON, Professor Andrew Robert Neonatal Unit, Department of Paediatrics, John Radcliffe Maternity Hospital, Oxford OX3 9DU Tel: 01865 221355 Fax: 01865 221366 Email: andrew.wilkinson@paediatrics.ox.ac.uk — MB ChB 1968 Birm.; MA Oxf. 1992; FRCP Lond. 1986; MRCP (UK) 1972; FRCPCH 1997; DCH Eng. 1972. Prof. of Paediat. Univ. Oxf. John Radcliffe Hosp.; Hon. Cons. Paediat. Oxf. Radcliffe NHS Trust; Fell. All Souls Coll. Oxf.

WILKINSON, Anita Margaret Southgate Surgery, 2 Forester Road, Southgate, Crawley RH10 6EQ Tel: 01293 522231 Fax: 01293 515655 — MB ChB 1988 Manch.; MRCP (UK) 1997; DCH RCP Lond. 1993. (Manch.) GP Crawley. Prev: Trainee GP/SHO (Geriat.) Crawley.

WILKINSON, Ann Fiona Rosemary 17 Austins Close, Market Harborough LE16 9BJ Tel: 01858 461910 — MB BS 1980 Lond.; DRCOG 1983. Prev: GP Birm.

WILKINSON, Anna Louise Poverest Medical Centre, 42 Poverest Road, St Mary Cray, Orpington BR5 2DQ Tel: 01689 833643 Fax: 01689 891976 — BM BS 1979 Nottm.; MRCGP 1983; Dip. Ther. Wales 1996. (Nottm.)

WILKINSON, Anne Barbara The Surgery, The Street, Wonersh, Guildford GU5 0PE Tel: 01483 898123 Fax: 01483 893104 — MB BS 1983 Lond.; MRCGP 1993; DCH Lond. 1988; DRCOG 1988. GP Prinicipal. Socs: MDU. Prev: GP Princip. Pk.wood Drive Surg., Hemel Hempstead.

WILKINSON, Anne Marie 27 Waringfield Crescent, Moira, Craigavon BT67 0FG — MB BCh BAO 1994 Belf.; DROG - 1996; MRCGP - 1998. (Queens - Belfast)

WILKINSON, Antony Edward Reid Hunter Health Centre, Andrew Street, East Kilbride, Glasgow G74 1AD Tel: 01355 906676 Fax: 01355 906676 — MB ChB 1987 Glas.; MRCGP 1991; DRCOG 1989. Prev: Trainee GP Skelmorlie.

WILKINSON, Audrey 438 Blackmoorfoot Road, Crosland Moor, Huddersfield HD4 5NS Tel: 01484 653520 — LRCPI & LM, LRCSI & LM 1952; MFCMI 1977; MFCM 1972; DPH Newc. 1966. (R.C.S.I.)

WILKINSON, Beatrice Jean Hadrian Clinic, Newcastle General Hospital, Westgate Road, Newcastle upon Tyne NE4 6BE — MB BS 1980 Newc.; MRCPsych 1988; DRCOG 1983. (Univ. Newc. u. Tyne) Cons. Psychiat. Hadrian Clinic Newc. Gen. Hosp. Prev: Sen. Regist. (Psychiat.) Newc.; Trainee GP Newc. VTS.

WILKINSON, Bernadette Shiela Department of Forensic Psychiatry, St. Nicholas Hospital, Newcastle upon Tyne — MB ChB 1983 Glas.; DRCOG 1986. Regist. (Psychiat.) Roy. Vict. Infirm. Newc.

WILKINSON, Beverley Anne 20 St Mary's Road, Worsley, Manchester M28 3RF — MB ChB 1994 Sheff.

WILKINSON, Brian Richard (retired) 22 Marlborough Road, Castle Bromwich, Birmingham B36 0EH Tel: 0121 747 8810 — MB BS Lond. 1951; MRCS Eng. LRCP Lond. 1951; FRCGP 1986, M 1965; DObst RCOG 1958. Prev: GP Shard End Birm.

WILKINSON, Bridget Ann 4 Londesborough Road, Market Weighton, York YO43 3AY Tel: 01430 873433 Fax: 01430 871466 — MB ChB 1988 Manch.; BSc (Med. Sci.) St. And. 1985; MRCGP 1992; DRCOG 1991. p/t Half time job-share Gen. Practitioner in Market Weighton. Prev: Health Developm. Off. Nainital, India.

WILKINSON, Carole Dawn 26 Mount Eden Park, Malone Road, Belfast BT9 6RB — MB BCh 1990 Wales; MRCGP 1994; DCH RCP Lond. 1995; DRCOG 1993.

WILKINSON, Charles Edward The Surgery, Chestnut Road, Sutton Benger, Chippenham SN15 4RP Tel: 01249 720244 Fax: 01249 721165 — MRCS Eng. LRCP Lond. 1975; Cert. Family Plann. JCC 1978. (Middx Hosp. Med. Sch.) Gen. Practitioner, Single Handed dispensing, Wilts. Health Auth.; Instruc. (Advanced Life Support in Obst.). Socs: Roy. Soc. Med.; CMAC Comm.; BMA. Prev: Police Surg. Chippenham Area; Clin. Asst. (PsychoGeriat.) S.mead Hosp.; Clin. Teach. Univ. Bristol.

WILKINSON, Charles Peter 19 Garland Road, Poole BH15 2LA — MB ChB 1997 Leic.

WILKINSON, Christopher David 135 Hubert Road, Selly Oak, Birmingham B29 6ET Tel: 0121 471 4645 — MB ChB 1988 Birm.

WILKINSON, Christopher Lindow The Caldecot Centre, King's Healthcare NHS Trust, King's College Hospital, Denmark Hill, London SE5 9RS Tel: 020 7346 4535 Fax: 020 7346 3486 Email: christopher.wilkinson@kcl.ac.uk; 1 Bryantwood Road, London N7 7BG Email: clwilkinson@csi.com — MB BS 1985 Lond.; MFFP 1993. Cons. Wom. Sexual Health, Family Plann. & Reproduc. Health Care & Genitourin. Med. King's Coll. Hosp. Lond.

WILKINSON, Clare Elizabeth 10 Mostyn Avenue, West Kirby, Wirral CH48 3HW — MB BCh 1980 Wales.

WILKINSON, Clare Elizabeth 30 Eborall Close, Warwick CV34 5QA — MB ChB 1992 Liverp.; BSc Liverp. 1989, MB ChB 1992; DRCOG 1995; MRCP 1997. (Liverpool) Specialist Regist. Rheum. & Gen. Med.

WILKINSON, Darrell Sheldon (retired) Whitecroft, Hervines Road, Amersham HP6 5HT Tel: 01494 433940 — MB BS Lond. 1946; MD Lond. 1947; FRCP Lond. 1964, M. 1947; MRCS Eng. LRCP Lond. 1942. Prev: Cons. Dermat. Aylesbury & High Wycombe Health Dists.

WILKINSON, David Parkside Surgery, Tawney Street, Boston PE21 6PF Tel: 01205 365881 Fax: 01205 357583 — MB ChB 1974 Ed.; MRCOG 1980.

WILKINSON, David (retired) Jelemy Tump, Ninevah Lane, Badsworth, Pontefract WF9 1AP Tel: 01977 643813 — MB ChB 1956 Aberd.

WILKINSON, Mr David 7 Moseley Wood Rise, Leeds LS16 7JA — MB ChB 1984 Leeds; MD Leeds 1993; FRCS Eng. 1990. Cons. Gen. & Vasc. Surg. Bradford Hosps. NHS Trust. Prev: Sen. Regist. N.. & Yorks. RHA.

WILKINSON, David Andrew Charles 17 Stoke Paddock Road, Bristol BS9 2DJ — MB ChB 1993 Birm.

WILKINSON, David Colin Cae'r Berllan, Llangristiolus, Bodorgan LL62 5PS Tel: 01248 750524 — BM BCh 1972 Oxf.; MA; MRCPsych 1978; DPM Lond. 1976. Cons. (Child & Adolesc. Psychiat.) Gwynedd AHA. Prev: Sen. Regist. (Child & Adolesc. Psychiat.) Roy. Manch. Childr. Hosp.

WILKINSON, David George Western Community Hospital, Walnut Grove, Millbrook, Southampton SO16 4XE Tel: 02380 475446 Email: dwilk2000@al.com; 18 Cobbett Road, Southampton SO18 1HH — MB ChB 1975 Birm.; FRCPsych. 1994, M 1981; MRCGP 1979. Cons. Old Age Psychiat. W.. Community Hosp. Soton.; Hon. Sen. Lect. Univ. of Soton.; Director Memory Assessm. and Research Centre www.marc.soton.ac.uk.

WILKINSON, David Gregor Academic Department of Psychiatry, The London Hospital Medical College, Turner St., London E1 2AD Tel: 020 7377 7344 — MB ChB 1975 Ed.; MPhil (Psychiat.) Lond. 1981; BSc Ed. 1973, MB ChB 1975; FRCP Ed. 1989; MRCP (UK) 1977; FRCPsych 1991, M 1980. Prev: Dir. Acad. Sub-Dept. Psychol. Med. N. Wales Univ. Coll. of Med.; Hon. Cons. Psychiat. Clwyd HA; Resid. Psychiat. Med. Res. Counc. Unit Epidemiol. Studies Psychiat. Ed.

WILKINSON

WILKINSON, David James Walnut House, Husthwaite, York YO4 3SY — MB BChir 1965 Camb.; BA, MB Camb. 1965, BChir 1964; DMRD Eng. 1971; FRCR 1975; FFR 1972. (Camb. & St. Mary's) Socs: Brit. Inst. Radiol. & Europ. Paediat. Radiol. Soc. Prev: Cons. Radiol. York Dist. Hosp. & Selby Dist. War Memor. Hosp.; Sen. Regist. (Radiol.) St. Geo. Hosp., Hosp. Sick Childr. & Roy.; Marsden Hosp. Lond.

WILKINSON, David John Department of Anaesthesia, St. Bartholomew's Hospital, London EC1A 7BE Tel: 020 7601 7518 Fax: 020 7601 7520; High Willow, 49 Spring Grove, Loughton IG10 4QD Fax: 020 8502 3887 Email: davidwilkinson1@compuserve.com — MB BS 1972 Lond.; MRCS Eng. LRCP Lond. 1971; FRCA 1976 Eng.; DObst RCOG 1973. (St. Bart.) Cons. Anaesth. Barts and the Lond. NHS Trust & Homerton Hosp. Trust. Lond. Socs: Hon. Sec. Assn. of Anaesth. (past); Brit. Anaesth. and Recovery Nurses Assn. (Ex-Pres.); Hon. Treas. Assn. Anaes. GB & Irel. Prev: Med. Dir. Day Surg. Centre St. Bart. Hosp.; Chairm. Dept of Anaesth. St. Bart. Hosp.

WILKINSON, Dawn Marsha St Stephens Centre, Chelsea and Westminster Hospital, 369 Fulham Road, London SW10 9NH Tel: 020 8746 8000; 31 Vartry Road, London N15 6PR — MB BS 1993 Lond.; DFFP 2000; Dip GU Med 2000; MRCP Lond. 1996. (St Georges Hospital Medical School) Specialist Regist. Genito-Urin. Med., Chelsea & W.minster Hosp., Lond. Prev: Regist. (Genitourin. Med.) Chelsea & W.minster Hosp. Lond.; SHO (GUM), Chelsea & W.minster Hosp., Lond.; SHO (Cardiol. St Marys Paddington Hosp.

WILKINSON, Debra Blythe 4A The High Street, Great Ayton, Middlesbrough TS9 6NJ — MB BS 1993 Newc.

WILKINSON, Douglas Allan Outeniqua House, 313 Woodstock Road, Oxford OX2 7NY Email: douglas.wilkinson@nda.ac.ox.uk — MB ChB 1985 Cape Town; BSc Cape Town 1980; MRCGP 1990; FRCA 1993; T(GP) 1991; DA (UK) 1988. Cons. Anaesth. Intens. Care Oxf. Prev: Sen. Regist. Oxf.; Regist. Rotat. (Anaesth.) Bristol; GP Vocational Train. Scheme Taunton, Som.

WILKINSON, Edith Mary (retired) 5 Badcall, Scourie, Lairg IV27 4TH Tel: 01971 502206 — MB BS Durh. 1942; FFA RCS Eng. 1954; DA Eng. 1951. Prev: Cons. Anaesth. Liverp. RHB.

WILKINSON, Elizabeth Jane The Health Centre, Midland St., Long Eaton, Nottingham NG10 1NY Tel: 0115 973 2370 Fax: 0115 946 3894; Grove House, 53 Grove Avenue, Chilwell, Nottingham NG9 4DZ Tel: 0115 925 5141 Fax: 0115 925 5141 — MB ChB 1973 Sheff.; MRCGP 1977. Screening Phys. Health Linx Pk. Hosp. Nottm. Socs: Nottm. M-C Soc. Prev: Trainee GP Doncaster VTS; Ho. Surg. Lincoln Co. Hosp.; Ho. Phys. Profess. Unit Sheff. Childrs. Hosp.

WILKINSON, Elizabeth Jane 31 Middlegate Court, Cowbridge CF71 7EF — MB BS 1985 Lond.; BSc Lond. 1982; MFPHM RCP (UK) 1994; MRCGP 1990; DRCOG 1989. (St. Mary's Hosp.) Sen. Med. Off. (Primary Healthcare Developm.) Welsh Off. Socs: BMA. Prev: Sen. Regist. (Pub. Health Med.) Mid Glam. HA; Trainee GP Bridgend VTS.

WILKINSON, Elizabeth Sarah British Airways Health Services, Waterside (HMAG), Po Box 365 UB7 0GB Tel: 020 8738 7745 Fax: 020 8738 9754 Email: elizabeth.s.wilkinson@britishairways.com; 3 Milton Road, Hampton TW12 2LL — MB ChB 1990 Manch.; 2000 AFOM; MRCGP 1995. (St Andrews/Manchester) Occupat. Phys. Brit. Airways Heathrow.

WILKINSON, Ellen Jane Fromeside Clinic, Blackberry Hill Hospital, Stapleton, Bristol BS16 2ED Tel: 0117 958 3678 — BM 1987 Soton.; MRCPsych 1993. Sen. Regist. (Psychiat.) Blackberry Hill Hosp. Bristol.

WILKINSON, Elspeth Catto (retired) The Stone Cottage, Gas House Lane, Morpeth NE61 1SR Tel: 01670 516387 — MB BS 1943 Durh.; MB BS (Hons.) Durh. 1943; DPM Lond. 1966. Prev: Cons. Child Psychiat. Qu. Eliz. Hosp. Gateshead.

WILKINSON, Emily Kate 8 Ember Lane, Esher KT10 8ER — MB BS 1998 Lond.

WILKINSON, Ewan Alastair John Liverpool Health Authority, 22 Pall Mall, Liverpool L36 AL — MB ChB 1980 Ed.; MFPHM 1996; DTM & H Liverp. 1984; DRCOG 1983. Cons. (Pub. Health Med.)Liverp. HA. Prev: Dist. Health Off., Malawi.

WILKINSON, Mr Francis Owen Wharton Moorside Farm, Moorside Lane, Pott Shrigley, Macclesfield SK10 5RZ Tel: 01625 73538 — MB BS 1947 Lond.; FRCS Eng. 1955. (Lond. Hosp.) Cons. Surg. Macclesfield & Dist. Hosp. Gp. Socs: Fell. Roy. Soc. Med. & Manch. Med. Soc. Prev: 1st Asst. Profess. Surg. Unit, Manch. Roy. Infirm.; Sen. Regist. Salford Roy. Hosp.; Urol. Regist. Preston Roy. Infirm.

WILKINSON, Frederick James (retired) The Stone Cottage, Gas House Lane, Morpeth NE61 1SR — MB BS 1950 Durh.; FRCGP 1976, M 1969. Prev: GP N.d.

WILKINSON, Gemma 257 Hinton Way, Great Shelford, Cambridge CB2 5AN — BM BS 1997 Nottm.

WILKINSON, George Colin (retired) Bankfield Surgery, Huddersfield Road, Elland HX5 9BA Tel: 01422 375537 Fax: 01422 370776 — MB ChB 1970 Leeds; MRCS Eng. LRCP Lond. 1970.

WILKINSON, Mr Glen Alexander Low Department of Cardiothoracic Surgery, Northern General Hospital NHS Trust, Herries Road, Sheffield S5 7AU Tel: 0114 271 4951; 21 Mayfield Heights, Off Brook House Hill, Sheffield S10 3TT Tel: 01142 229 5202 — MB ChB 1973 Birm.; FRCS Eng. 1978. Cons. Cardiothoracic Surg. N. Gen. Hosp. Sheff.; Hon Sen. Lect. Univ. of Sheff. Socs: Soc. Cardiothor. Surg. GB & Irel. Prev: Sen. Regist. (Cardiothoracic Surg.) W. Midl. RHA; Sen. Fell. Acting Instruc. (Cardiothoracic Surg.) Univ. Washington Hosp. Seattle USA; Lect. (Cardiothoracic Surg.) Lond. Hosp. Whitechapel.

WILKINSON, Gordon William Waddell 1F Reay Street, Inverness IV2 3AJ — MB ChB 1988 Aberd.

WILKINSON, Guy Matthew 13 Long Acre, Cuddington, Northwich CW8 2XP — MB ChB 1992 Liverp.

WILKINSON, Hazel Walnut House, Husthwaite, York YO61 4PY Tel: 0134 76 554 — MB BS 1966 Lond.; MRCS Eng. LRCP Lond. 1966; FRCPath 1989, M 1977. (St. Mary's) Cons. (Chem. Path.) York Health Dist. Prev: Sen. Regist. Yorks. RHA; Ho. Phys. Edgware Gen. Hosp.; Ho. Surg. King Edwd. VII Hosp. Windsor.

WILKINSON, Heather Louise 69 Lingmore Rise, Kendal LA9 7NR Tel: 01539 724767 — MB ChB 1995 Sheff. (Sheffield) Ho. Off. (Gen. Med.) W.morland Gen. Hosp. Kendal Cumbria; GP Regist. Lancaster VTS. Prev: SHO (Psychiat.) Ridge Lea Hosp. Lancaster; SHO (Paediat.) Roy. Lancaster Infirm.; GP Trainee Station Ho. Surg. Kendal.

WILKINSON, Helen Catrin 12 Woodkind Hey, Spital, Wirral CH63 9JZ — MB ChB 1991 Manch.; DRCOG 1994. Trainee GP Wirral.

WILKINSON, Helen Sarah Fisher Medical Centre, Millfields, Coach Street, Skipton BD23 1EU; 49 Otley Street, Skipton BD23 1ET Tel: 01756 69622 — MB BS 1984 Lond.; MRCGP 1989; DRCOG 1989. Prev: Trainee GP Airedale VTS.

WILKINSON, Henry Charles 20 Gainsborough Drive, Lawford Dale, Manningtree CO11 2JU Tel: 01206 391877 — MB BS 1990 Lond.; BSc (Marine Biol. & Zool.) Cardiff 1985; DCH RCP Lond. 1994. (Char., Cross & Westm. Med. Sch.)

WILKINSON, Iain Michael Stewart 6 High Green, Great Shelford, Cambridge CB2 5EG Tel: 01223 843856 — MD 1970 Manch.; MA Camb. 1977; BSc (Anat.) Manch. 1960, MD 1970, MB ChB 1963; FRCP Lond. 1981, M 1965. (Manch.) Cons. Neurol. Addenbrooke's Hosp. Camb. Socs: BMA & Assn. Brit. Neurol. Prev: Univ. Lect. (Neurol.) & Hon. Cons. (Neurol.) Manch. Roy. Infirm.; Sen. Res. Ho. Phys. Nat. Hosp. Qu. Sq.; Research Fell. in Cerebrovasc. Dis. Inst. Neurol. Qu. Sq.

WILKINSON, Ian Chadderton (Town) Health Centre, Middleton Road, Chadderton, Oldham OL9 0LH Tel: 0161 628 4543 Fax: 0161 284 1658 — MB ChB 1977 Bristol. Clin. Asst. (A & E) Roy. Oldham Hosp.

WILKINSON, Ian Boden Department of Clinical Pharmacology, University of Cambridge, Addenbrookes Hospital, Cambridge CB22 QP Tel: 01222 336806 Fax: 0870 1269863 Email: ibw2/@cam.ac.uk; The Old School house, West Wickham, Cambridge CB1 6RY — BM BCh 1993 Oxf.; MA Oxf. 1994, BA 1990; MRCP (UK) 1996. (Oxf.) Lect. clin. Pharm, Camb. unvi.; Hon. Cons. Phys., Addenbrookes Hosp. Cambr. Socs: Med. Res. Soc.; Brit. Pharmacological Soc.; Brit. Hypertens. Soc. Prev: Clin. Lecturesh. Med. Univ. Edin. W.. Gen. Hosp. Edin.; Clin. Lect. John Radcliffe Hosp. Oxf.; SHO (Med.) Qu. Med. Centre Nottm.

WILKINSON, Ian Louttit (retired) 18 Woodfield, Nash Lane, Belbroughton, Stourbridge DY9 9SW — MB ChB 1948 Birm.; MRCS Eng. LRCP Lond. 1948. Prev: Med. Off. Mary Stevens Matern. Home Stourbridge.

WILKINSON, Ivan Edward Corwen c/o 106 Beech Road, Stockport SK3 8HH — MB BS 1970 Lond.; MRCS Eng. LRCP Lond. 1969; MRCGP 1976; DIH Lond. 1990; Dip. Pract. Dermat. Wales 1990; DObst RCOG 1973; DTM & H Liverp. 1973; Cert. Av Med. 1981. (Guy's) Socs: Fell. Roy. Soc. Trop. Med. & Hyg.; BMA & Soc. Occupat. Med. Prev: SHO (Anaesth.) Chester Roy. Infirm.; SHO (Paediat.) Univ. Hosp. S. Manch.

WILKINSON, James Robert Wyndham Department of Respiratory Medicine, Eastbourne District General Hospital, Kings Drive, Eastbourne BN21 2UD Tel: 01323 417400 Fax: 01323 414993; Beeches Farm House, Sandhurst Lane, Little Common, Bexhill-on-Sea TN39 4RH Tel: 0142484 3109 — MB BS 1983 Lond.; MA Camb. 1983; MD Lond. 1993; MRCP (UK) 1986; FRCP (London) 2000. Cons. Gen. & Respirat. Med. E.bourne Hosps. NHS Trust. Socs: Brit. Thorac. Soc. Prev: Research Regist. Guy's Hosp. Lond.; Sen. Regist. Sir Chas. Gairdner Hosp. Perth, W.. Austral.; Sen. Regist. Soton. Gen. Hosp.

WILKINSON, Jane Dever Department of Child Health, Royal Hospital for Sick Children, Dalhair St, Yorkhill, Glasgow G3 8SJ Tel: 0141 201 0000 Fax: 0141 201 0837 Email: gcl159@clinmed.gla.ac.uk — MB ChB 1985 Aberd.; MRCP (Ireland). (Aberdeen) Assoc. Specialist (Cystic Fibrosis); Hon. Clin. Lect., Dept of Child Health, Glas. Univ. Socs: BMA; MRCPCH; MRCP (Irel.).

WILKINSON, Jane Elizabeth Margery Valentine Cottage, Banbury St., Kineton, Warwick CV35 0JU — BM 1989 Soton.

WILKINSON, Jane Frances York Road Group Practice, York Rd, Ellesmere Port CH65 0DB — MB ChB 1994 Liverp.; 1998 DFFP Lond.; 1998 DRCOG Lond.; 1996 DCH RCP Lond. p/t Gen. Practitioner (Princip.), York Rd Gp. Pract., Ellesmere Port. Prev: GP Regist. Wirral VTS.

WILKINSON, Jane Louise — MB ChB 1983 Manch. p/t Cons. Child & Adolesc. Psychiat. Chesterfield and N. Derbysh. Roy. Hosp. NHS Trust. Prev: Sen. Regist. (Child & Adolesc. Psychiat.) Sheff.

WILKINSON, Jane Mary 14 Leswin Road, London N16 7NL — MB BChir 1993 Camb.

WILKINSON, Jane Sally Tel: 01902 751420 Fax: 01902 747936; Rosegarth House, Clifton Road, Tettenhall, Wolverhampton WV6 9AP Tel: 01902 759377 — MB ChB 1974 Manch.; BSc St. And. 1971; MRNZCGP 1978; DCH Glas. 1977; DObst RCOG 1976. (St. And. & Manch.)

WILKINSON, Mr Jeremy Mark 34 Newbould Lane, Sheffield S10 2PL — MB ChB 1991 Sheff.; FRCS Eng. 1996. Specialist Regist. Orthop. Surg. N. Gen. Hosp. Sheff.

WILKINSON, Joan Oldham Family Health Services Authority, Lindley House, 1 John St., Oldham OL8 1DF Tel: 0161 626 4615 Fax: 0161 652 0182 — MB ChB 1957 Manch. Prev: Ho. Off. Oldham & Dist. Gen. Hosp. & Manch. Roy. Infirm.

WILKINSON, Joanna Ruth Rastrick Health Centre, Chapel Croft, Rastick, Brighouse HD6 3NA Tel: 01484 710853; 16 The Fairway, Fixby, Huddersfield HD2 2HU Tel: 01484 534763 — BM BS 1981 Nottm.; MRCGP 1986. (Nottingham)

WILKINSON, Joanne Sarah 1 Sunscales Av, Cockermouth CA13 9DY — MB ChB 1997 Manch.

WILKINSON, John (retired) 70 Craigleith Hill Gardens, Edinburgh EH4 2JH Tel: 0131 332 2994 — MB ChB 1941 Ed.; MD Ed. 1956; FRCP Ed. 1972, M 1957; MFCM 1979; DTM & H Ed. (Greig Medal) 1956. Vice-Pres., St Columba's Hospice, Edin. Prev: SCM Lothian HB.

WILKINSON, Mr John Arthur (cons. rooms) 4 Hulse Road, Banister Park, Southampton SO15 2JX Tel: 02380 334897; Beechwood, Church Lane, Braishfield, Romsey SO51 0QH Tel: 01794 67717 — BSc Wales 1945, MCh 1962, MB BCh 1948; FRCS Eng. 1957. Robt. Jones Prize & Gold Medal Brit. Orthop. Assn. 1961; Cons. (Orthop. Surg.) Soton. & S.W. Hants. Health Dist. & Lord; Mayor Treloar Hosp. Alton; Clin. Teach. Soton. Univ. Hosp.; ABC Trav. Fell. Brit. Orthop. Assn. Socs: Fell. Roy. Soc. Med.; Fell. Brit. Orthop. Assn. Prev: Sen. Regist. W.m. Hosp. Lond.; Regist. Roy. Nat. Orthop. Hosp.; Regist. Hosp. Sick Childr. Gt. Ormond St. Lond.

WILKINSON, John Darrell Department of Dermatology, Amersham General Hospital, Amersham HP7 0JD Tel: 01494 734600 Fax: 01494 734620; The Chiltern Hospital, London Road, Great Missenden HP16 0DG Tel: 01494 890890 Fax: 01494 890858 — MB BS 1972 Lond.; FRCP UK 1988, M 1975; MRCS Eng. LRCP Lond. 1972. (St. Thos.) Cons. Dermat. & Assoc. Clin. Dir. S. Bucks. NHS Trust; Hon. Lect. Univ. Lond. Socs: Eur. Environm. Contact Dermat. Research Gp.; Eur. Soc. Contact Dermat.; Mem. Brit Assn. Dermatol. Prev: Sen. Regist. (Dermat.) St. Thos. Hosp. Lond.

WILKINSON, Mr John Leonard, OBE (retired) Quince Cottage, Llysworney, Cowbridge CF71 7NQ — MB ChB 1948 Manch.; MD Manch. 1952; FRCS Eng. 1956; MRCS Eng. LRCP Lond. 1948; DTM & H Liverp. 1961. Prev: Sen. Lect. (Anat.) Univ. Coll. Cardiff.

WILKINSON, John Lindow (retired) Netherwood Cottage, Brookledge Lane, Adlington, Macclesfield SK10 4JU — MB ChB 1955 Leeds. Prev: SHO (Paediat.) & Obst. Ho. Off. W. Pk. Hosp. Macclesfield.

WILKINSON, John Robert Northern and Yorkshire public health observatory, Wolfson Research Institute, University of Durham Stockton campus, Stockton-on-Tees TS17 6BH Tel: 01642 385900 Fax: 01642 385906 Email: john.wilkinson@durham.ac.uk; Topside House, Marrick, Richmond DL11 7LQ Tel: 01748 884740 Fax: 01748 884975 Email: johnwilkinson@durham.ac.uk — MB ChB 1977 Ed.; MD 2001 Edin; MFCM 1987; MRCGP 1982; DRCOG 1980; FFPHM 1994. (Edinburgh) Director N.ern & Yorks. Pub. health observatory; Vis. Fell. Univ. of York; Vis.. Sen. Lect. Nuffield Inst. Univ. Leeds 1994. Socs: BMA; Soc. for Social Med.; Fac. of Pub. health Med. Prev: Dep. director of Pub. Health N. Yorks. health observatory; Cons. Pub. Health S. Cumbria HA; Dir. Pub. Health N.allerton HA.

WILKINSON, Jonathan James Arthur Harbury Surgery, Mill Street, Harbury, Leamington Spa CV33 9HR Tel: 01926 612232 Fax: 01926 612991 — MB ChB 1988 Birm.; MRCGP 1994. (Birm.)

WILKINSON, Mr Jonathan Mark Orthopaedic Directorate, Lincoln Hospitals NHS Trust, County Hospital, Greetwell Road, Lincoln LN2 5QY Tel: 01522 573217 Fax: 01522 573080; The Hall, Norton Disney, Lincoln LN6 9JP Tel: 01636 892011 — MB BS 1965 Lond.; FRCS Eng. 1972; MRCS Eng. LRCP Lond. 1965. (St. Bart.) Cons. Orthop. Surg. Lincoln Hosps. Prev: Sen. Regist. Rotat. (Orthop.) St. Bart. Hosp. Lond.; Regist. (Surg.) Ipswich Hosp.; Ho. Surg. St. Bart. Hosp. Lond.

WILKINSON, Julia Charlotte Fairfield, Bepton, Midhurst GU29 0NA — MB BCh BAO 1967 Dub.; MRCPsych 1973; DPM Eng. 1972. Cons. Adult Ment. Illness Graylingwell Hosp. Chichester. Prev: Sen. Psychiat. Regist. Roy. Edin. Hosp.; Sen. Psychiat. Regist. & Regist. (Psychiat.) Fulbourn Hosp. Camb.

WILKINSON, Kathleen Ann Norfolk & Norwich University Hospital NHS Trust, Colhey Lane, Norwich NR4 Tel: 01603 287086 Fax: 01603 287886 Email: kathy.wilkinson@norfolk-norwich.thenhs.com; Manor Moorings, 10 Yarmouth Road, Thorpe St Andrew, Norwich NR7 0EF Tel: 01603 434116 Fax: 01603 434116 — MB BS 1981 Lond.; FRCPCH 1999; MRCP (UK) 1989; FFA RCS Eng 1986; DCH RCP Lond. 1983. Cons. Paediat. Anaesth. Norf. & Norwich Health Care Trust. Socs: Assoc. of Paediat. Anaesth. Prev: Cons. Paediat. Intens. Care Unit & Paediat. Anaesth. Hosp. Sick Childr. Gt. Ormond St. Lond.

WILKINSON, Keith 16 Ballagarey Road, Glen Vine, Douglas IM4 4EA — MB ChB 1982 Liverp.

WILKINSON, Kenneth Norman 37 Aire Valley Drive, Bradley, Keighley BD20 9HY — MB ChB 1971 Leeds; BSc Leeds 1968, MB ChB 1971; MRCP (UK) 1975; DCH Eng. 1974. Cons. Paediat. Airedale Gen. Hosp. Steeton.

WILKINSON, Laura Margaret West of Scotland Breast Screening Centre, Stock Exchange Court, Nelson Mandela Place, Glasgow G2 1QT Tel: 0141 572 5833 Fax: 0141 572 5801; Laigh Monkcastle, Dalry Road, Kilwinning KA13 6PN — MB ChB 1984 Glas.; FRCR 1992. Cons. Radiol. W.. Infirm. Glas. & BrE. Screening Centre Glas.; Hon. Sen. Lect. Univ. Glas. Socs: Roy. Coll. Radiol. Prev: Sen. Regist. (Diag. Radiol.) W.. Infirm. Glas.

WILKINSON, Louise Sarah Radiology Dept, St Georges Hospital, Blackshaw Road, London SW17 0QT Tel: 020 8672 1255; 1 East Road, Kingston upon Thames KT2 6EJ — BM BCh 1987 Oxf.; BA Oxf. 1984; FRCR 1993. Cons. (diagnostic Radiol.) St Geo.s Hosp. Prev: Sen. Regist. (Diagn. Radiol.) Roy. Marsden Hosp.

WILKINSON, Lucille Marie 39 Christchurch Road, Norwich NR2 2BX — MB ChB 1990 Otago.

WILKINSON

WILKINSON, Marcia Isobel Pamela Gangies Farm, Gangies Hill, High Wych, Sawbridgeworth CM21 0LD Tel: 01279 721178 Fax: 01279 725724; Gangies Farm, Gangies Hill, High Wych, Sawbridgeworth CM21 0LD Tel: 01279 721178 — BM BCh 1943 Oxf.; MA Oxf. 1945, DM 1959; FRCP Lond. 1963, M 1946. Socs: Fell. Roy. Soc. Med.; Assn. Brit. Neurols.; (Ex-Pres.) Internat. Headache Soc. Prev: Cons. Neurol. Eliz. G. Anderson Hosp. Lond. & Hackney Hosp.; Dir. Regional Neurol. Unit E.. Hosp. Lond.; Sen. Regist. (Neurol.) Lond. Hosp.

WILKINSON, Marcus James The Farmhouse, 18 Crosshill, Codnor, Ripley DE5 9SR — BM BS 1985 Nottm.; MRCGP 1992.

WILKINSON, Margaret Anne (retired) — MB BS Lond. 1970; MSc (Neurochem.) Lond. 1974; MRCPsych 1977; DPM Eng. 1973; Acad. Dip. Gen. Biochem. Univ. Lond. 1966. Prev: Cons. Child & Adolesc. Psychiat. E. Berks. NHS Community Health Trust.

WILKINSON, Margaret Elizabeth The Coach House, Bolam, Morpeth NE61 3UA — MB ChB 1990 Ed.; MRCP (UK) 1993.

WILKINSON, Mark 24 Grasmere Drive, Liverpool L21 5JJ — MB ChB 1993 Liverp.

WILKINSON, Mark Jonathan Department of Histopathology, James Paget Hospital, Lowestoft Road, Gorleston, Great Yarmouth NR31 6LA — MB ChB 1982 Birm.; MRCPath 1990. Cons. Histopath. Jas. Paget Hosp. Trust. Prev: Lect. (Path.) Univ. Nottm.

WILKINSON, Mark Lawrence Guy's & St Thomas Hospital Trust, 1st Floor, College House, London SE1 7EH Tel: 0207 928 9292 Ext 7777 Fax: 0207 960 5543 Email: mark.wilkinson@gstt.sthames.nhs.uk; Tel: 020 8874 5330 Fax: 020 8870 8009 — MB BS 1974 Lond.; BSc Lond. 1971, MD 1985; FRCP Lond. 1992; MRCP (UK) 1977. (Middlx. Hosp.) Sen. Lect. & Cons. Gastroenterol. GKT Sch. Of Med. KCL. Guy's & St. Thos. Hosps. Lond. Socs: Brit. Soc. Gastroenterol. (Endoscopy Comm. Train. Off.); Internat. Assn. Study Liver; US. Soc.Gastrointestinal Endoscopy. Prev: Lect. Liver Unit King's Coll. Sch. Med. & Dent. Lond.; Regist. (Gastroenterol.) Middlx. Hosp. Lond.

WILKINSON, Martin John Brian The Harlequin Surgery, 160 Shard End Crescent, Shard End, Birmingham B34 7BP Tel: 0121 747 8291 Fax: 0121 749 5497; 249 Boldmere Road, Sutton Coldfield B73 5LL Tel: 0121 354 9973 — MB ChB 1982 Birm.; MMedSc Birm. 1994; FRCGP 1993, M 1986; DCH RCP Lond. 1985; DRCOG 1984. Clin. Lect. (Gen. Pract.) Univ. Birm.; Course Organiser E. Birm. VTS. Socs: Vice Chairm. Mid. Fac. Roy. Coll. GPs. Prev: Clin. Asst. (Paediat. Nephrol.) E. Birm. Hosp.; Trainee GP/SHO Centr. Birm. HA VTS; Trainee GP Sutton Coldfield & BromsGr..

WILKINSON, Mrs Mary Julia (retired) Church End House, 33 Church St., Tolleshunt D'Arcy, Maldon CM9 8TS Tel: 01621 860667 — MB BS 1959 Lond.; MRCP (UK) 1977; DCH Eng. 1963; DObst RCOG 1964. Prev: Cons. Community Paediat. Thorpe Coombe Hosp. Lond.

WILKINSON, Matthew Blackbird Leys Health Centre, 63 Blackbird Leys Road, Oxford OX4 6HL Tel: 01865 778244; 93 Church Road, Sandford-on-Thames, Oxford OX4 4YA Tel: 01865 774178 — MB ChB 1976 Manch. Prev: Med. Off. Save the Childr. Fund Nepal.

WILKINSON, Matthew (retired) 3 Arnhall Gardens, Dundee DD2 1PH Tel: 01382 669320 — MB BChir 1949 Camb.; MD Camb. 1956; FRCP Ed. 1974, M 1969; FRCP Lond. 1972, M 1951. Phys. Ninewells Hosp. Dundee; Lect. (Clin. Med.) Univ. Dundee. Prev: Phys. Ninewlls Hosp. Dundee.

WILKINSON, Maureen Gwendoline 171 Newton Drive, Blackpool FY3 8ND — MB ChB 1972 Bristol; MRCPsych 1979; DObst RCOG 1975.

WILKINSON, Maureen Jean 15 Camperdown Street, Broughty Ferry, Dundee DD5 3AA Tel: 01382 78881; The Whirlies, Kinnettles, Forfar DD8 1XF Tel: 01307 82367 — MB ChB 1965 Manch.; MRCGP 1976. (Manch.) GP Dundee. Prev: Ho. Surg. & Ho. Phys. St. Woolos Hosp. Newport; Ho. Phys. (Paediat.) St. Jas. Hosp. Balham.

WILKINSON, Michael Boyd Department of Anaesthetics, Northampton General Hospital, Cliftonville, Northampton NN1 5BD Tel: 01604 545671 Fax: 01604 545672; Cherry Tree Cottage, 84 Billing Road, Brafield on The Green, Northampton NN7 1BL Tel: 01604 891509 — MB BS 1985 Lond.; LMSSA Lond. 1984; FCAnaesth 1990. (St. Thos. Hosp. Lond.) Cons. N.ampton Gen. Hosp. Trust. Prev: Sen. Regist. Rotat. (Anaesth.) Newc.; Assoc. Prof. Duke Univ. Med. Center, USA.

WILKINSON, Mr Michael Charles Paul Department of Orthopaedic Surgery, King's College Hospital, Denmark Hill, London SE5 9RS Tel: 020 7346 3649; 14 Portman Avenue, E. Sheen, London SW14 8NX Tel: 020 8392 9552 Fax: 020 8392 2364 Email: mike.wilkinson@ukgateway.net — MB BS 1982 Lond.; BSc 1979 (Hons.) Lond.; FRCS Eng. 1986; FRCS (Orth.) 1994. (Westminster London) Cons. Orthop. Surg. King's Coll. Hosp. Lond. Socs: Fell. BOA; BASK. Prev: Sen. Regist. (Orthop.) Roy. N. Shore Hosp. Sydney NSW, Austral.; Sen. Regist. Rotat. (Orthop. Surg.) Char. Cross Hosp. Lond. & Regist. Rotat. (Orthop. Surg.) St Mary's Hosp. Lond.; SHO (Plastic Surg.) Qu. Mary's Hosp. Lond.

WILKINSON, Mr Michael James Swiers Royal Bolton Hospital, Minerva Road, Farnworth, Bolton BL4 0JR Tel: 01204 390538 Fax: 01204 390544; 8 Chelwood Mews, Chorley New Road, Lostock, Bolton BL6 4BF Email: mcquilk@wenderholme.doctors.org.uk — MB BS 1976 Lond.; BSc (Hons.) Lond. 1972, MS 1986, MB BS 1976; FRCS Eng. 1980. (Univ. Coll. Hosp.) Cons. Surg. Roy. Bolton Hosp. Socs: Fell. Assn. Surgs.; Fell. Assn. Upper G.I. Surg.; Fell. Roy. Soc. Med. Prev: Sen. Regist. (Surg.) NW Train. Scheme Salford HA; Research Fell. Christie Hosp. Manch.; Ho. Surg. St. Stephen's Hosp. Lond.

WILKINSON, Michael Simon The Maisonette, 57 South parade, Oakfield Road Clifton, Bristol BS8 2BA — MB BS 1996 Lond.

WILKINSON, Nafisa Badrudeen Department of Histopathology, St. James's Hospital, Leeds LS9 7TF Tel: 0113 206 4196 Fax: 0113 206 5429 — MB BChir 1984 Camb.; BA Camb. 1982; MRCPath 1993. Cons. in Gyn. Path. Prev: Lect. & Sen. Regist. (Histopath.) Univ. Leeds; Lect. & Sen. Regist. (Histopath.) Univ. Manch.; Regist. (Histopath.) NW RHA.

WILKINSON, Nicholas Mark Coleford Health Centre, Railway Drive, Coleford GL16 8RH Tel: 01594 832117; Millover, Main Road, Mile End, Coleford GL16 7BY Tel: 01594 835543 Email: nick@coleford.demon.co.uk — MB BS 1980 Lond.; MRCGP 1984; Dip. Ther. Wales 1996; DRCOG 1985. (Guy's) Prev: Clin. Asst. in endoscopy.

WILKINSON, Nicholas Michael Reginald 4 The Knoll, Billericay CM12 0NT — MB ChB 1990 Ed.

WILKINSON, Norman Victor (retired) Thorpe End, Almondbury, Huddersfield HD5 8TA Tel: 01484 427665 — MB BS 1952 Durh.; MRCPsych 1971; DPM Eng. 1956. Prev: Asst. Psychiat. Clifton Hosp. York.

WILKINSON, Patricia Ann Stacksteads Surgery, 20 Farholme Lane, Stacksteads, Bacup OL13 0EX Tel: 01706 873122 Fax: 01706 874152 — MB ChB 1989 Manch. GP Princip. Prev: GP Locum; GP Trainee, Burnley.

WILKINSON, Patricia Anne 45 Carsick Hill Crescent, Sheffield S10 3LS Tel: 0114 230 8612 — MB ChB 1972 Leeds; FRCA 1976. Cons. Anaesth. Roy. Hallamsh. Hosp. Sheff.

WILKINSON, Paul Daryll Environmental Epidemiology Unit, London School of Hygiene and Tropical Medicine, Keppel St., London WC1E 7HT Tel: 020 7927 2444 Fax: 020 7580 4524 Email: p.wilkinson@lshtm.ac.uk; 31B Adolphus Road, Finsbury Park, London N4 2AT Tel: 020 8809 4309 — BM BCh 1985 Oxf.; MSc Lond. 1991; MRCP (UK) 1989. Sen. Lect. (Environm. Epidemiol.) Lond. Sch. Hyg. & Trop. Med.

WILKINSON, Paul Oliver Ridgecourt, Court Rd, Newton Ferrers, Plymouth PL8 1DD — BChir 1996 Camb.

WILKINSON, Paul Robert 9 Rothley Avenue, Ainsdale, Southport PR8 2SS — MB BS 1988 Newc.; BMedSc Newc. 1987; MRCGP 1993; FRCA 1997. Specialist Regist. (Anaesth.) Roy. Vict. Infirm.; Pain Managem. Unit. Roy. Vict. Infirm. Prev: SHO (Anaesth.) Sunderland Gen. Hosp.; Trainee GP N.d. VTS.

WILKINSON, Pauline Northern Ireland Hospice, 74 Somerton Road, Belfast BT15 3LH Tel: 02890 781836 Email: information@inhospice.com — MB BCh BAO 1987 Belf.; MD Belf. 1995; MRCP (UK) 1991. p/t Cons. N.ern Irel. Hospice Belf.

WILKINSON, Professor Peter Charles 26 Randolph Road, Glasgow G11 7LG — MB BS Lond. 1956; FRSE; MD Lond. 1967. (Lond. Hosp.) Emerit. Prof. Cellular Immunol. Univ. Glas. Socs: Brit. Soc. Immunol. Prev: Vis. Prof. Rockerfeller Univ. New York; Lect. (Bact.) Lond. Hosp. Med. Coll.

WILKINSON, Peter John PHLS Trent, 29 Bridgford Road, West Bridgford, Nottingham NG2 6AU Tel: 0115 981 5544 Fax: 0115 981 5500 Email: pjwilkinson@trent.phls.nhs.uk; Hambledon House,

WILKS

Lodgefield Lane, Hoveringham, Nottingham NG14 7JQ Tel: 0115 966 4411 — MB BChir 1971 Camb.; MA Camb. 1969; FRCPath 1988, M 1976. (Camb. & King's Coll. Hosp.) Gp. Dir. PHLS Trent. Socs: Assn. Med. Microbiol.; Hosp. Infec. Soc.; Path. Soc. Prev: Cons. Microbiol. & Dir., Pub. Health Laborat. Nottm.; Cons. Microbiol. & Dir. Pub. Health Laborat. Plymouth; Cons. Sen. Lect. (Clin. Bact.) Univ. Bristol.

WILKINSON, Peter Maurice 12 Ramsdale Road, Bramhall, Stockport SK7 2PZ — MRCS Eng. LRCP Lond. 1964; MSc (Clin. Pharmacol.) Manch. 1973, MB ChB 1964; FRCP Lond. 1985; MRCP (UK) 1974; FRCR (Hon.) 1993. (Manch.) Cons. Clin. Pharmacol. Christie Hosp. & Holt Radium Inst. Manch.; Lect. (Clin. Pharmacol.) Manch. Univ. Prev: Vis. Prof. (Med. Oncol.) Sidney Farber Cancer Inst. Boston, USA; Lect. (Med.) Harvard Med. Sch.

WILKINSON, Peter Raymond 90 Graham Avenue, Patcham, Brighton BN1 8HD — MB BS 1982 Lond.; BSc (Hons.) Lond. 1979; MRCP (UK) 1987; MFPHM RCP (UK) 1996; Dipo.Tropical Med. And Hygiene Royal College of Physicians 1997. (Westm.)

WILKINSON, Peter Roger Ashford Hospital, London Road, Ashford TW15 3AA Tel: 01784 884279 Fax: 01784 884612 Email: peterwilkinson@doctors.org.uk; Email: peterwilkinson@doctors.org.uk — MB BS Lond. 1969; MD Lond. 1985; FRCP Lond. 1988, M 1973; MRCS Eng. LRCP Lond. 1969; DObst RCOG 1971. (Lond. Hosp.) p/t Cons. Cardiol. Ashford & St Peter Hosps. NHS Trust; Dir. Clin. Studies Imperial Coll. Sch. Med. Socs: Cardiac Soc. Prev: Sen. Regist. (Med.) Bristol Roy. Infirm.; Vis. Lect. Univ. Calif., San Francisco; Regist. (Med.) N.wick Pk. Hosp.

WILKINSON, Peter Stephen Bedford Road Surgery, 273 Bedford Road, Kempston, Bedford MK42 8QD Tel: 01234 852222 Fax: 01234 843558; 13 Cranfield Road, Wootton, Bedford MK43 9EB Tel: 01234 768434 — MB ChB 1981 Leic.; MRCGP 1985; DCH RCP Lond. 1985; DRCOG 1984.

WILKINSON, Peter Winston (retired) Culross, 15 kingsway, Gayton, Wirral CH60 3SN Tel: 0151 342 6864 — MD 1977 Leeds; MB ChB 1966; FRCP Lond. 1988; FRCPCH 1997; DCH Eng. 1968. Prev: Cons. Paediat. Arrowe Pk. Hosp. Wirral.

WILKINSON, Philip Ann 38 Oakwood Road, Sturry, Canterbury CT2 0LX — MB BS 1996 Lond.

WILKINSON, Philip Barr Oxfordshire Mental Healthcare NHS Trust, The Fulbrook Centre, Churchill Hospital, Old Road, Headington, Oxford OX3 7JU — BM BS 1986 Nottm.

WILKINSON, Raymond Walker (retired) 9 Granary Wharf, 57 Commercial Road, Weymouth DT4 8AL Tel: 01305 778967 Email: rupert.wilkinson@which.net — MB ChB 1945 Leeds; DCH Eng. 1948; FRCR 1975; FFR 1956; DMRD Eng. 1952. Prev: Cons. Radiol. Reading Gp. Hosps.

WILKINSON, Richard David Churchfields Surgery, Recreation Road, Bromsgrove B61 8DT Tel: 01527 872163; Robins Meadow, 43 Hanbury Road, Stoke Prior, Bromsgrove B60 4DW — MB ChB 1965 Birm.; MRCS Eng. LRCP Lond. 1965; DObst RCOG 1967. (Birm.) Hon. Phys. BromsGr. Cott. Hosp. Prev: Ho. Surg. & Ho. Phys. Qu. Eliz. Hosp. Birm.; Ho. Surg. Gen. Hosp. Birm.

WILKINSON, Richard Hanwell (retired) 26 Emden House, Barton Lane, Headington, Oxford OX3 9JU Tel: 01865 762973 — MB BChir 1946 Camb.; MA, MD Camb. 1952; MRCS Eng. LRCP Lond. 1946; FRCPath 1969, M 1964. Hon. Cons. Path. Oxf. HA. Prev: Cons. Chem. Path. Oxon. AHA (T).

WILKINSON, Robert Royal Infirmary, Blackburn BB2 3LR Tel: 01254 263555; (cons. rooms), Beardwood Hospital, Preston New Road, Blackburn BB2 7BG Tel: 01254 57666 — MB ChB 1975 Leeds; PhD Leeds 1972, BSc (Pharmacol.) (Hons.) 1966; BSc (Pharm.) (Hons.) Leeds 1965; FRCP Lond. 1992; MRCP (UK) 1978. Cons. Phys. (Gen. Med.) (s/i Endocrinol. & Diabetes) Blackburn, Hyndburn & Ribble Valley HA. Prev: Lect. (Clin. Med.) Univ. Birm. & Qu. Eliz. Hosp. Birm.; Regist. (Gen. Med.) Newc. AHA (T); Scientif. Staff MRC Mineral Metab. Unit Gen. Infirm. Leeds.

WILKINSON, Professor Robert Renal Clinical Investigation Unit, Freeman Hospital, Newcastle upon Tyne NE7 7DN Tel: 0191 223 1104 Fax: 0191 223 1233 Email: robert.wilkinson@tfh.nuth.northy.nhs.uk; Coach House, Bolam Hall, Whalton, Morpeth NE61 3UA Tel: 01661 881698 — MB BS (Hons.) Durh. 1963; BSc (Hons.) Durham. 1960; MD (Commend.) Newc. 1978; FRCP Lond. 1979, M 1967. (Newc.) Cons. Phys. & Prof. Renal Med. Univ. Newc. & Freeman NHS Trust & Roy. Vict.

Infirm. NHS Trust; Co. Chaiman, Extern. Refer. Gp. for Nat. Serv. Framework for Renal Dis. Socs: Assn. Phys. (Sen. Mem.); Internat. Soc. Hypertens.; Brit. Hypertens. Soc. Prev: Reader (Med.) Newc. Univ. Hosp.; Sen. Lect. (Med.) Newc. Univ. Hosps.; Trav. Fell. Med. Research Counc. Stanford Univ. Calif., USA.

WILKINSON, Robert Arthur Ryecroft, Caroline Road, New Inn, Pontypool NP4 5QJ Tel: 01495 53903 — LMSSA 1945 Lond. (St. Mary's)

WILKINSON, Sally Ann Southmead Hospital, Westbury-on-Trym, Bristol BS10 5NB Tel: 0117 950 5050 — MB ChB 1976 Bristol; BSc (Hons.) Bristol 1973, MB ChB 1976; MRCPsych 1983. Clin. Asst. (Psychiat.) S.mead Hosp. Bristol. Prev: Ho. Off. S.mead Hosp. W.bury-on-Trym & Ham Green Hosp. Bristol.

WILKINSON, Sarah Anne 8 Avondale Road, Ponteland, Newcastle upon Tyne NE20 9NA — BM BS 1994 Nottm.

WILKINSON, Sarah Louise 9 Gainsborough Road, Ipswich IP4 2UR — MB ChB 1993 Sheff.

WILKINSON, Sarah Louise 38 College Road, Upholland, Skelmersdale WN8 0PY — MB BS 1998 Lond.

WILKINSON, Simon David Midfield House, 75 Kidderminster Road, Hagley, Stourbridge DY9 0QN; 27 Hall Meadow, Hagley, Stourbridge DY9 9LE — MB ChB 1972 Birm. Socs: BMA. Prev: Trainee Gen. Pract. Abergavenny Vocational Train. Scheme; Ho. Phys. Worcester Roy. Infirm.; Ho. Surg. Gen. Hosp. Birm.

WILKINSON, Simon Malcolm 4 Londesborough Road, Market Weighton, York YO43 3AY Tel: 01430 873433 Fax: 01430 871466 — MB ChB 1988 Manch.; MRCGP 1992; DRCOG 1991. (Manchester) Gen. Practioner, Marketweighton; PCT & Area Prescribing Comm. Prev: Health Developm. Off. Nainital, India.

WILKINSON, Stephen Edward 44 Longlands Drive, Houghton-le-Spring DH5 8LR — MB BS 1991 Newc.

WILKINSON, Stephen Mark Department of Dermatology, The General Infirmary, Leeds LS1 3EX — MB BChir 1984 Camb.; MD Camb. 1995, BA 1982, MB BChir 1984; MRCP (UK) 1989; DRCOG 1987. Cons. Dermat. Leeds Gen. Infirm. Prev: Sen. Regist. (Dermat.) Skin Hosp. Manch.

WILKINSON, Stephen Paul Woodend Hospital, Aberdeen AB15 6XS Tel: 01224 556513 Fax: 01224 404019; 36 Brighton Place, Aberdeen AB10 6RS — MB BS 1979 Newc.; FRCP Ed. 1999; MRCP (UK) 1982. Cons. Geriat. Med. Grampian HB; Hon. Clin. Sen. Lect. Univ. Aberd. Socs: Brit. Geriat. Soc.; Aberd. M-C Soc. Prev: Sen. Regist. (Geriat.) Grampian HB; Regist. (Geriat.) Tayside HB; Research Fell. Dept. Med. Ninewells Hosp. Dundee.

WILKINSON, Stephen Percy Derriford Hospital, Plymouth PL6 8DH Tel: 01752 792686; RidgeCt., Court Road, Newton Ferrers, Plymouth PL8 1DD Tel: 01752 873190 — BSc (1st cl. Hons.) Lond. 1966, MD 1978, MB BS 1969; FRCP Lond. 1985. (King's Coll. Hosp.) Cons. Phys. Derriford Hosp. Plymouth. Socs: Brit. Soc. Gastroenterol. & Med. Res. Soc.; Assn. Phys. Prev: Cons. Phys. Glos. Roy. Hosp. Gloucester; Sen. Regist. Liver Unit King's Coll. Hosp. Lond.; SHO Radcliffe Infirm. Oxf.

WILKINSON, Tanya Sarah 27 Mucklestone Wood Lane, Loggerheads, Market Drayton TF9 4ED — MB ChB 1993 Manch.

WILKINSON, Theresa Dennis 128 Shepherds Bush Centre, London W12 8QX Tel: 020 8749 1882 — MB BS 1967 Lond.; MRCS Eng. LRCP Lond. 1966. (Guy's)

WILKINSON, Timothy John McLaughlin and Partners, 27-29 Derby Road, North End, Portsmouth PO2 8HW Tel: 023 9266 3024 Fax: 023 9265 4991; 2 Park Road, Purbrook, Waterlooville PO7 5ES Tel: 01705 663024 — MB BS 1980 Lond.

WILKINSON, William Hardman (retired) Baringo, The Keep Gardens, Dartmouth TQ6 9JA — MRCS Eng. LRCP Lond. 1951. Prev: Wing Cdr. RAF Med. Br., Surg. Specialist RAF Hosp. Ely.

WILKS, David Michael Worsley 32 Castlenau Gardens, Arundel Terrace, London SW13 8DU Tel: 020 8741 5325 Fax: 020 8563 7102 Email: michael@mwilks.demon.co.uk — MB BS 1972 Lond.; DObst RCOG 1974. (St. Mary's) Princip. FME Metrop. Police. Socs: Assn. Police Surg. (Chairm. Metrop. & City Gp.); Chairm. Med. Ethics Comm. BMA. Prev: GP Lond. & Richmond Surrey; Ho. Phys. & Ho. Off. (O & G) St. Mary's Hosp. Lond.; Ho. Surg. Wembley Hosp.

WILKS, David Peter Regional Infectious Diseases Unit, Western General Hospital, Crewe Road, Edinburgh EH4 2XU — MB BChir 1983 Camb.; MA, MD Camb. 1991; MRCP (UK) 1986; DTM & H RCP Lond. 1987. Cons. Phys. (Infec. Dis.) W.ern Gen. Hosp. Edin.

WILKS

Socs: Fell. Roy. Soc. Trop. Med. & Hyg. Prev: Sen. Regist. (Infec. Dis. & Gen. Med.) Addenbrooke's Hosp. Camb.; Research Regist. (Immunol.) Clin. Research Centre Harrow; Regist. (Med.) Univ. Coll. Hosp. Lond.

WILKS, Diana Bramhall Health Centre, 66 Bramhall Lane South, Bramhall, Stockport SK7 2DY Tel: 0161 439 8213 Fax: 0161 439 6398; 9 Davenport Park Road, Davenport Road, Stockport SK7 6JU — MB ChB 1973 Manch.

WILKS, Mr John (retired) 15 Lostock Junction Lane, Bolton BL6 4JR — MB BS 1942 Lond.; FRCS Eng. 1949; MRCS Eng. LRCP Lond. 1942. Cons. Surg. Bolton Hosp. Gp. Prev: Sen. Regist. Hosp. For Sick Childr. Gt. Ormond St.

WILKS, John Maurice (retired) The Spinney, Moult Hill, Salcombe TQ8 8LG Tel: 01548 842860 — MB BS 1946 Lond.; MRCGP 1966.

WILKS, Mark Monkspath, Limerstone, Newport PO30 4AA Tel: 01983 740887 — MRCS Eng. LRCP Lond. 1942. (Guy's)

WILKS, Martin ZENECA Agrochemicals, Fernhurst, Haslemere GU27 3JE Tel: 01428 655041 Fax: 01428 657130 Email: martin.wilks@aguk.zeneca.com — State Exam Med 1983 Hanover; PhD Surrey 1990; MD Hanover 1986. Med. Adviser, Zeneca AgroChem.s Fernhurst; Hon. Cons. Med. Toxicol. Guy's Hosp. Lond. Prev: Clin. Toxicol. ICI Centr. Toxicol. Lab. Macclesfield.; Asst. (Intern. Med.) Med. Sch., Hannover.

WILKS, Peter Robert Witley Surgery, Wheeler Lane, Witley, Godalming GU8 5QR Tel: 01428 682218 Fax: 01428 682218; Sandhills Corner, Wormley, Godalming GU8 5UF Tel: 01428 683918 Email: p.r.wilks@btinternet.com — MB 1978 Camb.; MA Camb. 1980, MB 1978, BChir 1977; MRCGP 1982; DRCOG 1981. Prev: Trainee GP Norf. & Norwich Hosp. VTS; SHO (Path.) Char. Cross Hosp. Lond.; Ho. Surg. & Ho. Phys. Char. Cross Hosp. Lond.

WILL, Andrew Marshall 1 Vale Road, Bowdon, Altrincham, WA14 3JA — MD 1992 Manch.; MB ChB 1978; MRCP (UK) 1983; MRCPath 1992. Cons. Paediat. Haemat. Roy. Manch. Childr. Hosp.

WILL, David John The Young People's Unit, Royal Edinburgh Hospital, Tipperlinn Road, Edinburgh EH10 5HF Tel: 0131 447 2011; 5 Warrender Park Terrace, Edinburgh EH9 1JA — MB ChB 1972 Ed.; FRCPsych 1995; MRCPsych 1977. Cons. Adolesc. Psychiat. Roy. Edin. Hosp. Socs: SAAP. Prev: Cons. (Child & Adolesc. Psychiat.) Roy. Infirm. Dundee; Asst. Prof. Dept. Psychiat. McMaster Univ. Canada; Sen. Regist. (Child & Adolesc. Psychiat.) Lothian Health Bd.

WILL, Eric John St. James's University Hospital, Beckett St., Leeds LS9 7TF Tel: 0113 206 4354 Fax: 0113 244 0499 Email: csjejw@stjames.leeds.ac.uk; Well Royd, Knott Lane, Rawdon, Leeds LS19 6JW Tel: 0113 250 9023 — BM BCh 1969 Oxf.; MA Oxf. 1972; FRCP Lond. 1989. Cons. Renal Med. St. Jas. Univ. Hosp. Leeds. Socs: Roy. Soc. Med.; Eur. Renal Assn. Prev: Lect. (Med.) Nottm. Gen. Hosp.; Sen. Regist. (Med.) Nottm. City Hosp.; FUNGO Research Fell. Univ. Hosp. Leiden.

WILL, George 21 Berryhill Drive, Griffnock, Glasgow G46 7AS — MB ChB 1943 Glas.; BSc, MB ChB Glas. 1943; FRFPS Glas. 1947; FRCP Ed. 1982, M 1962; FRCP Glas. 1967. (Univ. Glas.) Cons. Phys. Greenock & Dist. Hosps. Socs: Heberden Soc. & Roy. M-C Soc. Glas. Prev: Sen. Med. Regist. & Ho. Phys. Roy. Infirm. Glas.; Merchant Navy.

WILL, Malcolm Brodie 8 Alder Drive, Burghmuir, Perth PH1 1ER — MB ChB 1998 Glas.

WILL, Margaret 21 Berryhill Drive, Griffnock, Glasgow G46 7AS — MB ChB 1943 Glas.; BSc Glas. 1940, MB ChB 1943. (Univ. Glas.) Med. Asst. Cytol. Roy. Samarit. Hosp. Glas. Prev: Ho. Surg. Glas. Roy. Infirm. & Roy. Matern. Hosp. Glas.

WILL, Richard Trenton, Ford Road, Lanchester, Durham DH7 0SN — MB BS 1972 Lond.; FFA RCS Eng. 1977. (St. Geo.) Cons. (Anaesth.) Dryburn Hosp. Durh.

WILL, Robert George Tel: 0131 537 2128 Fax: 0131 343 1404; 4 St Catherine's Place, Edinburgh EH4 2XU Tel: 0131 667 3667 — MD 1985 Camb.; MA Camb. 1985, BA 1971, MB BChir 1974; FRCP 1994; MRCP (UK) 1978; FRCP(E) 1991. (Lond. Hosp.) Prof. Cons. Neurol. W.. Gen. Hosp. Edin. Socs: Scot. Soc. Phys.; Assn. Brit. Neurols. Prev: Sen. Regist. Guy's & Maida Vale Hosps. Lond.; Regist. (Neurol.) Nat. Hosp. Nerv. Dis. Lond.; Hon. Regist. (Neurol.) Dept. Clin. Neurol. Univ. Oxf.

WILL, Sheila Carol Catherine 1 Vale Road, Bowdon, Altrincham WA14 3JA — MB ChB 1978 Manch.; BSc St. And. 1975; MFPHM 1992.

WILL, Sheila Catherine The Darroch, Little Cantray, Culloden Moor, Inverness IV2 5EY — MB ChB 1978 Aberd.; MRCPsych 1982. Cons. Psychiat. Craig Dunain Hosp. Inverness. Prev: Sen. Regist. (Psychiat.) Roy. Edin. Hosp.; Regist. (Psychiat.) Craig Dunain Hosp. Inverness.

WILLAMUNE, Navaratne Bandara Northgate Hospital, Northgate St., Great Yarmouth NR30 1BU — MB BS 1973 Sri Lanka; MRCPsych 1983.

WILLAN, Alison Louise York Road Group Practice, York Road, Ellesmere Port, South Wirral CH65 0DB Tel: 0151 355 2112 Fax: 0151 356 5512; 37 Heath Drive, Upton, Wirral CH49 6LE — MB ChB 1991 Manch.; MRCGP 1995. (Manch)

WILLAN, John Curwen (retired) Health Centre, Carfax St., Swindon SN4 9LW Tel: 01793 692880 — MB BChir 1954 Camb.; BA, MB BChir Camb. 1954; MRCP Lond. 1957; DObst RCOG 1955. Prev: Asst. Lect. Path. St. Thos. Hosp.

WILLAN, Professor Peter Leslie Terence 30 Coniston Road, Gatley, Cheadle SK8 4AP Email: pwillan@talk21.com — MB ChB 1970 Birm.; FRCS Glas. 1976. Freelance Anat. Socs: Fell. Brit. Assn. Clin. Anat.; Anat. Soc. Prev: Prof. Anat. Univ. United Arab Emirates, Al-Ain; Sen. Lect. (Anat.) Univ. Manch.; Med. Off. (Surg.) Tameside Gen. Hosp.

WILLAN, William Kenneth (retired) 24 Longfield Road, Shaw, Oldham OL2 7HD — MB ChB 1953 Manch. Prev: Ho. Phys. Boundary Pk. Gen. Hosp. Oldham.

WILLARD, Christopher John Colston Arnewood Practice, Milton Medical Centre, Avenue Road, New Milton BH25 5JP Tel: 01425 620393 Fax: 01425 624219; Aubrey House, Keyhaven, Lymington SO41 0TL Tel: 01590 643219 — MB BS 1968 Lond.; MRCS Eng. LRCP Lond. 1968; DCH Eng. 1971; DObst RCOG 1971. (Guy's) Trainer (Gen. Pract.) & Regist. Course Organiser Soton.; Med. Off. New Forest Marathon. Prev: SHO (Obst.) FarnBoro. Hosp. Kent; SHO (Paediat.) St. Albans City Hosp.

WILLARD, Hilary Louise 65 Forest Road, Worthing BN14 9LR — MB BS 1993 Lond.

WILLARS, Christopher Mark 39 Hantone Hill, Bathampton, Bath BA2 6XD — MB BS 1998 Lond.

WILLATT, Mr David Jonathan ENT Dept, Hope Hospital, Eccles Old Road, Salford M6 8HD Tel: 0161 787 4758 Fax: 0161 787 4723 — MB 1980 Camb.; BChir 1979; FRCS Lond. 1985; MD Liverp. 1995. Cons. ENT Surg. Hope & Roy. Manch. Childr. Hosps. Salford HA; Hon. Clin. Lect. Univ. Sch. Med. Manch. Prev: Sen. Regist. (Otorhinolaryngol. Univ. Liverp.

WILLATT, Ian Duncan (retired) Crouch Readon, St. Patrick's Lane, Liss GU33 7HQ Tel: 01730 893316 — MD 1946 Ed.; MB ChB 1939; FRCGP 1973, M 1960. Prev: Regist. (Med.) Roy. Infirm. Chester.

WILLATT, Jonathon Myles 6 Grange Court, Main St., Egginton, Derby DE65 6HR — MB ChB 1997 Manch.

WILLATT, Richard Norman The Surgery, Southview Lodge, South View, Bromley BR1 3DR Tel: 020 8460 1945 Fax: 020 8323 1423; 9 Beadon Road, Bromley BR2 9AS — MB ChB 1973 Ed.

WILLATT, Ruth Annette Janie (retired) Crouch Readon, St Patrick's Lane, Rake Road, Liss GU33 7HQ Tel: 01730 893316 — MB ChB 1939 Ed.; BA (Hons.) Open 1977, BA 1974. Prev: Ho. Phys. E. Gen. Hosp. Leith.

WILLATTS, David George Six Bells Cottage, Upper Brailes, Banbury OX15 5AZ Tel: 01608 685363 — MB BS 1975 Lond.; MA Camb.; MRCS Eng. LRCP Lond. 1975; FFA RCS Eng. 1980. Cons. Anaesth. Horton Hosp. Banbury. Prev: Sen. Regist. (Anaesth.) St. Thos. Hosp. Lond.

WILLATTS, Sheila Margaret Intensive Care Unit, Bristol Royal Infirmary, Marlborough St., Bristol BS2 8HW Tel: 0117 923 0000 Fax: 0117 928 2098; 6 Westbury Park, Durdham Down, Bristol BS6 7JB Tel: 0117 974 3447 Fax: 0117 946 6429 Email: swillatts@compuserve.com — MB BS Lond. 1967; MD Lond. 1994; MRCP (UK) 1974; FRCP Lond. 1988; MRCS Eng. LRCP Lond. 1967; FRCA Eng. 1973; DObst RCOG 1969; DA Eng. 1969. (Univ. Coll. Hosp.) Ass Director, Intens. care unit; Counc. Coll. Anaesth. Vice-Pres. Socs: Assn. Anaesth.; Anaesth. Sect. RSM; Anaesth. Res. Soc. Prev: Cons. Anaesth. Bristol Roy. Infirm.; Sen. Regist. (Anaesth.)

King's Coll. & Brook Gen. Hosps. Lond.; SHO (Anaesth.) St. Helier Hosp. Carshalton.

WILLBY, Lesley Ann The Surgery, 59 Sheep St., Burford OX18 4LS; Frog Cottage, Green Lane, Milton-Under-Wychwood, Oxford OX7 6JY — MB BS 1982 Lond.; DRCOG 1986. (St. Geo. Hosp. Med. Sch. Lond.) GP Asst. Burford Surg. Oxf. Prev: GP Perth, Austral.

WILLCOCK, Gerald Arthur Toodle Cottage, Askham, Penrith CA10 2QJ — MB ChB 1954 Manch. (Manch.)

WILLCOCK, Roger Doidge (retired) The Elms, Buildwas Road, Ironbridge, Telford TF8 7DW — MB BS 1947 Lond.

WILLCOCKS, Julian Anthony James 85A The Street, Basingstoke RG24 7BY — MB BS 1992 Lond.

WILLCOCKS, Lisa Claire 76 Bournemouth Road, Poole BH14 0EY — BM BCh 1998 Oxf.

WILLCOX, Christine Heather The Red House, Lower Flat, 32 Daglands Road, Fowey PL23 1JN — MB BS Lond. 1964; MRCS Eng. LRCP Lond. 1964. (Roy. Free) Occupat. Phys. Cornw. Healthcare Trust & Cornw. Co. Counc. Socs: Soc. Occupat. Med. Prev: Dist. Occupat. Health Phys. NW Herts. HA; Med. Off. Kodak Ltd.

WILLCOX, Christopher Philip William The Health Centre, St. Peters Crescent, Selsey, Chichester PO20 0NN Tel: 01243 604321/602261 Fax: 01243 607996; Shaftgate, Paddock Lane, Selsey, Chichester PO20 9AZ — MB BChir Camb. 1966; MA Camb. 1966; DObst RCOG 1967. (Camb. & St. Mary's) Socs: BMA; (Ex-Pres.) Chichester Clin. Soc. Prev: Ho. Surg. St. Mary's Hosp.; Ho. Phys. King Edwd. Memor. Hosp. Ealing; Med. Off. Govt. Sabah E. Malaysia.

WILLCOX, Denys Roy Calder (retired) 8 Lady JaneCt., Cavendish Avenue, Cambridge CB1 7UW — MB BS 1949 Lond.; MRCS Eng. LRCP Lond. 1939; FRCPath 1969. Prev: Cons. Chem. Path. Harlow Dist. Hosps.

WILLCOX, Hilton Leonard, Group Capt. RAF Med. Br. Retd. (retired) Broomlea, Old Church Road, Cullen, Buckie AB56 4UZ Tel: 01542 40395 — MB ChB 1933 N.Z. Prev: PMO Rhodesian Air Train. Gp. RAF.

WILLCOX, Professor Hugh Nicholas Anson Neurosciences, Institute for Molecular Medicine, John Radcliffe Hospital, Oxford OX3 9DS Tel: 01865 222325 Fax: 01865 222402 Email: neurosciences@imm.ox.ac.uk; 74 Crescent Road, Temple Cowley, Oxford OX4 2PD Tel: 01865 779123 — MB BChir 1968 Camb.; PhD CNAA 1975; BA Camb. 1965, MA, MB 1969, BChir 1968. (Middlx.) Sen. Research Fell. (Neurosci.) Inst. Molecular Med. John Radcliffe Hosp. Oxf.; Research Lect. (Neurosci.) Univ. Oxf. Socs: Brit. Soc. Immunol. Prev: Lect. (Anat.) Newc.; Ho. Phys. Middlx. Hosp. Lond.

WILLCOX, Jeremy Robert Lower Newlands, Godwell Lane, Ivybridge PL21 0LE Tel: 01752 892600 — MB BS 1970 Lond.; MRCS Eng. LRCP Lond. 1972; DCH Eng. 1973. (St. Mary's) Cons. Genitourin. Med. Plymouth Torquay Hosps. Socs: Med. Soc. Study VD; Assn. Genitourin. Med. Prev: Lect. (Genitourin. Med.) Acad. Unit Middlx. Hosp.; Sen. Regist. (Genitourin. Med.) St. Thos. Hosp.; Surg. to P & O SN Company.

***WILLCOX, Merlin Luke** Shaftgates, Paddock Lane, Selsey, Chichester PO20 9AZ Email: merlinwillcox@hotmao;.com — BM BCh 1998 Oxf.; BM BCh Oxf 1998; BA 1995.

WILLCOX, Richard Neston Surgery, Mellock Lane, Little Neston, South Wirral CH64 4BN Tel: 0151 336 3951 Fax: 0151 353 0173; 26 Earle Drive, Parkgate, South Wirral CH64 6RZ Tel: 0151 336 6700 — MB ChB 1970 Liverp.; MRCGP 1977; DObst RCOG 1972. Clin. Asst. (Colposcopy) Roy. Liverp. Hosp. Prev: Regist. (Med.) Walton Hosp. Liverp.; SHO (Obst.) Liverp. Matern. Hosp.; Ho. Off. BRd.green Hosp. Liverp.

WILLCOX, Robert Health Solutions, 15 Broadlands Road, London N6 4AE Tel: 07977 068290 Email: health.solutions@virgin.net; 39 Charlbury Road, Oxford OX2 6UX Tel: 01865 512660 — MB BS 1972 Lond.; FOM RCP Lond. 1999, AFOM 1983; DTM & H Liverp. 1980. (Middlx.) Managing Dir. Socs: Fell. Roy. Soc. Med.; Soc. Occupat. Med. Prev: Gp. Med. Off. Cable & Wireless; Med. Off. Brit. Petroleum; Med. Off. Brit. Airways Med. Serv.

WILLCOX-JONES, Colin Tel: 01634 240295 Fax: 01634 245820; 3 Old Rectory Ground, Church Road, Offham, West Malling ME19 5NY Tel: 01732 842665 — MB ChB 1968 Ed.; DCH Eng. 1972; DObst RCOG 1971. (Ed.) Prev: Ho. Off. Roy. Infirm. Edin.

WILLDIG, Kathryn Mary Holmes Chapel Health Centre, London Road, Holmes Chapel, Crewe CW4 7BB; Woodheath Cottage, Whitecroft Heath Road, Lower Withington, Macclesfield SK11 9DF — BSc (Morbid Anat.) (Hons.) Manch. 1975, MB ChB 1977; MRCGP 1982; DCH RCP Lond. 1981; DRCOG 1980. (Manchester)

WILLDIG, Paul John Chance, Congleton Lane, Siddington, Macclesfield SK11 9LE — MB ChB 1976 Manch.; BSc (Physiol., Hons.) Manch. 1973, MB ChB 1976; MFOM RCP Lond. 1986, AFOM 1981; DIH Eng. 1981. Med. Off. W.. Area NCB; Hon. Clin. Asst. Shelton Chest Clin. Stoke-on-Trent. Socs: Soc. Occupat. Med. Prev: Ho. Off. (Neurosurg.) & Ho. Phys. (Haemat.) Manch. Roy. Infirm.

WILLDRIDGE, Jennifer 1 The Limekilns, Balgeddie, Glenrothes KY6 3QJ — MB ChB 1995 Glas.; BSc (Hons) Strathclyde 1987.

WILLE, Richard William Sarum House, 3 St Ethelbert St., Hereford HR1 2NS Tel: 01432 265422; 25 Broomy Hill, Hereford HR4 0LJ Tel: 01432 267242 — MRCS Eng. LRCP Lond. 1960; DObst RCOG 1962. (Guy's)

WILLEMS, Pierre Jacques Anthony St Marys House, Broad St., Wrington, Bristol BS40 5LA — LMSSA 1959 Lond.; DPM Eng. 1966. (Guy's) Sen. Regist. (Psychiat.) Oxf. RHB; Med. Adviser Oxf & Dist. Counc. on Alcoholism. Prev: Research Regist. (Alcoholism) Oxf. RHB.

WILLENBROCK, Philip Charles 13 Woodland Way, Wivenhoe, Colchester CO7 9AP Tel: 01206 823812 — BM BCh 1968 Oxf.; MA Oxf. 1968. (Lond. Hosp.) Prev: GP Camborne; SHO (Neurol.) Ch.ill Hosp. Oxf.; Ho. Off. Lond. Hosp.

WILLENS, Marni Northcote Surgery, 2 Victoria Circus, Glasgow G12 9LD Tel: 0141 339 3211 Fax: 014 357 4480 — MB ChB 1990 Glas.; DRCOG 1993; MRCGP 1995. (Glasgow) Partner N.cote Surg. Socs: Glas. LMC.

WILLERT, Emma Jane 17 Toucan Way, Basildon SS16 5ER — MB ChB 1997 Manch.

WILLETT, Christina Hill 75 Morven Road, Bearsden, Glasgow G61 3BY — MB ChB 1959 Glas. (Glas.)

WILLETT, Claire Jeanette 28 Monro Drive, Guildford GU2 9PS — MB BCh 1990 Wales; MRCGP 1994; DRCOG 1993; DCH RCP Lond. 1992. Prev: Trainee GP Hinchingbrooke Hosp. Huntingdon.

WILLETT, Frances Marion 13 Kerrison Place, Ealing, London W5 5NG — MB BS 1988 Lond.; BA Oxf. 1985; MRCP (UK) 1992. Dir. Clin. Research Cerebrus Wokingham.

WILLETT, Mr Keith Malcolm John Radcliffe Hospital, Headington, Oxford OX3 9DU Tel: 01865 220241 Fax: 01865 221231 — MB BS 1981 Lond.; FRCS Eng. 1985; MRCS Eng. LRCP Lond. 1981. (Charing Cross) Cons. Orthop. Trauma Surg. John Radcliffe Hosp. Oxf.; Cons. Orthop. Trauma Surg. Nuffield Orthop. Centre. Socs: Fell. BOA; (Pres.) Brit. Trauma Soc.; Soc. Exp. Witnesses. Prev: Trauma Fell. Sunnybrook Health Sci. Centre Toronto, Canada; Sen. Regist. (Orthop.) Char. Cross Hosp. Lond.; SHO Rotat. St. Bart. Hosp. Lond.

WILLETT, Mark Old Mill Surgery, Marlborough Road, Nuneaton CV11 5PQ Tel: 024 7638 2554 Fax: 024 7635 0047 — MB ChB 1984 Birm.

***WILLETT, Mark James** 11 Coberley Avenue, Davyhulme, Urmaston, Manchester M41 8QE — MB ChB 1994 Birm.

WILLETTS, Geoffrey Thomas Shipley, TD (retired) Hanway, 22 Clarry Drive, Sutton Coldfield B74 2QT — MB ChB 1948 Birm. Prev: Ho. Phys. & Ho. Surg. Gen. Hosp. Birm.

WILLETTS, Mr Ian Edward 338 Halesowen Road, Cradley Heath, Cradley Heath B64 7JT Email: gcq82@dial.pipex.com — MB ChB 1988 Manch.; MB ChB (Hons.) Manch. 1988; BSc (Hons.) Anat. Manch. 1985; FRCS Eng. 1993; FRCS Ed. 1993. Specialist Regist. (Paediat. Surg.) Leeds Gen. Infirm. & St. Jas. Univ. Hosp. Leeds; Hunt. Prof. RCS Eng. Socs: Assoc. Mem. Brit. Assn. Paediat. Surgs.; Brit. Transpl. Soc. Prev: Research Fell. (Paediat. Surg.) Nuffield Dept. Surg. Univ. Oxf.; Temp. Lect. (Anat.) Univ. Manch.; SHO Rotat. (Surg.) Qu. Med. Centre Nottm.

WILLETTS, Janet Margaret Shanklin Medical Centre, 1 Carter Road, Shanklin PO37 7HR Tel: 01983 862245 Fax: 01983 862310; Bagend, Slay Lane, Whitwell, Ventnor PO38 2QF Tel: 01983 730727 — MB BS 1979 Lond.; BSc (Hons.) Lond. 1976; MRCS Eng. LRCP Lond. 1979. (Guy's) Prev: GP Newport, I. of Wight.

WILLETTS

WILLETTS, Simon James Castlehill Health Centre, Castlehill, Forres IV36 1QF Tel: 01309 672233 — MB ChB 1987 Aberd.; MRCP (UK) 1993; MRCGP 1995. (Univ. Aberd.) Unrestricted Princip. - Grampian H.B. Socs: BMA.

WILLEY, Courtney Beresford Ingor, MBE, MC (retired) Heron Garth, Bleach Green, Egremont CA22 2NL Tel: 01946 820282 — MD Lond. 1952; MA Oxon. 1939, BM BCh 1937; FRCP Lond. 1970, M 1947. Prev: Cons. Phys. W. Cumbld. Hosp. Whitehaven.

WILLEY, Mrs Muriel Gladys (retired) Heron Garth, Bleach Green, Egremont CA22 2NL Tel: 01946 820282 — MB BS 1945 Lond.; DObst RCOG 1948. Prev: Med. Off. W. Cumbld. Family Plann. Clinics.

WILLEY, Richard Flynn Royal Lancaster Infirmary, Ashton Road, Lancaster LA1 4RP; Woodfield House, Moorside Road, Brookhouse, Lancaster LA2 9PN — MB ChB 1972 Ed.; FRCP 1991; FRCP Ed. 1988; MRCP (UK) 1974. Cons. Phys. Roy. Lancs. Infirm. & W.morland Gen. Hosp. Kendal. Prev: Sen. Regist. (Gen. Med.) Roy. Infirm. Edin.

WILLIAMS, Adela Mary 41 Winchendon Road, Fulham, London SW6 5DH Tel: 020 7736 6234 — MB ChB 1984 Bristol; DRCOG 1986. Prev: Trainee GP/SHO St. Albans VTS.

WILLIAMS, Professor Adrian Charles 53 Weoley Hill, Selly Oak, Birmingham B29 4AB Tel: 0121 472 0218 — MD 1978 Birm.; MB ChB 1972; FRCP Lond. 1986; MRCP (UK) 1974. Bloomer Prof. Clin. Neurol. Univ. Birm. Prev: Cons. Neurol. Qu. Eliz. & Selly Oak Gen. Hosps. Birm. & Manor Hosp. Walsall; Regist. & Sen. Regist. Nat. Hosp. Nerv. Dis. Lond.; Vis. Fell. Nat. Insts. Health Bethesda, USA.

WILLIAMS, Adrian Hyatt 11 BRoadlands Close, London N6 4AF Tel: 020 7267 3181; 5 Elm Terrace, London NW3 — MB BS 1975 Lond.; MRCGP 1981; DCH Eng. 1978. (Roy. Free) Socs: BMA. Prev: SHO (Psychiat.) & SHO (Paediat.) Roy. Free Hosp. Lond.; Trainee Gen. Pract. Lond.

WILLIAMS, Adrian John Elgar House Surgery, Church Road, Redditch B97 4AB Tel: 01527 69261 Fax: 01527 596856; Rivendell, 58 Wellington Road, Bromsgrove B60 2AX Tel: 01527 79741 — MB ChB 1980 Bristol; BSc (Hons. Pharmacol.) Bristol 1977, MB ChB 1980; MRCP (UK) 1984; DRCOG 1985; Cert Family Plann. JCC 1984. Socs: BMA & RCP. Prev: Trainee GP Worcester VTS; Ho. Phys. Profess. Med. Unit Bristol Roy. Infirm.

WILLIAMS, Adrian John Lane-Fox Respiratory Unit, St Thomas' Hospital, London SE1 7EH Tel: 020 7928 9292 Ext: 6856 Fax: 020 7922 8281 Email: asta@talk21.com; 8 Nightingale Square, London SW12 8QN Tel: 020 8673 4385 — MB BS Lond. 1969; FRCP Lond. 1989; MRCP (UK) 1971. (University College Hospital, London) Cons. Phys. & Clin. Dir. La.-Fox Respirat. Unit St. Thos. Respirat. & Sleep Med.; Hon. Sen. Lect. UMDS; Vis. Prof. UCLA. Prev: Prof. Clin. Med. & Dir. Pulm. & Critical Care W. L.A. VA Med Center & UCLA Med. Center, Los Angeles, USA.

WILLIAMS, Adrian Tudor Annette Fox Haematology Unit, Bradford Royal Infirmary, Duckworth Lane, Bradford BD9 6RJ Tel: 01274 364686; Mendip House, 127 Curly Hill, Ilkley LS29 0DT — MB BChir 1977 Camb.; MA 1978 Camb.; MRCP (UK) 1980; MRCPath 1986; FRCPath 1996; FRCP 1998. (St. Thos.) Cons. Haemat. Bradford Hosps. NHS Trust. Socs: BMA. Prev: Sen. Regist. (Haemat.) Guy's Hosp. Lond.; Regist. (Haemat.) King's Coll. Hosp. Lond.

WILLIAMS, Alan Clive Church View Surgery, Broadway Road, Broadway TA19 9RX Tel: 01460 55300 Fax: 01460 53999; Axhill House, Windmill Hill Lane, Ashill, Ilminster TA19 9NB Tel: 01823 480262 — MB BCh 1960 Wales; MRCGP 1968; DObst RCOG 1963. (Welsh Nat. Sch. Med.) Socs: BMA Chairm. Som. Div.; W Som. Med. Soc. Prev: Ho. Surg. (Urol.) United Cardiff Hosps.; Ho. Phys. E. Glam. Hosp.; Ho. Surg. (Obst.) Profess. Unit United Cardiff Hosps.

WILLIAMS, Alan Hugh Ferniehill Road Surgery, 8 Ferniehill Road, Edinburgh EH17 7AD Tel: 0131 664 2166 Fax: 0131 666 1075; 10 East Camus Road, Edinburgh EH10 6RE Tel: 0131 445 1223 — MB ChB 1985 Aberd.; DCCH RCP Ed. 1990; Dip Occ Med 1996. Phys. (Occupat. Health) S. E. Scotl. Blood Trans. Serv. & Protein Fractionation Centre, Edin.

WILLIAMS, Alan John Ty-Elli Group Practice, Ty Elli, Llanelli SA15 3BD Tel: 01554 772678 / 773747 Fax: 01554 774476; Grey Gables, Heol Ddv, Llanelli SA15 4RN Email: a.williams@easynet.co.uk — MB BS 1982 Lond.; MRCGP 1986.

WILLIAMS, Alan John Royal Bournemouth Hospital, Castle Lane E., Bournemouth BH7 7DW Tel: 01202 303626; Belle Heather, 166 Burley Road, Bransgore, Christchurch BH23 8DE — MB ChB 1975 Birm.; MD Birm. 1987; FRCP Lond. 1995; FRCP Ed. 1994; MRCP (UK) 1978. Cons. Phys. Roy. Bournemouth Hosp.; Hon. Lect. UCL. Socs: Brit. Thorac. Soc.& BMA. Prev: Sen. Regist. (Gen. Thoracic Med.) Mersey RHA; Sheldon Research Fell. E. Birm. Hosp.; Med. Regist. (Thoracic Med.) E. Birm. Hosp.

WILLIAMS, Alan Roy Macclesfield District General Hospital, Victoria Road, Macclesfield SK10 3BL Tel: 01625 421000/661820 Fax: 01625 661804; The Chase, Trouthall Lane, Plumley, Knutsford WA16 9RZ Tel: 01565 722434 — MB ChB 1975 Liverp.; MRCPath 1982; FRCPath 1992. Cons. Histopath. Macclesfield Dist. Gen. Hosp. & Home Office (Path.). Prev: Lect. (Path.) Univ. Liverp.; Regist. United Liverp. Hosps.

WILLIAMS, Mr Albert Frederick (retired) Pwll Crwn, Lon Yr Eglwys, Morfa Nefyn, Pwllheli LL53 6AR Tel: 01758 720285 — MB ChB (2nd cl. Hons.) Manch. 1939; BSc Manch. 1936; FRCS Eng. 1940; MRCS Eng. LRCP Lond. 1939. Prev: 1st Asst. Profess. Surgic. Unit, Manch. Roy. Infirm.

WILLIAMS, Aled (retired) Seawinds, 114 Ffordd Naddyn, Glan Conwy, Colwyn Bay LL28 5BJ — MB ChB 1957 Liverp.; FRCOG 1980, M 1967; DObst RCOG 1960. Prev: Cons. O & G Maelor Gen. Hosp. Wrexham.

WILLIAMS, Alex Olabode 37 Defoe Crescent, Colchester CO4 5LQ — MB BS 1985 Ibadan; MRCP (UK) 1993.

WILLIAMS, Alexander St Thomas Health Centre, Cowick Street, St. Thomas, Exeter EX4 1HJ Tel: 01392 676677 Fax: 01392 676677 — MB BS 1982 Lond.; MRCP (UK) 1985; MRCGP 1990; DRCOG 1989. Clin. Asst. (Respirat. Med.) Winford Hosp. Prev: Trainee GP Paignton; Regist. (Med.) Torbay Hosp.; SHO (O & G & ENT) Torbay Hosp.

WILLIAMS, Alexander Thomas Dunford 98 Harley Street, London W1N 1AF Tel: 020 7629 8340; Ridge House, Ballantyne Drive, Kingswood, Tadworth KT20 6EA Tel: 01737 353995 — MB BS 1968 Lond.; MSc (Distinc.) Lond. 1976; MRCS Eng. LRCP Lond. 1965; MFOM RCP Lond. 1979; DIH Eng. 1976; DObst RCOG 1975. (Univ. Coll. Hosp.) Med. Adviser Govt. Canada, Lond.; Med. Dir. Lond. Diagn. Centre; Assoc. Prof. Med. Univ. Nova Scotia. Socs: Fell. Roy. Soc. Med.; Soc. Occupat. Med. Prev: Med. Dir., Arctic Health Serv. Canada; Dir. Occupat. Health, Nova Scotia, Canada; Lect. Lond. Sch. Hyg. & Trop. Med.

WILLIAMS, Alison Claire — MB ChB 1988 Birm.; MRCGP 1993; DRCOG 1991.

WILLIAMS, Alison Jane Tel: 01728 860248 Fax: 01728 861300 — MB ChB 1989 Sheff.; MRCGP 1994; DRCOG 1992.

WILLIAMS, Alistair Robert William Department of Pathology, Edinburgh University Medical School, Teviot Place, Edinburgh EH8 9AG Tel: 0131 650 2957 Fax: 0131 650 6528 Email: alistair.r.w.williams@ed.ac.uk; 11 Corremic Drive, Edinburgh EH10 6EQ Tel: 0131 447 1481 Fax: 0131 447 2500 — MD 1988 Ed.; MB CHB Ed 1979; MB ChB Ed. 1979; MRCPath 1986; FRCPath 1997. Sen. Lect. (Path.) Univ. Edin. Socs: Path. Soc.; Brit. Gyn. Cancer Soc.; Internat. Soc. Gyn. Path.

WILLIAMS, Alun James The Practice Of Health, 31 Barry Road, Barry CF63 1BA Tel: 01446 700350 Fax: 01446 420795; Morfa, 12 Romilly Avenue, Barry CF62 6RB — MB BCh 1979 Wales; MRCGP 1987; DRCOG 1982.

WILLIAMS, Alun Rhys Tan-Y-Bryn, Heol-Y-Bryn, Rhigos, Aberdare CF44 9DJ — BM BCh 1994 Oxf.

WILLIAMS, Mr Alun Tudno ENT Department, Royal Infirmary of Edinburgh, Lauriston Place, Edinburgh EH3 9YW Tel: 0131 536 1000 Fax: 0131 536 1001 — MB BS 1989 Lond.; BSc Lond. 1988; FRCS (Otol.) 1996; FRCS Eng. 1996. (St. Thos. Hosp. Lond.) Specialist Regist. (Ear Nose & Throat) Edin. Roy. Infirm.

WILLIAMS, Alyn Christopher Prior Chapel Street Surgery, 93 Chapel Street, Billericay CM12 9LR Tel: 01277 622940/655134 Fax: 01277 631893; 8 The Knoll, Billericay CM12 0NT Tel: 01277 652841 — MB BS 1981 Lond.; BSc (Physiol.) Lond. 1978. Clin. Asst. (Rheum.) S.end Hosp. Trust.

WILLIAMS, Amanda Jane Melrose, Llwyncelyn Terrace, Nelson, Treharris CF46 6HF — MB BS 1989 Lond.

WILLIAMS, Andrew 39 Highfield Avenue, Appleton, Warrington WA4 5DX — MB ChB 1981 Birm.; MRCGP 1987.

WILLIAMS

WILLIAMS, Andrew Anthony 29 Lambardes, New Ash Green, Longfield DA3 8HX — BM 1992 Soton.; MRCP (UK) 1996. Regist. (Elderly & Gen. Med.) Dorset Co. Hosp. Dorchester.

WILLIAMS, Andrew Brian 70C Old Dover Road, London SE3 8SY — MB BS 1991 Lond.

WILLIAMS, Andrew David 25 Westaway Drive, Hakin, Milford Haven SA73 3EQ — MB ChB 1993 Birm.

WILLIAMS, Andrew George Woodbury, Bromley Lane, Chislehurst BR7 6LE — MB BS 1985 Lond.; MRCGP 1995. Clin. Commiss. Dir. Bromley Health. Socs: BMA & Christian Med. Fell.sh. Prev: SHO (Neurol.) Brook Gen. Hosp. Lond.; SHO (Gen. Med.) Orpington Hosp.

WILLIAMS, Andrew Ivor Lake Road Health Centre, Nutfield Place, Portsmouth PO1 4JT Tel: 023 9282 1201 Fax: 023 9287 5658 — MB BS 1987 Lond.; MRCGP 1991; DGM RCP Lond. 1990; DCH RCP Lond. 1990; DRCOG 1989.

WILLIAMS, Andrew James Medical Research Department, Zeneca Pharmaceuticals, Alderley Park, Macclesfield SK10 4TG Tel: 01625 514348; 48 Legh Road, Prestbury, Macclesfield SK10 4HX — MB ChB 1980 Liverp.; PhD CNAA 1975; BSc (Hons.) Lond. 1971. Chief Clin. Pharmacol. Zeneca Pharmaceut. Chesh.; Hon. Lect. (Med.) Manch. Univ. Med. Sch. Socs: Fell. Roy. Soc. Med.; Amer. Thoracic Soc.; (Meetings Sec.) Soc. Pharmaceut. Med. Prev: Sen. Clin. Pharmacol. Beecham Pharmaceut. Epsom; Lect. (Clin. Pharmacol.) St. Geo. Hosp. Med. Sch. Univ. Lond.

WILLIAMS, Andrew James Kevin Wester Marchbank, Mansfield Road, Balerno EH14 7JT — MB ChB 1980 Bristol; MD Bristol 1988, BSc (Hons.) 1977; FRCP Ed. 1995; MRCP (UK) 1983. Cons. Phys. (Gastroenterol.) St. John's Hosp. Livingston.

WILLIAMS, Andrew John Morriston Hospital, Heol Maes Eglwys, Cwmrhydyceirw, Swansea SA6 6NL Tel: 01792 703399 Fax: 01792 703716; Grove Cottage, Reynoldston, Gower, Swansea SA3 1AA Tel: 01792 390182 Email: ajwil@globalnet.co.uk — MB BS (Hons.) Lond. 1975; MD Lond. 1981; FRCP Lond. 1993; MRCP (UK) 1977. (Lond. Hosp.) Cons. Phys. (Renal Med.) Morriston Hosp. Swansea. Socs: Eur. Dialysis & Transpl. Assn.; Internat. Soc. Nephrol.; Renal ass. Prev: Sen. Regist. (Nephrol.) Lond. Hosp.; Lect. Cardiothoracic Inst. Lond.; Regist. (Med.) Qu. Mary's Hosp. Roehampton.

WILLIAMS, Mr Andrew Michael Royal National Orthopaedic Hospital, Brockley Hill, Stanmore HA7 4LP — MB BS 1987 Lond.; FRCS Eng. 1991; FRCS (Orth.) 1995. SenLect/Hon cons. Roy.Nat.Ortop.Hosps. Tanmore. Socs: Fell. Roy. Soc. Med.; Brit. Orthop. Sports Trauma Assn.; Assoc. Brit. Orthop. Assn. Prev: Sen. Regist. Roy. Nat. Orthop. Hosp. Stanmore; Clin. Lect. Roy. Nat. Orthop. Hosp. Stanmore.

WILLIAMS, Andrew Nason Consultant Paediatrician (Community Child Health), St Nicolas Park Clinic, Windermere Avenue, Nuneaton CV11 6HH; Chorley House, Back Commons, Clitheroe BB7 2DX Tel: 01200 426524, 02476 343337 Fax: 01200 426524 — BM BCh 1990 Oxf.; MSc 1999 Community Child Health (Warwick); BA (Hons.) Oxf. 1987; MRCP 1994 (UK); MRCP 1997. (Oxford) Cons. Paediat. (Community Child Health) N. Warks. NHS Trust; Hon. Sen. Clin. Fell., Birm. Childr.'s Hosp.; Hon. Visting Sen. Clin. Lect. Univ. of Warwick; Hon. Research Fell. Centre for Historical Studies, Univ. of Birm.. Socs: Brit. Soc. for the Hist. of Paediotrics & Child Health. Prev: Sen. Regist., Birm. Childr.'s Hosp.

WILLIAMS, Andrew Rhys Department of Anaesthetics, St George's Hospital, Blackshaw Road, Tooting, London SW17 0QT Tel: 020 8672 1255; 34 Beaufordt Avenue, Langland, Swansea SA3 4PB — MB BCh 1981 Wales; FFA RCSI 1989; DA (UK) 1985. Sen. Regist. (Anaesth.) St. Geo., Atkinson Morley & Gt. Ormond St. Hosps. Socs: Assn. Anaesth. Gt. Brit. & N. Irel. & Anaesth. Research Soc. Prev: Regist. (Anaesth.) Poole & Bournemouth Hosps.

WILLIAMS, Aneurin Gwyn Llanberis Surgery, High Street, Llanberis, Caernarfon LL55 4SU Tel: 01286 870634 Fax: 01286 871722; 3 Preswylfa, Llanberis, Caernarfon LL55 4LF Tel: 01286 870101 — MB BS 1983 Lond. (The London Hospital Medical Centre) Prev: GP Canning Town Lond.; SHO (ENT & Paediat.) St. John's Hosp. Chelmsford; SHO (A & E) Broomfield Hosp. Chelmsford.

WILLIAMS, Angharad Wyn Parc Glas Surgery, Bodorgan LL62 5NL Tel: 01407 840294; Plas Brain, Llanbedreoch LL76 8SJ Tel: 01248 450847, 0161 881 6715 Email: lindamontague@doctors.org.uk — MB BCh 1996 Wales; DRCOG; DFFP. (Univ. Wales Coll. Med.) GP, Anglesey. Socs: BMA. Prev: Ho. Off. (Surg.); Ho. Off. (Med.); SHO (A & E).

WILLIAMS, Ann Athel The Medical Centre, Kingston Avenue, East Horsley, Leatherhead KT24 6QT Tel: 0148 654151; (resid.), Dytchley's, The St, West Horsley, Leatherhead KT24 6HS Tel: 0148 652487 — MB BS 1960 Lond.; MRCS Eng. LRCP Lond. 1960. (Lond. Hosp.) Socs: BMA. Prev: Ho. Surg. & Ho. Phys. St. Luke's Hosp. Guildford.

WILLIAMS, Ann Elisabeth Wellers Cottage, Marringdean Road, Billingshurst RH14 9EJ — MB BS 1980 Lond.

WILLIAMS, Anne 33 Coalway Road, Penn, Wolverhampton WV3 7LU — MB BCh 1965 Wales.

WILLIAMS, Anne Elizabeth Warstones Healthcare, Pinfold Grove, Penn, Wolverhampton WV4 4PS Tel: 01902 575012 — MB ChB 1983 Birm.; MRCGP 1990. Prev: Trainee GP/SHO (O & G) New Cross Hosp. Wolverhampton.

WILLIAMS, Anne Marie Helene Thurston Road Surgery, 140 Thurston Road, Glasgow G52 2AZ Tel: 0141 883 8838 Fax: 0141 810 1511 Email: annemhwilliams@yahoo.co.uk; 5 Kirklee Gardens, Glasgow G12 0SG Tel: 0141 339 3234 Fax: 0141 339 3234 — MB BS 1981 Lond.; MRCGP 1990; DCH RCP Lond. 1989; DRCOG 1985. (Guy's, London) GP Princip.; GP Clin. Undergrad. Tutor. Socs: World Federat. Doctors; Scott. Counc. on Human Bioethics. Prev: Trainee GP Kilburn Lond. VTS; Mother & Child Health (Pacarán) Canete Valley, Peru.

WILLIAMS, Anthony Longford Street Surgery, Longford Street, Heywood OL10 4NH Tel: 01706 621417 Fax: 01706 622915; Edgecroft, Manchester Road, Heywood OL10 2NL — MB BCh 1974 Wales.

WILLIAMS, Anthony Brendon Flat 2, 13 Frederick Place, Bristol BS8 1AS — MB ChB 1986 Otago.

WILLIAMS, Anthony Charles Côte De Neige, 19 Hillside Avenue, Worthing BN14 9QR — MB BS 1974 Lond.; MRCS Eng. LRCP Lond. 1974; FFA RCS Eng. 1979. Cons. Anaesth. Worthing & S.lands Hosp.

WILLIAMS, Rev. Anthony David Social Security Department, PO Box 55, St Helier, Jersey JE4 8PE Tel: 01534 280000; Spindrift, Lasrande Route de la Cote, La Mare, St Clement, Jersey JE2 6FS Tel: 01534 729540 Fax: 01534 863729 Email: tonyw@cinergy.co.uk — MRCS Eng. LRCP Lond. 1963; MRCGP 1968; DObst RCOG 1965. (St. Mary's) Med. Off. Social Security Dept. St. Helier; Hon. Curate St. Helier Parish Ch. Socs: Jersey Med. Soc. Prev: GP Jersey; Obst. Jersey Matern. Hosp.

WILLIAMS, Anthony Ffoulkes Department of Child Health, St. George's Hospital Medical School, Cranmer Terrace, Tooting, London SW17 0RE Tel: 020 8725 2986 Fax: 020 8725 2858 Email: a.williams@sghms.ac.uk; 8 Aberdeen Wharf, 94 Wapping High Sreet, London E1W 2ND — MB BS 1975 Lond.; DPhil Oxf. 1987; BSc Lond. 1972; FRCP Lond. 1993; MRCP (UK) 1978; MRCS Eng. LRCP Lond. 1975; FRCPCH 1997. (Westm.) Cons. Neonat. Paediat. & Sen. Lect. St. Geo. Hosp. Med. Sch. Lond. Prev: Lect. (Child Health) Univ. Bristol; Research Fell. (Paediat.) Univ. Oxf.

WILLIAMS, Anthony Harold Elvin (retired) Cranesbie, 6 Dore Road, Dore, Sheffield S17 3NB — MB ChB 1956 Bristol; MEd Warwick 1984; FRCGP 1985, M 1962. Hon. Lect. (Gen. Pract.) Univ. Sheff. Prev: Med. Adviser Sheff. FHSA.

WILLIAMS, Anthony James Mounts Medical Centre, Campbell Street, Northampton NN1 3DS Tel: 01604 631952 Fax: 01604 634139; 17 Wymersley Close, Great Houghton, Northampton NN4 7PT — MB BS 1984 Lond.

WILLIAMS, Anthony John Barry Hospital, Colcot Rd, Barry CF62 8YH Tel: 01446 704110 — LLM 2001 Wales; MB BS Lond. 1970; FRCPsych 1995, M 1975. (Lond. Hosp.) Cons. Psychiat. Cardiff and Vale NHS Trust; Clin. Teach., Dept. of Psychol. Med., Univ. of Wales; Med. Mem., Ment. health review Bd. for Wales. Prev: Cons. Psychiat. St. Tydfils Hosp. Merthyr Tydfil & Towers Hosp. Leicester; Lect. (Psychiat.) Univ. Leicester.

WILLIAMS, Anthony John (retired) 2 Queen Square, Lancaster LA1 1RP Tel: 01524 843333 — MB ChB 1956 Liverp. Prev: Regist. (Med.) Sefton Gen. Hosp. Liverp.

WILLIAMS, Anthony Nicholas, Lt.-Col. Army Medical Directorate, Slim Road, Camberley GU15 4PQ Tel: 01276 412906 — MB BChir 1984 Camb.; MA Camb. 1983; MMedSc Birm. 1990; MFOM RCP Lond. 1992, AFOM 1990; DTM & H RCP Lond. 1988. Cons.

WILLIAMS

Occupat. Physic. Army Camberley; Cons. Occupat.al Phys. to 16 Air Assault Brig., Gl Chester. Socs: Soc. Occupat. Med. Prev: Commanding Off. 23 Parachute Field Ambul.; Staff Off. Med. Permanent Jt. HQ; Staff Off. Primary care Protect Team.

WILLIAMS, Anthony Paul 6 Walnut Close, Miskin, Pontyclun CF72 8RZ Tel: 01443 230171 Fax: 01443 230172 Email: sueandlary@supanet.com — MB BCh 1973 Wales; BSc Wales 1968; Cert. Family Plann. JCC 1976; MFCM 1989.

WILLIAMS, Anthony Peter 4 Oak Farm Close, Tetsworth, Thame OX9 7JA — MB BS 1992 Lond.; Dip. RCPath 1998 (London); MSc (Immunology) 1998. (Univ. of London); BSc (Pharmacol.) Lond. 1989; MRCP (UK) 1995. (Univ. Coll. Lond. & Middlx. Med. Sch.) Prev: Regist. (Med.) Univ. Hosp. Wales Cardiff; Specialist Regist. (Clin. Immunol.) Ch.ill & John Radcliffe Hosps. Oxf.

WILLIAMS, Antony John City Surgery, 187 City Road, Roath, Cardiff CF24 3WD Tel: 029 2049 4250 Fax: 029 2049 1968 — MB BCh 1957 Wales. (Cardiff)

WILLIAMS, Arfon Isfryn Surgery, Isfryn, Ffordd Dewi Sant, Nefyn, Pwllheli LL53 6EA Tel: 01758 720202 Fax: 01758 720083 — MB BCh 1991 Wales; MRCGP 1995. Socs: BMA. Prev: Trainee GP Pwllheli; SHO (O & G & Paediat.) Ysbyty Gwynedd Bangor.

WILLIAMS, Arthur Alun (retired) 3 Sovereign Close, Kingsend, Ruislip HA4 7EF Tel: 01895 677570 — MD Lond. 1948, MB BS 1946; FRCP Ed. 1962, M 1947; MRCS Eng. LRCP Lond. 1938. Hon. Cons. Phys. S. Tees Hosps. Prev: Cons. Phys. S. Teeside Hosps.

WILLIAMS, Arthur Hyatt, Maj. RAMC Retd. (retired) 29 St Johns Road, London NW11 0PE Tel: 020 8455 5682 Fax: 020 8458 2377 — MD 1949 Liverp.; MB ChB Liverp. 1938; FRCPsych 1971; DPM Eng. 1947. Prev: Hon. Dir. The Lond. Clinic of Psycho-Anal.

WILLIAMS, Arthur Jeffrey Department of Paediatrics, Glan Clwyd Dist. Hospital, Bodelwyddan, Rhyl Tel: 01745 583910 — MB ChB 1966 Birm.; FRCP Lond. 1989; MRCP (UK) 1974; DCH Eng. 1971. (Birm.) Cons. (Paediat.) Glan Clwyd Dist. Hosp. Bodelwyddan. Prev: Maj. RAMC; Paediat. Regist. Burnley Gen. Hosp.; Lect. in Child Health Alder Hey Childr. Hosp. Liverp.

WILLIAMS, Arthur Llewelyn John (retired) 5 Minera Road, Ffrith, Wrexham LL11 5LR Tel: 01978 756614 — MB BS 1959 Lond.; FFPHM 1986; DPH Wales 1966; DObst RCOG 1962; AKC; FRIPHH. JP 1981-. Prev: Dir. Pub. Health Med. & Chief Admin. Med. Off. Clwyd HA.

WILLIAMS, Arthur Warriner, CBE (retired) 16 Rose Lane, Cockermouth CA13 9DT Tel: 01900 826925 — MRCS Eng. LRCP Lond. 1929; MA Camb. 1934, BA 1926, MD 1938; FRCP Lond. 1955, M 1946; DTM & H 1931. Prev: Prof. of Med. Makerere Coll. Univ. E. Africa.

WILLIAMS, Babatunde Olabode 1 Fox Gardens, Lymm WA13 9EY — MB BS 1991 Ibadan.

WILLIAMS, Barbara Alice Reynolds 20 South Rise, Llanishen, Cardiff CF14 0RH — MB BCh 1962 Wales; FRCR 1978; DMRD Eng. 1975; DObst RCOG 1967.

WILLIAMS, Barbara Anne Pavilion Family Doctors, 153A Stroud Road, Gloucester GL1 5JJ Tel: 01452 385555 Fax: 01452 387905 — MB BS 1986 Lond.; DCH RCP Lond. 1989.

WILLIAMS, Barbara Anne Hill Brow, Main St., Tilton-on-the-Hill, Leicester LE7 9LF — MB ChB 1976 Dundee; MRCGP 1981.

WILLIAMS, Barbara Mary (retired) Bicknor House, High St., Stevenage SG1 3BG Tel: 01438 729122 — MB ChB 1946 Birm. Prev: Anaesth., Lister Hosp., Stevenage.

WILLIAMS, Barbara Mary (retired) Little Debden, Petham, Canterbury CT4 5NN Tel: 01227 700154 — MB BS Lond. 1954; MRCS Eng. LRCP Lond. 1954; DObst RCOG 1956; DA Eng. 1957. Clin. Asst. Anaesth. Canterbury Hosp. Gp. Prev: Ho. Phys. Med. Unit, St. Thos. Hosp. Lond.

WILLIAMS, Barrie St. John's Surgery, 56 Kidderminster Road, Bromsgrove B61 7JY Tel: 01527 71706 Fax: 01527 576022 — MB ChB Birm. 1965. (Birmingham) GP.

WILLIAMS, Benjamin James 50 Lady Edith's Avenue, Scarborough YO12 5RB; 212 Asmore Road, Queens Park, London W9 3DD Tel: 020 8969 1217 — MB BS 1993 Lond. (St Marys hosp) Specialist Regist. Anaesth. NW. Thames. Socs: Assn. Anaesth.

WILLIAMS, Benjamin James Flat 18, Rochdale House, 19 Slate Wharf, Manchester M15 4SX — MB ChB 1995 Birm.; ChB Birm. 1995.

WILLIAMS, Bernard Lincoln (retired) Brookfield, 23 Eyebrook Road, Bowdon, Altrincham WA14 3LH Tel: 0161 928 6016 — MB ChB 1948 Manch.; MB ChB (Hnrs.) Manch. 1948; DPath Eng. 1957; FRCPath 1971, M 1963. Hon. Cons. Path. Pk. Hosp. Davyhulme. Prev: Lect. (Path.) Univ. Manch.

WILLIAMS, Beryl Wyn Brecon Medical Group Practice, Ty Henry Vaughan, Bridge Street, Brecon LD3 8AH Tel: 01874 622121 Fax: 01874 623742; 3 Buckingham Place, Glamorgan St, Brecon LD3 7DL — MB BCh 1985 Wales; MRCGP 1989; DRCOG 1995; DGM RCP Lond. 1991; DCH RCP Lond. 1989.

WILLIAMS, Bethan 1 Plas Glen Rosa, Penarth CF64 1TS — MB BCh 1980 Wales. GP Barry.

WILLIAMS, Bethan Sketty Surgery, De la Beche Road, Sketty, Swansea SA2 9EA Tel: 01792 206862; 10 Brynderi Close, Penllergaer, Swansea SA4 1AG — MB BCh 1980 Wales; MRCGP 1984; DRCOG 1982. (Welsh Nat. Sch. of Med.)

WILLIAMS, Bethan Wyn 16 Belsize Road, Worthing BN11 4RH — MB BS 1987 Lond.

WILLIAMS, Bill Thomas Jordan 11 Northern Grove, West Didsbury, Manchester M20 8NL — MB ChB 1985 Manch. Regist. (Psychiat.) S. Manch. Univ. Dept., S. Manch. AHA.

WILLIAMS, Billie Innes (retired) Court Yard House, Church End, Bletchington, Kidlington OX5 3DL Tel: 01869 350171 Fax: 01869 350789 — MB BChir 1949 Camb.; PhD Lond. 1975, MSc (Distinc.) 1967; MA Camb. 1949; DO Eng. 1953. Prev: Hon. Lect. in Ophth. (Leverhulme Fell.) St. Mary's Hosp. Lond.

WILLIAMS, Brian David Morgan (retired) White Lea, Beech Close, Stratford-upon-Avon CV37 7EB Tel: 01789 296555 — BM BCh 1952 Oxf.; MRCGP 1964. Prev: Resid. Med. Off. St. Pancras Br. Univ. Coll. Hosp.

WILLIAMS, Brian Emlyn Burney Hatfield Road Surgery, 70 Hatfield Road, Ipswich IP3 9AF Tel: 01473 723373; 52 Anglesea Road, Ipswich IP1 3PW Tel: 01473 216257 — MRCS Eng. LRCP Lond. 1967; MRCOphth 1989; DO Eng. 1974. (Middlx.) Attend. Ophth. Optimex Laser Eye Centre Lond.; Hosp. Pract. (Ophth.) Ipswich Dist. Gen. Hosp. Prev: Med. Off. Louise Margt. Matern. Hosp. Aldershot; Med. Off. Camb. Milit. Hosp. Aldershot.

WILLIAMS, Brian John Marshfield Road Surgery, Marshfield Road, Chippenham SN15 1JU Tel: 01249 654466 Fax: 01249 462320; West End House, West End, Foxham, Chippenham SN15 4NB Tel: 01249 74634 Fax: 01249 462320 Email: barney@bykshed.freeserve.co.uk — BM BCh Oxf. 1966; MA Oxf. 1966; MRCS Eng. LRCP Lond. 1966; T(GP) 1991; Cert. Family Plann. JCC 1975; DObst RCOG 1970. (Oxf. & St. Mary's) Cas. Off. Wilts. HealthcareTrust Chippenham; Police Surg. Wilts. 'C' Div.; Clin. Med. Off. Chippenham Community Hosp. Socs: Chippenham Dist. Med. Comm. & Clin. Soc. Bath (Ex-Chairm.); Clin. Soc. Bath; Wilts. Forens. Med.Examinrs.

WILLIAMS, Brian Melville Avon Partnership, Occupational Health Service, Southmead Hospital, Westbury on Trym, Bristol Tel: 0117 959 5499 Email: williams_br@southmead.swest.nhs.uk — MB ChB 1982 Liverp.; MFOM 1998; AFOM RCP Lond. 1992. Cons. Occupat.al Phys., Avon Partnership Occupat.al Health Serv., Bristol. Prev: Med. Off. (Respirat. Dis.) Med. Bd.ing Centre Glas.

WILLIAMS, Brian Owen 15 Thorn Drive, High Burnside, Rutherglen, Glasgow G73 4RH Tel: 0141 634 4480 Fax: 0141 211 3465 — MB ChB 1970 Glas.; MB ChB (Commend.) Glas. 1970; MD Glas. 1984; FRCP Ed. 1991; FRCP Lond. 1989; FRCP Glas. 1983; MRCP (UK) 1973. (Glas.) Clin. Dir. & Cons. Geriat. Gartnavel Gen. Hosp. Glas. Socs: Brit. Geriat. Soc. (Pres. Elect.); FCPS (Pak) 1996; FRC SLT (Hon.) 1996. Prev: Sen. Regist. (Geriat. Med.) Vict. Infirm. Glas.; Sen. Regist. (Geriat. Med.) Stobhill Hosp. Glas.; Regist. (Med.) Vict. Infirm. Glas.

WILLIAMS, Brian Rees The Stewart Medical Centre, 15 Hartington Road, Buxton SK17 6JP Tel: 01298 22338 Fax: 01298 72678; Green Farm, King Sterndale, Buxton SK17 9SF Tel: 01298 70141 — BM BS 1976 Nottm.; DA Eng. 1981; DRCOG 1980.

WILLIAMS, Brian Richard 2 Park Road N., Middlesbrough TS1 3LF Tel: 01642 247008 Fax: 01642 245748; Briary Cottage, 7 Maltby Road, Thornton, Middlesbrough TS8 9BU Tel: 01642 592693 — MB ChB 1971 Ed. (Ed.) Socs: BMA.

WILLIAMS, Brian Thomas Department of Public Health Medicine & Epidemiology, University of Nottingham Medical School, Queen's Medical Centre, Nottingham NG7 2UH Tel: 01159 709326 Fax:

01159 709316 Email: b.t.williams@nottingham.ac.uk; Westover, Sheffield Road, Hathersage, Hope Valley S32 1DA — MB BS Lond. 1961; MD Sheff. 1973; FRCP Lond. 1990; FFPM RCP (UK) 1978, M 1974; DPM Eng. 1965; DPH Lond. 1964. (Westm.) Prof. Pub. Health Med. Univ. Nottm. Prev: Prof. Pub. Health Med. Univ. Sheff.; Sen. Lect. (Community Med.) Univ. Sheff.; Research Fell. (Med.) Inst. for Social Work Train. Lond.

WILLIAMS, Professor Bryan Department of Medicine, Clinical Sciences Building, Leicester Royal Infirmary, PO Box 65, Leicester LE2 7LX Tel: 0116 252 3183 Fax: 0116 252 3273 Email: bw17@le.ac.uk — MB BS 1983 Lond.; BSc (1st cl. Hons.) Lond. 1980; MD (Distinc.) Leicester 1996; FRCP Lond. 1995; MRCP (UK) 1986. (St. Mary's Hosp. Med. Sch.) Dir. Cardiovasc. Research Inst. Univ. Leicester. Socs: Assn. Phys.; Internat. Soc. Hypertens.; Brit. Hypertens. Soc. (Exec. Comm.). Prev: Sen. Lect. (Med.) Univ. Leicester; Lect. (Med.) & Hon. Sen. Regist. (Nephrol.) Leicester; Instruc. Med. Univ. of Colorado, Denver, USA.

WILLIAMS, Professor Bryan Davies Department of Rheumatology, University Hospital of Wales, Cardiff CF4 4XW Tel: 029 2074 3184 Fax: 029 2074 4388; Briar Bank, 18 Station Road, Dinas Powys CF64 4DF — MB BCh Wales 1966; MSc Birm. 1969; FRCP Lond. 1986, M 1969; FRCPath 1993, M 1992. Prof. & Cons. Rheum. Univ. Wales Coll. Med. Cardiff. Socs: Amer. Coll. Rheum.; Brit. Soc. Rheum.; Brit. Soc. Immunol.

WILLIAMS, Mr Bryn Terence Suite 204, Emblem House, London Bridge Hospital, 27 Tooley St., London SE1 2PR Tel: 020 7403 2150 Fax: 020 7403 4329; Kimberton, Warreners Lane, St. George's Hill, Weybridge KT13 0LH — MB ChB 1962 Birm.; FRCS Eng. 1967; MRCS Eng. LRCP Lond. 1962. Socs: Brit. Cardiac Soc.; Soc. Thoracic & Cardiovasc. Surgs.; Fell. Europ. Soc. Cardiol. Prev: Hon. Cons. Cardiothoracic Surg. to the Army; Cons. Cardiothoracic Surg. St. Thos. Hosp. Lond.; Sen. Regist. Nat. Heart & Chest Gp. Hosps. Lond.

WILLIAMS, Bryony Pauline Whitby Group Practice, Spring Vale Medical Centre, Whitby YO21 1SD Tel: 01947 820888 Fax: 01947 824100; Burnvale, Teapot Hill, Sandsend, Whitby YO21 3TF Tel: 01947 893004 — MB ChB 1983 Ed.; MRCGP 1988; Dip. IMC RCS Ed. 1992; DRCOG 1989.

WILLIAMS, Mr Carl John (retired) Hope Hospital, Stott Lane, Salford M6 8HD Tel: 0161 789 7373 — MB BS 1992 Lond.; BSc (Hons.) Med. Microbiol. Lond. 1989; FRCS 1997; FRCS 1998. Clin. Lect/Hon. Specialist Regist. Orthop. Surg. Prev: SHO (Gen. Surg.) Blackpool Vict. Hosp.

WILLIAMS, Carol Margaret Elizabeth Lime Tree Cottage, 19 Main St., Queniborough, Leicester LE7 8DB Tel: 0116 260 6228 — MB BS 1967 Lond.; MRCS Eng. LRCP Lond. 1965; DObst RCOG 1969. (Guy's)

***WILLIAMS, Caroline Emma** Burway House, 61 High St., Kintbury, Hungerford RG17 9TL Tel: 01488 657730; 19 Laitwood Road, Balham, London SW12 9QN Tel: 020 8488 3381 — MB BS 1996 Lond.

WILLIAMS, Caroline Jane 1 The Rowans, Aughton, Ormskirk L39 6TD — BM 1994 Soton.; MRCP (UK) 1999. (Univ. Soton.)

WILLIAMS, Caroline Joy 1 Russell Close, Winford, Bristol BS40 8EF Tel: 01404 42080 — MB BS 1988 Lond.; BSc (Nutrit.) Lond. 1985; DRCOG 1992. Trainee GP Harptree Pract. Bristol.

WILLIAMS, Catherine 22 The Turnways, Headingley, Leeds LS6 3DU — MB BS 1988 Newc.; MRCGP 1993; DCH RCP Lond. 1993.

WILLIAMS, Catherine Dilys 14 Kersley Road, London N16 0NP — MB BS 1987 Lond.

WILLIAMS, Catherine Elizabeth Mary c/o Bristol Eye Hospital, Lower Maudlin St., Bristol BS1 2LX Tel: 0117 923 0060 Fax: 0117 925 1421; 35 Haverstock Road, Knowle, Bristol BS4 2DA Tel: 0117 971666 — MB BS 1986 Lond.; BSc Lond. 1983, MB BS 1986; FCOphth 1991; PhD 1998; BMA; MPS. Cons.; Sen. Ophth., ALSPAC study, Inst. of Child health,Univ. of Bristol. Prev: Sen. Regist. (Ophth.), S. W.; MRC Research Fell. Bristol Eye Hosp.; Regist. (Ophth.) Bristol Eye Hosp.

WILLIAMS, Catherine Shan c/o Barrow Hospital, Barrow Gurney, Bristol BS48 3SG — MB BS 1985 Lond.; BSc (Hons.) Lond. 1980.

WILLIAMS, Cecil William Llewelyn (retired) Lanreath, The Wigdale, Hawarden, Deeside CH5 3LL Tel: 01244 532557 — MB ChB 1955 Liverp.; MRCGP 1968; DObst RCOG 1958. Hosp. Pract.

(Psychiat.) Maelor Gen. Hosp. Wrexham. Prev: Ho. Surg. & Ho. Phys. David Lewis N.. Hosp. Liverp.

WILLIAMS, Ceri 43 Elton Parade, Darlington DL3 8PJ — MB BCh 1979 Wales; BSc Wales 1976, MB BCh 1979; MRCPath 1985. Cons. Histopath. Memor. Hosp. Hollyhurst Rd. Darlington. Prev: Sen. Regist. (Histopath.) Univ. Hosp. Wales Cardiff & Roy. Gwent Hosp.; Newport.

WILLIAMS, Charles David The William Harvey Hospital, Ashford TN24 0LZ Tel: 01233 833331 Fax: 01233 616049; Stowting Court Stables, Stowting, Ashford TN25 6BA Tel: 01303 863344 — MB BChir 1978 Camb.; MA Camb. 1979; FRCP (UK) 1997; MD(Camb.) 1999. (Camb.) Cons. Phys. Diabetes & Endocrinol. William Harvey Hosp. Ashford; Hon. Sen. Lect. (Med.) GKT St. Thos. Hosp. Lond. Prev: Lect. & Sen. Regist. UMDS St. Thos. Hosp. Lond.

WILLIAMS, Charles Edward University Department of Radiodiagnosis, Royal Liverpool Hospital, Liverpool L69 3BX Tel: 0151 709 0141 — MB BCh BAO 1978 Dub.; FRCR 1985; FFR RCSI 1985. Sen. Clin. Lect./Hon. Cons. Radiol. Univ. Liverp. & Roy. Liverp. Hosp. Prev: Sen. Regist. (Diag. Radiol.) Leeds Gen. Infirm. & St. Jas. Hosp. Leeds.

WILLIAMS, Christina Janet Seymour 11 Frognal Way, London NW3 6XE Tel: 020 7435 4030 Fax: 020 7435 5636 Email: christopherwilliams@compuserve.com — MB BS Lond. 1965; FRCP Lond. 1992; MRCP (UK) 1970; MRCS Eng. LRCP Lond. 1965. (Guy's) Cons. Rehabil. & Disabil. Med.; Med. Adviser SCOPE; Mem. Med. Appeal Tribunal Serv. Socs: BMA; Brit. Soc. Rehabil. Med.; Liveryman Worshipful Soc. Apoth. Lond. Prev: Cons. Rheum. & Rehabil. Nat. Hosp. Nerv. Dis. Lond. & Bloomsbury & Islington HA & Roy. Hosp. for Neurodisabil. Putney; Sen. Regist. (Rheum.) Middlx. Hosp. Lond.

WILLIAMS, Christine Maria Moorefields Eye Hospital, City Road, London EC1V 2PD; 5 Rodney Gardens, Pinner HA5 2RS — MB ChB 1978 Dundee; FCAnaesth. 1990. Cons. Anaesth. Moorfields Eye Hosp. Lond. Socs: Roy. Soc. of Med.; Brit. Ophthalmic Anaesth. Soc.; Difficult Airway Soc. Prev: Sen. Regist. & Regist. (Anaesth.) Hammersmith Hosp. Lond.; SHO (Anaesth.) N.wick Pk. Hosp. Lond.

WILLIAMS, Mr Christopher Barrie The Park Hospital, Sherwood Lodge Drive, Arnold, Nottingham NG8 8RX Tel: 0115 978 7325; 25 Oundle Drive, Wollaton Park, Nottingham NG8 1BN Tel: 0115 978 7325 Fax: 0115 978 7325 — MB ChB 1962 Bristol; MD Bristol 1968; FRCS Eng. 1966. (Bristol) Cons. Gen. Surg. Nottm. City Hosp.; Clin. Teach. Univ. Nottm. Med. Sch. Socs: BMA. Prev: Sen. Regist. (Gen. Surg.) United Bristol Hosps.; Regist. (Surg.) Cardiff Roy. Infirm.; Ho. Surg. & Ho. Phys. Bristol Roy. Infirm.

WILLIAMS, Christopher Beverley Wolfson Unit for Endoscopy, St.Mark's Hospital, Northwick Park, Harrow HA1 3UJ Tel: 020 8235 4225 Fax: 020 8423 3588 Email: christopherwilliams@compuserve.com; 11 Frognal Way, Hampstead, London NW3 6XE Tel: 020 7435 4030 Fax: 020 7435 5636 Email: 100732.2460@compuserve.com — BM BCh 1964 Oxf.; MA Oxf. 1964; FRCP Lond. 1979, M 1968; MRCS Eng. LRCP Lond. 1965; FRCS 1999. (Univ. Coll. Hosp.) Cons. Phys. St. Mark's Hosp. for Intestinal & Colorectal Disorders Middlx. Socs: Fell. Roy. Soc. Med.; Brit. Soc. Gastroenterol.; Liveryman Soc. Apoth.

WILLIAMS, Christopher David Flat 2, 6 Jesmond Gardens, Jesmond, Newcastle upon Tyne NE2 2JN Tel: 0191 281 6721 — MB BS 1998 Newc.

WILLIAMS, Christopher John Glyn Hafan, Treforris Road, Dwygyfylchi, Penmaenmawr LL34 6RA — MB BS 1988 Lond.

WILLIAMS, Christopher John Department of Psychological Medicine, Administration Building, Garbnaval Roayl Hospital, 1055 Greab Western Road, Glasgow Gi2 0XH Tel: 0141 211 3912 Email: chris.williams@clinmed.gla.ac.uk — MB ChB 1988 Leeds; MD 2001 Leeds; BSc Leeds 1985, MMedSci (Clin. Psychiat.) 1994. (Univ. of Leeds) Sen. Lect., Univ. Galsgow - Hon. Cons. Psychiat., Glas. - Director of Glas. Instition for Psychosocial Interven.s (GIPSI) Glas.; Hon. Cons. Psychiat. Socs: Roy. Coll. Psychiat.; Brit. Psychol. Soc.; Brit. Assn. Behavioural & Cognitive Psychother. & UK Counc. Psychother. Prev: Lect. & Hon. Sen. Regist. (Psychiat.) Leeds Univ.; Regist. Rotat. (Psychiat.) Leeds HA.

WILLIAMS, Christopher John Royal United Hospital, Bath NHS Trust, Combe Park, Bath BA1 3NG Tel: 01179 685725 Fax: 01179 685725; Coombe Dene, 49 Coombe Lane, Stoke Bishop, Bristol BS9 2BL Tel: 01179 685725 Fax: 01179 685725 — MB BS 1996

WILLIAMS

Lond.; BSc Lond. 1993. (Kings College London) SHO (Med.) Roy. United Hosp. Bath; Assoc. Coll. Tutor.

WILLIAMS, Christopher John Cole Nova Scotia Cottage, Acaster Malbis, York YO23 2PY — MB BS 1985 Lond.; BSc Lond. 1982; MRCP (UK) 1990. Regist. Derbysh. Childr. Hosp.

WILLIAMS, Christopher John Hacon Cochrane Cancer Network, Institute of Health Science, PO Box 777, Oxford OX3 7LF Tel: 01865 226628 Fax: 01865 226765 Email: cwilliams@canet.org; The Triangle, Sibford Road, Hook Norton, Banbury OX15 5JU Tel: 01608 737765 — MB BS 1971 Lond.; DM Soton 1980; FRCP Lond. 1986; MRCP (UK) 1974; MRCS Eng. LRCP Lond. 1971. (St. Mary's) Co-ordinator, Cochrane Cancer Network, Inst. Health Sci. Oxf. Socs: Amer. Soc. Clin. Oncol.; Assn. Cancer Phys.s; Eur. Soc. Med. Oncol. Prev: Sen. Lect. & Hon. Cons. Phys. CRC Med. Oncol. Unit Soton. Gen. Hosp.; Postdoctoral Fell. Div. Oncol. Stanford Univ. Med. Centre, USA; SHO (Med. & Oncol.) St. Bart. Hosp. Lond.

WILLIAMS, Christopher John Harold Dr J M Beck and Partners, 21 Beaufort Road, Southbourne, Bournemouth BH6 5AJ Tel: 01202 433081 Fax: 01202 430527; Surf Sounds, 11 Percy Road, Bournemouth BH5 1JF Tel: 01202 398014 — MB ChB 1964 Birm.; MRCS Eng. LRCP Lond. 1964; MFCM 1974; DPM Eng. 1968. Hosp. Pract. (Psychiat.) King's Pk. Community Hosp. Bournemouth. Prev: SCM (Social Servs.) Dorset AHA; Regist. (Psychiat.) St. Ann's Hosp. Poole.; SHO (O & G) Co. Hosp. Hereford.

WILLIAMS, Christopher Philip Richard 7 Pavan Gardens, Ensbury Park, Bournemouth BH10 5JH — MB BCh 1995 Wales; MB BCh (Hons.) Wales 1995; MRCP (Lond.), 1998. SHO (Ophth.), Soton. Gen. Hosp. Prev: SHO (Gen. Med.), E. Glam. Gen. Hosp.

WILLIAMS, Christopher Richard 35 Bryony Road, Birmingham B29 4BY — MB BCh 1998 Wales.

WILLIAMS, Mr Christopher Richard Philip Orthopaedic Department, Royal Sussex County Hospital, Eastern Road, Brighton BN2 5BE Tel: 01273 696955 Fax: 01273 624297; Tel: 01825 791024 — MB BS 1985 Lond.; FRCS Eng. 1989. Cons. Orthop. Surg. Socs: Fell.BOA; BSSH. Prev: Sr. Fell. Hand Surg. Nottm.; Regist. (Orthop.) Basingstoke & Lord Mayor Treolar Hosps.; Regist. (Orthop.) P'boro. & Edith Cavell Hosps.

WILLIAMS, Christopher Robert Ashfield Surgery, Merthyr Mawr Road, Bridgend CF31 3NW Tel: 01656 652774 Fax: 01656 661187; Goodways, 78 Merthyr Mawr Road, Bridgend CF31 3NR Tel: 01656 653309 — MB 1977 Camb.; MA Camb. 1977, MB 1977, BChir 1977; DRCOG 1982. (St. Mary's) GP Bridgend. Prev: Trainee GP Bridgend VTS; Ho. Phys. Harold Wood Hosp.; Ho. Surg. N.wick Pk. Hosp. Harrow.

WILLIAMS, Christopher Vawer Somers Town Health Centre, Blackfriars Close, Southsea PO5 4NJ Tel: 023 9285 1202 Fax: 023 9229 6380 — MB BS 1977 Lond. (Middlesex Hospital)

WILLIAMS, Claire Ann 123 Southfield Road, Oxford OX4 1NY — MB BCh 1997 Wales.

WILLIAMS, Clare Rosemary Anaesthetics Department, St Helier Hospital, Carshalton Tel: 020 8644 4343; 16 Mansel Road, Wimbledon, London SW19 4AA — BM BCh 1971 Oxf.; BA, BM BCh Oxf. 1971; FFA RCS Eng. 1977; DObst RCOG 1973. Cons. Anaesth. St Helier Hosp. Carshalton.

WILLIAMS, Mr Claude Arthur Kingsley 64 Langstone Close, Babbacombe, Torquay TQ1 3TY — MB ChB 1962 Birm.; FRCS Ed. 1965; MRCS Eng. LRCP Lond. 1962.

WILLIAMS, Clive St Johns Lane Health Centre, St. Johns Lane, Bristol BS3 5AS Tel: 0117 966 7681 Fax: 0117 977 9676 — MB ChB 1972 Sheff.

WILLIAMS, Clive Propert The Grange, Vicarage Hill, Minera, Wrexham LL11 3YN — MD 1978 Liverp.; MB ChB 1969; MRCPath 1980. (Liverp.) Cons. (Chem. Path.) Maelor Gen. Hosp. Wrexham.

WILLIAMS, Colin 36 Albert Edward Road, Liverpool L7 8RZ — MB ChB 1991 Liverp.

WILLIAMS, Colin Anthony Portway Surgery, 1 The Portway, Porthcawl CF36 3XB Tel: 01656 304204 Fax: 01656 772605; 29 Danygraig Avenue, Porthcawl CF36 5AA Tel: 01656 784311 Fax: 01656 772605 — MB BCh 1968 Wales; DPD 1990. (Cardiff) Prev: SHO (Med.) Nevill Hall Hosp. Abergavenny; Ho. Surg. & Ho. Phys. (Paediat.) United Cardiff Hosps.

WILLIAMS, Mr Colin Roger (retired) Nuffield Hospital, Wood Road, Tettenhall, Wolverhampton WV6 8LE Tel: 01902 741526,

01902 754177 — MB BS 1963 Lond.; FRCS Eng. 1967. Prev: Research Fell. (Dept. Path.) Univ. Birm.

WILLIAMS, Craig Lester Cranage Department of Microbiology, Royal Alexandra Hospital, Corsebar Road, Paisley PA2 9PN Tel: 0141 580 4453 Fax: 0141 580 4242 Email: craig.williams@rah.sect.nhs.uk — MB ChB 1982 Liverp.; FRCP Ed. 1998; MRCP (UK) 1986; MRCPath 1991; FRCPath 2000; MD (Liverpool) 1999. Cons. Microbiologist Roy. Alexandra Hosp. Paisley; Hon. Research Fell. Univ. Glas.

WILLIAMS, Dafydd Fon 30 Harthill Avenue, Leconfield, Beverley HU17 7LN — MB BS 1982 Nottm.; BMedSci 1980. (Nottm.)

***WILLIAMS, Damian Carson** 32 Glyncollen Drive, Ynysforgan, Swansea SA6 6RS — MB ChB 1998 Birm.

WILLIAMS, Dan Shannon Stamford Hill Group Practice, 2 Egerton Road, Stamford Hill, London N16 6UA Tel: 020 8800 1000 Fax: 020 8880 2402 Email: dan.williams@gp-f84013.nhs.uk — MB BCh 1979 Witwatersrand. Princip., Gen. Pract.; Hosp. Practitioner Clin. Oncol., Chase Farm Hosp., Enfield, Middlx. Socs: Brit. Med.Assn. Prev: Lect. Gen. Med. Univ. Coll. Hosp. Lond.

WILLIAMS, Daniel Glyn Westcourt, 12 The Street, Rustington, Littlehampton BN16 3NX Tel: 01903 784311 Fax: 01903 850907 — MB BS 1990 Lond.; MRCGP 1994; DRCOG 1993. (St Bartholomews)

WILLIAMS, Professor Daniel Gwyn Department of Renal Medicine, Guy's Hospital, St Thomas St., London SE1 9RT — MD 1974 Wales; MB BCh 1963; FRCP Lond. 1978, M 1966. (Cardiff) Prof. Med. UMDS Guy's & St. Thos. Hosp. Lond.; Cons. Phys. Renal Dis. Guy's Hosp. Lond. Prev: SHO Med. Unit Cardiff Roy. Infirm.; Sen. Regist. Dept. Med. Radcliffe Infirm. Oxf.; Asst. Lect. (Med.) Roy. Postgrad. Med. Sch. Univ. Lond.

WILLIAMS, Daniel Harvey Redbrook, Llandevaud, Newport NP18 2AF — MB BCh 1998 Wales.

WILLIAMS, David Catterick Garrison Family Practice, Catterick Garrison DL9 3JF Tel: 01748 833904; Strangford House, 11 The Village Farm, Middleton Tyas, Richmond DL10 6SQ — MB ChB 1986 Birm.

WILLIAMS, David (retired) The Old Orchard, Saintbury, Broadway WR12 7PX Tel: 01386 852318 — MB BCh BAO 1951 NUI; DA Eng. 1958. Prev: Assoc. Specialist (Anaesth.) Kidderminster Gen. Redditch Hosps.

WILLIAMS, David 45 James Street, Lossiemouth IV31 6BZ — MB ChB 1983 Dundee; MD Ed. 1993; BMSc (Path.) Dund 1980; FRCP Ed. 1995; MRCP (UK) 1985. Cons. Med. & Gastroenterol. Doctor Gray's Hosp. Elgin. Socs: Brit. Soc. Gastroenterol. Prev: Clin. Tutor Hope Hosp. Salford.; Lect. (Med.) Univ. Sheff.

WILLIAMS, David Alastair Wyndham Southover, Bronshill Road, Torquay TQ1 3HD Tel: 01803 327100 — MB BCh BAO 1958 Dub.; MA. Prev: Regist. (Anaesth.) Torbay Hosp. Torquay; SHO (Anaesth.) Bristol United Hosps.; Surg. P. & O. Orient Lines.

WILLIAMS, David Anthony Blandford House Surgery, 7 London Road, Braintree CM7 2LD Tel: 01376 347100 Fax: 01376 349934; Boleyns, Church Lane, Bocking, Braintree CM7 5SE — MB BS 1978 Lond.; DRCOG 1981.

WILLIAMS, David Anthony North Nottinghamshire Health, Ransom Hall, Southwell Road W., Rainworth, Mansfield NG21 0ER Tel: 01623 676026 Fax: 01623 414117 Email: david.williams@nwha.nnotts-ha.tren.nhs.uk; 18 Private Road, Sherwood, Nottingham NG5 4DB — MB ChB 1980 Sheff.; MFPHM RCP (UK) 1995. CCDC. Prev: Train. Progr. Dir., Pub. Health. Med.

WILLIAMS, David Conon Salters Medical Practice, The Health Centre, Ombersley Street, Droitwich WR9 8RD — MB ChB 1971 Birm. Hosp. Pract. (GI Endoscopy) Ronkswood Hosp. Worcester. Prev: Med. Regist. Worcester Roy. Infirm.; Ho. Off. (O & G) Ronkswood Hosp. Worcester.

WILLIAMS, David Daniel Wyn Ingledene, Llandilo Road, Cross Hands, Llanelli SA14 6RR — MB BS 1962 Lond.; MRCS Eng. LRCP Lond. 1962. (Lond. Hosp.) Prev: Gp. Orthop. Regist. Brentwood Hosps. Gp.; Ho. Off. (Midw. & Gyn.) St. And. Hosp. Lond.; Ho. Surg. & Cas. Off. Poplar Hosp. Lond.

WILLIAMS, David Donald Rhys Cefn Coed Hospital, Swansea SA2 0GH Tel: 01792 561155 Fax: 01792 516478 — MD Lond. 1977, MB BS 1964; MRCS Eng. LRCP Lond. 1964; MRCPsych 1972; DPM Eng. 1968. (Lond. Hosp.) Cons. Psychiat. W. Glam. HA. Socs:

WILLIAMS

BMA; Welsh Med. Soc. (Y Gymdeithas Feddygol); IPA. Prev: Sen. Regist. WhitCh. Hosp. Cardiff & Morgannwg Hosp. Bridgend.

WILLIAMS, David Edward Sett Valley Medical Centre, Hyde Bank Road, New Mills, High Peak SK22 4BP Tel: 01663 743483; Dewsnaps, Chinley, High Peak SK23 6AW Tel: 01663 751175 — MB ChB 1973 Manch.; DObst RCOG 1975.

WILLIAMS, David Edward 43 Marine Drive, Barry CF62 6QP Tel: 01831 527949 — MB BS 1985 Lond.; BSc (Hons.) Biochem. Wales 1979. Med. Off. Subaru, Nissan & BMW Motor Racing Teams.

WILLIAMS, Mr David Gareth Holts Health Centre, Watery Lane, Newent GL18 1BA Tel: 01531 820689; Lower Farm House, Clifford's Mesne, Newent GL18 1JT Tel: 01531 821654 — MB BChir 1971 Camb.; MA, MB BChir Camb. 1971; FRCS Eng. 1977. (Guy's) Clin. Asst. Endoscopy Unit Cheltenham Gen. Hosp.; Family Plann. Surg. Glos. HA. Prev: Surg. Regist. Acad. Dept. Surg. Roy. Free Hosp. Lond.; SHO (Surg.) Roy. Cornw. Hosp. (City & Treliske) Truro; Surg. Regist. St. Helier Hosp. Carshalton.

WILLIAMS, David George 356 Crookesmoor Road, Crookes, Sheffield S10 1BH — MB ChB 1995 Sheff.

WILLIAMS, David Glyn 12 Green Park, Erodig, Wrexham LL13 7YE — MB BS 1990 Lond.

WILLIAMS, David Glyn Rushden Medical Practice, Adnitt Road, Rushden NN10 9TU Tel: 01933 412666 Fax: 01933 317666; 7 Manor Gardens, Stanwick, Wellingborough NN9 6PL Tel: 01933 460903 — MB BS 1984 Lond.

WILLIAMS, David Hugh Eglwysbach Surgery, Berw Road, Pontypridd CF37 2AA Tel: 01443 406811 Fax: 01443 405457; 1 Tir-y-Coed, Parc Nant Celyn, Efail Isaf, Pontypridd CF38 1AJ — MB BCh 1974 Wales; FRCGP 1994, M 1978; DCH Eng. 1977; DRCOG 1976. (Wales) GP; Course Organiser; GP VTS.

WILLIAMS, Mr David Hugh Orchard Cottage, Fownhope, Hereford HR1 4PJ — MB BS 1974 Lond.; BSc (Hons.) Lond. 1971, MB BS 1974; MChOrth Liverp. 1986; FRCS Eng. 1979. (Univ. Coll. Hosp.) Cons. Orthop. Surg. Hereford Hosps. & Robt. Jones & Agnes Hunt Orthop. Hosp. OsW.ry. Prev: Sen. Regist. Middlx. Hosp. & Roy. Nat. Orthop. Hosp. Lond.; Sen. Res. Harvard Combined Orthop. Train. Progr. Boston, U.S.A.

WILLIAMS, David Ian Gwent Child Psychiatric Service, Ty Bryn Adolescent Unit, St Cadocs Hospital, Caeleon, Newport NP18 3XQ Tel: 01633 436944 Fax: 01633 436834 Email: dave.williams2@gwent.wales.nhs.uk; Tel: 02920 655157 Email: dave.williams.2@ntlworld.com — BM 1988 Soton.; MSc Wales 1995; MRCPsych 1994. (Southampton University) Cons. (Child & Adolesc. Psychiat.). Prev: Sen. Regist. Rotat. (Child & Adolesc. Psychiat.) S. Wales.

WILLIAMS, Sir David Innes (retired) 66 Murray Road, Wimbledon Common, London SW19 4PE Tel: 020 8879 1042 — MB BChir 1942 Camb.; MA Camb. 1944, MD 1951, MChir 1945; FRCS Eng. 1944; Hon. FRCSI 1984; MRCS Eng. LRCP Lond. 1942; Hon FRCPCH 1997; Hon. FDS RCS Eng. 1986; Hon. FACS 1983. Prev: Cons. urological Surg., The Hosp. for sick Childr. Gt Ormond St.

WILLIAMS, Mr David James 5 Collingwood Close, Liswerry, Newport NP19 0JB — MB BS 1991 Lond.; FRCS Eno. 1995. (The London Hospital Medical College) Specialist Regist. Rot. (Gen. Surg.) W. Midl. Surgic. Socs: Roy. Soc. Med.; Assn. Surg. Train.; Rouleaux Club. Prev: Research Fell. (Vasc. Surg.) Bath; SHO (Orthop. & Surg.) Swindon; SHO (Neurosurg. & A & E) Sheff.

WILLIAMS, Mr David John The White Cottage, 15 High Road, Essendon, Hatfield AL9 6HT — MB BS 1965 Lond.; FRCS Eng. 1974. (St. Geo.) Cons. Orthop. Surg. Qu. Eliz. II Hosp. Welwyn Gdn. City & Hertford; Cons. Orthop. Surg. N.W. Thames RHA. Socs: Fell. Brit. Orthop. Assn.; Assoc. Fell. Brit. Soc. for Surg. of Hand; Fell. Roy. Soc. Med. Prev: Sen. Regist. Rotat. (Orthop.) Char. Cross & St. Mary's Hosps. W2.

WILLIAMS, David John Longfleet House Surgery, 56 Longfleet Road, Poole BH15 2JD Tel: 01202 666677 Fax: 01202 660319 — BM 1979 Soton.; DA Eng. 1981. (Soton.)

WILLIAMS, David John 13 Spencer Hill, Wimbledon, London SW19 4PA Tel: 020 8946 3785 — MB BChir Camb. 1964; FRCS 1999 ED; FRCA 2000; FRCP 1998 ED; MA Camb. 1965; FRCP Lond. 1982; MRCP (UK) 1970; FFAEM 1993; MRCGP 1972; FRCS 1997. (St. Thos.) Clin. Adviser t the Health Serv. Commr. (Ombudsman); Mem. Of Criminal Injuries Compensation Appeals Panel. Socs: Past Pres. Intercollegiate Fac. A & E Med.; (Ex-Pres.)

Brit. Assn. for Accid. & Emerg. Med.; Vice-Pres. Europ. Soc. Emerg. Med. Prev: Cons. i/c A & E Middlx. Hosp. Lond.; Resid. Med. Off. Middlx. Hosp. Lond. & Nat. Heart Hosp. Lond.; Clin. Dir. A & E Guy's & St. Thos. Hosp. Lond.

WILLIAMS, David John Department of Obstretics and Gynaecology, Imperial College of Science, Technology and Medicine, Chelsea and Academic Westminster hospital, 369 Fulham Road, London SW10 9NH Tel: 020 8237 5175 Fax: 020 8237 5089 Email: david.williams@ic.ac.uk; 1 Hearne Road, Strand on the Green, London W4 3NJ — MB BS 1984 Lond.; MRCP (UK) 1987. (The Royal London Hospital Medical College) Sen. Lect./Honourary Cons., Matern. Med., Imperial Coll. of Med., Lond. Socs: Internat. Soc. for the study of Hypertens. in Pregn.; Brit. Matern. and Fetal Med. Soc.; Sec. Macdonald Club Obst. Med. Gp. Prev: Lect. & Hon. Sen. Regist. (Nephrol.) Univ. Coll. Lond. Med. Sch.; Research Fell. (Anat. & Developm. Biol.) Brit. Heart Foundat. Univ. Coll. Lond.; Regist. (Nephrol.) St. Peter's Hosp. Lond.

WILLIAMS, David John 33 Greenmeadows Road, Madeley, Crewe CW3 9EY Tel: 01782 750305 — MB ChB 1990 Birm.; DA (UK) 1996; FRCA (UK) 1997. (Birm.) Specialist Regist (Anaesth.) Roy. Adelaide Hosp., Australia; Instruc. Advanced Paediat. Life Support; Instruc. Advanced Trauma Life Support. Prev: SHO (Anaesth.) Morriston Hosp. Swansea; Regist. (Orthop. Surg.) Univ. Teachg. Hosp. Lusaka, Zambia.

WILLIAMS, David John Michael Chalice Cottage, 90 The Street, Little Waltham, Chelmsford CM3 3NT Tel: 01245 360065 — MB BS 1976 Lond.; MBA Open Univ. 1995; FFA RCS Eng. 1982; FFA RCSI 1981. Cons. Anaesth. Mid Essex Hosp. Chelmsford. Prev: Cons. Anaesth. Broomfield Hosp. Chelmsford.; Sen. Regist. (Anaesth.) Lond. Hosp. Whitechapel; Sen. Regist. (Anaesth.) Hosp. for Sick Childr. Gt. Ormond St. Lond.

WILLIAMS, Mr David Keith Laser Vision, 22 Harley St., London W1G 9AP Tel: 020 7580 1200 Fax: 020 7580 1201 Email: laservisionuk@compuserve.com — MB BS 1965 Lond.; MRCS Eng. LRCP Lond. 1964; FRCSC 1973; FRCOphth 1989; FACS 1977; LMCC 1970. (Univ. Coll. Lond.) Cons. Ophth. Cromwell & Wellington Hosps. Lond.; Moorfields Eye Hosp. Lond. Socs: Roy. Soc. Med.; Amer. Soc. Cataract & Refractive Surg.; Roy. Soc. Of Cataract & Refractive Surg.

WILLIAMS, David Laurence Cherrybrook Medical Centre, Paignton TQ4 7SH Tel: 01803 844566 Fax: 01803 845244 Email: david.williams@cherry.enta.net; 33 Lancaster Drive, Paignton TQ4 7RP Tel: 01803 555630 — MB ChB 1978 Dundee; DA Eng. 1982; DRCOG 1981. Socs: Torbay Med. Soc. Prev: Trainee GP Exeter VTS; SHO (O & G) W. Suff. Hosp. Bury St. Edmunds; SHO (Anaesth.) Torbay Hosp.

WILLIAMS, David Llewelyn Department of Clinical Biochemistry, Royal Berkshire Hospital, Reading RG1 5AN Tel: 0118 987 7709 Fax: 0118 987 7755 Email: sasdwill@cix.compulink.co.uk — MB 1972 Camb.; MB BChir Camb. 1972; FRSC 1982; PhD Reading 1966; MA Camb. 1987, BA 1961; FRCPath 1991; CChem 1982. (Camb. & Oxf.) Dir. Path. & Cons. Chem. Pathol. Roy. Berks. & Battle Hosps. NHS Trust Reading; Vis. Prof. Univ. Reading. Socs: Assn. Clin. Biochems.; Assn. Clin. Paths. Prev: Cons. Chem. Pathol. St. Peter's Hosp. Chertsey & Ashford Hosp. Middlx.; Sen. Lect. (Clin. Biochem.) Univ. Surrey; Edr. Annals. Clin. Biochem.

WILLIAMS, David Lloyd The Surgery, 59 Sevenoaks Road, Orpington BR6 9JN Tel: 01689 820159 — MB BS 1978 Lond. Princip. Gen. Pract. Orpington. Prev: Ho. Surg. & Paediat. SHO Pembury Hosp.; Trainee Gen. Pract. Portsmouth Vocational Train. Scheme.

WILLIAMS, Mr David Lloyd Trelew, 73 Longogarth, Fferham, Benllech, Tyn-y-Gongl LL74 8TA Tel: 0124 88 52208 — MB BCh Wales 1965; FRCS Ed. 1975. Staff Grade (Orthop.) Glan Clwyd Hosp. St. Asaph. Prev: Regist. (Orthop.) Withington Hosp. Manch.

WILLIAMS, David Mansell The Health Centre, Stanwell Road, Penarth CF64; 18 Victoria Square, Penarth CF64 Tel: 01222 702301 — MB BCh 1965 Wales. (Cardiff) Prev: Sen. Ho. Phys. Profess. Med. Unit Cardiff Roy. Infirm.; Sen. Ho. Phys. Cardiothoracic Centre, Sully.

WILLIAMS, David Meredith (retired) Wycombe, Vaynor Road, Cefn Coed, Merthyr Tydfil CF48 2HE — MD 1961 Wales; BSc Wales 1942, MD 1961, MB BCh 1945; FRCP Lond. 1974, M 1952. Prev: Cons. Phys. Merthyr & Aberdare Hosps.

WILLIAMS

WILLIAMS, David Michael Jeremy, OStJ (retired) 6 Park Road, Barry CF62 6NU Tel: 01446 734925 Fax: 01446 734925 — MB BCh 1960 Wales; MD Wales 1978; FFOM 1992, MFOM 1981. Prev: Sen. Med. Off. B.P. Chem.s Ltd. Lond.

WILLIAMS, David Owen The Medical Centre, Kingston Avenue, E. Horsley, Leatherhead KT24 6QT Tel: 01483 284151 Fax: 01483 285814; Dytchleys, The St, West Horsley, Leatherhead KT24 6HS Tel: 0148 652487 — MB BS 1956 Lond.; MRCS Eng. LRCP Lond. 1956; DObst RCOG 1959. (Lond. Hosp.) Socs: BMA (Ex-Chairm. Guildford Div.). Prev: Hosp. Pract. Accid. Centre Roy. Surrey Co. Hosp. Guildford; Receiv. Room Off., Ho. Surg. & Res. Accouch. Lond. Hosp.

WILLIAMS, David Owen 16 Mitchell Avenue, Jesmond, Newcastle upon Tyne NE2 3LA Tel: 0191 811410 — MB ChB 1964 Birm.; FRCP Ed. 1983, M 1968; FRCP Lond. 1981, M 1968; MRCS Eng. LRCP Lond. 1964. (Birm.) Cons. Cardiol. Newc. HA. Prev: Brit. Amer. Research Fell. Miami USA; Hon. Sen. Regist. Cardiol. Qu. Eliz. Hosp. Birm.; Regist. in Cardiol. Sully Hosp.

WILLIAMS, David Paul The Surgery, Marshall House, Bancroft Court, Hitchin SG5 1LH Tel: 01462 420740 — MB ChB 1984 Liverp. SHO (O & G) N.d. HA. Prev: Trainee GP N.d. VTS.

WILLIAMS, Professor David Robert Rhys Nuffield Institute for Health, 71-75 Clarendon Road, Leeds LS2 9PL Tel: 0113 233 3453 Fax: 0113 233 3952 Email: hssdrrw@leeds.ac.uk; 12 Ellis House, Ellis Court, Harrogate HG1 2SH Fax: 01423 875606 — MB BS 1972 Lond.; MA Camb. 1988; PhD Durh. 1978; FRCP Lond. 1993; MRCS Eng. LRCP Lond. 1972; FFPHM RCP (UK) 1988, M 1982. Prof. Epidemiol. & Pub. Health Uni.Leeds. Socs: Mem. Bd. of Trustees, Diabetes UK; Vice-Pres. Int'l Diabetes Fed. Prev: Univ. Lect. Camb. Univ.; Addison Wheeler Research Fell. Univ. Durh.; MRC Train. Fell. Epidemiol. Dunn Clin. Nutrit. Centre Camb.

WILLIAMS, David Thomas Cascade Cottage, Pengam Road, Penpedairheol, Hengoed CF82 8BX — MB BCh 1990 Wales.

WILLIAMS, David Thomas Victoria Surgery, Victoria Road, Holyhead LL65 1UD; Bryn Teg, Gorad Road, Valley, Holyhead LL65 3BT Tel: 01407 742488 — MB BS 1982 Lond.; MRCGP 1987; DRCOG 1985. GP Holyhead.

WILLIAMS, David Thomas Arthur, OStJ (retired) Nythfa, 11 Bishop's Grove, Sketty, Swansea SA2 8BE Tel: 01792 204321 — MB BS Lond. 1956; DObst RCOG 1958.

WILLIAMS, David Tobias (retired) Tor-Na-Coille, 5 Walnut Grove, Kinfauns, Perth PH2 7UJ Tel: 01738 624629 Email: davidto@tinyworld.co.uk — MB ChB St. And. 1961.

WILLIAMS, David Trevor Huxley Biffins, Lane End, Hambleton, Godalming GU8 4HD — MB BS 1970 Lond.; MRCS Eng. LRCP Lond. 1970; FFHom 1997; DObst RCOG 1973. (St. Bart.) Socs: Brit. Soc. Med. Dent. Hypn; Accred.Mem.Brit.Med.Acupunc; Fell.Fac.Homeopathy.

WILLIAMS, David Vaughan South Forest Centre, 21 Thorne Close, Leytonstone, London E11 4HU Tel: 020 8535 6480 Fax: 020 8535 6481; 242 Malyons Road, Ladywell, London SE13 7XF Tel: 020 8690 7399 — MB BCh 1985 Wales; MRCPsych 1990. (University of Wales College of Medicine) Assoc. Specialist (Psychiat.) S. Forest Centre Lond. Prev: Clin. Asst. (Psychiat.) Claybury Hosp. NE Thames RHA; Regist. (Psychiat. & Ment. Handicap) Mid. Glam. HA; Ho. Off. (Gen. Med.) Clwyd HA.

WILLIAMS, Dean Thomas 20 Heathbrook, Llanishen, Cardiff CF14 5FA — MB BS 1990 Lond.

WILLIAMS, Deborah Lonkeda, Pen-Y-Walln, Pentyrch, Cardiff CF15 9SJ Tel: 01222 892398 — MB BS 1981 Newc. Retainer GP WhitCh. Cardiff. Prev: Trainee GP Ystrad Myroch.

WILLIAMS, Deborah Elizabeth Marine Surgery, 29 Belle Vue Road, Southbourne, Bournemouth BH6 3DB Tel: 01202 423377 Fax: 01202 424277; 2 Watcombe Road, Southbourne, Bournemouth BH6 3LT — MB BS 1974 Lond.; MRCGP 1978; DRCOG 1977. GP Bournemouth. Prev: Trainee GP Bath VTS; Ho. Phys. Univ. Coll. Hosp. Lond.

WILLIAMS, Deborah Innes The Lawson Unit, The Royal Sussex County Hospital, Eastern Road, Brighton BN2 5BE; 60 Osmond Road, Hove BN3 1TF — MB ChB 1984 Sheff.; MRCP (UK) 1987; DTM & H Lond. 1992. Cons. (GUM & HIV) The Roy. Sussex Co. Hosp. Brighton.

WILLIAMS, Deborah Lynne 8 Harold Hicks Place, Percy St., Oxford OX4 3OS — MB BCh 1987 Wales; MRCPsych 1992.

WILLIAMS, Denise Karen Department of Clinical Genetics, Birmingham Women's hospital, Edgbaston, Birmingham B15 2TG Tel: 0121 627 2630 Fax: 0121 627 2618 Email: denise.williams@blam-womens.thenhs.com; 18 Dark Lane, Stoke Heath, Bromsgrove B60 3BH Tel: 01527 872293 Email: moloneydenise@hotmail.com — MB BCh 1987 Wales; MRCP (UK) 1990; Dip. Human & Clin. Genetic Lond. 1992. (University of Wales, College of Medicine) p/t Cons. Clin. geneticist, Birm. Prev: Sen. Regist. Rotat. Trent Clin. Genetics Leicester Roy. Infirm. & City Hosp. Nottm.; Regist. Clin. Genetics Birm. Matern. Hosp.; Regist. (Paediat.) Leic. Roy. Infirm.

WILLIAMS, Denise Mary Box 181, Addenbrooke's Hospital, Hill Road, Cambridge CB2 2QQ Tel: 01223 245151 Fax: 01223 216966 Email: denise.williams@msexc.addenbrookes.anglox.nhs.uk; Tel: 01223 244299 — MB BCh 1980 Wales; FRCP Lond, 1997,MRCP (UK) 1983; MRCPCH. p/t Cons. Paediat. (Oncol.) Addenbrooke's Hosp. Camb.

WILLIAMS, Dennis Kenneth Treflan Surgery, Treflan, Lower Cardiff Road, Pwllheli LL53 5NF Tel: 01758 701457 Fax: 01758 701209 — MB ChB 1975 Liverp.; MRCGP 1983; DCH RCP Lond. 1982; DRCOG 1979. Gen. Practitioner; Clin. Director; Assoc. Post Grad. Organiser; Project Director N. Wales Telemed. Project.

WILLIAMS, Denys Ian (retired) Dundarroch, Brig O'Turk, Callender FK17 8HT Tel: 01243 552917 Fax: 01243 552917 — MB ChB Ed. 1956.

WILLIAMS, Derek Owen Chest Clinic, Ealing Hospital, Uxbridge Road, Southall UB1 3HW Tel: 020 8967 5381 Fax: 020 8967 5660; 31 Pinn Way, Ruislip HA4 7QG — MB BS 1972 Lond.; MRCP (UK) 1977. (Middlx.) Assoc. Specialist (Respirat. Med.) Chest Clinic Ealing Hosp. S.all & Chest & Allergy Clinic St. Mary's Hosp. Lond. Socs: Brit. Thorac. Soc.; Amer. Thoracic Soc.; Eur. Respirat. Soc. Prev: Research Fell. & Hon. Sen. Regist. (Respirat. Med.) Hammersmith Hosp. Lond.; Instruc. (Med.) N. W.. Memor. Hosp. Chicago, USA; Pulm. Fell. NW Univ. Chicago, USA.

WILLIAMS, Derfel Health Centre, Pen y Bont, The Roe, St Asaph LL17 0LU Tel: 01745 583208 Fax: 01745 583748; Bryn Arlais, Ffordd-Y-Bryn, Llanelwy, St Asaph LL17 0DD — BM 1986 Soton.; PhD Liverp. 1979, BSc (Hons.) 1974; MRCGP 1994; Dip. Palliat. Med. Wales 1993. (Southampton) Prev: SHO (Paediat.) Ysbyty Glan Clwyd; Clin. Med. Off. (Community Paediat.) Clwyd N. HA; Trainee GP Clwyd N. VTS.

WILLIAMS, Deric Haydn The Health Centre, Fender Way, Noctorum, Birkenhead CH43 9QS Tel: 0151 677 1034 Fax: 0151 604 0392; Crud y Mynydd, 4 Glas Goed, Cilcain, Mold CH7 5PP Tel: 01352 741765 — MB BS 1954 Lond.; MRCS Eng. LRCP Lond. 1954; MRCGP 1980; DPH Liverp. 1965; DObst RCOG 1958. (Guy's) Socs: Wirral Local Med. Comm. & Birkenhead Med. Soc. Prev: Sen. Asst. Div. Med. Off. Lancs. CC & Dep. MOH Kirkby UD; JHMO (Psychiat.) N. Wales Hosp. Denbigh; Ho. Surg. (O & G) Chester City Hosp.

WILLIAMS, Deryk John 8 The Knoll, Beckenham BR3 5JW — MB BS 1985 Lond.; BSc (Hons.) Lond. 1982, MB BS 1985.

WILLIAMS, Mr Desmond Patrick Commins 25 Antringham Gardens, Westfield Road, Edgbaston, Birmingham B15 3QL Tel: 0121 455 0025 — MB ChB 1947 Liverp.; FRCS Ed. 1960; DLO Eng. 1954. (Liverp.) Cons. ENT Surg. Birm. & Midl. ENT Hosp.; Sen. Clin. Lect. Birm. Univ.; Adviser Otolaryng. & Assessor RCS Eng. Socs: Fell. Roy. Soc. Med.; Counc. Brit. Assn. Otolaryng. Prev: Demonst. Physiol. Liverp. Univ. & Hon. Demonst. (Anat.) Camb. Univ.; Sen. Regist. United Bristol Hosps.; Cons. ENT Surg. Maidstone & Medway Hosps.

WILLIAMS, Dewi Rheinallt Cons. Anaesthetist, Dumfries & Galloway Royal Infirmary, Dumfries DG1 4UP Tel: 01387 246246; Little Garth, 8 Castle Douglas Road, Dumfries DG2 7NX — MB ChB Ed. 1987; FRCA 1993. (Ed.) Cons. Anaesth. Dumfries & Galloway Roy. Infirm. Dumfries. Socs: Intens. Care Soc.; Assn. Anaesth.; ESICM. Prev: SHO (Anaesth.) Ninewells Hosp. Dundee; Sen. Regist. (Anaesth.) Ninewells Hosp. Dundee.

WILLIAMS, Dominica Gale Old Road Surgery, Old Road, Abersychan, Pontypool NP4 7BH Tel: 01495 772239 Fax: 01495 773786; 7 Lime Trees Avenue, Llangattock, Crickhowell NP8 1LB Tel: 01873 810110 Fax: 01873 811606 — MB ChB 1965 Bristol; DObst RCOG 1967. (Bristol) GP Princip.; Clin. Asst. Co. Hosp. Pontypool. Socs: Fac. Fam. Plann. & Reproduc. Health Care; Fac.

WILLIAMS

Fam. Plann. & Reproduc. Health Care. Prev: GP Kingston & Richmond FPC; Clin. Med. Off. Gwent AHA.

WILLIAMS, Donald Gwynne, Capt. RAMC Retd. Claines, Skipton Old Road, Colne BB8 7AE Tel: 01282 865400 — MB ChB 1953 Birm.; FFCM 1981, M 1972; DPH Manch. 1970; DObst RCOG 1958. (Birm.) Socs: Fell. Manch. Med. Soc. Prev: DMO Blackburn Hyndburn & Ribble Valley HA; Area Specialist Community Med. (Health Care Plann. Informat.) Lancs. AHA; PMO Epidemiol. & Research Dept. Lancs. CC.

WILLIAMS, Doris (retired) 7 Pencoed Avenue, Pontypridd CF37 4AN — MB BS 1926 Lond.; MRCS Eng., LRCP Lond. 1923; DPH Wales 1926. Prev: Asst. Co. Sch. Med. Off. Glam. CC.

WILLIAMS, Dorothea Mary Oxford Street Surgery, Oxford Street, Aberaeron SA46 0JB Tel: 01545 570273 Fax: 01545 571625; Drefnewydd Farm, Aberaeron SA46 0JR Tel: 01545 570024 — MB ChB 1965 Birm.

WILLIAMS, Dorothy Jane 7 Hambledon Road, Southfields, London SW18 5UD — MB ChB 1979 Bristol.

WILLIAMS, Duncan Andrew Wirksworth Health Centre, St. John's St., Wirksworth, Derby — MB ChB 1992 Birm.

WILLIAMS, Duncan Howard Department of Anaesthetics, Christchurch Hospital, Private BAG 4710, Christchurch, New Zealand; Quarry Dene, 36 Church Lane, Bardsey, Leeds LS17 9DP Tel: 01937 572153 — MB ChB 1983 Sheff.; DRCOG 1986. Cons. (Anaesth.) ChristCh. Hosp. Prev: Regist. (Anaesth.) Waikato Hosp. Hamilton, NZ.

WILLIAMS, Duncan Meredydd Amman Valley Medical Practice, Graig Road Surgery, Gwann-Cae-Gurwen, Ammanford SA18 Tel: 01269 822231; Oaklands, Derwydd Road, Derwydd, Ammanford SA18 2TT Tel: 01296 850785 — MB BCh 1984 Wales; MRCGP 1988; DRCOG 1987.

WILLIAMS, Dylan Williams, O'Connor and Morgan, New Quay Surgery, Church Road, New Quay SA45 9PB Tel: 01545 560203 Fax: 01545 560916; Lake View, Oakford, Llanarth SA47 0RW Tel: 01545 580042 — MB BS 1978 Lond.; BSc Lond. 1975; DA (UK) 1984.

WILLIAMS, Dylan Wyn 36 Holland Street, Ebbw Vale NP23 6HZ — MB BCh 1990 Wales.

WILLIAMS, Dylan Wynne Department of Histopathology, University Hospital of Wales, Heath Park, Cardiff CF14 4XW — MB BS 1983 Lond.; PhD Wales 1988; BSc (Hons.) Lond. 1980, MB BS 1983; MRCPath 1991. Sen. Regist. (Histopath.) Univ. Wales, Coll. Med. Cardiff.

WILLIAMS, Earl Jon 20 Kingsley Avenue, Cannock WS12 4EA — MB ChB 1994 Leic.

WILLIAMS, Edith Hazel, OBE (retired) 12 Elm Close, Laverstock, Salisbury SP1 1SA Tel: 01722 328131 — MB BS Durh. 1941; DPH Lond. 1948; MFCM 1972; DCH Eng. 1949. Prev: Community Phys. Salisbury Health Dist.

WILLIAMS, Edna Elizabeth Dunster, The Grove, Burnham-on-Sea TA8 2PA — MB BCh 1943 Wales; BSc Wales 1940, MB BCh 1943. (Cardiff) Med. Off. Som. AHA. Socs: BMA. Prev: Ho. Phys. Morriston Hosp.; Asst. Med. Off. Middlx. CC & Carms. CC.

WILLIAMS, Edna May Community & Mental Health Trust, St. Mary's Hospital, Greenhill Road, Armley, Leeds LS12 3QE Tel: 0113 279 0121; 8 St. Winfreds Road, Harrogate HG2 8LN Tel: 01423 883404 — MB ChB 1976 Aberd. (Aberd.) Assoc. Specialist Community & Ment. Health Trust Leeds. Prev: SCMO Clwyd DHA.

WILLIAMS, Professor Sir Edward Dillwyn, KBE Thyroid Carcinogenesis Research Group, Strangeways Research Laboratories, Wort's Causeway, Cambridge CB1 8RN Tel: 01223 740180 Fax: 01223 411609 Email: louise@srl.com.ac.uk; Burford House, Hildersham, Cambridge CB1 6BU Tel: 01223 893316 — MD Camb. 1983, MB BChir 1953; FRCP Lond. 1977, M 1973; FRCPath. 1977, M 1965. (Lond. Hosp.) Emerit. Prof. Histopath. Univ. Camb; Jt. Director, Thyroid Carcinogenesis research Gp., Strangeways Laborat., Camb. Prev: Prof. Path. Univ. Wales Coll. Med.; Reader (Morbid Anat.) Roy. Postgrad. Med. Sch. Lond.

WILLIAMS, Professor Edward Idris, OBE Morecambe Bay Hospitals NHS Trust, Trust HQ, Westmorland General Hospital, Burton Road, Kendal LA9 7RG Tel: 01539 795366 Fax: 01539 795313 Email: idris.williams@k.bay-tr.nwest.nhs.uk; Barn Howe, Lyth, Kendal LA8 8DF Tel: 01539 568666 — MB ChB 1954 Manch.; MD Manch. 1973; FRCGP 1976, M 1965; DObst RCOG

1961. Emerit. Prof. Gen. Pract. Univ. Nottm.; Chairm. Morecambe Bay Hosp.s NHS Trust. Socs: Bolton Med. Soc. Prev: Sen. Lect. (Gen. Pract.) Univ. Manch.; Ho. Surg. (Orthop.) Manch. Roy. Infirm.; Ho. Surg. (Obst.) Bolton Dist. Gen. Hosp.

WILLIAMS, Edward James (retired) 24 Birkett Drive, Ulverston LA12 9LS Tel: 01229 583746 — MB ChB 1960 Leeds; MRCPsych 1973; DPM Leeds 1971. Prev: Hon. Cons. Psychiat. St. Luke's Hosp. for Clergy Lond.

WILLIAMS, Mr Edward John, RD Upper Meadow, Hedgerley Lane, Gerrards Cross SL9 7NP Tel: 01753 882651 — MB BS 1950 Lond.; MS Lond. 1965, MB BS 1950; FRCS Eng. 1958. (Lond. Hosp.) Cons. Surg. St. Mary's Hosp. Lond. & Wexham Pk. Hosp. Slough. Socs: Pres. Vasc. Surg. Soc. Gt. Brit. & Irel.; Europ. Soc. Vasc. Surg.; Assn. Surgs. Gt. Brit. & Irel. Prev: Asst. Dir., Surg. Unit St. Mary's Hosp. Lond.; Sen. Regist. (Surg.) Lond. Hosp.; Surg. Fell. Presbyt. St. Luke's Hosp. Chicago, USA.

WILLIAMS, Edward Robert (retired) Croft Cottage, West End, Bitteswell LE17 4UX Tel: 01455 557020 — MB BChir 1961 Camb.; MA, MD Camb. 1971; FRCP Lond. 1980, M 1963. Prev: Sen. Regist. (Med.) Bristol Roy. Infirm.

WILLIAMS, Professor Edward Sydney (retired) Little Hollies, The Close, Wonersh, Guildford GU5 0PA Tel: 01483 892591 — MB BS 1957 Lond.; PhD Lond. 1963, BSc 1950, MD 1971; FRCP Lond. 1979, M 1970; FRCR 1983. Prev: Prof. Nuclear Med. Univ. Lond.

WILLIAMS, Edwin Market Street Surgery, 3-5 Market Street, Caernarfon LL55 1RT Tel: 01286 673224 Fax: 01286 676405 — MB BS 1988 Lond. (Guy's) Socs: Cymdeithas Feddygol. Prev: Trainee GP Awdurdod Iechyd Gwynedd VTS.

WILLIAMS, Edwina Rachel Louise Department of Liaison Psychiatry & ICRF Psychosocial Ongology, 3rd Floor, Riddell House, St Thomas's Hospital, Lambeth Palace Rd, London SE1 Email: edwina.williams@kcl.ac.uk; 266 Camberwell New Road, London SE5 0RP Email: erlw@lineone.net — MB BCh 1988 Wales; Msc (Manch). Socs: MRCPsych.

WILLIAMS, Mr Eifion Vaughan 25 Heol-y-Coed, Rhiwbina, Cardiff CF14 6HQ — MB BCh 1988 Wales; FRCS Glas. 1994. SHO E. Glam Ch. Village. Prev: SHO (Gen. Surg.) Roy. Gwent Hosp.

WILLIAMS, Eileen Gibson Neish Glan Clwyd Hospital, Conwy and Denbighshire NHS Trust, Rhyl LL18 5UJ Tel: 01745 534969 — MB ChB 1977 Glas.; FFA RCS Eng. 1982. Cons. Anaesth. Glan Clwyd Hosp. Rhyl. Prev: Sen. Regist. (Anaesth.) Mersey RHA; Sen. Regist. (Anaesth.) Ysbyty Glan Clwyd Hosp. Rhyl.; Sen. Regist. (Anaesth.) Countess of Chester Hosp.

WILLIAMS, Eirlys Jean (retired) Broadway, 43 Southgate Road, Southgate, Swansea SA3 2DA Tel: 01505 2207 — LRCP LRCS 1951 Ed.; LRCP LRCS Ed. LRFPS Glas. 1951. Prev: Govt. Med. Off. Paediat. Unit Colon. War Memor. Hosp. Suva, Fiji.

WILLIAMS, Eirwen Nicholas Mill Cottage, Station Road, Welton, Daventry NN11 5JR — MB BS 1988 Lond.; DRCOG 1992.

WILLIAMS, Eleanor Mair Tabernacle Street Surgery, 4 Tabernacle Street, Skewen, Neath SA10 6UF Tel: 01792 817009 / 817573 Fax: 01792 321029; Ty-Gwyn, 33A Penywern Road, Neath SA10 7AW — MD 1981 Wales; BSc (Hons.) (Genetics) Wales 1971, MB BCh 1976; MRCGP 1991. Hon. Lect. (Med. Genetics) Welsh Nat. Sch. Med.; Hosp. Pract. (Med. Genetics) Welsh Nat. Sch. Med. Cardiff & Singleton Hosp. Swansea.; Med. FHSA. Prev: Ho. Off. Dept. Med. Llandough Hosp. Cardiff & Dept. Surg. Univ. Hosp. Wales Cardiff.

WILLIAMS, Eleri Catherine 30 Esher Avenue, Walton-on-Thames KT12 2TA — MB BS 1991 Lond.

WILLIAMS, Elisabeth Dorothy The Coach House, 31A Park Hill, Moseley, Birmingham B13 8DR Tel: 0121 449 0123 — MB ChB 1960 Birm. (Birm.)

WILLIAMS, Elisabeth Jane 7 Molesford Road, London SW6 4BX — MB BS 1989 Lond. SHO (Anaesth.) St. Geo. Hosp. Lond. Prev: SHO (Anaesth.) Watford Gen. Hosp. Herts.; Ho. Off. (Gen. Surg.) St. Helier's Hosp. Carshalton; Ho. Off. (Gen. Med.) New Cross Hosp. Wolverhampton.

WILLIAMS, Elisabeth Ruth 19 Allt-Yr-Yn Close, Newport NP20 5ED — BM 1995 Soton. SHO (Paediat.) Roy. Gwent Hosp. Newport.

WILLIAMS, Elizabeth Ann 14 High Street, Hawarden, Deeside CH5 3EF — BChir 1986 Camb.; MB 1987.

WILLIAMS, Elizabeth Ann The Gillies Health Centre, Sullivan Rd, Brighton Hill, Basingstoke RG22 4EH Tel: 01256 479747 Fax:

WILLIAMS

01256 320627; Sherfield End, Reading Rd, Shirfield on Luddon, Hook RG27 0JG — BM BCh 1978 Oxf.; MA Camb. 1978, BA 1975; MRCP (UK) 1982; MRCGP 1982; DRCOG 1981. Gen. Practitioner The Gillies & Overbridge Med. Partnership Basingstoke. Prev: Clin. Asst. (Oncol.) Basingstoke Dist. Hosp.; Non-Princip. GP Basingstoke.

WILLIAMS, Elizabeth Anne Intake Farm, Chevin End Road, Menston, Ilkley LS29 6BP — MB ChB 1975 Leeds. Assoc. Specialist Yorks. Regional Blood Transfus. Serv.

WILLIAMS, Elizabeth Anne 20 Trinity Street, Dorchester DT1 1TU Tel: 01304 251545; West Knighton House, West Knighton, Dorchester DT2 8PF — MB BS 1978 Lond.; DCH RCP 1984 London; MRCP 1981 (UK); MRCP (UK) 1981; DCH RCP Lond. 1984. (Middlx.) Princip. in Gen. Pract.

WILLIAMS, Elizabeth Carol Windermere Health Centre, Goodly Dale, Windermere LA23 2EG Tel: 015394 42496 Fax: 015394 48329; Old Heathwaite, Pk Road, Windermere LA23 2DH Tel: 015394 44740 Email: newsome1@globalnet.com — MB BS 1975 Newc.; MRCGP 1979; MFFP 1993; DRCOG 1978. GP Tutor Kendal. Socs: Brit. Med. Soc.; (Comm. Mem.) NW Soc. Sexual Med. & Family Plann. Prev: GP Sale; GP Trainee Newc. VTS; Clin. Med. Off. (Train., Family Plann. & Well Wom. Servs.) Manch.

WILLIAMS, Elizabeth Jane The Clapham Park Surgery, 72 Clarence Avenue, London SW4 8JP Tel: 020 8674 0101 Fax: 020 8674 2941 — MB BS 1982 Lond.; DRCOG 1993; DTM & H RCP Lond. 1989.

WILLIAMS, Elizabeth Jane Geufron, Llangollen LL20 8DY — MB ChB 1969 Birm.; DMRT Eng. 1972. (Birm.) SCMO (Radiother.) N. Staffs. Infirm. Prev: Sen. Regist. (Radiother.) N. Staffs.Infirm.; Clin. Asst. (Radiother.) N. Staffs. Infirm.; Regist. & Research Regist. Cookridge Hosp. Leeds.

WILLIAMS, Elizabeth Jean 29 Lambardes, New Ash Green, Longfield DA3 8HX — BM 1990 Soton.; BSc Psychol. (1st. cl. Hons.) 1989; MRCP (UK) 1993. M. R. C. Clin. Research Fell. Dept. Med. Univ. Soton. Prev: Regist. Rotat. (Gastroenterol. & Gen. Med.) Soton.; SHO Rotat. (Med.) Bournemouth & Poole.

WILLIAMS, Elizabeth Joan Department of Chemical Pathology, Princess of Wales Hospital, Coity Road, Bridgend CF31 1RQ Tel: 01656 752337 — MB BCh 1981 Wales; PhD (Med. Biochem.) Wales 1975, BSc (Hons.) Biochem. 1971; LLM 1993; MRCPath 1986. (Welsh National School Medicine) Cons. Chem. Path. P.ss of Wales Hosp. Bridgend.; Clin. Dir. (Pathol.) 1995-; PostGrad. Organiser/Clin. Tutor 1994-. Prev: Sen. Regist. (Med. Biochem.) Univ. Hosp. Wales. Cardiff.

WILLIAMS, Elizabeth Lloyd Thedford, Capel Llanilltern, Cardiff CF5 6JH — MB BS 1987 Lond. Trainee GP Devon VTS.

WILLIAMS, Elizabeth Mary (retired) Land Farm, Blackshaw Head, Hebden Bridge HX7 7PJ Tel: 01422 842240 Fax: 01422 842260 — MB BS Durh. 1963; DCH Eng. 1965.

WILLIAMS, Elizabeth Mary White Posts, Charlton All Saints, Salisbury SP5 4HQ — MB ChB 1970 Bristol; DCH Eng. 1973; DObst RCOG 1972.

WILLIAMS, Elwyn Brinley 4 Birch Tree Lane, Goostrey, Crewe CW4 8NS — MB BCh 1968 Wales; MFPM RCP (UK) 1991; Cardiff). Med. Dir. N. Europ. Wellcome Foundat. Ltd. Chesh.; Clin. Asst. (Diabetes) Manch. Roy. Infirm. Socs: Fell. Roy. Soc. Med.; Brit. Diabetic Assn.; Eur. Assn. Study Diabetes.

WILLIAMS, Emily Margaret Nuffield Department Anaesthetics, John Radcliffe Hospital, Headley Way, Oxford OX3 9DU — BM 1982 Soton.; FCAnaesth 1989; DCH RCP Lond. 1987. Cons. Anaesth. John Radcliffe Hosp. Oxf. Prev: Sen. Regist. (Anaesth.) Roy. Free Hosp. Lond.

WILLIAMS, Emlyn 71 Rodney Street, Liverpool L1 9EX Tel: 0151 708 8300 Fax: 0151 707 2047 — MB BS Lond. 1967; FRCP Lond. 1989, M 1971. (Char. Cross) Cons. Phys. (Rheum. & Rehabil.) Roy. Liverp. Univ. Hosp. & The Univ. Hosp. at Aintree; Cons. in Rehabil. Med. Roy. Preston Hosp., Preston. Socs: Brit. Soc. Rheum.; Brit. Soc. Rehabil. Med.

WILLIAMS, Emma Elizabeth Ellen 4 Oak Farm Close, Tetsworth, Thame OX9 7JA — MB BS 1992 Lond.; MRCGP London 1999; DFFP 2000; BSc (Physiol.) Lond. 1989; DCH RCP Lond. 1995. (Univ. Coll. & Middlx. Hosp. Med. Sch.) Clin. Asst., Palliat. Care, Sue Ryder Care Centre, Nettlebed, Henley on Thames; Gen. Practitioner Asst., The Crosskeys Pract., Chinnor; Locum Clin. Med. Off., Dept of Family Plann., Alec Turnbull Clinic, Oxf.

WILLIAMS, Erbin Hughes Llanishen Court Surgery, Llanishen Court, Llanishen, Cardiff CF14 5YU Tel: 029 2075 7025 Fax: 029 2074 7931; Llanishen Court Surgery, Llanishen, Cardiff CF14 5YU Tel: 01222 757025 — MB BCh 1973 Wales; MRCGP 1977; DObst RCOG 1975; Cert Contracep. & Family Plann. RCOG, RCGP &; Cert FPA 1976. Princip. in Gen. Pract.

WILLIAMS, Evan (retired) Cartref, Tudweiliog, Pwllheli LL53 8NA Tel: 01758 770329 — MRCS Eng. LRCP Lond. 1942; MFCM 1974; DPH Birm. 1947.

WILLIAMS, Evan David Glyndwr 10 Hillside Park, Bargoed CF81 8NL Tel: 01443 831009 — MRCS Eng. LRCP Lond. 1961; MB Camb. 1961, BChir 1960. (King's Coll. Hosp.)

WILLIAMS, Evelyn May Isobel Department of Public Health, Phadrangle, Liverpool L69 3GB Tel: 0151 794 5690 Fax: 0151 794 5700 Email: emiw@liv.ac.uk; 6 Chestnut Avenue, Crosby, Liverpool L23 2SZ — MD 1989 Lond.; MA Camb. 1979; MB BS 1978; FFPHM 1996; MFCM 1989. Sen. Lect. (Pub. Health) Univ. Liverp. Prev: Cons. Pub. Health Med. Oxf. RHA.

WILLIAMS, (Evelyn) Moira (retired) 7 Bennetts Copse, Chislehurst BR7 5SG Tel: 020 8467 9809 — MB BCh 1962 Wales; MRCPath 1974. Prev: Cons. Haemat. S. Lond. Blood Transfus. Serv.

WILLIAMS, F Gail Welsh Blood Service, Ely Valley Road, Talbot Green, Pontyclun CF72 9WB Tel: 01443 622016 Fax: 01443 622028 Email: gail.williams@wbs.wales.nhs.uk; The Hollies, 52 Kelston Road, Whitchurch, Cardiff CF14 2AH Tel: 02920 610158 — MB BS 1972 Lond.; LLM 1994; MRCS Eng. LRCP Lond. 1972; FRCPath 1991, M 1979; Cert. Family Plann. JCC 1976. Dir. Welsh Blood Serv. Socs: Fell. Roy. Soc. Med.; Hon. Sec. Brit. Blood Transfus. Soc. Prev: Cons. Blood Transfus. Welsh Regional Transfus. Centre Cardiff; Cons. Haemat. P. Chas. Hosp. Merthyr Tydfil; Lect. (Haemat.) St. Mary's Hosp. Lond.

WILLIAMS, Ffion Eleri 19 Parc Gwelfor, Dyserth, Rhyl LL18 6LN — MB ChB 1998 Liverp.; MB ChB Liverp 1998.

WILLIAMS, Frances 9 Pearson Road, Cleethorpes DN35 0DR — MB ChB 1988 Manch.; FRCA 1994. Assoc. Specialist (Anaesth.) Jas. Paget Hosp. Prev: Regist. (Anaesth.) Aberd. Roy. Infirm.; SHO (Anaesth.) Bradford Roy. Infirm.; SHO (Paediat.) Leeds Gen. Infirm.

WILLIAMS, Frances Mary Kingsley 75 Bennerley Road, London SW11 6DR Fax: 020 7223 8364; Research Haematology, 4th Floor North Wing, St. Thomas' Hospital, Lambeth Palace Road, London SE1 7EH Tel: 020 7928 9292 1439 Fax: 020 7928 5698 Email: f.williams@amds.ac.uk — MB BS 1992 Lond.; BSc Lond. 1991; MRCP (UK) 1995. (St. Mary's Hosp. Med. Sch.) ARC Clin. Fell. Lupus Research Unit Rayne Inst. St. Thomas' Hosp. Lond.

WILLIAMS, Frances Watcyn Hillside, Friog, Fairbourne LL38 2NX — MB BChir 1982 Camb.; MA Camb. 1982, MB BChir 1982; MRCP (UK) 1986; DTM & H Lond. 1991; MRCPCH 1997.

WILLIAMS, Frank Brynawel, LLangattock, Crickhowell NP8 1PY Tel: 01873 810200 — MB BCh 1973 Wales; MA Wales 1994, MB BCh 1973; FRCR 1979. (Cardiff) Cons. Radiol. Nevill Hall Hosp. Abergavenny.

WILLIAMS, Frank Aldwyn Benedict Melrose Surgery, 73 London Road, Reading RG1 5BS Tel: 0118 950 7950 Fax: 0118 959 4044 — MRCS Eng. LRCP Lond. 1968.

WILLIAMS, Frank Middleton Warner 3 Tudor Gardens, London W3 0DT Tel: 020 8993 2034 — MB BS 1949 Lond.; MRCP Ed. 1954; FRCP Ed. 1982. (Lond. Hosp. Med. Coll.) Prev: Cons. Phys. & Paediat. Med. Arts Centre, Geo.town, Guyana; Cons. Phys., Paediat. & Sen. Phys. Geo.town Hosp., Guyana.

WILLIAMS, Frank Richard Seafield of Raigmore, Inverness IV2 7PA Tel: 01463 711205 Fax: 01463 711205 — MB ChB Ed. 1969; BA Lond. 1962; BSc Ed. 1966; FRCR 1976; DMRD 1973; AKC. (Ed.) Cons. Radiol. Highland HB. Socs: Highland Med. Soc., Scott. Radiol. Soc. & BMA.

WILLIAMS, Gabrielle Joan Village Surgery, Station Road, Southwater, Horsham RH13 7HQ Tel: 01403 730016 Fax: 01403 730660; 5 Kingsfold Close, Billingshurst RH14 9HG Tel: 01403 784401 — MB ChB 1970 Leeds; DObst. RCOG 1972.

WILLIAMS, Gareth Heol Fach Surgery, Heol Fach, North Cornelly, Bridgend CF33 4LD Tel: 01656 740345 Fax: 01656 740872; Stormybrook Surgery, Waunbant Road, Kenfig Hill, Bridgend

WILLIAMS

CF33 6DE Tel: 01656 746611 — MB BCh 1977 Wales; MRCGP 1981.

WILLIAMS, Professor Gareth Clinical Sciences Centre, University Hospital Aintree, Liverpool L9 7AL Tel: 0151 529 2930 Fax: 0151 529 2931; Robinswood, Brow Lane, Lower Heswall, Wirral CH60 0DT Tel: 0151 342 2695 Fax: 0151 342 9300 Email: garethw@liv.ac.uk — MB BChir 1977 Camb.; FRCP Edin. 1999; MA Camb. 1978, MD 1986; FRCP Lond. 1991 (resigned 1998); MRCP (UK) 1979. Prof. Med. Univ. Liverp. & Hon. Cons. Phys. (Med.) Aintree Hosps. Liverp. Socs: Brit. Diabetes Assn.; (Comm.) Assn. Study Obesity. Prev: R.D. Lawrence Research Fell. Roy. Postgrad. Med. Sch. Lond.

WILLIAMS, Gareth David 39 St Annes Road, Formby, Liverpool L37 7AS — MB BS 1992 Lond. (St. Thos. Hosp. Med. Sch.) Specialist Regist. Anaesth. Leicester Teachg. Hosps.

WILLIAMS, Gareth David Vaughan Old Fire Station, Albert Terrace, Beverley HU17 8JW Tel: 01482 862236 Fax: 01482 861863 — MB ChB 1985 Leeds; FRCGP 1998; MRCGP 1989; DCH Glas. 1988; BSc Leeds 1988; DRCOG 1987.

WILLIAMS, Gareth Haydn 10 Winchmore Drive, Trumpington, Cambridge CB2 2LW — MB ChB 1987 Liverp.

WILLIAMS, Gareth Vaughan Darlington Memorial Hospital, Hollyhurst Road, Darlington DL3 6HX — MB BS 1973 Lond.; FRCP Lond. 1991; MRCP (UK) 1975. Cons. Phys. Darlington Memor. Hosp. Prev: Cons. Phys. Qu. Eliz. Hosp. Gateshead.

WILLIAMS, Gaynor Caroline Holycroft Surgery, The Health Centre, Oakworth Road, Keighley BD21 1SA Tel: 01535 602010 Fax: 01535 691313; Holycroft Surgery, Oakworth Road, Keighley BD21 1SA — MB ChB 1982 Leeds; BSc (Hons.) Leeds 1979, MB ChB 1982. Partner Gen. Pract.

WILLIAMS, Geoffrey Wynne Western Elms Surgery, 317 Oxford Road, Reading RG30 1AT Tel: 0118 959 0257 Fax: 0118 959 7950 — MB BCh 1977 Wales; MRCGP 1981; DRCOG 1980.

WILLIAMS, George (retired) 14 Tiverton Drive, Sale M33 4RJ — MB ChB 1949 St. And.; PhD Manch. 1965; MD St. And. 1957; FRCPath 1973, M 1964. Prev: Reader (Path.) Univ. Manch. & Hon. Cons. Path. Manch. Roy. Infirm.

WILLIAMS, Georgina Mary Court Road Surgery, Court Road, Malvern WR14 3BL Tel: 01684 573161; Hazeldene, 29 Richmond Road, Malvern WR14 1NE Tel: 01684 568297 — MB ChB 1991 Birm.; ChB Birm. 1991; DRCOG 1994; MRCGP 1996. GP Princip.; Sch. Med. Off. Malvern Girls Coll.; Clin. Asst. Gyn. Prev: SHO (O & G) Worcester HA; SHO (Paediat.) Sandwell HA; SHO & Ho. Off. (Med.) E. Birm. Hosp.

WILLIAMS, Geraint Llwyd, TD 20 South Rise, Llanishen, Cardiff CF14 0RH — MD 1970 Wales; MB BCh 1956; FRCOG 1977, M 1964.

WILLIAMS, Geraint Trefor 11 Cyncoed Crescent, Cyncoed, Cardiff CF23 6SW — MB BCh 1973 Wales; BSc (Hons.) Wales 1970, MD 1981, MB BCh (Hons.) 1973; FRCP Lond. 1991; MRCP (UK) 1975; FRCPath 1991, M 1979. Prof. Path. Univ. Wales Coll. Med. Cardiff; Hon. Cons. Path. Univ. Hosp. Wales Cardiff. Socs: Path. Soc. Gt. Brit. & Irel.; Brit. Soc. Gastroenterol. Prev: Lect. (Path.) St. Bart. Hosp. & St. Mark's Hosp. Lond.

WILLIAMS, Gerallt Todmorden Health Centre, Rose Street, Todmorden OL14 5AT Tel: 01706 815126 Fax: 01706 812693; The Lodge, Station Parade, Todmorden OL14 8PU Tel: 0170 681 5437 — MB ChB 1972 Ed.; MRCGP 1976; DObst RCOG 1975.

WILLIAMS, Mr Gerard Trevor 2 Bramway, Bramhall, Stockport SK7 2AP — MB ChB 1979 Bristol; FRCS Eng. 1983; ChM Manchester 1990. Cons. Vasc. Surg., N. Manch. Gen. Hosp. Prev: Regist. (Surg.) Univ. Hosp. S. Manch.

***WILLIAMS, Gethin Llewelyn** Glan Aber, Llanrhaeadr, Denbigh LL16 4LN — MB BCh 1994 Wales.

WILLIAMS, Gillian The Beeches, 67 Lower Olland Street, Bungay NR35 1BZ Tel: 01986 892055 Fax: 01986 895519; The Buck, Low Road, Earsham, Bungay NR35 2AG Tel: 01986 788470 — MB ChB 1971 Manch. (Manch.)

WILLIAMS, Gillian Ann The Surgery, Bramblys, Basingstoke RG24 8ND Tel: 01256 467778; The Surgery, Bramblys Grange, Basingstoke RG21 8UW Tel: 01256 467778 Fax: 01256 842131 — MB BS 1962 Lond.; MRCS Eng. LRCP Lond. 1962. (Westm.) Prev: SHO (O & G), & Cas. & Admissions Off. Roy. W. Sussex Hosp. Chichester; Ho. Phys. Rush Green Hosp. Romford.

WILLIAMS, Gillian Barbara Glyn The Surgery, Rockcliffe Court, Hurworth Place, Darlington DL2 2DS Tel: 01325 720605 — MB ChB 1980 Liverp.; MRCGP 1984; DCH RCS Lond. 1984; DRCOG 1983. GP Darlington.

WILLIAMS, Glenwynne (retired) 6 Houndean Rise, Lewes BN7 1EG Tel: 01273 475952 — MB BS Lond. 1958; MRCS Eng. LRCP Lond. 1958; FFCM 1981, M 1976; MPH Calif. 1968; DPH Sydney 1963; DObst RCOG 1961. Ref. Crematorium. Prev: Dep. Dir. Pub. Health E. Sussex HA.

WILLIAMS, Glyn Roger The Knowe, Templehill, Troon KA10 6BH — MB BS 1971 Lond.; MRCP (UK) 1976; DTM & H Eng. 1973. Cons. Phys. (Infec. Dis.) CrossHo. Hosp. Kilmarnock. Prev: Lect. (Infec. Dis.) Univ. Glas.; Regist. (Microbiol.) Hammersmith Hosp. Lond.; Regist. (Infec. Dis.) Coppetts Wood Hosp. Lond.

WILLIAMS, Mr Gordon 12 Derwent Road, Twickenham TW2 7HQ Tel: 020 8383 3218 Fax: 020 8383 3443 Email: g.williams1@rpons.ac.uk; 12 Derwent Road, Twickenham TW2 7HQ Tel: 020 8383 3218 Fax: 020 8383 3443 Email: gwilliams@hhnt.org — MB BS Lond. 1968; MS Lond. 1987; FRCS Eng. 1973; FRCS Edin 2000. (Univ. Coll. Hosp.) Cons. Surg. Urol. & Transpl. Unit Hammersmith Hosp.; hon Sen. Lect. Inst. of Urol., Middlx. Hosp. Socs: Roy. Soc. Med. (Counc. Urol. Sect.); Bd. of Chairmen Internal Soc. Urol.; Ex Mem. Counc. Brit. Assoc. Urol. Surg. Prev: Sen. Regist. (Urol. & Transpl.) Hammersmith Hosp. Lond.; Sen. Regist. Rotat. (Urol.) Norf. & Norwich Hosp.

WILLIAMS, Gordon Henry Gortnacally, Florence Court, Enniskillen BT92 1DB Tel: 01365 348702 — MB ChB 1975 Liverp.; DRCOG 1981; DCH Eng. 1978.

WILLIAMS, Gordon John Yorkshire Heart Centre, Leeds General Infirmary, Great George St., Leeds LS1 3EX Tel: 0113 392 5794 Fax: 0113 392 5265; Kinvara, 8 Thorp Arch Park, Thorp Arch, Wetherby LS23 7AN Tel: 01937 844516 Fax: 01937 541137 — MB BCh 1967 Wales; FRCP Lond. 1988; FACC 1988. (Cardiff) Cons. Cardiol. Regional Cardiothoracic Centre Killingbeck Hosp. & Seacroft Hosp. Leeds; Hon. Sen. Lect. Med. Univ. Leeds. Socs: Med. Research Soc. & Mem. Brit. Cardiac Soc. Prev: Ho. Phys. Med. Unit Cardiff Roy. Infirm.; Lect. (Cardiol.) Univ. Hosp. Wales Cardiff; Fell. (Paediat. Cardiol.) Hosp. Sick Childr. Toronto, Canada.

WILLIAMS, Graham Percival The Medical Centre, Badgers Crescent, Shipston-on-Stour CV36 4BQ Tel: 01608 661845; Home Farm, Cherington, Shipston-on-Stour CV36 5HS Tel: 01608 686414 — MB BS 1961 Lond.; MB BS (Hons. Distinc. Surg.) Lond. 1961; MRCS Eng. LRCP Lond. 1961; MRCGP 1972; DObst RCOG 1963. (Guy's) Clin. Asst. Ellen Badger Hosp. Shipston-on-Stour; Med. Off. Brit. Schs. Exploring Soc. Expedition. Socs: BMA. Prev: Ho. Off. (O & G) Lambeth Hosp.; Ho. Phys. Orpington Hosp.; Ho. Surg. Guy's Hosp.

WILLIAMS, Graham Richard Molecular Endocrinology Group, Imperial College School Science, Hammersmith Hospital, Du Cane Road, London W12 0NN Tel: 020 8383 3014 Fax: 020 8383 8306 Email: graham.williams@ic.ac.uk — MB BS 1984 Lond.; PhD Birm. 1993; BSc Lond. 1981; MRCP (UK) 1987; FRCP 1999. (St. Thos.) Reader in Trdociology, Imperial Coll. Humesintl Hosp.; Cons. Phys. Hammersmith Hosp. Lond. Prev: Lect. & Regist. (Med.) Qu. Eliz. Hosp. Birm.; Fell. Endocrinol. Harvard Univ. USA.

WILLIAMS, Mr Grant Burkhill Flat 3, 43 Wimpole St., London W1G 8AE Tel: 020 7935 6344 Fax: 020 7935 0477; The Manor of Pertenhall, Pertenhall, Bedford MK44 2SP Tel: 01480 860427 — MB BS Lond. 1957; MSc Lond. 1965, MS 1969; FRCS Eng. 1961; MRCS Eng. LRCP Lond. 1956. (Lond. Hosp.) Cons. Urol. Unit Harley St. Clinic; JP. Socs: Fell. Roy. Soc. Med.; Internat. Soc. Urol.; Eur. Soc. Urol. Prev: Cons. Urol. Char. Cross Hosp. & Roy. Marsden Hosp. Lond.; Sen. Regist. Lond. Hosp. & Inst. Urol. Lond.; Med. Cons. HM Inspretorate of Prisons.

WILLIAMS, Gregory 27 Blacon Point Road, Chester CH1 5LD — MB ChB 1989 Leic.

WILLIAMS, Mr Gregory Joel Peter 210 Castellain Mansions, Castellain Road, London W9 1HD — MB BS 1990 W. Indies; FRCS Eng. 1995.

WILLIAMS, Gwen Elizabeth (retired) 29 Margin Drive, Wimbledon, London SW19 5HA Tel: 020 8946 6640 — MB BCh 1956 Wales; BSc Wales 1952, MB BCh 1956.

WILLIAMS, Gwenlais Mary 14 Forest Close, Wendover, Aylesbury HP22 6BT — MB BS 1980 Lond.; MRCP (UK) 1984; MRCGP 1990;

WILLIAMS

Cert. Family Plann. JCC 1991; DRCOG 1990. GP Principle, Aston Clinton Surg., Aston Clinton, HP22 5LB. Prev: SHO (Neonat.) Oxf.; Regist. Rotat. (Paediat.) Bristol; SHO (O & G) Bath.

WILLIAMS, Gwilym Eryl Owen (retired) 68 Anstruther Road, Norfolk Park, Birmingham B15 3NP Tel: 0121 454 3297 — MD Liverp. 1939, MB ChB (1st cl. Hons.) 1937; FRCP Lond. 1963, M 1942. Hon. Cons. Phys. United Birm. Hosps. Prev: Clin. Lect. Univ. Birm.

WILLIAMS, Gwilym Rees (retired) Hedgerows, 20 Bramley Close, Ledbury HR8 2XP Tel: 01531 2990 — MB BCh 1943 Wales.

WILLIAMS, Harry 62 Old Edinburgh Road, Inverness IV2 3PG Tel: 01463 33536 — MB ChB 1945 St. And.; MD St. And. 1956, MB ChB 1945. (St. And.) Cons. Bacteriol. N. RHB (Scotl.). Socs: Soc. Gen. Microbiol.; Path. Soc. Gt. Brit. Prev: Asst. Lect. Univ. St. And.; Lect. Univ. Durban.

WILLIAMS, Mr Harry William George, OBE (retired) 1 Beau Rivage, Cley, Holt NR25 7RW Tel: 01263 740761 — MRCS Eng. LRCP Lond. 1939; FRCS Ed. 1947. Prev: Med. Adviser to Salvation Army.

WILLIAMS, Haydn John Sundon Medical Centre, 141/144 Sundon Park Rd, Luton LU3 3AH — MB BS 1993 Lond.; BSc Lond. 1990; MRCGP 1997; DRCOG 1996; DGM RCP Lond. 1995. (St. Mary's) Gen. Practitioner. Prev: SHP Palliat. Med., Isabel Hospice Welwyn Garden City; Trainee GP/SHO Lister Hosp. Stevenage VTS; Ho. Off. (Med., Surg. & Orthop.) Heatherwood & Wrexham Pk. Hosp.

WILLIAMS, Helen Catherine 9 Orkney Close, Calcot, Reading RG31 7YW — MB BS 1993 Lond.; MRPharmS 1988. (Charing Cross and Westminster)

WILLIAMS, Helen Diane The Manor House, Clifton-on-Teme, Worcester WR6 6EN; Tel: 01905 760637 Fax: 01905 760811 — BSc (Hons.) Lond. 1977; MB BS Lond. 1981; FFA RCS Eng. 1988. Cons. Anaesth. Worcester Roy. Infirm. Prev: Cons. Anaeth. Hereford; Sen. Regist. (Anaesth.) Qu. Eliz. Hosp. Birm.; Sen. Regist. Brighton HA.

WILLIAMS, Helen Frances 77a Hervey Road, London SE3 8BX — MB ChB 1989 Birm.; BSc Birm. 1988, MB ChB 1989; DRCOG 1994; T(GP) 1994; DGM RCP Lond. 1992. Prev: Trainee GP/SHO Greenwich & Bexley VTS.

WILLIAMS, Helen June 69 Clarence Road, Harborne, Birmingham B17 9JY — MB ChB 1995 Birm.; MB ChB (Hons.) Birm. 1995. (Birm.) SHO (Paediat.) Birm. Childr. Hosp.

WILLIAMS, Helen Mary Sefton Public Health Laboratory, Bowthorpe Road, Norwich NR2 3TX Tel: 01603 611816 Fax: 01603 620190 Email: hwilliams@nhs.phls.uk; Bramley, Chapel St, Barford, Norwich NR9 4AB — MB BCh 1979 Wales; FRCPath 1997; MRCPath 1987. Cons. Microbiologist PHLS Norwich. Socs: Regist. RCPath; Dir, Clin. Audit & Effectiveness RCPath (95-99).

WILLIAMS, Henrietta Megan c/o 41 Chandos Avenue, Ealing, London W5 4EP — MB BS 1985 Lond.; MFFP 1995; MRCGP 1990; Dip GU Med. 1997; DCH RCP Lond. 1990; DRCOG 1988. Prev: Regist. Genito Urin. Med. Radcliffe Infirm. Oxf.; GP Middlx. Lond.; GP Fell. HIV Barnet Frisa Lond.

WILLIAMS, Hilary Elaine 4 Quarry Place, Shrewsbury SY1 1JN Tel: 01743 272666 — MB ChB 1991 Liverp.

WILLIAMS, Hilary Frances 23 Castle Hill Avenue, Berkhamsted HP4 1HJ Tel: 01442 865291 — MB BS Lond. 1954; DObst RCOG 1956. (Middlx.)

WILLIAMS, Hilary Jane Ground Floor Flat, 1 Learmonth Gardens, Edinburgh EH4 1HD Tel: 0131 315 4173 Email: hils@ibm.net — MB ChB 1994 Sheff. Specialist Regist. Infec. Dis. Socs: MRCP (Ed.).

WILLIAMS, Mrs Honour Cynthia Imogen (retired) St. Mary's, High St., Bures CO8 5HZ Tel: 01787 227449 — MB ChB 1947 Birm.; MRCS Eng. LRCP Lond. 1948. Assoc. Specialist (Haemat.) Broomfield Hosp. Chelmsford. Prev: Ho. Phys. Mile End Hosp. Lond.

WILLIAMS, Howard Owen (retired) Roundwood, 3 Ashlyns Road, Frinton-on-Sea CO13 9ET Tel: 01255 672917 — BSc (Anat. & Physiol.) Wales 1941, MB BCh 1944. Prev: Cons. Phys. Whittington Hosp. Lond.

WILLIAMS, Hugh Iestyn Department of Clinical Pathology, General Hospital, Middlesbrough TS1 5JE — MB BChir 1948 Camb.; FRCPath 1977, M 1965; DCP Lond 1958. Cons. Path. S. Tees Health Dist. Socs: Path. Soc. Gt. Brit.; Fell. Roy. Soc. Med. Prev: Sen. Pathol. Inst. Med. Research, Kuala Lumpur, Malaya.

WILLIAMS, Hugh Jeremy Hyatt Grove Court, Upstreet, Canterbury CT3 4DD — MB BS 1970 Lond.; MB BS (Hons.) Lond. 1970; MRCP (U.K.) 1973; MRCPath 1977. (Guy's) Cons. (Haemat.) Maidstone Health Dist. Prev: Sen. Regist. (Haemat.) & Med. Regist. Guy's Hosp. Lond.; Asst. Lect. Dept. Pathol. Middlx. Hosp.

WILLIAMS, Mr Hugh Marshall BUPA hospital Elland, Elland Lane, Elland HX5 9EB Tel: 01484 428392 Fax: 01484 428392 Email: hmw@sunfaid.org; Email: hmw@sunfaid.org — MChOrth Liverp. 1971; MB BS Lond. 1962; FRCS Ed. 1969; FRCS Eng. 1970; MRCS Eng. LRCP Lond. 1962. (Char. Cross) Cons. Orthop. Surg. BUPA Hosp. Elland. Prev: Cons. Orthop. Surg. Huddersfield Roy. Infirm.; Sen. Orthop. Regist. Leeds Regional Train. Scheme; Regist. (Orthop.) Chester Roy. Infirm.

WILLIAMS, Hugh Oliver (retired) 80 Sheepcot Lane, Watford WD25 0EA Tel: 01927 372451 — MRCS Eng. LRCP Lond. 1948. Prev: Med. Dir. StanBoro. Private Hosp.

WILLIAMS, Mr Hugh Patrick 5 Harmont House, 20 Harley St., London W1G 9PH Tel: 020 7636 4406 Fax: 020 7636 5150 — MB ChB 1961 NZ; FRCS Eng. 1970; FCOphth Eng. 1990; DO RCS Eng. 1967; FRCOphth 1990. Cons. Ophth. Surg. Moorfields Eye Hosp. Lond.; Cons. Ophth. St. John & St. Eliz. Hosp. Lond.; Hon. Cons. Ophth. Surg. Moorfields Eye Hosp. Lond. Socs: Fell. Roy. Soc. Med.; Amer. Soc. Cataract & Refractive Surg.; UK & Irel. Soc. Cataract & Refractive Surg. Prev: Cons. Ophth. Surg. N. Middlx. Hosp. Lond.; Sen. Regist. Moorfields Eye Hosp. Lond.; Sen. Regist. Roy. Lond. Hosp.

WILLIAMS, Huw David 191 Clarendon Park Road, Leicester LE2 3AN — MB ChB 1998 Leic.; MB ChB Leic 1998.

WILLIAMS, Mr Huw Owain Llewellyn Royal Glamorgan Hospital, Llantrisant, Pontyclun CF72 8XR; Hendre Wenallt, St Athans Road, Cowbridge CF71 7HY — MB BCh 1982 Wales; FRCS Eng. (Orl.) 1989; FRCS Ed. (Orl.) 1988. Cons. ENT Roy. Glam. Hosp. M. Glam. Prev: Sen. Regist. (ENT) St. Bart. Hosp. Lond.; Regist. (ENT) Roy. Nat. Throat Nose & Ear Hosp. Lond.

WILLIAMS, Huw Powell Tel: 01325 354604 Fax: 01325 775445 Email: huw.williams@gp-j83016.nhs.uk; Mistletoe Cottage, 24 High St, Steeple Ashton, Trowbridge BA14 6EL Tel: 01380 870077 — MB BS 1976 Lond.; BSc Lond. 1973; MRCP (UK) 1980; MRCGP 1982; DRCOG 1981. (St. Mary's) Chairm., W. Wilts. Primary Care Trust Exec. Cmmittee; Clin. Asst. (Cardiol.) Roy. United Hosp. Bath. Socs: Spencer Wells Soc. Prev: Vice Chairm. Wilts. Health Auth.; SHO (Med.) Hammersmith Hosp. Lond.; Vis. Assoc. Prof. Dept. Family Med. Ohio State Univ. Coll. Med. Columbus, USA.

WILLIAMS, Hywel Glan Nant, 70 Cemetery Road, Porth CF39 0BL — MB BS 1972 Lond.; BSc Lond. 1969, MB BS 1972; MRCP (UK) 1978; DCH Eng. 1975; DObst RCOG 1974.

WILLIAMS, Professor Hywel Charles Department Dermatology, Queen's Medical Centre, Nottingham NG7 2UH Tel: 0115 924 9924 Fax: 0115 970 9003 Email: hywel.williams@nottingham.ac.uk; The Garden House, May Lodge Drive, Rufford, Newark NG22 9DE — MB BS 1982 Lond.; BSc Lond. 1979; MSc Lond. 1991; PhD Lond. 1995; FRCP 197. (Charing Cross Hospital Medical School) Prof. (Dermat.-Epidemiol.) Nottm. Socs: Brit. Assn. Dermat.; Pres. Internat. Dermato-Epidemiol. Assn.; Chairm. Brit. Epidermo-Epidemiol. soc. Prev: Sen. Lect. (Dermat.) Nottm.; Wellcome Research Fell. (Dermato-Epidemiol.) St John's Dermat. Centre.

WILLIAMS, Hywel Gareth Morris Craig Yr Wylan, Llanaber, Barmouth LL42 1AJ Tel: 01341 280226 — MB ChB 1961 Liverp.; DObst RCOG 1969. (Liverp.) Sessional Med. Off. Roy. Aero Estab. Llanbedr. Prev: Ho. Phys. & Ho. Surg. Liverp. Roy. Infirm.; Ho. Surg. (Obst.) Chester City Hosp.

WILLIAMS, Hywel Nicholas (retired) Bettws, Parrog, Newport SA42 0RX Tel: 01239 820559 Fax: 01239 820000 Email: bettws@ukonline.co.uk — MB BCh 1961 Wales; FRCGP 1983, M 1975; DObst RCOG 1963. Prev: Sen. Med. Off. Health Profess. Gp. Welsh Off. Cardiff.

WILLIAMS, Mr Hywel Rhys Dept. of Orthopaedics, York District Hospital, Wiggenton Road, York YO31 8HE — MB BCh 1987 Wales; FRCS 1997 ORTH; BSc (Hons.) Wales 1984; FRCS 1997; FRCS Eng. 1992. (Univ. Wales Coll. Med.) Cons. Dept. Orthop., York Dist. Hosp., York. Socs: Elbow & Shoulder Soc.; Brit. Orthop. Assn. Prev: Sen. Regist. St. James Univ. Hosp. Leeds & Leeds Gen. Infirm.; Fell. (Shoulder Surg.) Roy. Berks. Hosp. Reading; Sen. Regist. (Orthop.) St. Jas. Univ. Hosp. Leeds & Leeds Gen. Infirm.

WILLIAMS

WILLIAMS, Mr Hywel Thomas Whitbourne, 226 Malvern Road, St John's, Worcester WR2 4PA — MB BChir 1962 Camb.; MChir Camb. 1976, MA, MB 1962, BChir 1961; FRCS Eng. 1967. (Westm.) Cons. Urol. Worcester Roy. Infirm.

WILLIAMS, Ian Medical Centre, 12A Greggs Wood Road, Tunbridge Wells TN2 3JL Tel: 01892 541444 Fax: 01892 511157; 33 Dornden Drive, Langton Green, Tunbridge Wells TN3 0AE Tel: 01892 863040 — BM BCh 1982 Wales; MRCGP 1986; DRCOG 1986.

WILLIAMS, Ian Colin Martin The Health Centre, Green Lane, Corwen LL21 0AR Tel: 01490 412362 Email: ian.williams1@virgin.net — MB BCh 1989 Wales; MRCGP, 1984; DA. (University of Wales Coll. of Med.) GP Princip.; Clin. Asst. (Anaesth.).

WILLIAMS, Ian Geoffrey Department Sexually Transmitted Diseases, Royal Freeord University College Medical School, Mortimer Market Centre, Mortimer Market, London WC1E 6AU Tel: 020 7380 9893 Fax: 020 7380 9669; 263 Ice Wharf, 17 New Wharf Road, London N1 9RF Tel: 020 7278 6427 — MB ChB 1980 Manch.; BSc (Hons.) (Physiol.) Manch. 1977; MRCP (UK) 1984; FRCP 1998. (Manchester) Sen. Lect. (Genitourin. Med.) Roy. Freeord Univ. Coll. Med. Sch. & Camden & Islington Community Servs. NHS Trust & Univ. Coll. Lond. Hosps. Trust. Socs: MSSVO; (Exec. Comm.) BHIVA. Prev: Lect. (Genitourin. Med.) Univ. Coll. & Middlx. Hosp. Med. Sch. Lond.; Regist. (Med.) Qu. Alexandra & St. Mary's Hosps. Portsmouth; SHO (Med.) Univ. Hosp. S. Manch.

WILLIAMS, Ian Grindon Wellside Surgery, 45 High Street, Sawtry, Huntingdon PE28 5SU Tel: 01487 830340 Fax: 01487 832753; 22 Highfield Avenue, Alconbury Weston, Huntingdon PE28 4JS Tel: 01480 890002 Email: iang-williams@email.msn.com — MB BChir 1980 Camb.; MA Camb. 1982; AFOM RCP Lond. 1992; MRCGP 1985; DRCOG 1984. (Camb.) Div. Surg. St. Johns Ambul.; (Occupat. Health Phys.) Hinchingbrooke Healthcare NHS Trust. Socs: BMA; Soc. Occupat. Med.; Soc. Internet. in Med. Prev: Trainee GP P'boro. VTS; SHO (A & E) P'boro. Dist. Hosp.; Ho. Off. Addenbrooke's Hosp. Camb. & Huntingdon Co. Hosp.

WILLIAMS, Ian Lear Department of Cardiology, King's College Hospital, Denmark Hill, London SE5 9RS; 55 Nightingale Road, Farncombe, Godalming GU7 2HU Tel: 01483 420568 Fax: 01483 420568 Email: ilw1167@aol.com — MB BChir 1993 Camb.; MRCP (UK) 1995. (Camb. & St. Geo.) Specialist Regist. Rotat. (Cardiol.) Roy. Sussex Co. Hosp. Brighton. Prev: research fell. (Cardiol.) King's Coll. Hosp. Lond.; SHO (Cardiol.) Soton. Gen. Hosp.; SHO Rotat. (Gen. Med.) St. Richard's Hosp. Chichester.

WILLIAMS, Ian Michael 15 Spowart Avenue, Llanelli SA15 3HY — MB BCh 1986 Wales.

WILLIAMS, Ian Peter Argraig, Ael Y Garth, Caernarfon LL55 1HA — MB BCh 1991 Wales.

WILLIAMS, Ian Richard c/o Crofton Cottage, Broad St., Cuckfield, Haywards Heath RH17 5DX — MB ChB 1988 Bristol.

WILLIAMS, Ian Richard 10 Chepstow Close, Chippenham SN14 0XP — MB ChB 1993 Leic.

WILLIAMS, Ian Roger 18 Montagu Road, Formby, Liverpool L37 1LA — MB ChB 1966 Ed.; FRCP Lond. 1983, M 1969.

WILLIAMS, Ian Thomas Lloyd's Bank Ltd., 25 Camberwell Green, London SE5 7AB — MB BS 1966 Lond.; MRCS Eng. LRCP Lond. 1966. (King's Coll. Hosp.)

WILLIAMS, Ifor Pennant (retired) Primrose Cottage, Walberswick, Southwold IP18 6UP — MB BCh 1945 Camb.; MRCP Lond. 1947; DMRD Eng. 1952.

WILLIAMS, Ingeborg Eveline Ilse (retired) 6 Southcliff, Cliff Road, Falmouth TR11 4LY Tel: 01326 314676 — MD 1945 Hamburg; MRCS Eng. LRCP Lond. 1957; MRCPsych 1973; DPM Eng. 1964. Prev: Cons. Psychiat. (Psychogeriat. Med.) Barncoose Hosp. Redruth & St. Lawrence's Hosp. Bodmin.

WILLIAMS, Iola Ann Arrowe Park Hospital, Arrowe Park Road, Upton, Wirral CH49 5PE Tel: 0151 678 5111 Fax: 0151 606 9609 — MB BCh 1978 Wales; MRCOG 1984. Cons. O & G Arrowe Pk. Hosp. Merseyside. Prev: Sen. Regist. (O & G) Roy. United Hosp. Bath & Bristol Matern. Hosp.; Research Regist. (Reproduc. Endocrinol.) Roy. Free Hosp. Lond.; Regist. (O & G) P.ss Anne Hosp. Soton.

WILLIAMS, Iolo Gwerfyl (retired) 39 Radcliffe Road, Croydon CR0 5QJ Tel: 020 8654 5424 — MB BS 1940 Lond.; FRCP Lond. 1972, M 1948; MRCS Eng. LRCP Lond. 1938; FRCPath 1965, M 1963. Prev: Cons. Path. Woolwich Hosp. Gp.

WILLIAMS, Isobel Petrie St. Albans & Hemel Hampstead NHS Trust, Hemel Hampstead General Hospital, Hillfield Rd, Hemel Hampstead HP2 4AD Tel: 01442 287092 Fax: 01442 287092; The White Cottage, 15 High Road, Essendon, Hatfield AL9 6HT — MD Lond. 1983, MB BS 1965; FRCP 1987; MRCP (UK) 1971; DCH Eng. 1968. (St. Geo.) Cons. Phys. St. Albans & Hemel Hempstead NHS Trust; Chair STC G (I) M Lond., (N.).

WILLIAMS, Ivan Arthur (retired) Bucklands, Buckland-tout-Saints, Kingsbridge TQ7 2DS Tel: 01548 853141 — MB BS Lond. 1956; FRCP Lond. 1975, M 1959; DPhysMed. Eng. 1959. Prev: Cons. Rheum. & Rehabil. Tunbridge Wells HA.

WILLIAMS, Ivon The Hermitage, 32-34 Preston St., Shrewsbury SY2 5NY — MB BS 1962 Lond.; FFA RCS Eng. 1971; DA Eng. 1965. (St. Mary's) Cons. (Anaesth.) Roy. Shrewsbury Hosp. Prev: Regist. (Anaesth.) Char. Cross Hosp. Lond.; Sen. Regist. (Anaesth.) Char. Cross Hosp. Lond.; Specialist Anaesth. Groote Schuur Hosp. Cape Town.

WILLIAMS, Jacqueline Sheila 1 Carsons Close, Stretton on Fosse, Moreton-in-Marsh GL56 9SJ Tel: 01608 664205 Email: d.j.williams@gateway — MB ChB 1989 Birm.; MRCGP 1993; DRCOG 1991. (Birm.) GP Retainer. Socs: BMA. Prev: Trainee GP Harrogate; SHO (Gen. Med., Paediat., O & G & Psychiat.) Dumfries & Galloway Roy. Infirm.

WILLIAMS, Mr James Leigh Department of Ortho, Northern General Hospital, Herries Road, Sheffield S5 7AV; 40 Winchester Road, Sheffield S10 4EE Tel: 01142 302120 Fax: 01142 302120 — MB ChB 1992 Sheff.; FRCS 1997; FRCS 1997 (Ed.); BMedSci 1991. Specialist Regist. Orthop. Surg. N.ern Gen. Hosps. hef. Socs: BOA.

WILLIAMS, Jane Hollyhedge Farm, Main Road, Weston, Crewe CW2 5LD — MB ChB 1969 Manch.; DObst RCOG 1975; DPM Manch. 1973. Prev: Trainee GP Bolton VTS; Regist. (Psychiat.) Withington Hosp. Manch.

WILLIAMS, Jane Elizabeth 34 St Agnes Road, Cardiff CF14 4AP — MB BCh 1995 Wales.

WILLIAMS, Jane Mary 184 Norton Leys, Hillside, Rugby CV22 5RY — MB ChB 1979 Manch.; BSc St. And. 1976; MBA (Pub. Sector Managem.) Aston 1994.

WILLIAMS, Jane Stanley 2 Mallard Way, Rest Bay, Porthcawl CF36 3TS Tel: 0165 671 4031 — MB BCh 1951 Wales; BSc. MB BCh Wales 1951; DA Eng. 1954. (Cardiff) Prev: Sessional Clin. Med. Off. Mid Glam. Health Auth.

WILLIAMS, Janet 59 Sevenoaks Road, Orpington BR6 9JN — MB BS 1979 Lond. GP Orpington. Prev: Trainee GP Portsmouth VTS; Ho. Phys. Pembury Hosp.; Ho. Surg. Orpington Hosp.

WILLIAMS, Janet Barton House Health Centre, 233 Albion Road, London N16 9JT Tel: 020 7249 5511 Fax: 020 7254 8985; 172 Kyverdale Road, London N16 6PU Tel: 020 8806 1103 — MB ChB 1985 Manch.; MRCGP 1993; MRCPsych 1991.

WILLIAMS, Jason David Louis 3 Westmount Court, Corringway, London W5 3AE — MB ChB 1997 Manch.

WILLIAMS, Jeffrey Collwyn Richmond Clinic, 172 Caerleon Road, Newport NP19 7FY — MB BCh 1991 Wales; MRCGP 1995; DRCOG 1995.

WILLIAMS, Mr Jeremy Howard Accident and Emergency Department, West Wales General Hospital, Carmarthen SA31 2AF Tel: 01267 227007 Fax: 01267 227007; 6 Clos Yr Onnen, Abergwili, Carmarthen SA31 2JT Tel: 01267 238707 Email: jaydoc4@aol.com — MB BS 1986 Lond.; MA Oxf. 1992; FRCS 1992; FFAEM 1998. (St Bart.) Cons. (A & E) W. Wales Gen. Hosp.; Honourary Cons. A+E Morriston Hosp.,Swansea; Honourary Sen. Lect., Swansea Unviversity. Socs: Fell. Fac. A&E Med.; Fell. Fac. Pre Hosp. Care; Brit. Assn. Accid. & Emerg. Med. Prev: Sen. Regist. (A & E) Morriston Hosp. Swansea; Regist. (A & E) Russells Hall Hosp.; Regist. (A & E) Hosp. Birm.

WILLIAMS, Joanna Caroline 21 Golding Close, Wells BA5 2FL — BM BS 1998 Nottm.; BM BS Nottm 1998; BMedSci. (Notts)

WILLIAMS, Joanne Marie Clarendon House, Clarendon St., Hyde SK14 2AQ — MB ChB 1987 Manch.

WILLIAMS, John (retired) Holeyn Hall, Wylam NE41 8BQ Tel: 01661 853673 — MD 1964 Newc.; MB BS Durh. 1955; FRCGP 1980, M 1973. Prev: Hosp. Pract. Newc. Gen. Hosp.

WILLIAMS

WILLIAMS, John Arfon The Newlands, Penglais Road, Aberystwyth SY23 2EU — MB BS 1941 Lond.; MRCS Eng. LRCP Lond. 1941; MRCOG 1952, DObst 1948. (Guy's) Prev: Ho. Surg. Preston Hall Hosp. Maidstone; Ho. Phys. Joyce Green Hosp. Dartford; Squadron Ldr. RAFVR.

WILLIAMS, John Arthur 22 Severn Street, Welshpool SY21 7AD Tel: 01938 552222 — MB BS 1977 Lond.; BDS 1980; LDS RCS Eng. 1980; MRCS Eng. LRCP Lond. 1977; FDS RCPS Glas. 1980. (St. Bart.)

WILLIAMS, John Benedict 22 Bright Trees Road, Geddington, Kettering NN14 1BS — MB ChB 1996 Ed.

WILLIAMS, Professor John David Institute of Nephrology, University of Wales College of Medicine, Newport Road, Cardiff CF24 0SZ Tel: 029 2049 2233 Fax: 029 2045 3643 Email: williamsjd4@cf.ac.uk — MB BCh Wales 1973; MD Wales 1985; FRCP Lond. 1988; MRCP (UK) 1977. Prof. Nephrol. & Hon. Dir. Inst. Nephrol. Univ. Wales Coll. Med. & Cardiff Roy. Infirm. Prev: Postdoctural Research Fell. Harvard Med. Sch. Boston, USA.

WILLIAMS, John David Queen Elizabeth Hospital, Gayton Road, King's Lynn PE30 4ET Tel: 01553 613726; The Pightle, Leziate Drove, Ashwicken, King's Lynn PE32 1LT — MB BChir 1977 Camb.; MB BChir Camb. 1976; MA Camb. 1977; FRCP 1997, MRCP 1980. (Camb. & St. Bart.) Cons. Rheum. Qu. Eliz. Hosp. King's Lynn. Socs: Brit. Soc. Rheum. Prev: Sen. Regist. (Rheum.) Roy. Free & N. Middlx. Hosps. Lond.; Wellcome Research Fell. St. Bart. Hosp. Lond.; SHO Roy. Postgrad. Med. Sch. Lond.

WILLIAMS, John David 69 Victoria Park Road, London E9 7NA Tel: 020 8986 7046 — MD 1964 Liverp.; BSc Lond. 1951; MB ChB 1956; MRCP (UK) 1986; FRCPath 1981, M 1965; DCP Lond 1961. (Liverp.) Emerit. Prof. (Med. Microbiol.) The Univ. Lond.; Edr. Antibiotics Chemother. & Internat. Jl. Antimicrobial Agents. Socs: Past Pres. Internat. Soc. Chemother.; Past Pres. Federat. Europ. Soc. Chemother. & Infect.; Past Pres. Brit. Soc. Chemother. Prev: Prof. (Med. Microbiol.) Lond. Hosp. Med. Coll.

WILLIAMS, John David Gwynne (retired) 9 Castle Street, Ruthin LL15 1DP Tel: 01824 703242 Email: johndgwilliams@hotmail.com — MB ChB 1958 Manch.; DObst RCOG 1962. p/t Examg. Med. Practitioners, Disbility Med., Benefit Agency, N. Wales.

WILLIAMS, John Desmond Stablehouse, Wilderness Road, Chislehurst BR7 5EY Tel: 020 8467 3896 — MB BS 1949 Lond.; FRCP Lond. 1973, M 1954; MRCS Eng. LRCP Lond. 1949. (Guy's) Cons. Phys. Qu. Mary's Hosp. Sidcup & Orpington Hosp. Prev: Sen. Med. Regist., & Ho. Phys. & Asst. Ho. Surg. Guy's Hosp.; Research Assoc. in Med. Univ. Illinois Chicago U.S.A.

WILLIAMS, John Edmund 29 Margin Drive, Wimbledon, London SW19 5HA Tel: 020 8946 6640 — MB BCh 1955 Wales; BSc Wales 1952, MB BCh 1955; FRCP Ed. 1969, M 1961; FRCP Lond. 1982; FRCR 1975; FFR 1962 (Hon.) FFR RCSI 1988; DMRD Eng. 1960. (Cardiff) Dir. Depts. Diag. Radiol. St. Geo. Hosp. Lond.; Sen. Lect. & Chairm. Radiol. Teach. & Research Unit St. Geo. Hosp. Med. Sch. Lond. Socs: Fell. Roy. Soc. Med.; Brit. Inst. Radiol. Prev: Cons. Radiol. United Cardiff Hosps. & Clin. Teach. in Diag.; Radiol. Welsh Nat. Sch. Med.; Asst. Prof. Radiol. Univ. Washington, Seattle, U.S.A.

WILLIAMS, John Ellis 15 Edward Nicholl Court, Waterloo Road, Cardiff CF23 9BW Tel: 029 2049 3715 — MB BS 1985 Lond.; FRCA 1991. Cons. Anaesth. & Pain Managem. Roy. Marsden Hosp. Lond. Prev: Sen. Regist. (Anaesth.) Oxf. RHA; Vis. Asst. Prof. Dept. Anaesth. Univ. Maryland Hosp. Baltimore, Maryland, USA; Regist. (Anaesth.) St. Thos. Hosp. Lond.

WILLIAMS, John Frederick 62 West Stockwell Street, Colchester CO1 1HE Tel: 01206 369249 Fax: 01206 710661 — MB BS 1951 Lond.; BA Open 1991; MRCS Eng. LRCP Lond. 1951. (Westm.)

WILLIAMS, John Gareth Dros Dro, 5 Frondeg, Llanfairpwllgwyngyll LL61 5AX Tel: 01248 714831 — MB ChB 1966 Liverp.; MRCS Eng. LRCP Lond. 1966; FFR 1972; DMRD Liverp. 1970. (Liverp.) Cons. Radiol. Ysbyty Gwynedd, Bangor. Prev: Sen. Regist. (Radiol.) Univ. Hosp. of Wales Cardiff; Sen. Regist. Radiol. Alder Hey Childrs. Hosp. Liverp.

WILLIAMS, John Gareth The Grange Medical Centre, 39 Leicester Road, Nuneaton CV11 6AB Tel: 024 7632 2810 Fax: 024 7632 2820 — MB ChB 1986 Leic.; DCH RCP Lond. 1991.

WILLIAMS, John Gary Department of Health, NHS - ME, Quarry House, Quarry Hill, Leeds LS2 7UE Tel: 0113 254 5859; 47 Bryan Street, Farsley, Pudsey LS28 5JP — MB BS 1966 Lond.; PhD Adelaide 1992; MRCS Eng. LRCP Lond. 1966; FFA RACS 1977; FFA RCS Eng. 1972; DRCOG 1968. Sen. Med. Off. NHS - Managem. Exec. Leeds; Vis. Lect. (Med. Anthropol.) Dept. of Sociology & Social Anthropol. Univ. Keele. Socs: BMA. Prev: Sen. Specialist (Anaesth.) Roy. Adelaide Hosp. Austral.

WILLIAMS, John Gordon Halton General Hospital (NHS Trust), Runcorn WA7 2DA Tel: 01928 714567 Fax: 01928 753119 — MB ChB 1975 Liverp.; MD Liverp. 1982; FRCP Lond. 1993; MRCP (UK) 1978. Cons. Phys. Halton Hosp. Runcorn. Socs: Y Gymdeithas Feddygol & Brit. Thoracic Soc. Prev: Sen. Regist. BRd.green Hosp. Liverp.; Univ. Research Regist. Liverp. Univ.

WILLIAMS, Professor John Gordon School of Postgrad. Studies in Med. & Health Care, Maes-y-Gwernen Hall, Morriston Hospital, Swansea SA6 6NL Tel: 01792 703531 Fax: 01792 797310 Email: john.williams@pgms.wales.nhs.uk; Harford House, 3 Richmond Villas, Ffynone, Swansea SA1 6DQ Tel: 01792 462424 — MB BChir 1971 Camb.; MSc Lond. 1978; MA Camb. 1971; FRCP Lond. 1984; MRCP (UK) 1972. (St. Thos.) Prof. & Dir. Sch. of Postgrad. Studies Med. & Health Carelechyd Mogannwg Heath Auth., Univ. Wales Swans.; Cons. Gastroenterol. Neath Gen. Hosp.; Hon. Assoc. (Postgrad. Studies) Univ. Wales Coll. of Med. Socs: Brit. Soc. Gastroenterol.; Amer. Gastroenterol. Assn. Prev: Prof. of Naval Med. & Cons. Phys. RN Hosp. Haslar Gosport; Cons. Phys. RN Hosp. Plymouth; Hon. Sen. Regist. St. Thos. Hosp. Lond.

WILLIAMS, John Gordon St Lukes Surgery, Warren Road, Guildford GU1 3JH Tel: 01483 572364 Fax: 01483 304379; 148 London Road, Guildford GU1 1UF Email: j.g.williams@surrey.ac.uk — MB BChir 1972 Camb.; FRCGP 2001; MRCP (UK) 1974; MRCGP 1990; FRACP 1978. (Guys/Camb.) Prev: Regist. (Med.) Roy. Brisbane Hosp. Qu.sland; Austral.; Ho. Off. (Med.) Hillingdon Hosp. Middlx.; Ho. Surg. Guy's Hosp. Lond.

WILLIAMS, Mr John Graham New Cross Hospital, Wolverhampton WV10 0QP Tel: 01902 307999; The Homestead, Ash Hill, Compton, Wolverhampton WV3 9DR Email: jgw_chalponts@msn.com — MB BCh 1981 Wales; BSc (Human Anat.) Wales, 1978, MCh 1989, MB BCh 1981; FRCS Eng. 1985. Cons. Surg. Roy. Wolverhampton Hosps. NHS Trust. Socs: Assn. Coloproct. GB & Irel.; Assn. of Surg. BrSoc Gl. Prev: Lect. (Surg.) Univ. Birm. Qu. Eliz. Hosp.; Research Fell. Div. Colon & Rectal Surg. Univ. Minnesota, USA; Regist. (Surg.) Univ. Hosp. Wales Cardiff.

WILLIAMS, John Griffith Uplands Surgery, 48 Sketty Road, Uplands, Swansea SA2 0LJ Tel: 01792 298554 / 298555 Fax: 01792 280416; 145 Derwen Fawr Road, Swansea SA2 8ED — MB BCh 1961 Wales; DObst RCOG 1966.

WILLIAMS, John Haydn (retired) Y Bwthyn, Warwick Road, Leek Wootton, Warwick CV35 7QR Tel: 01926 853071 — MB BS Lond. 1952; DIH Soc. Apoth. Lond. 1959; MFOM RCP Lond. 1979. Prev: Regional Med. Off. Lond. Midl. Region BR.

WILLIAMS, John Henry Marlborough Medical Practice, The Surgery, George Lane, Marlborough SN8 4BY Tel: 01672 512187 Fax: 01672 516809 — MB BS 1991 Lond.; MRCGP 1995; DRCOG 1994; DFFP 1994. (St. George's) Prev: GP/Regist. Market HarBoro.; SHO (Paediat. & Med.) Leicester Roy. Infirm.; SHO (Rheum.) Leicester Gen. Hosp.

WILLIAMS, John Holman Bentley (retired) Eastbourne House, 118 Eastbourne Road, St Austell PL25 4SS Tel: 01726 65094 — MA BM BCh Oxf. 1957; DObst RCOG 1959; FRCGP 1982, M 1965. Prev: Med. Dir. Mt. Edgcumbe Hospice St. Austell.

WILLIAMS, John Humphrey Countess of Chester NHS Trust, Liverpool Road, Chester CH1 2BQ; The Spinney, Dicksons Drive, Newton, Chester CH2 2BR Tel: 01244 365000 — MB ChB 1968 Liverp.; FRCOG 1988, M 1975. Cons. (O & G) Chester HA.

WILLIAMS, John Ivor (retired) Cae Llwyd, Uwch-y-Garreg, Machynlleth SY20 8RP Tel: 01654 702165 — MB ChB 1932 Ed. Prev: Resid. Surg. Off. P'boro. & Dist. Memor. Hosp.

WILLIAMS, John Justin Caedre House, 38 Park St., Bridgend CF31 4AX Tel: 01656 2721 — MB BS 1953 Lond. (St. Geo.) Prev: Ho. Surg. Chase Farm Hosp. Enfield; Res. Obst. Off. & Ho. Phys. Neath Gen. Hosp.

WILLIAMS, Mr John Leighton (retired) White Croft, 170 Watt Lane, Sheffield S10 5QW Tel: 0114 230 4568 — MB BS 1949 Lond.; FRCS Eng. 1954. Prev: Cons. Urol. Surg. Roy. Hallamsh. Hosp. Sheff.

WILLIAMS, John Llewellyn Bronglais General Hospital, Aberystwyth, Aberystwyth Tel: 01970 672 3131 — MB BChir 1990 Camb.; MRCP (UK) 1992. Cons. Paediat.

WILLIAMS, Mr John Llewellyn, CBE Maxillofacial Unit, St. Richards Hospital, Chichester PO19 4SE Tel: 01243 831531 Fax: 01243 831544 Email: john.williams@tws-tr.sthames.nhs.uk; Cookscroft, Bookers Lane, Earnley, Chichester PO20 7JG Tel: 01243 513671 Fax: 01243 536108 — MB BS Lond. 1967; BDS Lond. 1961; FRCS Ed. 1991; MRCS Eng. LRCP Lond. 1967; FDS RCS Eng. 1966, LDS 1961; FRCS 1997; FRCA 1999. (Guy's) Cons. Oral & Maxillofacial Surg Roy.W. sussex NHS Trust, Worthing & S.lands NHS Trusr; Hon. Cons. Oral & Maxillofacial Surg. Qu. Mary's Hosp. Roehampton; Hon. Cons. Maxillofacial Surg. King Edwd. VII Hosp. Midhurst; Chairm. NCEPOD. Socs: Fell. Brit. Assn. Oral & Maxillofacial Surg. Pres. Elect; Pres Europ. Assn. Cranio-Maxillofacial Surg.; Pres. Brit. Assn. Oral.& Maxillofacial Surg. Prev: Vice-Pres. RCS Eng.; Dean Fac. Dent. Surg. RCS Eng.; Edr. Brit. Jl. Oral & Maxillofacial Surg.

***WILLIAMS, John Parry** 33 Durley Dean Road, Selly Oak, Birmingham B29 6SA — MB ChB 1995 Birm.

WILLIAMS, John Penfold Sheepmarket Surgery, Ryhall Road, Stamford PE9 1YA Tel: 01780 753151; Glebe Cottage, 45 West Street, Easton on The Hill, Stamford PE9 3LS Tel: 01780 481175 — MB BChir 1981 Camb.; MA Camb. 1982, BA 1978; MRCGP 1986; DRCOG 1985; DCH RCP Lond. 1984. (Camb. & St. Barts.) GP Stamford. Prev: Chief Medic Raleigh Expedition Patagonia; Trainee GP Overton, Hants.

WILLIAMS, Mr John Peter Rhys, MBE Princess of Wales Hospital, Bridgend CF31 1RQ; Llansannor Lodge, Llansannor, Cowbridge CF71 7RX Tel: 01446 772590 — MB BS 1973 Lond.; MRCS Eng. LRCP Lond. 1973; FRCS Ed. 1980. (St. Mary's) Cons. Trauma & Orthop. P.ss of Wales Hosp. Bridgend. Socs: Brit. Orthop. Assn.; BASK; BOSTA. Prev: Sen. Regist. (Orthop.) St. Mary's Hosp. Lond.; Regist. (Orthop.) & Regist. (Gen. Surg.) Univ. Hosp. Wales Cardiff.

WILLIAMS, Mr John Pritchard, RD (retired) Hillside Cottage, Queens Corner, Iping, Midhurst GU29 0PL Tel: 01428 741254 Fax: 01428 741254 — MB BChir 1950 Camb.; MChir Camb. 1959, MB BChir 1950; FRCS Eng. 1956. Hon. Cons. Urol. the Army. Prev: Cons. Urol. St. Peter's Hosps. & Greenwich Dist. Hosp. Lond. & King Edwd. VII Hosp. Off. Lond.

WILLIAMS, John Pritchard Gwernhefin, Glanhwfa Road, Llangefni LL77 7FA Tel: 01248 723260 — MB BCh 1962 Wales; MRCOG 1969, DObst 1964; FRCOG 1982. (Cardiff) Cons. O & G St. David's Hosp. Bangor. Socs: Welsh Obst. & Gyn. Soc. Prev: Regist. HM Stanley Hosp. St. Asaph & S.. Gen Hosp. Glas.; Sen. Regist. St. David's Hosp. Bangor.

WILLIAMS, John Rainsbury Erne Hospital, Enniskillen BT74 6AY Tel: 02866 324711 Fax: 02866 329655; Rossfad House, Ballinamallard, Enniskillen BT94 2LS Tel: 02866 388505 — MB BCh BAO 1966 Dub.; FRCP Lond., FRCP Ed. 1988; MRCP (UK) 1971. Cons. Phys. Erne Hosp. Enniskillen. Prev: Med. Specialist Kilimanjaro Christian Med. Centre Moshi, Tanzania.

WILLIAMS, Mr John Richard Department of Trauma and Orthopaedics/Surgery, The Medical School, Newcastle upon Tyne NE2 4HH Tel: 0191 222 5659 Fax: 0191 222 5659 Email: j.r.williams@ncl.ac.uk; 5 The Orchard, Coylam, Wylam NE41 8BS Tel: 01661 853649 Email: williams_john@msn.com — BM BCh 1986 Oxf.; MA Oxf. 1983; BM BCh 1986, DM 1997; FRCS Eng. 1990; FRCS (Orth.) Eng. 1997. (Oxford) Sen.Lect.Trauma.Orthop.Surg.; Hon. Cons. Orthop. Surg. Newc. upon Tyne Hosp. NHS Trust. Socs: Brit. Orthop. Assn.; Brit. Orthop. Research Soc.; Brit. Soc. Surg. Hand. Prev: Fell. Wrightington Hosp.; Regist. Nuffield Orthop. Centre NHS Trust Oxf.; Regist. (Orthop.) Stoke Mandeville Hosp. Aylesbury.

WILLIAMS, John Richard The Surgery, The Street, Holbrook, Ipswich IP9 2PZ Tel: 01473 328263 Fax: 01473 327185; Broadacres, Shotley Road, Chelmondiston, Ipswich IP9 1EE Tel: 01473 780565 — MB BS 1975 Lond.; MRCS Eng. LRCP Lond. 1975. (Char. Cross)

WILLIAMS, John Richard Burton (retired) The Old Bell House, London Road, St Ippolyts, Hitchin SG4 7NE Tel: 01462 454198 — MB BS 1946 Lond.; MD (Path.) Lond. 1952; MRCS Eng. LRCP Lond. 1946; FRCPath 1969, M 1964. Hon. Cons. Haemat. Lister Hosp. Stevenage. Prev: Cons. Haemat. Lister Hosp. Stevenage & Luton & Dunstable Hosp.

WILLIAMS, Mr John Sheldon The Health Centre, 10 Gresham Road, Oxted RH8 0BQ Tel: 01883 714361 Fax: 01883 722679 — MB BS 1979 Lond.; FRCS Eng. 1984; DRCOG 1985; DMJ (Clin.) 1996. (Kings Coll. Lond.) Police Surg. Surrey Police. Prev: Surg. Regist. W. Middlx. Univ. Hosp. Hounslow.; SHO (Med.) S. Middlx. Hosp.

WILLIAMS, Mr John Tanat 33 Coalway Road, Penn, Wolverhampton WV3 7LU Tel: 01902 341187 — MB BCh 1966 Wales; FRCS Ed. 1972. Cons. Surg. Russells Hall Hosp. Dudley. Socs: Fell. Assn. Surgs. Gt. Brit. & Irel.; Brit. Soc. Gastroenterol. Prev: Resid. Surgic Off. St. Marks Hosp. Lond.; Sen. Regist. Middlx. Hosp. Lond.; Post Grad. Fell. Univ. Calif. San Francisco.

WILLIAMS, John Tudor Newtons, The Health Centre, Heath Road, Haywards Heath RH16 3BB Tel: 01444 412280 — MB BS 1962 Lond.

WILLIAMS, John Walter Trades Lane Health Centre, Causewayend, Coupar Angus, Blairgowrie PH13 9DP Tel: 01828 627312 Fax: 01828 628253 — MB ChB 1968 St. And.; MRCGP 1975; DCH RCPS Glas. 1971; DObst RCOG 1969.

WILLIAMS, Mr John Wyn 104 Ffordd Naddyn, Glan Conwy, Colwyn Bay LL28 5BJ — MB BChir 1982 Camb.; MA Camb. 1984, MB BChir 1982; FRCS Lond. 1986; FRCR 1990.

WILLIAMS, Jonathan Adam Galloway Horse Fair Surgery, 12 Horse Fair, Banbury OX16 0AJ Tel: 01295 259484 Fax: 01295 279293; Holly Tree Farm House, Horley, Banbury OX15 6BJ — MB BS 1981 Lond.; DRCOG 1987; DCH RCP Lond. 1985.

WILLIAMS, Jonathan Craig 4 Bryn Celyn, Pontardawe, Swansea SA8 4LG — MB BCh 1993 Wales.

WILLIAMS, Jonathan David Portishead Health Centre, Portishead, Bristol BS20 6AQ Tel: 01275 847474 — MB ChB 1985 Bristol; 2001 LF Hom (Med); MRCGP 1989; DRCOG 1988; DCH RCP Lond. 1987.

WILLIAMS, Jonathan Graham Mill Top Farm, Mill Lane, Goosnargh, Preston PR3 2JX Tel: 01772 865414 — MB BChir 1974 Camb.; MA Camb. 1974; MRCS Eng. LRCP Lond. 1973; FFA RCS Eng. 1979. (Kings Coll. Hosp.) Cons. Anaesth. Preston HA. Prev: Sen. Regist. (Anaesth.) NW RHA; Lect. (Anaesth.) Univ. Calgary, Canada.

WILLIAMS, Jonathan Hyatt 43 Dyke Road Avenue, Hove BN3 6QA Tel: 01273 555284 Fax: 01273 563155 — MB BS 1967 Lond.; MRCS Eng. LRCP Lond. 1967; FFA RCS Eng. 1971; DA Eng. 1969. (Guy's) Cons. Anaesth. Brighton Health Dist. Socs: Assn. Anaesths.; BMA; Brit. Soc. Study Addic. Prev: Asst. Prof. Anaesth. Pk.land Hosp. Dallas, USA; Sen. Regist. King's Coll. Hosp. Lond.

WILLIAMS, Jonathan Owen Heaton 20 Wharton Street, London WC1X 9PT — MB BS 1992 Lond.; BSc 1980; MSC 1982; MRCGP 1996. (St Barts Lond) Hon Research Fell. UCL.

WILLIAMS, Jonathan Paul 24 Railway Drive, Sturminster Marshall, Wimborne BH21 4DQ — BM 1986 Soton. SHO (Paediat.) Poole Gen. Hosp.

WILLIAMS, Jonathan Wyn Meddygfa'r Llan, Church Surgery, Portland Street, Aberystwyth SY23 2DX Tel: 01970 624855 Fax: 01970 625824 — MB BS 1980 Lond.; MRCGP 1991; DRCOG 1984; DCH RCP Lond. 1983.

WILLIAMS, Joseph Brian (retired) 3 Maeshendre, Waunfawr, Aberystwyth SY23 3PR Tel: 01970 612210 — MB BCh 1957 Wales; DObst RCOG 1961. Prev: Ho. Surg. & Ho. Phys. Caerphilly & Dist. Hosp.

WILLIAMS, Joyce Kathleen Kingsfield Medical Centre, 146 Alcester Road South, Kings Heath, Birmingham B14 6AA Tel: 0121 444 2054 Fax: 0121 443 5856 — MB ChB 1985 Birm.; DCH RCP Lond. 1990; DRCOG 1989.

WILLIAMS, Judith Department of Paediatrics, Birmingham Heartlands Hospital Trust, Bordesley Green E., Birmingham B9 5SS Tel: 0121 766 6611 Fax: 0121 773 6458; The Dog House, 101 Old Station Road, Solihull B92 0HE Tel: 01675 443704 — MB ChB 1977 Liverp.; MD Liverp. 1993; MRCP (UK) 1981; DRCOG 1979. (Liverpool) Cons. Paediat. Birm. Heartlands Hosp. Trust. Socs: BTS; BMA; RCPH. Prev: Sen. Regist. (Paediat.) W. Midl. RHA; Hon. Research Fell. Roy. Childr. Hosp. Melbourne, Austral.

WILLIAMS

WILLIAMS, Mr Julian Peter 15 Clifton Street, Alderley Edge SK9 7NW — MB ChB 1989 Manch.; FRCS Ed. 1993. Specialist Regist. (Gen. Surg.) S. Manch. NW Region.

WILLIAMS, June Elizabeth Alice Earnswood Medical Centre, 92 Victoria Street, Crewe CW1 2JR Tel: 01270 257255 Fax: 01270 501943; 8 Mercer Way, Nantwich CW5 5YD — MB BS 1987 Lond.; DRCOG 1991.

WILLIAMS, Justin Hereward Gwilym Hellesdon Hospital, Drayton High Road, Hellesdon, Norwich NR6 5BE Tel: 01603 421421 Fax: 01603 421118 — MB BS 1988 Newc.; MSc (Environm. & Evolutionary Biol.) Glas. 1995. Regist. Rotat. (Psychiat.) Norf. Ment. Health Care NHS Trust Train. Scheme. Prev: SHO (Cas.) Middlesbrough Gen. Hosp.

WILLIAMS, Justin Marc 22 Park Terrace, Burry Port SA16 0BW — MB ChB 1994 Leic.

WILLIAMS, Karen Jayne Addiction Treatment Unit, 44 London Road, Gloucester GL1 3NZ Tel: 01452 891260 Fax: 01452 891261 — MB ChB 1986 Dundee; MRCPsych 1990. (Univ. Dundee) Cons. Psychiat. (Subst. Misuse) Addic. Treatm. Unit Glos. Prev: Sen. Regist. Rotat. (Psychiat.) W. Midl.; Regist. Rotat. All Birm. Psychiat. Scheme; SHO Rotat. Gloucester Psychiat. Scheme Coney Hill Hosp. Glos.

WILLIAMS, Katharine Nola (retired) Y Bryn, Beaumaris LL58 8EE Tel: 01248 810257 — MB ChB 1944 Birm. Prev: Assoc. Specialist (Geriat.) Gwynedd AHA.

WILLIAMS, Katherine Lorraine Summer Court, Newton, West Pennard, Glastonbury BA6 8NN — MB ChB 1995 Leic. Princip. Ho. Off. IC Unit Mt. Isa Base Hosp. Qu.sland, Australia.

***WILLIAMS, Katherine Mary** Brooklyn, Llancloudy, Hereford HR2 8QW — MB ChB 1995 Birm.

WILLIAMS, Kathryn Esther Washington House Surgery, 77 Halse Road, Brackley NN13 6EQ Tel: 01280 702436; Hill House, Wrightons Hill, Helmdon, Brackley NN13 5UF — MB BS 1980 Lond.; MFFP 1993; DA Eng. 1983. SCMO (Family Plann.) Oxf. Community NHS Trust.

WILLIAMS, Kathryn Mary 104 Cemetery Road, Porth CF39 0BH Tel: 01443 683501 — MB BCh 1987 Wales.

WILLIAMS, Kathryn Vivienne 29 Hazel Grove, Bacup OL13 9XT Tel: 01706 873212 — MB ChB 1977 Bristol; DA Eng. 1979.

WILLIAMS, Kay (retired) 26 Mercia Drive, Dore, Sheffield S17 3QF Tel: 0114 236 9384 Email: kaysden@aol.com — MB BS 1989 Newc. Prev: Ho. Off. (Gen. Med.) Freeman Hosp. Newc.

WILLIAMS, Kaye Llewellyn 92 Victoria Road, Warminster BA12 8HG Tel: 01985 212672 — MRCS Eng. LRCP Lond. 1959; DObst RCOG 1970. (W. Lond.) Hon. Clin. Teach. (Primary Med. Care) Med. Sch. Univ. Soton. Socs: Salisbury Med. Soc. Prev: Lt.-Col. RAMC.

WILLIAMS, Keith 7 Harbourside, Tewkesbury GL20 5DT — BM BS 1979 Nottm.; BMedSci (Hons.) 1977; FFPHM 1991, M 1989; MFCM 1984; FRCP Nottm. 1998.

WILLIAMS, Keith Nigel Anaesthetic Department, St. Thomas' Hospital, Lambeth Palace Road, London SE1 7EH Tel: 020 7928 9292 Fax: 020 7922 8079; 16 Mansel Road, Wimbledon, London SW19 4AA — MB BS 1980 Lond.; MA Camb. 1979; MRCS Eng. LRCP Lond. 1979; FFA RCS Eng. 1985. (St. Thos.) Cons. Anaesth. St. Thos. Hosp. Lond. Socs: Eur. Assn. Cardiothoracic Anaesth. & Brit. Computer Soc. Prev: Sen. Regist. Brompton Hosp.; Sen. Regist. N.wick Pk. Hosp.

WILLIAMS, Kelvyn Parry (retired) Wenallt, Capel Dewi Road, Llangynnwr, Carmarthen SA32 8AA — MB BCh 1947 Wales; MRCS Eng. LRCP Lond. 1947; DA Eng. 1956.

WILLIAMS, Kelwyn Daniel Norquay Wotton LawnHospital, Houton Rd, Gloucester GL1 3WL Tel: 01452 891500; 236 Mollison Way, Edgware HA8 5QY Email: kelwyn@kelwyn.freeserve.co.uk — MB BS 1987 Lond.; BSc Lond. 1984; MRCGP 1992; DCH 1992; MRCPsych. 1997. Specialist Regist. (Psych.) Wotton Lawn Hosp. Gloucester. Socs: BMA; MPS. Prev: Specialist Regist. Adult Psychiat. Barrow Hosp. Bristol.

WILLIAMS, Kenneth Gabriel 7 Crofton Court, Wellington Road, Bournemouth BH8 8JH — MRCS Eng. LRCP Lond. 1950.

WILLIAMS, Mr Kenneth Gwylym David 72 Wickham Way, Park Langley, Beckenham BR3 3AF — MB BS 1961 Lond.; FRCS Eng. 1970; MRCS Eng. LRCP Lond. 1961. (Char. Cross)

WILLIAMS, Kevin Rhydderch Willowbrook Health Centre, Cottingham Road, Corby NN17 2UR Tel: 01536 260747 Fax: 01536 402153; 7 Larkwood Close, Kettering NN16 9NQ Tel: 01536 511156 Fax: 01536 525684 Email: doctorw@aol.com — MB BS 1981 Lond. (St. George's) GP; Forens. Med. Examr. N.ants Police. Prev: Trainee GP Kettering VTS; Regist. (Med.) St. Albans City Hosp.

***WILLIAMS, Kimberley Jane** 106 Penland Road, Haywards Heath RH16 1PH Email: kimberley-williams@yahoo.com — MB BS 1998 Lond.; MB BS Lond 1998; BSc.

WILLIAMS, Kyra Ann 33 Chiswick Quay, Hartington Road, Chiswick, London W4 3UR — MB BS 1960 Lond.; MRCP (UK) 1980. (Char. Cross) Cons. Rehabil. Pk.side Health Trust & Cons. Younger Disabled Unit Willesden Hosp.; Assoc. Specialist Rheum. & Rehabil. N.wick Pk. Hosp. Prev: Clin. Asst. (Rheumat.) Char. Cross Hosp., Ealing Hosp., St. Peter's Hosp. Chertsey & Vict. Hosp. Woking.

WILLIAMS, Lars 13 Kierhill Road, Cumbernauld, Glasgow G68 9BH — MB ChB 1991 Aberd.

WILLIAMS, Laurence Glyn St Thomas Surgery, Rifleman Lane, St. Thomas Green, Haverfordwest SA61 1QX Tel: 01437 762162 Fax: 01437 776811; 1 Courtfield Drive, Simpson Cross, Haverfordwest SA62 6EQ Tel: 01437 710861 Email: 106550.472@compuserve.com — MB BS 1990 Lond.; PhD Lond. 1981; BSc (Hons.) 1978; MRCGP 1994; DCH RCP Lond. 1995; DRCOG 1993; DFFP 1993. Prev: Trainee GP W. Wales; Research Fell. (Med.) Profess. Unit. St. Barts. Hosp. Lond.; Ho. Off. (Med.) Wexham Pk. Hosp. Slough.

WILLIAMS, Layton Roy The Surgery, 560 Stratford Road, Sparkhill, Birmingham B11 4AN Tel: 0121 772 0284 — MB BCh 1962 Wales. (Cardiff.)

WILLIAMS, Leanne Marie 26 High Street, Abercarn, Newport NP11 5GQ — MB BCh 1995 Wales.

WILLIAMS, Lena Winnifred 5 Cramond Park, Edinburgh EH4 6PX — MB ChB 1943 Ed. Life Fell. Hunt. Soc. Socs: Fell. BMA. Prev: Clin. Asst. Obst. Dept. Whittington Hosp. Lond.; Ho. Surg. Dumphries & Galloway Roy. Infirm.; Maj. RAMC.

WILLIAMS, Leonard (retired) 11 Stanhope Road, Croydon CR0 5NS Tel: 020 8688 5957 — MB BS Lond. 1952; MRCGP 1976. Prev: Ho. Phys. Mayday Hosp. Croydon.

WILLIAMS, Leonard Hugh Paul 4 Highland Grove, Worksop S81 0JN Tel: 01909 484742 — BChir 1970 Camb.; MB 1971; MRCP (UK) 1972. Cons. Paediat. Worksop Hosp.

WILLIAMS, Lesley The Mote, Moat Lane, Taynton, Gloucester GL19 3AW — MB ChB 1985 Leic.; BA (Biol. Chem.) Essex 1975. SHO (O & G) Sheff. HA. Prev: Ho. Surg. & Ho. Phys. Kettering Gen. Hosp.

WILLIAMS, Lesley Seonaid (Patterson) Wellway Medical Group, Wellway, Morpeth NE61 1BY — MB ChB 1993 Aberd.; DRCOG 1999; MRCGP 2000. (Aberd.) p/t Asst. Gen. Practitioner, Wellway Med. Gp., Morpeth. Prev: GP Regist., N.umbria VTS, Newc., 1997-99; SHO Paediat., N. Tyneside Hosp., Newc.; SHO Paediat., Newc. Gen. Hosp., Newc.

WILLIAMS, Mr Leslie Arnold (retired) — MB BCh 1964 Wales; FRCS Ed. 1969; FFR 1972; DMRD Eng. 1970. Prev: Cons. Radiol. Dept. Radiodiag, Univ. Hosp. of Wales Cardiff & Cardiff Roy. Infirm.

WILLIAMS, Leslie Brian Department Radiology, Velindre Hospital, Whitchurch, Cardiff CF14 2TL; 13 Park Fields, Penyfai, Bridgend CF31 4NQ — MB BCh 1977 Wales; MA Camb. 1981; FRCR 1985; MRCP (UK) 1981. Cons. Radiol. Velindre Hosp. Cardiff.

WILLIAMS, Lewis John Furness General Hospital, Dalton Lane, Barrow-in-Furness LA14 4LF Tel: 01229 870870; Stank Villa, Stank, Barrow-in-Furness LA13 0LR Tel: 01229 831791 Email: docsw@globalnet.co.uk — MB ChB Dundee 1970; FFA RCS Eng. 1975. (Univ. Dundee) Cons. Anaesth. Furness Gen. Hosp.; Lead Clinician Furness Gen. Hosp.; Med. Advis. Furness Mt.ain Rescue Team. Socs: Fell. of the Roy. Coll. of Anaesth.s; Assn. Day Surg.

WILLIAMS, Mr Lewis Percival c/o Dr G Rebello, 9 Blackford Hill View, Edinburgh EH9 3HD — MB BS 1963 Madras; FRCS Ed. 1977; Dip. Orthop. Madras 1969. (Stanley Med. Coll.) Regist. (Orthop. Surg.) Fife Health Bd.

WILLIAMS, Linda Kennedy The Surgery, 8 Lavant Road, Chichester PO19 4RH Tel: 01243 527264 Fax: 01243 530607 — MB BS 1990 Lond.; PhD Lond. 1985, BSc 1978; MRCP (UK) 1994; DA (UK) 1995; MRCGP 1996. (St Bartholomews Hospital Medical

WILLIAMS

College) Princip. GP; Clin. Asst. (Cardiol.) St Richards Hosp. Cichester. Socs: BMA; RCEP; RCP. Prev: GP/Regist. Chichester; SHO (Anaesth. & Med.) St. Richards Hosp. Chichester.

WILLIAMS, Lisa The Turret Medical Centre, Catherine Street, Kirkintilloch, Glasgow G66 1JB Tel: 0141 211 8260 Fax: 0141 211 8264 — MB ChB 1990 Manch.

WILLIAMS, Lisa Amri Llwyn y Fedw Farm, Tyla, Govilon, Abergavenny NP7 9RU — MB BCh 1993 Wales.

WILLIAMS, Lisa Gwenan 15B Glenrafon Street, Bethesda, Bangor LL57 3AL — MB ChB 1993 Liverp.

WILLIAMS, Lisa Jane 29 Chesterfield Crescent, Leigh-on-Sea SS9 5PD — MB ChB 1994 Leic. SHO (Psychiat.) Fazakerley Hosp. Liverp. Prev: SHO (A & E) S.port Dist. Gen. Hosp.; Ho. Off. (Med.) Leicester Gen. Hosp.; Ho. Off. (Surg.) Geo. Eliot Hosp. Nuneaton.

WILLIAMS, Lora Young (retired) Quarry Dene, 36 Church Lane, Bardsey, Leeds LS17 9DP Tel: 01937 572153 — MB ChB 1954 Aberd.; MA Aberd. 1949, MB ChB 1954; DA Eng. 1958. Prev: Med. Off. Cancer Families Studies Epidemiol. Dept. Leeds Univ.

WILLIAMS, Louise Patricia 38 Salisbury Crescent, Oxford OX2 7TL — MB BS 1987 Melbourne.

WILLIAMS, Lucy Ann Cary c/o Maj R. D. Williams, 1 Regiment AAC WKSP BFPO 47 — MB BS 1990 Newc.; DA (UK) 1992. Prev: Clin. Asst. (Anaesth.) Salisbury Dist. Hosp.; SHO (Anaesth.) Yeovil Dist. Gen. Hosp.

WILLIAMS, Ludmila National Hospital, Queen Square, London WC1N 3BG — MUDr 1966 Prague; MSc Lond. 1990. Regist. (Med. Microbiol.) Nat. Hosp. Neurol. & Neurosurg. Qu. Sq. Lond.

WILLIAMS, Luke Robert 18 Rowan Lane, Skelmersdale WN8 6UL — MB ChB 1998 Manch.

WILLIAMS, Lynn Accident & Emergency Department, Queens medical centre, Nottingham NG7 2UH Tel: 0115 970 9153 — MB BCh 1980 Wales; BA Wales 1974, MB BCh 1980; FRCS Ed. 1987; FFAEM FFAEM 1993. Cons. A & E Qu.s Med. centre.

WILLIAMS, Mani Prabha HMP Bristol Prison, Cambridge Road, Bristol BS1 7AD Tel: 0117 942 6661 — MB BS 1978 Kakatiya, India; MB BS Kakatiya India 1978; FRCS Ed. 1985; LRCP LRCS Ed. LRCPS Glas. 1984.

WILLIAMS, Margaret Ashfield, Merthyrmawr Road, Bridgend CF31 3NW — MB ChB 1945 Manch. (Manch.) Socs: Coll. GP. Prev: Asst. Res. Med. Off. Crumpsall Hosp. Manch.; Asst. Res. Med. Off. Midw. & Gynaecol. Dept. Withington Hosp. Manch.

WILLIAMS, Margaret Eleanor 9 Llwyndern Drive, West Cross, Swansea SA3 5AP — MB BCh 1993 Wales; BSc Physiol. (1st cl. Hons.) Wales 1990. SHO (Cas.) Morriston Hosp. Swansea. Prev: SHO (Intens. Care) Univ. Hosp. Wales; SHO (Paediat.) Cardiff Roy. Infirm.; Ho. Off. (Neurol.) Univ. Hosp. Wales.

WILLIAMS, Margaret Elizabeth Marion Maple house, East Surrey Hospital, Canada Avenue, Redhill RH1 5RH — MB BS 1969 Lond.; MRCS Eng. LRCP Lond. 1969; DObst RCOG 1971; MRCP (U.K.) 1973. (King's Coll. Hosp.) Cons. community Paediat., Surrey and Sussex healthcare trust. Prev: SCMO (Community Child Health) Merton & Sutton HA.

WILLIAMS, Margaret Frances (retired) 4 Carlton Bank, Harpenden AL5 4SU Tel: 01582 763383 — MB BS 1963 Lond.; MB BS (Distinc. Surg., Obst. & Gyn.) Lond. 1963; MRCS Eng. LRCP Lond. 1963; DObst RCOG 1965. Prev: Ho. Surg. Univ. Coll. Hosp.

WILLIAMS, Margaret Louise Princess Road Surgery, 475 Princess Road, Withington, Manchester M20 1BH Tel: 0161 445 7805 Fax: 0161 448 2419; 118 Park Road, Timperley, Altrincham WA15 6TQ Tel: 0161 905 2046 — MB ChB 1986 Manch. Prev: Trainee GP Wythenshawe VTS; SHO (Paediat.) Stockport.

WILLIAMS, Margaret Novello 52 Merthyr Mawr Road, Bridgend CF31 3NR — MB BCh 1954 Wales.

WILLIAMS, Margaret Selina Isabel (retired) Birch Cottage, Torrington Close, Claygate, Esher KT10 0SB — MB BS Lond. 1953; MRCS Eng. LRCP Lond. 1953; DCH Eng. 1955. Prev: Med. Off. Europ. & Asian Hosp. Kampala, Uganda.

WILLIAMS, Margaret Valerie 6 Park Road, Barry CF62 6NU Tel: 01446 734925 — MB BCh 1960 Wales. (Cardiff) Socs: BMA; (Ex-Pres.) Barry Med. Soc.; (Ex-Pres.) Cardiff Med. Soc. Prev: GP Barry; Ho. Phys. (Paediat.) & Ho. Surg. Llandough Hosp. Penarth; Ho. Surg. (Obst.) St. David's Hosp. Cardiff.

WILLIAMS, Marian 66 Mill Hill, Waringstown, Craigavon BT66 7QP — MB BCh 1997 Belf.

WILLIAMS, Marie Elena South King Street Medical Centre, 25 South King Street, Blackpool FY1 4NF Tel: 01253 26637; 201 Layton Road, Blackpool FY3 8ES — MB ChB 1987 Manch.; MRCGP 1991. (Univ. Manch.) GP.

WILLIAMS, Marion Sheila 15 High Street, Yarm TS15 9BH — MB ChB 1995 Dundee; BMSc Dund 1992.

WILLIAMS, Marion Siobhan Collinge, Trolver Croft, Feock, Truro TR3 6RT — MB ChB 1978 Bristol; MRCGP 1984. Prev: SHO (Psychiat., Cas. & ENT) Roy. Cornw. Hosp. Treliske.

WILLIAMS, Marjorie Martin (retired) 1 Witham House, St. George's Avenue, Northampton NN2 6SF Tel: 01604 715364 — MB ChB 1927 Birm. Prev: Sen. Asst. MOH N.ampton.

WILLIAMS, Mark Aveley Medical Centre, 22 High Street, Aveley, South Ockendon RM15 4AD Tel: 01708 865640 Fax: 01708 891658; 18 St George Avenue, Grays RM17 5XB Tel: 01375 407493 Fax: 01708 891658 Email: mark@aveleymc.demon.co.uk — BM 1983 Soton. GP S. Ockendon. Prev: Trainee GP Ryde VTS; SHO (ENT) Luton Gen. Hosp.; SHO (Psych.) Worcester Newton Hosp.

WILLIAMS, Mark, Flight Lt. RAF Med. Br. Officers Mess, RAF Station Lyneham, Lyneham, Chippenham SN15 4PZ — MB ChB 1992 Leeds. Prev: Ho. Off. (Gen. Med.) Huddersfield Roy. Infirm.; Ho. Off. (Gen. Surg.) ScarBoro. Dist. Hosp.

WILLIAMS, Mark Andrew 23 Southcliffe Road, Christchurch BH23 4EN — MB BChir 1990 Camb.; MA Camb. 1991; MRCP (UK) 1993; FRCA 1997. Specialist Regist. Dept. Anaes. Soton. Prev: SHO Nuffield Dept. Anaesth. Oxf.; SHO (Intens. Care) Middlx. & Univ. Coll. Hosp. Lond.

WILLIAMS, Mark David Ardroy, 49 Summerhill, Kingswinford DY6 9JG — BM BS 1994 Nottm.

WILLIAMS, Mark Edward Beech Tree Surgery, 68 Doncaster Road, Selby YO8 9AJ — MB ChB 1983 Liverp.; MRCGP 1990; DCH RCP Lond. 1987; DRCOG 1985.

WILLIAMS, Mark Gill Wareham Surgery, Streche Road, Wareham BH20 4PG Tel: 01929 553444; 1 Woodlake Cottage, Bloxworth, Wareham BH20 7ET — MB BS 1989 Lond.; MRCGP 1994; DRCOG 1994; DFFP 1993. (St. George's Hospital, London) GP Wareham Surg., Dorset; Clin. Asst., Accid. & Emerg., Poole Hosp. NHS Trust, Poole.

WILLIAMS, Mark Howard 3 Saffron Close, Taunton TA1 3XW Tel: 01823 327863 Fax: 01823 327863 — MB BChir 1981 Camb.; MB BChir Camb. 1980; BA (Hons.) Camb. 1977, MA 1981; MRCGP 1988; MFPHM RCP (UK) 1993; DGM RCP Lond. 1988; DRCOG 1985; DCH RCPS Glas. 1984. (Camb. & St. Mary's) Cons. & Sen. Lect. (Epidemiol. & Pub. Health Med.) Univ. Bristol; Hon. Cons. (Pub. Health Med.) SW RHA. Socs: BMA; Fell. Roy. Soc. Med. Prev: Lect. (Epidemiol. & Pub. Health Med.) Univ. Bristol; Ho. Surg. Profess. Surg. Unit & Cardiovasc. Unit St. Mary's Hosp. Lond.

WILLIAMS, Mark Rees 1 Cheshire Close, Madeley, Telford TF7 5SP — MB BS 1997 Lond.

WILLIAMS, Martin 56 Northern Road, Cosham, Portsmouth PO6 3DP Tel: 023 92 373321 — MB BCh BAO 1963 Dub.; DObst RCOG 1966. (Trinity Coll. Dub.)

WILLIAMS, Martin Bodreinallt Surgery, Bodreinallt, Conwy LL32 8AT Tel: 01492 593385 Fax: 01492 573715 — MB ChB 1974 Bristol; DRCOG 1978; DA Eng. 1978.

WILLIAMS, Martin James The Cumbrian Clinic, West Cumberland Hospital, Whitehaven CA28 8JG Tel: 01946 523380; Low Hollins, Cockermouth CA13 9UX Tel: 01900 85251 — MB BChir 1965 Camb.; FRCP Lond. 1980, M 1968. (St. Thos.) p/t Cons. Phys. The Cumbrian Clinic W. Cumbld. Hosp. Whitehaven. Socs: Brit. Soc. Gastroenterol.; BMA. Prev: Cons. Phys. W. Cumbld. Hosp.; Sen. Regist. (Med.) Bristol Roy. Infirm. & Roy. United Hosp. Bath.

WILLIAMS, Martin James Ladywell Medical Centre, West Wing, Edinburgh EH12 7TB Tel: 0131 334 3602; Flat 3/5, Silver Mills, Stockbridge, Edinburgh EH3 5BF Tel: 0131 558 9190 — MB ChB 1991 Ed.; DCH 2000 (RCP); NRCGP 1999; BSc Ed. 1989; FRCS (A&E) Ed. 1997. Gen. Practitioner Ladywell Med. Centre W. Edin. Prev: SHO (Intens. Care) Qu. Margt. Hosp. Dunferline; SHO (A & E) Qu. Margt. Hosp. Dunfermline; Regist. (A & E) Roy. Infirm. of Edin.

WILLIAMS, Martin Kenneth 30 Brill Close, Maidenhead SL6 3EJ — MB BS 1994 Lond.

WILLIAMS, Mr Martyn Peter Lees Box 43, Addenbrooke's Hospital, Hills Road, Cambridge CB4 3TN — MB BS 1979 Lond.; FRCS (Paediat.) 1994; FRCS Ed. 1984. Cons. Paediat. Surg. &

WILLIAMS

Paediat. Urol. Addenbrooke's Hosp. Camb. Socs: Brit. Assn. Paediat. Surg.s; Brit. Assn. Paediat. Urol.s; Eur. Soc. Paediat. Urol. Prev: Sen. Regist. (Paediat. Surg.) Roy. Vict. Infirm. Newc.; Regist. (Paediat. Surg.) Roy. Liverp. Childr. Hosp.; Research Fell. Smith & Nephew Research Roy. Childr. Hosp. Melbourne, Austral.

WILLIAMS, Mary Angela Theresa ICRF, Ashley Wing, St James Univesity Hospital, Beckett St., Leeds LS9 7TF Tel: 0113 283 7089 — MB ChB 1970 Cape Town.

WILLIAMS, Mary-Claire 17 Bradfield Avenue, Bridgend CF31 4HL — MB BCh 1998 Wales.

WILLIAMS, Mary Llywela Oakley House, Maesycwmmer, Hengoed CF8 — MB BCh 1944 Wales; DObst RCOG 1947. (Cardiff) Asst. Med. Off. Mon. CC. Prev: Obst. Regist. St. Davids Hosp. Cardiff; Res. Med. Off. Derby City Hosp.; Ho. Surg. Warneford Gen. Hosp. Leamington Spa.

WILLIAMS, Mary Patricia 26 Riding Way, Woosehill, Wokingham RG41 3AH — MB BCh BAO 1975 NUI; MRCGP 1984; DCH RCSI 1979. p/t Clin. Med. Off. (Community Paediat.) Slough.

WILLIAMS, Matthew 106 Bowes Hill, Rowlands Castle PO9 6BS Tel: 01705 412565; 18 Barham Road, Petersfield GU32 3EX Tel: 01730 231610 — MB ChB 1993 Bristol; DA (UK) 1996; DCH RCP Lond. 1995. Specialist Regist. anaesth. Q A Hosp. Portsmouth. Socs: BMA; Train. Mem. Assn. AnE.h. Prev: SHO (Anaesth.) Roy. Devon & Exeter Hosp.; SHO (Paediat.) Taunton & Som.; Ho. Phys. Taunton.

WILLIAMS, Matthew Luke Llewelyn 41 Christchurch Road, Reading RG2 7AP — BChir 1996 Camb.

WILLIAMS, Matthew Peter Hill Cottage, Harlow Road, Roydon, Harlow CM19 5HH — MB BS 1988 Lond.

WILLIAMS, Medwyn Parc Glas, Bodorgan LL62 — MB ChB 1981 Liverp.; MRCGP 1985; DCH RCP Lond. 1984; DRCOG 1984. Prev: Trainee GP Gwynedd HA.

WILLIAMS, Melanie Microbiology Department, Frimley Park Hospital, Portsmouth Road, Frimley, Camberley GU16 7UJ Tel: 01276 604604 Fax: 01276 21547 — MB BS 1967 Lond.; MD 1982 Lond.; M 1980; MD Lond. 1982; MRCS Eng. LRCP Lond. 1967; FRCPath 1992, M 1980; MRCS Eng. LRCP 1967 Lond.; FRCPath 1992. (Char. Cross) Cons. Med. Microbiol. Frimley Pk. Hosp. Prev: Cons. Med. Microbiol. St. Jas. Hosp. Lond.; Sen. Lect. (Med. Microbiol.) St. Geo. Med. Sch. Lond.; Sen. Regist. (Bacteriol.) Glas. Roy. Infirm.

WILLIAMS, Meriel 5 Harford Court, Sketty, Swansea SA2 8DE — MB BCh 1952 Wales; MFCM 1973; DCH Eng. 1955; DObst RCOG 1959. SCMO W. Glam. AHA. Prev: Paediat. Regist. Morriston Hosp.

WILLIAMS, Merion Gwynne 45 Nursery Gardens, Staines TW18 1EJ — MB BS 1986 Lond.

WILLIAMS, Mr Michael Andrew Mayday University Hospital, Mayday Road, Croydon CR7 7YE Tel: 020 8401 3000; Wood End, 80 Welcomes Road, Kenley CR8 5HE Tel: 020 8660 0770 — MB BS 1975 Lond.; FRCS Eng. 1979; MRCS Eng. LRCP Lond. 1975. (St. Mary's) Cons. Gen. & Vasc. Surg. Mayday Univ. Hosp. Croydon. Prev: Research Regist. (Vasc. Surg.) St. Mary's Hosp. Med. Sch.; Sen. Regist. (Vasc. Surg.) St. Mary's Hosp. Harvard Schol.sh. Mass. Gen. Hosp., Boston.

WILLIAMS, Michael Andrew 22 Glencraig Park, Holywood BT18 0BZ — MB BCh 1998 Belf.

WILLIAMS, Michael Anthony Ashfield Surgery, Merthyr Mawr Road, Bridgend CF31 3NW Tel: 01656 652774 Fax: 01656 661187; Sudeley, Glanogwr Road, Bridgend CF31 3PF Tel: 01656 646861 — MB BS 1979 Lond.; Dip Sports Med 1999 Bath; DRCOG 1982; Dip. Med. Acupunc. BMAS 1998. (St. Mary's Hospital London) Socs: Brit. Med. Acupunct. Soc.; BMA; Brit. Assn Of Sports and Exercise Med.

WILLIAMS, Michael David Department of Haematology, Birmingham Children's Hospital, Steelhouse Lane, Birmingham B4 6NH Tel: 0121 333 9999 Fax: 0121 333 9841 — MD 1987 Liverp.; MB ChB 1977; FRCP 1997; FRCPath 1997. Cons. Haemat. Childr. Hosp. Birm.; Cons. Haemat. Birm. Woms. Hosp. Prev: Sen. Regist. (Haemat.) W. Midl. RHA.

WILLIAMS, Michael David Royal Hospital Haslar, Haslar Rd, Gosport PO12 2AA — MB ChB 1997 Sheff.

WILLIAMS, Michael Gill, Surg. Capt. RN 6 Queen Anne's Drive, Bedhampton, Havant PO9 3PG Tel: 01705 482647 — MB BChir 1957 Camb.; MA, MB Camb. 1957, BChir 1956; MRCS Eng. LRCP Lond. 1956; DO Eng. 1962; DObst RCOG 1958. (St. Mary's)

WILLIAMS, Michael James (retired) 48 Oakhill Road, Aberdeen AB15 5ES Tel: 01224 208046 — MB ChB Aberd. 1954; MD Aberd. 1965; FRCP Ed. 1993; FRCP Lond. 1976, M 1959. Prev: Cons. Phys. Aberd. Gen. Hosps.

WILLIAMS, Michael James Howard Watford General Hospital, Vicarage Road, Watford WD18 0HB Tel: 01923 217391 Fax: 01923 217279 Email: 101462.1205@compuserve.com — MB BS 1970 Lond.; FRCP Lond. 1990; MRCP (UK) 1973; MRCS Eng. LRCP Lond. 1970; DCH Eng. 1973. (St. Bart.) Cons. Paediat. (s/i Newborn) Matern. Wing Watford Gen. Hosp.; Clin. Dir. (Family Servs.) Mt. Vernon & Watford Hosps. NHS Trust; Dir. (Childr. Servs.) W. Herts.; Chairm. Exam. Bd. Dip. in Child Health RCP Lond. Socs: Roy. Coll. Paediat. & Child Health. Prev: Sen. Regist. (Paediat.) St. Mary's Hosp. Lond.; Chief Resid. (Paediat.) Childr. Hosp. Med. Centre, Boston, USA; Instruc. (Paediat.) Harvard Med. Sch. Boston, USA.

WILLIAMS, Michael John (retired) Stretton House, Church Oakley, Basingstoke RG23 7LJ Tel: 01256 780635 — MB BS 1957 Lond.; MRCS Eng. LRCP Lond. 1956; DObst RCOG 1958. Dep. Med. Ref. Basingstoke Crem. Prev: GP Basingstoke.

WILLIAMS, Michael Kingsley (Surgery), Gilbert House, 39 Woodfield Lane, Ashtead KT21 2BT Tel: 01372 276385; Sharston Lodge, Fortyfoot Road, Leatherhead KT22 8RN Tel: 01372 373315 — BM BCh 1958 Oxf.; MA (Engin. Sci.) Oxf..1956, DM 1968; MRCGP 1980; DIH Soc. Apoth. Lond. 1962; DObst RCOG 1959. (St. Mary's) Med. Off. Exide Batteries Ltd. Dagenham Dock. Prev: Sen. Lect. (Occupat. Health) Lond. Sch. Hyg. & Trop. Med.; Indust. Med. Off. Electric Power Storage Co. Swinton; Ho. Phys. (Med.) St. Mary's Hosp.

WILLIAMS, Michael Philip Department of Radiology, Derriford Hospital, Plymouth; Yeoland Down, Golf Links Road, Yelverton PL20 6BN — BM BCh 1979 Oxf.; MA Oxf. 1981; MBA (Health Exec.) Keele 1996; FRCR 1984. Cons. Radiol. Plymouth Hosps. NHS Trust; Clin. Dir. Med. Imaging. Prev: Clin. Tutor Univ. Bristol; Sen. Lect. (Radiol.) Roy. Marsden Hosp. Lond.; Sen. Regist. Addenbrooke's Hosp. Camb.

WILLIAMS, Mr Michael Richard Cumberland Infirmary, Carlisle CA2 7HY Tel: 01228 23444; The Old Vicarage, Rosley, Wigton CA7 8AU Tel: 016973 44255 — MB BS 1977 Lond.; DM Nottm. 1988; FRCS Eng. 1982; FRCS Ed. 1982. (The London Hospital Whitechapel) Cons. Surg. Cumbld. Infirm. Carlisle. Socs: Surg. Research Soc.; Brit. Assn. Endocrin. Surgs.; Assn. BrE. Surgs. Prev: Sen. Regist. (Surg.) W. Midl. RHA; Regist. (Surg.) Nottm. & Dudley Rd. Hosp. Birm.; Tenovus Research Fell. City Hosp. Nottm. BrE. Unit.

WILLIAMS, Michael Thomas Sweet Briars, East Dean Road, Lockrley, Romsey SO51 0JQ — MB BS 1991 Lond.; MRCP (UK) 1994. (St. Geo.)

WILLIAMS, Michael Vaughan Oncology Centre, Box 193, Addenbrooke's Hospital, Hills Road, Cambridge CB2 2QQ Tel: 01223 217020 Fax: 01223 217094 Email: michael.williams@addenbrookes.nhs.uk — MB BChir 1974 Camb.; MD Camb. 1984, MA 1974; MRCP (UK) 1975; FRCR 1982; FRCP 1997. (Lond. Hosp.) Cons: Clin. Oncol. Addenbrooke's Hosp. Camb.; Assoc. Lect. Clin. Sch. Univ. Camb; Head Clinician, W. Anglia Cancer Network. Prev: Clin. Director, Oncol. Centre, Addenbrooke's; Sen. Regist. (Radiother.) Velindre Hosp. WhitCh. Cardiff; Non-Clin. Research Scientist CRC Gray Laborat. Mt. Vernon Hosp.

WILLIAMS, Michael Wyn 9 East Avenue, Porthmadog LL49 9EN — MB BCh 1982 Wales.

WILLIAMS, Michelle Lola 68 Rugby Avenue, Greenford UB6 0EZ — MB BS 1993 Lond.

WILLIAMS, Miriam Ann Smeeton Road Health Centre, Smeeton Road, Kibworth, Leicester LE8 0LG Tel: 0116 279 3308 Fax: 0116 279 3320; 87 Weir Road, Kibworth, Leicester LE8 0LQ Tel: 0153753 3864 — MB BCh BAO 1971 NUI; MRCGP 1975; DCH RCPSI 1975.

WILLIAMS, Moira Anne Commins 3 Bryn-y-Coed, Hwfa Road, Bangor LL57 2BN Tel: 01248 361345; 25 Antringham Gardens, Edgbaston, Birmingham B15 3QL — MB ChB 1986 Birm. Community Child Health Med. Off. (Paediat.) Gwynedd Community Child Health Trust Caernarfon; Clin. Asst. (Haemat.) Ysbyty Gwynedd. Prev: Cas. Off. Ysbyty Gwynedd; SHO (Neurosurg.) Midl. Centre for Neurosurg. & Neurol. Smethwick; SHO (Otorhinolaryng.) Selly Oak Hosp. Birm.

WILLIAMS, Molly Therese (retired) 25A Chase Green Avenue, Enfield EN2 8EA — MB BS Lond. 1949; DObst RCOG 1951. Prev: Hon. Med. Off. GP Unit St. Michael's Hosp. Enfield.

WILLIAMS, Namor Wyn Department of Pathology, Singleton Hospital, Sketty, Swansea SA2 8QA Tel: 01792 205666; 24 Alexandra Road, Canton, Cardiff CF5 1NS — MB BS 1983 Lond.; BSc (Hons.) Lond. 1980; MRCPath 1992. (St. Bart.) Cons. Histopath. Swansea NHS Trust. Prev: Sen. Regist. (Histopath.) S. Glam. HA; Ho. Off. (Gen. Surg.) Crawley Hosp.; Ho. Off. (Gen. Med.) Whipps Cross Hosp. Lond.

WILLIAMS, Nefyn Howard Health Centre, Village Road, Llanfairfechan LL33 0NH Tel: 01248 680021 Fax: 01248 681711; Northcote, Pk Road, Llanfairfechan LL33 0AE — BM BCh 1985 Oxf.; MA Oxf.1982; MRCGP 1991; DCH RCP Lond. 1988; DRCOG 1987.

WILLIAMS, Neil Ashley 9 Bittell Road, Barnt Green, Birmingham B45 8LP — MB ChB 1989 Birm.

WILLIAMS, Neill Roger Etwall Surgery, Egginton Road, Etwall, Derby DE65 6NB Tel: 01283 732257 Fax: 01283 734876; 19 Willington Road, Etwall, Derby DE65 6JG Tel: 01283 732213 — MB BS 1971 Lond.; DFFP 1999; DObst RCOG 1973. (Univ. Coll. Hosp.) Socs: Derby Med. Soc. Prev: Ho. Surg. Univ. Coll. Hosp. Lond.; SHO (O & G) Burton-on-Trent Gen. Hosp.

WILLIAMS, Nerys Rhiannon — MB ChB 1984 Manch.; FRCP Lond. 1999; FFOM RCP Lond. 1995, MFOM, 1993, AFOM 1990; MRCGP 1988; DGM RCP Lond. 1987; DRCOG (Silver Medal) 1987; DCH RCP Lond. 1986. Sen. Med. Insp. & Head of EMAS; Mem. Edit. Panel Jl. Soc. Occupat. Med.; AFOM Examr. RCP Lond; Dep. Chief Examr. Fom RCP Lond.; Consg Occupat. Toxicol.. Dudley Rd. Hosp.; Hon. Sen. Clin. Lect. Inst. Occupat. Health Univ. Birm. Socs: Soc. Occupat. Med. Prev: Sen. Employm. Med. Advisor Health & Safety Exec.; Employm. Med. Advisor Health & Safety Exec.; Occupat. Phys. Wellcome Foundat. Ltd. Beckenham.

WILLIAMS, Mr Nicholas Department Plastic Surgery, Royal Victoria Infirmary, Queen Victoria Road, Newcastle upon Tyne NE1 4LP — MB ChB 1988 Leeds; BSc (Hons.) Leeds 1985; FRCS Eng. 1993; PHD 1999. (Leeds) p/t Cons. Plastic, Recontructive and Hand Surg., Roy. Vict. Infirm., Newc. upon Tyne. Socs: Assoc. Mem. Brit. Soc. Surg. Hand; Full Mem. Brit. Soc. Surg. Hand; Full Mem. Brit. Soc. Aesthetic Plastic Surg.s. Prev: Specialist Regist. Plastic Surg. N.. Gen. Hosp. Sheff.; Specialist Regist. Plastic Surg.Roy.Vict..Infirm.Newc.; Hand Fell., St.Jas. Uni. Hosp, Leeds.

WILLIAMS, Nicholas James 65 Manor Road, Woodley, Stockport SK6 1NS — MB BS 1994 Lond.

WILLIAMS, Nicola Moor Park Surgery, 49 Garstang Rd, Preston PR1 1LB Tel: 01772 252077 — MB ChB 1994 Dundee; MRCGP 2001; DFFP 1999. p/t GP Princip. Moor Pk. Surg. Preston; GP Assoc. at Lostock Hall Med. Centre, Leyland Rd, Lostock Hall, Preston.

WILLIAMS, Nicola Jane 21 Heol Aradur, Llandaff, Cardiff CF5 2RE; Ty Cornel, 21 Hedl Aradur, Llandaff, Cardiff CF5 2RE Tel: 01222 552249 Fax: 01222 308195 — MB BCh 1977 Wales; DRCOG 1979. (welsh nat.Sch.med)

WILLIAMS, Nicola Jane Gloucestershire Royal Hospital, Anaesthetic Department, Gloucester Royal Hospital, Great Western Road, Gloucester GL1 3NN Tel: 01452 394194 Fax: 01452 394485 — MB BS 1983 Lond.; BSc Lond. 1980; FRCA 1991. Cons. (Anaesth.) Gloucester Healthcare Trust.

WILLIAMS, Nicola Mary Flat 1, 163 New Kings Road, London SW6 4SN — MB BS 1994 Lond.

WILLIAMS, Nicolette 48 Ludlow Avenue, Luton LU1 3RW — MB BS 1991 Lond.

WILLIAMS, Mr Nigel University Hospitals Coventry & Warwickshire, Clifford Bridge Road, Walsgrave, Coventry LE2 4TG Tel: 024 76 602020 — BM BS 1986 Nottm.; ChM Manch. 1994; BMedSci Nottm. 1984; FRCS 1991; FRCS (Gen.) 1997. (Nottingham) Cons.Surg.; Sen. Lect., Univ. of Warwick. Socs: Assn. Surg.; Assn. Coloproctol. Prev: Tutor (Surg.) Univ. Manch.; Regist. Rotat. (Surg.) Leics.; SHO Rotat. (Surg.) Nottm.

WILLIAMS, Nigel Christopher Clarkson Surgery, De-Havilland Road, Wisbech PE13 3AN Tel: 01945 583133 Fax: 01945 464465; Dunnerdale House, 92 Church Road, Emneth, Wisbech PE14 8AF Tel: 01945 463446 Email: nigel.williams@ukonline.uk — MB ChB 1975 Liverp.; MRCGP 1982; DCH Eng. 1979. (Liverp.) Socs: BMA.

Prev: Trainee GP King's Lynn VTS; SHO (Med.) & Ho. Off. Walton Hosp. Liverp.

WILLIAMS, Nigel Dill 23 High Street, Wolstanton, Newcastle ST5 0EU — MB BCh BAO 1972 Belf. Cons. Microbiol. N. Staffs HA. Prev: Sen. Regist. (Med. Microbiol.) N.. Gen. Hosp. Sheff.; Regist. (Med. Microbiol.) & SHO (Path.) Roy. Vict. Hosp. Belf.; Ho. Off. Belf. City Hosp.

WILLIAMS, Nina Sunthankar Public Health, Iechyd Morgannwg Health, 41 High St., Swansea SA1 1LT Tel: 01792 458066 Fax: 01792 655364; 11 Westport Avenue, Mayals, Swansea SA3 5EA — MB BCh 1983 Wales; MSc (Community Child Health) Warwick 1996; DRCOG 1990; DCH RCP Lond. 1988; MFCH 1996. (Univ. Wales Cardiff) Specialist Regist. (Pub. Health). Socs: Fac. Community Health; Soc. Pub. Health; BAACH. Prev: Acting SCMO (Child Health) DHSS I. of Man; Trainee GP Hants.

WILLIAMS, Noël (retired) — MB BCh BAO 1947 NUI. Prev: SCMO N. Yorks. AHA.

WILLIAMS, Noreen Helen Walkley House Medical Centre, 23 Greenhow St., Walkley, Sheffield S6 3TN; 6 Hoober Road, Eccleshall, Sheffield S11 9SF — MB ChB 1979 Sheff. Prev: GP Trainee Sheff. VTS.

WILLIAMS, Norma Lottie Jean Suite One, 25 Weymouth St., London W1G 7BP Tel: 020 7636 5769 Fax: 020 7436 6076 — MB BS 1962 Lond.; MD Ohio 1969; MRCS Eng. LRCP Lond. 1962. (Guy's) Med. Dir. Amer. Wom. Health Center Lond. Socs: Fell. Roy. Soc. Med. Prev: Cons. Gyn. Ohio State Univ. Health Centre, Columbus, USA; Sen. CMO (Wom. Health) Lond. Boro. Tower Hamlets; Clin. Asst. Eliz. Garrett Anderson Hosp. Lond.

WILLIAMS, Norman Brian Department of Anaesthetics, Bristol Royal Infirmary, Marlborough St., Bristol BS2 8HW Tel: 0117 928 2163; 32 Old Sneed Park, Bristol BS9 1RF — MB BCh 1961 Wales; FFA RCS Eng. 1969; DObst RCOG 1963. Cons. Anaesth. Bristol Health Dist. (T). Socs: Fell. Roy. Soc. Med.; Assn. Anaesths. Prev: Sen. Regist. (Anaesth.) Bristol Health Dist. (T); Cons. Anaesth. Nchanga Consolidated Copper Mines Ltd. Kitwe, Zambia.

WILLIAMS, Norman Eric The Limes, Main St., Tinwell, Stamford PE9 3UD Tel: 01780 757273 Fax: 01780 757370 — MB (Distinc.) Camb. 1968, BChir 1967; MA Camb. 1968; FRCP Lond. 1995; MRCP (UK) 1971. (St. Thos.) Cons. Rheum. & Rehabil. P'boro. Hosp. & Addenbrooke's Hosp. Camb. Socs: BMA (Camb. Br.); BSR; NOS. Prev: Regist. (Rheum.) St. Thos. Hosp. Lond.; Regist. (Neurol.) & Ho. Phys. St. Thos. Hosp. Lond.

WILLIAMS, Professor Norman Stanley Academic Department of Surgery, St Bartholomew's & The Royal London School of, Medicine & Detistry, The Royal London Hospital, Whitechapel, London E1 1BB Tel: 020 7377 7079 Fax: 020 7377 7283 Email: n.s.williams@mds.qmw.ac.uk — MB BS 1970 Lond.; MS Lond. 1982; FRCS Eng. 1975; MRCS Eng. LRCP Lond. 1970. (Lond. Hosp.) Prof. Surg. St Bart. & The Roy. Lond. Sch. of Med. & Dent.; Hon Cons. Surg. The Roy. Hosps. NHS Trust. Socs: (Vice-Chairm.) Brit. Jl. Surg. Soc.; (Pres.) Ileostomy Assn. GB & Irel.; (Chairm.) UACCCR Colorectal Cancer Gp. Prev: Prof. Surg. Lond. Hosp. Med. Coll. & Hon. Cons. Lond. Hosp. Trust; Research Fell. Univ. Calif., Los Angeles, USA; Sen. Lect Univ. Leeds.

WILLIAMS, Norman Vincent (retired) Briarwood, Ty'r Winch Road, St Mellons, Cardiff CF3 9UU Tel: 01222 777481 — MB ChB 1935 Lond.; DPH Lond. 1939. Cons. Phys. Supt. Cefn Mably Hosp. Cardiff. Prev: Clin. Teach. Tuberc. Univ. Bristol.

WILLIAMS, Norton Elwy (retired) 80 Whitefield Road, Walton, Warrington WA4 6NB Tel: 01925 265889 — MB ChB Liverp. 1956; FFA RCS Eng. 1963. Prev: Sen. Regist. (Anaesth.) United Sheff. Hosps.

WILLIAMS, Olivia Anna 12A Southway, Lewes BN7 1LU — BM 1983 Soton.

WILLIAMS, Olivia Eugenie Flat 2, 22 Upper Tichbourne St., Leicester LE2 1GJ — MB ChB 1995 Leic.

WILLIAMS, Olwen (retired) 36 Millfields, Pentlepoir, Kilgetty SA68 0SA — MB BCh 1940 Wales. Deptm. Med. Off. Glam. CC. Prev: Ho. Phys. Med. Unit, & Ho. Surg. Gyn. & Obst. Unit. Roy. Infirm.

WILLIAMS, Olwen Elizabeth Department of Genitourinary Medicine, Wrexham Maelor Hospital, Croesnewydd Road, Wrexham LL13 7TD Tel: 01745 582314 Fax: 01745 582314 Email: o.e.williams@appleonline.net; Email: bethel@waitrose.co,

WILLIAMS

o.e.williams@appleonline.net — MB ChB 1983 Liverp.; MRCP (UK) 1988; Dip. Ven. Liverp. 1989. Cons. Genitourin. Med. Wrexham Maelor & Glan Clwyd, Rhyl; Hon. Lect. Univ. Hosp. Of Wales; Hon. Lect. Liverp. Univ. Socs: Hon. Asst. Sec. - Med. Soc. for the Study of Venereal Dis.s (MSSVD). Prev: Sen. Regist. & Regist. (Genitourin. Med.) Roy. Liverp. Hosp.; Lect. (Genitourin. Med.) Univ. Liverp.

WILLIAMS, Owain Aled Drury Cottage, Bilden End, Chrishall, Royston SG8 8RE — BChir 1994 Camb.

WILLIAMS, Owain Herbert Elfyn (retired) Cadlocks, Cadlocks Hill, Halstead, Sevenoaks TN14 7DU Tel: 01959 534410 — MRCS Eng. LRCP Lond. 1943; BS Lond. 1945. Prev: Surg. Regist. Guy's Hosp. Unit Orpington Hosp.

WILLIAMS, Owen Glynn (retired) Limeslade House, Limeslade Bay, Mumbles, Swansea SA3 4JE Tel: 01792 366652 — MB BS 1945 Lond.; BSc Wales 1942; MD Lond. 1951; FRCP Lond. 1975, M 1948; FCPath 1965. Home Off. Path. S. Wales & Mon.; Cons. Path. & Dir. of Laborat. Swansea Gen. & Singleton Hosps. Prev: Demonstr. (Path. & Bact.) Welsh Nat. Sch. Med. Cardiff.

WILLIAMS, Owen Martin Chingola, Tycroes LL63 5SW — MB BCh 1994 Wales.

WILLIAMS, Patricia, MBE Riverside Medical Practice, Ballifeary Lane, Inverness IV3 5PW; Seafield of Raigmore, Inverness IV2 7PA Tel: 01463 711205 — MB ChB Ed. 1968; MFFP 1993. Prev: SCMO (Family Plann.) Highland HB.

WILLIAMS, Patricia Grace Shiellow Grag, Sheillow Wood, Belford NE70 7PH — MB BS 1975 Newc.

WILLIAMS, Patricia Jill HMP Lewes, Brighton Road, Lewes BN7 Tel: 01273 477331 — MB BS 1976 Lond.; MRCS Eng. LRCP Lond. 1976; MRCPsych. 1981. (Roy. Free) Vis. Psychiat. HM Prison Lewes. Prev: GP Fordingbridge; Trainee GP Hants., FPC; Regist. (Psychiat.) Roy. Free Hosp. Lond.

WILLIAMS, Patrick Gilbert Noel Godolphin, Surg. Lt.-Cdr. RN Retd. Monteagle Surgery, Tesimond Drive, Yateley GU46 6FE Tel: 01252 878992 Fax: 01252 860677; 7 Knowles Avenue, Crowthorne RG45 6DU Tel: 01344 751290 Email: patwilliams77@hotmail.com — MB ChB 1975 Leeds; BSc (Hons.) (Physiol.) Leeds 1972; MRCGP 1984. (Leeds) Med. Director, Blackwater Valley Co-op.; Now former Hon. Tutor (Gen. Pract.) St. Geo. Hosp. Lond. Prev: Specialist in Med. RN.

WILLIAMS, Paul Glaxo Wellcome Research & Development Ltd, Greenford UB6 0HE — MB BCh 1970 Wales; MBA Brunel 1993; MD Lond. 1986; FRCPsych 1988, M 1975; DPM Eng. 1973. Dir. Med. Pract. Research Glaxo Research & Developm. Ltd. Socs: Fell. Roy. Soc. Med. Prev: Sen. Lect. Inst. Psychiat. Lond.; Sen. Regist. (Psychol. Med.) Middlx. Hosp. Lond.; Regist. (Psychiat.) Univ. Hosp. Wales Cardiff.

WILLIAMS, Paul Anthony Debyshire Constabullary, Butterly Hall, Ripley DE5 3RS Email: williamspaul@doctors.org.uk — MB ChB Leeds 1987; MRCGP 1992; DMJ 2000; LF Hons. (Med.) 2001; DRCOG 1991. Occupat.al Health Physcian; Homoeopathy. Socs: Police Surgs. Assn.; BMA; Fac. Med. Accupuncture Soc.

WILLIAMS, Paul Daniel — MB BS 1996 Newc.; DCH 2000; DTM & H 2001 Liverpool; MRCGP 2000; DFFP 2001. Locum Gen. Practitioner, Alma St. Med. Centre, Stockon-on-Teel.

WILLIAMS, Paul Eirian Medical Biochemistry & Imunology, University Hospital of Wales, Cardiff CF14 4XN Tel: 029 2074 8358 Fax: 029 2074 8331 Email: williamspe@cardiff.ac.uk — BM BCh 1979 Oxf.; MA Oxf. 1979, BA 1976, DM 1989; MRCP (UK) 1983; MRCPath 1993; FRCP 1998. (Univ. Oxf. Clin. Med. Sch.) Cons. Clin. Immunol. Univ. Hosp. Wales. Socs: Brit. Soc. Immunol.; Internat. Soc. Analyt. Cytol.; Brit. ass for allergy and Clin. Immunol. Prev: Sen. Regist. (Immunol.) W. Midl. HA; Research Regist. Blood Transfus. Centre Roy. Infirm. Edin.; Regist. (Thoracic Med.) Llandough Hosp. Penarth.

WILLIAMS, Paul Ford Dialysis Unit, Ipswich NHS Hospital Trust, Heath Road, Ipswich IP4 5PO Tel: 01473 704117 Fax: 01473 704117; 15 Broughton Road, Ipswich IP1 3QR Email: pwilliams@anglianet.co.uk — BM BCh 1976 Oxf.; MA Oxf. 1977, BM BCh 1976; FRCP Ed. 1991; MRCP (UK) 1978; FRCP Lond. (Oxford) Cons. Gen. Med. (Nephrol.) Ipswich NHS Hosp. Trust Ipswich & Addenbrooke's Hosp. Camb.

WILLIAMS, Paul Graham L'Aumone and St Sampson's Practice, Grandes Maisons Road, St. Sampson, Guernsey GY2 4JS Tel: 01481 245915 Fax: 01481 243179; Tyndale House, Les Vardes, St Peter

Port, Guernsey GY1 1BH — MB ChB 1983 Leic.; BSc Leic. 1981; MRCGP 1989; DCH RCP Lond. 1988; DRCOG 1987. (Leic.) GP Guernsey. Socs: Brit. Inst. Musculoskel. Med. Prev: SHO (Rheum.) Rotherham HA.

WILLIAMS, Paul Howard Moelfryn, Axton Lane, Axton, Holywell CH8 9DH Tel: 0174 56 86444 — MB ChB 1981 Liverp.; DCH RCP Lond. 1985. GP Prestatyn. Prev: Trainee GP Clwyd N. VTS; SHO (Gen. Med.) Whiston & St. Helens Hosps.; Ho. Off. (Gen. Med., Geriat., Gen. Surg. & Orthop.) Roy. Liverp. Hosp.

WILLIAMS, Paul Howard 11 High Street, Barford, Warwick CV35 8BU — BM BCh 1984 Oxf.; MA Camb. 1985.

WILLIAMS, Paul Martyn Medway Maritime Hospital, Windmill Road, Gillingham ME7 5NY Tel: 01634 830000; Keites Styles, Munns Lane, Hartlip, Sittingbourne ME9 7SY — BM BCh 1984 Oxf.; MA Camb. 1985; MRCP (UK) 1988. Cons. (Paediat.) Medway NHS Trust. Prev: Sen. Regist. (Paediat.) Mersey RHA.; Regist. (Paediat.) Adelaide Childr. Hosp. Adelaide, S. Austral.; Regist. (Paediat.) St. Jas. Univ. Hosp. Leeds.

WILLIAMS, Paul Raymond Upwell Health Centre, Townley Close, Upwell, Wisbech PE14 9BT Tel: 01945 773671 Fax: 01945 773152; Cartref, Town St., Upwell, Wisbech PE14 9AD Tel: 01945 772946 Email: paulwill@globalnet.co.uk — MB BS 1982 Lond.; BSc (Hons.) Lond. 1979, MB BS (Distinc.) 1982; MRCGP 1989; DGM RCP Lond. 1986. (St. Geo.) GP Wisbech.; Prescribing Lead Fenland PCG; GP Endoscopist Wisbech. Prev: Regist. (Gen. Surg.) Soton. Gen. Hosp.; SHO (Cardiothoracic Surg.) Brompton Hosp. Lond.; Anat. Prosector St. Thomas Hosp. Med. Sch.

WILLIAMS, Mr Paul Roger 94 Dogfield Street, Cardiff CF24 4QZ — MB BCh 1990 Wales; BSc (Physiol) UCC 1987; FRCS Eng. 1995.

WILLIAMS, Paul Simon 488 Gower Road, Killay, Swansea SA2 7DY — MB BS 1996 Lond.

WILLIAMS, Paul William The Church Street Practice, David Corbet House, 2 Callows Lane, Kidderminster DY10 2JG Tel: 01562 822051 Fax: 01562 827251 — MB ChB 1992 Birm.

WILLIAMS, Pauline Margaret Clinical Pharmacology Department, Greenford Road, Glaxo Wellcome plc, Greenford UB6 0HE Tel: 020 8966 3331 Fax: 020 8426 9383 Email: pmw23564@glaxwellcome.co.uk; Willow Barn, Elms Court, Little Wymondley, Hitchin SG4 7HP Tel: 01438 750340 — MB BCh 1990 Wales; Dip. Pharm. Med. RCP (UK) 1995. Sen. Research Phys. (CNS, Clin. Pharmacol.) Glaxo Wellcome plc Greenford.

WILLIAMS, Peter Peverell Park Surgery, 162 Outlands Road, Peverell, Plymouth PL2 3PR Tel: 01752 791438 Fax: 01752 783623; Home Park House, Landrake, Saltash PL12 5EN — MB BS 1980 Lond.; MRCP (UK) 1985.

WILLIAMS, Peter Yorkshire Street Health Centre, Yorkshire Street, Bacup OL13 9AE Tel: 01706 876644 — MB ChB 1977 Bristol; DRCOG 1982. Prev: Chairm. Rossendale PCG.

WILLIAMS, Peter Alexander Meredith 73 Mumbles Road, West Cross, Swansea SA3 5AA — MB BCh 1991 Wales.

WILLIAMS, Peter Ashley 248 Cyncoed Road, Cyncoed, Cardiff CF23 6RT — MB BCh 1978 Wales; MRCPsych 1982; MRCP (UK) 1982. Cons. Gen. Psychiat. & Community Psychiat. WhitCh. Hosp. Cardiff. Prev: Lect. Univ. Wales Coll. Med.; Wellcome Research Fell. & Hon. Sen. Regist. Univ. Hosp. Wales Cardiff; Regist. (Psychiat.) WhitCh. Hosp. Cardiff.

WILLIAMS, Peter David The Surgery, Butts Road, Bakewell DE45 1ED Tel: 01629 812871 Fax: 01629 814958 — MB BS 1997 Lond.; MRCGP 1997 Lond.; DFFP Cert CLAM. GP Partner.

WILLIAMS, Peter George The Surgery, 1 Arlington Road, Eastbourne BN21 1DH Tel: 01323 727531 Fax: 01323 417085 Email: peter.williams12@virgin.net; 1 Ashburnham Road, Eastbourne BN21 2HU Tel: 01323 728317 — MB BCh 1972 Wales; FRCGP 1999; MRCGP 1977; DFFP 1994; DObst RCOG 1976. (Welsh Nat. Sch. Med. Cardiff) GP; Tutor & Trainer (Gen. Pract.) E.bourne; RCGP Coll. Represen.; PCG Vice-Chairm.; LMC Chairm.; PGC Clin. Governance & Educat. lead. Socs: Assn. BRd.casting Doctors. Prev: Med. Off. RAF; SHO (Cas. & Accid. Surg.) Cardiff Roy. Infirm.; SHO (O & G) Univ. Hosp. of Wales Cardiff.

WILLIAMS, Peter Graham Castle Street Surgery, 39 Castle Street, Luton LU1 3AG Tel: 01582 729242 Fax: 01582 725192 — MB BS 1974 Lond.; PhD Lond. 1972, BSc (Physiol.) (1st cl. Hons.) 1969; MRCS Eng. LRCP Lond. 1974. (Char. Cross) Stud. Health Phys. Univ.

WILLIAMS

Luton. Prev: Resid. Med. Off. Lond. Clinic; SHO (Med.) Hammersmith Hosp.; SHO (Obst. & Med.) Brighton Health Dist.

WILLIAMS, Peter Howard Eaton Socon Health Centre, 274 North Road, Eaton Socon, St. Neots, Huntingdon PE19 8BB Tel: 01480 477111 Fax: 01480 403524; 54 High Street, Yelling, Huntingdon PE19 6SD — MB BS 1975 Camb.; MA Camb. 1975, MB 1975, BChir 1974; MRCGP 1986. Socs: MRCGP. Prev: GP Trainer Eaton Socon.

WILLIAMS, Peter Hugh Northenden Health Centre, 489 Palatine Road, Northenden, Manchester M22 4DH Tel: 0161 998 3206 Fax: 0161 945 9173; 28 Beech Avenue, Gatley, Cheadle SK8 4LS Tel: 0161 428 4464 — MB ChB 1967 Manch. (Manch.)

WILLIAMS, Peter Ian — MB ChB 1986 Liverp.; MSc 2001; FRCA 1993.

WILLIAMS, Peter Iorwerth 19 Bassaleg Road, Newport NP20 3EB Tel: 01633 267856 — MB BCh 1965 Wales; MD Wales 1981; FRCP Lond. 1993; MRCP (UK) 1971; MRCS Eng. LRCP Lond. 1965. (Cardiff) p/t Cons. Phys. Roy. Gwent Hosp. Newport; Private Pract. Newport; Expert Witness - within the fields of Rheum. Orthop. Med. Socs: Inst. Expert Witnesses.

WILLIAMS, Peter John Auchinlea House, Easterhouse, Glasgow G34 9PA Tel: 0141 771 3441 — MB BChir 1969 Camb.; MA Camb. 1970; MRCP (U.K.) 1975; MRCPsych 1980; FRCP 1999 Edinburgh. Cons. Psychiat., Pk.head Hosp. Glas. Prev: Staff Psychiat., Alberta Hosp., Edmonton, Canada; Cons. Psychiat. Dingleton Hosp. Melrose.

WILLIAMS, Peter Leslie Medway Hospital, Windmill Road, Gillingham ME7 5NY Tel: 01634 833904 Fax: 01634 833904; 9 Mansion Row, Brompton, Gillingham ME7 5SE — MB BChir 1974 Camb.; BA Camb. 1970; FRCP Lond. 1994; MRCP (UK) 1977. (St Thomas') Cons. Rheum. Medway Maritime Hosp., Gillingham. Prev: Sen. Regist. (Rheum.) Middlx., N.wick Pk. Harrow & Roy. Nat. Orthop. Hosps. Lond.

WILLIAMS, Peter Michael Gwynne Tinkers Lane Surgery, High Street, Wootton Bassett, Swindon SN4 7AT; The Shieling, Stoneover Lane, Wootton Bassett, Swindon SN4 8QX Tel: 01793 850157 Fax: 01793 848891 Email: peterwilliams@gp-j83029.nhs.uk — MB ChB 1974 Liverp.; MRCGP 1980; Cert. JCC Lond. 1979; DRCOG 1978. Trainer (Gen. Pract.) Wootton Bassett. Socs: MRCGP. Prev: Med. Off. Maj. RAMC; Med. Off. (Family Plann.) Wilts. AHA; Ho. Phys. & Ho. Surg. Whiston Hosp.

WILLIAMS, Peter Orchard, CBE (retired) Courtyard House, Bletchingdon, Kidlington OX5 3DL Tel: 01869 350171 Fax: 01869 350789 — MB BChir Camb. 1950; MA Camb. 1950; Hon. DSc Glas. 1992; Hon. DSc Univ. W. Indies 1991; Hon. DSc Birm. 1989; Hon. DM Oxf. 1992; Hon. DM Nottm. 1990; FRCP Lond. 1970, M 1952; MRCS Eng. LRCP Lond. 1950. Prev: Dir. The Wellcome Trust.

WILLIAMS, Peter Randall North Oxford Medical Centre, 96 Woodstock Road, Oxford OX2 7NE Tel: 01865 311005 Fax: 01865 311257; AlanCt., 13 Mill Lane, Old Marston, Oxford OX3 0PY — MB BChir 1971 Camb.; MA (Zool.) Nat. Sc. Trip., MB BChir Camb. 1971; MRCGP 1975. (Univ. Coll. Hosp.) Course Organiser Oxf. VTS.; Bd. of Dirs. Med. Defence Union. Prev: Partner Kentish Town Health Centre; Hon. Sen. Lect. (Gen. Pract.) Univ. Coll. Hosp. Lond.

WILLIAMS, Peter Rhys Jervis Ashfield, Merthyrmawr Road, Bridgend CF31 3NW Tel: 01656 2774 — MB BCh 1945 Wales; BSc, MB BCh Wales 1945. (Cardiff) Med. Off. to H.M. Forces Bridgend Area; Chairm. Min. of Pens. & Nat. Insur. Indust. Injuries Bds. Socs: Coll. GP. Prev: Surg. Specialist RAMC; Ho. Surg. Cardiff Roy. Infirm.; Asst. Res. Surg. Off. Mid. Glam. Hosp. Bridgend.

WILLIAMS, Peter Richard 29 Huntley Crescent, Winlaton, Blaydon-on-Tyne NE21 6EU — MB ChB 1998 Liverp.

WILLIAMS, Peter Stephen 17 Kale Close, West Kirby, Wirral CH48 3LE — MB ChB 1978 Manch.; MRCP (UK) 1981.

WILLIAMS, Peter Thomas 114 Harley Street, London W1N 1AG; 8 Devonshire Place, London W1N 1PB — BM BCh 1970 Oxf.; MA Oxf. 1970; MRCS Eng. LRCP Lond. 1970. Med. Dir. New Cavendish Centre Lond. Socs: Fell. Roy. Soc. Med.; Soc. Occupat. Med. Prev: Asst. Med. Dir. BUPA Med. Centres; MRC Research Fell. Dept. of Regius Prof. of Med. Oxf. Univ.; Resid. Med. Off. Middlx. Hosp. Lond.

WILLIAMS, Philip Anthony Dalton Royal Alexandra Hospital for Sick Children, Dyke Road, Brighton BN1 3JN Tel: 01273 328145 Fax: 01273 736685; 10 Sceptre, Towergate, London Road, Brighton BN1 6WT Tel: 01273 566926 Fax: 01273 566926 Email: paddywilliams@clara.co.uk — MB BS Lond. 1966; MRCS Eng. LRCP Lond. 1965; FRCA 1969. (Guy's) Cons. Anaesth. Brighton Health Care NHS Trust.

WILLIAMS, Philip David Rhodes Ashfield Surgery, Merthyr Mawr Road, Bridgend CF31 3NW Tel: 01656 652774 Fax: 01656 661187 — MB BS 1975 Lond.; MA Camb. 1975; MRCS Eng. LRCP Lond. 1975; MRCGP 1980. (St. Mary's) GP Mid. Glam. FPC; Mem. M. Glam. LMC. Prev: Cas. Off. & Ho. Phys. St. Mary's Hosp. Harrow Rd.; SHO (Gastroenterol.) Centr. Middlx. Hosp. Lond.

WILLIAMS, Mr Philip Mark Law Hospital NHS Trust, Carluke ML8 5ER Tel: 01698 361100 Fax: 01698 361593; Swn-y-Nant, Hermand, West Calder EH55 8QZ Tel: 01506 873714 Fax: 01506 873414 Email: philwill2927@abel.co.uk — MB BS Lond. 1986; FRCS (Orth.) 1996; FRCS Eng. 1990. (St. Geo. Hosp. Lond.) Cons. (Orthop.) Law Hosp. NHS Trust. Prev: Sen. Regist. Dundee Teachg. Hosps.; Clin. Fell. (Paediat. Orthop. & Trauma) Birm. Childr. Hosp. & Roy. Orthop. Hosp. Birm.; Career Regist. (Orthop.) Dundee & Perth.

WILLIAMS, Portia Louise 42 Seagrove Road, Portsmouth PO2 8AZ — MB BS 1998 Lond.

WILLIAMS, Priscilla Ashfield Surgery, Merthyr Mawr Road, Bridgend CF31 3NW; Llansannor Lodge, LLansannor, Cowbridge CF71 7RX Tel: 01446 772590 — MB BS 1973 Lond.; DFFP; MRCS Eng. LRCP Lond. 1973; DA Eng. 1977; DObst RCOG 1976. (St. Mary's) GP Bridgend. Socs: St Mary's Cambrian Soc. Prev: Research Asst. Orthop. Dept. Welsh Nat. Sch. Med. Cardiff.

WILLIAMS, Rachel Angharad 43 Hempstead Lane, Potten End, Berkhamsted HP4 2RZ — MB ChB 1997 Manch.

WILLIAMS, Rachel Margaret Ysbyty Gwynedd, District General Hospital, Bangor LL57 2PW Tel: 01248 384431; Bryn Goleu, Penmaen Park, Llanfairfechan LL33 0RL Tel: 01248 681742 Email: bryn@goleu.u-net.com — MB BS 1981 Lond.; MRCP (UK) 1985. (Guy's) Assoc. Specialist Ysbyty Gwynedd Dist. Gen. Hosp.

WILLIAMS, Raymond Iver John 26 Broomfield Road, Bexleyheath DA6 7PA Tel: 01322 21385 — MRCS Eng. LRCP Lond. 1950.

WILLIAMS, Raymond Stainton Tros y Gors, Waenfawr, Caernarfon LL55 4SD Tel: 01286 650317 Fax: 01286 650714; Liverpool House, Waenfawr, Caernarfon LL55 4YY Tel: 01286 650223 Fax: 01286 650714 — MB ChB 1968 Liverp.; MRCGP 1971. (Liverp.) Socs: BMA.

WILLIAMS, Rebecca Elizabeth Morlais The Spence Practice, Westcliff House, 48-50 Logan Rd, Bristol BS7 8DR Tel: 0117 944 0701, 01835 823655 Email: rebeccawilliams1@yahoo.com — BA 1991 Cantab.; MRCGP; BM BCh Oxf. 1994. (Cambridge '88-'91, Oxford '91-'94) GP Locum, Scott. Borders. Socs: MRCGP.

WILLIAMS, Rebecca Susan Oakhaven Hospice, Lower Pennington Lane, Lymington SO41 8ZZ Tel: 020 7249 8336 Email: beckywilliams@breathemail.net — MB BS 1994 Lond.; MRCGP 1999 Lond.; DFFP 1999; DCH RCP Lond. 1998. (University College London) p/t GP Retainer Lond. Prev: SHO (A & E) Roy. Free Hosp. Lond.; GP Asst. Lond.; St Marys Hosp. Lond., VTS Scheme.

WILLIAMS, Rex Darcy Alston 2 Penpoll Road, London E8 1EX — MB BS 1983 West Indies.

WILLIAMS, Rhiannon Eluned Wyn Llwyn Onn, Llangollen Road, Trevor, Llangollen LL20 7TF — MB ChB 1989 Liverp.

WILLIAMS, Rhoda 31 East Street, Tewkesbury GL20 5NR; 62 High Street, Weston, Bath BA1 4DB — BM 1994 Soton.; BM (Hons.) Soton. 1994; DCH RCP Lond. 1998; DRCOG 1999. (Southampton)

WILLIAMS, Mr Rhodri John Llewellyn Royal Glamorgan Hospital, Llantrisant, Pontypridd CF72 8XR Tel: 01443 443539; Hafod-Y-Fro, Sigingstone, Cowbridge CF71 7LP Tel: 01446 775326 — MB BCh 1978 Wales; MCh Wales 1988; FRCS Eng. 1982. Cons. Gen. Surg. Roy. Glam. Hosp. & BrE. Test Wales. Prev: Sen. Regist. (Gen. Surg.) Middlx. Hosp. Lond.; Lect. (Gen. Surg.) St. Mary's Hosp. Lond.; Clin. Research Fell. The Inst. Cancer Research.

WILLIAMS, Rhodri Wyn 50 Reedley Road, Bristol BS9 3SU — MB ChB 1997 Bristol; BDS Birm. 1990; FDS RCS Ed. 1994. SHO(ENT) S.mead Hosp. Prev: SHO (Gen. Surg.) W.on Gen. Hspital, W.on Super Mare; SHO (Orthop.) W.on Gen. Hosp. W.on Super Mare; Ho. Off. (Med.) W.on Gen. Hosp.

WILLIAMS, Mr Rhys Llewellyn 111 Ty Glas Road, Llanishen, Cardiff CF14 5EE — MB BS 1988 Lond.; FRCS Ed. 1992. SHO (A & E/Orthop.) Brighton HA. Prev: Ho. Off. (Surg./Orthop.) Luckfield Hosp. Haywards Heath; Ho. Off. (Med.) St. Helens Hosp. Hastings.

WILLIAMS

WILLIAMS, Rhys Meyrick (retired) Nethertor, 15 West Cliff, Southgate, Swansea SA3 2AN Tel: 01441 283423 — MB BS 1939 Lond.; MRCS Eng. LRCP Lond. 1937; FRCOG 1965, M 1948. Prev: Cons. O & G Singleton, Mt. Pleasant & Gorseinon Hosps.

WILLIAMS, Rhys Tudor (retired) (cons. rooms), 23 Anson Road, Manchester M14 5BZ Tel: 0161 224 8943 — MB BChir 1951 Camb.; FRCP Lond. 1972, M 1957. Prev: Med. Dir. Chesh. Community Healthcare Trust.

WILLIAMS, Richard Aelwyn Department of Rheumatology, Derbyshire Royal Infirmary, London Road, Derby DE1 2QY Tel: 01332 347171 Fax: 01332 254989; 31 Penny Long Lane, Derby DE22 1AX — BSc (Hons.) Lond. 1969, MB BS 1972; FRCP Ed. 1989; MRCP (UK) 1976. Cons. Rheumat. & Rehabil. Derby. Prev: Sen. Regist. (Rheum.) Middlx. Hosp. Lond.; Regist. (Med.) Univ. Hosp. Wales Cardiff; SHO (Paediat.) Cheltenham Gen. Hosp.

WILLIAMS, Richard Anthony James (retired) 1 Bridge Street Road, Lavenham, Sudbury CO10 9SH Tel: 01787 247682 — MRCS Eng. LRCP Lond. 1951; FFA RCS Eng. 1972; DA Eng. 1955. Prev: Cons. Anaesth. Roy. Infirm. Huddersfield.

WILLIAMS, Mr Richard Athelstan 8 Rotten Row, Great Brinkhill, Milton Keynes MK17 9BA Tel: 01525 261468 — MA, MB BChir Camb. 1951; FRCS Eng. 1957; FRCS Ed. 1957; MRCS Eng. LRCP Lond. 1950; DLO Eng. 1955. (Camb. & Middlx.) Prev: Cons. ENT Surg. Middlx. Hosp. Lond., Qu. Eliz. II Hosp. Welwyn & King Edwd. VII Hosp. for Off.s Lond.; Hon. Cons. Otolaryngol. to Army.

WILLIAMS, Richard Bartholomew Department of Rheumatology, Hereford County Hospital, Hereford HR1 2ER Tel: 01432 355444 Fax: 01432 364020; Stoke View, Shucknall Hill, Hereford HR1 3SL Tel: 01432 851438 — MB BS 1980 Lond.; FRCP 1997; MRCGP 1985; DRCOG 1985. Cons. Rheum. & Phys. Hereford Hosps. NHS Trust. Socs: Brit. Soc. Rheum. Prev: Sen. Regist. (Rheum.) Roy. Lond. Hosp.

WILLIAMS, Richard Charles Melville Street Surgery, 17 Melville Street, Ryde PO33 2AF Tel: 01983 811431 Fax: 01983 817215; Millbank Cottage, Horringford, Newport PO30 3AP Tel: 01983 865130 — MB ChB 1974 Liverp.; DAvMed. FOM RCP Lond. 1983; MRCGP 1980; DRCOG 1980. (Liverp.) GP Princip.; Trainer (Gen. Pract.) Ryde I. of Wight. Prev: Sen. Med. Off. RAF.

WILLIAMS, Richard Edward Alban Plas Afon, Glan-yr-Afon, Holywell CH8 9BQ — BM BS 1982 Nottm.; BMedSci (Hons.) Nottm. 1980; FRCP Lond. 1997. Cons. Dermat. Glan Clwyd Dist. Gen. Hosp. Bodelwyddan. Prev: Clin. Lect. (Dermat.) Univ. Glas.; Regist. (Dermat.) W.. Infirm. Glas.; Regist. (Gen. Med.) Clwyd N. HA.

WILLIAMS, Mr Richard Gareth Univ. Hospital Of Wales, Cardiff CF14 4XW Tel: 02920 742583; 16 Health Park Avenue, Cardiff Tel: 01752 769557, 02920 751718 — MB BCh 1983 Wales; MPhil Wales 1990; FRCS Eng. 1990; FRCS Ed. 1988. Cons. Otolaryngol. Univ. Hosp. Wales Cardiff. Prev: Cons. Groote Schuur Hosp. Cape Town; Sen. Regist. (ENT) Univ. Hosp. Wales; Regist. Roy. Gwent Hosp. Newport.

WILLIAMS, Richard Glyn 10 Priory Gardens, Bridgend CF31 3LB — MB BCh 1991 Wales.

WILLIAMS, Mr Richard Guilfoyle, TD 49 Manor Court Road, Hanwell, London W7 3EJ — MB BS 1949 Lond.; FRCS Eng. 1955; DLO Eng. 1954. (St. Mary's) Hon. Cons. ENT Surg. Hull Roy. Infirm.; Hon. Cons. (Oto-Rhino-Laryng.) Duchess Kent's Milit. Hosp. Catterick. Prev: Regist. Roy. Nat. Throat, Nose & Ear Hosp.; Lt.-Col. RAMC (V).

WILLIAMS, Richard James Willson 17 Westover Road, Westbury-on-Trym, Bristol BS9 3LY — MB ChB 1972 Birm.; MRCPsych 1976; DPM Eng. 1976. Cons. Child. & Adolsc. Psychiat. Roy. Hosp. Sick Childr. Bristol. Prev: Sen. Regist. Child & Adolsc. Psychiat. S. Glam. AHA.

WILLIAMS, Richard John Links Medical Centre, Restalrig Park Medical Centre, 40 Alemoor Crescent, Edinburgh EH7 6UJ Tel: 0131 554 2141 Fax: 0131 554 5363; 45 Morton Street, Joppa, Edinburgh EH15 2JA — MB ChB 1983 Ed.; MRCGP 1987.

WILLIAMS, Mr Richard John Niall Norwich — MB BS 1990 Lond.; FRCS Lond. 1994.

WILLIAMS, Richard Michael New Chester Road Surgery, 525 New Chester Road, Rockferry, Birkenhead CH42 2AG Tel: 0151 645 3464 Fax: 0151 643 1676; Wilmar Lodge, Gayton Lane, Gayton, Wirral CH60 3SH — MB ChB 1982 Liverp.; DCH RCP Glas. 1986; MRCGP 1987; DRCOG 1984. GP Wirral, Merseyside. Prev: SHO (Geriat. & Paediat.) Arrowe Pk. Hosp. Wirral.; SHO (O & G) Fazakerley Hosp.

WILLIAMS, Richard Michael Joseph Brookway, Sandylane, Oxted RH8 9LU Tel: 01883 712417 — BM BCh 1987 Oxf.; BA Oxf. 1984, BM BCh 1987; MRCP (UK) 1993.

WILLIAMS, Mr Richard Shôn The Old Boathouse, Faenol Park, Bangor LL57 4BP Tel: 01248 670178 Fax: 01248 670178 Email: shon.williams@breathemail.net; 12 Ffordd Gwyndy, Penrhos, Bangor LL57 2EX Tel: 01248 355381 Fax: 01248 355381 Email: gwilli1056@aol.com — MB BS 1989 Lond.; FRCS 1997. (UCMHMS) Special Regist. Mersey Deanery.

WILLIAMS, Richard William St Annes Road East, 24 St. Annes Road East, Lytham St Annes FY8 1UR Tel: 01253 722121 Fax: 01253 781121; 3 Shalbourn Road, St Annes-on-Sea, Lytham St Annes FY8 1DN Email: rww@shalpop.demon.co.uk — MB ChB 1983 Manch.; MRCGP 1988. Clin. Asst. (Ophth.) Vict. Hosp. Blackpool.

WILLIAMS, Richard Wyn Llidiart Gwyn, Bontnewydd, Caernarfon LL54 5TY — MB ChB 1972 Liverp.

WILLIAMS, Robat Ap-Iestyn Watkin, TD HM Prison Durham, Old Elvet, Durham DH1 3HU Tel: 0191 386 2621 ext 2339; 2 Pierremont Drive, Darlington DL3 9LZ Tel: 01325 252584 Email: dr.robat@dial.pipex.com — MB BS 1970 Lond.; LMSSA Lond 1970. (Lond. Hosp.) Med. Off. HM Prison Durh. Socs: Brit. Soc. Med. & Dent. Hypn. & Int. Soc. Hypn. Prev: Dir. Healthcare Purchasing S. Durh. HA; Unit Gen. Manager Community Unit Darlington HA.; Maj. RAMC (TA).

WILLIAMS, Mr Robert Southdowns House, 48 West Street, Storrington, Pulborough RH20 4EE Tel: 01903 742266 Fax: 01903 746395; North End Cottage, Greyfriars Lane, Storrington, Pulborough RH20 4HE Tel: 01903 744355 — MB BS 1977 Lond.; FRCS Eng. 1982; MRCP (UK) 1980; FCOphth 1989; DPMSA 1982; DO RCS 1981. (St. Bart.) Cons. Ophth. S.downs Med. Gp. Storrington, W. Sussex. Prev: Cons. Ophth. W. Sussex Eye Unit Worthing Hosp.; Sen. Regist. Moorfields Eye Hosp. Lond.

WILLIAMS, Robert Allen Mile Oak Clinic, Chalky Road, Portslade, Brighton BN41 2WF Tel: 01273 417390/419365 Fax: 01273 889192; Barrow Hill Farm, Barrow Hill, Henfield BN5 9DN Tel: 01273 491081 Email: bob.williams@drbobw.demon.co.uk — MRCS Eng. LRCP Lond. 1975; DA Eng. 1981. (St. Bart.) Prev: Regist. (Anaesth.) Roy. Sussex Co. Hosp. Brighton.

WILLIAMS, Robert Alun Menai Buckhurst Copse, Maiden Erlegh Drive, Reading RG6 7HP Tel: 0118 966 4959 — BM BCh 1972 Oxf.; PhD Lond. 1970; BSc (Hons.) Wales 1966; MA Oxf. 1976, BM BCh 1972; MRCP (UK) 1975; FRCPath 1991; MRCPath 1979; T (Path) 1991. Cons. (Histopath.) Roy. Berks. Hosp. Reading. Prev: SHO (Gen. Med.) N.wick Pk. Hosp. Harrow; Lect. (Clin. Path.) Univ. Oxf. Med. Sch.

WILLIAMS, Robert Clive 47 Anstruther Road, Edgbaston, Birmingham B15 3NW — MB ChB 1958 Bristol; MSc Lond. 1974; MRCS Eng. LRCP Lond. 1957; DIH Eng. 1974; DAvMed Eng. 1969; FFOM RCP Lond. 1997, M 1981. (Bristol) Socs: Soc. Occupat. Med. Prev: Chief Med. Off. GKN plc; Wing Cdr. RAF.

WILLIAMS, Robert Clive Anaesthetic Dept, Hermitage Lane, Maidstone ME16 9QQ Tel: 01622 729000 — MB BS 1989 Lond.; FRCA 1996. Anaesth.

WILLIAMS, Robert Delwyn, Capt. West Wirral Group Practice, 530 Pensby Road, Thingwall, Wirral CH61 7UE Tel: 0151 648 1174 Fax: 0151 648 0644; Heath Moor, 15 Beacon Lane, Heswall, Wirral CH60 0DG Tel: 0151 342 3276 — MB ChB 1956 Liverp.; DObst RCOG 1962. (Liverpool) Socs: BMA. Prev: SHO (O & G) Sharoe Green Hosp. Preston; Capt. RAMC; Ho. Surg. & Ho. Phys. Clatterbridge Gen. Hosp.

WILLIAMS, Robert Desmond (retired) Bicknor House, High St., Stevenage SG1 3BG — MB BChir 1948 Camb.; MRCS Eng. LRCP Lond. 1946. Prev: Ho. Phys. Mansfield & Dist. Gen. Hosp.

WILLIAMS, Mr Robert Edward Duncan (retired) BUPA Hospital, Jackson Avenue, Leeds LS8 1NT Tel: 0113 269 3939 Fax: 0113 268 1340 — MD 1965 Glas.; ChM 1964, MB ChB 1950; FRCS Eng. 1975; FRCS Ed. 1958. Prev: Cons. Urol. Surg. Gen. Infirm. Leeds & St. Jas. Hosp. Leeds.

WILLIAMS, Sir Robert Evan Owen (retired) Little Platt, Plush, Dorchester DT2 7RQ Tel: 01300 348320 Fax: 01300 348817 Email: robwill@bt.internet.com — MB BS 1940 Lond.; Hon. FRCPA 1977;

WILLIAMS

BSc Lond. 1937, MD 1945; Dr (hon. causa) Lisbon 1992; Hon. DSc Bath 1977; Hon. MD Uppsala 1972; FRCP Lond. 1966, M 1960; MRCS Eng. LRCP Lond. 1940; FFPHM 1976; FRCPath 1963. Prev: Dir. Pub. Health Laborat. Serv.

WILLIAMS, Robert Fraser (retired) 95 Moss Lane, Sale M33 5BS Tel: 0161 973 6046 — MB ChB 1955 Ed.; FRCPath 1975, M 1964. Prev: Cons. Microbiol. Monsall Hosp. Manch., Booth Hall Childr. Hosp. Manch. & Roy. Manch. Childr. Hosp. Pendlebury.

WILLIAMS, Robert Henry Morrah The Health Centre, Elm Grove, Mengham, Hayling Island PO11 9AP Tel: 023 9246 8413 Fax: 02392 637013 — MRCS Eng. LRCP Lond. 1974; BSc (Physiol.) Lond. 1971, MB BS 1974. (Guy's) Prev: Ho. Surg. Greenwich Dist. Hosp.; Ho. Phys. Poole Gen. Hosp.; Trainee Gen. Pract. Portsmouth Vocational Train. Scheme.

WILLIAMS, Robert Ian Treflan Surgery, Treflan, Lower Cardiff Road, Pwllheli LL53 5NF Tel: 01758 701457 Fax: 01758 701209; Bryn Eithin, Caernarfon Road, Pwllheli LL53 5YB Tel: 01758 701561 — MB BCh 1982 Wales; MA Camb. 1981; Cert. Family Plann. JCC 1984.

WILLIAMS, Robert Ian 21 Coryton Rise, Whitchurch, Cardiff CF14 7EJ Tel: 029 2069 2919 Fax: 029 2069 2919 Email: frondeg1@aol.com; University Hospital of Wales, Cardiff CF14 4WZ Tel: 029 2074 7747 — MB BCh 1991 Wales; MRCP (UK) 1995. (Univ of Wales Coll.Med) Specialist Regist. (Cardiol.) Univ. Wales Coll. Med. Cardiff. Prev: Regist. (Cardiol.) Roy. Gwent Hosp. Newport; SHO (Gen. Med.) Morriston Hosp. Swansea.

WILLIAMS, Robert John Grove Surgery, Grove Lane, Thetford IP24 2HY Tel: 01842 752285 Fax: 01842 751316 — LMSSA 1971 Lond.; DObst RCOG 1973. (Leeds) Prev: Regist. (O & G) Basildon Hosp.

WILLIAMS, Robert Kenneth Talbot Elderly Care Unit, Dorset County Hospital, Williams Avenue, Dorchester DT1 2JY Tel: 01305 263123; West Knighton House, West Knighton, Dorchester DT2 8PF Tel: 01305 852466 — MB BS 1976 Lond.; MRCP (UK) 1980. (Middlx.) Cons. Phys. (Geriat. Med.) Dorset Co. Hosp. Dorchester. Prev: Sen. Regist. N.wick Pk. & Middlx. Hosp. Lond.; Regist. Selly Oak Hosp. Birm.

WILLIAMS, Robert Lloyd 3rd Floor, 41 Home St., Edinburgh EH3 9JP — MB ChB 1993 Ed.

WILLIAMS, Mr Robert Lloyd 54 Ollerton Road, Bounds Green, London N11 2LA Tel: 020 8361 0188 — MB BS 1986 Lond.; FRCS (Orth.) 1996; FRCS Eng. 1990. (St. Bart.) Cons. Orthop. Surg. Univ. Coll. Lond. NHS Trust; Hon. Cons. Orthop. Surg. Lond. Foot Hosp. Socs: Fell. Roy. Soc. Med.; Fell. BOA. Prev: Sen. Regist. (Orthop.) Middlx. Hosp. Lond.; Regist. (Orthop.) Roy. Nat. Orthop. Hosp. Stanmore & Chase Farm Hosp.; Ho. Surg. St. Bart. Hosp. Lond.

WILLIAMS, Robert Meirion LLwyn-Y-Fedw, Tyla, Govilon, Abergavenny NP7 9RU Tel: 01873 831824 — MB BCh 1957 Wales; DPH 1962; MFCM 1972. (Cardiff) Cons. Pub. Health Med. M. Glam. HA. Prev: Med. Off. Health Merthyr Tydfil CBC.

WILLIAMS, Robert Pryce (retired) 273 Dobcroft Road, Sheffield S11 9LG Tel: 0114 236 2103 — MB BS 1958 Lond.; FRCP (UK) 1982, M 1970; MRCS Eng. LRCP Lond. 1957. Cons. Phys. (Geriat. Med.) N. Gen. Hosp. Sheff.; Hon. Lect. Dept. Med. Sheff. Univ. Prev: Med. Asst. (Geriat.) & Regist. (Path. & Med.) N.. Gen. Hosp.

WILLIAMS, Robert Stephen Ground Floor Flat, 96 Pembroke Road, Clifton, Bristol BS8 3EQ Tel: 0117 923 9283 — MB BS 1992 Lond.; MRCP (UK) 1996. (UCMSM) Specialist Regist. (Paediat.) S. W. Region.

WILLIAMS, Robin Derwent Maes-y-Vaynor, King St., Mold CH7 1LA — MRCS Eng. LRCP Lond. 1967; MRCGP 1980. GP Mold. Socs: Cas. Surgs. Assn. Prev: SHO (Orthop. Surg.) Birkenhead Gen. Hosp.; Ho. Off. Clatterbridge Hosp. Wirral.

WILLIAMS, Robin Edward Thomas Sidelands, Little Olantigh Rd, Wye, Ashford TN25 5DQ — BM BS 1997 Nottm.

WILLIAMS, Robin Huw Lloyd Tegfan, Parc Alexandra, Penmaenmawr LL34 6YH Tel: 01248 680040 — MB BS 1981 Lond.; MRCS Eng. LRCP Lond. 1981; DRCOG 1984.

WILLIAMS, Roger 64 Park Road., Hampton Hill, Hampton TW12 1HP — MB BS 1955 Lond. (St. Geo.) Capt. RAMC, RARO. Prev: Asst. Med. Off. Area 10 Middlx.; Ho. Surg. & Ho. Phys. Whipps Cross Hosp. Lond.; Capt. RAMC.

WILLIAMS, Professor Roger, CBE Institute of Hepatology, University College London, 69-75 Chenies Mews, London WC1E 6HX Tel: 020 7679 6510 Fax: 020 7380 0405 Email: roger.williams@ucl.ac.uk; 8 Eldon Road, Kensington, London W8 5PU Tel: 020 7937 5301 — MB BS 1953 Lond.; Hon. FRCPI 2001; Ac Med Sci 2000; MB BS (Hons. Distinc. in Med.) 1953; MD Lond. 1960; FRCP Ed. 1990; FRCS Eng. 1988; FRCP Lond. 1969, M 1957; MRCS Eng. LRCP Lond. 1953; FRACP 1991; Hon. FACP 1992. Dir. Inst. Hepatol. Univ. Coll. Lond.; Hon. Cons. Med. UCH.; Cons.Foundat. for Liver Research; Dir. Liver Unit Cromwell Hosp. Lond.; Cons. Emerit. to the Army. Socs: Assn. Phys.; (Ex-Pres.) Brit. Soc. Gastroenterol.; (Ex-Pres.) Brit. Assn. Study of Liver. Prev: Cons. Phys. King's Coll. Hosp. & Dir. Inst. Liver Studies King's Coll. Hosp. Med. Sch.; Prof. Hepatol. King's Coll. Sch. Med. & Dent. Lond.; Lect. (Med.) Roy. Free Hosp. Lond.

WILLIAMS, Roger Breeze Geufron Hall, Llangollen LL20 8DY Tel: 01978 860676 — MB ChB 1969 Birm.; BSc (Hons.) Sheff. 1964; MRCPath 1982. Cons. Histopath. Maelor Gen. Hosp. Wrexham Clwyd. Prev: Sen. Regist. (Histopath.) W. Midl. RHA.; Sen. Regist. (Chem. Path. & Histopath.) Leeds AHA (T); Sen. Regist. (Paediat. Path.) Sheff. AHA (T).

WILLIAMS, Roger Glyn (retired) Perivale, Higher Metherell, Callington PL17 8DD Tel: 01579 350737 Email: o+g@ukgateway.net — MB BS 1947 Lond. Prev: GP Bolton.

WILLIAMS, Mr Roger James Acresfield, Beechfield Road, Alderley Edge SK9 7AU Tel: 01625 582325 — MD 1976 Manch.; MB ChB 1967; FRCS Ed. 1973; FRCS Eng. 1974. (Manch.) Cons. Surg. N. Manch. Gen. Hosp.; RCS Eng. Tutor. Prev: Sen. Surg. Regist. & Tutor in Clin. Surg. Manch. Roy. Infirm.; Surg. Regist. Stepping Hill Hosp. Stockport.

WILLIAMS, Roger John The Chapel House, Mill Lane, Cloughton, Scarborough YO13 0AB — MB 1976 Camb.; BChir 1975; MRCP (UK) 1980; MRCPsych 1985. Cons. Child & Adolesc. Psychiat. Beck Ho. ScarBoro.. Prev: Sen. Regist. (Child & Adolesc.) Psychiat. Oxf. Regional Train. Scheme; Regist. Paediat. John Radcliffe Hosp. Oxf.

WILLIAMS, Roger John 4 Algitha Road, Skegness PE25 2AQ Tel: 01754 766766 Fax: 01754 760632 — MB BCh 1984 Wales.

WILLIAMS, Mr Roger Meyrick Horseleas, Bradfield, Reading RG7 6JA — BM BCh 1971 Oxf.; FRCS Ed. 1976; FRCS Eng. 1977; FRCOG 1991, M 1978. Cons. O & G Roy. Berks. Hosp. Reading. Prev: Sen. Regist. (O & G) John Radcliffe Matern. Hosp. Oxf.; Resid. Med. Off. Qu. Charlottes Matern. Hosp. Lond.; Regist. (O & G) King's Coll. Hosp. Lond.

WILLIAMS, Ronald Dennis Holton Road Medical Centre, 232 Holton Road, Barry CF63 4HS Tel: 01446 420222 Fax: 01446 749003 — MB BCh 1974 Wales; BSc Wales 1971, MB BCh 1974; MRCGP 1980; DRCOG 1976.

WILLIAMS, Ronald Edward (retired) 8 Heidegger Crescent, London SW13 8HA Tel: 020 8748 8137 — MB BChir 1954 Camb.; MA, MB Camb. 1954, BChir 1953; MRCP Lond. 1957. Sen. Med. Adviser, Min. Div., Ch. Eng. Lond.; Regional Med. Admissions Off. Prev: G.P Lond.

WILLIAMS, Rose Eleanor (retired) Mulberry, Station Road, Mayfield TN20 6BW — MRCS Eng. LRCP Lond. 1930; FFA RCS Eng. 1953; DA Eng. 1935. Prev: Cons. Anaesth. United Manch. Hosps. & Manch. RHB.

WILLIAMS, Rosemary Eve Daisy Lea House, Daisy Lea Lane, Lindley, Huddersfield HD3 3LP Tel: 01484 28392 — MB BS 1962 Lond.; MRCS Eng. LRCP Lond. 1962; MRCOG 1968. (St. Geo.) Assoc. Specialist Palliat.Med.Kukwood Hospice Huddersfield. Prev: Clin. Assoc. O & G Huddersfield.

WILLIAMS, Rosemary Gwendoline Orchard Cottage, Fownhope, Hereford HR1 4PJ — MB ChB 1975 Birm.; DRCOG 1978. Prev: Sen. Regist. (Community Med.) Paddington & N. Kensington Health Dist.

WILLIAMS, Rosemary Sian Risca Surgery, St. Mary Street, Risca, Newport NP11 6YS Tel: 01633 612666 — MB BCh Wales 1990; MRCGP 1996.

WILLIAMS, Mr Rowland James, OBE (retired) Llysfaen, Cardiff Road, Creigiau, Cardiff CF15 9NL Tel: 01222 890469 — MB BChir 1946 Camb.; BA Camb. 1941, MA, MB BChir 1946; FRCS Eng. 1948; MRCS Eng. LRCP Lond. 1944. Prev: Hon. Cons. Surg. E. Glam. Gen. Hosp.

WILLIAMS, Roy Stephen 2 Cefn Cantref, Brecon LD3 8LT — MB BCh 1995 Wales.

WILLIAMS

WILLIAMS, Royston Frank Woodview Medical Centre, 26 Holmecross Road, Thorplands, Northampton NN3 8AW Tel: 01604 670780 Fax: 01604 646208 — MB BS 1979 Lond.; MRCGP 1983.

WILLIAMS, Ruth Wells Park Practice, 1 Wells Park Road, London SE26 6JD Tel: 020 8699 2840 Fax: 020 8699 2552; 147 St. Leonards Road, Clarendon Park, Leicester LE2 3BZ — MB ChB 1989 Leic.; MRCGP 1995; DRCOG 1993.

WILLIAMS, Ruth Alison 2 Bear Close, Woodstock OX20 1JS — MB ChB 1985 Manch.

WILLIAMS, Ruth Elizabeth Department of Neurology, Great Ormond Street Hospital for Children, Great Ormond St., London WC1N 3JH Tel: 020 7405 9200 Fax: 020 7813 8255; 137 Wembley Hill Road, Wembley HA9 8DT Tel: 020 8902 5245 Email: ruth.williams@doctors.org.uk — BM BS 1985 Nottm.; DM Nottm. 1995; MRCP (UK) 1990; DCH RCP Lond. 1989. p/t Sen. Regist. (Paediat. Neurol.) Gt. Ormond St. Hosp. for Childr. Lond. Prev: Clin. Lect. (Paediat.) Univ. Coll. Lond. Med. Sch.; Wellcome Med. Grad. Research Train. Fell. Univ. Coll. Lond. Med. Sch.

WILLIAMS, Ruth Glyn Furnace House Surgery, St. Andrews Road, Carmarthen SA31 1EX Tel: 01267 236616 Fax: 01267 222673 — MB BCh 1982 Wales; MRCGP 1986; DRCOG 1985.

WILLIAMS, Ruth Laura Lodge Surgery, Normandy Road, St Albans AL3 5NP Tel: 01727 853107 Fax: 01727 862657 — MB BS 1993 Lond.; BSc Lond. 1990; MRCGP 1997; DRCOG 1996; DGM RCP Lond. 1995. (St. Mary's) GP Partner The Lodge Surg. St. Albans. Prev: GP Regist. Portmill Surg. Hitchin; SHO Lister Stevenge VTS; Ho. Off. (Surg. & Orthop.) Wexham Pk. & Heatherwood Hosp.

WILLIAMS, Sally Anne Orchard Medical Practice, Orchard Street, Ipswich IP4 2PU Tel: 01473 213261; Broadacres, Shotley Road, Chelmondiston, Ipswich IP9 1EE Tel: 01473 780565 — MB BS 1975 Lond.; MRCS Eng. LRCP Lond. 1975. (Char. Cross)

WILLIAMS, Sally Wynne Northern Birmingham mental helath Trust, Marsh Lane Centre, 79 marsh lane Erdington, Birmingham B23 6HY Tel: 0121 685 6817 — MB BCh 1988 Wales; MRCPsych 1994. (Wales College of Medicine) N. Birm. Ment. Health Trust.

WILLIAMS, Samuel Jonathan Selly Oak Hospital, Raddlebarn Road, Selly Oak, Birmingham B29 6JD Tel: 0121 627 1627 — Vrach 1973 Inst. of Paediat., Leningrad; Vrach Leningrad Inst. of Paediatrics USSR 1973; MMedSci (Surg. & Trauma) Birm. 1996; DPH Lond. 1978; DTM & H Liverp. 1974. Clin. Asst. (A & E, Orthop. Surg. & Traumatol.) S. Birm. HA; Hon. Fell. Inst. Accid. Surg. Birm. Socs: Fell. Roy. Inst. Pub. Health & Hyg.; Fell. Roy. Soc. Med. Prev: Lect. Teach. Hosp. Coll. Health Sc. Univ. Sokoto, Nigeria; Lect. (Med. Sc.) Univ. Jas., Nigeria; Clin. Asst. (Orthop. Surg. & Traumatol.) S. Birm. HA.

WILLIAMS, Sandra Jane Kingswood Surgery, Kingswood Road, Tunbridge Wells TN2 4UH Tel: 018920 863361; 85 Longmeads, Langton Green, Tunbridge Wells TN3 0AU Tel: 01892 863361 Fax: 01892 517597 — MB BS 1986 Lond.; MRCGP 1991; Cert. Family Plann. JCC 1988; DRCOG 1988. (Char. Cross)

WILLIAMS, Sara Catrin Rhydyfirian, Rhydyfelin, Aberystwyth SY23 4LU — BChir 1992 Camb.

WILLIAMS, Sarah 13 Aylestone Drive, Hereford HR1 1HT — BM BS 1992 Nottm.

WILLIAMS, Sarah Elin Wingfield, Penny Long Lane, Derby DE22 1AX — MB BCh 1998 Wales.

WILLIAMS, Sarah Elizabeth c/o 20 Swisspine Gardens, St Helens WA9 5UE — MB BS 1998 Lond.

WILLIAMS, Sarah Jane Riverside Surgery, 48 Worthing Road, Horsham RH12 1UD Tel: 01403 264848 — MB BS 1989 Lond.; DRCOG 1993. (Charring Cross & Westminster)

***WILLIAMS, Sarah Jane** 7 Kynnersley Lane, Leighton, Shrewsbury SY5 6RS — MB ChB 1998 Birm.

WILLIAMS, Sarah Perree 75 Labrador Drive, Poole BH15 1UY Tel: 01202 673918 — MB BChir 1994 Camb.; BSc St. And. 1991; MRCP (Lond.) 1997. (St. And. and Qus. Coll. Camb.) GP Regist. Poole; SHO (Obst. & Gyn.) Poole G. H. Prev: SHO (O & G) Poole GH; GP Tansen Mission Hosp. Nepal; SHO (Med.) Bournemouth.

WILLIAMS, Sarah Sian Occupational Health and Safety Unit, Royal Free Hospital, London NW3 2QG Tel: 020 7830 2524 — MB BS 1984 Lond.; MD 1997; MRCP (UK) 1987; MFOM RCP Lond. 1995, A 1989. (Univ. Coll. Hosp.) Cons. Occupat. Med. Roy. Free Hosp. Lond.

WILLIAMS, Scott Fraser Flat 10, 63 Lymburn Street, Glasgow G3 8PD — MB ChB 1991 Aberd.

WILLIAMS, Sean Roderick Rhys 1 Riverbank Close, Deeping-st-James, Peterborough PE6 8TL — MB ChB 1994 Leic.; BSc Leic. 1992.

WILLIAMS, Sharmistha Karina c/o Mrs. K. De Silva, 11 Caroline Close, Croydon CR0 5JU — MB BS 1988 Lond.

WILLIAMS, Sharon Louise 5 Altwood Bailey, Maidenhead SL6 4PQ — MB BS 1989 Lond.

WILLIAMS, Sian The Knowe, 43 Queen St., Perth PH2 0EJ — MB BCh BAO 1978 Belf.; DRCOG 1982. Clin. Asst. (Geriat. Med.) Perth Roy. Infirm.

WILLIAMS, Sian Emma 11 Percy Road, Boscombe, Bournemouth BH5 1JF Tel: 01202 398014; 27 Lander Close, Baiter Park, Poole BH15 1UL Tel: 01202 469446 Email: sew27@cwcom.net — MB BS 1997 Lond.; BSc 1996. (St Mary's Hospital) SHO (Paediat.). Prev: SHO (ENT), Poole; PRHO (Med.), Winchester; PRHO (Surg.), Chichester.

WILLIAMS, Sian Lloyd 9 Holroyd Road, Putney, London SW15 6LN — MB BS 1978 Lond.; MRCGP 1982; DFFP 1995; DCH RCP Lond. 1983; DRCOG 1982. (St. Bart.) GP Lond. Prev: Redhill GP VTS; Clin. Med. Off. (Child Health) Camberwell HA; Clin. Med. Off. (Family Plann.) Norwich.

WILLIAMS, Sian Margaret 33 Russet Gardens, Emsworth PO10 8DG — MB ChB 1990 Bristol. SHO (Psychiat.) St. Jas. Hosp. Portsmouth.

WILLIAMS, Sian Mia 6 Honeys Green Lane, Liverpool L12 9EW — MB BCh 1998 Wales.

WILLIAMS, Simon David St. Stephens House, 102 Woodfield Lane, Ashtead KT21 2DP Tel: 01372 272069 Fax: 01372 279123; 11 Homelands, Leatherhead KT22 8SU — MB BS 1983 Lond.; MRCGP 1989; DRCOG 1989. (St. Bart. Hosp.)

WILLIAMS, Simon Edward Beechlawn, 35 Woodthorpe Lane, Sandal, Wakefield WF2 6JG Tel: 01924 253685 — MD 1980 Lond.; MB BS 1970; FRCP 1992; MRCP (UK) 1975. (King's Coll. Hosp.) Cons. Phys. Med. & Respirat. Dis. Pinderfields Hosps. NHS Trust Wakefield. Socs: Brit. Thorac. Soc. Prev: Sen. Regist. Rotat. (Med. & Respirat. Dis.) Leeds & Bradford; Tutor (Med.) Hope Hosp. & Manch Univ.

WILLIAMS, Simon Geoffrey Royal Hallamshire Hospital, Glossop Road, Sheffield S10 2JF Tel: 0114 271 1900 Fax: 0114 271 1901; 12 Spoon Mews, Stannington, Sheffield S6 6NB Tel: 0114 233 6376 Email: simongwilliams@hotmail.com — MB ChB 1995 Sheff.; MRCP Lond. 1998. Research.Fell.Instit.Cardiovasc.Research. Univ.Leeds. Prev: SHO.Gen.Med.

WILLIAMS, Simon Graham John Dept of Medicine, Ipswich Hospital NHS Trust, Heath Road, Ipswich IP4 5PD — MB BS 1986 Lond.; MA 1987 Cantab; FRCP 2000; MD 1995 Lond. p/t Cons. Ipswich Hosp. NHS Trust. Prev: Sen. Regist. W. Middlx., Chelsea & W.m. Hosps.

WILLIAMS, Simon Haydn 137 New Hey Road, Wirral CH49 7NE — MB ChB 1994 Sheff.

WILLIAMS, Simon Timothy 4 Heron Close, Great Glen, Leicester LE8 9DZ — BM BS 1991 Nottm.

WILLIAMS, Simon Timothy Bowen 25 Loop Road, Beachley, Chepstow NP16 7HE — MB BCh 1997 Wales.

WILLIAMS, Sindy The Moorings, Peak Lane, East Preston, Littlehampton BN16 1RN — MB BS 1990 Lond.; MRCGP 1994. (St. Berts.)

WILLIAMS, Siôn Austin Gwynfa, Groesfawr, Llandyrnog, Denbigh LL16 4NB — MB BCh 1986 Wales; MRCGP 1993.

WILLIAMS, Sioned 65 Glan-y-Mor Road, Llandudno LL30 3PF — MB BCh 1994 Wales.

WILLIAMS, Stanley Robert (retired) 32 Hill Drive, Hove BN3 6QL — MB BS Lond. 1957; MRCS Eng. LRCP Lond. 1957; FFA RCS Eng. 1964.

WILLIAMS, Stephanie Jane Morecambe Health Centre, Hanover Street, Morecambe LA4 Tel: 01524 418418 — MB ChB 1992 Ed. (Edinburgh) GP Princip., Morecambe Health Centre. Prev: GP Regist. Roy. Lancaster Infirm.

WILLIAMS, Stephen The Larches, Wetherby Road, Bardsey, Leeds LS17 9BB — MB ChB 1979 Bristol; FFA RCS Eng. 1986.

WILLIAMS

WILLIAMS, Stephen Aled Runnymede Medical Practice, Newton Court Medical Centre, Burfield Road, Old Windsor, Windsor SL4 2QF Tel: 01753 863642 Fax: 01753 832180 — MB BCh 1980 Wales; MRCGP 1990; DRCOG 1985; DCH RCP Lond. 1983.

WILLIAMS, Stephen Clifford 8 Stour Close, Oadby, Leicester LE2 4GE — MB ChB 1992 Leic.

WILLIAMS, Stephen Gareth 2 Elm Cottages, Burleigh Lane, South Huish, Kingsbridge TQ7 3EF — MB BS 1985 Lond.; MRCGP 1994; DRCOG 1990; DCH RCP Lond. 1988. Prev: Ho. Phys. Qu. Eliz. II Hosp. Welwyn Garden City; Ho. Surg. Gloucester Roy. Hosp.

WILLIAMS, Stephen Harcourt Lowes Cottage, 74 Town Lane, Whittle-le-Woods, Chorley PR6 7DH — MB ChB 1979 Manch.

WILLIAMS, Stephen John Stoke Mandeville Hospital, Aylesbury HP21 8AL — MB BCh 1969 Wales; MRCP (U.K.) 1974. Prev: Sen. Regist. (Thoracic Med.) Brompton Hosp. Lond.; Regist. (Thoracic Med.) Brompton Hosp. Lond.; Regist. (Med. & Thoracic) S. Glam. AHA (T).

WILLIAMS, Stephen John Thompson Topsham Drive, Hill Road, Kilgetty SA68 — MB BS 1980 Lond.

WILLIAMS, Stephen Mark 63 Minny Street, Cathays, Cardiff CF24 4ET — MB BCh 1998 Wales.

WILLIAMS, Stephen Morriss The Garth Surgery, Westgate, Guisborough TS14 6AT Tel: 01287 632206 Fax: 01287 635112; The Spinney, Hutton Village, Guisborough TS14 8ER Tel: 01287 637416 Email: steven@argonet.co.uk — MB BS 1972 Newc.; MRCP (UK) 1978; MRCGP 1977. (Newc.) Princip. (Gen. Pract.) GuisBoro.; Cognitive Therapist The Whitecliffe Centre, E. Cleveland Hosp. Prev: Trainee Gen. Pract. Cleveland Vocational Train. Scheme; Ho. Phys. Cumbld. Infirm. Carlisle; Regist. (Med.) Palmerston N. Pub. Hosp., N.Z.

WILLIAMS, Stephen Padgett 179 Hubert Road, Selly Oak, Birmingham B29 6ET — MB ChB 1986 Birm.

WILLIAMS, Stephen Richard Trehwbwb, St Lythans, Cardiff CF5 6BQ — MB BCh 1985 Wales; BSc Wales 1980, MB BCh 1985. Trainee GP Newport Gwent. Prev: SHO (Cas.) Cardiff Roy. Infirm.

WILLIAMS, Stephen Richard The Health Centre, Lawson Street, Stockton-on-Tees TS18 1HX Tel: 01642 672351 Fax: 01642 618112 — MB ChB 1982 Leeds; MRCGP 1986; DCH RCP Lond. 1986; DRCOG 1984.

WILLIAMS, Steven The Curatage, 5 Pinfold Lane, Sowerby Bridge, Halifax — MB BS 1976 Lond.

WILLIAMS, Stuart Andrew Somerden Green, Chiddingstone, Edenbridge TN8 7AL Tel: 01892 870381 — BM 1989 Soton. SHO (A & E) W. Cornw. Hosp. Socs: BMA.

WILLIAMS, Stuart Michael 29 Purcell Road, Marston, Oxford OX3 0HB — BM BCh 1992 Oxf.; MRCP (UK) 1995. (Univ. Oxf.) Regist. (Radiol.) John Radcliffe Hosp. Oxf.

WILLIAMS, Mr Stuart Rhys ENT Department, Poole Hospital NHS Trust, Longfleet Road, Poole BH15 2JB Tel: 01202 665511 — MB BS 1976 Lond.; FRCS Eng. 1988; FRCS Ed. 1984; MRCS Eng. LRCP Lond. 1976; FFA RCS Eng. 1980.

WILLIAMS, Susan Department of Histopathology, Singleton Hospital, Sketty, Swansea SA2 8QA; 13 Parkfields, Peny Fai, Bridgend CF31 4NQ — MB BCh 1977 Wales; MRCPath 1985. Cons. Histopath. Singleton Hosp. Swansea NHS Trust.

WILLIAMS, Susan Anne Roathwell Surgery, 116 Newport Road, Roath, Cardiff CF24 1YT Tel: 029 2049 4537 Fax: 029 2049 8086 — BM 1989 Soton.; MRCGP 1994; DRCOG 1991. GP Roath Cardiff; Clin. Asst. (A & E) Cardiff Roy. Infirm. Prev: Asst. GP Penylan, Cardiff.

WILLIAMS, Susan Beris 35/7 Wood Lane, Beverley HU17 8BS — MB BS 1994 Lond.; MA Camb. 1993. (Cambridge and London) Research Fell. (Paediat. Surg.) Inst. of Child Health Lond. Prev: SHO (Cariothoracic Surg.) Roy. Brompton Hosp. Lond.

WILLIAMS, Susan Ebsworth High Street Surgery, 87 High Street, Abbots Langley WD5 0AJ Tel: 01923 262363 Fax: 01923 267374; Ashcroft, 186 Abbots Road, Abbots Langley WD5 0BL Tel: 01923 267840 — MB BS 1983 Lond.; MRCGP 1988; DCH RCP Lond. 1985; DRCOG 1985. Prev: Trainee GP Watford VTS.

WILLIAMS, Susan Elizabeth Leasowes, Clun, Craven Arms SY7 8QA — MB ChB 1997 Dundee. SHO A & E. P.ss Roy. Hosp., Telford, Shrops. Socs: Med. Defence Union. Prev: SHO Psychiat. Abeyshwym; SHO Med. Telford; SHO Surg. Telford.

WILLIAMS, Susan Elizabeth Long Barn Lane Surgery, 22 Long Barn Lane, Reading RG2 7SZ Tel: 01734 871377 Fax: 01734 750375 — MB ChB 1968 Sheffield.

WILLIAMS, Susan Gladys Kippax Hall Surgery, 54 High Street, Kippax, Leeds LS25 7AB Tel: 0113 286 2044 Fax: 0113 287 3970 — MB ChB 1989 Ed. (Edinburgh)

WILLIAMS, Susan Jane Senior and Partners, Morrab Surgery, 2 Morrab Road, Penzance TR18 4EL Tel: 01736 363866 Fax: 01736 367809; St Michaels, Trenow, Long Rock, Penzance TR20 8YQ Tel: 01736 710184 — MB BS 1985 Lond.; DRCOG 1989.

WILLIAMS, Susanne Maria (retired) Briar House, Weston Road, Bath BA1 2XT Tel: 01225 421509 — MB BS 1950 Lond.; MRCS Eng. LRCP Lond. 1950; DObst RCOG 1954. Prev: Clin. Med. Off. Child Health Bristol.

WILLIAMS, Tania Montgomery House Surgery, Piggy Lane, Bicester OX26 6HT Tel: 01869 249222 — MB ChB 1979 Liverp.; MSc Oxf. 1973; Cert. Prescribed Equiv. Exp. JCPTGP 1983.

WILLIAMS, Tegwyn Mel Caswell Clinic, Glanrhyd Hospital, Bridgend CF31 4LN Tel: 01656 662179 — MB BS 1983 Lond.; MRCPsych 1987. Cons. Forens. Psychiat. Bridgend & Dist. NHS Trust. Socs: Sec. Internat. Assn. Forens. Psychother. Prev: Sen. Regist. (Forens. Psychiat.) Wessex RHA.

WILLIAMS, Mrs Thelma (retired) Silverbrook, 50 Rhiwbina Hill, Rhiwbina, Cardiff CF14 6UQ Tel: 029 2062 6935 — MB BCh 1957 Wales.

WILLIAMS, Thomas Darlington Dewdown, Nempnett Thrubwell, Chew Stoke, Bristol BS40 8YF — MD 1954 Liverp.; BSc (Hnrs.) 1948, MB ChB 1951. (Liverp.) Sen. Lect. Physiol. Univ. Bristol; Cons. (Med. Sc.) Bristol Health Dist. (T). Socs: Physiol. Soc. Prev: Holt Fell. 1951; Med. Research Counc. Stud. 1951-3; Specialist Physiol. RAMC, At Army Operat.al Research Gp.

WILLIAMS, Thomas Dewi Meurig Prince Philip Hospital, Bryngwynmawr, Dafen, Llanelli SA14 8QF Tel: 01554 756567 Fax: 01554 749410; Llandeilo yr Ynys, Nantgaredig, Carmarthen SA32 7LQ Tel: 01267 290151 Fax: 01267 290102 Email: meurigwill@aol.com — MB BCh 1977 Wales; MA Oxf. 1976; MD Wales 1987; FRCP Lond. 1996; MRCP (UK) 1980. Cons. Phys. & Endocrinol. Carmarthenshire NHS Trust. Socs: Soc. Endocrinol. Prev: Lect. (Med.) Char. Cross & W.m. Med. Sch. Lond.; Research Fell. (Neuroendocrinol.) St. Mary's Hosp. Med. Sch. Lond.; SHO Roy. Postgrad. Med. Sch. Lond.

WILLIAMS, Thomas Henry Currer Nevill Hall Hospital, Abergavenny NP7 7EG Tel: 01873 852091 — MB BS 1972 Lond.; BSc (Hons.) Lond. 1969; FRCP Lond. 1995; MRCP (UK) 1976; FRCPCH 1997. Cons. Paediat. Nevill Hall Hosp. Abergavenny. Prev: Sen. Regist. (Paediat.) Leic. Roy. Infirm.

WILLIAMS, Thomas Ian Robertson Tregarthens, Little Weighton Road, Walkington, Beverley HU17 8TA — MB ChB 1970 St. And.; FFA RCS Eng. 1974. Cons. Anaesth. Hull & Beverley Health Dists. Prev: Anaesth. Sen. Regist. W.. Infirm. Glas.

WILLIAMS, Mr Thomas Meurig (retired) St John's Well, Great Barton, Bury St Edmunds IP31 2SU Tel: 01284 787250 — BM BCh 1934 Oxf.; FRCS Eng. 1936; MRCS Eng. LRCP Lond. 1934. Prev: Cons. Gen. Surg. W. Suff. Gen. Hosp. Bury St. Edmunds.

WILLIAMS, Thomas Neil 67 King George V Drive W., Cardiff CF14 4EF — MB BS 1985 Lond.; MRCP (UK) 1990; DTM & H Lond. 1988; DCH RCP Lond. 1988; PhD 1999. Research.Fell.Wellcome Trust.Nuffield.Dept.Med.Oxf/Rearch. Unit.Kenya; Lect. Paediat. Infect. Dis. St Marys. Hosp. Lond. Prev: Malaria Research N.. Dist. Hosp. Vanuatu, SW Pacific; Regist. (Paediat.) Whittington Hosp. Lond.

WILLIAMS, Mr Timothy Gabe The Independent Hospital, Fordcombe Road, Fordcombe, Tunbridge Wells TN3 0RD Tel: 01892 740040; Burnt Oak, Back Lane, Waldron, Heathfield TN21 0NN Tel: 014 353 2273 — MB BChir 1970 Camb.; MA, MChir Camb. 1983, MB 1970, BChir 1969; FRCS Eng. 1974. Cons. Surg. Kent. & Sussex Hosp. Tunbridge Wells. Prev: Sen. Surg. Regist. St. Thos. Hosp. Lond.; Ho. Surg. Surgic. Unit St. Thos. Hosp. Lond.; Surg. Regist. Ipswich Gp. Hosps.

WILLIAMS, Timothy John Department of Respiratory Medicine, Kettering General Hospital, Rothwell Road, Kettering NN16 8UZ; Willow House, 27A Warkton Lane, Kettering NN15 5AB — MB ChB 1969 Cambridge; MB ChB 1969 Cambridge.

WILLIAMS

WILLIAMS, Timothy Laurence 20 Clayworth Road, Newcastle upon Tyne NE3 5AB — MB BS 1990 Newc.; MB BS (Hons.) Newc. 1990, BMedSc (Hons.) 1987; MRCP (UK) 1993. Hon. Research Regist. (Neurosci.s) Univ. Newc. u. Tyne. Prev: SHO Rotat. (Med.) Newc.; Ho. Phys. Newc. Gen. Hosp.; Ho. Surg. Roy. Vict. Infirm. Newc. u. Tyne.

WILLIAMS, Tracey Elizabeth Jane Doctors Surgery, 40 St. Georges Crescent, Wrexham LL13 8DB Tel: 01978 290708 — MB ChB 1986 Manch.; DRCOG 1990. (Manch)

WILLIAMS, Trevor Dawson Oakengates Medical Practice, Limes Walk, Oakengates, Telford TF2 6JJ Tel: 01952 620077 Fax: 01952 620209 — MB BCh BAO 1982 Dub.; MRCGP 1988; DCH Dub. 1985.

WILLIAMS, Valerie 8 Ashdale Close, Alsager, Stoke-on-Trent ST7 2EN — MB ChB 1979 Manch.; FFA RCS Eng. 1983. Cons. Anaesth. N. Staffs. Roy. Infirm. Stoke-on-Trent.

WILLIAMS, Valerie Susan Seaton Hirst Health Centre, Norham Road, Ashington NE63 0NG Tel: 01670 813167 Fax: 01670 523889; 19 The Demesne, North Seaton, Ashington NE63 9TW — MB BS 1965 Lond.; MRCS Eng. LRCP Lond. 1965; MRCGP 1973; DCH Eng 1968; DObst RCOG 1968. (Roy. Free)

WILLIAMS, Vicki Erica Baugh House, Isle of Tiree PA77 6UN Tel: 01879 220323 — MB ChB 1991 Manch.

WILLIAMS, Mrs Victoria Louise The Park Medical Group, Fawdon Park Road, Newcastle upon Tyne NE3 2PE Tel: 0191 285 1763 Fax: 0191 284 2374 — MB BS 1989 Newc.

WILLIAMS, Vivien Nicola The Health Centre, Thatcham, Newbury RG18 3HD Tel: 01635 867171 Fax: 01635 876395 — MB BS 1979 Lond.; MRCGP 1984; DCH RCP Lond. 1983; DRCOG 1983. (St. Thos.) Socs: BMA; RCGP.

WILLIAMS, Wadad Tebeldy, 2 Cae Mawr, Penrhyncoch, Aberystwyth SY23 3EJ Tel: 01970 820060 — MRCS Eng. LRCP Lond. 1957. Prev: Dir. Khartoum Clinic & Harper Nursing Home Khartoum; Med. Off. Civil Hosp. Khartoum.

WILLIAMS, Walter (retired) Ty-Draw House, Blaencwm, Treherbert, Treorchy, Cardiff CF42 5DP Tel: 01443 771238 — MB BCh 1951 Wales. Prev: Gen. Practitioner.

WILLIAMS, Wendy Anne 5 Greenwood Road, Cardiff CF5 2QD — MB ChB 1987 Cape Town; T(GPP) 1992.

WILLIAMS, William 35 Abbey Gardens, London W6 8QR — MB BS 1993 Lond.

WILLIAMS, William David Cyril Dunns Lane Cottage, Evenjobb, Presteigne LD8 2SG — MB BS 1968 Lond.; FFA RCS Eng. 1974.

WILLIAMS, Mr William Gilbert (retired) 218 Myton Road, Warwick CV34 6PS Tel: 01926 491958 — MB BChir 1952 Camb.; MChir Camb. 1960, MA 1952; FRCS Eng. 1959. Prev: Cons. Cardiothoracic Surg. Walsgrave Hosp.

WILLIAMS, William Hugh (retired) Eelburn House, Westerdunes Park, Abbotsford Road, North Berwick EH39 5HJ Tel: 01620 892035 Fax: 01620 892035 — MB ChB 1960 Ed.; LRCP LRCS Ed. LRFPS Glas. 1960; DObst RCOG 1963. Prev: Med. Off. Fairmile Marie Curie Centre.

WILLIAMS, William Owen, OBE (retired) 103 Saunders Way, Sketty, Swansea SA2 8BH Tel: 01792 297664 — MB BCh 1945 Wales; BSc Wales 1942, MD 1958; FRCGP 1970. Prev: Hon. Dir. Epidemic Observation Unit RCGP.

WILLIAMS, Mr William Wood Broomfield Hospital, Court Road, Chelmsford CM1 7ET Tel: 01245 514824; 132 Broomfield Road, Chelmsford CM1 1RN — MB BS 1982 Lond.; BSc Lond. 1979; FRCS Eng. 1986; FRCS (Orth.) 1993. Cons. Orthop. Surg. Broomfield Hosp. Chelmsford.

WILLIAMS, Wyn Rowland Highways, Cayley Promenade, Rhos on Sea, Colwyn Bay LL28 4DU Tel: 01492 548268 Fax: 01745 534693 Email: wyn_r_williams@lineone.net — MB BS Lond. 1967; FRCP Lond. 1990; MRCP (UK) 1972; MRCS Eng. LRCP Lond. 1967. (Middlx.) Cons. Rheum. Glan Clwyd Hosp. NHS Trust. Socs: Brit. Soc. Rheum.& BMA. Prev: SHO, Regist. & Sen. Regist. Rheum. Dept. Middlx. Hosp. Lond.

WILLIAMS, Yvonne Failsworth Health Centre, Ashton Road W., Failsworth, Manchester M35 0HN Tel: 0161 682 6297 Fax: 0161 683 5861; 61 Redfearn Wood, Rochdale OL12 7GA — MB BCh 1987 Wales; MRCGP 1991; Cert. Family Plann. JCC 1991; Cert. Prescribed Equiv. Exp. JCPTGP 1991; DRCOG 1990. (Univ. Wales Coll. Med.) Clin. Asst. (Gen. Med.) Bury Gen. Hosp. Prev: Trainee GP Wrexham VTS; Resid. Med. Off. (Cas.) Katoomba NSW, Austral.; SHO (Cas.) Bury Gen. Hosp.

WILLIAMS, Yvonne Frances Saunders Grove Court, Upstreet, Canterbury CT3 4DD — MB BS 1970 Lond.; MB BS (Hons.) Lond. 1970; FRCP Lond. 1992; MRCP (UK) 1973; MRCS Eng. LRCP Lond. 1970; FRCPath 1989, M 1977. (Guy's) Cons. Haemat. Canterbury & Thanet Health Dist.

WILLIAMS-THOMAS, Frank Hugh (retired) Forest Surgery, 60 Forest Rd, Bordon GU35 0BP Tel: 01420 477733 Fax: 01420 477749 — MB BS 1967 Lond.; Cert. Family Plann. JCC 1975; DObst RCOG 1970. GP. Prev: SHO (Obst.) & Ho. Off. (Surg.) St. And. Hosp. Billericay.

WILLIAMSON, Alastair David Bamford Dept of Anaesthesia, Good Hope Hospital NHS Trust, Rectory Rd, Sutton B75 7RR Tel: 0121 378 2211 Email: alastair.williamson@goodhot.wmids.nhs.uk — MB ChB 1990 Birm.; MA Camb. 1990, BA (Hons.) 1987; FRCA 1996; DA (UK) 1993. Cons. Anaesth., Good Hope Hosp. NHS Trust.

WILLIAMSON, Andrea Elizabeth 23 Lochgreen Place, Kilmarnock KA1 4UY — MB ChB 1995 Glas.

WILLIAMSON, Andrew David 38 Crewe Road, Alsager, Stoke-on-Trent ST7 2ET Tel: 01270 882004 — MB ChB 1988 Manch.; BSc (Experim. Immunol. & Oncol.) Manch. 1985; MRCGP 1992; DRCOG 1991. Prev: Trainee GP Stockport; SHO Stepping Hill Hosp. Stockport.

WILLIAMSON, Andrew Rowan (retired) 8 Sutton Road, Howden, Goole DN14 7DJ Tel: 01430 430834 — MB ChB Ed. 1951; DCH Eng. 1957; DObst RCOG 1955. Prev: Clin. Asst. (Psychogeriat.) Goole & Dist. Hosp.

WILLIAMSON, Ann Helena Mary Pennine Medical Centre, 193 Manchester Road, Mossley, Ashton-under-Lyne OL5 9AJ Tel: 01457 832590 Fax: 01457 836083; Hollybank House, Lees Road, Mossley, Ashton-under-Lyne OL5 0PL Tel: 0145 783 2604 Fax: 0145 783 9363 Email: ann.williamson@zen.co.uk — MB ChB 1972 Bristol. GP Partner. Socs: Accred. Mem. Brit. Soc. of Med. & Dent. Hypn. (Hon. Sec.). Prev: Ho. Off. (Surg. & Med.) Oldham Roy. Infirm.; Ho. Off. (O & G) Oldham & Dist. Gen. Hosp.

WILLIAMSON, Mr Arthur William Rowe (retired) Cobden, Clarence Road, Tunbridge Wells TN1 1HE Tel: 01892 530509 — MB BS 1948 Lond.; MB BS (Hirs.) Lond. 1948; FRCS Eng. 1953. Hon. Surg. Tunbridge Wells Health Dist. Prev: Sen. Regist. Gen. Surg. & Urol. Guy's Hosp. Lond.

WILLIAMSON, Barbara Helen The Old Manor Barn, 2 Leatherbarrows Lane, Maghull, Liverpool L31 1AD — MB ChB 1971 Liverp. Staff Grace Doctor (Community Child Health) Roy. Liverp. Childr. Hosp.& Community Trust. Prev: Clin. Med. Off. S. Sefton HA.

WILLIAMSON, Mr Barry William Alexander Department Of General Surgery, Royal Alexandra Hospital, Corsebar Road, Paisley PA1 1DU Tel: 0141 887 9111 — MD 1980 Ed.; BSc (Hons.) Ed. 1970, MD 1980, MB ChB 1972; FRCS Ed. 1978. Cons. Surg. Roy. Alexandra Hosp. Paisley.

WILLIAMSON, Mr Bruce Christopher MacGregor (retired) Penarth, Nottingham Road, Melton Mowbray LE13 0NT Tel: 01664 565127 Email: bcmcgw@eurobell.co.uk — MB BS Lond. 1959; FRCS Eng. 1965. Prev: Surg. Asst. Melton & Dist. Memor. Hosp.

WILLIAMSON, Catherine 5th Floor, Clinical Research Building, Hammersmith Hospital, Ducane Road, London W12 0NN Email: c.williamson2@ic.ac.uk; 177 Blythe Road, West Kensington, London W14 0HL — MB ChB 1990 Manch.; MRCP (UK) 1993. Wellcome Advanced Clinic Fell. (Ostetric Med./Endocrinol.) Hammersmith Hosp., Lond. Prev: Specialist Regist. Endocrinol./Diabetes, Centr. Meddlesex Hosp., Lond.; Lect. Endocrinol., St. Mary's Hosp., Lond.; Research Fell., Muscular Endoncrinology, Hammersmith Hosp., Lond.

WILLIAMSON, Catherine 12 Cranberry Rise, Lovedough, Rosendale BB4 8FB Tel: 01706 231677 — MB ChB 1989 Liverp. Staff Grade Phys. (Adult Med.) Roy. Oldham Hosp. Prev: Regist. (Elderly Care) Burnley Gen. Hosp. & Hope Hosp. Salford; SHO (Med. & Elderly Care) Tameside Hosp.

WILLIAMSON, Catherine Jane Collingwood Surgery, Hawkeys Lane, North Shields NE29 0SF Tel: 0191 257 1779 Fax: 0191 226 9909 — MB BS 1986 Newc.; Cert. Med. Educat. Newc. 1999; MRCGP 1990; DRCOG 1988. Prev: Trainee GP N.umbria VTS.

WILLIAMSON, Charles James Francis Lloyd (retired) The Moorings, 14 Russells Crescent, Horley RH6 7DN Tel: 01293

WILLIAMSON

785371 Fax: 01293 785371 — MB BChir 1960 Camb.; MA Camb. 1960; MRCS Eng. LRCP Lond. 1961; DObst RCOG 1961; DA Eng. 1961. GP Adviser Surrey Oaklands NHS Trust. Prev: SHO (Anaesth.) Roy. Sussex Co. Hosp. Brighton.

WILLIAMSON, Colin MacGregor Felpham and Middleton Health Centre, 109 Flansham Park, Felpham, Bognor Regis PO22 6DH Tel: 01243 582384 Fax: 01243 584933 — MB BChir 1963 Camb.; BA, MB Camb. 1963, BChir 1962. (Westm.) Prev: Ho. Phys. (Med. & Paediat.) & Jun. Cas. Off. W.m. Hosp.

WILLIAMSON, Cortlandt Cecil Suffolk Health Authority, PO Box 55, Foxhall Road, Ipswich IP3 8NN Tel: 01473 323420 — BM BS 1986 Nottm.; MFPHM RCP (UK) 1995. Cons. Pub. Health Med. Suff. HA Ipswich.

WILLIAMSON, David Alexander James (retired) Rose Cottage, Woodside Lane, Lymington SO41 8FL Tel: 0159 673937 Email: davidwilliamson@onetel.net.uk — MD L 1946 Lond.; MD Lond. 1946, MB BS 1940; FRCP Lond. 1968; FRCPCH (Hon.) 1997; DCH Eng. 1947. Prev: Chief Asst. Med. Unit St. Bart. Hosp.

WILLIAMSON, David Bamford (retired) Job Hole, Kirkbymoorside, York YO62 6AZ Tel: 01751 431520 — MB ChB Ed. 1952; DObst RCOG 1957. Prev: Ho. Surg. Simpson Memor. Matern. Pavil. Edin.

WILLIAMSON, David James The Surgery, 1 Crawley Lane, Pound Hill, Crawley RH10 7DX Tel: 01293 549916 Fax: 01293 615382; 11 Selbourne Close, Pound Hill, Crawley RH10 3SA — MB ChB 1982 Bristol; MRCGP 1986; DRCOG 1986. GP Crawley; Clin. Asst. (Diabetes) Brighton HA. Prev: SHO Som. VTS; SHO (Accid & Emerg.) S.mead HA; Ho. Phys. S.mead HA.

WILLIAMSON, Mr David Martin Department of Orthopaedics, Princess Margaret Hospital, Okus Road, Swindon SN1 4JU Tel: 01793 426584; 17 Coxwell Road, Faringdon SN7 7EB Tel: 01367 240033 — BM BCh 1980 Oxf.; MA Oxf. 1981; FRCS Eng. 1984. Cons. Orthop. P.ss Margt. Hosp. Swindon. Prev: Sen. Regist, (Orthop.) Nuffield Orthop. Centre & John Radcliffe Hosp. Oxf.; Regist. (Orthop.) Nuffield Orthop. Centre Oxf.; SHO (Surg.) Roy. United Hosp. Bath.

WILLIAMSON, David Philip Harvey Grosvenor Medical Centre, Grosvenor Street, Crewe CW1 3HB Tel: 01270 256348 Fax: 01270 250786; 496 Crewe Road, Wistaston, Crewe CW2 6PZ — MB ChB 1976 Manch.

WILLIAMSON, David Watson Clifton Surgery, 151 Newport Road, Cardiff CF24 1AG Tel: 029 2049 4539 — MB ChB 1954 Ed.; FRCGP 1981; DObst RCOG 1956. Prev: Resid. Obst. Off. Cheltenham Matern. Hosp.; Ho. Phys. Chalmers Hosp. Edin.; Ho. Surg. Cheltenham Gen., Eye & Childr. Hosp.

WILLIAMSON, Deborah Kristine Thornborough House, South Kilvington, Thirsk YO7 2NP — MB ChB 1998 Manch.

WILLIAMSON, Diane Jane — MB ChB 1990 Ed.; MRCP (UK) 1994. Clin. Fell. in Dermat., Sunnybrook and Wom.s Coll. health Sci., Toronto, Ontario, Canada. Prev: Regist. (Dermat.) Univ. Hosp. Wales, Cardiff; SHO (Med.) Countess of Chester Hosp.; Sen. Regist. (Dermat.) Univ. Hosp. Wales, Cardiff.

WILLIAMSON, Dominic Brown House, Station Road, Eynsham, Oxford OX29 4HX — BM 1990 Soton.; MRCP 1993.

WILLIAMSON, Donald Mortimer Knolton Brow, 8 Ennerdale Road, Dewsbury WF12 7NE Tel: 01924 465382 Fax: 01924 465382 — MB ChB 1948 Leeds; MD Leeds 1962; MFOM RCP UK 1981; MRCGP 1968; DIH Soc. Apoth. Lond. 1958. Hon. Cons. Dermat. Gen. Infirm. Leeds & Pontefract HA; Cons. Occupat. Med. Socs: Brit. Assn. Dermat.; (Ex-Pres.) N. Eng. Dermat. Soc.; Brit. Soc. of Contact Dermatitis. Prev: Mem. NE Med. Appeal Tribunal Indep. Tribunal Serv. DSS; Sen. Regist. (Dermat.) Gen. Infirm. Leeds; Area Med. Off. (Sen. Med. Off.) Med. Serv. Nat. Coal Bd.

WILLIAMSON, Dorothy Eliza (retired) 67 Fenwick Road, Giffnock, Glasgow G46 6AX Tel: 0141 569 5017 — MB ChB 1952 Glas.

WILLIAMSON, Douglas John Eli Lilly and Co Ltd., Dextra Court, Chapel Hill, Basingstoke RG21 5SY Tel: 01256 315999 Email: d.williamson@lilly.com — MB ChB 1986 Ed.; MRCPsych. 1990. Assoc. Med. Dir. Eli Lilly & Co Ltd. Prev: Clin Research Phys. Lilly Industries Ltd.; Research Psychiat. MRC & Hon. Sen. Regist. Oxf. RHA; Research Regist. Crichton Roy. Hosp.

WILLIAMSON, Douglas MacGregor (retired) 46 BornCt., New St., Ledbury HR8 2DX Tel: 01531 635445 — MB ChB 1941 Aberd.

WILLIAMSON, Elizabeth J South Queensferry Group Practice, The Health Centre, Rosebery Avenue, South Queensferry EH30 9HA Tel: 0131 331 1396 Fax: 0131 331 5783; 35 Braehead Avenue, Edinburgh EH4 6QN — MB ChB 1977 Ed.; BSc Ed. 1974; MRCGP 1981; DRCOG 1979. GP Princip.

WILLIAMSON, Mrs Elspeth Mary (retired) Rose Cottage, Woodside Lane, Lymington SO41 8FL Tel: 01590 673937 — MB BS 1946 Lond.; DCH Eng. 1949. Prev: SCMO (Med. Genetics) Soton. Gen. Hosp.

WILLIAMSON, Emma Charlotte Mary Dept of Microbiology, St John's Hospital, Livingston Email: emma.williamson@wlt.scot.nhs.uk; Tel: 0131 225 6330 — BM BCh 1990 Oxf.; MSc Lond. 1995; MRCP (UK) 1993; MRCPath 1999. Cons. Microbiol. St John's Hosp., W. Lothian; Hon. Sen. Lect., Edin. Univ. Prev: Specialist Regist., Bristol.

WILLIAMSON, Ernest Robert Desmond (retired) 10/1 St Margaret's Place, Thirlstane Road, Edinburgh EH9 1AY Tel: 0131 446 9125 — MB BCh BAO 1949 Dub.; BA Dub. 1947. Prev: on Staff MRC Clin. Effects of Radiat. Research Unit W.. Gen. Hosp. Edin.

WILLIAMSON, Esther Jennifer Elizabeth 68 Westfield Road, Edgbaston, Birmingham B15 3QQ — MB BCh BAO 1975 Belf.; DCH RCP Lond. 1981; DRCOG 1977.

WILLIAMSON, George Henry (retired) 28A Moorend Park Road, Cheltenham GL53 0JY Tel: 01242 255388 — MB BCh BAO Belf. 1947; DPH Belf. 1967. Prev: Med. Off. DHSS.

WILLIAMSON, Gillian Florence Royal Marternity Hospital, Grosvenor Road, Belfast BT12 6BB — MB BCh BAO 1982 Belf.; MRCOG 1987. Assoc. Specialist Roy. Matern. Hosp. Belf. Prev: Regist. Craigavon Area Hosp. & Lagan Valley Hosp.

WILLIAMSON, Grace 25 Ballygomartin Road, Belfast BT13 3LA Tel: 01232 718841 — MB BCh BAO 1994 Belf.

WILLIAMSON, Mr Ian George Aldermoor Health Centre, Aldermoor Close, Southampton SO16 5ST Tel: 023 8079 7700 Fax: 023 8079 7767 — MD 1992 Ed.; MB ChB 1975; FRCS Ed. 1979; MRCGP 1986. Sen. Lect. (Primary Care) Univ. Soton.

WILLIAMSON, Ian James Royal Gwent Hospital, Glan Hafren NHS Trust, Newport NP20 2UB; 26 The Shires, Marshfield, Cardiff CF3 2AX — MB ChB 1986 Ed.; MD Ed. 1999; FRCP Ed. 1999; MRCP (UK) 1989; BSc (Hons.) Ed. 1984. (Ed.) Cons. Gen. Med. (Respirat. Med.) Roy. Gwent Hosp. Newport. Prev: Sen. Regist. (Respirat. Med.) S. Glam.; Career Regist. (Respirat. Med.) Gtr. Glas. HB; Regist. (Respirat. Med.) N.. Gen. Hosp. Edin.

WILLIAMSON, Professor James, CBE 8 Chester Street, Edinburgh EH3 7RA — MB ChB 1943 Glas.; DSc (Hons.) Rochester NY, USA 1989; FRCP Ed. 1959, M 1949. (Glas.) Emerit. Prof. Geriat. Med. Univ. Edin.

WILLIAMSON, James Frith The Brownhill Surgery, 2 Brownhill Road, Chandlers Ford, Eastleigh SO53 2ZB Tel: 023 8025 2414 Fax: 023 8036 6604; 3 Hawkers Paddock, Knapp Lane, Ampfield, Romsey SO51 9BT Tel: 01794 368084 — MB ChB 1975 Bristol; FFA RCS Eng. 1982. GP Chandlers Ford; Hosp. Practitioner, Dept. Anaesth., S.ampton Univ. Hosp. Trust. Prev: Trainee GP Soton.; Regist. (Anaesth.) Guy's Hosp. & Lewisham Hosp. Lond.; SHO (Anaesth.) Poole Gen. Hosp. Dorset.

WILLIAMSON, James Henderson (retired) 16 Southdown Court, Bellbanks Road, Hailsham BN27 2AT Tel: 01323 841868 — MB ChB Aberd. 1953; MA Aberd. 1946.

WILLIAMSON, James McIntyre (retired) 4 Castleton Crescent, Newton Mearns, Glasgow G77 5JX Tel: 0141 616 0204 — MB ChB 1953 Glas.; FRCP Ed. 1975, M 1962; FRCP Glas. 1971, M 1962; FRFPS Glas. 1958.

WILLIAMSON, James Sinclair (retired) Linden Lea, Middle Road, Lytchett Matravers, Poole BH16 6HJ Tel: 01202 625278 — MB ChB Glas. 1964. Prev: Regist. (Clin. Med.) Stobhill Gen. Hosp. Glas.

WILLIAMSON, Jean 18 Grange Street, York YO10 4BH — MB BCh BAO 1955 Dub. (T.C. Dub.)

WILLIAMSON, Mr John Ross Hall Hospital, 221 Crookston Road, Glasgow G52 3NQ; Highfield, 4 Balfleurs St., Milngavie, Glasgow G62 8HW Tel: 0141 955 0321 — MB ChB 1959; MD Ed. 1970; FRCS Glas. 1965; FCOphth. 1989; DO Eng. 1961. (Edin.) p/t Cons. Opth- Ross Hall Hosp.; Examr. Ophth. Fell. Glas. Socs: BMA; Scott. Optical Club. Prev: Ho. Off. Stirling Roy. Infirm.; SHO & Regist. Glas. Eye Infirm. Glas.; Cons. Ophth. Vict. & S.. Gen. Hosps. Glas.

WILLIAMSON, John 90 Lane Crescent, Drongan, Ayr KA6 7AH — MB ChB 1984 Glas.

WILLIAMSON

WILLIAMSON, John Bernard The MDU, 230 Blackfriars Road, London SE1 8PJ Tel: 020 7202 1563 Fax: 020 7202 1662 Email: williamsonj@the-mdu.com; 51 Astonville St, Southfields, London SW18 5AW — MB BS 1975 Lond.; Diploma in Community Emerg. Med. 1998 (University of Auckland); MRCS Eng. LRCP Lond. 1975; MRCGP 1980. (Guy's) Socs: Medico-Legal Soc. Prev: GP Auckland; GP Bury St. Edmunds; Clin. Asst. (Geriat.) W. Suff. Hosp.

WILLIAMSON, John Boyd, DSC Mainbrace, Druidstone Road, St Mellons, Cardiff CF3 6XD Tel: 029 207 7563 — MB ChB 1952 Ed.; Apptd. Fact. Doctor; Med. Off. Min. of Labour Rehabil. & Resettlem; Unit, Cardiff.

WILLIAMSON, John Bradley Department of Orthopaedic Surgery, Hope Hospital, Eccles Old Road, Salford M6 8HD Tel: 0161 787 4882 Fax: 0161 787 1754 Email: bwilliam@fs1.ho.man.ac.uk — MB ChB 1980 Manch.; FRCS Eng. 1984. Cons. Spinal Surg. Hope Hosp. Salford & Roy. Manch. Childr. Hosp.; Hon. Sen. Lect. (Orthop. Surg.) Univ. Manch. Socs: Fell. Brit. Scoliosis Soc.; Fell. Scoliosis Research Soc. Prev: Sen. Lect. (Orthop. Surg.) Manch. Univ.; Fell. (Spinal Surg.) Univ. of Hong Kong.

WILLIAMSON, John Charles Murdishaw Health Centre, Gorsewood Road, Murdishaw, Runcorn WA7 6ES Tel: 01928 712061 Fax: 01928 791988 — MB ChB 1974 Leeds.

WILLIAMSON, John David (retired) 9 Pembroke Crescent, Hove BN3 5DH Tel: 01273 776491 Fax: 01273207235 Email: jdw@pavilion.co.uk — MB ChB Sheff. 1968; DSc Sheff. 1988; FFPHM RCP (UK) 1993; MFCM 1980; MRCGP 1975; DObst RCOG 1970. Hon. Fell. Univ. Brighton; Trustee Standing Conf. on Pub. Health. Prev: Princip. Research Fell. (Pub. Health & Epidemiol.) Univ. Brighton.

WILLIAMSON, John Michael Steele Department of Pathology, The Hillingdon Hospital, Uxbridge UB8 3NN Tel: 01895 279562 — MB ChB 1980 Bristol; MRCPath 1986. Histopath. Hillingdon Hosp. NHS Trust. Prev: Sen. Regist. (Histopath.) Yorks. RHA; Lect. (Histopath.) Leeds Univ.

WILLIAMSON, John Richard Healdswood Surgery, Mansfield Road, Skegby, Sutton-in-Ashfield NG17 3EE Tel: 01623 513553 — MB ChB 1986 Sheff.; Cert. Family Plann. JCC 1989. (Sheffield) GP. Prev: GP Princip. Retford Notts; GP Trainee Alford Lincs.; SHO (Geriat.) St. Geo. Hosp. Lincoln.

WILLIAMSON, Mr John Robert William Glover Department of Obstetrics & Gynaecology, Rosie Unit, Addenbrooke's Hospital, Hills Road, Cambridge CB2 2QQ Tel: 01223 216221 Fax: 01223 586591 Email: johnwilliamson@chaucercamb.freeserve.co.uk; 8 Chaucer Road, Cambridge CB2 2EB Tel: 01223 360380 Fax: 01223 510021 — MB BCh BAO 1963 Dub.; MA Dub. 1967, BA 1963; MAO Dub. 1971; FRCSI 1967; FRCOG 1983, M 1970. (T.C. Dub.) Cons. Addenbrookes Hosp. Camb.; Assoc. Lect. Camb. Univ. Socs: Brit. Fertil. Soc.; Internat. Continence Soc. Prev: Sen. Regist. John Radcliffe Hosp. Oxf.; Regist. Rotunda Hosp. Dub.; Ho. Off. Roy. City of Dub. Hosp.

WILLIAMSON, Jonathan Timothy 29 Piccadilly, Scotforth, Lancaster LA1 4PX; Windsor Road Surgery, Windsor Road, Garstang, Preston PR3 1ED — MB ChB 1988 Manch.; MRCGP 1993; DRCOG 1993. GP Townsville Qu.sland, Austral. Prev: Trainee GP Manch.

WILLIAMSON, Julia Mary 84 Steepside, Radbrook Grove, Shrewsbury SY3 6DR — MB ChB 1985 Sheff.

WILLIAMSON, Julie Catherine 249 Hale Road, Hale, Altrincham WA15 8RE — MB ChB 1990 Glas.

WILLIAMSON, Karen Marie Department of Obstetrics & Gynaecology, Nottingham City Hospital, Hucknall Road, Nottingham NG5 1PB Tel: 0115 969 1169 Fax: 0115 962 7920 Email: kwillia2@ncht.org.uk — MB ChB 1983 Dundee; FRCS Ed. 1988; MRCOG 1989. (Dundee Univ.) Cons. Gynecological Oncologist Nottm. City Hosp. Socs: Brit. Gyn. Cancer Soc.; Inst. Gyn. Cancer Soc. Prev: Sub-Specialty Trainee (Gyn. Oncol.) Leicester Roy. Infirm.

WILLIAMSON, Katharine Frances 66 Cranmore Road, Chislehurst BR7 6ET — MB BCh 1973 Wales; DO Eng. 1978. Assoc. Specialist (Ophth.) Moorfields Eye Hosp. Lond.; Clin. Asst. (Diabetic Ophth.) FarnBoro. Hosp. Socs: MRCOphth.; Coll. Ophth. 1989. Prev: Clin. Asst. (Ophth.) Bromley Hosp.; SHO (Ophth.) Eye, Ear & Throat Hosp. Shrewsbury & St. Woolos Hosp. Newport.

WILLIAMSON, Katherine Mary Queen Alexandra hospital, Southwick Hill Road, Cosham, Portsmouth PO6 3LY Tel: 02392 286279 Email: gasgirl@btinternet.com; Holmsleigh, 4 Leith Road, Havant PO9 2ET Tel: 02392 477212 Fax: 02392 475974 — MB BS 1987 Lond.; FFA RCSI 1992; DA (UK) 1990. Cons. Anaesth., Portsmouth Hosp. NHS Trust. Prev: Specialist Regist. (Anaesth.) Univ. Hosp. Wales. Cardiff; Asst Prof. Anaesth. Indiana Univ. Div. of Pediatric Anesthesia & Critical Care Indianapolis, USA; Fell. (Paediat. Anaesth.) Childr. Nat. Med. Center Washington DC, USA.

WILLIAMSON, Kathryn Department of Elderly Psychiatry, St Cadoc's Hospital, Lodge Road, Caerleon, Newport NP6 1QX Tel: 01633 436700 — MB BS 1984 Lond.; MRCPsych 1991; DRCOG 1987. (St Mary's Hospital Medical School London) Cons. Psychiat. St. Cadoc's Hosp. Caerleon Newport. Prev: Sen. Regist. Rotat. (Psychiattry) S. Wales; Regist. Rotat. (Psychiat.) Bridgend; Trainee GP Bridgend VTS.

WILLIAMSON, Kelly Michelle 14 Blackthorn Crescent, Aberdeen AB16 5LU — MB ChB 1993 Aberd.

WILLIAMSON, Kenneth Noel Bamford Williamson and Partners, Jericho Health Centre, Walton Street, Oxford OX2 6NW Tel: 01865 429993 Fax: 01865 458410; 56 Parktown, Oxford OX2 6SJ Tel: 01865 310624 — BM BCh 1969 Oxf. (Oxf.) Tutor Univ Oxf. Dept of Primary Care. Prev: SHO (Accid. Serv.) Radcliffe Infirm. Oxf.; Gen. Med. Off. Govt. Seychelles; SHO (Obst.) John Radcliffe Hosp. Oxf.

WILLIAMSON, Kenneth Samuel Little Friars, Morning Thorpe, Long Stratton, Norwich NR15 2QL Tel: 01508 530373 — MB ChB 1957 Manch.; MSc Manch. 1960, MD 1970; FFOM RCP Lond. 1979. Socs: Fell. Roy. Soc. Med.; Soc. Occupat. Med. Prev: Dir. Occupat. Health & Hyg. Servs. Ltd.; Dir. Med. Servs. ICI plc.

WILLIAMSON, Lorna McLeod 157 High Street, Harston, Cambridge CB2 5QD — MB ChB 1987 Ed.; MRCP (UK) 1980.

WILLIAMSON, Lorraine Murray Flat 1/Left, 353 West Princes St., Woodlands, Glasgow G4 9EZ — MB ChB 1998 Glas.

WILLIAMSON, Lyn 17 Coxwell Road, Faringdon SN7 7EB Tel: 01367 240033 — BM BCh 1980 Oxf.; MA Oxf. 1981; MRCP (UK) 1983; MRCGP 1987; DCH RCP Lond. 1983; DRCOG 1982. Cons. Rheum., P.ss Marg. Hosp. Swindon; Dep. Director of Clin. Studies, Oxf. Univ. Med. Sch. Prev: GP Eynsham Oxf.; Regist. (Med.) Roy. United Hosp. Bath; Sen. Register in Rheum., Nuffield Orthop. Centre Oxf.

WILLIAMSON, Margaret Elaine 13 Kylintra Crescent, Grantown-on-Spey PH26 3ES — MB ChB 1973 Aberd.; MRCPsych 1977.

WILLIAMSON, Margaret Mary 10 Renshaw Road, Bishopton PA7 5HN Tel: 01505 862565 — MB ChB 1958 Glas. Prev: Ho. Phys. Oakbank Hosp. Glas.; Ho. Surg. Redlands Hosp. Glas.

WILLIAMSON, Mark Roy The Medical Centre, Hall Close, Marskeby-the-Sea, Redcar TS11 6BW Tel: 01642 482725; Beechwood, Victoria Terrace, Saltburn-by-the-Sea TS12 1HN Tel: 01287 622822 Fax: 01287 483334 — MB BS 1983 Lond.; MRCGP 1989.

WILLIAMSON, Mhari Bell The Health Centre, Charles Street, Langholm DG13 0JY Tel: 01387 380355 Fax: 01387 381211; 19 Whitaside, Langholm DG13 0JS — MB ChB 1978 Ed.; MRCGP 1994; DRCOG 1991. GP Princip.; Train. E. Cumbria VTS.

WILLIAMSON, Mr Michael Edward Ross Tides Reach, Shore Road, Wirral CH48 2JL — MB BCh 1987 Wales; BSc (Hons.) Wales 1984; FRCS Eng. 1991. Hon. Regist. & Research Fell. Univ. Leeds.

WILLIAMSON, Norman 1 Queen Square, Lancaster LA1 1RP — MB BS 1960 Lond.; MRCS Eng. LRCP Lond. 1960; DObst RCOG 1962. (St. Geo.) Socs: Brit. Soc. Immunol.; Brit. Soc. Allergy & Environm. Med. Prev: Cons. Immunol. Lancs. Immunol. Serv. Preston; Lect. (Experim. Path.) Univ. Birm.; Sen. Research Assoc. (Experim. Path.) Univ. Birm.

WILLIAMSON, Mr Peter Anthony St. George Hospital, Blackshaw Road, London SW17 0QT Tel: 020 87252052 Fax: 020 87253306 Email: peterawilliamson@yahoo.com — MB BS 1988 Lond.; FRCS Ed. 1994. (Middlesex Hospital) Cons. Surg., OtoLaryngol., St Geo.s Hosp. Lond.; Cons. Surg. OtoLaryngol., ST Helier Hosp., Carshalton, St Anthonys Hosp., Cheam, Pk.side Hosp. Wimbledon, Ashtead Hosp. Ashtead; Cons. Suurgeon, Head and Neck Surg., Roy. Marsden Hosp. Socs: Brit. Assn. Of Head and Neck Oncollgists. Prev: Specialist Regist. (ENT) S. and W. of Eng.; Fell. Head and Neck Surg., Roy. Marsdon Hosp. Lond.

WILLIAMSON, Peter David The Randolph Surgery, 235A Elgin Avenue, London W9 1NH Tel: 020 7286 6880 Fax: 020 7286 9787; 26 Kelly Street, Kentish Town, London NW1 8PH Tel: 020 7267 3135 — MB BS 1980 Lond.; MRCGP 1987.

WILLIAMSON, Richard Douglas Charles Wayside Surgery, 12 Russells Crescent, Horley RH6 7DN Tel: 01293 782057 Fax: 01293 821809 — MB ChB 1992 Leic. (Leic.)

WILLIAMSON, Professor Robin Charles Noel Department of Surgery, Imperial College School of Medicine, Hammersmith Hospital, London W12 0NN Tel: 020 7290 2977 (RSM), 020 7290 3920 (RSM), 020 8383 3210 Email: r.williamson@ic.ac.uk, robin.williamson@rsm.ac.uk; The Barn, 88 Lower Road, Gerrards Cross SL9 8LB Tel: 01753 889816 — MB BChir 1968 Camb.; MA Camb. 1968, BA (1st cl. Hons.) 1964, MD 1983, MChir 1978; Hon. PhD Mahidol Univ. 1994; FRCS Eng. 1972; Hon. FRCS Thailand 1992. (Camb. & St. Bart.) p/t Cons. Surg. Hammersmith Hosp. Lond.; Assoc. Dean Roy. Soc. of Med.; Prof. Surg. Imp. Coll. Sch. Med; Examr. in Primary FRCS Exam 1981-1988 & Intercollegiate FRCS Exam 1994-; Mem. Advisery Comm. Mason Med. Research Foundat. 1999; Mem. Intercollegiate Bd. in Gen. Surg. 1998. Socs: (Ex-Pres.) Pancreatic Soc.; (Ex-Pres.) Assn. Surgs. GB & Irel. (Chairm. Scientif. Comm.); (Pres) Europ. Soc. Surgs. Prev: Prof. Surg. Univ. Bristol & Hon. Cons. Surg. Avon HA & SW RHA; Sen. Regist. (Surg.) United Bristol Hosps. & SW RHB; Clin. & Research Fell. (Surg.) Mass. Gen. Hosp. & Harvard Med . Sch. Boston, USA.

WILLIAMSON, Rodney Ashton Road Surgery, 58 Ashton Road, Droylsden, Manchester M43 7BW Tel: 0161 370 1610 Fax: 0161 371 1258 — MB ChB 1971 Manch. GP Manch.

WILLIAMSON, Rodney Victor Wantage Mews, Main St., Middleton, Market Harborough LE16 8YU — MB BS 1986 Tasmania; MRCP (UK) 1994.

WILLIAMSON, Roland Hugh Bamford, Lt.-Col. Job Hole, Kirbymoorside, York YO62 6AZ Tel: 01751 431520 Email: hugh.williamson@virgin.net — MSc (Occupat. Health) Aberd. 1994; MFOM 1998; MRCGP 1990. (Univ. Ed.) Occupat. Med. (Army). Socs: Soc. of Occup. Med.; Roy. Soc. Med. Prev: RMO 1QO HLDRS./2SG; Ho. Off. (Gen. Med., Gen. Surg. & Orthop.) Bangour Gen. Hosp. W. Lothian; Occ Med Trainee (army).

WILLIAMSON, Ruth Hammersmith Hospital Imaging Department, Du Cane Road, London W12 0NN Tel: 020 8383 3389; 14 Brisbane Avenue, Wimbledon, London SW19 3AG Tel: 020 8540 3079 Email: ruth@williamson.demon.co.uk — MB BS 1989 Lond.; BSc Lond. 1986, MB BS 1989; MRCP (UK) 1992; FRCR 1997.

WILLIAMSON, Sally Suzanne Hardwicke House Surgery, Hardwicke House, Stour Street, Sudbury CO10 2AY Tel: 01787 370011 Fax: 01787 376521; Churchside Cottage, Little Waldingfield, Sudbury CO10 0SW Tel: 01787 247934 — MB BS 1981 Lond.; DRCOG 1984. (St. Thos.) Clin. Med. Off. Mid. Anglia Community Trust. Prev: SHO (O & G) St. Thos. Hosp. Lond.; Cas. Off. St. Peter's Hosp. Chertsey; Ho. Surg. St. Thos. Hosp. Lond.

WILLIAMSON, Scott Moray 40 Fortingall Place, Glasgow G12 0LT — MB ChB 1993 Ed.

WILLIAMSON, Sean Francis 9 Cringle Moor Chase, Great Broughton, Middlesbrough TS9 7HS — MB ChB 1988 Ed.; DA (UK) 1990; FRCA 1994. Cons. NeuroAnaesth. S. Cleveland Hosp. Middlesbrough.

WILLIAMSON, Sheila Anne Higgen (retired) 4 Castleton Crescent, Newton Mearns, Glasgow G77 5JX Tel: 0141 616 0204 — MB ChB 1956 Glas. Prev: Assoc. Specialist Ultrasonics Paisley Matern. Hosp.

WILLIAMSON, Shona Margaret Health Clinic, Mid Street, Bathgate EH48 1PT Tel: 01506 655155; 11 Riselaw Road, Edinburgh EH10 6HR Tel: 0131 447 5854 — MB ChB 1986 Ed.; MRCGP 1991; DRCOG 1989.

WILLIAMSON, Sigrun Karin Albertville Drive Surgery, 16 McCandless Street, Crumlin Road, Belfast BT13 1RU Tel: 028 9074 6308 Fax: 028 9074 9847; 13 Strathyre Park, Belfast BT10 0AZ Tel: 01232 601730 — MB BCh BAO 1973 Belf. (QUB)

WILLIAMSON, Sophia Louisa Harriet Queen Elizabeth Hospital, Gateshead NE9 6SX — BM 1989 Soton.; MRCPath 1998. Cons. Histopath., Qu. Eliz. Hopital, Gateshead.

WILLIAMSON, Stuart William Harvey Hospital, Ashford TN24 0LZ Tel: 01233 633331 — MB ChB 1967 Sheff.; MRCP (UK) 1972; FRCP Lond. 1996; DCH Eng. 1969; FRCPCH 1997. (Sheff.) Cons. Paediat. E. Kent Hosp.NHS Trust. Prev: Sen. Regist. King's Coll. Hosp. Lond.; Jun. Regist. (Paediat.) St. Thos. Hosp. Lond.

WILLIAMSON, Thomas Arthur (retired) 44 Erridge Road, London SW19 3JB Tel: 020 8540 7935 — MB BS 1947 Lond.; MRCS Eng. LRCP Lond. 1947; MRCGP 1973. Prev: Div. Surg. St. John's Ambul. Assn.

WILLIAMSON, Mr Thomas Hardie Ophthalmology, St Thomas' Hospital, Lambeth Palace Road, London SE1 7EH Tel: 020 7928 9292 Fax: 020 7922 8157 — MB ChB 1984 Glas.; MD Glas. 1995; FRCS Glas. 1988; FRCOphth 1988. (Univ. Glas.) Cons. (Ophth.) St Thomas Hosp. Lond.; Hon. Sen. Lect. UMDS. Prev: SHO (Ophth.) Aberd. Roy. Infirm.; SHO (Ophth.) Addenbrooke's Hosp. Camb.; Sen. Regist. Tennent Inst. Glas.

WILLIAMSON, Timothy James 9 Calton Road, Bath BA2 4PP Tel: 01225 420905 — MB 1969 Camb.; BChir 1968; DObst RCOG 1971. (St. Thos.) SCMO Bath & W. Community NHS Trust. Socs: Brit. Assn. Community Child Health; Brit. Assn. Community Drs in Audiol. Prev: SHO (Geriat.) St. Martin's Hosp. Bath; GP Bath; Med. Off. Nigerian Red Cross.

WILLIAMSON, Vincent Charles Department of Radiology, Arrowe Park Hospital, Upton, Wirral CH49 5PE Tel: 0151 678 5111 — MB ChB 1983 Wales; BSc 2000 (HonsOpen); FRCR 1989; DMRD Aberd. 1987. (Cardiff) Cons. Diagn. Radiol. Wirral Hosps. Merseyside. Socs: Assn. Chest Radiol.; Brit. Med. Assn.; Roy. Coll. of Radiologists. Prev: Sen. Regist. (Diagn. Radiol.) Liverp.; Regist. (Diagn. Radiol.) Aberd. Roy. Infirm.; SHO (Gen. Med.) Bishop Auckland Gen. Hosp.

WILLIAMSON, Walter (retired) Castle Hill House, Middleham, Leyburn DL8 4QW Tel: 01969 623302 — MRCS Eng. LRCP Lond. 1959; DObst RCOG 1963.

WILLICOMBE, Peter Richard PO Box 43, Civic Centre Road, Havant PO9 2AQ Tel: 023 9248 2124 Fax: 023 9247 5515; 10 Westbourne Avenue, Emsworth PO10 7QU — MB BChir 1975 Camb.; MA Camb. 1975; MRCP (UK) 1977; DRCOG 1982. (Camb. & Guy's) Hosp. Pract. (Med.) St. Mary's Hosp. Portsmouth. Prev: Regist. (Med.) St. Thos. Hosp. Lond.; SHO (Thoracic Med.) Brompton Hosp. Lond.; Ho. Off. (Med.) Guy's Hosp. Lond.

WILLIETS, Trevor Herbert Department of Pathology, Broadgreen Hospital, Thomas Drive, Liverpool L14 3LB Tel: 0151 228 4878 — MB ChB 1958 Birm.; MRCPath 1969. (Birm.) Cons. Pathol. E. Liverp. Hosp. Gp.; Hon. Clin. Lect. Univ. Liverp. Socs: Assn. Clin. Pathols. & Path. Soc. Prev: Regist. (Path.) Birm. Childr. Hosp. & Worcester Roy. Infirm.; Lect. in Bact. Univ. Leeds.

WILLIMOTT, Edith Jane Young Peoples Department, Newberry Centre, West Hare Hospital, Middlesbrough TS5 4EE Tel: 01642 352113 — MB ChB 1981 Aberd.; MRCPsych 1985. Cons. (Adolesc. Psychiat.) Newberry Centre, W. Hare Hosp., M'Boro. Prev: Sen. Regist. (Child & Family Psychiat.) Fleming Nuffield Unit Newc.; Regist. (Child & Adolesc. Psychiat.) Crichton Roy. Hosp. Dumfries.

WILLINGTON, Frederick Lane (retired) Innisfree, 40 Plymouth Road, Buckfastleigh TQ11 0DG Tel: 01364 642802 — MB BCh BAO (Hons.) Dub. 1939; MD Dub. 1960. Vis. Prof. (Geriat. Med.) Univ. W.. Ontario, Canada; Recognised Clin. Teach. (Geriat. Med.) Welsh Nat. Sch. Med. Cardiff. Prev: Cons. Phys. (Geriat. Med.) Univ. Hosp. Wales, Cardiff & St. David's Hosp. Cardiff.

WILLIS, Allan Trevor (retired) 16 Biddenham Turn, Biddenham, Bedford MK40 4AT — MD 1962 Melbourne; PhD Leeds 1956; DSc 1971; MB BS 1952; FRACP 1974, M 1966; FRCPA 1972; FRCPath 1976, M 1963; MCPA 1963. Prev: Dir. Pub. Health Laborat. Luton.

WILLIS, Andrew Charles The Diabetes Centre, Queen's Hospital, Belvedere rd, Burton-on-Trent DE13 0RB Tel: 01283 566333 Fax: 01283 593056 — MB BS 1987 Lond.; MRCP (UK) 1991. (St. Thomas' Hospital Me. School) Cons. Phys. in Gen. Med., Diabetes & Endocrinol., Burton Hosps. NHS Trust. Prev: Specialist Regist. (Diabetes & Endocrinol.) Walsgrave Hosp. Coventry; Specialist Regist. (Diabetes & Endocrinol.) Univ. Hosp., Birm.; Research Fell. (Diabetic Med.) Generla Hosp., Birm.

WILLIS, Andrew Peter David 8 Coombe Park, Sutton Coldfield B74 2QB — MB BS 1997 Lond.

WILLIS, Andrew William Dr A Willis and Partners, King Edward Road Surgery, Christchurch Medical Centre, King Edward Road, Northampton NN1 5LY Tel: 01604 633466 Fax: 01604 603227; 19 Thorburn Road, Northampton NN3 3DA Tel: 01604 412283 Fax: 01604 401260 — MB BS 1970 Lond.; MSocSc (Health Serv. Managem.) Birm. 1991; FRCGP 1995, M 1975; DCH Eng. 1973; DObst RCOG 1972. (Middlx.) Pres. NHS PCG Alliance. Prev: Liaison GP N.ants. HA; GP Computer Facilitator N.ants. FHSA; Chairm. Nat. Assn. Commiss. GPs.

WILLIS

WILLIS, Anthony John Percival (retired) 49 Crowstone Road, Westcliff on Sea SS0 8BG Tel: 01702 45974 — MB BS 1954 Lond.; MRCP Lond. 1959. Prev: Cons. Phys. S.end Hosp. Gp.

WILLIS, Antony Graham 41C Macfarlane Road, London W12 7JY — MB BChir 1993 Camb.

WILLIS, Audrey Spencer 2 Grovelands, Lower Bourne, Farnham GU10 3RQ — 1943 MRCS LRCP; MB BChir Camb. 1945; FRCP Lond. 1980, M 1954; DCH Eng. 1962. (Univ. Coll. Hosp.) Emerit. Cons. Phys. (Geriat. Med.) W. Surrey & NE Hants. HA. Prev: Sen. Regist. (Med.) Roy. United Hosps. Bath; Ho. Phys. (Med.) & Harker-Smith Regist. Univ. Coll. Hosp. Lond.

WILLIS, Brian Alexander Anaesthetic Department, University Hospital of Wales, Heath Park, Cardiff CF14 4WZ Tel: 029 2074 3255; 14 Heol Isaf, Radyr, Cardiff CF15 8AL — MB BCh 1981 Wales; PhD Wales 1968, BSc 1965, MB BCh 1981; FFA RCS Eng. 1985. Cons. Anaesth. Cardiff & Vale Trust; Clin. Dir. For Anaesth. Cardiff & Vale Trust, Cardiff. Prev: Sen. Regist. (Anaesth.) Univ. Hosp. Wales Cardiff.

WILLIS, Bryony Margaret Heather House, 21 Wantage Road, Wallingford OX10 0LR Tel: 01491 834327 Fax: 01491 834327 Email: bryonywillis@doctors.org.uk — MB BS 1975 Newc.; DRCOG 1978. Clin. Asst. (Fertil.) Oxf. RHA. Socs: Brit. Fertil. Soc.

WILLIS, Catherina Joanna 41C Macfarlane Road, London W12 7JY — MB BS 1993 Lond.

WILLIS, Charlotte Helen 1 Stafford Road, Brighton BN1 5PE — MB BS 1992 Lond.

WILLIS, Claire Elizabeth 9 St Ellens, Edenderry, Belfast BT8 8JN — MB BCh BAO 1991 Belf.

WILLIS, Claire Joanne 28 Wenden Road, Newbury RG14 7AE — MB BS 1996 Lond.

WILLIS, David Andrew Ware Road Surgery, 59 Ware Road, Hoddesdon EN11 9AB Tel: 01992 463363 Fax: 01992 471108 — MB BS 1979 Lond.; BSc (Hons.) Lond. 1970, MB BS 1979; DRCOG 1982. (Char. Cross) Prev: Trainee GP Welwyn Garden City VTS; Ho. Phys. St. Albans City Hosp; Ho. Surg. Wembley Hosp.

WILLIS, David Michael Ferryhill Medical Practice, Durham Road, Ferryhill DL17 8JJ Tel: 01740 651238 Fax: 01740 656291 — MB BS 1987 Newc.; MRCGP 1991; DCH RCP Lond. 1991; DRCOG 1990. Socs: BMA. Prev: Trainee GP Ulverston, Cumbria FPC.

WILLIS, Derek 41 Stutton Road, Tadcaster LS24 9HE — MB ChB 1993 Birm.; MB ChB (Hons.) Birm. 1993. (Birmingham) Socs: Roy. Coll. Phys. (Edin.).

WILLIS, Eunice Mary Weston Favell Health Centre, Weston Favell Centre, Northampton NN3 8DW Tel: 01604 409002 Fax: 01604 407034; 19 Thorburn Road, Weston Favell, Northampton NN3 3DA — MB BS 1970 Lond.; MB BS (Hons.) Lond. 1970. (Middlx.) Clin. Asst. (Infertil.) N.ants. Gen. Hosp. Prev: SHO (Paediat.) N.ampton Gen. Hosp.; Ho. Phys. (Gen. Med.) Salisbury Gen. Hosp.

WILLIS, Fenella Mai St George's Hospital, Blackshaw Rd, London SW17 0QT; 29 Alverstone Avenue, Wimbledon Park, London SW19 8BD — MB BS 1993 Lond.; 2000 DipPCPath; BSc 1990; MRCP 1996. (Roy. Free Hosp.) Specialist Regist. (Haemat.) St. Geo.'s Hosp., Tooting. Socs: Roy. Coll. Phys.; BMA; Brit. Soc. Haematol. Prev: Specialist Regist. (Haematol.) Mayday Hosp.; Specialist Regist. (Haematol.) St Helier's Hosp..; Specialist Regist. (Haemat.) Marsden Hosp.

WILLIS, Francis Peter (retired) Westow Lodge, Westow, York YO60 7LQ Tel: 01653 618204 Fax: 01653 618204 — MB BS Lond. 1950. Prev: Ho. Off. St. Mary's Hosp. & Roy. N.. Hosp. Lond.

WILLIS, Francis Robert Renal Unit, Royal Hospital for Sick Children, Yorkhill, Glasgow G3 8SJ Tel: 0141 201 0000 Fax: 0141 201 0859 — MB BS 1987 West. Austral.; FRACP 1994; DCCH RCP Ed. 1990; DCH RCP Glas. 1990. Sen. Regist. (Paediat. Nephrol.) Roy. Hosp. Sick Childr. Glas. Prev: Chief Regist. P.ss Margt. Hosp. Childr. Perth, W.. Austral.

WILLIS, Geoffrey Mark 12 Myrdle Court, Myrdle St., London E1 1HP — MB BS 1982 Lond.

WILLIS, Jacob 3 Broomhill Court, Belfast BT9 5HA Tel: 028 667221 — MD 1960 Belf.; MB BCh BAO 1956; FRCPath 1978, M 1966. (Belf.) Cons. Path. E. Health & Social Servs. Bd. Socs: Fell. Internat. Acad. Cytol.; Brit. Soc. Clin. Cytol. Prev: Sen. Regist. Path. N. Irel. Hosp. Auth.; Asst. Lect. Path. Qu. Univ. Belf.

WILLIS, James Alexander Ratcliffe Alton Health Centre, Anstey Road, Alton GU34 2QX Tel: 01420 84676 Fax: 01420 542975; Greenacre, 28 Borovere Lane, Alton GU34 1PB Tel: 01420 83416 Fax: 01420 83416 Email: jarwillis@compuserve.com — MB BS 1967 Lond.; FRCGP 1996, M 1973; DCH Eng. 1970; DObst RCOG 1969. (Middlx.) Prev: Ho. Phys. Middlx. Hosp.; Ho. Surg. Mt. Vernon Hosp. N.wood; Ho. Phys. (Paediat.) Whittington Hosp. Lond.

WILLIS, James Herbert Patrick c/o Lionel J. Lewis & Company, 117 Burnt Ash Road, London SE12 8RA — MB BS 1954 Lond.; FRCP Ed. 1972, M 1960; MRCS Eng. LRCP Lond. 1954; FRCPsych 1975.

WILLIS, Janet 1 Dunluce Avenue, Belfast BT9 7HR — MB BCh BAO Belf. 1978; MRCGP 1984; DCH Dub. 1984.

WILLIS, Janet Elizabeth (retired) Bradley Cross Farm, Bradley Cross, Cheddar BS27 3YU — MB ChB 1974 Sheff.; MRCGP 1979. SCMO (Child Health) S.mead HA. Prev: Trainee GP Bristol VTS.

WILLIS, Jennifer Mary Rae (retired) 5 Fenwick Close, Jesmond, Newcastle upon Tyne NE2 2LE — MB ChB Ed. 1957; DObst RCOG 1960; Cert FPA 1975. Prev: Clin. Med. Off. (Family Plann.) N. Tyneside AHA.

WILLIS, John Hodgson (retired) Wressle House, Brigg DN20 0BU — MB BS 1952 Lond. Prev: GP Brigg.

WILLIS, Kathryn Ann The Barn Surgery, Christchurch Medical Centre, 1 Purewell Cross Road, Christchurch BH23 3AF Tel: 01202 486456 — BM 1985 Soton. Prev: Trainee GP Bournemouth; SHO (Paediat.) Soton HA; SHO (Psychiat.) Salisbury HA.

WILLIS, Keith James 16 Southsea Avenue, Goring-bySea, Worthing BN12 4BN — MB ChB 1968 Birm.; MRCP (UK) 1972.

WILLIS, Kenneth Maddern 42 Great Bushey Drive, London N20 8QL Tel: 020 8445 2263 — MB ChB 1939 Liverp. (Liverp.) Prev: Med. Off. Roy. Infirm. Liverp. & Clatterbridge EMS Hosp.; RAFVR.

WILLIS, Laura Kathryn 27 Crawford Gardens, Horsham RH13 5AZ — MB BS 1998 Lond.

WILLIS, Linda Gertrude Francis Eglwysbach Surgery, Berw Road, Pontypridd CF37 2AA Tel: 01443 406811 Fax: 01443 405457; 14 Heol Isaf, Radyr, Cardiff CF15 8AL Tel: 01222 844459 Fax: 01222 844459 — MB BCh 1968 Wales; Dip. Palliat. Med. Wales 1991. (Cardiff) Hosp. Pract. (Anaesth.) E. Glam. Hosp. Pontypridd; Hosp. Pract. (Palliat. Med.) Y. Bwthyn Continuing Care Unit Pontypridd.

WILLIS, Malcolm David Fergus, Maj. RAMC Retd. Long Stratton Health Centre, Flowerpot Lane, Long Stratton, Norwich NR15 2TS Tel: 01508 530781 Fax: 01508 533030; Tawny Lodge, The Green, Wacton, Norwich NR15 2UN Tel: 01508 532358 Fax: 01508 530848 Email: malcwillis@hotmail.com — MB BS 1979 Lond.; MRCGP 1984. (St. Mary's) Prev: SHO (ENT, Dermat., Ophth., Accid & Emerg. & O & G) Camb. Milit. Hosp.

WILLIS, Marcia Pearl Louise 27 Winterbourne Road, Thornton Heath, Croydon CR7 7QX — MB BS 1996 Lond.; BSc Hons. (Neurosci.) 1993. (Royal Free Hospital London) Prev: SHO (A & E Med.) Chase Farm Hosp. Enfield; Ho. Off. (Orthop. & Gen. Surg.) Roy. Free Hosp.; Ho. Off. (Gen. Med. & c/o the Elderly) QE II Hosp. Kings Lynn Norf.

WILLIS, Mark Howard George Child and Family Clinic, St Peters House, Bricket Road, St Albans AL1 3JW — MB BS 1993 Lond.; BSc Lond. 1990, MB BS 1993.

WILLIS, Michael John 85 Castlecroft Road, Finchfield, Wolverhampton WV3 8BY — MB ChB 1985 Birm.; ChB Birm. 1985.

WILLIS, Michael Robert 72 Osmaston Road, Birkenhead CH42 8LP — MB ChB 1971 Liverp.

WILLIS, Peter Sunnybank, Stourbridge Road, Penn, Wolverhampton WV4 5NF — MB ChB 1978 Birm.; BSc (Hons.) Birm. 1973, MB ChB 1978.

WILLIS, Peter Burn Brae Surgery, Hencotes, Hexham NE46 2ED Tel: 01434 603627 Fax: 01434 606373; Wall Station, Wall, Hexham NE46 Tel: 01434 681045 — MB BS 1967 Newc.; DCH Eng. 1970; DObst RCOG 1969.

WILLIS, Peter Frederick (retired) 9 Westleigh Road, Barton Seagrave, Kettering NN15 5AJ Tel: 01536 614615 — MRCS Eng. LRCP Lond. 1950; FFA RCS Eng. 1963; DA Eng. 1957. Cons. Anaesth. Kettering & N.ampton Area Dept. Prev: Anaesth. Regist. Roy. Nat. Throat, Nose & Ear Hosp. & Whittington.

WILLIS, Peter John Valiant (retired) 44 Hemingford Road, London N1 1DB Tel: 020 7609 2479 — MB BS 1967 Lond.; MRCS Eng. LRCP Lond. 1966; DObst RCOG 1969. Prev: GP Lond.

WILLIS, Mr Ralph Glen Woodfield, Whitchurch Road, Chester CH3 6AE Tel: 01244 335756 — MB ChB 1983 Leeds; FRCS Ed. 1991; DRCOG 1995; DA (UK) 1994. (Univ. Leeds)

WILLIS, Richard John Salisbury Independent Medical Practice, 5 Wyndham Road, Salisbury SP1 3AA Tel: 01722 415444 Fax: 01722 415454; Felthams, Coombe Bissett, Salisbury SP5 4LE Tel: 01722 718512 — BM BCh 1972 Oxf.; MA Oxf. 1972; BA (Hons. Sch. Natural Sc.) 1969. (Oxf. & St. Bart.) InDepend. Gen. Practitioner. Prev: Regist. (Med.) Prof. Unit St. Barts. Hosp. Lond.; GP Tutor Salisbury HA; Mem. Wessex RHA Med. Advisery Comm.

WILLIS, Mr Robert Geoffrey Department of Urology, Royal Cornwall Hospital, Treliske, Truro TR1 3LJ Tel: 01872 252719 Email: robert.willis@rcht.swest.nhs.uk — MB ChB 1975 Bristol; MD Bristol 1989; FRCS Eng. 1980. Cons. Urol. Roy. Cornw. Hosp. Truro. Socs: Full Mem. Assn. Urological Surg.s; Mem. Brit. Med. Assn. Prev: Cons. Urol. Cumbld. Infirm. Carlisle.; Sen. Regist. (Urol.) Yorks. RHA.; Regist. (Urol.) Freeman Hosp. Newc. upon Tyne.

WILLIS, Robert Geoffrey Bainbridge (retired) 57 Green Lane, Buxton SK17 9DL Tel: 01298 24133 — MB ChB 1951 Liverp.; MRCS Eng. LRCP Lond. 1951; MRCGP 1971; DCH Eng. 1957; DObst RCOG 1956. Prev: SHO (Paediat.) Duchess of York Hosp. Babies Manch.

WILLIS, Stephen Arthur 25 Myers Road, Hillmorton, Rugby CV21 4BY — MB BChir 1993 Camb.; DRCOG 1998; MA Camb. 1993.

WILLIS, Thomas James (retired) Mellingey, Constantine, Falmouth TR11 5QH — MB BChir Camb. 1960; DA Eng. 1965; DObst RCOG 1965. Prev: Ho. Phys. & Ho. Surg. Lond. Hosp.

WILLIS-OWEN, Julia 8 Kashmir Close, New Haw KT15 3JD — MB BS 1993 Lond.; MRCGP 98; DRCOG 97; DFFP 98. Locum GP Surrey.

WILLISON, Hugh John University of Glasgow, Department of Neurology, Southern General Hospital, Glasgow G51 4TF Tel: 0141 201 1100 Fax: 0141 201 2993 Email: h.j.willison@udcf.gla.ac.uk; 3 Camstradden Drive W., Bearsden, Glasgow G61 4AJ Tel: 0141 943 1159 Fax: 0141 943 1159 — MB BS 1980 Lond.; PhD Lond. 1987, MB BS 1980; MRCP (UK) 1983; FRCP (UK) 1998; FRCP (Glas.) 1999. (Middlesex Hosp.) Wellcome Trust Research Leave Fell. & Reader (Neurol.) & Hon. Cons. Neurol. S.ern Gen. Hosp. Glas. Prev: Wellcome Sen. Research Fell. (Clin. Sci.) S.ern Gen. Hosp. Glas.; Fogarty Fell. Nat. Inst. of Health, USA; Clin. Lect. (Neurol.) S.ern Gen. Hosp. Glas.

WILLISON, Jean Campbell (retired) 1/1 Fettes Rise, East Fettes Avenue, Edinburgh EH4 1QH — MB ChB 1941 Ed.; MFCM 1972; DPH Glas. 1947; DCH Eng. 1948. Prev: Community Med. Specialist Lothian Health Bd.

WILLISON, Katherine Anna 23 The Rotyngs, Rottingdean, Brighton BN2 7DX — MB BS 1998 Lond.

WILLISON, Robert Gow (retired) 4 Nourse Close, Woodeaton, Oxford OX3 9TJ Tel: 01865 559109 Fax: 01865 559109 — BM BCh 1951 Oxf.; MA Oxf. 1951, DM 1968; FRCP Ed. 1971, M 1954; MRCP Lond. 1978. Prev: Cons. Clin. Neurophysiol. Nat. Hosp. Nerv. Dis. Qu. Sq. Lond.

WILLITS, David Glen Staithe Surgery, Lower Staithe Road, Stalham, Norwich NR12 9BU Tel: 01692 582000 Fax: 01692 580428; Pond Farm, Staithe Road, Sutton, Norwich NR12 9QU Tel: 01692 580616 Email: dands.willits@totalist.co.uk — MB BS 1960 Lond.; FRCGP 1990, M 1981. (Lond. Hosp.)

WILLMAN, Alan (retired) Middle Filham, Ivybridge PL21 0LR Tel: 01752 690011 — MB BS Durh. 1956; DObst RCOG 1962. Prev: GP Ivybridge.

WILLMAN, Antony Sean, Maj. RAMC Garrison Medical Centre, Salamanca Barracks BFPO 53 Tel: 00 357 263255 — MB BS 1990 Lond. GP Regist. BFPO 53.

WILLMER, Barbara Jane (retired) 60 Pine Avenue, West Wickham BR4 0LW Tel: 020 8777 3544 — MB BS Lond. 1959; MRCS Eng. LRCP Lond. 1958; DObst RCOG 1960. Prev: GP Croydon.

WILLMER, Jennifer Mary Barton Surgery, Lymington House, Barton Hill Way, Torquay TQ2 8JG Tel: 01803 323761 Fax: 01803 316920 — BM BCh 1984 Oxf.; MRCGP 1988; DCH RCP Lond. 1986; DRCOG 1986. (Oxford University Medical School)

WILLMER, Katherine Anne Cardiology Department, City General Hospital, Newcastle Road, Stoke-on-Trent ST4 6QG; 26 Mancroft Road, Tettenhall, Wolverhampton WV6 8RS — MB BS 1990 Lond.; MRCP (UK) 1993. Specialist Regist. Cardiol. Dudley Gp. Hosp. NHS Trust Wordsley Hosps. Tourbridge. Socs: Brit.Soc.Echocardio. Prev: Regist. (Cardiol. & Gen. Med.) Roy. Shrewsbury Hosp.; SHO (Gen. Med.) Dudley Rd. Hosp. Birm. & New Cross Hosp. Wolverhampton.

***WILLMOT, Mark Robert** 69 Victoria Road, Harborne, Birmingham B17 0AQ — MB ChB 1996 Birm.

WILLMOTT, Anne Margaret 86 Lorne Road, Leicester LE2 1YG Tel: 0116 270 0983 — MB ChB 1991 Leic.; MRCP (UK) 1995. Regist. (Paediat.) P'boro. Dist. Hosp.

WILLMOTT, Caroline Applegarth, Church Lane, Henbury, Bristol BS10 7QG — MB ChB 1995 Ed.

***WILLMOTT, Charles Harold Alan** 10 Harrow Road, Selly Oak, Birmingham B29 7DN — MB ChB 1995 Birm.

WILLMOTT, Frederick Edwin Department of Genitourinary Medicine, Royal South Hants Hospital, Southampton SO14 0YG Tel: 02380 825438 — MB BS 1964 Lond.; MCRS Eng. LRCP Lond. 1964; Dip. Ven. Liverp. 1970. (Guy's) Cons. Genitourin. Med. Roy. S. Hants. Hosp. Soton. Prev: Cons. Venereol. Leicester Roy. Infirm.; Cons. Venereol. Auckland Hosp. New Zealand.

WILLMOTT, James Henry Charles Daleacre House, Valley Drive, Chester CH2 1BP — MB ChB 1995 Manch.

WILLMOTT, Nicholas John Castle Mead Medical Centre, Hill Street, Hinckley LE10 1DS Tel: 01455 637659 Fax: 01455 238754 — BM BS 1975 Nottm.; BMedSci (Hons.) Nottm. 1974, BM BS 1975; MRCGP 1981; DRCOG 1978. Prev: Trainee Gen. Pract. Nottm. Vocational Train. Scheme; Brit. Red Cross Thailand 1979/1980.

WILLMOTT, Philip Andrew Penton House, Queen Anne St., Shelton, Stoke-on-Trent ST4 2EQ Tel: 01782 848642 Fax: 01782 747617; 10 Sutherland Drive, Newcastle ST5 3NB Tel: 01782 614879 — MB BS 1963 Lond.; MRCS Eng. LRCP Lond. 1963; DObst RCOG 1965. (King's Coll. Hosp.) Prev: Ho. Phys. King's Coll. Hosp.; Ho. Surg. Crewe & Dist. Memor. Hosp; Rural Leprosy Control Off. P.ss Zenebe Work Hosp., Addis Ababa.

WILLMOTT, Sara Louise Lawrence Hill Health Centre, Hassell Drive, Bristol BS2 0AN Tel: 0117 955 5241 Fax: 0117 941 1162 — MB BCh BAO 1966 Dub.; DA (UK) 1969.

WILLOCKS, Clare Margaret Glasgow Royal Maternity Hospital, 146-163 Rottenrow, Glasgow G4 0NA Tel: 0141 211 5400 Fax: 0141 211 5399 — MB ChB 1992 Glas.; BSc (Hons.) Glas. 1989. Specialist Regist. (O & G) W. of Scotl. Train. Scheme. Prev: SHO Glas. Roy. Infirm.

WILLOCKS, James (retired) 16 Sutherland Avenue, Glasgow G41 4JH Tel: 0141 427 6113 — MB ChB 1951 Glas.; MD Glas. 1963; FRCP Glas. 1978, M 1973; FRCOG 1969, M 1958. Prev: Cons. O & G Qu. Mother Hosp. & W.. Infirm. Glas.

WILLOCKS, Lorna Jane CDSC (Eastern), Institute of Public Health, University Forvie Site, Robinson Way, Cambridge CB2 2SR Tel: 01223 762037 Fax: 01223 331865 — MB ChB 1983 Glas.; MD Glas. 1995; MRCP (UK) 1986; MFPHM RCP (UK) 1995; FRCP 1998. Cons. Epidemiolog. (Communicable Dis.) CDSC (E.ern) Camb. Socs: Brit. Infec. Soc.; Pub. Health Med. Environm. Gp.; Assn. Pub. Health. Prev: Sen. Regist. (Communicable Dis. & Epidemiol.) Oxf.; Research Regist. Med. Research Counc. City Hosp. Edin.; Regist. (Infect. Dis.) City Hosp. Edin. & Ruchill Hosp. Glas.

WILLOCKS, Timothy 60 Arundel Mansions, Arundel Terrace, London SW13 8DS — MB BS 1984 Lond.

WILLOTT, Joanna Clare 32 Homefield Road, Exeter EX1 2QU — MB ChB 1998 Bristol.

WILLOUGHBY, Bruce Jamieson Biermont, Bingley Road, Menston, Ilkley LS29 6BD — MB BS 1993 Newc.

WILLOUGHBY, Cathryn Maria 13 Oxford Road, Farnborough GU14 6QT — MB BCh 1993 Wales.

WILLOUGHBY, Charles Peter 42 West Park Crescent, Billericay CM12 9EG Tel: 01277 656302 — BM BCh 1972 Oxf.; DM Oxf. 1980; BA (Physiol.) (1st cl. Hons.) 1969; MA 1972; FRCP Lond. 1992; MRCP (UK) 1975. Cons. Phys. & Gastroenterol. Basildon & Thurrock Gen. Hosps. Trust. Socs: Brit. Soc. Gastroenterol. Prev: Hon. Sen. Regist. (Gastroenterol.) Nuffield Dept. Clin. Med. John Radcliffe Hosp. Oxf.; Jun. Research Fell. Linacre Coll. Oxf.

WILLOUGHBY, Colin Eric 19 Shona Green, Ballymena BT42 4AT — MB ChB 1991 Liverp.; MB ChB (Hons.) Liverp. 1991; BSc (1st cl. Hons. Anat.) Liverp. 1988; FRCOphth 1996. (Liverpool) Specialist Regist. (Ophth.) Mersey Region.

WILLOUGHBY

WILLOUGHBY, John Michael Tait, RD (retired) 9 Longmeadow Drive, Ickleford, Hitchin SG5 3TJ Tel: 01462 432963 Email: mikewilby@aol.com — DM Oxf. 1974, MA, BM BCh 1962; FRCP Lond. 1979, M 1966; MRCS Eng. LRCP Lond. 1962. Cons. Phys. Pinehill Hosp. Hitchin; Chief Med. Off. Nat. Mutual Life Assur. Soc. Prev: Cons. Phys. Lister Hosp. Stevenage.

WILLOUGHBY, Roger Alastair Guy d'Eresby The Surgery, Mortimer, Reading RG7 3SQ Tel: 01734 332436 — MB BS 1960 Lond.; DA Eng. 1963. (St. Bart.) Prev: SHO (Anaesth.) Bromley Hosp.; Ships Surg. P & O Orient Line. & Union Castle SS Co.

WILLOUGHBY, Sara Jane Bandele Haematology Dept, Hereford County Hospital, Union walk, Hereford HR1 2ER Tel: 01432 355444 Ext: 4435 — MB BS 1988 Lond.; MRCP 1992; MRCPath 1997. (Roy. Free Hosp. Sch. of Med.)

WILLOUGHBY, Sarah Jane 7 Haughton Road, Woodseats, Sheffield S8 8QH — BM BCh 1994 Oxf.; MA Oxf. 1996, BA 1991. (OXF.) GP Regist. Sheff. VTS. Prev: SHO (O & G) Jessop Hosp. Sheff.; Ho. Off. (Med.) City Gen. Hosp. Stoke-on-Trent; Ho. Off. (Surg.) John Radcliffe Hosp. Oxf.

WILLOWS, Helen Westway Medical Centre, Westway, Maghull, Liverpool L31 0DJ Tel: 0151 526 1121 Fax: 0151 527 2631; 16 Hallmoor Close, Aughton, Ormskirk L39 4UQ Tel: 01695 571617 — BM 1987 Soton.; BSc (Biochem.) Hull 1979; MRCGP (Distinc) 1992; DRCOG 1990; Cert. Family Plann. JCC 1990. Prev: Trainee GP Havant Health Centre.

WILLOWS, Mary Anona 17 Lower Road, Milton Malsor, Northampton NN7 3AW — MB BS 1974 Lond. Staff Phys. (Palliat. Med.) N.ampton.

WILLOWS, Richard Ian Reid Delapre Medical Centre, Gloucester Avenue, Northampton NN4 8QF Tel: 01604 761713 Fax: 01604 708589; 17 Lower Road, Milton Malsor, Northampton NN7 3AW Tel: 01604 858653 Email: rickwill@nccnet.co.uk — MB 1975 Camb.; BChir 1974; MRCGP 1978; DRCOG 1978; FRCGP 1998. Course Organiser N.ampton VTS.

WILLOX, David George Addison Croftfoot Road Surgery, 44 Croftfoot Road, Glasgow G44 5JT Tel: 0141 634 6333; 14 Bradda Avenue, Burnside, Glasgow G73 5DE Tel: 0141 634 4566 — MB ChB 1981 Glas.; MRCGP 1985; DRCOG 1984. Exam. Phys. BUPA Med. Centre Glas. Socs: S.. Med. Soc. Glas.

WILLOX, Joanne Christine 74 Weymouth Drive, Glasgow G12 0LY — MD 1984 Glas.; MB ChB 1978. Clin. Asst. Cytopath., Vale of Leven Hosp., Alexandria. Prev: Clin. Research Fell. Dept. Clin. Oncol. Univ. Glas.; Regist. (Histopath.) Univ. Dept. Path., W.. Infirm., Glas.

WILLOX, Margaret Fairlie Carraig House, Snape, Bedale DL8 2TF — MB ChB 1982 Glas.; MRCGP 1987; DCH RCP Lond. 1986; DRCOG 1986.

WILLS, Adrian Jonathan 13A Kingsdown Road, Upper Holloway, London N19 4LT — MB BS 1986 Lond.; MD Lond. 1995; MRCP (UK) 1990.

WILLS, Alan Robert 32 Birch Avenue, Macclesfield SK10 3NU — BM BCh 1973 Oxf.; BA Oxf. 1970, BM BCh 1973; MRCPath. 1980. Cons. Microbiol. Macclesfield Dist. Gen. Hosp.

WILLS, Andrew Donald 24 Hazel Street, Leicester LE2 7JN — MB ChB 1998 Leic.; MB ChB Leic 1998.

WILLS, Carole Irene The Surgery, 1 Uxendon Crescent, Wembley HA9 9TW Tel: 020 8904 3883 Fax: 020 8904 3899; 7 Meadway Close, Hatch End, Pinner HA5 4AZ — MB ChB 1969 Manch.; BSc Manch. 1966, MB ChB 1969.

WILLS, Catherine Jane (Cowell) Queens Medical Centre, Nottingham NG7 2UH Tel: 0115 924 9924; 37 Moore Road, Mapperley, Nottingham NG3 6EF Tel: 0115 969 1176 — MB BS 1991 Lond.; BA Oxf. 1988; MRCP (UK) 1994. (Char. Cross Hosp. & West. Med. Sch.)

WILLS, Desiree Pamela (retired) 33 Comely Bank, Edinburgh EH4 1AJ Tel: 0131 343 2533 — MB ChB 1964 Glas.; MRCPsych 1973; DPM Eng. 1972. Nat. Mem. Criminal Injuries Compensation Appeal Panel. Prev: Cons. Child & Adolesc. Psychiat. W. Lothian Health Dist. & Roy. Hosp. Sick Childr. Edin.

WILLS, Diana Rosemary Child & Family Guidance Centre, Tanner St., Winchester SO23 8AD — MB ChB 1979 Liverp.; DCH RCP Lond. 1982.

WILLS, Dilys (retired) 131 Carisbrooke Way, Cyncoed, Cardiff CF23 9HU — MB BCh Wales 1954; FFR RCSI 1971; DCH Eng. 1962, DMRD 1968; FRCR 1970. Prev: Cons. Radiol. Bridgend Gen. Hosp.

WILLS, Emily The Surgery, 42 The Street, Uley, Dursley GL11 5SY Tel: 01453 860459; 18 High Furlong, Cam, Dursley GL11 5UZ Tel: 01453 544171 — MB ChB 1982 Bristol; MRCGP 1986; DCH RCP Lond. 1985. Asst. (Gen. Pract.). Socs: BMA. Prev: Trainee GP N. Devon VTS; Dist. Health Off. Rumphi, Malawi.

WILLS, Frances Anne Connaught House, Winchester & Eastleigh Healthcare NHS Trust, Ronsell Road, Winchester SO22 5DE Tel: 01962 824262 — MB BS Lond. 1981; MRCPsych 1989. Cons. Psych. Winchester & E.leigh NHS Trust.

WILLS, George Thomas The Old Court House, 4 Throwley Way, Sutton SM1 4AF Tel: 020 8643 8866; 36 The Avenue, Tadworth KT20 5AT Tel: 01737 3321 — MB BS 1959 Lond.; DObst RCOG 1961. (St. Bart.)

WILLS, Hugh Graham 85 Wigton Road, Carlisle CA2 7EP — MB BS 1967 Newc. Prev: Ho. Phys. Vict. Hosp. Blackpool; Ho. Surg. Roy. S. Hants. Hosp. Soton.

WILLS, Janet Frances 9 Leman Drive, Houston, Johnstone PA6 7LN — MB ChB 1979 Glas.; MRCGP 1983.

WILLS, John (retired) 50 Green Street, Hazlemere, High Wycombe HP15 7RA Tel: 01494 524181 — MB BS Lond. 1940; MRCS Eng. LRCP Lond. 1940; DObst RCOG 1946. JP. Prev: GP High Wycombe.

WILLS, Jonathan Stewart 37 Moore Road, Mapperley, Nottingham NG3 6EF Email: jswills@lineone.net — BM BCh 1991 Oxf.; BA (Hons.) Oxf. 1988; FRCA 1997. (Oxford) Regist. (Anaesth.) Qu. Med. Centre Nottm. Socs: Assn. Anaesth. Prev: Regist. (Anaesth.) Exeter; SHO (Anaesth.) Bristol; ITU SHO Nottm.

WILLS, Judith Claire 1 Dovecote Close, Red House Farm, Whitley Bay NE25 9HS; 37 Keyes Gardens, Jesmond, Newcastle upon Tyne NE2 3RA — MB ChB 1993 Leeds; MRCGP 1997; DRCOG 1996.

WILLS, Mr Leslie Charles (retired) — MB ChB 1966 Aberd.; FRCS Ed. 1972. Cons. ENT Surg. Aberd. Roy. Infirm.; Sen. Lect. ENT Aberd. Univ. Prev: Sen. Regist. ENT Dept. Aberd. Roy. Infirm.

WILLS, Mr Michael Ian Department of Urology, Walsgrave Hospital, Coventry CV2 2DX Tel: 02476 602020; Darracott, School St., Churchover, Rugby CV23 0EG — MB ChB 1977 Bristol; FRCS Eng. 1982. Cons. Urol. Walsgrave Hosp. Coventry. Socs: Brit. Assn. Urol.; Bristol. Urol. Inst.

WILLS, Patricia Mary Bellbrooke Surgery, 395 Harehills Lane, Leeds LS9 6AP Tel: 0113 249 4848; 14 Ivy Lane, Boston Spa, Wetherby LS23 6PD Tel: 01937 844 3118 — MB ChB 1975 Ed.; BSc (Med. Sci.) Ed. 1972; DA Eng. 1978; Cert. Family Plann. 1979. (Ed.) p/t Asst. GP, Bellbrooke Surg., 395 Harehills La., Leeds; Locum Clin. Med. Off., Family Plann., York Health Trust.

WILLS, Patrick Charles Station Road Surgery, 74 Station Road, West Wickham BR4 0PU Tel: 020 8777 8245; 115 Durham Road, Bromley BR2 0SP — MB BS 1989 Lond.; MSc Lond. 1993; MRCP (UK) 1995; MRCGP 1997; DFFP 1996; DGM RCP Lond. 1991. (King's Coll. Lond.) GP Princip.; Clin. Asst. (Genitourin. Med.) Beckenham Hosp. Socs: BMA. Prev: GP/Regist. Bromley VTS; SHO (Genitourin. Med.) Roy. Lond. Hosp.; SHO (Med.) Bromley Hosp.

***WILLS, Rachel Emma** Hawthorn Cottage, Bovey Tracey, Newton Abbot TQ13 9PT — MB ChB 1994 Birm.

WILLS, Simon John 18 Tanfield Road, Newcastle upon Tyne NE15 7DT — MB ChB 1993 Dundee.

WILLS, Valerie 23 Cholmley Gardens, Aldred Road, London NW6 1AG Tel: 020 7794 9370 — MD 1938 Prague; Cert JCC Lond. 1977. (Berlin & Prague) GP Lond. Prev: Sen. Med. Off. Roy. Boro. Kingston; Asst. Sch. & Matern. Child Welf. Off. Surrey CC; Med. Off. Kingston Co. Hosp.

WILLSDON, Helen Francis The Doctors House, Victoria Road, Marlow SL7 1DN Tel: 01628 484666 Fax: 01628 891206; Kings Dial Cottage, Medmenham, Marlow SL7 2EU — MB ChB 1975 Leeds; MRCGP 1986; MRCOG 1982.

WILLSHAW, Mr Harry Edward BUPA Parkway Hospital, Damson Parkway, Solihull B91 2PP Tel: 0121 704 1451; Burtons Farm Cottage, Malthouse Lane, Earlswood, Solihull B94 5DU Tel: 01564 702438 Fax: 01564 702438 — MB ChB 1971 Leeds; BSc Leeds 1967; FRCS Ed. 1977; FCOphth 1990. Cons. Ophth. Childr. Hosp. & Birm. & Midl. Eye Hosp.; Hon. Lect. Univ. Birm. Med. Sch.

WILLSHER, Thomas 99 Hopton Road, London SW16 2EL — MB BS 1996 Lond.

WILLSON, Garth 22 Brown's Way, Aspley-Guise, Milton Keynes MK17 8JA — MRCS Eng. LRCP Lond. 1978.

WILLSON, Gordon Frederick (retired) 7 Horncastle Road, Louth LN11 9LB Tel: 01507 609144 — MB BS 1943 Lond.; MD Lond. 1948; MRCS Eng. LRCP Lond. 1942; FFCM 1977, M 1974; DPH Lond. 1953. Prev: Area Med. Off. Dorset AHA.

WILLSON, Heather Jane Shepherd Spring Medical Centre, Cricketers Way, Andover SP10 5DE Tel: 01264 361126 Fax: 01264 350138; 10 Kingsmead, Anna Valley, Andover SP11 7PN — MB ChB 1982 Sheff.; DCH RCP Lond. 1986. Prev: SHO (Paediat.) Epsom Dist. Hosp.; SHO (Geriat.) Newmarket Gen. Hosp.; SHO (O & G) Addenbrooke's Hosp. Camb.

***WILLSON, Jeremy David** 143 Tiverton Road, Selly Oak, Birmingham B29 6BS — MB ChB 1998 Birm.

WILLSON, John Christopher Cottingham Medical Centre, 17-19 South Street, Cottingham HU16 4AJ Tel: 01482 845078 Fax: 01482 845078; 25 St Barnabas Drive, Swanland, North Ferriby HU14 3RL — MB ChB 1981 Liverp.

WILLSON, Lionel Arthur Herbert 23 The Avenue, Wanstead, London E11 2EE Tel: 020 8989 1245 — MRCS Eng. LRCP Lond. 1942. (Lond. Hosp.) Socs: BMA. Prev: Ho. Phys., &c. Roy. Sussex Co. Hosp. Brighton; Ho. Surg. Mile End Hosp.

WILLSON, Mr Peter David Department of Surgery, Kingston Hospital, Galsworthy Road, Kingston upon Thames KT2 7QV Tel: 020 8546 7711 Fax: 020 8546 4098 Email: peter.wilson@ekh-tr.sthames.nhs.uk — MB BS 1985 Lond.; BSc Lond. 1982; FRCS (Gen.) 1997; FRCS Eng. 1989. (Char. Cross & Westm.) Cons. (Surg.) Kingston Hosp. Qu. Mary's Hosp.; Hon. Lect. (Anat.) Imperial Coll. Lond. Socs: Fell. Roy. Soc. Med.; Assn. Endoscopic Surgs.; Assn. Surg. Prev: Sen. Regist. (Gen. Surg.) St. Marys Hosp. Lond.; Research Fell. Roy. Lond. Hosp.; Regist. Centr. Middlx. Hosp., Hillingdon Hosp. & Wexham Pk. Hosp.

WILLSON, Sarah Ann Culm Davy House, Henyock, Cullompton EX15 3UT — MB BS 1977 Lond.; MRCP (UK) 1979; FRCR 1983. (St. Bart.) Cons. Radiol. MusGr. Pk. Hosp. Taunton. Prev: Sen. Regist. (Radiol.) Middlx. Hosp. Lond.; Fell. Univ. Hosp. UCSD Med. Centre, San Diego, Calif., USA.

WILLSON, Thomas Hugh Burvill House Surgery, 52 Dellfield Road, Hatfield AL10 8HP Tel: 01707 269091 — MB BS 1984 Lond.; MA Oxf. 1983, BA 1979; DRCOG 1988. (Roy. Free) Prev: SHO St. Albans GP VTS.

WILLSON, William Wynne (retired) Hurst, Green Lane, Henley-on-Thames RG9 1LS Tel: 01491 573024 — BM BCh 1937 Oxf.; BA Oxf. 1937; LMSSA Lond. 1937; MRCGP 1959; DObst RCOG 1946. Prev: Ho. Phys., Ho. Surg. & 3rd Asst. (Path.) St. Mary's Hosp. Lond.

WILLSON-LLOYD, Joanne Mary 170 Dawlish Road, Birmingham B29 7AR Tel: 0121 689 5573 — MB ChB 1997 Birm. (Birm.) GP VTS Redditch.

WILLSON-PEPPER, Colin Raymond (retired) October House, Marsley heights Road, Kingsley Green, Haslemere GU27 3LU Tel: 01428 643285 — MB BS Lond. 1959; MSc (Community Med.) Lond. 1985; M Litt Oxf. 1970. Prev: Roy. Fleet Auxil.

WILLY, Diana Margaret Mitchell Manor Farm Medical Centre, Mangate Street, Swaffham PE37 7QN Tel: 01760 721700 Fax: 01760 723703; Hill House, North Pickenham, Swaffham PE37 8JZ, Tel: 01760 440679 — MB BS 1970 Lond.; MRCS Eng. LRCP Lond. 1970; DObst RCOG 1973. (Roy. Free).

WILM, Ann Ranghild Hawthorn Bank, 27 Glasgow Road, Denny FK6 5DW — MB ChB 1990 Glas.

WILMALASUNDERA, Neil Flat 17, Falconet Court, Wapping High St., London E1W 3NX — MB BS 1996 Lond.

WILMINGTON, Andrew Macgregor Church Road Surgery, 261 Church Road, Stannes on Sea, Lytham St Annes FY8 1EH Tel: 01253 728911 Fax: 01253 732114; 14 Arundel Road, Ansdell, Lytham St Annes FY8 1AF Tel: 01253 730301 — MB ChB 1984 Aberd.; MRCGP 1988; DRCOG 1987. Prev: Trainee GP Inverclyde Dist. Argyll & Clyde HB; Ho. Off. Co. Hosp. Oban.; Ho. Off. Woodend Hosp. Aberd.

WILMINGTON, Sheila MacIntosh 532 Paisley Road W., Glasgow G51 1RN; 16 Avondale Drive, Paisley PA1 3TN — MB ChB 1960 Glas.; DObst RCOG 1962.

WILMOT, Clare Julia May c/o E.T. Wilmot, 27 Church St., Barford, Warwick CV35 8EW Email: cwilmot@littletonhospital.org; 3501 Old Country Road, Waterford Vermont 0581, USA — MB ChB 1977 Bristol. Gen. Surg. Socs: AMA; BMA; ACS.

WILMOT, Elizabeth Frances St. Michael's Hospital, St. Michaels Road, Warwick CV34 5QW Tel: 01926 406733 Fax: 01926 406702 — MB ChB 1973 Birm.; MRCPsych 1984; DObst RCOG 1975. Cons. Psychiat. St. Michaels Hosp. Prev: Sen. Regist. Midl. Nerve Hosp. Birm.; Sen. Regist. Centr. Hosp. Warwick; Sen. Regist. Uffculme Clinic Birm.

WILMOT, John David Charles Beechwood Surgery, 57 John Street, Workington CA14 3BT Tel: 01900 64866 Fax: 01900 871561; 2 Greenside Cottages, Tallentire, Cockermouth CA13 0PR Tel: 01900 824774 — MB BS 1976 Newc.; FRCGP 1993, M 1980; DRCOG 1980; DCH RCPS Glas. 1979. Provost, Cumbria Fac. RCGP; Clin. Asst., Drugs and Alcohol, N. Cumbria Addictive Behaviour NHS Trust.

WILMOT, John Fabian Clarendon Lodge Medical Practice, 16 Clarendon Street, Leamington Spa CV32 5SS Tel: 01926 422094 Fax: 01926 331400 — MB ChB 1971 Birm.; MB ChB (Distinc. Psychiat.) Birm. 1971; FRCGP 1988, M 1975; DCH Eng. 1974; DObst RCOG 1973. (Birm.) Sen. Lect. (Primary Care) Sch. Postgrad. Med. Educat. Univ. Warwick Coventry; Vice-Chairm. Warks. MAAG Edit. Bd. Brit. Jl. of Gen. Pract. Socs: BMA; AUDGP; EGPRW. Prev: Sec. Gen. Pract. Research Club; Vis. Asst. Prof. Family Med. Univ. W.. Ontario, Canada; Course Organiser Coventry & Warks. VTS.

WILMOT, Rosalind Anne Oundle Surgery, Glapthorn Road, Oundle, Peterborough PE8 4JA Tel: 01832 273408; Town Farm House, Old Weston, Huntingdon PE28 5LL — MB ChB 1975 Liverp.; DRCOG 1978. (Liverpool) Socs: BMS. Prev: GP Cambs. & Soton.; Trainee GP Liverp. VTS.

WILMOT, Mr Thomas James (retired) Rathmore, 1A Knocksilla Park, Omagh BT79 0AR Tel: 01662 242244 — MB BS 1944 Lond.; MS Lond. 1950; FRCSI 1980; FRCS Eng. 1950; DLO Eng. 1948. Cons. ENT Surg. Omagh Co. Tyrone & Co. Fermanagh; Cons. Neuro-otol. Claremont St. Hosp. Belf. & Altnagelvin Hosp. Lond.derry.

WILMSHURST, Mr Andrew David Department of Plastic Surgery, Ninewells Hospital, Dundee DD1 9SY; 19 Hallowhill, St Andrews KY16 8SF — MB BS 1974 Lond.; FRCS Eng. 1980. (Univ. Coll. Hosp.) Cons. Plastic Surg. Ninewells Hosp. Dundee; Hon. Sen. Lect. Dundee Med. Sch. Prev: Sen. Regist. (Plastic Surg.) Salisbury Dist. Hosp.

WILMSHURST, Andrew Peter Kirriemuir Health Centre, Tannage Brae, Kirriemuir DD8 4ES Tel: 01575 753333 Fax: 01575 574230 Email: a.wilmshurst@kirnemuir.finix.org.uk — MB BChir 1989 Camb.; MRCP (UK) 1993; DRCOG 1997; MRCGP 1999. (Cambridge University)

WILMSHURST, Joanne Madeleine 133A Greenwich High Road, Greenwich, London SE10 8JA Tel: 020 8305 1694; Carters Cottage, Hangersley, Ringwood BH24 3JN Tel: 01425 473586 — MB BS 1989 Lond.; MRCP (UK) 1994. Specialist Regist. (Paediat. Neurol.) Guys Hosp. Prev: Lect. (Paediat.) Guys Hosp. Lond.; Regist. (Paediat.) Lewisham; Regist. (Paediat.) Canterbury.

WILMSHURST, Mark John The Priory Surgery, 326 Wells Road, Bristol BS4 2QJ Tel: 0117 949 3988 Fax: 0117 778250 — MB ChB 1989 Sheff.; MRCGP 1993; DRCOG 1993. Trainee GP Lincoln VTS.

WILMSHURST, Peter Thomas Royal Shrewsbury Hospital NHS Trust, Shrewsbury SY3 8XQ Tel: 01743 261108 Fax: 01743 261374 — MB ChB 1974 Manch.; BSc (Hons.) Manch. 1971; MRCP (UK) 1976. Cons., Cardiol.

WILMSHURST, Sally Louise 115 Stallards Close, Old Road, Bromyard HR7 4AX — MB ChB 1995 Manch.

WILNE, Brian David Harbury Surgery, Mill St., Harbury, Leamington Spa CV33 9HR Tel: 01926 612232 Fax: 01926 612991; Temple Cottage, Temple End, Harbury, Leamington Spa CV33 9NE — MB ChB 1962 Birm.; DObst RCOG 1965. (Birm.) Socs: BMA. Prev: SHO St. Geo. Hosp. Lincoln; Ho. Surg. Ipswich & E. Suff. Hosp. & Hull Matern. Hosp.

WILNER, John Marston The Church Street Practice, David Corbet House, 2 Callows Lane, Kidderminster DY10 2JG Tel: 01562 822051 Fax: 01562 827251; The Limes, Long Bank, Bewdley DY12 2QS Tel: 01299 405375 — MB ChB 1962 Birm.; FRCP Ed. 1994; MRCP (UK) 1967. (Birm.) Prev: Regist. (Med.) N. Staffs. Roy. Infirm. Stoke-on-Trent; Ho. Phys. & Regist. (Med.) Gen. Hosp. Birm.

WILSDON

WILSDON, John Bernard 11 Northumberland Avenue, Gosforth, Newcastle upon Tyne NE3 4XE — MB ChB 1974 Manch.; MRCP (UK) 1978; FRCR 1983; DMRD Eng. 1981. Cons. Radiol. Newc. Gen. Hosp.

WILSDON, Mr Kenneth Frank 7 Bentley Road, Cambridge CB2 2AW Tel: 01223 353094 — BM BCh 1939 Oxf.; MA Oxf. 1943, BM BCh. 1939; FRCS Ed. 1945. (Oxf. & King's Coll. Hosp.) Socs: Fell. Roy. Soc. Med. Prev: Surg. ENT Dept. Addenbrook's Hosp. Camb.; E.N.T. Regist. Radcliffe Infirm. Oxf.; Temp. Surg. Lt. R.N.V.R.

WILSDON, Ralph Bernard Nevil (retired) Easby House, Easby, Great Ayton, Middlesbrough TS9 6JQ Tel: 01642 722473 — MRCS Eng. LRCP Lond. 1940; MD Lond. 1950, MB BS 1941; FRCP Lond. 1971, M 1948. Prev: Cons. Phys. Middlesbrough Area (Newc. RHB).

WILSEY, Charlotte Mary Willasey 26 Braybrooke Road, Wargrave, Reading RG10 8DT Tel: 01189 402478 — MB BS 1991 Lond.; FRCA 1996. (King's College London)

WILSHAW, Mrs Hilary Anna Elmes Prospect House, 48 South St., Manningtree CO11 1BG — MB Camb. 1963, BChir 1962.

WILSKI-JALOSZYNSKI, Andrew Pembury Hospital, Tunbridge Wells TN2 4QJ; 4 Berkeley Road, Mount Sion, Tunbridge Wells TN1 1YR — Lekarz 1971 Warsaw; MRCPsych 1977; DPM Lond. 1975. Med. Dir. Invicta NHS Trust. Prev: Cons. (Psychiat.) Invicta NHS Trust; Lect. (Psychother.) Herts. Coll. Art; Sen. Regist. (Psychiat.), W.m. Hosp., Lond.

WILSON, Mr Adrian James Park View Cottage, Wash Hill, Wooburn Town, High Wycombe HP10 0JA Email: adrianwilson@btinternet.com — MB BS 1994 Lond.; BSc (Biochem.) Manch. 1989; FRCS Pt. I Eng. 1996; FRCS Pt 2 1998. (St. Bart.) SHO (Surg.) Wycombe Gen. Hosp. Bucks.; Specialist Regist. Orth. N.wick Pk. Prev: SHO (Orthop.) Roy. Berks.; SHO (Orthop.) Roy. Nat. Orthop. Hosp.; Demonst. (Anat.) Univ. Camb.

WILSON, Aileen Johnston (retired) 23 Beechlands Avenue, Glasgow G44 3YT — MB ChB Glas. 1964; MRCGP 1975; DPH Glas. 1967; DObst RCOG 1966. Prev: GP Glas.

WILSON, Alan (retired) 260 Brooklands Road, Manchester M23 9HD Tel: 0161 962 2124 — MB ChB 1952 Manch. Sch. Med. Off. William Hulmes Grammar Sch. Manch. Prev: SHO (Med.) Wythenshawe Hosp. Manch.

WILSON, Alan George (retired) The Old Mill, Mill Lane, Adderbury, Banbury OX17 3LW Tel: 01295 810340 — BSc (Special Physiol.) Lond. 1958, MB BS 1961; FRCP Lond. 1985, M 1964; MRCS Eng. LRCP Lond. 1961; FRCR 1975; FFR 1972; DMRD Eng. 1970. Prof. (Diagnostic Radio.) Univ. Lond. Prev: Prof. (Diagnostic Radio.) St Geo.'s Hosp. Lond.

WILSON, Alan Graham McTurk Summervale Medical Centre, Wharf Lane, Ilminster TA19 0DT Tel: 01460 52354 Fax: 01460 52652 — MB BS 1981 Lond.; MB BS London 1981; MA Cambridge 1982; MRCP (UK) 1985. (Royal Free Hospital School Medicine)

WILSON, Alan Hamilton 89 Bawtry Road, Bessacarr, Doncaster DN4 7AG — MB BS 1954 Lond.; FRCPsych 1990, M 1972; DPM Eng. 1964. Cons. Psychiat. Doncaster Roy. Infirm. & Loversall Hosp. Doncaster. Prev: Sen. Regist. Leeds Gen. Infirm. & St. Jas. Hosp. Leeds.

WILSON, Mr Alan James St. Mary's Wing, Whittington Hospital, Highgate Hill, London N19 5NF — MB ChB 1971 Birm.; MD Birm. 1983; MSc Glas. 1977; FRCS Glas. 1976. Cons. Surg. Whittington Hosp. Lond. Socs: Surg. Research Soc. Prev: Lect. Surg. King's Coll. Hosp. Lond.; CRC Research Fell. King's Coll. Hosp. Med. Sch. Lond.

WILSON, Alan Oliver Arneil (retired) 14 Cammo Hill, Barnton, Edinburgh EH4 8EY Tel: 0131 339 2244 Fax: 0131 339 2244 Email: o.wilson@virgin.net — MB ChB Ed. 1952; FRCPsych 1976, M 1971; DPM Eng. 1960. Cons. (Scotl.) Ex-Servs. Ment. Welf. Soc. Prev: Cons. Psychiat. Murrayfield BUPA Hosp. Edin.

WILSON, Alan Robin Muir Breast Screening Training Centre, City Hospital NHS Trust, Hucknall Road, Nottingham NG5 1PF Tel: 0115 969 1689 Fax: 0115 962 7707 Email: robinwilson@doctors.org.uk; 8 Meadow Way, Kinoulton, Nottingham NG12 3RE Tel: 01949 81509 Email: robinwilson@doctors.org.uk — MB ChB 1979 Dundee; FRCP Ed. 1993; MRCP (UK) 1982; FRCR 1987. Cons. Radiol. City Hosp. Nottm.; Vis. Prof. Radiol. Univ. of Derby. Socs: Roy. Coll. Radiol. (Sec. BrE. Gp.); (Past Sec.) Europ. Gp. for BrE. Cancer Screening.; Brit. BrE. Gp. Prev: Cons. Radiol. Univ. Hosp. Nottm.; Lect. (Radiol.) Univ. Hosp. Nottm.

WILSON, Mr Alan William 79 Tremona Road, Southampton SO16 6HS Email: alan.wilson2@virgin.net — BM 1993 Soton.; BDS Ed. 1985; FDS Ed. 1987; FRCS Lond. 1997. Specialist Regist. (Maxillofacial) QA Portsmouth.

WILSON, Mr Alastair 4 Halland Close, Crawley RH10 1SD — MB ChB 1976 Ed.; FRCS Eng. 1983; FRCS Ed. 1983. Regist. (Surg.) Roy. E. Sussex Hosp. Hastings. Socs: Fell. Roy. Soc. Med. Lond.; Fell. Roy. Med. Soc. Edin. Prev: SHO Emerg. & Accid. Dept. Lond. Hosp. Whitechapel; SHO (Gen. Surg.) United Norwich Hosps.

WILSON, Mr Alastair Osborne (retired) 211 Henley Road, Ipswich IP1 6RL — MB ChB 1947 Ed.; BSc Ed. 1946; FRCS Eng. 1961; FRCS Ed. 1953. Cons. Surg. Dudley Rd. Hosp. Birm. Prev: Sen. Regist. (Surg.) United Birm. Hosps.

WILSON, Mr Alastair Walter Rutique, Nethergate St., Harpley, King's Lynn PE31 6TW Tel: 01485 520914 Fax: 01485 520885 Email: alastair.wilson@btinternet.com — MB ChB 1973 Aberd.; FRCS Eng. 1980; FFAEM 1994. Clin. Dir. (A & E & Helicopter Emerg. Med. Serv.) Barts & the Lond. Socs: Brit. Trauma Soc. - Ex Pres.; Europ. Assoc. for Trauma and Emerg. Surg. - Vice Pres.(EATES). Prev: Sen. Regist. (Gen. Surg.) Lond. Hosp. Whitechapel & Old Ch. Hosp. Romford; Regist. (Gen. Surg.) Univ. Coll. & Brompton Hosps. Lond.

WILSON, Alexander John 8 Glebeland Close, West Stafford, Dorchester DT2 8AE — MB ChB 1985 Zimbabwe; BSc Natal 1980; LRCP LRCS Ed. LRCPS Glas. 1987; FFA RCSI 1992. Cons. Anaesth. W. Dorset Hosp. NHS Trust Dorchester. Prev: Sen. Regist. (Anaesth.) W. Midl.

WILSON, Alexander Murray 87 Stumperlowe Hall Road, Sheffield S10 3QS Tel: 0114 230 1220 Email: a.m.wilson@sheffield.ac.uk — MB ChB Bristol 1959; FFA RCS Eng. 1966; DRCOG 1961; Cert. Av Med. 1983. (Brist.) Cons. Anaesth. Sheff. Plastic Surg. Unit N. Gen. Hosp.; Hon. Clin. Lect. Univ. Sheff.; Mem. Air Transport Users Co. C.A.A. Prev: Head of Anaesth. Serv. Riyadh Milit. Hosp. Saudi Arabia.

WILSON, Mrs Alison Margaret 47 A Cambridge Road, Cambridge CB4 9NU Tel: 01223 352465 — MB BChir 1990 Camb.; BA (Hons.) Camb. 1988; MRCOG 1996. Flexible Trainee Specialist Regist. (O & G) Rosie Matern. Hosp., Camb., W. Suff. Hosp., Bury St Edmunds. Prev: Specialist Regist. (O & G), W. Suff. Hosp.; Regist. (O & G) Rosie Matern. Hosp. Camb.; SHO (Surg.) Chesterfield & N. Derbysh. Roy. Hosp.

WILSON, Alister Bryan Gartnavel Royal Hospital, Great Western Road, Glasgow G12 0XH — MB BCh BAO 1982 Belf.; MB BCh Belf. 1982.

WILSON, Amanda Jane The Health Centre, Canterbury Way, Stevenage SG1 1QH Tel: 01438 357411 Fax: 01438 720523 — MB BS 1984 Lond. Prev: Trainee GP N. Middlx. Hosp. VTS; Ho. Phys. Edgware Gen. Hosp.; Ho. Surg. Chase Farm Hosp. Enfield.

WILSON, Amanda Margaret 19 Drumgoose Road, Portadown, Craigavon BT62 1PH Tel: 01762 337964; 2/L 22 Hayburn Crescent, Glasgow G11 5AY Tel: 0141 334 6271 — MB ChB 1991 Glas. SHO (Cas.) Leeds Gen. Hosp. Prev: Ho. Off. (Surg.) Vict. Infirm. Glas.; Ho. Off. (Med.) Roy. Infirm. Glas.

WILSON, Andrew Alexander (retired) 45 Bothwell Road, Hamilton ML3 0BB Tel: 01698 281866 — MB ChB 1947 Glas.

WILSON, Andrew Carl Edenfield Centre, Prestwich Hospital, Bury New Rd, Prestwich, Manchester M25 3BL Tel: 0161 772 3684 Fax: 0161 772 3446 — MB ChB 1985 Leeds; MRCPsych 1989. Cons. Forens. Psychiat. N. W.ern Regional Forens. Serv.; Cons. Forens. Psychiat. Edenield centre,Ment. health trust of Salford. Prev: Sen. Regist. (Forens. Psychiat.) Reaside Clinic Birm.; Regist. Rotat. (Psychiat.) Merseyside RHA.

WILSON, Andrew Douglas Saffron Group Practice, 509 Saffron Lane, Leicester LE2 6UL Tel: 0116 244 0888 Fax: 01162 831405 — MB BS 1977 Newc.; MD Newc. 1991; MRCGP 1981; DRCOG 1979. Sen. Lect. Dept. Gen. Pract. & Primary Health Care Univ. of Leicester. Prev: Lect. (Gen. Pract.) Univ. Nottm.; GP N.. Med. Unit Univ. Manitoba.

WILSON, Mr Andrew Douglas Harold Blond McIndoe, Royal Free Hospital, Hampstead, London NW3 2QG Tel: 020 7794 0500 Email: adhwilson@hotmail.com; 19 Drumgoose Road, Portadown, Craigavon BT62 1PH Tel: 0141 337 2064 — MB ChB 1997 Glas.; MRCS 2000 Glasgow. (Glasgow) Plastic Surg. Research Fell., Blond McIndoe, Roy. Free Hoepital.

WILSON, Andrew Edgar James North Queen Street Surgery, 257 North Queen Street, Belfast BT15 1HS Tel: 028 9074 8317 Fax: 028 9075 4438; 3 Cricklewood Park, Belfast BT9 5GU Tel: 01232 663504 Email: aw@utrinternet.com — MB BCh BAO 1989 Belf.; MRCGP 1995; DFFP 1995; DRCOG 1994; DCH RCP Lond. 1993. (Queen's University Belfast)

WILSON, Andrew Gilmour Clark 147 Cregagh Road, Belfast BT6 0LB Tel: 028 457947 — MB BCh BAO 1952 Belf. Prev: Ho. Surg. & Ho. Phys. Belf. City Hosp.; Res. Med. Off. Roy. Lond. Homoeop. Hosp.

WILSON, Andrew Gordon, Capt. RAMC 2 Earlspark Drive, Bieldside, Aberdeen AB15 9AH — MB ChB 1992 Ed.

***WILSON, Andrew Kevin** 34 School Lane, Brereton, Sandbach CW11 1RN — MB ChB 1996 Birm.

WILSON, Andrew Malcolm Department of Clinical Pharmacology, University Dundee, Dundee Email: a.m.wilson@dundee.ac.uk; 17 Seymour St. (3F1), Dundee DD2 1HD — MB ChB 1992 Ed.; MRCP (UK) 1996. Clin. Lect. Univ. of Dundee. Socs: BMA; STS; MDU. Prev: Research Fell. Univ. Dundee; SHO (Med.) Hope Hosp. Manch. & Halifax Gen. Hosp.; Ho. Off. (Med.) Dumfries & Galloway Roy. Infirm.

WILSON, Andrew Peter Richard Department of Clinical Microbiology, University College Hospital, Grafton Way, London WC1E 6DB Tel: 020 7380 9516 Fax: 020 7388 8514 Email: peter.wilson@uclh.org — MB BS 1981 Lond.; MA Camb. 1981; MD Lond. 1987; MRCP (UK) 1984; MRCPath 1989; FRCPath 1997; FRCP (UK) 2000; FRCP FRCP (uk) 2000. (Univ. Coll. Hosp.) p/t Cons. & Hon. Sen. Lect. (Microbiol.) Univ. Coll. Lond. Hosps.; Hon. Sen. Lect. Lond. Sch. Hyg. & Trop. Med.; Hon. Cons. Whittington Hosp. Socs: Fell. Roy. Soc. Med.; Brit. Soc. Antimicrob. Chemother.; Hosp. Infec. Soc. Prev: Lect. & Hon. Sen. Regist. (Microbiol.) Univ. Coll. & Middlx. Hosps. Lond.; Research Regist. (Microbiol.) Univ. Coll. Hosp. Lond.; SHO (Med.) N.wick Pk. Hosp. Lond.

WILSON, Andrew Richard Health Centre, Townfield, Wilsden, Bradford BD15 0HT Tel: 01535 273227 Fax: 01535 274860; Townfield, Royd St., Wilsden, Bradford BD15 0HT — MB ChB 1985 Leeds; MRCGP 1991; DRCOG 1988. GP Bradford, W. Yorks. Prev: Trainee GP Bradford HA VTS.

WILSON, Andrew Stuart Parker Temple Cowley Health Centre, Templar House, Temple Road, Oxford OX4 2HL Tel: 01865 777024 Fax: 01865 777548 — BM 1989 Soton.; MRCGP 1994; DFFP 1993; DRCOG 1993. Prev: Trainee GP/SHO Soton. VTS.

WILSON, Andrew Thomas Schopwick Surgery, Everett Court, Romeland, Elstree, Borehamwood WD6 3BJ Tel: 020 8953 1008 Fax: 020 8905 2196; Donard, Letchmore Heath, Watford WD2 8EW Tel: 01923 854611 Fax: 01923 854611 Email: awilson@rpms.ac.uk — MRCS Eng. LRCP Lond. 1978; BSc, MB BS Lond. 1978; FRCGP 1994; DRCOG 1981. (Westminster) Examr. Roy. Coll. Gen. Pract.; Assoc. Dean (Postgrad. Gen. Pract.) N. Thames (W.); Mem. Edit. Bd. Ed. Postgrads. GP. Prev: GP Course Organiser N.wick Pk. Hosp. Harrow.

WILSON, Andrew Timothy Anaesthetic Department, Leeds Gen. Inf., Leeds LS1 3EX — MB ChB 1985 Leeds; FRCA 1991. Cons. Anaesth. & Intensivist, Leeds Gen. Inf. Socs: FRCA. Prev: Regist. Rotat. (Anaesth.) Sheff.

WILSON, Angela 42 South Avenue, Buxton SK17 6NQ — MB ChB 1988 Dundee.

WILSON, Angela Dorothy 27 North Linkside Road, Woolton, Liverpool L25 9NS — BM BS 1997 Nottm.; BMedSci Nottm. 1995. (Nottingham)

WILSON, Angela Ruth 10 Bourne End Road, Northwood HA6 3BS — MB BS 1975 Lond.; MRCPsych 1983; DRCOG 1977.

WILSON, Ann Health Centre, Academy St., Castle Douglas DG7 1EE Tel: 01556 2067; Lochaber, 65 Academy St., Castle Douglas DG7 1EE Tel: 01556 2656 — LRCPI & LM, LRSCI & LM 1965; LRCPI & LM, LRCSI & LM 1965; FRCOG 1989, M 1970, DObst 1967. (RCSI) Socs: BMA.

WILSON, Ann Ray Tamara (retired) 11 Larkswood Rise, Pinner HA5 2HH — MB BS 1961 Lond.; DPH 1964.

WILSON, Anna Stephenie The Gratton Surgery, Sutton Scotney, Winchester SO21 3LE Tel: 01962 760267 Fax: 01962 761138; Tioman, Stratton Road, St. Giles Hill, Winchester SO23 0JQ Tel: 01962 864102 Fax: 01962 877260 Email: dwilson155@aol.com — BM BCh 1971 Oxf.; BSc (1st cl. Hons.) Lond. 1968; MRCGP 1978; DFFP 1995; DTM & H RCP Lond. 1979; DCH RCP Lond. 1974; DObst RCOG 1973; FRCGP 1998. (St. Mary's and Oxford) p/t GP Trainer; GP SHO VTS Progr. Organiser and Wessex VTS; Sexual Heath and Child Protec. Local and Hants PCT; GP Mem. Hants. ACPC; Med. Stud. Teach. Soton. Univ.; Dep. Police Surg. Socs: Assoc. Mem. Inst. Psychosexual Med.; Fac. Community Health. Prev: Clin. Med. Off. (Community Health Serv.) Winchester HA & Wolverhampton HA; Chairm. Wessex Fac. Roy. Coll. GPs; Diplomat Bd. of Mem. Fac. of Family Plann. and Reproductive Health Counc.

WILSON, Anna Victoria 23 Beaconsfield Road, Clifton, Bristol BS8 2TS — MB ChB 1993 Bristol.

WILSON, Anne Merrall (retired) Kinnaird, London Road, Poulton, Cirencester GL7 5JQ — MB BS Lond. 1957; MRCS Eng. LRCP Lond. 1957; FRCPsych 1986, M 1972; DPM Eng. 1970. Second Opinion Apptd. Dr Ment. Health Act Commiss.; Ment. Health Act Commission. Prev: Cons. Psychiat. E. Glos. NHS Trust.

WILSON, Anne Moya Yatton Family Practice, 155 Mendip Road, Yatton, Bristol BS49 4ER Tel: 01934 832277 Fax: 01934 876085; 3 Silverstone Way, Congresbury, Bristol BS49 5ES Tel: 01934 833485 — MB ChB 1973 Glas.; MRCGP 1977; DCH RCPS Glas. 1977; DRCOG 1976. (Glas.) Socs: Roy. Coll. Gen. Pract.

WILSON, Anthony Ernest 8 The Paddock, Appleton Wiske, Northallerton DL6 2BE — MB BS 1965 Durh.; AFOM RCP Lond. 1984. Med. Off. Tees Div. Brit. Steel plc. Socs: BMA; BASICS; Soc. Occupat. Med. Prev: Regist. (A & E) Dundee Roy. Infirm.; Demonst. (Anat.) Dundee Univ.; Regist. (Cas. & Orthop.) Durh. Co. Hosp.

WILSON, Anthony Gerard Div. Of Genomic Medicine, Uni. Of Sheffield, Sheffield S10 2JF Email: a.g.wilson@shef.ac.uk; 1 Gladstone Mews, Ranmoor, Sheffield S10 3HS Tel: 01142 731402 Fax: 01142 712882 Email: a.g.wilson@sheffield.ac.uk — MB BCh BAO 1983 Queen's Uni., Belfast; MRCP 1986 UK; DCH 1988 RCPSI; PhD 1995 Shef. Sen. Lect. in Molecular Med/Rheum. Socs: Roy. Coll. Phys. Lond. & Brit. Soc. Rheum. Prev: ARC Research Fell. (Med. Fac.) Univ. Sheff.; Regist. & Lect. (Rheum.) N.. Gen. Hosp. Edin.; SHO (Cardiol., Neurol. & Rheum.) Roy. Vict. Hosp. Belf.

WILSON, Anthony James Thomas Drayton Medical Practice, Cheshire Street, Market Drayton TF9 3BS Tel: 01630 652158; 60 Main Road, Norton-in-Hales, Market Drayton TF9 4AT Tel: 01630 653426 — MB BS 1973 Lond. (Char. Cross) Prev: Trainee Gen. Pract. PeterBoro. Vocational Train. Scheme; Ho. Off. (Surg.) Profess. Unit Surg. & Ho. Off. (Med.) Char. Cross; Hosp. Lond.

WILSON, Anthony Robert (retired) Cedar House, Behoes Lane, Woodcote, Reading RG8 0PP Email: a.r.wilson@amserve.net — MB ChB 1956 Ed.; MRCGP 1975; MFCM 1974; DAvMed Eng. 1969. Prev: GP Woodcote Reading.

WILSON, Arlette Margaret 64 Watson Street, Aberdeen AB25 2SU — MB ChB 1988 Aberd.

WILSON, Arthur Claude (retired) Wateredge, Crosthwaite, Kendal LA8 8HX — MB ChB Glas. 1952; FRCOG 1974, M 1959. Prev: Cons. O & G N.. Sefton Health Dist. (S.port).

WILSON, Arthur Miles 74 The Avenue, Mortimer, Reading RG7 3QX — MB ChB 1998 Manch.

WILSON, Barbara Elizabeth Chapel Cottage, Chieveley, Newbury RG16 8XG — MB ChB 1944 Leeds.

WILSON, Bernard Gerard 15 Windsor Park, Belfast BT9 6FQ — MB BCh BAO 1979 Belf.

WILSON, Betty Nicol Child Development Centre, Bridgeton Health Centre, Abercromby St., Glasgow; 10 Ellergreen Road, Beardsen, Glasgow G61 2RJ — MB ChB 1979 Ed.; BSc (Med. Sci.) Ed. 1976, MB ChB 1979; MRCGP 1983; DRCOG 1982; LF (Hom.) Glas. 1995. SCMO (Child Health) Yorkhill NHS Trust. Socs: BMA; Vice-Chairm. BAAF Med. Adviser's Gp. Scotl. Prev: Clin. Med. Off. Forth Valley HB; Trainee GP S. Lothian VTS.

WILSON, Brian Andrew Langham Place Surgery, 11 Langham Place, Northampton NN2 6AA Tel: 01604 38162 Fax: 01604 602457 — MB BS 1985 Lond.; DRCOG 1987 GUYS.

WILSON, Bridget Elizabeth (Baldry) Birmingham Childrens' Hopsital, Steelhouse Lane, Birmingham B4 6NH; Email: oldfieldmanor@aol.com — MB ChB 1987 Sheff.; MRCP (UK) 1992. (Sheffield) Cons. In Paediatric Accid. & Emerg. Med. Birm. Childr.s' Hosp. Birm. Socs: Roy. Coll. Of Paediat. & Child Health. Prev: SHO Rotat. (Paediat.) Qu. Med. Centre Nottm. & Derby Childr. Hosps.; SHO Rotat. (Paediat.) Leicester; Trainee GP Redditch VTS.

WILSON

WILSON, Bridie Olivia (retired) Awelon, 22 Aber Drive, Craigside, Llandudno LL30 3AN Tel: 01492 549249 — MB ChB 1949 Birm.; MFCM 1974; DPH Manch. 1968; DObst RCOG 1953. Prev: Community Phys. Clwyd HA.

WILSON, Callum Stephen — MB ChB 1990 Dundee; FRCA 1995.

WILSON, Cameron MacKinnon Deepdale Road Healthcare Centre, Deepdale Road, Preston PR1 5AF Tel: 01772 655533 Fax: 01772 653414; 40 Preston Road, Grimsargh, Preston PR2 5SD Tel: 01772 651243 — MB ChB 1982 Glas.; DCH RCP Lond. 1988. Prev: Med. Off. RN.

WILSON, Carol Mildred 16 Cleaver Park, Belfast BT9 5HX — MB BCh BAO 1979 Belf.; MD Belf. 1986; FRCP Ed. 1995; MRCP (UK) 1983. Cons. Cardiol. Roy. Vict. Hosp. Belf. Socs: Brit. Cardiac Soc.; (Treas.) Irish Cardiac Soc.; (Hon. Sec.) Ulster Med. Soc.

WILSON, Caroline Jane c/o Gransha Hospital, Clooney Road, Londonderry BT47 6TF Tel: 01504 860261; Northfield House, Gransha Hospital, Clooney Road, Londonderry BT47 6TF Tel: 01504 860261 — MB ChB 1996 Stellenbosch. (University of Stellenbosch) SHO (Psychiat.) Gransha Hosp. Lond.derry. Prev: Jun. Ho. Off. Tygerberg Hosp. W.ern Cape, S. Africa.

WILSON, Caroline Lesley Department of Dermatology, St. James's University Hospital, Leeds LS9 7TF Tel: 0113 206 4900 Fax: 0113 206 4805 — MB BS 1982 Lond.; FRCP (UK) 1999; MRCP (UK) 1986; BSc (1st cl. Hons.) Lond. 1979, MD 1995. (Westm.) p/t Cons. Dermat. St. Jas. & Seacroft Univ. Hosp. NHS Trust Leeds. Prev: Sen. Regist. (Dermat.) Oxf. RHA & Hon. Regist. (Dermat.) Slade Hosp. Oxf.; Regist. (Med. & Dermat.) Stoke Mandeville Hosp.; SHO (Oncol.) Roy. Marsden Hosp.

WILSON, Mrs Caroline Samantha Grovehurst, Middle Lane, Denbigh LL16 3UW — MB ChB 1989 Birm.; MRCGP 1995. Asst. in Gen. Pract.

WILSON, Catherine Mary 33 Tweskard Park, Belfast BT4 2JZ — MD 1987 Belf.; MB BCh BAO 1976; FFA RCSI 1980. Cons. (Anaesth.) Ulster Hosp. Dundonald.

WILSON, Catherine Mary The Surgery, Oxenfoord Avenue, Pathhead EH37 5QD Tel: 01875 320302 Fax: 01875 320494; 8 Fala, Blackshiels, Pathhead EH37 5SY Tel: 01875 833296 — MB ChB 1977 Ed.; BSc Ed. 1974; Dip. Occ. Med. RCP Lond. 1997. GP Partner Pathmead Med. Pract. Pathmead, Midlothian; Occupat. Health Phys. Lothian NHS Occupat. Health Serv. Morelands, Astley-Ainslie Hosp. Edin. Prev: Trainee GP Edin. VTS; Regist. (Psychiat.) Roy. Edin. Hosp.; SHO (Psychiat.) Roy. Edin. Hosp.

WILSON, Catherine Sara Plot 7, Summerfield, Wattisfield Road, Walsham-Le-Willows, Bury St Edmunds IP31 3BD — MB BS 1982 Lond.

WILSON, Catherine Stewart Abington, 37 Ayr Road, Prestwick KA9 1SY — MB ChB 1977 Glas.; FFA RCSI 1981. Cons. Anaesth. N. Ayrsh. & Arran Trust.

WILSON, Catriona Edith Armadale Group Practice, 18 North Street, Armadale, Bathgate EH48 3QD Tel: 01501 730432; 3 Woodside Farm, Forrestfield, Airdrie ML6 7RY Tel: 01236 842539 — MB ChB 1987 Glas.

WILSON, Cedric James (retired) Thirty One, Beacon Road, Walsall WS5 3LF — MB BChir 1946 Camb.; MRCS Eng. LRCP Lond. 1946. Prev: Res. Surg. Off., Ho. Surg. & Anaesth. W. Bromwich & Dist. Gen. Hosp.

WILSON, Charles Antrim Hospital, 45 Bush Road, Antrim BT41 2RL Tel: 02894 424193 Fax: 02894 42423; 25 Bogroll Road, Ballymena BT42 4HH Tel: 02825 649260 — MB BCh BAO 1965 Belf.; FRCP Lond. 1994; MRCP (UK) 1970; FACC 1992. (Qu. Univ. Belf.) Cons. Cardiol. Antrim Hosp. Socs: Brit. Cardiac Soc.; BMA. Prev: Cons. Gen. Med. Waveney Hosp. Ballymena & Mid-Ulster Hosp. Magherafelt; Research Fell. (Cardiol.) & Sen. Regist. (Gen. Med.) Roy. Vict. Hosp. Belf.

WILSON, Charles Alexander Department of Forensic Pathology, Duncan Building, Daulby St., Liverpool L69 3GA Tel: 0151 706 4301 — MB ChB 1991 Sheff.; MRCPath 1997. (Sheffield) Lect. (Forens. Path.) Univ. Liverp.; Hon. Sen. Regist. (Histopath.) Roy. Liverp. Univ. Hosp. Socs: Assn. Clin. Path; Brit. Assn. Forens. Med. Prev: Regist Rotat. (Histopath.) N.. RHA.

WILSON, Charles Frederick (Surgery), 178 Roe Lane, Southport PR9 7PN Tel: 01704 28439; 50 Ryder Crescent, Hillside, Southport PR8 3AF Tel: 01704 78304 — MB ChB 1962 Liverp. (Liverp.) Socs: BMA & S.port Med. Soc. Prev: SHO Clatterbridge Hosp. Bebington; Regist. Cas. Roy. Liverp. Childr. Hosp.

WILSON, Charles Nicholas Farnham Medical Centre, 435 Stanhope Road, South Shields NE33 4JE Tel: 0191 455 4748 Fax: 0191 455 8573 — MB ChB 1971 Dundee; DObst RCOG 1974.

WILSON, Christina Isabella (retired) 75 Stewarton Drive, Cumbuslang, Glasgow G72 8DQ Tel: 0141 641 2195 — MB ChB 1948 Glas. Prev: SCMO Gtr. Glas. Health Bd.

WILSON, Christine Elizabeth Schopwick Surgery, Everett Court, Romeland, Elstree, Borehamwood WD6 3BJ Tel: 020 8953 1008 Fax: 020 8905 2196; Donard, Alderham Road, Letchmore Health, Watford WD25 8EW — BM 1976 Soton.; MRCGP 1982; DRCOG 1979. (Southampton)

WILSON, Christine Hilary Castledawson Surgery, Station Road, Castledawson, Magherafelt BT45 8AZ Tel: 028 7938 6237 Fax: 028 7946 9613 — MB BCh BAO 1973 Belf.; DRCOG 1977.

WILSON, Christine Shearer Auchinairn Road Surgery, 101 Auchinairn Road, Bishopbriggs, Glasgow G64 1NF Tel: 0141 772 1808 Fax: 0141 762 1274; 13 Ledcameroch Crescent, Bearsden, Glasgow G61 4AD — MB ChB 1983 Glas.; MRCGP 1987; DRCOG 1988; DCCH RCP Ed. 1988. (Glasgow) Prev: Trainee GP Livingston VTS; SHO (O & G) Stirling Roy. Infirm.; SHO (Infec. Dis.) Ruchill Hosp. Glas.

WILSON, Christopher Orthopaedic Department, BUPA Hospital, Cardiff CF23 8XL Tel: 029 2054 2655; 7 Palace Road, Cardiff CF5 2AF Tel: 029 2057 7117 Fax: 01222 577844 Email: chriswilson@cwilson.net — MB BS 1984 Lond.; BSc (Hons.) Lond. 1981, MB BS 1984; FRCS Orth. 1996; FRCS Ed. 1989. (Univ. Coll. Lond.) Cons. Trauma & Orthop. Surg.

WILSON, Christopher Claud Stevenson Cedarhill, Auchencloch, Banknock, Bonnybridge FK4 1UA Tel: 01324 840227 — MB ChB 1991 Aberd.; LR Hom Faculty homocop, June 1999. (Aberd.) SHO Rotat. (Med.) Roy. United Hosp. & Roy. Nat. Hosp. Rheum. Dis. Bath. Prev: SHO Rotat. (Med.) Worcester Roy. Infirm.; SHO (Neurosurg.) Radcliffe Infirm. Oxf.

WILSON, Christopher Edward Plympton Health Centre, Plympton, Plymouth PL7 2PS Tel: 01752 341474; Mansion 5, Mounthaven Village, Bitta Ford, Plymouth PC21 0XF Tel: 01752 345040 Email: chris@deanrd.global.net.co.uk — MB BS 1982 Nottm.; BMedSci Nottm. 1980, MB BS 1982; MRCGP 1986.

WILSON, Christopher John Thurlow, 9 Finchdean Road, Rowlands Castle PO9 6DA Tel: 023 9241 2350; Thurlow, 9 Finchdean Road, Rowlands Castle PO9 6DA Tel: 023 9241 2350 Email: wilson@thurlow.vispa.com — MB BS 1975 Lond.; DRCOG 1977. (Lond. Hosp.) Prev: Regist. (Paediat.) St. Mary's Hosp. Lond.; SHO Qu. Eliz. Hosp. Childr. Lond.; SHO (O & G) Lond. Hosp.

WILSON, Christopher John Francis Broomlands Brae, Stirches Road, Hawick TD9 7HF — MB ChB 1995 Sheff.

WILSON, Mr Christopher Reid 8A Ailsa Drive, Glasgow G42 9UL — MB ChB 1990 Glas.; FRCS Glas. 1994.

WILSON, Christopher Sean Church Walk Surgery, 28 Church Walk, Lurgan, Craigavon BT67 9AA Tel: 028 3832 7834 Fax: 028 3834 9331; 43 Kilmore Road, Lurgan, Craigavon BT67 9HT Tel: 01762 324789 Email: kilmorerd@supanet.com — MB BCh BAO 1979 Belf.; DRCOG 1982; DCH RCPS Glas. 1982. Gen. Pract. Princip.; Jt. Med. Dir. Craigavon & Banbridge Community Trust.

WILSON, Christopher William Homecroft Surgery, Voguebeloth, Illogan, Redruth TR16 4ET Fax: 01209 843707; Chy Bean, Harris Mill, Illogan, Redruth TR16 4JE Tel: 01209 213207 Fax: 01209 213207 Email: cwilson661@aol.com — MB BS 1974 Lond.; MRCS Eng. LRCP Lond. 1973; DA Eng. 1977; DObst RCOG 1975. (Westm.) Prev: SHO (Cas. & Anaesth.) Roy. Cornw. Hosp. (Treliske) Truro; SHO (Gyn.) Camborne-Redruth Hosp.

WILSON, Claire Louise Fairhill Medical Practice, 81 Kingston Hill, Kingston upon Thames KT2 7PX Tel: 020 8546 1407 Fax: 020 8547 0075; 12 Norman Avenue, St. Margaret's, Twickenham TW1 2LY Tel: 020 8892 3072 — MB ChB 1985 Bristol; MRCGP 1989; DCH RCP Lond. 1989; DRCOG 1988. Socs: BMA.

WILSON, Mr Colin The Ayr Hospital, Dalmellington Road, Ayr KA6 6DX Tel: 01292 610555 Fax: 01292 288952; 8 Southpark Road, Ayr KA7 2TL Tel: 01292 260772 — MB ChB 1979 Glas.; MD Glas. 1989; FRCS Glas. 1983; T(S) 1995. Cons. Surg. Ayr Hosp. Socs: Assn. & Surgs. GB & Irel.; Brit. Soc. Gastroenterol. Prev: Sen.

WILSON

Regist. (Gen. Surg.) Roy. Infirm. Glas.; Jun. Cons. Surgic. Gastroenterol. Groote Schuur Hosp., Cape Town, S. Afr.

WILSON, Colin Alexander Hunter Health Centre, Andrew Street, East Kilbride, Glasgow G74 1AD Tel: 01355 906622 Fax: 01355 906629 — MB ChB 1983 Glas.; MRCGP 1987; DRCOG 1986; Cert. Family Plann. JCC 1986.

WILSON, Colin Bryce Hollands and Partners, Bridport Medical Centre, North Allington, Bridport DT6 5DU Tel: 01308 421896 Fax: 01308 421109 — MB BS 1979 Lond.; DRCOG 1985; DO RCS Eng. 1984. (Westm.) Trainee GP Mullion VTS. Prev: SHO/Regist. Oxf. Eye Hosp.; SHO (Obst.) John Radcliffe Hosp. Oxf.; Ophth. Roy. Commonw. Soc. Blind, Grenada.

WILSON, Colin Moffat Lorn Medical Centre, Soroba Road, Oban PA34 4HE Tel: 01631 563175 Fax: 01631 562708; Clachbheo, Glenmore Road, Oban PA34 4NB Tel: 01631 562418 — MB ChB 1978 Glas.; FFA RCS Eng. 1982. Ltd. Specialist (Anaesth.) Lorn & Is.s Dist. Gen. Hosp. Prev: Regist. (Anaesth.) Vict. Infirm. Glas.

WILSON, Colin Rhodri Mactaggart, TD The Gateway, 4 Raynsford Road, Dallington, Northampton NN5 7HP — MB BS 1963 Lond.; MRCPsych 1972; DPM Eng. 1968. (St. Thos.) Cons. Psychiat. St. And. Hosp. N.ampton; Lt-Col. RAMC TA. Socs: Med. Soc. Lond.; (Pres.) N.ampton Med. Soc.; Yeoman Soc. of Apoth. Prev: Sen. Regist. (Psychiat.) Univ. Coll. Hosp. & Maudsley Hosp. Lond.; Research Sen. Regist. Univ. Coll. Hosp. & Hosp. Trop. Dis. Lond.; Regist. (Psychiat.) Univ. Coll. Hosp. Lond.

WILSON, Cyril Edward (retired) Aisling, 22 Croslands Park, Barrow-in-Furness LA13 9NH Tel: 01229 821718 — LRCPI & LM, LRCSI & LM 1950.

WILSON, Daniel Timothy Richardson Mill Stream Surgery, Mill Stream, Benson, Wallingford OX10 6RL Tel: 01491 838286; 2 Eyres Close, Ewelme, Wallingford OX10 6LA Tel: 01491 833556 — BM BS 1986 Nottm.; MPhil Nottm. 1985, BMedSci 1984; FRCGP 1995, M 1990; DCH RCP Lond. 1990; DRCOG 1989. Prev: Trainee GP N. Lincs. HA VTS.

WILSON, David Blackthorn Surgery, 73 Station Road, Netley Abbey, Southampton SO31 5AE Tel: 023 8045 3110 Fax: 023 8045 2747 — MB ChB 1968 Bristol; DObst RCOG 1970.

WILSON, David Bennett 30 Deramore Park S., Malone Road, Belfast BT9 5JY — MB BCh BAO 1971 Belf.; FFA RCSI 1977; DObst RCOG 1973.

WILSON, David Charles Department of Child Life and Health, University of Edinburgh, 20 Sylvan Place, Edinburgh EH9 1UW — MB BCh 1984 Belf.; MB BCh (Hons.) Belf. 1984; MRCP (UK) 1987; DCH RCP Lond. 1986.

WILSON, David Colin 164 Peel Brow, Ramsbottom, Bury BL0 0AX — MB ChB 1994 Ed.

WILSON, David Harold Grove House Practice, St. Pauls Health Centre, High St, Runcorn WA7 1AB Tel: 01928 566561 Fax: 01928 590212 — MRCS Eng. LRCP Lond. 1982. Prev: Trainee GP Halewood; SHO (A & E) BRd.green Hosp.; Ho. Off. St. Helen's Hosp.

WILSON, Mr David Hedley (retired) Lower Ackhill, Presteigne LD8 2ED Tel: 01544 267456 Email: d.h.wilson@btinternet.com — MB ChB Leeds 1951; FRCS Eng. 1988; FRCS Ed. 1964; FFAEM 1993; DTM Antwerp 1954. Prev: Dean Postgrad. Med. Educat. Univ. Leeds & Hon. Cons. Surg. A & E Leeds Gen. Infirm.

WILSON, Professor David Ian — MB BS 1984 Newc.; PhD Newc. 1996; BA Oxf. 1981; MRCP (UK) 1987. Prof. of Human Developm. Genetics, Soton. Univ., Soton.; Hon. Cons. in Clin. Genetics, Soton. Univ. Hosp. Trust. Socs: Brit. Soc. Human Genetics. Prev: MRC Clin. Scientist; Univ. of Newc.; Sen. Lect. (Med. Genetics) Dept. Human Genetics & Med. Univ. of Newc.

WILSON, Mr David Ian City Hospital, Hucknall Road, Nottingham NG5 1PJ Tel: 0115 969 1169 Fax: 0115 840 2601 — MB BS 1985 Lond.; FRCS Eng. 1990; FRCS (Plast.) 1998. (St. George's Hospital Medical School) Cons. Burns & plastic Surg. City Hosp. Notts. Socs: Brit. Burn Assoc. & Europ. Burn Assoc.; Amer. Burn Assoc.; Brit. Assoc. of Plastic Surg.s. Prev: Regist. (Burns & Plastic Surg.) City Hosp. Nottm.; Regist. (Plastic Surg.) Leicester Roy. Infirm.; SHO (Plastic Surg.) Sub-Regional Burns & Plastic Surg. Unit Plymouth.

WILSON, David Ian Talbot, MBE (retired) Quackers, Duck St., Child Okeford, Blandford Forum DT11 8ET Tel: 01258 861338 — MB ChB Ed. 1949; FRCGP 1980, M 1965. Med. Adviser Hall & WoodLa. Ltd. Prev: Chairm. Assn. GP Community Hosp. (Eng. & Wales).

WILSON, David John Nuffield Orthopaedic Centre, Windmill Road, Headington, Oxford OX3 7LD Tel: 01865 227257 Fax: 01865 227347 Email: david.wilson@noc.anglox.nhs.uk; Email: david.wilson@radiology.ox.ac.uk — MB BS 1976 Lond.; FRCP 1999; Hon. MA Oxf. 1985; FRCR 1983; MRCP (UK) 1980; BSc. (Human Physiol.) Lond. 1973; FRCP 1998. (King's Coll. Hosp.) Cons. Radiol. Nuffield Orthop. Centre & John Radcliffe Hosp. Oxf.; Sen. Clin. Lect. Univ. Oxf.; Asst. Edr. Clin. Radiol. Socs: Internat. Skeletal Soc.; Pres. Brit. Soc. Skeletal Radiol. Prev: Regist. & Sen. Regist. (Diag. Radiol.) John Radcliffe Hosp. Oxf.; SHO (Gen. Med.) Good Hope Hosp. Sutton Coldfield & MusGr. Pk. Hosp. Taunton.

WILSON, David Livingstone (retired) Cornerstone, 11 St Micheal Drive, Helensburgh, Glasgow G84 7SF Tel: 01436 677933 — MB ChB 1948 Glas.; FFPHM RCP (UK) 1981, M 1974; DPH Durh. 1962; DTM & H Liverp. 1951. Prev: Dist. Med. Off. Newc. HA.

WILSON, David Neill Rampton Hospital, Retford, Nottingham DN22 0PD Tel: 01777 247703 Fax: 01777 247737; Halam House, Halam, Newark, Nottingham NG22 8AG Tel: 01636 812177 Fax: 01636 812177 — MB BS Lond. 1970; LMSSA Lond. 1970; FRCPsych 1993, M 1979; DPM Eng. 1978. Cons. Psychiat. Prev: Sen. Lect. & Hon. Cons. Psychiat. Nottm. Univ.; Cons. Psychiat. (Ment. Handicap) Gloucester HA; Sen. Regist. Lea Hosp. BromsGr. & Lea Castle Hosp. Kidderminster.

WILSON, David Roy Derwent Surgery, Norton Road, Norton, Malton YO17 9RF Tel: 01653 600069 Fax: 01653 698014; 75 Middlecave Road, Malton YO17 7NQ Tel: 01653 692207 — MB BS 1964 Lond.; MRCS Eng. LRCP Lond. 1963; DObst RCOG 1965. (Guy's) Sen. Partner, Gen. Pract.; Hosp. Pract. (c/o Elderly) Malton Hosp. ScarBoro. & NE Yorks. Healthcare Trust. Socs: Hon. Treas. York Med. Soc.; BMA. Prev: Regist. (Neurol.) Pinderfields Gen. Hosp. Wakefield; Ho. Phys. Lewisham Hosp.; Ho. Surg. (Orthop.) Guy's Hosp.

WILSON, David Tinsley (retired) 15 Meadow Grove, Crawfordsburn, Bangor BT19 1JL — LRCP LRCS 1946 Ed.; LRCP LRCS Ed. LRFPS Glas. 1946.

WILSON, Deborah County Durham Health Authority, Appleton House, Lanchester Road, Durham DH1 5XZ — MB BS 1990 Newc.; MSc (Pub. Health) Newc. 1995; MFPHM 1997. Cons.Pub.healthMed.Communical Dis.Centro 1 Co. Durh. health Auth.

WILSON, Deborah Cosette 293 Higher Lane, Crank, St Helens WA11 8QU — MB ChB 1976 Liverp. Clin. Asst. Fazakerley Hosp. Liverp.

WILSON, Deborah Margaret 36 Redcraigs, Kirkcaldy KY2 6TR — MB ChB 1992 Ed.

WILSON, Derek (retired) Môr Isaf, Hardwicke, Hay-on-Wye, Hereford HR3 5HA Tel: 01497 831253 Fax: 01497 831599 — MB BS Lond. 1956; MRCS Eng. LRCP Lond. 1956; FRCGP 1977, M 1968; DObst RCOG 1960. Prev: GP Hay-on-Wye.

WILSON, Diana Frances St. Columba's Hospice, 15 Boswall Road, Edinburgh EH5 3RW Tel: 0131 551 1381 Fax: 0131 551 2771 — MB BS 1977 Lond.; MRCP (UK) 1981; MRCS Eng LRCP Lond. 1977; FRCR 1985. (St. Bart.) Cons. Palliat. Med. St. Columba's Hospice Edin. Prev: Cons. Palliat. Med. Winchester HA; Sen. Regist. St. Columba's Hospice Edin.

***WILSON, Diane Margaret** 106 Rosebery Road, Belfast BT6 8JF; 39 Alveston Road, Carryduff, Belfast BT8 8RP — MB BCh 1998 Belf.; MB BCh Belf 1998.

WILSON, Dirk Guy 20 Pace Close, Cardiff CF5 2QZ — MB BCh 1989 Wales.

WILSON, Dorcas c/o Mr M. Baker Professional Locum Services, The Broadway, London W6 7AF — MB BCh 1993 Witwatersrand.

WILSON, Doreen Mary (retired) Clunch Cottage, Lodge Road, Feltwell, Thetford IP26 4DL — MB BS 1954 Lond. Prev: Ho. Surg., Ho. Phys. & Cas. Off. Norf. & Norwich Hosp.

WILSON, Douglas Callan 23 Southerton Crescent, Kirkcaldy KY2 5ND — MB ChB 1969 Ed.; FFA RCS Eng. 1975; DObst RCOG 1971.

WILSON, Douglas George 11 Garden Street, Padiham, Burnley BB12 8NP — MB ChB 1985 Manch.

WILSON, Douglas George The Garth, 26 Blairforkie Drive, Bridge of Allan, Stirling FK9 4PH Tel: 01786 832181 — MB ChB 1952 Glas.; MFOM RCP Lond. 1978; DIH RFPS Glas. 1960; DObst RCOG 1954. Mem. Med. Appeals Tribunals. Prev: Civil Defence Adviser to

WILSON

Scott. Health Serv.; Head of Med. Servs. N.. Div., UK Atomic Energy Auth., Risley Nuclear Estab.; Sen. Med. Off. Dounreay Experim. Reactor Estab. UK Atomic Energy Auth.

WILSON, Douglas Scott MacGregor c/o The Practice Manager, The Queens Road Medical Practice, The Queens Road, St Peter Port, Guernsey GY1 1RH; Grange End Medical Practice, St. Peter Port, Guernsey — MB ChB 1979 Aberd.; MRCGP 1984.

WILSON, Duncan Henry The Village Surgery, 24-28 Laughton Road, Thurcroft, Rotherham S66 9LP Tel: 01709 542216 Fax: 01709 702356 — MB ChB 1984 Manch.; BSc (Med. Sci.) St. And. 1981. Prev: Trainee GP Preston Lancs.

WILSON, Duncan Robertson, Maj. RAMC Royal Brompton Hospital, Sydney St., London SW3 6NP Email: d.wilson@rbh.nthames.nhs.uk; 11 Coldstream Gardens, Putney, London SW18 1LJ Tel: 020 8877 9553 — MB ChB 1989 Dundee; MRCP (UK) 1994. Specialist Regist. Roy. Brompton Hosp. Lond. Socs: Brit. Thorac. Soc. Prev: Specialist Regist. Frimley Pk. Hosp. Surrey; Specialist (Gen. Med.) Camb. Milt. Hosp. Aldershot; SHO (ICU) Roy. Brompton Hosp.

WILSON, Edward Tel: 01382 60111; 29 Kirk Road, Newport-on-Tay DD6 8JD — MB ChB 1981 Glas.; FFA RCSI 1987. Cons. Anaesth. Ninewells Hosp. Dundee.

WILSON, Edward Adrian 23 Plymouth Road, Penarth CF64 3DA — MB ChB 1994 Manch.

WILSON, Edward Harold (retired) Awelon, 22 Aber Drive, Craigside, Llandudno LL30 3AN Tel: 01492 549249 — MB ChB Liverp. 1946; MD Liverp. 1954. Prev: Cons. Phys. (Geriat) Lancaster & E. Cumbria Health Dists.

WILSON, Mr Edward Timothy (retired) 6 Manor View, Croxteth Park, West Derby, Liverpool L12 0LT Tel: 0151 228 6513 — MD Jerusalem 1968; FRCS RCPSI 1978; MRCOphth 1988; DO RCPSI 1973; FRIPHH 1988. SCMO (Ophth.) St. Helens & Knowsley NHS Trust, Community Health Trust & Alder Hey Childr. Hosp.; Mem. St. Helens & Knowsley LMC. Prev: Lect. & Hon. Regist. Univ. Manch. Med. Sch.

WILSON, Eileen Cuthbertson 8 Barnford Crescent, Alloway, Ayr KA7 4UP — MB ChB 1978 Glas.

WILSON, Eileen Margaret (retired) 2 Earlspark Drive, Bieldiside, Aberdeen AB15 9AH Tel: 01224 869279 — MB ChB 1958 Aberd.; DA Eng. 1961. Prev: SCMO Tayside HB.

WILSON, Elaine Health Centre, Wardles Lane, Great Wyrley, Walsall WS6 6EW Tel: 01922 415515 — MB BS 1981 Lond.; MSc Community Paediat. Warwick 1992; DFFP 1993; DRCOG 1985. Prev: SCMO M. Staffs. HA.

WILSON, Elaine Anne Epilepsy Research Unit, Western Infirmary, Glasgow G11 6NT Tel: 0141 211 1925 Fax: 0141 211 1925; The Cairn, Crosshill St., Airdrie ML6 9DA — MB ChB 1988 Glas.; MRCGP 1994. Asst. Dir. Epilepsy Research Unit (Med.) W.. Infirm. Glas.

WILSON, Eleanor Mary Clachbeo, Glenmore Road, Oban PA34 4NB — MB ChB 1976 Glas. Clin. Med. Off. Family Plann. Clinic, W. Highland Hosp. Oban. Prev: Regist. (O & G) Rutherglen Matern. Hosp. Glas.; SHO (Anaesth.) Stobhill Hosp. Glas.

WILSON, Elena Macnaught Groves Ochard, The Common, Chipperfield, Kings Langley WD4 9BY — MB BS 1990 Lond.; BSc (Pharmacol.) Lond. 1987; MRCP (UK) 1993; FRCR 1998. (University College and The Middlesex London) Regist. (Clin. Oncol.) Mt. Vernon Hosp. N.wood Middlx. Prev: Regist. (Clin. Oncol.) Char. Cross Hosp. Lond.; SHO (Med.) The Whittington Hosp. Lond.

WILSON, Elizabeth New York Surgery, Brookland Terrace, New York, North Shields NE29 8EA Tel: 0191 258 5316 Fax: 0191 257 8231; 104 Birkdale, Whitley Bay NE25 9LZ — BM 1981 Soton.; MRCGP 1987; DRCOG 1984; Cert. Family Plann. JCC 1984. Socs: BMA.

WILSON, Elizabeth Anne 5 Hazeldene Drive, Bangor BT20 4RE — MB BCh BAO 1983 Belf.

WILSON, Elizabeth Anne Ringwood Health Centre, The Close, Ringwood BH24 1JY Tel: 01425 478901; 17 Shelley Close, Ashley Heath, Ringwood BH24 2JA — BM 1983 Soton.; DRCOG 1993. Clin. Med. Off. (Family Plann.) Hants. Prev: Trainee GP Ringwood Health Centre; SHO (O & G), P.ss Anne Hosp., Soton; SHO (A & E) & (Radiother. & Oncol.) Poole Hosp.

WILSON, Elizabeth Booth Galpins Road Surgery, 6 Galpins Road, Thornton Heath CR7 6EA Tel: 020 8684 3450 Fax: 202 8683 0439

— MB BChir 1962 Camb.; MA, MB Camb. 1962; BChir 1961; DObst RCOG 1963. (St. Geo.) Socs: BMA. Prev: Ho. Phys. Croydon Gen. Hosp.; Ho. Surg. Vict. Hosp. Childr. Lond. & Mayday Hosp. Croydon.

WILSON, Elizabeth Jean Department of Histopathology, St Barts Hospital, West Smithfield, London EC1A 7BE Tel: 020 7601 8850; 21 Parkside, Vanbrugh Fields, London SE3 7QQ — MB BS 1976 Lond.; BSc Lond. 1973; MRCP (UK) 1979; FRCR 1983. (Lond. Hosp.) Sen. Med. Off. & Specialist Clin. Servs. Div. DoH. Prev: Sen. Med. Off. DoH; Sen. Regist. (Radiother. & Oncol.) Lond. Hosp.; Regist. (Radiother. & Oncol.) Lond. Hosp.

WILSON, Elizabeth Margaret 12 Charter Approach, Warwick CV34 6AE — BM BS 1996 Nottm. SHO Med. Warwick Hosp.

WILSON, Elizabeth Marion 3 Little Heath Close, Audlem, Crewe CW3 0HX — MB ChB 1976 Manch.; BSc St. And. 1973.

WILSON, Elizabeth Mora Joan 9 Lindisfarne Road, Jesmond, Newcastle upon Tyne NE2 2HE Tel: 0191 281 0398 — MB ChB 1968 Aberd.; MFFP 1993; Cert. Family Plann. JCC 1977; DObst RCOG 1970. (Aberd.) SCMO (Contracep. & Sexual Health), Gateshead Health NHS Trust; Clin. Asst. (Colposcopy) Newc. u. Tyne & Gateshead HAs. Prev: GP Woking & Newc.; SHO (Gyn.) Roy. N.. Hosp. Lond.; SHO (Obst.) City of Lond. Matern. Hosp.

WILSON, Mrs Elizabeth Stanfield Bell (retired) 11 Westbourne Gardens, Glasgow G12 9XD Tel: 0141 334 3287 Email: libby@ewilson.fsnet.co.uk — MB BS Lond. 1949; MRCS Eng., LRCP Lond. 1949; FFFP 1993. Prev: Area Co-Ordinator Family Plann. Servs. (Incl. Domiciliary) Gtr. Glas. HB:.

WILSON, Elizabeth Sylvia 26 Bellshaugh Lane, Kelvinside, Glasgow G12 0PE Email: libbyirishrover@hotmail.com — MB ChB 1988 Glas.; BSc (Hons.) St. And. 1984; FRCS Glas 1992; FRCA Lond 1999. (St. Andrews and Glasgow) Specialist Regist. W.ern Infirm. Glas. Prev: SHO III (Gen. Surg.) W.. Infirm. Glas.; SHO Surg. Specialties Rotat. W.. Infirm. Glas.; Ho. Off. (Surg.) W.. Infirm. Glas.

WILSON, Ellen Elizabeth North House Surgery, North House, Hope Street, Crook DL15 9HU Tel: 01388 762945 Fax: 01388 765333; 20 Royal Grove, Crook DL15 9ER — MB ChB 1988 Liverp.; MRCGP 1992.

WILSON, Emma Georgina 66 Polwarth Ter, Edinburgh EH11 1NJ — MB ChB 1997 Birm.

***WILSON, Emma Jane** 10 Nea Road, Highcliffe, Christchurch BH23 4NA — MB ChB 1997 Manch.; BSc St. And. 1994.

WILSON, Ena (retired) Holywood Road Surgery, 54 Holywood Road, Belfast BT4 1NT Tel: 028 9065 4668 — MB BCh BAO 1960 Belf. p/t Hosp. Pract. (ENT) Ulster Hosp. Dundonald.

WILSON, Eoin David Shiplett Court Farm, Shiplate Road, Bleadon, Weston Super Mare BS24 0NY; Shiplett Court Farm, Shiplate Road, Bleadon, Weston Super Mare BS24 0NY — MB BS 1998 Lond.; BSc Human Biol & Basic Med Scis, Lond, 1995. (University College and Meddlesex School fo Medicine) RMO1 A&E(ITU)Gen. Med., Hornsby, Ku-Ring-Gai Hosp., Sydney, NSW, Australia. Socs: MPS and BMA; BMA.

WILSON, Esther Kencia, Cocklebury Road, Chippenham SN15 3NS — MB ChB 1996 Liverp.

WILSON, Esther Teresa Tel: 01382 462292 Fax: 01382 461052 — MB ChB 1983 Aberd. Clin. Med. Off. (Family Plann.) Dundee. Prev: GP Fraserburgh; Trainee GP Forresterhill & Peterhead; Clin. Asst. (Ment. Handicap) Ladysbridge Hosp. Banff.

WILSON, Ewen Hugh Charles 1/L, 52 White Street, Glasgow G11 5EA — MB ChB 1994 Glas.

WILSON, Fay Wand Medical Centre, 279 Gooch Street, Highgate, Birmingham B5 7JE Tel: 0121 440 1561 Fax: 0121 440 0060; 179 St. Andrews Road, Birmingham B9 4NB — MB ChB 1980 Birm.; MRCGP 1986; DCH RCP Lond. 1985; DRCOG 1984. (Birmingham) Med. Dir. Badger GP Out of Hours Co-op.

WILSON, Fiona Ann TIL, 19 Roxborough St., Glasgow G12 9AP — MB ChB 1998 Glas. PRHO Surg., Stobhill Trust, Glas. Prev: PRHO Med., Stirling Roy. Infirm.

WILSON, Fiona Margaret 14 Cammo Hill, Edinburgh EH4 8EY Tel: 0131 339 2244 Email: a.o.a.wilson@a.o.l.com — MB ChB 1955 Glas. (Glas.) Prev: Sen. Med. Off. (Community Ment. Health) Lothian HB; Asst. Psychiat. St. Nicholas Hosp. Newc.; Asst. Psychiat. & Regist. N.gate Hosp. Morpeth.

WILSON, Fiona Munro Chertsey Lane Surgery, 5 Chertsey Lane, Staines TW18 3JH Tel: 01784 454164 Fax: 01784 464360 — MB ChB 1990 Birm.

WILSON, Frances Olwen (retired) Gallimaufry, 22 Broad Oak Road, Worsley, Manchester M28 2TG Tel: 0161 794 1456 — MB ChB 1954 Birm. Prev: GP Manch.

WILSON, Francis William Govanhill Health Centre, 233 Calder Street, Glasgow G42 7DR Tel: 0141 531 8370 Fax: 0141 531 4431; 26 King's Park Avenue, Glasgow G44 4UP Tel: 0141 636 6836 — MB ChB 1962 Glas.; FRCGP 1985, M 1976; DObst RCOG 1964. (Glas.) Socs: S.. Med. Soc. & Roy. M-C Soc. Glas. Prev: Assoc. Adviser Univ. Glas.; Hosp. Pract. Cowglen Hosp. Glas.; Ho. Phys. Glas. Roy. Infirm.

WILSON, Mr Frank Yonderly, Tinacre Hill, Wightwick, Wolverhampton WV6 8DA Tel: 01902 763929 Fax: 01902 644821 Email: frankwilson@msn.com — MB BS 1971 Newc.; FRCS Eng. 1978; FRCS Ed. 1976. Cons. Otolaryngol. Dudley NHS Hosps. Trust & Roy. Wolverhampton Hosps. Trust. Socs: Roy. Soc. Med.; BMA; Brit. Assoc. of Otolaryngol. & Head/Neck Surg. Prev: Sen. Regist. (Otolaryngol.) Univ. Hosp. Wales Cardiff; TWJ Clin. & Research Fell. Univ. Calif. San Francisco, USA.

WILSON, Frank David 113 Denby Lane, Upper Denby, Huddersfield HD8 8UD Tel: 01484 861625 — MB BS Lond. 1956; MRCS Eng. LRCP Lond. 1956. (St. Thos.)

WILSON, Frederick Radford Health Centre, 1 Ilkeston Road, Radford, Nottingham NG7 3GW; 73 Cromwell Street, Nottingham NG7 4GJ Tel: 0115 978 9662 — MB BS 1951 Lond.; MRCS Eng. LRCP Lond. 1951; MRCGP 1963. (King's Coll. Hosp.) Med. Adviser & Med. Off. Trent Polytech.; Med. Adviser Raleigh Industs. Ltd. Nottm.; Med. Adviser Sturmey-Archer Ltd Nottm.; Nottm. PlayHo. Doctor. Socs: Brit. Stud. Health Assn. & BMA. Prev: GP Clin. Asst. Wom. Hosp. Nottm.; Cas. Off. King's Coll. Hosp.; Ho. Surg. E. Ham Memor. Hosp.

WILSON, Geoffrey David St Dunstan's Park Health Centre -, St Dunstan's Park, Melrose TD6 9RX Tel: 01896 822161 Fax: 01896 823151; Bridlewood, Fishers Lane, Darnick, Melrose TD6 9AS Tel: 0189682 3143 — MB ChB 1983 Ed.; MRCGP 1988; DRCOG 1987. Prev: Trainee GP N.umbria VTS.

WILSON, Geoffrey Donald Tel: 01323 727811 — MA Oxf. 1954, BM BCh 1952. (Oxf. & St. Thos.) Socs: BMA (late Chairm.); (late Pres.) E.bourne Med. Soc.; Fell. Roy. Soc. Med. Prev: Ho. Surg. & Ho. Phys. St. Mary's Hosp. E.bourne.

WILSON, Geoffrey Keith Greenshadows, Hancocks Mount, Ascot SL5 9PQ — MB ChB 1975 Birm.

WILSON, Geoffrey Ross Ashtead Hospital, The Warren, Ashtead KT21 2SB Tel: 01372 276161; Fax: 01372 800691 Email: plasticgrw@aol.co.uk — MB BChir 1976 Camb.; BA Camb. 1973; MA Camb. 1977; FRCS (Plast) 1993; FRCS Eng. 1981. (St. Geos. Hosp.) Cons. Hand, Plastic & Reconstruc. Surg. Chelsea & W.. Hosp. Lond.; Cons. Surg. (Hand, Plastic & Reconstruc.) Epsom Gen. Hosp. Surrey. Socs: BAPS; BAAPS; BSSH.

WILSON, George (retired) 50 Rowallan Drive, Kilmarnock KA3 1TU Tel: 01563 24892 — MB ChB 1950 Glas.; DA Eng. 1957. Prev: Cons. (Anaesth.) Ayrsh. & Arran Health Bd.

WILSON, George Martin 39 Carnreagh, Hillsborough BT26 6LJ — MB BCh BAO 1976 Belf.; MRCGP 1981; DRCOG 1978.

WILSON, George Morrison The Surgery, School Lane, Upton-upon-Severn, Worcester WR8 0LF Tel: 01684 592696 Fax: 01684 593122; Buryfield, School Lane, Upton on Severn, Worcester WR8 0LD Tel: 01684 592390 — MB ChB St. And. 1964. (St. And.) Vice-Chairm. Worcs. Health Auth. Prev: SHO Radcliffe Infirm. & Nuffield Orthop. Centre Oxf.; Demonst. (Anat.) Univ. St. And.; Ho. Surg. & Ho. Phys. Dundee Roy. Infirm.

WILSON, George Stephen (retired) 1 Gorse Road, Blackburn BB2 6LY Tel: 01254 56664 Email: george.wilson@cwcom.net — MB ChB 1955 Liverp. Prev: Assoc. Specialist (Genitourin. Med.) Bolton & Wigan AHAs.

WILSON, Georgina Harriette Mary 199 Victoria Rise, London SW4 0PF — MB BS 1995 Lond.

WILSON, Gerald Anthony 58 Priory Park, Belfast BT10 0AE Tel: 01232 627478 — MB BCh BAO 1992 Belf.; MRCGP 1996; DRCOG 1995; DGM RCPS Glas. 1994. Socs: BMA.

WILSON, Gerald Kingsley (retired) 32 St David's Road, Otley LS21 2AW Tel: 01943 464988 Email: shirleyandgerald@aol.com — MB BS 1957 Durh.; MB BS Durh., 1957; DPhysMed Eng. 1972. GP S. Shields. Prev: Med. Regist. Bradford Gp. Hosps.

WILSON, Gillian Elizabeth Young People's Department, Elmhill House, Royal Cornhill Hospital, Aberdeen AB25 2ZH Tel: 01224 681818; 16 Calsayseat Road, Aberdeen AB25 3UY Tel: 01224 630980 — MB ChB 1974 Glas.; MRCPsych 1978; Dip. Psychother. Aberd. 1981. Cons. Adolesc. Psychiat. Grampian HB.

WILSON, Gillian Mary (retired) Dewsbury District Hospital, Healds Road, Dewsbury WF13 4HS Tel: 01924 512000 Fax: 01924 512025 — MRCS Eng. LRCP Lond. 1965; MRCP (UK) 1972; FRCP 1988; FRCPCH 1997. Cons. (Paediat.) Dewsbury Health Dist., Dewsbury. Prev: Sen. Regist. (Paediat. & Developm. Med.) N.ampton Health Dist.

WILSON, Gillian Sara Portrush Medical Centre, 17 Dunluce Avenue, Portrush BT56 7DW Tel: 028 7082 2310 — MB ChB 1989 Sheff.; MRCGP 1994. p/t GP Retainer in Med. Centre in Portrush.

WILSON, Gillian Susan Lizbeth Northgate Surgery, Northgate, Pontefract WF8 1NF Tel: 01977 703635 Fax: 01977 702562; 3 The Coppice, Sherburn-in-Elmet, Leeds LS25 6LU Tel: 01977 685412 Fax: 01977 684804 Email: atulpatel@supanet.com — MB ChB 1983 Bristol; BSc Bristol 1980; DRCOG 1988; Cert. Family Plann. JCC 1988; DA (UK) 1985. Princip. GP. Dr. J.R.Waring & Partners, Pontefract. Socs: Local Med. Comm. -Nominee on.; Area Child Protec. Comm. Prev: GP Princip., Allerton Bywater, Castleford, Yorks; Retainer GP, N.gate Surg., Pontefract; Trainee GP Rawtenstall Health Centre Rossendale.

WILSON, Glenys Ruth Worcester Street Surgery, 24 Worcester Street, Stourbridge DY8 1AW Tel: 01384 371616; Rokeby, 62 Worcester Road, Hagley, Stourbridge DY9 0LD — MB BS 1987 Lond.

WILSON, Godfrey Everett Department of Histopathology/Cytopathology, 1st Floor, Clinical Sciences Building, Manchester Royal Infirmary, Manchester M13 9WL Tel: 0161 276 8812 Email: gwilson@labmed.cmht.nwest.nhs.uk — MB BCh BAO 1982 Dub.; MRCPath 1992. (TC Dub.) Cons. Histopath. Centr. Manch. Healthcare Trust.

WILSON, Graeme Bond Flat 1, 1 Highbury Road, Manchester M16 8PT — MB ChB 1994 Leeds.

WILSON, Graeme Eric Newham General Hospital, Plaistow, London E13 8SL — MB BCh 1988 Wales; MRCP (UK) 1992. (UWCM) Cons., Newham Healthcare Trust, Lond. Socs: Brit. Thoracic Soc. Prev: Regist. (Respirat.) Cardiothoracic Centre Liverp.; Sen. Regist. (Respirat.) Guy's & St. Thos. Hosp. Lond.; Hon. S.R., Roy. Brompton.

WILSON, Graham Allan Maclean 4 St Martins Avenue, Otley LS21 2AN — MB ChB 1991 Ed.; FRCA 1996.

WILSON, Graham Black Caldicot Medical Group, Gray Hill Surgery, Woodstock Way, Caldicot, Newport NP26 4DB Tel: 01291 420282 Fax: 01291 425853; 6 Queens Gardens, Magor, Newport — MB BCh 1979 Wales; MRCGP 1983.

WILSON, Graham Martin Ramsey Group Practice Centre, Grove Mount South, Ramsey IM8 3EY Tel: 01624 813881 Fax: 01624 811921; Ben Gairn, Lheaney Road, Ramsey IM8 2JF — MRCS Eng. LRCP Lond. 1977; BSc (Hons.) Lond. 1974, MB BS 1977; MRCGP 1981; DRCOG Lond. 1980. (St. Mary's)

WILSON, Graham Miller St Catherine's Surgery, St Pauls Medical Centre, 121 Swindon Road, Cheltenham GL50 4DP Tel: 01242 580668 Fax: 01242 707699 — MB ChB 1984 Birm.; MRCP (UK) 1987; MRCGP 1990.

WILSON, Guy (retired) Woodlands, 15 Pear Tree Lane, Maidstone ME15 9QY Tel: 01622 744660 — LMSSA Lond. 1934.

WILSON, Hanna Renate (retired) 3 Braybrooke Gardens, London SE19 2UN Tel: 020 8653 4794 — MB ChB 1950 Glas.; FRCPath 1977, M 1965. Prev: Cons. Pathol. Lewisham Gp. Laborat. Lewisham Hosp.

WILSON, Harold (retired) 1 ErringtonCt., Alma Road, Aigburth, Liverpool L17 6DP Tel: 0151 427 0275 — MB ChB Liverp. 1950; PhD Liverp. 1955, MD 1959. Prev: Sen. Lect. (Pharmacol.) Univ. Liverp.

WILSON, Harry (retired) Ling House, 130 Skipton Road, Keighley BD21 3AN Tel: 01535 605747 — MB ChB 1959 Sheff. Prev: Ho. Surg. O & G Vict. & St. John's Hosps. Keighley.

WILSON, Hayley Jo Anne 244 Goodyersend Lane, Bedworth, Nuneaton CV12 0HM — MB ChB 1992 Bristol.

WILSON

WILSON, Hazel Mary 18 Eastern Way, Elmswell, Bury St Edmunds IP30 9DP — MRCS Eng. LRCP Lond. 1954; DTM & H Liverp. 1961; DCH Eng. 1959.

WILSON, Heather Christine MRC Brain Repair Centre, Universoty Forvie Site, Robinson Way, Cambridge CB2 2PY Tel: 01223 331160 Email: hcw22@cam.ac.uk; Orion Cottage, 114 Coton Road, Grantchester, Cambridge CB3 9NX Tel: 01223 841259 — MB BS 1990 Lond.; MRCP (UK) 1993. (Guy's) Research. Reg. MRC Centre.Brain. Repair. Cambs; Specialist Regist. Neurol. SE.Thames. Region. Prev: Regist. (Neurol.) King's Coll. Hosp. Lond.; Regist. (Neurol.) Brook Gen. Hosp. Lond.; SHO Rotat. (Med.) E. Surrey Hosp. Redhill.

WILSON, Heather Norah University Health Service, University of Southampton, Building 48, Highfield, Southampton SO17 1BJ Tel: 023 8055 7531 Fax: 023 8059 3259; Oakdene, 16 Brookvale Road, Highfield, Southampton SO17 1QP Tel: 02380 584681 — MB BS 1979 Lond.; MRCGP 1988; FRCA Eng. 1984; DRCOG 1983. (Char. Cross) Socs: BMA. Prev: Trainee GP Soton.; Regist. (Anaesth.) Bristol HA.

WILSON, Mrs Henrietta Mabel (retired) 9 Highgrove, Wood Road, Tettenhall, Wolverhampton WV6 8LQ Tel: 01902 759169 — BA, BChir Camb. 1935. SCMO (Child Health & Family Plann. Servs.) Staffs. AHA.

WILSON, Herbert Kenneth 2 Newforge Dale, Belfast BT9 5QD Tel: 01232 660044 — MB BCh BAO 1965 Belf.; FFR RCSI 1983; FRCR 1975; DMRD Eng. 1972. (Qu. Univ. Belf.) Cons. Radiol. Ulster Hosp. Dundonald; Regional Postgrad. Educat. Adviser Roy. Coll. Radiol. for N. Irel. Socs: Fell. Ulster Med. Soc. Prev: Cons. Radiol. Roy. Vict. Hosp. Belf.

WILSON, Herbert William (retired) 43 Bamford Way, Bamford, Rochdale OL11 5NB Tel: 01706 640991 — MB ChB 1947 Manch.; FRCOG 1968, M 1954, DObst 1951. Prev: Cons. O & G Bury Dist. HA.

WILSON, Hilary (retired) 1 Golf Links Crescent, Newcastle BT33 0BE Tel: 01396 724029 — MB BCh BAO 1940 Belf.; MB BCh BAO (Hnrs.) Belf. 1940. Prev: Med. Asst. W.. Special Care Serv. Lond.derry.

WILSON, Hilary Elaine (Kerr) Centre for Rheumatic Diseases, Royal Infirmary, Glasgow G4 0SF; 11 Falkland Street, 1/L, Hyndland, Glasgow G12 9PY Tel: 0141 339 3396 Email: hilary@jings.com — MB ChB 1991 Glas. Clin. Research Fell. Socs: Brit. Med. Acupunc. Soc.; Roy. Coll. of Phys.s, Glas.; Brit. Soc. Rheum.

WILSON, Hilda Mary (retired) 56 Castle Grove Avenue, Leeds LS6 4BS Tel: 0113 275 2494 — MB ChB Leeds 1952. Prev: Sen. Med. Off. (Child Health) Leeds E. HA.

WILSON, Hugo Oliver 25 Harwood Close, Tewin, Welwyn AL6 0LF — MB BS 1997 Lond.

WILSON, Iain Henry Royal Devon and Exeter Hospital, Exeter EX2 5DW — MB ChB 1978 Glas.; FFA RCS Eng. 1983. Cons. Anaesth. Roy. Devon & Exeter Hosp. Prev: Lect. (Anaesth.) Lusaka, Zambia.

WILSON, Ian Wolverhampton Road Surgery, 13 Wolverhampton Road, Stafford ST17 4BP Tel: 01785 258161 Fax: 01785 224140 — MB ChB 1973 Birm. Med. Pract. (Gastroenterol. Endoscopy) Mid Staffs. HA. Socs: Midl. Gastroenterol. Soc.; Primary Care Soc. Gastroenterol.

WILSON, Mr Ian Clark 158 Wentworth Road, Harborne, Birmingham B17 9BX Tel: 0121 427 8251; University Hospital Birmingham NHS Trust, Queen Elizabeth Hospital, Edgbaston, Birmingham B15 2TH Tel: 0121 697 8309 — MB ChB 1982 Birm.; MD Birm. 1995; FRCS (CTh) 1994; FRCS Ed. 1987; FRCS Lond. 1987. Cons. Cardiothoracic Surg. Qu. Eliz. Hosp. Birm. Socs: Soc. Cardiothoracic Surg. of GB & Irel.; Internat. Soc. Heart & Lung Transpl. Prev: Research Fell. Johns Hopkins Hosp. Baltimore, USA; Transpl. Fell. (Cardiothoracic Surg.) Freeman Hosp. Newc.; Sen. Regist. (Cardiothoracic Surg.) W. Midl.

WILSON, Ian David 16 Corrie Court, Hamilton ML3 9XE — MB ChB 1991 Glas.; FRCS 1997.

WILSON, Ian David 9 Maxwell Road, London SW6 2HT — MB ChB 1985 Cape Town.

WILSON, Ian Donald Brynmelyn, Brynhoffnant, Llandysul SA44 6DS — MB BS 1972 Lond.; MRCS Eng. LRCP Lond. 1972; MRCPsych 1977.

WILSON, Ian Douglas (retired) Clova, 2 Lynwood Drive, Stalmine, Poulton-le-Fylde FY6 0PZ Tel: 01253 701282 — MB ChB 1955 St. And. Prev: Med. Off. DSS Blackpool.

WILSON, Ian George Department of Anaesthesia, St. James University Hospital, Leeds LS9 7TF Tel: 0113 243 3144 — MB ChB 1979 Dundee; FFARCS Eng. 1988; DA (UK) 1984; DRCOG 1982. Cons. Paediat. Anaesth. St. Jas. Univ. Hosp. Leeds.; Lead Clinician Anaesth. Prev: Lect. & Sen. Regist. (Anaesth.) Leicester; Trainee GP Airdrie VTS & Hawick VTS; SHO & Regist. (Anaesth.) Derbysh. Hosps.

WILSON, Ian John Pawaroo and Partners, The Old Forge Surgery, Pallion Pk, Pallion, Sunderland SR4 6QE Tel: 0191 510 9393 Fax: 0191 510 9595 — MB ChB 1984 Leeds.

WILSON, Ian Martin Shotfield Health Centre, Shotfield, Wallington SM6 0HY Tel: 020 8647 0031; 2A Court Hill, Chipstead, Croydon CR5 3NQ — MB BS 1980 Lond.

WILSON, Ian Robert Pain Management Service, Dewsbury & District Hospital, Halifax Rd, Dewsbury WF13 4HS Tel: 01924 512 058 — MB BS 1991 Newc.; 2001 PG Dip; FRCA 1998. (Newc.) Cons. in Pain Managem. & Anaesth. Socs: Assn. Anaesth. GB & Irel. (Mem. Anaesth. in Train. Comm.); BMA (Counc. Mem. & Pain Soc.). Prev: SHO (Anaesth.) Hope Hosp. & N. Manch. Gen. Hosp.; SHO (Anaesth.) Roy. Oldham NHS Trust; SpR (Anaesth.) Yorks. Deanery.

WILSON, Ian Stuart Guardian Street Medical Centre, Guardian Street, Warrington WA5 1UD Tel: 01925 650226 Fax: 01925 240633; 15 Francis Road, Stockton Heath, Warrington WA4 6EB — MB ChB 1981 Manch.; DRCOG 1984.

WILSON, Isabel Claire Welsh hearing Institute, Heath Hospital, Cardiff Tel: 029 2074 3471 — MB BCh 1991 Wales; MSc 1999 (Audiological Med.) UCL; FRCS (Orl.) Eng. 1996. p/t Specialist Regist. (Audiol. & Med.) Univ. Hosp. Wales. Socs: BMA. Prev: SHO (ENT) Roy. Gwent Hosp.; SHO ENT St Michaels Hosp. Bristol.

WILSON, Isabel Lilias (retired) 7 Ben Nevis Place, Kirkcaldy KY2 5RQ — MB ChB 1957 St. And.; MB ChB (Commend.) St. And. 1957, DPH 1960; MRC Schol. 1958-59. Prev: SCMO Fife Health Bd.

WILSON, Isobel Margaret Morningside Medical Practice, 2 Morningside Place, Edinburgh EH10 5ER Tel: 0131 452 8406 Fax: 0131 447 3020; 100 Morningside Drive, Edinburgh EH10 5NT Tel: 0131 447 1653 — MB ChB 1976 Ed.; BSc (Med. Sci.) Ed. 1973. (Ed.) GP; Med. Off. Geo. Watson's Coll. Edin. Socs: BMA. Prev: SHO (Paediat.) Roy. Hosp. Sick Childr. Edin.; SHO (Obst.) Elsie Inglis Matern. Hosp. Edin.; SHO (Cas.) Roy. Infirm. Edin.

WILSON, Ivor Vivian (retired) Anglers Lodge, Cliff Road, Hythe CT21 5XH Tel: 01303 268360 — MB BS Durh. 1951; FRCP Lond. 1974, M 1958. Prev: Cons. Phys. & Clin. Tutor SE Kent HA.

WILSON, Ivy Josephine Ama 206 Church Hill Road, East Barnet, Barnet EN4 8PP — BM BS 1998 Nottm.

WILSON, James (retired) Shaun, Firwood Road, Wentworth, Virginia Water GU25 4NG — MRCS Eng. LRCP Lond. 1933; MA, MB BChir Camb. 1937. Prev: Maj. RAMC.

WILSON, James (retired) 15 Campbell Road, Edinburgh EH12 6DT Tel: 0131 337 6763 — MB ChB 1952 Ed.; DObst RCOG 1956; BChir FFA RCS Eng. 1967. Cons. Anaesth. Roy. Infirm. Edin. Prev: Cons. Anaesth. Leeds Matern. Hosp. & United Leeds Hosps.

WILSON, James Campbell (retired) 10 Widewell Road, Roborough, Plymouth PL6 7DN Tel: 01752 787299 Fax: 01752 787299 — MB BCh BAO 1952 NUI; FRCP Lond. 1983; MRCP (UK) 1970; DCH Eng. 1968; DTM & H Eng. 1967.

WILSON, James Dickson Tupper (retired) 7 Hillview Place, Dollar FK14 7JG Tel: 0125 94 42508 — LRCP 1936 Ed.; LRCP, LRCS Ed., LRFPS Glas. 1936; DTM Liverp. 1937.

WILSON, James Harold Epsom General Hospital, Dorking Road, Epsom KT18 7EG Tel: 01372 204195 Fax: 01372 204199 — MB ChB 1972 Bristol; MRCPsych 1980. Cons. Psychother. Surrey Oaklands NHS Trust. Socs: Assoc. Mem. Lond. Centre for Psychother.; Inst. Gp. Anal. Prev: Cons. Psychother. Henderson Hosp. & Sutton Hosp.; Sen. Regist. (Psychother.) Henderson Hosp. & St. Geo. Hosp. Lond.; Regist. & Sen. Regist. (Psychiat.) Bethlem & Maudsley Hosp. Lond.

WILSON, Mr James Hubbard 101 Woodsford Square, London W14 8DT — MB BS 1985 Lond.; FRCS Eng. 1991.

WILSON, James Maxwell Glover (retired) Millhill House, 77 Millhill, Musselburgh EH21 7RP Tel: 0131 665 5829 — MB BChir

1938 Camb.; FRCP Ed. 1981; FRCP Lond. 1966, M. 1947; MRCS Eng. LRCP Lond. 1937; FFPHM 1972. Prev: Sen. PMO DHSS.

WILSON, James Moffett Templemore Avenue Health Centre, 98A Templemore Avenue, Belfast BT5 4GR Tel: 028 9020 4151; 18 Hampton Park, Belfast BT7 3JL — MB BCh BAO 1980 Belf.; MRCGP 1985; DRCOG 1983.

WILSON, Mr James Noel, OBE (retired) The Chequers, Waterdale, Watford WD25 0GP Tel: 01923 672364 — MB ChB (Hons.) Birm. 1943; ChM Birm. 1949; FRCS Eng. 1948; MRCS Eng. LRCP Lond. 1943. Hon. Cons. Orthop. Surg. Roy. Nat. Orthop. Hosp. Lond. & Nat. Hosps. Nerv. Dis. Qu. Sq. & Maida Vale; Vice-Chairm. IMPACT (UK): Prev: Prof. Orthop. Addis Ababa Univ. 1989.

WILSON, James Richard Maughan Red House, Rectory La, Hethel, Norwich NR14 8HD — MB ChB 1997 Bristol.

WILSON, Mr James Russell Department of Urology, York District Hospital, Wigginton Road, York YO31 Tel: 01904 631313; Tel: 01904 491466 — MB ChB 1992 Sheff.; MD 2000 Sheffield; FRCS Glas. 1997. (Sheffield) Specialist Regist. (Urol.) York Dist. Hosp. York. Prev: Specialist Regist. (Urol.) P.ss Roy. Hosp. Hull; Specialist Regist. (Urol.) Bradford Roy. Infirm., Bradford; Specialist Regist. (Urol.), St. James' Univ. Hosp. Leeds.

WILSON, Jane Gillian (retired) 2 Brettenham Crescent, Ipswich IP4 2UB — MB BS Lond. 1956; MRCS Eng. LRCP Lond. 1956; DCH Eng. 1959; BA Hons. Open Univ. 1990.

WILSON, Jane Karen Kingston Hospital, Galsworthy Road, Kingston upon Thames KT2 7QB Tel: 020 8546 7711 Fax: 020 8974 8388; 250 Sandycombe Road, Kew, Richmond TW9 3NP — MB BS 1982 Lond.; MD Lond. 1992; MRCOG 1988. (St. Thos. Univ. Lond.) Cons. O & G Kingston Hosp. NHS Trust. Prev: Sen. Regist. (O & G) Qu. Charlotte's & Chelsea Hosp. Lond.; Regist. (O & G) Guys Hosp. Lond. & Roy. Co. Hosp. Brighton.

WILSON, Jane Margaret 33 Hartington Grove, Cambridge CB1 7UA Tel: 01223 241587 Email: wilson.howarth@virgin.net — BM 1985 Soton.; MSc Oxf. 1979; BSc Plymouth 1975; DCH RCP Lond. 1992; DCCH RCP Ed. 1992. (Soton.) p/t GP Non-Princip.; Clin. Asst. Derm. Addenbrooke's Hosp. Camb. Socs: Fell. Roy. Soc. Trop. Med. & Hyg.; Brit. Travel Health Assn. Prev: Med. Assoc. AVSC Internat., Nepal; Health Adviser Water Aid, s. aSIA; Trainee GP Camb.

WILSON, Professor Janet Ann Department of Otolaryngology Head & Neck Surgery, Freeman Hospital, Newcastle upon Tyne NE7 7DN Tel: 0191 284 3111 Fax: 0191 223 1246 Email: janet.wilson@nuth.northy.nhs.uk; Oak House, 1 Jesmond Dene Road, Newcastle upon Tyne NE2 3QJ — MB ChB 1979 Ed.; BSc Ed. 1976, MD 1989; FRCS Eng. 1984; FRCS Ed. 1983; T(S) 1991. (Ed.) Prof. Otolaryngol. Head & Neck Surg. Univ. Newc. u. Tyne; Hon. Cons. Otolaryngol. Freeman Hosp. Newc. Socs: Roy. Soc. Med.; Brit. Assn. Otol.; Head and Neck Surgs. Prev: Cons. Otorhinolaryng. Roy. Infirm. Glas.; Lect. (Otolaryngol.) Roy. Infirm. Edin.

WILSON, Janet Diane Department of genitourinary medicine, The general infirmary at Leeds, Great George Street, Leeds LS1 3EX; 66 Main Street, Thorner, Leeds LS14 3BU — MB ChB 1980 Bristol; FRCP Lond. 1994; MRCP (UK) 1983. Cons. Genitourin. Med. Gen. Infirm. Leeds.

WILSON, Janet Eileen (retired) 2 The Courtyard, Walpole Court, Puddletown, Dorchester DT2 8TH — BM BCh Oxf. 1948; MRCPsych 1971; DPM Eng. 1962. Prev: Cons. Psychiat. Walthamstow Child Guid. Clinic Waltham Forest.

WILSON, Janet Elizabeth 4 Grand Prix Grove, Dundonald, Belfast BT16 2BD — MB ChB 1991 Ed.

WILSON, Janet Margaret Tamnaharrie, 41 Ballyhanwood Road, Dundonald, Belfast BT5 7SN — MB BCh BAO 1979 Belf.; MFFP 1993; MRCOG 1984; DRCOG 1981. Clin. Med. Off. E. Health & Social Servs. Bd.; Sen. Clin. Med. Off. Colposcopy Clinic Roy. Vict. Hosp. Belf.; Clin. Asst. (Genitourin. Med.) Roy. Vict. Hosp. Belf.

WILSON, Janie Margaret Cantilupe Surgery, 51 St Owen St., Hereford HR1 2JB — MB ChB 1979 Birm.; MRCGP 1985; DRCOG 1983; DFFP 1997.

WILSON, Jaqueline Ann St Johns Medical Centre, 62 London Rd, Grantham NG31 6HR Tel: 01476 590055; Chestnut House, 4 Manor Drive, Long Bennington, Newark NG23 5GZ Tel: 01400 282335 Fax: 01400 282335 — DRCOG 1991; BM BS 1988 Nottingham. p/t GP.

WILSON, Jason Alexander Dept of Anaesthestics, Charing Cross Hospital, Fulham palace Road, London W6 8RF Tel: 020 8846 7017 — MB BS 1986 Sydney; FRCA 1994. Cons. Anaesth. Char. Cross Hosp. Lond.

WILSON, Jean Freda 27 Marton Road, Bridlington YO16 7AQ Tel: 01262 73578 — MRCS Eng. LRCP Lond. 1939; BA Camb. 1936, MB BChir 1940; DPH Leeds 1942; DObst RCOG 1941.

WILSON, Jean Margaret (retired) Pond Cottage, Hoxne, Eye IP21 4LZ — MB BS Lond. 1946; MRCS Eng. LRCP Lond. 1945.

WILSON, Jean Sandra Nicol Street Surgery, 48 Nicol Street, Kirkcaldy KY1 1PH Tel: 01592 642969 Fax: 01592 643526 — MB ChB 1985 Ed.; MRCGP 1990; DRCOG 1987.

WILSON, Jeanie Livingston Darling (retired) 27 Gogo Street, Largs KA30 8BU Tel: 01475 672238 — MB ChB 1921 Glas. Prev: Ho. Surg. W. Norf. Hosp. King's Lynn & Roy. Infirm. Glas.

WILSON, Jennifer Jane Morris and Partners, 93 Queens Drive, Bedford MK41 9JE Tel: 01234 360482 Fax: 01234 219361; 2 Cornwall Road, Bedford MK40 3DH Tel: 01234 356644 Email: andy.jenny@tesco.net — MB ChB 1986 Leeds; MRCGP 1990; DTM & H Liverp. 1990; DRCOG 1989. Prev: Miss. with Baptist Miss. Soc.; Trainee GP Bradford VTS.

***WILSON, Jeremy Ian** 144 Howard Road, Leicester LE2 1XJ Tel: 0116 270 0825 — MB ChB 1998 Leic.; MB ChB Leic 1998.

WILSON, Mr Jeremy Paul Horstedpond House, Little Horsted, Uckfield TN22 5TR Tel: 01825 765406 Email: hipjpw@aol.com; Horstedpond House, Little Horsted, Uckfield TN22 5TR Tel: 01825 765406 Email: hipjpw@aol.com — MB Camb. 1958, BChir 1957; MA Camb. 1958; FRCS Eng. 1963; BA (Hons) York. 1996; MA Soton 1997. (Middlx.) Emerit. Cons. Surg. Qu. Mary's Hosp. Sidcup; Clin. Tutor St. Thos. Hosp. Med. Sch. Lond. Socs: Fell. Roy. Soc. Med. (Ex-Mem. Counc. Sect. Coloproctol.); Brit. Soc. Gastroenterol.; Ass of ColoProctol. Gt. Britain & Irel. Prev: Sen. Regist. (Surg.) Middlx. Hosp. Lond.; Regist. (Surg.) Norf. & Norwich Hosp.; Surg. Pathol. Middlx. Hosp. Med. Sch. Lond.

WILSON, Jillian Elizabeth Summervale Medical Centre, Wharf Lane, Ilminster TA19 0DT Tel: 01460 52354 Fax: 01460 52652; Ilford Bridges Farm, Stoklinch, Ilminster TA19 9HZ Tel: 01460 259266 Email: jewilson@lincone.net — MB 1985 Camb.; BChir 1984 Camb.; MRCGP 1988; DRCOG 1987. (Cambridge and St Thomas' London) p/t GP Princip.

WILSON, Joan 7 Cumnor Rise Road, Cumnor Hill, Oxford OX2 9HD Tel: 01865 862521; 2 Warblers Close, Constantia, Cape Town 7806, South Africa Tel: 0027 21 794 7984 Fax: 0027 21 794 3331 Email: drwilson@samedical.co.za — MB BS 1969 Lond. (University of London) Paediat. Pract., Cape Town, S. Africa. Prev: Cons. Paediat., J.G. Stijdon Hosp., Johannesburg; Regist. Paediat., J.G. Stijdon Hosp., Johannesburg; Regist. Paediat., Red Cross Childr.'s Hosp. Cape Town.

WILSON, Joan Mowbray (retired) 11 Mayfield Terrace, Edinburgh EH9 1RU Tel: 0131 662 1750 — MB ChB 1949 Ed.; MRCGP 1969. Prev: Assoc. Specialist Genitourin. Med. Roy. Infirm. Glas.

WILSON, Joanne Clare Culduthel Road Health Centre, Ardlarich, 15 Culduthel Road, Inverness IV2 4AG Tel: 01463 712233 Fax: 01463 715479; Tanela More, 45 Henrietta St, Avoch IV9 8QT Tel: 01381 620279 — MB ChB 1991 Liverp.; DRCOG; MRCGP. (Liverpool) GP Job Sharing Princip. Socs: BMA.

WILSON, Jocelyn Ann 167 Marlborough Crescent, Sevenoaks TN13 2HW — MB BS 1983 Lond.; BSc Lond. 1980, MB BS 1983; MRCGP 1987; DRCOG 1986. (Univ. Coll. Hosp.) GP Dartford. Prev: Trainee GP Qu. Marys Hosp. Sidcup.

WILSON, John (retired) Belair, 2 Cable Road, Whitehead, Carrickfergus BT38 9PX Tel: 01960 373458 — MB BCh BAO 1956 Belf.; FRCGP 1982, M 1968. Prev: GP Carrickfergus.

WILSON, John (retired) 8 Hunter Road, London SW20 8NZ Tel: 020 8946 8103 — MB BS 1956 Durh.; MB BS (Hons.) 1956; PhD Lond. 1965; BSc (Hons.) Durham. 1953; FRCP Lond. 1972, M 1958; FRCPCH 1997. Hon. Cons. Paediat. Neurol. Nat. Hosp. Nerv. Dis. Lond. Prev: Cons. Neurol. Gt. Ormond St. Childr. Hosp. NHS Trust Lond.

WILSON, John Alasdair Victoria Hospital, Hayfield Road, Kirkcaldy KY2 5AH Tel: 01592 643355 Fax: 01592 647087 Email: john.wilson9@which.net; Capelrig, Station Road, Kingskettle, Cupar KY15 7PX Tel: 01337 831262 Fax: 01592 647087 — MB ChB 1974 Ed.; MD Ed. 1988; FRCP Ed. 1990; MRCP (UK) 1979. (Ed.)

WILSON

Cons. Phys. (Gen. Med. & Gastroenterol.) Vict. Hosp. Kirkcaldy; Hon. Sen. Lect. (Biol. & Preclin Med.) Univ. St. And.; Univ. Clin. Teach. (Med.) Univ. Manch.; Mem. Clin. Teach. Staff (Fac. Med. Univ. Edin.). Socs: Brit. Soc. Gastroenterol.; Scott. Soc. Phys.; Caledonian Soc. Gastroenterol. Prev: Sen. Regist. (Gen. Med.) Ninewells Hosp. Dundee; Clin. Research Fell. McMaster Univ. Canada; Lect. (Clin. Pharmacol.) Univ. Dundee.

WILSON, John Allan 1 Forbes Road, Edinburgh EH10 4EF Tel: 0131 229 3786 — MB ChB 1980 Dundee; FRCP Ed. 1995; MRCP UK 1985; DRCOG 1982. (Dundee) Cons. Phys. Gen. & Geriat. Med. St. John's Hosp. Livingston.; Cons. Phys. Gen. Med. BUPA Murrayfield Hosp. Edin. Socs: Mem. Intercollegiate Acad. Bd. of Sports and Exercise Med..; Locality co-ordinator diploma exam in sports and exercise Med..; Fell. and Examr. Roy. Coll. of Phys.s of Edin.. Prev: Cons. Phys. Gen. & Geriat. Med. Bangour Gen. Hosp. Broxburn; Sen. Regist. (Geriat. & Gen. Med.) City Hosp. Edin.; Regist. (Geriat. Med.) City Hosp. Edin.

WILSON, John Andrew 11 Plewlands Gardens, Edinburgh EH10 5JS Tel: 0131 447 4697 — MB ChB 1991 Ed.; MRCP (UK) 1994.

WILSON, John Andrew 34 West Mill Rise, Walkington, Beverley HU17 8TP — MB ChB 1979 Leeds; BSc (Hons.) (Anat.) Leeds 1976; MRCPath 1986; Dip. Bact. Manch. 1984. Cons. Med. Microbiol. Pub. Health Laborat. Hull Roy. Infirm. Prev: Sen. Regist. Stoke Pub. Health Laborat.; Regist. Newc. Pub. Health Laborat.

WILSON, John Anthony Clark (retired) 7 Herevale Grange, Ellenbrook, Worsley, Manchester M28 1ZA Tel: 0161 799 3640 — MB ChB 1941 Ed.; FRCP Lond. 1973, M 1952; FRCP Ed. 1971, M 1950. Prev: Hon. Cons. Phys. Hope Hosp. Salford & Salford Roy. Hosp.

WILSON, John Atkinson (retired) 42 Childwall Park Avenue, Liverpool L16 0JQ Tel: 0151 722 2952 — MD 1967 Liverp.; MB ChB 1958; FRCP Lond. 1974, M 1962. Prev: Cons. Phys. Roy. Liverp. Hosp.

WILSON, John Beattie (retired) The Whins, Kinnel Banks, Lochmaben, Lockerbie DG11 1TD Tel: 01387 810679 — MB ChB 1943 Ed.; BSc (Hons. Path.) Ed. 1948, MD 1949; FRCP Ed. 1971, M 1949. Prev: Mem. Dumfries & Galloway HB 1976-1987.

WILSON, John Briddon (retired) Lovaine, Vendace Drive, Lochmaben, Lockerbie DG11 1QN Tel: 01387 810598 Email: j7aw@easicom.com — MB ChB Ed. 1964; FRCP Ed. 1982; MRCP (U.K.) 1971. Locum. Prev: Cons. Geriat. Dumfries & Galloway Roy. Infirm.

WILSON, John Campbell Grove Farm, 173 Dromore Road, Hillsborough BT26 6JA — MB BS 1996 Lond.

WILSON, John David (retired) 52 Jensen Road, Bracebridge Heath, Lincoln LN4 2QU Tel: 01522 524944 — MB ChB Manch. 1958; MRCPsych 1984; DPM Eng. 1963. Prev: Cons. Psychiat. Cheadle Roy. Hosp.

WILSON, John Fairlie Viewfield Lane Health Centre, Viewfield Lane, Selkirk TD7 4LJ Tel: 01750 21674 Fax: 01750 23176 — MB ChB 1972 Birm.; MRCP (UK) 1976; MRCGP 1980.

WILSON, John Frederick Millbarn Medical Centre, 34 London End, Beaconsfield HP9 2JH Tel: 01494 675303 Fax: 01494 680214 — MB ChB 1976 Bristol; MRCGP 1983. Clin. Asst. (Rheum.) Wycombe Gen. Hosp.

WILSON, John Gordon Gilbert Road Medical Group, 39 Gilbert Road, Bucksburn, Aberdeen AB21 9AN Tel: 01224 712138 Fax: 01224 712239; 9 Glen Road, Dyce, Aberdeen AB21 7FB — MB ChB 1979 Aberd.; MRCGP 1983.

WILSON, John Greer McTurk The Wooda Surgery, Clarence Wharf, Barnstaple Street, Bideford EX39 4AU Tel: 01237 471071 Fax: 01237 471059; Cross Fell, Raleigh Hill, Bideford EX39 3NX Tel: 01237 247 0082 Email: jgmwilson@cix.co.uk — MB BS 1976 Lond.; FRCGP 1999; MRCGP 1981. GP Tutor N. Devon. Prev: Ho. Surg. Roy. Free Hosp. Lond.

WILSON, John Ian Pinderfields Hospital NHS Trust, Wakefield WF1 4DG Tel: 01924 201688; 21 Fieldhead Paddock, Boston Spa, Wetherby LS23 6SA Tel: 01937 845778 — MB BS 1979 Lond.; BSc (Hons.) Lond. 1976, MD 1990; FRCP Lond. 1995; MRCP (UK) 1983. (Guy's) Cons. Cardiol. Pinderfields Hosp. Wakefield; Hon. Cons. Cardiol.Yorks. Heart Centre, Leeds; Hon. Sen. Lect. (Univ. of Leeds). Socs: Brit. Cardiac Soc. & Brit. Pacing & Electrophys. Gp.; Brit. Cardiovasc. Interven. Soc. Prev: Sen. Regist. (Cardiol.) Leeds Gen.

Infirm.; Research Fell. Univ. Leeds; Regist. (Med.) Centr. Middx. Hosp. Lond.

WILSON, John Kenneth 27 Cambridge Road, Middlesbrough TS5 5NG Tel: 01642 88102 — LMSSA 1943 Lond. (Univ. Coll. Lond.) Prev: Ho. Phys., Res. Anaesth. & Cas. Off. Stockton & Thornaby Hosp.; Sen. Ho. Surg. Gen. Hosp. Middlesbrough.

WILSON, John Lindsay 101 Woodsford Square, London W14 8DT Tel: 020 7603 6118; 101 Woodsford Square, London W14 8DT Tel: 020 7603 6118 — MB BS 1953 Lond.; FRCPsych 1974; DPM Eng. 1956. (Lond. Hosp.) Cons. Psychiat. Tavistock Clinic & Inst. Human Relats. Lond.; Sen. Tutor Inst. Psychiat. (Univ. Lond.); Hon. Cons. Maudsley Hosp. Lond. Prev: Clin. Fell. & Sen. Regist. Tavistock Clinic Lond.; Research Asst. Med. Research Counc.; Regist. Maudsley Hosp.

WILSON, John Malcolm Apartment 7, Great Bowden Hall, Leicester Lane, Market Harborough LE16 7HP — MB BChir 1977 Camb.; MA, MB Camb. 1977, BChir 1976; MRCP Ed. 1980.

WILSON, John Marshall (retired) The Health Centre, Priest Lane, Pershore WR10 1DR Tel: 01386 554567 — BM BCh Oxf. 1957; MA Oxf. 1957; MRCGP 1969; DObst RCOG 1960. Prev: Ho. Surg. Wom. Hosp. Wolverhampton.

WILSON, John Patrick 25 Brooklands Gardens, Whitehead, Carrickfergus BT38 9RS — MB BCh BAO 1996 Belf.

WILSON, John Robert Willoughby Larne Health Centre, Gloucester Avenue, Larne BT40 1PB Tel: 028 2826 1922 Fax: 028 2827 9560; 41 Wheatfield Heights, Ballygally, Larne BT40 2RT — MB BCh BAO 1984 Belf.; MRCGP 1988; DRCOG 1987; DCH RCPI 1986. Prev: Trainee GP Belf.; SHO (Gen. Med. & O & G) Craigavon Area Hosp.; SHO (Gen. Surg. & Paediat.) Craigavon Area Hosp.

WILSON, John Robertson Avon Medical Centre, Academy Street, Larkhall ML9 2BJ Tel: 01698 882547 Fax: 01698 888138; 7 Karadale Gardens, Larkhall ML9 1BE Tel: 01698 884873 — MB ChB 1977 Aberd.; MRCGP 1981.

WILSON, John Roslyn Muir (retired) Glenshee Cottage, Boquhan, Balfron, Glasgow G63 0RW — MB ChB 1949 Glas.; FFR 1971; DMRD Liverp. 1963; DMRD Eng. 1963. Prev: Cons. Radiol. Stobhill Gen. Hosp. Glas.

WILSON, John Russell Station Road Surgery, 99 Station Road, Redhill RH1 1EB Tel: 01737 761201 Fax: 01737 780510 — MB BS 1974 Lond.; MRCGP 1981. (St.Mary's Lond.) Princip. GP. Prev: Trainee GP Brook Gen. Hosp. Woolwich VTS.

WILSON, Mr John Samuel Pattison (cons. rooms) Cromwell Hospital, Cromwell Road, London SW5 Tel: 020 7370 4233; 16 Smith Street, Chelsea, London SW3 4EE Tel: 020 7636 5186 — LRCP LRCS 1946 Ed.; LRCP LRCS Ed. LRFPS Glas. 1946; FRCS Ed. 1959; FRCS Eng. 1973. Socs: Brit. Assn. Aesthetic Plastic Surgs. & Brit. Assn. Plastic; Fell. Roy. Coll. Med. Prev: Cons. Plastic. Surg. St. Geo., W.m., Roy. Marsden & Qu. Mary's Hosps. Lond.

WILSON, John Stanley (retired) Blairgarry, Callender FK17 8HP Tel: 01877 330121 — MB ChB 1944 Ed.

WILSON, John Thomas (retired) 2 Burlington Close, Dore, Sheffield S17 3NR Tel: 0114 236 4498 — MB ChB 1921 Ed.

WILSON, John Trevor Elgin Medical Centre, 10 Victoria Crescent, Elgin IV30 1RQ Tel: 01343 547512 Fax: 01343 546781 — MB ChB 1976 Aberd.; MRCGP 1981; DRCOG 1980.

WILSON, John Wardlaw 12 Glenorchill Place, Auchterarder PH3 1LR — MB ChB 1968 Glas.; DObst RCOG 1970; Cert. Family Plann. JCC 1982. Area Med. Adviser Benefits Agency. Edin. Prev: Med. Off. DHSS Lancs.; Gen. Pract. Auckland, New Zealand.

WILSON, John William Tel: 01292 267432; 10 Bellevale Avenue, Ayr KA7 2RP — MB ChB 1982 Aberd.; MRCGP 1987; DRCOG 1987. Prev: SHO (O & G) HM Stanley Hosp. Clwyd; Trainee GP E. Cumbria HA.

WILSON, Jonathan Mark 3 Windsor Road, Blackpool FY3 7SQ — MB ChB 1990 Manch.; BSc St And. 1987.

***WILSON, Jonathan Nicholas** 8 Hunter Road, London SW20 8NZ — MB BS 1994 Newc.; BMedSci (1st cl. Hons.) 1993; MRCP 1997.

WILSON, Jonathan Urquhart Department of Anaesthetics, Bedford Hospital, Kempston Road, Bedford MK42 9DJ Tel: 01234 355122; 26 Franklyn Gardens, Biddenham, Bedford MK40 4QE Tel: 01234 262966 Email: juw@globalnet.co.uk — MB BS 1980 Lond.; FFA RCS Eng. 1987. (St. Mary's) Cons. Anaesth. Bedford Hosp. NHS Trust. Prev: Cons. Anaesth. P.ss Mary's RAF Hosp. Halton; Squadron Ldr. RAF Med. Br.

WILSON, Joseph Rockfield Medical Centre, Doury Road, Ballymena BT43 6JD Tel: 028 25 638800 Fax: 028 25 633633 Email: dm.hopkins@p309.gp.n-i.nhs.uk — MB BCh BAO 1974 Belf.

WILSON, Joyce Isobel Griffin House, Watchmead, Welwyn Garden City AL7 1LT Fax: 01707 393132 — MB ChB 1979 Bristol; BSc (Hons.) Exeter 1965; MRCGP 1983; Dip. Palliat. Med. Wales 1993; DRCOG 1982. Cons. in pallative Med.; Hon. Cons Palliat. E+N Herts NHS Trust. Prev: Princip. GP Welwyn Garden City; Course Organiser Qu. Eliz. & Lister Hosp. Lond. VTS.

WILSON, Joyce Whitelaw Barrhead Health Centre, Barrhead, Glasgow; 30 Glenfield Avenue, Paisley PA2 8JH Tel: 0141 884 8245 — MB ChB 1983 Glas.

WILSON, Judith Ann Paediatric Unit, Northwick Park Hospital, Watford Road, Harrow HA1 3UJ Tel: 020 8869 2640 — MB BS 1965 Lond.; FRCP Lond. 1987, M 1969; MRCS Eng. LRCP Lond. 1965; DCH Eng. 1967. (St. Mary's) Cons. Paediat. N.wick Pk. Hosp.; Hon. Clin. Sen. Lect. ICMS. Prev: Sen. Regist. (Paediat.) & Regist. (Paediat.) St. Mary's Hosp. Lond.; Sen. Resid. Childr. Hosp. Med. Center Boston & Teach. Fell. Harvard; Med. Sch., U.S.A.

WILSON, Judith Frances (retired) Wyken, 173 Lache Lane, Chester CH4 7LU — MB ChB 1974 Birm. Prev: Lect. W. Chester Coll.

WILSON, Judy Ann (retired) Martins, School Lane, North Mundham, Chichester PO20 6LA Tel: 01243 785698 — MB BS 1957 Lond.; DA Eng. 1959. Med. Asst. (Anaesth.) St. Richards Hosp. Chichester. Prev: Ho. Phys. & Ho. Surg. S.lands Hosp. Shoreham-by-Sea.

WILSON, Julian Michael Overton Park Surgery, Overton Park Road, Cheltenham GL50 3BP Tel: 01242 580511; 64 Andover Road, Cheltenham GL50 2TN — MB BS 1987 Lond.; MRCGP 1992; Dip. Palliat. Med. Wales 1994; DRCOG 1991. Clin. Asst. in Palliat. Med. Prev: Cons. Palliat. Med. St. Davids Foundat. Newport, Gwent; Regist. (Palliat. Med.) Holme Tower Marie Curie Centre, Penarth; SHO (Palliat. Med.) St. Peter's Hospice Bristol.

WILSON, Julie Diane 6 Woodlands Mews, Knockmore Road, Lisburn BT28 2XS Tel: 02892 672848 — MB ChB 1990 Bristol; MRCGP 1996; DFFP 1996; DCH RCPSI 1995; DMH Belf. 1995; DRCOG 1994. (Bristol) GP Lisburn. Socs: BMA. Prev: Forens. Med. Off. Belf.

WILSON, June Patricia Independent Education Association Ltd., 91 Queen's Gate, London SW7 5AB Tel: 020 7373 5638 Fax: 020 7835 0771; 3 Fairgreen E., Cockfosters, Barnet EN4 0QR Tel: 020 8440 4402 — MB ChB St. And. 1956; MFHom 1975; DIH Eng. 1960; DPH Lond. 1959. (St Andrews) Med. Off. Indep. Educat. Assn. Ltd. Lond. Socs: BMA; Fac. of Homoeopathy.

WILSON, Justin Edward Howitt 6 Doone Close, Teddington TW11 9AG — MB BS 1996 Lond.

WILSON, Karen Ann Clach na Croise, Sollas, Lochmaddy HS6 5BU; Clach na Croise, Sollas, Lochmaddy HS6 5BU — MB ChB 1994 Aberd.; DRCOG 1997; MRCGP 1998. (Aberd.) GP Locum. Socs: RCGP. Prev: GP Regist. Inverness; SHO (Psychiat.) Craig Dunvain Hosp. Inverness; GP Regist. Inverness.

WILSON, Karen Geraldine Alma Cottage, Baldhoon Road, Laxey IM4 7NE — MB ChB 1991 Manch.; BSc (Hons.) Manch. 1988; MRCGP 1995; DRCOG 1994.

WILSON, Katharine Louise Springfield House, Bridge St., New Mills, High Peak SK22 4DN — MB ChB 1991 Leeds.

WILSON, Katherine Jane 41L Beaconsfield Road, Kelvinside, Glasgow G12 0NN Tel: 0141 339 4817 — MB ChB 1994 Liverp. (Liverpool University) GP Trainee Maryhill Health Centre Glas.

WILSON, Katherine Ruth Henley 24 Farndon Road, Oxford OX2 6RT Tel: 01865 510262 — MB BS 1967 Lond.; MRCS Eng. LRCP Lond. 1967; DA Eng. 1970. (Roy. Free) Med. Off. (Disabil. Med.) Mary MarlBoro. Centre Oxf. Prev: Ho. Surg. Roy. Free Hosp. Lond.; Regist. (Anaesth.) Addenbrooke's Hosp. Camb.; Med. Off. (Anaesth.) Nuffield Orthop. Centre Oxf.

WILSON, Kathleen Elizabeth Pathology Department, Monklands District General Hospital, Airdrie ML6 0JS Tel: 01236 748748 Fax: 01236 770117; 7 Karadale Gardens, Larkhall ML9 1BE Tel: 01698 884873 — MB ChB 1977 Aberd. Assoc. Specialist Histopath. Monklands Hosp. Airdrie.

WILSON, Kathryn Jane DME Box 135, Addenbrookes Hospital, Hills Road, Cambridge CB2 2QQ Tel: 01223 217785 Fax: 01223 217782 Email: jane.wilson@addenbrookes.anglox.nhs.uk — MB BS 1990 Lond.; MRCP Lond. 1994. (Roy. Free Hosp.) Cons. Phys. Dept of Med. for the elderly. Prev: Locum Cons. DME Addenbrookes Hosp.

WILSON, Keith McIver O'Neil Department of Haematology, University of Wales College of Medicine, Heath Park, Cardiff CF14 4XN Fax: 020 8643 7958 — MB BS 1985 West Indies; MRCP (UK) 1993; DRCPath 1996; MRCPath 1997. (Univ. West Indies) Clin. Sen. Lect. in Haemat., Univ. of Wales Coll. of Med.; Hon. Cons. Haematologist, Univ. of Wales and Welsh Blood Serv. Socs: Brit. Soc. Haematol. Prev: Sen. Regist. (Haemat.) The Roy. Marsden Hosp. NHS Trust Surrey; Sen. Regist. (Haemat.) St. Geo.'s Hosp. & Med. Sch. Lond.; Regist. (Haemat.) St. Geo. Hosp. & Med. Sch. Lond.

WILSON, Kenneth Charles Malcolm, Capt. RAMC Royal Liverpool Hospital, Prescot St., Liverpool L7 — MB ChB 1978 Liverp.; MPhil Lond. 1987; MRCPsych 1985. Cons. (Psychiat. of Old Age) Roy. Liverp. Hosp.

WILSON, Mr Kenneth William (retired) Warley Lodge, Warley Edge, Peter Lane, Halifax HX2 7RL Tel: 01422 360091 — MB ChB 1955 St. And.; FRCS Eng. 1962. Prev: Cons. Surg. Roy. Halifax Infirm. & Halifax Gen. Hosp.

WILSON, Kirsty Madeleine 20 Alder Avenue, Fenham, Newcastle upon Tyne NE4 9TB — MB BS 1996 Newc.

WILSON, Laurence Anthony Department of Neurology, Royal Free Hospital, Pond St., London NW3 2QG Tel: 020 7794 0500 — MB ChB 1967 Otago; FRCP Lond. 1989; FRACP 1978. (Otago) Cons. Neurol. Roy. Free Hosp. & Barnet Gen. Hosp. Lond. Prev: Cons. Neurol. Centr. Middlx. Hosp. Lond.; Sen. Regist. (Neurol.) Guy's Hosp. & Nat. Hosps. Nerv. Dis. Lond.; Regist. (Neurol.) Middlx. Hosp.

WILSON, Lawrence Joseph 1 Manor Av, Penwortham, Preston, Preston PR1 0XE — MB ChB 1997 Manch.

WILSON, Lesley The Poplaces, Westmount, St. Helier, Jersey JE2 3LP Tel: 01534 624832 Fax: 01534 624860 — MB BS 1976 Lond.; MRCPsych 1984 Lond. Cons. Old Age Psychiat. St. Helier, Jersey. Prev: Cons. Old Age Psychiat. Colindale & Napsbury Hosps.

WILSON, Mr Lester Francis Flat 5, 14 Dawson Place, London W2 4TJ — MB BS 1982 Lond.; BSc Lond. (Hist. Med.) 1979; FRCS (Orth.) 1994; FRCS Eng. 1987. Cons. Orthop. & Spinal Surg. Whittington Hosp. Lond. Prev: Sen. Regist. Roy. Nat. Orthop. Hosp. Stanmore; Regist. Univ. Hosp. Nottm.; Spinal Research Fell. Univ. Hosp. & Harlow Wood Orthop. Hosps. Nottm.

WILSON, Lewis Andrew The Health Centre, Victoria Road, Ulverston LA12 0EW Tel: 01229 582223; Schiehallion, 22 Fell View, Swarthmoor, Ulverston LA12 0XF Tel: 01229 584208 — MB BS 1980 Lond.; BA Lond. 1977; MRCGP 1984; DRCOG 1982; Cert. Family Plann. JCC 1982. (Univ. Camb. Lond. Hosp. Med. Coll.)

WILSON, Linda Grace 34 Redburn Drive, Shipley BD18 3AZ — MB ChB 1986 Leeds; MRCGP 1990; Dip. Palliat. Med. (Commend.) Cardiff 1993; DRCOG 1989. Regist. (Palliat. Med.) Yorksh. Region. Prev: Trainee GP Bradford HA VTS.

WILSON, Lockhart Lindsay 10 Highfield Road, Magherafelt BT45 5JD — MB BCh BAO 1986 Belf.

WILSON, Lorraine Mary Southampton General Hospital, Tremona Road, Southampton SO16 6YD; 79 The Hundred, Romsey SO51 8BZ — MB BCh BAO 1991 NUI; MRCP (UK) 1995; LRCPSI 1991. (Irel.) Specialist Regist. (Nuclear Med.) Soton. Gen. Hosp.

WILSON, Louisa Emma 29 Castle View Road, Canvey Island SS8 9FD Email: rocklobster@ozemail.com.uu — MB BS 1993 Lond.; BSc Lond. 1992, MB BS 1993; MRCP(Paed) 1996. (St Mary's London) Sydney Childr.'s Hosp., High St, Randwick, Sydney, NSW, Australia 2031(Paediat. Regist.).

WILSON, Louise The Surgery, Recreation Drive, Billinge, Wigan WN5 7L Tel: 01744 892205; 58A Wigan Road, Standish, Wigan WN6 0BA Tel: 01942 425618 — MB ChB 1979 Liverp.; DRCOG 1981.

WILSON, Louise 72 Queniborough Road, Leicester LE4 6GU — MB ChB 1993 Leic.

WILSON, Louise Caroline Unit for Clinical Genetics, Institute of Child Health, 30 Guilford St., London WC1N 1EH — MB ChB 1987 Manch.; BSc 1984 Biochemistry Manch.; MRCP (UK) 1991. Cons. (Clin. Genetics) Gt. Ormond St. Hosp., Lond.

WILSON

WILSON, Louise Elizabeth 6 Carolsteen Avenue, Helens Bay, Bangor BT19 1LJ — MB ChB 1986 Ed. Paediat. Intensivist Roy. Hosp. Sick Childr. Edin.; Sen. Lect. Fac. Med. Univ. Edin.

WILSON, Lucy Lillian 9 Laggan Road, Newton Mearns, Glasgow G77 6LP Email: luce3@hotmail.com — MB ChB 1998 Manch.; BSc (Hons) Met. Biol St And 1995.

WILSON, Lynda Ellen 7 Bronte Place, Stenhousemuir, Larbert FK5 4HN Tel: 01324 557175 — MB ChB 1996 Ed. SHO (Anaesth.), Rockhampton Hosp. Prev: SHO, O & G, Roy. Infirm., Edin.

WILSON, Lynda Mary Norwood Medical Centre, 360 Herries Road, Sheffield S5 7HD Tel: 0114 242 6208 Fax: 0114 261 9243; 27 Carsick View Road, Sheffield S10 3LZ — MB ChB 1978 Dundee; DRCOG 1981.

WILSON, Lynn 40 Sandhill Parade, Belfast BT5 6FH — MB BCh 1997 Belf.

WILSON, Lynn Margaret McIntosh, Gourlay and Partners, 1 India Place, Edinburgh EH3 6EH Tel: 0131 225 9191 Fax: 0131 226 6549; 95 Ravelston Dykes, Edinburgh EH12 6EY — MB ChB 1977 Ed.; BSc Ed. 1974, MB ChB 1977.

WILSON, Madeleine Ann Ambrose Avenue Surgery, 76 Ambrose Avenue, Colchester CO3 4LN Tel: 01206 549444 Fax: 01206 369910; 7 Richardson Walk, Colchester CO3 4AJ Tel: 01206 765510 — MB ChB 1983 Bristol; MB ChB Brist. 1983; MRCGP 1987; DCH RCP Lond. 1986. Prev: GP Manch.; Trainee GP Kenilworth; SHO (A & E & Geriat.) Dudley Rd. Hosp. Birm.

WILSON, Mairi Elizabeth Scott Burlington Road Surgery, 12/14 Burlington Road, Ipswich IP1 2EU; 48 Prittlewell Close, Ipswich IP2 9SP — MB ChB 1980 Aberd.

WILSON, Malachy Gerard Lister House Surgery, 35 The Parade, St Helier, Jersey JE2 3QQ Tel: 01534 36336 Fax: 01534 35304 — MB BCh BAO 1980 Dub.

WILSON, Margaret Fonab, 19 Appleton Avenue, Pedmore, Stourbridge DY8 2JZ Tel: 01384 396794 — MB ChB 1951 Glas.; DObst RCOG 1953; DA Eng. 1954. (Glas.) JP.

WILSON, Margaret (retired) 11 Bellevue Road, Kirkintilloch, Glasgow G66 1AL Tel: 0141 776 4229 — MB BS 1960 Lond.; MSc (Physiol.) Lond. 1958; MRCP (UK) 1970; DCH Eng. 1963. Prev: Gen. Practitioner Glas. G64 2AA.

WILSON, Margaret Cunningham Gibb Charlotte Street Surgery, 1 Charlotte Street, Dumfries DG1 2AG Tel: 01387 267626 Fax: 01387 266824; Riverside Cottage, Kelton, Dumfries DG1 4UA — MB ChB 1971 Aberd.; MRCGP 1986; DObst RCOG 1974. Med. Off. Occupat. Health Dept. Crighton Roy. Hosp. Dumfries.

WILSON, Margaret Lynne Brendon Hills Surgery, Torre, Washford, Watchet TA23 0LA Tel: 01984 640454 Fax: 01984 641164 — BM 1984 Soton.; MRCGP 1990.

WILSON, Marie Benedicta St David's Clinic, 2 Bramley Road, Ealing, London W5 4SS Tel: 020 8579 0165 Fax: 020 8579 0424; St. David's, 2 Bramley Road, London W5 4SS Tel: 020 8579 0165 — MB BS 1956 Madras; MRCP Lond. 1965; DObst RCOG 1961; DCH Eng. 1960. (Madras) Socs: Assoc. Mem. BMA; Med. Soc. Lond.; Hunt. Soc. Prev: SHO Glan Ely Hosp. Cardiff; SHO Acton Hosp. Lond.; Regist. Centr. Middlx. Hosp. Lond.

WILSON, Marie Elizabeth Easterhouse Health Centre, 9 Auchinlea Road, Glasgow G34 9HQ Tel: 0141 531 8150 Fax: 0141 531 8110; 2 Oban Drive, Glasgow G20 6AF — MB ChB 1981 Glas.; MRCGP 1991; MRCOG 1986. (Glasgow) GP Partner; Vocat. Studies Glas. Univ. Socs: Med. Wom. Federat. Prev: Trainee GP Kirkintilloch VTS; Regist. (O & G) W. Scotl.

WILSON, Mark Lower Street Health Centre, Lower Street, Tettenhall, Wolverhampton WV6 9LL Tel: 01902 444550/1 — MB BChir 1975 Camb.; MB Camb. 1975, BChir 1974; MA Camb. 1975; DRCOG 1978. (Char. Cross) Socs: BMA; Wolverhampton Med. Inst. Prev: SHO (Geriat. Med., O & G & A & E) Plymouth Gen. Hosp. (Freedom Fields Br.).

WILSON, Martin 312 Alcester Road S., Birmingham B14 6EN — BM BS 1994 Nottm.

WILSON, Mr Martin Cooper Homewood, 1 Barlow Fold Road, Romiley, Stockport SK6 4LH Tel: 0161 494 8634 — MD 1976 MB ChB 1969; MD Manch. 1976; FRCS Eng. 1973. Cons. Gen. Surg. Tameside Gen. Hosp. Lancs. Prev: Lect. in Clin. Surg. Univ. Edin.

WILSON, Martin Geoffrey Cleveland The Surgery, Station Road, Great Massingham, King's Lynn PE32 2JQ Tel: 01485 520521 Fax: 01485 520072; Red House Farm, Little Massingham, King's Lynn PE32 2JU Tel: 01485 520572 — MB BS 1974 Lond. Prev: Trainee GP/SHO King's Lynn Gen. Hosp. VTS; Ho. Phys. Whittington Hosp. Lond.; Ho. Surg. Dreadnought Seamans Hosp. Lond.

WILSON, Martin Thomson 22 Overton Drive, West Kilbride KA23 9LH — MB ChB 1978 Dundee; DRCOG 1982.

WILSON, Mary 23 Brackley Road, Monton, Eccles, Manchester M30 9LG Tel: 0161 281 2262; Department of Radiology, Withington Hospital, Nell Lane, Manchester M20 2LR Tel: 0161 291 4079 — MB BS 1978 Lond.; MRCS Eng. LRCP Lond. 1978; FRCR 1985. (St. Bart.) Cons. Radiol. S. Manch. Univ. Hosp. Trust. Prev: Sen. Regist. (Radiol.) N.W. RHA; Sen. Regist. (Radiol.) Nottm. HA.; Regist. (Radiol.) Nottm. HA.

WILSON, Mrs Mary Alexandra Marshall Chandos. 12 Parkside Mews, Hurst Road, Horsham RH12 2SA Tel: 01403 248747 — MB BS 1953 Lond.; MRCS Eng. LRCP Lond. 1953; DObst RCOG 1954. (Char. Cross) Prev: Ho. Surg. Harrow Hosp.; Resid. Obst. Off. Char. Cross Hosp. Lond.

WILSON, Mary Elizabeth 6 Butts Garth, Thorner, Leeds LS14 3DA — BChir 1995 Camb.

WILSON, Mary McKirdy 33 Tweskard Park, Belfast BT4 2JZ — MB BCh BAO 1938 Belf. (Qu. Univ. Belf.)

WILSON, Mary Shelagh The Health House, 1 Wootton Street, Cosham, Portsmouth PO6 3AP Fax: 023 9232 6379; Brooklyn Cottage, Commonside, Westbourne, Emsworth PO10 8TD Tel: 01243 375633 — BM 1982 Soton.

WILSON, Matthew Joseph Anthony Flat 25, Block 5, Griffin Close, Bristol Road S., Birmingham B31 2UY — BM BCh 1991 Oxf.; BA (Physiol. Sci.) Oxf. 1988. SHO (Cardiothoracic Surg.) Walsgrave Hosp. Coventry.

WILSON, MattJames 52 Abbotswood Road, London SW16 1AW Tel: 020 8769 4020 — MB BS 1997 Lond. (St Bartholomews Hospital) SHO Rotat. (Surgic.) Roy. Berks. Hosp. Lond. Rd. Berks. Prev: Ho. Off. (Med.) Colchester; Ho. Off. (Surgic.) Roy. Berks.

WILSON, Mrs Maureen Elizabeth (retired) Leewood, Leewood Road, Dunblane FK15 0DR Tel: 01786 822161 — MB ChB 1965 Glas.

WILSON, Melanie Patricia Bristol PHL, Department of Microbiology, Bristol Royal Infirmary, Bristol BS2 8HW Tel: 0117 928 2514; Hall Floor Flat, 32 Royal York Crescent, Bristol BS8 4JU — MB BS 1991 Lond.; DRCPath 1998. (St. Geo. Hosp. Med. Sch.) Regist. (Microbiol.) Bristol Pub. Health Laborat. Socs: Hosp. Infec. Soc.; Brit. Soc. Antimicrob. Chemother. Prev: SHO (Med. Microbiol.) Bristol Roy. Infirm. & Good Hope Hosp. NHS Trust Sutton Coldfield; SHO (Biochem.) Good Hope Hosp. NHS Trust Sutton Coldfield; Ho. Off. (Gen. Med.) Qu. Alexandra's Hosp. Cosham.

WILSON, Michael Anthony Longueville, Mill Hill, Huntington, York YO32 9PY Tel: 01904 768861 Fax: 01904 762012 — MB ChB Leeds 1958; FRCGP 1979, M 1966; DObst RCOG 1961. GP; Mem. A.B.P.I. Code of Pract. Appeal Bd.; Mem. Gen. Med. Counc. Socs: Fell. Roy. Soc. Med.; of Counc. BMA; York Med. Soc. Prev: Chairm. Gen. Med. Servs. Comm.; Dep. Chairm. Standing Med. Advis. Comm.

WILSON, Michael Anthony 11 The Comyns, Bushey Heath, Watford WD2 1HN Tel: 020 8950 3677 — MB BS 1950 Lond. (Middlx.) Med. Off. Bushey & Dist. Hosp.; Hosp. Pract. (Orthop.) Watford Gen. Hosp. & W. Herts. Hosp. Hemel; Med. Off. St. Margt.'s Sch. Bushey. Prev: GP Watford; SHO (Orthop.) Roy. Vict. Hosp. Bournemouth; Flight Lt. RAF.

WILSON, Michael David 25 Birch Polygon, Manchester M14 5HX — MB BS 1990 New South Wales.

WILSON, Mr Michael George (retired) Litfield House, Litfield, Clifton, Bristol BS8 3LS Tel: 0117 973 1323 — MB ChB Leeds 1940; ChM Leeds 1957; FRCS Eng. 1949; MRCS Eng. LRCP Lond. 1942. Hon. Cons. Surg. S.mead Hosp. Bristol, Wells & Dist. Hosp. & Clevedon Cott Hosp. Prev: Lect. (Clin. Surg.) Univ. Bristol.

WILSON, Michael John 37 The Ridgeway, Fleetwood FY7 8AH — MB ChB 1973 Manch.

WILSON, Michael Raymond 51 Carlton House, Western Parade, Southsea PO5 3ED Tel: 01705 863222 — BM 1981 Soton.

WILSON, Michael St George 9A Wilbraham Place, London SW1X 9AE Tel: 020 7730 5119; 2 Stanford Road, London W8 5QJ Tel: 020 7937 6973 — MB BChir 1959 Camb.; MRCS Eng. LRCP Lond. 1959; DObst RCOG 1963. (Westm.) Clin. Asst. (Dermat.) St. Mary's Hosp. Lond. Prev: Clin. Asst. Rheum Dept. W.m. Hosp.

WILSON

Lond.; Med. Off. Anaesth. Dept. Qu. Mary's Hosp. Hong Kong; Clin. Asst. ENT Dept. W.m. Hosp. Lond.

WILSON, Michael St George Kershaw Newton Surgery, Park Street, Newtown SY16 1EF Tel: 01686 626221/626224 Fax: 01686 622610; 8 Meadow Lane, Newtown SY16 2DU Tel: 01686 628786 — MB 1973 Camb.; BA Camb. 1969, MB 1973, BChir 1972; DRCOG 1977; DCH Eng. 1974. (St. Thos.) Prev: Ho. Surg. St. Thos. Hosp. Lond.; Ho. Off. (Paediat.) Essex Co. Hosp. Colchester; Ho. Surg. (Obst.) Roy. United Hosp. Bath.

WILSON, Michael Stanley (retired) Wycherts, West Hagbourne, Didcot OX11 0ND — MB BS 1953 Lond.; LMSSA Lond. 1952; DO Eng. 1958. Prev: Dir. Contact Lens Servs. & Assoc. Specialist Ophth. W.. Ophth. Hosp. Lond.

WILSON, Michael Stewart Dalkeith Medical Centre, 24-26 St. Andrew Street, Dalkeith EH22 1AP Tel: 0131 663 2461 Fax: 0131 561 5555; 17 Lasswade Road, Eskbank, Dalkeith EH22 3EE Tel: 0131 663 8845 — MB ChB 1973 Ed.; LMCC 1979; MRCGP 1981; DRCOG 1977; DCH RCPS Glas. 1975. GP Trainer (Paediat.) Sch. Community Paediat. Edin. Socs: Brit. Soc. Study of Infec.; Assoc. Mem. Fac. Homoeop.; Assn. Mem. Roy. Coll. Paediat. & Child Health. Prev: Regist. (Paediat.) Kingston Gen. Hosp. Kingston Ont. Canada; SHO (Med.) Roy. Hosp. Sick Childr. Edin.; Ho. Off. (Med.) W.. Gen. Hosp. Edin.

WILSON, Morven Patricia Flat 0/2, 4 Vinicombe St., Glasgow G12 8BG — MB ChB 1997 Glas.

WILSON, Neil Department of Cardiology, Royal Hospital for Sick Children, Yorkhill, Glasgow G3 8SJ Tel: 0141 201 0246 Fax: 0141 201 0853 Email: wilsonneil@aol.com; Beechwood, Bridge of Weir Road, Kilmacolm PA13 4NN Tel: 01505 874324 Fax: 01505 874324 Email: 100441.2742@compuserve.com — MB BS 1978 Lond.; FRCP Ed. 1995; MRCP (UK) 1982; DCH Glas. 1981; FRCP Ed. 1996. (St. Thomas') Cons. (Cardiol.) Roy. Hosp. For Sick Childr. Glas. Prev: Cons. (Paediat. Cardiol.) King Faisal Specialist Hosp. Riyadh, Saudi Arabia; Cons. (Paediat. Cardiol.) Killingbeck Hosp. Leeds; Sen. Regist. (Paediat. Cardiol.) Killingbeck Hosp. Leeds.

WILSON, Neil David Holycroft Surgery, The Health Centre, Oakworth Road, Keighley BD21 1SA; The Old Vicarage, Lothersdale, Keighley BD20 8EQ Tel: 01535 634952 — MB ChB 1975 Birm. (Birm.) GP Keighley.

WILSON, Mr Neil Imray Livingstone 92 Inveroran Drive, Bearsden, Glasgow G61 2AT — MB ChB 1977 Glas.; BSc Glas. 1975, MB ChB 1977; FRCS Glas. 1981; Dip Biomech (strath) 1987. Cons. and orthopaedic Surg.,Roy. Hosp. for sick Childr. and W.ern Infirm., Glas. Socs: BMA; Assoc. Mem. Brit. Orthop. Assn.; Mem. Brit. Scoliosiss Soc. Prev: Sen. Regist. (Orthop. Surg.) Vict. Infirm. Glas.; Regist. (Orthop. Surg.) Univ. Dept. W.. Infirm. Glas.; Jun. Ho. Off. (Med.) Profess. Unit. Stobhill Hosp. Glas.

WILSON, Niall Joseph Elliott Royal Liverpool University Hospital, Prescot St., Liverpool L7 8XP Tel: 0151 282 6856 Fax: 0151 282 6899; Tel: 0151 428 2646 — MB ChB 1991 Liverp.; BSc (Hons.) Liverp. 1988; MRCP (UK) 1995. (Liverpool) Cons. Dermat. Roy. Liverp. Univ. Hosp.; Hon.Clin. Lect. Dept. Of Med. Univ. Of Liverp. Socs: Brit. Assn. Dermat.; Liverp. Med. Inst.; Dowling Club. Prev: SHO (Histopath. & Med.) Roy. Liverp. Univ. Hosp.; Ho. Off. Roy. Liverp. Hosp.; Regist. (Dermat.) Roy. Liverp. Univ. Hosp.

WILSON, Nicholas Hedley Helios Medical Centre, 17 Stoke Hill, Stoke Bishop, Bristol BS9 1JN Tel: 0117 982 6060; 15 Normanton Road, Clifton, Bristol BS8 2TY — MB BS 1985 Lond.; BSc Lond. 1982; MRCGP 1993; DCH RCP Lond. 1990; DA (UK) 1989. (Westm.) Asst. GP; Sch. Doctor. Prev: Trainee GP Bristol.; Research Fell. Univ. W.minster Lond.

WILSON, Nicholas James The Old Town Surgery, 13 De La War Road, Bexhill-on-Sea TN40 2HG Tel: 01424 219323 — MB BS 1988 Lond.; DRCOG 1992.

WILSON, Mr Nicholas Muir Royal Hampshire County Hospital, Romsey Road, Winchester SO22 5DG Tel: 01962 825055 Fax: 01962 824640 — MB BS 1981 Lond.; BSc (Hons.) Lond. 1978, MS 1994; FRCS (Gen. Surg.) 1993; FRCS Eng. 1985. (St. Thos.) Cons. Gen. Surg. Roy. Hants. Co. Hosp. Winchester; Arris & Gale Lect. RCS Eng; Edr. Thrombosis, Gen. Surg. & Curr. Med. Literature. Socs: Fell. Roy. Soc. Med.; Fell. Assn. Surgs.; Fell. Vasc. Surgic. Soc. Prev: Sen. Regist. St. Thomas's Hosp. Lond.; Lect. St. Thos. Hosp. Lond.; Regist. Lond. Chest Hosp. & W.m. Hosp. Lond.

WILSON, Nicholas Stephen Market Deeping Health Centre, Godsey Lane, Market Deeping, Peterborough PE6 8DD — MB ChB 1986 Leic.; DTM & H Liverp. 1988. Socs: Fell. Roy. Soc. Trop. Med.

WILSON, Nicholas William Aidan — MB BS 1988 Newc.

WILSON, Nicola Jane 12 Rectory Road, Gosforth, Newcastle upon Tyne NE3 1XR — MB BS 1996 Lond.

WILSON, Nicola Margaret Royal Brompton Hospital, Paediatrics Department, Sydney St., London SW3 6NP Tel: 020 7351 8232 Fax: 020 7351 8763 Email: n.wilson@rbh.nthames.nhs.uk; The Old Mill, Mill Lane, Adderbury, Banbury OX17 3LW Tel: 01295 810340 — MRCS Eng. LRCP Lond. 1964; MB BS 1964; FRCPCH 1997; MD Eng. 1987; DCH Eng. 1967. (St. Geo.) p/t Hon. Cons. Paediat.

WILSON, Nigel Leith Stoneycroft Medical Centre, Stoneville Road, Liverpool L13 6QD Tel: 0151 228 1138 Fax: 0151 228 1653; 68 Winifred Lane, Aughton, Ormskirk L39 5DL Tel: 01695 423497 Email: wilsonul@liv.ac.uk — MB BChir 1982 Camb.; MB BChir Camb. 1981; MA Camb. 1982; AFOM RCP UK 1994; MRCGP (Distinc.) 1987; DRCOG 1985; Cert. Family Plann. JCC 1985. (Camb.) Occupat. Phys. Liverp. Univ. Prev: GP Bishop Auckland.

WILSON, Nigel Walton (retired) 14 Treadgold Street, London W11 4BP — MB BS 1980 Lond.; MA 1976.

WILSON, Mr Noel Vivian Department of Surgery, Kent & Canterbury Hospital, Ethelbert Road, Canterbury CT1 3NG Tel: 01227 766877; Horsehead Farm, Green Hills, Barham, Canterbury CT4 6JY — MB BS 1981 Lond.; MB BS Lond. 19; MS Lond. 1992; FRCS Eng. 1986. (St. Thos.) Cons. Gen. & Vasc. Surg. Kent & Canterbury Hosp. Socs: Vasc. Surg. Soc. GB & Irel.; Assn. Surg. Prev: Sen. Regist. & Regist. (Gen. Surg.) King's Coll. Hosp. Lond.; Sen. Fell. (Vasc.) St. Mary's Hosp. Lond.

WILSON, Norman Graham Michael Tel: 01270 582589 Fax: 01270 216330; The Warren, Berkeley Crescent, Wistaston, Crewe CW2 6QA Tel: 01270 568735 — MRCS Eng. LRCP Lond. 1966; DRCOG 1970; DA (UK) 1969. (Liverp.) Scheme Organiser, S. Chesh. VTS; Hon. Clin. Tutor, Dept. of Primary Care, Univ. of Liverp.; Hosp. Pract. (Anaesth.) Mid Chesh. Hosps. Trust; Mem. GPs in Asthma Gp. Socs: BMA (Pres Crewe Div.); Assoc. RCGP. Prev: Trainer (Gen. Pract.) Mersey Region.

WILSON, Mrs Olive Eversfield, Rockcliffe, Dalbeattie DG5 4QF Tel: 0155 663334 — M.B., Ch.B. Ed. 1943. (Univ. Ed.) Socs: BMA.

WILSON, Pamela Edith Haydock Medical Centre, Station Road, Haydock, St Helens WA11 0JN Tel: 01744 734419 Fax: 01744 454875 — MB ChB 1974 Manch.; DObst RCOG 1976; Cert. Family Plann. JCC 1983. (Manchester) Prev: SHO (Paediat.) & SHO (O & G) Wigan AHA.

WILSON, Mrs Patricia Caroline Gladwyns House, Sheering Road, Hatfield Heath, Bishop's Stortford CM22 7LL Tel: 01279 730184 Fax: 01279 739053; Gladwyns House, Sheering Road, Hatfield Heath, Bishop's Stortford CM22 7LL Tel: 01279 730256 Fax: 01279 739053 — MB ChB 1970 Birm.; MB ChB (Hons.) Birm. 1970; FRCOG 1990, M 1978. Consg. Gyn., Private Pract. At The Rivers Hosp., Herts. & St. John & St. Eliz., Lond. Socs: Counc. Mem. Of Indep.Doctors Forum; Brit. Soc. Colpos. & Cerv. Path.; Brit. Soc. Gyn. Endoscopy. Prev: Sen. Regist. Addenbrooke's Hosp. Camb.; Clin. Lect. (O & G) Clin. Sch. Camb.; Cons. O & G Essex & Herts. Health Servs.

WILSON, Patrick Antony Joseph 3 Mill Hill Road, Norwich NR2 3DP — MB BS 1984 Lond.; MRCP (UK) 1987; FRCR 1991.

WILSON, Patrick John Kevin 59 Myrtlefield Park, Malone Road, Belfast BT9 6NG Tel: 01232 660083; 19 Winston Drive, Portstewart BT55 7NW Tel: 0126583 3022 — MB BCh BAO 1945 Belf.; FRCGP 1980, M 1953; Assoc. Fac. Occupat. Med. RCP Lond. 1979; Lic. Fac. Occupat. Med. RCPI 1979. (Qu. Univ. Belf.) Hosp. Pract. Purdysburn Hosp. Belf. Med. Off. Bass Brewing Ltd.; Med. Off. DHSS Fell. Ulster Med. Soc. Socs: Soc. Occupat. Med. Prev: Clin. Asst. Med. Mater Infirm. Hosp. Belf.

WILSON, Patrick Pownall Bonnar and Partners, Sunnyside Surgery, Hawkins Road, Penzance TR18 4LT Tel: 01736 63340 Fax: 01736 332116; 3 St Michael's Terrace, Penzance TR18 2JP Tel: 01736 366234 — MB BS 1979 Lond.; MRCGP 1986; DRCOG 1985; DA Eng. 1982. (St. Thos.) Prev: Trainee GP Truro; SHO (Anaesth. & O & G) Treliske Hosp. Truro; SHO. (Cas.) Leicester Roy. Infirm.

WILSON, Patrick Ralph (retired) 5 Birlingham Close, Defford Road, Pershore WR10 1LZ Tel: 01386 556821 — LRCPI & LM,

WILSON

LRSCI & LM 1948; LRCPI & LM, LRCSI & LM 1948. Prev: Sch. Med. Off. Cornw. & Isles Of Scilly AHA.

WILSON, Paul Marybrook Medical Centre, Marybrook Street, Berkeley GL13 9BL Tel: 01453 810228 Fax: 01453 511778; The Bungalow, Canonbury Hill, Berkeley GL13 9BE Tel: 01452 810678 Email: paul.wilsondr@btinternet.com — MB ChB 1972 Bristol; 2001 Diploma in Prison Medicine; MRCGP 1976; DObst RCOG 1976. (Bristol) Med. Off. HM Prisons Leyhill & E.wood Pk.; Hon. Treas. Jenner Trust.; Apptd. Doctor to Health & Safety Exec. Ionising Radiat.s & Asbestosis. Socs: Roy. Soc. of Med. Prev: Trainee GP Teesside VTS; Ho. Surg. Bristol Roy. Infirm.; Ho. Phys. Cheltenham Gen. Hosp.

WILSON, Mr Paul Department of General Surgery, Royal Lancaster Infirmary, Lancaster LA1 4RP; Wood House, Wennington Road, Wray, Lancaster LA2 8QQ — MB ChB 1986 Birm.; MB ChB (Hons.) Birm. 1986; FRCS (Gen.) 1996; FRCS Ed. 1990. (Birm.) Roy. Lancaster Infirm. Prev: Cons. (Vasc. & Gen. Surg.) N. Manch. Gen. Hosp.; Sen. Regist. (Gen. Surg.) Roy. Oldham Hosp.; Sen. Regist. (Vasc. Surg.) Withington Hosp. Manch.

WILSON, Paul Anthony Abington, 37 Ayr Road, Prestwick KA9 1SY Email: the.wilsons@btinternet.com — MB ChB 1976 Glas.; FRCA 1982. Cons. Anaesth. N. Ayrsh. & Arran Trust. Socs: Assn. Anaesth.; Scott. Soc. Anaesth.; Intens. Care Soc.

WILSON, Paul Bayne 195 Sandown Road, Belfast BT5 6GX — MB BCh BAO 1979 Belf.

WILSON, Paul Bryan The Surgery, 232-234 Milton Road, Weston Super Mare BS22 8AG Tel: 01934 625022 Fax: 01934 612470; Shiplett Court Farm, Shiplate Road, Bleadon, Weston Super Mare BS22 0NY Tel: 01934 813412 — MB BS 1972 Lond.; DObst RCOG 1974. (Univ. Coll. Hosp.) Prev: Trainee GP Univ. Coll. Hosp. Lond. VTS.

WILSON, Paul Douglas The Surgery, Field Road, Stainforth, Doncaster DN7 5AF Tel: 01302 841202; The Lodge, St. Bartholomews Rise, Cantley Lane, Doncaster DN4 6LS Tel: 01302 533318 Email: paul@cantley.demon.co.uk — MB ChB 1979 Ed.; BSc (Hons.) Ed. 1976; MRCGP 1984; DRCOG 1984. (Ed.) Lect. (Gen. Pract.) Sheff. Univ.

WILSON, Paul Frederick Dodington Surgery, 29 Dodington, Whitchurch SY13 1EU Tel: 01948 662033 Fax: 01948 663428; Alport House, Alport Road, Whitchurch SY13 1NR Tel: 01948 662676 — MB BS 1971 Lond. Socs: BMA. Prev: SHO (O & G, Paediat. & Psychiat.) N. Middlx. Hosp. Lond.

WILSON, Paul Gerard 35 Willoughby Drive, Solihull B91 3GB Email: wilsonpg@globalnet.co.uk — MB ChB 1988 Birm.; MRCP (UK) 1992. Clin. Research Fell. Univ. of Birm. Prev: Regist. Rotat. (Gen. Med. & Gastroenterol.) Worcester Roy. Infirm. Selly Oak Hosp. Birm. & Qu. Eliz. Hosp. Birm.; SHO Rotat. (Med.) Chesterfield Roy. Hosp.

WILSON, Mr Paul Stephen ENT Department, North Staffordshire Hospitals NHS Trust, Newcastle Road, Stoke-on-Trent ST4 6QG Tel: 01782 552077 Fax: 01782 552895; Kirkstone House, Pinewood Road, Ashley Health, Market Drayton TF9 4PR Tel: 01630 672150 Fax: 01630 673631 — MB ChB Birm. 1983; FRCS (Orl.) Eng. 1989. Cons. (ENT Surg.) N. Staffs. Hosp. Trust; Hon. Research Fell. (Communication & Neurosci.) Univ. Keele.

WILSON, Paula Caroline 15 Quadrant Road, Glasgow G43 2QP — MB ChB 1993 Manch. Specialist Regist. Clin. Oncol. The Roy. Marsden Hosp Lond.

WILSON, Pauline Koinonia, 37 Kantersted Road, Lerwick ZE1 0RJ — MB ChB 1998 Aberd.

WILSON, Peter (retired) Randalls Cottage, 204 Catherington Lane, Catherington, Portsmouth — MB BS 1947 Lond.

WILSON, Mr Peter Kinnesswood, Withybush Road, Haverfordwest SA62 4BN — MB ChB 1956 Ed.; FRCS Eng. 1979; FRCS Ed. 1963. (Ed.) Cons. Withybush Gen. Hosp. HaverfordW.. Prev: Sen. Regist. in Gen. Surg. United Cardiff Hosps.

WILSON, Peter 23 The Warren Drive, Wanstead, London E11 2LR — MB BChir 1975 Camb.; MRCPath 1981. Sen. Lect. & Hon. Cons. Lond. Hosp. Med. Coll. & Newham Healthcare NHS Trust. Socs: (Exec. Counc. & Mem.ship Soc.) Assn. Clin. Path. Prev: Clin. Dir. Newham Healthcare; Gen. Manager (Acute Unit) Newham HA.

WILSON, Peter Bellingham Lowfell, Eaglesfield, Cockermouth CA13 0SD — MB BS 1968 Lond.; MRCPsych. 1981.

WILSON, Peter Charles 25 Bog Road, Ballymena BT42 4HH; 30 Linney Road, Bramhall, Stockport SK7 3JW Tel: 0161 439 7799 — MB ChB 1991 Manch. Specialist Regist. (O & G) N. W. Region.

WILSON, Peter David 27 Marton Road, Bridlington YO16 7AQ — MB ChB 1972 Leeds; BSc (Hons.) Leeds 1969, MB ChB 1972; MRCP (UK) 1976. Sen. Regist. (Dermat.) W.. Infirm. & Stobhill Hosp. Glas. Prev: Ho. Off. Profess. Med. Unit. St. Jas. Hosp. Leeds; Regist. (Dermat.) Roy. Vict. Infirm. Newc.; Research Fell. Dermat. Univ. Pennsylvania, PA, USA.

WILSON, Peter Edward Albion Road Surgery, 30 Albion Road, St Peter's, Broadstairs CT10 2UP Tel: 01843 862179 Fax: 01843 861317; Rosegarth, 15 St. Mildreds Avenue, Ramsgate CT11 0HX Tel: 01843 596456 — MB BS 1979 Lond.; DRCOG 1982. Med. Manager; E. Kent Doctors on Call.

WILSON, Mr Peter Ernest Heaton (retired) 5 Davenport Road, Coventry CV5 6QA Tel: 01203 677838 Fax: 01203 713822 — MB BS 1956 Lond.; FRCS Eng. 1966. Prev: Cons. Orthop. & Trauma Walsgrave Hosps NHS Trust.

WILSON, Peter Graham Torbay Hospital, Department Child Health, Vowden Hall, Lawes Bridge, Torquay TQ2 7AA Tel: 01803 655824 Fax: 01803 617174; Millcroft, Aish, Stoke Gabriel, Totnes TQ9 6PS Tel: 01803 782450 Fax: 01803 617174 — MB ChB 1975 Birm.; BSc Oxf. 1970; MFPHM 1997; MRCGP 1979. (Birm.) Community Paediat. & Child Health, Torbay Hosp., Torquay. Socs: Roy. Inst. Pub. Health and Hyg.; Brit. Assn. Community Drs in Audiol. Prev: SCMO (Child Health) S. Devon Healthcare NHS Trust Torbay; Sen. Regist. (Pub. Health) Bristol & W.on HA.

WILSON, Peter James Ligoniel Health Centre, 74A Ligoniel Road, Belfast BT14 8BY Tel: 028 9039 1690; 25 Broomhill Park, Belfast BT9 5JB Tel: 01232 660841 — MB BCh BAO 1978 Belf.; MRCGP 1983; DRCOG 1983.

WILSON, Mr Peter John Edgar Malyan (retired) Swallowshaw, The Street, Walberton, Arundel BN18 0PQ Tel: 01243 551316 — MB BS 1956 Lond.; FRCS Ed. 1962; FRCS Eng. 1962; MRCS Eng. LRCP Lond. 1956. Prev: Cons. Neurosurg. Morriston Hosp. Swansea.

WILSON, Peter Nicholas North End Medical Centre, 211 North End Road, West Kensington, London W14 9NP Tel: 020 7385 7777 Fax: 020 7386 9612 — MB BChir 1982 Camb.; MA, BChir Camb. 1981, MB 1982; MRCGP 1987.

WILSON, Peter Richard Birchwood Villa, Severalls Hospital, Boxted Road, Colchester CO6 4PA Tel: 01206 853535; Vaughans, Abberton Road, Layer de la Hayes, Colchester CO2 0LB Tel: 01206 34273 Fax: 01206 852022 — BM BCh 1960 Oxf.; MA, BM BCh Oxf. 1960; FRCP Lond. 1987, M 1968; DObst RCOG 1963. (St. Thos.) Cons. Phys. Geriat. Med., Stroke & Younger Disabled Servs. St. Marys Hosp. Colchester. Socs: Brit. Geriat. Soc. & Colchester Med. Soc.

WILSON, Peter Robert County Hospital, Hereford HR1 2ER; Stoneleigh, Bodenham, Hereford HR1 3HS — MB BS 1982 Lond.; MRCP (UK) 1985; FRCR 1989. Cons. Radiol. Co. Gen. Hosp. Hereford; Clin. Director of Combine Serv.s. Prev: Regist. Lond. Hosp. Whitechapel; SHO (Med.) OldCh. Hosp. Romford; SHO (Med.) Qu. Mary's Hosp. Sidcup.

WILSON, Philip Andrew Brendon Hills Surgery, Torre, Washford, Watchet TA23 0LA Tel: 01984 640454 Fax: 01984 641164 — BM 1984 Soton.; MRCGP 1989; DRCOG 1988.

WILSON, Philip Melvin Dunellan, Station Road, St Cyrus, Montrose DD10 0BQ — MB ChB 1969 Aberd.

WILSON, Philip Michael John Battlefield Road Surgery, 148 Battlefield Road, Glasgow G42 9JT Tel: 0141 632 6310 Fax: 0141 636 1180; 92 Earlbank Avenue, Glasgow G14 9DU — MB BChir 1984 Camb.; MB Camb. 1984, BChir 1983; DPhil Oxf. 1984, MA 1984; MRCP (UK) 1988; FRCGP 1997; MRCGP 1987; DCH RCP Lond. 1988. (Camb.) Research Fell. (Gen. Pract.) Glas. Univ.; Reviewer for Med. Monitor Magazine (Paediat. Topics).

WILSON, Philip Osmund Gill Department of Histopathology, 2nd Floor, N. Wing, St Thomas' Hospital, London SE1 7EH Tel: 020 7928 9292 Fax: 020 7401 3661; 29 Brackley Road, Beckenham BR3 1RB Tel: 020 8325 5617 — BM 1981 Soton.; MRCPath 1989. Cons. Histopath. & Cytol. Guy's & St. Thos. Hosp. Trust. Socs: BMA; Assn. Clin. Path.; (Hon. Asst. Sec.) BSCC. Prev: Lect. & Hon. Sen. Regist. (Histopath.) Roy. Free Hosp. Lond.; Regist. & SHO (Gen. Path.) Portsmouth Dist. Path. Serv.

WILSON

WILSON, Philippa Joseph Kateri c/o Dr M. Wilson, Department of Microbiology, Eastman Dental Institute, University of London, 256 Gray's Inn Road, London WC1X 8LD — BM BS 1995 Nottm.

WILSON, Piers Timothy John Anaesthetic Department, North Hampshire Hospital, Basingstoke RG24 9NA; Crocus Cottage, 10 Basingstoke Road, Ramsdell, Tadley RG26 5RB — MB BS 1983 Newc.; FFA RCS Eng. 1988. Cons. Anaesth. N. Hants. Hosp. Basingstoke. Prev: Sen. Regist. Rotat. (Anaesth.) Soton. & Basingstoke; Regist. (Anaesth.) Gt. Ormond St. Hosp. Lond. & Soton. Gen. Hosp.; SHO (Neonat. Med.) P.ss Anne Hosp. Soton.

WILSON, Ralph Noble, SBStJ (retired) Duffield House, Blind Lane, Breaston, Derby DE72 3BS Tel: 01332 875790 — MB BS Durh. 1943; DIH Soc. Apoth. Lond. 1961; DPH Lond. 1949. Prev: Med. Off. Stanton & Staveley Ltd.

WILSON, Raymond Gerrard 111 Moss Lane, Sale M33 5BU — MB BCh BAO 1979 NUI; MRCGP 1984; DCH RCP Lond. 1984.

WILSON, Reginald John Lyons (retired) Ballyward, Castlewellan BT31 9PS Tel: 01820 650203 — MD Belf. 1946, MB BCh BAO 1940 Belf.

WILSON, Richard George Longmead, 53 Sugden Road, Long Ditton, Thames Ditton KT7 0AD Tel: 020 8398 3987 — MB BS 1963 Lond.; FRCP Lond. 1984; MRCP (U.K.) 1970; MRCS Eng. LRCP Lond. 1963; DCH Eng. 1967. (St. Bart.) Cons. Paediat. Kingston Hosp. Kingston-upon-Thames; Hon. Cons. Paediat. Char. Cross Hosp. Lond.; Counc. Foundat. for Study of Infant Deaths. Socs: Brit. Soc. Allergy & Clin. Immunol. Prev: RMO Qu. Eliz. Hosp. for Childr. Lond.; Regist. Soton. Childr. Hosp.; RMO Roy. Free Hosp. Lond.

WILSON, Mr Richard Henry 9 Cranmore Gardens, Belfast BT9 6JL — MB BCh 1984 Belf.; MBC BCh BAO (Hons.) Belf. 1984; DRCOG 1987; FRCSI 1988.

WILSON, Richard Jeremy Malcolm Clydebank Health Centre, Kilbowie Road, Clydebank G81 2TQ Tel: 0141 531 6400 Fax: 0141 531 6336; 11A Westbourne Gardens, Glasgow G12 9XD Tel: 0141 357 0827 — MB ChB 1982 Dundee.

WILSON, Richard John Health Clinic, 407 Main Road, Dovercourt, Harwich CO12 4ET Tel: 01255 201299 Fax: 01255 201270 — MB ChB 1985 Glas.

WILSON, Richard John Wellspring Surgery, St. Anns Health Centre, St. Anns, Well Road, Nottingham NG3 3PX Tel: 0115 9505907/8 Fax: 0115 988 1582.

WILSON, Richard Jonathan Terry 7 New Walk Terrace, York YO10 4BG Email: jonathan@critbase.demon.co.uk — MB ChB 1984 Manch.; BSc St. And. 1981; FRCA 1992; DA (UK) 1989. (Manch. & St. And.) Cons. Anaesth. & Intens. Care York Dist. Hosp. Socs: Assn. Anaesth.; Intens. Care Soc.; BMA. Prev: Sen. Regist. (Anaesth.) York, Hull & Leeds; Regist. (Anaesth.) Leeds Gen. Infirm. & York Dist. Hosp.; SHO (Anaesth.) Camb. Milit. Hosp. Aldershot.

WILSON, Richard Malcolm Royal Hallamshire Hospital, Glossop Road, Sheffield S10 Tel: 0114 276 6222; 181 Millhouses Lane, Sheffield S7 2HD — MB ChB 1978 Dundee; MB ChB (Commend.) Dundee 1978; DM Nottm. 1985; FRCP Lond. 1993; MRCP UK 1981. Sen. Lect & Cons. Phys. (Gen. Med. & Diabetes) Dept. Med. Univ. Sheff. Socs: Brit. Diabetes Assn.; Eur. Assn. Study Diabetes. Prev: Lect. (Med. & Endocrinol.) Univ. Sheff.; Clin. Research Fell. Diabetes & Immunol. Univ. Hosp. Nottm.; Regist. (Gen. Med.) Ninewells Hosp. Dundee.

WILSON, Richard Raymond, VRD (retired) 5 Marks Mews, Castle Lane, Warwick CV34 4BQ Tel: 01926 493375 — MRCS Eng. LRCP Lond. 1942.

WILSON, Mr Richard Yelverton Department of Surgery, Furness General Hospital, Dalton Lane, Barrow-in-Furness LA14 4LF Tel: 01229 870870; Ashlands, Church Walk, Ulverston LA12 7EW Tel: 01229 586704 — MB BS Western Australia 1967; FRCS Eng. 1972. (West. Austral.) Cons. Urol. Furness Gen. Hosp. Cumbria, W.morland Gen. Hosp. Kendal Cumbria and Roy. Lancaster Infirm., Lancaster. Socs: Brit. Assn. Surgic. Oncol. (Full Mem.); Brit. Assn. Urol. Surg.; Brit Assoc. Urol.Surg. (Sect. of Oncol.). Prev: Lect. & Resid. Asst. (Surg.) Univ. Coll. Hosp. Lond.; SHO Univ. Hosp. S. Manch.; Ho. Phys. & Ho. Surg. Roy. Perth. Hosp., Austral.

WILSON, Robert (retired) 14 Forsyth Street, Greenock PA16 8DT Tel: 01475 27547 — MB ChB 1957 Glas. Prev: Cons. Clin. Biochem. Renfrewsh. Laborat. Serv.

WILSON, Robert Royal Brompton Hospital, Sidney Street, London SW3 6NP Tel: 020 7351 8338 Fax: 020 7351 8331 — MRCS Eng. LRCP Lond. 1979; MA Camb. 1980, MD 1987, MB 1979, BChir 1980; FRCP Lond. 1995; MRCP (UK) 1983. Reader & Cons. Phys. Nat. Heart & Lung Inst. & Roy. Brompton Hosp. Lond. Socs: Mem. of Brit. Thoracic Soc.; Mem. of Europ. Respirat. Soc.; Mem. of Amer. Thoracic Soc.

WILSON, Robert Alistair 10 Lisnagarvey Drive, Lisburn BT28 3DW — MB BCh BAO 1990 Belf.; MB BCh Belf. 1990.

WILSON, Robert Baird (retired) Mile Ash, Dumfries DG1 1JX Tel: 01387 252251 — MB ChB 1940 Glas.; BSc Glas. 1937, MB ChB (Hons.) 1940; FRCP Lond. 1970, M 1947; FRCP Ed. 1969, M 1961; FRCP Glas. 1967. Prev: Phys. Dumfries & Galloway Roy. Infirm.

WILSON, Robert Blue (retired) 15 Daleview Avenue, Glasgow G12 0HE Tel: 0141 576 1666 — MB ChB 1949 Glas.

WILSON, Robert Charles Duncan (retired) Old Dairy Cottage, Nutbourne Village, Pulborough RH20 2HE Tel: 01798 815294 Fax: 01798 815294 — MB ChB 1956 Aberd.; MD Canada 1960; LMCC Canada 1960; CCFP Canada 1972. Prev: Cons. Menopause & PMS Clinic Portland Hosp. Lond.

WILSON, Mr Robert George 7 Daltry Close, Yarm TS15 9XQ Tel: 01642 854841 — MB BS 1979 Newc.; MD Newc. 1987; FRCS Eng. 1984; FRCS Ed. 1984. (Newc.) Cons. Surg. S. Cleveland Hosp. Middlesbrough. Socs: Assn. Coloproctol.; Surgic. Research Soc.; BSG. Prev: Sen. Regist. N.. RHA; Sen. Research Assoc. & Demonst. (Anat.) Univ. Newc.; SHO (Gen. Surg.) Roy. Vict. Infirm. Newc.

WILSON, Mr Robert Graeme 25 Swanston Terrace, Edinburgh EH10 7DN — MB ChB 1980 Aberd.; ChM Aberd. 1991, MB ChB 1980; FRCS (Gen.) 1995; FRCS Ed. 1984. Cons. Surg. W.. Gen. Hosps. Trust Edin. Prev: Sen. Regist. (Gen. Surg.) Lothian HB.

WILSON, Mr Robert Irvine, MBE Spinney Cottage, 184 Finaghy Road Sth., Belfast BT10 0DH — MB BCh BAO 1938 Belf.; MB BCh BAO. Belf. 1938; FRCS Ed. 1947; FRCSI (ad eund.) 1974. (Belf.) Emerit. Prof. Qu. Univ. Belf. Socs: Fell. Brit. Orthop. Assn. & Ulster Med. Soc. Prev: Prof. (Orthop. Surg.) Qu. Univ. Belf.; Regist. Roy. Vict. Hosp. Belf. & P.ss Eliz. Orthop. Hosp. Exeter; Hon. Lt.-Col. RAMC.

WILSON, Robert James, Surg. Lt.-Cdr. RN Retd. 2 Old School Close, Birdham, Chichester PO20 7ER Tel: 01243 513859 — MB BS 1973 Lond.; MRCGP 1979; MRCS Eng. LRCP Lond. 1973. (Guy's)

WILSON, Robert James 1371 Warwick Road, Knowle, Solihull B93 9LW Tel: 01564 774412 — MB ChB 1957 Ed.; MB ChB (Hons.) Ed. 1957; MD Ed. 1973, BSc (Hons. Physiol.) 1954; FRCP Lond. 1982, M 1965; FRCP Ed. 1974, M 1962. Cons. Phys. Solihull Hosp. Prev: Sen. Regist. (Med.) Addenbrooke's Hosp. Camb.; Research Fell. (Cardiol.) Edin. Roy. Infirm.; Univ. Sen. Asst. Phys. (Investigative Med.) Univ. Camb.

WILSON, Robert John Lincolnshire HA, Cross O'Cliffe, Bracebridge Heath, Lincoln LN4 2HN Tel: 01522 515376 Fax: 01522 515364; 34 Kenyon Close, Heighington, Lincoln LN4 1GJ — MB ChB 1986 Glas.; MFPHM 1997; MRCGP 1990. (Glasgow) Cons. (Pub. Health Med.) Lincs. HA. Prev: Regist. (Pub. Health Med.) Leics. HA.

WILSON, Robert Richard 27 Iniscarn Park, Lisburn BT28 2BL — MB BCh BAO 1995 Belf.

WILSON, Robert Stanley Edward Lower Wood House, Lower Common, Longden, Shrewsbury SY5 8HB Tel: 0174 373657 — MB ChB 1968 Bristol; MA Wales 1990; BSc (Hons.) Bristol 1965, MB ChB (Hons.) 1968; FRCP Lond. 1985; MRCP (UK) 1972. (Bristol) Gen. Phys. Roy. Shrewsbury Hosp.; Unit. Med. Advis. W. Unit. Shrops.; Chairm. Dist. Audit Comm. Shrops. HA. Prev: Sen. Med. Regist., SHO (Med.) & Ho. Phys. & Ho. Surg. United Bristol; Hosps.

WILSON, Robin Butler The Health Centre, Banks Road, Haddenham, Aylesbury HP17 8EE Tel: 01844 291874 Fax: 01844 292344 — MRCS Eng. LRCP Lond. 1980 London; Lekarz 1976 Lodz; Lekarz 1976 Lodz.

WILSON, Robin John Abbey Surgery, 28 Plymouth Road, Tavistock PL19 8BU Tel: 01822 612247 Fax: 01822 618771 — MB BChir 1970 Camb.; MB BChir Camb. 1969; MA Camb. 1969; MRCP (UK) 1972; MRCGP 1982; DObst RCOG 1974; DCH Eng. 1973. (St. Thos.) Prev: Regist. (Paediat.) Plymouth Gen. Hosp.; Resid. Med. Off. W.m. Childr. Hosp. Lond.

WILSON, Rodney Pearson North Lane, Navenby, Lincoln LN5 0EH Tel: 01522 810221 — MB BS 1964 Lond.; DObst RCOG 1966.

WILSON

(Lond. Hosp.) Prev: Ho. Off. (Gen. Med. Surg. & O & G) Qu. Eliz. II Hosp. Welwyn Gdn. City; Ho. Off. (Gen. Surg.) Lond. Hosp.

WILSON, Roger Kyle 43 Surrey Street, Belfast BT9 7FR — MB BCh 1997 Belf.

WILSON, Mr Roger Stafford East Surrey Hospital, Canada Avenue, Redhill RH1 5RH Tel: 01737 768511; Ridge Green Farm, Kings Cross Lane, South Nutfield, Redhill RH1 5RL Tel: 01737 823200 Fax: 01737 823200 Email: rogerwilson@msn.com — MB ChB 1978 Birm.; FRCS Eng. 1983; FRCOphth 1989. Cons. Ophth. E. Surrey HA; Cons. Adviser Ophth. Civil Aviat. Auth. Socs: Fell. Roy. Soc. Med.; UK Intraocular Implant Soc. Prev: Sen. Regist. (Ophth.) W.. Ophth. Hosp. & Moorfields Eye Hosp. Lond.; SHO (Ophth.) Birm. & Midl. Eye Hosp.; Ho. Phys. Good Hope Gen. Hosp. Sutton Coldfield.

WILSON, Mr Ronald George (retired) Quality Assurance Reference Centre for Screening, General Hospital, West Gate Road, Newcastle upon Tyne NE4 6BE Tel: 0191 273 8811 — MB ChB 1961 Aberd.; MD Aberd. 1977; FRCS Ed. 1970. Prev: Cons. Surg. & Surg. Oncol. Gen. Hosp. Newc. & Newc. BrE. Screen. Unit.

WILSON, Rory Hugh 49 Kilmaine Road, Bangor BT19 6DT — MB BCh BAO 1994 Belf.

WILSON, Rosalind Mary (retired) Culm Park, Old Willand, Cullompton EX15 2RD Tel: 01884 33344 — MB BS Lond. 1951.

WILSON, Rowan Clare Department of Anaesthesia, St. James University Hospital, Beckett St., Leeds LS9 7 Tel: 0113 243 3144 Email: rwilson@epicure.u-net.com; Eltofts House, Carr Lane, Thorner, Leeds LS14 3HF Tel: 0113 289 3107 Fax: 0113 289 3800 — MB BS 1980 Lond.; MRCP (UK) 1984; FRCA 1989. (Univ. Coll. Hosp.) Cons. Anaesth. St. James Univ. Hosp. Leeds.; Hon. Sen. Lect. Univ. Leeds. Prev: Sen. Med. Off. Med. Educat., Train. & Staffing Div. Healthcare Directorate NHS Exec; Sen. Regist. Rotat. (Anaesth.) Yorks.

WILSON, Rowan Nicholas 12 St James Road, Prescot L35 0PF — MB BCh 1991 Wales.

WILSON, Ruth 91 College Road, Epsom KT17 4HH — MB ChB 1973 Leeds; BSc (Anat.) Leeds 1970, MB ChB (Hons.) 1973; MRCGP 1977; DObst RCOG 1975.

WILSON, Mrs Ruth Audrey (retired) Charnock Green, Wigan Lane, Heath Charnock, Chorley PR7 4DD Tel: 012572 63250 — MB ChB 1946 Manch.; MRCS Eng. LRCP Lond. 1946. Prev: Clin. Asst. Paediat. Roy. Albert Edwd. Infirm. Wigan.

WILSON, Ruth Edna Mary William Street Surgery, 67 William ST., Herne Bay CT6 5NR Tel: 01227 740000 Fax: 01227 742729; 33 Canterbury Road, Herne Bay CT6 5DQ Tel: 01227 368013 — MB ChB 1972 Glas.; DCH RCPS Glas. 1976; DObst RCOG 1975. BrE. Clinician Nat. BrE. Screening Progr. Kent & Canterbury Hosp.; Clin. Asst. (Oncol.) Kent & Canterbury Hosp.

WILSON, Ruth Pauline Elspeth Temple Cowley Health Centre, Templar House, Temple Road, Oxford OX4 2HL Tel: 01865 777024 Fax: 01865 777548 — MB ChB 1985 Leeds.

WILSON, Sally Ann 48 St Nicholas Drive, Shepperton TW17 9LD — MB ChB 1996 Bristol.

WILSON, Sally-Anne 12 Limetrees Gardens, Gateshead NE9 5BE Email: sally-anne.wilson@virgin.net — MB BS 1994 Newc. SHO (A & E) W.ern Bay Tauranga NZ. Socs: BMA; WIST. Prev: SHO (Med.) S. Tyneside Gen. Hosp.; SHO (A & E) N. Tyneside Gen. Hosp.; SHO (Urol. & Orthop.) Sunderland Dist. Gen. Hosp.

WILSON, Sally Ruth National Hospital for Neurology and Neurosurgery, Queen Square, London WC1N 3BG; 20 Oakington Road, London W9 2DH — MB BS 1983 Lond.; BSc (Hons.) Lond. 1980, MB BS 1983; FRCA 1988.

WILSON, Sam CNR Main & Centre STS, PO BOX 158, Pahiatua, New Zealand Tel: 00646 376 6466 Fax: 00646 376 6429; 110 Earlswood Road, Dorridge, Solihull B93 8RW — MB ChB 1976 Leeds; FRNZCGP; 2000 (Otago) Dip. GP. GP Pahiatua, Woodville & Eketakune, NZ. Prev: Med. Off. Suri Seri Begawan Hosp. Kuala Belait, Brunei; GP Coventry.

WILSON, Samuel John Simpson Lorna Doone, Praa Sands, Penzance TR20 9TQ — MB BS 1998 Lond.

WILSON, Sarah Stoneleigh, Bodenham, Hereford HR1 3HS — MB BS 1983 Lond.; DCCH RCGP 1995. Community Med, Off. Hereford Community Trust.

WILSON, Sarah Dorothy Straid, Ballyclare BT39 — MB BCh BAO 1946 Belf.; DPH 1960.

WILSON, Sarah Harriet 8 Meadow Way, Kinoulton, Nottingham NG12 3RE — MB ChB 1979 Dundee; BSc (Hons.) Dund 1974, MMSc 1976,; MFFP 1993; MFCM 1989; FFPHM 1998. Dir. Pub. Health Nottm. HA. Prev: Sen. Lect. (Pub. Health Med.) Univ. Nottm. Med. Sch.; Regist. (Community Med.) Trent RHA.

WILSON, Sarah Juliet Royal Victoria Hospital, Grosvenor Road, Belfast BT12 6BA Tel: 01232 240503; 2 Randal Park, Belfast BT9 6JJ — MB BCh BAO Belf. 1994; MRCO phtn 1998. SHO Ophth. Roy. Vict. Hosp. Belf.

WILSON, Sheena McRae 11 Inver Terrace, Muirhead, Dundee DD2 5LS Tel: 01382 580479 — MB ChB 1978 Dundee. Staff Grade O & G Ninewells Hosp. Dundee.

WILSON, Simon James Percy The Surgery, 1-3 Chequers Drive, Prestwood, Great Missenden HP16 9DU Tel: 01494 862858; Roseberry, Broombarn Lane, Great Missenden HP16 9JD Tel: 01494 864737 — MB BS 1991 Lond.; DRCOG 1996; MRCGP 1998. (Charing Cross & Westminster)

WILSON, Simon Paul White Gates, 37 Braidley Road, Bournemouth BH2 6JY Email: simon.wilson@dial.pipex.com — MB ChB 1995 Leeds; MA (Phil.) Leeds 1993, BSc (Chem Path.) 1991. (Leeds) Regist. (Psychiat.) Bethlem & Maudsley Hosps. Lond.

WILSON, Simon Russell "Fellside", Hale, Milnthorpe LA7 7BL Tel: 015395 63327 Fax: 015395 64059; Fellside, Hale, Milnthorpe LA7 7BL — MB ChB 1981 Manch. Prev: SHO W.morland Co. Hosp. Kendal & Lancaster Infirm.; Ho. Off. Vict. Hosp. Blackpool; GP Princip., Milnthorpe, Cumbria.

WILSON, Stanley Darrin 132 Upper Newtownards Road, Belfast BT4 3EQ — MB BCh BAO 1989 Belf.

WILSON, Stephanie Margaret (retired) 14 St Thomas Gardens, London NW5 4EX — MD 1964 Dub.; MB BCh BAO 1954; FRCPath 1976, M 1964. Prev: Cons. Histopath. St. Mary's Hosp. Lond.

WILSON, Stephen Geoffrey The Atkinson Morley Hospital, 31 Copse Hill, Wimbledon, London SW20 0NE Tel: 020 8946 7711; 91 College Road, Epsom KT17 4HH Tel: 01372 721062 Fax: 01372 721062 Email: s.wilson@doctors.org.uk — MB ChB 1973 Leeds; BSc (1st cl. Hons.) Physiol. Leeds 1970, MD 1981, MB ChB (Hons.) 1973; FRCP Lond. 1990; MRCP (UK) 1975. Cons. Neurol. Atkinson Morley's & Epsom Dist. Gen. Hosps.; Cons. & Hon. Sen. Lect. St. Geo. Hosp. Lond.

***WILSON, Stephen Jack** 30 Green Lane, Hucclecote, Gloucester GL3 3QU — MB ChB 1995 Birm.

WILSON, Stephen John Rosemount Medical Practice, 1 View Terrace, Aberdeen AB25 2RS Tel: 01224 638050 Fax: 01224 627308 Email: stephen.wilson@rosemount.grampion.scot.nhs.uk — MB ChB 1979 Aberd.; MRCGP 1983. (Aberd.) Prev: Offshore Doctor OMS Aberd.

WILSON, Stephen John Nuffield Dept. Of Anaesthetics, Oxford, John Radcliff Hospital, Headington, Oxford OX3 9DU Tel: 01865 741166 — MB ChB 1990 Bristol; FRCA 1999. Specialist Regist. (Anaesth.) Oxf. Socs: BMA; Assn. Of Anaesth. G. Brit.; Fell. Of Roy. Coll. Of Anaesth. Prev: Regist. (Anaesth.) N.ampton Gen. Hosp.

WILSON, Stephen Michael 6 Beaufort Grove, Morecambe LA4 6UF — MB ChB 1998 Ed.

WILSON, Stephen Robert C/o ISIS Centre, Little Clarendon St., Oxford OX1 2HS Tel: 01865 310744 Fax: 01865 310744 — MRCS Eng. LRCP Lond. 1968; MSc (Clin. Med.) Oxf. 1978; MSc (Economics) Lond. 1974; FRCPsych 1985, M 1974; DPM Eng. 1972. (Roy. Free) p/t Hon. Cons. Psychother. Ment. Healthcare Trust; Hon. Research Fell. Centre for Psychonalytic Studies Univ. Kent; Cons. Psychotherapist, Dept. Psychother. N.amptonshire. Prev: Cons. Psychotherapist Warneford Hosp. Oxf.; Cons. Psychiat. (Psychother.) Littlemore Hosp. Oxf.; Hon. Sen. Clin. Lect. (Psychiat.) Univ. Oxf.

WILSON, Stuart Jonathan 8 Selm Park, Livingston EH54 5NU — MB ChB 1993 Aberd. (Aberdeen)

WILSON, Mr Stuart William Department of Plastic Surgery, Pinderfields Hospital, Wakefield WF1 4DG — FRCS (Plast) 1997; MB ChB 1986 Sheff.; FRCS Eng. 1990; FRCS Glas. 1990; MRCP (UK). Cons. Plastic Surg., Withington Hosp. Prev: Sen. Regist. (Plastic Surg.) Pinderfield Hosp. Wakefield; Ho. Off. (Surg.) Roy. Hallamsh. Hosp. Sheff.; Ho. Phys. Lodge Moor Hosp. Sheff.

WILSON, Miss Susan Elaine 45A Samos Road, Anerley, London SE20 7TX Tel: 020 8325 3092 Email: susiew5000@aol.com; Department of Vascular Surgery, Leeds General Infirmary, Leeds LS1 — MB BS 1991 Lond.; BSc Lond. 1988; FRCS Eng. 1995. (Royal

WILSON-DAVIS

Free Hospital) Research Regist. (Vasc. Surg.) Leeds Gen. Infirm. Prev: Regist. (Gen. Surg.) Guy's Hosp. Lond.

WILSON, Susan Jane Vonda Queens Road Medical Practice, The Grange, St. Peter Port, Guernsey GY1 1RH Tel: 01481 724184 Fax: 01481 716431; Les Ruettes Farm, Les Ruettes, St. Andrews, Guernsey GY6 8UQ Tel: 01481 37142 — MB ChB 1979 Aberd.; MRCGP Ed. 1983.

WILSON, Susannah Louise 40 Ashford Drive, Ravenshead, Nottingham NG15 9DE Tel: 01623 794341 — BM BS 1995 Nottm. SHO (Gen. Med.) Nottm. City Hosp. VTS; SHO (Obst. & Gyn.) Grantham & Dist. Hosp.; SHO (Paediat.) Qu. Med. Centre Nottm.. Prev: Ho. Off. (Gen. Surg. & Urol.) Nottm. City Hosp.; Ho. Off. (Gen. Med.) King's Mill Hosp. Mansfield.

WILSON, Suzannah Yvonne 25 Lime Close, Harrow HA3 7JG — MB BS 1993 West Indies. SHO (Gen. Med.) Watford Gen. Hosp.

WILSON, Suzanne Denise 2 Hockley Cottages, The Heath, Hatfield Heath, Bishop's Stortford CM22 7EA — MB ChB 1991 Sheff.

WILSON, Sydney Gordon Forbes (retired) 2 Earlspark Drive., Bieldside, Aberdeen AB15 9AH Tel: 01224 869279 — MB ChB 1947 Ed.; MD Ed. 1960; FRCP Ed. 1967, M 1953; FRCPCH 1997. Prev: Cons. Paediat. Tayside HB & Sunderland Hosp. Gp.

WILSON, Sylvia Rosalys Wembley Disability Benefits Centre, Cannon Lincoln Building, Wembley HA9 0DL Tel: 020 8902 8822 Fax: 020 8903 5842; 6 Windrush Avenue, Bedford MK41 7BS — MB BS 1963 Lond.; MRCS Eng. LRCP Lond. 1963. (Roy. Free) Med. Off. Benefits Agency Med. Servs. Prev: Clin. Asst. Geriat. Unit Bedford Gen. Hosp.

WILSON, Tamsin Margaret Newbiggin Hall Farmhouse, Hexham NE46 1TA — MB BS 1984 Newc. Clin. Asst. (Anaesth.) Hexham Gen. Hosp.

WILSON, Terence Reginald, MC 27 Marton Road, Bridlington YO16 7AQ Tel: 01262 73578 — MB ChB 1939 Leeds.

WILSON, Teresa Anne Howitt Meadowbank, 12 Woodland Way, Weybridge KT13 9SW — MB BCh 1998 Wales.

WILSON, Thomas Daniel Partington 60 Binswood Avenue, Leamington Spa CV32 5RX — BChir 1995 Camb.

WILSON, Thomas Kyle Wishaw Health Centre, Kenilworth Avenue, Wishaw ML2 7BQ Tel: 01698 372201 Fax: 01698 371051; 22 Brownhill View, Newmains, Wishaw ML2 9QJ — MB ChB 1979 Glas.; MRCGP 1984.

WILSON, Thomas MacSkimming (retired) Benvenuti, 4 King Street, Oldmeldrum, Inverurie AB51 0EQ Tel: 01651 873091 — MB ChB 1944 Aberd. Prev: Principle in Gen. Pract., Bucksburn Aberd. 68/88.

WILSON, Thomas Scott (retired) 75 Stewarton Drive, Cambuslang, Glasgow G72 8DQ Tel: 0141 641 2195 — MD Glas. 1951, MB ChB 1944; FRCP Glas. 1979, M 1976; FFCM 1974; DPA Glas. 1959; DPH Glas. 1949; DIH RFPS Glas. 1949. Prev: SCM Gt.er Glas. Health Bd.

WILSON, Thomas Scott (retired) Tanglewood, St. Clements Hill, Truro TR1 1NU Tel: 01872 73719 — MD 1947 Belf.; MB BCh BAO 1940. Prev: Cons. Geriat. Phys. Cornw.

WILSON, Thomas Stephen (retired) 34 Malone Heights, Belfast BT9 5PG Tel: 02890 610042 — MB BCh BAO Belf. 1955; FRCPI 1987, M 1963; FRCPath 1977, M 1965. Prev: Cons. Bacteriol. Laborat. Belf. City Hosp.

WILSON, Timothy James Medway NHS Trust, Windmill Road, Gillingham ME7 5NY — MB BS 1973 Lond.; MRCS Eng. LRCP Lond. 1971; FFA RCS Eng. 1978. Cons. Anaesth. Medway Health Dist.

WILSON, Valerie Elizabeth Kensington Street Health Centre, Whitefield Place, Girlington, Bradford BD8 9LB Tel: 01274 499209; 26 Carrbottom Road, Greengates, Bradford BD10 0BB Tel: 01274 619184 Email: neasha@globalnet.co.uk — MB ChB 1977 Aberd. Clin. Asst. (Anaesth.) Leeds Gen. Infirm.

WILSON, Victor 1 James Close, Woodlands, London NW11 9QX — MB BS 1952 Lond. (Char. Cross) Socs: Ins. Med. Soc. Prev: Hosp. Pract. Dept. Dermat. Mt. Vernon Hosp. N.wood; Regist. & Ho. Phys. Dept. Dermat. Guy's Hosp. Lond.; Med. Off. Dept. Dermat. Hosp. Sick Childr. Gt. Ormond St.

WILSON, Virginia Sonia 49 Ovington Street, London SW3 2JA — MB BS 1980 Lond.; DCH RCP Lond. 1983.

WILSON, Mr William (retired) 34 Calderwood Road, Glasgow G43 2RU Tel: 0141 637 4898 — MB ChB Glas. 1952; FRCS Ed. 1958; FRCOphth. 1990; DO Eng. 1958. Ophth. Surg. Glas. Roy. Infirm. & Canniesburn Hosp. Glas. Prev: Ophth. Surg. Vict. Infirm. Glas. Ophth. Inst. & S.. Gen. Hosp. Glas.

WILSON, William (retired) Grosvenor House Nursing Home, 39 Duchy Road, Harrogate HG1 2HA Tel: 01423 523447 — MRCS Eng. LRCP Lond. 1932; BA Cantab. (Nat. Sc. Trip.) 1929, MA, MB BChir. Prev: Regional Med. Off. Min. of Health.

WILSON, William Adamson Melvin Charlotte Street Surgery, 1 Charlotte Street, Dumfries DG1 2AG Tel: 01387 267626 Fax: 01387 266824; Riverside, Kelton, Dumfries DG1 4UA — MB ChB 1972 Aberd.; MRCGP 1977; Dip. Forens. Med. Glas 1991.

WILSON, William Alan Rubislaw Place Medical Group, 7 Rubislaw Place, Aberdeen AB10 1QB Tel: 01224 641968 Fax: 01224 645738 — MB ChB 1968 Aberd.; MRCGP 1974.

WILSON, William Derek (retired) 8 Terregles Drive, Glasgow G41 4RN Tel: 0141 427 2374 — MB ChB Glas. 1950, DPH 1952; MFPHM 1972. Prev: Cons. Pub. Health Med. Roy. Hosp. for Sick Childr. Glas.

WILSON, William George The Retreat, Stourton Candle, Sturminster Newton DT10 2JN — MB BS 1990 Lond.

WILSON, William John Chesney Portglenone Health Centre, 17 Townhill Road, Portglenone, Ballymena BT44 8AD Tel: 028 2582 1551 Fax: 028 2582 2539 — MB BCh BAO 1977 Belf.; MRCGP 1981; DRCOG 1980. (Queens Univ. Belfast)

WILSON, William Murray (retired) 22 Courthill Street, Dalry KA24 5AN Tel: 01294 832165 — MB ChB 1948 Glas.; MRCGP 1960. Prev: Works Med. Off Roche Products Dalry.

WILSON, William Neil Willowfield Surgery, 50 Castlereagh Road, Belfast BT5 5FP Tel: 028 9045 7862 Fax: 028 9045 9785 — MB BCh BAO 1979 Belf.; MRCGP 1989.

***WILSON, William Richard** 49 Burnally Road, Limavady BT49 9DP Tel: 015047 227 44 Email: rwilson@doctors.net; 49 Burnally Road, Limavady BT49 9DP Tel: 015047 227 44 — MB BCh 1998 Belf.; MB BCh Belf 1998; BSC (Hons) Belf 1996.

WILSON, William Scott (retired) 20 Dingley Road, Edgerton, Huddersfield HD3 3AY — MB ChB 1942 Glas.; DPH 1947; MRCGP 1953. Prev: Res. Med. Off. Isolat. Hosp. & Sanat. Brighton & Roy. Infirm.

WILSON, William Thomas Cregeen Cooleen, Circular Rd, Jordanstown, Newtownabbey BT37 0RD; 195 Skegoneill Avenue, Belfast BT15 3LL — MB BCh BAO 1944 Dub.; BA Dub. 1943, MB BCh BAO 1944. (Dub.) Socs: Fell. Ulster Med. Soc.; BMA. Prev: Res. Med. Off. Roy. Vict. Hosp. Belf.; Capt. RAMC.

WILSON, Mr William Weatherston Charnock Green, Wigan Lane, Heath Charnock, Chorley PR7 4DD Tel: 012572 63250 — MRCS Eng. LRCP Lond. 1938; ChM Manch. 1959, MB ChB 1938; FRCS Eng. 1947. (Manch.) Surg. Emerit. Roy. Albert Edwd. Infirm. Wigan. Socs: Fell. Assn. Surgs. Gt. Brit. & Irel. & Manch. Med. Soc. Prev: Surgic. Chief Asst. Christie Hosp. & Manch. Roy. Infirm.; Mem. Ct. Examrs. RCS Eng.; Capt. RAMC.

WILSON, Mr Willoughby, OBE Raheen, 1 Church Avenue, Jordanstown, Newtownabbey BT37 0PJ Tel: 01231 63277 — MB BCh BAO 1946 Belf.; FRCSI 1969; FRCS Ed. 1952. (Qu. Univ. Belf.) Cons. Surg. Roy. Vict. Hosp. Belf. Socs: Vice-Pres. Med. Defence Union; Fell. Assn. Surgs.; BMA & Ulster Med. Soc. Prev: Ho. Phys. & Ho. Surg. Roy. Vict. Hosp. Belf.; Orthop. Ho. Surg. Musgrave Pk. Hosp. Balmoral.

WILSON, Yvonne Teresa 34 Malone Heights, Belfast BT9 5PG — MB ChB 1984 Dundee; FRCS Glas. 1988; FRCS (Plast.) 1996. Cons. Plastic Surg. Birm. Childr.'s Hosp. B'ham. Prev: Cons. (Plastic Surg.) St. Johns Hosp. Livingston & Roy. Hosp. for Sick Childr. Edin.; Sen. Regist. (Plastic Surg.) St. Johns Hosp. Livingston.; Regist. (Plastic Surg.) N.. Gen. Hosp. Sheff.

WILSON-CROOME, Jonathan Wilson Iona, Smugglers Lane, Furzehill, Wimborne BH21 4HB — MB BS 1975 Lond.; MRCGP 1982; DRCOG 1981. (Char. Cross) Chief Med. Off. Prime Med. Bournemouth. Socs: Roy. Coll. Gen. Pract. & BMA. Prev: GP Fremington N. Devon; Med. Off. RAF.

WILSON-DAVIS, Margaret Lilian 14 Ballygallum Road, Downpatrick BT30 7DA Tel: 01396 615168 — MB BS 1965 Newc.; FFA RCSI 1969; FFA RCS Eng. 1969. (Newc.) Prev: Cons. (Anaesth.)

WILSON-HAFFENDEN

Whiteabbey Hosp.; Sen. Regist. (Anaesth.) Roy. Vict. Hosp. Belf.; Sen. Regist. (Anaesth.) Sheff. HA.

WILSON-HAFFENDEN, Carolyn Fay Cambridgeshire Health Authority, St Johns, Thorpe Road, Peterborough PE3 6JG Tel: 01733 882288 Email: fay.haffenden@nwanglia.anglox.nhs.uk; Hill Farm House, 20 Chishill Road, Heydon, Royston SG8 8PW — MB ChB 1976 Ed. Cons. Pub. Health Med. NW Anglia Health Auth. Socs: Fac. Pub. Health Med. Prev: Sen. Regist. (Pub. Health Med.) Beds.

WILSON-HOLT, Mr Nicholas John Royal Cornwall Hospital, Treliske TR1 3JW Tel: 01872 253903; Duchy Hospital, Penventinnie Lane, Pen, Truro TR1 3UP Tel: 01872 226100 — MB BS 1982 Lond.; BSc (Hons.) Lond. 1979; FRCS (Ophth.) Glas. 1986; FRCOphth 1989. Cons. Ophth. Surg. Roy. Cornw. Hosp. Trust.; Freeman Scholsh. Middlx. Hosp. Med. Sch. Prev: Sen. Regist. & Vitroretinal Fell Moorfields Eye Hosp. Lond.; Resid. Surgic. Off. Moorfields Eye Hosp.

WILSON JONES, Alexander Catherine Rose Longfield, Fairfield Lane, West End, Woking GU24 9QX — MB ChB 1995 Bristol. Prev: Ho. Off. (Med.) Treliske Hosp. Cornw.; Ho. Off. (Surg.) S.mead Hosp. Bristol.

WILSON JONES, Charlotte Frances The Maudsley Hospital, Denmark Hill, London SE5 8AZ — MB BCh 1991 Wales; MRCPsych 1996. (Univ. Wales Coll. Med.) Specialist Regist. Comm. Psychiat. The Maudsley Hosp Lond.; Hon. SOR liaison Psychiat. to St. Christophers Hospice, Sydenham, Lond. Socs: BMA; Roy. Coll. Psychiat. Prev: Sen. Regist. Bethlem & Maudsley Adult Psychiat. NHS Trust, Lond.; Clin. Research Fell.Psychiat. Kings Coll. Lond. & Inst. of Psychiat.; Regist. (Psychiat.) Bethlem & Maudsley NHS Trust.

WILSON JONES, Nicholas Anthony Hugh Joseph Longfield, Fairfield Lane, Woking GU24 9QX — MB BCh 1996 Wales.

WILSON-MACDONALD, Mr James St. Luke's Hospital, Latimer Road, Headington, Oxford OX3 7PF Tel: 01865 288866 Fax: 01865 744520 Email: jwmac@onetel.net.uk; Culham Manor, Culham, Abingdon OX14 4LZ Tel: 01235 527009 Email: james.w@btclick.com — MB ChB 1978 Bristol; MCh 1990; FRCS Eng. 1982. Cons. Orthopaedic Surg., Nuffield Orthopaedic Centre, Oxf. OX3 7LD. Socs: Brit. Scoliosis Soc. Exec.; Brit. Assn. Of Spine Surg.s; Brit. Cervical Spine Soc. Prev: Cons. Orthop. Surg. Norf. & Norwich Hosp.

WILSON-NUNN, David Laurence Addenbrooke's Hospital, Hills Road, Cambridge CB2 2QQ Tel: 01223 245151; 25 Out Risbygate, Bury St Edmunds IP33 3RJ Tel: 01284 724216 Email: davidwilsnunn@globalnet.co.uk — MB BChir 1992 Camb.; PhD Camb. 1990; BA Oxf. 1987; FRCA 1997. Specialist Regist. (Anaesth.) Addenbrooke's Hosp. Camb.

WILSON-SHARP, Cecil Derek (retired) St. Peter's Croft, 4 Charles Moor, Stockton Lane, York YO31 1BE Tel: 01904 33890 — MB BS 1945 Lond.; DMRD 1950. Prev: Cons. Radiol. in Admi/c Essex Co. Hosp. & Others.

WILSON-SHARP, Rosalind Claire Pinderfields General Hospital, Aberford Road, Wakefield WF1 4DG Tel: 01924 201688; 2 Dunstarn Drive, Leeds LS16 8EH — MB BS 1975 Lond.; MRCP (UK) 1979; FRCR 1983. Cons. Radiol. Pinderfields Gen. Hosp. Wakefield.

WILSON-SMITH, Elaine Margaret Dept of Anaesthetics, John Radcliffe Hospital, Oxford OX3 9DU — MB BS 1988 Lond.; FRCA 1995. (Guys) Specialist Regist. Anaesth. John Radcliffe.Hosp.Oxf. Socs: Mem. BMA. Prev: Spec Reg Anaesth.Alder hey Hosp.Liverp.

WILSON-STOREY, Mr Derrick Royal Hospital for Sick Children, Sciennes Road, Edinburgh EH9 1LF Tel: 0131 536 0000 Fax: 0131 536 0665 — MD 1988 Sheff.; MB ChB 1978 Sheff.; FRCS Ed. 1983. (Sheffield) Cons. Paediat. Surg. Roy. Hosp. Sick Childr. Edin. Socs: Brit. Assn. Paediat. Surg.; Scott. Soc. Paediat. Surg. Prev: Sen. Regist. & Clin. Tutor (Paediat. Surg.) Childr. Hosp. Sheff.; Regist. (Paediat. Surg.) Edin.; Regist. (Gen. Surg.) Barnsley HA.

WILTER, Pierre Hendrik Willow Court, Marsham Lane, Gerrards Cross SL9 8HD Tel: 01753 899096 Fax: 01753 899095 Email: pierre@wa-global.com — MB ChB 1980 Cape Town; BSc (Med.) Cape Town 1975; MBA Open 1991. (Cape Town) Cons. Health Care Managem. PriceWaterHo.Coopers Lond. Prev: Med. Dir. HM YO1 & RC Feltham Middlx.; Clin. Asst. (Forens. Psychiat.) Regional Secure Unit St. Bernards Hosp. Lond.; Regist. (Psychiat.) Middlx. Hosp. & St. Bernards Hosp. Lond.

WILTON, Alison Yvonne Department of Community Paediatrics, 3/5 Craven Road, Reading RG1 5LF Tel: 01734 862277 Fax: 01734 750297; 7 St. Johns Road, Mortimer, Reading RG7 3TR Tel: 01734 331201 — MB ChB 1982 Birm.; MRCP (UK) 1987. Cons. Paediat. (Community Child Health) Reading. Prev: Sen. Regist. (Community Paediat.) E. Anglia RHA; Clin. Research Regist. Univ. Birm.; Hon. Regist. (Paediat.) Dudley Rd. Hosp. Birm.

WILTON, Anthony 47 Caemawr Gardens, Porth CF39 9DB — MB BCh 1982 Wales.

WILTON, Ben John 74 Mayflower Lodge, Regents Park Road, London N3 3HX Tel: 020 8346 0447 — MRCS Eng. LRCP Lond. 1934. (St. Bart.) Socs: BMA. Prev: Occupat. Health Adviser Scholl UK Ltd., Initial Servs. Ltd., Metro Color Ltd. etc.; Employm. Med. Adviser EMAS; Apptd. Fact. Doctor.

WILTON, Howard John West View House, 26 Callis Court Road, Broadstairs CT10 3AF Tel: 01843 862624 — MB BS 1971 Lond.; FFA RCS Eng. 1977. (King's Coll. Hosp.) Cons. Anaesth. Canterbury & Thanet DHA. Socs: Obst. Anaesth. Assn.; BMA (Hon. Sec. E. Kent Div.). Prev: Anaesth. Sen. Regist. Portsmouth & Soton. Health Dist.

WILTON, Joseph Frederick Lisson Grove Health Centre, Gateforth St, London NW8 8EG Tel: 020 7262 1366 Fax: 020 7258 1943; 28 Winscombe Street, London N19 5DG — MB BS 1977 Lond.; BSc (Microbiol.) Reading 1969; MRCS Eng. LRCP Lond. 1977; MRCGP 1982; DRCOG 1980; DCH Eng. 1979. (St. Bart.) GP Princip. Lisson Gr. Health Centre Lond.; Course Organiser GP Ho. Off. in Gen. Pract.; Coordinator Further Educat. & Support for Non-Princip. KCW Health Auth. Prev: Trainee GP Kentish Town Health Centre.

WILTON, Mr Timothy James 81 Friargate, Derby DE1 1FL; Hillcrest, 22 Castle Hill, Duffield, Belper DE56 4EA — MB BS 1978 Lond.; BA (Hons.) Oxf. 1975; FRCS Eng. 1983; MA(Hons) Oxf. 1995. (University College Hospital) Cons. Orthop. Surg. Derbysh. Roy. Infirm.; Clin. Teach. Nottm. Uni. Med. Sch. Socs: Fell. Orthop. Assn.; Treas. Brit. Assn. Surg. Knee. Prev: Sen. Regist. (Orthop.) Derbysh. Roy. Infirm. & Harlow Wood Orthop. Hosp.; Regist. (Orthop.) Univ. Hosp. & Harlow Wood Orthop. Hosp. Nottm.; Regist. Surg. Train. Scheme Welsh Nat. Sch. Med. Cardiff.

WILTSHAW, Eve, OBE (retired) The Cottage, Overnoons, Bexley Hill, Petworth GU28 9DZ — MB BCh 1951 Wales; MD Wales 1969; FRCP Lond. 1981, M 1971; FRCOG 1990. Prev: Cons. Phys. Roy. Marsden Hosp. Lond.

WILTSHIRE, Christopher Robert (retired) Dairy Farmhouse, Somersham Road, Bramford, Ipswich IP8 4NN Tel: 01473 832559 Fax: 01473 832559 — MB BS 1970 Lond.; FRCP Lond. 1993; MRCP (UK) 1973; FRCR 1976. Prev: Regist. (Radiother.) Middlx. Hosp. Lond.

WILTSHIRE, Edwin Julian Mark Whitchurch Road Medical Centre, 210-212 Whitchurch Road, Heath, Cardiff CF14 3NB Tel: 029 2062 1282 Fax: 029 2052 0210; 3 Rhydypenau Road, Cardiff CF23 6PX — MB BCh 1984 Wales; MRCGP 1988; DRCOG 1987.

WILTSHIRE, Robin James Abbott Laboratories, Abbott House, Norden Road, Maidenhead SL6 4XE Tel: 01628 644322 Fax: 01628 644185; 1 Hayward Place, Hedsor rd, Bourne End SL8 5EP Tel: 01628 526074 — MB ChB 1992 Birm.; BSc (Pharm.) Birm. 1989; Msc Aberdeen 1999. (Birmingham) Med. Advisor Abbot Laboratories Maidenhead. Socs: BRAPP. Prev: Med. Off. Brit. Antarctic Survey.

WILTSHIRE, Susan Jane Department of Anaesthesia, The Ipswich Hospital NHS Trust, Heath Road, Ipswich IP4 5PD Tel: 01473 712233; Dairy Farm House, Somersham Road, Bramford, Ipswich IP8 4NN Tel: 01473 832559 — MB BS Lond. 1970; FFA RCS Eng. 1975. (Roy. Free) Cons. Anaesth. Ipswich Hosp. Prev: Sen. Regist. (Anaesth.) Ipswich Hosp. & Addenbrooke's Hosp. Camb.; Regist. (Anaesth.) Lond. Hosp.

WIMALARATNE, Bala Manage Daya Sisil 98 Chase Way, Southgate, London N14 5DG — MB BS 1977 Sri Lanka; FFA RCS Eng. 1986; DA Eng. 1980.

WIMALASIRI, Robert Wijepala 5 Grove Lane, Kingston upon Thames KT1 2SU — MB BS 1962 Ceylon; MRCP (UK) 1987.

WIMALASUNDERA, Herbert Harischandra Gordon House Surgery, 78 Mattock Lane, Ealing, London W13 9NZ Tel: 020 8567 0631 — MB BS Ceylon 1961.

WIMALASUNDERA, Ruwan Chinthaka 43 Tudor Drive, Kingston upon Thames KT2 5NW — MB BS Lond. 1991; BSc Lond. 1988; MRCOG Lond. 1996. (King's College Hospital) Clin. Research Fell. Imperial Coll. Med. Sch. Nat. Heart & Lung Inst.; Dept. Clin. Pharmacol. St Mary's Hosp. Lond.

WIMALASURIA, Sarath Bandula 2 Firsby Avenue, Croydon CR0 8TL Tel: 020 8654 5003 — MBBS Celon; DTM & H Liverp.

WIMBLETON, Penelope Ann 14 Stanley Road, Bournemouth BH1 4SB — MB ChB 1989 Manch.

WIMBORNE, David (retired) 1 Darley Avenue, West Didsbury, Manchester M20 2XE — MB BS 1951 Lond.; LMSSA Lond. 1945. Hon. Cons. (Path.) Salford Roy. Hosp. Prev: Cons. Path. Salford Roy. Hosp.

WIMBORNE, Jonathan Mark 5 James Street, Morecambe LA4 5TE — MB ChB 1988 Manch.; MRCGP 1993.

WIMHURST, Mr James Anthony 7 Auckland Road, Cambridge CB5 8DW Email: woodwim@compuserve.com — MB BChir 1992 Camb.; FRCS 2001 (Tr. & Orth.); MChir 2000; MA Camb. 1992, MB BChir 1992; FRCS (Eng.) 1996. (Cambridge) Specialist Regist. (Trauma & Orthop.) E. Anglian Rotat. Addenbrooke's Hosp. Socs: Assoc. Mem. BOA; Brit. Orthop. Train. Assn. Prev: Specialist Regist. (Trauma & Orthop.) Norf. & Norwich; Specialist Regist. (Trauma & Orthop.) Addenbrooke's; Specialist Regist. (Trauma & Orthop.) Ipswich.

WIMHURST, John Alan (retired) The Warren, Elmcroft Lane, Felixstowe IP11 9LX — MB BS Lond. 1962; DObst RCOG 1964. Clin. Asst. Bartlet Hosp. Felixstowe. Prev: Clin. Asst. (A & E) Ipswich Hosp.

***WIMPENNY, Joanne Louise** 10 Ryal Close, Ockbrook, Derby DE72 3TG — MB ChB 1998 Birm.

WIMPERIS, Jennifer Zeala Norfolk & Norwich Hospital, Brunswick Road, Norwich NR1 3SR Tel: 01603 287866 Fax: 01603 286918 Email: jennie.wimperis@norfolk-norwich.thenhs.com; 420 Unthank Road, Norwich NR4 7QH — MB BS 1979 Lond.; BA Oxf. 1976; DM Oxf. 1987; FRCP; FRCPath. Cons. Haemat. Norf. & Norwich Hosp.

WIN, J M T Coggeshall Road Surgery, 9 Coggeshall Road, Braintree CM7 9DD Tel: 01376 552508 Fax: 01376 552690 — MB BS 1975 Med Inst (I) Rangoon; MB BS 1975 Med Inst (I) Rangoon.

WIN, Maung Tun c/o Lloyds Bank, 6 Pall Mall, London SW1Y 5NG — MB BS 1949 Rangoon.

WIN, Swe Swe Family Health Care Centre, 1 East Anglian Way, Gorleston-on-Sea, Great Yarmouth NR31 6TY Tel: 01493 662130 — MB BS 1972 Med Inst (I) Rangoon; MB BS 1972 Med Inst (I) Rangoon.

WIN HLAING, Dr Burma Hills Surgery, Ashridge Road, Wokingham RG40 1PH Tel: 0118 978 5854 Fax: 0118 978 2215 — MB BS 1975 Med. Inst. (I) Rangoon.

WIN KO, Dr 38 Woolaston Avenue, Cardiff CF23 6HA — MB BS 1973 Med. Inst. Rangoon.

WIN MAUNG, Dr HMP Whitmoor, March Tel: 01354 660653 — MB BS 1967 Med. Inst. (III) Mandalay; FRCP Ed. 1987; MRCP (UK) 1973. Sen. Med. Off. HMP Whitmoor, March. Prev: Sen. Med. Off. HMP Full Sutton York.; Med. Off. HM Prison Serv. Hull; Cons. Phys. & Med. Supt. Toungoo, Burma.

WINARSO, Paulus 15 Lowerfold Way, Rochdale OL12 7HX — MB ChB 1976 Birm.; FRCR 1983; DMRD 1981.

WINAYAK, Kamal 92 Heston Road, Heston, Hounslow TW5 0QP — MB BS 1987 Lond.

WINAYAK, Varendar Kumar The Medical Centre, 192 Twickenham Road, Hanworth, Feltham TW13 6HD Tel: 020 8979 3058 — MB BS 1978 Lond.; DRCOG 1982; MFFP 1982. (Univ. Coll. May. Med. Sch. Lond.) GP Lond. Prev: SCMO Margt. Pyke Centre Lond.; Med. Off. Marie Stopes Hse. Lond.; Cons. Phys. BUPA Med. Centre Lond.

WINBOW, Adrian John Godden Green Clinic, Godden Green, Sevenoaks TN15 0JR Tel: 01732 763491 Fax: 01732 763160 Email: adrianwinbow@haysgrove.prioryhealthcare.co.uk; Fax: 01732 838775 — MB BS 1969 Newc.; MRCPsych 1976; T(Psych) 1991; DPM Eng. 1975; FRCPsych 1998. (Newc.) Cons. Psychiat, Godden Green Clinic; Cons. Psychiat. Hartswood Hosp. Brentwood; Cons. Psychiat. Shirley Oaks Hosp., Croydon; Cons. Psychiat. Nuffield Hosp., Tunbridge Wells. Socs: BMA & Brit. Soc. Med. & Dent. Hypn. Prev: Sen. Regist. (Psychiat.) Leics. DHA (T); Regist. (Psychiat.) St. Nicholas' Hosp. Newc.; Ho. Surg. & Ho. Phys. Roy. Vict. Infirm. Newc.

WINBURN, Philip E I 26 Oakhurst Drive, Newcastle upon Tyne NE3 4JS — MB BS 1947 Durh. (Newc.) Prev: Hosp. Pract. (Orthop.) Ashington Hosp.; Asst. Lect. (Anat.) Roy. Free Hosp. Med. Sch. Lond.; Ho. Surg. Roy. Vict. Infirm. Newc.

WINCESLAUS, Soosaipillai Joseph Kent & Sussex Hospital, Mount Ephraim, Tunbridge Wells TN4 8AT Tel: 01892 26111; 31 Byng Road, Tunbridge Wells TN4 8EG — MB BS 1969 Ceylon; FRCOG 1993, M 1978. Cons. Genitourin. Med. Kent & Sussex Hosp. Tunbridge Wells; HIV Phys., Kent & Sussex Hosp. Tunbridge Wells. Prev: Sen. Regist. (Genitourin. Med.) Lond. Hosp.

WINCEWICZ, Andrzej Marian 92 Harley Street, London W1N 1AF; 119 Hatherley Court, Hatherley Grove, London W2 5RG Tel: 020 7229 5691 — MB BS 1967 Med.; MB BS Med. Acad. Bialystok 1967; LMSSA Lond. 1977; DRCOG 1983. Prev: Regist. (O & G) Newham Matern. Hosp. Lond. & St. Mary's Hosp. Wom. Lond.; Regist. (O & G) Qu. Mary's Hosp. Sidcup.; Asst. (O & G) City Hosp. Torun, Poland.

WINCH, Timothy Miller's Cottage, Ratham Lane, West Ashling, Chichester PO18 8DL — MB ChB 1987 Aberd.

WINCHESTER, Elizabeth Natalie Marten (retired) 4 Brook Manor, Turners Hill Road, East Grinstead RH19 4 LX Tel: 01342 301 645 Fax: 01342 315 592 Email: 106153.2474@compuserve.com — MB ChB 1962 Sheff.; MRCPsych. 1982. p/t Ass. Specialist Child Psychiat., Coventry, Rugby, Nunneaton. Prev: Assoc. Specialist (Child Psychiat.) N. Warks., Rugby & Coventry HAs.

WINCHESTER, John Paul Theale Medical Centre, Englefield Road, Theale, Reading RG7 5AS Tel: 0118 930 2513 Fax: 0118 930 4419; 64 Horseshoe Road, Pangbourne, Reading RG8 7JL Tel: 01734 984 2583 — MB BS 1986 Lond.; MRCGP 1991; DCH RCP Lond. 1989. (University College London) Clin. Asst. (Rheum.) Battle Hosp. Reading. Prev: Trainee GP Hay-on-Wye & Talgarth; SHO (O & G) Hillingdon Hosp.; SHO (A & E) Whittingdon Hosp. Lond.

WINCHESTER, John Sefton (retired) 4 Brook Manor, Turners Hill Road, East Grinstead RH19 4LX Tel: 01342 301645 Fax: 01342 315 592 Email: jswinchester@compuserve.com — MB ChB 1962 Sheff.; MRCPath 1982. GP, Covent. Prev: SHO St. Geo. Hosp. Lond.

WINCHESTER, Sandra Lesley 31 Montclair Drive, Liverpool L18 0HD Tel: 0151 722 6395 — MB ChB Liverp. 1967; DObst RCOG 1969. (Liverp.) SCMO (Community Child Health - Special Needs) Roy. Liverp. Childr. NHS Trust. Socs: Foundat. Mem. Fac. Community Health; Soc. Pub. Health; Assoc. Mem. Roy. Coll. Paediat. & Childhealth. Prev: Clin. Med. Off. Liverp, HA; SHO Roy. Liverp. Childr. Hosp.; Ho. Off. Sefton Gen. Hosp. Liverp.

WINCHURCH, Stuart Ronald Carlton Street Surgery, Carlton Street, Horninglow, Burton-on-Trent DE13 0TE Tel: 01283 511387 Fax: 01283 517174; The Barn, Sutton on the Hill, Ashbourne DE6 53A Tel: 01283 733283 — MB ChB 1979 Liverp.; MB ChB (Hons.) Liverp. 1979; DA (UK) 1986; DRCOG 1981. (Liverpool) GP; Hypnother. Counselling. Prev: Anaesth./ITU Gen. Med.

WINDALL, Karen Margaret Tyn PwllBank, Bodedern, Holyhead LL65 3PB — MB ChB 1981 Leeds; DA (UK) 1985. GP David Lewis Centre for Epilepsy Chesh.

WINDEBANK, Kevin Patrick Department of Child Health, Sir James Spence Institute, The Royal Victoria Infirmary, Newcastle upon Tyne NE1 4LP Tel: 0191 202 3026 Fax: 0191 202 3060 Email: k.p.windebank@ncl.ac.uk — BM BCh 1977 Oxf.; DM Oxf. 1999; MA Oxf. 1987; MRCP (UK) 1983. Sen. Lect. in Child Health Univ. of Newc. upon Tyne; Hon. Cons. Paediat. Oncol. Roy. Vict. Infirm. Newc. Upon Tyne. Socs: Fell. RCP; Fell.RCPCH; Histocytosis Assn. Prev: Lect. (Paediat. Oncol.) Dept. Child Health Med. Sch. Newc.; Fell. (Paediat. Haemat. Oncol.) Mayo Clinic Rochester Minnesota, USA.

WINDEBANK, William John, SBStJ Derbyshire Royal Infirmary, London Road, Derby DE1 2QY Tel: 01332 347141 — MB ChB 1966 Glas.; BSc (Hons. Physiol.) Glas. 1963; FRCP Lond. 1994; FRCP Glas. 1980; MRCP (UK) 1970. (Glas.) Cons. Phys. (Thoracic Med.) Derbysh. Roy. Infirm. Derby. Socs: Europ. Resusc. Counc.; Scott. Thoracic Soc.; Brit. Thorac. Soc. Prev: Regist. (Med.) Med. Centre Respirat. Investig. Roy. Infirm. Glas.; Ho. Phys & Ho. Surg. Glas. Roy. Infirm.

WINDER, Professor Anthony Frederick Department of Molecular Pathology and Clinical Biochemistry, Royal Free & University College Medical School, UCL, Pond St., London NW3 2QG Tel: 020 7830 2258 Fax: 020 7830 2235 Email: tony_w@rfhsm.ac.uk; Burtons Wood, Burtons Lane, Chalfont St Giles HP8 4BA Tel: 01494 763522 — BM BCh 1963 Oxf.; PhD Lond. 1971; BA (Hons.) Oxf. 1959, MSc 1962, MA 1963, DM

WINDER

1982; FRCP 1997, M 1988; FRCPath 1985. (Oxf. & St. Mary's) Prof. Chem. Path. & Human Metab. Univ. Lond.; Hon. Cons. Roy. Free Hampstead NHS; Hon. Chairm. Family Heart Assn. Socs: (Ex-Pres.) Assn. Clin. Path.; Assn. Clin. Biochem.; Brit. Hyperlipid. Assn. Prev: Chairm. RSM Forum on Lipids in Clin. Med.; Sen. Lect. (Chem. Path.) Inst. Ophth. Univ. Lond.; Hon. Reader (Path. & Med.) Univ. Leics.

WINDER, John Hugh (retired) 13 Westbourne Crescent, Highfield, Southampton SO17 1EA Tel: 01703 556514 — MB ChB 1956 Leeds; DObst RCOG 1958; FFA RCS Eng. 1965; DA Eng. 1962. Prev: Cons. Anaesth. Soton Univ. Gp. Hosps.

WINDER, Stephen Eye Department, A Floor, Royal Hallamshire Hospital, Glossop Road, Sheffield S10 2JF Tel: 0114 271 1900; 6 Cortworth Road, Ecclesall, Sheffield S11 9LP Tel: 0114 236 2847 — MB BS 1987 Lond.; FCOphth 1992. (St. Thos. Hosp. Med. Sch.) Sen. Regist. (Ophth.) Roy. Hallamsh. Hosp. Sheff. Prev: Regist. (Ophth.) Aberd. Roy. Infirm.; SHO (Ophth.) Univ. Hosp. Nottm.

WINDHABER, Robin Alan James 37 Allensbank Road, Heath, Cardiff CF14 3PN — MB BCh 1998 Wales.

WINDLE, Mary Frances Staunton Group Practice, 3-5 Bounds Green Road, Wood Green, London N22 8HE Tel: 020 8889 4311 Fax: 020 8826 9100 — MB BS 1976 Lond.; BSc Lond. 1973; MRCGP 1983; DRCOG 1982.

WINDLE, Mr Richard Department of Surgery, Glenfield General Hospital, Groby Road, Leicester LE3 9 — MD 1979 Bristol; MB ChB 1969; FRCS Eng. 1974. Cons. Surg. Leics. HA.

WINDLE-TAYLOR, Mr Paul Carey Nuffield Hospital, Plymouth PL6 8BG Tel: 01752 775861 Fax: 01752 768969 — MB BChir 1972 Camb.; MA Camb. 1972; MRCS Eng. LRCP Lond. 1972; FRCS Eng. 1976; MBA Plymouth 1994. (St. Thos.) Cons. Otolaryngol.Derriford Hosp., Plymouth. Socs: Corr. Mem. Amer. Acad. Otolaryngol. Head & Neck Surg. Prev: Sen. Regist. Roy. Lond. Hosp. Whitechapel; Sen. Regist. Roy. Nat. Throat, Nose & Ear Hosp. Lond.; Regist. Gough Cooper Dept. Neurol. Surg., Nat. Hosp. Nerv. Dis.

WINDMILL, Maria Elaine 97 Princes Avenue, Walderslade, Chatham ME5 8AY — MB ChB 1995 Dundee.

WINDRAM, Jonathan David 7 The Oval, Hartlepool TS26 9QH — MB ChB 1998 Glas.

WINDROSS, Peter Michael Chelsea and Westminster Hospital, 369 Fulham Road, London SW10 9NH Tel: 020 8746 8000; Flat 12, 697 Garratt Lane, London SW17 0PD Tel: 020 8947 6856 — MB BS 1996 Lond. (Charing Cross & Westminster Med. Sch.) SHO (Trauma & Orthop.) Chelsea & W.minster Hosp. Lond. Prev: SHO (A & E) Char. Cross & Hammersmith Hosps. Lond.

WINDRUM, Philip 47 Vara Drive, Belfast BT13 3BY — MB ChB BAO 1994 Belf.

WINDSOR, Mr Alastair Colin James St Mark's Hospital, Watford Rd, Harrow HA1 3 Tel: 020 8235 4028 Fax: 020 8235 4001; 38 Highfield, Grimsdyke Manor, Oxhey Lane, Bushey WD1 5DZ — MB BS 1986 Lond.; MD Lond. 1995; FRCS Eng. 1991; FRCS Ed. 1990. (St. Marys Hospital London) Cons. Surg., St Mark's Hosp. Prev: Sen. Lect. & Hon. Cons. Surg. St. James Hosp. Leeds.

WINDSOR, Alastair Macdonald 13 Cherry Street, Stratton Audley, Bicester OX27 9AA — MB ChB 1985 Wales; MRCP (UK) 1989; FRCA 1993.

WINDSOR, Angus Cameron MacDonald Roseville, Fresh Water East Road, Lamphey, Pembroke SA71 5JX — MB BCh 1961 Wales; FRCP Lond. 1994; FRCP Glas. 1981, M 1966; MRCP Lond. 1967. (Cardiff) Cons. Phys. Bristol Roy. Infirm. Socs: Brit. Soc. Research on Ageing; Brit. Geriat. Soc. Prev: Hon. Sen. Lect. Med. Brist. Roy. Infirm.

WINDSOR, Barry Patrick George (retired) 25 Keith Road, Bournemouth BH3 7DS Tel: 01202 527102 — MB BS 1960 Lond.; DObst RCOG 1962. Prev: Ho. Surg. Middlx. Hosp. Lond.

WINDSOR, Mr Colin William Ombler (retired) Willow House, The Common, Lower Broadheath, Worcester WR2 6RH — MB ChB 1956 Birm.; ChM Birm. 1968; FRCS Eng. 1962; MRCS Eng. LRCP Lond. 1956. Cons. Surg. Worcester Roy. Infirm. Prev: Surg. Lt. RN.

WINDSOR, Hugh (retired) 57 Main Street, Hanworth, Feltham TW13 6SZ Tel: 020 8893 8151 — MB BS 1970 Lond.; LRCPI & LM, LRCSI & LM 1970; DCH RCPSI 1972. Prev: Chief Med. Off. Salvation Army Chikankata Hosp. Mazabuka, Zambia.

WINDSOR, Jeremy 18 Ashleigh Gardens, Barwell, Leicester LE9 8LE — MB ChB 1998 Sheff.

WINDSOR, John Peter Walter 38 St Philip's Road, London E8 3BP — MB BS 1975 Lond.; FFA RCS Eng. 1981. Cons. Anaesth. Whipps Cross Hosp. Lond. Prev: Sen. Regist. Lond. Hosp.

WINDSOR, Katherine Twyn Simon Farm, Argoed, Blackwood NP12 0JA — MB BCh 1989 Wales.

WINDSOR, Margaret Joan (retired) Willow House, The Common, Lower Broadheath, Worcester WR2 6RH Tel: 01905 333651 Fax: 01905 333382 — MB ChB 1956 Birm.; MRCS Eng. LRCP Lond. 1956; MFFP 1993. Phys. i/c Health Screening Dept. BUPA S. Bank Hosp. Worcester. Prev: Clin. Dir. (Family Plann.) Worcester & Dist. HA.

WINDSOR, Patricia Ann Roseville, Fresh Water East Road, Pembroke SA71 5JX — MB BCh Wales 1963. (Cardiff)

WINDSOR, Phyllis Margaret Tel: 01382 660111 Fax: 01382 632885; Cach-A-Cheile, The Holdings, Kinfauns, Perth PH2 7JU — MB BS 1977 Lond.; MB BS Lond. 1977; BSc (Hons.) Lond. 1974, MD 1986; FRCR 1984. (St. Mary's Hospital Medical School, London) Cons. & Hon. Sen. Lect. Dept. Radiother. & Oncol. Ninewells Hosp. Dundee; Club doctor Dundee Football club, Dundee. Socs: Fell. of Roy. Coll. of Radiol.; Scott. Radiological Soc.; Europ. Soc. for Therapeutic Radiol. and Oncol. Prev: Lect. (Clin. Oncol.) Univ. Edin.

WINDSOR, Rachael Elizabeth 86 Westcombe Hill, Blackheath, London SE3 7DT — MB BS 1994 Lond.; BSc Hons 1991; MRCP 1997. (St Georges Hospital) Specialist Regist. (Paediat.).

WINDSOR-MARTIN, David Andrew Queen Elizabeth II Hospital, Howlands, Welwyn Garden City AL7 4HQ — BM 1993 Soton.

WINEHOUSE, Jonathan 11 Sandmoor Lane, Leeds LS17 7EA — MB BCh BAO 1990 NUI; LRCPSI 1990.

WINER, John Boyle Department of Neurology, Queen Elizabeth Hospital, Edgbaston, Birmingham B15 2TH Tel: 0121 472 1311 — MB BS 1978 Lond.; MD Lond. 1986, MSc (Immunol.) 1985; FRCP Lond. 1995; MRCP (UK) 1980. (Middlx.) Cons. Neurol. Univ. Hosp. NHS Trust Birm.; Sen. Lect. Univ. Birm. Socs: Fell. Roy. Soc. Med.; Brit. Soc. Immunol.; Assn. Brit. Neurol. Prev: Sen. Regist. Nat. Hosp. Nerv. Dis. & St. Mary's Hosp. Lond.; Regist. (Neurol.) Guy's Hosp. Lond.

WINFIELD, Alan George (retired) Milemead Down Road, Tavistock PL19 9AQ Tel: 01822 612699 — MB BS 1953 Lond.; MRCS Eng. LRCP Lond. 1953; DA Eng. 1957.

WINFIELD, David 2 Becketts Stables, Shrivenham, Swindon SN6 8EY — BM BS 1996 Nottm.; BMedSci Nottm. 1994. (Nottingham)

WINFIELD, David Alfred 1 Chorley Drive, Sheffield S10 3RQ — MB ChB 1967 Sheff.; FRCP Lond. 1986; FRCP Ed. 1985; MRCP (UK) 1974; FRCPath 1986, M 1973. Cons. Haemat. Sheff. Health Auth. (T). Socs: Brit. Soc. Haematol. & Assn. Clin. Path. Prev: Cons. Haemat. Derbysh. AHA; Sen. Regist. (Haemat.) United Sheff. Hosps.

WINFIELD, Frances Isabel Buchanan (retired) 20 Foxgrove Avenue, Beckenham BR3 5BA — MB ChB Ed. 1936. Prev: Med. Off. Lond. Boro. Greenwich & Inner Lond. Educat. Auth.

WINFIELD, Jane The Surgery, 3 Heyward Road, Southsea PO4 0DY Tel: 023 9273 7373; 13 Selsey Avenue, Southsea PO4 9QL Tel: 01705 755812 — BM 1976 Soton.; MRCGP 1983; DCH Eng. 1979; DRCOG 1978; MFHom Lond. 1992.

WINFIELD, John Little Gatehouse, Gatehouse Lane, Hathersage, Sheffield S32 1BQ — MB ChB Leeds 1972; MRCP (U.K.) 1975; FREP. Cons. Rheum., Roy. Hallamshire Hosp., Sheff.; Lect. in Rheumatology, Univ. of Sheff. Socs: BMA; Brit. Soc.Rheumatol.; Midl. Rhuematol. Soc.

WINFIELD, Philip John Wright The Westgate Medical Centre, Braddon Close, Westgate, Morecambe LA4 4UZ Tel: 01524 832888 Fax: 01524 832722 — MB ChB 1981 Manch. (Manchester)

WINFREY, Peter Marsden Kisiizi Hospital, PO Box 109, Kabale, Uganda; 9 Duck Street, Elton, Peterborough PE8 6RQ Tel: 01832 280728 — MB BS 1985 Lond.; MRCGP 1989; DTM & H Lond. 1992; DObst Otago 1990. (St Mary's, London) Socs: Roy. Soc. Trop. Med. & Hyg.; BMA; RCGP. Prev: SHO (Anaesth.), Peterboro., UK; Med. Off., Kagando Mission Hosp., P.B. Kasese, Uganda; Med. Off. Kapuna Mission Hosp. Gulf Province, Papua New Guinea.

WING, Antony John (retired) 16 Fairacres, Roehampton Lane, London SW15 5LX Tel: 020 8878 8824 Fax: 020 8878 6332 —

BM BCh 1958 Oxf.; MA Oxf. 1958, DM 1969; FRCP Lond. 1976, M 1965. Prev: Cons. Renal Phys. St. Geo.'s Hosp. Lond.

WING, Lorna Gladys National Autistic Society, SCD Centre, Elliot House, 113 Masons Hill, Bromley BR2 9HT Tel: 020 8466 0098 Fax: 020 8466 0118 — MB BS Lond. 1952; MD Lond. 1965; MRCS Eng. LRCP Lond. 1952; FRCPsych 1980, M 1972; DPM Eng. 1956. (Univ. Coll. Hosp.) Cons. Nat. Autistic Soc. Lond. Prev: Hon. Cons. Maudsley Hosp. Lond.; Mem. Scientif. Staff Med. Research Counc.

WINGATE, Anthony Peter (retired) Mickleden, Linton, Ross-on-Wye HR9 7RY — MB BChir Camb. 1944; DPH Eng. 1960.

WINGATE, Professor David Lionel G1 Science Research Unit, 26 Ashfield St., London E1 2AJ Tel: 020 7377 0977 Fax: 020 7375 2103 Email: d.l.wingate@mds.qmw.ac.uk; Sydney House, 7 Pilgrims Lane, London NW3 1SJ Tel: 020 7435 6101 Fax: 020 7419 7066 — BM BCh 1960 Oxf.; MSc Oxf. 1959, DM 1979, MA 1960; FRCP Lond. 1979, M 1967. (Oxf. & Middlx.) Prof. Gastrointestinal Sci. Univ. Lond.; Dir. Gastrointestinal Sci. Research Unit St. Bart. & Roy. Lond. Hosps. Sch. Of Med. Socs: Brit. Soc. Gastroenterol. & Amer. Gastroenterol. Assn.; Fell. Roy. Soc. of Arts. Prev: Sen. Lect. (Physiol.) Lond. Hosp. Med. Coll.; Reader (Gastroenterol.) Univ. Lond.; Research Asst. Gastroenterol. Unit Mayo Clinic Rochester, USA.

WINGATE, John Peter City Hospital NHS Trust, Dudley Road, Birmingham B18 7QH Tel: 0121 554 3801; 35 Selly Wick Road, Selly Park, Birmingham B29 7JJ Tel: 0121 471 4896 — MB BS 1973 Newc.; FRCR 1982. Cons. Radiol. City Hosp. Birm.; Hon. Sen. Clin. Lect. Univ. Birm. Prev: Sen. Regist. (Radiol.) Birm. Hosps.; SHO (Med.) Hull Gp. Hosps.; Ho. Off. Newc. Gen. Hosp.

WINGATE, Verity Anne (Surgery), 21 Woodthorpe Road, Kings Heath, Birmingham B14 6EF Tel: 0121 444 2054 Fax: 0121 443 5856; 35 Selly Wick Road, Selly Park, Birmingham B29 7JJ Tel: 0121 471 4896 — MB ChB 1979 Birm.

WINGATE-GRAY, Elisabeth 1 South Side, Shadforth, Durham DH6 1LL — MB BS 1968 Newc. (Newc.)

WINGFIELD, Caroline Ann Bramblefield Cottage, 33 Church Lane, Rode, Bath BA11 6PN — BM BCh 1988 Oxf.; MA Oxf. 1988; MRCGP 1992; DFFP 1993; Cert. Family Plann. JCC 1991; DRCOG 1991.

WINGFIELD, David John Charles The Brook Green Medical Centre, Bute Gardens, London W6 7BE Tel: 020 8237 2800 Fax: 020 8237 2811; 5 Poplar Grove, London W6 7RF Tel: 020 7603 4200 — MB BS 1985 Lond.; MA Oxf. 1987; MRCGP 1989; DCH RCP Lond. 1989; DRCOG 1988. (St. Mary's Lond. & St. Peter's Coll. Oxf.) GP Princip.; Research Fell. (Gen. Pract.) Char. Cross & W.m. Med. Sch.; Research Ldr. for W. Lond. Research Network. Socs: BMA; Hon. Sec. N. & W. Lond. Fac. Roy. Coll. Gen. Practs.; Brit. Hypertens. Soc. Prev: Trainee GP St Stephens & W.m. Hosps. Lond. VTS.

WINGFIELD, John George (retired) Heverlee House, Shalden, Alton GU34 4DU — MB BCh Wales 1959; MRCOG 1967; FRCOG 1981, M 1967; MRCS Eng. LRCP Lond. 1960. Prev: Cons. O & G W. Middlx. Hosp. Isleworth.

WINGFIELD, Susan Nicola The Cottage, Caldecott, Wellingborough NN9 6AR Tel: 01933 460807 — MB ChB 1985 Sheff.; MRCGP 1989; DRCOG 1989. Socs: BMA. Prev: SHO (Radiother.) Leics. HA; SHO (Med.) Sheff. HA; Ho. Off. N.. Gen. Hosp. Sheff.

WINKLER, John Lewis 4 Kensington Mansions, Trebovir Road, London SW5 9TF Tel: 020 7373 2029 — MB BS 1944 Lond.; MRCS Eng. LRCP Lond. 1944. (Lond. Hosp.) Socs: W Lond. M-C Soc. Prev: Clin. Asst. (Med. & Surg.) W.m. Childr. Hosp.

WINKLEY, Linda Mary Oaklands Centre, Child & Adolescent Department, Selly Oak, Birmingham B29 6JD Tel: 0121 627 8321 Fax: 0121 627 8684 — MB ChB Birm. 1965; MRCS Eng. LRCP Lond. 1965; FRCPsych 1989, M 1973; DPM Eng. 1972; DObst RCOG 1967; DCH Eng. 1967. (Birm.) Cons. Psychiat. Birm. Childr. Hosps.; Hon. Sen. Clin. Lect. Univ. Birm.

WINN, Caroline Rachel York House, Romsey Road, Awbridge, Romsey SO51 0HG Tel: 01794 340139 Email: winncr@cardiff.ac.uk; York House, Romsey Road, Awbridge, Romsey SO51 0HG Tel: 01794 340139 — MB BCh 1998 Wales. SHO (Med.) P.ss of Wales Hosp., Bridgend, Cardiff. Prev: Ho. Off. Med. (Llandough, Cardiff); Ho. Off. Surg. (Morriston, Swansea).

WINN, John Henry Royal Victoria Hospital, Belfast BT12 6BA; Tel: 02892 638961 Email: j.h.winn@doctors.org.uk — MB BCh BAO 1988 Belf.; MB BCh Belf. 1988; FFA RCSI 1996. (Qu. Univ. Belf.) Cons. (Anaesth.) in Trauma. Roy. Vict. Hosp. Belf. Socs: BMA; Assn. Anaesth. Prev: Locum Cons. Card. Anaesth. St. Geo. Hosp. Lond.; Clin. Fell. Cardiac Anaesth. Harefield Hosp. Middlx.

WINN, Neil Barrie 111 Albion Road, Idle, Bradford BD10 9QL Tel: 01274 620375 — MB ChB 1975 Sheff.; MRCGP 1979; DRCOG 1977.

WINN, Pauline Imogen Margaret (retired) 32 Nero Court, Justin Close, Brentford TW8 8QA — MB ChB 1950 Ed.; MRCPsych 1973; DPM Eng. 1960. Prev: Assoc. Specialist St. Bernard's Hosp. S.all.

WINNARD, James Alan 21 Station Road, Eston, Middlesbrough TS6 9EW Tel: 01642 467093 Email: winnie01@globalnet.co.uk — MB ChB 1995 Manch. (Univ. Manch.)

WINNER, Simon Jeremy Department of Clinical Geratology, The Radcliffe Infirmary, Oxford OX2 6HE Tel: 01865 311188 Fax: 01865 224815 Email: simon.winner@geratol.ox.ac.uk — MB BChir 1975 Camb.; MB BChir Camb. 1974; MA Camb. 1975; MRCP (UK) 1977; FRCP Lond. 1997. (Univ. Coll. Hosp.) Cons. Phys. (Gen. Med. & Clin. Geratol.) Radcliffe Infirm. & John Radcliffe Hosps. Oxf.; Hon. Sen. Clin. Lect. Univ. Oxf. Med. Sch. Prev: Clin. Lect. (Geriat. Med.) Nuffield Dept. Clin. Med. Univ. Oxf.; Specialist Phys. Papua New Guinea; Regist. (Med.) Univ. Coll. Hosp. Lond. & Whittington Hosp. Lond.

WINNETT, Andrew Robert Douglas 5/3 Arlington Road, Mornington Crescent, London NW1 7ER — MB BS 1990 Queensland.

WINNEY, Robin John Renal Unit, Royal Infirmary, Lauriston Place, Edinburgh EH3 9YW Tel: 0131 536 2305 Fax: 0131 536 1541 Email: r.j.winney@ed.ac.uk; 74 Lanark Road W., Currie EH14 5JZ Tel: 0131 449 2382 — MB ChB 1968 Ed.; MRCP (UK) 1971; FRCP Ed. 1980. Cons. Renal Phys. (Med. Renal Unit) Edin. Roy. Infirm.; lead Renal Serv.s, Edin. Roy. Infirm.

WINNICOTT, Harry David (retired) 1 Mallender Drive, Knowle, Solihull B93 9BX Tel: 01564 774265 — MB BS Lond. 1958. Prev: GP Birm.

WINNIFRITH, Tabitha Jessie Ann 10 Stockmore Street, Oxford OX4 1JT — MB BS 1993 Camb.; MRCGP 1999 (UK); MA Camb. 1994, BA (Hons.) 1990; MRCP (UK) 1996. (Roy. Lond. Hosp.) p/t GP Retainer in Oxf. Prev: SHO (Old Age Psychiat.) Fulbrook Centre Oxf.; Med. SHO Leics.

WINNING, Andrew James West Middlesex University Hospital, Twickenham Road, Isleworth TW7 6AF Tel: 020 8565 5337/8 — BM BCh 1977 Oxf.; DPhil Oxf. 1974, BA 1970, MA, BM BCh 1977; FRCP Lond. 1993; MRCP (UK) 1979. (Oxf. & Lond.) Cons. Phys. W. Middlx. Univ. Hosp. Isleworth & Ashford Hosp. Middlx. Socs: Med. Res. Soc. & Brit. Thoracic Soc. Prev: Lect. & Hon. Sen. Regist. Char. Cross & W.m. Med. Sch. Lond.; Regist. St. Thos. Hosp. Lond.; Med. Research Counc. Schol. Univ. Laborat. of Physiol. Oxf. & Inst. Physiol. Milan, Italy.

WINNING, James (retired) Bon Secours Hospital, Mansionhouse Road, Glasgow G41 3DW Tel: 0141 632 9231 — LRCP LRCS 1948 Ed.; LRCP LRCS Ed. LRFPS Glas. 1948; DO Eng. 1961. Prev: Cons. Ophth. Glas. Roy. Infirm. & Monklands Dist. Gen. Hosp.

WINNING, Timothy John Berato, Barrs Brae, Kilmacolm PA13 4DE Tel: 01505 874473 — MB ChB 1970 Aberd.; FFARCS Eng. 1975. Cons. Anaesth. Inverclyde Roy. Hosp. Greenock. Socs: Assn. Anaesth. Gt. Brit. & Irel. Prev: Cons. Anaesth. E. Gen. Hosp. Edin.; Hon. Lect. Univ. Zimbabwe.

WINOCOUR, Bertram (retired) Flat 6, The Hollows, Ayr Road, Giffnock, Glasgow G46 7JB — LRCP LRCS 1948 Ed.; LRCP LRCS Ed. LRFPS Glas. 1948.

WINOCOUR, Peter Howard Department of Medicine, Queen Elizabeth II Hospital, Welwyn Garden City Tel: 01707 328111 Fax: 01707 365191 — MB ChB 1979 Glas.; MD Glas. 1989; MRCP (UK) 1982; FRCP Lond. 1998. Cons. Phys. Epot & N. Herts NHS Trust; Hon. Sen. Lect. Roy. Free Hosp. Sch. Med. Socs: Brit. Diabetic Assn.; Comm. Mem. Brit. Hyperlipidaemia Assn. (Ex-Off.); Comm. Mem. Assn. Brit. Clin. Diabetesl. Prev: Lect. Univ. Newc.; Tutor (Med.) Hope Hosp. Manch.; Research Fell. Univ. Manch.

WINOKUR, Benjamin (retired) 8 Highwood Avenue, Leeds LS17 6ES Tel: 0113 268 8536 — MB BCh Witwatersrand 1949;

WINPENNY

DPM Eng. 1968. Prev: Cons. Psychiat. (Ment. Handicap) Meanwood Pk. Hosp. & Fieldhead Hosp.

WINPENNY, Helen Claire 143A Kingston Road, London SW19 1LJ — MB BS 1993 Lond.; BSc Lond. 1990, MB BS (Distinc. Med.) 1993.

WINROW, Adrian Mark Crake Trees, Crosby Ravensworth, Penrith CA10 3JL Tel: 01931 715274 — MB ChB 1993 Leeds. Trainee Psychiat. Leeds.

WINROW, Andrew Philip Department of Paediatrics, Kingston Hospital, Galsworthy Road, Kingston upon Thames KT2 7QB Tel: 020 8546 7711 Fax: 020 8974 6295 Email: awinrow@kingstonhospital.nhs.uk; 412 Staines Road, Twickenham TW2 5JA Tel: 020 8898 7911 Email: apwinrow@twickers412.freeserve.uk — MB BS 1986 Lond.; FRCP; BSc (Hons.) Lond. 1983; MRCP (UK) 1990. (Char. Cross & Westm.) Cons. Paediat. Kingston Hosp. Kingston upon Thames; Med. Dir. Kingston Hosp. NHS Trust. Prev: Sen. Regist. (Paediat.) St. Mary's Hosp. Lond.

WINSEY, Audrey Mackay 4 Cambridge Road, Langland, Swansea SA3 4PE — MB ChB 1959 Aberd.; DA Eng. 1963. (Aberd.) Prev: Anaesth. Regist. King Geo. Hosp. Ilford.

WINSHIP, Anna Zuleika 1 Dudley Road, London N3 2QR — BM BS 1992 Nottm.

WINSHIP, Kulsum Abdulla (retired) 1 Dudley Road, Finchley, London N3 2QR Tel: 020 8346 3829 Fax: 020 8346 3829 — LRCPI & LM, LRSCI & LM 1956; LRCPI & LM, LRCSI & LM 1956; FRCP Ed. 1988; MRCP Ed. 1965; FFPM 1989; FFPHM RCP (UK) 1988, M 1972; DCH Eng. 1958. Chair. BrE. Cancer Advisery Comm. Barnet Health Auth. Lond. Prev: Sen. Med. Off. Med. Control Agency DoH.

WINSHIP, Shelagh Mary c/o Department of Anaesthesia, Perth Royal Infirmary, Perth PH1 1NX; 23 Muirton Bank, Perth PH1 5DW — MB ChB 1985 Sheff.; FANZCA 1996; FRCA. 1992; FFA RCSI 1991. (Sheff.) Cons., Perth Roy. Infirm. Socs: Anaesthetic Research Soc.; Intens. Care Soc. Prev: Specialist Regist. (Anaesth.) Merseyside; Ltd. Specialist Belford Hosp. Fort William.

***WINSLADE, Claire Georgina** Scania, Links Road, Lowestoft NR32 4PQ — MB ChB 1998 Manch.; MB ChB Manch 1998; BSc 1995.

WINSLET, Professor Mark Christopher University Dept Surgery, Royal Free Hospital, Pond Street, London NW3 2QG — MB BS 1981 Lond.; MS Lond. 1988; FRCS Eng. 1985; FRCS Ed. 1985. (Roy. Free Hosp. Sch. Med.) Prof. Surg. & Hon. Cons. Surg. Roy. Free Hosp. Sch. Med. Lond. Socs: Fell. Roy. Soc. Med.; BMA; Counc. Mem. Assn. Coloprotol. GB & Irel. Prev: Sen. Lect. & Hon. Cons. Surg. Roy. Free Hosp. Sch. Med. Lond.; Lect. & Sen. Regist. (Surg.) Univ. Birm. & United Birm. Hosps.; Regist. (Surg.) Leics. Hosps.

WINSLOW, George Stewart Stratheden Hospital, Cupar KY15 5RR — MB ChB 1971 Glas.; MRCPsych 1981. Cons. Fife Psychiat. Serv. Prev: Cons. Psychiat. Stratheden Hosp. Cupar.

WINSLOW, Lee Manchester Royal Infirmary, Oxford Road, Manchester M13 9WL Tel: 0161 276 1234 — MB ChB 1988 Leeds; FRCA 1993. Cons. cardiothoracic Anaesth., Manch. Roy. Infirm.

WINSLOW, Leon John Lennard The School House, Radway, Warwick CV35 0BS Tel: 01295 670357 — MB ChB 1964 Birm.; MRCS Eng. LRCP Lond. 1964. Prev: Flight Lt. RAF Med. Br.

WINSLOW, Nicholas Robert Scots Gap Surgery, Scots Gap, Morpeth NE61 4EG Tel: 01670 74216 Fax: 01670 774388 — MB BS 1982 Newc.; BMedSc Newc. 1979, MB BS 1982; MRCP (UK) 1985; DGM RCP Lond. 1986; MRCGP 1987; DRCOG 1988. Socs: Brit. Geriat. Soc. Prev: Trainee GP Coldstream; Research Fell. Univ. Newc. upon Tyne.

WINSNES, Paul Frederick Bridge Surgery, St. Peters Street, Stapenhill, Burton-on-Trent DE15 9AW Tel: 01283 563451 Fax: 01283 500896; Rose Cottage, Chapel Lane, Rolleston-on-Dove, Burton-on-Trent DE13 9AG Tel: 01283 812686 — MB 1973 Camb.; BA Camb. 1969, MB 1973, BChir 1972; DRCOG 1978. (St. Thos.) Prev: Ho. Off. (O & G), Ho. Off. (Paediat.) & SHO (Psychiat.) St.; Thos. Hosp. Lond.

WINSON, Mr Ian Geoffrey Gifford House, Wooton Road, Rangeworthy, Bristol BS37 7NB — MB ChB 1978 Sheff.; FRCS Ed. 1983. Cons. Orthop. & Trauma Surg. S.mead Hosp. Bristol. Socs: Fell. BOA. Prev: Lect. & Sen. Regist. (Orthop.) Sheff.; Regist. (Orthop.) Brist. Roy. Infirm.; Regist. (Gen. Surg. & Orthop.) Cardiff.

WINSON, Maxwell David Woodside Cottage, Marsh Lane, Acton, Nantwich CW5 8PH Tel: 01270 628915 — MB ChB 1967 Liverp.; MB ChB (Hons.) Liverp. 1970; BSc (1st cl. Hons.) Liverp. 1967; FRCP Lond. 1990; MRCP (UK) 1974. Cons. Phys. Leighton Hosp. Crewe. Socs: Brit. Thoracic Soc. Prev: Sen. Regist. (Gen. & Thoracic Med.) Llandough Hosp. Cardiff; Regist. (Gen. Med.) Nottm. City Hosp.; Lect. (Path.) Univ. Liverp.

WINSPEAR, Michael The Laurels Medical Practice, 28 Clarendon Road, St Helier, Jersey JE2 3YS Tel: 01534 733866 Fax: 01534 769597 — MB ChB 1988 Ed.; MSc Newc. 1983; BSc (Hons.) Salford 1982; MRCGP 1992; DRCOG 1991.

WINSPUR, Mr Ian Hand Clinic, 29-31 Devonshire St., London W1N 1RF Tel: 020 7486 7131 Fax: 020 7486 0090; 8 Tennyson Court, 12 Dorset Square, London NW1 6QB Tel: 020 7402 6308 Fax: 020 7402 6308 — MB ChB Ed. 1969; FRCS Ed. 1974; FACS 1981; LLM 2000. Cons. Hand. Surg. King Edwd. VII Hosp. Midhurst & Devonshire Hosp. Lond. Socs: Brit. Hand Soc.; Amer. Soc. Surg. Hand. Prev: Asst. Clin. Prof. Plastic Surg. Univ. Colorado; Cons. Hand Surg. Cottage Hosp. Santa Barabara, Calif., USA.

WINSTANLEY, Alison Michelle 6 New Street, Tiddington, Stratford-upon-Avon CV37 7DA — MB BS 1998 Lond.

WINSTANLEY, Claire Sophia Timbers, Warwick Road, Stratford-upon-Avon CV37 0NR — MB BS 1993 Newc.

WINSTANLEY, David Pierre (retired) 63 Weald Road, Brentwood CM14 4TN Tel: 01277 226809 — BM BCh Oxf. 1948; MRCP Lond. 1953; MRCPath 1963.

WINSTANLEY, Mr John, MC, TD (retired) 10 Pembroke Villas, The Green, Richmond TW9 1QF Tel: 020 8940 6247 — MB BS 1951 Lond.; FRCS Eng. 1957; FRCOphth 1988. Hon. Cons. Ophth. Surg. St. Thos. Hosp. Lond. Prev: Hon. Cons. Ophth. MoD (Army).

WINSTANLEY, Mr John Henry Robert 50 Crossfield Drive, Manchester M28 2QQ Tel: 0161 790 2070 — MD 1992 Liverp.; MB ChB (Hons.) 1981, BDS 1974; FRCS Eng. 1987; FRCS Glas. 1985; FDS RCPS Glas. 1978. Cons. Surg. Roy. Liverp. Univ. Hosp. & BRd.green Hosp. Liverp. Socs: Surgic. Research Soc. & Brit. Assn. for Cancer Research. Prev: Sen. Regist. (Gen. Surg.) Mersey Region.

WINSTANLEY, Maria Therese — MB ChB 1979 Liverp.; MRCP (UK) 1982; DTM & H Liverp. 1989.

WINSTANLEY, Peter Andrew Department of Pharmacology and Therapeutics, University of Liverpool, Liverpool L69 3GE Tel: 0151 794 5544 Fax: 0151 794 5540 Email: peterwin@liv.ac.uk; 105 Druids Cross Road, Liverpool L18 3HN Tel: 0151 722 2710 — MB ChB 1979 Liverp.; MB ChB (Hons.) Liverp. 1979; MD Liverp. 1989; MRCP (UK) 1982; DTM & H Liverp. 1988; FRCP (UK) 1997. (Liverpool) Reader Clin. Pharmacol. Univ. of Liverp. Socs: Fell. Roy. Soc. Trop. Med.; Brit. Pharm. Soc. Prev: Sen. Lect. (Clin. Pharmacol.) Univ. Liverp.; Clin. Lect. Nuffield Dept. Med. Oxf.

***WINSTANLEY, Ronald Peter** 1 Pine Road, Manchester M20 6UY Tel: 0161 445 6480 — MRCS Eng. LRCP Lond. 1959; FDS RCS Eng. 1955; LDS Manch. 1951.

WINSTANLY, Derek Miles 63 Albion Gate, Albion St., London W2 2LA — MB ChB 1973 Pretoria.

WINSTOCK, Adam Rohan National Addiction Centre, Institute of Psychiatry, Addiction Science Building, 4 Windsor Walk, London SE5 Tel: 020 7703 6333 Fax: 020 7703 6333 — MB BS 1991 Lond.; MS Lond. 1999; BSc Lond. 1988; MRCP (UK) 1994; MRCPsych 1997. SpR S. Lond. & Maudsley; Clin. Lect. NAC, IOP, KCL; SpR in Med. Educat. GK Med. Sch. 99/2000. Socs: Roy. Soc. Study of Addic. & Alcohol; Lond. Toxicology Gp.; Int. Harm Reduction Alliance. Prev: Regist. (Pscyhiatry) Maudsley Hosp. Lond.; Regist. Nat. Alcohol Unit Bethlem Roy. Hosp.; SHO (Med.) Hammersmith.

WINSTOCK, Mr Donald (retired) 33 West Heath Avenue, London NW11 7QJ Tel: 020 8455 0619 — MB BS Lond. 1956; BDS (Hons.) Lond. 1948; FRCS Ed. 1985; MRCS Eng. LRCP Lond. 1956; FDS RCS Eng. 1959. Hon. Cons. Oral Surg. St. Bart. Hosp., Middlx. Hosp. & Edgware Gen. Hosp Lond; Sen. Lect. & Hon. Cons. Oral Surg. UMDS Guy's & St. Thos. Hosps. Lond. Prev: Sen. Regist. (Oral Surg.) St. Thos. Hosp. Lond.

WINSTOCK, Grant Bruce Milo 249 Garratt Lane#, London SW18 4UE Tel: 020 8870 1341, 020 8870 8907 — MB BS 1982 Lond.; DMJ; MRCGP. (London) Forens. Med. Examr.

WINSTON, Alan 11 Fruin Avenue, Newton Mearns, Glasgow G77 6HA — MB ChB 1994 Glas.

WINSTON, Anthony Philip University Department of Psychiatry, Brandon Unit, Leicester General Hospital, Leicester LE5 4PW Tel: 0116 258 4751 Fax: 0116 258 4752 — MRCS Eng. LRCP Lond. 1987; MRCS Eng LRCP Lond. 1987; MRCPsych 1995. Lect. (Psychiat.) Univ. Leicester.

WINSTON, Christopher Mark — MB BS 1980 Lond.; BSc Lond. 1977; MRCPsych 1987; T(Psych) 1992. (Char. Cross Hosp.) Cons. Psychiat. St. Tydfil's Hosp. Merthyr Tydfil; Assoc. Dir. Roy. Coll. Psychiat. Research Unit (Wales) St. Tydfil's Hosp. Prev: Lect. (Psychiat.) Med. Sch. Harare, Zimbabwe; Sen. Regist. (Psychiat.) WhitCh. Hosp. Cardiff & E. Glam. Hosp. M. Glam.

WINSTON, Ian 137 Camberwell New Road, London SE5 0SU — MB BS 1998 Lond.

WINSTON, Mr Maurice Elyis (retired) 16 St John Street, Manchester M3 4EA Tel: 0161 834 4282 Fax: 0161 835 1465 — MB ChB 1938 Ed.; FRCS Ed. 1945. Cons. Orthop. Surg. Manch. Prev: Cons. Orthop. Surg. Bolton Gp. Hosps.

WINSTON, Michael Patrick 43 Hilbre Road, Wirral CH48 3HB — MB BChir 1994 Camb.

WINSTON, Raymond (retired) 211 Battersea Bridge Road, London SW11 3AP Tel: 020 7223 5579 — MRCS Eng. LRCP Lond. 1942; FRCGP 1985. Prev: Capt. RAMC.

WINSTON, Professor Robert Maurice Lipson Hammersmith Hospital, Du Cane Road, London W12 0HS Tel: 020 8383 4155 Fax: 020 8749 6973; 11 Denman Drive, London NW11 6RE — MB BS 1964 Lond.; MRCS Eng. 1964 LRCP Lond. 1964; FRCOG 1983, M 1971. Prof. Fertil. Studies Roy. Postgrad. Med. Sch. Lond.; Cons. Gyn. & Obst. Hammersmith Hosp. Lond. Socs: Fell. Roy. Soc. Med.; Comm. Mem. Brit. Fertil. Soc.; Fell. Acad. Med. Prev: Reader (Fertil. Studies) Inst. O & G 1981-86; Prof. (Gyn.) Univ. Texas, USA.

WINSTON, Sarah Rosemary 43 Hilbre Road, Wirral CH48 3HB — MB BChir 1993 Camb.

WINSTONE, Raymond (retired) Reeves, Queen Camel, Yeovil BA22 7NQ Tel: 01935 850440 — MB ChB 1954 Bristol; MRCGP 1968; DCH Eng. 1958; DObst RCOG 1959. Prev: Ho. Off. Childr. Hosp. Soton.

WINTER, Adrienne Elisabeth (retired) Mickledore, 25 The Whiteway, Cirencester GL7 2ER Tel: 01285 655929 Fax: 01285 655929 Email: awinter@mickledore.com — MB BChir Camb. 1964; MA Camb. 1964; DObst RCOG 1966. Prev: GP, St Peter's Rd. Surg.,Cirencester.

WINTER, Miss Alison Specialist Registor in General Surgery, West of Scotland; Email: alisondavid@msn.com — MB ChB 1993 Glas.; FRCS Ed 1998. (Glas.) Specialist Registr Gen. Surg., W. of Scotl. Socs: Med. & Dent. Defence Union Scotl.; BMA; Assn. Surg.s in Train. Prev: SHO (Surg.) W. Glas. Hosp. Univ. NHS Trust; Sen. Health Off. (Accid. & Orthop. Surg.) Glas. Roy. Infirm.; Sen. Health Off. (Surg.) Hairmyres Hosp. Co. Kilbride.

WINTER, Andrew John Department GU Medicine, Sandyford Iniative, 6 Sandyford Place, Glasgow G3 7NB Tel: 0141 211 8608 Fax: 0141 211 8609 Email: andy.winter@glacomen.scot.nhs.uk — BM BCh 1989 Oxf.; MRCP (UK) 1992; PhD (Birm.) 1997. Cons. In Genito-Urin. Med. and HIV, Glas. Prev: Clin. Research Fell. (Infec.) Univ. Birm.; Specialist Regist. (Med.) W. Midl.

WINTER, Angela The Cambridge Medical Group, 10A Cambridge Road, Linthorpe, Middlesbrough TS5 5NN Tel: 01642 851177 Fax: 01642 851176; 12 Rosemoor Close, Marton-in-Cleveland, Middlesbrough TS7 8LQ — MB BS 1987 Newc.; MA (Med. Sci.) Camb. 1988; MRCGP 1991; DRCOG 1991. Prev: Trainee GP Cleveland VTS.

WINTER, Christina Wei Mei International Product Safety & Pharmacovigilance, Glaxo Wellcome Research & Development, Greenford Road, Greenford UB6 0HE Tel: 020 8966 3240 Fax: 020 8423 2097; 15 Woodbank Avenue, Gerrards Cross SL9 7PY Tel: 01753 888118 — MB BCh BAO 1975 Dub.; MD Dub. 1984; Dip. Pharm. Med. 1996. (TC Dub.) Head, Safety Phys. Gp. Internat. Product Safety & Pharmacovigilance Glaxo Wellcome Research & Developm. Greenford. Socs: Brit. Assn. Pharmaceut. Phys.; Med. Res. Soc. Prev: Lect. (Cardiovasc. Studies) Univ. Leeds; Safety Coordinator Aire Study (Clin. Trial); Demonst. (Physiol.) TC Dub.

WINTER, Craig David 87 Mayflower Way, Ongar CM5 9BB — MB BChir 1992 Camb.

WINTER, David Paul (retired) Little Lea, Turners Hill Road, East Grinstead RH19 4LX Tel: 01342 325374 — MB BS 1960 Lond.; MSc Lond. (Occupat. Med.) 1982, MB BS 1960; Specialist Accredit. Occupat. Med. JCHMT 1986; DIH Eng. 1981; MFOM RCP Lond. 1985, A 1981; DObst RCOG 1962. Prev: Med. Adviser Rentokil Gp. plc E. Grinstead.

WINTER, Emma 4 The Open, Leazes Square, Newcastle upon Tyne NE1 4DB — MB BS 1996 Newc.

WINTER, George 2 Bronwydd Avenue, Penlyn, Cardiff CF23 5YA Tel: 029 2048 2222 — MB ChB 1948 Bristol; MRCGP 1967. Mem. Bd. S.E. Wales Fac. RCGP. Socs: BMA (Mem. Exec. Comm.). Prev: Ho. Surg. S.mead Hosp. Bristol; Res. Med. Off. St. Mary's Hosp. Portsmouth; Res. Obst. Off. Sunnyside Matern. Hosp. Cheltenham.

WINTER, Professor Gerald Bernard (retired) Eastman Dental Institute, Eastman Dental Hospital, Gray's Inn Road, London WC1X 8LD — MB BS Lond. 1958; BDS 1955; FRCPCH 1997; FFD RCSI 1986; FDS RCS Eng. 1962; DCH Eng. 1960. Prev: Dean & Dir. Studies Inst. Dent. Surg.

WINTER, Gordon Robert (retired) Pennyroyal, 11 Pipers Close, Cobham KT11 3AU Tel: 01932 864622 — MRCS Eng. LRCP Lond. 1962; LMSSA Lond. 1962; DObst RCOG 1964. Prev: Ho. Surg. O & G Epsom Dist. Hosp.

WINTER, Heather Rosemary Department of Public Health & Epidemiology, The Medical School, University of Birmingham, Edgbaston, Birmingham B15 2TT Tel: 0121 472 1122; 66 Prospect Road, Moseley, Birmingham B13 9TD — MB BCh BAO 1982 Belf.; MD Belf. 1995; MRCOG 1987. Lect. (Pub. Health Med.) Inst. Pub. & Environm. Health Univ. Birm.; Sen. Regist. W. Midl. RHA.

WINTER, Helen Livingstone 10 Hillneuk Avenue, Bearsden, Glasgow G61 3PZ — MB ChB 1970 Glas. Clin. Med. Off. (Community Child Health) Yorkhill Trust.

WINTER, Jack Westwood 10 Hillneuk Avenue, Bearsden, Glasgow G61 3PZ — MB ChB 1997 Glas.

WINTER, John (retired) 9 The Downs, Blundellsands, Liverpool L23 6XS — MD 1956 Liverp.; MB ChB 1941, MRad 1948; DMRD Eng. 1948. Prev: Cons. Radiol. Mersey RHA.

WINTER, John Anthony Cooper Wingate Medical Centre, 79 Bigdale Drive, Northwood, Liverpool L33 6YJ Tel: 0151 546 2958 Fax: 0151 546 2914 — MB ChB 1969 Liverp.; MRCGP 1980; AFOM RCP Lond. 1982; DIH Soc. Apoth. Lond. 1981. (Liverp.) p/t Med. Adviser Brooke Bond Foods Manch.; Med. Adviser Samuel Banner & Co. Ltd., Balfour Beatty Ltd., BASF Liverp., Rathbone PLC. Socs: Soc. Occupat. Med. Prev: Med. Adviser Birds Eye Walls Ltd. Liverp.

WINTER, John Barry Mark Haemophilia Centre, Kent & Canterbury Hospital, Ethelbert Road, Canterbury CT1 3NG Tel: 01227 766877 Fax: 01277 783167 Email: mark.winter@kch-tr.sthames.nhs.uk — MB BS 1973 Lond.; FRCP Eng. 1991; MRCP (UK) 1976; MRCS Eng. LRCP Lond. 1973; FRCPath 1992, M 1980. (Guy's) Cons. Haemat. & Dir. Haemophilia Centre Canterbury & Thanet HA; Hon. Sen. Lect. Univ. Kent. Socs: Brit. Soc. Haematol.; World Federat. Haemophilia; Brit. Soc. Haemostasis & Thrombosis. Prev: Lect. (Haemat.) Middlx. Hosp. Med. Sch. & Hon. Sen. Regist. Middlx. Hosp. Lond .; Lect. (Haemat.) Guy's Med. Sch. & Hon. Sen. Regist. Guy's Hosp. Lond.

WINTER, John Hirst Kings Cross Hospital, Cleppington Road, Dundee DD3 — MB ChB 1974 Birm.; BSc Birm. 1971, MD 1983; FRCP Ed. 1996; FRCP Glas. 1995; MRCP (UK) 1978. Cons. Phys. Dundee Teachg. Hosps. NHS Trust.

WINTER, John Keith Joshua 26 Orchard Lane, Newtownards BT23 7PQ Tel: 01247 822427 — MB BCh BAO 1978 Belf.; DGM RCPS Glas. 1998. (Queens Univesity Belfast)

WINTER, John Malcolm Salters Meadow Centre, Rugely Road, Chase Terrace, Burntwood WS7 8AQ Tel: 01543 682611 Fax: 01543 675391 — MB ChB 1971 Manch. GP; Bd Mem. Lichfield & Burntwood PCG. Socs: Lichfield.Med.Soc.

WINTER, John Michael Cirencester Hospital, The Querns, Tetbury Road, Cirencester GL7 1UY Tel: 01285 655711 Fax: 01285 884623; Mickledore, 25 The Whiteway, Cirencester GL7 2ER Tel: 01285 655929 Fax: 01285 655929 Email: mwinter@mickledore.com — MB BS 1962 Lond.; MRCP (UK) 1973; MRCS Eng. LRCP Lond. 1962; DCH Eng. 1966; DObst RCOG 1964. (St. Bart.) p/t Hosp. Pract. (Med.) Cirencester Hosp. Socs: Christian Med. Fell.ship; Assur. Med. Soc.; Roy. Soc. Med. Prev: GP (Princip.

WINTER

& Trainer) St Peter's Rd. Surg. Cirencester, 1974-2000; Med. Off. Ngora (Ch. of Uganda) Hosp. 1966-1968; Regist. (Med.) Hull Hosp. 1972-1974.

WINTER, Julian Peter Ashlea, 5 Fairlands Way, Cheddar BS27 3NW; 242 Low Lane, Horsforth, Leeds LS18 5QL Tel: 0113 258 9741 — MB ChB 1995 Leeds; MRCP (UK), 1999. (Leeds Univ.) SHO (Gen. Med.) Leeds Gen. Infirm. Prev: SHO (A & E) Leeds Gen. Infirm.; SHO (Med. for Elderly) St. Jas. Univ. Hosp. Leeds.

WINTER, Lee Nigel Palace Road Surgery, 3 Palace Road, London SW2 3DY Tel: 020 8674 2083 Fax: 020 8674 6040; 3 Palace Road, Streatham Hill, London SW2 3DY — MB BS 1990 Lond. (St. Geo.) Prev: Trainee GP Mayday Hosp. Croydon VTS.

WINTER, Lesley Joy Abigail — MB ChB 1995 Leeds; DRCOG 2000; MRCGP 2001; DFFP 2000. (Leeds) p/t GP Asst., Bradford Family Plann. Off., Densbury.

WINTER, Michael David Whitburn Health Centre, 1 Weavers Lane, Whitburn, Bathgate EH47 0SD Tel: 01501 740297 Fax: 01501 744302; 2 Craigmount Court, Edinburgh EH4 8HL — MB ChB 1980 Ed.; MRCPsych 1986; MRCGP 1984; DRCOG 1982. Socs: Chairm. Lothian LMC. Prev: Regist. (Psychiat.) Bangour Village Hosp. Broxburn.

WINTER, Peter John (retired) Angel Farm, Newland St., Coleford GL16 8NA Tel: 01594 837036 — MB BS 1961 Lond.; MA Camb. 1961; FRCP Lond. 1981, M 1968; FRCR 1975; FFR 1972; T(R) (CO) 1991; DMRT Eng. 1970. Cons. Radiother. Guy's Hosp. Lond. Prev: Cas. Off. & Ho. Phys. Guy's Hosp.

WINTER, Philippa Rachel Xanthe Shrewsbury Road Surgery, 20 Shrewsbury Road, Craven Arms SY7 9PY Tel: 01588 672309 Fax: 01588 673943 — MRCS Eng. LRCP Lond. 1976; DFFP 1997.

WINTER, Richard Keith Department of Radiology, Royal Glamorgan Hospital, Ynysmaerdy, Llantrisant, Pontyclun CF72 8XR Tel: 01443 443371 Fax: 01443 218454, 01443 443367 Email: richard.winter@pr-tr.wales.nhs.uk; 12 Cae Garw, Thornhill, Cardiff CF14 9DX Tel: 02920 522924 Email: richard@rkwinter.freeserve.co.uk — MB BCh Wales 1977; FRCS Eng. 1982; FRCR 1986. Cons. Radiol. Roy. Glam. Hosp. RCT.

WINTER, Robert James University Hospital, Queen's Medical Centre, Nottingham NG7 2UH Tel: 0115 924 9924 Fax: 0115 970 9910 Email: bob.winter@nottingham.ac.uk; 6 Ascott Gardens, West Bridgford, Nottingham NG2 7TH Tel: 0115 945 5828 — BM BS 1982 Nottm.; DM Nottm. 1995, BMedSci (Hons.) 1980; MRCP (UK) 1986; FFA RCS Eng. 1987. Cons. Intens. Care Med. Univ. Hosp. Nottm. Prev: Sen. Regist. (Anaesth.) Trent RHA; Research Fell. Bristol Roy. Infirm.

WINTER, Robert James David Respiratory Medicine Unit, PO Box 40, Addenbrooke's Hospital, Cambridge CB2 2QQ Tel: 01223 217079; Fax: 01767 677364 — MB BS 1977 Lond.; BSc (Hons.) Lond. 1974, MD 1987; FRCP Lond. 1995; MRCP (UK) 1979. Cons. Phys. Addenbrooke's Hosp., Camb. Prev: Cons. Phys. Barnet & Edgware Gen. Hosp.; Sen. Regist. (Respirat. Div.) Hammersmith Hosp. Lond.; MRC Train. Fell. Lond. Chest Hosp. & St. Mary's Hosp. Lond.

WINTER, Professor Robin Michael Institute of Child Health, 30 Guilford St., London WC1 1EH Tel: 020 7242 9789 Fax: 020 7813 8141 Email: rwinter@ich.ucl.ac.uk; 29 Grange Road, Bushey, Watford WD23 2LQ Tel: 01923 252203 — MB BS 1974 Lond.; BSc Lond. 1971; FRCP Lond. 1990; MRCP (UK) 1976. Prof. Clin. Genetics & DysMorphol. Inst. Child Health Lond. Socs: BMA; Clin. Genetics Soc. Prev: Cons. Clin. Geneticist N.wick Pk. Hosp. Middlx.; Post-doctoral Fell. (Genetics Med.) Coll. Virginia, USA.

WINTER, Roger Andrew The Avenue Surgery, 1 The Avenue, South Moulsecoomb, Brighton BN2 4GF Tel: 01273 604220/606214 Fax: 01273 685507; 10 Deans Close, Woodingdean, Brighton BN2 6RN — MB ChB 1986 Birm.; DRCOG 1990; Cert. Family Plann. JCC 1990; DCH RCP Lond. 1989. (Birmingham) Prev: Trainee GP Kidderminster VTS; SHO (Paediat., O & G, A & E) Birm.

WINTER, Steven Michael Jarvis and Partners, Westbrook Medical Centre, 301-302 Westbrook Centre, Westbrook, Warrington WA5 8UF Tel: 01925 654152 Fax: 01925 632612 — MB ChB 1983 Sheff.; MRCGP 1988; DRCOG 1987. Socs: Accred. Mem. Brit. Med. Acupunc. Soc. Prev: Trainee GP Wirral VTS; Ho. Off. (Surg. & Med.) Chesterfield & N. Derbysh. Roy. Hosp.

WINTER, Stuart Charles Alec 6 Ashbury Cl, Henley-in-Arden, Solihull — MB ChB 1997 Bristol.

WINTER, Susan Jane The North Wales Hospital for Nervous Mental Disorders, Denbigh LL16 5SS — MB BS 1982 Lond.; BSc (Hons.) Lond. 1979, MB BS 1982.

WINTER-BARKER, John Paul St. Marys Surgery, Applethwaite, Windermere LA23 1BA — MB ChB 1985 Glas.

WINTERBORN, Claire Justine 18 Westmorland Road, Harrow HA1 4PL — MB BS 1998 Lond.

***WINTERBORN, Rebecca Jane** Top Flat, 4 Cambridge Park, Redland, Bristol BS6 6XN Tel: 020 7974 2732 Email: rwinterborn@hotmail.com — MB ChB 1998 Bristol.

WINTERBOTTOM, Keith Frederick Winterbottom and Partners, The Health Centre, 97 Derby Road, Stapleford, Nottingham NG9 7AT Tel: 0115 939 2444 Fax: 0115 949 1751; Doctor's Corner, 205 Russell Drive, Wollaton, Nottingham NG8 2BD Tel: 0115 928 3201 — MB BChir 1968 Camb.; MA Camb. 1968. (Univ. Coll. Hosp.)

WINTERBOTTOM, Paul Michael Heathfield, 30 Denmark Road, Gloucester GL1 3HZ Tel: 01452 891350 Fax: 01452 891341 — MB ChB 1985 Leeds; MRCPsych 1992. Clin. Dir Severn NHS Trust Learning Disabil. Directorate; Cons Psychiat. in the Psychiat. of Learning Disabil. W. Gloucestershire; Cons Psychiat. to Relate Gloucestershire. Prev: Sen Reg S W. RHA; Regist. (Gen. Psychiat.) Yorks. RHA.

***WINTERBOTTOM, Peter Mark** 65 Oxford Street, Woodstock OX20 1TJ Tel: 01993 811291 Fax: 01993 811291 Email: fatboyblim@hotmail.com — MB BS 1996 Newc.

WINTERBURN, Ruth Bewley Drive Surgery, 79 Bewley Drive, Liverpool L32 9PD Tel: 0151 546 2480 Fax: 0151 548 3474 — MB ChB 1975 Liverp.; MRCGP 1982; DCH Eng 1978.

WINTERINGHAM, Tresca 6 Knoll Court, Knoll Hill, Bristol BS9 1QX — BM BCh 1961 Oxf.

WINTERS, Amanda Claire Elizabeth 24 Blane Drive, Milngavie, Glasgow G62 8HG — MB ChB 1993 Aberd.

WINTERS, Zoe Ellen 4 Canal Street, Jericho, Oxford OX2 6BQ — MB BCh 1984 Witwatersrand.

WINTERSGILL, Eleanor Mary Severn NHS Trust, Rikenel, Montpellier, Gloucester GL1 1LY Tel: 01452 891023 Fax: 01452 891020; 10 The Cherry Orchard, Staverton, Cheltenham GL51 0TR — MB BS 1967 Lond.; MB BS (Hons.) Lond. 1967; MRCS Eng. LRCP Lond. 1967; DCH RCP Lond. 1985; DCCH RCP Ed. 1985. (St. Bart.) Cons. Paediat. (Community Child Health) Severn NHS Trust Glos. Socs: BMA; Brit. Paediat. Assn.; BACCH. Prev: Clin. Head (Community Paediat.) Glos. HA; Manager (Community Paediat.) Glos. HA; Ho. Phys. & Ho. Surg. Rochford Gen. Hosp.

WINTERSGILL, Peter (retired) 28 Westfield Avenue, Oakes, Huddersfield HD3 4FN — MRCS Eng. LRCP Lond. 1951. Prev: Sen. Med. Off. Huddersfield HA.

WINTERTON, Anthony John (retired) Greystones, Greenway Park, Chippenham SN15 1QG Tel: 01249 443144 — MB BS 1954 Lond.; MRCS Eng. LRCP Lond. 1954; MRCGP 1965; DObst RCOG 1955; DCH Eng. 1956. Locum GP. Prev: GP Chippenham.

WINTERTON, Elizabeth Anne Tretherres, St. Allen, Truro TR4 9QX — MB BS 1974 Lond. (King's Coll. Hosp.) Clin. Asst. (Rehabil.) St. Michael's Hosp. Hayle. Prev: Clin. Med. Off. Cornw. & Isles of Scilly HA.; Ho. Phys. Plymouth Gen. Hosp. (Greenbank Sect.); Ho. Surg. Roy. Cornw. Hosp. (Treliske) Truro.

WINTERTON, Ian Stewart Gosforth Memorial Medical Centre, Church Road, Gosforth, Newcastle upon Tyne NE3 1TX Tel: 0191 285 1119 — MB BS 1971 Newc.; MRCGP 1975; DObst RCOG 1973; FRCGP 1999. Prev: Trainee GP Newc. VTS; Ho. Surg. Newc. Gen. Hosp.; Ho. Phys. Roy. Vict. Infirm. Newc.

WINTERTON, Michael Charles Tretherres, St. Allen, Truro TR4 9QX Tel: 01872 540354 — MB BS 1959 Lond.; FRCP Lond. 1979, M 1966; MRCS Eng. LRCP Lond. 1959. (King's Coll. Hosp.) Cons. Phys. Roy. Cornw. Hosp. Treliske Truro.

WINTERTON, Sandra Gosforth Memorial Medical Centre, Church Road, Gosforth, Newcastle upon Tyne NE3 1TX Tel: 0191 285 1119 — MB BS 1971 Newc. Prev: Ho. Phys., Ho. Surg. & SHO (O & G) Hexham Gen. Hosp.

WINTERTON, Simon John Dorset County Hospital, Williams Avenue, Dorchester DT1 2JY Tel: 01305 255114 Fax: 01305 254778; Elwell Lea, 710 Dorchester Road, Upney, Dorchester DT3 5LA Tel: 01305 813000 Fax: 01305 816100 Email: simon.winterton@talk21.com — MB BS 1982 Lond.; BA Oxf. 1979;

MRCP (UK) 1986; FRCP 1998. (St. Mary's) Cons. Cardiol. Dorset Co. Hosp. Dorchester. Socs: Brit. Cardiac Soc. & Brit. Cardiovasc. Interven. Soc.; Brit. Pacing & Electrophysiol. Gp. Prev: Regist. (Cardiol.) Lond. Chest Hosp.; Research Fell. & Hon. Regist. (Cardiac) St. Mary's Hosp. Lond.; Regist. (Gen. Med.) Hillingdon Hosp.

WINTLE, Christopher James The Rogerstone Practice, Chapel Wood, Western Valley Road, Rogerstone, Newport NP10 9DU Tel: 01633 893272 Fax: 01633 895079; The Limes, Fields Pk Road, Newport NP20 5BH — MB BCh 1968 Wales. (Cardiff) Prev: GP Trainee GP Unit Welsh Nat. Sch. Med. Cardiff; SHO (Gen. Med.) St. David's Hosp. Cardiff; Ho. Surg. Dept. Urol. & Ho. Phys. Cardiff Roy. Infirm.

WINTLE, Fiona Caroline 2 Aspland Road, Hyde SK14 5LS — MB ChB 1998 Manch.

WINTLE, Jennifer Margaret The Limes, Fields Park Road, Newport NP1 5BH — MB BCh 1970 Wales; DObst RCOG 1972. Prev: SHO (O & G) & Ho. Phys. Roy. Gwent Hosp. Newport; Ho. Surg. & Ho. Phys. St. Woolos Hosp. Newport.

WINTLE, Matthew Edward 17 Picton Street, Kenfig Hill, Bridgend CF33 6EF — MB BCh 1997 Wales.

WINTLE, Richard Vivian 17 Picton Street, Kenfig Hill, Bridgend CF33 6EF — MB BS 1992 Lond.; MSc (Diagn. Imaging) Oxf. 1994.

WINTLE, Trevor Clifford Medical Centre, Reading Road, Wallingford OX10 9DU Tel: 01491 35577 — MRCS Eng. LRCP Lond. 1965; MA Camb. 1966, MB BChir 1965; FRCGP 1986, M 1980; DObst RCOG 1968. (St. Mary's) Clin. Asst. (Rheum.) Battle Hosp. Reading; Gen. Pract. Trainer Reading VTS; Course Organiser Reading GP VTS.

WINTON, Donald Bain The Love Street Medical Centre, 40 Love Street, Paisley PA3 2DY Tel: 0141 889 3355 Fax: 0141 889 4785; 8 Hawick Avenue, Paisley PA2 9LD Tel: 0141 884 4999 — MB ChB 1961 St. And. (St. And.) Sen. Partner.

WINTON, Elizabeth The Sheiling, 6 Bryntirion Hill, Bridgend CF31 4DA Tel: 01656 653818 — MB BCh BAO 1944 Belf.; MB BCh BAO (Hnrs.) Belf. 1944. (Belf.) Prev: Sen. Extern Surg. & Ho. Surg. Roy. Vict. Hosp. Belf.

WINTON, Francis Edgar Phoenix Day Hospital, Hospital Rd, Bury St Edmunds IP33 3NR Tel: 01284 725333 x 2385 — MB BS 1980 Lond.; BSc. Lond. 1977; MRCPsych 1984; FRCPsych FRCPsych, 1980. Cons. Rehabil. & Gen. Psychiat. W. Suff. Hosp. Socs: Hon. Sec. of Rehabil. and social phychiatry Sect. of Roy. Coll. of Psychiat.s. Prev: Cons. Lincoln. Co. Hosp.; Sen. Regist. Maudsley Hosp. Lond.; Hon. Sen. Regist. Inst. Psychiat. Maudsley Hosp. Lond.

WINTON, John Miller Lauder (retired) 57 Forfar Road, Dundee DD4 7BE Tel: 01382 451114 — MB ChB 1947 St. And.

WINTON, Margaret (retired) Green Lane House, 1 Green Lane, Davenham, Northwich CW9 8HT — MB ChB 1949 Leeds. Prev: SCMO Crewe Health Dist.

WINTON, Pamela Elizabeth 6 Sycamore Way, Moulsham Lodge, Chelmsford CM2 9LZ Tel: 01245 281403 — MB ChB 1997 Aberd.; BSc Med Sci, 1995.

WINTONIUK, Diane Mary Old Road Surgery, Old Road, Abersychan, Pontypool NP4 7BH Tel: 01495 772239 Fax: 01495 773786 — MB BS 1989 Lond.

WINWARD, John McGregor The Atherstone Surgery, 1 Ratcliffe Road, Atherstone CV9 1EU Tel: 01827 713664 Fax: 01827 713666; Brookfield, Main Road, Sibson, Nuneaton CV13 6 — MB BS 1982 Lond.; DRCOG 1986; Cert. Family Plann JCC 1986.

WINWOOD, Paul John Royal Bournemouth Hospital, Castle Lane E., Bournemouth BH7 Tel: 01202 303626 Fax: 01202 704909 Email: paul.winwood@rbch-tr.swest.nhs.uk — MB BS 1985 Lond.; BSc (Hons.) Lond. 1984; DM Soton. 1994; MRCP (UK) 1988; FRCP 2000; FRCP Edin 2000. (London Hospital Medical College) Cons. Phys. & Gastroenterol. Roy. Bournemouth Hosp.; Hon. Sen. Lect. Univ. Soton.; UnderGrad. tutor Bournemouth; NACC Med. Adviser Dorset Bondi. Socs: Brit. Soc. Gastroenterol.; Brit. Assn. for Study Liver; BMA. Prev: Lect. & Hon. Sen. Regist. (Med. & Gastroenterol.) Soton. Gen. Hosp.; MRC Trav. Fell. Liver Center Laborat. Univ. Calif. San Franciso, USA; Regist. Rotat. (Gen. Med. & Gastroenterol.) Soton. & Bournemouth Gen. Hosps.

WINWOOD, Robert Sidney (retired) Mellstock, 18 Dale Gardens, Woodford Green IG8 0PB — MB BS 1957 Lond.; FRCP Lond. 1978, M 1964. Prev: Cons. Phys. Whipps Cross Hosp. Lond. & Hon. Vis. Cardiol. St. Bart. Hosp. Lond.

WINYARD, Graham Peter Arthur NHS Management Executive, Quarry House, Quarry Hill, Leeds LS2 7PD; 15 Clifton Road, Winchester SO22 5BP — BM BCh 1971 Oxf.; FRCP Lond. 1989; FFPHM 1987, M 1981; MRCP (UK) 1975. Med. Dir. NHS Managem. Exec. Leeds. Prev: Regional Med. Dir. & Dir. Pub. Health Wessex RHA.

WINYARD, Paul Julian Douglas 102 Cobbold Road, Shepherds Bush, London W12 9LL Tel: 020 8740 4588 — BM BCh 1986 Oxf.; MA Camb. 1987, BA (Med. Sci.) 1983; MRCP (UK) 1990. Research Fell. & Hon. Sen. Regist. (Nephrol.) Hosp. Childr. Gt. Ormond St. Lond. Prev: Regist. Qu. Eliz. Hosp. Childr. Hackney; Regist. (Paediat. Haemat & Oncol.) Hosp. Sick Childr. Gt. Ormond St. Lond.; Exchange Regist. Childr. Hosp. Philadelphia, USA.

WIPAT, Krishna 51 Sandringham Road, Gosforth, Newcastle upon Tyne NE3 1QB — MB BS 1996 Newc.

WIRATUNGA, Edward Basil Pandukabhaya St Helens & Knowsley HA, Cowley Hill Lane, St Helens WA10 2AP Tel: 01744 457234 Fax: 01744 457339; 28 Hornby Lane, Liverpool L18 3HH — MB BS 1965 Ceylon; MCommH Liverp. 1977; MFPHM RCP (UK) 1989; MFCM RCP (UK) 1986. Cons. Communicable Dis. Control St. Helens & Knowsley HA. Socs: BMA. Prev: WHO Fell. People's RePub. China & UK; Med. Off. Health Sri Lanka & Nigeria.

WIRTH, Maria Alexandra Dumbarton Road Surgery, 115 Dumbarton Road, Glasgow G14 9PY Tel: 0141 211 9045 Fax: 0141 211 9047 — MB ChB 1982 Glas.; MRCOG 1983.

WISBY, Lee Robert 3 Cherry Cottages, School Road, Hastings TN35 5BQ — BM 1995 Soton.

WISCOMBE, Kieron Aubrey Raymond Munro Medical Centre, West Elloe Avenue, Spalding PE11 2BY Tel: 01775 725530 Fax: 01775 766168 — MB BS 1985 Lond.; 2000 FlmcRCSEd; MRCGP 1989; DRCOG 1988; DCH RCP Lond. 1987; Dip. IMC RCS Ed. 1989. (St. Mary's Hosp. Lond.) p/t GP Princip. Lincs Clin. Asst. (Acc. & Emerg.); PCG Exec. Bd. Mem. Socs: BASICS. Prev: Trainee GP Windsor VTS.

WISDOM, Anthony Rodwell Genitourinary Medicine, Newham Hospital, London E13 8SL Tel: 020 7363 8146; 24 St. Albans Road, London NW5 1RD Tel: 020 7482 2442 — MB BS Lond. 1954. (Lond. Hosp.) Cons. Genitourin Med. Newham Hosp. Lond. Socs: Fell. Hunt. Soc.; Med. Soc. Study VD. Prev: Cons. Genitourin Med. Barking, Havering & Brentwood HAs; Sen. Regist. (VD) St. Mary's Hosp. Lond.; Surg. Lt. RNVR.

WISDOM, Paul Nigel 35 Kings Road, Coltishall, Norwich NR12 7DX — BM BS 1985 Nottm.

WISDOM, Rosemary Jean (retired) Wykeham House, 11 Mill Hill, Alresford SO24 9DD Tel: 01962 732237 — MB BS 1953 Lond.

WISDOM, Stephen John Cresswell Maternity Hospital, Rosevale St., Dumfries DG1 2ES Tel: 01387 246246 — MB ChB 1982 Ed.; FRCOG 2001; BSc (Med. Sci.) Ed. 1980; MRCOG 1989. Cons. (O & G) Dumfries & Galloway Roy. Infirm. & Cresswell Matern. Hosp. Socs: Brit. Med. Ultrasound Soc.; Brit. Matern. and Foetal Med. Soc. Prev: Regist. (O & G) Glas. Roy. Matern. Hosp. & Glas. Roy. Infirm.

WISE, Arlene 146 Archerhill Road, Knightswood, Glasgow G13 3JH — MB ChB 1998 Glas.

WISE, Brian George 6 Chichester Close, East Wellow, Romsey SO51 6EY — MB BS 1987 Lond.; MRCOG 1994; MD Lond. 1996. Cons. (Obst & Gyn) William Harvey Hosp., Ashford Kent. Socs: Roy. Soc. Med.; Internat. Continence Soc.; BMA. Prev: Regist. Rotat. SW Thames Region; Research Fell (Urodynamics) King's Coll. Hosp. Lond.

WISE, Christopher Foston Longrigg Medical Centre, Leam Lane Estate, Gateshead NE10 8PH Tel: 0191 469 2173 Fax: 0191 495 0893; 16 Moor Place, Gosforth, Newcastle upon Tyne NE3 4AL — MB BS 1984 Newc.; MRCGP 1988; DRCOG 1988; Cert. Family Plann. JCC 1987.

WISE, David (retired) 10 Gretaside, Keswick CA12 5LG — MB BChir 1952 Camb.; MD Camb. 1960; FRCP Lond. 1980, M 1954. Prev: Cons. Phys. W. Hill Hosp. Dartford.

WISE, David 75 Arlington Avenue, London N1 7BA — MB ChB 1991 Manch.; BSc (Psychol.) 1st cl. Hons. CNAA Lond. 1985. SHO (Surg.) W. Cornw. Hosp. Penzance. Prev: SHO (Med.) W. Cornw. Hosp. Penzance; SHO (A & E, Trauma & Orthop.) Treliske Hosp. Truro & Leighton Hosp. Chesh.; Lect. (Anat.) Manch. Univ. Med. Sch.

WISE

WISE, David Graham Denham Grove Medical Centre, 3 Vale Avenue, Grove, Wantage OX12 7LU Tel: 01235 770140 Fax: 01235 760027; 14 Truelocks Way, Charlton Heights, Wantage OX12 7EG Tel: 01235 768606 — MB ChB 1977 Bristol; MB ChB (Hons.) Bristol 1977; MRCGP 1981; DCH Eng. 1981; DObst. RCOG 1980.

WISE, Mr David Ian (retired) 44 Plymouth Wharf, London E14 3EL Tel: 020 7987 9958 — MB BS 1966 Lond.; FRCS Eng. 1972; MRCS Eng. LRCP Lond. 1966. Prev: GP Worthing.

WISE, Mr David Ian Huddersfield Royal Infirmary, Acre St., Lindley, Huddersfield HD3 3EA Tel: 01484 482214; The Old Inn, Flush House Lane, Holmbridge, Holmfirth, Huddersfield HD7 1QD Tel: 01484 682713 — MB ChB 1982 Leic.; FRCS (Orth.) 1993; FRCS Eng. 1988; FRCS Glas. 1987. Cons. Orthop. Surg. Huddersfield Roy. Infirm.

WISE, Helen Jayne 13 Market St, Poole BH15 1NA Email: helwise@aol.com — BM 1994 Soton. Specialist Regist. (Anaesth.). Socs: Assn. of Anaesth.s; Intens. Care Soc. Prev: SHO (Anaesth.).

WISE, Mr Kenneth Stanley Hadyn The Old Rectory, Upper Icknield Way, Saunderton, Princes Risborough HP27 9NJ Tel: 01844 343241 Fax: 01844 344314 — MB BS Lond. 1963; FRCS Eng. 1970. (St. Bart.) Cons. Orthop. Surg. S. Bucks. Trust. Socs: Fell. BOA & Brit. Soc. Surg. Hand.; Brit. Cervical Spine Soc.; World Orthopaedic Concern. Prev: Sen. Regist. (Orthop.) Wessex Orthop. Train. Scheme; Asst. Lect. St. Bart. Hosp. Med. Coll.

WISE, Lindsay Karen 8 Cottesmore Gardens, Leigh-on-Sea SS9 2TG — MB BCh 1993 Wales.

WISE, Marcus Seall 231 Cherry Lane, Lymm WA13 0TA — MB ChB 1990 Manch.

WISE, Mr Martin Portsmouth Hospitals NHS Trust, Queen Alexandra Hospital, Cosham, Portsmouth PO3 6QS Tel: 023 92 286000; Chellow Bank, 4 Ranvilles Lane, Catisfield, Fareham PO14 3DS Tel: 01329 842768 — MB ChB 1973 Bristol; MD Bristol 1986; FRCS Eng. 1977. (Bristol) Cons. Surg. Socs: Assn. Surg.; Brit. Assn. Surg. Oncol.; Brit. Transpl. Soc.

WISE, Matthew Peter 17 Hobart Close, High Wycombe HP13 6UF — MB BChir 1990 Camb.; MA Camb. 1991, MB BChir 1990; MRCP (UK) 1993; DPhil Oxon. 1998.

WISE, Michael Erwin Jan Pitt House, North End Avenue, London NW3 7HP Email: j@wisepsych.freeserce.co.uk — MB BS 1992 Lond.; MRCPysch 1997; MSc 1998. (UMDS) Specialist Regist. Hammersmith Hosp. Socs: BMA; Jun. Doctors Negotiating Comm.; Comm. on Community Care. Prev: Research Fell. Lewisham & Guy's MHT; Regist. (Psychiat.) Guys & Lewisham MHT; SpR BKC&W MHT.

WISE, Peter Hermann 67 Chartfield Avenue, London SW15 6HN Tel: 020 8246 6802 Fax: 020 8246 6802 Email: peter@ali-ham.demon.co.uk — MB BS Adelaide 1959; PhD Lond. 1969; FRCP Lond. 1978, M 1961; FRACP 1972, M 1963. (Adelaide) Hon. Cons. Phys. (Endocrinol.) Char. Cross Hosp. Lond.; Hon. Sen. Lect. Imperial Coll. Sch. Med. Socs: Eur. Assoc. St. Diab.; Fell. Roy. Soc. Med.; Soc. Endocrinol. Prev: Assoc. Prof. Med. & Dir. Endocrinol. Flinders Univ. Med. Centre; S. Australia.

WISE, Raymond Percy (retired) Holmfield House, Farnham, Blandford Forum DT11 8DE Tel: 01725 516436 — MB BS 1952 Lond.; MRCS Eng. LRCP Lond. 1952; FFA RCS Eng. 1956; DA Eng. 1954. Cons. Anaesth. St. Thos. Hosp. Lond. Prev: Sen. Regist. (Anaesth.) St. Thos. Hosp. Lond.

WISE, Professor Richard Department Microbiology, City Hospital Trust, Dudley Road, Birmingham B18 7QH Tel: 0121 507 4255 — MB ChB Manch. 1966; MD Manch. 1981; FRCPath 1986, M 1974; FRCP (Hon) 1998. Cons. Med. Microbiol. City Hosp. Trust Birm.; Hon. Prof. Clin. Microbiol. Univ. Birm.; Specialist Adviser Hse. of Lords 1997-8. Socs: Pres. Brit. Soc. Antimicrobial Chemother. Prev: Regist. (Bact.) Hammersmith Hosp. Lond.; Research Fell. (Microbiol.) Univ. Brit. Columbia; Ho. Off. (Surg. & Cardiol.) Manch. Roy. Infirm.

WISE, Richard James Surtees Wellcome Department of Cognitive Neurology, Institute of Neurology, Queen Square, London WC1N 3BG Tel: 020 7833 7456; 33 Ladbroke Gardens, London W11 2PX — BM BCh 1974 Oxf.; DM Oxf. 1986; MRCP (UK) 1977. Wellcome Sen. Clin. Research Fell. Inst. Neurol. Lond.; Cons. Nat. Hosp. Neurol. & Neurosurg. Lond.; Sen. Lect. Roy. Free Hosp. Med. Sch. Lond. Prev: Cons. Char. Cross Hosp. & Centr. Middlx. Hosp. Lond.; Sen. Regist. & Regist. Nat. Hosp. Nerv. Dis. Lond.; Research Regist. Roy. Postgrad. Med. Sch. Hammersmith Hosp. Lond.

WISE, Valerie Anne Helvellyn, Clovelly Road, Beacon Hill, Hindhead GU26 6RW — MB ChB 1982 Manch.

WISELKA, Martin Joseph Department of Infection and Tropical Medicine, Leicester Royal Infirmary, Leicester LE1 5WW — BM BCh 1982 Oxf.; PhD 1995; MA Camb. 1983, MD 1992; MRCP (UK) 1985; FRCP (uk) 1999. (Oxford) Cons. Infec. Dis. Leicester Roy. Infirm.; Sen. Lect. Dept. of Microbiol. and Immunol. Uiversity of Leicester. Socs: Brit. Infec. Soc.; Brit. HIV Assn.; Soc. for Gen. MicroBiol. Prev: Wellcome Trust Clin. Research Fell. & Sen. Regist. (Infec. Dis.) Univ.Leics.; SHO (Med.) Qu. Med. Centre Nottm.

WISELY, Catherine Macdonald (retired) 5 Hillway, Westcliff on Sea SS0 8QA Tel: 01702 76505 — MB ChB Ed. 1956; FFA RCS Eng. 1966; DA Eng. 1960. Prev: Cons. Anaesth. S. Essex Hosp. Gp.

WISELY, Mr Edward Hugh (retired) 5 Hillway, Westcliff on Sea SS0 8QA Tel: 01702 476505 — LRCP Lond. MRCS Eng.1957; FDS RCS Eng. 1960, LDS 1946. Cons. Oral Surg. S.end-on-Sea Hosp. Prev: Sen. Regist. Qu. Vict. Hosp. E. Grinstead & Roy. Dent. Hosp. Lond.

WISELY, Ivan Charles Fraser Brimmond Medical Group, 106 Inverurie Road, Bucksburn, Aberdeen AB21 9AT Tel: 01224 713869 Fax: 01224 716317; 1 Rubislaw Den N., Aberdeen AB15 4AL Tel: 01224 317750 Fax: 01224 322004 — MB ChB Aberd. 1967; DA Eng. 1970.

WISELY, Joanna 5 Hillway, Westcliff on Sea SS0 8QA Tel: 01702 76505; 3f2 80 Montrose Park, Edinburgh EH10 4NG Tel: 0131 228 6588 — MB ChB 1994 Ed.; DRCOG 1998. (Edin) GP Reg.

WISELY, Nicholas Alexander 8 Old Oak Street, Didsbury, Manchester M20 6RH Tel: 0161 446 2783 Fax: 0161 438 0720 Email: nik@nikw.demon.co.uk — MB ChB 1992 Ed.; FRCA 1998. (Univ. Ed.) Specialist Regist. Train. Rotat. N. W. Region. Socs: Fell. Roy. Med. Soc.; Train. Mem. Assn. Anaesth.; Scott. Soc. Anaesth. Prev: SHO (Anaesth.) St. John's Hosp. Livingston; SHO Rotat. (Anaesth.) SE Scotl. Sch. Anaesth.

WISEMAN, Alfred Malcolm 10 Shilton Garth Close, Old Earswick, York YO32 9SQ — MB BS 1970 Lond.

WISEMAN, Ann Juliet 3 Holmdene Avenue, Mill Hill, London NW7 2LY — MRCS Eng. LRCP Lond. 1961; AFOM RCP Lond. 1978; MFCM 1974; DPH Eng. 1965. (Guy's) Sessional Med. Off. Regional Depts., Dept. Health & Dept. Soc. Sec. Socs: Hunt. Soc. Prev: Sen. Med. Off. Barnet AHA; Deptm. Med. Off. Lond. Boro. Enfield; Med. Off. Blood Transfus. Serv.

WISEMAN, Aviva Woodrow Farm Cottages, Woodrow, Amersham HP7 0QH Tel: 01494 724734 Email: avivawiseman@compuserve.com — MRCS Eng. LRCP Lond. 1945. (King's Coll. Hosp.)

WISEMAN, Claire Elizabeth 33 Seafield Road, Rustington, Littlehampton BN16 2JH — MB ChB 1985 Sheff.; DFFP 1996. (Sheff.) Clin. Med. Off. Contracep. & Sexual Health Dept.; Worthing Priority Care NHS Trust Worthing W. Sussex.

WISEMAN, Denis Buchanan (retired) 32 Freemans Close, Stoke Poges, Slough SL2 4ER Tel: 01753 663543 — MB ChB 1941 Ed. Prev: Resid. Phys. Roy. Infirm. Edin.

WISEMAN, Elizabeth Claire 10 Priory Close, Ruskington, Sleaford NG34 9ED; 142 Howard Road, Leicester LE2 1XJ — MB ChB 1997 Leic.

WISEMAN, Elizabeth Sarah 78 Poole Crescent, Birmingham B17 0PB — MB ChB 1995 Birm.; ChB Birm. 1995.

WISEMAN, Hazel Gwendoline (retired) Treverbyn Vean, Two Waters Foot, Liskeard PL14 6HN Tel: 01579 321656 — MB ChB 1949 Glas.; MFOM RCP Lond. 1984; DIH Eng. 1982; DCH Eng. 1966; DObst RCOG 1954. Prev: Dist. Occupat. Health Phys. City & Hackney HA.

WISEMAN, Janet The Hollies, Griffiths Green, Claverley, Wolverhampton WV5 7BG — MB ChB 1977 Birm.

WISEMAN, Jennifer Ruth 15 Back Lane, Haslingfield, Cambridge CB3 7JN Tel: 01223 871635; 29 St Chad's Rise, Headingley, Leeds LS6 3QE Tel: 0113 278 0418 — MB BS 1988 Newc.; MRCGP 1994; Dip. Palliat. Med. Wales 1997. (Newc.) Specialist Regist. Rotat. (Palliat. Med.) Yorks.

WISEMAN, John Woodside Medical Group B, 80 Western Road, Woodside, Aberdeen AB24 4SU Tel: 01224 492828 Fax: 01224 276173 — MB ChB 1979 Aberd.

WISEMAN, Louise Catherine 10 Ferring Street, Ferring, Worthing BN12 5HJ — MB BS 1997 Lond.; BSc 1994. (St marys hosp.Imperial.Coll) SHO Anaesth. P.ss. Roy.Hosp.Haywards Heath.

WISEMAN, Malcolm Raymond Department of Child Psychiatry, Guy's Hospital, St Thomas St., London SE1 9RT — MB 1977 Camb.; MA Camb. 1976, BA 1973; MRCPsych 1982. Cons. Child & Adolesc. Guy's Hosp. Lond.

WISEMAN, Martin Fitzalan Medical Centre, Fitzalan Road, Littlehampton BN17 5JR Tel: 01903 733277 Fax: 01903 733773 — MB BS 1984 Lond.

WISEMAN, Professor Martin Jeremy Department of Health, 80 London Road, London SE1 6LW Tel: 020 7972 5325 Fax: 020 7972 5153 Email: mjwiseman@doh.gov.uk; 20 Barnmead Road, Beckenham BR3 1JE Email: mjwiseman@comuserve.com — MB BS 1975 Lond.; MRCP (UK) 1977; MRCS Eng. LRCP Lond. 1975; FRCP 1998; FRCpath 1999. (Guy's) Princip. Med. Off. & Head of Nutrit. Unit DoH; Hon. Sen. Lect. (Human Nutrit.) Lond. Sch. Hyg. & Trop. Med.; Vis. Prof. Human Nutrit. Univ. Soton. Socs: Brit. Diabetic Assn.; Nutrit. Soc. Prev: Hon. Sen. Regist. Guy's Hosp. Lond.; Regist. (Med.) Roy. Vict. Hosp. Boscombe & W.m. Hosp. Lond.; Sen. Ho. Phys. (Gen. Med.) N.. Gen. Hosp. Sheff.

WISEMAN, Oliver 16 Edmunds Walk, London N2 0HU — MB BChir 1995 Camb.; MA Camb. 1996. (Addenbrooke's Hosp. Camb.) Demonst. (Anat.) Univ. Camb. Prev: SHO (A & E) Watford Gen. Hosp.; Ho. Off. (Gen. Med.) N.ampton Gen. Hosp.; Ho. Off. (Gen. Surg.) Addenbrooke's Hosp. Camb.

WISEMAN, Paul Jeremy Talbot Hampstead Group Practice, 75 Fleet Road, London NW3 2QU Tel: 020 7435 4000 Fax: 020 7435 9000; The Cromwell Hospital, Cromwell Road, London SW5 0TU Tel: 020 7370 4233 — MB BS 1982 Lond.; MRCGP 1987; Cert. Family Plann. JCC 1985.

WISEMAN, Penelope Anne Barnet & Chase Farm NHS Trust, Barnet General Hospital, Wellhouse Lane, Barnet EN5 3DJ Tel: 020 8732 6718 — MB BS 1981 Lond.; MA Oxf. 1978; FRCP; MRCP (UK) 1984; FRCP 1998. (Oxford) p/t Cons. in Med. for the Elderly, Barnet Hosp., Barnet.

WISEMAN, Raymond 2 St Baldred's Crescent, North Berwick EH39 4PZ Tel: 01620 892775 — MB ChB 1964 Aberd.; FRCPath 1982, M 1970; Dip. Bact. Lond 1970. (Aberd.) Cons. Bact. St. John's Hosp. Livingston; Hon. Sen. Lect. (Bact.) Edin. Univ. Prev: Cons. Bact. Bangour Gen. Hosp. Broxburn; Lect. (Bact.) Univ. Aberd.; Sen. Bact. Pub. Health Laborat. Luton.

WISEMAN, Richard Ansel Slough Place, Cuckfield, Haywards Heath RH17 5JD Tel: 01444 454312 Fax: 01444 416609 — MRCS Eng. LRCP Lond. 1960; PhD Lond. 1969; FFPM RCP (UK) 1991; DTM & H Eng. 1964; DObst RCOG 1961. Managing Dir. HOGENS Ltd. W. Sussex; Hon. Sen. Lect. Dept. of Epidemiol. & Populat. Health; Lond. Sch. Hyg. & Trop. Med. Lond. Socs: Fell. Roy. Soc. Med. Prev: Managing & Med. Dir. Schering Chems. Ltd. W. Sussex; Lect. Lond. Sch. Hyg. & Trop. Med; Research Fell. Med. Unit Hosp. Trop. Dis. Lond.

WISEMAN, Simon Martin St. Paul's Road Medical Centre, 248-250 St Paul's Road, Canonbury, London N1 2LJ Tel: 020 7226 6333 — MB BS 1972 Lond.; MRCGP 1991. (Univ. Coll. Hosp.) Gen. Practitioner St. Pauls Rd. med. Centre Lond. N1 2LJ; GP Tutor Whittington Hosp. Lond.; Hon. Clin. Lect. Dept. Primary Care & Populat. Sci. Roy. Free & Univ. Coll. Med. Sch. Lond. Prev: Hosp. Pract. Regional Alcoholism & Drug Dependence Unit St. Bernards Wing Ealing Hosp. Lond.; SHO Shenley Hosp.; Ho. Surg. King Geo. Hosp. Ilford.

WISHART, Eva Hanna 99 Oakfield Road, Birmingham B29 7HW Tel: 0121 472 1768 — MB BS 1957 Lond.; MRCS Eng. LRCP Lond. 1957; MFFP 1993; DObst RCOG 1960. (Univ. Coll. Hosp.) SCMO S. Birm. HA; Clin. Asst. (Ultrasound) Sandwell Hosp. Socs: BMA. Prev: Research Fell. (Med.) Qu. Eliz. Hosp. Birm.; Regist. (Microbiol.) Hosp. Sick Childr. Gt. Ormond St. Lond.

WISHART, Mr Gordon Cranston Cambridge Breast Unit, Box 97, Addenbrooke's Hospital, Hills Road, Cambridge CB2 2QQ Tel: 01223 216315 Fax: 01223 586932 Email: gordon.wishart@addenbrookes.nhs.uk — MB ChB 1983 Ed.; FRCS 2001 Eng.; MD Ed. 1992; FRCS (Gen.) 1995; FRCS Glas. 1987. Cons. BrE. and Endocrine Surg., Addenbrook's Hosp., Camb. Socs: Assn. Surg.; Brit. Assn. Surg. Oncol. (BASO); BASO BrE. Gp. Prev: Cons. Gen. Surg. P.ss Roy. Hosp. Haywards Heath; Sen. Regist. (Gen. Surg.) W. Scotl. Higher Surgic. Train. Scheme; Sen. Regist. (Surg.) W.. Infirm. Glas.

WISHART, Helen Millar (retired) 14 Townsend Crescent, Kirkcaldy KY1 1DN Tel: 01592 263276 — MB ChB 1954 St. And. Prev: O & G Ho. Surg. Cresswell Matern. Hosp. Dumfries.

WISHART, Ian Herbert The Health Centre, Crieff PH7 3SA Tel: 01764 2283; Woodhaven, East Craigmuir, Madderty, Crieff PH7 3NZ Tel: 01764 683396 — MB ChB 1959 St. And.; MRCGP 1974; DObst RCOG 1971. Hon. Med. Off. Crieff & Dist. Hosp. & Glenalmond. Coll. Prev: SHO (Gen. Med.) Murray Roy. Hosp. Perth; Ho. Phys & Ho. Surg. Perth Roy. Infirm.; Ho. Surg. Forth Pk. Matern. Hosp. Kirkcaldy.

WISHART, Katharine Cecilia Hainton House, 66 West St., Kings Cliffe, Peterborough PE8 6XA — MB BS 1985 Lond. Socs: RCGP.

WISHART, Mrs Manijeh Seradji Warrington District General Hospital, Lovely Lane, Warrington WA5 1QG Tel: 01925 35911; North Cheshire Hospital, Stretton, Warrington WA4 4LU Tel: 01925 265000 — MD 1973 Teheran; FRCS Eng. 1983; FCOphth 1988. Cons. Ophth. Surg. Warrington Dist. Gen. Hosp. Socs: Oxf. Ophth. Soc. & Overseas Doctors Assn. Prev: Clin. Research Asst. Inst. Ophth. Moorfields Eye Hosp. Lond.; Regist. (Ophth.) OldCh. Hosp. Romford; SHO (Ophth.) Manch. Roy. Eye Hosp.

WISHART, Maria Olivia 3 Victoria Road, Cambridge CB4 3BW — BChir 1992 Camb.

WISHART, Marion Gardiner (retired) 48 Blake Hill Crescent, Lilliput, Poole BH14 8QS Tel: 01202 707598 — MB ChB Ed. 1947; FFA RCS Eng. 1954; DA Eng. 1950. Prev: Assoc. Specialist (Anaesth.) Poole Gen. Hosp.

WISHART, Mary Lower Sent, Oakwood Hill, Dorking RH5 5NB — MB ChB 1954 Glas.; BSc Glas. 1950, MB ChB 1954. (Glas.) Clin. Asst. Geriat. Unit Redhill Gen. Hosp. Prev: Asst. Lect. Physiol. Univ. Glas.; Jun. Ho. Off. Killearn Hosp. & Stobhill Gen. Hosp. Glas.

WISHART, Mr Peter Knight St. Pauls Eye Unit, Royal Liverpool Hospital, Prescot St., Liverpool L7 8XP Tel: 0151 706 3968 Fax: 0151 706 5861; Lourdes Hospital, 57 Greenbank Road, Liverpool L18 1HQ Tel: 0151 733 7123 Fax: 0151 735 0446 — MB ChB 1976 Aberd.; FRCS Glas. 1982; FCOphth 1988; DO Eng. 1980. Cons. Ophth. Surg. St. Paul's Eye Unit Roy. Liverp. Univ. Hosp. Trust. Socs: N. Eng. Ophth. Soc. Prev: Resid. Surgic. Off. Moorfields Eye Hosp. Lond.; Sen. Regist. King's Coll. Hosp. Lond.

WISHEART, Mr James Dunwoody (retired) 3A Southfield Road, Westbury-on-Trym, Bristol BS9 3BG Tel: 0117 962 3918 — MB BCh BAO 1962 Belf.; BSc (Hons.) Belf. 1959, MCh (Hons.) 1974; FRCS Eng. 1984; FRCS Ed. 1967; DObst RCOG 1964. Prev: Cardiothoracic Surg. Roy. Infirm. Childr. Hosp. Bristol.

WISLEY, Alexander Barclay Finlayson Street Practice, 33 Finlayson Street, Fraserburgh AB43 9JW Tel: 01346 518088 Fax: 01346 510015; Craigielea, Commerce Lane, Fraserburgh AB43 9LF Tel: 01346 516738 Fax: 01346 510015 — MB ChB 1975 Aberd. (Aberdeen University) Phys. Fraserburgh Hosp.

WISMAYER, Emma Cecile Datchet, St. Georges Lane, Sandwich CT13 9JS — MB BCh 1990 Wales.

WISNIOWIECKA, Anna Uphill, Ardens Grafton, Alcester B49 6DR Tel: 01789 772710 — BM BCh 1977 Oxf.

WISSA, Atef Halim 10 Creek Road, South Woodham Ferrars, Chelmsford CM3 5GU — MB BCh 1975 Ain Shams; LRCP LRCS Ed. LRCPS Glas. 1983.

WISTOW, Trevor Edwin William Flat A, 39 Mount Adon Park, Dulwich, London SE22 0DS Tel: 020 8693 9567; 44 Mile End Road, Godmanchester, Norwich NR4 7QX Tel: 01480 219743 Fax: 01603 504627 Email: twisto@aol.com — MB BS 1986 Lond.; BSc Lond. 1983, MB BS 1986; MRCP (UK) 1989. (The Royal Free Hospital) Cons. Cardiol. Norf. & Norwich Hosp., Norwich. Prev: Sen. Regist. (Med.) Toowoomba, Qu.sland, Austral.

WISZNIEWSKA, Ruth Heather 42 Arnall Drive, Henbury, Bristol BS10 7AP — MB ChB 1994 Bristol; DRCOG 1996. Prev: SHO (Psychiat.) W.on Gen. Hosp. W.on Super Mare; SHO (ENT & O & G) St. Michaels Hosp. Bristol; SHO (Ophth.) Bristol Eye Hosp.

WITANA, Jaika Sali Department Audiological Medicine, St George's Hospital, Tooting, London SW17 0QT Tel: 020 8725 1988 Fax: 020 8725 1874; 8 Parish Gardens, Hagley Road, Pedmore, Stourbridge DY9 0DS — MB BS 1979 Sri Lanka; FRCSI 1990; MS Sri Lanka 1991. (University of Sri Lanka, Colombo) Specialist Regist.

WITANA

(Audiological Med.). Socs: Brit. Assn. Audiol. Phys. (Full); Brit. Soc. Audiol.; MPS.

WITANA, Kung Yu 52 Doctors Residences, James Paget Hospital, Lowestoft Road, Great Yarmouth NR31 6LA — MB BS 1979 Colombo.

WITCHALLS, James Raymond Bupa Health Screening Centre, Battle Bridge House, 300 Gray's Inn Road, London WC1X 8DU Tel: 020 7837 6484 Fax: 020 7837 6797; Maddox Farm, Little Bookham St, Little Bookham, Leatherhead KT23 3BU Tel: 01372 454197 — MB BS 1967 Lond.; MRCS Eng. LRCP Lond. 1968; DObst RCOG 1972. (St. Bart.) Sen. Phys i/c BUPA Health Screening Centre Lond.; Chairm. Pioneer Health Centre Ltd.; Governor Albert Schweitzer Hosp. Lambarene Gabon. Socs: Pres. Internat. Assn. Friends Albert Schweitzer; Roy. Soc. Med. Prev: Med. Off. Albert Schweitzer Hosp. & Leprosarium Lambarene Gabon; Med. Cons. to the Juno Mission.

WITCHER, John William Regional Transfusion Centre, Southmead Road, Bristol BS10 5ND Tel: 0117 950 7777; 4 Anchor Way, Pill, Bristol BS20 0JY — MB ChB 1969 Bristol; DA Eng. 1973. Staff Phys. Blood Servs. SW Bristol. Socs: Fac. Anaesth. Prev: GP Bristol; Clin. Asst. (Anaesth.) Bristol.

WITCOMB, Alexandra Helen 50 Falmouth Road, Evington, Leicester LE5 4WH — MB BS 1989 Lond. SHO (Paediat.) Centr. Middlx. Hosp. Lond.

WITCOMBE, John Brian Bradstone House, Amberley, Stroud GL5 5AQ Tel: 01453 872220 — MB BS 1966 Lond.; MRCS Eng. LRCP Lond. 1966; FRCR 1975; DMRD Eng. 1973; DCH Eng. 1969. (St. Thos.) Cons. Radiol. Glos. Roy. Hosp. Gloucester. Prev: Sen. Regist. (Radiol.) Radcliffe Infirm. Oxf.; Vis. Asst. Prof. Radiol. Univ. Colorado Med. Center, Denver, USA; Sen. Lect. (Paediat. Radiol.) Univ. Manch.

WITCOMBE, Keith Barrington Forbes (retired) 7 Longdown Lane N., Ewell, Epsom KT17 3HY — MB ChB 1945 New Zealand; FRCP Ed. 1994, M 1951. Prev: Psychiat. The Manor Hosp. Epsom.

WITCOMBE, Shirin (retired) 7 Longdown Lane N., Ewell, Epsom KT17 3HY Tel: 01372 815297 — MRCS Eng. LRCP Lond. 1949.

WITHAM, Elizabeth Alice (retired) 31 Egerton Road, Lymm WA13 0PA Tel: 01925 754707 — MB ChB 1955 Liverp. Prev: SHO (Med.) War Memor. Hosp. Scunthorpe.

WITHAM, Fiona Mary Queen Alexandra Hospital, Cosham, Portsmouth PO6 3LY Tel: 023 92 286030 Fax: 023 92 286895 Email: fiona.witham@qmail01.porthosp.swest.nhs.uk; 63 Lower Mead, Herne Farm, Petersfield GU31 4NR — MB BS 1988 Lond.; BSc Lond. 1985; MRCP (UK) 1991; FRCR 1994. Cons. Radiol. Qu. Alexandra Hosp. Portsmouth. Socs: BMA; BSSR; ESSR. Prev: Sen. Regist. (Radiol.) Soton. Univ. Hosp.; Regist. (Radiol.) Kings Coll. Hosp. Lond.; SHO (Diabetes, Endocrinol., Metab. Med. & Chest Med.) St. Thos. Hosp. Lond.

WITHANA, Kithsiri Amarananda Chase Farm Hospital NHS Trust, The Ridgeway, Enfield EN2 8JL Tel: 020 8967 5903; 27 Westpole Avenue, Cockfosters, Barnet EN4 0AX Tel: 020 8292 6873 — MB BS 1962 Ceylon; FRCP 1996 (L); FRCPCH 1997; MRCP (UK) 1973; DTCH Liverp. 1980; DCH RCP Lond. 1971. Cons. Paediat. Chase Farm Hosps.

WITHANA, Ranjith Jayantha Department of Haematology, Whipps Cross Hospital, Leytonstone, London E11 1NR — MB BS 1969 Ceylon; DPath Eng. 1978. (Ceylon) Regist. (Haemat.) Whipps Cross Hosp. Lond. Socs: Assoc. Mem. RCPath. Prev: Regist. (Path.) Mt. Vernon Hosp. N.wood; Regist. (Path.) W. Middlx. Hosp. Isleworth; Med. Off. (Haemat.) Nat. Blood Transfus. Serv. Sri Lanka.

WITHECOMB, Julie Louise 25 Southdown Road, Brighton BN1 6FH — MB BS 1986 Lond.

WITHERINGTON, Elizabeth Mary Angela 190 Melton Road, Nottingham NG2 6FJ Tel: 01329 847015 — MB BChir Camb. 1986; MA Camb. 1986; MRCGP 1990; DRCOG 1989; DGM RCP Lond. 1989. Prev: GP Jubilee Surg. Titchfield Hants; Clin. Asst. (Geriat.) Qu. Alexandra Hosp. Portsmouth; Trainee GP Portsmouth VTS.

WITHEROW, Fraser Norman 2FR, 32 Oxford Street, Edinburgh EH8 9PL — MB ChB 1994 Ed.

WITHEROW, Helen 988 Richmond Hill, Richmond TW10 6RJ — MB ChB 1993 Bristol; BDS Birm. 1984.

WITHEROW, Mr Peter James (retired) Litfield House, 1 Litfield Place, Clifton, Bristol BS8 3LS Tel: 0117 973 1323 Fax: 0117 973 3303 — MB ChB 1958 Birm.; FRCS Eng. 1966. Prev: Sen. Regist. Robt. Jones & Agnes Hunt Hosp. OsW.ry.

WITHEROW, Mr Ross O'Neill 26 Harmont House, 20 Harley St., London W1G 9PJ Tel: 020 7935 1252 Fax: 020 7637 5373 — MB BS 1968 Lond.; MS Lond. 1981; FRCS Eng. 1973; FEBU 1992. (Univ. Coll. Hosp.) Cons. Urol. St. Mary's Hosp. Lond.; Sen. Clin. Lect. St. Mary's Hosp. Univ. Lond. Socs: Fell. Roy. Soc. Med.; BAUS. Prev: Lect. & Hon. Sen. Regist. (Urol.) Lond. Hosp.; Resid. Surg. Off. St. Peters Hosps.; Postgrad. Research Fell. (Urol.) Univ. Calif. San Francisco, USA.

WITHERS, Andrew Walter James The Grange Practice, Allerton Clinic, Wanstead Crescent, Allerton, Bradford BD15 7PA Tel: 01274 541696; 3 Kendal Avenue, Moorhead, Shipley BD18 4DU Email: andy-withers@compuserve.com — MB ChB 1982 Leeds; MRCGP 1986; DRCOG 1985. Prev: Trainee GP Bradford VTS; Ho. Surg. Pinderfields Gen. Hosp. Wakefield; Ho. Phys. Bradford Roy. Infirm.

***WITHERS, Angela Julie** 17 Aran Close, Harpenden AL5 1SW — MB BS 1998 Newc.; MB BS Newc. Upon Tyne 1998.

WITHERS, Anthony Francis Dennis Royal Crescent Surgery, 11 Royal Crescent, Cheltenham GL50 3DA Tel: 01242 580248 Fax: 01242 253618 — MB BChir 1965 Camb.; MA Camb. 1968, MB BChir 1965. (Camb. & Lond. Hosp.)

WITHERS, Mr David Geoffrey (retired) The Sign of the Dolphin, Westerleigh, Bristol BS37 8QQ Tel: 01454 312122 — MB ChB 1964 Bristol; FRCS Ed. 1969; DObst RCOG 1970.

WITHERS, David James Warren Lodge, The Roundway, Rustington, Littlehampton BN16 2BW — MB BChir 1982 Camb.

WITHERS, Digby Paul The Health Centre, White Hart Close, Buntingford SG9 9DQ Tel: 01763 271362 Fax: 01763 272878; Woodstock, Hare St, Buntingford SG9 0EQ — MB BS 1972 Newc.; BSc Newc. 1968; DRCOG 1985; DTM Antwerp 1981. Socs: Fell. Roy. Soc. Med. Prev: SHO (Obst. & Paediat.) Leicester Gen. Hosp.; Med. Off. Hôpital de la CBFZ, Pimu, Zaïre; Ho. Phys. & Ho. Surg. Roy. Vict. Infirm. Newc.

WITHERS, Dominic John 15 Kersley Road, London N16 0NP — MB BS 1987 Lond.

WITHERS, Eleanor Jane Arbury Road Surgery, 114 Arbury Road, Cambridge CB4 2JG Tel: 01223 364433 Fax: 01223 315728 — MB BCh 1985 Wales; MRCGP 1989; DRCOG 1991; DCH RCP Lond. 1989.

WITHERS, Joanna Elizabeth The Bield, Hotley Bottom Lane, Great Missenden HP16 9PL — BM BCh 1990 Oxf.

WITHERS, Keri Jane 43-45 High Street, Codicote, Hitchin SG4 8RA — MB BS 1987 Lond.; MRCPsych 1994; DCH RCP Lond. 1990; DRCOG 1997; DFFP 1997; MRCGP 1998. (Roy. Free Hosp. Sch. Med.) GP Princip. Prev: Sen. Regist. (Child & Adolesc. Psychiat.) Tavistock Clinic Hampstead; Regist. (Psychiat.) P. Henry Hosp. Sydney, Austral.; SHO (Paediat.) Chase Farm Hosp. Enfield.

WITHERS, Mark Richard 323 Brincliffe Edge Road, Sheffield S11 9DE — MB ChB 1988 Leic.

WITHERS, Michelle 42 Frensham Road, Crowthorne RG45 6QH — MB BS 1998 Lond.

WITHERS, Nicholas John Department of Respiratory Medicine, Royal Devon And Exeter Hospital, Barrack Rd, Exeter Ex2 5DW Tel: 01392 402827 Fax: 01392 402828; 162 Wimbledon Park Road, London SW18 5UG Tel: 020 8874 2170 — MB BS 1988 Lond.; DM 1998 Soton.; MRCP (UK) 1991. Cons. Paediat. with an interest in Respirat. Med., Roy. Devon And Exeter Hosp., Exeter. Prev: Sen. Registra, Respirat./Gen. Med., Bristol Hosp.; Research Fell. Soton. Univ. Med.

WITHERS, Peter Anthony 54 Churston Close, Westbury Park, Newcastle ST5 4LP — BM 1987 Soton.; T(GP) 1993.

WITHERS, Richard Alan Yaxley Group Practice, Yaxley Health Centre, Landsdowne Road, Yaxley, Peterborough PE7 3JX Tel: 01733 240478 Fax: 01733 244645; Field Farm House, Bullock Road, Washingley, Peterborough PE7 3SJ Tel: 01733 244780 — MB BS 1983 Lond.; BSc Lond. 1978; MRCGP 1988; AFOM RCP Lond. 1995; DCH RCP Lond. 1986; DRCOG 1986. (Univ. Coll. Hosp.) Force Med. Adviser Cambs. Constab. Prev: Trainee GP P'boro. VTS; Ho. Surg. N.ampton Gen. Hosp.; Ho. Phys. Whittingdon Hosp. Lond.

WITHERS, Ronald John Adams and Partners, The Health Centre, Tavanagh Avenue, Portadown, Craigavon BT62 3BU Tel: 028 3835 1393 — MB BCh BAO 1978 Belf.; MRCGP 1982.

WITHERSPOON, Edward William 25 Potwell Gardens, The Hooks, Henfield BN5 9UY Tel: 01273 494979 Email: w.witherspoon@tinyworld.co.uk — MB ChB 1949 Birm.; FFPM RCP (UK) 1990; DTM & H RCPS 1969. Cons. Iatrogenic Disorders Contract Agencies UK, USA. Socs: Fell. Med. Soc of Lond.; Fell. Roy. Soc. Of Health; Fell. Roy. Soc. Med. Prev: Med. Dir. Warner Lambert/Pk.e Davis UK, Europe, Afr.; Wellcome Med. Dir. Austral. & NZ; Maj. RAMC Middle E. Land Forces.

WITHERSPOON, Paul 1A Ravelston Place, Edinburgh EH4 3DT — MB ChB 1997 Glas.

WITHEY, John Sandford (retired) Lane End Farm, Hightown, Ringwood BH24 3DY Tel: 01425 472036 — MB BS 1955 Lond.; DObst RCOG 1959.

WITHEY, Josephine Mary Heavitree Health Centre, South Lawn Terrace, Exeter EX1 2RX Tel: 01392 431355 Fax: 01392 498305; 2 Riversweet House, Topsham, Exeter EX3 0BE — MB BS 1977 Lond.; DA 1980. (St Marys Hospital Medical School) Princip. Gen. Pract.,.

WITHEY, Simon John 70/72 Westbourne Terrace, London W2 6QA — MB BS 1984 Lond.; MS Lond. 1997, MB BS 1984. Sen. Regist. (Plastic Surg.) Pan Thames Train. Scheme. Socs: Fell. RCS; Fell. Roy. Soc. Med. Prev: Research Regist. & Regist. Rotat. (Gen. Surg.) St. Geo. Hosp. Lond.

WITHINGTON, Brian Richard Hebburn Health Centre, Campbell Park Road, Hebburn NE31 2SP Tel: 0191 483 5533 Fax: 0191 428 1826 — MB BS 1977 Newcastle; MB BS Newc. 1977. (Newcastle) GP Hebburn, Tyne & Wear.

WITHINGTON, Brian Stephen 40 Megson Way, Walkington, Beverley HU17 8YA — MB BCh BAO 1989 Belf. SHO (Anaesth.) P.ss Mary's RAF Hosp. Halton.

WITHINGTON, Peter Stuart Department of Anaesthetic and Intensive Care, The Royal London Hospital, London E1 1BB Tel: 020 7377 7725 Fax: 020 7377 7126 Email: p.s.withington@mds.qmw.ac.uk; 29 Meynell Road, Hackney, London E9 7AP Tel: 020 8533 4051 Fax: 020 8533 4051 Email: psw@hackney.u.net.com — MB BS 1979 Lond.; FFA RCS Eng. 1983. (The London Hospital Medical College) Sen. Lect. & Hon. Cons. (Anaesth. & Intens. Care) Roy. Lond. Hosp. Socs: Assn. Anaesth.; Intens. Care Soc.

WITHNALL, David Mersea Road Surgery, 272a Mersea Road, Colchester CO2 8QY Tel: 01206 764374 Fax: 01206 765667; 157 Maldon Road, Colchester CO3 3BJ — MB BS 1974 Lond.; FRCGP 1997, M 1979. (St. Bart.) Hosp. Practitioner (Endoscopy) Colchester Gen. Hosp. Socs: Primary Care Soc. Gastroenterol. Prev: Trainee GP Colchester VTS; Ho. Phys. Connaught Hosp. Lond.

WITHNELL, Allan (retired) Compton Court, Compton Green, Redmarley, Gloucester GL19 3JB Tel: 01531 822330 — MB ChB Manch. 1951. Prev: Area Med. Off. Glos. AHA.

WITHRINGTON, Robin Henry 45 The Street, Ash, Canterbury CT3 2EN Tel: 01304 812080 — MB BCh BAO 1973 Dub.; BA Dub. 1971; MRCP (UK) 1978. Cons. (Rheum.) Canterbury & Thanet DHA. Prev: Sen. Regist. St. Marys Hosp. Lond. & Roy. Nat. Orthop. Hosp. Lond.

WITKIEWICZ, Tadeusz Stefan Department of Anaesthesia, Hairmyres & Stonehouse Hospitals NHS Trust, East Kilbride, Glasgow G75 8RG Tel: 0141 220292; 21 George Allan Place, Strathaven ML10 6EH Tel: 01357 521145 — Lekarz 1978 Warsaw. Staff Grade Anaesth. Hairmyres & StoneHo. Hosps. NHS Trust E. Kilbride; Specialist Anaesth. (Poland) 1985. Socs: Dip. Europ. Acad. Anaesthesiol. Prev: Staff Grade Anaesth. Law Hosp. Carluke.

WITNALL, Albert Peter (retired) Ysgubor Wen, Machynlleth SY20 8JA Tel: 01654 702228 — MB ChB 1961 Birm.

WITNEY, Raymond Lamprey (retired) 59 Northwood Road, Whitstable CT5 2HA Tel: 01227 272094 — MRCS Eng. LRCP Lond. 1938; BA Camb. Prev: Temp. Capt. RAMC.

WITT, Jacqueline Middleton Blackthorn Medical Centre, St. Andrews Road, Barming, Maidstone ME16 9AL Tel: 01622 726277 Fax: 01622 725774; Yard Cottage, Fant Farm, Maidstone ME16 8DE Tel: 01622 728008 — MB ChB 1982 Sheff.; MRCGP 1987; DRCOG 1986. Prev: SHO (O & G) N.. Gen. Hosp. Sheff.; SHO (Gen. Med.) S.port Gen. Infirm.

WITT, Mr Johan Delf The Middlesex Hospital, Department of Orthopaedics, Mortimer St., London W9 2QP Tel: 020 7380 9293 Email: jwitt@compuserve.com; 110 Sutherland Avenue, Maida Vale, London W9 2QP — MB BS 1983 Lond.; FRCS (Orth.) 1992; FRCS Eng. 1987. Cons. Orthop. Surg. & Hon. Sen. Lect. The Middlx. Hosp. & Univ. Coll. Lond. Socs: Fell. Roy. Coll. Surg.; Fell. BOA. Prev: Sen. Regist. (Orthop. Surg.) King's Coll. Hosp. Lond.; Sen. Resid. Mass. Gen. Hosp., USA; Clin. Fell. Harvard Med. Sch., USA.

WITT, Judith Karen 16 Westdale Gardens, Manchester M19 1JD — MB ChB 1998 Liverp.

WITTE, Klaus Karl August 129 Port Road E., Barry CF63 9PX — MB BS 1994 Lond.; MRCP (UK) 1997. (King's Coll.) Specialist Regist. (Cardiol.) Roy. Gwent Hosp. Newport. Prev: SHO (Cardiol.) UHW NHS Trust Cardiff; SHO (Chest Med.) Llandough Hosp.

WITTEK, Mrs Irena Hanna 21 Streatham Close, Leigham Court Road, London SW16 2NQ — MB ChB 1948 Poland; MB ChB Polish Sch. of Med. 1948; DCH Eng. 1953.

WITTELS, Peter Louis 6 Whitwick Moor, Thringstone, Coalville LE67 8NS — MB BS Lond. 1970; MRCS Eng. LRCP Lond. 1970; MRCGP 1975. (Lond. Hosp.) Non-Princip. Locum in GP & Med. Examr. in the Benefits Agency. Prev: SHO A & E Unit St. Leonard's Hosp. Lond.; Trainee GP Boston Lincs. VTS.

WITTMANN, Frederick William (retired) Burley, 22 The Chase, Reigate RH2 7DH Tel: 01737 762141 — MB ChB 1959 Glas.; FFA RCS Eng. 1964; DA Eng. 1962. Cons. (Anaesth.) New E. Surrey Hosp. Prev: Regist. (Anaesth.) Redhill Gen. Hosp. & United Birm. Hosps.

WITTRAM, Conrad Magnolia, Old Shaw Lane, Shaw, Swindon SN5 5PH Tel: 01793 770459; Magnolia, Old Shaw Lane, Shaw, Swindon SN5 5PH Tel: 01793 770459 Email: wittram@hotmail.com — MB ChB 1986 Liverp.; FRCR 1993; DMRD Liverp. 1991; FRANZCR 1998; American Board Radiol 1998; USMLE Step 1 & Step 2 1999. Asst. Prof./ Head Thoracic Radiol. Boston Univ. Prev: Fell. (Thoracic Radiolology) Univ. Toronto, Canda; Fell. (Clin. Radiol.) Univ. Alberta Hosp., Canada; Lect. (RadioDiag.) Univ. Liverp.

WITTS, Emma Jane 15 Beech Av, Chichester PO19 3DR — MB ChB 1997 Manch.

WITTS, Helena Maria Greenhills, The Green, Pitton, Salisbury SP5 1DZ Tel: 01722 712383 Fax: 01722 712574 Email: djwitts@global.co.uk; The Three Swans Surgery, Rollestone St, Salisbury SP1 1DX Tel: 01722 333548 — MB BS 1991 Lond.; MRCGP 1996 (Distinc.); DRCOG 1993. (Char. Cross & Westm.) Partner, GP Salisbury. Socs: Wessex Fac. of Coll. of GPs Salisbury Med. Soc.; Salisbury LMC Represent. Wiltsh. LMC. Prev: SHO (Psychiat.) Old Manor Hosp. Salisbury; SHO (Paediat.) St. Mary's Hosp. Portsmouth; SHO (O & G) P.ss Anne Hosp. Soton.

WITTS, Simon James Grovehurst Surgery, Grovehurst Road, Kemsley, Sittingbourne ME10 2ST Tel: 01795 430444 Fax: 01795 410539; 28 New Road, Chatham ME4 4QR — MB BS 1989 Lond.; MRCGP 1995; DTM & H Liverp. 1991. Prev: Trainee GP Maidstone Hosp.; Resid. Med. Off. Hauyra Khassa Hosp. Cochabamba, Bolivia.

WLODARCZYK, Krzysztof Kazimierz Sabden & Whalley Medical Group, 42 King St., Whalley, Clitheroe BB7 9SL Tel: 01254 823273 Fax: 01254 824891; 34 Straits Lane, Read, Burnley BB12 7PQ Tel: 01282 770052 — MB ChB 1986 Manch.; MRCGP 1990; DRCOG 1990; DCH RCP Lond. 1988; Cert. Family Plann. JCC 1988. (Manchester)

WOBER, Hilali Antony 18 Boathouse Reach, Henley-on-Thames RG9 1TJ Tel: 01491 578117 Fax: 01491 636271 Email: wm@doctors.org.uk — MB BS 1965 Lond.; MFOM RCP Lond. 1981; DAvMed FOM RCP Lond. 1972; DRCOG 1969. (St. Mary's) Cons. Occupat. Phys.Univ Coll Lond. Chasefarm Hosp Enfield, CMO QBE Health; Dir. of WM Health Internat. Ltd. Socs: Roy. Aeronaut Soc.; Aerospace Med. Assn. Prev: Med. Off. Roy. Air Force Med. Br.

WOBI, Bukar Department of Paediatrics, Wexham Park Hospital, Wexham, Slough SL2 4HL Tel: 01753 634603 Fax: 01753 634602; 2 Larchwood, Heatherwood, London Road, Ascot SL5 8AA Tel: 01334 27874 — MB BS 1979 Nigeria; MRCP (UK) 1991; DTCH Liverp. 1985. Assoc. Specialist (Paediat.) Heatherwood & Wexham Pk. Hosps. Trust. Prev: Regist. Heatherwood & Wexham Pk.; SHO (Paediat.) Chesterfield & N. Derbysh. Roy. Hosps.; SHO (Paediat.) Macclesfield.

WOERLEIN, Christoph Flat 32, Fellsdyke Court, Sheriff Hill, Gateshead NE9 6SX — State Exam Med 1994 Kiel.

WOFFENDEN, Laura Rachel Dodbrook House, Millbrook, Torpoint PL10 1AN — MB ChB 1998 Leeds.

WOFFINDIN

WOFFINDIN, Joyce Highfield Close Surgery, 4 Highfield Close, Seascale CA20 1HF — MB ChB 1985 Dundee; MRCGP 1990; Dip. Sports Med. Lond. 1990.

WOGU, Godwin Udo Ezechuku 41 Lynne Way, Northolt UB5 5UP — MB BCh BAO 1972 Dub.

WOHL, Miriam Ann 35 St James Road, Leicester LE2 1HR Tel: 0116 255 4316 Fax: 0116 240 4243 Email: miriamwohl@hotmail.com; Reservoir View, Saddington, Leicester LE8 0QH Tel: 0116 240 4243 Fax: 0116 240 4243 — MB ChB 1972 Glas.; Cert. Family Plann. JCC 1981; MSTAT. (Glasgo University) Med. Off. BAMS Midl.; Medico-legal Expert; Mem. Disabil. Living Alswana Advis. Bd. Socs: Soc. Of Teach. Of Alexander Technique. Prev: Med. Off. Brit. Red Cross Soc.; Med. Off. Pregn. & Gyn. Advis. Serv. Lond.; Med. Off. Pregn. Advis. Serv. Lond.

WOHL, Myer 86 Alexandra Park Road, London N10 2AD Tel: 020 8883 4800 — MRCS Eng. LRCP Lond. 1942. (St. Bart.) Socs: Brit. Psychoanal. Soc. Prev: Cons. Brent Consult. Centre (Educat. Dept. Lond. Boro. Brent).

WOJCIECHOWSKI, Mieczyslaw Kazimierz 42 Park Drive, Bradford BD9 4DT — MB ChB 1947 Polish Sch. of Med. Cons. Anaesth. Leeds RHB. Socs: Assn. Anaesths. Gt. Brit. & Irel.; Yorks. Soc. Anaesths. Prev: Res. Anaesth. Roy. Infirm. Edin.; SHO (Gen. Surg. & Cas.) Roy. Bucks. Hosp. Aylesbury; Anaesth. Regist. Roy. Bucks. & Assoc. Hosps. Gp.

WOJCIUK, Jerzy 35 Breck Road, Blackpool FY3 9DL — LRCP LRCS Ed. LRCPS Glas. 1997.

WOJNAROWSKA, Fenella Theta Department of Dermatology, The Churchill, Oxford Radcliffe Hospital, Oxford OX3 7LJ Tel: 01865 228259 Fax: 01865 228260; Piddington Place, Piddington, Bicester OX6 0PY — BM BCh 1973 Oxf.; MA Oxf. 1972, MSc 1971, BM BCh 1973; DM Oxf. 1995; FRCP Lond. 1993. (St. Mary's) Cons. Dermat. The Ch.ill, Oxf. Radcliffe. Hosp.; Reader Dermat. Univ. Oxf. Prev: Sen. Clin. Lect. (Dermat.) Univ. Oxf.; Sen. Regist. St. John's Hosp. Dis. Skin Lond.; Regist. (Dermat.) St. Mary's Hosp. Lond.

WOJTULEWSKI, Jan Andrzej 16 Cranborne Avenue, Eastbourne BN20 7TS — MB BS 1963 Lond.; FRCP Lond. 1987; MRCP (U.K.) 1971; MRCS Eng. LRCP Lond. 1963. (Westm.) Cons. Rheum. E.bourne Health Dist. Prev: Sen. Regist. W.m. Hosp. Lond.; Med. Regist. Roy. Masonic Hosp. Lond.; Res. Med. Off. Amer. Hosp. Paris.

WOKO, Ellis Chinatu 77 Burnley Road, London NW10 1EE — MB BS 1996 Lond.

WOKO, Mr Samuel Chinatu The Surgery, 77 Burnley Road, London NW10 1EE Tel: 020 8452 7689 — MB BCh BAO 1960 Dub.; FRCS Ed. 1969.

WOLANCZYK, Witold Jozef (retired) Eldene Health Centre, Eldene, Swindon SN3 3RZ — MB BCh BAO 1955 NUI. Prev: Ho. Off. Roy. Matern. Hosp. Belf. & Roy. Belf. Hosp. Sick Childr.

WOLDMAN, Simon Jack 23 Poplar Avenue, Glasgow G77 5QZ; 53 Grampian Gardens, Dyce, Aberdeen AB21 7LF — MB ChB 1989 Glas.; MRCP 1993. Specialist Regist. Cardiol. W.. Scot. Rotat.

WOLF, Andrew Robert Department of Anaesthesia, Royal Hospital for Sick Children, Yorkhill, Glasgow G3 8SJ — MB BChir 1980 Camb.; FFA RCS Eng. 1985. Assoc. Prof. Anaesth. Penn. State Univ., USA; Dir. Pediat. Anaesth. & IC Hershey Med. Center., USA. Prev: Lect. (Anaesth.) Univ. Bristol.

WOLF, Anton Lilac Cottage, 147 Waddicar Lane, Melling, Liverpool L31 1DS Tel: 0151 546 3377 — LRCP LRCS 1955 Ed.; LRCP LRCS Ed. LRFPS Glas. 1955. Prev: Ho. Phys. Mill La. Hosp. Wallasey & Vict. Centr. Hosp. Wallasey; Sen. Ho. Off. O & G Gen. Hosp. Ashton-under-Lyne.

WOLF, Eugene 25 Wayland Avenue, London E8 2HP Tel: 020 7254 4988 — MD 1943 Czechoslovakia; MA Camb. 1946; FRCPsych 1972. Socs: Gp.-Analyt. Soc.; Fell. Roy. Soc. Med. Prev: Sen. Lect. Acad. Dept. Psychiat. & Hon. Consult. Middlx. Hosp. Lond.; Vis. Prof. Memor. Univ. Newfld., Canada; Maj. RAMC, Command Psychiat.

WOLF, Paulus A 10 Hayden Walk, Oadby, Leicester LE2 4TL — Artsexamen 1988 Maastricht; Artsexamen 1988 Maasricht.

WOLF, Rebecca Cassandra 5 St Johns Cl, Morton, Bourne PE10 0PA — MB ChB 1997 Sheff.

WOLFE, Carey Spencer Vine Surgery, Hindhayes Lane, Street BA16 0ET Tel: 01458 841122 Fax: 01458 840044; Welham Rise, Charlton Mackrell, Somerton TA11 7AJ — MB BChir 1981 Camb.; MRCP (UK) 1984; DRCOG 1989. (St. Thos.) GP Practitioner Princip.; GP Orthopaedic Specialist Meridip PCT. Socs: Brit. Soc. Rheum.; Roy. Coll. Phys.; Brit. Assn. for Sport in Med. Prev: Regist. (Med.) Soton. HA; Regist. (Rheum.) St. Thos. Hosp. Lond.

WOLFE, Charles David Alexander Division of Public Health Sciences, GRT School of Medicine Guy's Campus, London SE1 3QD Tel: 020 7955 5000 Fax: 020 7403 4602 Email: charles.wolfe@kcl.ac.uk; 48 West Square, London SE11 4SP — MB BS 1978 Lond.; MD Lond. 1990; MRCS Eng. LRCP Lond. 1978; FFPHM RCP (UK) 1996; FRCOG 1988. (Roy. Free Medical and Dental School London) Reader (Pub. Health Med.) Guy's, King's & St Thomas' Sch. of Med. Lond.; Dir. Of Research and Developm., Guy's & St Thomas Hosp.

WOLFE, Ingrid Johanna Flat 7, 19 Frognal, London NW3 6AR — MB BS 1997 Lond.

WOLFE, James Godiva Cottage, Evesham Road, Salford Priors, Evesham WR11 5UU — MB ChB 1996 Liverp.

WOLFE, Jason Flat 3, 3 Clifton Road, Crouch End, London N8 8HY Tel: 020 8348 2825 Email: jwolfe@clara.net — MB BS 1993 Lond. (London) SHO Plastic Surg St Andrew Unit Chelmsford. Prev: SHO Rotat. (Surg.) Hammersmith Hosp. Lond.; SHO Rotat. (Surg.) P.ss Alexandra Hosp. Harlow.

WOLFE, Mr John Henry Nicholas 66 Harley Street, London Tel: 020 7580 5030 Fax: 020 7631 5341 Email: jwolfe@uk-consultants.co.uk; 1 Westcroft Square, London W6 0TB Tel: 020 8741 9035 Fax: 020 8746 3069 — MB BS 1971 Lond.; MS Lond. 1981; FRCS Eng. 1975. (St. Thos.) Cons. Surg. St. Mary's Hosp. Lond.; Hon. Sen. Lect. Roy. Postgrad. Med. Sch. Hammersmith; Hon. Cons. (Surg.) Roy. Brompton Hosp.; Cons. Surg. Edwd. VII Hosp. for Off. Lond.; Mem. Edit. Bd. Europ. Jl. Vasc. Surg.; Vice Pres. Vase Div. UEMS. Socs: (Counc.) Vasc. Soc. GB & Irel. (Chairm. Vasc. Advis. Comm.); (Counc.) Assoc. Surg. GB & Irel.; Hon. Corr. Mem. Soc. Vascula Surg. USA. Prev: Sen. Regist. (Surg.) St. Thos. Hosp. Lond.; Research Fell. Harvard Med. Sch. Boston, USA; SHO St. Jas. Hosp. Balham.

WOLFE, Rev. Kenneth Wesley (retired) 40 Greenfield Avenue, Spinney Hill, Northampton NN3 2AF Tel: 01604 406369 — MB BCh BAO 1942 Belf. Prev: Cas. Off. Radcliffe Infirm. Oxf.

WOLFE, Martin James The Medical Specialist Group, PO Box 113, Alexandra House, Les Frieteaux, St Martin's, Guernsey GY1 3EX — MB BS 1973 Lond.; FFA RCS Eng. 1978. (Middlx.) Prev: Cons. Anaesth. N. Derbysh. HA & Rampton Hosp. Notts.; Cons. Anaesth. Bassetlaw HA.

WOLFE, Ronald Rutland Place Surgery, 21 Rutland Place, Glasgow G51 1TA Tel: 0141 427 3121 Fax: 0141 427 7600 — MB ChB 1977 Ed.

WOLFE, Samantha Sarah Braeside, Main St., Thornton le Moor, Northallerton DL7 9EA — MB ChB 1997 Leic.

WOLFENDALE, Katherine Dilys 115 Station Road, Marple, Stockport SK6 6PA — BM BS 1997 Nottm.

WOLFENDALE, Margaret Rose 19 Lower Way, Great Brickhill, Milton Keynes MK17 9AG Tel: 01525 261647 — MB BS 1956 Lond.; MD Lond. 1980; MRCS Eng. LRCP Lond. 1955. (Roy. Free) Prev: Cons. Cytopath. Stoke Mandeville Hosp. Aylesbury.

WOLFENDALE, Richard Ellis (retired) Easter Invervar, Glenlyon, Aberfeldy PH15 2PL Tel: 01887 877214 — MB BChir 1952 Camb.; MRCS Eng. LRCP Lond. 1952. Prev: Ho. Surg. Manch. Roy. Infirm.

WOLFENDEN, Brian Anthony (retired) Field End, 2 Manor Farm Cottages, Marsworth, Tring HP23 4LN Tel: 01296 661698 — MB ChB 1949 Manch.; MRCGP.

WOLFERSTAN, Martin Accident & Emergency Department, South Tyneside District Hospital, Harton Lane, South Shields NE34 0PL — MD 1969 Columbia; MA (Hons.) Camb. 1964; BA (Hons.) 1960.

WOLFF, Anna Layla Email: ds_a_l_wolff@hotmail.com — MB ChB 1987 Manch. (Manchester)

WOLFF, Anthony Herbert 26 Quernmore Road, London N4 4QX Tel: 020 8340 9510 — MB BS 1980 Lond.; BSc Lond. 1977, MB BS 1980; MRCP (UK) 1985; FCAnaesth. 1989. (Univ. Coll. Hosp.) Sen. Regist. (Anaesth.) Roy. Free Hosp. Lond. Prev: SHO (Gen. Med.) Lond. Hosp.; Lect. (Physiol.) Lond. Hosp. Med. Coll.; Regist. (Gen. Med.) Lond. Hosp.

WOLFF, Antonia Child & Family Centre, Maas Road, Northfield, Birmingham B31 2PR Tel: 0121 476 6969 — BSc Lond. 1978, MB

BS 1981; MRCP (UK) 1987; DCH RCP Lond. 1983. Cons. Community Paediat. Child & Family Centre Birm.

WOLFF, Christopher Bancroft 52 Victoria Park, Cambridge CB4 3EL Fax: 01462 742893 — MB ChB 1962 Sheff.; PhD Lond. 1975; MRCP Lond. 1969; FRCP 1998. (Univ. Sheff.) Hon. Cons. Clin. Physiol. Guy's Hosp. Lond./Cons. St. Thomas's Hosp, Sherrington Sch.; Hon. Clin. Research Fell. Clin. Phys. Balts & the Lond. Socs: Physiol. Soc.; Med. Res. Soc.; Int. Soc. For Oxygen transport to tissues. Prev: Clin. Research Fell. Kings Coll. Hosp. Lond.

WOLFF, Elizabeth Patricia Fay Bridge Lane Health Centre, 20 Bridge Lane, Battersea, London SW11 3AD Tel: 020 7585 1499 Fax: 020 7978 4707; Flat 5, The Priory, 225 Bedford Hill, Balham, London SW12 9HU — MB ChB 1993 Sheff.; DRCOG 1995. GP Battersea Lond.; Clin. Asst. Genito-Urin. Med.

WOLFF, Geoffrey Simon MRC Social, Genetic & Develop. Psychiatry Research Centre, Institute of Psychiatry (Social Psychiatry Section), De Crespegny Park, London SE5 8AF Email: g.wolff@iop.bpmf.ac.uk — MB ChB 1985 Manch.; BSc (Hons) (Anat.) Manch. 1982; MD Manch. 1995; MRCPsych 1990; DCBT 1997. (Manch.) Sen. Regist. Gen. Adult Psychiat. (Eating Disorders Unit) Bethlem & Maudsley (NHS) Trust Lond.; Attached worker, MRC Social, Genetic & Developm. Psychiat. Research Centre (Social Psychiat. Sect.), Inst. of Psychiat. Lond. Socs: MRCPsych. Prev: Clin. Scientist, MRC Social, Genetic & Developm. Psychiat. Research Centre; +Inst. Psychiat. Lond.; Hon. Sen. Regist. Maudsley & Bethlem (NHS) Trust Lond.

WOLFF, Isidor (retired) 71 Milverton Road, Giffnock, Glasgow G46 7LQ Tel: 0141 638 1512 — LRCP LRCS Ed. LRFPS Glas. 1942.

WOLFF, Jill (retired) 53 Danbury Street, Islington, London N1 8LE Tel: 020 7226 0748 — MB ChB 1950 Birm. Prev: Clin. Asst. Roy. N. Hosp. Lond.

WOLFF, Linda Elisabet Bonnybridge Hospital, Falkirk Road, Bonnybridge FK4 1BD Tel: 01324 814685 Fax: 01324 815652; 19 Castle Road, Dollar FK14 7BE — MB ChB 1982 Ed.; MRCPsych 1987; DRCOG 1985. Cons. Psychiat. (Old Age Psychiat.) Bellsdyke Hosp. Larbert. Prev: Sen. Regist. (Psychiat.) Gtr. Glas. HB.

WOLFF, Professor Otto Herbert, CBE 53 Danbury Street, London N1 8LE Tel: 020 7226 0748 — MB BChir 1943 Camb.; MD Camb. 1954; FRCP Lond. 1962, M 1948; MRCS Eng. LRCP Lond. 1943; DCH Eng. 1949; BM BS FRCPCH (Honorary) 1996. (Univ. Coll. Hosp.) Emerit. Prof. Child Health & Dean Inst. Child Health Lond. Socs: Fell. Roy. Soc. Med.; (Ex-Pres.) Brit. Paediat. Assn.; MRCPCH. Prev: Cons. Phys. Hosp. Sick Childr. Gt. Ormond St. Lond.; Reader (Paediat. & Child Health) Univ. Birm.

WOLFF, Sulammith (retired) 38 Blacket Place, Edinburgh EH9 1RL Tel: 0131 667 7811 Fax: 0131 662 0337 Email: h.walton@edu.ad.uk — BM BCh Oxf. 1947; MA Oxf. 1950; FRCP Lond. 1972, M 1951; FRCPsych 1972; DPM Lond. 1958; DCH Eng. 1949. Prev: Cons. Child. Psychiat. Roy. Hosp. Sick Childr. Edin.

WOLFF-MACDONALD, Elisabeth Marie 3 Dawson Place, London W2 4TD — MD 1983 Amiens.

WOLFIN, Michael Benjamin 11 Calton Avenue, London SE21 7DE — MB BS 1989 Lond.

WOLFLE, Andrew Donald The Nook Surgery, Withyham Road, Groombridge, Tunbridge Wells TN3 9QP Tel: 01892 863326 Fax: 01892 863985; Glen Andred Lodge, Corseley Road, Groombridge, Tunbridge Wells TN3 9PN — MB BS 1988 Lond.; MRCGP 1993; DRCOG 1993. Prev: Trainee GP Roy. Tunbridge Wells VTS; Ho. Phys. Guys Hosp.; Ho. Surg. Greenwich Dist. Hosp.

WOLFMAN, Leonard Charles Underlea Stables, North Sudley Road, Mossley Hill, Liverpool L17 6BT — MB ChB 1947 Liverp. (Liverp.) Hon. Capt. RAMC; Hosp. Pract. Psychiat. Liverp. Drug Dependency Clinic. Socs: Liverp. Med. Inst.

WOLFMAN, Michael John Longrove Surgery, 70 Union Street, Barnet EN5 4HT Tel: 020 8441 9440/9563 Fax: 020 8441 4037; 9 Park Road, New Barnet, Barnet EN4 9QA Email: mikewolf-y-wsfoundation@btinternet.com — MB ChB 1982 Liverp.; DRCOG 1988; Cert. Family Plann. JCC 1988. Clin. Asst. (A & E) Barnet Gen. Hosp.; Clin. Asst. Lond. Hospice; Club Doctor Barnet FC; Vice-Chairm. Williams Foundat.; Mem. Idiopathic Infantile Hypercalcaemia Foundat. (Mem. Med. Comm.).

WOLFMAN, Stuart Samuel Underlea Stables, North Sudley Road, Mossley Hill, Liverpool L17 6BT — MB ChB 1978 Liverp.; MRCP (UK) 1981.

WOLFSON, Martin Stephen The Surgery, 28 Claremont Road, Surbiton KT6 4RF Tel: 020 8399 2280 Fax: 020 8390 0371; 11 St Leonards Road, Surbiton KT6 4DE Tel: 020 8399 7484 — MB BS 1974 Lond.; BSc Lond. 1971, MB BS 1974; MRCP (UK) 1977; MRCGP 1982; DRCOG 1981. (Westm.) Occupat. Health Cons. St. Anthonys Hosp. Prev: Regist. (Med.) Guy's Hosp. Lond.; SHO (O & G) Dulwich Hosp. Lond.; SHO (Med.) St. Thomas Hosp. Lond.

WOLFSON, Richard, KStJ, Capt. RAMC Retd. (retired) 7 Eglinton Drive, Giffnock, Glasgow G46 7NQ Tel: 0141 638 4220 Fax: 0141 638 4222 Email: dick@jenni5.freeserve.co.uk — LRCP LRCS Ed. LRFPS Glas. 1947; BCH Ed. 1960; DA Eng. 1963. Anaesth. StoneHo. Hosp. Prev: Clin. Asst. (Anaesth.) Edin. Roy. Infirm.

WOLINSKI, Alexander Peter X-Ray Department, Russells Hall Hospital, Dudley Tel: 01384 456111; Gorse Green Cottage, Gorse Green Lane, Belbroughton, Stourbridge DY9 9UH Tel: 01562 730939 — MB ChB 1978 Birm.; FRCR 1984. Cons. Radiol. Dudley Hosps. Socs: Brit. Inst. Radiol.; Brit. Soc. Interven.al Radiol. Prev: Sen. Regist. (Radiol.) Plymouth Gen. Hosp. & Bristol Roy. Infirm.; Regist. (Radiol.) Bristol Roy. Infirm.

WOLKIND, Stephen Nathaniel Flat 2, Helmsley, 7 Cleveland Road, London E18 2AY — MB BS 1962 Lond.; MD Lond. 1972; FRCPsych 1979, M 1973; DPM Eng. 1966. (Middx.) Prev: Sen. Lect. (Clin. Psychiat.) Lond. Hosp. Med. Coll.; Sen. Regist. (Psychiat.) Lond. Hosp.; Regist. (Psychiat.) United Camb. Hosps.

WOLL, Nora Kathleen, MBE (retired) Hedgehope, Church Lane, Bottesford, Nottingham NG13 0EJ — MB BS 1938 Durh. Prev: Capt. IMS.

WOLL, Penella Jane Cancer Research UK Department of Clinical Oncology, University of Nottingham, City Hospital, Hucknall Road, Nottingham NG5 1PB Tel: 0115 969 1169 Ext: 47297 Fax: 0115 962 7923 Email: penella.woll@nott.ac.uk — MB BS 1980 Newc.; PhD Lond. 1990; BMedSc (Hons.) Newc. 1977; MRCP (UK) 1983; Spec. Accredit. Med. Oncol. JCHMT 1992; Spec. Accredit. Gen. Med. JCHMT 1992; FRCP 1998. Reader (Clin. Oncol.) Univ. Nottm.; Hon. Cons. Med. Oncol. City Hosp. Nottm. Socs: Assn. of Cancer Phys.s (Sec.). Prev: Lect. (Med. Oncol.) Univ. Manch. & Christie Hosp.; Clin. Research Fell. Imperial Cancer Research Fund & Guys Hosp. Lond.

WOLLASTON, John Francis The Tower, Elsdon, Newcastle upon Tyne NE19 1AA Tel: 01830 520179 Fax: 01830 520179 — MB BS 1969 Newc.; MFOM RCP Lond. 1997, A 1980; DIH Soc. Apoth. Lond. 1978. (Newcastle Upon Tyne) Cons. Occupat. Phys. Indust. & Organisational Health. Socs: Soc. of Occup. Med.; Roy. Soc. Of Med. Prev: Managing Dir. & Princip. Med. Advisor AMARC Occupat. Health & Safety Serv.; Chief Med. Off. & Dir. Occupat. Health & Safety Servs. Brit. Ship Builders; Med. Off. RN.

WOLLASTON, Oenone Hilda (retired) The Staithe, 38 Cross Lane, Mossley, Congleton CW12 3JX Tel: 01260 271318 Email: oenonew@tinyworld.co.uk — MB BS 1958 Lond.; MRCGP 1975; Cert. Family Plann. JCC 1960. GP Amea Health Auth.; GP Stoke-on-Trent; Family Plann. Prev: Child Med. Off. AHA.

WOLLASTON, Sarah Chagford, Newton Abbot TQ13 8BW Tel: 01647 433320 Fax: 01647 432452 — MB BS 1986 Lond.; BSc (Path.) Lond. 1983; MRCGP 1992; DRCOG 1991. (UMDS (Guys)) Princip. in Gen. Pract. (p/t); Dep. Police Surg. Prev: Trainee GP Bristol.

WOLLASTON, Sophie Leonora River Place Group Practice, River Place, Essex Road, London N1 2DE Tel: 020 7530 2100 Fax: 020 7530 2102 — MB BS 1988 Lond.; BSc Lond. 1985; DCH 1991; DRCOG 1992; MRCGP 1994.

WOLLNER, Leo (retired) 16 Blenheim Drive, Oxford OX2 8DG Tel: 01865 557109 — MB BS 1951 Lond.; FRCP Lond. 1974, M 1957; MRCS Eng. LRCP Lond. 1951. Hon. Cons. Phys. Oxf. HA (T). Prev: Cons. Phys. (Gen. & Geriat. Med.) John Radcliffe Hosp. & Radcliffe Infirm. Oxf.

WOLLNER, Sylvia Helen (retired) 16 Blenheim Drive, Oxford OX2 8DG Tel: 01865 557109 — MB BS 1952 Lond. Prev: Assoc. Specialist (Geriat. Med.) Radcliffe Infirm. Oxf.

WOLMAN, Basil (retired) 29 Ashfield Lodge, Palatine Road, Didsbury, Manchester M20 2UD Tel: 0161 445 3500 — MB ChB Manch. 1941; MD Manch. 1951; FRCP Lond. 1972, M 1944; MRCS

WOLMAN

Eng. LRCP Lond. 1942; FRCPCH 1997; DCH Eng. 1947. Cons. Paediat. The Bridge Child Care Cons. Lond. Prev: Cons. Paediat. Booth Hall Childr. Hosp. Manch.

WOLMAN, David (retired) 48 Hall Road E., Liverpool L23 8TU — MB ChB 1950 Manch. Prev: SHO (Phys.) Roy. Albert Edwd. Infirm. Wigan.

WOLMAN, Richard Ian 17 Old Barrack Yard, London SW1X 7NP Tel: 020 7235 1711 Fax: 020 7823 1681; 24 Wilton Row, London SW1X 7NS Tel: 020 7235 6006 Fax: 020 7235 5440 — MB ChB 1981 Cape Town; DPM (S. Afr.) Cape Town 1981; Inceptor Roy. coll. Psychiat. (Cape Town and St. Georges Tooting) Private Cons. Med. Psychotherapist. Socs: BMA.

WOLMAN, Roger Louis Royal National Orthopaedic Hospital Trust, Brockley Hill, Stanmore HA7 4LP Tel: 020 8954 2300 Email: rwolman@rnoh-tr.org — MB ChB 1981 Manch.; MD Manch. 1990; MRCP (UK) 1984; FRCP (UK) 1998. (Manch.) Cons. Sports Med. & Rheum. Roy. Nat. Orthop. Hosp. Lond.; Cons. Brit. Olympic Med. Centre; Sen. Lect. UCL. Prev: Sen. Regist. (Rheum. & Rehabil.) Roy. Nat. Orthop. Hosp. Lond.; Regist. Brit. Olympic Med. Centre N.wick Pk. Hosp. Middlx.; Regist. (Gen. Med. & Rheum.) Middlx. Hosp. Lond.

WOLMUTH, Henry (retired) 2 Torver Road, Harrow HA1 1TQ Tel: 020 8427 3943 — MD 1939 Paris.

WOLPE, Alexander Paul Gudgeheath Lane Surgery, 187 Gudgeheath Lane, Fareham PO15 6QA Tel: 01329 280887 Fax: 01329 231321; 33 Common Lane, Titchfield, Fareham PO14 4DA — MB ChB 1982 Birm.; MRCGP 1987; DRCOG 1985.

WOLSEY, Lotte Andrea Frolund 5 Coventry Road, Newton Hall, Durham DH1 5XD Tel: 0191 386 1610 — MB ChB 1995 Sheff.; MB ChB (Hons.) Sheff. 1995; DCH 1998. (Sheffield) SHO (Obstetrics & Gyn.) Centr. Middlx. Hosp. Socs: Med. Defence Union; BMA. Prev: SHO (A & E) St. Geos. Hosp. Tooting; SHO (Med.) W. Middlx. Univ. Hosp.; SHO (Paediat.) Centr. Middlx. Hosp.

WOLSLEY, Karen 8 Belmont Park, Belfast BT4 3DU — MB BCh. BAO 1992 Belf.

WOLSTENCROFT, Philip John, Surg. Lt. RN 36 Smithy Croft, Houghton, Carlisle CA3 0NS Tel: 01228 28098 — MB ChB 1989 Birm. Squadron Med. Off. RN. Prev: Ho. Phys. RNH Haslar; Ho. Surg. Birm. Accid. Hosp.

WOLSTENCROFT, Rachel Frances Cober View, Old Hill, Helston TR13 8HT Tel: 01326 565766 — MB ChB 1997 Manch.

WOLSTENHOLME, Allan Grant (retired) Airlie Cottage, Mayfield TN20 Tel: 01435 3169 — LMSSA 1944 Lond. Prev: Med. Regist. Hellingly Hosp. Hailsham.

***WOLSTENHOLME, James Henry** 18 Scammerton, Wilnecote, Tamworth B77 4LA — MB ChB 1996 Birm.

WOLSTENHOLME, Roger James Royal Albert Edward Infirmary, Wigan WN1 2NN — MB BS 1974 Lond.; BSc (Hons.) (Pharmacol.) Lond. 1971; FRCP Lond. 1994; FRCP Ed. 1985; MRCP (UK) 1978; MRCS Eng. LRCP Lond. 1974; Dip. Sports Med. Scotl. 1993; DTM & H Eng. 1979. (Westm.) Cons. Phys. Roy. Albert Edwd. Infirm. Wigan; Assoc. Prof. Aga Khan Univ. Hosp. Karachi, Pakistan. Socs: Brit. Thorac. Soc.; Brit. Soc. Clin. Allergy & Immunol.; Brit. Assn. Sport & Med. Prev: Lect. (Respirat. Dis.) Univ. Edin.; Med. Off. (Min. Overseas Developm.) Maldive Is.s; Ho. Phys. W.m. Hosp.

WOLSTENHOLME, Virginia 45 St Lukes Avenue, London SW4 7LG — BM 1993 Soton.

WOLTMANN, Gerrit 30 Bambrook Close, Desford, Leicester LE9 9FY — State Exam Med 1989 Hannover; MRCP (UK) 1994. Regist. (Respirat. Med.) Glenfield Hosp. Leicester.

WOLTON, Ann Dorothy Maple Cottage, Water Lane, Somerton TA11 6RG — MB ChB 1986 Sheff.

WOLVERSON, Adam Stuart Nottingham City Hospital NHS Trust, Nottingham NG2 6QH Tel: 0115 969 1169; 7 Aira Close, Gamston, Nottingham NG2 6QH Tel: 0115 981 5241 — BM BS 1988 Nottm.; BMedSci Nottm. 1986; FRCA 1996. Specialist Regist. (Anaesth.) City Hosp. Nottm. Socs: Intens. Care Soc.; Assn. Anaesth.; Eur. Soc. Anaesth. Prev: SHO (Gen. Med.) Univ. Hosp. Nottm.; SHO (Anaesth.) Univ. Hosp. Nottm.; Regist. (Anaesth.) Univ. Hosp. Nottm.

WOLVERSON, Keith 33 Hobby Close, East Hunsby, Northampton NN4 0RN — MB BS 1996 Lond.

WOLVERSON, Mr Richard Lane City Hospital, Birmingham B18 7QH Tel: 0121 554 3801 — MB BS 1974 Lond.; MS Lond. 1986, MB BS 1974, BDS 1970; FRCS Eng. 1978. Cons. Gen. Surg. City Hosp. Birm.; Arris & Gale Lect. RCS Eng; Clin. Sen. Lect. Univ. Birm. Med. Sch. Socs: Fell. Assn. Surgs. Prev: Cons. Gen. Surg. Dudley Rd. Hosp. Birm.; Sheldon Clin. Research Fell. Dudley Rd. Hosp. Birm.; Regist. (Surg.) Dudley Rd. Hosp. Birm.

WOMACK, Christopher Department of Pathology, Peterborough District Hospital, Thorpe Road, Peterborough PE3 6DA Tel: 01733 874648 Fax: 01733 874791 Email: chris.womack@pbh-tr.anglox.nhs.uk — MB BS 1978 Lond.; FRCPath 1996, M 1984; T(Path) 1991. Cons. Path. P'boro. Dist. Hosp. Socs: Assn. Clin. Paths.; Brit. Soc. Clin. Cytol.; Internat. Acad. Path. Prev: Sen. Regist. (Histopath.) Univ. & City Hosp. Nottm.; Regist. (Histopath.) St. Mary's Hosp. Manch.; SHO (Path.) Manch. Roy. Infirm.

WOMACK, Mr Nigel Richard Pinderfields Hospital, Aberford Road, Wakefield WF1 4DG; Kingswood House, 3 The Drive, Adel, Leeds LS16 6BG Tel: 0113 261 3198 — MB BS 1978 Lond.; BSc (Hons.) Lond. 1975, MB BS (Hons.) 1978, MS 1988; FRCS Eng. 1981; MRCS Eng. LRCP Lond. 1978. (Guy's) Cons. Gen. Surg. Pinderfields Hosp. Wakefield. Prev: Sen. Regist. (Surg.) Leeds; Lect. (Surg.) Lond. Hosp.; MRC Research Fell. Leeds Gen. Infirm.

WOMERSLEY, Adrienne Margaret Elizabeth (retired) Barns Close House, Amberley, Stroud GL5 5AG Tel: 01453 874100 Fax: 01453 874104 — MB BCh BAO 1979 Belf.

WOMERSLEY, Barbara Jean 37 Shakespeare Road, Acton, London W3 6SF — MB BS 1956 Lond.; BSc (Physiol.) Lond. 1953, MB BS 1956. (St. Bart.)

WOMERSLEY, Deborah Susan 8 School Road, Himley, Dudley DY3 4LG — BM BS 1988 Nottm.

WOMERSLEY, Hester Clare Kohinur, Old Mill Road, Chelston, Torquay TQ2 6HW Tel: 01803 605508 — MB ChB 1991 Manch.; BSc (Med. Sci.) 1st cl. Hons. Physiol. St. And. Univ. 1988; MRCPsych, June 1998. Specialist Regist. in Old Age Psychiat. Shelton Hosp. Prev: Regist. (Gen. Psychiat.) WhitCh. Hosp. Cardiff; SHO (Old Age Psychiat.) Chorley Dist. Gen. Hosp.; SHO (Gen. Psychiat.) Roy. Oldham Hosp.

WOMERSLEY, John Greater Glasgow Health Board, 350 St Vincent St., Glasgow G3 8YU Tel: 0141 201 4815 Fax: 0141 201 4733 Email: john.womersley@glasgow-hb.scot.nhs.uk; 22 Lochend Road, Bearsden, Glasgow G61 1DX Tel: 0141 942 7149 Email: john@womet.freeserve.co.uk — MB ChB 1966 Glas.; PhD Glas. 1974, BSc 1963; FRCPS Glas. 1991; FFCM 1985, M 1977; DPH Glas. 1976. (Glas.) Cons. Pub. Health Med. Gtr. Glas. HB; Hon. Clin. Lect. Pub. Health Glas. Univ. Socs: BMA. Prev: SCM Gtr. Glas. HB & Lanarksh. HB; Lect. (Physiol.) Univ. Glas.

WOMERSLEY, John Samuel Bassett St Brannocks Road Medical Centre, St. Brannocks Road, Ilfracombe EX34 8EG Tel: 01271 863840 — MB BCh BAO 1981 Belf.; MRCGP 1986.

WONG, Albert 163 Hennessy Road, 5/Fl., Wanchai, Hong Kong Tel: 2511 1239 Fax: 2511 0099; 73 Darwin Court, 16-24 Gloucester Avenue, London NW1 7BQ Tel: 020 7284 3387 — MB BS 1974 Lond. (Westm.) GP Hong Kong; Chairm. Hosp. Gov. Comm., Chesh. Home, Hong Kong. Socs: BMA & Hong Kong Med. Assn. Prev: SHO (Obst. & Gyn.) St. Lukes Hosp. Guildford; Cas. Off. St. Stephens Hosp. Lond.; Med. Off. Univ. Surg. Unit Hong Kong Univ.

***WONG, Alexander Kai Ming** 5 Bournbrook Road, Selly Oak, Birmingham B29 7BL — MB ChB 1994 Birm.

WONG, Alice Khin Mar Win 70 Norwood Road, Southall UB2 4EY; 162 Shakespear Avenue, Hayes UB4 0BP — MB BS 1970 Rangoon; MB BS Rangoon, Burma 1970; DRCOG 1979.

WONG, Alison Po Ling Falmouth Road Surgery, 78 Falmouth Road, London SE1 4JW Tel: 020 7407 4101/0945 Fax: 020 7357 6170 — MB BS 1990 Lond.; MRCGP 1994; DRCOG 1993.

WONG, Andrew No. 9, Andrew St., Liverpool L4 4DS Tel: 01510284 7850 — MB BS 1987 Singapore; M Med (Anaesth.) 1996; FRCA 1997. (Nat. Univ. Singapore) Specialist Regist. (Anaesth.).

WONG, Aric Shiu-Quan Castle House, Castle Road, Horsell, Woking GU21 4ET — MB BS 1984 Lond.; MRCGP 1989. Trainee GP Horsley VTS.

WONG, Cheong Yee The Surgery, 105 Carslake Road, London SW15 3DD Tel: 020 8785 6440 Fax: 020 8788 2063 — MB BS Lond. 1969; DObst RCOG 1972; DCH Eng. 1971. (Univ. Coll. Hosp.) Prev: SHO (Paediat.) N. Middlx. Hosp. Edmonton; SHO (O & G) P.ss

Alexandra Hosp. Harlow; SHO (Anaesth.) King Edwd. Memor. Hosp. Ealing.

WONG, Chi Chown 16 Russell Court, Cambridge CB2 1HW — BChir 1996 Camb.

WONG, Mr Chi Ho Department of Cardiothoracic Surgery, University Hospital Birmingham, Queen Elizabeth Medical Centre, Edgbaston, Birmingham B15 2TH Tel: 07050 609664 Fax: 0121 627 2542 Email: c.h.wong@bham.ac.uk; 116 Preston Road, Standish, Wigan WN6 0HY Tel: 01257 400919 Fax: 0121 627 2542 — MB BChir 1992 Camb.; MA Camb. 1992, BA 1989; FRCS Eng. 1996; FRCS Ed. 1996. (Univ. Camb.) Regist., Dept. of Cardiothoracic, Univ. Hosp., Birm.; RCS Eng. Research Fell.sh.; Fell. MRC Cyclotron Unit, Hammersmith Hosp. Lond. Socs: Fell. Roy. Soc. Med. Mem. Heart Surg. Forum; Fell. Soc. Cardiothoracic Surgs. GB & Irel.; Heart Surg. Forum. Prev: SHO Regional Spinal Unit, Roy. Orthop. Hosp.; Research Fell. (Surg.) Dept. of Cardiothoracic Surg. Univ. Birm.; SHO Rotat. (Surg.) Univ. Birm. Hosp. Trust.

WONG, Chi-Hung 28 Ferndale View, Doncaster DN5 8HG — MB ChB 1990 Sheff.

WONG, Chi Kuen Oxford Road Medical Centre, 25 Oxford Road, Burnley BB11 3BB Tel: 01282 423603 Fax: 01282 832827; 78 Lindsay Park, Worsthorne, Burnley BB10 3SQ — MB ChB 1979 Manch.

WONG, Chieh Lee 72 Beckhill Walk, Leeds LS7 2RW — MB ChB 1997 Leeds.

WONG, Chin Yuan 9 Gateside Close, Cardiff CF23 8PB — MB BCh 1990 Wales; MRCOG 1996.

WONG, Chiu Ming The Surgery, 105 Bellenden Road, London SE15 4QY Tel: 020 7639 9622 Fax: 020 7732 0870 — MB BS 1988 Lond.

WONG, Chiung Ing 72 Beckhill Walk, Meanwood, Leeds LS7 2RW — MB ChB 1998 Manch.

WONG, Chong Peng 14 St Kildas Road, Harrow HA1 1QA — MB BS 1967 Lond.; DObst RCOG 1972. (Roy. Free) Prev: Ho. Off. (O & G) Lewisham Hosp.; Ho. Phys. (Paediat.) Roy. Free Hosp.; Obst. Ho. Surg. Roy. Free Hosp. Lond. (Liverp. Rd. Br.).

WONG, Mr Christopher Kwan Ming c/o C P Armstrongs Secretary, Frenchay Hospital, Frenchay Park, Bristol; 29 Cefn Onn Meadows, Lisvane, Cardiff CF14 0FL Tel: 01222 689674 — MB BCh 1992 Wales; FRCS (Eng.) 1996. Specialist Regist. Rotat. SW Region. Socs: BMA; Fell. RCS; ASIT. Prev: Specialist Regist. (Gen. & Vasc. Surg.) Treliske Hosp. Truro; SHO (Gen. Surg.) Univ. Hosp. Wales Cardiff; SHO (Trauma & Orthop. & A & E) Cardiff Roy. Infirm.

WONG, Chun Fung 29 Bracewood Gardens, Croydon CR0 5JL — MB BS 1996 Lond.

WONG, Conroy Allan Department of Respiratory Medicine, City Hospital, Hucknall Road, Nottingham NG5 1PJ Tel: 0115 969 1169 Email: mfzcw@unix.ccc.nottingham.ac.ud; 8 Finsbury Road, Arnold, Nottingham NG5 9QF Tel: 0115 926 1068 — MB ChB 1985 Otago; FRACP 1994; Dip. Obst. Otago 1988. Research Fell. (Respirat. Med.) Univ. of Nottm.; Hon. Sen. Regist. Respirat. Med. City Hosp. Nottm. Socs: Brit. Thorac. Soc.; Thoracic Soc. of Australia & New Zealand (TSANZ).

WONG, David Chuen Ho 11 Wolfe Crescent, London SE16 6SF — MB BS 1992 Lond.

WONG, David Jungmain Flat 11, 6 Riverview Place, Glasgow G5 8EB — MB ChB 1992 Glas.

WONG, Ee Min 1 Chinnocks Wharf, 42 Narrow St, Limehouse, London E14 8DJ — MB BS 1988 Lond.; FRCA 1993. (London Hospital Medical College) Cons. Anaesth. Prev: Sen. Registr., St Bart's; Regist. (Anaesth.) St Bart. Hosp. Lond.; SHO (Anaesth.) Whipps Cross Hosp. & Roy. Lond. Hosp.

WONG, Elizabeth Mandarin, Pewley Point, Pewley Hill, Guildford GU1 3SP; Dermatology Department, Royal Surrey County Hospital, Guildford GU2 7XX — MD 1987 Lond.; MB BS 1976; MRCP (UK) 1979; FRCP 1997; Specialist Accredit. Dermat. JCHMT 1984. (Univ. Coll. Hosp.) Cons. Dermat. Roy. Surrey Co. Hosp. & Haslemere Hosps. Socs: Fell. Roy. Soc. Med.; Brit. Assn. Dermat.; BMA. Prev: Sen. Regist. & Lect. St. John's Hosp. Dis. Skin & Inst. Dermat. Lond.; Regist. (Med. & Dermat.) FarnBoro. Hosp.; Regist. (Dermat.) Guy's Hosp. & St. John's Hosp. Lond.

WONG, Folk-Man 45 Mall Chambers, Kensington Mall, London W8 4DZ — MB BS 1996 Lond.

WONG, Foong Han Doctors Mess, Worthing Hospital, Lyndhurst Road, Worthing BN11 2DH — MB BS 1996 Queensland.

WONG, Gavin Anthony Ernest Kai-Cheung Flat 2 Albert Court, 7 Elm Grove, Didsbury, Manchester M20 6PQ — MB ChB 1993 Dundee; MRCP (UK) 1996.

WONG, Gen Tat 4 Cotlands Green, Dunmurry, Belfast BT17 0BF Tel: 01232 626279 Fax: 01232 626279 — MB BCh BAO 1992 Belf.

WONG, Geoffrey Richard Chee Keong 16 Norland Place, London W11 4QG — MB BS 1993 Lond.; MA Camb. 1990. (UMDS) GP Asst.; Research Fell. Roy. Free & Univ. Coll. Med. Sch. UCL.

WONG, Grace Elaine Royal Surrey County Hospital, Egerton Road, Guildford GU2 7XX — MB BS 1993 Lond.; MRCP.

WONG, Grace Josephine Wing San 10 Aylmer Road, London N2 0BX — MB BS 1990 Lond.

WONG, Hoi Shing 15 Morningside, Washington NE38 9JH — MB ChB 1993 Manch.

WONG, Hok John Department of Clinical Biochemistry and Immunology, Kingston Hospital, Galsworthy Road, Kingston KT2 7QB Tel: 020 8934 3292 Email: jwong@kingstonhospital.nhs.uk — MB BCh BAO 1976 Dub.; FRC Path 1996; MSc Surrey 1980; MA Dub. 1980, MB BCh 1976; MRCPath. 1984. (Trinity College, Dublin University) Cons. Chem. Path. Kingston Hosp. Prev: Sen. Regist. (Chem. Path.) Char. Cross Hosp.

WONG, Ing Hin Alton House, Ayr Hospital, Dalmellington Road, Ayr KA6 6DX — MB ChB 1997 Glasgow.

WONG, Ismail Kien Chiong 73 Denison Road, London SW19 2DJ — MB BS 1998 Lond.

WONG, Mr Jackson Yan Wing Department of Paediatrics, Leicester Royal Infirmary, Leicester LE1 5WW Tel: 0116 541414; 11 Devonia Road, Oadby, Leicester LE2 4UJ Tel: 0116 271 2808 Fax: 0116 271 2808 Email: jw28@le.ac.uk — MB BS Lond. 1987; MB BS Lond. 1987; MRCP (UK) 1993; MRCP (UK) 1993; DCH RCP Lond. 1993; DCH RCP Lond. 1993; MRCPCH 1995; FHKAM (Paediat.) 1998; MHKCPaediat. 1998. (St. Mary's Hosp. Med. Sch. Univ. Lond.) Specialist Regist. (Paediat.) Leicester Roy. Infirm. Socs: BMA; Brit. Respirat. Soc.; Fell. Hong Kong Acad. Med. (Paediat.). Prev: Clin. Research Fell. (Paediat. Respirat. Med.) Dept. Child Health Univ. Leicester & Hon. Sen. Regist. Leicester Roy. Infirm.; Regist. (Paediat.) Hammersmith Hosp. & Qu. Charlotte & Chelsea Hosp. Lond.; Regist. (Paediat.) Lewisham Hosp. Lond.

WONG, Jacqueline Michelle Flat 5, 2 Lancaster Grove, London NW3 4NX — MB BChir 1990 Camb.; MB Bchir (Cantab) 1990; MA (Cantab) 1991.

***WONG, Jason Kar Wai** 16 George IV Street, Cambridge CB2 1HH — BChir 1998 Camb.

WONG, Jason Kin Fai 178 Whitehouse Road, Barnton, Edinburgh EH4 6DB — MB ChB 1998 Aberd.

WONG, Jen-San 37 Spring Pool, Warwick CV34 4UP Tel: 01926 497179 — MB ChB 1998 Leic.; MB ChB Leic 1998. (University of Leicester Medical School) SHO (Trauma & Orthop.) Alexandra Hopital, Redditch. Prev: Pre-Registration Ho. Off., Leicester Roy. Infirm., Leicester LE1 5WW.

WONG, John Soo Kiam The General Medical Centre, Surgery Lane, Hartlepool TS24 9DN; 6 Grantham Avenue, Hartlepool TS26 9QT — MB ChB 1983 Aberd.; MRCP (UK) 1988. Prev: Regist. (Gen. Med.) CrossHo. Hosp. Kilmarnock & Aberd. Roy. Infirm.; SHO (Med.) St. Luke's Hosp. Huddersfield.

WONG, Mr Julian Chi Leung 58 Langton's Wharf, The Calls, Leeds LS2 7EF — MB ChB 1991 Aberd.; FRCS Glas. 1996. Lect. (Surg.) Dept. Surg. Univ. Manch. Withington Hosp.; Specialist Regist Rotat. (Gen. Surg.) N. W. Region. Prev: SHO (Surg.) Acad. Unit Castle Hill Hosp.; SHO Rotat. (Surg.) Leeds Gen. Infirm.; Ho. Off. (Med. & Surg.) Aberd. Roy. Infirm.

WONG, Kayan Catherine Fazakerley Hospital, Longmoor Lane, Liverpool L9 7AL Tel: 0151 525 5980; 2A The Fairway, Alsager, Stoke-on-Trent ST7 2AZ Tel: 01270 872544 — MB ChB 1991 Liverp.; BSc (Hons.) Liverp. 1986. SHO (Med. & Rheum.) Fazakerley Hosp. Liverp. Prev: Ho. Off. (Med., Surg., Geriat. & Urol.) Fazakerley Hosp. Liverp.

WONG

WONG, Kenneth Kak Yuen 37 Mount Pleasant Road, London NW10 3EG — MB ChB 1992 Ed. SHO (Urol.) Freeman Hosp. Newc. u. Tyne.

WONG, Kirstin Elizabeth Brown Rigg, Halton Hall Gardens, Halton, Lancaster LA2 6LP — MB BS 1992 Lond.; DCH 1995; DRCOG 1996; MRCGP 1997; DFFP 1997. (Imperial College London)

WONG, Lai Hong 4 The Leazes, Sunderland SR1 3SW — MB ChB 1997 Sheff.

WONG, Leslie c/o MRC Tissue Bank, Imperial College School of Medicine, Hammersmith Hospital, Du Cane Road, London W12 0NN — MB ChB 1966 Otago.

WONG, Lin Hieng Royal Wrnwall Hospital, Truro, Cornwall TR1 3LJ Email: john.wong@RCHT.swest.nhs.uk; Email: johnlhw@netscape.net — MB BCh 1993 Wales; MRCP 1997. (Univ Wales) Specialist Regist. Gastroenterol. W. Midl. Traing. Scheme.

WONG, Mr Ling Sen 21 Furrows Close, Littlethorpe, Leicester LE9 5JR Tel: 0116 275 2228 Fax: 0121 627 2449 Email: lswong@hotmail.com; 14 Barclay Square, Renfrew PA4 8DY Tel: 0141 886 5381 — MB ChB 1989 Glas.; FRCS Ed. 1993; MD 1998. (Glasgow) Specialist Regist. Qu. Eliz. Hosp. Birm.; Specialist Regist. Selly Oak Hosp. Birm. Socs: Brit. Assn. Sugic. Oncol.; Assn. Surg. Train.; Assn. Coloproctol. Prev: Specialist Regist. (Gen. Surg.) Walsgrave Hosp. NHS Trust; Specialist Regist. Geo. Eliot Hosp. Nuneaton; Research Regist. (Gen. Surg.) Walsgrave Hosp. Coventry.

WONG, Locke Tse 30D South Hill Park, London NW3 2SB — MB BS 1996 Lond.

WONG, Man Kit Faith House Surgery, 723 Beverley Road, Hull HU6 7ER Tel: 01482 853296 Fax: 01482 855235; Shalom, 40 Badgers Wood, Cottingham HU16 5ST Tel: 01482 843293 — MB ChB 1987 Glas.

WONG, Margaret Mary Eye Unit, The Ayr Hospital, Dalmellington Road, Ayr KA6 6DX Tel: 01292 442384; 1 Knowle Road, Maidstone ME14 2BA — MB BS 1985 Med. Inst. (I) Rangoon; FRCS Ed. 1995; FRCOphth 1995. Staff Ophth. Ayr Hosp. Prev: SHO Kent & Sussex Hosp., Kent Co. Ophth. Hosp. Maidstone & Roy. Eye Infirm. Plymouth.

WONG, Maria Ka Yee Flat 9 Albert Court, 20 Stoneygate Road, Leicester LE2 2AD — MB ChB 1993 Leic.

WONG, Matthew Chi-Chung 21 Weald Lane, Harrow HA3 5EU — MB BS 1998 Lond.

WONG, Michael — MB ChB 1991 Manch.; MRCGP 1995; DFFP 1994; DRCOG 1994. (Manch.) Prev: GP Ripley; Trainee GP Oldham; SHO (O & G) Bolton HA.

WONG, Michael Kwai Yew Brownrigg, Halton Hall Gardens, halton, Lancaster LA2 6LP Tel: 01524 811358 Fax: 01524 811358. Email: mike@brownrig.demon.co.uk — MB BS 1992 Lond.; MRCGP 1997; DRCOG 1996; DCH 1996; DFFP 1997. (Imperial College) GP Assoc.

WONG, Nelson Chi-Kit 11 Greemwood Close, Ashwellthorpe, Norwich NR16 1HB — MRCS Eng. LRCP Lond. 1978; MB BS Lond. 1978; MRCP (UK) 1981.

WONG, Newton Alexander Chiang Shuek Department of Pathology, University of Edinburgh Medical School, Teviot Place, Edinburgh EH8 9AG Tel: 0131 650 3001 — MB ChB 1993 Bristol; MRCP 1996.

WONG, Nga Chung 4 The Leazes, Sunderland SR1 3SW Email: wongnc@netvigator.com — MB BS 1993 Newc. GP & Res. Med. Off. Union Hosp., Hong Kong. Socs: BMA.

WONG, Nyet Song Theresa 32 Barshaw Gardens, Appleton, Warrington WA4 5FA Tel: 01925 604035 Fax: 01925 604035 — MB BCh 1994 Wales; AFRCS. (Univ.Wales.Coll.Med) SHO Gen. Surg. Countess of Chester. Hosp. Prev: SHO (Gen. Surg.) Warrington. Gen. Hosp.; SHO (Plastics) Whiton Hosp.; SHO (Orthop.) Roy. Liverp. Univ. Hosp.

WONG, Oi Yee 16 The Beeches, Off Woodhead Drive, Cambridge CB4 1FY — MB BChir 1994 Camb. (Camb.) SHO Rotat. (Paediat.) Addenbrooke's Hosp. Camb.

WONG, Patricia Agnes Crabbs Cross Surgery, 38 Kenilworth Close, Crabbs Cross, Redditch B97 5JX Tel: 01527 544610 Fax: 01527 540286 — MB BS 1982 Lond. (Lond.) Prev: Trainee GP Redditch; SHO (Gen. Psychiat.) Barnsley Hall Hosp. BromsGr.; SHO (Geriat. & A & E) Dudley Rd. Hosp. Birm.

WONG, Patricia Che 4 Hayfield Gardens, Birmingham B13 9LE — MB ChB 1995 Birm.; ChB Birm. 1995.

WONG, Patrick Department of Anaesthetics, Queen Victoria Hospital, Holtye Road, East Grinstead RH19 3DZ — MB BS 1993 Lond.

WONG, Paul Tong Yin 110 Norman Road Surgery, Smethwick, Smethwick B67 5PU Tel: 0121 429 1373 & 021 420 2727 Fax: 0121 434 4549; 14 Greening Drive, Edgbaston, Birmingham B15 2XA — MB ChB 1978 Birm.; MRCS Eng. LRCP Lond. 1978.

WONG, Mr Phooi Kit Flat 5, 14 Hatherley Grove, London W2 5RB — MB BS 1986 Lond.; FRCS Eng. 1990. Socs: Fell. Roy. Soc. Med. (Comm. Mem. Clin. Sect.).

WONG, Quintin Kwing Kee North Brink Practice, 7 North Brink, Wisbech PE13 1JR Tel: 01945 585121 Fax: 01945 476423; The Old Vicarage, Barton Road, Wisbech PE13 4RP Tel: 01945 585121 Fax: 01945 476423 — MB BS 1985 Lond.; MRCGP 1990; DRCOG 1989. (Royal Free Hospital School of Medicine, London) Princip. Gen. Pract. Prev: Trainee GP. Qu. Eliz. Hosp. King's Lynn Norf.

WONG, Richard Chiang Wen Flat 2, 8 Rooney Mansions, Clifton, Bristol BS8 4HY — MB ChB 1989 Bristol; MB ChB (Hons.) Bristol 1989.

WONG, Richard Keng Mun — MB BChir 1995 Camb.; MA 1996; MRCP (UK) 1998. (Camb.) Specialist Registar (Med.) Leicester Roy. Infirm. Prev: SHO (Derm) Leicester Roy. Infirm.; SHO (Endocrine) Leicester Roy. Infirm.; SHO (Neurol.) Leicester Roy. Infirm.

WONG, Robina Yu-Chu 10 Herongate, Benfleet SS7 5SG — MB BS 1993 Lond.

WONG, Roger Anthony Counselling & Support Team, Brownlee Centre, 1053 Great Western Road, Glasgow G12 0YN Tel: 0141 211 1085 Fax: 0141 211 1097; 6 Ellon Way, Paisley PA3 4BW Tel: 0141 887 9997 — MB ChB 1983 Glas.; MRCPsych 1988. Clin. Coordinator, HIV Counselling & Support Team Glas. Prev: Clin. Med. Off. HIV Counselling Clinic Edin.; Regist. (Psychiat.) Gartloch Hosp. Glas.

WONG, Mr Sai Hung David Lindley, Lever Causeway, Storeton, Wirral CH63 6HT Tel: 0151 608 6613; 48 Rodney Street, Liverpool L1 9AA Tel: 0151 709 4319 Fax: 0151 709 2727 — MB ChB 1978 Liverp.; FRCS Eng. 1983; MRCP Lond. 1981; MRCS Eng. LRCP Lond. 1978; FRCOphth. 1989. Cons. Ophth. St. Paul's Eye Hosp. Liverp.; Hon. Clin. Lect. (Ophth.) Univ. Liverp. Prev: Sen. Regist. & Regist. Moorfields Eye Hosp. & St. Thos. Hosp. Lond.; Regist. & SHO St. Pauls Eye Hosp. Liverp.; Ho. Off. Roy. Liverp. Hosp.

WONG, Samuel Chun Kong Ophthalmology Department, Kings Mill Hospital, Sutton-in-Ashfield NG17 4JL — BM BS 1991 Nottm.

WONG, Sarah Jane 11 Cullera Close, Northwood HA6 3SE — MB BS 1998 Lond.

WONG, See Chang 10 Bellevue Grove, Edinburgh EH7 4DD — MB BS 1988 Melbourne.

WONG, See Mei Christina 14 Clos Hendre, Rhiwbina, Cardiff CF14 6PN — MB ChB 1994 Bristol.

***WONG, Selena** 47 Hough Road, Kings Heath, Birmingham B14 6HL — MB BS 1998 Lond.; MB BS Lond 1998.

WONG, Simon Chi On Flat 2/L, 25 Queensborough Gardens, Hyndland, Glasgow G12 9QP — MB ChB 1995 Glas.

WONG, Siu Ling 402B New World Tower, 18 Queen's Road Central, Hong Kong, Hong Kong Tel: 00 852 25251251 Fax: 00 852 28400165; 3 Harvesters Way, Weavering, Maidstone ME14 5SH — MB BS 1986 Lond.; MRCGP 1990; DRCOG 1989; DCH RCP Lond. 1988. (Lond. Hosp. Med. Coll.)

WONG, Soo Kim 95-97 Crawford Street, London W1H 2HJ — MB BS 1985 Lond.; MRCGP 1989; DRCOG 1988. Socs: BMA; Roy. Coll. of Gen. Practitioners. Prev: Trainee GP Edgware Gen. Hosp. VTS.

WONG, Stephen Phooi Yew 5 Chancellor's Walk, Cambridge CB4 3JG — BM BS 1994 Nottm.

WONG, Steven Bak-Siew Glenfield Hospital NHS Trust, Groby Road, Leicester LE3 9QP Tel: 01533 871411; 33 Waldale Drive, Leicester LE2 2AR Tel: 01533 708707 — MB ChB 1992 Leicester. SHO (Orthop.) Glenfield Hosp. NHS Trust.

WONG, Suzanne Yuk Siu 37 Whiteacre Close, Thornhill, Cardiff CF14 9DG — MB BS 1997 Lond.

WONG, Sze Chai Peter Department of Cardiology, University Hospital Aintree, Lower Lane, Liverpool L9 7AL Tel: 0151 525 5980 Fax: 0151 529 2724 — MB BS 1989 Lond.; MRCP 1993 UK; MD 2000 London; BSc Lond. 1986. (The London Hospital Medical College) Cons. Cardiol. & Phys. in Gen. Med. Socs: Med. Defence

Union; Brit. Cardiovasc. Interven. Soc.; Brit. Soc. Of Echocardiography. Prev: SpR Train. -W. Midl.s; SHO Rotat. (Med. & Dermat.) Hull HA.; Ho. Off. (Surg.) Broomfield Hosp. Chelmsford Hosp.

WONG, Terence Hor Ga Institute of Liver Studies, King's College Hospital, Bessemer Road, London SE5 — MB BChir 1991 Camb.; MA Camb. 1991. MB BChir 1991; MRCP (UK) 1993. Specialist Regist. Inst. Liver Studies King's Coll. Hosp. Lond. Prev: Specialist Regist. Guildford Roy. Surrey Co. Hosp. Guildford; Clin. Research Fell. Inst. Liver Studies King's Coll. Hosp.; SHO (Med.) St. Bartholomews Hosp. Lond.

WONG, Timothy Hong Tak Flat 9, Blair Court, Boundary Road, London NW8 6NT Tel: 020 7586 4827 — BChir 1986 Camb.; MB 1987.

WONG, Tui Iar 14 Strutt Road, Sheffield S3 9AG — MB ChB 1986 Sheff. Regist. Rotat. (Psychiat.) Sheff. HA Train. Scheme; Regist. (Acute Adult Psychiat.) Middlewood Hosp. Sheff.

WONG, Tung-Shing 13 Parkside, Finchley, London N3 2PJ — MB BS 1976 Hong Kong; DPM Eng. 1982. Staff Grade Psychiat. Lambeth Healthcare NHS Trust. Socs: Affil. Roy. Coll. Psychiats.

WONG, Voi Shim Department of Gastroentrology, Royal Liverpool University Hospital, Prescott St., Liverpool L7 8XP Tel: 0151 706 2000 Fax: 0151 706 5896 Email: vsw1000@cus.cam.ac.uk; 2nd Floor Flat, 38 Shrewsbury Road, Oxton, Birkenhead CH43 2HZ Tel: 0151 653 0040 Fax: 0151 706 5896 — MB ChB 1987 Manch.; MD 1998; BSc St. And. 1984; MRCP (UK) 1991. (Univ. Manch) Sen. Regist. (Gen. Med. & Gastroenterol.) Roy. Liverp. Univ. Hosp. Socs: Med. Defence Union; Brit. Soc. of Gastroenterol.; Roy. Soc. Med. Prev: Research Regist. (Gastroenterol. & Hepat.) Addenbrooke's Hosp. Camb.; Regist. (Gen. Med. & Gastroenterol.) St. Jas. Univ. Hosp. Leeds; SHO Fairfield Gen. Hosp. Bury.

WONG, Way Main Flat 1, York House, Queen Alexandra Hospital, Cosham, Portsmouth PO6 3LY; 16 Fayre Road, Fareham PO16 0UB — MB 1984 Camb.; BChir 1983; MRCP (UK) 1987. SHO (A & E) Sunderland Dist. Gen. Hosp.

WONG, William Chi Wai Flat2 12 Westbourne Gardens, London W2 5PU Tel: 020 7792 0636 — MB ChB 1993 Ed.; DFFP 1996; DCH 1998; MRCGP 1999. Socs: BMA; MRCGP; Steer. Comm. Mem. CMIR.

WONG, Wilson Dept of Nephrology & Transplantation, 5th Floor thomas & Guys Hospital, London SE1 9RT Tel: 020 7855 5000 — MB BS 1988 Lond.; BSc (1st cl. Hons.) Lond. 1985, MB BS 1988; MRCP (UK) 1991; DPhil 1997. Sen.Lect.Hon.Cons.Nephrol.

WONG, Mr Wing Zou 5 Shackleton Way, Bowbrook Park, Shrewsbury SY3 8SW Tel: 01743 270119 Email: wingzon@hotmail.com; 20 Jalan Ramah, Taman Gembira, Jalan Kuchai Lama, Kuala Lumpur, Malaysia Tel: 00 60 3 7804697 — MB ChB 1988 Glas.; FRCS Ed. 1992. (Univ. Glas.) Regist. (Surg.) Higher Surgic. Trainee, Qu. Eliz. Hosp. Prev: Regist. (Surg.) Higher Surgic. Trainee Dudley.

WONG, Wo Yuen 58 Langtons Wharf, Leeds LS2 7EF — MB ChB 1993 Leeds.

WONG, Yat Wing Room 64, Musgrave & Clark House, Royal Victoria Hospital, Grosvenor Road, Belfast BT12 6BA; 23 Upper Malone Park, Belfast BT9 6PP — MB BCh BAO 1995 Belf.

WONG, Mr Yin Lun Allen 2 High Street, Baldock SG7 6AR — MB ChB 1985 Glas.; FRCS Ed. 1990; FRCS Glas. 1990.

WONG, Yuen Fong Solomon 14 Wigton Green, Leeds LS17 8QR — MB ChB 1988 Dundee.

WONG, Yuk Ki 8 Deanfield Close, Hamble, Southampton SO31 4JJ Email: yw2@soton.ac.uk — MB ChB 1990 Manch.; BSc (Hons.) Manch. 1987, MB ChB 1990; MRCP (UK) 1993. Specialist Regist. (Cardiol.) Soton Gen. Hosp. Prev: Regist. (Cardiol. & Med.) St. Mary's Hosp. Portsmouth; SHO (Med.) Birch Hill Hosp. Rochdale.

WONG CHING HWAI, Shim Yan Walton Hospital, Rice Lane, Liverpool L9 1AE — MB ChB 1984 Manch.; MRCP (UK) 1988.

WONG HONG CHAI, Mr Flat 4, 26 Elsham Road, London W14 8HB — MB 1977 Camb.; BChir 1976; FRCS Ed. 1982; MRCP (UK) 1980. Francis & Renee Hock Fell. Retinal Dis. Moorfields Eye Hosp. Lond. Prev: Resid. Surgic. Off. Moorfields Eye Hosp. Lond.

WONG KAM-KEE, Simon 10 Aylmer Road, Hampstead Garden Suburb, London N2 0BX Tel: 020 8340 9371 — MB BS 1960 Hong Kong; MRCP Ed. 1965; DCH RCPS Glas. 1964.

WONG KIM MENG, Dr House 24, Western Court, 100 University Place, Glasgow G12 8SQ — MB BS 1987 New South Wales.

WONG LAI CHENG, Dr 13 Hitherwood Drive, College Road, London SE19 1XA — MB BS 1979 Lond.

WONG LUN SANG, Angela San-Youn 143 Balls Pond Road, London N1 4BG — MB BS 1994 Lond.

WONG-LUN-SANG, Stella 53 Atkins Road, London SW12 0AH — MB BS 1998 Lond.; MB BS Lond 1998.

WONG SUNG LUNG, Aaron Amersham General Hospital, Wheilden St., Amersham HP7 0JD — MB BS 1991 Melbourne.

WONG-YOU-CHEONG, Jade Janette 12 Attwood Road, Timperley, Altrincham WA15 7NJ Tel: 0161 980 7826 — MB ChB 1984 Manch.; BSc (Hons.) Manch. 1982, MB ChB (Hons.) 1984; MRCP (UK) 1987; FRCR 1991. Sen. Regist. Rotat. (Radiol.) N. W.. RHA. Socs: Fell. Manch. Med. Soc. Prev: Regist. (Radiol.) N. W.. RHA; SHO (Cardiothoracic Med.) Wythenshawe Hosp. Manch.; SHO (Gen. Med.) Manch. Roy. Infirm.

WONGTSCHOWSKI, Karl Georg Julius 20 Tarranbrae, Willesden Lane, London NW6 7PL Tel: 020 8459 3649 — MD 1924 Berlin.

WONKE, Beatrix Department of Haematology, Whittington Hospital, Highgate Hill, London N19 5NF — MD 1964 Zurich; LMSSA Lond. 1970; FRCPath 1988, M 1976; FRCP FRCP 1999. Cons. Del The Whittlingttonn Hosp. NHS Trust; Hon. Cons. Roy. Free Hosp. Lond.; Clin. tutor UCLH. Socs: Roy. Coll. Pathol.; Roy. Coll. Phys.s.

WONTUMI, Joseph Asiedu c/o Miss Parbury, T.A.T.D., British Council, 65 davies St., London W1Y 2AA — MB BS 1966 Lond.

WOO, Bing-Chung 6 Glenside Drive, Wilmslow SK9 1EH — MB ChB 1992 Leeds.

WOO, Dominique Grace Sue Ryder Palliative Care Home, Staunton Harold Hall, Staunton Harold, Ashby-de-la-Zouch LE65 1RT Tel: 01332 862798 Fax: 01332 864877 — BM BS 1990 Nottm.; BMedSci (Hons.) Nottm. 1988. (Nottm.) Staff Grade Phys. (Palliat. Med.) Sue Ryder Palliat. Care Home Staunton Harold. Prev: SHO (Gen. Med.) Derbysh. Roy. Infirm.; SHO Palliat. Med. Leics. Hospice; Clin. Asst. Palliat. Med. Marie Curie Centre Caterham.

WOO, Ka Chung Dawson 3 Belgrave Square, London SW1X 8PH — MB BS 1988 Lond.

WOO, Martin Payen Red Lion House Surgery, 86 Hednesford Road, Heath Hayes, Cannock WS12 5EA Tel: 01543 502391 Fax: 01543 573424; The Grange, Cannock Wood Street, Rawnsley, Hednesford, Cannock WS12 5PW Tel: 01543 685573 — MB ChB 1978 Birm.; DRCOG 1982.

WOO, Michael Ting Chung Red Roofs, 31 Coton Road, Nuneaton CV11 5TW Tel: 024 7635 7100 Fax: 024 7664 2036 — MB BChir 1975 Camb.; BA, MB BChir Camb. 1975; MRCP (UK) 1978; MRCGP 1980.

WOO, Professor Patricia Mang Ming Departments of Molecular Pathology & Medicine, University College London Medical School, 46 Cleveland St., London W1T 4JF Tel: 020 7504 9148 Fax: 020 7436 0783; 319 Lonsdale Road, Barnes, London SW13 9PY — MB BS 1972 Lond.; PhD Camb. 1979; BSc Lond. 1969; FRCP Lond. 1991; MRCP (UK) 1975; FRCPCH 1997. (Char. Cross) Prof. Paediat. Rheum. UCLH & Gt. Ormond St. Hosp. Childr. Lond.; Hon. Cons. Phys. Hosp. for Sick Childr. Lond. Socs: Fell. RSM; Fell. Coll. Paediat. & Child Health; Counc. Mem. Brit. Soc. Rheum. Prev: Head Molecular Rheum. MRC Clin. Research Centre Lond.; Research Fell. Div. Cell. Biol. Childr. Hosp. Med. Centre Boston, USA; Sen. Regist. (Med. & Rheum.) Guy's Hosp. Lond.

WOO, Pick Ngor 2 (1/R) Fortingall Avenue, Glasgow G12 0LR — MB ChB 1993 Glas.

WOO, Yook Mun Renal Unit, Western Infirmary, Dunbarton Road, Glasgow G11 6NT; T/L Flat, 21 Queensborough Gardens, Glasgow G12 9PP — MB BS 1992 Sydney; MRCP (UK) 1996. Regist. (Nephrol.) W.. Infirm. Glas. Socs: Scott. Renal Assn.; Renal Assn.

WOOD, Adrian Robert (retired) 5 Cross Road, Birchington CT7 9HN Tel: 01843 841661 — MB BS Lond. 1938; MRCS Eng. LRCP Lond. 1938.

WOOD, Agnes Pool Penicuik Health Centre, 37 Imrie Place, Penicuik EH26 8LF Tel: 01968 672612 Fax: 01968 671543; Martyrs Cross, Penicuik EH26 0NJ Tel: 01968 73799 — MB ChB 1976 Ed.; MRCGP 1980; DRCOG 1979. Socs: Mem. of the Soc. of orthopaedic Med.

WOOD

WOOD, Alan Edward (retired) 31 St Margaret's Street, Rochester ME1 1TU Tel: 01634 400358 Email: aewood1@tinyworld.co.uk — MB BS 1953 Lond.; FRCGP 1973, M 1960. Prev: Sen. Med. Off. DHSS.

WOOD, Mr Alan Jeffrey The Royal Hospitals Trust, St. Bartholomew's Hospital, West Smithfield, London EC1A 7BE Tel: 020 7601 7119 Fax: 020 7601 7117; 34 Circus Road, St Johns Wood, London NW8 9SG — MB BS 1975 Lond.; FRCS Eng. 1980; MRCS Eng. LRCP Lond. 1975. (St. Bart.) Cons. Cardiothoracic Surg. St. Bart. Hosp. Lond.; Cons. Cardiothoracic Surg. Lond. Chest Hosp. & Roy. Lond. Hosp.

WOOD, Alasdair Guy Park Lane Surgery, 8 Park Lane, Broxbourne EN10 7NQ Tel: 01992 465555; 1 Long Grove Close, Broxbourne EN10 7NP Tel: 01992 441649 — MB ChB 1989 Leic.; DFFP 1995. Gen. Pract. Princip., Pk. La. Surg., Broxbourne. Prev: Clin. Asst., Psychiat.

WOOD, Alison Jane Department of Child & Adsolescent Psychiatry, Duchess of York Childrens Hospital, Nell Lane, West Didsbury, Manchester M20 Tel: 0161 447 3131; 26 Moorfield Road, West Didsbury, Manchester M20 2UY Tel: 0161 434 5155 — MB ChB 1984 Leeds; 1995 (Dip HSM) Open Univ.; MD 1999 Manchester; MSc Psychiat. Manch. 1992; MRCPsych 1988; DCH RCP Lond. 1990; DRCOG 1990. Cons. & Hon. Clin. Lect. (Child & Adsolesc. Psychiat.) S. Manch. Univ. Hosps. NHS Trust. Socs: Roy. Coll. Psychiat. Prev: Tutor & Hon. Sen. Regist. (Child & Adolesc. Psychiat.) Roy. Manch. Childr. Hosp.; Sen. Regist. (Child & Adolesc. Psychiat.) NW RHA Train. Scheme; Trainee GP Macclesfield Dist. Gen. Hosp.

WOOD, Alison Janet Strathpeffer Medical Practice, The Surgery, Strathpeffer IV14 9BA Tel: 01997 421455 Fax: 01997 421172 — MB ChB 1983 Aberd.; MRCGP 1986; DRCOG 1984.

WOOD, Alison Karen — MB ChB 1995 Manch.; 1985 (Physics BSC I) London. (Manch.) Sen. Ho. Officier, CHS, Sheff. Socs: MDU.

WOOD, Amanda Catherine 23 Beaumont Road, St. Judes, Plymouth PL4 9BL; 20 Torr Crescent, Hartley, Plymouth PL3 5TW — MB ChB 1984 Manch.

WOOD, Andrea Amersham Health Centre, Chiltern Avenue, Amersham HP6 5AY Tel: 01494 434344 — MB ChB 1985 Leic.

WOOD, Andrew John Warneford Hospital, Oxford OX3 7JX Tel: 01865 245651; 93 St. Marks Road, Henley-on-Thames RG9 1LP — MB BCh 1981 Oxf.; MA Camb. 1981; DM Oxf. 1988, MB BCh 1981; MRCP (UK) 1984.

WOOD, Andrew Mayne Fernbank, The Common, Dinas Powys CF64 4DL — MB BS 1983 Lond.; BSc Lond. 1980, MB BS 1983; MRCP (UK) 1987; FRCR 1990.

WOOD, Andrew Michael The Health Centre, Bunny Lane, Keyworth, Nottingham NG12 5JU Tel: 0115 937 3527 Fax: 0115 937 6781; 35 Selby Lane, Keyworth, Nottingham NG12 5AQ Tel: 0115 937 2406 — MB ChB 1979 Glas.; BSc Glas. 1976; MRCGP 1983.

WOOD, Angela Clare Haematology dept, James Cook University Hospital, Marton Rd, Middlesbrugh T34 3BW — MB BS 1987 Newc.; MD 1999 Newcastle; MRCP 1991; MRCPath 1998. Cons. Haemat. James Cook Univ. Hosp., MiddlesBoro. Socs: Med. Soc. Haematol.

WOOD, Angela Margaret (retired) North West Lung Centre, Wythenshawe Hospital, Southmoor Road, Manchester M23 9LT Tel: 0161 946 2834 — MD 1978 Manch.; MB ChB 1965; FRCP Lond. 1992; MRCP (UK) 1970; DObst RCOG 1968.

WOOD, Angus Donald Graham Poole Hospital NHS Trust, Longfleeb Road, Poole BH15 2JB Tel: 0116 274 5003 Email: veronicakiddle@yahoo.co.uk; 36 Seafield Road, Friars Cliff, Christchurch BH23 4ET — MB BS 1985 Lond.; MRCP (UK) 1988; FRCR 1993. (Westm. Med. Sch.) Cons. Radiol. Poole Hosp. Prev: Lect. (Magnetic Resonance Imaging) Lond. Hosp. Med. Coll.; Sen. Regist. (Radiol.) Soton. Gen. Hosp.

WOOD, Ann Mabel North Ridge Medical Practice, North Ridge, Rye Road, Hawkhurst, Cranbrook TN18 4EX Tel: 01580 753935 Fax: 01580 754452; 22 Joyce Close, Cranbrook TN17 3LZ Tel: 01580 715112 — MB ChB 1981 Glas.; MRCPsych 1986. (Glas.) Gen. Practitioner; Sch. Med. Off.

WOOD, Anna Elzbieta Central Middlesex Hospital, Acton Lane, Park Royal, London NW10 7NS — MB BS 1985 Lond.; MRCP (UK) 1990; DRCPath 1995. Hon. Research Regist. (Haemat.) Centr. Middlx. Hosp. NHS Trust.

WOOD, Anna Francesca 41 Eaton Road, Alsager, Stoke-on-Trent ST7 2BQ — BM BS 1994 Nottm.

WOOD, Annette Lynne Birmingham Health Authority, 213 Hagley Road, Birmingham B16 9RG Tel: 0121 695 2350 — MB BCh 1986 Wales; MFPHM RCP (UK) 1995; MRCGP 1990; DRCOG 1990. Cons. Pub. Health Med. Birm. HA. Prev: Sen. Regist. (Pub. Health Med.) W. Midl. RHA.

WOOD, Anthony Millard (retired) Spindrift, 101 Orchary Avenue, Parkstone, Poole BH14 8AN Tel: 01202 740695 — MB BS Lond. 1955. Prev: GP Colchester.

WOOD, Antony John 26 Bentley Way, Stanmore HA7 3RP Tel: 020 8954 3060 — MB BS 1956 Lond.; MFCM 1973; DPH Bristol 1965. (Westm.) PMO (Health Educat.) Brent & Harrow AHA. Socs: BMA & Soc. Community Med. Prev: Med. Lect. Health Educat. Counc.; 1st Asst. Epidemiol. Bristol Co. Boro.; Asst. MOH Dudley Co. Boro.

WOOD, Armorel Wendy Tulscroft, Poplar Lane, Bransgore, Christchurch BH23 8JE Tel: 01425 674415 — MB BS 1986 Lond.; MA Oxf. 1983; Cert. Family Plann. JCC 1989. Clin. Asst. (Rheum. & Rehabil.) Roy. Bournemouth Hosp. Prev: SHO (Psychiat.) City Hosp. Truro; SHO (Med. for Elderly) York Dist. Hosp.; SHO (Cas.) Winchester.

WOOD, Arthur Brian (retired) 31 Heights Drive, Linthwaite, Huddersfield HD7 5SU — MRCS Eng. LRCP Lond. 1944; MRCGP 1959.

WOOD, Barbara Louise Psychotherapy Department, Maudsley Hospital, Denmark Hill, London SE5 8AZ Tel: 020 7919 2384/5 — MB BS 1987 Lond.; MRCP (UK) 1991; MRCPsych 1994. p/t Sen. Regist. (Psychother.) Maudsley Hosp. Lond.

WOOD, Beatrice Gillian Starcross, Great Austins, Farnham GU9 8JG Tel: 01252 715272 — MB ChB 1962 Aberd. (Aberd.) Occupat. Health Phys. Frimley Pk. Hosp. NHS Trust; Sen. Clin. Med. Off. Well Wom. & Family Plann. Clinics N.; Downs Community Health Unit.

WOOD, Benjamin Stuart Blachford (retired) 3 Kingsfield, Lymington SO41 3QY Tel: 01590 672967 — BM BCh 1941 Oxf.; DM Oxf. 1951, BA, BM BCh 1941; FRCP Lond. 1966, M 1948; DCH Eng. 1948. Prev: Cons. Paediat. Birm. Centr. Health Dist. (T).

WOOD, Brian Haydon 25 Churchill Mews, St. Peters Marina, Newcastle upon Tyne NE6 1BH Tel: 0191 224 1296 — MB ChB 1993 Aberd.; MRCP (UK) 1996. Regist. (Geriat. & Gen. Med.) Newc. Gen. Hosp.

WOOD, Brian Robert Craigmillar Medical Group, 106 Niddrie Mains Road, Edinburgh EH16 4DT Tel: 0131 536 9500 Fax: 0131 536 9545 — MB ChB 1975 Ed.

WOOD, Bridget Caroline Oakhaven Hospice, Lower Pennington Lane, Lymington SO41 8ZZ Tel: 020 7249 8336 Email: beckywilliams@breathemail.net; 36 Seafield Road, Friars Cliff, Christchurch BH23 4ET — MB BS 1984 Lond.; BA Camb. 1981; MRCGP 1988; FRCR 1993; DRCOG 1986. p/t Cons. Palliat. Med. & Med. Dir. Oakhaven Hospice Lymington. Prev: Sen. Regist. (Palliat. Med.) Wessex Region; Regist. (Radiother. Oncol.) Roy. S. Hants. Hosp.; Regist. (Palliat. Care) St. Christophers Hospice Lond.

WOOD, Bridget Mary (retired) Dormington House, Dormington, Hereford HR1 4ES Tel: 01432 850543 Fax: 01432 850543 Email: john.b.wod.@lineone.net — MB BS 1960 Lond.; 1960 MB BS Lond.; 1960 MRCS Eng. LRCP Lond.; 1977 FFA RCS Eng.; 1964 DA Eng. Prev: Clin. Dir. (Critical Care) & Cons. Anaesth. Sandwell Dist. Gen. Hosp.

WOOD, Carine Henriette Department of Anaesthetics, Guy's Hospital, St Thomas St., London SE1 9RT Tel: 020 7955 4051 Fax: 020 7955 8844 Email: carinewood@gstt.sthames.nhs.uk; 36 Earl's Court Square, London SW5 9DQ Tel: 020 7370 6939 Fax: 020 7835 2081 Email: carinewood@vizzavi.net — MD 1980 Paris; FRCA 1987; FFA RCSI Dub. 1985. Cons. Paediatric Anaesth. Guy's & St. Thos. NHS Trust Lond. Socs: Fell. Roy. Soc. Med.; Soc. Clin. Française.; Fell. Roy. Coll. Anaesth. Prev: Sen. Regist. Char. Cross & W.m. Hosps.; Regist. Hammersmith & Edgware Hosps.; Regist. N.wick Pk. Hosp.

WOOD, Charles Geoffrey Millard The Surgery, Roman Way, Billingshurst RH14 9QZ Tel: 01403 782931 Fax: 01403 785505; Beke Glade, Marringdean Road, Billingshurst RH14 9HF Tel: 01403

WOOD

782440 Fax: 01403 786691 Email: chosliew@epulse.net — MB BS 1978 Lond. (St. Mary's Hosp.) Clin. Asst. (Dermat.) Worthing Hosp.

WOOD, Charles Roger (retired) Ethnam Cottage, Ethnam Lane, Sandhurst, Cranbrook TN18 5PS Tel: 0158 085 850 360 — MRCS Eng. LRCP Lond. 1942. Prev: O & G Ho. Surg. King Edwd. VII Hosp. Windsor.

WOOD, Charlotte Elizabeth Brooklea Health Centre, Wick Road, Brislington, Bristol BS4 4HU Tel: 0117 971 1211; 4 Napier Road, Bristol BS6 6RT Tel: 0117 973 3572 — MB BS 1981 Lond.; BA Oxf. 1978; MRCGP 1986; DFFP 1996; DRCOG 1985. Prev: GP Bedminster; Trainee GP Avon VTS.

WOOD, Christina Clare 3 Bassingham Road, London SW18 3AF — MB ChB 1991 Leic.

WOOD, Christine Bernadette Ashville Medical Centre, 430 Doncaster Road, Barnsley S70 3RJ Tel: 01226 216000; 96 Bluebell Ave, Penistone, Sheffield S36 6LQ Tel: 01226 765644, 0208 958 2564 Email: barry@knee.demon.co.uk.(barry@knee.demon.co.uk — MB ChB 1976 Sheff. p/t Asst. GP Penistone./ GP Partner at (Princip. Asnville Med. Centre Barnsley).

WOOD, Christine Dorothy Salisbury Palliative Care Services, Salisbury District Hospital, Salisbury SP2 8BJ Tel: 01722 336262 Fax: 01722 338015 Email: christine.wood@shc-tr.swest.nhs.uk — MB BCh 1978 Wales; FRCP (UK) 1981. p/t Cons. Palliat. Med. Salisbury Dist. Hosp. Prev: Med. Dir. Salisbury Macmillan Unit; Research Fell. Med. Coll. & Sen. Regist. (Med. Oncol.) St. Bart Hosp. Lond.; Hosp. Rotat. (Med.) Lond. Hosp.

WOOD, Mr Christopher Barry Department of Surgery, Wexham Park Hospital, Slough SL2 4HL Tel: 01753 633000 Fax: 01753 691343 — MD 1984 Wales; MB BCh 1970; FRCS Ed. 1974. Hon. Cons. Surg. Wexham Pk. Hosp. Slough. Prev: Sen. Lect. (Surg.) Roy. Postgrad. Med. Sch. Lond.; Lect. (Surg.) Roy. Infirm. Glas.; Research SHO (Surg.) Univ. Hosp. Wales Cardiff.

WOOD, Christopher Bryan Somerset 38 Church Crescent, Whetstone, London N20 0JP Tel: 020 8368 6951 Fax: 020 8368 6951 — MB BChir 1958 Camb.; BChir 1957; FRCP Lond. 1973, M 1963; FRCPCH 1997; DCH Eng. 1959. (Camb. & St. Bart.) Emerit. Prof. Child Health Barts and The Lond. Qu. Mary's Sch. of Med. and Dent.; Hon. Cons. Paediat. Roy. Hosps. Trust, Homerton Hosp. Trust & Childr. Trust Tadworth Ct. Socs: Fell. Roy. Soc. Med.; BMA; Brit. Thorac. Soc. Prev: Lect. & Sen. Lect. (Child Health) Univ. Bristol; Research Fell. Paediat. Research Unit Guy's Hosp. Lond.; Regist. Evelina Childr. Hosp. (Guy's Hosp.) Lond.

WOOD, Christopher Giles Agars 138 Campbell Road, Florence Park, Oxford OX4 3NT — MB ChB 1985 Bristol.

WOOD, Christopher Holman (retired) Small Acres, Poplar Lane, Bransgore, Christchurch BH23 8JE Tel: 01425 672747 Fax: 01425 674941 — MB ChB 1956 Bristol. Prev: Ho. Surg. & Ho. Phys. Bristol Roy. Infirm.

WOOD, Christopher John Michael St John's Surgery, Main Road, Terrington St. John, Wisbech PE14 7RR Tel: 01945 880471 Fax: 01945 880677 — MB BS 1972 Lond.; MRCS Eng. LRCP Lond. 1972; MRCPsych 1977; DPM Eng. 1976. (St. Bart.)

WOOD, Christopher Mark Clarendon Wing, Belmont Grove, Leeds LS2 9 Tel: 0113 243 2799; 7 Laurel Hill Grove, Colton, Leeds LS15 9EL Tel: 0113 260 3874 — MB BS 1986 Lond.; BA Camb. 1983; MRCP (UK) 1990. Lect. & Hon. Sen. Regist. (Paediat.) Leeds Gen. Infirm. Socs: Paediat. Research Soc. Prev: SHO (Paediat. Cas.) St Thos. Hosp. Lond.; SHO (Paediat.) St. Jas. Univ. Hosp. Leeds.

WOOD, Mr Christopher Patrick Langton Wrenwood, Park Avenue, Hartlepool TS26 0DZ — MB BS 1969 Lond.; FRCS Eng. 1976. (St. Bart.)

WOOD, Christopher Robert 442 Blackness Road, Dundee DD2 1TQ Tel: 01382 667547 — BM BS Nottm. 1995. SHO Surgic. Rot., Dorset Co. Hosp. Prev: Emerg. Med. Re. (Newc.); SHO (A&E) Leeds Gen. Infirm.; SHO (A&E) W. Cumbld. Hosp.

WOOD, Clare Mairi Park Avenue Medical Centre, Park Avenue, Dundee DD4 6PP Tel: 01382 462222 Fax: 01382 452866 — MB ChB 1992 Dundee.

WOOD, Colin Samuel (retired) Crumlin medical centre, Crown st, Crumlin NP11 4PQ Tel: 01495 244633 Fax: 01495 249118 — MB BCh 1974 Wales; MSc Surrey 1981. Staff Phys. N. Downs Hosp. Caterham. Prev: Specialist (Disabil. Med.) Benefits Agency Med. Serv. DSS Sutton.

WOOD, Damian Mark St mary's Hospital, Hathforsage Road, Manchester M13 0JH — MB ChB 1995 Manch.; DCH 1998. Clin. Fell. Paediat. St Mary's Hosp. Manch.

WOOD, Mr Daniel Nigel 32 Westcliff Drive, Leigh-on-Sea SS9 2LB Tel: 01702 715022 Email: don.wood@virgin.net — MB BS 1994 Lond.; FRCS Eng. 1998. (St. Bart.) Research Fell.Instit.Oncol. Lond. Prev: SHO (Gen. Surg.) S.end Gen. Hosp.; SHO (Intens. Care) Qu. Alexandras Hosp. Portsmouth; SHO (A & E) Roy. Surrey Co. Hosp. Guildford.

WOOD, Professor David Allan Cardiac Medicine, Imperial College School of Medicine, Dovehouse St., London SW3 6LY Tel: 020 7351 8859 Fax: 020 7351 8856 — MB ChB 1974 Dundee; MSc (Epidemiol.) Lond. 1981; FRCP Lond 1991; FRCP Ed. 1991; MRCP (UK) 1979. Prof. Clin. Epidemiol. Nat. Heart & Lung Inst. Univ. Lond.; Hon. Cons. Cardiol. Roy. Brompton & Bromley Hosps. Prev: Sen. Lect. (Med.) Univ. Soton.; Wellcome Research Fell. (Clin. Epidemiol.) Cardovasc. Research Unit Univ. Edin.

WOOD, David Cecil The Surgery, Station Road, Knebworth SG3 6AP Tel: 01438 812494 Fax: 01438 816497; 29 Heath Lane, Codicote, Hitchin SG4 8YE Tel: 01438 820824 — MB ChB 1972 Aberd.

WOOD, David George Edwin The Cottage, Eglwysbach, Colwyn Bay LL28 5UD — MB ChB 1970 Bristol; MRCS Eng. LRCP Lond. 1969; MRCGP 1977.

WOOD, David James The Laurels, 11 High St., Misterton, Doncaster DN10 4BU — MB BS 1988 Lond.

WOOD, David Michael 8 Newlands Close, Horley RH6 8JR Tel: 01293 785446 — MB ChB 1997 Bristol; MB ChB (Hons.) Bristol 1997. (Univ. of Bristol) John Racliffe Med. SHO Rotat. Oxf. Prev: Ho. Surg. Derriford Hosp. Plymouth; Ho. Phys. Bristol Roy. Infirm. Bristol.

WOOD, David Nugent 17 New Road, Brixham TQ5 8BL Tel: 01803 2731 — MB BS 1958 Lond.; MRCGP 1970; MRCS Eng. LRCP Lond. 1958; AKC 1988. (St. Geo.) Prev: Ho. Phys. Stoke Mandeville Hosp. Aylesbury; Ho. Surg. St. Geo. Hosp. Lond.; Med. Off. Mildmay Miss. Hosp. Lond.

WOOD, David Richard Ellern Mede Centre for Eating Disorders, 31 Totteridge Common, London N20 8LR Tel: 0208 959 7774 Fax: 0208 959 6311 Email: david.wood@ellernmede.org; Fax: 0208 959 6311 Email: david.wood@ellernmede.org — MB BS 1975 Lond.; MRCPsych 1984; DRCOG 1978. (Char. Cross) Cons. Child & Adolesc. Psychiat. & Psychotherap. Socs: Inst. Gp. Anal.; Family Systems Div. Tavistock Soc. Psychother.; Assn. Child Psychol. & Psychiat. Prev: Cons. Child Psychiat. Hemel Hempstead; Sen. Regist. Tavistock Clinic Lond.; Regist. (Psychiat.) The Lond. Hosp. Whitechapel.

WOOD, David Robin Hayes Grove Priory Hospital, Prestons Road, Hayes BR2 7AS Tel: 020 8462 7722 Fax: 020 8462 5028; Tel: 01689 851054 Fax: 01689 858368 — MB ChB Ed. 1962; MRCP Lond. 1969; MRCP Ed. 1967; FRCPsych. 1997; MRCPsych 1972; DPM Eng. 1972; FRCP Ed 1996. (Ed.) Cons. Psychiat. & Asst. Med. Dir. Priory Hosp. Bromley, Kent. Socs: Fell. Roy. Soc. Med. Prev: Cons. Psychiat. & Med. Dir. Ravensbourne NHS Trust; Sen. Regist. Maudsley Hosp. Lond.; Regist. (Neurol.) N.. Gen. Hosp. Edin.

WOOD, David Stanley, MBE (retired) 36 Highfields, Llandaff, Cardiff CF5 2QB Tel: 01222 566248 — MB BCh Wales 1951; BSc Wales 1947. Prev: Ho. Phys., Cas. Off. (Surg.) & Ho. Surg. (O & G) Cardiff Roy. Infirm.

WOOD, David Wildman (retired) The Health Centre, High St., Bedworth, Nuneaton CV12 8NQ Tel: profess. Bedworth 315432 — MRCS Eng. LRCP Lond. 1953.

WOOD, David William 12 Cedar Drive, Durham DH1 3TF — MB ChB 1971 St. And.; FRCA 1975. Cons. Anaesth. Durh. HA. Prev: Sen. Regist. (Anaesth.) N.. RHA; Regist. (Anaesth.) Cardiff.

WOOD, Diana Frances The Medical Unit, The Royal London Hospital, Whitechapel, London E1 1BB Tel: 020 7377 7110 Fax: 020 7377 7636 — MB ChB 1980 Birm.; MD Birm. 1992; FRCP 1996; MRCP (UK) 1983. (Birmingham) Sen. Lect. in Med. & Hon. Cons. Endocrinologist, Barts and the Lond. Qu. Marys Med. Sch. Univeristy of Lond. Prev: Lect. (Clin. Endocrinol.) St. Mary's Hosp. Med. Sch. Lond.

WOOD, Diana Frances Warden Lodge Surgery, 63 Albury Ride, Cheshunt, Waltham Cross EN8 8XE Tel: 01992 441649; 1 Long

WOOD

Grove Close, Broxbourne EN10 7NP — MB BS 1989 Lond.; DFFP 1994. Gen. Practitioner.

WOOD, Dorothy Anne School Lane Surgery, School Lane, Washingborough, Lincoln LN4 1BN Tel: 01522 792360 Fax: 01522 794144; The Old Barn, Manor Road, Washingborough, Lincoln LN4 1BQ Tel: 01522 792360 — MB ChB 1978 Ed.; MRCGP 1982; DRCOG 1981; DCH Eng. 1982.

WOOD, Mr Edward Hamilton (retired) 7 Maes Rhosyn, Rhuddlan, Rhyl LL18 2YW — MB ChB 1961 Birm.; DObst RCOG 1963; FRCS Ed. 1968. Cons. Surg. Clwyd N. Health Dist.

WOOD, Edward Vaughan 101 Lightwater Meadow, Lightwater GU18 5XJ — MB ChB 1996 Liverp.

WOOD, Edwin Charles The Writtle Surgery, 16A Lordship Road, Writtle, Chelmsford CM1 3EH Tel: 01245 421205 Fax: 01245 422094 — MB BS 1985 Lond.; MRCGP 1990; DRCOG 1989.

WOOD, Eleanor 104 Manchester Road, Bury BL9 0TH — BChir 1996 Camb.

WOOD, Elizabeth Cowan 3 Kingsfield, Lymington SO41 3QY Tel: 01590 672967 — MB ChB 1940 St. And. (St. And.) Prev: Med. Asst. Rubery Hill Hosp. Birm.; Research Asst. (Paediat. & Child Health) Univ. Birm.; Ho. Surg. Dundee Roy. Infirm.

WOOD, Elizabeth Moody 95 Dulwich Village, London SE21 7BJ Tel: 020 8693 3836 — MB BS 1968 Lond.; MRCP (UK) 1979; MRCS Eng. LRCP Lond. 1968; DTM & H Liverp. 1976; DCH Eng. 1972. (Middlx.) Staff Grade Paediat. Qu. Mary's Hosp. Sidcup. Prev: SHO (Paediat.) & Regist. (Paediat.) St. Mary's Hosp. Portsmouth.

WOOD, Emma Frances 105a Kilburn Park Road, London NW6 5LB — MB BS 1997 Lond.

WOOD, Eric (retired) 286 Frederick Street, Oldham OL8 4HG Tel: 0161 624 6179 — MB ChB Manch. 1945.

WOOD, Eric Robert Miller 3 Lovers Walk, Dumfries DG1 1LR — MB BS 1975 Newc.

WOOD, Evelyn John (retired) 21 The Avenue, St. Margarets, Twickenham TW1 1QP Tel: 020 8892 4566 — BM BCh 1939 Oxf.; MA, BM BCh Oxon. 1939.

WOOD, Fiona Jane The Field House, Thorrington Road, Great Bentley, Colchester CO7 8QR — MB ChB 1986 Liverp. Staff Grade (Community Paediat.).

WOOD, Frances Ann The Surgery, Gaywood House, North St, Bedminster, Bristol BS3 3AZ Tel: 0117 966 1412 Fax: 0117 953 1250; 17 Cricklade Road, Bishopston, Bristol BS7 9EW — MB ChB 1976 Bristol; DRCOG 1980.

WOOD, Fraser Thomas 3 Kingswood Grove, Kingswells, Aberdeen AB15 8AH — MB ChB 1993 Glas.

WOOD, Frederick Brian Gaylor (retired) Jacaranda, Chapel Lane, Bransgore, Christchurch BH23 8BN — MB ChB 1955 Sheff.; DPH Leeds 1967. Prev: Cons. Communicable Dis. Control Kent.

WOOD, Garth Riddiough 40 Harley Street, London W1 1AB Tel: 020 7255 1909; 18 Cunningham Place, London NW8 8JT Tel: 020 7289 2254 — MB BS 1978 Lond.; MA Camb. 1964; LMSSA Lond. 1978. (Roy. Free) Socs: Fell. Roy. Soc. Med. Prev: Regist. (Psychiat.) Priory Hosp. Roehampton Lond.; Regist./SHO (Psychiat.) Univ. Coll. Hosp. Lond.; Assoc. Research Fell. (Clin. Pharmacol.) Univ. Coll. Lond.

WOOD, Geoffrey Campbell Dale View Health Centre, Dale View, Caistor, Market Rasen LN7 6NX Tel: 01472 851203 Fax: 01472 852495 — MB BS 1981 Lond. (St Georges) Prev: Trainee GP Carshalton VTS; Med. Off. & Dist. Med. Off. St. Francis Hosp. Katete, Zambia.

WOOD, Geoffrey Holman (retired) Polmener, Mullion, Helston TR12 7DH Tel: 01326 240308 — MB ChB Bristol 1952. Prev: Hon. Med. Adviser (Lizard-Cadgwith Lifeboat) RNLI.

WOOD, Geoffrey Michael 341 Marine Road, Morecambe LA4 5AB — MB ChB 1957 Manch.

WOOD, Gilbert Health Centre, 276 Darton Lane, Mapplewell, Barnsley S75 6AJ; 21 Southcroft, Upper Denby, Huddersfield HD8 8UA — MB ChB 1951 Leeds. Prev: Res. Anaesth. Off. Infirm. Doncaster; Ho. Phys. Ackton Hosp. Pontefract & Gen. Infirm. Pontefract.

WOOD, Gillian Elizabeth Woodhouse Medical Centre, 7 Skelton Lane, Woodhouse, Sheffield S13 7LY Tel: 0114 269 0025 — MB ChB 1988 Sheff.; MRCGP 1992.

WOOD, Gordon McKenzie George Eliot Hospital, Nuneaton CV10 7DJ — MB ChB Leeds 1977; BSc Leeds. 1974, MD 1989; FRCP Lond. 1995; MRCP (UK) 1980. (Leeds) Cons. Phys. Geo. Eliot Hosp. Nuneaton. Prev: Sen. Regist. (Gen. & Geriat. Med.) Dudley Rd. Hosp. Birm.; Regist. Profess. Med. Unit St. Jas. Univ. Hosp. Leeds.

WOOD, Mr Graham Allan Canniesburn Hospital, Bearsden, Glasgow G61 1QL Tel: 0141 211 5787 Fax: 0141 211 5652 Email: gawood@publiconline.co.uk; Abbotsford, Broomknowe Road, Kilmacolm PA13 4HX Tel: 01505 873954 Fax: 01505 873954 — MB ChB 1978 Dundee; FDS RCS Eng. 2000; BDS Glas. 1968; FRCS Ed. 1985; FDS RCPS Glas. 1973. Cons. Oral & Maxillofacial Surg. Canniesburn Hosp. Glas.; Sen. Lect. (Oral & Maxillofacial Surg.) Univ. Glas.; Clin. Prof. Oral & Maxillofacial Surg. Univ. Texas, Houston, USA. Socs: Fell. Brit. Assn. Oral & Maxillofacial Surg.; Fell. Internat. Assn. Oral & Maxillofacial Surgs.; BMA. Prev: Cons. N. Wales Hosps.; Regist. Canniesburn Hosp. Glas.; Ho. Off. (Plastic Surg.) Dundee Roy. Infirm.

WOOD, Graham Colin Avondale Unit, Royal Preston Hospital, Sharoe Green Lane, Preston PR2 9HT Tel: 01772 716565 — MB ChB 1979 Ed.; BSc (Hons.) Ed. 1976; MPsychMed Liverp. 1992; MRCPsych 1989; MRCGP 1983. Cons. Psychiat. Guild Community Healthcare NHS Trust Preston. Prev: GP Newton-le-Willows Merseyside.

WOOD, Graham John (retired) 4 Cobden Crescent, Southampton SO18 4EW — MB BS 1973 Lond.; FFA RCS Eng. 1978; T(Anaes.) 1991. Prev: Cons. Anaesth. King Faisal Specialist Hosp. Riyadh, Saudi Arabia.

WOOD, Greg 49 Chandos Road, East Finchley, London N2 9AR — MB BS 1988 Lond. Sen. Health Off. Psychiat. DKH Catterick, N. Yorks. Prev: Princip. Med. Off. HMS Osprey Portland.

WOOD, Harry Joseph (retired) Holly Court, Kenyon Close, Stratford St Mary, Colchester CO7 6LJ Tel: 01206 322574 Email: happy@hjwood.demon.co.uk — MB BChir 1954 Camb.; MRCS Eng. LRCP Lond. 1954; DObst RCOG 1956.

WOOD, Hazel Anne Queen Elizabeth II Hospital, Howlands, Welwyn Garden City AL7 4HQ Tel: 01707 328111 — MB ChB 1979 Leeds; MRCPsych 1984. Cons. Psychiat. Old Age Qu. Eliz. II Hosp. Welwyn Garden City. Prev: Sen. Regist. (Psychiat.) Pk.side HA.; Sen. Regist. (Psychiat.) Yorks. RHA.; Regist. (Psychiat.) Leeds Rotat. Train. Scheme.

WOOD, Helen Mary Borras Park Surgery, Borras Park Road, Wrexham LL12 7TH Tel: 01978 352341 Fax: 01978 310294 — MB BCh 1983 Wales.

WOOD, Helen Mary Plas Goulbourne Farmhouse, Holt Road, Llan-Y-Pwll, Wrexham LL13 9SA — MB BCh 1983 Wales; DRCOG 1985.

WOOD, Ian Hendrie Young Townhead Surgery, 6-8 High St., Irvine KA12 0AY Tel: 01294 73131; Kincraig, Kilwinning Road, Irvine KA12 8SU — MB ChB 1959 Glas.; DObst RCOG 1961. (Glas.)

WOOD, Ian Robertson St Andrews Hospital, Billing Road, Northampton NN1 5DG Tel: 01604 29696; The Malt House, 2 Bishopstone Rd, Stone, Aylesbury HP17 8RF — BM BCh 1975 Oxf.; MA Oxf. 1970, BM BCh 1975; BS Yale 1968; MRCP (UK) 1976; MRCPsych 1980. cons. Psychiat. (Adult Ment. Health) St. Andrews Hosp. N.ampton. Prev: Cons. Psychiat. Aylesbury Vale.

WOOD, Isobel Janet 10 Johnsburn Park, Balerno EH14 7NA Tel: 0131 449 4177 — MB ChB 1951 Ed.; BSc St. And. 1946. (Edinburgh) Med. Asst. BrE. Screening Clinic Edin.

WOOD, James Challoner (retired) 'Fir Trees', Mill Lane W., Elloughton, Brough HU15 1JJ Tel: 01482 668546 — MB ChB Aberd. 1944. Prev: Ho. Surg. & Ho. Phys. Sutton Annexe, Roy. Infirm. Hull.

WOOD, James Graham Top Flat, 10 North Road, West Kirby, Wirral CH48 4DF — MB ChB 1994 Ed. Ho. Off. (Gen. Med.) Roy. Infirm. Edin. Prev: Ho. Off. (Paediat. Surg.) Roy. Hosp. Sick Childr. Edin.

WOOD, Mr James Jeremy The North London Nuffield Hospital, Cavell Drive, Uplands Park Road, Enfield EN2 7PR Tel: 020 8366 2122; 35 Muswell Road, Muswell Hill, London N10 2BS Tel: 020 8442 0472 — BM BCh 1974 Oxf.; MA Oxf. 1974, DM 1988; FRCS Eng. 1980. Cons. Enfield & Haringay BrE. Screening Progr. Socs: Brit. Assn. Surg. Oncol. Prev: Sen. Regist. (Gen. Surg.) St. Bart.

WOOD

Hosp. Lond.; Regist. (Gen. Surg.) Whipps Cross Hosp. Lond; Research Fell.sh. Harvard Med. Sch. Boston, USA 1983-5.

WOOD, James Leslie (retired) Burnsall, Skipton BD23 6BS Tel: 01756 720227 — MRCS Eng. LRCP Lond. 1948. Prev: SHMO (Ophth.) St. Jas. Univ. Gp. Hosps. Leeds.

WOOD, Jane Diana Dudley (retired) Vrogain, Park St., Denbigh LL16 3DE — MB BS 1961 Lond.; FRCP Lond. 1994; FRCP Glas. 1985, M 1965. Prev: Cons. Phys. c/o Elderly Glan Clwyd Dist. Gen. Hosp. Trust.

WOOD, Jason Mortimer 6 Whiteway Drive, Exeter EX1 3AN — MB BS 1993 Lond.; BSc (Hons.) Lond. 1990. (The Royal London Hospital) Prev: Ho. Off. (Med.) Brookfield Hosp. Chelmsford Essex; Ho. Off. (Surg.) P.ss Alexandra Hosp. Harlow & St Margt.s Hosp. Essex.

WOOD, Jennifer Mary (retired) 6 Keelam Lane, Keighley BD20 6DE — MB ChB 1963 Liverp.; DTM & H Liverp. 1964.

WOOD, Jeremy Paul Royal Bolton Hospital, Minerva Road, Farnworth, Bolton BL4 0JR; 12 Churchwood Road, Didsbury, Manchester M20 6TY Email: jezden@hotmail.com — MB ChB 1992 Manch.; FRCA, 1998. (Manchester) Cons. Anaesth. with an interest in Intens. Care Roy. Bolton Hosp. Socs: Intens. Care Soc. Mem. Assn. of Anaesth.s Mem. Prev: N.est Regional Specialist Regist.

WOOD, Joanne 541 Acklam Road, Acklam, Middlesbrough TS5 7HH — MB ChB 1996 Ed.

WOOD, Joanne Morag 48 Roman Way, Dunblane FK15 9DJ — MB ChB 1980 Glas.; DA (UK) 1985. Staff Grade (Anaesth.) Falkirk & Dist. Roy. Infirm.

WOOD, Johanna Mary 10 The Woodlands, Chelsfield Park, Orpington BR6 6HL Tel: 01689 851054 — MB ChB 1979 Manch. GP Retainer, Chelsfield, Kent; Health Correspondent Woman Alive; Health/Media Speaker Premier Radio. Socs: GPWA.

WOOD, John (retired) 16 Park Road, Deeping St James, Peterborough PE6 8ND — MB ChB 1954 Ed. Prev: Dir. Med. Dept. Brit. Counc.

WOOD, John Albert The Surgery, Austin Rise, netherhall, Leicester LE5 1HJ Tel: 0116 241 6392; 49 Linden Drive, Evington, Leicester LE5 6AJ — MB BS Lond. 1966; MRCS Eng. LRCP Lond. 1966; MRCGP 1975; DObst RCOG 1969. Br. Med. Off. Leics. Br. Brit. Red Cross. Prev: Asst. Br. Med. Off. Leics. Br. Brit. Red Cross Soc.; SHO (Paediat.) Leicester Roy. Infirm.; SHO (O & G) Good Hope Hosp. Sutton Coldfield.

WOOD, John Battersby (retired) Dormington House, Dormington, Hereford HR1 4ES Tel: 01432 850543 Fax: 01432 850543 Email: john.b.wood@lineone.net — BM BCh Oxf. 1960; FRCP Lond. 1979, M 1966. Prev: Cons. Phys. Hereford Co. Hosp.

WOOD, Mr John Bernard Flat 22, 1 Stewart St., London E14 3EX Tel: 020 7538 4951 — MB BS 1991 Lond.; BSc (Hons.) Basic Med. Sci. & Anat. Lond. 1987; FRCS Ed. 1995. Career Regist. Rotat. (Orthop. Surg.) Guy's Hosp. Lond. Socs: Brit. Assn. Sport & Med.; Brit. Assn. Immed. Care Schemes; Brit. Orthop. Train. Assn. Prev: SHO (Gen. Surg.) Joyce Green Hosp. Kent; SHO (Cardiothoracic Surg.) Roy. Brompton Nat. Heart & Lung Hosp. Lond.; SHO (Plastic Surg.) St. Thos. Hosp. Lond.

WOOD, John Derek 77 Blakeney Road, Sheffield S10 1FD — MB BS 1992 Lond.

WOOD, John Gervase (retired) Pinkneys Farm House, Fressingfield, Eye IP21 5SA Tel: 01379 586504 — BM BCh 1958 Oxf.; MA Oxf. 1958. Prev: Princip. GP Oxf.

WOOD, John Hay (retired) 24 The Villas, London Road, Stoke-on-Trent ST4 5AQ Tel: 01782 411700/44237 — MB ChB 1942 Aberd.; DPH 1947.

WOOD, John Kevin Yardley Wood Health Centre, 401 Highfield Road, Yardley Wood, Birmingham B14 4DU Tel: 0121 474 5186 Fax: 0121 436 7648; 83 St. Bernards Road, Solihull B92 7DF — MB ChB 1973 Birm.

WOOD, John Ramsay The Hollies, Auchenblae, Laurencekirk AB30 1XR Tel: 0156 12 220 — MB ChB 1953 Aberd.; FRSE 1980; Dip. Soc. Med. Ed. 1968. Prev: Wing Cdr. RAF Med. Br.

WOOD, John Reginald Pinecones, Salisbury Road, St Margaret's Bay, Dover CT15 6DP Tel: 01304 853386 Fax: 01304 853686 Email: pinecones@compuserve.com/jrwpinecones@cs.com — MB BChir 1954 Camb.; BA Camb. 1950, MA 1980; MRCS Eng LRCP Lond. 1953; MFOM RCP Lond. 1980; MRCGP 1963; DIH Soc. Apoth. Lond. 1971; DObst RCOG 1955. (Guy's) Med. Off. (Occupat. Health) Medway Hosp. Socs: Soc. Occupat. Med.; W Kent M-C Soc.; Roy. Soc. Med. Prev: Course Organiser Lond. (Brook Hosp.) VTS; Med. Off. Woolwich Bldg. Soc.; Apptd. Fact. Doctor Greenwich Dist.

WOOD, John Richard Linthorpe Road Surgery, 378 Linthorpe Road, Middlesbrough TS5 6HA Tel: 01642 817166 Fax: 01642 824094; 63 Hemingford Gardens, Leven Park, Yarm TS15 9ST Tel: 01642 786895 — MB ChB 1980 Dundee; MRCGP 1984; DRCOG 1983.

WOOD, John Roland Gastrointestinal & Metabolic diseases, Glaxowellcome R & D, Stockley Park W., Uxbridge Tel: 020 8990 8201 Fax: 020 8990 8150; Linden House, 4 Fulmer Drive, Gerrards Cross SL9 7HJ — MRCS Eng. LRCP Lond. 1978; PhD Lond. 1988, BSc (Hons.) 1973, MB BS 1978; FFPM RCP. (King's Coll. Hosp.) Dir Therapeutic Develop & product Strategy; Hon. Sen. Lect. Roy. Free Hosp. Sch. Med. Lond. Socs: Brit. Soc. Gastroenterol. & Physiol. Soc. Prev: Regist. Liver Unit King's Coll. Hosp. Lond.; SHO Brompton Hosp. Lond.; SHO Nat. Hosp. for Nerv. Dis. Lond.

WOOD, John Vaughan 101 Lightwater Meadow, Lightwater GU18 5XJ — MB ChB 1998 Manch.

WOOD, Jonathan Altham Brooklea Health Centre, Wick Road, Brislington, Bristol BS4 4HU Tel: 0117 711211 — BChir 1981 Camb.; 1999 Dip in Med Sci (Gen Practt) Birm.; DCH RCP Lond. 1985; DRCOG 1985.

WOOD, Jonathan Mark David 16A Harriotts Lane, Ashtead KT21 2QH — MB ChB 1998 Manch.

WOOD, Jonathan Stuart Square Surgery, 66 The Square, Hartland, Bideford EX39 6BL Tel: 01237 441200; Burley House, 10 Tudor Close, Northam, Bideford EX39 3QD Tel: 01237 421138 — MB ChB 1987 Sheff.; MRCGP 1992; DRCOG 1994. GP Hartland. Prev: SHO Barnsley Dist. Gen. Hosp. VTS; Ho. Off. (Gen. Med. & Surg.) Barnsley Dist. Gen. Hosp.

WOOD, Joseph Keith Department of Haematology, BUPA Hospital, Gartree Road, Leicester LE2 2FF Tel: 0116 265 3663 Fax: 0116 265 3673 Email: kwood-hs@bupa.com; Heather Lodge, 87 Gartree Road, Oadby, Leicester LE2 2FE Tel: 0116 270 7888 — MB ChB Manch. 1962; FRCP Lond. 1985; FRCP Ed. 1978, M 1969; MRCP (UK) 1971; FRCPath 1982, M 1970. (Manch.) Cons. Haemat.Bupa and Nuffield Hosp.s Leicester; Hon. Sen. Lect.Path.. Univ. of Leicester. Socs: Mem.(Chairm. & Past Pres.) Leicester Med. Soc.; Brit. Soc. Haematol.; Brit. Blood Transfus. Soc. Prev: Lect. (Haemat.) Univ. Edin.; Regist. (Haemat.) Univ. W. Indies; Regist. (Clin. Haemat.), Ho. Phys. & Ho. Surg. Roy. Infirm. Manch.

WOOD, Joyce Dorothy Garth Soar, Talsarnau LL47 6UW Tel: 01766 770227 — MB BS 1952 Lond.; MRCS Eng. LRCP Lond. 1952; MFCM 1974; DCH Eng. 1956; DPH Lond. 1960; DObst RCOG 1956. (Guy's)

WOOD, Julie Anne 8 Friars Close, Colchester CO4 4SA — MB BS 1994 Lond.

WOOD, Katie Anne 45A Uplands Road, London N8 9NN — MB BS 1996 Lond.

WOOD, Katrina Mackay 4 Borras Park Road, Wrexham LL12 7TG — BM BCh 1989 Oxf.

WOOD, Mr Kenneth (retired) 10 Johnsburn Park, Balerno EH14 7NA Tel: 0131 449 4177 — MB ChB 1951 Ed.; MB ChB (Hnrs.) Ed. 1951, DMRD 1964; BA Open Univ. 1997; FRCS Ed. 1957; FRCR 1991. Prev: Cons. Radiol. Bangour Gen. Hosp.

WOOD, Kenneth Albert Carrick CMHT, 57 Pydar Street, Truro TR1 2SS Tel: 01872 356000 — MB ChB 1983 Bristol; MSc Keele 1992; MRCPsych 1987. Cons. Psychiat. Cornw. Healthcare NHS Trust. Socs: Brit. NeuroPsychiat. Assn. Bioethics. Prev: Cons. Psychiat. Highland HB; Lect. (Psychogeriat.) Univ. Newc.; Cons. Psychiat. Grampian Primary Care Trust.

WOOD, Kenneth Duncan (retired) Bridge House, Snape, Bedale DL8 2SZ Tel: 01677 470529 — MB ChB 1939 Leeds. Prev: GP Spennymoor.

WOOD, Mr Kenneth Fowler Royal Infirmary, Leicester LE1 5WW Tel: 0116 258 6701 Fax: 0116 252 3123; 26 Southernhay Road, Leicester LE2 3TJ Tel: 0116 270 3081 — MB ChB (Hons.) Leeds 1946; DSc Leic 1980; ChM Leeds 1961; MD Washington Univ. St. Louis 1947; FRCS Eng. 1952. (Leeds & Washington Univ. St. Louis) Emerit. Cons. Surg. Roy. Infirm. Leicester & Leicester Gen. Hosp.; Edr. of Bull. of the Med. Sch. Univ. of Leicester. Socs: Fell. Assn. Surgs.; BMA. Prev: Cons. Advisor Med. Audit Trent Regional HA &

WOOD

Leics. HA.; Regional Postgrad. Dean Trent RHA; 1st Asst. Profss. Surg. Unit. Sheff. Roy. Infirm.

WOOD, Kenneth Michael Hampstead House, Corbridge NE45 5PD Tel: 01434 632359 — MB BS 1947 Durham.

WOOD, Mr Laurence Edward Peter Walsgrave Hospital, Coventry; 6 Dalton Road, Earlsdon, Coventry CV5 6PB Tel: 0121 777 8550 — MB ChB 1976 Liverp.; FRCS Eng. 1981; MRCOG 1990; DTM & H Liverp. 1982. Cons. (O & G) Univ. Hosp.s of coventry & Warks.; Hon. Sen. Lect., Univ. of Warwick; O & G Train. Progr. Director Univ. Hosp. of Coventry & Warks.; Assoc. Postgrad. Dean for Med. Educat. W. Midl.s Region. Prev: Director of Educat. Nat. Counc. Governance Support Team.

WOOD, Miss Lisa Foxhill, The Old Rope Walk, Tetbury GL8 8XG; Stable Cottage, Turpins Hill Farm, Heddon on the Wall, Newcastle upon Tyne NE15 0JX Tel: 01661 852073 Email: 106745.607@compuserve.com — MB ChB 1993 Birm.; BA (Hons.) Camb. 1990; FRCS 1997. (Birmingham) Specialist Regist. (Orthop.). Socs: Med. Protec. Soc. & BMA; BOA. Prev: SHO (Plastics) RUI/RGH; SHO (Orthop.) Sunderland; SHO (Cardiothoracic Surg.).

WOOD, Margaret Columbia University, College of Physicians & Surgeons, 630 West 168th Street, P & S Box 46, New York 10032, USA Tel: 00 1 212 3053117 Fax: 00 1 212 3053296 Email: woodmar@cpmail-nz.cis.columbia.edu; 77 Strathern Road, Broughty Ferry, Dundee DD5 1PG — MB ChB 1970 St. And.; FFARCS Eng. 1974; Dip. Amer. Bd Anaesth. 1996. Prof. & Chairm. Dept. Anesthesiol. Columbia Univ. Coll. Phys. & Surgs. NY, USA. Socs: Pres. Assn. Univ. Anaesth. 1996-1998; Anaesth. Res. Soc. & Amer. Soc. Anaesth. Prev: Prof. Anesthesiol. Vanderbilt Univ., Nashville, TN, USA.

WOOD, Margaret Ann Wilverley, 22 High St, Castor, Peterborough PE5 7BB — BM BS 1987 Nottm.; BMedSci Nottm. 1985. Clin. Asst. (Rheum.) P'boro. Prev: Trainee GP P'boro. VTS; Ho. Off. (Med. & Surg.) Roy. Vict. Hosp. Bournemouth.

WOOD, Margaret Caie (retired) 7 Pinefield, Inchmarło, Banchory AB31 4AF Tel: 01330 825952 — MB ChB 1947 Aberd.; MFCM RCP (UK) 1973; DObst RCOG 1952. Prev: Community Phys. (Child Health) Wirral HA.

WOOD, Margaret Elizabeth Ramblin, Yearngill, Aspatria, Carlisle CA7 3JX Tel: 0169 73 21161 — MB BS 1975 Lond.; MRCS Eng. LRCP Lond. 1975; DRCOG 1978. (Univ. Coll. Hosp.)

WOOD, Margaret Laura Rotherham District General Hospital, Moorgate Road, Oakwood, Rotherham S60 2UD Tel: 01709 820000 Fax: 01709 304481 Email: woodsec.@rgh-trent.hns.uk — MB ChB 1977 (Hons.) Sheff.; FRCP Lond. 1995; MRCP 1980. p/t Cons. Dermat. Rotherham Dist. Gen. Hosp.

WOOD, Marion Elizabeth Department of Haematology, Colchester General Hospital, Turner Road, Colchester CO4 5JL — MB BS 1980 Lond.; FRCP 1998; 2000 FRCPath. Cons. Haemat. Colchester Gen. Hosp. Prev: Sen. Regist. (Haemat.) Roy. Free Hosp. Lond.

WOOD, Mark Bailey 118 Ringwood Road, Christchurch BH23 5RF — MB BChir 1990 Camb.; MA Camb. 1989, MB BChir 1990.

WOOD, Mark Edward Scarness Cottage, Bassenthwaite, Keswick CA12 4QZ — BChir 1996 Camb.; MB 1997; MA 1998. (Cambridge) SHO (Paediat.) Newc.

WOOD, Martin James 118 Craigmount Avenue N., Edinburgh EH4 8HJ — MB ChB 1997 Aberd.

WOOD, Martin John Department of Infection & Tropical Medicine, Birmingham Heartlands Hospital, Birmingham B9 5ST Tel: 0121 4243354 Fax: 0121 4241309 Email: m.j.wood@bham.ac.uk; Rook Farm, Meer End, Kenilworth CV8 1PW Tel: 01676 534180 Email: martinwood@doctors.org.uk — BM BCh Oxf. 1970; MA Oxf. 1970; FRCP Ed. 1994; FRCP Lond. 1987; MRCP (UK) 1973. (Oxf. & St. Mary's) Cons. Phys. Birm. Heartlands Hosp.; Hon. Sen. Clin. Lect. Dept. Infec. Univ. Birm.; Pres. Br.Soc Antimicrobiol. Chemother. Socs: (Counc.) Brit. Soc. Antimicrobiol. Chemother.; Brit. Infec. Soc. Prev: Lect. (Med.) Lond. Hosp. Med. Coll.; Lect. (Med. Microbiol.) Lond. Hosp. Med. Coll.; Edr-in-chief Jl. Antimicrobiol Chemother.

WOOD, Mary Polmener, Mullion, Helston TR12 7DH — MB ChB 1952 Bristol. (Bristol) Prev: Cas. Off. S.mead Hosp. Bristol; Res. Med. Off. Bruce Melville Wills Memor. Hosp. Bristol; Civil Med. Pract. Depot. King's Afr. Rifles Nakuru, Kenya.

WOOD, Mary Elspeth (retired) Eastlea, Harlow Road, Roydon, Harlow CM19 5HE — MSc (Physiol.) Lond. 1950, MB BS 1955;

MRCS Eng. LRCP Lond. 1955; DCH Eng. 1959. Prev: Regist. (Paediat.) S.end Gen. Hosp.

WOOD, Mary Margaret (retired) 38 Church Crescent, Whetstone, London N20 0JP Tel: 020 8368 6951 Fax: 020 8368 6951 Email: margaret@christaret.demon.co.uk — BM BCh 1957 Oxf. Prev: Assoc. Specialist (Microbiol.) Watford Gen. Hosp.

WOOD, (Mary) Philippa Woodview Medical Centre, 26 Holmecross Road, Thorplands, Northampton NN3 8AW Tel: 01604 670780 Fax: 01604 646208 — MB BS 1977 Newc.; MRCGP 1984; DA Eng. 1980. Prev: Clin. Med. Off. (Child Health) Newc.; Regist. (Geriat. & Gen. Med.) Dryburn Hosp. Durh.; Regist. (Anaesth.) Dryburn Hosp. Durh.

WOOD, Matthew John Andrew Universtiy of Oxford, Department of Human Anatomy, South Parks Road, Oxford OX1 3QX — MB ChB 1987 Cape Town.

WOOD, Matthew Laurence Berry Anaesthetic Department, Queen Alexandra Hospital, Cosham, Portsmouth PO6 3LY; 90 Broyle Road, Chichester PO19 4BE — MB ChB 1984 Manch.; MRCP (UK) 1988; FRCA 1988. Cons. Anaesth. Qu. Alexandra Hosp. Portsmouth. Socs: Assn. Anaesth. & Obst. Anaesth. Soc.; Assn Dent. Anaesth. Prev: Sen. Regist. (Anaesth.) St. Geo. Hosp. Lond.; Regist. (Anaesth.) Char. Cross Hosp. Lond.

WOOD, Melanie 118 Acre Lane, Brixton, London SW2 5RA; 75b Nightingale Lane, London SW12 8LY — MB BS 1996 Lond.; MRCP 1999. (Charing Cross & Westminster)

WOOD, Michael Charles Ridgeways, The Stream, Catsfield, Battle TN33 9BD — MD 1941 Dub.; MA Dub. 1947, BA 1936, MB BCh BAO 1937; DMR Lond 1947. (T.C. Dub.) Emerit. Cons. Croydon AHA. Prev: Cons. Radiol. Lewisham Hosp. Gp.; Dep. Dir. X-Ray Dept. Roy. Marsden Hosp. Lond.; Surg. Lt. Cdr. RNVR.

WOOD, Michael Johnson Dundonald Medical Practice, 9 Main Street, Dundonald, Kilmarnock KA2 9HF Tel: 01563 850496 Fax: 01563 850426; 15 Kilnford Crescent, Dundonald, Kilmarnock KA2 9DW — MB ChB 1985 Glas.; MRCGP 1989.

WOOD, Michael Keith 11 Fortinbras Way, Chelmsford CM2 9JA — MB BS 1992 Lond.; BSc (Hons) 1989; MRCP 1996. Specialist Regist. (Thoracic Med.) N. E. Thames Region. Prev: SHO (A & E) Mayday Univ. Hosp. Thornton Heath.

WOOD, Michael Richard Duncan Health Centre, Bishops Close, Spennymoor DL16 6ED Tel: 01388 811455 Fax: 01388 812034; Tel: 0191 373 4317 Fax: 01388 812034 — MB BS 1974 Newc.; MA 1999 Durham; MRCGP 1978. (Newc.) GP Sen. Partner; Company Med. Off. Black & Decker Ltd. Co. Durh. Socs: BMA; Roy. Coll. Gen. Pract.

WOOD, Michael William Wellesley (retired) Wickham Orchard, Overdale Road, Willaston, Neston, South Wirral CH64 1SZ Tel: 0151 327 4779 Fax: 0151 327 4779 — MB BChir 1940 Camb.; MD Camb. 1949; FRCP Lond. 1970, M 1947; MRCS Eng. LRCP Lond. 1940. Cons. Phys. Clatterbridge Hosp. Bebington; Vis. Cons. Phys. Hoylake Cottage Hosp. Prev: Chief Asst. (Med.) W. Middlx. Hosp.

WOOD, Miriam Anne Mount Street Surgery, 69 Mount Street, Coventry CV5 8DE Tel: 024 7667 2277 Fax: 024.7671 7352; 6 Dalton Road, Earlsdon, Coventry CV5 6PB Tel: 024 76 673841 — MB ChB 1977 Liverp.; DTM & H Liverp. 1982. (Liverp.) GP Coventry.

WOOD, Monica Jane School Lane Surgery, School Lane, Washingborough, Lincoln LN4 1BN Tel: 01522 792360 Fax: 01522 794144; Woodlands, Barff Road, Potterhanworth, Lincoln LN4 2DU Tel: 01522 791726 — MB BS 1980 Lond. Prev: Trainee GP Lincoln VTS.

WOOD, Nicholas James 19 Ivygreen Road, Manchester M21 9FF — MB BS 1994 Lond.

WOOD, Nicholas John Lauriel Bank, 37b Castle Road, Kendal LA9 7AU Tel: 01593 734702 Email: njwood1@hotmail.com — MB ChB 1991 Manch. Police Surg. Cumbria Constab. Kendal; Clin. Asst. Cas. Kendal; Med. Adviser to Benefits Agency; Clin. Asst. S. Cumbria Community & Ment. Health Trust.

WOOD, Nicholas Simon 55 Brighton Terrace Road, Crookes, Sheffield S10 1NT Tel: 0114 266 3479 — MB ChB 1991 Sheff.; MRCP (UK) 1997. Clin. Research Fell. - Neonatology Univ. Nottm. Dept. Child Health City Hosp. Nottm.

WOOD, Professor Nicholas William National Hospital for Neurology & Neurosurgery, Queen Square, London WC1N 3BG Tel: 020 7837 3611 Fax: 020 7278 5616 Email: n.wood@ion.ucl.ac.uk

WOOD

— MB ChB 1986 Birm.; FRCP 2000; PhD Camb. 1995; MRCP (UK) 1989. Prof. & Hon. Cons. Neurol. Nat. Hosp. Neur. Hosp. Lond. Socs: Assn. Brit. Neurols.; Edit. Bd. Mem. Movement Disorder Soc.; Amer. Soc. Human Genetics. Prev: Sen. Lect. & Hon. Cons. Neurol. Nat. Hosp. Neurol. & Neurosurg. Lond.; Regist. (Neurol.) Nat. Hosp. Neurol. & Neurosurg. Lond. & Addenbrooke's Hosp. Camb.; Lect. (Neurol.) Inst. Neurol. Nat. Hosp. Neurol. & Neurosurg. Lond.

WOOD, Nicola Rachel Dil Kushi, Windsor Lane, Little Kingshill, Great Missenden HP16 0DP; 3 Woodbank, Little Lane, Loosley Row, Princes Risborough HP27 0TS — MB ChB 1998 Bristol. PRHO High Wycombe Stoke Mandeville Hosp. Socs: Exec. Comm. BMA Bucks.Div.

WOOD, Mr Nigel The Great Sutton Medical Centre, Old Chester Road, Great Sutton, South Wirral CH66 3PB Tel: 0151 339 2424; Jalna, Upper Raby Road, Neston, South Wirral CH64 7TZ — MB ChB 1979 Liverp.; BSc (Hons.) Anat. Liverp. 1975, MB ChB 1979; FRCS Ed. 1984; MRCGP 1990; DRCOG 1989; Cert. Family Plann. JCC 1989.

WOOD, Nigel Charles Arden Medical Centre, Albany Road, Stratford-upon-Avon CV37 6PG Tel: 01789 414942 Fax: 01789 296427; Park House, Clopton House Gardens, Stratford-upon-Avon CV37 0QR Tel: 01789 296993 — MB BS 1978 Lond.; MRCP (UK) 1981; DRCOG 1985. (St. Thos.) Prev: Regist. (Med.) Leeds Infirm.; SHO (Med.) Kidderminster & Dist. HA.

WOOD, Nigel Ewart (retired) Timbers, Sandy Bank, Riding Mill NE44 6HU Tel: 01434 682457 — MB BS 1944 Durh.; MRCGP 1953; DObst RCOG 1949. Prev: Orthop. Ho. Surg. & Ho. Phys. Hexham Gen. Hosp.

WOOD, Nigel Ian Jaunty Springs Health Centre, 53 Jaunty Way, Sheffield S12 3DZ Tel: 0114 239 9453; 100 Howard Road, Sheffield S6 3RW Tel: 0114 234 4142 — MB ChB 1977 Sheff.; DRCOG 1980.

WOOD, Nigel Robert Health Centre, Holmes Road, Broxburn EH52 5JZ; Manuel Mill Farm, Burnbridge, Linlithgow Bridge, Linlithgow EH49 6JF — MB ChB 1976 Ed.; BSc (Med. Sci.) Ed. 1973, MB ChB 1976; MRCGP 1980; DRCOG 1978.

WOOD, Noel Waldo (retired) Morley Health Centre, Corporation St., Morley, Leeds LS27 9NB Tel: 0113 2522051/525646 — MRCS Eng. LRCP Lond. 1953.

WOOD, Patrick Arthur Terence (retired) Coopers, 9 St Edmunds Place, Ipswich IP1 3RA Tel: 01473 230495 — MD 1961 Lond.; MB BS 1944; DObst RCOG 1951. Prev: Nuffield Trav. Fell. For Gen. Practs. 1961-62.

WOOD, Paul Albert Avery Hodson and Partners, Park Farm Medical Centre, Allestree, Derby DE22 2QN Tel: 01332 559402 Fax: 01332 541001 — BM BS 1988 Nottm.; BMedSci (Hons.) 1986; DRCOG 1991.

WOOD, Paul Louis Edward Rockingham Wing, Kettering General Hospital, Rothwell Road, Kettering NN16 8UZ Tel: 01536 492900 Fax: 01536 492871; The Old Vicarage, Dingley Road, Great Bowden, Market Harborough LE16 7ET Tel: 01858 432069 Fax: 01858 431746 Email: plwoldvic@compuserve.com — MD 1990 Leicester; MB ChB 1980 Liverpool; Dip Ven 1983 Liverpool; FRCOG 1998; MRCOG 1985. (Liverp.) p/t Cons. O & G Kettering & Dist. Gen. Hosp. Socs: Expert Witness Inst. Prev: Lect. & Hon. Sen. Regist. (O & G) Univ. Leic.

WOOD, Paul Raymond Major Injuries Unit, Birmingham General Hospital, Steelhouse Lane, Birmingham B4 6NH — MB BCh 1980 Wales; FFA RCS Eng. 1986.

WOOD, Pauline Elizabeth Ann (retired) Heather Lodge, 87 Gartree Road, Oadby, Leicester LE2 2FE Tel: 0116 270 7888 — MB BS 1963 Lond.; DA Eng. 1967. Assoc. Specialist (Anaesth.) Leicester Roy. Infirm. Prev: Clin. Asst. Leics. Hospice.

WOOD, Penelope Clare 8 Balmoral Terrace, Heaton, Newcastle upon Tyne NE6 5YA — MB BS 1996 Newc.

WOOD, Peter 4 Orchard Court, Longniddry EH32 0PE — MB ChB 1970 Ed.; BDS 1964; FDS RCS Ed. 1973. (Ed.) Lect. Oral Med. & Oral Path. Univ. Sch. Dent. Edin. Socs: BMA; Roy. Odonto-Chir. Soc. Scotl. Prev: Lect. (Oral Med.) Univ. Edin.; Ho. Off. Roy. Infirm. Edin.; Regist. Edin. Dent. Hosp.

WOOD, Peter James 118 Hampton Court Road, Birmingham B17 9AG — MB ChB 1989 Birm.

WOOD, Peter John Caldwell 8 Ravensbourne Drive, Chelmsford CM1 2SJ; Beauchamp House Surgery, 37 baddow Road, Chelmsford CM2 0DB Tel: 01245 262255 Fax: 01245 262256 — MB BS 1983 Lond.; DTM & H Liverp. 1988; DRCOG 1987. (Middlx.) SHO (Med. for Elderly) Airedale Gen. Hosp. Steeton. Prev: Med. Dir. Kisiizi Hosp. Kabale, Uganda.

WOOD, Peter John Watson The Grange Consulting Rooms, 92 Whitcliffe Road, Cleckheaton BD19 3DR Tel: 01274 878600 Fax: 01274 869898 Email: drwood@the-grange.org.uk — MB BS 1971 Lond.; MRCS Eng. LRCP Lond. 1971; MRCPsych 1978; DPM Eng. 1978; FRCP FRCPsych 2000. (St. Bart.) Indep. Cons. Forens. Psychiat. Bradford.

WOOD, Mr Peter Laurence Rolls Wrightington Hospital, Wigan WN6 9EP Tel: 0125725 6232 Fax: 0125725 3809 Email: admin@wrightington.org.uk; Orchard Cottage, 25 Canal Bank, Lymm WA13 9NR Email: plrwood@yahoo.com — MB BS 1971 Lond.; FRCS Eng. 1976; MRCS Eng. LRCP Lond. 1971. (Char. Cross) Cons. Orthop. Surg. Wrightington Hosp. Wigan. Socs: Eur. Soc. Foot and Ankle Surgs.; Fell. BOA. Prev: Fell. Orthop. Surg. St. Luke's Episcopal Hosp. Houston, Texas; Sen. Regist. (Orthop.) NW RHA.

WOOD, Peter Trevor, MBE, Maj. RAMC Retd. Chagford Health Centre, Chagford, Newton Abbot TQ13 8BW Tel: 01647 433320 Fax: 01647 432452 — MB ChB 1983 Bristol; MRCGP 1988; DFFP 1994; Dip. IMC RCS Ed. 1994; Dip. Pract. Dermat. Wales 1994; DCCH RCP Ed. 1993; DRCOG 1989; DA (UK) 1987. Prev: Sen. Med. Off. SHAPE BFPO 26 & Family Med. Centre BFPO 23; SHO (O & G) Roy. Shrewsbury Hosp.; Trainee GP/SHO (Anaesth., Paediat. & Geriat.) Roy. Devon & Exeter Hosp.

WOOD, Philip Frank Brambles, 15A Townside, Haddenham, Aylesbury HP17 8BQ Tel: 01844 290878 — MB BCh 1966 Wales; MRCGP 1970; FFPM RCP (UK) 1992; Dip. Pharm. Med. RCP (UK) 1980; DObst RCOG 1969; DCH Eng. 1968. Med. Dir. Anthra Pharmaceut. Europe. Prev: Med. Dir. Wellcome UK & Bristol-Myers Squibb Pharmaceut.

WOOD, Philip Fraser Anderson Union Brae Surgery, Union Brae, Tweedmouth, Berwick-upon-Tweed TD15 2HB Tel: 01289 330333 Fax: 01289 331075 — MB ChB 1982 Dundee; LFHom RCP Lond. 1996; MRCGP 1987. Socs: Brit. Med. Acupunct. Soc.

WOOD, Philip Henry Nicholls Bephillick, Duloe, Liskeard PL14 4QA Tel: 01503 264635 — MB BS Lond. 1955; FRCP Lond. 1978, M 1971; FFPHM 1989; FFCM 1972. (St. Bart.) Emerit. Dir. Arthritis & Rheum. Counc. Epidemiol. Research Unit Univ Manch. Prev: Hon. Prof. Community Med. Univ. Manch.; Asst. Research Prof. Med. State Univ. N.Y. Buffalo, USA; Ho. Phys. Brompton Hosp. Lond.

WOOD, Philip Meldrum Laurel House Surgery, 12 Albert Road, Tamworth B79 7JN Tel: 01827 69283 Fax: 01827 318029 — MB BS 1967 Lond.; MRCS Eng. LRCP Lond. 1967; MRCP (UK) 1972.

WOOD, Philip Michael Dawson Department of Clinical Chemistry and Immunology, Leeds General Infirmary, Great George Street, Leeds LS1 3EX Tel: 0113 392 2340 — MB BS 1991 Newc.; MRCPath 2001; DPhil Oxon. 1997; BMedSc (Hons.) Newc. 1988; MRCP (UK) 1994. Specialist Regist. (Clin. Immunol.) Birm. Heartlands Hosp. Birm. Prev: Research Fell. Molecular Immunol. Gp. Nuffield Dept. Med. Oxf.; SHO (Med.) Newc. Hosps.

WOOD, Philip Milton Wood, The Surgery, Chapel Road, Aldborough, Norwich NR11 7AA Tel: 01263 768602 Fax: 01263 761340; Smithy Cottage, The Loke, Bessingham, Norwich NR11 7JR — MB BChir 1984 Camb.; MA Camb. 1985, BA 1981. Prev: SHO Gt. Yarmouth & Waveney, Norwich & P'boro. HAs.

WOOD, Philippa Jane University Hospital of North Durham, North Road, Durham DH1 5TW Tel: 0191 333 2333 Email: philippa.j.wood@lineone.net; 3 Rose Acre, Shincliffe, Durham DH1 2NT Tel: 0191 383 2410 — MB BS 1985 Lond.; FRCA 1990; DA (UK) 1987. (Char. Cross & Westm.) Cons. Anaesth. Univ. Hosp. of N. Durh. Socs: Mem. of Obstetric Assn. of Anaesth.s. Prev: Sen. Regist. (Anaesth.) Middlx. Hosp. Lond.

WOOD, Rachael Jane Information & Statistics Division, Common Services Agency, Trinity Park House, South Trinity Rd, Edinburgh EH5 3SQ — MB ChB 1993 Ed.; BSc (Med. Sci.) Ed. 1991; Dip. Obst. RCPT Lond. 1997; DCH RCP Lond. 1996; DTM & H Liverp. 1994; DFFP 1997. (Ed.) p/t Specialist Regist. Pub. Health Med., S. E. Scotl. Train. Scheme. Socs: Fell. of the Roy. Soc. of Med. Prev: SHO (O & G) E. Gen. Hosp. Edin.; SHO (Med.) E.. Gen. Hosp. Edin.; SHO (Paediat.) Stirling Roy. Infirm.

WOOD

WOOD, Rachel Mary Flat 10, Arundel House, 21 Lawn Road, Portswood, Southampton SO17 2ER; 1 Hunters Mead, Hawkesbury Upton, Badminton GL9 1BL — BM 1998 Soton.; BM Soton 1998. PRHO Gen.Med.Roy.Bournemouth.Hosp. Prev: PRHO Gen.Surg.Poole.Gen.Hosp.

WOOD, Rachel Sarah 15 Wasley Close, Fearnhead, Warrington WA2 0DH — MB BS 1998 Newc.

WOOD, Raymond Anthony Berry Wraysdale House Surgery, Wraysdale House, Coniston LA21 8ES Tel: 015394 41205 — LRCPI & LM, LRSCI & LM 1971; DObst RCOG 1974. (RCSI) GP Coniston. Socs: Irish Coll. Gen. Pract.; BMA; Assoc. Mem. RCGP. Prev: Princip. GP Merseyside; Ho. Off. (Med. & Surg.) & SHO (O & G) Birch Hill Hosp. Rochdale; GP & GP Tutor King Fahd Milit. Hosp. Jeddah, Saudi Arabia.

WOOD, Rebecca Jane 103 Hunter House Road, Sheffield S11 8TX Tel: 0114 268 2159 — MB ChB 1991 Sheff.; DRCOG 1996.

WOOD, Rhian Copper Beeches, Theescombe Lane, Amberley, Stroud GL5 5AZ Tel: 01453 872671 — MB BS 1976 Lond.; MRCS Eng. LRCP Lond. 1976.

WOOD, Professor Richard Frederick Marshall, RD (retired) Clinical Sciences Centre, Northern General Hospital, Herries Road, Sheffield S5 7AU Email: p.m.king@Sheffield.ac.uk — MB ChB 1967 Glas.; MA Oxf. 1981; MD Glas. 1976; FRCS Glas. 1972; FRCS Eng. 1972; T(S) 1991. Prof. Surg. Univ. Sheff. & Hon. Cons. Surg. N.ern Gen. Hosp. NHS Trust. Prev: Prof. Surg. St. Bart. Hosp. Med. Coll. & Hon. Cons. Surg. Bartholomews NHS Trust.

WOOD, Richard Hamilton (retired) The Surgery, Moor View, Hinderwell, Saltburn-by-the-Sea TS13 5HH — MB BS 1971 Lond. Prev: GP Saltburn-by-the-Sea.

WOOD, Richard Holman (retired) Morva, Gillan, Manaccan, Helston TR12 6HG Tel: 01326 231560 — MB ChB 1948 Bristol. Prev: Clin. Asst. Chelmsford & Essex Hosp.

WOOD, Richard John Rhinns Medical Centre, Port Charlotte, Isle of Islay PA48 7UD Tel: 01496 850210 Fax: 01496 850511; Coultorsay House, Isle of Islay PA49 7UN Tel: 01496 850298 — MB BS Lond, 1966; MRCS Eng. LRCP Lond. 1966; DObst RCOG 1968. (Lond. Hosp.) GP Princip. Prev: SHO (Obst.) St. John's Hosp Chelmsford; Ho. Phys. & Ho. Surg. Roy. Cornw. Hosp. Treliske.

WOOD, Mr Richard Mountford Thellusson 1 Plough Court, Roskrow, Penryn TR10 9AP Tel: 01326 378298 Fax: 01326 375622 Email: rmtwood@aol.com — MB BS Lond. 1966; FRCS Ed. 1973. (St. Bartholomews Hospital) Prev: GP Hong Kong.

WOOD, Richard Neil Ashley Gateacre Brow Surgery, 1 Gateacre Brow, Liverpool L25 3PA Tel: 0151 428 1851 — MB ChB 1983 Bristol; MRCGP 1992; DRCOG 1991; DA (UK) 1986. Prev: Trainee GP Blackpool VTS; S.C.C. Roy. Navy.

WOOD, Rita Maxine Bank View, Bilham Road, Clayton West, Huddersfield HD8 9PA — MB ChB 1992 Sheff.

WOOD, Robert Allen Heady Hill Surgery, Heys Lane, Heywood OL10 3RB Tel: 0161 761 1775; 10 Mount Pleasant, Nangreaves, Bury BL9 6SP — MB ChB 1988 Manch.; MRCGP 1993; DFFP 1993.

WOOD, Professor Robert Anderson (retired) Ballomill House, Abernethy, Perth PH2 9LD Tel: c — MB ChB 1963 Ed.; BSc (Hons.) Ed. 1961; FRCS Ed. 1994; FRCP Glas. 1997; FRCP Ed. 1976, M 1966; FRCPsych 1999. Treas. RCP Edin.; Head of Counc. & Managem. Comm. MODUS; Mem. Criminal Injuries Compensation Appeal Panel. Prev: Cons. Phys. Perth & Kinross Health Dist.

WOOD, Mr Robert Anthony Bowness Ward 10, Ninewells Hospital and Medical School, Dundee DD1 9SY Tel: 01382 660111 Fax: 01382 633994; Lubnaig, 442 Blackness Road, Dundee DD2 1TQ Tel: 01382 667547 — MB ChB Leeds 1965; FRCS Ed. 1981; FRCS Eng. 1971; MRCP (London) 1969. Cons. Surg. Dundee Teachg. Hosp. Trust; Hon. Sen. Lect. (Surg.) Ninewells Hosp. Dundee. Socs: Surgic. Research Soc.; Brit. Soc. Gastroenterol. Prev: Lect. (Surg.) Univ. Hosp. of Wales Cardiff; Regist. (Surg.) Norf. & Norwich Hosp.; SHO (Med.) York City Hosp.

WOOD, Robert Brockwell 18A North Street, Silsden, Keighley BD20 9PQ — MB ChB 1987 Leeds.

WOOD, Robin UKAEA, Harwell, Didcot OX11 0RA Tel: 01235 435296 Fax: 01235 435018; 6A Gravel Lane, Drayton, Abingdon OX14 4HY — MB ChB 1971 Sheff.; MFOM Eng. 1982; DIH Eng. 1980. Chief Med. Adviser Ukaea. Socs: Soc. Occupat. Med.

WOOD, Robin Gaythorn Bramma Drayton Medical Practices, The Health Centre, Cheshire Street, Market Drayton TF9 3BS Tel: 01630 652158 — MB ChB 1971 Manch.; DObst RCOG 1973.

WOOD, Sally — MB BS 1986 Lond. Trainee GP Burley Wharfedale. Prev: Trainee GP Addingham.

WOOD, Sally Margaret Westway Surgery, 1 Wilson Road, Ely, Cardiff CF5 4LJ Tel: 029 2059 2351 Fax: 029 2059 9956; 32 St Michael's Road, Llandaff, Cardiff CF5 2AP Tel: 029 2056 5884 — MB BS 1982 Lond.; MRCGP 1986. Forens. Med. Examr. Socs: Cardif Medico-Legal Soc.; Roy. Soc. Med.; (Sec.) Cardiff Med. Soc.

WOOD, Sarah Augusta Claremont Clinic, 459-463 Romford Road, Forest Gate, London E7 8AR Tel: 020 8522 0222 Fax: 020 8522 0444; 74 Clavering Road, London E12 5EX Tel: 020 8925 1895 Email: gussett74@aol.com — MB BS 1980 Lond.; BSc Lond. 1977, MB BS 1980. (London)

WOOD, Sarah Elizabeth 'Woodbank', Slades Road, Golcar, Huddersfield HD7 4NE Tel: 01484 652659 Fax: 01484 845080 Email: drswood@hotmail.com — MB ChB 1996 Leeds. SHO/GP Registr. (O & G), HGH. Prev: SHO (A&E), Ryde Hosp.; SHO (Paediatr.), Huddersfield.

WOOD, Miss Sarah Jane 7 Auckland Road, Cambridge CB5 8DW Email: woodwin@compuserve.com — MB BChir 1993 Camb.; MA Camb. 1993; FRCS (Eng.) 1996. (Cambridge) Research Regist. (Urol.) Inst. Urol. & Nephrol. Lond. Socs: Brit. Assn. Urol. Prev: SHO (Gen. Surg. & Urol.) Hinchingbrooke Hosp. Huntingdon.

WOOD, Sarah Morwenna — MB BS 1991 Lond.; BA Oxf. 1983; MRCP (UK) 1994. Clin. Lect./Hon SpR Univ. of Edin. S. E. Scotl. Postgrad. Med. Educat. Bd. Roy. Infirm. of Edin.

WOOD, Sheila Alice (retired) 10 Grange Road, Bushey WD23 2LE Tel: 01923 228055 — MB BS 1954 Lond.; MRCS Eng. LRCP Lond. 1954; DObst RCOG 1956. Prev: Late GP Hemel Hempstead.

WOOD, Sheila Margaret Ballomill, Abernethy, Perth PH2 9LS Tel: 0173 885201 — MB ChB 1965 St. And. (St. And.) Regist. (Med.) Perth & Kinross Health Dist. Prev: Ho. Phys. St. Chas. Hosp. Lond.; Ho. Surg. Vict. Centr. Hosp. Wallasey; Asst. Lect. in Path. Univ. Dundee.

WOOD, Mr Simon Harold Charing Cross Hospital, Fulham Palace Road, London W6 8RF Tel: 020 8846 1720 — MB BS 1986 Lond.; FRCS 1990 ed.; FRCS 1997 ((Plast.)). Cons. Plastic Surg., Char. Cross Hosp., Lond.; Cons. Plast. Surg., St Mary's Hosp., Paddington, Lond. Socs: Brit Assn. Of Plastic Surg.; Brit. Assn. Of Head & Neck Oncologists. Prev: Sen Regist. (Plastic Surg.) Addenbrookes. Camb.

WOOD, Simon Jon 18 Mardley Hill, Welwyn AL6 0TN; 17 Sandfield Road, Gateacre, Liverpool L25 3PE Tel: 0151 421 1245 — MB ChB 1990 Liverp.; MRCOG 1995. (Liverpool) Research Fell. Reproductive Med. Unit Liverp. Wom.s Hosp.

WOOD, Simon Marshall (retired) 3 St Leonards Road, Exeter EX2 4LA Tel: 01392 437435 — MB BChir 1964 Camb.; MD Birm. 1974; MRCS Eng. LRCP Lond. 1963; FRCOG 1981, M 1968, DObst 1966. Prev: Cons. O & G Roy. Devon & Exeter Hosp.

WOOD, Simon Morley 3 Barnby Avenue, York YO10 4HX — MB ChB 1980 Leeds; MRCPsych 1984; MMedSc Leeds 1985.

WOOD, Simon Murray 9 Heathfield Road, Chelmsford CM1 7BZ — MB BS 1993 Lond.; BSc (Hons. Human Genetics) Lond. 1992. SHO (Med. for Elderly People) Whipps Cross Hosp. Lond. Prev: SHO (A & E) Basildon Hosp. Essex; SHO (Psychiat.) E. Ham Memor. Hosp.; Ho. Off. (Surg.) Homerton Hsop. Lond.

WOOD, Stephanie Joan Northfield Health Centre, Northfield Road, Narberth SA67 7AA Tel: 01834 860316 Fax: 01834 861394; 4 Minwear Wood, Martletwy, Narberth SA67 8AA Tel: 01437 541305 — MB ChB 1983 Bristol. GP Narberth. Prev: Trainee GP Withybush Hosp. HaverfordW..

WOOD, Stephen 4 Jubilee Cottages, Throwley Forstal, Faversham ME13 0PJ; 4 Jubilee Cottages, Throwley Forstal, Faversham ME13 0PJ Tel: 01795 890485 — MB BS 1979 Lond.; BSc Lond. 1976, MB BS 1979; MRCPsych 1983. (Guy's) Sen. Lect. (Psychiat.) UMDS Guy's Hosp. Lond. & Acad. Psychiat. Unit Canterbury; Med. Dir. Canterbury & Thanet Community Healthcare NHS Trust; Cons. Psychiat. St Martin's Hosp. Canterbury. Prev: Cons. Psychiat. Ment. Health Advice Centre Lewisham.

WOOD, Stephen Donnington Health Centre, 1 Henley Avenue, Oxford OX4 4DH Tel: 01865 771313; 12 Old High Street, Headington, Oxford OX3 9HN Tel: 01865 741211 — BM BCh 1971

WOODCOCK

Oxf. (St. Thos.) Tutor (Gen. Pract.) Oxf. Univ. Prev: SHO Cheltenham Gen. Hosp. & Ch.ill Hosp. Oxf.; Ho. Surg. St. Thos. Hosp. Lond.

WOOD, Stephen Jarvis Tyndale Oak Lodge, Lower Shockerwick, Bath BA1 7LW Tel: 01225 742376 Email: stephenandjeanne@waitrose.co.uk — MB ChB 1977 Birm. Cons. Med. Advisor to Brit. Inst. for Brain Injured Childr. Bridgewater Som. Prev: GP Wells Som.; Occupat. Health Phys. Herrison Hosp. Dorchester; Occupat.al Health Phys., Brit. Aerospace, Bridgewater, Som.

WOOD, Mr Stephen John ENT Department, Southmead Hospital, Bristol; 26 Clarendon Road, Redland, Bristol BS6 7EU — MB ChB 1987 Bristol; FRCS Eng. 1994; FRCS Ed. 1992; FRCS Eng. 1992; FRCS (ORL) 1998. Specialist Regist. Rotat. (Otolaryngol.) SW Region/ Cons. Sen. Lect. & Hon. Cons. Otolaryngol., Head & Neck Surg.; Fell. in Head & Neck Surg., Toronto Gen. Hosp. Prev: Clin. research fell., Bristol Roy. Infirm.; SHO Rotat. (Surg.) Bristol Roy. Infirm.; Demonst. (Anat.) Bristol Univ.

WOOD, Mr Stephen Keith (retired) 4 Hook Water Close, Chandlers Ford, Eastleigh SO53 5PS Email: skwchf@compuserve.com — MB ChB 1958 Manch.; FRCS Ed. 1968; FRCS Glas. 1965. Prev: Hon. Cons. Soton. Univ. Hosp. Trust.

WOOD, Stuart Fotheringham Dumbarton Road Surgery, 1264 Dumbarton Road, Glasgow G14 9PS Tel: 0141 959 6311 Fax: 0141 954 9759 — MD 1985 Glas.; MB ChB 1973; FRCGP 1986, M 1978. Sen. Lect. Gen. Pract. Univ. Glas.; GP Glas. Prev: SHO (Med.) Stobhill Gen. Hosp. Glas.; Ho. Surg. Glas. Roy. Infirm.; Ho. Phys. Stobhill Gen. Hosp. Glas.

WOOD, Suzanne 62 Priory Road, Linlithgow EH49 6BS — MB ChB 1997 Glas. SHO (Paediat.) St Johns Hosp. Livingston. Socs: BMA. Prev: PRHO (Med./Surg.) St Johns Hosp. Livingston; SHO (A+E) St Johns Hosp. Livingston.

WOOD, Suzanne Anne c/o Doctors Mess, Chesterfield and North Derbyshire Royal Hospital, Calow, Chesterfield S44 5BL — MB ChB 1997 Sheff.

WOOD, Sylvia Allena (retired) Chimes Cottage, Sandside, Kirkby-in-Furness LA17 7UA Tel: 01229 889133 — MB ChB 1959 Manch. Prev: Regist. (O & G) Mpilo Hosp. Bulawayo, Rhodesia.

WOOD, Terence Alwyn The Health Centre, Testwood Lane, Totton, Southampton SO40 3ZN Tel: 023 8086 5051 Fax: 023 8086 5050; Rackenford, Pikes Hill Avenue, Lyndhurst SO43 7AX — MB ChB 1966 Bristol; MRCGP 1976. Prev: Ho. Phys. & SHO Dept. Path. S.mead Hosp. Bristol; Ho. Surg. Roy. Infirm. Bristol.

WOOD, Thomas Alan 11 Reece Mews, London SW7 3HE Tel: 020 7584 0650 — MB 1967 Camb.; BChir 1966; FRCPath 1987, M 1974. (Camb. & St. Bart.) Med. Dir. Selfusion Autologous Blood Serv. Prev: Dep. Dir. S. Lond. Blood Transfus. Centre; Hon. Cons. (Blood Transfus.) St. Geo. Hosp. Lond.; Lect. (Haemat.) St. Geo. Hosp. Med. Sch. Lond.

WOOD, Timothy Campbell (retired) 20 Greys Close, Cavendish, Sudbury CO10 8BT — BM BCh 1955 Oxf.; MA, BM BCh Oxf. 1955; FRCGP 1985, M 1976; DObst RCOG 1959. Med. Off. Merchant Taylor's Sch. Prev: GP Watford.

WOOD, Timothy Charles Anthony The Barn Surgery, Newbury, Gillingham SP8 4XS Tel: 01747 824201 Fax: 01747 825098 — BM 1986 Soton.; MRCGP 1992; DRCOG 1992.

WOOD, Vernon (retired) Oratava, Castle Douglas DG7 1PE Tel: 01556 600221 Email: dr.wood@tesco.net — MB ChB 1966 St. And. Private Involvem. in sports Med. Prev: GP Clifton Nottm. & Mansfield Notts.

WOOD, Wendy Elizabeth Ann The Garden Flat, 1 Talbot Place, Blackheath, London SE3 0TZ — MB BS 1968 Lond.; FRCPath 1994; MRCPath 1982. Assoc. Specialist in Chem. Path. Greenwich Dist. Hosp.

WOOD, William Matthew 5 Cavensish Street, Chorley PR6 0RU — MB ChB 1968 Ed.

WOOD-ALLUM, Clare Alison 29 Matchless Close, Northampton NN5 6YE — BM BCh 1997 Oxf.

WOODALL, John Trevor (retired) 89 Broad Street, Canterbury CT1 2LU Tel: 01227 470185 — MB BS 1946 Lond.; FRCGP 1971; DObst RCOG 1953. Prev: GP St. Paul's Cray.

WOODALL, Nicholas Alexander 94 Kestrel View, Weymouth DT3 5QZ Tel: 01305 814352 Fax: 01305 814352 — MB BS 1995 Lond. (St George's Hosp. Med. Sch., Lond.) Locum GP.

WOODALL, Nicholas Mark 9C Upton Close, Norwich NR4 7PD — MB ChB 1980 Liverp.; FFA RCS Eng. 1985. Cons. Anaesth. Norf. & Norwich Hosp. Prev: Sen. Regist. (Anaesth.) Middlx. Hosp. Lond.; Clin. Instruc. Univ. Calif., USA.

WOODALL, Peter Lyndon South Liverpool Child & Family Consultation Team, T Ward, Alder Hey Children's Hospital, Eaton Road, Liverpool Tel: 0151 228 4811 — MB ChB 1985 Manch.; MRCPsych 1991; Dip. Psychother. Liverp. 1991. Cons. Child & Adolesc. Psychiat. Roy. Liverp. Childr. NHS Trust.

***WOODALL, Rachel Louise** 101 Heywood Old Road, Middleton, Manchester M24 4QL; Flat 1, 28 Hallville Road, Allerton, Liverpool L18 0HR — MB ChB 1997 Liverp.

WOODBRIDGE, Kenneth (Surgery), 6 Townsend Road, Southall UB1 1EX Tel: 020 8574 2794 Fax: 020 8893 5463; 13 Lodge Close, Englefield Green, Egham TW20 0JF Tel: 01784 435232 Fax: 01784 893 5463 — MB BCh Wales 1960. (Cardiff) Med. Off. Ultra Electronics. Greenford (Communicats.) & Ultra (Loudwater). Socs: Assoc. Mem. RCGP; Assoc. Mem. Soc. Occupat. Med.

WOODBRIDGE, Kevin Francis New Manse Surgery, Linklet House, North Ronaldsay, Orkney KW17 2BE Tel: 01857 633226 Fax: 01857 633207 — MB ChB 1972 Manch. Prev: SHO (Med.) Withington Hosp. Manch.

WOODBRIDGE, Michael 17 Orchard Road E., Northenden, Manchester M22 4FQ — MB BChir 1993 Camb.

WOODBRIDGE, Peter A (retired) c/o National Westminster Bank, 5 Meads St., Eastbourne BN20 7QT — MB BS 1952 Lond.; MRCS Eng. LRCP Lond. 1952. Prev: Hosp. Pract. (Dermat.) E.bourne Health Dist.

WOODBRIDGE, Sylvia (Surgery), 2 Baxters Close, Leicester LE4 0QR Tel: 0116 235 3579; 302 Leicester Road, Cropston, Leicester LE7 7GT Tel: 0116 235 6574 — MB BS 1951 Lond.; MRCS Eng. LRCP Lond. 1951; CPH 1953. (Roy. Free)

WOODBURN, Alastair George Medical Centre, 12 East King Street, Helensburgh G84 7QL Tel: 01436 673366 Fax: 01436 679715; 55 John Street, Helensburgh G84 9LZ Tel: 01436 3366 — MB ChB 1971 Glas.; BSc Glas. 1967, MB ChB 1971; MRCGP 1975; DObst RCOG 1973.

WOODBURN, Caroline Boreland Farm, Hollybush, Ayr KA6 7ED — MB ChB 1998 Glas.

WOODBURN, Elizabeth Mary Alice Ballyalbana, Ballyclare BT39 — LRCP LRCS 1962 Ed.; LRCP LRCS Ed. LRFPS Glas. 1962.

WOODBURN, Mr Kenneth Robert Professorial Surgical Unit, Level 10, Western Infirmary, Glasgow G11 6NT Tel: 0141 211 2122 Fax: 0141 334 1826; Bishopmills Court, 210 Old Dumbarton Road, Glasgow G3 8QB — MD 1994 Ed.; MB ChB 1985; FRCS Glas. 1989. Career Regist. (Surg.) W. Scotl. HST; Regist. (Surg.) W.. Infirm Glas. Prev: Regist. (Surg.) Ayr Hosp.; Regist. (Vasc. Surg.) Glas. Roy. Infirm.; Regist. (Surg.) Vict. Infirm. Glas.

WOODBURN, Kirstie Jane Roayl Victoria Hospital, Craigleith Road, Edinburgh EH4 2DN Tel: 0131 537 5000 — BM BCh 1988 Oxf.; MA Oxf. 1985; MRCPsych 1993; MD Ed. 1997. Cons. in Old Age Psychiat. Edin. Prev: Wellcome Clin. Research Train. Fell. (Psychiat.) Univ. Edin.

WOODBURY-SMITH, Marc Ronald c/o Medical Personnel Department, Tatchbury Mount, Calmore, Totton, Southampton SO40 2RZ — MB ChB 1993 Dundee.

WOODCOCK, Arthur Sutton (retired) Dale Garth, Queens Drive, Heswall, Wirral CH60 6SH Tel: 0151 342 4378 — MB ChB 1944 Leeds; MD (Distinc.) Leeds 1955; FRCPath 1970, M 1964; FRCOG (ad eundem) 1984.

WOODCOCK, Professor Ashley Arthur North West Lung Centre, Wythenshawe Hospital, Manchester M23 9LT Tel: 0161 291 2398 Fax: 0161 291 5020 — MB ChB 1975 Manch.; BSc (1st cl. Hons. Physiol.) Manch. 1972, MD 1982; FRCP Lond. 1992; MRCP (UK) 1977. (Manch.) Cons. Phys. Wythenshawe Hosp. Manch./Prof. Resp. Med. Uni. Manch.; Dir. Regional Dept. of Respirat. Physiol. & Sleep Laborat. Socs: Eur. Respirat. Soc.; Chairm. Clin. Assembly. Prev: Cons. Phys. Manch. Roy. Infirm.; Sen. Regist. Brompton Hosp. Lond.; Specialist Phys. Gen. Hosp. Bandar Seri Begawan, Brunei.

WOODCOCK, Barrie Ewart University Hospital Aintree, Longmoor Lane, Liverpool L9 7AL; 12 Hartley Road, Birkdale, Southport PR8 4SA — MB ChB 1977 Birm.; MA (Physiol. Scs.) Oxf.; FRCP Lond. 1995; MRCP (UK) 1980; FRCPath 1996, M 1984. Cons. haematologist, Aintree Hosps. NHS Trust; Hon. Lect. Univ. Liverp.

WOODCOCK

Prev: Cons. Haemat. S.port & Ormskirk NHS Trust; Sen. Regist. Rotat. (Haemat.) Sheff. HA; Regist. (Haemat.) Roy. Hallamsh. Hosp. Sheff.

WOODCOCK, Barrington Morton The Oaklands, Liverpool Road, Fiveways, Neston, Wirral CH62 6EL — MB ChB 1968 Bristol; DCH Eng. 1973.

WOODCOCK, Clive John Longfield Road Surgery, 1 Longfield Road, Harpfields, Stoke-on-Trent ST4 6QN Tel: 01782 616587 Fax: 01782 719108; 54 The Avenue, Hartshill, Stoke-on-Trent ST4 6DA Tel: 01782 614272 — MB BS 1978 Lond.; BSc Lond. 1975; FRCGP 1995, M 1984; Dip. Sports Med. Glas. 1992; DRCOG 1981. (St. Bart.)

WOODCOCK, David Roy Peel House Medical Centre, Avenue Parade, Accrington BB5 6RD Tel: 01254 237231 Fax: 01254 389525; 61 Tarn Avenue, Lynwood Park, Clayton-le-Moors, Accrington BB5 5XT Tel: 01254 386064 — MB ChB 1984 Manch.; BSc (Med. Sci.) St. And. 1981; Cert. Family Plann. JCC 1987; DRCOG 1986.

WOODCOCK, Emma Mary 130 Brighton Road, Godalming GU7 1PL — MB BS 1990 Lond. SHO (A & E) St. Geo. Hosp. Lond.

WOODCOCK, Justine Frances Namwen, Hoyle Hill, Beare Green, Dorking RH5 4PS — MB BS 1992 Lond. Cas. Off. Roy. Sussex Co. Hosp. Brighton.

WOODCOCK, Kevin Rowland 18 Stoke Road, Winchester SO23 7ET Tel: 01962 862122 Fax: 01962 622533; Royal Hampshire County Hospital, Winchester SO22 5DG Tel: 01962 863535 Fax: 01962 824826 Email: kevin.woodcock@weht.swest.nhs.uk — MB BS Lond. 1965; MRCP (UK) 1971; MSc (Social Med.) Lond. 1973; MFPHM RCP (UK) 1974; MFPM RCP (UK) 1989. (St. Mary's) Cons. Genitourin. Med. Roy. Hants. Co. Hosp. Winchester. Socs: Fell. Roy. Soc. Med.; Fell. Roy. Soc. Health; Fell. Scientif. & Med. Network. Prev: Pharmaceut. & Medico-Legal Cons. Serenissima Medica Winchester; Cons. & Sen. Lect. (Venereol.) Soton. Univ. Hosps.; Community Med. Specialist (Informat. & Plann.) Kensington, Chelsea & W.m. HAs.

WOODCOCK, Malcolm Gareth Lewin, Flight Lt. RAF Med. Br. MDHU Peterborough Eye Department, Peterborough District Hospital, Peterborough Tel: 01733 874000; 42 Empingham Road, Stamford PE9 2RH Tel: 01780 482268 — BM 1995 Soton.; BSc (Hons.) Soton 1994. (University of Southampton) SHO (Opthalmology) PeterBoro. Dist. Hopsital. Prev: Jun. Med. Off. RAF Laarbruch, Germany.

WOODCOCK, Nicholas Paul 37 Leadley Croft, Copmanthorpe, York YO23 3YX — MB ChB 1994 Leeds.

WOODCOCK, Patrick Willis 66 Tachbrook Street, London SW1V 2NA Tel: 020 7834 0654 — MB ChB 1943 Birm.; MRCS Eng. LRCP Lond. 1944. (Birm.)

WOODCOCK, Peter James Ribblesdale House Medical Centre, Market Street, Bury BL9 0BU Tel: 0161 764 7241 Fax: 0161 763 3557 — MB ChB 1973 Manch. GP Bury.

WOODCOCK, Peter John 14 Laverdene Drive, Sheffield S17 4HH — MB ChB 1989 Sheff.

WOODCOCK, Philip Alan Michael 15B Thurlow Park Road, London SE21 8JB — MB BS 1980 Lond.

WOODCOCK, Reuben Cyril (retired) 6 The Woodlands, Lostock, Bolton BL6 4JD Tel: 01204 495276 — MB ChB 1943 Leeds; FRCPath 1967; DCP Lond 1951; DPath Eng. 1954. Prev: Cons. Pathol. Bolton Hosp. Gp.

WOODCOCK, Sean Anthony Aiden 56 Hague Street, Glossop SK13 8NS — MB BS 1991 Lond.

WOODCOCK, Susannah Mary Old Rectory, Sowton, Exeter EX5 2AG Tel: 01392 367423 — MB BS 1952 Lond.; MRCP Lond. 1958. (Roy. Free) Socs: Assn. Brit. Neurols. Prev: Neurol. Manch. RHB; Sen. Regist. (Neurol.) United Birm. Hosps.; Res. Med. Off. Maida Vale Hosp. Nerv. Dis.

WOODCOCK, Thomas Edward Department Anaesthesia, Southampton General Hospital, Tremona Road, Southampton SO16 6YD Tel: 02380 777222 — MB BS 1978 Lond.; FFA RCS 1982. (Char. Cross Hosp.) Cons. (Anaesth. & Intens. Care) S.ampton Univ. Hosp. NHS Trust. Prev: Sen. Regist. (Anaesth.) SW RHA; Regist. Clin. Shock Study Gp. W.. Infirm. Glas.; Fell. (Anaesth.) Univ. W.. Ontario, Canada.

WOODCOCK, Vanessa Emma 55 Windle Gr, Windle, St Helens WA10 6HP — MB ChB 1997 Liverp.

WOODD-WALKER, Robert Basil (retired) 35 Lexden Road, Colchester CO3 3PX Tel: 01206 571896 — MB BChir Camb. 1959; FRCP Lond. 1982, M 1966; MRCS Eng. LRCP Lond. 1960; DCH Eng. 1964; FRCPCH 1997. Prev: Cons. Paediat. Gen. Hosp. Colchester.

WOODER, Margaret Louise The Limpet, 6 Overcliff, Port Isaac PL29 3RZ — BM 1976 Soton.; MRCOG 1982. Resid. Med. Off. Duchy Hosp. Truro Cornw. Prev: Resid. Med. Off. Portland Hosp. Wom. & Childr. Lond.

WOODFIELD, Marie Celia Hinchingbrooke Health Care NHS Trust, Hinchingbrooke Park, Huntingdon PE29 6NT — BChir 1995 Camb.

WOODFIELD, Martyn Little Penquite, Lostwithiel PL22 0HX; Stillmoor House, Bodmin PL31 2QP Tel: 01208 79059 — MB BCh 1984 Wales; BSc Wales 1979, MB BCh 1984; MRCGP 1989.

WOODFORD, Ann Riverside, Nesfield Road, Ilkley LS29 0BE Tel: 01943 608193 Fax: 01943 608193 Email: cfh@chasholdsworth.prestel.co.uk — MB ChB 1962 Manch. (Manch.) Clin. Asst. (Anaesth.) Airedale Gen. Hosp. Socs: BMA. Prev: Ho. Surg. & Ho. Phys. Kingston Hosp.

WOODFORD, Charles Philip 2 Deepfields, Radbrook, Shrewsbury SY3 6DP — MB BS 1974 Lond.; DCH RCP Lond. 1983; DRCOG 1980. (Lond. Hosp.)

WOODFORD, Derek The Surgery, Church Lane, Elvington, York YO41 5AD; The Old Rectory, Elvington, York YO4 5AD Fax: 01904 608710 — MB BS 1965 Lond.; MRCS Eng. LRCP Lond. 1965; DObst RCOG 1968. (King's Coll. Hosp.)

WOODFORD, Henry John The Old Rectory, Elvington, York YO4 5AD — MB BS 1996 Lond.

WOODFORD, Sarah Louise Newnham College, Cambridge CB3 9DF — BChir 1996 Camb.

WOODFORDE, Alec Robert (retired) Knowlewood, 4 Warren Close, Ringwood BH24 2AJ — MRCS Eng. LRCP Lond. 1933.

WOODFORDE, Christopher Simon John Peelhouse Lane Surgery, 1 Peelhouse Lane, Widnes WA8 6TW Tel: 0151 424 6221 Fax: 0151 420 5436 — MB ChB 1991 Liverp.; BSc (Hons.) Liverp. 1986. (Liverp.) Gen. Pract. Widnes; G.P. Fell. In Resp. Health for Halton P.C.T., Chesh..; Director of R.E.A.C.H. Progr. (Resp. Excellence Across Clin. Care in Halton). Socs: Med. Protec. Soc.; BMA; BASICS.

WOODGATE, Donald John Cardiac Department, Basildon Hospital, Basildon SS16 5NL Tel: 01268 533911 Fax: 01268 520392 — MB BS 1958 Lond.; FRCP Lond. 1979, M 1964; DA Eng. 1961. (Lond. Hosp.) Cons. Phys. & Cardiol. & Clin. Dir. Cardiol. & Pharmaceut. Servs. Basildon & Thurrock HA. Socs: Brit. Cardiac Soc. Prev: Sen. Regist. (Med.) Roy. Free Hosp. Lond.; Sen. Regist. (Cardiol. & Thoracic Med.) Roy. Free Hosp. Lond.; Ho. Surg. Lond. Hosp.

WOODGATE, Jane Elizabeth Woodgate and Packham, Fairfield Surgery, High Street, Burwash, Etchingham TN19 7EU Tel: 01435 882306 Fax: 01435 882064; Cople Cottage, Burwash Weald, Etchingham TN19 7LA — MB BS 1981 Lond. Prev: Trainee GP Tunbridge Wells VTS.

WOODGATE, Mark 25B Brighton Road, Stoke Newington, London N16 8EQ — MB BS 1992 Lond. Regist. (Psychiat.) Roy. Lond. Hosp. Lond. Socs: Inceptor Roy. Coll. Psychiat.

WOODGATE, Mrs Moira Margaret (retired) 7 The Drive, off Mill Road, Deal CT14 9AE Tel: 01304 363532 — MB BCh BAO Dub. 1940. Prev: GP, Surbiton, Surrey.

WOODGATE-JONES, Noel Philip (retired) High Hallsannery, Bideford EX39 5HE Tel: 01237 421432 — MRCS Eng. LRCP Lond. 1937. Hon. Maj. RAMC. Prev: Ho. Surg. Harrow & Wealdstone Hosp.

WOODGATE-JONES, Timothy Woodgate-Jones and Partners, The Surgery, Mount Street, Bishops Lydeard, Taunton TA4 3LH Tel: 01823 432361 Fax: 01823 433864 — MB BS 1964 Lond.; MRCS Eng. LRCP Lond. 1964.

WOODGER, Bruce Arthur 53 Dowanside Road, Glasgow G12 9DW Tel: 0141 339 1092 — MB ChB 1946 Glas.; FRIC 1972; FRCPath 1968; DPath Eng. 1954. (Glas.) Cons. Path. Monklands Dist. Gen. Hosp. Coatbridge. Socs: Assn. Clin. Pathols. & Assn. Clin Biochem. Prev: Capt. RAMC; Cons. Path. Hairmyres Hosp. E. Kilbride; Sen. Lect. Path. Univ. Nairobi, Kenya.

WOODHALL, Andrew John Vernon House, Vernon Road, Heckmondwike WF16 9LU Tel: 01924 402091 — MB BS 1976

Lond.; BSc Bristol 1967; MSc Lond. 1970, MB BS 1976; DRCOG 1979. (Roy. Free)

WOODHALL, Cynthia Ruth Whiston Hospital, Warrington Road, Prescot L35 5DR Tel: 0151 430 1452 Fax: 0151 430 1902 — MB ChB 1971 Manch.; FRCP Lond. 1995; MRCP (UK) 1979; MRCPCH 1979; DRCOG 1977. p/t Cons. Paediat. Whiston & St. Helens Hosps. Merseyside. Socs: Liverp. Paed. Soc.; Manch. Med. Soc. Prev: Sen. Regist. (Paediat.) NW RHA; Fell. (Neonat. Paediat.) Dalhowsie Univ. Halifax, Canada; Tutor (Child Health) Manch. Univ.

WOODHAM, Colin Henry Radiology Department, The John Radcliffe Hospital, Headington, Oxford OX3 9DU — MB BS 1975 Lond.; BSc (Physics) CNAA 1965; MRCS Eng. LRCP Lond. 1975; FRCR 1984. (St. Bart.) Regist. Dept. Radiol. Radcliffe Infirm. Oxf.; Cons. John Radcliffe Hosp. Headington Oxf.

WOODHAM, Michael John 16 Tyrone Road, Southend-on-Sea SS1 3HF — MB BS 1980 Newc.; FFA RCS Lond. 1986. Cons. Anaesth. S.end Hosp. S.end-on-Sea. Prev: Sen. Regist. (Anaesth.) St. Geo. Hosp. Lond.

WOODHAMS, Anna Mary 50 Beverley Terrace, Cullercoats, North Shields NE30 4NU — MB BS 1996 Newc.

WOODHAMS, Lara Jessica The Brambles, 6 Carline Court, Northampton NN3 3RJ — MB BS 1998 Lond.

WOODHAMS, Richard William Talofa, 127 Bentswood Road, Haywards Heath RH16 3PP — MB BS 1991 Lond.; DFFP 1994; DRCOG 1993.

WOODHAMS, Simon David 12 Chatfield Road, Cuckfield, Haywards Heath RH17 5BB — MB BS 1990 Lond.

WOODHEAD, Anne Elizabeth 25 Drakes Way, Portishead, Bristol BS20 6LD Tel: 01272 844594 — MB ChB 1972 St. And.; DObst RCOG 1974.

WOODHEAD, Christopher James 68 Somerton Drive, Erdington, Birmingham B23 5ST — MB ChB 1982 Birm.

WOODHEAD, David Magnus John Meopham Medical Centre, Wrotham Road, Meopham, Gravesend DA13 0AH Tel: 01474 814811/814068 Fax: 01474 814699 — MB ChB 1990 Manch.

WOODHEAD, Jill Louise 28 Hungerford Road, Bournemouth BH8 0EH — MB ChB 1997 Sheff.

WOODHEAD, Jonathan Wickham (retired) Upper Magdalen, Allington Park, Bridport DT6 5DD Tel: 01308 423365 — MRCS Eng. LRCP Lond. 1951. Prev: SHO (Obst.) Newmarket Hosp.

WOODHEAD, Mark Andrew Manchester Royal Infirmary, Oxford Road, Manchester M13 9WL Tel: 0161 276 4381 Fax: 0161 276 4989 Email: woodhead@central.cmht.nwest.nhs.uk — MB BS 1979 Lond.; BSc (1st cl. Hons.) Lond. 1976; DM Nottm. 1988; FRCP Lond. 1996; MRCP (UK) 1982. (King's Coll. Hosp.) Cons. Phys. (Respirat. & Gen. Med.) Manch. Roy. Infirm. Socs: Brit. Thorac. Soc. (Sec. Research Comm. 1993-1996); Eur. Respirat. Soc. (Head Respirat. Infec. Sect.). Prev: Sen. Regist. (Respirat. & Gen. Med.) St. Geo. & Brompton Hosps. Lond.; Research Regist. Notts. HA; Ho. Phys. King's Coll. Hosp. Lond.

WOODHEAD, Nicholas Jesse Uplands Medical Practice, Bury New Road, Whitefield, Manchester M45 8GH Tel: 0161 766 8221 Fax: 0171 796 2417; Tel: 0161 766 8526 — MB ChB Manch. 1969.

WOODHEAD, Nicola Jane Valkyrie, Whitepost Lane, Meopham, Gravesend DA13 0TH — MB ChB 1990 Manch. SHO (Psychiat.) Maidstone Priority Care Trust. Prev: SHO (O & G) St. Mary's Hosp. Manch.

WOODHEAD, Patricia Jane Weston General Hospital, Uphill, Weston Super Mare BS23 4TQ — BM 1979 Soton.; 2000 MBA University of Bath; MRCP (UK) 1982; FRCR 1986. Cons. (Radiol.) W.on Gen. Hosp. W.on Super Mare; Exec. Med. Director, W.on Health Trust. Prev: Regist. & Sen. Regist. (Radiol.) Univ. Coll Hosp. Lond.; Vis. Lect. Univ. Michigan, USA.

WOODHEAD, Peter Michael Hainslack Farm, Skipton Old Road, Colne BB8 7ER — MB BS 1983 Lond. Regist. Dept. Radiol. Leicester Roy. Infirm.

WOODHEAD, Richard Leslie The Yorkshire Clinic, Bradford Road, Bingley BD16 1TW Tel: 01274 560311; 6 Bankfield Drive, Nab Wood, Shipley BD18 4AD Tel: 01274 586315 — BM BCh Oxf. 1966; MA Oxf. 1966; FRCP Lond. 1984, M 1969. (Univ. Coll. Hosp.) Prev: Cons. Phys. Roy. Infirm. & St. Luke's Hosp. Bradford; Sen. Regist. (Med.) Leeds Gen. Infirm.; Regist. (Med.) Univ. Coll. Hosp. Lond.

WOODHEAD, Robert Barry Croft House Surgery, 5 Croft House, 114 Manchester Road, Slaithwaite, Huddersfield HD7 5JY Tel: 01484 842652 Fax: 01484 348223; The Spinney, 63 Woodside Road, Beaumont Park, Huddersfield HD4 5JF — MB ChB 1975 Manch.; MRCGP 1987; DRCOG 1978.

WOODHEAD, Roderick John Group Surgery, Normans Place, Off Regent Road, Altrincham WA14 2AB Tel: 0161 928 2424; 9 Thorley Lane, Timperley, Altrincham WA15 7BJ Tel: 0161 980 5011 — MB ChB 1963 Manch.

WOODHEAD, Roxie 15 Moorfield Gardens, Chapeltown, Pudsey LS28 8BW Tel: 0113 256 5477 — MB ChB 1948 Leeds. (Leeds) Socs: Bradford M-C Soc. Prev: Med. Off. Community Health Serv. Bradford HA; Ho. Phys. & Ho. Phys. Med. Profess. Unit, St. Jas. Hosp. Leeds; Ho. Phys. Paediat. Dept. Leeds Gen. Infirm.

WOODHEAD, Zoe Mary Surgery, Normans Place, Off Regent St., Altrincham WA14 2AB Tel: 0161 928 2424; 9 Thorley Lane, Timperley, Altrincham WA15 7BJ Tel: 0161 980 5011 — MB ChB 1963 Manch.

WOODHOUSE, Bruce Andrew Dyneley House Surgery, Newmarket Street, Skipton BD23 2HZ Tel: 01756 799311 Fax: 01756 707203; Newton Head, Bank Newton, Gergrave, Skipton BD23 3NT Tel: 01750 749421 Email: bwoodhouse@totalise.co.uk — BM BS Nottm. 1989; BMedSci Nottm. 1987; MRCGP (Distinc.) 1993. Clin. Asst. Lieriatrics,Airedale NHS Trust. Prev: Trainee GP Airedale VTS; SHO (Orthop.) Airedale Gen. Hosp.; Ho. Off. (Med.) Nottm. Univ. Hosp.

WOODHOUSE, Carolyn Mary 22 Dennyview Road, Abbots Leigh, Bristol BS8 3RB Tel: 01275 373726 — MB ChB 1971 Bristol; MRCGP 1977; D.Occ.Med. RCP Lond. 1996. Med. Team Ldr. Med. Serv. SEMA Grp.

WOODHOUSE, Christopher John Hulme House Medical Centre, 175 Royce Road, Hulme, Manchester M15 5TJ Tel: 0161 226 0606 Fax: 0161 226 5644; 44 Kingston Road, Didsbury, Manchester M20 2SB — MB BCh BAO 1982 Belf.; DRCOG 1987; DCH RCP Lond. 1987; MRCGP 1991.

WOODHOUSE, Mr Christopher Richard James Lister Hospital, Chelsea Bridge Road, London SW1W 8RH Tel: 020 7730 6204 Fax: 020 7730 6204; 14 Crescent Grove, London SW4 7AH Tel: 020 7622 4441 Fax: 0207 622 4665 Email: cwoodhouse2@coompuserve.com — MB BS 1970 Lond.; FRCS Eng. 1975; MRCS Eng. LRCP Lond. 1970; FEBU 1993. (Guy's) Reader in Adolesc. Urol. & Hon. Cons. Urol. Inst. Urol. Middlx. Hosp. Lond.; Cons. Urol. Roy. Marsden Hosp. Lond.; Hon. Cons. Urol. Hosp. for Childr. Gt. Ormond St.; Hon. Cons. Urol. UCL Hosp. Socs: Fell. Roy. Soc. Med.; Brit. Assn. Urol. Surg.; Amer. Urol. Assn. Prev: Cons. Urol. St. Geo. Hosp. Lond.; Sen. Regist. (Urol.) St. Peter's Hosps. (Inst. Urol.) Lond.; Regist. (Surg.) Lond. Hosp.

WOODHOUSE, Joan Suzanne (retired) 180 Lichfield Road, Rushall, Walsall WS4 1ED — MB ChB 1945 Birm.

WOODHOUSE, John County Durham HA, Appleton House, Lanchester Road, Durham DH1 5XZ Tel: 0191 333 3232 Fax: 0191 333 3222; 2 Highbury, West Jesmond, Newcastle upon Tyne NE2 3BX — MB BS 1984 Newc.; MA Oxf. 1980; MSc (Pub. Health) Newc. 1991; MFPHM RCP (UK) 1992; MRCGP 1988; DRCOG 1987. Dir. (Pub. Health) Co. Durh. HA. Prev: Cons. Pub. Health Phys. N.. & Yorks. RHA; Sen. Regist. (Pub. Health Med.) N.. RHA.

WOODHOUSE, Josephine Cecilia 3 Grimston Park Mansion, Grimston Park, Tadcaster LS24 9DB Tel: 01937 835360 — MB ChB 1975 Leeds.

WOODHOUSE, Julian Isidoro Jose Antonio — MB BS 1992 Lond.; MRCGP 1992 Lond.; DFFP Roy Free Hosp. Sch. Med. 1998. (Roy. Free Hosp. Med. Sch.) RMO 2nd BN The Roy. Gurkha Rifles. Prev: Resid. Med. Off. & Dep. Post Master; S. Georgia (Brit. Antarctic Territory); Regtl. Med. Off. The Roy. Dragoon Guards.

WOODHOUSE, Kenneth Walter University Department of Geriatric Medicine, Llandough Hospital, Cardiff Tel: 029 2071 6985 Fax: 029 2071 1267 Email: woodhousekw@cardiff.ac.uk — MD 1985 Newc.; BM (Hons.) Soton 1977; FRCP Lond. 1990; MRCP (UK) 1979; T(M) 1991. Prof. Geriat. Med. & Vice Dean Med. Univ. Wales Coll. Med. Cardiff. Socs: Brit. Pharm. Soc. & Brit. Geriat. Soc. Prev: Cons. Phys. & Sen. Lect. in Med. (Geriat.) & Clin. Pharmacol. Roy. Vict. Infirm. & Univ. Newc.; MRC Trav. Fell. Dept. Clin. Pharmacol. Karolinska Inst. Stockholm; MRC Train. Fell. Depts. Med. & Clin. Pharmacol. Univ. Newc.

WOODHOUSE

WOODHOUSE, Mark Noel 86 Crosby Street, Cale Green, Stockport SK2 6SP — MB ChB 1988 Manch.

WOODHOUSE, Mervyn Ashley (retired) Well Cottage, 43 Dorchester Road, Frampton, Dorchester DT2 9NF — MB ChB Birm. 1955; FRCPath 1977, M 1965. Prev: Cons. Pathologist, W. Dorset Gen. Hosp.s NHS TRUS.

WOODHOUSE, Monica Mary (retired) Well Cottage, 43 Dorchester Road, Frampton, Dorchester DT2 9NF — MB BS Lond. 1957; MRCS Eng. LRCP Lond. 1956. Prev: Clin. Asst. in Psycho-Geriat. W. Dorset HA.

WOODHOUSE, Paul Anthony Old Barn, Pond Farm, East Peckham, Tonbridge TN12 5NA — MB ChB 1986 Ed.; BA Oxf. 1983.

WOODHOUSE, Peter Robert Department of Medicine for Elderly, West Norwich Hospital, Bowthorpe Road, Norwich NR2 3TU Tel: 01603 288002 Fax: 01603 288571 Email: peter.woodhouse@norfolk-norwich.thenhs.com — BM 1983 Soton.; DM Soton. 1995; MRCP (UK) 1989; FRCP Lond. 1999. Cons. Geriat. Med. Norf. & Norwich Healthcare Trust; Hon. Sen. Lect. Univ. of E. Anglia. Socs: Brit. Geriat. Soc. Prev: Sen. Regist. (Gen. & Geriat. Med.) & Research Fell. (Clin. Gerontol.) Addenbrooke's Hosp. Camb.; Lect. (Physiol.) Lond. Hosp. Med. Coll.

WOODHOUSE, Phillip 22 Grinton Road, Stockton-on-Tees TS18 5HE — MB ChB 1998 Leic.

WOODHOUSE, Sarah Jane Lilac Cottage, Wymondham Road, Wreningham, Norwich NR16 1AT — MB ChB 1987 Liverp.

WOODHOUSE, Wendy Jane Child & Adolescent Psychiatry Department, Princess Margaret Hospital, Okus Road, Swindon SN1 4JU Tel: 01793 536231 — MB BS 1986 Lond.; MRCP (UK) 1990; MRCPsych 1992. Cons. Child & Adolesc. Psychiat. P.ss Margt. Hosp. Swindon. Prev: Sen. Regist. (Child Psychiat.) Maudsley Hosp. Lond.

WOODIER, Neville Christopher Pencefn, Llanddona, Beaumaris LL58 8UB Tel: 01248 811282 — MB ChB (2nd Cl. Hnrs.) Liverp. 1954. (Liverp.) Prev: Ho. Surg. & Ho. Phys. Liverp. Roy. Infirm.; O & G Ho. Surg. Mill Rd. Hosp. Liverp.

WOODING, Daniel Francis Peter (retired) Mansion House Surgery, Abbey St., Stone ST15 8YE Tel: 01785 815555 — MB BS Lond. 1954; DObst RCOG 1957.

WOODING, Nicholas James 8 Barkers Lane, Wythall, Birmingham B47 6BU Tel: 01564 823539 Email: nickkiwales@hotmail.com — BM BCh 1990 Oxf.; DTM & H 1996 Liverpool; MA 1997 Oxford; MRCGP 1996; BA Open 1996; BA Oxf. 1987; DRCOG 1993. Socs: Christian Med. Fell.sh. Prev: GP Trainee, Sydenlam Green Health Centre; GP VTS, Lewisham Hosps.

WOODING, Regan Mary Susan Well Close Square Surgery, Well Close Square, Berwick-upon-Tweed TD15 1LL Tel: 01289 356920 Fax: 01289 356939 Email: regan.wooding@gp-a84026.nhs.uk — MB BS 1981 Lond.; DRCOG 1983. GP Berwick upon Tweed.

WOODING, Simon Charles Long Clawson Medical Practice, The Surgery, The Sands, Long Clawson, Melton Mowbray LE14 4PA Tel: 01664 822214/5 — BM BS 1987 Nottm.; MRCGP 1992; DCH 1993. (Nottm.) GP Melton Mowbray.

WOODING, Stephen James 14 Eccleshall Road, Walton, Stone ST15 0HN — MB BS 1983 Lond.; BSc (Pharmacol.) Lond. 1980.

WOODINGS, David Francis Medicines Control Agency, Market Towers, 1 Nine Elms Lane, London SW8 5NQ Tel: 020 7273 0148 Fax: 020 7273 0195; Eastweald, 59 Valley Road, Ipswich IP1 4EG Tel: 01473 254220 — MB BChir 1969 Camb.; MA, MB Camb. 1969, BChir 1968; MRCP (UK) 1971; FRCPS Glas. 1991; FFPM 1989; FRCPath 1986, M 1974; FRCP Lond. 1997. (Camb. & Middlx.) Sen. Med. Off. Med. Control Agency Lond. Socs: Fell. Roy. Soc. Med.; Brit. Soc. Haematol. Prev: Med. Dir. Schwarz Pharmaceut. Ltd. Chesham; Sen. Research Phys. Glaxo Gp. Research Ltd. Ware; Lect. (Haemat.) St. Geo. Hosp. & Med. Sch. Lond.

WOODINGS, John Trevor (retired) London Road Medical Centre, 2 London Road, Uppingham, Oakham LE15 9TJ Tel: 01572 823531 — MB ChB 1965 Ed.; DA Eng. 1967.

WOODINGS, Pamela Louise 92 Adderley Road, Clarendon Park, Leicester LE2 1WB; 56 Leicester Road, Uppingham, Oakham LE15 9SD — MB ChB 1991 Leic.; MRCP (UK) 1994. Regist. (Oncol.) W.on Pk. Hosp. Sheff. Prev: SHO (Oncol.) Roy. Marsden Hosp. Sutton.; SHO Rotat. (Med.) Leicester.

WOODLAND, John Rheumatology Department, Standish Hospital, Stonehouse GL10 3DB; The Stocks., 5 Cleeve Road, Gotherington, Cheltenham GL52 9EW — MB BS 1969 Lond.; FRCP Lond. 1989; MRCP (UK) 1972; MRCS Eng. LRCP Lond. 1969; T(M) 1991. (Guy's) Cons. Rheum. Glos. HA. Socs: Brit. Soc. Rheum. Prev: Sen. Regist. (Rheum.) Lond. Hosp.

***WOODLAND, John Michael** 18 Common Road, Wincanton BA9 9HU — MB ChB 1995 Birm.

WOODLAND, Richard John Temple (retired) 8 Hurstmere House, Hurstmere Close, Grayshott, Hindhead GU26 6TT Tel: 01428 5297 — MRCS Eng. LRCP Lond. 1943; MB BChir Camb. 1940; MA Camb. 1940; LMCC 1950; DA Eng. 1978.

WOODLEY, Alan George Grove Health Centre, 129 Dundee Road, Broughty Ferry, Dundee DD5 1DU Tel: 01382 778881 Fax: 01382 731884; 67 Marlee Road, Broughty Ferry, Dundee DD5 3EU Tel: 01382 739820 — MB ChB 1976 Dundee; MRCP (UK) 1982; DCH RCP Lond. 1982. Hon. Med. Adviser, Dundee Br. RNLI.

WOODLEY, Helen Elizabeth Leeds General Infirmary, Great George St., Leeds LS1 3EX; The Cottage, Mill Lane, Pool-in-Wharfedale, Otley LS21 1LR Tel: 0113 284 3401 — MB BChir 1991 Camb.; BA (Hons.) Camb. 1987, MA, MB 1991, BChir 1990. SHO Rotat. (Gen. Med., Radiother. & Oncol.) Cookridge Hosp.

WOODLEY, Joan Margaret 2 Manor Road, Ipswich IP4 2UX Tel: 01473 251210 — MB BS 1954 Lond.; MRCS Eng. LRCP Lond. 1954.

WOODLIFF, Hugh Jackson Markholme, Keswick CA12 5PW — MB ChB 1950 Ed.; FRCP Ed. 1971; MRCP (UK) 1954; FRCPath 1974, M 1963.

WOODMAN, Alastair Michael 19 Quarry Road, Belfast BT4 2JD — MB BCh 1998 Belf.

WOODMAN, Professor Ciaran Bernard John Centre for Cancer Epidemiology, Kinnaird Road, Manchester M20 — MB BCh BAO 1977 NUI; MD 1990; MRCOG 1986; MFPHM 1988. Prof. Cancer Epidemiol. Univ. Manch. Prev: Sen. Lect. (Cancer Epidemiol.) Univ. Birm.; Lect. ((Social Med.) Univ. Birm.

WOODMAN, Geoffrey Francis Gordon (retired) Farrowsheals, 16 Linden Acres, Longhorsley, Morpeth NE65 8XQ Tel: 01670 788229 Email: woodman@northland.fsnet.co.uk — MB BS Durh. 1952; MRCGP 1970. Prev: Hosp. Pract. (Geriat.) Morpeth Cottage Hosp.

WOODMAN, Graham John Bronllys Hospital, Bronllys, Brecon LD3 0LY Tel: 01874 711255; Copthorne, Llanshall Lane, Knighton LD7 1LW — MB ChB 1980 Birm.; BSc Bristol 1970; MRCGP 1984; DRCOG 1982. (Birm.) Prev: DRS Ksiff, Woodman & Cross; Wylcwh St Surg.; Powys LD7 1AD.

WOODMAN, Jacqueline Rachel 22 Eden Drive, Oxford OX3 0AB — MB ChB 1991 Stellenbosch.

WOODMAN, Michael John The Health Station, 21a Brand St., Hitchin SS5 1JE Tel: 01462 459595 Fax: 01438 435373 Email: thehealthstation@netscapeonline.co.uk — MB BS Lond. 1970; DFFP 1994; DRCOG 1972. (St. Mary's) Socs: Assur. Med. Soc.; Nat. Assn. Family Plann. Doctors.

WOODMAN, Miriam Manchester Health Authority, Gateway House, Piccadilly S., Manchester M60 7LP Tel: 0161 237 2812 Fax: 0161 237 2813 Email: woodman@manchester.nwest.nhs.uk — MB BCh BAO 1978 NUI; MFPHM RCP (UK) 1987. Cons. Pub. Health Manch. Health Auth.; Hon. Clin. Lect. Univ. Manch. Prev: Cons. Pub. Health Kidderminster Health Auth.; Sen. Regist. (Community Med.) Centr. Birm. Health Auth..

WOODMAN, Timothy John The Health Centre, Holding Street, Rainham, Gillingham ME8 7JP Tel: 01634 262333 — MB BS 1981 Lond.; DRCOG 1984. SHO (Paediat.) S. W. Surrey HA. Prev: Trainee GP Witley; SHO (O & G) Medway HA; SHO (A & E) Cuckfield Hosp.

WOODMANSEY, Annica Louise 23 Weeping Cross, Stafford ST17 0DG Email: pacdwoodm@aol.com — MB ChB Sheff. 1986; DCH RCPS Glas. 1989. Prev: Staff Grade Paediat. (A & E) Sheff. Childr. Hosp. NHS Trust.; Staff Grade, Community Paediat., S. Staffs. Healthcare NHS Trust, Stafford Centr. Clinic.

WOODMANSEY, Paul Arnold Staffordshire General Hospital, Weston Road, Stafford ST16 3SA Tel: 01785 230677 Fax: 01785 230677 — MB ChB 1986 Sheff.; MD Sheff. 1995, BMed Sci. (Hons.) 1983; MRCP (UK) 1989; FRCP Lond 2000. Cons. Cardiol. M. Staffs. NHS Trust; Hon. Cons. Cardiol. N. Staffs. NHS Trust. Socs: Brit. Cardiac Soc.; Brit. Soc. of Echocardiography; Brit. Pacing &

Electrophysiol. Gp. Prev: Regist. (Cardiol.) Leeds Gen. Infirm.; Research Regist. (Cardiol.) Roy. Hallamsh. Hosp. Sheff.

WOODNUTT, Mr David John 8 Talygarn Street, Heath, Cardiff CF14 3PT Tel: 029 2038 7092 Fax: 029 2038 7092 — MB BS 1990 Lond.; MPhil Open 1993; BSc (Hons.) Bristol 1982; FRCS Eng. 1994. Regist. (Orthop.) Cardiff Roy. Infirm. Prev: SHO (A & E) Derbysh. Roy. Infirm.; Ho. Off. Char. Cross Hosp. Lond. & Barnstaple & N. Devon Dist. Hosps.

WOODROFFE, David (retired) 57 Wensleydale Road, Hampton TW12 2LP — MB BS Lond. 1954. Prev: GP Middlx.

WOODROFFE, Frederick James (retired) Swanton Lodge, Swanton St, Bredgar, Sittingbourne ME9 8AS Tel: 01622 884434 Email: f.woodroffe@btclick.com — MSc (Gen. Biochem.) Lond. 1975, MB BS (Hons.); FRCP Lond. 1978, M 1966; MRCS Eng. LRCP Lond. 1961. Prev: Phys. Chase Farm Hosp. Trust.

WOODROFFE, Guy Campbell Woodroffe, Dixon and Raitt, Ravenswood Surgery, New Road, Forfar DD8 2AE Tel: 01307 463558 Fax: 01307 468900 Email: drwoodroffe@ravenswood.finix.org.uk; Rockcliffe, 2 Bankhead Road, Forfar DD8 3JP Tel: 01307 467596 Email: guycw@supanet.com — MB ChB 1985 Ed.; MRCGP 1989; DFFP 1996; DObst RCPI 1990. (Ed.) Princip. GP. Socs: Life Mem. Roy. Med. Soc. Prev: SHO (Paediat.) Burnley Gen. Hosp.; Trainee GP Hawick VTS; SHO (Med.) Edenhall Hosp. Musselburgh.

WOODROFFE, Janet Betty Seamura, Smallwood Hey Road, Pilling, Preston PR3 6HJ Tel: 01253 790109 — MB ChB 1943 Liverp.; DA Eng. 1954. (Liverp.) Socs: Fell. Manch. Med. Soc.; Liverp. Med. Inst. Prev: Cons. Anaesth. Preston HA; Regist. (Anaesth.) Chester Hosp. Gp.; Res. Anaesth. Preston Roy. Infirm.

WOODROFFE, Robert William North End Surgery, High Street, Buckingham MK18 1NU Tel: 01280 813239 Fax: 01280 823449; Hanover Barn, Hanover Farm, Addington, Buckingham MK18 2JW Tel: 01296 715607 Fax: 01296 715607 Email: roffe@globalnet.co.uk — MB BS 1971 Lond.; BSc (Hons.) Lond. 1968, MB BS 1971; MA Keele Univ. 1993. (St. Thos.) Med. Off. Buckingham Hosp.; Asst. Dep. Coroner (Milton Keynes). Socs: BMA. Prev: SHO (Med. & Oncol. & O & G) I. of Thanet HA; SHO (Cas.) St. Thos. Hosp. Lond.

WOODROFFE, Susan Aileen Rockcliffe, 2 Bankhead Road, Forfar DD8 3JP Tel: 01307 467596 — MB ChB 1985 Ed.; MRCGP 1989; DRCOG 1988. Socs: Life Mem. Roy. Med. Soc. Prev: Trainee GP Edin.; SHO (Med.) Edenhall Hosp. Musselburgh; SHO (Cas., O & G, Paediat. & Psychiat.) W.. Gen. Hosp. Edin.

WOODROOF, Gerard Martin Fenwick Chipton Barton, Dittisham, Dartmouth TQ6 0HW Email: gerard.woodroof@sdevonhc-tr.swest.nhs.uk — MB BS 1979 Lond.; MSc Lond. 1984, BSc (Hons.) 1976; FFOM RCP Lond. 1995, MFOM 1987, AFOM 1985; MRCS Eng. LRCP Lond. 1979. (Guy's) Cons. Occupat. Phys. Torbay Hosp. Torquay & Derriford Hosp. Plymouth.

WOODROW, Charles Jonathan 94 Milton Park, London N6 5PZ Tel: 020 8341 9780; Division of Infectious Diseases, St. George's Hospital Medical School, London SW17 0RE Tel: 020 8725 5834 Fax: 020 8725 3487 Email: cwoodrow@sghm5.ac.uk — MB BS 1993 Lond.; BA (Hons.) Camb. 1990; MRCP Lond. 1996. Clin. Research Fell. St Geo.'s Hosp. Med. Sch. Lond. Socs: BMA. Prev: SHO (Renal) St. Mary's Hosp. Lond.; SHO (Respirat. Med.) The Lond. Chest Hosp.; SHO (Rheumat. & Neurol.) Hammersmith Hosp. Lond.

WOODROW, David Frederick (retired) 47 Shooters Hill, Pangbourne, Reading RG8 7EA — MB BS 1969 Lond.; MRCS Eng. LRCP Lond. 1969; FRCPath 1994. Prev: Sen. Lect. (Histopath.) Char. Cross & W.m. Med. Sch. Lond.

WOODROW, Elizabeth Ann 21Cyprus Avenue, Belfast BT5 5NT — MB BCh BAO 1988 Belf.; DRCOG 1992; MRCGP Belf. 1993; DCCH 1995; DFFP 1998. (Queen's University Belfast) Clin. Med. Off. (Community Paediat.) Glengormley. Socs: BMA; Fac. Fam. Plann. & Reprod. Health Care. Prev: Asst. GP Whiteabbey Health Centre.

WOODROW, Graham Renal Unit, Leeds General Infirmary, Great George St., Leeds LS1 3EX Tel: 0113 392 2375 Fax: 0113 392 6560 — MB ChB 1986 Leeds; FRCP 2001; MD Leeds 1997; MRCP (UK) 1989. Cons. (Renal Med.) Leeds Gen. Infirm.; Hon. Sen. Clin. Lect. Univ. of Leeds. Socs: Brit. Renal Assn.; Eur. Dialysis & Transpl. Assn. Prev: Sen. Regist. (Renal & Gen. Med.) Withington Hosp.

Manch.; Research Regist. & Regist. (Med.) Leeds Gen. Infirm.; Regist. (Renal) Nottm. City Hosp.

WOODROW, Ivan Henry Rupert (retired) New Holding, Steppes Hill, Langton Matravers, Swanage BH19 3ET — MB BCh BAO 1944 Dub.; BA Dub. 1942, MB BCh BAO 1944. Prev: Res. Med. Off. Gen. Hosp. S. Shields.

WOODROW, Janice Marian Health Centre, Lake Lock Road, Stanley, Wakefield WF3 4HS Tel: 01924 822328 Fax: 01924 870052; The Poplars, Aberford Road, Stanley, Wakefield WF3 4AG — BM BS 1980 Nottm.; BMedSci. Nottm. 1978, BM BS 1980; MRCGP 1984.

WOODROW, Joseph Charles Woak Hill, St. Davids Lane, Noctorum, Birkenhead CH43 9UD Tel: 0151 652 4989 — MB ChB Leeds 1948; MD Leeds 1961; FRCP Lond. 1971, M 1953. (Leeds) Emerit. Prof. Dept. Med. Univ. Liverp. Socs: Assn. Phys. & Brit. Soc. Rheum.; Liverp. Med. Inst. Prev: Hon. Cons. Phys. Roy. Liverp. Hosp. & BRd.green Hosp. Liverp.; Prof. Rheum. Univ. Liverp.

WOODROW, Sarah Louise 41 Orchard Street, Cambridge CB1 1JS — MB BS 1991 Lond.; BSc (1st cl. Hons.) Lond. 1988; MRCP (UK) 1993. (Char. Cross & Westm. Hosp. Lond.) Regist. (Dermat.) Addenbrooke's Hosp. NHS Trust Camb. Socs: BMA; Train. Mem. Brit. Assn. Dermat. Prev: SHO (Dermat.) Ealing Hosp.; SHO (Endocrinol. & Geriat.) Roy. Free NHS Trust.

WOODROW, Susan Patricia 5 Westfield Lane, Wigginton, York YO32 2FZ — MB ChB 1977 Leeds. SCMO (Occupat. Health) York Dist. Hosp. Prev: Princip. GP Easingwold Health Centre.

WOODRUFF, Mr Geoffrey Harold Addison Department of Ophthalmology, Leicester Royal Infirmary, Leicester LE1 5WW — MB BS 1976 Lond.; BSc (Hons.) Lond. 1973; FRCS Ed. 1983; FRCOphth 1988. Cons. Ophth. Univ. Hosps. Leicester; Hon. Sen. Lect. Univ. Leicester. Socs: Fell. Roy. Coll. Ophth.; Roy. Soc. Med. Prev: Sen. Regist. (Ophth.) Tennent Inst. Glas.; Fell. (Paediat. Ophth.) Hosp. for Sick Childr. Toronto, Canada.

WOODRUFF, Michael James Flat 8, Kennedy Court, Tapton Crescent Road, Sheffield S10 5DA — MB ChB 1994 Sheff.

WOODRUFF, Peter Waller Rolph University of Sheffield, Academic Department of Psychiatryt, The Lngley centre, Norwood Grange Drive, Sheffield S5 7JT — MB BS Newc. 1981; MRCP (UK) 1985; MRCPsych 1991; PhD (Lond) 1998. Prof. of Gen. Adult Psychiat., Univ. of Sheff.; Hon. Cons. Psychiat. Sheff. NHS Trust. Socs: Liveryman Worshipful Soc. Apoth.; Fell. Med. Soc. Lond. Prev: Asst. Prof. Univ. Maryland, USA; Lect. King's Coll. Hosp. Med. Sch. Lond.; Regist. Maudsley Hosp. Lond.

WOODRUFF, Simon Addison 7 Hazlitt Road, London W14 0JY — MB BS 1991 Lond.

WOODS, Alexander Jamison 8 Meadow Park, Crawfordsburn, Helens Bay, Bangor BT19 1JN Tel: 0289 185 3376 — MB BCh BAO Belf. 1952; DA Eng. 1961; LM Coombe 1953. Mem. Fac. Anaesth. RCS Eng. Prev: Ho. Off. Moyle Hosp. Larne & Belf. City Hosp.; Sen. Ho. Off. Whiteabbey Chest Hosp.

WOODS, Alison Hellier 35 Highfield Road, Dunkirk, Nottingham NG7 2JE — BM BS 1996 Nottm.

WOODS, Amanda Jane Silverton Surgery, Silverton, Exeter EX5 4HX Tel: 01392 860176; Bridel Cottage, Shobrooke, Crediton EX17 1AZ — MB ChB 1979 Dundee; BSc St. And. 1974.

WOODS, Amanda Jayne (retired) Summerfield, 15 Langcliffe Avenue, Harrogate HG2 8JQ Tel: 01423 536038 — MB ChB 1983 Birm.; MRCP (UK) 1987; MRCGP 1989. Prev: SHO (Paediat.) Birm. Childr. Hosp.

WOODS, Amanda Louise 5 Melville Avenue, Wimbledon, London SW20 0NS Tel: 020 8946 9870 — MB BS 1986 Lond.; MRCP (UK) 1989.

WOODS, Andrew Duncan 81 Shakespeare Way, Taverham, Norwich NR8 6SL — MB BS 1992 Lond. Ho. Phys. Heatherwood Hosp. Ascot.

WOODS, Andrew Wilson 30 St. Anmore Ave, Lanark ML11 7HB — MB ChB 1989 Ed.; FRCA 1995. (Ed.) Specialist Regist. Anaesth. Vict. Infirm. Glas. Socs: MRCAnaesth.; Assn. Anaesths.

WOODS, Brian Terence Annandale Surgery, 239 Mutton Lane, Potters Bar EN6 2AS Tel: 01707 644451; 69 Calder Avenue, Brookmans Park, Hatfield AL9 7AJ Tel: 01707 664822 Email: 113111.544@compuserve.com — MB BS Lond. 1966; MRCGP 1975. (Lond. Hosp.) Potters Bar Hosp. Prev: Hosp. Pract. (Orthop.)

WOODS

Barnet Gen. Hosp.; Regist. (Accid. & Orthop.) Barnet Gen. Hosp.; Ho. Surg. (Gyn.) Chase Farm Hosp. Enfield.

WOODS, Caroline Mary 2 St Mary's Gardens, Battle Hill, Battle TN33 0DB Tel: 014246 3559; 96-98 High Street, Heathfield TN21 8JD Tel: 014352 4999 — BM 1979 Soton.; DRCOG 1983. Prev: Trainee GP Hastings HA VTS.

WOODS, Christopher James Locking Hill Surgery, Locking Hill, Stroud GL5 1UY Tel: 01453 764222 Fax: 01453 756278; 22 Paul's Rise, North Woodchester, Stroud GL5 5PN — MRCS Eng. LRCP Lond. 1978; BSc (Pharm.) Lond. 1975, MB BS 1978; DRCOG 1985; DA (UK) 1981.

WOODS, Christopher John The Halliwell Surgery, Lindfield Drive, Bolton BL1 3RG Tel: 01204 523642 Fax: 01204 384204; 103 Holcombe Old Road, Holcombe, Bury BL8 4NF — MB ChB 1976 Manch.; MRCGP 1984.

WOODS, Claire Lisa 8 Piperhill, Ayr KA7 4XB — MB ChB 1993 Ed. SHO (Anaesth.) Sunderland Roy. Hosp. Sunderland. Prev: SHO (Med.) Wansbeck Gen. Hosp. N.umberland; SHO (Anaesth.) Wansbeck Gen. Hosp. N.umberland.

WOODS, Colin Gerard (retired) 22 Kirk Close, Oxford OX2 8JN Tel: 01865 54516 — MB ChB 1951 Leeds; BSc (Hons.) Leeds 1948; FRCPath 1975, M 1964. Prev: Cons. Path. Nuffield Orthop. Centre Oxf.

WOODS, Colin John (retired) 19 Sandringham Road, Lytham St Annes FY8 1EZ Tel: 01253 725545 — MB ChB 1962 Liverp.; FRCP Lond. 1981, M 1968. Prev: Cons. Paediat. Vict. Hosp. Blackpool.

WOODS, Mr David Anthony Department of Orthopaedics, Princess Margaret Hospital, Okus Road, Swindon SN1 4JN Tel: 01793 426133 Email: david.a.woods@lineone.net; Tanyard House, Chilton Foliat, Hungerford RG17 0TG Tel: 01488 683830 Email: david.awoods@uneoe.net — MB ChB 1986 Sheff.; BMedSci Sheff. 1985; FRCS Glas. (Orth.) 1996; FRCS Eng. 1991. (Sheff.) Cons. Orthop. Surg. P.ss Margt. Hosp. Swindon. Socs: Girdlestone Orthop. Soc.; BOA.

WOODS, David Granville St Marys Surgery, 37 St. Mary's Street, Ely CB7 4HF; 25 Fieldside, Ely CB6 3AT Tel: 01353 663554 — MB BS 1973 Lond.; MRCS Eng. LRCP Lond. 1973; MRCGP 1978; DRCOG 1978. (Westm.) Prev: Sen. Med. Off. RAF Binbrook; SHO (O & G) RAF Hosp. Wegberg; Unit Med. Off. RAF Wildenrath.

WOODS, David Mack Forest Road Health Centre, 8 Forest Road, Hugglescote, Coalville LE67 3SH Tel: 01530 832109 — MB BS 1977 Lond.; MRCS Eng. LRCP Lond. 1976. (Guys Hospital Medical School)

WOODS, David Richard 207 Cardigan Lane, Leeds LS6 1DX Tel: 0113 278 4685 — MB ChB 1990 Leeds. Prev: Ho. Off. (Surg.) Camb. Milit. Hosp.; Ho. Off. (Med.) St. Jas. Hosp. Leeds.

WOODS, Declan John bVine Cottage, 3 Hallaton Road, Medbourne, Market Harborough LE16 8DR Tel: 0185 883776 — MB ChB 1975 Leeds; FRCR 1983. Cons. Radiol. Kettering Gen. Hosp. Prev: Sen. Regist. (Radiol.) W. Midl. RHA.

WOODS, Donald Pierpoint Sweet Briar, Ovington, Alresford SO24 0RE Tel: 01962 732729 — BM BCh 1954 Oxf.; MA Oxf. 1954; FRCGP 1981, M 1963; Cert. Av. Med. 1987; DObst RCOG 1956. (Oxf. & Lond. Hosp.) Prev: Ho. Phys., Ho. Surg. & Res. Accouch. Lond. Hosp.

WOODS, Elizabeth Anne — MB ChB 1981 Leeds; MRCGP 1990; Cert. Community Paediat. Sheff. 1990; DRCOG 1987; DCH RCP Lond. 1985. (Leeds) Socs: BMA; RCGP; Soc. Orthop. Med. Prev: SHO (O & G) Luton & Dunstable Hosp.; SHO & CMO (Paediat.) Community Child Health Sheff. HA; SHO (Geriat. Med.) Univ. Manch.

WOODS, Geoffrey Thomas (retired) 490 Rayleigh Road, Eastwood, Leigh-on-Sea SS9 5HZ Tel: 01702 525644 — MB BS 1949 Lond.; MRCS Eng. LRCP Lond. 1949; DLO Eng. 1951.

WOODS, Hubert Frank Department of Medicine & Pharmacology, The Royal Hallamshire Hospital, Sheffield S10 2JF Tel: 0114 273 7623 Fax: 0114 272 1104; 68 Ivy Park Road, Ranmoor, Sheffield S10 3LD Tel: 0114 230 1829 — BM BCh 1965 Oxf.; DPhil Oxf. 1971, BM BCh 1965; BSc Leeds 1962; FRCP Ed. 1991; FRCP Lond. 1978 FFPM RCP UK 1989; MRCP (UK) 1968. Prof. Clin. Pharmacol. & Therap. Univ. Sheff.; Sir Geo. Franklin Prof. Med.; Dean Fac. of Med. & Dent. Univ. Sheff. Med. Sch.; Hon. Cons. Phys. Sheff. AHA (T).

WOODS, Ian Yungarra, Ferryman's Walk, Nether Poppleton, York YO26 6HZ — MB ChB 1979 Manch.; FFA RCS Eng. 1983. Cons. Anaesth. York HA. Socs: Brit. Assn. Anaesth.; Intens. Care Soc. Prev: Sen. Regist. (Anaesth.) N. W.. RHA; Regist. (Anaesth.) Roy. Cornw. Hosp. Truro; SHO (Anaesth.) Withington Hosp. Manch.

WOODS, Ian Malcolm McClure Long Lane Medical Centre, Long Lane, Liverpool L9 6DQ Tel: 0151 530 1009 — MB ChB 1976 Dundee. Hon. Med. Adviser Liverp. City Mission.

WOODS, Jacqueline Lee Penelope Isogroup International, 33 rue Arsène Houssaye, Paris 75008, France Tel: 00 33 1 53 53 53 00 Fax: 00 33 1 42 89 64 70; Pooh Corner, Loudwater. Lane, Loudwater, Rickmansworth WD3 4HX Tel: 01923 896717 Fax: 01923 896818 — MB BS 1987 Lond.; MA Camb. 1988; MBA Insead 1992.

WOODS, James Crerar Dr Moss and Partners, 28-38 Kings Road, Harrogate HG1 5JP Tel: 01423 560261 Fax: 01423 501099 — MB ChB 1982 Dundee; MRCGP 1988.

WOODS, James Patrick 35 Ailesbury Crescent, Belfast BT7 3EZ — MB BCh BAO 1984 Belf.; BSc (Hons.) Belf. 1981; MRCGP 1990; DRCOG 1990. Med. Off. DHSS Belf.

WOODS, Jennifer Mary Department Anaesthetics, Level 04, Derriford Hospital, Derriford Road, Plymouth PL6 8DH Tel: 01752 792691 Fax: 01752 763287 Email: anaesthesia@phnt.swest.nhs.uk — MB BS 1973 Lond.; FFA RCS Eng. 1981; DA Eng. 1977; DObst RCOG 1976; Cert. Family Plann. JCC 1976. (Roy. Free) Cons. Anaesth. SW RHA. Socs: Assn. Anaesth. Gt. Brit. & Irel. & Soc. Anaesth. SW Region. Prev: Sen. Regist. (Anaesth.) Bristol & W.on HA.

WOODS, Jill Kathryn High Street Surgery, 60 High Street, Lurgan, Craigavon BT66 8BA Tel: 028 3832 4591 — MB BCh BAO 1992 Belf.

WOODS, John Declan 18 Harberton Park, Belfast BT9 6TS — MB BCh BAO 1986 Dub.; BA Dub. 1986, MB BCh BAO 1986; MRCP (UK) 1990.

WOODS, John Joseph (retired) Ridge Farm, Brinscombe Lane, Membury, Axminster EX13 7JP Tel: 01297 33046 — MB BCh BAO 1941 NUI. Prev: Cons. Anaesth. Airedale Gen. Hosp.

WOODS, John Oliver (retired) The Mall, Armagh BT61 9AU Tel: 01861 523165 — MD Belf. 1967, MB BCh BAO 1959; FRCGP 1979, M 1968; DObst RCOG 1961; DCH RCPS Glas. 1966. Prev: Provost NI Fac. RCGP.

WOODS, Jonathan Philip Gartnavel Royal Hospital, 1055 Great Western Road, Glasgow G12 0XH Tel: 0141 334 6241; Beechknowe, Barclaven Road, Kilmacolm PA13 4DQ Tel: 01505 872744 — MB ChB 1981 Manch.; BSc (Med. Sci.) St. And. 1978; MRCGP 1986; DRCOG 1984; MRCPsych 1988.

WOODS, Katherine Mary Department of Anaesthetics, University Hospital of Wales, Heath Park, Cardiff CF14 4XW Tel: 029 2074 7747; 4 Cyncoed Crescent, Cyncoed, Cardiff CF2 5SW Tel: 029 2075 7357 — MB BChir 1988 Camb.; MA Camb. 1988, MB BChir Camb. 1988; FRCA 1992. Sen. Regist. (Anaesth.) Univ. Hosp. Wales Cardiff. Prev: Regist. Rotat. (Anaesth.) Bloomsbury HA.

WOODS, Kathleen Rose Dept. of Anaesthetics, Glasgow Royal Infirmary, North Glasgow University Hospitals NHS Trust, Castle St, Glasgow G4 0SF Tel: 0141 211 4000 Ext: 4620; 27 Gleniffer Drive, Barrhead, Glasgow G78 1JA — MB ChB 1995 Glas. SHO (Anaesth.), Glas. Roy. Infirm.; ACLS - Instruc. Socs: BMA & IMO. Prev: SHO (A & E), St Jas. Hosp., Dub.; SHO (A&E) Roy. Alexandra Hosp. Paisley; SHO (A&E) Nat. Childr.'s Hosp. HarCt. St. Dub.

WOODS, Kathryn Anne 19 Hill Top Road, Oxford OX4 1PB — MB BS 1988 Lond.; MB BS Lond. (Hons.) 1988; MRCP (UK) 1991. (St. Bart.) Lect. (Paediat. Endocrinol.) & Hon. Sen. Regist. Oxf. Univ. & John Radcliffe Hosp. Prev: Research Fell. (Paediat. Endocrinol.) St. Bart. Hosp. Lond.; Regist. (Paediat.) Qu. Eliz. & Gt. Ormond St. Hosps. for Sick Childr. Lond.

WOODS, Professor Kent Linton Department of Medicine & Therapeutics, Clinical Sciences Building, Leicester Royal Infirmary, Leicester LE2 7LX Tel: 0116 252 3126 Fax: 0116 252 3108 Email: klw@le.ac.uk; 10 Knighton Drive, Stoneygate, Leicester LE2 3HB Tel: 0116 221 8144 Fax: 0116 270 0287 — MB BChir 1972 Camb.; MA Camb 1973, MD 1980; MS Harvard 1983; FRCP Lond. 1988; MRCP (UK) 1974. (Camb. & Birm.) Prof. Therap. Univ. Leicester; Cons. Phys. Leics. Roy. Infirm.; Dir. NHS Heath Techn. Asses. Prog (P/T). Socs: Assn. Phys.; Brit. Cardiac Soc.; Brit. Pharm.

Soc. Prev: Lect. (Therap. & Clin. Pharmacol.) Univ. Birm.; MRC/Lilly Internat. Trav. Fell. (Epidemiol.) Harvard Univ.; MRC Train. Fell. (Med.) Univ. Birm.

WOODS, Lesley Anne Department of Anaesthetics, City Hospital Trust, Hucknall Road, Nottingham; 44 Rodney Road, West Bridgford, Nottingham NG2 6JH Tel: 0115 923 5834 — MB ChB Manch. 1984; FCAnaesth 1990. Cons. Anaesth. City Hosp. Trust Nottm. Socs: Assn. Anaesth.; Obst. Anaesth. Assn. Prev: Sen. Regist. (Anaesth.) Roy. Hallamsh. Hosp. Sheff.; Fell. (Intens. Care) Academisch Ziekenhuis Groningen, Netherlands; Regist. (Anaesth.) Roy. Hallamsh. Hosp. Sheff.

WOODS, Lynne Church Close Surgery, 3 Church Close, Boston PE21 6NB Tel: 01205 311133 Fax: 01205 358986 — MB ChB 1977 Sheff.

WOODS, Mary Rosaleen The Brandon Centre, Cheadle Hospital, Royal Walk, Cheadle ST10 1NS Tel: 01538 487546 Fax: 01538 487544 — MB ChB 1980 Ed.; BSc Ed. 1977; MRCPsych 1987; MRCGP 1984; DRCOG 1983. Harplands Hosps., Stoke-on-Trent. Prev: Sen. Regist. (Psychiat.) N. Staffs.; Regist. (Psychiat.) Roy. Edin. Hosp.

WOODS, Michael John West Bridgford Health Centre, 97 Musters Road, West Bridgford, Nottingham NG2 9PX Tel: 0115 9811858/5666 Fax: 0115 982 6448; The Willows, 43 Jessops Lane, Gedling, Nottingham NG4 4BQ Tel: 0115 952 5114 — BM BS 1979 Nottm.; MRCGP 1984. Hon. Lect. Dept. of Gen. Pract.

WOODS, Paul Julian Church Close Surgery, 3 Church Close, Boston PE21 6NB Tel: 01205 311133 Fax: 01205 358986 — MB ChB 1977 Sheff.; MRCGP 1981.

WOODS, Paul Michael Holbrook Surgery, Bartholomew Way, Horsham RH12 5JB Tel: 01403 755900 Fax: 01403 755909; 13 Purton Road, Horsham RH12 2HB — MB BS 1991 Lond.; MRCGP 1995; DFFP 1995. (Roy. Lond. Hosp. Med. Coll.) Socs: BMA; Med. Defence Union. Prev: Trainee GP Horsham.

WOODS, Peter Michael 52 Wimpole Road, Colchester CO1 2DL; Yew Tree House, Higham Road, Stratford St. Mary, Colchester CO7 6JU — MRCS Eng. LRCP Lond. 1976; BSc (Hons. Biochem. & Physiol.) Lond. 1972, MB BS 1976. (Westm.)

WOODS, Mr Robert Rex Church View Surgery, 30 Holland Road, Plymstock, Plymouth PL9 9BW Tel: 01752 403206; Barn Farm House, Barn Wood, Plymstock, Plymouth PL9 9NH — MB BS 1978 Lond.; MA Oxf. 1973; FRCS Ed. 1982. (St. Bart.) GP; Hosp. Practitioner (Endoscopy), Derriford Hosp., Plymouth.

WOODS, Rosemary Coxhoe Medical Practice, 1 Lansdowne Road, Cornforth Lane, Coxhoe, Durham DH6 4DH Tel: 0191 377 0340 Fax: 0191 377 0604 — MB BS 1978 Newc.; MRCGP 1982; DRCOG 1981. GP Coxhoe Co. Durh.

WOODS, Sarah Jane 4B Morningside Place, Edinburgh EH10 5ER — MB ChB 1996 Ed.

WOODS, Sharon Jane 15 West Mall, Clifton, Bristol BS8 4BQ — MB BS 1988 Lond.; MRCP (UK) 1993.

WOODS, Sheelagh Catherine Patricia Deeny Anaesthetics Department, University College Hospital, Gower St., London WC1E 6AU Tel: 020 7387 9300 Fax: 020 7380 9816; 16 Sudeley Street, London N1 8HP Tel: 020 7837 3981 — MB BCh BAO 1966 NUI; FFA RCS Eng. 1973; FFA RCSI 1973. Cons. Anaesth. Univ. Coll. Hosp. Lond. Socs: Obst. Anaesth. Assn. & Europ. Soc. Regional Anaesth. Prev: Sen. Regist. (Anaesth.) Univ. Coll. Hosp. & Hosp. Sick Childr. Gt. Ormond St.; Regist. (Anaesth.) St. Mary's Hosp. Lond. & Univ. Coll. Hosp. Lond.

WOODS, Sheelagh Kathleen Mary (retired) Armagh Health Centre, Dobbin Lane, Armagh BT61 1ER Tel: 01861 522663 — MB BCh BAO 1930 Belf.

WOODS, Sheila Mary 3 Gainsborough Court, Skipton BD23 1QG — MB ChB 1982 Manch.; MB ChB (Hons.) Manch. 1982; BSc St. And. 1979; MRCP (UK) 1985; MRCGP 1991; DRCOG 1990. GP Skipton. Prev: Med. Off. St. Paul's Hosp. Kashikishi, Zambia.

WOODS, Susan Elizabeth 4 Frenchs Road, Cambridge CB4 3LA — MB BChir 1993 Camb.

WOODS, Susan Elizabeth Dig Street Surgery, Dig Street, Hartington, Buxton SK17 0AQ Tel: 01298 84315 Fax: 01298 84899 Email: susanwoods@gp-c81082.nhs.uk; 2 Goldhill Cottages, Goldhill, Tansley, Matlock DE4 5FG Tel: 01629 56378 Fax: 01629 56378 Email: sue@2-goldhill.fsnetco.uk — MB ChB 1978 Liverp.; DRCOG 1983.

WOODS, Tina Louise 153 Mains Lane, Poulton-le-Fylde FY6 7LB — MB BS 1993 Newc.

WOODS, Tracey Oriole Child & Family Services, (North West Team) Seymour House, 41-43 Seymour Terrace, Seymour St., Liverpool L3 5TE Tel: 0151 707 0101 Fax: 0151 708 9200 — MB ChB 1985 Liverp.; MSc. Manch. 1995; MRCPsych 1990. Cons. Child & Family Psychiat. Alder Hey Roy. Liverp. Childr. NHS Trust. Prev: Sen. Regist. (Child & Adolesc. Psychiat.) Manch.; Research Regist. (Child & Adolesc. Psychiat.) Univ. Manch.; Regist. Rotat. (Psychiat.) Manch.

WOODS, William Graham Kilkeel Health Centre, Knockchree Avenue, Kilkeel, Newry BT34 4BS Tel: 028 4176 2601 Fax: 028 4176 3308 — MB BCh BAO 1973 Belf.

WOODS, Mr William Gustave Arnold Worthing Hospital, Park Avenue, Worthing BN11 2DH — BM BCh 1974 Oxf.; MA, BM BCh Oxf. 1974; DM Oxf. 1987; FRCS Eng. 1978.

WOODSEND, Robert Gervase (retired) Staithe Barn, Brancaster Staithe, King's Lynn PE31 8BP Tel: 01485 260 — MRCS Eng. LRCP Lond. 1943; BA Camb. Prev: Ho. Phys., Res. Med. Off. & Asst. Med. Regist. W.m. Hosp.

WOODSFORD, Paul Vincent Ty-Cerdd, 29 Cae Rex, Llanblethian, Cowbridge CF71 7JS Tel: 0144 63 773305 & profess 0443 218218 — MB BS 1973 Lond.; FFA RCS Eng. 1979. (St. Mary's) Dir. Intens. Care Unit & Cons. Anaesth. E. Glam. Dist. Gen. Hosp. Socs: Fell. Fac. Anaesth. RCS Eng.; Assn. Anaesth. & Welsh Intens. Care Soc. Prev: Sen. Regist. (Anaesth.) Nottm. HA (T); Sen. Specialist (Anaesth.) P.ss Alexandra Hosp. RAF Wroughton.

WOODSIDE, Robert, RD (retired) Flat 10 Wallace Court, 39 Wallace Road, Broadstone BH18 8NF Tel: 01202 691132 — MB BS 1951 Lond.; MRCS Eng. LRCP Lond. 1951. Prev: Sen. Med. & Health Off. Hong Kong Govt.

WOODSIDE, Robert Monckton (home), Healdswood House, Skegby, Sutton-in-Ashfield NG17 3FR Tel: 01623 517479 — MRCS Eng. LRCP Lond. 1943. (Guy's) Med. Off. Leicester & Nottm. Racecourses. Socs: Fell. Roy. Soc. Med.; BMA & (Ex-Pres.) Mansfield Med. Soc. Prev: Mem. DHSS Med. Bd.ing Panel for War Pension & Indust. Injuries; Out-pat. Off. Guy's Hosp.; Ho. Surg. Guy's U.S.A. Hosp. Seal.

WOODWARD, Mr Alan 53 Parc Bryn Derwen, Llanharan, Pontyclun CF72 9TU — MB BCh 1983 Wales; FRCS Ed. 1987.

WOODWARD, Albert Kenneth (retired) Fleetwith, 29 Suckling Green Lane, Codsall, Wolverhampton WV8 2BP Tel: 01902 843747 Email: k.and.j.woodward@classicfm.net — MB ChB Birm. 1957; DObst RCOG 1959.

WOODWARD, Alison Jane Rothschild House Surgery, Chapel St, Tring HP23 6PU Tel: 01442 822468; The Old House, 38 Station Road, Ivinghoe, Leighton Buzzard LU7 9EB Tel: 01296 668444 — MB BS 1976 Lond. (Middlesex) Princip., Gen. Pract. Rothscild Ho. Surg., Tring Herts. Prev: SO Empangeni Provin. Hosp. Empangeni Natal SA; Phys. & Surg. Chas. Johnson Memor. Hosp. Nqutu, Kwazulu, S. Afr.; SHO (ENT) Cheltenham Gen. Hosp. / A+E Cheltenham Roy. Hosp.

WOODWARD, Andrew Christopher 28 Wellington Street, Hillside, Edinburgh EH7 5ED Tel: 0131 556 6474 Email: baly@woowar.demon.co.uk — MB ChB 1993 Ed.

WOODWARD, Mrs Audrey Mary Woodlands, Swainsea Lane, Pickering YO18 8NF — MB ChB 1951 Leeds; MRCP Ed. 1956; DCH Eng. 1954. SCMO ScarBoro. HA. Prev: Asst. Res. Med. Off. Birm. Childr. Hosp.; Regist. Profess. Unit Sheff. Childr. Hosp.; Asst. MOH & Sch. Med. Off. City Oxf.

WOODWARD, Catherine Mary Department of Public Health Medicine, Avon Health Authority, King Square House, King Square, Bristol BS2 5EE — BSc (Biochem.) Leeds 1982, MB ChB 1985; MFPHM RCP (UK) 1994; DCH RCP Lond. 1987. Cons. in Pub. Health Med., Avon Health Auth.; Lect. (Pub. Health Med.) Univ. Cape Town. Socs: BMA & Soc. Social Med. Prev: Wessex Region Train. Scheme in Pub. Health Med.; Winchester DHA VTS.

WOODWARD, Cathryn Louise Queen Elizabeth Hospital, Edgbaston, Birmingham B15 2T Tel: 0121 472 1311 — MB ChB 1992 Birm.; FRCR 2001 (UK); MRCP (UK) 1995. p/t Regist. (Clin. Oncol.) Qu. Eliz. Hosp. Birm. Prev: SHO (Gen. Med.) Sandwell Hosp. Birm.; SHO (Oncol. & Radiother.) Cookridge Hosp. Leeds; SHO (A & E) City Hosp. Birm.

WOODWARD

WOODWARD, Charlotte Elisabeth Louise 4 Sunning House, London Road, Sunningdale, Ascot SL5 9QN Tel: 01344 20699 — MB ChB 1991 Leic.; MRCGP 1995. Socs: Med. Protec. Soc.; BMA. Prev: Trainee GP Stratford upon Avon; SHO (O & G) Birm. Matern. Hosp. & Wom. Hosp. Birm.; SHO (Psychiat.) Qu. Eliz. Psychiat. Hosp.

WOODWARD, Claire Louise Flat 5, 12 Oakfield Grove, Clifton, Bristol BS8 2BN; 89 Kennington Avenue, Bishopton, Bristol BS7 9EX — MB ChB 1989 Manch.; MRCP (UK) 1994; MRCGP 1996; DCH RCP Lond. 1992. (Manch.) GP. Socs: Brit. Paediat. Assn.

WOODWARD, Mr David Alan Keith (retired) 1 Ferndale Drive, Kenilworth CV8 2PF Tel: 01926 512094 — MB ChB 1958 Birm.; FRCS Eng. 1964. Licenced Teach. (Anat.) MoH; Assoc. Adviser Gen. Profess. Train. Dept. Postgrad. Med. Educat. Univ. Birm. Prev: Cons. Gen. & Vasc. Surg. Walsgrave Hosp. Coventry.

WOODWARD, David Keith Department of Anaesthetics, Northern General Hospital, Herries Road, Sheffield S5 7AU Tel: 0114 243 4343; Tel: 0114 262 0547 Fax: 0114 262 0547 — MB ChB 1986 Leeds; MRCP (UK) 1989; FRCA 1994. (Univ. Leeds) Cons. Anaesth.,N.. Gen. Hosp. Sheff. Prev: Sen.Reg. (Anaesth) The Alfred Hosp.Melbourne; Lect.,P. of Wales Hosp. Shatin,Hong Kong.

WOODWARD, Elisabeth Anne The Surgery, 20 Westdale Lane, Gedling, Nottingham NG4 3JA; 10 Retford Road, Sherwood, Nottingham NG5 1FZ Tel: 0115 960 5743 — BM BS 1988 Nottm.; BMedSci Nottm. 1986; MRCGP 1992.

WOODWARD, Jeremy Mark Lydbrook, Rowney Green Lane, Rowney Green, Alvechurch, Birmingham B48 7QS — MB BChir 1990 Camb.; MA, MB BChir Camb. 1990. Prev: Ho. Phys. St. Thos. Hosp.; SHO (Cardiol.) Hammersmith Hosp. Lond.

WOODWARD, John 57 Greenville Drive, Maghull, Liverpool L31 7DF — MB ChB 1978 Liverp.

WOODWARD, John Wakerley Sidcup Health Centre, 43 Granville Road, Sidcup DA14 4TA Tel: 020 8302 7721 Fax: 020 8309 6579; 33 Rectory Lane, Sidcup DA14 4QN Tel: 020 8302 9970 Fax: 020 8302 2224 — MB BS 1962 Lond.; FRCGP 1985, M 1974; DCH Eng. 1965; DObst RCOG 1964. (St. Thos.) Socs: BMA. Prev: Ho. Surg. Roy. Waterloo Hosp.; Ho. Phys. W. Kent Hosp. Maidstone; Ho. Off. (Obst.) Brit. Hosp. Mothers & Babies Woolwich.

WOODWARD, Mr Mark Nicholas Long Acre, Alveston, Stratford-upon-Avon CV37 7QN Tel: 01789 293780 — BM 1992 Soton.; BM (Hons.) Soton. 1992; FRCS Eng. 1996. (Soton.)

WOODWARD, Natalie Anne Michaela 21 Beechcroft Court, Beechcroft Avenue, London NW11 8BP — MB BS 1997 Lond. GP.

WOODWARD, Nicholas Arthur (retired) Bridge House Medical Centre, Scholars Lane, Stratford-upon-Avon CV37 6HE Tel: 01789 292201 Fax: 01789 262087 — MB ChB 1962 Birm.; MRCS Eng. LRCP Lond. 1962; DObst RCOG 1964; FFA RCS Eng. 1968; DA Eng. 1965. Hosp. Pract. (Anaesth.) S. Warks. Health Dist. Prev: Squadron Ldr. RAF Med. Br.

WOODWARD, Philippa Jane 12 Mayfield Close, Walton-on-Thames KT12 5PR — BChir 1991 Camb.

WOODWARD, Rosalind Mary 8 Brookfield Gardens, Sarisbury Green, Southampton SO31 7DT — MB BS 1967 Lond.

WOODWARD, Roy Bennett Spread Initiative Department, Liverpool Health Authority, Hamilton House, 24 Pall Mall, Liverpool L3 6AL Tel: 0151 236 4620 Fax: 0151 258 1264 Email: spreadini@yahoo.com; 4 Butterfield Gardens, Aughton, Ormskirk L39 4XN Tel: 01695 576965 Email: roy@butterfield4.demon.co.uk — MB ChB Liverp. 1969; FRCGP 1995, M 1978. (Liverp.) Princip. Maghull Merseyside; Spread Initiative Co-ord. NW Region. Prev: Med. Adviser Sefton HA.

WOODWARD, Siân Glasfryn, Pentre Cilcain, Mold CH7 5PE — MB BCh 1981 Wales. GP Trainee Clwyd HA.

WOODWARD, William Marshall Royal Cornwall Hospitals Trust, Treliske Hospital, Department of Anaesthesia, Treliske, Truro TR1 3LJ Tel: 01872 253134 Fax: 01872 252480 Email: william.woodward@rcht.swest.nhs.uk; Primrose Cottage, Greenwith Road, Perranwell Station, Truro TR3 7LU Tel: 01872 864104 — MB ChB 1985 Sheff.; FRCA 1992; DA (UK) 1988. (Sheffield) Cons. (Anaesth./IC) Roy. Cornw. Hosp. Truro, Cornw. Prev: Sen. Regist. Rotat. (Anaesth.) Bristol; Lect. (Anaesth.) Univ. Sheff.; Regist. Rotat. (Anaesth.) Sheff.

WOODWARD-COURT, Rodney Ian Heene and Goring Practice, 145 Heene Road, Worthing BN12 4PY Tel: 01903 235344 Fax: 01903 247099; 33 Lansdowne Road, Worthing BN11 4NF Tel: 01903 502135 — MB BS 1972 Lond. (Char. Cross) Prev: Med. Off. Ngora (Ch. of Uganda) Hosp.; SHO (Geriat.) Char. Cross Hosp. Lond.; Ho. Surg. W. Lond. Hosp.

WOODWARDS, Mr Robert Timothy Michael Maxillofacial Unit, North Manchester NHS Trust, Central Drive, Manchester M8 5RB Tel: 0161 720 2143 Fax: 0161 720 2284; 210 The Grand, 1 Aytoun St, Manchester M1 3DA Tel: 0161 236 7090 Fax: 0161 236 7090 Email: bob-woodwords@hotmail.com — MB BCh 1987 Wales; BDS Birm. 1978; FRCS Ed. 1990; FDS RCS Eng. 1983. (Univ. Wales) Cons. Oral & Maxillofacial Surg. Manch. NHS Trust & Rochdale NHS Trust; Hon. Clin. Teach. Univ. Manch. Fac. Med.; Postgrad. Clin. Tutor N. Manch. NHS Trust; Clin. Director head and neck Surg. N. Manch. NHS trust. Socs: Fell. Brit. Assn. Oral & Maxillofacial Surg.; Liveryman Worshipful Soc. Apoth. City of Lond.; BMA. Prev: Sen. Regist. (Oral & Maxillofacial Surg.) Qu. Mary's Univ. Hosp. Lond.

WOODWARK, Catherine 24 Cunningham Hill Road, St Albans AL1 5BY — MB ChB 1981 Bristol.

WOODWORTH, Andrea Elizabeth 83 Griffiths Close, Swindon SN3 4NP — MB BCh 1985 Wales; MRCGP 1990. Trainee GP Nevill Hall Hosp. Abergavenny. Prev: SHO (c/o Elderly) Nevill Hall Hosp. Abergavenny.

WOODYARD, Mr John Edward (retired) 32 Knowle Road, Stafford ST17 0DP Tel: 01785 665941 — MB Camb. 1956, BChir 1955; FRCS Eng. 1961; FRCS Ed. 1961; DObst RCOG 1957. Prev: Cons. Orthop. Surg. Dist. Gen. Hosp. Stafford.

WOODYATT, Christopher Prust 4 Centurion Way, Brough HU15 1AY Tel: 01482 667108 Fax: 01482 665090; 53 Church Street, South Cave, Brough HU15 2EP Tel: 01430 423173 — MB ChB 1969 Leeds; MB ChB (Hons.) Leeds 1969; BSc (Hons.) Leeds 1966; FRCGP 1993, M 1974; DObst RCOG 1972; DCH Eng. 1971. (Leeds) Prev: Ho. Phys. Profess. Unit Birm. Childr. Hosp.; Concise Organiser Hull GP VTS Scheme.

WOODYER, Mr Anthony Bartlam Windy Harbour Cottage, Woodhead Road, Glossop SK13 7QE Tel: 01457 855239 Fax: 01457 855239 — MB ChB 1972 Ed.; ChM Ed. 1985; FRCS Eng. 1978; FRCS Ed. 1977. Cons. Surg. Tameside Gen. Hosp. Ashton-under-Lyne.

WOOF, William Richard Corbett Medical Practice, 36 Corbett Avenue, Droitwich WR9 7BE Tel: 01905 795566 Fax: 01905 796984; 7 Richmond Hill, Worcester WR5 1DP — MB BS 1986 Lond.; MRCGP 1991; M Med.Sci. Birm. 1998. Clin. Lect, (Gen. Pract.) Univ. Brimingham; Clin. Asst. St. Richards Hospice Worcester. Prev: Clin. Research Fell. (Gen. Pract.) Univ. Birm.; Trainee GP Harefield Ho. Surg. Worcester; SHO (O & G) Worcester Roy. Infirm. VTS.

WOOFF, Derek James Stranraer Health Centre, Edinburgh Road, Stranraer DG9 7HG Tel: 01776 706566; Lochwood, 36 Larg Road, Stranraer DG9 0JE Tel: 01776 705778 Email: kifian@aol.com — MB ChB 1980 Glas.; MRCGP 1984; DRCOG 1987; DCH RCP Lond. 1984. (Glasgow)

WOOKEY, Brian (retired) Pontcae Surgery, Dynevor Street, Georgetown, Merthyr Tydfil CF48 1YE Tel: 01685 723931 Fax: 01685 377048 — MB BCh 1961 Wales; MRCGP 1980.

WOOKEY, Brian Eric Penny Liquorpond Street Surgery, 10 Liquorpond Street, Boston PE21 8UE Tel: 01205 362763 Fax: 01205 358918 — MB BS 1961 Lond.; FRCGP 1980, M 1969; DObst RCOG 1963. (Middlx.) Chairm. Trent Regional Med. & Dent. Comm. Socs: BMA; Counc. Nat. Assn. of HAs.

WOOKEY, Sarah Lucy Mary West Bar Surgery, 1 West Bar Street, Banbury OX16 9SF Tel: 01295 256261 Fax: 01295 756848; Waggonners Cottage, Sandford Common Farm, Sandford St. Martin, Chipping Norton OX7 7AE Tel: 0160 863673 Fax: 0160 863417 Email: sarahw@andromedalight.co.uk — MB BCh BAO 1983 Belf.; MRCP (UK) 1990; MRCGP 1988; DFFP 1997; DCH RCP Lond. 1985; DRCOG 1985. (Belf.) GP Banbury.

WOOL, Rosemary Jane, CB Wicken House, 105 Weston Road, Aston Clinton, Aylesbury HP22 5EP Tel: 01296 630448 Fax: 01296 632448 Email: rjw@wicken.nildram.uk — MB BS Lond. 1960; FRCPsych 1987, M 1974; DPM Eng. 1973; DObst RCOG 1965. (Char. Cross) Hon. Sec. Gen. Internat. Counc. Prison Med. Servs.; Med. Adv. To Dept. Leg. Affairs, Counc. Of Europe. Socs: Roy. Soc. Med., Internat. Counc. Prison Med. Servs.; BMA. Prev: Head of

Educ. & Train. Dept of Addict. Behaviour, St. Geo.s's Hosp. Med. Sch.; Dir. of Health Care Prison Serv.

WOOLARD, Fiona Elizabeth Kennoway Medical Group, Jordan Lane, Kennoway, Leven KY8 5JZ Tel: 01333 350241 Fax: 01333 352884 — MB ChB 1987 Manch.; BSc (Med. Sci.) St. And. 1984.

WOOLAS, Kenneth Dixon Gayfield, Portsdown Hill Road, Cosham, Portsmouth PO6 1BE Tel: 023 92 375178 Fax: 023 92 375178 — MB BS Durh. 1945; AFOM RCP Lond. 1982; Cert. Av. Med. 1974. (Univ. Durh.) Med. Off. MoD & Marconi Defence Systems; Air-Med. Examr. Civil Aviat. Auth. & FAA (USA) & Canada. Socs: Assur. Med. Soc.; Anglo-Amer. Med. Soc. Prev: Capt. RAMC.

WOOLAS, Mr Robert Philip Gayfield, Portsdown Hill Road, Cosham, Portsmouth PO6 1BE Tel: 023 92 375178 — MB BS 1982 Lond.; MD Lond. 1995; FRCS Glas. 1987; FRCS Ed. 1987; MRACOG 1991; MRCOG 1990. Cons. Gyn. Oncol. St. Mary's Hosp. Portsmouth. Socs: Fell. Roy. Soc. Med.; Coun. Mem. Brit. Gyn. Cancer Soc.; Internat. Gyn. Cancer Soc. Prev: Fell. Roy. Marsden Hosp.; Regist. Roy. Lond. Hosp.; Resid. Med. Off. Qu. Charlottes Hosp.

WOOLAWAY, Martin Charles 64 Highfield Lane, Southampton SO17 1RJ — MB BS 1973 Lond.; MSc Lond. 1980, MB BS 1973; MFCM 1985.

WOOLCOCK, Jacqueline Anne New Pond Row Surgery, 35 South St., Lancing BN15 8AN Tel: 01903 752265; 6 Beach Road, Shoreham-by-Sea BN43 5LJ Tel: 01273 453540 — MB BChir 1963 Camb.; MRCP (UK) 1965; MRCS Eng. LRCP Lond. 1963; T(GP) 1993. (New Hall Cambridge, Westminster Hospital) GP Partner; Family Plann. Doctor Worthing Priority Care NHS Trust. Prev: SHO (Med.) Manch. Roy. Infirm.; Med. Off. Dohnavur Fell.sh. Hosp. Dohnavur Tirunelveli Dist. Tamil Nadu, India.

WOOLDER, Sara Louise The Coatham Surgery, 18 Coatham Road, Redcar TS10 1RJ Tel: 01642 483495; 'Edinbane', 11 Cringle Moor Chase, Great Broughton, Middlesbrough TS9 7HS Tel: 01642 710684 — MB BS 1988 Nottm.; BMedSci 1986; MRCGP 1992; DRCOG 1992. (Nottingham)

WOOLDRIDGE, Wilfred John 3 Lyndhurst Drive, Hale, Altrincham WA15 8EA — MB ChB 1984 Manch.; FRCA 1992; DA (UK) 1989. Cons. Cardiothoracic Anaesth. Wythenshawe Hosp. Manch. Socs: BMA. Prev: Sen. Regist. (Anaesth.) NW Region.

WOOLER, Mr Geoffrey Hubert, TD (retired) Shaw Grange, 19 Shaw Lane, Headingley, Leeds LS6 4DH Tel: 0113 275 9356 — MD Camb. 1947, MA, MB BChir 1938; Hon. MD Szeged Univ. Hungary 1983; FRCS Eng. 1941; MRCS Eng. LRCP Lond. 1937. Hon. Thoracic Surg. Leeds Gen. Infirm. Prev: Thoracic Surg. United Leeds Hosps.

WOOLF, Adrian Spencer Developmental Biology Unit, Institute of Child Health, 30 Guildford St., London WC1N 1EH; 15A Hanley Road, London N4 3DU — MB BS 1981 Lond.; MB BS (Hons. Med.) Lond. 1981; MA Camb. 1982; MD Lond. 1989; MRCP (UK) 1984. Cons. & Sen. Lect. Inst. Child Health Lond. Socs: Internat. Soc. Nephrol.; Amer. Soc. Nephrol. Prev: Research Fell. Div. Nephrol. UCLA Sch. Med. Los Angeles, USA; Regist. (Med.) Middlx. Hosp. Lond.

WOOLF, Alison Mary North Cardiff Medical Centre, Excalibur Drive, Thornhill, Cardiff CF14 9BB Tel: 029 2075 0322 Fax: 029 2075 7705; 3 Clun Terrace, Cathays, Cardiff CF24 4RB Tel: 029 2038 2614 — MB BCh 1988 Wales; MRCP (UK) 1991; MRCGP Lond. 1996. GP N. Cardiff Med. Centre Cardiff. Socs: BMA; MDU. Prev: GP Regist. Cardiff; Regist. (Haemat.) W. Midl.; SHO (Med.) W. Glam. HA.

WOOLF, Professor Anthony Derek Duke of Cornwall Rheumatology Department, Royal Cornwall Hospital, Truro TR1 3LJ Tel: 01872 253792 Fax: 01872 222857 Email: woolfa@dialin.net; Rope House, Point, Devoran, Truro TR3 6NS Tel: 01872 864442 Fax: 01872 870099 — MB BS 1975 Lond.; BSc Lond. 1972; FRCP Lond. 1994; MRCP (UK) 1979. (Lond. Hosp.) Cons. Rheum. Cornw. & I. of Scilly HA; Hon. Prof. Postgrad. Med. Sch. Univ. of Plymouth. Socs: Brit. Soc. Rheum.; Eur. League Against Rheumatism (Mem. Exec. Comm.); Bone & Jt. decade int. Steering Comm. & Tresur. Prev: Sen. Regist. (Rheum.) Roy. Nat. Hosp. Rheum. Dis. Bath & Bristol Roy. Infirm.; Regist. (Gen. Med. & Rheum.) Guy's Hosp. Lond.

WOOLF, Mr Anthony John (retired) 51 Maresfield Gardens, Hampstead, London NW3 5TE Tel: 020 7794 6365 Fax: 020 7431 9286 — MB BS 1956 Lond.; FRCS Eng. 1959; MRCS Eng. LRCP Lond. 1948; FRCOG 1969, M 1956, DObst 1949. Hon. Lect. (Obst. & Gyn.) St. Bart. Hosp. Med. Coll. Lond.; Examr. RCOG; Examr. & Lect. Centr. Midw. Bd.; Examr. Obst. & Gyn. Conj. Bd. & Univ. Lond. Prev: Hon. Cons. Gyn. Homerton Hosp.

WOOLF, David Andrew Peterborough District Hospital, Thorpe Road, Peterborough PE3 6DA Tel: 01733 874246 Fax: 01733 874001 — MB BS 1983 Lond.; BSc (1st cl. Hons. Physiol.) Lond. 1980; MRCP (UK) 1986; FRCPCH 1997. (St. Thos.) Cons. Paediat. P'boro. Dist. Hosp.; Honourary Cons. paeditrician Respirat. Med., Gt Ormond St Hosp. Socs: FRCPCh. Prev: Sen. Regist. (Paediat.) Hosp. Sick Childr. Gt. Ormond St. Lond.; Lect. (Child Health) & Hon. Sen. Regist. Inst. Child Health & Hosp. Sick Childr. Gt. Ormond St. Lond.; Regist. Rotat. (Paediat.) Lond. Hosp. & Newham Gen. Hosp.

WOOLF, Ernest (retired) 11 Chessington Court, Charter Way, London N3 3DT Tel: 020 8346 5355 — MRCS Eng. LRCP Lond. 1937. Prev: Cons. Chest. Phys. Havering Health Dist.

WOOLF, Jesmond Clive (retired) 21 Cremorne Road, Chelsea, London SW10 0NB Tel: 020 7352 6505 — MB BS Lond. 1950. Prev: RAF Med. Br., Ho. Surg. St. Mary Abbots Hosp. Kensington.

WOOLF, Josephine Kay Scratchwood House, Barnet Lane, Elstree, Borehamwood WD6 3QU Tel: 020 8953 0900 — BM BCh 1975 Oxf.; MA Oxf. 1975; MRCGP 1979; DRCOG 1978. (Univ. Coll. Hosp.) Specialist (Psychosexual Med.) Roy. Free Hosp. & Caryl Thos. Clinic. Harrow Wealdstone; Clin. Asst. Roy. Free Hosp. Sexual Problems Clin. Socs: Inst. Psychosexual Med. Prev: Trainee GP Lond. VTS; GP Twickenham; Med. Edr. Matern. & Child Health.

WOOLF, Margery Philippa Sidney (retired) Doctor's House, Leighland, Roadwater, Watchet TA23 0RP — BM BCh Oxf. 1950; MA Oxf. 1955. Indep. Pract. Psychiat. Som. Prev: Cons. Psychiat. (long term locum) Yeovil Dist. Hosp.

WOOLF, Professor Neville University College London Medical School, Gower St., London WC1E 6BT Fax: 020 7383 2462 Email: n.woof@ucl.ac.uk; 53 Dunstan Road, London NW11 8AE — MB ChB Cape Town 1952; PhD Univ. Lond. 1961; M Med (Path) 1957; FRCPath 1976, M 1964. Vice-Dean Fac. Clin. Sci. Univ. Coll. Lond.; Bland-Sutton Prof. Histopath. UCL Med. Sch. Socs: Path. Soc. & Antibody Club. Prev: Reader (Experim. Path.) & Sen. Lect. in Morbid Anat. St. Geo. Hosp. Med. Sch. Lond.

WOOLF, Patricia Mollie (retired) 122 Elmer Road, Bognor Regis PO22 6LJ Tel: 01243 586870 — MB BCh BAO Dub. 1951; DCH Eng. 1954. Prev: Regist. Qu. Eliz. Hosp. Childr. Lond.

WOOLF, Peter Grahame 2a Vanbrugh Hill, London SE3 7UF Tel: 020 8858 5798 Fax: 020 8293 9998 — MRCS Eng. LRCP Lond. 1952; FRCPsych 1979, M 1971; DPM Eng. 1955. (Middlx.) Med. Mem. Ment. Health Rev. Tribunal. Socs: Soc. of Clin. and Social Psychiat. Prev: Cons. Psychiat. Darenth Pk. Hosp. Dartford; Vis. Psychother. HM Youth Custody Centre Rochester & HM Prison Cookham Wood; Hon. Cons. Psychiat. Bethlem Roy. & Maudsley Hosps. Lond.

WOOLF, Rex Lee 48 Broxash Road, London SW11 6AB; Pegtyles, 14 Penington Road, Beaconsfield HP9 1ET Tel: 01494 670490 — MB BS 1988 Lond.; FRCA 1993; CCST 1997. Cons. Anaesth. Wrexham Pk. hosp. Bucks; Hon. Cons. UCLH. Socs: BMA; ICS; ACTA.

WOOLF, Simon 116 Mitchley Avenue, Sanderstead, South Croydon, Croydon CR9 2HH Tel: 020 8657 6565 — BM 1979 Soton.; MRCGP 1985. GP Croydon.

WOOLF, Mr Victor John North Middlesex Hospital, Sterling Way, London N18 1QX Tel: 020 8887 2000; 94 Bickenhall Mansions, Baker St, London W1U 6BS Tel: 020 7935 9086 Fax: 020 7935 9086 — MB BS 1981 Lond.; FRCS Orth 1997; FRCS Ed. 1988; FRCS Eng. 1988. (Univ. Coll. Hosp.) Cons. (Orthop. Surg.) N. Middlx. Hosp. Socs: Fell. Roy. Soc. Med.; Fell. BOA. Prev: Sen. Regist. Rotat. (Orthop.) Middlx., Stanmore & Gt. Ormond St. Hosps.; Regist. Rotat. (Orthop.) Roy. Free Hosp. Lond.

WOOLFALL, Philip 18 Marlbourough Ave, Newcastle upon Tyne NE3 2HT Email: philip.woofell@ncl.au.uk; 18 Marlbourough Ave, Newcastle upon Tyne NE3 2HT — MB ChB 1992 Leeds; MRCP(UK) London 1996. Specialist Regist. Diagnostic Radiol., Freeman Hosp., Newc.

WOOLFENDEN, Emma Catherine Wolfelee, Bonchester Bridge, Hawick TD9 8JQ — MB ChB 1991 Sheff.

WOOLFENDEN

WOOLFENDEN, Jean Flett (retired) Claremont Parkway Residential Home, Holdenby, Kettering NN15 6XE Tel: 01536 484494 — MB ChB 1935 Aberd. Prev: Ho. Surg. Co. Matern. Hosp. Bellshill.

WOOLFENDEN, Mr Kenneth Alan 48 Rodney Street, Liverpool L1 9AA Tel: 0151 709 2079; Riverside, Manorial Road, Parkgate, South Wirral CH64 6QW Tel: 0151 336 7229 — MB ChB 1973 Liverp.; FRCS Eng. 1978; FEBU 1992. Cons. Urol. Roy. Liverp. Hosp. Socs: Assoc. Mem. Liverp. Med. Inst.; Birkenhead Med. Soc. Prev: Ho. Phys. & Ho. Surg. Sefton Gen. Hosp. Liverp.; Sen. Demonst. (Anat.) Univ. Liverp.; Regist. (Cardiothoracic Surg.) BRd.green & Fazakerley Hosps.

WOOLFENDEN, Margaret (retired) 795 Liverpool Road, Ainsdale, Southport PR8 3NU Tel: 01704 578383 Email: m.parker@merseymail.com — MB ChB 1942 Liverp. Prev: Resid. Med. Off. S.port E.M.S. Hosp.

WOOLFORD, David John 23 Burley Road, Oakham LE15 Tel: 01572 2449 — BM BCh 1949 Oxf.; MA, BM BCh Oxon. 1949; DObst RCOG 1950. (Lond. Hosp.) Med. Off. Rutland Memor. Hosp. Oakham; Local Treasury Med. Off.; Anaesth. Off. Rutland Memor. Hosp. Oakham. Prev: Capt. RAMC; Clin. Obst. Off., Ho. Phys. & Ho. Surg. Lond. Hosp.

WOOLFORD, Marcus Christian David Park Drive Health Centre, 2A Park Drive, Leicester Forest East, Leicester LE3 3FN Tel: 0116 289 8111; 18 Faire Road, Glenfield, Leicester LE3 8EA Tel: 0116 231 1899 — MB ChB 1985 Leic.; MRCGP 1989; DRCOG 1988. Prev: Trainee GP Syston; SHO (A & E) Leic. Roy. Infirm.; SHO (O & G) Leic. Gen. Hosp.

WOOLFSON, Gerald 97 Harley Street, London W1N 1DF Tel: 020 7935 3400 Fax: 020 7487 3834 Email: geraldwoolfson@comp.com; 56 Redington Road, London NW3 7RS Tel: 020 7794 1974 — MB ChB Cape Town 1954; FRCP Glas. 1980, M 1963; FRCPsych 1979, M 1971; DPM Eng. 1958. (Cape Town) Cons. Psychiatr. St. Chas. Hosps. Lond.; Cons. Psychotherap. HM Prison Holloway; Hon. Cons. Psychiat. & Sen. Lect. Hammersmith Hosp. & Roy. Postgrad. Med. Sch. Lond. Socs: Fell.Roy. Soc. Med.; Fell. Roy. Soc. Med. Prev: Cons. Psychiat. W. Pk. Hosp. Epsom; 1st Asst. Dept. Psychiat. St. Geo. Hosp. Lond.; Regist. Depts. Surg. & Neuropsychiat. Groote Schuur Hosp. Cape Town.

WOOLFSON, Harold (retired) 19 Chessington Lodge, Regents Park Road, London N3 3AA Tel: 020 8343 0551 — LRCP LRCS Ed. LRFPS Glas. 1950; FRCP Lond. 1989; FRCP Ed. 1980; FRCP Glas. 1979; MRCP (UK) 1967; DCH RCPS Glas. 1964. Hon. Cons. Dermat. Brook Gen. Hosp. Lond. Prev: Cons. Dermat. Brook Gen. Hosp. Lond.

WOOLFSON, Julian Department of Obstetrics & Gynaecology, Queen Mary's Hospital, Sidcup — MB ChB 1971 Birm.; MRCOG 1978; FRCOG 1991. Cons. (O & G) Qu. Mary's Hosp. Sidcup. Prev: Sen. Regist. Oxf. RHA; Regist. Matern. Dept. Roy. Berks. Hosp. Reading.

WOOLFSON, Peter Ivor 4 Barbondale Close, Whittle Hall, Warrington WA5 3HU — MB ChB 1989 Manch.; BSc 1986; MRCP 1992; MD 1999. Specialist Regist. Cardiol. Manch. Roy. Infirm. Socs: Med. Res. Soc.; Brit. Soc. Echocardiogr. Prev: Sp Reg.Cardio.Roy.Bolton.Hosp; Research Fell.Cardiovasc.Meds.tepping Hall Hosp.Stockport; Med.Reg.Trafford Gen.Hosp.Manch.

WOOLFSON, Robin Gideon Tel: 020 7380 9366 Fax: 020 7380 9199 Email: r.woolfson@ucl.ac.uk; Tel: 020 7435 1406 — MB BChir Camb. 1984; MD Camb. 1991; MRCP (UK) 1987; FRCP Lond. 1999. (Cambridge University, St. Thomas' Hospital Medical School) Cons. Nephrologist, UCLH; Cons. Nephrologist Whittington Hosp. Trust.

WOOLFSON, Stephen Benjamin 11Midhurst Avenue, London N10 3EP — MB BS 1988 Lond.

WOOLGAR, Justin David 96 Lyes Green, Corsley, Warminster BA12 7PA — MB ChB 1990 Leeds.

WOOLGAR, Melanie Joy 16 Great Bounds Drive, Southborough, Tunbridge Wells TN4 0TP — MB ChB 1983 Bristol.

WOOLGROVE, Cyril George Tresco, 4 Priorfields, Ashby-de-la-Zouch LE65 1EA Tel: 01530 412320 — MB ChB 1939 Birm.; FFCM RCP (UK) 1974, M 1964; DPH Manch. 1946. (Birm.) MOH SE Derbysh. RDC & Long Eaton UDC; Sch. Health Serv. & Environm. Refer. to Handicaps, Housing & Family Health. Socs: Fell. Soc. MOH & Manch. Med. Soc. Prev: Med. Off. Birm. RHB; Sen. Asst. MOH &

Sen. Sch. Med. Off. Coventry; Dep. MOH & Dep. Sch. Med. Off. Co. Boro. Reading.

WOOLHOUSE, Ian Stewart 2 Mill Rise, South Gosforth, Newcastle upon Tyne NE3 1QY — MB BS 1993 Newc.

WOOLICH, John Gevenson The Surgery, 26A Park Road, Harlesden, London NW10 8TA Tel: 020 8965 5255 Fax: 020 8965 9080; 24 Sidmouth Road, London NW2 5JX Tel: 020 8459 4661 — MB BS 1959 Lond.; MRCS Eng. LRCP Lond. 1960; MRCGP 1975; DObst RCOG 1962. (Westm.) Socs: BMA. Prev: Resid. Med. Off. Watford Matern. Hosp.; Ho. Phys. & Ho. Surg. St. Albans City Hosp.

WOOLLACOTT, M The Surgery, 57 Dowsett Road, Tottenham, London N17 9DL — MRCS Eng. LRCP Lond. 1967 London; MRCS Eng. LRCP Lond. 1967 London.

WOOLLACOTT, Susan 89 Highgate West Hill, London N6 Tel: 020 8340 8228 — MB ChB 1965 Leeds; MRCPsych 1972; DPM Eng. 1970. (Leeds)

WOOLLAM, Christopher Henry Morgan Department of Anaesthetics, Norfolk & Norwich Hospital, St Stephens Road, Norwich NR1 — MB BS 1968 Lond.; FFA RCS Eng. 1973. (St. Thos.) Cons. Anaesth. Norf. & Norwich Hosp. Socs: Hosp. Cons. & Specialists Assn. & Assn. Anaesth. GB & Irel. Prev: Sen. Regist. Berks. AHA; Sen. Regist. & Regist. Nuffield Dept. Anaesth. Radcliffe Infirm. Oxf.

WOOLLAM, Victoria Anne Morgan Downing Street Surgery, 4 Downing Street, Farnham GU9 7NX Tel: 01252 716226 Fax: 01252 322338; Sandhills Corner, Wormley, Godalming GU8 5UF Tel: 01428 683 3618 — MB BS 1979 Lond. (Char. Cross) Clin. Asst. (Dermat.) Farnham Hosp.

WOOLLANDS, Ian Gordon Medical Centre, Corus, Scunthorpe Works, Brigg Road, Scunthorpe DN15 1BP Tel: 01724 403472 Fax: 01726 403469 Email: ian.woodlands@corusgroup.com — MB ChB 1983 Leic.; BSc Sheff. 1977; AFOM RCP Lond. 1989; MRCGP 1987. (Leic.) Head of Occupat.al Health; Dir. Kaizen Med. Serv. Ltd. Socs: Soc. Occupat. Med.; Brit. Register of Complementary Practitioners - Chinese Med.; ISSSEEM. Prev: Technical Dir. Hazlewood Foods plc; Occupat. Phys. Brit. Steel. Scunthorpe.

WOOLLARD, Adrian John 9 Oaklands Drive, Penwortham, Preston PR1 0XY — MB ChB 1998 Manch.

WOOLLARD, Ann Elizabeth Merton Lodge Surgery, West Street, Alford LN13 9DH Tel: 01507 463262 Fax: 01507 466447; Claythorpe Manor, Claythorpe, Alford LN13 0DU Tel: 01507 450042 — MB BS 1981 Lond.; MRCGP 1985. (Royal Free Hospital) Clin. Asst. (Dermat.) Louth Co. Hosp. Lincs. Prev: Trainee GP Pilgrim Hosp. Boston VTS; Ho. Surg. MusGr. Pk. Hosp. Taunton; Ho. Phys. Treliske Hosp. Truro.

WOOLLARD, Bruce Pargeter Pennys Lane Surgery, Pennys Lane, Cranborne, Wimborne BH21 5QE Tel: 01725 517272 Fax: 01725 517746; Lower Meadow Cottage, Tarrant Launceston, Blandford Forum DT11 8BY Tel: 01258 830511 Fax: 01258 830511 Email: brucewoollard@compuserve.com — MB BS 1988 Lond.; DFFP 1994; DRCOG 1994. (St. Mary's Hospital Paddington) Clin. Asst. (Obst. & Gyn.) Blandford Hosp. Prev: SHO (O & G) W. Dorset Hosp.; Trainee GP Wimborne Dorset; Clin. Asst. (Dermat.) Poole Gen. Hosp.

WOOLLARD, Christopher Mark 9 Oaklands Drive, Penwortham, Preston PR1 0XY — MB ChB 1995 Liverp.

WOOLLARD, Susan Jane Community Child Health, Mulberry House, Alder Hey Childrens Hospital, Eaton Road, Liverpool L12 2AP Tel: 0151 228 4811; 41 Paradise Lane, Freshfield, Liverpool L37 7EH — MB ChB 1978 Manch.; FRCPCH; DCH Eng. 1981. Cons. Community Paediaiat. Roy. Liverp. Childr. Hosp. Socs: Fac. Comm. Health. Prev: SCMO (Child Health) Liverp.; Clin. Med. Off. (Child Health) Salford.

WOOLLASTON, Kevin Alan Harold Yardley Green Medical Centre, 75 Yardley Green Road, Bordesley Green, Birmingham B9 5PU Tel: 0121 773 3737; 16 Arnold Grove, Shirley, Solihull B90 3JR — MB ChB 1984 Manch.

WOOLLASTON, Marion Ethel Frances Four Vine Place, Brighton BN1 3HE Tel: 01273 737578 — MRCS Eng. LRCP Lond. 1942; BSc Lond. (Physiol.) 1938; FRCPsych. 1981, M 1972; DPM Eng. 1952. (King's Coll. Hosp.) Hon. Cons. Psychiat. Char. Cross Hosp. Lond. Socs: Fell. Roy. Soc. Med. Prev: Cons. Psychiat. Char. Cross. Hosp.

Lond.; Regist. (Psychiat.) St. Ebba's Hosp. Epsom & Banstead Hosp. Sutton.

WOOLLER, David Michael Whalebridge Practice, Health Centre, Carfax Street, Swindon SN1 1ED Tel: 01793 692933; 10 Callas Rise, Wanborough, Swindon SN4 0AQ Tel: 01793 790528 — MB ChB 1966 Sheff. Clin. Asst. (A & E) P.ss Margt. Hosp. Swindon; Med. Off. Pinewood Sch. Bourton. Prev: Doctor to Brit. Men's Alpine Ski Team; Ho. Phys. & Cas. Off. & SHO (Orthop.) Roy. Hosp. Sheff.; SHO (Orthop.) King Edwd. VII Orthop. Hosp. Sheff.

WOOLLER, Dennis John Alfred The Whittington Hospital, Highgate Hill, London N19 5NF Tel: 020 7288 5464 Fax: 020 7288 5417 Email: dennis.wooler@whittington.thenhs.com; 65 Dresden Road, London N19 3BG Tel: 020 7272 2413 Fax: 020 7686 0967 Email: djawooller@aol.com — MB BS 1981 Queensland; FANZCA 1992; FFARACS 1992; DA (UK) 1986. (Queensland) Cons. Anaesth. & Dir. (Day Surg.) Whittington Hosp. Lond. Socs: Austral. Soc. Anaesth.; Ass. Anaesth.; BMA. Prev: Cons. Anaesth. Gold Coast Hosp. S.port, Austral.

WOOLLETT, Richard John Manor Brook Medical Centre, 117 Brook Lane, London SE3 0EN Tel: 020 8856 5678 Fax: 020 8856 8632 — MB BS 1984 Lond.

WOOLLEY, Alan William, MBE (retired) South Mill, Dulcote, Wells BA5 3NU Tel: 01749 676257 — MB ChB 1935 Bristol; MRCS Eng. LRCP Lond. 1935. Prev: Ho. Surg. & Ho. Surg. (ENT) Roy. Infirm. Bristol.

WOOLLEY, Andrew Charles Springfield, Street Road, Glastonbury BA6 9EG — BM BCh 1996 Oxf.; MA Camb. 1997; MRCP 1999. SHO (Med.) Soton. Gen. Hosp.

WOOLLEY, Birgit Victoria Road Surgery, 50 Victoria Road, Worthing BN11 1XB Tel: 01903 230656 Fax: 01903 520094; 30 Nutbourne Road, Worthing BN14 7HS Tel: 01903 204710 Email: birgit@birgit.freeserve.co.uk — State Exam Med 1992 Heidelberg; DRCOG 1996; MRCGP 1997; Dip. Psychol. Heidelberg 1977. (Heidelberg) GP Princip. Socs: Med. Protec. Soc.; BMA; RCGP. Prev: GP Regist. Sompting; SHO (Gen. Med.) Worthing Hosp. VTS.

WOOLLEY, Christopher Michael 24 Newfoundland Road, Gabalfa, Cardiff CF14 3LA Tel: 029 2052 2796 — MB BCh 1994 Wales. Prev: Ho. Off. (Surg.) Neville Hall Hosp.; Ho. Off. (Med.) E. Glam. Hosp.

WOOLLEY, Emma Jane 113 West Vale, Little Neston, South Wirral CH64 0SF; The Hayloft, 8 Hanns Hall Farm, Wilaston, Chester CH64 2TQ — MB ChB 1997 Liverp.; BDS Sheff. 1988; FDSRCS (Eng.) 1994. (Liverpool) SHO.Orth. Socs: BMA; Assoc. BAOMS. Prev: Pre-Regist. Ho. Off. Wirral Hosps. NHS Trust; Sen. Ho. Off. (Surg.); SHO.Oral & Maxill.Surg.

***WOOLLEY, Jacqueline Louise** 21 Lon Y Bryn, Eitminog, Bangor LL57 2LD — MB BCh 1996 Wales.

WOOLLEY, James Barry Senior House Officer, The Maudsley Hospital, Denmark Hill, London SE5 8AZ Email: j.woolley@doctor .com — MB BS 1996 Lond.; BSc (Hons.) Lond. 1995. (St. Mary's Hosp. Med. Sch.) SHO (Psychiat.), The Maudsley Hosp., Lond. Prev: SHO (Med.) Roy. Free Hosp. Lond.; Ho Surg. N.wick Pk. & St. Mark's Hosp., Harrow, Middlx.; Ho. Off. Med. Ealing Hosp. Middlx.

WOOLLEY, Michael James The Medical Centre, 37A Heaton Road, Heaton, Newcastle upon Tyne NE6 1TH Tel: 0191 265 8121 Fax: 0191 276 6085; 5A Colbeck Terrace, Tynemouth, North Shields NE30 4BW — MB ChB 1982 Liverp.

WOOLLEY, Paul David Tel: 0161 291 4939 Fax: 0161 291 4604 Email: paul.woolley@zetnet.co.uk; Rosebank, Temple St, Padfield, Glossop SK13 1EL — MB ChB 1981 Sheff.; FRCP Lond. 1996; MRCP (UK) 1985; DFFP 1996; DRCOG 1984. Cons. Genitourin Med. Withington Hosp. Manch. Prev: Sen. Regist. & Research Regist. (Genitourin. Med.) Roy. Hallamsh. Hosp. Sheff.

WOOLLEY, Sarah Louise Birmingham Childrens Hospital, Edgbaston, Birmingham B4 6; 11 Lapwing Drive, Hampton-in-Arden, Solihull B92 0BF Tel: 01675 443385 — MB ChB 1990 Birm.; MRCP (UK) 1995; MRCPCH 1996. SHO (Paediat.) Birm. Childr. Hosp. Socs: Brit. Diabetic Assn. Prev: SHO (Paediat. & Neonat.) Addenbrooke's Hosp. Camb.; SHO (Paediat. & Neonat.) New Cross Hosp. Wolverhampton; Regist. (Diabetes & Endocrinol.) Singleton Hosp. Swansea.

WOOLLEY, Steven Michael 46 Riley Road, Yard Wood, Birmingham B14 4JH Tel: 0121 474413 — MB ChB 1997 Birm. SHO Gen. Surg., Birm. Heartlands Hosps. Prev: SHO (A & E) Birm.

Heartlands Hosp.; Ho. Off. (Surg.) Birm. Heartlands Hosp.; Ho. Off. (Med.) Alexandra Hosp. Redditch.

***WOOLLEY, Thomas** 25 Roy Square, London E14 8BY Tel: 020 7538 3613; c/o P. E. Woolley, 62 Alfriston Road, London SW11 6NW Tel: 020 7228 3633 — MB BS 1995 Lond.

WOOLLEY, Vivian Lloyd (retired) Y Ddol, 21 Lon-y-Bryn, Eithinog, Bangor LL57 2LD Tel: 01248 352158 — MB BCh 1964 Wales; FRCP Lond. 1990; MRCP (UK) 1970; FRCPCH 1997; DCH Eng. 1969. Cons. Paediat. Gwynedd Hosp. Prev: Sen. Regist. (Paediat.) United Cardiff Hosps.

WOOLLEY, Wendy (retired) 45 Stanneylands Drive, Wilmslow SK9 4EU Tel: 01625 523553 — MB BS Lond. 1947. Prev: Clin. Asst. Dept. Rheum. Withington Hosp. Manch.

WOOLLONS, Andrew David The Surgery, 75 Longridge Avenue, Saltdean, Brighton BN2 8LA Tel: 01273 305723 Fax: 01273 300962 — MB ChB 1987 Bristol; MRCGP 1993; DRCOG 1991; DCH RCP Lond. 1990.

WOOLLONS, Arjida Department of Dermatology, Worthing and Southlands NHS Trust, Lyndhurst Road, Worthing BN11 2DH Tel: 01903 205111 Fax: 01903 823721 — MB BS 1987 Lond.; MD 2001; MRCP (UK) 1993. (Guy's, London) Cons. Dermatol., Worthing & S.lands NHS Trust. Socs: BAD; BSID; BSPD. Prev: Specialist Regist. (Dermat.) Brighton Health Care NHS Trust & St. John's Inst. Dermat. Lond.; Regist. (Neurol.) Hurstwood Pk. Neurol. Centre; SHO Rotat. (Gen. Med.) Kent & Canterbury Hosp.

WOOLLONS, Martin John Pensby Road Surgery, 349 Pensby Road, Pensby, Wirral CH61 9NL Tel: 0151 648 1193 Fax: 0151 648 2934 — MB BS 1992 Lond.

WOOLMORE, Michael John Frank (retired) 457 Wellingborough Road, Northampton NN3 3HW Tel: 01604 713908 Email: michael@woolymed.demon.co.uk — MB BS Lond. 1959; MRCS Eng. LRCP Lond. 1959; MRCGP 1975; DObst RCOG 1964. Prev: GP N.ampton.

WOOLNER, Catherine Anne University Health Service, University of Southampton, Building 48, Highfield, Southampton SO17 1BJ Tel: 023 8055 7531 Fax: 023 8059 3259 — MB ChB 1987 Birm.

WOOLNER, Harold William 4/1 Craufurdland, Braepark Rd, Edinburgh EH4 6DL Tel: 0131 317 7596 — LRCP LRCS 1944 Ed.; LRCP LRCS Ed. LRFPS Glas. 1944; DPH Ed. 1952. Med. Off: Scott. Home & Health Dept. seconded to Ment. Welf. Commiss. Scotl. Prev: Sen. Health Off. W.. Region Nigeria; Sen. Med. Off. Fife CC; RAMC.

WOOLNOUGH, Melanie Jane Heatherlea, 5 Lucas Road, High Wycombe HP13 6QE — MB ChB 1998 Sheff.

WOOLRICH, Louise Helen 21 Haddon Crescent, Beeston, Nottingham NG9 5JU — MB ChB 1992 Bristol.

WOOLRYCH, Jonathan Michael 20 Nightingale Road, Godalming GU7 3AG — MB BChir 1990 Camb.

WOOLRYCH, Michael Ernfrid (retired) 20 Nightingale Road, Godalming GU7 3AG — BM BCh 1958 Oxf. Prev: Ho. Off. (Paediat.) Radcliffe Infirm. Oxf.

***WOOLRYCH, Rachel Susan** Breaconside Farm, Moniaive, Thornhill DG3 4DZ — BChir 1994 Camb.; BA Camb. 1992.

WOOLSEY, Siobhan Marie 12 McGreavy Drive, Lurgan, Craigavon BT66 6LS Tel: 01762 342030 — MB BCh BAO 1995 Belf.; MB BCh Belf. 1995.

WOOLTERTON, Mark Clive Avenue Road Surgery, 2 Avenue Road, Warley, Brentwood CM14 5EL Tel: 01277 212820 Fax: 01277 234169; 114 Woodman Road, Brentwood CM14 5AL — MB BChir 1989 Camb.; MA Camb. 1990; MRCP (UK) 1992; MRCGP 1994.

WOOLTORTON, Mr Stephen John St Thomas Road Health Centre, St. Thomas Road, Newquay TR7 1RU Tel: 01637 878599; Tregosse, Wheal Friendly, St Agnes TR5 0SR Tel: 01872 552601 — MB BS 1974 Lond.; BSc (Physiol.) Lond. 1970; FRCS Eng. 1979; MRCS Eng. LRCP Lond. 1974; DRCOG 1976. (Westm.) Prev: GP. I. of Scilly; Med. Off. & Sen. Med. Off. St. Helena.

WOOLVEN, David William Brading (retired) The Glebe House, Clothall, Baldock SG7 6RE Tel: 01462 790335 — MB ChB (1st Cl. Hons.) Liverp. 1952; DObst RCOG 1954.

WOOLVERIDGE, Ann Patricia (retired) 7 Monmouth Square, Olivers Battery Road N., Winchester SO22 4HY Tel: 01962 853506 — MRCS Eng. LRCP Lond. 1968; MRCGP 1974. Prev: Squadron Ldr. RAF Med. Br.

WOON

WOON, Mr Wai Hong 3 Tern Park, Collingham, Wetherby LS22 5LY — MB BChir 1982 Camb.; MRCP (UK) 1984; FRCOphth 1990; FRCS Ed. 1988. Cons. Ophth. Leeds Gen. Infirm.

WOOSTER, Edgar Gerald 28 Holly Grove, London SE15 5DF Fax: 020 7635 0448, 020 7732 8517 — MB BChir 1957 Camb.; MRCP Lond. 1960; FRCPsych 1981, M 1971; DPM Lond. 1963. (St. Bart.) Socs: Assoc. Mem. Brit. Psychoanalyt. Soc.; Mem. Gp. Analytic Soc. (Lond.). Prev: Cons. Psychiat. Lond. Univ. Centr. Inst. Stud. Health Serv.; Cons. Psychotherapist St. Geo. Hosp. Lond.; Sen. Regist. (Psychother.) Maudsley Hosp. Lond.

WOOSTER, Joanne Clare 7 Kenilworth Road, Blundellsands, Liverpool L23 3AD; 5 Charles Street, Boxmoor, Hemel Hempstead HP1 1JH — MB BS 1996 Lond.

WOOSTER, Sarah Louise 28 Hawthorn Road, Hale, Altrincham WA15 9RG Email: doctorjrm@aol.com — MB ChB 1988 Sheff. Regist. Rotat. (Med. Microbiol.) NW RHA.

WOOTHIPOOM, Wit 28 Princes Gate, London SW7 — MB BS 1973 Lond.; MRCP (UK) 1977.

WOOTLIFF, Alan Brian 10 St Regis Heights, Firecrest, West Heath Road, London NW3 7NE — MB ChB Manch. 1956. (Manch.) Prev: Clin. Asst. Dept. Rheum. E. Lond. Gp. Hosps.; Ho. Phys. Memor. Hosp. Darlington; Ho. Surg. St. Mary Abbot's Hosp. Lond.

WOOTTON, Alan (retired) Redwood House, Fiery Lane, Uley, Dursley GL11 5DA — MB ChB 1956 Birm.; DObst RCOG 1963. Prev: GP Dursley.

WOOTTON, Alison Catherine The Surgery, Station Road, Langbank, Port Glasgow PA14 6YA; Newton Farm, Kilmacolm PA13 4TE — MB BS 1973 Newc. Prev: SHO (Obst.) Forth Pk. Matern. Hosp. Kirkcaldy; Regist. (Geriat.) Bridge of Weir Hosp.; Ho. Surg. Gt. Yarmouth & Gorleston Gen. Hosp.

WOOTTON, Ian David Phimester (retired) Cariad Cottage, Cleeve Road, Goring, Reading RG8 9DB Tel: 01491 873050 — MB BChir 1945 Camb.; PhD Lond. 1950; MA Camb. 1945; FRCP Lond. 1974, M 1969; FRCPath 1972, M 1963; FRSC 1956. Prev: Univ. Lond. Prof. Chem. Path. Roy. Postgrad. Med. Sch. Lond.

WOOTTON, Mr James Robert Maelor General Hospital, Croesnewydd Road, Wrexham LL13 7TD — MB BS 1981 Lond.; BSc (Hons. Pharmacol.) Lond. 1979, MB BS 1981; FRCS Eng. 1985. (St. Bart.) Regist. (Orthop. Train. Scheme) Robt. Jones & Agnes Hunt Orthop.; Hosp. OsW.ry. Prev: Regist. (Orthop.) Gwynedd Hosp. Bangor.

WOOTTON, Julia Clare St. Nicholas Hospice, Macmillan Way, Hardwick Lane, Bury St Edmunds IP33 2QY Tel: 01284 766133 Fax: 01284 752709 — BM 1985 Soton.; BEd Lancaster 1972; Dip. Palliat. Med. Cardiff 1996. (Southampton) Med. Dir. St. Nicholas Hospice; Cons. Palliat. Med. W. Suff. Hosp., Hardwick La., Bury St. Edmunds, IP33 2QY. Socs: Assn. for Palliat. Med.; Fell. Roy. Soc. of Med.; Brit. Med. Assn. Prev: Assoc. Specialist St. Lukes Hospice Basildon Essex.; G.P. Princip., Bournemouth, Dorset.

WOOTTON, Leslie William 81 Ash Tree Drive, West Kingsdown, Sevenoaks TN15 6LW Tel: 01474 852100 Fax: 01474 854549; 15 Mamignot Close, Bearstead, Maidstone ME14 4PT Tel: 01622 735939 — MRCS Eng. LRCP Lond. 1967; DO 1994 Maidstone; DObst RCOG 1969. (Sheff.) Lect. NESCOT. Socs: Fell. Roy. Soc. Med. Prev: Ho. Surg. Wharncliffe Hosp. Sheff.; Ho. Phys. (Neurol.) Fulwood Annexe Roy. Hosp. Sheff.; Ho. Off. (Obst.) Jessop. Hosp. Sheff.

WOOTTON, Mary (retired) Redwood House, Fiery Lane, Uley, Dursley GL11 5DA Tel: 01453 860371 — MB ChB Birm. 1956. Prev: GP Dursley & Cas. Off. Stroud Gen Hosp.

WOOTTON, Matthew Alan Dept. Of Anaesthetics, Yeovil District General Hospitarl, Higher Kingston, Yeovil BA21 4AT Tel: 01935 384246 — MB BS 1990 Lond.; BSc (Hons. Physiol.) Newc. 1984; FRCA 1996. Cons. Anaesth. Yeovil Dist. Gen. Hosp. Som.

WOOTTON, Oonagh Rosemary The Doctors Centre, 41 Broomwood Road, Orpington BR5 2JP Tel: 01689 832454 Fax: 01689 826165; 20 Hamilton Road, Sidcup DA15 7HB Tel: 020 8302 5942 — MB ChB 1965 Sheff. (Sheff.) Clin. Asst. (Haemat.) Qu. Mary's Hosp. Sidcup. Prev: Asst. MOH & Sch. Med. Off. Sheff.; Cas. Off. Roy. Hosp. Sheff.; Ho. Phys. (Dermat.) Sheff. Roy. Infirm.

WOOTTON, Polly Beaton 8 Kingswood Gardens, Leeds LS8 2BT — MB BS 1997 Newc.

WOOTTON, Romola Isabel (retired) Harvington, 10 Bell Road, Walsall WS5 3JW Tel: 0121 357 2067 — MB ChB 1959 Birm. Prev: Cons. Pub. Health Med. Walsall HA.

WOOTTON, Russell Philip New Surgery, Bridge of Weir Road, Kilmacolm PA13 4AP Tel: 01505 872844 Fax: 01505 872299; Newton Farm, Kilmacolm PA13 4TE — MB BS 1972 Newc. Med. Off. Epileptic Centre Quarriers Homes Bridge of Weir. Prev: Cas. Off. Vict. Hosp. Kirkcaldy; Ho. Off. Sunderland Gen. Hosp.

WORAH, Rekha Church Lane Medical Centre, Orchid Rise, Off Church Lane, Scunthorpe DN15 7AN Tel: 01724 864341 Fax: 01724 876441 — MB BS 1977 Patna. Trainee GP Hull.

WORBY, Malcolm Eric (retired) New Road Surgery, New Road, Brightstone, Newport PO30 4BB Tel: 01983 740219 Fax: 01983 741399 — MB BS 1970 Lond.; MRCS Eng. LRCP Lond. 1970. Prev: Sen. Med. Off. UK Atomic Energy Auth.

WORDEN, Jenifer Ann 320 Birmingham Road, Sutton Coldfield B72 1DP — MB ChB 1985 Manch.

WORDEN, Richard John Wayfarers, Pilgrims Way, Broad St., Hollingbourne, Maidstone ME17 1RB — MB BS 1961 Lond.; MRCS Eng. LRCP Lond. 1961; DObst RCOG 1963. (Guy's) Med. Adviser Appeals Serv., tribunel appeals for Disabil. awareness. Prev: GP Chatham; Ho. Off. (Obst.) Mile End Hosp.; Ho. Surg. & Ho. Phys. St. Olave's Hosp. Lond.

WORDEN, Timothy William John The Docs, 55-59 Bloom Street, Manchester M1 3LY Tel: 0161 237 9490 Fax: 0161 228 3164; Tel: 0161 792 9151 — BM BS 1979 Nottm. (Nottingham)

WORDLEY, Anthony Richard Ivy Grove Surgery, 1 Ivy Grove, Ripley DE5 3HN Tel: 01773 742286 Fax: 01773 749812; The Kennels, Alderwasley, Belper DE56 2RB Tel: 01629 822315 — MB BS 1979 Lond.; Cert Family Plann. JCC 1984. (St. Thos.) Socs: Derby Med. Soc.

WORDSWORTH, Andrew Damian 54 Wimblington Road, March PE15 9QN Tel: 01354 660044 Email: andrew@docwords.freeserve.co.uk — BM BS 1988 Nottm.; BMedSci, Nottm, 1986. Assoc. GP, Cambs. Fens; Med. Examr., Benefits Agency; Occupat. Health Phys. GWPadley; Police Surg. Camb.shire Constab.

WORDSWORTH, Professor Bryan Paul Seddon Ward, Nuffield Orthopaedic Centre, Oxford OX3 7LD Tel: 01865 740062 Fax: 01865 742186 Email: paul.wordsworth@well.ox.ac.uk; Tollgate Cottage, Lower Heyford, Bicester OX25 5PE Tel: 01869 340794 — MB BS 1975 Lond.; FRCP Lond. 1996; MRCP (UK) 1978. (Westm. Med. Sch. Lond. Univ.) Clin. Reader (Rheum.) Nuffield Dept. Clin. Med. Univ. Oxf. & Hon. Cons. Rheum.; Sen. Tutor, Green Coll. Oxf. Univ.; Prof. (Rheumatol.) Univ. Oxf. Socs: Brit. Soc. Rheum.; UK Skeletal Dysplasia Gp. Prev: Sen. Regist. (Rheum. & Rehabil.) Nuffield Orthop. Centre Oxf.; Regist. (Rheum.) Middlx. Hosp. Lond.; Regist. (Med.) Mayday Hosp.

WORDSWORTH, Jennifer Mary Central Health Clinic, 1 Mulberry St., Sheffield S1 2PJ Tel: 0114 271 6790 Fax: 0114 271 6791 — MB ChB 1965 Sheff.; MFFP 1993. (Sheffield) Cons. Family Plann. & Reproduc. Health Care Community Health Sheff. NHS Trust; Dir. Sexual & Reproductive Health, Community Health Sheff. NHS Trust; Director of the Div. of child and community Serv.s. Socs: Coun. Mem., Brit. Menopause Soc.; Fac. Community Health; Fell. Roy. Inst. Pub. Health & Hyg. Prev: Med. Off. Family Plann. Assn.; GP Tideswell Derbysh.; Director of sexual + reproductive health, Sheff. NHS Trust.

WORDSWORTH, Matthew Thomas 50 Cork Lane, Glen Parva, Leicester LE2 9JS — MB ChB 1991 Birm.; ChB Birm. 1991.

WORDSWORTH, Ruth Frances (retired) St. Marys Convent, Wantage OX12 9DJ Tel: 01235 771053 — MRCS Eng. LRCP Lond. 1937; DTM Calcutta 1939. Prev: Med. Miss. USPG Diocese, Poona.

WORDSWORTH, Victor Pargiter (retired) 11 Fiddicroft Avenue, Banstead SM7 3AD Tel: 01737 211762 — MRCS Eng. LRCP Lond. 1948; DA Eng. 1953; FFA RCS Eng. 1954. Prev: Cons. Anaesth. Croydon Gp. Hosps.

WORGAN, Mr Douglas Heath house, Minstead, Lyndhurst SO43 7GP Tel: 02380 812311 — MB BCh Wales 1960; MRCS Eng. LRCP Lond. 1960; FRCS Eng. 1969; FRCS Ed. 1966. Cons. ENT Surg. Soton. Univ. Gp. Hosps. Socs: (Counc.) Roy. Soc. Med.; Brit. Assn. Otol. Prev: Sen. Regist. (ENT) Char. Cross Hosp. Gp.; Ho. Surg. St. Jas. Hosp. Balham & Birm. Accid. Hosp.

WORKMAN, Alan Robert Heol Fach Surgery, Heol Fach, North Cornelly, Bridgend CF33 4LD Tel: 01656 740345 Fax: 01656 740872; Montrose, Heol-Yr-Orsaf, Kenfig Hill, Bridgend CF33 6EQ Tel: 01656 746135 — MB BCh 1984 Wales; DRCOG 1987.

WORKMAN, Alexander James Gordon Health Centre, 14 Market Place, Carluke ML8 4BP Tel: 01555 771012; Wintons, 33 West Avenue, Carluke ML8 5AE Tel: 01555 771877 — MB ChB 1972 Ed. (Edinburgh) Prev: SHO (Cas.) Derbysh. Roy. Infirm. Derby; Ho. Off. (O & G) E.. Gen. Hosp. Edin.; Ho. Off. (Med. Paediat.) Leith Hosp. Edin.

WORKMAN, Clare Louise Occupational Health Department, University of Stirling, Stirling; Nether Shannochill, Aberfoyle, Stirling FK8 3UZ Tel: 01877 382924 — MB ChB 1979 Leeds; BSc (Hons.) Leeds 1976; D.Occ.Med. RCP Lond. 1995. (Leeds Univ.) Occupat. Health Phys., Lothian Primary Healthcare NHS Trust; Occupat. Health Phys. (PT), Company Health Ltd., Blackpool. Socs: Soc. Occupat. Med.; BMA. Prev: Occupat. Health Phys., Salus, Lanarksh.; Occupat. Health Phys. Preston NHS Trust; Med. Off. DSS Leeds.

WORKMAN, Irvin Clarence Eugene Department Child & Family Psychiatry, London Road, Canterbury CT1 8LZ — MB BS 1977 Bangalor; MB BS Bangalore 1977; MRCPsych 1985. Cons. Child & Adolesc. Psychiat. Canterbury Kent.

WORLD, Lt. Col. Michael John, Lt.-Col. RAMC Department of Military Medicine, Royal Defence Medical College, Fort Blockhouse,, Gosport PO12 2AB Tel: 02392 765660 Fax: 02392 765653; 46 Munnings Drive, College Town, Sandhurst GU47 0FN Tel: 01276 34023 Email: 106201.1307@compuserve.com — MB ChB 1972 Lond.; BSc (1st cl. Hons. Physiol.) Lond. 1969, MD 1981; FRCP Lond. 1992; MRCP (UK) 1975; MRCS Eng. LRCP Lond. 1972. (Roy. Free) Prof. Milit. Med. & Cons. Phys. Roy. Hosp. Haslar Gosport. Socs: Renal Assn. Prev: Asst. Prof. Dept. Internal Med. Riyadh Univ. Saudi Arabia; Lect. (Med.) Lond. Hosp. Med. Coll.; Ho. Phys. (Med.) Dept. Neurol. Roy. Free Hosp. Lond.

WORLDING, Jane Department Radiotherapy & Oncology, Leicester Royal Infirmary, Leicester — BM 1990 Soton.; BSc (Hons.) Physiol. Sheff. 1985; MRCPI 1996. (Soton.) Specialist Regist. (Radiother. & Clin. Oncol.) Leicester Roy. Infirm. Prev: SHO Rotat. (Med.) Leicester; SHO (A & E) Portsmouth.

WORLEY, George Anthony 51 Ravenscroft Street, London E2 7QG — MB BS 1990 Lond.

WORLOCK, Arnold Brook House, Berrick Salome, Oxford OX44 6JQ Tel: 01865 891121 — MB BS 1955 Durh. (Newc.) Chairm. Shield Diagnostics Ltd, Biocompatibles Ltd & Cygnus Venture Partners; Maj. RAMC (T & AVR). Socs: Fell. Roy. Soc. Med. Prev: Sen. Adviser Health Care Pruden. Bache Capital Funding Lond. & NY.; Dir. Wellcome Foundat. Ltd. Lond.; Chairm. Wellcome Diag. Ltd.

WORLOCK, Frederick Cecil (retired) Brooklands, Fladbury, Pershore WR10 2QP — MB BChir 1958 Camb.; MA Camb. 1958; MRCS Eng. LRCP Lond. 1957.

WORLOCK, Michael Stanley Gould (retired) Watersmeet, Cackle St., Nutley, Uckfield TN22 3DU Tel: 0182 571 2740 — MRCS Eng. LRCP Lond. 1949.

WORLOCK, Mr Peter Harrison Trauma Service, John Radcliffe Hospital, Headington, Oxford OX3 9DU Tel: 01865 220231 Fax: 01865 221231 — MB BS 1976 Newc.; DM Nottm. 1987; FRCS Ed. 1981; FRCS Eng. 1981. (Univ. Newc. u. Tyne) Cons. Trauma Surg. John Radcliffe Hosp. Oxf.; Civil Cons. Orthop. Trauma RAF. Socs: Fell. BOA; Brit. Orthop. Research Soc. (Mem.); Brit. Trama Soc. (Mem.). Prev: Cons. Orthop. Surg. Sunderland Dist. Gen. Hosp.; Lect. (Orthop. & Accid. Surg.) Univ. Nottm. & Hon. Sen. Regist. Univ. Hosp. Nottm. & Harlow Wood Orthop. Hosp. Mansfield; Clin. Fell. (Orthop. & Trauma Surg.) Sunnybrook Med. Centre & Regional Trauma Unit Univ. Toronto, Ontario, Canada.

WORMALD, John Leathard (retired) 95A Coniscliffe Road, Darlington DL3 7ES Tel: 01325 464378 — MB BS 1940 Durh. Prev: Orthop. Ho. Surg. Roy. Vict. Infirm. Newc.

WORMALD, Peter John (retired) Kasauli Pines, Highwood, Ringwood BH24 3LZ — MRCS Eng. LRCP Lond. 1938; MA Camb. 1947, MD 1954, MB BChir 1938; FRCPath 1969. Prev: Dir. Pub. Health Laborat. Odstock Hosp. Salisbury.

WORMALD, Philip Nigel 37 Elm Grove Road, Exeter EX3 0EJ — MB ChB 1953 Birm.; BSc (Hons.) Birm. 1950, MB ChB 1953; DObst RCOG 1958. (Birm.) Prev: SHO Med. Profess. Unit & Ho. Phys. & Ho. Surg. Qu. Eliz. Hosp. Birm.; SHO City Birm. Fev. Hosp.

WORMALD, Mr Richard Piers Leslie Department of Ophthalmic Epidemiology, Moorfields Eye Hospital, 162 City Road, London EC1V 2PD Tel: 020 7566 2818 Fax: 020 7608 6925; 35 Ellington Road, London N10 3DD — MB BChir 1977 Camb.; BA Camb. 1974, MB 1978 BChir 1977; MSc (Epidemiol.) Lond. 1989; FRCS Glas. (Ophth.) 1985. Hon. Cons. & Sen. Lect. Moorfields Eye Hosp. Lond. Prev: Sen. Lect. & Hon. Cons. W.. Ophth. Hosp. & St. Mary's Med. Sch. Lond.; Sen. Regist. & Regist. Moorfields Eye Hosp. Lond.; Lect. (Preven. Ophth.) Inst. Ophth. Lond.

WORMAN, Audrey June (retired) 3 Wilmot Cottages, Park Road, Banstead SM7 3DH — MB BS 1947 Lond.; MRCS Eng. LRCP Lond. 1946; DCH Eng. 1951.

WORMINGTON, Elsie Marjorie (retired) Beech House, Queens St., Culworth, Banbury OX17 2AT — MB ChB Birm. 1949.

WORMLEY, Robert Lee Dullshot House Surgery, 12 The Parade, Epsom KT18 5DW Tel: 01372 726361 — MB BS 1989 Lond.

WORMSLEY, Kenneth Geoffrey (retired) 12 Cherry Tree Close, High Salvington, Worthing BN13 3QJ Tel: 01903 693031 Fax: 01903 261789 — MB BS 1961 Lond.; DSc Lond. 1974, BSc (Hons.) 1947, MD 1961, MB BS 1951; FRCP Lond. 1973, M 1956. Prev: Cons. Phys. Dundee Teach. Hosps.

WORMSLEY, Susan Jane 3 Belmont Court, 93 Highbury New Park, London N5 2HA — MB ChB 1988 Leeds; MRCGP 1996; DRCOG 1994.

WOROPAY, Sarah Jane The Cannonhill Lane Medical Practice, 153 Cannon Hill Lane, Raynes Park, London SW20 9BZ Tel: 020 8542 5201 Fax: 020 8540 9049; 14 Manor Gardens, Merton Park, London SW20 9AB — MB BS 1982 Lond.; MRCGP 1986; DRCOG 1985. (St. Geo. Hosp. Med. Sch.)

WORRALL, Anne-Marie 22 Rectory Gardens, Wollaton Park, Nottingham NG8 2AR — MB BS 1974 Lond.; MMedSci Nottm. 1993; MRCS Eng. LRCP Lond. 1974; MPH Nottm. 1995; Dip. Med. Educat. Dund 1991; DRCOG 1978; Dip. Health Mgt. Keele 1996. (St. Mary's)

WORRALL, Anthony (retired) Hillcrest, 73 Townend, Cheadle, Stoke-on-Trent ST10 1PG Tel: 01538 3161 — MB ChB 1960 Birm. Prev: Police Surg. Cheale.

WORRALL, Ernest Paterson 11 Upper Bourtree Drive, Burnside, Rutherglen, Glasgow G73 4EJ — MB ChB 1966 Glas.; FRCPsych 1988, M 1973; DPM Ed. & Glas. 1971. (Glas.) Med. Dir. The priory Hosp. Glas. Prev: Cons. Psychiat., S.ern Gen. Hosp., Glas.; Sen. Lect. (Psychol. Med.) Univ. Glas.; Lect. (Psychiat.) Univ. Dundee.

WORRALL, Jennifer Garner Rheumatology Department, Whittington Hospital NHS Trust, Highgate Hill, London N19 5NF Tel: 020 7288 5740 Fax: 020 7288 5550; 10 Carysfort Road, London N8 8RB Tel: 020 7348 9454 — MB BS 1979 Lond.; BSc (Econ) Lond. 1972, MD 1993; FRCP (UK) 2000. Cons. Whittington Hosp. Lond. Prev: Sen. Regist. N.wick Pk. Hosp.; Wellcome Clin. Research Fell. Middlx. Hosp. Lond.; Sen. Regist. Middlx. Hosp. Lond.

WORRALL, Margaret Ann Cunningham Oldham and Partners, Manor House Surgery, Manor Street, Glossop SK13 8PS Tel: 01457 860860 Fax: 01457 860017; 3 Blackshaw Road, Old Glossop, Glossop SK13 7SL — MB ChB 1965 Glas. (Glas.)

WORRALL, Stanley Michael (retired) Ash Close, Plough Lane, Lowdham, Nottingham NG14 7AT Tel: 0115 966 3319 — MRCS Eng. LRCP Lond. 1953; MA, MB BChir Camb. 1953; FRCGP 1987, M 1973; DObst RCOG 1959.

WORRALL-DAVIES, Anne Elizabeth Academic Unit of Child & Adolescent Mental Health, 12A Clarendon Road, Leeds LS2 9NN Tel: 0113 295 1760 Fax: 0113 295 1761 Email: annewd_leedscmht@btinternet.com — MB ChB 1985 Leeds; MD Leeds 1996, MMedSci 1990; MRCPsych 1989. Sen. Lect. (Child & Adolesc. Psychiat.) Leeds; Hon. Cons. Child Psychiat. Leeds. Prev: Sen. Regist. (Child & Adolesc. Psychiat.) Yorks. RHA; Tutor (Psychiat.) Univ. Leeds; Regist.& SHO Rotat. (Psychiat.) St. Jas. Univ. Hosp. Leeds.

WORRALL-KENT, Lindsey Sian University of Birmingham, Department of Psychiatry, Birmingham B15 2QZ Tel: 0121 627 2165 — MB ChB 1989 Aberd.; MRCPsych 1995; Phd Birm. 2998. Research Fell. Univ. Birm.

WORRELL, Mr John Accident & Emergency Department, North Hampshire Hospital, Aldermaston Road, Basingstoke RG24 9NA Tel:

WORRELL

01256 473202; 42 Manor Road, Sherborne, St. John, Basingstoke RG24 9JN — MB BS 1974 Lond.; FRCS Eng. 1981. Staff Grade (A & E) N. Hants. Hosp. Basingstoke. Prev: Sen. Regist. (A & E) Qu. Alexandra Hosp. Portsmouth.

WORRELL, Simon Jonathan 89e Clapham Common South Side, London SW4 9DJ — MB BS 1993 Lond.

WORSDALL, Andrea Kate 49 Chaldon Road, London SW6 7NH — MB ChB 1989 Bristol.

WORSDALL, Guy Mark Westfield Surgery, Waterford Park, Radstock, Bath BA3 3UJ Tel: 01761 436333; 36 Furlong Close, Midsomer Norton, Bath BA3 2PR — MB ChB 1982 Bristol; DRCOG 1988; DA (UK) 1985.

WORSELL, Karen Elizabeth Castleton Health Centre, 2 Elizabeth Street, Castleton, Rochdale OL11 3HY Tel: 01706 658905 Fax: 01706 343990; 22 Wheelwright Drive, Smallbridge, Rochdale OL16 2QQ — MB ChB 1980 Birm.; MRCGP 1984. (Birmingham) GP Rochdale.

WORSEY, Catherine Juliet 6 Exton Road, Nottingham NG5 1HB Tel: 0115 960 6851 — MB ChB Liverp. 1992. SHO (Cas.) Kings Mill Hosp. Mansfield, Notts. Prev: SHO (Health c/o Elderly) Nottm. City Hosp.; SHO (Psychiat.) Mapperly Hosp. Nottm.; Ho. Off. (Med. & Surg.) Arrowe Pk. Hosp. Merseyside.

WORSFOLD, Belinda Jane — MB ChB 1995 Bristol; MA Oxf. 1986; DRCOG 1997.

WORSLEY, Adrian Paul Kings Mill Centre for Health Care Services NHS Trust, Sutton-in-Ashfield NG17 4JL Tel: 01623 25515 — MB BS Lond. 1980; BSc (Hons.) Lond. 1977; MRCP (UK) 1984; DCH RCP Lond. 1982. Prev: Sen. Regist. (Paediat.) Roy. Alexandra Hosp. Sick Childr. Brighton; Lect. (Neonat.) Bristol Matern. Hosp.; Sen. Regist. (Paediat.) King's Coll. Hosp. Lond.

WORSLEY, Alison Margaret 4 Seacombe Road, Sandbanks, Poole BH13 7RJ — MB BS 1975 Lond.; BSc Lond 1972; MRCP (UK) 1978; MRCPath 1984. (Middlx.) Cons. Haemat. Poole Gen. Hosp. Prev: Sen. Regist. (Haemat.) Hammersmith Hosp. Lond.; Leukaemia Research Fund Clin. Train. Fell. MRC Leukaemia Unit; Hammersmith Hosp. Lond., Fell. (Haemat.) Mt. Sinai Hosp. NY.

WORSLEY, Andrew Peter Diabetic Department, Lewisham Hospital, Lewisham High St., London SE13 6LH Tel: 020 8333 3000; Beechwood Lodge, Shire Lane, Orpington BR6 7EU — MD 1993 Lond.; MB BS 1979; MRCP (UK) 1984. Cons. Phys. Lewisham Hosp. Lond.; Hon. Sen. Lect. Guy's & St Thos. Lond. Socs: Brit. Diabetic Assn. Prev: Sen. Regist. (Gen., Metab. & Molec. Med.) Clin. Research Centre N.wick Pk. Hosp. Harrow; Sen. Clin. Research Fell.sh. (Diabetes) Middlx. Hosp. Lond.

WORSLEY, David Eric, Brigadier late RAMC Retd. 10 Old College Close, Beccles NR34 9LY Tel: 01502 718151 — MB ChB Bristol 1952; FFOM 1982, M 1981; FFCM 1979, M 1975. Socs: Soc. Occupat. Med.; BMA. Prev: Col. Commandant RAMC; Dir. Army Prevent. Med.; Cdr. HQ AMS (TA).

WORSLEY, Gillian Elizabeth Whitchurch Health Centre, Armada Road, Bristol BS14 0SU Tel: 01275 832285 Fax: 01275 540035 — MB ChB 1981 Bristol; MRCGP 1985; DRCOG 1983.

WORSLEY, Mark Henry 6 Melville Terrace, Stirling FK8 2ND Email: m_worsley@demon.co.uk — MB ChB 1982 Glas.; FFA RCS Eng. 1986. Cons. Anaesth. Stirling Roy. Infirm. Prev: Sen. Regist. (Anaesth.) Roy. Infirm. Edin.

WORSLEY, Richard (retired) 12 King Edward Avenue, Lytham St Annes FY8 1DP Tel: 01253 725050 — LMSSA 1947 Lond.; MRCGP 1961. Local Treas. Med. Off. Prev: Ho. Surg. St. Jas. Hosp. Leeds.

WORSLEY, Simon David Tel: 01493 414141 Fax: 01493 656253 — MB ChB 1976 Bristol; BSc (Hons.) (Cell. Path.) Bristol 1976; DRCOG 1985. Prev: GP. HM Forces VTS.; Sen. Med. Off., HQ Hereford Garrison.

WORSLEY-WINTERINGHAM, Rosemary Jeannette (retired) Glannant, Gwernogle, Carmarthen SA32 7RZ Tel: 01267 202390 Email: rjww@btinternet.com — MB BS 1967 Lond. Drug & Alcohol Abuse Counsellor Washoe Med. Centre Reno, USA.

WORSSAM, Anthony Ralph Holtby (retired) Yearnor Mill, Worthycombe, Porlock, Minehead TA24 8JL — MB BChir 1948 Camb.; FRCP Lond. 1977, M 1953; FRCPath 1970, M 1963. Prev: Sen. Regist. Path. St. Bart. Hosp.

WORSTMANN, Therese Queen's Hospital, Belvedere Road, Burton-on-Trent DE13 0RB Tel: 01283 566333 Fax: 01283 593014; 23 Beacon Road, Rolleston, Burton-on-Trent DE13 9EF Tel: 01283 812787 — MB BS 1977 Lond.; FRCS Ed. (Ophth.) 1983; MRCS Eng. LRCP Lond. 1977; FRCOphth 1989; DO RCS Eng. 1982. (St. Bart.) Cons. Ophth. Burton Hosps. Trust. Prev: Sen. Regist. (Ophth.) E. Anglian RHA; Regist. (Ophth.) Roy. Hallamsh. Hosp. Sheff.

WORSWICK, John Cowgill 108 St Mark's Road, Bush Hill Park, Enfield EN1 1BB — MRCS Eng. LRCP Lond. 1953; MA Camb. 1948.

WORT, Ian (retired) Wystra Del, Coverack, Helston TR12 6TH Tel: 01326 280501 — MB ChB 1954 Liverp.; DObst RCOG 1956. Prev: Research Regist. (Dermat.) Truro, Penzance, Redruth & Helston Gp. Hosps.

WORT, Margaret Elizabeth (retired) 9 Leonard Court, Edwardes Square, London W8 6NL Tel: 020 7603 9636 — MB BS 1949 Lond.; DObst RCOG 1953. Prev: Ho. Surg. Roy. Free Hosp. Lond.

WORT, Michael John Withybush General Hospital, Haverfordwest SA61 2PZ Tel: 01437 764545 Fax: 01437 773655 — BM BS 1977 Nottm.; BMedSci Nottm. 1975; FFA RCS Eng. 1983. Cons. Anaesth. & Pain Relief Withybush Gen. Hosp. HaverfordW.. Prev: Cons. (Anaesth.) RAF Hosp. Halton; Cons. (Anaesth.) RAF Hosp. Wegberg; Hon. Sen. Regist. & Hon. Regist. (Anaesth.) Frenchay Hosp. Bristol.

WORT, Rosalyn Louise Occupational Health Department, Withybush General Hospital, Fishguard Road, Haverfordwest Tel: 01437 773217 — BM BS 1977 Nottm.; BMedSci Nottm. 1975; MRCGP 1983; AFOM RCP Lond. 1995; DRCOG 1982; MFOM RCP Lond. 1998. (Nottingham university medical school) Cons.Occup.Phys. Withybush Gen. Hosp. HaverfordW. Pembrokesh. Socs: Soc. Occupat. Med.; Assn. Local Auth. Med. Advis.; Assn. Nat. Health Serv. Occupat. Phys - Sec. to Welsh Granp of Anhops.

WORT, Stephen John 107 King's Road, Higher Bedington, Wirral CH63 8LX — MB BS 1993 Lond.

WORTERS, Alastair Robin (retired) Linthill Farmhouse, Eyemouth TD14 5TG Tel: 01890 752045 — MB BS 1952 Lond.; MRCS Eng. LRCP Lond. 1952; FRCPsych. 1981, M 1971; DPM Eng. 1958. Prev: Cons. Psychiat. Manor Hosp. Epsom; Regist. Dept. Applied.

WORTERS, Jonathan Robin 69 Pickering Road, West Ayton, Scarborough YO13 9JE — MB BS 1978 Lond.; MRCP (UK) 1980; MRCGP 1989; DRCOG 1987. (Middlx.)

WORTH, Austen Jonathan Jacob 2 Orchard Close, Oxton, Southwell NG25 0SR — BM BCh 1997 Oxf.; BA Oxf. (Oxford) SHO (Paediat.) St. Geo.'s Hosp. Lond.; SHO (Neonatocogy) St Geo.'s Lond. Prev: Ho. Off. (Surg.) Cumbld. Infirm. Carlisle; Ho. Off. (Med.) John Radcliffe Hosp. Oxf.

WORTH, Christopher Thomas Calderdale & Kirklees HA, St. Luke's House, Blackfootmoor Road, Huddersfield HD4 5DR Tel: 01484 466024 Fax: 01484 466111; Lower Ellistone's Mill, Saddleworth Road, Greetland, Halifax HX4 8NF — BM BS 1983 Nottm.; BMedSci Nottm. 1981; MFPHM RCP (UK) 1991; MRCGP 1987; T(PHM) 1992; T(GP) 1991; FFPHM RCP (UK) 1997. (Nottingham) Dir. Pub. Health Calderdale & Kirklees HA; Vis. Prof. Univ. Huddersfield. Prev: Dir. (Pub. Health) W. Yorks. Health Auth.; Lect. (Pub. Health Med.) Univ. Nottm.; Hon. Sen. Regist. (Pub. Health Med.) Trent RHA.

WORTH, David Philip York District Hospital, Wigginton Road, York YO31 8HE; York Email: david.p.worth@excha.yhs-tr.northy.nhs.uk — MD 1987 Sheff.; MB ChB Sheff. 1975; FRCP Lond. 1994; MRCP (UK) 1978; DCH Eng. 1977. Cons. Phys. York Dist. Hosp. Prev: Sen. Regist. (Med.) Yorks. RHA.

WORTH, Jean Margaret Moston Lodge Childrens Centre, Countess of Chester Hospital, Liverpool Road, Chester CH2 1UL Tel: 01244 364801; 14 Orchard Croft, Guilden Sutton, Chester CH3 7SL — MB ChB 1972 Sheff.; MB ChB Sheffield. 1972. Assoc. Specialist (Community Paediat.) Countess of Chester Hosp. Socs: Assoc. Mem. Coll. Paediat. & Child Health. Prev: Trainee GP Hull VTS; Ho. Phys. N.. Gen. Hosp. Sheff.; Ho. Surg. Hull Roy. Infirm.

WORTH, Karen Vivien Radford Health Centre, 1 Ilkeston Road, Radford, Nottingham NG7 3GW; 54 Watcombe Circus, Sherwood, Nottingham NG5 2DT Tel: 0115 969 1830 Email: shalom@zetnet.co.uk — BM BS 1988 Nottm.; BMedSci Nottm. 1986; MRCGP 1993. Lect. Divison GP Nottm. Med. Sch.

WORTH, Paul Francis 53 Railwayside, Barnes, London SW13 0PN Tel: 020 8878 2458 Email: p.worth@ion.ucl.ac.uk — BM BCh 1992 Oxf.; MRCP (UK) 1995. (Oxf.) Hon. Clin. Asst. & Research Regist. Nat. Hosp. Neurol. & Neurosurg. Lond. Prev: Regist. (Gen. Med.) Epsom Gen. Hosp.; Regist. (Neurol.) Atkinson Morley's Hosp. Lond.

WORTH, Penelope Jane Thornfield House, Hodgson Lane, Upper Poppleton, York YO26 6DY — MB ChB 1979 Leeds.

WORTH, Mr Peter Herman Louis (retired) 31 Wimpole Street, London W1G 8GS Tel: 020 7935 3593 Fax: 020 7224 1957 Email: phlwotrh@line.onc.net — MB 1961 Camb.; BChir 1960; FRCS Eng. 1967. Cons. Urol. Surg. Univ. Coll. Lond. Hosp. Trust & King Edwd. VII Hosp.; Hon. Sen. Lect. Inst. Urol. Lond. Prev: Sen. Regist. St. Paul's Hosp. Lond.

WORTH, Richard Christopher Countess of Chester Hospital, Liverpool Road, Chester CH2 1UL Tel: 01244 366441 Fax: 01244 366455 — MB ChB 1971 Sheff.; MD Sheff. 1983; FRCP Lond. 1989; MRCP (UK) 1974; DObst RCOG 1973. Cons. Phys. Countess of Chester Hosp. NHS Trust. Socs: Fell. Roy. Soc. Med.; Brit. Diabetic Assn.; Soc. Endocrinol. Prev: Sen. Regist. (Med.) Sheff. HA; Research Fell. Roy. Vict. Infirm. Newc.; Regist. (Med.) Newc. HA.

WORTH, Mr Richard William 1A Gwendolen Avenue, Putney, London SW15 6EU — BM BCh 1975 Oxf.; MA. DPhil Oxf. 1973, BM BCh 1975; FRCS Eng. 1979; MRCOG 1981. Cons. (O & G) Epsom Dist. Gen. Hosp. Prev: Sen. Lect. (O & G) Char. Cross & W.m. Med. Sch. Lond.; Cons. (O & G) Qu. Mary's Univ. Hosp. Lond.; Sen. Regist. (O & G) Chelsea Hosp. Wom. & Qu. Charlotte's Hosp. Wom. Lond.

WORTHINGTON, Andrew Ralph (retired) Abbotswood, Sandy Lane, West Runton, Cromer NR27 9NB Tel: 01263 837545 — MB ChB 1952 Leeds; MFCM RCP (UK) 1972; DTM & H Eng. Lond. 1963. Prev: Brigadier late RAMC Retd.

WORTHINGTON, Professor Brian Stewart c/o Academic Radiology, University Hospital, Queens Medical Centre, Clifton Boulevard, Nottingham NG7 2UH; Cliff Cottage, Belper Road, Shirland, Alfreton DE55 6AG Tel: 01773 834096 — MB BS Lond. 1963; BSc (Hons. Physiol.) Lond. 1960; FRS (1998); MRCS Eng. LRCP Lond. 1963; FFR (Rohan Williams Medal) 1969; DMRD Eng. 1967; F.Med Sci 1998. (Guy's) Emerit. Prof. Diagn. Radiol. Univ. Nottm.; Examr. Roy. Coll. Radiol. & DMRD Univ. Liverp.; Hon. Cons. Neuroradiol. Univ. Hosp. NHS Trust. Socs: Hon. Mem. Radiol. Soc. Iceland & Finland; Brit. Inst. Radiol.; Soc. Magnetic Resonance in Med. (Gold Medal 1990) (Fell. 1997). Prev: Sen. Regist. (Diag. Radiol.) Lond. Hosp.; Ho. Phys. & Ho. Surg. Guy's Hosp.; Ho. Phys. Whittington Hosp. Lond.

WORTHINGTON, Cathryn Anne Avondale Surgery, 3-5 Avondale Road, Chesterfield S40 4TF Tel: 01246 232946 Fax: 01246 279803; 14 Southfield Avenue, Chesterfield S41 0LX — MB ChB 1990 Liverp.

WORTHINGTON, Edmund Guy Barker (retired) Langley House, Hutton Buscel, Scarborough YO13 9LN Tel: 01723 864512 — MRCS Eng. LRCP Lond. 1952; MRCGP 1960; DObst RCOG 1954. Prev: Cas. Off. Leeds Pub. Disp. & Hosp.

WORTHINGTON, Elspeth Frances 69 Ashbourne Road, Aigburth, Liverpool L17 9QQ Tel: 0151 726 0000 Email: eworthington@ukonline.co.uk — MB BChir 1991 Camb.; MA Camb. 1992, BA 1988; MRCP (UK) 1995. (Camb.) Specialist Regist. A&E Arrowe Pk. Hosp. Socs: Fell. Fac. A & E Med.; Med. Protec. Soc.; BMA. Prev: Specialist Regist. (A & E) Whiston Hosp.; Specialist Regist. (A & E) Alder Hey Childr.'s Hosp.; SHO (A & E) Roy. Liverp. Univ. Hosp.

WORTHINGTON, John Robert Maltby Moss Lane Surgery, Moss Lane, Madeley, Crewe CW3 9NQ Tel: 01782 750274 Fax: 01782 751835 — MB BS 1974 Lond.; BSc (Physiol.) Lond. 1971, MB BS 1974; DCH Eng. 1976. (Roy. Free)

WORTHINGTON, Jonathan Mark 15 Greenland Crescent, Larne BT40 1HE — MB BCh BAO 1995 Belf.

WORTHINGTON, Joy 34C Albyn Court, Tradespark, Nairn IV12 5PY — MB ChB 1995 Glas.

WORTHINGTON, Lisa Maria Flat 4, Princess Rise, London SE13 7PW — MB BS 1991 Lond.

WORTHINGTON, Pamela Ruth Ashtree Cottage, Wardlow, Tideswell, Buxton SK17 8RP — MB ChB 1992 Leeds.

WORTHINGTON, Ross Charles Health Centre, Bond St., Englefield Green, Egham TW20 0PF Tel: 01784 437671; 4 Chestnut Drive, Egham Hill, Egham TW20 0BJ — BM BCh 1979 Oxf.; MA Oxf. 1983, BM BCh 1979.

WORTHINGTON, Sidney The Surgery, The Street, Wonersh, Guildford GU5 0PE Tel: 01483 898123 Fax: 01483 893104; Mulberry Cottage, Wonersh, Guildford GU5 0PB Tel: 01483 892676 — MB BChir 1967 Camb.; MA Camb, 1967; DCH Eng. 1971; DObst RCOG 1969. (Guy's) Prev: Ho. Phys. (Gen. Med. & Infec. Dis.) Hither Green Hosp.; Ho. Surg. (Gen. Surg.) Kent & Sussex Hosp. Tunbridge Wells; Ho. Surg. (O & G) N. Middlx. Hosp.

WORTHINGTON, Mr Tim Rees 2 Rectory Close, Church Lane, Farndon, Chester CH3 6PS — MB ChB 1993 Birm.; FRCS 1997. Simpson Research Fell. Roy. Coll. of Surgs. Hammersmith Hosp.

WORTHLEY, Paul Burrswood, Groombridge, Tunbridge Wells TN3 9PY Tel: 01892 863637 — MB BS 1976 Lond.; Dip. Palliat. Med. Wales 1996; DCH RCP Lond. 1989. Resid. Phys. Burrswood Christian Centre for Healthcare & Min. Prev: Regist. (Paediat.) Adelaide Childr. Hosp.

WORTHY, Eric (retired) 28 Burnt Stones Drive, Sheffield S10 5TT — MB BChir 1963 Camb.; BMedSci Sheff. 1968; FRCPath 1987, M 1969. Prev: Cons. Chem. Path. Sheff. Childr. Hosp.

WORTHY, Jonathan Nigel 15 Queensberry Avenue, Hartlepool TS26 9NW — MB BS 1992 Newc. SHO (Paediat.) Dryburn Hosp. Durh. Prev: SHO (A & E & Surg.) Shotley Bridge Gen. Hosp. Consett & S. Cleveland Hosp. Middlesbrough; Hosp. Pract. (A & E, O & G & Anaesth.) Goulburn Valley BaseHosp. Shepparton Vict., Austral.

WORTHY, Sylvia Anne Radiology Dept, Royal Victoria Infirmary, Queen Victoria Road, Newcastle upon Tyne NE1 4LP Tel: 0191 232 5131 — MB BS 1986 Newc.; MRCP (UK) 1989; FRCR 1992; DMRD Liverp. 1991. Cons.Radiol.Roy.Vict.,InfirmNewc. Socs: RCR. Prev: Regist. (Radiol.) Merseyside & W. Midl. RHAs; SHO Rotat. (Gen. Med.) Durh.; Sen. Regist. Rotat. (Radiol.) N.. RHA.

WORTHY, Thomas Stanley Bransdale, 19 Creskeld Drive, Bramhope, Leeds LS16 9EJ Tel: 0113 267 2623 — MB BChir 1957 Camb.; PhD Camb. 1957; FFR 1962; DMRT Eng. 1960. (Camb. & Middlx)

WORTLEY, Pamela Mary Church View Medical Centre, Silksworth Terrace, Silksworth, Sunderland SR3 2AW Tel: 0191 521 1753 Fax: 0191 521 3884; 9 Thornhill Terrace, Sunderland SR2 7JL Tel: 0191 510 2456 — MB BS Newc. 1970; MFFP 1993; MRCGP (Distinc.) 1989. Trainer (Gen. Pract.) Sunderland; Chairm. Sunderland LMC; Mem. Sunderland S. PCG. Prev: Non Exec. Dir. Sunderland HA & Health Commiss.; SCMO Sunderland HA.

WORWOOD, Graham 17 Celyn Gr, Cardiff CF23 6SH — MB BCh 1997 Wales.

WOSORNU ABBAN, Dzifa The Alexandra Hospital, Woodrow Drive, Redditch B98 7UB Tel: 01527 503030 Fax: 01527 512000 Email: dzzifa.abban@alex-tr.winids.hns.uk; Email: dzifa@foxfields.freeserve.co.uk — MB ChB 1984 Glas.; MD Glas. 1995; MRCP (UK) 1987; FRCP (Lon) 2000; FRCP (Glas) 2000. (Glas.) Cons. Gen. Med. & Cardiol. Alexandra Hosp. Redditch. Socs: Collegiate Fell.. RCPS Glas.; BMA; Brit. Cardiac Soc. Prev: Sen. Regist. Vict. Infirm. Glas.; Clin. Research Fell. Univ. Birm.; Career Regist. (Cardiol.) Selly Oak Hosp.

WOSTENHOLM, David Kenneth The Annunciation Vicarage, 89 Washington St., Brighton BN2 2SR Tel: 01273 681341 Email: hanover@mistral.co.uk — MB ChB 1980 Ed.; BTh (Hons.) Soton. 1988. Parish Priest Ch. of the Annunciation Brighton. Prev: Curate St. Margts. Ch. Leytonstone, Lond.

WOTHERSPOON, Andrew Charles Department of Histopathology, Royal Marsden NHS Trust, Fulham Road, London SW3 6JJ Tel: 020 7352 7348 Fax: 020 7352 7348; 11 Rye View, High Wycombe HP13 6HL — MB BCh 1984 Wales. Cons. Histopath. Roy. Marsden NHS Trust Lond. Prev: Sen. Lect. (Histopath.) Roy. Postgrad. Med. Sch. Lond.; Lect. (Histopath.) Univ. Coll. Lond. Med. Sch.; Sir Jules Thorn Fell. (Histopath.) Univ. Coll. & Middlx. Sch. Med.

WOTHERSPOON, Fiona 15 Copley Dene, Bromley BR1 2PW; Marchmont, Rectory Drive, Alphington, Exeter EX2 8XJ Tel: 01392 431823 — BM 1994 Soton.; MRCP (UK) 1997. (Southampton University) Specialist Regist. (Diabetes & Endocrinol.Treuske Hosp truro Cornw.

WOTHERSPOON, James Macdonald Langdale, 16 Ayr Road, Whitecraigs, Glasgow G46 6RY Tel: 0141 638 1638 — LRCP LRCS 1945 Ed.; LRCP LRCS Ed. LRFPS Glas. 1945; MFHom 1949. (Anderson Coll. Glas.)

WOTHERSPOON, John 55 Buckingham Road, Maghull, Liverpool L31 7DN — MB ChB 1986 Liverp.

WOTHERSPOON, Mark Gavin Kingsclere Health Centre, Kingsclere, Newbury RG20 5UX Tel: 01635 296000 Fax: 01635 299282; Berthas Cottage, Hannington, Basingstoke RG26 5UA Tel:

WOTHERSPOON

01635 297867 — MB BS 1985 Lond.; Dip. Sports Med. Lond 1992.

WOTHERSPOON, Matthew 2 Longrigg, Wardley, Felling, Gateshead NE10 8QJ — LRCP LRCS 1949 Ed.; LRCP LRCS Ed., LRFPS Glas. 1949.

WOTHERSPOON, Rona Hunter 20 Bishopsmill Court, 208 Old Dumbarton Road, Yorkhill, Glasgow G3 8QB — MB ChB 1997 Glas.

WOTHERSPOON, William Campbell Northumbria Healthcare NHS Trust, Wansbeck General Hospital, Ashington NE63 9JJ Tel: 01670 521212 — MB ChB 1974 Aberd.; FRCR 1981; DMRD Aberd. 1978. Cons. (Radiol.) Wansbeck Gen. Hosp. Socs: Fell. Roy. Coll. Radiols.; Brit. Med. Ultrasound Soc. Prev: Sen. Regist. (Diag. Radiol.) Newc. AHA; Trainee Regist. (Diag. Radiol.) Aberd..

WOTTON, Linde Diana Goddards Green, Angley Road, Cranbrook TN17 3LR Tel: 01580 715507 — MB BChir 1979 Camb.; MRCPsych 1982.

WOTTON-MCTURK, Peter Howard 26 Raven Court, Hatfield AL10 8QN — MB ChB 1964 Ed.; DPM Eng. 1970. Cons. Child Psychiat. Warwick Health Dist.

WOUDA, Mirjam The Group Practice, Health Centre, Springfield Road, Stornoway HS1 2PS; 5A Scotland Street, Stornoway HS1 — Artsexamen 1993 Amsterdam.

WOULDS, Merla 9 St Faiths Ct, West Pde, Lincoln LN1 1QZ — MB ChB 1997 Sheff.

WOWKONOWICZ, Krystyna (retired) 79b Englewood Road, London SW12 9PB Tel: 020 8673 4674 — Med. Dipl. Warsaw 1945; DMRD Eng. 1949. Prev: Cons. Radiol. Qu. Mary's Hosp. Sidcup.

WOYKA, Winifred Jane Graham Harrow Health Care Centre, 84-88 Pinner Road, Harrow HA1 4HZ Tel: 020 8861 1221 Fax: 020 8427 4915 Email: rufus@harrow55.freeserve.co.uk; 52 Pebworth Road, Harrow HA1 3UD — MB BChir 1979 Camb.; MA Camb. 1980; MRCGP 1983. (Cambridge) Socs: BMA. Prev: Trainee GP Roy. Free Hosp. Lond. VTS; Ho. Phys. Addenbrooke's Hosp. Camb.; Ho. Surg. P'boro. Dist. Hosp.

WOZENCROFT, David Wilfred Edward Jenner Unit, Peterborough District Hospital, Thorpe Road, Peterborough PE3 6DA Tel: 01733 874696 Fax: 01733 875802 — MB BS Lond. 1971; MRCS Eng. LRCP Lond. 1971; MRCPsych 1978; DA Eng. 1975. (Westm.) Cons. Child & Adolesc. Psychiat. P'boro. Dist. Hosp.

WOZENCROFT, Enid Myra (retired) Croftwold, 42b West Common, Harpenden AL5 2JW Tel: 01580 4330 — MB BS 1954 Lond.; MRCS Eng. LRCP Lond. 1954; DObst RCOG 1955. Prev: Med. Off. Harpenden Family Plann. Clinic.

WOZNIAK, Mr Andrew Peter 40 Braeside, Beckenham BR3 1SU — MB BS 1976 Lond.; FRCS Ed. 1984; MRCS Eng. LRCP Lond. 1975. (Guy's)

WOZNIAK, Edward Richard St Mary's Hospital, Milton Road, Portsmouth PO3 6AD Tel: 023 92 286000 Fax: 023 92 866101 — MB BS 1974 Lond.; BSc Lond. 1971; FRCP Lond. 1993; MRCP (UK) 1978; FRCPCH 1997; DCH Eng. 1979. (Lond. Hosp.) Cons. Paediat. St. Mary's Hosp. Portsmouth. Socs: Examr. Roy. Coll. Paediat. & Child Health; Regional Adviser Roy. Coll. Paediat. and Child Health. Prev: Research Fell. (Child Health) Inst. Child Health; Hon. Sen. Regist. Hosp. Sick Childr. Gt. Ormond St. Lond.; Sen. Regist. (Child Health) Soton. Gen. Hosp.

WOZNIAK, Irena Anna 31 Elizabeth Road, Moseley, Birmingham B13 8QH — MB ChB 1978 Birm.

WOZNIAK, Janusz Tadeusz Kingsfield Medical Centre, 146 Alcester Road South, Kings Heath, Birmingham B14 6AA Tel: 0121 444 2054 Fax: 0121 443 5856; 7 Carpenter Road, Edgbaston, Birmingham B15 2JT — MB ChB 1971 Birm.; MRCP (U.K.) 1974.

WOZNIAK, Sarah Woodgate Valley Practice, 61 Stevens Avenue, Woodgate Valley, Birmingham B32 3SD Tel: 0121 427 6174 Fax: 0121 428 4146; 7 Carpenter Road, Edgbaston, Birmingham B15 2JT — MB ChB 1974 Birm.; DObst RCOG 1976.

WOZNIAK, Teresa Crown St Surgery, 1-23 Crown St, Alton W3 8SA Tel: 020 8992 1963; Tel: 01983 551239 Email: mrhiow@aol.com — MB BChir 1982 Camb.; MA Camb. 1982; MRCGP 1989; DRCOG 1985. p/t GP.

WRAGG, Andrew 61 The Chine, London N21 2EE Tel: 020 8360 6629 — MB BS 1994 Lond.; BSc (1st cl. Hons.) Pharmacol. Lond. 1991. Ho. Off. St. Bart. & Homerton Hosps. Lond. Prev: Ho. Off. Bath.

WRAGG, Christopher Michael 5 Dunstan Hill, Kirton in Lindsey, Gainsborough DN21 4DU — MB ChB 1976 Liverp.; DCH Eng. 1980; DTM & H 1980; DRCOG 1979.

WRAGG, Mr Peter George Doctors Surgery, Forge Close, Hayes, Bromley BR2 7LL Tel: 020 8462 1601 Fax: 020 8462 7410; 91 Hayes Road, Bromley BR2 9AE Tel: 020 8460 2933 — MRCP Eng. LRCP 1968 Lond.; BSc (Anat.) Lond. 1964, MB BS 1968; FRCS Eng. 1975. Socs: BMA; Roy. Coll. of Surg.s; Med. Defense Union. Prev: Surg. Hôpital Protestant Dabou, Ivory Coast; Sen. Regist. (A & E) Portsmouth HA.; Princip. GP, Burford, Oxf.shire.

WRAGG, Simon Derek 56 Chirgwin Road, Truro TR1 1TT — MB BS 1984 Lond.; FCAnaesth 1989.

WRAIGE, Elizabeth Anne 62 St James's Avenue, Beckenham BR3 4HG — MB BS 1990 Lond.

WRAIGHT, Edwin Philip (retired) 51 Glisson Road, Cambridge CB1 2HG Tel: 01223 52610 Email: philip.wraight@ntlworld.com — MB BChir Camb. 1966; PhD Camb. 1970, MA 1965; FRCR 1990; DMRT Eng. 1971. Prev: Cons. Nuclear Med. Addenbrooke's Hosp. Camb.

WRAIGHT, Sara Katherine Firs House Surgery, Station Road, Impington, Cambridge CB4 9NP Tel: 01223 234286 Fax: 01223 235931; 51 Glisson Road, Cambridge CB1 2HG Tel: 01223 526210 — MB BChir 1983 Camb.; MA Camb. 1969; MRCGP 1987; DRCOG 1985.

WRAIGHT, William John Stable House, Winkfield Road, Brookside, Ascot SL5 7LT Tel: 01344 882082 — MB BS 1973 Lond.; MRCS Eng. LRCP Lond. 1973; FFA RCS Eng. 1978; DObst RCOG 1975. Cons. Anaesth. E. Berks. Health Dist. Prev: Sen. Regist. (Anaesth.) Roy. Free Hosp. Lond.; Regist. (Anesth.) Birm. Health Dist. (T); Regist. (Anaesth.) Plymouth Gen. Hosp.

WRAITH, James Edmond Westfield, 257 Worsley Road, Swinton, Manchester M27 0YE Tel: 0161 281 2206 Email: ed.wraith@ntlworld.com; Willink Biochemical Genetics Unit, Royal Manchester Children's Hospital, Manchester M27 4HA Tel: 0161 727 2137 Email: ed@willink.demon.co.uk — MB ChB 1977 Sheff.; MRCP (UK) 1980; FRCPCH 1998. Dir. Willink Biochem. Genetics Unit Roy. Manch. Childr. Hosp. Prev: Cons. Paediat. Roy. Manch. Childr. Hosp.; Clin. Fell. Murdoch Inst. Roy. Childr. Hosp. Melbourne, Austral.

WRANGHAM, Melita Royal London Hospital, Whitechapel, London E1 1BB; 69 Sweetcroft Lane, Hillingdon, Uxbridge UB10 9LF — MB BS 1996 Lond.; BSc (Hons) Lond. 1994. (London Hospital Medical College) SHO (Paediat.) Roy. Lond. Hosp. Whitechapel. Prev: SHO (A & E) Univ. Coll. Hosp. Lond.

WRATE, Robert Milo Young People's Unit, Royal Edinburgh Hospital, Morningside Place, Edinburgh EH10 5HF Tel: 031 537 6380 Fax: 031 537 6102 — MB BS 1969 Newc.; FRCPsych 1987, M 1974; DPM Eng. 1972. Cons. Adolesc. Psychiat. Roy. Edin. Hosp.; Hon. Sen. Lect. Dept. Psychiat. Univ. Edin. Prev: Asst. Prof. Dept. Psychiat. McMaster Univ. Ont. Canada; Regist. (Psychol. Med.) Roy. Vict. Infirm. Newc.; Research Assoc. Dept. Psychol. Med. Univ. Newc.

WRATHALL, Gareth James Frenchay Hospital, Frenchay Pk Road, Bristol BS16 1LE Tel: 0117 970 1212 Email: gareth.lynn@cwcom.net; Tel: 0119 944 1404 Email: gareth.lynn@cw.net — MB BS 1988 Lond.; FRCA 1994. Cons. (Anaesth. & IC Med.) Frenchay Hosp. Hosp. Socs: BMA & Assn. Anaesth.; Intens. Care Soc. Prev: Sen. Regist. (Anaesth. & Intens. Care Med.) S. & W. RHA; Regist. & SHO (Anaesth.) S. Birm. HA; SHO (Med.) Swindon HA.

WRATHER, Susan Elizabeth Heathdale Cottage, Kingsley Road, Frodsham, Warrington WA6 6AR — MB ChB 1992 Manch.

WRATTEN, Juliette Claire Little Pixhall, Hawkhurst, Cranbrook TN18 4XT — MB ChB 1998 Ed.

WRAY, Mr Arnold Richard 13 Dunnwood Park, Prehen, Londonderry BT47 2NN — MB BCh BAO 1973 Belf.; FRCS Ed. (Orth.) 1982; FRCS Eng. 1978; FRCS Ed. 1977. Cons. (Orthop. Surg.) Altnagelvin Hosp. Lond.derry.

WRAY, Mr Christopher Charles Airedale General Hospital, Steeton, Keighley BD20 6TD Tel: 01535 651308; Westfield House, Marton Road, Gargrave, Skipton BD23 3NL Tel: 01756 749303 — MB ChB 1976 Leeds; FRCS Ed. 1981. Cons. Orthop. Surg. Airedale

Gen. Hosp. Socs: BOA; Brit. Soc. Surg. Hand. Prev: Sen. Regist. (Orthop.) Leicester Roy. Infirm.

WRAY, Professor David MacFarlane Glasgow Dental Hospital & School, 378 Sauchiehall St., Glasgow G2 3JZ Tel: 0141 2119700 Fax: 0141 211 9834 Email: d.wray@dental.gla.ac.uk; 2 Queensgate, 125 Dowan Hill street, Glasgow G12 9DN Tel: 0141 334 0021 — MB ChB 1976 Glas.; MD Glas. 1982; FDS RCS Ed. 1987; FDS RCPS Glas. 1979, BDS 1972; F. Med Sci 1998. (Glasgow) Prof. Oral Med. & Dean of Dent. Sch. Univ. Glas.; Hon. Cons. Gtr. Glas. HB. Prev: Sen. Lect. (Oral Med. & Oral Path.) Univ. Edin.

WRAY, Mr Denis Gage (retired) 11 Clifford Road, Poynton, Stockport SK12 1HY Tel: 01625 872537 Fax: 01625 872537 — MB ChB 1950 Ed.; MCh Orth. Liverp. 1961; FRCS Ed. 1960. Prev: Cons. Orthop. & Traum. Surg. Stockport AHA.

WRAY, Donald George Salisbury House Surgery, Lake St., Leighton Buzzard LU7 1RS Tel: 01525 373139 Fax: 01525 853006; The Craddocks, Heath Road, Leighton Buzzard LU7 3BW Tel: 01525 377153 — MB ChB Ed. 1959; DObst RCOG 1961. (Ed.) Socs: BMA. Prev: SHO (Paediat.) Shrodells Hosp. Watford.; Ho. Phys. E.. Gen. Hosp. Edin.; Resid. Med. Off. Watford Matern. Hosp.

WRAY, Gillian Mary Helen 35 Merrivale, London N14 4TE — MB BS 1988 Lond.

WRAY, Gordon 10 Penleonard Close, Exeter EX2 4NY Tel: 01392 59506 — MB ChB 1958 St. And.; MB ChB (Commend.) St. And. 1958; FFA RCS Eng. 1965. (St. And.) Cons. Anaesth. Roy. Devon & Exeter Hosp.

WRAY, Heather Ann 78 Westfield Drive, Loughborough LE11 3QL Tel: 01509 550133 — MB ChB 1974 Manch.; DObst RCOG 1976.

WRAY, Joan Mary Colvin 6 Grasmere Road, Alderley Edge SK9 7US Tel: 01625 582772 — MRCS Eng. LRCP Lond. 1932. (Roy. Free) Socs: Sec. Med. Wom.s Fell.ship.

WRAY, John Robert Edward 12 Hillside Road, Southport PR8 4QB — MB ChB 1985 Liverp.; Dip. IMC RCS Ed. 1989; DRCOG 1990; Cert. Av. Med. 1989.

WRAY, Kenneth Alexander Armitage (retired) 1 Southern Dene Close, Tilehurst, Reading RG31 6ND Tel: 0118 425748 — MB BChir 1945 Camb.; MRCP Lond. 1946; MRCS Eng. LRCP Lond. 1945. Indep. Lect. Health & Retirement. Prev: Ho. Phys. & Path. Asst. Lond. Hosp.

WRAY, Mary Isobel (retired) 2 Venetian House, 47 Warrington Crescent, London W9 1EJ Tel: 020 7286 2388 Fax: 020 7286 2388 — MB BS Lond. 1948; MRCS Eng. LRCP Lond. 1948; DMRD Eng. 1952. Prev: Cons. i/c Radiol. Barnet Gen. Hosp.

WRAY, Michael Bayes 14 Heightside Avenue, Newchurch, Rossendale BB4 9HA Tel: 01706 223151 — MB BCh BAO 1962 Dub.; BA, MB BCh BAO Dub. 1962; DObst RCOG 1964. (T.C. Dub.) Socs: BMA. Prev: SHO Mid-Ulster Hosp. Magherafelt & W. Som. Hosp. Minehead; Ho. Off. Roy. City Dub. Hosp.

WRAY, Pamela Mary (retired) 30 Constable Road, Ipswich IP4 2UW Tel: 01473 258071 — MB ChB 1946 Sheff.; MD Sheff. 1959; MRCS Eng. LRCP Lond. 1946; FRCOG 1982, M 1954, DObst 1948. Prev: Venereol. Ipswich & E. Suff. Hosp.

WRAY, Richard Conquest Hospital, The Ridge, St Leonards-on-Sea TN37 7RD Tel: 01424 755255; 8 The Dene, Chowns Hill, Hastings TN35 4PD Tel: 01424 752021 — MB ChB Leeds 1967; FRCP Lond. 1988; MRCP (UK) 1970. Cons. Phys. (Cardiol.) Hastings & Rother NHS Trust & Hon. Cons. Cardiol. King's Coll. Hosp. Lond. Socs: Brit. Cardiac. Soc.; Brit. Assn. Med. Managers. Prev: Sen. Regist. (Cardiol.) Leeds Gen. Infirm.; MRC Jun. Research Fell. & Hon. Regist. & Ho. Phys. Hammersmith Hosp.

WRAY, Robert Harold Mount Baker, Moneymore, Magherafelt BT45 7TX — MB BCh BAO 1981 Belf.; MRCGP 1985; MICGP 1985; DObst RCPI 1985; DRCOG 1984. GP Cookstown.

WRAY, Ruth Mary 25 Lyme Regis Road, Banstead SM7 2EY Tel: 01737 356814 — MB ChB 1956 Liverp.; MRCPath 1976. Med. Off. Banstead FPA Clinic Surrey. Prev: Assoc. Specialist (Haemat.) St. Helier Hosp. NHS Trust Carshalton; Regist. (Path.) St. Helens & Croydon Hosp. Gps; SHO (Surg. & Orthop.) Mossley Hill Hosp. Liverp.

***WRAY, Sarah Lesley** Cutlers Hill House, Higher Greenway Lane, Sidmouth EX10 0LY; 142 RussellCt., Woburn Place, London WC1H 0LP Tel: 020 7837 1870 — MB BS 1998 Lond.; MB BS Lond 1998.

WRAY, Stephen Queens Road Medical Practice, St Peter Port, Guernsey GY1 1RH; Vieux Port, Le Rocher Road, St. Martins, Guernsey GY4 6EL — MB ChB 1984 Leic.; MRCGP 1989; DCH RCP Lond. 1988. Prev: Med. Off. Popondetta, Papua New Guinea; Trainee GP Aberystwyth VTS.

WREFORD, Jonathan Moore Health Centre, Moore Health Centre, Moore Road, Bourton on the Water, Cheltenham GL54 2AZ Tel: 01451 829242 Fax: 01451 820532; 3 The Green, Northleach, Cheltenham GL54 3EX Tel: 01451 860200 Email: wreford@globalnet.co.uk — MB BS 1987 Lond.; DRCOG 1992. (St. Bart.)

WREGLESWORTH, Janet Kay Grove House, St. Paul's Health Centre, High St., Runcorn WA7 1AB Tel: 01928 566561; 2 Hunts Lane, Grappenhall, Warrington WA4 2DT Tel: 01925 266094 — MB ChB 1988 Liverp.; Cert. Family Plann. JCC 1994; T(GP) 1993. Prev: Ho. Off. (Gen. Med. & Gen. Surg.) Clatterbridge Hosp. Merseyside.

WREN, Alison Margaret 73 Heaton Street, Prestwich, Manchester M25 1HH — MB BS 1993 Newc.

WREN, Christopher Department of Paediatric Cardiology, Freeman Hospital, Newcastle upon Tyne NE7 7DN Tel: 0191 223 1082 Fax: 0191 213 2167 Email: christopher.wren@tfh.nuth.northy.nhs.uk — MB ChB 1975 Birm.; MRCP (UK) 1978. Cons. Paediat. Cardiol., Freeman Hosp & GOSH.

WREN, Damian Richard Atkinson Morleys Hospital, Copse Hill, Wimbledon, London SW20 0NE Tel: 020 8946 7711; Vynes Cottage, The Green, Pirbright, Woking GU24 0JE — BM BCh 1979 Oxf.; BA Oxf. 1976, DM 1988, BM BCh 1979; FRCP 1999; MRCP 1982. Cons. Neurol. Atkinson Morleys Hosp. & Frimley Pk. Hosp. Prev: Sen. Regist. Nat. Hosp. Neurol. & Neurosurg. Qu. Sq. & Kings Coll. Hosp. Lond.

WREN, Esmé Maria 21 Amber Court, Holland Road, Hove BN3 1LU Tel: 01273 771133 — MB ChB Liverp. 1945; MD Liverp. 1953; FRCP Lond. 1972, M 1949; DObst RCOG 1947. (Liverp.) Mem. Brighton & Hove Med. Clinic. Socs: BMA. Prev: Cons. Phys. Hove Gen. Hosp., Brighton Gen. Hosp., Bevendean Hosp. Brighton & Lady Chichester Hosp. Hove; Regist. (Med.) Liverp. United Hosps. & Nat. Heart Hosp. Lond.; Research Fell. Med. Liverp. Univ.

WREN, Margaret Monksgate, Hardacre Lane, Whoittle-le-Woods, Chorley PR6 7PQ — MB BS 1945 Lond.; DCH Univ. Lond. 1947. (Roy. Free) Asst. Sch. Med. Off. Lancs. CC (No. 4 Area). Prev: Med. Regist. Sefton Gen. Hosp. Liverp.

WREN, Marie Elizabeth Lister Fertility Unit, Lister Hospital, Chelsea Bridge Road, London SW1W 8RH — MB BS 1980 Lond.; MRCOG 1985. Fertil. Specialist Lister Fertil. Unit Lister Hosp. Lond.

WREN, Mary Catherine Gleadless Medical Centre, 636 Gleadless Road, Sheffield S14 1PQ — MB ChB 1987 Sheff. Prev: Trainee GP Sheff. VTS.

WREN, Maurice William Godfrey, RD 43 Links Lane, Rowlands Castle PO9 6AE — MRCS Eng. LRCP Lond. 1960; MB ChB Liverp. 1960, DMRD 1964; FRCR 1975; FFR 1967. Cons. Radiol. Portsmouth & S.E. Hants. Health Dist.

WREN, Peter John James, VRD, OBE, KStJ 8 Wardle Court, Whittle Hall Farm, Whittle-le-Woods, Chorley PR6 7DQ; 8 Wardle Court, Whittle Hall Farm, Whittle-Le-Woods, Chorley PR6 7DQ — MD 1967 Liverp.; FRCGP 1971. (Liverp.) DL; JP.; Med. Off. Eaves La. Geriatr. Hosp. Chorley; Responsible Med. Off. Lisieux Hall Ment. Nurs. Home; Co. Commr. Duke of Lancaster Dist. St. John Ambul. Brig. Socs: MIBiol; Genetical Soc.; C.Biol. Prev: Surg. Lt.-Cdr. RNR; Ho. Phys. Sefton Gen. Hosp. Liverp.; Nuffield Research Asst. Univ. Liverp. Med. Sch.

WREN, Siobhan Mairead Elizabeth Alencon, 43 Links Lane, Rowlands Castle PO9 6AE — MB BS 1996 Lond.

WRENCH, Ian James Royal Hallamshire Hospital, Sheffield S10 Tel: 0114 2711 900 — MB ChB 1987 Sheff.; PhD Sheff. 1987; BMedSci Sheff. 1983; FRCA 1994. Cons. Roy. Hallamsh. Hosp. Sheff. Socs: BMA & Med. Defence Union; FRCA Anaesth. Prev: Sen. Regist. Sheff.; Regist. (Anaesth.) Nottm.; SHO (Med.) York Dist. Hosp.

WRENCH, James Ross Edwin Hay on Wye Surgery, Forest Road NP8 1ST Tel: 01497 822100; 72 Parkland Drive, Oadby, Leicester LE2 4DG Tel: 01873 812124 Email: gmatharu66@tiscali.co.uk — MB BS 1991 Lond.; MRCGP 1999 U.K; BSc (Immunol.) Lond. 1988; MRCP (UK) 1996; Dip Child Care Roy Coll. Child Health + Paed

WRENCH

1999. (Univ. Lond. & Char. Cross & Westm. Hosp.) GP Princip. Hay on Wye & Talgorth. Socs: Scott. Heart and Arterial Dis. Risk Protec. Prev: Resid. Regist. (Med. & ITU) Som. Hosp. Greenpoint, Cape Town, S. Afr.; Cardiac Fell. Papworth Hosp. Camb.; SHO (Med.) Addenbrooke's Hosp. Camb.

WRENCH, John Gibson NHS Highland, Assynt House, Beechwood Park, Inverness IV2 3HG; 42 Castlehill Gardens, Inverness IV2 5DL — MB ChB 1970 Ed.; FRCP (Glas) 2001; MSc (Community Med.) Ed. 1985, BSc (Med. Sci.) 1967; MRCP (UK) 1973; FFPHM RCP (UK) 1996, M 1988; MRCGP 1976; DObst RCOG 1975; FRCP (Ed) 1997. (Edinburgh) Director of Pub. Health & Health Policy, NHS Highland, Inverness; Hon. Sen. Lect. (Pub. Health Med.) Univ. Edin.; Hon. Sen. Lect. (Pub. Health) Univ. of Aberd. Socs: Convenor Scott. Affairs Comm.; Fac. Pub. Health Med. Prev: Cons. Pub. Health Med. Forth Valley HB; Hon. Clin. Tutor (Med.) Univ. Edin.; GP Livingston.

WRENCH, Rosanne 24 Main Street, Hartford, Huntingdon PE29 1XU — MB BChir 1981 Camb.; PhD Aston Univ. 1973, BSc 1970.

WRENN, Paul Anthony Michael The Ashes, Tamworth Road, Over Whitacre, Coleshill, Birmingham B46 2PG — MB ChB 1978 Birm.

WRESSELL, Susan Elizabeth Newcastle City Health Trust, Fleming Nuffield Unit, Burdon Terrace, Newcastle upon Tyne NE2 3AE Tel: 0191 219 6429; 44 St. Georges Terrace, Jesmond, Newcastle upon Tyne NE2 2SY — MB BS 1983 Newc.; MRCPsych 1987. Cons. Child & Adolesc. Psychiat. Fleming Nuffield Unit Newc. u. Tyne; Hon. Lect. (Child Health) Newc.

WRIDE, Jonathan Peter Home Farm, Oxton, Kenton, Exeter EX6 8EX — MB BCh 1987 Wales; BSc (Hons) Wales 1982; MRCGP 1992. SCMO Addic.s Serv. Community Trust Exeter. Prev: Trainee GP Torbay VTS; Clin. Med. Off. Community Ment. Health Team Paignton.

WRIGGLESWORTH, Peter Bennet (retired) 186 Warbeck Hill Road, Blackpool Tel: 01253 51611 — MB ChB 1958 Manch.; DCH Eng. 1963; DObst RCOG 1964. Prev: Capt. RAMC (Nat. Serv.) Hong Kong.

WRIGHT, Alan Charlton (retired) 11 Malting Court, Brewery Street, Stratford-upon-Avon CV37 0TJ Tel: 01789 263879 — MB ChB 1950 Ed.; DIH Soc. Apoth. Lond. 1964. Prev: GP Worksop.

WRIGHT, Alan Duncan George Anaesthetic Department, Law Hospital, Carluke ML8 5ER Tel: 01698 361100; 466 Lanark Road W., Balerno, Edinburgh EH14 5AE Tel: 0131 449 4500 — MB ChB 1973 Ed.; FFA RCS Eng. 1979. (Edinburgh) Cons. Anaesth. Law Hosp. Carluke.

WRIGHT, Alan Finlay 5 Lynedoch Place, Edinburgh EH3 7PX — MB ChB 1971 St. And.; MRCPsych 1980.

WRIGHT, Alan John Hudshaw House, Hexham NE46 1HZ — MB BS 1975 Lond.; MRCP (UK) 1979; MRCS Eng. LRCP Lond. 1975. Cons. Phys. Gen. Hosp. Hexham. Socs: Assn. Phys. (N.. Br.) & Brit. Geriat. Soc. Prev: Sen. Regist. (Gen. & Geriat. Med.) Newc. HA.

WRIGHT, Alan John Benefits Agency, Arden House, Gosforth, Newcastle upon Tyne NE3 3BP Tel: 0191 223 3064; 88 Stoneybeck, Bishop Middleham, Ferryhill DL17 9BN Tel: 01740 651319 — MB BS 1976 Newc.; MRCGP 1980. Med. Adviser NE Benefits Agency. Prev: Med. Servs. Manager NE Benefits Agency; Med. Off. Benefits Agency DSS Newc. u. Tyne; GP Ferry Hill Chilton.

WRIGHT, Alan Vincent 36 Queen Street, Wairoa, New Zealand; c/o 33 Brinkinfield Road, Chalgrove, Oxford OX44 7QX — MB BS 1983 Lond.; MRCGP Lond. 1987; DCH RCP Lond. 1985. Prev: GP Nottm.; Med. Off. St. John's Hosp. Mzuzu, Malawi.

WRIGHT, Alasdair Ross Greasby Health Centre, Greasby Road, Greasby, Wirral CH49 3AT Tel: 0151 678 3000 Fax: 0151 604 1813 — MB ChB 1994 Manch.; BSc (Hons.) Phys. & Sports Sci. Glas. 1989; Dip. Sports Med. RCS Ed. 1997; DCH RCP Lond. 1998; DRCOG 1998; DFFP 1998; MRCGP 1999. G.P Pricipal, Greasby Health Centre, Greasby Rd, Greasby, Wirral. Socs: BMA. Prev: GP/Regist. Guildford; G.P Princip., Linden Hall Surg., Newport, Shrops.

WRIGHT, Alexander David Diabetics Centre, University Hospital Selly Oak, Raddlebarn Road B29 6JD Email: a.wright@bmres.org.uk; 72 Fitzroy Avenue, Harborne, Birmingham B17 8RQ Tel: 0121 427 7406 Email: a.wright@bmres.org.uk — MB BChir 1962 Camb.; MRCS Eng. LRCP Lond. 1961. p/t Hon.cons phys, Univ hosp. Birmg. Prev: Sen. Lect. (Med.) Univ. Birm.; Cons phys.walsall hosp.trust.

WRIGHT, Alexander Finlay, MBE The British Journal of General Practice, 14 Princes Gate, Hyde Park, London SW7 1PU Tel: 020 7581 3232 Fax: 020 7584 6716 Email: journal@rcgp.org.uk; 5 Alburne Crescent, Glenrothes KY7 5RE Tel: 01592 753139 Fax: 01592 753139 Email: gx77@dial.pipex.com — MB ChB 1958 Glas.; MD Glas. 1981; LRCP LRCS Ed. LRFPS Glas. 1957; FRCGP 1985; DObst RCOG 1960. Edr. Brit. Jl. Gen. Pract. Prev: Chairm. Clin. & Research Div. RCGP Lond.

WRIGHT, Alexander Justin 210 Welford Road, Leicester LE2 6BD — MB ChB 1995 Leic.

WRIGHT, Alison Lesley Flat C, 232 Otley Road, Leeds LS16 5AB — MB ChB 1990 Leeds.

WRIGHT, Alistair Kenneth John Roxburgh Street Surgery, 10 Roxburgh Street, Galashiels TD1 1PF Tel: 01896 752557 Fax: 01896 755374 — MB ChB 1981 Ed.

WRIGHT, Alwyn Peter (retired) 7 Grey Towers Drive, Nunthorpe, Middlesbrough TS7 0LS — MB BS 1952 Lond.; FFOM RCP Lond. 1983, M 1979; DObst RCOG 1954; DIH Soc. Apoth. Lond. 1959. Prev: Cons. Occupat. Phys.

WRIGHT, Mr Andrew Accident & Emergency Department, Doncaster Royal Infirmary, Doncaster DN2 5LT Tel: 01302 366666; 17 Poppyfields Way, Branton, Doncaster DN3 3UA — MB ChB 1974 Baghdad; FRCS Ed. 1986; LMSSA Lond. 1986. Cons. A & E Med. Doncaster Roy. Infirm. Socs: Brit. Assn. Accid. & Emerg. Med.; BMA; Med. Protec. Soc.

WRIGHT, Andrew David Priory Fields Surgery, Nursery Road, Huntingdon PE29 3RL Tel: 01480 52361 Fax: 01480 434640 — MB BS 1993 Lond.; MA Cantab. 1994; MRCGP 1998; DCH 1997; DRCOG 1998; DFFP 1997; DGM 1996. (University College and Middlesex School of Medicine)

WRIGHT, Andrew Hugh Ravenswood Doctors Surgery, Thomson Avenue, Johnstone PA5 8SU Tel: 01505 331979 Fax: 01505 323444 — MB ChB 1984 Glas.; MRCGP 1988; DRCOG 1987. Prev: Trainee GP Paisley VTS; Ho. Surg. Hairmyres Hosp. E. Kilbride Glas.; Ho. Phys. Roy. Alexandra Infirm. Paisley.

WRIGHT, Andrew John Ladybridge Surgery, 10 Broadgate, Ladybridge, Bolton BL3 4PZ Tel: 01204 653267 Fax: 01204 665350; 1 The Hoskers, West Houghton, Bolton BL5 2DW — MB ChB 1983 Sheff.; MRCGP 1989; DCH RCP Lond. 1990; DRCOG 1986.

WRIGHT, Andrew John Hampton Hill Medical Centre, 23 Wellington Road, Hampton TW12 1JP Tel: 020 8977 0043 Fax: 020 8977 8691 — MB ChB 1976 Bristol; MRCGP 1981; DCH Eng. 1980. (Bristol) Vice-Chairm. Twickenham/Teddington/Hampton PCG. Socs: Med. Ass. Soc. Prev: IT Dir. Kingston & Richmond Multifund; Cons. NHS Centre for Clin. Coding Middlx.; Tainee GP Kettering VTS.

WRIGHT, Andrew Leslie Yeadon Health Centre, 17 South View Road, Yeadon, Leeds LS19 7PS Tel: 0113 295 4040 Fax: 0113 295 4044 — MB ChB 1981 Leeds; BSc (Hons.) Physiol. Leeds 1978; DRCOG 1987. GP Leeds.

WRIGHT, Andrew Leslie St. Lukes Hospital, Little Horton Lane, Bradford BD5 0NA Tel: 01274 365547 Fax: 01274 365529 — MB ChB 1981 Sheff.; BMedSci (Hons.) Sheff. 1979; FRCP Lond. 1995; MRCP (UK) 1984; MRCS Eng. LRCP Lond. 1981. Cons. Dermat. Bradford Roy. Infirm. & Airedale Hosp. Steeton. Prev: Sen. Regist. (Dermat.) Rupert Hallam Dept. Dermat. Sheff. HA; Hon. Clin. Tutor Univ. Sheff.; Regist. (Dermat.) Edin. Roy. Infirm.

WRIGHT, Andrew Martin The Surgery, 34 Teme Street, Tenbury Wells WR15 8AA Tel: 01584 810343 Fax: 01584 819734 — MB 1973 Camb.; BChir 1972; MRCP (UK) 1977; DRCOG 1978.

WRIGHT, Andrew Ronald Department of Radiology, St Mary's Hospital, Praed St., London W2 1NY Tel: 020 7886 6363 Fax: 020 7886 6363 — MB BS 1981 Lond.; MA Oxf. 1976; MRCP (UK) 1985; FRCR 1989; T(R) (CR) 1991. (University College Hospital London) Prev: Cons. Radiol./Sen. Lect. W.ern Gen. Hosp. Edin.

WRIGHT, Andrew Timothy Wright and Partners, Heald Green Medical Centre, Finney Lane, Heald Green, Cheadle SK8 3JD Tel: 0161 436 8384 Fax: 0161 493 9268 — MB ChB 1985 Manch.; BSc (Med. Sci.) St. And. 1982; AFOM 1997; MRCGP 1990. (Manch.) Socs: Brit. Med. Acupunct. Soc.; Soc. Occupat. Med. Prev: Princip. GP; Trainee GP Stockport VTS; SHO (O & G) Tameside Gen. Hosp.

WRIGHT

WRIGHT, Ann Compton Crosburn House, Main Road, Long Bennington, Newark NG23 5DJ — MB BS 1962 Lond.; MRCS Eng. LRCP Lond. 1962; DObst RCOG 1964. (Roy. Free)

WRIGHT, Ann Margaret 8 Croft Gardens, Holywood BT18 0PD — MB BS 1986 Lond.

WRIGHT, Ann Penelope (retired) The Moor, Westfield, Hastings TN35 4QR Tel: 01424 754913 — MB BS 1956 Lond. Prev: Childr. Ho. Off. Radcliffe Infirm. Oxf.

WRIGHT, Anna Jane Highfield Health Centre, 2 Proctor Street, off Tong Street, Bradford BD4 9QA Tel: 01274 227700 Fax: 01274 227900 — MB ChB 1980 Leeds; BSc (Hons.) Leeds 1977; MRCGP 1984; DCH RCP Lond. 1984; DRCOG 1982. (Leeds)

WRIGHT, Anthony Quarry Ground Surgery, Broadway, Edington, Bridgwater TA7 9JB Tel: 01278 722077 Fax: 01278 722352 — BM 1978 Soton.; FRCGP 1998; MRCP (UK) 1982; MRCGP 1986; DRCOG 1985.

WRIGHT, Anthony Health & Safety Executive, Kiln House, Pottergate, Norwich NR2 1DA Tel: 01603 615711 Fax: 01603 761436 Email: tony.wright@hse.gov.uk; Cantley House, Cantley Lane, Cringleford, Norwich NR4 6TF Tel: 01603 452041 — MB BChir 1964 Camb.; MA, MB Camb. 1964, BChir 1963; MFOM RCP Lond. 1989; DIH 1981; DObst RCOG 1966; FFOM 1999. (Camb. & St. Bart.) Sen. Med. Insp. Health & Safety Exec. Norwich. Socs: Norwich M-C Soc. & Soc. Occupat. Med. Prev: SHO (O & G) St. Mary's Hosp. Kettering; Ho. Surg. & Ho. Phys. S.end Gen. Hosp.; GP Norwich.

WRIGHT, Professor Anthony Institute of Laryngology & Otology, 330 Grays Inn Road, London WC1X 8EE Tel: 020 7915 1308 Fax: 020 7837 9279 Email: anthony.wright@ucl.ac.uk; 4 Grange Road, Highgate, London N6 4AP Tel: 020 8340 5593 — MRCS Eng. LRCP Lond. 1974; DM Oxf. 1986, BM BCh 1974; LLM Wales 1995; FRCS Eng. 1995; FRCS Ed. 1979. Prof. Otorhinolaryng. & Dir. Inst. Laryngol. & Otol. Univ. Coll. Lond.; Hon. Cons. Otol. Roy. Nat. Throat, Nose & Ear Hosp. Lond. Prev: Cons. Otol. Roy. Free Hosp. Lond.

WRIGHT, Anthony Thomas Stanley Hathaway Surgery, 32 New Road, Chippenham SN15 1HR Tel: 01249 447766 Fax: 01249 443948; The Stable House, Rowden Lane, Chippenham SN15 2NN Tel: 01249 447994 Email: jan.tony@btinternet.com — MB ChB 1979 Sheff.; MRCGP 1987; DA Eng. 1983; DRCOG 1982; DCH RCP Eng. 1982. Clin. Med. Off. Chippenham Community Hosp.

WRIGHT, Antony Marcus Bourne Galletly Practice Team, 40 North Road, Bourne PE10 9BT Tel: 01778 562200 Fax: 01778 562207; 34 Grampian Way, Grantham NG31 8FY Tel: 01476 564255 — MB BS 1992 Newc.; MRCGP 1997; DFFP 1997; BMedSc. Newc. (Newc.)

WRIGHT, Arthur Edwin, TD (retired) The Old Smithy, Westboat, Warden, Hexham NE46 3SB Tel: 01434 605847 — MB BS 1948 Durh.; MD Durh. 1957; FRCPath 1973, M 1964; Dip. Bact. Lond 1958; DPH Durh. 1954. Hon. Cons. Newc. HA (T); Hon. Lect. (Microbiol.) Univ. Newc. Prev: Dir. Pub. Health Laborat. Newc.

WRIGHT, Barbara Yvonne The Beeches, 6 Westbury Gardens, Higher Odcombe, Yeovil BA22 8UR — MB BS 1971 Lond.; MRCS Eng. LRCP Lond. 1971; DA Eng. 1978; DObst RCOG 1974.

WRIGHT, Barrie James Pettigrew (retired) 31 High Street, Dorchester-on-Thames, Wallingford OX10 7HN Tel: 01865 340029 — MRCS Eng. LRCP Lond. 1958; LMSSA Lond. 1956. Prev: Cas. Off. & Ho. Phys. & Ho. Surg. Harold Wood Hosp.

WRIGHT, Benjamin Accident & Emergency Department, Westminster Hospital, Dean Ryle St., London SW1P 2AP — MB BS 1991 Lond.

WRIGHT, Brian Eric Morden (retired) The Hermitage, Metheringham, Lincoln LN4 3HA Tel: 01526 20569 — MRCS Eng. LRCP Lond. 1957. Prev: Ho. Surg. Vict. Hosp. Swindon.

WRIGHT, Brian John (retired) 13A Ashburton Road, Gosport PO12 2LH Tel: 01705 580106 Email: bjwright@freenet.co.uk — MB BS Lond. 1951; FRCGP 1983, M 1968; DObst RCOG 1958. Prev: Ho. Phys. (Gen. Med. & Neurol.) & Ho. Surg. St. Geo. Hosp.

WRIGHT, Bryan Keith 17 Stanley Grove, Ruabon, Wrexham LL14 6AH — MB ChB 1991 Birm.; ChB Birm. 1991.

WRIGHT, Camilla Jane Evelyn 26 Everington Street, London W6 8DU — MB ChB 1994 Leeds.

WRIGHT, Carl Houghton Plas Gwyn, Gannock Park, Deganwy, Conwy LL31 9PZ — MB ChB 1970 Liverp.; FRCR 1976; DMRD Liverp. 1973. Cons. Radiol. Glan Clwyd Hosp. Bodelwyddan. Socs: BMA & Brit. Inst. Radiol. Prev: Sen. Research Fell. X-Ray Dept. St. Thos. Hosp. Lond.; Sen. Fell. (Diag. Radiol.) Univ. Kansas Med. Centre.

WRIGHT, Carol Jane 143 Portland Road, Bournemouth BH9 1NG — MB BS 1988 Lond.; MRCP (UK) 1993.

WRIGHT, Caroline Isobel (retired) Flat 3, 9 Pembroke Avenue, Hove BN3 5DA — MD 1927 Lond.; MB BS 1923; MRCS Eng. LRCP Lond. 1922, DPH 1924. Prev: Med. Insp. Childr. Dept. Home Office.

WRIGHT, Caroline Jane 55 Church Road, Wickham Bishop's, Witham CM8 3JZ — BChir 1993 Camb.

WRIGHT, Caroline Margaret 23 Dart Close, Upminster RM14 1PR Tel: 017082 26268 — MB BS 1986 Lond. PHO (Gen. Surg.) P.ss Alexandra Hosp. Brisbane, Austral. Prev: PHO (Surg.) Rockhampton Base Hosp., Austral.; PHO (Urol. & Gen. Surg.) Nambar Gen. & Gold Coast Hosps., Austral.; SHO (Transpl. & Gen. Surg.) Qu. Eliz. II Hosp. Birm.

WRIGHT, Catherine Hutton (retired) 5 Pingle Avenue, Millhouses, Sheffield S7 2LP — MB ChB 1933 Glas.; DPH 1938. Prev: Sen. Asst. Med. Off. Matern. & Child Welf. Sheff.

WRIGHT, Catherine Jane Norwich Primary Care Trust, Little Plumstead Hospital, Norwich NR13 5EW Tel: 01603 711227 Fax: 01603 711202 Email: catherine.wright@norwich-pct.nhs.uk — BM 1987 Soton.; Cert. MHS 1999; MRCPsych 1992. Cons. (Psychiat.) Learning Disabilities.

WRIGHT, Charles Edward Quercy, Broadway, Wickham Skeith, Eye IP23 8LT Email: charles.wright2@virgin.net — MB BS 1992 Lond.; BSc Lond. 1989, MB BS 1992; MRCGP 1998. (London Hosp) Socs: BMA & MDU; RCGP.

WRIGHT, Charles Mark Vernon Portslade Health Centre, Church Road, Portslade, Brighton BN41 1LX Tel: 01273 422525/418445 Fax: 01273 413510 — MB BS 1974 London; MRCS Eng LRCP Lond 1974. (London) GP Brighton.

WRIGHT, Charles Richard Longshaw House, Billinge, Wigan WN5 7JA Tel: 01744 892417 — MB ChB 1933 Liverp.; MRCS Eng. LRCP Lond. 1933. (Liverp.) Prev: Ho. Surg. Stanley Hosp. Liverp.; Res. Med. Off. Mill Rd. Infirm. Liverp.; Maj. RAMC.

WRIGHT, Charles Stewart Weatherley 37 Corfton Road, Ealing, London W5 2HR Tel: 020 7935 2477 — MB BChir 1969 Camb.; MA, MB Camb. 1969, BChir 1968; MRCS Eng. LRCP Lond. 1968; FRCOG 1987, M 1973. (Camb. & St. Mary's) Cons. (O & G) Hillingdon Hosp. Uxbridge; Hon. Sec. Spencer Wells Soc. Socs: Fell. Roy. Soc. Med. (Hon. Sec. Sect. Obst. & Gyn.). Prev: Sen. Regist. St. Mary's Hosp. Lond.; Res. Surg. Off. Hosp. Wom. Soho Sq. Lond.; Res. Med. Off. Qu. Charlottes Matern. Hosp. Lond.

WRIGHT, Charles William The Medical Centre, 2 Francis Street, Doncaster DN1 1JS Tel: 01302 349431 Fax: 01302 364558 Email: dr.wright"gp-c86025.nhs.uk; Estate Cottage, 6 Mosham Road, Blaxton, Doncaster DN9 3AZ Tel: 01302 770345 — MB BS 1974 Lond.; BSc (Hons.) Lond. 1977; FRCS Eng. 1981; MRCS Eng. LRCP Lond. 1974; MRCGP 1988. (St. Bart.)

WRIGHT, Charlotte Margaret Peach Unit, QMH Tower, Yorkhill Hospital, Glasgow G3 8SJ Tel: 0141 2016927 Fax: 0141 2016943 Email: charlotte.wright@clinmed.gla.ac.uk; 26 York Street, Summerhill, Newcastle upon Tyne NE4 6ET Tel: 0191 273 6832 — BM BCh 1982 Oxf.; MSc Lond. 1992; MD Newc. 1996; BMedSc Newc. 1979; MRCP (UK) 1987. Sen. Lect.(Community Child Health) Univ.Glas.; Hon. Cons. Community Child Health, Yorkhill child Health Care Trust. Socs: Fell. Roy. Coll. Paediat. & Child Health; Paediat. Research Soc.; Soc. for Social Med. Prev: Wellcome Train. Fell. (Child Health) Newc.; Regist. (Paediat.) Brighton HA & Guy's Hosp. Lond.

WRIGHT, Christine Janet Haematology dept, City Hospital, Dudley Road, Birmingham B18 7Q — MB ChB 1986 Bristol; MRCP (UK) 1991; Dip RCPatch 1998; MRCPath 1999. Cons. Haematologist, City Hosp., Dudley Rd., Birm. Prev: Regist. (Haemat.) Birm. Hosp.; Sen. Regist. (Haemat.) Uni. Hosp. Birm.

WRIGHT, Christopher Division of Pathology, School of Pathological Sciences, University of Newcastle upon Tyne, Royal Victoria Infirmary, Newcastle upon Tyne NE1 4LP Tel: 0191 232 5131 Fax: 0191 222 8100 — MB BS 1983 Newc.; PhD Newc. 1994, MB BS 1983, BMedSci 1980; MRCPath 1990. Sen. Lect. (Perinatal Path.) Univ. Newc. u Tyne.

WRIGHT

WRIGHT, Christopher James (retired) 2 Old Hall Croft, Gargrave, Skipton BD23 3PQ Tel: 01756 749699 Email: cjwright@doctors.org.uk — MB ChB 1965 Leeds; FFA RCS Eng. 1969; DA Eng. 1967. Prev: Sen. Regist. (Anaesth.) Leeds RHB.

WRIGHT, Christopher John George Deerbrook Surgery, 114-116 Norwood Road, London SE24 9BB Tel: 020 8674 4623 Fax: 020 8678 6236; 56 Amberley Gardens, Stoneleigh, Epsom KT19 0NG — MB ChB 1985 Ed.; BSc Ed. 1984. (Edinburgh)

WRIGHT, Christopher Mark 5 Gorsewood Drive, Hakin, Milford Haven SA73 3EP — MB BS 1994 Lond.

WRIGHT, Colin The Ridge Medical Practice, 3 Paternoster Lane, Great Horton, Bradford BD7 3EE Tel: 01274 502905 Fax: 01274 522060; 93 Smith Avenue, Wibsey, Bradford BD6 1HA — MB BS 1980 Newc. Socs: Amer. Soc. Laser Med. & Surg.

WRIGHT, Colin Ernest 55 South Road, South Ockendon RM15 6NX — MB BS 1953 Lond.

WRIGHT, David, MC (retired) 28 Manor Road, Hemingford Grey, Huntingdon PE28 9BX — MB ChB Glas. 1941.

WRIGHT, David 2 Dryburn Park, Durham DH1 5AD — MB ChB 1983 Sheff.; MD Sheff. 1992, BMedSci 1982; MRCP (UK) 1986. Cons. Rheum. N. Tees Health NHS Stockton-on-Tees. Socs: Brit. Soc. Rheum. Prev: Sen. Regist. N.. RHA.

WRIGHT, David Department of Haematology, Pontefract General Infirmary, Pontefract WF8 1PL — MB BCh 1983 Wales; BSc Wales 1980; MRCP (UK) 1987; MRCPath 1994; MD 1998. Cons. Haemat. Pontefract Gen. Hosp. Prev: Sen. Regist. (Haemat.) Roy. Liverp. Univ. Hosp.; Research Regist. UK REF Laborat. Withington Hosp. Manch.

WRIGHT, David Alexander 9 Bellevue Court, Bellevue Gardens, Brighton BN2 2AN — MB ChB 1989 Manch.; MRCP (UK) 1992. Regist. (Gen. Med.) Worthing Hosp. Prev: SHO (Gen. Med.) Univ. Hosp. S. Manch.; SHO (Gen. Med.) Wythenshawe Hosp. Manch. & Burnley Gen. Hosp.; SHO (Nephrol.) St. Thos. Hosp. Lond.

WRIGHT, David Arthur (retired) — MB BS 1952 Lond.; MRCS Eng. LRCP Lond. 1952. Med. Off. Foster Wheeler Ltd. Prev: Clin. Asst. ENT St. Mary's Hosp. & Paddington Green Childr. Hosp.

WRIGHT, Mr David Arthur Mount Alvernia Hospital, Harvey Road, Guildford GU1 3LX Tel: 01483 561315 Fax: 01483 538230 Email: davidwright3@compuserve.com; Eastbury Farm House, Compton, Guildford GU3 1EE Tel: 01483 810343 Fax: 01483 538230 Email: davidwright3@compuserve.com — MB BChir 1960 Camb.; MA Camb. 1960; FRCS Eng. 1966; MRCS Eng. LRCP Lond. 1959. (Camb. & Guy's) ENT Surg. Mt. Alverna Hosp. Guildford.; Cons. ENT Surg. King Edwd. VII Hosp. Midhurst; Civil. Cons. ENT. Advis. to the Army. Socs: Fell. Roy. Soc. Med. (Ex-Pres. Sect. Otol.); Master Brit. Acad. Conf. Otolaryngol. 2003. Prev: Pres.Brit.Assn.Otol, Head & Neck Surg.; Sec.Gen.ORL Eur.Union.Meds.pecial.; Mem.Senate.Surg.Roy.Coll.

WRIGHT, Mr David Dakin Iorwerth Surgicare Ltd., Dralda House, Crendon St., High Wycombe HP13 6LS Tel: 01494 511911 Fax: 01494 511922; Juniper House, 2 Austenwood Close, Daws Hill Lane, High Wycombe HP11 1PT Tel: 01494 523216 Email: david@juniper238.freeserve.co.uk — MB BS 1978 Lond.; BSc (Physics in Med.) Lond. 1975; FRCS Eng. 1983. Med. Dir. Surgicare Ltd. Socs: Roy. Soc. Med. (Steering Comm. Venous Forum). Prev: Lect. (Surg.) Char. Cross Hosp. & W.m. Med. Sch. Lond.; Regist. (Surg.) Qu. Mary's Hosp. Roehampton; Regist. (Surg.) Basingstoke Dist. Hosp.

WRIGHT, David Eric (retired) 125 Monkhams Avenue, Woodford Green IG8 0ER Tel: 0208 504 0357 — MB BS 1952 Lond.; MRCS Eng. LRCP Lond. 1953. Hosp. Pract. (Dermat.) Barking Hosp. & King Geo. Hosp. Ilford. Prev: Ho. Surg. Ophth. Dept. & Emerg. Off. Lond. Hosp.

WRIGHT, David Graham (retired) 29 Bloomfield Avenue, Bath BA2 3AB Tel: 01225 427920 — MB BS 1963 Lond.; FRCP Lond. 1981, M 1967; MRCS Eng. LRCP Lond. 1963. Prev: Cons. Geriat. St. Martins Hosp. Bath.

WRIGHT, David Harold, CBE East Backstonegill Farm, Dent, Sedbergh LA10 5TE Tel: 015396 25073 — MSc Lond. 1989, MB BS 1970; MFOM RCP Lond. 1993, A 1989; FFOM RCP Lond 1999. (St. Thos.) Cons. Occupat.al Phys. Post Office Employee Health Servs.; Mem. Ct. of Governers Lond. Sch. of Hyg. & Trop. Med. Socs: Fell. Roy. Soc. Med.; Soc. Occupat. Med.- Hon Sec. Prev: Regtl. Med. Off. Roy. Scots Dragoon Guards; Chief Med. Off. UN Protec. Force, Yugoslavia.

WRIGHT, David James Thomas Gillies and Overbridge Medical Partnership, Brighton Hill, Sullivan Road, Basingstoke RG22 4EH Tel: 01256 479747; Yew Tree House, Long Parish, Andover SP11 6PT Tel: 01264 720598 — MB BS 1978 Lond.; MRCS Eng. LRCP Lond. 1977; MRCGP 1985; DRCOG 1982; DCH Lond. 1982. (Guys) Prev: Trainee GP Brighton VTS.

WRIGHT, David John Donnington Medical Practice, Wrekin Drive, Donnington, Telford TF2 8EA Tel: 01952 605252 Fax: 01952 677010 — MB ChB 1989 Manch.; BSc (1st cl. Hons.) Med. Biochem. Manch. 1986; MRCGP 1993; DCH RCP Lond. 1992; DRCOG 1991.

WRIGHT, David John Anaesthetic Department, Western General Hospital, Edinburgh EH4 2XU Tel: 0131 537 1661 Fax: 0131 537 1021; 20 Lennox Row, Edinburgh EH5 3JW Tel: 0131 552 3439 — MB BS 1968 Lond.; MRCS Eng. LRCP Lond. 1968; FFA RCS Eng. 1974; DA Eng. 1971. (St. Bart.) Cons. Anaesth. W.. Gen. Hosp. Edin.

WRIGHT, David John Oaklands House, Sheldons Lane, Hook, Basingstoke RG27 9QZ — MB BS 1992 Lond.

WRIGHT, David Julian Maurice Department of Medical Microbiology, Charing Cross Hospital, Fulham Palace Road, London W6 8RF Tel: 020 8846 7256 Fax: 020 8846 7261 Email: d.jwright@ic.ac.uk — MB BS Lond. 1961; MD Lond. 1973; FRCPath 1991, M 1982. (Middlx.) Cons. Microbiologist Char. Cross Hosp. Lond.; Reader (Med. Micro.) Imperial Coll. Sch. of Med.

WRIGHT, David Justin Killinbeck Hospital, York Road, Leeds LS14 6UQ Tel: 0113 264 8164; Rose Cottage, Brook Hill, Bildon, Shipley BD17 6NS Tel: 01274 584731 — MB ChB 1990 Leeds; MRCP (UK) 1994. (Leeds) Research Fell. (Cardiol.) Killingbeck Hosp. Leeds.

WRIGHT, Mr David Malcolm Western Infirmary, Dumbarton Road, Glasgow G11 6NT Tel: 0141 211 2806; 45 McLean Place, Paisley PA3 2DG — MB ChB 1989 Glas.; MB ChB Ed. 1989; BSc (Hons.) Glas. 1986; FRCS Ed. 1993. Specialist Regist. (Gen. Surg.) W. of Scott. Higher Surgic. Train. Scheme. Prev: SHO W.ern Infirm. Glas.

WRIGHT, David Poulter (retired) The Butts, High Bank, Porlock, Minehead TA24 8NS Tel: 01643 862975 — MB ChB 1948 Leeds; MRCGP 1964. Prev: Princip. GP Nailsea.

WRIGHT, David Robert 8 Maris Green, Great Shelford, Cambridge CB2 5EE — BM 1990 Soton.

WRIGHT, David Sheldon The Surgery, April Cottage, High Street, Buxted, Uckfield TN22 4LA Tel: 01825 732333 Fax: 01825 732072 — MB BS 1987 Lond.; BSc (Biochem.) Lond. 1984; MRCGP 1991; DGM RCP Lond. 1989. Prev: Trainee GP Whipps Cross Hosp. Lond. VTS.

WRIGHT, David Smethurst Inzievar Surgery, 2 Kenmore Street, Aberfeldy PH15 2BL Tel: 01887 820366 Fax: 01887 829566 Email: dr.dwright@inzievar.finix.org.uk; Tigh N'Acheonan, Dull, Aberfeldy PH15 2JQ Tel: 01887 820465 Email: drdwright@hotmail.com — MB ChB 1973 Dundee; MRCP 1976 Edinburgh, UK. (Dundee) GP Aberfeldy, Perthsh.; Sessional paynet for 'c/o the elderly' Aberfeldy Community Hosp.

WRIGHT, David Stephen, OBE, OStJ, Surg. Capt. RN Retd. 9 Ashburton Road, Alverstoke, Gosport PO12 2LH Tel: 023 9258 2459 Email: dswright@talk21.com — MB BS 1959 Lond.; MSc Salford 1973; FRCP Lond. 1989; FFOM RCP Lond. 1983, M 1978; MFCM RCP (UK) 1974; DIH Soc. Apoth. Lond. 1968; DPH Lond. 1967. (St. Bart.) Cons. Occupat. Phys. Hants. Socs: Fell. BMA; Soc. Occupat. Med. Prev: Chief Med. Off. Brit. Petroleum Co. plc; Dean Fac. Occupat. Med.; Prof. Naval Occupat. Med.

WRIGHT, David Wood Whiteman's Surgery, Whitefriar's Street, Perth PH1 1PP Tel: 01738 627912 Fax: 01738 643969; 8 Strathearn Terrace, Perth PH2 0LS — MB ChB 1973 Dundee; BSc Ed. 1968; MRCGP 1978; DRCOG 1976. Prev: SHO (Anaesth.) Ninewells Hosp. Dundee.

WRIGHT, Deirdre Jane 6 Manland Avenue, Harpenden AL5 4RF — MB BS 1981 Lond.; BSc Lond. 1978, MB BS 1981; MRCP (UK) 1986; FRCR 1988. Cons. Radiol. Luton & Dunstable Hosp. Prev: Sen. Regist. (Radiol.) Guy's Hosp. Lond.

WRIGHT, Professor Dennis Howard Faculty of Medicine, Southampton General Hospital, Tremona Road, Southampton

WRIGHT

SO16 6YD Tel: 023 8079 4856 Fax: 023 8079 6603; Brae House, 31 Chilbolton Avenue, Winchester SO22 5HE Tel: 01962 863778 Fax: 01962 869530 Email: denniswright@totalise.co.uk — MB ChB (Hons.) Bristol 1956; BSc (Physiol. Hons.) Bristol 1953, MD 1964; FRCPath 1977, M 1965. (Bristol) Emerit. Prof. Path. Univ. Soton.; Hon. Cons. Haematopath. Roy. Bournemouth & ChristCh. Hosps. NHS Trust; Locum Cons. Path. Soton. & SW Hants. HA. Prev: Reader (Path.) Univ. Birm. & Makerere Univ. Coll., Uganda; Ho. Surg. & Ho. Phys. Bristol Roy. Infirm.

WRIGHT, Derek Geoffrey Green Lane Surgery, 2 Green Lane, Belper DE56 1BZ Tel: 01773 823521 Fax: 01773 821954 — MB ChB 1985 Leeds; MRCGP 1991; DRCOG 1990; DCH RCP Lond. 1989; DA (UK) 1987. Hosp. Practitioner; Babington Hosp., Belper, Derbysh. Socs: Derby Med. Soc. Prev: GP Wirksworth Health Centre Derbysh.; Trainee GP Colchester Gen. Hosp. VTS; Ho. Off. Rotat. (Anaesth.) St. Jas. Univ. Teach. Hosp. & York Dist. Hosp.

WRIGHT, Derek Halton Highfield, 14 Queen's Park Road, Burnley BB10 3LB Tel: 01282 424736 — MB ChB Manch. 1947. (Manch.) Prev: Ho. Surg. Gen. Surgic. Unit & Radium Inst. Burnley Vict. Hosp.; Med. Off. Prestwich Hosp.

WRIGHT, Donald Geoffrey 33 Mount Pleasant Road, Newtownabbey BT37 0NQ — MB BCh BAO 1986 Belf.

WRIGHT, Donald Robert (retired) 5 Meadow Lane, Milton Keynes Village, Milton Keynes MK10 9AZ Tel: 01908 661960 — BM BCh 1954 Oxf.; MA, BM BCh Oxf. 1954; MRCGP 1967. GP Cons. Med. Defence Union. Prev: Resid. Med. Off. St. Pancras Hosp. & Univ. Coll. Hosp. Lond.

WRIGHT, Dorothy Elizabeth 3 Kingswood Avenue, London NW6 6LA — MB BS 1952 Lond.; MRCS Eng. LRCP Lond. 1951. (Roy. Free) Prev: Ho. Off. Univ. Coll. Hosp. W. Indies, Jamaica; Ho. Surg. Roy. Free Hosp. Lond.

WRIGHT, Douglas 7 Wake Green Road, Moseley, Birmingham B13 9HD Tel: 0121 449 0300; 3 St. Agnes Road, Moseley, Birmingham B13 9PH Tel: 0121 449 4870 — MB ChB 1956 Birm.; MRCS Eng. LRCP Lond. 1956; DObst RCOG 1957; DMJ Soc. Apoth. Lond. 1969. (Birm.)

WRIGHT, Douglas David Wye Valley Surgery, 2 Desborough Avenue, High Wycombe HP11 2BN Tel: 01494 521044; 16 Abbots Way, High Wycombe HP12 4NR Email: dougw@vossnet.co.uk — BM 1988 Soton.; MRCGP 1994; DCH RCP Lond. 1993.

WRIGHT, Douglas Milne Kirkham Health Centre, Moor Street, Kirkham, Preston PR4 2DL Tel: 01772 683420 — MB ChB 1978 Dundee; MRCGP 1983.

WRIGHT, Edwina Caroline 119A Cumnor Hill, Oxford OX2 9JA — MB BS 1998 Lond.

WRIGHT, Elaine Catherine 15 Woodcote Park Avenue, Purley CR8 3ND Tel: 020 8660 4220 — MRCS Eng. LRCP Lond. 1955; MD Lond. 1980, MB BS 1955; FRCPsych 1984, M 1971; DPM Eng. 1961. Cons. Psychiat. St. Lawrence's Hosp. Caterham. Prev: Cons. Psychiat. Fountain & Carshalton Hosp. Gp.

WRIGHT, Elizabeth 5 Lynedoch Place, Edinburgh EH3 7PX — MB ChB 1973 Dundee; DCH RCPS Glas. 1975.

WRIGHT, Elizabeth Ann Department of Radiology, Countess of Chester Hospital, Liverpool Road, Chester CH2 1UL Tel: 01244 365000; Sakura, 2 Demage Lane S., Upton-by-Chester, Chester CH2 1EQ Tel: 01244 380711 — MB BCh BAO 1976 Belf.; FRCR 1990; DMRD Liverp. 1987. Cons. Radiol. Chester Hosp. Prev: Sen. Regist. (Radiol.) Mersey Region; Regist. (Radiol.) Roy. Liverp. Hosp.

WRIGHT, Elizabeth Dorothy Department Microbiology, West Suffolk Hospital NHS Trust, Hardwick Home, Bury, St Edmunds BN11 2DH Tel: 01284 713000 Email: liz.wright@wash-tr.sthames.nhs.uk — MB BS 1981 Lond.; MSc Lond. 1986, BSc 1971; PhD Glas. 1975; MRCPath 1986; FRCP FRCPath 1997. (Roy. Free) Cons. MicroBiol. W. Suff. Hosp. Bury, St Edmunds. Prev: Sen. Regist. (MicroBiol.) Qu. Mary's Hosp. & St. Geo.'s Hosp. Lond.; Cons. Microbiologist Worthing Hosp. Worthing.

WRIGHT, Elizabeth Julie Woodlands, Delph Lane, Aughton, Ormskirk L39 5EB Tel: 01695 423920 — MB BS 1980 Newc.; FFA RCS Eng. 1985; DA (UK) 1982. Cons. Anaesth. Aintree Hosp. Liverp.

WRIGHT, Ellen Sylvia Queen Elizabeth Hospital, Stadium Road, Woolwich SE15 — MA Oxf. 1980; MB BS Lond. 1985; FRCA 1990. p/t Cons. (Pain Managem.) Greenwich Dist. Hosp. Lond.; GP Princip. Vandrugh Hill Health Centre, Vandrugh Hill, Greenwich SE10. Socs: FRCA; BSMDH; BMA. Prev: Regist. (Anaesth.) Roy. Marsden Hosp., Qu. Charlottes Hosp. & St. Mary's Hosp. Lond.; GP principle, Greenwich SE10 0HZ.

WRIGHT, Eluned Marion Department of Anaesthetics, Llandough Hospital, Penlan Road, Penarth CF64 2XX Tel: 01222 711711 — BM BCh 1983 Oxf.; BA Oxf. 1980; FRCA 1988. Cons. Anaesth. Llandough Hosp. Cardiff. Prev: Sen. Regist. (Anaesth.) Univ. Hosp. Wales Cardiff.

WRIGHT, Eric Arthur 5 Sion Hill, Bath BA1 2UF Tel: 01225 420851 — MB BS 1944 Lond.; DSc Lond. 1976, MD 1952; FRCP Lond. 1974, M 1949; LMSSA Lond. 1944; FRCPath 1966, M 1954. (Guy's) Emerit. Prof. Univ. of Lond. Socs: Fell. Roy. Soc. Med. Prev: Prof. Morbid Anat. King's Coll. Hosp. Med. Sch. & Cons. Path. Kings Coll. Hosp.; Reader & Cons. Path. St. Mary's Hosp. Lond.; Research Fell. Harvard Univ. Med. Sch.

WRIGHT, Eric Paul Department of Microbiology, Conquest Hospital, The Ridge, St Leonards-on-Sea TN37 7RD Tel: 01424 755255 Fax: 01424 758022 Email: wright.paul@har-tr.sthames.nhs.uk — MB ChB 1975 Liverp.; FRCPath 1993, M 1982; Dip. Bact. (Distinct.) . Manch. 1980. (Liverp.) Cons. Microbiol. Conquest Hosp. St. Leonards-on-Sea. Socs: BMA; Assn. Med. Microbiol. (Pub.ats. Sec.); Hosp. Infect. Soc. Prev: Asst. Med. Microbiol. Luton Pub. Health Laborat.; Trainee Med. Microbiol. Liverp. Pub. Health Laborat.; Ho. Off. (Med. Surg.) Fazakerley Hosp. Liverp.

WRIGHT, Eric Walter (retired) 3 Queen's Avenue, Woodford Green IG8 0JE Tel: 020 8504 2016 Email: wright.3qa@virgin.net — MB ChB Ed. 1947; FFPHM 1989; FFCM 1979, M 1972; DPH Ed. 1952. Prev: Area Med. Off. Redbridge & Waltham Forest HA.

WRIGHT, Ernestine Abioseh 3 Penroy Avenue, Manchester M20 2ZH — MB ChB 1990 Manch. SHO (Gen. Med.) Wythenshawe Hosp. Manch. Socs: BMA.

WRIGHT, Ethel May 7 Church Farm Garth, Leeds LS17 8HD Tel: 0113 273 7472 — MB ChB 1951 Leeds; DCH Eng. 1957.

WRIGHT, Fiona 36 Burnside Court, Bearsden, Glasgow G61 4QD — MB ChB 1994 Glas.

WRIGHT, Fiona Alison 102A Osbaldeston Road, London N16 6NL Tel: 020 8806 8574 — MB ChB 1987 Bristol. Sen. Regist. (Pub. Health Med.) N. Thames Region. Socs: BMA. Prev: Research Asst. (Social Policy) Univ. Bristol; SHO (A & E) Cardiff Roy. Infirm.; Ho. Phys. S.mead Hosp. Bristol.

WRIGHT, Fiona Alison 3 St Margaret's Road, Swindon SN3 1RU — BM 1998 Soton.

WRIGHT, Fiona Judith (3FR) 13 Cargil Terrace, Trinity, Edinburgh EH5 3ND — MB ChB 1991 Aberd.

WRIGHT, Francine Joy Lodge Medical Centre, 1A Grange Park Avenue, Leeds LS8 3BA Tel: 0113 265 6454 Fax: 0113 295 3710 — MB ChB 1986 Leeds; DRCOG 1990. Prev: Trainee GP Bradford VTS.

WRIGHT, Francis George de Longsden Norfolk Clinical Research, Staithe House, East Harbour Way, Burnham Overy Staithe, King's Lynn PE31 8JE Tel: 01328 730064 Fax: 01328 730064; Staithe House, Burnham Overy Staithe, King's Lynn PE31 8JE Tel: 01328 738236 — MB BChir Camb. 1959; LMSSA Lond. 1958. (St. Mary's) Socs: BMA. Prev: Med. Off. Uganda Med. Serv.

WRIGHT, Frank Bowen (retired) 23 Mereheath Lane, Knutsford WA16 6AW Tel: 01565 651838 — MB ChB Liverp. 1943; MRad. Liverp. 1949; FRCR 1982; DMRD Eng. 1949. Prev: Cons. Radiol. Warrington, St. Helens & Knowsley HAs.

WRIGHT, Frank William, MBE Norfolk Park Health Centre, Tower Drive, Sheffield S2 3RE Tel: 0114 276 9661 Fax: 0114 276 9471 Email: frank.wright@virgin.net; 72 Grove Road, Sheffield S7 2GZ Tel: 01442 362569 Fax: 01442 362569 Email: frank.wright@virgin.net — MB ChB Sheff. 1960. (Univ. Sheff.) Trainer (Gen. Pract.) Sheff.; Clin. Asst. Dermat. Roy. Hallamsh. Hosp. Sheff. Socs: Sheff. M-C Soc. (Pres. Elect). Prev: Clin. Asst. Renal Unit Lodgemoor Hosp. Sheff.; Regist. Birm. Accid. Hosp.; SHO (Gen. Surg.) N. Gen. Hosp. Sheff.

WRIGHT, Fraser George Dunblane Medical Practice, Well Place, Dunblane FK15 9BQ Tel: 01786 822595 Fax: 01786 825298 — MB ChB 1987 Aberd.; BSc Hons. Aberd. 1982. SHO (A & E) Stirling Roy. Infirm. Prev: Ho. Off. (Surg.) Stirling Roy. Infirm.; Ho. Off. (Med.) Raigmore Hosp. Inverness & Belford Hosp. Fort William.

WRIGHT

WRIGHT, Frederick Keith (retired) Bron y Garth, 31 Fforddlas, Prestatyn LL19 9SG Tel: 01745 854358 Email: fkwright@doctors.org.uk — MB ChB (Hons.) Birm. 1959; FRCP Lond. 1979, M 1965. Appeals Serv. (p/t). Prev: cons phys Glan Clwyd Hosp. NHS Trust.

WRIGHT, Frederick Richard (retired) Pasir Pandang, 20A Grey Point, Helen's Bay, Bangor BT19 1LE Tel: 01247 853727 Fax: 01247 853727 Email: fred.r.w@lineone.net — MB BCh BAO 1953 Belf.; FFR RCSI 1981; FRCR 1975; FFR 1966; DMRD Eng. 1960. Hon. Cons. Ulster Hosp. Dundonald. Prev: Cons. Radiol. Ulster, N. Down & Ards Hosps. Unit.

WRIGHT, Frederick Wynn Charfield, Cassington Road, Eynsham, Oxford OX29 4LH Tel: 01865 881496 — BM BCh 1954 Oxf.; DM Oxf. 1974; FRCP Lond. 1996; MRCP Lond. 1958; FRCR 1975; FFR 1961; DMRD Eng. 1958. (Oxf.) Cons. Radiol. Oxon. HA (T); Clin. Lect. (Radiol.) Univ. Oxf. Socs: Brit. Inst. Radiol.; Brit. Nuclear Med. Soc. Prev: Vis. Staff Radiol. Henry Ford Hosp. Detroit, USA; Regist. (Radiol.) United Oxf. Hosps.; Ho. Phys. & Cas. Off. Radcliffe Infirm. Oxf.

WRIGHT, Gary David Flat 21, 38 Windsor Park, Belfast BT9 6FS — MB BCh BAO 1987 Belf.

WRIGHT, Gavin Anthony Keaton 19 Caversham Avenue, London N13 4LL — MB BS 1996 Lond.

WRIGHT, Geoffrey David Stamp East Dean Cottage, East Dean, Salisbury SP5 1HH — MB ChB 1973 Birm.; DM Soton. 1986; BSc Birm. 1970, MB ChB 1973; MRCP (UK) 1978; FRCP 1999. assoc. med. Dir. Glaxo Wellcome UK; Hon. Cons. Neurol. Raddcliffe Infirm.Oxf. Socs: BMA, N. Eng. Neurol. Assn. & S. Eng. Neurol. Assn. Prev: Sen. Regist. (Neurol.) Radcliffe Infirm. Oxf.; Regist. (Neurol.) Radcliffe Infirm. Oxf.; Research Regist. Wessex Neurol. Centre Soton. Gen. Hosp.

WRIGHT, Geraldine Margaret Queen Mary's University Hospital, Roehampton Lane, Roehampton, London SW15 5PN; 21 Devonhurst Place, Heathfield Terrace, London W4 4JB — MB BS 1978 Lond.; BSc Lond. 1975; MRCP (UK) 1983; FRCP (UK) 1997. (Roy. Free) Sen. Lect. Char. Cross & W.m. Med. Sch. Lond.

WRIGHT, Gillian Ruth (retired) Glen Alainn, Treaslane, Portree IV51 9NX Tel: 01470 532392 — MB BS Lond. 1957; DObst RCOG 1959.

WRIGHT, Gladys Frances Ballymena Health Centre, Cushendall Road, Ballymena BT43 6HQ Tel: 028 2564 2181 Fax: 028 2565 8919; 57 Tullygarley Road, Ballymena BT42 2JA — MB BCh BAO 1983 Belf.; MRCGP 1992; DRCOG 1990; DCH Dub. 1990. Prev: GP Smithfield Med Centre, Ballymena.

WRIGHT, Gordon Herbert (retired) 68 de Freville Avenue, Cambridge CB4 1HU — MRCS Eng. LRCP Lond. 1942; MB BChir Camb. 1951; MD Camb. 1954. Fell. Clare Coll. Prev: Assoc. (Anat.) Univ. Pennsylvania.

WRIGHT, Grace Elliot (retired) 7 Rothley Close, Ponteland, Newcastle upon Tyne NE20 9TD Tel: 01661 22118 — MB BS 1926 Durh. Prev: Med. Off. Wom. Welf. Clinic (Family Plann. Assn.) Newc. &.

WRIGHT, Graham 17 Greenwood, 31 Princes Way, Wimbledon, London SW19 6QH — MB BS 1977 Lond.; BSc Lond. 1974, MB BS 1977. SHO (Ophth.) Mayday Hosp. Thornton Heath. Prev: Ho. Surg. Frimley Pk. Hosp.; Ho. Phys. Roy. Hants. Co. Hosp. Winchester.

WRIGHT, Graham Alexander Lagmhor Surgery, Little Dunkeld, Dunkeld PH8 0AD Tel: 01350 727269 Fax: 01350 727772; Mansewood, Oak Road, Birnam, Dunkeld PH8 0BL Tel: 01350 727135 — MB ChB 1982 Ed.; MRCGP 1986. Clin. Asst. (Gastroenterol.) Perth Roy. Infirm. Prev: GP Fife; SHO (Paediat. Med.) Law Hosp. Carluke Lanarksh.; Cas. Off. (SHO) Vict. Hosp. Kirkcaldy.

WRIGHT, Mr Graham Charles Stairhill Farm, Moorlake, Crediton EX17 5EL — MB BS 1980 Lond.; FCOphth 1991; FRCS (Ophth.) Ed. 1990.

WRIGHT, Graham Robert Riverton Medical Centre, 145 Palmerston St., Riverton, Southland 9654, New Zealand Tel: 0064 3 2348990 Fax: 0064 3 2348990 Email: graham.wright@xtra.co.nz; 17 Lime Grove, Royston SG8 7DJ Tel: 01763 246800 Email: graham.wright@dial.pipex.com — BM BS 1989 Nottm.; MRCGP 1995; T(GP) 1995. (Nottm.) GP Princip. Riverton Med. Centre. Prev: Partner Donneybrook Med. Centre.

WRIGHT, Hayley Suzanne Honeysuckle House, Oakwood, Hexham NE46 4LE — MB ChB 1987 Leic.; MRCGP 1991; DRCOG 1991. (GP Retainer) Prev: Trainee GP N.umbria VTS.

WRIGHT, Heidi Elizabeth 6 Talgarth Close, Oakwood, Derby DE21 2RX — MB ChB 1992 Dundee.

WRIGHT, Helen 18 Grosvenor Terrace, Bootham, York YO30 7AG Tel: 01904 621679 — MB BS 1973 Lond. (Guy's)

WRIGHT, Helen Gail 5 Chandos Terrace, Avington, Winchester SO21 1DD Email: helenwright@chandosterrace.freeserve.co.uk — MB ChB 1993 Manch.; MRCGP 1999; BSc (Med. Sci.) St. And. 1990. GP Locum. Socs: Treaswer of Basingstroke Sessional GPs Gp.

WRIGHT, Helen Mary Inzievar Surgery, 2 Kenmore Street, Aberfeldy PH15 2BL Tel: 01887 820366 Fax: 01887 829566 — MB ChB 1976 Aberd.; DRCOG 1979.

WRIGHT, Helen Mary Bridgemill Farmhouse, Beal, Berwick-upon-Tweed TD15 2RN Tel: 01289 381300 Email: scotdoc-hmwright@hotmail.com; P.O. Box 2887, Pertu, Western Australia WA 6001, Australia — MB ChB 1995 Glas.; DCH Glas. 1996; MRCP Glas. 1998. Paediat. Regist. P.ss Margt. Hosp. Childr. Perth. W. Australia. Prev: SHO (Paediat.) CrossHo. Hosp. Kilmarnock; Ho. Off. (Gen. Med.) Ayr Hosp.; SHO Roy. Hosp. For Sick Childr. Yorkhill, Glas.

WRIGHT, Helena Margaret Elizabeth 6 Starborough Cottages, Station Road, Dormansland, Lingfield RH7 6NL — MB ChB 1989 Leic.

WRIGHT, Mr Henry Beric (retired) Brudenell House, Quainton, Aylesbury HP22 4AW Tel: 01296 655250 Fax: 01296 655250 — MB BS 1942 Lond.; FRCS Eng. 1955; MRCS Eng. LRCP Lond. 1942; MFOM RCP Lond. 1978. Lect. Retirem. & Ageing Problems. Prev: Chairm. BUPA Med. Centre & Governor BUPA.

WRIGHT, Henry John (retired) Kekewich House, 1 View Road, London N6 4DL — MB BCh BAO 1939 NUI; MRCGP. Prev: Gen. Practitioner Nuneaton Warks.

WRIGHT, Henry William (retired) Avalon, Drunzie, Glenfarg, Perth PH2 9PE Tel: 01577 830641 — MB ChB Ed. 1952; DObst RCOG 1956.

WRIGHT, Henry William Newton Port Surgery, Newton Port, Haddington EH41 3NF Tel: 01620 825497 Fax: 01620 824622 — MB ChB 1983 Ed.; MRCGP 1988; Dip. Obst Otago 1986. (Edinburgh)

WRIGHT, Hugh Edward Maida Vale Medical Centre, 40 Biddulph Mansions, Elgin Avenue, London W9 1HT Tel: 020 7286 6464 Fax: 020 7266 1017; 112 Hamilton Terrace, St John's Wood, London NW8 9UP Tel: 020 7289 6413 — MB BS 1984 Lond.; DRCOG 1999; DEM RCP Lond. 1999; MRCGP 1998; COAF Eng. 1997. (St Mary's London) GP Princip. Maida Vale Med. Centre Lond.; Clin. Med. Off. Pk.side Health; Private GP Wright Private Med. Pract. Lond. Socs: Fell.Roy. Soc. of Med. Prev: SHO OtoLaryngol. Centr. Middlx. Hosp. Lond.; SHO O & G Crawley Hosp. Sussex; SHO Geriat. Redhill Hosp. Surrey.

WRIGHT, Ian Alec 34 Beacon Square, Emsworth PO10 7HU — MB BS 1976 Lond.; MRCGP 1980; DRCOG 1979.

WRIGHT, Ian Conrad Kings House, 14 New Road, Romsey SO51 7LN Fax: 01794 517875 — MB ChB 1992 Bristol.

WRIGHT, Ian Cosmo Institute of Psychiatry, De Crespigny Park, Denmark Hill, London SE5 8AF Tel: 020 7919 3535 — MB BChir 1990 Camb.; MA Camb. 1991, MB BChir 1990; MRCP (UK) 1992; MRCPsych 1995; MSc Lond. 1995. Wellcome Clin. Train. Fell. Inst. of Psychiat.; Hon. Sen. Regist. Maudsley Hosp. Prev: Lect. Inst. of Psychiat.; Regist. (Psychiat.) Maudsley Hosp.; SHO (Neurol.) Radcliffe Infirm. Oxf.

WRIGHT, Ian Gavin Department of Anaesthetics, Harefield Hospital, Harefield, Uxbridge UB9 6JH Tel: 0189 582 3737 — MB ChB 1977 Rhodesia; LRCP LRCS Ed. LRCPS Glas. 1977; FFA SA 1983. Cons. (Anaesth.) Harefield Hosp. Prev: Cons. (Anaesth.) Groote Schuur Hosp. & Red Cross Childr. Hosp. Cape Town.

WRIGHT, Mr Ian Peter 2 painters Place, Shrewsbury SY3 5PT Email: ipwright@globalnet.co.uk — MB ChB 1994 Manch.; BSc (Immunol. & Oncol.) Manch. 1991; FRCS Eng. 1998. Specialist Regist. Trauma Orthop. OsW.ry Rotat. Socs: BOA. Prev: SHO (Surg.) Whiston Hosp. Merseyside; Ho. Off. Wythenshawe Hospial Manch.; SHO Orthop.Alder Hey Childr.s Hosp.

WRIGHT

WRIGHT, James Alexander Morrison (retired) Haslemere House, Golf Links Road, Yelverton PL20 6BN Tel: 01822 852323 — MB BCh BAO NUI 1957; FRCP Lond. 1982, M 1969.

WRIGHT, James Courtney (retired) 22 Briercliffe Road, Stoke Bishop, Bristol BS9 2DB Tel: 0117 968 6142 — LRCP LRCS 1949 Ed.; LRCP LRCS Ed. LRFPS Glas. 1949.

WRIGHT, James Duncan (retired) c/o St Anne's Surgery, 161 Station Road, Herne Bay CT6 5NF Tel: 01227 361114 — MB ChB 1952 Liverp.; MRCS Eng. LRCP Lond. 1952.

WRIGHT, James Michael 246 Springfield Road, Chelmsford CM2 6BS — MB BS 1998 Lond.

WRIGHT, Jane Catherine 114 Wickham Avenue, Cheam, Sutton SM3 8EA — MB ChB 1988 Bristol. SHO (Radiother. & Oncol.) Roy. Hosp. Wolverhampton.

WRIGHT, Jane Elizabeth Mary Moreton Health Clinic, 8-10 Chadwick Street, Wirral CH46 7XA Tel: 0151 677 1207 Fax: 0151 604 0372 — MB ChB 1983 Liverp.; DRCOG 1987.

WRIGHT, Janet Barbara Maternity Unit, Bradford Royal Infirmary, Duchworth Lane, Bradford Tel: 01274 542200 — MB BS 1991 Lond.; MRCOG 1997; BSc Lond. 1988. (St. Geo. Hosp. Med. Sch.) Specialist Regist. (O & G) Yorks.

WRIGHT, Janet Frances 30 Dunleady Park, Dundonald, Belfast BT16 1JU — MB BCh BAO 1992 Belf.

WRIGHT, Janet Ruth Fernville Surgery, Midland Road, Hemel Hempstead HP2 5BL Tel: 01442 213919 — MB BS 1980 Lond.; MRCGP 1984; DRCOG 1985. (King's Coll. Hosp.) GP Hemel Hempstead. Prev: GP Cirencester; Volunteer Community Health Project S.. India; Regist. (Terminal Care) St. Joseph's Hospice Lond.

WRIGHT, Janine Louisa Basement Flat, 79 Barnsbury St., Islington, London Email: janine.wright@virgin.net — MB BS 1990 Lond.; MRCP (UK) 1995. p/t Regist. (Med. & Gastroenterol.) Middlx. Hosp. Socs: BMA. Prev: SpR Med. & Gastroenterol., King Geo. Hosp.; Spr Med. & Gastroenterol., Middlx. Hosp.

WRIGHT, Jayne Margaret 45 Donaghaguy Road, Warrenpoint, Newry BT34 3PR — MB BCh BAO 1981 Belf.; FFA RCSI 1985. Cons. Anaesth. Daisy Hill Hosp. Newry.

WRIGHT, Jean Isobel 34 Hockcliffe Street, Leighton Buzzard LU7 — MB ChB 1962 Aberd.

WRIGHT, Jean Margaret (retired) 11 Elms Avenue, Lytham St Annes FY8 5PW Tel: 01253 735673 — MB ChB 1956 Liverp.; DObst RCOG 1960. Prev: SCMO Blackpool Child Developm. Centre.

WRIGHT, Jeremy Torquil St. Peter's Hospital, Guildford Road, Chertsey KT16 0PZ Tel: 01932 872000 Fax: 01483 875462 Email: jwrighta@cix.compulink.co.un; SIGIRI, College Lane, Woking GU22 0EW Tel: 01483 715699 Fax: 01483 724833 Email: jwrighta@cix.compulink.co.uk — MB BS 1971 Lond.; MRCS Eng. LRCP Lond. 1971; FRCOG 1991, M 1977; MBA 1996. (Univ. Coll. Hosp.) Cons. O & G St. Peter's Hosp. Chertsey; Comm. Mem. BSGE. Prev: Sen. Regist. (O & G) W. Middlx. Univ. Hosp. & Char. Cross Hosp. Lond.; Regist. (O & G) Whipps Cross Hosp. Lond.; Resid. Med. Off. Qu. Charlotte's Matern. Hosp. Lond.

WRIGHT, Joan Mary Birmingham University Medical Practice, Elms Road, Edgbaston, Birmingham B15 2SE Tel: 0121 414 5111; Cowsden Croft, Upton Snodsbury, Worcester WR7 4NX Tel: 01905 60515 — MRCS Eng. LRCP Lond. 1955. (Birm.) GP Birm. Univ. Health Centre; Med. Off. Family Plann. Assn. Clinics. Prev: Ho. Phys. & Ho. Surg. Little Bromwich Hosp.; Med. Off. Blood Transfus. Serv. Birm.

WRIGHT, Joan Patricia (retired) The Castle, Castle Edge, New Mills, High Peak SK22 4QF Tel: 01663 742364 — MB ChB 1952 Manch.; FRCP Ed. 1985, M 1962; DCH Eng. 1954. Prev: Cons. Paediat. Cardiol. Manch. Roy. Infirm. & St. Mary's Hosp. Manch.

WRIGHT, Joanna Mary 16 College Avenue, Leicester LE2 0JF Tel: 0116 255 4224 — MB ChB 1991 Leic.; MRCGP; DFFP 1997. GP Locum Non-Princip.

WRIGHT, John 7 Woodlands Court, Gateshead NE11 0YG — MB ChB 1987 Dundee.

WRIGHT, John (retired) The Garth, 10 Tynedale Terrace, Benton, Newcastle upon Tyne NE12 8AY — MB BS 1955 Durh. Med. Mem. Appeals Serv. Prev: Ho. Phys. Hosp. Sick Childr. (Fleming Memor.) Newc.

WRIGHT, John Alan West Wirral Group Practice, Winterdyne, Rocky Lane, Heswall, Wirral CH60 0BY Tel: 0151 342 2557 Fax: 0151 342 9384 — MB ChB Liverp. 1965; DObst RCOG 1967; DTM & H Liverp. 1966. (Liverp.) Prev: Ho. Surg. (O & G) Chester City Hosp.; Ho. Phys. (Trop. Dis.), Ho. Phys. & Ho. Surg. Sefton Gen. Hosp.

WRIGHT, John Barry Debenham Limetrees Child & Family Unit, 31 Shipton Road, York YO30 6RF Tel: 01904 652908 Fax: 01904 632893 — MB BS 1985 Lond.; MMedSc Leeds 1994; MRCPsych 1991; MRCGP 1989; DCH RCP Lond. 1989; MD Lond. 2000. (St. Bartholomew's Hospital) Cons. Child & Family Psychiat. York. Socs: York Med. Soc. Prev: Sen. Regist. Rotat. (Child Psychiat.) Leeds.

WRIGHT, John Brennan 202 Camberwell Grove, London SE5 8RJ Tel: 020 7733 0104 Fax: 020 7733 0104; 202 Camberwell Grove, London SE5 8RJ Tel: 020 7733 0104 Fax: 020 7733 0104 — LAH 1959 Dub.

WRIGHT, John Brian (retired) 8 Windsor Road, Chorley PR7 1LN Tel: 01257 265419 Email: john_b.wright@totalise.co.uk — MB ChB Manch. 1963. Prev: Ho. Off. Manch. Roy. Infirm., Leigh Infirm. & Bishop Auckland Gen. Hosp.

WRIGHT, John David (retired) 26 Highgate Avenue, Fulwood, Preston PR2 8LL — MB ChB 1963 Manch.; MSc Manch. 1972; FRCOG 1981, M 1968, DObst. 1965. Prev: Clin. Tutor (Obst.) Univ. Manch.

WRIGHT, John Denham, MBE (retired) 21 Waterdale, Compton, Wolverhampton WV3 9DY Tel: 01902 422564 Fax: 01902 422564 — MB BS 1962 Lond.; FFPHM RCP (UK) 1983, M 1972; DPH Lond. 1966; DCH Eng. 1964. Prev: Cons. Pub. Health Med. Wolverhampton HA.

WRIGHT, Mr John Edward 44 Wimpole Street, London W1 7DG Tel: 020 7580 1251 — MD 1962 Liverp.; MB ChB 1956; FRCS Eng. 1967; DO Eng. 1965. (Liverp.) Cons. Ophth. Surg. Moorfields Eye Hosp. City Rd. Lond.; Cons. Ophth. Surg. Roy. Nat. Throat Nose & Ear Hosp. Lond. Socs: Fell. Roy. Soc. Med.; Amer. Acad. Ophth. Prev: Cons. Ophth. Surg. St. Mary's Hosp. Lond.; Res. Surg. Off. Moorfields Eye Hosp. City Rd. Br. Lond.; Capt. RAMC.

WRIGHT, Mr John Edward Charles 50 Wimpole Street, London Tel: 020 7486 8964 Fax: 020 7486 7918 — MB BS Lond. 1958; FRCS Eng. 1964; MRCS Eng. LRCP Lond. 1958. (King's Coll. Hosp.) p/t Cons. Cardiothoracic Surg. The Heart Hosp.; Hon. Cardiac Surg. Lond. Hosp. Socs: Soc. Thoracic & Cardiovasc. Surg. & Cardiac Soc. Prev: Sen. (Surg.) Regist. Nat. Heart Hosp.; Harvard Research Fell. Mass. Gen. Hosp., USA; Med. Off. RAF.

WRIGHT, John Edward Denham 22 Botanical Road, Hunters Bar, Sheffield S11 8RP Email: jedw@globalnet.co.uk — MB ChB 1993 Sheff.; FRCS (Eng) 1997. Sprontnopaedics Rotat., Trent.

WRIGHT, John Francis The Health Centre, Melbourn Street, Royston SG8 7BS Tel: 01763 242981 Fax: 01763 249197 — MB BS 1984 Lond.; MA Camb. 1985, BA 1981; MRCGP 1991; Dip. Occupat. Med. 1997. (Churchill Camb. & St.Thos.)

WRIGHT, John Geoffrey Charles Heart Unit, Birmingham Children's Hospital, Steelhouse Lane, Birmingham B4 6NH Tel: 0121 333 9443 Fax: 0121 333 9441 Email: john.wright@bham.childrens.wmids.nhs.uk — MB BChir 1975 Camb.; MA Camb. 1972; FRCP Lond. 1994; MRCP (UK) 1977; FRCPCH 1996. Cons. Paediat. Cardiol. Childr. Hosp. Birm.; Hon. Sen. Lect. Univ. Birm.; Cons. Cardiol. (Fetal Med.) Univ. Birm. Prev: Sen. Regist. (Paediat. Cardiol.) Roy. Liverp. Childr. Hosp.; Resid. Med. Off. Nat. Heart Hosp. Lond.

WRIGHT, John Henry (retired) 5 Haywards Close, The Heath, Glossop SK13 7AZ — MB ChB Liverp. 1957; FFA RCS Eng. 1963. Cons. Anaesth. Withington & The Christie Hosp.

WRIGHT, Mr John James 55 Robyns Way, Sevenoaks TN13 3ED — MB BS 1966 Lond.; FRCS Eng. 1975. Prev: Regist. (Neurosurg.) Roy. P. Alfred Hosp., Sydney; SHO (Gen. Surg.) Redhill Gen. Hosp.; Ho. Phys. Norwich Hosp.

WRIGHT, Mr John Kenneth (retired) 71 St Annes Road E., Lytham St Annes FY8 1UR Tel: 01253 723084 — BSc 1939, MB ChB Manch. 1942; FRCS Eng. 1950; MRCS Eng. LRCP Lond. 1942. Hon. Cons. Orthop. & Traum. Surg. Blackpool Health Dist. Prev: Examr. Orthop. Nurs. Certif., Jt. Exam. Bd. & Brit. Orthop. Assn.

WRIGHT, Mr John Lawson William, RD 152 Harley Street, London W1N 1HH Tel: 020 7935 0444 Fax: 020 7224 2574; Winsland Mews House, Branstone Rd, Richmond TW9 3LB Tel: 020 8948 3968 Fax: 020 8940 0708 — MB ChB 1964 Bristol; MBA Open 1992; FRCS Eng. (Orl.) 1971; FRCS Ed. 1968; DObst RCOG 1966. (Bristol) Hon. Cons. Surg. Otolaryngol. St. Mary's Hosp.

WRIGHT

Lond.; Civil. Cons. Otolaryngol. RN; Cons. Otolaryngol. to Gibraltar Govt. Prev: 1st Asst. (Otolaryngol.) Radcliffe Infirm. Oxf.; Clin. & Research Fell. Harvard Med. Sch.

WRIGHT, John Patrick — MB BCh BAO NUI 1986; MD NUI 1995; LRCPSI 1986; MRCPsych 1993. (Nat. Univ. Irel. RCSI) Head Clin. Neurosci.,Eli Lilly Ltd. Europe; Sen. Lect. City & Hackney Community Serv. NHS Trust (Oct. 1997 to date); Sen. Lect. Inst. Psychiat. Univ. Lond. (April 1997 to 2000). Socs: Fell. Roy. Soc. Med.; Brit. Assn. Psychopharmacol.; World Psychiat. Assoc. Immunol. in Psychiat. (Comm. Founder).

WRIGHT, John Paul 38 Streatham Common N., London SW16 3HR — MB ChB 1993 Leeds.

WRIGHT, John Paul Bradford Royal Infirmary, Duckworth Lane, Bradford BD9 6RJ Email: johnwright@bradfordhospitals.nhs.uk; 6 Esholt Avenue, Guiseley, Leeds LS20 8AX — MB ChB 1987 Leeds; BSc (Hons.) Leeds 1987; MRCP (UK) 1990; MFPHM RCP (UK) 1996; MPH Leeds 1994. Cons. Clin. Epidemiol. Bradford Roy. Infirm.; Edr. Brit. Jl. of Clin. Governance. Prev: Sen. Regist. (Pub. Health Med.) York; Med. Off. Good Shepherd Hosp., Swaziland.

WRIGHT, John Rodney 59 Deighton Lane, Batley WF17 7EU — MB ChB 1965 Leeds. (Leeds)

WRIGHT, John Stephen (retired) 11 Elms Avenue, Lytham St Annes FY8 5PW — MD 1972 Liverp.; MB ChB 1958; FRCP Lond. 1979, M 1966; DObst RCOG 1963. Prev: Cons. Cardiol. Vict. Hosp. Blackpool.

WRIGHT, John Steven Eastville Health Centre, East Park, Bristol BS5 6YA Tel: 0117 951 1261 Fax: 0117 935 5056 — MB ChB 1987 Bristol; BSc Sheff. 1971; MB ChB (Hons.) Bristol 1987; DRCOG 1991.

WRIGHT, John Stuart (retired) The Health Centre, Beeches Green, Stroud GL5 4BH Tel: 01453 764696 — MB BS 1969 Lond.; MRCGP 1976; DObst RCOG 1975.

WRIGHT, John Trevillian (retired) Silverthorn, Blocks Corner, Hatfield Heath, Bishop's Stortford CM22 7AX Tel: 01279 730366 — BM BCh 1945 Oxf.; DM Oxf. 1953; FRCP Lond. 1964, M 1947. Prev: Cons. Phys. (Gen. Med. & Gastroenterol.) Lond. Hosp.

WRIGHT, John Watson Cowdenbeath Medical Practice, 173 Stenhouse Street, Cowdenbeath KY4 9DH Tel: 01383 518500 Fax: 01383 518509 — MB ChB 1970 St Andrews; MB ChB St And. 1970. (St Andrews) GP Cowdenbeath, Fife.

WRIGHT, John William Royal Surrey County Hospital, Guildford GU2 5XX Email: john.wright@surrey.ac.uk; 8 Critchmere Vale, Haslemere GU27 1PS Tel: 01428 642142 — MB BS 1967 Lond.; MSc (Clin. Biochem.) Surrey 1974; FRCP; MRCP (U.K.) 1971; MRCS Eng. LRCP Lond. 1967; MRCPath 1976. (Guy's) Cons. (Clin. Biochem.) Roy. Surrey Co. Hosp., Guildford; Reader in Metab. Med., Univ. of Surrey, Guildford GU2 7XH. Socs: Assn. of Clin. Biochem.s; Diabetes UK; Brit. Hyperlipidaemia Assn. (Hon. Treas.). Prev: Regist. (Med.) St. Luke's Hosp. Guildford; Resid. (Med.) Penna. Hosp. Philadelphia, U.S.A.; Ho. Surg. Guy's Hosp. Lond.

WRIGHT, Jonathan Gordon Royal Liverpool Hospital, Prescot St., Liverpool L7 8 Tel: 0151 706 2000 — MB ChB 1987 Sheff.; BMedSci (Hons.) Sheff. 1987; MRCP (UK) 1990. Sen. Regist. (Haemat.) Roy. Liverp. Hosp.

WRIGHT, Jonathan Graham 17 Battersby Close, Yarm TS15 9RX — MB BS 1983 Newc.; DRCOG 1986.

WRIGHT, Jonathan Mark Tel: 01782 612375 Fax: 01782 714036 — MB ChB 1982 Birm.; DRCOG 1988; MPhil 2000; MRCGP 1988; DCH RCP Lond. 1987. Gen. Practitioner.

WRIGHT, Judith Ann Reading Room Cottage, Shilton, Oxford — BM BCh 1972 Oxf.

WRIGHT, Judith Anne Cropredy Surgery, 18 Station Road, Cropredy, Banbury OX17 1PP Tel: 01295 758372 Fax: 01295 750435; Magpies, Lower Farm Lane, Mollington, Banbury OX17 1BJ Tel: 01295 750724 — MB ChB 1982 Leic.; DRCOG 1987.

WRIGHT, Judith Anne Gillian 30 Smith Street, London SW3 4EP Tel: 020 7352 6860 — MB BS 1958 Lond.; MRCS Eng. LRCP Lond. 1958. (Guy's) Clin. Med. Off. Pk.side. Socs: BMA. Prev: Clin. Med. Off. Kensington, Chelsea & W.m. AHA; Ho. Phys. Sheff. Roy. Infirm.; Ho. Surg. Wharnecliffe Hosp. Sheff.

WRIGHT, Judith Clare 35 Moor Road, Prudhoe NE42 5LL — MB ChB 1993 Leic.; FRCA Lond. 1997. Specialist Regist. (Anaesth.) Glas. Roy. Infirm.

WRIGHT, Judith Margaret Saddleworth Medical Practice, The Clinic, Smithy Lane, Uppermill, Oldham OL3 6AH Tel: 01457 872228 Fax: 01457 876520 — MB ChB 1975 Manch.; MRCGP 1987. GP Uppermill.

WRIGHT, Julia Vanessa Cross Plain Surgery, 84 Bulford Road, Durrington, Salisbury SP4 8DH — BM 1991 Soton.; MRCGP 1996; DFFP 1996. p/t Partner in Gen. Pratice.

WRIGHT, Julian Francis Hawthorn Medical Centre, May Close, Swindon SN2 1UU; Beechcroft, Common Platt, Lydiard Millicent, Swindon SN5 5LB — MB ChB 1972 Manch.; LF Hom 1997; DObst RCOG 1974. Prev: SHO Cheltenham Childr. Hosp.; Ho. Phys. Univ. Hosp. S. Manch.; Ho. Surg. Manch. Roy. Infirm.

WRIGHT, Julian Robert 148 Weaste Lane, Salford M5 2JJ — MB BS 1994 Lond.; BSc (Hons.) Lond. 1991; MRCP 1998. Locum. Reg. Nephrol. Gen. Med.Hope Hosp. Salford. Socs: MDU & BMA; RCP. Prev: Ho. Off. (Renal & Gen. Med.) Withington Hosp. Manch.; Ho. Off. (Surg.) Barnet Gen. Hosp. Lond.; SHO Rotat. (Gen. Med.) N. Staffs. Hosps. Trust Stoke-on-Trent.

***WRIGHT, Juliet Elizabeth** 9 Bellevue Court, Bellevue Gardens, Brighton BN2 2AN Tel: 01273 696955 ext 7064 Email: wrightplc@aol.com — MB BS 1994 Lond.

WRIGHT, Justine Anne Mona Cottage, Hughes Lane, Harvington, Evesham WR11 5NH Tel: 01386 870324 — MB ChB 1993 Leic. Regist. (Anaesth.) Waikato Hosp. Hamilton NZ. Prev: SHO (Anaesth.) Harrogate Dist. Hosp.; SHO (Anaesth.) Waikato Hosp. Hamilton, NZ.

WRIGHT, Kavin John Cricketfield Surgery, Cricketfield Road, Newton Abbot TQ12 2AS Tel: 01626 208020 Fax: 01626 333356 — MB BS 1970 Lond.; MRCGP 1978; DRCOG 1977; DCH Eng. 1977. (St. Geo.)

WRIGHT, Kelso Cooper 29B Esplanade, Greenock PA16 7RU Tel: 01475 725112 — LRCP LRCS Ed. LRFPS Glas. 1960. Prev: Princip. GP Port Glas. 1965-1997.

WRIGHT, Kelvin Donald A&E Dept, Wexham park Hospital, Wexham St., Slough SL2 4HL Tel: 01753 634022; Wycombe General Hospital, Queen Alexandra Road, High Wycombe HP11 2TT Tel: 01494 526161 — MB BS 1992 Lond.; FRCS Eng. 1997; Dip. IMC RCS Ed. 1998. (King's Coll. Lond.) Specialist Regist. (A & E) Wexham Pk. Hosps.lough; St. John Ambul. Brig. Div.al Surg. St. Pancras Div.; Trauma Instruc. Two Shires Ambul. NHS Trust; Immediate Care Doctor-Berks, Ambul. Socs: Brit. Assn. Immed. Care Schemes. Prev: SHO (Intens. Therap.) Char. Cross Hosp. Lond.; SHO (Surg.) Roy. Lond. Hosp.; SHO (Orthop.) Homerton Hosp. Lond.

WRIGHT, Kenneth James Thomas 48 High Street, Hadleigh, Ipswich IP7 5AL Tel: 01473 828976 Fax: 01473 829059 Email: kenwright@doctors.org.uk; 48 High Street, Hadleigh, Ipswich IP7 5AL Tel: 01473 828976 — BM BCh 1961 Oxf.; MPhil (Psychiat.) Lond. 1969; BA (Animal Physiol., 1st cl. Hons.) Oxf. 1959; MRCPsych 1973. (Oxf. & Middlx.) Indep. Cons. Gen. Psychiat. & Psychoanalyt. Hadleigh Suff. Socs: Assoc. Mem. Brit. Psychoanalyt. Soc. Prev: Cons. Psychiat. Severalls Hosp. Colchester; Sen. Lect. & Hon. Cons. Psychother. Acad. Dept. Psychiat. Middlx. Hosp. Lond.; Sen. Regist. (Adult Psychiat.) Tavistock Clin. Lond.

WRIGHT, Mr Kenneth Urquhart University Hospital of North Durham, North Road, Durham DH1 5TW Tel: 0191 333 2333; 3 Park View, Oakenshaw, Crook DL15 0ST — MB ChB 1984 Manch.; BSc St. And. 1981; FRCS (Orth.) 1996; FRCS Ed. 1990. (Univ. Manch.) Cons. Orthop. Surg. Dryburn Hosp. Durh. Prev: Sen. Regist. & Regist. (Orthop.) N.. Region; PeriFell.sh. Regist. Wolverhampton.

WRIGHT, Kerr Richard The Schoolhouse, Bridgefoot, Dundee DD3 0PH — MB ChB 1984 Ed.; DRCOG 1989. GP Dundee.

WRIGHT, Lesley Anne Somerville Medical Practice, 4 Somerville, Poulton Road, Wallasey CH44 9ED Tel: 0151 638 9333 Fax: 0151 637 0291 — MB ChB 1979 Manch.

WRIGHT, Linda 33 Glenmore Avenue, Toryglen, Glasgow G42 0EH — MB ChB 1992 Glas. GP Toryglen.

WRIGHT, Linda The Consulting Rooms, 21 Neilston Road, Paisley PA2 6LW; Strathmore, 24 Donaldfield Road, Bridge of Weir PA11 3JG — MB ChB 1984 Glas.; MRCGP 1988; DRCOG 1987; DCH RCPS Glas. 1987. (Glasgow) Prev: GP Glas. N. VTS; Ho. Phys. Hairmyres Hosp. E. Kilbride; Ho. Surg. Stobhill Gen. Hosp. Glas.

WRIGHT, Lionel Percy John Drumkeeran, 333 Ewell Road, Surbiton KT6 7BX Tel: 020 8399 1192 — MB BS Lond. 1948; MRCS Eng. LRCP Lond. 1942; Foundat. MRCGP 1953. (Guy's) Socs:

BMA. Prev: SHO (Surg.) St. John's Hosp. Lewisham; SHO (Surg.) St. Bart. Hosp. Rochester; Capt. RAMC 1943-5.

WRIGHT, Lucille Patricia BP PLC, Breakspear Park, Breakspear Way, Hemel Hempstead HP2 4UL Tel: 01442 225097 Fax: 01442 223878 Email: wrightlp@bp.com — BM BS 1984 Nottm.; BMedSci Nottm. 1982; MFOM RCP Lond. 1994, AFOM 1992. (Nottingham) Regional Med. Director, BP plc. Prev: Sen. Employm. Med. Adviser Health & Safety Exec. Luton.; Employm. Med. Adviser Health & Safety Exec. Luton.

***WRIGHT, Lynn Mary** Flat 17, 9 Central Grove, Mount Vernon, Glasgow G32 0SP Tel: 0141 778 9282 — MB ChB 1996 Manch.

WRIGHT, Lynne Marie Pencester Surgery, 10/12 Pencester Road, Dover CT16 1BW Tel: 01304 240553; Cherry Tree Cottage, West Hougham, Dover CT15 7AT — MB ChB 1986 Liverp.; BSc Liverp. 1981, MB ChB 1986; DRCOG 1990.

WRIGHT, Malcolm (retired) 87 Belfield Road, Epsom KT19 9TF Tel: 020 8394 2728 — MB ChB 1951 Leeds; MRCS Eng. LRCP Lond. 1951; FRCPsych 1987, M 1971; DPM Eng. 1961. Prev: Cons. Psychiat. Long Gr. Hosp. Epsom & Roy. Hosp. Richmond.

WRIGHT, Malcolm Harold George Cedar House Surgery, 14 Huntingdon Street, St. Neots, Huntingdon PE19 1BQ Tel: 01480 406677 Fax: 01480 475167; Tudor House, Eynesbury, St. Neots, Huntingdon PE19 2TA — MB ChB 1969 Liverp.; MRCGP 1975. (Liverp.) GP Cedar Ho. Surg.; Course Organiser VTS Hinchin Brooke Hosp. Socs: Brit. Med. & Dent. Hypn. Soc. Prev: Ho. Phys. & Ho. Surg. Roy. S.. Hosp. Liverp.; SHO (O & G) & SHO Renal Unit Sefton Gen. Hosp. Liverp.

WRIGHT, Mr Malcolm Oliver 72 Cammo Grove, Barnton, Edinburgh EH4 8HA Tel: 0131 339 7005 — MB ChB 1966 Manch.; FDS RCS Ed. 1993; FRCS Ed. 1987. (Manch.) Sen. Lect. (Physiol. Med.) Sch. Univ. Edin. Prev: Ho. Phys. & Ho. Surg. Manch. Roy. Infirm.

WRIGHT, Maree 11 Durham Close, Paignton TQ3 2QN Tel: 01803 663156 — BM BS 1989 Nottm.; FRCA 1996.

WRIGHT, Margaret Chestnut Cottage, Drayton Parslow, Milton Keynes Tel: 0129 672520 — MB BS 1965 Lond.; MRCPsych 1989; DPM Eng. 1972; DCH Eng. 1968. (Oxf.) Cons. (Child Psychiat.) Milton Keynes Health Dist.; Pk. Sch. Pottersbury Sch. (Rudolph Steiner). Prev: Sen. Regist. (Child Psychiat.) St. Thos. Hosp. Lond.; Regist. (Psychiat. & Paediat.) Qu. Mary's Hosp. Childr. Carshalton.

WRIGHT, Margaret Elizabeth Liberty Mutual health research complex, Foresterhill Road, Aberdeen AB25 2ZP Tel: 01224 669000 Fax: 01224 669030 Email: lizwright@aers.aon.co.uk; Email: liz@wright_47.prestel.co.uk — MB ChB 1980 Glas.; MSc Aberd. 1994; MFOM RCP Lond. 1996, AFOM 1993. (Univ. Glas.) Sen. Occupatonal Phys. AON Occupat. Health Ltd. Aberd.; Clin. Lect. (Environm. & Occupat. Med.) Univ. Aberd.; hon Cons. in Occupat.al Med. Grampian Univ., Aberd. Socs: Soc. Occupat. Med.; Inst. Occupat. Safety & Health. Prev: Occupat. Phys. Grampian Healthcare NHS Trust.

WRIGHT, Margaret Elizabeth 14 Westcliffe Road, Roker, Sunderland SR6 9NW Tel: 0191 548 2472 — MB ChB 1937 Liverp. (Liverp.) Prev: Ho. Phys. Roy. Liverp. Childr. Hosp.; Ho. Surg. & Obst. Ho. Surg. Liverp. Roy. Infirm.

WRIGHT, Margaret Mary James Paget Hospital, Gorleston, Great Yarmouth NR31 6LA Tel: 01493 600611 Fax: 01493 452753 Email: maggie.wright@jpaget.nhs.uk; 127 Corton Road, Lowestoft NR32 4PR Tel: 01502 561834 Fax: 01493 432753 Email: maggie.wright@jpaget.nhs.uk — MB ChB 1978 Dundee; BSc (Hons.) Dund 1973, MB ChB 1978; FFA RCS Eng. 1982. (Dundee) Cons. Anaesth. Gt. Yarmouth & Waveney HA. Prev: Hon. Cons. (Anaesth.) Jas. Paget Hosp. Gorleston Gt. Yarmouth; Sen. Regist. (Anaesth.) Hammersmith Hosp. Lond.; Regist. (Anaesth.) Ninewells Hosp. Dundee.

WRIGHT, Marie Helen Isobel (retired) 10 Rutland Terrace, Stamford PE9 2QD Tel: 01780 755718 — MB ChB 1942 Glas. Prev: Clin. Asst. PeterBoro. Dist. Hosp.

WRIGHT, Marjorie Frances Lind (retired) The Firs, Reynoldston, Swansea SA3 1BR Tel: 01792 390188 — MB ChB 1962 St. And.; DObst RCOG 1964; DA Eng. 1965. Prev: Med. Advis. Dept. Transport.

WRIGHT, Mark 44 Sleigh Road, Sturry, Canterbury CT2 0HT; Flat 1, 15 Milton Avenue, Highgate, London N6 5QF Tel: 020 8348 6786 Email: mwright433@aol.com — MB BS 1994 Lond.; BSc 1991; MRCP 1997. (St Bart.) Specialist Regist. (Gastroenterol.).

WRIGHT, Mark John 22 Brentford Road, Birmingham B14 4DQ — MB ChB 1991 Sheff.; MRCP (UK) 1995. Regist. (Renal Med.) Leeds Gen. Infirm. Prev: Regist. (Renal Med.) Hull Roy. Infirm.

WRIGHT, Mr Mark Renouf Princess Alexandra Eye Pactice, Chalmers Street, Edinburgh EH3 Fax: 0131 536 1674; 15 John Street, Edinburgh EH15 2EB Tel: 0131 669 1760, 01865 557693 — MB ChB 1985 Aberd.; FRCS Ed. 1993. Cons. Ophth. PAEP & St John's Hosp., Livingston.

WRIGHT, Martin Portugal Place Health Centre, Portugal Place, Wallsend NE28 6RZ Tel: 0191 262 5252 Fax: 0191 262 5252 — BM BS 1986 Nottm.; BMedSci 1983; MRCGP 1991. GP Wallsend Tyne & Wear Trainee GP N.d. VTS.

WRIGHT, Martin Wilden (retired) Downsview, 59 High St., Chipstead, Sevenoaks TN13 2RW — MB ChB 1963 Manch.; DPH Eng. 1966; DObst RCOG 1965. Prev: Sen. Med. Off.and SCMO and Sen. Med. Off. (Occupat. Health) E. Surrey HAFPC Oxted Health Centre Surrey.

WRIGHT, Mary Elizabeth Clark Burcot House, Blunsdon St Andrew, Swindon SN25 2DY Tel: 01793 721487 — MB ChB 1953 St. And.

WRIGHT, Mary Frances 293 Brownhill Road, London SE6 1AE — M.B., B.S. Lond. 1943.

WRIGHT, Maureen Edith St Johns Lane Health Centre, St. Johns Lane, Bristol BS3 5AS Tel: 0117 966 7681 Fax: 0117 977 9676; 40 Somerset Road, Knowle, Bristol BS4 2HU Tel: 0117 971 6940 — BM BCh 1974 Oxf.; Cert. Family Plann. JCC 1976. Prev: Community Med. Off. (Family Plann.) S.mead HA.; Clin. Asst. (Genitourin. Med.) Bristol Roy. Infirm.; Princip. GP Lambeth, S.wark & Lewisham FPC.

WRIGHT, Maxwell James (retired) 21 Keston Gardens, Keston BR2 6BL Tel: 01689 851222 — MB ChB Ed. 1950; DMRD Eng. 1955. Recognised Teach. Univ Lond. Prev: Cons. Radiol. Greenwich Dist. Hosp.

WRIGHT, Mea Wallace (retired) The Butts, High Bank, Porlock, Minehead TA24 8NS Tel: 01643 862975 — MB BCh BAO Belf. 1950; DObst RCOG 1953. Prev: GP Nailsea.

WRIGHT, Michael George 10 Harley Street, London W1G 9PF Tel: 020 7467 8345 Fax: 020 7467 8312 Email: micheal-wright@lineone.net; 12 Den Close, Beckenham BR3 6RP Tel: 020 8658 3201 Fax: 020 8658 3201 Email: micheal-wright@lineone.net — MB BS Lond. 1963; FRCP Lond. 1994; MRCP (UK) 1973; MRCS Eng. LRCP Lond. 1963. (Lond. Hosp.) Cons. Rheum. & Rehabil. Newham Health Dist. & Roy. Lond. Hosp.; Cons. Rheum. & Rehabil. Nat. Dock Labour Bd. Socs: Brit. Assn. Rheum. & Rehabil.; BMA; BIMM. Prev: Sen. Regist. King's Coll. Hosp. Lond.; Resid. Med. Off. W.m. Hosp. Lond.; Ho. Surg. Lond. Hosp.

WRIGHT, Michael James 37 Old Doune Road, Dunblane FK15 9BU — MB ChB 1987 Ed.; MSc Univ. Newc. 1994; MRCP (UK) 1990. Clin. Fell. Centre for Med. Genetics Johns Hopkins Hosp. Baltimore, USA. Prev: Research Regist. (Human Genetics) Newc.

WRIGHT, Michael John Central Street Health Centre, Central Street, Countesthorpe, Leicester LE8 5QJ Tel: 0116 277 6336; 15 Cosby Road, Countesthorpe, Leicester LE8 5PD — MB BS 1969 Lond.; MRCS Eng. LRCP Lond. 1969; DA Eng. 1974; DObst RCOG 1971. (Char. Cross)

WRIGHT, Michael John Croft House Surgery, 5 Croft House, 1145 Manchester Road, Slaithwaite, Huddersfield HD7 5JY Tel: 01484 842652 Fax: 01484 348223; Stoneycroft, 21 Rumbold Road, Edgerton, Huddersfield HD3 3DB Tel: 01484 532168 — MB BChir 1973 Camb.; MA Camb. 1973; DObst RCOG 1974. (Camb. & Middlx. Hosp.) GP. Socs: Hudds. Med. Soc.; BMA (Treas. & Chairm. Huddersfield Div.). Prev: Clin. Asst. (Dermat.) Huddersfield Roy. Infirm.; Trainee GP Huddersfield VTS; Ho. Phys. & Ho. Surg. Bedford Gen. Hosp.

WRIGHT, Michael John Andrew 2 Leather Street, Long Itchington, Rugby CV47 9RD; Flat Three, Beecholme Court, 143 Lichfield Road, Four Oaks, Sutton Coldfield B74 2RY Tel: 0121 308 0833 — MB ChB 1989 Ed.; BSc (Hons.) Ed. 1986. SHO (Med.) Manor Hosp. Walsall. Socs: BMA (Powar Doctors).

WRIGHT, Michael Joseph 22 Doves Yard, London N1 0HQ — MB BCh BAO 1955 Belf.; MRCGP 1971; DA Eng. 1960; DObst RCOG 1959. (Queens Univ. Belfast) p/t Locum GP. Socs: Fell. RSM.

WRIGHT

Prev: Squadron Ldr. RAF Med. Br.; Chairm. Barking, Havering & Brentwood LMC & BMA.

WRIGHT, Mr Michael Peter Frigg's Mill, 116 Bath Road, Stroud GL5 3NX Tel: 01453 764847 — BM BCh 1954 Oxf.; BA (Physics) Oxf. 1943, BM BCh 1954; FRCS Ed. 1964. (Oxf.) Med. Legal Reporting. Socs: Cas. Surgs. Assn.; Internat. Surg. Soc. Prev: Cons. A & E Glos. Roy. Hosp.; Sen. Regist. Thoracic Unit St. Geo. Hosp. Lond.; Research Asst. Accid. Serv. Radcliffe Infirm. Oxf.

WRIGHT, Michelle 1 Barns Road, Budleigh Salterton EX9 6HJ — MB BS 1989 Lond.; DA (UK) 1992.

WRIGHT, Nathanael Marcus James 72 Gorsey Croft, Eccleston Park, Prescot L34 2RT — MB ChB 1989 Leeds.

WRIGHT, Nathaniel James Selborne Flat 25, Ravenswood, 1 Spath Road, Manchester M20 2GA — MB ChB 1995 Manch.

WRIGHT, Neil John Mayfield Surgery, 54 Trentham Road, Longton, Stoke-on-Trent ST3 4DW Tel: 01782 599147 — MB ChB 1984 Bristol; DRCOG 1987; Cert. Family Plann. JCC 1987. Prev: Trainee GP Stockport; SHO (Elderly Med.) Bolton Gen. Hosp.; SHO (O & G & A & E) Wythenshawe Hosp. Manch.

WRIGHT, Neil Peter 37 Endcliffe Rise Road, Ecclesall, Sheffield S11 8RU — MB BChir 1989 Camb.; MRCP (UK) 1992. Lect. Paediat. Sheff. Childr. Hosp. Prev: Spec Regist. (Paediat.) Sheff. Childr. Hosp.

WRIGHT, Neil Richard 53 Dudsbury Road, West Parley, Wimborne — MB ChB 1987 Leic.; BSc Leic. 1984, MB ChB 1987.

WRIGHT, Neville Bryce X-Ray Department, Royal Liverpool Children's NHS Trust, Alder Hey, Eaton Rd, Liverpool L12 2AP — MB ChB 1986 Liverp.; FRCR 1992; DMRD Liverp. 1991. Cons. Paediat. Radiol. Liverp. Childr. Hosp. Socs: Fell. Roy. Coll. Radiol.; BMA; Brit. Soc. of Paediatric Radiol. Prev: Sen. Regist. (Radiol.) N.. Region; Research Fell. (Paediat. Radiol.) Univ. Liverp.; Regist. (Radiol.) Mersey Region.

WRIGHT, Neville Frank Winding Bank, Silloth, Carlisle CA7 4PS — MB ChB 1982 Manch.; BSc (Physiol.) Manch. 1979, MB ChB 1982.

WRIGHT, Nicholas 9 Burnett Close, Winchester SO22 5JQ Tel: 01962 866626 Fax: 01962 866626 — MB BChir Camb. 1957; FRCP Lond. 1987, M 1961; FRCPsych 1983, M 1971; DPM Eng. 1959. (St. Thos.) Cons. Forens. Psychiat. Private Pract., Winchester. Prev: Cons. Psychiat. Marchwood, Priory S.ampton; Cons. Psychiat. Wessex RHA; Sen. Regist. (Psychol. Med.) & Regist. (Neurol. & Psychol. Med.) St. Thos. Hosp. Lond.

WRIGHT, Professor Nicholas Alcwyn Imperial College School of Medicine, Hammersmith Campus, Du Cane Road, London W12 0NN Tel: 020 8383 3200 Fax: 020 8383 3203 Email: n.wright@ic.ac.uk; ICRF Laboratories, 44 Lincoln's Inn Fields, London WC2A 3PX Tel: 020 7269 3065 Fax: 020 7269 3091 — MB BS 1965 DURH; MB BS Durh. 1965; PhD Newc. 1975; MA Oxf. 1979; DSc Newc. 1985; MD Newc. 1973; FRCPath 1986, M 1974; MACP 1998; F MED1998; FRCS 1999. (Newc.) Dep. Princip. & Vice-Princip. for Research Imperial Coll. Sch. Med. Lond.; Head Histopath. Unit ICRF Lond. Socs: Path. Soc.; Brit. Soc. Gastroenterol.; Brit. Assn. Cancer Research. Prev: Dean Roy. Postgrad. Med. Sch. Lond.; Prof. Histopath. Univ. Lond.; Dir. (Clin. Research) ICRF Lond.

WRIGHT, Nicola Jane Friarsgate Practice, Friarsgate Medical Centre, Friarsgate, Winchester SO23 8EF Tel: 01962 853599 Fax: 01962 849982 — BM 1987 Soton.; DRCOG 1990. p/t GP. Socs: MRCGP. Prev: SHO (A & E) Salisbury Gen. Infirm.; SHO (O & G, Paediat.) Roy. Hants. Co. Hosp.; Ho. Off. (Med.) Roy. Hants. Hosp.

WRIGHT, Nicola Stephanie 36 Vergette Street, Peterborough PE1 4DL Tel: 01733 751962 — BM 1994 Soton. Ho. Phys. P.ss Margt. Hosp. Swindon.

WRIGHT, Noel Diamond, OBE (retired) 1 Upper Croft Road, Holywood BT18 0HJ Tel: 02890 422308 — MB BCh BAO Belf. 1945; FRCGP 1967. Prev: Mem. Gen. Med. Counc.

WRIGHT, Mr Norman Lesley The Dove House, Old Pembroke Farm, High St., Burwell, Cambridge CB5 0HB — MB BCh BAO Belf. 1953; MRCP Lond 1959; Dobest RCOG 1955; MD Belf 1957; FRCS Edin 1961.

WRIGHT, Olwen Louise 14 Ardmore Heights, Holywood BT18 0PY — MB ChB 1994 Ed.

WRIGHT, Pamela Louise East Hill Surgery, 78 East Hill, Colchester CO1 2RW; Beech House, Church Road, Layer De La Haye, Colchester CO2 0EN Tel: 01206 734074 — MB BS 1982 Lond.; DRCOG 1986. (St Mary's Lond.) Socs: Colchester Med. Soc. Prev: Trainee GP Colchester VTS; Hon. Off. Edgware Gen. Hosp. & Wexham Pk. Hosp.

WRIGHT, Patricia Augusta Pathology Department, University of Wales College of Medicine, Heath Park, Cardiff CF14 4XN Tel: 029 2074 7747; 26 Windsor Avenue, Radyr, Cardiff CF15 8BY Tel: 029 2084 3720 — MB BS 1987 Lond.; BSc (1st cl. Hons.) Lond. 1984, MB BS 1987. Lect. (Path.) Univ. Wales Coll. Med. Cardiff. Socs: Path. Soc.; Amer. Assn. Advancem. Sci.

WRIGHT, Patrick James 3 Mayes Walk, Yarm TS15 9TU — MB ChB 1981 Dundee; DRCOG 1983; DCCH Ed. 1984. Trainee GP Cleveland VTS. Socs: Assoc. Mem. RCGP.

WRIGHT, Paul Barnaby Plas Gwyn, Gannock Park, Deganwy, Conwy LL31 9PZ — MB ChB 1998 Bristol.

WRIGHT, Paul Francis Cornwall Road Surgery, 15 Cornwall Road, Dorchester DT1 1RU Tel: 01305 251808 — MB BS 1973 Lond.; BDS 1968; DRCOG 1977. (The London Hospital) p/t Assoc. Dir. For GP Postgrad. Educat. Wessex; Course Organiser & Trainer GP Dorset VTS; Chair. S.W. Dorset PCT Exec. Socs: Fell. Roy. Soc. Med.; Exec. Mem. Nat. Assn. Course Organisers. Prev: Lect: (Dent. Anat.) 1967; Lect. (Oral Path.) 1968; Sen. Lect. (Primary Care).

WRIGHT, Paul Hastings Holts Health Centre, Watery Lane, Newent GL18 1BA Tel: 01531 820689 — MB ChB 1968 Liverp.; DObst RCOG 1971. Prev: Ho. Surg. & Ho. Phys. Leicester Roy. Infirm.; SHO O & G MusGr. Pk. Hosp. Taunton.

WRIGHT, Paul Kingsley 41 Well Lane, Heswall, Wirral CH60 8NQ — MB ChB 1998 Aberd.

WRIGHT, Paul Richard 22 Brentford Road, Birmingham B14 4DQ — MB ChB 1994 Leic.

WRIGHT, Pauline Montgomery 24 Ayr Road, Giffnock, Glasgow G46 6RY — MB ChB 1991 Glas.

WRIGHT, Penelope Jane Wapping Health Centre, 22 Wapping Lane, London E1W 2RL Tel: 020 7481 9376 — MB BS 1985 Lond.; MA Camb. 1986; MRCGP 1991; DRCOG 1987.

WRIGHT, Mr Peter (retired) Southbrook Court, Southbrook Lane, Bovey Tracey, Newton Abbot TQ13 9NB Tel: 01626 835233 — MB BS Lond. 1955; FRCP Lond. 1994; FRCS Eng. 1964; MRCS Eng. LRCP Lond. 1955; FRCOphth 1989; DO Eng. 1959. Hon. Cons. Ophth. Surg. Moorfields Eye Hosp. Lond.; Hon. Cons. Ophth. Surg. KCH Lond. Prev: Pres. Roy. Coll. Ophth.

WRIGHT, Peter Andrew Public Health Laboratory, Royal Preston Hospital, Preston PR2 9HG Tel: 01772 710113 Fax: 01772 710166 Email: paw@presphl.demon.co.uk — MB ChB Manch. 1968; FRCPath 1988, M 1976. Cons. Microbiol. Pub. Health Laborat. Serv. Socs: Assn. Clin. Path.; Assn. Med. Microbiol. Prev: Cons. Microbiol. Blackburn; Cons. Bact. Glas. Roy. Infirm.; Hon. Clin. Lect. Univ. Glas.

WRIGHT, Mr Peter Dennis 30 Elmfield Road, Gosforth, Newcastle upon Tyne NE3 4BA Email: peter.wright@ncl.ac.uk — MD 1974 Newc.; MB BS 1967; FRCS Eng. 1971. (Newc.) Cons. Surg. & Sen. Lect. Dept. Surg. Univ. Newc. Freeman Hosp. Prev: Wellcome Surg. Research Fell. Dept. Surg. Univ. Newc.; Vis. Asst. Prof. Surg. Harvard Med. Sch. Boston, U.S.A.; Lect. in Surg. (Dept. Surg.) Univ. Newc.

WRIGHT, Peter George Yardley Hackwood Partnership, Essex House, Worting Road, Basingstoke RG21 8SU Tel: 01256 470464 Fax: 01256 357289; Fenimore, 61 Northfield Road, Sherfield-on-Loddon, Hook RG27 0DS — MB BS 1981 Lond.; BSc Lond. 1978; MRCGP 1985; DRCOG 1985. (Univ. Coll. Hosp. Med. Sch.)

WRIGHT, Peter Henry 23 Gordon Mansions, Torrington Place, London WC1E 7HF Tel: 08700 327051 Email: peter.wright4@virgin.net; 23 Gordon Mansions, Torrington Place, London WC1E 7HF — MB BS 1968 Lond.; MSc (Occupat. Med.) 1982; MRCP (UK) 1971; MFOM RCP Lond. 1988, AFOM 1986; MRCS Eng. LRCP Lond. 1968. (Univ. Coll. Hosp.) Med. Policy Adviser, Dept. for work and Pens.; Cons. Occupat. Prev: Cons. Phys. & Chest Phys. Sandwell DHA; Sen. Regist. (Thoracic Med.) Lond. Chest Hosp.; Sen. Regist. (Gen. Med.) St. Thos. Hosp.

WRIGHT, Peter James Department of Anaesthetics, Daisy Hill Hospital, Hospital Road, Newry BT35 8DR Tel: 028 3083 5000 — MB ChB 1976 Sheff.; MSc 2000 Cardiff; FFA RCS Eng. 1980. Cons. (Anaesth.) Daisy Hill Hosp. Newry. Socs: Pain Soc.; Brit. Med. Acupunct. Soc. Prev: Cons. & Regist. (Anaesth.) Roy. Hallamsh.

WRIGHT

Hosp. Sheff.; Sen. Regist. (Anaesth.) Roy. Vict. Hosp. Belf.; Research Fell. Montreal Neurol. Hosp. Canada.

WRIGHT, Peter John The Surgery, Greenwich Avenue, Hull HU9 4UX Tel: 01482 374415 Fax: 01482 786462; 20 Spencer Close, Hedon, Hull HU12 8HE — MB ChB 1983 Leeds; DRCOG 1986.

WRIGHT, Peter Louis The Hollies, 11 Albion Hill, Loughton IG10 4RA Tel: 020 8508 6540 Fax: 020 8508 6540 Email: drplwright@doctors.org.uk — MB BChir 1960 Camb.; MA Camb. 1964; FRCP Lond. 1978, M 1963. (Lond. Hosp.) Hon. Cons. Phys. Whipps Cross Hosp., Leytonstone. Socs: BMA. Prev: Lect. Med. Unit Lond. Hosp.; Cons. Phys. Whipps Cross Hosp., Leytonstone.

WRIGHT, Peter Malcolm Colin Department of Anaesthesia, Freeman Hospital, Heaton Road, Newcastle upon Tyne NE7 7DN Tel: 0191 222 6982 Fax: 0191 222 8988 Email: p.m.c.wright@ncl.ac.uk — MB BCh BAO 1983 Belf.; MD Belf. 1992; FFARCSI 1987. (Queens University Belfast) Cons. Anaesth. Freeman Hosp.; Sen. Lect. (Anaesth.) Univ. of Newc. Prev: Asst. Prof. Anaesth. Univ. of Calif., San Francisco.

WRIGHT, Peter Norman Alexandra Group Medical Practice, Glodwick Health Centre, Glodwick Road, Oldham OL4 1YN Tel: 0161 909 8400 Fax: 0161 909 8414; 18 Lincoln Close, Ashton-under-Lyne OL6 8BS Tel: 0161 339 2885 Email: pnmdocspot@aol.com — MB ChB 1978 Manch.; DRCOG 1982. (Manch.)

WRIGHT, Mr Peter Randell (retired) 20 Streatley Lodge, Whitehouse Road, Oxford OX1 4QF Tel: 01865 726630 — BM BCh Oxf. 1942; MA Oxf. 1942; FRCS Eng. 1948. Prev: Cons. Orthop. Surg. Canterbury & Thanet & SE Kent Health Dist.

WRIGHT, Richard Edward Caterham Valley Medical Practice, Eothen House, Eothen Close, Caterham CR3 6JU Tel: 01883 347811 Fax: 01883 342929; 12 Manor Avenue, Caterham CR3 6AN Tel: 01883 345182 — MB BS 1990 Lond.; MRCGP 1996; DRCOG 1994. (St. Thomas's Hospital Medical School) Prev: Trainee GP/SHO E. Surrey Hosp. Redhill VTS; SHO (Med.) & Ho. Phys. Battle Hosp. Reading; Ho. Surg. Basingstoke Dist. Hosp.

WRIGHT, Richard Geoffrey Department of Occupational Health, Carmarthen & District NHS Trust, West Wales General Hospital, Carmarthen SA31 2AF Tel: 01267 235151 Fax: 01267 227427; Berwyn, 71 Saron Road, Saron, Ammanford SA18 3LH Tel: 01269 595478 — MRCS Eng. LRCP Lond. 1970; FRCS Ed. 1977; AFOM RCP Lond. 1981; FRIPHH 1982; FRSH 1982. (Guy's) Sen. Occupat. Phys. & Dir. Occupat. Health Serv. Carmarthen & Dist. NHS Trust; Occupat. Health Co-ordinator Welsh Water Auth.; Med. Adviser Fire Brig., Co. Counc. & W. Wales Ambul. Trust. Socs: Fell. Roy. Soc. Med. (Sect. Occupat. Med.); Fell. Roy. Soc. Health; Soc. Occupat. Med. Prev: Sen. Med. Off. Gp. Occupat. Health Centre, BP Research Centre Sunbury; Sen. Med. Off. BP Petroleum Developm. (UK) Ltd. Aberd.; Regist. (Surg.) Bradford Roy. Infirm.

WRIGHT, Richard Michael 52 Avondale Road, Gorleston, Great Yarmouth NR31 6DN — MB ChB 1991 Leic.

WRIGHT, Richard William Maylin Tel: 01904 624404 Fax: 01904 651813; 18 Grosvenor Terrace, York YO30 7AG — MRCS Eng. LRCP Lond. 1972; MRCP (UK) 1978. (Guy's) Med. Off. Bootham Sch. York.; Clin. Asst. (Haemat.) York Dist. Hosp. Socs: Brit. Soc. of Med. and Dent. Hypn. Prev: Med. Off. Coll. Ripon & York St. John.

WRIGHT, Robert (retired) 6 Ashlong Grove, Halstead CO9 2QH Tel: 01787 472468 — MB BChir 1940 Camb.; BA Camb. 1936. Prev: Ho. Phys. Manch. Roy. Infirm. & Crumpsall Hosp. Manch.

WRIGHT, Robert Anthony Dept. Of Cardiology, South Cleveland Hospital, Marton Road, Middlesbrough TS4 3BW Tel: 01642 282491 — MB ChB 1985 Ed.; MD Ed. 1996; MRCP (UK) 1988. (Univ. Ed.) Conds. Cardiol. S. Cleveland Hosp. Socs: Bris. Cardiac Soc.; Brit. Cardiovasc. Interven. Soc. Prev: Cons.Phys.The Ayr Hosp.; Sen. Regist. (Cardiol. & Gen. Med.) Roy. Infirm. Edin. & W.. Gen. Edin.; Lect. (Cardiol.) Univ. Edin. & Roy. Infirm. Edin.

WRIGHT, Robert Desmond 70 Church Road, Dundonald, Belfast BT16 2LW Tel: 01232 3142 — MB BCh BAO 1945 Belf. (Belf.)

WRIGHT, Robert Edward Richard The Ulster Community Hospitals Trust, Belfast BT16 1RH Tel: 02890 484511; 171 Ballylesson Road, Belfast BT8 8JU Tel: 02890 826905 — MB BCh BAO 1985 Belf.; FRCR 1992; FFR RCSI 1991. (Queen's Univ. Belfast) Cons. Radiol. Clin. Director, Clin. Diagnostics Directorate.

Socs: Ulster Radiological Soc.; Ulster Med. Soc.; Europ. Assoc. of Radiol. Prev: Sen. Roy. Vict. Hosp. Belf.

WRIGHT, Robert William Ormskirk Street Surgery, 51A Ormskirk Stret, St Helens WA10 2TB Tel: 01744 29209 — MB ChB 1988 Liverp.; DRCOG 1992.

WRIGHT, Ruth The Maternity Unit, Ipswich Hospital, Heath Road, Ipswich IP4 5PD Tel: 01473 703016/7; Bryher, St. Mary's Park, Bucklesham, Ipswich IP10 0DY Tel: 01473 659434 — MB BS 1953 Lond. (Roy. Free) SCMO Ipswich Hosp. Family Plann. Serv.; Dep. Police Surg. E. Suff.; Instruc. Doctor Nat. Assn. Family Plann. Doctors. Prev: Clin. Asst. Ipswich Hosp. Family Plann. Serv.; Dept. Med. Off. Suff. AHA.

WRIGHT, Simon Andrew Hodge Road Surgery, 2 Hodge Road, Worsley, Manchester M28 3AT Tel: 0161 790 3615 Fax: 0161 703 7638 — MB BS 1987 Lond.; MA Camb. 1988; MRCP (UK) 1990.

WRIGHT, Simon Ralph 56 Hunter Hill Road, Sheffield S11 8UE — MB ChB 1983 Sheff.; MRCPsych 1988. Clin. Lect. (Psychiat.) Univ. Sheff.

WRIGHT, Simon Ronald Aspley Medical Centre, 511 Aspley Lane, Aspley, Nottingham NG8 5RW Tel: 0115 929 2700 Fax: 0115 929 8276 — MB ChB 1980 Dundee; DRCOG 1983; MRCGP 1984; DCH RCP Lond. 1984.

WRIGHT, Stanley Charles Falkirk & District Royal Infrimary, Major's Loan, Falkirk FK1 5QE Tel: 01324 624000 Fax: 01324 616020; 4 Coxburn Brae, Bridge of Allan, Stirling FK9 4PS Tel: 01786 832152 — MB BCh BAO 1977 Belf.; MD Belf. 1988; FRCP Ed. 1993; MRCP (UK) 1982; DRCOG 1983. Cons. Phys. Falkirk Roy. & Dist. Roy. Infirm.; Hon. Sen. Lect. Univ. Edin. Socs: Brit. Thorac. Soc.; Scott. Thoracic Soc.

WRIGHT, Stephen 26 The Crescent, Maidenhead SL6 6AH; Ipsen International, Kensington House, 66 Hammersmith Road, London W14 8UD Tel: 020 7559 2159 — MD 1988 Camb.; MA Camb. 1977; MRCP (UK) 1979; Dip. Pharm. Med. RCP (UK) 1992; MFPM 1992. (London) Sen. Vice-Pres. Clin. Research & Developm. Ipsen Internat. Prev: Cons. Sen. Lect. Roy. Free Hosp. Lond.

WRIGHT, Stephen Alexander 26 Sheepwalk Road, Lisburn BT28 3XQ — MB BCh 1998 Belf.

WRIGHT, Stephen David 7 Byron Road, London W5 3LL — MB ChB 1985 Dundee; MSc (Haemat.) Lond. 1991. Socs: Assoc. Mem. Clin. Path.

WRIGHT, Stephen Edward 26 Pinegarth, Ponteland, Newcastle upon Tyne NE20 9LF — MB ChB 1997 Sheff.; MRCP 2001. Europ. SHO exchange scheme (Gen. Med.), St. Bartholomews Hosp., Lond. & L'Hopital Cantonale de Geneve, Geneva. Prev: SHO Rotat. (Gen. Med.) Roy. Vict. Infirm. Newc.

WRIGHT, Stephen Geoffrey Hospital for Tropical Diseases, Mortimer Market, off Capper St., Tottenham Court Road, London WC1E 6AU Tel: 020 7387 4411 Fax: 020 7388 7645 Email: swright@ishtm.ac.uk — MB BS Lond. 1968; FRCP Lond. 1991; MRCP (UK) 1973; MRCS Eng. LRCP Lond. 1968; DCMT . Lond. 1971. Cons. Phys. Hosp. Trop. Dis.; Phys. King Edwd. VII's Hosp. For Off.; Hon. Sen. Lect. (Clin. Sci.) Lond. Sch. Hyg. & Trop. Med. Prev: Sen. Regist. Hosp. Trop. Dis. Lond.; SHO N.wick Pk. Hosp. Harrow; Ho. Off. (Neurosurg. Studies) Nat. Hosp. Nerv. Dis. Lond.

WRIGHT, Prof Stephen Geoffrey Faculty of Health, St Martin's College, Lancaster LA1 3JD — MB ChB 1985 Liverp.

WRIGHT, Stephen John Seacroft Road Surgery, Seacroft Road, Mablethorpe LN12 2DT Tel: 01507 473483 Fax: 01507 478865 — MB ChB 1986 Leic.; MRCGP 1990.

WRIGHT, Stewart John Willow Green Surgery, Station Road, East Preston, Littlehampton BN16 3AH Tel: 01903 758152 Fax: 01903 859986; 52 Sea Lane, East Preston, Littlehampton BN16 1NE Tel: 01903 786096 — MB BS 1983 Lond.; DCH RCP Lond. 1987; DRCOG 1986. (St. Mary's) Prev: Trainee GP Thanet VTS.; SHO (A & E) Roy. Berks. Hosp. Reading; Ho. Surg. Hillingdon Hosp. Uxbridge.

WRIGHT, Stuart Lloyd 184 Park Road, Bearwood, Smethwick B67 5HU — MB ChB 1989 Birm. Med. Off. (Cas.) Geo. Town Hosp., Cayman Is.s.

WRIGHT, Susan Frances Jane Tel: 01962 732345 Fax: 01962 736034 — MB BChir 1989 Camb.; MRCGP 1994; DRCOG 1992. GP Princip. Alresford. Prev: Trainee GP Winchester VTS.

WRIGHT, Susan Jane 6 Womersley Road, London N8 9AE — MB BS 1984 Lond. Regist. (Anaesth.) Middlx. Hosp. Lond.

WRIGHT

WRIGHT, Suzanne Gaenor 17 Battersby Close, Yarm TS15 9RX — MB BS 1984 Newc.; DRCOG 1986. Trainee GP Cleveland VTS. Socs: BMA & Med. Defence Union. Prev: SHO (A & E) Qu. Eliz. Hosp. Gateshead; SHO (O & G) N. Tees Gen. Hosp. Stockton-on-Tees; SHO (Psychiat.) St. Lukes Hosp. Middlesbrough.

WRIGHT, Tanya Ruth 115 Coleraine Road, Portstewart BT55 7HR — MB ChB 1996 Dundee.

WRIGHT, Thomas John Wyatt Alexander 35 Highgrove Drive, Ballyclare BT39 9XH Tel: 0196 03 42011 — MB BCh BAO 1981 Belf.; MRCGP 1986; DCH Dub. 1985. (Belfast)

WRIGHT, Thomas Paul Markethill Health Centre, Newry St., Markethill, Armagh BT60 1TA Tel: 028 3755 1306 Fax: 028 3755 2148; 62 Ballyloughan Road, Ahorey, Portadown, Craigavon BT62 3TA — MB BCh BAO 1985 Belf.; MRCGP 1990; DRCOG 1989; DCH Dub. 1988. (Belf.)

WRIGHT, Timothy Freeman Scapa Medical Group, Health Centre, New Scapa Road, Kirkwall KW15 1BQ Tel: 01856 885445 Fax: 01856 873556; Westbank, St. Ola, Kirkwall KW15 1TR Tel: 01856 872606 — MB BS 1971 Lond.; DObst RCOG 1976. (Roy. Free) Clin. Asst. (Obst.) Balfour Hosp. Kirkwall; Obst. Ultrasound Balfour Hosp. Kirkwall; Non-Exec. Dir. Orkney HB; Mem. Scott. Auth. Airmed. Examrs. Socs: Brit. Med. Ultrasound Soc. Prev: SHO (Obst.) Vale of Leven Hosp. Alexandria.

WRIGHT, Timothy Grant Sigiri, College Lane, Woking GU22 OEW — MB BS 1972 Lond.; MRCP 1977; MCRS Eng. LRCP Lond. 1972.

WRIGHT, Timothy Samuel 22 Telegraph Lane, Claygate, Esher KT10 0DU — MB BS 1998 Lond.

WRIGHT, Tony 73 Trinity Road, Taunton TA1 3JJ — BM 1991 Soton.

WRIGHT, Trevor (retired) Fields Farm, Ashford Road, Bakewell DE45 1GL Tel: 01629 813966 — MD Belf. 1946, MB BCh BAO 1940; DCH Univ. Lond. 1947. Prev: Cons. Phys. (Handicap. Childr.) Childr. Hosp. Sheff.

WRIGHT, Vanessa Mary Barts & The London NHS Trust, Royal London Hospital, Whitechapel Road, London E1 1BB Tel: 020 7377 7000 Ext: 3911 Fax: 020 7377 7743; 28 Empire Wharf, 235 Old Ford Road, London E3 5NQ Tel: 020 8981 5844 — MB BS Lond. 1966; FRCS Eng. 1972; FRACS (Paed. Surg.) 1976. Cons. Paediat. Surg. Barts & The Lond. Hosp.; Cons. Paediat. Surg. UCL Hosp. Prev: Sen. Regist. Roy. Childr. Hosp. Melbourne, Austral.; Regist. Qu. Mary's Hosp. for Childr. Carshalton & Univ. Coll. Hosp. Lond.

WRIGHT, William Millfield Medical Centre, 63-83 Hylton Road, Sunderland SR4 7AF Tel: 0191 567 9179 Fax: 0191 514 7452; 7 McLaren Way, West Herrington, Houghton-le-Spring DH4 4NP Tel: 0191 584 0717 — MB BS 1977 Newc.; MRCGP 1981; DRCOG 1980. GP Sunderland FPC. Socs: BMA.

WRIGHT, William Bryce (retired) Mill End Cottage, Northleach, Cheltenham GL54 3HJ Tel: 01451 860681 — MB ChB 1950 Glas.; FRCP Lond. 1979, M 1966; FRCP Ed. 1971, M 1955. Prev: Cons. Geriat. S. W.. RHA.

WRIGHT, William Michael Antony (retired) The Moor, Westfield, Hastings TN35 4QR Tel: 01424 754913 — MB BChir 1956 Camb.; MA, MB Camb. 1957, BChir 1956. Prev: Obst. Ho. Surg. St. Paul's Hosp. Hemel Hempstead.

WRIGHTON, Mr John Derek (retired) Cleaves Cliff, 39 Bowleaze Coveway, Preston, Weymouth DT3 6PL Tel: 01305 832418 Fax: 01305 832418 — MB BS 1956 Lond.; FRCS Eng. 1967; DObst RCOG 1958. Hon. Cons. Orthop. W. Dorset Gp. Hosps. & Weymouth & Dist. Hosp. Prev: Sen. Regist. (Orthop.) P.ss Eliz. Orthop. Hosp. Exeter & City.

WRIGHTON, Ronald John (retired) Stream House, Cootham, Storrington, Pulborough RH20 4JT Tel: 01903 742909 — MB BS 1959 Lond.; MB, BS Lond. 1959; MRCP Lond. 1963; FFPHM 1983. Prev: Dir. Pub. Health Mid Downs HA.

WRIGHTSON, Fiona Michelle 48 Cumberland Avenue, Goring-by-Sea, Worthing BN12 6JX — MB ChB 1998 Leic.

WRIGHTSON, Lynne Dr Hewish, Dangare and Partners, The Health Centre, Bartholomew Avenue, Goole DN14 6AW Tel: 01405 767711 Fax: 01405 768212 — MB ChB 1983 Aberd.; MRCGP 1989; DRCOG 1986.

WRIGLEY, David George Email: dgw@preesall.freeserve.co.uk; Fax: 0870 1338796 Email: dgw@preesall.freeserve.co.uk — MB ChB 1997 Sheff.; MRCGP 2001. (Sheffield) NonPrincip. GP, Lancaster, Lancs. Prev: SHO (A & E), Roy. Lancaster Infirm.; Ho. Off. (Surg.), Chesterfield; Ho. Off. (Med.), Oban.

WRIGLEY, Edward Thornton Freshfields, Keepers Lane, Codsall, Wolverhampton WV8 — MB BS 1971 Lond.; DObst RCOG 1974.

WRIGLEY, Edwin John (retired) White Walls, Golf Links Lane, Selsey, Chichester PO20 9DP Tel: 01243 602426 — MB BS 1954 Lond. Prev: Dist. Med. Off. N. Nigeria.

WRIGLEY, Emma Caroline Farndon, 15 Riddings Road, Hale, Altrincham WA15 9DS — MB ChB 1986 Manch.; MFFP 1995; MRCOG 1991. Specialist Regist. (O & G) Wythenshawe Hosp. Prev: Specialist Regist. (O & G) Roy. Surrey Co. Hosp.; Research Fell. (Gyn. Oncol.) Christie Hosp. Manch.; Regist. (O & G) Mersey RHA.

WRIGLEY, Fenella Kate 7 Fountain Road, London SW17 0HG Tel: 020 8682 2471 — MB BS 1996 Lond.; BSc (Hons.) Clin. Sci. Lond. 1995. (St. Geo. Hosp. Med Sch.) SHO Paediat.

WRIGLEY, Mr James Hall (retired) Walnut Tree Cottage, Church Hill, Marnhull, Sturminster Newton DT10 1PU Tel: 01258 820265 — MB ChB Ed. 1944; FRCS Ed. 1948. Prev: Cons. Surg. Bishop Auckland Gen. Hosp.

WRIGLEY, Katrin University Health Service, University of Southampton, Building 48, Highfield, Southampton SO17 1BJ Tel: 023 8055 7531 Fax: 023 8059 3259; 35 Hursley Road, Chandlers Ford, Eastleigh SO53 2FS — MB ChB Bristol 1972. GP Univ. Soton. Health Serv. Prev: GP Portswood Soton.; Trainee GP Bristol VTS; SHO (Psychiat.) Glenside Hosp. Bristol.

WRIGLEY, Mark William c/o Department of Anaesthesia, The Central Middlesex Hospital, Abbey Road, Park Royal, London NW10; 18 May Road, Twickenham TW2 6QP Tel: 020 8894 3432 — MB BS 1982 Lond.; FFA RCS Eng. 1987. Cons. Anaesth. Centr. Middlx. NHS Trust. Socs: Assn. Anaesth. Prev: Sen. Regist. Middlx. Hosp. Lond.; Regist. (Anaesth.) Qu. Charlottes Matern. & Middlx. Hosps. Lond.

WRIGLEY, Peter Francis Martyn Old College House, All Saints Court, Church Lane, Pannal, Harrogate HG3 1NH Tel: 01423 879442 Fax: 01423 879442 Email: peter@wrigley.net — BM BCh 1964 Oxf.; PhD Lond. 1970, BSc 1961; FRCP Lond. 1979, M 1967. (Univ. Coll. Lond. & Magdalen Oxf.) Socs: Assn. Cancer Phys.; Liveryman Soc. Apoth.; ASCO Emerit. Prev: Cons. Phys. (Med. Oncol.) St. Bart. Hosp. Lond.; Dir. Postgrad. Oncol. Train. & Educat. Research Sch. Med. St. Jas. Univ. Hosp. Leeds; Sen. Lect. & Imperial Cancer Research Fund Fell. ICRF Med. Oncol. Unit St. Bart. Hosp. Lond.

WRIGLEY, Richard Alan Waterloo Health Centre, 5 Lower Marsh, London SE1 7RJ Tel: 020 7928 4049 Fax: 020 7928 2644 — MB BS 1986 Lond.

WRIGLEY, Sophia Ruth Derriford Hospital, Derriford Road, Plymouth PL6 8DH Tel: 01752 777111 — MB ChB 1983 Bristol; DCH RCP Lond. 1986; DRCOG 1985. p/t Cons. Anesthetist Derriford Hosp., Plymouth. Socs: Anaest. Res. Soc.& Assn. Anaesth.; Assn. Paediat. Anaesth. Prev: Cons. Anaesth. Roy. Lond. Hosp.; Sen. Regist. Rotat. (Anaesth.) Univ. Coll. Hosp. Lond.

WRIGLEY, Susan Margaret 187 Moorgate Road, Rotherham S60 3AX Tel: 01709 382852 — MB ChB 1974 Birm.; BSc (Med. Biochem.) Birm. 1971; MRCGP 1979. Socs: BMA. Prev: Trainee GP Rotherham VTS; SHO (Med.) Qu. Alexandra Hosp. Cosham; Ho. Off. (Surg.) Halifax Gen. Hosp.

WRITER, Martin Darrell Levett 21 Queensmead Road, Bromley BR2 0ER — MB BS 1991 Lond.; DFFP 1996; DRCOG 1995; DCH RCPS Glas. 1994. (St. Bart.) Socs: Roy. Coll.

WROBLEWSKA, Maria Helena 142 Kings Road, Old Trafford, Manchester M16 9WT; 167 Springfield Crescent, Edgeware, London HA8 8SH — MB BS 1996 Lond.; BSc (Hons.) Psychol. Lond. 1990. (Univ. Coll. Lond.) GP Regist. Edgeware Lond. Prev: SHO (Paediat.) Barnet Gen. Hosp. Lond.; SHO (A & E) Barnet Gen. Hosp. Lond.; Ho. Off. (Surg.) Barnet Gen. Hosp. Lond.

WROBLEWSKI, Professor Boguslaw Michael Centre for Hip Surgery, Wrightington Hospital, Wigan WN6 9EP Tel: 01257 256286 Fax: 01257 256291; The Coach House, Tan House Close, Parbold, Wigan WN8 7HH — MB ChB 1960 Leeds; FRCS Ed. 1966. (Leeds) Cons. Orthop. Surg. Centre for Hip Surg. Wrightington Hosp. Wigan; Prof. Orthop. BioMech. Univ. Leeds 1992. Socs: Fell. BOA; Internat. Hip Soc.; (Pres.) Brit. Hip Soc. Prev: Regist. (Surg.) Leeds Gen. Infirm.; Regist. Robt. Jones & Agnes Hunt Orthop. Hosp. OsW.ry. Sen. Orthop.; Regist. Birm. Roy. Orthop. Hosp.

WROE, Anna Caroline The Vicarage, Coldwell Park Drive, Gateshead NE10 9BY — MB ChB 1997 Birm. Med. Ho. Off. Good Hope Hosp. Sutton Coldfield. Prev: Med. HO. Off.

***WROE, Christopher James** 2 Kings Avenue, Gatley, Cheadle SK8 4JN Email: cwroe@cs.man.ac.uk — BChir 1996 Camb.; MB 1996; MA 1998.

WROE, Stephen John New Southgate Surgery, Buxton Place, off Leeds Road, Wakefield WF1 3JQ Tel: 01924 334400 Fax: 01924 334439; Midsett Cottage, Brockswood Court, Walton, Wakefield WF2 6RD — BM BCh 1985 Oxf.; MA Oxf. 1988; DRCOG 1988.

WROE, Stephen Joseph Department of Neurology, Ipswich Hospital, Ipswich IP4 5PD Tel: 01473 704006 Fax: 01473 704004; 31 Graham Road, Ipswich IP1 3QE Tel: 01473 413451 — MB ChB 1979 Liverp.; MD Liverp. 1993; FRCP Lond. 1996; MRCP (UK) 1983. (Liverp.) Cons. Neurol. Ipswich Hosp. & Addenbrooke's Hosp. Camb. Socs: Internat. League Against Epilepsy; Liverp. Med. Inst.; Assn. Brit. Neurolog. Prev: Sen. Regist. (Neurol.) Nat. Hosp. Qu. Sq. & Guy's Hosp. Lond.; Lect. (Clin. Pharmacol.) Univ. Wales Coll. Med. Cardiff; Regist. (Neurol.) Walton Hosp. Liverp.

WRONG, Professor Oliver Murray Flat 8, 96-100 New Cavendish St., London W1W 6XN Tel: 020 7637 4740 Fax: 020 7637 7006; Email: oliverwrong@compuserve.com — BM BCh Oxf. 1947; DM Oxf. 1964; FRCP Ed. 1970; FRCP Lond. 1967, M 1951. (Oxf.) Emerit. Prof. Med. Univ. Coll. Lond.; Vis. Prof. Med. Univs. Harvard & Sherbrooke 1974, Toronto & McGill 1976. Socs: (Ex-Sec.) Renal Assn. Prev: Prof. Med. Univ. Dundee; Sen. Lect. (Med.) Roy. Postgrad. Med. Sch. Lond.; Chairm. Nat. Kidney Research Fund.

WROTH, Richard Peter Chesterfield Royal Hospital, Chesterfield S44 5BL Tel: 01246 552284 — BM 1987 Soton.; FRCA 1994. Cons.(Anaesth.), Chesterfield Rjoyal Hosp. Prev: Sen. Regist. (Anaesth.) N. Trent Region; Research Regist. (Anaesth.) Roy. Hallamsh. Hosp. Sheff.

WROUGHTON, Marjorie Anne (retired) 30 Royal Standard House, Standard Hill, Nottingham NG1 6FX Tel: 0115 941 7771 Fax: 0115 941 7771 Email: wroughton@royalstandard.fsnet.co.uk — MB ChB 1955 Sheff. Prev: Assoc. Specialist (Dermat.) Univ. Hosp. Nottm.

WROUT, John Dawson Taunton Road Medical Centre, 12-16 Taunton Road, Bridgwater TA6 3LS Tel: 01278 444400 Fax: 01278 423691; Willow House, Ham, Creech St Michael, Taunton TA3 5NZ Tel: 01823 443055 Email: jwrout@cix.co.uk — BM BCh 1971 Oxf.; MA Oxf. 1971; MICGP 1988; FRCGP 1997, MRCGP 1976; DFFP 1993; DObst RCOG 1973. (Guy's) Princip. GP; Assoc. Regional Adviser (Summative Assessm.) Glos., Avon & Som.; Clin. Asst. (Rheum.) Bridgwater Hosp; Examr. MRCGP; Extern. Examr Cert. Fam.pract.Kuwait. Socs: W Som. Med. Club. Prev: Course Organiser Som. VTS; Examr. DRCOG & MICGP; RCGP Coll. Tutor Som.

WU, Alexandra 1 Meadow Bank, Primrose Hill, London NW3 3AY — MB BS 1983 Lond.

WU, Eugene Brian 6 Lambert Jones Mews, Barbican, London EC2Y 8DP Tel: 020 7628 9660 — MB BS 1993 Lond.; MRCP (UK) 1996. (United Med. & Dent. Sch. Lond.) Reg Cardiol. Guys & Thomas. Prev: SHO (Med.) Frimley Pk. Hop.; SHO (A & E) N. Middlx. Hosp.; Ho. Off. (Surg.) Frimley Pk. Hosp.

WU, Felix Siu-Man 6B Peak Hill Gardens, London SE26 4LE — MB ChB 1992 Sheff.

WU, Frederick Chung-Wei Department of Endocrinology, Manchester Royal Infirmary, Manchester M13 9WL Tel: 0161 276 8750 Fax: 0161 276 8019 Email: frederick.wu@man.ac.uk — MB ChB 1972 Ed.; BSc (Hons.) Ed. 1970, MD 1983; FRCP Lond. 1995; FRCP Ed. 1989; MRCP (UK) 1974. (University of Edinburgh) Sen. Lect. (Endocrinol.) Univ. & Roy. Infirm. Manch.; Hon. Cons. Phys. Manch. Roy. Infirm. & St. Mary's Hosp. Manch. Prev: MRC Clin. Sci. MRC Reproduc. Biol. Univ. Edin.; Sen. Regist. (Endocrinol. & Diabetes) Roy. Infirm. Edin.; Hon. Sen. Regist. (Endocrinol.) & MRC Clin. Research Fell. (O & G) Univ. Edin.

WU, Gladys 9 Craven Lodge, 15-17 Craven Hill, London W2 3EN — Medico Cirujano Peru 1970.

WU, Grace Yuen Man Old Home 3, Room 68, Doctors Residence, North Staffordshire Hospital Management, The Limes, Hartshill Road, Stoke-on-Trent ST4 7PS — MB ChB 1992 Bristol.

WU, Kenneth Hoong Jee 37 Ashburton Road, Birkenhead CH43 8TN — MB ChB 1997 Liverp.

WU, Kin-Chung 155 Trehafod Road, Pontypridd CF37 2LL — MB BCh 1997 Wales.

WU, Wing Cheng Kenneth 71 New Edinburgh Road, Uddingston, Glasgow G71 6AB — MB ChB 1991 Manch.

WUBETU, Tebabu 37 Merley Gate, Morpeth NE61 2EP — MB BCh BAO 1984 Belf.; MRCOG 1989. SHO Belf. City Hosp. Socs: BMA.

WULF, Regina 3 New Bridge Avenue, Tettenhall, Wolverhampton WV6 0LW; Victoria Hospital, Accomodation Office, Whinney-Heys-Road, Blackpool FY3 8NR Tel: 01253 300000 — State Exam Med 1993 Frankfurt. Sen. SHO (O & G) Vict. Hosp. Blackpool. Prev: SHO (O & G) Birm. Wom.s Hosp.

WULFF, Christian Hertel Department of Clinical Neurophysiology, Poole Hospital, Longfleet Road, Poole BH15 2JB Tel: 01202 442965 Fax: 01202 442762 Email: cwulff@poole-tr.swest.nhs.uk; 39 Dunkeld Road, Talbot Woods, Bournemouth BH3 7EW Tel: 01202 763293 — MD 1971 Copenhagen. Cons. Clin. Neurophysiol. Poole Hosp. Dorset.

WULFF, Douglas Edward 12 Hollyfield Road, Sutton Coldfield B75 7SG — MB BCh 1975 Witwatersrand.

WUNNA, R The Surgery, 148 Castleford Road, Normanton WF6 2EP Tel: 01924 223636 Fax: 01924 220252 — MB BS 1973 Rangoon; MB BS Med Inst (I) Rangoon 1973. (Rangoon) GP Normanton, W. Yorks.

WUNSCH, Claire Margaret Abbotswood Medical Centre, Defford Road, Pershore WR10 1HZ Tel: 01386 552424; 27 Head Street, Pershore WR10 1DA — MB ChB 1983 Manch.; MRCP (UK) 1987; MRCGP 1992; DRCOG 1991. Prev: Trainee GP Pershore; Regist. (Paediat.) E. Glam. Hosp. Pontypridd & Wellington Hosp., NZ; SHO (O & G) Worcs. Roy. Hosp.

WURM, Peter Kettering General Hospital, Rothwell Road, Kettering NN16 8UZ — State Exam 1991 Aachen; MD Aachen 1993; MRCP (UK) 1995.

WURM, Reinhard Engelbert 5 All Saints Road, Sutton SM1 3DA — MD 1990 Essen; State Exam Med. 1984.

WURR, Catherine Jane West Leeds Child & Adolescent Mental Health Team, Cringlebar House, 415 Bradford Road, Leeds LS28 7HQ Tel: 0113 295 4111 — MB ChB 1987 Leeds; MMedSci. Leeds 1992; MRCPsych. 1992. Cons. Child Adolesc. Psychiat. Child & Adolesc. Ment. Health Serv.s, Leeds; Sen. Clin. Lect. Univ. Leeds. Socs: ACPP. Prev: Sen. Regist. (Child Adolesc. Psychiat.) Yorks. RHA; Trainee Gen. Psych. Bootham Pk. Hosp. York VTS; Ho. Phys. Leeds Gen. Hosp.

WURR, Elizabeth Mary (retired) 70 Melrose Road, Norwich NR4 7PW Tel: 01603 457323 — MB ChB Birm. 1966; BA (Hons.) Open 1989, BA 1984.

WUSU, Oladipo Olusegun Hunponu 76 Dobbies Road, Bonnyrigg EH19 2AZ — MB ChB 1962 Glas.; MD Glas. 1970, MB ChB 1962; FRCP Glas. 1979, M 1977; MFCM RCP (UK) 1974; DPH Glas. 1967.

WYATT, Ann (retired) 9 Vancouver House, 44 Barrack Road, Christchurch BH23 1PF — MB BS Lond. 1947; MRCS Eng. LRCP Lond. 1946; FRCGP 1983, M 1953. Prev: GP Princip. 1955-85.

WYATT, Mr Arthur Powell (retired) The Cottage, 72 Camden Pk Road, Chislehurst BR7 5HF Tel: 020 8467 9477 Fax: 020 8467 9477 — MB BS 1955 Lond.; FRCS Eng. 1960. Prev: Cons. Surgic. Greenwich healthcare Trust.

WYATT, Ben Timothy Brig Royd Surgery, Brig Royd, Ripponden, Sowerby Bridge HX6 4AN Tel: 01422 822209 — MB BS 1985 Lond.; BSc Lond. 1982; MRCGP 1992; DRCOG 1990; DCH RCP Lond. 1989. Hosp. Pract. (Clin. Haemat.) Halifax.

WYATT, Caroline Marie 2 Garden Close, Givens Grove, Leatherhead KT22 8LU — BM BCh 1998 Oxf.

WYATT, Edward Henry (retired) 16 St James Road, Melton, North Ferriby HU14 3HZ Tel: 01482 633606 — MB BS Lond. 1951; FRCP Lond. 1991; FRCP Ed. 1977, M 1967; MRCS Eng. LRCP Lond. 1951; DTM Antwerp 1954; DObst RCOG 1953. Prev: Cons. Dermat. Roy. Hull Hosps. Trust.

WYATT, Elma Priscilla (retired) 16 Casterbridge Road, Dorchester DT1 2AQ — MB BChir 1957 Camb.; MRCS Eng. LRCP Lond. 1957; DObst RCOG 1964. Retd. Gen. Practioner, Dorchester Dorset.

WYATT, Geoffrey Paul Meadowville, 13 Guisborough Road, Great Ayton, Middlesbrough TS9 6AA Tel: 01642 722379 — MB ChB 1973 Liverp.; MRCP (UK) 1978; DCH Eng. 1976. Cons. Paediat. Middlesbrough Gen. Hosp. Prev: Sen. Regist. (Paediat.) Soton. & Portsmouth Hosps.; Clin. Tutor (Child Health) Univ. Manch.; SHO

WYATT

(Paediat.) Coronation; Hosp. Univ. Witwatersrand, Johannesburg, S. Africa.

WYATT, George Bernard School of Tropical Medicine, Pembroke Place, Liverpool L3 5QA Tel: 0151 708 9393 Fax: 0151 707 2052 Email: gwyatt@liv.ac.uk — MB BS 1957 Lond.; FRCP Lond. 1977, M 1961; MRCS Eng. LRCP Lond. 1957; FFPHM 1989; FFCM 1980, M 1974; DTM & H Liverp. 1964; DCH Eng. 1959. (Univ. Coll. Hosp.) Sen. Lect. (Trop. Med.) Liverp. Sch. Trop. Med.; Clin. Dir. (Trop. Med.) Roy. Liverp. Univ. Hosp. Trust; Cons. Phys. Trop. Med. Aintree Hosps. Trust; Civil Cons. Trop. Med. RAF. Socs: Fell. Roy. Soc. Trop. Med. & Hyg.; Internat. Epidemiol. Assn. Prev: Prof. (Community Med.) Univ. Papua New Guinea Port Moresby; Sen. Regist. (Med.) Univ. Coll. Hosp. Ibadan, Nigeria; Ho. Surg. Univ. Coll. Hosp. Lond.

WYATT, Hilary Anne Dept of Child Health, Kings College Hospital, Denmark Hill, London SE5 9RS Email: hilary.wyatt@kcl.ac.uk; 84 Tannsfeld Road, London SE26 5DG — MB BS 1984 Lond.; MRCP (UK) 1988; DCH RCP Lond. 1988; MRCPCH. (Westm.) Prev: Clin. & Research Fell. (Cystic Fibrosis) King's Coll. Hosp. Lond.; Regist. (Child Health) All St.s Hosp. Chatham & King's Coll. Hosp. Lond.; Assoc. Specialist (Cystic Fibrosis) Dept. Child Health King's Coll. Hosp. Lond.

WYATT, James Andrew 24 Sheendale Road, Richmond TW9 2JJ — MB BCh 1958 Wales; DCH Eng. 1963.

WYATT, Jean Louise (retired) 9 Adelaide Terrace, Waterloo, Liverpool L22 8QD Tel: 0151 474 5661 — MB ChB (Hons.) Bristol 1960; MRCGP 1983; DCH Eng. 1978; DTM & H Liverp. 1964. p/t Occasional Locums. Prev: Med. Off. Univ. Health Servs. Univ. Papua New Guinea, Port Moresby.

WYATT, Jeremy Crispin School of Public Policy, University College London, 29 Tavistock Square, London WC1H 9EZ Tel: 020 7504 4986 Fax: 020 7504 4998 Email: jeremy.wyatt@ucl.ac.uk; 12 Greville Park Road, Ashtead KT21 2QT Tel: 01372 273634 — MB BS 1980 Lond.; BA Oxf. 1977, DM 1991; MRCP (UK) 1983; FRCP 1999. (Oxf. & Westm.) Sen. Fell. Health Policy; Dir. Knowledge Managem. Centre; Sen. Research Fell. Centre for Statistics in Med. Univ. Oxf. Socs: (Pres.) Europ. Soc. Artific. Intelligence Med.; (Vice Chairm.) Brit. Med. Informatics Soc.; Fell. Amer. Coll. Med. Informatics. Prev: Med. Informatics Cons. ICRF, 1992-97; MRC Train. Fell. Stanford Univ. 1991-92; Lect. (Med. Informatics) Nat. Heart & Lung Inst. Lond.

WYATT, John Douglas (retired) 4 Cringleford Chase, Norwich NR4 7RS Tel: 01603 501939 — MRCS Eng. LRCP Lond. 1958; MA Camb. 1961, MB 1958, BChir 1957; LMCC 1975; Cert. Family Plann. JCC 1977; DObst RCOG 1960; Cert. Av. Med. 1975. Prev: Sen. Med. Off. H.M. Prison Norwich.

WYATT, Professor John Stephen Department of Paediatrics, University College London Medical School, Rayne Institute, 5 University St., London WC1E 6JJ Tel: 020 7209 6113 Fax: 020 7209 6103 Email: j.wyatt@ucl.ac.uk; 84 Queens Drive, Finsbury Park, London N4 2HW — MB BS 1978 Lond.; BSc Lond. 1975; FRCP Lond. 1993; MRCS Eng. LRCP Lond. 1978; MRCP (UK) 1981; FRCPCH 1997; DCH RCP Lond. 1984. (St. Thos. Hosp., Univ. Lond.) Hon. Cons. & Prof. Neonat. Paediat. Univ. Coll. Lond. Prev: Sen. Lect. & Lect. (Paediat.) Univ. Coll. Lond.

WYATT, Mr Jonathan Paul Forensic Medicine Unit, Medical School, Teviot Place, Edinburgh EH8 9AG Tel: 0131 650 3288 Fax: 0131 650 6529 Email: j.wyatt@ed.ac.uk — MB ChB Sheff.; MB ChB Sheff. 1986; BMedSci (Clin. Physiol.) Sheff. 1984; FRCS Ed. 1992. (Sheff.) Research Fell. (Forens. Med.) Univ. Edin.; Mem. Fac. A & E Med. (Mem. Represen. Bd.). Socs: Brit. Accid. & Emerg. Trainees Assn. (Scott. Represen.). Prev: Sen. Regist. (A & E) Roy. Infirm. Edin.; Regist. (A & E) W.. Infirm. Glas.; Regist. (Surg.) Edin. Roy. Infirm. Assoc. Hosps.

WYATT, Judith Irene Pathology Department, St. James's University Hospital, Beckett St., Leeds LS9 7TF Tel: 0113 206 4571 Fax: 0113 206 5429 Email: judy.wyatt@gw.sjsuh.northy.nhs.uk — MB ChB 1979 Bristol; MRCPath 1986. Cons. Histopath. St. Jas. Hosp. Leeds.

WYATT, Martin Thomas Tree Lodge, 40 Brean Down Avenue, Weston Super Mare BS23 4JQ — MB ChB 1974 Bristol.

WYATT, Megan Glen 30 Balmoral Drive, Barrow-in-Furness LA13 0HX — MB BCh 1989 Witwatersrand.

WYATT, Mr Michael Graham Freeman Hospital, High Heaton, Newcastle upon Tyne NE7 7DN Tel: 0191 284 3111 Fax: 0191 213 1968 Email: mike.wyatt@tfh.north.northy.nhs.uk; 22 Adeline Gardens, Gosforth, Newcastle upon Tyne NE3 4JQ Tel: 0191 285 6858 Email: mikewyatt@lineone.net — MB BS 1982 Lond.; MD Newc. 1993; MSc (Med. Sci.) Glas. 1985; FRCS Eng. 1987; T(S) 1994. (Newcastle 77/82) Cons. Gen. & Vasc. Surg. Freeman Hosp. Newc. u. Tyne. Socs: Vasc. Surg. Soc.; Eur. Soc. Vasc. Surg.; Assn. Surg. Prev: Sen. Regist. (Gen. Surg.) SW HA; Research Fell. Bristol Roy. Infirm.; Regist. Frenchay Hosp. Bristol & Derriford Hosp. Plymouth.

WYATT, Miss Michelle Elizabeth 44 Broomwood Road, London SW11 6HT — MB BChir 1993 Camb.; MA Camb. 1993; FRCS (Oto.) Eng. 1997; FRCS Eng. 1996. (Camb. Univ.) Specialist Regist. N. Thames Region.

WYATT, Miriam Louise The Abbey Practice, The Family Health Centre, Stepgates, Chertsey KT16 8HZ Tel: 01932 561199 Fax: 01932 571842 — BM BS 1990 Nottm.; MRCGP 1995; DRCOG 1994; DGM RCP Lond. 1991.

WYATT, Nell Victoria Station Approach Health Centre, Station Approach, Bradford-on-Avon BA15 1DQ Tel: 01225 866611; Brew Cottage, Green Lane, Turleigh, Bradford-on-Avon BA15 2HH — MB BS 1992 Lond.; MRCGP 1995; DRCOG 1996; DCH RCP Lond. 1995. (Univ. Coll. & Middlx. Sch. Med. Lond.) GP Princip. Bradford-on-Avon.

WYATT, Paul Henry 9 Adelaide Terrace, Liverpool L22 8QD — MB ChB 1994 Sheff.

WYATT, Richard, RD Glenfield Hospital, Groby Road, Leicester LE3 9QP Tel: 0116 287 1471; 40 Fairfield Crescent, Glenfield, Leicester LE3 8EH Tel: 0016 287 0170 Fax: 0116 287 0170 — MB BS 1966 Lond.; MRCS Eng. LRCP Lond. 1966; FFA RCS Eng. 1973; DA Eng. 1969. (St. Mary's) Cons. Anaesth. Glenfield Trust Hosp. Leicester. Socs: Vice-Pres. BAODA; Assn. Anaesths.; Pain Soc. Prev: Sen. Regist. (Anaesth.) Sheff. AHA (T); Ho. Off. St. Mary's Hosp. Lond.; Surg. Lt. RN (Anaesth. Specialist).

WYATT, Richard Damon 3 Orchard Close, March PE15 9DF — MB BS 1998 Lond.

WYATT, Richard Henry 30 Balmoral Drive, Barrow-in-Furness LA13 0HX — MB BCh 1990 Witwatersrand.

WYATT, Robert John The Surgery, Marsh Lane, Misterton, Doncaster DN10 4DL Tel: 01427 890206 Fax: 01427 891311; Heljen House, Caves Lane, Walkeringham, Doncaster DN10 4LS Tel: 01427 891218 — MB ChB 1974 Sheff.; MRCP (UK) 1978. Prev: Clin. Asst. (Gen. Med. & Endocrinol.) Doncaster Roy. Infirm.

WYATT, Robert Miles Poundwell Meadow Health Centre, Poundwell Meadow, Modbury, Ivybridge PL21 0QL Tel: 01548 830666 Fax: 01548 831085 — MB BS 1979 Lond.; DRCOG 1982.

WYATT, Sarah Suzanne Hampton Lodge, Warwick CV35 8QT Tel: 01926 492521 — MB BChir 1991 Camb.; MRCP (UK) 1993; FRCA 1997. Regist. (Anaesth.) Soton. Gen. Hosp. Prev: SHO (Anaesth.) Soton. Gen. Hosp.; SHO (Anaesth.) Roy. United Hosp. Bath; Regist. (Med.) Chas. Gardiner Hosp. Perth, W.. Austral.

WYATT, Susan Elizabeth Belmont House, 3/5 Belmont Grove, Leeds LS2 9DE Tel: 0113 392 5169 Fax: 0113 392 6219 — MB BS 1977 Lond.; MB BS Lond. 1974; BSc Lond. 1974; MRCP (UK) 1981; DCH Eng. 1979. (Kings Coll. Hosp. Med. Sch. Lond.) Cons. Community Paediat. Leeds Healthcare. Prev: Sen. Regist. (Community Paediat.) Oxf. RHA; Sen. Regist. (Paediat.) Univ. Coll. Hosp. Lond.; Regist. (Haemat.) Roy. Postgrad. Med. Sch. Lond.

WYATT, Susan Jane St Augustines Medical Practice, 4 Station Road, Keynsham, Bristol BS31 2BN Tel: 0117 986 2343 Fax: 0117 986 1176 — MB BS Lond. 1970; MRCS Eng. LRCP Lond. 1970; MRCGP 1977; DCH Eng. 1975; DA Eng. 1973. (Univ. Coll. Hosp.) Prev: Med. Intern Coney Is. Hosp. New York, USA; SHO (Paediat.) Hull Roy. Infirm.; SHO (Cas.) Edgware Gen. Hosp.

WYATT, Suzanne Twyn Simon Farm, Argoed, Blackwood NP12 0JA — MB BCh 1993 Wales.

WYATT, Thomas Andrew Latham House Medical Practice, Sage Cross Street, Melton Mowbray LE13 1NX Tel: 01664 854949 Fax: 01664 501825 — MB ChB 1985 Liverp.; MRCGP 1989; Dip. IMC RCS Ed. 1990. Mem. (Vice-Chairm.) Rutland & Leics. Accid. Care Schehem (Affil. to BASICS); Clin. Asst. (Rheum.) Leicester Gen. Hosp. Socs: BASICS; Primary Care Rheum. Soc.

WYBORN, Alison Jane Nerina The Timbers, 66 Burwood Road, Walton-on-Thames KT12 4AL; Cambridge House, 3 Southampton Road, Romsey SO51 8AD — BM 1990 Soton.; MRCGP 1995; DRCOG 1994; DFFP 1994; DCH RCP Lond. 1993. (Soton.) GP Asst. The Grattan Surg. Hants.; GP Asst. Endless St. Surg. Salisbury. Prev: Trainee GP Nightingale Surg. Romsey Hants.; SHO (Psychiat.) Salisbury; SHO (O & G) St. Mary's Hosp. Portsmouth.

WYBORN, Mary Vinnien Thomson Ivy Street Medical Practice, 5 Ivy Street, Ipswich IP1 3QW Tel: 01473 254718 Fax: 01473 287790 — MB BS 1971 Lond.; MRCS Eng. LRCP Lond. 1972; DA Eng. 1975; DObst RCOG 1973. (St. Mary's) Prev: Clin. Asst. (Anaesth.) Huntingdon Co. Hosp.; Regist. (Anaesth.) Addenbrooke's Hosp. Camb.; Regist. (Anaesth.) & SHO Hillingdon Hosp. Uxbridge.

WYBREW, Maria Elizabeth Wentworth Street Surgery, 15 Wentworth Street, Huddersfield HD1 5PX Tel: 01484 530834; Brook House Farm, Clough Road, Golcar, Huddersfield HD7 4JX — MB ChB 1985 Manch.; MB ChB (Hons.) Manch. 1985; BSc (Hons.) Manch. 1982. (Manchester)

WYBREW, Robin Wilfrid James Wentworth Street Surgery, 15 Wentworth Street, Huddersfield HD1 5PX Tel: 01484 530834; Brook House Farm, Clough Road, Golcar, Huddersfield HD7 4JX — MB ChB 1983 Manch.; MRCGP 1988; Dip. Clin. Hypn. (Distinc.) Sheff. 1991. (Manchester)

WYCHERLEY, Christine Rebecca Sidney Powell Avenue Family Health Centre, Sidney Powell Avenue, Westvale, Kirkby, Liverpool L32 0PL Tel: 0151 546 5103 Fax: 0151 547 2729; 1 Tennyson Drive, Billinge, Wigan WN5 7EJ — MB ChB 1977 Liverp.

WYCHRIJ, Oryst Brook Haven, Princess of Wales Hospital, Stourbridge Road, Bromsgrove B61 0BB Tel: 01527 488284 Fax: 01527 488281 — MB ChB 1975 Birm.; MRCPsych 1981. Cons. Psychiat. Elderly BromsGr. & Redditch.

WYCLIFFE-JONES, Keith Culduthel Road Surgery, Ardlarich, 15 Culduthel Road, Inverness IV2 4AG Tel: 01463 712233 — MB ChB 1983 Ed.; BSc (Med. Sci) 1981; FRCGP 1994, M 1987; DRCOG 1986.

WYCLIFFE-JONES, Stephen Christopher Ashley (retired) 7 Morven Road, Inverness IV2 4BU Tel: 01463 235880 — MB BS 1949 Lond.

***WYDENBACH, Kirsty Ann** 16 The Ridgeway, Fetcham, Leatherhead KT22 9AZ Tel: 01372 372587 — MB BS 1998 Lond.; MB BS Lond 1998; BSc Lond. 1995.

WYER, Anthony Ian Dorset County Hospital, Williams Avenue, Dorchester DT1 2JY Tel: 01305 251150 Email: ian.wyer@doctors.org.uk — MB BS 1998 Lond.; MB BS Lond 1998; BA. (St Barts/Roy.Lond.Hosps)

WYER, Jonathan Francis 23D Bromell's Road, Clapham, London SW4 0BN Tel: 020 7720 6114 — MB BS 1990 Lond. SHO (Paediat.) Qu. Mary Hosp. Childr. Sutton.

WYER, Simon Richard 19 Westlands, Comberton, Cambridge CB3 7EH — MB BCh 1998 Wales.

WYETH, Simon Walter Faversham Health Centre, Bank St., Faversham ME13 8QR Tel: 01795 532192; 27 Abbey Street, Faversham ME13 7BE — MB BS 1983 Lond.; MRCGP 1987; DCH RCP Lond. 1986; DRCOG 1985.

WYGANOWSKA, Maria Ewa Teresa 13 Squirrels Heath Avenue, Gidea Park, Romford RM2 6AD — LRCPI & LM, LRSCI & LM 1953; LRCPI & LM, LRCSI & LM 1953.

WYKE, Barry Darrell 25 Boundary Road, London NW8 0JE Tel: 020 7624 0491 — MD 1965 Sydney; MB BS (Hons.) 1945. (Sydney) Dir. Neurol. Research Unit RCS Eng.; Sen. Lect. Applied Physiol. Inst. Basic Med. Scs. Univ. Lond.; Mem. Bd. Studies in Physiol. Univ. Lond.; Examr. (Physiol.) Exam. Bd. in Eng. Socs: Brain Research Assn. Internat. Assn. Study Pain.; DHSS Working Gp. Back Pain. Prev: Fell. Rockefeller Foundat. 1948; Beit-Memor. Research Fell. 1949-50; Clin. Research Asst. Nuffield Dept. Surg. Oxf. 1949-50.

WYKE, Margaret Elizabeth Watling Vale Medical Centre, Burchard Crescent, Shenley Church End, Milton Keynes MK5 6EY Tel: 01908 501177 Fax: 01908 504916; 7 Rylstone Close, Heelands, Milton Keynes MK13 7QT Tel: 01908 314227 — MB BS 1978 Lond.; MRCS Eng. LRCP Lond. 1978; DRCOG 1982. Prev: Trainee GP Bedford VTS; Ho. Off. (Med.) Wexham Pk. Hosp. Slough; Ho. Off. (Surg.) Burton Gen. Hosp.

WYKE, Peter Leonard (retired) Trefynant Hall, Trefynant Park, Acrefair, Wrexham LL14 3SR Tel: 01978 822867 — MB BS 1978 Lond.; LLM Wales 1993; MA Camb. 1978, BA 1974; MFOM RCP Lond. 1993, A 1987; C Eng 1965; FIMechE 1996, M 1962; FIChemE 1996, M 1994, G 1960; Spec. Accredit. Occupat. Med. JCHMT 1995. Prev: Sen. Med. Off. (Toxicol.) Imperial Chem. Indust. Ltd. (Chem. Polymers Ltd.).

WYKE, Richard John The Ipswich Hospital, Heath Road, Ipswich IP4 5PD Tel: 01473 712233 — MB BS 1972 Lond.; MD 1983 Lond.; FRCP 1995 Lond.; MRCP 1975 UK; AKC. (St. Geo.) Cons. Phys. & Gastroenterol. Ipswich Hosp. Prev: Sen. Regist. (Gen. Med.) Walsgrave Hosp. Coventry; Research Fell. Liver Unit King's Coll. Hosp. Lond.; Regist. (Gen. Med.) Leeds Gen. Infirm.

WYKES, Catherine Beatrice 27A Canonbury Square, London N1 2AL — MB BS 1993 Lond.

WYKES, Clare Elizabeth 6 Byng Road, Tunbridge Wells TN4 8EJ Tel: 01892536421 Fax: 01892536421 — MB BS 1998 Lond. (LHMC (University of London))

WYKES, Emma Louise Clattwm, Trefnant, Denbigh LL16 5UP — BChir 1996 Camb.

WYKES, Faye Cara 18 Monkhams Lane, Woodford Green IG8 0NS — MB BS 1998 Lond.

WYKES, Kathryn Jane Liverpool Road Health Centre, 9 Mersey Place, Liverpool Road, Luton LU1 1HH Tel: 01582 31321 — MB ChB 1989 Liverp.; MRCGP 1993. Trainee GP Wycombe HA VTS.

WYKES, Peter (retired) Beech House Surgery, Beech House, 69 Vale Street, Denbigh LL16 3AY Tel: 01745 812863 Fax: 01745 816574 — MB BS 1968 Lond. Prev: Ho. Phys. St. Geo. Hosp. Lond.

WYKES, Peter Revill The Surgery, 1 Waynflete Square, London W10 6UX Tel: 020 8969 1242 Fax: 020 8968 3045 — MB BS 1956 Lond.; MRCS Eng. LRCP Lond. 1956; DA Eng. 1958. (Westm.) Socs: Assoc. Mem. Roy. Soc. Med: Prev: Med. Regist. Gordon Hosp. (W.m. Hosp.); Regist. St. Jas. Hosp. Balham; Ho. Surg. W.m. Hosp. Gyn. Dept.

WYKES, Mr Philip Robert 23 Avon Road, Hale, Altrincham WA15 0LB — MB ChB 1993 Bristol; FRCs 1998. Specialist Regist. Orthop. N. W. Rotat.

WYKES, Richard James Clattwm, Plas Chambers Road, Denbigh LL16 5UP; 32 Gerald Street, Wrexham LL11 1EL — MB BS 1993 Lond.; DRCOG 1996. SHO (Gen. Med.) Wrexham; GP Regist. Wrexham Area. Prev: SHO (Paediat.) Wrexham; SHO Timam, New Zealand; SHO (O & G) Wrexham.

WYKES, Timothy Robert (retired) 11 Clarence Road, Ventnor PO38 1NE Tel: 01983 855740 — MRCS Eng. LRCP Lond. 1967; MA Dub.; LMCC 1972. Prev: Surg. Chief Off. Roy. Fleet Auxilliary Serv. (Merchant Navy).

WYKES, Mr William Nicholas Ross Hall Hospital, 221 Crookston Road, Glasgow G52 3NQ Tel: 0141 810 3151; 20 Merrylee Road, Newlands, Glasgow G43 2SH — MB ChB 1976 Bristol; FRCS Eng. (Ophth.) 1983; FRCOphth 1988; DO RCS Eng. 1982. Cons. Ophth. & Clin. Dir. S.. Gen. Hosp. Glas. Socs: UKISCRS; BOPA; SOC. Prev: Sen. Regist. Univ. Hosp. Wales Cardiff & St. Woolos Hosp. Newport; Regist. P.ss Alexandra Eye Pavil. Edin.; SHO (Ophth.) N.ampton Gen. Hosp.

WYLD, Lynda Walker Edge Farm, Walker Edge, Bolsterstone, Sheffield S36 4ZA — MB ChB 1990 Sheff.; FRCS Eng. 1994; FRCS Ed. 1994.

WYLDE, Edith Margaret (retired) Chapel Cottage, Wetherden, Stowmarket IP14 3LB Tel: 01359 240372 — MB ChB 1950 St. And.; DObst RCOG 1952; DA Eng. 1955. Prev: MO i/c Matern. & child health,Kuala Lumpur.

WYLDES, Michael Peter 89 Marsh Lane, Solihull B91 2PE Tel: 0121 705 9986 Email: wyldes@compuserve.com — MB ChB 1983 Leic.; BA Oxf. 1980; MA Oxf. 1992; MRCOG 1988; DAdvObstUltrasound RCR/RCOG 1993. Cons. O & G Birm. Heartlands Hosp.; Sen. Lect. (Obst. & Gyn.) Birm. Univ. Socs: Brit. Med. Ultrasound Soc.; Brit. Gyn. Endoscopy Soc. Prev: Sen. Regist. Manor Hosp. Walsall; Regist. (O & G) Centr. Birm. & S. Birm. Hosps.

WYLIE, Alan Scott Room F17, Primary Care Trust, Stobhill Hospital, Glasgow Tel: 0141 531 3231 — MB ChB 1985 Aberd.; MRCPsych 1990; Dip. Forens. Med. Glas. 1995. Cons. & Hon. Sen. Lect. (Psychiat.) Glas. Community & Ment. Health Care Trust. Socs: Soc. Study Addic. to Alcohol & Other Drugs. Prev: Sen. Regist. &

WYLIE

Hon Lect. (Psychiat.) Glas. HB; Assoc. Psychiat. Lond.; Regist. (Psychiat.) Warlingham Pk. Surrey.

WYLIE, Anne Margaret Hunter Health Centre, Andrew Street, East Kilbride, Glasgow G74 1AD Tel: 01355 906676 Fax: 01355 906676; 9 Moor Road, Eaglesham, Glasgow G76 0BA Tel: 01355 303597 — MB ChB Glas. 1990; MRCGP 1994; DRCOG 1993.

WYLIE, Cecilia Elizabeth Community child health, Maple House East Surrey Hospital, Canada Avenue, Redhill RH1 5RH Tel: 01737 768511 Ext: 6872; 72 Hazelwick Road, Crawley RH10 1NH — MB ChB 1982 Dundee; DRCOG 1984. SCMO (Child Health) E. Surrey HA Redhill.

WYLIE, Cedric Robert Robertson (retired) 73 Stockton Lane, York YO31 1JA Tel: 01904 421055 — MB ChB Glas. 1957; MRCP Ed. 1963. Prev: Cons. Haemat. York Health Dist.

WYLIE, Professor Charles Murray 26 Clarence Way, Horley RH6 9GT Tel: (01293) 771038; 1607 Dicken Drive, Ann Arbor MI 48103, USA Tel: 00 1 3137692632 — MB ChB Glas. 1947; MD Glas. 1957; FFCM RCP (UK) 1972; FFPHM RCP (UK) 1990; DTM & H Eng. 1958; DrPH John Hopkins 1956. (Glas.) Indep. Pract. (Geriat. Med.) Ann Arbor Michigan, USA; Prof. Emerit. Pub. Health Administ. & Prof. Health Gerontol. Univ. Michigan Sch. Pub. Health, Ann Arbor, USA. Socs: Fell. Amer. Pub. Health Assn.; Fell. Amer. Geriat. Soc. Prev: Assoc. Prof. Pub. Health Administ. Johns Hopkins Univ. Sch. Hyg. Baltimore, USA; Lt-Cdr. Med. Corps USN Washington, USA.

WYLIE, David Wright (retired) 11 The Highway, Sutton SM2 5QT — BSc (Hons.) Glas. 1946, PhD 1949, MB ChB 1953. Prev: Chairm. & Pres. Europ. Div. Sterling Drug Inc.

WYLIE, Eric Samuel Black Moor Road Surgery, Mawdesley, Ormskirk L40 2QE Tel: 01704 822240 — MB ChB 1954 Liverp. (Liverp.) Prev: Ho. Phys. Clatterbridge Hosp.; Obst. Ho. Surg. Ormskirk Co. Hosp.; Sen. Ho. Off. Alder Hey Childr. Hosp. Liverp.

WYLIE, Fiona Mary Shearer Flat 4, 12 Brittany Road, St Leonards-on-Sea TN38 0RD — MB BS 1990 Lond.

WYLIE, Gordon Leonard 3 Calton Road, Lyncombe Hill, Bath BA2 4PP Tel: 01225 429247 — MB ChB 1949 Glas. (Glas.) Socs: BMA. Prev: Surg. Lt.-Cdr. RN; Ho. Surg. W.. Infirm. Glas.; Ho. Phys. Roy. Infirm. Worcester.

WYLIE, Graeme Woodland View Surgery, Woodland View, West Rainton, Houghton-le-Spring DH4 6RQ Tel: 0191 584 3809 Fax: 0191 584 9177; 6 Marsham Close, Cleadon Village, Sunderland SR6 7PP Tel: 0191 536 2702 — MB ChB 1983 Sheff.; MB ChB (Hons.) Sheff. 1983; BSc Sheff. 1983; MRCGP 1987; DRCOG 1987; Cert. Family Plann. 1987. Aurthur Hall Gold Medal Path. 1981. Prev: Ho. Phys. (Profess. Med. Unit) N.. Gen. Hosp. Sheff.; SHO (Gen. Med. Rotat.) Freeman & Newc. Gen. Hosps. Newc. u. Tyne; Trainee GP N.umbria VTS.

WYLIE, Graham Leatham Parexel Lts, River Court, 50 Oxford Road, Denham,, Uxbridge UB9 4 Tel: 01895 23800 Fax: 01304 618299 Email: graham_wylie@sandwich.pfizer.co; Red Tiles, Beauchamps Lane, Nonington, Dover CT15 4EZ — MB BS 1987 Lond.; BSc Lond. 1982. (St. Bart. Hosp. Lond.) Med. Dir.- Europe N.sea Region. Socs: BMA- Full Mem.; RCM. Prev: Business & Quality Developm. Manager Pfizer Ltd. Sandwich; Clin. Developm. Operat. Manager Pfizer Ltd. Sandwich; Dir. Pfizer Inc. New York.

WYLIE, Mr Ian Gordon The London Imaging Centre, 11 Wimpole St., London W1M 7AB Tel: 020 7580 5255; 44 Cronks Hill Road, Redhill RH1 6LZ Tel: 01737 245990 — MB BS 1961 Lond.; FRCS Ed. 1968; MRCS Eng. LRCP Lond. 1961; FRCR 1975; FFR 1972; DMRD Eng. 1970. (St. Mary's) Cons. Radiol. Roy. Lond. Hosp. Socs: Eur. Soc. Neuroradiol. & Brit. Soc. Neuroradiols. Prev: Ho. Surg. St. Mary's Hosp. Lond.; Regist. (Gen. Surg.) SE Metrop. RHB; Sen. Regist. (Radiodiag.) Lond. Hosp.

WYLIE, Iris Lorraine 38 Derrycreevy Road, Dungannon BT71 6RZ — MB BCh BAO 1997 Belf.

WYLIE, James Pinson 7 Dyott Road, Moseley, Birmingham B13 9QZ — MB BS 1990 Lond.; MRCP (UK) 1993. SHO (Clin. Oncol.) Christie Hosp. Manch. Prev: SHO (Med.) S. Warks. Hosp.

WYLIE, Jennifer Margaret Great Ayton Health Centre, Rosehill, Great Ayton, Middlesbrough — MB BS 1988 Lond. SHO (Accid & Emerg.) Middlesbrough Gen. Hosp. Prev: Ho. Off. (Surg.) Harrogate Dist. Hosp.; Ho. Off. (Med.) Derbysh. Roy. Infirm.

WYLIE, John Buchanan 10 Southlands, Holmes Chapel, Crewe CW4 7EU Tel: 01477 35787; 10 Southlands, Holmes Chapel, Crewe CW4 7EU Tel: 01477 35787 — MB ChB 1963 Glas.; MRCGP 1972; DA Eng. 1968; DObst RCOG 1965.

WYLIE, Judith Haematology Department, Darlington Memorial Hospital, Holyhurst Road, Darlington DL3 6HX Tel: 01325 380100 — MB BS 1983 Newc.; MRCP (UK) 1988. Staff Grade (Haemat.) Darlington Memor. Hosp. Prev: Sen. Regist. (Genitourin. Med.) Sunderland Dist. Gen. Hosp.; Regist. (Haemat. & Gen. Med.) Sunderland Roy. Infirm.

WYLIE, Kevan Richard Porterbrook Clinic, 75 Osbourne Road, Nether Edge, Sheffield S10 3TL Tel: 0114 271 6671 Fax: 0114 271 8693 Email: k.r.wylie@sheffield.ac.uk — MB ChB 1985 Liverp.; MMedSc Leeds 1991; MRCPsych 1989; MHSM 1992; DFFP 1993; MD 1999. Cons. Psychiat. Sheff. Socs: Inst. Health Servs. Managem.; Soc. for Scientif. Study of Sexuality; Accred. Mem. BASMT. Prev: Sen. Regist. (Psychiat.) Yorks. RHA; Regist. Rotat. (Psychiat.) Leeds; SHO (A & E) Walton Hosp. Liverp.

WYLIE, Lesley Anne — MB ChB 1988 Ed.

WYLIE, Myra (retired) 11 The Highway, Sutton SM2 5QT — BSc Glas. 1949, MB ChB 1954. Prev: Med. Off. Lond. Boro. Sutton.

WYLIE, Paul Gerard 19 Shalloch Park, Doonfoot, Ayr KA7 4HL — MB ChB 1981 Dundee; MRCGP 1985; FFA RCSI 1993; DA (UK) 1991; DRCOG 1983. Cons. AnE.hetist, Ayrsh. & Arran Hosp.s. Socs: Assn. Anaesth.; Glas. & W. Soc. of AnE.hetists; Scott. Intens. Care Soc. Prev: Sen. Regist. (Anaesth.) N. & Yorks. Region.; Regist. Rotat. (Anaesth.) Vict. Infirm. Glas.; GP Hemel Hempstead.

WYLIE, Philip Arthur Lawson 2 West Walks, Dorchester DT1 1RE — MB ChB 1984 Bristol; BSc Bristol 1981; MRCP (UK) 1987; DTM & H RCP Lond. 1993; DCH RCP Lond. 1987. Cons. Paediat.

WYLIE, Robert Daryll Stewart Camps Bay House, Downderry, Torpoint PL11 3LG — MB ChB 1984 Aberd.

WYLIE, Robert Malcolm Church Lane Surgery, 24 Church Lane, Brighouse HD6 1AS Tel: 01484 714349 Fax: 01484 720479 — MB ChB 1978 Leeds; MRCGP 1982; DRCOG 1981. Clin. Asst. (Genitourin. Med.) Huddersfield. Socs: BMA.

WYLIE, Ronald John (retired) flat 6D, Pollokshields Square, Pollokshields, Glasgow G41 4QT Tel: 0141 423 9713 Fax: 0141 423 9713 Email: rwyhe2@doctors.org.uk — MB ChB Glas. 1957; DA RCPSI 1966; DObst RCOG 1961.

WYLIE, Sandra (retired) 16 Shorelands, Greenisland, Carrickfergus BT38 8FB Tel: 02890 862072 — MB BCh BAO 1950 Belf.; FRCGP 1980. Prev: Res. Med. Off. Roy. Vict. Hosp. Belf.

WYLIE, Stewart 61 Noblehill Avenue, Dumfries DG1 3HS — MB ChB 1993 Glas. SHO (A & E) Ayr Hosp.; SHO (Obst. & Gyn.) Greenock Inverclyde. Prev: Ho. Off. (Med.) CrossHo. Hosp.

WYLIE, Susan St Margarets Health Centre, St. Margaret's Drive, Auchterarder PH3 1JH Tel: 01764 662614/662275 Fax: 01764 664178 — MB ChB 1987 Ed.; MRCGP 1994; DRCOG 1992; DCH RCPS Glas. 1992; DA (UK) 1989. Prev: Trainee GP Alloa; SHO (Anaesth. & Med.) Ashington Gen. Hosp.

WYLIE, Thomas Alan (retired) The Old Schoolhouse, Moneydie, Luncarty, Perth PH1 3HZ Tel: 01738 437 Email: alpha@wylie3demon.co.uk — BSc (Pure Sci.) Glas. 1941, MB ChB 1943; MRCPsych 1972; DPM Lond. 1950. Cons. Psychiat. Murray Roy. & Murthly Hosps. Perth. Prev: Regist. (Trainee Specialist) Kingseat Ment. Hosp.

WYLLIE, Professor Andrew David Hamilton Department of Pathology, Tennis Court Road, Cambridge CB2 1QP Tel: 01223 333691 Fax: 01223 339067 Email: ahw21@cam.ac.uk — DSc Aberd. 1998; FRS 1995; FRCP Ed. 1993; FRSE 1991; FRCPath 1987, M 1975; PhD Aberd. 1975, BSc 1964; MRCP (UK) 1971; MB ChB Aberd. 1967. (Aberd.) Prof. of Path. & Head of Dept. of Path. Univ. of Camb. Socs: Path. Soc.; Amer. Assn. Cancer Research; Found. Mem. Acad. Med. Sci. Prev: Head Dept. Path. & Prof. Experim. Path. Univ. Edin.; Research Fell. Cancer Research Campaign; Lect. (Path.) Edin. Univ.

WYLLIE, Anne Margaret 9 Crawford Crescent, Uddingston, Glasgow G71 7DP Tel: 01698 324377 — MB ChB 1960 (Hons.) Aberd.; FRCS Ed. 1966; DO Eng. 1963. Cons. Ophth. Lanarksh. Health Bd. Socs: Scott. Ophth. Club. Prev: Sen. Regist. (Eye) Aberd. Gen. Gp. Hosps.; Lect. (Ophth.) Univ. Manch.

WYLLIE, Brendan Warren (retired) Lower Wythall, Walford, Ross-on-Wye HR9 5SD Tel: 01989 57755 — MB BCh BAO 1941 Dub.; BA, MB BCh BAO Dub. 1941. Prev: Med. Off. Matern. & Child Welf. Clinics Rolvenden & Wittersham.

WYLLIE, David Hamilton 37 Thorsby Road, Walkley, Sheffield S6 2PG — MB BS 1992 Lond.; MRCP (UK) 1995. Hon: Regist. (Rheum.) Roy. Hallamsh. Hosp. Sheff.

WYLLIE, Miss Frances Jane 12 Glamis Drive, Dundee DD2 1QL Tel: 01382 668700 — MB ChB Ed. 1975; FRCS Ed. 1979. Med. Off. (Plastic Surg.) Dundee Roy. Infirm. Socs: Profess. Assoc. Brit. Assn. Plastic Surgs.; Assoc. Mem. Brit. Soc. Surg. Hand. Prev: Fell. Louisville Hand Surg. Kentucky, USA; Regist. Burns Unit Birm. Accid. Hosp.; Regist. (Plastic Surg.) Bangour Gen. Hosp.

WYLLIE, George Alexander McHarg (retired) Overbeck, 7 Old Godley Lane, Halifax HX3 6XQ Tel: 01422 359692 — MB ChB Glas. 1961; FRCOG 1980, M 1967. Prev: Cons. (O & G) Halifax Gen. Hosp.

WYLLIE, James Hamilton 2 James Street, Edinburgh EH15 2DS — MB ChB 1997 Ed.

WYLLIE, Professor John Hamilton 10 Seaview Road, Cummingston, Burghead, Elgin IV30 5YU Tel: 01343 835946 Fax: 01343 835946 Email: jh_wyllie@tesco.net — BSc Aberd. 1954, MD (Hon.) 1961, MB ChB (Hon.) 1957; FRCS Eng. 1964; FRCS Ed. 1964. (Aberd.) Emerit. Prof. Surgic. Studies Univ. Coll. Lond. Med. Sch. Prev: Hon. Cons. Gen. Surg., Whittington Hosp. & UCL Hosp.s; Wolfson Lect. in Surg. Biochem. RCS Eng.; Lect. (Surg.) Univ. Aberd.

WYLLIE, Jonathan Peter Department of Neonatology, South Cleveland Hospital, Marton Road, Middlesbrough TS4 3BW Tel: 01642 850850; 42 Langbaurgh Road, Hutton Rudby, Yarm TS15 0HL — BSc (Hons.) Experim. Immunol. & Oncol. Manch. 1983, MB ChB 1986; FRCP. Cons. Neonat. S. Cleveland Hosp. Middlesbrough. Socs: FRCP; FRCPCH.

WYLLIE, Sheila Margery Jane Department of Ophthalmology, Scunthorpe General Hospital, Cliff Gardens, Scunthorpe DN15 7BH Tel: 01724 282282; 10 The Old Estate Yard, Normanby, Scunthorpe DN15 9JA Tel: 01724 720298 — MB BS 1961 Lond.; MRCS Eng. LRCP Lond. 1961. (St. Mary's) Clin. Asst. in Ophth. Scunthorpe War Memor. Hosp.; Med. Off. (Sch. Health Serv.) Humberside AHA; Med. Off. Family Plann. Assn. Clinic Scunthorpe. Mem. BMA.

WYMAN, Mr Andrew Northern General Hospital, Herries Road, Sheffield S5 7AU Tel: 0114 226 6985 Fax: 0114 271 4480 — MB ChB 1982 Sheff.; MD Sheff. 1992; FRCS Eng. 1986. Cons. Surg. N. Gen. Hosp. Sheff. Prev: Sen. Regist. (Surg.) Roy. Hallamsh. Hosp. Sheff.; Vis. Lect. (Surg.) Chinese Univ. Hong Kong; Lect. (Surg.) Univ. Sheff. & N.. Gen. Hosp. Sheff.

WYMAN, Arthur Lewis (retired) 65 Nassau Road, Barnes, London SW13 9QG Tel: 020 8748 6670 — MD 1940 Lond.; MB BS 1935; FRCP Lond. 1970, M 1940. Prev: Phys. Char. Cross Hosp. Lond.

WYMAN, David Anthony Park Lane Surgery, 8 Park Lane, Broxbourne EN10 7NQ; 22 Graham Avenue, Broxbourne EN10 7DP Tel: 01992 443979 — MB BS 1974 Lond.; MRCS Eng. LRCP Lond. 1974; DObst RCOG 1976. (Westm.) Clin. Asst. (Diabetes) Qu. Eliz. II Hosp. Welwyn Gdn. City. Socs: Roy. Soc. Med.

WYNANDS, R W A Filey Surgery, Station Avenue, Filey YO14 9AE Tel: 01723 515881 Fax: 01723 515197 — Artsexamen 1988 Rotterdam; Artsexamen 1988 Rotterdam.

WYNCOLL, Duncan Lloyd Andrew Intensive Care, East Wing, St. Thomas Hospital, Lambeth Palace Road, London SE1 7EH Tel: 020 7960 5843 Fax: 020 7960 5843 — MB BS 1989 Lond.; DICM 1998; EDIC 1997; FRCA 1994. Cons. Intensivist Dept. A Intens. Care St. Thomas Hosp. Lond. Socs: Intens. Care Soc.; Europ. Soc. of Intens. Care Med.; Soc. of Critical Care Med. Prev: SHO (Anaesth.) Guy's Hosp. & Lewisham Trust Hosp.; Sen. Regist. Kings Hosp. Liver Unit, Lond.; Sen. Regist. Dept of Anaesth., Guys Hosp. Lond.

WYNDHAM, Jonathan Gabriel 2 Hill Rise, London NW11 6NA — MB BS 1973 Lond.; MRCP (UK) 1979; DCH Eng. 1977. (Westm.) Prev: Ho. Phys. Qu. Mary's Hosp. Roehampton; SHO (Clin. Chem. & Haemat.) N.wick Pk. Hosp. Harrow; SHO (Paediat.) St. Stephen's Hosp. Fulham.

WYNDHAM, Michael Trevor Lane End Medical Group, 25 Edgwarebury lane, Edgware HA8 8LJ Tel: 020 8958 4233 Fax: 020 8905 4657 — MB BS 1978 Lond.; MRCS Eng. LRCP Lond. 1978; MRCGP 1983; DRCOG 1980. (Westm.) Course Organiser Barnet & Edgware Gen. Hosp. VTS. Prev: Clin. Asst. (Thoracic) N.wick Pk. Hosp. Harrow.

WYNE, Khalid Osman Abeer 34 Morden House, London Road, Morden SM4 5HH — MB BS 1993 Lond.

WYNES, Christopher William Sutton Hill Medical Practice, Maythorne Close, Sutton Hill, Telford TF7 4DH Tel: 01952 586471 Fax: 01952 588029; Field Lane, Kemberton, Shifnal TF11 9LW Tel: 01952 586471 — MB BS 1965 Lond.; MB BS (Hnrs. Med.) Lond. 1965; MRCS Eng. LRCP Lond. 1965. (King's Coll. Hosp.) Socs: BMA. Prev: Med. Off. Internat. Grenfell Assn. N.W. River Labrador; Ho. Phys. & Ho. Surg. Dulwich Hosp.

WYNESS, Phyllis Jane 101 Newark Street, Greenock PA16 7TW — MB ChB 1969 Aberd. SHO Larkfield Hosp. Greenock.

WYNFORD-THOMAS, David Wynford Department of Pathology, University of Wales College of Medicine, Cardiff CF14 4XN Tel: 029 2074 2700 — MB BCh 1978 Wales; PhD Wales 1982; MRCPath 1987. Prof. Path. Univ. Wales Coll. Med. Cardiff.

WYNICK, David Department of Medicine, Bristol University, Marlborough St., Bristol BS2 8HW Tel: 0117 928 3396 Fax: 0117 928 3976 Email: d.wynick@bris.ac.uk; 19 Old Sneed Park, Bristol BS9 1RG Tel: 0117 928 3396 Fax: 0117 928 3976 Email: d.wynick@bristol.ac.uk — MB BS 1983 Lond.; BSc (Hons.) Lond. 1980, MD 1994; MRCP (UK) 1986; PhD 1998; FRCP 1998. (Middlx.) Sen. Lect. & Hon. Cons. Bristol Roy. Infirm.; Hon. Sen. Lect. RPMS. Prev: MRC Clin. Scientist Roy. Postgrad. Med. Sch.; Regist. Rotat. (Med.) Hammersmith Hosp. Lond.; Wellcome Trust Train. Fell. Roy. Postgrad. Med. Sch. Hammersmith Hosp. Lond.

WYNICK, Sarah Pennina Child & Family Department, Tavistock Clinic, 120 Belsize Lane, London NW3 5BA Tel: 020 7435 7111; Email: sarahw@doctors.org.uk — MB BS 1988 Lond.; BSc Lond. 1985. p/t Cons. (Child & Adolesc. Psychiat.) Tavistock Clinic Lond. Prev: Regist. (Psychiat.) Roy. Free Hosp. Train. Sch.; Sen. Reg. Tavistock Clinic.

WYNN, Gregory Robert Melford Park Farm, Alpheton, Sudbury CO10 9BN Tel: 01284 828747 — MB BS 1996 Lond.; BSc (Neuroanat.) Lond. 1992. (Lond.) SHO Rotat. Kings Lynn. Socs: MDU; BMA.

WYNN, Jeremy Benet Flat 2, Victoria Court, Victoria Avenue, Disbury, Manchester M20 1FR — MB ChB 1986 Manch.

WYNN, John Stephen 41 The Downs, Altrincham WA14 2QG Tel: 0161 928 0611 Fax: 0161 927 9175; Hill Croft, Chelford Road, Great Warford, Alderley Edge SK9 7TL Tel: 01625 582553 Fax: 01625 582553 — MB ChB 1975 Manch.; FRCP 1999; FRCOG 1996; MRCP (UK) 1981; MRCOG 1981; DCH Eng. 1979. (Manch.) Cons. O & G Wythenshawe Hosp. Manch. Socs: N. Eng. Obst. & Gyn. Soc.; Brit. Soc. Gyn. Endoscopy; Sale Med. & Dent. Soc. Prev: Sen. Regist. (O & G) Freedom Fields Hosp. Plymouth; Sen. Regist. (O & G) Groote Schuur Hosp. Cape Town; Regist. (O & G & Neonat. Med.) St. Mary's Hosp. Manch.

WYNN, Marie Dorothy 113 Newland Park, Hull HU5 2DT Tel: 01482 341410 Fax: 01482 341410 — MB ChB Liverp. 1951; DCH Eng. 1955.

WYNN, Michael 34 Orrok Park, Edinburgh EH16 5UW Tel: 0131 666 1353 — MB ChB Aberd. 1964. (Aberd.) Med. Manager, Med. Servs., Sema Gp., Edin. Prev: GP Edin.

WYNN, Nwe Nwe Willow House, 23 Grosvenor Road, Aldershot GU11 1DL Tel: 01252 350387; 22 Windermere Walk, Heatherside, Camberley GU15 1RP Tel: 01252 505887 — MB BS 1980 Med. Inst. (I) Rangoon; MRCPsych 1995. SCMO Gen. Adult Psychiat.

WYNN, Patrick 28 Aberford Road, Bramham, Wetherby LS23 6QN — MB ChB 1992 Manch.

WYNN, Philip Adrian 6 Heatherstones, Queensgate, Halifax HX3 0DH — MB ChB 1990 Aberd.

WYNN, Robert Francis Royal Manchester Children's Hospital, Hospital Way Manchester Tel: 0161 727 2172 — MB BChir 1989 Camb.; MRCP (UK) 1992; MRCPath 1997. Cons. Paediatric Haematologist Roy. Manch. Childr.s Hosp.

WYNN, Simon Mostyn Hayden 4 Maris Drive, Burton Joyce, Nottingham NG14 5AJ — BM BS 1988 Nottm.; BMedSci 1986; MRCP (UK) 1993; DFFP 1994; MRCGP 1993.

WYNN, Professor Victor 21 Redington Road, Hampstead, London NW3 7QX — MB BS 1944 Melbourne; MD Melbourne 1953; FRCP Lond. 1974, M 1967; FRCPath 1967, M 1964. Chairm. Wynn Inst. for Metab. Research; Emerit. Prof. Human Metab. Lond. Univ. Socs: Assn. Phys. & Med. Research Soc.; Assn. Path.; Assn. Clin. Biochem. Prev: Prof. Human Metab. Univ. Lond. at St. Mary's Hosp. Lond.; Civil Cons. (Human Metab. & Endocrinol.) RAF & Med. Serv. Brit.

WYNN-JONES

Airways; Dir. Alex. Simpson Laborat. Metab. Research St. Mary's Hosp. Med. Sch. Lond.

WYNN-JONES, Dylan Y Gaer Wen, Cae Meta, Llanrug, Caernarfon LL55 3AY Tel: 01248 671925 — MB BS 1996 Lond.; BSc (Hons.) Lond. 1993; part 1 MRCP 1998. (St George's Hospital Medical School) SHO (Med.) P.ss of Wales Hosp. Bridgend.

WYNN-JONES, John Well Street Surgery, Well Street, Montgomery SY15 6PF Tel: 01686 668217 Fax: 01686 668599; The Lions, Lions Bank, Montgomery SY15 6PT Tel: 01686 668569 Fax: 01686 668569 — MB BS 1975 Lond.; BSc (Hons.) Lond. 1972; MRCS Eng. LRCP Lond. 1975; MRCGP 1979; DCH Eng. 1978; DRCOG 1978. (Guy's) Clin. Dir. Team TeleMed. Project Powys; CME Tutor N. Powys; Bd. NHS Staff Coll. Wales. Socs: (Sec.) Montgomery Med. Soc.; RCGP (Comm. Mem. Rural Task Force).

WYNN-MACKENZIE, David Michael The Shaftesbury Practice, Abbey View Medical Centre, Salisbury Road, Shaftesbury SP7 8DH Tel: 01747 856700 Fax: 01747 856701; Tout Hill House, Tout Hill, Shaftesbury SP7 8LX Tel: 01747 854051 Email: david.wynn-mackenzie@talk21.com — MB BS 1976 Lond.; MRCP (UK) 1978; MRCGP 1983; DRCOG 1981; DCH Eng. 1979. (Middlx.) Prev: SHO (Med.) Roy. Free Hosp. Lond.; SHO (Paediat.) Middlx. Hosp. Lond.; SHO (Obst.) Centr. Middlx. Hosp. Lond.

WYNN PARRY, Christopher Berkeley, MBE British Association Fot, Performing and Medicine, 169 Shaffes Gury Avenue, London WC2H 8JL Tel: 020 7240 3331; 51 Nassau Road, London SW13 9QG Tel: 020 8748 6288 — BM BCh 1947 Oxf.; MA, DM Oxf. 1954, BA 1947; FRCS Eng. 1978; FRCP Lond. 1972, M 1959; DPhysMed Eng. 1950. (Oxf.) p/t Cons. Rheum. Brit. Assn. for Permorming & Med.; Cons rheumatologist to Brit performing Arts med trust Lond. Socs: Fell. Roy. Soc. Med.; Brit. Soc. Surg. Hand; Brit Assoc. Reum. Prev: Dir. (Rehabil.) King Edw. VII Hosp. Midhurst & Roy. Nat. Orthop. Hosp. Lond.; Gp. Capt. RAF Med. Br.

WYNN-WILLIAMS, David Llewelyn, SBStJ Roper and Partners, Syston Health Centre, Melton Road, Syston, Leicester LE7 2EQ Tel: 0116 260 9111 Fax: 0116 260 9055; Vine House, Chapel St, Syston, Leicester LE7 1GN Tel: 0116 260 8333 — MB BChir 1963 Camb.; BA Camb. 196; MRCGP 1974; DObst RCOG 1964. (Camb. & King's Coll. Hosp.) Socs: BMA; Leic. Med. Soc. Prev: Cas. Off. King's Coll. Hosp. Lond.; SHO Vict. Childr. Hosp. Hull; Clin. Asst. (Med.) LoughBoro. Gen. Hosp.

WYNNE, Afshan c/o Mr K.S. Wynne, South Tyneside District General Hospital, Harton Lane, South Shields NE34 0PL — MB BS 1982 Punjab; MRCOG 1994.

WYNNE, Arthur Theodore (retired) 103 New City Road, Glasgow G4 9JX — MB ChB 1932 Birm.; BDS (Hons.) Birm. 1928, LDS 1927; FDS RCS Eng. 1949. Prev: Med. Off. (Dent. Adviser) Dept. Educat. & Sc.

WYNNE, Austen Trevor Health Centre, 407 Main Road, Dovercourt, Harwich CO12 4ET Tel: 01255 201299 — MRCS 1976 London; MB BS 1976 London; FRCP 1976 London; FRCS 1981 (Ed) Edinburgh. (Royal Free) GP Princip.; Clin. Asst. Orthapaedics, Colerater Dist. Gen. Hosp.

WYNNE, Catherine Sophia Department of Paediatrics, St James's University Hosital, Beckett St., Leeds LS9 7TF Tel: 0113 243 3144; 25 Woodlea Garth, Meanwood, Leeds LS6 4SG — MB ChB 1997 Leeds.

WYNNE, David McGregor 18 Fettercairn Gardens, Bishopbriggs, Glasgow G64 1AY — MB ChB 1998 Glas.

WYNNE, Hilary Anne Royal Victoria Infirmary, Queen Victoria Road, Newcastle upon Tyne NE1 4LP Tel: 0191 232 5131 — MB BS 1980 Lond.; BA Camb. 1977; MD Newc. 1991; FRCP Lond. 1995; MRCP (UK) 1983. Cons. Phys. (Geriat.) Roy. Vict. Infirm. Newc. u. Tyne.

WYNNE, Ian Charles Patterdale Lodge Medical Centre, Legh Street, Newton-le-Willows WA12 9NA Tel: 01925 227111 Fax: 01925 290605; 123 Ashton Road, Newton-le-Willows WA12 0AH — MB ChB 1976 Bristol; MRCGP 1986.

WYNNE, Jane Margery Clarendon Wing, Leeds General Infirmary, Leeds LS2 9NS Tel: 0113 292 6106 Fax: 0113 392 6219 — MB ChB Leeds 1969; FRCP Lond. 1992; MRCP (UK) 1973. (Leeds) Cons. Community Paediat. Leeds Gen. Infirm. & Hon. Sen. Lect. (Clin. MLeeds. Prev: Lect. (Child Health & Community Paediat.) Leeds Univ.; Sen. Regist. (Paediat.) Kings Coll. Hosp. Lond. & Roy.

Alexandra Hosp.Sick Childr.; Brighton; Regist. (Paediat.) Nottm. City Hosp. & Childr. Hosp. Nottm.

WYNNE, John Stuart Wellington Medical Centre, Bulford, Wellington TA21 8PW Tel: 01823 663551 Fax: 01823 660650; Headweir, Washford, Watchet TA23 0LB Tel: 01984 640743 — MB ChB 1983 Leic.; MRCGP 1988. (Leicester) GP Partner Wellington Med. Centre Wellington; Clin. Asst. (Urol.) MusGr. Pk. Hosp. Taunton Som. Prev: GP S. Ct. Minehed Som.

WYNNE, Mr Kamil Shameen Shields General Hospital, Harton Lane, South Shields NE34 0PL Tel: 0191 202 4014 Fax: 0191 202 4081; 239 Sunderland Road, South Shields NE34 6AL Tel: 0191 455 9827 — MB BS 1982 Punjab; FRCS Ed. 1987; FRCS Eng. (King Edward Medical College Lahore, Pakistan) Cons. Surg.

WYNNE, Richard Charles Warren Broughton, 14B Fairlands Road, Stourbridge DY8 2DD Tel: 01384 371999 Fax: 01384 371812 — LMSSA 1970 Lond.; BSc St. And. 1961; FRCGP 1992, M 1974; DObst RCOG 1972. (Leeds) Benefits Agency Examg. Med. Pract. Med. Servs., Manc.; Private Homeopathic Doctor. Socs: Assoc. Mem. Fac. Homoeop. Prev: Trainee GP Ipswich VTS; SHO (O & G) Ipswich Gp. Hosps.; Ho. Phys. & Ho. Surg. Pinderfields Hosp. Wakefield.

WYNNE, Ronan D'Arcy 15 White Furrows Cotgrave, Nottingham NG12 3LD — MB BS 1972 Newc.; BSc (Hons. Physiol.) Newc. 1969; FFPM RCP (UK) 1992; Dip. Pharm. Med. RCP (UK) 1982. (Newcastle upon Tyne) Med. Dir. Fujisawa Pharmaceut. Co Ltd Europ. Clin. Research Centre Lond. Prev: Head of Clin. Pharmacol. Knoll Pharmaceut. Nottm.; Hon. Clin. Asst. (CVS Med.) Univ. Hosp. Nottm.; Sen. Research Phys. Clin. Investigat. Dept. The Boots Company Nottm.

WYNNE, Rosemary Anne Broughton, 14B Farlands Road, Stourbridge DY8 2DD — MB BS 1965 Lond.; MRCS Eng. LRCP Lond. 1965; MRCOphth 1991; DO RCS Eng. 1969. (King's Coll. Hosp.) Clin. Asst. (Ophth.) Guest Hosp. Dudley & Kidderminster Gen. Hosp.; Ophth. Med. Pract. Ludlow Shrops. Socs: Anthroposop. Med. Assn.; Midl. Ophthalm. Soc. Prev: Med. Off. Pk. Attwood Therap. Centre Trimpley; SHO (Ophth.) King's Coll. Hosp.

WYNNE, Sian Philippa Morgan 29 Elm Drive, Wirral CH49 3NP — MB ChB 1991 Birm.; BSc Birm. (Pharm.) 1988, MB ChB (Hons.) 1991; MRCP (UK) 1994. Trainee GP/SHO (Med.) Merseyside VTS.

WYNNE-DAVIES, Ruth (retired) 2 Dale Close, St. Ebbe's, Oxford OX1 1TU Tel: 01865 727525 Email: ruth@wynne-davies.fsnet.co.uk — BA Oxon. 1997; MB BS Lond. 1953; PhD Ed. 1973; FRCS Eng. 1960. Hon. Cons. Med. Genetics Ch.ill Hosp. Oxf. Prev: Reader (Orthop.) Genetics Research Univ. Edin.

WYNNE EVANS, Barbara Karyn Caeherbert Lane Surgery, Caeherbert Lane, Rhayader LD6 5ED Tel: 01597 810231 Fax: 01597 811080; Bryn Llewenydd, Rhayader LD6 5LT Tel: 01597 810313 — MB ChB 1969 Liverp. (Liverp.) Prev: Ho. Phys. & Ho. Surg. Wrexham, Powys & Mawddach Gp. Hosps.; Med. Off. (Gen. Duties) Anglo-Amer. Co. Kitwe, Zambia.

WYNNE-JONES, Geraint Rhoslan Surgery, 4 Pwllycrochan Avenue, Colwyn Bay LL29 7DA Tel: 01492 532125 Fax: 01492 530662 Email: rhoslansurgery1@netscapeonline.co.uk — MB ChB 1980 Liverp.; DRCOG 1984. (Liverpool)

WYNNE-JONES, Guy Alexander Flat 2, 144 Kennington Lane, London SE11 4UZ Email: guy.wynne-jones@virgin.net — MB BS 1993 Lond.; FRCS 1998; PhD Lond. 1990.

WYNNE-JONES, Melanie Louise Stockport Road Medical Practice, 50 Stockport Road, Marple, Stockport SK6 6AB Tel: 0161 426 0299 Fax: 0161 427 8112; 2 Jessop Drive, Marple, Stockport SK6 6QB Tel: 0161 427 7194 — MB ChB 1978 Manch.; MRCGP 1991; DRCOG 1982. Freelance Med. Jl.ist Chesh.; GP Trainer. Prev: GP Gatley & Runcorn.

WYNNE-ROBERTS, Caroline Rosales Seager Morgan c/o Lloyds Bank, Victoria House, Southampton Row, London WC1B 5HR — MB BS 1961 Lond.; LMSSA Lond. 1960. (Roy. Free) Socs: Amer. Rheum. Assn.; New York Acad. Sci. Prev: Assoc. Prof. (Rheum.) S.. Illinois Univ. Sch. Med. Springfield; Staff Phys. & Rheumatol. Veterans Admin. Hosp. Pittsburgh; Chief, Electron Microscopy Unit Veterans Admin. Hosp. Pittsburgh.

WYNNE-SIMMONS, Anne Penelope Mary 34 Dartmouth Row, London SE10 8AW Tel: 020 8694 2320 — MB BS 1971 Lond.; MRCS Eng. LRCP Lond. 1971; MFHom RCP Lond. 1985; MRCGP 1979; DCH Eng. 1973. (Roy. Free) Homoeop. Phys. Lond.

WYNNE-WILLIAMS, Hilary Victoria 18 Tyler Court, Shepshed, Loughborough LE12 9SJ — MB BS 1968 Lond.; MRCS Eng. LRCP Lond. 1968. Prev: SHO (Obst.) Univ. Coll. Hosp. Lond.

WYNROE, John Christopher Nab Top Farm, Dale Road, Marple, Stockport SK6 6NL — BM 1994 Soton.

WYNROE, Ralph Forbes, Group Capt. RAF Med. Br. Retd. 31 Dobbins Lane, Wendover, Aylesbury HP22 6DH Tel: 01296 622217 — MB ChB 1932 Liverp.; DMRE 1935; FFR RCSI 1962. Socs: Fac. Radiol. & Brit. Inst. Radiol. Prev: Cons. Radiol. RAF Med. Br.; Ho. Surg. & Ho. Phys. Liverp. Stanley Hosp.

WYNROE, Susan Iris Romiley Health Centre, Chichester Road, Romiley, Stockport SK6 4QR Tel: 0161 430 2573 Fax: 0161 406 7237; Nab Top Farm, Dale Road, Marple, Stockport SK6 6NL Tel: 0161 427 6569 — MB ChB 1966 Manch.; MRCGP 1978; DA Eng. 1970; DObst RCOG 1969. Socs: BMA. Prev: Regist. (Anaesth.) Crumpsall Hosp. Manch.

WYNTER, Meriel Jennifer Claire Otford Medical Practice, Leonard Avenue, Otford, Sevenoaks TN14 5RB Tel: 01959 524633 Fax: 01959 525086; The Gables, 41 Zion St, Seal, Sevenoaks TN15 0BD — MB ChB 1988 Dundee; DRCOG 1992; DCH RCP Lond. 1991. Socs: Med. & Dent. Defence Union Scotl.

WYON, Agnes May (retired) Ford Cottage, Thirlby, Thirsk YO7 2DJ Tel: 01845 597466 — MB ChB 1937 Leeds; DObst. RCOG 1938. Prev: Med. Off. (Family Plann. & Child Welf.) N. Yorks. AHA.

WYPER, John Forrester Brown (retired) Stable End, Blackhills, Leochel-Cushnie, Alford AB33 8LQ Tel: 01339 883468 — MB ChB 1938 Glas.; BSc. Glas. 1935, MB ChB 1938; FRCOG 1957, M 1942. Prev: Cons. Gynaecol. & Obstetr. Grampian Health Bd.

WYSE, Colin Terris (retired) Seaholme, Chapel Green Road, Earlsferry, Leven KY9 1AD — MB ChB 1951 St. And.

WYSE, Matthew Kevin Walsgrave NHS Trust, Clifford Bridle Road, Coventry CV2 2DX Tel: 024 76 538952 — MB BS 1990 Newc.; FRCA 1995. Cons. anaesth. Walsgrave Hosp. Coventry. Socs: BASICS.

WYSE, Sheena Dobson Chubbs Farm, Pound Lane, Burley, Ringwood BH24 4EF Tel: 01425 402298 — MB ChB 1967 Manch.; FFA RCS Eng. 1972. (Manch.) Prev: Cons. Anaesth. Groote Schuur Hosp. Cape Town, S. Afr.; Regist. (Anaesth.) Brompton Hosp. Lond. & Univ. Coll. Hosp. Lond.

WYTHE, Paul County Practice, Barking Road, Needham Market, Ipswich IP6 8EZ Tel: 01449 720666 Fax: 01449 720030 — MB ChB 1974 Liverp.; DTM & H Liverp 1994.

WYTHERS, Deborah Jayne 25 St Mary's Road, Tickhill, Doncaster DN11 9NA Tel: 01302 742503 Fax: 01302 752293; 120 Broom Road, Rotherham S60 2SU Tel: 01709 375947 — BM BS 1992 Nottm.; MRCGP 1996.

XAVIER, Alfredo Bruno College Street Surgery, College Street, Southampton SO14 3EJ Tel: 023 8033 3729 Fax: 023 8022 7233; Xaviers, Canada Road, West Wellow, Romsey SO51 6DE — MB ChB 1970 Leeds; BSc (Hons.) Lond. 1963; MRCS Eng. LRCP Lond. 1970. (Univ. Leeds) Prev: Regist. (Gen. Med.) Dorset Co. Hosp. Dorchester; SHO St. Mary's Hosp. Leeds; Ho. Off. (Med., Neurol. & Surg.) Chapel Allerton Hosp. Leeds.

XAVIER, Dennis Francis (cons. rooms), 62 Wimpole St., London W1 Tel: 020 7935 8400; 27 Lawrie Park Road, Sydenham, London SE26 6DP Tel: 020 8778 8702 — MB ChB 1967 Baghdad. (Baghdad) Clin. Asst. Orthop. Dept. Hackney Hosp. Lond.

XAVIER, Patrick Lloyd Culbert (retired) 24 Cherry Gardens, Billericay CM12 0HA Email: xaps@aol.com — MB BS 1970 Lond.; BSc (Physiol., Hons.) Lond. 1967; FRCR 1981. Prev: Cons. Oncol. and Radiother. OldCh. Hosp. Romford.

XAVIER, Richard James Harrison (retired) Birnam Lodge, Nursey Road, Loughton IG10 4EF Tel: 020 8508 1393 — MRCS Eng. LRCP Lond. 1952.

XAVIER, Stephanie Christine Yvonne Sita (retired) 3 Woodland Place, Hemel Hempstead HP1 1RD — MB BS 1964 Ceylon. Prev: Clin. Asst. (Histopath.) Hemel Hempstead Gen. Hosp.

XAVIER, Surahi Marisha St Lukes Surgery, Warren Rd, Guildford GU1 3JH Tel: 01483 572364; 1 Lake Cottages, The Green, Shamley Green, Guildford GU5 0UJ Tel: 01483 894126 — MB BS 1993 Lond.; MRCGP 1999; DRCOG 1998; DFFP 1998. (UMDS (United Medical & Dental Schools of Guy's & St. Thomas) p/t Half Time Princip. in Gen. Pract.; Clin. Asst., Genito-Urin. Med., Farnham Rd Hosp., Guildford, Surrey.

XENITIDIS, Kiriakos Department of Psychological Medicine, Institute of Psychiatry, De Crespigny Park, London SE5 8AF Tel: 020 7740 5287 Fax: 020 7701 9044 Email: sphakix@iop.bpmf.ac.uk — Ptychio latrikes 1984 Athens; MSc Univ. Lond. 1995; MRCPsych 1993. Cons. Psychiat. Hon. Sen. Lect. Prev: Sen. Regist. Maudsley & Guys NHS Trusts; Regist. & SHO (Psychiat.) Univ. Edin.; Research Fell. & Hon. Sen. Regist. (Psychiat.) Inst. Psychiat. Lond.

XENOPHOU, Xenakis c/o Mr Filshie's Secretary, B Floor East Block, Queen's Medical Centre, Nottingham NG7 2UH — MB BS 1986 Adelaide.

XERRI, Salvino 23 Brighton Road, Crawley RH10 6AE Tel: 01293 523383 Fax: 01293 553560; 10 Trinity Close, Pound Hill, Crawley RH10 3TN Tel: 01293 883910 — MD 1976 Malta. (Roy. Univ. Malta)

XIFARAS, George Paul 58 Purnells Way, Knowle, Solihull B93 9EE Tel: 0156 453977 — Med. Dipl. 1961 Univ. Athens; MRCS Eng. LRCP Lond. 1969; FFA RCS Eng. 1969. (Univ. Athens) Cons. Anaesth. W. Birm. Gp. Hosps. Prev: Sen. Regist. Anaesth. Birm. United Hosps. & Birm. RHB; Regist. Anaesth. & SHO Anaesth. Aberd. Teachg. Hosps.

XUEREB, John Henry Division of Molecular Histopathologics, Box 231, John Bonnett Clinical Laboratories (Level 3), Addenbrooke's Hospital, Hills Road, Cambridge CB2 2QQ Tel: 01223 762607 Fax: 01223 762610 Email: jhx1000@cam.ac.uk; 1 Capstan Close, Cambridge CB4 1BJ Tel: 01223 522762 — MD 1990 Newc.; FRCPath 1999; MA Camb. 1994; MD Malta 1984; MRCP (UK) 1981; MRCS Eng. LRCP Lond. 1977; MRCPath 1990; T(Path) 1991. (Roy. Univ. Malta) Sen. Lect. (Neuropath.) Univ. Camb. & Hon. Cons. Neuropath. Addenbrooke's Hosp. Camb.; Fell. and Dean St Catharine's Coll. Camb. Socs: Fell. Roy. Soc. of Med.; Brit. NeuroPath. Soc. Prev: Sen. Regist. (Neuropath.) Addenbrooke's Hosp. Camb.; Regist. (Neuropath. & Neurol.) Region. Neurol. Centre Newc. Gen. Hosp.; Regist. Profess. Med. Unit Manch. Roy. Infirm.

YAAKUB, Roselina 38 Housefield, Willesborough, Ashford TN24 0AF — MB ChB 1988 Liverp.

YACOB, Mr Nadir Youshow 6 Longdales Road, New Carron Village, Falkirk FK2 7EQ — MB ChB 1976 Mosul, Iraq; FRCS Ed. 1990; CABS 1988. (The Arab Board for Medical Specialisation) Staff Surg. (Surg./Urol.). Socs: Assoc. Mem. BAUS; Scott Urol. Soc.

YACOB, Z M Colliers Wood Surgery, 58 High Street Colliers Wood, London SW19 2BY Tel: 020 8540 6303 — MB ChB 1972 Baghdad.

YACOUB, Mr Makram Ghanam 41 Coppice Lane, Willenhall WV12 5RT — MB ChB 1982 Alexandria; FRCSI 1993.

YACOUB, Sophie Flat 10, Arundel House, 21 Lawn Road, Portswood, Southampton SO17 2ER — BM 1998 Soton.

YADAV, Anupam 25 Winchester Close, Woolton, Liverpool L25 7YD — MB ChB 1996 Manch.

YADAV, Desh Gaurav Sheffield Road Surgery, 170A Sheffield Road, Barnsley S70 4NW Tel: 01226 293232 Fax: 01226 280432 — MB BS 1960 Patna. GP Barnsley, S. Yorks.

YADAV, Hans Raj The Surgery, 192 Tudor Drive, Kingston upon Thames KT2 5QH Tel: 020 85490061 Fax: 020 8549 9488 — MB BS 1964 Delhi. (Maulana Azad Med. Coll.) Socs: BMA. Asst. Surg. Grade I Ordnance Factories, India.

YADAV, J K Earle Road Medical Centre, 131 Earle Road, Liverpool L7 6HD Tel: 0151 733 5538 Fax: 0151 733 6914.

YADAV, Mr Shambhu Narayan Lorn & Island District General Hospital, Glengallan Road, Oban PA34 4HH Tel: 01631 567500 Fax: 01631 567133 — MB BS 1972 Bihar; MS Bihar 1975; FRCS Glas. 1980. Cons. Surg. (Gen. Surg.) Lorn & Is.s Dist. Gen. Hosp. Oban. Socs: Assn. Surg.; W Scotl. Surgs. Assn. Prev: Lect. (Surg.) Univ. Papua, New Guinea.

YADAV, Surinder Singh 5 Britland Close, Barnsley S75 2JP — MB ChB 1994 Liverp.

YADAVA, Rajendra Prasad Merton Surgery, Merton Street, Longton, Stoke-on-Trent ST3 1LG Tel: 01782 322966 Fax: 01782 322914 — MB BS 1964 Patna; FRCGP 1997; MFFP 1995; DCH RCPS Glas. 1972; DTM & H Eng. 1967. (P. of Wales Med. Coll.)

YADEGAR, Mr John 2 Linnet Close, Bushey, Watford WD23 1AX — MB BS 1991 Lond.; FRCS Eng. 1995; FRCSI 1995. SHO (Transpl. Surg.) Addenbrooke's Hosp. Camb.

YAGER, Robert Stewart (retired) 19 Vicarage Gardens, Scunthorpe DN15 7BA Tel: 01724 856378 — MB BS 1948 Durh.

YAGER

YAGER, Thomas Andrew Tel: 01379 898295; Bridge House, Bury Road, Rickinghall, Diss IP22 1EJ Tel: 01379 890233 — MB BS 1982 Lond.; MA (Philosophy of Healthcare) Wales 1994; MRCGP 1988; DRCOG 1985.

YAGHAN, Mr Rami Jalal Kalajari 2/2, 16 Blantyre Street, Glasgow G3 8AP — MB BS 1986 Jordan; FRCSI 1992.

YAGNIK, Romesh Dayashanker 356 James Reckitt Avenue, Hull HU8 0JA Tel: 01482 796121; Tel: 01428 791163 — MB BS 1966; FRCS 1970 (Ed.); MD 1971 USA; 1971 (ECFMG) USA. (B.J. Medical College Ahmedabad (GUJ) India) GP Princip. (full time '74); Vasconist, Minor Surg., I/A Pericuticular Surg. -on contract NHS. Prev: Urol. & Vasc. Surg. '72-'74, Ahmedabad (GUJ) India.

YAHIA, Abdalla Osman Dorothy Pattison Hospital, Alumwell Close, Walsall WS2 9XH Tel: 01922 858000 Fax: 01922 858085; 415 Birmingham Road, Walsall WS5 3NT Tel: 01922 648456 Fax: 01922 648456 — MB BS 1978 Khartoum; MRCPsych. 1992; DPM RCPSI 1989. (Khartoum University, Sudan) Cons. (Psychiat.) Walsall Community Health NHS Trust W. Midl.s. Prev: Sen. Regist. Rotat. NE Thames; Regist. (Psychiat.) St. Matthew's Hosp. Burntwood Walsall; Regist. & SHO (Psychiat.) St. Clement's Hosp. Ipswich.

YAHIA, Bahaa Eldin Abbas Abdel Salam 14 The Terraces, Northwick Park Hospitals, Watford Road, Harrow HA1 3UJ — MB BCh 1981 Cairo; MRCP (UK) 1996.

YAHYA, Anwar Eaglestone Health Centre, Standing Way, Eaglestone, Milton Keynes MK6 5AZ Tel: 01908 679111 Fax: 01908 230601 — MB BS 1966 Lucknow.

YAKELEY, Jessica Wood The Maudsley Hospital, Psychotherapy Unit, Denmark Hill, London SE5 8AZ Tel: 020 7919 2385, 020 7919 2514 — MB BChir 1990 Camb.; MA Camb. 1990; MRCP (UK) 1993; MRCPsych 1996. (Univ. Camb. Trinity Coll. & Univ. Coll. Middlx. Sch. Med.) Specialist Regist. (Psychother.) Maudsley Hosp. Lond.; Assoc. Mem. of Brit. Psychoanalytic Soc. Prev: Regist. Rotat. (Psychiat.) Maudsley Hosp. Lond.; SHO Rotat. (Psychiat.) Maudsley Hosp. Lond.; SHO Rotat. (Neurol. & Med.) Roy. Free Hosp. Lond.

YALE, Vijaydev 104 Sudbury Court Road, Harrow HA1 3SQ Tel: 020 8904 2937 — MB BS 1974 Bangalore; DLO RCS Eng. 1986.

YALLOP, Deborah 4 Old Hall Close, Trowse, Norwich NR14 8TB — MB BS 1998 Lond.

YAM, Tat Shing 2 Greenvale, Dunmurry, Belfast BT17 9LR — MB BCh BAO 1994 Belf.

YAMEY, Gavin Mark 56B Market Place, London NW11 6JP — MB BS 1994 Lond.

YAMIN-ALI, Richard Glenn 60 Baronscourt Road, Carryduff, Belfast BT8 8BQ Tel: 01232 814803 — MB BCh BAO 1992 Belf.; FFARCSI 1997.

YAN, Christopher 216 Widney Manor Road, Solihull B91 3JW — MB ChB 1998 Aberd.

YAN AUNG, Dr 4 Deepdale, Leigh WN7 3EG — MB BS 1972 Med. Inst. (I) Rangoon.

YANAH, Mr David Kwame 134 Grove Road, London E17 9BY — MB BS 1967 Durh.; FRCS Ed. 1977; FRCS Eng. 1979. (Newc.) Regist. (Gen. Surg.) St. And. Hosp. Lond. Prev: SHO (Orthop.) Blackburn Roy. Infirm. & Whipps Cross Hosp. Lond.; SHO (Surg.) Hull Roy. Infirm.

YANDELL, Caroline Jane 8 Breach Road, Bristol BS3 2BD — MB ChB 1997 Bristol.

YANEZ PEREZ, Leopoldo Manuel Eldene Health Centre, Eldene, Swindon SN3 3RZ Tel: 01793 22710 — LRCP LRCS 1961 Ed. (W. Lond.) Socs: BMA.

YANG, Donald Matthew 258 Neath Road, Briton Ferry, Neath SA11 2SL — BM 1994 Soton. SHO (Rehabil. Med.) Rookwood Hosp. Cardiff. Prev: SHO (Gen. Med.) Caerphilly & Dist. Gen. Hosp.; SHO (Paediat. & ENT) Univ. Hosp. Wales Cardiff.

YANG, Yit Chiun Royal Liverpool University Hospital, Prescot St., Liverpool L7 8XP — MB ChB 1988 Aberd.; FRCOphth 1993. Regist. (Ophth.) Roy. Liverp. Univ. Hosp. Prev: SHO (Neurosurg.) Nat. Hosp. Lond.; SHO (A & E) Leicester Roy. Infirm.; Demonst. (Anat.) Univ. Leicester.

YANNEY, Michael Peter 32 Fitch Court, Laburnum Road, Mitcham CR4 2ND — MB BS 1993 Lond.

YANNI, Mr Dimitri Hassan c/o Bromely Hospital, Cromwell Hospital, Bromley BR2 9AJ Tel: 0208 687442 — MB BS 1983 Lond.; FRCS Eng. 1988; FRCS Ed. 1987; FRCS (Orth.) 1992. (Guy's) Cons. (Orthop. & Hand Surg.) Bromely Hositals NHS Trust. Socs: Fell. Roy. Soc. Med.; Fell. Brit. Elbow & Shoulder Soc. Prev: Sen. Regist. (Orthop. Surg.) SE Thames Train Progr.; Sen. Regist. Cappagh Orthop. Hosp. Dub.; Fell. (Hand Surg.) Pulvertaft Hand Centre Derbysh. Roy. Infirm.

YANNI, Mr George Armia Wellhouse NHS Trust, Barnet General Hospital, Wellhouse Lane, Barnet EN5 3DJ Tel: 020 8440 5111; 16 Holmstall Avenue, Edgware HA8 5JH Tel: 020 8205 2410 — MB BS 1980 Khartoum; FRCS Ed. 1991. Regist. (Surg.) Barnet Gen. Hosp. Herts. Prev: Regist. (Surg.) Edgware Gen., Univ. Coll. & Middlx. Hosps. Lond.

YANNI, Ghada 55 Avondale Road, Bromley BR1 4HS — MD 1991 NUI; MB BCh BAO 1984; LRCPI & LM, LRCSI & LM 1984; MRCPI 1986. Sen. Regist. (Rheum. & Gen. Med.) Guy's Hosp. Lond. Prev: Research Lect. (Rheum.) Univ. Coll. Dub.; Regist. (Rheum. & Gen. Med.) Beaumont Hosp. Dub.; SHO Rotat. (Med.) St. Laurence's Hosp.

YANNI, Mr Omar Nicolas William Harvey Hospital, Ashford TN24 0L — MB BS 1989 Lond.; FRCS Ed. 1993.

YANNY, L B Lister House, 473 Dunstable Road, Luton LU4 8DG Tel: 01582 571565 Fax: 01582 582074 — MB BCh 1972 Cairo.

YAP, Beng Khiong 11 Kerscott Road, Manchester M23 0GD — MB ChB 1992 Dundee.

YAP, Boon Hung 100 Southgrove Road, Sheffield S10 2NQ — MB ChB 1984 Sheff.

YAP, Mr John Yin Ming Royal Brompton Hospital, Sydney St., London SW3 6NP Tel: 020 7352 8121 Email: ct.jw@virgin.net — MB ChB 1986 Glas.; FRCS Glas. 1991; MD (Glas.) 1999. (Glasgow) Specialist Regist. Cardiothoraric Surg., Roy.Brompton Hosp., Lond. Socs: BMA; RCSP (Glas.).

YAP, Lip Kee 44 Cairnside, West Cults, Aberdeen AB15 9NZ Tel: 01224 861394 — MB BS 1977 Singapore. Regist. (O & G) Grampian Health Bd.

YAP, Lok Bin 91 Ravenshaw Street, London NW6 1NP — BM BS 1998 Nottm.

YAP, Peng Lee Edinburgh & SE Scotland, Regional Blood Transfusion Centre, Royal Infirmary, Edinburgh EH3 9HB Tel: 0131 536 5302 Fax: 0131 536 5301 — MB ChB 1974 Ed.; PhD CNAA 1980; BSc (Hons.) Ed. 1971. MB ChB 1974; FRCP Ed. 1994; FRCPath 1993, M 1980. Cons. Blood Transfus. & Immunol. Edin. & SE Scotl. Blood Transfus. Centre; Sen. Lect. Univ. Edin. Prev: Roy. Soc. Med. Foundat. Vis. Prof.; MRC Clin. Research Fell. 1976-79.

YAP, Soong Loy Maypole Health Centre, 10 Sladepool Farm Road, Kings Heath, Birmingham B14 5DJ Tel: 0121 430 2829 Fax: 0121 430 6211; 77 Hay Lane, Shirley, Solihull B90 4TZ Tel: 0121 745 9244 Fax: 0121 745 9244 — MB ChB 1987 Dundee. Prev: Trainee GP/SHO (Gen. Med.) Walsgrave Gen. Hosp. Coventry VTS; Ho. Off. (Gen. Med. & Surg.) & SHO (ENT & Psychiat.) Walsgrave Hosp. Coventry.

YAP, Sue Ching 25 Abbey Road, Beeston, Nottingham NG9 2QF — BM BS 1998 Nottm.

YAP, Yee Guan 36 Fitzroy Crescent, Chiswick Place, Chiswick, London W4 3EL — BM BS 1992 Nottm.; BMedSci (Hons.) Nottm. 1990; MRCP (UK) 1996. (Univ. Nottm. Med. Sch.) Brit. Heart Foundat. Research Fell. (Cardiol.) St Geo.'s Hosp. Med. Sch. Lond. Socs: Fell. Roy. Soc. Med. Prev: Clin. Research Fell. (Cardiol.) St. Geo. Hosp. Med. Sch. Lond.; SHO (Gen. Med.) St. Geo. Hosp. Lond.; SHO (Neurol.) Atkinson Morley Hosp. Lond.

YAPANIS, Michael 7 Heddon Road, Barnet EN4 9LD — MB ChB 1991 Ed.

YAPP, Julia Anita 3 Snowdrop Valley, Crich, Matlock DE4 5BT — MB BS 1991 Lond.; DRCOG 1993.

YAPP, Julie Kencot Lodge, Kencot, Lechlade GL7 3QX; 37 Brook St, Winsor, Brisbane, Queensland 4030, Australia Tel: 07 3861 1585 — MB BCh 1988 Wales; DCH RCP Lond. 1992; DRCOG RCOG 1993; MRCGP RCGP 1995. (Cardiff)

YAPP, Paula Anthea 191 Monmouth Road, London N9 0LE; 11 Spellbrooke, Hitchin SG5 2NB Tel: 01462 627788 — MB BS 1992 Lond.; DRCOG 1996. Phys. (Drug Safety) Roche Products Welwyn Garden City. Socs: Med. Sickness Soc. Prev: GP Locum; GP Regist. N. Finchley; SHO (Paediat.) VTS Barnet.

YAPP, Thomas Rowland Kencot Lodge, Kencot, Lechlade GL7 3QX; 37 Brook St, Winsor, Brisbane, Queensland 4030, Australia Tel: 07 3861 1585 Email: bigtom.y@bigpond.com — MB BCh 1988 Wales; MRCP (UK) 1992. (Cardiff) Vis. Fell., Clin. Sci.s &

YARROW

Liver Unit, Qu.sland Inst. of Med. Research. Prev: Specialist Regist. (Uni. Hosp. Wales, Cardiff.

YAQOOB, Mohammed Ali 27 Neville Street, Cardiff CF11 6LP — MB BCh 1992 Wales.

YAQOOB, Mohmad Eaton Place, 47 White Elme Road, Danbury, Chelmsford CM3 4LR — MB BS 1973 Bombay; FRSH 1983.

YAQOOB, Najma 54 Station Road, Birmingham B14 7SR — MB ChB 1991 Birm. SHO (Med.) Dudley HA.

YAQOOB, Rabia GP Direct, 5/7 Welback Road, West Harrow, Harrow HA2 0RH Tel: 020 8515 9300 Fax: 020 8515 9300; 33 Kingsway, Wembly Park, Wembley, London HA9 7QP — MB BS 1991 Lond.; MRCGP 1998; DRCOG 1996; DCH RCP Lond. 1995; DFFP 1994. (Univ. Coll. & Middlx. Sch. Med. Lond.) GP Princip. GP Direct. Prev: SHO (O & G) Chase Farm Hosp. Enfield; SHO (Paediat.) Chase Farm Hosp. Trust Enfield; SHO (A & E) WellHo. Trust Barnet Gen. Hosp.

YAQUB, Mohmad The Health Centre, Cliffe Road, Brampton, Barnsley S73 0XP Tel: 01226 753321 Fax: 01226 753321 — MB BS 1968 Jammu & Kashmir.

YAQUB, Sami Ullah 18 Malford Grove, London E18 2DX — MB BS 1990 Lond.

YAQUB, Zia Ullah 18 Malford Grove, London E18 2DX — MB BS 1997 Lond.

YAR KHAN, Sayeed Afridi The Rooms, Elemran, Aston Lane Shardlow, Derby DE72 2GX Tel: 01332 792871 Fax: 01332 793310 Email: sayeedyar@aol.com; Elemran, 5 Aston Lane, Shardlow, Derby DE72 2GX Tel: 01332 792871 Fax: 01332 792871 Email: 101667.2717@compuserve.com — MB BS 1956 Punjab; BSc Bombay 1949; MS Punjab 1962; MRCPsych Eng. 1973; T(Psychiat.) 1991; DPM Eng. 1972. (King Edwd. Med. Coll.) Indep. Cons. Derby; Unit Med. Represen. to Gen. Managem. Team. Socs: BMA. Prev: Cons. Psychiat. Aston Hall Hosp. Aston-on-Trent; Regist. & SHO (Psychiat.) Severalls Hosp. Colchester; Sen. Regist. Roy. E.. Co. Gp. Hosps. Essex.

YARDLEY, Denis Noel Alma Road Surgery, 68 Alma Road, Portswood, Southampton SO14 6UX Tel: 023 8067 2666 Fax: 023 8055 0972 — MB ChB 1967 Liverp.

YARDLEY, Mr Mark Peter John ENT Department, Royal Hallamshire Hospital, Glossop Road, Sheffield S10 2JF — MB BCh 1984 Wales; FRCS Ed. 1989; MPhil Sheff 1996. Cons. (ENT) Roy. Hall Hosp. Sheff.; Cons. (ENT) Sheff. childr.'s Hosp.; Hon. Lect. Univ. Sheff.

YARDLEY, Michael Hilton Lyngford Park Surgery, Fletcher Close, Taunton TA2 8SQ Tel: 01823 333355 Fax: 01823 257022; 27 Avon Close, Taunton TA1 4SU Tel: 01823 275726 — BM BCh 1972 Oxf.; MA Oxf. 1982, BA 1969; MRCGP 1980; DFFP 1994; DLO RCS Eng. 1982; DRCOG 1981. (Oxford) Hon. Med. Off. W. Som. Railway. Prev: Trainee GP Taunton VTS; SHO (ENT) MusGr. Pk. Hosp. Taunton; Med. Off. St. Lucy's Hosp. Tsolo Transkei.

YARDLEY, Ralph Andrew Castle Mead Medical Centre, Hill Street, Hinckley LE10 1DS Tel: 01455 637659 Fax: 01455 238754; 32 Winchester Drive, Burbage, Hinckley LE10 2BB Tel: 01455 634471 — MB ChB 1965 Birm.; MRCP (UK) 1973; DCH Eng. 1968. (Birm.) Prev: Regist. (Paediat.) Leics. AHA (T); SHO Neonat. Paediat. Sorrento Matern. Hosp. Birm.; SHO Med. Groby Rd. Hosp. Leicester.

YARDLEY-JONES, Mr Anthony Chelsea and Westminster Hospital, 369 Fulham Road, London SW10 9NH Email: ayj@yardleyjones.com — MB ChB 1975 Liverp.; PhD Surrey 1988; FRCS Ed. 1979; FFOM RCP Lond. 1993, MFOM 1984; DIH Soc. Apoth. Lond. 1981; DIH Eng. 1981; Cert Av. MoD (Air) & CAA 1980; Dip. Med. Acupuncture. (Liverpool) p/t Cons. in Occupat.al Med. Chelsea and W.minster Hosp., Lond.; Consg. Occupat.al Toxicologist, Nat. Poisons Inf. Serv., Birm.; Hon. Sen. Clin. Lect. (Occupat. Health) Univ. Birm.; Hon. Cons., King's Coll. Hosp. Occ Health Dept. Socs: Soc. Occup. Med.; Fell. Amer. Coll. Occupat. & Environm. Med.; Regist. Toxicol. Brit. Toxicology Soc. Prev: Chief Med. Adv., Burmah Castrol Trading Ltd, Swindon; Sen. Occupat. Med. Adv. Shell UK Ltd.; Regist. (Surg.) Regional Neurosurg. Unit Walton Hosp. Merseyside.

YARDUMIAN, Dorothy Anne Department of Haematology, North Middlesex Hospital, Sterling Way, London N18 1QX Tel: 020 8887 2428; Church Farm House, Luffenhall, Walkern, Stevenage SG2 7PX — MD 1988 Lond.; MB BS (Hons. Obst. & Gyn. & Path.) 1979; MRCP (UK) 1982; MRCPath 1988; FRCP 1996; FRCPath. 1996. Cons. Haemat. N. Middlx. Hosp. Lond. Prev: Lect. & Sen. Regist. (Haemat.) Middlx. Hosp. Med. Sch. Lond.

YARDY, Neil David East Kent Hospitals NHS Trust, Dept. Anaesthesia, William Harvey Hospital, Kennington Road, Ashford TN24 0LZ Tel: 01233 633331 Fax: 01233 616118 — MB BS 1987 Lond.; FRCA 1996. (Guy's Hospital Medical School) Cons. Anaesth., E. Kent Hosps. NHS Trust. Socs: Fell. Roy. Coll. Anaesth.; Assn. Anaesths.; Difficult Airway Soc. Prev: GP Canterbury & Thanet HA.; Specialist Regist. (Anaesth.) N. W. Region.

YARGER, Nishi 101 Ellesmere Road, London NW10 1LH — MB BS 1994 Lond.; BSc. (University College London) Regist. (Child & Adolesc. Psychiat.) N.wick Pk. Hosp. Harrow, Middlx.

YARHAM, Dorian David Portcullis Surgery, Portcullis Lane, Ludlow SY8 1GT Tel: 01584 872939 Fax: 01584 876490; Birchlea, Caynham, Ludlow SY8 3BJ Tel: 01584 875423 Fax: 01584 876240 Email: shropdoc@dyarham_demon.co.uk — MB ChB 1984 Glas.; MRCGP 1988; DRCOG 1987. (Glas.) Med. Adviser Ludlow Hosp.; Non-Exec. Dir. & Chairm. Shrops. Drs. Co-Op. Socs: BMA; Chir. Soc. Glas. Prev: SHO James Paget Hosp. Gt. Yarmouth VTS; Ho. Off. (Med.) Glas. Roy. Infirm.; Ho. Off. (Surg.) Stobhill Gen. Hosp. Glas.

YARNALL, David John Queen Square Surgery, 2 Queen Square, Lancaster LA1 1RP Tel: 01524 843333 Fax: 01524 847550; 54 High Road, Halton, Lancaster LA2 6PS Tel: 01524 811025 — MB ChB 1976 Bristol; MRCGP 1980; DCH Eng. 1979. (Bristol) GP Lancaster; Crowd Doctor Reebok Stadium Bolton Wanderers FC; Course Organiser Lancaster GP VTS. Prev: Med. Off. CECIB Heysham.

YARNALL, Nicholas John, Surg. Lt.-Cdr. RN 14 Branton Hill Lane, Aldridge, Walsall WS9 0NR Email: drnjy@drnjy.demon.co.uk — MB ChB 1991 Leeds; DRCOG 1998. (Leeds Uni. Med. Sch.)

YARNELL, John William Gordon Department of Epidemiology & Public Health, Mulhouse Building, Queen's University of Belfast, Grosvenor Road, Belfast BT12 6BJ Tel: 01232 894614 Fax: 01232 231907; Greenmount, 267 Kingsway, Dunmurry, Belfast BT17 9EL — MB ChB 1968 Manch.; MD Manch. 1981; MFCM 1979; DPH Bristol 1972. Sen. Lect. (Epidemiol.) Qu. Univ. Belf. Socs: Soc. Social Med.; Eur. Soc. Cardiol. (Working Gp. Epidemiol. & Preven.); Internat. Soc. & Federat. Cardiol. Prev: Mem. Scientif. Staff, MRC Epidemiol. Unit Cardiff.

YARNELL, Stephanie (Surgery), 51 Crossland Road, Chorlton, Manchester M21 9DU Tel: 0161 860 4745 — MB ChB 1988 Manch.; MRCGP 1993; DCH RCP Lond. 1992. Socs: BMA.

YARNLEY, Paul Arthur IMASS LTD, 10 Southway Lane, Roborough, Plymouth PL6 7DH Tel: 01752 782211 Fax: 01752 782299 Email: imass@mass.freeserve.co.uk — MB BS 1976 Lond.; AFOM RCP Lond. 1993. Clin. Dir. Indust. Med. & Safety Serv. Ltd. Socs: Soc. Occupat. Med.

YARNOLD, John Robert 27 Killieser Avenue, London SW2 4NX — MB BS 1972 Lond.; MRCP (UK) 1974; FRCR 1977. Sen. Lect. & Hons. Cons. Inst. Cancer Research & Roy. Marsden Hosp.

YARR, Julie Elaine 9 Beanstown Road, Lisburn BT28 3QS — MB BCh 1997 Belf.

YARR, Nicholas Tudor North Road Medical Practice, 182 North Road, Cardiff CF14 3XQ Tel: 029 2061 9188 Fax: 029 2061 3484 — MB BCh 1980 Wales; MRCGP 1984; DRCOG 1984.

YARR, Susan Nicola 18 Dowshire Park, Hillsborough BT26 6HB — MB BCh BAO 1990 Belf.; MRCP (UK) 1993; MRCGP 1995; DRCOG 1996.

YARRANTON, Helen Thrombosis & Haemostasis Research Unit, University College Hospital London, 98 Chienes Mews WC1E 6HX Tel: 0207 380 9581 — MB ChB 1993 Bristol; MRC Path 2001; MRCP (UK) 1996. (Bristol) Research Regist. Haemat. Prev: Specialist Regist. (Haemat.) Camb.

YARROW, Andrew David Beech House Surgery, 2 Ash Tree Road, Knaresborough HG5 0UB Tel: 01423 542580 Fax: 01423 864450 — BM BCh 1972 Oxf.; DRCOG 1977.

YARROW, Dudley Ernest (retired) Little Winsford, Woodland Rise, Sevenoaks TN15 0HY Tel: 01732 61817 — MB BChir 1938 Camb.; MRCS Eng. LRCP Lond. 1936; DCH Eng. 1945. Prev: Capt. RAMC.

YARROW, Hal 27B Devonshire Street, London W1N 1RJ Tel: 020 7935 1694; West Green, Preston, Hitchin SG4 7UB — MRCS Eng., LRCP Lond. 1935. (St. Bart.) Med. Dir. Dermal Labs Ltd. Socs: Fell.

YARROW

RSM; BMA. Prev: Ho. Surg. Gravesend & N. Kent Hosp.; Clin. Asst. St. Johns Skin Hosp. Lond.; Police Surg. & Pub. Vaccinator.

YARROW, Simon Home Farm Cottage, 6 High St., Weston, Towcester NN12 8PU Tel: 01295 760069 — BM BCh 1993 Oxf.; FRCA 1999; DA (UK) 1996. Specialist Regist. in Anaesth., Oxf., Deaney. Prev: SHO (Anaesth. & ITV) Univ. Hosp. Birm.; SHO (Anaest) City Hosp. Birm.

YARWOOD, Gary David Princess Elizabeth Hospital, Guernsey GY4 6UU Tel: 01481 725241 — MB BS 1985 Lond.; FRCA 1990. (St Bart.) Cons. Anaesth. & Dir. Intens. Care Qu. Eliz. Hosp. Guernsey. Socs: Assn. of Anaesth.s GB and Irel.; Intens. Care Soc. Prev: Sen. Regist. (Anaesth.) St. Bart. Hosp. Lond.

YARWOOD, Rosemary Manor Park Surgery, Bell Mount Close, Leeds LS13 2UP Tel: 0113 257 9702 Fax: 0113 236 1537; Beechwood, 18 Rockwood Rd, Calverley, Pudsey LS28 5AA — MB ChB 1984 Leeds; MRCGP 1989. Prev: Trainee GP Pinderfields Gen. Hosp. Wakefield VTS; SHO (A & E, Paediat., Obst. & Psychiat.) Pinderfields Gen. Hosp. Wakefield; SHO (Anaesth.), Ho. Phys. & Ho. Surg. Pinderfields Hosp. Wakefield.

YARWOOD SMITH, Colin Hugh Wychbury Medical Centre, 121 Oakfield Road, Wollescote, Stourbridge DY9 9DS Tel: 01562 882277; 12 Cochrane Close, Pedmore, Stourbridge DY9 0ST Tel: 01562 884706 — MB ChB 1981 Birm.; MRCGP 1985; DRCOG 1985; Cert. Family Plann. JCC 1985. (Birmingham) Chairm. Dudley LMC; Chairm. Stourbridge PCG. Socs: BMA (Ex-Chairm. Dudley Div.). Prev: Trainee GP Wycombe DHA VTS; Ho. Surg. Kidderminster Dist. Gen. Hosp.; Ho. Phys. Med. Profess. Unit Qu. Eliz. Hosp. Birm.

YASEN, Mr Thamir Howaydi Royal Victoria Hospital, Poole Road, Westbourne, Bournemouth BH4 9DG Tel: 01202 761332 — MB ChB 1974 Baghdad; FRCS (Ophth.) Glas. 1986; DO RCPSI 1984.

YASHODA, Punreddy c/o Dr K.R. Reddy, 12 Langholme Close, Wigan WN3 6TT — MB BS 1967 Osmania.

YASIN, Khaled Mustafa Brentford Health Centre, Boston Manor Road, Brentford TW8 8DS Tel: 020 8321 3822 Fax: 020 8321 3808; 1 Daver Court, Mount Avenue, London W5 1PL — MB BS 1982 Lond.

YASIN, Tahsin 77 Broom Park, Teddington TW11 9RR — MB ChB 1983 Glas.

YASSA, Janet Ghobrial Sheffield Children's Hospital, Sheffield S10 2TH — MRCS Eng. LRCP Lond. 1970.

YASSEEN, Baheig El Sir Mohamed 36 Streatham Common, London SW16 3BX — MB ChB 1965 Ain Shams.

YASSIN, Raouf (retired) Mallards, The Rickyard, Shutford, Banbury OX15 6PR — MB ChB 1956 Cairo; LMSSA Lond. 1964. Prev: SHO (Med., Paediat. & Surg.) Horton Gen. Hosp. Banbury.

YASSIN KASSAB, Mr Mouhamad Room 56, Cavell Court, C23, Nottingham University Hospital, Queens Medical Centre, Nottingham NG7 2UH — MD 1987 Damascus; FRCS Ed. 1992.

YATE, Brian Hugh Whitlera, Dryslwyn, Carmarthen SA32 8SJ — MB ChB 1968 Manch.

YATE, Paul Michael Anaesthetics Department, London Hospital, Whitechapel, London E1 1BB — MB BS 1974 Lond.; FRCA Eng. 1979. Cons. Anaesth. Roy. Hosps. NHS Trust. Prev: Sen. Lect. & Hon. Cons. (Anaesth.) Lond. Hosp. Med. Coll.

YATE, Robert Michael Whitlera, Dryslwyn, Carmarthen SA32 8SJ — MB BCh 1995 Wales.

YATES, Alan Paul Beman Anaesthetic Department, St. James' University Hospital, Beckett Street, Leeds LS9 7TF — MB BS 1978 Lond.; FFA RCS Eng. 1983. Cons. Paediat. Anaesth. St. Jas. Univ. Hosp. Leeds.; Sen. Lect., Sch. of Med., Univ. of Leeds.

YATES, Andrew Department of Anaesthetics, Queen Alexandra Hospital, Cosham, Portsmouth PO6 3LY Tel: 023 92 286279 Fax: 02392 286681; Rosina Cottage, Church Road, Newtown, Fareham PO17 6LE Tel: 01329 835218 — MB BS 1975 Lond.; FFA RCS Eng. 1983. (St. Thos.) Cons. Anaesth. Portsmouth Hosps. NHS Trust; Ass. Clin. Dir. Theatres, Portsmouth Hosp. NHS Trust. Socs: Assn. Anaesth.; Soc. Naval Anaesth.; Vice-Pres. AODP. Prev: Cons. Anaesth. Roy. Naval Hosp. Haslar; PMO HMS Ark Roy. & HMY Britannia.

YATES, Andrew John 88 Framingham Road, Sale M33 3RJ — MB ChB 1981 Sheff.; MRCPath 1992. Cons. Histopath. Tameside Gen. Hosp. Prev: Sen. Regist. (Histopath.) N. W.. RHA.

YATES, Mr Anthony James 24 Hawthorn Avenue, Lenzie, Glasgow G66 4RA Tel: 0141 776 4502 — MB ChB 1966 Ed.; FRCS Ed. 1971. Cons. Urol. Surg. Stobhill Gen. Hosp. Glas. Socs: Fell. Europ. Bd. Urol.; Brit. Assn. Urol. Surgs. Prev: Surg. Sen. Regist. (Urol. Dept.) Glas. Roy. Infirm.; Regist. Rotat. (Surg.) S. E.. RHB Scotl.

YATES, Brendan Davidson — MB ChB 1979 Otago; BA (Hons.) Otago 1984; FFPHM 1990; MPH Glas. 1988. Cons. Pub. Health Med. NHS Exec. S. W. Bristol. Prev: Cons. in Pub. Health Med. S. W. RHA; Cons. in Pub. Health Med. N.ern and Yorks. RHA; Cons. in Pub. Health Med. Yorks. RHA.

YATES, Bryan Hulme 115 Wingrove Road, Newcastle upon Tyne NE4 9BY — MB BS 1998 Newc.

YATES, Charles Michael (retired) 25 Bloomfield Terrace, London SW1W 8PQ Tel: 020 7730 3650 — MB BChir 1953 Camb.; MA Camb. 1986, BA (Hons.) 1950, MB BChir 1953. Prev: Med. Cas. & Ho. Surg. St. Thos. Hosp. Lond.

YATES, Mr Christopher John Percy Wellington Health Centre, Chapel Lane, Wellington, Telford TF1 1PZ Tel: 01952 244740; The Mill House, High Ercall, Telford TF6 6BE Tel: 01952 770394 — MB BS 1971 Lond.; FRCS Eng. 1977; MRCS Eng. LRCP Lond. 1971; DRCOG 1982. (St. Bart.) Prev: Regist. Rotat. (Surg.) St. Geo. Hosp. Lond.; Research Fell. (Periferal Vasc. Unit) St. Jas. Hosp. Lond.; Regist. (Surg.) Leicester Gen. Hosp.

YATES, Mr Colin Department of Oral & Maxillofacial Surgery, Wexham Park Hospital, Slough SL2 4HL Tel: 01753 634076 Fax: 01753 691343; Squirrels, Hatton Hill, Windlesham GU20 6AD Tel: 01276 472100 — MB ChB 1972 Birm.; BDS Birm. 1963; FDS RCS Eng. 1967. Cons. Oral & Maxillofacial Surg. Heatherwood & Wexham Pk. Hosps. Trust; Specialty Tutor E. Berks. RCS (Eng.). Socs: Fell. Brit. Assn. Oral & Maxillofacial Surg.; BMA & BDA. Prev: Sen. Regist. (Oral & Maxillofacial Surg.) King's Coll. Hosp. Lond. & Mass. Gen. Hosp. Boston, USA; SHO (Oral Surg.) Hosp. Sick. Childr. Lond.; Ho. Surg. Birm. Accid. Hosp.

YATES, David Anthony University Hospital Birmingham NHS Trust, The Queen Elizabeth Hospital, Department of Neuroradiology, Edgbaston, Birmingham B15 2TH Tel: 0121 472 1311 Fax: 0121 627 2578; The Cottage, 6 Cotton Church Lane, Cotton Hackett, Rednal, Birmingham B45 8PT Tel: 0121 445 1293 — BM BCh 1970 Oxf.; BA Oxf. 1968; FRCR 1980. Cons. Radiol. Qu. Eliz. Hosp. Birm.; Hon. Sen. Lect. Univ. Birm. Socs: Brit. Soc. Neuroradiol.; Sen. Mem. World Federat. of Intervent. & Therap. Neuroradiol.; Fell. RCRadiol.

YATES, David Anthony Hilton Adams Cottage, Bramshott, Liphook GU30 7SJ Tel: 01428 723075 Fax: 01428 723075 — MB BS 1953 (Hons.) Lond.; MD Lond. 1963; FRCP Lond. 1974, M 1957; DPhysMed Eng. 1960. (St. Thos.) Emerit. Phys. St. Thos. Hosp. Lond.; Emerit. Rheum. HM Armed Forces. Socs: Fell. Roy. Soc. Med. (Ex-Pres. Rheum. Sect.); (Ex-Pres.) Brit. Soc. Rheum. Prev: Cons. Rheum. King Edwd. VII Hosp. Offs. Lond.; Cons. Phys. St Thomas Hosp. Lond.; Regist. (Thoracic Med.) & Cas. Off. St Thomas Hosp.

YATES, David Beresford Taunton & Somerset Hospital, Musgrove Park, Taunton TA1 5DA Tel: 01823 342132 Fax: 01823 344542; Vexford Court, Higher Vexford, Lydeard St. Lawrence, Taunton TA4 3QF Tel: 01984 656735 Email: dbyates@doctors.org.uk — MB BS 1967 Lond.; MRCS Eng. LRCP Lond. 1967; FRCP Lond. 1983; MRCP (UK) 1970. (King's Coll. Hosp.) Cons. Phys. Taunton & Som. Hosp. Socs: (Counc.) Brit. Soc. Rheum.; (Pres.) SW Wessex & S. Wales Rheum. Soc.

YATES, David Geoffrey 10 Melrose Avenue, Seaton Delaval, Whitley Bay NE25 0JR — MB BS 1991 New South Wales.

YATES, David Herbert Wintergreen, St.. Jidgey, Wadebridge PL27 7RE Tel: 01208 812391 — MB ChB 1949 Manch.; FRCPsych 1986; DPM Eng. 1960. (Manch.) Cons. Psychiat. St. Lawrence Hosp. Bodmin. Socs: Fell. Roy. Soc. Med. Prev: Sen. Regist. Mapperley Hosp. Nottm.

YATES, David Owen Jary, Yates and Brown, Well Street Medical Centre, Well Street, Cheadle, Stoke-on-Trent ST10 1EY; Vinewood Farm, Marlpit Lane, Denstone, Uttoxeter ST14 5HH Tel: 01889 591185 Email: vinewood@btinternet.com — MB ChB 1976 Dundee; MRCGP 1981. (Dundee) Clin. Asst. (Elderley Care) Cheadle Hosp.

YATES, David William Kent and Sussex Hospital, Tunbridge Wells TN4 8AT — BM 1977 Soton.; FFA RCS Eng. 1982. Cons. Anaesth. & Intens. Care Tunbridge Wells. Prev: Lect. Univ., Zimbabwe.

YATES

YATES, Professor David William Hope Hospital, Salford, Manchester Tel: 0161 787 4842 Fax: 0161 787 4842 Email: dyates@fs1.ho.man.ac.uk; 22 Westminster Road, Eccles, Manchester M30 9EB — MB BChir 1967 Camb.; MD Camb. 1990, MA 1967; MChOrth Liverp. 1975; FRCS Eng. 1972; FRCP 1998. (St. Thos.) Prof. Emerg. Med. Manch. Univ.; Hon. Cons. Emerg. Med. Hope Hosp. Salford; Mem. Scientif. Staff N. W.. Injury Research Centre.

YATES, Eric John, DSC (retired) The Weir House, Boat Lane, Welford-on-Avon, Stratford-upon-Avon CV37 8EN Tel: 01789 750546 — MB ChB 1938 Manch. Prev: Ho. Surg. Ancoats Hosp. Manch.

YATES, Francis Alexander (retired) Pine Corner, Poynings, Brighton BN45 7AQ Tel: 01273 857376 — MB BS Lond. 1952; MRCS Eng. LRCP Lond. 1952. Prev: Ho. Phys. Bolingbroke Hosp. Lond.

YATES, Frank Wright 1 Rivington Lane, Headless Cross, Anderton, Chorley PR6 9HQ Tel: 01257 483042 Fax: 01257 482642 — MRCS Eng. LRCP Lond. 1960; LMSSA Lond. 1957. (Liverp.)

YATES, Geoffrey Alan Belmont Farm, Great Harwood, Blackburn BB6 7UY — MB BS 1991 Lond. (St George's)

YATES, Gordon 75 Stoke Road, Shelton, Stoke-on-Trent ST4 2QH Tel: 01782 745325 Fax: 01782 747617; Wyndowne, Bedcraft, Barlaston, Stoke-on-Trent ST12 9AL Tel: 01782 372155 Fax: 01782 747617 — MRCS Eng. LRCP Lond. 1956; MA, MB BChir Camb. 1956; DIH Soc. Apoth. Lond. 1963. (Camb. & Middlx.) Indep. Cons. Occupat. Med. Stoke-on-Trent. Socs: BMA & N. Staffs. Med. Inst. Prev: Ho. Surg. Middlx. Hosp.; Ho. Phys. N. Middlx. Hosp. Lond.; Nuffield Trav. Fell. 1968.

YATES, Helen Anne Grosvenor Medical Centre, 23 Upper Grosvenor Road, Tunbridge Wells TN1 2DX Tel: 01892 544777 Fax: 01892 511157; Tel: 01892 536913, 91514 530373 — BM 1989 Soton.; MRCGP 1995; DRCOG 1993. p/t Asst. GP Tunbridge Wells.; GP Princip. Prev: Trainee GP Tunbridge Wells VTS.

YATES, Helena Louise 33 Mackenzie Gardens, Brechin DD9 6DG — MB ChB 1969 Sheff.; FFA RCS Eng. 1973.

YATES, Mrs Janette Avril 18 Union Street Surgery, Kirkintilloch, Glasgow G66 1DH Tel: 0141 776 1238; The Ferns, 24 Hawthorn Avenue, Lenzie, Kirkintilloch, Glasgow G66 4RA Tel: 0141 776 4502 — MB ChB 1966 Ed.

YATES, John Benjamin Alexander Wintergreen St Judgey, St Issey, Wadebridge PL27 7RE — MB ChB 1994 Glas.

YATES, John Robert Watson Department of Medical Genetics, Box 134, Addenbrookes Hospital NHS Trust, Hills Road, Cambridge CB2 2QQ Tel: 01223 216446 Fax: 01223 217054 — MB BS 1977 Lond.; MA (Physics) Oxf. 1970; FRCP Lond. 1994; MRCP (UK) 1981. (Univ. Coll. Hosp.) Reader (Med. Genetics) Univ. Camb.; Hon. Cons. E. Anglian Med. Genetics Serv. Addenbrooke's Hosp. Camb. Prev: Cons. Med. Geneticist W. Scotl. Regional Genetics Serv.; Hon. Clin. Lect. Univ. Glas.

YATES, Judith Anne Wand Medical Centre, 279 Gooch Street, Highgate, Birmingham B5 7JE Tel: 0121 440 1561 Fax: 0121 440 0060 — MB ChB 1975 Birm.; DRCOG 1979. GP Birm.

YATES, Kenneth Philip The Surgery, Mill Hoo, Alderton, Woodbridge IP12 3DA — MB ChB 1974 Manch.

YATES, Mabel 5 St Catherines Walk, Leeds LS8 1SB Tel: 0113 266 8801 — MB ChB 1956 Leeds. (Leeds) Med. Panel Mem. of the Appeals Serv. Prev: Princip. Clin. Med. Off. Leeds E. HA; SCMO (Hearing Impairm.) Leeds E.. HA; Ho. Phys. Geriat. & Ho. Surg. ENT & Ophth. St. Jas. Hosp. Leeds.

YATES, Mark Timothy Longdon, Shipley Road, Southwater, Horsham RH13 7BQ — BM BS 1996 Nottm. SHO, Orthalmology, W. Norwich Hosp., Norwich.

YATES, Mark William 12 Avon Close, Taunton TA1 4SU Tel: 01823 256512 — MB BS 1986 Monash.

YATES, Martin 16 The Sycamores, Bramhope, Leeds LS16 9JR — MB BS 1985 Newc.; MRCP (UK) 1994; MRCPsych 1990. Regist. (Gen. Med.) Roy. Gwent Hosp. Newport.

YATES, Mhairi Stewart 15 Lee Fold, Tyldesley, Manchester M29 7FQ — MB ChB 1991 Liverp.

YATES, Michael David The Surgery, 239 Mosley Common Road, Boothstown, Worsley, Manchester M28 1BZ Tel: 0161 790 2192 Fax: 0161 799 5046 — MB BS 1967 Lond.; MRCS Eng. LRCP Lond. 1967. (Westm.) GP Churston Ferrers Brixham. Prev: SHO (O & G) Canad. Red Cross Hosp; Paediat. W.m. Childr. Hosp. Lond.; Ho. Surg. Qu. Mary's Hosp. Roehampton.

YATES, Michael John Frimley Green Medical Centre, 1 Beech Road, Frimley Green, Camberley GU16 6QQ Tel: 01252 835016 Fax: 01252 837908; 156B Frimley Green PD, Camberley GU16 6NA Tel: 01252 835254 — MB BS 1972 Lond.; BSc Lond. 1969; MRCGP 1981; DObst RCOG 1974. (St. Geo.) Prev: Ho. Phys. & SHO (O & G) St. Geo.'s Hosp. Tooting; Ho. Surg. Ashford Hosp., Middlx.

YATES, Michael Simon The Pines, 71B Westhall Road, Warlingham CR6 9HG — MB BS 1987 Lond.

YATES, Moira Jean (Thompson) St George's Surgery, 46 a Preston New Rd, Blackburn BB2 6AH Tel: 0125 453791 — MB ChB 1992 Ed.; MRCGP 1996; DFFP 1996; DRCOG 1995. Socs: RCGP (NW Eng. Fac.); BMA; Scott. Family Plann. Assn. Prev: Trainee GP Inverness-sh. VTS.

YATES, Muriel Grace (retired) Bryn Aber, Nantgwynant, Caernarfon LL55 4NW — MB ChB Ed. 1949; DCH Eng. 1951. Prev: Asst. MOH Surrey CC.

YATES, Nicholas The Kintbury Medical Practice, Kintbury Surgery, Newbury Street, Kintbury, Hungerford RG17 9UX Tel: 01488 658294; 5 Halfway, Bath Road, Newbury RG20 8NG Tel: 01488 658092 — MB BS 1975 Lond.; BSc (Ophth. Optics) Manch. 1969; MRCGP 1980; DCH Eng. 1980; DRCOG 1980. Prev: Regist. (Paediat.) Ninewells Hosp. Dundee; Ho. Surg. & Ho. Phys. (Paediat.) St. Thos. Hosp. Lond.

YATES, Paul Anthony 118 Doveleys Road, Salford M6 8QW — MB ChB 1982 Bristol.

YATES, Peter Albert Academic Unit of Child & Adolescent Psychology, 3rd Floor QEQM, St Mary's Hospital, Norfolk Place, London W2 1PG Email: p.yates@ic.ac.uk — MB ChB 1989 Cape Town; MRCPsych 1996. Specialist Regist. Child & Adolesc. Psychiat. Gt. Ormond St Hosp., Lond.; Hon. Clin. Research Fell., Acad. Unit of Child & Adolesc. Psychiat., Imperial Coll. Sch. Of Med. @ St Mary's, Lond.

YATES, Peter Anthony 457 Lawnmarket, Edinburgh EH1 2NT Tel: 0131 225 2635 — MB ChB 1957 Manch.; MSc, MB ChB Manch. 1957. (Manch.) Lect. (Path.) Univ. Edin. Prev: Med. Off. Inst. Aviat. Med. RAF FarnBoro., Hants. Research Fell.; (Path.) Johns Hopkins Univ. Baltimore, U.S.A.

YATES, Philip Blood Transfusion Centre, Aberdeen Royal Infirmary, Foresterhill, Aberdeen AB25 2ZW Tel: 01224 685685 — MB ChB 1979 Manch.; FRCP Ed. 1995; MRCP (UK) 1984; FRCPath 1997; MRCPath 1988. (Manch. Univ.) Cons. Transfus. Med. Aberd. & NE Scotl. Blood Transfus. Serv. Aberd. Prev: Assoc. Specialist (Transfus. Med.) Aberd. & NE Scotl. Blood Transfus. Serv.; Sen. Regist. Rotat. (Haemat.) Bristol Roy. Infirm.; Regist. (Haemat.) W.. Gen. Hosp. Edin.

YATES, Philip Andrew Orchard Medical Centre, Macdonald Walk, Kingswood, Bristol BS15 8NJ Tel: 0117 980 5100 Fax: 0117 980 5104 — MB ChB 1979 Bristol; MRCGP 1984; DFFP 1996; DRCOG 1982. (Bristol) Chair S. E. Gloucestershire PCG.

YATES, Philip David 220 Belmont Road, Bolton BL1 7AZ — MB ChB 1991 Manch.

YATES, Rachel Helyn Theresa 65 The Fairway, Saltburn-by-the-Sea TS12 1NG — MB ChB 1993 Liverp.

YATES, Rachel Olwyn Nethergreen Road Surgery, 34-36 Nethergreen Road, Sheffield S11 7EJ Tel: 0114 230 2952 — MB ChB 1974 Sheff.; BSc Sheff. 1969.

YATES, Richard William Peel Hilo House, St. Clements Coast Road, St Clement, Jersey JE2 6SA Tel: 01534 22381 — MB BS 1953 Lond.; MRCS Eng. LRCP Lond. 1953. (Guy's)

YATES, Robert William Michael 34 Reckitt Road, London W4 2BT — MB BCh 1988 Witwatersrand.

YATES, Robert William Smith Kilmory, 22 Ralston Road, Bearsden, Glasgow G61 3BA — MB ChB 1977 Glas.; MRCOG 1984. Lect. Dept. O & G Univ. Liverp. Prev: Regist. Infertil. Clinic Roy. Infirm. Glas.; Research Regist. Univ. Glas. Dept. O & G Roy. Infirm. Glas.

YATES, Robert Wright Paediatric Intensive Care, Royal Manchester Childrens Hospital, Pendlebury, Manchester M27 4HA Tel: 07092 274407; 31 Stapleton Avenue, Heaton, Bolton BL1 5ET Email: robert.yates@man.ac.uk — MB BS 1986 Lond.; MSc Univ. Lond. 1996; MRCP (UK) 1990; FRCPCH 1996; DA (UK) 1991. (Roy. Free) Cons. Paediat. Intens. Care Manch. Childr. Hosps. Prev: Sen.

YATES

Regist. (Paediat. Intens. Care) Gt. Ormond St. Hosp. Lond.; Regist. (Paediat.) Chelmsford; Regist. (Anaesth.) Roy. Lond. Hosp.

YATES, Roger Alan Zeneca Pharmaceuticals, Medical Research Department, Macclesfield SK10 4TG Tel: 01625 582828; 3 Racecourse Park, Wilmslow SK9 5LU Tel: 01625 520246 — MB BChir 1971 Camb.; PhD Bristol 1976; MA Camb. 1972; MRCP (UK) 1977; FFPM RCP Lond. 1993; MFPM RCP Lond. 1990. Sen. Clin. Pharmacol. Zeneca Pharmaceuts. Div. Alderley Pk. Prev: Clin. Research Asst. (Therap. & Clin. Pharmacol.) Qu. Eliz. Hosp. Birm.; MRC Jun. Research Fell. Dept. Pharmacol. Bristol Univ.

YATES, Rowena Catharine 2 The Horseshoe, York YO24 1LX Tel: 01273 707546 — MB BS 1965 Lond.; MRCS Eng. LRCP Lond. 1965. (Guy's) Clin. Asst. (Psychiat.) Clifton Hosp. York. Prev: Regist. Dept. Child Psychiat. St. Jas. Hosp. Leeds; Regist. (Psychiat.) St. John's Hosp. Stone.

YATES, Sarah Mounts Medical Centre, Campbell Street, Northampton NN1 3DS Tel: 01604 631952 Fax: 01604 634139; 39 Aldwell Close, Wootton, Northampton NN4 6AX — MB BS 1968 Lond.; MRCS Eng. LRCP Lond. 1968; DFFP 1993. Prev: Lect. Univ. Malta.

YATES, Sarah Catherine Longdon, Shipley Rd, Southwater, Horsham RH13 7BQ — BM 1997 Soton. (Soton) GP Trainee.

YATES, Sarah Catriona 24 Sandy Lane, Lymm WA13 9HQ — MB ChB 1991 Liverp.; MB ChB 1991 Liverp.

YATES, Stewart Paul Barnsley District General Hospital, Gawber Road, Barnsley S75 2EP Tel: 01226 730000 — MB ChB 1983 Sheff.; BMedSci 1980; FRCR 1990; T(R)(CR) 1991. Cons. Radiol. Barnsley Dist. Gen. Hosp. Prev: Sen. Regist. (Radiol.) Sheff. HA; Regist. (Med.) Rotherham Dist. Gen. Hosp.

YATES, Susan Felicity Bryn Aber, Nantgwynant, Caernarfon LL55 4NW — MB BS 1977 Lond.; MRCGP 1983; DRCOG 1980; DCH Eng. 1979. Clin. Med. Off. Child Health Servs. Paddington & N. Kensington HA; Clin. Asst. Paediat. Home Care Unit Paddington Green Childr. Hosp. Prev: GP Trainee VTS St. Mary's Hosp.; SHO (Psychiat.) Roy. Free Hosp. Lond.; Cas. Off. Roy. Sussex Co. Hosp. Brighton.

YATES, Sylvia Helen (retired) Gemini, Lanham Lane, Winchester SO22 5JS Tel: 01962 861681 Email: johngeminjoy@aol.com — MB ChB 1952 Sheff.; Acad. DPH Univ. Lond. 1956. Prev: SCMO Winchester HA.

YATES, Mrs Victoria Mary Orchard Cottage, 40 Leighton Beck Rd, Beetham, Milnthorpe LA7 7AX Tel: 01539 564129 — MB ChB 1974 Sheff.; FRCP Lond. 1993; MRCP (UK) 1976. Cons. Dermat. Roy. Lancaster Infimary. Prev: Cons. Dermat. Blackburn Roy. Infirm.; Sen. Regist. (Dermat.) Skin Hosp. Manch.; Sen. Regist. & Regist. (Dermat.) Stobhill Hosp.

YATES, Wendy Ann Cytology Department, Clinical Sciences Building, Manchester Royal Infirmary, Oxford Road, Manchester M13 9WL Tel: 0161 276 8819 Fax: 0161 276 6348; 3 Racecourse Park, Wilmslow SK9 5LU Tel: 01625 520246 — MB BChir 1971 Camb.; MA Camb. 1972, MB BChir 1971; DFFP 1996; DObst RCOG 1973. (Cambridge) Clin. Asst. (Cytol. & Colposcopy) St. Mary's Hosp. Manch.

YATES-BELL, Mr Andrew John (retired) King's College Hospital, Denmark Hill, London SE5 9RS — MB BChir 1959 Camb.; BA Camb. 1959; FRCS Eng. 1966. Hon. Cons. Urol. King's Health Dist. (T). Prev: Regist. (Surg.) St. Peter's Hosp. Lond.

YAU, Chi Yuen 2A Harvesters Close, Gillingham ME8 8PA — MB BChir 1992 Camb.

YAU, Kar-Man Raymond 76 Rofant Road, Northwood HA6 3BA — BM 1993 Soton.

YAU, King Wai Royal National Orthopaedic Hospital NHS Trust, Brockley Hill, Stanmore HA7 4LP — MB ChB 1981 Birm.; FRCA 1986.

YAU, Susan Zi May 34 Wonford Street, Exeter EX2 5DL — MB ChB 1998 Bristol.

YAU, Wing Him The Surgery, Rough Road, Kirkstanding, Birmingham B44 0VY; 14 Lapworth Drive, New Oscott, Sutton Coldfield B73 6QG — MB ChB 1980 Ed.; DRCOG 1984; DCH RCP Glas. 1982; Cert. Family Plann. JCC 1983.

YAU, Mr Yun-Hom 74/5 Orchard Brae Avenue, Edinburgh EH4 2GA Tel: 0131 623 2895 Fax: 0131 466 0608 Email: yhyau@msn.com — MB ChB 1994 Ed.; FRCS Ed. 1998; FCS (HK) 1998. (Univ. Ed.) Regist. (Neurosurg.) W.ern Gen. Hosp. Edin.; BST (Roy. Infirm. of Edin. & P.ss Marg. Rose Hosp. Edin.). Prev: SHO (Gen. Surg.) E. Gen. Hosp. & Roy. Infirm. Edin.; BST SE Scotl. Rotat.; SHO (A & E) Roy. Infirm. Edin.

YAU, Yun Yin 10 Barned Court, Maidstone ME16 9EL — MB BS 1997 Lond.

YAXLEY, Katharine Mary Fulwood Clinic, Lytham Road, Preston PR2 4JB Tel: 01772 401300; 61 Beechfield Avenue, Wrea Green, Preston PR4 2NX Tel: 01772 681619 — BM 1985 Soton.; DCH RCP Lond. 1990. (Soton.) p/t Staff Grade Practitioner (Community Paediat.), Preston acute Hosp.s NHS Trust. Prev: Staff Grade Pract. (Community Child Health) Norwich Community Health NHS Trust; Clin. Med. Off. (Community Child Health) Norwich Community Health NHS Trust; Ho. Off. (Gen. Med., Cardiol., Urol. & ENT) Norf. & Norwich Hosp.

YAZDANI, Monwar Shariar South West Herts Health Centre, Oxhey Drive, South Oxhey, Watford WD1 6SF Tel: 020 8421 5224.

YAZDANI, Qudsia 10 Ashby Road, Tamworth B79 8AG — MB BS 1972 Punjab.

***YAZDIAN-TEHRANI, Hamid** 3 Somerhill Road, Hove BN3 1RP Email: docham@hotmail.com — MB BS 1998 Lond.; MB BS Lond 1998.

YEALLAND, Susan (retired) 9 Clarkson Road, Cambridge CB3 0EH — MB BS 1949 Lond.; MRCS Eng. LRCP Lond. 1949; DO Eng. 1975.

YEAMAN, William Taylor McKenzie (retired) 22 Jedburgh Road, Dundee DD2 1SR Tel: 01382 668601 — MB ChB 1955 St. And.

YEANDLE, Martin Paul 1 Bayford Drive, Shrewsbury SY1 3XQ Tel: 01743 363423 — MB BS 1995 Lond. GP Regist. Ch. Stretton Med. Centre.

YEANG, Yvonne Yee Wan 30 Deansway, East Finchley, London N2 0JF Tel: 020 8883 6951 Fax: 020 8883 6951 — MB ChB 1971 Ed.; BSc (Med. Sci.) Ed. 1968, MB ChB 1971; MRCP (UK) 1974; Dip. Pharm. Med. RCP (UK) 1986; FFPM 1995. (Edinburgh University) Dir. Clin. Investig. Pharmaceut. Company.

YEAP, Joo Seng Room 3 Upper Wing, Louise Fleishchmann Building, Royal National Orthopaedic Hospital, Brockley Hill, Stanmore HA7 4LP — MB BCh BAO 1992 Belf.

YEAP, May Lynn Flat B32, Leicester Royal Infirmary Staff Residence, Walnut St., Leicester LE2 7GJ; 2 Priory Road, Clifton, Bristol BS8 1TX — MB ChB 1995 Bristol. SHO (A & E) Roy. Infirm. Leicester. Socs: Med. Defence Union; BMA; Med. Protec. Soc. Prev: Ho. Off. (Surg.) Bristol Roy. Infirm. & S.mead Hosp.; Ho. Off. (Med.) Bristol Roy. Infirm.

YEARSLEY, Deborah Margaret Marlborough Medical Practice, The Surgery, George Lane, Marlborough SN8 4BY Tel: 01672 512187 Fax: 01672 516809; Fairways, 28 The Thorns, Osbourne Chase, Marlborough SN8 1DY Tel: 01672 512965 — MB BCh 1985 Wales; DRCOG 1991. Prev: Trainee GP Ramsbury Wilts.

YEARSLEY, John Kenneth Noel, MC (retired) 46 Middlebridge Street, Romsey SO51 8HL Tel: 01794 522317 — MB BS 1952 Lond.; DTM & H Liverp. 1954. Prev: GP Ramsgate, Kent.

YEARSLEY, Richard Henderson Thornhills Medical Group, 732 London Road, Larkfield, Aylesford ME20 6BQ Tel: 01732 843900 Fax: 01732 872633 — MB BS 1983 Lond.; MRCGP 1995; DRCOG 1987. (St. Bart.) Prev: Ho. Surg. Luton & Dunstable Hosp.; Ho. Phys. St. Bart. Hosp. Lond.; Gen. Resid. Roy. Newc. Hosp. Austral.

YEATES, Caroline Elizabeth Swn y Gwynt, Day Hospital, Tir y Dail Lane, Ammanford SA18 3AS Tel: 01269 595473 — MB BS 1984 Lond.; DRCOG 1988. Staff Grade Doctor (Psychiat.) Swn y Gwynt Day Hosp. Ammanford.

YEATES, Christopher Laurie 14 Parbroath Road, Finglassie, Glenrothes KY7 4TH Tel: 01592 772625 — MB ChB 1974 Dundee; MSc (Occupat. Med.) Univ. Lond. 1984; BSc (Med. Sci.) St. And. 1971. Benefits Agency Med. Off., Benefits Agency Med. Servs. Argyle Hse., Lady Lawson St., Edin. Prev: Med. Off. Atomic Weapons Research Estab. Aldermaston.; SCMO (Occupat. Health) N. Beds. HA; Regist. (Diag. Radiol.) Withington Hosp. & Manch. Roy. Infirm.

YEATES, Curtis Bernstein Big J's Supermarket, Lower Harbour St., Falmouth Post Office, Trelawny, Jamaica; 2 St. Lawrence House, Melville Road, Edgbaston, Birmingham B16 9NQ Tel: 0121 454 6840 — MB BS 1989 West Indies; BSc (Hons.) New York 1984; MRCP (UK) 1994.

YELLOWLEES

YEATES, Dorothy Jean Glenwood Health Centre, Napier Road, Glenrothes KY6 1HL Tel: 01592 756631; 14 Pabroath Road, Finglassie, Glenrothes KY7 4TH Tel: 01592 772625 — MB ChB 1978 Dundee. Clin. Med. Off. Fife HB. Socs: Fac. Comm. Health. Prev: Clin. Med. Off. Basingstoke & N. Hants. Health Dist.; Clin. Med. Off. Luton.

YEATES, Francis Alexander The Thorndike Centre, Longley Road, Rochester ME1 2TH Tel: 01634 817217; 27 Beresford Road, Kits Coty, Aylesford ME20 7EP Tel: 01634 861374 — MB BS 1982 Lond.; DRCOG 1987.

YEATES, Mr Hugh Alan 2 Inver Park, Holywood BT18 9NF — MB BCh BAO 1971 Belf.; FRCS (Orthop.) Ed. 1980; FRCS Ed. 1976. Cons. Orthop. Surg. Musgrave Hosp. Belf.; Cons. Orthop. Surg. Ulster Hosp. Dundonald. Socs: Brit. Orthop. Assn. & Ulster Med. Soc.

YEATES, Sybil Ruth (retired) 185 Lawrie Park Gardens, London SE26 6XJ Tel: 020 8778 8148 — MB BS 1947 Lond.; MRCS Eng. LRCP Lond. 1946; FRCPCH 1997. Prev: Cons. Optimum Health Trust Lond.

YEATMAN, Alison West Suffolk Hospital, Hardwick Lane, Bury St Edmunds IP33 2QZ; Caius Cottage, Bardwell Road, Barningham, Bury St Edmunds IP31 1DF — MB BS 1991 Lond.

YEATMAN, Mr Mark Frenchay Hospital - Bungalow 1, Frenchay Park Road, Bristol BS16 1LE — MB BS 1989 Lond.; BSc (Hons.) Lond. 1986; FRCS Eng. 1993. (St. Thos. Hosp. Med. Sch.) Cardiovasc. Research Fell. (Surg.) Duke Univ. Med. Center Durh. N. Carolina, USA. Prev: Surgic. Fell. Transpl. Unit Papworth Hosp. Camb.; SHO (Surg.) St. Mary's Hosp. Lond. VTS.

YEATMAN, Nigel William Johnathan 1C Tredegar Square, Bow, London E3 5AD Tel: 020 8980 4181 — MB BS 1974 Lond.; BSc Lond. 1972, MB BS 1974; MRCP (UK) 1978; DCH Eng. 1977; DRCOG 1976. (Lond. Hosp.) Lect. (Immunol.) Lond. Hosp. Prev: SHO (Cas.) Whipps Cross Hosp. Lond.; SHO (Paediat.) Lond. Hosp.

YEBOAH, Owusu Kwasi 27 Riverholme Drive, Ewell West, Epsom KT19 9TG Tel: 020 8224 2662; 22 Beaufort Way, Epsom KT17 2PS — Vrach 1967 Moscow; Vrach People's Friendship Univ. Moscow 1967; MSc Trop. Med. Liverp. 1973; DTM & H Liverp. 1971.

YEDLA, Suryaprakash Rao c/o Dr S. Motha, 41 The Sutton, St Leonards-on-Sea TN38 9RA — MB BS 1975 Andhra.

YEE, Amah Tyrone Road Surgery, 99 Tyrone Road, Thorpe Bay, Southend-on-Sea SS1 3HD Tel: 01702 582670 Fax: 01702 589146 — MB BS 1965 Dacca; MRCS Eng. LRCP Lond. 1983.

YEE, Kok Meng Flat 701, Endsleigh House, Bedford Hospital, South Wing, Kempston Road, Bedford MK42 9DJ; Flat 701, Endsleigh House, Bedford Hospital, South Wing, Kempston Road, Bedford MK42 9DJ — MB ChB 1993 Ed.

YEE, Main Ching 40 Chapel Road, Weldon, Corby NN17 3HP — MB ChB 1992 Leicester.

YEE, Mee Lian Flat 1, Trident Court, 3 Gilbertstone Avenue, Birmingham B26 1LD — MB ChB 1983 Sheff.

YEGANEH-ARANI, Erfan Church Grange Surgery, Brambeys Drive, Basingstoke RG21 8QN; 32 Ellenborough Road, London N22 5HA — MB ChB 1995 Manch.; DRCOG 1998. (Manchester) SHO (O & G) N. Hants. Hosp.; GP Regist. Ch. Grange Basingstoke Surg. Socs: Med. Protec. Soc. Prev: SHO (Pub. Health Med.) N. & Mid Hants. Health Auth.; SHO (Psychiat.) Roy. J. Hants Hosp.; SHO (Med.) Burnley Gen. Hosp. Lancs.

YEGHEN, Tullie King's College Hospital, Denmark Hill, Lewisham High St., London SE5 Tel: 020 7737 4000; 20 Stokenchurch Street, London SW6 3TR Tel: 020 7736 8400 — MB BS 1986 Lond.; BA Oxf. 1982; MRCP (UK) 1990; DRCPath 1993. Sen. Regist. (Haemat.) King's Coll. Hosp. Lond. Prev: Sen. Regist. (Haemat.) Lewisham Hosp. NHS Trust Lond.; Research Fell. (Haemat. & Microbiol.) Roy. Free Hosp. Lond.; Regist. (Haemat.) St. Geo. Hosp., Roy. Marsden. Hosp. & Roy. Surrey Co. Hosp.

YEH, James Shue-Min 71 Plover Way, London SE16 7TS Tel: 020 7252 3899 Fax: 020 7252 3899 Email: yeh-james@hotmail.com; 153-155 Bradstow Way, Broadstairs CT10 1AR Tel: 01843 865483 Fax: 01843 865483 — MB ChB 1995 Ed.; BSC Ed 1993; MBCHB Ed 1995 (Class Medal, Sloggies Prize in Gen. Pract. & Dorothea Walpole Mem. Prize in Gen. Pract.); MRCP (UK) 1998; ALS Cert 1999. (Ed.) SHO (Gen. Med.) King's Coll. Hosp. Lond.; SHO Oncol. Myertein Inst. of Oncol. Middlx. Hosp. Uni. Coll. Lond. Hosp., Lond. Socs: Fell.Roy.Soc.Med.; BMA; RCP. Prev: Ho. Off. (Gen. Surg. &

Gen. Med.) Roy. Infirm. Edin.; SHO Neurol. & Neurosurg., King's Coll., Lond. Gen. Med. & HIV & Geriatic Med., Lond.

YEH, Mr John Sho-Ju The Queen Elizabeth Newnscience Centre, Edgbaston, Birmingham B15 2TH Tel: 0121 472 1311 Email: j.s.yeh@bham.ac.uk; 11 Metfield Croft, Birmingham B17 0NN Tel: 0121 426 1724 Fax: 0121 426 1724 — MB BChir 1989 Camb.; MA Camb. 1991, BA (Hons.) 1987, MB BChir 1989; FRCS Ed. 1994. (University of Cambridge) Specialist Regist., Neurosurg., The Qu. Eliz. NeuwSci. Centre, Birmingham; Hon. Clin. Lect. Univ. Birm. Socs: Assoc. Mem. of Soc. fo Brit. Neurol. Surg.s; Brit. Cervical Spine Soc.; Fell. Roy. Coll. Surg. Edin. Prev: Research Regist. (Neurosurg.) Midl. Centre for Neuosurg. & Neurol. Warley.; SHO (Surg.) N. Staffs. Roy. Infirm. Stoke-on-Trent; Ho. Phys. (Gen. Med. & Haemat.) & Ho. Surg. (Urol. & Gen. Surg.) Addenbrooke's Hosp. Camb.

YEH, Peter Shue-Yen 71 Plover Way, London SE16 7TS Tel: 020 7252 3899 Fax: 020 7252 3899 Email: yehpeter@hotmail.com; 15 Kestell Drive, Cardiff CF11 7BF Tel: 029 2066 5931 Fax: 029 2066 5931 Email: yehpeter@hotmail.com — MB BChir 1992 Camb.; MRCOG 2001 London; MA Camb. 1993, BA (Hons.) 1989; DFFP Lond. 1997. (Camb.) Regist. (O & G) Hammersmith Hosp. NHS Trust Lond.; McLoghlin Schol. RCS Eng. Socs: Brit. Fertil. Soc.; Roy. Soc. of Med.; Brit. Soc. of Gyn. Endoscopy. Prev: Regist. (O & G) Oxf. Radcliffe Hosp. NHS Trust; SHO (O & G) Roy. Lond. Hosp. & St. Bart. Hosp. Lond.; Ho. Off. (Gen. Med. & Haemat.) Addenbrooke's Hosp. Camb.

YELD, Rophina Owen Southbourne Surgery, 337 Main Road, Southbourne, Emsworth PO10 8JH Tel: 01243 372623 Fax: 01243 379936 Email: rophina.yeld@gp-h82078.nhs.uk — MB BS 1987 Lond.; DFFP 1994; DRCOG 1993. (Charing Cross and Westminster) GP at S.bourno Surg. Prev: Trainee GP S.bourne, Hants.; SHO (A & E) St. Richards Hosp. Chichester; SHO (Anaesth.) Poole Gen. Hosp.

YELDHAM, Denise Linda The Lawels, Newton Abbot Hospital, 62 East Steet, Newton Abbot TQ12 4PT Tel: 01626 357335 — MB ChB 1975 Leeds; BSc Leeds 1972; MRCPsych 1979. (Leeds) Cons. Psychiat. S. Devon Healthcare Trust. Socs: Assoc. Mem. Brit. Assn. Psychother. Prev: Med. Dir., Cons. Psychiat. & Psychother. Pk.lands Ment. Health Servs. Mid-Surrey HA; Cons. Psychiat. & Psychother Ment. Illness Mid. Surrey HA; Sen. Regist. (Adult Psychiat.) St. Geo. Hosp. Lond.

YELL, Jennifer Anne Leigh Infirmary, The Avenue, Leigh WN7 1HS Tel: 01942 264015 Fax: 01942 264016; Cushendall, Belmont Road, Hale, Altrincham WA15 9PT Tel: 0161 928 0057 — MB ChB 1985 Cape Town; MRCP 1987 UK; MD 1998 Cape Town; FRCP 2000 UK. Cons. Dermat. Wrightington Wigan & Leigh NHS Trust & Salford Roy. Hosps. Manch. Socs: Brit. Assn. Dermat.; Brit. Soc. Study VD; BSID. Prev: Sen. Regist. & Regist. (Dermat.) Oxf. Radcliffe Hosp.; Fell. (Dermat.) Univ. N. Carolina Chapel Hill, USA.

YELLAND, Mr Andrew Nigel Porter Breast Unit, Royal Sussex County Hospital, Eastern Road, Brighton BN2 5BE Tel: 01273 696955; 72 Woodland Drive, Hove BN3 6DJ Email: ayelland@pavilion.co.uk — MB BS 1986 Lond.; MS Lond. 1994; FRCS Ed. 1993. (St. George's) Lead Cons. BrE. Surg. Roy. Sussex Co. Hosp. Brighton. Socs: BrE. Surgs. Gp.; Roy. Soc. Med.; Assn. Surg. Prev: Regist. Rotat. (Surg.) S. Thames (W.); Research Fell. (Med. Oncol.) Char. Cross & W.m. Med. Sch. Lond.

***YELLAND, Elizabeth Sian** 51 Drymen Road, Bearsden, Glasgow G61 2RN — MB ChB 1994 Glas.

YELLIN, Sharon Diana Leeds Health Authority, Blenheim House, West One, Duncombe St., Leeds LS1 4PL; 19 The Avenue, Roundhay, Leeds LS8 1JG — BM BCh 1986 Oxf.; MFPHM RCP (UK) 1993; MPH Leeds 1992; MRCGP 1997. Cons. Pub. Health Med. Leeds HA.

YELLON, Trevor John 6 The Drive, London NW11 9SR — MB BS 1998 Lond.

***YELLOP, Lisa Jane** 5 The Rookery, Deepcar, Sheffield S36 2NE Tel: 0114 288 5916 — BM BS 1994 Nottm.

YELLOWLEES, Alexander John Priory Hospital, Langside Rd, Glasgow Tel: 01738 621151 Fax: 01738 440431 Email: alex.yellowlees@onet.co.uk; Tel: 01738 440431 — MB ChB 1977 Ed.; MPhil Ed. 1984, BSc (Med. Sci.) 1974; MRCPsych 1981. (Ed.) Med. Director Priory Hosp., Glas.; Hon. Lect. Univ. Stirling; Hon. Sen. Lect. Univ. of Dundee. Socs: Som. Eating Disorder

YELLOWLEES

Assn.(Patron). Prev: Cons. Psychiat. Murray Roy. Hosp. Perth; Sen. Regist., Regist. & SHO (Psychiat.) Roy. Edin. Hosp.

YELLOWLEES, Gillian Mary MHET Melburn Lodge, Borders General Hospital, Melrose TD6 9BS Tel: 01896 827105 Fax: 01896 827114 — MB ChB 1983 Bristol; MRCPsych 1988. (Bristol) p/t Cons. Psychiat. (Old Age) Borders Primary Care Trust Melrose. Prev: Sen. Regist. (Psychiat.) Newc.; Sen. Regist. Rotat. (Psychiat.) Bristol; Regist. (Psychiat.) Wonford Ho. Hosp. Exeter.

YELLOWLEES, Sir Henry, KCB (retired) 33 Lea Road, Harpenden AL5 4PQ — BM BCh Oxf. 1950; MA Oxf. 1950; MRCS Eng. LRCP Lond. 1950; FRCP Ed. 1993; FRCS Eng. 1984; FRCP Lond. 1971, M 1966; Hon. FRCPS Glas. 1974; Hon. FRCPsych 1977; FFCM 1972. Prev: Chief Med. Off. DHSS Educat. Sci. & Home Off.

YELLOWLEES, Ian Henry Borders General Hosptial, Melrose TD6 9BS; Tel: 01835 822428 Email: ian.yellowlees@virgin.net — MB ChB 1983 Bristol; BA (Hons.) Engin Sci. Oxf. 1977; MPhil (Engineering) 1990; FCAnaesth 1989. Cons. Anaesth. Borders Gen. Hosp. Prev: Sen. Regist. Rotat. (Anaesth.) Newc.; Regist. (Anaesth.) Bristol; Lect. (Engin. Sci.) Univ. Exeter.

YELLOWLEES, Walter Walker, MC (retired) The Cottage, Alma Avenue, Aberfeldy PH15 2BW Tel: 01887 820277 — MB ChB Ed. 1941; FRCGP 1970. Prev: RMO 5th Bn. Qu. Own Cameron Highlanders.

YELLOWLEY, John Crisp (retired) 30 Lumsdaine Drive, Dalgety Bay, Dunfermline KY11 9YU Tel: 01383 824870 — MB ChB 1952 Ed.

YELLOWLEY, Thomas William 106 Edge Hill, Ponteland, Newcastle upon Tyne NE20 9JQ — MB BS 1961 Durh.; DObst RCOG 1963.

YELNOORKAR, Kamalakar The Galleries Health Centre, Town Centre, Washington NE38 Tel: 0191 416 7032 — MB BS 1968 Marathwada. (Marathwada) GP Washington, Tyne & Wear.

YEN, Mr William 49/50 Leinster Gardens, Bayswater, London W2 3AT — MB BS 1959 Lond.; FRCS Eng. 1964; FRCS Ed. 1963; MRCS Eng. LRCP Lond. 1959.

YENTIS, Irvan Lavender Wall, 12 Warren Road, Ickenham, Uxbridge UB10 8AA Tel: 01895 235867 — MB BS 1947 Lond.; MD Lond. 1950; FRCP Lond. 1973, M 1951; FRCR 1975; FFR 1957; DMRD Eng. 1953. (Guy's) Socs: (Ex-Pres.) Windsor & Dist. Med. Soc. Prev: Dist. Clin. Tutor E. Berks. HA; Cons. Radiol. King Edwd. VII Hosp. Windsor & Wexham Pk. Hosp. Slough; Sen. Regist. (X-Ray Diag.) Univ. Coll. Hosp. & Hosp. Sick Childr. Gt. Ormond St. Lond.

YENTIS, Steven Marc Magill Department of Anaesthesia, Chelsea & Westminster Hospital, 369 Fulham Road, London SW10 9NH Email: syentis@ic.ac.uk — MB BS 1984 Lond.; BSc Lond. 1981, MD 1994; FRCA 1989. (Univ. Coll. Hosp.) Cons. Anaesth. Chelsea & W.m. Hosp. Lond. Prev: Sen. Regist. (Anaesth.) Char. Cross & W.m. Hosps. Lond.; Regist. (Anaesth.) St. Mary's Hosp. Lond.

YEO, Ai-Lyn Penthouse Flat 12, Block 4, Portman Mansions, Chiltern St., London W1M 1PW — MB BChir 1988 Camb.

YEO, David Woon Tjun 412 Park W., London W2 2QT — MB BS 1998 Lond.

YEO, Elaine Ruth Abernethy House, 70 Silver Street, Enfield EN1 3EP Tel: 020 8366 1314 Fax: 020 8364 4176; 9 Glebe Avenue, Enfield EN2 8NZ Tel: 020 8363 1019 — MB ChB 1972 Birm.; MRCGP 1984; DCH Eng. 1975; DObst RCOG 1974. GP Course Organiser Enfield VTS. Prev: Ho. Off. (Obst.) & SHO (Paediat.) N. Middlx. Hosp. Lond.

YEO, Hazel Eunice Dorothy Pennells and Partners, Gosport Health Centre, Bury Road, Gosport PO12 3PN Tel: 023 9258 3344 Fax: 023 9260 2704 — MB BS 1978 Lond.; BSc Lond. 1975; MRCGP 1982; DRCOG 1980. (Univ. Coll. Hosp.) Prev: GP Guildford; SHO (Paediat. & ENT) Roy. Surrey Co. Hosp. Guildford.

YEO, Jane Elizabeth Tilehurst Surgery, Tylers Place, Pottery Road, Tilehurst, Reading RG30 6BW Tel: 0118 942 7528 Fax: 0118 945 2405; 9 Norman Avenue, Henley-on-Thames RG9 1SG Tel: 01491 577915 — MB BS 1961 Lond.; MRCS Eng. LRCP Lond. 1961; MRCGP 1983. Prev: GP Barbados.

YEO, Kok Cheang, CMG (retired) 10 Rowbarns, Battle TN33 0JQ Tel: 01424 772803 — MB BS Hong Kong 1925; MD Hong Kong 1930; DPH Camb. 1928; DTM & H Eng. 1927. Prev: Asst. Psychiat. St. Ebba's Hosp. Epsom.

YEO, Nigel James 19 Leopold Road, Crawley RH11 7BN — MB BS 1998 Lond.

YEO, Patricia 122 Ruskin Park House, Champion Hill, London SE5 8TL — MB ChB 1992 Sheff.

YEO, Mr Richard Adams Farm, Sandrock Hill, Crowhurst, Battle TN33 9AY Tel: 01424 830255 — MB BChir 1959 Camb.; MChir Camb. 1967, MA, MB 1959, BChir 1958; FRCS Eng. 1962; MRCS Eng. LRCP Lond. 1958. (Westm.) Hon. Cons. Gen. Surg. Conquest Hosp. St. Leonards-on-Sea. Socs: Sec. Brit. Surg. Stapling Gp.; Surg. Vasc. Soc. of Gt. Brit. & Irel. Prev: Cons. Gen. Surg. Roy. E. Sussex & St. Helen's Hosps. Bexhill Hosp. & Rye Hosp.; Res. Surg. Off. Brompton Hosp.; Sen. Regist. (Surg.) King's Coll. Hosp. Lond.

YEO, Richard Castle Hill Hospital, Castle Hill Road, Cottingham HU16 5JQ Tel: 01482 875875; Bank House Farm, Main St, Etton, Beverley HU17 7PQ Tel: 01430 810459 — MB BS 1968 Lond.; FRCOG 1987, M 1973; DObst RCOG 1970. (St. Geo.) Cons. O & G E. Yorks. Hosp.s Trust Hull. Socs: Lond. Obst. & Gyn. Soc.; Hull Med. Soc. Prev: Sen. Regist. (O & G) Char. Cross Hosp. Lond.; Regist. (O & G) Pembury Hosp.; SHO (O & G) P.ss Margt. Hosp. Swindon.

YEO, Seng-Jin 3F Portman Mansions, Chiltern St., London W1U 5AH — MB BS 1984 Newc.

YEO, Seng Tee 31 Wyncote Court, Jesmond Park Est., Newcastle upon Tyne NE7 7BG — MB BS 1991 Newc.

YEO, Siaw Ing Flat 36, Campania Building, Atlantic Wharf, 1 Jardine Road, London E1 9WE Tel: 020 7790 3180 — MB BS 1993 Lond.; MRCP (UK) 1996. (UMDS Guy's and St. Thos. Hosps.) Specialist Regist. (Rheum. & Med.) S. Thames. Prev: Clin. Research Fell. (Rheum.) King's Coll. Hosp.; SHO (Rheum.) Lewisham NHS Trust.

YEO, Victor 122 Ruskin Park House, Champion Hill, London SE5 8TL — MB BChir 1991 Camb.; MA Camb. 1992.

YEO, Wilfred Winston Section of Clinical Pharmacology & Therapay, University Department Medicine & Pharmacology, Floor L, Royal Hallamshire Hospital, Glossop Road, Sheffield S10 2JF Tel: 0114 271 3789 Fax: 0114 272 0275 Email: w.w.yeo@sheffield.ac.uk; 7 Glebe View, Barlborough, Chesterfield S43 4WF Tel: 01246 570454 — MB ChB 1984 Sheff.; BMedSci (Hons.) Sheff. 1983; MRCP (UK) 1987; MD 1996, Sheff. Sen. Lect. in Med., Clin. Pharmacol. & Thrapeutics; Hon. Cons. Phys., Centr. Sheffield, Univ. Hosp. Trust. Socs: Brit. Pharm. Soc.; Brit. Hypertens. Soc.; Clin. Sec. BPS. Prev: Sen. Regist. & Lect. (Med. & Pharmacol.) Roy. Hallamsh. Hosp. Sheff.; Research Regist. (Pharmacol. & Therap.) Roy. Hallamsh. Hosp. Sheff.

YEOH, Mr Lam Hoe St. Helier Hospital, Wrythe Lane, Carshalton SM5 1AA Tel: 020 8296 2565 Fax: 020 8644 968 — MB BS 1976 Singapore; MSc Manch. 1988; FRCS (Otol.) Eng. 1982; DLO Eng. 1979. Cons. Audiol. Phys. Merton & Sutton HA. Prev: Sen. Regist. (Audiol. Med.) Mersey RHA; Sen. Regist. (Otorhinolaryng.) Mersey RHA; Regist. (ENT) St. Bart. Hosp. Lond.

YEOH, Michael John Department of Anaesthetcis, Salisbury District Hospital, Odstock Road, Salisbury SP2 8BJ — MB BS 1991 Melbourne.

YEOMAN, Andrew David The Rectory, Merthyr Mawr Road N., Bridgend CF31 3NH — MB BCh 1998 Wales.

YEOMAN, Colin Michael Highpoint, Church Lane, Thropton, Morpeth NE65 7JB — MB ChB 1994 Manch.

YEOMAN, Guy Beatty Oldland Surgery, 142 High St., Oldland Common, Bristol BS30 9QQ Tel: 0117 932 4444 Fax: 0117 932 4101 — MB BS 1990 Lond.; MRCGP 1994; DRCOG 1993. (GP Princip. Bristol) Trainee GP Ivybridge.

YEOMAN, Lindsey Jane Department of Radiology, Barnsley District General Hospital, Gawber Road, Barnsley S75 2EP Tel: 01226 730000 — MB BS 1983 Lond.; MRCP (UK) 1986; FRCR 1990; T(R) (CR) 1991. Cons. Radiol. Barnsley Dist. Gen. Hosp. Prev: Cons. Radiol. City Hosp. Nottm.

YEOMAN, Neil Christopher 14 Meynell Gardens, London E9 7AT — MB BS 1987 Lond.

YEOMAN, Patrick Michael 8 Frog Lane, Plungar, Nottingham NG13 0JE — MB BS 1976 Lond.; FFA RCS Eng. 1981. Cons. Anaesth. Univ. & City Hosps. Nottm.

YEOMAN, Peter David Blyth Health Centre, Thoroton Street, Blyth NE24 1DX Tel: 01670 396560 Fax: 01670 396579 — MB ChB 1983 Manch.; BSc St. And. 1980; DRCOG 1986. (St Andrews & Manchester) Bd. Mem. PCG. Prev: SHO (Paediat.) Cumbld. Infirm.;

SHO (O & G) Newc. Gen. Hosp.; Ho. Off. (Med.) Lewis Hosp. Stornoway.

YEOMAN, Roger Willow Surgery, Coronation Rd, Downend, Bristol BS16 Tel: 0117 970 9500; 26 West Mall, Clifton, Bristol BS8 4BG Tel: 0117 973 7552 — MB ChB 1986 Manch.; D.A Coll. Anaestetists 1991; BSc Med. Sci. 1983, St. And. (St. Andrews/Manchester) Socs: Cossham Med. Soc.

YEOMANS, Julian David Ian Somerset House, Manor Lane, Shipley BD18 3BP Tel: 01274 531536 Fax: 01274 770779 — MB ChB 1985 Manch.; BSc St. And. 1982; MMedSc Leeds 1992; MRCPsych 1990. Cons. Psychiat. (Adult Psychiat.) Bradford Community Health Trust. Prev: Sen. Regist. (Adult Psychiat.) Yorks. Region; Hon. Tutor (Psychiat.) Univ. Leeds.

YEOMANS, Neil Paul 6 Leopold Drive, Bishops Waltham, Southampton SO32 1JU — MB ChB 1998 Leeds.

YEOMANS, Steven John Tel: 0191 257 2765; 35 The Broadway, Tynemouth, North Shields NE30 2LL — MB BS 1992 Lond.; BA Oxf. 1989; MRCP (UK) 1997. (Guy's Hosp., Lond. Univ.) Specialist Regis., (Gen. & Geriat. Med.), Bishop Auckland Hosp. Socs: Brit. Geriat. Soc. Prev: Specialist Regist., S. Cleveland Hosp.; Specialist Regist., Sunderland Roy. Hosp.; Specialist Regis., N. Tees Hosp.

YEONG, Chee Chew Warrington Hospital NHS Trust, Lovely Lane, Warrington WA5 1QG Tel: 01925 662457; 24 Greenway, Appleton, Warrington WA4 3AD Tel: 01925 604899 — MB BCh BAO 1982 Dub.; MRCP (UK) 1987; FRCR 1992; T(R) (CR) 1993. Cons. Radiol. Warrington Hosp. NHS Trust. Prev: Sen. Regist. N. Staffs. Hosp.

YERASSIMOU, Pamela Marcella 15 Belmont Court, 93 Highbury New Park, London N5 2HA — MB BCh 1994 Wales.

YERBURY, Christopher Michael Grange Road Surgery, Grange Road, Bishopsworth, Bristol BS13 8LD Tel: 0117 964 4343 Fax: 0117 935 8422 — MB BS 1985; BSc Lond. 1982; MRCGP 1993; DRCOG 1992; DCH RCP Lond. 1988. (U.C.H, London) GP Bristol. Prev: GP VTS, Bath; Med. Off. Kikuyu Hosp. Kenya.; Med. Off. Eshowe Hosp. Zululand.

YERBURY, Grace Margaret Timber Close, Church Lane, Oakley, Bedford MK43 7RP Tel: 01234 825432 — MB BS 1954 Lond.; MPhil Cranfield Univ. 1993; MRCS Eng. LRCP Lond. 1954; DObst RCOG 1956; DCH Eng. 1957. (Middlx.) Socs: Fell. Roy. Soc. Med.; Brit. Paediat. Assn. Prev: Regist. (Paediat.) Addenbrooke's Hosp. Camb.; Assoc. Paediat. Bedford Gen. Hosp.; Med. Co-ordinator Child Developm. Centre Bedford.

YERBURY, Nicholas Olyffe New Court Surgery, Borough Fields Shopping Centre, Wootton Bassett, Swindon SN4 7AX Tel: 01793 852302 Fax: 01793 851119 — MB BS 1972 Lond.; MRCS Eng. LRCP Lond. 1972; MRCGP 1979; DObst RCOG 1974. (Guy's) Socs: Soc. Apoth. Lond. Prev: Sen. Med. Off. RAF Lyneham; Ho. Off. (Obst.) Roy. Sussex Co. Hosp. Brighton; Ho. Off. (Paediat.) S.mead Hosp. Bristol.

YESUFU, Aminu Omonikhe 279 Katherine Road, London E7 8PP — MBBS Ibadan, Nigeria; MRCOG. (Ibadan, Nigeria) Socs: G.M.C. Prev: Staff Grade Obst.& Gynae., St Cross Hosp., Rugby,January 1997.

YETTON, William Rex (Surgery), 4 St Peters Place, Brighton BN1 4SA Tel: 01273 606006 Fax: 01273 623896; 49 The Droveway, Hove BN3 6PR Tel: 01273 558274 — MRCS Eng. LRCP Lond. 1973; FFA RCS Eng. 1980. GP Brighton. Prev: Regist. (Anaesth.) Roy. Sussex Co. Hosp. Brighton.

YEUNG, Eric Sze Tsun 44 Castle Grove, Portchester, Fareham PO16 9NZ — MB BS 1996 Lond.

YEUNG, John Ngai Man Whittington Hospital, Highgate Hill, London N19 5NF Tel: 020 7272 3070; 108 Clarence Gate Gardens, Glentworth St, London NW1 6AL Tel: 020 7724 1299 — MB ChB 1988 Ed.; MBA Warwick 1990; MRCP (UK) 1992. SHO (Paediat.) Whittington Hosp. Lond. Prev: SHO Rotat. (Med.) Battle & Roy. Berks. Hosps. Reading; Ho. Off. (Med.) Dumfries & Galloway Roy. Infirm.; Ho. Off. (Surg.) W.. Gen. Hosp. Edin.

YEUNG, Justin Ming-Chi 11 Hazelmere Grove, Lenton, Nottingham NG7 2EH — BM BS 1996 Nottm.

YEUNG, Shun May Flat 16, 45 Barkston Gardens, London SW5 0ES — MB BS 1991 Lond.

YEUNG, Stephen Roy The General Infirmary at Leeds, Great George Street, Leeds LS1 3EX — MB ChB 1968 Leeds; Dip. Pract. Dermat. Wales 1991. Assoc. Specialist Dermat., Leeds Teachg. Hosps. NHS Trust. Prev: Research Clin. Asst. (Neurol.) Leeds Gen. Infirm.; Ho. Phys. Leeds Gen. Infirm.; Ho. Surg. St. Jas. Hosp. Leeds.

YEUNG KUATE PIN, Yew Kim Block 1, Flat 3, Yorkhill Court, Royal Hospital for Sick Children, Yorkhill, Glasgow G3 8SJ — MB ChB 1984 Glas.

YEUNG TAM SANG, Stella 20 Victoria Terrace, Leeds LS3 1BX — MB ChB 1989 Leeds.

YEUNG-WYE-KONG, Mr Chin-Kian Pontefract General Infirmary, (Pinderfields and Pontefract Hospital Trust), Friarwood Lane, Pontefract WF8 1PL Tel: 01977 600600; Green Knoll, Pontefract Road, Ackworth, Pontefract WF7 7EL — MB ChB 1969 (Hons.) Leeds; FRCS Eng. 1975; FRCS Ed. 1974. Cons. Surg. Pontefract Gen. Infirm. Pinderfields & Pontefract Hosp. Trust. Prev: Sen. Regist. (Surg.) Leeds & Bradford Health Dists.; Research Fell. Univ. Dept. Surg. Leeds Gen. Infirm.; Surg. Regist. Nottm. AHA (T).

YEW, Bernard Fan Leong Brooklyn Court, Woking GU22 7TQ — MB BCh BAO 1993 Belf.

YI, Chung-Yiu Guy's Hospital, St. Thomas St., London SE1 9RT Tel: 020 7955 5000 — MB 1992 Camb.; BChir 1991; MA Camb. 1993; MRCP (UK) 1995. SHO (Renal Med.) Guy's Hosp. Lond.

YIALLOUROS, Michael 2 Camlet Way, Barnet EN4 0LH Tel: 020 8440 1628 Fax: 0208 447 1627 Email: alxtn@globalnet.co.uk — Ptychio Iatrikes 1971 Thessalonika.

YIANGOU, Mr Constantinos Queen Alexandra Hospital, Cosham, Portsmouth PO6 3LY Tel: 02392 286000 Fax: 02392 228 6547 — MB BS 1987 Lond.; BSc (Hons.) Lond. 1984; FRCS Eng. 1991; FRCS (Gen Surg.) 1999. (St. Mary's Hosp. Med. Sch.) Cons. Surg. Qu. Alexandra Hosp., Portsmouth; ATLS Instruc. RCS Eng; Cons. Surg., Bupa Hosp. Portsmouth. Socs: BMA; Brit. Assn. Of Surgic. Oncol. Prev: Sen. Specialist Regist. (Gen. & Oncol. Surg.) Lister Hosp. Stevenage; Specialist Regist. (Gen. Surg.) Hemel Hempstead Hosp.; Sen. Specialist Regist. (Gen. & BrE. Surg.) Char. Cross Hosp. Lond.

YIANGOU, Georgia Grosvenor House, 147 Broadway, West Ealing, London W13 9BE Tel: 020 8567 0165/5172 Fax: 020 8810 0902; 11 St. Michaels Avenue, Wembley HA9 6SJ — MB ChB 1981 Manch.; Cert. Family Plann. JCC 1982.

YIANNAKOU, John Yiannakis 10 Raglan Street, Kentish Town, London NW5 3DA — MB ChB 1986 Dundee.

YIANNI, John 9 Newman Road, Hayes UB3 3AL — MB BS 1996 Lond.

YICK, David Chee Kong 11 Lords Way, Copperfields, Exeter EX2 5UD — BM BS 1996 Nottm.

YIEND, Margaret Elizabeth The Jays, Lynwood Road, Lydney GL15 5SG — MB ChB 1950 Leeds. (Leeds) Asst. MOH Matern. & Child Welf. Plymouth.

YIH, Jean-Paul Lai Bong 34A Belsize Road, London NW6 4RD — MB BS 1990 Lond.; MA Oxf. 1993. SHO Moorfields Eye Hosp. Lond. Prev: SHO (Ophth. & Plastic Surg.) Hosp. Childr. Gt. Ormond St. Lond.; SHO (Neurosurg. & Ophth.) Roy. Lond. Hosp.

YII, Mr Michael Yang Yong Cardiothoracic Surgical Unit, Royal Postgraduate Medical School & Hammersmith Hospital, Du Cane Road, London W12 0HS Tel: 020 8743 2030; 16 Vellacott House, Du Cane Road, London W12 0UQ Tel: 020 8746 0627 — MB BS 1990 Melbourne; FRCS Eng. 1994. Research Regist. (Cardiac Surg.) Roy. Postgrad. Med. Sch. & Hammersmith Hosp. Lond.

YIN YIN WIN, Dr 6 Burnsall Close, Brackendale, The Droveway, Pendeford, Wolverhampton WV9 5RU; Wall Lane House Young People's Centre, St. Edwards Hospital, Cheddleton, Leek ST13 7EB — MB BS 1979 Med. Inst. (I) Rangoon; MRCPsych 1996.

YING, Ian Alaistair Ashby Clinic, Collum Lane, Scunthorpe DN16 2SZ Tel: 01724 271877; 135 Moorwell Road, Scunthorpe DN17 2SX Tel: 01724 840742 Fax: 01724 840742 — MB BS 1963 Lond.; MRCS Eng. LRCP Lond. 1967; MRCOG 1969. (St. Bart.) Prev: Cons. O & G Geo.town Hosp. Guyana; Regist. (O & G) Beckenham Matern. & Beckenham Gen. Hosps.

YIP, Alex Shing Biu 48 Childebert Road, London SW17 8EX — MB BS 1981 Lond.; MRCP (UK) 1984. (St. Bart.) Regist. (Med.) Roy. United Hosp. Bath. Prev: SHO (Cardiol.) Lond. Chest Hosp.; Ho. Phys. Whipps Cross Hosp. Lond.; Ho. Surg. St. Bart. Hosp. Lond.

YIP, Brigitte Department of Medicine for the Elderly, Hairmyres Hospital, Glasgow G75 8RG Tel: 0141 522 0292 Fax: 0141 523 4064; 31 Leicester Avenue, Kelvindale, Glasgow G12 0LU — MB ChB 1985 Glas.; MRCP (UK) 1989. Cons. (Phys. in Geriat. Med.) Hairmyres Hosp. E. Kilbride.

YIP

YIP, Mr Kevin Man Hing 2 Lovell Place, Surrey Quays, London SE16 6QQ Tel: 020 7252 0779 — MB BS 1986 Lond.; FRCS 1990. Regist. (Orthop. Brook Hosp. & Greenwich Dist. Hosp. Prev: SHO (Surg. Unit.) Qu. Mary's Hosp. Sidcup; SHO (Acad. Surg. Unit.) Roy. Marsden Hosp.; SHO (Orthop.) Mayday Hosp. Croydon.

YIP, Lai-Ching Kathleen 28 Highbury Road, Glasgow G12 9DZ — MB ChB 1987 Ed.; MRCGP 1991. Prev: Med. Off. (Community Paediat.) Optimum Health Servs. Lond.; SHO (Obst.) Paisley Matern. Hosp.; Trainee GP Greenlaw Med. Centre Paisley.

YIP, Richard Ying Wai 10 Hancroft Road, Bennetts End, Hemel Hempstead HP3 9LL Tel: 01442 236693 — MB BChir 1990 Camb.; MRCGP 1994. Socs: Brit. Med. Acupunct. Soc. Prev: Trainee GP Hemel Hempstead.

YIP, Yee Yan c/o 62 Elmslie Point, Ackroyd Drive, Mile End, London E3 4LD — MB BS 1967 Hong Kong; DTM & H Liverp. 1968.

YISA, Mahazu Ajayi 81 Claydon Drive, Beddington, Croydon CR0 4QX — MB BS 1976 Ibadan; MRCP (UK) 1984.

YIU, Carolyn Anne Cornerways Surgery, 50 Manor Road, Beckenham BR3 5LG Tel: 020 8650 2444; 56 Barnfield Wood Road, Park Langley, Beckenham BR3 6SU Tel: 020 8658 1739 — MB BS 1975 Newc.; MRCGP 1979.

YIU, Mr Chu Yiu Greenwich District Hospital, Vanbrugh Hill, Greenwich, London SE10 9HE Tel: 020 7288 3405 Fax: 020 7288 5030 Email: c.yiu@ucl.ac.uk — MB BS 1976 Lond.; BSc (Hons.) Anat. Lond. 1973, MS 1990; FRCS Eng. 1981. (Univ. Coll. Hosp.) Sen. Lect. & Cons. Surg. Whittington Hosp. Lond. Cons. Srg. Greenwich Dist. Hosp. Lond.. Socs: Brit. Assn. Surg. Oncol; Assn. Coloproctol.; St. Mark's Assn. Prev: Sen. Regist. (Surg.) UCL Med. Med. Sch..; Regist. (Surg.) Chase Farm Hosp. Enfield Middlx.; Wellcome Lect. (Surg.) Sch. Med. Univ. Coll. Lond.

YIU, Cynthia Oi San The Hurley Clinic, Ebenezer House, Kennington Lane, London SE11 4HJ Tel: 020 7735 7918 Fax: 020 7587 5296 — MB BS 1983 Lond.; MRCGP 1995; DCH RCP Lond. 1991.

YIU, Hsiang-Sung, Robert 35 Hendon Avenue, Finchley Central, London N3 1UJ Tel: 020 8349 2360 — MB BS 1955 Hong Kong.

YIU, Mr Patrick 26 Woodberry Way, North Finchley, London N12 0HG — MB BS 1989 Lond.; BSc (Hons.) Lond. 1986; FRCS Eng. 1994. (UMDS Guy's & St. Thos.) Research Regist. (Surg.) Middlx. & Univ. Coll. Hosps. Lond. Socs: BMA; Roy. Soc. Med.; Roy. Coll. Surg. of Eng. Prev: Regist. (Cardiothoracic) Lond. Chest Hosp.

YOGALINGAM, Muttukumaru 182 Upper Shoreham Road, Shoreham-by-Sea BN43 6BG Tel: 01273 591183 — MB BS 1971 Ceylon. (Ceylon)

YOGANATHAN, Kathirgamanathan 24 Rhydydefaid Drive, Sketty, Swansea SA2 8AJ Tel: 01792 204615 — MB BS 1981 Sri Lanka; MRCS Eng. LRCP Lond. 1989; MRCP (UK) 1988; FRCP 1998. Cons. Phys. (Genitourin. Med.) Singleton Hosp. Swansea. Prev: Sen. Regist. (Genitourin. Med.) King's Coll. Hosp. Lond.

YOGANATHAN, Malarmagal 24 Rhydydefaid Drive, Sketty, Swansea SA2 8AJ Tel: 01792 204615 — MRCS Eng. LRCP 1988 Lond.; MRCS Eng LRCP Lond. 1988; DFFP 1995. Clin. Asst., (ENT & Rheum.). Prev: Locum Staff Grade Phys. in Elderly Care, Hill Ho. Hosp., Swansea.

YOGARAJAH, Subraya Chettiar Department of Radiology, Milton Keynes General Hospital, Milton Keynes MK6 5LD Tel: 01908 660033 — MB BS 1966 Ceylon; FRCR 1976; DMRD Eng. 1975. (Colombo) Cons. Radiol. E. (Glas.) Health Dist.; Hon. Clin. Lect. (Radiodiag.) Univ. Glas. Socs: Brit. Inst. Radiol. & Brit. Med. Ultra-Sound Soc. Prev: SHO (Med.) Haslemere & Dist. Hosp.; Regist. (Radiol.) & Sen. Regist. (Radiol.) Roy. Infirm. Glas.

YOGARAJAH, Yogamala 105A Cottenham Park Road, London SW20 0DS — MRCS Eng. LRCP 1988 Lond.; MRCS Eng LRCP Lond. 1988.

YOGARATNAM, Sarojinidevi 3 Churchill Close, Aylestone Hill, Hereford HR1 1DH Tel: 01432 352308 Fax: 01432 276527 Email: yogaratnam@btinternet.com — MB BS 1973 Sri Lanka. Clin. Asst. Gen. Hosp. Hereford.

YOGASAKARAN, Bhuwaneswari Sivakumarie Luton & Dunstable Hospital, Lewsey Road, Luton LU4 0DZ — MB BS 1974 Sri Lanka; FFA RCS Eng. 1982.

YOGASAKARAN, Namasivayam Registrar in Anaesthetics, Princess Alexandra Hospital, Harlow CM20 1QX; 38 Sheldon Avenue, Clayhall, Ilford IG5 0UD — MB BS 1974 Ceylon; FFA RCSI 1984; DA Eng. 1981.

YOGASUNDRAM, Sanath Naresh The Old Bakery, 25 West St, Easton on the Hill, Stafford PE9 3LS Tel: 01780 753898 — MB ChB 1990 Leic.; BSc (Hons.) Leic. 1987; MRCGP 1995. Partner GP. Prev: PeterBoro. VTS; SHO Rotat. (Med.) P'boro. VTS.; SHO Wollongong Hosp. NSW, Austral.

YOGASUNDRAM, Mr Yoganathan 4 Winmarleigh Road, Ashton, Preston PR2 1ET Tel: 01772 726992 — MB BS 1958 Ceylon; FRCS Eng. 1965; FRCS Ed. 1964. (Ceylon) Assoc. Specialist (Surg.) N. W. RHA. Prev: Tutor in Surg. Univ. Ceylon; Regist. (Orthop.) Gen. Hosp. Colombo.

YOGENDRAN, Logesvaran Clinical Pharmacology, Glaxo Wellcome Research and Development Ltd, Greenford UB6 0HE Tel: 020 8966 2696 Fax: 020 8966 4363 Email: ly15106@glaxowellcome.co.uk; 11 Hawthorn Drive, Harrow HA2 7NU — MB BS 1983 Colombo; MRCP (UK) 1989. Sen. Research Phys. (Clin. Pharmacol.) Glaxo Research & Developm. Greenford,Middlx. Socs: Fell. Roy. Soc. Med.

YOGESWARAN, Pararajasingham 82 Hillside Road, Northwood HA6 1PZ — BM 1994 Soton.

YONACE, Adrian Harris Bournemouth Nuffield Hospital, 65-67 Lansdowne Road,, Bournemouth BH1 1RW Tel: 01202 291866 — BM BS 1975 Nottm.; BMedSci (Hons.) Nottm. 1973; FRCPsych 1994, M 1980. (Nottm.) Cons. Psychiat. Private Pract.; Hon. Cons. Roy. Bournemouth and Poole Gen. Hosp.s; JP; Ment. Health Review Tribunal; SOAD Ment. Health Act Commiss. Prev: Cons. Psychiat. St. Ann's Hosp. Poole; Cons. & Hon. Sen. Lect. Frien Hosp. & Roy. Free Hosp. Sch. Med. Lond.; Lect. & Hon. Sen. Regist. Roy. Free Hosp. & Regist. Maudsley Hosp.

YONG, Agnes Siew Mee 28A Benbow Road, London W6 0AG — MB BCh BAO 1990 Belf.; MRCP (UK) 1993. Regist. (Haemat.) Hammersmith Hosp. Lond.

YONG, Audrey Alice 7 Park Drive, Wickford SS12 9DH — MB BS 1991 Lond.; FRCS 1995. (St Bartholomew's)

YONG, Chee Heng Medical Residency, Morriston General Hospital, Heol Maes Eglwys, Cwmrhyceirw, Swansea — MB ChB 1987 Ed.

YONG, Collin Kah Khion 21 Stephenson Close, Leamington Spa CV32 6BS — MB ChB 1989 Leic.

YONG, Diana Elizabeth Jane 39 Avebury Avenue, Leicester LE4 0FQ Tel: 0116 253 9488 Email: yong@dial.pipex.com — MB ChB 1989 Aberd.; MRCP (Paediat.) (UK) 1993. Specialist Regist. (Paediat.) Leicester. Prev: Specialist Regist. (paeds) PeterBoro. Dist. Hosp.; Hon. Clin. Lect. Univ. Aberd.; Staff Grade Neonat. Aberd. Matern. Hosp.

YONG, Jamy Lap 3 Roxby Court, Craiglee Drive, Atlantic Wharf, Cardiff CF10 4AG Tel: 029 2049 0526 Email: jlyong@aol.com — MB BCh 1995 Wales. (University of Wales College of Medicine)

YONG, Kwee Lan Flat 28, Corringham, 13-16 Craven Hill Gardens, London W2 3EH — MB BS 1984 Lond.

YONG, Lynette 6E Stuart Towers, Maida Vale, London W9 1UF — MB BS 1994 Lond.

YONG, Patrick Foh Khing c/o 11 Brocas Close, London NW3 3LD — MB ChB 1998 Bristol.

YONG, Pauline Poh Lin St Mary's Surgery, James Street, Southampton SO14 1PJ Tel: 023 8033 3778 Fax: 023 8021 1894 — BM 1985 Soton. SHO (O & G) Dorchester. Socs: BMA, Prev: Ho. Off. Isle of Wight & E. Dorset HA.

YONG, Sin Chuen 23 Cairns Road, Sheffield S10 5NA Email: w.yong@sheffield.ac.uk; 54 Jalan Terasek Tiga, Bangsar Baru, Kuala Lumpur 59100, Malaysia — MB ChB 1991 Dundee; BMSc (Hons.) Dund 1988; MRCP (UK) 1995. Specialist Regist. N. Trent Paediat. Rotat. Socs: Med. & Dent. Defence Union Scotl.; BMA; MRCPCH. Prev: Research Regist. (Neonate) Jessop Hosp. for Wom., Sheff.; SHO Sheff. Childrs. Hosp.

YONG, Sze Ming 8/7 West Powburn, Edinburgh EH9 3EN — MB ChB 1998 Ed.

YONGE, Geoffrey Pragnell, TD (retired) Foxhollow, Merlewood Drive, Chislehurst BR7 5LQ Tel: 020 8467 6117 — MB BS 1949 Lond. Prev: Chief Med. Off. Provident Mutual Life Assur. Assn.

YOON, Jeannie Swee Lynn 1 Addison House, Grove End Road, London NW8 9EH — MB BS 1986 Lond.

YOON, Lai Lan 31 Ashleigh Manor, Windsor Avenue, Belfast BT9 6EJ — MB BCh BAO 1992 Belf.

YOONG, Adrian Kah Hean Department of Histology, Birmingham Women's Hospital, 1st Floor Laboratories, Edgbaston, Birmingham B15 2TG Tel: 0121 627 2729 Fax: 0121 607 4721 — MB BChir 1983 Camb.; FRCPath 1999; T(Path) 1991; MRCPath 1991; MA Camb. 1985. (Cambridge) Cons. Gyn. Histo/Cytopath. Birm. Wom.'s Hosp.; Hon. Sen. Clin. Lect. Univ. of Birm.

YOONG, Ann Fui-En Department of Obstetrics & Gynaecology, St. Mary's Hospital, Newport PO30 5TG Tel: 01983 534348 — MB ChB 1983 Birm.; FRCOG 2001; MD Birm. 1993; MRCOG 1988. Cons. (O & G) St. Mary's Hosp. I. of Wight. Prev: Lect. O & G St. Mary's Hosp. Manch.; Research Fell. (Reproduc. Physiol.) St. Bart. Hosp. Lond.; Regist. (O & G) Wom. Hosp. Liverp.

YOONG, Soo Yee Zetland House, Friarage Hospital, Northallerton DL6 1JG; 27 Copperclay Walk, Easingwold, York YO61 3RU — MB ChB 1982 Aberd.; MMedSc Leeds 1997; MRCP (Paediat.) Glas. 1992; DCH RCP Lond. 1986. (Univ. Aberd.)

YOONG, Wai Cheong 72 Winchfield Drive, Birmingham B17 8TR — MB BCh BAO Belf. 1987; MRCOG 1995. Clin. Research Fell. Dept. of O & G Roy. Free Hosp. Lond. Prev: Rotat. Regist. (O & G) W. Midl.

YORK, Ann Helen Child & Family Consultation Centre, Richmond Royal, Kew Foot Rd, Richmond TW9 2TE Tel: 020 8355 1984 Fax: 020 8355 1977 Email: ann.york@kdc-tr-sthames.nhs.uk — MB BS 1982 Lond.; MRCPsych 1987. (Roy. Free) Cons. Child & Adolesc. Psychiat. Child & family consultation Centre, Richmond; Hon. Sen. Lect., Child & Adolesc. Psychiat., St Geo. Hosp. Med. Sch. Lond (P/T). Socs: Mem. of Roy. Coll. of Psychiat.s. Prev: Sen. Regist. (Child Psychiat.) St. Geo. Hosp. Lond.; Clin. Asst. (Addic.) Qu. Mary's Hosp. Lond.; Regist. (Child Psychiat.) Ealing Child Guid. Ealing.

YORK, Anthea Hilary Queens Road Surgery, Earls Colne, Colchester CO6 2RR Tel: 01787 222022; The Cottages, Lamarsh Road, Bures CO8 5EW Tel: 01787 227490 — MB ChB 1969 Birm.

YORK, Elizabeth Louise Treetops, Bathold Rd, Radstock, Bath BA3 3HF Tel: 01761 432693 — MB ChB 1996 Ed. SHO Med., Frenchay Healthcare NHS Trust. Prev: SHO S. E. Scotl.

YORK, James Richard Brynhyfryd Surgery, Brynhyfryd Square, Brynhyfryd, Swansea SA5 9DZ Tel: 01792 655083; 29 Bryn Hedydd, Llangyfelach, Swansea SA6 8BS — BM BS 1988 Nottm.; MRCGP 1992. Prev: Trainee GP York VTS.

YORK, Josephine Helen The Cottages, Lamarsh Road, Bures CO8 5EW — MB ChB 1998 Sheff.

YORK, Stephen Arthur Paternoster Lane Surgery, 11 Paternoster Lane, Bradford BD7 3DS Tel: 01274 573696/572573 Fax: 01274 521605; Arrowbutt Lee, Catherine House Lane, Luddenden Dean, Halifax HX2 6XB — MB ChB 1976 Leeds.

YORK, Stephen Peter High Street Surgery, 75 High Street, Minster, Ramsgate CT12 4AB Tel: 01843 821333 Fax: 01843 823146 — MB BS 1986 Lond.

YORK, Susan Mary 1 Southview Gardens, Ravenshead, Nottingham NG15 9GB — BM BS 1976 Nottm.

YORK-MOORE, David William Litchdon Medical Centre, Landkey Road, Barnstaple EX32 9LL Tel: 01271 23443 Fax: 01271 25979 — MB BS 1976 Lond.; MRCGP 1982; DRCOG 1981. (London Hospital) Prev: Trainee GP N. Devon VTS.

YORKE, Peter Harold (retired) The Old Coach House, Buttery Lane, Teversal Village, Sutton-in-Ashfield NG17 3JN — MB BS 1958 Durh. Med. Off. Notts. Water Bd. & Alan Smith Gp. Nottm. Prev: Dent. Anaesth. for Sch. Dent. Serv.

YORKE, Reginald Angelo (retired) Briardale, 3 Wicks Lane, Formby, Liverpool L37 3JE Tel: 01704 8 72187 Email: wd71@dial.pipex.com — MB ChB 1954 Liverp.; FRCGP 1996, M 1988. Prev: Regist. (Med.), Ho. Surg. & Ho. Phys. Liverp. Roy. Infirm.

YORKE, Ronald James Health Centre, Civic Centre, Ebbw Vale NP23 6EY; Errigal, Bryn Deri Road, Ebbw Vale NP23 6DG — MB BCh BAO 1947 Dub. (Dub.)

YORKE, Sydney Clifford Brookfield Anna Freud Centre, 21 Maresfield Gardens, London NW3 5SD Tel: 020 7794 2313; Fieldings, Paper Mill Lane, South Moreton, Didcot OX11 9AH Tel: 01235 814555 Fax: 01235 814555 Email: clifford.yorke@virgine.net — MRCS Eng. LRCP Lond. 1946; FRCPsych 1981, M 1971; DPM Lond. 1951. (King's Coll. Hosp.) Hon. Cons. Psychiat. Anna Freud Centre Lond. Socs: Fell. Roy. Soc. Med.; Brit. Psychoanal Soc. Prev:

Cons. Psychotherap. Psychiat. Unit Watford Gen. Hosp.; Cons. Psychotherap. Napsbury Hosp.

YORKSTON, Neil James Stockton Hall Psychiatric Hospital, The Village, Stockton on the Forest, York YO3 9UN — MB BS 1952 Sydney; FRANZCP 1990; FRACP 1973, M 1956; FRCPsych 1979, M 1971; DPM Eng. 1962; DTM & H Sydney 1957. Cons. Psychiat., Stockton Hall Psych. Hosp, York; Emerit. Prof. Psychiat. Univ. Brit. Columbia Vancouver, Canada. Socs: Co-Winner, Soc. of Psychother. Research Award. Prev: Cons. Psychiat. S. Durh. Health Care NHS Trust Darlington; Prof. Dept. Psychiat. Univ. Brit. Columbia, Canada; Assoc. Prof. Psychiat. & Med. Univ. Minnesota Minneapolis, USA.

YORSTON, Caroline Mary Didcot Health Centre, Britwell Road, Didcot OX11 7JH Tel: 01235 512288 Fax: 01235 811473; 2 Chestnut Avenue, Radley College, Abingdon OX14 2HS Tel: 01235 520081 — MB ChB 1988 Bristol; MRCGP 1994; DRCOG 1993; DFFP 1993; DCH RCP Lond. 1991. (Univ. Bristol) Prev: Trainee GP Oxf. & Exeter VTS.

YORSTON, Graeme Andrew St. Andrew's Hospital, Billing Road, Northampton NN1 5DG Tel: 01604 616000 Fax: 01604 616015 Email: graeme.yorston@standrew.co.uk — MB BS 1986 Lond.; BSc (Hons.) Lond. 1983; MRCPsych 1994. (Westm.) Cons. Old Age Psychiat., St. And.Hosp., N.ampton. Socs: Brit. Assn. for Psychopharmacol. Prev: Cons. (Old Age Psychiat.) Lanarksh.; Sen. Regist. (Psychiat.) Oxf.; Regist. (Psychiat.) Fife.

YORSTON, Jessie Campbell Luibeg, Gardeners Lane, East Wellow, Romsey SO51 6BB — MB ChB 1953 Aberd.; MD Aberd. 1956. (Aberd.) Prev: Med. Off. (Family Plann.) Hants. AHA; Garden Research Fell. (Midw.) Aberd. Univ.; SHO (Anaesth.) Aberd. Roy. Infirm.

YORSTON, Malcolm Bruce (retired) Luibeg, Gardeners Lane, East Wellow, Romsey SO51 6BB Tel: 01794 512054 — MB ChB 1953 Aberd.; FFA RCS Eng. 1961; DA Eng. 1955. Prev: Fell. (Teach. Media) Univ. Soton.

YORSTON, Robert Allan (retired) Templehall, Longforgan, Dundee DD2 5HS Tel: 01382 360242 — MB ChB 1951 St. And.; DLO Eng. 1960. Prev: Assoc. Specialist (ENT) Ninewells Hosp. Dundee.

YOSEF, Hosney Mohamed Ahmed Ali Beaton Oncology Centre, Western Infirmary, Dumbarton Road, Glasgow G11 6NT — MB BCh 1965 Cairo; FRCR 1973; DMRE Cairo 1968. (Cairo) Cons. (Radiother. & Oncol.) Gtr. Glas. Health Bd.

YOUAKIM, Sherif Samir Fayez 1 Admiral Gardens, Knowle Hill, Kenilworth CV8 2XJ — MB ChB 1983 Alexandria.

YOUART, Ann Haematology Department, Hartlepool General Hospital, Holdforth Road, Hartlepool TS24 9AH — MB BS 1975 Newc.; MRCP (UK) 1978; FRCPath 1996, M 1985; DMRT Eng. 1980. Cons. Haemat. Hartlepool Gen. Hosp. Prev: Sen. Regist. Haemat. Nottm.

YOUD, David James Brookroyd House Surgery, Cook Lane, Heckmondwike WF16 9JG Tel: 01924 403061 — MB ChB 1978 Manch.

YOUDALE, Dennis Auguste (retired) Oak House, Oak Lane, Minster-in-Sheppey, Sheerness ME12 3QP Tel: 01795 872723 — MB ChB Leeds 1955; DObst RCOG 1957. Prev: SHO (O & G) Fulford & Matern. Hosps. York.

YOUDAN, Michael Eric Northcroft Surgery, Northcroft Lane, Newbury RG14 1BU Tel: 01635 31575 Fax: 01635 551857 — BM BCh 1972 Oxf.; MA; MRCGP 1977. Prev: Trainee GP PeterBoro. VTS.

YOUELL, Adrien George (retired) 3 The Lakeside, Blackwater, Camberley GU17 0PQ Tel: 01276 36642 Email: agyou@neural.demon.co.uk — MB BCh BAO Dub. 1970; MA Dub. 1973. Prev: Fell. (Path.) AFIP Washington DC.

YOUELL, Anthony The New Surgery, 42 Duke Street, Formby, Liverpool L37 4AT Tel: 01704 876363 Fax: 01704 833808 — MB ChB 1964 Liverp.; DObst RCOG 1967. Prev: Ho. Surg. & Ho. Phys. Roy. S.. Hosp. Liverp.

YOUELL, Catherine Dorothy 4 Holmer Down, Woolwell, Plymouth PL6 7QW — MB BS 1980 Lond.; MRCGP 1985.

YOUENS, John Edward Bentley Bretton Health Centre, Rightwell, Bretton, Peterborough PE3 8DT Tel: 01733 264506 Fax: 01733 266728; 25 The Rookery, Orton Wistow, Peterborough PE2 6YT Tel: 01733 239659 — MB BCh 1979 Wales; DRCOG 1989; DCH RCP Lond. 1988. Prev: Regist. (Clin. Biochem.) New Adenbrooke's Hosp. Camb.; Med. Off. Brit. Antartic Survey.

YOUHANA

YOUHANA, Mr Aprim Yousif Cardiac Centre, Morriston Hospital, Morriston, Swansea SA6 6LN Tel: 01792 704126 Fax: 01792 704141; 28 Joiners Road, Three Crosses, Swansea SA4 3NY Tel: 01792 875804 — MB ChB 1977 Baghdad; FRCS (Cth.) 1995; FRCS Ed. 1990. (Badhdad) Cons. Cardiothoracic Surg. Cardiac Centre Morriston Hosp. Swansea. Socs: Soc. Cardiothoracic Surgs. GB and Irel.; Roy. Soc. Med. Prev: Cons. Cardiothoracic Surg. Roy. Hosps NHS Trust. Lond.; Sen. Regist. Roy. Brompton Hosp.; Sen. Regist. Lond. Chest Hosp.

YOUKHANA, Ishow Skharia Royal Hospital For Sick Children, Yorkhill G15 6PX Tel: 01268 593422, 0141 201 0827 Email: iyoukham@ntlworld.com; 4 Fobbing Farm Close, Basildon SS16 5NP Tel: 01268 593638 — MB ChB 1974 Mosul; FRCA 1994; DA (UK) 1991. Cons. Anaesth. Basildon Hosp., Basildon, Essex. Socs: BMA; MDU; Assn. of Anaesth.s of Gt. Britain & Irel. Prev: Regist. (Anaesth.) Yeovil Dist. Hosp.; Specialist Anaesth 1987-90; Regist. (Anaesth.) Qu.'s Med. Centre Nottm.

YOUL, Bryan Douglas 50 Lady Somerset Road, London NW5 1TU.

YOULE, Michael Simon 19 Strahan Road, London E3 5DA — MB ChB 1984 Sheff.; BMedSci Sheff. 1983, MB ChB 1984.

YOULTEN, Lawrence John Francis London Allergy Clinic, 66 New Cavendish Street, London W1G 8TD Tel: 020 76379711 Fax: 020 75809749 Email: l-a-c@lineone.net; Periteau House, High St, Winchelsea TN36 4EA Tel: 01797 224045 Fax: 01797 222694 Email: lyoulten@aol.com — MB BS 1961 Lond.; PhD Lond. 1968; FRCP Ed. 1992; MRCS Eng. LRCP Lond. 1961; FFPHM RCP (UK) 1993. (Guy's) Cons. and Director, Lond. Allergy Clinic; Emerit. Cons., Dep of Allergy & Clin. Immunol.; Vis. Cons.. Dep of Allergy & Clin. Immunol., Addenbrookes Hosp., Camb. Socs: Brit. Soc. Allergy & Clin. Immunol. (Mem.). Prev: Dir., Clin. Pharmacol. Compliance Smith Kline Beecham Pharmaceuts.; Sen. Lect. (Pharmacol.) Inst. Basic Med. Scs. RCS Eng.; Sen. Lect. (Physiol.) Lond. Hosp. Med. Coll.

YOUNAN, Mr Fekry Hemaya Hazel Oak, 2 Blythewood Close, Knowle, Solihull B91 3HL Tel: 01564 774518 — MB ChB 1969 Cairo; FRCS Eng. 1978. (Kasr El Eni) Assoc. Specialist Warwick Hosp. NHS Trust; Cons. Surg. King Faisal Milit. Hosp. Khamis Mushat, Saudi Arabia. Prev: Asst. Prof. Surg. King Saudi Univ. Abha, Saudi Arabia; N. Eng. Research Soc. Regist. (Surg.) Med. Sch. Univ. Newc.

YOUNG, Adrian Charles Bletchingdon Road Surgery, Bletchingdon Road, Islip, Kidlington OX5 2TQ Tel: 01865 371666 Fax: 01865 842475; Wirepool Cottage, Oddington, Kidlington OX5 2RA Tel: 01865 331284 — MB BS 1974 Lond.; BSc Lond. 1971, MB BS 1974; DRCOG 1977. (Char. Cross) Prev: Trainee GP Mid-Sussex VTS.

YOUNG, Alan George St Giles Road Surgery, St. Giles Road, Watton, Thetford IP25 6XG Tel: 01953 889134/881247 Fax: 01953 885167 — MB BS 1969 Lond.; BSc (Anat.) Lond. 1966, MB BS 1969; MRCGP 1974; DObst RCOG 1975. (Univ. Coll. Hosp.) Prev: Ho. Phys. & Ho. Surg. Univ. Coll. Hosp. Lond.

YOUNG, Alasdair Patrick Flat 4/R, 5 University Avenue, Glasgow G12 8NN — MB ChB 1998 Glas.

YOUNG, Alastair Cushnie BUPA Hospital, Russell Road, Whalley Range, Manchester M16 8AJ Tel: 0161 226 0112 Fax: 0161 226 1187 Email: ac.young@talk21.com; Oakleigh, 3 Euxton Hall Gardens, Euxton, Chorley PR7 6PB Email: acyoak@btinternet.com — MB ChB; FRCP Lond. 1985; MRCP (UK) 1970. (Aberdeen) Cons. NeUrol. BUPA Private Pract., Manch. Hosp. & 57 Chorley New Rd. Bolton; Private Med. & Medico-Legal Pract., Neurol., Manch. & Bolton. Socs: Fell. Manch. Med. Soc.; Mem. Assoc. Of Brit. NeUrol.s; Mem. Acad. of Experts. Prev: Cons. Neurol. Salford Roy. & Bolton Roy. NHS Trusts; Sen. Regist. (Neurol.) Oxon HA; Regist. (Med.) Aberd. Gen. Hosps.

YOUNG, Alexander Harley (retired) 22 Eden Park Drive, Batheaston, Bath BA1 7JJ — MRCS Eng. LRCP Lond. 1964; BDS Glas. 1955; FDS RCS Eng. 1959; FDS RCS Ed. 1959. Clin. Lect. (Dent. Surg.) Univ. Bristol Dent. Hosp. Prev: Cons. (Oral & Maxillofacial Surg.) Bath Health Dist. & Bristol & W.on Health Dist. (T).

YOUNG, Alexander Muir Morton Alyth Health Centre, New Alyth Road, Alyth, Blairgowrie PH11 8EQ Tel: 01828 632317 Fax: 01828 633272; Boglea House, Alyth, Blairgowrie PH11 8NU Tel: 01828 632442 — MB ChB 1973 Dundee; MRCGP 1981. (Dundee) Clin. Asst. (Diabet.) Ninewells Hosp. Dundee. Prev: Trainee GP Dundee VTS.

YOUNG, Professor Allan Hunter School of Neurosciences, Division of Psychiatry, Royal Victoria Infirmary, Newcastle upon Tyne NE1 4LD Tel: 0191 227 5108 Email: a.h.young@ncl.ac.uk — MB ChB 1984 Ed.; MPhil Ed. 1990. MB ChB 1984; PhD Ed. 1996; MRCPsych 1988. Sen. Lect. Univ. Newc. Prev: Research Fell. & Hon. Sen. Regist. (Psychiat.) Univ. Edin.; Clin. Lect. (Psychiat.) Univ. Oxf.

YOUNG, Allan Russell Castlemilk Health Centre, 71 Dougrie Drive, Glasgow G45 9AW Tel: 0141 531 8585 Fax: 0141 531 8596; Allanvilla, 2 Threestanes Road, Strathaven ML10 6DX Tel: 01357 21165 — MB ChB 1965 Glas.; DObst RCOG 1972. (Glas.)

YOUNG, Amanda Jane Albion House Suegery, Albion Street, Brierley Hill DY5 3EE Tel: 01384 70220 Fax: 01384 78284; Green Bank, 18A Stone Lane, Kiner, Stourbridge DY7 6EG Tel: 01384 872899 — MB BS 1987 Lond.; BSc (Hons) Lond. 1984; MRCGP 1991; DRCOG 1989. (University College London)

YOUNG, Amber Elizabeth Russel North Bristol NHS Trust, Dept. of Anaesthesia, Frenchay Hospital, Bristol BS16 1LE Tel: 0117 970 2020 Fax: 0117 957 4414 Email: amber.young@dial.pipex.com; Clifton Retreat, Clifton Hill, Clifton, Bristol BS8 1BN Tel: 0117 974 5220 Fax: 0117 957 4414 Email: amber.young@dial.pipex.com — MB ChB 1987 Bristol; BSc Bristol 1984; FRCA 1993. (Bristol) Cons. Paediat. Anaestetist, Frenchay Hosp., Bristol; Chairm. Paediatric Standards Comm. Socs: Paed. Intens. Care Soc.; Intens. Care Soc.; Brit. Burns Assn. Prev: Sen. Regist. (Paediat. Anaesth.) Roy. Childr.'s Hosp. Melbourne, Australia; Research Regist. (Neuro. & Intens. Care) Frenchay Hosp. Bristol; Post Fell.sh. Regist. (Paediat. Anaesth.) Gt. Ormond St. Hosp. Childr. NHS Trust.

YOUNG, Mr Andrew Buchanan (retired) 46 Darnley Road, Glasgow G41 4NE Tel: 0141 423 6814 — MB ChB 1950 Glas.; FRCS Glas. 1979; FRCS Ed. 1959. Prev: Cons. Orthop. Surg. Glas. Roy. Infirm.

YOUNG, Andrew John Silver Springs Medical Practice, Beaufort Road, St Leonards-on-Sea TN37 6PP Tel: 01424 422300/426464 Fax: 01424 436400; High Firs, Silverhill Avenue, St Leonards-on-Sea TN37 7HG Tel: 01424 752640 — MB BS 1975 Lond.; MRCS Eng. LRCP Lond. 1974; MRCGP (UK) 1981; DRCOG 1977. (St. Bart.) GP Trainer Hastings. Prev: SHO (Paediat.) Qu. Mary's Hosp. Childr. Carshalton; SHO (O & G) N.ampton Gen. Hosp.; Ho. Surg. FarnBoro. Hosp. Kent.

YOUNG, Andrew Jonathan 15A Morton Way, London N14 7HS — MB BS 1993 Lond.

YOUNG, Angeline Mary Rubislaw Medical Group, 7 Rubislaw Place, Aberdeen AB10 1QB Tel: 01224 641968 — MB ChB 1983 Aberd.; MRCGP 1987; DRCOG 1986. Clin. Asst. Aberd.

YOUNG, Ann Shona 1 Bagnall Cottages, Cinderhill Road, Bulwell, Nottingham NG6 8SD — MB ChB 1992 Ed.; MB ChB Ed.1992. Specialist Regist. (Anaesth.) Qu. Med. Centre Univ. Hosp. Nottm.

YOUNG, Anna Catriona Micaela The Surgery, Denmark Street, Darlington DL3 0PD Tel: 01325 460731 Fax: 01325 362183 — MB BCh BAO 1989 NUI; DRCOG 1992.

YOUNG, Anna-Mary 28 Woodborough Road, London SW15 6PZ — MB BS 1998 Lond.

YOUNG, Anne Elizabeth Ann Cottage, Kilmeston, Alresford SO24 0NW Tel: 01962 771472 Fax: 01962 771899 Email: graham.cresswell@bigfoot.com; The Surgery, Doctors Lane, West Meon, Petersfield GU32 1LR Tel: 01730 829333 Fax: 01730 829229 — MB ChB 1974 Glas.; DRCOG 1985.

YOUNG, Anne Hall (retired) 20 Claremont Drive, Hartlepool TS26 9PD Tel: 01429 279446 Email: brian@bguttridge@freeserve.co.uk — MB BS 1959 Durh.; MFCM 1974; DPH Durh. 1964. Prev: Dep. MOH & Dep. Princip. Sch. Med. Off. Hartlepool Co. Boro.

YOUNG, Anne Mortimer (retired) 1 The Beeches, Lydiard Millicent, Swindon SN5 3LT Tel: 01793 770483 Fax: 01793 771556 — MB BS 1954 Lond.; BSc (Anat.) Lond. 1952, MB BS 1954; DHMSA 1982; DPM Eng. 1966. Prev: Assoc. Specialist Seymour Clinic Swindon.

YOUNG, Mr Anthony Elliott King Edward VII Hospital, Beaumont St., London W1G 6AA Tel: 020 7580 3612 Fax: 020 8244 5467 Email: anthony.yung@gstt.sthames.nhs.uk; Fax: 020 8244 5467 — MB BChir 1968 Camb.; MChir Camb. 1979, MA 1969; FRCS Eng. 1973. (St. Thos.) Cons. Surg. Guy's & St. Thos. Hosp. Trust; Cons.

Surg. King Edwd. VII's Hosp., Lond. Socs: Fell. Roy. Soc. Med.; BMA; BASO. Prev: Sen. Regist. St. Thos. Hosp. Lond.; Fell. Harvard Med. Sch. & Peter Bent Brigham Hosp. Boston, USA.

YOUNG, Mr Antony John 2 Berners Mansions, 34-36 Berners Street, London W1T 3LU Email: tony.young@ucl.ac.uk — MB BS 1994 Lond.; FRCS Eng. 1998. (UCLMS) Specialist Regist., Urclog, William Harvey Hosp. Ashford, Trent.

YOUNG, Professor Archie University of Edinburgh, Geriatric Medicine, 21 Chalmers St., Edinburgh EH3 9EW Tel: 0121 536 4535 Fax: 0131 536 4536 Email: a.young@ed.ac.uk — MB ChB 1971 Glas.; MB ChB (Commend.) Glas. 1971; BSc (Hons.) Glas. 1969, MD 1983; FRCP Lond. 1989; FRCP Glas. 1985; MRCP (UK) 1973. Prof. Geriat. Med. Univ. of Edin. Socs: Med. Res. Soc. & Europ. Soc. Clin. Investig.; Amer. Coll. Sports Med. Prev: Brit. Counc. Vis. Prof. Univ. Zimbabwe 1990; Prof. Geriat. Med. Roy. Free Hosp. Sch. Med.; Clin. Lect. & Hon. Cons. Phys. Univ. Oxf.

YOUNG, Mr Austen (retired) Fairways, Ynyslas, Borth SY24 5JX Tel: 01970 871234 — MB ChB 1937 Ed.; FRCS Eng. 1948; FRCS Ed. 1946. Prev: Aural Surg. Roy. Infirm. Sheff. & Childr. Hosp. Sheff.

YOUNG, Barry Philip Medical Centre, Craig Croft, Chelmsley Wood, Birmingham B37 7TR Tel: 0121 770 5656 Fax: 0121 779 5619 — MB ChB 1983 Birm.; DCH RCP Lond. 1986.

YOUNG, Barry Stuart Avondale Surgery, 5 Avondale Road, Chesterfield S40 4TF Tel: 01246 232946 Fax: 01246 556246 — MB ChB 1976 Sheff.; MRCGP 1981; DRCOG 1980. GP Chesterfield; Company Doctors Stage Coach Bust Company Med. Therapeutic Research.

YOUNG, Basil (retired) 81 Woolton Hill Road, Liverpool L25 4RE — MRCS Eng. LRCP Lond. 1951; MRCGP 1968. Prev: Med. Pract. (Dermat.) Newsham Gen. Hosp. Liverp.

YOUNG, Brian Keith Shelley Surgery, 23 Shelley Road, Worthing BN11 4BS Tel: 01903 234844 Fax: 01903 219744; Oliver's Cottage, 141 The St, Patching, Worthing BN13 3XF Tel: 01903 871251 Fax: 01903 871251 Email: youngbk@pavilion.co.uk — BM BS 1980 Nottm.; BMedSci Nottm. 1978; MRCGP 1984; DCH RCP Lond. 1984; DRCOG 1982. (Univ. Nottm.)

YOUNG, Caroline Jayne — MB ChB 1992 Birm.; MRCGP 1998; DFFP 1996; BPharm (Hons.) Nottm. 1986. (Birmingham) p/t GP Princip.; Civil. Med. Practitioner RAF Stafford; Occupat.al Health Phys. Spool Pottories; Occupat.al Health Phys. Tarmac. Socs: Pharmaceut. Soc. & BMA. Prev: Locum GP UK & New Zealand; SHO (Orthop.) N. Staffs. Hosp. Centre; GP Trainee Hall Gr. Surg. WGC.

YOUNG, Carolyn Anne The Walton Centre for Neurology & Neurosurgery, Lower Lane, Fazakerley, Liverpool L9 7LJ Tel: 0151 529 5711 Fax: 0151 529 5512 — MB ChB 1985 Bristol; BSc (Hons.) Bristol 1982; MRCP (UK) 1989; Euro. Dipl. Of Rehab. Med, 1994; MD 1998; FRCP 1998. (Bristol) Cons. Neurol. Walton Centre for Neurol. & Neurosurg. Merseyside. Socs: Assn. Brit. Neurol.; Edu. Comm. Mem., Brit. Soc. Rehabil. Med.; World Federat. Neurol. Sec. Neurol. Rehab. Research Gp. Prev: Sen. Regist. (Neurol. & Rehabil.) & Higher Train. Post Merseyside RHA; Regional Regist. Rotat. Merseyside.

YOUNG, Catharine Janet The Old Vicarage, Llancarfan, Barry CF62 3AJ Tel: 01446 751175 Fax: 01446 751265 — MB ChB 1980 Manch.; MRCGP 1985; DRCOG 1983. Police Surg. S. Wales; Prison Medicial Off. Prev: Forens. Med. Examr. Metrop. Police; Clin. Asst. (Genitourin. Med.) Herts. & Essex Hosp. Bishop's Stortford; Staff Grade (A & E) N. Middlx. Hosp.

YOUNG, Catherine Ann Holmer Surgery, 22 Wycombe Road, Holmer Green, High Wycombe HP15 6RY Tel: 01494 718318 Fax: 01494 713222; Crinan Cottage, Manor Road, Penn, High Wycombe HP10 8JB Tel: 01494 816425 Fax: 01494 816425 — MB ChB 1964 Glas. GP Holmer Green. Prev: Ho. Surg. S.. Gen. Hosp. Glas.; Ho. Phys. Roy. N.. Hosp. Inverness.

YOUNG, Catherine Margaret Pershore Health Centre, Priest Lane, Pershore WR10 1RD Tel: 01386 502030 Fax: 01386 502058 — MB ChB 1984 Leic.; DRCOG 1987. (Leic.) Princip. In Gen. Pract. Socs: Med. Protec. Soc. Prev: Trainee GP Kettering VTS.

YOUNG, Catherine Pamela Rasharkin Health Centre, 10 Moneyleck Road, Rasharkin, Ballymena BT44 8QB Tel: 028 2557 1203 Fax: 028 2557 1709; Windyridge, Finvoy, Ballymoney BT53 7JW Tel: 0126 65 71203 — MB BCh BAO 1971 Belf.; MB BCh BAO (Hons.) Belf. 1971; MRCP Glas. 1979; DCH RCPS Glas. 1973. Sessional Med. Off. (Paediat.) Route Hosp. Ballymoney.

YOUNG, Christine Anne Viewpark Health Centre, Burnhead Street, Uddingston, Glasgow G71 5SU Tel: 01698 813753 Fax: 01698 812062 — MB ChB 1983 Dundee. (Dundee) Socs: Med. Protec. Soc. Prev: SHO (Med. & Surg.) St. Michael's Hosp. Hayle; SHO (Paediat.) Inverclyde Roy. Hosp. Greenock; SHO (Psychiat.) Ravenscraig & Inverclyde Roy. Hosp. Greenock.

YOUNG, Christopher Donald Central Surgery, Brooksby Drive, Oadby, Leicester LE2 5AA Tel: 0116 271 2175 Fax: 0116 271 4015; 1 Pinetree Gardens, Oadby, Leicester LE2 5UT — MB BS 1982 Lond.; DRCOG 1984. (St Mary's Lond.) Princip. GP & Sen. Partner. Socs: Leic. Med. Soc.

YOUNG, Mr Christopher Paul Department of Cardiothoracic Surgery, St. Thomas' Hospital, London SE1 7EH Tel: 020 7928 9292 Fax: 020 7922 8077 Email: chris@cpyoung.demon.co.uk — MD 1991 Sheff.; MB ChB 1980; FRCS Eng. 1984. Cons. Cardiothoracic Surg. & Hon. Sen. Lect. St. Thos. Hosp. Lond. Socs: Soc. Cardiothoracic Surgs. GB. & Irel.; Edit. Bd. Soc. Cardiovasc. Surg. Prev: Sen. Regist. (Cardiothoracic Surg.) Hosp. Sick Childr. Gt. Ormond St. Lond.; BHF Jun. Research Fell. Rayne Inst. St. Thos. Hosp. Lond.

YOUNG, Claire Alexandra 19 Woodbine Road, Gosforth, Newcastle upon Tyne NE3 1DD — MB BCh 1992 Wales; MRCP (UK) 1996. Prev: SHO (Gen. Med.) Univ. Hosp. Wales.

YOUNG, Claire Fiona Middlesborough General Hospital, Middlesbrugh; 13 Haldane Terrace, Jesmond, Newcastle upon Tyne NE2 3AN Tel: 0191 281 7309 Email: cfyoung@jesmond10.freeserve.co.uk — MB ChB 1995 Glas.; MRCS (Eng.) 1998. Specialist Regist. (Orthop.) MiddlesBoro. Gen. Hosp. Prev: SHR (Orthop) Newc. Gen. Hosp.; SPR (Orthop.) Wansbeck Gen Hosp.; SPR (Orthop.) Cumbld. INF.

YOUNG, Claire Sutherland Psychiatric Unit, Longlet Cantre, Norwood Grange Drive, Sheffield S5 7JT Tel: 0114 226 1530 — MB ChB 1982 Manch.; MRCPsych 1994. Cons. Old Age Psychiat. N.ern Gen. Hosp., Sheffield. Prev: Regist. (Psychiat.) Roy. Dundee Liff Hosp.

YOUNG, Colin Mark 249 Holywood Road, Belfast BT4 2EW — MB BCh BAO 1986 Belf.

YOUNG, Mr Cyril John, TD, Deputy Lt. Queen Elizabeth Hospital Trust, Stadium Road, Woolich, London SE18 4QH Tel: 0208 836 4501 Fax: 0208 836 4504; 75 Hornfair Road, London SE7 7BB Tel: 020 8319 2567 — MRCS Eng. LRCP Lond. 1966; MSc Surrey 1977; FRCOG 1988, M 1972. (King's Coll. Hosp.) Cons. O & G Qu. Eliz. Hosp. Woolich; Rep.Dep.Lieut.L.B.Greenwich. Socs: Soc. Apoth.; W Kent M-C Soc. Prev: Cons. O & G Greenwich Dist. Hosp.; Cons. Obst. Brit. Hosp. Mothers & Babies Lond.; Sen. Regist. (O & G) Qu. Charlotte's Hosp. Wom. Lond.

YOUNG, Professor Daniel Greer Department of Paediatric Surgery, RHSC Yorkhill NHS Trust, Glasgow G3 8SJ Tel: 0141 201 0169 Fax: 0141 201 0858; 49 Sherbrooke Avenue, Glasgow G41 4SE Tel: 0141 427 3470 — MB ChB 1956 Glas.; FRCS Glas. 1975; FRCS Ed. 1962; DTM & H Liverp. 1959; FRCPCH 1996. Prof. Paediat. Surg. Univ. Glas.; Hon. Cons. Surg. Roy. Hosp. Sick Childr. Glas. Socs: (Ex-Pres.) Roy. M-C Soc. Glas.; (ex-Pres.) Brit. Assn. Paediat. Surg.; (Ex-Chairm.) W. of Scot. Surg. Assn. Prev: Sen. Regist. & Resid. Asst. Surg. Hosp. Sick Childr. Gt. Ormond St.; Sen. Lect. (Paediat. Surg.) Inst. Child Health Lond.; Hon. Cons. Surg. Hosp. Sick Childr. Gt. Ormond St. & Qu. Eliz. Hosp. Hackney.

YOUNG, David Alan The Surgery, 2 Gregson Avenue, Gosport PO13 0HR Tel: 01329 232446 Fax: 01329 282624 — MB ChB 1974 Bristol.

YOUNG, David Anthony (retired) Restormel, Penpol, Devoran, Truro TR3 6NW Tel: 01872 865433 — MB BS Lond. 1957; MRCS Eng. LRCP Lond. 1958; FFA RCS Eng. 1967; FFA RCSI 1966; DA Eng. 1959. Prev: Cons. Anaesth. Bromley HA & Clin. Dir. (Anaesth. & Allied Servs.) Bromley Hosps. NHS Trust.

YOUNG, David John 5 Thingwall Road E., Thingwall, Wirral CH61 3UY — MB ChB 1980 Liverp.

YOUNG, David Robertson Milliken and Young, The Surgery, Castlehill Loan, Kippen, Stirling FK8 3DZ Tel: 01786 870369 Fax: 01786 870819 — MB ChB 1983 Glas.; MRCGP 1987. Prev: GP Cumnock.

YOUNG, David Wallace Laxey Clinic, 19 New Road, Laxey IM4 7BG Tel: 01624 781350; Rock Rose, Ballacollister Heights, Laxey — MB ChB 1973 Glas.; BSc (Hons.) Biochem. Glas. 1969,

YOUNG

MB ChB 1973. Prev: Sen. Med. Off. St. Helena Is., S. Atlantic; GP Broxburn W. Lothian.

YOUNG, David William Young and Partners, The Ryan Medical Centre, St. Marys Road, Bamber Bridge, Preston PR5 6JD Tel: 01772 335136 Fax: 01772 626701; Oakleaf, Kellet Lane, Bamber Bridge, Preston PR5 6AN — MB ChB 1975 Dundee.

YOUNG, David William City Hospital NHS Trust, Birmingham B18 7QH Tel: 0121 554 3801 Fax: 0121 523 6125 — MD 1983 Manch.; MB ChB 1963; FRCP Lond. 1982, M 1967; MFCM RCP (UK) 1982. (Manch.) Phys. Birm. City Hosp. NHS Trust; Sen. Clin. Lect. Univ. Birm.; Clin. Adviser Informat. Policy Unit NHS Exec. Prev: Lect. (Med.) Univ. Birm.; MRC Clin. Research Fell. Qu. Eliz. Med. Centre Birm.; Regist. Qu. Eliz. Hosp. Birm.

YOUNG, Derek William 11 Orkney Drive, Kilmarnock KA3 2HP — MB ChB 1995 Glas.

YOUNG, Donald James Reid 5 Woodside Gardens, Clarkston, Glasgow G76 7UG — MB ChB 1998 Manch.

YOUNG, Donya Carolyn Denise The Surgery, 2 Manor Road, West Wickham BR4 9PS Tel: 020 8777 1293 Fax: 020 8776 1977; 9 Bishops Avenue, Bromley BR1 3ET Email: donyayoung@arsenalfc.net — MB BS 1985 Lond.; DFFP 1995; MRCGP 1990; DRCOG 1988. (King's College Medical School, London) Prev: Trainee GP FarnBoro. Hosp. VTS.

YOUNG, Douglas Gordon 98 Main Street, Methven, Perth PH1 3QP — MB ChB 1989 Dundee.

YOUNG, Duncan Niel The Health Centre, Dunning Street, Stoke-on-Trent ST6 5BE Tel: 01782 425834 Fax: 01782 577599; The Gables, Alsager, Stoke-on-Trent ST7 2HT — MB ChB 1991 Sheff.; BSc Dund 1986; MRCGP 1997. Prev: GP Regist. Sheff.

YOUNG, Edward 68 Beech Lane, Earley, Reading RG6 5QA — MB BS 1961 Lond.; MRCS Eng. LRCP Lond. 1961; FFA RCS Eng. 1969; DA Eng. 1965; DObst RCOG 1963. (Guy's) Cons. Anaesth. W. Berks. Health Dist. Prev: Sen. Regist. (Anaesth.) United Oxf. Hosps.; Ho. Phys. Pembury Hosp.; Ho. Surg. New Cross Hosp.

YOUNG, Eileen Barbara Barr (retired) Vectis Lodge, 74 Victoria Road S., Southsea PO5 2BN Tel: 02392 821682 — BM BCh 1953 Oxf.; MA Oxf. 1957, BM BCh 1953; FRCGP 1981, M 1968. Prev: Princip. GP Portsmouth.

YOUNG, Elaine Anne 75 Higher Lane, Lymm WA13 0BZ Email: phemsted@aol.com — MB ChB 1988 Liverp.; MRCP (UK) 1992; FRCR 1998. Specialist Regist. (Clin. Oncol.) Christie Hosp. Withington. Prev: Trainee Radiother. Christie Hosp. Withington.

YOUNG, Elizabeth Anne West Barton Farm, Horwood, Bideford EX39 4PB Tel: 01271 858495 — MB ChB 1970 Sheff.; DCH RCP Lond. 1972. Sch. Med. Off. N. Devon HA. Prev: Clin. Med. Off. Trafford HA; SHO (Paediat.) Childr. Hosp. Sheff. & Jenny Lind Hosp. Norwich; Ho. Off. (Gen. Med.) N.. Gen. Hosp. Sheff.

YOUNG, Elizabeth Helen 2 Gayton Close, Trumpington, Cambridge CB2 2JY — MB BS 1996 Lond.; BSc Lond. 1993. (UCL) Med. SHO Addenbrooke's Hosp. Camb. Socs: Christ. Med. Fell.sh.; MDU.

YOUNG, Eric Thomson (retired) Holly Lodge, Fulbeck, Morpeth NE61 3JT Tel: 01670 512052 — MB ChB 1959 Glas.; FRCP Ed. 1975, M 1963; FRCP Glas. 1974, M 1963; FRCP Lond. 19/7, M 1964. Cons. Phys. N.d. AHA & Newc. AHA (T). Prev: Sen. Regist. (Med.) Roy. Vict. Infirm. Newc.

YOUNG, Fergus Ian Department of Pathology, Cumberland Infirmary, Newtown Road, Carlisle CA2 7HY Tel: 01228 523444 — MB ChB 1985 Dundee. Cons. (Histopath.) Cumbld. Infirm. Carlisle.

YOUNG, Fiona Marianne Church Hill Cottage, West Overton, Marlborough SN8 4ER — MB ChB 1990 Manch.

YOUNG, Francis Louis Dermot (retired) 32 Granville Court, Granville Road, Eastbourne BN20 7EE Tel: 01323 723926 — MRCS Eng. LRCP Lond. 1940; DPM Eng. 1948. Prev: Dir. Psychogeriat. Servs. Nova Scotia Hosp. & Cons. Psychiat. Halifax Co. Regional Rehabil. Centre, Canada.

YOUNG, Frank Maurice (retired) Dormy Cottage, 5 Fortune Hill, Knaresborough HG5 9DG Tel: 01423 862411 — MB BS Lond. 1960; MRCS Eng. LRCP Lond. 1960; DObst RCOG 1964. Prev: Ho. Phys. & Cas. Off. St. Geo. Hosp. Lond.

YOUNG, Frederick Robert Mackinlay (retired) The Hollies, 55 Victoria Road, Macclesfield SK10 3JA Tel: 01625 427592 — MB BS 1945 Lond. Hon. Cons. Med. Hypn. Prev: RAFVR.

YOUNG, Freida (retired) Flat 9, 46 Lancaster Gate, London W2 3NA Tel: 020 7262 1888 — MB BS 1933 Lond.; MB BS (Hnrs.) Lond. 1933; MRCS Eng. LRCP Lond. 1933; FRCPath 1964; DCP Lond 1941. Prev: Pathol. Willesden Gen. Hosp., E. Ham Memor. Hosp. & Pinderfields Gen.

YOUNG, Gail — MB ChB 1985 Sheff.; MRCGP 1990; T(GP) 1991; DRCOG 1989; DCH RCP Lond. 1988; Cert. Family Plann. JCC 1988. (Sheff.)

YOUNG, Gavin Leslie Temple Sowerby Medical Practice, Temple Sowerby, Penrith CA10 1RZ Tel: 017683 61232 Fax: 017683 61980 — MB BS 1975 Lond.; MA Oxf. 1980; FRCGP 1993, M 1980; DRCOG 1979. (Univ. Coll. Hosp.) Socs: Founder Mem. (Ex-Chairm.) Assn. Community Based Matern. Care; Fell. Roy. Soc. Med.

YOUNG, Gavin Robert Department of Neurology, Middlesbrough General Hospital, Ayresome Green Lane, Middlesbrough TS5 5AZ Tel: 01642 850850 — MB ChB 1987 Manch.; MD Manch. 1997; MRCP (UK) 1990; MD Manchester 1997. (Manchester) Cons. Neurol. Middlesbrough Gen. Hosp.

YOUNG, George Brims Greenbank Surgery, 1025 Stratford Road, Hall Green, Birmingham B28 8BG Tel: 0121 777 1490 Fax: 0121 778 6239; 44 Cheswick Way, Cheswick Green, Solihull B90 4HE Tel: 01564 702965 Email: young44@compuserve.com — MB BS 1980 Lond.; MRCGP 1984; DRCOG 1983. Chairm. Hall Green PCG; GP Trainer Birm. Socs: Exec. Mem. NHSPCG Alliance (PREV NACGP). Prev: Chairm. Hall Green GP Commiss.ing Project; GPCA Chest Med. Birm. Chest Clinic; Trainee GP/SHO E. Birm. Hosp. VTS.

YOUNG, Mr George Ivan (retired) 38 Magheralave Road, Lisburn BT28 3BN Tel: 02892 664166 — MB BCh BAO Belf. 1949; FRCS Ed. 1956; FRCS Eng. 1956; Cons. Surg. Lagan Valley Hosp. Lisburn. Prev: Surg. Fell. Lahey Clinic Boston, U.S.A.

YOUNG, Glenda Kaye (retired) 21 Sealand Court, Shorts Reach, The Esplanade, Rochester ME1 1QH Tel: 01634 845834 — MB BS Lond. 1961. Prev: Clin. Asst. (Psychother.) Canterbury & Thanet Community Healthcare Trust.

YOUNG, Grace Maria North Staffordshire Hospital Emergency Department, Windsor House, 223 Princes Rd, Hartshill, Stoke-on-Trent ST4 7JW Tel: 01782 554503 Fax: 01782 747179; 15 Sidmouth Avenue, The Brampton, Newcastle ST5 0QN Tel: 01782 711509 — MB ChB 1982 Birm. Assoc. Specialist (A & E), N. Staffs Hosp. NHS Trust. Prev: SHO (Anaesth.) E. Birm. Hosp.

YOUNG, Mr Graeme Bruce (retired) 5 Tipperlinn Road, Edinburgh EH10 5ET Tel: 0131 447 7318 — MB ChB Ed. 1939; FRCS Ed. 1947; FRCR 1975; FFR 1964; DMRD Ed. 1961. Prev: CMO Mission Hosp. Jalna Deccan, India.

YOUNG, Graham The Surgery, High Street, Kemnay, Inverurie AB51 5NB Tel: 01467 642289 Fax: 01467 643100; 18 Fetternear View, Kemnay, Inverurie AB51 5JF Tel: 01467 642681 — MB ChB 1972 Aberd.; FRCGP 1992, M 1977; DObst RCOG 1976. (Aberdeen) Staff GP Inverurie Hosp.

YOUNG, Mrs Gwyneth Vivien Wright 63 Lee Road, London SE3 9EN Tel: 020 8852 1921 Fax: 020 8244 5467 — MB BS 1969 Lond.; MRCPCH 1997; DCH Eng. 1971. (St. Thos.) Assoc. Specialist (Paediat.) Greenwich Dist. Hosp. & Qu. Eliz. Hosp. Lond. Socs: Harveian Soc. & Med. Soc.; BACCH & Brit. Paediat. Assn. Prev: SHO (Paediat.) & Ho. Phys. Kingston Hosp.; Ho. Off. (Surg.) St. Thos. Hosp. Lond.

YOUNG, Hamilton Nat (retired) 19 Kingston Road, Bridlington YO15 3NF Tel: 01262 401372 — MB ChB Glas. 1958; DA Eng. 1965; DObst RCOG 1960. Prev: GP (Robt.son Young Mundy and Harris).

YOUNG, Harry Lawrance 15 Blythwood Road, Crouch Hill, London N4 4EU — MB BS 1952 Lond.

YOUNG, Heather Mary c/o South Warwickshire Hospital, Lakin Road, Warwick CV34 5BW Tel: 01926 495321; 2 Woodbine Cottages, Wedgenock, Warwick CV35 7PX Tel: 01926 410452 — MB ChB 1990 Otago. (Univ. Otago Med. Sch.) SHO Rotat. (Med.) S. Warks. Hosp. Warwick; Assoc. Coll. Tutor S. Warks. Socs: (Ex-Treas.) NZ Med. Wom. Assn. Prev: SHO (O & G) Arrowe Pk. Hosp. Wirral.

YOUNG, Helen Kathryn 6 Cooper Crescent, Enniskillen BT74 6DQ — MB ChB 1993 Ed.

YOUNG, Helen Louise St Andrews, Herbert Road, Chelston, Torquay TQ2 6RW — MB BCh 1998 Wales.

YOUNG

YOUNG, Helen Sara Department of Dermatology, Hope Hospital, Stott Lae, Salford, Manchester M6 8HD — MB ChB 1994 Manch.; MRCP 1997. (Manchester University) Specialist Regist. Dermat., Hope Hosp., Manch. Prev: SHO (Dermat.) Hope Hosp., Manch.; SHO Rotat. (Gen. Med.) Hope Hosp. Manch.; SHO (Cardiothoracic Med.) Wythenshawe Hosp. Manch.

YOUNG, Hoi Wah Soon Khow 33 Eriskay Avenue, Newton Mearns, Glasgow G77 6XB; 24 Longpark Place, Eliburn, Livingston EH54 6TU Tel: 01506 419116 Email: soon@skyoung.freeserve.co.uk — MB ChB 1989 Glas.; FRCS; FRCR. Specialist Regist. Radiol.

YOUNG, Howard (retired) 6 Kinfauns Drive, High Salvington, Worthing BN13 3BL — MB ChB Birm. 1952.

YOUNG, Mr Howard Anthony 24 Albyn Place, Aberdeen AB10 1RW Tel: 01224 595993 Fax: 01224 584797 Email: info@albynhospital.co.uk; 18 Edgehill Road, Aberdeen AB15 5JH Tel: 01224 324554 Email: howlou@lineone.net — MB BS 1968 Newc.; FRCS Eng. 1974. (Newc.) Cons. Otolaryngol. & Head & Neck Surg. Grampian Univ. Hosps. NHS Trust; Vis. Otolaryngol. Orkney & Shetland Health Bds.; Hon. Sen. Clin. Lect. (Otolaryngol.) Aberd. Univ.; Cons. Otolaryngol & head and neck Surg., at Albyn Hosp., Aberd. Socs: Fell. Roy. Soc. Med. (Mem. Otol. & Laryngol. Sect.); Scott. Otolaryngol. Soc.; Brit. Assn. Otol. & Head & Neck Surg. Prev: Regist. (Otolaryngol.), Ho. Surg. & Ho. Phys. Roy. Vict. Infirm. Newc.; Sen. Regist. (Otolaryngol.) Tayside HB; Hon. Lect. (Otolaryngol.) Univ. Dundee.

YOUNG, Mr Howard Lewis School of Postgraduate Medical & Dental Education, University of Wales College of Medicine, Cardiff CF14 4XN Tel: 029 2074 4934 Fax: 029 2075 4966 Email: younghl1@cf.ac.uk; 56 Cheriton Drive, Thornhill, Cardiff CF14 9DF Tel: 029 2075 9313 Email: hlyoung@netcomuk.co.uk — MB ChB 1973 Dundee; MBA Open 1993; ChM Dund 1983; FRCS Eng. 1978. (Univ. Dundee) Vice Dean Sch. Postgrad. Med. & Dent. Educat. & Hons. Cons. Surg. Socs: Fell. Assn. Surgs.; Surgic. Research Soc.; Assn. Coloproctol. Prev: Sub-Dean & Dep. Dir. Postgrad. Med. Educat. for Wales & Hon. Cons. Surg.; Sen. Lect. & Lect. (Surg.) Univ. Wales Coll. Med. Cardiff; Clin. Research Off. (Surg.) Welsh Nat. Sch. Med. Cardiff.

YOUNG, Hugh Boyd (retired) 22 Broomvale Drive, Newton Mearns, Glasgow G77 5NN — MB ChB 1942 Glas. Prev: Cons. Phys. Lyle Ship Managem. Glas.

YOUNG, Iain McGregor 2nd Floor Left, 116 Novar Drive, Glasgow G12 9SX — MB ChB 1991 Glas.; MRCP (UK) 1996. (Glasgow) Specialist Regist. (A & E) W. of Scotl. Socs: Brit. Assn. Accid. & Emerg. Med.; Fac. Accid. & Emerg. Med.

YOUNG, Professor Ian Douglas Department of Clinical Genetics, Leicester Royal Infirmary, Leicester LE1 5WW Tel: 0116 258 5736 Fax: 0116 2586 057 Email: iandyoung@hotmail.com; Email: iandyoung@hotmail.com — MB BS 1973 Lond.; MD Lond. 1981, MSc 1978, BSc (Hons.) 1970; FRCP Lond. 1989; MRCP (UK) 1976; DCH Lond. 1976. Cons. Clin. Genetics & Vis. Prof., Leicester Roy. Infirm. Socs: Clin. Genetics Soc. & Europ. Soc. Human Genetics. Prev: Sen. Lect. (Clin. Genetics) Univ. Leicester; Sen. Regist. (Med. Genetics) Univ. Hosp. Wales Cardiff; Clin. Fell. Hosp. Sick Childr. Toronto, Canada.

YOUNG, Mr Ian Edward 4/9 South Elixa Place, Edinburgh EH8 7PG Tel: 0131 659 5375 — MB ChB 1992 Ed.; FRCS Ed. 1996. (Ed.)

YOUNG, Ian Malcolm Department Reproductive Physiology, St. Bartholomew's Hospital, 51 Bartholomew Close, London EC1A 7BE — MB BS 1972 Lond.

YOUNG, Professor Ian Stuart Department of Clinical Biochemistry, Royal Victoria Hospital, Belfast BT12 6BA Tel: 012890 263106 Fax: 012890 236143 Email: i.young@qub.ac.uk — MB BCh BAO 1985 Belf.; BSc (1st cl. Hons.) Biochem. Belf. 1982, MD 1994, MB BCh BAO 1985; MRCP (UK) 1988; MRCPath 1992; FRCP Lond. 1998; FRCPath 2000. Prof. of Med., Qu.'s Univ. Belf.; Cons. Clin. Biochem. Roy. Gp. Hosps. Belf. Prev: Sen. Lect. (Clin. Biochem.) Qu. Univ. Belf.

YOUNG, Mr Ian William (retired) 1 The Beeches, Lydiard Millicent, Swindon SN5 3LT Tel: 01793 770483 — BM BCh 1954 Oxf.; MA Oxf. 1954; FRCS Eng. 1962. Prev: Cons. Orthop. & Accid. Surg. P.ss Margt. Hosp. Swindon.

YOUNG, Ian Wilson 294/4 Craigcrook Road, Edinburgh EH4 7BA Tel: 0131 336 3604 — MB ChB 1967 Ed. (Ed.) Exam. Med. Pract.

Benefits Agency Med. Servs. Edin.; Med. Adviser, Recruit Selection Centre, Glencorse Barracks, Penicuik; Sessional Med. Off. Edin. & S. E. Scotl. Blood Transfus. Serv. Socs: BMA. Prev: Clin. Asst. Haemophilia & Haemostasis Centre Roy. Infirm. Edin.; Princip. GP Folkestone.

YOUNG, Isaac 8 Ashfield Lodge, Palatine Road, Didsbury, Manchester M20 2UD — MB ChB 1939 Leeds. Prev: Cas. Off. Stockton & Thornaby Hosp.; Asst. Med. Off. Hollymoor Emerg. Hosp.; Med. Off. RAFVR 1940-46.

YOUNG, Isobel Margaret (retired) 56 Broomwell Gardens, Monikie, Dundee DD5 3QP Tel: 01382 370451 — MB ChB 1947 St. And. Prev: Med. Ref. Scott. Home & Health Dept.

YOUNG, James Andrew (retired) Ninewells Hospital and Medical School, Dundee — MB ChB 1960 Glas.; FRCP Glas. 1981, M 1965; MRCP Lond. 1966. Prev: Cons. Paediat. Neurol. Ninewells Hosp. Dundee.

YOUNG, James Crawford 49 Ravelston Road, Bearsden, Glasgow G61 1AX — MB ChB 1971 Glas.; FRCP Glas. Cons. Phys. (Geriat. Med.) S.. Gen. Hosp. Glas.

YOUNG, James David Dr Moss and Partners, 28-38 Kings Road, Harrogate HG1 5JP Tel: 01423 560261 Fax: 01423 501099 — MB ChB 1977 Sheff.; MB ChB (Sheff.) 1977; FRCGP 1991, M 1981; DRCOG 1980. Prev: Trainee GP Harrogate VTS; Ho. Surg. Roy. Hosp. Sheff.; Ho. Phys. St. Geo. Hosp. Lincoln.

YOUNG, Mr James Drummond Harding South Kinrara, Fairmount Terrace, Perth PH2 7AS Tel: 01738 625343 — MB ChB 1964 Liverp.; FRCS Ed. 1970; FRCOphth 1988. Cons. Ophth. Dundee Teach. Hops. NHS Trust. Prev: Cons. Ophth. Tayside HB.

YOUNG, James Graham Watergates, Ashbourne Road, Blackbrook, Belper DE56 2DA — BM BCh 1993 Oxf.; FRCS Eng. (Oxf.) Specialist Regist. (Urol.), Char. Cross Hosp., Hammersmith, Lond. Prev: SHO (Urol.) Kent & Canterbury Hosp. Canterbury; SHO (Gen. Surg.) Roy. Berks. Hosp. Reading.

YOUNG, James Jack 15 King Street, Paisley PA1 2PR Tel: 0141 889 3144; Creggan, Arthur Road, Paisley PA2 8AZ Tel: 0141 889 9831 — MB ChB 1956 Glas.

YOUNG, James Richard 51 Beech Court, Darras Hall, Ponteland, Newcastle upon Tyne NE20 9NE — MB BS 1962 Durh.; FFR 1968; DMRD Eng. 1966. (Newc.) Cons. Radiol. Qu. Eliz. & Freeman Trust Hosps.; Clin. Lect. Radiol. Newc. Univ.; Clin. Dir. BrE. Screening & Assessm. Centre Gateshead. Prev: Cons. Radiol. i/c Radiol. Qu. Eliz. Hosp. Gateshead.

YOUNG, James Richard Keeling Street Doctors Surgery, Keeling Street, North Somercotes, Louth LN11 7QU Tel: 01507 358623 Fax: 01507 358746; 3 Meteor Road, Manby, Louth LN11 8UB Tel: 01507 328784 Fax: 01507 328784 Email: jyoung7234@aol.com — MB BS 1983 Lond.; DFFP 1995; DRCOG 1987. (Roy. Free) Socs: Assoc. Mem. RCGP; BMA; Fell. RSM. Prev: Trainee GP Harrogate; SHO (O & G) York Dist. Hosp.; SHO (ENT Surg.) Roy. Gwent Hosp. Newport.

YOUNG, Jane Elizabeth 65 Lethbridge Road, Wells BA5 2FW — MB BS 1994 Lond.

YOUNG, Jane Frances Hampton Medical Centre, Lansdowne, 49a Priory Road, Hampton TW12 2PB Tel: 020 8979 5150 Fax: 020 8941 9068; (branch Surgery) Tangley Medical Centre, 10 Tangley Pk Road, Hampton TW12 3YH — MB BS 1968 Lond.; MRCS Eng. LRCP Lond. 1966; DFFP 1993; DObst RCOG 1968. (St. Mary's) Med. Off. Hampton Sch. Middlx.

YOUNG, Janet Cecilia Josephine 37 Nightingale Avenue, Cambridge CB1 8SG — MB BS 1955 Lond.; MRCS Eng. LRCP Lond. 1955.

YOUNG, Janet Margaret Seivwright Church Street Surgery, St Mary's Courtyard, Church Street, Ware SG12 9EF Tel: 01920 468941 Fax: 01920 465531 — MB BS 1976 Lond.; BSc Lond. 1973, MB BS 1976; MRCP (UK) 1979; MRCGP 1988.

YOUNG, Jason Christopher 2 Gayton Close, Trumpington, Cambridge CB2 2JY — MB BS 1996 Lond.; BSc Lond. 1993. (UCL) SHO (Anaesth.) W. Suff. Gen. Hosp. Bury St. Edmunds. Socs: Christ. Med. Fell.sh.; BMA.

YOUNG, Jean Lady Eden Resource Centre, Cockton Hill Road, Bishop Auckland DL14 6EN Tel: 01388 609350; 39 Newlands Avenue, Bishop Auckland DL14 6AJ Tel: 01388 602495 — MB BS 1958 Durh. (Newc.) Clin. Asst. (Psychiat The Day Hosp.Bishop Auckland co.Durh. Prev: Clin. Asst. Winterton Hosp. Sedgefield

YOUNG

Cleveland; Regist. (Adult Psychiat.) Winterton Hosp. Sedgefield; Regist. (Child & Family Psychiat.) Darlington Memor. Hosp. & Bishop Auckland Gen. Hosps.

YOUNG, Jean Isobel Lanark Doctors, Health Centre, South Vennel, Lanark ML11 7JT Tel: 01555 665522 Fax: 01555 666857 — MB ChB 1972 Aberd.; MRCGP 1984; DObst RCOG 1975; DCH RCP Lond. 1975.

YOUNG, Jean McIver 41 Beechwood Drive, Broomhill, Glasgow G11 7ET Tel: 0141 357 6600 — MB ChB 1952 Glas.; LFHom 1997 (Licenciate). Socs: LFHOM. Prev: Clin. Med. Off. W.. Health Dist.; Med. Off. Lanarksh. CC; Ho. Surg. Roy. Hosp. Sick Childr. Glas.

YOUNG, Jean Morrison The North Glasgow University Hospitals NHS Trust, Glasgow G11 0YN; 79 Campsie Gardens, Clarkson, Glasgow G76 7SF — MB ChB 1983 Glas.; MRCP (UK) 1986. (Bristol) Specialist Regist. (Gen. Internal Med. & Geriat. Med.) N. Glas. Univ. Hosps. NHS Trust. Socs: Soc. Occupat. Med.; Brit. Geriat. Soc. Prev: Sen. Regist. (Gen. & Geriat.) Longmore Hosp. Edin. Sen. Regist. (Geriat.s) Vict. Infirm. NHS Trust Glas.; Regist. (Geriat.) Lightburn Hosp. Glas.; Regist. (Med. & Neurol.) Inst. Neurol. Sci. S.. Gen. Hosp. Glas.

YOUNG, Jennifer Ann Department Pathology, Medical School, University of Birmingham, Birmingham B15 2TT Tel: 0121 414 4016 Fax: 0121 414 4019; 18 Frederick Road, Edgbaston, Birmingham B15 1JN Tel: 0121 455 7775 — MB BCh BAO 1961 Dub.; MA, MD, Dub. 1982, BA; FFPath RCPI 1985; FRCPath 1998. (T.C. Dub.) Sen. Lect. (Path. & Cytopath.) Univ. Birm.; Edit. Bd. Mem. Cytopath. & Diagn. Cytopath. Socs: Internat. Acad. Cytol. Pathol. Soc. GB & Irel.; Vice-Chairm. Brit. Soc. Clin. Cytol. Prev: Sen. Regist. (Path.) Qu. Eliz. Hosp. Birm.; Research Regist. (Cytol.) Glas. Roy. Infirm.

YOUNG, Jennifer Margaret Ball Tree Surgery, Western Road North, Sompting, Lancing BN15 9UX Tel: 01903 752200 Fax: 01903 536983; 64 Mill Road, Lancing BN15 0QA — MB ChB 1973 Birm. (Birm.) GP Lancing. Socs: BMA.

YOUNG, Joanna Hilda Grangemead, 1 Hawthylands Rd, Hailsham BN27 1EU Tel: 01323 442144 Fax: 01323 847822 — MB BS 1985 Lond.; MRCPsych 1992. (St Georges, London) Staf Psychiat.(Old Age), E.bourne & Co. Healthcare NHS Trust. Prev: Staff Psychiat. (Forens.) Ashen Hill Hailsham; Staff Psychiat. E.bourne & Co. Healthcare (NHS Trust).

YOUNG, Joanna Mary 70 South Street, Greenock PA16 8QJ — MB ChB 1998 Glas.

YOUNG, Joanne Community Paediatrics, Borders General Hospital, Melrose TD6 9BS Tel: 01896 826000; Lyme House, 51 Shedden Pk Road, Kelso TD5 7AW Tel: 01573 226107 — MB ChB 1980 Glas.; MPhil 2000 Glas. Staff Grade (Child Health) Roxburghsh. Prev: Med. Off. BTS; SHO (Anaesth.) Dudley Rd. Hosp. Birm. & E. Birm. Hosp.; Ho. Off. (Surg.) St. Chad's Hosp. Birm.

YOUNG, John (retired) 24 Westholme Avenue, Aberdeen AB15 6AA — MB ChB 1942 Ed.

YOUNG, John (retired) 21 Furners Mead, Henfield BN5 9JA Tel: 01273 2708 — MB ChB 1921 Glas.; DPH Camb. 1922. Prev: MOH Leics. & Rutland Comb. Dists.

YOUNG, John Archibald — MB ChB 1973 Aberd.; MRCGP 1977. (Aberd.) GP Princip. Alva; Trainer (Gen. Pract.) Alva. Socs: BMA; Roy. Coll. Gen. Pract. Prev: Trainee GP Aberd. VTS; Resid. Ho. Off. City Hosp. Aberd. & Aberd. Roy. Infirm.

YOUNG, Professor John Braithwaite Department of Medicine for Elderly, St. Luke's Hospital, Bradford BD5 0NA Tel: 01274 734744 Email: johnyoung@bradfordhospitals.nhs.uk — MB BS 1977 Lond.; MSc Lond. 1989, MBA (Open Univ.) 1995; FRCP Lond. 1994; MRCP (UK) 1980. Cons. Phys. St. Luke's Hosp. Bradford; Assoc. Prof. Sheff. Inst. for stuides on Ageing (SISA); Vis. Prof. Nuffield Inst. for Health, Leeds; Prof. Assoc., Sch. Health Care Studies, Bradford.

YOUNG, John Charles Norwood Medical Centre, 99 Abbey Road, Barrow-in-Furness LA14 5ES Tel: 01229 822024 Fax: 01229 823949 — MB ChB 1987 Dundee.

YOUNG, John Dewar Consett Medical Centre, Station Yard, Consett DH8 5YA Tel: 01207 216116 Fax: 01207 216119; Shortycroft, Stocksfield NE43 7SB — MB BS 1977 Newc.; BMedSc 1974; MRCGP 1988.

YOUNG, John Duncan Nuffield Department of Anaesthetics, Radcliffe Infirmary, Woodstock Road, Oxford OX2 6HE Tel: 01865 224772 Fax: 01865 794191 — BM 1979 Soton.; DM Soton. 1992; FFA RCS Eng. 1984. (Soton.) Clin. Reader (Anaesth.) Univ. Oxf.

YOUNG, John Hildreth Merck Sharp & Dohme, Hertford Road, Hoddesdon EN11 9BU Tel: 01992 452341 Fax: 01992 479191 Email: john_young@merck.com — MB BS 1968 Lond.; FRCP Lond. 1990; MRCP (UK) 1973; FRCPath 1993, M 1982; FFPM 1990; Dip. Biochem. Lond 1965. (St. Thos.) Med. Dir. Merck, Sharp & Dohme Ltd. Socs: Brit. Soc. Rheum. & Brit. Geriat. Soc. Prev: Lect. (Chem. Path.) Univ. Soton.; Regist. (Med.) N.wick Pk. Hosp. Harrow; Regist. (Chem. Path.) Hosp. Sick Childr. Gt. Ormond St. Lond.

YOUNG, John Howard Ball Tree Surgery, Western Road North, Sompting, Lancing BN15 9UX Tel: 01903 752200 Fax: 01903 536983; 64 Mill Road, Lancing BN15 0QA — MB ChB 1977 Birm.; MB ChB Birm. 1972 FFA RCS Eng. 1977. (Birm.)

YOUNG, John Murray, OStJ, Surg. Capt. RN Retd. (retired) 29 Kennedy Crescent, Alverstoke, Gosport PO12 2NL Tel: 023 9258 0168 — MRCS Eng. LRCP Lond. 1956; DPhil Oxf. 1971; MFCM 1974; MFOM 1978; MFPHM 1990; FFOM RCP Lond. 1987. Prev: Cons. Occupat. Phys. Gosport.

YOUNG, John Murray Miller (retired) Cairngorm, 20 Lyons Lane, Appleton, Warrington WA4 5JG — MB ChB 1952 Glas.; MRCGP 1968.

YOUNG, John Peter Russel Lyndale, 32 The Rise, Sevenoaks TN13 1RQ Tel: 01732 460115 — MD 1971 Camb.; MPhil Lond. 1969; MA Camb. 1970, MD 1971, MB 1963, BChir 1962; FRCP Lond. 1987, M 1969; FRCPsych 1986, M 1971. (St. Thos.) Prev: Emerit. Cons. in Psych. Med., Guys & St. Thos. NHS Trust.

YOUNG, Mr John Riddington, OStJ, TD Department of Otolaryngology, North Devon District Hospital, Raleigh Park, Barnstaple EX31 4JB Tel: 01271 322736; West Barton Farm, Horwood, Bideford EX39 4PB Tel: 01271 858495 — MB ChB 1970 Sheff.; MPhil 2001 Brussels; FRCS (Otol.) Eng. 1976; DLO Eng. 1974. Sen. Cons. ENT Surg. N. Devon Hosp. Barnstaple; Col. (Commanding Off.) 211 Wessex Field Hosp. RAMC (V); Area Surg. (N. Devon) St. John Ambul. Brig. Socs: Mackenzie Soc. Prev: Sen. Regist. (ENT Surg.) Manch. Roy. Infirm.

YOUNG, John Robert Burns 65A Links Lane, Rowlands Castle PO9 6AF Tel: 01705 412009 — MB ChB 1960 Glas.; FFA RCS Eng. 1967; DObst RCOG 1962. Cons. Anaesth. Portsmouth Gp. Hosps.

YOUNG, Jolyon David The Dewerstone Surgery, Hampton Avenue, St Marychurch, Torquay TQ1 3LA Tel: 01803 323123/314240 Fax: 01803 322001 — MB ChB 1981 Birm.

YOUNG, Jonathan Charles 76 Montpellier Park, Edinburgh EH10 — B Med Newc NSW 1987.

YOUNG, Juanita Jane, Maj. RAMC Revilo, Maybourne Rise, Mayford, Woking GU22 0SH — MB BS 1985 Lond.; MRCGP 1990; DCH RCP Lond. 1988. SHO (Gen Med.) Camb. Milit. Hosp. Aldershot; GP Aldershot VTS. Prev: SHO (Paediat.) Regtl. Med. Off. Army.

YOUNG, Katharine St Paul's Road Medical Centre, 248 St Paul's Road, Islington, London N1 2LJ Tel: 020 7226 6333 — BM BCh 1990 Oxf.; MA Oxf. 1994; MRCGP 1994; DCH RCP Lond. 1992.

YOUNG, Katharine Elizabeth Mowbray House, Crook DL15 9JG — BM BS 1994 Nottm.; BMedSci Nottm. 1992. SHO (A & E) N. Tyneside Gen. Hosp. N. Shields. Prev: Ho. Off. (Gen. Med.) King's Mill Hosp. Mansfield; Ho. Off. (Gen. Surg.) Wansbeck Gen. Hosp. Ashington.

YOUNG, Katrina Elizabeth Magdalen Medical Practice, Lawson Road, Norwich NR3 4LF Tel: 01603 475555 Fax: 01603 787210; Church Farm, Church Lane, Eaton, Norwich NR4 6NW Tel: 01603 457302 — MB ChB 1972 Aberd.

YOUNG, Katrina Mary St Marys Surgery, 37 St. Mary's Street, Ely CB7 4HF; 81 Downham Road, Ely CB6 3DY Tel: 01353 610870 — MB BS 1985 Lond.; DA (UK) 1993. Prev: SHO (ENT & Anaesth.) Cheltenham Gen. Hosp.; Resid. Med. Off. Grafton Cone Hosp., Austral.; Clin. Asst. (Anaesth.) Hinchingbrooke Hosp. Huntingdon.

YOUNG, Keith The Surgery, High Street, Epworth, Doncaster DN9 1EP Tel: 01427 872232 Fax: 01427 874944 — MB ChB 1976 Sheff.; MRCGP 1980; DRCOG 1980.

YOUNG, Keith Adam Department of Rheumatology, City Hospital, Waverley Road, St Albans AL3 5PN Tel: 01727 866122 Fax: 01727 897572; 36 Platts Lane, London NW3 7NT — MB BChir 1972 Camb.; MA Camb. 1969; FRCP Lond. 1991; MRCP (UK) 1975.

YOUNG

(Camb. & St. Geo.) Cons. Rheum. St. Albans & Hemel Hempstead NHS Trust. Socs: Brit. Soc. Rheum. Prev: Sen. Regist. (Rheum.) Middx. Hosp. Lond.; Regist. (Neurol.) Centr. Middx. Hosp. Lond.

YOUNG, Keith Digby, OBE, OStJ (retired) Holloways, Priors Marston, Rugby CV47 7RS Tel: 01327 260287 — MRCS Eng. LRCP Lond. 1940; BA (Hons.) Camb.; FFCM 1977, M 1972; DPH Bristol 1961; TDD Wales 1953. Prev: Surg. Lt.-Cdr. RNVR.

YOUNG, Keith Evans 52 St Michaels Road, Llandaff, Cardiff CF5 2AQ — MB BCh 1958 Wales; DObst RCOG 1961. (Cardiff) Prev: Ho. Phys. Roy. Infirm. Cardiff; Ho. Surg. (Obst.) St. David's Hosp. Cardiff.

YOUNG, Keith Richard Consultant Obstetrician and Gynaecologist, Scunthorpe and Goole NHS Hospitals Trust, Cliff Gardens, Scunthorpe DN15 7BH Tel: 01724 282282 — MB BS 1973 Lond.; FRCOG 1993. Cons. O & G Scunthorpe & Goole Hosps. Trust. Socs: Brit. Soc. Colpos. & Cerv. Path.; Brit. Soc. Gyn. Endoscopy. Prev: Cons. O & G RAMC.

YOUNG, Keith Stewart (retired) Chester House, 24 Bell Lane, Kesgrave, Ipswich IP5 1JQ Tel: 01473 624306 — MB BChir 1962 Camb.; MA Camb. 1962; DCH Eng. 1964; DObst RCOG 1964. Prev: SHO (Paediat.) & Ho. Surg. (Obst.) Ipswich & E. Suff. Hosp.

YOUNG, Mr Kenneth Andrew 16 Brierie Gardens, Houston, Johnstone PA6 7BZ Tel: 01505 615251 — MB ChB 1990 Glas.; FRCS Ed. 1995. Specialist Regist. (Orthop. Surg.) W. Scotl. Train. Scheme.

YOUNG, Kenneth Herbert McKenzie, OBE, Brigadier late RAMC Retd. (retired) 58 Forest Drive, Theydon Bois, Epping CM16 7EZ Tel: 01992 812337 — MB BCh BAO 1946 Dub.; FRCGP 1977, M 1972; DTM & H Eng. 1972; DPH NUI 1964. Prev: Director of Army Gen. Pract.

YOUNG, Lesley Jane Department of Geriatric Medicine, Sunderland Royal Hospital, Kayll Road, Sunderland SR4 7TP; Broadbeck, Leazes Villas, Burnopfield, Newcastle upon Tyne NE16 6HW Email: lesleyyoung99@hotmail.com — MB BS 1989 Newc.; MRCP (UK) 1992; Dip. Med. Sci. (Newcastle) Cons. Geriat. Socs: Brit. Geriat. Soc.

YOUNG, Lesley Rita London Weekend Television, South Bank TV Centre, London SE1 9LT Tel: 020 7261 3132 Fax: 020 7261 3132; 26 Strawberry Hill Road, Twickenham TW1 4PU Tel: 020 8891 0638 — MB BS 1970 Lond.; MRCS Eng. LRCP Lond. 1970; DObst RCOG 1973. (St. Mary's) Med. Off. Lond. Weekend Television; Med. Off. P&O Bulk Shipping. Socs: Soc. Occupat. Med.

YOUNG, Linda Anne 84 Glenview Road, Nab Wood, Shipley BD18 4AR — MB BChir 1977 Camb.; MA, MB Camb. 1977, BChir 1976.

YOUNG, Lindsay Fiona 6 Lidgettmount, Roundhay, Leeds LS8 1EX — MB BS 1987 Lond.

YOUNG, Lindsey Margaret 20 Halfway Street, West Kilbride KA23 9EQ — MB ChB 1985 Glas.

YOUNG, Lorna Bruce Manchester Eye Hospital, Oxford Road, Manchester M16 8AJ; 8 Winton Road, Bowdon, Altrincham WA14 2PB Tel: 0161 927 7469 — MB ChB 1975 Ed.; DO Eng. 1980. Assoc. Specialist. Ophth. Socs: MRCOphth. Prev: Assoc. Specialist Ophth. P.ss Alex. Eye Pavilion Edin.

YOUNG, Malcolm John Bridgeflat, Bridge of Weir PA11 3SJ Tel: 0150 587 2595 — MB ChB 1970 St. And.; FRCP Glas. 1985; MRCP (UK) 1973. Cons. Dermat. Argyll & Clyde Health Bd.

YOUNG, Margaret Anne Rena Tel: 01776 706566; Orchardton, Garlieston, Newton Stewart DG8 9DE Tel: 01988 600612 — MB ChB 1980 Glas.; BA Open 1996; MRCGP 1984. (Glasgow)

YOUNG, Marie Jane 30 Cairngorm Gardens, Aberdeen AB12 5BS — MB ChB 1989 Aberd.

YOUNG, Mark Andrew St John's House Surgery, 28 Bromyard Road, Worcester WR2 5BU; 14 Upper Ferry Lane, Callow End, Worcester WR2 4TL Tel: 01905 831218 — MD 1990 Manch.; MB ChB 1975; MRCP (UK) 1981. (Manchester) GP Princip. Socs: Brit. Hypertens. Soc.; Assur. Med. Soc.

YOUNG, Mark Andrew Stapenhill Surgery, Fyfield Road, Stapenhill, Burton-on-Trent DE15 9QD Tel: 01283 565200 Fax: 01283 500617; The Fieldings, 51 Main St, Rosliston, Swadlincote DE12 8JW — BM BS 1984 Nottm.; BMedSci Nottm. 1982, BM BS 1984; MRCGP 1989; Cert. Family Plann. JCC 1988. GP Burton-on-Trent. Prev: SHO (Anaesth.) Leighton Hosp. Crewe.

YOUNG, Martin Paul Alistair Department of Histopathology, St. George's Hospital Medical School, Cranmer Terrace, London SW17 0RE Tel: 020 8725 5265 Email: mpayoung@aol.com; 3 Charlesworth Place, Eleanor Grove, Barnes, London SW13 0JQ Tel: 020 8392 8611 — MB BS 1980 Lond.; BSc Lond. 1977; MRCPath 1994; MRCOG 1987. (St. Geo.) Cons. Histopath. St. Geo. Hosp. Med. Sch. Lond.; Cons. Histopathol. & Cytopathol. St. Geo. Hosp. Lond. Socs: Assn. Clin. Path.; Path. Soc. Prev: Lect. & Hon. Sen. Regist. Univ. Coll. Lond. Med. Sch.; Regist. (Histopath.) Univ. Coll. Hosp. Lond.; SHO (Path.) Manch. Roy. Infirm.

YOUNG, Mary Joanna 16 Buccleuch Close, Guisborough TS14 7LP — BM BS 1992 Nottm.; DRCOG 1996; MRCGP 1997. GP Non-Princip., Weymouth.

YOUNG, Matthew James 2 Manor Road, West Wickham BR4 9PS; 9 Bishops Avenue, Bromley BR1 3ET — MB BS 1986 Lond.; BSc Lond. 1983; MRCGP 1990; DRCOG 1990. (Univ. Lond. & Westm.) GP Adviser for GP Newspaper Lond. Prev: Trainee GP/SHO Qu. Mary's Hosp. Sidcup VTS; Ho. Surg. Mayday Hosp. Croydon; Ho. Phys. Qu. Mary's Hosp. Lond.

YOUNG, Matthew John Department of Diabetes, Royal Infirmary of Edinburgh, Lauriston Place, Edinburgh EH3 9YW — MB BS 1985 Newc.; MD Newc. 1994; MRCP (UK) 1989. Cons. Phys. & Diabetologist Roy. Infirm. Edin. Socs: Brit. Diabetic Assn. & Europ. Assn. Study Diabetes. Prev: Sen. Regist. Glas. Roy. Infirm.; Research Fell. Manch. Roy. Infirm.; Regist. N.. Gen. Hosp. Sheff.

YOUNG, Maura Fiona 19 Waterfoot Road, Magherafelt BT45 6LF — MB BCh 1997 Belf.

YOUNG, Michael 21 Sealand Court, Shorts Reach, The Esplanade, Rochester ME1 1QH — MB BS 1961 Lond.; MRCS Eng. LRCP Lond. 1961; DObst RCOG 1965. (Roy. Free) Assoc special. (Palliat. Med.) Heart of Kent Hospice Aylesford. Socs: BMA; Assn. Palliat. Med. Prev: GP Rochester; Cas. Off. & Ho. Surg. St. Bart. Hosp. Rochester.; Ho. Surg. & Phys. Lond.

YOUNG, Mr Michael Harry 12 Park Road, Padyr, Cardiff CF15 8DG Tel: 029 2084 2975 — MB ChB 1960 (Hons.) Sheff.; MD (Commend.) Sheff. 1964; FRCS Eng. 1966. Cons. Orthop. Surg. S. Glam. AHA (T). Socs: Fell. Brit. Orthop. Assn.; Brit. Orthop. Research Assn. Prev: Research Fell. Toronto W.. Hosp. Canada; Lect. in Orthop. Surg. Univ. Edin. & Hon. Sen. Regist. Roy. Infirm.; Edin. & P.ss Margt. Rose Orthop. Hosp. Edin.

YOUNG, Michael John Young, Ellis and Overton, 41 David Place, St Helier, Jersey JE2 4TE Tel: 01534 723318 Fax: 01534 611062; 3 Albermarle, LA Grande Route Des Sablons, Groyville, Jersey JE3 9FP Tel: 01534 851256 Fax: 01534 857642 — MB BS 1957 Lond.; MRCS Eng. LRCP Lond. 1956. (Guy's) Socs: MRCGP; Jersey Med. Soc. Prev: SHO (Gen. Med.) P.ss Beatrice Hosp. Lond.; Ho. Phys. (Paediat.) & Ho. Surg. Guy's Hosp.

YOUNG, Michael Peter Northlands Wood Surgery, 7 Walnut Park, Haywards Heath RH16 3TG Tel: 01444 458022 Fax: 01444 415960 — MB BChir 1970 Camb.; MRCP (UK) 1973; MRCGP 1980; DCH Eng. 1974; DObst RCOG 1974. (Univ. of Camb. Univ Coll. Lond.)

YOUNG, Myer (retired) 61 Hamilton Terrace, London NW8 9RG Tel: 020 7286 1220 — MRCS Eng. LRCP Lond. 1927.

YOUNG, Nathaniel Stuart 6 Sackville Way, West Berg Holt, Colchester CO6 3DZ Tel: 01206 570371 — MB BS 1964 Lond.; MRCS Eng. LRCP Lond. 1964. (Guy's)

YOUNG, Nicholas James Sevenposts Surgery, 326A Prestbury Road, Prestbury, Cheltenham GL52 3DD Tel: 01242 244103; 34 Kings Road, Cheltenham GL52 6BG — MB ChB 1983 Birm.; DRCOG 1987.

YOUNG, Nicholas John Holly Lodge, Fulbeck, Morpeth NE61 3JT — BM BS 1992 Nottm.

YOUNG, Nicola Department of Medical Microbiology, F Floor, Royal Hallamshire Hospital, Glossop Road, Sheffield S10 2JF Tel: 0141 271 3767 — MB ChB 1992 Manch.; BSc St. And. 1989; MRCPath 2001 London; DTM & H, Lond. 1998. Specialist Regist. (Med. Microbiol.) Roy. Hallamshire Hosp. Sheff. Prev: Regist. (Med. Microbiol.) N.. Gen. Hosp. Sheff.

YOUNG, Mr Nigel John Alexander Clementine Churchill Hospital, Harrow HA1 3RX Tel: 020 8422 3464 — MB BS 1968 Lond.; FRCS Eng. 1977; FRCOphth. 1988. (Middx.) Cons. Ophth. Watford Gen. Hosp. Prev: Cons. Ophth. Centr. Middx., N.wick Pk. & Mt. Vernon Hosps.; Chief Clin. Asst. Moorfields Eye Hosp. Lond.; Res. Surg. Off. Moorfields Eye Hosp. Lond.

YOUNG

YOUNG, Norman (retired) 71 The Broadway, Walsall WS1 3EZ Tel: 01922 622144 Fax: 01922 622144 Email: normanyoung@excite.co.uk — MB ChB 1950 Glas.; DObst RCOG 1954; MRCGP 1963; LMCC 1969. Prev: Ho. Phys. & Ho. Surg. Stobhill Hosp. Glas.

YOUNG, Pamela Joy (retired) 22 Dumpton Gap Road, Broadstairs CT10 1TA — MB ChB Leeds 1964; DObst RCOG 1967; DPM Eng. 1972.

YOUNG, Pamela Ruth Greyfriars Surgery, 25 St. Nicholas Street, Hereford HR4 0BH Tel: 01432 265717 Fax: 01432 340150; Yew Tree Villa, Cobhall Common, Allensmore, Hereford HR2 9BN Tel: 01432 343292 — MB ChB 1983 Birm.; DRCOG 1986; MRCGP 1989. Prev: Trainee GP Shrewsbury; SHO (Psychiat.) Tokanwi Hosp. New Zealand; SHO (Paediat. & O & G & Geriat.) & Cas. Off. Roy. Shrewsbury Hosp.

YOUNG, Patricia Margaret Edinburgh Sick Children's NHS Trust, Community Child Health Services, 10 Chalmers Crescent, Edinburgh EH9 1TS Tel: 0131 536 0000 Fax: 0131 536 0570; 35 Fox Covert Avenue, Edinburgh EH12 6UQ Tel: 0131 316 4010 — MB ChB 1983 Dundee; MRCGP 1987; DFFP 1993; T(GP) 1991; Cert. Family Plann. JCC 1986; DCH RCP Lond. 1986. Staff Grade Paediat. Edin. Sick Childr.'s NHS Trust (p/t). Socs: Soc. Pub. Health; Fac. Community Health; Assn. Research in Infant & Child Developm. Prev: GP Partner & GP Asst. Hull; SCMO Hull & Holderness Community Health Care Trust; Trainee GP Hull VTS.

YOUNG, Patrick Michael 1 Cardington Drive, Heath Farm Estate, Shrewsbury SY1 3HD — MB BS 1984 Lond.

YOUNG, Peter Frank Little Arowry Cottage, Little Arowry, Hanmer, Whitchurch SY13 3DD — MB ChB 1984 Ed. SHO (O & G) Shrops. HA. Prev: SHO (Med.) P.ss Roy. Hosp. Telford.

YOUNG, Peter Frederick Pallion Health Centre, Hylton Road, Sunderland SR4 7XF Tel: 0191 567 4673 — MB BS 1964 Durh. (Newc.) Socs: Sunderland W. End Med. Soc. Prev: SHO (O & G) Sunderland Gen. Hosp. & SHO (ENT) Roy. Vict. Infirm. Newc.; Ho. Phys. Gen. Hosp. Newc.

YOUNG, Peter Jeffrey 17 Branksome Road, Norwich NR4 6SN — MB ChB 1990 Ed.

YOUNG, Peter John William (retired) Boundary House Surgery, Mount Lane, Bracknell RG12 9PG Tel: 01344 483900 Fax: 01344 862203 — MB BChir 1963 Camb.; BA Camb. 1959.

YOUNG, Peter Nesbitt Cheltenham General Hospital, Sandford Road, Cheltenham GL53 7AN Email: peter.young@egnhst.sorg.uk; 112 Linden Avenue, Prestbury, Cheltenham GL52 3DS Tel: 01242 520459 Email: pnyoung@argonet.co.uk — MB BChir 1964 Camb.; FFA RCS Eng. 1971; DObst RCOG 1968. (Univ. Coll. Hosp.) Cons. Anaesth. Cheltenham Gen., Glos. Roy. & Tewkesbury Hosps. Prev: Sen. Regist. (Anaesth.) Middlx. Hosp. Lond.; Regist. (Anaesth.) Soton. Univ. Gp. Hosps. & Mid-Sussex Gp.; Hosps.

YOUNG, Peter Timothy Haylodge Health Centre, Neidpath Road, Peebles EH45 8JG Tel: 01721 720380 Fax: 01721 723430; 19 Morning Hill, Peebles EH45 9JS — MB ChB 1984 Glas.; MRCGP 1990. Prev: Trainee GP Glas. VTS.

YOUNG, Peter Westgate Plumstead Health Centre, Tewson Road, Plumstead, London SE18 1BB Tel: 020 8854 1898 Fax: 020 8855 9958 — MB BS 1975 Lond.; MRCS Eng. LRCP Lond. 1974; DRCOG 1977.

YOUNG, Philip Charles, Surg. Lt.-Cdr. RN Royal Hospital Haslar, Gosport PO12 2AA Tel: 01705 584255 Email: 106225.1276@compuserve.com — MB BS 1985 Lond.; FRCA 1995. Cons. Anaesth.; Hon. Cons. (ITU) Oxf. Radcliffe NHS Trust. Socs: BMA; Assn. Anaesth. Prev: Hon. Sen. Regist. Oxf. Radcliffe NHS Trust.

YOUNG, Rachel Caroline 19 Leigh Hill Road, Cobham KT11 2HS — MB BS 1990 Lond.

YOUNG, Mr Richard Aretas Lewry West Middlesex University Hospital, Twickenham Road, Isleworth TW7 6AF Tel: 020 8565 5768 Fax: 020 8287 2778 Email: youngral@compuserve.com; 26 Strawberry Hill Road, Twickenham TW1 4PU Tel: 020 8891 0638 Fax: 020 8287 2778 — MB BChir 1968 Camb.; FRCS Eng. 1972; MRCS Eng. LRCP Lond. 1967. (Camb. & St. Mary's) Cons. Surg. W. Middlx. Univ. Hosp. Lond.; Recognised Teach. Univ. Lond.; Examr. Find MB, BS Lond. Socs: Fell. Roy. Soc. Med.; Fell. Assn. Surgs.; Vasc. Surgic. Soc. Prev: Sen. Regist. (Surg.) St. Mary's Hosp. Lond.; Bernard Sunley Research Fell. RCS Eng.; Regist. (Surg.) Roy. Free Hosp. Lond.

YOUNG, Mr Richard Charles 1 Broomsleigh St, West Hampstead, London NW6 1QQ Email: ryoung@mcindoeud.demon.co.uk — BM BCh 1993 Oxf.; MA Camb. 1994; FRCS Eng. 1995. (Oxf.) Research Fell., Blond Mcindoe Laboratories, Roy. Free Hosp. Lond. Prev: SHO (A & E) John Radcliffe Hosp. Oxf.; SHO Rotat. (Surg.) Frenchay Hosp. Bristol; Demonst. (Anat.) Univ. Camb.

YOUNG, Richard Edward 25 Lawmarnock Crescent, Bridge of Weir PA11 3AS — MB ChB 1971 Glas.; MRCP (UK) 1977. Cons. Phys. Geriat. Med. Argyl & Clyde HB. Prev: Regist. (Med.) W. Infirm. Glas.; Research Asst. Univ. Dept. Med. & SHO (Cardiol.) W. Infirm. Glas.

YOUNG, Richard John Paston Surgery, 9-11 Park Lane, North Walsham NR28 0BQ Tel: 01692 403015 Fax: 01692 500619; Home Farm, Barton Turf, Norwich NR12 8BQ Tel: 01692 536475 — MB BChir 1989 Camb.; MRCGP 1993; DRCOG 1992. Course Organiser Norwich VTS.

YOUNG, Robert Alasdair Brims Parkway Centre, Parkway, Havant PO9 1HH Tel: 01705 471661 Fax: 01705 498291 Email: al@old-forge.demon.co.uk — MB ChB 1972 Glas.; MRCPsych 1976. Cons. Psychiat. Pk.way Centre Pk.way Havant; Hon. Clin. Teach. Soton. Univ. Med. Sch. Prev: Regist. St. Crispin Hosp. N.ampton; Sen. Regist. St. Jas. Hosp. Portsmouth & (Psychiat.) Roy. S. Hants. Hosp. Soton.

YOUNG, Mr Robert Andrew Michael 23 Millvale Road, Hillsborough BT26 6HR Tel: 01846 682387; Department of Urology, Craigavon Area Hospital, Craigavon BT63 5QQ Tel: 01762 334444 — MB BCh BAO 1983 Belf.; MD Belf. 1993; FRCSI 1987; FRCS (Urol.) 1996. (Queen's University Belfast) Cons. Urol. Craigavon Area Hosp. Socs: Brit. Assn. Urol. Surg.; BMA & Ulster Med. Soc. Prev: Sen. Regist (Urol.) Belf. City Hosp.; Regist. (Surg.) Roy. Vict. Hosp. Belf.; Research Fell. Roy. Vict. Hosp. Belf.

YOUNG, Robert Douglas (retired) Highfield, Silverdale, Carnforth LA5 0SQ Tel: 01524 701234 Fax: 01524 701234 — MB ChB Ed. 1943; MD Ed. 1958; FRCP Ed. 1971, M 1950. Prev: Cons. Phys. Lancaster & S. Cumbria Health Dists.

YOUNG, Robert Henry Julian Pen-y-cae, 14 Maes Cadwgan, Creigiau, Cardiff CF15 9TQ — MB BS 1991 Lond.; MRCGP 1996.

YOUNG, Robert Kyle Barr Brunthill Farm, Fenwick, Kilmarnock KA3 6HX Tel: 01560 700242 — MB ChB 1966 Glas.; FFA RCS Eng. 1971. (Glas.) Cons. Anaesth. N. Ayrsh. Dist. Gen. Hosp. Prev: Sen. Regist., Regist. & SHO (Anaesth.) Glas. Roy. Infirm.

YOUNG, Robert Marryat New House Surgery, 142A South Street, Dorking RH4 2QR; Puffins, Newdigate Road, Beare Green, Dorking RH5 4QN Tel: 01306 711920 — MB BS 1976 Lond.; MRCS Eng. LRCP Lond. 1975; DRCOG 1978. (St. Mary's) Prev: Trainee GP Lond.; SHO (Cas. & O & G) St. Mary's Hosp. Harrow Rd.; SHO (Anaesth.) Worthing Hosp.

YOUNG, Roger Christopher (retired) Yennadon Spinney, Dousland, Yelverton PL20 6NA Tel: 01822 777 — MB BS 1956 Lond.; DObst RCOG 1958; DA Eng. 1960. Prev: Ho. Phys. Warneford Hosp. Leamington Spa.

YOUNG, Ronald (retired) Westfield House, Calow, Chesterfield S44 5AD Tel: 01246 73845 — LMSSA 1954 Lond. Prev: Sen. Ho. Off. (Ophth.), Ho. Phys. & Ho. Surg. (Gyn.) Derby Roy.

YOUNG, Rowena 22 Edenpark Drive, Batheaston, Bath BA1 7JJ Tel: 01225 858212 — MB BS 1966 Lond.; MRCS Eng. LRCP Lond. 1966; DObst RCOG 1968. (Roy. Free) Assoc. Specialist Roy. United Hosp. Bath. Socs: BMA; Brit. Diabetic Assn. (Med. & Scientif. Sect.). Prev: Ho. Surg. (Obst.) S. Lond. Hosp.; Ho. Phys. W. Kent Gen. Hosp. Maidstone; Ho. Surg. Roy. Free Hosp. Lond.

YOUNG, Russell Andrew c/o Hull Royal Infirmary, Anlaby Road, Hull HU3 2JZ Tel: 07930 193617 Email: winfield19@aol.com; 5 Albert Terrance, Beverley HU17 8JU Tel: 01482 882146 — MB ChB 1997 Manch. SHO (Gen. Surg.) Hull Roy. Infirm. Prev: Ho. Off. (Gen. Med.) Trafford Gen. Hosp. Manch.; SHO Orthpaedics; SHO (A&E).

YOUNG, Russell Murray Department of Chemical Pathology, Queen Alexandra Hospital, Cosham, Portsmouth PO6 3LY Tel: 023 92 286349 Fax: 023 92 286265 — BM BS 1976 Nottm.; FRCPath 1995; Dip. Health Managem. Keele 1993; BMedSci Nottm. 1974. Cons. Chem. Path. Portsmouth Hosps. NHS Trust.; Assoc. Clin. Dir.

YOUNG

(Path.) Portsmouth Hosp. NHS Trust. Socs: Hon. Sec. Assn. Clin. Pathol.; Assn. Clin. Biochem.

YOUNG, Ruth Amelia (retired) 5 The Manor House, Upper Green, Tettenhall, Wolverhampton WV6 8QJ Tel: 01902 756168 — MB ChB Glas. 1946, DPH 1949. Prev: Gen. Practitioner Wolverhampton.

YOUNG, Lady Ruth Eleanor (retired) Cleeve Hill Nursing Home, Cleeve Hill, Cheltenham GL52 3PW Tel: 01223 352650 — MRCS Eng. LRCP Lond. 1936; BSc 1930, MB BS Lond. 1936; MRCPsych 1972; DPM Eng. 1961. Prev: Med. Asst. (Psychiat.) Addenbrooke's Hosp. Camb.

YOUNG, Samuel Knibb, SBStJ (retired) 39 Newlands Avenue, Bishop Auckland DL14 6AJ Tel: 01388 602495 — LMSSA Lond. 1954; MA Camb. 1954. Prev: Ho. Surg. (Obst.) Bishop Auckland Gen. Hosp.

YOUNG, Sandra Hurst Holly Lodge, Fulbeck, Morpeth NE61 3JT Tel: 01670 512052 — MB ChB 1961 Glas. (Glas.) Clin. Asst. (Dermat.) Roy. Vict. Infirm. Newc., Tynemouth Vict. Jubilee Infirm. & N.Id. AHA. Prev: SHO Dept. Dermat. Vict. Hosp. Glas.; Ho. Off. Ballochmyle Hosp. Mauchline.

YOUNG, Sara Camilla (retired) 19 Kingston Road, Bridlington YO15 3NF Tel: 0126 401372 — MB ChB Sheff. 1963. Prev: SCMO E. Yorks. Community Healthcare.

YOUNG, Sarah Catherine Russel 30A Kemplay Road, Hampstead, London NW3 1SY Tel: 020 7794 7983 — MB BS 1991 Lond.; BSc Lond. 1986, MB BS 1991. Prev: SHO (O & G) Hammersmith Hosp. Lond.; SHO (Med.) Johannesburg Hosp., SA.

YOUNG, Sarah Louise Doctors Surgery, Forge Close, Hayes, Bromley BR2 7LL Tel: 020 8462 1601 Fax: 020 8462 7410; 13 Beadon Road, Bromley BR2 9AS — MB BS 1986 Lond.; MA Oxf. 1983; DRCOG 1992; DCH RCP Lond. 1989. Socs: BMA.

YOUNG, Sarah Margaret 8 Oxford Road, Teddington TW11 0PZ — BM BS 1998 Nottm.

YOUNG, Sean Patrick New Surgery, Victoria Street, Pontycymer, Bridgend CF32 8NW Tel: 01656 870237 Fax: 01656 870354; Llangeinar House, Bttius Road, Llangeinar, Bridgend CF32 8PH — MB BS 1989 Lond.; MRCGP 1994. Prev: Trainee GP/SHO (Psychiat.) M. Glam. VTS.

YOUNG, Sharon Moiran Midgley University Health Service, University of Edinburgh, Richard Verney Health Centre, 6 Bristo Square, Edinburgh EH8 9AL Tel: 0131 650 2777 Fax: 0131 662 1813; 8 Succoth Place, Edinburgh EH12 6BL — MB ChB 1979 Ed.; DCCH RCP Ed. 1985.

YOUNG, Sheila Haxby & Wigginton Health Centre, The Village, Wigginton, York YO32 2LL Tel: 01904 760125; 6 The Willows, Strensall, York YO32 5YG — MB BS 1982 Newc.; DRCOG 1988.

YOUNG, Shina Ann Birchwood Surgery, Birchwood, Arisaig PH39 4NJ Tel: 01687 450258 — MB ChB 1967 Aberd. Prev: Clin. Med. Off. Highland HB; GP Kinlochleven; Resid. Roy. Aberd. Hosp. Sick Childr. & Woodend Hosp. Aberd.

YOUNG, Simon John Brenkley Avenue Health Centre, Brenkley Avenue, Shiremoor, Newcastle upon Tyne NE27 0PR Tel: 0191 251 6682 Fax: 0191 219 5700 — MB ChB 1989 Manch. GP Newc.

YOUNG, Simon John The Health Centre, Station Approach, Bradford-on-Avon BA15 1DQ Tel: 012216 6611; Tower House, Pomeroy Lane, Wingfield, Trowbridge BA14 9LJ Tel: 01225 769551 — MB ChB 1972 Leeds; DRCOG 1979. GP Bradford-on-Avon.

***YOUNG, Simon Peter** 165 Cornhill Drive, Aberdeen AB16 5HN — MB ChB 1998 Aberd.; MB ChB Aberd 1998.

YOUNG, Stephanie Kim 11 Sheridan House, Wincott Street, London SE11 4NY — MB ChB 1992 Otago; MRCPsych 2000.

YOUNG, Mr Stephen Kenrick South Warwickshire Hospital, Lakin Road, Warwick CV34 5BW; Sussex Gardens, Grafton Lane, Binton, Stratford-upon-Avon CV37 9TZ — MB BChir 1979 Camb.; FRCS Ed. 1983. Cons. Orthop. Surg. S. Warks. Hosp. Prev: Sen. Regist. (Orthop.) Bristol Roy. Infirm.

YOUNG, Steven Charles Tel: 01555 840293 Fax: 01555 840024; 9 Ash Grove, Carnock, Dunfermline KY12 9JT — MB ChB 1978 Dundee; MRCPsych 1987. Cons. Psychiat. State Hosp. Carstairs Lanarksh.

YOUNG, Steven Jackson Oakham Medical Practice, Cold Overton Road, Rutland, Oakham LE15 6NT Tel: 01572 722621; Lyndon View, 12 Church St, Wing, Rutland, Oakham LE15 8RS — MB ChB 1979 Manch.; MSc Sports Med. Nottm. 1994; MRCGP 1988;

DRCOG 1987. Clin. Asst. (c/o Elderly & Fract. Clinic) Rutland Memor. Hosp. Oakham.

YOUNG, Steven James 2 Threave Place, Newton Mearns, Glasgow G77 6YD — MB ChB 1989 Glas.; FRCA 1994; DA (UK) 1992. SHO (Anaesth.) Hairmyres Hosp. E. Kilbride.

YOUNG, Stuart Shepherdson 9 Longmans Lane, Newgate St., Cottingham HU16 4EA Tel: 01482 876700 — MB ChB 1952 Sheff.; MRCS Eng. LRCP Lond. 1952; DCH Eng. 1956; DObst RCOG 1956.

YOUNG, Susan Dorothy 223 Preston Road, Clayton-le-Woods, Chorley PR6 7PT — MB ChB 1977 Manch.

YOUNG, Susan Elizabeth Jean (retired) 51 Wilton Road, London N10 1LX — MB BCh BAO 1958 Dub.; MRCP (UK) 1971; Dip. Bact. Lond 1973; DCH Eng. 1961. Specialist in Community Med. (Epidemiol.) Communicable Dis.

YOUNG, Susan Forsyth Hunter Health Centre, Andrew Street, East Kilbride, Glasgow G74 1AD Tel: 01355 906611 Fax: 01355 906615 — MB ChB 1988 Glas.

YOUNG, Susan Margaret 301 Westmount Road, Eltham, London SE9 1NR — MB ChB 1990 Leic.

YOUNG, Susan Miranda Department of Genitourinary Medicine, Kings Mill Hospital, Mansfield Road, Sutton-in-Ashfield NG17 4JL Tel: 01623 622515 Ext: 4095 — MB ChB 1977 Dundee; MRCPI 1988; Dip. Ven. Liverp. 1984. (Univ. Dundee) Prev: Sen. Regist. (Genitourin. Med.) Leic. Roy. Infirm.; Regist. (Genitourin. Med.) Roy. Liverp. Hosp. & Arrowe Pk. Hosp. Upton.

YOUNG, Mr Terence Willifer (retired) 1 Canon Drive, Barnack, Stamford PE9 3EG Tel: 01780 740347 — MB BChir 1956 Camb.; MA, MB BChir Camb. 1956; FRCS Eng. 1963. Prev: Cons. Surg. PeterBoro. Dist., Stamford & Rutland Hosps.

YOUNG, Thomas Behnam 3A Horn Lane, London W3 9NJ Tel: 020 8993 2313 — MB ChB 1970 Mosul; FRCS Glas. 1980.

YOUNG, Thomas William Stewart 24 Bell Lane, Kesgrave, Ipswich IP5 1JQ — MB ChB 1994 Leeds.

YOUNG, Timothy Stuart Staveley Temple Sowerby Medical Practice, Temple Sowerby, Penrith CA10 1RZ Tel: 017683 61232 Fax: 017683 61980 — MB ChB 1982 Ed.; DRCOG 1986. Clin. Asst. (Ophth.) Cumberld. Infirm. Carlisle. Prev: Trainee GP Fife Health Bd. VTS.

YOUNG, Torrence Martyn (Tod) (retired) Department of Anaesthetics, Manchester Royal Infirmary, Oxford Road, Manchester M13 9WL Tel: 0161 276 4551 Fax: 0161 273 5685 — MB BS Lond. 1950; MRCS Eng. LRCP Lond. 1950; FFA RCS Eng. 1956; DA Eng. 1954. Prev: Hon. Cons. Anaesth. Manch. Centr. Dist.

YOUNG, Venetia Emma Beech Lodge, Carleton Clinic, Carlisle CA1 3SU Tel: 01228 602392; Eden Croft, Temple Sowerby, Penrith CA10 1RZ Tel: 017683 61647 Fax: 017683 61980 Email: youngjckvg@compuserve.com — MB BS 1975 Lond.; BSc Lond. 1972; MRCGP 1979; DRCOG 1979. (Univ. Coll. Hosp.) Clin. Asst. (Family Psychother.) Carleton clinic. Carlisle; Dip. Family Ther.

YOUNG, Mr Vincent Kieran Coleraine Road, Maghera BT46 5HZ; 4 Avondale Lawn, Carysfort Avenue, Blackrock, Dublin, Republic of Ireland Tel: 00 353 1 833420 — MB BCh BAO 1986 Dub.; FRCS Eng. 1990; FRCSI 1990. Regist. (Gen. Surg.) Waterford Regional Hosp.

YOUNG, Violet Boyle (retired) Orphir, Main Road, Rhu, Helensburgh G84 8RB Tel: 01436 820698 — MB ChB Glas. 1941; DA Eng. 1944. Prev: Med. Off. Blood Transfus. Serv. Glas.

YOUNG, William Alister Miempoint House, Bromley, Bexley and Greenwich, Child and Adolescent Mental Health Service, Memorial Hospital Shooters Hill, London SE18 3RZ Tel: 0208 836 6418 Fax: 0208 836 6436; 60 Craigerne Road, Blackheath, London SE3 8SN Tel: 020 8853 4863 Fax: 020 8853 0022 Email: byoung@dircon.co.uk — MB ChB 1983 Manch.; MRCP (UK) 1987; MRCPsych 1989; DCH RCP Lond. 1985; FRCPCH 1999 UK. p/t Cons. Child & Adolesc. Psychiat. Bromley, Bexley & Greenwich Child & Adolesc. Ment. Health Serv. Lond.; Cons. Adolesc. Psychiat. and Clin. Director, Oakview Adolesc. Unit, St Mary Cray, Orpington, Kent BR5 4ES. Socs: Mem. of Roy. Coll. of Psychiatrists; Fell. Roy. Coll. of Paediat. and Child Health; Comm. Mem. of Assn. for Child Psychol. & Psychiat. Prev: Sen. Regist. (Child & Family Psychiat.) Tavistock Clinic Lond.; Regist. (Psychiat.) Maudsley Hosp. Lond.; SHO (Paediat.) Qu. Eliz. Hosp. Lond.

YOUNG

YOUNG, William Brewitt (retired) Black Charles Barn Cottage, Underriver, Sevenoaks TN15 0RY — MB BChir Camb. 1941. Prev: Ho. Surg. Mildmay Miss. Hosp. Lond.

YOUNG, William Cunningham (retired) 43 Portland Place, Hamilton ML3 7JU Tel: 01693 286112 — MB ChB 1935 Glas.; MFCM 1973; DPA Glas. 1952; DPH Glas. 1939. Prev: Dist. Med. Off. Motherwell & Lanark Health Dist.

YOUNG, William David Viewfield Medical Centre, 3 Viewfield Place, Stirling FK8 1NJ Tel: 01786 472028 Fax: 01786 463388 — MB ChB 1969 Glas.; MRCOG 1977. Clin. Asst. (Genitourin. Med.) Orchard Hse. Health Centre Stirling. Prev: Regist. (O & G) Stirling Roy. Infirm. & Stobhill Gen. Hosp. Glas.; Regist. (Biochem.) Qu. Mother's Hosp. Glas.

YOUNG, William Hayward 15 Nottington Court, Weymouth DT3 5BL Tel: 01305 812818; 15 Nottington Court, Weymouth DT3 4BL — MRCS Eng. LRCP Lond. 1967; BSc Lond. 1961; AKC 1971; DMRT Eng. 1972. (Westm.) p/t Indep. GP Weymouth. Socs: BMA & Assn. Palliat. Med. Prev: Sen. Regist. (Radiother.) Christie Hosp. & Holt Radium Inst. Manch.; Regist. (Radiother.) St. Bart. Hosp. Lond.; Regist. (Radiother.) Roy. Marsden Hosp. Lond.

YOUNG, William Morrison Douglas Street Surgery, 1 Douglas Street, Hamilton ML3 0DR Tel: 01698 286262 — MB ChB 1980 Aberd.; MRCGP 1984; DRCOG 1983.

YOUNG, Windsor Tudor X Ray Department, Princess of Wales Hospital, Bridgend CF31 1RQ Tel: 01656 752425; Old Cogan Hall, Sully Road, Penarth CF64 2TQ — MB BCh 1980 Wales; MRCP (UK) 1983; FRCR 1988; FRCP 1998. (Welsh National School Medicine) Cons. Radiol. P.ss Wales Hosp. Bridgend. Prev: Sen. Regist. (Radiol.) Univ. Hosp. Wales.

YOUNG, Yvonne 24 Brackendale, London N21 3DG — MRCS Eng. LRCP Lond. 1958.

YOUNG, Yvonne Maria 40 Mount Road, London SW19 8EW — MB BS 1983 Lond.; BSc (Hons.) Lond. 1980, MSc 1990, MB BS 1983. Cons. Comminicable Dis. Control/Publ. Health Med. Prev: Research Regist. (Microbiol.) W.m. Hosp. Lond.; Regist. (Pub. Health Med.) SW Thames RHA.

YOUNG-HARTMAN, Marrigje 5 Fairlands Park, Coventry CV4 7DS Tel: 02476 418684 — Artsexamen 1981 Amsterdam; Cert. Community Paediat. Warwick 1984; Dip. Community Paediat. Warwick 1986. (Univ. Amsterdam) SCMO (Child Health) Coventry HA. Prev: Occupat. Health Phys. S. Warks. HA; SHO (Paediat.) & Ho. Off. Coventry DHA.

YOUNG MIN, Marie Sandra Department of Haematology, Birmingham Heartlands Hospital, Bordsley Green East, Birmingham B9 5SS; 27 Blackwood Road, Bromsgrove B60 1AN — MB ChB 1991 Birm.; BSc (Hons) Birm. 1988; MRCP (UK) 1994. Specialist Regist., Birm. Heartlands Hosp.

YOUNG MIN, Steven Andrew Newcastle General Hospital, Newcastle upon Tyne NE4 6BE Tel: 0191 273 8811; 172 Osborne Road, Jesmond, Newcastle upon Tyne NE2 3LE Tel: 0191 281 7593 — BM BCh 1994 Oxf.; BA (Hons.) Oxf. 1991. SHO (Med.) Newc. Gen. Hosp.

YOUNG-SNELL, Andre John Edward Day Hospital, Irvine Unit, Bexhill Hospital, Holliers Hill, Bexhill-on-Sea TN40 2DZ — MB BS 1988 Lond.

YOUNGE, Paul Andrew Emergency Department, Frenchay Hospital, Bristol BS16 1LE Tel: 0117 959 5112 Email: paul.younge@north-bristol.swest.nhs.uk — BM 1987 Soton.; BSc (Hons.) 1981; MRCP (UK) 1993; DA (UK) 1989; FFAEM 1998. Clin. Fell. Paediat. Emerg. Med., Cons. in Emerg. Med.; Clin. Lect. in Child Health; Sen Lect. in Emerg. Med. Prev: Clin. Fell. (Paediat.) ICU, Bris. Childr.'s Hosp.; Specialist Regist. (Emerg. Med.) Bris. Roy. Infirm.

YOUNGER, Jane Mary 7 Ormiston Gardens, Belfast BT5 6JD — MB ChB 1998 Liverp.

YOUNGER, Kirsten Alexandra Tandrup, Hill View Road, Claygate, Esher KT10 0TU; Epsom General Hospital, Dorking Road, Epsom KT17 7EG Tel: 01372 735735 Ext: 6062 — MB BS 1983 Lond.; BSc (Physiol. with Basic Med. Sci) Lond. 1980; FRCR 1990. (Lond. Hosp.) Cons. Radiol. Epsom Gen. Hosp. Prev: Regist. (Radiol.) St. Geo. Hosp. Lond.; SHO Rotat. (Surg.) Roy. Surrey Co. Hosp. Guildford.

YOUNGHUSBAND, Andrea Joan Broadway Medical Group, 164 Great North Road, Gosforth, Newcastle upon Tyne NE3 5JP Tel: 0191 285 2460; Hawthorn Cottage, East Heddon, Newcastle upon Tyne NE15 0HD — MB BS 1985 Newc.; MRCGP 1990.

YOUNGHUSBAND, Mr John David Oakmere, 20A Sinah Lane, Hayling Island PO11 0EY Tel: 01705 465721 — MB BChir 1939 Camb.; FRCS Ed. 1940; MRCS Eng. LRCP Lond. 1937. (St. Thos.) Prev: Cons. Surg. Portsmouth & S.E. Hants. Health Dist.

YOUNGMAN, Charlotte Ann Park View, Park Lane, Lapley, Stafford ST19 9JT Tel: 01785 840043 — MB BS 1982 Lond.; BSc (Hons.) Lond. 1979, MB BS 1982; Cert. Family Plann. JCC 1984. (St. Marys) GP Wolverhampton. Prev: SHO (Psychiat., O & G & Dermat.) Wolverhampton HA.

YOUNGMAN, James Robert 15 Corinne Road, London N19 5EZ — MB BS 1990 Lond.

YOUNGMAN, Lisa Margaret 51 Chepstow Road, Leicester LE2 1PB — MB ChB 1997 Leic.

YOUNGMAN, Patrick Michael Ellis Cherry Trees, Victoria Mill Road, Framlingham, Woodbridge IP13 9EG Tel: 01728 621510 — MB BS 1959 Lond.; MRCS Eng. LRCP Lond. 1949; FFA RCS Eng. 1961; DA Eng. 1955. (Univ. Coll. Hosp.) Socs: Fell. Roy. Soc. Med.; BMA. Prev: Emerit. Cons. Anaesth. Roy. Nat. Orthop. Hosp. Lond.; Cons. Anaesth. Hendon Gp. Hosps.; Regist. (Anaesth.) Univ. Coll. Hosp. Lond.

YOUNGMAN, Peter Robert Hamilton Road Surgery, 201 Hamilton Road, Felixstowe IP11 7DT Tel: 01394 283197 Fax: 01394 270304; The Cottage, Thorpe Common, Trimley St Martin, Felixstowe IP11 0RZ Tel: 01394 273688 — MB BS 1977 Lond.; BSc Lond. 1974, MB BS 1977; DRCOG 1981; DCH Eng. 1980. (Middlx.)

YOUNGS, Elizabeth Rosa Public Health Laboratory, County Hospital, Lincoln, St Anne's Road, Lincoln LN2 5RF Tel: 01522 528607 Fax: 01522 546997 — MB ChB 1977 Manch.; DBact. 1982; FRCPath 1995; BMedSci 1974; MRCPath 1984. (St. Andrews & Manch.) Laborat. Dir. Cons. Med. Microbiol. Pub. Health Laborat. Lincoln.

YOUNGS, Giles Robert Dept. Public Health, NHS Executive (Eastern), Capital Park, Fulbourn, Cambridge CB1 5XB Tel: 01223 597749 Fax: 01223 597718 Email: giles.youngs@doh.gsi.gov.uk; Kopsey Cottage, Rattlesden Road, Drinkstone, Bury St Edmunds IP30 9TL — MB BChir 1966 (Hons. Path.) Camb.; MA Camb. 1967, MD 1972; FRCP Lond. 1982, M 1969. (Camb. & Lond. Hosp.) p/t Med. Mem., Regional (E.ern) Prison Health Task Force. Prev: Cons. Phys. (Med. & Gastroenterol.) Countess of Chester Hosp. Chester.; Sen. Regist. (Med.) Soton. Gen. Hosp.; Ho. Phys. Profess. Med. Unit Lond. Hosp.

YOUNGS, Jane Claire Higherfield, Horrabridge, Yelverton PL20 7RW — MB ChB 1997 Birm.

YOUNGS, Mr Robin Peter Gloucestershire Royal Hospital, Great Western Road, Gloucester GL1 3NN Tel: 01452 394205 Fax: 01284 713428 Email: ryoungs@anglianet.co.uk — MB BS 1980 Lond.; MD Lond. 1993; FRCS Eng. 1984; MRCS Eng. LRCP Lond. 1980. (Westminster) Cons. Otolaryngol. W. Suff. Health Dist.; Vis. Lect. Inst. Laryngol. & Otol. Univ. Lond. Socs: Fell. Roy. Soc. Med. Prev: Sen. Regist. (ENT) St. Bart. Hosp. Lond.; Regist. (ENT) St. Mary's Hosp. Lond.; TWJ Research Fell. Univ. Toronto, Canada.

YOUNGS, Sarah-Louise Emma Charlotte Lockwood Springfold, Cherry Tree Road, Rowledge, Farnham GU10 4AB — MB ChB 1994 Birm.; MRCGP 2000; MBCHB Birm.1994; DFFP 1998; DRCOG 1999. GP Principle; Med. Off. at Cheltenham Ladies Coll. Prev: GP Reg. Cheltenham.

YOUNGSON, Elaine Margaret 23 Highbury Avenue, Rowley Regis B65 9PN — MB ChB 1986 Ed. GP Princip. Prev: Trainee GP Livingston; SHO (Paediat.) Falkirk Roy. Infirm.; SHO (Psychiat.) Bangour Village W. Lothian.

YOUNGSON, Professor George Gray Royal Aberdeen Children's Hospital, Cornhill Road, Aberdeen AB25 2ZG Tel: 01224 681818 Fax: 01224 550642 Email: ggyrach@abdn.ac.uk; Birken Lodge, Bieldside, Aberdeen AB15 9BQ Tel: 01224 861305 — MB ChB 1973 Aberd.; PhD Aberd. 1979, MB ChB 1973; FRCS Ed. 1977. (Univ. of Aberdeen) Cons. Paediat. Surg. Grampian Univ. Hosps NHS Trust; Regional Adviser RCS of Edin.; Hon. Prof (Paediat. Surg.) Univ. of Aberd. Socs: Assn. Surg.; Brit. Assn. Paediat. Surg. Prev: Lect. (Surg.) Aberd. Univ.; Resid. (Cardiac Surg.) Univ. W.. Ontario & Fell. Clin. Surg. Hosp. Sick Childr. Toronto, Ontario, Canada.

YOUNGSON, Robert Murdoch, Col. late RAMC Retd. (retired) 26 St Leonard's Avenue, Blandford Forum DT11 7NY Tel: 01258 452465 Email: robert_youngson@compuserve.com — MB ChB Aberd. 1951; FRCOphth 1988; DO Eng. 1965; DTM & H Eng. 1964. Full-time Med. & Sci. Writer. Prev: Cons. Ophth. Qu. Eliz. Milit. Hosp. Lond.

YOUNIE, George Grant, TD (retired) 5 Laurelwood Avenue, Aberdeen AB25 3SY Tel: 01224 636491 — MB ChB 1948 Aberd.

YOUNIE, Mai Louise Amanda 1 All Saints Road, Thurcaston, Leicester LE7 7JD — MB ChB 1997 Bristol. SHO (A&E). Prev: Ho. Off. (Surg.); Ho. Off. (Med.); SHO Orhopaedics.

YOUNIS, Mr Farouk Mustafa (cons. rooms), 129 Harley St., London W1N 1DJ Tel: 020 7487 4897 Fax: 020 7224 6398 Email: fmyounis@aol.com; 4 Langton Avenue, Whetstone, London N20 9DB Tel: 020 8446 1672 Fax: 020 7224 6398 Email: fmyounis@aol.com — MB ChB 1971 Baghdad; FRCS Eng. 1977. Cons. Surg. P.ss Grace Hosp. & Hosp. of St John & St Eliz. Socs: Fell. Roy. Soc. Med.; BMA; Fell. Assoc. Surg. GB & Irel. Prev: Cons. Surg. Whittington Hosp (Locum); Regist. (Gen. Surg. & Urol.) Huddersfield Roy. Infirm.; Regist. (Gen. Surg.) Whittington Hosp. Lond.

YOUNIS, Naveed 58 Norton Street, Manchester M16 7GR — MB ChB 1993 Manch.

YOUNIS, Yasmeen 156 Queens Road, Halifax HX1 4LN — MB ChB 1997 Dundee.

YOUNUS, Mr Naeem 36 Buckland Road, Leyton, London E10 6QS — MB BS 1990 Punjab; FRCS Ed. 1995.

YOUSAF, Rauf 16 Yew Tree Close, Lords Wood, Chatham ME5 8XN Tel: 0973 671151 — MB ChB 1995 Dundee.

YOUSEF, Zaheer Raza 25 Pollards Close, Goffs Oak, Cheshunt, Waltham Cross EN7 5JP; Flat, Alpika Court, Saunders Road, London SE18 1NT Tel: 020 8355 7755 Email: zyousef@dircon.co.uk — MB BS 1992 Lond.; BSc (Hons.) Lond. 1988, MB BS 1992; MRCP Lond. 1996. Clin. Research Fell. (Cardiol.) Guy's & St. Thos. Hosps. Lond.

YOUSIF, Abdul Ridha Salman 14 Bowyer Walk, Ascot SL5 8QS — MB ChB 1970 Baghdad.

YOUSIF, Emad Habib 15 Harvest End, Stanway, Colchester CO3 5YX — MB ChB 1971 Baghdad; MRCPsych 1985; T(Psych) 1991. Cons. Psychiat. (Learning Disabil. Psychiat.) New Possibilities NHS Trust.

YOUSIF, Nasif El Galeim Flat 6, Donne Court, Orpington Hospital, Sevenoaks Road, Orpington BR6 9JU Tel: 01689 27050 ext. 2105 — MB BS 1979 Khartoum; MRCP (UK) 1985.

YOUSIF, Safa'a Toma Department of Medicine, St. Mary's Hospital, NSH Trust, Newport PO30 5TG Tel: 01983 524081 Fax: 01983 822569; 4 Oaklands Close, Ryde PO33 4HJ Tel: 01983 883499 — MB ChB 1978 Mosul; MRCP (UK) 1994. Gen. Med. & Elderly Care.

YOUSIF, Sami Yousif 9 Southwold Spur, Slough SL3 8XX — MB ChB 1973 Baghdad; MRCPI 1991.

YOUSSEF, Evelyn Elia Birmingham and Midland Eye Centre, Dudley Road, Birmingham B18 7QU Tel: 0121 554 3801; 3 Becontree Drive, Baguley, Manchester M23 9WQ — MB BCh 1976 Assiut; FRCSI 1992.

YOUSSEF, Gamal El-Din Mohamed Piccadilly Farm, Piccadilly Lane, Mayfield TN20 6RH — MB BCh 1970 Ain Shams; DA 1973.

YOUSSEF, Professor Hanafy Ahmed Mahmoud (retired) Medway Hospital, Windmill Rd, Gillingham ME7 5NY Tel: 01634 830000 Fax: 01634 830082 — MRCS Eng. LRCP Lond. 1974; MRCPsych 1972; DMedRehab RCP Lond. 1989; DGM RCP Lond. 1988. Prof. Psychiat. Fac. Med. Sci. Univ. W. Indies, Trinidad; Cons. Psychiat. Medway Hosp., Gillingham, Kent. Prev: Cons. Psychiat. & Clin. Tutor St. Davnet's Hosp. Monaghan, Irel.

YOUSSEF, Hanei Mohamed Hosny Ali 17 The Green, Radyr, Cardiff CF15 8BR Tel: 029 2084 2781; 17 The Greend, Radyr, Cardiff CF15 8BR Tel: 02920 842781 — MB ChB 1972 Alexandria; FRCOG 1997, MRCOG 1984; DGO Dub. 1977. Locum Cons., Obst. and Gyn. Dept., Nottm. City Hosp., Hucknall Rd., Nottm. Socs: Brit. Fertil. Soc. & Brit. Menopause Soc. (former). Prev: Cons. (O & G) and Acting Chief (O&G) King Abdul Aziz Hosp. &Oncol.Centre Jeddeh Saudi Arabi; Cons. Obst. and Gynaecologist Wictoria Sq. Med. Centre suite 216 2345 10th Avenue W. P. Albert Canada; Chief (O & G) Yanbu, Saudi Arabia.

YOUSSEF, Haney 5 Poppyfield Ct, Coventry CV4 7HW — MB ChB 1997 Birm.

YOUSSEF, Professor Hussein Abd El Fattah El Sayed Whipps Cross University Hospital, Whipps Cross Road, Leytonstone, London E11 1NR Tel: 020 8535 6614 Fax: 020 8535 6467; Corner Garth, Nursery Road, Loughton IG10 4EF Tel: 020 8508 6029 Fax: 020 8508 6029 — MB ChB 1964 Egypt; 2001 MRCA, England; FCCM (USA) 1994; FFA RCSI (Irel.) 1974; FACA (USA) 1982; FICS (USA) 1980; DA (UK) 1973; DA (Denmark) 1971; CA (Norway) 1968. (Alexandria Egypt) Cons. Anaesth. Whipps Cross Univ. Hosp. Lond. Socs: Fell. Assn. Anaesth. GB & Irel.; Fell. Amer. Soc. Anaesthesiol.; Fell. Amer. Soc. Critical Care Med. Prev: Prof. & Cons. Anaesth & Critical Care Med. Kuwait Univ. Fac. of Med.; Cons. Paediat. Anaesth. Min. Pub. Health Kuwait; Cons. Anaesth Edgware Hosp., Lond., Eng.

YOUSSEF, Mr Magdy Mohamed Kamal Ibrahim 7 Roebuck Close, Ingleby, Barwick, Stockton-on-Tees TS17 0RZ Tel: 01642 762336 — MB BCh 1979 Cairo; FRCS Glas. 1989. Assoc. Specialist Hartlepool Gen. Hosp.

YOUSSEF, Samir Morcos (retired) — MB BCh 1958 Ain Shams; MRCS Eng. LRCP Lond. 1979; DMedRehab Eng. 1978; DTM & H Ain Shams 1964. Prev: Regist. (Rehabil.) Raigmore Hosp. Inverness.

YOUSSEF, Youssef Yacoub Lady Close, Warrington Road, Mere, Knutsford WA16 0TE Tel: 01565 830517 — MB ChB 1964 Alexandria; FFA RCSI 1973; DA Eng. 1973. Cons. (Anaesth.) N. (Manch.) Health Dist.; Hon. Lect. Univ. Manch. Socs: Assn. Anaeth. Gt. Brit. & Irel.; Obst. Anaesth. Assn.; Pain Soc. of G.B. & Irel. Prev: Coll. Tutor.

YOUSU KUNJU, Mohamed Glynebwy Surgery, James Street, Ebbw Vale NP23 6JG Tel: 01495 302716 Fax: 01495 305166; 5 Green Street, Victoria, Ebbw Vale NP23 8WR Tel: 01495 309505 Email: kunju@btinternet.co.uk — MB BS 1974 Kerala. (Trivandrum Medical College, University of Kerala)

YOUSUF, Enver Yunus 35 Sutherland Avenue, London W9 2HE — MB BS 1994 Lond.; BSc (Hons.) Lond. 1991.

YOUSUF, Mr Ishrat Muhammad Chesterfield Royal Hospital & NHS Trust, Chesterfield S44 5BL Tel: 01246 277271; 15 Blackthorn Close, Hasland, Chesterfield S41 0DY Tel: 01246 551853 Fax: 01246 551853 Email: ishrat@ishrat.fsnet.co.uk — MB BS 1983 Karachi; FRCSI 1991. (DOW Medical College, Karachi) Staff Grade (ENT) Chesterfield Roy. Hosp. Prev: SHO (ENT) Dudley Rd. Hosp. Birm. & Sunderland Dist. Gen. Hosp.; SHO (Gen. Surg.) Neville Hall Hosp. Abergavenny.; Regist. (ENT) Stoke Mandeville Hosp. Aylesbury.

YOUSUF, Kolothum Thodi 7 Bridle Hey, Nantwich CW5 7QE — MB BS 1976 India.

YOUSUFF, Mr Anser Mohammed 27 Laxton Garth, Kirkella, Hull HU10 7NN Email: yousuff@aol.com — MB BS 1986 Madras; FRCS Glas. 1991; Dip Urology Lond. 1994. Staff Grade Urol., Roy.Hull.NHS.Trust, Hull. Prev: Act. Regist.Urol., Burton Hosp.; Regist.sur.Stockport/Trafford/Ashton-tyme.

YOUSUFZAI, Noor Mohammad (retired) BUPA Hospital, Little Astor, Sutton Coldfield B74 3HP — MB BS 1963 Sind; FRCPsych 1991, M 1973; DPM Eng. 1970. Cons. Psychiat. BUPA Hosp. Little Astor. Prev: Cons. Psychiat. Dorothy Pattison Hosp. Walsall Burntwood Psychother. Unit Bloxwich Hosp. Walsall.

YOXALL, Charles William Neonatal Intensive Care Unit, Liverpool Womens Hospital, Crown St., Liverpool L8 7SS Tel: 0151 708 9988 Fax: 0151 702 4082 Email: c.w.yoxall@liv.ac.uk; Email: bill.yoxall@lwh-tr.nwest.nhs.uk — BM BS 1986 Nottm.; BMedSci Nottm. 1984; MRCP (UK) 1990; MD 1998 Liverpool. Cons. Neonat. Paediat. Liverp. Wom.s Hops. Liverp.; Hon. Lect. Dept. Child Health Univ. Liverp.; Hon. Cons. Paediat. Roy. Liverp. Childs. Hosp. Liverp. Socs: Eur. Soc. Paediat. Research; Neonat. Soc.; MRCPCH. Prev: Lect. Dept. Child Health, Univ. Liverp.; Clin. Research Fell. (Neonatol.) Univ. Liverp.; Regist. (Paediat.) Mersey Region.

YOXALL, James Henry Blackbrook Surgery, Lisieux Way, Taunton TA1 2LB Tel: 01823 259444 Fax: 01823 322715; West Lodge, Pitminster, Taunton TA3 7AZ Tel: 01823 421396 — MB BS 1977 Lond.; DRCOG 1980.

YU, Carmen Chia-Wen 14 Hillary Rise, Barnet EN5 5AZ — MD 1994 Camb.; MA (Hons.) Camb. 1985, MD 1994, MB BChir 1984; MRCP (UK) 1988.

YU

YU, Christopher Bing On 9 Magnolia Place, Montpelier Road, London W5 2QQ — MB BS 1991 Lond.

YU, Danny Yiu Fung 85 Gatehead Road, Crosshouse, Kilmarnock KA2 0JH — MB ChB 1987 Ed. SHO (Med. & Gastroenterol.) Warrington Dist. Gen. Hosp. Prev: SHO (Neurol.) Hull Roy. Infirm.; SHO (Cardiol.) Hull Roy. Infirm.; SHO (Nephrol.) P.ss Roy. Hosp. Hull.

YU, Dominic Fergus Quok Ching King's College Hospital, Denmark Hill, London SE5 Tel: 0207 346 3331; Fax: 0208 810 7545 Email: dominic.yu@ukgateway.net — MB BS 1991 Lond.; FRCR 2001; MRCPI 1997. Specialist Regist. (Diagnostic Radiol.) King's Coll. Hosp. Prev: SHO (Gen. Med.) Medway Hosp.; SHO (Gen. Med.) Chase Farm Hosp.; SHO (A & E) Watford Gen. Hosp.

YU, Dominic Shu Lok 70 Leybourne Avenue, London W13 9RA — MB BS 1996 Lond.

YU, Gloria Kiu Ying Orpington Hospital, Sevenoaks Road, Orpington BR6 9JU Tel: 01689 815087 Fax: 01689 815165 — MB BS 1983 Lond.; MRCP (UK) 1987. Cons. Med. Elderly Bromley Hosps. NHS Trust. Prev: Sen. Regist. (Geriat. Med.) King's Coll. Hosp. Lond.

YU, Koa Hung Green Wrythe Surgery, 411a Green Wrythe Lane, Carshalton SM5 1JF Tel: 020 8648 2022 Fax: 020 8646 6555; 24 The Highway, Sutton SM2 5QT Tel: 020 8661 6242 — MB BS 1980 Colombo. GP Surrey.

YU, Ling Faang Marfleet Group Practice, 350 Preston Road, Hull HU9 5HH Tel: 01482 701834; PO Box 13954, Kota Kinabalu, Sabah 88845, Malaysia Tel: 00 60 88 245088 — MB ChB 1990 Glas.; MRCP (UK) 1995; MSc Wales 1997; DDSc Wales 1996. (Glasgow).

YU, Mark Meng Lun 52 Calderon Road, London E11 4EU Tel: 020 8558 7773 — MB BS 1966 Lond.; LMSSA Lond. 1964; MD Peking 1969. Cons. Acupunc. Clinic Dartford E. Health Centre; Dean Acad. Chinese Acupunc. Socs: BMA. Prev: Cons. Hampstead Acupunc. Centre Lond.; Cons. Acad. Chinese Acumpunc. & Acad. Chinese Med.

YU, Raymond Chi Hung 99 Harley Street, London W1G 6AQ — MB 1983 Camb.; BChir 1982; MRCP (UK) 1988.

YU, Shee Hung 27 Chestnut Close, London N14 4SG Tel: 020 8447 9452 — MB BS 1975 Sri Lanka; LRCP MRCS Eng. LRCP Lond. 1979; DRCOG 1984.

YU, Sui Cheung 24 Aspen Close, London W5 4YG — MB ChB 1992 Leeds; BSc Leeds 1989, MB ChB 1992. (Leeds) Med. Off. Dept. Anaest.& IC, P. of Wales Hosp. Hong Kong; Adjunct tutor Chinese Uni. of Hong Kong.

YU HO YAM, Henry Golden Pine, Charles II Place, 77 King's Road, Chelsea, London SW3 4NG Tel: 020 7352 6499 — MB BS 1966 Lond.; LMSSA Lond. 1964; FRACS 1973.

YUCE, Metin 7 Derwent Drive, Purley CR8 1ER Tel: 020 8660 7715 — Tip Doktoru 1963 Istanbul.

YUDKIN, Gillian Diana James Wigg Group Practice, Kentish Town Health Centre, 2 Bartholomew Road, London NW5 BX Tel: 020 7530 4747 Fax: 020 7530 4750 Email: gillian.yudkin@gp-f83023.nhs.uk; 28 Huddleston Road, London N7 0AG Tel: 020 7607 3855 — MB BChir 1967 Camb.; DCH Eng. 1971. (Camb. & Univ. Coll. Hosp.)

YUDKIN, Professor John Stephen 28 Huddleston Road, London N7 0AG Tel: 020 7607 3855 — MD 1975 Camb.; MB BChir 1967; FRCP Lond. 1988, M (UK) 1971. (Camb. & Univ. Coll. Hosp.) Prof. Med. Univ. Coll. Lond. Socs: Med. Res. Soc. & Brit. Diabetic Assn. Prev: Cons. & Sen. Lect. (Gen. Med. & Diabetes) Whittington & Univ. Coll. Hosps. Lond.; Lect. Metab. & Endocrine Unit Lond. Hosp. Med. Coll.; Sen. Lect. Fac. Med. Univ. Dar es Salaam, Tanzania.

YUE, Arthur Man-Hin 41 Kings College Court, 55 Primrose Hill Road, London NW3 3EA — BM BCh 1994 Oxf.; MA Oxf. 1996; MRCP (UK) 1997. (Oxf.) Specialist Regist. Rotat. (Cardiol.) Wessex & SW Thames. Socs: Brit. Echocardiogr. Soc.

YUEN, Alan Wah Cheong 9 Elmwood Park, Gerrards Cross SL9 7EP — BM BCh 1977 Oxf.; MA Camb. 1978; MRCP (UK) 1979; FFPM RCP (UK) 1996; MRCGP 1982. (Oxf. Med. Sch.) Manager Global Licensing. Prev: Head CNS Sect. Clin. Research.

YUEN, Albert Kin-Chung 134 Gillespie Road, London N5 1LP — MB BS 1994 Lond.

YUEN, Conrad Hong Wai 20 Moel Famau View, Liverpool L17 7ET — MB ChB 1994 Liverp.; MRCOphth 1997. SHO (Ophth.) St Paul's Eye Unit Roy. Liverp. Univ. Hosp. Prev: SHO (Ophth.) S.port & Formby NHS Trust S.port Gen. Infirm. (Eye Unit); SHO (Ophth.) Glas. Roy. Infirm. NHS Trust; Ho. Off. Aintree Hosp.

YUEN, Kevin Choong Ji Diabetes Centre, Ipswich Hospital NHS Trust, Heath Road, Ipswich IP4 5PD Tel: 01473 621644; 31 Dewar Lane, Kesgrave, Ipswich IP5 2GJ Tel: 01473 621644 — MB ChB 1993 Sheff.; MRCP (UK) 1997. (Sheff.) Specialist Regist. (Diabetes/Endocrinol.) Ipswich Hosp. Socs: MDU. Prev: SHO (Diabetes/Endocrinol.) Ipswich Hosp.; SHO (Clin. Biochem.) Ipswich Hosp.; SHO (Geriat.) Ipswich Hosp.

YUGAMBARANATHAN, Kandiah 7 Harefield Close, Enfield EN2 8NQ — MB BS 1978 Colombo, Sri Lanka; MRCP (UK) 1993.

YUILL, George Martin (cons. rooms), 16 St John St., Manchester M3 4EA Tel: 0161 834 2554 — MB ChB 1965 Manch.; BA Open 1988; BSc (Physiol.) Manch. 1962, MB ChB 1965; FRCP Lond. 1982, M 1968; Cert. Av Med. MoD (Air) & Civil; Aviat. Auth. 1979. (Manch.) Cons. Neurol. N. Manch. Gen. Hosp.; Lect. Med. Univ. Manch. Socs: Assn. Brit. Neurols. & N. Eng. Neurol. Assn.

YUILL, Gordon McLellan Flat 2, Tall Trees, Mersey Road, West Didsbury, Manchester M20 2PE Tel: 0161 718 1949 — MB ChB 1994 Manch.; BSc (Hons.) Manch. 1991. (Manchester) Specialist Regist. Anaesth., N. W. Rotat. Socs: MRCAnaesth.; Assn. Anaesth. Prev: SHO (Anaesth.) Stepping Hill Hosp.; SHO (Anaesth.) Roy. Oldham Hosp.

YUILL, Robert Alexander Border Medical Ltd., 10 Hunters Walk, Canal St., Chester CH1 4EB — MRCS Eng. LRCP Lond. 1970. Med. Examr. to Civil Aviat. Auth.

YUILLE, Frances Anne Pascoe Western General Hospital, Crème Road, Edinburgh EH4 2XU Tel: 0131 537 1000; Poldrait, Preston Rd, Linlithgow EH49 6QL Tel: 01506 842124 — MB BS 1987 Lond.; MRCP (UK) 1990; FRCR 1994. Cons. in Clin. Oncol. W.ern Gen. Hosp. Eninburgh.

YUILLE, Pamela Mary Bridgnorth Medical Practices, Northgate House, 7 High Street, Bridgnorth WV16 4BU Tel: 01746 767121 Fax: 01746 765433; Underton Cottage, Underton, Bridgnorth WV16 6TY — MB BS 1975 Lond.; MRCP (UK) 1978; MRCGP 1982; DRCOG 1980.

YUILLE, Tom Dalling Glan Clwyd Hospital, Bodelwyddan, Rhyl LL18 JUJ Tel: 01745 334225 Fax: 01745 534194 Email: drtom.yuille@cd-tr.wales.nhs.uk — MB BS 1969 Lond.; MRCP (U.K.) 1972. (Roy. Free) Cons. Paediat. Conwy & Denbighsh. NHS Trust.

YUKSEL, Bulend Barnet and Chase Farm Hospital NHS Trust, The Ridgeway, Enfield EN2 8JL Tel: 020 8366 6600 Fax: 020 8967 5903; 40 Leaside Avenue, Muswell Hill, London N10 3BU Tel: 020 8444 7276 — Tip Doktoru 1980 Istanbul; MD Istanbul 1984; FRCPI 1997; MRCPI 1994; FRCPCH 1997; DCH RCP Lond. 1990. (University Istanbul) Cons. (Paediat. Neonatol) Barnet and Chase Farm Hosp. Enfield; Assoc. Prof. Univ. Istanbul 1993; Hon. Teach., Univ. Coll. Lond. Hosps., 1996 onwards. Socs: Eur. Respirat. Soc. (Sec., Neonat. & Paediat. Intens. Care Grp.); Amer. Thoracic Soc.; Neonat. Soc. Prev: Clin. Research Fell. & Hon. Sen. Regist. King's Coll. Hosp. Lond.; Specialist (Paediat.) Univ. Istanbul 1984.

YULE, Adrian John Royal Hampshire Hospital, Romsey Rd, Winchester SO22 5DG; Hunters Chase, Rockbourne Road, Coombe Bissett, Salisbury SP5 4LP — MB BCh 1989 Wales. SHO (Paediat.) Winchester. Prev: SHO (Ophth.) Cardiff.

YULE, Alexander Graeme St Julians Medical Centre, 13A Stafford Road, Newport NP19 7DQ Tel: 01633 251304 Fax: 01633 221977; 12 Llangorse Drive, Rogerstone, Newport NP10 9HJ — MB BCh 1988 Wales. (Wales) GP Princip.; Clin. Asst. Drugs Project in Newport; Med. Off. Cross IGMS Rugby Club.

YULE, Constance Margaret (retired) 8 Ash Tree Grove, Bolton Le Sands, Carnforth LA5 8BD Tel: 01524 822070 — MB ChB 1949 Aberd.

YULE, Diana Pratt (retired) 3 Abbey Farm, St Bees CA27 0DY Tel: 01946 823155 — MB ChB (Distinc.) St. And. 1945; DObst RCOG 1946. Prev: Assoc. Specialist W. Cumbld. Hosp.

YULE, George William Golder (retired) Orchard Cottage, Little Longstone, Bakewell DE45 1NN Tel: 01629 640414 — MRCS Eng. LRCP Lond. 1953; AFOM RCP Lond. 1983; DObst RCOG 1956. Works Med. Adviser & Appt. Doctor (lead Regulat.s) H.J. Enthoven's Lead Smelter Darley Dale. Prev: Clin. Asst. (Orthop.) Devonsh. Roy. Hosp. Buxton.

ZACHARY

YULE, Ian Golder 14 Malthouse Court, Thornham, Hunstanton PE36 6NW — MB ChB 1954 Manch.; DPH 1962; FFCM 1973; DCH Eng. 1960. Dist. Med. Off. & Dir. Serv. Plann. Aylesbury Vale HA. Socs: BMA. Prev: Area Med. Off. Bucks. AHA; Area Med. Off. & Div. Sch. Med. Off. W. Essex Health Area & MOH; Saffron Walden Boro. & RD.

YULE, Mr James Herbert Burton (retired) 216 Newton Drive, Blackpool FY3 8JE Tel: 01253 32880 — BM BCh 1947 Oxf.; MCh Oxf. 1961, MA BM BCh 1947; FRCS Eng. 1954. Prev: Cons. Surg. Blackpool & Fylde Hosp. Gp.

YULE, Joan Matthewson 17 Mellerstain Road, Kirkcaldy KY2 6UB — MB ChB 1995 Aberd.

YULE, John Charles Rutherford House, Langley Park, Durham DH7 9XD Tel: 0191 373 1386 Fax: 0191 373 4288 — MB BS 1970 Newc.

YULE, Mr Robert (retired) 4 Copperfield Court, New St., Altrincham WA14 2QF Tel: 0161 928 5878 — MB ChB 1949 Ed.; FRCS Ed. 1956; FRCOG 1974, M 1957. Prev: Cons. Cytopath. Christie Hosp. & Holt Radium Inst. Manch.

YULE, Robert Martin 14 Station Road, Hest Bank, Lancaster LA2 6HP — MB ChB 1975 Dundee.

YULE, Steven Murray Eisai Ltd., 3 Shortlands, London W6 8EE; The Foothills, Church Rd, Tostock IP30 9PA Email: richard@west25.freeserve.co.uk — MB ChB 1986 Dundee; PhD 1996 Univ. of Newcastle; BMSc Dund 1983; MRCP (UK) 1989. Med. Adviser, Oncol.

YULE, Steven Robert — MB ChB 1989 Aberd.; MRCP (UK) 1992; FRCR 1996. Cons. Radiologist, Aberd. Roy. Infirm. Prev: Regist. (Radiol.) HA Manch.; SHO (Med.) Aberd.

YULE, Susan Frances The Lofts, 24 Ash Lane, Collingtree, Northampton NN4 0ND — MB ChB 1998 Leeds.

YULE-SMITH, Annabel Louise Church Street Surgery, Church Street, Hibaldstow, Brigg DN20 9ED Tel: 01652 650580; West Farm, Hunts Lane, Hibaldstow, Brigg DN20 9EH — BM BS 1987 Nottm. (Nottm.) Socs: BMA.

YULL, Derek Neil 1 Nightingale Road, Rickmansworth WD3 7DE — MB BS 1994 Lond.

YUNAS, Sohail 2-D Mossfield Road, Birmingham B14 7JB — MB ChB 1994 Liverp.

YUNG, Bernard Man-Chak Department of Respiratory Medicine, Basildon & Thurrock Hospital., Nether Mayne, Basildon SS16 5NL — MB BCh 1988 Wales; MD 2001 London; MRCP (UK) 1991. Cons. Phys., Basildon Hosp. (Gen. & Resp. Med.). Socs: Brit. Thorac. Soc. Prev: Specialist Regist. (Gen. & Respirat. Med.) Barnet Gen. Hosp.; Clin. Tutor & Research Fell. (Respirat. Med.) Roy. Brompton Hosp. & Nat. Inst. Heart & Lung Dis. Lond.; Clin. Research Fell. (Cystic Fibrosis) Sect. Respirat. Med. Univ. Wales Coll. Lond.

YUNG, Mr Man Wah The Ipswich Hospital, Ear, Nose & Throat Department, Heath Road Wing, Ipswich IP4 5PD Tel: 01473 712233 — MB BS 1978 Hong Kong; PhD Liverp. 1987; FRCS Ed. 1982; DLO RCS Eng. 1980. Cons. Otorhinolaryng. Ipswich Hosp. NHS Trust, Ipswich. Socs: Politzer Soc.; Euro. Acad. In Otol. & Neuro-Otol. Prev: Lect. (Otorhinolaryng.) Univ. Liverp. 1986-1987; Sen. Regist. (ENT Surg.) Roy. Liverp. Hosp.

YUNG, Sui Yin Ruth c/o Mr. S. Tang, 56 Eighth Avenue, Newcastle upon Tyne NE6 5YB — MB BS 1985 Newc.

YUNUS-KHIZR, Syed Arif Ahmed 23 Selbourne Close, Liverpool L18 2XU — MB BS 1962 Osmania; MRCS Eng. LRCP Lond. 1975; MRCP (UK) 1975.

YUSAF, Baber Stowmarket Health Centre, Violet Hill Road, Stowmarket IP14 1NL Tel: 01449 776000 Fax: 01449 776005 — MB BS 1982 Lond.; BSc Lond. 1979; DRCOG 1988. (The Lond. Hosp.) GP Stowmarket.

YUSOF, Alvin Idrishah Flat G, 49 Bellshaugh Gardens, Kelvinside, Glasgow G12 0SA — MB ChB 1994 Glas. (Univ. Glas.) SHO Rotat. (Psychiat.) Woodilee Hosp. N. Glas. Train. Scheme. Socs: BMA.

YUSOFF, Farhanah Crosshouse Hospital, 41 Simpson St., Kilmarnock KA2 0BE Tel: 01563 21133 — MB ChB 1993 Glas.

YUSUF, Hafsa Ahmed Flat 2 Essex House, Harold Wood Hospital, Gubbins Lane, Romford RM3 0BE — MB ChB 1994 Glas.

YUSUF, Imtiaz Ahmed Maybury Surgery, Alpha road, Maybury, Woking GU22 8HF Tel: 01483 728757 Fax: 01483 729169; Plymlea, Triggs Lane, Woking GU22 0EH — MB BS 1984 Lond.; D.Occ.Med. RCP Lond. 1995; AFOM RCP 1997. (Char. Cross) Occupat. Health Phys. Brit. Airport Auth. Heathrow; GP. Socs: Soc. Occupat. Med. Prev: Med. Advisor (Occupat. Med.) Roy. Surrey Co. Hosp.; Ho. Surg. Hertford Co. Hosp.; Ho. Phys. Char. Cross Hosp. Lond.

YUSUF, Mr Mohammed Ormskirk & District General Hospital, Wigan Road, Ormskirk L39 2AZ — MB BS 1960 Lucknow; MS (Orthop.) Lucknow 1963, MB BS 1960; FRCS Ed. 1976. (G.S.V.M. Med. Coll. Kanpur) Prev: JHMO Promenade Hosp. S.port; SHO Orthop. & Accid. Dept. N. Staffs. Roy. Infirm. Stoke-on-Trent; SHO Orthop. & Genito-Urin. Unit Wrightington Hosp. Wigan.

YUSUF, Muhammad Najib Richmond Community Healthcare, Hamlet, Kew Foot Road, Richmond TW9 2TE Tel: 020 8940 3331 Fax: 020 8940 2490; 30 Stewart Close, Hampton TW12 3XJ Tel: 020 8941 6059 Fax: 020 8941 6059 Email: najib.yusuf@which.net — MB BS 1978 Sri Lanka; LRCP LRCS Ed. LRCPS Glas. 1985. (Univ. Sri Lanka) Assoc. Specialist in Community, Paediat., St Geo.'s Healthcare, NHS Trust. Socs: Roy. Coll. Paediat. & Child Health; MRCPCH. Prev: Sen. Staff Community Paediat. Richmond, Twicknham & Roehampton Healthcare Trust; SCMO Greenwich Healthcare NHS Trust.

YUSUF, Mrs Saadat Ahmed Junaid 60 Kewstoke Road, Willenhall WV12 5DL Tel: 01922 400838 Fax: 01922 445106 — MB BS 1965 Punjab. (Fatima Jinnah Med. Coll. Lahore)

YUSUF, Sarah Flat 7, Westfield Hall, Hagley Road, Birmingham B16 9LG — MB BS 1992 Lond. (St Geoges Hosp. Lond.) Specialist Regist. (Radiol.).

YUSUF, Shamil 28 Daventry Road, Manchester M21 0ZP — MB ChB 1995 Manch.

YUSUF, Mr Syed Waquar 10 Appledore Avenue, Wollaton, Nottingham NG8 2RE Tel: 0115 928 9094 — MB BS 1987 Karachi; FRCS Eng. 1991. Vasc. Research Fell. Univ. Hosp. Nottm. Socs: Assoc. Fell. Amer. Coll. Angiol.; Internat. Soc. Endovasc. Surg.

ZABETAKI, Eleni 46 Fairfield Crescent, Edgware HA8 9AH — Ptychio latrikes 1988 Patras.

ZABIHI, Mr Tahmoures Department Orthopaedics, South Cleveland Hospital & Middlesbrough General Hosp., Middlesbrough Tel: 01642 850850 Ext: 5914; 5 Welburn Grove, Ormesby, Middlesbrough TS7 9BN Tel: 01642 325937 — MD 1968 Tehran; MS (Orthop.), MS (Gen. Surg.) Tehran 1968, MD 1955. Staff Grade Surg. S. Cleveland Hosp. Middlesbrough Gen. Hosp.; Assoc. Specialist S.T.H.A. MiddlesBoro. Gen. Hosp. Socs: Brit. Orthopaedic Assn.

ZACHARAKIS, Nikolaos Queens Medical Centre, Galen Court F25, Flat 6, Nottingham NG7 2UH — Ptychio latrikes 1984 Athens.

ZACHARIA, Ajit Yhomas 16 Chedworth Road, Nettleham Park, Lincoln LN2 4SL — MB BS 1983 Kerala.

ZACHARIAH, Jolly Central Milton Keynes Medical, 1 North Sixth Street, Central Milton Keynes, Milton Keynes MK9 2NR Tel: 01908 605775 Fax: 01908 676752; 16 Haltonchesters, Bancroft, Milton Keynes MK13 0PF — MB BS 1977 Mysore; MRCS Eng. LRCP Lond. 1981. (J.J.M. Med. Coll.)

ZACHARIAH, Mr Samuel Raymond THe Surgery, 89 Gubbins Lane, Harold Wood, Romford RM3 0DR Tel: 01708 346666 Fax: 01708 381300; 48 Chelmsford Road, Shenfield, Brentwood CM15 8RJ — MB BS 1971 Calcutta; FRCS Eng. 1979.

ZACHARIAH, Shanti Elizabeth 17 Westrick Walk, Wrenside, Prestwood, Great Missenden HP16 0RZ — MB BS 1968 Lond.; MRCS Eng. LRCP Lond. 1968; FFA RCS Eng. 1981; DA Eng. 1975. Assoc. Specialist (Anaesth.) Wycombe Gen. Hosp. Bucks.

ZACHARIAS, John Trent View Medical Practice, 45 Trent View, Keadby, Scunthorpe DN17 3DR Tel: 01724 782209 Fax: 01724 784472; 7 The Dell, Silica Lodge, Scunthorpe DN17 2XB Tel: 01724 850120 Fax: 01724 850120 Email: joh.zacharias@btclick.com — MB BS 1967 Bangalor; MB BS Bangalore 1967. (Bangalore) Prev: SHO (O & G) Fulford Matern. Hosp. York; SHO (Gen. Surg.) & SHO (Gyn.) W. Cumbld. Hosp. Whitehaven.

ZACHARIAS, Peter Lindsay Ardinamar, Budworth Close, Oxton, Birkenhead CH43 9TJ — MB ChB 1971 Liverp.

ZACHARY, Anne Rosemary Portman Clinic, 8 Fitzjohn's Avenue, London NW3 5NA Tel: 020 7794 8262 Fax: 020 7447 3748; 13 West Park Road, Kew Gardens, Richmond TW9 4DB Tel: 020 8876 7531 — MB BS 1975 Lond.; MRCS Eng. LRCP Lond. 1975; MRCPsych 1982; DRCOG 1977; FRCPysch 1998. (Roy. Free) ConsPsych.in.Psychother. Portman Clinic Lond. Socs: Assoc. Mem.

ZACHARY

Brit. Psychoanalyt. Soc. Prev: Sen. Regist. (Psychother.) Cassel Hosp. Lond.; Regist. (Psychiat.) Roy. Free Hosp. Lond.; Locum Cons.Psychother.Maudsley Hosp.Lond.

ZACHARY, John Bransby Barnsley District General Hospital, Gawber Road, Barnsley S75 2EP Tel: 01226 730000 — BM BCh 1973 Oxf.; BA Oxf. 1967, MA 1973; MRCS Eng. LRCP Lond. 1972; FRCR 1980; DMRD Eng. 1977; DObst RCOG 1975. (Oxf. & Lond. Hosp.) Cons. Radiol. Dist. Gen. Hosp. Barnsley.

ZACHARY JENNINGS, Caroline Michelle 33 Trewince Road, London SW20 8RD — MB BS 1994 Lond.

ZACK, Philip 49 Selby Road, Carshalton SM5 1LE — MB BS 1993 Lond.

ZADEH, Mr Hamid G West Middlesex University Hospital, Twickenham Road, Isleworth TW7 6AF Email: zadeh@zadeh.co.uk — MB BS 1987 Lond.; FRCS Eng. 1991; FRCS (Orth) 1997. (Guy's Hospital) Cons. Orthop. Surg., W. Middlx. Univ. Hosp. Socs: Assoc. Mem. BOA; RCS (Eng.). Prev: Specialist Regist. Roy. Nat. Orthop. Hosp. Trust Rotat.

ZADIK, Elena (retired) 131 The Avenue, Leigh WN7 1HR Tel: 01942 673488 — MB ChB Sheff. 1943. Prev: Clin. Asst. (Anaesth.) Wigan & Bolton Health Dists.

ZADIK, Paul Michael 8 Spout Copse, Sheffield S6 6FB — MB BCh 1974 Oxf.; MSc (Med. Microbiol.) Lond. 1981; MRCPath 1982. Cons. Microbiol. Pub. Health Laborat. N. Gen. Hosp. Sheff.

ZADIK, Sarah Anne Selborne Road Medical Centre, 1 Selborne Road, Sheffield S10 5ND — MB ChB 1977 Ed.; BSc (Med. Sci.) Ed. 1974; MRCP (UK) 1981; MRCGP 1987; DCH RCPS Glas. 1979. (Edinburgh) p/t GP Princip. Sheff. Health.

ZADOO, Kishori Lyndhurst Drive Surgery, 53 Lundhurst Drive, Leyton, London E10 6JB Tel: 020 8539 1663 Fax: 020 8556 1977 — MB BS 1970 Jammu & Kashmir.

ZADOROZNY, Vanda Lorraine 15 Protea Gardens, Titchfield, Fareham PO14 4TJ — MB BS 1991 Lond.; BSc Lond. 1988. (St. Bart. Hosp.)

ZAFAR, Afia 41 Greenburn Park, Lisburn BT27 4LS — MB BS 1982 Karachi.

ZAFAR, Mr Fawad Sabooh 12 New Staffs Residence, City General Hospital, Hilton Road, Stoke-on-Trent ST4 6QG — MB BS 1985 Punjab; FRCS Glas. 1990; FRCSI 1990. Regist. (Urol.) Roy. Shrewsbury Hosp. Prev: Regist. (Urol.) Hammersmith Hosp. Lond.; Regist. (Gen. & Urol.) Ealing Hosp. Lond.

ZAFAR, Muhammad Hanif 9 Lincoln Avenue, London SW19 5JT — Vrach 1985 Kuban Med. Inst.

ZAFAR, Mr Muhammed Rafay c/o Mr K. Siddiqi, 16 Rancliffe Avenue, Keyworth, Nottingham NG12 5HY — MB BS 1986 Karachi; FRCSI 1993.

ZAFAR, Noreen 19 St David's Close, Worksop S81 0RP — MB BS 1990 Punjab; MRCOG 1995.

ZAFAR, Shaheen Atia Hospital, 48 Malir Township, Kala Board, Karachi 37, Pakistan; 103 Legahory Court, Craigavon BT65 5DF Tel: 01762 345737 — MB BS 1981 Karachi; MRCOG 1989. Regist. (Obst. & Gyn.) Roy. Matern. Hosp. Belf. Socs: Ulster Obst. & Gyn. Soc. Prev: Regist. (Obst. & Gyn.) Lagan Valley Hosp. & Craigavon Area Hosp.

ZAFAR, Syed Ali The Surgery, 192 Charles Road, Small Heath, Birmingham B10 9AB Tel: 0121 772 0398 Fax: 0121 772 4268 — MB BS 1967 Bihar; MRCP (UK) 1976. (Darbhanga Med. Sch., Bihar) Hosp. Pract. Diabetic Clin. Birm.

ZAFAR, Syed Sibte 25 Oswald Street, Rochdale OL16 2LA — MB BS 1984 Pakistan.

ZAFAR, Tahira 30 City Way, Rochester ME1 2AB Tel: 01634 818449; 332A, Lane 4, Peshawar Road, Rawalpindi, Pakistan Tel: 00 92 51 474765 Email: azmalik@hotmail.com — MB BS 1978 Punjab; MRCPath 1994. (King Edward Med. Coll. Pakistan) Cons. Haemat. Armed Forces Inst. Path. Rawalpindi, Pakistan.

ZAFAR, Mr Waheed Uz Staff Urologist, Macclesfield District General Hospital, Victoria Road, Macclesfield SK10 3BL Tel: 01625 421000; 16 Brampton Avenue, Macclesfield SK10 3DY Tel: 01625 265727 Email: farahjuly@aol.com — MB BS 1983 Punjab; BSc Islamia 1980; FRCSI 1990. Staff Urol. Macclesfield Dist. Hosp. & Vict. Roy. Hosp. E. Chesh. NHS Trust. Socs: Brit. Assn. Urol. Surgs. Prev: Regist. (Urol.) Portsmouth Hosps. NHS Trust; SHO (Urol.) E. Yorks. NHS Trust; SHO (Urol.) Macclesfield Dist. Gen. Hosp.

ZAFER, Ibtsam Mohamed Zaki 9 Horsley Close, Epsom KT19 8HB Tel: 013727 21233 — MB BCh 1963 Cairo; DA 1971. Anaesth. E. Surrey & Mid. Surrey HA. Socs: Assn. Anaesth. Gt. Brit. & Irel.

ZAFFAR, Mahmood Ahmad (retired) 7 Lavender Swwep, London SW11 1DY — MB BS 1954 Punjab. Locum Gen. Practitioner. Prev: SHO Mayo Hosp. Lahore.

ZAFFAR, Muzaffar 7 Lavender Sweep, London SW11 1DY Tel: 020 7223 7475 Email: muzaffarz@hotmail.com; 7 Lavender Sweep, London SW11 1DY Tel: 020 7223 7475 — MB BS 1996 Lond.; BSc (Hons.) Lond. 1993. (Charing Cross and Westminster) SHO (GP Train. Scheme) Mayday Univ. Hosp. Lond. Socs: BMA. Prev: Hse. Surg. St. Peter's Hosp. Chertsey; Hse. Phys. Chelsea & W.minster Hosp. Lond.

ZAHANGIR, Mohammed Monkland District General Hospital, Monkscourt Avenue, Airdrie ML6 0JS Tel: 01236 787787 Fax: 01236 760015; 6 North Avenue, Carluke ML8 5TR Tel: 01555 751034 — MB BS 1966 Dacca; MRCPsych 1975; DPM Eng. 1974. (S.S. Med. Coll.) Cons. Psychiat. Lanarksh. Health Bd.

ZAHEEN, Mr Mohammad 9 Homewood Drive, Hensingham, Whitehaven CA28 8JG — MB BS 1984 Peshawar; FRCS Glas. 1990; FCOphth 1990.

ZAHEER, Pervez Cinderford Health Centre, Dockham Road, Cinderford GL14 2AN Tel: 01594 598020 — MB BS 1964 Karachi. (Kerachi) GP Cinderford, Glos.

ZAHEER, Mr Syed Asghar The Briery, 3 Orchard Place, Rectory Rd, Wokingham RG40 1DW Tel: 0118 979 2902 — MB BS 1954 Lucknow; BSc Allahabad 1949; FRCS Eng. 1962; FRCS Ed. 1961. Chief Cons. Surg. & Urol. Igbinedion Hosp. & Med. Research Centre Okada, Nigeria. Socs: Fell. Internat. Coll. Angiol. (NY) 1967; Fell. Assn. Surgs.; Sen. Mem. Brit. Assn. Urol. Surgs. Prev: Cons. Surg. E. Antrim Gp. Hosps.; Cons. Surg. Merthyr & Aberdare Gp. Hosps.; Regist. (Surg.) SE Kent Gp. Hosps. & Withington Hosp. Manch.

ZAHER, Samir Abd El-Azim Flat 2/01, 91 Greenock Road, Paisley PA3 2LF Tel: 0141 840 1757 — MB BCh 1965 Cairo.

ZAHIR, Mr Abol Ghassem 152 Harley Street, London W1N 1HH Tel: 020 7935 2477 Fax: 020 7224 2574; 72 Onslow Gardens, Muswell Hill, London N10 3JX Fax: 020 8883 6027 — MB BS 1964 Lond.; FRCS Eng. 1967; MRCS Eng. LRCP Lond. 1962; Specialist Accredit (Orthop.) RCS Eng. 1973. (Lond. Hosp.) Cons. Orthop. Surg. Whipps Cross (Forest Healthcare). Socs: Fell. Roy. Soc. Med. & BOA. Prev: Cons. Orthop. Tehran Clinic, Iran; Sen. Regist. (Orthop.) Lond. Hosp.

ZAHIR, Keyvan Enfield & Haringey Health Agency, Alexander Place, Lower Park Road, New Southgate, London N11 1ST Tel: 020 8361 7272 Fax: 020 8361 6126; 72 Onslow Gardens, Muswell Hill, London N10 3JX Tel: 020 8365 2430 Fax: 020 8883 6027 — MD 1967 Tehran; FFCM 1993, M 1985; DPH Lond. 1970. Dir. (Pub. Health Med.) Enfield & Haringey Health Agency. Prev: Dir. Pub. Health New River HA; Specialist (Community Med.) Haringey HA; Sen. Regist. NW Thames RHA.

ZAHIR, Maryam Edgware Community Hospital, Burnt Oak Broadway, Edgware, Edgware HA8 0AD Tel: 020 8732 6566 Fax: 020 8732 6474; 58 Blake Road, London N11 2AH Tel: 020 83682 990 Email: maryamzahir@netscapeonline.co.uk — MB BS 1984 Lond.; BSc McGill 1979; MRCP Paediat. (UK) 1989; DCH RCP Lond. 1987. (The Royal London Hospital) Cons. Community Paediat. Barnet Healthcare NHS Trust. Socs: Roy. Coll. Paediat. & Child Health; Eur. Assn. Childh. Dis. Prev: Lect. (Community Paediat.) Camberwell HA; Regist. (Paediat.) St. Mary's Hosp. Lond.; SHO (Neonat.) Hammersmith Hosp. Lond.

ZAHIR, Mr Mohammed Wythenshawe Hospital, Southmoor Road, Manchester M23 9LT Tel: 0161 946 2836; 20 Rhodes Street, Halifax HX1 5ET — MB ChB 1986 Manch.; FRCS Ed. 1993. Sen. Regist. S. Manch. Univ. Hosps. Prev: Regist. (A & E) Fazakerley Hosp. Liverp.; Regist. (A & E & Gen. Med.) Sir Chas. Gardner Hosp. Perth, W. Austral.

ZAIB, Sajid Ali 3 Whitelands Way, High Wycombe HP12 3EH — MB BS 1994 Lond.

ZAIDI, Mr Abul Abbas District General Hospital, Moorgate Road, Rotherham S60 — MB BS 1968 Sind; FRCS Glas. 1978; FCOphth 1989; DO RCPSI 1971. (Liaquat Med. Coll. Hyderabad) Cons. Ophth. Surg. Dist. Gen. Hosp. Rotherham. Prev: SHO (Ophth.)

ZAKHOUR

Maelor Gen. Hosp. Wrexham; Regist. (Ophth.) Chester Roy. Infirm.; Sen. Regist. Roy. Eye Hosp. Manch.

ZAIDI, Mr Ahsan Zafar c/o Mr. S.M. Rasheed, 13 Dalmeny Crescent, Hounslow Tel: 020 8847 4210 — MB BS 1972 Aligarh; MB BS Aligarh Muslim 1972; FRCS Eng. 1979; LRCP LRCS Ed. LRCPS Glas. 1980. Prev: Gen. Surg. & Chief Surg. Civil Hosp. Khamees Mushayt Saudi Arabia; Regist. (Gen. Surg.) N. Middlx., Lond. & Roy. Lancs. Infirm.

ZAIDI, Amir Masood 3 The Forge Mews, 501-503 Wilmslow Road, Withington, Manchester M20 4AW — MB ChB 1989 Manch.

ZAIDI, Farhan Husain 28 Bedford Road, South Woodford, London E18 2AQ — MB BS 1994 Lond.; MB BS (Hons.) Lond. 1994; FRCS Eng. 1997. SHO (Surg.) UCL Hosps. Lond. Socs: Middlx. Hosp. Med. Soc. Prev: SHO (Cardiothoracic Surg.) St. Bart. & Roy. Lond. Hosps.; SHO (A & E) UCH Lond.; Ho. Phys. N. Middlx. Hosp. Lond.

ZAIDI, Iram 55 Daybrook Road, London SW19 3DJ — MB BS 1994 Lond.

ZAIDI, Mone Biochemical Medicine, St. George's Hospital Medical School, Tooting, London SW17 0RE Tel: 020 8682 3380 Fax: 020 8784 2946; 33 Oakwood Park Road, Southgate, London N14 6QT Tel: 020 8886 8867 — MB BS 1984 Lucknow; PhD Lond. 1987, MD 1991; FRCPI 1994, M 1993; MRCPath 1990. Sen. Lect. & Cons. St. Geo. Hosp. Med. Sch. Lond.; Research Worker Physiol. Laborat. Univ. Camb. Socs: Amer. Soc. Bone & Mineral Research & Soc. Endocrinol. UK. Prev: Lect., Sen. Regist., Regist. & Research Schol. Endrocrine Unit Dept. Chem. Path. Roy. Postgrad. Med. Sch. Lond.

ZAIDI, Nerjis Huma 10 Halvis Grove, Manchester M16 0DX — MB ChB 1994 Manch.

ZAIDI, Sarwat Eastwood Surgery, 348 Rayleigh Road, Eastwood, Leigh-on-Sea SS9 5PU Tel: 01702 525289 Fax: 01702 520134; 91 Eastwood Road, Leigh-on-Sea SS9 3AH Tel: 01702 476543 — MB BS 1962 Punjab; DRCOG 1976; DFFP 1996.

ZAIDI, Syed Ali Raza 19 Arbour Way, Hornchurch RM12 5BS — MB BS 1968 Karachi; MB BS Karachi, Pakistan 1968; FFA RCSI 1975.

ZAIDI, Syed Babar Abbas Head of Healthcare Services, HM Prison, Barrack Square, Gloucester GL1 2JN Tel: 01452 529551 Fax: 01452 310302 — MB BS 1970 Dacca; Dip. Addic. Behaviour Lond. 1992; DPM Eng. 1982. Head Health Care Servs. HM Prison Gloucester. Socs: Med. Protec. Soc. Prev: Clin. Asst. (Psychiat.) E. Dyfed HA.

ZAIDI, Mr Syed Husain Afzal Department of Cardiothoracic Surgery, University Hospital of Wales, Heath Park, Cardiff CF14 4XW; 40 Bishops Road, Trumpington, Cambridge CB2 2NH — MB BChir 1991 Camb.; MA Camb. 1991; FRCS Eng. 1994. (Camb. & Guy's Hosp.) Specialist Regist. (Cardiothorac. Surg.) Univ. Hosp. Wales Cardiff. Socs: Roy. Soc. Med. & Internat. Soc. Heart & Lung Transpl. Prev: Transpl. Research Fell. Papworth Hosp.; Regist. Cardiothoracic St. Bart.'s Hosp. Lond.

ZAIDI, Syed Husain Jamal Dept. of Obstetrics & Gynaecology, Conquest Hospital, The Ridge TN37 7RD Tel: 07974004923 Email: zaida.jamal@har-tr.stthomas.nhs.uk — MB BS 1987 Lond.; MD 2000; MRCOG 1992. (King's College Lond.) Cons. Obst.&Gyn @ Congnect Hosp., The Ridge, E.Sussex &BUPA Hosp., Hastings. Socs: Brit. Fertil. Soc.; Internat. Soc. Ultrasound in Obst. & Gyn.; Brit. Soc. Gyn. Endoscopy. Prev: Sen. Regist. (O & G) John Radcliffe Hosp. Oxf.; Regist. (Clin. Research) King's Coll. Hosp. & Lond. Wom. Clinic. Harley St.; Regist. (O & G) King's Coll. Hosp. Lond.

ZAIDI, Syed Ishrat Ali St Nicholas Health Centre, 57 Canterbury Way, Stevenage SG1 4QH Tel: 01438 357411; 54 Dowlands, Stevenage SG2 7BH — MB BS 1962 Karachi; DA Eng. 1973. (Dow Med. Coll.) Prev: Med. Off. H.H. Agha Khan Hosp. Mombasa, Kenya; Regist. (Anaesth.) Stafford Gen. Infirm.; SHO (Anaesth.) Roy. Hosp. Wolverhampton.

ZAIDI, Syed Masoodul Hasan Kilmarnock Infirmary, Kilmarnock; Accident & Emergency, Crosshouse Hospital, Kilmarnock KA2 0BE Tel: 01563 521133 — MB BS 1961 Karachi. Cons. A & E CrossHo. Hosp. Kilmarnock. Socs: BMA; BAEM.

ZAIDI, Syed Mohammad Nawab 87 Farnham Road, Guildford GU2 7PF Tel: 01483 68715 — MB BS 1968 Karachi; MRCPsych 1972; DPM Eng. 1982; DPM Eng. 1971. (Dow Med. Coll.) Cons. Psychiat. Brookwood Hosp. Knaphill.

ZAIDI, Syed Mohammad Zafar 118 Albert Road, Jarrow NE32 3AG Tel: 0191 489 7002 Fax: 0191 428 5640 — MB BS 1983 Karachi. (Kerachi) GP Jarrow, Tyne & Wear.

ZAIDI, Syed Nayyar Abbas 10 Halvis Grove, Manchester M16 0DX — MB ChB 1990 Manch.

ZAIDI, Syeda Talat Abbas Kent Elms Health Centre, Rayleigh Road, Leigh-on-Sea SS9 5UU Tel: 01702 421888 Fax: 01702 421818; 335 Eastwood Road N., Leigh-on-Sea SS9 4LT Tel: 01702 529817 — MRCS Eng. LRCP Lond. 1978.

ZAIDI, Zafar Husain 28 Bedford Road, South Woodford, London E18 2AQ Tel: 020 8989 3090 — MB BS 1955 Lucknow; FRCP Ed. 1980, M 1965; DCH Eng. 1960. (King Geo. Med. Coll.) Cons. Paediatr. Barking Hosp., King Geo. Hosp. Ilford & OldCh. Hosp. Romford. Socs: Brit. Paediat. Assn. Prev: Chief Resid. (Paediat.) Univ. Ottawa Gen. Hosp., Canada; Ho. Phys. Hosp. Sick Childr. Gt. Ormond St. Lond.; Prof. & Head, Dept. Paediat. Univ. Aligarh, India.

***ZAIN, Amir Azlan** 23 Tattershall Drive, Beeston, Nottingham NG9 2GP; 17 Templemead, Witham CM8 2DF — BM BS 1997 Nottm.; BMedSci. (Hons.) Nottm. 1995.

ZAINUDDIN, Ani Amelia 44 Helmsley Road, Sandyford, Newcastle upon Tyne NE2 1DL Tel: 0191 261 8944 Fax: 0191 261 8944 . Email: zainuddin@aol.com — MB BS 1996 Newc. (News.-u-Tyne) SHO Dept. O & G Directorate of Wom.'s Servs. Newc.-u-Tyne. Socs: BMA; Med. Protec. Soc. Prev: Surg. Ho. Off. Med. Ho. Off. S. Tyneside Dist. Hosp. Tyne & Wear.

ZAINUDDIN, Idris Abdulkader Flat 21, Gatehill Court, 166 Notting Hill Gate, London W11 3QT Tel: 020 7229 6404 Fax: 020 7221 2691; Maimoon Manzil, 10 The Glebe, Worcester Park KT4 7PF Tel: 020 8335 4051 Fax: 020 8335 4152 — MB BS 1962 Punjab; DOMS Vienna 1966. Socs: BMA. Prev: Clin. Asst. Roy. Eye Hosp. Lond.; SHO (Ophth.) Sunderland Eye Infirm. & Ophth. Hosp. Maidstone.

ZAIREEN, Wan Nurdiana 47 Tiree, East Kilbride, Glasgow G74 2DR — MB BCh 1997 Belf.

ZAJICEK, John Peter Department of Neurology, Derriford Hospital, Plymouth PL6 8DH — MB BS 1984 Lond.; PhD Camb. 1993; BA Camb. 1981; MRCP (UK) 1987. Cons. Neurol. Derriford Hosp. Plymouth; Hon. Sen. Lect. Univ. of Plymouth. Prev: Clin. Lect. Addenbrooke's Hosp. Camb.

ZAKANI, Regina Upton Road Surgery, 30 Upton Road, Watford WD18 0JS Tel: 01923 226266 Fax: 01923 222324 — State Exam Med 1988 Hamburg. GP Princip. Upton Rd. Surg. Watford.

ZAKARIA, A K M The Surgery, 50 Upper Road, London E13 0DH Tel: 020 8552 2129 Fax: 020 8471 4180 — MB BS 1969 Dacca; MB BS 1969 Dacca.

ZAKARIA, Faris Benjamin Peter First Floor Flat, 15 Meithuen Park, London N10 2JR — MB BS 1990 Lond.

ZAKARIA, Ghulam Yusufzai Afghania House, 35 Marlings Park Avenue, Chislehurst BR7 6QN Tel: 020 8850 2779 — MB BS 1962 Karachi; MD Jalal-Abad 1975; BSc Peshawar 1956; DCH RCPS Glas. 1968. Managing Sec. Afghania Educat. Trust. Socs: GP Research Gp.; BMA & BDA. Prev: Research Asst. Lennard Hosp. FarnBoro.; Clin. Asst. (Diabetol.) Greenwich Dist. Hosp.; Clin. Asst. (Diabetol.) W.hill Hosp Dartford.

ZAKARIA, Mohamed Yahia Withybush Hospital, Haverfordwest SA61 2PZ — MB BCh 1980 Cairo.

ZAKARIA, Mohd Idzam 38 Southbank Road, Manchester M19 1PX — MB ChB 1998 Manch.

ZAKARIA, Mr Muhannad Rasheed Muhammad 6D Neville Street, London SW7 3AR — MB ChB 1973 Mosul; FRCS Ed. 1983; MRCOG 1982.

ZAKARIA, Nada Abdalla 11 Ruskin Court, 4 Champion Hill, London SE5 8AH Tel: 07881 824914 Fax: 020 7738 6960 Email: nadawho@hotmail.com — MB BS 1989 Khartoum, Sudan; MRCP (UK) 1994. (University of Khartoum) Research Regist. (Sp R Gastro/GIM), Inst. of Liver Studies, King's Coll. Hosp. Lond. Socs: MRCP (UK); MDU. Prev: SpR Gastroenerology, Liver Unit, King's Coll. Hosp. Lond.; SpR Gastroenterol., Qu. Mary's Hosp. Roehampton; SpR Gastroenterol., Ashford Hosp. Middlx.

ZAKHOUR, Hani Arrowe Park Hospital, Upton, Wirral CH49 5PE; Holmsea, 9 Linnets Way, Heswall Lower Village, Wirral CH60 9JW Tel: 0151 342 3657 Fax: 0151 604 1733 Email: hanizak@dial.pipex.com — MD 1973 Prague; MD Charles Univ. Prague 1973; MRCS Eng. LRCP Lond. 1979; FRCPath 1993, M

ZAKI 1982. (Charles Univ. Prague) Cons. Path. Arrowe Pk. Hosp. Wirral; Assoc. PostGrad. Dan Mersey Deanery Liverp.; Director of PostGrad. Educat. Wirral Hosp. Turst. Socs: Internat. Acad. Path.; Assn. Clin. Path.; Pres. NW Br. Assn. of Clin. Pathol. Prev: Sen. Regist. (Histopath.) N.. Gen. Hosp. & Clin. Tutor (Morbid Anat.) Univ. Sheff.; Regist. (Histopath.) Wythenshawe Hosp. Manch.; Resid. Clin. Path. Booth Hall Childr. Hosp. Manch.

ZAKI, Afza 35 Launceston Road, Perivale, Greenford UB6 7EX — MB BS 1996 Lond.

ZAKI, Aida Said Stechford Health Centre, 393 Station Road, Stechford, Birmingham B33 8PL Tel: 0121 784 8101 Fax: 0121 785 0565 — MB BCh 1970 Alexandria; Family Planning Certificate. GP Gen. Pratitioner. Prev: GP Since 1988; 1974-1978 Gyn. & Obstetric; 1978-1986 Anacsthetics.

ZAKI, Mr Graeme Anderson Maxillofacial Unit, Queen Alexandra Hospital, Cosham, Portsmouth PO6 3LY Tel: 023 92 286466 Fax: 023 92 286089 — MB BS 1983 Lond.; FRCS 1988 Ed.; FDS RCS 1986 Eng.; BDS 1976 Lond. Cons. Oral & Maxillofacial Surg. Qu. Alexandra Hosp. Portsmouth. Socs: Fell. Brit. Assn. Oral & Maxillofacial Surg.; BMA. Prev: Sen. Regist. St. Geo. Hosp. Lond.

ZAKI, Irshad 19 Knightsbridge Crescent, Stirchley, Telford TF3 1BN — BM BS 1987 Nottm.; BMedSci (Hons.) Nottm. 1985; MRCP (UK) 1990. Cons. (Derm) Solihull & Heartlands Hosp. Prev: Sen. Regist. (Dermat.) Nottm.

ZAKI, Mohammed Dilnasheen, Pyle Hill, Mayford, Woking GU22 0SR — MB BS 1969 Delhi. (Maulana Azad Med. Coll.)

ZAKI, Mona Morad Ramzy Northern Residence, Singleton Hospital, Sketty, Swansea SA2 8QA — MB BCh 1988 Cairo; MRCOG 1995.

ZAKI, Mr Nazieh Nageh Duchess of Kents Hospital, Catterick Garrison DL9 4DF Tel: 01748 832521 Fax: 01748 873011; 49 Frenchgate, Richmond DL10 7AE Tel: 01748 825062 — MB BCh 1972 Assiut; FRCS Glas. 1982; FRCS Ed. 1982. Cons. ENT Surg. Duchess of Kent's Hosp. Catterick Garrison. Socs: Brit. Assn. Otol. & Head & Neck Surg.; Fell. Roy. Soc. Med.; BMA.

ZAKI, Shereen 33 Cheam Road, Epsom KT17 1QX — MB BS 1991 Lond. SHO (Cardiol.) Cardiothoracic Centre Liverp. Prev: SHO (Gen. Med.) Joyce Green Hosp. Dartford Kent; SHO (A & E) Newham Gen. Hosp. Lond.; Ho. Off. (Surg.) Roy. Cornw. Hosp. Treliske.

ZAKI AHMED, Syed Mohammad Malinslee Surgery, Church Road, Malinslee, Telford TF3 2JZ Tel: 01952 501234 Fax: 01952 594555; 19 Knightsbridge Crescent, Stirchley, Stirchley, Telford TF3 1BN — MB BS 1962 Osmania; DPH Osmania 1967. (Gandhi Med. Coll.) Socs: BMA & Overseas Doctors Assn.; Small Practs. Assn. Prev: Asst. Prof. Gandhi Med. Coll. Hyderabad, India; Asst. MOH Municip. Corpn. Hyderabad; Asst. Surg. Urban Family Plann. Clinic Hyderabad.

ZAKI-KHALIL, Ihab Ahmed Victoria Hospital, Whinney Heys Road, Blackpool FY3 8NR — MB ChB 1975 Cairo; MRCOG 1988; DRCOG 1986. Regist. (O & G) Torbay Hosp. Torquay. Prev: Regist. (O & G) Grimsby Dist. Gen. Hosp.

ZAKLAMA, Magued Sabet, Maj. RAMC (retired) Birch Hill Hospital, Rochdale OL12 9QB Tel: 01706 77777 — MB BCh 1970 Cairo; FRCOG 1992, M 1977. Cons. O & G Rochdale Dist. HA. Prev: Cons. O & G Brit. Milit. Hosp. Hannover, BFPO 33.

ZAKRZEWSKA, Joanna Maria Oral Medicine, Bart. & the London Dental Institute NHS Trust, Turner St., London E1 2AD Tel: 020 7377 7035 Fax: 020 7377 7627 — MB BChir 1980 Camb.; MD Camb. 1990; BDS Lond. 1972; FFD RCSI 1991; FDS RCS Eng. 1980. (Camb.) Sen. Lect. & Hon. Cons. Bart Lond. Dent. Inst. Socs: Fell. Roy. Soc. Med.; Brit. Soc. Oral Med.; Internat. Assn. Study of Pain. Prev: Cons. & Hon. Sen. Lect. (Oral Med.) E.man Dent. Hosp. & Univ. Coll. Hosps. Camden & Islington NHS Trust; Cons. Camden & Islington Community NHS Trust; Hon. Cons. Nat. Hosp. Neurol. & Neurosurg. Lond.

ZAKRZEWSKI, Henryk John Pendleside Medical Practice, Clitheroe Health Centre, Railway View Road, Clitheroe BB7 2JG Tel: 01200 421888 Fax: 01200 421887; Craigmore, Eastham Street, Clitheroe BB& 2HY Tel: 01200 426583 Fax: 01200 421887 Email: john.zakrzewskp@gp-p81067.nhs.uk — MB ChB 1990 Manch.; MRCGP 1994; DFFP 1993; DRCOG 1993. (Univ. Manch.) GP Princip. Pendleside Med. Pract., Clitheroe Lancs.; GP Trainer. Socs: (Treas.) Blackburn & Dist. Med. & Dent. Soc. Prev: Asst. GP Pendleside Med. Pract. Clitheroe; Trainee GP Montague Health Centre Blackburn; Trainee GP/SHO Qu. Pk. Hosp. Blackburn VTS.

ZAKRZEWSKI, Kajetan Krzysztof Hayes Grove Priory Hospital, Prestons Road, Hayes, Bromley BR2 7AS Tel: 020 8462 7722 Fax: 020 8462 5028 Email: kzakrzewski@hotmail.com — Lekarz 1974 Warsaw; MRCPsych 1987; Specialist Psychiatrist 1983, Institute of Psychiatry & Neurology Exam. Board Warsaw. Cons. Anaesth. Roy. Hallamshire Hosp. Socs: BMA; Roy. Coll. Psychiatr. Prev: Cons. Psychiat. Leics. Ment. Health Servs. & E.bourne Co. NHS Trust; Cons. Psychiat. & Alcoholism, Warsaw, Poland; Specialist Psychiat. Inst. Psychait. Neurol. Warsaw.

ZAKY, Saroj 17 Doncaster Close, Coventry CV2 1HW — MB BS 1973 Rajasthan.

ZALA, Navin Naran Marling Way Surgery, 117 Marling Way, Gravesend DA12 4RQ Tel: 01474 533201; 128 Elaine Avenue, Rochester ME2 2YP — MB BS 1975 Poona; DObst 1980. (BJ Med. Coll.) Clin. Asst. (Paediat.) Gravesend & N. Kent Hosp.; Vis. Med. Off. Community Ment. & Handicap Unit Dartford & Gravesham HA. Prev: SHO (Gen. Med.) Gravesend & N. Kent Hosp.; Trainee GP Dartford VTS.

ZALIDIS, Sotirios The Surgery, 52B Well Street, London E9 7PX Tel: 020 8985 2050 Fax: 020 8985 5780; 140 Powerscroft Road, Clapton, London E5 0PR Tel: 020 8986 9479 — Ptychio latrikes 1973 Athens; MRCP (UK) 1982. Socs: Soc. Psychosomatic Research; Balint Soc.

ZALIN, Anthony Maurice Vine Cottage, Vine Lane, Clent, Stourbridge DY9 9PH — MD 1976 Camb.; MA Camb. 1966, MD 1976, MB 1970, BChir 1969; FRCP Lond. 1983; MRCP (UK) 1971. Cons. Phys. Corbett & Wordsley Hosps. Stourbridge. Prev: Lect. (Med.) Univ. Birm.

ZALIN, Mr Harold (retired) 13 Heathfield Close, Church Road, Potters Bar EN6 1SW Tel: 01707 651522 — MB ChB 1937 Liverp.; FRCS Ed. 1947; DLO Eng. 1945. Prev: Cons. Surg. ENT Walton Hosp. Liverp.

ZAMAN, Ahmed Darwen Health Centre, Union Street, Darwen BB3 0DA Tel: 01254 778377 Fax: 01254 778372; 121 Manor Road, Darwen BB3 2SN Tel: 01254 702319 — MB BS 1962 Dacca; BSc Dacca 1955, MB BS 1962. (Dacca Med. Coll.) GP Blackburn; Clin. Asst. (Psychiat.) & Clin. Asst. (Geriat.) Qu.'s Pk. Hosp. Blackburn; Trainer Family Plann. Assn. Socs: Fell. Inst. Psychiat. Prev: SHO (Med.) Maelor Gen. Hosp. Wrexham; Regist. (Infec. Dis. & Geriat.) Ladywell Hosp. Salford; SHO (Chest & Med.) Lodge Moor Hosp. Sheff.

ZAMAN, Anwar Ghaus 132A Barnsley Road, Hemsworth, Pontefract WF9 4PG Tel: 01426241202 — BM BCh 1986 Oxf.; MA Camb. 1987; MRCP (UK) 1989; FRCOphth 1991. Cons. Ophth. Surg., Qu.s Med. Centre Nottm. Prev: Vitreuretinal Fell., Moorfields Eye Hosp.; utreoretinal Fell., Manch. Roy. Eye Hosp.; Sen. Regist. Ophth., Qu.s Med. Centre.

ZAMAN, Ashrif Cheyenne 85 Vickers Road, Sheffield S5 6WA — MB ChB 1995 Sheff.

ZAMAN, Azfar Ghaus 132A Barnsley Road, Hemsworth, Pontefract WF9 4PG — MB ChB 1985 Leeds; BSc Leeds 1982, MB ChB 1985; MRCP (UK) 1988. Tutor (Cardiovasc. Med.) Univ. Leeds. Prev: Regist. (Gen. Med.) St. Jas. Univ. Hosp. Leeds.

ZAMAN, Herbert Winthrop River Surgery, 110 London Road, River, Dover CT16 3AB; White Horses, Cliff Road, Kingsdown, Deal CT14 8AJ Tel: 01304 373397 — MB BS 1967 W. Indies; ECFMG Cert 1976. Locum GP. Socs: Fell. Roy. Soc. Med. Prev: GP Princip.

ZAMAN, Khalid Holly House, Nunroyd, Heckmondwike WF16 9HB — BM BS 1996 Nottm.

ZAMAN, Maqsuda 15 Sylvandale Avenue, Manchester M19 2FB — MB ChB 1992 Liverp.

ZAMAN, Mohammed Asaduz 116 Kedleston Road, Derby DE22 1FX Tel: 01332 362221 — MB BS 1957 Dhaka; FRCPsych 1989, M 1973; DPM Eng. 1969. (Dhaka Med. Coll.) Cons. Psychiat. Kingsway Hosp. Derby. Prev: Prison Med. Off. (Forens. Psychiat.) Home Off.; Assoc. Specialist (Gen. Psychiat.) Morgannwg Hosp. Bridgend.

ZAMAN, Mohammed Justin Samuel Middlesex Hospital, Mortimer St., London W1T 3AA — MB BS 1997 Lond.

ZAMAN, Nasser Ali Derby Lane Medical Centre, 30 Derby Lane, Derby DE23 8UA Tel: 01332 773243 — MB ChB 1989 Manch.

ZAMMIT-TABONA

ZAMAN, Neelofer Yasmin 132A Barnsley Road, Hemsworth, Pontefract WF9 4PG — MB ChB 1989 Leeds; MRCP ed 1993; BSc (Hons) Path. 1986. (Leeds University Medical School)

ZAMAN, Qaisar HMP Strangeways, Southall Road, Manchester M60 9AH Tel: 0161 834 8626 — MB BS 1972 Peshawar, Pakistan. GP HMP Strangeways Manch.

ZAMAN, Quazi Abul Mansur Mahbubuz 153 Park Road, Hornsey, London N8 Tel: 020 8340 7940; 104 Shrewsbury Road, New Southgate, London N11 2JU Tel: 020 8368 8619 — MB BS 1953 Dacca; FRCP Glas. 1983; FRCP Ed. 1982; MRCP (Ed.) 1963; MRCP (Glas.) 1961. Socs: BMA & Overseas Doctors Assn. Prev: Phys Conservation of Manpower Unit (Treatm. Alchohol Dependency) Lond.; Cardiol. Cardiac Life Line Lond.; Prof. Cardiol. Inst. Postgrad. Med. & Research Dhaka, Bangladesh.

ZAMAN, Rashid Imperial College School of Medicine, Division of Neurosciences & Physiological Medicine, Paterson Centre, 20 South Wharf Road, London W2 1PD Email: r.zaman@ic.ac.uk; 265 Mill Road, Cambridge CB1 3DF Email: rash@peak88.freeserve.co.uk — MB BChir 1988 Camb.; MB Camb. 1988, BChir 1987; MRCPsych 1996; MRCGP 1991; DGM RCP Lond. 1989; LMSSA Lond. 1986; BSc (Hons.) St. And. 1980. (Cambridge) Lect. & Hon. Specialist Regist. Div. of Neurosci.s & Physiol. Med. Imperial Coll. Univ. of Lond.; GP Camb.; Psychiat. Research Lond. Socs: BMA; Roy. Coll. Psychiatr.; Internat. Soc. Transcranial Stimulation. Prev: Regist. (Psychiat.) Char. Cross Hosp. Lond.; Research Regist. Leavsden Hosp. Herts.; Regist. & SHO (Psychiat.) Char. Cross Hosp. Lond.

ZAMAN, Saira Judith 17 Brentwood Avenue, West Jesmond, Newcastle upon Tyne NE2 3DQ — MB BS 1996 Newc.

ZAMAN, Salman Mohammad Radiology Department, Leighton Hosptial, Middlewich Road, Crewe CW1 4QJ Tel: 01270 612153 Fax: 01270 612156 Email: salman.zaman@virgin.net — MB BS 1985 Peshawar; MRCP (UK) 1990; FRCR 1995. (Khyber Med. Coll. Peshawar) Cons. Radiol. Mid. Chesh. Hosps. Trust. Prev: Sen. Regist. & Regist. Sheff. Radiol. Train. Scheme; SHO Rotat. (Med.) Camb.; SHO Rotat. (Med.) Hull.

ZAMAN, Shahid Hassan Department of Anatomy, University of Bristol, Bristol BS8 1TD — MB ChB 1985 Sheff.; PhD Camb. 1993; BMedSci (Hons.) Sheff. 1983; MRCP (UK) 1994. SHO Psychiat., Bristol; Hon. Research Fell., Univ. of Bristol. Prev: Hon. Regist. (Neurol.) Addenbrooke's Hosp. Camb.; Regist. (Chem. Path.) Univ. Hosp. Wales; SHO (Geriat. Med.) Cardiff Roy. Infirm.

ZAMAN, Shamas 114 Spencer Street, Keighley BD21 2QB — MB ChB 1995 Leic.

ZAMAN, Sonya Rownak Green Acre, Brookhouse, Laughton, Sheffield S25 1YA — MB BS 1998 Lond.

ZAMAN, Syed Nuru Elderly Care Unit, Southampton General Hospital, Tremona Road, Hampshire, Southampton SO16 6YD Tel: 02380 794329; Email: syed@haarlem.freeserve.co.uk — MB BCh BAO 1988 NUI; MRCP (UK) 1992. (Roy. Coll. Surgs. Irel.) Cons. Phys. in Elderly Care, Elderly Care Unit, S.ampton Gen. Hosp. Socs: Brit. Geriat. Soc. Prev: Sen. Regist. (Med & Geriat.) Wessex; Regist. (Med.) Broomfield Hosp. Chelmsford.

ZAMAN, Tahir Mahmood 596 Bromford Lane, Birmingham B8 2DS — MB ChB 1990 Manch.; BSc (Hons.) Manch. 1987, MB ChB 1990.

ZAMAN, Tariq Mahmood 162 Cherrywood Road, Bordesley Grove, Birmingham B9 4UN — MB ChB 1988 Dundee.

ZAMAN, Zahur Department of Clinical Chemistry, University Hospitals Leuven, Catholic University of Leuven, Herestraat 49, Leuven B-3000, Belgium Tel: 00 32 16 343390; 38 Milton Lawns, Chesham Bois, Amersham HP6 6BH Tel: 01494 726110 — MD 1985 Louvain; PhD Soton. 1973, BSc (Hons.) Physiol. & Biochem. 1969. Cons. Chem. Path. Univ. Hosps. Leuven, Belgium; Reader Catholic Univ. Leuven, Belgium. Prev: Sen. Regist. (Chem Path.) Centr. Middlx. & St. Mary's Hosps. Lond.; Research Fell. Sc. Research Counc. Univ. Soton.; Sen. Research Fell. Dept. Med. Catholic Univ. Louvain, Belgium.

ZAMANIS, Nikolaos 41 Aldbourne Road, London W12 0LW — Ptychio latrikes 1988 Athens.

ZAMANTHANGI, Jadeng Mani The Surgery, 30 Church Road, Manor Park, London E12 6AQ Tel: 020 8478 0686 Fax: 020 8478 1666 — MB BS 1966 Gauhati. (Gauhati) SHO Emerg., Cas. & Orthop. Dept. E. Ham Memor Hosp. Prev: Ho. Off. Med. Dept. Bruntsfield Hosp. Edin.; SHO Geriat. Dept. E.. Gen. Hosp. Edin.

ZAMAR, Antonios Camille c/o York Clinic, Guy's Hospital, St Thomas St., London SE1 9RT; 6 Highgrove Court, 69 Pk Road, Beckenham BR3 1QR — MB BCh 1989 Cairo; MRCS Eng. LRCP Lond. 1992; MRCPsych 1994. Research Fell. Hayes Gr. Priory, UMDS Guy's & St. Thos. Hosps. Lond.

ZAMBANINI, Andrew Department of Clinical Pharmacology, NHLI, Imperial College, St. Mary's Hospital, Praed Street, London W2 1NY Tel: 020 7886 6827 Fax: 020 7886 2207 Email: a.zambanini@ic.ac.uk — MB BS 1991 Lond.; 2001 CCST Clin. Pharmacol. & Therap.; MRCP (UK) 1995. (St. Geo. Hosp. Med. Sch. Lond.) Clin. Research Fell. in Clin. Pharmacol. NHLI, Imperial Coll., Lond. Socs: Roy. Coll. Phys.; Lond. Hypertens. Soc.; Roy. Soc. Med. (Fell.). Prev: Sen. Regist., Clin. Pharmacol., Chelsea & W.m. Hosp. Lond.; Research Fell. (Cardiovasc.) Green La. Hosp., Auckland, New Zealand; Regist. (Gen. Med.) Chelsea & W.minster & Watford Hosp.

ZAMBARAKJI, Mr Hadi Jihad Department of Ophthalmology, Whipps Cross Hospital, London E11 1NR Tel: 020 8539 5522 Fax: 020 8535 6466; 10 Lowndes Square, Flat 20, London SW1X 9HA Tel: 020 7259 6765 Email: hzambarakj@aol.com — MB ChB 1990 Dundee; FRCOphth 1995. (Dundee) Specialist Regist. (Ophth.) N. Thames Rotat. Socs: BMA; MRCOphth.; Med. & Dent. Defence Union Scotl. Prev: Fell. (Diabetic Retina Ophth.) Qu. Med. Centre Nottm.; SHO (Ophth.) Char. Cross Hosp. Lond.; SHO Stirling Roy. Infirm.

ZAMBLERA, Dante 224 Friern Road, East Dulwich, London SE22 0BB — MB BCh BAO 1988 NUI; LRCPSI 1988. Regist. (O & G) Guys & St. Thos. Hosp. Lond.

ZAMBON, Maria Caterina Virus Reference Laboratory CPHL, 61 Colindale Avenue, Colindale, London NW9 Tel: 020 8200 4400 Fax: 020 8200 1569 Email: mzambon@phls.co.uk — BM BCh 1989 Oxf.; PhD Univ. Lond. 1984. (Oxford) Cons. Virologist Virus Ref. Laborat. Centr. Pub. Health Lab. Lond. Socs: Soc. Gen. Microbiol.

ZAMENHOF-NIETUPSKA, Olga Eugenia 29 Rooksmead Road, Sunbury-on-Thames TW16 6PD Tel: 0193 27 89099 Fax: 01932 789099 — Med. Dipl. Warsaw 1935; MFCM 1973; DPH Bristol 1961. Hon. Cons. King's Coll. Hosp. Lond. Prev: Princip. Med. Off. Lambeth CC.

ZAMIR, Rebecca Jayne 7 Chatsworth Drive, Tutbury, Burton-on-Trent DE13 9NS — BM BS 1993 Nottm.

ZAMIRI, Iraj 225 Lake Road W., Cardiff CF23 5QY Tel: 029 2075 8316 — MD 1973 Newc.; MB BS Durh. 1964; MRCS Eng. LRCP Lond. 1964. (Newc.) Sen. Lect. Welsh Nat. Sch. Med. & Hon. Consult. Univ. Hosp. Wales; Hon. Cons. Pub. Health Laborat. Cardiff.

ZAMIRI, Mozheh 27 Lonsdale Terrace, Newcastle upon Tyne NE2 3HQ — MB ChB 1996 Ed.

ZAMIRI, Parisa 31 Alison Road, London W3 6HZ — MB BS 1991 Lond.

ZAMMIT, Stanley George Broom House, Rumble St., Monkswood, Usk NP15 1QG — BM BCh 1993 Oxf.

ZAMMIT, Vincent (Surgery) 50 Church Road, Ashford TW15 2TU Tel: 01784 254041; 10 Sheperds Close, Shepperton TW17 9AL Tel: 01932 243337 — MD 1965 Malta; MRCGP 1987; Cert. Family Plann. JCC 1978.

ZAMMIT-MAEMPEL, Ivan Department of Radiology, Freeman Hospital, Newcastle upon Tyne NE7 7DN; 19 Baronswood, Gosforth, Newcastle upon Tyne NE3 3UB — MB ChB 1982 Manch.; MRCP (UK) 1985; FRCR 1988. Cons. Radiol. Freeman Hosp. Newc. u. Tyne. Prev: Sen. Regist. (Radiol.) NW RHA; Regist. (Radiol.) NW RHA; SHO (Med.) Wythenshawe Hosp.

ZAMMIT-MAEMPEL, Joseph George The Meadow Fields Practice, Chellaston Park, Snelsmoor Lane, Chellaston, Derby DE73 1TQ Tel: 01332 700455 Fax: 01332 700628; Longlands Farm, 19 Main St, Findern, Derby DE65 6AG Tel: 01283 703203 — MB ChB 1984 Dundee; DRCOG 1987; DCH RCPS Glas. 1986.

ZAMMIT-TABONA, Michael Victor Lanhael House, 34 High St., Toft, Cambridge CB3 7RL — MB 1976 Camb.; MA Camb. 1975, MB 1976, BChir 1975; MRCP (UK) 1978; Dip. Pharm. Med. RCP (UK) 1986. Med. Dir. & Vice-Pres. Europe, Smithkline Beecham Pharmaceut. Socs: Brit. Thorac. Soc. & Amer. Thorac. Soc. Prev: Research Fell. (Respirat. Med.) Univ. Brit. Columbia, Vancouver; Regist. (Med.) Hammersmith Hosp.; SHO (Med.) Kent & Canterbury Hosps.

ZAMMITT, Nicola Naomi 34/2 Clerk Street, Edinburgh EH8 9HX — MB ChB 1998 Ed.

ZAMORA EGUILUZ, Maria Christina Leyton Green Neighbourhood Health Service, 180 Essex Road, Leyton, London E10 6BT Tel: 020 7539 0756 Fax: 020 7556 6902 — MB ChB 1981 Birm.

ZAMORA VICENTE DE VERA, Francisco Javier Colchester General Hospital, Turner Road, Colchester CO4 5JL — LMS 1990 U Autonoma Madrid.

ZANDER, Karine Marguerite 39 Chestnut Road, London SE27 9EZ — MB ChB 1993 Bristol. SHO (Med.) Frenchay Hosp. Bristol.

ZANDER, Lucas Immanuel Department of General Practice, UMDS (St. Thomas), 50 Kennington Road, London SE11 Tel: 020 7735 5881; 39 Chestnut Road, London SE27 9EZ Tel: 020 8670 4901 — MB 1961 Camb.; BChir 1960; FRCGP 1982, M 1969; DCH Eng. 1964; DObst RCOG 1964. (St. Mary's & Camb.) Sen. Lect. Dept. Gen. Pract. St. Thos. Hosp. Med. Sch. Lond. Socs: Roy. Soc. Med. (Ex-Pres. Gen. Pract. Sect.).

ZANE, Jeffrey Neil Colne House Surgery, 99A Uxbridge Road, Rickmansworth WD3 2DJ Tel: 01923 776295 Fax: 01923 777744; 16 Dunsmore Way, Bushey, Watford WD23 4FA Tel: 020 8950 6705 Fax: 020 8950 1112 Email: dryulu@globalnet.co.uk — MB BS 1972 Lond.; MRCS Eng. LRCP Lond. 1972; DA Eng. 1974. (Univ. Coll. Hosp.)

ZANGOURAS, Dasos Thefanous Delfryn, Crundale, Haverfordwest SA62 4DF — MB BS 1995 Lond. Prev: Pembrokesh. Gen. Pract.; VTS 1996-1999.

ZANIEWSKI, Francis Teodor 2 Braemar Mansions, Cornwall Gardens, London SW7 4AF — MB BS 1973 Lond.; MRCP (UK) 1976; MRCS Eng. LRCP Lond. 1973; DCH Eng. 1975. (St. Thos.)

ZAPATA, Luis Camilo 31 Riverside Road, Oxford OX2 0HT — MB BS 1994 Lond.

ZAPATA-BRAVO, Enrique Milton Keynes Hospital, Standing Way, Milton Keynes MK6 5LD Tel: 01908 660033 Fax: 01908 243853; 31 Riverside Road, Oxford OX2 0HT Tel: 01865 721933 Fax: 01865 724645 — Medico Cirujano 1964 Chile; MSc Oxf. 1984; MRCPsych 1987; AFOM RCP Lond. 1983. Cons. Psychiat. Oxf. RHA; Med. Dir. Milton Keynes Community NHS Trust.; Acad. Tutor RCPsych. Milton Keynes. Prev: Cons. Psychol. Med. Oxf.; Cons. WHO Brazzaville; Dir. Hosp. del Torax Santiago.

ZAPHIROPOULOS, George Constantine Walsgrave Hospitals NHS Trust, Clifford Bridge Road, Coventry CV2 2DX — MB ChB Alexandria 1961; LMSSA Lond. 1967; FRCP Lond. 1985; MRCP Lond. 1969. Cons. Rheum. Coventry & Nuneaton Hosps., Walsgrave Hosps. NHS Trust & Geo. Eliot Hosp. NHS Trust. Socs: Brit. Soc. Rheum.; Midl. Rheum. Soc.; W Midl. Phys. Assn. Prev: Sen. Regist. (Rheum.) Guy's Hosp. Lond. & Roy. Sussex Co. Hosp. Brighton; Regist. (Med.) Roy. Vict. Hosp. Bournemouth.

ZAR, Nuzhat 23 The Highgate, Newcastle upon Tyne NE3 4LS — MB BS 1989 Newc.

ZARAGOZA CASARES, Pablo 22 Colston Road, East Sheen, London SW14 7PQ — LMS 1994 U Complutense Madrid.

ZARD, Chantal Maurice 2 Chiltern Close, Croydon CR0 5LZ — MB BS 1989 Lond.

ZARDIS, Michalakis Chris Testvale Surgery, 12 Salisbury Road, Totton, Southampton SO40 3PY Tel: 023 8086 6999/6990 Fax: 023 8066 3992; Little Busketts, 184 Woodlands Road, Woodlands, Southampton SO40 7GL — BM 1984 Soton.; MRCP (UK) 1987; MRCGP 1990; DRCOG 1989. Prev: SHO (Paediat. Cardiol.) Soton. & SW Hants. HA.

ZAREMBA, Eleanor Lois Stonewold, Hunton Road, Catterick Garrison DL9 3NN — MB BS 1998 Lond.

ZARGAR, Bashir Ahmad 12 Turnbury Close, Branston, Burton-on-Trent DE14 3GZ Tel: 01283 539603 — MB BS 1967 Kashmir. Clin. Med. Off. (Gen. Psychiat.) Premier Health Trust Burton-on-Trent. Prev: Clin. Med. Off. (Community Health) Blackpool, Wyre & Fylde HA.

ZARGAR, Ghulam Akbar 18 Langport Close, Fulwood, Preston PR2 9FE — MB BS 1976 Sind.

ZARGAR, Ghulam M Druids Heath Surgery, 27 Pound Road, Druids Heath, Birmingham B14 5SB Tel: 0121 430 5461 — MB BS 1967 Patna.

ZARIFA, Mr Zuhair Khalil Custom House Surgery, 16 Freemasons Road, London E16 3NA Tel: 020 7476 2255 Fax: 020 7511 8980; 5 Ffordd Hendre, The Ithens, Wrexham LL13 7EZ — MB ChB 1976 Ain Shams; FRCS Glas. 1985.

ZARKA, Zaki Anas 101 College Dean Close, Derriford, Plymouth PL6 8BP — MD 1984 Aleppo.

ZARNOSH, Mohammad Royal Eye Unit, Kington Hospital, Galsworthy Road, Kingston upon Thames KT2 7QB; 12 Manor Drive N., New Malden KT3 5PB — MB BS 1968 Punjab; MB BS Punjab (Pakistan) 1968; DO Eng. 1975. (Nishter Med. Coll. Multan) Clin. Asst. (Ophth.) Kington Hosp. Prev: SHO (Thoracic Med.) Aintree Hosp. Liverp.

ZARO, Mushtaq Ahmad The Surgery, 6-7 Aspen Court, Belvoir Park Road, Cleethorpes DN35 0SJ Tel: 01472 291977 — MB BS Janu & Kashmir 1969; MD Kasmir Univ. 1977; DCCH Sheff. 1994. GP Med. Off. GTFC.

ZAROD, Mr Andrew Peter 14 St John Street, Manchester M3 4AZ Tel: 0161 834 9900; 31B Carrwood Road, Bramhall, Stockport SK7 3LR Tel: 0161 485 3100 — MB ChB 1973 Liverp.; FRCS Ed. 1980; FRCS Eng. 1980. Cons. ENT Surg. N. Manch. Healthcare Trust and Centr. Manch. and Manch. Childr.'s Univ. Hosps. Socs: Founder Mem. (Ex-Counc. Mem.) Brit. Assn. Paediat. Otorhinolaryngol.; Roy. Soc. Med. (Vice-Pres. Sect. Laryngol. & Rhinol.). Prev: Lect. (Anat.) Univ. Manch.

ZARYCKYJ, Michael 3 Stockdove Wood, Cleveleys, Thornton-Cleveleys FY5 2JP Tel: 01253 866978 — MB ChB 1978 Manch. GP St. Anne's on Sea.

ZATMAN, Perry 104 Kimberley Road, Penylan, Cardiff CF23 5DN Tel: 01222 337701 Email: perryzatman@msn.co — MB BS 1991 Lond.; BSc Manch. 1986. Specialist Regist., Radiol. Uni. Hosp. Of Wales. Prev: SHO (Orthop.) Cardiff Roy. Infirm.

ZATMAN, Syeda Tahsin Fatima 13 Fernbank Close, Stalybridge SK15 2RZ — MB BS 1992 Lond.

ZATOUROFF, Michael 145 Harley Street, London W1G 6BJ Tel: 020 7935 4444 Fax: 020 7935 2725 — MB BS 1961 Lond.; FRCP Lond. 1982, M 1966; MRCS Eng. LRCP Lond. 1961; DCH Eng. 1964. (Lond. Hosp.) Hon. Sen. Lect. (Med.) Roy. Free Hosp. Lond.; Lect. (Med.) Lond. Foot Hosp.; Examr. Med. Soc. Chiropodists; Examr. Med. Conjt. Bd. Eng. Socs: (Counc.) Med. Soc. Lond.; Sec. Osler Club. Prev: Regist. (Med.) Roy. N.. Hosp. Lond.; Regist. Univ. Coll. Hosp. Ibadan; Phys. Kuwait Govt.

ZAVODY, Maria 42 Buckland Avenue, Slough SL3 7PH Tel: 01753 523575 — MD 1963 Pecs Hungary. Staff Psychiat. Huntercombe Manor Hosp. Taplow. Prev: Regist. (Psychiat.) Pk. Prewett Hosp. Basingstoke.

ZAW, Win 9 Friarwood Lane, Pontefract General Infirmary, Pontefract WF8 1DX; 9 Friarwood Lane, Pontefract WF8 1DX Tel: 01977 600600 — MB BS 1984 Med. Inst. (I) Rangoon; MRCP (UK) 1995; DCH RCP Lond. 1994.

ZAW WIN, Dr 53 Taunton Way, Stanmore HA7 1DJ — MB BS 1971 Med. Inst. (I) Rangoon. (Med. Inst. (I) Rangoon) SHO (Anaesth.) ScarBoro. Hosp.

ZAYYAN, Mr Kasimu Sanusi 218 Sandycombe Road, Kew, Richmond TW9 2EQ Tel: 020 8948 7823 — MB BS 1983 Nigeria; FRCS Ed. 1990; FRCSI 1990.

ZBRZEZNIAK, Wiktor Stanislaw Caythorpe Surgery, 52-56 High Street, Caythorpe, Grantham NG32 3DN Tel: 01400 272215 Fax: 01400 273608; The Surgery, 52 High St, Caythorpe, Grantham NG32 3DN Tel: 01400 72215 — MB BS 1985 Lond.; BSc (Hons.) Lond. 1982; MRCGP 1989; DCH RCP Lond. 1988. Prev: Trainee GP Lincoln VTS; Ho. Phys. & Ho. Surg. Guy's Hosp. Lond.

ZDZIARSKA, Caroline Anne Child Health Department, Mansfield Community Hospital, Stockwell Gate, Mansfield NG18 5QJ Fax: 01623 424062; 45 Haddon Road, Ravenshead, Nottingham NG15 9EZ — BM BS 1988 Nottm.; BMedSci Nottm. 1986; MRCGP 1994. (Nottm.) Community Paediat. (Staff Grade) Centr. Healthcare Trust Notts. Socs: BACCH. Prev: GP.

ZEALLEY, Andrew King (retired) Viewfield House, 12 Tipperlinn Road, Edinburgh EH10 5ET Tel: 0131 447 5545 Fax: 0131 447 5545 — MB ChB 1959 Ed.; FRCP Ed. 1974, M 1963; FRCPsych 1979, M 1971; DPM Ed. 1966. Prev: Cons. Psychiat. Roy. Edin. Hosp.

ZEALLEY, Helen Elizabeth, QHP, OBE Lothian Health, Deaconess House, 148 Pleasance, Edinburgh EH8 9RS Tel: 0131 536 9163

Fax: 0131 536 9164; Viewfield House, 12 Tipperlinn Road, Edinburgh EH10 5ET Tel: 0131 447 5545 Fax: 0131 447 5545 Email: helen.zealley@lhb.scot.nhs.uk — MB ChB 1964 Ed.; MD Ed. 1968; FRCP Ed. 1987; FFPHM 1980, M 1974; DCCH RCP Ed. (Hons) 1982; Dip. Soc. Med. Ed. 1973. Chief Admin. Med. Off. & Dir. Pub. Health Lothian HB; Hon. Sen. Lect. Univ. Edin. Prev: SCM Lothian HB; Med. Off. Scott. Counc. Postgrad. Med. Educat.; Regist. Regional Virus Laborat. City Hosp. Edin.

ZEALLEY, Ian Alexander Freeman Hospital, Freeman Road, Newcastle upon Tyne NE7 7DN Tel: 0191 284 3111; 76 Holly Avenue, Jesmond, Newcastle upon Tyne NE2 2QA Tel: 0191 281 3334 — MB ChB 1991 Ed.; BSc (Med. Sci.) (Hons.) Ed. 1989; MRCP (UK) 1994; FRCR 1997. Regist. Rotat. (Radiol.) N. & Yorks. Region. Socs: (Ex-Jun. Pres.) Roy. Med. Soc. Edin. Prev: SHO Rotat. (Med.) Newc. Teach. Hosps.; Ho. Phys. & Ho. Surg. Roy. Infirm. Edin.

ZEALLEY, Kirsten Elizabeth 12 Tipperlinn Road, Edinburgh EH10 5ET Tel: 0131 447 5545 Fax: 0131 447 5545 — MB ChB 1991 Dundee; MRCGP 1997; DCH RCP Lond. 1994; DFFP 1997. (Dundee) Prev: GP/Regist. Inch Pk. Surg. Edin.; SHO (Psychiat.) Roy. Edin. Hosp.; SHO (O & G) Gosford Hosp. NSW, Austral.

ZEALLEY, Monica Margaret (retired) The Old Vicarage, Southstoke, Bath BA2 7DU Tel: 01225 832080 — MB ChB 1946 Ed.

ZEB KHAN, Aurang Birch Hill Hospital, Birch Road, Rochdale OL12 9QB Tel: 01706 377777 Fax: 01706 755663; 23 Hawthorn Road, Rochdale OL11 5JQ Tel: 01706 44290 — MB BS 1978 Peshawar; MCPS Pakistan 1982; DCH Dub. 1985; DCH Punjab 1980. (Khyber Med. Coll. Peshawar) Staff Grade (Paediat.) Birch Hill Hosp. Rochdale. Prev: Regist. (Paediat.) W. Dorset Gen. Hosp., Altanegalvin Area Hosp. N. Irel. & Waterford Regional Hosp. Irel.

ZEBOUNI, Luay Nasrat Peter Royal National Hospital for Rheumatic Diseases, Upper Borough Wells, Bath BA9 1RL Tel: 01225 465941; 24 Rufford Close, Harrow HA3 8UX Tel: 020 8907 1420 — MB ChB 1973 Baghdad; DMedRehab RCP 1984 Lond.; MRCPI 1987; MPhil 1990 Leeds. (Baghdad University Medical School) Specialist Regist. Rehabil. Med., Roy. Nat. Hosp. for Rheumatic Dis.s, Bath. Socs: Brit. Soc. Rehabil. Med.; Brit. Med. Assn.

ZEBRO, Tadeusz Julian Microprep Pathology Laboratory, Ross House, Church Street, Wistow, Huntingdon PE28 2QE Tel: 01487 823131 Fax: 01487 824484 — Lekarz Krakow 1953; MD 1st Med. Inst. Moscow 1956; FRCPath 1980. Cons. Histopath. Microprep Laborat. Servs. Huntingdon. Socs: Assn. Clin. Path.; Eur. Soc. Pathol. Prev: Cons. Histopath. Hinchingbrooke Hosp. & Cromwell Clinic Huntingdon; Vis. Prof. & Hon. Cons. Path. King's Coll. Hosp. Med. Sch. Lond.; Vis. Prof. Inst. Path. Giessen Univ. Med. Sch. W. Germany.

ZECKLER, Sharon-Rose The Wall House, Mongewell Park, Wallingford OX10 8DA — MB BS 1996 Lond.

ZEEGEN, Ronald, OBE Westminster & Chelsea Hospital, 369 Fulham Road, London SW10 9NH Tel: 020 8237 8007 Fax: 020 8237 5007; 36 Clare Lawn Avenue, East Sheen, London SW14 8BG Tel: 020 8876 4622 — MB BS 1962 Lond.; FRCP Lond. 1980, M 1967; MRCS Eng. LRCP Lond. 1964; DObst RCOG 1964. (St. Bart.) Cons. Phys. (Gen. Med. & Gastroenterol.) W.m. & Chelsea Hosp. & The Lister Hosp. Lond.; Hon. Cons. Gastroenterol. Roy. Marsden & Brompton Hosps. Lond.; Hon. Cons. Phys. Roy. Hosp. Chelsea. Socs: BMA & Brit. Soc. Gastroenterol. Prev: Sen. Regist. (Med.) W.m. Hosp. Lond.; Research Fell. & Sen. Regist. (Med.) St. Bart. Hosp. Lond.; SHO Roy. Free Hosp. Lond.

ZEGLAM, Adel Moh Ben Intergrated Child Health Services Unit, Memorial Hospital, Shooters Hill, London SE18 3RZ Tel: 020 8856 5511; 2 Jenner House, Restell Close, London SE3 7UW — MB BCh 1981 Al Fateh; MRCPI 1991; MRCPCH 1996; DCH RCPI 1988. Paediat. Greenwich Health Care Trust. Socs: Libyan Soc. Paediat.; Assn. for Research in Infant & Child Developm. Prev: Staff Grade (Paediat.) Greenwich Health Care Trust; Regist. (Paediat.) Brook Gen. Hosp. & Greenwich Gen. Hosp. Lond.; Regist. (Paediat.) Cavan Gen. Hosp. Irel.

ZEGLEMAN, Fiona Elizabeth 4 Wester Coates Avenue, Edinburgh EH12 5LS Tel: 0131 337 1900 — MB ChB 1980 Ed.; MRCPsych 1985.

ZEIDAN, Marwan Moorfields Eye Hospital, City Road, London EC1V 2PD Tel: 020 7253 3411 — Approbation 1971 Leipzig. (Univ. Leipzig, Germany)

ZEIDER, Mr Paul Alfred The Surgery, 3 Candover Street, London W1W 7DE Tel: 020 7636 4311 — MB ChB 1969 Sheff.; FRCS Ed. 1975; MRCOG 1974.

ZEIDERMAN, Mr Michael Richard Southport & Ormskick NHS Trust, Town Lane, Kew, Southport PR8 6NJ Tel: 01704 704252; Email: mz@zeiderman.freeserve.co.uk — MB ChB 1978 Liverp.; BSc (Hons.) Liverp. 1975, ChM 1988; FRCS Eng. 1982. (Liverpool) Cons. Gastroenterol. & Gen. Surg. S.port & Ormskick NHS Trust; Clin. Lect. (Surg.) Univ. of Liverp.; Mem. Ct. of Examr.s Roy. Coll. of Surg.s of Eng. Prev: Lect. Univ. Dept. Surg. N.. Gen. Hosp. Sheff.; Lect. & Hon. Sen. Regist. Sheff. & Chesterfield Hosp.; Research Fell. Leeds Gen. Infirm. 1983-5.

ZEIDLER, Martin Dieter CJD Surveillance Unit, Western General Hospital, Crewe Road, Edinburgh EH4 2XU Tel: 0131 332 2117 Fax: 0131 343 1404; 20 High Lawn, Devizes SN10 2BA — BM 1989 Soton.; MRCP (UK) 1993. Research Regist. (Creutzfeldt-Jakob Dis. Surveillance) Unit W.. Gen.Hosp. Edin. Prev: SHO (Med.) Roy. United Hosp. Bath; SHO (Neurol.) Roy. Devon & Exeter Hosp.

ZEILMAKER, Cornelis 4 Walters Mead, Ashtead KT21 2BP — Artsexamen 1987 Leiden.

ZEIN SANCHEZ, Miss Maria Pilar 66 Awel Mor, Llanedey Rn, Cardiff CF23 9QB Tel: 01222 540059 Fax: 01222 540019; c/o San Emilio 4 Bajo, 28017, Madrid 28017, Spain Tel: 00 34 1 7252776 — LMS 1991 Madrid; MBBS 1991. (Fac. Med. of Madrid Autonomous Univ.) SHO (Anaesth.) Univ. Hosp. Of Wales Cardiff. Socs: Jun. Trainee Mem. Roy. Coll. Anaesths.; Jun. Trainee Mem. Assn. Anaesths. of Eng. and Irel. Prev: SHO (Anaesth.) James Paget Hosp. Norf.; SHO (Basic Surg. Rotat.) James Paget Hosp. Gt. Yarmouth, Norf.; SHO (A & E) Maidstone Gen. Hosp. Kent.

ZEINELDINE, Ahmed Amr 109 Commercial Way, London SE15 6DB Tel: 020 7703 6460 Fax: 020 7701 2266 Email: amr.zeineldine@dial.pipex.com; 99 Great Brownings, College Road, London SE21 7HR Tel: 020 8670 7488 Fax: 020 8488 7872 Email: amr.zeineldine@which.net — MB ChB 1975 Alexandria; MRCGP 1989; T(GP) 1994. Socs: Diplomate Fac. Family Plann. RCOG. Prev: Trainee GP Lond.; GP Riyadh Armed Forces Hosp.

ZEITLIN, Professor Harry UCL, Academic Department of Psychiatry, Wychelm House, Hamstel Road, Harlow CM20 1QX; 3 West Grove, Greenwich, London SE10 8QT Tel: 020 8692 6403 Fax: 020 8691 9477 Email: hhz@msn.com — MRCS Eng. LRCP Lond. 1962; MD Lond. 1983, MPhil 1971, BSc (Hons. Physiol.) 1959; FRCP Lond. 1988, M 1967; FRCPsych 1972, M 1972. (Lond. Hosp.) Prof. Child & Adolesc. Psychiat. Univ. Coll. Lond.; Hon. Cons. N. E. Essex, Ment. Health. Socs: Fell. Roy. Soc. Med. Prev: Reader (Child Psychiat.) Char. Cross & W.m. Med. Sch. Lond.; Sen. Regist. Childr. Dept. Maudsley Hosp. Lond.; Regist. Lond., Maudsley, & S.end Gen. Hosp.

ZEITLIN, Helen Claire Avonbury, 16 High St., Bidford-on-Avon, Alcester B50 4BU — MB BS 1971 Lond.; MRCP (UK) 1974; MRC Path 1979.

ZEITLIN, Susan Rose Lower Farm Cottage, Lower Farm Lane, Ampfield, Romsey SO51 9BP; 22 Abbey Close, Crapstone, Yelverton PL20 7PX Tel: 01822 854823 — MB BS 1977 Lond.; FRCPC 1985.

ZEITON, Mr Asaid Ali Royal Lancaster Infirmary, Ashton Road, Lancaster LA1 4RP Tel: 01524 65944 — MB BCh 1981 Al Fateh; FRCS Ed. 1992.

ZEITOUN, Mr Hisham 9 Moelwyn Avenue W., Kinmel Bay, Rhyl LL18 5DR Tel: 01745 353177 Email: rzi@lgobalnet.co.uk — MB ChB 1984 Alexandria; FRCS Glas. 1993; FRCS (ORL-NNS) Glos 1998; 17PHIP, Keele Uni. 1998; 17S (ORL) Alexandria 1989. (Alexandria University Egypt) Cons. Otolaryngologist, Head & Neck Surg., NHS Trust, N. Wales.

ZEITOUNE, Mr Samir Moussa 32 Stanbrook Road, Monkspath, Solihull B90 4UT Tel: 0121 745 7712 — MB ChB 1968 Alexandria; FRCS Glas. 1982.

ZEKI, Mr S M 4 Highburgh Road, Glasgow G12 9YD — MB ChB 1971 Baghdad; MSc (Med. Sci.) Glas. 1990; FRCS Glas. 1986; FRCOphth 1993; DO RCS Eng. 1980. Prev: Sen. Regist. Rotat. W. Midl.; Sen. Regist. & Regist. (Ophth.) Tennent Inst. Ophth. Glas.

ZELAYA-MENDIVIL, Gonzalo Felipe Tigh-Na-Mara, Kirkton, Glenelg, Kyle IV40 8JR Tel: 01599 522272 Fax: 01599 522272 —

ZELENKA

Medico Cirujano San Andres, Bolivia 1970. Princip. GP Glenelg. Prev: Assoc. GP Scourie Durness.

ZELENKA, Robert Martin Accident and Emergency Department, Friarage Hospital, Northallerton, Northallerton DL6 1JG Tel: 01609 763334; The Old School Cottage, Great Smeaton DL6 2EY Tel: 01609 881357 Email: robzelenka@lineone.net — MB BS 1988 Lond.; MA Oxf. 1981; MRCGP 1994; DFFP 1994. (Guy's) Assoc. Specialist in A&E Med., Friargate Hosp., N.allerton, N. Yorks DL6 1JG. Prev: Trainee GP Harrogate VTS; SHO (Orthop.) Friarage Hosp. N.allerton; SHO (Psychiat.) Harrogate Dist. Hosp.

ZELIN, Jill Margot Sexual Health Centre, St Bartholomews Hospital, West Smithfield, London EC1A 7BE Tel: 020 7601 8090 Fax: 020 7601 8601 Email: j.zelin@bartsandthelondon@nhs.uk — MB BCh 1984 Wales; MFFP; MRCOG 1991; Dip GU Med. Soc. Apoth. Lond. 1990. p/t Cons. Genitourin. Med. St. Bart. Hosp. Lond. Prev: Sen. Regist. (Genitourin. Med.) St. Bart. Hosp. Lond.

ZELISKO, Richard Stephen 1 Edinburgh Drive, Ickenham, Uxbridge UB10 8QY — MB BS 1975 Lond.

ZEMAN, Adam Zbynek James Dept. of Clinical Neur.Sciences, Western General Hospital, Edinburgh E44 2XU Tel: 0131 537 1167 Email: adam.zeman@ed.ac.uk — BM BCh 1984 Oxf.; BA 1979 Oxf; DM 1994 Oxf; MRCP 1987 UK. Cons. Neurol., W.ern Gen. Hosp., Ed.; Sen. Lect. Univ. Ed. Socs: Assn. Of Brit. Neurol.; Brit. NeuroPsychiat. Assn.; Brit. Sleep Soc. Prev: Sen. Regist. (Neurol.) Addenbrooke's Hosp. Camb.; Regist. Nat. Hosp. for Neurol. & Neurosurg. Qu. Sq. Lond.; Regist. (Neurol.) Radcliffe Infirm. Oxf.

ZENTLER-MUNRO, Patrick Luke Department of Medicine, Raigmore Hospital, Inverness IV2 3UJ Tel: 01463 704000 Fax: 01463 705460; Brae House, Canonbury Terrace, Fortrose IV10 8TT Tel: 01381 620039 — MB BChir 1972 Camb.; MA 1973, MD 1985; FRCP Ed. 1989; MRCP (UK) 1975. Cons. Radiol. Airedale Gen. Hosp.; Hon. Clin. Sen. Lect. Univ. Aberd. Med. Sch.; Asst. Edr. Drug Therap. Bull. Prev: Hon. Clin. Asst. Brompton Hosp. Lond.; Sen. Regist. St. Geo. Hosp. Lond.; Research Fell. St. Geo. Hosp. Med. Sch. Lond.

ZEPEDA, Armando Ramon 323 Skircoat Green Road, Halifax HX3 0NA Tel: 01422 54874 — MD 1973 El Salvador.

ZEPPETELLA, Giovambattista St Josephs Hospice, Mare St., London E8 4SA Tel: 020 8525 6060 Fax: 020 8985 4711 Email: jzeppetella@stjh.org.uk — MB BS 1985 Lond.; BSc (Hons.) Lond. 1981; MRCGP 1991. (University College London) Cons. Palliat. Med. St. Joseph's Hospice Lond.; Hon. Barts and the Lond. NHS Trust.

ZERAFA, R Paston Health Centre, Chadburn, Peterborough PE4 7DH Tel: 01733 572584 Fax: 01733 328131 — MD 1967 Malta.

ZERMANSKY, Adam James 2 Wigton Grove, Leeds LS17 7DZ Tel: 0113 268 3802 — MB ChB 1994 Birm.; MRCP 1998.

ZERMANSKY, Arnold Geoffrey Dib Lane Practice, 112A Dib Lane, Leeds LS8 3AY Tel: 0113 295 4650 Fax: 0113 295 4663; 2 Wigton Grove, Leeds LS17 7DZ Tel: 0113 268 3802 Email: arnoldz@easynet.co.uk — MB ChB 1970 (Hons.) Leeds; MRCGP (Distinc.) 1978; DObst RCOG 1972. Hon. Sen. Research Fell. Univ. Leeds, Chair E. Leeds PCG; Tutor (Gen. Pract.) Univ. Leeds; Mem. Leeds LMC. Socs: (Ex-Pres.) Leeds Jewish Med. Soc. Prev: Med. Adviser Leeds FHSA; Gp. Mem. Leeds E. Dist. Managem. Bd. & Chairm. Leeds E. Dist. Med. Comm.

***ZERMANSKY, William Simon** 2 Wigton Grove, Alwoodley, Leeds LS17 7DZ — MB ChB 1998 Birm.

ZEWAWI, Mr Ali Salem Flat A, 43 Rectory Road, Crumpsall, Manchester M8 5EA — MB BS 1976 Garyounis, Libya; FRCSI 1990.

ZEYA, Kyaw 6 Burnsall Close, Pendeford, Wolverhampton WV9 5RU Tel: 01902 781096 — MB BS 1979 Med. Inst. (I) Rangoon; LRCP LRCS Ed. LRCPS Glas. 1986.

ZEYLSTRA, Onno Nanou 11 Wellington Park, Montrose DD10 8QG — Artsexamen 1988 Amsterdam.

ZEZULKA, Alexander Vratislav Airedale Hospital, Skipton Road, Steeton, Keighley BD20 6TD Tel: 01535 292018 Fax: 01535 292019 — MB BS 1977 Lond.; FRCP 1999; MD Lond. 1993; MRCP (UK) 1980; BSc (Physiol.) Lond. 1974. (Westm.) Cons. Cardiol. Airedale Hosp. Steeton W. Yorks. Socs: Brit. Cardiac Soc.; Brit. Cardiac Interven.al Soc.; Brit. Pacing and Electrophysiol. Soc. Prev: Sen. Regist. & Regist. (Cardiol.) Leeds Gen. Infirm.; Sen. Regist. (Med.) Profess. Med. Unit, Leeds Gen. Infirm.

ZIA-UL-HASAN, Dr 4 Abbots Way, Westlands, Newcastle ST5 2ET — MB BS 1984 Peshawar; MRCP (UK) 1994.

ZIA, Moohammad Imran 60 Knotts Green Road, London E10 6DE — MB BS 1996 Lond.

ZIA, Mubashar 48 St Kilda Drive, Jordanhill, Glasgow G14 9LT — MB BS 1986 Punjab; FFA RCSI 1993.

ZICCHIERI, Francesco Luigi Robin Lane Medical Centre, Robin Lane, Pudsey LS28 7DE Tel: 0113 295 1444 Fax: 0113 295 1440; Woodland Villas, 84 Bachelor Lane, Horsforth, Leeds LS18 5NF — MB ChB 1985 Leeds; MRCGP 1989. Prev: SHO (Ophth.) Bradford Roy. Infirm.

ZICKERMAN, Anna Maria 6 Aber Road, Stoneygate, Leicester LE2 2BA Tel: 0116 270 9565 Fax: 0116 270 9565 — MB ChB 1994 Leic. (Univ. Leicester) VTS Regist. (Rotat.) O & G, Leicester Gen. Hosp.; Flexible Trainee. Prev: SHO Rotat. (Med.) Leicester; SHO (Cardiol.) Glenfield Gen. Hosp.; SHO (Respirat. Med.) Glenfield Gen. Hosp.

ZIDEMAN, David Anthony, QHP, CStJ 31 Moss Lane, Pinner HA5 3BB Email: d.zideman@hhnt.org — MB BS 1972 Lond.; FIMC RCS Ed, 2000; BSc (Hons.) Lond. 1969; FFA RCS Eng. 1976; Dip. IMC RCS Ed. 1995. (Lond. Hosp.) Cons. Anaesth. Hammersmith Hosp. & Hon. Sen. Lect. (Anaesth.) Imperial Coll. Sch. of Med.; Chief of Serv. for Anaesth., Hammersmith Hosps. Trust. Socs: Sec. of Eur. Resusc. Counc.; Vice Chairm. BASICS; Exec. Comm. - Resusc. Counc. (UK). Prev: Sen. Regist. (Anaesth.) Hammersmith Hosp. Roy. Postgrad. Med. Sch.; Fell. (Anaesth.) Hosp. Sick Childr. Toronto, Canada; Regist. (Anaesth.) St. Mary's Hosp. Lond.

ZIEGLER, Emma Samantha Mary 27 Love Lane, Petersfield GU31 4BP — MB ChB 1988 Bristol. (Bristol) Specialist Regist. (Occupat. Health) Camb.

ZIELINSKI, Richard Antoni 3 Fell Grove, Birmingham B21 8JQ — MB ChB 1993 Birm.; ChB Birm. 1993.

ZIERVOGEL, Mark Allan (retired) 2 Robinsfield, Balmore Road, Bardowie, Milngavie, Glasgow G62 6ER Tel: 01360 622268 Email: ziervogel@uk.gateway.net — MB ChB 1969 Glas.; BSc Natal 1959; FRCR 1975; FFR 1974; DMRD Eng. 1972. Prev: Cons. Radiol. Roy. Hosp. Sick Childr. Glas. & Stirling Roy. Infirm.

ZIGMOND, Anthony Stephen High Royds Hospital, Menston, Ilkley LS29 6AQ — MB ChB 1975 Birm.; MRCPsych 1979. Cons. Psychiat. Leeds W.. HA (T).

ZIGMOND, David North Aisle Medical Centre, St James Church, Thurland Road, London SE16 4AA Tel: 020 7237 4066 Fax: 020 7740 1031 — MB ChB 1969 Birm.; MRCGP 1976; DPM Eng. 1975. p/t Liaison Psychiat. Hammersmith Hosp. Socs: Inst. Transactional Anal.; Assn. of Gp. and Individual Psychother. Prev: Sen. Lect. NE Lond. Polytechnic; Vis. Tutor Brit. Postgrad. Med. Federat.; Hon. Lect. Roy. Postgrad. Med. Sch. Lond.

ZIKO, Adel Aly Osman 57 Rectory Lane, Bury BL9 7TA — MB BCh 1980 Ain Shams, Egypt; MRCP (UK) 1994.

ZILAHI, Clara Clotilde 31 Wimbotsham Road, Downham Market PE38 9PE — MB 1956 Camb.; BChir 1955; FRCS Eng. 1965.

ZILKHA, Kevin Jerome Cromwell Hospital, Cromwell Road, London SW5 0TU Tel: 020 7460 5668 Fax: 020 7460 5669 — MB BS 1953 Lond.; MD Lond. 1962; FRCP Lond. 1970, M 1958; MRCS Eng. LRCP Lond. 1953. (Guy's) Emerit. Hon. Neurol. King's Coll. Hosp. Lond.; Emerit. Hon. Phys. Nat. Hosp. Qu. Sq. Lond. Socs: Fell. Roy. Soc. Med.; Assn. Brit. Neurols. Prev: Hon. Neurol. Army & Roy. Hosp. Lond.; Sub-Dean Inst. Neurol. Qu. Sq. Lond.; Ho. Phys. (Neurol.) Guy's Hosp. Lond.

ZILKHA, Timothy Robert Tarr House, Kingston St Mary, Taunton TA2 8HY — MB BS 1984 Lond.; FCAnaesth. 1990. (Guy's) Cons. Anaesth. Taunton & Som. Hosps. Socs: Assn. Anaesths.; Harveian Soc. Prev: Sen. Regist. (Anaesth.) & Research Fell. (Pain Relief) King's Coll. Hosp. Lond.; Regist. (Anaesth.) St. Bart. & S.end Gp. Hosps.

ZILLWOOD, Sarah Jane 28 Malling Avenue, Broughton Astley, Leicester LE9 6QS — MB ChB 1989 Leic.

ZILVA, Professor Joan Foster (retired) 30 Lavington Court, 77 Putney Hill, London SW15 3NU Tel: 020 8789 1585 Email: jzilva@aol.com — MB BS 1951 Lond.; BSc (Special Physiol.) Lond. 1947, MD 1958; FRCP Lond. 1971, M 1955; FRCPath 1974, M 1964. Emerit. Prof. Chem. Path. Univ. Lond.; Hon. Cons. Chem. Path. Riverside HA. Prev: Prof. Chem. Path. Char. Cross & W.m. Med. Sch.

ZIMBLER, Nicoletta 23 Rosebery Crescent, Jesmond, Newcastle upon Tyne NE2 1EU — MB ChB 1991 Leic.; MRCP (UK) 1994. SHO (Anaesth.) Sunderland Dist. Gen. Hosp. Prev: SHO (Infec. Dis.) Dundee; SHO (Med.) Nottm.

ZIMMER, Stanley 29 Burn Road, Darvel KA17 0DB — MB ChB 1970 Glas.; FFA RCS Eng. 1974. Cons. Anaesth. N. Ayrsh. & Arran NHS Trust.

ZIMMERN, Ronald Leslie Public Health Genetics Unit, Strangeways Research Laboratory, Worts Causeway, Cambridge CB1 8RN Tel: 01223 740228 Fax: 01223 740200 Email: vou.zimmern@srl.cam.ac.uk; Hall Farm House, Great Abington, Cambridge CB1 6AE Tel: 01223 891996 — MB BChir 1972 Camb.; MA Camb. 1976; FRCP Lond. 1992; MRCP (UK) 1973; FFPHM RCP (UK) 1993; MFCM 1987. (Middlx.) Dir., Pub. Health Genetics Unit; Assoc. Lect. Univ. Camb; Cons. in Pub. Health Med. Socs: Brit. Assn. Med. Managers (Bd. Dir.) & Roy. Soc. Med. Prev: Cons. Pub. Health Med. Addenbrooke's Hosp. Camb.; Hon. Sen. Regist. (Neurol.) Addenbrooke's Hosp. Camb.; Sen. Regist. (Community Med.) Camb. HA.

ZINCKE, Horst Department of Uro-Oncologic Surgery, Health Care International (Scotland) Ltd., Beardmore St., Clydebank G81 4HX — State Exam Med 1966 Frankfurt.

ZINKIN, Pamela Margaret 45 Anson Road, London N7 0AR — MB ChB 1956 Leeds; FRCP Lond. 1981.

ZINNA, Rosario Federico 23 Wharfedale Road, Westbourne, Bournemouth BH4 9BT — MD 1948 Naples; LAH Dub. 1970; MRCPsych 1971; Dip. Amer. Bd. Psychiat. & Neurol. 1965; Dip. Psych. McGill 1960; ECFMG Cert. 1962. (Naples) Cons., W. of Eng. Laser Centre, Som. Nuffield Hosp., Taunton. Socs: Corresp. Mem. Amer. Med. Psychiat. Assns.; BMA. Prev: Clin. Tutor Duke Univ. Med. Sch., Univ. N. Carolina Med. Sch. & Dartmouth Coll. Med. Sch., U.S.A.

ZINTILIS, Spyros Andrea London Road Surgery, 49 London Road, Canterbury CT2 8SG Tel: 01227 463128 Fax: 01227 786308; 31 Longacre, Chestfield, Whitstable CT5 3PQ Tel: 01227 792452 Fax: 01227 792132 Email: spyros@epulse.net — MD 1973 Athens; MRCS Eng. LRCP Lond. 1975.

ZIPRIN, Anna Elisabet 6 The Closes, Haddenham, Aylesbury HP17 8JN — MB ChB 1992 Manch.

ZIPRIN, Jennifer Hilary 5H Castlebar Park, Ealing, London W4 1DD Tel: 0208 930 1103 Email: jenny@3iprin.freeserve.co.uk; 20 Christchurch Road, Malvern WR14 3BE — MB BCh 1993 Wales; MRCP Paeds. Specialist Regist. Neonatology Univ. Coll. Hosp. Lond. Prev: SPR Paediat. Hillingdon Hosp. Lond.

ZIPRIN, Paul 4A Churchfield Road, London W13 9NG Tel: 020 8566 0877 Email: paul@ziprin.freeserve.co.uk — MB BCh 1992 Wales; FRCS (Eng) 1996. NW Thames Specialist Regist. Rotat. (Surg.). Prev: Regist (Gen. Surg.) Roy. Gwent Hosp.; SHO (Gen. Surg.) Cardiff Roy. Infirm.; SHO (Urol.) Cardiff Roy. Infirm.

ZIRK, Maia Helga 15 Beechwood Close, Leicester LE5 6SY — Med. Dipl. Tartu 1944.

ZIYADI, Nadia Fatima Adnan 166 Buckswood Drive, Gossops Green, Crawley RH11 8JF — MB ChB 1984 Baghdad, Iraq.

ZIYAIE, Dorin 11 Minard Crescent, Dundee DD3 6LH — MB ChB 1993 Dundee.

ZLOTNIK, Joanna Marcia Catherine 34 Ridgeway Road, Salisbury SP1 3BU Tel: 01722 335423 — MB ChB 1966 Ed.; FRCS Eng. 1971; FRACS 1972.

ZMYSLOWSKI, Andrzej Jerzy 24 Chester Avenue, Southport PR9 7ET — MB BS 1980 Newc.; Dip.Med.Ac 1997; MRCGP 1984; DCCH RCGP 1984; DRCOG 1983; Cert. Family Plann. JCC 1983. p/t Med. Exam. for Benefits Agency Med. Serv.; Registered Med. Examr. Gen. Counc. Brit. Shipping; Indep. Acupunc. Pract. Socs: Brit. Med. Acupunct. Soc. Prev: Med. Off. P & O Lines; GP Houghton-le-Spring; Indep. Acupunc. Co. Durh.

ZOBAIR, Mike Swan Street Surgery, 35-41 Swan Street, Longtown, Carlisle CA6 5UZ Tel: 01228 791202 Fax: 01228 791942 — MB BS 1968 Patna. (P. of Wales Med. Coll.) GP Princip. Single Handed; Civil Med. Pract. MoD Establ. Socs: BMA; SPA. Prev: SHO Gen. Med. Chester-le-St., Durh.; Ho. Off. (Gen. Surg.) Sunderland Gen. Hosp.; SHO (Gen. Med., ENT & Eyes) Patna Med. Coll. Hosp., India.

ZOHA, Mir Moin 24 Queen Elizabeth Drive, London N14 6RD — MB ChB 1992 Birm.

ZOHDY, Mr Gamal West Wales General Hospital, Carmarthen SA31 2AF Tel: 01267 227749 Fax: 01267 227414 Email: zgamal@yahoo.com — MB ChB 1982 Alexandria, Egypt; FRCS Ed. 1993. (Alexandria Coll. of Med.) Assoc. Specialist (Ophth.). Prev: Staff Grade (Ophth.) Shrops. HA; Regist. (Ophth.) W. of Scotl.

ZOLCZER, Laszlo Department of Orthopaedics, Mayday University Hospital, London Road, Croydon CR7 7YE Tel: 020 8401 3000 Fax: 020 8401 3100 — MD 1985 Semmelweis, Hungary; Hungarian Trauma & Orthop. Board 1990. Staff Surg. (Orthop.) Mayday Univ. Hosp. Somey. Socs: Brit. Orthop. Assn.; Hungarian Trauma & Orthop. Assoc. Prev: Sen. Regist. (Orthop.); Regist. (Orthop.).

ZOLKIPLI, Zarazuela 15B Canonbury Square, London N1 2AL — MB ChB 1996 Ed.

ZOLLINGER-READ, Paul John Mount Chambers, 92 Coggeshall Road, Braintree CM7 9BY Tel: 01376 553415; 2 Grove Field, Braintree CM7 5NS — MB BS 1986 Camb.; MA Camb. 1986; DCH RCP Lond. 1991; DRCOG 1990; DGM RCP Lond. 1989.

ZOLLMAN, Catherine Esther 11 Cliftonwood Crescent, Bristol BS8 4TU Tel: 0117 921 1247 — MB BS 1989 Lond.; BA (Physiol. Sci.) Oxf.1986; MRCP (UK) 1992. Dir. Med. Educat. Servs. Research Counc. for Complementary Med. Lond.; GP Montpelier Health Centre, Bristol. Prev: GP/Regist. Montpelier Health Centre Bristol; Regist. (Oncol. Med.) Qu. Eliz. Hosp. Birm.; SHO (Paediat. Oncol.) Bristol Childr. Hosp.

ZOLTIE, Mr Nigel Accident & Emergency Department, Leeds General Infirmary, Great George St., Leeds LS1 3EX Tel: 0113 392 6470 Fax: 0113 392 2810 Email: nigel.zoltie@leedsth.nhs.uk — MB ChB 1977 Bristol; FRCS Ed. 1982; FFAEM 1994. Cons. A & E Leeds Gen. Infirm.; Hon. Sen. Clin. Lect. (A & E) Leeds Univ. Prev: Regist. (Plastic Surg.) W. Norwich Hosp.; Sen. Regist. (A & E) Leeds.

ZOLTOWSKI, Mr Janusz Andrzej Highfield Surgery, Holtdale Approach, Leeds LS16 7RX Tel: 0113 230 0108 Fax: 0113 230 1309 — Lekarz 1970 Warsaw; MPhil Leeds 1982; FRCS Ed. 1977.

ZOMA, Asad Abood Stonehouse Hospital, Stonehouse, Larkhall ML9 3NT Tel: 01698 794042 Fax: 01698 791379 Email: a.zoma@clinmed.gla.ac.uk; 43 Garvel Road, Milngavie, Glasgow G62 7JD — MB ChB 1971 Baghdad; FRCP Lond. 1999; FRCP Glas. 1989; MRCP (UK) 1979. (Baghdad) Cons. Phys. (Rheum.) Hairmyres & StoneHo. Hosps. NHS Trust Hosp. Scotl.; Sen. Clin. Lect. Univ. of Glas. Socs: Brit. Soc. Rheum.; Fell.Amer. Coll. Rheum. Prev: Sen. Regist. (Gen. Med. & Rheum.) Roy. Infirm. Glas.; Regist. (Gen. Med.) Gartnavel Gen. & W.. Infirm. Glas.

ZOMAS, Athanassios Academic Department of Haematology & Cytogenetics, Royal Marsden Hospital, Downs Road, Sutton SM2 5PT Tel: 020 8642 6011; 8 Salisbury House, Bessborough Gardens, Pimlico, London SW1V 2HJ Tel: 020 7821 0350 — Ptychio latrikes 1988 Thessalonika. Hon. Sen. Regist. (Haemat.) Roy. Marsden Hosp.; Hon. Regist. (Haemat.) St. Geo. Hosp. Med. Sch. Lond.

ZOOB, Betty Constance (retired) 5 Kenbrook House, Kensington High St., London W14 8NY Tel: 020 7602 3329 — MB BS Lond. 1944. Prev: Clin. Asst. Bloomsbury Rheumat. Unit. Arthur Stanley Ho. Lond.

ZOOB, Cyril Lionel Timbers, Sycamore Close, Fetcham, Leatherhead KT22 9EX — MB BS 1954 Lond. (St. Mary's) Clin. Asst. (ENT) Kingston Hosp. Prev: Ho. Surg. ENT Dept. St. Mary's Hosp. Lond.; Ho. Phys. King Edwd. Memor. Hosp. Ealing.

ZOON, Elizabeth 137 Humberston Avenue, Humberston, Grimsby DN36 4ST — Artsexamen 1989 Rotterdam.

ZORAB, John Stanley Mornington (retired) Holmray Cottage, Park St., Iron Acton, Bristol BS37 9UJ Tel: 01454 228757 Fax: 01454 228295 Email: jzorab@compuserve.com — MRCS Eng. LRCP Lond. 1956; FFA RCS Eng. 1963; DA Eng. 1959. Emerit. Cons. Anaesth. Frenchay Hosp., Bristol.; Edr. Europ. Acad. Anaesth. Newsletter; Sect. Edr. Curr. Opinion in Anaesthesiology. Prev: Cons. Anaesth. & Med. Dir. Frenchay Hosp. Bristol.

ZORAB, Walter John (retired) Flat 18, Village Gate, Southampton Hill, Fareham PO14 4BJ Tel: 01327 847351 — MRCS Eng. LRCP Lond. 1939. Prev: Ho. Phys. (Midw. & Anaesth.) White Lodge Hosp. Newmarket.

ZORAB, William Guy (retired) 271 Old Worting Road, Basingstoke RG22 6NX Tel: 01256 461757 — LMSSA 1937 Lond. Prev: Ho. Surg. P. of Wales (Greenbank) Hosp. Plymouth.

ZORIC

ZORIC, Bozena St Peter's Hospital, Guilford Road, Chertsey KT16 0PZ — MD 1982 Zagreb; MSc 1996 Lond.; MRCP (UK) 1987. Cons. Paediat. Prev: Sen. Regist. (Paediat.) Soton.; Regist. Nottm. City Hosp.; Research Fell. (Paediat.) MRC Nottm.

ZOSMER, Nurit Ratzoni Samuel 5 Western Avenue, London NW11 9HG — MD 1983 Tel Aviv, Israel.

ZOTKIEWICZ, Marek Jozef Bentcliffe, 9 Devonshire Road, Hope, Salford M6 8HY — MB ChB 1982 Manch.; BSc (Hons.) Manch. 1979. Dir. of Health Care Servs. HM Prisons Garth & Wymott Leyland, Preston.

ZSCHOCKE, Anna Mary 9 Glenn Parade, Belfast BT11 8FD — MB BCh BAO 1993 Belf.

ZSIGMOND, Andrew Consulting Rooms, 43 Rodney Street, Liverpool L1 9EW Tel: 0151 709 7441 Fax: 0151 708 0526 Email: doctor@zsigmond.co.uk — MRCS Eng. LRCP Lond. 1962; MFOM RCP Lond. 1979; Cert Av Med MoD (Air) & CAA; Aviat. Auth. 1974. (Liverp.) Authorised Med. Examr. Civil Aviat. Auth., Fed. Aviat. Admin. & Civil Aviat. Auth., Canada; Med. Examr. RAF Liverp.; Asbestos Cons. Liverp. Socs: (Ex-Pres.) Liverp. Med. Inst. 1995-96; (Ex-Chairm.) Assn. Aviat. Med. Examrs. 1998-2000. Prev: Ho. Phys. Walton Hosp. Liverp.; Ho. Surg. (Orthop.) Roy. S.. Hosp. Liverp.; SHO (Radiother.) Clatterbridge Hosp. Bebington.

ZU SOLMS-BARUTH, Caroline-Mathilde Elisabeth (retired) Barn Cottage, The Green, Bledington, Chipping Norton OX7 6XQ — MB ChB 1961 Stellenbosch; MSc Cape Town 1955. Prev: GP Banbury.

ZUBAIDI, Sara 47 Moira Terrace, Edinburgh EH7 6TD Tel: 0131 660 2711 — MB ChB 1993 Ed. SHO (A & E) Hull Roy. Infirm. Prev: SHO (Psychiat.) St. Jas. Univ. Hosp. Leeds; Ho. Off. (Surg.) W.. Gen. Hosp. Edin.; Ho. Off. (Med.) Falkirk & Dist. Roy. Infirm.

ZUBAIRU, Mohammad Bankole The Health Centre, Braithwell Road, Maltby, Rotherham S66 8JE Tel: 01709 798822 — Vrach 1972 1st Leningrad Med. Inst. USSR. (Leningrad) Socs: BMA & Soc. Occupat. Med. Prev: Area Sen. Med. Off. S. Yorks. Brit. Coal; Dep. Area Med. Off. S. Midl. Area Nat. Coal Bd.; Regist. (A & E & Orthop.) N. Lincs. HA.

ZUBERI, Mohammad Mustafa, CBE 1A Davenham Avenue, Northwood HA6 3HW — MB BS 1953 Punjab (Pakistan); FFOM RCP Lond. 1986; DPH Lond. 1964; DIH Eng. 1968. (King Edwd. Med. Coll. Lahore) p/t Cons. Occupat. Health Medicentres, Lond. Socs: Soc. Occupat. Med. Prev: Cons. Occupat. Health BUPA Occupat. Health; Med. Adviser Health Policy Health & Safety Exec.; Regional Dir. & Dep. Dir. Med. Servs. Health & Safety Exec.

ZUBERI, Sameer Mustafa Fraser of Allander Neurosciences Unit, Royal Hospital for Sick Children, Yorkhill, Glasgow G3 8SJ Tel: 0141 201 0141 Fax: 0141 201 9270 Email: sameer.zuberi@yorkhill.scot.nhs.uk — MB ChB 1989 Ed.; MRCP (UK) 1992; MRCPH 1997. (Ed.) Cons. (Paediat. Neurol.) Roy. Hosp. Sick Childr. Glas.; Hon. Sen. Lect. in Child Health, Univ. of Glas. Socs: Roy. Coll. Phys. Edin.; MRCPCH; Brit. Paediat. Neurol. Assn.

ZUBERI, Shahid Akhtar 5 Tennent Lodge, North Road, Bellshill Hospital, Bellshill ML4 3JN Tel: 01698 747290 ext 244 Fax: 01698 747292 — MB BS 1982 Karachi; MD Pennsylvania. (Dow Med. Coll. Karachi, Pakistan) Staff Paediat. Monklands & Bellshill Hosps. Prev: Resid. Paediat. Hershey Med. Center, Pennsylvania State Univ. Childrs. Hosp. Hershey, P.A. USA.

ZUBIER, Claire Mary Patricia 74 Garnock Hill, Black's Road, Belfast BT10 0AW — MB BCh BAO 1993 Belf.

ZUBIER, Francis Aziz 74 Garnock Hill, Blacks Road, Belfast BT10 0AW — MB BCh BAO 1992 Belf.

ZUCK, David Craigower, St. Andrew's Close, Woodside Avenue, London N12 8BA Tel: 020 8445 4685 Email: fy96@dial.pipex.com — MB ChB 1945 Birm.; FFA RCS Eng. 1953; DHMSA Lond. 1975; DA Eng. 1948. Hon. Cons. Anaesth. Enfield Dist.; Fell. Fac. Hist. Med. Soc. Apoth. Lond. Socs: Fell. Roy. Soc. Med.; Assn. Anaesths. - Pask Cert. of Honour; (Ex-Pres.) Hist. Anaesth. Soc. Prev: Capt. RAMC Graded Anaesth.; Sen. Cons. Anaesth. Chase Farm Hosp. Enfield.

ZUCKERMAN, Professor Arie Jeremy Royal Free & University College Medical School, Royal Free Campus, Rowland Hill St., London NW3 2PF Tel: 020 7830 2579 Fax: 020 7830 2070 Email: a.zuckerman@nfc.ecl.ac.uk — MB BS 1957 Lond.; MB BS (Hons.) 1957; MSc (Genetics.) Birm. 1962, BSc (Hons.) 1953, DSc (Experim. Path.))1973; MD Lond. 1963; FRCP Lond. 1982, M 1978; MRCS Eng. LRCP Lond. 1957; FRCPath 1977, M 1965; Dip. Bact (Distinc.) 1965; DObst RCOG 1958. (Roy. Free) Prof. Med. Microbiol. Univ. Lond.; Dir. WHO Collaborating Centre for Ref. & Research on Viral Dis.; Cons. Med. Microbiol. Roy. Free. Hampstead NHS Trust; Hon. Cons. Virol. Nat. Blood Auth.; Non-Exec. Dir. Roy. Free Hampstead NHS Trust; Dir. Anthony Nolan Bone Marrow Trust; Edr.-in-Chief Jl. Med. Virol. & Jl. Virol. Methods. Socs: Soc. Gen. Microbiol.; Amer. Assn. Study Liver Dis. Prev: Princip. & Dean Roy. Free & Univ. Coll. Med. Sch.; Squadron Ldr. RAF Med. Br.; Prof. Microbiol. Lond. Sch. Hyg. & Trop. Med.

ZUCKERMAN, Charles Howard Zuckerman, Felderhof and Ali, Northfield Health Centre, 15 St Heliers Road, Northfield, Birmingham B31 1QU — MB BS 1971 Lond.; FRCGP 1993, M 1976; DObst RCOG 1975; DCH Eng. 1975. Sec. Birm. LMC. Prev: Regist. Guy's Hosp. Lond.; Ho. Surg. St. Pancras Hosp. Lond.; Ho. Phys. St. Jas. Hosp. Lond.

ZUCKERMAN, Jane Nicola Royal Free & University College Medical School, London NW3 2PF Tel: 020 7830 2999 Fax: 020 7830 2268 — MB BS 1987 Lond.; MD Lond. 1996; MFPM (Royal College of Physicians) 2000. Head & Hon. Cons. Acad. Centre for Travel Med. & Vaccines; Sen. Lect. & Elective Tutor Roy. Free & Univ. Coll. Med. Sch., Lond.; Dir. Clin. Trials Centre Roy. Free & Univ. Coll. Med. Sch.; Med. Dir. The Roy. Free Travel Health Centre. Socs: Brit. Assn. Pharmaceut. Med. Res. Soc.; RCP UK Fac. of Pharmaceutical Med.; Brit. Infec. Soc. Prev: Sen. Research Fell. Roy. Free Hosp. Sch. Med. Lond.; Clin. Research Fell. Occupat. Health Unit Roy. Free Hosp. Lond.; Regist. & SHO (A & E & ITU) Roy. Free Hosp. Lond.

ZUCKERMAN, Mark Adam Dulwich Public Health Laboratory & Department of Medical Microbiology, King's College School of Medicine & Dentistry, East Dulwich Grove, London SE22 8QF Tel: 020 8693 3005 — MB BS 1985 Lond.; MSc (Clin. Microbiol. Lond.) 1990, BSc (1st cl. Hons. Microbiol.) 1980; MRCP (UK) 1989; MRCPath 1993. (University College Hospital) Cons. Virol. & Hon. Sen. Lect. Dulwich PHL & Med. Microbiol. King's Coll. Sch. of Med. & Dent. Prev: Regist. (Med. Microbiol.) The Lond. Hosp.; SHO (Med.) Ipswich Gen. Hosp.; Ho. Surg. Stoke Mandeville Hosp.

ZUHA, Roslin 3 The Paddock, Hove BN3 6LT — MB BS 1994 Lond.

ZUHRIE, Shadman Riaz Northwick Park & St Mark's NHS Trust, Watford Rd, Harrow HA1 3UJ Tel: 020 8235 4231 Fax: 020 8426 6002 Email: rzuhrie@mds.qmw.ac.uk; 16 Duffield Close, Harrow HA1 2LG Tel: 020 8424 0160 — MB BS 1971 Poona; PhD Lond. 1991. (Armed Forces Med. Coll.) MRC Clin. Scientist & Hon. Clin. Assist. Med., N.wich Pk. & St Mark's NHS Trust Middlx. Socs: MBA; BMS (Menopause Soc.); SSM (Social Medium). Prev: MRC Clin. Scientist & Hon Sen. Regist. MRC, Epidemiol. Med. Care Unit. St Bartholmews Hosp. Lond.; Research Regist. Clin. Immune Defic. Dis, Research Gp., MRC Clin. Research Centre, N.wich Pk. Hosp. Middlx.

ZUK, John Albert Tel: 0191 333 2457 — MB ChB 1983 Dundee; BMSc (Hons.) Dund 1980; BMSc (Hons.) Dund 1980; MRCPath 1989; FRCPath 1998. Cons. Histopath & Cytopath. Dryburn Hosp. Durh. Socs: ACP & Brit. Div. IAP. Prev: Sen. Regist. (Histopath.) Mersey Region; Regist. (Histopath.) Leic. Roy. Infirm.; Cons. Histopath. & Cytopath. Univ. Hosp. N. Durh.

ZUK, Ronald Joseph Department of Histopathology, Monklands District General Hospital, Monkscourt Avenue, Airdrie ML6 0JS — MB ChB 1981 Dundee; BMSc 1978 (Hons.) Dundee; MRCPath 1989.

ZULFIKER, Sharif Omar Flat 12 Albert House, Hinchingbrooke Park, Huntingdon PE29 6NS — MB BCh 1993 Wales. GP Regist. VTS Hinchingbrooke NHS Trust Cambs.

ZULUETA MADINABEITIA, Luis Sandwell District General Hospital, West Bromwich B71 4HJ Tel: 0121 553 1831; 39 Avern Close, Tipton DY4 7ND Tel: 0121 557 3991 — LMS 1989 Basque Provinces. Clin. Asst. (Anaesth.) Sandwell Dist. Gen. Hosp. W. Bromwich. Prev: Clin. Asst. Geo. Eliot Hosp. Nuneaton; SHO Sandwell Dist. Gen. Hosp.

ZUMLA, Professor Alimuddin Centre for Infectious Diseases, Royal Free University College London Medical School, Windeyer, Institute Room G41, 46 Cleveland St., London W1T 4JF Tel: 020 7679 9187 Fax: 020 7679 9311 Email: a.zumla@ucl.ac.uk — MB ChB 1979 Zambia; BSc 1976 Zambia; MSc 1981 Lond.; MRCP 1984 Lond.; PhD 1987 Lond.; FRCP 1995 Lond.; FRCP 1999 Ed. Prof. of Infec. Dis. & Int. Health Univ. Coll. Lond., Roy. Free & Univ. Coll.

Med. Sch.; Cons. Phys. (Infec. Dis.) Univ. Coll. Lond. Hosps. Trust; Hon. Prof. Inst. of Child Health Lond. Socs: Internat. Union Against Tuberc. & Lung Dis.; Brit. Soc. Immunol.; Fell. Roy. Soc. Trop. Med. Hyg. Prev: Vis. Prof. & Utzam Dir. Sch. Med. Univ. Zambia; Assoc. Prof. Centre for Infec. Dis. Univ. Texas, Houston, USA; Sen. Regist. (Clin. Immunol. & Rheum.) & Hon. Lect. Roy. Postgrad. Med. Sch.

ZUREK, Andrew Alexander Antoni Weaver Vale Practice, Hallwood Health Centre, Hospital Way, Runcorn WA7 2UT Tel: 01928 711911 Fax: 01928 717368 — MB ChB 1964 Ed.; MRCGP 1976. (Ed.) Prev: Hon. Clin. Lect. (Med.) Univ. Liverp.; Sen. Clin. Lect. (Gen. Pract.) Univ. Liverp.

ZUREK, Andrew Maria 38 Queen Victoria Road, Westbury Park, Bristol BS6 7PE Tel: 0117 923 8222 Email: andy@zed1.freeserve.co.uk — MB BChir 1991 Camb.; MRCP (UK) 1994. (Camb.) Clin. Research Fell./Hon. Regist. (Respirat. Med.) Soton. Univ. Prev: Regist. (Respirat. Med.) Glos. Roy. Hosp.; Regist. (Med.) S.mead Hosp. Bristol; Regist. (Med.) MusGr. Pk. Hosp. Taunton, Som.

ZURGANI, Mr Abdulkarim 17 Oliver Road, Walthamstow, London E17 9HL — MB BCh 1980 Alfateh; FRCS Ed. 1994.

ZURICK, Natasha Jane Weald Cottage, Sheerwater Avenue, Woodham, Addlestone KT15 3DP — MB ChB 1994 Bristol; BSc Bristol 1991, MB ChB 1994.

ZURUB, Amer Ahmad Health Centre, High Street, Bedworth, Nuneaton CV12 8NQ Tel: 024 7631 5432 Fax: 024 7631 0038; 17 Chilworth Close, The Poplars, Nuneaton CV11 4XE Tel: 01203 351363 Email: amer@zurub.freeserve.co.uk — MB BCh BAO 1988 NUI; LRCPSI 1988. (RCSI) Socs: Med. Protec. Soc.

ZUTSHI, Derek Wyndham 36 Eton Court, Eton Avenue, Hampstead, London NW3 3HJ Tel: 020 7722 6316 — MB ChB 1957 Bristol; FRCP Lond. 1991, M 1967; DObst RCOG 1959. Socs: Fell. Roy. Soc. Med.; Fell. (Ex-Pres.) Hunt. Soc.; Fell (Ex-Counc.) Med. Soc. Lond. Prev: Cons. Phys. Rheum. P. of Wales' & St. Ann's Hosps. Lond.; Sen. Regist. (Rheum.) Lond. Hosp.; Ho. Phys. Profess. Med. Unit Bristol Roy. Infirm.

ZUTSHI, Mr Mohan Krishen 9 Meyricks, Coed Eva, Cwmbran NP44 6TU Tel: 01633 675421 Fax: 01633 675421; 57 Priory Gardens, Ealing, London W5 1DY Tel: 020 8997 4198 — MB BS 1957 Agra; FRCS Eng. 1969; FRCS Glas. 1967 FRCS Ed. 1966; FICS 1973. (S.N. Med. Coll.) Socs: Fell. Roy. Soc. Med.; BMA. Prev: Regist. (Surg.) Gen. Hosp. Burton-on-Trent; Sen. Cons. Surg. & Head (Surg.) Gen. Hosp. Pondicherry, India & St. Martha's Hosp. Bangalore, India.

ZUTSHI, Risheshwar Nath (retired) 40 Villiers Crescent, Eccleston, St Helens WA10 5HR Tel: 01744 27177 — MB BS Lucknow 1948; BSc (Allahabad India) 1942. Prev: GP St. Helens.

ZWARTOUW, Carol Louise Rosser and Partners, Crewkerne Health Centre, Middle Path, Crewkerne TA18 8BX Tel: 01460 72435 Fax: 01460 77957; Little Plot, Silver St, Misterton, Crewkerne TA18 8NG — MB BS 1978 Lond.; DRCOG 1981; DA Eng. 1981.

ZWI, Morris Child & Family Consultation Centre, Richmond Royal Hospital, Kew Foot Road, Richmond TW9 2TE Tel: 020 8355 1984 Fax: 020 8355 1977 Email: morris.zwi@kdc-tr.sthames.nhs.uk; Email: m.zwi@blueyonder.co.uk — MB BCh 1982 Witwatersrand; MRCPsych 1989. (Witwatersrand) Cons. Child & Adolesc. Psychiat. Richmond Roy. Hosp. Socs: Centre for Evidence Based Ment. Health; Child Psychiat. Research Soc. Prev: Sen. Regist. Child & Adolesc. Psychiat., N. W. Thames Rotat.; Regist. Psychiat., Barnet Rotat.

ZWINK, Patricia Jessie Swan Woodthorpe, St. Mary's Avenue, London E11 — MB ChB 1944 St. And.

ZWINK, Mr Roger Bryan Accident & Emergency Department, Broomfield Hospital, Chelmsford CM1 7ET Tel: 01245 514601 Fax: 01245 514223; Maggotts, Pleshey, Chelmsford CM3 1HY Tel: 01245 231256 — MB BCh 1981 Wales; BDS Wales 1972; FRCS Ed. 1987; FFAEM 1994; FDS RCS Eng. 1976. (Welsh Nat. Sch. Med.) Cons. A & E Broomfield Hosp. Chelmsford; Recognised Clin. Teach., Univ of Camb. Sch. of Clin. Med.,; Regional Adviser N. Thames (E.) Fac. of Accid. and Emergencey Med. Prev: Sen. Regist. (A & E) OldCh. Hosp. Romford; Regist. (Oral & Maxillo-Facial Surg.) Welsh Nat. Sch. of Med. Cardiff.

ZYCH, Zdenek Princess Alexandra Hospital, Harlow CM20 1QX Tel: 01279 444455 Fax: 01992 577558; Holly Bushes, 5a Tower Road, Epping CM16 5EL Tel: 01992 572760 Fax: 01992 572760 — MRCS Eng. LRCP Lond. 1970; FFA RCS Eng. 1974; DA Eng. 1972.

ZYLSTRA, Heinrich Johan 20 Grange Close, Godalming GU7 1XT — MB ChB 1983 Cape Town.

ZZAMAN, Kazi Ansaru Zaman, Marus Bridge Health Centre, Highfield Grange Avenue, Wigan WN3 6SU — MB BS 1962 Calcutta.

Index by Postal District: London

E1
Ahmed, A U
Ananda Rajan, R
Anderson, S R
Andrews, J T
Ang, S C
Apaolaza Corral, M I
Auer, R L
Baithun, S I A
Banatvala, N
Barry, M J
Bates, A W
Batra, S
Bavetta, S
Beedham, T
Beer, N R
Bennett, G C J
Berry, C L
Bhattacharya, S
Bhowal, G
Bhui, K S
Bhusari, G S
Bingham, S J
Bone, M P
Booy, R
Boucher, B J
Bradley, P F
Brearley, J D M
Brennan, M L
Breuer, J
Brohi, K H
Bromham, C E
Brown, P L
Butler, P
Carr, S B
Carter, J L B
Carter, Y H
Cartwright, R
Carty, E
Cavenagh, J D
Cerio, R
Chan, Y-C C
Chaput De Saintonge, D M
Chawdhery, M Z
Chiew, Y F
Chikanza, I C
Chong, P F S
Chow, P C M
Coats, T J
Coghlan, K M
Cohen, R D
Collier, C J
Collins, J W
Colvin, B T
Colvin, M P
Connolly, A A P
Coppack, S W
Cotter, F E
Cotter, J
Cross, F W
Crouchman, P W F
Cugnoni, H L
Culpitt, S V
Cunningham, J
Curtis, D
Curtis, J L
David, L A
Davies, F C W
Davies, G E
Davies, K N
Dean, N R
Dean, T S
Desai, S
Dodd, S M
Dorudi, S
Drewery, H K
Dunford, A P
Earlam, R J
Eckersley, A J P
Eccles, S J A
Edge, J C
Edmondson, M E
Engert, D J
Fairclough, P D
Farthing, M J G
Fearnley, J M
Feather, A
Feldman, R A
Flynn, P J
Forster, G E
Fowler, C G
Friedman, E P
Gamble, E A
Geddes, J F
Ghobrial, S A F
Gibbons, A E
Gil Orozco, S M
Glynn, M J
Godkin, A J
Goh, B T
Goldhill, D R
Gompertz, P H
Graham, P Y
Grange, W J
Gutteridge, C N
Habershon, R B
Ham, R J
Hamilton, P
Hamlyn, P J
Hanbury, C J
Haq, H A
Hardee, P S G F
Hardy, J P
Harris, B R
Harris, B T
Harris, R J
Hartley, S M
Hasan, K
Hathorn, M K S
Healey, S
Healy, M T
Hellewell, S A
Hird, M F
Hossain, M N
Houston, T C
Huang, J K C
Hughes, S M
Hull, S A
Hutchison, I L
Ingram, D A
Jacobson, R A
Jago, L J
Jawad, A S M
Jenkins, S C
Jones, J O
Junaid, I
Kadirkamanthan, S S
Karamadoukis, L
Karim, J
Keatinge, W R
Keir, M I S
Kelly, M P
Kempley, S T
Khan, H
Kidd, B L
Knowles, C H
Koeze, T H
Kopelman, P G
Kozlowska, W J
Kuitert, L M E
Kumar, R
Lai, M M R
Lee, K Y
Leigh, I M
Leigh, M F M
Lishman, S C
Littlejohns, J H
Lynch, E E
McAnena, O J N P
McCrea, D
McEwan, A
McLellan, N J
Makin, C M I
Malhotra, A
Mannix, P A
Marsden, J
Marsh, F P
Marshall, A G
Martin, J E
Mifsud, A J
Miles, S A D
Misra, D C
Mitchell, R T C
Moganasundram, S
Mooney, D J
Mulcahy, H
Murfitt, J B
Murphy, M B
Mylonopoulou, M
Navarro-Weitzel, I C
Newland, A C
O'Shea, P J
Odetoyinbo, O A
Okun, T O
Orteu, C H
Paige, D G
Paspatis, G
Paterson, I D
Pelluet, E J
Pickard, R S
Pollok, R C G
Ponnampalam, M S
Porter, D S
Powell-Tuck, J
Powell, K J
Prince, J A
Probst, A F
Proby, C M
Quinn, S J
Raftery, M J
Rampton, D S
Read, T R C
Redstone, C D
Rees, A J
Reynard, J M
Richards, M W
Ring, H A
Ritter, J M N
Rosen, M H
Rossi, M
Roy, E H
Rudge, C J
Ryan, A
Sabin, H I
Safir, J G
Sandhu, H S
Sanghi, A
Sashidharan, R
Saulsbury, N K G
Scarborough, M
Scheimberg Schiff, I B
Scott, G
Shah, S
Sheaff, M T
Sheikh-Sobeh, M
Shepherd, S
Silk, J M
Simpson, H L
Sivapathasundaram, V
Skinner, C J
Snodgrass, G J A I
Soin-Stanley, S A J
St John, M A F
Stanway, A T
Strunin, L
Sturt, T M
Swash, M
Szilagyi, R Z
Taylor, K W
Taylor, S J C
Tebboth, L I J
Thakkar, C H
Thakore, J H
Thompson, D H M
Toh, K-W
Trumper, M J
Uddin, K
Van Den Bosch, C A
Van Der Oest, C H
Van Lieshout, T A
Venus, M R
Vincent, M E
Walker, R W H
Walsh, M S
Walters, E A
Ward, H L
Webborn, A D J
Welch, S B
Whitton, T J
Wilkinson, D G
Williams, N S
Willis, G M
Wilmalasundera, N
Wingate, D L
Withington, P S
Wood, D F
Wrangham, M
Wright, P J
Wright, V M
Yate, P M
Yeo, S I
Zakrzewska, J M

E2
Adekanmi, A A
Ahmed, S
Applebee, J C
Arnott, A S
Aw, T C
Bann, S D
Barnes, N C
Bate, L V
Boddington, J D
Brewer, N J
Brooks, A P
Burbridge-James, W L
Chin, T L N
Cooke, S D
Corbett, D S
Craig, G W
Di Salvo, C
Drye, N D
Dutt, G C
Flanagan, K L
Gant, L J
Groves, I P
Hett, C L
Hindmarsh, A C
Hooi, Y S
Howard, D C
Jakeman, P
Kielty, R A
Kristeleit, R S
Kumar Gupta, A
Liew, W L
Louca, P
McKeogh, M M
Macleod, D P
McNally, L M
Martin-Ortiz, R
Mead, A G
Meadway, J V
Midgley, C J
Nunns, M E B
O'Hara, J
Patel, R M
Payne, M R
Peat, S J
Phillips, C F
Pollen, R M
Rackstraw, S A
Rahman, R
Roberts, C H
Robertson, F J
Rogers, G
Schofield, Z J
Seabra Oliveira, A M
Sellars, N A
Sheldon, M G
Silva, A
Tahalani, R P
Timmis, A D
Tregaskes, S N
Turbitt, D A
Viney, R M M
Wark, K J
Warshow, U M M
Webster, G K
Whittington, D A
Wilcox, F J
Worley, G A

E3
Adams, K J
Ashby, M W
Bass, N J
Benfield, H
Best, T B N
Boocock, O K
Boomla, S
Bowles, C J A
Brock, C S
Browning, M
Budhdeo, S M
Burnett, A C
Burns, S C
Callaghan, M S D
Caudwell, R
Chen, R P T
Cheung, V Y N
Clinch, J G
Cobb, A M
Cockman, P J
Cookson, J C
Cox, K L
Dass, J M H
Davis, J E
De Jode, M G
Dent, J T
Edwards, C M B
Edwards, M J J
Everington, A H
Farrelly, G A
Feldman, J D
Foo, K Y
Gill, A P
Gill, M W
Glover, G R
Glover, M T
Grant, L J
Green, E L
Hall, E J
Hancox, N
Haque, R A
Hardiman, J H
Haroon-Ur-Rashid, Dr
Heath, E I
Henderson, K I M
Howard, R J
Howell, S R
Johnson, R
Jones, E A
Jonsson, K E
Jumaily, A G
Kirchner, V
Lawlor, E F
Li, P-L
Lightowlers, S K
Lim, K A
McGovern, I
McGown, A D
Mantell, A E
Moffat, M D
Parry, A R J
Phillips, J N
Pratt, C F W
Rashid, R-U
Reading, P J
St John, M D F
Stansfield, D P
Steel, J R
Stern, J M
Taylor, B
Thom, A W R
Tibble, J A
Vilarino-Varela, M J
Yeatman, N W J
Yip, Y Y
Youle, M S

E4
Aitchison, D J M
Amin, N S
Armstrong, B P
Bedwell, S
Britt, C P
Burgess, S P
Cave, G V
Challis, M T
Choi, B
Choudhury, B M
Collingwood, K E
Dadabhoy, M E
Dadabhoy, S M
Davis, P A
Drake, D
El-Gadra, A H A
Farah, F L
Forwood, C M
Garwood, A
Gavaghan, S W M
Gavin, J M
Grenville, M
Griffiths, N C
Hardman, E W
Harvey, R M
Hooper, B M
Hybel, A P
Kayani, J T
Kendall, B E
Khalaf, M S
Khan, S B
Khare, K C
Koczan, P J
Kumar, S S
Lloyd Roe, C A
Michael, W D A
Mital, D
Myers, T R
Nandi, B C
Ormerod, S J
Phillips, R
Pringle, A
Putt, C M
Raiman, J D
Raiman, J A J
Scowen, M K
Shaw, J D R
Sheikh, I
Taylor, S D D
Telesz, A M
Todd, A A J
Walsh, M L
West, S E

E5
Absolon, C J
Ahmad, K Z
Alexander, C M
Aquilina, J
Arulampalam, T H A
Bates, P D
Carter, J E
Clarke, J O
Cogan, R
Collier, D J
Cronin, A J
Daly, R J
Duggal, B
Duggal, M S
Eastaway, J A
Ekecowa, U I
Elkouby, K
Feder, G S
Gordon, D R
Greenhalgh, I
Griffiths, C J
Highton, C
Ibrahim, A T
Jankowska, A M
Johnston, H C
Jones, C E
Kapur, K V
Khatri, A K
Lipner, A E
Lyle, R C H
Mahon, J N
Oganwu, S O
Okoreaffia, A C
Perry, A C
Perry, R J
Petrou, M S
Pickhaver, K M
Prenelle, I
Rakshit, A K
Rama Mohana Rao, D
Rickets, M
Rubner, P
Salcedo, A A
Shui, E M Y-L
Singh, S K
Spruyt, O W
Stanley, P B
Wallis, D E
Watkins, S
White, R I
Whyte, N J D

E6
Alam, A

London, E14

Baiju, D S
Bamgbala, A M
Barnabas, A J
Barnardo, A M A
Bower, S J
Chalabi, N
Chidambaram, A
Davison, C M
Dubal, P R
Emeagi, C N
Eshun, J E
Fernando, M P
George Samraj, P N
Gibbs, K J
Goose, G L
Greet, D M
Hussain, S T
Kapur, S
Kohli, B
Krishnamoorthy, L
Lawrie, J A
Lewis, D A A
Mandavilli, S
Meadows, H G
Naish, J C-M
Nandakumar, C G
Ojukwu, N J
Orimoloye, A O
Patel, H S
Patel, N R
Powell, T A
Rafique, F
Salako, A O
Samanta, A K
Seaton, A T
Stanowski, R
Umachandran, V
Vidhyadharan, A
Walker, C L
Watt, D E
Waugh, R E M

E7

Abbott, S M
Abrahamson, D
Ahmed, A
Akinloye, O T
Bapna, G
Basit, A
De Souza, A T
Driver, N R
Duffett, R S
Farrukh, A A R
Friel, C M
Hasici, E
Ishaq, A S
Ivinson, S
Joyce, C
Khan, S A
Lam Kin Teng, L T
Mahendran, S
Manam, A
Mazarelo, J A X
Moussa, M M H
Munro, M H W
O'Moore, G R
Pandya, H C
Patel, A
Patel, D
Patel, R
Patel, Y I
Rafiq, S S
Rashid, Y
Robinson, K A
Ruhi, S O
Sheriff, M K M
Sherwood, S M
Silver, N C
Sinha, B K
Somorin, A O
Striesow, H H
Swedan, S K S
Uddin, M M
Wood, S A
Yesufu, A O

E8

Ajuied, A
Benn, R S
Brook, D W
Cahill, M F A
Caplin, L A
Cooper, S A
Cowley, S J
Darnley, B J M
Fade, P Z
Finnerty, M J G
Fontaine, E J
Gupta, K C

Halcox, J P J
Hendricks, Y J
Heyse-Moore, L H
Highton, R S J
Hopson, A S M
Jackson, K
Jarrett, L
Kirton, J L
Lee, R M
Mdingi, G V
Murphy, M C
Palmer, Z E
Patil, M B
Phillips, L A
Pilkington, A C
Read, J M
Ribeiro, M D C
Sanfey, J J
Senior, R S
Tibrewal, S P
Todd, M J A
Toon, P D
Vincent, J A
Wales, N M
Williams, R D A
Windsor, J P W
Wolf, E
Zeppetella, G

E9

Adireddi, V S P
Aitken, M J
Amos, R J
Andreyev, H J N
Armstrong, G H
Aung, S
Azaz, A M A
Balakrishna, J
Bays, S M A
Bliss, W H
Bodenstein, M E
Bothamley, G H
Bower, R C
Bucknall, J L
Bull, R H
Butler, I A
Charles, H J
Chatterjee, A P
Choi, A Y S
Choi, D M A
Cohen, R M
Coleman, J W
Costeloe, K L
Cowden, F
Cullinan, T P
Cumming, I R
Cumming, K J
Curry, N S
De Souza, B A
Dean, P J
Desai, K B
Dex, E A
Dorman, E K
Egan, S A
Erskine, K J
Fang, S H
Forrester, A
Gibson, R J
Green, S C
Grun, L M
Guha, M K
Gurtin Zorkun, D
Hamid, S S
Harrad, J D
Highton, C R
Holland, M E
Husain, S M
Hutt, N C
Jones, P S
Joseph, S
Julian, P A C
Karcher, A M
Kelly, C A
Kittler, Z K
Kong, K C
Leaver, E J
Leaver, J M
Lehmann, A B
Leslie, K S
McCarthy, D M
Mikhail, S W I
Mootoo, R V
Mustafa, M
Niayesh, M H
Olusanya, A A A
Patel, G H
Patel, H G
Peirce, K S
Petterson, L E

Power, L M
Prasad, R
Pugh, G G
Purkiss, M E
Rajakulasingam, K
Ratnam, D S
Rizvi, S P J
Roberts, P C
Roper, J
Salter, M S
Singer, R
Timmis, P K
Tobias, G J
Tollins, A P
Tunstall Pedoe, D S
Vafaie, K
Van Der Heiden, E R J
Van Velsen, C L
Washington, A J
Watson, J D
Watson, S J
Whittaker, A J
Yeoman, N C
Zalidis, S

E10

Abora, Y Y
Adams, W
Ali, S M
Allybocus, S A H
Anjaneyulu, K
Ariff, M H I
Bennett, M
Biss, G C
Biswas, A
Bose, K
Casey, D R
Crowe, M B
Das, P K
Das, R
Dhillon, P S
Dutta, S N
Fernandes, D A
Hafeez, I
Hill, B
Huddart, M J
Kalra, T K K
Kapoor, D
Kapoor, R
Khawaja, S S
Lath, S
Mallick, G
Mallick, K B
Pal, G S
Pandit, S N
Phillips, S
Radix, J C A
Ramsis, H E
Sen, S K
Singh, J C I
Sun Wai, W Y S
Wey, E Q
Younus, N
Zadoo, K
Zamora Eguiluz, M C
Zia, M I

E11

Abraham, M A
Adam, S A
Adly Habib, N
Ahmed, A U
Aiyegbusi, M
Akin-Olugbade, O
Akramuzzaman, M
Ali, L
Alstead, E M
Amin, M R
Amin, R T
Anderson, C C
Annan, H G
Arulefela, M M
Ashley, E J
Aswani, K
Atando, S W
Athreya, K
Aveling, W
Baillie, C T
Balkind, J
Bari, N
Beasley, I F R
Bewley, A P
Bickerstaff, M C M
Bjorndal, B E
Blair, C P
Bohra, C G
Boruch, L A
Botha, A J
Branley, H M

Brearley, S
Brent, W M
Bright, C M
Browning, M J
Cantrell, W D J
Carroll, J M A
Castle, S G
Chalabi, G
Chalapathy, A S
Chattopadhyay, B
Choudhury, M A H
Clayton, H M
Cotterill, A M
D'Oyley, D A
Darkwah, J A
Das-Gupta, M
Dawda, P
Dawidek, G M B
Donnelly, S P
Dorran, J A
Doshi, S
Doyle, D V
Duggan, A J
Duncan, B B A
El-Hadi, A A R A
Evenson, J
Ezekwesili, R A
Fagin, L H
Ferdinandus, E L C
Frankel, E
Gadhvi, H M
Gauci, C A
Gavalas, M C
George, H B-L
Gibbon, K L
Gilmour, R F
Goldie, B S
Goodbourn, C G M
Hamilton-Farrell, M R
Hassan, S
Hasslocher, D
Herbert, M B
Hines, J E W
Hird, K H
Hogan, J C
Hotton, M E
Hunt, M T
Hurley, P D
Hussain, K
Hussain, S A
Hutchings, A
Islam, A K M S
Jacklin, M C
Jackson, M E
Jacobs, D S
Jain, C
Jestico, J V
Jones, S E
Kafetz, K M
Kavanagh, M
Kenyon, G S
Khan, H N
Khan, M A
Khan, M S H
Khan, N
Kiyani, T M
Lamba, M S
Larcher, V F
Lim, S C
Littler, B O
McClelland, H K
Mansi, E G
Matthews, W C
Meadows, C I S
Melville, R L
Muir-Taylor, D J
Muir-Taylor, J H
Mukherjee, B N
Mulcahy, B D
Murray, K E
Nagpal, V S
Norris, G F
O'Callaghan, E M
O'Carroll, A-M
O'Donnell, C J
O'Farrell, J M
Owen, R A
Pahwa, B K
Partridge, M R
Paul, I P
Prasad, L R
Rajah, M I I
Ramaswamy, S
Rattan, D S
Ray, N
Reading, N G
Reed, A R
Roberts, C M
Robinson, S E

Russell, S S
Samuel, M
Sandhu, S S
Savla, N C
Sawyerr, A M
Shaikh, A A
Shalet, M
Sharma, P
Siggins, P C
Silas, A M
Singh, R
Singh, T
Soole, M J
Stables, A B J
Storring, R A
Sudderuddin, A
Taylor, R F H
Thomas, P A
Togobo, A K
Tranmer, L S
Travers, W I E
Walshe, M B A
Wijeyekoon, S P
Williams, D V
Willson, L A H
Wilson, P
Withana, R J
Youssef, H A E F E S
Yu, M M L
Zambarakji, H J

E12

Alagrajah, P
Alvares, C L
Ambris, M G
Avery, D J
Dalrymple, A
Dhariwal, S K
Ethell, M E
Farnham, F R
Gill, H K
Gopakumar, C G
Graham, P
Gunathilagan, G J
Hussain, A A
Jones, P T C
Kapur, N
Mridha, K B
Mridha, M S A
Nasralla, A H K
Ojagbemi, F O
Pople, A R
Raina, C P
Ramesh, N
Rees, J E
Sai Sankar, N
Shekar, S
Shetty, M K
Sohi, M S
Staunton, T H F
Sullman, B
Thirumamanivannan, G
Vijaya, V
Zamanthangi, J M

E13

Abbas, K F
Addai, S A
Ahmed, A U
Ahmed, Z
Al-Mudallal, G B
Allgrove, J
Andrew, C J
Arumugam Ratnam, L
Aturu, B R
Baffour-Kodua, M O A
Basu, I
Basu, S K
Beaver, M R
Bewaji, A F
Bhagrath, M S
Boulton, J M
Brown, R C M
Buscombe, J A
Chaudhuri, B B
Chohan, S S
Dolan, T G
Gadel Rab, R R
Gelding, S V
George, G H M
Gohil, J
Gonsai, R B
Gwynne, M V P
Halberstadt, I
Hallam, P L
Hanmer, O J
Higgins, R G
Kalhoro, S
Ko, M L B

Leung, Y-L
Littlejohns, D W
McGhee, T D
Madipalli, S
Mahir, M S
Maynard, A H
Mihaimeed, F M A
Naftalin, A A
O'Shaughnessy, T C
Packe, G E
Patel, J
Pauleau, A
Pradhan, V S
Princewill, O M
Rao, M V
Sahin, A
San, K K
Santana Garcia, R
Shahidi, M M
Shirsalkar, A M
Silverman, L S
Smith, R F A
Srinivasan, M
Suliman, A M H
Tan, K M
Umrani, W M
Velupillai, S
Venugopal, R
Vijayaraghavan, S
Wilson, G E
Wisdom, A R
Zakaria, A K M

E14

Absolon, C M
Adusu-Donkor, A
Allibone, J B
Allred, J E
Atkin, P A
Baker, C J
Barraclough, M A
Basu, H K
Belsey, J D
Bennett-Richards, P J
Betteridge, C L M
Boomla, K R F
Byrom, H J
Caulfield, M J
Chandr-Ruang-Phen, P
Chok, S L-M
Chong, C F
Cirolli, R G M
Crombie, J L
Daniels, B J
Devonald, H C
Dobbing, C J
Doig, K M
Dos Santos, A V L
Douglas, N A
Edwards, O H P
Epstein, L J
Farrand, S R
Fraser, K E
Giles, I P
Gould, M G
Hall, G J
Harrison, C
Hart, H C V E
Jackson, J M
John, C R
Kanagasabay, R R
Kayzakian, A M
Ketley, J B
Khan, Z A
Kinsler, R A
Kirby, D A
Kotecha, K
Lamb, P M
Lea-Cox, C M
Lee, S
Lethbridge, W J
Linford, S
Livingstone, A E
Lunniss, P J
Lyon-Maris, J J
McAteer, E J
Mahajan, V D
Nagrath, K D
Owa, A O
Owen, D A L
Parsons, S L F
Perry, J D
Pietroni, T L
Playford, V J
Porter, H
Qureshi, T M
Rahi, S L
Ray, N L
Richardson, J R

London, E15

Robbins, S P
Robson, J P
Sarkar, B
Schilling, C J
Seh Yang Loong, Dr
Self, J E
Sharma, A
Shukla, A C
Siriwardena, D K
Speldewinde, D C M
Taylor, J R
Thormod, C E
Ting, P Y C
Vickers, A R
Walton, S
Whitley, T B H
Wise, D I
Wood, J B

E15

Bhowmik, P R
Brohi, A Q
Chang, M K L
Farook, G
Fleming, M E
Kennedy, D D M
Khan, M S J
Lalude, O A
Najam Ud Din, Dr
Ojuro, I V
Pashankar, D S
Pashankar, F D
Qadri, A Q
Rahman, A R
Shah, A M
Uzoka, K A O

E16

Adedeji, E A
Adeyemi, M S
Barco Marcellan, J M
Comyns, M J
De Cocq, D F F
Edginton, S
Irelewuyi, O A
Jones, J O E
Lwin, T
Palav, S S
Patel, B P
Quigley, I G
Ryanna, K B W
Saha, M
Sehra, R T
Seneviratne, G N
Seneviratne, K B C
Shore, E M
Siddiqui, N
Zarifa, Z K

E17

Afzal, M
Akuffo, E O
Arasaradnam, R P
Arastu, N
Bailey, J
Barker, J P
Barnes, N R
Barrett, R V
Belton, P A
Birrell, W L
Bishop, R A
Coomarasamy, D
Cooney, S
Darko, K
Delany, M G
Deva, A
Dhital, R P
Evans, M D E
Fullilove, S M
Gardner, A
Garelick, A I
Georgiou, G
Gracias, C J L
Gupta, R K
Gupta, U
Hadley, R S
Holman, J E
Horne, A D
Howie, S M
Huda, M F
Ibrahim, A
Isaacs, S
Jabbar, F
Jethwa, R N
John, T M
Kariyawasam, H H
Kawar, P M
Khalid, A F A
King, C A J
Lindall, S

Malhotra, A K
Malik, Z I
Monteiro, R F
Omololu, A G
Oraelosi, F N O
Pagadala, V
Parsons, M A
Payne, H A
Rajput, P B
Ray, J C
Reeve, A C
Rowse, N J
Seedat, N I
Shah, M R
Shah, R B
Shantir, D Y A-R
Sheikh, A Q
Shoaibi, A T
Siddiqui, A M
Sinason, M D A
Sloczynska, C W
Sowemimo, G M
Stearns, E J E
Stolar, M
Subramanian, P B
Sureshkumar, T
Swedan, H I
Taylor, G A W
Tennekoon, M
Tsokodryi, C
Yanah, D K
Zurgani, A

E18

Amini, A
Atun, R A
Brafield, A J E
Chard, D T
Cohen, J
Collins, J A
Dempsey, C M
Dus, V
Edwards, J G
Franklin, J J
Galloway, M J
Gimblett, M L
Hanley, M L
Hillenbrand, F K M
Hilton, A H
Hines, K C
Howlett, S F J
Johannsson, H E
Karim, M R
Kulhalli, V
Kumar, S
Lawrence, D
McKenzie, S A
McNeill, J M
Masani, V D
Mirchandani, M V
Moiz, M
Munjal, S
Nandy, S K
Nokes, T J C
Penfield, B
Philp, T
Rather, G M
Routledge, R
Ryan, J M
Shabestary, S M
Shah, M V
Shaw, S A
Smith, S D
Staley, M
Staniforth, A D
Stapley, M L
Tejani, S
Thompson, AV
Webster, F
Whitfield, C D
Whitfield, K M
Wolkind, S N
Yaqub, S U
Yaqub, Z U
Zaidi, F H
Zaidi, Z H

EC1

Abdelaziz, M M
Abdullah, S
Abrams, S M L
Aitken, C C
Al-Sudani, M L
Alesci, G
Anderson, J
Anderson, J V
Andrea-Barron, D R
Andreou, P S
Angell-James, J E

Armstrong, P
Assi, A
Baines, P S
Barton, K
Beaconsfield, M
Beddow, E C L
Bessant, D A R
Bird, A C
Born, G V R
Brelen, H M
Briffa, R M
Britton, K E
Bruce, T J R
Buckley, R J
Carr, C A
Carroll, S R
Catarino, P A S D R A
Charteris, D G
Chew, S-L
Coakley, J H
Cooke, E D
Cooling, R J
Cordeiro, M F
Cottrill, C P
Crake, T
Croft, N M
D'Auria, D A P
Dambo, K U
Daniel, R D
Dart, J K G
Das, S S
Dauncey, M K
Davies, N P
Deahl, M P
Dickinson, C J
Dilkes, M G
Dinan, T G
Domizio, P
Doust, P J
Dowler, J G F
Drake, W M
Driver, H E
Farrugia, D C
Fells, P
Ficker, L A
Franks, W A
Freedman, P S
Gair, E J
Gallagher, C J
Galton, D J
Gartry, D S
Geoghegan, C J
Gilbert, C E
Glenn, M S
Gormley, F C
Granowska, M
Greenhough, S G
Grossman, A B
Guymer, R H
Hajioff, S
Halliday-Bell, J A
Hardie, R M
Harris-Jones, R D L
Hincks, S S M
Hine, D J
Holt, B A U
Howell, P R
Hudson, C N
Hughes, J L
Hulbert, M F G
Ihenacho, A O
Ind, T E J
Ionides, A C W
Jacks, A S
Jacobs, I J
Jeffries, D J
Jenkins, P J
Jeyarajah, A R
Johnson, C-A
Johnson, G J
Johnston, L B
Jurek, P M P
Kadim, M Y
Kamal, D S
Kapadia, S B
Kapur, A
Kelsey, S M
Khaw, P-T
Kingston, J E
Kon, C H
Kwan, S L A
Landers, A M
Langford, R M
Larkin, D F
Leaver, P K
Lee, M J T
Lehmann, E D
Lehmann, O J
Levene, R

Lightman, S L
Lipkin, G W
Lister, T A
Litchfield, P
Loh, C P L
Lowe, D G
Lower, A M
Lugone, H A
Luthert, P J
Macaulay, D E S
MacCallum, P K
McGavin, D D M
MacGregor, E A
MacIntyre, I
McLaren, D S
McNeish, A S
Malpas, J S
Marks, R R D
Martinez, A E
Miller, G J
Miller, N E
Mirakian, R M
Monson, J P
Moodaley, L C M
Moore-Gillon, J C
Mulholland, B
Murdoch, I E
Myint, F P-O
Nagendran, K
Neaman, G M
Newell-Price, J D C
Newman, L T
Nolan, W P
Norton, A J
Nutting, C M
O'Byrne, S R T
Okhravi, N
Oliver, R T D
Ong, K-B
Oza, A M
Palazzo, F F
Parkin, J M
Parmar, D N
Patel, P
Patterson, L J
Pearson, R M
Perry, N M
Pinching, A J
Powell, M E B
Pozzilli, P
Prentice, M B
Prior, P F
Pritchard, N C B
Propper, D J
Psychari, S
Quigley, C S M
Rao, K A
Rimmer, B K
Rodriguez Arnao, J
Ruckert, L A L
Rudd, R M
Sachs, J A
Saldanha, C B R
Sanderson, I R
Sauvage, J A M
Savage, M O
Sayer, J W
Schilling, R J
Schwartz, E C
Sethi, A S
Shafford, E A
Shah, P
Sheaff, P C
Shingadia, D V
Sigston, P E
Smith, L F F
Sourial, A S A
Steele, J P C
Stevens, J D
Sullivan, P M P
Tabaqchali, S
Tate, A T
Thexton, P J
Tuft, S J
Turner, T H
Upton, K M
Vasserman, D
Vinnicombe, S J
Viswalingam, N D
Votruba, M
Wald, N J
Waters, A H
Watkiss, J B
Weaver, M G
Webb, J A W
Wedzicha, J A
Wells, C A
Wells, P
White, D A

White, P D
Wilkins, M R
Wilkinson, D J
Williams, C M
Wilson, E J
Wood, A J
Wormald, R P L
Young, I M
Zeidan, M
Zelin, J M

EC2

Alusi, G
Bell, P A
Brackenridge, R D C
Brown, S E
Buchanan, M
Bullough, J
Cannell, L B
Chambers, D R
Chard, T
Collier, P M
Cowie, C M
De Zulueta, M E
Delis, K
Easton, A L T
Emerson, T R
England, N W J
Evans, M R E
Fingret, A L M
Fischl, E A
Flack, N J
Fletcher, C L
Forman, C W
Griffiths, M A
Hanly, J F
Harries, A V K
Harvey, A M
Hasan, M A-M
Horder, J M
House, J M
Jones, C
Kelly, D
Landon, J
Lumley, J S P
Lunniss, R J
Lyons, V L
MacGillivray, D
McRae, S C C
Makings, E A
Marshall, N W
Moffat, R J R
Murphy, A M
Murphy, E
Newton, J M
Pollen, A G
Preston, J W P
Richards, J M
Royan, C N
Roythorne, C
Shetty, A K
Showghi, S
Tay, E S W
Terry, A E
Thomas, D R B
Tofts, E J
Wallington, D M
Walsh, D I
Wilcox, D T
Wu, E B

EC3

Arnison-Newgass, P
Boylan, T M
Chesney, R
Cunningham, G A B
Edmonds, C M D
Guider, P J
Lohn, M S
McGrath, J G
Macleod, G A
O'Donoghue, M G
Spier, G W
Stacey, A C E
Thompsell, A A B
Vaile, E
Van Horick, H
Webb-Wilson, G J

EC4

Agius-Ferrante, M-T
Campbell, I D
Cheverton, P D
Cooper, J R B
Cunard, M A
Dawood, R M
Ferrante, A M A
Ferriday, U T
Friston, M H
Gill, C R W

Gorog, D A
Hurley, R
Lowther, J
Marshall, I B
O'Grady, J
Pollock, E M M
Powers, M J
Samaratunga, V S
Solomon, F S
Taylor, S W

N1

Addous, A
Adrangi, B
Asteriades, H E
Badia Vallribera, L
Bain, B J
Banerjea, P
Bannerman-Lloyd, F
Barkham, D W
Barton, A C G
Baumgarten, S
Beaumont, B R
Beckett, H D
Bhargava, A
Bhatti, N
Blackwood, N J
Bloor, I A M
Booth, P J
Boyd, N R H
Braithwaite, S A
Bromage, M-C C
Brooker, C B
Bunt, R J
Bushman, J A
Candlin, R E
Casson, D H
Cattell, C A
Chan Tun Lun, A-F
Chapman, M J
Chianelli, M
Cikurel, K
Clements, E A F
Cochrane, G A
Cole, P V
Collier, B B
Collinson, N E
Colvin, D R
Connolly, J O
Cranitch, J A
Croxson, S A C
Dacie, J E
Dana, E C
Davies, S
De Couteau, M E
Dean, A D
Deighan, A J
Dixon, J A
Docherty, J N
Duggan, P J
Eigener, K F E
Erwin, D C
Esan, O O
Evans, J P M
Evans, R C
Fahey, J D
Fenton, T R
Fidler, S J
Findley, I L
Fleetwood, M E
Ford, C G
Foster, P M M
Fox, B D
Frank, M
Franks, L M
Fuller, J H S
Furness, A G
Ganesan, V
Garway-Heath, D F G
Gillies, L
Gillis, S
Giwa, S O
Goldberg, R G
Gore, J C P
Grandison, A L
Gupta, N
Gwinnell, E F
Hagdrup, N A
Hai, S A
Harrison, S M
Hassim, C E
Haughey, S J
Haynes, B
Heath, C D
Helm, M R D
Henry, J
Heyman, J
Hickling, J A
Hillman, K A

London, N6

Hoad, D J
Hodes, D T
Hollander, R
Holt, V J
Hopkins, R J
Hossain, A
Howling, S J
Hunter, J V
Hurwitz, B S
Hutchins, R R
Indapurkar, N R
Jacks, M E
James, I G
Jenkins, C D G
Jenkins, S H
Jenkins, S M
Jolliffe, V M L
Jones, P H M
Kavanagh, J
Khazne Charimo, Z
Kouimtsidis, C
Kouvarellis, D S
Laban, C A
Laing, G J
Lambert, C
Lawson, J O N
Lemonsky, I
Lessof, M H
Livingston, J P
Lloyd-Owen, S J
Lloyd, J K
MacBean, A L
McCartney, P R
McEnery, G
McGilligan, J A
McGoldrick, S
McLoughlin, I C
Maheswaran, M
Marley, R T C
Marshall, J S
Mayer, M
Meerstadt, P W D
Michael, D
Miflin, G K
Mills, S M
Milner, Q J W
Montemagno, R
Moody, J M
Morgans, M E
Narayanan, S
Nayer, P
Njoku, P E
Nye, J F
O'Connor, P D H
O'Driscoll, C M
O'Rourke, L E
Pandit, A
Pedder, J R
Peppercorn, P D
Pilston, M J
Pote, A H
Poulsen-Hansen, A G
Pracy, J P M
Qureshi, K M
Qureshi, R N
Reese, A J M
Rivas, P H
Roberts, J V
Rosen, E D
Rottenberg, G T
Rowlands, S C
Roy, S
Sandhu, K
Sattar, D A
Scott, L V
Seal, D V
Semao, M A
Sennett, K J
Shanson, R L
Sharman, J
Shiels, A M
Siegruhn, G C
Simon, R D B
Skalicka, A
Skelly, C M
Skinner, J I
Slater, N D
Smillie, D C
Spackman, D R
Speight, L
Stacey, C M
Stafford, C J
Stewart, K H
Stibe, E
Stirland, A M
Summerfield, K E
Taylor, J F
Tench, C M
Thompson, P B

Tibble, M J K
Umaria, N
Varley, B Q
Varma, R
Watson, G M T
Weinbren, H
Welsby, I J
Wise, D
Wiseman, S M
Wolff, J
Wolff, O H
Wollaston, S L
Wright, M J
Wykes, C B
Young, K

N2

Abrams, A B
Akita, A G M
Anderson, L D
Andrews, S J
Assem, E-S K E-S A
Baker, L D
Baron, D N
Bloomer, J M
Bourne, G L
Braham, A N
Brooks, H R
Camara, B S
Conrad, K K
Dakin, P K
Dalton, I S
Davies, G J
Dezateux, C A
Dick, A F
Dong, B
Ehigie-Osifo, E
Ellis, H
Fairhead, I A
Fallon, P K
Fox, M F R
Freaker, W A
Freedman, S
Gelfer, R A
Gibeon, S
Goldberg, A A J
Gregson, R S I
Hanouka, A
Harris, W C
Healy, T J
Hon, E H C
Hon, P H T
Ioannou, N
Isenberg, H
Isenberg, L A
Jacobs, J J
Jacobs, J
Jampel, H H
Jampel, L
Josephs, I
Kashi, I
Kelly, T
Kennedy, C O
Kreel, L
Lada-Grodzicka, H M
Lee, P
Leigh, M E M
Lewis, S R
Livingston, G A
Lucas, R N
McNicol, F J
Marcus, R
Marouf, E T S
Matharu, M S
Mellins, R A
Morgan, M
Mouchizadeh, J
Naidoo, R O M
Nathan, N L
Ng, P C
Osrin, D
Powell, A
Prasad, V
Qureshi, N M
Rabin, N K
Rappaport, R A
Renton, P
Rinsler, A H
Rogers, K B
Rund, R L
Salkind, M R
Samad, E M A-M
Samanta-Laughton, M
Shadwell, R N
Shore, P M
Simon, J
Singarayer, K N
Singer, A
Slesenger, J P

Smith, C W L
Spencer, M J
Steinberg, S D
Stewart, B A
Sutton, I
Sutton, V E
Tailor, R
Tang, S C
Tarnesby, G M S
Timmis, J B
Tobin, J A
Tong, T
Tong, T
Twena, D M
Ugboma, I A F
Veitch, A M
Wagner, S D
Wai, A S-Y
Wilcox, T
Wilkinson, A H
Wiseman, O
Wong Kam-Kee, S
Wong, G J W S
Wood, G

N3

Banerjee, P
Bangham, C E
Beatus, D
Bejekal, R A
Bentley, M S
Bousquet, P M
Boyton, R J
Bradley, J J
Burke, S
Cavendish, A
Cavendish, J A
Chak, M H G
Chan, A H
Chandrapal, K E
Chowdhury, N I
Christodoulou, A A
Cronin, E
Dana, A
David, G
Davison, R M
Desai, S R
Droller, B
Durden, N P
Dvorkin, L S
Eltom, N K
Elton, C
Ezra, H
Faith, C N
Fernandez, R
Foley, C L
Foley, P E
Garretts, M
Giannoulatos, S
Gibbons, E M
Gilbert, A
Gimmack, G
Gluck-Bardi, S
Glynn, R H
Gower, A J
Hague, D E
Hamzah-Sendut, I
Harkin, E J
Hart, C A
Herxheimer, A
Herxheimer, J C G
Hockman, N
Ismail, A R
Jarrett, A
Kay, D L
Kazemi, A-R
Keane, P M
Keidan, I J
Khan, S
Kochhar, N
Koso-Thomas, O A
Lawrence, D
Levin, G E
Mehta, P
Meltzer, M L
Mohamed, R
Mooncey, S
Morris, N H
Morris, S R
Mukherjee, R K
Mukherjee, S
Mumtaz, F H
Mumtaz, T
Nataraju, M R
Okonkwo, N A
Pandya, K K
Patel, N
Pelendrides, E
Perkins, A L

Perlow, B W
Popat, U R
Prasad, S
Radcliffe, J J
Rahman, F A
Ramachandran, M
Rashid, A H
Rathore, C K
Rees, H L
Robinson, A C
Rogol, S
Ross, M
Rowlands, A E
Sadana, A
Saville, M K
Scott, B D
Scott, K
Shah, L D
Shah, M N
Shah, V P
Siddiqui, K H
Spiro, M
Stacey, S M
Stoll, H
Talwatte, B Y
Talwatte, D B B
Tan, P H
Thangaraj, I L
Tonucci, D F M
Varnava, A M D
Vigano, P C
Vyas, D K
Wang, R Z
Watkins, G O
Wayne, N D
Weyman, C
Wilton, B J
Winship, A Z
Wong, T-S
Woolfson, H
Yiu, H-S R

N4

Alam, M S
Ali, M
Amarasena, G A C
Anyamene, N A
Arfeen, Z-U
Ariff, B B
Banu, S P
Barbenel, D M
Bartella, L
Broadhead, M W
Carver, R T
Chinyama, N C
Chow, J Y-N
Davies, D W L
Ekwuru, M O
Haas, J M
Harris, S J A
Hockey, J S
Hotonu, O E O
Hubbard, A D
Hubbard, M
James, E A
Jones, P H
Kar, G S
Khan, G M
Krisnamurthy, M
Kwok, Q S K
Li Ting Wai, L S
Lipitch, H S
Ma, R M M N
Mack, D J
McKane, W S
Masterson, S W
Meghani, S
Morrison, I R
Newman, P J
Nubi, W A O
O'Brien, F E
Patel, P C
Portanier, J
Porte, M E
Ruhul Amin, M A K M
Sanders, F E
Shah, N S
Shier, D L
Streather, C P
Teo, S G
Ullah, K M S
Varughese, R T J
Vijayakumar, M
Wolff, A H
Young, H L

N5

Alexander, N
Anand, V

Bakar, N B A
Bataille, V
Bennett, S D
Blane, D B
Brookes, C I O
Calder, P R
Caller, H A
Casasus Borrell, T
Challands, J F
Collie, M H S
Crawford, T A
Dervish, H
Dimmock, S A
Dock, V J
Dutton, J A E
Foord, M L
Gawronski, J G S
Goldsack, C
Gupta, S P
Hunningher, A
Hussain, S M
Indar, R A
Jacobs, F K S
Kaplan, J
Krishnamurthy, A K
Magnifico, F
Mathen, L C
Morrison, H E
Mullen, M J
Nicholson, R H
Patel, J D
Perera, S R
Phillips, D M
Singer, N E
Slack, S J
Smirl, J E
Spicer, R F E H
Stone, J C
Trosser, A
Warren, A K
Wearne, I M J
Whitlock, P R
Wormsley, S J
Yerassimou, P M
Yuen, A K-C

N6

Addenbrooke, T E A
Aitken, C H
Alberman, E D
Alimo, E B D
Andrews, L H
Armstrong-James, D P H
Baig, L
Baker, R S
Bardsley, I M
Bates, M A E J L
Bax, M C O
Beardwell, N A
Beaugie, A V
Beaugie, J M
Bernhardt, L W
Boohan, T L
Brant, H A
Bretland, P M
Briffa, J P J
Broadhurst, E R
Brough, G M
Browne, E F
Bruce, J T
Chan, K K L
Chataway, A M
Chataway, S J S
Cheng, A
Chesshyre, M H
Choudhry, S O
Clemente Meoro, M D C
Collie-Kolibabka, E
Collie-Kolibabka, G A
Cook, J
Cooper, C P
Cowen, D D
Crockard, M C A
Davies, E
Davies, J M
Dawid, F E
Denford, J D
Dickie, S J
Dukes, S A
Feldman, M M
Ferner, R E
Frank, N J
Frankl, A R
Galton, C J
Galton, J S
Gibbons, R K
Gilchrist, E

Graham, A J
Graham, R L
Grant, C M
Greenwold, N K H
Grover, N
Grüneberg, A L
Handler, C E
Harbin, L J
Harding, K R
Harding, L
Harlow, P A
Harrod, S T S-C
Hindley, C P
Hinton, A E
Hoffbrand, B I
Holtby, V C
Hosie, G P
Howitt, G B
Hudson, H N G
Jacob, S J
James, E C W
Jelenowicz, E
Johal, P S
Johnston, R L
Jones, E M
Jordan, L M
Keeble, T
Knowlden, M J
Knowlden, P R
Kong, J H B
Lam, W W-L
Lambert, J E M
Lanham, J G
Latimer-Sayer, E G
Levi, J
Levine, D
Lewis, E
Ling, C S
Lloyd-Thomas, H G L
Lloyd-Thomas, R M
Lowe, D A
Lunken, C R
Malik, M A
Mamaloukas, E
Margulies, H H
Mayer, R D
Meadows, C A
Meyer, N A
Mikhailidis, A M
Mindlin, M J
Mulvany, S R
Myers, D S
Myerscough, N
Nandi, L R S N
Neil, A B
Ng, J C M
Nonoo-Cohen, C
O'Riordan, E J
Obertelli, A
Ong, E G P
Pallister, W K
Patel, K
Patel, R S
Paterson, M T
Pathmanathan, Y
Pearse, P A E
Peart, S
Pomson, H R
Pondes, S
Prudo-Chlebosz, R R Z
Riddell, J D
Riley, L C
Robertson, S M
Rockall, T A
Romanos Betran, M T
Rosen, J-P D
Rosen, M R
Roxburgh, R A
Rushman, N R
Rustin, J K
Sankey, A O
Schmidt, A E
Schon, F E G
Semenov, R A
Shaw, C A
Sheppard, B S
Sheridan, C H
Shove, D C
Sidhu, S K
Silman, R E
Smith, S M
Smits, M M
Spankie, A C
Steen, C A
Stern, G
Swinhoe, J R
Tatnall, F M
Taylor, J
Thackray, A C

London, N7

Thum, A M E
Tyszczuk, L T
Uhr Delia, J A
Urquhart, R P M
Van Wyk, A L
Vicary, F R
Wainwright, D
Wainwright, S J
Webster, G J M
Willcox, R
Williams, A H
Woodrow, C J
Wright, H J

N7

Amin, D J
Asher, P N
Bantock, H M E
Barrett, M D A
Battle, G N
Berry, J
Chow, W C
Coutinho, M L P
Cripwell, M T
Crook, T J
Davidson, D
Dockery, F
Dopfmer, U
Eagleton, F M B
Edoman, S
Emmanuel, A V
Emmanuel, J S
Evans, M L
Fainman, D
Field, P M
Funnell, M S
Getachew, U
Grender, B C
Gupta, V K
Haigh, D J G
Hall, I S
Harbinson, P L
Hart, J K
Hart, P E
Hau, Y G
Hayes, M E B
Hewitt, J
Hilton, A I
Hopper, A H
Howard, J M
Hubscher, I
Hunt, S T
Hussein, A A G
Jayasena, S D
Jemec, B
John, L H
Joshi, C S
Kinsella, L M J
Krause, U
Krywawych, M N
Lyall, E G H
Manktelow, A R J
Manktelow, C
Marinker, M L
Mpanga, L A Z
Nguyen, C T
Oakley, G M
Ogundipe, E M
Ozcariz Eizaguirre, J M
Patel, A
Patel, R N
Quinton, L
RamcHandra, K
Rea, J N
Savage, A W G
Sayer, G L
Sills, M D
Sinclair, S I G
Sitaras, D
Storey, S M
Tarlow, J
Tarlow, S
Tatham, M E
Tounjer, I A
Uhegwu, N
Yudkin, J S
Zinkin, P M

N8

Adeniran, F G A
Ahmad, K S
Ali, T M M I
Amlot, N
Avraamides, P C
Bardani, I
Beck, E R
Beck, R O
Benson, K J
Berk, C

Blackburn, T D V
Blass, D M
Boyd, R J
Broomhead, C J
Brown, J G
Buchthal, A B
Busaidy, F S
Caleb, J V
Campkin, M R
Coleman, K A
Cooper, J A
Dangoor, E
Datta, D
Davies, J R
Derounian, N G P
Dhorajiwala, D
Dolman, W F G
Eccles, N K
Ellerby, M J
Fehler, B M
Fitzgerald, J M
Giotakis, I
Gittins, C S
Gothard, S C
Greenbury, E
Gueret-Wardle, T
Hasenson, B A
Hassiotou, A
Hill, S A
Hindson, N A
Jacobs, E D
Jefferies, N J
Johns, J
Jones, G
Jones, G V
Jootun, N
Klassnik, B
Korner, J
Locke, I
Lodge, P J
McCartney, S A
Maneksha, S
Marriage, S C
Masters, D
Matsakis, M
Meek, J H
Miles, D W
Moorey, H C
Munro, J M
Niazi, S
Nikolopoulos, J
Oli, J M
Onyeabo, B C
Paine, M A
Perera, C A M
Photos, E
Ramgoolam, N
Rosenthal, D
Rosenthal, J J
Rosin, R A
Rubra, T D
Sampson, A
Sharma, S
Shashikanth, S
Sher, C
Skogstad, H
Smith, C C
Smith, S D C
Stock, D J
Stock, R D
Strycharczyk, K J
Talat, M
Trew, J M
Walker, A
Waugh, J J S
Weston, C E
Wolfe, J
Wood, K A
Wright, S J

N9

Amin, K A
Anyanwu, A C
Boast, N R
Bolcina, A L
Bumrah, R S
Clare, D
Exworthy, T P N
Francis, R S
Ghazi, A H
Gill, D P
Gnananandan, J
Herekar, S R
Jones, A S
Jones, A
Jowett, S A
Kattan, G V
Logan, M B
Meltzer, E S

Mistry, C R
Philippou, G N
Pillai, K O
Pillai, S W
Reshamwalla, D K N
Roy Burman, B P
Sampat, V J
Schapira, A L
Singer, R V J
Smith, I A
Sternberg, S
Warren, J S
Yapp, P A

N10

Abrams, M E
Addy, N
Amlot, P L
Benians, R C
Berzon, D
Betts, J C
Blackstone, V H
Blend, D M
Brecker, N A
Brocklesby, S J
Brown, D W G
Brueton, R N
Buffey, A D
Burt, D E R
Chaloner, E J
Chesser, E S
Christian, P K
Christopher, E
Clarke, A L
Cohen, C R G
Corridan, B J P
Corridan, N P
Das, C K
Davies, D V
Demades, J
Dorling, A
Dzumhur, S
Economides, V A
Farrow, S C
Finch, R J
Foley, M F
French, S L
Friedmann, B
Funaki, A
Gerrard, T J
Greig, J
Hale, R B
Harris, K J
Hatjiiosif, R
Healy, R
Hill, J P
Hinton, E A
Howard, R S
Isaacson, R
Jackson, A A
Jaumdally, J-U-D R
Jones, H M
Karim, A
Karunaratne, D C P
Kell, P D
Kichlu, J K
Kiernan, W E S
Kolocassides, K G
Laverick, S
Lawes, D A
Levine, S
Lewis, S N
Lockey, D J
Luka, A
Luthra, A
MacGowan, J R
MacQuillan, J G
Malleson, S M
Mantides, G E
Marks, R J
Menzies, E A D
Mitchell, S C M
Mootoosamy, I M
Mulkis, H B
Murphy, C L
O'Donoghue, D M
Pearson, R F
Piachaud, R A
Putris, S H
Richardson, T A
Robinson, K J
Rotblat, F
Russell, A G
Russell, M S A
Safranek, M M S
Salkind, S R
Segal, H M
Sharfuddin, I
Sharma, R C

Shaw, J C L
Sivakumar, T
Solomons, N
Sudell, J M
Swale, J
Taylor, T H
Trompeter, S
Van Hagen, T C
Warley, M A
Waterhouse, E T
Weatherley, P L
Werth, F
Wohl, M
Woolfson, S B
Young, S E J
Zakaria, F B P

N11

Adamson, E
Albon, L I M
Brooks, J
Corcoran, D
Deshmukh, B A
Dickie, C H
Dimitrakos, M-A
Goraya, A
Haidar, A
Hamilton, S J
Harrison, W A
Holt, L W J
Khumri, A
Lawal, O
Lee, C T
Lewis, R M
Mansfield, J D
Maroof, Dr
Oboth Owino, N
Ofori, J A B
Okonkwo, S I
Parmar, S J
Patel, S M
Plunkett, C N
Rifkin, S
Rouse, A J
Saglani, S
Schamroth, A J
Selwyn, V G
Shah, S M
Sherman, L M
Siddiqui, G K
Singh, R
Smith, G W T
Thillainathan, S
Thiruvudaiyan, P
Twine, M R
Waldron, G
Waldron, H A
Williams, R L
Zahir, K

N12

Abdul-Ghani, A K M
Ahmed, A R
Alterman, J
Amdurer, M A
Astruc, D M N
Baker, J
Barnes, S J
Barrett, P J
Berkovitz, S R
Besherdas, K
Bezuidenhout, P B
Bhatia, S
Brett, C J S
Brull, D J
Brunner, M D
Burney, S R M
Chan, K S
Chan, S S Y
Chari, P
Chari, S
Cheah, E K L
Cheung, K Y P
Chong, A Y-L
Cogman, D M H
Corcoran, J S
Daitz, A R
Dardis, P M
Deboutte, D
Devos, S E
Diamond, E M
Docherty, S M
Douglas-Wilson, I
Farooque, P G B
Fish, M
George, B
George, P M
Gokhale, S N
Goulden, N J

Goulden, P K
Govewalla, P
Guindi, G
Jarvis, E T
Jennings, S J
Jones, N
Jordan, A J
Klein, A A
Leighton, M H
Liu, E N-W
Liu, R S N
Mahadeshwar, S S
Maybin, K J
Ming, H Y
Mohapatra, J R
Mok, H L-H
Momoh, J A
Myttas, N
Nabarro, J M
Ng, B K W
Oddy, M J
Olaitan, A
Parker, A M
Patel, A
Patel, R S
Peisach, C M
Ray, C K
Richards, L M E
Riley, C E
Salasa, M H
Sargent, C S
Sebastianpillai, N J
Sharif, M
Sharland, D E
Singh, A K
Skia, B
Smith, H R
Stein, H
Stephens, C A
Strouthos, M
Tang, Y-T K
Tauzeeh, S M
Tornari, K C
Van Der Sande, M A B
Wee, A A B L
Weingarten, N J
Yiu, P
Zuck, D

N13

Achike, D I O
Ahmed, A A S M
Ahmed, A
Ali, K M
Ali, T
Crossley, H
Dick, A R
Doctor, N H A
El-Oush, T M M
Gibbs, J G
Gupta, S
High, J E
Kolman, P C
Kouloumas, G
Leedham, S
Llahi Camp, J M
Makinde, O
Malone, T B A
Naik, P N
Nandadeva, P G
Nicholaou, T A
O'Mahony, J F
Obiekwe, M N
Osman, R
Patel, M H
Patel, T B
Sinha, K M
Sole, S L
Tan, K C B
Tsavellas, G
Van Der Knaap, J
Warren, L M
Wright, G A K

N14

Abedi, M K A
Aetheris, P S
Ahmad, S N
Ali, S A
Amarasinghe, L M
Amarasinghe, M A
Anderton, E
Annaradnam, R J
Ara, B K
Aristodemou, A
Bashir, K
Behr, H L
Brener, N D
Broster, G M

Campbell, A C H
Caplan, H
Cattell, H R
Chau, B L
Coffey, M S
Corley, M
Cowen, J
D'Souza, L R
Daitz, H
Dancyger, A M
De, S K
El Ashry, A A
Eldridge, C D
Engel, H O
Fletcher, W D
Geffin, B B
George, M J
Haikel, S M S
Hamid, M S M
Harris, E A E
Helwa, S A I
Ho, N C Y
Ho, V C L
Howell, D C J
Islam, M N
Islam, V
Ismail, H
Ismail, H
Ismail, I H M
Jarvis, K J
Jayaratnam, A S V R
Kaleel, M F
Kaleel, M F H
Kay, J Z
Khan, T B
King, A-M
Kiss, I S
Kooner, P
Lakhani, N N
Lau Lai Lin, L
Lipkin, B D
McClure, J L
Mangaleswaradevi, R G
Marcus, N J
Muhundhakumar, S
Muhunthakumar, P
Murphy, M E
Neehall, D J
Ninis, N
Niranjan, N
Ong, Y T
Owino, E W J
Patel, P G
Pati, J
Phadnis, S G
Phillips, R L
Pollock, E G
Prothero, D
Rasiah, N J
Richardson, E J L
Robinson, G M
Seal, A N
Seal, L J
Sebastianpillai, C
Sebastianpillai, F B Y
Shaddick, R A
Shah, D K L R
Sheldon, L A
Sissou, P
Smith, G D
Sonigra, H K
Synge, J
Thomas, J M
Turk, J L
Turk, T
Van Someren, R N M
Veale, D M W C
Watts, V K
Wimalaratne, B M D S
Wray, G M H
Young, A J
Yu, S H
Zoha, M M

N15

Afghan, K
Bateman, A W
Bilginer, H T
Blanchard, M R
Callan, A F
Caplan, R S
Chadwick, J M
Chowdhury, D H
Chowdhury, H
Dickinson, M J
Fenton, K A
Furlong, R C S
Ghosh, A K

London, NW1

Ghosh, D
Hawkes, G I N
Hazelwood, S R
Hemmings, C P
Hoar, A C D
Holmes, D A
Ikwueke, J K
Isorna, V
Kirk, M
Kundu, D K
Lingam, S
Majewski, A A
Mukhopadhyay, D N
Nageswaran, A S
Oji, K N
Oke, O O
Pal, D
Pandya, J K
Phimester, M E
Popat, R T
Portsmouth, S D
Rachman, S C
Read, J H M
Rohan, J S
Sabat, A L
Seargeant, J M
Shaw, T B
Sivasinmyananthan, K
Smith, W G
Thambapillai, A J
Wheeler, A J

N16

Ansorge, R
Bench, M T
Bohn, P M
Bouchet, V A
Bradbury, A G
Brandner, B
Browne, N B
Buchin, E M
Carr, J B
Caviston, P M
Chong, J A
Chowdhury, F B
Clayton-Jolly, A J
Clouter, G
Collins, C M P
Connolly, A M
Coote, N M A
Cross, L C
Dalton, M J T
Davidson, K
Dell, A J
Derrett, C J
Dewhurst, A T
England, R
Evans, T K A
Faire, G M
Faruhar, M
Fisher, H
Fitzpatrick, M J
Foster, C S
Gadhvi, M R
Gadhvi, N M
Gangola, R L
Garner, G M
Goodhart, L C
Graffy, J P
Green, S G
Gupta, S P
Hindley, M C
Jaffer, N
Jamieson, A
Kambitsis, N
Kay, P T S
Keene, A D
Kiernan, S J R
Kleeberg, B K
Kleeberg, C S
Lamb, G
Leibel, D J
Levy, A L
McKie, J M
Madge, S J
Mallick, J K
Maloney, C
Mann, N G
Marks, C M
Mitchell, H J
Morton, A D
Osen, H E
Phelan, D R
Prasad, S N
Press, V R
Qureshi, M A H
Ramanna, M
Rasburn, B
Sargent, C B

Sibtain, A
Spitzer, J
Virjee, S
Waldman, L J
Weinstock, S
Wilkinson, J M
Williams, C D
Williams, D S
Williams, J
Withers, D J
Woodgate, M
Wright, F A

N17

Abomeli, D O
Agyeman, K
Amato, G A
Augustt, A G
Barnett, P
Bastianpillai, L S K
Cave, D R
Chan, S K W
Crowley, M P
Curtin, J T
Dadzie, O E
Dowler, S A
Ebigbo, A P M
Edelston, R H
Henderson, A M
King, E
Lindsay, M S
Louka, L
Marotta, S
Mazzon, S
Moossun, H
Morrison, C M
Ngo, T C
Parkinson, S H
Pereira, J M D S
Pierre, S L
Piller, W K
Ranmuthu, A H
Svenne, D
Udenkwo, G
Woollacott, M

N18

Al-Dabbagh, L T
Ali, T T
Alsford, L J
Alwan, A H
Aziz, M N
Borgstein, R
Davies, S A
Deo, S I
Dixon, P J
Drabu, Y J
Evans, F A
Fowlis, G A
Girgis, F L
Goodyear, H M
Hiew, S C C
Hirst, D K
Husien, A M A
Ithayakumar, E S
Jeffery, R C S
Karp, S J
Khan, A
Kumaran, T O
Lester, E
Luckit, J K
Makker, H K
Mansell, E J B
Mehtar, S
Millar, A D
Mitchell, A B S
O'Brien, B P
Onwubalili, J K
Patel, B C
Ranmuthu, P
Rees, J A
Sala, C
Seara Escudero, J
Shah, H R
Silver, M E
Sinclair, H D
Stoker, D L
Sultana, A A
Sundaresan, M L
Thapar, R
Thiagarajah, K A
Tindall, H
Viswanathan, M
Weithers, E C
Woolf, V J
Yardumian, D A

N19

Aarons, S D
Ardeshna, K M

Arnold, A M
Ashley-Miller, M
Atia, W A
Bacarese-Hamilton, I A
Baldeweg, S
Banerjee, A
Barnes, S D
Beatson, S M
Bebbington, P E
Bell, S D
Bernardis, C K
Bielawska, C A
Blake, S M
Brady, R
Brett, B T
Campbell, M F S
Chase, J C C
Chaudhuri, R
Cheung, C M G
Chong Siew Foon, E
Coppola, W G T
D'Arrigo, W L
Dacre, J E
Dalton, J
Darley, M P
Dennell, L V A
Desai, S A
Desmond, N M
Din, R R
Dinner, L
Dufton, K E
Durrant, K J
Ellis, D G
Evans, N D
Feeney, J T
Floyd, D C
Foo, M W-Y
Fraser, R J
Gluck, T A
Grande, M J
Grant, D S
Greenhalgh, P M
Gregson, R M C
Hadfield, E V A P
Hakhamaneshi, D
Hales, H J
Hannam, S
Hanson, L G
Hardman, S M C
Hargreaves, C G
Harvey, N S
Haselden, S P
Heaton, G M A
Helman, C G
Heman-Ackah, C A
Hennigan, J T
Henson, G L
Hoult, J E
Ihamah, F E
Ingham Clark, C L
Inwald, A C M
Jacobs, S R
Jaswon, M S
Jolowicz, K
Jukes, M M R
Kalra, D
Kateb, H J
Kelsey, M C
Ko, A H N
Koya, M R
Kyei-Mensah, A A A
Lock, M R
Lock, S H
Mackinnon, H S
McLure, C E
Mansell, M E
Martin, J R
Martinez-Alier, N G
Miller, R A
Mills, P R
Mitchell, P O
Mitchell, S J
Modell, C B
Modell, M
Morgan, A A
Morgan, H
Mountford, L
Nesbitt, S J
Olateju, M A O
Panch, G
Parker, N E
Patterson, D L H
Persad, K
Radwan, T A H
Rands, G S J
Restrick, L J
Riches, L A
Roberts, J E
Robins, A W

Robinson, I F
Ross, A M
Roussak, J B
Seckl, M J
Semrau, U
Shah, M R
Singer, A
Southgate, L J
Stevens, J P
Sullivan, C M
Tan, S-Y
Taylor, L C R B
Thomas, M R
Ticktin, S J
Tucker, S K
Varley, R A
Vos, A L
Walters, K R
Wills, A J
Wilson, A J
Wonke, B
Wooller, D J A
Worrall, J G
Yeung, J N M
Youngman, J R

N20

Bayreuther, J L
Bennett, S
Brigden, W W
Callaghan, B D
Cambell, J F
Chandhok, V R
Chrysopoulo, M T
Creer, D D
Davidson, R A
Davis, P W
Dyer, N C
Eisen, S M
Emond, R T D
Flynn, F V
Free, D G C
Fujita, Y
Goldman, M H
Grantley, B
Green, E C
Griffith, J D A-H
Gross, G
Hayward, A E
Hirsh, J
Hobsley, M
Howells, B K
Howells, J C
Howells, T H
Jankowska, P J
Jeffreys, P A
John, P D L
Kapur, S B
Katz, R E
Kenefick, J S
Lawlor, M G
Leontiades, G M
Lever, C G
Lindsay, M D
Lubin, J R
Lucas, E A
Lumley, K
Maxwell, J R
Milnthorpe, J C
Olver, J J
Page, F M L
Peters, N
Phillips, B L D
Poobalasingam, N
Price, H
Quilliam, P
Sampson, R D
Scurr, A J
Scurr, C F
Seevaratnam, N S
Shaikh, N A
Silk, J
Smith, H G
Viapree, R O
Wallace, M H
Ward, S L
Welch, R F
Whiter, A J
Whiter, G L
Willis, K M
Wood, D R
Wood, M M

N21

Abdel Khalek, A I
Ballah, N D
Banim, R H
Bhattacharyya, M R
Binysh, H

Bodger, W M
Chakraborty, A
Chitra, A
Cooper, E J
Craigmile, D A
De Silva, R K
De Thierry, A E L
Durcan, G B
Edhem, I
Elias, T H
Farmer, J A M
Fletcher, I H
Freeman, M J
Georgallou, M
Golara, M
Gormley, S J
Haikel, M S
Halil, O
Harris, R D
Harte, K M
Hendry, W G
Herriott, M
Herriott, T D
Hume, R C
Huq, K K
Jash, K
Jenkins, G C
Jenkins, M D
Jesuthasan, M
Jones, H S J
Jones, M O
Karia, N
Krass, I M
Ling, K S L
Maciolek, J S
MacKenzie, G D
MacPhail, M
Makuloluwe, C L K
Masters, A B
Mottalib, E A
Nolan, F C
Noor, R
North, J R
Olakanpu, O A
Perera, W A T E
Raithatha, R
Samtani, A
Selwood, J E
Sethi, P
Shah, P R
Shah, P
Shah, R C
Sheville, E
Siriwardene, S K
Sirri, T N
Stern, G M
Stewart, D
Thomson, J L S
Trathen, D P
Tudberry, R A
Watkins, M E
Wiggins, L J
Wijesinghe, D P
Wragg, A
Young, Y

N22

Acharya, R J
Aldulaimi, D M
Bodhinayake, B
Botros, H
Christoforou, C
Clarke, P C
Cleanthis, T M
Connolly, G M M
Dave, M S
De Rooy, L J
Deeney, H N
Douglas, B C
Eren, E
Ferguson, E M
Graham, N W
Hasan, H I
Higgins, C J
Hoque, A T M M
Jadeja, A K
Jalloh, S S
Jurangpathy, M F
Kamal Nor, N
Kaya, B
Kaya, E
Koziol, L F S
Man, F W A
Manheim, V H
Marasco, M
Matheson, P J
Moitra, R K
Ong, K K L
Pantazis, A

Patel, H M
Paun, S M
Preston, P J
Raza, M
Salek Haddadi, A A
Samarasinghe, L
Scott, A J
Sivananthan, N
Sothi, S
Soutter, P G
Steinberg, S
Stekelman, S
Strommer, T R
Sultana, K
Theodorou, M
Visavadia, B G
Windle, M F

NW1

Agathokleous, K
Akinyanju, O O
Al-Adnani, M S
Alberti, K G M M
Alcorn, R J
Allinson, R N
Andersen, S L
Antoniades, C G G
Anwar, F S
Arnold, K G
Arnold, N
Assheton, S J
Avery, N R
Awad, W I I
Aziz, M V
Bahl, M R
Bakshi, N
Baraitser, P
Barker, M A
Barker, V
Barlow, J S
Basnett, I N
Bellman, M H
Benaim, S
Berger, P L
Blades, H R
Bloom, P A
Booth, C C
Bowman, M J
Bradley, E A
Brennan, E
Brockbank, M H
Brogan, P A
Buchanan, A J
Carlton, O H
Castell, F A
Cathcart, S J
Cawley, R H
Chakrabarty, S
Challoner, T E
Chan, S M T
Collier, L H
Connor, H E
Cook, C A G
Cook, G C
Cope, H M
Corbett, M C
Corcuera Maza, M A
Coren, A
Cowan, D A
Cowan, G O
Cox, P J
Crystal, S C
Cullum, A R
Dally, A G
Darbyshire, J H
Datta, D
Davidson, J
Davis, A A
Davis, H J
Davis, R M E
Dinning, W J
Dobbs, P M
Doherty, J F
Down, J F
Drummond, P M
Duguid, I G M
Dunlop, L J
Eapen, E
Edmunds, L E S
Elphinstone, P E
Faghihi Naraghi, A M
Fairhead, S M
Ferguson, C N
Fikree, M A
Fletcher, A P
Girling, D J
Giunti, P
Gledhill, R C
Goodstone, A S

London, NW2

Gordon, I
Granger-Taylor, C P
Gray, T B
Greaves, S
Gregory-Evans, K
Grimaldi, B D F
Grüneberg, R N
Hackett, G H
Hailstone, J D
Harbord, R B
Harris, D N F
Hecker, K V
Hegazi, M A
Hennelly, K J
Herst, E R
Hoffman, R
Hooper, H J
Hoque, M
Horder, E J
Huang, A
Jain, S
Jenkinson, A D
John, L M
Joyce, C M M
Joyston-Bechal, S
Kaleem, N
Kanaan, R A A
Katz, A W
Kemp, K S A
Kerr, I E
Kurbaan, A S
Kyriacou, E
Lakasing, L
Landeck, A
Latchman, M Z
Lawrence, C J
Lawrie, H S L S
Layland, W R
Lee, N B
Lee, S
Lieberman, G
Lindsay, K D
Ling, K L C
Lo, S K
Lockey, E
Longden, P B
Loud, S G
McCormack, S M G
McCullagh, G M
McDonald, W I
McVie, J G
Mahler, R F
Malaki, F
Malik, R
Marsh, H P
Martin, C B
Miller, J W
Mills, A M
Moore, D A J
Morris, J E
Morrison, R C
Morrison, S C
Nadarajah, S
Nagle, C J
Nightingale, D
O'Donnell, J G M
Oliver, B K
Ormerod, W E
Ormston, R M A
Orsi, C R
Osmond-Clarke, F
Panama, K
Parry, E H O
Peirce, N S
Peters, D
Petrou, P P
Pickard, C A M
Pietroni, P C
Pollock, R M
Puxon, C M
Qamar, A
Ragge, N K
Rao, S K
Ratcliffe, G E
Ray, N
Rees, W L L
Reid, A J C
Renfrew, I
Roques, T W
Rose, J H
Rosenthal, A N
Roux, B R
Sabeti, H
Sanderson, P J
Sangala, W O O
Scarffe, J H
Senanayake, I P
Sharpe, R M
Shaw, K L

Shina, A G
Shute, J T
Siddiqi, N I
Simmons, N A
Skensved, H
Smaje, L H
Smith, E R
Smith, S M
Sohn, L
Southall, T R
Steiner, M C
Taylor, P A
Taylor, R W M
Teoh, S K
Thompson, C M
Trevor-Roper, P D
Uprichard, W J N
Vernon, P R
Walker, A E
Wander, A P
Waters, M F R
Watkeys, J E M
Watson, E N
Wedeles, E H
Weston, T E T
Whitcombe, E M
White, M
Whittle, M A
Winnett, A R D

NW2
Abenyeka-Nunma,
P O K O
Adebayo, A B
Agranoff, J
Ahuja, A
Ajdukiewicz, K M B
Al-Musawi, D M M
Al Sahlani, U Y A
Allen, R L
Amin, Y K
Andrawis, N F
Appiah, L K
As'Ad, S M
Baghai-Ravary, R
Barter, J A
Bashey, A
Bennett, J A
Berzon, D B
Biggs, S
Brennan, M T
Brzechwa-Ajdukiewicz,
A A
Bunn, A W
Bunn, D I G
Burch, A M
Chaudhury, S D
Coates, S M
Cohen, J
Cohen, N A
Craig, A P
Dalsania, A V
Datoo, M M A
Davidson, B R
Davis, L
De Kare-Silver, N S
Dresser, T H
Dudley, A F
Elmiyeh, B
Erskine, A W F
Ezquerro Adan, A
Faal, M A
Fernando, N P
Florin, L C
Forbat, S M
Frosh, B J
Ganny, A S
Gilston, A
Gomes, J A
Guercken, N
Guercken, T P
Halsted, C J
Hart, F D
Hassan, M A
Haynes, K G
Heuschkel, R B
Houston, M E
Howard, M R
Husain, S T
Imeson, J
Isaacs, J D
Izegbu, V A E
Jeswani, T A
Jolles, M A
Joshua-Amadi, M I
Joslin, J M
Kahtan, S R
Kayani, R M
Khan, Z

Lepski, G R
Lodhi, M A K
McCollum, M P
Mahatane, J R
Marre, L
Marshall, J R
Martin, S M
Mehta, K A
Mehta, R K
Mitchley, S E
Najim, Z N
Negus, R P M
Neoman, I F Z
Nesa, Q U
Nissenbaum, H
Nwozo, J C
O'Donovan, M R
Oliver, M T
Onyeador, M I
Osakwe, E A
Parris, R J
Patel, M K
Perinpanayagam, R M
Phelan, M S
Phellas, R
Pinner-Harth, J A
Prempeh, T B
Qureshi, A I
Raby, A M
Rahman, F Z
Rainbow, D J
Raja, M A K
Rakshi, J S
Ranade, J U
Rawal, R S
Richman, G
Robinson, A L
Robson, G
Rudge, P J
Rutter, G G R
Samarasinghe, K P B
Sathia, U L
Schelvan, C S K
Sebastianpillai, M R
Segall, J J
Shah, S
Shah, U U
Shah, U R
Sheth, J G
Siriwardhana, S A
Skelker, M H
Slome, J J
Smith, N P D
Sorungbe, A O O
Spirman, M
Talmud, J C
Taylor, J
Thackray, J E
Thiru, C N
Thomas, J M
Thursfield, S R
Tilley, J M
Twaddle, J L T
Ukachukwu, I
Vaghela, H M
Wadhwa, P
Wamuo, I A
Ward, P A
Weisz, G M
White, D M

NW3
Achkar, J C
Ackerman, L E
Adler, J L
Adler, M A
Ahmed, S M
Akerele, O F
Akinsola, S A
Al-Damluji, S
Al-Turki, S A
Aldouri, M A W
Ali, A A
Allum, C A
Altschulova, H J
Ameen, A A
Amoils, S
Amrolia, P J
Anderson, C R S
Anderson, E S
Angel, A M
Annis, H M
Anthony, A
Arendt, G J
Aung Hpyoe, Dr
Bahri, A K
Bailey, J N R
Baillod, R A
Baker, D M

Balakrishnan, I
Balcombe, J N
Bannister, B A
Bardsley, E M
Bark-Jones, E M H
Barker, D A
Barkley, D E H
Barnes, E J
Bates, S J
Bayes, A R R
Beary, M D
Beckles, M A
Begent, R H J
Behr, E R
Bell, C L
Belsham, P A
Bendor, A M
Bennett, H R
Bentley, T J
Berelowitz, M O
Berger, L A
Berstock, R L
Bevan, K E
Bird, A S
Birnstingl, M A
Bivona, D
Black, C M
Black, J M
Blakeley, C J
Bonner, C V
Bostock, T S V
Boukalis, A
Bouloux, P-M G
Bourne, S
Bowen, E M
Bowler, J V
Bradley, E F
Bradley, S M O
Brafman, A H
Braimbridge, M V
Brett, E M P
Bridgewater, J A
Brook, A
Brook, J H R
Brown, G N
Bruce, A
Bruggen, C P L
Brumfitt, W
Burke, O C A
Burling, S A
Burman, A M
Burroughs, A K
Burton, B J L
Buscombe, J R
Butterworth, M S
Byng-Hall, J J
Calatayud Revert, A
Cannon, M
Caplin, M E
Carr-Brion, J M H
Carter, S M
Casserley, J D A
Caufield, H M
Chan Seung Chi, S
Chan, C S Y
Chan, O
Chan, V
Chanrai, M
Chao, D
Chapman, J T V
Chapman, M V
Chee Keng Jin, A
Chen, W
Cheng, G C W
Choi, S P
Choong, K S S
Clayton, W J
Cockcroft, A E
Cohen, A
Cohen, H
Cohen, S
Cohn, A S
Collee, G G
Collett, S
Conrad, R J
Cooke, M
Cormack, M A
Cox, S J
Cree, J A
Croft, G A
Crow, J C
Crowcroft, A
Cubes Montoro, J
Cummings, G E
Curtis, C J
Cwynarski, K L
Daly, M B
Daniel, J R
Danso, M A

Davenport, A
Davey, C C
Davids, Z-U-N
Davidson, T I
Davies, A E
Davies, A G
Davies, C M
Davies, S E
Davis, S
Davison, H W
Davison, P M
Daya, H
De Mare, P B
Deery, A R S
Dennys, E
Denton, C P
Dick, R
Dimitriou, C
Dirmeik, B F
Djazaeri, B
Djazaeri, B
Dooley, J S
Dorward, N L
Dowd, G S E
Downie, P M
Drake, B E N
Duchen, L W
Duncan, D D
Dunn, J
Durge, N N
Durkin, C A
Dusheiko, G M
Dytham, A J
Eastwood, D M
Eber, T R
Economides, D L
Edwards, S E
Eid, C S
Eid, N H
Eisen, T G Q
Ellis, J M
Elmhirst, S I
Evans, A L
Evans, R J
Evans, T R
Fairclough, A D
Fancy, N E
Faraj, K S
Farfan, G A
Farouk, M O
Fatnani, D T
Feinmann, C
Feldmann, P J
Fernando, O N
Fielder, M H
Fielding, J
Finlay, S C
Fleischman, A P
Florin, D A
Flynn, D M
Flynn, R J
Fogarty, A B
Fok, D H S
Foong, J
Foster, J W
Foster, S
Fox, S B
Francis, G E
Frankel, T L
Freedman, A
Freedman, J
Gabriel, G
Galton, E M G
Gertner, G
Ghosh, J M
Gibb, E L
Gibbs, J M
Gillespie, S H
Ginsberg, L
Ginsburg, J
Goddard, N J
Goldblatt, B
Goldin, J M
Gosling, R D
Gracey-Whitman, L J
Grant, H C
Grasse, A S M
Greig, E R
Griffin, S
Griffiths, P D
Gulati, S
Gyorffy, G
Hallgarten, R J
Hamilton, G
Hamilton, M I R
Hamon, M D
Harper, N C
Harris, M J
Harrison-Read, P E

Hart, P M A
Hayman, A W
Heaton, J M
Heelan, B T
Hellings, P M
Henderson, J H
Henryk Gutt, R
Heron, M
Higgitt, A C
Higgs, B D
Hilson, A J W
Ho, R L-M
Ho, S S M
Ho, S W T
Hobson, R P
Hodgson, P E
Hodkinson, A C
Hoffbrand, A V
Hoffbrand, S E
Holt, S G
Hood, C
Hood, J R
Hopkins, P
Hopman, E M
Horgan, L F M
Horton, J P
Huang Yun Pui, B
Hughes, J R
Humphrey, J R
Hussain, M
Hutchings, S L
Hyett, J A
Hyman, S
Hymanson, E N
Ioannidis, A
Ioannidis, C
Irish, C J
Jackson, D J
Jacobs, M G
Jaffe, R
Jaikaran, E S
Jakubski, R J A
James, G J
Jareonsettasin, T
Jarmulowicz, M R
Johnson, A M
Jones, A L
Jones, C L
Jones, J A
Jones, J M
Jones, M M
Jourdan, I C
Jourdan, M H
Kallberg, M H
Kampfner, F B E
Kasinski, K L J
Katopi, D
Katsarma, E
Katz, F
Katz, J R
Kelly, A
Kenton-Smith, J
Kernoff, P B A
Keshav, S C
Khan, N Q
Khan, S R
Khara, M
Khoo, P C
Kibbler, C C
Kiely, N M
Killaspy, H T
King, M B
Kingdon, E J
Kinston, M A
Kinston, W J
Kirk, R M
Kleinman, R L
Koh, T N
Koh, T W
Kohn, M R
Koso-Thomas, O M
Kraemer, J W S
Kreindler, J R
Krijgsman, B
Kurowska, A C
Kurzer, L
Laniado, M E
Laqueur, S R
Laurence, A D J
Laurence, D R
Laurence, N J I
Law, R R
Law, R
Lawson, J M M
Le Quesne, L P
Leddy, K
Lee, A L
Lee, C A
Lee, D R

London, NW6

Lee, M A G H
Lefford, F
Leigh, E D
Lewis, A A M
Lewis, E
Li, S K
Lim, C J
Lim, P S C
Lindsay, A
Lindsey, C R W
Lipman, M C I
Little, B C
Lloyd, B W
Lloyd, S K W
Lobl, E F
Loo Wing Hing, H
Lopez Hijos, C
Lotzof, K G
Loughridge, F A
Lozewicz, S
Lucas, C
McCarthy, J E
MacDonald Burns, D C
McFadyen, A
McGuinness, A M
McIntyre, N
McLean, A G
McLean, A M
Maclean, A B
McMurry, S A
Magos, A L
Majzlisz, A
Malek, B
Malhotra, U
Mallett, S V
Martin, J P
Martin, M D
Mason, H M C
Meer, S
Meeson, A
Meeson, B
Mehta, A B
Menachem, S
Mendonca, L M
Meyer, R E
Mikhael Matta, W H
Mikhail, G W I
Mikhailidis, D
Miller, C L
Milton, J E
Miranda Fernandez, F J
Mollison, P L
Montanez, A
Moore, K P
Morgan, E R M
Morgan, M Y
Morgan, N D
Morgan, S L
Morris, D C
Morris, S D
Mouzas, G L
Mudrewicz, J
Murch, S H
Naoum, H G
Nathan, B E
Natt, R S
Nazareth, I
Nelson, T R
Newby, J C
Newsholme, W A
Ng, R L H
Nohl-Oser, H C
Noktehdan, N
Nonis, C N A
Nwose, M O
O'Neill, C M B
Obholzer, A M
Ogunbiyi, O A
Oguz, C
Okolo, S O
Oon, L L E
Ordman, A J
Orrell, R W
Osborn, D P J
Owen, N J
Pachmayr, H K
Pachmayr, J
Parbhoo, S P
Parsons, T M C
Patch, D W M
Patrick, M P H
Pattani, S M
Payne, N D G
Peachey, T D
Peek, I M
Pepys, E O
Pepys, M B
Perry, D J

Philipp, A B
Phillips, W G
Pierce, C M
Pigott, J L
Pigott, K H
Pincus, C T
Pines, D
Platts, A D
Poole, S M
Poon, W K M
Potter, M N
Pounder, R R E
Powis, S H
Prais, S S
Prelevic, G
Prentice, H G
Psimenou, E
Pugh, J L
Rabson, D
Raeburn, J R
Randall, R I
Raschid, M S
Rau, D
Raven, P W
Reed, J R
Rees, L H
Rees, M C
Rees, P H
Regan, J L
Reid, W M N
Renwick, S R
Revell, P A
Robinson, P H
Rodger, J C
Rolles, K
Rowlatt, C
Rubio Lainez, C R
Sacks, M D
Samuel, O W
Sandford, J M
Savage, P T
Sayer, C S
Schott, J M
Scott, E M
Scott, P D C
See Chye Heng, A
Senanayake, L F N
Sewell, W A C
Shamash, A
Sharma, A K
Shaw, E H
Shein, I G
Sheldon, J H
Shenai, M S
Shenfield, F
Shieff, C L
Shiu, K Y
Siddiqi, A
Sienkowski, I K
Silver, C P
Simons, R S
Simpson, K M
Simpson, T D
Skarbek, C A C
Skioldebrand, J L
Sklar, J
Smailes, C L
Smeeth, L
Smith, M E
Snowdon, B A
Sofi, M A
Speight, R G
Stang, F
Stanley, C A
Steele, A S V
Stegen, G
Stewart, H
Stoll, L J
Stone, A B
Stone, R M E
Stone, S P
Storr, C
Stratton, R J
Stuart-Smith, S J
Stuart, A B D
Suppree, D A
Sutcliffe, A G
Sutton, D
Swain, A F
Swain, C P
Sweeten-Smith, B A
Sweny, P
Tai, N R M
Tam, T C
Tan, P C
Tanner, M A
Taylor, C P F
Taylor, D
Taylor, S E

Temple, N O T
Thammongkol, K
Thomas, J R L
Thomson, M A
Tibballs, J M
Tormey, V J
Toszeghi, A D
Tuck, S M
Tuckman, E
Turjanski, N R
Turner, J J O
Tyrer, M J
Van Someren, V H
Vaz, O K
Verma, S
Violet, J A
Vivian, A J
Vizza, E
Wajed, S A
Walker-Smith, J A
Walker, E M
Warbey, V
Warner, T T
Watkinson, A F
Watts, J D
Webber, I T A
Webster, A D B
Weich, S R
Weller, M P I
Wheeler, D C
Whiteway, A J
Whittaker, S J
Wijesuriya, N C
Williams, C J S
Williams, S S
Wilson, A D H
Wilson, L A
Winder, A F
Winslet, M C
Wise, M E J
Wiseman, P J T
Wolfe, I J
Wong, J M
Wong, L T
Woolf, A J
Wootliff, A B
Wu, A
Wynick, S P
Wynn, V
Yong, P F K
Yorke, S C B
Young, S C R
Yue, A M-H
Zachary, A R
Zuckerman, A J
Zuckerman, J N
Zutshi, D W

NW4

Abdul-Kadir, R A
Aggarwal, R K
Al-Dabbagh, Z T N
Alijani, M
Almeida, A Z
Alper, J
Aronica, G F
Aziz, V M
Baker, G
Bashir, F A
Benepal, T S
Benjamin, C A
Benjamin, E D
Burney, A S
Byrne, P G
Cardash, T K
Chatrath, V M
Cohen, M
Cooke, A H
Cooper, K S
Cooper, S H
Copeland, G G
Crosby, C P
Curwen, I H M
Dako, K O
Datoo, S A L
Davarashvili, T I
Davis, C P
Davis, H
Duke, C J B
Evans, K R
Fernando, B S
Fox, S D
Fraser, K E
Gilchrist, N E
Glatt, M M
Goldman, J H
Gosain, R K
Graf, K A
Graham, H

Graham, K E
Grant, A J
Gregory, G K
Hart, P S
Hoffbrand, C R
Holder, B
Hunt, L B
Hyman, H B
Ihara, T
Jaffe, V
Jaja, D M
Jerichower, F F
Jolic, G
Jones, P E
Joshi, R
Josse, S E
Katz, G
Kessel, A S
Khonji, A A
Kielty, V J
Kleinberg, S R
Kohli, B L
Kohli, S K
Kotecha, K M
Krasner, D H
Krestin, M
Lauffer, G L
Lawson, S E
Leader, S O
Mailoo, R J
Mair, J M
Mallucci, P L
Markiewicz, M
Maxwell, V B
Milofsky, R
Missakian, S K
Musgrave, M S
Mustafa, A
Ogunyemi, O A O
Okaro, C O
Osuagwu, F I
Pambakian, Y E L A
Patel, S A
Patel, V
Peters, E M
Popat, J T
Qureshi, Z
Rahmanie, N
Ray, S
Raymond, G P M
Razzaq, N
Rees, J D S
Rose, G A
Rosenberg, J N
Ruben, D H
Sakkadas, A
Samuel, J L
Samuel, S
Saperia, J
Sarma, R C
Sarma, U C
Schwartz, J S
Shah, H R
Shah, R M
Shapiro, L
Shelat, C C
Sheng, M H-T
Solomon, L A
Stein, G
Steuer, L R
Sudan, S
Taylor, E
Thrower, P A
Toledano, H
Townsley, W
Upadhyay, V A
Uzoka, A A E
Waydenfeld, S W
Weiniger, C F
Whitton, T
Wilkes, A

NW5

Alnaes-Katjavivi, P H
Amiel, S M
Asen, K M
Ashworth, N P
Barker, G R
Blackburn, V M M
Boyce, W J
Bunker, J R
Casburn-Jones, A C
Castle, M Z D
Cleverley, J R
Collins, H A
Copeland, B I
Craft, N
Davis, J C
Davison, M

Dean, J
Dean, Z-U
Deys, C M
Dickinson, C M
Dixon, G L J
Dixon, S M
Dormandy, T L
Dow, A M
Empson, B D
Farmer, M
Fitzpatrick, C M
Fleming, C
Fox, M P
Freudenberg, S
Gaminara, E J
Gillams, A R
Gough, S L
Graham, N
Graham, P J
Graham, S H
Grant, D M
Gunasekara, R D
Hajioff, J
Hale, A D
Halford, S E R
Hannan, F M
Hawting, R A
Heath, I C
Hill, D S
Hinshelwood, B G
Hollick, E J
Hughes, B C
Hunt, S J
Imber, C J
Ivens, D R
Jegadeva, A N
Jennings, E A L
Keyvan-Fouladi, M
Klouda, A T
Koperski, M T
Kubiangha, B O
Kwan, J W Y
Leff, A P
Lockett, C J
Lowe, J N
Lucas, D N
Luttrell, S R R
McCall, J M
Macdonald, M
Macgregor, D R
McNaught, A S
Mariotti, P
Marks, F M
Matthewman, P J
Mehta, A
Moran, M M
Moyes, B A
Myat, J M
Oswald, I H S G
Palmer, S C
Patel, P
Posner, P J
Rahman, S
Ramachandran, S
Rich, E M
Richman, N S
Riddell, A F
Robbins, S A
Roberts, O A
Robinson, K A
Roedling, A S
Rose, C D L
Sackville West, J E
Sayer, M M R
Schneidau, A
Sinclair, N E
Sinha, S
Sinha, S K
Smith, T M
Steel, A C
Summerfield, D A
Tendall, J D
Toeg, D
Underwood, T J
Wakeham, N R
Wilson, S M
Yiannakou, J Y
Yudkin, G D

NW6

Abraham, M D
Afridi, S K
Akerele, O
Ames, D J
Angeloglou, M
Ansell, E
Asafu-Adjaye, D S
Ashdown, A C
Ballaro, A P C

Banks, M R
Barnett, J M
Basir, N
Berry, M G
Binks, M H
Blenkinsopp, P F
Blesovsky, L T
Braude, W
Braunold, G A
Briffa, A C
Britton, R S
Brookes, J L
Budewig, K
Burgoyne, P W
Burman Roy, S A
Calaminici, M
Cantons, C A
Caparrotta, L
Caplan, A
Carey, P A
Carulli, M T
Casey, V C
Chan Chung-Chi, Dr
Chandler, K E
Chandler, S E
Cohen, S L
Coker, F B A
Cooper, H
Crème, M L
Cunningham, F L
David, L T
Davis, J A
De Zulueta, P C B
Desai, A
Dettori, H L
Di Luca, C
Eames, S A
Edmondson, C R
Elliott, S M
Eneli, A C
Esterson, A
Farah, A E T
Fatemi Langroudi, B
Footerman, D S
Ford, C H
Fox, K F
Gallagher, C M
Gill, M W
Goldberg, G J
Gottlieb, I
Gotto, J
Gozali, S
Grant, A J
Grasse, M E M
Griffith, G D W
Gumpel, S M
Hales, P C
Halpern, H S
Hammad, M K A H H
Hardenberg, J A
Hijazi, I S A-G
Hill, J M
Hillier, J E
Hinshelwood, L S
Hitchings, A E
Hobdell, R A
Holmes, M J
Howell, A
Humphrey, S J
Iliffe, S R
Jepson, A M
Judge, M R
Kane, H E
Kansagra, D M
Keane, F
Keays, R T
Kehoe, M J
Kelly, B T
Keys, D W
Khan, Z P
Kudrati, M E
Kustow, B
Lazanakis, M S
Le Roux, P H
Lee, C C-Y
Lee, V
Lester, M T
Leung, G K K
Levy, D M
Levy, M J
Levy, W
Lightstone, H L
Lim, H-M S
Lim, J C M
Lovell, D
Lucas, J M
Luksenberg, S R
Mabadeje, A F B
MacDermot, K D

London, NW7

McGuinness, O E
Magara, G
Mahmood, K
Mallett, P
Marcus, E
Marshall, N
Maxwell, S L
Miller, H R
Molloy, C C
Morris, M G A
Morris, P D
Morton, O
Motamed, M
Munnelly, S M
Murphy, E
Murray, E
Muthulingam, S
Nathan, M P
Nunez Miret, O
O'Connor, P M
O'Sullivan, E P
Obichere, A
Offer, M
Osrin, I
Parkes, H R
Pelekoudas, N
Pelling, M X
Pokorny, M R
Potter, J M
Powis, M R
Qubaty, M A-M
Ramsay, S J
Ranganathan, S C
Ray, S
Reinald, F N C
Richman, D M
Robinson, D J C
Rosenfelder, A F
Sandby-Thomas, M G
Scatchard, K M
Segall, J M
Semmler, J M
Shah, M V
Shah, N I
Shakokani, A A
Shaw, F M
Sherif, T E B A F
Skoblo, M
Smith, A M
Smith, D K
Smith, G L
Smith, S C
Solomons, S
Spencer, L L
Stein, A G
Stratton, M R
Summerskill, S C W
Sumption, C A
Tate, A L
Taylor, H L
Thomson, B J
Tobias, M
Tonnesmann, M E H P
Tooth, B
Trefzer, S
Vijeyasingam, R
Vites, J
Wainhouse, C L
Ward, K F
Watson, T P
Wayne, A N
Whitworth, J A G
Wills, V
Wongtschowski, K G J
Wood, E F
Wright, D E
Yap, L B
Yih, J-P L B

NW7

Adler, K A
Albert, P J R
Antebi, D
Armstrong, A
Arora, N
Aslan, T
Bailey, D A
Bala Subramanian, V
Balidis, M
Bangham, A M
Bernstein, L S
Beynon, H L C
Brown, B E
Burke, J B G
Carswell, W A
Claasen, G
Cogman, M M H
Crawford, C E
Cuttell, P J C

Dawson, J D
De Lord, D A
Dimson, H P
Durojaiye, O M
Fairweather, D V I
Faulkner, P
Fields, P A
Figa, S A
Fletcher, N
Flower, S P
Fluck, N C
Fluck, S L
Frost, D K
Gandamihardja, T A-K
Goldsmith, E
Gomes, M F A
Gordon, W
Greenbaum, A S
Gupta, R
Henderson, D C M
Hitchcock, S-C
Hopper, P K
Imtiaz, F
Jackson, A D M
Joshi, D A
Joshi, N D
Joshi, N D
Khan, S N
Lagnado, M L J
Lai Chung Fong, P
Lange, M J
Levy, J
Lewis, D S
Lineen, P M
Lloyd, M H
Lumb, R A
McDermott, E
Magri, J
Markandya, O P
Maruthainar, N
Milner, P J
Mirza, H
Mitchell, D N
Mulholland, J M
Murad, J
Nandi, R
Newman, M J
Nixon, J
Oduro-Yeboah, A
Osman, E M
Pei Yaw Liang, G
Pei, K C B
Pei, Y M D
Peter, J L T
Pine, R C
Remington, G A
Remington, K N
Reynolds, M A
Reynolds, W H
Robles, A
Rosefield, A R
Roualle, H L M
Sawdayee-Azad, A
Shaper, A G
Sinclair, E L
Singer, J
Sirisena, U N H
Sood, M K
Stidolph, N E
Sundle, M M
Tapeldin, M E
Tang, Y C
Taylor, E G
Thompson, D G
Thwaites, S V
Tobias, A R
Urwin, J E
Valentine, N J
Valentine, P W M
Watson, M
White, J M
Wijetilleka, A B S A
Wiseman, A J

NW8

Abadi, D I
Abdel Aal, N M Y
Abrams, W M
Afridi, A K
Aichroih, P M
Al-Barjas, H S A
Al-Duri, Z A A A K
Al-Simaani, M T
Alam, K
Alorda Boscana, M M
Alvarez, A S
Amis, S J
Anderson, G
Antoniou, A K

Bakker, A A
Beukes, A J
Bhattacharya, K
Black, P D
Blau, J N
Bolger, O H
Brennan, D J J
Brown, R A
Campbell, M D
Chambers, R F
Chan, E Y-L
Chan, Y-C
Charkin, S M
Chau, G K-O
Chazan, A A
Cheah, E-G
Cheesman, A D
Conran, M B
Constantinidou, M
Conway, J S
Cram, L A
Darkins, A W
De Fonseka, S E
Dick, J R F
Doniach, I
Dunn, C J
El Sayed, T F E B
Elias, D A
Elton, A
Emery, R J H
Fisher, G C
Fortune, F
Freedman, L
French, A J
Garfinkel, H A
Gillingham, N S
Glazer, G
Godfrey, M P W
Gold, M
Golding, A M B
Golding, C E M
Graham, J M
Grahame, R
Grubb, C
Harris, D W S
Hodges, H C
Hong, A S L
Hughan, I C
Hunt, S R
Jackson, I M
Jacobs, L
Jacobson, U
Jarman, B
Jepson, E M
John, L C H
Jones, I C
Kanoria, S
Kauffmann, E A
Kazi, T
Kennedy, R K I
Khan, A
Lam, F H T
Landau, H H
Lavelle, E T
Legg, N J
Lever, E G
Levin, A
Lewis, K H
Lim, C C
Lister, D A
Love, M B
Love, W E
Lowick, S J
Lyons, J D
Lyons, M J
Mackay, J A
Mallon, E C
Masani, J J N
Mason, A A
Maurice-Williams, R S
Mehta, A R
Miles, A I
Mintz, H G
Mira, S A
Mitra, A N
Mohammed, I
Mulla, N A
Nancekievill, D G
Nieman, E A
Nwakakwa, V C
Oldenshaw, P J
Pal, C
Panos, G Z
Panos, M Z
Phillips, J M
Quinn, D W
Ralph, D J
Ratnaval, N
Ratnavel, S

Rogol, B
Rosalki, J R
Rosen, A
Ross, A
Ross, L
Rosswick, R P
Sarner, M
Schuff, G H
Seifert, M H
Shahdadpuri, V D
Sharp, M A
Sheinman, B D
Shellim, M A
Shirlaw, N A
Silove, Y M
Singh, J K
Singh, R
Smith, G M
Snell, W M
Soh, J K
Sonnabend, J A
Sonoda, I L
Soyer, J A
Stone, L D
Super, P
Tan, Y K
Teoh, L-K K
Thorne, N A
Todes, C J
Tothill, A U
Vecht, R J
Wasan, B S
Watts, R W E
Wayne, C J
Wilkins, R A
Wilton, J F
Wong, T H T
Wyke, B D
Yoon, J S L
Young, M

NW9

Abdullah, A M
Ahmed, G M S U
Ahmed, S
Alpren, C G
Amakye, C A
Bachelani, A
Brownleader, S M
Burnett, A C
Cahalin, P A
Catchpole, M A
Chandran, V
Chandrasekara, B S D
Chapman, L E
Cheeroth, S R
Cheeroth, S A
Chong, I
Contreras, M
Cookson, B D
Dave, D V
De Silva, M
Deshpande, H B
Dinshaw, D
Dutta, J
Ehrenstein, J S
El-Saghier, A A F
Elazrak, S M H
Evans, B G
Finlay, B R
Fitzgerald, A M
Fox, A S
Fry, T
Fung-A-Fat, A G E
Furtado, A
Gallagher, L M
Gandhi, P
George, R C
Gill, O P N
Guhadasan, R
Harpalani, V B
Harrison, J F
Hewitt, P E
Heyse-Moore, J P
Huehns, E R
Hunyi, S J
Irfan, S A
Johnson, P M
Kaul, A
Kearney, J W
Kelsey, W A
Kirkbride, H A
Knowles, S M
Kumar, P V
Lamba, M K
Lloyd, R V
Madi, M S
Makhecha, R L
Martin Palma, E

Mathew, G
Mathew, N G
Modi, A J
Moore, M C
Morafa, O A
Mortimer, P P
Newby, R T
Ng Chieng Hin, S M C
Nicoll, A G
Nwachukwu, I A
O'Brien, S J
O'Mahony, M C
Odejinmi, F O
Ofoe, V D
Om Prakash, M
Onuoha, O O
Pang, L S C
Patel, J
Pattani, S K
Pundit, M
Qureshi, N A
Ramanan, R
Ray, S
Raza, N
Regan, A F M
Richards, D
Rousseau, S A
Rowe, B
Rub, R
Scott, J R
Selwyn, A
Shah, A H
Shah, J
Shah, U
Shah, Y Z
Shibu, M M
Sim, F M
Smith, P D
Sobti, U K
Stanwell Smith, R E
Steele, S
Tobiansky, R I
Towuaghantse, E
Turnberg, L A
Vadgama, S
Vetpillai, M
Vetpillai, S
Vogel, M
Walford, D M
Wall, P G
Warwick, R M
Watson, J M
Wexler, D M
Whitingum, G L

NW10

Abboudi, Z H
Abdalla, A H
Abrahams, L N
Agbim, O G
Akinosho, B O
Akmal, M
Amerasinghe, C N
Aminu, A K
Amobi, C A E
Annan, N T
Armar, N A
Arnold, A E
Athow, A C
Ayles, H M
Badiani, D
Bain, G A
Baldota, S Z
Ball, S T
Bansel, J K
Beaconsfield, T
Beale, T J
Bell, R A
Bellew, M V
Bhide, A V
Bose, U
Bowman, P
Boyce, M J
Brook, M G
Bumby, A F
Carne, A J
Cayley, A C D
Cheong-Leen, R
Coffman, D A
Cummings, T A
Curtis, M
Dalby, M C D
Dancy, C M
Davies, D D
Davies, S C
De Roeck, N J
Depala, B T
Deshmukh, S B
Dharia, R R

El-Sadig, S E G
Erskine, M K
Evans, B J
Eza, D E
Ezeh, I U
Fletcher, M D
Fletcher, S D
Frost, P G
Gellert, A R
Gellert, S L
Gillbard, G D
Godward, S
Green, D M
Grenfell, A
Habib, M
Hakim, M-S M-H
Harlow, F-H D
Hine, A L
Ho, S J
Ho, V K
Hollingdale, J P
Howells, H V
Humphries, P D
Ibrahimi, M-Q
Igboaka, G U A
Irani, G S
Israni, G K
Johnston, F A B
Joseph, J P
Joshi, R
Kapoor, A
Kay, L
Kerslake, S
Khadra, K A
Khatri, G N
Kirollos, C T
Kirubaharan, K
Kong, E K C
Korkodilos, M
Levy, S G
Loftus, J K M
Low, J K
Lubega, S L
McKee, L A
McManus, R J M
Maddison, I D
Mak, V H F
Mallik, D
Manning, E A D N B
Markham, G C
Marks, A J
Marks, L
Marks, M M
Marris, R
Murugesu, I
Nancarrow, J G
O'Brien, M S G
Ogakwu, M O
Ogugua, V O
Ojo, A A
Padarajhee, N S
Parkar, H B
Patel, C S
Patel, C
Patel, I P
Patel, P J
Patel, S B
Pearse, M
Peter, A M
Phillips, W S
Powell, R B
Prosser, R E
Ramdahen-Gopal, S
Ramjoorawon, M
Ray Chaudhuri, K
Richardson, A
Riordan, J F
Robayo Castillo, L V
Roberts, A J
Rolfe, L M
Russell, L
Ryan, K E R
Ryan, N M A
Salmasi, A-M
Samani, S
Samuel, N W G
Schwartz, R H
Shabrokh, P
Shafi, M S
Shah, D
Shapiro-Stern, P R
Sharma, A
Shaw, B E
Sherman, D I N
Shorvon, P J
Singh, S P
Sklar, E M
Slater, K E
Tachakra, S S

London, SE1

Tan, S
Thacker, B G
Thompson, S M
Toh, C T
Varghese, G U P
Veiras, M B
Vergnaud, S
Warren, P D
Warrington, S J
Wijetunge, A
Woko, E C
Woko, S C
Wong, K K Y
Wood, A E
Woolich, J G
Yarger, N

NW11

Abdul Ghani, P P
Abramov, S
Adler, J S
Adler, S
Adomakoh, N K P
Ahmad, S
Amin, L I
Andrew, M
Angell, C L
Armonis, A
Arsenopoulou, I
Asaria, R H Y
Atkin, N B
Atkinson, H D E
Beck, A
Been, J B
Benjamin, A R
Bethlehem, A K
Blanchon, B J R
Bloch, L G
Blom, P S
Bose, N K
Bowen, R A
Brar, S S
Brenner, B N
Bruegel, J
Buckman, L
Burger, J M
Campbell, E D R
Campbell, S
Caplin, M
Carlos, A J
Catania Aguero, S
Cavendish, M N
Chalk, B-Z
Cheong, F M
Chow, P Y
Clark, M
Clein, E M
Cockburn, A S
Cohen, A
Cohen, R J
Cohen, S I
Cohen, V
Croft, E
Curwen, J L
Da Costa, G I B
Davis, S
Day, B L
De Souza, M V
De Souza, V C
Desai, S J S
Dietch, D M
Dollery, C T
Donovan, C F
Dubowitz, D J
Dubowitz, G
Dubowitz, L M S
Duckworth-Smith, H C
Duckworth, G W
Dutt, S
Eccleston, S E
Elgar, J D
Elliott, A
Evans, A T
Fahmy, S I
Firth, H L
Fisher, M
Flores De Laurnaga, B
Foley-Comer, A J
Foo, I S M
Frank, J R
Gandhi, M N
Garrett, K R
Gergel, I P
Gilks, A W
Gishen, F S
Gledhill, J A
Gledhill, M T
Gold, D B
Goldberg, M

Golden, B J
Goldin, J G
Goldman, A
Goldman, E
Goldwater, S
Goodchild, H
Gordon, G
Greenberg, M
Greenstein, A S
Greenstreet, Y L A
Grossmark, K R
Gubbay, A D
Gubbay, M
Harper, S J
Harris, C
Harris, M
Harverd, L B
Heald, S C
Herbert, P J
Highman, J H
Highman, W J
Hill, D W
Hill, J M
Hochhauser, D
Homa, B
Hooper, P A
Ibrahim, F
Ilari, L
Jayaweera, R L A
Jayaweera, R D
Jenkins, J S
Kabeli, S
Kates, W E
Kaufman, D
Kaufman, L
Kay, S
Kennedy, F M
Kessel, M S
Khan, I U H
Kirklin, D L
Kucheria, R
Kurer, M H J
Kwapong, A O
Kwong, A
Lake, L M M
Lalvani, M
Lawson, N J
Laznowski, A
Lewin, S A
Lindop, P J
Liu, C K L
Long, C W
Majid, S
Malhotra, M
Mathur, A
Meghjee, S P L
Mellins, D H
Meyer, D L
Mond, C T
Moross, T
Morris, W R
Moss-Morris, S B
Mukherjee, E
Mushin, A
Nadal, M J
Newland, L A
Oberman, A S
Ong, C
Onnie, C M
Ononye, L A
Osborn, T W
Page, C M
Parikh, A M
Patel, B C
Patel, M M
Patel, N R
Phillips, C J
Porter, D R
Price, E H
Ramphul-Gokulsing, S K
Ratnasabapathy, L
Ray, S
Raza, K
Rhodes, E
Roberts, B L
Robinson, P D
Rogers, D J S
Rosen, S D
Rosenfelder, E
Rothenberg, T M
Rowbury, C A
Roy, P
Russell, N H
Sacks, B I
Sacks, G P
Sanati, M
Sanders, K
Sautelle, A C

Scheuer, P J
Seltzer, A A
Shah, J C
Shah, N K
Shah, S N
Shah, S P K
Shanson, B
Shanson, D C
Sharman, V L
Sheridan, M R
Shukla, K K
Sifman, M
Steiner, J
Stern, M
Stoll, B A
Tarsh, E J
Teller, R H M
Thomas, M E M
Titmas, J M
Tobert, A
Townley, A D
Trivedi, S K
Tunkel, S A
Valman, H B
Vandervelde, E M
Varchevker, J A
Vinayagum, S R
Warman, L H
Weber, J
Wengrowe, N E
Williams, A H
Wilson, V
Wyndham, J G
Yamey, G M
Yellon, T J
Zosmer, N R S

SE1

Aaalamani, H
Abbs, I C
Acharya, B
Adam, A N
Agathonikou, A
Agrawal, M R
Ahmed, A A
Alcock, E L
Amin, D M
Anderson, D R
Anderson, H J
Andrews, V
Archibong, E I
Atkinson, S H
Baker, E J
Baker, R J
Bankes, M J K
Barker, J N W N
Barkley, A S J
Barnett, M B
Baron, I D
Barrington, S F
Barrow, J
Bateman, N T
Bauer, P
Beale, R J
Beaney, R P
Beckley, J
Beechey-Newman, N
Beecroft, N M
Bejon, P A
Bennie, M J
Bewley, S J
Beynon, T A
Bialas, I
Biggart, S A W S
Bihari, D J
Bingham, J S
Bingham, J B
Bird, C F
Biswas, G
Black, M M
Blauth-Muszkowski, C I A
Boardman, A P
Bolton, J P G
Borek, B T
Borzyskowski, M
Bosley, C M
Boulton, J E
Bouras, N
Bradbeer, C S
Braude, P R
Breathnach, A S
Breathnach, S M
Brennand-Roper, D A
Bridgwood, W G
Briscoe, O V
Brooks, M
Brunjes, H O
Bucknall, C A

Burnand, K G
Burney, P G J
Buxton, N J
Cade, H J
Cahill, J M
Calman, F M B
Calver, D M
Cameron, C R
Campion, A M
Carr, R
Carroll, P V J
Catto, G R D
Chambers, J B
Champion, M P
Chan, K
Chang, S H-L
Chappell, L C
Chelliah, J V
Chevretton, E B
Chia, H M Y
Chong, W H
Chowdhury, P
Chua, W M
Church, A B
Ciclitira, P J
Clark, A G B
Clark, K G A
Clark, T B
Clarke, D G
Clarke, S E M
Clayden, G S
Cochrane, G M
Coleman, R
Colover, J
Coltart, D J
Connaughton, M
Connell, P A
Cook, G J R
Cooke, R A
Cooper, A L
Cooper, B M S
Corr, L A
Corrigall, R J
Corrigan, C J
Cowling, M G
Cox, A D
Cranston, I C P
Cremona-Barbaro, A
Crook, M A
Crowson, R A
Cunningham, C S
Cunningham, D G
Curry, P V L
Curson, S
D'Cruz, D P
Da Graca Menino Gloria, M L
Daniels, J G
Davies, C J
Davies, G M
Davies, T W
Davis, A R
Dawe, S A
Day, V
De Ruiter, A
Demetroulis, C
Dervos, H D
Dickson, J P
Djurovic, V
Dobbs, J
Dodhia, H
Doherty, S J
Donnan, S P B
Dowling, R H
Doyle, P J
Dratcu, L
Drury, A E C
Duncan, J K
Dussek, J E
Eady, R A J
Earnshaw, P H
Ebringer, A
Eckle, I
Elkington, N M
Evans, A V
Evans, M R W
Eykyn, S J
Fagg, N L K
Farmer, C K T
Fentiman, I S
Ferguson, J S J
Ferro, A
Fisher, M J
Fishlock, D J
Fleischer, F
Fletcher, C D M
Flinter, F A
Flora, H K
Fogelman, I

Fonseca, E E
Forbes, M J
Fotiadou, M
Fraser-Andrews, E A
Fraser, H M
Fraser, J S
Free, C J
French, G L
Fry, A H
Fryer, J A
Gabriel, C M
Gabriel, J R T
Gadd, E M
Gaind, R
Garnham, I R C
Ghosh, G J
Giannelli, F B
Gill, A D S
Gill, J A
Gleeson, M J
Goldsmith, D J A
Graham, E M
Grammena, P
Gransden, W R
Gray, D C
Greaves, M W
Griffiths, M A
Gruden, G
Guerin, M D
Gulliford, M C
Gunasekara, H L
Haig, J
Hamann, W C
Hamed, H H A
Hammond, C J
Hampson, N
Haq, M R
Harari, D
Harborow, P W
Harris, A N G
Harris, M B
Harris, S J
Harrison, C N
Hay, R J
Haycock, G B
Heathcock, R M
Heatley, F W
Heppenstall, J F
Herbert, A
Hicks, B H
Hilton, R M
Ho, W T V
Hodgkiss, A D
Hodgson, S V
Holloway, J B
Holt, G M
Hopkinson, N S
Hopper, J M
Hoyle, C F
Hughes, G R V
Hughes, R A C
Hughes, S E
Hunt, B J
Hunter, D N
Hussain, K
Islam, M T
Izatt, L P
Jackson, B T
Jackson, G
Jamieson-Craig, T K
Jamieson, C P
Jamieson, C W
Janse Van Rensburg, M
Jarvis, D L
Jenkins, B S
Jewell, D P A
Jezzard, R G
Johnson, J-A
Joiner, C L
Jones, A J
Justins, D M
Kaiser, A M
Kanabar, D J
Karalliedde, L D
Kavalier, F C
Keable-Elliott, D A
Keen, H
Khader, M A B A
Khamashta, M A
Khan, L N
Khan, S S
Khor, T T G
Kindness, H M J
Kinirons, M T M
Kirby, N G
Kmiot, W A
Kneale, B J
Kobza Black, A

Kopelman, M D
Koutroumanidis, M
Kovalic, A J
Kubba, A A
Kulasegaram, R
Laidlaw, D A H
Lakhani, A D H
Lamas, C D C
Lambiase, D P
Landau, D B
Landfester, C
Langford, K S
Lankester, T E
Lavender, H A
Leach, R M
Lee, C
Lee, S L C
Lee, T H
Lee, Y-C
Leeds, A R
Leese, E J
Lehner, T
Leigh, T H
Leighton, M A
Lekakis, G
Lennox, P A
Leon Villapalos, J
Leslie, M D
Levy, S J
Lewis, G H
Lewis, P J
Lewis, R R
Liew, E C L
Lin, J-P
Linton, R A F
Lipsedge, M S
Lloyd, C P
Lloyd, J
Lo, R S-K
Lowy, C
Ludgate, S M
Mabey, D M
Mcalonan, G M
McCarthy, M M
McColl, Dr
MacDonald, D M
MacDonald, L M
McGibbon, D H
McGovern, M
McGrath, J A
MacGreevy, B M C
McGregor, J M
McGuinness, C L
McLuckie, A
MacMahon, E M E
Madan, R
Maisey, M N
Mander, B J
Mangtani, P
Mant, T G K
Marber, M S
Mark, I R
Markey, A C
Markowe, H L J
Marlowe, K H S
Marrs, T C
Marsh, M J
Marshall, S A
Martin, F C
Martin, L J
Maryon-Davis, A R
Mascarenhas, L J
Master, D R
Mathews, J A
Mawer, C
Mayer, E
Maynard, R L
Mekawi, L M F
Mellerio, J E
Mellor, J
Metcalf, S W
Meyer, F J
Midgley, D Y
Milburn, H J
Millard, T P
Millis, R R
Milner, A D
Milner, D G G
Mishra, M
Misra, K K
Morgan, J R
Morgan, L
Morgan, M F
Motto, S G A
Muhammad, S N
Mulvey, M J
Mundy, A R
Naftalin, R J
Nath, B K

London, SE2

Nelson-Piercy, C
Newton, N I
Ng, S T
Norwood, F L M
Nunan, T O
Nunn, D
O'Brart, D P S
O'Brien, M D
O'Connell, M E A
O'Donnell, P J
O'Sullivan, D G M
O'Sullivan, G M
Owen, W J
Palmer, H E
Panayi, G S
Parikh, K S
Parnaby-Price, A
Parsons, R S
Patel, D
Pattison, J M
Payne, C O
Pearce, A C
Pearson, A D
Pearson, T C
Peel, M R
Peet, S E E
Penman Splitt, M C
Perkin, M A
Peters, B S
Pettigrew, R A
Phipp, I D
Pietroni, R A Y
Pither, C E
Plunkett, T A
Pocock, C F E
Pohl, K R E
Polani, P E
Polychronis, A
Pope, F M
Porter, J S
Poston, R N
Potter, J G
Povlsen, B
Powrie, J K
Powroznyk, A V V
Priest, T D
Pritchard, J
Psarra, A
Qureshi, S A
Radclyffe, V G
Rakhit, R D
Ramachandra, S
Ramirez, A J
Ramsay, R L
Rankin, S C
Rao, M R
Razzaque, M
Reddy, M
Redfearn, A
Redfearn, P M
Redwood, S R
Reed, L J
Rees, P J
Reid, C J D
Reidy, J F
Rejman, A S M
Reynolds, F J M
Richards, A
Richards, M A
Ridley, D M
Rigden, S P A
Ritter, J M
Robb, S A
Robinson, R O
Rodgers, C A
Roth, C E
Rowlands, E C
Rowsell, A R
Roxburgh, J C
Rubens, R D
Russell-Jones, R D
Russell, R E K
Rycroft, R J G
Ryle, A
Rymer, J M
Sabroe, R A
Sacks, S H
Salimee, S G
Salisbury, D M
Saunders, A J S
Saunders, P J
Savidge, G F
Scarisbrick, J J
Schey, S A
Schneider, H J
Scott-Mackie, P L
Setterfield, J F
Seymour, A-M F
Shaheen, S O

Shanti Raju, K
Sharief, M K
Sharland, G K
Sharpe, E E
Shaw, M C
Shepherd, P S
Sherry, E N
Shilling, J S
Simcock, R A J
Simpson, J M
Singh, S D
Siva Prakash, P G
Skidmore, F D
Smales, E
Smith, G N
Smith, M J M
Smith, S J
Sonksen, P H
Soo, S S
Spector, R G
Spector, T D
Spencer, J D
Staffurth, J N
Stavropoulos, N
Steer, S E
Stefan, M D
Stern, C M M
Stock, D G
Stone, I M
Summers, L K M
Sundaresan, V
Tan, K-H
Taylor, J D
Taylor, P R
Tebbs, E M
Teo, C E-S
Thadani, H
Thé, I T
Thoburn, C R
Thompson, A E
Thompson, R P H
Tibby, S M
Tilzey, A J
Timothy, A R
Tolhurst, D E
Tong, D
Tonge, K A
Torry, R
Toynton, S C
Treacher, D F
Treasure, T
Trigg, C J
Tulloh, R M R
Tungekar, M F M Y
Turnbull, S M
Turner, A
Twitchen, M J
Twort, C H C
Ungar-Sargon, J Y
Van Amelsvoort, T A M J
Van Den Hurk, P J
Van Der Aa, N
Vassiliadis, N
Vaughan, J M M
Velazquez Guerra, M D
Venn, G E
Verikou, K
Vernon, J A
Viberti, G F
Waddle, K
Wale, L W
Walker, S C
Wallis, D N
Walsh, R M
Wang, J E H
Ward, J
Wareing, M J
Waring, M
Waterstone, M P M
Watson, J P
Watson, M S
Webb-Peploe, M M
Webb, J F W
Webb, M C
Wedley, J R
Whincup, H H
Whitmore, B L
Widdicombe, J G
Wierzbicki, A S
Wight, A L
Wilkinson, M L
Williams, A J
Williams, B T
Williams, D G
Williams, K N
Williamson, J B
Williamson, T H

Wilson, P O G
Wiseman, M R
Wiseman, M J
Wolfe, C D A
Wong, A P L
Wong, W
Wood, C H
Wrigley, R A
Wyncoll, D L A
Yi, C-Y
Young, C P
Young, L R
Zamar, A C

SE2

Al-Zaidy, A K
Anand, P
Bore, J C
Cannon, W J
Gravestock, S M
Menezes, G R
Milstein, P A
Monksfield, P A
Pulsford, D R
Robinson, S J
Smith, C C M
Todd, V A
Troughton, V A

SE3

Ahmed, S S
Anand, R
Aravinthan, J
Arnold, R W
Bains, J J S
Bassi, S K
Begum, J A
Black, P J
Borooah, P R
Butler, E P
Chapman, P
Chesterton, J R
Chowienczyk, P J
Cobb, B
Colvin, L J
Condon, J A
Coote, M J A N
Cuddigan, B J
Cumberland, A G
Davies, N H
Deane, H L E
Dhadly, M S
Diaz Ojeda, M H
Doshi, R
Egan, H M
Elliott, R M
Erskine, J F
Exon, P D
Fender, L J
Field, B C T
Field, E S
Forster, E D
Fyfe, A E
Ghoorahoo, H I
Gillbard, J
Good, C J
Gregory, F P
Groves, B
Guest, R M
Guppy, A E
Harrison, T A
Hartley, R B
Hay, J F
Heliotis, M
Hickey, E M
Holland-Gladwish, J J
Hooper, A
Hooper, S E
Hordern, B W
Houghton, S H
Huang, C P
Huang, D C S
Huddy, J E
Illingworth, C D
Infantone, L
Jackson, P G
Jenkins, D
Jennings, J M
Jewkes, D A
Jewkes, R F
Johnson, K E
Jones, H I
Jones, O B C
Kailey, L K
Kalairajah, M
Kalairajah, Y
Krall, K
Lach, H
Lantin, H

Lee, S R
Loehry, J K
McCarthy, C A
McCullagh, A G
McKee, S N K
McLennan, A C
McNicholas, F C P
Macphie, D L
McShane, C D
Maisey, I C
Makkar, B S
Manna, V K
Megias Martin, E M L
Mehta, M S M
Melchor Ferrer, C
Mikhail, W I
Miller, A L C
Mitchell, E J
Montgomery, A C V
Mori, K
Morton, M A S
Moscuzza, F
Muhammad, L M
Munro, M
Murphy, E L C
Mustapha, A A
New, D I
O'Connell, B
O'Riordan, J B A
Offerman, E L
Omer, M I
Patel, S K
Pell, H
Penney, C C
Pereira, E P
Petty, L G
Plana Vives, F
Powell, M B
Power, C C
Price, T R
Proud, R D
Purdy, B
Radcliffe, H
Rahman, S M L
Ramsay, A S
Refsum, E
Ricketts, D
Roberts, A P
Ross, J R W
Ross, O C
Rowntree, C
Rowntree, M
Sales, J M
Saunders, K B
Schnepel, B
Scott, D F
Senior, D F
Sievers, I M
Skyrme, A D
Smith, S G T
Songhurst, L Z
Sotiriou, S
Stephenson, M T
Stevenson, K E
Stoker, T A M
Stokes, T C
Sutaria, P D
Thilagarajah, M
Thomas, A J
Thomas, D
Thompson, A B R
Thompson, I R
Thompson, M M H
Thomson, A D
Turner, A J
Unsworth, N J
Vollum, D I
Wallis, P G
Ward, D G
Wengraf, C L
Westwick, R J
Whitfield, G P
Williams, A B
Williams, H F
Windsor, R E
Wood, W E A
Woolf, P G
Woollett, R J
Young, G V W

SE4

Alderman, E W R
Asherson, P J E
Ballsdon, J C
Bolam, M J
Byrne, P R
Cahn, A P
Chan, S Y Y
Fakoya, A O

Fellows, E W
Griffiths, M P
Haines, D H
Jagathesan, R
Jiao, L
McCullagh, M M M
McIntyre, D H
Majid, F
Malde, G M
Mearns, M B
Neal, F R
Parker, J H
Parsons, D L T
Pawlowska, E
Reshi, S H
Rosenfeld, S
Sagay, A S
Saper, J
Smith, S M
Sobolewski, O A
Springer, S E
Watts, A M

SE5

Abas, M A
Aclimandos, W A I
Adair, A
Ahmed, A M M
Aitchison, K J
Al-Chalabi, A
Al-Sarraj, S T
Alarcon Palomo, G
Allin, M P G
Amiel, S A
Amusan, K A
Ansari, N A
Ansari, N Z
Ashley, E M C
Ayling, R M
Bacon, L E
Bailey, A J
Bailey, C S
Bailey, P J
Baker, H J W
Balendran, P
Ball, C S
Ball, D M
Banerjee, S S
Barnes, P R J
Barrett, C H R
Begley, E A
Bellingham, A J
Benjamin, I S
Bernard, S H
Berry, H E
Bhatt, G B
Bhugra, D K M L
Bidmead, J P
Bindman, J P
Bindra, R
Binnie, C D
Bird, J
Birtchnell, J A
Biswas, U
Bjarnason, I T
Booton, P
Bowden, P M A
Bowles, M J
Boyd, A S
Bras, P J
Brex, P A
Briess, D A O
Brown, A S T
Brown, R M
Browning, L E
Brownsdon, C E
Buchanan, A W
Buchanan, C R
Buckland, M S
Bullock, P R
Buxton-Thomas, M S
Cairns, H S
Casewell, M W
Cavanagh, J B
Cervilla Ballesteros, J A
Chan, D H Y
Chandler, C L
Chau, N-M
Checkley, S A
Child, F J
Chin, D T-E
Chitkara, N
Chong, M S
Chong, N H V
Choy, E H S
Chukwuemeka, A O
Cleare, A J
Clough, C G

Cohen, A T
Cole, E D E J
Compson, J P
Connan, F H
Connor, S E J
Conway, J L C
Costello, J
Cottam, S J C
Cotton, H M
Coutts, M A
Crane, J L
Crayford, T J B
Crick, R P
Critchley, G R
Critchlow, D G
Cross, Z E
Crouchman, M R
Crowther, S D
Curson, R
Curtis, V A
D'Alba, R
Dare, J R
Davenport, M
David, A S
Davies, R A
Davies, S N
Davison, S E
Davison, S C
Dawson, A
Dawson, J M
Dayanandan, R
De Meeus, J-B
De Zulueta, F I S
Deasy, N P
Desai, J B
Desai, S
Devane, S P
Devereux, S
Devlin, J
Dickinson, L
Dowell, J K
Driver, M
Driver, M V
Durston, R S
Easterbrook, P J
Eben, F
Eddleston, A L W F
Edmonds, M E
Edmonds, P
Edwards, E J
Edwards, J G
Elkington, H M
Ellis, C M
Ellison, Z R
Elwes, R D C
Evans, B M
Evans, J A
Evanson, R L
Fabre, J W
Fahy, T A
Farrell, M P
Fenwick, P B C
Ferguson, J D
Fife, A J
Finch, E J L
Fisher, A P
Fleminger, S
Forbes, L J L
Forgacs, I C
Fraser, S C A
Gall, N P
Gardner, W N
Garrett-Anderson, D
Garrett, J R
Gayle, C M
Ghufoor, Z
Gibb, D M F
Ginsburg, R
Glucksman, E
Goldberg, D P B
Gonde, J E
Goodman, R N
Goodwill, C J
Granger, A C P
Gray, B J
Green, D W
Greenough, A
Griffin, M
Grime, P R
Groom, A F G
Groves, P A
Gullan, R W
Gunn, J C
Gurm, H S
Ha, Y W M
Hadfield, P J
Hadzic, N
Hakkak, M S
Hambley, H

London, SE13

Harris, P E
Harrison, P M
Harry, R A
Hart, I J
Harwood, D M J
Harwood, G
Hasan, N
Hassan, M H
Healy, M R
Height, S E
Henderson, R C
Hendry, B M
Heyman, I
Higgins, E M
Holmes, C L
Homolka, M P P
Honavar, M
Hopkins, D F C
Hopster, D J
Howard, L M
Howard, R J M W
Howells, R B
Huggon, I C
Hugh-Jones, P
Hughes, M W
Hutchinson, G A
Hutchison, D C S
Jadresic, D P
James, H T I
Janota, I
Jayakrishnan, A G
Jeffree, M A
Jenkins, R
Jermy, K V
Jewitt, D E
Jones, M B
Jones, N A E
Joseph, S E O
Juhasz, Y C
Jurkovic, D
Kalra, L
Kelly, A J
Kelly, C P
Kelly, D M C
Kerwin, R W
Klein, S
Krasucki, C G
Lader, M H
Langdon, J D
Lantos, P L
Lawton, F G
Layton, D M
Lee, F H-T
Leech, S C
Lees, C C
Leff, J P
Leigh, P N
Limb, S P
Lingford-Hughes, A R
Lloyd, C M
Lo, S K
Lovestone, S H
Lucas, P A
Lucey, J V
Lyons, A J
McCarthy, K J
McCune, R E
MacDonald, B K
McDonald, E M P
McDonnell, N P
McEwan, J A
McGinley, E
McGregor, A M
McGuffin, P
McGuire, P K
McNerny, T M
McKenzie, N C
MacKinnon, A G
Macvicar, A D L
Maden, A
Maiden, H K
Malligannis, P
Man, W D-C
Marks, I M
Marrinan, M T
Marsh, M S
Marshall, E J
Marshall, W J
Martin, A J
Martin, J F
Mascunan Perez, P
Massil, H Y
Maynard, D D
Meldrum, B S
Melissari, E
Messent, J J
Messent, M
Michaelis, C
Mieli Vergani, G

Mills, K R
Misch, P A
Mitchard, J R
Mohamed Rela, S
Moniz, C F
Moorey, S
Mortimer, J M P
Mostyn, P A
Moxham, J
Muiesan, P
Mulvin, D W
Munro, J C
Murphy, K C
Murphy, S M
Murray, R M
Nash, R M
Natucci, M
Neeleman, J
Ng Hock Oon, P
Ng, V W K
Nikitakis, N N
Noble, P J
Noble, P R
Noshirvani, H F
O'Brien, I M
O'Connor, B J
O'Dowd, L R
O'Grady, J G M
Olajide, O O
Ong, P J L
Osborne, S A
Pagliuca, A
Palmer, C
Park, H G J
Parkin, J R
Parmar, H
Parsons, J H
Parton, M J
Patel, A G
Patel, A J
Paul, T
Pearson, N R
Pearson, R E
Peebles, D M
Perez Celorio, I
Peters, T J
Phillips, M L
Phillips, S L
Philpot, M P
Philpott-Howard, J N
Pocock, J
Polkey, C E
Polkey, M I
Pollock, L E
Pollock, S S
Ponte, J C
Poore, P D
Portmann, B C
Pouria, S
Prasad, S
Price, J F
Purves, A M
Rahman, S
Redkar, R G
Reiss, D
Rennie, J M
Retzlaw, E
Reynolds, E H
Reynolds, P A
Reynolds, P M
Richardson, P J
Ridsdale, L L
Rifkin, L
Riordan Eva, P
Robinson, S
Romilly, C S
Rood, J P
Rosemen, J J
Rowell, A M
Rushton, D N
Russell, M A H
Rutter, M L
Saha, M
Salisbury, J R
Salman, M S
Samuel, M C
Sangala, A V
Santiago, J C
Saunders, D E
Sayal, K S
Seaman, J A
Sedgwick, J V
Shafafy, M
Shah, A M
Sham, P C
Sharland, R J
Sharma, T
Shaw, F D
Shaw, S C

Sheehan, B D
Sheikh, A
Sidhu, P S
Sigurdsson, E
Simonoff, E A
Sinha, J
Skinner, J A M
Springer, J
Stagkou, A
Stephens, A D
Stewart, R J
Strang, J S
Strong, A J
Subotsky, F E
Sutherby, E K
Tabet, N T
Tanner, S P
Taylor, A M
Taylor, C B
Taylor, E A
Taylor, R E
Tenant-Flowers, M
Thein, S L
Thomas, J N
Thomas, N W M
Thomas, S M
Thompson, P M
Thomson, D S
Thorncroft, G J
Titler, J M
Travis, M J
Treasure, J L
Trill, A S
Turner, L
Upton, K E
Virji, A A N
Von Kaisenberg, C S L
Vougas, V
Wade, J J
Wainwright, R J
Waterstone, J J
Watkins, P J
Watson, D-M K
Watts, P M
Webster, P M
Welch, J M
Wendon, J A
Werneke, U
Wessely, S C
Wheatley, E A
Whitehead, M I
Wickstead, D H
Wilkinson, C L
Wilkinson, M C P
Williams, I L
Williams, I T
Wilson Jones, C F
Winston, I
Wolff, G S
Wood, B L
Woolley, J B
Wright, I C
Wright, J B
Wyatt, H A
Xenitidis, K
Yakeley, J W
Yates-Bell, A J
Yeo, P
Yeo, V

SE6

Abang-Taha, A B
Akinbolue, O S
Akomea-Agyin, C
Allan, P E M
Allen, M C
Alonso Urrutia, A M
Amiruddin, K M
Augustine, A S
Ayeko, M O
Bennett, P J
Dare, C
Doble, N S
Entwistle, H J
Grabinar, J
Heathcote, J A
Heron, J G F
Higginson, I J
Hollington, C E
Hughes, E F
Hussain, H M
Ismail, K
Joseph, M J G
Lasoye, T A
Lee, J F
Macauslan, K M
McCredie, J E
McIntosh, D M
Mangan, C M

Mills, A W
Mireskandari, K
Misselbrook, D P
Modern, G M
Modern, N
Modi, M C
Nguyen, T D
Noltie, A C K
O'Connor, K B
O'Neill, P A
Pavar, J S
Pektas, T
Ragupathy, M
Shanaz, M
Sharpe, D S
Soto Malet, V
Stell, I M
Surridge, N J
Thomas, M R
Twort, R J
Weston, J C
White, P T
Wright, M F

SE7

Abel, D C
Barker, K
Browne, D G
Corston, S H
Dickson, E J
King, L A
Ohlsen, J C
Palmer, S J
Parkash, V K
Parsons, M S J
Patel, M K
Santos, J P D
Skelton, M L
Skelton, M O

SE8

Batra, B K
Caffrey, E A
Dace, J M B
Gandhe, A J
Hashmi, K Z
Ikogho, O O
Jain, A K M
Joannou, P
Khan, O
Klemperer, F J
Mitra, S
Mohamedali, A
Olobia, E V A
Ong, T B
Patel, J
Rafique, S F A
Sanghera, S
Smith, N H

SE9

Abel, H B
Agarwal, V
Alcalay, M
Ameen, M
Baksh, M
Berndt, E
Boddy, J L
Boomla, D F
Brahmbhatt, G A
Brett, J E
Campbell, P I
Carver, N
Chase, N B A
Cochrane, A A
Durve, D V
Edghill, H B
Evans, D P
Evans, J D
Evans, M M M
Fortune, D C
Hack, H H A
Hack, M E
Horton, G F
Hutton, W W
Jarrett, P H
Kawooya, B
Kenny, D A
Khanam, A N
Lal, J
Lazim, T R
Livingstone, J S
McCarthy, K
Mahfuth, Z S
Martin, R K
Massey, R M
Masters, D K
Mbubaegbu, C E
Miller, J D
Mulvaney, J K

Owen, W A
Pearlgood, M
Rendell, C M
Saldanha, G J F
Sandrasagra, V
Sennik, S K
Shahab, K L
Shobowale, F O
Singer, M H
Singh, H
Sithamparanathan, T
Sizer, E
Surenthiran, S S
Taylor, M J
Taylor, R L
Thenuwara, C D
Varma, C
Varma, R B
Wade, C B
Young, S M

SE10

Ahmed, I
Ali, M S
Barclay, G A
Bennett, E P T
Bennett, P J
Brown, A P
Chandrasena, T G S R N
Cochran, G O
Cox, D E
Davies, J K
Demetriou, M
Evans, A N W
Farquharson, M
Gomez-Reino Sanchis, J M
Hale, J M
Haque, Q S M
Harris, A J
Ireland, R M
Janmohamed, K M I
Karnicki, J
Kemp, J R
Lannas, P A
Leane, M G
Lee, J A
Lesnik Oberstein, S Y
Lindsay, I
McCarthy, K H
McNie, H M M
O'Riordan, S E
Perks, N F
Perry, N D
Phillips, A M
Phillips, H M
Phillips, P M
Power, S J
Ratnarajan, N
Ratnarajan, S T
Richards, T J L
Ryan, M J
Seymour, W M
Sivagnanam, C
Smith, A D
Stott, R B
Sweet, P R
Teall, A J
Thomas, A L
Tibrewal, S B
Tiptaft, R C
Wilkinson, A C H
Wilmshurst, J M
Wynne-Simmons, A P M
Yiu, C Y

SE11

Allen, D K
Ashworth, M
Badger, K M
Barnick, C G W
Bottomley, C P E H
Bruce, R C H
Campbell, J L
Cantillon, C J P M
Collins, A D
Cutting, C W M
Cutting, H A
Dudley, F L
Earnshaw, G
Falkov, A F
Fitzpatrick, S A
Foley, P T
Fourie, H
Gaspar, H B R
Gerada, C
Ghosh, M

Glynn, O E G
Harker, R J
Harrison, N A
Henwood, N D
Hunt, T M
James, S
Jones, R H
Kadri, A O
Kerwick, S W
Khorsandi, S E
Lees, M
Loader, P J
Lorek, A K
Lovell, M J
McLeod, A D M
Madan, A K
Martin, W N
Mercurio, G G
Murdoch, E
Olayemi, A O
Parsons, R L
Pelfrene, E
Poole, D
Ross, E M
Rossor, E B
Sayour, S
Scrutton, M J L
Shaffer, J
Smyth, J M
Spencer, G T
Staunton, C R
Summers, P D
Tangang, V N
Theodore, C M
Timms, P W
Tynan, M J
Van Reenen, S
Walsh, D M
Waltham, M
Wass, V J
Weddell, J M
West, H
Wynne-Jones, G A
Yiu, C O S

SE12

Balachandran, S
Bamberger, D C
Bentham, J C P
Byford, S
Davison, S C
Ellis, D B
Ghuran, A V
Helm, E J
John, R I
Kenning, B R
Khanem, N M
Kreeger, C G
Lawson, C M
McAllister, W T B
McCarthy, O R
MacDonagh, I R J
Malik, Y D
Mehmet, S
Mian, I
Morgan, D S
Mukerjee, K
Ong, F G-C
Seth, P
Stark, J P
Taylor, K A
Thurairatnam, D N
Uhama, J N
Whitworth, M
Willis, J H P

SE13

Aitken, E M
Al-Janabi, T A J
Alister, M E
Bahri, A H
Ball, C J
Bharaj, H S
Birch, D J
Blower, P W
Boss, G
Byng, R N
Cargill, A F
Choudhury, M M
Coogan, J S V S R
Cooney, J M
Daman Willems, C E
Del Amo Valero, J
Dissanayake, S B
du Peloux Menagé, H G
Dudley, J M
Dykes, E H
Eiser, N M

London, SE14

Evans, R G
Farrington, T
Fidler, H M
Garvie, D C
Gibbs, S E M
Goddard, N P
Gore, R V
Gostling, A C
Haines, H M
Harris, T M
Heath, M L
Hill, M D
Holloway, G
Hossain, A T M A
Hossain, Z A
Huggon, A-M
Isaac, M T
Jack, T C L
Jackson, P D
Jacobs, B R
Kabir, A M N
Kabir, J M M
Kennedy, D C M
Kenny, P A
Khalpey, Z I
Khwaja, F A
Kingsley, G H
Knott, P D
Lam, J S J
Lanigan, C J M
Lettington, W C
Lewis, S J
Linsell, J C
Lockwood, C M
McBrien, F E F
Mohammed, S A
Mounty, E J
Mukherjee, A
Nayeem, N
Needham-Bennett, H W A
Norton, J
O'Donohue, J W
O'Sullivan, A G
Ogufere, W E
Okugbeni, G I
Page, J M
Petriccione Di Vadi, P
Phillips, M G
Pierpoint, S
Plugge, E H
Prince, M J
Rashid, H I
Roberts, A P
Roberts, J M
Roe, C M
Ross, A P
Roulson, C J
Sajjanhar, T
Sakka, S A A
Salama, N Y
Sands, A M
Sarker, P
Savvas, M
Seth, R V
Shaw, S J
Shelton, D M
Siddique, D B
Singh, S
Smith, C H
Songo-Williams, R A
Stacey, S G
Starke, I D
Stevens, T G
Stroobant, J
Suddle, A R
Toye, R
Uduku, N O-A
Viaqappan, G M
Walker, G A
Wellesley, A J
Worsley, A P
Worthington, L M

SE14

Almeida, E J J
Almeida, N M
Banks, P A
Blackie, P J
Bruce Ja Ja, D F
Charmanas, M G
Chesterman, L P
Dargan, P I
Dias, S A N
Gordon-Brown, A D
Haire, A R
Himid, K A
Humm, T E
Jenkins, R G

Jeyanathan, S
Jones, A L
Kandavel, R
Karalliedde, S
Karlman, I M
Kulkarni, K A
McColl, J L
MacDermott, A J
MacFarlane, A E
Maisey, N R
Martin, P
Murray, V S G
Palin, C
Persaud, R A P
Pickard, S J
Pochin, R S B
Sarder, M O G
Sayyah-Sina, K
Selvanathan, G A J
Shah, B B
Tiwary, R N
Tome De La Granja, M B

SE15

Abel, K M
Abeysinghe, A D
Akintade, L K
Allen, R G
Alyas, F
Amir-Ansari, K
Ayodele, S O
Banjo, A A
Birch, F
Butler, H V S
Chappiti, S S
Coan, K M
Craig, R P
Crawshaw, A
Do, M K
Dobbie, C R
Donohue, S M
Effiong, P
Feazey, A J
Ford, J E
Gersten, A E
Graham, J H
Heatley, C J
Hossain, M
Hutchinson, N P
Huynh, P S N
Iriyagolle, I M R C
Iu, M
Kapadia, B
Kumar, S
Lomas, D M
Lupton, M G F
McLellan, D G
Marks, P
Matheson, D M
Mehta, P P
Morris, R J C
Murday, A J
Murday, V A
Pratt, T
Rakowicz, A S
Reyburn, H W
Roe, Y O W
Sales, R C
Seeraj, E C
Seevaratnam, M S
Sekweyama, S G G
Simmons, J
Spindler, J J
Stimmler, A
Stolkin, C
Tan, S W
Vorster, T N
Watson, F J
Watson, H S
Weeramanthri, T B
Wieland, S S L
Wong, C M
Zeineldine, A A

SE16

Abbasi, K A
Ahmed, S
Allen, M J
Anifowoshe, S O
Beales, P I
Bell, A J
Bhatt, J N
Burton, C M
Chamberlin, A J
Chauhan, D S
Clark, B R
Coles, D R
Coyle, F M

Donmall, R C
Easter, R A
Fawibe, O O
Fenuyi, I A A
Ferguson, J K
Gammon, M
Gangoli, S V
Gradillas, V
Haas, P A
Harding, L D
Hegarty, D D
Holden, P J
Jagathesan, T
Jani, F M
Jani, P
Jansen, K L R
Kadhim, R Y
Kanagalingam, J
Kandiah, N
Kelly, J C
Kent, A S H
Kho, B C
Kirkpatrick, A H
Kirkpatrick, W N A
Kooy, S A
Li, A M
Lo, S H-S
Manam, V R
Marrinan, P J M M
Moses, D V K
Nalla, J
O'Neill, E V
Otty, C J
Patel, S M
Rahman, M A A
Rheem, J Y
Richards, E R
Ringrose, D K
Ross, J R
Sandhu, C
Shiv Shanker, V
Stamenkovic, S A
Stoner, E A
Then, K Y
Thomas, M R
Wijetunge, D B
Wong, D C H
Yeh, J S-M
Yeh, P S-Y
Yip, K M H
Zigmond, D

SE17

Abdoolcader, T
Al-Isa, A A H I
Besson, J A O
Bethapudy, S R
Brew-Graves, E H
Brown, J R I
Croft, M S
Davenport-Jones, C I
Diffley, F S
Eddy, B A
Evans, B E K
Glasper, A J
Haigh, C S
Herzmark, V J
Higgs, R H
Hodges, J M
Jones, J R
Kay, S
Kian, K
Kiernan, E J
Klimek, J V
Lask, B D
Mackay, J E
Maycock, A J
Nixon, S J
Noohu Kannu, A
Oakervee, H E
Page, E A
Pryor, A D
Quick, D G C
Rao, N
Robinson, S P
Round, L
Samudri, M F
Sangowawa, O O
Thomas, W K

SE18

Aggarwal, R P
Agnihotri, S
Aston, N O F
Banerjee, S
Bath, R
Bragman, S G L
Brox, G A
Buntwal, N E

Burch, R J
Cameron, M L
Cetti, N E
Chadha, M S
Char, D N
Chinduluri, C M R
Coakley, P G L
Colvin, S
Dickens, E L
Divall, S F
Edmonds, N R V
Ferraris, G M C
Ghosh, S K
Gibbs, C J
Gray, N
Groves, C R
Gupta, S K
Hafeez, A
Hill, J C
Holmes, S-E J
Hughes, R K F
Hussain, S
Hussien, A M M A
Jenkins, J H
Johnston, J D
Khan, A
Laganowski, H C
Le Ball, K M
Lester, P K
McDermott, B C
Mather, M
Mohamed, A M S
Mohammed, Y I
Nagendran, R
Nicholson, W J
Njuki, F I
Okocha, C
Onyali, K O
Parikh, J
Patel, B K
Patel, R K
Pinto, T
Pollock, I
Rached, S T
Raphael, N
Roden, C E
Saleem, S
Seehra, C S
Seehra, T K
Sellappah, S
Sen, A
Shah, B A
Shakespeare, C F
Singh, S P
Smith, J R G
Spencer, M E
Sri Krishna, M
Sri Krishna, R
Srinivas, K G
Steadman, P W M
Tanega, R R M
Taylor, M B
Venn-Treloar, J M
Veysey, M J
Wahba, H F
Watkin, P M
Wiggin, T R
Young, C J
Young, P W
Young, W A
Zeglam, A M B

SE19

Al-Hadithi, B A K
Arvin, B
Bennett, S
Bolade, I O A
Chan, C L H
Cheung, B Y Y
Choyce, A
Condon, J R
Deegan, K M
Diver, A O
Elliott, M K
Fakim, A
Fanous, S F V B
Field, I T
Flynn, A G
Gatward, C C
Gebrial, W N
Goberithan, P D
Gray, C J
Heyer, E J
Hickin, L A
Hirst, G
Holden, A
Jacobs, B W
James, L E
Khandwala, S

Lams, E J
Lidgey, S I
Luff, R H
Macdonald, I
McNeillis, N J D
Mahdi, A M
Mortimer, C B
Ng Cheng Hin, P
Nunn, P A
Onojie-Oraka, A
Patel, R N
Patel, V C
Roditi, E
Sharma, M A
Sinha, S K
Sivathasan, S
Smith, S E
Somalingam, R
Tan Eng Looi, C
Taylor, C L
Trivedi, R S
Virdi, D S
White, P T
Wilson, H R
Wong Lai Cheng, Dr

SE20

Brooks, S J
Davda, K G
Fishtal, A
Fox, V J C
Hellyar, A G
Manidas, S
Mason, J H
Nalliah, S J
Prasad, P N
Silva, P S
Sutton, R B O
Wheeler, D W
Wilson, S E

SE21

Anderson, A R
Ansari, H N R
Aranki, D A
Aranki, S F I
Archer, S E
Assersohn, L C
Athanassiou, S
Baker, S J
Black, J W
Bradbeer, T M
Broughton, S J
Cawson, R A
Chow, C
Cook, J V
Davidson, M J
Dejong, M J
Di Ceglie, D
Di Ceglie, G R
Doig, R J
Drake, D P
Duff, S E
Edeh, J C T
Evans, T G J R
Fieldhouse, R D
Fleminger, J J
Fleminger, R
Flower, G P
Ford, G R
Forster, K B
French, J C
Gamsu, H R
Goulston, R F
Grubnic, S
Gupta, R
Hamilton, E B D
Hargrove, R L
Harwin, B G
Hatton, M A
Healy, A A P
Hill, S M
Holden, C A
Hollis, D G H
Howard, K A
Howell, C W
Hulf, J A
Jenner, C S
Johns, N G
Kakkar, A K
Karalliedde, J L
Katugampola, S M
Kerkar, R A
Kiln, M R
Lams, B E A
Lams, P M
Leonard, R A
Leung, W C D
Lim, J C S

Llewelyn, D E H
Lynn, C R
McCaul, J A
Macdonald, A J D
McKelvey, T P H
Mahon, C C W
Mann, S N
Mantell, B S
Marsden, P
Meisner, P
Miller, S C
Moberly, P
Morgenstern, F-S
Myers, S R
Nicolaides, K H
Pearce, F M
Pegrum, A C
Pemberton, J
Pemberton, P L
Pentney, M J
Perry, C M
Polkey, A E
Price, D E
Raeburn, J N
Redmond, M J
Rohatiner, A Z S
Roseveare, M P
Rothman, D
Rowe, V B
Ryan, J M
Sandberg, S U T
Siddique, A B M
Sidey, M C
Sivanandan, M
Skinner, T G
Smith, J A J
Soni, N C
Spence, M P
Starr, D R P
Steger, A C
Taggart, L P
Tamale Ssali, E G
Turvill, J L
Turvill, S B
Wakely, C
Walters, H L
Walters, S J
Watson, C M
Webb, J R
Whooley, D J
Woflin, M B
Wood, E M
Woodcock, P A M

SE22

Abbas, A
Adam, G
Adelman, S
Ahmed, M J
Ajay, R A
Akpobome, G
Alexander, A M
Amir-Ansari, B
Babington, W S
Barlow, D
Barlow, N P
Barrett, D
Bhatia, A
Blackburn, A M
Breen, C P M B
Brooks, M D
Bryce, K A
Carucci, P
Chauhan, N
Clark-Jones, A
Cliffe, J M
Close, J C T
Corbett, S A
Costello, M C L
Cowmeadow, F P
Cranston, R D
Crowcroft, N S
Cure, S M F
Curran, I E
Curtis, L D
Dalgliesh, D
Davies, A
Dewji, H
Dimitriou, G
Draper, A G
Drobniewski, F A
During, M E
Edwards, R E
Egun, A A
Ellis, S M
Elston, W J
Emanuel, K E V
Evans, J M
Fowler, H M

London, SW2

Francis, D M
Gallagher, N J
Ghufoor, W N
Graham, H J
Grant, S A
Gulliford, T J G
Gupta, R P
Haq, M I
Hicks, A E
Hill, J P
Hitchins, J E
Ibrahim, S
Ilves, P J
Jackson, S H D
Kavadia, V
Kon, S P
Lal, A S
Leung, C H B
Lewis, S J
Lim, D P
Lim, M
Luce, P J
McCormick, D C
Macdougall, I C
McHenry, E A
MacKeith, J A C
McKenzie, K J
Mallinson, C
Manos, J
Nimmo, A J
Nowiak, Z
Osborn, D M
Parbhoo, I
Parbhoo, K
Patey, R A
Perkins, H D
Pettingale, K W
Pritchard, M J
Rhodes, B
Rogers, A D
Rogerson, M E
Round, J E C
Ryan, D J
Saleem-Uddin, M A
Saunders, J P
Scoffings, D J
Scorer, R M
Scott, D L
Stenhouse, P D
Stubbings, R
Sundaram, S
Swift, C G
Tegner, H
Thomas, J L
Thompson, R J
Wainford, C M
Waller, S C
Walton, T J H
Westall, G P
Wistow, T E W
Zamblera, D
Zuckerman, M A

SE23

Ahmed, C M
Bomford, A B
Bonner, K M
Bradshaw, C R
Brodie, C
Chawla, R L
Chow, W C S
Cottrell, C K
Crown, I W
Cudlip, S A
Dein, S L
Dilly, P N
Edwards, M V
Fogazzi, G B
Greenbaum, L
Hampshire, J C
Hickey, M A J
Hu, M T M
Hyatt, P J
Israel, J
Khan, U
Koay, C B
Ledger, S
Machin, V G
McLeod, J A
Morris, M W
O'Sullivan, N T
Oldershaw, K L
Patel, N R
Rosenberg, D A
Rowland, R M
Schroeder, K E M
Sleight, E
Slovick, S
Soile, D O

Sykes, A C
Van Cooten, S E
Venning, M A
Wheeler, J H

SE24

Ball, S P
Bean, J
Blackburn, T K
Blackman, G M
Bowen, E F
Brindley, G S
Brooke, D N
Cameron-Wood, R A
Chantler, J M
Chieveley-Williams, S A
Chinegwundoh, J O M
Dasan, R
Deasy, H C A
Dhingra, J K
Dick, M C
Dickinson, G
Donegan, J L M
Ellsbury, G F
Evanson, E J
Finn, A P
Frater, N E
Galdos Tobalina, M P
Gleeson, J M
Hampton, A C
Hanna, S J E
Hargreaves, E J
Hornsey, J M
Houghton, M A
Hughes, G J
Hussain, F F
Ish-Horowicz, M R
Joashi, U C
Jones, P R
Kasaka, N
Kelleher, A A
Kemp, R A
Kulkarni, A K
Lasserson, E M
Ledger, D H
Levine, M B
Levine, R
McClintock, T L
Meares, T M
Morris, M S D
Naraynsingh, P A
Noble, P L
O'Flynn, D C
Pallecaros, A S
Papapanagiotou, G
Peakman, M
Plimmer, M M
Rathbone, R G
Rayner, H C A
Rennie, J A
Richards, J M
Riley, U B G
Roberts, L S A
Robertson, D E
Roth, M G
Ruiz, R G G
Saunders, A P G
Scaravilli, N
Scott, S B C
Shaffi, S
Silverman, A M
Steele, J M B
Stephens, D
Stevens, M J
Tamvakopoulos, G S
Tovey, D I
Wright, C J G

SE25

Ackland, P
Allan, E M
Ameerally, P J
Arjun, N V L
Armstrong, J B O
Attard, A C
Barber, K W
Bhatti, F N K
Cooper, V M
Critchley, P A
Cutler, N A L
Dhoat, J S
Dhoat, N
Dunnet, R
Emara, M M K
Furnell, P M
Jackson, P M
Jahangir, M T
Jupp, G F

Khan, A R
O'Hara, S V
Ogedegbe, A J
Pickup, J C
Shipolini, A R
Sondhi, R
Spicer, J E A
Srivastava, G

SE26

Allen, K R
Austin, B M
Barnes, S
Batrick, N C
Bell, T
Bewick, M
Campbell, J E
Chaudhri, B B
Cheal, C
Christie Brown, J S
Christie Brown, M E
Clarke, S D
Cole, R B W
Cordery, R A
Da Fonseca, J M G
Dammers, F J H
Dunlop, R J
Edwards, P A
Edwards, W G
Ellington, N C
Essex, B J
Evans, A G
Fisher, B H
Gibbs, L M E
Gothard, J W W
Hassan, Z-U
Hughes, P L
Kangesan, K
Kellett, J M
Kok, K W
Liew, C F
Liew, L C H
Lindo, D O N S J
Lindo, J A
Mercer, M D
Nesbitt, A
Noble, C J
Noon, C F
Nurse, A M
Platman, A M
Raeside, D A
Rakhit, A
Redenham, A J
Robinson, F O
Saunders, C M S
Sikorski, J J
Snowden, S A
Sykes, N P
Thickett, D R
Thomas, S E
Wakeling, A
Wakeling, M
Whitworth, G R
Williams, R
Wu, F S-M
Yeates, S R

SE27

Acton, K J
Ashley, M H
Ashley, P M
Beresford, H
Bruce, A E
Choyce, J
Dawson, S J
Daynes, T J
Doa, W
Ewen, J M
Gardner, A K
Hawxwell, S G
Haxby, E J
Hu, Y J
Pounds, F J
Rampersad, R F
Sapuay, B C
Singh, N
Smith, N H
Vanier, T M
Vaz, F M
Zander, K M

SE28

Asafu-Adjaye, H B
Chalmers, J A C
Cristofoli, L E
Kennedy, J M
Lewins, P G
Lobley, C F M
Wheeler, D M

SW1

Abdalla, H I
Abdul Aziz, A B Z
Acheson, F M
Alexander, F M
Amery, J E
Andrews, B G
Archer, G M D
Ashe, A G R
Athanassiou, E
Atherton, F
Bache, X J S
Bailey, H J
Bailey, V F A
Baker, L V
Barber, A D
Barnardo, P D
Barshall, C E
Bates, P F
Bayliss, R
Beal, J H B
Bearn, P E
Bewley, B R
Bewley, T H
Bezulowsky, V
Bodsworth, S A
Bone, A
Bram, G
Breuning, S G E
Brewer, C L
Brewerton, D A
Broomfield, A A
Brouckaert, S M
Brown, C J R
Browne, D R G
Brunton, K S
Bryans, S A
Budden, J M
Bushnell, M G
Cannon, R
Carter, J T
Cecil, M R
Chapman, J
Chapman, T T
Chaudhry, T A
Cheng, W
Chirgwin, M E
Chiu, C K F
Chong, G W
Collier, G H
Coltart, T M
Copeman, P W M
Corall, I M
Cowen, J
Cox, H E
Criswell, M I
Cutting, J C
Davey, T J
Davidson, M J F
Dicker, A P
Donaldson, L J
Doran, P S
Dorrell, W
Dow, C
Du Mello Kenyon, E M
Easmon, C J
East, J A
Edmondson, K W
Eggleton, D A
Elphinstone, L H
Ernaelsteen, D A M
Etherington, R H
Fairley, E W R
Ferguson Smith, J
Fergusson, I L C
Ferris, M M
Fitz-Clarence, H
Fitzmaurice, S
Fogelman, F
Foot, V H
Foster, D H C L
Fox, L
Fryatt, R J
Furness, M J
Gafar, A H
Garber, I H
Garcia-Lozano Gomes, F J
Garcia, S P
Gayner, J R
Goddard, P F
Godfrey, G
Graff, C T
Grech, M P
Grech, P
Greenburgh, A L
Gwynne-Jones, M
Hamers, R H A
Hammond, J

Hancock, R P D
Handforth, J
Hanratty, J F
Harding, M J H
Harley, J R
Harvey, C J
Hazlewood, J G
Helps, S A F
Herbert, D C
Herman, A M
Hickey, M U
Hsin, M K-Y
Hudson, T G
Hunt, J P H
Hussein, S E
Ilbert, R C
Ind, J E
Jennings, G A
Jerjian, J C
Jones, I J
Joy, A
Kalbasi, H
Kalina, M A
Kapff, P D
Kapila, M
Kendell, R E
Keys, L
Kidner, S B
King-Lewis, P W
Kingman, C E C
Kingston, F E
Kirker, J M
Knapman, P A
Kong, S-K
Kwok, J
Laing-Morton, P A
Langley, C N M
Lee Kar Cheuk, L
Lee, M R
Levinson, C M
Lew-Gor, S T W
Lillywhite, L P
Lloyd-Harris, Q L G
Longfield, M
Ludford, C N
Lyndsay, D M
McAlinney, P G
McDonald, I O
McDonald, J
McKerrow, M M
McKiernan, D C
McKiernan, M J
McLaren, A R H
McOwan, A G
Macpherson, D A
Madan, I
Maniera, D M
Mathias, J C
Mayou, B J
Mehra, R L
Menzies, R C
Miller, S A S J
Mills, S B
Mitchell, A J
Moriarty, J
Mostad, H
Muir, J A H
Muir, V R-J
Munday, J E L
Myers, N J
Negus, D
Neville, A M
Noone, V
O'Connell, D
O'Connell, U
O'Keeffe, A G
Ogunsanwo, O A O
Oram, J J
Osborne, G E N
Padfield, N L
Pao, C S-L
Pattison, J R
Pattison, P B
Payne, J G
Peacock, C
Phillips, C E W
Phillips, R H
Platt, H S
Poncia, J
Price, G D L
Pryor, J P
Pugh, K E
Raffaelli, P I
Ragoowansi, R H
Rankine, S E
Reed, J L
Reeve, J
Renner, N E A
Rice, N S C

Richings, J C H
Rinsler, M G
Roberts, J R L
Russo, M
Saakwa-Mante, K
Salt, B D
Sandberg, M D A
Saraki, O A A
Sarkar, S P
Scott, J E
Scurr, J H
Seddon, I H
Shanks, J M
Sieratzki, J H
Sippert, A
Slotover, M L
Smith, J R
Sodipo, J O
Somasundaram, V
Sopher, S M
Squires, N F
Stables, P R J
Starita, C
Staughton, R C D
Stone, C M
Store, F R
Studd, J W W
Sweeney, M G
Tannock, T C A
Tao, M
Tayler, E M
Tew, J S T
Thomas, J M
Thornton, R
Timms, I G O
Tiner, R S
Tlusty, P J
Tonge, J L
Triay, C H
Troop, P A
Unwin, A B
Van Der Walt, L
Van Tooren, R
Vandendriesen, N M
Vaskovic, T
Vaughan, G F
Velkes, V L
Vernon, G R P A
Volkers, R C
Walden, P A M
Waters, M R
Wedgwood, J
Wells, J C
Wheeler, P J
Wilson, M S G
Win, M T
Wolman, R I
Woo, K C D
Woodcock, P W
Woodhouse, C R J
Wren, M E
Wright, B
Yates, C M

SW2

Agranoff, D D
Ah-Moye, G R
Andlaw, M R
Bennett, D S
Britton, A L
Brooks, T A V
Chakrabarti, B K
Chatoo, S B
Chaudhari, S A
Cohen, J R
Cook, M
Davis, L A
Denny, S J
Estyn-Jones, H
Eyears, J M
Fairclough, P J
Farrugia, P
Fernandez Panos, M
Freeman, S V
Fuller, M D
Geh, S Y V
Georgiou, M
Giwa-Osagie, O O
Guinane, M J
Hayfron-Benjamin, J M S
Hewes, D K M
Jamil, M A Q
Kayes, M I
Kouriefs, C
McCarthy, S P
Magonet, H
Mancey-Jones, M S
Mir, N

London, SW3

Moore, N L
Newton, A A T
Osmond, E C
Patel, V C
Peringer, J E
Pinder, M
Rainey, A J
Roberts, C D
Ruttley, M-E
Saif, M R
Scott, C R
Shannon, C N
Shannon, G M
Slater, M A
Thomas, P B
Tilzey, S E
Utting, S M
Vincent, C M A
Waschk, G
Watson, C O N
Webb, S E
Whyte-Venables, M
Wilkie, C E
Winter, L N
Wood, M
Yarnold, J R

SW3

Abd Allah, S A H
Al-Nasiri, N
Alexander, C
Allen, M J
Andrews, J
Archer, C D
Archer, D J
Assoufi, B K
Balfour-Lynn, I M
Barata, L M
Barnes, P J
Beam, J G
Benson, C
Beresford, N W
Blake, P R
Boffard, K D
Bolger, A P
Bordat, S P E
Bradfield Stowell, P
Brass, H U
Brazil, L C A
Broadley, K E
Brown, G
Burman, J F
Bush, A
Carson, H E A
Carson, J
Catovsky, D
Celin, G
Cheung, D L C
Chisholm, D G
Chung, K F
Clark, S J
Clarke, M J
Coats, A J S
Cole, P J
Collins, P
Corrie, L A C
Corrin, B
Cowie, M R
Crichton, P
Datnow, A D
Daubeney, P E F
Davey, J B
Davies, S W
Davys, M G D
De Lorenzo, F F
De Souza, A C
Devchand, D
Dickinson, A M
Doherty, A P
Donaldson, R M
Douek, M
Du Bois, R M
Durham, S R
Edwards, L
El Oakley, R M
Ellis, P A
Ellison, C
Evans, T W
Feldman, S
Ffytche, D H
Finney, S J
Fisher, C
Flather, M D
Fogg, K J
Fox, K M
Galbally, B P
Geddes, D M
Gerlis, L M
Gibson, D G

Gillbe, C E
Goldstraw, P
Gordon, A J
Gormley, M A
Graneek, B J
Grange, J M
Green, M
Greening, J E
Greenwood, C H
Griffiths, M J D
Gui, G P
Hammer, E
Hansel, T T
Hansell, D M
Haq, S E A
Harmer, C L
Harrington, K J
Harris, P C
Hartley, R H R
Haselden, B M
Hawley, K E
Hay, M A
Herford, T
Hickey, H B M
Holesh, S A
Hollis, M E
Hon, J K F
Hong, A
Hooper, R J L
Horsewood-Lee, S M
Howe, L J
Howland, C E
Howland, E J
Hussein, J R
Jahangiri, M
Johnston, D J B
Johnston, S R D
Jones, F P
Jungels, A L
Kakkar, S K
Kaprelian, R R
Kay, A B
Keogh, B F
Kilner, P J
King, T J
Kontogianni, I
Ladas, G
Lazari, M A
Leslie, R D G
Li, K
Lim, S
Liu, H C E
Longmore, D B
Lovett, P D
McDonald, J C
Macgregor, J E
McGuiness, C N
Macrae, D J
Maini, A
Mainwaring, P N
Majo, O
Mann, A H
Mannion, E M
Matutes Juan, M E
May, O S
Miller, D E
Mitford-Slade, F D
Moat, N E
Mokbel, K
Money-Kyrle, J F
Moskovic, E C
Muir, J M H
Newman Taylor, A J
Northridge, G H
Nowell, J L
Nurock, L M
Oliver, M F
Olsen, E G J
Ostermann, M E
Page, N G R
Panting, J R
Parry-Jones, N
Parvis, A H
Pasha, N
Pennell, D J
Pierce, J F
Poole-Wilson, P A
Powell-Brett, C F
Power, J
Puebla Alonso, M A
Purcell, I F
Rakus, M R
Rigby, M L
Robarts, W M
Rosano, G M C
Rose, A J
Rosenthal, M
Rowan, C A C
Russell, J P A

Sachdeva, R
Sacks, N P M
Scallan, M J H
Searle, A E
Shearer, R J
Shembekar, M V
Sheppard, M N
Shinebourne, E A
Simonds, A K
Singh, S
Skewes, D G
Soulioti, A M A
Southcott, A M
Stevenson, M C
Swanston, J S K
Thomas, D J
Thomas, S R
Till, J A
Trott, P A
Turner, J S
Tutt, A N J
Underwood, S R
Van Zyl, J E
Vella Bonello, L M
Venables, K M
Verrill, M W
Wallace, W M
Watters, K J
Webb-Peploe, K M
Weil, E
Wilson, D R
Wilson, N M
Wilson, R
Wilson, V S
Wood, D A
Wotherspoon, A C
Wright, J A G
Yap, J Y M
Yu Ho Yam, H

SW4

Aitken, D M
Allt-Graham, J
Ashton, P S
Bailey, E A
Balazs, J R
Ball, R
Bernard, F E P
Bickerstaff, H E
Blake, A J
Brain, P D
Brough, D I
Burton, C A L
Butler, R S
Calder, I
Callaghan, I M
Carey, B J
Cassidy, L
Child, C S
Choudhuri, K
Clark, A
Coffey, D P
Cotton, M H
Cullen, E S
Curran, D P M
Cutter, W J
D'Arcy, C A
Davies, N J
Dyer, B J
Edwards, B M F-A
Ferentinos, A
Forsythe, S L
Fraser, S A
Garnery, D
Gerrard, D J
Ghosh-Chowdhury, N
Gilham, P A
Glanville, T A
Glasson, C
Hacking, M B
Hanekom, W V H
Hanscheid, T
Harper, J R
Haworth, S G
Haywood, P T
Healy, J C
Heenan, P N
Henderson, H W A
Hughes, K R
Hull, D A
Johnston, I B
Keane, M A R
Keating, A R
Khurshid, M N
Lamuren, T E
Lascelles, K P
Lewis, R J
Little, G F J
Low, N M

MacDiarmid, D
McDonagh, M J
McKenzie, R J
McLachlan, A J
Majeed, F A
Marsh, A M
Mathers, D
Miskry, T S
Mould, T A J
Munden, A
Neuber, M
Oteng-Ntim, E
Patel, R
Phillips, R J W
Prahalias, A A
Rodgers, M E
Sharif, H
Shelock, C F M
Shepherd, S T
Smith, S M E
Sunthankar, G
Vass, N N
Vogt, J
Waight, C T
Wallat, W
Walsh, E M
Walsh, R
West, J A
Whittet, S E
Williams, E J
Wilson, G H M
Wolstenholme, V
Worrell, S J
Wyer, J F

SW5

Al-Haddad, H B
Almeida, A M
Amias, A G
Awwad, A M
Batool, M
Bentley, D
Bester, P K
Biadene, G
Bricka, C
Brooke Barnett, J W
Cantor, D D
Claoue, C M P A
Crock, H V
De Siena, P M
Dewast-Gagneraud, C
Dols Peerillo, S
Dzik-Jurasz, A S K
El Borai, M R
El-Gamel, A M H M
El Shafei, H M A
Emiliani, O
Faridan, P
Fiamanya, W K
Glazebrook, W R
Grande, R A
Hamann, N A A J
Harling, J D
Ho, K M T
Howard, E R
Ibrahim, S A H
Iqbal, M M
Irving, J D
Irving, J
Keaney, F P S
Khadjeh-Nouri, D
Kulathilake, A E
Ladbrooke, T E
Lancaster, M J
Lewis, C A
Lhopitallier, O M
Lowrey, S
Mahmood, S M
Mallett, P J
Mansour, F
Martin, V M
Minasian, H
Mooney, V M B
Morris, N F
O'Brien, K M
Odgers, P B
Paterson, F W N
Peries, A
Periyasamy, T
Pickard, B H
Qureshi, M A
Ramishvili, A
Ramsay, I D
Room, G R W
Rose, G S
Rothman, M T
Rub, A
Simons, E G
Skeggs, D B L

Tabrizi, S J
Wallace, C E
Yeung, S M
Zilkha, K J

SW6

Ahmed, M
Ahrens, G N
Allan, M P
Arunasalam, P
Atkinson, J A
Aw Yong, Y M
Bailey, A J M
Bailey, C F
Baraniecka, V T
Barron, D J
Benfield, J E C
Bilagi, P S S K
Blair, G
Buchanan, G N
Buckley, J F
Burgess, E H
Calamvokis, J G
Caldas, C M S D S
Chan, K A
Chappatte, O A
Chaudhry, A N
Cheshire, E R D
Christian, W J
Clegg, J M
Cowper, D M
Cruikshanks, P J
Daborn, A K
Davis, E J
De Sousa, L A S
Deeming, K F
Dellaportas, C
Dove-Edwin, I A
Downs, M H
Draper, H L
Dunwoody, M W O
Duquesney, R F
Eccles, S J
Edwards, S C
Elliott, C L
Eltringham, I
Elverson, H J
Evans, M A L
Fahy, D M
Fairweather, D K
Fellows, A H J
Fleming, D C
Forster, N J
Frain, J D J
Freeman, G K
Gilchrist, F C
Gimlette, T M D
Gossain, J B
Gunston, E L
Gunther, A L
Harington, M
Harper-Wynne, C L
Harris, N A
Harrop-Griffiths, J L
Henderson, A D
Hill, N A H
Hoban, B L
Holmes, P M
Homfray, T F R
Howsam, S E
Hung, T C-W
Hussain, Z
Inchley, J P
Jackson, E A
Jameson, B
Jelley, A P
Jenkins, R T
Johnston, A K
Jones, A T
Karwatowski, S P
Keown, P J
Key, P R
Khambatta, R B
Klosok, J K
Ladenburg, H I
Lawley, G C
Lawson, R I
Low-Beer, N M
Lyons, F M
McAndrew, F C M
McMichen, H U S
McMichen, I K S
McNicholas, T J
MacSweeney, D A
Malkin, J C
Mangwana, K L
Mantafounis, A
Marshall, R E K
Martin, A

Mee, S J
Meenan, J K P
Mehrotra, R
Millen, J S
Miskelly, F G
Morgan, N F A D
Mulcahy, A J
Murphy, D M
Muthiah, R N
Nageh, T
Newton, J H
O'Farrell, N
O'Shea, D B
Orr, G M
Palfrey, A J
Paris, S T
Patel, A
Patel, S D
Peckett, W R C
Peters, J M
Peters, R M
Philipp, E E
Pickering, A E
Playfair, M L
Pool, A J
Porter, J D H
Powrie, S E
Pugh, H E J
Pugh, S F
Rahmat Pour
Montared, M
Redhead, J B G
Rezvani, K
Robbie, D S
Robinson, I E
Roomi, R
Ross, P J
Roylance, R R
Sandison, A
Scriven, A J
Selvarajan, B S
Serafy, A
Singhal, S
St John Of Bletso, H J
Stone, A F M
Stroudley, J L
Thomas, K
Trenfield, S M
Urbaniak, D
Vigars, S P
Walker, E J
Walker, G R
Warden, M G
Wasfi, F M
Webb, L J
Westcott, M C
Westwell, S L
Wildman, S M C
Williams, A M
Williams, E J
Williams, N M
Wilson, I D
Worsdall, A K

SW7

Adams, A R
Al-Khawaja, I M S
Alexander, P D
Archard, J C
Auden, R R
Bareille, J-P
Bassett, J M
Baudon, J J
Bealing, C L B
Bhagat, K
Bobat, R A
Boreham, J J C
Boyle, N H
Caro, C G
Carritt, C A K
Cela, E
Cheung, B
Cheung, H
Chu, S K
Clark, T J H
Critchley, J M
Darzi, A W
Dauncey, J K
Day, M H
Deane, T H W
Delorme, E J
Dorward, P S
Edwards, C R W
Eltesham, S
El-Meligy, D A N
Flood, A
Freedman, S A
Geraud, C
Ghadimi, H

London, SW13

Gillon, R E Z
Good, C D
Gowland, D N
Hargrove, R C A
Hawawini, A
Hughes, A F A
Husband, V M
Innes, C A
Jairaj, P
Judge, R
Kayton, D M E
Kazantzis, G
Khater, M S E D
King, H L
Kinston, P
Kirkham, A P S
Kotak, A
Lalloo, U G
Ledingham, S J M
Lefever, R
Lemut, H
Levene, M M
Levin, A G
Loon, N
Luxen, A A J
McKeown, M D
Mahmud, T
Marris, N D
Marston, J A P
Marston, S
Michel, C C
Mina, F S
Murad, J S
Neri, M
Owen, J T
Papamichael, D
Perepeczko, B
Rawlinson, M P G
Rowley, P D
Sabroe, I
Sarker, S K
Sethi, T J
Sharpe, L D
Staight, G B
Stott, C J
Swann, A B
Viegas, M
Watrelot, A
Weinreb, I R
Wells, F
West, J R C
Wilson, J P
Wood, T A
Wright, A F
Zakaria, M R M
Zaniewski, F T

SW8

Ala, A J K
Astroulakis, Z M J
Aylett, S O
Barker, R M
Barratt-Johnson, M F R
Baxter, G A
Blakeney, I F A
Bowker, T J
Branker, M D
Burgess, P A
Cheshire, N J
Cohen, D G
Collins, J D
Costa, D
Crawley, M A
Dhillon, R S
Down, M W F
Dunne, J
Emberson-Bain, D I
Haase, G
Halley, P B
Harrison-Woolrych, M L
Harrison, P J
Hawkins, C E A
Heath, C P M
Hudson, M M T
Jefferys, D B
Job, S A
Joseph, T A S
Law, J E
Lawrence, A G
Laws, C J
Le Fanu, J R
Lee, E H
Logan, P J A
Losa, I E
McClelland, R L
MacFarlane, D A
MacLennan, I P B

Macrae, M B
Matthews, J G
Mitchell, I A
Muhammad, H A
Nath, A
Odumosu, T A
Onwuchekwa, W O
Page, M C
Parikh, C
Peacey, J M
Phillips, I
Powell, M
Powlson, M
Robinson, N M K
Saidin, D
Sedar, M I
Singh, S S
Skuce, A M
Smith, C L
Smith, I W
Speirs, C F
Steen, J S M
Taylor, S J
Thallon, A J
Thatcher, M J
Trawin, C C
Tylden, E
Viswanathan, A C
Warren, P D
Wharam, J
Woodings, D F

SW9

Abaecheta, A-M N
Abaecheta, H C
Adeoba, S A
Alikhan, R
Angus, D A P
Atkinson, S A
Azuonye, I O
Beck, N A
Bennette, J G
Berlyn, R A D
Boocock, A M
Bradley, L J
Breach, C S
Browne, N D F
Bruml, S K
Burchardt, A G
Casey, K G
Church, R S
Corry, D G
Cresswell, B E
Crocombe, M J
Davies, N J
Dunning, V I
Edwards, H G
Fong, J J
Garland, N H
Halse, G G
Hawthorne, S W
Henderson, M J
Hitchens, J
Hopkinson, K A
Hutchinson, N A
Jenkins, C J R
Joseph, J V
Khan, A G
Konzon, N I
Lee, H K P
McCarthy, D P J
McCoy, R N
McGinn, E P
Maxwell, N J
May, S D
McCready-Hall, L P
Moloney, C M
Ndegwa, D G
Nwaboku, H C I
O'Flynn, D W
Patel, H J
Patel, S N
Pillai, K C
Prendergast, K F
Ruben, P E
Rust, P A
Savage, R A
Sheeran, J M
Starczewska, M
Stokes, M L
Toyne, A
Van Den Berk, J C L M
Varsanyi, G
Vowles, R H
Wallis, R M
Wickremesinghe, S S
Wicks, R M

SW10

Abrahamson, E L
Adekunle, O O
Allen-Mersh, T G
Amin, Z
Anderson, J R
Asboe, D
Ayida, G A
Ball, S G
Barltrop, D
Barton, S E
Basquill, J G
Bell, J R G
Benatar-Catillon, J
Biddulph, D R
Bispham, A
Boag, F C
Booth, S J
Bower, M D
Bridges, J E
Bridges, N A
Bridgett, C K
Brinkley, D M
Browne, R E
Bunker, C B
Burkill, G J C
Carter, A E S
Catalan, J
Cavanagh, J
Cavanagh, P A
Chambers, M T
Chinn, R J S
Claxton, A P
Coghlan, B A
Collins, J V
Cooper, B J
Costello, C E M
Cox, S
Dakin, M J
Dill-Russell, P C
Dinneen, M D
Durbridge, J A
El-Refaey, H A
Emerson, P A
Etchegoyen, A
Evans, S C
Farmer, R D T
Farrar, S E
Feher, M D
Fell, I M E
Fisher, M J
Fleet, M S
Fox, P A
Gazzard, B G
Georgiou, C
Gibberd, F B
Gilleece, Y C
Haddad, M J Y
Hadden, R D M
Hall, T
Hargreaves, P I
Harris, I K
Harrison, M C
Hawkins, D A
Hopper, S A
Hossain, J
Hulme, A L
Hunter, M R A
Inge, K S-K
Isaacs, A J
Jackman, J G
Johnson, M R
Joshi, N
Kaddoura, S
Kampers, W T
Karolyi, B M G
Kaye, S A
Kazim, H A A
Kennedy, A M D
Khan, M M T
Kovar, I Z
Kreppel, M
La Paglia, J E
Lant, A F
Lavelle, J R
Lawson, A D
Levin, J
Lowe, J C
McCall, J
MacCormack, S M
Macnair, M E
Madden, N P
Maguire, M
Mahendran, B
Mallal, G M
Manisali, M
Margarson, M P
Martin, D L
Meehan, J P

Menon, R R
Miao, Y M
Mitchell, S M
Morgan, D J R
Morris, A K
Napier, K C
Newman, C G H
Nordin, A J
Nott, D M
O'Connor, K A
Palmer, M K
Panay, N
Papayannakos, E
Patel, K
Patterson, A E J
Pelly, M E
Penn, Z J
Penrice, J M
Petropoulios, M-C
Pozniak, A L
Rakhit, D J
Rees, T S
Roberts, N E M
Schulte, A C
Scotland, A D
Sedgwick, E
Sender, H
Sender, S N
Shah, P L
Sharpe, B D
Shaw, F E
Sinclair, E A
Singer, J D
Skinner, R R
Sleigh, G
Stafford, M K
Stanford, H M
Stanford, M R
Steer, P J
Sweeney, B J G
Thomas, V J E
Thompson, J N
Thomson, G A
Thorpe-Beeston, J G
Vaile, H G
Van Leuven, B D
Vonau, B U
Voss, S B
Walsh, J C
Wastell, C
Wild, R N
Wilkinson, D M
Williams, D J
Windross, P M
Woolf, J C
Yardley-Jones, A
Yentis, S M
Zeegen, R

SW11

Abokarsh, K
Ahad, N I
Ainley, C C
Ameke, I N
Artley, M L
Bevan, D H
Bourke, S K
Bradshaw, W W
Brigden, C E
Brock, J E C
Budd, A J
Butler-Manuel, S A
Butt, R
Carruth, J S
Chittick, D G H
Churcher, J D
Coker, C B A O
Collino, C E
Cook, C B
Cramp, H A
Cramp, M E
Creamer, J D
Creamer, K L
Davis, B A
Dent, K J
Dimond, C W
Dunwoody, J E O
Durham, M G
Eden, J C P
El Beze, Y S
Elgar, D E
Ellin, C
Ellingham, M J
Elmslie, F V
Falworth, M S
Fernando, S B
Fife, K M
Finch, D G
Fitzgerald, S F

Flis, C M
Frazer, C K
Freeman, S P
Gazzard, J A
Geary, S C
Ghosh, D B
Gibson, A R
Gill, S
Given-Wilson, R M
Goldberg, C D S
Gordon, E M
Grannell, J
Griffiths, A W
Grundy, A
Gulati, R K
Haddock, J A A
Halfpenny, D M
Hall, M K
Halliday, K E
Hanbury-Webber, R
Hemming, A E
Hicklin, L-A C
Honeyman, A E
Hossain, A B M M
Hunt, J L
Islam, G
Israel, M S
Jayamanne, D G R
Joakes, M
Johnson, E A
Johnson, M C
Keating, F S J
Khan, D B A
Khulusi, S
Kinmonth, R J
Klaye, T O
Kleinberg, K
Levitt, C
Litewski, J I
Littlewood, E M
Lofts, J A
MacCallum, N S
Macsweeney, S T R
Mbamalu, D P
Meacock, W R
Meares, H D D
Mills, R J
Monahan, A M
Muttalli, M
Nesdale, A D
North, S L P
O'Dwyer, A-M
Owens, D F
Parry, T M
Pattabhi, J
Penge, D J
Price, M L
Puvinathan, H
Rees, C N
Robinson, J F
Robinson, S C
Rogers, P T
Ron, M A
Rowson, N J
Salim, A
Salim, S H
Savage, R A
Schofield, A D R
Scott-Fleming, M S
Scott, M F
Shah, W A
Shakir, N A
Shaw, S E
Smellie, W J B
Snape, E E
Sporik, R B
Stavron, K J
Surawy, A J
Taghizadeh, A K
Todd, J A
Walden, A P
Walsh, E A M
Waters, J S C
White, L A M
Wilkins, H A
Williams, F M K
Winston, R
Wolff, E P F
Woolf, R L
Wyatt, M E
Zaffar, M A
Zaffar, M

SW12

Ahsan, A N
Akah, F B C
Akbar, N
Antwi, D N K
Baretto, J M

Baretto, R L
Bartley, C W
Biswas, D
Blair, A M
Bower, P J
Brinkmann, D A
Brosnan, C M
Carey, A H
Cartwright, R H
D'Art, Y M
Darowski, A
Djerkovic, G S
Egan, A C
Ellis, S I
Ferguson, C N
Gillespie, S M
Green, P G
Haire, K M
Hall, T B
Halligan, M S F
Hamblin, L G
Hamblin, M T
Han, L-Y
Haque, S E
Heriot, J A
Imam, A
Jeanes, A C
Johns, J
Jopson, C J
Keatings, V M
Kirwan, J F
Koh, B C
Laakkonen, V
Lapsley, D H M
Lapsley, M
Law, A K
Lea, K S
Leaker, B R
Leung, R S
Li Saw Hee, F L
Lipowsky, R
Lloyd, G W L
Lobo, C E
McLachlan, S
McManus, K M
Macmichael, C J
Magnall, R J
Manikon, M I
Marshall, S J
Mazhar, M
Mazhar, N A
Morgan, A T
Morris, K A
Mughal, M S
Nelson, J D
Ng Sui Hing, N Y K
Nicholas, P L
Okusi, D
Parry-Jones, A J D
Patel, K M
Patel, S
Peach, C J D
Qazi, N A
Rahman, M S
Ratcliffe, P W
Reid, K
Ribeiro, C A
Robinson, G E
Rosen, B K
Saggar, D P
Salt, N J
Salter, P A
Serajuddin, M
Shah, N C
Shariff, A T
Singh, P
Smith, S J L
Tan Phoay Lay, C
Torossian, F S B
Turner, A W M
Vowles, R E
Websdale, B H
Wheldon, H S
Wong-Lun-Sang, S
Wowkonowicz, K

SW13

Ahmad, A
Almond, E
Bartlett, N A
Beales, P H
Berman, L H
Bloom, D S
Botting, J P
Britton, T C
Browne, G P R
Burnett, L J B
Burton, M
Cavanagh, S R

London, SW14

Creese, R
Doherty, P F
Elkington, A G F
Elkington, J R S
Elkington, S G
Ellman, T J
Faulkner, M A L
Fender, G R K
Flood, R J
Gibson, P W
Harries, M
Hassan, T H A
Heymann, T D
Hockney, E A
Janikoun, S H
Johnson, L
Jones, D R
King, P A
Krimholtz, A
Lee, M W Y
Lewis, E A
Maguire, A C
Main, A M
Makey, A R
Martineau, A R
Mathias, T W
Metaxas, N
Minton, N D
Moult, P J A
Muntarbhorn, S
Nicholas, S C
Oliver, C D
Olney, S M
Palacci, A E
Palazzo, M G A
Plant, M J
Powell, K D
Reay, A
Redstone, D
Reid, S
Rice-Jones, M C
Ross Erro, A-L
Saklatvala, J
Smith, R N C
Tangye, S R
Tasker, H Y
Theodorou, N A
Tubbs, S C
Waters, H
Watson, J
White, W D
Wilks, D M W
Williams, R E
Willocks, T
Worth, P F
Wyman, A L

SW14

Adams, P J
Al-Yassiri, M M H
Barnes, P K
Barton, F H
Beard, C A S
Boheimer, K
Brand, A J O
Brown, K L
Brown, S A
Bullen, C
Bunje, H W
Bush, J L
Carter, A E
Casey, H B
Castello-Cortes, A H
Clarke, J A
Craighill, A R
Crollick, A J
Davies, A E M
De Burgh-Thomas, A G
Dob, D P
Duncan, D F J
Ellison, M M
Emery, E R J
Emmerson, J A
Frosh, A C
Geffen, T J B
Grayson, C E A
Gregory, S M
Henry, M J
Ismail, F
Jezierski, M R
Johnson, I A
Kaczmarski, R S
Kidd, A L
Krimholtz, M J
Lambert, H P
Lewis, N U
Lloyd, A M
MacDonald, A

Mahomed Keshavjee, S N
Miller, W
Mofeez, M A
Moore, F P
Nicholson, J A
Parkins, R A
Pryce-Jones, E
Rana, A M
Rundle, P K
Shalom, A S
Shalom, J I K
Sharaf, T F A
Shoults, C
Smith, M V
Spence-Sales, D
Squire, A M
Strickland, P
Thilagarajah, R
Thomas, H M
Tomlinson, D R
Uwechue, J L E
Walter, N
Warren, C J
Watts, C C W
Weeks, R L
Wellesley, H A L
Zaragoza Casares, P

SW15

Aarons, B M
Adam, R
Ahmad, S
Ahmed, Y
Al-Ahmad, S K Y
Al Mahdy, H
Al-Sager, A H J
Amin, S N O
Andersson, L C
Andrews, K
Arden, M L
Arthur, R M F
Avison, J D
Bailey, C R
Bain, W E S
Baker, C L
Balassa, G
Bale, R J
Ballard, R M
Barnes, E S
Barnes, E A
Barnes, P R
Bass, C S
Beales, J M
Bearn, V M
Bennett, E D
Bhide, A M
Black, E A
Boultbee, J E
Bowen, P L
Bradley, L J
Bradshaw, A J
Bradstreet, C M P
Brook, N E
Brown, E M
Bulstrode, N W
Burt, L
Cadogan, F
Calwell, W P K
Chan, J J K
Chau, I T M
Chess, E J
Chua, D P L
Clarke, E A
Clement, A
Cockerell, O C
Collins, M N
Collyer, J
Cory, J E S
Cowie, V A
Craggs, D F
Cropley, I M
Cull, A D
Curson, D A
Dashti, H
Davies, G I
Day, J M C
De Boer, R F A
Deas, S C
Dennis, D L
Drzymala, M K
Duncan-Whyte, J
Edge, M
Edwards, K J T
El Dabouni, M A M
Elliott, P M
Evans, O G
Farrell, T G
Fasser, E

Festa, M S
Fitzgerald, A J
Fitzmaurice, M
Flett, E H
Georgiannos, S
Gil Rivas, S
Gray, M E R
Grice, C A
Gupta, R R
Haddo, O
Halileh, S O M
Hammond, R J
Hannan, M M
Harding, L
Harrison-Hansley, E J
Harrop-Griffiths, A W
Harvey, P
Heath, V C F
Hedayati, B
Heriot, A G
Hickey, J B
Horby, P W
Horn, M E C
Hoveyda, F
Hoveyda, N
Huff, A G
Islam, S
Janosi, M
Jasani, A F
Kataria, M S
Kelly, D H W
Khadra, A
Kilduff, R C
Kimberley, A P S
Kirkland, A A L
Kleanthous, K L
Kooner, M
Lebus, J C M
Lewington, W E
Lim, E J
Lister, P J
Lumley, K P S
McAnally, D
McKee, K J
McKenzie, D J
Major, A
Mallya, B
Manjula, G
Marquand, P B
Martin, A C
Mathews, C J
Mavalankar, A P
Mayou, S C
Mendonca, D R
Mireskandari, M
Moore, P C L
Morton, K E
Moul, P E
Naudeer, S F M
Navamani, A S
Ngan, H
Nirmalan, R
North, S M
O'Neill, J M B
O'Reilly, M A R
Pantin, P L
Paulding, E A
Payne, F M
Pearson, R H
Pigott, B
Plumley, S M
Pollert, J
Pourgourides, E K
Pugh, D R
Ramon Valcarcel, B
Ratnayake, B C N
Ray, S A
Redding, W
Riccio, M
Richardson, H J
Rimmer, C J
Roberts, D
Roberts, J M
Roberts, J H M
Robinson, K P
Roet, B C
Russell, A L
Ryan, S M
Scarlett, N J D
Schafler, K F
Searle, C W A
Shanahan, S E E
Shore, E C
Shur, E
Simmons, C A
Sindall, F M
Sooriakumaran, S
Speirs, J M
Spooner, T C

Stilgoe, J R
Sweetman, B S
Sweetman, S M
Swierczynski, S
Tan, S-Y
Taylor, P J
Temple, S E
Theodossi, A
Thompson, D C
Thomson, M E
Watters, O F
Wattie, M L
Watts, T C
White, S J
Williams, S L
Wise, P H
Wong, C Y
Worth, R W
Wright, G M
Young, A-M
Zilva, J F

SW16

Addo, J K
Adeboyeku, D U
Afzal, M M
Ah Chong, A K
Ahmed, M
Aka, A K
Akoojee, E
Allen, S
Amin, M
Amure, A O
Ashby, P M
Ashton, F J V
Baker, E H
Barrett, P P
Bentley, C R
Beranek, M D
Berman, R
Beumelburg, N J
Beyzade, B
Blacklay, H C
Blair, D A
Blankson-Beecham, G
Brett, J M
Calder, F R
Chaudhary, M F
Choukroun, C
Christian, E C
Clarke, K
Clarke, S
Climie, R P
Cohen, A C
Cross, T G
Cummings, I G
De Almeida, S T L
Desai, N
Duff-Miller, D B
Duncan, E H
Edwards, R
Eliatamby, S R-K
Fernando, A M R
Foster, T R
Freeman, J
Gajjar, A
Gata Diaz, A I
Graham, A S
Graham, M H
Groen, B G S
Gunasuntharam, T
Halsey, D J
Hasan, R
Hayes, J
Healey, J
Hirsch, E A
Hoque, K A
Howitt, J B
Huggins, E M
Jaswal, J S
Kaba, R A
Keane, M F
Keappock, C G A
Kerr, A M
Kessling, W
Lee, S B J-P
Levy, C A
McElligott, A J
MacIver, M
Mackenzie, S J
Madhav, R T
Mahadevan, D
Marszalek, H B
Masterton, J W
Modder, J V J
Mullin, M M
Myint, T T
Nadeem, F
Newell, A M B

Nowicki, M T
Nzegwu, G O
Obiyan, M E I
Osborne, P P
Otuteye, E T
Parton, E Q
Patel, B R
Patel, C T
Patel, S
Patel, S M
Peck, A B
Phipps, J A
Pollak, B
Pollock, A M
Popert, S J
Potter, A N
Potter, D R
Raghunath, J V
Raghunath, N J
Rahman, Y
Roberts, P J
Sadek, M
Saleemi, M A
Samarasinghe, A M
Samarasinghe, C R
Samarasinghe, D G
Savage, S J
Schapira, D J
Sharma, A O
Silver, T
Simon, E E
Steele, A P H
Szekely, G
Talati, F
Tanweer, K
Thomson, P G
Todd-Pokropek, C J
Towers, J F
Trivedi, S
Vickers, B A J
Vyas, A
Wallace, E L M
Ward, D W
Watt, D B S
Watt, L L
Weatherup, J
Willsher, T
Wilson, M
Wittek, I H
Wright, J P
Yasseen, B E S M

SW17

Abayawardana, R D
Abou Saleh, M T
Adam, E J
Adams, F R A
Ahmad, I
Ahmad, R N
Ahmed, A
Ahmed, M I
Aitken, P H L
Akbany, J
Akram, F
Al-Saady, N M M
Ala, A
Alam, S
Alford, P F
Almeida, B M
Anderson, C J
Anderson, R
Anson, K M
Axford, J S
Bahl, S
Bain, M D
Baldacchino, A M
Ball, J A S
Ball, S E
Barker, D S
Barlow, F M
Bedford Russell, A R
Belli, A-M
Bennett, M A
Benton, M A
Bernal, S J
Bijlani, N
Bircher, M D
Birthistle, K A J
Bland, J L
Boddy, S-A M
Bolton, J S
Borgstein, B M E
Bose, M
Bourne, T H
Bowen, A L
Boyd, R D H
Brecker, S J D
Bridle, S H
Brook, H D D

Brown, R W
Buckenham, T M
Burge, C K
Burke, A W
Burns, T P
Calvert, P T
Calvert, S A
Camm, A J
Campion, H C R
Caoles, U F
Capps, S N J
Cappuccio, F P
Carrasco, M P
Cashman, J N
Chalmers, A G W
Chambers, T J
Chandrasekaran, V
Chang, R W S
Chaplin, R H
Chapman, R C
Checinski, K M
Child, A H
Chow, W M J
Chowdhury, S
Chowns, J C
Christopher, J A
Clifton, A
Cloud, G C
Coates, A R M
Coles, J A
Colgan, J F
Collier, J G
Collinson, P O
Constable, P H
Corbishley, C M
Costa-Michael, M
Courtenay, K P
Cox, I D D
Crawley-Boevey, E E
Crusz, T A M
Curry, I J
Dalgleish, A G
Damaskinidou, K
Dash, A
Dashwood, C S
Davies, M J
Dawson, H A R
Day, A C
De Caestecker, J S
De Silva, L S
Dhiman, A
Domoney, C L
Donohue, E P G
Dormandy, J A
Dove, D S
Drummond, C R
Drummond, D C
Drummond, L M
Dumonde, D C
Dundas, D D
Dunsmuir, W D
Durban, J R
Eastman, N L G
Eastwood, J B
El-Kholy, A A-K A-F
El-Sayeh, H G S K
Elanchenny, N
Elanchenny, P
Elliman, D A C
Evans, C L
Fahey, C A
Fairbank, A C
Farnsworth, G M
Farrer, K M
Featherstone, J
Fegan-Earl, A W
Fernando, A R
Fernando, M D A K S
Field, C M
Finlayson, C J
Fisher, N R
Fitzpatrick, G S M
Foran, J P M
Foster, O J F
Foulds, N C
Franklin, M
Gallagher, M M
Ganeshalingham, R
Garcia Asensio, M D P
Garcia Rodriguez, R
Gateley, D R
Gavrielides, I
Ghaem-Maghami
Hezaveh, S
Ghodse, A H
Glynn, J C
Goldenberg, S M
Goodwin, C S
Gordon-Smith, E C

London, SW19

Griffin, G E
Griffiths, J R
Grounds, R M
Hall, G M
Ham, J A
Hamilton-Fairley, D
Hamilton, P A
Hammond, J E
Hampson-Evans, D C
Hanafiah, Z
Hanspal, J S
Harris, F E
Harris, P A
Hartikainen, J E K
Hartley, H M
Harvey, F A H
Harvey, I
Hastie, I R
Hawkins, R L
Hay, P E
Heath, P T
Heenan, S D
Hennessey, F A
Hermon-Taylor, J
Heron, C W
Hill, G N
Hill, P D
Hilson, G R F
Hindley, P A
Hinton, E A
Holliman, R E
Hollins, S C
Hollyman, J A
Holmes, S J K
Hubble, D
Hughes, N C
Hughes, P M
Humphrey, M E D
Hunter, G
Hussain, I R
Hutchinson, L R
Hutchinson, S E
Hwang, D T W
Iheanacho, I O
Izzard, M E
Jacobson, R R
Jarman, C M B
Jazzrawi, R P E
Jeffrey, I J M
Jones, K J
Jones, P W
Jordan, G M
Joyce, M E
Judge, J E
Kadambari, S R
Karmani, M S
Keane, C J
Keen, D V
Kenny, S J
Kent, A J
Kessar, P
Khan, Q-U-A
Khan, S A
Khaw, K-T
Kidd, M
Kiely, P D W
Killoughery, M P
Kingdom, C C
Kirkland, P M
Klijnsma, M P
La Porta, S E
Lacey, J H
Laczko-Schroeder, T J
Larkin, G B R
Last, K
Lau, R K W
Laugharne, R A
Lawrence, W H
Lee Khet Leong, D
Lee, K S
Leicester, R J
Liban, J B
Lofts, F J
Lovell, R A
Macallan, D C
McCorkell, S A
McCoubrie, M
MacGregor, G A
McKenna, W J
MacPhee, I A M
Madden, B P
Magner, V C
Mahroof, H M
Malik, M H K
Mansi, J L
Mantovani, C P
Marsden, R A
Marsh, J C W
Maxwell, J D

Melville, D M
Mezey, G C
Middleton, I A
Midgley, S N
Minattur, D J
Mitchell-Heggs, N A
Mitchison, D A
Mitton, S G
Monga, A K
Morgan, R A
Morgan, S V
Morley, H L
Morris, C M
Mortimer, P S
Moss, A L H
Moss, P S
Mughal, M S
Mughal, N J
Mukherjee, R A S
Muralitharan, V
Murdoch, L J
Nadarajah, T
Naqvi, S B
Nemeth, W
Newton, C R
Nowak, K
Nussey, S S
O'Callaghan, P A
O'Flynn, N M
O'Riordan, J A
O'Toole, J J
Oakeley, P S
Oakeshott, P
Obel, O A
Okafor, B E
Oliveira, D B G
Olugbile, A O B
Oyebode, B O
Paine, P A
Panahloo, A A
Parker-Williams, E J
Patel, P C
Patel, U
Pathmabaskaran, S
Patton, M A
Pearce, J M F
Philips, B J
Pilcher, J M
Pillay, T M
Plange, T N
Porter, S-A M
Powell, B W E M
Prime, K P
Pumphrey, C W
Rahman, M
Rajadurai, V
Rajalingam, U P
Rayner, C F J
Razis, P A
Redmill, B S
Rehman, Z
Reid, S F
Rhodes, A
Rice, P S
Rich, P A
Richardson, P S
Robertson, S J
Rogers, D J
Rostron, C K
Rowland, E
Roy, P K
Ruggier, R
Sagar, S M
Saggar, A K
Saleemi, S A
Saxena, S K
Sayer, R E
Scott, K A
Shafi, A I
Shah, F N
Shannon, M S
Sharland, M R
Sharma, A K
Sharpe, C C
Shepherd, R T
Sherman, Y
Shiraz, M
Sibthorpe, R J
Singer, D R J
Singh, R
Sinha, M K
Sivarajan, K
Skillern, L H
Smith, E E J
Snashall, S E
Spry, C J F
Stanton, A W B
Stark, M M
Starkey, C N

Stevens, J R D
Strachan, D P
Styles, C J
Sultan, M S
Sunil Babu, V
Sutton, B A
Szolach, M R
Tham, S W
Thomas, V A
Thompson, G M
Thurlbeck, S M
Thurlow, A C
Tibbs, C J
Tilley, R C
Tomlinson, L A
Tomlinson, M A
Trojanowski, A
Turk, J
Turner, D R
Twisleton-Wykeham-Fiennes, A G
Uddin, J M
Ugwumadu, A N
Vallance, P J T
Van Besouw, J-P W G
Varghese, D
Vince, J
Vinestock, M D
Vyvyan, H A L
Wadey, L P
Walters, D V
Wansbrough-Jones, M H
Warwick, H M C
Westlake, A S
Whincup, P H
White, G J
Wilbraham, D G
Wilkinson, L S
Williams, A R
Williams, A F
Williamson, P A
Willis, F M
Witana, J S
Wrigley, F K
Yip, A S B
Young, M P A
Zaidi, M

SW18
Adamson, D L
Aderinto, J B
Afaq, M A
Auty, F T
Bamber, D B
Bamford, N J
Banfield, G K
Barthes-Wilson, E L
Battley, C J
Bavar, G
Baxter, N C
Bell, P A J
Bickerton, A S T
Bobak, S A
Bovill, I P
Bradley, U P
Bradley, W N
Brana, N
Bull, M E
Burbidge, M J
Chapman, E P
Chow, K Y
Christie, C L
Coffey, T A
Cooper, Y
Costales, E L
Cumberbatch, J B
Cumberland, M A
Dale, C
Davies, A J
Davies, B A
Deuchar, A J
Ewen, R A
Freeling, P
Gibbons, C R
Gibson, A T
Girgis, A J
Goddard, J
Gomez, C K R
Gomez, K R
Gordon, D H
Gorman, J J
Guyer, M F
Hagger, R W
Haider, S M J
Hamlet, M R
Harris, T J
Hollamby, R G
Horwood, N

Iadevita, G
Ilves, A C
Jacobs, S
Jones, N
Khan, M-U H
Kidd, G T B
Lawrence, E S
Lewis, S
Lynch, B A
McCrone, H E M
McKay, D R
Millington, G W M
Morgan, N H
Nicholas, A M
O'Connell, J M
O'Neill, R
Oliver, R E
Onoche, A O
Ostlere, L S
Patel, L C
Patel, M B
Penny, J A
Perraudeau, M K
Perry, N
Phillips, A A
Quarmby, J W
Rashid, M A
Redelinghuys, J
Reis, J L
Reis, M
Roberts, L M
Robertshaw, H J
Robinson, M D
Roche, C J H
Rousseau, N C
Rudzinski, B M
Sadojee, A A
Scott, G M S
Serafini, F
Seymour, H R
Shah, C S
Sherry, V F
Shorten, J B
Siddiqi, S A
Sinfield, C J
Solan, N L
Sullivan, A K
Taylor, H P
Vreede, E
Waite, J C
Walker, M C
Ward, E S
Ward, L
Weinstock, N G
Whitehead, S C
Wilcock, F M
Williams, D J
Winstock, G B M
Wood, C C

SW19
Aguado Sagarribay, M
Allen, J M S
Anson, J A R
Appadurai, I R
Atkins, M J
Ayub, M S
Aziz, N
Baig, M N
Baillie, C J A
Bakowska, A J
Balasingam, V
Ball, D H
Balsingham, S
Bending, M R
Bett, N J
Bettridge, R F
Biswas, D
Blegay, R N
Blonstein, L H
Bolton, J G F
Bonar, J A
Bonn, J A
Booth, T R
Bossowska, I J
Bowen, J A P
Boyd, J D
Bruckner, F E
Bulman, W K
Bunting, R M
Butler, E B
Butt, M W
Byrne, J W
Cadsky, O
Capra, M
Cattermole, H R
Chakrabarti, U
Chakravarty, S K
Choi, W H

Chua, S-E
Chuaqui, P B
Clarke, J T
Cock, S
Coleman, C M
Conway, S K
Crichton, B M
Cross, J A
Cundy, P R
Cunningham, A R
Cunningham, S F
Cuthbert, N D
Dacie, J V
Dadarkar, P
Darke, K F
Darr, A J
Davidson Parker, J J
Davidson, D G C
Davies, D D
De Alwis, L C
De Beer, D A H
De Souza, N M
De Winter, E
Devan, V R
Dhillon, S
Dias, S G A
Dick, G M
Dinsmore, J E
Dirmikis, H
Dooley, D
Drury, A
Dunfield-Prayero, A C
Earle, J H O
Elstub, J
Emerson, E M
Evans, A L
Fanning, J
Farrington, G H
Feilding, E L
Field, A M
Flynn, P E
Forsyth, D S
Freeman, E J K
Frenkiel, A L
Gaillard, B
Gentili, N
Gnanapragasam, J
Gnanapragasam, J B
Gnanapragasam, V C
Gomez, G
Gray, T J P
Greenfield, P M
Gyi Khin Ma, Dr
Hafizi, S
Hamilton-Paterson, U T
Hamilton, M A
Haq, S H
Hargreaves, M
Harper, I D R
Hasan, H A R
Headley, S R T
Henderson, E R
Heron, T G
Hill, L C
Homer, D R M
Howell, D D
Hutton, P A N
Iya, D
Jackson, S A
Jacobs, H B
Jajbhay, M
Jamil, M
Jay, B S
Johnson, M W
Jones, H W
Jones, J R
Jones, P M
Jones, T N
Joshi, A K
Joyce, E L
Jupp, S M
Kanapathippillia, R
Kelly, T W J
Kendall, J S M
Kenyon, K L
Khan, S
Langley, K J C
Leigh, G I
Li, W-Y
Livesey, S A
Lomax-Simpson, J M
Luksch, M
McKinnon, M E
McLaughlin, C A
Magee, A G
Marchant, D E
Marsh, H T
Mather, D C

Matsuda, T
Message, S D
Millard, R E
Mills, F C A
Mistry, F D
Moloney, E F
Moorthy, I T
Morris, S C
Mosaheb-Mohammadi, A
Moss, M C
Mulcahy, R P C
Munsie, A J
Murphy, H C
Mushin, J S
Nabijee, A H A A
Naha, B
Nandanwar, C
Nanson, E M
Neil, A F
Nortley, E R W
Ntountas, I
O'Neill, D
O'Neill, M F J
O'Riordan, M D
Ohri, A K
Osborne, A W H
Pandit, L C
Paremain, G P
Parry, J M
Paton, N I J
Paul, J R
Payne, J P
Payne, N L
Pickard, H M
Plimmer, A L
Plimmer, W N
Portas-Dominguez, L-C
Post, F
Powell, S N
Provost, G C
Qureshi, M S
Rabbin, D C
Raghavan, M
Rahman, S G
Rajakariar, R
Ransome (Mrs Heron), J
Ratnasingam, L
Ray, D K
Reddy, G
Rees, M
Rege, K P
Reynolds, J F
Reynolds, M W
Rhind, P F
Richards, B W
Rippingale, C
Roberts, G C
Roberts, I F
Robertson, W B
Robinson, G T M
Robinson, S C
Robson, B E C
Roche, D W
Rudd, A G
Rutter, D A
Sabbat, J K M
Salahuddin, A
Saleem, I
Salmon, L F W
Sanders, G M
Sanders, J
Sanderson, I M
Saville, S
Schiffer, G
Schofield, C B
Scoble, J E
Scott, O L S
Sibbel-Linz, A-K
Singh-Ranger, D
Singh-Ranger, G
Sithaparanathan, S
Skeete, H J
Skull, A J
Small, M
Smallwood, R I L
Soin, B
Soni, R
Sornalingam, N
South, P W
Spencer, T M
Stammers, T G
Stavrou, M
Steven, C M
Sundaralingam, J
Sundkvist, T P H
Taussig, D C
Taylor-Roberts, T D

London, SW20

Taylor, A M
Taylor, C G
Taylor, J
Tennant, R C
Terrell, V
Thanga, V
Tilsed, J V T
Trepte, N J B
Tudor Miles, A P T
Tun, M S
Udwadia, Z
Vasudeva, A K
Vergano, J B
Wake, A M
Wake, M C
Waldman, N S
Wallat-Vago, S B
Walsh, J A
Watson, H P
Watt, J
Webb, H E
Welply, G A C
West, G F
White, G M
Whitehead, V B
Williams, D I
Williams, D J
Williams, G E
Williams, J E
Williamson, T A
Winpenny, H C
Wong, I K C
Wright, G
Yacob, Z M
Young, Y M
Zafar, M H
Zaidi, I

SW20

Ahmad, S F
Ahrens, P M
Allum Lai-Fook, J T
Appulingam, K
Ashe, N D
Ayub, N A
Aziz, M M
Bell, B A
Bierer-Sharp, D
Borthwick, S D
Brierly, R D
Britton, J A
Burling, M B
Byles, N S
Bynevelt, M
Cairns, L M
Chandi, A
Chengappa, K S
Chill, C S
Clarke, J A
Clarke, J M H
Clifton, A G
Craig, G M
Crisp, A H
Crook, S J
De Wilde, S J
Dhalla, N H K
Edwards, D R L
Emsden, A E M
Entekhabi-Fard, O
Evans, D L
Evans, S M
Fleming, P R
Freeman, H M
Gabe, C I
Gardner, A R
Ghauri, A S K
Gnanaratnam, J
Gonsalves, O J
Gowing, N F C
Grieve, J P
Grimble, I T
Halden, P J
Hamilton, P G
Hardie, R J
Harnett, P R
Hartley, I C R
Hashmi, H M
Hennessey, C M
Holmes, P A
Jacob, S
Jarzembowski, M K
Khan, R M
Kingsmill, J C
Kolendo, J
Kozielski, Y M
Lawlor, T
Lemberg, M W
Lewis, A K
Lewis, T L T

McCaffrey, B J
McCaffrey, S
Marshall, J
Mason, G J
Misir, S M
Monahan, E C
Moore, A J
Morgan, H
O'Connor, M D
Pandit, R
Patel, D
Pateman, J
Penrice, L M
Perkins, R M
Peters, A J
Peters, D A
Portelly, J E
Puvinathan, S A
Radway, C J
Reddy, K M
Rhodes, L U N
Roberts, J A
Rohde, S P
Rozewicz, L M
Sarsam, S A A
Schwartz, M S
Senthuran, S
Serena Sanchez, R
Sheth, P K S
Sivayoham, N
Sri Ganeshan, M
Stapleton, S R S J
Stone, P C
Stroud, C E
Thevathasan, L J
Thompson, P J
Tsang, F J
Tulloch, A D
Tupper, A D
Ubhi, V S
Venkatesan, D
Wait, H J
Webber, L M
Wheelan, L
Wilson, J
Wilson, S G
Woods, A L
Woropay, S J
Wren, D R
Yogarajah, Y
Zachary Jennings, C M

W1

Abecassis, M
Abood, E A
Abraham, R R
Abramovich, S J
Achan, N V
Achan, P
Achan, V
Acheson, J F
Adams, B G
Adams, P W
Adeniyi-Jones, R O C
Adiseshiah, M
Afshar, F
Akle, A
Akle, C A
Al-Ani, H M
Alhejazi, M B R H
Almeyda, J J R
Amakye, J
Ames, P R J
Anthony, S
Appleby, B P
Armstrong, N P I
Arnott, S J
Ashby, P H
Astley, B A
Atkinson, F G
Awty, M D
Aylward, G W
Baath, L-E
Badrawy, G A
Bailey, C M
Bailey, C S
Baker, G H B
Baker, H
Baker, L R I
Balcon, R
Balfour-Lynn, L P
Banim, S O
Barker, S G E
Barlow, A D
Barretto, J H
Baskerville, P A
Basra, D S
Bates, G
Baum, M

Bayoumi, H M
Bekhit, S M
Bekir, J S
Bengani, K S
Bentovim, A
Bernstein, D C
Berry, H
Besser, G M
Betteridge, D J
Beynon, G P J
Bingold, A C
Bischoff, R E H
Bishop, C C R
Bishop, C
Blach, R K
Black, A D
Blackburne, J S
Blackie, R A S
Blair, A A D
Blanshard, C
Bleehen, S S
Bloom, S L
Bloomer, A C S
Blott, M J
Boag, A G
Bomanji, J
Bond, S A
Booth, H L
Bor, S
Bosanquet, C
Botros, F N
Boulos, P B
Bourke, B E
Bowen, J E
Bowen, M L
Bowerman, J E
Bown, S G
Box, J E
Boyde, T R C
Bradbrooke, S A
Brain, C E
Brazier, D J
Breach, N M
Brendel, S C
Brennan, M E B
Brenton, D P
Bret Day, R C
Briggs, J H
Briggs, P C
Bright, H
Bristow, A S E
Broadbent, J A M
Bromley, L L
Brook, C G D
Brookes, G B
Brookes, J A S
Brooks, J H
Brostoff, J
Brough, M D
Browett, J P
Brown, D G
Buchanan, J
Buckley-Sharp, M D
Bucknill, T M
Bull, T R
Bullock, E E
Bultitude, M I
Burton-West, K E
Bush, K
Butcher, P J A
Byers, P D
Byrne, M A S
Calnan, C D
Campbell, L B
Campos Costa, D
Cardozo, L D
Carpenter, R
Carruthers, G B
Carruthers, M E
Carter, M E
Carter, M J
Carter, S S C
Cass, P L
Cassone, A M
Catterall, A
Chalstrey, J
Chamoun, V
Chantarasak, N D
Chao, W S-C
Chapman, K
Chapman, M
Chapman, R
Charles, L M
Charmandari, E
Chase, H D
Chignell, A H
Choy, Y S
Christie Brown, J R W
Churchill-Davidson, D

Cibulskis, R P
Clark, M L
Clarke, C R A
Clarke, P D
Clayden, G E
Clein, L J
Clements, R V
Clyne, M J
Clynick, F E
Cnattingius, J A
Cobb, J P
Cochrane, J P S
Cockburn, H A C
Coden, J A
Cohen, B
Cohen, B
Cohen, S
Coleridge Smith, P D
Collin, J R O
Collins, J G
Collins, M L
Colville, J R
Connolly, R C
Conway, G S
Cooper, B S
Cooper, R M
Cope, D H P
Court, S A
Cowan, D B
Cowan, M L
Cowie, D B H
Coxon, A Y
Craft, I L
Cranswick, G N H
Crawley, E M
Cream, J J
Croft, C B
Croft, R J
Croker, J R
Cronin, E
Crooks, R A J
Crown, J M
Crown, S
Croxson, R S
Cullen, N M
Currie, J C M
D'Silva, R P
D'Souza, R E
Dajani, I A M T
Dalrymple, J O
Dancey, E-J
Daniel, R
Darby, D J W
Dartey, P K W
Das-Gupta, R
Davey, G
Davies, A E
Davies, A E
Davies, C M D
Davies, D G
Davies, D M
Davies, D W
Davies, D W L
Davies, G
Davies, J E
Davies, R
Davies, T S G
Dawson, J R
Dawson, P
Day, J H
Daya, S M
De Bono, E F C P
Deman, E J
Diggory, P L C
Dilke, T F W
Dingle, M L D
Dische, F E
Dixon, J
Douch, G
Douek, E
Douek, E E
Dow, J D
Dowd, P M
Drewry, H R
du Vivier, A W P
Duchesne, G M
Dunaway, D J
Dutt, T P
Dymond, D S
Dymond, G S
East, C A
Edgar, M A
Edmonds, J A T
Edmondson, P C
Edmondson, S J
Edwards, J C W
Ehrenstein, M R
Eisenhandler, S J
El-Sherbini, R M

Elias, J A
Ell, P J
Ellahee, N
Ellingsen, J D
Ellis, F G
Emberton, M
Empey, D W
Enderby, D H
England, J P S
Enslin, R C
Eskander, A A
Ettlinger, P R A
Evans, C J
Evans, D G
Evans, I M A
Evans, J N G
Evans, M J
Falcon, M G
Farjo, B K P
Farjo, N P F
Farrag, M Z A E R
Farthing, A J
Feitelson, Z
Fenton, D A
Fermont, D A
Ferrett, C G
ffytche, T J
Field, L H
Fine, J H
Fison, P N
Fitzgerald O'Connor, A F
Foale, R A
Ford, S P
Forecast, D J
Forman, G H
Forman, R G
Foster, J M G
Fotheringham, T
Fowler, P B S
Frank, O S
Frankland, A W
Fraser, I R
Freeman, H L
Friedman, D E I
Frith, K M
Frossard, R J
Fry, L
Furlong, R J
Gabriel, S S
Gander, D R
Gardner, D A
Garson, J A
Gawler, J
Gaya, H
Gaze, M N
George, C F
George, P J M
George, R J D
George, S W
Gerlis, L S
Ghaffari, K
Ghatak, S K
Ghilchik, M
Ghosh, J C
Gil-Rodriguez, J A
Gilkes, J J H
Gillard, M G
Gilmore, O J A
Gilmour, B D
Glenville, B E
Glynne, A
Gold, S C
Goldstone, J C
Goodhardt, L S
Gordon, A B
Gould, D C
Graham, D F
Graham, J M
Grant, H R
Gravett, P J
Greenbaum, R
Greene, A M
Greenwood, M H
Greer, A J
Greeves, J A
Gregor, Z
Grespi, L
Greville, A C
Griffiths, W A D
Grindle, C F J
Grobbelaar, A O
Gross, M
Grossmann, M E
Grover, R
Groves, R W
Guéret Wardle, D F H
Guillebaud, J
Gurling, H M D

Gustavson, E H
Gwinner, P D V
Gyselinck, P
Haacke, N P
Haas, D S
Haddad, F S
Hall-Craggs, M A
Hall, A J
Hallin, R G
Hamid, S
Hamilton, A M
Hammond, C R
Harcourt, J P
Hardwick, P B
Harland, S J
Harper, P G
Harrington, K F
Harris Hendriks, J M
Harris, A M
Harris, J R W
Harris, M N E
Harris, M
Harris, N H
Harrison, M A
Harrison, M J G
Hart, R A
Hassiotis, A
Hatfield, A R W
Hatton, M J
Havard, C W H
Hawley, P R
Hazell, J W P
Healey, N J
Heard, C R
Henckel, J
Hend, M F A
Henry, M M
Hensher, R W
Herman, S S
Hickey, J D
Hill, A F
Hilton, P J
Hitchings, R A
Ho, B M L
Hobbs, J T
Hogewind, G L
Hollingworth, B A
Honey, M
Hooper, A A
Hosking, G P
Howard, C H
Howat, D D C
Howell, R J S
Hudson, J R
Hugh, D J
Hughes, A F R
Hughes, L
Hungerford, J L
Hunt, D M
Hunter, P A
Huskisson, E C
Hutton, J N T
Hyatt, D W
Hykin, P G
Infield, J A
Ingram, G S
Ioannides, C
Irvine, D H
Isaacs, A D
Isenberg, D A
Isworth, R A
Jackson, A M
Jackson, N R
Jacobs, H S
Jadav, J S
Jadhav, S S
Jagger, J D
James, D G
James, D R
James, P L
Janetos, P J
Janikoun, S G
Jasani, M K
Jelliffe, A M
Jeya-Prakash, A
Johns, M E D
Johnson, J R
Johnson, N M
Jones, B M
Jones, D M
Jones, O W
Jory, D W
Jory, W J
Joseph, H T
Joyce, B
Joyston-Bechal, M P
Kaisary, A V
Kallis, P
Kapadia, L H

London, W2

Kaplan, B
Kapur, N
Karanouh, D D
Katona, C L E
Katz, D R
Katz, M
Kaufmann, P
Kay, L A
Keene, M H
Kelleher, C J
Kellett, M J
Kells, G H G
Kemp, H B S
Kendall, S
Kenig, M
Kennedy, K W
Kenney, A
Kerr- Muir, M G
Kersley, H J
Khalife-Rahme, R
Khambata, A S
Kharbanda, R K
Khawaja, Y R
Khwaja, M G
Kilborn, J R
Kili, S A
King, J D
King, T T
Kingdon, A J
Kingsley, D P E
Kinnear, P E
Kirby, R S
Kirkham, J S
Kirwan, E O G
Klaber, M R
Knight, M J
Knowlden, R P
Kocjan, G
Kolvekar, S K
Konotey-Ahulu, F I D
Kost, E
Kotowski, K E
Kourtis, M
Kraft, T
Kreeger, L C
Krikler, D M
Kurtz, A B
Kurzer, M N
Kushalappa, C K
Kwok, K D
Lagrelius, A S
Lai, L M
Lam, S J
Lancaster, R
Lange, L S
Langley, J F A
Larbalestier, N P
Laurence, M
Lavelle, R J
Lavy, J A
Lawrence, R E
Laws, I M
Lawson Baker, C J
Layton, C A
Leader, G L
Leathem, A J
Ledermann, E K
Ledermann, J A
Lee, J P
Lee, N E
Lee, S M
Lees, W R
Leigh, M E
Leng, C P
Leonard, J N
Leonard, T J K
Leslie, T A
Levene, S
Levy, I S
Lewis, B
Lewis, B W
Li, A S L
Libby, G W
Lim, F T K S
Lincoln, J C R
Lindholm, K-E
Lisle, J R
Littlewood, R M
Liversedge, R L
Lloyd-Davies, R W
Lloyd, G G
Lloyd, G J
Lloyd, U E
Lodge Patch, I C
Loeffler, F E
Logan, M A J
Lovat, L B
Loveday, M O
Lovell, A T

Lucire, Y
Luder, J
Luke, I K
McAra, A C
Maccabe, J J
MacCarthy, J A
McDonald, E L
Macdonald, N-J
Mace, M C
McEwan, J R
McGovern, C F M
McGrath, J
McHugh, J D A
Mackay, I S
Mackenzie, P W
Mackie, I A
Mackinnon, D M
Mackinnon, J
Mackintosh, C E
Maclean, A D W
MacLoughlin, P V A
McMillan, D L
McNab Jones, R F
MacSweeney, J E
Magee, P G
Magovern, P M J
Maguire, A
Mahendra, B
Mak, I Y H
Mallinson, C N
Mallinson, M
Maltz, M B
Malvern, J
Mandel, J E
Mann, F B
Mansell, M A
Maratos, J
Marsh, R J
Marston, R A
Marwood, R P
Mason, P G W
Mason, P W
Mason, R R
Mathalone, M B R
Matti, B A
Maxwell, H
May, M W
Maynard, J D
McHardy-Young, S
Meadows, J C
Meleagros, L
Mellett, P G
Menzies-Gow, N
Michelagnoli, M P
Migdal, C S
Millar, J M
Millar, K N C
Miller, M H
Millis, E A W
Millner, W F
Mills, P G
Milroy, C
Milroy, E J G
Mindell, J S
Misiewicz, J J
Mitchell, G
Mitchell, H
Mitchell, V S
Moncrieff, Z E
Monty, C P
Moore-Gillon, V L
Moran, J D
Morgan, B M
Morgan, D
Morgan, R J
Morley, T R
Morris, V H
Morrison, G A J
Muir, J R
Muirhead-Allwood, S K
Mullins, M M
Mullins, M K
Mumtaz, H
Mundy, A J
Murphy, D A
Murphy, H M
Murray-Lyon, I M
Murray, D
Mushin, A S
Mythen, M G
Nag-Chaudhury, S R
Nagasubramanian, S
Nagiube, A F
Natali, C
Nauth-Misir, R R
Naylor, C H
Nazeer, S
Nebhrajani, J
Nebhrajani, V T

Neild, G H
Neild, J E
Nemeth, C H
Newman, J H
Newton, J R
Newton, M A
Newton, W K
Nicholls, R J
Nicolle, F V
Nield, D V
Nisbet-Smith, A P
Nissen, J J
Nixon, J E
Nixon, P G F
Noordeen, M H H
O'Brien, J P
O'Connell, J P J
O'Doherty, C S J
O'Donoghue, N
O'Driscoll, P M
O'Neill, G F A
Oakley, N W
Ohri, R
Okoro, D B
Olobo-Lalobo, J H
Oram, D H
Orbach, N
Ormrod, J
Ornstein, M H
Osborne, J L
Osho, O F
Page, E D
Page, J E
Panting, G P
Pardy, B J
Pariente, D
Paris, A M I
Parker, G
Parkhouse, H
Parsons, D W
Paton-Philip, P
Pattison, C W
Pavlou, C
Pawson, M E
Pedley, J E
Pereira, S P
Perring, M A
Persoff, D A
Petty, H R
Peyman, M A
Pfeffer, J M
Phelan, M R
Phelan, M B
Phillips, K D
Pilcher, R
Pinker, G D
Pitcher, D C R
Plowman, P N
Pollock, R C
Porter, K K
Power, J W
Pragnell, C A
Price, J D
Price, J D
Price, L A
Price, S L
Primavesi, R J
Prinja, A
Prvulovich, E M
Pugh, M A
Quest, I M
Quiney, R E
Radcliffe, A
Radcliffe, G J
Rahmathunisa, A A
Raine, G E T
Raji, A M
Ralph, D J
Ramage, C M H
Ramsbottom, N
Ransley, P G
Raphael, M J
Ratsey, D H K
Razavi, L M
Read, F E
Redgment, C J
Redstone, I
Rees, G M
Rehman, A J
Resek, G E
Reynolds, T J
Rhys Evans, P H
Rickards, A F
Rickards, D
Ridley, D S
Rivlin, A
Roberts, A H
Roberts, D N
Robertson, M J S

Robertson, M M
Robinson, D K
Robinson, T W E
Rockall, A G
Rodriguez De La Sierra, L
Rogers, J
Roodyn, L
Rook, G A W
Rosalki, S B
Rose, F C
Rose, G E
Rosen, R C
Rosin, R D
Ross, D N
Rossdale, D
Rowbotham, H D
Rowland Payne, C M E
Rubens, M B
Rubin, A P
Rudolf, N M
Rushman, R W
Russell, R C G
Rustin, M H A
Ryan, P D
Sabetian, M
Sainsbury, J R C
Salah, M W
Salmon, P R
Salt, J C
Samuel, A M
Sanders, R
Sanders, S
Saraogi, K K
Sarkany, I
Saunders, C M
Saunders, M T
Savin, G E
Sawyer, C N
Schetrumpf, J R
Scholes, G B
Schulenburg, W E
Schutte, P K
Scott, W A
Sebagh, J-L
Sebastian, J
Seear, M
Seifert, R
Selby, L M
Sellors, P J H
Semple, J C
Sergeant, H G S
Setchell, M E
Shah, N S
Shah, P J R
Shaikh, A A
Shanahan, D
Shannon, A
Shaw, C D
Shephard, E
Shephard, E P
Shepherd, J H
Sherwood, M P
Shiers, L G P
Shine, I B
Shuker, M T
Sidaway, M E
Siddins, M T B
Silk, D B
Sillers, B R
Silver, J
Silverstone, A C
Simpkin, P
Simpson, A G
Simpson, J K
Simpson, S R
Sims, C D
Sinclair, L
Slevin, M L
Smith, Dr
Smith, J H
Sogliani, F
Soliman, Y M
Solomons, B E R
Somerville, W
Sommerfield, J
Somper, J D
Sood, S C
Southward, N R
Spalton, D J
Speechly-Dick, M E
Spence-Jones, C
Spiro, S G
Spittle, M F
Sporton, S C E
Spoudeas, H A
Springall, R G
Spurrell, R A J
Stamp, T C B

Stanek, J J
Stanford, J L
Stanley, N N
Stanton, S L R
Starr, M J
Starr, P A J
Stearns, M P
Steel, A E
Stein, R C
Stephens, J W
Stern, G M
Stoker, D J
Stonehill, E
Strachan, J C H
Strigner, A E
Stuart Morrow, C
Sturridge, M F
Stuttaford, I T
Sullivan, M F
Sutcliffe, J C
Sutcliffe, N
Sutton, R
Swanton, R H
Swedan, M I
Sweetnam, D I S
Swire, N
Syada, M
Szabolcsi, A E
Szekely, F H
Tabone-Vassallo, M
Talerman, H J
Tang, D W K
Taor, W S
Tappouni, F R
Tattari, C
Taylor, D S I
Taylor, E
Taylor, I
Taylor, J C
Taylor, J O M
Teasdale, E L
Temperton, H C
Thakur, E
Thom, M H
Thomas, M G W
Thomson, D J R G
Tinker, J
Towers, M K
Towler, H M A
Townsend, C
Tucker, A K
Tucker, S M
Tufnell, G
Tunio, A M
Tunnadine, L P D
Turner, M S
Ungar, S C
Unwin, R J
Uppal, R
Vaizey, C J
Van Oldenborgh, H M
Vandenburg, M J
Vandendriessche, M A W
Vanhegan, G M
Vanhegan, J A D
Vermeire, C
Vesselinova-Jenkins, C K
Vickers, R H
Viel, M
Viel, R
Wade, T H H
Wadsworth, T G
Waldman, A D B
Walesby, R K
Walker, P E
Wallace, S A
Walmsley, K M
Walshe, J M
Ward, D E
Ward, K N
Ware, J W
Warren, R A
Waterhouse, N
Waters, K J
Watkin, B C
Watkin, J E
Watkins, E S
Watson, A
Watson, D M
Watson, N A
Webb, A R
Welldon, E V
Wellwood, J M
Weston, M J
Whelan, J S
White, A G
White, H

White, I R
White, S A
Whitelocke, R A F
Whiteson, A L
Whitfield, H N
Whitfield, P J
Wignall, B K
Williams, A T D
Williams, D K
Williams, G B
Williams, H P
Williams, N L J
Williams, P T
Wincewicz, A M
Winspur, I
Witherow, R O N
Wong, S K
Wontumi, J A
Woo, P M M
Wood, G R
Woolfson, G
Worth, P H L
Wright, J E
Wright, J L W
Wright, M G
Wrong, O M
Wylie, I G
Yarrow, H
Yeo, A-L
Yeo, S-J
Youlten, L J F
Young, A E
Young, A J
Younis, F M
Yu, R C H
Zahir, A G
Zaman, M J S
Zatouroff, M
Zeider, P A
Zumla, A

W2

Abdalla, S H
Abdullah, H S N
Acha Gandarias, P
Al-Onaizy, Z Y
Alexander, H P M
Alexander, R F
Alexander, S M
Alexander, S L
Alexopoulou, A
Anderson, S T B
Aref-Adib, F
Arora, S
Atkinson, S
Aylin, P P
Balakrishnan, J A
Ball, J A
Barghouti, W Y
Beesley, M L S
Bell, A
Bell, S S J
Berlin, A P
Bevan, P J
Beveridge, I G
Bharucha, M-P E
Bilagi, P
Blake, J C
Bradley, J W P
Britto, J F
Buck, A E
Buckman, A
Cairns, T D H
Caraher, M M
Cattell, V
Chalhoub, N M Y
Chambers, W M
Chambler, A F W
Chapple, J C
Cheshire, N J W
Chew, A-L
Chin, J E
Chiotakakou, E
Chong, K K
Clifford, K A
Cobb, E I
Collinge, J
Coren, M E
Corlett, S K
Coulter, C A E
Cowan, D L
Craig, F
Crofton, M E
Cronje, W H
Cunningham, D A
Damant, H G
Das Gupta, S
Davies, H T
Deal, J E

London, W3

Doo, A K
Duckworth, G J
Eastcott, H H G
Ebrahim, I O
Eckersley, J R T
El-Farhan, M H
Elder, A H
Elkeles, R S
Elliott, P
Epenetos, A A
Epstein, J
Espir, M L E
Evans, D J
Fairney, A
Faliakos, S
Farmer, S F
Faust, S N
Feizi, O
Fitzharris, P F
Flanagan, A M
Flitcroft, D I
Fluxman, J D
Franks, S
Gadelrab, R R
Gandhi, N D
Gangar, K F
Garralda Hualde, M E
Gautama, S
Gilling-Smith, C M-T L
Glyn, J H H
Goater, N L
Goldin, R D
Goldman, J M
Goon, P K C
Gorchein, A
Greenwell, F P
Guy, M A
Habibi, P
Hadjiminas, D
Hadjinikolaou, L
Hakim, N
Haldane, M
Hamilton, R D
Hansell, A L
Harris, J E
Hart, R
Hartley, S L
Hassan, A H A
Heggessey, L S
Hemingway, H J S
Henebury, R E D
Henry, J A
Hewitt, C A H
Hickey, M
Higham, J M
Hodes, M
Holdsworth, G M C
Holmes, A E
Hoogsteden, L
Hopkins, C E O
Horn, A R
Hoth, T
Huang, Y L E
Hughes, A D
Hulme, B
Hussain, W
Hussein, J
Indar, R
Ismail, A H
Jeffery, K J M
Jepson, A P
Joffe, M
Johnson, M A
Johnston, D G
Jones, D M
Jones, R M
Joseph, P L A
Judge, D J
Kadas, T
Kalodiki, E
Kammerling, R M
Kampmann, B
Karimjee, S
Karmi, G
Kessell, M
Khaliq, S A
Khullar, V
Killick, C J
Klynman, N L
Kon, O M
Kong Yao Fah, S K
Kroll, J S
Kropach, K
Kwan, J S K
Kwan, M C-H
Kywe, H
Lacey, C J N
Lack, G
Lamb, G M

Lamba, H S
Langdon, N
Latif, Z
Lau, Y K
Lawson, S S
Lee, D M
Lee, W S
Leyton, H R
Lishman, E J
Lissauer, T J
Llewelyn, M J
Lomax, D M
McCarthy, M I
McEvedy, C J B
Mackey, S P
McLean, C J
MacLeod, K G A
Maconochie, I K
Maguire, H C F
Main, J
Maini, S
Mansfield, A O
Markides, V
Marriott, S V L
Martinez Burgui, J A
Maru, L
Mason, J
Mathias, C J
Mavroudis, L
Mayet, J
Messinezy, M D
Mikou, P
Mitchell, D M
Mok, M H H
Montgomery, S A
Morgan, I S
Mowbray, J F
Moyes, S T
Murad, A S
Murphy, K W
Musajo, F G
Nadel, S
New, H V
Newberry, D J
Nicolaides, A N
O'Hare, R
O'Sullivan, F E
Oberoi, A
Odunuga, B A
Olufunwa, P B
Openshaw, P J M
Palmer, A B D
Papageorgiou, P
Papas, K
Patel, K S
Patel, S A
Pellerito, R
Percy, D B
Peters, N S
Philip, G E
Platt, M W
Poulter, N R
Powles, A V
Purssell, N R
Rajab, H
Reed, A M
Rees, R G
Refson, J S
Regan, L
Rice, A S C
Ritsou-Zavolia, K
Rivers, R P A
Robinson, S
Rosedale, N
Rottenberg, S G
Rowlands, E N
Royo Moya, J
Sala, M J
Sanderson, A L
Saxsena, S P
Schachter, M
Schonfield, S
Schulte-Frohlinde, P J
Scott, S L
Seed, W A
Selby, S B
Sever, P S
Sharbawi, R B
Shaw, J F
Shawis, T N
Sheridan, D J
Shortall, T N
Shroff, K J
Shum, W K
Siddique, F H
Silva, D
Simpson, J E P
Sinclair, M J
Smith, M R

Smyth, C L
Smyth, D P L
Snell, M E
So, E
Sondheimer, J
Soucek, S
Spathis, A O
Spyrou, N
Stanbridge, R L
Stanton, A V
Stevenson, J C
Summerfield, J A
Tabandeh, H
Taffinder, N J
Tan, S C
Taub, P-S A
Taylor-Robinson, D
Taylor, G P
Taylor, S M
Teare, J P
Tegos, T
Teoh, T G
Thiru, Y
Thom, S A M
Thomas, H C
Thomas, H J W
Thomas, P R
Thompson, E M
Thompson, P K
Thursz, M R
Tolley, N S
Touquet, R
Trihia, H
Tweedy, M H
Tyrer, P J
Usmani, O S
Vale, J A
Venkat Raman, N
Vine, A M
Vranakis, K
Wakelin, S H
Walker, M M
Wall, L E
Walters, M D S
Wansa, S
Ward, H
Watkins, R P F
Webb, S A R
Weber, J N
Weir, J G
Wickramasuriya, J P
Wilson, L F
Winstanly, D M
Withey, S J
Wolff-MacDonald, E M
Wong, P K
Wong, W C W
Wright, A R
Wu, G
Yates, P A
Yen, W
Yeo, D W T
Yong, K L
Young, F
Zaman, R
Zambanini, A

W3

Annadani, S R
Arora, G S
Azzopardi, D
Baber, P M
Bakala, A I
Bayney, R D
Boakye, L K A
Borrows, R J
Brooks, P J
Burns, A
Cabot, K L
Campbell, A M
Campbell, B J
Campbell, E
Chambers, M M
Chong, P
Cincotta, R B
Collier, I F
Crawford, C L
Dabrowska, M W
Datta, S N
Davies, C D
Dehghani, M
Dhatt, M
Dougall, D R
Douglass, C A
Evans, J A
Gang, J M M
German, K A
Goodall, J D
Harari, O A

Hassanaien, M M
Haverty, P F
Henderson, C
Howes, J P
Ickringill, J C W
Jacobs, E B A
Jeffreys, G E S
Jones, C R
Kaur, S
Kazzaz, H J S A
Khan, A W
Khan, N Z
Khashaba, A M H
Kolokithas, D
Koziell, S
Lai, H M
Laurie, A S
Liow, R Y L
McGovern, U B
McKeigue, S J
Magner, E H
Mahadeva, R
Martinez, J
Measday, I F
Minasian, M
Morrell, J E
Pambakian, N H
Papee, E
Pullaperuma, S P
Reddy, C P
Rimmer, D M D
Rimmer, Y L
Robinska, E M
Saujani, A V
Shahrabani, R M J
Shennan, A H
Sinha, B P
Smith, M A
Sobhy, Y M
Spencer, S M
Takhar, G S
Taraba, P
Triscott, A P
Ukra, H A H R
Vowles, J E
Wielogórski, A K
Williams, F M W
Womersley, B J
Young, T B
Zamiri, P

W4

Abeyakoon, D R
Adams, E W
Al-Benna, S
Albertyn, R D
Anderson, F M
Anderson, J M
Baker, C B
Bannon, M J
Barnes, S K M
Barton, M
Beaconsfield, R
Bennett, D M
Bennett, N C
Beresford, D N L
Betancor Martinez, M
Bhatt, V B
Bullen, P J
Burbidge, N V
Bushby, A J R
Campion, H M R
Chan, S T K
Chandran, B S
Chiu, D C
Chiverton, S G
Choudhuri, D
Clarkson, N
Cole, A S
Colfor, A M
Colson, S J
Connell, R J
Cooper, J E
Cowap, J A
Cowie, C M
Cronin Pozwolski, M J
Czajkowski, M A
Dark, C H
Datta, N
Datta, S P
Davis, J R
Devine, A R Y
Doulia, E
Dumskyj, M J
Edmonds, E V J
Edmunds, S E
Edwards, K M J
Ellis, J W M
Evans, D P

Ezekwe, C K C
Garcia-Praderas, I
Gardiner, C A
Garrard, P
Gibb, I E
Gilvarry, A M
Goodey, F J
Groves, C J
Guntis, E
Hall, S A
Halliday, M W
Harris, M F
Heinsheimer, R J
Hirst, S L
Holderness, Y M
Hughes, G V
Hunt, S M
James, C E
James, D C O
Jansen, A
Jones, E F
Joyce, A
Jungalwalla, H N
Kaplan, M J
Keen, J W
Kelly, H B
Khalifa, W
Khalique, S
Killeen, M A
Kirtchuk, G H
Konieczko, K M
Lander, D K
Lechler, R I
Levison, A V
Lim, W W D
Lockett, M J
Long, S G
Louis, J L
Lyons, R A
McCormack, M
MacDonald, R S
Maginnes, J J D
Marshall, S E M
Matthews, S H M
Mendes Da Costa, C J
Milojkovic, D
Moseley, I F
Moussa, R
Munro, A R
Murdoch, I A
Nimenko, W J
Owen, R
Packard, R S
Paszkowska, K
Patel, H
Patel, M B
Pattison, J
Pejovic, I
Phelan, M B
Pigott, J D
Polkinghorne, K R
Porto, L O D R
Proner, B D
Rackow, F I
Reinstein, D Z
Ridgway, E S
Rizvi, N
Roberts, E F
Rocker, M D
Rogers, C
Rubens, D H
Rumian, A P
Rumian, R
Salama, A D
Sangar, V K
Sargent, A M F
Shah, B R
Shah, S N
Shaw, P J
Simone, J J L
Smith, I
Sowray, J H
Soysa, P N
Stableforth, C F
Stevens, A J
Stracey, D M J
Szyszko, J M
Taggart, P I
Taylor, W J
Thakrar, N A
Thompson, P M
Thomson, R D A
Thuraisingham, J C
Venkatesham, G
Ventresca, G
Vroegop, P G
Vyvyan, M L
Walden, S J
Wasan, H S

Wasan, P K
Waygood, A R
Weber, A M
Whiten, C J
Williams, K A
Yap, Y G
Yates, R W M
Ziprin, J H

W5

Abadir, W F
Abbasi, A-H
Abeyasinghe, N I
Al-Saidi, N H M
Ali, S H
Allan, S E
Allen, C M
Allen, G M
Aluvihare, V R
Amin, M A
Anderson, A L
Ashby, D R
Atalla, R K
Aziz, M R A
Azzopardi, J G
Balasegaram, M V
Balasegaram, U
Ball, K P
Bark, C M
Baruch, U B H
Beardow, R V
Benierakis, C
Bereza, M J
Bradley, L A
Broomhead, L R
Burnand, N J
Buxton, P A
Campbell, S
Campbell, T J
Carlisle, R
Carter, F E
Chao, R P W
Charitou, A
Cienska, P
Coghill, N F
Cogill, G O
Creagh, M F
Crooks, J
Crowley, C J
Dalal, R R
Dalal, S R
Danillowicz, A
Dapres, P
Das, L
Dave, J
Dave, R
Davies, M S
Day, A M
De Rosa, S S
Dhillo, W S
Dixon, P J V
Dowling, M
Downer, J P
Duff-Miller, M T
Dundon, E A
Dunkley, A B
Dureja, A
Dybas, B
Edwards, E A
Einhorn, B
Engler, C F
Evans, D C M
Farley, K L
Francis, H W S
Fraser, A C
Ghosh, G K
Giam, N K L
Giannas, J
Gill, J S
Gittins, J C
Greene, L A
Greenway, R A C
Grewal, P S
Hamilton, J A
Hampton, R W D
Hanslip, J I
Haque, S J
Harding, C S J E
Harper, E S
Harvey, A E
Hayes, K B
Hayman, G R
Heal, J G F
Hennebry, M C
Hennebry, S
Higgins, S J
Hiwaizi, F S
Hogarth, M B
Holbrook, D M A

London, W9

Holdcroft, A
Horner, R
Hunt, K D
Irvine, S M T
Jeffery, R M R
Johnson, D S
Jones, M R
Kaler, S S
Kamalarajah, B
Kamalarajah, S
Karim, Q N
Karthikesalingam, M P
Karthikesalingam, S
Kearns, J L
Keddilty, J T H
Khehar, S
Khorasani, M H
Knox, K L
Kochan, M D
Kohn, A D
Krasucki, R E
Kyriakou, K P
Laskiewicz, B M
Lauder, M M
Lawes, R J
Leigh, M E
Lenox-Smith, A J
Li, C K-C
Lloyd, D
Logan, B
Lucas, C M
Lydon, C
McDermott, U M C
McLaughlin, J E
McLure, H A
Malik, O
Mallik, S
Mander, D S
Mangion, J
Masthi, A
Mata, S K
Meer, H
Melikian, N
Mendel, D J
Meurer-Laban, M M
Mitko, A Z
Mohamed, G E Y
Nadersepahi, A
Nafie, S A E-A A
Nakhla, L S
Neave, F
Norwid-Niekraszewicz, H
Nussbaum, F H
O'Callaghan, A C
O'Regan, D J
Oldfield, W L G
Oliver, R E W
Owen, M J
Pakarian, B F
Pande, M
Patel, G A A M
Paul, N K
Peatfield, R C
Pezeshkian, H
Philp, B M
Pietroni, R G
Pisko-Dubienski, J
Pope, S J
Pride, N B
Rampling, M J
Ramsamy, T
Rashid, W
Rawson, A B
Reddy, R
Richmond, P J M
Roberts, I
Robinson, R J
Rogers, D A
Rogers, Z J
Rollason, S B
Ryder, M H
Sapsford, R N
Sarwar, M N
Sharma, S
Sherafat, H
Shindler, E
Shnyien, N K
Siddiqi, M N
Sikorski, J M
Simpson, A B
Simpson, J C
Smallman, J M B
Smith, G S J T
Smith, R J H
Soutzos, T
Stephenson, D T
Sturge, J C
Sturge, R A

W6

Swan, J H
Teuten, A R
Thexton, R
Toale, E
Trivedi, V J
Tung, M-Y
Twomey, J L
Verne, J E C W
Walji, S F
Whitehead, A P
Whitehead, P T
Willett, F M
Williams, H M
Williams, J D L
Wilson, M B
Wright, C S W
Wright, S D
Yu, C B O
Yu, S C

W6

Agius, E V
Ahmad, M
Alaghband Zadeh, J
Alexander, S
Ali, S F
Alusi, S H
Arrigoni, P B
Artus, J M
Asplund, O A O
Ault, E A
Azadian, B S
Bagshawe, K D
Banati, R B
Banks, L C
Barling, J M
Barney, S H R
Barrett, S P
Bartels, A R D
Bench, C J
Bennett, P R
Beynon, J A
Billett, A F
Birtle, A J
Blunt, S B
Bojanic, S
Bolton, A
Boolell, M
Brown, E A
Brown, J L
Burt, L G
Carby, A E
Charity, K M
Choudhury, M A Q
Choudree, S U D
Christmas, T J
Chua, S M
Clarke, F
Clarke, P M
Clifford, C P
Colquhoun, I R
Combe, E A
Coombes, R C D S
Coomes, E N
Cope, A P
Courtenay-Mayers, B B P
Crimlisk, S N
Crowhurst, J A
Cummin, A R C
Dalrymple, S D
David, A L M
Davies, A H
Davies, S E
Davis, A
de Wardener, H E
Deacon, M B
Dellal, V M
Dennis, R T
Dharmawardene, S B
Di Pasquale, A B
Doran, G R
Dovey, Z S
Duff, I S
Dutta, R L
Edmonds, D K
Edwards, C J
Evans, P J D
Fauvel, N J
Feldmann, M
Ferguson, V M G
Fernandes, P F R
Fisk, N M
Fitzgerald, T J
Fleck, A
Flood, A J
Foadi, M D
Forester, A J
Fortin, C H G

Fotiadis, R J
Francis, N D
Frank, J W
Franklin, I J
Frazer, A N L
Fuller, A P
Gaer, J A R
Geh, J I
Getachew, H
Gibbs, J S R
Gibson, A J
Gladdish, S J
Glaser, M G
Glees, J P
Glickman, S
Glover, M
Gopinath, S
Gordon, J S
Goubran, G F
Gower, P E
Green, A N
Green, R
Greenhalgh, R M
Guiloff, R J
Guz, A
Hamblett, C J
Hanham, I W F
Harper, F V L
Harrington, D J
Harris, R L
Hart, N
Hashim, H
Hayward, M P
Heath, A
Heymann, K G
Hirsch, S R
Ho, S-A
Howard, J V
Hrouda, D
Hucker, J C
Hughes, R A
Hughes, S P F
Husain, M
Illingworth, R D
Impallomeni, M G
Ion, L E
Isaac, D L
Jamieson, I W
Jankowski, S K
Janssen, J-C J M I
Jarvis, S C
Jaye, P D
Johnson, P V
Joyce, E M
Joyce, S
Jukes, S E
Kennard, C
Khalil, N M
Koppel, J I
Kroker, P B
Lane, R J M
Lawson, L L
Lessey, K J P
Letsky, E A
Lim, C H
Linjawi, S
Lurring, E M
Lynch, V M
McCartie, J D
MacDonald, D H C
McEwan, J A M
MacInnes, L E
McKee, H J
McLaren, S A U
McLean, K A
McPhillips, M A
Maier, M
Maini, R N
Maitra, B
Mak, I Y N
Mann, P T
Manson, A J
Maraj, B H
Matthews, T D
Mendoza, N D
Michaud, R J
Millington, H T
Misra, R R
Mizen, C S
Mohith, A B
Montgomery, D H
Morgan, R E
Morley, S J
Mulligan, T J
Mur Laffon, D
Naguib, M E N
Nanchahal, J
Newlands, E S
Newson, D H

Noble, M I M
Norman, B J
Nuthall, T R A
O'Neill, R J
Olver, J M
Owens, C M
Palmieri, C
Paradinas, F J
Park, A J
Percival, N J
Perkin, G D
Persaud, M C
Pett, S J
Phelan, M C
Phillips, M E
Powell, C G B
Pritchard, C A
Proll, S
Ramsay, J W A
Ratcliffe, M J H
Razzak, A H M H W M
Reder, P
Rees, B W
Rees, H C
Retsas, S
Riaz, Y
Rice-Edwards, J M
Roddie, M E
Roddin, M J
Roney, S M
Roohanna, R
Rose, G L
Ross, G M
Rudge, S D E
Rugg, S A M
Salt, P J
Sanderson, J D
Scriven, J E
Seed, M
Shakir, R A W
Shaoul, D D R
Shaoul, E
Sharma, M
Sharma, R
Sheikh, A
Shnier, D
Shousha, M S M
Simon, D W N
Sinnett, H D
Slater, L B
Smith, J J
Smith, N A
Smith, Y L O
Southcott, B M C
Srivastava, R N
Steiner, T J
Steuer, A
Stewart, J S W
Su, R C W
Tan, S V S-M
Taubel, J
Taylor, A
Taylor, D G
Taylor, P C
Taylor, S D
Thomson, S D
Thomsen, H
Thuluvath, P J
Tipples, M K
Trendell-Smith, N J
Venables, E M
Wade, J P H
Walton, I G
Ward, P M
Watson, D G A
Wetton, C W N
Wheatley, D P
White, J F
Whitehouse, J M A
Williams, W
Wilson, D
Wilson, J A
Wingfield, D J C
Wood, S H
Wright, C J E
Wright, D J M
Yong, A S M
Yule, S M

W7

Baldock, J E
Ballard, J
Bennett, C N
Bennett, D N
Bery, J
Crinnion, J N
Cummings, T M
Derham, R J M

Dhillon, A P
Ellis, R D
Freeman, A L
Garcia Cifuentes, B
Gill, G S
Hallums, A L
Hereward, J M
Hereward, J O
Jackson, A E
Kyrionymou, G
Larbi, E D
Lees, A R
Lewandowska, A
Lewanski, C R
Light, F W
Low, G A
Malik, M A
Naish, R
Pambakian, A L M
Pambakian, H
Pambakian, S
Perinpanayagam, S T V
Pinney, S A
Raheja, S K
Robertson, D M W
Sahota, O S
Sanderson, R W A
Sivaramalingam, T R
Stapleton, S
Stewart, R C
Thomas, C S
Waldes, R M
Williams, R G

W8

Alderson, E H
Allan, A J
Baird, P R E
Barrow, E
Belcher, J R
Bell, M
Bevan, J S
Bozek, T
Bronsdon, C E
Burrows, A M
Candelier, C K
Clark, S K
Cockett, F B
Cohen, A S
Cole, M L
Corbett, P C
Dahdal, M T E
Dajani, F F
Dalley, V M
De Brito, A J F
Dimitriadis, I
Doidge-Harrison, K J
Dornhorst, A C
Dornhorst, H M
Ernys-Roberts, H M
Ernsting, J
Farnham, C W E
Freeman, R T
Gomersall, C D
Hamlyn, E M
Hammond, R O
Hargreaves, D G
Harris, T E
Hashemian, H A
Hayes, J M
Ijaz, S
Jameel, H A A-H
Kang, C H
Kaye, G S
Kealey, G T E
Khammar, G S
Kiernan, P J
Kimerling, J J
Kitiyakara, C
Kurtz, Z
Larsen, F
Lasa Georgas, A E
Lea, G
Lee, S K
Lessing, D N
Lopez-Ibor Alcocer, M I
MacGreevy, B I P
Malhas, M H
Malhas, S M
Martin, J
Middleton, B R
Moloney, M-C
Moore, J C G
Moore, S P G
Morrissey, P M
Mundy, M
Nour-Eldin, F

O'Brien, E M D
O'Connell, J F
O'Sullivan, J C
Pawlikowski, T R B
Peterson, D C
Refson, A R
Romanis, R D W
Ross, E J
Rossdale, R A
Sachs, M
Samaan, N M
Scott, O C A
Sefton, A M
Sharara, A M
Smith, J B
Smith, M P
Stanowski, M
Tahbaz, A
Tambakopoulos, D
Thammaratnam, A K
Thompson, J R
Tsao, S S-L
Waterlow, J C
Watson, M
Westaby, D
Whittall, G W
Wong, F-M
Wort, M E

W9

Abrams, D J R
Adams, D L
Adams, M A C
Adshead, J M
Bancroft, R J
Barreto, A
Barry, S M E
Basham, S C
Bearsted, C J
Beaton, F J
Beetles, C
Berger, A J
Bevington, R L S
Bliss, J P
Borton, C
Brennan, F J
Brennand, D J
Brookes, B I
Bull, D R
Cantrell, P J
Carey Smith, R L
Chan, J P L
Church, S M
Cockkinos, P
Congreve, K A M
Constantinou, J
Corbett, M
Crowley, S
Curtis, R N M
Cusano, C
Davies, P A
De Silva, P S
Dexter, S L
El-Gazzar, Y A S
Elvin, E J
Fraser, J I C
Fung, Y Y
Galbraith, A W
Garfield, A M
Garner, J S
Gibson, D J
Gibson, P E
Giles, M J
Gorham, T J
Hart, S K
Haughton, N D
Helme, M A
Hepper, F J
Hicks, R A
Hidalgo Simon, M A
Hirsh, A V
Ho-Asjoe, M S K W
Honey, S E
Houghton, J M
Houghton, S L
Idowu, O L
Ishaque, J S
Ismail, K
Jepson, A S
Johnson, M A
Jones, E C A
King, P M
Kitchen, V S
Kopelowitz, L
Lawal, A H
Leader, A R
Lin, M K K
Linehan, T P
Lloyd-Jones, E B

London, W10

Lockie, J
Losseff, N A
McGilligan, J M P
McGilligan, R C
Malone, A A
Meir, N S
Miles, M M
Miles, M V
Moorhead, J F
Nelson, P D
Newton, S E
Noble, W S
Nolan, J C
Owen-Reece, H
Panteleaki, A
Payne, S K
Pirie, A
Poole, A J
Poole, T R G
Puttick, M I
Quilliam, R P
Qureshi, M
Ratip, S
Rich, P M
Richards, C A
Richards, S C
Robson, M G
Roeves, A J
Rucklidge, M W M
Rutter, P
Sahota, K K
Sarnicki, M A
Sawtell, I J
Siva, A
Sorour, G A
Spiro, D M
Stafford, M T
Stormont, F C
Sunderland, M H
Symons, S B V
Taherzadeh, O
Tennant, S J
Toubia, N F
Uppal, R S
Vanden Driesen, M M
Varawalla, N Y
Vats, A
Vogel, M W
Wallace, N E
Wei, C W
Williams, G J P
Williamson, P D
Witt, J D
Wray, M I
Wright, H E
Yong, L
Yousuf, E Y

W10

Abbas, W S
Ahmed, N
Anderson, D J
Ardern, M H
Bordin, P
Bradbury, M G
Brunner, I C
Burton, R C
Butler, R E
Chang, Y H
Chin, C A
Dathi, H H M
De Ruiter, J M
Densham, E P
Doyle, J M
Duke, P J
Eagger, S A
Gillespie, H M
Gillespie, H R E
Hack, M A
Harrison, M L
Hasford, C
Heydari, A
Higgitt, A C
Jalisi, Q Z H
Jasani, N
Kelso, I J
Lam, T H
Mackney, P H
Melnik, L
Melville, C S A
Michael, T T E
Myers, K G
Naysmith, A
Nijhar, A
O'Rawe, M G D
Ormerod, A E
Perinpanayagam, K N
Rahman, M L
Ramasamy, N

Rose, F G
Sadler, G D
Sash, L
Sheldon, C S
Smith, G N
Smith, P C C
Swade, S N
Turner, G I
Wald, D S
Webb, S C
Wykes, P R

W11

Al-Khyatt, M K H
Ali, M I Z
Alikhani, S
Ansari, S
Arnold, F J L
Bashford, A J
Beard, R W
Beatley, W M
Beejay, N U A
Bell, R W
Besse, C P
Bloom, C A
Bonwitt, C
Britten, C M
Brosens, J
Calman, C R
Chapman, J N
Cheng, W C W
Chin, P C C
Chowdhury, S
Christie, G I G
Chung, M M
Datnow, E L
Dawson, M E
De Mowbray, M S
Demetriou, R S
Dias, V O
Dzendrowskyj, P
Edgley, R S
El-Kabir, D J
Emanuel, R W
Farrimond, J G
Foong, L C
Foyle, M F
Gillies, E A D
Glynn, A A
Holden, S J
Houang, E T
Hutt, R S A
Hyde, T A
Ibrahim, S M Y
Iqbal, F
Jackson, G D M
Jenkins, G R
Kazi, A B
Khan, M A
Kuteesa, W M A
Lascelles, P T
McDonagh, L M
McParland, M G
Mansi, M N
Mellon, C F M
Mitchell, A W M
Mohamad, J A
Mok, C A K Y
Mummery, C J
Nathan, P W
Nayani, T H
Norman, A R F
O'Connell, B A
O'Connor, C M I
Oviedo Exposito, M L
Pearl, B A
Pettifer, B J
Picard, J J
Preziosi, J J
Price, D B
Radcliffe, S A
Ramsden, S S
Raval, M P
Reid, P J
Rendall, M
Rosenthal, J M
Rowntree, R S
Rutter, T M
Salkeld, S A
Schachter, J
Scurr, M J
Seemungal, B M
Shoenberg, E
Shoenberg, P J
Simpson, E D L
Soboniewska, K M T
Stallard, J M
Steele, A C
Stride, J S C

Stringer, K R
Udwin, E L
Viviers, L
Wadsworth, S J
Waldron, J P
Wassif, W S
Watson, D
White, J C
Wijaysinghe, D
Wilson, N W
Zainuddin, I A

W12

Abel, P D
Adam, E C
Ahmad, R A S
Ahmed, M
Aichinger, G
Ainley, T C
Aitman, T J
Al-Hamali, S A
Albrecht, T
Allen, A R
Allison, D J
Anderson, J R
Anjarwalla, N K A
Assogbakpe-Tevi, C
Bacon, R C
Badat, A A
Baldock, G J
Bantick, R A
Barakat, M T
Basarab, M
Bates, A L
Beatt, K J
Bevan, R K
Blank, S C
Blomley, M J K
Bloom, S R
Boecker, H
Bogle, R G
Botelho De Gusmao De Moraes, M F
Botto, M
Bourdillon, P J
Bratby, M J
Breen, N J
Briffa, V
Brooks, D J
Bryan, E M
Bulpitt, C J
Burns, A
Camici, P G
Canisius, D S D
Ceballos Baumann, A O
Chadha, S
Chapman, P T
Chapman, V J
Chu, A C
Chung, A S
Clutterbuck, E J
Coker, R K
Coleman, D V
Cook, H T
Cosgrove, D O
Cowan, F M
Cox, P M
Craddock, C F
Cruwys, M J
Cummings, C S
Curati-Alasonatti, W L
Dalley, C D
Dandapat, R
Das-Gupta, S
Davies, K A A
De La Fuente Pereda, J
Deacock, S J
Dhanjal, M K
Dokal, I S
Dornhorst, A
Dowdeswell, K A
Drewett, S J
Drury, R E F
Epstein, R J
Evans, T J
Feldman, R G
Fermie, P G
Fluke, R W
Forbes, S J
Forton, D M H
Frankton, S
Friedland, J S
Fullerton, S A
Fusi, L
Garg, A
Gaskin, G
Gates, C D
Gbeckor-Kove, D M

Girgis, S I
Glynne, P A
Goldstone, A P
Goodchild, K A
Gothard, P K
Grippaudo, V M
Hall, F C L
Hall, R J C
Harvey, D R
Haskard, D O
Hawkins, P N
Hawkins, T E
Hemingway, A P
Hodes, C B
Holmes, M R
Hornick, P I
Howard, J K
Huddy, J M M
Hughes, J M B
Hughes, T P
Ind, P W
Jackson, J E
Jenkins, I H
Johnson, I B
Jolly, R V
Jones, B
Kanfer, E J
Keyani, J A
Kirby, S A
Kolomainen, D F
Kumar Surendran, S
Kuwani, T
Laffan, M A
Lalani, E-N M A
Lavery, S A
Leckie, M J
Lefroy, D C
Lemoine, N R
Lewis, M
Lighten, A D
Lightstone, E B
Linardou, H
Lindsay, J O
Lockwood, G G
Lowe, E M
Lynn, J A
Maalouf, E F
McClure, N A
MacDermot, J
McIndoe, G A J
McKenna, C L
Makgoba, M W
Mallucci, G R
Marcus, C
Martyn-Johns, D
Mason, J C
Meeran, M K
Miller, S
Miracle Echegoyen, J X
Modi, N
Morrison, P A
Morrison, R S
Moses, G
Muntoni, F
Naoumova, R P
Nihoyannopoulos, P
Nikolaou, D
O'Donovan, M
O'Gallagher, D M B
Oakley, C M
Oun, H A M
Panoskaltsis, T
Papakostas, P
Partridge, S E
Paternostro, G
Paterson-Brown, S
Piccini, P
Pickering, M C
Pitt, A E
Plaat, F S
Polak, J M
Price, N M
Puri, B K
Pusey, C D
Ramrakha, P S
Rayner, S A
Razack, A H B A
Redfern, D R M
Richardson, R J
Roberts, I A G
Robertson, N J
Robinson, B H
Rogers, T R F
Ross, E C
Rutherford, M A
Samuel, M
Scott, J
Sellu, D P
Sethurajan, A

Shadbolt, C L
Shah, K R
Shah, R N H
Shariff, S B
Shaunak, S
Shaw, R J S
Shovlin, C L
Sigurdsson, H H
Singer, J M
Smith, P L C
Soleimani, B
Soutter, W P
Spencer, J
Sriskandan, S
Stavri, G T
Stephen, G W
Stern, J S
Strickland, N H
Taheri, S
Tam, F W-K
Tateossian, J K
Taylor-Robinson, S D
Taylor, K M
Teh, J L Z
Thillainayagam, A V
Thomas, H
Thompson, G R
Thomson, M A
Tierney, J
Trew, G H
Trikas, A
Tuddenham, E G D
Uppal, G S
Uppal, S
Valentine, L
Van Iddekinge, B
Vassiliou, G S
Vernon, C C
Vigushin, D M
Vyse, T J
Walker, E K L
Walport, M J
Warrens, A N
Waxman, J H
Wilkinson, T D
Williams, G R
Williamson, C
Williamson, R C N
Williamson, R
Willis, A G
Willis, C J
Winston, R M L
Winyard, P J D
Wong, L
Wright, N A
Yii, M Y Y
Zamanis, N

W13

Adams, B K
Azoo, N M
Bailey, S M
Baker, W N W
Bassi, S
Bayer, J M
Beetles, E A
Beitverda, Y
Belcher, P E
Bernstein, I A
Bhatti, M A
Biel, E M
Blyth, T P
Boerger, T-O
Buck, M
Burna Asefi, M S
Chamberlain, A L
Clarke, D C K
Clarke, S A
Cominos, M
Coucher, J R
Courrier, M Y
Cowen, D S
Dasoju, R
Denis, R B
Dhillon, G
Drepaul, L R M
Duckworth, L A
Duff, M C
Estreich, L
Fuller, J H
Gopal, B
Gordon, A C
Gordon, G
Gordon, H
Hare, J F
Harris, J V
Hooftman, L W F
James, S M
Janes, S M

Jarosz, J M
Jazrawi, H H
Kitchener, P A
Kosciesza, E
Lau, P H-H
Lazarov, D
Lemoine, L
Lui, A L S
Lyon, A K
McPartlin, D W
Majekodunmi, O O
Mankoo, K S
Markham, J J
Mason, S J
Master, B R
Mitchell, C
Murray, M
Narozny, R H
Nazerali, G A
Nunoo-Mensah, J W
O'Donohue, M B
Osman, Z
Oyediran, M A
Pathansali, R
Picchioni, M M
Porter, E J B
Price, A B
Rai, R S
Randall, D G S
Ridings, P C
Romano, P
Russell, D A
Saary, M
Salam, S
Saunders, Y
Seneviratne, S
Shah, A K
Shennan, D H
Shotts, A
Sidhu, V S
Soldini, M J F
Stevens, M A
Sukhia, V D
Thomas, D K
Travis, P J
Waters, S H
Watrasiewicz, K E
Watson, A C
Webster, G A M
Wilkin, D J W
Wimalasundera, H H
Yiangou, G
Yu, D S L
Ziprin, P

W14

Adams, C E A
Adewoyin, T O A
Alexandrou, D
Avrane, J-J
Badrek-Amoudi, A
Batarec, A J E
Beardshaw, J A
Binysh, J K
Bourke, K A
Bullen, S A
Campion, J E
Carleton, H C S
Carne, S J
Chao, M A
Chappell, B G
Chen, S D M
Clark, M P
Clarke, J C K
Clubb, E M F-S
Clubb, R A
Collins, L
Colquhoun, M C E S
Cotter, P A
Davidson, A W
Davison, M M
Dickinson, R
Dornan, V I P
Dua, J S
Edrich, C L
Elliott, C
Ettlinger, N E
Fahmy, H
Fennelly, E D
Frenkel, J
Ghazanfar, R
Giles, A J H
Greenhalgh, R
Handscombe, M C
Harbord, M W N
Harris, J S E
Herman, J S
Holloway, I P
Hood, D J

London, WC1

Horne, A W
Ind, S H
Jackson, G N B
Kanani, M
Kerr, B A
Khan-Gilbert, H
Kohner, E M
Lande, R J
Lau, A W K
Lewis, D J
Low, S W W
Lyon, J A
McCollum, A
McEvedy, C P
Macvie, S I
Malik, N N
Martinez Campos, E
Metcalfe, A M
Miller, H C
Milne, A G
Miner, E N S
Mitchell, T N
Moir, J G
Montgomery, A J
Morley, M
Muhiudeen, H A
Nash, G F
Nichol, G M
Nihal, A
O'Brady, D S
O'Driscoll, M C
O'Hara, L J
Ogunbiyi, T A J
Oon, V J H
Oshodi, M A
Patwardhan, K
Pease, H W S
Power, E L
Raj, S J
Rao, R M
Richardson, B
Rosbotham, J L
Roth, D M L
Salukhe, T V
Sastre Cabrer, J A
Saxena, V
Schofield, E M
Scoones, F H
Scuplak, S M
Shanks, W
Sharma, A
Sims, H
Sofaer, D
Thompson, W C R
Timbury, M C
Trent, S L
Turner, C
Vakis, S
Vogel, L
Von Onciul, J
Watts, K C
Weggelaar, J S
Wilson, J H
Wilson, J L
Wilson, P N
Wong Hong Chai, Dr
Woodruff, S A
Zoob, B C

WC1

Adler, M W
Ahmad, S
Albanese, A
Albert, D M
Alcoreza Oliva, M I
Alibhai, A A
Allam, J
Allam, M
Allason-Jones, E
Allford, S L
Alvarez Parra, G E
Amin, S
Anagnostopoulos, A-V
Andersen, P A
Anderson, R H
Andersson, N R
Arden, G B
Assi, G
Atherton, D J
Aynsley-Green, A
Babu-Narayan, S V
Bagary, M S
Banfield, C C
Baranowski, A P
Barker, R A
Barnicoat, A J
Bavin, D J
Baxendale, H E
Beavis, J P

Behrens, R H
Bellingan, G J
Benn, P D
Benton, J S
Bernard, T
Bingham, R M
Biscoe, T J
Bitner-Glindzicz, M A K
Black, A E
Black, N A
Boralessa, R
Botma, A M
Botwood, N A J
Bowden, R N
Bowyer, J D
Boyd, S G
Bradley, D J
Bremner, F D
Bronstein, A M
Brown, A S J M
Brown, M M
Brown, P
Bryan, S J C
Bull, C
Burmester, M K
Burstein, N
Cadge, B A
Cale, C M
Cameron, F J
Caplan, H L
Carnall, D J
Carney, P J E
Casey, A T H
Cass, H D
Cassell, J A
Chan, C-T J
Chan, D
Chan, M Y
Chaturvedi, N
Chawda, S J
Chessells, J M
Chiodini, P L
Chisholm, J C
Chong, W K
Chorbachi, M R
Churchyard, A J
Clarke, A E
Clayton, P T
Cohen, H
Cohen, S L
Coleman, M P
Collins, J E
Collis, I
Colville, C C
Copp, A J
Corbett, E L
Cordery, R J
Cornah, R A
Corney, G
Costello, A M L
Cowan, F M
Craven, M J
Crean, V S J
Cremaschini, G
Crockard, H A
Cross, J H
Cruz Arteaga, J C
Cutts, F T
Daly, P E
Daniel, S E
Dattani, M T
Davies, J M
Davies, M C
Davies, R C
Davies, R A
De Leval, M R
De Sica, A
De Sousa, C M C P
De Swiet, M
Dearden, A R
Desai, M M
Devile, C J
Dickson Mabon, J
Dillon, M J
Dinwiddie, R
Dolan, R J
Dollery, C M
Donald, A K
Donaldson, J A
Duchen, M R
Duffy, P G
Duncan, J S
Eagleton, T M
Easmon, C S F
Ebrahim, G J
Eden, H Y
Elliott, A M
Elliott, C A

Elliott, M J
Ellis, D S
Everitt, A D
Facer, E K
Fasoli, L
Feather, S A
Felton, J M
Fernandez Moya, E
Fertleman, C R
Fish, D R
Fisher, L F
Fisher, P A G
Fistein, J L
Foreman, J C
Forouhi, N G
Fowler, C J
Frackowiak, R S J
French, P D
Fryssira, E
Gardiner, R M
Gibb, D M
Gibson, E E
Gilbert, R E
Gillett, G T
Gilson, R J C
Giovannoni, G
Glaser, D R
Glover, W J
Glynn, J R
Goadsby, P J
Godfrey, M
Godlee, F N
Goldberg, I J
Goldman, A J
Goldstone, A H
Goodman, F R
Gration, J C D
Greenberg, M P
Greenwood, R J
Griffiths, M H
Groves, P H
Hagard, S
Haines, A P
Hall, A J
Hall, C M
Halvorsen, R T L
Hann, I M
Harding, B N
Harding, S R G
Harkness, R D
Harkness, W F J
Harper, J I
Harrison, N W
Harrop-Griffiths, K
Hart, A J
Hartley, B E J T
Harvey, R J
Hasan, F A
Hasan, R S
Hatch, D J
Havard, J D J
Hawdon, J M
Hawkins, S A
Hayward, R D
Healy, C M J
Heard, S R
Henrichsen, T A
Herberg, L J
Hesketh, T M
Hickman, S J
Hill, A P
Hill, R A
Hill, S M
Hinchcliffe, R
Hirsch, N P
Hobart, J C
Hopper, C
Horncastle, R A
Horton, R C
Hossain-Ibrahim, M K
Hough, C F
Houghton, A M
Houlden, H J
Hourihane, J O B
Houssemayne Du Boulay, E P G
Howard, D J
Inwald, D P
Irani, T N
Isaacson, P G
Iyer, K R
Jaffe, A
James, A
Jarman, P R
Jauniaux, E
Jeene, H J E
Jelley, R Y
Jennings, N K
Jennings, R M

Johnson, M R
Jones, A M
Jones, R E
Judah, J D
Kaluba, J B L
Kapila, P
Kapoor, R
Kent, D G
Khan, N L
Kiely, E M S G
Kilby, A M
Kilpatrick, T J
King, M J
Kinton, L
Kiriakakis, V
Kirkham, F J
Kitchen, N D
Klein, N J
Kratimenos, M L K
Kroon, S M
Kullmann, D M
Küpper, A-L
Lachelin, G C L
Lakhani, S
Lamont, P J
Land, J M
Langdon, M L
Lange, K J H
Larner, A J
Larsen, C H
Lau, L K S
Lavelle, C
Ledermann, S E
Lee, P J
Lees, A J
Leiper, A D
Leonard, J V
Leonardi, G S
Levinsky, R J
Levitt, G A
Libri, V
Liesner, R J
Limaye, S V
Limousin, P
Linch, D C
Lindley, K J
Lloyd-Thomas, A R
Lob-Levyt, J P
Lockwood, D N J
Logan, G S
Loke, M Y
Lomas, D E
Loudon, D R
Lucas, D J
Lucas, S B
Lund, V J
Luxon, L M
Mabey, D C W
Macallister, R J
MacArdle, B M
McCarthy, M J
McElhinney, J M
McGregor, R M V
Machin, S J
McHugh, K
McKee, C M
McKeigue, P M
McLean, A E M
McManus, I C
McMichael, A J
McMorrow, S M
McNeilly, R A
Macpherson, M M
Madden, E J
Mahlati, S S G
Mahoney, P F
Maini, M
Malin, A S
Malone, M M T
Mantoudis, E
Marazzi, E
Marmot, M G
Marnane, C N
Maskey, S P C
Meade, T W
Meeks, M G
Mellado Calvo, N
Mercey, D E
Merry, R T G
Michaelis, L J
Michaels, L
Michalski, A J
Milla, P J
Millar, M R
Miller, R F
Miotti, A M
Miotti, F A
Misra, V P E
Mitchell, H S

Moghissi, A J
Mok, Q Q
Montgomery, H E
Moran, N F
Morris, H R
Morris, J N
Moss, F M
Muller, W G
Mundy, P G
Murray, N M F
Naftalin, A P
Naim, T
Nandi, P R
Naoumov, N V
Nathanson, V H
Nazroo, J Y
Neale, G
Neville, B G R
Newman, L
Newton, M C
Ng, C Y
Nicholls, D E
Nicholson, A C
Nischal, K K
Njovu, M
Noah, N D
Norman, P M
Novelli, M R
Novelli, V
Nyiri, P J
O'Brien, P A
O'Donoghue, B M
O'Flynn, P E
O'Higgins, P
O'Riordan, J I
Obasi, A I N C
Okonkwo, O O
Omara-Boto, T C A
Paice, E W
Paine, M A
Pal, D K
Palaniappan, R
Pandya, P
Parkinson, M C
Patel, A
Patterson, K G
Peckham, C S
Peckham, M J
Pembrey, M E
Penrose, C V
Petros, A J
Phelps, P D
Pierro, A
Pigott, N B
Pillaye, J
Pitt, M C
Plant, G T
Pollock, J R
Porter, S R
Poskitt, E M E
Powell, M P
Pramstaller, P P
Prichard, B N C
Pritchard, J
Quinn, N P
Raglan, E M
Rahi, J S
Rahman, S
Rai, V S
Raine, R A
Rajput, K M
Ramsay, A D
Ratcliffe, S G
Rea, P A
Redington, A N
Rees, G E
Rees, J H
Rees, L
Rees, P G
Rehman, A M
Reinhardt, A K
Revesz, T
Reynolds, E O R
Richens, J E
Ridgway, G L
Rieberer, G C
Risdon, R A
Roberts, A J
Roberts, I G
Robinson, A J
Rodeck, C H
Ross, D A
Rossdale, M R
Rosser, E M
Roughneen, P T M
Rudge, P
Russell-Eggitt, I M
Ryan, J M
Sander, J W A D S

Sarasola Lopetegui, J A
Scadding, G K
Scadding, J W
Scaravilli, F
Schapira, A H V
Scher, H
Schindler, M B
Schott, G D
Scott, R J
Seeley, H F
Segal, A W
Segal, T Y
Sethi, D
Sharrack, B
Shekerdemian, L S
Shelley-Smith, N J
Shields, S A
Shipley, M E
Shorvon, S D
Shukla, P B
Shulman, C E
Singer, M
Singh, D
Singh, M B
Sirimanna, K S
Sisodiya, S M
Skolar, P J
Skuse, D H
Smith, M
Smith, S J M
Solanki, G A
Solomon, S M E
Somerville, F
Sonksen, P M
Souhami, R L
Spitz, L
Spoulou, V
Stanhope, R G
Stanton, A J
Stark, J
Steer, J A
Stephenson, J M
Stevenson, V L
Stewart, A L
Stewart, G W
Stirling, L C
Strobel, S
Stuart, K L
Sumner, E
Suri, D
Surtees, R A H
Sury, M R J
Swerdlow, A J
Taheri, S
Tatman, M A
Taylor, J F N
Thekekara, A G
Thomas, D G T
Thomas, J A
Thomas, M L
Thomas, P K
Thompsett, C
Thompson, A J
Thompson, D N P
Thompson, E J
Thorpe, J W
Thrasher, A J
Tinker, A
Tomkins, A M
Tonks, A M
Trimble, M R
Trompeter, R S
Tsam, L
Tully, J M
Vallance-Owen, A J
Van Doorn, C A M
Van Paesschen, W
Van'T Hoff, W G
Vaughan, J P
Vaz Pato, M
Vellodi, A
Vergani, D
Veys, P A
Wadley, J P
Wagg, A S
Walker, I A
Ward, A A
Ward, R H T
Warren, V J
Watkins, L D
Webb, D K H
Webber, R H
Wei, T C M
Westcott, G F
Wharton, B A
White, S R
Whitehead, B F
Whitmore, A V

London, WC2

Wilkinson, P D
Williams, I G
Williams, J O H
Williams, L
Williams, R
Williams, R E
Wilson, A P R
Wilson, L C
Wilson, P J K
Wilson, S R
Winter, G B
Winter, R M
Wise, R J S
Witchalls, J R

Wood, N W
Woods, S C P D
Woolf, A S
Woolf, N
Wright, A
Wright, P H
Wright, S G
Wyatt, J C
Wyatt, J S
Wynne-Roberts, C R S M

WC2

Aylward, M

Basu, D B
Bavetta, F
Bloom, M
Bond, K E
Bosman, D H
Briggs, P W
Brown, P M R
Byrne, M B
Chatamra, K
Debuse, M J
Eadie, S P
Ellis, P S
Fender, E
Garner, J F

Goodge, A
Hale, A S
Heap, E L
Henderson, M
Hilton, J A M
Holland, W W
Jones, D S D
Jones, G C O B
Jones, R H
Kelt, J D
Lee, C P
Martin, I J
Milliken, T D A
Missen, G A K

Mitchell, J L
Morris, C B
Morris, P J
Ng, T T C
Okech, M
Ough, R W
Rady, N A
Ratnavel, R
Rawlins, M D
Sawney, P E
Sinnatamby, C S
Skinner, R K A M
Smith, J H W
Stidolph, P N

Stone, R J
Szarewski, A M
Tacconelli, F
Thomas, R D
Toy, J L
Warren, J B
Wedderburn, L R
Whitear, J R
Whitear, S-N
Wynn Parry, C B

Index by Town

Abbots Langley
Abuelela, H M A K
Baldwin, L J
Ghosh, S K
Gray, P
Hamid, Z
Isaac, I C O
Kotecha, S
Lang, E-M
Mariz, S D M
Neighbour, R H
Oladipo, A
Ousta, B N
Peck, M A
Simmons, P M
Stafford, N J
Swanwick, T
Tomson, P R V
Williams, S E

Aberaeron
Barfield, S
Davis, P M
Evans, D O
Herbert, H
Herbert, M H
Jones, A M
Price-Jones, J C
Thomas, R G
Williams, D M

Aberdare
Ali, S A
Ashraf, M
Bowen, C R
Bradley, A C
Campbell-Taylor, M D
Chattopadhyay, S K
Cheung, C W
Codd, I M M
Davies, C L
Davies, G C
Davies, M P
Dietzel, T
Evans, A D
Foster, M G
Gandy, C P
George, P K
Gratton, D M
Griffiths, B E
Griffiths, E
Haldar, N A
Harris, D S
Hawkins, M P
Imtiaz, S M
Jenkins, R D
Kermeen, R S
Mahmud, S
Menon, A G
Morgan, V E
Nawaz, M
Noah, S B
Oberai, S K
Rahman, S O
Richards, A F
Richards, P R
Sahai, I B
Sahai, S N
Shah, S A
Shah, V
Thomas, D D
Torrance, C J
Veerayya, Y
Vijayakumar, P
Wardrop, A G
Williams, A R

Aberdeen
A'Hara, L J
Abu-Omar, Y
Acevedo Merino, M
Adam, A
Adey, G D
Affleck, I R
Affleck, R B
Ah-See, A K-N
Ah-See, K W
Ahsan, S F
Aiken, Y
Aitchison, V A
Aitken, H
Al-Busaidy, S Z
Al-Jabiry, H H S
Albert-Recht, F
Alderson, P M
Alexander, E R
Alipour-AlmacHavan, K
Allan, D S
Allan, K M
Allan, T M
Allen, J C
Alozairi, O
Anderson, V
Armstrong, L
Ashcroft, G P
Ashcroft, G W
Ashton, E M
Ashton, H R
Atcheson, S F
Athawes, R W B
Auchterlonie, I A
Avenell, A
Ayliffe, P R
Baker, A R
Baker, L
Balch, N J
Barber, A B
Barker, S L
Barkham, M N
Barr, J M
Barrett-Ayres, A M
Barton, S
Basu, A
Beebeejaun, H R
Bell, D J
Bendomir, A
Bennett, F M
Bennett, N B
Berrisford, R J
Berrow, L C
Bevan, J S
Beveridge, M E
Beveridge, S
Bewsher, L K
Bewsher, P D
Bexley, K A
Binnie, N R
Bishop, H S
Bisset, A M
Bisset, W M
Blaiklock, C T
Blaiklock, J S
Blair, D W
Blake, J G
Blessing, K
Boddie, D E
Booth, P
Boshier, A J
Bowring, A
Boyd, J A
Boyle, P
Bremner, M H
Broadbridge, C T J
Brooker, I M
Brooks, M E
Broom, J
Brown, A N
Brown, B
Brown, D
Brown, I M
Bruce, A W
Bruce, D M
Bruce, G A M
Brunt, M E A
Brunt, P W
Brunton, J N
Buchan, K M
Buchan, M F
Buchanan, C E
Bullough, C H W
Burgul, R
Burnett, J B C
Burrell, J M
Byers, G F
Byrne, A W
Cadwgan, A M
Calder, S A
Calder, W N
Callender, J S
Callender, P A
Campbell, A G M
Campbell, A M
Campbell, D M
Campbell, M A
Canavan, K S
Cargill, R I
Carson, L S
Carty, J
Caruana, P
Caskey, F J
Cassidy, J
Casson, W R
Castello Cortes, H P
Catto, W D
Caughey, D A
Chadha, Y C
Chalmers, G C
Chalmers, M E
Chan, M W
Chapman, A D
Charleson, F
Chee, Y L
Chesney, R B
Chew, G K
Chin, S K
Choudhuri, U K
Christie, S M
Chrystal, K M R
Church, J R M
Church, W H
Clark, A S
Clark, C M
Clark, E D
Clarke, G J
Clegg, E J
Close, C T
Cohen, N P
Coleman, R J
Collie, W M
Conner, C E
Connon, E A F
Cook, D H M
Cook, R
Coomansingh, D P
Cooper, A J
Cooper, G
Cooper, G G
Cooper, J G
Cooper, J K
Cooper, K G
Copland, M
Copland, S A
Cornwell, G
Corse, J O
Cosgrove, J M
Costen, M T J
Cougan, C A
Cox, A D
Cozens, J A
Craig, A
Craig, C M
Craig, L M
Craig, S W
Craik, M C
Cranfield, K A W
Croal, B L
Crofts, H R
Crooks, L W
Cross, K S H
Cross, S J
Cruickshank, M E
Crum, J E
Culligan, D J
Cumming, C A
Cumming, R P
Curnow, J
Currie, J M
Cusick, E L
Cutler, F J
Daly, C D
Danielian, P J
Dargie, H E
Dark, A
Davey, K A M
Davidson-Lamb, N J
Davidson-Lamb, V C
Davidson, A I
Davidson, J C
Davidson, J F
Davidson, M I
Davidson, P E
Davidson, R D
Davidson, S G
Davidson, T B
Davidson, V
Dawson, A
Dawson, A A
Dawson, L R
De Beaux, J L M
De Silva, D C
Dean, J
Deans, A K
Deans, H E
Deans, S P
Dempsey, O J P
Devereux, G S
Dharmendra, M S
Dick, A D
Dick, F D
Dickson, C J
Dickson, R E
Docherty, E M
Doherty, P M
Doig, W J
Donald, I
Donald, R T
Donald, S A
Donaldson, W B M
Donnelly, R P
Douglas, A
Douglas, A M S
Douglas, J G
Drummond, R D
Duffty, J H
Duffty, P
Duffus, E C
Duffus, P R S
Duncan, K A
Duncanson, K C
Duthie, B W
Duthie, I
Duthie, R A
Eagles, J M
Eastmond, C J
Easton, E A
Ede, R J F
Edward, J
Edward, V E M
Edwards, S L
El Tahir, A M M
Ellis, C J
Emslie, L M
Evans, D E
Ewen, S W B
Falconer, A E
Falconer, H R
Farquharson, J M
Farquharson, M
Faulkner, G E
Fawcett, M
Fenwick, D K F
Ferguson, J
Ferguson, K
Ferguson, W J
Finlayson, A I
Finlayson, J K
Finnie, J S
Flett, G M M
Flett, M E
Fogiel, P C
Foo, A M L
Foote, A V
Forbes, A A
Forrest, N
Forrester, M
Forsyth, L
Fowler, D
Fowler, L R
Fowlie, D G
Fraser, A K
Fraser, A M
Fraser, A
Fraser, C
Fraser, C D A
Fraser, D E
Fraser, W R
Freeland, W A
Friend, J A R
Furnace, G F
Furnace, J
Gall, A
Galloway, D B
Galloway, W H
Gardiner, A Q
Garton, F M
Gates, L J
Gauld, G D
Gautam, L M
Gautam, P C
Geider, S
George, H M
Gerrard, J M
Gerrie, L M
Gibb, M W
Gibson, H F
Gibson, P H
Gibson, S J
Gilbert, F J
Gilchrist, A C
Gillies, P M
Glazener, C M A
Glenesk, A D
Gold, A E
Goldbeck, R
Gordon, A K
Gordon, J G G
Gordon, N L M
Gordon, R B
Gould, I M
Grant, A M
Grant, C E
Grant, L
Grant, R W
Grant, S H
Grant, S B
Grattidge, I R
Gray, A G
Gray, D W G
Gray, E S
Greaves, M
Green, A F
Green, C L
Green, F D
Gregory, H
Greiss, M A M
Grieve, A A H
Grieve, D R
Grieve, J H K
Griffin, M
Grimshaw, J M
Gunnyeon, W J
Guthrie, G M
Guthrie, V J
Hadden, K M
Haddow, A M
Haetzman, M L
Haites, N E
Hall, M H
Hamilton, M E
Hamilton, M P R
Hamilton, R J
Hamilton, S J C
Hancock, S E
Hannaford, P C
Harcourt, J E
Harper, D R
Harris, D E
Hart, D D
Harvie, J P
Hay, A D
Hay, I C
Hay, J L
Hayworth, A J C
Helms, P J
Henderson, A J W
Henderson, I M
Henderson, J G
Henderson, M H
Hendry, M J
Hendry, W T
Hepburn, H
Herriot, R
Hewison, R A C
Hewitt, C D
Hewitt, J B
Heys, S D
Hill, J
Hillis, G S
Hinton, H A
Hinton, L
Hiscox, J A
Hivey, S E
Hobbs, S A
Hobson, E E
Hobson, R P
Holder, P A
Holmes, J D
Hourston, A J D
Howarth, F P
Howe, E G
Howe, G W B
Howie, H C
Hunter, A
Hunter, D I
Hunter, J D
Hunter, M M
Hurman, D C
Hussey, J K
Hutton, L S
Ibojie, J O
Imlach, M
Imray, J M
Ingram, E A
Inkster, J E
Innes, A H
Innes, G
Innes, J R S
Irvine, W
Ismail, S K
Jacobs, P
James, I E
James, W P T
Jameson, S A
Jamieson, A D
Jamieson, K L
Jandial, V
Jeffrey, R R
Jennings, K P
Johnson, J W
Johnston, A
Johnston, A M
Johnston, C V M
Johnston, G M
Johnston, J N
Johnston, P W
Jones, P F
Jones, T R
Kaawach, W F
Kam, H K V
Kay, D T
Keech, J P
Keenan, R A
Keilloh, D A
Kelly, F
Kelty, C J
Kemp, M S M
Kennedy, N S
Kernohan, N M
Kerr, K M
Khadilkar, A S
Khan, A L
Khan, H R
Khan, I H
Khaund, R R
Khir, A S M
Kidd, A M J
Kiehlmann, P A
Kiehlmann, T A
Kindley, A D
King, B C
King, D J
King, P M
Kirk, H J
Klopper, A I
Kluth, D C
Knight, D J
Knight, E
Knight, J C
Knox, F M

Aberdovey

Koruth, N M
Koruthu, A
Kreutzer, B R L
Krukowski, Z H
Laing, R B S
Laird, S A
Lamberton, G E
Lamberton, R B
Lamont, H J
Lang, G D
Larmour, P A
Lau, C S
Lawton, K
Le Fevre, P D
Le Poidevin, D
Ledingham, W M
Lee, E S
Lee, P K-C
Lee, S W M
Lees, D I
Lees, G M
Lefevre, K E
Legg, C M
Legg, R J
Legge, J S
Legge, M B
Leiper, D B
Lennox, A S
Leslie, P D
Lessels, S E
Levitt, C S A W
Lewis, H B M
Lewis, R J
Lian, C S
Liddell, C R W
Liddell, E J
Light, C J
Lim, K P
Lloyd, D J
Logan, G D
Lolley, J
London, H M
Lowit, I M
Luk, T L
Lumsden, C J
Lyle, A
Lynch, D J L
Lynch, M M
Lynch, S J
Macaskill, I A M
McAteer, D S
Macaulay, I I
McCaffery, T M
McCallum, F E
Maccallum, K J M
McCarthy, S A
McCheyne, A J
McCheyne, J
McClintock, M J
McClinton, S
McColgan, C M J
McConnell, D T
McConville, P M
McCrone, L A
McCullough, K A
McDiarmid, A J
MacDonald, A G
MacDonald, A F
McDonald, G A
McDonald, J M
MacDonald, P J
McFarlane, C
McFarlane, H J
Macfarlane, L M
McGill, D J
MacGregor, C
MacGregor, D M
McGugan, E A
McHardy, D A
McHardy, K C
Macilwain, I F
McIntosh, S A
McKay, A R
McKay, C E
McKay, E
Mackay, K M
McKean, M E
McKee, I A
Mackenzie, A R
Mackenzie, A S
Mackenzie, C L
McKenzie, H
MacKenzie, J M
Mackenzie, J D
Mackenzie, S E
McKerachér, R D
McKinlay, A W
MacKinlay, M E
MacKinnon, J R

Macklin, A S
Maclean, A M
Maclean, G D
McLean, J A
Maclean, M N
Macleod, A M
Macleod, D M
Macleod, E
Macleod, M J
McLeod, S A
Macleod, T N N
Maclure, A M R
McMann, P M
Macmillan, J C
Macmillan, S J S
MacNaughtan, I P J
Mcneil, G
Macphee, S J
McPherson, H
MacPherson, J B
McRuvie, G M
Mahy, I R J
Mair, D J
Mair, D R
Maitland, J M
Malcolm, L
Marwick, D M
Matheson, A B
Mathieson, D
Mawdsley, J H
Maxwell, A J
Maxwell, D G
Messer, D E
Metcalfe, M J
Metcalfe, W
Michie, V C A
Miedzybrodzka, Z H
Milburn, C J
Millar, H R
Miller, G D
Mills, K L G
Milne, A D
Milne, M R
Milne, R M P
Milton, A M
Mishriki, S F
Moffat, L E F
Molloy, J S
Moore, S J
Morrison, F S
Mowat, N A G
Muir, M S
Munro, A J
Munro, C
Munro, L R
Munro, M J
Murdoch, E A H
Murdoch, H B
Murphy, C A
Murphy, E
Murray, A D
Murray, C
Murray, G
Murray, J B
Murray, S
Mutch, W J
N'Dow, J M O
Needham, G
Newlands, W J
Newnham, D M
Nicholson, A P
Nicol, A G
Nicoll, K S
Nicolson, M C
Nunez, D A
O'Hanrahan, T J
O'Kelly, T J
Ogg, F L M
Ogston, D
Ogston, K N
Olley, P C
Olson, I A
Olson, J A
Olson, S
Ormerod, A D
Orr, J D
Orr, M J
Otto, M H
Owen, J A
Page, J G
Palin, A N
Park, K G M
Parkin, D E
Parry Davies, M F
Paterson, J G
Patey, R E
Payne, S N L
Pearson, D W M
Pennington, T H

Petrie, M X P
Petrie, M C
Philip, R A
Philip, W J U
Phull, E A
Phull, P S
Pirie, C M
Pitt, E S
Porteous, J M
Porter, B J
Pratt, M A
Prentice, A C
Prime, A J
Primrose, W R
Proctor, K G F
Provan, C D
Provan, J
Qureshi, A M
Raffan, A W
Rait, D E
Ralston, S H
Rashid, M
Ratcliffe, M A
Ray, P K
Read, J R M
Reary, S
Reed, J M
Rees, A J
Reid, A
Reid, C
Reid, D M
Reid, J A
Reid, J P
Reid, T M S
Reith, H L
Reith, W
Rennie, A M
Renny, N M C
Renshaw, P R
Repper, J A
Rhind, G B
Rhodes, P M
Richards, D W L
Richardson, F M
Richardson, F
Richardson, J R
Riddell, R E
Ritchie, A M
Ritchie, A M
Ritchie, C W
Ritchie, G D
Robbie, R B
Roberts, S C
Robertson, A
Robertson, A J
Robertson, C
Robertson, D E
Robertson, E A
Robertson, G S
Robertson, K
Robertson, S F
Robinson, J G
Rodger, S J N
Ronald, A L
Rose, C
Rose, S
Ross, A M
Ross, A M
Ross, D G
Ross, D I
Ross, E T
Ross, H S
Ross, I S
Ross, I
Ross, J A S
Ross, S
Ross, W A
Rossi, M K
Russell, E M
Russell, G
Rutherford, J A S
Rutherford, M C
Sagias, F
Samuel, L M
Sarwar, M I M
Saunders, N J
Scorgie, R E
Scotland, J J
Scotland, T R
Scott, C J
Scott, G B
Scott, J
Scott, S T
Seton, D L
Seymour, D G
Seymour, R M
Shafi, M T
Shand, J S
Shand, L M

Shanks, M F
Shaw, J A M
Shearer, A F
Sheehan, C
Shepherd, F G G
Shepherd, G A A
Shirley, P J
Shirriffs, M J
Shirriffs, G G
Short, D S
Short, J A
Showell, N M
Sim, A J W
Simpson, J G
Simpson, S A
Simpson, T W
Simpson, W G
Sinclair, C D
Sinclair, P
Sinclair, T S
Sinnathuray, K R
Skinner, C K
Slessor, D M
Smail, P J
Smart, A R T I
Smart, L M
Smith, A P M
Smith, B H
Smith, C A
Smith, C C
Smith, F W
Smith, G
Smith, H
Smith, H P
Smith, I
Smith, I C
Smith, J M
Smith, M G
Smith, N
Smith, W C S
Smyth, E H
Snape, P E
Soper, F R C
Soutar, A L D
Soutter, W
Spence, E M
Spence, F M
Srivastava, P
St. Clair, D M
Stalder, C M
Stanbridge, J E
Stark, G P
Starr, K J
Stephen, G
Stephen, W T
Stephen, W S Y
Stephenson, R N
Stevenson, C W
Stewart, C
Stewart, M
Stewart, R J G
Steyn, J H
Stirling, I B
Stockdale, E J N
Stott, S A
Strachan, F M
Strachan, P A
Strachan, R
Sulawany, T I A
Sutherland, A G
Sutherland, B
Sutherland, H W
Sutherland, J G
Sutherland, L M
Swami, K S
Tan, W B
Tayebjee, M H
Taylor, A J
Taylor, F A
Taylor, G A
Taylor, G W
Taylor, M
Taylor, R J
Taylor, V E
Taylor, W E
Telfer, J M
Templeton, A
Terris, M
Terry, P B
Thomas, D P C
Thompson, A J
Thompson, C A
Thompson, W D
Thomson, A R
Thomson, S M J
Thorpe, A P
Tou, S I H
Trotter, P M
Tunstall, M E
Turnbull, P J

Turner, A R
Tuttle, S
Tweedlie, I K
Valentine, M J
Van Woerden, H C
Vang, S K
Veitch, D Y
Vickers, M A
Viswanathan, M J
Walker, F
Walker, S A
Wallace, E D
Wallace, J D
Wallage, S
Wallis, J F E M
Walshe, E T
Ward, P R
Wareham, V A
Warrender, T
Warrington, J
Watson, A J M
Watson, D P B
Watson, H G
Watson, M S
Watson, P A F
Watson, W A
Watt, A H
Watt, M J
Watt, M M
Watt, R M J
Wearden, D J
Webster, J
Webster, J
Webster, K
Wedderburn, S
Weissen, P R
Welluppillai, S
Weston, A N
Wetherly, J M R
Whalley, L J
White, J C
White, M I
White, M
Whitelaw, D E
Whitter, A E
Wilkie, M J
Wilkinson, A T
Wilkinson, S P
Williamson, K M
Wilson, A G
Wilson, A M
Wilson, E M
Wilson, G E
Wilson, J G
Wilson, S J
Wilson, W A
Wisely, I C F
Wiseman, J
Wood, F T
Wright, M E
Yap, L K
Yates, P
Young, A M
Young, H A
Young, J
Young, M J
Youngson, G G
Younie, G G

Aberdovey

Davies, T T
Sayes, R M

Aberfeldy

Dougall, H T
Griffith, D H S
Harrold, J A
Hunter, D W
Inglis, A
McBride, H M
MacGregor, D M
Paterson, R M
Pitchforth, A E
Riddell, D I
Riddell, M J
Stark, G D
Taylor, Z L
Wheater, R A
Wolfendale, R E
Wright, D S
Wright, H M
Yellowlees, W W

Abergavenny

Abdel-Massih, R S
Alfaro Garcia, G M
Babiker, S E D M
Balboa, S
Bapuji Rao, V
Beard, H

Bhatia, A G
Birdi, P K
Blackett, R L
Borg, A
Bowden, B G
Bracchi, A L C A M
Bracchi, R C G
Buczek, L A
Burrows, D J
Carbarns, N J B
Cave, W P
Clements, J M M
Coldrey, P A
Concha, E M
Cross, N C
Das, I
Davies, B S
Davies, D L
Davies, H G
Davies, P L
Dawson, A J
Dawson, L K
Dennis, C A
Deshpande, P V
Edwards, G J
Edwards, M
Edwards, P W
El Gaid, I S
El-Serafy, N I
Eriam, M S
Evans, E C
Everest, M P
Fairweather, S J
Falkner, J D
Farrington, R M
Fielding, S
Fone, D L
Frazer, A C
Fry, D I
Gibbon, G J
Gilbertson, C
Griffiths, A D
Griffiths, W S
Gruffudd-Jones, D M
Hargest, R
Harrell, M E
Harrell, R
Heneghan, C P H
Hodge, R C
Hosen, S C
Howell, S
Hulme, C E
Hutchison, S J R
Jackson, W D
Jenkins, N H
Jennings, J S R
Jones, D G H
Jones, I E
Jones, I G
Josephidou, M
Keely, G M J
Kellett, R J
Kerr, M P
Khanna, PB
Killeen, N C J
Kocan, M K
Lavis, M S
Lawson, J M
Lee, A M A
Lewis, J K
Lewis, R M L
Linton, S M
Lutter, P F
Maddocks, J
Mahmood, A
Martin, M J
Meredith, A S
Morgan, R
Musa, B S
Nalini, V
Natarajan, D
O'Byrne, G A
Parker, A
Parker, R J
Parker, T F J
Pickford, S
Plumb, J M
Poddar, S
Proctor, E
Queen, K B
Raichoudhury, B S
Reed, D H
Reynolds, J H
Rich, D A
Richard, B L
Robins, G
Rolfe, A B
Rolfe, S E
Rose, H M

Alexandria

Saafan, A A M
Sampson, S R M
Saunders, J
Sinha, A
Skea, G K
Snell, T P
Srinivasan, K
Staples, V J
Stokes, I M
Stucke, S K
Taylor, D C
Thomas, G O
Ueberhorst, A
Walker, R W
Warren, S W
Weekes, C A
Weeks, R A
Wheatley, R J
Williams, L A
Williams, R M
Williams, T H C

Abergele

Battersby, J M
Charles, T J
Clarkson, N C
Davies, H O
Dromey, J F
Edge, J M
Edwards, S G
Garnett, A G G
Hakeem, A A
Honeybun, J J
Innes, H E
Jamil, A
Jones, T R
McCormack, J G
Percy-Hughes, H C
Riding, B E J
Riding, J E
Roberts, A P
Salisbury, J B
Smith, I C E
Srinivasan, J
Stockport, J C

Aberlour

Bonnyman, S D
Caldwell, J S
Cammack, A E
Dennis, T
Duncan, G G
Ellis, S J
Green, H M
Johnston, N M
Lawrence, J
McDowall, D J
Miller, D J
Purdie, N L
Whyment, W H

Abertillery

Clatworthy, M R
Dexter, C G
Hossain, N A
Hossain, S A
Howell, R D
Narang, S K
Pagadala, R K R
Roy, C H
Venn, C S
Venn, S J

Aberystwyth

Amole, A A
Atrah, H I A R
Awad, S A M M
Axford, A T
Boswell, G V
Brookes, J-P C M
Burroughes, A M
Callaghan, B M L
Callaghan, P
Cleland, E M
Colbourn, C
Cunningham, D A
Daniels, C K
Davies, E J
Davies, G S
Edwards, C D
Edwards, D R
Edwards, R B L
Evans, A
Evans, R
Gardner, P T
Gerrard, F E
Godfrey-Glynn, P M N
Griffiths, J J
Haddad, S K
Henderson, R M

Hooper, C A
Hosker, I T
Hughes, E T
Hughes, J H
Humphreys, S W
Jackson, D S
Jones, C E M
Jones, J A
Jones, P D
Khoo, K T
Lewis, D M
Lloyd, H S
Lloyd, J B
Lord, M G
Lotfi, G
Meredith, A D
Mishra, K P
Morgan, G W
Morris, M B
Morus, L C
Muller, R K G
Murdoch, W I
Myles, R W
Narain, M A
Nicholls, H
Price, M A
Rhys, A
Roberts, B A
Roberts, D B
Roberts, R S C
Roberts, W J C
Sahni, K
Saleh, A J
Slade, K
Smart, F A
Thomas, B I E
Thomas, K
Vivian-ab-Ewart, V R
Walters, D D
Williams, J A
Williams, J L
Williams, J W
Williams, J B
Williams, S C
Williams, W

Abingdon

Adams, L R
Allan, E A
Allinson, H S
Auckland, C R
Barwood, P F
Bryant, J E
Casemore, V A
Casson, R T
Cave, R J S
Cherry, J
Chipperfield, A
Cox, A H
Cox, V A
Crosbie, W A
Crossley, N R
Cullington, D E
Davis, C J F
Davis, E L
Dixon, A D
Duffield, J E
Dugdale-Debney, F W
Dunn, J M
Dyson, E D
Edge, C J
Elwig, N H
Evans, A J
Evans, R F
Finch, E A
Gibbs, D D
Govier, K L
Graves-Stanwick, T R
Hampson, S C
Hart, M H
Herdman, J R E
Hodgson, D C
Hodgson, H J
Hughes, M
Jenkins, A J
Keeling, A L
Kelion, A D
Kendall, J C C
King, S J
Kinsler, V A
Laing, A H
Lambert, B G
Lapwood, S G
Lea, J R
Lynch-Blosse, R H
McDougall, A C
McEvett, C A
McGuire, M
McMichael, C F

May, D R
Meinhard, E A
Moore, J N B
Moyses, C
Mulla, M M
Murray, J L
Norris, J G H
Ogg, C S
Otterburn, D M
Pathinayake, B D A C
Pedrazzini, S-L
Pembridge, B T
Perrins, D J D
Phillips, D J
Pinches, R S
Pope, M H M
Rendall, D C S
Reynolds, T D R
Robertson, P M
Rockett, M P
Safranek, P M
Saxby, J R B
Schofield, D J
Schulte, A C
Scott, B O
Shah, T
Sharma, A
Shepperd, R A
Smith, W R
Sperry, H J
Sperry, L M
Spriggs, A I
Stein, F C
Studholme, K M
Tan, P S T
Tate, P H L
Thorne, A
Thorne, R J T
Tilley, J A
Verjee, S A K S
Vivian, P C
Waddy, D C
Waters, B H T
Waters, C M
Westwood, L K
Whiting, F E

Aboyne

Auld, M I R
Clarke, P B
Cook, A M
Dawson, H
Dunbar, C M
Glass, J
Kynoch, R M
Lindsay, G F
McCance, K J
McGregor, A M
McGregor, M M
Robertson, J L
Starritt, D R
Taylor, J L
Taylor, M B
Taylor, R M

Accrington

Batra, G S
Bhat, G M
Brown, N
Cunningham, S L
Dixon, J H
Field, V K
Grady, A K
Grime, L P
Gupta, R C
Gupta, S K
Hewitt, K M
Hipwell, M C
Jawad, A A A-J
Joseph, P K
Kapenda, A Y
Karim, N
Karim, S I
Karim, S I-U
Kelly, A M
Krishna Murti, L
McCarthy, M J
Manjooran, F
Manjooran, T
Manuel, A
Mills, S S
Mitchell, A P
O'Brien, T E B
Ojha, R R
Quinn, P W
Seymour, L K
Smith, A C
Turner, W J
Tuxford, K

Wallworth, R A
Ward, C A
Westwood, G R
Woodcock, D R

Acharacle

Houston, R J
Masson, W D

Achnasheen

Arnold, P A
Livingston, E

Addlestone

Carter, S E
De Netto, M-A K
Denison, D M
Godrich, J E
Zurick, N J

Ailesbury

Taylor, A R

Airdrie

Ahmed, A
Al-Ghita, H
Alagar, S P
Angus, M M M
Atkinson, J
Beshr, A S M S
Bodane, A K
Butt, M A
Cargo, P E
Carlin, G F
Cassie, R
Cockburn, T A
Cook, R J
Crawford, J G
Curle, J M
Darroch, J N
Dimascio, R P R
Dobbie, C M
Douglas, W S
Dunn, B P
Duthie, J A
Dutta, K
Evans, C D
Gardiner, D S
Gibb, F D M
Gilbert, T J
Gopinathan, V
Gray, H G M
Gupta, G
Guse, J V
Halliday, J
Hamilton, A S S
Hammersley, N
Harrower, A D B
Howatson, S R
Hughes, K
Imrie, J E A
Inglis, M D
Innes, D T
Jardine, S L
Jarvie, F E
Johnston, H G
Johnston, P M
Johnston, S A
Johnstone, P A
Kennedy, N
Kluge, G H
Laird, B J A
Lees, C T W
Lough, J R M
Lwanda, J L
McAlpine, L G
McAvoy, N C
MacDonald, A
MacInnes, A N
McIntyre, J E
McIntyre, J M
Mackenzie, R E
McKerlie, L C
McKillop, H T
McLaren, I
McPhail, N J
Maculloch, S M
Mathew, G
Matthews, D M
McLaughlin, M-J
Milligan, J
Mills, E E
Monaghan, M T
Murphy, J A
Oni-Orisan, J E A
Orr, D J
Orr, P S
Osman, M K
Paterson, P
Paton, R M

Paulus, U
Pollock, E E
Pollock, J M M
Prach, A T
Reid, V T
Roberts, J E
Ross, P M D
Schultz, S S
Scullion, W
Sharma, R A
Shilliday, I R
Siddiqui, M F
Siddiqui, M F
Smith, J H L
Soutar, R L
Sugden, C J
Teo, N B
Thompson, J
Todd, W T A
Wainwright, N J
Walker, D
Walker, L
Wallers, K J
Watson, W H
Weerackody, R P
Wilson, K E
Zahangir, M
Zuk, R J

Alcester

Armitage, J P
Beasley, C L
Bulchand, R
Cavanagh, J G J
Chaffey, R F
Dencer, D
Doherty, P J
Embley, C
Haden, R M
Harman, K E
Harman, S A
Madge, A F
Nava, P L
Neville, T P
Popplewell, J A
Popplewell, M
Premchand, V B
Rennie, K M
Singh, M B
Singh, P D
Tudor, R G
Wisniowiecka, A
Zeitlin, H C

Aldeburgh

Ball, S C
Barrick, D N
Boswell, A M
Collins, M T
Coventry, K
Dalrymple, J G M
Fife, J G
Figgis, M M
Fox, D G R
Hine, J L
Jamieson, J A
Johnstone, F L
Johnstone, M D
Little, W R
Lock, S P
Lyon, J B
McGough, J G
Morgan, L C
Newill, R G D
Simmonds, S-J
Soutar, C J W
Standley, T D A
Tait, I G
Tait, J F
Turnbull, A L

Alderley Edge

Arnold, C L
Barry, E S
Chaudry, I H
Clough, P H
Davidson, J
Dutton, J E M
Edward, G W
Fallon, L M
Finch, E L
Gardiner, J S
Gibson, J M
Hall, H E
Hammonds, R M
Henderson, S
Hennessey, T D
Hirst, G C
Macdonald, D J H
Mackenzie, S P

Merchant, S D
Mohindra, S
Moore, P E
Newton, E R
O'Callaghan, P J
Pratt, B A
Renton, P H
Sambrook, P
Taylor, J A
Thompson, H E
Tobias, M
Walton, G M
Williams, J P
Williams, R J
Wray, J M C

Alderney

Fegan, W G
Hunt, P W
Mark, J F
Price, H M
Roper, M
Scott, A
Seymour, R N
Stocker, J C
Waters, S D M

Aldershot

Anderson, D R
Bartlett, S G A
Bergman, B P
Brigg, P D
Brooks, C E
Brown, W
Campbell, R M
Capanni, P D
Carpenter, M E
Cristofani, P J
Croft, A M J
Davis, L C
Deakin, D T F
Ebrahim, N
Evans, T C J
Fahmy, M
Gonçalves-Archer, H C
Gruebel Lee, D M
Head, J E
Hilditch, J
Innes, A C
Jamieson, I W
Keeling, J D
Kingston, F R A
Lansley, P H
Law, K V
Leopold, C A
Lohia, S
MacLeod, M D
Morgan-Jones, D J
Nikitik, C
Nithyanandhan, G
O'Callaghan, S E
Pallant, J M
Paterson, R A
Pearson, C A
Riggs, M
Robertson, B
Robinson, I H
Romaya, B F
Scantlebury, B
Sceats, G P
Scott, M J
Shalley, M J
Shaw, A J
Sherwood, K E
Stewart, T D S
Whatmough, P M
Wictome, J
Wynn, N N

Alexandria

Al-Khafaji, M N M
Barber, T S
Baxter, A D
Bell, M H
Cameron, A E
Campbell, L
Campbell, P M
Carmichael, H A
Clark, D P
Clarke, I S
Cowie, T N
Cox, H
Dancer, S J
Douglas, G A
Dunn, J A
Dunn, S
Easy, W R
Fabling, M
Flett, S R
Forbes, F

Alford, Aberdeenshire

Guthrie, C E
Harper, A S
Hassan, K
Haxton, M J
Herd, G W
Hunter, C A P
Johnson, G
McCruden, D C
McGlinchey, I
Mackay, N S D
McLachlan, K R
MacRae, M M
Maiden, N L
Mamdani, G H
Manning, N T
Marsh, L M
Murray, E L
Nassar, A H M
Peacock, J E M
Robertson, E W
Sajid, M
Scott, W J C
Scullion, M
Series, J J
Shand, J M
Shouler, P J
Sievert, J
Simpson, M P
Singer, D M F
Taylor, R C
Towlson, K L
Trust, P M
Tully, A M

Alford, Aberdeenshire

Payne, G S
Reid, J S H
Watt, G L

Alford, Lincolnshire

Allis, D E
Bartlett, P J
Carter, I M
Carter, S
Charlton, K
Ferguson, D W
Haslett, P J
Spenceley, K R
Woollard, A E

Alfreton

Bingham, M S
Blyth, J M
Broderick, M M
Burstow, A C
Duffield, M W
Garden, I A
Gruffydd, D R
Gundkalli, A A
Gundkalli, I
Hill, J P
Hills, E S
Holland, D D
Holtham-Taylor, D A
Kelman, M B
Lawrence, R A A R
McCane Whitney, J A
McKay, N P
MacNab, A
Meakin, A H
Noronha, M D
Parkin, T
Richmond, G A
Round, P H
Smith, P G
Sowerby, H A
Taylor, D W
Tippetts, R
Tipping, P J
Townend, R H M
Veale, M J

Alloa

Bailey-Smith, R
Bhatti, G C G
Borland, D S
Borrowman, J
Clark, J M
Collins, I P
Dullea, B C A
Green, F R
Greig, J E W
Hood, G J
Johnstone, F M
Kirk, D P
Macgregor, J
MacInnes, P
Massey, J B
Moses, R G

Musk, D C
Patrick, A G
Proctor, S J R
Rasul, S
Sime, L A
Stirling, K W
Walters, W D
Ward, A L
Webster, R W J

Almondsbury

Munro, A E B

Alness

Bain, R M
Baxter, P N
Carracher, S J
Dolan, P
Hutton, J F
Jackson, J D
Macdonald, J

Alnwick

Blaiklock, R A
Brannigan, M
Bridge, A J
Brown, C R
Brown, R C A
Campbell, F D
Clark, J G
Davison, D C
Dodd, M J
Dodd, S J
Fortune, W A
Fraser, G S
Fraser, J C
Guy, M J
Hogg, P J
Kohler, H M
Lishman, S H
Lyons, G J
McKenna, A M
McKenna, K
Mackichan, N D
Mitford, E
Peberdy, M
Renner, S L
Robertson, E
Smith, M
Stevenson, C J
Vardy, E R L C
Webster, C C

Alresford

Brill, G C
Cassidy, S J
Catto, A F
Clark, M J
Cribb, R A
Crosse, S M
Dobbie, S N
Dore, A J K
Durand, A C
Fairley, C J
Ferris, E A E
Fuller, H W C
Gosse, C N
Green, D H
Green, D J
Hall, Z M
Happel, J S
Happel, S M
Hill, D M
Holland, P
Hollyhock, V M C
Hurley, J D
Hurley, S Y
Isbister, A R
Lowman, A C
McKeogh, J
Mann, C V
Masters, A J
Moore, W P N
Odell, R M
Read, J M
Sandison, A L
Sandler, R
Sargent, J H P S
Sargent, P M
Seaburne-May, M P
Shaw, C S
Stebbing, J E
Stokes, P J
Sword, L J
Tanner, S J
Thorpe, S C
Wisdom, R J
Woods, D P
Young, A E

Alston

Dawson, M J
Robinson, T D

Alton

Amery, A H
Barry, N A
Bethell, H J N
Biss, K
Burch, P
Collins, C L
Cunliffe, P N
De Quincey, M M
Dean, S J
Evans-Prosser, C D G
Everett, C B
Fletcher, V J
Frankel, R J
Hall, M J
Hamilton, J M I
Hayward, M G
Hill, H J
Hopwood, P N
Isaac, P W
Kelly, L F
Lewis, J E
Louden, S F
Macnamara, M
Mannings, R A D
Martin, A M
Myers, S F
Over, J M
Rickard, A J
Robson, D C
Shortt, E P H
Stubbington, H L
Sword, A J
Terry, K J
Thomas, C P
Wassef, M A-E
Watters, S R
White, N J
Willis, J A R
Wozniak, T

Altrincham

Adams, M E
Adams, P H
Al-Khaffaf, H S
Al-Safar, J A
Aldean, I M A
Allred, J P
Alvi, A R
Anderson, P C B
Anderton, J M
Awan, S K
Aziz, K
Bailey, P J
Bainbridge, D
Banks, I C
Beardsmore, J D
Bee, P
Belloso Uceda, A
Bernstein, J M
Bhatt, A M
Bhatt, M K
Biswas, S
Botterill, I D
Boughdady, I S I
Bowman, R A
Bromley, E J T
Brooke, W E
Brown, I C
Brown, J D K
Brown, J J
Buck, P
Burns, J
Butler, J D
Cairns, T S
Cameron, P M
Caplan, B
Carroll, K B
Cave, S B
Chan, K T
Cheah, T-S
Cheyne, E H L
Cheyne, L R P L
Chung, A S
Claxton, A R
Coates, L E
Cohen, C B
Conboy, A O
Condliffe, H A
Connell, R
Connolly, K M
Conroy, P T
Corlett, A J
Craske, J
Cutts, M W J

Da Cunha, F A L
Dark, J F
Davies, C J
Davitt, M C
Davy, R A
Dawson, S F
De Lacy, S E
Denton, R
Derlien, J A L
Desai, M S
Desai, S C
Dover, B
Drabble, J E
Drabu, G J
Duthie, V J
Edmonds, O P
Edmonds, P P F
Edwards, P D
El-Kafrawy, U
Ellington, C A
Elliott, C E
Ellul, J
Estcourt, T
Evans, A E J
Evans, A K
Evanson, E F
Falconer, J M
Falconer, P J
Falconer, W J
Fitzgerald, C H
Fitzgerald, J J
Foster, B
Frank, T L
Franklin, C B
Franklin, D
French, R A
Furrows, D C
Furrows, S J
Ghaneh, P
Gilbert, B
Gillett, R
Gilman, M M
Ginever, D M
Gosling, R H
Grady, K M
Gratwick, L C
Greene, M J
Greenwood, B K
Gregory, M W
Griffin, Y
Hallack, I M
Hallas, S F
Halpern, I B
Hanley, R C M
Haslett, R S
Haslett, R C
Herrington, L M
Heywood, M W
Hilton, R M
Holmes, P
Hoosen, Y
Huddlestone, L
Hyde, E A M
Iglesias Alvarez, M
Ingram, J C
Jackson, A
Jacovelli, J B
Jellinek, D C
Jenkins, S
Jessup, G
Johnson, C M
Johnson, T W
Johnston, J S
Jolley, S P
Jones, M T
Jones, P E
Jones, R A C
Kelly, J
Kelman, C G
Kiel, A W
Kiel, J E
King, A T
King, S L
Klass, H J
Klein, L E
Krysiak, P
Ladha, S S
Laha, S
Laha, S K
Laitt, R D
Landes, C J
Lee, B V
Lee, K G
Leech, G
Leggate, J R S
Lennie, M E
Lieberman, I
Lloyd-Jones, E M
Lloyd, M J

Lord, N P
Lukeman, P J
Ma-Fat, R
McCorkindale, J W
Macdonald, B N
McIntyre, D
MacIver, J E
McKenna, M J
McKinnon, K A
Mackrodt, K M
McNab Jones, S E
Mahmood, N
Manns, J J
Marsden, A R
Marshall, B E
Martin, C P
Menon, S
Morgan, J R
Morgenstern, G R
Morrod, D A
Moss, P
Moyo, C
Mrozinski, R A
Naik, C S
Naik, S M
Newson, L R
Nicholson, D A
Norman, S A
Norris, K J
O'Connor, J P B
O'Driscoll, D P
Oleesky, S
Ormerod, J E H
Owen, G E
Parbrook, M J
Parkinson, D W
Parks, R J
Pasterski, J K
Patel, M
Paterson, S L S
Paterson, W
Pathak, P N
Pearson, D J
Pearson, D
Pengelly, C D R
Phillips, G
Phillips, J
Portnoy, B
Pumphrey, J H
Rahmanou, P
Rampling, C M
Remington, S A M
Reynolds, S M
Rich, J
Richardson, M J
Rickman, A J
Robinson, M C
Robinson, S P
Roland, J
Rothera, M P
Rowland, G F
Rowley, D E M
Russell, E M
Russell, J G B
Saleh, R
Salmons, P H
Santaniello-Newton, A
Scarsbrook, A F
Shamas-Ud-Din, S
Shaw, J
Shekelton, F A
Sheridan, A J
Shipston, A M
Shipston, J E
Sieff, I
Sin, J P Y
Singh, I P
Smith, B G
Smith, J H J
Smith, S
Southworth, S A
Sperry, D A
Spurrell, M T
Stewart, H S
Sutherland, H C
Swerdlow, M
SymcOx, H A
Taylor, A E
Taylor, E P M
Temple, R H
Thompson, A M S
Thompson, E E M
Thompson, G S
Thomson, S P S
Tighe, N J
Tolhurst-Cleaver, C L
Toon, C G E
Trask, M D
Trehan, A

Turnbull, J C
Tytler, J A
Varley, E M
Vasa, S A
Vincent, J A
Waddell, J
Weighill, P A
Wells, S L A
West, S L
Westwood, C
Whale, K
Wheatley, A H
Whorwell, P J
Wilkins, G S
Will, A M
Will, S C C
Williams, B L
Williamson, J C
Wong-You-Cheong, J J
Woodhead, R J
Woodhead, Z M
Wooldridge, W J
Wooster, S L
Wykes, P R
Wynn, J S
Yule, R

Alva

Abel, G A
Byrne, A J
Collier, F
Crocket, A
Hay, G I
Hurry, R A
Illingworth, M J
Johnston, F I

Ambleside

Acheson, E J
Acheson, H W K
Andrew, R A
Bailey, I S
Birket, I J
Bishop, E S
Bowen, G W
Colville, B
Colville, E A
Crossley, D R
Dalton, M B
Davies, P J
Davis, L R
Earnshaw, D H
Eldridge, J R
Forrester, M B T
Forrester, R M
Harris, M T M
Hazelden, A
Hill, A S
Jackson, A H
Kehoe, C P
Kirkwood, J M
Lawrence, V J
Mathieson, A E T
O'Connell, G
Robson, M
Shaw, W M H
Smith, R I
Stanley, J R
Warburton, R A

Amersham

Barnes, K L
Barnes, R J
Batten, C
Bennett, N J
Blenkinsopp, W K
Brooks, J M H
Brown, A J
Buchanan, G E
Burgess, J M
Burne, B H
Capper, J W R
Carter, P A
Carter, V L
Champ, C J
Chesworth, A J
Chesworth, C J
Coady, A T
Coates, P J B
Couch, A L
Curling, O M
Davies, C J W
Davies, D L
Davison, P S
Dellow, A C
Enright, S M
Ferguson, D M
Ferraro, A J
Fieldsend, R C
Foote, A A

Ashbourne

Forti, A D
Fraser, I M
George, S A
Gibbs, A E R
Gough, D
Gray, J
Hall, M L
Haydon, D A
Helps, E P W
Higgs, B
Hynes, K A
Jenkins, J C
Jenner, P N
Kanga, S B
Kilgour, J L
Kingsbury, Q D
Kingsbury, S L
Lambert, H E
Lamont, R F
Laube, S
Lilley, C S
McMullan, J J
Mangat, H K
Marren, P A
Morris, E H
Nash, C J
Neal, B L
Orton, D I
Pienaar, G F
Poullis, A P
Sapsford, R A
Scorey, J
Skinner, D V
Slater, A J
Stackwood, D A
Stevens, R J
Summers, L A
Tarin, P J
Thompson, S G
Thorne, S J
Vassallo, C M
Vesely, M J J
Wall, R A
Ward, E
Wayte, J A
Weaver, A E
Webber, M G
Whittaker, C A
Wilkinson, J D
Wiseman, A
Wong Sung Lung, A
Wood, A

Amlwch

Austin, B N
Griffith, B A
Jones, S T
King, A H
Owen, J P
Snead, A R
Thomas, A

Ammanford

Bizby, L J
Capper, W M
Coombe, A D
Davies, A J
Edwards, A L
Evans, D A
Griffiths, J S
Griffiths, M J
Jenkins, R W
Jones, G J
Jones, S
Lewis, B R
Mason, B W
Morgan, T K
Morris, H D
Morris, P
Murfin, D E
Parry, J D
Powell, F I
Rahman, K M
Rees, J C
Richards-Jones, M C
Rowlands, H W D
Salisbury, R D
Sheehan, G P
Smith, D E
Thomas, G
Watkin, A R
Williams, D M
Yeates, C E

Andover

Allan, M J
Armstrong, A J M
Arthur, J P B
Batham, D R
Blyth, A G
Bond, S
Bruford, M K
Bryan, T A
Carr, S A
Clarke, S H C
Cleland, W P
Collins, P A
Cook, A E
Daley, S E
Davies, G C
Davies, L A L
Davies, T M
Deacon, R C
Evans, R R
Ford, H R C
Gailey, D A H
Gaitonde, M D
Gardiner, J C
Govier, C B E
Greig, A D
Griffiths, R J
Hall, R W
Hamilton, A J
Harries-Brown, R A
Hay, E D A
Hickey, S
Hobhouse, S L
Hoole, P M
Howe, I
Humphreys, M F
Irwin, W J
Islam, A M
Jackman, J S G
James, T R
Johnston, D
Lambert, R
Lockwood, M J
Loudon, G M
Mann, J N
Marriott, J
Marval, M J
Matheson, R M
Merrington, J C
Mitchell, J E
Mitchell, P M
Needham, V H
O'Halloran, P D
Pack, G J
Pawley, A F
Perry, I C
Porter, G D
Potter, A R
Rossiter, M A
Ryle, F R
Shields, R S D
Stone, M
Venables, P
Verity, J C T
Waddell, T R
Walker, A M
Wallis, C J
Wells, R D W
Wessely, T L
Wheywell, R
Wilkins, C J
Willson, H J

Anglesey

Roberts, E L
Thomson, H R

Annan

Abd Karim, Z
Baillie, N A
Byers, D L
Elder, J W H
Fisher, D J R
Henderson, J D
Kelly, N G
Kerr, J S
Kieran, W J G
Lapka, B A
McCallum, E M
MacKay, R H
Maggiori, T K
Millar, S
O'Reilly, F W
Paul, D H
Paul, H E
Ross, S D
Taylor, M C

Anstruther

Angus, A R
Brunton, C
Bumbra, J S
Clark, I W
Clark, M L
Dorrance, H R
Douglas, J M

Francis, C P
Hodge, I L D
Hughes, J I
Hunt, A C
Kennedy, A S L
Kyle, A W
Livingstone, J
McGonigal, J A
Marston, D J W
Mitchell, A V
Nisbet, N H
Ross, A
Ross, P W
Scott, D B
Tarvet, F
Weir, J

Antrim

Addis, W D
Alderdice, J M
Ashe, R G
Bigley, G J
Bittar, W
Black, I H C
Brown, J H
Browne, R J
Brownlees, W
Carson, J G
Clyde, H C
Critchlow, S G
Crossan, I
Currie, R E S
Cusick, P B
Daly, J G
Delap, T G
Dickson, M C
Dripps, K
Duff, Y R
Elliott, T P
Fawcett, R L
Ferguson, J A J
Ford, B N
Freeman, T
Furlong, M B
Gaffney, M J P
Galway, J P
Gamble, W
Garstin, W I H
Greeves, C M
Gregg, W V H
Henry, G
Hill, D H
Hogg, W
Howard, P B
Hughes, G
Humphreys, W G
Hunter, P
Hutchinson, W D
Jenkins, J G
Kapur, D K
Kearney, M P
Kelly, C B
Kennedy, A
Kenny, B D
Kernohan, R M
Leyden, P E F
Lim Hoe Kee, J
McAloon, J
McBrien, M E
McCabe, R E
McCartney, K N
McCaughey, M
McClelland, C J
McClelland, H R
McCloskey, M
McGimpsey, S J
McGinnity, M G A
McIlroy, G H C
McKeown, P P J
McLarnon, J F
McLeod, H N
McMillen, R M
MacPherson, J E
Mannion, M F
Marriott, C M
Moss, J E
Nelson, H F J
Nelson, W M
Nicholson, J
O'Gorman, C J
O'Loan, M D
Osman, M F A
Potter, P E
Rainey, D S
Robb, J J
Stewart, J H H
Stinson, R
Toner, G G
Trouton, T G

Turk, G N
Turner, M D
Watson, M R
Weir, D A
Whiteside, M C R
Wilson, C

Appin

McNicol, D
McNicol, I D
Mathieson, D A M

Appleby-in-Westmorland

Box, B
Delap, P
Leitch, J B
Sharpe, G F
Sharpe, K T

Arbroath

Anderson, C J B
Bird, S P G
Boyd, E J S
Carney, C J
Cherry, J S
Clark, H
De Voil, C W B
Duncan, A A
Duncan, W
Forbes, L J W
Gray, M W
Hornsby, A H
Inglis, J D A
Keddie, K M G
Langlands, J M
Ledson, M A
McKay, C M
Manson, G I
Moffat, G L
Muir, G L
Ogilvie, J R
Reid, P J
Smith, W R
Speirs, R B
Stuart, I
Sutherland, G M
Taylor, H M
Walker, R J
Ward, A E
Weir, I G C

Archeracle

Buchanan, M E

Ardgay

Crabb, G R
Hamblet, K M
Lumsden, W
Macdonald, K J
Macdonald, P M
Mair, C J
Mair, J M

Ardrossan

Clark, P
Craig, R
Haggerty, G
Johnstone, C P
Kerr, K
McGuire, A Y
McGuire, M
Mackay, F W
Merry, A J
Raghavendra, K
Russell, D K R
Russell, J S
Weetman, M G
Weir, G
Whyte, M D R
Wight, A M

Arisaig

Cramp, G J
Tiarks, J C
Young, S A

Arlesey

Lonergan, F J

Armagh

Allen, J M
Anderson, R
Beckett, E P
Beggs, J I
Bergin, S P
Bloomer, S E
Canning, U B
Carlile, R M
Cartmill, J L
Cassidy, C E
Cole, E P

Colvin, P W B
Conway, G L
Corrigan, D B
Dorman, D E
Dorman, E S
Dorman, L A
Dorman, R H
Douglas, K M J
Eames, M H A
Edwards, D J
Fearon, E D
Fee, P M
Fitzsimons, O
Foster, G D
Gaffney, S S M
Garvin, C C
Gillespie, B A
Gillespie, J F
Gray, P L
Heatley, W A G
Jones, M N R
Kellett, P S
Knipe, C W D
Leetch, R J
Lowry, J
McAlinden, E S
McAlinden, P M
McAllister, C
McBride, S J
McCahon, R A
McCall, J M S
McClung, J P
McCollum, W R K
McConnell, V P M
McConnell, W B
McConville, J P
McConville, J M
McCormack, M C
McElnay, R E
McEvoy, M P C
McGuinness, J F
McMullan, J E
McNally, M S
Magee, T F
Maguire, J
Marshall, K M
Marshall, N C
Mayne, D G
Millar, K J
Mitchell, M A
Morrow, D
Morrow, J
Nicholson, G M
O'Hagan, A H
O'Hagan, F T
O'Neill, J J
O'Reilly, G V
O'Reilly, R
Paisley, J C
Plunkett, G B
Plunkett, N P
Reaney, E A
Reilly, R P
Robinson, F L
Sam, G J
Scott, K W
Shirley, D S L
Smyth, A E
Spence, T A
Steed, A J
Telford, A M
Thompson, J B
Tohani, V K
Turtle, A M
Walsh, J B
Watters, F M
Whelan, L M
Woods, J O
Woods, S K M
Wright, T P

Arrochar

Fettes, P H
Troup, D F

Arthog

Francis, H
Ramsden, G D

Arundel

Chapple, K S
Coles, M K
Eve, R H
Farquhar-Thomson, D R
Foulkes, A
Gibbs, R G J
Humphry, T M
Jenkins, M E C
Larsen, T A

Levantine, A V
Lichtensteiger, L
Michell, A W
Michell, D R
Mott, A N
O'Hanlon, N M P
Palmer, R M
Peters, D J
Priestman, G M
Stenson, K
Thompson, K C
Turnbull, T A
Waite, C G
Wilson, P J E M

Ascot

Afzal, N
Al-Chalabi, T
Armstrong, P M C
Bevan, C A
Burgess, N D S
Collins, H A
Coode, P E
Cook, G W
Craze, A L
Davies, R J
Deane, G
Dempsey, B M
Denny, S
Drake, N B
Dunne, P J
Elliott, B A
Fanning, A P
Ferrero, T M
Furness, R H S
Gall, R G
Galton-Fenzi, F C E
Gatha, D N
Gillespie, A V
Grace, K L R
Gracey, L R H
Green, B J
Griffiths, B J
Gunther, H N C
Gunther, M H D
Harding, J W
Hoad, C F
Hussain, M A
Jones, G D
Khaksar, S J
Khudados, E S S
Kingsmill Moore, J M
Lansley, M J
Lask, J P
Leighton, E J
Lloyd, N C J
Luck, C A
McDonald, D G
McMath, W K T
Natorff, B L
Norminton, D R H
Rasheed, A
Rawlinson, J R
Reid, G D
Selvey, D M
Sexton, S A
Sheikh, N
Sherley-Dale, A C
Smith, M J
Sodhi, R K
Spring, J E
Stephens, R E
Tasker, G D
Tomlinson, A M
Walker, D M
Warren, J B
Whitfield, P N
Whittington, A M
Wilson, G K
Woodward, C E L
Wraight, W J
Yousif, A R S

Ashbourne

Ashworth, J R
Baines, D A
Bates, B J
Billington, S A M
Bridge, M-L T
Constable, G N
Dance, B M
Dent, K S
Dixon, H M
Erskine, R J
Fenwick, H C
Gage, P R
Geary, R J
Ghadiali, H H
Ghadiali, H N

Ashby-de-la-Zouch

Hanson, R J
Harvey, J A
Henshall, T D
Joel, C E
Kirtley, P R
Macleod, I S C S
MacLeod, S M
Martin, S J
Nel, T P
Ogley, R
Parker, D A
Richardson, C M
Shepherd, S J
Starey, N H L
Tattersall, E P
Thomas, D R
Thomas, K E
Tomlinson, R C
Tothill, C L
Ward, D R
Wedgwood, J P

Ashby-de-la-Zouch

Addison, J
Clifton, C J
Davies, R A
Happel, S
Harrison, P L
Jordan, T E
Matthews, A R
Minhas, R S
Patel, S P
Randev, P
Randev, P K
Short, M P
Singh, M P
Smith, C E
Sood, M
Speegler, W J
Stedman, W J
Tailor, H
Woo, D G
Woolgrove, C G

Ashford, Kent

Abdurahman, M F S
Abson, E P
Addison, R L
Al-Maarof, M S M
Al-Shaikh, B 2 T
Allenby, K
Bafadhel, Z A
Banks, J C
Bates, T
Bernhardt, J R C
Blacklay, J B
Bradley, G W
Brook, M G
Buckenham, M G
Bull, P W
Bushnell, T G
Busk, C M A
Butler-Gallie, S P
Chance, P S G
Chianakwalam, C I
Chissell, S A
Chrispin, K H
Church, W E
Clark, J E
Cocker, M
Colledge, I D
Colledge, R E J
Cooney, J A
Corfield, N S
Coulson, E A M
Cowley, C
Davies, C C A
Davies, J O
Davies, W J
Dia, R S
Divekar, A B
Dove, S J
Dundas, C W
Dunnet, W J S
Dutton, J G
Eggleden, J C
Evans, C H
Fairley, J W
Farrell-Roberts, M G J
Flack, G S
Fox, A R
Freeston, U H
Frohn, M J N
Frohnsdorff, K G E
Gardner, M C
Ghulam, S J
Greaves, B P
Green, C P
Hamer, M S F

Hardwick, R O F
Harper, K J
Harris, J L
Hensman, E R
Hetigin, A J
Horn, N J
Horn, S H
Husain, S M S
Insall, R L
Irvine, C
Jones, L E L
Kamalvand, K
Kazmi, S M A
Klim, E A
Koria, R
Kosowski, K
Lai, A K T
Lake, J
Lawson, C W
Learmont, J G
Levi, S R
Li, K C
Linkin, A C
Lister, T P
Littledale, R M
Lloyd-Smith, W
Lock, M
Long, C M M
Lunn, M P T
Macdonald, A M
Mackey, C J
Malladi, K S
Mann, C J V D
Menon, R
Michaels, T M
Michie, I F
Miles, J P
Miller - Jones, C M H
Miller, J D C
Mirza, G H
Moffat, W J
Morey, R G
Morris, A J R
Morris, J E
Muir, C U
Muir, F H
Munro, N A R
Newton, T
Nuttall, J S
O'Neill, C
Paciorek, P M
Parker, S L
Pearce, M S
Percival, R H
Phipps, M E
Pinnock, R G
Poplett, N D
Porter, C A
Powell, C D
Pragnell, A A
Price, C A
Ralfs, I G
Rampton, A J
Reddy, C R
Roud, P L
Rowan, R A
Rowden, K W
Ruaux, C D
Ryley, J P
Sands, M J
Sapsford, D
Scaysbrook, P R
Seaton, J E V
Setty, M V S
Sewell, J R
Shah, V N
Shakir, S A W
Shanvill, D E
Sherry, C C
Shrivastava, R K
Singh, A K
Smith, R A
Smithard, D G
Standley, H S
Stanley, T M
Stewart, C M
Stossel, C A
Taylor, A H
Tidnam, P F
Tolba, M A-A
Traill, C G
Turner, C M
Ursell, W
Vella, M A
Vogel, M L
Waitt, R H F
Waller, R
Waluube, D D F
Webb, W M

Webster, D J
Webster, F B
Weeks, M A
Wheeler, P C G
Whitby, W S
White, C A
White, C P
Williams, C D
Williams, R E T
Williamson, S
Yaakub, R
Yanni, O N
Yardy, N D

Ashford, Middlesex

Adams, A J
Aldous, J C
Aweid, A M S
Bailey, B M W
Bellamy, E A
Belstead, J S
Belstead, S M
Bond, H R
Bramble, B
Butt, S
Carter, M C N
Couch, J R
Das, A
Dawson, J C
El Ashouri, A R
Ellis, B W
Farmer, I S
Furniss, M J P
Garner, A
Grosssmith, C M
Hamdan, N M A
Horner, J
Irani, M S
Joseph, J
Kandela, P
Keenan, C E S
Khan, S
Kirk, N R
Kisembo-Lule, E
Kulkarni, R P
Matthew, J
Meekings, E L
Moore, R G W
Newberry, D J
Ofori-Atta, P
Paul, L
Rees, J E
Reiff, D B
Roushdi, H R I M
Sandrasagra, A J R
Sidhu, D S
Sinnerton, R J
Skeldon, I
Stewart, G M
Surtees, H F A
Thornton, J R
Turner, P J
Waite, K E
Whitaker, G B
Wilkinson, P R
Zammit, V

Ashington

Amin, S M
Bagott, M J
Beattie, W H
Bell, A D
Bradburn, D M
Caisley, P J
Carr, M
Cleverley, S J
Conn, A G
Cox, J G C
Crook, P R
D'Souza, R C M
Daly, M E
Daniel, C
Derrick, S-A
Dewar, M S
Drummond, P M
Fraser, G B
Gedney, I
Gilfillan, L J
Gillespie, J
Gregory, W L
Hatch, T
Henry, J A
Higham, P D
Hobbs, J J
Hodgson, J
Innes, A R
Jones, S M G
Lambourn, R J
Lauckner, D I

Laurenson, J A
Lavin, T A
Leitch, J M
McCubbin, A T G
Neilly, I J
Osunkoya, A O
Oxby, A D
Parkins, D R J
Partington, P F
Rasoul, M S
Rennison, C M
Roberts, A E
Saba, T S Z
Sellers, J
Senarath Yapa, R S
Sill, P R
Smith, D A
Williams, V S
Wotherspoon, W C

Ashtead

Anderson, A M
Anderson, W J
Bailey, M J
Barr, E L
Boardley, A C
Chilton, M H
Claridge, G B
Cobb, A G
Denman, P
Eldridge, S B J
Evans, G M
Gillespie, I H
Hallifax, E S
Hartnoll, G
Hurley, P R
Inglis, M S
Jones, H W
Lee, M D
Leslie, M
Lewis, C K
Lidgey, D A R
Litman, C L
Lowes, J J
McArdle, B
Maclean, R
McNamara, L
MacTavish, S D
Mavrikios, A
Miller, S E P
Mitchell-Heggs, P F
Moore, J A
Papadopoulos, A J
Phillips, A M
Poundall, C E
Robb, G H
Soden, K A
Southam, J A
Stephenson, C A
Stephenson, J R
Taylor, E J S
Taylor, F G M
Taylor, R S
Williams, M K
Williams, S D
Wilson, G R
Wood, J M D
Zeilmaker, C

Ashton-under-Lyne

Allan, G
Arya, R
Basnayake, P
Bayman, D C
Bhachu, H S
Biswas, B
Biswas, C
Boyes, B E
Brammah, T B
Brandts, H H
Burke, D K
Campbell, C H
Chand, K
Chopra, M P
Choraria, B R
Chudgar, N O
Clark, S J
Clothier, P R
Coates, M
Coote, J H
Creedon, R J
Creighton, F J
Dalal, N
Dalal, R B
Davies, B C
Davis, B L
Dixon, G R
Edge, A N
El Safadi, N

Ellenbogen, S
Freeman, J S
Fynn, S P
Garcia-Ormaetxea, M
Goldthorp, W O
Greenhough, C M
Haque, M E N
Hesten, F J
Husaini, M H
Hutton, A J
Idrees, F
Ilyas, M
Iserloh, H J
Jackson, W J
Jenkins, L K
Jolobe, O M P
Kenyon, W I
Kerr, I F W
Kokiet, S J
Kollimada, A R
Kushlick, A
Laird, G S
Lopetegui Mendizabal, M A
MacCowan, J S R
McDade, G
Massarano, A A
Mistry, K
Morrell, M T
Munro, D I
Needham, E
Nelson, S A
Nunns, D
O'Mullane, N M
Oliver, F
Parham, A L
Patel, G R
Pena, M A
Pyburn, R E
Rajendram, S
Rakicka, H
Reynolds, P A M
Rhodes, R J
Roberts, J K
Rubner, J V
Rushton, S J
Sadik, S M
Sara Rivero, J
Shaw, C M
Shoo, E E
Simpson, J
Smith, P A
Spanos, V
Sridhar, J
Stagg, M J
Telfer, I
Tewari, S K
Tiwari, K
Unsworth, P F
Wan Ho Hee, H
Watson, A J S
Wells, P A
Williamson, A H M

Askam-in-Furness

Barker, J M
Jain, P R
Lewis, M

Atherstone

Alam, S Z
Beavon, P
Bone, A M
Boulstridge, L J
Chant, B W
Chapman, K M
Cheetham, A M
Clemons, M J
Farn, K T
Gooding, T N
Hull, J M
Roberts, A W
Thomson, A S
Weston, D A
Winward, J M

Attleborough

Craig, J P
Croot, G M
Howard-Alpe, G M
Knowles, J O
Leach, B M
Lindner, R H
Main, T J
Martin, A A
Martin, H M
Oxley, C F S
Scase, A E
Thornton, R J

Auchterarder

Brown, F O
Burnett, J P
Cameron, E W
Carswell, M A W
Carter, S J
Crease, G A G
Day, J R S
Dick, R
Dickson, J D
Donaldson, D E
Dow, G R
Flanagan, W L
Grant, J A
Kelly, D R
Laird, J C
Lind, M I
Lowry, T G
MacDonald, C W
Macdonald, J S
McKelvie, G B
MacLarty, H J
McLeay, G F
Martin, C W
Matthews, A E
McGregor-Robertson, G S
Mechie, S M
Morton, C A
Paterson, R W
Richardson, I M
Robertson, A J
Stevenson, P
Watkins, S M K
Watson, A S
Wilson, J W
Wylie, S

Augher

Bingham, M T
Clarke, R C N

Aughnacloy

McCord, W C
McCord, W D G

Aviemore

Berkeley, J S
Berkeley, M I K
Checkley, B H B
Drinkwater, J B
Garraway, W M
Irvine, G E
Jachacy, G B
Langmuir, M M
Langran, M
MacDonald, N J
MacNeill, A
Patterson, A C
Stewart, A C
Stewart, K M
Tonkin, R W

Avoch

Anderson, E M
Todd, A W

Axbridge

Fernandez, R H P
Flew, T J
Friend, J P D
Frost, S M
King, R
Lewis, M S
Montefiore, D G
Nicholl, S
Partridge, C

Axminster

Brown, H C
Bugler, R A
Cobley, T D D
Cotton, J M
Evans, D N
Henley, G D
Hillyard, E H
Hodges, S R
Hodges, Y M B
Malcolm, R B
Meijer, E C M
Parkinson, G H
Soothill, J F
Taylor, P A
Taylor, P J R
Vann, J A
Woods, J J

Aylesbury

Abou Rayya, A R M
Adams, J N
Adlard, P

Ballasalla

Ahmed, N
Ammar, M A W
Andrew, B
Ashworth, M F
Attwood, A I
Baez Gandia, J A
Bailey, B N
Bakhshi, K N
Balfour, A J C
Balfour, P J T
Ballantyne, P T
Banerjee, R
Banwell, P E
Baruch, J D R
Beck, G S
Beesley, H S
Benjamin, L
Betmouni, M K
Bhowmick, B
Birchenough, S J
Black, H J
Blackwell, J N
Boakes, A J
Bodley, R N
Booth, A
Bowen, B M
Bransbury, A J
Brown, R S
Burwood, D F S
Butland, H J
Cahill, J F B
Cairns, R J
Cameron, D F
Campbell, C D
Carpenter, J L
Champ, R C
Chappel, J A
Chaubal, N D
Cheung, D S-H
Chung, T W H
Clare, T D
Clarke, J
Clements, J M
Cloherty, J K
Cloke, A
Collins, P
Coombes, S J
Corcoran, H M
Coull, A J
Cox, G J
Cox, H J E
Cox, S N
Crabtree, J M
Currie, I
Curtis, M O
Danton, S J
Davies, L C
Davies, M M
Davis, R D
Derry, F
Desai, S N
Dhannaraj, S
Donnelly, J M
Dooley, B G
Dooley, S
Downey, W R H
Downs, R E
Drury, D A N
Duckworth, M T
Durkin, C J
Edge, W G
Edmonds, S E
Edwards, P J
Edwards, R S
Ejikeme, I F
Enright, E R
Ernst, E M C
Evans, A B
Evans, B-J
Ewan, G D S
Forman, C H
Frankel, H L
Gammon, A P J
Gardner, B P
Garrod, J A
Gillett, A P
Gordon, J F
Goy, J A
Graham, A
Graham, C T
Griffiths, P A
Guest, L S
Hammond, K C
Handley, C
Harding, P J
Haroon, M
Harries, W J L
Harris, N M
Hawken, W J

Henderson, E A
Henderson, N J
Hens, M
Heywood, A J
Hill, A M
Hoffmann, K A
Holdich, S Y
Hollis, L J
Holmes-Smith, L I
Isaac, J S
Jackson, G J
James, C B
Jamous, M A
Jennings, D A
Johnson, K L
Jonas, E G G
Jones, T L
Kalia, R
Karmali, J
Kennedy, D M
Kennedy, N D
Kiff, P S
Kindell, C
King, B R H
King, R C
Knight, A H
Lamb, C T
Lambros, T A
Law, S A T
Lea-Wilson, G M
Leeper, R Q
Leyland, M D
Lindsay, M K M
Linley-Adams, S L
Lloyd, C T
Loosemore, M P
Mackenzie, G F
Mackenzie, J F
Mackenzie, J M
Maclachlan, A C
McLaskey, S
MacLeod, E L
Marr, J
Marsh, A J N
Marshall, J P
Mayon-White, V A
Melvin, C A
Middleton, G G A
Millo, J L B
Mitchell, K J
Mlynek, C R
Moorman, C M
Moreton, P W
Muldoon, C G
Mulholland, M N C
Newton, E K
Noone, C
Norton, R C
Nuseibeh, I M
O'Connor, I M T J
O'Driscoll, J C
O'Hea, A M
Ochoa Grande, J
Packham, J C
Padel, A F
Painter, S C
Pannikar, K K
Parge, F M E
Parsons, T D
Patterson, J A
Paul, M
Peacock, T G
Peberdy, R J
Peile, E B
Phillips, R C
Phillipson, H O
Plummer, R B
Powell, J A
Pryse, J G
Pryse, R D
Puszet, J
Rainford, D J
RamcHandani, P G
Ratnavel, R C
Record, C
Reed, R A
Reid, B A
Reid, M B
Renfrew, A C
Ribes Pastor, P
Riley, C C
Riley, D M
Rizzo-Naudi, J L
Roberts, A H N
Roberts, F E V
Robertson, L J
Robinson, J G
Roden, T G V
Sadler, J C

Sale, J P
Savage, P E
Schuman, A N
Scott, G A
Scott, K L
Scott, M J L
Segui Real, B
Shaikh, G F
Shanmuganathan, K
Shanmuganathan, M
Sharif, R A M
Shepard, C L
Shield, M J
Shine, B S F
Sikdar, T
Slocombe, G
Smith, C M
Smith, C M
Smith, K L
Smith, R G
Smith, R S
Smith, V M
Spence, J M
Stott, D G
Stradling, H A
Stradling, P A
Subramaniam, K P
Sullivan, M E
Sutton, J C
Talbot-Smith, A J
Taylor, A E
Tewson, E T C
Tewson, J
Theobald, A J
Thirlwall, M
Thiyagarajan, C A
Thomas, S M
Tinnion, S A
Trower, C S G
Tudway, A J C
Turner, A R
Turner, M
Tweedie, J H
Usherwood, M M
Vasi, V
Vogelzang, S A
Wakefield, M A
Walker, S R
Walters, A M
Ward, S J
Warwick, R J
Watson, A
Watt, A D
Watt, D C
Webley, M
Weldon, M J
White, C S
Whittington, J M
Williams, G M
Williams, S J
Wilson, R B
Wood, P F
Wool, R J
Wynroe, R F
Ziprin, A E

Aylesford

Ayers, D E
Bergmann, M
Bowen, R L
Brown, J S
Cantor, T J
Charlesworth, W G
Chesover, D F
Cochrane-Dyet, C E
Forsythe, D T
Gray, R N M
Humphreys, S
Mackie, A
Palmer, A P
Parkes, C A
Rana, B S
Ridsdill Smith, R M
Shakespeare, K M
Swann, R I A
Yearsley, R H

Ayr

Adamson, M W
Afzal, M
Afzal, T
Ahmad, K
Al-Aummran, M E
Alcorn, N J
Alexander, R G
Armitage, E
Ashcroft, J L
Auld, W H R
Bain, R

Balachandran, C
Bass, J C
Beattie, A B
Beattie, N G M
Begg, J A
Berry, I E
Blair, M
Bowbeer, J
Brown, C J
Brown, H C
Browne, K W
Bunting, R W
Campbell, M S
Candlish, W
Carswell, T M
Clark, N M
Collier, D A W
Craig, A D
Craig, J A
Creaney, K L
Creaney, W J
Culver, J M
De Mey, R D
Dixon, E M
Doherty, J
Douglas, R J
Dowell, R C
Downie, T J
Ducat, W
Duerden, J W N
Duncan, G
Dunne, B J
El Morsy,
H A E-H A E-H
Emery, E J
Evans, M R
Ferguson, A E
Ferguson, J T
Fernando, L
Flowerdew, J A
Forsyth, M T
Fraser, M H
Fraser, S
Gaikwad, G A
Galloway, J B W
Gaskell, A
Gemmill, J D
Gibson, D H
Gibson, F M
Gilliland, S J
Glencross, J F
Gow, A C
Grant, E D M J
Grant, P K
Hannah, A C
Hardie, R A
Hendry, S W
Hollins, G W
Holms, J S M
Huda, A S
Huda, Q
Huda, S S
Hughes, H E
Hunter, J S
Hunter, T W
Inglis, M R
Jackson, R E
Jamdar, S
Jeffries, C A
Johnston, E J
Johnston, S E
Jousset, M N A M-
Kemp, E G
Kennedy, A J C
Kennedy, G E
Kerr, K I
Kerr, S P J
Kettlewell, J
Kothari, S H
Kyaw Khin Saw, Dr
Large, D F
Lawrie, I G
Lennox, B
Linden, D
Linton, C M
Logan, M C
Lumsden, A S
Lusman, D
McCabe, C G
McCamily, J
McClelland, A
McClure, J A
McClure, J P
McGee, T C
McGinty, A D
McHardy, J
Mackie, N F T
MacLeod, A G
McMahon, R

McNally, P
McNally, S J
McNicol, I F
McTaggart, W A
McVeigh, G
Madden, A M
Maher, M M C V
Mann, E A
Martin, S W
Meddings, R N
Meiklejohn, B H
Miller, H J B
Miller, J B
Moore, J M
Morison, N
Morrall, J T F
Morrison, D M
Morrow, J J
Muir, R F
Muirhead, A M
Muirhead, C S M
Murdoch, J M
Murray, E L A
Murray, J G S
Murray, J L
Murray, K N
Nelson, J
Niblock, J L
Nicol, W A
Nicoll, W D
O'Sullivan, B C
Osborne, K N A
Park, K A
Paterson, A W
Paterson, F C
Paterson, G W H
Paterson, J C
Paterson, R C
Paterson, R W W
Paul, J
Pieper, H
Potter, R S
Rae, P S
Rennick, C B
Rennie, A R
Reynolds, P M G
Robertson, G J
Rose, J D R
Russell, J D
Russell, T V N
Ryan, D A
Salih, K M
Scott, D C C
Shah, P
Shaw, M K
Shearer, P E
Simpson, A C
Smellie, M K R
Sood, R K
Stevens, P G
Stewart, G
Swanson, F M
Swanson, I M
Taylor, D
Ter Morshuizen, R E I
Thompson, C
Thomson, R S
Wall, J P
Watson, G S
Watson, J M
Watt, C M E
Whatmore, P B
White, A A J
Williamson, J
Wilson, C
Wilson, E C
Wong, I H
Wong, M M
Woodburn, C
Woods, C L
Wylie, P G

Bacup

Gordon, C
Greenwood, J D
Islam, M H
McCloy, R F
Sattar, N
Sharma, Y
Wilkinson, P A
Williams, K V
Williams, P

Badminton

Butler, M O
Hope, B M
Mitchelmore, A E

Bagshot

Bremner, P A

Caukwell, S L
Croft, D
Donaldson, K M
Fox, S E
Lander, S J
Posner, J

Bakewell

Ashton, M G
Bartlett, N C
Bendefy, I M
Birkinshaw, K L
Blakey, D H
Chadwick, M S
Cohen, A
Cosgrove, I M
El Demir, M S
Gardner, I
Gilmore, E J
Griffiths, J A
Harris, G C
Holloway, J
Lewis, D R
Lockhart, O A
MacKenzie, J
Martys, C R
Mason, R E A
Newton, J C B
Pennington, G W
Pickard, R J
Platt, N D
Smith, G H
Stephenson, I
Stuart, O M
Turner, M A
Williams, P D
Wright, T
Yule, G W G

Bala

Davies, R M
Jones-Evans, D H
Jones-Evans, R A
Jones, T
Lazarus, D H
Roberts, I E

Baldock

Ahmed, A
Bhide, P D
Castell, E O
Cockburn, M K F
Dorrell, C E
Hall, H I
Hoffman, M G
Korgaonkar, S V
Macrae, I F
Masood, M R
Moynihan, F D
Nevison, J
Old, S E
Outhoff, K
Parkinson, H
Russell, S C J
Sawyer, E J
Seymour, J E A
Stanley, R S G
Thomas, M M
Trathen, B C
Wong, Y L A
Woolven, D W B

Balerno

Beattie, C M M
Boddy, K
Boyd, D H A
Dickson, M J
Fergusson, N S
Henderson, W K
Jackson, J E Z
Krauth, G A
Millar, C G
Ogilvie, I M
Rae, S M
Ritchie, C A M
Tervit, N M
Williams, A J K
Wood, I J
Wood, K

Ballachulish

McKenzie, J P M
McKenzie, W
Macleod, R

Ballasalla

Bailey, N M
Blackman, A M
Brockington, C F
Brockington, J M
Hockings, J E

Ballater

Scott, J A
Taggart, C C

Ballater

Armstrong, S M
Crawford, P M
Cruickshank, D M
Cruickshank, G R
Cumming, A K
Fallowfield, T L
Fulton, W F M
Glennie, E M
McLeod, E D J
Manson, W G C
Porter, I A
Scudamore, J H

Ballindalloch

Aldridge, O R V
Crowley, D J
Derounian, J N
Fraser, K B

Ballycastle

Farnan, C A
Guzhar, A R
Hunter, A M
Killough, E A
McCaughan, U M
McKinley, P M
McIister, M S
McNulty, D M C
O'Kane, J G P
Plumb, R D
Ryan, J J T
Sherlock, K E
Stewart, C D

Ballyclare

Baird, G V
Baird, H
Baird, S H
Bell, G S
Bill, R H
Bill, S M E
Cameron, J D
Clarkson, I P
Craig, M
Crooks, G M
Darrah, A C
Dawson, C A
Doherty, J F
Easy, A J
Gardiner, E W
Ghosh, R M
Gilmore, W A
Glass, D T
Green, R G H
Hill, M J
Jefferson, W W
Jenkinson, H A
Kinahan, K B
Laird, J D
Logan, J H C B
Luney, S R
Ly, M H
McAteer, C O
McClintock, R
MacFarlane, S E
McIlmoyle, C A
McIlrath, J P
Manderson, J E
Minford, E J
Moore, J
Munro, P I
O'Kane, E M
Rea, R D
Robinson, H
Stirling, J A
Thompson, T J
Vine, R J
Whitehead, E M
Wilson, S D
Woodburn, E M A
Wright, T J W A

Ballymena

Agarwala, R P
Agarwala, S
Alexander, B K
Allen, D J
Allen, G J
Armstrong, H M
Armstrong, K J
Armstrong, M G
Armstrong, S T
Bailie, W T
Bali, I M
Bali, S
Barker, R C

Barr, R S
Barr, S H
Beckett, M
Black, I M
Black, J H A
Black, M C
Boyce, S A
Bunting, L
Burnside, P
Cameron, D
Carey, S A
Carlisle, H A I
Clark, P J
Clarkson, L
Cubitt, E D
Dace, J S
Davison, L B S
Delargy, K P
Dick, C M
Dick, P T H
Doyle, D C
Dundee, R C
Flanagan, P G M
Fox, P J
Gardiner, G D
Gaston, W D M
Gilchrist, A
Glover, B D
Grainger, D J
Harper, J
Heggarty, P C
Hogg, J H
Hopkins, D M
Hunter, J B
Hutchinson, S P
Johannsen, K
Johnston, D J
Johnston, R S
Johnston, R E
Jones, W N
Kaytar, J
Kaytar, T
Kennedy, D M
Kennedy, F D
Kennedy, J P
Kenny, R J
Khanna, S
King, R
Laird, W H
Love, H E S
Low, B K
Lowry, J
Lowry, M
MacCartney, C
McCaughern, J
McCleery, M
McCluney, N A
McCollam, M P
McCoy, K J
McCrea, J A S
McCready, D V
McCusker, D P
McFarland, J R L
McGahey, D T
McGavock, E
McKelvey, J
McKelvey, J K
McKelvey, R D
McKillen, J M
McLoughlin, K H
McManus, O B
McMullan, M G
McMullan, N J
McNeill, O A
McQuillan, J D
McSparran, A J M
McSparran, J A
McWilliams, E A
Magowan, M C
Magowan, T D
Marshall, M
Mercer, B E A
Mudd, D G
Neely, R A
Newell, J
O'Hanlon, S
O'Hara, M G
O'Kane, W P
O'Neill, N P
Orr, C I K
Patterson, B G
Pothanikat, M G
Purce, E J
Ramsey, T L
Rea, R E
Redmond, M R
Redmond, R A A
Redmond, V A
Reid, J A

Ritchie, W A H
Russell, M W
Russell, S G
Simpson, A H
Simpson, J D
Sinclair, C J
Smith, J J
Smyth, N W
Stewart, R A
Tawia, A
Thompson, K J
Torrie, E C
Turtle, F
Vercoe-Rogers, J P
Waldron, G J M
Watson, J D
Willoughby, C E
Wilson, J
Wilson, P C
Wilson, W J C
Wright, G F
Young, C P

Ballymoney

Adams, J R
Boyd, F
Boyd, K L
Burns, R A
Fannin, E S
Finlay, H M
Flynn, J G
Gaston, J T
Hardy, T J
Harvey, W R
Henderson, R E
Johnston, D W H
Johnston, J E
Johnston, R J
Kwok, L S
Lee, D T
McCartney, R N J
McCartney, W A
McConnell, P
McVicker, J D
Matthews, J G W
Moles, M R
Murdock, O W N
O'Kane, M P
O'Sullivan, B M P
Pollock, M A
Robb, J D
Robb, J D A
Robinson, J H W
Sterne, A P
Virapen, M P
Wallace, J A

Ballynahinch

Ashton-Jennings, C A
Bailie, A G
Banks, I G
Bassett, J W
Beatty, H G
Christy, M W D
Courtney, C H
Courtney, J M
Ferguson, R W
Gillespie, P H
Gunn, S C
Harrison, R T S
Harrison, T J
Hilman, S J
Hopkins, M R
Lowry, I H
McAdam, J G
McGlew, J M
McGrath, E P
McKay, A P
McKelvey, J M
McKinley, A G
Mills, E M
Nirodi, P
Nirodi, V N
Norris, W A
O'Duchon, O
O'Gorman, E C
Ross, R W D
Sands, F M
Scott, R
Smyth, E F
Watson, S J
Watterson, B R

Bamburgh

Hull, C J
Johnson, J C

Bampton

Allport, S J

Biggs, R P
Bray, M
Cole, A D
Dainty, A R
Harper, E
Head, M O C
Landray, R
Mackenzie, R M
Owen, D J
Perry, M G
Ward, N A L

Banbridge

Allen, B D
Auld, J E
Boyce, C A
Carlisle, R J T
Cassidy, C A
Cocks, G R
Connolly, K
Cupples, A I
Cupples, B B
Deeny, E
Downey, A C
Graham, K E
Hawkins, E
Hollinger, M J
Hopkins, J P
Huey, M J
Knight, E D
McCandless, W
McConville, R M
McCreedy, A E
McCurdy, A M
McKenna, K E
Mallon, J H
Marsh, A M B
Mawhinney, C
Moran, I B
Moran, M B
Morrow, B A
Murray, L J
Murray, L A B
Murray, M A E
Ramsey, J K
Ramsey, P J
Robinson, T J
Taylor, D H

Banbury

Adam, R J
Addison, S L
Aickin, C P
Ainslie, R S
Aldous, M R
Allison, N Q
Alzua Blanco, J M
Appleton, G V N
Arnold, I R
Bayona Bayona, F
Bell, R A F
Bentley, S
Biggam, G J
Boyle, D S
Budd, B M
Budd, D W G
Canty, S H
Capehorn, D M W
Chalmers, J S
Chamberlain, S K
Comfort, A
Copcutt, E G
Cordingley, J L
Cornwall, L J
Courtenay, M J F
Crawford, P
Cull, T W B
Davenport, C F
Davies, A E
Day, C W
Eatock, E M
Edwards, H A M
Ellis, A J
Elphick, M
Evans, C P
Everatt, J C D C
Everatt, S
Farrar, E B
Fergusson, M L
Garud, S P
Gate, B
George, G J C
Gilchrist, R A S
Gillham, N R
Golden, E C E
Goode, A F
Granne, I E
Greywoode, G I N
Griffiths, C L

Griffiths, H
Hall, C J
Harris, D M
Harris, M A M
Harrison, J M
Hauer, T
Haynes, S A
Heath, S
Holt, C S
Holt, K S
Hughes, A W
Hunter, M F
Hyslop, D A
Jackson, D J
Kemp, S H
Keys, P F
Kilpatrick, H K R
Kilpatrick, M
Laird, E R
Large, S H
Laurie, P S
Le Roux, A E
Lehman, R S
Lehmann, N J P
Leitch, K M
McAuliffe, G L
MacLaren, D M
Mahy, N J
Mann, C
Mann, R Q
Marcovitch, H
Marshall, T P
Martinez Romero, F J
Mason, G P H
Miller, S J
Moran, S F
Mullard, K S
Munro, N R
Narayana, P L
Ng Cheng Hin, H S
Nicholls, J S D
North, C E
O'Connor, A P
O'Donnell, H F
O'Farrell, A M
O'Farrell, B D
Orr, M M
Parsons, P W
Patton, M K
Pile, R J
Pollard, J P
Raffle, P A B
Reid, N G B
Rivers, J S
Robinson, E A
Robinson, S L
Rodrick, I W
Rogers, S J
Rojo Llanos, M
Ruddock, F S
Rush, R A J
Rust, N D
Shafighian, B
Shapley, R
Shaw, R E
Sheybany, S
Shia, G T-W
Simms, S A R
Smith, S R
Spackman, D D
Stanislas, J M C
Tasker, J A
Taylor, G Y
Thornley, B A
Tideswell, D J
Ward, A M V
West, J D P
Wheeldon, P T
White, A B
White, D J
Whitehead, T C
Whitwell, E A
Wignell, D J
Willatts, D G
Williams, J A G
Wookey, S L M
Wormington, E M
Wright, J A

Banchory

Barclay, D G
Bayliss, A P
Bayliss, M A
Brynes, G D
Campbell, N C
Carroll, A L
Carroll, D S
Cassie, G F
Donald, K J

Ferguson, I M
Gibson, J I
Herd, J
Johnston, A W
Johnston, S J
Jordan, G
Kentish, L E
McCance, P F
McCrone, M G
McGarity, J F
Mackay, J F
Maclean, A F
Mair, F F
Mennie, G H
Morton, K M
Pearson, M J
Philip, J F
Proctor, D W
Watson, A V R
Watt, S J
Webster, N R
Wood, M C

Banff

Allan, N J W
Anderson, J E
Bruce, C E
Campbell, R J
Chung, C W
Covins, C M
Innes, G D D
Lees, R F B
McBain, A P
Mandal, K C
Mitchell, G A
Ross, J B
Wallace, E A H

Bangor, County Down

Anderson, G H I
Archer, K L
Archer, L J
Bailie, R K
Baird, W J S
Baker, R C
Ball, G M
Ballard, J D
Beckett, N
Bingham, G P
Blair, P H B
Bleakney, R R
Bownes, I T
Brennan, R M W
Brooks, S
Brown, A P
Brown, F R B
Bryans, R
Cairns, P N E
Calwell, R
Campbell, G A M
Carroll, R A
Carson, R E
Chambers, C A
Christy, J R O
Conn, A J
Connolly, F G
Craig, V
Crawford, G M
Crowe, J A
Crowther, S M
Davidson, J M
Dinsmore, E A
Doran, G
Douglas, J H E
Drew, J L
Dunne, P A
Edwards, M D
Elliott, H
Fee, J G
Fulton, A J
Garland, J M
Gault, L D
Gibson, C
Gildea, E
Gilmore, C P
Gilmore, W R
Glenn, D R J
Gorman, J H
Graham, P J K
Gray, D A
Green, J M
Guy, D D
Haggan, R N
Hainsworth, A M
Harbinson, S A
Hardy, C L
Harper, S
Haslett, W H K

Barnsley

Heaney, A E
Hill, C
Hill, P J
Hilliard, O R
Hinds, S
Holmes, B J
Hull, D R
Hunter, J
Jones, D D
Jordan, N P D
Kennedy, M N
Kerr, H
Killiner, W S
Laird, T P
Lavery, H A
Lavery, J T
Lightbody, C J
Logan, R
Loughrey, C M J
Lowy, C R
Lynas, T H
McAuley, W J
McBride, R J
McBride, S T
McCalister, A
McClelland, A M
McCoubrey, M A
McGrane, C T
McGrattan, B M
McKnight, J E
McManus, D K
McMinn, S A
Majury, N T
Mannis, N D
Maybin, A J A
Millar, E I
Millar, S P
Millar, W J R
Miller, J
Moore, D I
Moore, M C
Moore, M D
Mulholland, M L E
Murphy, A L
Murphy, F M
Murray, A J F
Nesbitt, S F
Nicol, P A
O'Keeffe, D
Page, A B
Patterson, G J
Patterson, R N
Phipps, B M
Redmill, D A
Reid, R D
Rennie, I M
Rogers, H J
Sharpe, T D E
Slater, R M
Stewart, J
Stout, A W
Thompson, K R
Todd, C
Todd, S A
Turner, J
Walford, G A
Wetherall, L M
Wilson, D T
Wilson, E A
Wilson, L E
Wilson, R H
Woods, A J
Wright, F R

Bangor, Gwynedd

Adams, C J
Al-Awa, A O
Baldwin, C D
Barr, G S
Bates, A B
Bebb, D G
Benfield, G F A
Birch, P D
Bloodworth, L L O
Bolton, L M
Booth, P J
Botman, A G M
Bowen-Jones, A
Brown, S R
Caulkell, J P
Chowdhury, M W R
Corson, J D
Crawford, R C
Davies, D J C
Davies, R R
Devakumar, M
Devaraj, K S
Ebrahim, M A
Edwards, N I

Elliston, P R A
Evans, D M
Flood, C P
Fowell, A J
Francis, A F
Gavel, F F G V
Gilleece, M H
Hardy, T K
Harris, T J B
Healy, D T M
Heinersdorff, N R
Hodges, N
Horn, J S M
Hughes, J A
Hughes, R C E
Ibrahim, F I
Iqbal, J
Johnston, J G
Jones, D A
Jones, D P A H
Jones, G L
Jones, I W
Jones, M W
Jones, R M
Kassab, S C
Kinahan, P J
Korn, H E T
Kurian, G V
Langmaack, C H
Leeson, S C
Lewis, J A
Lloyd-Evans, G N
Lynch, F K
McCann, V J
MacFarlane, A W
McMonagle, T M M
McSweeney, L
Maddison, P J
Madkour, M B E-D
Mammen Korulla, B
Mehta, H K
Mehta, M H
Miles, L
Mithan, W J
Morris, A R
Mortimer, J A
Mossa, F
Moyse, M
Naunton Morgan, J C
Nickson, P J
Ohri, P N
Oldale, K N M
Owen, B C
Owen, O E
Owen, R W
Owens, E W
Parry, R
Pennant-Lewis, R
Poeppinghaus, V J I
Powell, T G
Price, L J R
Prichard, D R
Radford, A M
Roberts, D P W
Roberts, E
Roberts, G E W
Roberts, L R
Roberts, M A
Roberts, M E
Rosser, C
Savage, M C
Seale, J R C
Shambrook, A S J
Singh Josson, K
Slater, M
Spill, W F
Sriwardhana, K B
Stuart, N S A
Subash Chandran, R
Tillson, C
Tivy-Jones, P
Vaughan, A R
Walker, A M
Watkin, G T
Wayte, D M
Whiteley, G S W
Williams, L G
Williams, M A C
Williams, R M
Williams, R S
Woolley, V L

Banstead

Adams, P N
Ahmad, M
Archibald, R M
Arduino, L A
Banerjee, D K
Banerjee, S

Basu, R
Carr, E F
Cartwright, H F
Digby, S T C
Douglas, G J E
Eldin, A M I S
Fielder, H C
Gallagher, H
Geer, P L
Hayes, K M
Heard, R N S
Hollowood, K
Kirk, H L
Lancefield, K S
McCurdie, I M
Majumder, J L
Mansfield, J R
Murphy, M K
Nathan, L A
Nunan, M R
Pande, S K
Pearson, P J T
Perlman, F J A
Pienkos, A V
Planche, T D
Powles, R L
Till, R J W
Tinton, M M
Wordsworth, V P
Worman, A J
Wray, R M

Banwell

Mee, M S

Bargoed

Baig, M Z
Caesar, E
Caesar, N
Das, N
Datta, B N
Majumdar, S K
Prior, G T J
Todd, C
Watkins, N R
Williams, E D G

Barking

Abudu, I A
Ahmad, H
Ahmed, A B J
Akinola, S E
Ali, M M
Baghla, D P S
Barclay, G
Booth, H C
Chopra, A S
Gupta, S N
Harvey, L J
John, A
John, K
Kateck, V H
Massey, H J O
Mathur, P
Moazzez, K
Moghal, I A
Nguyen, D D H
Pajwani, N P
Parikh, N S
Purkis, A E
Rahmatullah Khan, Dr
Sainsbury, J
Seth, P V
Shaw, J G H
Sheril, D B
Thomas, G L
Tolia, K J
Tote, S P
Uncle, K A
Watts, C J

Barmouth

Bradley, M C S
Hassan, S P
Haworth, R A
Hickey, M S
Short, S P
Taaffe, P
Whitehead, W H
Williams, H G M

Barnard Castle

Austin, P G
Cherry, W J B
Cuthbert, C R
Dry, D S
Fordy, K
Hamilton, F J
Harrison, C M S
McIntosh, A B

Nainby-Luxmoore, J C
Pickworth, K H
Ritson, A M
Ross, A M
Ross, I H
Ryan, P M
Smith, A H
Stewart, P D
Welch, F M
White, J J

Barnet

Alan, T S
Amasanti, D
Anchor, S C
Armstrong, R F
Arunachalam, S
Baig, K A
Baker, K W
Barnes, A J
Bell-Gam, Dr
Bell, D J
Berger, J
Berney, S I
Bird, R L R
Bloomfield, A E
Bolton, J P
Bradford, A T
Bradley, J C
Breeze, R W
Briggs, T P
Brown, E G
Bunce, C J
Burn, M J L
Burns, R
Carstairs, J L
Cartmell, E L
Chamberlain, M J
Chawishly, S A
Clarke, S W
Cohen, N H
Cooper, S M
Cope, J
Curran, P M
Dar, V K
David, L S
Davies, A C
Davies, J R E
Davis, N
El Jabbour, J N
Evans, J
Fage, V A A
Ferris, B D
Fine, W
Fox-Male, P
Fox, D B
Fuller, G
Garland, M H
Garsin, M D
Goodman, J
Goodwin, R W
Gray, K E
Greenbaum, R A
Gugenheim, J M
Hanks, G N
Harvey, D M
Hill, C M
Ibrahimi, G S
Johnston, I E
Joseph, L R
Kamath, B S K
Kanabar, S D
Khan, A A R
Khan, S
Khiroya, D V
Khiroya, V P
Kidson, I G
Kinloch, J D
Kirk, A
Kumar, G
Kurien, J
Lagnado, E A
Lai Chung Fong, P
Laufer, N E
Laurent, S J
Law, N W
Lawrence, B H
Leahy, A C B
Lee, F Y K
Lehovsky, A J
Leslie, A
Levy, N A
Lindsey, S K
Ling, Y B
Livingstone, D A
Loh, A
Lupin, L
McGowan, P R
Mackay, K H

Mackay, R M
Males, S M
Marcus, A J
Margerison, N J
Maudgal, D P
Merzer, R
Milaszkiewicz, R
Miles, S J
Miller, A
Milne, A M D
Minchin, A J
Moman, R B
Monkman, D S
Moore, S J
Mortimer, P E
Moss, I S
Natkunarajah, S
Natkunarajah, S
Nicholls, M D W
Nieto Velillas, J J
Nikapota, H M V L B
Norris, J C
Norton, K R
Ostberg, J E
Painter, A N
Pal, M
Patalay, T
Patel, M K
Patel, S
Pavey, S K
Pearson, A J G
Philippson, M E A
Powney, J G
Prior, A W
Raman, C
Ranasinghe, D U
Ranasinghe, N
Rean, Y M
Ribet, P W L
Ribet, R P
Rosenbaum, N L
Rossouw, D J
Roth, S C
Russell, R C
Ryan, F M
Sanchez Benitez, A
Sanghani, V V
Savege, P B
Shafi, G
Shah, S S
Shanthakumar, R E
Sharkawi, E
Sheridan, P J
Simmons, P H
Sireling, L I
Sittampalam, G
St. John Smith, P
Stacey, B S F
Strawbridge, L C
Sturridge, B F
Symons, I E
Tait, D
Tanner, P A S
Tello Arenas, E
Tham, N
Thambapillai, R
Thomas, H J W
Troyack, A D
Vellodi, C
Virchis, A E
Watson, L C A
Watt, S J
Watts, N
Weir, W R C
Weston, P M
Wilson, I J A
Wiseman, P A
Wolfman, M J
Yanni, G A
Yapanis, M
Yiallouros, M
Yu, C C-W

Barnetby

Grant, B M
Vora, A

Barnoldswick

Evans, A J
Holmes, S G T
Huxley, P A
Jackson, S M

Barnsley

Aboobakar, B
Acton, T J
Ahmad, A
Al-Bazzaz, M K I M
Allen, D J
Allen, K W

Alvarez Escurra, M F
Alvarez Iglesias, M
Amonkar, J A
Appelqvist, I P
Athale, D M
Balac, N
Ballingall, D A T
Banerjee, K
Bannister, J J
Baxter, A P
Beck, J M
Bell, A R
Bell, C
Bell, N J
Bennett, R I
Bhartia, R R
Bhaskara Rao, B
Bhaskaran, N C
Birinder, K T
Birkinshaw, R I
Birks, D V
Bodhe, M M
Booth, D
Bothwell, J E
Bothwell, R A
Bradbury, R A
Bridger, C A
Bryant, P A
Bryant, V M
Bullimore, D W W
Burgin, M I
Burton, E J
Burton, S J
Carlin, E M
Chan Lam, J M F D
Chaudhry, T A
Chow, G C S
Claydon, P J
Clifton, D I
Coup, A J
Courtney, M E
Crouch, E C
Crowe, M
Czepulkowski, E C
Darby, D C
Davis-Reynolds, L M R
Davison, R C
Dehadray, M G
Eldred, J B
Fahmy, T M
Firth, S H
Foster, J
Franklin, J S Q
Freeborn, C M
Gear, S L
Gill, N P
Glover, S C
Goh, G C
Granger, K A
Griffiths, J D
Harban, J
Harrison, K M
Harrison, K
Healey, T
Heyes, T G
Hirst, W S J
Hoda, M Q
Hooson, T K
Hossain, M A
Hourihane, B
Izhar Ul Qamar, Dr
Jain, V K
Johnson, M E
Jones, T H
Kakoty, P C
Keini, K S
Kershaw, D A
Khan, G H
Khan, M A
Kini, K K
Krishnaswamy, C K
Lane, P F
Lavender, A
Law, C E
Leabeater, B F
Lee, D E
Leese, C W
Leigh, J
Littler, W W
Loh, R Y M
Lottfallah, H N
McDonald, A R
McDonald, K W
McFeely, D F
McNicholas, J L
Mahatme, S S
Mahatme, S B
Marshall, A D R
Matuk, M D

Barnstaple

Maxwell, W G S
Mehta, B M
Menezes, A R
Metson, J R
Mian, R S
Middleton, F H
Miller, A J
Mills, H
Mitra, S
Mondal, K N
Morris, I R
Myint, Y
Naish, C
Narasimha Rao, M V S
Nayyar, N A
Ng Ping Cheung, J-P
North, C
O'Carroll, A
O'Dwyer, P F
O'Reilly, B N
O'Sullivan, D J
Oddy, C G
Ostrowski, J L
Palmer, N W
Panezai, J U R
Parkes, G
Pearson, V
Pick, J T H
Piper, I H
Pollock, A L
Poon, P Y A
Poonawala, S S
Prasad, Y N
Price, A G
Price, E R
Puttagunta, B
Quincey, C
Ravi, A
Ravi, S
Reed, P D
Reid, M V
Richards, F A
Robertson, J G
Rose, D
Roy, R
Roy, S S
Ruddlesdin, C
Ruiz Fito, J R
Sagar, J L
Sattar, S A
Sattar, S A
Scargill, M A
Senior, D C
Sheridan, J A B
Shrivastav, D P
Sirs, M R
Sillifant, K L
Singh, D
Singh, R P
Singh, R V
Smith, A K
Spencer, H D
Sriramulu, V
Swinhoe, C F
Sykes, L
Tambar, B K
Taylor, A B
Thomas, S E
Tyerman, G V
Tyerman, P F
Vaghani, J T
Varley, R
Vinod Kumar, I
Waddington, R T
Wahedna, I
Wakefield, V A
Waldock, F J
Walker, A
Walker, J A
Ward, A S
Way, B G
Weatherill, J
Wickham, M H
Wilkerson, J N
Wood, C B
Wood, G
Yadav, D G
Yadav, S S
Yaqub, M
Yates, S P
Yeoman, L J
Zachary, J B

Barnstaple

Alexander, H M
Ashton, M G
Attock, B
Averns, H L
Ayres, R G

Azimuddin, K
Baker, A W T
Bannister, M
Barber, S G
Bargery, A
Barker, A J
Barker, J R
Barlow, A
Barron, E K
Barwise, K
Bastiaenen, H L R
Beer, R J S
Bigge, T L
Bluett, N H
Bosley, A R J
Boss, J M
Boucherat, A
Bourne, R
Boyle, A H W
Brennan, N
Buchanan, I
Bull, A D
Bunney, R G
Burgess, W
Cartmell, M T
Claydon, E J
Cole, R H L
Compton, N J
Cowman, J E
Davies, J H
Dickson, J
Dodds, J M
Duke-Cox, N M
Eckford, S D
Enoch, B E
Forster, S J
Forster, T W H
Fox, Z D
George, G
George, M
Gibson, R A
Hardy, M T
Hart Prieto, M C
Harvey, D R
Hawkins, M J
Helsby, J
Holman, R A
Holmes, J A
Hooper, C A
Horman, L M
Howlett, A J
Hubbard, H C
Hughes, M P
Hunt, S J
Jack, I F M
Kaliciak, A I
Kalsi, B S
Kandasamy, K
Kay, M
Lavalette, D P
Laycock, G J A
Le Dieu, H R
Leiper, R G
Lewin, I G
Lindsay, E D
Loader, B W
McCabe, J G
McCaie, C P
MacCaig, J N
McElderry, E M
Malcolm, B
Markham, N I
Marston, J A
Matthews, H C
Miller, A L
Miller, J E
Mills, C L
Moore, G E
Moore, P C H
Moran, A
Morgan, M R
Myers, S
Nicholson, S D
O'Donovan, N P
Oliver, M H
Osborne, C L E
Osborne, D B R
Partridge, J P
Payne, R F
Peet, J S
Porterfield, J S
Quinton-Tulloch, J C
Reynolds, R J
Reynolds, Z M
Ridd, M J
Roberts, G A
Roberts, T L
Ross, C M D
Rutter, M J

Sadek, R I M
Sanderson, A J
Saunders, J M
Sewell, M S
Sinclair, B J
Smith, P F
Socrates, A
Sowden, G R
Speirs, G E
Spencer, P D
Suresh Shetty, V
Taylor, C P
Treble, N J
Treweeke, P S
Turner, J G
Van Buren-Schele, M
Walder, A D
Watt, R M
Wheble, A M
White, J C
Whittle, E R
York-Moore, D W
Young, J R

Barrhead

Capaldi, A D
Garrigan, C T
Gemmell, W E
McAleer, M
Mitchell, M B
Morton, I C
Naven, T
Nicholson, A F

Barrow-in-Furness

Abdullah, S H
Allan, D
Allington, M D
Ashcroft, A J
Ashcroft, C N
Ball, C S
Baqai, A N
Boardman, A J
Brewer, L
Brookes, D B
Burden, M F
Campbell, C A
Cockshott, C U
Coker, D M
Courtman, N H
Crawshaw, P J S
De Clercq, S M
Dieker, A
Earnshaw, G
Egan, J A
El Tawil, H M M G
Fryers, T
Glew, M
Gore, R B
Govenden, V
Green, C J
Harrison, R
Hasan, M R-U
Hay, A W
Hearn, H J
Hodkinson, J N
Ivey, A T
Jackson, J H
Jeelani, G
Joglekar, V M
Jolliffe, G C
Kamalanathan, V
Keating, J J
Knott-Craig, J L
Knox, D D
Lee Cheong, L F L
Lindley, J G
Maalaw, M M
Mabrook, A F
MacDonald, B R
McGroarty, V
Macheta, A T
MacLeod, A R
McQuillan, S T
Mangal, A
Manthri, S
Mandel, S N
Memon, Y
Mohammed, O E N
Murugappan, N
Nasmyth, D G
Ni Chuileannain, F M
Nugent, E M
Nugent, J J
O'Donovan, I A M
Oldham, T P
Page, A
Pai, K G
Partridge, S M

Patel, M C
Puvi, N
Puvirajasingham, S
Puvirajasingham, S
Rathi, R K
Robinson, K M
Rogerson, J W
Rogerson, S H
Rothnie, D W
Sayer, N J
Shapland, D E P
Sharples, P J
Shaw, C P
Stoney, P J
Story, T W
Taylor, A
Todd, D
Tupper, C H
Vaidya, R B
Wear, I J
Wiejak, A P
Williams, L J
Wilson, C E
Wilson, R Y
Wyatt, M G
Wyatt, R H
Young, J C

Barrow-upon-Humber

Chapman, C D

Barry

Baig, A
Brook, J F
Brown, G G
Bugler, H
Burlitt, E M
Chapman, J R
Coleman, M A T
Coyle, F M
Coyle, J M A
Davies, D
Davies, E J
Davies, G F
Davies, S H
Doherty, E F
Donaghy, C E
Donnison, P E I
Evans, J G
Fitzgerald, P A
Harfoot, D A
Hartley, E D M
Holgate, S K
Hooper, R A
Hortop, S E
Hughes, A
Jones, S D
Keble-Williams, G
Lennox, C K B
Lindsay, S D
Luen, S C
McGill, E V A
Morgan, S D
Parker, S J
Parr, E J
Richards, L F
Sareen, S D
Smith, S J
Staff, C J
Stephens, D S
Stott, J R
Sullivan, M A L
Sutton, L J
Tasker, D G
Walton, E E
Weatherup, A
Williams, A J
Williams, A J
Williams, D E
Williams, D M J
Williams, M V
Williams, R D
Witte, K K A

Barton-upon-Humber

Bacon Kinsella, C E
Ball, J B
Birtwhistle, T J C
Dickinson, J A
Jaggs-Fowler, R M
Lobacz, R M
Macmillan, F N
Pemberton, J
Ridgway, D M
Robertson, J S
Robertson, M C
Rowles, N

Basildon

Agombar, A C
Agrawal, A
Agrawal, R L
Ali, A
Ali, P M
Barton, I K
Bass, R S
Bell, R J
Biswas, K
Biswas, S K
Catterall, M D
Cavaroli, M E
Chajed, G
Chan, A W C
Chan, T Y K
Chopra, A
Colby, R
Collier, D S J
Colliver, D W
Cook, L
Cornforth, B M
Cotta, R G
Coward, L J
Craig, V A
Das, K S V
David, A C
Davis, M D
Denham, A
Dhadli, D K
Dikimli, A
Eade, P F
Easton, D M
Evely, T K W
Galea, C
Gendi, N S T
Gertner, D J
Gordon, P W N
Goyal, R L A
Griffin, A B
Gulamali, I H
Gupta, G R
Hastings, L A
Hopcroft, K A
Jas, B B
Jeddy, T A
Jenner, G H
Karia, S J
Kerrigan, P J C
Kunde, D P
Latif, A
Lee, H Y
Lefevre, D C
Lehner, K G
Lennox, I A C
Linehan, I P
Lockwood, C A
Lowe, M R
McFarlane, S H
Mampilly, J
Marshall, R B
Martin, C J
Martin, P B
Maunder, R F
Memon, W M
Millins, S
Milwood, A J E
Mitchell, A J
Morgan, S H
Moulds, A J
Murphy, V J
Murray, A M
Newport, N G
Nimmo, S
Palit, J
Patel, P C
Pereira, C M
Peters, M G
Prem Swarup, I J
Pretty, M A
Punchihewa, V G
Purdie, H R M
Pusey, R J
Rahman, M L
Rajan, K T J
Rao, H S
Rawlingson, C J
Rubie, N G
Rylah, L T A
Sage, R J
Saw Myint, Dr
Sharief, N N Y
Sharpe, R A
Sims, M A
Singh, P K
Singhal, H
Smith, R B
Spraggins, D
Targett, J P G

Tarn, M
Taylor, H W R
Thillainadarajah, P
Utting, H J W
Vohra, A
Vyas, J K
Wake, C A
Wakeman, R
Watts, E J
Whitehead, J P
Willert, E J
Woodgate, D J
Yung, B M-C

Basingstoke

Acres, D J
Adamson, G
Adeosun, A S
Adler, V
Aertssen, A M G
Allen, J F
Allen, P L
Armstead, S P
Aronstam, A
Ashworth, J S
Ashworth, M E
Assadourian, R
Aston, D L
Bajwa, R
Bates, R G
Batten, C O
Baxter, P J C
Beck, R S
Bell, J W
Bennett, D A
Bernstein, J J
Beswick, R E
Birtwistle, S M
Bishop, A J
Blade, P D
Blanshard, J D
Booth, L V
Boswell, P A
Bowen, S P
Brain, G R H
Brian, J
Britton, A E M
Britton, J M
Brooklyn, T N
Brown, C W W
Browne, R J S
Burgess, E J
Button, P D
Calderon Pelayo, R
Cameron, A H
Carman, S J
Carney, A
Church, J P
Cochrane, T R C
Cole, A T
Cole, L M
Coppin, R J
Crone, A M
Cummins, E L
Darmady, J M
De Mars, C
Dent, C J
Dent, T H S
Dixon, C G
Eastwood, C J
Eustace, J D
Faithfull-Davies, D N
Fallon, A T S
Farquharson, S M
Fisher, E P
Fraser, N B
Freeman, H J
Gall, J
Geach, A R
Gould, S W T
Gowers, L E
Green, I L
Greenslade, J H
Guy, R J C
Hamber, B H
Harding, C M
Haselden, J E
Heald, R J
Hearn, C E D
Hettiaratchy, S W
Heys, M
Hilditch, H
Hiorns, P E
Hoar, D H M
Hogan, A M
Hudson, S W
Hudson, W S
Hullah, D
Hunter, E M M

Bath

Hurley, J E
Iffland, C A
Ilangovan, P B
Ilesley, I C
James, A M
James, P D
Jamil, S
Jardine-Brown, K
John, T G
Johnston, R H
Jones, S H
Jones, T J H
Jones, V J I
Keightley, S J
Kingan, J G
Knight, D K S
Knowles, P M
Knowles, S P
Koch, S
Lacey, N A
Lane, P K
Lee, A C
Levy, T M
Lindsay, J A
Lloyd, P C
Lorge, R E
Lyon, J S
McGonigal, G
McKinlay, K P
McLay, I A B
Macve, J S
Maltby, J D
May, A-M
Milne, A E
Mitchell, A T
Mitchell, M I
Moolgaoker, A S
Moran, B J
Morrell, R R J
Moss, D
Moss, M L
Mostafid, A H
Munro, D F
Murphy, A J
Mycock, H D
Myles, B J
O'Neill, H M-J
O'Sullivan, G F M
O'Sullivan, M J B
Ollerhead, K J
Pagdin, J C
Pal, C R
Panday, K
Parker, J C
Parker, R L E
Patel, S
Patterson, G M
Payne, D N R
Payne, P R
Phalke, I M
Plant, G R T
Platt, K A
Plowman, P E
Pooler, A F W M
Preston, H G
Pronk, A
Quew, R A
Ramage, J K
Rathod, S L
Readett, D R J
Rees, J
Rees, M
Reid, C G
Render, C A
Richards, A B
Richardson, J
Ridsdale, P A
Rimington, M R
Robins, D W
Rowlands, A B
Roy, A
Roy, L
Sacco, D F
Sandy, C J
Sayer, T R
Shaw, G M
Shawe, D J
Shelley, D F
Shelley, J C
Simpson, A
Skeggs, P L
Skinner, E G
Smedh, R K
Sorby, N G D
Spencer, G M
Spraggs, P D R
Squire, J M
Stebbing, M A
Stedman, S A

Stephenson, D A
Stranks, G J
Summers, L J
Sweeney, O J
Sykes, C F G
Teall, J G
Thomas, N P
Thomson, K D
Todd, G P A
Tovey, F I
Tristram, S J
Trueman, R S
Tupper, D J L
Turner, R G
Upchurch, S
Vanita, Dr
Vinitharatne, J K P
Walters, P J
Walters, R O
Waring, N J
Warren, P A
Wells, J K G
Werry, D M
Wigfield, R E
Wilkins, D F
Willcocks, J A J
Williams, E A
Williams, G A
Williamson, D J
Wilson, P T J
Worrell, J
Wright, D J T
Wright, D J
Wright, P G Y
Yeganeh-Arani, E
Zorab, W G

Bath

Abu Zaid, E-H A
Adams, M J
Ahmed, A W
Alabaster, C J
Alexander, A G
Allan, M D
Amos, C
Amour, A A
Anderson, M I
Antcliff, R J
Aplin, C G
Archer, P
Aston, S J
Atkinson, P J
Austin, V M A
Avery, A F
Baer, R M
Bagley, S R V
Bailey, D A
Baird, M B
Bamford, D S
Barclay, J A
Bardner, D J
Barton, B J J
Bassett, P M
Bateman, D E
Bates, T S
Batten, K L
Batterham, I A
Beaven, J T
Bell, R C
Bender, L E
Bennett, J M
Bennett, P F
Bennett, P N
Berrisford, C E
Bevan, C M
Beviss, J E
Bhalla, A K
Bhardwaj, R
Biddlestone, L R
Billson, A L
Binzenhofer, J
Bishay, M S K
Blackmore, J E
Blackstock, J
Blain, C R V
Blake, D R
Bliss, P
Blunt, M J
Bointon, G B H
Bollon, M E
Booth, P J
Botham, J R W
Bottomley, M B
Boucher, K J
Bovill, B A
Britton, D C
Bromwich, H L
Brooks, J D
Brooks, S J

Brown, A M
Bruce-Jones, W D A
Bubna-Kasteliz, B
Budd, J S
Bunbury, D E
Burditt, A F
Byrne, J W
Cadbury, A-L
Cahill, T E
Calin, A
Calin, H J
Canter, R J
Capper, R
Carr, D W R
Carter, A C
Casanova Coll, F
Cash, H C
Cashman, J P
Cave, D A
Chalmers, A H
Chapman, J A
Charles-Chilcott, R J
Charlton, C A C
Christie, I W
Clark, M I H
Clark, N
Clark, T W
Clarke, A K
Clarke, S
Claxton, N B
Cockshoot, D
Collins, A J
Colville, I A
Conner, T A E
Conway, B M
Cook, S J
Cooper, A M
Cooper, D J
Cooper, S J
Cornish, J M M
Cosgrove, P V F
Cottee, C S
Cottman, S B
Coulter, G G
Craft, T M
Craig, P M
Cromby, J W
Crook, A E
Cumpsty, C E
Cumpsty, J R
Curtis, K
Darch, G R
Davies, C E F
Davies, J
Davies, J A
Davies, W R
Davis, M
Dawson, K
Deane, L S
Denbow, M L
Denham, R H G H
Denny, R S H
Dinwoodie, J M
Divall, P A W
Donovan, A D
Dorman, S
Douglass, S J
Dow, L
Downie, C J C
Dowson, D I
Dragowska, E M
Duignan, M
Dunkerley, D R
Dunlop, D A B
Dunlop, D C
Dunn, R B
Dunster, G D
Eavis, P M
Edwards, E A
Ellis, D H
Eustace, J
Ewbank, J A
Fallon, K M
Farrant, J M
Fickling, W E
Finlay, R D
Fitzgerald, J H
Fleming, R J K
Foley, M B N
Freeman, M J
Fryett, D C
Fuge, C A
Gage, R J B
Galimberti, A
Galizia, E J
Gallegos, C R R
Gardner, P A
Gentles, H
Gibbs, Z K

Giddins, G E B
Gilbert, J H
Gilby, E D
Gillberry, M A
Gillies, F C L
Gillies, R M
Glaser, S
Glew, D
Goddard, D A
Goodwin, A P L
Goulder, R V H
Grabham, R E
Graham, A J
Graham, A A
Gray, J D
Green, P J
Griffiths, J D
Griffiths, J M
Groenhuysen, C
Groves, S J
Gupta, K J
Hallett, A M
Hamling, H M-C
Hamling, J B
Hampton, J
Handel, J M
Hansell, J
Hansell, P
Hanson, B E
Harbinson, N K
Harding, R D
Hardman, J A R
Harries, A J
Harries, J M
Harris, M F
Harris, T J
Harrison, K J
Hartley-Brewer, V F
Hartley, J D
Hayes, A L
Hayes, L M
Hayward, S J
Head, A J
Hersch, E
Hertlein, R A
Heywood, A J
Hicks, E R
Hill, S L
Hillen, R S
Hills-Wright, P A
Hirschowitz, L
Hodson, R S
Holman, J G S
Horn, C K
Horrocks, M
Houghton, H J
Howell, G P
Howell, M E
Howlett, D M
Howse, N L
Hubbard, W N
Hudson-Jessop, P
Hughes-Davies, D I
Hughes, L S
Humphries, E A M
Hyde, P J
Hyzler, C A
Irish, W T
Irons, D J
Jackson, A C
Jackson, F P
Jackson, G E
Jackson, H J
Jackson, M B
Jacobson, S K
James, J R
Jameson, A I
Jameson, R J
Jelley, T M
Jennings, P J F
Jiggins, M P
Johns, W A
Johnson, M R
Johnson, N
Johnson, T M
Jones, C B
Jones, C D
Jones, D E P
Jones, J P
Jones, N C R
Jones, P A
Jones, R
Jones, R W
Jones, S W
Judge, C B
Karanjavala, J D
Kaye, A
Kennaway, C V
Kingston, P

Kirkup, J R
Kitching, P A
Kitson, S R
Knechtli, C J C
Knowles, J K
Korendowych, E
Kotecha, Y J
Kremer, J K
Laverty, T A
Law, F D
Leach, C L
Leahy, E P
Lechi, A
Legassick, R A
Lenton, S W
Letcher, A M
Lewis, I
Lim, A B H
Lloyd, D B
Lovell, C R
Luck, J
Lutterloch, M J
Lyons, P R
McAllen, C J P
McClean, A N
McClemont, W F
McCrea, J
MacDougall, M H
McHugh, L A
McHugh, N J
Mackay, G H
McKechnie, E J
McKim, D S
McKim, R S
McMaster, V J
McNab, M A
Maddox, P R
Magee, P T
Maguire, K M
Mahto, R S
Maken, S
Malthouse, M E
Malthouse, S R
Mann, J B
Mann, P G
Mansfield, B G
Manton, H C
Marjot, R
Matlhaga-Nyoni, B M
Matthews, B E
Matthews, N I L
Mauri Sole, I
Mayor, A H
Medworth, S
Meehan, C J
Metcalfe, G C
Michael, B
Miller, A M
Millington, C
Milner, P C
Minas, H P
Moisey, C U
Monro, A D
Montgomerie, J
Moore, D C
Moore, G D C
Morgan, K F H
Morrice, A A G
Morris, J C
Morrison, M
Morrison, P J M
Mowat, J S S
Muddiman, M J
Mundy, F H
Murison, I C
Murphy, C M
Murray, S R
Musgrove, H E
Neill, A E
Newman, N
Nixon, J
Noakes, M J
Nolan, J P
North, P C
Novak, S A
Nulliah, K
O'Brien, A T J
Oliver, M I
Orpen, I M
Osborne, J P
Padkin, A J
Page, M J
Parr, M J A
Paterson, M P
Pauli, H M
Payton, C D
Pearson, A V A
Pearson, M L
Peden, C J

Pemberton, D P
Perry, N K
Peters, C D
Phillips, B H
Pike, A A
Pilton, D W
Pizey, N C D
Playfair, J R
Pointing, T D
Pollock, K J
Poor, S J
Porter, R J
Potter, R G
Pozo, J L
Pratt-Johnson, J H
Price, L E N
Price, M R J
Priestman, S
Proffitt, C M
Protheroe, D T
Provan, A B
Radford, S R
Randell, M
Randell, W D
Reckless, J P D
Redman, A G O
Redman, L R
Redman, S P
Rees, J H
Reynolds, N J
Richardson, J C
Roberts, M B
Robertson, D A F
Robinson, B L
Rolls, R L
Rooney, N
Rose, D S C
Rose, H J
Ross, A C
Rudd, P T
Rumball, C L
Rye, S
Salter, M W A P
Sammes, H R
Sanchez-Andrade Bolanos, J M
Sandeman, A P
Savine, R
Schnetler, J F C
Schofield, H M
Schofield, T L
Scott-White, L A
Scott, R
Seagger, R M
Seagger, R A
Self, J J
Seppelt, I H
Servant, C T J
Sharman, S L
Shaw, L J
Sheppard, C A
Sholapurkar, S L
Simpson, N
Simpson, T J P
Singer, C R J
Singh Ranger, R
Skrine, R L
Slack, R W T
Slinn, R M
Smith, A
Smith, J
Smith, J C
Smith, J G
Smith, M N
Smith, P K W
Souter, A J
Spear, G E
Speed, D E M
Speed, M A
Spelman, J F
Spencer, C M
Spurling, S G
St. John, J I
Stagg, C E
Standing, B L
Stanton, R A
Stewart, D J
Stewart, M S
Straughan, D W
Sweetenham, D M
Sykes, P H
Tan, R S-H
Tate, J J T
Taylor, P J
Terry, S W W
Terzis, G
Thomas, C L
Thomas, J
Thomas, R D

Bathgate

Thompson, M G
Thomson, D M M
Thomson, I G
Thorley, A P
Tighe, J R
Tighe, S M
Tilley, J S
Todd, I P
Tonge, H M
Tovey, G H
Tower, S E
Towers, J S
Tuckey, J P
Turnbull, A R
Turner, A C
Turner, J F
Tyrrell, J C
Umpleby, H C
Usman, F
Valentine, J P
Wakefield, G S
Waldron, J
Walker, D J
Walker, G D
Walker, J M
Watkins, S P
Watson, D P H
Watson, M
Wayte, C
Webb, S E
Webber, S M
Weller, S D V
Wernham, C M
Wexler, S A
Weyndling, J M
Wharton, R L
White, A
White, D M
Whitfield, B E
Widdowson, E J
Wilde, J M
Wiles, I D
Willars, C M
Williams, C J
Williams, S M
Williamson, T J
Wingfield, C A
Worsdall, G M
Wright, D G
Wright, E A
Wylie, G L
York, E L
Young, A H
Young, R
Zealley, M M
Zebouni, L N P

Bathgate

Adams, G J H
Al-Ubaid, K S
Bader, R
Bell, P C
Brady, B M
Brown, K J
Carlaw, W G
Chaudhury, A J
Cook, A J C
Duncan, I D
Easter, H J
Ferguson, A
Ferguson, S R
Gallagher, B A
Gunn, J F
Hay, D J
Ibrahim, M
James, B K D
Kerr, A M
Laird, G W
Lees, J S
Macaulay, D
McCallum, J M
McCollum, D
MacGillivray, D
McKinstry, B H
McKitterick, M J
McNutt, A P W
Merrilees, H F
Milne, S M
Mooney, J K
Murphy, A M
Musk, C S
Porter, L J
Ritchie, V
Robertson, C M M
Russell-Smith, E D
Ruxton, A M
Sibbald, B
Sibbald, D S

Sneddon, L M
Stewart, C M
Thomson, J
Toellner, C B
Tydeman, G S J
Wallace, J A K
Williamson, S M
Wilson, C E
Winter, M D

Batley

Ashraff, N N
Ashraff, Y N
Barker, D R
Bham, A Y
Bham, Y G M
Bottomley, S E
Broughton, A D D
Cowie, I W R
Desai, P M
Dutta, S
Elders, M K
Fowers, D E
Ghanchi, F D
Gillson, S T
Glover, P D
Grunwald, H
Haque, M E
Haughie, R G
Houghton, C S
Jones, J F M
Kalla, V K
Kundu, C R
Lawler, J S
Lawson, S J
Lidhar, J K
Lidhar, K S
Lobb, B R
Longmore, T B
Lynch, B D
Lynch, M P
McCormack, R F
Mackereth, A C
Miller, P A
Mishra, A K
Mohanraj, M
Mullhi, P S
Mulrennan, S
Rajpura, A
Rajpura, A
Scales, M F
Stonawski, B
Walker, E C
Walker, J E
Warwick, J R
Wright, J R

Battle

Akers, P S
Beal, R J
Belcher, N G
Campbell, D A
Corser, P J W
Green, P F
Griffith, D G C
Hargreaves, C D
Jardine-Brown, T
Justice, R J
Kemm, I S J
Leece, J G
Lister, J B
Lloyd-Jones, D
Long, D
Macpherson, G
Merrick, C D
Mogan, J E
Pembrey, M R
Rademaker, J W
Rice-Oxley, C P
Rivett, J G
Rivett, P M
Roberts, G R E
Silva, L U
Stern, S R
Underhill, T J
Vale, K E
Wakeford, N A A
Watson, J
Wood, M C
Woods, C M
Yeo, K C
Yeo, R

Beaconsfield

Agbeja, A M
Amin, C L
Apperley, J F
Balmforth, J R
Bayliss, M A
Blackmore, S J

Bradnock, K M
Brodie, D P
Brown, S P
Bulger, J M
Burley, D M
Butcher, A S F
Bywaters, E G L
Churn, M J
Coggan, A M
Cox, S A L
Crawford, D S
Crawford, J L
Dalton, J I F
Davies, K E
Dell, R J
Donald, J G
Donnelly, R J
Elliott, C
Fletcher, G R L
Gallagher, S K
Gau, D W
Gau, G S
Gibbs, S L
Giles, E L
Glover, J D
Grover, E R
Hagger, A O
Hall, A G
Hambly, E M
Hambly, J F E
Hardy, J
Hargrave, D R
Harris, G
Hart, R A
Hayek, A H J
Hern, E E
Holdstock, S
Horn, R F H
Jones, R D
Joy, P J
Lang, G S
Lister, J
Lomax, S H M
Lord, P H
McDade, H B
McDermott, H W
McGirr, B P
Mackenzie, V F
McPherson, G A D
McVey, V M
Marsden, D A
Musaji, M A
Roberts, P D
Sacks, B A
Sherry-Dottridge, F G
Slater, S D
Smith, H N
Stanworth, S J
Stoneham, M D
Thomas, S I
Tytherleigh-Strong, G M
Walker, B J
Watters, R M
Watts, A B
Westcott, T
Widgington, N J
Wilson, J F

Beaminster

Clarke, R J
Goodhart, R A G
Green, J T H
Hudson, M K G
Kettell, J A
Payne, J M V
Robinson, T W
Sinclair, E R
Smith, C H

Beauly

Baecker, T E
Fergusson, R S C
Finlayson, J A
Forsyth, R S
Fullerton, L A
Graham, M J
Grigor, M J
Habermann, F F
Hawco, M J
Iwaszko, J
Janssens, M
Kane, I A
Kane, T P C
McIntyre, A J
McLardy, J
MacLean, I G
MacLeod, M
MacVicar, J

Paul, N
Whittle, E J

Beaumaris

Dubberley, J
Fowell, A
Grace, P H
Jones, E L
Jones, H W
Jones, R Y
Macvicar, S
Parry, D H
Pringle, M
Richards, G
Riley, A H
Roberts, G I
Roberts, H G
Vousden, J E
Waite, H C
Williams, K N
Woodier, N C

Beaworthy

Al-Doori, A A A-M
Bowden, L J
Filer Cooper, R
Human, M S
Miller, S W M

Bebington

Thomas, J

Beccles

Battye, I R
Berry, P S
Bubb, A R
Bungay, E K
Cadman, S
Coleman, R A
Collins, G W
Douglas, K D S
Dunbar, K P L
Duncan, R W
Frears, J F
Gibbs, R G
Gilbert, M C
Harrison, D A
Holly-Archer, F K M
Hopkins, C J
King-Davies, A A
King-Davies, D H
Kinsey, W L
Latoy, J J
Morton, T J
Osborne, C D I
Pitt, J M
Rintoul, R C
Sargen, F E
Seel, J R
Smith, P R
Wells, A L

Beckenham

Abdullah, V
Abraham, D M
Apostolov, K
Aps, C
Armitage, A R
Atkinson, S W
Baker, A J
Barnett, H C
Bayer, M
Bearn, J A
Bernadt, M W
Binning, S C
Birch, D M L
Blakely, A P L
Blower, D E
Boakes, J P
Britto, J A
Broadfield, J B
Bugler, J A
Buttriss, C J
Campbell, A C
Carroll, K P C
Cassar, S D
Corrin, S A
Daly, H C S
Davidson, S P
Dean, B C
Dheansa, B S
Dignan, A P
Donald, J L
Dunachie, P A
Dyer, K E
Eayrs, P J
Ephson, P M J
Feroze, R M
Fisher, M F
Fitt, C S

Fitzpatrick, D G
Fowle, A S E
Fowle, L L
Freeman, C
Frimpong, G A A A
Funnell, N J
Gale, R F
Gibson, T J
Gilbert, A M
Glanfield, M D
Glenister, P W
Gnanachelvan, S
Gordon, H L
Graham, C R
Grint, P C A
Harper, K H
Harris, L S
Harris, V G
Heaton, N D
Higton, D I R
Hind, A W
Holder, S E
Holloway, F
Hoo, C A
Horgan, M M
Horwood, E
Hurn, B A L
Husain, S S-Y
Hutchinson, D B A
Ilo, O A
Jaisri, S S P
James, J D
James, P R
Jani, M R
Johnson, C
Kamalanathan, F A
Kandavel, R
Kaye, A M
Kazmi, S M N A
Kelleher, K G
Kerawala, J J
Latham, J
Letley, E
Levinson, N
Lishman, W A
Little, C P
Little, V
McColl, C L
Maclean, I F
McQueen, J
McWilliams, S E
Maini, R
Malhi, G
Mansfield, L E
Manuel, J B
Martin, J R
Medcalf, M S
Mercer, D M
Morton, W A
Motahar, M M
Mozley, C R
Naylor, R
Newman, M
Norton, M R
Nunnerley, H B
Onen, T S
Pandya, D
Parker, M T
Pitt-Payne, J H
Pook, J A R
Radley, W H
Rajap, T I
Reddy, K P
Restorick, H M
Reveley, A
Richardson, J F
Richardson, T
Ross, A
Sampson, S A
Shipsey, E M
Shipsey, M J
Simmons, I G
Soodeen, P I
Staniforth, A S C
Stone, C J
Stonham, J
Swann, J C
Tempest, J E
Thompson, J
Tilsley, D W O
Tinson, R E
Tranter, A W
Trezies, A J H
Underhill, H C
Vella, R
Wagstyl, J W
Ware, R J
Wells, R A
Welsh, B M

Williams, D J
Williams, K G D
Winfield, F I B
Wozniak, A P
Wraige, E A
Yiu, C A

Beckermet

Cheetham, R B
Dixon, E H M
Lewis, M A

Bedale

Ashworth, J
Baird, J W
Beaumont, N
Bell, R E
Church, H D V
Collier, C N
Fisken, J M
Fletcher, B R G
Henshaw, M B A
Laybourne, B J
Roberts, G R
Rounding, A
Rounding, M S
Thompson, J M
Thompson, M J
Wasilewski, A W
Willox, M F
Wood, K D

Bedford

Agarwalla, B
Agrawal, A T
Agrawal, M L
Agrawal, P
Agrawal, S G
Agrawal, T
Aldrich, I D
Allingham, J P
Anderson, J M
Atkinson, P R T
Attia, F F
Au, K H-K
Aylward, J G
Baker, A S
Baker, P A
Baldwin, H C
Barber, A R
Barnes, P M
Barter, S J
Batty, D M
Bazeley, B J
Beeden, A G
Berman, J W
Besag, F M C
Bhamra, G S
Binns, J C
Black, F S
Blackshaw, A J
Blackshaw, M J
Bogle, G D
Bone, J W
Brookes, N R
Brooks, A S
Brown, G M
Buchanan, A A
Buckingham, C J
Budden, G C
Bude, A
Burtt, G J
Butlin, J A
Butterworth, E A
Callam, M J
Cambridge, G C
Cameron, E A
Cashman, A J
Chakrapani, R
Charfare, G H G M
Clark, E C
Clark, R W
Cochrane, J G
Colebrook, M
Coles, S R
Coombes, A M A
Cooper, I C
Cooper, J P
Cooray, P G
Cosford, P A
Crawford, A D
Crawford, B J F
Curnock, A L
Dalton, A M
Dangoor, A M
Daniels, D G
Davies, M H
Davies, R J E
Dawson, J P
De Groot, W T

Belfast

Deane, S E
Didier, H P
Disher, A D R
Done, A R
Dorling, B
Dutton, D A
Dyer, B B
Edwards, W J
Egan, A M
Elliman, A M
Elson, C J
English, G M
English, G M
Eyears, L W S
Fardell, S J
Farhoud, J S L
Fenske, M
Ferguson, A W
Ferguson, S A
Fisher, F F
Fitch, L E
Fleming, M C
Foley, E I
Foley, R J E
Fox, J M
Frampton, M C
Fraser, C V
Fuad, F
Gallivan, R J
Ganczakowski, S K
Ganesh, I S
Garside, J P
Gaunt, V P
George, D M
Gillett, G B
Glaze, M E
Gnanakumaran, G
Godbole, V
Godbolt, A K
Gooding, R G
Gordon, E A C
Gray, A P
Greenish, B V I
Grice, G C
Griffith, T P
Hadfield, J I H
Haggie, S J
Hamilton, B H
Haque, S
Harland, A I
Harling, R E
Harries, A M
Harrison, J
Hassard, J R
Haywood, R J
Haywood, R M
Hedges, J I
Hedges, K M
Hemy, L M
Hicks, I P
Hoare, T J
Hood, J E
Hopper, C
Howard, D J
Howell, A P
Howes, D T
Hughes, S P
Hurst, J
Hyder, M N
Indra Kumar, K
Inskip, T G
Iqbal, M
Jackson, R F
Jaiswal, R S
James, P S
Janjua, F C
Jones, B G
Jones, C J
Jones, S R
Jones, T M
Josephs, J
Kanungo, S M
Kathane, R H
Kavan, R
Kedward, J F
Kelly, M B
Khanbhai, A T
Khiani, M L
Khokher, T H
King, R G P
Kirubakaran, S
Kotecha, N
Kruszewska, J W M
Kukendrarajah, K
Leigh, M
Leonard, S J
Lessell, C B
Lindo, D G
Lindsay, J I

Ling, H-L
Liu, D W H
Lobb, M O
Lockley, W J
Lotay, N S
Lowe, S W
Lua, S H
Luthra, D S
MacInnes, R E
Mackellar, B N
McNamara, P A
Main, R E W
Malden, M A
Manford, M R A
Markar, H R
Marner, S P
Martin, W A
Mason, R C S H
Mee, W M
Mehta, R D
Miller, R G
Mooly, A S
Monk, B E
Monks, D C
Morris, R H
Morrish, N J
Moxon, R A
Munno, A
Murdie, W
Murphy, J P
Murray, R M B
Mutch, A F
Naeem, S M
Nagreh, B K
Nawal, H C S
Nayar, V K
Neale, E J
Nel, G
Niblett, D J
Nicol, L G
Nixon, C J
Noel, M G B
Norris, R
O'Neill, E M
O'Rourke, M H
Oakley, R H
Obara, L G
Odunsi, L O
Ogborn, A D R
Onyekwuluje, C E
Parkes, J C
Parry Okeden, P C U
Parson, D A
Parsons, D C S
Patel, A G
Peacock, B
Pettman, S B
Pienkowski, C F
Pocha, M J
Pope, I M
Prior, M
Rae, S A
Rajapakse, A D P
Rawlins, R D
Read, N E
Reddy, J
Rees, D C
Reynolds, S F
Rhodes, D J
Riding, W D
Riley, T B H
Rimmer, D B
Roberts-Thomson, J H
Rochford, J J
Ross, F M
Rowe, P G
Rupasinghe, E P
Ryan, R P
Sahai, C M
Samel, V P
Saparamadu, P V D D
Sattiarajah, A I
Saunders, J H B
Shah, D K
Shankar, A N
Shankar, S
Shanmugaratnam, K
Sharrock, J K C
Simmonds, M J
Singhal, A
Sivabalan, T
Sizer, J M
Skipper, D
Small, D J
Smith, J J M
Smyly, E M B
Snape, J W F
Snape, S L
Soni, I R

Soni, V K
Sowerby, R F
Spies, J A
Sprott, M M
Stanton, J R
Steynor, G R
Stow, S L
Suddle, A N
Sydenham, D J
Tatman, P J
Taylor, F R
Thomas, H L
Thomas, M J
Todd, M M
Todd, O R
Toovey, A J
Toovey, A R
Tredget, J M
Tree, J R
Trounson, W N
Ungaro, A R
Valentine, J C
Villatoro Lopez, E A
Wali, J D
Wallace, R M
Wallis, M
Walters, M
Waterfall, N B
Webster, L K
Wheldon, D B
White, N A
White, W T
Wijayaratne, W M T
Wilden, S D
Wilkins, I A
Wilkins, M J E
Wilkinson, P S
Willis, A T
Wilson, J J
Wilson, J U
Yee, K M
Yerbury, G M

Bedlington

Abbey, H B
Cape, A M
Forster, D P
Harris, P J S
Harrison, J
Hawthorne, P S
Hobson, J E
Marshall, C M
Mather, J F
Munro, E W
Sen, I
Starkey, G
Starkey, K G
Summers, D J
Tallantyre, P M
Taylor, F J B
Todd, J

Bedworth

Menage, J

Beith

Brodie, K M
Campbell, L M J
Isbister, G I
Jamieson, A
McCarroll, S E
Madsen, S
Morrissey, A F
Morrissey, M S C
Peggie, D A

Belfast

Abdo, K R
Abraham, H M
Abram, W P
Acheson, D J
Acheson, N
Acton, J D
Adair, A I
Adair, I V
Adair, J J
Adair, N S S
Adair, R A
Adair, S R
Adams, D A
Adams, G
Adams, H E
Adams, J H
Adams, M G
Addidle, M
Addley, K
Agnew, L M
Akhtar, A S
Alcorn, J R M
Alderdice, D K
Alderdice, J T
Alexander, J P
Ali, A
Allen, A R
Allen, D C
Allen, G S
Allen, G E
Allen, I V
Allen, J D
Allen, J A
Allen, M J
Anderson, L C
Anderson, N H
Anderson, R J
Anderson, W J A
Andrews, C T
Anjum, J I
Annamalai, G
Archer, D B
Ardill, A C
Armstrong, A M
Armstrong, D L
Armstrong, D K B
Armstrong, F T
Armstrong, M A
Armstrong, R
Atkinson, R J
Atkinson, S
Austin, S J
Bailey, I C
Bailie, A G
Bailie, C A L
Bailie, K E M
Bailie, L M
Bailie, N
Baird, D J R
Baird, R H
Bakry, M A A
Ball, J A C
Ball, P A
Bamber, J H
Bamber, M D
Bamford, D H
Bamford, K B
Bannon, D
Barbour, J V R
Barr, R J
Barros D'Sa, E A
Barros D'Sa, V F
Baylis, P M
Beattie, D C
Beatty, O L
Bell, A
Beirne, D M
Beirne, P K
Beirne, P A
Bell, A H
Bell, A L
Bell, B A
Bell, D J A
Bell, J D
Bell, J M
Bell, K R
Bell, P F
Bell, P M
Bell, P
Bentley, A J
Beringer, T R O
Best, B G
Best, R M
Beverland, D E
Bew, M
Bharucha, H
Bhat, K K
Bieler, Z A
Biggart, J D
Bill, K M
Bingham, E A
Black, A J
Black, C E
Black, E A
Blair, T M
Bolton, D S
Bolton, P W
Bolton, S D J
Bond, E B
Bonnar, G E
Boreland, G J
Bowden, J B
Bowers, M J
Boyd, C S
Boyd, D D
Boyd, H G M
Boyd, J S
Boyd, N A M
Boyd, S A S
Boyd, T H
Boyle, D D
Boyle, D M
Boyle, J P
Boyle, M M I
Bradley, J A G
Bradley, P
Bradley, T
Brady, M M M
Breach, J F
Breach, M J W
Brady, K A
Breene, E R
Brennen, M D
Bridges, J M
Briggs, G M
Briscoe, M
Brooker, D S
Brooks, C A
Brotherston, T M
Brown, H M
Brown, H C
Brown, J G
Brown, J A
Brown, P T K
Brown, S
Brown, T
Brown, W M
Browne, F W A
Browne, G A
Browne, J N
Bruce, I N
Bryson, C A
Buchanan, H K
Buchanan, T A S
Buckley, M R E
Bunting, B M
Burke, B E
Burns, G E
Burrows, B D
Burrows, D
Burton, J T
Busby, R E
Byrne, L J P
Byrnes, C K C
Byrnes, D P
Byrnes, S M A
Byrnes, T J D
Cairns, A P
Cairns, C M
Calderwood, C J
Calderwood, J W
Callaghan, M J
Callender, B E
Callender, M E
Calwell, D E
Cameron, R I
Campbell, D K
Campbell, D H
Campbell, J E
Campbell, L M
Campbell, M
Campbell, W I
Canavan, D A
Carabine, U A
Carnaghan, L E
Carser, J E
Carson, C A
Carson, D J
Carson, F D G
Carson, I W
Carson, J M
Carton, P F
Casement, M E
Casey, Y A
Cashell, C F
Cashell, M P
Caskey, G M
Cassidy, E E
Caughley, L M
Cavanagh, S A
Chakravarty, B
Chambers, S A
Chambers, S J
Chan, S K
Chan, W S
Chan, W C
Chapman, C J D
Chapman, D G
Chapman, R C
Cheah, F S
Chee, T O C
Cheng, K E
Cheuk, C
Cheung, C C
Chew, E W
Chew, M W
Chew, Y H
Cheyne, D B
Chidrawar, M M
Chin, T M M
Choo, D S F
Christie, E M
Christie, S N
Chua, R K W
Cinnamond, M J
Clarke, E W
Clarke, G S E
Clarke, J I M
Clarke, J C
Clarke, J C
Clarke, K E
Clarke, R S J
Clements, J G
Clements, R A
Clements, W D B
Cleugh, P A
Cochrane, B A
Cochrane, D J
Cole, C M
Cole, T B
Colgan, B J
Colleary, G
Collier, J F
Collins, A J
Collins, C J
Collins, D D M
Collins, F J
Collins, J P
Collins, K M
Collins, V C A
Colton, F M E
Colville, J
Compton, S A
Conn, P G
Connolly, C K
Connolly, J D R
Connolly, J H
Connolly, J P
Connolly, M J
Connolly, N P
Convery, P N
Conway, B R
Conway, K P
Conway, M F
Coogan, M
Cooke, E A
Cooke, J-L
Cooke, R S
Cooper, J
Cooper, S J
Coppel, D L
Corbett, J R
Corcoran, J D R
Corkey, C L
Corr, J F
Corrie, P R
Corry, I S
Cosgrove, A P
Cosgrove, S D
Coulson, S M
Coulter, J E M
Courtney, P A
Cowie, G H
Coyle, D J
Coyle, J M
Coyle, V M
Craig, B F
Craig, B G
Craig, C L
Craig, J J
Craig, J S
Crane, J
Crawley, U C
Crean, P M
Cromey, G M
Cromie, A J
Crone, M D
Crookes, R E
Croskery, S E
Crossin, C M
Crossin, J D
Crossin, T C
Crothers, J G
Crowther, G R
Crozier, C L
Cruickshanks, S T
Culbert, M A
Cullen, B M
Cullen, C M
Cummings, A J
Curran, F P
Curran, H J M
Currie, J N
Currie, W P
Curry, R C
Cuthbert, R J G
D'Arcy, F G
Dallas, A J
Dalzell, G W N
Darby, B J

Belfast

Dargan, C B
Darragh, J H
Darragh, P G
Davis, R I
Dawson, J F
Dawson, N F
Dearden, C H
Deasy, D M
Deeney, S
Deignan, E B
Dempsey, S I
Devendra, D
Deyermond, R E
Diamond, A M
Diamond, M C
Diamond, P J
Dick, A C
Dick, A G
Dick, C J
Dillon, P J
Dilworth, G R
Dinsmore, W W
Diong, K-L
Dixon, R T
Dobson, G
Doherty, C C
Doherty, G M
Doherty, J K
Doherty, M M
Doherty, S P
Dolan, J J
Dolan, L M
Dolan, O M
Donaghy, J F
Donaldson, R A
Donaldson, S N
Donnelly, C S
Donnelly, D E
Donnelly, G M
Donnelly, M J
Donnelly, M C
Donnelly, M
Donnelly, R P
Donnelly, U M
Doran, N F
Dornan, S J
Dougan, J P
Douglas, J F
Dowey, K E
Downey, B G
Downey, M P
Downing, R R C
Doyle, J
Doyle, S M
Droogan, A G
Duddy, M E
Duffin, M S
Duffy, C M
Dugan, J P
Duncan, C G
Dunlop, D J
Dunlop, J M
Dunlop, K A
Dunlop, P A
Dunlop, R
Durkan, V J R
Dynan, C E
Dynan, K B
Eakin, R L
Eakins, W A
Edgar, J D M
Eedy, D J
Egan, J
Ekin, E H
Ekin, W H
El Agnaf, M R
El-Gaddal, A A H
Elliott, P
Emanuel, M Q
English, B
English, F C
Esmonde, T F G
Essandoh, R S
Eu, T Y
Evans, A E
Evans, J R
Evans, N D
Fair, B E
Falls, N B T
Fannin, T F
Farling, P A
Farnan, B J
Farnan, E P
Farnan, T B
Farrell, J G
Faulkner, P R
Fee, J P H
Feenan, S D
Ferguson, C J S
Ferguson, H R
Ferguson, K
Fetherston, M S
Field, C M B
Finlay, F O
Finlay, S R
Finnegan, J M
Finney, E J
Fisher, R B
Fitch, C M
Fitch, M
Fitzpatrick, K T J
Fitzpatrick, M S
Flanagan, N M
Flannery, D J
Fleming, G A
Fleming, J C
Flett, R H
Flynn, P A
Fogarty, B J
Fogarty, D G
Fogarty, P P
Fon, L J
Foo, A W
Foo, L K
Forbes, J M
Foster, P A H M
Foster, P A
Foy, C J
Frazer, D G
Frazer, M J L
Frew, N C
Froggatt, P
Fryers, S G
Fullerton, K J
Fulton, D I
Fulton, R J
Fulton, T T
Gallacher, C
Gallagher, A
Gallagher, E J
Gallagher, G M
Gallagher, P F
Galloway, R M
Gardiner, C M
Gardiner, K R
Gardiner, V R
Gardner, C S
Gavin, A T
Gawley, S P
George, K A
George, R R
Gibbons, M J
Gibson, F M
Gibson, J M
Gibson, R
Gibson, S F
Giles, C M
Giles, C J
Gillespie, I A
Gillespie, P E
Gillespie, S F
Gilligan, C J
Gilligan, M T
Gilliland, A E W
Gillvray, K E
Gilmer, S O
Gilmore, D H
Gilmore, I R
Gilmour, C A
Gilroy, D G
Glackin, S
Glasgow, A C A
Glasgow, J F T
Gleadhill, D N S
Gleadhill, V F D
Glenfield, J E
Glover, P J
Goldsmith, E C
Gordon, D J
Gordon, D S
Gorman, C C
Gorman, C C
Gormley, G J
Gormley, M J J
Gormley, P J A
Gormley, S M C
Gough, A D
Gough, F C
Gough, P J
Gracey, S E
Graham, A C
Graham, A N J
Graham, A
Graham, C J
Graham, D A
Graham, D T
Graham, E A
Graham, E L
Graham, M E
Graham, R
Grant, B
Gray, J E
Gray, R C
Gray, W J
Green, J N S
Greer, A M
Greeves, L G
Gregory, A L
Grey, A C
Gunna, B R
Gunning, L M
Guy, R L
Guy, S E
Hadden, D R
Hadden, D S M
Haire, M
Hall, D M
Hall, J D I
Hall, J G
Hall, J A
Hall, J C
Hall, R
Halliday, C
Halliday, H L
Halliday, J A
Hamill, B A
Hamilton, D
Hamilton, E A
Hamilton, I S
Hamilton, J W
Hamilton, M S
Hampton, M A
Hampton, S M
Handley, J M
Hanley, P D
Hanna, E V
Hanna, P R
Hanna, W A
Hannon, R J
Harbinson, M T
Harland, R W
Harley, I J G
Harley, J M G
Harper, E E
Harper, G K
Harper, K W
Harper, M A
Harper, R
Harris, P G
Harris, W E
Harrison, C
Hart, D C
Hart, P M A
Harvey, C F
Haslam, L J
Hawthorne, P W
Hayes, D
Heaney, L G
Hegan, P D
Henderson, J M C
Henderson, J D
Henderson, S A
Hendron, J G
Henry, J F
Henry, M E C
Henry, P G
Henry, R W
Herdman, G J
Herity, N A
Herron, B M
Herron, K
Heylings, D J A
Hickey, M C A
Higgins, J A
Higgins, S M
Higginson, J D S
Hill, A E
Hill, C M
Hill, D A
Ho, T S
Hoey, D P W
Holmes, E J
Holmes, L M R
Holterman, K A
Hooks, I C
Hopkins, M R
Horner, G F B
Houghton, J P
Houston, J K
Houston, K E
Houston, R F
Howe, J P
Huda, U
Hughes, D A
Hughes, D M
Hughes, J A F
Hughes, M L
Hughes, R
Humphreys, R O
Hunter, A J
Hunter, C M
Hunter, D C
Hunter, J
Hunter, O G
Hunter, S J
Huntley, L E
Hurwitz, D S
Hutchison, T H
Hyland, M A
Hyland, P N
Hynes, J M
Irvine, A
Irvine, A D
Irvine, A K
Irvine, G J G
Irvine, G M
Irvine, J J B
Irwin, A W
Irwin, D G
Irwin, E A
Irwin, J W S
Irwin, R B
Irwin, S T
Jackson, C H D
Jackson, W E
Jamieson, R
Janes, E S
Jefferson, J C
Jefferson, J A
Jhagroo, R R
Johnson, M J
Johnston, G D
Johnston, J M
Johnston, J R
Johnston, L E
Johnston, P B
Johnston, P G
Johnston, P W
Johnston, S D
Johnston, T G
Jones, F G C
Jones, M
Jones, P
Jong, M
Kealey, W D C
Keane, H M I
Keane, M T
Keane, P F
Kee, F
Kee, M A A
Keilty, S R
Keith, D B
Kelly, B E
Kelly, E R
Kelly, J E
Kelly, J E M
Kelly, L S
Kelly, M M T
Kelly, M G
Kelly, M C
Kelly, R E
Kelly, S A T M
Kendrick, R W
Kennedy, J A
Kennedy, J A
Kennedy, M T
Kennedy, P
Kennedy, P T
Kennedy, T G
Kenny, L M
Kernohan, M M
Kerr, A G
Kerr, A N
Kerr, A
Kerr, D N
Kerr, H
Kerr, K M
Kerr, P P
Kerr, R V C
Kerrigan, B M
Kervick, G N
Kettle, P J
Keys, C M
Khan, K
Khoo, B C H
Khoo, S M-L
Khosravi-Nezhad, B
Khosraviani, K
Kidd, A M
Kidwai, B J
Kilbane, M P J K
Kilgore, H J
King, C M
King, D J
King, K R
King, S M
King, T C F
King, W F I
Kinney, A M
Kirk, C D
Kirk, G R
Kirk, K S
Kirk, S J
Kirkpatrick, A
Kirkpatrick, D H
Kitara-Okot, P
Knight, C M
Knox, E W
Knox, L M
Kuan, Y C
Kyle, E A
Kyle, S J
Lai, H K
Lalsingh, I R
Lambe, D E
Lambert, R G W
Lamki, H M N
Lasa Gallego, M A
Lau, L L
Lavelle, A E
Laverick, M D
Lavery, A G
Lavery, P E
Lawler, A M
Lawson, J T
Leddy, F
Lee, A L
Lee, B
Lee, D E T
Lee, J T-S
Lee, S M
Leggett, J J
Leggett, P F
Leitch, A J
Lenfesty, J P
Lennox, J D
Leonard, A G
Leonard, N
Lewis, A E
Lewis, H G
Lewis, J N
Lewis, M A
Li, A H-Y
Lim, C T S
Lim, C C
Lim, P L
Lim, Y Y
Lindsay, K G
Ling, T C
Little, J M
Little, M A
Livingstone, A F
Loan, W C
Loane, B J
Loane, R A
Lockie, P D
Logan, J I
Logan, J S
Logan, M-L
Lotery, A J
Lotery, H E
Loughran, P G
Loughrey, A C B
Loughrey, C B M
Loughrey, C M
Loughrey, C M
Loughrey, M B
Loughrey, P G
Loughridge, E A
Loughridge, J C H
Loughridge, R J
Loughridge, W G G
Lovell, S L
Lowry, J P S
Lowry, K A
Lowry, K G
Lowry, P P
Lowther, D J
Lua, Y C
Lundy, G P P
Lynas, R F A
Lynas, W J
Lynch, G M
Lynch, J V
Lynch, T H
Lyness, R W
Lyons, A R
Lyons, H A
Lyons, J D M
Lyons, M S
Lyons, S M
Lyttle, J A
Lyttle, K D L
McAlea, P M
McAleer, J J A
Mcaleese, J J
McAlinden, M G
McAllister, A S
McAllister, J M
McArdle, L
McAtamney, D G
McAteer, J A
McAteer, M P
McAughey, J M
MacAuley, A M
McAuley, D F
MacAuley, D J
Macauley, D C
McAuley, D M
McAuley, E M J
Mcauley, M R
McBride, M O
McBride, W T
McCabe, N E E
McCafferty, F G
McCaffrey, J E
McCallion, K
Mccallion, W A
MacCallum, W A G
McCance, D R
McCann, J P
McCarroll, C P
McCarthy, B T
McCarthy, M A
McCarthy, M D
McCartney, E M
McCartney, M
McCarty, D
McCarty, H A
McCaughern, S G
Mccaughey, C P J
McCaughey, M
McCauley, A A M
McCay, N M
McClean, M
McCleery, A J
McCleery, M R
McClelland, R
McClelland, W M
McClements, B M
McCloskey, B V
McCloskey, M S
McCloy, M P
McCluggage, J R
McClure, K A
McClure, M C
McClure, N
McCluskey, C
McCluskey, D R
McCollum, J S C
McComb, D W
McConkey, C D
McConkey, M J
McConnell, L A
McConnell, R G C
McConway, J H F
McCormack, S R E
McCourt, K C
Mccoy, E P
McCoy, G F M
McCracken, N
McCracken, S R C
McCrea, G W
McCreesh, G A
McCrory, D C
McCullagh, C D
McCullagh, M R
McCullins, M E
McCune, K H
McCutcheon, A
McDonald, G H
McDonald, P A
McDonnell, A
McDonnell, C M
McDonnell, G V
McDowell, W A
McEldowney, U J
McElhenny, B E
McElwaine, A V
McElwee, C S E
McEntee, S H
McErlane, J R C M
McEvoy, J D
McEvoy, M D
McEwen, E A M
McFarland, G L
McFarland, M A
McFarland, R J
McFaul, P B
McFerran, K
McGarrity, S J
McGarry, C J P
McGarry, P J
McGarvey, L P A

Belfast

McGeough, P T
McGeown, J G
McGeown, M G
McGibben, B F
McGibbon, S P
McGinn, C M S
McGinnity, F G
McGlade, K J
Mcgleenon, B M
McGlennon, D M
McGonigle, R J
McGouty, E C
McGovern, G J M
McGovern, J M
McGovern, M C
McGovern, S M M
McGovern, T D
McGovern, V M
McGowan, D J
MacGowan, S W
McGrath, K J
McgRead, A J
McGrogan, P J
McGuffin, K M
McGurk, C T
McHenry, S M
McHugh, C J
McHugh, J A
McHugh, J O P
McHugh, S J A
McIlrath, E M
McIlrath, R A
McIlroy, R L
McIver, M S
McIvor, E M H
McIvor, P J
McKaigue, J P
McKane, W R
McKay, A C
McKee, C H W
McKee, R H
McKeever, G J K
McKelvey, A
McKelvey, S T D
McKenna, D J J
McKenna, G L
McKenna, J F
McKenna, M P
McKenna, M P
McKenna, S M M
McKeown, D S P
McKeown, E F
McKeown, P B
McKeown, R P
McKernan, M F
McKie, L D
McKinney, K A
McKinney, M S
McKinstry, A R
McKinstry, C S
McKnight, A G
McKnight, F E W
McLarnon, R S W
McLaverty, D M
MacLennan, B A
McLeod, S
McLeod, W J
McLorinan, G C
McLoughlin, C M
McLoughlin, C C
McLoughlin, J C
McLoughlin, J S
MacMahon, J
McMahon, N M
McMahon, R
McManus, D T
McManus, J
Macmanus, M P
McMaster, J I
McMechan, S R
McMillan, J A
McMillan, J C
McMillan, M I
McMillen, H K
McMillin, W P
McMordie, E A M
McMullan, M J
McMullan, P F
McMullen, E A
McMullin, M F
McNaboe, E J D
McNally, D P G
McNally, J R A
McNamee, D A
McNamee, H M
McNarry, A F
McNeill, S I
McNicholl, B P G
McNutt, C E

Macpherson, C
Macsorley, M P
MacSorley, P J
McVeigh, G E
McVeigh, L M
McVicker, J M
Magee, A C
Magee, G D
Mageean, A M
Magennis, H M
Magill, E A
Maguire, P
Maguire, D F
Maguire, O T
Maguire, W A
Maini, A K
Mairs, A P
Maitland, J E
Major, K J
Malik, J Z
Manderson, L L
Mangan, B G
Mangan, C M
Manoharan, G
Manwell, M K C
Mark, M C
Markey, G M
Marsh, D R
Marshall, B A
Marshall, C A
Marshall, D F
Martin, A C
Martin, D
Martin, G R C
Martin, J B
Martin, M F T
Martin, P S
Masroor, T
Mathews, H M L
Matthews, C F
Matthews, S J
Maw, R D J
Mawhinney, H J D
Mawhinney, S
Maxwell, A P
Maxwell, R J
Maynard, S J
Mayne, E E
Mee, J D
Meenagh, C P
Meenan, G W
Mellotte, M E
Meroown, I B A
Mercer, C I
Mestel, A L
Middleton, A M N
Millar, J K
Miller, R L
Milligan, K R
Milligan, S
Milliken, J A H
Mills, D M J
Minford, H D F
Mirakhur, M
Mirakhur, R K
Mitchell, D J
Mitchell, E
Mitchell, R M S
Moffett, J C
Molloy, M E
Monaghan, C A
Moncrieff, E M
Montgomery, D A D
Montgomery, E A
Montgomery, S A
Moohan, V P
Moon, A R
Moore, A L
Moore, J E M
Moore, J E
Moore, S P
Moore, V C
Moorehead, C N S
Moorehead, R J
Morgan, B J F
Morison, J E
Morris, K
Morris, T C M
Morrison, P J
Morrison, R L
Morrow, J I
Morrow, V S
Moynihan, P
Muldoon, O T
Mulgrew, J A
Mulholland, C K
Mulholland, H C
Mulholland, K C
Mulholland, M I

Mulholland, M G
Mullally, B
Mulvenna, B A
Murdock, E M
Murnaghan, M E
Murphy, B G
Murphy, G J J
Murphy, M F
Murphy, R D
Murphy, T F B
Murray, B
Murray, J M A
Murtagh, E G
Murtagh, H B
Murtagh, J G
Murtagh, J
Murthy, K
Mustafa, M A B
Nagar, H A
Neagle, E H
Neary, J T
Neeson, C
Neill, J G
Nelson, J K
Nelson, J K
Nelson, K A
Nelson, M G
Nelson, W E
Nelson, W M
Neoh, K H P
Nethercott, R G
Newlands, L C
Nicholas, J
Nicholas, R M
Nicholl, H J M
Nicholl, R M
Nicholls, D P
Nicholson, M J
Noh, M B M
Nolan, C P
Norris, A M
Nugent, A M
O'Connor, B G
O'Connor, M G
O'Connor, P J
O'Doherty, A J
O'Donnell, M T
O'Gorman, C
O'Hagan, S
O'Hagan, S J
O'Hara, M D
O'Hare, D M
O'Hare, M P
O'Kane, A E
O'Kane, D J
O'Kane, D
O'Kane, H F G
O'Kane, H O
O'Kane, J M
O'Keeffe, D B
O'Keeffe, U B
O'Loan, A A
O'Neill, B M
O'Neill, E G J
O'Neill, F A
O'Neill, G D
O'Neill, H F
O'Neill, T W
O'Rawe, A M
O'Rawe, B M A
O'Reilly, M J
O'Rourke, D M
O'Sullivan, A K
O'Sullivan, J F
Odling-Smee, G W
Ogbobi, S E
Oneill, M F
Ong, G M L
Ong, H Y
Ong, S H
Ong, Y L
Ong, Y L
Orr, D H
Oryema, M B
Osterberg, P H
Owusuansa, N
Park, R M
Parke, R C
Parke, S C
Parks, L
Parks, T G
Passmore, A P
Patterson, A
Patterson, A S
Patterson, D G
Patterson, G C
Patterson, V H
Patton, L
Patton, W C

Paulin, M N M
Paxton, L D
Peden, K I
Pedlow, P J
Pendleton, A
Perrin, M E
Phair, I C
Phillips, A S
Pinkerton, F
Pinkerton, J H M
Pitt, J B
Porter, M A
Porter, W D
Power, M J P
Price, J H
Primrose, E D
Quah, S P
Quinn, F M
Quinn, M J
Quinn, S R
Rafferty, C G
Rafferty, M S
Rainey, G J
Rainey, G W
Rainey, N A
Rainey, R S
Ramsay-Baggs, P
Ramsey, H C
Ramsey, J A
Ramsey, J C P
Ranaghan, E A
Rankin, M G
Rankin, S J A
Raphael, A M
Rea, G R
Rea, I M
Redmond, O A B
Refsum, S E
Reid, A J M
Reid, I A C
Reid, J E
Reid, J E
Reid, M A
Reid, M M
Reid, P T
Reilly, P
Renfrew, C W
Rethinasamy, E L
Richardson, R J
Richardson, S G
Riddell, G
Riddell, J G
Riddell, J W
Ritchie, I S D
Robb, D E
Roberts, M J D
Roberts, R N
Roberts, S D
Robertson, J H
Robinson, F E
Robinson, F L J
Robinson, J M
Robinson, K A
Robinson, R K
Rocke, L G
Rodden, N D
Roddie, K A
Rodgers, C
Rodgers, L M
Rodgers, S A
Rodrigues, R J C
Rogan, J T
Rogan, S M
Rooney, A
Rooney, P J
Ross, A M
Ross, R W D
Rowan, I G
Rowan, M G
Rowney, W R
Rudralingam, V
Ruiz Herrero, A L
Rusk, R A
Russell, C F J
Russell, J C
Russell, M F
Rutherford, J R
Rutherford, M E
Rutherford, W H
Ryan, A M
Ryan, R J
Sadler, M A
Salathia, K S
Salters, M
Samuel, M
Sandhu, S K
Savage, D M
Savage, J M
Sawh, B

Sawhney, B B
Scally, B G
Scally, M J
Scoffield, J L
Scott, A C
Scott, C E
Scott, J N
Scott, K C
Scott, K W
Scott, L C
Scott, M J
Scott, M E
Scott, T J
Seymour, G G
Shamoun, O S A M
Shanks, R G
Shannon, J M
Sharkey, J J M
Sharkey, P J
Sharma, P
Sharp, E
Sharpe, D R K
Shaw, R A
Shaw, V J E
Shaw, Y P
Shearer, K
Shearer, R M
Shepherd, D R T
Shepperd, H W H
Sherrard, E S M
Sherwood, J I
Shields, E G
Shields, M D
Shiels, A M K
Short, M E C
Shum, P L
Silvestri, G
Simpson, D I H
Simpson, R
Singh, S
Sinnott, B S
Sivananthan, S S
Skan, D I M
Skelly, R T
Sloan, J M
Sloan, M K
Sloan, S
Sloan, S C
Small, C
Small, F M
Small, J O
Small, R B
Small, U R
Smith, D J
Smith, P
Smyth, E T M
Smyth, F
Smyth, F B
Smyth, J S
Smyth, R
Spence, R A J
Spence, S D
Spencer, E F A
Stamm, R G W
Steele, E K
Steele, I C
Steele, P S
Steele, W K
Steen, H J
Stevens, A B
Stevenson, H M
Stewart, A J
Stewart, F J
Stewart, M C
Stewart, P C
Stewart, R C
Stewart, T J
Stout, R W
Stranex, S
Swain, A
Swain, K B
Swain, W D
Swallow, M W
Swan, K O
Swann, M A
Sweeney, D
Sweeney, L E
Sweet, D G
Taggart, A J
Taggart, C M
Taggart, H M
Talbot, P S
Tallon, G M
Tan, K S
Tan, M C S
Tang, R Z-G
Tate, S
Tay McGarry, G S
Taylor, I C

Taylor, R H
Taylor, T C
Tennet, H M
Tham, T C K
Thompson, A W
Thompson, A J
Thompson, A M
Thompson, E M
Thompson, E J
Thompson, G H
Thompson, M A
Thompson, N S
Thompson, R N J
Thompson, W
Thornbury, G D
Thornbury, K D
Thornton, C M
Thornton, M
Thornton, P D
Thornton, W D
Toal, B J
Todd, D O
Tohill, J
Tohill, M P
Toland, J M P
Toner, J G
Toner, P G
Tracey, M E
Traub, A I
Trethowan, B A
Trimble, F M
Trimble, M
Trimble, P H C
Trimble, W G C
Trinick, T R
Troup, I M
Tsang, W C
Tsang, W K
Tubman, T R J
Turner, G
Twinem, G S
Ullah, R M
Urquhart, A D
Vallely, S R
Vaughan, P K
Wadgaonkar, P S
Walby, A P
Walker, N J P
Walker, P T
Walker, S H
Walker, W H A
Wallace, R B
Wallace, R J
Wallace, W F M
Walsh, I K
Walsh, M Y
Ward, R P S
Warke, T
Wasson, C
Waterman, M R
Waters, H M
Watkins, D C
Watson, J D
Watt, E
Watt, M
Watters, J P
Weatherup, J
Weaver, J A
Webb, C H
Webb, S W
Wells, M D
White, B J
White, D W
White, D S
White, J A
White, S T
Whiteside, R J
Wiggam, M I
Wilde, J C
Wilkinson, A J
Wilkinson, C D
Wilkinson, P
Williamson, G F
Williamson, G
Williamson, S K
Willis, C E
Willis, J
Willis, J
Wilson, A E J
Wilson, A G C
Wilson, B G
Wilson, C M
Wilson, C M
Wilson, D B
Wilson, E
Wilson, G A
Wilson, H K
Wilson, J M
Wilson, J E

Belford

Wilson, J M
Wilson, L
Wilson, M M
Wilson, P J K
Wilson, P B
Wilson, P J
Wilson, R H
Wilson, R I
Wilson, R K
Wilson, S J
Wilson, S D
Wilson, W N
Wilson, Y T
Windrum, P
Winn, J H
Wolsley, K
Wong, G T
Wong, Y W
Woodman, A M
Woodrow, E A
Woods, J P
Woods, J D
Wright, G D
Wright, J F
Wright, R D
Wright, R E R
Yamin-Ali, R G
Yarnell, J W G
Yoon, L L
Young, C M
Young, I S
Younger, J M
Zschocke, A M
Zubier, C M P
Zubier, F A

Belford

Ashby, D W R
Brown, G M
Evans, J C
Gill, D K
Gill, S J
Miller, E C
Miller, S N
Morrison, D
Pawson, R H
Upjohn, C H C
Warrander, A
Williams, P G

Bellshill

Bradshaw, T A
Browning, J D
Cameron-Mowat, G
D'Netto, M
Duncan, E M
Elder, A G
Fletcher, L O A
Gallagher, M
Gordon, H K
Kelly, C A
Lindsay, K
McKibbin, C M
McLenachan, W M
Muir, W J
Ritchie, S A
Zuberi, S A

Belper

Atherton, S J
Barkham, M H
Batty, R
Bold, T A W P
Brabiner, D
Brentnall, C J
Brett, M J E
Bruzaud, J D
Burke, F D
Chapman, M G T
Fairweather, J E
Giovannelli, M A
Hanson, S A
Harris, R C
Leyland, B
McKenzie, E M B
McLachlan, S G
Millward, E L
Nathan, P A
O'Flanagan, P H
Rutherford, J M
Stephenson, J D
Stevens, C E
Taylor, I R
Venables, M G M
Ward, J R
Wright, D G
Young, J G

Belvedere

Adagra, M B
Adrian, C K
Ali, M F
Beckley, G A J
Bruce, E
Camp, B J
Dave, R J
De Waal, F
Kapur, S K
Mandl, S A
Marus, A G F
Pattison, D C
Roy, S R
Sehgal, N N
Taylor, E C

Bembridge

Barker, C S
Cuddigan, J H P
Kaula, C V
McComb, P E F
Swinstead, P D
Thomas, D S

Benbecula

Dessouki, N R R

Benfleet

Acres, D I
Baker, R J N
Bendkowski, B
Betts-Brown, A
Bunney, J A
Cardwell, M E
Coombes, A G A
Dhingra, S K
Gardiner, R A
Gill, S S
Gupta, S K
Gutteridge, H J
Hawker, P G
Hiscock, S C
Holloway, I A
Leahy, P D
Lemmens, J A
Lester, M J
McGladdery, J A
Mott, H W
Patel, R M
Pilsworth, R
Pope, J A F
Simpson, M E
Smith, M J
Smithson, D L
Tan, L A
Taylor, R E
Timms, R L
Trotter, G G
Waiwaiku, K N
Wessels, H M A H
Wilde, J P
Wong, R Y-C

Berkeley

Davies, N F
Higgs, S J
James, F E
Joyce, D N
Longstaff, A J
Walshe, P B
Wilson, P

Berkhamsted

Aitchison, E I
Andrews, C J
Baker, G M
Banerji, A K
Benjamin, A
Calnan, J S
Chuter, G S J
Conway, Z F
Corbin, C J
Crawfurd, M A
Currie, C L A
Dalton, R S J
Evans, J B
Evans, S C
Fleming, H C
Franc, N L
Freedman, D B
Garner, A J J
Garratt, A
Garratt, C D
Hallan, L A
Harbord, K W M
Harris, J E
Hill, G G
Lees, W
Manton, H E

Meyer, P C
Monsell, F P
Nath, A R
Ormiston, I N R
Ponsonby, C E
Ramsay, B
Rees, D C
Rennie, I G
Rice-Edwards, S A
Roythorne, J P
Sargaison, J M
Saunders, K M
Squire, A J
Staunton, M H
Suchy, K C
Taylor, R A
Thiriwall, A S
Thornber, A J
Tutty, C L
Underwood, T J
Walker, R I
Ward, A M
Williams, H F
Williams, R A

Berwick-upon-Tweed

Alison, A C
Binnie, G A C
Bottone, N P
Bromly, A C
Cheek, B N
Drummond, A W
Fisken, J
Gunning, D P
Johnson, C D G
Knight, R A
McMahon, J B
Mather, R F
Mitchell, J H
Reavley, P D A
Robertson, L E
Semple, G A
Sinclair, T M
Smith, B C H
Spink, M
Watson, I F
Watson, J M
Wood, P F A
Wooding, R M S
Wright, H M

Betchworth

Belton, E M
Crawshaw, J W A
Jenner, G J
Kober, P H
Mathews, B H
Newton, W B
Rawson, L E
Sevenoaks, T A
Webster-Smith, C S
Whiteley, J S

Betws-y-Coed

Chown, C S M
Evans, C
Metcalfe, R E
Park, A V

Beverley

Adams, R H M
Ali, M A
Ali, S A
Almond, D J
Bashir, B A R
Bawn, B L
Bestley, J W
Beynon, B
Bibby, K E S
Bradshaw, J D
Branton, J F
Caldwell, P J
Carruthers, S C
Chapman, R D
Chorlton, I
Clayton, G L
Clifton, J
Clint, S A
Cooper, D D
Dale, S S
Dale, S P
Donnan, R H C
Donohue, J S
Drew, P J
Ellett-Brown, H
Gillespie, J R
Gillespie, J M
Glover, K J
Goddard, U K

Griffin, S C
Hardisty, P
Harley, A M
Hartley, W C
Heslop, R W
Hibbert, C L
Hill, S A
Hogg, D C
Horrocks, P
Huckvale, B F
Hunter, R E
Hutchinson, W A
Ikin, P N
Ilangaratne, J B
Imrie, M J
Jones, P G
Kennan, N M
Kerin, M J
Klein, H
Lee, P W R
Lewis, C M P
McCollum, R D
McDonnell, H
Mann, S L
Marwah, K S
Mayne, M G
Meanley, D A
Medley, D R K
Medley, J M
Meek, A E
Menon, M
Milner, A C
Mitchell, G
Mixer, P R
Montgomery, D A
Moran, A G
Morris, P J
Murphy, B A M
Nyawo, B
Patmore, J E
Phillips, K
Ratnavel, C D
Robertson, R T
Rowland, G P
Ryan, D H
Sargison, K D
Shaw, J N
Shearing, L J
Slade, A M
Smith, J S
Sowerby, M K J
Stafford, H G
Stafford, N D
Stephenson, M R
Stirling, J G
Stirling, V A
Sugars, K H
Suri, H S
Sutton, D R
Sutton, R J
Thornhill, S J
Tomkinson, J S
Underwood, A D
Wade, A
Walters, M I
Weatherill, W F
Weldon, D P
White, A S C
Williams, D F
Williams, G D V
Williams, S B
Williams, T I R
Wilson, J A
Withington, B S

Bewdley

Ball, J G
Ball, P M
Bidgood, R A
Cooper, J H
Dutton, P M E
Dyson, J A
Frow, J A
Gordon, E G
Gottschalk, B
Green, C A
Hall, R J
Holloway, B J
Inglis, I M
Jones, H E
Kean, L H
Kumar, R
Lillie, R
McLachlan, C J H
Meggy, J M
Montandon, P E
Mulder, F A
Orange, M
Paton, J S H

Prince, C B
Robertson, J A
Robinson, D W
Rumley, S J
Walker, A A
Walley, M R

Bexhill-on-Sea

Al-Ansary, Y
Ashby, S M
Brown, E
Butterfield, J K
Chalkias, I
Craig, G R
Crawford, J A
Dewhurst, P D
Eaton, J C R
Elias, R G
Emmanuel, J H
Gower, J
Grace, A H
Graham, E W
Grant, P W
Hadley, L A-A
Harrison, K M
Hawley, W L
Hunter, G M
Innes, E H
Jay, J W W
Kinch, H W A
Kramer, S
Kremer, D J
Lacey, E M
Lawton, D J
Ludwig, Z J
McGee, F C
Mackie, J H K
Maloney, F E
Maxwell, T G
Moore, G W
Munro, W S
Murphy, W R H
Myrddin-Evans, T O W
Nash, T G
Newell, D N
Plumley, P F
Plumpton, H P
Radwan, R R M I
Rajanathan, E
Ramachander, C B
Robinson, M K
Sanford, W
Schofield, R
Scott, L G
Sharma, R
Singh, G
Sitwell, I A H
Smith, G M
Southward, S P
Thompson, A J
Thompson, A R
Thomson, A G
Thomson, S R
Thurston, J V
Vernon, P H
Waller, J G
Walter, N R
Warden, D J
Watson, D B D
Wilson, N J
Young-Snell, A J E

Bexley

Ahmad, S
Ayto, R M
Banerjee, A
Banerjee, T K
Barker, A F
Beer, M D
Boomla, R F
Chan, J M W
Cota, A M
Coutinho, E J
Critchley, M J
Goulstone, W
Guryel, E H
Harty, M A
Head, M C
Hirons, J M
Hoogewerf, M
Isherwood, S C
Malone, S T
Meilak, A A
Mendonca, S
Natha, D J
Owen, S
Pyszora, N M
Raine, G J
Saiz, A M B

Simmons, R L L
Skarsten, A R H
Spensley, C A
Srinivas, R K
Sykes, R A
Thavapalan, N D
Thenuwara, C
Virdee, M S
Walter, I M
Wedderspoon, A D
Wesley, H M M

Bexleyheath

Adam, J
Andrews, M J
Berg, S N
Buck, J E
Cameron, E A
Chase, P N
Chase, S B
Chowdhury, A M
De Souza, P B
Dhatariya, K K
Easwar, M D
Forshaw, H B B
Goddard, C A
Griffin, A E
Hammatt, M D
Harrison, N S C
Hatfull, D M
Joyner, N
Kumar, S K
Kutar, S S
Maizels, D W
Malone, A M
Malpass, E L
Martin Martinez, J G
Mehta, M M
Nour, H
Perera, D C
Pollock, J A
Quarterman, E A
Rajaratnam, S
Rajshekhar, M S
Routh, C D
Shah, H K
Sharma, K
Singh, R
Stoate, H G A
Streetly, A
Strevens, M J
Thavapalan, M
Thomas, J C
Tolhurst, J
Watts, M R
Whitehead, G A
Williams, R I J

Bicester

Abbott, C J A
Ainsworth, Q P
Anderson, T W D
Attwood, S P
Bailey, R C
Bartlett, G E
Bennett, L S
Bliss, G A S
Bonner, P M
Bonner, S E
Brooks, A S B
Burgess, S A
Cox, G H
Crammer, J L
Curry, M J
Duncan, G
Ealing, J E P
Ealing, K M
Flintan, B A
Fox, R A
Gale, R G
Galuszka, J A
Gibson, A F B
Grimshaw, D R
Halsey, C
Hannon, D G
Horne, C A
Jackman, J R
Jones, J R
Langstaff, R J
Martin, H P L
Matthews, S M
Miller, B J
Moncrieff, G C
Moore, P J
Murphy, A E H
Murphy, E F H
O'Duffy, D
Radatz, S
Ragheb, E A A

Ridley, N T F
Robbins, S E
Rowlands, A
Sanders, R S
Sargent, H M
Sargent, N W
Saunders, L J
Saunders, T H
Stephenson, R H
Talbot, J M
Thompson, N
Tofts, L J
Tunbridge, A J
Tunbridge, F K E
Van Stigt, E S
Wait, C M
Weaver, H P
Williams, T
Windsor, A M

Bideford

Atkinson, E
Belsey, G
Bradbeer, P J
Brown, K P
Brummitt, P J
Buckland, R H
Candler, S C
Candler, T O
Clayton, M R
Cook, G T J
Cracknell, M M
Daly, G A
David, J C C
Dean, R P
Diamond, A J
Durward, D F
Ford, R G
Ford, S G
Gooda, S E
Herriott, S L
Hill, S G
Hunt, R F
Knight, G
Latham, A
Loder, R E
Loka-Saleh, R M
McKean, W T S
Mason-Walshaw, K R
Mayers, C P
Medway, T A
Milburn, D W
Moore, A
Moore, E M
Pritchard, K A
Roby Jones, C
Shaw, G F
Southgate, B A
Spencer, G S
Turner, J J
Wilson, J G M
Wood, J S
Woodgate-Jones, N P
Young, E A

Biggar

Bewsher, M R
Browning, J A
Cameron, F S
Cameron, J A
Carvel, D R
Dobbie, A E
Elder, A M
Elder, M G
Fulton, H S
Goldie, A M D
Gourlay, R G
Hughes, R A
Leitch, R G
McGregor, P G
May, J M B
Munro, A M
Pasqual, R S H
Porter, B B
Rodger, K A
Tiley, M J
Walterson, L I
Watt, A M

Biggleswade

Bharti, R K
Carroll, G A
Chowdhary, U M
Dowsett, A O
Evans, C M
Feast, S M
Low, A C S
Marshall, F T
Mason, R B S
Murnal, S B

Robertson, W G
Stambach, T A
Taylor, A J

Billericay

Afifi, A
Almond, M K
Brown, F M
Butler, S J C
Chatterjee, K L
Chatterjee, S
Clear Hill, B G R
Cockcroft, J H J
Copsey, M D
Das Gupta, A L
Das Gupta, R
Davies, G
Denham, M M
Durani, S K
Fernie, T C
Frew, J M
Garner, A
Gibbs, E P
Griffiths, P
Gupta, C P
Hayden, P G
Herath, N L B
Holman, A J L
Hui, W L
Jones, M I
Jones, S
Kellock, W M
Knight, J S
Kukathasan, P
Kumar, S
Kwan, D K Y
Lai, S H-L
Langmead, F L
Lawrence, C J
Lazell, G J
Lee, S P-C
McAllister, R M R
McDonald, J K
McGoldrick, A N
Miles, E H S
Moiemen, N S M
Morley, C
Nadarajah, K
Nicholas, A
Pain, V M
Pollard, M A
Porter, C I
Roberts, J K
Sarfraz, A M
Sarfraz, M-U-H
Shen, R N
Sirotakova, M
Sofoluwe, G O
Thomson, L F
Tin Loi, S F
Ware, S J
Wilkinson, N M R
Williams, A C P
Willoughby, C P
Xavier, P L C

Billingham

Adebayo, A O
Chatterjee, P P K
Clish, D
Constable, A
Elborough, A Y
Fenwick, S
Fordham, J N
Gartner, C P
Geoghegan, H F
Gittens, M J
Goorbarry, M D
Gosalia, N H
Irvine, A J
Joyce, C A
Lockey, K N
Longwill, J M
Murphy, R S
O'Donoghue, J P
Reynolds, R P
Ritchie, P
Sinclair, J A G
Walton, L J
West, S C

Billingshurst

Balme, G M
Barber, N J
Broughton, M D
Crabb, S J
Drummond, J
Dunlop, K J
Jones, N J
Leach, A R

Lowe, M J
Margetts, G
Margetts, J P
Meanock, C I
Piper, A J
Polwin, P J S
Rouse, D A
Sichel, G R M
Tabb, P A
Vine, J
Williams, A E
Wood, C G M

Bilston

Adma, L
Anandakumar, P
Cosgrave, E N
De, S K
Hossain, M
Jhass, L S
Kumar, S
Lal, C
Morris, T A
Rangel, R L
Sharma, S V
Than, M
Tinsa, J S

Bingley

Andrews, E C
Bairstow, T E
Beck, I
Bradbury, J A
Busby, C R
Claxton, B A
Comerford, D G
Davies, A B
Dawe, B C E
Dean, A J
Duke, F C
Eyton-Jones, J
Findlay, J M
Findlay, P A
Flockton, E A
Froggatt, D L
Gabbitas, S M
Harden, S V
Haslam, G H
Hassan, F A
Hattam, S A L
Hollins, P J
Holms, W
Hopkins, D J
Horsfield, M J
Jeffrey, R F
Jennings, K L
Jones, S E
Jowett, L J
Kennedy, J R
King, A J
Knappett, P A
Lambert, R C
Larsen, C J
Lloyd, M D
Ludlow, E L
Newton, D A G
Price, J J
Pushpangadan, M
Rai, N
Robson, K H
Selby, R O
Tang, D T S
Thorburn, R N
Tuffnell, D J
Vesey, J
Vesey, R J
Wallis, G G
Woodhead, R L

Birchington

Bird, H C H
Drummond, J S
Eddington, J
Eddington, W A
Fletcher, M W
Garland, J K
Gleed, D I L
Hanafy, M E E D
Hayden, J T D
Ikhena, S E
Jackson, N C
O'Donoghue, E
Rao, C R
Turtle, J B
Wood, A R

Birkenhead

Alauddin, K
Amily, G S
Appleby, C

Arthur, C P
Austen, J M
Blaney, J A
Blaney, S P A
Boylan, B G
Brayley, M
Brodbin, C
Burrows, M M
Caslin, A W
Charles, E J
Clayton, R D
Cookson, I B
Coombs, D M
Courtney, D B
Cullen, M
Cummins, A
Cunningham, J L
Davies, J A
Davies, L
Davies, M G
De Hoxar, V M
Delaney, S G J
Dillon, I J
Dixon, T A
Dobbins, S T
Dodd, M D
Douglas, H M
Dow, J M
Dow, S C
Durrant, W
Edwards, E M H
Edwards, R W
Ellis, B R
Eyre, F J H
Fallowfield, R E
Farooqi, A A
Ferguson, R E
Franklin, J
Freeman, M J
Friedmann, A C
Galvani, D W
Garewal, S S
Grant, P J
Green, D H
Green, M J
Greenfield, J E
Hall, R S
Hardaker, E A
Harding, S G
Harding, S
Harris, N L
Hedges, P J
Hill, D R
Hilton, R C
Holley, J M
Howard, J E
Hughes, P A
Jones, W W
Karyampudi, P
Karyampudi, R S
Kidd, C M T
Klenka, H M
Leigh, R F
Lewis, A H
Lowe, D C
McCarey, A G
McElroy, B J
McGill, P P B
Mairs, P P
Mantgani, A B
Martin, R V
Massey, K
Mawdsley, J
Mawdsley, R
Moorhouse, J
Murray, J H
Naughton, M D
Noorpuri, R S
O'Connor, G J
Onion, C W R
Oolbekkink, M
Owens, V B
Owers, D L
Owers, F M
Owers, M H
Page, C A
Paymaster, N J
Payne, J H
Pelosi, L
Raines, R J H
Ranasinghe, C L
Ratnaike, N D A
Ream, J E
Renwick, J A
Roberts, M L
Romaniuk, D A
Roper, J P
Rowlands, A G
Ryall, C J

Salahuddin, M
Satchithananthan, S
Seager, J
Selby, R L
Selvarajah, D T
Seymour, P J
Smethurst, F A
Smurthwaite, D
Soe Aung, Dr
Stevens, L E
Strang, L
Sturgess, R P
Syed, M F
Tan, A T-L
Taylor, A J
Taylor, B W
Thomas, J G
Vaillant, C H
Vangikar, M M
Vogwell, P C
Walker, C V S
Walters, A E
Wardale, J G
Whalley, J T
Williams, D H
Williams, R M
Willis, M R
Woodrow, J C
Wu, K H J
Zacharias, P L

Birmingham

Aas, O G B
Abbas, S
Abdul Cader, A H M
Abdullahi, A T
Abrams, L D
Abrol, V
Abudu, A T
Acharya, M P
Ackroyd, R S
Acland, P R
Adak, A K
Adams, C
Adams, J L
Addy, D P
Adlakha, S
Adu, D
Adwani, S S
Affie, E M
Afnan, A M M
Aggarwal, S P
Agwu, S C
Ahamed, H A
Ahamed, M
Ahee, P R
Ahmad, N
Ahmad, S
Ahmad, S Z
Ahmad, Y
Ahmed, A H
Ahmed, B
Ahmed, I
Ahmed, M M
Ahmed, Q W
Ahmed, R I
Ahmed, R
Ahmed, S
Ahmed, Z
Ainsworth, J R
Aitchison, F A
Ajimal, S K
Akbar, A
Akhtar, A
Akhtar, R
Al-Aaraji, Y M S
Al-Ansari, I K
Al-Haboubi, N Y A
Al-Ibrahim, J
Al-Kadi, K
Al-Mawali, S H
Al-Rifai, H A
Ala, F A
Alam, M
Alauddin, M
Aldridge, F R
Alexander, F G
Ali, A
Ali, A H M S
Ali, Z
Allan, A-M T
Allan, P M
Allan, R N
Allaway, E J
Allen, C H
Allen, M P
Allin, D M
Allington-Smith, P J
Allroggen, H

Allt, J E
Alonzo, K H R
Alton, H M
Aluwihare, N P
Ambasht, D P
Ambekar, A A
Amey, H
Amin, U R
Amir, W P
Anderson, B M M
Andrews, H A
Anees, N W
Anfilogoff, N H
Ansari, M Z R H
Anthony, R L
Anwar, M
Appiah, S K
Appleford, J K
Archer, V R
Arif, M H
Arif, M R
Arif, S
Arkell, D G
Armitage, L E
Armstrong, F M
Armstrong, H J
Armstrong, L B
Arnold, A J
Arora, G R
Arora, K J
Arora, P P
Arundell, L E
Ashcroft, M E
Ashton, C J
Ashton, J
Ashton, W D
Asif, M
Asif, M
Asker, D C
Aslam, A
Asquith, J R
Asquith, P
Aston, R H R
Atewah, R M
Atherton, P J
Atkins, G
Atwal, S S
Aukland, A
Austin, J D R
Auth, M K-H
Aveyard, P N
Aw, T-C
Aylin, D R
Ayres, J G
Azam, S
Aziz, O M K
Bache, C E
Bacon, P A
Badawi, H I
Badger, I L R
Baghdadi, S H N
Bagshaw, O N T
Bailey, G M
Bain, I M
Bainbridge, E T
Bains, J
Baird, M S
Bajaj, B P S
Bajpai, A C
Bakhshi, S S
Ball, E W
Ball, J A
Ballantyne, S L
Ballesteros Jeronimo, M S
Baloch, K G
Bamford, N A
Bancroft, G N
Bancroft, J
Bandara, D S P K
Bandopadhyay, S
Bandyopadhyay, B C
Bandyopadhyay, S
Banerjee, D J
Banerjee, S K
Banerjee, S K
Banks, M J
Bansel, J K
Bansel, J S
Barber, J M P
Barber, K J
Barber, P J
Bareford, D
Barford, D J
Barker, G M
Barnes, S J
Barnett, A H
Barnett, B
Barnett, E R

Birmingham

Barraclough, C R
Barratt, D J
Barret, C M
Barrett, J S
Barrett, K E
Barrett, T G
Barron, J A
Barry, J S
Barry, R J A
Bartlett, M A
Basak, S
Basil, K-T
Batch, A J G
Bate, C
Bates, G D L
Bath, S S
Bathla, V
Batra, S
Batta, K
Baxter, M A
Bayliss, H G
Beach, J R
Beath, S V
Beatson-Hird, J F
Beattie, J M
Beazley, M F
Beedie, M A
Beeken, S A
Beevers, D G
Begum, H
Beighton, P G
Belhag, M A A
Benbow, J A
Benham, J D
Benham, M
Bennett, J
Bennett, J M
Bennett, M
Bennett, R J
Benson, S R C
Bent, J A
Bentsi-Barnes, A
Berovic, M N
Berriman, J-A
Berry, K
Betts, T A
Bevan, P G
Beyer, P M
Bhadri, A D
Bhardwaj, M K
Bhari, J K
Bhaskar, V A P
Bhatia, R K
Bhatt, K B
Bhattacharyya, B
Bhatti, R A
Bhatti, S
Bhimji, Y S
Bhomra, D S
Bhullar, M S
Bickley, P
Bindal, T
Bindman, E
Bion, J F
Birch, L J
Bird, A P
Bird, R
Birkill, R J
Birmingham, J S
Birmingham, L S
Birt, C A
Birtle, J
Bishay, E S S
Bissenden, J G
Biswas, H
Biswas, S
Biswas, S
Blackford, R D
Blaggan, A S
Blake, D H
Bland, N C
Bleetman, A
Blissitt, L C
Blows, M
Bluck, G M
Bluglass, J M K
Bluglass, R S
Blunt, S M
Boden, J M
Boden, J L
Bodicoat, S P
Bond, G M
Bond, M
Boniface, K J
Bonser, R S
Boorman, D G
Booth, I W
Bora, D
Borg-Bartolo, P P
Bosworth, M R
Botha, R A
Boughton, B J
Boulter, A R
Bowater, G B
Bowden, G
Bowden, M I
Bowman, S J
Boyce, D E
Bracewell, R M
Bradberry, S M
Bradbury, A W
Bradbury, M J E
Bradby, G V H
Bradford, A P J
Bradish, C F
Bradley, S A
Bradshaw, K A
Bradwell, A R
Brain, D J
Bramhall, S R
Brammer, R D
Brawn, C M
Brawn, W J
Brearey, S P
Brewer, D B
Brewin, M D
Brierley, A F M
Briffa, N P
Bright-Thomas, R M
Bright-Thomas, R J
Bright, P
Brinksman, S
Bromley, P N
Brookes-White, P J S
Brookes, E J
Brookes, S K
Brookes, V S
Broomhead, M E
Brown, A M S
Brown, G T
Brown, G J
Brown, J B
Brown, M
Brown, N P
Brown, R M
Brown, S E
Browne, S D
Brueton, L A
Bruton, L A
Bryan, R T
Bryson, P H R
Buchanan, D D
Buchanan, I S
Buckels, J A C
Buckley, A M
Budh-Raja, V P
Buick, R G
Buist, L J
Bull, J P
Buller, N P
Bulso, V
Burdon, A W
Burdon, M A
Burge, A
Burge, P S
Burges, D C E
Burke, D P A
Burke, S J
Burls, A J E
Burman, J H
Burns, B V
Burrows, F G O
Busby, S C
Butcher, A J
Butler, J A M
Butler, L
Cabrera Abreu, J C
Cadbury, N L
Cader, M Z
Cadigan, D V
Cadigan, P J
Calderwood, D K O D
Calderwood, R O D
Calderwood, V S
Caldwell, W G D
Cameron, J
Campbell, A J G
Campbell, C M
Campbell, F E
Canham, N L E
Cant, I M
Carey, M P
Carlish, S
Carmalt, M H B
Carnie, J C
Carolan, E G
Carroll, A M
Carruthers, D M
Carter, R A
Carter, S R
Carter, S R
Cartmill, A D
Carver, E D
Cash, A J
Cash, D G
Cash, H T
Caskey, M J
Cassam, K
Casson, P A
Caswell, L P
Cathcart, M
Cathcart, V H
Cave, N S
Chadwick, V L
Chakma, I B
Chan, K K
Chan, N T-Y
Chan, S Y
Chander, A
Chaparala, B C
Chapman, A L N
Chapman, S
Charon, J-P M
Chaudary, A H
Chaudhary, S M
Cheel, C
Cheema, M N
Cheng, K K
Cherry, R C
Cheung, G W Y
Cheung, R C-Y
Child, D L
Child, V M
Chilton, A P
Chilvers, J P
Chitnis, A J
Chokshi, N C
Chokshi, U N
Chong, A Y
Chong, C L
Choudry, A A
Choudry, G A
Chowdhary, S
Chowdhury, T A
Christodoulou, C
Chu, W W-C
Chudley, S M
Chukwulobelu, R N
Clancy, J M P
Clarke, D J
Clarke, G R
Clarke, H G
Clarke, J R
Clarke, P F F
Clarkson, M E
Clay, S N
Cleasby, M J
Clifton, P J M
Clutton-Brock, T H
Cobb, R A
Cockel, R
Cockerham, R
Cocks, H C
Cockwell, P
Coddington, T
Coe, T R
Colabawalla, H M
Cole, F
Cole, T R P
Coleman, G M
Coleman, N S
Coley, V P
Collard, J M
Colley, J J
Collingham, K E
Collins, P L
Collis, J L
Colloby, P S
Combes, N J
Commander, M J
Commander, R A D
Condie, R G
Condley, M
Conlon, M H
Conrad, V A
Considine, J
Cook, D M
Cook, J
Cook, M A
Cooke, A M
Cooke, H B J
Cooke, M A
Cooper, C
Cooper, H M
Cooper, J F
Cooper, M R
Cope, R V
Corfan, E
Corkery, J J
Cormac, I D
Corrie, T
Cotterill, C P
Court, B V
Cowan, C B
Cowan, E M M
Cowan, M A
Coward, A D
Coward, C M A
Cox, D A
Cox, P A
Coyle, M E
Crabtree, N L
Craddock, N J
Craigen, M A C
Cramer, E J
Cranston, D S
Crawford, S L
Cresswell, D
Crocker, C B
Crocker, C S
Crocker, J
Crombie, C M
Crooks, S W
Crosland, J M
Cross, V H
Crowe, P M
Crowley, N L H
Cruickshank, F R T
Cullen, L
Cullen, M H
Cullingworth, T M
Cunliffe, I A
Cunningham, M J I
Curran, R C
D'Silva, M R
D'Urso, P J
Dadheech, H H
Dadheech, V K
Dakin, M C
Dalal, B M
Dale, R C
Dalton, D J N
Daly, A S J
Daly, J E
Daly, P J
Damoa-Siakwan, S A
Daniell, P A
Daniels, A M
Das, G
Dasgupta, S R
Datta, S
David, M D
Davidson, S L
Davies, A J
Davies, A L
Davies, A M
Davies, C M
Davies, J A H
Davies, J T
Davies, J H
Davies, M E B
Davies, M H
Davies, P H
Davies, Q
Davies, R R
Davies, S R
Davies, H
Davies, J M
Davis, R
Dawkins, D M
Dawson-Edwards, P
Dawson, D E
Dawson, K G
Daya, P
Dayal, M S
Daymond, P W R
De Giovanni, J V
De Wildt, G R
De, S
Deacon, K R
Dean, C
Deas, M C
Debelle, G D
Debenham, S E
Deiry, A A
Dekker, P J
Del Bene, R
Delaney, B C
Deluz, J E
Dennis, V
Denton, A
Derrick, G M
Derrington, P M
Derry, D D
Desai, H C
Desai, M
Deshmukh, S C
Desveaux, J-C
Deuchar, N J
Devine, A
Dewsbury, J A
Dhamija, S K
Dhariwal, A S
Dhingsa, R
Dhother, S S
Dibdin, E M
Dicker, B J
Diwan, S P
Doble, R A
Dodson, P M
Doggett, J M
Doherty, J D H
Doherty, N J
Dominey, J A
Donaldson, A
Donaldson, I
Donnelly, H M
Donovan, I A
Dorricott, N J
Doughty, H-A
Dover, M S
Downes, M K
Dowson, L J
Doyle, M A
Drake-Lee, A B
Drake, S M
Drayson, M T
Drever, W M H
Du Feu, M
Dubash, D H
Duddy, M J
Dudley, P M
Dullehan, R M S
Dunne, F P M
Dunstan, C M
Dunstan, E J
Durbin, G M
Durkin, D J
Durston, G W
Dutt, K K
Dwarakanath, L S
Dyer, C A E
Dyer, P H
Eagle, C D
Eardley, K S
Eberle, S
Ebert, F H
Eccleshall, S C
Eccleston, D B
Eckhardt, S H
Edge, R
Edmunds, J M
Edmunds, J P
Edward, M G
Edwards, G J
Edwards, J J
Edwards, J H
Edwards, S C
Ehtisham, J
Ehtisham, M
Ehtisham, S
Eke, A J
El-Farok, M O
El Mankabady, S F
El-Sheikh, O A-E A
Elcock, S K
Elgon, J J A
Elias, E
Elliott, C M
Elliott, C I
Elliott, S C
Elliott, T S J
Ellis, C J
Ellwood, H L
Ely, J C J
Emens, J M
Emery, D G
Empson, K
England, E J R
England, S J
Engledow, A H
English, A
English, M W
Enriquez Puga, A
Escofet Martinez De Arenzana, X
Etherington, I J
Evans, D F
Evans, H M
Evans, M L
Evans, R C
Evans, R
Evans, R F
Ewer, A K
Exon, D J
Ezikwa, F Z
Faisal, K N M A
Faisal, N A
Farhadian, F
Farmer, A J
Farmer, C M
Farndon, P A
Faroqui, M H
Farr, M
Farrar, D J
Farrell, M M
Faull, C M
Fawcett, C J
Felderhof, J C
Fenton, T W
Ferguson, D I
Ferguson, W J
Fernando, I N
Ferner, R E
Ferrando, A
Fertig, O
Fessey, B M
Field, S K
Field, S J
Fielder, A R
Finn, R M
Fisher, E W
Fitzmaurice, D A
Fleming, D M
Fletcher, R I
Fletcher, R F
Flinn, R M
Flint, G A
Fogell, A M
Fogell, M
Ford, D R
Forgan, R C
Forsey, P R
Forster, P M
Foulds, I S
Fownes, H E
Fox, J E
Fox, S J
Fraise, A P
Fraise, M C
Francis, A E
Francis, G H
Franklyn, J A
Freeman, P E
Frempong, J
French, G C
Fung, C C-C
Gaballa, N E
Gabra, G S
Gabriel, S G J
Gaik Cheng Ooi, Dr
Gallacher, K G
Gallacher, T
Gammage, M D
Gandhi, I K
Ganiwalla, T M J
Gannon, M X
Garcia De Vinuesa, C
Gardner-Medwin, J M M
Gardner, G T G
Gargya, S C
Gaspar, A S
Gaspar, D
Gaspar, K
Gaspar, L S
Gasson, G B
Gaston, C H
Gattas, A A
Gazis, A G
Gearty, J C
Gee, H
George, R H
Giannakis, I
Gibbons, P J
Gibson, J M
Giddings, P
Gill, J K
Gill, M J
Gill, S K
Gillies, A J
Gilmour, E
Gittins, P R
Gladwell, S R F
Glaholm, J
Glass, A
Glass, R G
Glithero, P R
Glover, M
Glover, R A
Goadby, J W
Gohil, N M
Gohil, S
Gol, B

Birmingham

Gold, L M
Goldin, J H
Goldman, M D
Goldstein, A R
Goldstein, A L
Goldstein, J E
Gonsalves, P
Gonzaga, R T
Goode, N J
Goodman, M H
Goodyear, P A J
Gordon, C
Gordon, W L
Gore, J
Gornall, P
Gospel, R L
Goswami, V P
Gough, A C
Gould, M J
Gourevitch, A
Gourevitch, D
Gowar, J P
Graham, R J
Graham, T R
Grainger, C R
Grant, C A
Grant, I J M
Gray-Henry, D-M A
Gray, J
Green, M A
Green, S H
Gregg, E M
Gregory, K S
Greig, J M
Griffith, J F
Griffith, M E
Griffith, S
Griffiths, A C
Griffiths, A
Griffiths, F D
Griffiths, K J
Griffiths, M P
Griffiths, P R
Griffiths, R K
Grimer, R J
Grocutt, M S J
Grundy, R G
Guest, P J
Guirguis, H M
Gupta, A K
Gupta, J K
Gupta, T N
Gyde, O H B
Haas, D J
Hadley, J W
Hafeez, A
Hafeez, F
Hahn, A M
Haider, F S
Haigh, S F
Hakeem, A G
Hales, A D M
Hall, D J
Hall, J M
Hall, M G
Hall, P
Hallissey, M T
Hambleton, D
Hamer, A R
Hamilton, H
Hamilton, P A
Hammersley, R L
Hammond, L A
Hamnett, E
Handford, D J
Handy, S
Hanif, M
Hankin, J E
Haq, I U
Hardie, A D
Harding, L K
Hardwick, J M
Hardy, R G
Harland, S P
Harley-Mason, G R
Haroon, A M
Harrington, J M
Harris, D M
Harris, P
Harris, Q
Harrison, G R
Harrison, J F
Harrison, M A M
Harrison, R F
Harrison, R G
Hart, D P
Hart, R O
Harvey, T C
Hashmi, F S

Hashmi, M
Hasler, J C
Hassan, M S U
Hassan, M S U
Hassan, U S
Hawes, G C B
Hawker, C F
Hawker, J I
Hawkey, P M
Hawkins, D J
Hayes, G S
Heafield, M T E
Heath, C M
Heath, C W
Heath, D A
Heatherington, J E
Hegarty, M A
Heitmann, M
Hell, J A
Henshall, S M
Heritage, J H
Hero, I
Heslop, J M
Hettiaratchy, S P
Hewitt, M L
Hibbert, G R
Hickman, M D
Higgins, J R A
Hijazi, L
Hill, A C
Hill, F G H
Hill, H S
Hill, P R
Hill, S O
Hinder, S A J
Hirsch, M V
Hiscock, E
Hobart, A G
Hobbs, F D R
Hocking, M D
Hockley, A D
Hodgson, C
Hodgson, J
Hofmann, H A
Hollier, K P
Hollingworth, T
Hone, J H
Honeybourne, D
Honeyman, M M
Hooper, C L
Hooper, M B
Hope-Ross, W M
Hopkins, J D
Hopkinson, R B
Horry, G M
Horton, G
Horton, V C
Hosty, G S
Houghton, A C
Houghton, P G
Houlihan, J F
Hoult, E A
Hourani, A H I
Howells, J H
Howells, R E J
Howes, D M
Howie, A J
Hubscher, S G
Huddleston, R E
Huengsberg, M
Huggins, L J
Huggins, N J
Hughes, J M
Hughes, M A
Hughes, S J
Hughes, T J
Hulten, M A
Hulton, S-A
Humphreys, M S
Humphries, J A
Hunt, E
Hussain, A
Hutton, P
Hvidsten, S J
Hyde, C J
Hyde, J M E
Hyde, J A J
Hylton, S M
Hyman, B M
Ibrahim, Z H Z
levins, F A
levins, R A
Iles, P B
Imlah, N W
Indwar, C
Insley, J
Iqbal, A
Iqbal, J
Irani, S A

Ireland, P S
Irgin, S M
Irwin, E M
Isaac, D T
Isaac, S
Isaacs, B
Iskander-Gabra, S D
Islam, N
Ismail, A
Ismail, T
Itrakjy, A S J M A
Iyengar, P G
Jackowski, A
Jackson, A P F
Jackson, S A
Jacobs, A G
Jacobs, G J
Jaffer, K
Jain, R
Jairaj, M B
Jaitly, V K
Jajoo, J N
Jamaluddin, M
Jameel, S Y
Jameel, T
James, J M
James, N D
James, P J
James, S R N
Jamieson, D G
Jamieson, G K R
Janardhan Reddy, S R
Jankowski, J A Z
Jaron, A E G
Jasinghe, R
Jassel, G S
Jeavons, M P
Jefferson, J M
Jefferson, M
Jemahl, S
Jenkins, D W
Jenkins, P J
Jenkinson, H C
Jeskins, G D
Jessop, H C
Jeys, L M
Jheeta, A S
Jheeta, B S
Jhittay, P S
Jobanputra, P
John, P R
Johnson, A P
Johnson, I S
Johnson, J W E
Johnson, R J
Johnson, S A
Johnson, S A
Johnston, D H
Jones, A F
Jones, A G
Jones, B
Jones, E L
Jones, E F
Jones, G S
Jones, H H
Jones, M M
Jones, M C
Jones, R L
Jones, S L
Jones, S E F
Jones, T J J
Jordan, J A
Jordan, P J
Jordan, R P
Jordan, R H A
Joseph, M
Joshi, K
Joshi, M D
Joshi, S M
Jubb, R W
Jukes, D S
Kahn, A
Kai, J P
Kamal, M
Kandula, D R
Kandula, V
Kane, K F
Kanekal, K V
Kannan, A J
Kapadia, M K
Kapur, R V
Karamdad, D R
Karim, M B
Karzoun, F K
Kathuria, U C
Kaur, B
Kavi, L A
Kay, A D
Kay, J

Kayani, J A
Kayente, M L
Kaylan, A S
Keeble, M
Keegan, A A M
Keighley, D M
Keighley, M R B
Kelly, D A M
Kelly, J
Kelly, L M
Kemm, J R
Kendall, M J
Kennedy, J
Kenney-Herbert, J P
Kenton, A R
Kenyon, B
Keogh, B E
Kerr, D J
Kersley, J B
Keshri, R
Ketkar, V H
Kett, D W
Khair, O A G B M
Khaira, J S
Khalid, A
Khalid, S
Khalid, U K
Khalil Marzouk, Y F
Khan, A
Khan, G
Khan, I
Khan, J A
Khan, K S-E-Z
Khan, M
Khan, M I
Khan, M S
Khan, M A
Khan, R
Khan, S A
Khanduri, S
Khanna, K A
Khattak, S S
Khattak, S H
Khin-Maung-Zaw, Dr
Khoobarry, K C
Kilby, M D
Kinch, D
King, A M
King, B R
King, M J
Kingman, H M
Kinshuck, D J
Kirk, J M W
Kirkby, G R
Kirkwood, J L
Knausenberger, H-P
Knight, G
Knowles, M G
Knowles, P J
Kong, K L
Kong, N
Kordan, M A
Kos, K
Kpiasi, E O
Kubik, N A
Kulshrestha, M K
Kulshrestha, R P
Kumar, S
Kumble, J R
Kuo, M J-M
Kurtz, J B
Labinjo, K O
Laird, M J
Lakhani, M Y
Lamond, I
Lampert, I
Lander, A D
Lander, B J
Landray, M J
Lane, P J L
Langford, Dr
Langford, R J
Langman, M J S
Langrick, A F
Lanham, J R C
Lanigan, S W
Lashen, H A M A
Latham, T B
Latief, T N
Latif, S A
Latthe, M M
Latthe, M M
Latthe, M A
Lau, E W Y
Law, D P F
Lawrence, G D
Lawrence, M P
Lawrence, N J H
Lawrence, R P

Laws, P E
Lawson, S E
Lazar, T
Lea, D C J
Lea, R A
Learmonth, D J A
Lee Pek Wan, Dr
Lee, A J
Lee, C Y
Lee, J M
Lee, J R
Lee, M J R
Lee, S J
Leggott, M J
Leigh, C
Lengua Quijandria, C A
Leone Ganado, A
Leslie, A
Lester, H E
Lester, J S
Lester, R L
Lester, W A
Levi, N A
Levick, P L
Lewis, H M
Lewis, M
Lewis, M
Lewis, M E
Lidder, P G
Lidher, J
Liebling, A J
Liebling, L I
Liew, L C W
Light, R J
Liley, A
Lilford, R J
Lilley, J-P
Lindsay, J A
Lines, L M
Linney, S F
Lip, G Y H
Lip, P L
Littler, W A
Liu, M C
Llewellyn, C G
Lloyd, A L
Lloyd, B E M
Lloyd, S C
Lloyd, V A
Lockley, M R
Loffeld, A
Loftus, C E
Logan, I S
Loizou, E
London, D R
London, J
Lonergan, J G
Lopez Sanchez, C
Loudon, R F
Loughridge, C J
Lovesey, E M
Low-Beer, T S
Low, D C
Lowe, A L
Luckas, M J M
Luckman, K E
Luckraft, G G
Lucy, M H
Ludman, P F
Luesley, D M
Lumley, L C
Mabley, A M
McCafferty, I J
McCarthy, D F
McCollum, D H
McConkey, B
McCrann, U G
McDonnell, J H
McDougall, S H
Macerola, G
McFarland, P E V
Macfarlane, D W R
McGarry, J M
McGovern, D A
McGrath, C C B
McGuinness, P J N
Machin, P
McHugo, J M
McIlroy, W H H
McKechnie, R L
McKee, S A
Mackenzie, A A
McKeown, C M E
McKeown, S J
Mackie, J G
McKiernan, P J
MacLennan, I C M
MacLeod, J

MacLeod, R A L
McLeod, T J
McMaster, P
McMinn, F J
McMullan, P J V
Macnamara, M A M
McNamara, M J
McNeish, I A
MacPhail, C V
MacPherson, L K R
McQuillan, E J
McShane, L M
MacVie, M H
Madhotra, R
Magee, C M
Magnay, A R
Magnay, K L
Mahendra, P
Maher, E R
Maher, M G
Maheswaran, V
Mahmood, Y
Majevadia, D K
Makin, A J
Makins, D J B
Malik, A Q
Malik, N M
Malins, A F
Malone, P C
Manaseki-Holland, S
Mangat, K S
Mangham, D C
Manji, M
Manley, V C
Mann, A-B
Mann, C H
Mann, J R
Mansfield, H N
Mant, J W F
Manu, M
Manuchehri, K
Manyweathers, V J
Marino, A
Marks, D S
Marlow, C E
Marns, R S
Marok, I S
Marr, J E
Marsden, J R
Marshall, A C
Martin, J P
Martin, K L
Martin, N A J
Martin, S H
Martin, U
Mashhoodi, N
Mason, A D
Masood, M
Massar, C G
Massey, P M O
Matharoo, H
Matheou, N
Mathews, E T
Mattar, R G
Matthews, P M
Mattu, G S
Matyka, K A
Mayer, A D
Mayer, P P
Mayor, V
Meakin, L C
Meer, L C
Mehta, R R
Melikian, F R
Melikian, V
Mendelsohn, R A
Messahel, F M A
Meux, S C S
Mewar, D
Meyer, C H A
Meyer, H C K
Mg Mg Lat, Dr
Michael, J
Midya, T S
Milford, D V
Millar, C L
Milledge, D T
Miller, J A L
Miller, L F
Miller, M R
Miller, P A
Milligan, D W
Millington, D
Millns, J P
Mills, M W
Milo-Turner, G
Mina, M T
Mina, M M M
Minwalla, F

Birmingham

Mishra, M N
Miskin, N
Miskin, S J
Misra, P K
Misra, U S
Mistry, T P
Mitchell, R D
Mohan, C B
Monaghan, A M
Moonga, P S
Moore, G F
Moore, J R M
Moore, P A S
Moore, S J
Moraitou, E
More, I S
Morgan, D R
Morgan, E J
Morgan, M E I
Morgan, S D
Morland, B J
Morley, R L
Morreau, P N
Morris, N G
Morris, S B
Morrison, H M
Morrison, I D
Morrison, J M
Mortiboy, D E
Mortimer, A T
Mortimer, M J
Morton, D G
Morton, J E V
Mosquera Lopez De Larrinzar, A
Mosquera, D A
Moss, C
Moss, J L M
Moss, M S
Moss, P A H
Mottershead, L M
Moussa, K T
Moxon, C P
Moy, R J D
Moysey, J C
Muayed, R M H
Mughal, S
Mukerji, B D
Mukherjee, S
Mulcahy, T M
Mulik, R B
Mullhi, D
Mulligan, P J
Mulligan, T S
Munday, S J
Munden, A C
Munkley, R M
Mupanemunda, R H
Murphy, M S
Murphy, P D
Murray, A T
Murray, D C
Murray, J A
Murray, J A
Murray, P I
Murray, R G
Mushin, S E
Muss, D C
Myskova, I A
Mzimba, Z S
Nadjat-Shokouhi, M A A
Nagle, C J
Nagle, R E
Nagrani, R
Najada, S F
Najak, B G H
Nall, P T
Nalpas, A C
Nancarrow, J D
Nandi, D K
Nankivell, M
Narayan, B S
Narayan, P
Narhlya, P K
Naseem, M
Nathavitharana, C P G
Nathavitharana, K A
Nattrass, M
Naughton, P E
Nazem, A B M
Nazir, M
Nazki, M T
Neuberger, J M
Newman, J
Newrith, C R F
Newth, S J
Newton, J R
Nicholl, D J

Nicholl, P T
Nicholls, A M H
Nicol, D B
Nithi, K A
Nithiyananthan, R
Nitzke, F J
Niven-Jenkins, N C
Nixon, H K
Nkuo, K
Norman, A M
North, J P
Notghi, A
Nye, M Y L
Nyholm, E S
O'Brien, C M
O'Brien, D C
O'Brien, J M
O'Brien, K
O'Brien, P M
O'Connell, J E
O'Dea, J F
O'Donnell, D
O'Donovan, D J C
O'Driscoll, A M
O'Driscoll, D J
O'Gara, M G
O'Gorman, M E
O'Hara, J N
O'Leary, M M
O'Reilly, P J
O'Shea, J G
Oates, G D
Obeid, M L
Obeng, M A
Oetiker, U
Ojha, A
Oliver, R J
Olliff, J F C
Olliff, S P
Oppenheim, E M
Orsborn, R C
Osman, K H E
Owen, A J
Owen, C A
Owen, J J T
Owen, K R
Owen, K C
Oyaide, O M
Oyebode, O A
Page, A J
Page, M M
Pahor, A L
Pal, P
Pal, P K
Palsingh, J
Pandit, S S
Pankhania, R
Panton, S
Papini, R P G
Paramanathan, K
Paramanathan, S
Parashar, K
Pardoe, I S
Parekh, S
Parikh, D H
Parikh, S
Park, C A
Parker, B D
Parker, F G
Parker, K J
Parkes, J
Parle, H J E
Parle, J V
Parmar, S
Parnaik, V G
Parry, D L
Parsonage, M J
Patel, A R A
Patel, A
Patel, C
Patel, H
Patel, J N
Patel, R C
Paterson, J T
Patodi, S K
Pattni, B L
Paul, A
Paw, R C
Payne, E S
Payne, M N
Payne, M L
Payne, R J
Peake, D R
Pearce, D E
Pearman, K
Pears, P E
Pearson, A J
Pearson, G A
Pearson, J R

Peet, A C
Penfold, S E
Pennington, E
Pennington, S J
Pentecost, B L
Perkins, G D
Perkins, S L
Perry, I
Pettit, D R
Phelps, S R
Philip, W M
Phillips, C R
Phillips, S M A
Pickworth, F J
Pickworth, S M
Pillay, D
Piqueras Arenas, A I
Pirie, A M
Pitt, M P I
Plant, P A
Platt, C C
Platt, S G
Plewes, J L
Pogmore, J R
Pollock, G T
Poltock, T L
Pomeroy, R T
Poole, C J
Porter, K M
Porter, M F
Pourgourides, E
Poyner, K G
Pradhan, C B
Prais, L
Prasad, A
Prasad, K T
Prasad, P
Prasher, V P
Pratt, J D
Price, A R
Prime, C F
Pritchard, T R
Proops, D W
Prosser, G H
Pugh, L J L
Pugh, M T
Puleston, R L
Pullan, D S B
Puntis, H
Qureshi, M H S
Raafat, F
Rabb, L M
Radcliffe, K W
Radvanyi, M
Rafiq, M
Rahber, M S
Rahim, A
Rahman, A S M M
Rahman, F
Rahman, H U
Rahman, I
Rahman, M H
Rahman, S-A
Rai, H S
Raichura, V K
Raine-Fenning, N J
Raine, R A
Raj, G R
Raja Lope, R J
Raja, J H
Rajesh, P B
Rajput, S
Rajput, V K
Rajput, V K
Ralston, C S
Ralston, G R D
Ramachandram, R S
Ramani, P
Ramarao, M V
Rami Reddy, S
Ramjohn, M A
Ramsay, D H E
Rana, K
Rana, T A
Randhawa, V
Rankin, E C C
Rao, V
Rashid, A
Rati, N
Raut, S L
Ravindrababu, G
Ray, S
Rayner, H C
Rayner, I R
Rayner, M M
Rayner, P H W
Rayton, E L
Raza, K
Rea, D W

Reddy, K S P
Reddy, N S
Redfearn, E
Redlich, M J H
Redman, H K A
Reece, R J
Reed, A
Rees, A H
Rees, E N
Rees, G L
Rehmany, K M
Reid, A P
Reid, R E G
Rewhorn, I D
Reynolds, A L
Reynolds, J H
Riaz, A
Rice, P F
Richards, N T
Richards, P W
Richings, C I
Rickards, E H G
Riddell, P L
Riddington, D W
Ridgway, J C
Ridley, C C S
Rigby, M T
Riley, E T
Riley, P L
Riordan, F A I
Riordan, M F
Rippin, J D
Roberts, A C
Roberts, G M
Roberts, H
Roberts, K E
Roberts, K D
Roberts, M
Robertson, A S
Robertson, D N
Robertson, P A
Robertson, P W
Robinson, A L
Robinson, B H B
Robinson, J S
Robinson, S J
Robson, C H
Robson, N J
Rock, I W
Rodgers, R T B
Rodrick, C J
Rodrigues, A J
Rogers, J M
Rogers, S N
Rogowski, P
Rooney, M J
Roper-Hall, M J
Roper, H P
Roper, P H
Rose, J H
Rose, S J
Rosenfield, M
Ross, A M
Ross, J D C
Rothery, D J
Rouse, A M
Rowe, J
Rowlands, D C
Rowntree, C J
Roy Choudhury, M
Roy, A
Roy, H
Roy, M
Roylance, J
Ruby, A
Rummens, L J
Rummens, S D
Rumsey, J M A
Rushton, D I
Russell, G S J
Russell, I D
Russell, S H
Russell, S E
Rutter, L C
Ryatt, K S
Ryder, C A J
Ryder, R E J
Rylance, G W
Sabir, N M
Sadler, P
Saeed, T
Saeed, Z P
Sahay, P K
Saigol, M
Saigol, M Y
Saikia-Varman, N
Saikia, S
Saini, M S
Saini, M S

Sajjad, A
Sakhuja, S B
Saksena, S C
Salama, A A K
Salamat, A A
Salar, T A
Saldanha, L J
Saleem, M A
Sales, T S
Salib, S S E
Salim, M
Salim, S N
Salmon, D N
Salt, P J
Samarasinghe, L A
Sambatakakis, A
Sandhu, S S
Sandilands, D W I M
Sandler, D
Sandrasegaran, K
Sanghera, J S
Sangra, R A S
Sankarayya, N
Sarmah, B D
Sarwar, S
Sashidharan, S P
Saunders, D M
Saunders, E J
Saunders, P B
Savage, C O S
Sawers, R S
Schuppler, P E R
Scotcher, S M
Scott-Cook, H R
Scott, R A H
Scott, S J
Seakins, E C
Sealey, M M
Searle, S J
Segall, M S
Sellarajah, A
Sempa, A V
Sen-Gupta, T
Sengupta, R
Seth, A
Settatree, R S
Seymour, A H
Shafi, M I
Shafiq, M
Shah, A U
Shah, B M
Shah, F
Shah, J L
Shah, M J
Shah, N K
Shah, P R
Shah, V M
Shah, Z H
Shahmanesh, M
Shahmanesh, M
Sham, S-Y
Shameem, M
Shankernarayan, M G
Shannon, J R
Shannon, N L
Shannon, S W
Shapiro, J A
Shapiro, L R
Sharif, K W S
Sharma, A
Sharma, A
Shastri, M M
Shaw, M J
Shaylor, P J
Shehmar, M
Shelton, F C
Sheppard, M C
Sherlaw, J A
Sherrington, J M
Shervington, J P
Sherwood, N A
Shieff, E
Shields, P L
Shinkwin, C A
Shinner, G
Shinton, R A
Shipman, P A M
Shire, H
Shorrock, C J
Shumsheruddin, D M
Siddeeq, M U
Sidhom, A T M
Sidhu, R S
Siggins, D W
Siggins, G F G
Sigurdsson, A S
Sills, J A
Silove, E D
Silverman, S H

Simkiss, D E
Simms, M H
Simms, M S
Simon, P D
Simons, D M
Simpson, M
Sinclair, A S
Singal, A
Singh, G
Singh, P
Singh, S P
Singh, S
Singh, S
Singhal, S
Sinha, A K
Sinha, M
Sintler, M P
Sipple, M A
Siriwardena, G J A
Skingle, I S
Skinner, A M M
Slaney, G
Slater, N A J
Slator, R C
Smallwood, H M
Smart, C J
Smart, S J
Smith, A G
Smith, A M
Smith, A
Smith, B S
Smith, B H
Smith, E K
Smith, E G
Smith, G R
Smith, J E M
Smith, J E
Smith, K J
Smith, L J A
Smith, M R
Smith, N A
Smith, P R
Smith, R V
Smith, R N
Smith, S R G
Smith, S A
Smith, U M
Smyth, M G M
Sneath, R J S
Sneath, R S
Sobti, A K
Solari, J R
Somasundara-Rajah, J
Somasundara-Rajah, K
Somerset, D A
Somerset, R B
Sood, M R
Soon, Y
Southwood, T R
Souza Faria, F P
Spanner, R M
Spannuth, F
Sparkes, J M
Spiller, P A
Spray, C H
Sreeram, N
Srivastava, A S
Stableforth, D E
Stannard, W A
Stanton, E C R
Stark, E G
Stark, P J
Starkie, C M
Starritt, M P
Stedman, J K
Stedman, S R
Steedman, G
Steele, R T
Stern, S
Sterne, A J
Steven, N M
Stevens, A J H
Stevens, M C G
Stevenson, I H
Stewart, D G
Stewart, P M
Stirling, A J
Stockley, R A
Stoddart, B C
Stokes-Lampard, H J
Stokes, M A
Stonelake, P S
Strain, T B H
Strang, G E M
Strange, S W
Straughan, J K
Strouhal, P D
Stuart-Smith, K

Blackburn

Stumper, O F W
Sturman, S G
Subhie, N
Sud, S K
Suggett, N R
Suleman, N A
Sullivan, C A
Sunderland, R
Sungum-Paliwal, S
Super, P A
Sutherland, G A
Sutton, G A
Swaby, D S A
Swain, A J
Swain, D G
Swales, N V
Swani, M S
Swanston, A C N
Sweeney, H R
Syed, A B
Syed, N Y
Sylvester, A R
Symonds, J M
Tadros, W S
Takes, H M
Tan, C Y
Tandon, N K
Tandon, U R
Tavares-Mott, N E
Taylor-Shewring, D A
Taylor, A P
Taylor, C M
Taylor, C J C
Taylor, D G B
Taylor, E I R
Taylor, F T
Taylor, J L
Taylor, J M
Taylor, K G
Taylor, L D
Taylor, M H
Taylor, S A
Taylor, S L
Taylor, W
Teale, G R
Temple, J G
Temple, M J L
Temple, R M
Thake, A I S
Thakur, S
Thambyrajah, J
Than Than Swe, Dr
Thandi, K S
Thebridge, P J
Theodoulou, G S
Thethy, R S
Thind, I
Thomas, A M C
Thomas, E
Thomas, M K
Thomas, P A
Thompson, A G
Thompson, A K
Thompson, A P
Thompson, I M
Thompson, R D
Thompson, R A
Thompson, S M
Thomson, H J
Thorne, S A
Thornhill, R J
Thornton, M E
Thwaites, A J
Tibbits, J C N
Tierney, J N
Tillman, R M
Timoney, N
Tinkler, R
Titley, O G
Todd, R S
Toogood, S J
Tooth, E A
Toozs-Hobson, P M
Tovey, P J
Townend, J N
Toyn, C E
Tricklebank, B
Trimble, K T
Trivedi, K M
Trotter, S E
Tsakonas, D
Tse, W Y
Tubbs, O N
Tudor, M M
Tudor, V S
Turner, E A
Turner, E S
Turner, N O
Turner, P R W

Turpin, P J
Tyagi, A K
Udokang, M J
Ullyatt, K J
Unsworth, J
Uppal, H S
Usher-Somers, N
Usmani, I
Usselmann, B M
Vachhani, M K
Vaile, J C
Vaja, K H
Vale, J A
Valsalan, U
Van Marle, W
Van Mourik, I D M
Vasi, S C
Vatish, R K
Veness, A M
Venkat, K R
Venkatesan, P
Venugopal, S
Verity, D H
Verma, A N
Verma, A
Verma, A
Verma, S K
Verma, S
Virdee, M S
Vo, V T
Vora, A K
Waddell, C A
Wade, O L
Wadhwa, H K
Wagstyl, S
Wainscott, G R D
Waite, M A
Wake, M J C
Wali, G
Walji, M-T I
Walker, S L
Walker, W E
Wall, R A
Wallace, D M A
Wallace, P A
Wallis, P J W
Walsh, A R
Walshe, A D
Walt, H J
Walt, R P
Walters, S
Walton, K W W H
Ward, D J
Ward, J P Q
Wardlaw, M M S
Wardle, A D
Warfield, A T
Wasserberg, J
Wassmer, E
Waters, R A
Watkins, R A
Watkins, S J D
Watkinson, J C
Watkinson, M
Watson, D N
Watson, E A J
Watson, K A
Watt, J M
Wearn, A M
Weaver, J B
Webb, D R
Webb, F E
Webster, K
Weddell, D J
Weeks, M C
Weil, J G
Weiner, G M
Weller, M D
Weller, P H
Weller, T M A
Wells, M B
West, R J
Wheatley, K E
Wheeley, S M
White, A C
White, D J
White, R J
Whitehouse, S J
Whiteley, J T
Whiting, J L
Whittaker, C M
Whittington, R M
Whittle, M J
Whyte, J A
Wiggins, M R
Wigley, E J
Wijnberg, A W A
Wilcox, C
Wilcox, R G
Wilcox, R M L

Wild, N J
Wildbore, P M
Wilde, J T
Wilkes, M P
Wilkey, A D
Wilkinson, B R
Wilkinson, C D
Wilkinson, M J B
Williams, A C
Williams, C R
Williams, D K
Williams, D P C
Williams, E D
Williams, G E O
Williams, H J
Williams, J K
Williams, J
Williams, L R
Williams, M D
Williams, N A
Williams, R C
Williams, S W
Williams, S J
Williams, S P
Williamson, E J E
Wilson-Lloyd, J M
Wilson, B E
Wilson, F
Wilson, I C
Wilson, M
Wilson, M J A
Winer, J B
Wingate, J P
Wingate, V A
Winkley, L M
Winter, H R
Wise, R
Wiseman, E S
Wishart, E H
Wolff, A
Wolverson, R L
Wong, C H
Wong, P C
Wood, A L
Wood, J K
Wood, M J
Wood, P R
Wood, P J
Woodhead, C J
Wooding, N J
Woodward, C L
Woodward, J M
Woollaston, K A H
Woolley, S L
Woolley, S M
Worrall-Kent, L S
Wozniak, I A
Wozniak, J T
Wozniak, S
Wrenn, P A M
Wright, C J
Wright, D
Wright, J M
Wright, J G C
Wright, M J
Wright, P R
Wylie, J P
Yap, S L
Yaqoob, N
Yates, D A
Yates, J A
Yau, W H
Yee, M L
Yeh, J S-J
Yoong, A K H
Yoong, W C
Young Min, M S
Young, B P
Young, D W
Young, G B
Young, J A
Youssef, E E
Yunas, S
Yusuf, S
Zafar, S A
Zaki, A S
Zaman, T M
Zaman, T M
Zargar, G M
Zielinski, R A
Zuckerman, C H

Bishop Auckland

Airlie, K R
Alam, M M
Alcock, D J
Andrew, J D
Andrew, M C
Baliga, K V S

Bateson, M C
Benstead, S E
Bentley, T M
Bibby, C B
Bolton, G M
Bowron, P
Bremner, I S
Chandrasiri, R B C M
Chauhan, M
Cottrell, A J
Deytrikh, N
Downs, C T
Drath, M C
Eccleston, E C
Fairclough, B E
Ferguson, A J A
Findlay, S M
Finnighan, E-A
Ford, G D
Forge, J A
Fox, E A
Fox, J V
Gandhi, N J
Gash, S R
Gomersall, C R
Gonsalves, H J B
Hackett, M T C
Harris, D
Heath, G
Hema Kumar, J
Hetherington, A
Holden, H M
Howells, L
Jayasekera, L A G
Johnson, M K
Johnston, A M
Jones, P M
Jones, S R
Kandiah, B J
Khan, S H
Lamb, W H
Langford, D C
Lees, W
Lewis, A
Lewis, M A
Liddell, A S
Limb, D G
Lloyd, I G
Lumb, S A
McCulloch, A J
McGregor, G S
Macleod, A H
McManners, R
Mahdi, K S
Mees, G P
Mehrzad, A A
Needham, I C
Newall, N
Orr, P K
Pickworth, J C
Pike, B R
Pindolia, N K
Prentice, M C
Pugh, K
Rajasooriyar, W
Ramachandran, V
Roberts, C
Robertson, F
Robertson, I
Robinson, K B
Sarkar, D
Schumann, E C
Scott, C M
Sivayokan, P
Smellie, W S A
Smith, H L
Spurr, J I
Stephen, J G
Stewart, A L
Stewart, M P M
Stock, S E
Vijayaraghavan, S
Vose, H C
Walker, W I
Waller, D C E
Ward, M A
Weerasinghe, B D
Young, J
Young, S K

Bishops Castle

Bryce-Smith, R
Gillett, A S
Gurney, J D
Howell, N C B
Penney, A P S J
Penney, G N S J

Bishop's Stortford

Agarwal, S
Al-Fattal, S M A S
Arafa Ali, K A L
Baas, A A G
Bhuller, A S
Bradbury, N J L
Carew, R I
Carrick, P A
Chauhan, A
Chisnall, A
Clarke, I R
Clarke, J A
Clemans-Gibbon, T M
Cooke, C J
Crowe, G H
Currey, J
Dain, A V
Davies, R G
Davis, R A
Degun, W J
Dennis, A S
Dixon, J A
Dolling, M
Donnelly, J S
Dove, P R
Emmett, V E
Ensor, G F
Fawcett, I M
Fitness, S J
Gilchrist, I C
Goldspink, M H F
Greenlees, F R
Halliwell, E L
Hardwick, M J
Hardy, J D
Harling, R M
Hickman, P J
Hope, C J
Hutchings, K N
Jabbar, N K A
Jellis, T S
Jenns, M A
Jordan, A F
Kapadia, Y K
Kent, R V
Leiper, E J R
Leiper, M D
Lewin, R A
Lightman, D J
Lloyd, J E
McKenzie, J G
Madigan, M R
Mand, H S
Meyrick, J
Moore, P J
Morgan, B
Morgan, M W E
Morris, E C
Nutley, P G
Oates, N R
Orton, K A
Orton, P K
Pandor, S B
Payne, R F
Poirier, H
Price, D M C
Raine, J M
Rayner, J M
Rogers, M J
Schofield, J G
Scott, L A
Sequeira, J M
Shah, D B
Shaw, K
Spooner, K J
Stephens, M D B
Tischkowitz, M D K-E
Todd, R M
Trivedi, K G
Van De Walle, J G J
Visuvanathan, S
Wallace, J T
Watson, A T
Whetstone, S
Wilson, P C
Wilson, S D
Wright, J T

Bishopton

Alexander, J O
Bennie, A M
Boyce, J
Doak, W M
Dooley, J M
Downie, F B
Dudgeon, V E
Gowling, G E
Gray, D G

Gray, J S
Hodgson, M E
MacGregor, C A
Masterton, J G
Miller, J
Williamson, M M

Bitteswell

Williams, E R

Blackburn

Adams, A M
Adhya, N R
Agarwal, K N
Ahmad, T U
Ahmed, M M
Al Ani, F S S
Ali, A A
Ali, M O
Amarasinghe, G P W
Amran Bin Marzuki, Dr
Apaloo, F K B
Aravind, S P
Ariyaratnam, S
Ashe, P J
Azfar, S S
Bahia, H I
Balasubramanian, M
Bani-Hani,
K E-D H A A
Banik, S
Barker, R F
Barrie, J L
Bennett, N O
Benson, J W T
Benson, R C
Bhattacharjee, G B
Bhojani, I H
Bristow, A I
Brown, E L
Brun, C
Buckley, N G E
Burch, K L
Burke, P E
Burn, K E
Butler, S V
Bux, Z M
Carter, P S
Chadwick, E
Chandler, J A
Chattopadhyay, T
Chattree, S
Cherry, J R
Chorlton, M I
Chowdhury, M A P
Clark, C E
Clarke, S J
Clarkson, S
Critchley, E M R
Critchley, H D
Critchley, M
Crowley, B
Datta, M K
Datta, S
Davenport, G A
Davey, R J
Dawson, C R
De, A K
Dervan, M F
Dugmore, W N
Duong, T V
Earnshaw, D P
Emmott, R S
Evans, D A
Fairhurst, H J
Fakhry, H A G
Farooq, H M
Fielding, A
Fletcher, L M
Fossard, C
Fourie, P G
Fox, D J
Gamble, A R
Gargye, U
Garwood, P J
Gavan, D R
George, T K
Gilligan, S J
Goetzee, A E
Goodall, D
Gooder, P D
Goodfellow, P B
Grayson, R P
Green, R M
Grimes, D S
Grundy, M
Gunn, S D
Gupta, D
Hamlin, G W

Blackpool

Hancock, S A
Handley, J
Haq, Z
Hardy, C I
Hardy, S C
Hardy, S K
Harrington, M L
Hartley, R C
Hodkinson, P S
Holden, C L
Holme, V J
Hossain, M O S M
Hudson, C
Hutton, E M
Islam, N
Jadhav, S D
Jeyaseelan, S
Jones, D A
Jones, E
Jones, G R
Jones, R P
Jones, R C
Joseph, S N
Joshi, S V
Juhasz, A G
Karim, H
Karim, M R
Karim, T
Kaur, S
Khan, F
Khan, M S
Khan, Z U
Kirkpatrick, H W
Kirkpatrick, L T
Knowles, A C
Koneru, U S
Kratter, F E
Kumar, A
Kundu, B N
Kundu, S
Ladlow, M E
Lea, M H
Lewis, F W
Lomax, S R
Lowe, S E
Lowrie, I G
Lynch, D A F
McCraith, J A
McEwan, A B
Magell, J
Mahoney, C F K
Mahoney, M P
Maiti, S K
Marlborough, J J C
Maskell, A P
Mene, A R
Minto, G W
Misra, N
Mohammed, T
Moodie, I J
Moss, P D
Mousdale, S
Mowbray, C H
Mukherjee, C
Mukherjee, S K
Mukherji, D J
Murdoch, A J M
Murray, D B
Myers, A
Nagpal, N
Nagpal, S
Nandakumar, E
Nataraj, V
Neilson, D
Nicholson, R W
Nylander, A G E
O'Donovan, P A
O'Reilly, M P
Okpara, C C
Ormerod, L P
Osman, M
Owen, C M
Paley, J D
Paley, W G
Panikkar, J
Parry, A K
Patel, M P
Paton, R W
Pearce, S
Perera, G S G S
Phillips, E B
Phillips, J K
Pimblett, G H
Platt, A M
Pollock, R S
Premraj, K
Prescott, R J
Privonitz, D M
Probert, C B

Rahman, M A
Rahman, M
Rakshit, B C
Randall, J C
Rao, K C
Rashed, N F
Rautray, R C
Rautray, R
Ravat, F E
Read, L
Reddy, Dr
Reed, P F
Rehman, S A
Rimmer, S
Roberts, N A
Roberts, T A
Romachney, P
Rooney, R G
Rose, D J A
Royle, J D
Rushton, C E
Russo, P
Sarodia, U A
Schram, C M H
Searson, J J
Shah, F Z
Sharma, M
Siddiqui, A I A
Singh, R K
Sivagnanam, T
Sivayoham, I S
Sivayoham, S
Smerdon, A C
Smith, C P
Smith, D
Smith, N A
Soliman, E S
Spink, M S
Teh, L-S
Thambar, I V
Timms, M S
Timothy, H R
Timson, I
Trafford, P D
Tresadern, J C
Upton, S N
Valluri, P
Vaughan, S T A
Vijayakumar, A
Virdi, R P S
Walmsley, P N H
Walsh, G P
Walsh, J
Walsh, M F
Ward, R L
Watson, R J
Weerakone, R S
Wemyss-Holden, G D
Whyte, I D
Wilkinson, R
Wilson, G S
Yates, G A
Yates, M J

Blackpool

Abellan-Antolin, F J
Adinkra, J P
Allman, M B
Anandappa, A J A
Anderson, W J
Apaloo, E C
Arrowsmith, P J
Arya, M
Arya, S
Arya, S C
Ashworth, R N
Au, J K K
Aulakh, H S
Avasthi, R B
Awbery, S M
Baloch, A G
Barlow, D J
Bedell, J
Beet, P L
Bell, H J T
Bennett, H G B
Bevis, C R A
Bibby, R J
Billington, P
Birtles, T D
Biswas, P K
Boak, M
Bolton, M
Bonsell, E M
Bowyer, P K
Brooks, A
Brown, S
Bury, R W
Byrd, L M

Byrne, S
Calvert, C A D
Calvert, J S
Campbell, C D
Caramitsos, J T
Carroll, E
Chamberlain, M E
Chandra, V
Charles, D P
Charles, W J
Chatterjee, J P
Chattopadhyay, P K
Choudhury, A K
Clarke, C W M
Clewlow, R M
Cookson, A J
Cooper, J D
Cornah, M S
Costello, F T
Counsell, D J
Cox, B G
Crookenden, D
Curtis, P D
Cushing, S
Dabrowski, M T
Dale, G
Dale, M C
Davie, A M
Dewis, P
Dickinson, E B
Donne, R
Duncan, A J
Dunne, J A
Duthie, R
Duthie, S J
East, A M P
Eccleston, I M
Edwards, V A
Eggington, W R O
El-Jabri, M
Ellis, S K
Evans, C G
Faux, P A L
Fewster, S D
Finucane, U A
Flanagan, N G
Flegg, P J
Forster, D M
Furniss, A E
Gadallah, E F
Gandhi, R G
Garstang, A R
Gibb, I A M
Green, K L
Greenaway, W E
Greiss, G G
Guirguis, A F A
Hall, S L
Harper, N G
Harrison, D
Harrop, H J
Harrop, S N
Hausser, B I
Haworth, D A
Haworth, D G
Haydar, A A S
Hayes, B
Hayes, P J
Hayes, S D A
Heath, J C D
Hemmings, S C
Hiles, A
Hinchcliffe, D E
Hindley, C J
Hoadley, G M
Horton, S J R
Hulme, A V
Humber, J C
Humphries, C A
Hunt, J S
Inmonger, J
Iqbal, M
Ireland, D
Isaacs, P E T
Jensen, P
Johnson, A G
Johnson, G W
Jowitt, M D
Kane, T P
Kay, D S G
Kazi, G A
Kelly, P D
Kelsey, P R
Khawaja, U L
Kirkham, I C
Kitching, C
Lake, P J
Lambert, I K
Lau, S C

Leather, K E
Lee, E M
Lee, L K
Lehane, D F
Levine, W H C
Li Kam Wa, T C
Lippmann, M E M
Liu, S M
Lord, B M
Lowson, T A
Lucking, M T
Lunn, M K
Lynch, R
Lynch, S
Macbeth, A J
McConachie, I W
McGovern, A J
Mackay, J D
McLoughlin, S J
Madan, K K
Madan, S
Mannion, S J
Martin, M H
Matthews, J J
Meichen, F W
Miller, H S
Miller, J
Milne, J R
Mistry, D D
Molodynski, C J
Montgomery, D P
Moore, R
Morcos, M I
Morgan, R J M
Muir, J G
Murray, D G
Naguib, M A E-A A
Nasr, E F
Neary, P J
Newiss, L P
Nigam, A
Nolan, J A
O'Donnell, M J
O'Reilly, J F
Ong, K T
Parham, A L S
Parikh, R K
Parker, M A
Parker, S P
Parkinson, G F
Parr-Burman, S J
Perricone, V
Pettit, S H
Pollock, J E
Pollock, W S T
Powell, M L
Prakash, H
Preskey, M S
Priestley, E
Qualtrough, J E
Raines, M F
Randall, N P C
Ravi, S
Reed, G P
Rees, A N
Riding, G S G
Riding, K J
Robb, A K
Roberts, D H
Rogan, E
Rogan, P M
Rothwell, P J N
Rowlands, A J
Rudnick, L R
Saeed, A M
Salah, I H I
Sampath, S A C
Sarkar, P K
Saunders, E H
Saunders, M G
Scott, C W
Scott, I W H
Sedgwick, M
Self, M C
Shanmugasundaram, O
Shearer, S A
Shravat, B P
Smith, S T
Smythe, R
Srivastava, A
Srivastava, S P
Steel, A
Steel, M R
Suriya, A
Tait, W M
Thomas, M R
Thompson, G
Tun, S T
Vardy, P I

Vasudev, K S
Vyse-Peacock, A
Walker, M C M
Walshaw, C F
Ward, T W
Wells, R A
Wheatley, R
Wilcox, F L
Wilkinson, M G
Williams, M E
Wilson, J M
Wojciuk, J
Wrigglesworth, P B
Yule, J H B
Zaki-Khalil, I A

Blackwood

Datta, B N
Emerson, S C
Harris, C
Jayadev, A
Jones, R
Khan, B
Lloyd, A L
Nash, J T
Ray, D K
Rogers, J H P
Sahni, P
Shah, I S
Shah, S H
Sheen, M
Sweetman, J A
Thompson, W
Waheed, A
Windsor, K
Wyatt, S

Blaenau Ffestiniog

Boyns, A R
Dafydd, R E
Evans, O W
Jones, H R
Jones, J R K
Lambert, C G
Maxwell, D M
Morgan, J R
Parry, T
Wells, D G

Blaenavon

Buffett, G J G
Grant, D P
Griffiths, R B
Hemming, C
Islam, M S
Khan, A K M S
Lewis, T L
Lewis, W

Blairgowrie

Buchanan, E U
Buchanan, J G S
Burgess, H J L
Burke, D
Caldwell, D C
Callaway, E J
Cathro, A J M
Dallas Ross, W P
Delahunty, C
Dick, J B C
Downie, S E
Dunbar, J M
Dunbar, O M J
Dunn, H E
Faloon, K
Ferrier, D W
Forbes, H F
Gilmour, F B
Gilruth, A J M
Greig, G C
Hart, M R D
Haxton, H A
Hind, V M D
Huddleston, I
Jack, J F B
Mackay, J M
McNeill, G P
McNeill, K E M
McPherson, E C
MacVicar, M
Martin, R K
Martindale, M M
Milne, A J
Morris, M J
Pyle, R L
Reid, I C
Scott, M C
Shaw, J M A
Sim, I J
Slater, W J

Stewart, C T
Swanson, W C
Waddell, D L
Williams, J W
Young, A M M

Blakeney

Gibbs, M
Oakley, J E

Blandford Forum

Allum, G J
Armand Smith, N G
Beadsmoore, E J
Benazon, L
Billington, M J
Blevins, T C S
Bosworth, P
Burlton, D A
Cade, A N
Chan, K H M
Clarke, J J
Clements, J
Cogbill, K L
Creagh-Barry, M J W
Davies, J V
Davies, J V
Ellery, S M
Evans, J M
Ford, M S
Gelder, A D
Hillier, E W
Hillier, M J H
Kenny, T J W
Lester, J A
Meyrick Thomas, R H
Norman, T
Norris, E M
Oliver, P O
Percival, G N
Pestridge, A D
Prior, R J
Richardson, S M
Scorey, P D
Stockings, F E
Swan, P A
Thomas, A M
Walton, M J
Ward, R F
Wilson, D I T
Wise, R P
Youngson, R M

Blaydon-on-Tyne

Banerji, A
Bloxham, C A
Bolas, R
Duggal, R P
Freer, M C
Gibson, A L
Jackson, R
Johnson, R M
Kattan, J C
Khanna, R
Lowery-Leigh, G
McKay, S
Mackie, J H
McWilliams, J E
Matheson, D J
Oliver, G
Orr, A J
Robson, S
Warnakulasuriya, K M R D S
Williams, P R

Blyth

Allen, J S
Anderson, S B
Carr, R
Charlton, R M
Cochran, L
Dodds, W R
Eynon, D M
Fletcher, H J
Ghosh, J K
Gittins, S
Henderson, C A
Hussain, Z
Johri, R
Kimmitt, J
McCollum, R W
McEvedy, P A
Morgan, D C
Murphy, R A
Rawes, G D
Redfearn, A
Sukumaran Nair, C
Turner, J P
Urquhart, A S

Bordon

Westgarth, D
Yeoman, P D

Boat of Garten
Murray, A C
Riach, I C F

Bodmin
Ball, D R
Bruce, J D
Bruce, W R
Buckley-Evans, J D
Collins, V M
Coulthard, C W S
Cox, P J R
Eastwood, N J B
Evans-Jones, R J
Farrar, D I
Hignell, S P
Hogbin, P A
Koch, B
Maguire, J
Owen, N T P
Partington, A G
Rouncefield, A M
Spicer, C C
Stead, M S
Stokes, S A K
Symeonakis, A
Tullberg, H T W
Watkins, S J O

Bodorgan
Lee, E
Roberts, J M
Wilkinson, D C
Williams, A W
Williams, M

Bognor Regis
Afridi, K W
Ahmed, E R
Amaladoss, A S P
Barnes, N W
Behraznia-Berelian, A
Berelian, S
Bradstock-Smith, M R
Bratt, C C
Brennan-Benson, P
Cahill, C
Callaway, P L
Condon, K H
Coupland, T G
Dalgleish, J G
Darling, T W
Ellis, E A
Esslemont, A
Evans, C A S
Fletcher, M
Fox, C M
Fox, M H
Fulton, R
Furlepa, K A
Gibson, J R M
Gilbert, R G
Graham-Evans, J N
Greenway, J H
Hanan, P M
Heaton, W R
Houston, R
Jackson, R A
Kerr, S A
Kipling, M L
Kirk, R S
Lavender, A J
Lean, A T
Linton, D E
Lloyd, O W
Macarthur, A
McLoughlin, J N
Marnell, M B
Mather, S D
Miles, J P
Muir, A P J
Naylor, A M A
Nisbet, N W
O'Kelly, F J
Parker, W N B
Paterson, F N
Price, J R
Rehman, F U
Ridley, M G
Robinson, A
Robinson, G R E
Rogers, W J
Shaw, M M
Sheerboom, D J
Sodera, V K
Sole, P W
Sommerville, P

Southgate, H J
Southwood, M C
Southwood, W F W
Speer, P G
Spence, K A E
Spurrier, P D
Tapp, G R
Trepess, J N
Wallis, P
Warren, J N
Warwick-Brown, R
Weeks, R F
Whitelaw, E M
Whitelaw, J D A
Williamson, C M
Woolf, P M

Boldon Colliery
Aitken, G J
Cole, F R
Hall, W
Simpson, J H
Thornley-Walker, E G A

Bolton
Adam, Y
Ahmad, S I
Ainley-Walker, P F
Allamby, D L
Allan, A E
Allan, J D D
Allan, W R
Allanson, M J
Anderson, P
Anderson, S M L
Ariff, A
Aspbury, J N
Aspinall, R J
Aston, R
Atcha, A W
Atcha, S
Atcha, Z I
Baker, F
Baker, P
Bancroft, K
Banerjee, A
Banerjee, A K
Banks, A J
Barben, M R
Barrett, A A
Basu, J K
Bene, J
Benjamin, M S
Berry, S G
Bishop, H M
Bisset, D L
Bisset, J M
Board, T N
Bolt, J C D
Bora, R
Bowman, F M
Boyd, A A W
Bradford, J M
Bratt, A
Brenchley, S A
Briggs, S R
Brocklebank, M C
Brookes, C N
Brough, R A
Brown, M C
Brownlee, M R
Bullen, T F
Bullough, R
Bunn, D T
Buttoo, S
Bydder, M
Caldwell, I D
Chan, K-K
Chandra, M
Chandrappa, M H
Charidemou, C
Chia, K V
Chishti, J M
Chowdhury, M
Clarke, K M
Cooper, M M
Cooper, R M
Counsell, G A
Craig, S K L
Crank, A
Cranna, R A
Cross, P A
Dady, I M
Dakshinamurthi, M
Das, D
Daud, A S
Dave, A K
Dave, V K

Davies, A J
Davies, D
Davies, M R P
Daw, E G
Dawson, R J
Dean, J D
Delamore, I W
Dennard, D L
Derbyshire, M J
Dey, M P
Downes, B
Doyle, S J
Dryburgh, P A
Duncalf, H A
Earnshaw, C J
Ellis, A G
Ellis, J E
Ellis, M
Ellis, P J
Farrand, R J
Farrell, A M
Fasnacht, M
Faulkner, G S
Ferguson, G H
Fildes, G
Fildes, S L
Finn, J O
Firth, J
Fletcher, C L
Fletcher, M S
Flynn, M J
Ford, P M
Fraser, A J
Fraser, A H
Freeman, M
Galea, F
Garewal, S
Gartside, M W
Gatenby, J
Gent, R N
Glass, S
Godden, D P
Godden, D R P
Gowland, M R
Green Hemmings, C E
Green, J J
Greenhalgh, C B
Greenhalgh, S
Gulati, R
Habashi, F A
Hafizullah, M
Hailwood, R A
Hailwood, S M
Hall, J M
Hall, M J
Hall, S A
Hamer, I E
Hamilton, S L
Hanif, S T
Hardman, J L
Hargreaves, S P
Harris, J
Harris, R P
Harrison, R W
Hartley, R C
Hartopp, I K
Haslam, D W
Haslam, I F
Haslam, N
Hawks, A M
Healey, H
Hearn, G M
Hearn, K C
Henderson, A A
Henderson, J J
Hendy, B
Hendy, C
Higgins, B
Higgins, M C
Hobbiss, J H
Hodgson, S P
Holly, L J
Hopkins, R E
Hopkinson, J M
Hossain, M
Hunt, R A
Hutchesson, A C J
Iliff, A M
Ingram, G E
Isaac, T C
Jack, E M
Jackson, R J
Jagannath, P
James, I G V
Jarvis, A M
Jayasekera, A I
Jayasekera, D S
Jip, J
Jiva, M I

Johnson, I A T
Johnson, J D
Johnston, T O
Jones, D K
Jones, I N
Jones, J R
Joyce, E A
Kay, A L
Kearney, R T
Kelly, S P D D
Kent, L N
Kenward, S E
Khan, A M
Khan, S H
Khwaja, M S
Killcross, A
Kirby, J A L
Korlipara, K R
Kumar, D
Lad, R P
Lamb, A K
Lancashire, G S
Langton, J
Leather, G D
Leaver, N M
Lentin, M
Lipscomb, K J
Liratsopulos, G
Litherland, D J
Littlewood, R
Liversedge, S N
Loomba, Y
Lowe, J
Lowry, J C
Lynch, T
Lyon, A L
McAuley, D E
McCallum, A S R
McClaughlin, J
McGlade, M P
McKenna, M A
McKenna, T D
McKenzie, C J
Mackinnon, C J
McLardy, G
McLean, G F A
McMillen, J E
Mahindrakar, N H
Mallott, L M
Mangrolia, R D
Mann, C L A
Marles, P J
Marriott, F P S
Marshall, B
Martin Gonzalez, J E
Mathew, S
Maxwell, A J
Mercer, C P
Mitchell, R G
Mobb, G E
Moriarty, K J
Morrison, A M
Morton, W S
Moulton, C
Muhammad, J K
Mukherjee, D
Munshi, S A B
Murphy, D J
Naqvi, S M H
Naqvi, S N H
Navaratnam, Y
Needham, J A
Newgrosh, B S
Newman, B M
Ng Man Kwong, G
Nicholson, J A H
Northover, T H
O'Keeffe, L J
Odonga, F
Ogbo, V I
Ogden, G H
Oghoetuoma, J O
Onwudike, M
Openshaw, D R
Ormiston, P J
Ostick, D G
Page, J
Panja, S R
Parr, P J
Patel, D M
Patel, K J
Patel, V K
Patel, V N
Peacock, J
Pearson, J M
Perkins, B
Perry, E M
Petrie, P J
Phillips, G M

Phillips, J P K
Pope, I J
Pownall, P J
Poynor, M U
Prabhu, S
Prasad, A
Price, E W
Priest, P J
Rae, P J
RamcHandani, M
RamcHandani, P
Ratcliffe, F H
Reading, J G
Regan, C M
Reilly, S M
Reynard, A J
Roberts, J W
Robinson, J
Roddie, A E
Rodgers, M E R
Rowe, S D
Rowlands, F M
Ryan, J P
Ryan, W G
Sabrine, S F
Sarkar, S
Sarker, D
Saul, P A
Schofield, C P
Scott, P J
Searby, G J
Seddon-Smith, R I
Senarath Yapa, S C
Senior, T P M
Service, E
Settle, P
Shannon, T E
Shaw, S A G
Sheldon, H E
Sheppard, I J
Sidat, I A G M
Siddiqui, T N
Silvert, B D
Simmons, C M
Simmons, W H
Simpson, R A
Singh, S
Singh, V M M
Smith, G P
Smith, M C
Smith, N J
Smith, S C
Smyth, J W
Somerville, D M
Spurr, D
Steele, M
Stirk, N J
Strong, P M
Szulec, Z J
Tabor, J E
Tankard, J G
Taulke-Johnson, T D
Taylor, A
Taylor, D B S
Taylor, J
Thalange, N K S
Thomas, C F L
Thompson, J T
Thompson, L
Tomkinson, J S
Tuck, J S
Tun Min, Dr
Umebuani, V C
Vali, A M
Varghese, C M
Varker, J A
Varley, S C
Wadey, J A E
Wakefield, C J
Walker, J R A
Walker, P M
Walker, R J
Wall, D A
Wallis, S W J
Walmsley, T A
Ward, P J
Ward, S M
Wardman, L E
Warner, J G
Watson, R
Watt, R W
Webster, R C
Wells, S
West, C G H
Wheatley, E C
Whittle, J K
Widaa, A R
Wildman, M J
Wilkinson, M J S

Wilks, J
Wood, J P
Woodcock, R C
Woods, C J
Wright, A J
Yates, P D

Bo'ness
Acheson, A J
Barry, J E
Crichton, A-M
Easton, D V M
Gilmour, M F W
Hitchcock, R H
McCullough, M E
Onori, K M
Park, D J
Park, J
Paton, J
Proudlove, R
Sargent, T S P

Bonnybridge
Anderson, S C
Blair, E M
Colgan, J M
Dick, A N
Dyer, C F
Dyer, R S
McCalister, B
McCalister, P W
Murray, M D
Rankin, J
Reilly, T
Weir, J A
Wilson, C C S
Wolff, L E

Bonnyrigg
Brown, I D
Clarke, F J
Condie, R
Dalgleish, J
Dickson, G C
Dyson, F M H
Heggie, L J
Innes, R B
Keith, M A
Lamb, S G
Munro, N H
Norton, A M
Rogers, K A
Rother, P
Sattar, N
Smart, I S M
Thomson, G G J
Watkinson, H L
Wusu, O O H

Bootle
Ali, A
Beck, R A
Chung, K M
Goldberg, D O
Jha, K K
Kapoor, R G
Lalgee, C H
McCormick, C G S
McGrane, C E
McGrane, M
Misra, G K
Murphy, K E
Newman, T A
Osman, J
Rawbone, R G
Roberts, A W
Roope, Y A
Sinha, N K
Sinha, S K
Srivastava, P K
Stokell, R A
Stone, L D
Swarbrick, J G
Vinchenzo, A

Bordon
Beaumont, K M
Beech, P A
Binns, H
Booth, F M
Boswood, S B
Copping, D M
Dilley, M D
Dunkley, A H
Grice, M J
Izard, R
Kani, W
Read, Z H
Rose, J S

Borehamwood

Watkinson, W M F
Williams-Thomas, F H

Borehamwood
Adeboye, K A O
Behrman, S A
Bellau, A R
Bennett, P E
Binks, F A
Campbell, I A
Cremin, P M
Cushion, J E L
Dattani, R T
Drake, A J
Edwards, M R
Elliott, S C
Gaunt, D R
Goddard, A V
Goddard, D M
Graham, J W
Grant, S C
Harrison, R A
Henderson, E C E
Hirsch, L
Howe, C J
Jacobson, B L
Lewin, J H
Livingston, S I
Longbourne, J R
Makanjuola, A D
Makanjuola, A O
Marks, J H
Nicholson, C A
Price, E M
Pugh, D A
Rayat, S
Rose, J D
Smith, A L B
Spring, J T
Thomson, S D
Venison, T D
Wilson, A T
Wilson, C E
Woolf, J K

Boroughbridge
Jones, O G

Borth
Davies, A G
Davies, D L
Davies, M B
Davies, W C
Fish, S E
Young, A

Boscastle
Abbott, P R
Garrod, G D
Jarvis, C A N
Weir, D A D

Boston
Abdel Khalek, M N A
Adeyemi, O A
Al-Fallouji, M A R
Allwood, A C L
Allwood, C R L
Andrews, N J
Arayomi, J O
Banerjee, A R
Barrie, W J
Basu, S N
Baxter, I C
Bediako-Ntim, K A
Bee, N J
Benn, S V A
Beswick, T A
Bexton, M D R
Bloom, I R B
Boldy, D A R
Boughey, O M S
Boughey, W N F
Brackenridge, J D
Brocklehurst, J R
Brown, F J
Bull, C S
Burks, C G
Busch, T A H
Chalmers, E P D
Chapman, R
Chatterjee, S C
Cheung, L C B
Clay, J C
Cope, J T
Cope, S F
Crawford, M J
Cressey, J M
Datta, S
Dawson, P J

Dichmont, E V
Doddrell, A I
Dogra, K S
Durrant, D C S
Ejaz, T
Elwood, C M
Fairman, M J
Forrest, A M
Garden, G M F
Garg, N
Germer, M D
Germer, S
Gill, K P M
Gray, P J
Green, D F
Green, J P
Griffiths, C J
Hanumara, S K
Harris, P J
Hartshorn, J
Hassan, H S A
Holmes, P R
Hunt, B P
Jones, R
Kelly, C
Khin Khin Nwe, Dr
Kirk-Smith, P R J
Kurri, P R
Lamb, W R
Latchem, R W
Layfield, J N
Leckie, G B
Loudon, K W
McAlindon, S
Mackin, J R
Malcolm, P N
Mangion, D
Massey, C I
Massey, J M
Matiti, H H
Meacock, D J
Minhas, T-W H A
Mortlock, A J
Nolan, M S R
Norton, A C
Nyman, C R
Olczak, S A
Palit, T
Parkin, N D
Patnaik, B K
Pereira, E D
Pettit, J R
Polling, M R
Rainford, P J
Rance, D B
Razzak, M S A
Refaat, R F
Rhys-Davies, S T
Sagar, D A
Sankey, E A
Savory, J N
Savory, S J
Serrano Sanchez, A
Shah, S M
Shaheen, A A M
Shrivastava, B D
Sobolewski, S J
Spencer, N G
Spittal, M J
Steel, K C M
Taffinder, L D
Teo, R E C
Thomas, J
Thompson, C E R
Trayers, M M
Turner, D T L
Turner, L D
Walling, M R
Wallis, J H
Warren, C E J
Watson, J A S
Westmore, G A
Wheatley, S R
Wilkinson, D
Woods, L
Woods, P J
Wookey, B E P

Bourne
Bevan, S F
Beveridge, V L
Briggs, B A
Burgess, P C
Burr, C R
Deasy, J B
Elder, R A
Finn, R C
Halliday-Pegg, S M
Harris, J C

Islam, M A
Khan, A R
King, P T
Pace, I G
Palmeri, P
Patel, R B
Pears, C R
Premkumar, G
Redding, W H
Sharman, W A
Sneath, P H A
Stitson, R N M
Sweetnam, C W
Turnbull, N B
Wallace, D A
Wheatley, I M
Wolf, R C
Wright, A M

Bourne End
Bentley-Thomas, C A
Biles, J P
Buxton, S H
Church, J C T
Church, M R T
Church, S M
Fergusson, D A
Fewster, E J
Flanagan, K T
Havelock, T P
Henderson, J E
Hussain, T
Knight, S E
Lee, L J
Slack, R A
Varney, P A
Watkins, D J
Wheater, M J

Bournemouth
A'Ness, T L
Abdalla, H O
Abel, J A K
Abrew, K M C
Adams, R C
Ahmed, K A G
Al-Saab, J J M
Alagna, N
Alder, T A
Alders, F M
Aldwinckle, R J
Allen, S C
Alsadi, M R H
Andrews, B T E
Armitage, M
Baggett, C J
Bagnall, P J
Baldwin, F J
Barker, P G
Barraclough, A C
Beck, J M
Bell, R A
Bellamy, D
Bellamy, S
Benson, R A
Bentley, K D
Beswick, I C
Bevan Jones, T M
Bintcliffe, D J L
Blakeaway, C
Blaszczyk, A
Bolam, S S G
Brad, L D A
Bramble, F J
Brewer, A
Bridgman, N M
Bridgman, W M
Broad, C P
Bromley, P A
Brookes, K R
Brookes, S V
Brown, G E
Brownlow, A H
Caplin, G
Carter, C J M
Cavan, D A
Chadwick, H A
Charlesworth, P H
Chau, W F
Cheesman, A M
Clark, W A
Cook, M C
Cotton, W J
Cowan, J F E
Cowley, N M
Cox, I M
Craig, E S
Creasey, D P
Creasy, T S

Cremin, W D
Crichton, D A
Crockett, C J
Darley, M B
Davies, C
Davies, T
Davison, C R N
Dickson, D M
Dorrell, E D
Dunkelman, H M
Dutton, P
East, K R
Edwards, A J
Edwards, G A
El-Dars, L D
El Dars, M K
El-Dars, N
Emmitt, K M
Etchells, D E
Evans, P
Eve, L A
Fila, C
Fisher, J A
Fisher, J F
Fitzmaurice-Petty, G L
Flack, S T
Foot, A S
Fozard, J B J
Frank, H J
Freedman, I
Freeth, M O
French, E
French, P F
Friedmann, A I
Gannon, I D
Gant, C E
Gardiner, A O P
Garside, L J
Gibson, J F J
Goodgame, K W M
Goodwin, H
Goodwin, M I
Gordon, J
Gould, J M
Granger, J D
Gregory, D G
Grice, A S
Gunson, O S
Hamblin, T J
Hamilton, M L
Hammer, J L
Hardie, A W
Harding, J C
Harling, M E
Hartley, R H
Hassan, K M R
Head, J M
Heatley, I H
Heatley, K A
Hobson, J H
Hooper, W L
Hopkinson, N D
Hoyle, J R
Hughes, D M
Hughes, M C
Hurren, C M
Hurren, S R S
Hutchings, A
Hutchinson, G E
Irwin, N C
Jack, K I
Jackson, P H
Jaffe, G V
Jarvis, H
Jenkinson, D F
Jensen, N E
Jeyatheva, D N
Johnson, T C
Joshi, J B
Jowett, R L
Joy, H M
Kennedy, J J A
Kernohan, J G
Kerr, D
Kidman, S P
Killick, S B
King, R A
Kingsley, M
Kissen, L H
Knighton, J D
Knighton, K H
Langsdale, G A
Lawrance, R J
Lesley, B A
Levitt, A M
Lindall, K
Linnard, C A
Loehry, C A E H
McErlain, M J

McFetrich, A J
McGill, N A
McKinstry, C E
McNulty, R R
Mahmoud, M A-R
Martin, M J
Masding, M G
Maytum, C M
Mecklenburgh, P E
Mellor, M J
Michel, M Z H
Miller, S
Millward, J
Moreland, B O
Morris, A H C
Morris, M M
Murdoch, S
Myint, H
Nandra, J S
Nelemans, I
Newman, J L
Ni'Man, M N
Nicholson, A G
Nicholson, I G
Nicholson, J G
Norris, C D
O'Connor, M J C
Ogden, A S
Oscier, D G
Owen, S J
Owens, C T
Pampiglione, J S
Panton, N T M
Parham, D M
Parker, S W
Parkin, L P M
Parvin, S D
Pearce, N S
Peel-White, A L
Penn, M A
Pennell, S C
Perkins, P D
Pettiford, G H
Phillips, J J
Poulton, D J
Pratt, D R
Price, N C
Pryce, L S
Purkis, J J M
Raikes, A S
Ramsay, M W
Raymond, M P
Raza, T H
Reynolds, M J
Rintoul, D M M
Rogers, B
Rogers, S A
Rozkovec, A
Salloum, M S
Sanderson, C J
Scales, A H
Scheri, L B
Scott, A D
Scott, J W
Scrivener, S L
Scull, D A
Searle, G F
Sekhar, C J R
Seligman, S A
Shahid, A
Shaw, A A A
Shaw, M B
Shepherd, D F C
Sheridan, J J
Sim, D G
Singh, A
Skene, A I
Skivington, M A
Slade, G M
Sly, J M
Small, J H
Smith, M C
Smith, S
Southgate, J J
Spreadbury, K V H
Steel, S J
Styles, R V
Surridge, J G
Sword, A C
Sylvester, S E
Tawn, D J
Taylor, G G
Taylor, H M
Taylor, P
Tetley, G
Thomas, J B T
Thomas, S M
Thomson, R K
Thurston, A M

Torquati, F R
Tunstall, N R
Turnbull, P
Turner, J A M
Van Hasselt, G L M
Vartan, C P
Venkiteswaran, R
Vicario Ruiz, F
Wadams, S J F
Walker-Date, S E
Waters, J M
Watkins, J M
Watson, J M
Weaver, R D
Whitwell, J
Widdicombe, N J
Williams, A J
Williams, C J H
Williams, C P R
Williams, D E
Williams, K G
Williams, S E
Wilson, S P
Wimbleton, P A
Windsor, B P G
Winwood, P J
Woodhead, J L
Wright, C J
Yasen, T H
Yonace, A H
Zinna, R F

Bow Street
Owen, H G
Rhys, G
Roy, P B

Bowmore
Farrington, R L
Latta, D
Macdonald, M R S
MacDonald, M R

Brackley
Bennett, C L
Burdon, P J
Burrough, S J
Byles, P H
Chidwick, D A
Cordingly, K A M
Dhital, K K
Fry, A J
Kennerley, P C
McGurk, M N
Mayhew, J C
O'Beirne, K
Orme, R M E
Perrott, C S
Quiney, I D
Rathborne, A C
Rundle, J A
Shirazi, J E
Stephens, J
Stevens, P J
Thomas, C W I T E
Turpin, D
Waterfall, J M
Widdowson, F J M
Wijayawardena,
M A S S
Williams, K E

Bracknell
Afolami, S O
Atkinson, C M
Baker, W J
Barrett, J
Bartlett, J M
Beckley, R A
Bell, A R
Briggs, E D
Caird, C J
Chambers, J P
Clayton, A H
Crisp, K E
Curry, K M
Emery, P K
Evans, E C
Faunch, E T
Franks, C R
Gennery, B A
Green, R L
Hall, A K
Hammerton, S P
Hanson, G A
Henman, M E
Holmes, D J
Houston, A C
Jady, K
Johnson, O

Brecon

Kade, C
Kassianos, G
Keeling, T J
Knight, M G S
Koelman, R J
Lapham, G P
Lawrence, J J
Leather, M S
Macaulay, O O
McBurnie, P R
McCoubrey, I A
McDonald, C F
Machray, A J
Metson, D
Mitchell, A C S
Mitchell, P B
Moriarty, J M A
Murray, J W L
Newton, K J W
Nielsen, K S
Norman, D P
Northover, S C
Nuvoloni, M C C
Orr, J F
Pardhanani, G
Patchett, U M M
Pegrum, H L
Perry, L J
Powers, L A
Ranscombe, B J
Readings, S M
Ricketts, K J
Rogers, C E
Ross, D N
Schiff, A A
Slemp, M C
Smith, M J
Stirling, J S
Tay, K S
Tobin, M J W
Tong, W
Trowbridge, M D
Verma, N
Weir, G
Young, P J W

Bradford

Abbas, N F
Abbas, S K
Abbasi, S F S
Abbasi, Z
Acton, H M
Ahmad, M
Ahmed, I
Akhtar, S A
Akhtar, S
Alemi, A A
Alemi, C M
Ali, S M
Amarendra, V
Anderson, B D
Anikin, V A
Ansari, M I
Armstrong, J K
Ashley, J R
Ashman, L M
Ashurst, N H
Atherton, P J
Atkinson, P L
Atukorala, A W
Auty, S J
Azam, A
Azam, M
Bargh, J H
Barker, D J
Barnes, C A
Barnes, F C
Bartle, E O
Baruah, A
Baruch, M R
Basu, A
Bateman, S P
Bates, D J
Batman, P A
Baugh, S J
Bavington, A J
Bavington, J T
Bell, G A
Bembridge, J L
Bembridge, M
Beresford, N M
Bickford Smith, P J
Bindu, A
Blackburn, S D
Bollen, S R
Booth, A C
Bothra, J
Bowring, N A C
Boyden, J E

Bracken, P J
Bradley, C
Bradley, P A
Brierley, E J
Brierley, S A
Bromley, S E
Brooke, M D
Brooksbank, A J
Brown, B J
Brown, G M
Brown, P M
Budd, S T
Byrne, C
Callaghan, R T
Callander, W H
Calvert, R J
Cann, M L
Cavaliere, V
Chatfield, S L
Chin, D
Chitsabesan, S
Chohan, N S
Chowdhury, S B
Clark, J A
Clark, R
Cohen, M S
Cole, A J
Cole, B W
Cole, H K C
Coley, K
Collingwood, G A
Collins, J B
Collis, K V
Connolly, A L
Connolly, C M
Connolly, J M
Corry, P C
Cowan, C L
Cramp, P G W
Crossland, W D
Daley, A G
Dalton, P K
Danby, J
Datta, R
Datta, S
Davidson, G M
Davidson, R I
Davies, T J
Davison, J A
Dawson, A D G
De Mowbray, S S
Dean, K M L
Dedrick, S H
Devonport, H
Dharma Rajah, S
Dutta, A
Dyer, P M
Eastwood, A B
El Azab, A E S A
El Eliwi, R A
Ellis, M P J
Emms, J R
Eshwari, C G
Evans, C S
Evans, E C
Fairbrass, M J
Fenwick, I E
Fieldhouse, D C
Flannigan, G M
Foo, I T H
Franklyn, P P
Gaguine, D S
Garnie, E M K
Gavin, F M
Gilkar, G M
Gill, J C
Ginbey, D W
Goel, A
Gouldesbrough, D R
Gowa, S
Green, S D R
Griffiths, A O
Gupta, U
Haigh, D
Haile, A
Hall, R J
Hamilton, J B
Hanif, S M
Hanna, S N
Hansen, A T
Haque, S M
Hardaker, J C
Harris, C P
Harrop, F M
Haskins, C L
Henderson, A A
Henderson, L J
Hewson, L A
Hill, S R A

Hillary, G M
Hingston, C F
Hipps, G
Horsman, B A
Hossain, M M
Hossain, U
Howarth, B
Howcutt, M T
Hughes-Guy, L
Hughes, A
Hunter, S A
Husain-Qureshi, S
Hussain, S
Ihsan, F
Ilyas, M
Ismail, A H I M
Jandu, I
Jayatilake, N A
Jenkins, M
Jenkinson, S E
Jennings, S J
Jepson, K
Johnston, C A
Johnstone, W A
Jones, J M
Joyce, K J
Kamill, P G O
Karet, B J
Karunakara, M
Keeler, J F
Kellett, H S
Kennedy, S
Khan, A
Khan, A A
Khan, A
Khan, I A
Khan, M H
Khan, M A
Khan, N
Khan, S I
Khara, B R
Khatoon, A
Khwaja, S A I
King, S
Latif, A B
Lealman, G T
Lee, J E
Leedham, W G
Lennard, R F
Lilford, V A
Lindsay, H S J
Lishman, D C
London, E M
London, K M
MacDermott, J P A
McEvoy, A W
McEvoy, J F
McInroy, R A
Macintosh, M C M
McKean, E J G
McKenzie, A B
McLindon, J P
McRoberts, W
McWhinney, P H M
Maddison, J L
Maddy, A
Mahmood, M
Mahmood, T
Mahomed, I
Majid, A
Majid, S M
Malhotra, R K
Malik, T H
Mall, K P
Manchester, S G
Manning, A P
Marcham, C D
Margerson, M R
Margerrison, C D
Marsh, P J
Martin-Hirsch, D P
Masood, A
Masood, M B
Matthew, A M
Mayfield, M P
Mearns, A J
Mellors, P A
Melson, R D
Mewasingh, D
Micallef, C
Michie, C A H
Miciak, J
Mihajlovic, S
Mills, G A
Milne, H B
Mistry, A
Modi, D S
Moochhala, H S
Moreea, S M

Morley, C A
Morrison, G W
Moulson, A J
Mughal, Z A
Nair, B
Nasir, T U K
Nawaz, R M
Neale, M L
Neasham, J
Newmark, J C P
Newmark, P A
Newton, L J
Nigam, R
Noble, B A
Obiechina, N E
Oke, A O
Okeahialam, M G
Ossei-Gerning, N
Overend, G S
Parapia, L G H
Parkinson, B F
Parnell, C
Passant, W S G
Paterson, C L
Patterson, C J
Patterson, J A
Paul, N
Peacey, S R
Pennington, E R
Philip, J
Pinder, C A F
Pond, M N
Price, S A
Qureshi, M A
Qureshi, M T
Raine, A
Raine, C H
Ralph, W H
Rand, R J
Rashid, A A W
Rashid, R
Raybould, R H
Rehman, J
Rehman, M J
Rennie, P R
Reynell, P C
Riley, G A
Rimington, J E
Roberts, A M
Roberts, J
Robertshaw, D E
Robinson, K D
Ross, M
Rout, D J
Rowlands, C J
Rushton, A
Russon, L J
Ryley, H E
Sabir, M S
Saed, E A-H
Sanderson, G D
Sanderson, H
Sandhu, K S
Sargant, E F R
Schallreuter, K
Senior, E M
Shah, S T K
Shaw, D L
Sheldon, K P
Shepherd, R I
Shoesmith, D J
Sides, A P
Sides, C A
Sidra, R S
Sinclair, P M
Singh, B K
Singh, I M
Singh, J P
Singh, N K
Singh, V
Sloan, B E
Smith, K T E
Smith, M L
Smith, R A
Spiers, M R
Stephens, E C P
Stinson, I R
Strachan, C D S
Strachan, D R
Strang, I G
Suleman, A S
Sullivan, J M
Swapp, H G
Symons, N J H
Taylor, S E
Temperley, C
Terry, H J
Thomas, P F
Thornhill, W C

Throssell, J A
Timmons, M J
Todd, F N
Tooby, H A
Towers, S M
Trikha, S P
Tucker, A G
Tucker, J S
Turner, S M
Upile, T
Van Duijn, N
Venables, A J
Venkatesh, U R
Venters, N D
Vijaykumar, U
Vize, C E
Vowden, P
Wade, I R
Wade, M J
Walker, N G
Wallace, S
Walsh, M J
Ward, T
Warlow, J J
Wason, A-M
Watson, E J
Watters, A T
Webster, J C T
Welford, J R F
White, S I
Williams, A T
Wilson, A R
Wilson, V E
Winn, N B
Withers, A W J
Wojciechowski, M K
Wright, A L
Wright, A J
Wright, C
Wright, J B
Wright, J P
York, S A
Young, J B

Bradford-on-Avon

Allen, R L
Batty, S C
Bell, F G
Bolt, J M
Carter, V
Catt, V E
Charlesworth, D N
Christie, E A
Cox, J A
Ellis, D A
Flight, R J
Gamble, K R
Gough, N A
Heap, D C
Heffer, J S
Higgs, C M B
Johnson, E B
Kendrick, C H
Mason, A M S
Matthews, R J
Narang, V P S
Needham, P R
Newstead, J S
O'Reilly, M
Patrick, J
Pett, R J
Phillips, S M
Snow, A R
Thomas, M H
Wilkins, D C
Wyatt, N V
Young, S J

Braintree

Antcliff, A C
Archer, G K
Bracebridge, S P
Carter, J A
Cowburn, P J
Cutts, A M
Evans, D M
Gibson, C V
Gibson, I G L
Hildrey, A C C
Horobin, S R
Jackson, M D
Jackson, W L M
King, R L
Knapman, F M M
Kyaw Htun, Dr
Littler, W I
Martin, R H
Mayo, R E P
Meakin, R P

Meesters, H J R
Paterson, J R
Pereira, N B M
Purdie, A V
Reynolds, C P
Richardson, J S
Runacres, A S R
Rushton, S C
Shaw, I C
Slater, J E
Soares, A-M R
Summers, S K
Williams, D A
Win, J M T
Zollinger-Read, P J

Brampton

Atkinson, L J
Beazley, J M
Bestwick, J R
Blakeman, T M
Burn, J C
Byers, M
Gray, P J
Howorth, P J N
Low, G D
Nelson, L D
Nicholson, S
Royle, J
Thorne, D H
Wagstaff, R J
Weaving, P G

Brandon

Blenkinsopp, E M
Campman, G H
Cockshott, A M
Daley, T P
Hicks, T M
Perry, J G
Pugh, C J
Warren, A E

Braunton

Beresford West, T B H
Bradford, H R
Dissevelt, A C E
Francis, A
Gray, M J J
Howell, J K
Loveden, L M
Luxton, B P
Moore, D G
Pearse, H A C
Pote, J
Regester, P T
Stracey, P M
Vale, J C
Vale, R J
Waters, C G
Wheble, V H

Brechin

Adams, S A
Allison, C W
Andrews, E N
Andrews, M
Buckley, J R
Callaghan, T S
Cowan, M
Donald, L A
Duff, A R
Fernandez, D B
Frost, S A H
Gillanders, I A
Grant, D A
Greig, H D
McInnes, A M
Mahon, I M
Martin, R W Y
Oswald, A G
Rickhuss, P K
Shaw, A M
Slater, P A
Stein, L
Tainsh, J A
Thomas, A D
Tulloch, J A
Valentine, N W
Weekenborg, M-A
Yates, H L

Brecon

Asver, M A
Bacon, R W
Birch, R J
Cavenagh, A J M
Clowes, C I
Cooper, P J
Coppock, J M

Brentford

Coppock, W A
Davies, C D
Davies, E
Davies, J A J
Dimyan, W A
Dunn, A M
Evans, A V
Evans, M
Faulkner, P O
Ford, E M S
Gardner, Z N C
Goodger, R C
Goodger, V R
Gooding, P S
Greig, R H
Griffith, D J O
Griffiths, M J
Hargest, E L
Hart, D P
Harvey, K C
Heard, J
Heneghan, M B J
Hill, B J
Jackson, A S
Johnson, D B
Jones, D L
Jones, E J
Jones, J K
Menon, J A
Mulhall, P P
O'Reilly, S
Owen, R E
Price, K J P
Rees, D G
Rowland, H A K
Scott, P W B
Snow, P J
Somerville, G
Strong, J D E
Thomas, W H
Vulliamy, C B
Wainwright, A J
Wainwright, D T
Williams, B W
Williams, R S
Woodman, G J

Brentford
Al-Shakir, A M
Alves Teixeira, J M
Bowden, A D
Chisholm, J M
Davies, H W
Dignan, F J
Galvin, F D M
Haslett, C
Hill, J F
Horton, R J
Jones, D A
Lane, S M
Maclean, H R C
Murphy, A L
Neequaye, A R
Neequaye, J E
Oatham, C E
Pugh, H M
Revell, C P
Rowley Jones, D
Ruggles, R M
Ryan, P J J
Stevens, D J C
Sykes, J E
Wellwood, M R
Winn, P I M
Yasin, K M

Brentwood
Ababio, S N
Ainsworth, D P
Al-Hasani, A J
Apps, M C P
Ariyanayagam, I J
Ariyanayagam, S
Bashir, P M
Battey, G S
Bennett, S M V
Berry, S I
Booth, R T
Boralessa, H
Bowler, P J
Bradbury, V D
Brock, D M
Brock, T P
Brown, R
Burton, E R
Butcher, J H
Butler, N S
Cannon, P
Carter, C M W B C

Cervi, P L O
Chaloner, J M
Chatterjee, D S
Clough, L A
Coull, D B
Croft, R P
Curtis, J
Daly, R M
Davies, A M
Davies, D N
De Alwis, K H
Dennehy, H A
Dima-Okojie, S I
Dryden, M M
Duce, D J
Dunne, F J
Ekanayake, A T
Evans, C A W
Evans, D E W
Evans, J D
Fanning, M
Feakins, M J
Fernando, H G
Fife, D G
Goodfellow, A E
Gordon, A J
Gorman, A M
Graham, C
Gray, A G
Gupta, R
Hamilton, H C
Hamilton, M A
Handel, B M
Handel, C C
Harper, C A
Hepton, S K
Heeravisenti, C
Hildebrand, S C
Hill, J T
Hillman, G W
Holkar, V E
Horti, J M
Hoyle, M J
James, R E S
Jeffery, R M
Jennings, S J
Karim, A S A
Karunanayake, M G S
Kassab, R D
Kersey, H J G
Kochhar, M S
Leahy, E S
Lee, J
Lewis, E R
Li, R S K
Lissmann, M R
MacCarthy, C D
McDonald, A F
McGown, F M
McGown, M P
McKinnon, M D
Mathur, S B
Mead, K I
Medlock, J M
Moore, R G W
Motley, B M
Moul, D J
Mulkern, P D
Murray, J J
Naeem, A A
Nauth-Misir, T N
Navaratnam, S
Neill, S V
Nicolaou, A J
O'Driscoll, T G
O'Reilly, B J
Oakey, J S
Outten, P R
Pandit, D R
Parsons, P H I
Patel, B
Peskett, S A
Plaha, H S
Prinn, M G
Purches, A C
Puvanendran, K
Race, J W
Ribeiro, B F
Richardson, J C W
Ridpath, J
Ritchie, J K
Scott-Russell, A M
Sexton, C R
Sexton, N J
Sikabbubba, J M
Sloan, S B
Sridharan, D R
Steddon, S J
Steer, G L

Stephens, J D
Strachan, S R
Swift, J L
Tallack, J A
Tate, M E
Taylor, J L
Thomas, D A
Tuppen, J J
Varma, R
Villiers, C
Walton, M E
Walton, S J
Watson, J
Watts, S J
Wenger, R J J
Winstanley, D P
Woolterton, M C

Bridge of Weir
Aitchison, W R C
Allister, A H
Anderson, J M
Arnot, A D W
Barclay, S R
Binning, A R
Blair, A M R
Crawford, J M
Findlay, J N
Geddes, C M
Geddes, N K
Gemmell, J A
Goudie, H M
Hunter, C J
Lawson, P M
Leiberman, D P
Lightbody, T D
McBain, R H
Macdonald, J B
McFarlane, E S
McKay, C J
McLaren, G I
Maclean, D G
Mullen, R J
O'Kane, G
Pollock, J S S
Rentoul, J R
Shepherd, H J
Smith, J L
Tatek, J
Taylor, K A
Van Der Lee, A J
Young, M J
Young, R E

Bridgend
Abse, D
Ali, I M
Anthony, J R
Ashpole, K J
Balfour, R P
Banerji, C
Barr, D B
Barrett, R M
Bartholomew, G H
Bartlett, N
Bassett, S D
Baynham, T D W
Beale, D J
Beckett, P A
Bhargava, J P
Blackall, D H
Bowyer, F M
Boyce, J M H
Brodie, S W
Burgess, B J
Chappell, A G
Chivers, S E
Clarke, E J
Collis, A A
Coulter, D F
Coyle, P J
Craven, A
Crockett, J
Cuthill, J M
Danson, S P P
Davies, A
Davies, A I
Davies, C E
Davies, G
Davies, H F
Davies, J P
Davies, K M
Davies, R H
Davies, T J
Dawkins, J C
Devalia, V
Donagh, J G F
Dowse, J L A
Edwards, C D

Edwards, P D L
English, E M
Evans, D A
Evans, G W
Evans, L J
Evans, O
Evans, R A
Evans, W H M
Farrell, S H
Fletcher, P C
Foster, D R
Fowler, A W
Gataure, P S
Gibson, P R H
Gilmartin, L M D
Goodwin, A
Griffiths, E A
Griffiths, J L
Gwilliam, G M
Hadley, R J
Hambly, P B
Hapgood, A I
Hapgood, G C
Hasan, D
Hashmi, M S
Higgs, J M
Hughes, D W
Hughes, S
Hunter, C C
Jagger, P T
James, K C B
James, S H
James, W
Janas, M A
Johnson, R C
Jones, A
Jones, C J H
Jones, D C
Jones, J S
Jones, J P
Jones, M J T
Jones, R H T
Joseph, F G
Judd, D
Katugampola, S L
Koppel, S M
Kwan, W Y
Lewis, J H J
Llewellyn, D C M
Lloyd, A T
Lloyd, S M
Logan, R A
Lord, M M L
McCann, R J
McHugh, P M
McHugh, R J
McHugh, S
Madelin, S K
Manning, A
Mason-Williams, J
Mason, C H
Meredith-Smith, A
Miller, J S
Miller, M D
Mohajer, S K P
Morgan, C A
Morgan, L R
Morgan, R O
Morris, J S
Morris, L M
Morris, P G
Morris, R W
Nelson, B L P
Nicholas, M
O'Connor, I
Obaid, M P
Obaid, S L
Obaidullah, M
Osborne, J A
Owen, R E
Pace, D
Parry, D S
Patel, G K
Powner, H R
Price, A
Price, D B
Price, G V
Pritchard, G A
Pyees, C A
Quick, C A
Raha, S K
Rahman, A Z M M
Rahman, N A
Raijiwala, N T
Rees, A M
Reilly, T A A
Richards, G L
Richards, T V H
Roberts, C

Roberts, N I
Roberts, S A
Rowland, A M
Rowland, J F
Rushworth, F H
Sarvotham, R
Shanmugasundaram, G
Singhal, K
Smillie, J F
Sollis, M E
Stamatakis, J D
Sultan, K
Thomas, D J
Thomas, K
Thomas, R I
Tidley, M G
Timlett, R H J
Vasu, V
Ware, D A
Waters, I R
Watura, J C
West, S A
White, A M
Wilkins, W E
Williams, C R
Williams, E J
Williams, G
Williams, J J
Williams, J P R
Williams, M
Williams, M N
Williams, M-C
Williams, M A
Williams, P R J
Williams, P D R
Williams, P
Williams, R G
Williams, T M
Wintle, M E
Wintle, R V
Winton, E
Workman, A R
Yeoman, A D
Young, S P
Young, W T

Bridgnorth
Ashcroft, D
Blayney, J E
Burke, L P
Carvell, S P
Cotter, J
Dalton, M H
Downs, A M R
Eveson, J G
Gibbs, R H
Gillie, C P
Goodall, M S
Groves, R C C
Hammerton, M D
Hammerton, W
Hughes, R G
Kneen, L C
Lloyd-Jones, M
Mackie, G
Magill, M J
Martin, S L
Parsonage, W A
Patel, Y A
Reeves, E M
Sandhu, N S
Seeley, A J
Smith, P E
Sykes, T C F
Torkington, A P J
Turnbull, M H F
Weston, J L
Yuille, P M

Bridgwater
Aird, P M
Airey, N J
Allen, H M
Barnes, J S
Barrington, P M
Bennekers, J E C
Bray, E L
Bray, N J
Budd, J D
Chandler, W G
Cheek, C M
Comber, M G
Constable, G D
Cooke, D I
Cortissos, E
Creamer, K A
D'Ambrumenil, P L
Deakin, H L
Di Mambro, S L M

Dorrett, S
Douglas Smith, B J
Douglass, A W R
Dovey, J K
Evans, R L
Fergusson, G M
Gardiner, S
Goldie, A M
Green, A M
Hall, M H
Hansford, P K
Hayne, P S
Hincks, M E
Hooper, A I
Hooper, R I
Hynes, D M
Ives, C L
Jago, H M
Johnson, M F
Johnson, R D
Lambert, R J
Lawler, C E
Lee, B E
Lee, R J
Legat, P
Lemmens, G W
Macadam, C F
McEwen, L M
Mann, R J
Matthews, D T
Molyneux, A R
Mumford, A D
Ni Fhlaithbheartaigh, E M
Ogle, J L
Osborne, C J
Paisley, A C
Parratt, J
Peel, G W B
Pepperell, J C T
Reed, A E R
Reed, P D
Richardson, D E R
Roberts, S E K
Rooke, D K
Slack, J
Slack, W W
Smart, M A
Stevenson, G R
Swindall, H J
Tanner, G P G
Tanner, H
Taylor, T M W
Tilsley, G N W
Tilsley, T M
Todd, K R
Todd, O I
Tolhurst, S J M A
Tottle, J A
Wade-Thomas, R
Watson, R H
Wright, A
Wrout, J D

Bridlington
Armstrong, D J
Barton, E A
Bayne, J B
Bowden, D F
Broadhurst, C
Burridge, D N
Calaghan, N P
Clarke, A J
Cookson, R P
Farley, K T J
Francis, A C
Gillespie, J R
Harris, P A
Hart, M W
Hickson, D E G
Hillman, J G
Knox, D A
Lucey, J D
McLaren, G L
McLaren, R J H
MacNab, H K
Mattock, R P
Meldrum, H R P
Memon, M A
Mundy, P
Nasar, M A
Nisbet, A M
Osman, Y M
Ravindra Bose, S S B
Ridley, P D
Robertson, A S
Robertson, A
Robertson, A S
Robertson, M

Bristol

Rudd, K K
Schofield, R
Sinha, C
Sinha, R S K
Talbot, A W
Walker, F H
Wallam, T D
Watson, A J S
Watson, R M
Webster, M R
Whitehead, J P S
Wilson, J F
Wilson, P D
Wilson, T R

Bridport

Apted, F I C
Barter, A P
Beckers, M J J
Beckers, S R
Burt, B M
Carter, R G
Cottrill, P H
Crawshaw, E G A
Crook, A
Hollands, J J C
Horowitz, J I
Kennedy, C C
King, J G
Lane, B K
Laven, L E D
Linnell, P M
Lintner, B
Lintner, J K
Longley, J I
Millar, A B
Napper, A M S
Neame, R L
Nugent, S
Orton, P K L
Platt, I T
Pratt, C L G
Rossiter, S K
Shipton, B M
Skellern, E P
Skellern, G
Smyth, P W J
Thomson, M
Walker, C D
Webb, P G
Wilson, C B
Woodhead, J W

Brierley Hill

Ahmed, N W
Bundred, M A
Clarke, B W
Craggs, I F
Edwards, C R
El-Sayad, A R A H
Faux, D H R
Fernandes, C
Hafiz, A
Khazagwale, A K
Leung, V K Y
Patel, J A
Plant, S J
Reed, I A
Rigler, M S
Russell, J A
Shah, H V
Shah, R M
Smith, K M
Sumaria, M K M
Thornton, A J
Young, A J

Brigg

Aggarwal, A D
Burscough, J F
Chester, D W
Crompton, B A
Crowe, N A
Edmondson-Jones, M
Foxton, R H
Hill, A
Ibbotson, S L
Iuel, B M
Leitch, T W
Lloyd, S
Matthews, T K
Norris, P E
Proctor, K S
Reid, F M
Stanley, D E
Stringer, R
Sutton, P A
Topping, J S
Travers, A F
Warriner, S J

Whitaker, A S
Whitaker, V S
Willis, J H
Yule-Smith, A L

Brighouse

Allison, R M
Brook, A C
Chambers, S J
Farrow, S
Gatecliff, J R
Gay, D A T
Gorman, P J
Gurr, J M
Higson, M
Jain, N K
Lamming, R E M
Lawson, J H
Martin, S
Mason, A D
Mason, L E
Matischen, G M
Mattocks, A N
O'Carroll, P J A
Quarcoo, S T
Rajjayabun, P H
Sharma, N K
Wilkinson, J R
Wylie, R M

Brighton

Aawar, O A
Abraham, A J
Abraham, R A R
Acheson, R M
Adams, N J
Aiton, N R
Ajavi, A A
Alder, S
Allen, C D
Allenby, L M
Altman, K
Ames, W A
Amess, P N
Anderson, K J
Anderson, K J
Ap Ivor, T D
Appanna, N
Ashton-Key, M R
Aston, J E
Atkinson, D C
Austera, J
Ayling, G Z
Baker, B S
Banieghbal, B
Banner, J V
Barley, M G
Bartlett, C I
Bartlett, P D
Beasley, J V
Beesley, C J
Bell, M E
Bentley, M R
Beresford-Jones, P R
Bhermi, A J
Bintcliffe, I W L
Bird, N
Black, A A
Bloomfield, D J
Bodkin, J R
Bowie, J E
Bowman, G O
Bowskill, R J
Boyd, J
Boyd, O F
Bradley, R J
Bradshaw, M J
Bridger, S
Brittain, G P H
Brown, A K
Brown, C F
Browne, D J
Bryant, C M
Bryant, G D R
Bryson, A F
Burns, R
Burt, R W
Carter, H R
Chaikin, M J
Chamberlain-Webber, J A A S
Chang, Y F
Cherukuri, A K
Child, C S B
Churchill, D R
Clark, A N G
Clarke, J N
Clarke, S A
Clarkson, P J

Clifford, G J
Cobb, H E
Cockcroft, M
Coe, C D
Combe, A J
Copp, T A
Cordingly, M R
Corner, A J
Cottingham, R L
Craigie, I T
Crichton, A R C
Crossman, I G
Culliford, L D
Cuming, K V
Curtis, A
Darley, C R
Dart, D E
Davey, A J
Davidson, C
Davies, H J
De Souza, R G J
De Winter, J G
Deady, J M
Denis Le Seve, P A
Derrick, E K
Devlin, P N P
Dew, A E
Dodge, G S
Domoney, S R
Doshi, M K
Doyle, T N
Drake, H F
Duncan, J R
Dunne, R D C
Eadie, E J
Earl, D F
Ebbetts, J H
Eckstein, M B
Edwards, M K R
Elcock, D H
Elvidge, J B
Evans, A H
Evans, N A P
Fallowfield, J A
Farhoumand, N
Farrington, A G
Fernandes, L
Firth, S M
Fish, A N J
Flewett, T P
Forsyth, A T
Fraser, G A
Fry, A
Gainsborough, N
Garewal, C
Garrett, W V
George, J Y
Ghani, M
Gilhooly, G
Gillman, D H
Goldberg, L C
Good, H W W
Goyne, R L
Gray, H D
Gray, R
Green, B
Green, D J M
Gumpert, J R W
Gutjahr, C
Habgood, C M
Hacking, R S
Hale, P C
Halford, J
Hallam, L
Hanington, E L I
Harden, A F
Harper, D R
Harries, M L
Harris, I M
Harris, S
Hartley, J P R
Hawker, C E
Hayward, C R W
Haywood, S
Helps, P J
Hermitage, A P
Herold, J
Hildick-Smith, P M
Hollis, P R
Holmberg, S R M
Homer, P M
Howells, M
Hoyle, A N
Humphrey, A
Hunter, R M
Hurst, P A E
Hutchesson, E A
Hyams, A B
Hyde-Forster, I

Ickeringill, M G
Iggo, N C
Ing, R P
Ingram, A S
Iversen, S A
Jackson, M B
Jackson, T L
Jarvis, K R
Jenkins, D
Jenkins, D R
Juli, C F
Kahan, A
Kanal, L
Karnicki, M T
Kaye, S L
Keating, E J
Kelleher, D I F
Kenney, I J
Kenny, M W
Kerr, G A
Kershaw, G R
Khan, N A
Khot, A S S
King, A L
King, C J
King, E J
Kingswood, J C
Kirkham, N
Kirkland, B
Knott, M H
Kramer-Hermann, E-B
Kumar, M A
Kuper, M B
Kushwaha, R S
Lamah, M
Larcombe, P J
Larner, T R G
Leake, R A
Lee, W
Levack, F C
Lewis, B
Lewis, C C
Lewis, J
Lipscombe, S L
Livesey, E A
Lopes, A V
Ludsegged, A
Lyall, R A
McConnell, R
McDonnell, E D
McLeod, B K
McNally, S A
Macoun, S J R
MacRorie, N D
MacRorie, R A
Male, I A
Mangat, S S
Meade, P F
Melville, E D
Mendonca, M J T
Mensing, C N
Montgomery, J C
Mull, A
Murugasu, E
Mustill, A L
Myers, D N E
Neilson, F M
Newman, G H
Newman, P L
Nisbet, A P
Norman, M A
Norris, R M
O'Connor, F A
O'Hara, J
O'Neal, H
Oyarzabal Amigo, M F
Paisley, J M
Panja, S K
Papasavvas, G K
Parikh, J K
Parish, S P E
Parker, M B
Parnham-Cope, D A
Parry, M G
Parsley, J
Patel, N K
Pateman, J A
Patton, N D
Paul, J
Perez-Avila, C A
Perkins, B A W
Perry, F M
Phillips, D L
Pierce, E L
Price, G J
Price, M L
Pritchard, H W
Pugsley, W B
Punja, A N

Purchase, S M
Ragab, S
Ralph, I
Ramadas, R
Ransom, P A
Rich, A E
Roberts, C E A
Robertson, H A M
Robinson, D S
Robinson, E M O K
Robinson, R E M
Rockwell, S R
Roderic-Evans, J E
Rosenberg, M A J
Rowan, J
Rubin, G
Rubin, J
Rustom, R
Saadah, E S M
Sacks, S L
Sagar, P J
Saphier, E
Saunders, M G
Saunders, N C
Sayani, M I
Sayers, W J H
Schulze, K R
Seddon, P C
Shah, A C
Shah, R
Shaheen, J S O
Sharp, M J A
Sharpstone, D R
Shears, M-R B
Sibbald, D M
Slattery, M A
Smith, A J
Smith, A M
Smith, N F
Sonksen, C J
Spurrell, J R R
Spurrell, P A R
Srinivasan, S
Sripuram, S G
Stalker, M J
Staniforth, P
Stead, C A
Stern, M
Street, M J
Studd, C
Supple, D L
Sutcliffe, V A
Sutton, C J
Swaine, C N
Tayler, D H
Tee, D E H
Thom, B T
Thomas, P J
Thompson, M W B
Thorp, T A S
Titley, R G
Tranter, R M D
Tredgold, B
Tresilian, K E
Trounce, J Q
Twohig, M M
Usher, H-E
Van Ryssen,
J S M W P
Vaughan, N J A
Vickers, S F
Vincent, R
Vokins, C G
Voyce, M E
Walters, M T
Warburton, M C
Warburton, T H M
Warden, K H
Waters, A M
Watson, C A
Watson, P M
Weighill, J S
Weir, F J
Weir, R J S
Wells, A A
Whale, W R
White, H A
White, S M
Whitehead, J A
Wickham, L J
Wilkinson, P R
Williams, C R P
Williams, D I
Williams, P A D
Williams, R A
Willis, C H
Willison, K A
Winter, R A
Withecomb, J L

Woollaston, M E F
Woollons, A D
Wostenholm, D K
Wright, C M V
Wright, D A
Yates, F A
Yelland, A
Yetton, W R

Bristol

Abrams, P
Ackroyd, C F
Adams, E J
Adams, K J
Adamson, B D
Addison, S J
Addleson, D J
Ahmad, N
Ahmed, M
Akerman, P L
Al-Mufti, R A W M L
Al-Tai, S H I
Al Wakeel, G M
Alderson, D
Aldren, J T
Aleeson, R
Alexander, J I
Alexander, K M M
Ali-Khan, A S
Allen, C S
Allen, P E
Allen, P L
Alonso Madrazo, C
Alsop, K R
Amar, K A K A
Amure, Y O
Anderson, D N
Anderson, E G
Anderson, R S
Andersson, C S
Andrews, H S
Andrews, J H
Ansell, D B
Anstey, E J
Anthony, P
Appleton, A S
Archer, C B
Arkell, S M
Armstrong, S J
Arney, K B
Arnold, R P
Arnott, M S M
Arul, G S
Ash-Miles, J A
Ashworth, M T
Aspinall, R L
Atherton, M T
Atkins, J L
Atkins, R M
Atkins, S E
Atter, C C
Awadzi, G
Axson, D M
Aycart Valdes, E R
Aylard, A P
Aylard, P R
Azurmendi Sastre, V
Backhouse, M F
Bacon, J M
Badger, G
Bagshaw, P J
Bailey, C C
Bailey, D J G
Bailey, H B M
Bailey, J A
Bailey, J C
Bailey, J E
Bailey, P B
Bailward, T A
Baird, A M
Baird, R D
Baird, R N
Baker, A R
Baker, I A
Bakker, P A G
Baldwin, D L
Baldwin, R J
Bannister, G C
Barber, M J
Barber, R D
Barclay, R F
Barham, C P
Barkley, A C
Barley, V L
Barlow, G M
Barnes, A D
Barnes, E
Barnes, H E
Barrett, A J

Bristol

Barry-Braunthal, J A
Barry, R E
Barwell, J R
Barwell, P J
Barwell, W B A
Basava Kumar, D G
Baskett, P J F
Bassi, S C
Bates, J H J
Bates, M
Batstone, G F
Baxter, I T
Bayley, G L
Bayley, J L
Bayly, G R
Bazeley-White, D L
Beare, N A V
Bebb, R L
Begley, P J
Bell, C J
Bell, C R W
Bell, K F
Ben-Shlomo, Y
Bench, L J
Benger, J R
Bennet, E G
Bennett, E M
Bennett, J A
Bennett, J A
Bennett, R M
Beresford, R J A
Beringer, R M
Berkley, R J
Berry, P J
Bevir, T A
Bicknell, P G
Biddulph, G
Bigwood, F V
Bigwood, M T G
Bingley, P J
Binns, C E
Birch, K
Birchall, J E
Birchall, M A
Bird, J M
Bird, J M
Bird, S A A
Birkett, P B L
Bishop, N L
Bisson, D L
Black, A M S
Black, S M
Blacker, C V R
Blackwell, M M
Bland, P M
Blazeby, J M
Blewitt, N
Blom, A W
Bloss, D E
Blythe, A J
Bobrow, C S
Bodard, S J
Bodman, A P
Bolger, C M
Bolsin, S N C
Bolt, J L
Bolt, S H
Bolton, A
Bolton, J
Bonnet, M S
Booker, D A
Boone, D L
Boreham, P A
Borhanzahi, K
Bose, A
Boultbee, D R R
Bowden, J E
Bowen, J T
Bowen, R L
Bowes, J B
Bowie, M J
Bowler, V A
Bown, N J
Box, M P
Box, O M
Boycott, A
Boyd, J
Boyd, K E
Boyles, A F
Bradfield, J W B
Bradfield, P C
Bradley, B A B
Bradley, R J B
Bradley, S N
Bradshaw, J R
Bragg, J M
Bragonier, R
Brain, S P
Branfoot, K J

Bredow, M-T
Bremner-Smith, A T
Brett, M T
Brierley, L M
Briggs, J C
Briggs, J A
Brightley, K M
Brindle, P M
Britten, S
Britten, S R
Broadway, S M
Brokate, A
Bromham, B
Bromley, J
Brooks, J R
Brosh, S J
Brown, A C
Brown, C A
Brown, E M
Brown, I M
Brown, J
Brown, J M
Brown, M V
Brown, P S
Brown, R A
Brown, R P M
Brown, R M
Brownridge, C E
Bryan, A J
Buckingham, R A
Buckley, P A
Buckner, J I
Buhrs, E G J
Bunting, R A
Burd, D A R
Burd, E
Burke, D M
Burke, G A A
Burke, M M
Burke, S P
Burman, D
Burn, S C
Burness, J H
Burney, P J
Burnham, W H
Burns-Cox, C J
Burrow, J E
Burston, G R
Burston, J I
Burt, V A
Burton, C J
Burton, J L
Bush, J T
Buston, M H
Butler, A V J
Butler, N R
Buttar, P S
Byrne, A
Byron, M A
Caddick, J F
Cadman, M
Cahill, D J
Caine, S E
Cairns, P A
Callaway, M P
Callow, G
Cameron, M-Y
Campbell, C J
Campbell, C P
Campbell, M J
Candish, C G
Capel, J P
Caputo, M
Carey, R J
Carney, L J
Carnie, P W
Carpenter, P K
Carr, R J
Carrington, D
Carson, K G S
Carswell, A M
Carswell, F
Carter, J A
Carter, M
Carter, S E
Carter, S M
Carter, T E
Case, C P
Cash, I D
Caswell, H J
Cates, M E
Catterall, J R
Causton, A W
Causton, J C
Cawthorn, S J
Cayton, H R
Celestin, L R
Cembrowicz, S P
Cemlyn-Jones, M W

Cemlyn-Jones, P M
Cervantes, A J
Chadwick, S A
Chamberlain Webber, R F O
Chambers, A N
Chambers, J
Chambers, S
Chambers, T L
Chan, K X-H
Chan, S K M
Chandler, R J
Chandna, A
Changizi, R
Chatakondu, S C
Chatakondu, S
Chauhan, M L
Cheesman, M G
Cheetham, E J
Chesney, D S
Chesser, T J S
Cheung Ming Hon, M
Chillistone, D J D
Chowdhury, M I
Christie, A W
Christie, J M L
Churchill, A J
Cianfarani, S
Cilasun, O
Clamp, J R
Clark, A J B
Clark, C I M
Clark, J E
Clark, J B
Clark, M E
Clarke, G J
Clarke, S P
Clarke, S K R
Clavert, K L
Clayton, T J
Clement, J A I T
Clement, M J
Clifford, J
Cloote, A H
Clough, J R
Coakham, H B
Coates, D P
Cobby, M J D
Cobby, T F
Cochrane, B
Cochrane, D F
Codling, B W
Coggins, R P
Cohen, A M
Cohen, M A H
Coleby, E M
Coleman, P D
Coles, C J
Coles, R E
Collett, A S
Colley, J R T
Collins, K G
Collis, R J
Colman, A R
Combe, G M
Coniam, S W
Connor, A P
Conrad, J M
Constantinides, H
Conway, P J
Cook, C K L
Cook, D A G
Cook, N J
Cook, S D
Cook, T
Cooke, L B
Cooling, H S
Cooper, J J
Cooper, R A
Cooper, S J
Coote, E A
Corcoran, M T K
Cordell, A J
Corner, B D
Cornes, J S
Cornes, P G S
Cornwell, J C
Corrall, R J M
Costello, J C
Coulson, A
Coulson, C
Coulson, T J
Cowan, F J
Coward, R J M
Cox, C M
Cox, D E
Cox, G L
Cox, J W
Craig, J V

Craig, J K
Craig, N J
Creamer, P
Creed, D S
Crichton, N R
Crick, J C P
Cripps, T R
Crook, B R M
Crooks, J
Crossley, G E M
Crossley, J
Crow, I S
Crowley, J M G
Crowley, T
Crown, A L
Crowne, E C
Croxson, S C M
Culling, J A
Cunliffe, J L
Cunningham, D M
Curran, A L M
Currie, A D M
Currie, L J
Cussen, W D
Dacombe, C M
Daglish, M R C
Dalton, G R
Daly, R S
Daniel, R M
Daniels, K R
Darby, M
Darbyshire, P J
Darcy, M K
Darlaston, L M
Darley, E S R
Darvill, D R
Darwent, M
Das, V K
Davey-Smith, G
David, M G J
Davidson, E J
Davidson, R G
Davies, D I
Davies, G G
Davies, I M
Davies, J
Davies, N
Davies, V M
Davis, A
Davis, G J
Davis, L R
Davison, P A
Dawkins, C E
Dawson, N J
Day, A
Day, C L
Day, P J
Dayan, C M
De Berker, D A R
De Cothi, G A
De Fonseka, C P
Deakin, G J
Dean Revington, P J
Dedman, P A
Degens, G C
Delaney, R J
Dennis, B I
Dennison, M
Denton, K J
Denton, R S
Derbyshire, H R
Di Mambro, A J
Diamond, J P
Dibdin, S J
Dickens, A J G
Dickson, D M
Dickson, M H
Dickson, R R
Dieppe, P A
Difford, F
Dinani, S
Disley, P J
Dix, P J
Dixon, A R
Dixon, J C
Dixon, J H
Dixon, N M
Dobbie, J A
Dobson, L
Donald, C C
Donald, F A
Doney, I E
Doris, J F
Dos Remedios, I D M
Douek, I F
Douglas, N T E
Dowdeswell, H J
Dowling, A
Dowling, S F O

Down, R C E
Downes, P W E
Dowse, C T
Dowson, S R
Doyle, M J
Draycott, T J
Dresser, I G
Du Heaume, J C
Duck, J L
Dudderidge, T J
Dudley, C R K
Dudley, J A
Duff, M C
Duke, L C
Duke, N C
Dumbell, M
Duncan, A W
Duncan, K R
Dunn, A N
Dunn, A J
Dunn, P M
Dunnett, J M
Dunnett, I A R
Dunnill, M G S
Dunning, B H
Durdey, P
Durrant, G M
Dutton, H R
Dwarika, W M
Dwerryhouse, S J
Dwight, J F S J
Dwyer, N A
Eames, P G
Early, D F M
Early, P E
Eastaugh-Waring, S J
Eastman, F V
Easty, D
Easty, M J
Eaton, J M
Ebrahim, S B J
Eccles, M J
Eckert, H
Eddison, D M
Eddison, R M
Edwards, N
Egginton, A M
Eldridge, J D J
Eley, E A
Ellingham, K E
Ellingham, R B
Elliott, C
Ellis Jones, E
Ellis, C
Ellis, J C
Elphick, J
Elstow, G A
Eltringham, W K
Emmanuel, E
Emond, A M
Emsley, S P
Entrican, J H
Erskine, K F
Esler, R
Espiner, H J
Estela-Ferrero, C M
Evans, B R W
Evans, E M
Evans, G A
Evans, J C W
Evans, J L
Evans, S J
Evely, R S
Ewins, D
Eyers, P S G
Eyre-Brook, A L
Eyre-Brook, E M
Fahey, T P B
Falk, S J
Farey, H K
Farnall, E A
Farndon, J R
Farndon, M A
Faulkner, D
Fearon, H C
Febry, G N
Feest, T G
Felce, D W
Feller, R
Fenn, S E
Fenton, J A
Ferguson, I T
Ferguson, J W
Ferguson, S A C
Fernandes, F J
Fernandez De Castillo Torras, B
Ferris, J D
Feuchtwang, A C

Fielding, A S
Fields, R
Filik, R
Findlay, A M
Finn, A H R
Finn, H P
Flanagan, P M
Fleming, D G
Fleming, J O
Fleming, P J
Fligelstone, J S
Follows, P M
Foot, A B M
Forbes, K
Ford, M R W
Ford, S M
Foreman, P S
Fornear, J E
Forrest, M J
Forrester-Wood, C P
Fosbury, S J F
Foster, D M
Foster, H L
Foster, L M
Foubister, W J
Fowler, A L
Fowler, C A
Fowles, S J
Fox, A B E
Fox, C A
Fox, D P
Fox, D H
Frank, J D
Frankel, S J
Franklin, T C
Fraser, I D
Fraser, S E
Freeman, B J C
Freeman, S L
Frewer, J D
Frewin, T
Frost, N A
Gaal, E
Gale, E A M
Gandhi, B P
Gandhi, K B
Ganly, S A
Gardiner, P V
Gardner, I C
Gardner, K A
Gargan, M F
Garner, J E
Garrett, T
Garrod, T J
Gellett, L R
George, M J
Gepi-Attee, S
Germon, T J
Gething, E
Ghosh, A R
Gibbs, C E
Gibbs, G H R
Gibbs, I E
Gibson, A G F
Gill, A A
Gill, S S
Gillatt, D A
Gillespie, E M
Gillespie, W A
Gilmore, K J
Gingell, J C
Ginn, H E
Glastonbury, R R
Gleeson, R E
Glew, C
Glew, S S
Glover, D A
Glover, S C
Goddard, P R
Godfrey, I B
Godfrey, P S A
Godfrey, P F
Goffin, R B
Goldie, D J
Goldie, M W
Goldstraw, E J
Goldsworthy, L L
Golledge, J
Gollin, T J
Gompels, M M A
Goodden, G F C
Goodland, D S
Goodman, N W
Goodman, S E
Goodrick, M J
Gordon, J R
Gordon, U D
Gough, K R
Gough, R

Bristol

Gould, T H
Goulding, T J
Goyder, N P
Graham, A L
Graham, E M
Graham, J D
Granier, S K
Grant, D A
Grant, L J P
Gray, H C
Gray, J F
Gray, J R
Gray, S F
Green, A M
Green, A J
Green, M E
Green, P R
Green, R E
Green, S M
Greene, J R T
Greenhalgh, K L
Greenhouse, P R D H
Greenslade, G L
Greenwood, H
Greenwood, S R
Gregory, M
Grenfell-Shaw, J M
Grenfell, P M
Grey, R H B
Grice, G L
Grier, D J
Griffith, N W
Griffiths, M V
Grimaldi, C B
Grindey, C A
Grubb, J
Gruenewald, P
Grundy, P L
Guest, J
Guest, P G
Guilding, T M
Gujral, S S
Gumb, J P
Gunnell, D J
Gunner, T
Gutteridge, G J
Guy, P R
Habib, F
Haddy, C E L
Hadfield, R J H
Haggett, T I
Hale, B M
Halford, J M
Halford, M E H
Hall, C M
Hall, C R
Hamilton-Wright, H M
Hamilton, M A
Hamm, R S
Hammer, B
Hancock, J E
Hancock, J P
Hanks, G W
Hanmer, R L
Hannon, M A
Harbord, P N
Hardiman, G V
Harding, K A
Harding, R J
Hardy, H D
Hardy, J R W
Hare, L
Hargreaves, H M
Harland, R F
Harling, C C
Harlow, E D
Harman, I P
Harper, S J
Harrad, R A
Harries, H J
Harris-Lloyd, C M
Harris, G J C
Harris, P P
Harrison, E
Harrison, G L
Harrison, J E
Harrison, L S
Harrison, M D I
Harrison, V M
Hart, J C D
Hartnell, V H
Hartog, M
Harvey, J E
Harvey, R F
Hasler, J C
Hatton, C E
Hatzis, T
Havers, A R
Hawkins, I A

Hawkins, R E
Hawkins, T J
Hawley, R M
Haworth, J M
Haworth, J M A
Hayes, A M
Hayes, F M
Hayes, J R
Hayes, R A
Heading, C M
Healy, M P
Hearing, S D
Hearn, K P
Heath, R W
Heidelmeyer, C F
Hellier, P A
Hellier, W P L
Hellings, R M
Helliwell, V C
Hembry, J N
Hemmings, M A
Henning, J D R
Hepburn, P R
Herapath, G C K
Herborn, A
Herod, S J
Herron, M L
Hetzel, M R
Hewer, R L
Hewes, J C
Heyderman, R S
Heywood, P
Hibbert, V L
Hicks, J A
Higgins, A S
Higgs, S A
Hill, B W
Hill, C M
Hills, M W
Hilton, M P
Hinds, G E
Hine, C E
Hine, I D
Hinton, R A
Hobbs, A
Hockey, B J
Hodges, C
Hoffman, A-L
Hoffman, C L
Hoffman, J N
Hoffman, N J
Hoffman, R J
Hogg, D C
Hogg, G P
Hoghton, M A R
Hoh, H B
Holden, N E S
Holdsworth, J E
Holland, D E
Holland, R K
Holland, S M
Holliday, D B
Hollingworth, P
Holloway, J E
Holmes, K M
Homewood, J M
Hooper, N R J
Hopton, P S
Hopwood, J A
Hopwood, S
Horner, P J
Horrocks, C T
Horton, R E
Hosking, E-J
Houghton, K J
Houghton, L M
House, W
Hovey, T M
Howe, A M
Howe, R A
Howell, S J
Hows, J M
Hoysal, N
Hoyte, C A E
Hubble, M J W
Hudson, J G
Huggins, K
Hughes-Games, J S
Hughes, C W
Hughes, D G
Hughes, G
Hughes, R C W
Hughes, S
Hull, M G R
Humphreys, N
Humphries, A B D
Hung, I F-N
Hunter, J D
Huskisson, L J

Hussain, N
Hutchings, M S
Hutchinson, M J
Hutter, J A
Hyde, J P
Hynam, P
Ibrahim, K
Ibrahim, N B N
Iles, R A
Iles, S
Illingworth, S C
Inward, C D
Irvine, C E W
Irvine, G H
Izhar, M
Jackson, L M
Jackson, M
Jackson, N J
Jacobs, D Y
Jahfar, S C
James, A M G
James, H A
James, J A
James, J A
James, L
James, M C
James, S C
Jardine, P E
Jefferson, K P
Jefferson, N R
Jeffrey, D R
Jelfs, J P
Jenkins, G M
Jenkins, I A
Jenkins, J M
Jephcott, C R
Jetha, H C
Jethwa, P
Jewell, M D
Jewkes, J
Jeyasingham, K
Jobanputra, R
Joels, L A
Johar, M A
John, N G
Johns, N M
Johnson, C J H
Johnson, D P
Johnson, D M
Johnson, R S
Johnson, R W
Johnstone, C G
Johnstone, J C
Jones, A J
Jones, A M
Jones, C M
Jones, E V
Jones, E M J
Jones, G L
Jones, J J
Jones, J V
Jones, J V
Jones, J D
Jones, J E
Jones, K E
Jones, M S
Jones, M L
Jones, N
Jones, R
Jordan, L M
Jordan, S C
Joy, R
Joy, V J
Kabala, J E
Kalfayan, P Y
Kane, L A
Kane, N M
Karabatsas, K
Kay, A R
Kaye, G S
Kaye, J I
Keane, D P
Keen, G
Kelland, S A
Kellas, A R P
Kemp, H J
Kemple, T J
Kendall, C E
Kendall, J M
Kenealy, J M
Kennedy, C T C
Kennedy, R P
Kenney, B A K
Kenny, J R
Kent, N J
Kenwright, P
Kerfoot, N E
Kershaw, D M L
Kershaw, H C

Kessler, D S
Khabaza, E
Khan, F
Khan, S
Khan, S N
Khong, C H
Khong, S-Y
Kindleysides, A
Kingham, D
Kings, G A
Kingston, J M
Kinmont, J C
Kinsella, S M
Kirkpatrick, A J J
Kirkpatrick, B L
Kirkup, M E M
Kirwan, J R
Kitching, D F
Knight, C J
Knights, S E
Koehli, N
Koh, S H
Koutentis, C A
Krischer, J M
Krishnapillai, R
Kutt, E
Kvalsvig, A J
Kyle, M V
Kyle, P M
Kyriakides, T
Lafferty, E M
Lahiri, S K
Laird, D B
Lalla, S C
Lam, P S E
Lambert, M V
Lambert, P A
Lambert, R G
Lamont, M M
Lamont, P M
Lancaster, J F
Langdon, I J
Langfield, J A
Langton Hewer, S C
Langton, F A
Laszlo, G
Latham, I A
Latham, S G
Lau, D F
Lauder, G R
Laue, B
Laurence, R Q
Lavelle, A B
Laverty, S E
Lavin, E P
Law, R C
Lawes, M J
Lawlor, D A
Lawrence, J C
Lawrence, T M
Lawson, D N
Lawson, R H
Laxton, C H
Leaf, A A
Leahy, T C
Lear, J T
Lear, P A
Learmonth, I D
Leary, P M
Lee, E C
Lee, R C
Lee, T D
Leigh, J
Leitch, A
Lench, P A
Lesley, S W
Leslie, I J
Levy, A
Lewis, C M
Lewis, D R
Lewis, G M
Lewis, H J
Lewis, T T
Lewis, V E
Ley, B E
Li, S T B
Lightman, S L
Lim, B K
Lim, H H
Lindahl, A J
Lindeck, J F
Ling, R H L
Linter, S P K
Lismore, J R
Liversedge, N H
Lloyd, J G
Lloyd, W H
Loader, J S
Lockyer, J S

Lockyer, M S
Lodge, B C
Longhurst, S E
Lopez, A
Lounamaa, R H K
Love, S
Loveday, E J
Lowis, S P
Lowrey, S
Luders, K S
Lunt, P W
Lunts, E S
Lupton, H A
Lush, B S
Lush, M A
Lush, R J
Luty, J S
Lyburn, I D
Lyell, V R
Lynch, L M
Lyons, A F M
Lyons, C
Lyons, M
McBride, E V
McBride, P A
McCafferty, I J
McCaldin, M D
McCarron, P G
McClatchey, A
McCormick, B A
McCracken, D
McCracken, M
McCulloch, N A
Macdonald, A J R
Macdonald, R D
McEvoy, S C
MacGillivray, I
MacGowan, A P
McGowan, M T
McGraw, M E
Macintyre, A E R
Macipe, M E
Mackenzie Crooks, D J
Mackenzie, E F D
Mackenzie, J C
Mackintosh, M A
McLeod, F N
McMahon, J E
McMahon, R J
McOmie, H
McPherson, M R
Macpherson, R I
Macquire-Samson, I M P J
McQuoney, P A
McRobert, M S
McSparron, R A
McVey, F K
McWatters, V
Madden, A P
Maendl, A C J
Mahood, C V M
Mahyoub Abbas, M A
Main, J A
Main, P G N
Mair, J M
Majeed, G S
Majid, M A
Makins, R J
Malcolm, G P
Male, P
Malhotra, R
Malki, A A-E-H G
Mallory, S
Malone, J D
Manara, A R
Mancero, S
Mandeville, J E
Mansfield, K B
Mansfield, N C
Margetts, L J
Mark, S D
Markham, D H
Markham, R H C
Marks, D I
Marmion, V J
Marsh, P J J
Marshall, D E
Marshall, J
Marshall, P J
Martin, A G
Martin, R P
Martin, V C
Martindale, S J
Masheder, S
Mason, C F
Mason, E E
Mason, G M
Massey, S R

Mather, F E
Mather, H G
Mather, S J
Mathieson, P W
Mathison, A C
Mathison, D M
Maw, A R
Maxa, D W
Maxwell, R B H
Mayes, A J
Meadows, P S
Meads, A E
Mediratta, N K
Meehan, S
Meek, S J
Mehta, D
Melichar, J K
Meller, R H C
Memel, D S
Menage, M J
Mendhan, J E
Menke, T
Mercer, M H
Mercer, N S G
Metcalf, J V
Metcalfe, M W
Miall, C H I
Mian, I H
Millar, A B
Millar, B A
Miller, S E
Mills, C A
Mills, M S
Milne, J D
Milne, M R
Minors, J D
Mitchell, D C
Mitchell, J P
Mitchell, T J F
Mitchell, W B
Mitcheson, J I H
Moncrief, A C
Monk, C R
Montague, A P
Montague, R F
Montgomery, S M
Moon, D J
Moore, A G
Moore, N J
Moore, P J
Moorman, N E
Moralee, P
Moreno Garcia, J
Morgan, F
Morgan, H G
Morgan, J H C
Morgan, J D T
Morris, E W
Morris, E A J
Morrison, P A
Morse, M H
Moss, J A
Moss, T H
Mostafa, M A A
Mountford, R A
Mudawi, A M
Muir, R M
Mumford, D B
Munday, C A
Munro, D S
Munro, E N
Murdoch, J B
Murphy, E M
Murphy, K P M
Murphy, P J
Murray, J R
Mussett, J M
Mutch, H J
Myers, P P V
Myles, J S
Naish, J M
Naish, N
Nandwani, N
Nash, A P
Nation, C B M
Naughton, C A
Naysmith, M C
Ndirika, A C
Neal, D M
Neale, P M
Neale, R D
Neatby, G O M
Negus, A G
Nelson, I W
Nereli, B E
Ness, A R
Neubauer, K A
Newbery, F E
Newman, C A

Bristol

Newman, H F V
Newman, J H
Newton, H S
Ng, S Y
Nicholas, M
Nicholls, G
Nicholls, K
Nichols, K C
Nicholson, E M
Nicholson, H D
Niven, P A R
Norfolk, G A
Norman, H M M
Norman, J M
Norman, M L
Norman, M A
Norman, S P
Norman, S
Norton, R H
Norton, S A
Nowers, M P
Nutt, D J
Nutt, N R
O'Brien, C M
O'Brien, M
O'Carroll, M G
O'Connor, S
O'Hara, G V
O'Higgins, F M
O'Higgins, J W
O'Leary, A J
O'Leary, D P
O'Mahony, M Y
O'Neill, P J
Oakhill, A
Oakland, C D H
Oakley, G A
Obi, B C
Odum, S
Ogunnaike, O B
Ohlsson, V
Oke, S C
Oliver, E J H
Oliver, S E
Oliwiecki, S
Oram, M
Orde, M M
Orlando, A
Ormerod, F
Ormerod, I E C
Orton, B F
Orton, R W
Osborne, N J R
Osborne, S F
Ostins, A W
Otton, S H
Over, D C
Owen-Jones, J L
Owen, G
Owen, J H
Owen, W I
Oxley, J D
Paddon, A M
Page, F B
Page, K I
Page, S J
Paine, T F
Pamphilon, D H
Pandit, J C
Papacostopoulos, D
Papouchado, M
Pardoe, J L
Pardoe, R B
Parke, M E C
Parker, A S
Parker, J
Parker, L R C
Parker, M
Parker, S E
Parkinson, J M T
Parmenter, J G
Parnham, A
Parrott, J P S
Parry, A J
Parry, H R
Parry, M O L
Part, M
Partridge, D R
Patel, K C
Patel, P S
Patel, S D
Paterson, C F
Paterson, J P
Paterson, T A
Pattison, H F
Paul, I R
Pauli, M A
Pawade, A M
Paxton, C P C

Payne, C J I
Payne, N E S
Payne, P A G
Peach, A H S
Peachey, R D G
Peacock, G F
Pearce, K J
Pearcy, R M
Peat, D S
Peel, D J
Pegg, G C
Pell, G M
Pemberton, P E
Penning-Rowsell, V W
Pennock, C A
Penny, E M F
Penny, J B
Pentlow, B D
Pepper, S H
Pereira, A M
Persad, R A R
Peters, A R
Pettit, E K
Pheby, D F H
Philipp, R
Phillips, D G
Phillips, S M
Phillips, W R
Pickering, V
Pickett, D A
Pieczora, M S
Pike, J
Pimm, M H J
Pinkney, J H
Pirotta, D A
Pitman, M A
Pizer, B L
Plowman, J R
Plummeridge, M J
Plunkett, L
Pomirska, M B
Pople, I K
Portas, C D
Porteous, D J
Porteous, R
Porter, D G
Porter, H J
Porter, I J
Porter, K
Porter, L
Potokar, J P
Potokar, T S
Potter, E S
Pottinger, R F
Potts, M J
Poulsom, W J
Pounsford, J C
Powell, D G M
Powell, L A
Powell, P D A
Price, C H G
Price, C G A
Price, C J S
Price, D M
Price, J
Price, S P
Pridie, J M
Primrose, P A
Probert, C S J
Prophet, M J
Pryn, S J
Prys-Roberts, C
Prys-Roberts, C O
Przemioslo, R T
Puleston, B M
Purkiss, R H
Purves, H J
Quinn, M J
Raffety, R C
Rahman, M A
Rahman, S N
Raistrick, E R
Randall, M E H
Rasanayagam, S R
Rashid, I
Rashid, R
Ratliff, A H C
Rawlings, K
Rawlinson, G V
Rawlinson, J N
Rawlinson, S M
Raynal, A L
Rayter, Z
Read, K G
Reading, C A
Record, C A
Redmond, J V
Ree, C J
Rees, C A

Rees, G J G
Rees, H J
Rees, J R
Rees, J S
Rees, J R E
Rees, R
Reeve, M
Reeves, G E
Reeves, R W K
Reid, C D
Reid, D L L
Reid, J W
Reifenberg, N A
Revington, P J
Reynolds, N M
Rice, G A
Rich, M G
Richards, C M
Richards, P S M
Richards, T D
Richardson, S A
Ridler, S L
Ridley, P
Rigby, H S
Riley, K
Ring, N P
Roberts, A S
Roberts, C M
Roberts, C J C
Roberts, C J
Roberts, D G V
Roberts, D M
Roberts, G I
Roberts, J B M
Roberts, S K
Robertson, R J
Robinson, B
Robinson, D C
Robinson, D E
Robinson, P J
Roche, K P M
Roddie, R K
Rodgman, M E
Roe, A M
Rogers, D G C
Rogers, J E G
Rogers, J C
Ronson, J G
Rooth, F G
Rooth, J A
Rosengren, H
Ross, A J
Rossdale, M G P
Routledge, T A
Rowley, C
Rowley, S A
Rowsell, R M
Roy, B F
Royston, V H
Russell, G A B
Russell, J A O
Russell, S R
Ryan, A G
Sacks, L J
Sadler, J A
Sage, C H
Sahay, S
Sale, S M
Salisbury, C J
Salmon, G M
Sammut, D P
Sampson, M T
Samuels, A
Sandeman, D R
Sanders, A D
Sanders, D J
Sandford, J J
Sandhu, B K
Sandry, R J
Sandry, S A
Sansom, J E
Sant, A M
Sarangi, P P
Sarma, K P
Sartori, R A
Sasada, M P
Saunders, E S
Saunders, M W
Saunders, P W
Saungsomboon, D
Savage, J R
Savage, P E
Sawford, R W
Scally, G J
Scanlon, J M
Schaefer, J A
Schembri Wismayer, F
Schofield, E C
Schuster Bruce, M J L

Schutt, W H
Scott-Moncrieff, C M
Scott, A J
Scott, B A
Scott, G L
Scott, M P Y
Scott, P J Y
Scull, T J
Searle, J M
Seddon, J M
Seddon, J D M
Self, F R
Sellick, C S
Senior, C J
Sephton, E A
Sexton, R J
Seymour-Shove, R
Shah, M J
Sharp, D J
Sharrard, H E
Sheard, T A B
Sheffield, E A
Shepherd, A M
Shepherd, S G
Shepherdson, D
Sheppard, C J
Shere, M H
Sherman, L
Sherriff, R J
Sheshgiri, J B
Shield, J E H
Shield, J P H
Shinde, S
Shlosberg, C B
Short, C A
Short, D J
Shutt, L E
Shyamapant, S
Sias, A
Sibley, G N A
Sidebotham, P D
Siemaszko, C O
Silbiger, C A
Silvey, H S
Silvey, S J
Simmonds, M R
Simmonds, M N
Simons, P S
Simpson, A L
Simpson, P J
Sims Williams, H G
Sinton, W S
Skelton, D A W
Skew, B L
Skinner, A V
Slack, N F
Slade, P R H
Slade, R R
Sloan, D R
Smalldridge, J
Smalldridge, N J F
Smeeton, A K
Smith, A J
Smith, C S
Smith, D G A-E
Smith, D L
Smith, F C T
Smith, G F
Smith, J E
Smith, J M
Smith, K C P
Smith, P J B
Smith, P M
Smith, P A
Smith, R M
Smith, S J
Smith, S M
Smith, T J T
Smithson, J E
Smithson, S F
Smyk, D
Smyth, G T C
Snow, J A
Solomon, L
Soodeen, D E
Soodeen, S J
Soothill, P W
Spare, T J
Sparks, W B
Speller, D C E
Spence, D S
Spence, R W
Spencer, R C
Spicer, R D
Spurling, B M
Stableforth, P G
Stambuli, P M
Stanley, D J P
Stanley, O H

Stannard, C F
Stansbie, D L
Stapleton, C
Steele, T
Steiner, M R
Stellakis, M L C
Stephens, A D
Stephenson, C R
Sternberg, M P
Stevenson, B J
Stevenson, J
Steward, C G
Stimpson, G G
Stock, P R
Stoddart, H
Stoddart, P A
Stone, D W G
Stotesbury, S N
Strang, J I G
Struthers, C A
Stuart, A G
Stuart, E L
Stubbs, P D
Styles, C L
Sullivan, J G
Summerskill, W S M
Sutcliffe, M C
Sweerts, M I E
Swingler, R
Swithinbank, D W
Swithinbank, L V
Syed, N A
Sykes, P M
Sylvester, D G H
Sylvester, P A
Symes, M O
Tait, C P
Tallis, P M
Tam, B S M
Tan, C
Tan, S Y
Tanser, A R
Tarleton, D E B
Tate, D W
Tattan, T M G
Tavare, A J
Tawodzera, P B-C P
Taylor, C
Taylor, J D M
Taylor, J S W
Taylor, M J
Taylor, N W G
Taylor, P A
Taylor, R A
Taylor, R G
Taylor, S D
Telling, J P
Teo, H T H T C
Terry, D M S
Than, S
Tharmaratnam, D
Thiagarajan, J
Thin Kyu, Dr
Thomas, C W
Thomas, H M
Thomas, J S
Thomas, K A
Thomas, K D
Thomas, L A
Thomas, M S
Thomas, M S
Thomas, M G
Thomas, P W
Thomas, S J
Thomas, T A
Thompson, C S
Thompson, E A
Thompson, E C M
Thompson, K M
Thompson, M J
Thompson, M H
Thompson, S A
Thomson, J L G
Thomson, T K
Thornley, P
Thornton, M J
Thornton, P G N
Thorpe, J
Thorpe, P L P
Tierney, P A
Tilley, A J
Timoney, A G M
Titcomb, D R
Tizard, E J
Tobias, J H
Tobin, G W
Todd, E J
Todman, E
Toma, A

Tometzki, A J P
Tomison, A R
Tomlinson, J M
Tomlinson, M J
Tomson, C R V
Totham, A
Townsend, P L G
Treloar, E J
Tremaine, K J
Trenfield, J D S
Tribe, E M
Tricks, C D
Trinder, J
Truscott, J H
Tsai-Goodman, B
Tuffrey, C
Tunstall, S R
Turner, R J
Twigg, S J
Tyldesley, R C
Umarji, S I M
Underwood, S M
Undrill, G M
Unsworth, D J
Upton, M W M
Vaggers, S D
Vahdati-Bolouri, M
Van Asch, P
Van'T Hoff, H C
Vassallo, A A
Vaughan, J R
Vernon, J M
Vickers, J H
Vickery, C J
Vickery, C W
Vickery, I M
Virjee, J P
Voss, M
Vranjkovic, V
Vyas, S K
Waddell, A N
Wakeley, C J
Walburn, M B
Walford, N Q
Walker, J V
Walker, P C
Walker, P R
Walker, S C B
Walker, W L
Wallace, C A
Waller, T J
Walley, B M
Wallington, T B
Walsh, D S
Walsh, E M
Walter, E J
Walters, F J M
Walters, J H
Ward, A M
Ward, A J
Ward, C L C
Ward, G R
Ward, J A
Ward, L L
Wardle, P G
Warin, W A
Warinton, A D
Warner, D L
Warr, C A
Warr, E E
Warr, R P
Warren-Browne, C Y
Warren, S A F
Washington, J S
Watkins, C J
Watson, G W
Watson, M J
Watt, E M
Watt, F A
Watt, F K
Watt, G C
Watt, I
Watts, A R
Watts, D P
Watts, D R
Watts, H R
Watts, M R
Weale, A E
Webb, A J
Webb, D A
Webb, E J
Webb, J C J
Webb, J M
Webb, M E
Webster, F L
Wehner, H E
Weil, D M
Weinbren, M J
Weir, J N M

Weir, P M
Welbourn, H F
Welbourne, J
Weller, R M
Welsh, M A
Wensley, S K
West, S H
Whaley, A P
Whallett, D J
Whallett, E J
Wheatley Price, M
Wheatley, A M
Wheeler, A
Whipp, E C
Whitaker, N T
White, H
White, M T
White, R J
Whitehead, P J
Whitelaw, A G L
Whiteside, B G
Whitfield, M J
Whittaker, K W
Whitton, T L
Whitwell, F D
Whone, A L
Wickert, A J
Wickremaratchi, M M
Wigfield, C C
Wight, D J
Wilde, R P H
Wiley, D J
Wilkins, D G
Wilkins, P H
Wilkinson, D A C
Wilkinson, E J
Wilkinson, M S
Wilkinson, S A
Willatts, S M
Willems, P J A
Williams, A B
Williams, B M
Williams, C J
Williams, C E M
Williams, C S
Williams, C
Williams, J D
Williams, M P
Williams, N B
Williams, R W
Williams, R J W
Williams, R S
Williams, T D
Willmott, C
Willmott, S L
Wilmshurst, M J
Wilson, A V
Wilson, A M
Wilson, M P
Wilson, M G
Wilson, N H
Winson, I G
Winteringham, T
Wisheart, J D
Wiszniewska, R H
Witcher, J W
Witherow, P J
Withers, D G
Wong, C K M
Wong, R C W
Wood, C E
Wood, F A
Wood, J A
Wood, S J
Woodhead, A E
Woods, S J
Woodward, C M
Woodward, C L
Worsley, G E
Wrathall, G J
Wright, J C
Wright, J S
Wright, M E
Wyatt, S J
Wynick, D
Yandell, C J
Yates, P A
Yeatman, M
Yeoman, G B
Yeoman, R
Yerbury, C M
Young, A E R
Younge, P A
Zaman, S H
Zollman, C E
Zorab, J S M

Brixham

Acheson, E A

Acheson, P
Amos, H E
Ansley, D G H
Avery, P J
Baxter, N
Binnie, M C
Bromige, R M
Brown, K R M
Brown, L M M
Brown, R M
Grime, P D
John, T C
Johnson, P B
Kew, L D
Langley, D C
Langley, P S
Lee, E J
McConnell, M B
Montgomery, R W
Morgan, J H S
Murray, S J
Paton, A N
Pile, H F
Powell, M R
Sutton Coulson, T
Tapp, M J F
Washington, R J M
White, D M D
Wood, D N

Broadstairs

Adam, E J
Ajayi, J D
Arnold, C S
Bachlani, M M
Barter, R W
Bean, J N
Beheshti, R
Briant, B A
Brierley, R P
Brooker, A E W
Brown, T W
Butler, M F
Cardwell, M D
Chastell, D J M
Clark, A R L
Cook, D M
Cook, J A M
Cook, R M M
Corti, K D F
Cunard, A J K
Cutting, R J
Davies, M
Ferguson, A
Fraser, K M
Gill, R S
Gledhill, J R
Goldberg, S M
Gunn, K P
Hartt, A S
Heath, E
Herron, J T
Hewitson, M W A
Jepps, J M A
Karunadasa, A T R K
Limentani, A E
Loveless, J A
Macaulay, R B
McAvoy, B J T
McBean, J B
McBean, M S
Marshall, A
Marshall, D I
Martin, T S
Nairac, B L
Pheils, P J
Rose, C
Ruben, M
Sahadevan, S
Shariff, S Y
Slator, D A
Spittlehouse, K E
Stacpoole-Ryding, F
Standeven, P A H
Stephen, I B M
Toosey, J B M
Voysey, M M
Webster, G W
Wilson, P E
Wilton, H J
Young, P J

Broadstone

Briggs, M W
Cartwright, L N
Davies, H C R
Dinley, R R J
Drake, B E
Dudding, G J

Dutson, M E J
Ellis, C J K
Fleming, P A
Jones, J H A
Lawrence, J S
Marsh, K E
Nixon, S M
Ortega, L S
Panda, J K
Panda, V P
Pharaoh, J M
Richardson, M I
Saynor, A M N
Shakespeare, R M
Sharp, N S
Timmis, R G
Warren, S J
Watkins, A J
West, R
Woodside, R

Broadway

Bloch-Ashbridge, K M
Bloch, T P S
Connell, A M S
Corbett, H V
D'Agapeyeff, A P
Dootson, P H
Edgar, B M
Fitzgibbon, S M
Houghton, C C
Juckes, T R B
Juckes, W R
McFall, I C
Mockler, E M
Moore, M M
Orr, B M
Shaw, A C
Smith, D M
Townshend, N W N
Williams, A C
Williams, D

Brockenhurst

Barnes, F M
Benson, R J
Birt, C H
Browne, D S
Clinton-Jones, G B
Diwakar, V
Godfrey, I M
Green, R V
Hayley, W D
Horsfall, T J M
Humby, E M
Jones, N F
Kilsby, E B
Lang, J R
Lawrence, K M
McColl, M T C
Moss, S J
Newbury, L
Pearce, D J
Roberts, M A
Ross, J K
Sparrow, P M
Stevenson, B J
Thomas, V L

Brodick

Blesovsky, A
Brown, M M
Buchanan, R A
Cumming, A
Grassie, A D
Grassie, E H S
Guthrie, E L
Halstead, J
Kerr, M M
MacLeod, S M B
MacVicar, F T
Martin, J A M
Saint-Yves, I F M
Shaw, I L
Sloss, G A
Starks, J M
Thompson, W T
Tinto, B A
Tinto, R G
Wallace, W M M
Whitla, D R

Bromley

Ahmed, Q Z
Al-Chalabi, N
Allen, P R
Arnold, S J
Arora, A
Arul, D R
Asante, M A

Barratt, S D
Bassett, D J
Berman, G L
Berman, N A
Best, E A
Best, M H
Bhinda, H P
Bird, S F
Birmingham-McDonogh, S M L
Bone, D H
Bradley, M D
Breese, E O
Broadhead, J C
Broom, A M
Browne, P H
Burville, L M
Cameron, J M
Carp, G W
Castell, R
Castles, W J B
Chamberlain, H M
Chang, Y-C
Chester, A W
Clift, D C
Collins, M E
Colt, J M R
Comper, S J
Condon, H A
Coombes, S K
Cornish, E M
Cornwell, W B
Couper, E H
Cox, A
Crook, J M
Cundy, J M
Darby, P W
Davies, N E
Davies, T D W
Davis, K E
Dawkins, G P C
De Cothi, E M
Dhadly, P P S
Eapen, V
Eason, J R
Edmonds, G M
Ellice, R M
Ellinger, J W
Ellul, J P M
Erhardt, C C
Fathulla, B B
Fergusson, D A N
Fernando, E C K
Fisher, E J
Fowler, T J
Fox, M B
Franklin, A
Fry, I K
Gent, E D
Ghali, F A M
Gleave, C M T
Gnanachelvan, K
Gowenlock, A J
Graham, P C
Gray, P J P
Guckenheim, P D L
Gupta, B N
Gupta, D
Guram, N S
Hadley, E M
Hall, S E
Hamid, S
Hamilton, M J H
Hanna, L S
Harrison, M C
Harvey-Smith, E A
Haughey, N M
Hazra, D
Hedley, R M
Hibbert, G S C
Higgs, S I L
Hill, N C W
Hobbs, A C
Hollis, P
Holt, R I G
Hoskins, E A
Hunt, J B
Hunter, J E
Jalajam, M P
Jamall, O A
Jeanes, A L
Jegamohan, K
Jenkins, A P
Jenkins, V M
Job, M C H
Jones, N C
Kahlon, K S
Kalgutkar, S K
Kandiah, D

Kapadia, A P
Kaur, I
Kendall, G
Kenyon, J B
Kessel, B L
Kharade, M A
King, J B
King, P B
King, P M
Ladd, G H Y
Lamparelli, M J
Langford, E J
Lawson, W T W
Leather, A J M
Leather, S C
Lewis, B S
Lewis, K M
Littlewood, J M
Lord, J E
Lumley, P W
Luong, C B
Lutman, D H
Lyttle, M E A C
MacCann, E
McCarthy, K
Maciejczak, D
MacKillop, A J J
MacLeod, M J
Mahendrarajah, A
Malekniazi, D
Marmery, V J
Martin, A
Martin, R J
Matthews, M A
Medcalf, J F
Medcalf, J M
Meire, H B
Michael, W F
Midwood, C J
Minty, C A
Moore, D A
Morcos, S N
Muir, J N
Mullally, J J
Murphy, J M
Murphy, P J
Nackasha, E P
Narayan, K
Neelamkavil, D P S
Ng, L V-L
Nurse, D E
O'Brien, D D
O'Sullivan, K M C
Osborn, S V
Ostlere, M
Owen, R A
Page, J E
Patel, A B
Patel, C R
Patel, J V
Patel, R K
Payne, N M
Peebles, D J
Percy, A J L
Pereira, D A S P
Prasad, K
Predolac, O D
Priddle, E S
Pritchard, E L
Procter, L
Pulley, M S
Purcell, P
Quastel, A S
Quirk, J A
Radford, R C
Rajamenon, A
Rakowicz, S P
Rao, V R K
Rashid, A
Ratneswaren, N
Rault, J P R
Reed, H
Russell, G F M
Ryba, P C J
Samuel, M S
Satkurunath, G
Saunders, R C O
Sawicka, E H
Scott, C S-L
Sebel, J
Sehmi, S K
Selby, M R
Selvanathan, E S
Selway, J R
Shah, J K R
Shahnawaz, G
Sharma, K K
Sharples, C J
Sheppey, M C

Bromsgrove

Shivanathan, S
Singh, H
Singh, N
Sivagnanasundaram, S
Smith, H D
Smith, I F
Smith, M R W
Smith, S M
Spiby, J
Spurr, J J
Staffurth, J F
Staffurth, J S
Statham, H C
Stein, G S
Surenthiran, S
Swift, M R
Tampiyappa, T N
Tatford, E P W
Tattersfield, H G
Taylor, P A
Tharmaseelan, K
Thomas, A M K
Timothy, J I
Tseng, E H Y
Turvey, A J
Van Gelderen, D S
Vasey, J M
Vine, P R
Wegstapel, H
Whiteside, W N
Willatt, R N
Wing, L G
Wotherspoon, F
Wragg, P G
Writer, M D L
Yanni, D H
Yanni, G
Young, S L
Zakrzewski, K K

Bromsgrove

Ashton, F
Aust, T R
Bailey, S R
Banerjee, A
Banerjee, S
Benn, A
Blacker, J P D
Blackwell, D H
Blunt, R J
Borastero, E W
Brooksbank, H A
Buchanan, E H
Byrnes, R
Bywater, B
Chakraverty, R C
Cheetham, J N H
Chidley, K E
Coles, V R
Collins, S J
Cooke, R A
Crooks, M P
Dale, J E
Dowley, S P M
Dowley, W G H
Dykes, P A
Dykes, P W
Eardley, M L
Evans, A J
Evans, H A
Fellowes, M A
Filer, A D J
Finnegan, J A
Goldman, I G
Goodwin, A J
Gorman, S L
Grove, L H
Hall, F J
Hallows, M R
Hayes, G M
Heath, C D
Hicken, G J
Hill, A T
Hill, L E
Horton, S J
Hotham, D S
Jack, D A
Jack, J W
Jack, O P
Jack, R A F
Jackson, J R
James, V H C
Jenkins, R M
Jones, S R
Kenchington, N S
Kidsley, S G
Latham, D M
Laxton, C J S
Leci, M K

Bromyard

Leigh, B A
Lewin, J S
McIlveen, D J S
McIlveen, S M
Mills, M J
Morgan, D W
Morgan, P A P
O'Neill, D
Penfold, B M
Pryke, D S E
Quinton, P J
Radcliffe, M E
Reddie, E M
Reeve, J L
Schirrmacher, U O E
Scott, P V
Sefton-Fiddian, P
Sheasby, M J
Smith, M T
Spires, R C S
Swire, H
Wall, L T
White, F M
White, H M
Whiteford, L J
Wilkinson, R D
Williams, B
Wychrij, O

Bromyard

Barnes, J M
Boddington, D G
Brockington, I F
Bull, L
Clear, M R
Crosskey, P H
Ganderton, P
Ilsley, J K
Kirrage, D C
Lamerton, S M
Scott, S F O
Spicer, N A A
Tait, I J
Wilmshurst, S L

Brora

Fortune, M H
Main, M M

Broseley

Bhageerutty, J D
McCarthy, M U

Brough

Allen, S P
Arrowsmith, J S
Blair, R E
Bray, J H
Carrick, G H
Cast, J E I
Charlson, M J
Charlson, P B
Cook, T
Dobson, E M
Ferguson, R A
Harper, C L
Hart, W A
Hodgson, B
Joseph, A E P
Livesey, J P
Livesey, S H
Lucas, K
Macpherson, H
Marshall, S R
Mathew, B G
Partridge, S
Purdy, G M
Richardson, W N
Rosenberg, F G
Savage, A C
Searle, S M
Smith, S L
Somerville, G W
Spencer, J
Storrs-Fox, P
Summerton, A M
Tinker, N R
Tod, I A A
Whiting, J M S
Wood, J C
Woodyatt, C P

Broughton-in-Furness

Bates, T H
Calverley, E H
Harvey, S C
Hopkinson, J J
Parsons, G J

Broxbourne

Blackman, M
Condon, R N H
Dignan, J E P
Hale, B C
Hiscock, B M V
Manlow, C J
Mukherjee, A
Sheridan, J S
Watt, N K
Wood, A G
Wyman, D A

Broxburn

Atkinson, M C
Buchan, G I
Coffey, I W
Ferguson, T H
Fowler, G
Heath, L
Hendry, J D
Kent, B
Lewis, B
Lyons, G L
MacLardy, I H
McRae, F C
Mawdsley, E M
Nimmo, J F
Russell, J C
Salisbury, K
Santer, P M
Semple, S M
Singh, A D
Sives, D A
Wood, N R

Bruton

Genton, H E
Hawkins, A L
Nicole, T M
Player, M H
Taylor, J A

Brynmawr

Nookaraju, K

Buckfastleigh

Barton, T J
Draper, C A
Dunstan, E R R
Edwards, P D
Hedger, J R
Kealy, M R
Moore, D A
Oxtoby, S J
Rice, E A
Towers, J R
Willington, F L

Buckhurst Hill

Adamson, M I
Ah-Moye, M
Alexander-Sefre, F
Allum, T G L
Arif, S
Barnardo, A N
Briggs, A C
Collett, P M R
Crown, M P
Daniel, C A
Dodd, P P
Eve, J P
Fieldman, N R
Heavens, M A C
Hussain, I
Jackson, E R
Keane, B
Kennedy, J M
Leahy, J D
Liao, S
McAuliffe, T B
McEwen, A M
McMillan, A-M
Moss, C E
Nunneley, J B
Osborough, F
Patel, K M
Pietroni, M C
Ross, G A W
Ruben, S T
Sewell, R C T
Singh, M
Slater, A J
Stuart, R D
Taylor, G B
Taylor, J S G
Thomas, A M
Thomas, D J B
Tranmer, C
Vere, D W

Viniker, D A
Walker, A

Buckie

Arnould, K M
Foster, N M E
Gallacher, W A
Hood, C M
Jaffrey, W G A
MacLeod, M C
McClintock, M G
Mair, W G P
Martin, M S
Menzies, C
Morrison, R M
Morrison, S G
Morrison, S J F
Pringle, G M
Rennie, J A
Scott, A W M
Silbergh, A E
Stoker, N R B
Tuckerman, J G
Walker, L
Willcox, H L

Buckingham

Austin, M W
Brown, C R
Cash, C J C
Clark, W I C
Coatesworth, A
Dickson, R N
Elwell, C M
Evans, B A
Fairfield, J J
Fraser, D F
Harrington, R W E
Heppell, R M
Jones, R O
Largent, T
McDonald, N J
McMullan, A D
Mason, M R
Mason, P D
Mathews, S R
Murphy, P A
Murphy, U M
Murray, B J
Preston, A E
Pritchard, G R G
Richardson, D
Robb, E
Robins, A E
Rudd, M I
Simons, G D
Spencer, M A P
Straker, D M
Stranks, S J
Suddes, K P
Taylor, A V G
Taylor, A R
Thorpe, K F
Tizzard, S P
Trafford, P J
Watson, A
Wetherill, M H
Whittington, J R
Woodroffe, R W

Buckley

Attree, R C
Botham, S A
Bradley, H J
Cartwright, N
Chadwick, J M
Clarke, W B
Hoggins, G R
Hopkins, R S
Hughes, T R T
Lucas, R M
Manson, M D
Speakman, P F
Spencer, C W
Tansley, A G

Bucknell

Harrison, J F
Kandasamy, K E

Bude

Batty, C G
Blood, A M O
Brown, A J
Cook, N C
Forrest, A K
Giles, D P V L
Gurd, D E P
Haddon, P W
Hammond-Evans, J M

Lake, M
Morwood, C I
Moss, A Y D
Munks, A W
Munks, J
Register, P W
Rowlands, A M
Sweet, D J
Thres, G V

Budleigh Salterton

Allen, J M
Archer, N E R
Aucott, D J
Benson, J A G
Buxton, A V
Cooper, C M H
Davis, T S
Dixon, J E R
Evans, D M
Fletcher, S E
Franklin, S
Hargreaves, T
Harland, R
Hart, M W
Henderson, E P
Hobbs, J L
Hughes, S
Huish, C C
John, A H
Lewis, A A G
Mejzner, R H
Nancekievill, L
Pocklington, S L
Reese, J M
Ross, F K
Rothnie, N G
Rowland, A J
Scott, A H
Simmons, M R
Smith, F R
Sykes, D W
Taylor, G E
Thomson, C W
Ward, I V I
Wright, M

Builth Wells

Coles, P F C
Davies, S D L
Davies, V B
Edmondson, C L
Gibbins, R L
Harriss, A R W
Jones, R J B H
Nash, M J
Parker, H G
Pugh, F V
Pugh, J K
Pugh, V T
Watson, T M

Bungay

Emerson, A R
Emerson, R G
Goss, B M
Hand, C H
Lewis, C A
McRory, J P
Mangat, K S
Self, A E
Sethia, K K
Williams, G

Buntingford

Banks-Smith, H R
Bryant, J G
Handysides, N S P
Lancaster, P A
McNamara, S A F O
Muir, I S
Partington, M J
Whitaker, B L
Withers, D P

Bures

Cattermole, R W
Magnus, I A
Patey, D G H
Pilgrim, L L
Williams, H C I
York, J H

Burford

Drayer, N M
Irving, J M R
Jeffs, J V
Mackenzie, F M
Sharpley, O J
Sims, E H
Slater, C

Smith, S P
Willby, L A

Burgess Hill

Barker, G M
Broadley, C E
Carter, J R
Cheng, M-N
Claiden, M
Daniels, N L
Eastman, K E
Ebbage, J C
Elliot, J V
Gankerseer, S A
Gigli, C
Harman, F E M
Harrop, J E
Holwell, I A
Hornby, R C
Longthorne, P N
Lyle, P T W
MacGuire, J D
Mahapatra, K C
Napier, J C
Pepera, T A A
Plant, S H
Rahman, M K
Read, J M
Roche, D F E
Ross, B
Siddiqui, U A
Turton, C W G
Whelan, R M

Burnham-on-Crouch

Bailey, K L
Elkin, A C
Harris, S J
Jayasekara, K S
Kamlow, F J
Ketteley, S J
Latif, M H
Phillips, J D
Phillips, S
Shaw, I J P

Burnham-on-Sea

Armin, R H
Charlwood, G P
Childs, D R
Evans, P A
Gauld, D A
Green, M J
Hall, H W
Hicks, M H M
Holl, S G
Johnston, S L
Matthews, N K
Sampson, H C R
Thomas, A L
Thomson, M R
Walker, M A
Wildbore, R D
Williams, E E

Burnley

Abdul-Nabi, M J
Abou-El-Farag, A M
Ahmad, S M
Al-Amin, M
Al-Dawoud, A A F
Ali, S T
Anafi, R F
Arif, N
Asghar, N M
Ashworth, F J
Ateaque, A
Avivar Fernandez, M B
Bailey, D W
Bailey, S
Barker, T M
Barsby, M R
Bayton, E A
Beech, K J
Berry, C M
Best, R A
Bezboruah, P P
Biswas, S R N
Brelsford, K J
Brew, J R
Brierley, A J
Brown, I H
Burke, M J
Calow, C E
Clark, E J
Cleasby, S J
Collins, L J
Cooke, B E
Corke, R T
Corkhill, S E

Coulson, I H
Craig, A E
Craven, N M
Cruickshank, J M
Crumbleholme, G K
Dabir, Z M
Daly, B M
Dalziel, E A
Das, R
Das, S
Deegan, S P
Dennison, A J N
Dennison, J M A
Dickens, G B
Dilraj Gopal, T R
Donald, C J M
Dooldeniya Perera, D
Downes, J
Durkin, M A
Fraser, D J
Gadsby, J B
Ghosh, S K
Graveston, N H
Green, A T
Gross, E
Gupta, S N
Hajela, V P
Hamer, F C
Hanna, M I
Haq, A
Haq, K S
Hartley, P C
Hartley, S J
Hassan, A
Haworth, R E
Hebden, S
Hyatt, R H
Hyder, C K Z
Inglis, T C M
Iqbal, J
Jain, J N
Jenkins, A J
Kendra, J R
Kenyon, S T
Khan, L U R
Khan, N A
Khatu, B V
Kirby, J M
Kumar Singh, P K
Langton, S G
Lauret, M A
Limaye, P
Limaye, S H
Littley, M D
Lockwood, E
Lolayekar, D T
Lotha, L M
McDevitt, M W
McGeorge, A
McGeorge, R S
Mackenzie, T H M
Mahady, I W
Mahady, V E
Malik, S
Masanjika, J P
Maung, M
Mellody, J
Merry, P H
Milne, I L
Mirza, I F
Mirza, M
Molyneux, D H
Narayana, V
O'Hagan, D P
Ogden, J R
Phillips, G E H
Rajarathna Setty, R S
Raza, S S
Rhodes, P C
Robertson, J G F
Rusius, C W
Rusius, J
Sahu, R C
Salman, W D
Sayers, C L
Schmitgen, C
Schmitgen, G
Seavers, J E
Seavers, P
Seeney, B
Shah, R K
Shahid, M
Singh, N
Singh, R K
Singh, S K
Singh, S
Sinha, R P
Smith, M V
Stewart, A P O

Bury St Edmunds

Summers, D J
Sundararajan, P
Sutcliffe, R C
Swann, A
Swann, I L
Syed, I A
Tattersall, N
Taylor, J P
Thistlethwaite, D
Tripathi, D N
Vilches Moraga, A
Vohra, S
Walton, M R
Watts, J C
White, D J
Whittaker, K
Wilson, D G
Wong, C K
Wright, D H

Burntisland

Adam, W S
Bates, D T
Bell, M D
Brown, G R
Chishti, M K
Chishti, Z J
Cochrane, A J
Duncan, D
Fleming, L E M
Forbes Smith, P A
Halliday, I M
Hamill, A M
Hunter, A S
Kay, V J
Lees, S
McCrae, W M
McCrea, W
Macdonald, J H B
Mackinnon, N A M
Mowbray, A
Myles, J C
Sinclair, K
Spence, A J
Stirling, G M
Weir, R M L

Burntwood

King, J C
Reynolds, C E
Winter, J M

Burry Port

Anderson, P M
Davies, R J
Gower, G E
Hughes, D G
Jones, C J M T
Lodha, L A
Morgan, C I
Thomas, F J
Williams, J M

Burton-on-Trent

Allebone, P
Allen, C
Allsop, P
Anderson, J D
Atkinson, M G W
Balcombe, N R
Baldock Grimes, S M
Barlow, H J
Barrow, A S
Benn, J J
Black, A
Bradbury, E L
Bucknall, T E
Butchart, G D
Camac, J C
Cartwright, P H
Charles, D
Chaturvedi, R
Chawdhary, S
Cleary, J J L
Collier, S L
Corfield, R A
Crittenden, F K
Crosse, J M
Davies, F W T
de Castella, H C
Dickey, J M
Dickson, D E
Dimetri, A E Z
Dixon, T P
Doyle, P T
Dutton, G C D
El-Khanagry, M F F
Ellerton, J D R
Farrar, C D
Flanagan, N J

Free, G
Gent, K S
Ghori, M U
Gompertz, R H K
Goodwin Hudson, E E
Green, D M
Green, G A
Green, L C
Greenwood, C M
Gregory, B A
Grey, J M
Guirguis, R S
Gunstone, C C
Gunstone, E M
Hall, C J
Hann, H C L
Hannon, M C
Hardy, R M
Harrison, A R
Harrison, R J
Heal, C M
Heath, A C
Hextall, R A
Hill, J D
Hingorani, T V
Holgate, P W
Hopper, J M
Horton, R M
Hughes, M W
Hughes, M E R
Hunter, B J
Irwin, M W
Jacob Samuel, T
Jenkins, R G
Johns, A M
Jones, P L
Jordan, A D
Judd, O F
Kamath, U M
Kasthuri, N
Khan, H A
Khan, M A
Knowles, V M
Laban, S J
Lapper, J
Lathbury, W C
Law, H M
Law, S D
Lobb, C J
Lockwood, J A F
Long, J M
Luft, G A N
Lydon, R J
Lydon, Y H F
Mager-Jones, J
Manzoor, A
Martin, J W
Masani, H M
Matharu, G S
Millar, S W
Miller, J M
Mills, A M
Minn Din, Z
Mirfattahi, M M B
Moloney, P G
Murray, C A
Nanda, K K
Nelson, H M
Newton, M P
Nik Abdullah, N A I
Nweke, A J
O'Dwyer, F G J
Oakley, W E
Oates, J
Okoye, D O C
Patel, G B
Paul, M B
Pearson, R M G
Pelekouda, E
Pidsley, C G L
Pinhorn, A
Piracha, A
Porter, A J
Rafique, A
Rau, U B N
Rauf, A
Reisner, C
Reynolds, T M
Roberts, A I
Roberts, I
Robinson, P N
Rockley, T J
Rose, L
Rushton, A M
Saleem, M
Saweirs, M W
Saweirs, W M
Scheel, T A
Seigel, J F

Sellens, K F
Sharkey, J
Sheldon, J W S
Sher, M
Shipman, J A J
Shore, I
Singanayagam, J
Skinner, H D
Smith, I B
Smith, K L
Spencer-Jones, J M
Spencer-Jones, R G
Spencer, N M
Srivastava, P C
Staley, F M
Stenhouse, C W
Stevenson, M P
Stokes, M J
Storey, N
Street, M N
Swaminathan, M
Tansey, J M
Taylor, J H
Taylor, W R
Thomas, D M
Thompson, A C
Tombs, D G
Trelinski, M J
Vickers, W J
Waddy, E M
Walker, N L
Wallace, M E
Watmough, D
Webb, C A
Wellstood-Eason, M J H
White, J A
White, J C
Whitney, J D W
Why, H J F
Wilkin, L M
Wilkin, W M
Willis, A C
Winchurch, S R
Winsnes, P F
Worstmann, T
Young, M A
Zamir, R J
Zargar, B A

Bury

Adamson, C L
Ahmed, S
Al-Nashi, M E
Anjum, I A
Apte, S R
Ashraf, S
Baig, M K
Baig, S
Bansal, A
Bashir, A A
Best, C T
Beveridge, A J
Bhalla, K
Bhalla, P
Bhatt, G S
Bhatt, G K
Bhatt, P R
Bowers, S L
Bradburn, J C
Bradbury, S L
Brammer, C G
Brandrick, J T
Brewood, A F M
Brigg, D J
Britton, C A
Buchanan, M J
Bugg, G
Burt, J H
Butt, K S
Cade, M S
Chidambaram, V
Chui Yew Cheong, C Y
Cleary, P M
Clough, R K
Cole, D R
Contractor, N
Cornmell, C A
Cotton, J L
Cumarasamy, K
Danson, J A
Dark, P M
Dawson, N J
De Sousa, B A
De Sousa, E L
De Vial, S R
Deakin, H
Demetriou, A

Devlin, J C
Dewar, N
Dockrell, J C
Doyle, J
Duce, C L
Duggan, D R
Duthie, J S
Dutt, S
El-Malek, E A A
Ellison, M F
Eltoft, M E
Evans, S A
Finnegan, M J
Fletcher, D P
Fletcher, K L
Fletcher, P F
Fraser, J P
Frassek, B
Freschini, D L
Gadiyar, V
Garg, N
Garson, P A R
Gormally, J
Gosall, G S
Grey, M R
Hammonds, G
Hampson, J R
Haraz, M H B A
Harbottle, J A
Harris, D E
Harvey, G C
Hashemi, M Z
Haworth, K S
Hayden, J
Herd, M E
Higgins, A P
Hill, A D
Holly, H J
Hough, M
Hudson, P C
Hughes, R D
Hurst, J R
Iqbal, P K
Jackson, J C
Jackson, P A
Jenkins, S A P
Joseph, N
Kan, Y-M
Karwowski, I S
Khan, A M
Khan, M
Kirby, D P J
Kirkham, S K
Kotak, P K
Kroll, L
Kyffin, D N
Lal, D P S S
Lal, S
Lam, W K
Leahy, M M P
Lippett, S C
Livingstone, J
Livsey, J E
Lo, S V
Loomba, B K
Lyons, A J
McCurdie, M J
McGivney, R C V
McGowan, A K
MacKechnie, D W M
Mackinnon, A S R
Mackinnon, G
Mamoowala, H E
Martin, N J C
Martinez Hernandez, A
Mattison, M L
Maudsley, I S
Mirza, S R
Molyneaux, A M
Mottershead, B
Mukherji, D K
Mulvey, P
Mutucumarana, C S
Narendran, R
Neininger, P D R
Norman, P R
North, P J
O'Callaghan, K M
O'Connor, F
O'Regan, J M M
Oates, B C
Opitz, E
Paris, J A G
Parton, A B
Pearson, K W
Phillips, B S
Pressler, J M
Rolli, M-J
Russell, A J

Saab, M
Sanchez Del Aguila, M J
Sarkar, D
Sarkar, S K
Savage, M W
Seigleman, M
Sethi, P
Shekar, C
Siegler, S A
Sims, A J
Sinha, S K
Sinniah, A R
Smith, A C
Smith, S M
Sopher, B J
Standing, P A
Stokes, R A
Stone, F
Stoner, J M
Subbiah, S
Sullivan, A L
Summers, E M
Sumner, A H
Tan, G D
Thaker, K K
Thornton, S J
Tolan, E L
Turck, W P G
Vijayakumar, S
Wadhwa, V K
Wake, C R
Wakefield, R M
Watts, J P
Wheater, A W
Wilson, D C
Wood, E
Woodcock, P J
Ziko, A A O

Bury St Edmunds

Abu-Haneeffa, M
Adams, C N
Adams, P J
Alam, N A
Arjani, K A
Astall, E C
August, A C
Aung, T T
Bannon, R P
Barabas, A
Barnet-Lamb, M
Bedford, A F
Bedford, M A
Biedrzycki, T
Bird, O J
Blunt, M C
Booth, S A
Boothby, C B
Bower, E L
Bowling, P I V
Boys, J E
Bracegirdle, J
Bradford, H W
Bradley, R K
Brain, A R
Brereton-Smith, G
Broadhurst, A D
Brookes, M T
Brown, S M
Bruton, J A
Burgess, J
Burns, A M
Cannon, J C
Cantlay, J S
Chow, A E
Clark, J D A
Clelland, C A
Clibbon, J J
Coles, R E A
Cooledge, J S
Cooledge, R C
Cooper, C B
Crickmore, C T
Danckwerts, R E
Darley, J S
Darrah, E R A
Davies, J A
Dean, P R
Dean, R S
Dodds, E J A
Dring, C M
Drummond, R C
Dunne, C T P
Edgar, P C
Edwards, S K
Evans, I E L
Evans, I E
Evans, P R

Fasler, J J
Field, J M
Finn, P J
Finn, P S
Foord, R D
Gardiner, M F
Gibson, J E
Giles, C E
Giles, R W H
Godwin, R J
Goldby, F S
Gove, J R W
Grace, K R
Grace, T
Graham, H M
Green, C R H
Greener, J S
Greener, W A
Grove, L M
Guard, B C
Gull, S E
Guy, J M
Hadley, P A
Haider, Z S
Hall, J D
Hamshere, R J
Handfield-Jones, S E
Harben, P R
Harpur, N C W
Harrison, P D
Harston, A P B
Hart, C D
Haslewood, S M
Hayden, M J
Herron, D M
Heywood, L J
Hickson, L P
Hobby, L J L
Hodgson, C C
Hopkinson, G P
Hughes Hallett, I
Hutton, R A
Jackson, J M
Jones, R C
Jordan, K
Kasbarian, A
Keeling, N J
Kelvin, G
Kennedy, C L
Kerrigan, G N W
Kilner, P B
King, B J
Knowles, J E A
Lamb, R J
Lambert, E L
Langford, R A
Lee Pek Yuk, G
Lewis, G M
Lister, R
Little, W R
Livermore, A L
Lockyer, M J
Lowe, S S
Mabin, D C
McBrien, M P
Mackenzie, K M
McLoughlin, J
Main, B J
Maitland, B W
Majeed, J F
Mangnall, R
Martin, M M R
Martin, S C
Mason, A M
Mason, A
Mason, J R
Masters, J E
Matheson, K H
Mauger, J S
May, S A
Mayer, C N
Merry, G P
Mistry, M K
Moffat, J R
Moody, A M
Motha, J T
Mumford, J W
Newell, J R L W
Nicholls, A
Nicolson, A
Nikam, D B
Noble-Jamieson, C M
Nutten, H E
O'Brien, P W
O'Flynn, R R
O'Reilly, D T
Odegaard, E R
Oliver, S F
Othman, W M

Bushey

Pearson, D A
Penfold, N W
Pereira, J F
Pigott, H W S
Porteous, M J L F
Prigg, N J
Rai, K
Raton Lunn, S M
Recaldin, S
Rees, D A
Reynolds, G A
Riddick, A C P
Rix, G H
Robinson, R C
Robling, S-A
Russell, A J
Russell, L K
Rutherford, J
Rycroft, N E
Sach, M
Sauvage, A D P
Sawyer, R J
Scott, A P
Scott, H M
Scott, R E
Sengupta, A
Sharpe, C E
Siklos, P W L
Sjolin, S U
Slade, J M
Slade, J M
Slattery, Z T
Smith, C
Smith, R M L
Soper, R H
Spencer, P J
Stroud, D S
Tasker, W J
Taylor, K C G
Teo, H S
Thompson, A M S
Thompson, J B
Thompson, M G
Tolland, E M
Urquhart, J C
Van Den Brul, P J
Vassilas, C A
Wade, R V
Wallace, E C
Ware, A W
Waters, F S
Watkins, P H
Watson, D H
Watson, L J
Webb, T E
West, R J
Wignall, O J
Wilkins, M L
Williams, T M
Wilson, C S
Wilson, H M
Winton, F E
Wootton, J C
Yeatman, A

Bushey

Crowlesmith, J D
Fennelly, M E
Wood, S A

Bushmills

Dunlop, M L
Kinley, J G
Nicholl, B
Wee, S-C

Buxton

Astill, P H
Barrett, P D
Best, E A
Beswick, I P
Blakey, K
Blomfield, S J W
Bradbury, E M
Brandreth, A R
Bridge, A L
Briggs, A P
Campbell, P J
Collier, A J
Cox, P J
Culshaw, J A
Culshaw, M C
Doig, C M
Edwards, A J
Fitzsimmons, C R
Graham, S M
Haddon, J
Hallam, C A
Hardman, M
Hardman, S F

Harry, J D
Hartley, A W
Hockenhull, C H
Hollick, J R
Howell, N J
Jones, R W
Kay, S M
Kidd, H M
Kidd, M L
King, S F
Lunn, G R
Mark, C T
Patrick, A A
Pearson, L A
Reeves, D
Reynolds, M A
Sharpe, E A B
Short, P R D
Smallbone, D F
Stirling, R J
Sutcliffe, G R M
Swinhoe, D J
Weir, K M
Williams, B R
Willis, R G B
Wilson, A
Woods, S E
Worthington, P R

Caernarfon

Bee, R W
Coates, W E
Crabtree, P G E
Davies, R H
Dyson, E
Ellis, G G
Ellis, T
Evans, G M
Evans, J G
Farquhar, G N
Griffiths, G
Gutting, P A
Holland, H T
Huws, N O
Jones, H W
Jones, J M
Jones, J S
Jones, K R
Jones, M W
Jones, O P
Jones, P
Jones, W A
Littlejohn, D I
Llwyd, E M
McCann, K
Morgan, J
Morgan, L G
Morgan, P R
Oddy, A V
Owen, M
Owen, M E
Owen, T J
Owens, G W
Parry-Jones, G
Parry, A L
Parry, E E
Parry, M I
Parry, R
Parry, W G W
Pierce, E W
Pritchard, D A R
Pritchard, M
Rees, K S
Roberts, D W
Roberts, H L
Roberts, S M
Roberts, W O
Stephens, P J
Thomas, M
Thompson, J C B
Tickle, E K
Warrell, D W
Watson, S J
Williams, A G
Williams, E
Williams, I P
Williams, R S
Williams, R W
Wynn-Jones, D
Yates, M G
Yates, S F

Caerphilly

Abou-Zeid, S M A-H
Ahmad, H B
Allan, D E
Anderson, R A
Bailey, D S
Bashar, N A

Bignall, J A
Chapman, M D
Chidgey, M A
Cox, C J C
Crossley, J W
Davies, D R
Davies, J M P
Davis, D H J
Doulah, M A U
El Garib, A E M H
Evans, S E
Ferguson, S D
Griffiths, M
Haldar, M S
Harney, P J
Harper, R J
Hourihan, B M
James, N M
Jayawickrama, N S
Jenkins, D
Jones, R
Lewis, J W
Morgan, P D
O'Dwyer, J S
Owen, P A
Pathak, P K
Penrose, G L
Reid, A
Roberts, C J
Salam, S
Shannon, J L
Stout, T V
Thevathasan, M
Thomas, E W
Thomas, J P D
Thomas, J
Tudor, G R
Turner, R G
Watson, H P
Watt, A

Caerswys

Green, M W
Howell, T M
Smith, S M L B
Wallbank, G R

Cairndow

Basu, T K
Borland, P M J
Craik, J E
Kilpatrick, R J
MacLean, M
Peel, F C
Thomson, W S T

Caithness

Muirhead, D G

Caledon

Oliver, A

Calise

Macdonald, C E

Callander

Gibson, I M
Mathewson, K G
Scott, R M
Strang, G D M

Callender

Baillie-Hamilton, P F
Barron, C M
Finlay, H H M
Malone, D
Scott, A M-L
Strang, C D
Watkins, O
Wilson, J S

Callington

Bartram, J W
Chaplin, S
Payne, J A
Steggles, B G
Thomas, O M
Warren, E J
Williams, R G

Calne

Beale, N R
Bishop, D S
Clarke, B P
Dilley, J C
Gough, S L
Hatherley, C C A
Kirkbride, A
Lawson, P R
Lawson, R P
Leach, R M C
Lovell, A G

Money-Kyrle, R S
Pritchard, S A
Sandford-Hill, A M
Searle, M A
Sharp, O P
Stalker, D J
Taudevin, E J
Thornton, A S

Calstock

Bowie, A N
Fitzgerald, M B

Camberley

Al-Khalaf, S S I
Al-Rawaf, S A A
Allen, G M
Allera, D
Alston, W C
Alton, P A
Andrew, J H
Andrews, D M
Anis, M A I
Ashbrooke, A B
Attenborough, J
Bajwa, N P S
Bala, K
Baligh, H M A
Bancroft, D G
Barker, S E
Barnes, R M
Barrie, E
Bartlett, C I S
Bernstein, S
Beynon, D W G
Blackman, R H
Booth, B P
Bown, R L
Boyd, M J
Briant, E R
Brinklow, K A
Brown, K J
Buchan, R N M
Buchanan, P L
Chakrabarti, G N
Chissell, H R
Chiswell, R J
Cockburn, J E
Collinson, J R
Cook, R J
Corbet Burcher, E A
Coulson, M L
Coulter, S A
Crichton, D G
Cumberland, N S
Cureton, P C
Cureton, R E
Davidson, J A
Davies, M H
De Ferrars, R J M
Debrah, K M
Dempster, D W
Denham, P L
Denton, S E
Dias, D R C
Divan, A M
Dohne, S F
Donovan, B
Drever, I R
Drury, R R
El Mahallawy, M H A A
Embling, K F
Evans, K M
Fabricius, P J
Ferguson, B M
Fernando, D S
Fisher, M G P
Freshwater, D A
Galbraith, S N
Garai, O F
Garber, S A
Gibb, A D
Gill, M E C
Goddard, G F
Gordon, E
Govind, A
Grady, K B
Graham, S J
Green, A D
Griffiths, M F P
Gudgeon, A M
Hadley, N S
Hague, N J
Hall, J R W
Harris, J R
Hashim, A A A
Hassan, G A E-S M
Hawley, A

Hawthorne, M E
Hay, J I
Hearn, D L
Hearn, F J
Hey, G B
Hinton, R M
Hoad, N A
Hodgetts, T J
Hogben, R K F
Holdbrook-Smith, H A
Holden, C E A
Holgate, J A
Holliman, S M
Holmes-Smith, J G
Howard, F M
Hull, J B
Humphreys, D M
Ineson, N
Ingram, R K
Jakeman, R D
Jennings, C S
Jewitt, J A L
Jolliffe, D S
Jonathan, D A
Jones, S R
Joshi, P
Kabir, Y A E-M
Keightley, A M
King, S J
Knight, R K
Kumar, R
Lal, A B
Leopold, P W
Lewis, J
Lothe, K J
Loucas, K
Lowes, T
Lucas, M A
Lyon Dean, C W
McClenahan, A F
McCombe, A W
Mayall, M N A
Millar, W S
Montgomery, B S I
Moorthy, B
Mundy, K I
Murrow, J N
Nadarajah, R
Naerger, H G A
Neill, F E
Nethercliffe, J M-S
Nicol, E R M
Niemiro, L A K
Noyelle, R M
O'Leary, D A
O'Sullivan, D P D
Oliver, P J R
Ooi, R G B
Orr, J E K
Ottley, V R
Paley, M R
Papp, M
Patel, U S
Paterson, I M
Paton, D S
Peers, L
Pike, J M
Pinder, D C
Porter, A M W
Porter, C J
Price, B A
Pugh, P J
Rahman, M K A
Rawle, P R
Raymond-Jones, J G
Reilly, P A J
Renbourn, E T
Restall, J
Roberts, G D
Roberts, P
Robinson, G M
Roche, N A
Rust, N E
Rutherford, J
Simpson, R G
Singh, S
Sleator, D J D
Smart, P C
Smith, C E T
Sreenivasa Rao, P M
Starr, R L
Strudley, M R
Sukumaran Nair, P K
Sukumaran Nair, S
Tandon, M K
Tanner, C C
Teale, T E
Teasdale, D H
Tettenborn, M A

Ticehurst, A C
Tiller, G
Tong, J L
Toplis, P J
Trippe, H R
Uheba, M A
Upadhyay, A K
Van De Pette, J E W
Waine, J M
Wang, T W-M
White, I L
Williams, A N
Yates, M J

Camborne

Agnew, A N D
Ahling-Smith, H E M
Barton, S R
Bergin, J R
Blake, I D
Brooks, J W
Cheetham, P
Collins, W E
Cotton, S A
Crellin, D W
Dowling, K A
Emberton, A
Harvey, R A
Hawker, L B
Henderson, K J
Hindley, J A
Hughesdon, A G
Keech, T P
Lay, E T
McCabe, C R
MacDonald, K E
Perkins, P J
Relf, C M
Thomas, J E
Whiting, S L

Cambridge

Abad Alejandre, J
Abrahams, M J
Abrahams, P H
Acerinl, C L
Addison, P D
Addo, S E
Adey, E M
Adlam, D M
Adlam, S A
Ah-See, S-Y W
Ahluwalia, J S
Aiken, C G A
Airey, M S
Akagbosu, L C
Alderson, M L
Alderson, T S J
Alexander, G J M
Alexander, S J C
Allen, C M C
Allen, L E
Allison, M E D
Amure, B O
Anderson, C H
Anderson, J B
Anderson, J R
Anderson, J M
Anderson, J C
Anderson, M R
Anderson, S L
Andreasen, M-J
Andrews, M J D
Aparicio, S A J R
Appleton, D S
Appleyard, W J
Aravot, D J
Arends, M J
Arno, J
Arrowsmith, J E
Arscott, J
Ashurst, N J
Atkinson, J N C
Attwood, C M
Backhouse, H L
Badcock, D J
Baglin, T P
Bailey, A R
Bailey, P A
Baldwin, E C
Baldwin, P J W
Ball, S J A
Ballance, G A
Ballantine, D M
Bangham, R B
Bankes-Page
Chapman, C A
Baralle, D

Cambridge

Barber, D T C
Barclay, K E
Barclay, S I G
Barnard, M J
Barnard, S A
Barnes, J L C
Barnes, R J
Barratt, A J
Bartlett, D W
Bass, S P
Bastable, R B
Bateman, A M
Bateman, P J
Batstone, G R D
Battersby, A J
Bavalia, K
Baxter, P J
Baynes, K C R
Bearcroft, P W P
Beardsall, K
Beattie, S L
Beatty, C
Behr, S B
Bell, D
Bell, I F
Bell, M A C
Bennett, A M D
Bennett, A C
Bennett, C M
Benson, J A
Benson, J R
Bentham, P W
Bentley, S
Berrios, G E
Bertram, R C R
Bettinson, H V
Bhojani, J P
Biggs, J S G
Bilton, D
Birch, M C
Birdi, I
Birks, E I
Birks, K A
Birtwistle, S
Bisset, J A
Blaine, F
Blandford, N S
Bleehen, N M
Bobrow, L G
Bobrow, M
Boissard, J M
Bolland, J L M
Bolton, P F
Boniface, S J
Booth, P M
Booth, S
Borer, E F
Bowman, R J C
Boyle, J J
Bradley, J A
Bradley, J R
Brain, A J L
Brant, J M
Brassett, C
Brayne, C E G
Brecknell, J E
Brennan, L
Brett, M
Brice, J H
Brieger, J E G
Brimblecombe, P R
Brinsden, P R
Britton, P D
Broadley, S A
Brodie, D A
Brodie, G D
Brook, C P B
Brook, S S
Brooks, E R
Brown, A I P
Brown, C K
Brown, C H
Brown, D L
Brown, I
Brown, M J
Brown, N M
Browning, C J
Buchan, I E
Budd, E O
Bufton, K E
Bullmore, E T
Bullock, K N
Bunn, R G
Burgen, A S V
Burnet, N G
Burnford, R P
Burrell, C G
Burrows, N P
Burton, G J
Burton, M H
Butcher, A
Butler, A J
Butterworth, J L
Buttery, P C
Cahir, J G
Calder, I M
Calladine, M R H
Calloway, S P
Calne, R Y
Camilleri-Ferrante, C
Campbell-Hewson, G L
Campbell, D I
Campbell, G A
Campbell, H M
Carmichael, A J
Carmichael, J
Carne, C A
Carrell, R W
Carrell, T W G
Carroll, N R
Cary, N R B
Cassidy, A D
Cawdry, N G I
Chacko, B G
Challen, A D
Chaloner, A B
Champion, R H
Chan Lee Gaik, Dr
Chang, D
Chaouat, A
Chatterjee, V K K
Cheney, G T
Cheriyan, J
Chester, G H
Chester, S C
Chesworth, T J
Chilvers, E R
Ching, H S
Chippindale, R M
Choksy, S A
Christley, H M
Chua, V W T
Church, R B
Clark, A T
Clark, D H
Clements, A L
Coates, O A
Cocheme, M A X
Coleman, N
Coles, A J
Coles, C E
Coles, J P
Collins, V P
Compston, J E
Condliffe, A M
Conlan, D P
Connolly, D L
Conochie, B C
Constant, C R
Cooper, C M
Cooper, J
Corbett, M F
Corbett, M J
Corkery, F M
Cormack, G C
Cornish, F E
Corrie, P G
Corston, P B
Cosgrove, M P
Coulden, R A R
Cowley, H C
Cox-Maksimov, D C T
Cox, E J C
Cox, T M
Cozzi, E
Craig, J I O
Craigen, A A
Crawford, I E M
Crawford, L M
Crawford, R A F
Cressey, P F
Crisp, A J
Crosbie, A D
Crosse, J O
Croucher, P E
Culank, L S
Cullum, S-J
Cummings, G E
Currie, J
Cutler, G M
D'Amore, A
Dalton, K J
Daly, M M
Dandy, D J
Dansie, A R
Darnborough, J
Davey, P P
Davies, R G
Davies, T W
Davison, B C C
Davy, D M
Dawnay, N A H
Dawson, I H P
De Lacey, P A
De Vries, P J
Dean, J H
Deans, C L
Debenham, P J
Dening, T R
Denman, F M C
Dennis, C M
Desselberger, U
Dickson, L S
Diston, C F
Dixon, A K
Dixon, C M
Dixon, J M
Dodsworth, H
Doherty, C B
Dolan, A L
Donagh, A C
Donovan, D H
Dourish, M P
Dowson, J H
Doyle, P W
Drake, B J
Draper, J
Duff, C H
Duncan, G D
Dunning, J J
Dyce, J M
Earl, H M
East, M M
Eaton, S M
Eckstein, P A
Edgar, A C D
Edwards, D J
Edwards, O M
Edwards, S G M
El Tahir, E F M M
Elder, C T
Elliott, M L
Elliott, R W
Ellis, P D M
Elton, N H
Emberson, C
Emerson, D
Emerson, M S
English, M C
English, T A H
Evans, C A
Evans, G
Evans, K A
Evans, P M
Everett, A A
Everett, W G
Ewan, P W
Exley, A R
Falk Van Rooyen, I
Farmer, J
Farnell, J E
Farquhar-Smith, W P
Farrant, C G C
Farrington, M
Ferguson-Smith, M A
Fersht, N L
Fertig, A
Ffrench-Constant, C K
Fingleton, P G
Firth, H V
Firth, J D
Fisher, A F
Fisher, P M
Fistein, E C
Fitzsimons, J T
Fleming, H A
Fleming, W R
Flinn, A J
Flint, J E
Flynn, P D
Foggensteiner, L
Fontana, A
Ford, E H R
Forsyth, D R
Foweraker, J E
Fox, G M
Francis, D P
Francis, J D
Francis, P E Q
Frayling, I M
Freeman, A H
Freeman, R A V
Friend, J H
Froggett, S M
Fynes, M M
Gair, R W
Gaitonde, E J L
Galbraith, N S
Galbraith, P S
Gandhi, M K
Gandy, G M
Gant, R M
Gardner, R
Gardner, T D
Garlick, G G
Gaston, C M
Gaston, J S H
Gelson, A D N
Georgiou, T
Gibbs, P
Gibson, T
Gidwani, F N
Gilbert, L K
Gilder, F J
Giles, A P
Gillard, E S E
Gillard, J H
Gillham, M I
Gilligan, D
Gilmore, A M C
Gimson, A E S
Girling, D M
Glazebrook, C W
Gleave, J R W
Glover, D R
Glynn, I M
Godsiff, L S
Goh, S-G J
Goldbeck-Wood, S J
Goldsmith, P
Goodyer, I M
Gordon-Brown, J
Gordon, D N
Gould, J M
Grace, A A
Graeme-Barber, M
Graham, A J
Graham, J E
Grange, R V
Grant, C J
Grant, I
Grant, J W
Gray, R F
Gray, S J
Green, A R
Gregory, C A
Gresham, G A
Gresham, G M
Grey, P L
Griffin, D R
Griffin, S V
Griffin, S J
Griffith, F M
Griffiths, M E
Grimshaw, K M
Grounds, A T
Groves, A M
Grubb, H E S
Gunning, K E J
Gupta, A K
Gurnell, M
Gwynn, A M
Habib, S B
Habib, S E
Hackett, G A
Hagley, M
Hague, G C
Haigh, B
Haigh, E
Hales, C N
Hall, B I
Hall, N R
Halliday, S E
Hamdi, I A K M
Hamilton, D C
Harcombe, A A
Hardwick, R H
Hardy, C S
Hardy, D G
Hardy, I
Harper, J M
Harris, P A
Harrison, N G
Harrison, R L
Harrison, R J
Harten-Ash, V J
Hartley, L M
Hashim-Iqbal, H
Hassan, J
Hatfield, A D
Hatsiopoulou, O
Hawkins, T D
Haycock, P
Haydock, S F
Hayhoe, F G J
Hazleman, B L
Henderson, A
Herbert, J
Herrick, M J
Hewlett, J L
Hewlett, T G
Hickling, J B
Higgins, J N P
Hignett, C L
Hill, D J
Hill, D A
Himsworth, R L
Hirschfield, G M
Hitchcock, C T
Ho, L W
Hobbiger, S F
Hobby, J L
Hodges, J R
Hodgson, O E F
Hogg, N J
Holland, A J
Holland, C M
Hollings, A H
Holme, P
Holmes, A E
Holmes, J R
Holmes, S M
Hopkins-Jones, D G
Horn, G
Horn, N M A
Howell, J E
Huang, C L-H
Hubbard, S C M A
Huber, M J E
Hugh-Jones, M C
Hughes, D R
Hughes, I A
Hughes, M
Hughes, V C
Humphreys, A J
Hung, C T
Hunt, C R
Hunt, N J
Hunt, T J
Huntbach, J A
Hunter, J O
Hussey, A S
Hutchinson, H C
Hutchinson, P J A
Hyde, J B
Hymas, N F S
Iles, R W
Iregbulem, L M
Irwin, M S
Isherwood, D L
Jackson, J M C
Jackson, R S
Jaffa, A J
James, B
James, C J
James, D C
Jamieson, N V
Jamieson, V L
Jandziol, A K
Jayawardena, B
Jayne, D R W
Jenkins, D P
Jenkins, Y C
Jenks, C E
Jessop, F A
Johnstone, K I
Johnstone, R D
Jones, D H
Jones, J G
Jones, L M
Jones, P B
Jones, R M
Jones, S E
Jorgensen, T A
Josse, J D
Kaloo, P D
Karet, F E
Keast-Butler, J
Keene, G S
Kellow, N H
Kelsall, A W R
Kelvin, R G
Kennedy, D J
Kenney, C G
Kent, C J
Kett-White, C E R
Kettle, M A
Keynes, R J
Keynes, W M
Khan, J
Khaw, K-T
Kidd, S B
King, A J
King, A
King, D K
King, M S
Kingsley Pillers, E M
Kingsley, N A
Kinmonth, A-L
Kirker, S G B
Kirkpatrick, P J
Kirollos, R W M
Klein, J R
Klinck, J R
Knapton, P M
Kneeshaw, J D
Kodicek, J H
Kok, A
Kuczynska, A-M E J
Kuczynska, M J
Kuczynski, A
Kumararatne, D S
Lachmann, H J
Lachmann, P J
Lachmann, R H
Lachmann, S M
Lai, R Y K
Laing, R J C
Lalli, C A
Lam, R W F
Lamb, W T
Lamberty, B G H
Lamberty, F
Lane, S
Lannes, B
Large, S R
Latcham, F
Latcham, R W
Latimer, M D
Latimer, P R
Lattimore, C R
Lawson, C R
Lawton, C A
Lee, T S
Leeder, P C
Leggatt, V J
Lennox, G G
Lessan, N G
Lever, A M L
Levick, M P
Levine, G
Lewis, E J
Lewis, G A
Lillicrap, M S
Lindop, M J
Linehan, G M
Lockett, G A
Loke, Y W
Lomas, D A
Lomas, D J
Lomas, J A
Lomas, P E S
London, M
Lovett, E
Lowe, D I
Lowe, M D
Lucas, S J
Ludlam, H A
Lum, L C
Lyon, A R
Macartney, F J
McCabe, J A
McClure, R J
McConachie, C F J
McDonald, C J
MacDougall, M J
McDougall, S M
Macfarlane, M P
Macfarlane, R
McGettigan, H C
MacGibbon, R
Machen, J M
McIntyre, K E
McIntyre, K R
Mackay, J
McKay, J M
Mackay, J H
McKee, T A
McKenna, P J
McKenna, P J
McKeown, J M I
McLean, A C J
McNaughton, E L
Macrae, A D
Mahaffey, A M
Maibaum, A
Maimaris, C V
Malekottodjary, N M
Males, A G
Males, R
Malik, S N
Mallet, C M
Mallet, M L
Maloney, E J E

Camelford

Mantle, M
Marcus, N K K
Marcus, R E
Marcus, S F
Marks, J
Marriott, R M
Marsden, D P
Marshall, A E
Martin, K J
Martin, P J
Masina, M H
Matheson, L A
Mathews, T
Matthews, C H
Matthews, C J
Matthewson, M H
Meggitt, B F
Meldrum, D J
Menon, D K
Merchant, E B N
Merricks, M J
Meyer, P A R
Middleton, S J
Miles, B J
Millar, A J W
Miller, R
Mills, A J D
Mills, D J O
Mills, I H
Milne, K
Milstein, B B
Milton, P J D
Minhas, P S
Minshull-Beech, C S
Minto, C L
Mitchell, A J
Mitchell, A L
Mitchell, A U
Mitchell, J N
Mitchinson, M J
Moffat, D A
Moffatt, J L
Mole, J R
Monahan, E B
Moore, A T
Morgan, R H
Morris, P J
Morris, S A
Moseley, R P
Muller, D J
Mulroy, S E
Munglani, R
Murphy, P J
Nagington, J
Naima, S J
Namasivaym, S
Nashef, S A-M
Nasser, S M S
Navaratnam, V
Negrette, J L
Neill, A-M
Nelson, P D
Newell, J P
Newman, D K
Newport, M J
Newsom, S W B
Newton, P J
Ng, C S
Nicholl, C G
Nicholson, J C
NiemcZuk, P
Ninkovic, M
Nkonge, F M K S
Norris, P G
Nussey, A P
Nutbourne, P A
Nyman, J A
O'Donnell, E A
O'Donnell, D R
O'Donovan, D G
O'Leary, D A
O'Rahilly, S P
O'Reilly, A J
O'Shaughnessy, K M
O'Sullivan, D M
Oakeshott, S
Obey, P A
Oduro-Dominah, A
Offen, D N
Ogg, T W
Ogilvie, A D
Ogilvy-Stuart, A L
Oh, V M-S
Okhai, M F
Oliver, H W L
Oram, S B
Orton, W T
Osborn, C
Ostenfeld, T

Ovington, N R
Owen, T M
Owens, J
Paddison, D J
Paine, D S
Panegyres, P K
Parameshwar, K J
Parish, C
Park, G R
Park, R J
Parker, A P J
Parker, I R
Parkin, I G
Parkinnen, S A
Parkinson, E J
Parkyn, J
Parry, A J
Parry, M W
Parums, D V
Patel, H C
Patel, J S
Patel, K J
Patient, C J
Paw, H G W
Pawley, J J
Paxton, P J
Paykel, E S
Pencheon, D C
Pepke-Zaba, J W
Peppiatt, T N
Perera, S D
Perrett, A G
Perrin, V L
Perry, J R
Petch, M C
Peters, A M
Peters, D K
Petrie, G M
Petrie, K
Petter, J R
Pharoah, F M
Pharoah, P D P
Philipson, R S
Phillips, J
Pickard, J D
Picken, S
Pименidis, D
Pinnington, J
Polack, C
Polkinhorn, M E
Ponder, B A J
Poole, S B
Popham, P A B
Powell, J F
Power, D M
Powles, J W
Praseedom, R K
Prentice, A
Pullen, B W
Pulvertaft, R W
Purr, J M
Purushotham, A D
Pye, M J
Pye, R J
Rabey, G P
Ralevic, D
Ranasinghe, R S
Ranasinghe, W A E P
Randall, T M K
Rankin, A
Rankin, J
Rankin, N E
Rann, S F
Rao, G S
Rashbass, J L
Ravichandran, D
Ray, J L
Raymond, F L
Reacher, M H
Reader, J G
Reading, J M
Redfern, C E
Redwood, M D
Reed, M G P
Reed, N J H
Rees, J K H
Reid, E A L
Reiss, H E
Richards, D A
Richards, S D
Ridsdill Smith, G P
Ridsdill-Smith, W P
Rigg, E L
Rigg, K J
Ritchie, A J
Roberts, C P
Roberts, D S
Roberts, G E
Roberts, J S C

Roberts, J T
Roberts, M T M
Roberts, S O B
Robinson, A H N
Robinson, F M
Robinson, R E
Robinson, S M
Robson, J M
Roe, P G
Roper, G P
Roscoe, J D
Rose, H F
Ross Russell, R I
Rosser, A E
Roth, M
Rothwell, S E
Round, C E
Rowland, M G M
Rubenstein, D
Rubery, E D
Rubinsztein, J S
Rudd, J H F
Ruddock, J M
Rudenski, A S
Ruel, A H
Rushton, N
Rushton, R J
Rushton, S M
Russell, S J
Saich, A J
Sale, J E
Salisbury, R S
Salmon, R P
Sanders, C R
Sandford, R N
Sansome, A D
Sapsford, D J
Sarkies, N J C
Sartori, P C E
Satchithananda, D K
Saumarez, R C
Sawcer, S J
Sayeed, R A
Scadeng, M
Schiebaan, E
Schoeman, J
Schramm, C J
Scolding, N J
Scott, J D
Scott, P M
Scully, R
Seaman, M J
Seed, M J
Selzer, G H
Sepe, V
Set, P A K
Shapiro, L M
Shaw, R W
Sheard, R M
Sheares, K K K
Sheldrick, J H
Shepherd, B C
Shepherd, J S
Sherriff, H M
Sherwood, T
Shneerson, A
Shneerson, J M
Short, M B
Sills, O A
Silverman, B H
Silverman, J D
Simpson, R M
Sinha, N
Sinha, S
Sinnatamby, R
Sissons, J G P
Smailes, C M
Smellie, A S
Smellie, W A B
Smith, A D
Smith, F G
Smith, G C S
Smith, I E
Smith, S K
Smith, T A
Snead, M P
Socolovsky, M
Soh, V A L
Soilleux, E J
Somers Heslam, J
Sonnex, C
Soo, K G
Spooner, V J
Staunton, R M
Stebbing, B
Steed, S S
Stein, P E
Stephens, C J
Stephenson, C M E

Sterling, J C
Stevens, J F
Stewart, A J
Stewart, S
Stone, D L
Stovin, P G I
Stovin, S E
Stumbles, D E
Sturges, M
Subramaniam, S D
Sule, B A
Summers, I M R
Suter, C M
Swami, A B
Tai, C-C
Tan, L T
Tan, M W L
Tangney, A-M
Tasker, A D
Tasker, R C
Tate, P A
Tavare, S M
Tayabali, M
Taylor, A J
Taylor, C E D
Taylor, C H
Taylor, I
Taylor, L K
Tempest, H V
Terlevich, A
Tewson, P J
Thirunavukkarasu, S
Thomas, C M
Thomas, G J
Tidswell, A T
Tiley, C G
Toase, P D
Tobin, G B
Todd, P M
Tolley, M E
Toms, A P
Toogood, C M
Tooze, R M
Torpey, N P
Townsend, K C
Towriss, M H
Traub, M M
Treip, C S
Trump, D
Tsui, S S L
Tuckfield, C J
Tudor, J
Turner, J M
Turner, M W H
Turner, P S
Tweedale, J L
Upjohn, A C
Upjohn, G M
Vaishnaw, A K
Valente, J E
Vallance-Owen, J
Varty, K
Verghese, R
Verity, C M
Verney, G I
Vickers, D W
Villagran Moreno, J M
Villar, R N
Wada, I
Wade, J D
Wagstaff, A E
Walker, M A
Walker, N A
Wallace, B A
Wallwork, J
Walsh, C M
Walter, C J S
Walton, J D
Warburton, E A
Ward, M
Wareham, N J
Warren, A J
Warren, A R
Warren, R M L
Waters, A
Waters, F H
Waters, J K
Waterworth, P D
Watsham, C M P
Watson, A B
Watson, M E C
Watson, P S
Watson, P G
Webster, S G P
Weissberg, A
Weissberg, P L
Welbourn, E
Welch, T P
Welham, K L

Wentworth, J M
Werno, A M
West, D J
Whale, R
Wharton, A J
Wheeler, T K
Wheeler, V A
White, C
Whitehead, A L
Whitehead, S H
Whitfield, J J
Whittle, E
Wight, D G D
Wight, N J D
Wight, W J
Wilkey, B R
Wilkins, A
Wilkinson, G
Wilkinson, I M S
Wilkinson, I B
Williams, D M
Williams, E D
Williams, G H
Williams, M P L
Williams, M V
Williamson, J R W G
Williamson, L M
Willocks, L J
Wilsdon, K F
Wilson-Nunn, D L
Wilson, A M
Wilson, H C
Wilson, J M
Wilson, K J
Wimhurst, J A
Winter, R J D
Wiseman, J R
Wishart, G C
Wishart, M O
Withers, E J
Wolff, C B
Wong, C C
Wong, O Y
Wong, S P Y
Woodford, S L
Woodrow, S L
Woods, S E
Wraight, S K
Wright, D R
Wright, G H
Wright, N L
Wyer, S R
Wyllie, A D H
Xuereb, J H
Yates, J R W
Yealland, S
Young, E H
Young, J C J
Young, J C
Youngs, G R
Zammit-Tabona, M V
Zimmern, R L

Camelford

Garrod, A C
Haddon, J E
Hrynaszkiewicz, A
Richardson, J P S
Rowe, A I

Campbeltown

Cook, K M
Elder, M R
Hall, M D
Hyndman, A M
Jackson, R N
Lazarus, M
Leask, J T S
Macaulay, F M
Macdonald, R W D
Rae, R M
Ropper, D N
Sommerville, R G
Wallace, A D

Cannock

Abdullah, A J J
Apta, R D
Ballinger, P M
Banerjee, N L
Berriman, T J
Chapman, P
Conmey, M M
Farr, D R
Gallimore, J R
Gibbins, S R
Hands, S J
Holbrook, J A P
Hulme, L V
McMorrow, J F P

Morgan-Hough, C V J
Murugan, M
Nicklin, S
Price, T
Saha, S K
Sainsbury, J A
Satchwell, V J
Sathia, P J
Sathia, P
Sathia, U
Selvam, A
Singh, P K
Sitther, B H
Speedie, C A
Thaker, P K
Thompson, A J
Threepuraneni, G
Verma, A
Warburton, A L
Williams, E J
Woo, M P

Canonbie

Baker, C D
Dearing, R M
Mann, P J
Rose, A J
Tinker, M D

Canterbury

Aaronricks, P J F
Abdool Raman, A C D
Ainslie, J A
Al-Hasani, M K A-K
Alhassan, S E-D A
Ananda Balendran, V
Andrew, N C
Andrewes, J F
Armstrong, H E
Ashman, E
Askwith, J H
Baines, A R
Baker, C D
Baker, C
Baker, G R C
Bamber, R W K
Barley, P E
Batty, G M
Baxter, J S R
Bayley, A C
Beaton, A
Beats, B C
Beaumont, A C
Biggs, P E
Black, J A
Black, M M
Black, M E
Blanco Davila, R
Bland, J D P
Bliss, S M G
Bobba, J R
Bodger, W A H
Bowen, E
Bradburn, B G
Brett, T J E
Broad, E A L
Broadley, J N
Brown, S A
Browne, N P
Burrowes, P W
Byrom, H
Byrom, K
Byrom, R G
Cameron, A
Carmichael, P
Carpenter, G I
Carter, A R
Caswell, S J
Cave, J D H
Cave, M A
Chatoor, R
Cheese, J A
Chowdhury, S R
Christie, B G B
Christodoulou, C C
Claridge, M
Cleobury, J F
Coakley, A J
Cocks, E M
Colchester, A C F
Collier, J
Collins, R E C
Coltart, R S
Cook, C C H
Coopamah, L D
Cornelius, P G
Crawford, K P E
Crawley, B E
Curtis, E W

Cardiff

Das, P K
Datta, D C
Davies, N W S
Davis, J M
De Cock, R
Di Biasio, N
Didehvar, R
Downes, M O
Dowse, S C
Drake, S R
Drouot, J E
Eaves, D L
Edwards, R S
Ellis, S B A
Entwisle, K G
Evans, J W H
Eve, M D
Farley, M D
Fegent, J A
Field, S
Flynn, M D
Foord, A L
Forbes, G B
Forsythe, J M
Freij, R M
Fullman, P M
Gable, D R
Garrett, C J
Garsed, M P
Gawler, T J
Gibson, A G
Goddard, K A
Goggin, M J
Goka, A K J
Gough, J H C
Greaves, D J
Greaves, S J
Grice, D J P
Hall, F M
Hamilton, A G
Harvey, M S
Heddle, R M
Heller, A J
Herraiz Morillas, R
Hettiarachchi, S P
Higgs, W S
Hildick-Smith, M
Hill, A
Hilliard, T N
Hoda, A W
Hodges, M R
Holbrook, B W
Horton-Szar, D A J
Housden, P L
Hughes, J A
Hughes, W L
Hussain, M F
Hussain, S A
Irwin, K Z
Jackson, D B
John, E B
Johnson, A J
Jones, D M
Jones, G L
Jordan, A C
Kalidindi, S
Kerr, J
Kinnersley, D S
Kittle, D J
Kurstjens, S P
Laing, R T R
Lamb, C J
Larkin, V J
Learner, J M
Lewin, K
Lilley, J
Little, S R C J
Livesey, P G
Lloyd-Roberts, R E
Lloyd, R J
Long, D R
Lorimer, J
Love, E R
Lythall, D A
McGibney, D
McIvor, J E M
Mackenzie, E C
Mackinnon, J C
Macklin, A V
Macklin, C P
McWilliams, R N
Mahapatra, P K
Manson, G
Maryosh, J A A
Matheson, P
Mikhail, A S I S
Milligan, M P
Milligan, P M
Mitchell, D B

Mithal, N P
Molony, M
Molony, P E
Morrison, I D
Moskovits, P E
Muller, A F
Muller, M A
Murray, K H A
Nash, I T
Nashef, L
Neales, K E
Newson, T P
Nichols, M J
Nicholson, J A B
Noble, T C
Norman, M H
Nosenzo, I
O'Sullivan, C C
Ogilvie, A C F
Oldreive, P D
Oliver, J L
Opdam, H I
Owen, A
Padgham, N D
Panahloo, H A
Panayides, S M
Panday, S
Parks, Y A
Pay, G V
Pay, J A
Peebles, J P
Peebles, R A
Plummer, W P
Potter, J M
Pratt, D G
Pritchard, J G
Proctor, E A
Prosser, D I
Puleston, J M
Rake, M O
Reed, F S
Rehling, G H
Richardson, H
Richardson, M H
Riddall, M W
Ridley, N M
Roberts, B K
Roberts, C I
Roberts, M W
Robertson, B R
Royston, R G
Saleh, M I
Salmon, C R
Sarkhel, R P
Sarkhel, S T
Sawitzky, C
Schlien, M
Shah, B A
Shaw, K A
Shere, S
Sigurdsson, R G
Simmonds, R
Smedley, H M
Smith, A M
Smith, A R
Snow, J T
Somer, K G R
Sorefan, O M A
Sprangemeyer, D
Spratley, T A
Srinivas, S
Starbuck, M J
Stevens, M R C
Stevens, P E
Stewart, R M
Stillman, K
Storrs, T J
Strange, F G S C
Sturgess, I
Sultana, S
Sykes, P H
Tamimi, N A M
Tasou, A
Thompson, J B C
Thurrell, W P
Townsend, J A
Turle, G C
Tyler, P A
Vernon, P L H
Walker, A E
Walkington, R P E
Warren, M D
Way, C F
Weatherley, A
Wells, J A
Wetherell, R G
Whiting, B H
Wickham, E A
Wijesurendra, C S

Wijesurendra, I T
Wilkins, P
Wilkinson, P A
Williams, B M
Williams, H J H
Williams, Y F S
Wilson, N V
Winter, J B M
Withrington, R H
Woodall, J T
Workman, I C E
Wright, M
Zintilis, S A

Canvey Island

Aslam, M
Aung, T D J
Ghauri, J B
Jena, R
Kanapathippillai, S
Levy, A J
Limage, S J
McCarthy, T J
Machacek, K A
Patel, D S
Patel, S H
Rahman, H U
Skeet, W A G
Sughra, G
Swami, P M
Tay Za Aung, Dr
Vavrecka, M J F
Wilson, L E

Cardiff

Abdel-Nabi, A G H A G
Abdullah, M F
Abel, J V
Abel, R J
Abideen, S
Abolade, B K
Abouharb, A T
Abusrewil, F M
Adams, H
Adams, M
Addicott, L S
Adisesh, L A
Adjepong, S E
Affley, B T
Aggarwal, O P
Ahmad, A B
Ahmad, S
Ajayi, B A
Al-Jader, L N
Al-Shirawi, A H
Al-Wafi, A A
Alberti Marono, J
Alcolado, J C
Aldridge, C R
Aleem, M
Ali, M S A H
Allanby, C W
Alldrick, M D
Allim, A S
Allouni, S
Amer, K M A
Amodeo, P A
Amso, N N J
Anand, V T
Anderson, D J W
Andrew, M
Andrews, J D
Anwar, A M G E
Ap Gwilym, E R M
Arana Galdos, M A
Archer, H L
Arif, M
Armstrong, T S H
Ashworth, D R
Atkins, S J
Attwood, S J
Aubrey, D A
Austin, T R
Aymat Torrente, A
Azzu, A A
Baban, V
Backer, H
Badminton, M N
Baghomian, A
Bagshaw, M J M
Baker, J H E
Baker, K L
Bako, A M
Ballard, C G
Barber, M A
Barlow, N H
Barnes, R A
Barr, C S

Barr, S M
Barr, V J
Barrett-Lee, P J
Barrett, I T
Barry, A J
Barry, B W
Barry, J E S
Barry, J D
Barton, D M
Basheer, A
Batt, M C
Baynham, P R W
Beattie, R B
Bebbington, A
Beck, M
Beck, P
Bedwani, S J
Bellamy, R J
Benedict, C
Bennett, A J
Bensusan, D
Bentley, D P
Bentley, R P
Bentley, R P
Benton, I J
Benzimra, R E
Bevan, M A
Bhal, P S
Bhogal, J
Bibi, R B
Billing, V C
Bisson, J I
Black, J J A
Blackman, D J
Bleasdale, A M S
Bleasdale, R A
Bleehen, R E
Bloomfield, M C
Blower, A C
Bodger, J N
Bongilli, J S
Borysiewicz, L K
Bose, P
Bowen, D R
Bowen, R G
Bragg, E A
Braithwaite, P A
Bratton, M L
Breckenridge, I M
Brew, E F M
Brewster, A E
Brooks, R M
Broughton, J M
Broughton, R B K
Broughton, S F
Brown, E S
Brown, H M
Brown, I M
Brown, N K
Brown, N J
Browning, M R
Buchan, K G
Bufton, H J S
Bullen, K R
Bunce, N H
Burnett, A K
Burr, M L
Burrell, C C
Burrell, C D
Burt, G A
Burt, R M
Burwell, D R
Bustam, A Z
Butchart, E G
Butler, C C
Butler, J L
Byron, M G
Cadman, D A
Cairns, H
Callaghan, A L
Callaghan, R R
Callen, N R
Camara Xardone, P M
Cameron, I R
Camilleri, J P
Cantor, R
Capstick, M E L
Cardno, A G
Carr, K Z T
Carter, K M
Carter, R L
Cartlidge, P H T
Casali, G
Casey, R C E
Chakravarty, R D
Chan, W I
Chandrani, R
Chang Chau-Lap, C
Chant, D J

Chapman, J A
Charles, H M J
Chaudhary, S N
Chaudhry, W N
Chawla, J C
Cheang, P P
Chellaram
Hathiramani, K G
Chen, S C J
Chin, S S
Chivers, M E
Chowdhury, M M U-H
Chowdhury, M R
Chubb, H L
Chubb, L V
Chung, T Y
Ciampolini, I
Clark, G S
Clark, M H
Clarke, A J
Clarke, A J
Cline, W
Clyburn, P A
Cochlin, D L
Cockcroft, J R
Cocks, D W N
Coekin, S E
Cohen, S S
Cole, K E
Coleman, S P
Coles, E C
Coles, G A
Coles, P F
Colgate, R E T
Collier, G M
Collins, P D
Collins, P W
Collis, R E
Conboy, V B L
Conlon, F V
Conroy, M C
Contractor, N K
Cook, D S
Cook, E A
Cooke, B E D
Cooper, A M
Cooper, O
Corbett, J
Corcoran, E
Cotter, M
Courtney, E M
Coutts, W E
Cox, D A
Coyle, E F
Craig, B R
Craigmyle, M B L
Crane, J A
Creaby, M M
Creese, K H
Creighton Griffiths, P M C
Crocombe, J M
Crosby, D L
Crosby, G
Crowe, L J
Cunningham, N
Curran, E F
Cuthill, A R
Daniels, A W
Daniels, H F
Daniels, I R
Daoud, Z A-S
Darmani, A A
Das, S
Datta, S N
David, C
David, M Y
Davidson, J M
Davies, C
Davies, C S
Davies, C E
Davies, D G L
Davies, D K L
Davies, E G
Davies, E L
Davies, G A
Davies, H J
Davies, H E
Davies, H W
Davies, I H
Davies, J S
Davies, J A
Davies, J S
Davies, J M
Davies, J O C
Davies, J S
Davies, J H
Davies, K R
Davies, M

Davies, M
Davies, M
Davies, M R
Davies, N J
Davies, S E
Davies, S J
Davies, S G
Davies, S P
Davies, W T
Davis, N C
Davison, A M
Dayananda, K S S
De Alwis, E
De Lloyd, L J
Deb, S
Delicata, R J
Dexter, A M
Dey, P
Dhaliwal, J K
Dhallu, T
Dharmasena, A D
Dharmasena, H P
Dickinson, L
Diez-Rabago Del Barrio, M V
Dimpel, H L
Dingley, L D
Dixon, S F
Dolby, A E
Donaldson, A J
Douglas-Jones, A G
Doull, I J M
Doyle, C
Drayton, M R
Duerden, B I
Duff, E J
Duffy, P J
Dunford, C
Dunlop, D G
Dunne, J A
Dunne, N M
Duthie, H L
Duthie, M
Duthie, P I
Dwarakanath, B S S
Dyer, J R W G
Dymond, C M
Dymond, D C
Edwards, A T
Edwards, E A
Edwards, E D
Edwards, J
Edwards, P H
Edwards, R P
Edwards, R T M
Edwards, S M
Eickmann, C
El-Khatieb, M M H
El Khogia, A M
El Mahayni, N M R
El-Shaboury, A-H M
El-Taranissi, M A F A A
Elder, G H
Elder, S H
Elgadi, S M A
Elliott, H R
Ellis, A G
Elsarrag, M E
Elwood, P C
Elwyn, G J
Emery, L L
England, R C D
Enoch, M D
Entwistle, D M
Esmail, M M A
Evans, A R
Evans, A
Evans, C E
Evans, C L
Evans, C
Evans, D E N
Evans, D L
Evans, D G
Evans, D H
Evans, D L
Evans, D M D
Evans, G
Evans, H O
Evans, J M
Evans, J
Evans, K T
Evans, L T I
Evans, M A
Evans, M H
Evans, M R
Evans, N A
Evans, P M S
Evans, R E

Cardiff

Evans, R J
Evans, R O N
Evans, R C
Evans, R H
Evans, S A
Evans, S G
Evans, S L
Evans, S M
Evely, C L
Everest, S F
Fagan, D
Fairclough, J A
Farley-Hills, E M
Farmer, A E
Farrell, A M
Farrier, J N
Fegan, C D
Fenn, N J
Fenton-May, J M
Fenton, J C B
Ferguson, T G
Feyi-Waboso, A C
Fielding, P A
Findlay, C M
Findlay, G P
Finlay, A Y
Fisher, D J H
Fisher, M
Flackett, L K
Flynn, A J
Fortt, R W
Foster, D W
Foster, M E
Fowler, J C M
Fox, R
Foy, J G D
Foy, J M
Fraser, A G
Fraser, E D
Fraser, W I
Freedman, A R
Frost, A
Fudge, B J
Fuge, B
Gaffney, C C
Gajraj, M
Gallivan, M P
Gallop-Evans, E M L
Gandhi, P S
Gantley, J M
Garrett, J G
Gayer, S J
Gelder, C M
George, A M
George, L D
Gibbon, F M
Gibbs, C R
Gilbert, W S
Gildersleve, C D
Gill, J S
Gilmour, J P
Glascoe, S P
Glover, G
Goble, N M
Gomez Bordas, L A
Goodfellow, J
Goodfellow, R M
Goodfellow, S J
Goodwin, G L
Goodwin, N
Goodwin, R G
Goodwin, V H
Gopala Krishna, P
Gordon, T L
Gough, M A
Gouldson, R
Gourlay, R P
Graham, F M O
Graham, G P
Graham, J A
Graham, J G
Graham, P A
Graham, V H J
Granger, M E
Gravell, R M
Gravelle, I H
Gray, M F
Gray, M Y
Green, E N
Green, J M J
Green, M F
Gregory, J W
Grey, J E
Griffin, P J A
Griffith, I P
Griffith, T M
Griffiths, B
Griffiths, D F R
Griffiths, E H
Griffiths, G B
Griffiths, J J
Griffiths, K U
Griffiths, M C
Griffiths, R
Griffiths, S G
Groom, P J
Groves, A H
Groves, N D
Groves, P H
Grundy, P F
Grzybowska, P H
Guillem, A W
Guiney, M
Gulliford, J A G
Gunawardena, S M
Hadjikoutis, S
Hallwood, R L
Haley, A J L
Hall, J E
Hall, R
Ham, J C
Ham, M F
Hambly, P R
Hamilton, S A
Hanif, J
Hanna, C L
Harding, K G
Harding, L J E
Hariharan, K
Harmer, M
Harper, D G
Harper, M
Harper, P S
Harries, I G
Harries, J
Harries, S E M
Harris, B B
Harrison, C A
Harrison, M D
Harrison, S K
Harry, G
Harse, J B
Hart, P R
Hart, S M
Hasan, K
Haslam, J C
Hatfield, R H
Hauke, A H
Havard, C
Havard, E M M
Hawthorne, A B
Hawthorne, K
Hayes, G J
Hayes, T M
Heard, G E
Heavens, C
Held, I
Helsby, W G
Henderson, A H
Henson, S E
Henton, N J
Hermann-Smith, J A
Hibbard, B M
Hibbard, E D
Hicks, C E
Higgins, M A G
Hiley, D A
Hill, K J
Hillier, J
Hilling, G A L
Ho, S F
Hocking, J A
Hodzovic, I
Holden, B M
Holland, J W
Holme, S A
Holmes, H P
Holt, M D
Holt, P J A
Hombal, J W R
Hope, D A
Hopkins, C L
Hopkins, R
Hopkins, S D
Hopkins, T
Hopkinson, I
Horner, S E
Hosking, G E
Hourihan, M D
Houston, H L A
Howard, A J
Howarth, P J
Howe, T M
Howell, T K
Howells, C H L
Howells, D
Howells, R M
Huddart, S N
Hughes, D L
Hughes, D J
Hughes, J D
Hughes, J L
Hughes, J N P
Hughes, L E
Hughes, M
Hughes, O D M
Hughes, R C
Hughes, T A T
Humphries, A M
Hunt, M O
Hunter, J W
Hunter, P J
Hurle, R A
Hurley, R
Hutton, K A R
Hyett, C A
Inman, C G
Ions, E
Isaacs, S L
Ismail, S M
Jackson, E F
Jackson, P M
Jacobs, I D
Jacobs, R
Jacobson, L D
Jain, S C
Jain, S
Jamal, A S
Jamal, Z
James, A
James, D R
James, G R
James, H W H
James, J A
James, S
Jamil, N F
Jani, B R
Jani, J J
Jasani, B
Jawad, M S M
Jawad, N H
Jefferson, M J
Jeffs, A C
Jenkins, A I R
Jenkins, B J
Jenkins, B J
Jenkins, C
Jenkins, D M
Jenkins, D R L
Jenkins, H R
Jenkins, J R
Jenkins, L R
Jenkins, M P E
Jenkins, M W
Jenkins, P L G
Jenkins, S A
Jenkins, T H
Jenkins, T D O
Jessop, J D
Jewkes, F E M
Johansen, E M
Johansen, K A
Johl, P P
John, A W
John, N E
John, P A
Johnson, J A
Johnson, J
Johnson, M L
Johnston, K R
Jones Williams, W
Jones, A R
Jones, A M L
Jones, A
Jones, A M
Jones, A
Jones, D L
Jones, D L
Jones, D R
Jones, D R
Jones, D T
Jones, E C
Jones, G H
Jones, G S
Jones, H L
Jones, H O
Jones, J I L
Jones, J V
Jones, M R
Jones, M
Jones, N K
Jones, P L
Jones, P W
Jones, R M
Jones, R G
Jones, R D
Jones, S
Jones, V
Jordan, G J
Judodihardjo, H
Kamarylzaman, S B
Kamath, S K
Kant, M
Kapp, E M
Karseras, A G
Kay, A J
Kaye, P D
Keen, M R
Keh, C H L
Kell, W J
Kellam, A M P
Kerby, C
Kerby, I J
Kerkar, N R
Key, S J
Khallaf, A A
Khan, N A
Khan, T
Khatib, H A
Khatib, M J
Killeen, N C
Kini, U S
Kinnersley, P
Kirby, A H
Kirk, C R
Kirov, G K
Kite, J E
Klentzeris, L D
Knight, A G
Knight, B H
Knoyle, P A
Kontos, K
Krimmer, M H
Krishnamurti, D
Kshetry, L D
Kumar, P
Laidlaw, S T
Laidler, P
Lane, A G
Lane, C M
Lane, I F
Latto, I P
Lawrence, M S
Lawrie, B W
Lawson, J G
Lawton, H L
Layzell, J C M
Lazarus, G F
Lazarus, J H
Lazda, E J
Leadbeatter, S
Lee Hai Leong, Dr
Lee, E S G
Leeson, N A
Lehner, P J
Leung, H Y
Lewis, C G E
Lewis, D H
Lewis, D K
Lewis, D M
Lewis, G
Lewis, G H
Lewis, H
Lewis, J E
Lewis, J M
Lewis, M J
Lewis, M
Lewis, M E
Lewis, M H
Lewis, S M
Li, W C W
Lim Su Ping, R
Lim, F K B
Lim, J T K
Lim, K C-K
Lim, P O
Lindley, P L
Lindsey, H C
Lindsey, M
Lipetz, C
Livingstone, M D
Llewellyn, J O
Llewelyn, A A
Llewelyn, M B
Lloyd-Jones, S J
Lloyd, A R
Lloyd, D C F
Lloyd, E
Lloyd, G E
Lloyd, H A
Lloyd, H J
Lloyd, I W
Lloyd, K N
Lloyd, P A R
Lloyd, R H G
Lloyd, S D
Lloyd, T H L
Lo, S N
Logan, S W
Logan, V K
Longstaffe, J E
Lonnon, J A
Lord, R H H
Loudon, M M
Lovett, W C D
Lowe, G L
Lowe, K J
Ludlow, E J
Lukaris, C P
Lush, S G
Lyne, P N D
Lyons, I
McBeth, C
McCann, N
McCarthy, G M T
McCleary, W L
McCracken, D
MacCulloch, M J
McDowell, IFW
McHugh, L J
Mackie, I G
McKirdy, H C
McKirdy, M L
Maclaren, A M
Maclean, A C W
Maclean, A
McLean, M J
McLoughlin, N P T
McPherson, R J E
McQueen, I N F
McSweeney, K G P
MacVicar, G
Maheson, M V S
Majoe, P
Malik, S
Manley, R
Mannari, N S
Mansel, R E
Manuel, A R G
Manuel, D D
Marks, J
Marks, R
Marsh, H S
Marshall, G E
Martin Oliver, M J
Martin, J C
Martinez, G
Masani, N D
Mason, M D
Mason, S J
Masterson, M
Mathew, V
Matthews, F J
Matthews, P
Matthews, P N
Maughan, T S
Maxwell, C A
Mayo, H G
Mead, B M
Meades, D C
Meghani, D K
Mehta, D K
Meldrum, C H
Meldrum, J A K
Metters, A J F W
Meyrick, R S
Millar-Jones, D J
Mills, P V
Mills, R G S
Millward, D
Minton, D K
Mir, M A
Mischel, E L
Mitchell, G M
Mitchell, I F A
Mitchell, S H M
Moffat, D B
Moghal, A M
Mohamed, M Y
Monaghan, S P
Moore, R H
Morey Canellas, J
Morgan, B P
Morgan, C
Morgan, D L
Morgan, G F
Morgan, J E
Morgan, P
Morgan, S M
Morgan, S J S
Morgan, S J
Morris, G
Morris, R L
Morris, S J
Morris, T J
Morris, W B
Morse, R E
Morton, W H
Moselhi, M
Moss, L J
Motley, R J
Mott, A M
Mowle, S H
Mudge, M
Munro, J A
Murrin, K R
Myerson, N A
Nam, S
Narang, I
Nayar, R N
Naysmith, J H
Neal, J W
Nelson-Owen, M E C
Newell, R L M
Newman, G M
Newman, S E
Ng, W T
Ng, W S
Nokes, L D M
Nolan, M E
Norton, C A
Nowayhio, F A
Nunez-Avellaneda, J R
Nunley, C I
O'Doherty, D P W
O'Donovan, M C
O'Dowd, B J
O'Dwyer, H S
O'Sullivan, M
Obaji, A K K
Oelmann, G J
Ogden, J N
Oldham, T A
Oliver, D J
Ong, J P L
Orakzai, N
Oretti, R G
Owen, A M
Owen, D C
Owen, M J
Owens, E P
Owens, R P
Palmer, D J W
Palmer, S R
Pandya, H
Parab, S B
Parekh, S J
Parkinson, D J
Parry-Morton, M
Parsons, A S
Parsons, J M
Pathy, D J G
Pawley, M K
Payne, E H
Payne, E M M
Payne, E E
Pearce, A V
Pearson, J F
Pearson, J R
Pegge, N C
Pegler, G
Penny, E P
Penny, W J
Peters, J R
Petterson, J A
Phillips, A O
Phillips, S
Phillips, S
Picken, D K W
Pickersgill, T P
Pierrepoint, M J
Pierry, A A
Pilz, D T
Pippen, C A R
Pitt, D J
Place, D G
Plant, M J
Porteous, A O R
Poynton, C H
Preest, A R B
Premawardhana, L D K E
Presley, R
Price, M M
Price, M A
Prichard, J E
Pritchard, M H
Probert, D E
Procter, A M
Prokop, R
Pryce, I G
Pugh, C N
Pugh, D H O
Pugh, S C

Carlisle

Puntis, M C A
Quine, S M
Rafter, M J
Raghunathan, K
Raghupati, R
Rahman, W
Ramsahoye, B H
Rattigan, S M
Ravine, D
Rawlinson, F M
Raybould, A D
Razouqi, B M
Read, M S
Reddy, D P
Reed, E A
Rees, A
Rees, B M
Rees, B I
Rees, H G
Rees, J A E
Rees, J I S
Reeves, D M
Rhoden, H M
Rhodes, P
Rhys, G M
Ribeiro, C D
Richards, C J
Richards, D A
Richards, E D J
Richards, F M
Richards, H J
Richards, M H J
Richards, R M
Richards, R P
Richards, S
Richards, S H
Richmond, J K
Richmond, P W
Ridha, B H
Rimmer, A J
Rishko, A J
Rivron, M J
Roach, H D
Robbe, I J
Roberts, A
Roberts, A W
Roberts, A J
Roberts, B C
Roberts, B N
Roberts, C J
Roberts, G M
Robertson, M W
Robertson, S W
Robinson, B G
Robinson, C J
Robinson, D K
Robinson, L G
Robinson, M D
Robinson, T
Roblin, D G
Roblin, M W
Rochfort, A M C
Rogers, A
Rogers, C
Rogers, J A
Rogers, M T
Rosen, M
Rothwell, A C
Routledge, P A
Rowlands, N C
Roy, W S
Rubin, L B
Rudge, P
Rudling, J L
Ruttley, M S T
Ryan, A G M J
Ryder, R C
Rye, A D
Sabir, A W
Sabir, A T W
Sadiq, S S Q
Sadler, S J
Sage, M
Sagoo, S S
Sakel, R
Salmon, R L
Salter, D G
Salter, R J
Sambhi, R T S
Sampson, J R
Samuels, A J L
Sarnobat, M S
Sarnobat, S R
Saunders, K
Savage, P M
Sayer, C A
Scanlon, M F
Scarle, T J B
Scherf, C F

Scholey, J A
Scolding, K J
Scorer, R C
Scott, A K
Scourfield, J
Secker Walker, J
Shah, H V
Sharma, S K
Sharma, S
Sheehan, P B
Shehadeh, E S
Shelling, D
Shepherd, E H
Sheraton, T E
Shewring, D J
Shewring, J I
Shewring, S A
Shone, G R
Shortland, G J
Shrivastava, S K
Siddall, B L
Sim, K T
Sim, M F V
Simpson, B A
Sinclair, A J
Singh, H
Singh, H B
Sinha, A K
Sinha, S
Skone, J F
Skyrme, M L
Skyrme, R J
Smail, S A
Smart, J A
Smith, A T
Smith, G C
Smith, J S
Smith, J C
Smith, L-A
Smith, P E M
Smith, P H
Smith, R
Smith, R A
Smithies, M N
Soukias, N
Sparks, R A
Stacey, M R W
Staniforth, J
Stephen, J R
Stephens, S D G
Stephenson, T P
Stevenson, A I
Steward, J A
Stock, D
Stone, A M
Stone, R L
Stoodley, N G
Stork, A F
Stott, N C H
Sullivan, B A
Sullivan, S C
Sultana, K
Sultana, R
Summers, Z
Sumption, J C
Sumption, N J
Sweetland, H M
Sykes, D A
Sykes, H E
Syson, A
Tan, K L
Tan, K H-V
Tanaka, H
Tang, W Y
Tapper-Jones, L M
Taylor, C
Taylor, S C
Thapar, A
Thom, N K
Thomas, A M
Thomas, A
Thomas, A S M
Thomas, C E
Thomas, D M
Thomas, D R
Thomas, D C
Thomas, G A O
Thomas, G V
Thomas, H O
Thomas, J A
Thomas, J A B
Thomas, M
Thomas, M J
Thomas, M J E
Thomas, M
Thomas, O R
Thomas, R H
Thomas, S B
Thomas, T H

Thomas, W G
Thompson, C K
Thompson, J E
Thompson, P W
Thompson, T H R
Thompson, W M
Tiwari, R
Tjandra, J J
Todd, G B
Todd, J N
Todd, S E
Tomkins, S E
Trigg, S E E
Triggs, A J
Tudor Jones, R
Tufail, A
Tweddel, A C
Tye, T E
Umapathy, K
Upadhyaya, R R
Vaid, S
Valabhji, P
Van Der Voort, J H
Vasanthakumari, S
Vaterlaws, A L
Vaughan, D L J
Vaughan, R S
Verrier Jones, K
Vetter, N J
Vig, S
Vujanic, G
Wainwright, J R
Wakeling, J A
Wakely, D
Wakely, I K E
Walker-Baker, L
Waller, J A
Walsh, M C
Walters, R F
Ward, D A
Ward, D E
Ward, N W
Warner, J T
Wat, D S-C
Watermeyer, S R
Watkins, W R
Watson, M R
Watson, M W
Watts, K A
Watura, R
Weaver, C M
Weaver, S R
Webb, E V J
Webster, D J T
Webster, V J
Weightman, W M
Weisl, H
Wenham, G A
West, S C
Westall, W G
Westlake, H E
Westlake, J D
Westmoreland, D
Wheeler, M H
Wheeler, M T K
Wheeler, R A E
Whiston, R J
Whitaker, G
White, S V
Whittaker, J A
Whittaker, S M
Whitten, L
Whitten, M P
Wigley, A M
Wiles, C M
Williams, A J
Williams, B A R
Williams, B D
Williams, D T
Williams, D
Williams, D W
Williams, E V
Williams, E L
Williams, E H
Williams, G L
Williams, G T
Williams, J E
Williams, J D
Williams, J E
Williams, L B
Williams, N J
Williams, N V
Williams, P E
Williams, P R
Williams, P A
Williams, R L
Williams, R G
Williams, R I
Williams, R J

Williams, S M
Williams, S R
Williams, S A
Williams, T
Williams, T N
Williams, W
Williams, W A
Williamson, D W
Williamson, J B
Willis, B A
Wills, D
Wilson, C
Wilson, D G
Wilson, I C
Wilson, K M O N
Wiltshire, E J M
Win Ko, Dr
Windhaber, R A J
Winter, G
Wong, C Y
Wong, S M C
Wong, S Y S
Wood, D S
Wood, S M
Woodhouse, K W
Woodnutt, D J
Woods, K M
Woolf, A M
Woolley, C M
Worwood, G
Wright, P A
Wynford-Thomas, D W
Yaqoob, M A
Yarr, N T
Yong, J L
Young, H L
Young, K E
Young, M H
Young, R H J
Youssef, H M H A
Zaidi, S H A
Zamiri, I
Zein Sanchez, M P

Cardigan

Allan, D P
Cohen, L
Cuddigan, A S
David, O J
Fischer, C M
Griffiths, S R
Hemington, A
James, D W
Jones, D G G
Knight, S N K
Mandry, D R
Noakes, J P L
Rees, E G
Rendle, D E
Russell, B T
Stephens, N G
Thomas, S E M
Thomas, S G
Tindle, J E
Vernon, J D S

Carlisle

Adam, G P
Allison-Bolger, V Y
Amin, S
Amos, T A S
Anderson, J G
Ashton, H
Ashton, J R
Asquith, C E
Athey, G N
Athey, R J
Attarwala, U
Baker, C M
Barber, H M
Barber, L M
Barnes, D W
Barnsley, R J
Bearn, M A
Beastall, A
Bell, H J
Bennett-Jones, D N
Billett, J S
Black, A D F
Black, J B M
Bolson, P F
Bomford, W B N
Bone, J A
Brammah, A L
Briggs, M A
Brignall, C G
Britton, J N
Britton, N R
Brodie, C A

Brookes, C E
Brown, A A
Buckley, F B
Burke, D A
Calvert, N I R
Carr-Saunders, E M
Casson, P A
Cawley, N
Chandre Gowda, H K
Chin, P-L
Christie, G L
Clark, D R
Clark, I J
Clark, M G
Clark, N L
Clough, H A
Cole, A
Cole, T P
Corrigan, C
Cowley, M L
Cox, N H
Cumming, J A
Davies, D G
Davies, D P
De Cornet, L C
Deeble, J
Depla, D N
Deshpande, S K
Dias, T F
Dickson, U K
Dobson, J M
Donaldson, T H
Dorken, P R
Dunckley, H G
Dyson, P
Edgar, A J
Edge, J M H
Edwards, A D
Evans, A T G
Ewbank, J A
Fallaw, C R F
Faux, J W
Foster, J C
Foxworthy, J V
French, J A
Frizzell, R A
Frost, J C
Furlong, L R
Galloway, D W
Gardner, D W
Garland, J E M
Garner, M I
George, J
Goold, M F
Gordon, J E
Gowda, C K
Graham, W H
Grainger, I M
Hallewell, C L
Hand, D W
Harker, C G
Harrison, J F
Hasan, M-U
Hasan, S Q
Haworth, J
Haworth, J N
Hay, S R
Hayes, D G
Herrick, A C
Herrmann, K
Hindle, J M
Hipple, L J
Hoddy, D W
Holdsworth, A C
Holmes, K M
Honeyman, W P
Horne, A R
Horobin, R H
Huggins, C L
Hutcheson, P M
Inglis, A
Ions, G K
Jackson, J E
Jardine, G W H
Jayawardena, G M U
Jennings, P G
Jimenez Camara, V C
John, M R
Jolly, G M
Jones, D F
Jones, R M
Keir, S L
Kennedy, S
Kerss, I M S
Kewley, M A
Kidd, C E
King, A L
King, P H M
Kirke, C N

Knowles, M A
Koussa, F C
Large, D M
Lawley, R
Leesley, D A
Lewis, C K
Lightfoot, R J
Loftus, J
Long, E D
Lord, C
Ludlam, R B
McClay, W J A
Macdonald, A J
McDowell, J F
MacFadzean, J A C
Mackay, T I
Mackenzie, G M
McKenzie, Y
Maclean, A B
McNeill, R H
McStay, K C
Margerison, L N
Marshall, R A
Marshall, R E
Mead, P A
Merrick, M M
Milton, J C
Mitchell, C P
Moffat, J S
Moles, D J
Morgan, W H
Morley, K D
Murphy, R C W
Murrant, N J
Murray, A C
Murray, I H F
Murray, R H
Mustchin, C P
Mythili, K
Neal, G
Newbery, J M
Nicoll, J J
Noblett, J J
Nolan, J A
O'Brien, H A W
Orr, M J
Palmer, J G
Palmer, V F
Patel, P K
Paterson, A W
Paterson, W D
Patterson, C
Pattinson, C P
Payne, M R
Paynter, A S
Pearson, S E
Peduzzi, R D
Philp, L D
Popple, A W
Pritchard, G C
Putnam, G D
Raimes, S A
Raitt, G P
Rangecroft, R G
Reay, S
Reed, R C
Reid, F M
Reid, W
Rickerby, E J
Rigby, M F
Rippon, C
Roberts, M H W
Roberts, S A
Robson, A K
Roddick, I A
Rodgers, R C
Ross, M G
Rushton, D G
Sabir, O M E
Salisbury, M S
Salter, R H
Saxton, J S
Scott, S W
Scroggie, B M R
Sells, M F L
Sethi, B P
Sevar, R
Shanks, A B
Shetty, T T
Shirtcliffe, P M
Simpson, E M M
Singh, T M
Sixsmith, M
Slinger, K M A
Smith, K P
Smith, R P S
Stanley, B S
Stitt, G W
Storr, J N P

Carluke

Storr, T M
Stride, P C
Strover, A R M
Stuart, P
Swain, R A H
Swindells, A
Tait, K F
Taylor, P J
Taylor, M C
Terrell, J D
Thom, M G
Thomas, C M
Thomson, J C
Tidmarsh, M D
Tiplady, P
Turner, M A
Twomey, M P K
Tzabar, Y H
Ward, D B
Weaving, H C
Wheatley, D S
Wheatley, P K
Wheeler, D V
White, M J
White, P M
Whiteley, J
Wholley, V G
Wicks, R
Wigmore, N P
Williams, M R
Wills, H G
Wolstencroft, P J
Wood, M E
Wright, N F
Young, F I
Young, V E
Zobair, M

Carluke

Arnott, S
Baldwin, S H G
Bell, A
Ben-Younes, A H
Bezem, M F
Boyd, J C
Buck, L M
Burns, J M
Campbell, H
Cannon, J D
Chaubey, S
Chhabda, P S
Christie, I R
Christie, L C
Crossan, E M
De Giorgi, L
Frame, W D
Galloway, R J
Gazi, T F
Gemmill, S
Graham, A J
Guha, S
Gulati, B S
Gunn, I R
Guthrie, G M
Hacking, L
Haque, M S
Hendry, A
Hodsman, N B A
Holder, E S
Howard, M E
Innes, A C
Jabbal, S S
Jackson, A W
Kaiqobad, R M
Kay, J F
Kennedy, G
Khan, M A M
Lynas, A M
McCallion, J
McCallion, J S
Mackenzie, A I
Mackintosh, C L
Milne, A J
Munro, R A L
Murray, M G S
O'Brien, I A D
Ofili, G U
Ong, K O
Paterson, E H
Pattnaik, D K
Peterkin, M A
Rajendra, M
Redpath, J B S
Rennie, G G
Rennie, M L
Rieley, T C
Robertson, A C
Robertson, R H
Scott, J J

Shajahan, P M
Sharma, B D
Stewart, J F N
Teoh, Y P
Wallace, J R
Williams, P M
Workman, A J G
Wright, A D G

Carmarthen

Adamson, A I
Ahmed, A M
Al-Abdullah, A F I
Allen, G M
Arvind, A S R
Atkinson, R W
Bartlett, C G
Battu, V R
Bennett, M
Black, R J
Bloomfield, T H
Brennan, D R
Briggs, G D
Brown, P M
Carter, S H
Chan, S-P
Chapman, T H
Chatterji, S
Coleman, M C
Cornah, P R
Crane, J E
Cressey-Rodgers, J F
Cumber, P M
Daniel, O
Davidson, L A G
Davies, A L
Davies, D A
Davies, D M G
Davies, E W
Davies, G W M
Davies, G R
Davies, T M
Davis, B R
Denholm, R B
Derry Thomas, J P
Dowling, M A
Edwards, H
Eustace, J R
Evans, C J
Evans, H A
Eynon, A M
Farr, J
Forman, S M
Gana, B M
Gibbin, P P
Gibby, S A
Goriah, S A
Gravelle, I P
Greenacre, J A
Greenlaw, G J K
Grey, I E M F
Griew, A R
Griffith, M J
Griffiths, S E
Griffiths, W G
Gupta, D
Haley, A H
Harries, D K
Hasan, M A S
Herbert, J L
Hill, W S
Hitchcock, M
James, W M
Jenkins, I R
John, C L
John, E L
Johnson, S J
Johnson, S R
Jones-Davies, G A
Jones, C
Jones, C A M
Jones, D W M
Jones, D
Jones, E
Jones, E W
Jones, M H
Jones, S C
Jones, T M B
Jose, K
Kanapathy Raja, M S
Kinnear, J C
Laxton, A G P
Laxton, C J
Lewis, A L
Lewis, G H
Lewis, G E
Lindsay, A M
Locker, A P
Loxdale, H A R

Loxdale, H K R
Loyden, C F
McGinley, J F
Magee, T M
Male, E J
Maliphant, H B
Martinez Pascual, R M
Masoodi, M N
Mistry, P G
Morgan, N J
Morgan, S
Morriss, G W
Murphy, D L
Murphy, J K
Murphy, R C
Murray, J P
O'Riordan, B G M
Owen, D W
Owen, G
Potter, H A
Rees, A
Rees, J H T
Rees, R L
Rees, T W
Reynolds, G M
Rimell, P J
Rincon Aznar, C
Riordan, P M A M
Ritchie, W N
Roberts-Harry, T J
Roberts, G
Rowlands, I G
Russell, D R
Salam, I
Salinas, J
Sargeant, M P
Saxena, V R
Scourfield, D B
Scourfield, D
Sheridan, W G J
Simmons, M D
Stephens, C L
Tan Tong Khee, Dr
Taube, M
Thirunawarkarisu, K S
Thomas, C W
Thomas, D H
Thomas, J M
Thomas, M V
Thomas, M A
Thomas, T P L
Thomson, W
Tirunawarkarisu, K P
Turtle, M J
Varnadeva, P
Velmurugiah, V
Walapu, M F M
Walker, M
Wallace, L
Wan, S K H
Warren, P M
Warren, S
Wilding, H I
Wilkins, M F
Williams, J H
Williams, K P
Williams, R G
Wright, R G
Yate, B H
Yate, R M
Zohdy, G

Carnforth

Abraham, N J
Agababian, A A
Baird, R B
Bates, P
Beagan, M M
Bennett, P W
Benson, H G
Blewitt, R W
Brown, D J
Bryan, S R
Burnett, J M P
Burnett, T S
Cash, K J
Clarke, J M
Coles, M E
Cowell, M A C
Crosfill, F M
Davies, A H
Docton, R K E
Duddle, C M
Findlater, J
Fleetwood, A L
Fletcher, M M
Fletcher, S
Fowden, A
Gent, N S C

Granger, C E
Gray, P F
Griffiths, N R
Hall, A W I
Hall, P J I
Halsey, J P
Hampson, J L
Hargreaves, N
Hinson, E L
Hobbs, G A T
Hodgson, L M
James, F A
John, R W
Johnson, J A
Kelly, J F
Kopcke, D H F
Lakeland, D A
Longley, J P
Lowson, K
McConnell, A T
Matchett, A A
Mathews, W G
Matthews, T S
Meiring, J K
Mercer, K A
Morgan-Capner, K
Morris, A D
Morris, J A
Park, W G
Partington, A
Paul, H M P
Placzek, M M
Pollock, H B
Pollock, R
Redpath, D
Robinson, R E
Scott, L T
Severn, A M
Sewell, R N
Shakespeare, J
Sheals, G
Smith, E A
Sykes, O M
Theobalds, J R
Thomas, D G
Till, C B W
Torkington, M J
Turnbull, G A
Walker, G P
Wall, W H J
Whitehead, J S W
Wickenden, G H
Young, R D
Yule, C M

Carnoustie

Boswell, J
Cain, A J
Campbell, L
Clark, M F
Crosby, F R G
Easton, A I M
Gallon, M E
Halliday, G M
Hutcheon, S D
Jess, G E
Lata, H
Leslie, H
McKendrick, A D
Morton, L J
Robb, O J
Thornton, P W

Carr Bridge

Adamson, K H
Boxx, P J
Shaw, K J

Carrickfergus

Addis, S R D
Anderson, M R
Andrews, W J
Baird, T A
Bolton, L H
Bradley, S
Buckley, O M
Calwell, A M I
Calwell, A I J
Campbell, H S
Courtney, D
Crothers, E D
Darragh, P M
Davison, D N
Dixon, N D
Erskine, R I
Esler, J R D
Ferguson, J R
Ferres, C J
Gordon, D V
Green, D F

Hunter, K
Hutchinson, A F
Lewis, A
Linden, P G J
Logan, I D
Mcallister, J G
McCaughan, J F G
McCluggage, W G
McCrory, C A W
McDonald, L J
McKnight, J
MacLoughlin, J H
McRoberts, R J
Mahood, K M
Moffatt, W H
Morgan, S A
Rainey, J C A
Robinson, W J E
Russell, C H
Ryans, R I
Shahidullah, B S
Sloan, D J
Smith, S P
Stone, M P
Sutcliffe, J E L
Turkington, J R A
Vahid Assr, M D
White, J S
Wilson, J
Wilson, J P
Wylie, S

Carshalton

Akinmade, O
Ali Khan, N F
Andrews, P A
Assinder, F R S C
Atallah, M G
Attard, M T
Baig, S N
Bansal, A S
Barron, J L
Barry, J J G
Behrens, J
Benson, M J
Bird, J
Blewitt, S D
Boardman, D R
Boyd, P J R
Brown, J M
Byrne, P D
Catling, J S
Chegwidden, R J D
Cheong-Leen, P
Chesser, J J S
Citron, N D
Clancy, R M
Clarke, M F
Cockbain, J M R
Cooke, D A P
Cooke, N T
Dar, A
Dar, S
Das, S K
Ditri, A
Doyle, A P
Duke, O L
Estreich, S
Favre, A
Field, R E
Fouque, C A
Froley, A F
Galloway, A
Ghaznavi, A H
Gilford, H J
Goel, K L
Goel, R K
Halfhide, C P
Harland, C C
Hastie, A L
Hebrero Matobella, E
Hickish, T F G
Hodson, N J
Howard, P J
Hyer, S L
Jones, C R
Jones, G D T
Kavanagh, T G
Khan, F
Khong Yang-Sui, M
Kwan, J T C
Lazarus, K C
Lees, J F
Ling, S
Liu, M Y
McGowan, M E L
McWhinney, N A
Madina, T
Mantell, J

Marsden, M R
Maynard, J P
Mercieca, J E
Mody, R
Mohiud-Din, F
Mohiud-Din, S M
Mojiminiyi, O A
North, E A
Ogilvie, D
Orchard, R T
Patel, D J
Patel, S R
Penna, L K
Philip, G
Pinto, A P R
Pujara, M S
Quinton, C F
Radford, P
Ravetto, M P C
Rhind, R A
Ringer, W S
Roberts-Harewood, M-R D
Rodin, D A
Ross, L D
Rudolphij, A J
Sharma, M
Shellim, A J
Shephard, E R
Sherriff, E A
Siala, M-D
Silva, N C
Singarajah, C U
Singh, L N
Slater, P C-A
Smith, A R C
Stevens, K L H
Stockwell, M A
Sultan, V
Tayar, R
Taylor, J D
Thomas, P R S
Toosy, T H
Varney, V A
Verma, A
Warren, M E
Wartan, S W
Whaley, K E
Wheildon, M H
Wilcox, A H
Williams, C R
Yeoh, L H
Yu, K H
Zack, P

Carterton

A'Court, C H D
Clough, F C
Jones, N M
Reid, G E
Sheehan, J P A
Wilkinson, A R

Castel

Balls, J L
Bisson, M A
Cameron, I A
Clark, R N W
Frank, R
Gee, I B
Hanna, R G J
Mowbray, E S M J I
Rey, C H J
Swainston, D G

Castle Cary

Collins, D P
Depla, W M A
Dunlop, H A
Farquhar, A J
Jayasuriya, A L N
Ketley, A M D
Parker, J M
Roylance, M K

Castle Douglas

Armstrong, W H
Baird, H M
Cameron, K A
Carmichael, I A
Carson, E A
Charlesworth, R
Christie, C F
Clarke, I L
Clarke, M D B
Davidson, I W
Forbes, A A
Forsythe, W I
Freeth, H D
Gregor, C B

Chelmsford

Halliday, K C R
Johnstone, G M
Jones, B G
King, M
Law, B
Law, R G
Livingstone, S E
McCormick, J S C
Malone, C M
Neil, J R K
Neil, S P
Oliver, N M
Paterson, M C W
Purdie, G
Robertson, D J
Scott, P J
Smith, A E
Sproat, L M E
Timperley, J C
Walker, K R
Wilkinson, A P D
Wilson, A
Wood, V

Castlebay
Campbell, M E
Hidson, J M
Robarts, J H
Savory, J C
Sinclair, A-M

Castlederg
Bailie, R W A
Cotter, A G P
Duggan, B J
Garvey, J
Johnston, C D
McElroy, R G
McHugh, R
O'Hare, B J
O'Hare, I P

Castleford
Aldridge, G R
Atkinson, R
Bance, H R
Butler, I
Cuttell, E J
Gallagher, P
Godridge, A C
Gopinathan, K K
Henein, R R
Lee, J D
Lloyd, C
McClintock, C B
Minocha, D
Nambiar, S C
Prasad, A
Ravindran, A
Sanzeri, M
Sloan, R E G
White, D A

Castletown
Brewis, V T
Brittain, G J C
Brittain, P
Burdett, A G
Carson, E G
Harris, S A
Kirkham, C S
McVerry, E A
Rennie, F M
Rimington, J
Smith, P H
Swainson, S M

Castlewellan
Chestnutt, J A J
Magorrian, M T
Ward, P G
Wilson, R J L

Caterham
Bantick, G L
Bennett, R A
Branford, O A
Brocklebank, A-M N
Cole, B W
Crispin, S A
Defriend, K P
Dodson, H J
Drost, F
Dunnet, E L
Dunnet, W N
Fabricius, J M
Hanbury, W J
Heath, M T
Howard, J V
Hunnybun, J M
Hunnybun, J

Hutchinson, A
Irvine, R E
Khan, A M
Lazarus, N R
Lewis, J M
Lister, I S
Livesey, B
McKeran, R O
Middleton, C L
Miller, A J
Moore, W E D
Munro-Faure, A D
O'Brien, F C
Oliver, R A M
Peermahomed, R
Posford, P C A
Reay-Jones, M H H
Roberts, P F
Sinclair, R D
Walls, N J
Wand, P J
Ward, K A
Wright, R E

Catterick Garrison
Anderson, J
Anderson, R M L
Barker, C T
Conroy, M
Cox, V M
McAllister, P D
Neal, L A
Phillpotts, I S T
Robertson, D G
Russell, D
Turner, M A
Williams, D
Zaki, N N
Zaremba, E L

Cemaes Bay
Macleod, H
Owen, R E
Shaw, T J

Chalfont St Giles
Allison, N
Barratt, P M
Cooke, N P
Cosgrove, J L
Dixon, W M
Freeman, V
Fung, D A
Harmer, D
Heywood, D
Holton, T S
Kennedy, K E
Lawrence, D A S
Loh, R S K
McAllen, M K
Potter, J D F
Sutherland, S C
Webber, A M

Chard
Beaven, J H
Bowie, C
Davies, S J
Down, A G
Eales, M J
Evans, J M
Freeston, W
Gamm, F G S
Glanvill, A P
Glanvill, M E
Goddard, C L
Harris, S W
Jones, D R H
Montague, I A
Paxton, A M
Rees, A
Reeves, R G W
Roberts, P J
Saintey, P A
Staveley, C D
Tresidder, A P T
Tyson, C M

Chatham
Ahern, M D
Ahmad, O A F
Aslam, T
Badiger, R V
Beeby, D I
Bellary, S V
Broom, T
Callebaut, G E H
Chan, K N
Chaudhry, M A
Cohen, J

Craig, A V
Dabestani, M
Davis, F C
Douglas, M K
Foy, D M
Gopalji, B T
Hanson, L M H
Hay, A J
Howard, C G
Hussain, A
Iles, S E
Imlach, A A
Janse Van Vuuren, N
Jennings, P J
Jewitt, D D E
Jha, A B
Jones, E R
Judge, S
Karim, M M
Khan-Lodhi, N
Khan, M A
Lal, A
Lewis, A M
McWilliams, L F
Mahapatra, K S
Mahmood, A
Mansour, N Y
Mansueto, V
Masand, M
Merwaha, R
Modha, P G
Mohamed, M S H
Morton, V J
Nathan, N
Norris, R W
Ogueh, O
Qureshi, K N
Raval, J K
Raval, P B
Raval, V P
Sethi, C S
Sethi, J K
Shaikh, R A
Shariff, U M
Sharma, A
Shum, C M
Simmons, H O
Sinha, G C
Soutter, L P
Stearns, A H
Schwedziuk, P
Talavlikar, P H
Tooby, D J
Tucker, B R
Tucker, P J
Ukachi-Lois, J O
Vibhuti, R
Virdee, B S
Webb, P J
Windmill, M E
Yousaf, R

Chathill
Patterson, S M
Spark, M G

Chatteris
Childs, A J
Duguid, B
Herbert, A T
Massey, A M O
Szekely, J M
Watts, S J

Cheadle
Abdulezer, T R
Adam, N M
Adams, J R
Aggarwal, R
Ajmal, M
Almond, D P
Aslam, N F
Atkinson, N H
Baron, M
Bazley, P D
Bennett, C A
Black, R L
Bowman, A H
Boyd, J
Brady, J L
Cahill, A
Carroll, R N P
Chapman, P J L
Chaudhry, A A
Colgan, S M
Connolly, P T
Cowie, R A
Cox, J
Craig, R D P
Crewe, H J

Cumming, W J K
Dakin, E M
Dalpadado, L S G
Darroch, R A
Das, A
Davidson, D G D
Davies, C P
Davison, A J
Day, J F
De Kretser, D M H
Deakin, D P
Dean, K M
Deiraniya, A H K
Delaney, J A
Depares, J
Dickens, C M
Doherty, C H
Donaghy, M C
Downie, P
Drake, S P
Dunlop, P M
Duthie, M B
Early, P F
Ellis, J
Fitzgerald, J J A
Fletcher, R H
Fraser, N C
Fuller, A R
Gaon, D
Gardner, R W
George, B
Gilbert, D J
Glicher, S R
Goodwin, S H J
Gore, P J
Gowland, E
Grant, E M
Gupta, A P
Haines, J F
Hambleton, G
Hambleton, K M
Hardman, A
Hatimy, U A
Hendry, J
Higson, V L
Hopkins, S M
Hudson, G R
Hunter, M D
Hussain, I
Ingleby, I
Isherwood, M J
Jackson, H
Jobling, A J
Johnson, S M
Jones, A E
Jones, B
Keenan, J
Khan, S A
Kiely, G P
Knox, G M
Lang, D M
Lansbury, J
Lee, S J
Lemon, J G
Leslie, S A
Lewis, D M
Lewis, M J V
Lim, K M Y
Lord, G M
Lord, R H
Lund, S T
MacCarthy, J M
McFarlane, T
McGirr, P W
McKeown, S P
McLaren, J E
McLauchlan, D G
Maclellan-Smith, I
Mamelok, J P
Markham, D E
Mather, A J
Meigh, J A
Miller, T C
Mirski, T I M
Mishra, K
Moore, S J
Morewood, G A
Morgan, R J
Mottershead, M S
Myatt, T S
Naeem, N S
Nassar, W Y
Newbon, S
Ng Huang, S C P
O'Driscoll, J B
O'Gorman, P J
Oldale, M J
Oommen, P K
Patel, S J

Payne, C R
Pemberton, C J
Pollard, D E
Priest, A V
Priestley, G S
Radcliffe, D
Ream, J A
Richardson, K A
Rigg, J D
Roberts, E D
Rowlands, A K
Rowlands, D J
Russell, J R
Sandars, J E
Sanderson, J H
Sassoon, J H
Seabrook, R J
Seeley, S K
Shalet, S M
Shepherd, J N
Sillince, C
Simpson, R S
Simpson, S M
Smith, W D
Strachan, A N
Strachan, E J
Stretton, T B
Sutton, J K
Swainson, C J
Sykes, J R
Sylvester, B S
Taylor, A K
Testa, H J
Thorne, J A
Turnberg, D
Tweedle, D E F
Wade, M W P
Walsh, S M
Weatherby, E D
Webb, A K
Webb, L J
Webster, A P
Weiner, C A
Wensley, R T
Whiteson, S D
Whittaker, J S
Woods, M R
Wright, A T

Cheddar
Blakeney-Edwards, N P
Davies, T E
Dingley, E R
Hincks, J R
Smith, E J
Thomas, S Y A
Willis, J E
Winter, J P

Chelmsford
Acorn, D J
Acton, J A
Agarwal, A
Ahmad, S
Ahmed, M A
Ahmed, W
Akhurst, J M
Al Janabi, K J S
Alexander, W L
Ali, N R
Allan, H F
Anderson, C S
Anfield, A C D
Ansermino, J M
Archer, M
Bagchi, R
Bailey, M C
Bakewell, S M
Balmer, B D
Banks, A
Bannon, L
Barron, E T
Baugh, O H A
Baylis, T M
Bazett, M A
Bell, M P
Bell, T A G
Bevan, C J
Birn-Jeffery, J
Blainey, A D
Blizzard, J W
Boggon, R P
Boira Segarra, M B
Boon, C S
Booth, J T
Boyle, R J
Bradbury, P G
Brain, A G C
Brain, H P S

Brann, L R
Bridgman, J C
Bridgman, J F
Brook, V
Brown, M T
Brown, P D
Bruce, K M
Bulkeley, J D L
Cacket, N E
Campbell, D W
Carter, J A
Cass, S
Chad, R K
Clark, G
Clesham, G J
Collins, C J
Constantin, A M L
Cook, S G
Cooper, N I
Cordell-Smith, J A
Cormack, J F
Coumbarides, A M
Crisp, T A
Cummins, T A
Cunnah, D T E
Cunniffe, G A
Dann, C F
Daruwala, P D
Davies, P J
Davies, R A
Davis, M E
Davis, M K
Dawton, A J
De Meza, P
De Ville, K M
Dilley, S P
Doherty, S T
Duffy, M
Duku, A Y
Durcan, J J
Durrani, M
Dyson, A E
Eaton, J E
Edelsten, M
Emerick, S C
Essien, A R
Everett, S C
Fallowfield, M E
Faure-Walker, S A V
Ferguson, J L
Fisher, J M
Flemming, A F S
Forbes, D I
Forbes, R D
Forde, I
Frame, J D
Franklin, A J
Garrod, P J
Garvey, J C
Gaskell, W G
Gittos, M J B
Goodfellow, C F
Gopakumar, C K
Grant, F M
Greene, M L
Griffith, D W
Guttikonda, A
Guttikonda, K L
Guy, J
Guy, L M
Hale, B E C
Hall, N C
Handy, J L
Hanson, B C
Hariram, P
Harpur, J E
Harverson, A R V
Harverson, G
Harvey, M H
Hashmi, S T A
Hashmi, S Z A
Hatton, C-L
Heywood-Waddington, M B
Hock Heng Tham, Dr
Hooper, D M
Hopkins, P A
Huddy, N C
Huddy, V J
Hughes, J S
Hume, E M
Hunt, N G
Ingold, S R
Iskander, C M
Ivermee, S P
Ives, A J
Iwuagwu, F C
Jackson, G M
Jader, S N

Cheltenham

Jegede, A A
Jenkins, G W
Johnson, P D
Jonas, M
Kamala, K
Kelly, D A
Kelly, R A
Kiff, K M
King, D S
Klaber, M C V
Lach, S
Lafferty, K
Lanman, I R
Leaver, S A
Lewi, H J E
Lewis, H A
Lints, A V
Lipscomb, A P
Little, J C
Logan, A
Longhurst, H J
Lotay, R K
Lyall, H A
McAllister, P D
Macbeth, J N
McCarthy, P R
Macgregor, M F
McLean, G E
Mahesh Babu, R N
Manickasamy, T A
Marrett, J E
Mathai, J T
Maxwell, J F
Melamed, R
Merritt, J L
Middleton, M I
Miranda Caraballo, J I
Monsell, N J
Mookerjee, R P
Moore, C J
Morgan, B H
Morley-Jacob, C A
Moss, P M
Murphy, E A
Murray, C
Murray, D M
Murray, M
Nadra, A
Naraghi, A H
Nickol, K H
Niranjan, N S
North, M A
Noury, S A M
Oak, M K
Onwude, J L
Ooi, L G S
Osborne, D R
Pace-Balzan, A
Pain, A N
Panagiotopoulos, I
Partington, C K
Passani, S
Pateman, M T
Patterson, M
Pauffley, J H
Peck, D J
Peck, S
Philpott, G J
Pickard, T M
Picton, T A
Pirrie, J M
Pitt, B M
Pluck, J C
Qureshi, A S
Qureshi, S
Ramlee, N N H
Ramsay, H V
Randell, R
Rao, V R
Ravi, M
Richardson, N G B
Robarts, P J
Roberts, M E
Robson, E J
Ross, A H M
Rushbrook, S M
Russell, S M
Salmon, K M
Salom De Tord, R
Santhiapillai, D
Sarjudeen, M T
Sauven, P D
Savage, C S
Savage, N A
Saverymuttu, S H
Seager, F G M
Short, A I K
Singh, C B
Singh, G
Sinha, A
Sisson, J R
Sommerlad, B C
Sommerlad, M G
Soria, A
Spence, M R
Spilsbury, R A
Spurr, M J
Srinivasan, A M
Stallwood, M I
Stern, P M
Stevens, S A
Stewart, N A R
Steyn, M P
Su, A P C C
Sutcliff, J R H
Swallow, J H
Tamlyn, G W
Tarjuman, M
Taylor, M F S
Teare, E L
Tetstall, A P
Tettmar, R E
Than, M
Thorn, J L
Thoung, M T
Thway, Y
Timmins, A C
Tiwari, A
Tiwari, I
Toes, N A
Towers, E M
Towson, N B D
Tucker, S E
Tuite, J D
Turk, K A D
Utting, J A
Vincent, N R J
Vucevic, R
Wagle, S G
Walker, M P
Walmsley, D A
Ward-Booth, R P
Ward, P J
Whitney, R W
Wickramasinghe, S G M
Williams, D J M
Williams, W W
Winton, P E
Wissa, A H
Wood, E C
Wood, M K
Wood, P J C
Wood, S M
Wright, J M
Yaqoob, M
Zwink, R B

Cheltenham

Ackroyd, A
Adams, J F R
Ainscow, D A P
Aldridge, C S V H
Allfrey, C F
Allum, W E
Anderson, J T
Andrews, C M
Anstee, B H
Anthony, R A J
Aung Thu, Dr
Barker, G N
Batten, J H
Bennett, I M
Bennett, J M
Benstead, K
Bialas, M C
Billings, R A
Black, D
Blake, G M
Blundell, E L
Bohm, Y H
Bond, R
Bouzyk, P C A
Bowley, R N
Brampton, W J
Bramwell, J C
Briers, P J
Bristol, J B
Brooks, K M
Brown, E F
Brudney, C S
Brunskill, J M E
Buckley, W E G
Bugaighis, A E
Bunting, J S
Burgess, C C
Burgess, L M
Burkett, J D
Burvill-Holmes, P
Caldwell, J A
Campbell, A J
Capell, E A
Carpenter, M
Carter, J J B
Carter, T J
Casey, W F
Chapman, D C
Chapple, R
Chapple, R D
Cheetham, D R
Chodera, J C
Christmas, T K J
Church, C A
Church, L D
Clarkson, J M
Clarkson, K R
Cogger, V E S
Collyer, S P
Cooper, M A
Copp, M V
Copps, C A
Counsell, R
Court, S E
Cowen, C J
Cox, A-M
Cranna, F M
Cummin, C G
Cunliffe, D R
Curtis, K W
Dagger, T
Dalton, R J
Darling, A H
Davies, P H
Davies, S L
Day, A J
De Courcy, J G
De Gressi, S
De Moor, M M A
Deering, A H
Delaney, G M
Delaney, T J
Delhanty, M H V
Dick, A M
Disney, J N
Dixon, G E
Douglas, D R
Dring, S M
Duthie, A V E
Dye, H K
Dykes, R M
Eaton, D J
Edmondson, S G
Edwards, H E
Elliott, S A
Ellis, C A
Ellis, M F S
Ellis, R H
Elyan, S A G
Evason, A R
Eynon, C A
Fairhurst, A M
Field, J
Fielding, P D
Fletcher, P J
Flowers, C S
Flynn, J F
Forsyth, H M
French, V I
Froggatt, R C
Galey, S M
Gazet, A C
Gee, A S
Gibson, F A M
Gibson, J M
Gilbert, H W
Gillett, A P
Giraldi, D J
Glen, R T
Glover, L A
Gompertz, R M H
Goodman, A J
Goodrum, D T
Goodrum, E J
Green, A R
Griffiths, A D
Gubbay, N
Hamilton-Ayres, M J J
Hamilton, D C M
Hamilton, J W
Hande, H R S
Hanna, E M
Hanna, F A
Harding, E V
Harper, J R
Harrison, J M
Harrod, R R
Harrop, M
Hart, C T
Harvey, P D
Haseler, C M
Haynes, S
Healy, T J G
Henson, A
Higgins, P M
Hill, E L
Hills, M M
Hiorns, M P
Hodges, R N
Hollands, J M
Hollands, R D
Holmes, D M
Honeywill, S
Honneyman, F D
Howes, A C
Hoyle, G
Htin Aung, Dr
Huber, C P P
Hurn, J D
Hurst, T J A
Hyatt Williams, M G
Hyatt Williams, R
James, A M
James, B G
James, G S E
Jaycock, P D
Jeffrey, D I
Jones, M B S
Jones, R L
Joyce, M
Karadia, S
Kerr-Wilson, R H J
Kinder, R B
Kinder, S M M
King, B G
King, K I
King, M D
Kirkpatrick, J N P
Kloer, J
Kloer, M J
Kloer, P J
Knights, A L
Kurlbaum, P
Laidlaw, J D D
Laidlow, E H
Lamden, C S J
Larsson, E M
Lascelles, F C
Latham, F
Leddy, J M
Lee, S A
Lennox, W M
Liebert, I J
Llewellyn, T D
Lloyd, D J
Lyle, D W
Lyle, R W
McCarthy, K P
McGrath, J C
McKellar, A K
Mackenzie, E P
McKenzie, I F
Mackinnon, H M
Mackinnon, J G
MacKinnon, M D
Mackintosh, G I S
McMinn, S G E
McNaught, A I
McPherson, I S
McSwiney, M M
Marlow, J H
Marshall, B S M
Marshall, J A
Marson, D
Martin, A
Martin, D G
Martin, K
Mather, C M P
Mathers, R G
Matthew, G K
Mayne, N M C
Meade-King, M L
Medland, L F
Mehta, C P
Meyrick, J S
Milroy, S E C
Minett, A R
Mitchell, E A
Moate, T J R
Mohankumar, S
Moliver, A A
Moliver, S
Moore, C G
Moore, J B
Morgan, A G
Morgan, P D
Morison, N J
Morphew, K J
Morris, B D A
Morrow, P C
Mortimore, I L
Mount, J H
Murphy, E A
Neill, D J
Nelson, S A B
Nicholas, M E
Nicolson, B R
Nijjar, R S
O'Conor, H M N
O'Leary, C M
Odam, R
Olver, J D
Ong, J
Ormerod, T P
Owen, J R
Owen, K L
Pascall, A
Passant, C D
Pearce, S L
Pearson, J G
Penketh, A R L
Penny, E C
Perkins, C S
Pillai, M B
Pomeroy, A
Poskitt, K R
Pratt, S F
Price, D G
Price, E D P
Price, N C
Pugh, V L
Pygott, Y M
Quekett, J T S
Radbourne, B M
Rahill, M T C
Raitt, E J
Ramsay, I D
Ranger, M
Rawstorne, S
Rees, R J W
Reilly, M C
Rice-Evans, E I
Richards, M J
Ritchie, P A
Robinson-White, C M
Robinson, C P
Robinson, F M
Roch-Berry, C S B
Rogers, R S B
Rooker, G D
Ropner, R J R
Roscoe, P
Ross, A
Rouse, G M
Routh, G S
Rowles, S V
Russell, H C
Ryley, S P
Sanchez-Moyano Lea, J M
Sanders, H E
Sanderson, P M
Saunders, A
Sawers, H A
Sawers, J S A
Scanlon, P H
Scott, S J
Seddon, G B
Shepherd, S F
Sherringham, P E C
Skelsey, E L
Skillman, J M
Slimmings, P G
Sloan, F J
Smellie, V R
Smith, S P
Soltau, D H K
Stedeford, J C
Steele, N A
Sutton, M
Sweet-Escott, M W
Thompson, C L
Thompson, J B
Thomson, D S
Thomson, R G
Thornett, J A
Timlin, C E
Todd, K H
Topliss, C J
Treharne, A E
Tribley, A R
Tribley, K D
Trueman, M D
Ursell, K M
Van Rooyen, E
Vernon-Smith, J W
Wadsworth, F M E
Wand, J S
Watkins, D J
Watt, W A
Webb, M R
West, R M
West, S L
West, S E
Whitham, S E
Whyman, M R
Wickham, H E H V
Williamson, G H
Wilson, G M
Wilson, J M
Withers, A F D
Wreford, J
Wright, W B
Young, N J
Young, P N
Young, R E

Chepstow

Allison, R J
Dallimore, J N
Daly, M H
Davies, H L
Dickson, W A
Edwards, T J
Gibbon, G V
Gray, B M
Hancox, D J
Hawkins, P
Hilton, P J
Jacks, S M
Jacks, T A
Jacques, M A
Jenkins, K
Jones, N J P E
Jones, P H
Jones, R H
Jovasevic, B
Kimble, F W
Lougher, L J
Lunn, J N
Matthews, C N A
May, J E
Merrick, J M
Moore, E J
Morton, P P
Oldham, J C
Pendleton, A P M
Penney, M D
Pullen, F J
Rees, E H
Reynolds, M T P
Roberts, P
Saphier, H
Savage, C
Seale, A N
Tayton, K J J
Thompson, P D
Twamley, H W J
Van Buren, A E
Watkins, O H
Williams, S T B

Chertsey

Aggarwal, R
Amua-Quarshie, N
Barnes, D
Batchelor, P M
Baxter, M A
Beeson, A A
Bennett, C E
Blewitt, N J
Bowyer, J J
Britton, M G
Brodribb, P F
Burns, J P J
Butler, B
Canty, M C
Castleton, B A
Chin, K H
Chong, H P
Cole, R S
Coward, F B
Coyer, J
Crawshaw, P A G
Creagh, T M
Davidson, D G
Davidson, S M
Dawson, S J
Dhenin, G H
Donaldson, D R
Elias, A H
Evans, J A
Evans, R J
Farjad Azad, F
Finch, P J

Chesterfield

Fluck, D S
Fowle, A J
Franciosi, P G
Fuzzey, G J J
Gelman, W
Glover, J R
Greaves, K
Grundy, H C
Haddad, D F
Hadikoumi, I
Hadley, J M
Hall, G M
Hall, M
Hennessy, R E
Ho, P P
Hollingsworth, R P
Houlton, P G
Hung, W Y-C
Jamruth Bibi, A B
Jones, K D
Joy, M D
Kanagasabay, S
Kumar, P
Long, C A
McQuade, B N
Mallinson, E A
Manaktala, K J R
Manjubhashini, S
Mann, H M
Mantel-Cooper, N
Martin, P B
Maxfield, H S
Michael, S A
Nackasha, W L
Neill, S M
Newman, K J H
Newton, R C F
Nordstrom, M E
North-Coombes, D P
O'Shaughnessy, D F
Patil, K P
Penketh, R J A
Rafferty, A M
Rana, P S
Rizvi, S S A
Sarris, I
Sebestik, J P
Seehra, K K
Sharma, V
Silver, D M
Singh, A P
Singh, S
Stuart, F M
Taylor, A F
Thomas, M H
Towie, H G
Turner, P
Weston, J A B
Wright, J T
Wyatt, M L
Zoric, B

Chesham

Appleby, M I
Aulaqi, A A M
Baxter, T
Bishop, A P
Boast, P W
Clegg, B V
Cooper, N C
Davies, A P
Dineen, R A
Fabre, R A
Firth, R M
Flint, P J
Hatfield, M
Heywood, S K
Jordan, R A
King, S M
Masters, G L
Middle, G B
Morris, A E
Mowat, K J
Norman, M
Paul, M L H
Payne, G P I
Phibbs, P A T
Rashiq, H N
Roberts, J P
Russell, T
Singh, J P
Stevens, D C
Tovey, R B
Usher, S M
Verrinder, C J L
Wilkie, J N

Chessington

Clarke, S C

Currie, A P
Edgar, F M
Elford, M T
Gibb, J K
Gray, J E
Jayasekera, N
Khan, K A
Lyons, A J
Riley, S J
Somanathan, L
Udal, M S
Visva Nathan, S

Chester

Adams, E J
Adams, R M
Ahmed, J
Al Shamma, F A S
Alfonsi, V P
Allen, J T D
Amin, A W A K
Anderson, L E
Anscombe, B G
Armstrong, S
Arnold, R T
Ashton, A J E
Assheton, D C
Baker, C M
Baker, M A H
Ball, E M P
Barnard, C S
Barrondo Azcorra, M
Battersby, N C
Beckitt, T A
Bender, S
Berry, E
Berry, J
Bertram, A
Billings, A C
Birchett, S H
Biske, E M
Blacklock, N S
Blake, A C
Blakely, J J A
Bland, A K
Bobic, V
Bodsworth, H
Boothroyd, E C
Bottomley, W
Bourne, M W
Bowles, S A
Bowyer, J D
Boyd, J P
Bradshaw, D J
Braithwaite, I J
Bronnert, N H
Brookes, R
Brown, L G
Bulgen, D Y
Bullough, A S
Burke, M M
Bushell, K E
Butcher, J M
Byam, J E
Cabrera Cabrera, A R
Cain, J E
Campbell, A J P
Campbell, D
Campbell, S H
Carter, L
Charles-Jones, J E D
Charles-Jones, S M D
Cherry, J M
Childs, D
Chitty, R N
Cliff, A M
Clough, J V
Coals, J
Coghlan, S F E
Conway, D S G
Cook, M A T
Cope, T M
Cornforth, C M
Cotgrove, A J
Cotter, H M J
Coughlin, L B
Coyle-Gilchrist, M M
Coyle, P R
Craven, B M
Creagh-Barry, P C P
Cresswell, A D
Crinyion, I J
Cunliffe, C H
Curphey, J M
Curtis, J M
Cuthill, I M
Da Gama-Rose, B M
Dalzell, A J C
Danczak, E M

Daniels, I S
Davidson, J S
Davies-Humphreys, J
Davies, R M
Davies, T J
Davis, P B M
De Cossart, L M
Deas, K S
Debray, R
Demnitz, U H
Dennitts, P J
Dhital, S K
Dignon, N M
Dowling, C J
Dowling, P
Doyle, G J
Duffin, D N
Duffin, L B
Dunbavand, A
Duncan, R K
Dunn, H D
Ellerby, S E
Elliott, A E
Emmerson, L F
Evans-Jones, F G
Evans-Jones, J G
Evans-Jones, L G
Evans, S P
Ewins, D L
Fairweather, S H E
Fantom, E S
Farrall, D L
Fergusson, N V
Finnerty, J P
Fisher, C D
Fleming, L J
Forbes, A M
Forrest, E T S
Forsyth, M C
Foster, G E
Fowler, A
Franks, A R
Fryar, C P
Galaud, J B
Gardiner, M R
Gentle, S M
Ghebrehewet, S
Gibbs, J M
Gilmore, C
Golder, N D B
Gowers, S G
Gray, K E C
Griffith, A W
Griffiths, M D
Guest, V J
Guinan, K T
Hafez Amin, H E S
Hargreaves, W J
Harlin, S J
Harris, N A
Harris, P G
Harrison, D A
Harvey, I A
Hassanein, M M A
Hayward, E L
Hodgson, J
Hogan, G M
Holland, J L
Holley, G E
Holliday, T D S
Holme, C-A
Hood, J S
Hopkins, W D
Houghton, J E
Hughes, A C
Hughes, I L
Hunter, P R
Inchley, D C
Ingham, H
Jameson, P M
Jap-A-Joe, H K
Jayaram, R
Jayaram, V K
Johnston, M N
Jones, A J
Jones, D A L
Jones, J I W
Jones, R D
Jones, V W
Joyce, P K
Judge, J F
Kane, J F
Kaufman, A L
Kaye, S N
Keeping, I M
Kenyon, W E
Kini, K N
Langrick, H E
Larmour, P F

Lee, R M
Leech, S G
Leng, G
Lloyd, H M
Logan, A S C
Lowrie, M J S
Lugton, J H
Lush, D
McBride, M
McCaig, R H
McClure, E A
McClure, R H
McCormack, M J
McDonald, P C
Macdonald, S E
McGeorge, D D
Mackay, A M
Mackinnon, N A
McNutt, A R J
Madden, J S
Maitland, A H
Makower, R M
Malik, S
Manche, M
Mannion, P T
Meachim, S M
Mead, G E
Mendelsohn, S S
Mills, B
Milner, P M
Minshall, I R
Mishra, P K
Monk, D N
Morgan, N K
Muirhead, R
Myskow, M W
Nathan, R N
Naylor, S E
Nelson, R A
Neukom, C R
Nicholson, D G
O'Donnell, J
O'Mahony, C P
O'Sullivan, J P
Oliver, P J
Overton, C
Owen, R A
Owen, S J
Padmakumar, B
Parry, J C
Pascall, O J
Peattie, A B
Pennington, J H
Poole, P M
Powell, C S
Powell, D L
Pownall, C
Prebble, S E
Pullin, A V
Ratcliffe, D S
Ramsdale, J E
Reid, P G
Riley, L M
Roaf, R
Roberts, S A
Robertson, M F
Rogers, A J
Rogerson, I M
Rowe, B R
Roylance, P D
Russell, I J B
Russell, I A
Ryan, S R
Saunders, T P
Scanlan, J
Schofield, C E
Scott, P
Seddon, D J
Sedgwick, M L
Self, R J
Setty, P H R
Shanahan, A P
Simpson, B J
Simpson, R J
Sinha, B N
Sissons, C E
Sissons, D A
Sissons, G R J
Sivananthan, A
Skilton, R W H
Skues, M A
Smith, A L
Smith, B J
Smith, W D F
Sowerby, R G
Spencer, H F
Spencer, M G
Stanley, J D
Statham, J A

Steele, P R M
Stephens, J M
Stewart, A G
Stewart, R C
Stronach, A J
Swallow, M D
Swanson, M A
Taylor, C J
Taylor, M L
Temple-Murray, A P
Temple, L J
Thelwell, J R
Thomas, A
Thompson, B A
Thompson, M W
Thompson, R E
Thompson, V
Thornton, L
Tighe, S Q M
Todd, R W
Tonge, B L
Tonge, V
Towers, S H
Tsekouras, A
Turner, A
Turner, S L
Tutton, M K
Wakeley, J C N
Walker, D J
Warren, E
Weatherley, R E
Wentel, J D
Westlake-Guy, C H
Wetherell, G A
White, G B
Whiteoak, K L W
Williams, G
Williams, J H
Willis, R G
Willmott, J H C
Wilson, J F
Worth, J M
Worth, R C
Worthington, T R
Wright, E A
Yuill, R A

Chester-le-Street

Alexander, K
Bennett, C J
Bowman, S J
Bray, J A
Brockington, J M
Collings, P A J
Colman, G
Cookey, N C
Crackett, G
Derrick, J P
Douglas, A R H
Duke, A M
Duke, W A
Espie, J T
Espie, P J
Featherstone, G L
Fletcher, P T
Garcia-Miralles, J R
Gollings, A J
Grimson, T A
Hall, R S
Herring, D W
Holmes, C J
Hughes, J M
Johnston, T P S
Leung, S O M
Lilly, R J
Lombard, D C
McGillivray, K
Mackay, V E
McMichael, J L
Marsden, S N E
Morrell, J R D
Nair, R R
Norman, J B
Owen, T D
Powney, A
Preston, J G
Rahman, S
Rhys Evans, G
Robinson, A B
Shave, N R
Shirbhate, N C
Sinclair, S
Steele, J W
Sullivan, A
Thein Thein Wynn, Dr
Timmons, M T G
Tubmen, H
Underwood, M C

Vincent, P W
Wheatley, R

Chesterfield

Adams, D P
Ahmed, K A
Ahson, A A
Aiken, R A
Ainsworth, A J
Alam, M M
Aldred, P R
Allen, C C
Allen, D
Allen, T R
Anderson, D I
Andrew, M F
Apaya, J A
Archer, A G
Asher, J N
Atkins, J-A L
Aucott, W R
Ayyash, H
Aziz, N H
Babirecki, M
Bailey, R C
Baker, G C W
Banning, M D
Bardsley, D
Beauchamp, C G
Bell, E O
Bescoby-Chambers, N J C
Bethell, A N
Bhalla, D
Bhattacharyya, R N
Black, D W
Blagden, M D
Booth, C J
Bose, J C
Boucher, N R
Bourne, J T
Bradley, M A
Brooks, D J
Bryant, M J
Bullock, J
Bullock, J
Campbell, J P R
Carley, J M
Chand, A D
Chawla, V
Cheam, E W S
Chedumbarum Pillay, O D
Chew, D
Church, E J
Clark, D J
Clarke, U S
Collin, R C L S
Collins, G
Colver, G B
Contardi, P A
Cook, J P
Cook, N J
Cooper, C M
Coup, A
Coyle, J B
Cresswell, J L
Crowther, P S
Cunnane, J G
Dale, J I H
Dastidar, B G
Dave, D
Davie, H P
Davies, S J
Day, C D
De Carteret, J R
Dias, B G
Dilley, S E
Dods, I M
Dornan, M G
Dowsett, S J
Dowson, C M
Dunphy, N W
Durward, H D
Early, N E
Elmore, D M
Else, C P
Ennis, K A B
Eustace, R W
Evans, M
Everett, C F
Fairburn, K
Fermer, F E
Fey, C M
Fowler, C S
Fraser, P A
Freeman, W H
Garbutt, D
Gardner, J A

Chichester

Gedge, A S
Gell, I R
Ghosh, S
Gillam, S C
Glaves, J
Goodwin, D P
Grant, J S
Gray, P B
Gray, W J
Green, M A
Groves, J B
Grundman, M J
Hadfield, J W
Hadfield, S C
Hammerton, J
Hanwella, J S
Harley, D H
Harries, S J
Hawley, C L
Hehir Strelley, M E
Herrick, A M
Heston, J P
Holt, S
Howell, E S
Hughes, D E
Hughes, H O
Humphries, T A
Ibrahim, I F
Iqbal, P
Jackson, C W P
Jackson, M G
Jackson, P C
Jaiswal, R C
James, M J
Jassim, D A A
Jones, W A K
Kale, N J
Keith, P R
Kellock, S L
Kemp, C E
Kimmins, B A G
Knowles, T K
Krishna Kumar, P
Lambert, K J
Lambert, W G
Langan, S
Leary, B D J
Lendrum, K
Leveckis, J
Livesey, A E
Livings, R R
Lloyd, S
Lockie, D
Loveday, J H
Lowe, T
Lower, B M
McConnell, T J D
McConville, A E
McCullough, I M
McDonnell, J M
McKenna, D M
McKenzie, B C
McNab, D A
Madden, C A
Makkison, I
Mallett, D S
Mann, J R
Markus, K
Mason, S M
Masters, P W
Matthews, A P M
May, M S
Medcalf, P
Mee, R A
Millar, J D C
Miller, P E
Mishra, A D
Mitton, D J
Mohamad, K K F
Moon, J A
Morgan, R J
Morrell, N W
Murray, S
Murton, M D
Nair, K V
Narayana Swamy, B G
Natt, A L
Neep, R J
Neofytou, S K T
Nissenbaum, S H
Nofal, F M
O'Neill, P
Oluwajana, F M
Palmer, A
Parker, A P
Parnacott, S M
Parratt, J R
Parry, J C
Parthasarathy, P B
Patel, C B B
Patel, S
Perera, A N R
Pilcher, C J
Pratap, R
Preece, P M
Preston, H S
Price, D A
Raby, C
Ray Chaudhuri, R
Ray, S C
Rayner, P R
Reid, K M
Rengan, D C
Reuter, S
Richardson, R P S
Riches, E
Roberts, I F
Rowlands, R P
Russ, S A
Ryan, D
Ryan, J B
Sandler, D A
Saunders, S
Scotland, H W F
Searle, J M
Sen, R N
Sengupta, S K
Serrell, I R
Sharma, A K
Sharma, G
Shaw, W A
Sheikh, A Z
Shelswell, A E
Shrestha, B K
Simms, J M
Singleton, C D
Sivarajan, V
Smith, A E R
Smith, T
Snee, K
Spencer, D J
Spencer, M R
Start, R D
Stevens, J D
Stevens, P J
Stewart, R M
Stirland, J D
Talati, V R
Tan, Y M
Thambirajah, G R
Thickett, K M
Thomas, K
Thornton, D M
Thurstan, J W
Tromans, P M
Tsang, G M K
Tyler, R M
Tyler, S S A
Underwood, M
Van Der Heijden, L P J
Varma, R K
Walker, A E
Walters, R B
Walton, R D
Webster, J
Whalley, S A
Wilbourn, G
Wood, S A
Worthington, C A
Wroth, R P
Young, B S
Young, R
Yousuf, I M

Chichester

Aldridge, J F L
Allen, D R
Allen, R D
Allen, S J E
Amesbury, B D W
Anderson, D E W
Archer, E
Ashby, C R
Ashby, E C
Ashby, P M
Ashford, N S
Atkins, M
Banfield, P J
Banuls Pattarelli, M
Barnett, A L
Barratt, F M
Bateman, C J T
Bell, F J
Bennett, S V
Berry, P A
Betts, N E
Bevan, P C
Beynon, J L
Binsted, E A
Birtchnell, S A
Birtley, E J
Bishop, M P
Blackwell, M
Blackwell, V C
Bonsey, M M F
Bower, H D
Bowyer, R C
Bracewell, M A
Bradbury, P A
Bradley, J M
Brigden, W D
Britton, J P
Bromley, L M
Brownfield, R N
Buchanan, I Y
Burton, P J C
Buxton, R S J
Candy, D C A
Carpenter, J P
Carruthers, L R B
Carter, P G
Cavanagh, S P
Chadwick, K C
Chai, D T C
Challis, R E
Child, T J
Clarke, B M
Clarke, P D
Coburn, P R
Coffin, F R
Collins, D R
Collins, M D
Collis, J W
Condon, H C
Conroy, B
Conroy, J M
Conyers, A B
Copsey, A
Corke, A R
Covell, T
Cowan, J B
Crinion, A R
Cripps, N P J
Crossman, R P
Deavall, T
Dempster, S J
Dennis, S C R
Dewhurst, A G
Dormer, M J S
Dunlop, B N B
Dzikowski, W K
Edmond, M C
Edwards, T G
Elliott, B
Ellis, S J
Ely, B S
Fairley, A
Feetham, M E G
Fernando, K T M
Fernando, S M
Fieldhouse, R M A
Findlay, A M T
Ford, J C
Fox, P D
Gethen, R C R
Gilbert, M E
Gomez, B K
Gomez, M P G A
Gordon-Watson, M A
Gorrie, G H
Graham, K T
Greenwood, M C
Greenwood, W E
Gregory, A B
Greig, M A
Hagen, D L
Haigh, R A
Hammans, S R
Hammond, T J
Hargreaves, J
Harries, B J
Harris, R
Hartland, S J
Hartree, C J
Harvey, A J
Hawkins, M J
Hawkins, W
Hester, R F
Hewetson, M J T
Hide, D
Hill, R P
Hoare, D M
Holman, R A E
Hooker, J G
Hooper, M
Hounsome, C E
Howarth, M W
Howlett, R A
Hunniford, Y E
Ivatts, S H
James, S L
Janes, S L
Jenkins, A J D
Johnson, P A
Johnstone, C I
Johnstone, T
Jones, C M
Kay, D N
Kelly, G S-B
Kelly, J
Kelly, S K
Kennedy, D J
Kennett, K
Lacey, C D
Lacey, M J
Lacey, M L
Lake, A C
Lamont, C A R
Lartey, J P A
Laseinde, O O
Latcham, P R
Lavender, C P
Lee, G B
Leegood, H M J
Lewis, F J
Lidstone, V L
Lotinga, J K
Lotinga, K H M
Low, N M H
Lytton, A
McDonald, P F
McDowall, J
McGuinness, C L
McHale, S P
Macpherson, D W
Madden, G J
Mallam, W D C
Martin, K W
Matthews, M B
Matthews, N E V
Medhurst, M R
Miller, K A
Miller, P G
Milligan, H E
Missen, A J B
Missen, J C
Mitchell, P H
Moffitt, V K
Morrison, I M
Mortimer, K E
Morton, S J
Mulatero, C W
Mullett, S T H
Muris, E
Murphy, A
Murphy, C F
Murphy, D J L
Murphy, M M
Murray, T G S
Nicholls, D R
Nicholls, M W N
Nott, M R
O'Brien, J I
O'Keeffe, K A
O'Shea, J K
O'Sullivan, J P
Orr, M J
Owen-Smith, B D
Pailthope, D B L
Palmer, D J
Paterson, J C
Paterson, R G
Payne, A
Perrin, C E
Platts, H A
Poate, T W J
Pointon, G I
Poots, G G L
Pratt, P L
Price, J M
Purse, P A
Quiney, J R
Quinnell, P M
Quinnell, T G
Reader, A M
Reid, C J
Reid, D E B
Rice-Oxley, M
Richardson, J C
Ridley, C M
Ross, D J
Rotz, B
Sainsbury, P
Sartory, F B
Scott, R A P
Sears, A H
Shand, D
Shapiro, E B A
Shipsey, C M
Siddle, S G
Simpson, R D
Simson, J N L
Smith, C
Smith, E M
Snell, J K
Solan, K J
Spence, A J
Spencer, M C
Spender, Q W
Stevens, D J W
Stewart, J D M
Stirling, P W M C
Stott, J A V
Stross, W P
Stupple, J M G
Styles, M E
Tamlyn, G J
Tanner, J A
Taylor, L J
Taylor, T M
Tilney, H S
Towers, B M
Townend, J R L
Townsend, R F
Turner, G A
Van Arenthals, A J S
Vardy, D L
Venn, S N
Walford, F R
Walker, F C E
Wallace, A C M
Ward, D J
Ward, S P
Wartnaby, H
Watford, N C T
Watts, G V
Watts, J S
Webb, A J
Weeks, M L
White, E
Whitehouse, R J
Whiteside, J D
Whittaker, B E
Whittaker, P J D
Wightman, S
Wild, D
Willcox, C P W
Williams, J L
Williams, L K
Wilson, R J
Winch, T
Witts, E J
Wrigley, E J

Chigwell

Ansari, S A
Beling, G E A
Brandman, S
Cameron-Mowat, C
Celaschi, D A
Chana, J S
Chattopadhyay, U
Chitra, G
Chopra, P S
Dandekar, S S
Dauid, L M
Davies, R M E
Farzaneh-Far, A
Finer, J
Flasz, M H
Hamal, A
Hing, C B
Inayat, Dr
Jackson, J A
Jain, A S
Jain, A K
Jumani, A N
Kwarko, H A
Lall, K S
Lee, R A
Lillywhite, A V
Lillywhite, E K
Maxwell, R
Memon, M A
Mestel, J
Modle, W J
Osen, J S
Osen, M A
Patel, D P
Qureshi, A H
Rajah, V
Roback, S D
Rushton, G J
Schapira, R C
Sharma, A
Singh, S
Strehle, E-M
Weatherstone, R M
Weera, C R W

Chinnor

Ball, K E
Hood, C A
Hood, C A
Knightley, M J
Stamp, S A

Chippenham

Allard, L L
Allen, P
Barter, J A W
Barton, T C
Bevan, R G B
Blake, K I
Bools, C N
Bridgens, J P
Bright, E B
Brosch, J A
Brown, N H
Brunyate, P H
Cartwright, J
Constantine, S J
Dewland, P M
Eastes, H J
Firman, M A
Gaunt, R M C
Grandison, I M
Hartington, K
Heaton, J C
Henry, W S
Holbrook, A G
Jennings, V L
Jones, M R
Kay, J T M
Keatings, B T
Lashford, A M
McCarron, E E
McCay, N J P
McCormack, N W
McCune, C A
McKibbin, A R
Marshall, R
Meudell, C M
Mills, K F
Moore, M T
Morgan, J E
Morley, C E
Muir, R F
Netherwood, A J
Ninan, G M
Nowlan, W A
Page, C J
Page, L J
Paish, N R
Palmer, R B
Patrick, G M
Pickthall, P D
Prees, K A
Russell, J G
Scott-Jupp, C E
Short, E S
Smith, J M
Stanton, E F
Stevens, D M
Stokoe, M A
Watson, C J
While, R S A
Whyatt, N D
Wilkinson, C E
Williams, B J
Williams, I R
Williams, M
Wilson, E
Winterton, A J
Wright, A T S

Chipping Campden

Ballantyne, J R
Brook, W A D
Button, P M
Clarkson, J-M
Denning, A M
Devas, M B
James, M J
Johnson, B E
MacFadyen, W A L
Olliff, J M
Sim, D W
Smith, J A
Stuart, G K
Sykes, D
Walker, J M
Wallbank, W A
Walsh, ND

Clitheroe

Ware, J M
Watson, D A

Chipping Norton
Banstead, C A
Bayliss, H J
Bond, H E K
Davidson, A
Davison, P H
Edwards, D R
Edwards, J E
Elliott, C A
Everett, V J
Freeth, R K
Goves, J R
Hall, W L
Harbinson, R D
Hebden, A L
Hornby, C J
Keenan, C
Keenan, M F
Moore, J G
Moran, P A
Nixon, D P
Packer, J M V
Pargeter, J M
Parker, F B W
Paul, E H M
Peniket, A J
Platten, M C
Queenan, M B
Rihan, R S
Scott, G
Somaiya, R S
Steel, A M
Tritton, D F
Walker, J R
Walton, J A
Watson, N P
Zu Solms-Baruth, C-M E

Chislehurst
Agarwal, P C
Ambache, N
Ambache, S M E
Aziz, M
Baker, S S
Barbary, N S
Becker, W G E
Brander, E A S
Brown, J J S
Bryant, A J
Campbell, D R
Carr, D A
Choong, M L O
Colleypriest, B J
Datta, V
Deacon, C
Dean, E A
Denvir, L
Edmondson, S J
Evans, I L
Gregory, I D R
Griffin, G A
Griffin, T D
Gupta, V K
Hamblyn, N C
Hattotuwa, K L
Higgins, P M
Hitman, G A
Isaacson, H P
Jessiman, I M
Kamdar, B B
Kelly, A T B
Lindley-Jones, M F H
Maddocks, A C
Magrath, H P
Mahesh, Dr
Marten, R H
Morrison, R J G
Mukadam, G A
Mules, F M
Olley, L M
Parson, A F
Perks, R D
Powell, C R
Proffitt, D
Qazi, F A
Rainer, E H
Ratneswaren, S
Rehm, A
Rub, H-U
Savine, R L E
Sevitt, I
Shackleton, J E
Shah, A H
Shah, N
Sharma, P

Sharma, S K
Sichel, R J S
Simmonds, W B G
Sivakumar, B
Terry, J
Trueman, G B
Wasty, S W H
Watkins, M D
Williams, A G
Williams, M
Williams, J D
Williamson, K F
Yonge, G P
Zakaria, G Y

Choppington
Cameron, E A
Dawson, A J
MacDonald, W P
Parker, B L
Sanderson, P W
Thomas, M I
Turner, W M
White, T

Chorley
Abbott, P
Ahmed, K
Ainsworth, P
Almond, W R
Astle, D L
Baghdjian, R B
Barker, C
Bell, S C
Bennett, A M
Bennett, R J C
Black, D J
Blake, P M
Brade, D A
Brown, A K
Burford, S A
Calleja, M A
Clarke, C B
Clarke, J F B
Crossley, S L
Damas Mora, J M R
Dare, E K
Drake, I M
Edwards, S J
El Halhuli, O A E R S
Estill, W O
Evison, M N
Evison, R A
France, M M
Gale, M S J
Gallagley, A
Galletly, S C
Garnett, S M
George, P P
Griffiths, B
Hall, I M
Halstead, G A
Hamilton, M
Hartley, R D
Heald, S J
Hilton, S N
Howarth, D E
Hronis, V G
Hunt, A E
Hunter, J T
Hussain, S A
Imam, S H
Inglis, P R
Iyengar, M O N
Jones, L S
Katic, B M
Kelly, G A
Kelly, G A
Khanna, V K
Knapp, J A
Lamden, K H
Leonard, I J
Lofthouse, J A
Lord, S R
Lyons, R M
McAllister, D M
Madi, S I
Mainey, V G
Manji, A K
Marsden, D M
Marsden, K
Maybury, J W
Maybury, N K
Mohammed, A
Montero Garcia, J M
Morgan-Capner, P
Mughal, M M
Mulholland, K M
Mumford, P A
Mutch, A J

Ne Win, Dr
O'Donnell, E L
Phillips, K A
Pinheiro, N L
Platt, J A
Robinson, L J
Ross, D
Salpekar, P D
Sambrook, A M
Sambrook, A J
Savage, M E
Scott, J M
Service, M A
Shah, V S
Sharma, V N
Sloan, M A
Smith, I G
Soe Than Myint, Dr
Spinks, B C
Stockwell, R C
Symes, J E
Symes, S R
Tasker, M
Tembe, D P
Troop, A C
Vaidya, K S
Valiant, K A
Venkatasubba Rao, S
Wallis, S C
Walsh, J M
Ward, W C
Watmough, P J
Whalley, J
Whalley, J A
Whitaker, H J
Williams, S H
Wilson, R A
Wilson, W W
Wood, W M
Wren, M
Wren, P J J
Yates, F W
Young, S D

Christchurch
Ahmad, M
Archard, G E
Aveyard, S C
Barnett, T J
Birch, H E W
Blaikley, A B
Blick, A H
Boyd, A P M
Cantlie, J
Carey, N F
Carr, N
Clarke, J M
Cocks, R A
Collier, J D
Collins, S C P
Coupe, S C
Critchley, E
Deane, E W
Debenham, E J R
Dunne, K A
Dunnill, R P H
Edwards, K
Ellerton, D A
Elphick, P R
Evans, A J
Faldu, V
Fielding, S F
Fulford, L G
Gamper, M A
Gamper, N H
Gardner, E K
Garnham, J R
Gay, J C C
Gilbertson, R C
Gregson, J P
Haden, R
Halder, S R
Hall, K E
Hamdi, S S
Harris, J D C
Haydon, E G
Hickish, A E
Hickish, G W
Hodgson, L E
Jenkinson, R
Josephs, L K
Kay, T A
Kelly, B J
Kelso, W
Kent, J H C
Klein, G
Lee, J M
Livingstone, M
Lloyd-Thomas, A R

Lodge, L C
Louli, A Y
McCarthy, K
McGowran, D P
Menzies, A R
Nell, J L
Oliver, J M
Pearce, P E
Pillinger, J E T
Pugh, E M G
Pugh, R J
Rana, B S
Rana, M Z K
Randall, F M
Rangaswamy, V
Reeve, S D
Rhodes, G A
Rogers, D J
Savage, N J
Scott-Jupp, R M
Scott-Jupp, W M
Scott, J D
Smith, F M S
Smith, P C H T
Speirs, A T O
Sugarman, I D
Tallant, N P
Tang, Y Y M
Terry, C M
Thomas, R L
Tuddenham, A D
Walden, A
White, A S T
White, J S
Williams, M A
Willis, K A
Wood, A W
Wood, C H
Wood, F B G
Wood, M B
Wyatt, A

Chulmleigh
Beer, M H
Bowman, C R
Brown, B A
Burke, J E T
Cox, J D
Fisher, S R
Kemp, N H
Wielink, R C A D

Church Stretton
Allan, N C
Anderson, D G
Bartlett, K
Beach, J F
Beach, J W
Bowdler, S R
Brown, I A R
Cook, L R
Copson, E R
Griffiths, C C
Hooper, P J
Howard, J A
Malone, C J
Parker, J
Parker, T G
Peer, E J
Plumptre, A M M
Quinlivan, R C M
Robinson, K A
Rushton, P F
Sefton, E M
Turner, G M A
West, C A
West, D R S

Cinderford
Adams, J M
Arthurs, D
Burrows, C D M
Gadsby, I C
Lane, D M
Lyden, C J
Roberts, R C
Shaw, D G
Zaheer, P

Cirencester
Barnes, L J
Barton, S
Beales, D M
Beales, D L
Bergin, J H E
Binfield, P M
Black, M L
Cameron, E A
Chapel, A J
Coffey, P E

Coleridge, H C C
Davies, R N
Davis, I R
Drysdale, S W
Dukes, C S
Duncumb, C E
Duncumb, R E
Evans, D J
Evans, M
Evans, P M
Evans, R I
Fielder, L V
Fox, G C
Gale, D G L
Goldie, C J
Gomara, C J B
Grant, N J C
Grantham, C F
Hawkins, M
Hewett, H E
Hewett, M F
Higgins, P G
Hutchison, C R
Jacob, M P
James, F E
Jardine, C V
Jenkins, J C
Jones, J H
MacKinnon, A D
MacKinnon, J R
Marriott, C M
Mathias, S R
Miller, J E
Mitchell, D C
Moorhead, P M
O'Donovan, E C
Patterson, L C
Patuck, D
Patuck, F
Pawson, R M
Postlethwaite, R
Price, P A
Pritchard, L J H
Ramsay, J R S
Robson, C E
Sedgwick, J M W
Sethi, R
Simpson, I J
Sullivan, T J
Tallon, J G J
Thomson, A C P D
Thurston, N
Townsend, H R A
Troughton, A H
Veale, M H D
Waddell, J A
Waters, I R
Watkinson, M C
Whittles, S E
Wigfield, M F
Wilson, A M
Winter, J M

Clackmannan
Bowman, A M
Gray, R D
Jackson, L S
Macphail, D I
Scott, V A
Thomson, I B

Clacton-on-Sea
Barry, M P
Bowsher, F M
Buchanan, L A
Burton, D J
Carter, M D
Cochrane, W H
Colquhoun, J H C
Cox, S
Cullen, T J
Dawson, C C
Faerestrand, H I
Faerestrand, W M
Farrow, R J
Feldmar, G L
Flood, A G
Garas, S F
Garside, J M
Geddes, D M
Grange, A R
Guille, J L
Halstead, D E
Haxton, C A
Howden, P
Hunt, J W
Ishaq, A M
Kibbler, M A R
Leach, J N

Letton, D J
Letton, P H J
Lineen, J P P
Littlemore, A J
McCurdy, J F
Mackenzie, A D C
MacMillan, S J
Mann, M
Mathias, R D
Morrison, A J
North, C D
Sarathchandra, C B
Shiers, C
Stewart, A G E M
Sweeney, G A
Tan, S
Turner, R W

Cleator
Thursz, A D
West, N C

Cleckheaton
Appleton, P M
Barson, J K
Brayshaw, S A
Crosbie, E G
Fox, G S
Greenwood, A
Hatfield, S J
Kelly, D
Khan, M S A
Marsh, J M
Midgley, R S-J
Rix, K J B
Stringer, J
Sykes, J A
Vallow, P W
Wood, P J W

Cleethorpes
Ahluwalia, S
Bhaduri, S K
Choudhury, P
Crombie, R N
Dailey, L
David, H
Doldon, J L
Horsburgh, J D
Lavin, R J
Purser, P C
Rees, A L
Sarkar, D
Singh, K P
Singh, N P
Sutherland, I A
Ward, P J K
Williams, F
Zaro, M A

Clevedon
Baker, V N
Barley, J
Blackwell, A M
Bullock, R D
Ford, J J
Gilmore, J M
Green, D
Hampton, T J
Hime, M C
Horner, G R
Horry, P A
How, G C
Hylton, L C
Jameson, B N
McCrae, J S
MacLeod, A I
Marshall, N C
Miller, I S
Nicholas, F E
Norman, V E
Parfitt, C J
Patrick, E A S
Payne, F B
Pill, S H C
Rukunayake, G N C
Russell, C I F
Stewart, E J
White, G P

Cliftonville
Bissessar, E A

Clitheroe
Ackroyd, M A M
Ainsworth, B
Awan, R J
Bartle, M R
Brown, A M
Burns, J
Bywater, N S

Clogher

Carter, J A F
Crawford, M J
Cronin, M A
Crowther, A
Eddleston, M P
Flatley, M
Fogg, C J
Franks, K N
Freeman, R A
Gavan, J
Golding, T M
Hardy, J
Harrison, CM
Hart, I
Heaton, W M
Henderson, R T S
Higson, R J
Higson, W A
Hodgson, G A
Holgate, S
Huson, A S
Hutchison, B T N
Hutchison, S J
Ibbotson, I J
Kelly, H B
Lansdell, R
McCree, T
Mackean, W G
McKinlay, W J D
McLaughlin, J
McMeekin, N H
Manson, I W
Maw, M C
Morris, S J
Neville, R J
Porter, C
Porter, J H
Purnell, K L
Ramage, I
Razzaque, M A
Rees, G
Royle, C
Saunders, J
Smith, B
Smith, M M
Stalker, R
Stanley, I R
Turner, I M
Wlodarczyk, K K
Zakrzewski, H J

Clogher
Boyd, W H
Irvine, A P

Clydebank

Addis, B J
Anderson, M I M
Beard, N D O
Bell, D R
Chatzigrigoris, P
Clark, A A
Clark, J F
Clarke, E A
Clegg, B D
Crawford, G M
Doverty, M R
Duffy, P S
El Fighi, A A M
Fleming, J M
Fletcher, M A
Gorrie, S M
Harper, P I
Hearns, S T
Hollier, L H
Houston, D R
Jaberoo, D W
Khogali, K A
Lawrie, G M
Light, J K G
Linggood, R M
McCall, J M
McDevitt, A G
McKenzie, J
Maclean, N M
Miller, A H
Mitchell, E I
Polding, A
Potter, A W
Rahman, A Q M H
Ramayya, P
Ray, D A A
Rogerson, G G
Ross, R M
Sardi, A
Sarmiento, A
Simpson, D B
Spence, D G
Sutcliffe, N P
Templeton, L M
Veidenheimer, M C
Wade, A G
Wilson, R J M
Zincke, H

Coalisland

Garvin, J S M

Coalville

Baker, J
Chawda, N J
Hammond, T M
Hazlehurst, G J
Hepplewhite, E A
Horsburgh, C
Jolleys, J V
Khirwadkar, P M
Lawrence, R W
Lewis, A M
Morgan, L M
Muir, W W
Newman, D J
Robinson, I C
Wittels, P L
Woods, D M

Coatbridge

Agnew, M
Bakhtyari-Nejad-Esfahani, A
Bawa, S S
Bell, D W
Brankin, E
Buonaccorsi, E C
Connolly, S A
Coull, R S
Daisley, S E
Docherty, J V
Feeney, J
Flanigan, J J
Fraser, S M
Grewal, A S
Holt, S M
Hutchison, F C E
McCabe, E A
McCarron, B N
McGowan, J D
McIntyre, L M
McMorris, S
Marcuccilli, F
Marcuccilli, N S
Morcos Hanna, M Y
Ooi, K H
Park, D J
Picozzi, G L
Picozzi, J
Rooney, C
Singh, K B P
Turnbull, E B

Cobham

Abraham, C M
Allen, R J
Austen, J C
Bailey, C
Baird, I M
Bell, J G
Chambers, J C
Chisham, M
Desor, M I N
Dunlop, A V
Eliopoulos, F B
Glover, D N
Gompels, B M
Hawkins, S F S C
Hobbs, M D B
Huchzermeyer, P M
Jefferies, S M M
Johnston, F G
Kelly, J A
Knudsen, E T
Kumar, S
Lane, V M
Lehmann, F M
Lewin, J M
Littlejohn, M J
Lytle, J D M
McClure, P S
MacDougall, I S
Meurisse, F L A
Nguyen, D M
Nguyen, H B
Phillips, T T B
Raphael, O R
Robinson, M J
Robinson, O P W
Small, Y J
Stuart, L M
Trent, M P

Watson, A
Winter, G R
Young, R C

Cobo

Biggins, P
Razzak, D

Cockburnspath

Brown, J A H

Cockermouth

Berrill, W T
Bird, A R
Bird, K S
Bird, T
Campbell, G C
Clarkson, D G
Claxton, A
Cockersole, F J
Coote, S E
Cowan, N R L
Desert, S A
Dowsland, M H
Drouet, C J
Dutta, S K
Edwards, A N
Edwards, P J
Eldred, A E
Eynon, S M
Eyre, T A
Fearfield, L A
Fletcher, T
Frazer, R S
Gilchrist, S
Hardie, J L
Hargreaves, A
Herd, E B
Hodson, M J
Holloway, D E
Horder, E A
Hossain, M A
Hossain, S
Howarth, J P
Jones, A P
Lavender, M C
Lees, D M
Lobb, P M M
Marks, H M R
Mason, A R
Metcalfe-Gibson, C
Nield, J
Parkes, J G
Pearson, A J
Roberts, M B R
Rogers, A M
Shaw, N A
Style, A M
Thomson, C
Travis, A
Wandless, R J
Whiteley, J
Wilkinson, J S
Williams, A W
Wilson, P B

Colchester

Aberdour, K R
Adcock, F A
Ahmad, N
Aitken, J M
Al-Dabbagh, M A T
Al-Sad, H M H H
Alam, A N
Alder, H
Alderton, M J
Anderson, E A
Arrindell, A P
Ashok Kumar, T L
Backhouse, C M
Baldwin, S P
Baloch, K H
Baloch, N
Banna, A
Banyard, B D
Barkham, J D T
Barnes, L S
Barnes, M J
Bashir, A
Bateman, D J
Bateman, D J A
Beauchamp, J E
Beckingsale, A B
Bennett, V S
Bentley, J P
Berry, W M
Bevan, A T
Bevan, J C
Blaxill, J M
Bodmer, C W
Bohannan, P J
Booth, C M
Boots, M A
Bown, S D
Bradley, J A
Brayley, N F
Brogan, D P
Brown, J W
Brown, J A
Burt, E H W
Bush, A M
Byrne, P A C
Carlyon, L
Carr, P J
Casale, F F
Cavenagh, N F
Chambers, C
Chanarin, L M
Chanarin, N
Chapman, P J
Claridge, P M
Clark, D G C
Clubb, V J
Cockwell, K
Colclough, A B
Collingwood, P D
Conn, P C
Conway, M E
Cope, A I
Coulson, R W S
Coutts, M A
Cowan, R E
Coxhead, M S
Coxhead, N
Crocket, B M
Cross, X H
Cullen, T H
Curry, S
Cutler, R C
Daunt, S O N
Davidson, A G H
Davidson, F S
Davidson, N J H
Davies, C F
Davies, G L S
De Silva, G K C
De Silva, R J
Dixon, N T
Dixon, P E
Dixon, S J
Dixon, S M
Dobree, C H
Donald, J
Doney, A S F
Donnelly, C M
Dowson, H M P
Doyle, R
Duffy, S M
Eames, G M
Eddy, J W
Edwards, L J
Eldridge, M G
Elrington, G M
Elston, A C
Elston, R A
Emerson, B M
Emery, P J
Etherington, K A
Evans-Jones, J C
Farnworth, H E
Fellows, C P
Ferguson, A L
Finch, S A B
Firth, J B
Foreman, J T
Forsyth, M C
Fox, R
Fox, V E N
Frampton, M A
Freeman, A M
Gamble, D
Gamble, G E
Gatland, J C
Gay, F W
Gear, P
George, M D
Ghosh, I R
Gibbs, M L
Gilbert, C R
Gittos, R A B
Goodwin, A M
Gould, M
Grant, J
Graves, V
Gray, J D
Gray, P W S
Green, J B M
Greville, N R
Griffin, R W
Griffiths, J J
Grimm, B W
Guiver, I M
Gunawardena, S A
Gunetilleke, L
Hale, J C P
Hall, C B
Hall, E
Hall, S
Hamilton, M
Handley, A J
Handley, S A J
Hare, M F
Hargreaves, M J
Hayhoe, S H J
Henderson, D J
Hester, K H C
Hickman, M P
Hilton, N J
Hine, K L
Hinshelwood, R D
Hoodboy, S A
Howells, J G
Howes, T Q
Huber, J P
Hudson, R C
Hughes, N J
Hume, A C
Hunt, M J N
Irwin, E B
Jacklin, F R
James, H M
Jayaratnam, A V H
Jeffries, J D
Johnson, G T
Jones, C E B
Jones, J M E
Jones, M R C
Justice, A A
Kennedy, W P U
Khan, A R
Khetarpal, B K
King, W D
Kitchen, P
Konarzewski, W H
Kong, H A
Laing, R I
Lamont, D A
Landsmeer, R E
Lawrenson, G W
Lennard-Jones, A M
Lind, J F
Loeffler, M D
Lothian, A W R
Lucas, C J
Macallan, C R
McBride, T M
McCarthy, M J
MacDonald, L M
MacDonnell, S P J
McFerran, D J
McGinty, M J
McKeever, C S T
Mackenzie, S I P
Maclean, B S
McLoughlin, T A W
Macmillan, S I E
MacNeill, F A
McRae, R D R
Mahon-Daly, L M E
Marfleet, J C
Marossy, D
Marsh, S K
Marshall, A S
Marshall, P A
Marshall, W
Masters, A P
Matthes, P A
May, A R L
Meanley, J A
Meanley, T H
Menzies, D
Middleton, H O
Millar, D M
Milne, D R M
Milne, S E
Monk, M C
Moore, D J
Moore, M H
Morris, A H
Morrison, D L
Mossop, H E J
Motson, R W
Mukerji, A K
Mukerji, S
Mulenga, H P S
Murphy, M J
Murray, B
Murray, P A
Myers, D M
Myers, G J C
Nizamani, S
Novak, M R
O'Callaghan, E G
O'Callaghan, U C
Ogilvie, A J
Orr, N W M
Owen, J D
Owens, J M
Palmer, E G
Parker, G D
Parker, J A R
Paros, N L
Parry, C W K
Parthasaradhi, K
Patel, A C
Patient, P S
Phillips, M G A
Pickering, R S
Pinkey, B
Podmore, M D
Polak, L
Ponty, R
Poole, R R G
Pratt, W R
Pringle, T G
Rajan, S
Rajapakse, D
Ramster, D G
Ranasinghe, D N
Ranasinghe, P N I
Ranawat, N S
Rao, M
Rasool, I
Rasor, P A
Read, D J
Robinson, A F
Robinson, N C
Rogger-Amies, A M
Ross-Marrs, R P
Rudge, S D
Rudra, T P
Rushbrook, L A W
Ryan, J F
Sagar, S A
Salter, H A
Sanderson, D A
Sanderson, J G
Sarathchandra, S F
Seddon, J
Shah, S Z H
Shearer, J M L
Sheldrick, C M
Shuttleworth, D
Sihra, B S
Singh, R K
Singh, S D
Slawson, J A
Smerdon, G T
Smith, A I
Smith, C N
Smith, C M
Smith, J M
Smith, M A
Snell, M J
Snell, P
Snook, N J
Spooner, L L R
Spowage, P M
St. Joseph, A V
Stannard, E J
Stedman, S L
Steeds, J H
Steiner, N B M
Stephens, D D
Strowbridge, N F
Studdy, J D
Swainston, R M
Sweet, H S
Symons, J C
Tarala, C T
Taylor, B O T
Thavabalan, P B
Thibaut, R E
Thomas, C E
Thomas, D J
Thomas, T L
Thompson, D D
Thompson, M A
Thomson, S J
Thorogood, A
Tillett, A J
Tilley, R E
Toms, R M
Treharne, I A L
Tucker, D L
Tucker, K E
Tucker, P M

Coulsdon

Tupper-Carey, D A
Turner, N A
Urwin, G
Vernon, M S
Wakely, J N
Wall, M
Walshe, J
Ward, W D
Welsh, S F
Whyte, A P
Wilbraham, K
Willenbrock, P C
Williams, A O
Williams, J F
Wilson, M A
Wilson, P R
Withnall, D
Wood, F J
Wood, J A
Wood, M E
Woodd-Walker, R B
Woods, P M
Wright, P L
York, A H
Young, N S
Yousif, E H
Zamora Vicente De Vera, F J

Coldstream
Marynicz, P
Schleypen, P F H M J
Sproule, B J
Veitch, E M H

Coleford
Barton, M E
Camp, J J
Cummins, B D
Ford, L I
Jones, D R H
Longley, R H
Nagle, P J
Nagle, P J
Portman, E
Simpson-White, R
Steiner, D A
Walters, S M
Wilkinson, N M
Winter, P J

Coleraine
Adams, S M
Beck, A W
Beck, A W
Bell, M A
Bonnar, B C
Brown, J A
Brown, J S
Brown, M G
Burns, R W
Church, A W E
Clarke, L W A
Coleman, E
Connor, B W D
Cooper, A R
Dane, T E B
Davies, E A
Dixon, L J
Donnelly, M E C
Ellard, M A
Finnegan, O C
Friel, A M
Fyvie, K R J
Ghaie, S S
Glass, R
Hadden, I J
Henderson, J E
Henderson, W A
Holland, C G
Holmes, K D
Holmes, W
Hope, E A M
Huey, S
Hunter, P
Hunter, R F
Hutchinson, S J
Irwin, K R
Johnston, D G
Kapur, K
Kelly, S G
Kerr, A H
Kerr, A I K
Kerr, J B K
Lee, B C
McAuley, R G
McClenahan, M C
McFetridge, L D
McGahan, A M
McGavock, H
McGlade, J F X

McGowan, W A W
McGrath, D R
McGurk, G M
McLaughlin, J
McMaster, I J
Marshall, G P M
Martin, R P
Mathews, W
Matthews, R S
Meharg, W
Mitchell, B W
Montgomery, R C
Moore, R H
Nevin, L J
Newman, C E
Nicholl, M E
Nutt, D J P
O'Donnell, H E
Orr, D S A
Orr, K G
Orr, R D
Pollock, C L
Quiery, A F J
Quinn, Z E
Rollins, M D
Scally, C M
Shannon, E N
Sharieff, S F
Siberry, H M
Sinnamon, D G
Stewart, D G T
Stewart, H E
Symington, J J M
Telford, K J
Temple, M E
Temple, R W
Thompson, M K J
Thompson, R E B
Topping, W A
Torrens, J K
Tracey, T J
Turner, T B
Wali, J
Wallace, S
White, M H R

Colne
Bower, I
Bryson, J R
Cooper, A K
Cowpe, T V
Cox, P T
De Vries, H
Dick, D G
Duari, M
Haythornthwaite, M J
Jackson, R S
Kenny, R
Kerridge, F J
Kirby, G V
McHugh, A T
Mason, M J M
Miller, P G
Mitchell, A D
Northridge, C S
Phillips, R C S
Sahar, M A
Singh, R C P
Spencer-Palmer, C M
Spencer, A E
Sulaiman, S M U
Turner, H M
Turner, W M L
Watson, C C
Watson, H D
Williams, D G
Woodhead, P M

Colwyn Bay
Al-Shabender, M
Algawi, K D M
Armer, M L
Arthur, J L
Ashcroft, K
Barry, P
Brave, I H
Breese, V L
Bretland, M J
Brooks, J W
Burton, M M
Corkery, P B
Corkery, P H
Cowell, E W
Cowell, T R W
Crawford, D J
Davies, E
Davies, H R G
Davies, W R A
Edwards, M

Evans, A B A
Evans, J D A
Farah, A G
Frost, C S
Groves, L A
Gupta, B K
Hammad, E M E S
Hardman, F G
Harper, G L
Harper, J
Hindle, C M
Hughes, E P
Hughes, M M
Humphreys, E W
Jones, G W
Jones, G H
Kelly, K J
Kiehn, B
Klimach, V J
Laraman, C
Lloyd, D H O
McIlroy, P W J
Malik, A E D T M
Midgley, J M
Owen, K
Owen, R
Parry-Williams, A W
Popat, D
Powell, M A
Ratcliffe, M J
Reynolds, R
Robinson, S N
Rouse, E C
Rouse, R T
Sissons, H M
Thackray, C P
Townley, D W
Widdowson, D J
Williams, A
Williams, J W
Williams, W R
Wood, D G E
Wynne-Jones, G

Colyton
Askew, M F
Badger, F G
Brown, N C
Carmichael, D S
Clarke, D B
Davidson, C M
Green, P C
Jones, J R
Thomas, D O

Congleton
Argent, C J
Atkin, K J
Baker, T H
Bennett, P H
Bromley, P T
Brooks, J B S
Brough, D W
Carter, E A
Daly, R C
Delany, B H
Dutton, A C
Edees, S
Fray, D
Gokhale, V L
Goodwin, P J
Green, A N F
Harry, T V A
Hesketh, M
Highland, A M
Jesudason, E C
Jesudason, J S
Kay, G E
Leese, P G
McLean, J H
Norris, M G
Rigby, P J
Rosson, A K
Sivakumaran, S R
Taylor, C M
Thomson, C M
West, D R
Wollaston, O H

Coniston
Wood, R A B

Consett
Anderson, E J
Astley, D A
Bright, S T
Cameron, K S
Chapman, D W
Douglass, U E
El-Gasim, M H A

Elliott, J C
English, S P J
Flynn, E J
Forsyth, J I M
Frazer, M W
Hamilton, J R
Hamilton, S J
Hasan, S
Iqbal, A
Jack, W
Jakubovic, M O
Johnston, B
Langston, C J
Levick, J F
Levick, S
Macdonald, J M
Mason, J J
Mountford, J A
Murray, A W
Nave, E W
Petterson, D M
Petterson, T
Porteous, I B
Raine, C
Rao, C S
Riley, P D
Robinson, H I
Sambasiva Rao, G
Shah, P R
Stevenson, W J
Thiede, B
Turner, J
Tyerman, K S
Walker, A K
Welsh, L
Whitfield, E M
Young, J D

Conwy
Arthur, T I F
Barber, V E
Barnard, R E
Basil, A V
Bell-Davies, D E
Bellamy, J L
Crawford, A H
Davies, H L
Edwards, P J
Evans, J G
Gillan, R U
Gilmore, R
Grout, P
Harrison, E T
Howell, F R
Hunter, S G
Jones, D A
Kraaijeveld, L M-A
Leask, H J G
Luff, D A
McCabe, D J M
Mackereth, R M
Mackereth, S W
Mitchelson, P A
Osborne, B V
Parry, D C
Parry, J J
Statham, R
Taylor, E
Wainwright, J
Whitley, L L
Williams, M
Wright, C H
Wright, P B

Cookham Rise
Birdi, A Z

Cookstown
Acharya, K P
Barnes, S A
Black, J H
Black, R G
Burns, F J
Corrigan, J C
Curry, P A
Dalzell, M C
Doonan, J F
Duff, A
Finch, R S
Flanigan, P P J
Gilfillan, R C
Hamilton, R J
Irwin, A I
Irwin, P B
Johnston, T C
Linton, T E C
McBride, J B
McKeever, G T M
Mullan, R P
O'Kane, J B

O'Reilly, J A
Smyth, J E
Wallace, M A F

Corbridge
Berrington, A W
Berrington, J E
Caird, J D D
Calder, V H
Cowling, B E
Crack, L A
Cunningham, W F
Dickinson, P H
Dykins, R J
Egan, M J
Harle, D G
Irving, P M
Josephs, J
King, R
Kingett, R W J
Manship, J M M
Melrose, T M
Michelmore, K F
Morley, A R
Perry, J J
Postlethwaite, K R
Swaddle, M
Waddell, F M
Walters, P L
Wood, K M

Corby
Appleton, C R
Baxter, R D
Beric, V
Bhattacharya, B R
Bowie, I M
Buckingham, P V
Graham, C
Harris, A R
Harris, T J N
Hart, J J
McCahill, J P
MacDonald, J L
Marsh, D I
Maxim, O V
Mellor, J G
Misra, S C
O'Neill, A
O'Neill, J D
Palmer, D A
Partington, C T
Passmore, A M
Sumira, R P
Treharne, I R
Turner, D C
Wade, S
Wadsworth, S M
Whittaker, R N
Wilczynski, P J G
Williams, K R
Yee, M C

Cornhill-on-Tweed
Harvey, W J

Cornwall
Wong, L H

Corsham
Allan, E B
Baker, H E
Bullen, J A
Burrell, S J
Burrowes, W L
Cowie, A S
Daniel, P G
Davey, G J
Drummond, R C F
Green, D M
Gruffydd-Jones, K
Hatherell, M J
Henderson, P A
Hobbs, C B
Johnson, W D K
Kelley, S P
Leyden, H E
MacArthur, D J
Mohr, S J J R
Starr, L M
Walker, S J

Corwen
Davies, E J J
Deady, R
Gibbs, B P
Gibbs, M L
Park, K C
Pope, U C
Roberts, D G

Sharkey, A G
Williams, I C M

Cottingham
Ahmad Turkistani, I Y
Ashley, S D
Avery, G R
Bowden, H F
Cain, T J
Cale, A R J
Campbell, M S
Chia, P S
Clark, A L
Clark, J P
Clarke, P D
Colbridge, T J
Coope, S R
Cowen, M E
Crosby, M E
Culbert, B D
Duthie, G S
Dyet, L E
Eckersley, P S
Elliott, L
Evans, P
Exon, M E
Farnsworth, T A
Finlay, M E
Foggitt, K D
Fox, J N
Gower, S N
Greenstone, M A
Guvendik, L
Hall, C E
Hargreaves, S A
Harkness, G J
Harmer, R H
Hart, N B
Haworth, C M
Hopper, D L
Howard, J S
Hussain, S R
Hutchinson, C M
Johnson, G S
Joshi, U Y
Karunaratne, W U
Kastelik, J A
Kaye, G C
Kieran, D N B
Knox, J
Korab-Karpinski, M R
Liew, W K
MacDonald, A W
McGivern, D V
Mahapatra, T K
Main, A
Michie, E W
Michie, H R
Mohiuddin, S A
Mohsen, A M M A
Monson, J R T
Morgan, M
Morice, A H
Moxon, C
Munro, M F
Murtagh, G P
Nair, K K
Nanda, B S
Neligan, P H
O'Hare, P M
Pearson, L
Philpott, M G
Pollock, C G
Redington, A E
Reiss, S H
Richmond, I
Robson, J
Russell, J D
Shaw, C J
Shields, M L
Such, A
Sutton, P A
Thind, J
Tomlinson, I W
Tsai, H H
Webb, A T
Wharton, I P
Whitehead, P
Willson, J C
Yeo, R
Young, S S

Coulsdon
Alexander, W B
Asirdas, S R N
Banerjee, B
Boffa, P B J
Brogan, V M
Chesser, D T S

Coventry

Chitkara, S C
Craddock, D
Cruickshank, I D
Goddard, M J
Harvey, H R
Haywood, G S
Heber, K R
Irfan, M
Iu, P C
Johnston, M J
Khan, J A
Lace, E J
Landsborough, D
McAleese, P J G
McAllister, W J
MacCallum, R
Murphy, D J
Northfield, T C
Padayachee, M
Partridge, E D
Patel, S V
Pearce, R
Powles, J W
Price, A B
Ramakrishnan, K P
Rooke, A W M
Sawyer, A N
Silverton, K L
Smith, A G L
Smith, M L W
Stewart, A D
Stirland, H
Sundararajan, K
Takhar, B
Titford, J E
Von Backstrom, A G

Coventry

Ackroyd, E B
Agarwal, I C
Aggarwal, P
Ahmed, I
Ahmed, Z P
Al-Bayati, A H A R
Al-Chalabi, A N
Aldersley, M A
Aldridge, M J
Ali, S
Ali, T
Allan, P S
Allen, M E
Ansari, E A
Ansari, M Z A
Ansari, N A
Anyanwu, A L
Archer-Hall, J F C
Armstrong, L E
Atherton, D J
Atwal, A S
Awonuga, A O
Ayub, W
Baguant, N K
Ballantine, R J
Bambridge, P R
Barbieri, M
Barclay, A J G
Barclay, G
Barfield, L J
Barker, P J
Barnett, M M
Barros D'Sa, A A J
Bastock, J M
Bastow, N M
Basu, S N
Batten, J
Bayman, I W
Beaumont, P A
Been, M
Bellamy, E P D
Benning, R
Bera, S K
Berry, C
Berth-Jones, J
Bhambra, M K
Bhandal, M S
Blacklock, A R E
Blakemore, M E
Bland, G J
Bland, J W
Bloo, J M
Boateng, K E
Bodalia, B
Bodalia, R
Bogahalande, S
Booker, J M
Booth, C
Booth, L J
Borman, C A
Borman, E M

Bowman, D M
Brady, P A
Brain, N D
Brennan, M E
Brown, P W
Brown, W F
Burley, N M J
Burrows, A J
Calder, I G
Calder, S J
Camm, M J
Carr, C M
Carson, E J
Cattle, D S
Chadwick, E J
Chaggar, H S
Chandra Mohan, V J
Chandy, J
Chaudhry, A Y
Chen, K
Cherry, R J
Chohan, B P S
Choksey, A B
Choksey, M S
Choudree, A C
Christodoulou, C
Cietak, K A
Clarke, G K
Cleaver, M H
Clegg, J
Clowes, D P
Clowes, R L
Coad, N A G
Cockerill, M J
Coe, A W
Cole, B
Cooke, M W
Coole, L
Coolican, M A
Cooper, G M
Coppock, J E
Coppock, J S
Cordle, J E
Cottrill, A C
Court, G A
Cowan, E W H
Cowley, A D
Craggs, L A
Cunnington, P M D
Dadhania, M R
Dale, J R
Dann, T C
Dawda, V G
Dawes, D L
De Silva, G E F
De Souza, T J
Dean, F M
Deegan, T F
Defas, G
Desai, K M
Dewsbury, E
Dhillon, M S
Dhillon, S K
Dickson, T D
Dilip Kumar, R
Dimitri, P J
Dimitri, W R
Docker, C
Done, J M
Donegan, A M
Dooley, P T
Dorricott, J I
Dosanj, R S
Dosanjh, H S
Douzenis, A
Downing, M E N
Dukes, H M
Duncan, A A
Dunn, M W
Durr, C S
Dutta, R K
Ebrahim, D W
Ecob, C C
Ecob, E A
Edmunds, M E
Edwards, R B
El-Saghir, M A
Elton, R J
Emery, J C
Essex, C
Evans, C M
Evans, D R
Evans, H C
Exon, S M
Ezzat, A A
Farooq, A
Feltbower, A R
Ferryman, S R
Fink, C G

Fish, D C
Fletcher, S
Foguet Subirana, P R
Francis, K S
Franks, A L
Fraser, I A
Fulford, K W M
Garala, M
Garry, G M
Geddes, G B
Ghosh, P K
Gill, H K
Girvan, R B
Gold, M R
Gonzalez Sanz, N
Goodfellow, T
Gough, M W R
Goulden, G W
Gray, C T
Greenwood, R S
Grewal, R S
Grieve, R J
Griffin, P J
Griffiths, F E
Guha, T
Gunstone, R F
Halder, S R
Halliday, B L
Halls, P J
Hamilton, R J
Harkness, M C H
Harris, J B
Hasan, S
Hazarika, P D
Heer, A S
Herd, A M
Hibberd, M L
Higgins, R M
Hill, M N
Hillhouse, E W
Ho, L
Ho, Y M
Hobson, S
Hocking, M L
Holt, M C
Holton, K M
Horn, P J
Hughes, Z L
Hussain, M J
Hutton, R M
Igwiloh, C O K
Ilchyshyn, A
Imray, C H E
Irwin, C J R
James, R
Jamie, D B
Jarratt, D
Jaspal, M S
Jayaratnam, M
Jetty, U
Jones, D G
Jones, D A
Jones, L E
Jones, R D
Jones, W K
Jotangia, T P
Judelsohn, F A
Judge, G S
Kakad, K L
Kalloor, G J
Kandaswamy, S
Kanji, H K
Kapwepwe, S
Kashi, S H
Katti, S S
Kavia, S
Keane, C C
Kearney, S E
Keenan, J
Kelly, C
Kennedy, C R
Kennedy, N M J
Kenyon, P S
Khalifa, Y
Khan, A M
Khara, B S
Kilshaw, L A
Kirkham, C J
Kishori, A
Kisnah, V P
Klocke, R
Kolacki, B M T
Krikler, S J
Kukreja, A S
Kukreja, N
Kukreja, R K
Laird, A N
Lal-Sarin, R R
Lam, F T

Lawford, C V P
Lawton, M E
Lea, P M
Lee, R N
Leung, H K H
Leung, H H-Y
Lewis, M
Lockett, G W E
Loft, D E
Long, R J
Louden, J D
Lovatt, W P
Ludlow, B P
Lupton, S C
Lyall, S S
McAleese, G A
Macartney, J C
McCulloch, W J D
Macdonald, I
Macdougall, C F
Mace, C J
Maciejewski, A
McIntosh, J S
Mackie, F D
McLachlan, K P
MacLean, J
MacNamara, A F M
Macpherson, J H
Madan, H
Madhu, K R
Maheson, A
Majevadia, S K
Mangaleswaran, K
Mangat, K S
Marsh, R M
Marston, G M
Mason, B E
Mason, M J
Matthews, M J
Mehta, R L
Mirza, Z A
Mishra, K
Misra, V K
Mistry, B P
Mistry, D K
Mitchell, A D
Morris, J C
Morris, R
Morris, R M J
Mulholland, P J
Mulrooney, P
Munro, R M
Murrin, R J A
Murthy, B V R N
Muruganinrajah, S
Mwale, E M Y
Nahl, S S
Navin, W P
Newbold, K M
Njie, B M
Norton, R
Nwokolo, C U
O'Brien, J A
O'Brien, P W M
O'Hara, R J
O'Sullivan, J F X
Obaid, S
Oliver, C B D
Onyirimba, F C
Osman, F
Page, G W
Pai, M S
Paige, P G
Pandya, H K
Parfitt, G G
Parker, C E
Parker, R W
Parker, S J
Parmar, J S
Parr, S M
Patel, J M
Patel, K
Patel, M P
Patel, P
Patel, P J
Patel, R
Patel, S J
Pathan, M A
Payne, L R
Perez De Albeniz, A J
Perlik-Kolacki, D B
Pickin, M C
Ponsford, J R
Porter, J M
Priddy, R J
Purnell-Mullick, S
Quabeck, G
Rahman, A
Rai, H S

Rajput, R S
Rakhit, S
Ramachandra, R R
Ramsden, K L
Ranu, N S
Rauchenberg, P M
Rhodes, C A
Richards, P E I
Richards, S M
Richardson, W
Riddoch, D
Ritchie, F A
Rivers, D
Robbins, M C O
Robert, P S
Roberts, P N
Robinson, R E
Rosin, M D
Rubython, E J
Ryan, A P
Saad, K F G
Sadrani, P J
Saeed-Ahmad, S
Sahota, J K
Sandhu, J S
Sandoz, M D
Sathyanarayana, C N
Selwyn, E M
Shad, S K
Shaeena, P R
Shah, V S
Shahabuddin, M
Shanmugalingam, V
Shariff, A G
Sharp, M A
Shatwell, W J
Sheard, S C
Shehu, A
Sheikh, M A
Shergill, N S
Sherlala, K H
Shields, S D
Shillinglaw, D
Shine, D F
Shiu, M F
Short, A K
Siddiqui, N A
Sihota, J S
Simmonds, E J
Singh, S
Singh, S
Singh, S S
Singh, T
Sitjes Llado, N
Slibi, M
Smith, H M
Smith, J L
Smith, R C
Smithers, A J
Snead, D R J
Snowdon, J C
Sood, T S
Soomro, M
Spalding, T J W
Spencer, N J
Spokes, G A
Spokes, R M
Srodon, P D
Stableforth, P J
Stansbie, J M
Stanworth, P A
Stirling, H F
Stockdale, A D
Stone, K M
Strantzalis, G
Subhani, M
Sullivan, W R
Sultan, M
Sumner, A W
Taggart, C M
Tan, B B
Tan, B C
Tansey, A K P
Taylor, S A
Taylor, S W C
Thacker, S L
Thavasothy, M
Thavasothy, R
Thevendra, S
Thin Thin Aye, Dr
Thompson, I D
Thomson, K T
Thornton, D A
Thornton, S
Tilbury, J G
Tin Min Ohn, Dr
Tran, A T H
Trent, R S
Turner, S M

Vallet, E A
Venkataraman, M
Viira, D J
Vishwanath, M R
Vlachtsis, H
Vohrah, A R
Wade, A A H
Wade, P J F
Wallace, M E H
Walton, A M
Ward, I J
Ward, J A
Webster, S J
Wellings, R M
Whatmore, W J
Wheatley, K A
Whibley, H K
White, M E E
Whiteman, S M
Wijesundera, R L
Wilkins, E M
Williams, N
Wills, M I
Wilson, P E H
Wood, L E P
Wood, M A
Wyse, M K
Young-Hartman, M
Youssef, H
Zaky, S
Zaphiropoulos, G C

Cowbridge

Adams, K G
Allman, A C J
Armstrong, R L
Blayney, J D M
Bowrey, D J
Bradshaw, R B
Broughton, L A
Cohen, D A
Davis, A R
Dent, C M
Dowdle, J R
Edwards, M
Elliott, S E
Evans, A G
Evans, C E
Evans, D H C
Evans, S
Fardy, C H
France, J E
Graham, I M
Hedges, A R
Hinde, G B
Houghton, I
Howells, E B
Howells, K L
Jenkins, E K
Jones, B S
Jones, D A S
Jones, D I
Jones, J P
Jones, P W
Jones, R D
Kavanagh, R
Kemble, H R
Lever, J
Lewis, T D C
Llewellyn, R
Longstaff, J
Longstaff, M A
McDowell, M J
McGovern, D J L
Mather, E A
Meller, K E B
Naysmith, C
Newham, J R T
Nicholas, J M
O'Hanlon, T M
Page, M D
Pardoe, T H
Plummer, S J
Pugh Williams, S
Rees, J H M
Rees, R W M
Sheridan, C M
Stuart, T M
Taylor, C L
Taylor, J M
Thomas, A O
Thomas, D G
Thomas, P H
Todd, A J
Varma, P N
Watkins, T G L
Webb, D B
Wilkinson, E J

Wilkinson, J L
Woodsford, P V

Cowdenbeath
Alcock, J
Choudhury, N K
Choudhury, R
Cross, W A
Dunn, A
Johnston, M A
McRobbie, I A
Paterson, L M
Wright, J W

Cowes
Biggs, D T
Bisset, J G V
Boll, M D O
Boll, M D
Browne, P P M
Chopra, R
Clements, S D
Coleman, C M
Finch, E A M
Freytag, C U
Galpin, G W
Hinchliffe, J
Kaiser, G M
Khopkar, D D
McDonald, R S
Noble, H A
Orr, B W G
Stainer, G
Stainer, M R
Stewart, G D
Swarbrick, R H

Cradley Heath
Chaggar, J S
Gripton, G
Jones, H A
Mahon, J P
Muthuveloe, D W
O'Brien, D J
Willetts, I E

Craigavon
Adams, G F
Adams, J D
Anderson, S J E
Armstrong, V L
Bailie, N A
Barr, J W R
Bell, J A
Best, J A
Best, S
Best, S J
Bingham, A R
Black, R J
Black, V E
Bronte, J E
Brown, N A
Bruce, J H
Budd, S K
Bunting, H E
Burnett, J A
Burnett, R A
Burns, H
Campton, J L
Carl, I L
Carson, G F
Carson, P E R
Cash, W J
Chada, N
Chambers, M F
Clarke, S E
Collins, A T
Connolly, M
Conran, T M
Craig, S E
Creane, J G
Critchlow, M R
Cupples, M E
Damani, N N
Davidson, M E
Davin, D W
Davis, E M
Dawson, T A J
Dickie, A W
Dillon, J M
Dobson, W
Doyle, M F
Dunseith, P G S
Eakin, J M
Egerton, F
Eldon, J
Elliott, J M
English, S A
Evans, A J
Evans, C E D

Farnon, C M
Galway, J E
Gawarikar, S B
Geddis, A E
Geddis, C J
Geddis, T H
Golchin, K
Good, B J
Good, P D
Gormley, J D
Gracey, D G R
Graham, J L
Grant, V E
Grier, D G
Hall, S J
Hamilton, A J
Hamilton, R A
Hanratty, B
Hanratty, C G
Heasley, R N
Henderson, F E
Higazey, M A M
Horan, M A
Houston, S J
Hunter, D M
Hunter, H S
Hutchinson, M E J
Irwin, W D B
Jamison, C A
Jennings, J E
Kilduff, K M
Landy, S J
Lappin, K J
Lee, R J E
Lemon, S E
Lennon, S P
Livingstone, K
Logan, R A
Lowry, D W
Lowry, D S
McAlpine, K W H B
McAnallen, C
McAnallen, J G
McAteer, E J
McAuley, S M
McCaffrey, M J
McCann, E
McCann, G J
MacCarthy, D
McCaughey, W
McCleane, G J
McClure, T C
McConaghy, M D
McConaghy, P M
McConnell, J P
McConville, K F
McConville, M T
McCourt, M Y
McCourt, M W G
McCrory, M
McCune, N S C
McDonald, C M
McGoldrick, V M C
McGucken, P B
McGuigan, J A
McKeveney, P J
Mackle, C P
Mackle, E J
Mackle, R A
McLoughlin, D C
McNamee, B T
McNutt, N R
MacSorley, F J
Madan, A
Maguire, S H
Martin, K R G
Mathews, C W
Mathews, J W
Miller, R G A
Miller, V A
Mitchell, D M
Mockford, B J
Moriarty, A J
Morton, M R J
Murugan, S P
Mussen, J A
Nelson, S D
Nugent, A G
O'Brien, A
O'Kane, B M
Orbinson, H M
Orr, D A
Orr, I A
Overend, J
Parker, E J E
Parker, S J
Patterson, J A
Patton, D T
Patton, M

Rice, R H
Ritchie, C M
Sabherwal, P
Sami, S A
Sharpe, P C
Sharpe, S W
Shaw, C L
Shepherd, C W
Shields, G L
Sidhu, H K
Simpson, J A
Somerville, J E
Southwell, A G
Stewart, A
Stirling, W J
Sullivan, V A
Tay, T W
Thompson, I M
Thompson, W B
Thomson, M P
Tipping, C G
Titterington, M B
Troughton, A M J
Troughton, K E V
Vallely, C T J
Walker, N W
Wallace, W D
Warnock, D S
Webster, K
Weir, C D
Wharton, E V
Wilkinson, A M
Williams, M
Wilson, A M
Wilson, C S
Withers, R J
Woods, J K
Woolsey, S M

Craighouse
Acres, G M
Garrett, S M
Johnson, J M S
Merz, L H

Cramlington
Ahmed, A B M E
Ainsworth, S B
Benbow, H G
Brown, D M G
Cripps, E J
Davison, E P
Dickinson, G M
Dove, A P
Dunbar, G
Elliott, J
Elliott, W D
Fail, M
Ferguson, E M
Foster, L A
Green, P A T
Henry, A
Jewitt, J A
Khan, M A U
Khan, U Z
Kuruvilla Zachariah, K
Laing, J A
Leith, D
McKenzie, S A
Macmillan, J D R
Maddison, P
Nargol, A V F
Parkin, S G
Patton, M
Prank, C J
Quayle, S E
Quinn, T G
Reddy, K S
Scott, S M
Thompson, G H
Waddell, J M
Ward, C C
Watson, J P

Cranbrook
Al-Kassim, N
Badcock, D J C
Beale, A J
Blundell, R J
Brettingham, L C
Brodie, N H
Butler, C R
Butler, H J
Cony, B G
Crowe, D J
Cubison, T C S
Davies, M S
Dean, S C
Dewing, C R
Dibble, J B

Digby, R J
Emmanuel, V
Ginn, A E
Grant, A C
Hefni, M A
Hindmarsh, D J
Hooper, J M D
Hudd, N P
Hugo, A B
Hussell, J G
Hussell, T A
Jepp, K
Kefford, P J
Kefford, R H
Lewis, C J R
Llewellyn, H
Locket, S
McEwan, G D
McGlone, K J
McGuire, E J
Macpherson, D S
Mahadevan, S
Moore, E
Nesfield, J C B
Norton, K G
Oakley, J C
Penny, G
Player, P V
Potu, P
Quaife, J
Richards, A E S
Scotcher, L M
Sharkey, D E
South, L M
South, P J
Trayling, A P A
Van Der Plas, F P
Warrilow, W H E
Wood, A M
Wood, C R
Wotton, L D
Wratten, J C

Cranleigh
Bratty, C A
Bundy, M J
Cameron, D
Christie, D
Clark, M L
Fawkner-Corbett, R
Gibbs, A J
Glover, R E
Hamer, H M
Hart, C J
Hawkins, N W
Hawley, R T
Ingham, J F
King, R H
Kirkpatrick, S R
Knight, F R S
Kolind, A L
Lewis, R J W
Lynch, T M
Mitchell, W A L
Myhill, M D H
Price, R N
Read, J M
Staines, F H
Verdon, J H
Wightman, S J

Craven Arms
Appleby, D J
Bell, J H
Challiner, J
Davidson, J M
Elliott, J R
Garlick, M J
Garman, J G
Gray, J C S
Higgs, K P
Johnson, S E
Kydd, J L
Lambert, S P
Leonard, E M
Leonard, J C
Leonard, R C
Record, D M
Stanford, C A
Williams, S E
Winter, P R X

Crawley
Abayomi, E M-J
Abdel-Hadi, S E A M
Adams, S P R
Addie, C E
Alexander, P
Alexander, R
Anderson, I P

Armstrong, J E
Atkinson, P I
Baigent, J K
Bailey, R J
Ball, A B S
Bennett, G
Bevan, K
Bhargava, A
Birch, J K
Blechynden, J C
Bower, S M
Brightwell, C G
Burgess, C S
Caldbeck, C R
Carter, C A
Carter, S J
Chhaya, B C
Child, J A
Chorley, S J
Clemens, N J
Clifford, A D
Clout, A
Clout, I R
Cooper, A L
Craik, J I O B
Croucher, L C
Davies, J M C
De La Mota Nicolas-Correa, M D P
Donnellan, I M
Duxbury, B J M
Evans, S A
Foley, H M
Gerard, E M
Gleeson, C M A
Goodwin, D M
Goodwin, R J
Gossage, A A R
Greaves, P
Greenway, P
Haworth, R N
Hawrych, A B
Hiam, R C
Higgins, N S
Hill, D A
Hoare, R W
Hobbs, L J
Hopkins, N F G
Hornung, E A
Huarte Pano, J I
Hunter-Craig, C J
Hurrell, K J
Husain, T
Jackson, N W
Johnstone, F C
Kansagra, B A
Kansagra, I B
Kansagra, K B
Khakhar, M B
Khanna, S
Kirwan, E P
Leigh, R K
Leigh, T R
Lenton, E B
Lewis, I G
Litchfield, J A
Luke, J R
Lyle, D J R
McIntosh, I D
McIntosh, K R
Mackey, J P P
Mohabir, N A
Mohamed, A H
Mufti, M M
Murray, P V
Mutsaerts, J F M
Myint Thein Khine, Dr
Nandi, A C
Newman, V J
Oliver, J E
Pallett, J L
Palmer, C R
Pannu, G S
Parker, A L
Parker, S M
Peard, M C
Phillips, R C
Piper, P C
Procter, M S
Radford, B J
Rafi, I
Rafique, A
Rivers, M D
Rofail, S D
Rose, S E
Roy, A
Royds-Jones, J A
Sattianayagam, A
Schirge, A S

Crewe

Shah, S
Singh, D R
Sinha, R K
Smith, R D
Smith, W C
Sneddon, J F
Sortsis, A
Spoto, G
Stapley, S A
Stillman, P
Stone, C D P
Storer, N R
Strube, A G
Strube, G
Suntharanathan, A
Sutaria, N
Thirkettle, J L
Thom, P M
Thomas, G H
Tin, N K
Truter, K W C
Turner, B C
Turner, R
Turner, R C
Turner, S L
Vallon, A G
Veerabangsa, M
Vekes, K
Venkataratnam Babu, K
Vethanayagam, S
Vinson, P S
Vive, J U
Waldron, M J
Ward, R J
Watson, S V
Wellbelove, P A
Weston-Burt, P M
Weston, J
Whitten, S M
Wilkinson, A M
Williamson, D J
Wilson, A
Xerri, S
Yeo, N J
Ziyadi, N F A

Crediton
Anderson, C
Anderson, J M E
Berridge, P D R
Berrington, W P
Blackman, S E-A
Blight, K J
Brice-Smith, J
Bull, P M
Davidson, J L
Davies, J E
Friend, H M
Hall, A M
Johnstone, C A P
Kekwick, C A
Kent, C P
Marshall, J
Maycock, C H
Murphy, M H
Niklaus, L J
Rodd, C D
Selley, P J
Shorney, J S
Shorney, N M
Smith, C F
Stephenson, R E
Thurlow, B P
Twomey, P J G
Westwood, P A
Wright, G C

Crewe
Armatage, R J
Atkins, S L
Bache, J B
Barnett, C J
Bevan, J R D
Bevan, S J
Blakebrough, I S
Blanco Rodriguez, I
Board, P N
Booth, P A
Brady, V P J
Brooks, N C
Brough, S J S
Brown, R M
Calderhead, R J
Calvey, T A J
Calvey, T N
Chambers, D K
Chundrigar, T
Clarke, M J

Crewkerne

Cooper, J G
Cooper, J
Cooper, M S
Currie, R D
Davies, J E
Davies, J M
Deans, J A J
Dingle, A F
Dobson, H S
Dodds, P A
Doherty, A G
Doring-Basso, S
Edwards, B A
Ellison, J A
Evans, S E
Evennett, P M
Farrell, A J
Felmeden, D C
Felmingham, J E
Ferrington, D F
Findlay-Domes, E
Findlay, C D
Freeman, L B
Freeman, M R
Gay, S P
Gillies, R M
Göpfert, M J
Gould, A A
Gray, J L
Guerenu Carnevali, J A
Guy, A J
Hall, J I
Hall, K H
Hamilton, D L
Hands, D H
Hensel, E A
Hill, J
Hill, O J
Hodgson, D I
Hossack, I I
Howard, J C
Hudson, M F
Huffon, B R
Hunt, C P
Hyde, K R
Hynes, E F
Irvine, A W
Jackson, A D
Jeyadevan, K S
Jeyadevan, N N
Jones, H W
Jones, J H
Jones, K E
Lane, M B
Lawrence, M
Leaver, E P
Lewis, P
Lind, J
Linney, M J
Lloyd, D
Lloyd, J
Lockwood, F H
London, I J
Lovatt, G L
Lovett, J W T
McDonald, A D
McKavanagh, M
McKay, J S
Malins, T J
Mallya, S
Martin, A J
Matin, M P
Mattison, A E
Mennim, P G
Millward, R G
Milsted, R A V
Mitchyn, M
Moriarty, B J
Mukhopadhyay, T K
Musgrove, C
Nahabedian, A M
Neugebauer, M A Z
Nicol, A
O'Donoghue, M A T
O'Driscoll, M
O'Sullivan, G P
Oleshko, C G
Patel, N
Patterson, M J L
Pearce, P A
Pegg, D J
Pettit, W J
Piggott, A
Potter, C R G
Power, A B
Pugh, A
Radha, R
Redfern, T R
Rigby-Jones, T

Roberts, S L
Robinson, M P
Robinson, P
Sackey, A H
Sagar, M V
Salisbury-Trelawry, J M
Sampson, M R
Scally, J
Scheepers, B D M
Scott, G I
Scott, W G
Selvachandran, S N
Selvadurai, L R N
Sergiwa, A
Sharma, P
Shridhar, S
Smirk, T W
Smith, D G
Smith, T G
Spooner, A L
Stephens, G P
Stirling, W N
Tate, S R
Thomas, D G
Thompson, J
Thomson, A P J
Thornton, M C
Timothy, I
Torrens, R L
Trowler, E P
Vickers, G A
Vickers, J C
Vishweshwar Rao, H V R
Walker, J
Watson, C A
Watson, J M
West, B
Willdig, K M
Williams, D J
Williams, E B
Williams, J
Williams, J E A
Williamson, D P H
Wilson, E M
Worthington, J R M
Wylie, J B
Zaman, S M

Crewkerne

Balian, B H
Bevan-Mogg, K J
Camsey, J M
Fenlon, C M
Field, M W
Gilson, R A J
McInerney, M A
Priest, P
Rosser, J G
Zwartouw, C L

Criccieth

Hodgkinson, V
Jonathan, O M
Jones, E T
Jones, H W E
Roberts, G H
Webb, J G

Crickhowell

Braeman, C
Gregory, D W
Herdman, G J S
Hommers, M
Humphreys, R C
Jerram, K L
Jones, D R B
Jones, O S
Kakas, M A
Lewis, R I
Maguire, T K
Moesen, J R
Monahan, P R W
Paton, D H H
Porter, T
Pryce Thomas, R L
Saundby, E
Saundby, R P
Shand, W S
Stoker, C J
Taylor, M E
Waring, J R
Williams, F

Crieff

Barrowman, M
Bradley, E
Bushby, D R P
Cleghorn, J

Cooper, J A
Corbett, R A
Crabbie, E M
Denny, F
Dick, J F
Don, J B
Dowie, A N
Ewing, P A
Fyfe, G
Fyfe, I M
Gaskell, D E
Gerrard, G
Graham, J L
Jeffery, S
Johnston, A M
Johnston, J H
McEwan, C
McFarlane, A S U
Macindoe, W L
McLeod, G G
McPhail, L M
Martin, A E
Martin, D
Miller, J S
Mitchell, D G
Morrison, A
Morrison, E E
Murray, R H S
Osborne, P M
Penny, J L
Randfield, R S
Sales, J D
Savage, G
Sutherland, G
Tipton, C M
Webster, A L
Wishart, I H

Cromarty

Hendry, C M
Hussey, S
Matheson, I U
Pern, P O

Cromer

Arbuthnot, J H
Becker, F
Burrows, J R
Croton, C S
Ding, C D
Griffiths, J D V
Lee, K
Lennox, A M
Lennox, V C
Norman, W A
Oliver, R M
Ripley, P
Smith, A G
Symes, M H A
Worthington, A R

Crook

Banerjee, A K
Banerjee, A K
Banerjee, A K
Barmby, D S
Carney, M R
Catterick, D I
Chadwick, E T
Chesters, E W
Clarke, J A
Foulds, J W
Gayer, M A
Holbrook, G D
Khan, C F
Marshall, M
Middleton, R A
Peverley, P M
Proud, J J
Sarnaik, B S
Sarnaik, N B
Wilson, E E
Young, K E

Crowborough

Ankrett, V O
Asprey, J C
Baldwin, L N
Briffa, J E
Bruce, C E J
Clarke, E M
Cobb, P C
Crosbie, B J
Davies, J O G
Doherty, J E
El-Nagieb, O M
Elliott, J A
England, A
Foinette, K M R
Fox, R M

Gallannaugh, S C
Golton, M J
Hall, D K
Halliday, N P
Leedham, G D
Loftus, D A
McGillivray, J L
Marriott, P J
Morgan, J
Morris, J V
O'Connell, M C
Pereira, J A
Price, T W
Priestman, K G
Priestman, L F G
Routh, J E
Ruck, C S K
Sampson, C S
Scott, C H M
Sinclair, K G A
Smith, S E
Spencer, M A
Stokes, C E
Taylor, S J
Thornton, B A
Thornton, V G
Ussher, C W J
Vine, R S
Watkins, R C
Watney, D M
Watts, M E

Crowthorne

Adshead, G M J
Basson, J V
Chau, E P W
Cheung, M S-M
Crampton, A
Cundill, J G
Damania, A
Davies, A G
Doherty, A J
Edwards, W J
Forshaw, D M
Fox, W T A
George, A
Gupta, A J
Hind, E J
Horne, A S
Humphreys, S A
Illes, S A
Illingworth, C S
Johns, A R
Layng, J E
Lee, W E
Lord, W J H
McGauley, G A
McGrath, P G
Mason, F L
Meux, C J
Minne, C C M
Mohan, D J
Murray, K J
Oakley, C J
Payne, A J
Perry, J R
Robinson, M W
Singh, M P
Smith, G K
Spanswick, R
Thomas, R S L
Veeramani, R
Vermeulen, J W
Wearing, E A
Withers, M

Croxley Green

Aurora, M

Croydon

Abbot, H P
Abbott, A
Abhayaratne, R N
Abili, O B
Abulafi, A-M
Acevedo, I A
Adabie, K H
Adcock, G N
Ahmadani, H
Akanga, J M C
Al-Sheikhi, A R J
Amarasekara, R N S
Amonoo-Kuofi, K
Ansari, A R
Aquilina, C
Armstrong, J T
Ashley, E A
Atayi, M A
Ayliffe, W H R
Baker, G P

Balendran, N
Barnes, J
Barretto, C J
Baruya, M
Barzanji, A J
Baskaran, B
Beal, V E D
Bees, N R
Bentley, H E
Berry, D W
Bhat, Y
Birley, D M
Booker, M W
Bootes, J A H
Bowen-Wright, H E
Brightwell, P
Brookes, C M
Bruce, M P
Bruijlants, B
Burke, D V
Butts, D J
Byrne, P J
Cambridge, N A
Canepa-Anson, R
Carter, N J
Chandra, G
Chang, Y L
Charlton, P P
Chaudery, N
Cheema, A A
Chen, F F F
Clarke, A M
Clementson, G
Coppen, M J
Cottrall, K
Courtenay-Evans, R J
Crouch, L
Crowe, M J
Cutting, D A
D'Souza, A C
Darko, D A
Darougar, S
Dave, S S
Davies, M R
De Alwis, D V
De Silva, N T
Derodra, J K D
Desai, I T
Diggory, P
Dixit, B B
Doig, A D
Eason, J R
Ebbs, S R
Ede, J N
Eid, T M
El Beshty, M M
Elliman, A J
Elton, S
Epie, G M
Fernandes, A T
Fisher, G R
Ford, N T
Francis, G G
Fyvie, A D
Gardiner, D A
George, S E
Gow, P C
Gray, J G
Griffin, M H
Griffith, D N W
Hall, J M
Hanifa, Y
Harrison, J
Hart, S M
Hashemi, K
Hayes, M J
Heidari-Khabbaz, N
Henry, R A
Hill, J J
Hoskins, M C
Howell, S D
Hrbacek, F J
Htay Nyunt Kyi, Dr
Hughes, J E
Hughes, J G
Husbands, S D
Hussain, S
Ikpoh, A C A
Jagamohan Reddy, G
Jayamanne, I L
Jayaratne, B S S
Joseph, S P
Kam, K Y E
Karim, N B
Kashif Al-Ghita, F A A
Kemp, T J
Khan, K A
Khan, S H
Knibb, A A A

Knight, J R
Kooner, H S
Krysa, J
Kulanayagam, P C
Lam, Y H
Lennard, R H
Lowe, S
McCrea, D W K
Madziwa, D
Magrath, I M
Mahesan, G S
Mahran, R M A
Manjiani, J D
Manoharan, S
Mansuri, M G
Marsh, G D J
Massoud, M S
Mayahi, L
Mendall, M A
Mendis, W W G P
Mian, M R
Miller, A C
Miranda Palomino, J F
Monks, P S
Morgan, L M
Morley, A J M
Motiwala, H G
Mowbray, M A S
Mufti, F H
Murray, C T A
Nath, R
Navaratnarajah, M
Nawrocki, A
Ng Cheng Hin, P Y
Ng, C L L
Ng, S H
Nievel, J G
Noronha, H D S
Northfield, R R
Ogunmuyiwa, T A
Orrell, C J
Owen, A M
Palmer, R N
Patel, P R
Patel, V R
Patel, Y S
Paul, S N
Pawa, C M
Peebles-Brown, A E
Persaud, R D
Price, R K
Puvanendran, P
Ramasubbu, K
Ramaswamy, A C
Rapoport, A
Rathwell, C A
Ratnarajah, M R
Ratnasinghe, D D
Ravishankar, G
Redvers, A
Reilly, M M
Ridout, A B
Salama, N S I
Salerno, J O
Salerno, J A
Sand, P R
Saravanan, K
Sarkany, R P E
Sathananthan, K
Seward, H C
Shah, P N
Shaikh, S S
Shaikh, S A
Shakir, S A W
Shanks, J E
Shanmugaraju, P G
Sharif, M
Sheen, A J
Shenoy, A N
Shindler, J S
Siddiqui, A R
Simenacz, M A
Sinclair, A M
Smahliouk, P
Smaldon, D L
Sneary, M A B
Sornalingam, C
Soutter, A P
Spink, F R
Sreetharan, M
Stacey, A G
Suganthi, D P
Talwar, M
Tan, J L
Tarn, A C
Tay, H H
Tharmarajah, P
Thatcher, P G
Thawda Win, Dr

Theano, G
Thiagalingam, N
Timans, A R
Todd, B J
Toosy, A T
Treml, J
Trew, R J
Tross, S Z
Tuffill, S G
Vaja, R
Vajpeyi, U S
Varughese, M A
Verstraten, L
Wade, C C
Waitt, D J
Walker, K P
Wallace, E J
Walton, D P
Warren, S J
Weighell, R D
Wesson, I M
White, M S
White, S
White, T G E
Whitfield, R J
Wilcock, C J
Williams, I G
Williams, L
Williams, M A
Williams, S K
Willis, M P L
Wimalasuria, S B
Wong, C F
Woolf, S
Yisa, M A
Zard, C M
Zolczer, L

Crumlin
Armstrong, C J
Carey, F M
Gallagher, H J
Gallagher, J P
Gallagher, J P
Gallagher, O T
Hughes, D M
Hyndman, R W
Kelly, M M
Larkin, C J
MacCreanor, C M
McDermott, B M L
McLean, T W B
McQuillan, C
O'Neill, C P
Roughton, S A
Scott, C W D
Sinclair, J S
Thompson, G
Thompson, L E
Thomson, J H
Weir, J M
Wood, C S

Crymych
Lovett, K F

Cullompton
Ball, L J
Bellamy, J E
Bodger, M A
Couldrick, M W
Cruickshank, J G
Davis, S V
Fairrie, A J
Farmer, C E
Gabriel, P
Griffin, J H L
Harris, H M
Hook, P C G
James, M L
Jenner, D R
Lake, B M
McLintock, D M
Martin, A M
Rew, R J
Rhys-Davies, N
Rushton, N P
Smith, A G
Straughan, S J
Trussell, R R
Willson, S A
Wilson, R M

Cumnock
Adams, R A
Bhatkar, R L
Boyd, R J I
Burley, J A
Chaplin, D A
Christie, I T

Christie, J H
Christie, L H
Currie, G P
Findlay, C A
Hasan, M T
Latoria, J K
Latoria, R
Lockens, R
Low, K M
Macnair, C F
MacNair, D M B
Macnair, J A
Macnair, J M
Naczk, A
Ramsay, I
Smith, B A
Strath, I D
Weir, J C R

Cupar
Adams, D W S
Allison, A S
Anderson, J F
Anderson, L J
Arbuckle, E
Arthur, J
Barlow, H C
Blyth, A C
Booth, D J W
Brand, M A J T
Brown, M M
Brown, S M
Cachia, P G
Cardno, G W
Cardno, N
Cavanagh, P J
Cooper, N
Cottrell, D A
Cruickshank, A
Dakin, H E
Donald, J G
Drummond, W
Duncan, M C L
Dunne, N M A
Field, M A S
Findlay, A
Gourley, P E M
Graeme, P D
Graham, D J M
Grant, H S
Grant, L J
Gray, A J
Gray, D A
Griffiths, L K
Hardie, L A E
Hargreaves, P N
Hargreaves, V S
Harry, R M
Hartridge, G
Hendry, C V
Hendry, D W W
Hendry, M D
Hogg, I K
Hyland, J M
Ince, A H
Kenny, N M
Kerr, J A
King, W J
Lendrum, R D C
Leonard, K A
McBlane, A C
MacDonald, D
Macdonald, L M
McFarlane, J A C
McGregor, H M
McGregor, H T
MacManaway, P J
MacPherson, S A
Melhuish, R O
Melville, E M
Melville, R M
Mercer, J C G
Mills, S I
Neilson, D R
Pickard, M A
Pollington, G D
Provan, D H
Pryde, A N M
Robertson, L M
Rochow, S B
Rowling, D E
Saunders, C J P
Sawers, J D
Scott, E A H
Seaman, J L
Shannon, V C
Sherret, I R
Soppitt, H S
Taylor, D L

Thomson, M F
Warner, B G
Wightman, D
Winslow, G S

Currie
Andrews, D
Arthur, A E
Church, M A
Clinkenbeard, J M
De Lima, V R F
Dennis, G A M
Kerr, I J
McColl, A D
McGavigan, P P
McGrath, W D
Page, C A
Potter, M A
Scott, E C
Venters, G L
Wallace, W F

Cwmbran
Allen, L M
Alvi, N-S F
Baldwin, R J T
Birchley, D W
Busby, H I
Butcher, J L
Davies, R A
Davies, S S
Davies, T S
Ensaff, S
Evans, H S
Fok, M E
Holgate, G P
Hunter, S
Hussain, R I
Kabeer, A W A
Kabeer, A A K
King, J L
Kinnaird, T D
Law, P J
Lohfink, A B
McKay, F H
Morgan, N A
Nicell, D T
Nirmal, D L
Nolan, W P
Paramagnanam, N
Roberts, G A
Rowlands, P J
Sathya, H C
Shah, R B
Skitt, R C
Smith, S A
Thear-Graham, M R
Thomas, B E
Thurgood, M C
Vermaak, Z A
Warrington, R
Wharton, E
Wilcox, B
Zutshi, M K

Dagenham
Abaniwo, N M
Asadullah, M
Ashraff, S M M
Baird, S R
Bajpai, S
Beheshti, B
Bishop, D A
Connell, T E
Cusack, M R
Dijkuizen, R S
Ellul, N
Fateh, M
Ghosh, T K
Gosai, P M
Heinink, P A
Henderson, H J
Hora, S
Hora, S C
Jaiswal, D P
Johnston, R D
Junaid, K N
Junaid, R A
Kadva, A B
Kalra, R S
Kaulu, K K
Khan, G M A A
Kiely, N T
Kugapala, G
Kumar, A
Kumar, M
Kumar, S
Mitra, A K
Mittal, A K
Mohan, T C

Quansah, B B
Roy, M
Saxena, D
Wijekoon, J B

Dalbeattie
Burton, S D
Burton, T P
Carrie, D I B
Cowe, L
Dodd, D
Ewart, M
Freeth, A I
Golen, Z
Kelly, J
Marshall, D M
Munro, G H M
Munro, J M
Neilson, D J C
Patrick, I T
Pflanz, S
Rogers, W J B
Rose, E
Wilson, O

Dalkeith
Binnie, J A H
Black, A
Capperauld, I
Chisholm, H K
Copp, P A J
Court Brown, C M
Dennis, C A R
Drever, J C
Glencross, A H
Glidden, J M
Grant, N C R
Ireland, V M E
McLean, K
McLean, N P
Marshall, W D
Miller, J N
Mok, J Y Q
Murray, M E D
Murray, M J
Robertson, D
Smart, L
Wilson, M S

Dalmally
Mackay, D J

Dalry
Andrews, I M
Arnott, A H
Arnott, G L
Bell, D
Kirke, E M
Law, M J A
Stevenson, J
Taylor, J A
Wilson, W M

Dalton-in-Furness
Amos, C E
Johnson, R N
Maguire, J C
Qazi, A A

Darlington
Abu-Rajab, R B
Adams, G
Ali, A S M
Alief, L R J
Apps, A J L
Bagshaw, I M M
Bainbridge, J M
Barnes, E W
Barnett, M B
Beeton, C
Berenguer Pellus, J V
Berry, J
Biggin, A E
Birnie, T
Bishop, D G M
Bosanquet, H G
Bottomley, D H
Bradey, N
Bradshaw, J
Braid, J
Bray, G P
Broadbent, C
Brock, J
Brookes, J L
Brown, C D
Bruggink, E M A
Buckley, S A E
Burdis, B D
Burkart, C B
Burton, L L
Byrne, W H T

Cannon, P G
Carpenter, R F
Carr, A E
Carr, P H
Carrick, H J
Carter, F C
Caver, H C
Chan, L
Chan, T
Charlton, R S
Chou, C W K
Clason, A E
Connolly, C K
Cooper, M W
Davison, C P
Dillon, E
Dixon, H H
Drummond, R S
Duncan, C J
El Awage, A E S Y
Elliot, J W
Enoch, D A
Fenwick, K W H
Finnie, S M
Fuat, A
Gabb, P
Gooch, I J
Gunning, K A
Haidon, J L
Handyside, W B
Hargreaves, M J
Hargreaves, R J
Hargroves, D R
Harker, R A G
Harris, C A
Harris, G
Harsha, B S
Haslam, J D
Haw, D S
Henderson, R G
Henderson, T E
Hindmarsh, J R
Hodgson, J D S
Hopkins, J S
Htun Nyunt, R
Huda, A H M Q
Husain, S A
Hutchon, D J R
Izzat, A B
James, R D
Jeavons, D A
Jones, A B
Kukreja, N
Lam Shang Leen, G
Langham, P J
Latimer, J
Laws, J O
Lincoln, K A
Little, J D
McIlhinney, S E
Mackenzie, M S
Mallinder, P A
Marsh, G N
Marshall, A J
Martin, I C A
Martin, S D
Mather, J S
Maughan, J H
Melrose, D M
Melrose, W M
Metcalfe, G J G
Michie, A F
Mitchell, R A
Monro, J S C
Montgomery, A
Mowbray, P
Munshi, S
Murphy, J J
Naismith, S M
Neville, A C
Neville, M J
Neville, W
Nicholson, G
Oluwole, M O K
Pallister, I
Parameswaran, R
Peart, E J
Penney, B F
Pheara, J
Potter, G J A
Pugh, E J
Rajah, P A N
Reed, M R
Rhodes, M
Richardson, S S
Robson, E G
Robson, M C
Rosin, L J
Ruckley, R W

Russell, D
Saha, S
Said, J R
Sathananthan, D
Sathananthan, N
Satyavadanan, B S
Scott, F M
Senanayake, G
Senthilnathan, G
Shaw, A
Singleton, G J
Sloss, J M
Spark, J I
Stahl, T J
Stephenson, K D
Stephenson, M A
Stevens, R C H
Stevenson, G C
Stone, S A
Strong, D A
Sturman, J M
Suri, Y P
Talluri, S C
Tan, Y M
Tarelli, S V
Taylor, I H
Taylor, W D
Thakur, I M
Townshend, J M
Trewby, P N
Trewhella, M J
Tulloch, C J
Turnbull, J C
Tyre, N W F
Uitenbosch, M
Upshall, R T P
Wade, R
Wade, S J
Waldin, I E G
Waller, I S
Walton, D A
Watson, C
Weerasinghe, S
Whittaker, A M
Whittaker, M G
Wilkie, J L
Williams, C
Williams, G V
Williams, G B G
Wormald, J L
Wylie, J
Young, A C M

Dartford
Aburn, S P
Alban Davies, H
Alsmeier, C J
Andrews, V E
Baines, M J
Beazley, P M C
Bhargava, S
Bhatia, P P K
Bhatia, P S
Brace, C H
Brooke, D B M
Browne, S E
Burne, J C
Corbett, D J R
Cressall, S F M
Cybulska, E
Dave, S R
Davies-Wragg, C
Davis, A E
Delport, B C
Denholm-Young, H M
Dickinson, I K
Dickinson, K A
Ede, R J
Edward, R H
Enchill-Yawson, M K
Farquhar, C W
Fernandes, N B
Fernando, P H Q
Fitzpatrick, W J F
Fraser, J A
Gladman, M A
Godfrey, R G
Grant, C E
Greer, B L
Gunasingham, V
Hamblyn, M J
Harding, C K
Harding, W G
Harryman, Dr
Herring, J
Hood, J
Hudson, J H
Hunt, A B
Hunter, F M

Dartmouth

Husaini, T A
Huxham, C D
Jamall, A
Jeans, V C
Jones, D R
Jones, M H
Khakoo, A A
Khan, M M
Kirk, J M E
Koo, C K
Lawrence, D J
Lawrence, D A
Lawrie, J E
Lawrie, R S
Leyshon, A
McCann, M G
McElearney, N L G
McIrvine, A J
Mackenzie, G D
Madill, S A
Mathew, V M
Melia, W M
Mohan, A J S
Mohan, S
Morgan, S A
Muhammad, F A
Nicolson, J A
Osman, A K A
Pahuja, S
Parker, M C O
Parrott, J M
Parry, G M
Patel, D C
Patel, H R
Patel, H
Patel, R A
Patel, T P
Peiris, M L Q
Pepelassis, D
Peppiatt, R
Perry, N
Pimenta, N G
Pimenta, S M
Prendergast, M T A
Protopapas, M
Pugh, H W
Pyle, S J
Rana, A K
Rashid, A M F
Rawcliffe, J F X
Rose, S L
Saheed, A H
Sarkar, J C
Scott, J F
Seaton, J S
Selvaratnam, M A
Sen, S M
Shamprasadh, V
Sharma, R
Shaw, A C
Shetty, A
Shora, B S
Short, D H
Short, N L
Sikdar, N
Slater, A J
Stewart, M
Symes, J B L
Thebe, P R
Thuraisingham, R C
Toth, M
Watts, J A E
West, C H
Westbrook, S J
Wickens, C L
Wild, D

Dartmouth

Anderson, A C
Ashton, E G
Bann, R F
Barrell, S R
Ellerby, R
Eynon-Lewis, A J
Fairlie-Clarke, G A
Fenton, J S
Giblin, M
Giblin, M M
Golledge, N H H
Gray, J M
Green, J E
Keane, W G
Kent, S G
Lees, K P
Lockerbie, G D
McKibbin, B
Pearson, C J P
Poole, G W
Poole, J
Roberts, J C
Ross, M P
Shalders, K
Shatwell, B L
Taylor, E H
Taylor, J B
Wilkinson, W H
Woodroof, G M F

Darvel

Kondol, A J
Montgomery, S J
Rait, E A
Robertson, M A
Sargaison, M F R

Darwen

Ahmed, E
Ahmed, S
Alam, S K
Andrews, D M
Bidwell, J C
Bolton, A
Burrows, C
Butterworth, D J
Dalton, C R
Griffin, J N
Higab, M G B
Hirst, A M
Jagandesham, P
Memon, M I
Mills, A
Morlese, J F
Morris, P J
Patel, R
Schofield, I J
Sinclair, A A
Storey, A B
Zaman, A

Daventry

Beer, T C
Boulton, D J
Craig, A J
Cripps, C M
Davies, M G
El Hadidi, M M E E
Ewart, H
Gardiner, P S
Graham, C M
Harding, T A C
Herbert, K C
Hill, R R W
Jeffers, L M
Justice, J M
Kirkham, S E
Lovatt, C J
Mackichan, I D
Maurice-Smith, N J
Middleton, P H
Moser, J B
Pound, D P B
Redpath, A M
Rookledge, M M
Sewell, J M
Silverman, A J
Sims, R J A
Verso, N E
Voeten, F
Williams, E N

Davyhulme

Sykes, P A

Dawlish

Alborough, E A
Bradshaw, M K
Brook, G K
Clements, A J P
Diprose, J
Diprose, R H
Donovan, W M
Dorkins, C E
Irvine, C D
James, A J B
Oxborrow, S M
Pajovic, S
Raby, P R
Rutherford, A K D
Whitehead, J R E

Deal

Allen, W H
Barron, H L
Beach, G R
Booker, K M N
Bulmer, J N
Cockrill, J N
Dunn, J M E F
Dyer, J K
Farrer, C J

Forte, V J C
Frischman, W J
Heeley, M E
Hoffmann, F
Hollingsbee, E R
Ison, E
Joslin, C C
Joslin, J E M
Kaduruwane, E N
Lee, M A
Maginn, S
Mannings, H W P
Pond, J B
Rafla, M
Rawlings, K L
Russell, S A
Rutherford, S J
Ryder, S-A
Scholfield, D P
Scott, A L
Sharp, J F
Sharvill, N J
Sheffield, D G
Smith, G M
Sparrow, I R C
Summerhayes, J W
Ustianowski, P A
Viney, M T
Walter, M V
Whitfield, R G S
Woodgate, M M

Deeside

Barlow, G D
Basu, S C
Cameron, M C
Carson, P C
Currie, A E
Curry, J A
Donaldson, M
Drew, P J T
Dreyer, C P
Dyer, T J
Fells, J F
Gavin, M J
Gavin, M J
Gavin, W B J
Graham, C M
Harney, M A J
Jeffries, M G
Jolly, W
Jones, C W
Jones, D T
Jones, T M W
Jones, W R S
Jordan, A F
Kamaly-Asl, Y
Markey, B M
Morris, D E
Pritchard, R M
Rathbone, N
Roberts, D F
Roberts, D Y
Salt, A
Skilbeck, B
Stiggelbout, H J
Tannahill, M M
Williams, C W L
Williams, E A

Denbigh

Aiken, D A
Appleton, F
Banks, R
Bishop, J M
Davies, C R
Davies, M W
Evans, M E
Eve, J L
Fry, N M
Giles, M A
Griffiths, R W
Hackett, P L
Heaton, A
Jackson, F B
Jenkins, S E
Jones, D G
Jones, J
Jones, R H
Jones, R W
Karunakaran, K
Krasner, C D
Lister, R F
Lynch, J B
Macgregor, A H
Madoc-Jones, J C
Marshall, A G
Mosa, M A M
Needham, P R G

Owen, G W
Parry, D E
Parry, E
Roberts, B
Roberts, J M
Roberts, R J
Rodgers, B
Rowe, A J S
Salusbury, C A
Sheers, R
Thomas, H M
Thomas, J C
Thomas, J G
Trevelyan, T R
Turczanska, E
Watkin, H
Webb, R D
Webb, T B
Wilkins, S W
Williams, S A
Wilson, C S
Winter, S J
Wood, J D D
Wykes, E L
Wykes, P
Wykes, R J

Denny

Anderson, A R
Blyth, T H
Boyd, M N
Campbell, I K
Craig, I F
Davidson, A
Deuchar, R A
Donaldson, S W
Downs, F M
Flynn, F M
Giles, G M
Kay, D H
Kay, P A
McElhinney, A S J
McGettigan, J T
McLean, K F
Michels, A M J
Ryrie, G E
Slann, H E R
Smith, J R
Wilm, A R

Derby

Abrahams, J W
Adams, N M
Adamson, E A
Aitchison, P J M
Aiton, C G
Allen, G R
Allen, L J
Allen, R A
Ambrose, J S
Ancliff, P M
Anderson, C M
Anderson, T
Anderson, W A
Appaiah, M C
Archer, S J
Arthur, R G
Arulkumaran, S
Asar, A H
Ashby, J H
Ashcroft, J S
Ashworth, J M
Askew, A E
Atkin, M P
Bailey, G R
Bainbridge, L C
Bainbridge, M A
Bains, H S
Bakshi, J
Banbury, J E
Baron, J H
Barrett, S
Barron, D A
Barron, N M
Barton, B W
Basi, S K K
Bateman, J R M
Bates, B J
Bates, R C E
Bavister, P H
Bawden, M J
Bedford, E M
Bell, M M
Beltran De Guevara Martinez, M L
Benjamin, P D
Benson, B M
Bentley, G C
Berrisford, R C

Bertram, A
Bhowmik, M M
Binnie, D J
Birtwell, A J
Black, I L
Blacker, P A
Blackshaw, G L
Blackwall, M C H
Bland, E S
Bland, S A
Bleiker, T O
Blissett, J E
Boddy, P J
Booth, D F
Bowden, P W
Bradfield, R M
Brewin, J E
Brooks, A J
Brown, A G
Brown, H M
Browne, M N K
Budgen, J P B
Bullock, D W
Burn, S
Burnett, K J
Busfield, H M B
Bush, J A
Bushby, A F
Butler, G
Byrne, P H
Cagney, B M M
Callum, K G
Calthorpe, D A D
Cameron, S
Campbell, D W
Cargill, A O
Cargill, J
Cartwright, D P
Chakraborti, A
Chakraborti, P K
Chamberlain, S T
Chapman, M A S
Chapman, R L K
Charlton, J A
Charlton, J C
Chawla, O P
Chelliah, P J
Chen, H C
Chilka, S Y
Chilton, C P
Choonara, I A
Choudhury, A R
Chowdhury, P A H
Chowdhury, S M I
Chua, C B
Church, R D
Clark-Maxwell, P A
Clark, D I
Clark, M H
Clarke, D P
Clayton, A R
Clulow, C
Coate, C E H
Cocker, J
Cohen, G F
Cohen, M E L
Cole, A T
Collar, B
Cooke, D
Cooper, R E
Coupe, R M
Cowlishaw, P J
Cox, J R
Cox, J
Cozens, N J A
Crompton, J G
Crossley, A W A
Crowder, L E
Cust, M P
Dalton, D M
Daniells, J J
Daniels, S M
Dann, N
Dann, W L
Darnell, R
Davidson, G A
Davies, J
Davies, P B
Davies, S L
Davies, T G G
Dawson, J S
Day, H M M
De Nunzio, M C
Derrington, M C
Dew, S E
Dhadda, B S
Disney, D J
Dixon, W G
Docherty, P T C

Dodd, K L
Dodsley, D R
Donaldson, J C
Donnelly, R
Doris, E J
Dua, R
Duthie, J
Edwards, R B
Edyvean, I K
Edyvean, R J F
Eglitis, H M
Eisenberg, J N H
Elgar, R J
Ellis, S R
Elsherbini, M M
Evans, A G
Evans, D J
Evershed, T A
Farmer, D
Farrell, K A
Farrow, R J
Fellick, J M
Ferrer, I R
Fey, R E
Field, S Y
Fieldhouse, M L
Filer, J L
Fisher, S A
Fletcher, J D
Fletcher, V L
Fluck, R J
Forde, M E
Foreman, E A
Forster, M C
Forster, N D
Forsyth, S M
Foskett, L A
Foster, J H
Foster, N J
Fowlie, A
Fox, J R
Fraser-Moodie, W A
Fraser, T W G
Freeman, B
Freeman, J R
French, G W G
Fyall, A A
Game, L M
Gardner, I D
Gartside, J M
Gayed, S L
Gembali, M
George, J R G
Gilchrist, A M
Girn, S S
Godridge, H
Goh, D K Y
Golding, D J
Golding, P R
Goldsmith, R
Goodall, P
Goodwin, J F
Gopee, K D R
Gorman, W P
Gray, J M
Grenville, J S
Gurling, K J
Guthrie, D
Guy, R
Haddow, A M
Hale, W M
Hall, R I
Hamilton, W D E
Hammond, F K
Hands, B G
Hanna, N P
Harper, R D
Harris, A P
Harrop, A J
Harrop, J S
Harvey, C M
Hay, J M
Hayes, I P
Hayes, P D
Hayton, M I
Heappey, M
Henry, A P J
Herberts, P J D
Heron, A T
Hewitson, E H
Hewitt, R I
Hill, P A
Hillary, I A
Hinwood, D C
Hirst, R E
Ho, B Y M
Hobday, S R
Hocknell, J M L
Hodgkins, J

Diss

Hodson, P B
Hogg, J R
Holliday, C M
Holliday, H W
Holloway, R
Holloway, S A
Holmes, G K T
Hope, D T
Hopper, I P
Hopton, S S
Horden, P J
Horner, M E A
Horry, P E
Horton, E B
Hough, A
Howard, P W
Howarth, N J
Howell, D A
Howell, P J
Howells, D P M
Hudgins, D
Hughes, J
Hunt, D J
Ibrahim, F R
Iddon, P W
Iftikhar, S Y
Isherwood, J P
Jack, B A
Jackson, S N J
James, P D
James, R A
Jefferson, D
Jefferson, R D
Jibodu, M O
Jibodu, O A
John, T M
Jones, K
Jones, T L
Joshi, A A
Kapila, I
Karia, D J
Karim, U H A
Kazmi, F A
Kazmi, M A
Keeley, V L
Keeling, C J
Keeling, M
Keen, J J
Kelsey, R E
Kennedy, J L
Keys, S S S
Khalil, N G
Khan, A Q A
Khan, J A
Khan, M Z G M
Khosla, S
Khullar, S K
Kiani, S H
Kinsella, H P
Kirupananthan, S
Klukowski, A K
Komocki, E C
Korday, S N
Lacey, P G
Langham, B T
Lansbury, L E
Lavelle, R H
Law, A T
Lawson, I J
Ledbury, J
Leeson, P M
Lenehan, R M
Leveaux, V M
Leyshon, V N
Liasides, E C
Lim, N P Y
Little, S W
Lloyd, C G
Long, J
Lowe, P A
Lunn, A J F
McCance, A J
McCance, S L
McFarlane, H W
MacFarlane, J C
McGhee, M
McGibbon, I
McGrath, C M P
McIntyre, D
McIntyre, J W
Mackaness, C R
McKenny, J G
McKernan, A M
McLean, K A
Macleod, G F
Maginnis, C M
Majumdar, B
Malhi, S S
Marak, W K

Marshall, T J
Matthews, H L
Matthews, I W
Matthews, J I
Maung Maung Tun, N
Mayne, S
Millar Craig, J A
Millar-Craig, M W
Miller, M T V
Minford, J E
Miralles, R E
Mitchell, D C
Moar, A K
Monteiro, J L
Moore, J K
Mordey, P L
Morks, T H W
Morris, P A
Morrissey, J J
Morrissey, W J
Morton, R E
Moss, P J
Muhiddin, K A L
Mukhopadhyay, S
Mulvey, D A
Munson, K W
Murphy, M A C
Murray-Leslie, C F V
Murray, D P
Mylvahan, N
Napier, J F
Nash, J R
Nath, M
Navaratnam, R M
Nelson, C S
Newell, P A
Newland, R D P
Newton, R J
Nichols, G J
Nicholson, J
Nickson, H
Norton, B
O'Donoghue, A E M A
O'Reilly, M K
O'Reilly, S C
O'Rourke, E J
Oppong, A C K
Orchard, J M
Orr, R L
Otim-Oyet, D
Owen, R T
Panton, S
Parkes, I R
Patel, K C
Patel, P K
Patel, R C
Patton, G
Paul, G
Paveley, W F
Pavlidis, S
Peacock, I D A
Pearson, W J C
Pengiran Tengah, D S N A
Perko, C D
Piotrowicz, A J K
Piotrowicz, A L M
Plessas, S
Poll, D J
Pore, P S
Pore, S V
Pound, N
Prabhu, M A
Pritty, P E
Pryce, J C
Quinnell, R C
Raabe, H-C
Rahman, F R
Rajakumar, R
Ralph, S J
Ramzan, M
Rao, K
Ratcliffe, A B
Ratcliffe, V A
Ratnayaka, B D M
Rawal, O P
Rayment, A
Rayner, S S
Redlaff, L
Reeder, S-J
Regan, M R
Reynolds, J R
Rivers, J A
Rixom, J A
Roberts, A D G
Robertshaw, J K
Robertshaw, K A
Robinson, I A
Robinson, J F C

Robinson, K F
Rogers, P N
Rogerson, D
Rossiter, J M
Rowan-Robinson, M N
Rowles, J M
Ruggins, N R
Russell, W F
Sarath Mohan, M
Sayal, C
Schroven, I
Scothern, G E
Scott, I V
Scott, T N B
Scrivener, L E
Searle, A E
Sebastian, M
Semeraro, D
Shand, I R
Sharp, J F
Shaukat, M N
Shepherd, M C
Sherman, M A
Sibbering, D M
Simmons, M H
Singh, D N P
Singh, H P
Singh, K S P N
Sinha, L
Sinha, S
Sisodia, N
Skidmore, J R
Smailes, R A
Smalley, D M
Smith, A P
Smith, A D A
Smith, F D
Smith, H J
Smith, K
Smith, M R
Smith, P G L
Smith, R E
Snape, J
Spincer, J
Squirrell, C A
Sreevalsan, S K
Sreevalsan, S K
Staley, P K
Stanley-Smith, S P
Stark, R A
Steele, G A
Stephenson, C M
Stephenson, D K
Stephenson, M G
Sterland, M E
Stevenson, J M
Stoddard, D R
Stuart, I P
Stuart, K C
Stuart, R
Summers, G D
Summerscales, A
Sumner, K R
Sykes, R V
Sykes, S G
Symonds, I M
Tamizian, O
Tangri, C
Tatla, T
Taylor, G J
Taylor, K M
Terrell, E S
Thacker, S P
Thomas, D A
Thomas, G D
Thomson, D J
Thornicroft, S G
Tindall, M J
Tran, M N
Tresidder, J S
Tuckley, C M
Turnbull, A E
Turner, C B
Turner, G M
Uings, A E
Vater, M
Verma, R
Vijan, S G
Vinayagamoorthy, M
Vinayagamoorthy, P
Voice, A
Walsh, J T
Wanger, K M
Ward, C D
Warner, C E J
Warrack, J H
Warren, S S
Watkinson, S E
Weir, N U

Wells, D T
Wharton, P J
Wheatcroft, M S
Whitaker, R
Whitehall, A L
Whitehead, S M
Wicks, M H
Wight, H S C
Wigley, A
Willatt, J M
Williams, D A
Williams, N R
Williams, R A
Williams, S E
Wilson, R N
Wilton, T J
Windebank, W J
Wood, P A A
Wright, H E
Yar Khan, S A
Zaman, M A
Zaman, N A
Zammit-Maempel, J G

Dereham

Abell, C A
Bailie, H C
Carroll, R L
Carroll, S M
Clemo, J
Colman, J E R
Cooper, S F
Crampton, S A
Dun, M
Ewing, J M
Grahame-Clarke, C N E
Hanson, D S
Harvey, E M
Hibberd, S C
Hodge, A L
Hughes, R J R
Humphreys, J R H
Jackson, A O
Jones, E A
Jones, H W
Kreeger, A J
Langman, D A H
Lavelle, K G
Lee, A J
MacNair, A D
Marais, A D R
Marczewski, A G
Mathias, D H
Meade, B W
Michie, C
Moore, S C
Mourin, K A A
Rose, C J
Stafford, E A
Strickland, P J
Sugathadasa, J E
Sutton, A J
Taylor, S J
Thorneley, C W
Tracey, C A
Turner, S D
Van Dyk, J J
Webb, K R

Devizes

Akhtar, M A
Archer, R D J
Ashford-Brown, W H
Atkins, P J
Bird, M C C
Clayton, J P
Cogan, J F
Dawkins, R
Dunbar, P G
Fearnley, J D O
Featherstone, J M
Flood, J E
Foxen, E H M
Godfrey, J M
Godwin, L C
Gompels, M A B
Hallward, C G
Hamid, E A H M
Heaton-Renshaw, J S
Hollway, J C
Hollway, T E
Jackson, P D
Janes, N C
Kilpatrick, W G
Kuber, U A
Lindon, R G
Lodge, G J
Madigan, E A

Meredith, S G
Miller, J D T
Nash, J C
Nelson, S J
New, J W
Osborn, H M
Palmer, R L B
Pearce, R A J
Price, S
Pullen, J E
Purcell, B L
Reid, N C
Riley, N P
Sandford-Hill, R C S
Saunders, D R S
Siggers, S H
Spencer Jones, C J
Stevens, D G
Tully, E M K
Twiner, D A N
Vize, C M
Watson-Jones, D L
Watson, C
Whelehan, J M

Dewsbury

Ahmad, M
Ahmad, M
Angus, P D
Ansari, N-U-H
Asmal, Y Y V
Asmar, M A A A
Balasunderam, S
Balasunderam, S
Barnes, S M
Booya, N H
Brook, J
Brown, S A
Bullimore, S P
Cathcart, D B
Chapple, M R
Conway, C A
Craig, I R
Crockett, A L
Currie, D C
Dadibhai, E I
Davies, H F
De Silva, P A
Dhir, S
Evans, J M
Evans, M
Farooqui, T M
Ford, G P
Gordinsky, T J
Gorham, P F
Goulden, P
Gowda, R
Goyal, A
Hamwi, M W
Hicks, J
Hodgkinson, N A
Hordon, L D
Kalli, M
Kemp, T M
Khaliq Masood, A
Khan, Z H
Kumarasena, H A D
Lovegrove, J E
Mackay, P M
Maher, O
Mathur, G N
Medley, S N
Mehrotra, A P
Miles, S M
Myers, N A
Nanabawa, H I
O'Daly, E F
Osman, G O
Patel, Y V S
Rahman, M F
Rajpura, A I
Rehman, S-U
Robinson, C D
Shah, M
Shea, J G
Smith, P A
Smyllie, J H
Steel, D
Stephenson, R
Sutherland, W G M
Taylor, E G
Thimmegowda, H
Trehan, A K
Twist, D C
Wetherill, J H
Williamson, D M
Wilson, G M
Wilson, I R

Didcot

Asbury, J F P
Barrett, J M
Batty, B J
Beswick, K B J
Corps, D J
Couldrick, W G R
Deaney, C N
Delfosse, J B
Greenslade, P D
Haas, A J
Hawthorne, S E
Hooper, R W H
Hornsby, I C
Jackson, W F
Kershaw, J A
Lai, K
Lee, A M
McFarlane, J P
Millar, J M
Moore, S J
Nowell, H J
Richardson, I H
Rowbotham, M D
Ryan, E
Salzman, N G
Scott, D M
Spiro, J G
Tennent, T G
Thaung, C M H
Thompson, V M
Wade, A O
Wagner, A J
Wilson, M S
Wood, R
Yorston, C M

Dinas Powys

Andrews, J
Azami, J
Bater, A S
Cherry, A W
Chilcott, J L
Crane, M D
Curran, E
Davies, N P
Davies, R
Elmes, P C
Harvey, J S
Hilary-Jones, E P
Jackson, S
Jenkins, J D
Jenkins, J R E
Jones, H H G
Jones, J A G
Jones, K S
Kilpatrick, G S
Laurence, K M
Lewis, A G
Liddell, M B
Mackay, K R
Matthews, S J
Monypenny, I J
Monypenny, I G
Price-Davies, R
Robinson, M E
Sampeys, C S
Seel, E H
Smith, P M
Stears, A J
Thomas, S
Watkins, D M
Wood, A M

Dingwall

Allison, D K M
Black, D M C
Black, D K M
Davidson, A J L
Eagleson, K W
Haddow, I F G
Hayward, J D
Jackson, A
Macdonald, H M
Mack, M B
McKenna, M F
Maclean, H
McRorie, J
Millar, J S
Morrison, I A
Rasdale, P
Reid, K J
Roberts, S J
Ross, C M
Scott, E R

Diss

Bawden, R H F
Burke, S C
Chandler, O J

Dolgellau

Clarke, S M
Cooke, T D
Cordeaux, W L
Drake, S E
Foster, R M
Garton, F P A
Grogono, R M
Gunaratna, I J
Hassan, A G
Hayward, J M
Hopkins, S M
Hume, I M
Jones, A D
Leftley, P A
Lewis, R C D
Mason, H V
Nixseaman, D H
Rawlence, P D
Roth, D J
Rowell, S S
Schopflin, K E
Stevenson, I N B
Twite, M D
Veneto, B
Walsh, J
Wheble, S M

Dolgellau

Bradley, J N
Challen, P D
Edwards, J J
Fisher, J M
Hellawell, G O
Hilton, S M
Hopkins, J P
Lawson, T M
Martin, H M
Ogden, T L
Owen, S H
Roberts, I E
Roberts, J G
Thomas, N A

Dollar

Allan, F
Baughan, P M
Borrowman, E H
Bridges, A B
Galloway, I W Y
Gordon, V W C
Holdsworth, R J
Houston, N M
Hunter, K W
Jackson, L A
Logan, S M
Logan, W
Mok, V S
Morgan, J P
Pearson, M G
Randfield, H F
Reid, C R G
Risk, W J
Rodger, G N
Wilson, J D T

Donaghadee

Beckett, H E
Bunting, S
Groves, A M
Johnston, G W
Larkin, J A M
Long, E D
Macafee, A L
McClelland, J A E
Majury, C W
Miller, J
Neill, R A
Rutherford, J H
Smyth, M S
Walker, S

Doncaster

Abbas, M
Adams, L M
Addey, K M
Ahmad, S
Ahmad, S
Al-Khatib, M
Al-Najar, M A W A H
Ali-Khan, M V
Alkayali, R M
Anim-Addo, A
Attwood, M D
Baddoo, W A
Baig, M K
Baig, M W
Bajorek, M F W
Bake, A J
Banga, B S
Banga, R
Barbour, P
Bardhan, G
Barker, S R
Barrett, V L
Baskar, B
Beal, J A
Benson, P J
Benton, N M
Berry, A W
Bittiner, S B
Blacklock, A P
Blake, S C
Bloore, C M
Bolton, R P
Bonham, T J
Booth, S J
Borrill, M A
Boucherat, R
Boyle, R T
Bradley, A E
Bradley, J M
Brennan, K
Britten, L D
Brophy, C S
Brown, D J
Brownson, A J
Brownson, G M
Buckle, R J
Burne, J M
Burroughs, E A
Burton, A C
Carmichael, J C G
Carreck, G C
Chadha, D K
Chaffe, A G M
Chandler, G P
Chandrasekhar, T V
Charnock, R B
Chaudhary, R P
Chib, S C
Chikhani, C G A
Clark, A J
Clark, R
Cleeve, V J
Colbeck, W J
Coleman, M C
Conchie, A F
Connor, G J
Cook, P H E G
Coombes, G B
Cope, M A
Corlett, J R
Crooks, R N
Cubbon, D H
Cunliffe, L F
Cuschieri, R J
Dahanayake, S B M
Dahanayake, W D
Dakin, G H
Daly, F W M H
Das, P D
Davey, R S
Daw, N S
De Groot, S J
Deere, J J
Desai, S P
Desai, V S
Dexter, A
Dinakaran, S
Dobson, R B
Doran, K W
Dua, I S
Dua, P
Dua, R S
Duffield, J S
Eddison, P F
Eden, D J
Emms, N W
Erskine, W
Evans, K J
Everitt, B M
Fadra, S A
Fagg, P S
Falk, R M
Farmer, S E
Farrow, C O
Faruqi, M T
Fearns, D C
Fearns, J M
Fearns, S N
Felton, J C
Fenton, G R
Fenton, P A
Field, P M
Field, W D
Fisher, A M
Fitton, D C
Forbes, A L
Fullwood, H F
Furlong, O C
Gallagher, J M
Gibson, D A
Gilbert, J
Gillespie, A M
Glaves, P
Godley, H D
Goni, R A
Goodhead, D G
Goodyear, J E
Gordon, D J
Graves, A C
Griffiths, M A
Hadjikakou, A P
Hall, J L
Hamlin, R A
Hancocks, M E
Haq, M S
Harding, G M
Harris, J J
Hasenfuss, M F
Hattab, M M
Hawkswell, J C
Helm, R H
Heslip, M R
Hezseltine, D
Hill, G M
Hirpara, R H
Ho, A K-M
Hooper, K H
Hosker, J P
Howard, F A
Howarth, E
Howarth, J K
Hoy, C M
Huckett, E C A
Hughes, K B
Hughes, M E
Hughes, T J
Humby, F C
Hurley, P J
Inglis, J
Inglis, S A
Inman, A J
Inman, S R
Islam, G
Jackson, B E
Jackson, J H
Jadhav, P R
Jagadish, T S
Jenkinson, M D
Johnson, A M
Jones, E W
Jones, R L D
Jordan, P R
Karwa, R K
Kayarkar, V V
Kaye, K
Kell, S W
Kerr, I P
Kesseler, G
Ketchin, G S
Key, C
Khan, A
Khan, A U
Khan, M A
Khan, S
Kilvington, K A
Kingston, M A
Kirby, S
Kolli, L R
Kouchouk, A A
Kulkarni, G R
Kumar, P N H
Kurien, G
Lambert, J R
Latif, S
Le Vann, A M
Lee, K M S
Leggett, R J E
Leigh, R J
Leitch, S G
Lockyear, S K
Lomax, W
Love, P W
McDougall, K M M
McGrath, H M
Machin, A J
McIlwraith, W
McKenna, B J
Mackenzie, D S
Mackenzie, J
MacKillop, N G
Mackinlay, J Y
McMahon, C
Madan Benarji, T
Majumdar, G
Majumdar, K N
Makol, O P
Marsh, V C
Marshall, A J
Marshall, B A
Marshall, G F G
Martin, P C
Matthews, J G
Mian, T A
Middleton, N M
Miller, A M
Milne, B R
Mitchell, D
Mitra, S
Moore, J M
Moores, W K
Moss, T R
Mozdzierz, W J
Murphy, F
Nelson, J P
North, P E
Northwood, D
O'Horan, P
O'Leary, M
Oakshott, G H L
Orridge, H W
Outwin, G R
Owen, R P
Pande, S K
Pardoe, R F
Paskins, J R
Patel, B M
Patterson, E R E
Payne, G E
Phillips, S L
Pilgrim, J A
Pittaway, A J
Platts, K A
Pollock, J S
Porter, R W
Pramanik, P
Prasad Reddy, K
Psaila, J V
Qureshi, N
Raithatha, H H
Rajathurai, A
Rajathurai, T
Ramgoolam, M
Redden, J F
Rigby, K A
Roberts, J H
Roberts, J E
Robinson, R J
Rockett, H E
Rodgers, L J
Rogers, S
Rogers, T K
Ross, D
Saddler, N J
Saha, S K
Salama, N D
Saunders, I M
Savage, D
Savage, J
Sayer, J M
Scott, S R
Sellars, N R
Seth, A K
Sewell, P F J
Shannon, P E
Sharp, J E
Sharp, M W
Sheehan, A L
Sheikh, M E
Shepherd, J B M
Sherburn, V E
Shetty, A
Shetty, R
Silvester, N W H
Simonds, G W
Sinclair, N M
Singh, S
Smyllie, H C
Sowden, M C
Stalker, R
Stannard, P A
Stewart, D J A
Subhani, M
Sunderland, H
Sutherland, M V
Sykes, K B
Sykes, R S
Tahir, S M
Taneja, A
Taylor, H F
Taylor, M P
Taylor, M R
Tomlinson, G N
Townend, I R
Train, J J A
Turner, N A
Turner, S
Umapathee, P
Urruty, J-P
Van Der Lijn, R
Walker, D
Walker, M
Ward, C J
Ward, D A
Ward, P J
Ward, S
Watson, G M
Watson, M G
Webb, R F
Weeks, I R
Weller, S
Wellings, D
Whale, C I
Whittlestone, T H
Wildgoose, K
Wilson, A H
Wilson, P D
Wong, C-H
Wood, D J
Wright, A
Wright, C W
Wyatt, R J
Wythers, D J
Young, K

Dorchester

Adams, K J
Al-Hilali, M M A
Andrew, D S
Anscombe, A M
Armitage, P L
Arnall-Culliford, J M
Ashfield, R P
Bailey, A P
Bailey, E H
Baird, P W
Ball, A J
Ball, S E
Barker, D A
Barker, M R S
Barlow, I W
Barlow, J M
Bawden, S L
Bell, W A G
Belsham, A J
Bhide, M
Boardman, C J
Boon, F W
Boucher, J
Bowering, A R
Boyle, A M E
Bray, L C
Brooks, R F
Bruce-Jones, P N E
Brueton, N R
Buck, A C
Cain, D L
Camm, P R
Campion-Smith, C R
Carbones Casanovas, F X
Carey, W D H
Cartwright, F S
Chall, D
Chase, A O
Chesney, D
Clay, M E
Cleaver, C P
Clifford, R D
Collins, P A
Collyer-Powell, K J
Coode, W K
Cornaby, A J
Cove, D H
Cove, R D
Cox, H J
Daoud, R A
De Silva, K P
Debenham, G
Dick, D H
Dixon, K
Dobbs, J F R
Dooley, M M P
Doyle, A R
Edwards, T J
El Komy, A A H A
Fahmy, M E E-D S
Fleet, J C
Fleury, R A
Flowerdew, A D S
Flowerdew, S M
Ford, G R
Fox, P G
Foxell, R M
Francis, G J
Gallimore, G R
Gendy, R K
Gibbens, C L
Gibbens, G L D
Gill, K J
Gilliver, A
Glaisyer, J M
Goonetilleke, C R
Goulden, S E
Gourley, D G
Graham, M D
Groom, S N
Hall, G
Hankin, R G
Harker, N J
Harker, P
Hebblethwaite, R P E
Helliwell, M G
Hollis, J N
Hooper, E J
Hopford, R L S
Hopkin, N B
Hughes, T O
Hunt, D C E
Iftikhar, M
Ingram, S M
Iparragirre, B
Jarrett, E B
Jeffery, P J
Johnson, A J
Johnson, M G
Johnston, P G B
Kassab, A S M
Knight, H-P F
Krishnamurthy, P
Lane, S M
Lascelles, B D
Lawson, R L
Lim, K S
Ling, D
Little, J A
McAllen, P M
McConnell, W D
Mackay-James, M A
McNicol, G P
McNicol, S M
McShane, C B
Mahoney, M
Matthews, M W B
Meikle, D D
Millner, C B E
Mitchell, A E
Mitchell, R G
Moosa, A H
Murray, E O
O'Neill, D W J
Pearce, M Q
Phillips, G D
Pilcher, R K
Porter, G P
Potter, V A J
Pulletz, M C K
Purvis, R J
Raza, M N
Rees, P H B
Riddoch, A J
Romanes, G J
Salvi, A E K
Scott, S T
Shattock, G M
Simpson, S W
Sloan, R H
Small, F T
Smith, N C
Snell, E S
Somani, N R
Somani, N
Sowerby, P R
Stanley, S
Stevenson, J
Stoot, C J
Tadros, A N
Taylor, J E
Taylor, M J
Taylor, P N
Thomas, G D
Thomasson, J E R
Vaughan-Jackson, O J
Veasey, D A
Vines, J R
Vulliamy, D G
Wakeham, C T
Walters, F J H
Webb, A J
Wiley, P F
Williams, E A
Williams, R E O
Williams, R K T
Wilson, A J

Wilson, J E
Winterton, S J
Woodhouse, M A
Woodhouse, M M
Wright, P F
Wyatt, E P
Wyer, A I
Wylie, P A L

Dorking

Adams, K J
Alloway, R
Arnold, P C
Blockey, G J
Booth, D
Boothroyd Brooks, B G
Boothroyd Brooks, E M
Bramwell, E C
Budd, P P
Castaldi, P
Chalker, E J
Chappell, R H
Clarke, I A
Clissold, E
Collins, C D
Cornish, G F
Curties, R T L
Farmer, M A
Gledhill, R F
Goode, I M P
Guthrie, G M
Gwyther, S J
Hardwick, C
Hare, N C
Hornung, R G
Jago, A J
Jeffcoate, S L
Jefferies, S D B
Jepson, G J
Kingsley-Jones, J
Kober, S J
Livingstone, A V
Loveless, S R
Menzies, R D
Mills, E J
Monella, S C
Morrow, M
Mulgirigama, L D
Orr, R G
Pare, C M B
Parkes, W R
Phipps, P H
Price, S A
Rasmussen, J G C
Revel, J-C A
Reynard, T J W
Savage, S J
Scott, H J
Sells, E L
Sells, H
Stanley-Jones, J K V
Thomas, C W
Thomas, H G
Thompson, J R
Tomkins, J G
Tomlinson, S J
Venn, R M
Wheeler, W F
Wishart, M
Woodcock, J F
Young, R M

Dornoch

Aitchison, K J
Campbell, D E
Mitchell, R M
Nash, R W
Robertson, S J T
Sutherland, J H

Douglas

Abdulrahman, A O A
Adair, T M
Alcock, A M
Ashton, E K
Batey, N R
Beatson, T R
Berry, R J
Biggart, M J
Birkin, N J
Blackman, C M
Blankert, M H L
Booth, J B
Bourdillon, R E
Bradley, V P
Brownsdon, D J
Bruce, A
Bull, D M
Chalmers, D H K

Chatfield, A H
Clague, R B
Cousins, B A
Crerand, J
Cretney, J D
Cromar, D M
Cullen, J P
Danher, J
Daniels, J K
Dowman, C G
Evans, G
Evans, P F
Fayle, R J S
Featherstone, R M
Fenton, C M
Ferguson, F T
Gardner, L D
Garvey, C N
Gavin, N G S
Green, A D L
Hamm, R E D
Hampton, G
Harding, F W
Harris, B D
Harrison, N A
Harrison, P A
Harrop, M C
Hillas, C
Hinds, J C D
Hockings, N F
Hogg, R P
James, D
Kerr, R J N
Kerruish, T B W
Khan, E G
Khuraijam, G S
Kissack, C M
Lang, A E
Lee, A M
Lee, J O
McCrory, J W
Manuja, S L
Maung Cho, Dr
Morley, T S
Moroney, L H E
Murray, C R H
Newton, P G
Nicholls, C R
Nightingale, O D
Ninan, A C
O'Malley, D N
Pickering, F C
Pilling, A C
Plews, N R
Ritson, R H
Rolfe, J M
Skelly, F J
Stevens, D B
Stone, A K
Swan, E
Swan, J
Thavarajah, V M
Townsend, A S
Vaughan, A R S
Wardle, J K
Wilkinson, K

Doune

Cordwell-Smith, C B
Henderson, P M N
Jardine, C K H
McAlpine, J A
Rose, P F
Sawyer, D H
Swinney, G E
Thetford, D E A

Dover

Anderson, A M
Bahadur, T
Bahinipaty, L
Baillie-Johnson, H R
Ballinger, M B
Bradley, S D
Bundy, A G
Carey, A
Chaudhuri, S
Cloke, D J
Collins, M
Davis, R J L
Del Bianco, G
Dillistone, E
Dodd, I H
Elwood, J H
Farebrother, L A
Goddard, I M
Graham, J L T
Hodnett, S F
Jain, S C

Jenkins, D
Johnstone, J R
Jones, M E P
Kelly, B A
Kumi, G O
McSwiggan, G V
Melhuish, R J
Meynell, E W
Meynell, G G
Morris, J I J
Mottershead, A C
Naterwalla, R H
Neylon, J J
O'Muirithe, B P
Pepper, K M
Pollitt, J D
Premnath, P
Premnath, R
Radcliffe, D W J
Raman, S
Rauz, R-U-A
Rauz, S
Raynes, R H
Roulston, P
Smith, D
Snell, A D
Stellon, A J
Thompson, R J
Tippu, N I
Torrance, T C
Turner, D J
Ward, K J
Waters, S S
Welch, E F J
Wood, J R
Wright, L M
Zaman, H W

Downham Market

Bungay, A W
Cassels, A H
Chase, N J
Cvijetic, B P
Garner, P
Gent, T M
MacKichan, A H T
Sconce, J C A
Scott, R D
Sheppard, C T
Zilahi, C C

Downpatrick

Archbold, J A A
Bain, D A
Barr, E G
Baxter, H
Bell, J C
Boggs, R E
Boyd, J S
Brown, E
Cheung, H C
Creaney, J
Cunningham, E L
Deeny, A P
Donnan, K E
Doris, J P
Foy, J M
Foy, W T
Gaffney, B P
Glass, C E
Glass, G M
Grebbell, F S
Hamill, G
Hamill, J A
Hamill, J P
Hamill, V A
Hanna, B C
Hannah, B A
Harney, A-M
Harney, E J
Hayes, O M
Ingram, R M
James, W V
Kelly, M I
Kirk, J E J
Lamberton, M H
Leavy, A M
MacAleenan, F A
MacAleenan, N A
McCaw, T
McDaniel, D
McDowell, M J
McGill, J U
McGoldrick, H P M
McGrady, B J
McIntosh, H Y
McMullan, R
Magennis, C E
Magill, R B

Milhench, M R
Moore, P R J
Mulhall, M M
Murphy, M
Murphy, P G
O'Connor, S A
O'Reilly, G M
O'Toole, C E K
Phillips, M R
Riordan, M E P
Sheridan, M C
Smiley, C C
Stevenson, T H
Stewart, J C M
Stewart, M J
Storey, R G N
Whitehead, H M
Wilkie, A W
Wilson-Davis, M L

Driffield

Anderson, S J
Ascroft, N O
Beal, T A
Brotherston, J
Clarke, A D
Clarkson, G C
Crawford, A N
Crumpton, M
Crumpton, N E
Dawber, E E
Fawcett, G M
Freeman, R C
Goodlass, J
Guest, K A
Heaton, C H
Jollie, I A D
Kelly, S E
Kidd, J T
Knowles, J A
Loqueman, N
Low, J S M
Lynn, P R A
Monks, I M
Pickering, N
Richardson, P C
Senior, D
Sissons, C L
Sykes, A J
Thomas, D T
Towers, S J
Vincini, C
Walker, Z A
Walster, V M J
Wigglesworth, D F

Droitwich

Adcock, A V
Blake, A
Bradshaw, T
Brown, J F
Brown, R
Brownridge, D S
Cleak, D K
Cottell, K M
Dykes, C J
Edmondson, H D
Elliott, N M
Ellson, C R
Entwistle, C
Fernell, D M
Franklin, M E
Freeman, M J
Grave, G F
Hadley, J S
Hamer, J D
Horn, A C
Hossain, A M M
Jenkins, N E
Jones, G E S
Kameen, A F
Keeble, M M
Kelly, A J
Kenyon, A C W
Kerton, I L
Kinsman, R I
Kramer, H
Lancashire, M J
McCloskey, B G
McGregor, A
McKie, D J
Marshall, A T
Mitchell, E B
Neville, M L
Newsholme, R G
Oakley, R J
Pashley, J K
Pidsley, G K
Rawcliffe, P J

Read, L
Rennie, C D
Rogers, J B
Rosser, P M
Russell, R G
Sawyer, J P C
Smart, J C
Smith, C
Smith, P S
Stephens, L S
Strover, A E
Tarlo, L
Tomlinson, C J
Turner, P J
Vardi, G
Wild, S M
Williams, D C
Woof, W R

Dromore

Atchison, E M
Beggs, L H
Cargin, J A
Connery, J A
Corbett, G D A
Cull, M E
Drake, A T
Drake, M B G
Forsythe, T
Hearty, R T
Hinds, G M E
Kenny, C J
Kirby, J M
McNeice, R A
O'Rourke, K P
Paisley, J A
Patterson, A B
Rice, P F
Robinson, S D
Ruddell, N J
Shannon, G E M
Sweeney, C M
Walsh, S J

Dronfield

Allamby, P R
Baddoo, H H K
Barrowcliffe, D G
Bladon, C J
Bull, R E
Davidson, M J
Earl, R C
FitzGerald, M G
Foroughi, M
Green, M
Harvey, G M
Hawley, S K
Hughes, W Y
Lether, V A
Park, A J
Parsons, C E M
Spooner, C A
Taylor, C L
Verel, A C M

Drybrook

Good, C D
Hooper, A J

Dudley

Acquah, E K
Al-Rabban, S F
Anandakumar, P
Ananthanarayanan, V
Andrews, R
Arkell, L J
Bansal, N
Blackman, A J
Bowen, J C
Brettell, P B V
Broad, M V J
Butt, M S M
Cartwright, J
Cartwright, S T
Christie, J L
Collins, J B
Conlon, D M
Conlon, W P
Craggs, J E
Cullen, P E
De Silva, D T
Desai, J
Dimopoulos, V
Doherty, M J
Dukes, I K
Elwell, D
Emtage, L A
Farmer, M
Favill, E J
Fisher, N C

Dukinfield

Flahn, G N
Funkel, H
Gali, M H A
Gee, R W
George, D E
George, N J R
Georgui, M M
Gibson, J R B
Gnanadurai, T V
Goel, I P
Grimley, R P
Gupta, P D
Gupta, R
Gurney, P W V
Haddon, A L
Hamlyn, A N
Hampson, W T
Harris, G R
Harrison, P
Huish, Z K
Husain, R A
Ingle, P R
Ingle, U P
Irani, S
Irfan, H
Jain, S K
James, D A
Jayatunga, A P
Jones, B J M
Kevern, A B
Khan, J M
Kuligowski, M
MacAviney, M A M
Marriott, R G
Mittal, V K
Moors, A H
Morrill, P O
Nagendran, V
Norcott, H C
Oliver, P S
Oliver, R
Oram, D A
Pall, J
Parkes, A W
Parres, H
Parry, D G
Patel, R
Perera, R K
Poole, C J M
Porter, A M
Potamitis, T
Quinlan, M
Randall, J
Rao, V M K
Reed, I T D
Richardson, S G N
Robertson-Steel, I R S
Rowse, A D
Sant, K G
Saunders, W A
Savage, A P
Scriven, P M
Shaikh, Z A
Shather, N A
Shave, R M
Shipsey, S J
Shovlin, W M
Smart, V M
Sonksen, J R
Spencer, G
Spiers, R J
Stevenson, M M
Suharwardy, J M A
Swatkins, S
Warrington, N J
Whallett, A J
Whear, N M
White, H J
White, N C
Whitehurst, P
Wild, S P
Wolinski, A P
Womersley, D S

Dukinfield

Ali, F S M
Asthana, A
Douglas, C A
Dowling, T I
Kelly, B J
Ketchin, A
Malik, D
Marr, D H
Milner, D
Procter, J C
Roylance, M H
Toyn, J L

Dulverton

Dulverton
Berry, E M
Burton, L
Constable, F
Goodwin, F R
Hunter, J O
Morgan, G L
Murphy, F W
Peck, J D W
Thomson, R G

Dumbarton
Alcorn, T
Barlow, T H
Berry, C
Bidwell, L A M
Boyd, A S
Braidwood, E A
Byrne, F J
Byrne, J A
Byrne, M A
Cairns, E E
Campbell, E C
Crawford, E G
Doig, A
Downie, J F
Eadie, J A
Foote, S J
Logan, D R
Lynn, K N
McCulloch, I N
Maciver, S A H
Mackenzie, J A
McMaster, T
McNamee, R N
McNamee, S A
Mason, M R
Mitchelson, A V
Morton, D E
Murray, W
Peacock, M L
Rainey, V
Renshaw, S B H
Roberts, A E
Schreiber, J A
Stevenson, J G
Sweeney, J M
Thomas, M M
Wales, R M
Wallace, A D
Walsh, S M M
Watson, J M

Dumfries
Adams, J C
Armstrong, H E
Auld, A R
Auld, C D
Bailey, P A M
Balfour, W D
Ball, D R
Baptist, G P
Beaumont, C G
Bedford, G J B
Bedford, J W
Bennie, D B
Bone, F J
Bonn, G
Breen, D A
Brewster, H A
Brown, C A
Bruce, V R
Bryson, I
Buchan, C C
Buisson, J S
Burton, J W
Cameron, I A
Carey, S J
Carruthers, J W
Cathcart, J B T
Cathcart, R A
Chalmers, J G
Christie, A B
Christie, M L
Clayton, P
Clow, D J
Clyde, J W
Cochran, J B
Cowie, I D S
Currie, H D
Currie, R A
D'Ambrogio, M S
Dale, B A S
Dang, R K B
Dewar, C S
Dewar, D A E
Dewar, E F H
Donachie, F M
Downie, A

Drever, E A
Evans, D A
Falconer, J A G
Fellowes, E C
Ferguson, K M
Finlayson, A J K
Flint, E F
Flockhart, D R
Frain-Bell, L
Garcia-Baquero
Merino, M T
Gardiner, C A
Geals, M F
Gibson, I H
Gibson, J L
Gibson, J C
Gordon, F H
Gordon, G
Gordon, R G
Graham, J M
Grant, C I
Grey, J
Grieve, R M K
Gurney, M F
Gysin, J
Halliday, B W
Halliday, S P
Hamilton, D H
Hassall, L E S
Hay, I F C
Henderson, M A
Holden, R
Holt, M C W
Howell, J A
Howie, G M
Hutchison, G B
Hutchison, P G
Irving, M A M
Isles, C G
Isles, R M
Jamieson, C
Johnson, J K
Johnston, L F E
Jones, D N
Jones, S
Kennedy, J A
Kiely, D G
Kirk, J F
Law, P J
Lawrence, J R
Little of Morton Rig, J C
Lowry, W S
Luffy, A M
Lyon, A R
McCreadie, R G
McCullough, A M
MacDonald, E M
McFadden, P M
McFadzean, J J
McGrouther, R J
McKay, D A
McKechnie, J M
Mackie, J I
Maclean, I H
McMahon, M J
Maggiori, L A E
Martin, L C
Mason, J M
Meek, R
Mensah, P K A
Metcalfe, S F
Morris, S
Morrison, R
Morton, M L
Muir, I M
Neilson, J
O'Brien, F G M
Pancham, P K
Park, R W
Paterson, I E
Paterson, J R
Penman, W A
Perkins, V
Powell, E F
Powell, J C
Power-Breen, P A
Power, B J
Power, N R
Rafferty, P
Reid, J M
Rizvi, S T M
Robertson, S E
Robson, J E
Russell, S J M
Rutherford, J S
Saad, K J
Sabur, R Y
Sajid, S A

Sanderson, H
Seright, W
Shearer, M G
Shroufi, S
Simpson, J D
Simpson, R M
Smith, D P
Smith, F E W
Smith, I G
Spafford, P J D
Stark, A N
Steele, G J
Steele, J D T
Stirling, G S
Strachan, D A
Stubbs, J R C
Syme, W S
Tait, G W
Taylor, D D
Taylor, S B
Thomson, A M
Thomson, R B
Tilak-Singh, D
Toolis, F
Train, J D
Train, T S R
Unyolo, P M
Waite, A
Waite, F T J
Walls, A D F
Walter, R D
Waterhouse, J
Watson, G D
Watson, N T B
Waugh, E M
White, J M
Williams, D R
Wilson, M C G
Wilson, R B
Wilson, W A M
Wisdom, S J
Wood, E R M
Wylie, S

Dunbar
Badger, T R
Black, C N
Brewster, A M
Cassels, D A
Gordon, A I
Hare, E H
Horn, C R
Macdonald, I
Rogers, M E

Dunblane
Abercrombie, M R
Auld, J
Barnes, J F
Bengough, E A
Buchan, D A
Butts, S L
Crow, Y J
Crowther, I A
Dunbar, K M
Dunbar, P J A
Gardiner, A J S
Garrett-Cox, R G
Gray, S M
Hamilton, B
Herbert, J M
Kennedy, W W
Kerr, A L
King, I
Kirkpatrick, R
McCallan, S E
McCallum, D A L
McCurrach, D M
McGarva, J
McNeill, A
McShane, L J
Mallace, B
Pemberton, D A
Pollock, A M
Price, F J
Reavey, J
Rodger, R A
Roxburgh, D A
Smith, C M
Stewart, N G
Swan, W G
Trench, A
Watson, R G
Wood, J M
Wright, F G
Wright, M J

Dundee
Abu-Bakra, M A J
Adam, J D

Adamson, D J A
Adlakha, H L
Adlakha, S
Agustsson, P
Al-Allaf, A W Y S
Al-Dabbagh, A S K
Al-Sanjari, N A G A
Alishahi, S
Allardice, S M
Allcock, P A
Allen, M-F
Allison, R H
Andersen, R M
Anderson, J M
Anderson, J M
Anderson, J A
Arblaster, L A
Arnold, C W B
Arthur, I D
Arthur, S J
Aslam, M
Aungle, J C
Aungle, P G
Avison, G G
Azam, H U
Baharani, J B
Bain, D J G
Bain, J
Ballinger, C B
Banerji, S
Bannister, J
Barr, A D
Barthram, C N
Basra, S
Baxby, K
Beale, J P
Beattie, P E
Begg, J D
Belch, J J F
Berry, C L
Birrell, A L
Birrell, D H
Blair, R L
Block, J
Block, R
Bloodworth, S B
Blumsohn, A
Bonnar, S E
Bowen, D T
Bree, S E
Brookes, E M
Brown, A A M
Brown, A D
Brown, D W H
Brown, E H
Brown, P I
Brown, S V
Bruce, D A
Bruce, J T
Bruce, L E
Bryce, J G
Bryden, A M
Buchan, A B
Buckney, M N M
Cairns, M
Cameron, F M L
Cameron, L
Cameron, R C P
Carroll, C M
Carswell, A H P
Cater, J I
Cavanagh, J
Cezanne, H H
Chakraverty, S C
Chan, R H F
Chan, Y Y
Charlett, P J
Che Abdullah, S T
Checketts, M R
Chishti, K K
Chong, Y M
Church, J E
Clark, R A
Clarke, R
Coid, D R
Coleiro, J A
Colvin, B A J
Colvin, B C
Colvin, J R
Colvin, M A
Connolly, C M N
Cook, A M
Copland, A M
Cormie, C A
Coull, S L
Coventry, D M
Crichton, J A
Crighton, A J
Crighton, A D

Crofts, S L
Crowder, A M
Curr, E A
D'Arrigo, C
Dally, H L
Dance, J C
Das, S
Das, S
Dauleh, M I M
Davey, P G
Davidson, D L W
Davidson, H A
Davis, B C
Davis, M H
Dawson, A J
Day, R K
De Zeeuw, F J
Deery, C H
Dent, J A
Dewar, J A
Dick, H M
Dick, P H
Dillon, J F
Dillon, P A
Dimitriu, V-N
Doherty, S B
Doig, S N
Donald, J M
Donaldson, K J
Donaldson, L
Donoghue, C N
Dorling, J S
Dorward, D W T
Dorward, W F M
Dow, E
Duff, C J S
Duffy, M C
Duke, S L
Dunbar, A P
Dunbar, D S
Duncan, I D
Duncan, M R
Dunkley, M P
Dymock, B A
Dymock, T
Eljamel, M S
Ellis, E
Ellis, J D
Ellison, L E
Emslie-Smith, A M
Emslie-Smith, D
Emslie-Smith, K M
English, J B
Esparon, J A
Evans, A T
Evans, L M
Fairlamb, A H
Fan, K
Farquharson, C A J
Farrell, J H
Fee, M C D
Fellowes, J L
Ferdinand, R D
Fergus, C J Y
Ferguson, E A
Ferguson, G
Ferguson, J
Ferguson, J B
Ferguson, J G
Fergusson, R A
Findlay, D J
Finnigan, J P
Flavahan, C
Fleming, R A
Fletcher, F
Fletcher, J D
Florey, C D V
Fogarty, M Y
Forbes, C D
Forbes, J H D
Forbes, R B
Forrester, A C
Forrester, A G
Forrester, J C
Forsyth, C C
Forsyth, J S
Forsyth, J D J
Foster, J
Foulbister, G C
Fowlie, H C
Fox, P
France, A J
Frankland, H W J
Franklin, V L
Franks, U
Freeman, C A
Freshwater, K H
Frew, J S
Galloway, A J

Gardiner, Q
Gardiner, S
Gardiner, W M
Garmany, D H
Garmany, H
Gelly, K J
Gemmell, D F
Gentleman, D R
George, M J A
Ghosh, U K
Gibb, A G
Gillespie, L M
Gillespie, N D
Golden, P N H
Goodall, H B
Goodman, C M
Gorman, L J
Gossip, J M
Goudie, B M
Goudie, D R
Graham, J G I
Grant, K P M
Grant, P C
Grant, P W
Gray, M
Green, C M
Greene, S A
Griffiths, P D
Grimmer, C
Grimmond, L M C
Guha, P K
Gunn, A
Gusa Lavan, S G
Guthrie, W
Haining, R E B
Hajipour, L
Halhead, G E
Hall, P A
Hamilton, W F D
Hankinson, C A
Hanna, G B
Hannah, S R
Hanslip, J L
Harden, R M
Harper, I A
Harper, J F W
Harris, M G
Harrold, A J
Hartmann, D
Haut, F F A
Hawney, E C
Hayes, M G
Henderson, L M
Henman, P D
Herring, A J
Hew, W S R
Hewick, S A
Hewitt, P M
Hindley, M O
Ho, M
Ho, S W L
Hogg, M C
Holland, S
Hopwood, D
Hopwood, S E
Houston, J G
Howie, A J
Howie, G F A
Howie, P W
Hsu, P P
Hu, S
Huang, D S W
Hulbert, J K M
Hume, R
Hunt, V J
Hunter, J E
Hunter, S M
Hussain, S S M
HussellBee, K M
Hutchison, G J
Hutchison, G L
Ibbotson, S H
Inglis, K T
Innes, J S
Irwin, J
Iyngkaran, T
Jaafar, H M I B
Jain, A S
James, G B
James, P B
Jamieson, J S
Jamieson, W C
Jeffers, R F
Jeffrey, D E
Johnston, B B
Johnston, D A
Johnston, R N
Jones, K D
Jones, M C

Dunkeld

Jones, P A
Jung, R T
Kavi, J
Kazmi, S A-H
Kenicer, K J A
Kennedy, D W
Kennedy, M S
Kerr, L M
Kerr, M R
Key, B
Khan, J A
Khong, T K
Kilgallon, B
Kirkpatrick, A P
Kirkpatrick, M R
Knight, D G
Knox, J D E
Kyeremateng, S P K
Lafferty, M E
Laing, D E
Lall, R
Lamb, G C
Lamb, J S
Lang, S
Leadbitter, H
Leary, A C
Ledingham, I M
Leese, G P
Leese, R A
Leiper, J M
Leong, M Y
Leslie, G A M
Leslie, J R S
Levack, I D
Levin, C A
Levison, D A
Levison, J L
Levison, S E
Lewis, A H O
Lo, M C K
Locke, J W
Locke, R M
Lockwood, P
Loftus, J A
Lorimer, S
Lowe, E M
Lowe, J G
Lowe, K G
Lowe, L M
Lucocq, J M
Lyall, M H
McAllion, S J
McAndrew, E M
McCallum, D S
McCarthy, R
McCartney, C J L
McClymont, W
MacConnachie, A A
McConnell, K D
McCormack, D J
MacCormack, J G
MacCowan, H A S
McCowat, L C
McCulloch, A S
McCulloch, J M
McCullough, J B
McDevitt, D G
McDevitt, J M
MacDonald, M G
MacEwen, C J
McEwen, J
McEwen, J R
McGeechan, A T
McGhee, C N J
MacGillivray, J B
McGlone, L
McGowan, D W
McGowan, S W
MacGregor, A M
MacGregor, K L
McGrory, F
McHarg, A M
McHarg, J F
MacIntyre, J M
Mackenzie, A J
McKenzie, J A
Mackenzie, N
McKenzie, S A S
Mackinnon, A J
McLaren, E J
Maclean, D
Maclean, P J
McLean, S M
McLellan, A
McLoughlin, P M
Macmillan, A I M
McMurdo, M E T
McNaughton, E
McNicholas, M J

Macpherson, E S
Macrae, W A
MacWalter, R S
Magro, J J
Main, G
Malcolm, J B
Malcolm, R M
Malik, S
Man, I W-P
Manthri, P R
Maple, C
Marr, T C K
Marshall, D C
Marshall, M
Martindale, J P
Mathew, P
Mathewson, Z M
Matthews, K
McEwan, M S R
Meikle, J N
Mellish, R W E
Mennie, G S
Menzies, I C
Miller, A S C
Miller, D C
Miller, M J R
Milne, A W
Milne, M K
Mitchell, H E
Mitchell, J F O
Mitchell, L H
Mitchell, P E G
Mitchell, R G
Montgomery, A J
Moore, E E M
Morley, S M
Morris, A M
Morrison, A
Morrison, W G
Motwani, N S
Mowat, D H R
Mowle, D H
Muir, A H
Murdoch, G
Mustafa, A M
Naasan, A
Naidu, S
Naismith, K I
Narasapur, S L
Nathwani, D
Neal, P
Neville, R G
Newton, J R
Newton, R W
Nichol, N M
Nicoll, L M
Nimmo, M J
Noaman, L A
O'Donoghue, C R
O'Leary, T D
Ogilvie, K E
Okhai, A A H
Oliver, T B
Orange, G V
Owen, L E
Parratt, D
Patel, N B
Paterson, C R
Paton, C C
Payne, R J
Peacock, D A
Pegg, S M
Pennington, C R
Petrie, R X A
Pickard, C
Pippard, M J
Porter-Boveri, K A M
Prain, J H
Prakash, U
Preece, P E
Pringle, S D
Pringle, T H
Proctor, I
Prodhan, C R
Prophet, L E
Proudfoot, D J
Proudfoot, E M
Proudfoot, F B
Pullar, T
Purdie, C A
Purvis, M S
Quinn, K
Rae, A S L
Rae, G B
Raffle, E J
Raj, M
Rajendran, S
Ramachandran, N K
Ramage, L

Ramsay, A E
Rankin, E M
Ravikumar, A
Reddy, C K
Reid, A H
Reid, D C
Reynolds, N
Richards, J P
Richmond, J D
Rippon, A G
Ritchie, D K
Ritchie, R T
Roberts, J
Roberts, R C
Robertson, A J
Robertson, N A
Robson, C J
Robson, J P
Rorie, D A
Rorrison, H W
Rosbottom, R
Rose, J
Ross, E M
Rowley, D I
Russell, D W
Ruta, D A
Ruthven, J L
Ryan, M F
Ryder, K O
Sachdev, N H
Sadler, D W
Saggar, K D
Salisbury, J
Sanders, A F
Sanderson, J B
Saqr, L S
Savage, A J
Save, V E
Scahill, S J
Scallan, K C
Scanlan, P H
Scott, A
Scott, K N L
Scott, R F
Scott, S S
Scullion, J E
Scullion, L T
Seaton, R A
Seftel, A L
Semple, M M
Senior, P A
Sharma, M M
Sharpe, G D M
Shaw, D
Shearer, A J
Shearer, K H
Shepherd, C
Simonsen, H
Simpson, A I
Simpson, I M
Simpson, N S
Sinclair, B L
Sinclair, S
Siu, S K L
Slane, P W
Small, R G
Smeaton, N C
Smith, A H W
Smith, D R W
Smith, G D
Smith, H L
Smith, R
Smith, R W
Smith, R N
Smith, W D
Snadden, D
Sohail Sahibzada, A
Soo, S
Spencer, J
Spiers, E M
Spruce, B A
Stalker, A M
Stayte, D J
Staziker, A C
Steele, B D
Steele, R J C
Steele, S M
Stewart, C I L
Stewart, C P U
Stewart, D P
Stewart, J L
Stewart, J
Stonebridge, P A
Struthers, A D
Sturrock, A M
Summers, G
Summers, R
Sutherland, M S M
Suttie, K Y

Swanson, A J G
Swingler, R J
Symon, M A
Taig, C E M
Taig, C
Taig, D R
Talpahewa, S P
Tan, K S
Tarnow-Mordi, W O
Taylor, A
Taylor, J H
Taylor, P B
Taylor, T W
Taylor, W J
Thakore, S B
Thompson, A M
Thomson, A J M
Thomson, E S
Thomson, J M D
Thomson, M A R
Thomson, R
Thulbourne, T
Thurairajah, K
Tiffin, P A C
Todd, A S
Todd, A-M
Todd, J A
Toller, R A
Townell, N H
Travell, R M
Treliving, L R
Tulloch, A K
Tunstall-Pedoe, H D
Tunstall-Pedoe, O D
Underwood, C L
Uqlat, L N E
Uriel, A J
Urquhart, G E D
Urquhart, J M
Vaid, M A E
Veitch, T
Vernon, J P
Vernon, M M
Vincent, D S
Walker, P J
Walker, W F
Wallace, D J
Ward, M C
Watson, A D
Watson, A M
Watson, G C
Watson, J M
Watson, Y M R
Weaver, J P A
Weir, C J
Wheeldon, T J
White, C B
White, K D
White, P S
Whiteside, C E
Whiteside, J B
Whittle, T L F
Wigfull, J R
Wilcock, M A
Wildsmith, J A W
Wilkinson, M
Wilkinson, M J
Wilmshurst, A D
Wilson, A M
Wilson, S M
Winter, J H
Winton, J M L
Wood, C R
Wood, C M
Wood, R A B
Woodley, A G
Wright, K R
Wyllie, F J
Yeaman, W T M
Yorston, R A
Young, J A
Ziyaie, D

Dunfermline

Adams, W E
Alexander, A C A
Alexander, D
Allan, S J R
Anderson, H E
Anderson, T J
Angus, C W G
Auras, A
Austin, A E
Barton, C H
Birkinshaw, K J
Bray, J C
Briggs, S J
Brown, A G
Brown, T M

Brownlie, R
Brunton, J M
Burt, G F
Burt, J R
Burt, J R F
Calder, J
Cameron, I A N
Campbell, J
Carter, R G
Chan, Y K
Chigaru, C
Christmas, E R
Claisse, A Z
Conway, N T
Cook, P
Copeland, C L
Curry, P D
Daniel, T
Darjee, R
Dean, B
Downie, F D H
Duncan, R W
Duthie, P C
Edwards, P M P
Emery-Barker, J A
Evan-Wong, L A
Farrar, S M
Firth, C E
Fleet, M S
Fletcher, G M
Gallacher, J B
Garvie, S J
Gilbert, S S
Gillespie, G D
Gilmore, D R
Gowans, M
Grant, S M T
Hadoke, J K
Hamilton, Y M H
Hendry, G I
Hendry, M W
Hicks, J D
Hill, C
Hill, M G
Holligan, E M
Howd, A
Hyde, A J A
Jamieson, A
Jenkins, D A S
Johnston, B E
Johnston, C A B
Johnston, G
Jones, B J
Jones, D G
Kao, R N P
Keston, R B
Kumar, S
Laggan, M J
Langham, M I
Lawson, A A H
Lester, R B
Lyall, J B F
Lyth, D R
Macaulay, K E C
McCrone, C C
McCrone, C J
MacEwen, A C
McGovern, A W
MacIsaac, A B
Mackay, K M
Mackay, S K
MacLeod, D C
McMinn, C S
Major, K A
Malcolm, W N
Malone, K D S
Marks, R C
Mason, I L
Mathie, I H
Mathie, Y M
Moxey, J E
Moy, J R
Murdoch, G E
Ness, T M
Nicholas, M P
Niven, C F
O'Regan, M B
Oliver, C J R
Park, M J
Paszkiewicz, J M
Patel, G J
Petrie, S E
Peyton, P A
Prentice, L-A
Proudfoot, M C
Reid, S R
Robertson, I P C
Robertson, M I
Ross, A G

Russell, S C
Rutherford, R A
Scott, M R
Scott, T M
Seaman, F M
Selby, C D
Shah, S K
Shaw, D R
Sinclair, A
Smith, D M W
Soutter, C I
Stuart, F M
Thomas, I G
Thores, O A
Toal, E M
Turner, A R
Walker, M W
Walsh, J P
West, A M
Whyte, A S
Yellowley, J C

Dungannon

Allely, P R
Baird, T J
Barbour, P M
Bogues, B E
Brodison, A M
Campbell, R
Casey, F
Coogan, K
Corr, F M
Costello, L M
Cullen, M E
Cummings, D H
Currie, A A
Donaghy, S M
Elliott, C S
Gallagher, M E
Gamble, W J
Girvin, F G
Gribben, T M
Hackett, P J
Hagan, P M
Haughey, J P
Herron, A
Herron, M J
Hobson, L A
Hughes, S
Hunter, C F
Jenkinson, W R
Johnston, I H
Johnston, S E
Jones, A M
Kelly, E
Kennedy, H M
Kennedy, M
Logan, J M
Logan, J J
McAliskey, D P
McCammon, L C
McCoy, B G
McGuinness, B
MacHenry, J C R M
McIvor, D E L
McKay, J J
McKenna, P H
McKeown, P F
McLoughlin, U M
McMenemy, P L
McNeill, H G
McQuade, E
McShane, A M
McVeigh, J E
Marshall, P
Millar, E J
Mitchel, B M
Murphy, P P
Nelson, M E K
Nugent, T P J
O'Loughlin, M A
Orr, M A G
Palmer, J M
Peyton, J W R
Pothanikat, G
Rodgers, A A
Rodgers, D A
Sands, C J
Streahorn, D
Thompson, M R
Tierney, J P
Ward, C C
Watson, J
Watson, M S
Wylie, I L

Dunkeld

Binnie, D S
Brooks, J E

Dunmow

Buckingham, J
Donnelly, J D
Hannay, P W
Howie, T
Mackie, J F
Silburn, J N
Silburn, M D W
Wright, G A

Dunmow

Castleden, L S
Davies, P G
Griffiths, R L
Hartgill, J C
Hartgill, T W
Healy, D W
Hood, S V
Howlett, R W
Hudson, I R B
Hughes, S A
Jackson, J S B
McCartney, C A
McGlashan, I A
McGlashan, K A
Malone, A H
Miller, R
Morris, R
Nunn, R A
Penny, R M
Pinchen, C J
Pugh, E C
Rankin, G L S
Rawes, J C L
Raybould, S A
Slack, C C
Slack, M C
Stevens, J A
Tailor, R A
Tayler, M J
Tee, M K
Turner, D R
Vernon, J G
Warren, C B M
Weller, M A

Dunoon

Adamson, D M R
Alstad, K S
Anderson, A
Bruce, S P
Campbell, P T
Carter, F J
Clark, C M
Horton, G R
Johnston, D I
Johnston, S M
Keen, J C
Lawson, C A
Lilley, I N
Moen, C R
Pearce, J M
Raghavaiah, L S
Robertson, J T
Smith, A C A
Stewart, A J
Stewart, J G H
Thomson, A W
Turner, A R
Weir, J T
Wilkie, W J

Duns

Aitken, W B
Auld, B M
Davis, D M S
Dobie, V J S
Fingland, I W W
Fowles, R G
Gray, K J
Hall, G H
Hatrick, H
Macallister, D J
McCann, S R
Main, P T
Mitchell, D L
Mitchell, L I S
Needham, C D
Redpath, A J
Ross, E J W
Sim, G
Sim, S M
Taylor, C M
Thomson, S W

Dunstable

Astin, T W
Bell, J R
Benedikt, N A
Berry, J E
Bilton, K

Bodhani, H D
Carter, G B
Carter, M I
Chowdhury, U K
Costin, S B
Cro, R J
Curt, N E
Dashore, J P
Day, M J I
Donald, A
Freeman, K A
Fsadni, J
Gabriel, R W
Goutam, P K
Haq, M F
Harrold, B P
Hassan, P C
Hawking, K M
Henderson, A G
Hodgson, A L
Jackson, P G
Jones, M R
Long, A C
Mackay, I R
Mallik, A K
Neal, R C
O'Toole, O B
Pal, U
Perkins, J D A
Peters, J
Prendergast, J M
Price, S V
Quartly, C F
Rees, H
Reyner, L J
Robinson, R C
Rothwell-Jackson, R L
Shah, C N
Shah, R
Speakman, H M A
Standen, A S
Stein, S M
Sykes, C M
Towler, J M
Twivy, S B
Ward, P J
Warriner, S E
Weir, W M

Durham

Acquilla, S D
Adamson, R J
Akindolie, O
Alifieri, E
Allison, D
Ancliff, J E
Anderson, G E
Anderson, J E
Atkinson, W J
Aye, C C
Baldasera, M A
Banks, J G
Barnes, A J
Barnes, S E
Beard, J R
Beggs, G C
Bernard, P M
Bexon, W H
Birrell, K G
Birrell, V L
Boll, S
Buxton, C S J
Carr, M M
Cartner, R
Catty, R H C
Cave, M H
Chapman, W E
Charters, J W
Cheeseman, S J
Chester, P G
Chuck, A J
Clark, A D
Clark, J A
Clark, M W
Clifford, D G
Conway, V G
Cook, A J M
Cook, P J
Cooper, M H
Cooper, R
Corrigan, J K
Cotes, J E
Craddock, S C
Cunliffe, T P
Dabrowska, J
Darling, B M
De Silva, C
Desai, S M
Dixon, J L

Docherty, T B
Dowson, S
Duffey, P O F
Duncan, C G
Dunning, P G
Dunstone, G H
Earnshaw, M A
Ehtisham, M
Ellis, W R
English, P J
Erdmann, M W H
Fisher, C J
Flanagan, P A
Glover, M E
Gooding, M
Gorton, R K
Graham, G S
Green, M R
Greenwell, D G
Gururaj Prasad, K B
Hammond, R J
Hand, R W
Harrington, J
Harrison, J H
Harrison, J E
Hart, J M
Hart, T
Hawthorn, I E
Hazell, M J
Heath, D V
Helliwell, G M
Herd, A N
Heslop, M
Hickson, G M
Holland, J A
Holmes, E J
Horton, A J
Hossain, M A
Hubbard, M P
Hurly, K
Hutchinson, F H
Ibbott, J M
Irons, D W
Irving, H M
Ive, H
Jackson, R M
James, S
Jones, D W
Judson, M L
Kaushik, V Y
Keane, T K
Keenan, F M
Kemball, H J
Kirkup, W
Lake, P M J
Lamballe, A K
Lane, M R
Leaver, A A M
Lewthwaite, P W
Lodge, A
Lorimer, J D
Lothian, M
Ludkin, S
McAndrew, P E
McConnell, F K
McDonald, G E S
McGlade, D R
Macintyre, A
McLean, A T M
McLean, D
Maddison, B
Maddison, G M
Mahto, N K
Maini, V
Maloney, D J L
Maloney, G
Mangion, P
Mansfield, S D
Mansour, S H S
Marsden, P J
Martin, S J S
Maung, S W
Milne, B E
Milne, P
Mitchell, R W D
Mithilesh, S
Moran, P
Moss, S A
Munro, G
Munro, J S
Munro, N C
Murray, R W
Nagi, S S
Neely, R D G
Neilson, F M C
Noel, I
Osborne, E M
Osborne, K A
Pascall, C M E

Patel, A S
Patel, K M
Pearce, S J
Peel, P H
Phipps, A J
Porter, A C
Prescott, R W G
Quasim, M
Raetz, H P
Ramakrishna, G M D
Ramarao, P
Ray, P
Rhind, J R
Rippon, L M
Robb, S
Robertshaw, B A
Robertson, D C F
Rocker, P B
Rodriguez Garcia, F J
Roper, N A
Ross, W M
Rowlands, I D H
Ruffett, D I
Ryan, J M
Sandall, D
Sanders, E
Sanjeeva Rao, V
Selby, N M
Sinclair, S A
Siriwardana, N C P
Slowe, J J
Smart, D W
Smart, S R S
Smith, D R S
Smithson, J R
Snashall, P D
Speight, A N P
Spencer, I
Stephenson, C
Stewart, H V
Stokoe, E
Sutherland, I A K
Tatham, P C
Tattersall, P H
Terry, G
Thalayasingam, B
Thomas, D G
Thomas, D G
Thompson, C S
Thompson, S J
Turner, H D
Twite, S J
Underwood, I R
Vallance, J H
Wagstaff, E
Wagstaff, J K
Walker, D
Walton, P R
Walton, S E
Wandless, I
Wardropper, A G
Watkinson, S A P
Watson, S J W
Way, M C
Weatherill, D
Welsh, G H
Whalley, F E
White, C
White, D R
Whitfield, S J
Whyte, S D
Wilford, N J
Will, R
Williams, R A-I W
Wilson, D
Wingate-Gray, E
Wolsey, L A F
Wood, D W
Wood, P J
Woodhouse, J
Woods, R
Wright, D
Wright, K U
Yule, J C

Dursley

Alvis, S J
Bewley, J S
Burk, A
Cole, G J
Coplin, J C
Curtis Hayward, K S
Duraisingam, G
Frankau, T G
Freeman, M J
Gornall, C B
Hall, E W
Hill, A J
Jones, B C

Kenny, D
Lewis, R M
McDowell, M J
Opher, S J
Prowse, R B
Rix, S P
Roberts, J K
Steel, J A P
Wardell-Yerburgh, T C
Wills, E
Wootton, A
Wootton, M

Dyffryn Ardudwy

Vickers, C F H

Dymock

French, R J
Grant Duff, L G
Lunn, H F
Mason, J E

Ealing

Patel, P R
Warren, A J
Whitehurst, A M

Earlston

MacDonald, S L

East Boldon

Baines, D L
Benton, K
Board, H R
Clark, D
Cooper, D G
Crabtree, H L
Dhar, R
Fawzi, H W
Forster, I D M
Ghosh, N
Ghosh, S
Howard, J J
Killen, B U
Moffitt, P A
O'Dair, G N
O'Dair, J D
Obonna, R
Reed, L
Saleh, S S A

East Cowes

Andrews, C J A
Clarke, H L
Davies, M L R
Gillan, S A

East Grinstead

Allen, J P
Arnstein, P M
Ashworth, C
Avery, C M E
Aylesbury, H E
Bainbridge, D R
Barham, C J
Bateman, R M
Belcher, H J C R
Bellamy, S J
Berkovitch, A P
Boorman, J G
Bowley, N B
Brooks, K J
Brown, A E
Brown, J M
Chapman, S E
Chapple, S A
Christopher, B W C C
Cobbett, J R
Cullen, K W
Curran, J E
Diba, A
Digges, C N O N
Dunstan, R J R
Edwards, A F
Enderby, G E H
Enskat, A R D
Erlam, A R
Exadaktilos, A
Farquhar, J K
Fisher, J I
Foulger, V A L
Franklin-Adams, J I
Genevieve, M Y
Gilbert, P M
Hoare, G L
Hoe, W K-C
Jones, I T N E
Jones, S M
Khilkoff-Choubersky, A
Lavery, K M
Mackenzie, A A J

Malcolm, A D
Martin, A
Micallef, A M
Moshegov, C N
O'Hara, F R
Parkhouse, N
Patel, H P
Peck, B J
Pickford, M A
Powell, R M
Robertson, C G
Robertson, H J
Smith, C M
Smith, R W
Squires, S J
Stevens, P J
Sugden, J J
Teo, T-C
Van Gelderen-Swart, A G
Venn, P J
Vevers, J J
Whitmarsh, V B
Winter, D P
Wong, P

East Linton

Batters, W G
Cameron, J M W
Davenport, A
Durie, T B M
Guy, D
Hare, K M

East Molesey

Brant, S E
Britton, S E
Brown, K A C
Browne, G R W
Collie, I F
Coxon, I D
Dunster, C
Fleck, D G
Gajraj, M K
Gajraj, N M
Galvan De La Hoz, A
Glanville, S B C
Gray, J
Hamill, J S
Jacobs, R A
Jeffcoate, C M
Kapoor, A
Marks, K A
Pall, H S
Palmer, M S M
Paramothayan, B N
Parry, M A M
Ploye, P M
Robak, K R
Rowe, T L
Tapping, P J

Eastbourne

Abraham, A J
Adoki, I I
Adolph, M P N
Ahmed, S A
Al Hajaj, W H
Allan, S M
Anderson, H J
Argent, V P
Argiriu, P
Ashby, C P
Bangert, S K
Barkworth, F B S
Barnes, J D
Beeney, M A R
Bell, T J
Bending, J J
Bhattacharya, A
Bhattacharya, V V
Bishai, I A H
Bland, L W
Bloor, G K
Bonnici, A V
Bowry, R
Brennan, B P M
Brooks, P L
Brown, G C
Bruins, J
Canagaratnam, N
Carney, D P
Caroe, J W
Casey, J M I H
Chapman, D J
Chelvarajah, R
Chowcat, N L
Chui, D K C
Churcher, A
Clark, R F

Edinburgh

Clarke, H J
Cole, N M
Cook, A J
Cook, J H
Cook, J S
Cooke, R P D
Cookey, I P
Cordin, C W
Coutts, G M
Cowie, A G A
Curry, P S
D'Arcy, J C
Davidson, J M
De Muinck Keizer, J W
Deery, R W
Dickens, P R
Dodds, M
Dugan, U M
Dunk, A A
Durrani, A-R
Durrani, A J
Elliott, D H
Emslie, A J
Evans, G H C
Evans, S K
Evason, M R
Eyre, S J
Fan, Y S
Farnan, N D
Field, E C
Flight, D J
Folwell, G A J
Forster, R A
Francis, K M J
Freedman, B A M
Frisby, P A
Fuggle, A R
Fuller, J R
Gaffney, M S J
Garlick, D J
George, L
Gietzen, T W
Gilmour, A M
Ginimav, S P
Gonzalez Polledo, J
Gover, P A
Gow, A H F
Grace, R J
Graham-Brown, K E
Grant, M
Hadley, I M
Hall-Smith, R G
Hargreaves, J N
Haworth, D J
Heizman, K
Henley, F A
Hester, J B
Hewitt, W
Hobbs, S D
Horton, E W
Hughes, D V
Hunt, C B M
Hunter, F G
Hurter, L E
Inayat, M
Isibor, F O
Jack, A H
Jackson, L V
James, S E
Kamugisha, C K
Kelleher, B J
Kinder, J
King, T A
Kinniburgh, N A
Kisler, J D
Kochanowski, S J
Lawrence, W T
Leeson, K E
Liddell, K
Livingston, S
Lofts, J A
Lytton, S T
McGregor, R R
McNaughton, I C
Malak, T M
Mallagh, D E
Marchbank, N D P
Marshall, M F P
Martyr, J W
Mason, C H
Masotina, A
Matin-Siddiqi, S A
Maxwell, D L
Miller, W G
Moffat, C J C
Monteoliva Murga, V
Murray, H G S
Murray, M E
Myerson, K R

Mynott, M J
Nahhas, A S
Nash, P J
Nicholls, S
Nicoll, S J B
Noble, G E
O'Donnell, M J
O'Sullivan, P F
Parker, A P
Paterson, I W
Plumb, A P
Powley, J M
Prosser, J K
Rabuszko, J P
Rajendra, S
Reddy, G S
Redondo Campos, A R
Reid, D A C
Rhodes, J
Ribbons, R M C
Richards, D J
Richardson, T N A
Robertson, D E
Ross, K R
Ruffell, E A
Rutland, E
Salam, M A
Sallomi, D F
Sargant, N R
Sasada, K
Saunders, M P
Savvas, S
Scarisbrick, P H
Shawcross, J
Sheikh, M A
Shepherd, C D
Shepherd, P R
Simpson, J M W
Singh, K
Squires, M J
Steer, B
Stewart, A N
Stockton, M G
Stoodley, B J
Sulke, A N
Sullivan, A
Surtees, S J
Sutherland, I B
Swan, J D
Taha, A S A
Tasharrofi, R
Thomas, H F
Trembalowicz, F C
Valentine, B H
Vandenwijngaerden, S
Venn, P H
Verghese, K L
Vickery, K
Viveash, D M
Waddy, R S
Walmsley, A J
Walter, M
Ward, J P
Warren, G A R
Waters, S J
Watson, G M
Watson, N A
Wearmouth, E M
Westlake, A C
Wigfield, W J
Wilkins, J L
Wilkinson, J R W
Williams, P G
Wojtulewski, J A
Woodbridge, P A

Eastleigh

Acton, P M
Aley, M C
Anderson, D F
Arden, C D
Bacon, S E
Balachandra, K
Bellenis, C
Black, G H
Bland, C J
Bodagh, I Y O
Brodrick-Webb, C A
Brough, B J
Browning, A C
Burbidge, A A
Carter, R C
Castro, K A
Cawley, M I D
Chaplin Rogers, S P
Chojnowska, E I
Chojnowski, A J
Clark, L-J
Colmsee, M R

Connolly, E A
Courtney, P M
Cowan, A R
D'Arcy, A H E
Dakeyne, M A
Das, A
Drabu, R K
Dulay, J S
Dunger, G T
Dunsford, M L
Egan, J N T
Ezad, L
Ezad, M A
Farmer, I F
Fitchet, M Q
Foote, G A
Forrest, L V
Fox, A D
Frank, T G
Gardner, A C
Gavin, J
Gibson, J I
Gnanapragasam, J J
Godfrey, P K
Goodbody, R A
Gorrod, E R
Graham, J M
Greenhalgh, J H
Gregory, K L
Gupta, M P
Hall, R L
Harris, R A
Harvey, A R
Hegan, H
Hill, D O
Hillam, A C
Hollyhock, W M
Holman, J J
Hood, W A F
Hounslow, N J
Humphries, S A
Illis, L S
Jenner, C E
Jones, L C
Kell, G
Latham, J M
Lavanchy, O R
Levitt, M J
Liakos, G M
Lockhart, D L
Luff, A J
Lupton, K J
McAulay, J
McCarthy, M E
Malloch, J D
Manners, J M
Massy, J R
Moffitt, D L
Monnery, L
Murphy, D P
Olson, J J
Onyekwere, C U C
Parkes, J
Patel, P
Peckham, C L
Pickvance, N J
Proverbs, A G
Rickenbach, M A
Robinson, S M
Rogers, M J
Roseveare, C D
Rowen, D
Royle, G T
Sadler, C J
Sadler, M A
Salmon, A P
Scott, P J
Scott, T P
Tansley, M C
Taylor, R D
Titcomb, M L
Turner, A M
Walker, J
Ward, S A P
Watkins, A D
Watt, J M
Weavind, G P
Whitmey, R J
Whyte, S P
Williamson, J F

Ebbw Vale

Alford, G
Bissett, D C B
Davies, S W
Goddard, L
Hunt, L E
Jain, A K
Katz, D M

Khan, M R
Mohindru, A C
Morgan, J H
Morgan, W D
Neville, K F
Rice, K J
Sodhi, S S
Turner, D
Varshney, G K
Wasim, M
Williams, D W
Yorke, R J
Yousu Kunju, M

Edenbridge

Bayley, T R L
Beare, R L B
Bradley, K J
Broadhead, R L
Brown, J K
Brudenell, M J R
Bywater, H C I
Eclair-Heath, C M
Edwards, A H
Gillespie, M M
Ilsley, M D
Jones, B R
Kelly, K B
King, L E
Mackintosh, I
Martin, G
Milner, B S
Morrison, S J
Russell, A O
Shaw, J H T
Spear, B S
Williams, S A

Edgbaston

Das, I

Edgware

Ahluwalia, S M S
Ajitsaria, R
Al-Rais, S H
Alam, D K
Alam, S K
Alexander, R E
Amin, S P
Anderson, J E
Annear, J M
Bard, V
Barnard, M E
Beney, J C
Braham, D L
Briggs, B H J
Caplin, H
Chakraborty, C
Challis, D M
Chan, S Y
Cheng, B
Clark, M M
Cooklin, M
D'Costa, R A F J
David, A B
Davies, H J
Davis, S
Dey, A
Endbinder, J S
Fernandes, A L C
Ferris, M
Festenstein, J B
Feuchtwang-Foy, J N H
Gainza, C F A
Ganesh, T
Goldmeier, D
Gondhia, A
Goonawardana, P R
Gordon, H
Gugenheim, P S
Harman, W B
Hikmatullah, S
Hommel, L
Hopkins, W B
Hornik, R J
Hossain, S
Huelser, R E
Ikkos, G
Ismailjee, F
Jain, P
Kapacee, D R C
Kapadia, K K
Kapse, A A
Kapse, N A
Kawsar, M
Kearney, T M
Keni, M
Keni, N
Kirpalani, G

Kitsberg, A A
Kohll, S J M
Kolhatkar, L M
Kumar, K
Kurian, K M
Kutschbach, J M B
Landau, J E
Li, J
Littlestone, W
McDougall, A V
Makanji, H
Malik, A
Manning, A D
Manning, G L
Manzur, K M A
Marples, D D R
Maybaum, S W
Mei Yuk Luk, Dr
Miller, H
Moodaley, D
Nagpaul, S
Narendran, P
Nevrkla, E J
O'Shea, E M A
Pampel, M M
Parsons, G M
Parthipan, K
Patel, A M
Patel, A N
Patel, S
Patel, S B
Patel, S K
Pinto, Z A
Platt, S R
Psiachou-Leonard, E
Reeback, J S
Roberts, L L
Rosenberg, D
Rozewicz, E
Saldanha, M B Y
Sanyal, A
Saraf, I M
Sbano, H
Scambler, S M
Schipperheijn, J A M
Scobie, J Q
Shah, J
Shah, K
Shah, K K
Shah, N
Shah, R C
Shamsuddin, A B
Sharman, G
Shelley, S A
Shukla, D K
Sivasanker, K
Small, N M W
Songra, A K
Stanton, J A
Stephenson, L K
Subhani, S
Susman, M D
Susman, R D
Taktak, S G
Taylor, R A R
Thanabalasingham, B
Tharumaratnam, D B
Trafford, P A
Van Rooyen, A
Varughese, P S
Virdee, T S
Wagman, L
Weinbrenn, G H
Wyndham, M T
Zabetaki, E
Zahir, M

Edinburgh

Abernethy, P
Abernethy, P J
Abraham, A
Achara, N I
Ackerman, E K
Adam, E I
Adam, H M
Adams, A D
Adams, L J
Affleck, R L
Affolter, J T
Ahmed, S F
Airlie, M A A
Aitken, J
Aitken, R J
Aitken, R E G
Akram, A P
Akroyd, S A
Akyol, A M
Al-Shahi, R
Aldridge, J P
Aldridge, L M
Aldridge, R D
Alexander, W D
Alfonzo-Ngwenya, A V M
Alhadi, H A A
Allan, A G L
Allan, D J M
Allan, J R
Allan, P L P
Allan, S R
Allison, M E
Alston, R P
Aly, H E B M
Anderson, A D G
Anderson, A M
Anderson, C E
Anderson, E D C
Anderson, E M
Anderson, E A M
Anderson, J A M
Anderson, K M
Anderson, K D
Anderson, M E
Anderson, M G
Anderson, M R
Anderson, N H
Anderson, P E
Anderson, R A
Andrews, J M
Andrews, R C
Angus, M M
Annan, F J
Annan, I H
Annan, J H
Annand, J C
Archibald, F L M
Armstrong, E M
Armstrong, M W J
Armstrong, P J
Arnold, E S
Arnstein, F E
Arthur, A G
Arthurson, I H
Ashfaq, I
Ashley, R H
Ashmore, A M
Ashworth, B
Athwal, B S
Auckland, K J
Avery, B J
Aw, J
Ayles, A C M
Aylward, R L M
Ayub, M
Bailey, L
Bain, D
Bain, E M
Bain, M R S
Bain, S S R
Baird, D T
Baird, J B B
Baird, J D
Balfour, R F
Ballantyne, A
Ballantyne, J A
Bancroft, P J
Bancroft, T P
Banyard, J E
Barber, M D
Barclay, G P T
Barclay, J M
Barlee, R J
Barnes, C F
Barr, D G D
Barron, M C
Barry, H M
Bartolo, D C C
Bashir, F A
Bashir, W A
Bateman, D N
Bath, L E
Bathgate, A J
Baylis, P J
Beach, C A D
Beamish, D
Beaton, D M
Beattie, T F
Becher, J-C
Beedel, A
Begbie, M M
Begg, A C
Beggs, I
Bell, A M R
Bell, D A
Bell, J D
Bell, J E
Bell, K
Bell, L

Edinburgh

Bell, M M
Bell, M F J
Bell, N J
Bellamy, C O C
Bembridge, B A
Benediktsson, R
Bennison, J M
Bennison, J M
Benton, E C
Benton, T F
Benzie, S J
Berg, J N
Berger, G E
Best, J J K
Beveridge, G W
Bickler, C B
Billcliff, N
Binnington, E S
Bird, C C
Birkett, E S
Bisset, A F
Bisset, W H
Bissett, E M
Black, F M
Black, G
Black, R N H
Black, W D
Blackwell, C D
Blackwood, D R
Blaikie, K J
Blair, A S
Blair, S C
Blake, S J
Bloomfield, P
Bloomfield, S M
Blundell, G
Bodasing, N
Boeing, L
Bolland, W T
Bolton, R E
Bond, A J
Bond, I D
Bonne, W R
Boon, N A
Boron, I
Bouchier, I A D
Bouki, K
Bourke, P J
Bowler, G M R
Bowman, A
Box, S A
Boyd, G
Boyd, J T
Boyd, K J
Boyd, W D
Boye, G L
Bracewell, A C E
Bradbury, M D
Bradbury, P
Bradshaw, F M
Branson, K M H
Bremner, A R F
Breslin, L
Brettle, R P
Brewster, D H
Brewster, N T
Briggs, L M
Briglmen, C J
Brittenden, J
Brittenden, J
Broadbent, M R
Brockington, A R
Bronte-Stewart, C M
Brookman, C A
Brotherston, K G
Brough, M D
Brown, A D G
Brown, A S
Brown, A H
Brown, C
Brown, D R
Brown, D T
Brown, D B
Brown, D C
Brown, E L R
Brown, H C
Brown, J C R
Brown, K J A
Brown, K E
Brown, L M
Brown, O J
Brown, R W
Brown, S
Brown, T S
Browne, G M
Browning, G G P
Bruce, J
Bruce, M S
Brush, J P

Brydon, R A
Brydone, G F C
Buchan, A S
Buchan, J A
Buchanan, R B
Buck, S M
Buckley, E G
Bull, M W
Bunney, M H
Burgoyne, J
Burnel, A J
Burnett, H M
Burnett, R
Burnett, R C S C
Burnett, W H
Burns-Brown, I L
Burns-Brown, J
Burns, J E
Burns, S M
Burt, A J
Burt, J P
Bury, J K
Busuttil, A
Butler, A E
Butler, A C
Buttery, R C
Buxton, P K
Byrne, M P
Cacciatori, M
Cairns, C J S
Cairns, D A
Cairns, M J
Cairns, P F
Calder, A A
Calder, M A
Calder, S K
Caldwell, H M
Calvert, J M
Calvert, S H S
Cameron, A V
Cameron, D A
Cameron, E W J
Cameron, G
Cameron, H S
Cameron, J M
Cameron, K M
Cameron, S C
Cameron, S T
Campbell, A S
Campbell, C D
Campbell, D A
Campbell, F A
Campbell, H
Campbell, I D
Campbell, J P M
Campbell, J A
Campbell, R C H
Campbell, R
Campbell, W A
Cannon, N
Cantley, P M
Caplin, B D
Carey, F A
Carmichael, G L M
Carrie, M
Carroll, J P M
Carruthers, D B
Carter, T A H
Casasola, R J
Casey, J J
Cash, J D
Cash, M P
Cassie, A B
Catnach, J
Cavanagh, J T O
Caves, N D
Cay, E L
Cay, S E B
Chaddock, M E
Chadwick, A E P
Chalmers-Watson, C E
Chalmers-Watson, J I
Chalmers-Watson, T A
Chalmers, H A
Chalmers, J W T
Chalmers, J
Chalmers, R T A
Chalmers, S R
Chalmers, T M
Chapman, B J
Chapman, D G
Chapman, J S
Chapman, M E
Chapman, N C
Charnley, N G
Chaudhry, M T
Chawla, H B
Cheesman, C A
Chetty, U

Cheung, J S-Y
Chevassut, T J T
Chew, I S H
Chia, S
Chick, J D
Chin, D M F
Chiswick, D
Chowings, J S
Christie, J
Christie, J E
Christie, P A
Chrystall, D M
Chua, S S W
Chui, E-C
Clark, A J E
Clark, C R
Clark, D J
Clark, E
Clark, R M
Clark, V A
Clarke, A L
Clarke, B F
Clarke, R L
Clegg, G R
Clive, S
Clouter, M A
Cobain, E J
Cohen, K D J W
Coia, J E
Cole, J S
Cole, S K
Colledge, N R
Collee, J G
Collingham, N T
Colver, H M
Colvin, L A
Comiskey, G A
Conacher, E I
Conacher, W D H
Conlon, C F
Connan, A L
Connolly, K C
Cook, R E
Cookson, D T
Coombes, J L
Cooper, E S
Cooper, E J
Copland, E J
Copland, W A
Corbett, G T
Cormack, C R H
Cornbleet, M A
Cosgrove, L E
Coupe, S M
Coupland, M D C
Cowan, C
Cowan, D L
Cowan, J T
Cowan, J
Cowan, M G
Cowan, S
Cowell, M M
Cox, N M
Cozens, A L
Craig, G
Craigmile, J A
Cramond, S A C
Craven, J M
Crawford, A S
Crawford, C E H
Crawford, D H
Crawford, M C
Crean, A M
Creed, J J
Cremona, F R
Cresswell, J E
Crichton, A
Crichton, J H M
Crichton, T I
Crispin, J D
Crispin, J R
Critchley, H O D
Crofton, E C
Crofton, J W
Crofts, F M
Crofts, T-J
Crompton, G K
Cronin, H M B
Crookes, D P
Crosbie, P A J
Crosswaite, A G
Cruikshank, J G F R
Cubie, A
Cull, R E
Cullen, A K
Cullen, C P
Cullen, J F
Cullen, M J
Cullinane, S C

Cummine, D P
Cumming, A
Cumming, A D
Cunningham-Burley, R A
Cunningham, M
Cunningham, S
Cupples, W A
Curnier, A P R
Currie, C T
Currie, I H
Currie, I S
Currie, J M
Currie, J R M
Curtis, A
Da Costa, J A G
Dabb, R G
Dahele, A V M
Dahele, M R
Dale, F M
Dalkin, T J
Dall, G F
Dames, G
Davenport, R J
Davidson, A W
Davidson, D J
Davidson, E D L
Davidson, E M
Davidson, F B
Davidson, I A
Davidson, K E
Davidson, K L
Davidson, K
Davidson, M G
Davie, E G
Davie, I T
Davies, M J
Davies, P E
Davies, S J
Dawson, H L
Dawson, L K
De Beaux, A C
De Beaux, I
De Burgh, M J A
De Souza, J M A
Dean, S M
Deans, R A
Deary, I J
Deehan, S C
Delahooke, T E S
Delgado Martin, M B
Delvaux, A
Denison, F C
Denison, R S
Dennis, M S
Dennis, R E
Denvir, M A
Deuchars, J A
Devey, L R
Dhall, P
Dhillon, B
Dhillon, V B
Diamond, R L
Dick, H E R
Dick, N C
Dickson, A A
Dickson, E M
Dickson, J E A
Dickson, J
Dickson, M A S
Dickson, R I
Dickson, T E
Dimigen, M
Din, N A
Dinwoodie, D L
Dinwoodie, H P
Dixon, J M J
Dixon, R E J
Dobbie, J W
Dobbin, A E
Dobson, G A
Dodd, K W
Dodds, A D
Doherty, V R
Doig, A
Dolan, A
Donald, A G
Donald, J B
Donald, P M
Donald, S M
Donaldson, D B
Donaldson, I M L
Donaldson, K
Donaldson, L M
Donaldson, S M
Donaldson, W
Donat, R
Donnelly, J G
Donnelly, M P

Donnelly, S C
Donovan, W R
Doris, A B
Douds, F H A
Dougall, H K
Douglas, A J
Douglas, A C
Douglas, M J
Douglas, N J
Doull, D H
Dow, R J
Dowling, N J
Downie, R G
Doyle, D
Drake, A J
Draper, M H
Drever, G F
Drever, J H
Drewitt, D J N
Drewitt, H P
Drummond, D C
Drummond, G B
Drysdale, C F
Duffy, N J
Duncan, J G
Duncan, J A T
Duncan, L J P
Duncan, L E
Duncan, M E
Duncan, W
Duncan, W C
Dundas, K C
Dundas, S
Dunhill, Z M
Dunlop, A
Dunn, J L
Dunn, M J G
Dunn, S M
Durkacz, K P
Duvall, E
Dyer, J A T
Dyson, R G
Ebmeier, K P
Eckford, I B C
Edington, J H R
Edmunds, A T
Edmunds, W T
Edwards, H V
Eglinton, D J
El Hag, O A O
El-Khatib, A R R
Elder, A T
Ellis, R A
Elmubarak, M Y
Elswood, R
Emmanuel, F X S
Emond, M W
Ennis, J E
Ennis, J S A
Erridge, S C
Errington, J R
Errington, M L
Eunson, G J
Evans, A S
Evans, C D J
Evans, G C
Evans, J
Evans, J I
Evason, S E
Ewart, D W
Ewing, D J
Ewing, F M E
Fabbroni, G
Faccenda, J F
Fair, J F
Fairhurst, K
Falconer, J S
Fallon, M T
Falzon, M
Fananapazir, K
Farah, H H
Farmer, K D
Farquharson, D I M
Farquharson, E M L
Faulding-Bird, H M
Fawcett, P G
Fearon, K C H
Fentiman, G J
Fenton, I M K
Fenton, I S
Ferguson, A
Ferguson, M J
Ferguson, S M
Ferguson, S C
Fergusson, R J
Fernandez Dair, N
Fettes, M R
Findlow, D
Fink, G

Finlayson, N D C
Finnie, L R
Fisher, J A C
Fitzgerald, T
Fitzmaurice, B
Fitzpatrick, D R
Flapan, A D
Fleck, B W
Fleming, C F
Fleming, P A
Fleming, S
Fletcher, A J
Flynn, A B
Flynn, P M
Follett, G F
Foo, H S L
Foo, I T H
Forbes, G I
Forbes, K
Forbes, N F
Forbes, W
Fordyce, D T
Forfar, I M L
Forfar, J O
Forrest, A P M
Forrest, J G
Forrester, J M
Forsyth, K C
Foster, C A
Fouyas, I
Fowkes, F G R
Fowler, J W
Fox, K A A
Foy, R C
Francis, C M
Francis, R R M
Franks, D M
Franks, K L
Fraser, A K
Fraser, D R K
Fraser, G M
Fraser, H S F
Fraser, J
Fraser, M
Freeman, C P L
Freeman, J A
Freestone, S
Freshwater, J V
Frew, D
Fried, M J
Frier, B M
Fulford, P E
Fulton, C A
Fulton, P M
Gabra, H
Galea, G
Gallivan, P R
Garden, O J
Gardiner, J
Gardiner, K J
Gardner, D L
Garner, J A M
Gaskell, P A
Gatiss, S-J
Gebbie, A E
Gebbie, H H
Geddes, M C
Geddes, N A
Gemmell, H M
George, C M
George, F O
Geraghty, J R
Gerow, E R
Ghaly, A F F
Ghosh, S
Gibb, A P
Gibbs, S M
Gibson, D A
Gibson, J N A
Gibson, P H
Gibson, R J
Gilchrist, J J
Gilchrist, M L
Gillespie, I N
Gillespie, R J S
Gillespie, T A
Gillies, T E
Gillingham, F J
Gillon, J
Gilmore, M M
Gilmour, H M
Gilmour, S H
Gilmour, W M
Gilray, G
Glasby, M A
Glasier, A F
Glaze, R C J
Glen, E M
Glen, J L

Edinburgh

Glen, S K
Gold, H J
Gonzalez Prieto, M C
Gooday, H M K
Gordon, A
Gordon, A C
Gould, J C
Gourlay, K A
Gourley, C M
Gow, G
Gowans, G T
Gowans, I D
Graham, A D
Graham, L J C
Grainger, J E J
Grant, D J
Grant, I S
Grant, L J C
Grant, N A
Grant, R
Grant, S M
Grant, S M
Grant, W E
Gray, D A
Gray, H C
Gray, J A
Gray, R S
Gray, S K R
Green, B K W
Green, R H A
Greene, J D W
Greening, A P
Greenwood, J
Greer, J R
Gregor, A
Grieve, D C
Grieve, F J
Griffiths, J M T
Grigor, H
Grigor, J
Grigor, K M
Gronski, M J
Grubb, M A
Grubb, N R
Gruer, R
Gunn, A A
Gunn, J M
Gunn, W J
Gurmin, V J
Guthrie, B
Guthrie, C E M
Guthrie, I M K
Gutierrez Rodriguez, A
Guy, S E
Habeshaw, M J
Hailey, J A
Hall, A M
Hall, M S
Hall, R J P
Hallam, N F
Halloran, E M
Halpin, S
Halson, E R
Hamann, I D
Hamer-Hodges, D W
Hamill, A M
Hamilton, A R
Hamilton, H R
Hamilton, J M S
Hamilton, J
Hamilton, M I
Handyside, R
Hanley, J P
Hannaford, P F
Hannon, P A C
Hanson, M F
Hardie, C L
Hargreave, T B
Harkin, C
Harkness, R A
Harper, L B
Harris, P A
Harrison, A M
Harrison, A R
Harrison, C G
Harrison, D J
Harrison, J M
Harrison, N
Harrison, R E
Hart, S P
Harunarashid, H
Harvey, F M K
Haslam, C J
Haughney, M G J
Hawkins, J W
Haycock, K E
Haydon, G H
Hayes, P C
Hayward, R L

Heading, R C
Henderson, C E A
Henderson, K
Henderson, K M
Henderson, L F
Henderson, N C
Henderson, R N
Henderson, R E
Hendry, S J
Henriksen, P A
Henry, C N M
Hepburn, T
Hepple, P A
Herbert, I
Herd, R M
Hewitt, A N M
Hill, J
Hill, Q A
Hintjens, K L
Hoare, P
Hodgson, M M
Hoffmann, B R F
Holland, C J S
Holland, P J P
Hollingdale, E E
Hollis, S
Holloway, A J
Holmes, C P
Holton, D W
Holton, F A
Homer, D E
Hook, A C P
Hooper, G
Hope, J G
Hopkins, A W
Horn, H M
Horne, A M
Horne, D C
Horne, N W
Horne, P M
Hornibrook, S C
Horsburgh, G
Horsburgh, J C
Horsfall, H S C
Hosie, J E
Housley, E
Howard, G C W
Howard, R G
Howie, C R
Howie, C C M
Howie, G M
Howie, J G R
Howitt, L F
Hoyle, J A
Huby, C L
Hudson, I N
Hughes, J
Hughes, J E
Hughes, K I
Hughes, M L
Hughes, P
Hughes, R G
Hughson, D R
Hume, S M
Hunter, A J C
Hunter, I
Hunter, J M
Hunter, J A A
Hunter, N J F
Huntly, B J P
Hurley, P A
Hurst, J R
Hurst, N P
Hutchison, A F
Hutchison, E J
Hutchison, J K
Hutton, C L
Ihekwaba, F N
Iliffe, A L
Illingworth, D G
Illingworth, S G M
Inglis, J H C
Inglis, S A
Ingram, S M
Innes, E M
Innes, J
Innes, J A
Insley, M L
Inwood, J M
Ip Min Wan, D
Ireland, A S
Ireland, H M
Ironside, J W
Ironside, J A D
Ironside, M J
Irvine, D S
Irvine, W J
Irving, R J
Ismail, A M

Ives, J C J
Jack, H L
Jack, W J L
Jackson, P D
Jackson, S E
Jacques, A H
Jalan, A R
Jalan, R
Jamie, G M
Jamieson, M B
Jamieson, N S D
Jamieson, W S
Jamnicky, L
Jan, S Y
Jappy, M E
Jawaheer, G
Jeffrey, J C S
Jellinek, E H
Jenkins, A M
Jenkins, J
Jenkins, M G
Jigajinni, M V
Jodrell, D I
Johns, R H
Johnson, C R
Johnson, G A
Johnson, H
Johnson, P R E
Johnston, P O
Johnstone, E C
Johnstone, F D
Johnstone, M M
Jolliffe, D W
Jolly, M M P
Jones, C W
Jones, D B
Jones, I A
Jones, N V
Jones, R D G
Jones, R I A
Jordan, L J
Kanwar, S
Kaufman, M H
Kay, R W
Kearney, P P
Keating, F A
Keating, J F
Keay, A J
Keel, A M
Keeling, J W
Keighley, J E
Kellett, R J
Kelly, B A
Kelly, C A
Kelly, K P
Kelly, P
Kelman, J R
Kelman, L
Kelnar, C J H
Kemp, I W
Kennedy, R I
Kent, J A
Kent, V J
Ker, J S
Kerr, A I G
Kerr, A W S
Kerr, J M
Kerr, N G D
Keys, J A
Khalifa, B E B
Khan, M A
Kidd, S L
Kilpatrick, R
King, M R G
King, N E
Kirkpatrick, A E
Kirkup, J R
Kirkwood, H L S
Kirwan, E V
Kitchin, A H
Knox, K W
Knox, M I R
Kondracki, S G
Krajewski, A S
Kreitman, N B
Kuenssberg, B V
Kunkler, I H
Kurt-Elli, S L
Labinjoh, C
Laing, I A
Lakhdar, A A
Lam Shang Leen, C
Lam, W L
Lamb, D I H
Lamb, I
Lamb, K
Lamb, P J
Lamb, W L
Lambert, C M

Lambie, A T
Lambie, S H
Lammie, G A
Lang, C C E
Lang, F H
Lang, H M
Lang, J A
Langa Ferreira, B A
Langdale-Brown, B
Langridge-Smith, J E
Langsley, N
Langton, M S B
Lapraik, M R
Large, A H D
Latham, T
Laurence, A R
Lawrie, S M
Lawson, C S
Lawson, G M
Lawson, R A
Lawson, S R
Le Maitre, J P
Learmonth, A C
Leckie, A M
Leckie, S M
Ledingham, J G
Lee, A
Lee, D
Legge, R I
Leitch, J E B
Lello, G E
Leonard, P A
Leonard, R C F
Leslie, P C
Lessells, A M
Lessells, K M
Leung, C H S
Leung, R C-Y
Levack, P A
Lever, M J
Lewin, C A
Liddell, M L
Liddle, R E
Lilley, C D
Lim, C S
Lim, W C
Lindsay, R S
Lingam, R N
Liston, W A
Little, F A
Little, K
Littlechild, P
Littlewood, D G
Livingston, S C
Livingstone, J R B
Lloyd, E L
Lloyd, F H
Lodge, A M
Lodge, M C
Logan, A
Logan, M R
Logie, L J
Loh, D L
Lopez Manas, J M
Lorenzo Gallego, S
Lorge, M A
Lorimer, S M R
Lossock, F H
Loudon, J A Z
Loudon, J B
Loudon, J D O
Loudon, N B
Low, G W Y
Lowry, L M
Ludlam, C A
Lueck, C J
Lumsden, G R
Lumsden, W H R
Lundholm, E O
Luqmani, R A
Lurie, P S
Lyall, R M
Lyon, A J
Lyon, W M M
McAlister, C A
McAndrew, G M
McAndrew, L J H
McArdle, C S
Macari, A C
Macartney, M M
Macaulay, A
Macaulay, R A A
McAuslane, S E
McBirnie, J M
McCabe, S
McCallum, H G
McCallum, J R
MacCallum, L R
McClelland, D B L

McClure, J H
McCool, H J
McCord, N
McCowen, E M
McCracken, A J
McCrae, A F
McCrea, M
McCulloch, G J
McCulloch, I M
McCullough, C T
McCutcheon, C
McDermid, G
McDermott, R A
McDevitt, C S
McDiarmid, M H
McDonald, C F
MacDonald, E
Macdonald, H W
Macdonald, I D
MacDonald, J
Macdonald, K L
MacDonald, L A
MacDonald, M K
MacDonald, S P J
MacDougall, G M
McDougall, J B
MacDougall, M W J
MacDougall, R H
MacDuff, A
McFadyen, I J
Macfarlane, R M
Macfie, J A
Macfie, J L B
McGalloway, B A
MacGilchrist, A J
MacGillivray, G
MacGillivray, N
McGoogan, E
McGovern, G P
MacGregor, A B
McGregor, A H
McGregor, C J
McGregor, G
McGregor, J C
McGuigan, C C
McGuigan, P S
McGurn, B
McHale, S J
MacHale, S M
McHardy, G J R
McHardy, V U
McIlwaine, G G
McIlwaine, G M
MacIndoe, N L
McIntosh, A H
McIntosh, A F
McIntosh, A M
McIntosh, C A
McIntosh, C E
McIntosh, N
McIntosh, S A
McIntosh, W G
MacIntyre, D J
MacIntyre, I M C
McIntyre, J C
MacIntyre, J C
McIntyre, M A
Macintyre, S C
McKain, A D
Mackay, A
Mackay, A R
Mackay, G R
McKay, I I
Mackay, P C
Mackay, T W
Mackean, M J
McKeating, E G
McKee, I H
MacKenney, P J
Mackenzie, A
McKenzie, A G
Mackenzie, C J R
MacKenzie, C D
Mackenzie, J
MacKenzie, J R
Mackenzie, J E
McKenzie, K J
Mackenzie, P A P
Mackenzie, S B P
Mackenzie, S J
Mackenzie, S
Mackenzie, S
Mackenzie, W C
McKeown, D W
Mackie, C F
Mackie, J E W
Mackie, S E R
McKimmie, S J
MacKinlay, G B

MacKinlay, G A
Mackinnon, H F
Mackinnon, H L
Mackinnon, R K J
McKnight, J A
MacLachlan, D C
McLaren, D B
MacLaren, F B
MacLaren, I F
McLaren, J A
McLaren, J S
McLaren, K M
McLaren, R C
McLarty, I J
McLay, K
McLean, A M
Maclean, C M U
McLean, C M
McLean, I P
Maclean, M H
MacLean, M E
Maclean, N
Maclean, S S
Maclean, W K
McLellan, S A
McLennan, J M
MacLennan, W J
MacLeod, A D
MacLeod, C M
Macleod, D A D
Macleod, H M
Macleod, I B
Macleod, J G
Mcleod, K A
MacLeod, K G
Macleod, M R
Macleod, M A
McLeod, N W
MacLullich, A M J
McMaster, M J
McMillan, A
McMillan, E
Macmillan, I M M
McMillan, J H
Macmillan, M A B
McMillan, S A
McMillan, T M
Macnab, J L
MacNee, W
MacNeil, C
McNeill, S A
McNeillage, J A
Macnicol, M F
McNiven, A C
McPartlin, G M
MacPhail, H N
Macpherson, A G H
MacPherson, H D
Macpherson, S G
McPhillips, M A
McQueen, M M
MacQueen, M
MacRae, W R
McRorie, E R
McSwan, E
MacTaggart, M M
McVean, A E
McVie, D H
McVie, M W
McWilliam, J M
Magin, S C
Magnusdottir, E M
Main, T D
Maingay, C H
Malcolm-Smith, N A
Manders, D N
Mankad, P S
Manson, J S
Manson, T W
Manson, W G
Mantravadi, K M
Maran, A G
Maran, N J
Mardon, J
Marsden, A K
Marsh, J L
Marshall, A F
Marshall, H
Marshall, J A G
Marshall, T G
Martin, A C
Martin, H M
Martin, L V H
Martin, R D
Martindale, H C
Mason-Apps, S P
Mason, J K F
Masson, A H B
Masson, M N

Edinburgh

Masterton, G
Masterton, R G
Matheson, G H
Matheson, J M
Matheson, L M
Matheson, M
Matthews, A G
Matthews, A J
Matthews, J D
Mattick, A P
Maule, M M
Maynard, C A
McCall-Smith, E D A
Mealy, K
Mee, B
Meekison, L A
Mehigan, C
Melvin, W D
Mends, D R B
Menon, G
Mepham, S O
Merino, S V
Merricks, E K
Metcalf, J
Middleton, S
Middleton, W G
Midgley, S
Miles, C S
Miles, D N
Miles, H L
Miles, R S
Miles, W F A
Millar, A M
Millar, G T
Millar, J A M
Millar, J T
Millar, M Y I
Millar, S A I
Miller, C J
Miller, H C
Milligan, G R
Mills, A R
Mills, R P
Millwater, C J
Milne, A R
Milne, A C
Milne, C A
Milne, J A
Milne, J B M
Milne, K G S
Mishra, P
Mitchell, A
Mitchell, C
Mitchell, D H
Mitchell, I D C
Moffat, I A
Moffat, R C E
Moffoot, A P R
Mohan, M
Moir, A T B
Moir, F M
Moir, S B
Monaghan, H
Moor, S
Moores, A H
Moores, C R
Moorhead, A
Moralee, S J
More, M
Morgan, K P
Morley, H S
Morris-Mancor, C J
Morris, E J B
Morris, J A
Morrison, A G
Morrison, A
Morrison, D P
Morrison, F M
Morton, C M
Morton, C P J
Morton, D N
Morton, E W F
Morton, I M
Morton, S L
Morton, V L M
Moses, A G W
Moultrie, S J
Mounstephen, A H
Mountain, D A
Moussa, S A
Muir, B B
Mukherji, P S
Mumford, C J
Munro, A L
Munro, F D
Munro, H D R
Murchison, J T
Murdoch, J M
Murdoch, R A F

Murie, J A
Murphy, C M
Murphy, R R
Murphy, T J C
Murphy, W G
Murray, D M
Murray, H M
Murray, I E L
Murray, J G
Murray, J E
Murray, K
Murray, M
Murray, N S
Murray, S A
Myrscough, P R
Myint, K
Myles, L M
Myskow, L M
Nagle, R S
Nally, A P
Neades, G T
Neil, A E
Neil, A J
Nelson, F R
Nevard, C H F
Newby, D E
Newsam, A G
Newsam, J E
Nicholson, S
Nicol, E F
Nicoll, J A
Nimmo, A F
Nimmo, G R
Nimmo, I G R
Nimmo, J
Nimmo, S M
Nisbet, R M
Nisbet, W H
Nixon, S J
Noble, I M
Norman, J E
Northridge, D B
Norton, B
Nuki, G
Nussey, F E
Nutton, R W
O'Connell, U C
O'Donnell, M
O'Hanlon, P E
O'Hare, A E
O'Neill, J M
O'Neill, K M
O'Neill, O B
O'Neill, W M
O'Regan, M E
O'Sullivan, M G J
O'Toole, L
Ody, A W
Ogilvie, M M
Ojar, D H
Olday, S J
Oliver, C W
Oliver, M Y
Orr, J A
Orr, J D
Orr, S C
Osborne, A B
Osifodunrin, O O O
Ostrowski, N M J
Oswald, J
Owen, M
Owens, D G C
Oxenham, H C
Paisley, A M
Palmer, K S
Palmer, K R
Palmer, N D
Palmer, P A
Papachryostomou
Evgenikos, M
Parker, A C
Parker, S S
Parris, J B
Parris, M R
Parry, K M
Pascoe-Watson, D
Passmore, R
Patterson-Brown, S P
Paterson-Brown, S
Paterson, A
Paterson, B C
Paterson, D R
Paterson, F M
Paterson, I
Paterson, J W
Paterson, J D
Paterson, M W
Paterson, P M M O
Paterson, S M

Paton, E R L
Patrick, A W
Patterson, J S
Pearce, H L
Pearce, M M
Pearson, M
Pearson, M M
Pearson, S J
Peat, M L
Pedder, C E
Pendreigh, G M
Penman, I D
Pentland, B
Pepper, S J
Pereira, M L
Perez Sales, S
Perez, J M
Perry, C H
Perry, R C M
Peters, J A
Peutherer, J F
Phanjoo, A L
Phelps, R G
Philip, L
Phillips, C I
Phillips, H A
Phillips, J
Phillips, J E
Pilkington, A
Plant, W D
Player, D A
Plevris, I
Plews, D E
Pollok, A J
Polson, H W M
Pope, D G
Porteous, M E M
Potter, J L
Potts, S G
Pound, S E
Prasad, B R
Prasad, P
Premnath, Dr
Prendergast, A E
Prescott, L F
Price, A
Price, G M
Price, G C
Price, J F
Price, M
Price, R F
Price, W H
Prince, K L
Prossor, I M
Proudfoot, A T
Pugh, G C
Pugh, K J
Purdue, B N
Quaba, A A-R A
Quinn, A N K
Quinn, T J
Raczkowski, R M
Radley, S
Rae, A R M
Rae, H H
Rae, P W H
Rafi, M A
Rajack, S M
Ramdeehul, A R
Ramkissoon, A M
Ramo, M P
Ramsay, D A
Ramsay, L J
Ramsay, R G
Rankine, A E
Rashbass, P
Rasool, T P
Ratcliff, R A W
Ravisekar, O
Ray, D C
Ray, R E
Razzaq, G
Read, H S
Redhead, D N
Redpath, C J
Reeves, I C
Regan, C C
Reichardt, O S
Reid, A G
Reid, A G
Reid, D A
Reid, F M
Reid, K A
Reid, W A
Reid, W J
Reiss, J E
Reive, A R
Rennie, L M
Rennie, N J

Renton, M C
Reynish, W P
Rhein, H M
Rhind, G B
Rhodes, J K J
Richards, J P
Richardson, J M
Riches, H I
Richmond, D W
Richmond, J
Rigden, J
Rigg, R C
Rimmer, C S
Rimmer, S
Rintoul, R C
Ritchie, C M D
Ritchie, E L
Ritson, E B
Robb, J E
Robbins, A G
Roberton, C J
Roberts, J
Robertson, A A
Robertson, A E
Robertson, G D
Robertson, G
Robertson, I D
Robertson, J R
Robertson, J M
Robertson, K
Robertson, M J C
Robertson, P J
Robertson, P
Robinson, C M
Robinson, R A
Robison, C
Robson, J S
Robson, M J A
Roddie, P H
Rodgers, A J C
Rodgers, H J
Rogan, C A
Rogers, C E
Rookwood, K J
Rooney, M M E
Rose, E M
Rose, M
Rosie, H A
Ross, F M H
Ross, I R F
Ross, J A
Ross, J M H
Ross, J M
Ross, J M
Ross, L A
Ross, P J
Ross, R A K
Ross, R S
Ross, S M
Rothwell, P M
Rourke, A
Rowney, D A
Royle, H M
Ruckley, V A
Rushmer, R J
Russell, E B A W
Russell, G T
Russell, H B L
Russell, J F A
Russell, K A
Russell, L F M
Russell, R K
Russell, T
Ruth, M J
Rutledge, M L C
Rutledge, P
Ryan, M F
Ryan, M P
Rycroft, H D
Sa'Ad, Z A
Sadler, K M
Sahu, P
Sala Tenna, A M
Salem, R J
Sander, C R
Sandercock, P A G
Sanders, D S A
Sanders, R
Sanderson, R J
Sandison, D R
Sangra, M S
Santana Hernandez, D J
Santini, A J A
Sargent, W
Savill, J S
Savin, J A
Saweirs, W W M
Scarth, L G
Schneider, V

Schofield, O M V M
Sclare, G
Scobie, W G
Scott, A
Scott, A C
Scott, C J
Scott, D H T
Scott, E A J
Scott, G J C
Scott, G R
Scott, G G G
Scott, J H S
Scott, M
Scott, P A
Scott, P M
Scott, R M
Scott, R J
Scott, S C M
Scudder, C C
Searl, C P
Seaton, A
Seaton, D A
Seckl, J R
Seiler, E R
Sellar, R J
Sellar, W T K
Seth, S A
Seton, R F
Seyfollahi, S
Shand, A G
Sharp, J C M
Sharpe, F M
Sharpe, M C
Sharwood-Smith, G H
Shaw, J F
Shaw, R J
Shaw, T R D
Sheehan, S M
Shepherd, A M
Shepherd, P C A
Shepherd, W C
Shiels, R M
Shortt, N L
Sim, J S N
Sime, J L
Simmonds, P N
Simmons, C M
Simon, E J
Simpson, C A
Simpson, D L
Simpson, H
Simpson, K J
Simpson, N
Simpson, R J
Simpson, W A
Sinclair, A A
Sinclair, C J
Sinclair, F M
Sinclair, I S R
Sinclair, W W
Singh, J
Singh, K K
Sinha, S
Skelton, C E
Skene, C G
Skinner, B C
Skinner, F M
Skinner, J
Skinner, R
Slater, B C S
Slater, E M
Slater, E
Slater, K D
Slatford, K
Slawson, K B
Small, C M
Small, M J
Small, M S S
Small, W P
Smart, G E
Smith, A N
Smith, A I
Smith, A D S
Smith, A F
Smith, B J
Smith, D L
Smith, G
Smith, I J M
Smith, I I
Smith, J K
Smith, J
Smith, J L
Smith, L A
Smith, R G
Smith, S E
Smith, T J S
Smithson, N J
Smyth, J F
Sneddon, D J C

Somerville, E M
Song, S H
Soutar, C A
Soutar, I
Souter, W A
Southam, J C
Sowler, E M K
Speirs, N T
Spence, A A
Spens, H J
Spiller, J A
St. John, H E
Stanley, M C
Stansfield, M H
Starkey, I R
Statham, P F X
Steel, R M
Steers, A J W
Stein, K W T
Stenson, B J
Stephenson, R N
Sterrick, M J M
Stevenson, A J M
Stevenson, A G
Stevenson, D J D
Stevenson, J E
Stevenson, J S K
Stevenson, L V
Stewart, A R
Stewart, A J
Stewart, A J
Stewart, B J C
Stewart, E A
Stewart, G A
Stewart, G T
Stewart, I C
Stewart, J P
Stewart, L H
Stewart, M D C
Stewart, R A L
Stewart, R A
Stewart, W G
Steyn, J P
Stilley, D
Stirling, A M
Stirling, S C
Stockman, P K
Stone, J
Storey, D
Strachan, D G
Strachan, M W J
Strong, J A
Struthers, R A
Stuart, P C
Stuart, W P
Sudlow, E M
Sudlow, M F
Sumeray, M S
Summers, D M
Sutherland, A B
Sutherland, G R
Sutherland, J K
Sutherland, K A
Sutherland, R W
Swainson, C P
Swan, H T
Swann, D G
Swarbrick, P J
Syed, A H
Sykes, C J
Sym, J C B
Symmers, W S C
Tait, A C
Tait, I B
Tait, W A
Tam, C K M
Tan, J C-G
Tan, S Y
Tannahill, A J
Tarar, M N
Tay, C C K
Taylor Brown, M
Taylor, D M
Taylor, F J
Taylor, J C G W
Taylor, J
Taylor, L M
Taylor, S G
Telfer, A H
Telfer, J R C
Temple, C M
Tennick, J R
Than Nyunt, M P
Theodosiou, C A
Theodosiou, L J
Therapondos, G P
Thomas, A E
Thomas, E C
Thomas, H M

Enfield

Thomas, H B W
Thomas, J G
Thomas, J S J
Thomas, M W
Thomas, M J C
Thompson, C I
Thompson, E J
Thompson, J R
Thompson, J M
Thompson, M J
Thompson, M J
Thomson, A J
Thomson, C M
Thomson, D M
Thomson, D G
Thomson, K J
Thomson, K J
Thomson, L D G
Thomson, L A
Thomson, M K
Thomson, P G
Thomson, S A
Thomson, S
Thomson, W I
Thorn, J B
Thow, M E
Thyne, D H S
Tidman, J S M
Tidman, M J
Ting, A Y-H
Tipper, R J
Todd, I C
Todd, J R C
Todd, R G
Todd, W G
Toft, A D
Toft, N J
Tolley, D A
Tolley, M S
Torrance, A M E
Torrance, M H
Torres, M D R C
Tothill, S A
Treasure, W
Trevelyan, M H
Tripp, J C S
Trotter, S H
Tulloch, D E
Tulloch, D N
Tulloch, L J
Turnbull, C M
Turnbull, G L
Turnbull, L W
Turner, A N
Turner, D
Turner, M L
Turney, T M
Twiddy, P J
Twigg, J P D
Tybulewicz, A T
Underwood, J R
Upton, P A
Uren, N G
Uttley, J M C
Uttley, W R
Valle, A M
Varma, K B
Varma, M
Varma, S
Vaughan, G T
Venters, B
Virgo, M A
Voss, K L
Wade, F A
Wakefield, C H
Walayat, M
Walbaum, P R
Walker-Kinnear, M H
Walker, B R
Walker, D D
Walker, D E
Walker, D E
Walker, G A
Walker, J C
Walker, J D
Walker, J
Walker, R B W
Walker, S W
Walker, S A
Walker, W S
Wall, L R
Wallace, A M
Wallace, C J
Wallace, G M F
Wallace, I W J
Wallace, M A
Wallace, N W
Wallace, W H B
Wallis, C B

Walls, E W
Walls, J V M
Walmsley, F J
Walmsley, S R
Walpole, R H
Walsh, E G
Walsh, J S J
Walsh, T S
Walton, H J
Ward, H J T
Wardlaw, J M
Waring, A B
Waring, W S
Warlow, C P
Warnock, S M
Warwick, M M
Waterer, S C
Watson, C E
Watson, D L
Watson, F E
Watson, G M
Watson, K C
Watson, L M
Watson, M L
Watson, N
Watson, P A
Watson, R A M
Watt, B
Watt, G
Watt, K P
Watt, S J
Watts, D A
Webb, D J
Webb, J N
Weir, D M
Weller, R P J B
Welsby, P D
Wenham, V C
Wharton, S B
Whatling, P J
Whimster, J H
White, A
White, I R
White, L J
White, P G
Whitfield, A
Whitley, M W
Whittle, A T
Whittle, I R
Whittle, J R S
Whitwell, J R
Whitworth, C E
Whitworth, D M
Whyte, H
Widdowson, J
Wight, R M
Wightman, A J A
Wigmore, S J
Wild, S R
Wildgoose, C D
Wilkinson, J
Wilks, D P
Will, D J
Williams, A H
Williams, A R W
Williams, A T
Williams, H J
Williams, L W
Williams, L P
Williams, M J
Williams, R J
Williams, R L
Williamson, E R D
Williamson, J
Wills, D P
Wilson-Storey, D
Wilson, D C
Wilson, D F
Wilson, E G
Wilson, F M
Wilson, I M
Wilson, J
Wilson, J M
Wilson, J A
Wilson, J A
Wilson, L M
Wilson, R G
Winney, R J
Witherow, F N
Witherspoon, P
Wolff, S
Wong, J K F
Wong, N A C S
Wong, S C
Wood, B R
Wood, M J
Wood, R J
Woodburn, K J
Woods, S J

Woodward, A C
Woolner, H W
Wrate, R M
Wright, A F
Wright, D J
Wright, E
Wright, F J
Wright, M O
Wright, M R
Wyatt, J P
Wyllie, J H
Wynn, M
Yap, P L
Yates, P A
Yau, Y-H
Yong, S M
Young, A
Young, G B
Young, I E
Young, I W
Young, J C
Young, M J
Young, P M
Young, S M M
Yuille, F A P
Zammitt, N N
Zealley, H E
Zealley, K E
Zegleman, F E
Zeidler, M D
Zeman, A Z J
Zubaidi, S

Egham

Allen, E B
Baker, G A E
Bethel, R G H
Burmanroy, S
Elliott, J V
Galazka, L S
Galazka, N M I
Hawk, L J
Kidd, S J
Latimer, B H
Morris, R O
Nicholson, P J
Palmer, J P
Pavesi, L A
Priestley, V R
Purkait, S K
Salmon, R P
Sharpe, J C
Stuart, M A E
Taylor, S G
Vaughan-Davies, S L
Warwicker, P M
Whiteley, J D
Worthington, R C

Egmanton

Tragen, D

Egremont

Bewick, M
Creed, A L N
Gallacher, R H
Galloway, F D
Goodman, S E
Heijne Den Bak, J
Hunter, W T
Jakobson, R A
Strain, J W
Veitch, J W
Willey, C B I

Elgin

Addison, J
Albiston, E M
Anderson, D J S
Anderson, D M
Attenburrow, A A
Bagnall, R A
Bedford, S J
Beedie, E J A
Blain, A M
Bredell, P M
Brown, D F
Brown, K M
Cameron, M A
Cartwright, B L
Chen, T M C H
Craig, E
Dawson, G A W
Dewar, M E
Duthie, G M
Esson, G A C
Evans, D C
Fell, L F
Findlay, P F
Gammie, H D

Gammie, J W
Gunn, I G
Harper, I
Hart, C L
Hawkins, J L
Henderson, M G
Hodges, A E
Hornsby, C A
Houliston, M D
Hrisha, G S
Johnston, M I
Jones, E A
Langmuir, R M
Lim, M-N
Lowe, R J
McBain, I
MacDonald, J C M
MacDonald, W G
MacEachen, M L
McFarlane, C
McFarlane, D E
Macfarquhar, I A
McIntyre, R
McLauchlan, A J W
MacLeod, R D M
McPherson, A
Maitland, H M
Miller, J D B
Milne, G G
Mitchell, F L
Mobbs, J M
Morrison, G W
Morrison, W M
Morrison, Y A
Murtagh, M
Nash, C H
Navani, S
Nehra, P
Nicol, J W
Pearson, R L
Race, J
Rae, I W
Ritchie, G M
Robertson, J G
Rodger, A B
Sangster, I D
Scott, M J
Simpson, A I
Sinclair, D B
Smith, J R
Stewart, R D M
Taylor, G R
Taylor, J C
Taylor, J S
Tennant, N J
Todd, J O
Trew, J M
Trythall, J
Walker, K J
Welsh, J
Wilson, J T
Wyllie, J H

Elland

Bylina, E P
Clarkson, J E
Cockcroft, G A
Holroyd, J B M
James, T E
Macfarlane, J B
Modgill, V K
Naz, E M
Naz, F
Spencer, S F
Wilkinson, G C
Williams, H M

Ellesmere

Andrews, R B
Greville, E A M
MacGregor, D
Morgan-Jones, R L
Newton, S J
Northmore-Ball, MD
Oakley, D E
Richards, P A
Southern, D A
Wess, J M

Ellesmere Port

Faulks, G
Frazer Cox, M
Powell, R A
Wall, C E
Wearne, J P
Wilkinson, J F

Ellon

Aitken, J E B
Bell, R M R

Brown, P J
Burgess, C S
Burnett, R J
Chisholm, R I
Donaldson, A E
Duncan, J A
Fowler, T M
Hardie, R H
Laing, A G
Mackay, D I
McKerchar, D J
Mackie, L
Morrison, W J
Murphy, P A
Pearson, A R
Penney, G C
Pucci, M J
Rennie, A G R
Riddler, S J
Simpson, I T
Stephen, H J
Sutherland, J F W
Walker, D M

Ely

Ambrose, E R
Aniskowicz, J S
Aylott, C L
Baker, I H
Barltrop, A H
Beer, R W G
Bond, C A
Bucher, T J P
Byrne, M M
Cheng, S E
Coupé, L C
Dixey, J M D
Dober, M H
Douglas, A S
Dunn, A J
England, M
Few, A S
Findlay, S C
Frost, D M
George, A M
Harding, S E
Hobson, J F
Holt, J
Holton, W R
Howard, J E
Howells, D M G
Hughes, J M
Hughes, T C
Kenny, P
King, S L
Lindsay, I D
Lynch, V J
McBryde, C W
McCormack, D H P T
McCorquodale, L J
McHugh, J
Manning, A G V
Marczewski, L Z
Martin, A P
Maurice-Smith, J M
Mee, S E
Merrifield, A J
Mills, C A
Molyneux, A H
Morgan, A M
Mumford, N G
Newrick, C W
Norris, K L
O'Connell, C R W
Partha, J
Ragu, H K S
Shackleton, J R
Smith, H L
Stewart, A J
Stringer, B M
Taylor, S C
Tiwari, I B
Webb, W J S
White, N K
Woods, D G
Young, K M

Emsworth

Allen, P
Atkinson, C L
Baker, N J
Bale, R N
Barnard, R L H
Bateman, J E
Bateman, N D
Bowen, A H
Brooks, E M T
Brown, M M
Carey, L

Collings-Wells, J S
Cowan, C M
Craigie, D M
Crundwell, N B
Cummins, S J G
Dorrian, U T
Edsell, M E G
Farer, C A
Foley, M E M
Gale, C W
Giles, S L
Griffiths, W E G
Harris, A S
Hertzog, J L
Hollis, M J
Ingram, D L
Kelway, S P
Kirkham, P W
Kitchen, C V
Knight, K E
Lawson, A
Levis, R D
McDonald, G E
MacHale, J J
Maile, W B D
Millar, J G B
Mitchell, J D
Mountford, L O
Newman, P M
Nixon, K H
Richardson, I A
Ryland, J M
Seymour-Jones, J A
Seymour, E J
Shannon, C J
Speed, C A
Sussex, J E
Sutherland, I C
Thomas, A L
Thomas, D J
Thomas, P M A
Tibbs, P G
Tilley, E A
Timms, D P
Townsend, A C
Vaughan, R J
Verdon, P E
Vinnicombe, J
Wilkins, P S W
Williams, S M
Wright, I A
Yeld, R O

Enfield

Agwunobi, A O
Akinkunmi, A
Amarin, J O
Amin, N
Andrews, H T T
Appleton, H
Archibald, D A A
Arnold, J A
Atkinson, D W
Attalla, F E
Balachandran, T
Barnes, M A
Barnes, P
Baynes, C
Beeharry, R
Benjamin, L D
Brown, B A
Bryant, C A
Bukhari, N A S
Bull, R K
Bull, T M
Carmi, M A M B
Carrick, J C
Chahal, R
Challis, J H
Chan Kin, T M
Chan, K H
Chang, C T N
Chopra, J
Clark, E
Conacher, R S R
Connaughton, J T
Copland, R F P
Craig, A R
D'Souza, A S
Davies, R H
Day, C J
De Taranto, N E
Devereux, M H
Dias Weerasinha, R N
Dissanayake, H R M
Donnelly, P F
Downes, E G R
Duignan, I J C M
Eldon, H M

Enniskillen

Erkeller-Yuksel, M F
Fajemisin, B A
Farag, M Z M
Fryszman-Fenton, A J
Gardham, J R C
Garland, B
Garner, B J
Gaukroger, M C
Glynn, A
Gocman, M C
Golin, M
Gomes, A N V
Goodspeed, A H
Gopalakrishnan, G
Grace, D L
Griffin, A J
Grock, K K A
Habashi, S
Hadji-Stylianou, R
Hamilton, L W E
Hampton, N R E
Handa, N
Hare, J M S
Harlow, R A
Harvey, D C M
Head, J E
Hinchley, G W
Hindley, C B
Hitchings, S R
Hitchings, V
Howell, D I
Iqbal, A
Jackson, A E
Jackson, R A
James, K K
Jayran Nejad, Y
Jenkins, M G
Jepson, C M
Jones, G R B
Kanse, P T
Kaplan, S A
Karvounis, S-S
Kataria, B
Kearns, A
Keating, P G D
Kelland, P
Kember, M J
Kennedy, H G
Khiroya, R C
Knott, L J
Knowles, R L
Konig, S
Lai, K Y-C
Larkin, S C
Love, S V
Macartney, N J D
McLay, J S
McQueen, J E
Mandersloot, G F
Marks, A S
Martins, S L
Matthews, R F J
Mazumder, R
Meek, D B
Menagé, M J A
Menzies, L J
Mier Jedrzejowicz, A K
Mikhail, H M T
Mok, A W-F
Moosvi, R S
Moran, E
Moran, P A
Morcos, M Y
Morganti, K M
Mummery, R V
Munro, B F
Mussa, M Y
Nagy, B M C
Nduka, S A
Newton, P M
Nichol, W D
Nicholas-Pillai, A
O'Mahony, P H M
Osborne, M J
Palaniappan, S
Panjwani, S
Patel, S R
Pathan, A H
Pavlou, S
Plummer, Y M
Pollock, I
Prout, J R
Rafiq, S M
Rahman, A T M L
Ramanathan, P
Ratnarajah, K
Ravindran, A
Reid, A S
Reid, H A S

Rice, N E
Ridge, A T
Rohan, C F
Roland, M
Rooban, R A
Roux, H J
Rubenstein, I D
Rubenstein, P
Salih, H
Salmon, J R
Sandell, J M
Savage, D E
Scurlock, H J
Shah, A R
Sharkey, J
Shaw, S
Shenouda, N A
Shepherd, H R
Shridhar, S
Sidhu, G S
Simmons, P A M
Sinniah, A T
Soutter, P A M
Spencer, R E
Stanton, M B
Stone, K H
Subanandan, P
Subrahmanyam, P C
Syed, A
Taylor, A R
Taylor, L B
Theivendra, M
Theron, J S
Tolliss, D A R
Tuthill, D P
Valls Ballespi, J
Varatharaj, J
Verma, D K
Walgama, S K L
Walker, R E
Ward, M W N
Warren, S J
Watkin, L A
Weinstein, A F
Whittaker, W E
Williams, M T
Withana, K A
Wood, J J
Worswick, J C
Yeo, E R
Yugambaranathan, K
Yuksel, B

Enniskillen

Abdel Aziz, S I A
Armstrong, J D
Asghar, M M
Auterson, T N
Blake, P N
Bothwell, J E
Boyd, J D
Boyle, C B
Brady-Henry, M B
Brady, M C I
Brady, P J
Caithness, J S
Campbell, M E
Casey, N E
Cassidy, J P
Cathcart, M E H
Cheah, S S
Cody, M W J E
Conneally, P
Connor, E
Cromie, W N
Cunningham, M M
Curran, K
Darling, J R
Day, D E M
Deeny, E D M
Devlin, K F
Dolan, F M
Elliott, M E L
Forster, E M H
Forster, S W H
Frizelle, P C
Gallagher, A B
George, M G
Gilroy, J B
Graham, C W
Groves-Raines, J C
Halahakoon, W L D
Harrold, P F M
Herdman, C G
Jentsch, T
Johnston, J A
Johnston, J M
Keaney, A A M
Kelly, J F

Kerr, D J
Kiernan, T F
King, L J
Kirby, A M
Kirby, J M
Kyle, S G W
Leary, R T
Long, R M
Lynch, P N
McAleer, B G A
McCaffrey, P E
McCaw, C J
McCollam, J
McConville, M E
McCusker, E
McCusker, J A
McDermott, B A
McGowan, P J A
McManus, B M
McManus, T E
Maddock, C A M
Maguire, C J F
Mallon, M J
Marshall, S G
Mellotte, M
Millar, A J D
Montague, J J
Mulhern, F J
Mulholland, J E T
Mulligan, G R
Mulligan, P M
Murphy, L G
Murray, M J
O'Dolan, C A
O'Donohoe, J M
O'Hare, C V
O'Hare, R A
O'Reilly, P J D
Pippet, D J
Porteous, P J
Rahman, M M
Rea, M A
Reidy-Brady, N M
Richey, E E
Rogers, J
Rogers, J P
Scott, M J
Sides, K M
Smyth, M G
Stewart, W E
Strahan, J
Sweeney, C J
Sweeney, K M M
Towell, A
Treacy, P J
Varma, M P S
White, A B
Williams, J R
Young, H K

Epping

Abraham Mathews, A
Amen, A A A
Ashaye, O A
Ashford, A L
Barker, D A V
Barrie, M A
Bolton, P J
Brown, G
Burling, S J
Casaubon Alcaraz, F J
Chapman, R A M
Darcy, J A
Dawkins, R S
Dempsey, E M
Evans, F J H
Gold, J-A
Higham, C
Hill, J D
Hynds, W R G
Jenkins, A W R
John, C E H
Jones, R M
Kopelman, H
Lan Keng Lun, K F
Letcher, R G M
Longton, M A
Longton, R H
Lowry, D M
Mayer, A-P T
Morris, R W
Norman, G A H
O'Connor, D M E
Pradhan, R M
Richards, G J
Richards, J M
Roy, B K
Scott, S C C
Shepherd, D T S

Stanhill, V
Walker, Z
Waller, J F

Epsom

Allum, W H
Badami, A J
Bailey, R D
Baird, J E
Baldwin, M J
Baldwin, S J
Barker, R J
Beach, H
Beadles, W I
Beckaya, A
Bellenger, W S
Bendig, J W A
Bishay, S S
Blewett, M L R
Bonner-Morgan, G R
Bottomley, N
Boughton, P R
Brown, J
Buchan, I C
Bunn, M N
Burkhardt, A
Burton, R H
Canton, L C
Charig, C R
Chen, A W Y
Chen, B
Churchill, M P
Clancy, T
Clark, I D
Clarke, D J
Clarke, G C M
Cleeve, H J W
Cobb, R A
Connolly, F H
Cooper, P J
Coppen, A J
Cowlard, R J
Cunningham, J A
Darlington, L G
Davis, P A
Desborough, J P
Diedericks, R J
Dutta, S
Edwards, J A
El-Dosoky, A M R A
Ellis, C E G
Elrahman, I H A A
English, P M B
Etherington, J
Evans, H C
Ewah, B N
Falkowski, W
Farooqi, M R
Flower, J F
Ford, P N
Free, A J
George, C D
Goddard, R K
Gould, S R
Gregory, A M
Hammond, P J
Harris, D M
Harun, S
Hastle, J A
Hay, G C
Haydon, S C
Hayes, M A
Hayward, A J
Hayward, C M M
Henderson, G A
Hermon, G A
Holbrook, J
Hopkins, G O
Hosegood, J F
Howard, C M
Howlett, D C
Howlett, K A
Hughes, S G
Imms, F J
Irvine, A T
Jayasena, K
Jayawardhana, S R
Jones, D W
Jones, L
Kakumani, V
Katesmark, M
Katiyar, A K
Leaver, D G
Lim, A G
Liyanage, P P
Lord, M E
Lucie-Smith, R E B
Macarthur, H C
McCullough, T K

McFarland, R J
Mackay, C J
McKee, N D
McNeill, D L M
Mahadevan, M
Markose, V M
Matthews, A J
Matthews, T J
Miller, A L
Misch, K J
Mistry, M R
Mitchell, H J
Mitchell, P A
Mitchell, S C
Mok, D W H
Moore, S
Morrell, D C
Morrell, J M
Morton, E E
Narang, K K
Nicholls, J M
Nicholson, S
Nightingale, M D
Obomanu, W A I
Odemuyiwa, O
Omar, M E-D
Orton, J J
Oyston, M G
Pais, W A
Pattinson, C J
Perkins, H H B
Plumley, T A
Pooley, A S
Protheroe, S M
Ranasinha, K W
Ranganath, L R
Rangedara, D C
Ransom, W T M
Ravago, E
Rees, J A
Reynolds, J C
Richardson, T
Richmond, P W
Robb, P J
Roberts, S A
Rollin, A-M
Rollin, H R
Rundle, S K
Salem, N
Samuel, R K G
Satkunanayagam, V
Scarlett, J F
Schramm, L H
Semple, M J
Senhenn, J S A
Sevenoaks, M R
Sevitt, M A
Seymour, A L
Shankar, S
Shanmuganathan, T
Sharpe, A P
Shephard, E A
Sheriff, S
Sheth, T R
Silva, F B
Smith, E E
Sneath, P
Sreetharan, M
Steventon, P N
Stott, R A P
Suleman, S K
Swift, R I
Temple, L N
Thomson, M T
Thornton-Smith, A N
Tom, J P
Totman, M B
Trevan, A C
Twyman, R S
Walker, J L
Walker, R M H
Ward, C
Waters, F M
Watts, R
White, M C
Wijewardena, H C
Wilson, J H
Wilson, R
Wormley, R L
Wright, M
Yeboah, O K
Zafer, I M Z
Zaki, S

Erith

Arnaot, M R Z
Browning, S M
Chopra, R K
Dhatariya, R C

Fok, W W F
Franklin, V
Ghosh, M H
Kailey, S S
Le Geyt, J D
McIntyre, M R
Mehrbakhsh, A
Nandra, K S
Nguyen, H
O'Neill-Byrne, K
Patel, V S
Roberts, P J
Sullivan, L F

Erskine

Afuakwah, J K
Aikman, M
Carlyle, J E
Griffith, D B
Hanley, T-A
Harris, C A
Harris, L J W
McFadyen, T
McGavigan, M E
Meiklejohn, D J
Nsofor, B I
Stewart, J B
Tabony, W M
Tarrant, P D

Esher

Ainslie, D
Al-Jezairy, A I K
Andersen, U H
Barnardo, A T
Barton, F L
Bates, T D
Bodger, D H
Breathnach, A S
Bull, B I
Busby, E R
Bushell, B W M
Bustamante Sainz, S
Cansick, J C
Crockford, A
Cross, J M
Dance, P J
Dixon, M H N
Evans, J C
Fawcett, B K
Forrester, P C
Franks, Q B
Fyfe, A L A
Gannon, M C
Gavins, P W
Gibson, I D
Goldsack, A M
Hall, C A
Hamilton-Davies, C
Hancock, J M
Harding, D G R
Harper, C A
Hendry, J A
Hirsch, P O
Holden, A M
Hoy, A M
Hui, F C
Hutton, M D C
Johnson, P K
Kamboj, A S
Karim, A
Kearsey, S Y
Leach, J B
Leach, R D
Leary, R M
Lingwood, M M
Looi, D B-E
Low, I H
Lucas, C F
McGinn, O M
Main, A C
Marsh, M E
Mearing-Smith, T M
Moores, N S
Munnelly, J T
Munro, N M
Mustapha, N M
North-Smith, M H
Owen, P J
Patel, H F
Radford, M J
Rhodes, E L
Robinson, P D
Rodgers, F M
Sanchez, M-J
Shine, A M
Sim, H G
Smith, G B
Spooner, J B

Eyemouth

Stanbury, R M
Steel, C N
Stewart, A
Thorns, A R
Wales, E
Wilkinson, E K
Williams, M S I
Wright, T S
Younger, K A

Etchingham
Cowey, A J
Fairhurst, J A
Gilbert, C P
Knight, H C
McKay, K B
O'Neill, D F
Packham, B A
Packham, D A
Walters, G
Woodgate, J E

Evesham
Ashton, R M
Astley, W C
Bartholomew, J
Bartholomew, M
Bennett, E
Burton, G
Cox, M J
Cross, H M
Cross, R L
D'Arcy, C M R
Doran, J S
Edwardes, J A
Grant, D S
Grant, S C
Gregorowski, L F
Harris, D A
Henry, I J
Herold, D C
Jackson, N R
Johnson, S J
Jones, D A
Jones, S J
Lloyd, J H
Logan, P J
Manuel, J
Milner, J C G
Nava, G
Ounsted, C M
Pollitt, P G H T
Richards, L E J
Serenyi, A G
Shore, K M
Smith, I L T
Swindlehurst, A L
Wolfe, J
Wright, J A

Exeter
Abbood, K H
Abdel Rahman, I E
Adams, S J
Adcock, C J
Adey, J
Adkins, C T
Alcock, N S
Amin, R
Anderson, R J
Anthony, P P
Arshi, H
Austin, P M
Ayres, R C S
Bailey, A M
Baines, R
Baker, P J S
Ballard, P K
Barnes, A P
Barnes, S L
Barnett, A M
Bartlett, S J
Barton, J S
Bayliss, C R B
Beaman, M
Beasley, P
Beck, W A
Berry, C B
Berry, J A
Beynon, R P
Bhanji, S
Bhatia, N
Bisson, M J
Bisson, P G
Black, S E
Bland, R
Blewett, A E
Bliss, P
Boaden, R W
Bogdanovic, M D
Bolden, F M
Bolden, K J
Booth, R A D
Bradley-Smith, G C
Bradley, M K
Bradley, N C A
Branton, D W
Brennan, J
Brightwell, A P
Briscoe, M H
Broad, G J
Brown, A M E
Brown, W S
Browne, S R
Bunkall, S C
Bunker, T D
Bussey, A L
Butler, N G P
Cahill, M J
Calder, M W
Campbell, W B
Campling, J M
Cantrell, G L
Carless, A G M
Channing, E W M
Chapman, O G
Choon, S C
Cichon-Feldman, B M
Clamp, A R
Claridge, M T
Clarke, H C
Clarke, T A P
Clarke, T J
Clarke, W L
Clarkson, K G
Clarkson, R L
Clarkson, W B
Clay, A
Clements, C L
Clunie, J M J
Coleman, J R
Coleman, L J
Colley, N V
Collyer, D R
Colmer, J P
Colville, A
Conn, D A
Cook, M E M
Cooper, M J
Coote, J M
Cope, N J
Corkill, R J
Cox, P J A
Crowe, C A S
Cumming, J E
Dainton, J N
Daly, A J
Daneshmend, T K
Daniel, S
Daniel, V
Danin, J C
Davis, J B
Dawrant, J M
Dawrant, M L
Day, C J E
De Boer, R C
De Carteret, S L
Dean, J W
Debeer, P
Devaraj, V S
Dick, C L
Donovan, J F
Douglas, A M
Drewe, C D
Dudbridge, S B
Dunn, J M
Edwards, J M
Edwards, J R
Eggleton, J D P
Elzik, C S
Ernst, E
Eskander, R I
Evans, A
Evans, L J
Evans, P H
Evans, S E
Ewings, S A
Fahmy, F S
Faircloth, H O
Featherby, E A
Fenwick, G M
Ferguson, A D
Ferguson, B M
Fernando, G C A
Ffooks, O O F
Finlay, D T
Fiorentini, T
Forber, K W
Foster, E A
Foster, W P
Fox, J H
Francis, J G
Fredriksson, S T
Freer, T H
Fuest, M
Fursdon, D M
Fursdon, P
Gallwey, P L G
Gandhi, M M
Gardner-Thorpe, C C
Gardner-Thorpe, C
Gardner-Thorpe, S M R
Gardner, N H N
Garland, J M
Garrard, O N I
Garth, R J N
Gilbert, J
Giles, S H
Goh, K L
Goodman, A G
Gopal, R
Greenwood, B P
Gutowski, N J
Halford, J G
Hall, G H
Hall, M S
Halpin, D M G
Hamad, S N
Hamilton-Wood, C
Hamilton, W T
Hampshire, M S B
Hanington, S J
Harington, J M
Harries, S R
Harrill, J G M
Harrison, A J
Hart, A M
Hart, J C C
Hattersley, A T
Hawkins, G F C
Heal, P C
Helliar, N H
Heming, J R
Hemsley, A G
Henry, C M T
Herdman, J
Heron, W C
Hewin, D F
Hicks, T
Hill, R F
Hilton, D C W
Hoey, P R
Holding, J
Holman, H M
Holman, R A
Holme, C O
Honan, W P
Hong, A
Hooper, D C
Hopwood, B C
Horton, I A
Howard, I T
Hudson, A J R
Hudson, A J
Hughes, A G
Hulin, S J
Irvin, T T
Jabarin, Z S
Jack, A
Jacob, J S H
Jacoby, R K
James, M A
Jameson Evans, D C
Janssen, A
Jefferies, A E
Jefferiss, C D
Jeffreys, O M E
Johnson, D S
Jolles, S R A
Jolliffe, P H G
Jones, A M B
Jones, G B
Joyner, M V
Joyner, S E
Kay, P H
Kealey, L E
Keen, C E
Keenan, J
Keith, J R
Keith, M S
Kemp, A M
Kent, E M
Kernick, D P
Key, H
Khanna, R M E
King, C F
Kinsella, D C
Knight, J W H
Knox, A J S
Knox, C S J
Lamb, P D
Lang, M R M
Langley, G E
Lawn, E N
Lee, A
Lee, A J
Lee, R W H
Leeder, D S
Leete, R J
Leger, B J
Lillicrap, J S
Ling, R S M
Lloyd, G K
Lloyd, J K
Lloyd, K R
Lloyd, M W
Loden, A E
Lowings, E A
Lydon, A P M
McBay, I W
McClelland, L C
McConville, R J
McCorkindale, R A
McCrindle, D C
McCullagh, P J
Mackenzie, K G P
McKinnel, S R
McKnight, D O
McLaren, S
McLauchlan, C A J
McLean, E K
McLean, M D
Macleod, K M
McNinch, A W
Magill, H G
Malim, P F
Malloch, D K
Malone, T J L
Mann, R S C
Marshall, F P F
Marshall, M N
Martin, M R
Meredith, M J
Merrick, A W
Midgley, A K
Miller, J R
Mitchell, S J
Mole, M R
Montgomery, C D
Moodie, S J
Moody, R H
Moore, G J M
Morgan, G M
Morgan, M S
Morgan, W I C
Moss, R C S
Mossop, G W E J
Moxon, G W
Munn, J
Murdock, J R
Musson, F A
Mynn Htyn, Dr
Nicholls, A J
Northover, R P
Norton, M R
O'Sullivan, M E
Oades, P J
Onyett, R M
Orme, R C E
Orrell, R F E
Osborne, P B
Owen, M R
Packer, T F
Pagliero, K M
Pallett, J M
Palmer, H J G
Palmer, J H
Parker, Y-M A
Parkyn, T M
Pearce, V R
Pearse, A G E
Pearse, E
Pearson, S W
Penn, S A
Pepper, B J
Perkins, J H
Perriss, B W
Plummer, H
Pocock, M A J
Pocock, R D
Powis, R A
Purday, J P
Quicke, J
Ragbir, M
Ragi, E F E
Rains, S G H
Ramell, M D
Reaves, C S
Reaves, E C
Rees, J E G
Regan, J M
Renninson, J N
Renouf, A C D
Riad, H N
Rich, P M
Richards, F G
Richardson, D E M
Richardson, J S
Ridler, B M F
Ridley, A R
Riordan, T
Roberts, C J
Roberts, F L
Robinson, T J
Rogers, A R
Rolfe, M G
Rosser, V C E
Rossiter, A
Round, A P
Rowland, C G
Russell, D J
Rutter, J A
Saddler, J M
Salzmann, M B
Sandhar, B K
Savage, P E A
Saxby, P J
Schoolmeesters, B
Schranz, P J
Scott, A P B
Sen, J
Sharpe, D P
Sharpe, I T
Shaw, D B
Sheehan, D J
Sheldon, C D
Sheldon, J C
Shewell, P K
Simcock, P R
Simpson, J H
Simpson, R H W
Smallwood, N N
Smith, A E
Smith, L D R
Smith, M J
Smith, R C
Spencer, H
Spyer, G
St. Johnston, C F
Stead, J W
Steele, R J F
Stewart, M M
Stone, C A
Stott, M A
Stowell, G M
Sturley, R H
Sturrock, G D
Sweeney, K G
Talbot, N J
Taylor, R L
Teasdale, A R
Telford, R J
Theobald, J A
Thomas, G
Thomas, K M J
Thomas, R D
Thompson, J F
Thomsitt, J
Thorne, C P
Tillett, R I L
Timms, J W M
Timperley, A J
Toy, E W
Travers, P R
Tribukait, U
Tripp, J H
Turner-Warwick, R T
Turner, C
Turner, R J
Turnpenny, P D
Van Nimmen, B
Van Staden, G N
Varian, J A
Vercoe, M G S
Vercoe, S
Von Arx, O A
Vowles, K D J
Vowles, M
Walker, A C
Walker, J A
Walker, J Y
Wallen, G D P
Wallis, M M
Walters, A J
Warin, A P
Warin, J M
Watkins, P F A
Watson, M B
Watson, T M
Weatherley, C R
Webber, J E
Weekes, A J
West, J H
West, P G
White, A R
Wilkie, J R
Wilkins, L K
Williams, A
Wilson, I H
Withers, N J
Withey, J M
Wood, J M
Woodcock, S M
Woods, A J
Wormald, P N
Wray, G
Wride, J P
Yau, S Z M
Yick, D C K

Exmouth
Argent, J D
Beed, M J
Blyth, R I K
Clements, P W
Codd, K L
Davis, J A
De Kretser, A J H
Debenham, T R
Disney, M E
Dixon, J T
Donald, R G
Doyle, M K
Enright, H M
Fewings, P E
Garwood, N
Gooding, S M D
Hepburn, J A C
Hopkins, R J
Hull, M G
Johnson, M J
Johnston, N F A
Jones, J M
Kay, S R
Laney, D R
Lewis, A P
Lupprian, K G
May, C J
Mulvihill, H E
Nicholson, M E J
Nicholson, T F
Price, H J
Price, S R
Quinn, P M
Richmond, G O
Ring, S M
Ross, S D J
Sanderson, L
Scott, C L
Spiers, D R
Stubbings, C A
Stubbings, S M
Telfer, J R
Urwin, K
Ward, S

Eye
Chase, D R
Colley, S P
Cooper, P H
Eckersley, E
Ellis-Jones, M
Goodge, B M
Holmes, S J
Innes, J R F
Macmillan, F K
Morris, J A C
Read, G M
Thirlwell, C
Vaudrey, B
Vicary, D J
Wilson, J M
Wright, C E

Eyemouth
Dorward, I M
Dorward, J A
Fenty, M A
Harrison, M F
Laidlaw, J P
Macdonald, J A
Mason, A P
Nicoll, A M
Nicoll, F J

Fairbourne

Swan, I L H
Worters, A R

Fairbourne
Williams, F W

Fairford
Benzie, A S
Bingham, C
Frazer, D C
Gardiner, A E
Knights, M J G
Lunney, D C
Sabourin, A C

Fakenham
Bennett, D J N
Browne, K W
De Marco, P
Evans, A M
Fleming, L B
Johnson, N A
Joshi, M
Nichols, J B
Reinhold, P H
Taylor, A B W

Falkirk
Acheson, H F
Ainsworth, J H S
Anderson, S W
Ark, S S
Arthur, I S
Ball, C M
Barnes, S
Barth, C
Bennett, K M E
Birch, A D J
Borg Grech, V
Briggs, E W W
Broome, I J
Brown, E
Brown, H G
Brown, J S
Bruce-Smith, J
Bryce, J C
Brzeski, M S
Buchanan, L M
Casero Alonso, F J
Clafferty, R A
Close, S A
Colvin, J W
Cordeiro, N J V
Crawford, G
Crichton, F J B
Crookston, A
Crowe, A M
Cusworth, E J
Dodds, G
Duncan, P L
Edwards, G P
Edwards, S J
Evans, S M
Ewing, R G
Ewins, C M
Fairgrieve, B D
Fairley, L F
Fischbacher, E
Gardner, H W
Gilbert, J
Gilbert, R A F
Gillespie, J F
Gillespie, M D
Glen, K A
Grant, K A
Hargreaves, A D
Harris, N W S
Harvey, J M
Haywood, H A
Henderson, G I R
Hendrie, G J
Hogarth, E D A
Holliday, M P
Howland, N J
Hunter, I
Jack, M E
Johnston, V J
Kerr, G D
Kerr, I M
Khurana, C
Khurana, I K
Krosnar, A
Krosnar, S C
Laurie, G A
Law, R G
Lehany, G P
Leonard, J D
Lim, J A
Lim, P C-K
Luke, W M
McCabe, E M
McCall, A C
McDonald, A
Macdonald, I S
MacFlynn, G M P
McGhee, C
McGlynn, J M
MacGregor, I G
McInnes, G K
McLean, G S
McManners, J
MacNab, M S P
McSorley, P D
Maguire, N M
Martin, M G
Merrick, B M
Middlemiss, S A
Millar, E
Millar, J S
Miller, P A R
Miller, W D W
Morrison, D
Morrison, R A
Moses, P C
Multani, S S
Murdoch, P S
Nadeem, R D
Naismith, D A
Nimmo, T W
Ogilvie, C K
Oram, M C H
Orr, K M
Osborne, C J
Peddie, M M
Peden, N R
Ramsay, D M
Ramsay, K
Reekie, A E M
Reekie, E H
Reid, J
Robb, H M
Robertson, A A
Robertson, A
Salatian, M
Sandilands, L J
Scott, A D
Scougal, I J
Shanks, H A C
Shields, M F
Smillie, M W
Smith, R C
Stewart, J D
Stewart, M P D
Thomson, R C G
Toop, W J
Turner, P
Underwood, G H
Waldron, S M
Westfield, M B
White, W G
Whitelaw, C A
Wright, S C
Yacob, N Y

Falmer
Cohen, J

Falmouth
Barwell, T E
Blundell, J A T
Burnett, P
Camm, C E
Cheetham, C E
Clover, A M
Collins, J R
Corbett, A C
Davies, S W V
Davis, G W
Dommett, P G
Downey, A
Downey, K S
Grais, M
Griffin, M
Hichens, S M
Hindley, F
Hyland, J
James, R D G
Jones, H
Killeen, D M
Lester, A A
Macdonald, L J
McGhie, A S
MacGregor, R G S
Miller, D G
Morris, M
Price, P E
Proctor, I R D
Reeves, M A
Roberts, A B

Roberts, C E P
Roberts, P
Rotheray, A D
Rowe, A J
Ryder, G H
Sage, F J
Sellwood, K
Sellwood, N H
Shepperd, M J
Shirley, M
Siddall, H S C
Simcock, A D
SimcOck, D E
Sindell, J A
Slater, P D
Stacpoole, H A
Thomas, D K
Thomas, J K
Timmins, W L
Wight, V L
Williams, I E I
Willis, T J

Fanworth
Burn, J L

Fareham
Allen, N J
Ashton, R E
Baldock, N E
Barnard, K D
Barr-Taylor, P
Bass, B H
Bayliss, S G
Bellenger, N G
Bellenger, R A
Bostock, J F
Brims, F J H
Carling, J R
Carling, W H
Chaderton, N H
Chatwin, H C
Chaudhuri, S
Chilvers, D M
Christie, I G
Clark, A D
Clark, R C
Clarkson, S J
Coleman, H
Colquhoun Flannery, W
Coote, A L
Crowley, M
Daoud, J B
Diggens, S E
Dixon, K E
Douglas, T G C
Dover, R W
Du Feu, G J C
Dunbar, D A
Dunton, A K N
Dunton, M J
Durrani, A
Durrant, D A E
Ellis, E L
Evans, S A
Farr, A G
Foggitt, A C
Foot, J L
Franklen-Evans, M U
Gill, P K
Gonem, M N H
Gordon, A C
Griffiths, S J
Hahn, H J A
Harley, J E
Harris, F E
Henry, C
Hillam, G H
Hollinghurst, D
Hopkins, P N
Howell, R D
Hoxey, K L A
Hughes, R M
Jackson, A R
Jonas, M M
Jones, C
Jordan, B L
Kershaw, R
Kershaw, S
Kyd, K L
Lambert, F R
Lambert, V M J
Larmer, S D
Larson, A G
Lowe-Ponsford, F L
Lusznat, R-M G
MacAdam, R C A
McLean, A D

McMillan, J A
Mears, H J
Moon, J A
Moon, J R A
Moore, A L
Munden, A J
Murrison, A W
Mushens, E J
Nagvekar, V
Nelson, R
O'Byrne, J J
O'Connell, W J
O'Grady, J C
Ormsby, J M
Packman, C C
Page, K M
Pai, K S
Paterson, A J
Pechal, A J
Polson, R G
Potiphar, D W
Prosser, J G S
Prout, W G
Quarry, D P
Rayner, S A L
Richards, P L
Robins, S J
Ronayne, K L
Ross, R J
Samarajiwa, H K
Schopp, M J
Sewell, N B
Shaw, G D
Shaw, K M
Shepherd, T H
Sims, J S
Sinclair, D J
Sirr, H C R
Smallwood, S H
Sommerville, G P
Sotheran, W J
Southern, K J H
Stewart, M D
Swanson, N C P
Tandy, J C
Taylor, A V
Taylor, M E
Tenters, M T
Thomas, R C
Tibble, H C
Toleman, S E
Topham, L G
Tottle, S
Tucker, A J
Wade, N R
Walmsley, B H
Walmsley, T
Ward, C T
Ward, T P
Warner, J R
Webster, E M
Wolpe, A P
Yeung, E S T
Zorab, W J

Faringdon
Bartholomew, G J
Cartwright, S R
Chesterton, L J
Craighead, I B
Douglas, A M R
Erskine, S P E
Gardner, S G
Hatcher, H J
Heanley, C P
Holdsworth, F E
Humphreys, L M
Last, S E M
Pang, E N-O
Pinches, P J E
Scott-Brown, G
Stenhouse, J N
Stewart, B J A
Warner, M D
Watters, M P R
Williamson, L

Farnborough
Ahmed, M A
Barnard, S A
Beck, S C
Bellamy, R C T
Boorman, S R
Caird, G R
Carvalho, A
Cave, A M
Curran, A
Cusack, C F
Damms, M M

Davies, J W
De Verteuil, J A
Draper, M R
Draper, P D
Dyson, E H
Eggeling, I T
Fairbairn, O J
Ferguson, N R
Foster, H
Gibbons, A N
Hargreaves, U
Headley, C A
Heywood, S A
Hughes, N J
Kay, W D
Kayll, J N
Kimber, J R E
Linton, L S K
Linton, S P
Lyall, H
Maclay, W P
Marshall, C B
Martin, F X
Martin, T E
Micklethwaite, G
Nejo, T A
Opie, N J
Poots, D F J
Prior, A J
Ramachandran, K
Reid, J E
Sales, N R
Sarvesvaran, J S
Sarvesvaran, R
Simon, J W
Smyth, M
Spicer, D D M
Stack, M M
Stott, J R R
Stuart, I M
Sumner, T L
Sutherland, I A
Tanner, K J
Toms, M E
Vakil, P A
Walshe, G M
Welch, R A
Whitcher, H W
Willoughby, C M

Farnham
Abbas, T
Adams, P J
Ainsworth, C A
Ainsworth, R W
Aldridge, A J
Allan, J R
Anderson, J T
Austin, A J
Bandara, I S
Beare, B C
Bird, K L
Blagden, S P
Blundell, F J
Bourne, R R A
Boydell, J H
Braithwaite, J M
Brown, D
Burton, S L
Byren, J C
Callaghan, A W
Carriere, G
Carter, J W
Carvill, J M
Chadha, A-N C
Christmas, A R
Clarke, S
Collier, F I
Cothay, D M H H
Coull, J T
Davidson, A F
Davidson, E S
Davies, S J M
Davies, W G
Dempster, J B
Diaper, E D J
Elliott, A J
Elliott, A J
Elwood, J S
Evans, C R
Evans, M E
Evans, R N
Fahmy, A I
Fawcett, H F
Fawcett, W J
Felix, R H
Fergus, M C
Fisher, N J
Fisher, R L

Fox-Russell, P M
Fozard, J R
Giles, P R
Gomez, J R
Gooding, A
Govan, J A A
Gudgeon, J E A
Guy, M P
Harrison, J G M
Haskins, T D
Head, F F
Henry, D O
Hodgson, M C
Holmes, B J
Holt, D I
Hoy, C H A
Hurrell, F C
Ibrahim, A J
Ibrahim, I K
Inman, S E
Jagger, D B
Jenkins, S L
Johnson, P A
Joiner, I M
Kelleher, M F H
King, D M
Laidlaw, I J
Lallemand, R C
Lambert, P M
Lynch, N P
MacAdam, A D
McClay, A O
Macfarlane, H D
Mackenzie-Ross, R K
McLeod, C D
Massouh, H
May, W J
Mehta, M K
Mendus-Edwards, E
Meyer, J S B
Milligan, G M
Milne, C H C
Moore, J W A
Morris, C B
Narula, Y P
Newell Price, J C
Newell Price, S R
O'Donnell, H
O'Donnell, J J
O'Dowd, C E
Ody, C L M
Palfrey, E L H
Parker, P M
Partridge, R J
Payne, M J
Phillips, E H D
Powell, L J
Price, R D
Pritchard, M C
Pryke, J R
Quin, M M
Quin, N E
Raw, A J A
Regan, K J
Ridley, P J
Rishworth, V C
Roberts, H J M
Robinson, P C
Russell, C J
Russell, M J M
Rutter, K R P
Sackwood, S
Salzmann, M M
Scott-Perry, S J
Scott, J M
Scriven, J M
Shelford, G C O
Smyth, E H J
Spink, M
Standring, A F
Straiton, J M
Sturdy, M L L
Sushila, S
Swage, T H
Tibbott, C W
Walker, A A
Walker, J
Wallace, I W
Walter, L S
Way, M
Whelan, R J H
White, D G
Whittingham, M A
Wood, B G
Woollam, V A M
Youngs, S-L E C L

Faversham
Barnes, A D

Frinton-on-Sea

Bennett, A M H
Capoore, H S
Chopra, G
Chopra, M S
Crofts, N F
Curry, R D
Cwynarski, M T
Dawson-Bowling, P R
Edney, R J
Everest, N J
Hodgkiss, R V
Kesson, R A
Knowles, P A
Logan, L C
Lynch, C G M
Lynch, M A
Macpherson, R B
Mendel, D
Moore, D J
Moore, J E
Potter, V J
Reichhelm, T
Scarlett, A J
Taylor, A J
West, A G
Wood, S
Wyeth, S W

Felixstowe

Baluch, C J
Barker, S B
Beaton, K C
Bennett, J
Bostock, A D
Clarke, B M G
Craner, M J
Davenport, R A
De Cleen, M
Feltwell, S R J
Forde, H H
Holloway, G J T
McKee, W B
McMurray, J
Moon, D N L
Pearce, K W
Powell, K U L
Reed, T J
Reid, I R D
Rowe, F J
Sherlock, A
Silovsky, K
Sudell, W A
Tempest, L C
Watson, P
Youngman, P R

Feltham

Amarasinghe, A R
Anderson, I R
Aswani, G T
Ayala Gonzalez, A
Bhullar, B K
Chopra, S
Dagg-Heston, R
Ghosh, A K
Gill, P S
Gunathilaka, H S
Howes, N R
Hussain, T
Hutchings, M W
Kotian, P D
Lynch, C M
McInnes, E G
Malik, T Y
May, R D
Meagher, M A
Mecci, Z H
Moran, J R
Muzafer, M H
Navani, L
O'Connor, J B
Patel, V N
Rosten, B M D
Rosten, M H
Scopes, I
Sen, S K
Stent, V M
Takeda, S
Winayak, V K

Ferndale

Banerjee, P
Dutta, R
Guhaniyogi, S B
Lloyd, M
Nath, K
Rahman, M
Sengupta, S

Ferndown

Adams, L A
Adlington, B
Ah Kine, P K
Barcellos, A A
Bennett, S F
Blackmore, J M S
Chippindale, L
Crook, S M
Davenport, E J
Green, R K
Jenkins, N M W
Ladd, J E
Laishley, R F
Liebling, P O
Luckie, M J
McPhail, A L
Mallett, R
Molina Navarro, C
Paine, D H D
Pilling, P J
Rees, C R
Sander, P N
Sarwar-E-Alam, A K M
Timberlake, T

Ferryhill

Cadigan, P
Denton, M
Drew, S C
Hall, N A
MacDougall, B K
Merson, P J
Moore, H E
Oakenfull, A G P
Orlandi, M
Schneeloch, B
Stevenson, G
Tijsseling, A C
Welsh, H
Willis, D M

Ferryside

Griffiths, D R
Jenkins, D M G
O'Donnchadha, B P

Filey

Ablett, J J L
Donovan, A G
Garnett, J F P
Hazledine, C
Hinson, D S
Hunt, P
McIlroy, R J
Meeson, M D
Nunn, B R
O'Leary, G
Pawson, M E
Richardson, D L
Shepherd, C M
Skitt, B
Valentine, D A
Wynands, R W A

Fishguard

Bushell, A C
Chapman, P J
Davies, D B
Davies, N G
Dunn, D M
Evans, H D
Halstead, J
Lewis, E H
MacGeoch, C M
Owen, D N H

Fivemiletown

Berney, A G
McKeagney, K E
McKibbin, C
Rutledge, E M

Fleet

Arscott-Barber, J A
Aubrey, D R
Barker, S S
Barnes, T C
Basher, M J S
Beal-Preston, R M C
Benson, A P
Bhabutta, R K
Billinge, V A
Bricknell, M C M
Bromley, C L
Clark, N A D
Clarke, S A
Coombe, D H
Darbyshire, I N
De Glanville, T B
Fraser, J H

Garsed-Bennet, D J C
Gillespie, A
Goldring, S T
Hamann, J C H
Hannington-Kiff, J G
Healey, J C
Hector, R M
Heffernan, S
Henderson, K
Higgins, C J C
Hoare, C F
Hoare, J M
Howard, P
King, S
Lees, L A
McElligott, H F
McOwan, M M
McVeigh, C M
Michel, A B
Moore, H S
Murphy, J F D
Parkinson, K A
Pearson, I B
Prior, A R J
Reader, D C
Roper, J
Saxton, T N
Sharp, A L H
Slater, J C
Swift, M A
Taylor, A H
Tilly, H V
Tollett, B J
Townsend, L Z
Waters, R J
Webb, J F
Weeks, D C
Wickenden, P D

Fleetwood

Ali, S M
Armour, A L
Carpenter, P G
Clark, R J
Ewart, C H
Fairhead, S
Grenier, H P
Hardwick, J L
Hockings, M
Kirk, S J
Natrajan, K
Page, M J S
Ramesh, C
Rowley, E
Singleton, N J
Smyth, R A C
Spencer, M
Tse Sak Kwun, P C
Whiteside, A
Wilde, S
Wilson, M J

Flint

Barnard, W K H
Cochrane-Smith, R A W
Daniel, P
Davies, C P
Fenner, J N
Kapoor, J C
Latif, F
MacKirdy, J E
Mathews, E D
Rehman, Z-U

Fochabers

Budge, C C
Cameron, D J C
Ewing, C P
Kennedy, A-M
McNie, H
Pakenham, R W
Pimley, S K
Scott, C R
Sutherland, G P

Folkestone

Allen, K E
Amin, Y Y
Arulanantham, N Y
Attara, G A
Bailey, A D
Beckett, M E
Birks, E J
Blaxland, N N
Blinston Jones, M P
Burrow, D E M
Calver, G D
Catto, C E
Counsell, G F

Cox, M C L
Dallin, V J
Deane, A M
Degorrequer-Griffith, T B H
Evans, D P
Ewer, F
Ewing, D A
Farrow, D J
Felstead, S J
Fernandes, M A A M
Findlay, G H
Goodman, J L
Goodwin, A M
Goodwin, D P
Govier, E A
Heffernan, J
Hossain, M A
Immelman, R E
Inglis, P M
Jackson, D
Jackson, R G M
Jedrzejewski, J A
Jequier, P W
Jones, E R L
Jones, S M
Keown, D
Khine-Smith, M C K
McComiskey, C A
McGregor, B L
McPartlin, J F
Madar, R I
Maddaford, K J
Mallett, E
Marlowe, M J
Mathers, R P
Maung Yay, Dr
Montgomery, D
Morris, I J L
Musselwhite, D H
Neild, V S
Nicholson, G M
Pool, K R S
Rand, D F
Read, P
Ribet, L P
Roberts, G A
Robertson-Ritchie, H
Sheikh, N A
Sholl, P P
Simpson, E
Sudheer, K
Trace, T
Veenhuizen, P G
Veenhuizen, P A
White, K J

Fordingbridge

Ashby, J B B
Atherton, W G
Bailey, D S G M
Barron, J N
Bennett, B
Buckley, C V
Cooke, S S
Creek, I M
Davies, M C R
Dodds, G
Gannon, M J
Hensel, C M
Hensel, J A
Hughes-Davies, T H
Knight, C E
Kuttler, A D S
Lobb, M
Mccallum, M
Marshall, J R
Matcham, N J
Morris, H J L
Newstead, S M
Ogg, A J
Percy, H G
Ridley, N A
Shephard, N W
Smedley, G T
Smith, S
Staunton, E B
Straton, R H
Straton, T
Vickery, M H
Wardley, J R
Watson, S L
Whitehead, M N

Forest

Jamison, D G
Neubert, F R
Reilly, S J

Forest Row

Aitken, H W
Bjorn, J M
Carnegie, G F M
Del Mar, A R
Gaillemin, O S G R
Gray, C R W
Josephson, J-M
Martin, D A
Miller, S A
Twentyman, L R

Forfar

Beveridge, J B
Burnett, W
Burt, D P
Cohen, C
Cruickshank, L D
Davies, F J M M
Devereux, S L M
Dick, P R
Dixon, A
Edmond, H L
Edwards, A I
Erskine, F M
Houghton, A
Houghton, E S
Kerr, F M
Laidlaw, H L
Lawrie, J A
McAreavey, M J
McAughtrie, A E
MacCallum, K S
MacDonald, A J A
McPhail, I J
McWilliam, L S
Milne, D
Mitchell, L D N
Morris, A H M
Nolan, J A C
Peel, W J
Pennie, D D
Peterkin, C W G
Raitt, N
Smith, D M
Smith, W T M
Wake, D J
Watts, M C
Woodroffe, G C
Woodroffe, S A

Forres

Anderson, E
Anderson, J A
Angel, H R M
Barr, E J
Bates, A
Bayliss, P A
Bone, C E
Carstensen, O
Cousins, M A
Devlin, B J
Fraser, A S
Govan, G
Hay, W
Hutchison, S
Johnson, D S
Kennedy, R J
Kerr, D
McMullen, B J
Mead, D E
Morgan, H M
Paterson, F L
Renwick, A A
Roy, L K M
Sabiston, M A
Sneddon, D T
Stevenson, D
Stewart, R J
Thomson, A S
Troup, D I
Wallace, J
Willetts, S J

Fort Augustus

Farmer, I D
Hunter, W
Skeoch, J E

Fort William

Baggallay, A J
Douglas, J D M
Foxley, M E M
Goodall, J A D
Irving, E W
Lachlan, G W
Lachlan, M
Leeson-Payne, C E S
Leeson-Payne, C G
McArthur, C A

Macdonald, D
MacDonald, E C
McKay, J
Mackintosh, D J
Massie, A
Merry, E C
Munro, D J
Robinson, C
Roy, H L
Roy, M
Scott, D A
Sedgwick, D M
Shirley, J
Smith, A D
Tangney, D J
Tregaskis, B F

Fortrose

Beasley, R A
Blair, J W
Blair, R G
Fraser, U S
Howes, J A
Imrie, A H
Lloyd, N M
MacGregor, A M
MacIver, E M
Robb, A L
Robertson, J W
White, S M

Fowey

Causey, G
Coombs, J R
Hamilton, M H
Luther, A M
Mann, A J
Middleton, A
Nyman, V A
Ross-Mawer, J H R
Skeens, E M
Skeens, E C
Skerrett, F D
Waldron, J W
Waldron, M J
Willcox, C H

Fraserburgh

Beattie, A G
Bichan, R M
Crockett, C S
Dick, M J W
Duthie, R M
Forbes, W
Fowler, H M
Gordon, G S
Kinnon, J F
Lee-Mason, F V A
Logan, R M
McLeman, D
McPherson, J R
Massie, R R
Murray, R S M
Packham, G B
Smith, A R
Steele, W M
Strachan, G M
Tweedie, D M
Watt, A N
Wisley, A B

Freshwater

Barrett, A R
Magee, K J
Marshall, J C
Moffat, W C
Scivier, A
Sheard, P H W
Thomson, G E
White, D H
Whitmore, J L

Frimley

Hendrickse, A D
Johnstone, AJ

Frinton-on-Sea

Badock, G B
Clark, G A
Davies, J S
Davies, N M
Ellis, E W W
Elvin, G H
Exworth, D B
Fludder, V
Forrai, G L
Hamilton-Paterson, J
Harrison, I D
Learmont, D
McMullen, H L
Moore, G S

Frizington

Shiers, D
Slade, M G
Stubbs, A
Stubbs, V M
Wall, M T
Williams, H O

Frizington

Donald, C
Graham, E
Jackson, A
McKay, W G
Watkinson, L N

Frome

Begley, M D
Blacklidge, R D
Booth, A C
Bungay, D M
Chesterfield, M P
Clacey, R P
Colville, J F
Devlin, E M
Ellis, C J
Ellis, J A J
Griffiths, R L
Gumbley, M
Hall, C L
Henderson, V E
Holden, P E
Hunt, M A
Jelly, J R
Joy, D
Kenyon, R C
Kingston, H M
Knight, F J
MacGregor, C
May, P A
Merry, T L
Millar, J M
Moxon, J E U
Muscat, S
Rawlins, D C
Scheurmier, N I M
Scotchman, F G V
Sherrington, P
Taylor, J C
Vose, M A
Whitehead, N F

Gaerwen

Bowden, D F
Davidsson, H J
Fairhurst, B J
MacQuisten, S
Thomas, G D

Gainsborough

Basu, S K
Beaman, R E
Bedford, T A
Bird, R A
Brears, O B
Brown, P C
Carmichael, C M
Clarke, S L
Devine, A
Devitt, P M
Done, B B
Done, K L
Fickling, K A
Hale, E G
Hockey, J A
Hoggard, N
Hunt, C S
Hyde, P R
Jolly, D A
Kademani, Y
Lannon, P G
Lawley, B J
Linnell, P E
McCabe, M J
Maunders, D P
Morris, M-A M
Nicklin, M J
Padley, R G
Patanwala, S K
Pearson, A R
Pearson, R J
Percival, I D
Pollard, M
Procter, A M
Procter, G S
Rees, H W
Taiwo, C B
Walker, A P
Ward, W
Warnes, G D
Wilkins, R A
Wragg, C M

Gairloch

Denovan, E D B
Kyle, J
Macrae, D J
Marshall, A L
Robertson, R H
Smith, Y

Galashiels

Anthony, T B
Arbuckle, G M
Borthwick, J B
Brown, M I
Cormie, P J
Cramond, P M
Crockett, P S
Cross, M D
Cross, R A
Douglas, E W S
Glenfield, J R
Gollock, J M
Greenwood, C A
Johnston, J R
Johnston, R L
Johnstone, A V
Kerr, A D
Leaver, R J
Lindsay, M K
Maclaine, G N
Miller, I I A
Miller, R A
Owen, D J
Pollok, A
Pringle, D L D
Rodger, F E
Rodgers, F R
Smith, R R
Soutter, R I
Timperley, L R
Wright, A K J

Galston

Calder, E J M
Dean, W M F
Loudon, I
McCall, J S
McWhirter, J W
Nicoll, W S
Robertson, J L

Garndolbenmaen

Jenkins, J T M C

Garve

MacLeod, A
Whitteridge, S M

Gateshead

Aird, I A
Antrobus, J N
Arthur, J B G
Ashour, H Y H
Austin, A H
Barer, D H
Basu, A S
Beeby, A R
Bhaskaran, A R
Bhaskaran, U
Bird, C M
Bone, D
Bonnington, R M
Bowman, A
Bowman, D E
Browell, D A
Browne, B D P
Brumby, P
Bryson, J M
Calvert, S
Cassidy, P D
Chalmers, J E
Chambers, I R
Chandnani, M T
Chilaka, V N
Clarke, A J
Cock, C E
Comerci, G
Condie, W H
Congera, G P
Coorsh, J C
Cope, M T
Cox, R A
Crawford, B W D
Crawford, M
Cross, N
Cross, P A
Cunliffe, W J
Dalgleish, J
Daniels, S P
Dawson, C J
Dodds, S R

Dorani, B
Dowson, T
Dutta, D K
Eccles, J B
Errington, D R
Errington, M G
Eseonu, O C
Fairs, R G
Fearby, S
Field, S M
Fisher, R J
Foster, I O
Francis, R C
Fullerton, G D
Galloway, H J
Gardner, C A
Gilbert, P S
Groom, H M
Hanson, G H G
Hardstaff, R M
Harrison, D A
Harrison, R W S
Hart, F J
Henley, D F
Heycock, C R
Hoare, S
Holmes, A
Hood, M P
Hudson, S J
Hughes, T
Hunt, A J
Ilyas, M
Imam, S M
Jackson, I D
Jackson, J B
Jones, K P
Kanu, F C S
Kaura, A
Kaura, V C
Kell, W
Kelly, C A
Kennan, E
Kenny, C
Killen, J W W
Kumar, A
Kunju, M P K
Lambert, K H
Leahy, D A
Leon, C M
Liston, J E
Lopes, A B
Lunt, L G
Lustman, F
Mcauley, F T
McErlane, F E
McHutchon, A
McKay, M
McManners, I
May, H A
Miller, T
Moran, P F
Morris, N A
Muthu Krishnan, N
Naik, R
Naylor, F L
Newby, M P
Newby, V J
Nicolle, A L
Nutting, L M
O'Cuill, M B
Ormerod, H J V M
Orritt, S G C
Pannu, U S
Pattekar, B D
Paxton, A E
Pike, E E
Postlethwaite, D L
Prudhoe, K
Ranu, H K
Reveley, C H
Rickards, M
Rizwi, M T A
Robinson, A C J
Robson, J C
Rutenberg, S M
Schumm, B A
Scott, A M
Scott, C D
Shankar, N
Shenfine, C
Sherratt, M
Siddiqui, M G
Singh, K J
Smith, D D
Smith, D A
Smith, L
Stack, W C
Steele, A M
Stefan, M A

Streit, C E
Suchdev, M S
Tailor, A J
Tasker, B E
Tate, J
Tetlow, S
Thompson, P
Uberoi, R
Varghese, M A
Ward, P J M
Warwick, J S
Williamson, S L H
Wilson, S-A
Wise, C F
Woerlein, C
Wotherspoon, M
Wright, J

Gatwick

Bleeze, K G
Cooke, J N C
Evans, A D B
Johnston, R V
Spencer, J P G

Gerrards Cross

Airey, T P
Aldwinckle, T J
Allan, G
Amin, S
Armstrong, J W
Barber, R T
Bartkiewicz, A J
Baxendine, D M
Bell, G S
Bray, S J
Britt, J R
Burton, R M
Butcher, S J
Chandra, A
Chandra, A K
Churchman, I R
Clayton, P P
Dean, A E
Dhesi, G S
Fiddian, A P
Forsyth, S
Foskett, R A
Foster, K E
Fowler, G R J
Gathercole, R
Ghouze, A
Graham, A M
Grassick, B D M
Gregory, P R
Grieve, D K
Grimshaw, B S
Gristwood, I
Hall, M A
Harrison, E L
Hart, A M
Hell, S C
Heywood, R L
Hughes, M J
Irwin, P F
Jackson, E B
James, A H
Johal, J S
Kennedy, H C
Kingdom, L G
Kitteringham, L J
Leaver, S
Mackenzie Ross, A D
Mackinnon, S
Marsh, B T
Mason, B A
Michell, E P G
Minassian, D
Myant, A
Myant, N B
Ogden, W S
Patel, S R
Paul, S S
Pilbrow, L K
Pope, R T
Pye, G F
Quiney, M J
Rakhit, M K
Regan, R J
Robertson, S J
Ross, D
Sales, J E L
Seimon, J W M D J
Sheridan, J V
Shotbolt, J P
Smallwood, E H
Stalder, G P M
Thomas, C C
Townsend, E R

Try, J L
Turner, N S
Westcott, E D A
Whittle, R J M
Whitwell, G S
Williams, E J
Wilter, P H
Yuen, A W C

Gilford

McMullen, J V

Gillingham, Dorset

Bett, A J
De Caestecker, P E A
Denman, E E
Fawcett, K J R
Freeland, M S
Groom, M R
Jacobs, P B
Lewis, G D
Longden, D E
Mole, K F
Sage, H
Short, M A
Warren, R J
Wood, T C A

Gillingham, Kent

Adams, K J
Addy, N C
Adesida, O A
Adlam, D
Ahmed, A I H
Al-Sinawi, A A H S
Anderson, E
Asiain Urrizola, J M
Badrinath, M R
Bakshi, P
Beattie, A M
Beerstecher, H J
Belcher, H E
Bewicke, R W
Bhatti, S A
Blanco Rojo, C
Bloor, A J C
Bui, T A
Buist, R J
Butler, C M
Corall, J M
Cox, S J
Damri, M
Davis, J P
Day, R C
Day, S
Debenham, M J
Dharni, D S
Dholakia, R P
Dillon, M
Diwakar, K N
Ducker, D A
Duckett, J R A
Dunbar, I J C
El Kary, S I
Fernando, W S B P
Ferrin, L V
Fleetcroft, J P
Frances, V
Frank, M J
Garousha, S A
Gluckman, P G C
Grant, J L
Griffith, E
Gupta, J
Hahn, S
Halpern, S M
Haque, M E
Haroon, S K
Hasan, K
Haworth, K L
Hayes, J P L A
Hayward, M J
Hogg, L M
Hoile, R W
Hoque, H M R
Hughes, G E
Imam, N
Jana, P P
Joshi, S
Karim, M
Karim, N
Karim, Y
Karwal, N
Khan, O
Kooiman, E D H
Lakshman, J C
Landham, T L
Lindley, R P
Littlewood, M J
Mahmud, S Z

Manuel, P D
Mason, M A
Meyer, J E
Moll, E L
Mongwa, S L
Moore, D M
Morrice, A E
Mufti, G R
Mukherjee, K
Nagmoti, V G
Naseem, M S
Norman, S G
Oliver, R M
Palmer, J H
Parwani, G S
Patel, C P
Patel, M G
Patel, S S
Patel, S C
Penman, D G
Penrose-Stevens, A
Prendergast, M P
Procter, E A
Quatan, S M H
Quigley, M C
Qureshi, M-U-D
Qureshi, S M
Rahman, M
Randall, B J
Rastomjee, C D
Reddy, K
Reddy, N
Rinaldi, C A
Rishi, N P
Rucinski, J
Ryan, P J
Sarmotta, J S
Scobie, I N
Segwagwe, M
Selvan, S T
Shaunak, L N
Shetty, A A
Silhi, R B
Simpson, D A
Singh, A K
Singh, B N
Sivathasan, S
Smith, A
Stewart, A G
Stout, R J
Sumner, C
Suresh, K
Symonds, R L
Tsang, W-M
Varada Reddy, P S
Velamati, M D
Verheul, M R
Wahab, M A
Watkin, J
Weiner, N
Welland, H A
Wilcox, A-M C
Williams, P M
Williams, P L
Wilson, T J
Woodman, T J
Yau, C Y
Youssef, H A M

Girvan

Anderson, D G
Barr, G W
Brown, N M
Cowell, G G
Green, G F
Kirkwood, H L
McFadyen, E P
McLannahan, I F G
Malloch, T
Mathieson, J
Maxwell, H L
Moore, C D
Smith, T C G
Strachan, G R
Strachan, J W

Glasgow

Aaron, D A R
Abbas, A C
Abbas, A
Abbas, G
Abedin, K J
Abel, B J
Abernethy, J
Abrami, G
Abu-Heija, A T H K
Abu-Seido, H-E-D A A
Abu-Sitta, G
Adam, J S

Glasgow

Adams-Strump, B J
Adams, B W
Adams, E A P
Adams, F G
Adams, K M
Adams, T J
Addis, G M
Addis, G J
Adjei, S S
Adler, B J
Adlung, B
Afuakwah, R J
Agrawal, A D
Ahmad, M T
Ahmad, T
Ahmed, O N
Ahmed, R
Ahmed, S I
Ahmed, S
Ahmed, S
Ainslie, W G
Aitchison, M
Aitken, E M
Aitken, I C
Akhtar, M
Akhter, R
Akhter, Z
Al-Alousi, L M E
Al-Badran, L
Al-Badran, R H
Al Bahnasawy, L M S
Al-Jilaihawi, A N A
Al-Kaabi, J K A
Al-Kadhimi, A R J H
Al-Khabori, M A J
Al-Khan, J A M
Al-Maharzi, A M
Al-Mulla, F R
Al-Qadri, M A S
Al-Roomi, L
Al-Salmi, H N Y
Al-Shamma, M R R
Alam, M F
Alam, T A
Alcock, S R
Alcorn, D L
Alcorn, D J
Alexander, A M
Alexander, C A
Alexander, C I
Alexander, R J T
Alexander, W D
Algie, T A
Alguero, L
Ali, A
Ali, A
Ali, H O M
Ali, S K
Allahabadia, A
Allahabadia, A
Allahabadia, J K
Allam, B F
Allam, S
Allan, D B
Allan, G W
Allan, J G
Allan, J H
Allen, D K
Allen, J M
Allison, A G
Allison, H E
Allison, M E M
Almutairi, S
Alves, C B
Alwan, M A R
Amin, V S
Anand, C L
Anderson, A A S
Anderson, A S
Anderson, B G
Anderson, C E
Anderson, D L
Anderson, D E
Anderson, E M
Anderson, E J F
Anderson, E G
Anderson, H M
Anderson, I W R
Anderson, J M
Anderson, J S
Anderson, J H
Anderson, J R
Anderson, J R
Anderson, J S
Anderson, M W
Anderson, P J
Anderson, W D
Anderson, F
Andrew, D S

Ang, C K
Antebi, R
Anwar-Ul-Haq, M
Anwar, A E
Anwar, M
Anwar, S
Apiliga, M T
Arbab-Zadeh, A
Archer, S C
Arfan, A
Arguelles Arias, J A
Armstrong, I A
Armstrong, J L
Arnold, R A
Arthur, D S
Arul, A
Asbury, A J
Asghar, B
Ashley, A M
Ashley, E A
Ashmead, J D
Ashraf, S
Ashrafuzzaman, B M K A
Aslam, A
Auld, A
Auld, M H
Austin, A V
Aylmer, A T
Aylmer, D A
Azmy, A A M F
Azuh, V I
Bacsich, P
Bahrin, N R
Baig, M H
Baillie, D
Bain, A K
Bain, C A L
Bain, D J
Bain, K E
Bain, W H
Baird, D R
Baird, J W
Baird, J E C
Baird, J A
Baird, K S
Baker, M
Balaji, M
Baldwick, C M
Balfour, A E
Balkrishna, N
Ballantyne, D
Ballantyne, J P
Ballantyne, J P
Ballantyne, R
Ballingall, C
Balmain, S
Bamforth, C I
Bancewicz, D
Banerjee, A K
Banerjee, S
Banham, S W
Bankowska, U Z
Barber, J H
Barber, J M
Barbour, M P
Barclay, G J L
Barker, J
Barlow, G
Barlow, M
Barlow, P
Barnes, F J
Barnes, J
Barnes, M F L
Barnett, D N
Barr, A S
Barr, G T D
Barr, J B
Barr, M C
Barran, D A N
Barrett, A
Barrett, B G J
Barrett, C F
Barrett, H A
Barrett, K F
Barrett, M C F
Barrett, R
Barrett, S V
Barrie, A A O
Barrie, R
Barton, J
Bashir, A A
Bath, J C J L
Baxter, F J
Baxter, G M
Baxter, R H
Beard, K
Beardsley, S J
Beaton, C M

Beattie, A D
Beattie, G J
Beattie, G M
Beattie, J O
Beattie, R M
Beattie, S C
Beattie, T J
Beckhurst, C A
Bedi, C I
Bedi, T S
Beesley, S A
Begg, C J
Begg, T B
Behan, C M H
Behan, W M H
Belcher, O P P R
Bell, C A
Bell, E
Bell, G
Bell, G T
Bell, J M
Bell, L C
Benaran, C
Benbow, S J
Bennet, A C
Bennet, G C
Bennett, N L M
Bennie, E H
Bennie, P F
Berardelli, C E
Berg, G A
Bergin, R L
Berkeley, P R
Berrie, A K
Berry, F
Berry, M M
Best, C J
Best, W A
Beveridge, E J
Beydals, J
Beynon, J A
Bhachu, H S
Bhandari, S
Bhatia, N
Bhatt, A
Bhattacharya, J J
Bhatti, N T
Bhawal, R
Bhopal, A S
Bidwell, J P
Biggart, R J
Bigrigg, M A
Bilsland, D J
Bingham, B J G
Bingham, J
Binnie, B
Binns, J K
Birkmyre, A C
Bishop, A
Bissett, J D
Bissett, J J
Bissett, S M
Bissoonauth, S
Black, C J M
Black, C
Black, C K
Black, E A
Black, M
Black, R A L
Blackhurst, G
Blackwood, D L
Blair, A M
Blair, A J
Blair, A M
Blair, A J
Blair, D L
Blair, J A S
Blair, J M
Blair, S J A
Blatchford, M E
Bleasby, C J F
Blincow, A H
Blockey, N J
Bloom, S J
Blyth, M J G
Blyth, M
Boag, J W
Boddy, F A
Bogan, J G
Bolt, J M W
Bond, M R
Bone, I
Bong, J L
Bonnes, T M
Boom, S J
Booth, J C D
Booth, M G
Booth, R H
Borland, G A W

Borthwick, J M
Bouch, C J K
Boulton-Jones, J M
Boulton-Jones, J R
Boulton-Jones, R V
Bowman, C M
Bowring, S A C
Boyce, S H
Boyd, A L
Boyd, C
Boyd, F F
Boyd, G
Boyd, J F
Boyd, M J W
Boyd, M A
Boyd, W P
Boyle, D
Boyle, K C
Boyle, K
Boyle, M A
Boyle, M A
Boyle, S C
Boyne, I C
Bradford, E M W
Brady, A J B
Braidwood, A S
Brandon, A-M
Bransby-Zachary, M A P
Brebner, H
Brechin, S
Bree, M M
Bremner, A D
Brennan, A F
Brennand, J E
Briggs, C
Briggs, E M
Briggs, J D
Brij, S O
Brittliff, J
Brodie, A F
Brodie, D J
Brodie, M J
Brogan, R T
Bronte-Stewart, J M
Brookes, M T
Brookes, R W
Brooksbank, K L
Brown, A J
Brown, B
Brown, D A
Brown, D H
Brown, D J G
Brown, D R P
Brown, D M
Brown, D C
Brown, G J
Brown, G A
Brown, G L
Brown, I D M
Brown, I G
Brown, I L
Brown, J A
Brown, J H
Brown, K M
Brown, M R
Brown, R C
Brown, R M
Brown, S M R
Brown, S A
Brown, S E
Brown, S J
Brown, T
Brown, W C
Brown, W R
Browne, B H
Browne, M K
Browning, G G
Browning, J J
Browning, J P
Browning, J G
Browning, R
Bruce, C L M
Bruce, D J
Bruce, E J
Bruce, H T
Bruce, S J
Bryan, S A
Bryce, I G
Bryden, F M
Bryden, H S
Bryden, J S
Brydie, D H
Brydie, S E
Brydon, C W
Bryson, A
Bryson, G W
Bryson, M S
Buchanan, M E B

Buchanan, M M
Buchanan, M D
Buchanan, W M
Bucknall, C E
Buksh, K
Bullock, M R R
Bundi, R S
Burden, A D
Burgoyne, M
Burke, A M
Burleigh, E A
Burnett, E B
Burnett, R A
Burns, H J G
Burns, J W
Burns, J M A
Burns, M F
Burns, P S
Burrell, H E
Burrow, M A L
Burton, A E
Burton, K A
Bush, A C
Butler, J G
Butler, S J
Butt, A M
Butt, N M
Byford, D M
Byrne, D S
Byrne, G C
Byrne, J C
Cadenhead, A L
Cairns, T
Calder, C B
Calder, J F
Calder, N J
Caldwell, A J
Caldwell, J C
Caldwell, W F
Callaghan, M W
Calman, K C
Calvert, M H
Cameron, A D
Cameron, E
Cameron, H J
Cameron, H A
Cameron, I T
Cameron, M G
Cameron, N M
Camilleri, I G
Campbell-Brown, M B
Campbell, A C W
Campbell, A T
Campbell, A J
Campbell, A C
Campbell, A M
Campbell, A P
Campbell, B C
Campbell, C D
Campbell, C
Campbell, C W
Campbell, D A F
Campbell, D G S
Campbell, D S
Campbell, D S
Campbell, D
Campbell, F A
Campbell, G J
Campbell, G
Campbell, G A M
Campbell, H C
Campbell, I C
Campbell, J A
Campbell, J L
Campbell, J C
Campbell, J G
Campbell, J M
Campbell, L M
Campbell, S A
Campbell, S E
Camrass, H J
Candy, J M
Canning, G J
Canning, G P
Canning, M
Cannon, R N
Capell, H A
Caplan, R P
Caponigro, F
Carachi, R
Cargill, J S
Carlile, D
Carlyle, A V
Carmichael, J
Carmichael, R M
Carnon, A G
Carrick, D G
Carrick, L A
Carroll, G

Carswell, G F
Cartlidge, E A
Cartlidge, I J
Carty, C A
Carty, M J
Cassels, M C
Cassidy, J
Cassidy, M
Cassie, G
Castle, E A
Cathcart, A
Catto, M E
Caulfield, S F
Cavallo, A V
Caven, E A
Cavoura, C
Chakrabarti, H S
Chalmers, A M
Chalmers, E A
Chalmers, F A
Chalmers, G L
Chalmers, G W
Chalmers, W N
Chan, P K H
Chandrachud, H R
Chandrasekaran, S
Chang, J W
Chapman, R M
Chappell, A M
Chatfield, M M
Chatfield, W R
Chaudhri, O S
Chaudhry, M A
Chaudhry, S R
Chazan, N
Cheah, P Y
Chen, C X
Cheriyan, S
Cherry, L A
Cheyne, A J
Chiah, K S
Chiah, S A
Chiang, C C P
Chin, K-F
Chisholm, I M
Chisholm, J K
Chita, B S
Chong, D
Chong, P S
Chong, T-Y
Choudhery, V P
Chowaniec, A M
Chowdhury, M M M
Chowdhury, M
Chowdry, A S
Christian, M T
Christie, A
Christie, C A
Christie, J M
Christie, L J
Christie, S F
Christison, D
Christison, M K
Christmas, D M B
Chui Wan Cheong, P L
Chumas, P D
Chung, D A
Church, A C
Church, H
Church, J A
Church, M V
Clancy, B
Clapham, P
Clare, F B
Clark, C E
Clark, C J
Clark, C
Clark, C
Clark, D
Clark, G A
Clark, H B
Clark, L A
Clark, L J
Clark, P
Clarke, J G
Clarke, P T
Clegg, S K
Cleland, L C
Clements, R
Clifford, D J
Climie, P B
Clinton, E
Clubb, C
Cobbe, S M
Cochran, D P
Cochran, K M
Cochrane, L M
Cochrane, L M
Cochrane, M J B

Glasgow

Cochrane, R A
Cockburn, A F
Cockburn, F
Cohen, H N
Coia, D A
Cole, A T
Coll, L
Collie, S J
Collins, J W
Collins, K E
Colquhoun, A D
Colquhoun, I W
Colville, D R
Colville, R L K
Conn, A K
Conn, H S
Conn, J G
Connaughton, K J
Connell, A C
Connell, A F
Connell, J M C
Connell, L E
Connell, R A
Conner, A N
Conner, J T
Connolly, C E
Connolly, C M
Connolly, M A
Connolly, P J
Connor, J M
Connor, J M
Connor, R A C
Conroy, S
Convery, C
Conway, D I
Conway, E J
Conway, V A
Cook, G
Cook, J E
Cooke, L D
Cooke, T G
Cooper, A F
Cooper, B
Cooper, S-A
Cooper, S M
Copeland, L E K
Corbett, R H
Corcoran, G D
Cordiner, C M
Cordiner, J W
Corfield, A R
Corrigan, D L
Cossar, D F
Cossar, J H
Costello, P A
Cotton, M M
Cotton, P
Courtney, C A
Cousland, G
Coutts, J A P
Coutts, N A
Coutts, S B
Cowan, C A
Cowan, E B
Cowan, J B
Cowan, M S
Cowan, M D
Cowburn, P J
Cowden, J M
Cowie, F J
Cowie, R G
Coyle, A C
Coyle, H E
Craig, A D
Craig, M B
Cram, L P
Crampsey, V R
Crawford, C M
Crawford, J A
Crawford, L A
Crawford, L E
Crawford, M
Crawford, P J
Crawford, R
Crawford, S C
Crean, G P
Crocket, G T
Crombie, A
Cron, A M
Crooks, J E
Crorie, J W
Crosbie, D I
Crossling, F T
Crowther, J A
Cruickshank, A M
Cruickshank, D M
Cruickshank, M C W
Cuchel, M
Cuddihy, T P

Cuddihy, V
Cullen, A S
Cullen, M P
Cullen, T J O H
Culshaw, M A
Cumming, D M
Cumming, R L C
Cumming, S A
Cunning, B W
Cunningham, A A
Cunningham, R S
Cunningham, R B
Cunnington, A-L
Cupples, P A
Curran, A J
Curran, J D
Curran, J E
Currie, P F
Curry, G W
Cuthbert, D A
Cuthbert, J W
Cutler, B
D'Silva, M C
D'Silva, R
Dabydeen, L
Dabydeen, S W Y
Dagg, K D
Dall, L M
Dalling, R
Daniel, M K
Dargie, H J
Dargie, R
Darlow, J M
Das, A C
Das, R
Das, S
Datta, J B
Datta, S
Daud, S M
Davda, A N
Davda, N S
Davidson, B K S
Davidson, C B
Davidson, F A
Davidson, G W
Davidson, H R
Davidson, I T
Davidson, J K
Davidson, K G
Davidson, M C
Davidson, M W A
Davidson, R
Davidson, S M
Davidson, W K
Davie, A P
Davie, C A
Davie, J W
Davies, D L
Davies, G J
Davies, N P G
Davis, J A
Dawe, R S
Dawes, P F H
Dawoud, R A
Dawson, M F
Dawson, R D
Day, R E
De Bono, H A
De Caestecker, L
De Casso Moxo, M D C
De Courcy, R L
Deacon, A D
Deane, R F
Debono, J S
Deeny, M
Deighan, M P
Deighan, M J
Deighton, F W G
Dell, A E
Dely, C J
Desai, G
Deshpande, N P
Deshpande, P M
Deubel, E L
Devanney, M C
Devers, M C
Devine, B L
Devine, J
Devine, J F
Devine, M M
Devine, M B
Devlin, M F P
Dewar, K M S
Dhami, D S
Dhiya, S
Diaper, C J M
Dick, C P C
Dick, D H

Dick, E S
Dickson, E J
Dinardo, L R B
Dobson, C C
Dobson, H M
Docherty, A J
Docherty, D J
Docherty, J G
Docherty, R C
Dochery, A
Dodds, M
Doherty, A M
Doherty, B M M
Doherty, P A
Doherty, S M
Doig, G J
Doig, H P
Doig, W B
Doig, W M
Dominiczak, A F
Dominiczak, M H
Donald, J R
Donaldson, L
Donaldson, M D C
Donnelly, J W
Donoghue, C
Doraiswamy, N V
Doran, C A
Dougall, A J
Dougall, H G G
Dougall, H I
Dougall, J R I R
Dougan, M A
Doughty, J C
Douglas, A M
Douglas, E P
Douglas, J L
Douglas, K W
Douglas, R N C
Dove, P M
Dover, S B
Dow, J S M
Dow, T G B
Dowers, A D
Downey, M G
Downie, A C
Downie, A C
Downie, C J
Doyle, A S P
Doyle, D
Drainer, E K
Draper, I T
Drummond, M B
Drummond, M W
Drummond, R S
Drury, J K
Dryburgh, F J
Drysdale, R G
Duddy, M A
Dudgeon, J C
Dudley, E A
Duff, G M
Duffy, M
Duffy, M T
Duffy, P H
Duke, E M C
Dummett, N J
Dunachie, S J
Duncan, A C
Duncan, C L
Duncan, J R
Duncan, J
Duncan, M R
Duncan, M S
Duncan, R
Duncan, R D D
Dunleavy, M J
Dunlop, G F
Dunn, A J
Dunn, F G
Dunn, I B
Dunn, J M
Dunn, J M
Dunn, J J
Dunn, L T
Dunn, M B
Dunn, M C
Dunn, N G
Dunn, R
Dunn, R A
Dunn, R T
Dunn, S G M
Dunn, T J
Dunnigan, M G
Dunsmuir, R A
Dunwoodie, W M
Durnin, J V G A
Durward, W F
Duthie, B A M

Duthie, F R
Duthie, J C
Duthie, N J
Dutta, S
Dutton, G N
Dyker, A G
Dyker, G S
Dyker, K E S
Dykes, A C
Dynan, Y M
Dysart, J G
Eason, A R R
Eason, S M
Easson, M T
Easton, J C
Eatock, F C
Eddowes, H A
Edgar, C B
Edmond, P
Edwards, B A
Edwards, C
Edwards, D J
Edwards, G F S L
Edwards, R D
El Attar, A
El-Lemki, M A M
Elder, R L
Elias-Jones, M C B
Ellahi, R T
Ellamushi, H E I
Elliott, H L
Ellis, G
Ellison, J
Elms, S T
Esler, D J
Evans, I L
Evans, S E
Evans, S M
Evans, T J
Evans, T R J
Eves, S C
Ewart, P A
Ewen, G
Ewen, S J
Ewins, A M
Fadaly, A-H A
Fagan, C
Fairchney, A
Fairgrieve, R
Fairley, A
Fairlie, A B
Fairlie, H
Fairweather, R A
Fakhoury, V A
Fallon, C W
Fallon, H M
Fallon, M Y
Farish, G
Farquharson, D
Farrell, A M
Farrell, A A
Farrow, J
Fawzi, H H
Fazzi, U G
Featherstone, C J
Fegan, P G
Felix, D H
Fell, E
Fell, N
Fellows, K P
Fenton-Lee, C A
Fergie, I
Fergie, N
Fergus, G C
Ferguson, A M
Ferguson, A E
Ferguson, A G
Ferguson, D R
Ferguson, D J M
Ferguson, E
Ferguson, J W
Ferguson, J C
Ferguson, M C
Ferguson, R J
Ferguson, S K A
Fergusson, T E S
Fern, A I
Fernie, C G M
Ferrell, W R
Field, M
Fife, J
Fife, R
Fife, R J A
Finch, A K
Findlay, J S
Findlay, K
Finlay, E R
Finlay, I G
Finlay, W E I

Finlayson, M J W
Finnegan, A A
Finney, A A W
Fish, R R J
Fisher, B M
Fisher, K H
Fitch, W
Fitchett, A A
Fitzpatrick, A P
Fitzpatrick, J J
Fitzpatrick, J P
Fitzpatrick, M O
Fitzpatrick, R G
Fitzsimmons, G M
Fitzsimons, E J
Fitzsimons, P A
Flanigan, C M
Flanigan, P G
Fleming, F W
Fleming, G
Fleming, M
Flowers, A-M
Flynn, E M
Flynn, M-A
Foley, C A
Foo, L F
Forbes, M C
Ford, A D
Ford, L B
Ford, S J
Forrest, A E M
Forrest, A
Forrest, C A
Forrest, J A H
Forrester, A W
Forrester, P B
Forsyth, A
Forsyth, A
Forsyth, A C
Forth, A J
Foster, J E
Fouad, A A M M
Foulds, W S
Foulis, A K
Foulis, K
Fowlie, J E
Fox, E G
Fox, J G
Fox, R
Frame, A H
Frame, D W
Frame, J
Frame, M A
Frame, M H
Frame, M Y
Frame, W T
Francis, R
Franklin, I M
Fraser, A A
Fraser, C P
Fraser, E M
Fraser, G
Fraser, G M
Fraser, J
Fraser, K C B
Fraser, L D
Fraser, M A M
Fraser, M H
Fraser, N G
Fraser, P A
Fredericks, B J
Freedman, H J
Freeland, R
Freer, C B
Fu, Y L
Furneaux, J
Fyfe, A H B
Fyfe, E L
Fyfe, W M
Gaballa, M A A
Gabri, R A M I
Gaffney, D
Gajree, A K
Galbraith, J
Galbraith, S L
Galbraith, S B
Galea, P F
Gallatsou, E
Gallagher, S J
Gallagher, A P
Gallagher, D M
Gallagher, G A
Gallagher, J
Gallagher, J M C
Galloway, D J
Galloway, P J
Gammack, E A J
Gan, J H
Gan, Y C

Gandhi, R A
Gardee, M R
Gardiner, H M
Gardiner, T B
Gardner, E R
Gardner, F
Gardner, H
Gardner, T M
Garrett, M M
Garrett, W
Garrioch, M A
Garthwaite, M E K
Garvie, A C E
Garwood, E J
Gattens, M
Gaudoin, M R
Gavin, A R
Gavin, M P
Gaw, A
Gaw, N J
Geddes, C C
Geddes, I C
Geddes, K M
Geddes, P M
Geddes, S M
Gemmell, A J
Gemmell, J M M
Gemmell, J A
George, M I
George, W D
Gerber, A
Gerber, H
Ghosh, K
Ghosh, P
Ghosh, S K
Ghouri, N A
Gibson-Smith, B K
Gibson-Smith, S
Gibson, A J
Gibson, A A M
Gibson, B E S
Gibson, H
Gibson, I W
Gibson, J
Gibson, N A
Gibson, R G
Gibson, S L M
Gilhooly, T C
Gilchrist, C A M
Gilchrist, C R
Gilchrist, I N
Gilchrist, J
Giles, M D
Gilhooly, C J
Gilhooly, M V
Gillani, N
Gillen, D
Gillen, J
Gillespie, A J F
Gillespie, E
Gillespie, G
Gillespie, G
Gillespie, G N
Gillespie, J A
Gillespie, J S
Gillies, C
Gillies, G W A
Gillies, M A M
Gillis, C R
Gilmartin, G
Gilmore, M C
Gilmour, D G
Gilmour, H N
Girdwood, R W A
Gladden, M H
Glancy, C I H
Glancy, S J
Glanville, T J
Glasser, A I
Glasser, J M
Glasspool, R M
Glavin, R J
Glen, A A
Glen, A C A
Glen, P A S
Goddard, M J
Goel, K M
Goh Huat Seng, M
Going, J J
Going, S M
Goldberg, A
Goldberg, D J
Goldberg, J A
Goldberg, S H
Goldie, A S
Goldie, J G S
Goldie, J
Goldin, E J
Goldring, J R

Glasgow

Goldthorp, S L
Gooch, C L
Goodfield, N E R
Gordon, D
Gordon, D
Gordon, E R
Gordon, I M H
Gordon, J A
Gordon, J
Gordon, J N
Gordon, J S
Gordon, M W G
Gordon, M M
Gordon, R A
Gordon, S M J
Gorrie, M J
Goswami, D
Goudie, D E
Goudie, R B
Goudie, S G
Goudie, S E G
Goudie, T A
Gourlay, J C
Goutcher, C M
Govan, J
Gow, R L
Gracie, S W
Graham-Service, D M
Graham, A M R
Graham, A R
Graham, A S
Graham, D I
Graham, I K
Graham, I A
Graham, J
Graham, J
Graham, J F
Graham, R D
Graham, W M
Granet, D
Granger, J M
Grant, I R
Grant, J J
Grant, P T
Grant, S W
Grant, S A
Gray, A J R
Gray, F M
Gray, G R
Gray, J A
Gray, J K M
Gray, K E
Gray, M M
Gray, R M
Gray, R F
Gray, T M
Green, B
Green, M S
Greenhill, M D
Greenhill, R
Greenhorn, D J
Greer, A
Greer, I A
Greig, K
Greig, L D
Grewal, G K
Grierson, D J
Grieve, C
Grieve, R G R
Griffiths, H L
Grigor, K C
Grist, N R
Groden, R E
Grom, I A P
Grossart, K W M
Grosset, D G
Grosset, K A
Gruer, L D
Gruszecka, K A T
Gunneberg, C
Gunneberg, N
Gupta, D
Gupta, M
Gurbanna, B A
Gurling, S R
Guse, G E W
Gusterson, B A
Guthrie, C I
Guthrie, E
Guyer, B S
Habeshaw, T
Haddock, G
Haddow, K A R
Hadley, K M
Hadley, M D M
Hagan, C M
Haggerty, S J
Haggith, A K
Hague, R A

Haigh, J S E
Hair, A
Hajivassiliou, C A
Haldane, D J
Haldane, G J
Hall, D J
Hall, G L
Hallam, D L
Halliday, J C
Halstredt, K A
Hamayun, M P
Hamblen, D L
Hamid, S K
Hamill, E A
Hamilton, A M S
Hamilton, E F
Hamilton, G W
Hamilton, G M
Hamilton, J D
Hamilton, J G
Hamilton, J A
Hamilton, J A
Hamilton, S
Hamilton, W
Hammer, H M
Hamoudi, H H
Hamoudi, A H
Handa, J L
Handa, U
Hanlon, M E
Hanlon, P W
Hannah, A H
Hannah, E G
Hannah, J A
Hannah, L E
Hannah, P M
Hannay, J A F
Hanretty, K P
Hansell, D T
Harchowal-Muir, V S K
Harden, K A
Hardie, M J
Hardie, M R W
Hardman, R J
Harkins, L
Harkins, M
Harkness, A
Harley, E C
Harnett, A N
Harper, A C
Harper, A M
Harper, C M
Harper, M P
Harper, W F
Harries, D P
Harris, F E
Harris, M C
Harris, M I
Harrison, D M
Harrison, H P C
Harrison, J M
Harrison, P G W
Harrison, S C
Harrison, S J
Hart, A M
Hart, B J
Hart, D M
Harvey, A M R
Harvey, K J
Harvie, A
Hassail, F
Hassan, K S
Hastie, G S
Hathorn, I A
Hatter, T J
Haughney, J A F
Hawksworth, C R E
Haworth, G
Hawthorn, R J S
Hay, E J
Hay, J H
Hay, L A
Hay, M H C
Hay, W M
Hay, W I
Hayes, C M J
Headden, E A
Healy, K M
Hegde, R
Hems, T E J
Henderson, A P K
Henderson, B T H
Henderson, F
Henderson, H R
Henderson, J R
Henderson, J J
Henderson, L K
Henderson, M K P
Henderson, R W

Henderson, R
Henderson, S C
Henderson, T F
Henderson, W I F
Hendry, C
Hendry, D S
Hendry, J G B
Hendry, J M
Hendry, R B
Henry, G P
Hepburn, M
Hepburn, M E
Hepple, S E
Herbison, J
Herrington, R N
Herron, J J
Hickey, K M
Hide, T A H
Higgins, A
Higgins, M J
Higgins, S P J
Higney, M C
Hilditch, W G
Hillan, K J
Hillis, W S
Hinnie, J
Ho Buu, K-T
Ho, G-T
Ho, J T F
Hodelet, N P
Hodge, C H
Hodge, G J K
Hodge, W R
Hogg, H B T
Hogg, K-J
Hogg, P
Hogg, R B
Hoh, C S L
Holden, R J
Holden, R M
Holland, B M
Holms, C M
Honings, F P G C
Hood, J
Hood, V D
Hooper, D K B
Hooper, K M
Hooper, L A
Hope, A T
Hopkinson, Z E C
Horgan, A F
Horgan, M P
Horgan, P G
Horne, G M
Horne, J
Hosie, G A C
Hosie, J
Hossain, T
Houghton, D J
Houghton, M
Houston, F M
Houston, V
Howat, A M
Howat, C
Howat, R C L
Howat, T P
Howat, T W
Howatson, A G
Howells, J
Howie, E B
Howie, F M C
Hubbard, K E
Hughes, K S
Hughes, M J
Hughes, M
Hughes, R L
Hughes, V E
Hughson, A V M
Huisman, A N
Hukin, S L
Hullin, M G
Hume, M A
Hume, R
Hung Kwok Choi, M J A
Hunter, C B
Hunter, G W G
Hunter, J A
Hunter, M A
Hunter, R
Hunter, R D
Hussain, N
Hussain, Z
Hutchison, A S
Hutchison, A G
Hutchison, B M
Hutchison, D A
Hutton, I
Hutton, M M

Hyde, R A
Ibrahim, F H
Ijomah, G C N
Imrie, C W
Imrie, F R
Imrie, G J
Imrie, W L
Ingham, D G
Inglis, A C
Inglis, A I
Inglis, M E
Ingram, I M
Ingram, R R
Ip, J C K
Ip, P P C
Ireland, A J
Ireland, J M M
Ireland, R W
Irshad, N
Irvine, B W H
Irvine, M-L
Irvine, R W
Irvine, S A
Irwin, G J
Isa, A Y
Ishak, M A
Ismail, I S
Ismail, S A
Jack, D A
Jack, P M
Jackson, A P
Jackson, D J
Jackson, G A
Jackson, H J
Jackson, J A
Jackson, L E C
Jackson, R
Jackson, S A
Jackson, T F M
Jacobs, L
James, A M
James, A S
James, E A
James, J M
James, K S
James, W B
Jamieson, D G
Jamieson, G A
Jamieson, H T
Jamieson, I D M
Jamieson, M E
Jamieson, M P G
Jamieson, R R
Jandial, S
Jaques, B C
Jardine, A G
Jarrett, P M
Jarrett, R F
Jarvie, A
Jauhar, P
Jay, J L
Jay, M J H
Jeffrey, J S
Jeffrey, P M
Jenkins, S C
Jennett, S M
Jennings, K
Jheeta, J S
Jobst, K A
Johnmian, C J
Johnpulle, A F S
Johnson, C O
Johnson, D T
Johnson, M K
Johnston, A M
Johnston, A N
Johnston, C E
Johnston, F A
Johnston, G
Johnston, R A
Johnstone, C
Johnstone, J A
Johnstone, W A
Jones, B L
Jones, C C
Jones, D G
Jones, G E
Jones, G C
Jones, I G
Jones, R D
Jones, S
Jordan, M T
Jordan, P
Jorgensen, M E
Joseph, S
Joyce, C C L
Jubb, L G
Juhasz, P L
Junor, B J R

Junor, E J
Jury, C S
Kaleba, J
Kamat, N D
Kamel, H M H
Kamming, D
Kasem, K F
Kausar, M S
Kausar, S
Kavanagh, D
Kay, A J F
Kean, D M
Keane, J A
Keddie, J
Keeble, W
Keen, C M
Keenan, M
Keighley, B D
Kell, M R
Kell, R A
Kelly, B P
Kelly, C J G
Kelly, G M
Kelly, I G
Kelly, J L
Kelly, L C
Kelly, M D
Kelly, M P
Kelly, M H
Kelly, R C C
Kempsill, G R J
Kennedy, A
Kennedy, A C
Kennedy, D H M
Kennedy, E M M
Kennedy, H B
Kennedy, H C
Kennedy, I M
Kennedy, J H
Kennedy, J A
Kennedy, M M
Kennedy, M
Kennedy, P G E
Kennon, B
Kenny, G N C
Kent, F J
Kent, M A
Kenyon, N J
Ker, G J
Ker, N D
Kerr, A M
Kerr, E A
Kerr, I C
Kerr, I B
Kerr, I F
Kerr, J I
Kerr, J M
Kerr, J
Kerr, K A M
Kerr, K J
Kerr, M H
Kerr, M M
Kerr, R E I
Kerr, W J
Kershaw, P W
Kesson, A J
Kesson, C M
Kestin, I G
Khan, A F M
Khan, A B
Khan, M D R
Khan, S N
Khan, S A J
Khand, A
Khand, R
Khanna, R
Kidd, D W
Kidd, P H
Kidd, V E
Kiddie, J M
Kilpatrick, A W A
Kim Lin Lim, Dr
Kincaid, R J
Kincaid, W C
King, B B
King, G C
King, J P
King, L-G C
King, S A
Kingsmore, D B
Kinnear, F B
Kinninmonth, A W G
Kinsella, J
Kirk, A J B
Kirk, C M
Kirk, D
Kirkland, I B
Kirkness, C M
Kirkpatrick, J J R

Kirkwood, I
Kirkwood, W S
Kleinglass, A H
Kneale, E M
Knill-Jones, R P
Koch, J E
Kochar, A
Kohi, Y M
Koppel, D A
Korsah, P K G
Kraszewski, A
Krause, A A
Krishnan, P
Kubba, A K
Kuhan, V
Kyle, A
Kyle, K F
Kyle, P M
Lafferty, T G
Laing, M S
Laird, L
Laird, S
Lake, D B
Lalloo, D
Lamb, E W B
Lamb, G W A
Lamb, K S R
Lamont, I C
Lan-Pak-Kee, L Y K
Land, J H
Lang, S C
Lang, W
Lang, W
Langan, C E
Langan, J J
Langhorne, P
Langridge, S J
Lanigan, D J
Lappin, S J
Larkin, J G
Larkin, M P
Lartey, E H
Lau, P F
Laude, A
Lauder, J C
Laughland, A W
Laughland, A P
Laurie, A N
Laurie, M
Lawrie, S M
Lawrie, T D V
Lawson, A A
Lawson, D H
Lawson, R A
Lean, M E J
Leanord, A T
Leask, R G S
Leckerman, A
Ledingham, M-A
Lee, A F C
Lee, A C
Lee, A J
Lee, F D
Lee, J C L
Lee, J
Lee, K M
Lee, S J
Lee, W R
Leeper, W J
Lees, A W
Lees, J T
Lees, J C
Lees, K R
Lees, N W
Leggate, P A
Legge, S
Leitch, J J
Leith, J M
Leman, J A
Leng, J E
Lennox, C A
Lennox, I M
Leonard, M
Leonard, M J
Leslie, C A
Leslie, D W
Leslie, H C
Leslie, K
Leslie, M E
Leung, E W-Y
Leven, C F
Leventis, J
Lever, A F
Lever, R S
Levin, R L
Levy, B
Levy, I A
Levy, J
Levy, R D

Glasgow

Lewis, A M
Lewis, G D
Lewis, J M D
Lewis, M T
Lewis, R F M
Leyland, K G
Li Yim, D F M
Li, K-W K
Liang, J
Liddell, A R
Liddle, E J
Liew, B S
Lim, C F
Lim, V Y T
Lim, Y H
Lindop, G B M
Lindsay, A C
Lindsay, E L S
Lindsay, G
Lindsay, J M
Lindsay, K W
Lindsay, K A
Lindsay, N J F
Ling, S C
Lingam, K
Lingam, S M K
Links, M
Litherland, J C
Litton, A
Livingston, E
Livingston, M G
Livingston, V S
Livingstone, D
Livingstone, E D
Livingstone, H W
Lockhart, E P
Lockhart, G D
Lockhart, M C
Lockie, W J
Logan, J A
Logan, R W
Logue, J A
Long, J R
Lorimer, A R
Loudon, J C
Love, G H
Love, W C
Lovett, J M
Low, E J
Low, R A L
Lowe, G D O
Lu, J C Y
Lucie, N P
Luck, J F
Lui, G J L
Lukman, H
Lumsden, M A
Lunan, C B
Lunan, H R
Lupton, M F
Ly, I S S
Lyall, H
Lyle, D L N
Lynas, A H
Lynas, G J
Lynch, B
Lynch, J
Lyon, S C
Lyons, D
Lyons, J C
M'allistev, K F
McAlavey, P S
Macalister, A
McAlpine, A C
McAlpine, C H
McAlpine, C J
McAlpine, H M
McAlpine, S G
MacAndie, C
MacAndie, K
MacAnespie, H
MacAra, L M
Macarthur, A D D
MacArthur, A A
MacArthur, G E
McArthur, J D
McAspurn, M V
McAulay, E M
Macaulay, L
MacBain, G C
MacBain, K H
MacBrayne, J
Macbrayne, J F
McBurnie, V A
McCabe, R J R
McCaffery, K
McCall, A
McCallum, M M
MacCallum, R D

McCallum, R W
McCallum, S M
McCandlish, H E
McCann, C M
McCann, G
McCann, S J
McCann, W
McCarlie, I
McCarry, N W
McCarter, D H A
McCartney, D J
McCaul, J A
McClure, E C
McClure, I M
McClure, K R
McCluskie, M A F
McCluskie, R A
McColl, D
McColl, K E L
McConnell, J M
McConnell, V A
MacCormick, A S
McCormick, M F
McCreath, B J
McCreath, C M
McCreath, G T
McCreath, S W
McCrosson, F M
McCruden, E A B
McCubbin, T D
McCue, E C
MacCuish, A C
MacCuish, S K
McCurley, J
McCutcheon, A R
McDermott, J M
McDevitt, J
McDevitt, R L
McDiarmid, J G M
McDonagh, M F
McDonagh, T A
Macdonald, A G
Macdonald, A G
Macdonald, A C
Macdonald, A M
MacDonald, A
McDonald, C F M
Macdonald, D J F
MacDonald, E
Macdonald, E B
MacDonald, G J
Macdonald, H E
Macdonald, I M
Macdonald, I K G
Macdonald, J C
McDonald, J C H
McDonald, J E
McDonald, J S
McDonald, K J
Macdonald, M E
MacDonald, M L
MacDonald, M G
Macdonald, P D
Macdonald, R M
McDonald, S W
Macdougall, A I
McDougall, A
McDougall, A N
McDougall, C
McDougall, J W
MacDougall, J Y
Macdougall, M C
McDougall, N
McDougall, S J
McDougall, V M
Mace, A T M
McEachan, J E
McElhone, J J
McElroy, K
McElvanney, A M
McEntegart, A
McEntegart, M B
McEwan, A J
McEwan, H P
MacEwan, T H
McEwen, J
McEwen, J M
McFadyen, M B
Macfarlane, D W
McFarlane, D B
MacFarlane, G P
Macfarlane, G N
McFarlane, J H
Macfarlane, P S
McFarlane, T
McFatter, F B
McGarrity, J D
McGarrity, M

McGarry, F J
McGarry, G W
McGarry, J A
McGavigan, A D
McGavigan, J
McGeoch, P D
McGeorge, A P
McGettrick, S M
McGhee, D P
McGhie, J
McGibbon, J S L
McGill, P E
McGillivray, D
MacGillivray, R C
McGillivray, W H
McGinley, A L
McGirr, E M
McGivern, C
McGlone, G C
McGlone, M C
McGonigal, A
McGowan, A R
McGowan, M P
McGown, D S
McGrath, A M
MacGregor, A M
MacGregor, A R
MacGregor, A F S
McGregor, E A
MacGregor, F B
McGregor, F M
MacGregor, K E
McGregor, K A
McGregor, M S
Macgregor, S E
McGuinness, J B
McGuire, J N
McGurk, F M
McGurk, S F
McHattie, I
McHenry, P M
McHugh, O C
McIlhenny, C
McIlroy, E A
McIlroy, H A
McIlwaine, L M
McIndoe, S E
Macinnes, B N
McInnes, G C
McInnes, G T
McInnes, I B
McInroy, D C
Macintosh, I D
MacIntyre, D
McIntyre, J M
McIntyre, K J
MacIntyre, P D
McIntyre, W Q
Mack, A E
Mack, A J
Mack, D S
Mack, K M
McKail, T J
McKane, J P
McKay, A J
Mackay, A J
MacKay, C K
Mackay, E J
Mackay, G V
Mackay, H M
Mackay, H P
McKay, I
Mackay, I M
Mackay, I R
Mackay, I G
McKay, J H
Mackay, J E
McKay, K
Mackay, K J
McKay, S E
Mckay, V
MacKeachan, F
McKean, S J C
McKean, W P
McKechan, K F
McKechnie, M D J
McKechnie, S A
McKee, A H
McKee, P B
McKee, P J W
McKee, R F
McKeeve, G
McKellar, J B M
McKellar, N J
McKendrick, L
Mackenna, B R
McKenna, E A
McKenna, K J
McKenna, M P

Mackenzie, A G
Mackenzie, A M
Mackenzie, A M
Mackenzie, F M
Mackenzie, I
Mackenzie, J A B
Mackenzie, J F
Mackenzie, K
Mackenzie, P C
Mackenzie, P A
Mackenzie, R J
Mackenzie, R A
MacKenzie, S
McKeon, J T
McKeon, S C
McKeown, A C
McKeown, R C
Mackie, C M
Mackie, E M
Mackie, M R
Mackie, R M
McKillop, A C
McKillop, J H
McKillop, K D
MacKillop, N A
McKimmie, P L F
McKinlay, G C
McKinlay, K H
McKinlay, S
Mackinnon, A D M
McKinnon, C
MacKinnon, H B
Mackintosh, C J
Mackintosh, L N M
Mackintosh, W A
McKirdy, M J
Mackle, J
Macklon, N S
McKnight, D W
McKnight, J M
McLachlan, D D
MacLachlan, I S M
MacLachlan, J S
Maclachlan, R S
McLaren, A D
McLaren, D
McLaren, E H
MacLaren, I R
McLaren, J
McLauchlan, J H
McLaughlin, E
McLaughlin, F K
McLaughlin, I M
McLaughlin, I S
McLaughlin, K J
McLaughlin, M E
McLaughlin, M R
McLaughlin, S F
McLaughlin, T
Maclaurin, J C
McLay, A L C
McLay, W D S
Mclean, A N
McLean, A H
Maclean, G P
MacLean, J A
MacLean, M J
MacLean, P S
MacLean, R A S
Maclean, S A
McLearie, S
McLeish, I S
McLeish, R D M
McLellan, A R
McLellan, D
McLellan, D M
McLellan, D R
McLellan, E M
Maclennan, A C
McLennan, A J
McLennan, C
MacLeod, A
MacLeod, A L
MacLeod, C M B
MacLeod, D J
MacLeod, D
McLeod, F
McLeod, G A
Macleod, H E
Macleod, I A
McLeod, L S
Macleod, M C M
MacLeod, R
Macleod, U M
McLintock, T T C
McLuskey, P W
McMahon, A J
McMahon, D J
McMenemin, R M

Macmichael, F H
McMichael, J F
Macmillan, A H M
McMillan, A C
Macmillan, C
McMillan, J
McMillan, K
McMillan, L J D
McMillan, M A
McMillan, N C
Macmillan, R M
Macmillan, S B
McMurray, D A
McMurray, J J V
McNab, S M
Macnab, W R
McNally, A M
McNally, D M
McNamara, N J
McNaught, E I
McNaught, P L
MacNaughton, M C
MacNaughton, R J
McNay, M B
McNee, A
McNeil, H
McNeil, I R R
McNeil, N
MacNeill, A D
MacNeill, D R
McNeill, R J
McNeish, C I M
McNeish, G
McNicol, A M
McNicol, I J
McNicol, J A
McNicol, L R
McNicol, M F
McNicol, R A
McNicoll, I T
McPhaden, A R
MacPhail, A K
McPhater, A
Macphee, G J A
McPhee, S G
MacPhee, W P
Macpherson, A C
MacPherson, C K
Macpherson, C M
McPherson, E A
Macpherson, I
Macpherson, M C
MacPherson, M J
Macpherson, S C
Macpherson, S G
McQuaker, I G
McQueen, A
Macrae, C M
Macrae, K A
Macrae, M E
MacRae, W J
MacRitchie, J D
MacSween, M P
MacSween, R N M
MacSween, R M
McTaggart, H
MacTavish, A S
Mactier, H
Mactier, R A
MacVicar, S M
McWilliam, R C
McWilliam, R J
Madhok, R
Madhok, V K
Madi, A M
Madigan, M M
Magowan, W S
Maguire, A M
Maguire, J M
Maguire, S F
Mahal, P S
Mahalingam, S
Mahmoud, O A R
Mainds, C C
Mair, M I
Mair, R M
Mairs, J G
Makin, A P
Malata, C M
Malcolm, M R
Malcolm, M K
Malcolm, R S
Malik, H Z
Malik, M I A
Mallinson, A C
Mallon, E A
Mallon, J M
Mamode, N
Manchanda, L

Manchip, A J
Mandeville, R P
Mani, C
Mann, T S
Mansbridge, D C
Mansouri, M
Mardon, J M
Marinaki, P
Marks, R
Marney, Y M
Marsh, D R G
Marsh, J I
Marshall, A J
Marshall, A J
Marshall, A M
Marshall, J W V
Marshall, J M
Martin, A C
Martin, B J
Martin, C L
Martin, G M
Martin, J H
Martin, J I
Martin, L J
Martin, N
Martin, W G
Masterson, E
Masterton, G
Mather, J G
Mathers, A M
Matheson, J A
Matheson, W M
Mathewson, W B
Mathieson, A G
Mathieson, M A
Matthew, T B
Maule, B H
Maule, J H
Maxwell, H
May, B J
McLaughlin, A-M
Mealyea, M T M
Meek, D
Meek, R M D
Meggs, A M
Mehra, A P
Meighan, A A S
Meighan, D P
Mellon, A
Melrose, D
Melrose, H G
Melville, I D
Menzies, G F
Mercer, K J
Merriwether, F J
Metcalfe, I R
Metcalfe, R A
Michaelson, H
Michels, G A
Midgley, N M
Midgley, P C
Miles, B M
Millan Serrano, R
Millar, A J
Millar, A Y
Millar, B A
Millar, E A
Millar, G
Millar, S
Miller, A G B
Miller, C D
Miller, D C
Miller, J E
Miller, J C
Miller, J M
Miller, K J
Miller, R
Milligan, J A
Milligan, K E
Mills, P R
Milne, R
Milne, S E
Milroy, R
Minhas, H B
Minnis, H J
Mires, J-E
Mishra, S
Misra, P C
Misra, S
Mitchell, A C
Mitchell, A C
Mitchell, A G
Mitchell, C M
Mitchell, H R
Mitchell, J R
Mitchell, K M
Mitchell, R
Moar, R W
Moffat, K J

Glasgow

Moffett, A W G
Moffett, M
Mohammed, N
Mohammed, R
Mohammed, Y
Moir, J S
Molloy, M B
Molloy, R G
Monaghan, P B
Mone, A J
Mone, J G
Monie, R D H
Moore, J M
Moos, K F
Moran, F
Moran, N F
Morar, S
More, I A R
More, M B
Morgan, A H
Morgan, H G
Morgan, M
Morley-Davies, A J
Morley, P
Morley, W N
Morrice, M S
Morris, A R
Morris, A J
Morris, S T W
Morrison, A C M
Morrison, A E
Morrison, C E
Morrison, D A N
Morrison, D S
Morrison, G B
Morrison, J D
Morrison, J M
Morrison, J M
Morrison, J L
Morrison, J L
Morrison, L M
Morrison, M
Morrison, S
Morrow, H M
Morton, A L
Morton, E D
Morton, M J S
Morton, N S
Morton, R
Moss, J G
Moss, N M
Moule, B
Mowat, A M
Mowat, C
Mowat, E M
Mowat, W
Moyes, E C
Moylan, T L
Mucci, B
Muhammad Taib, R H
Muir, A J
Muir, D F
Muir, F
Muir, K W
Muir, M G
Mukherjee, S K
Muldoon, D G
Mulhearn, J F
Mullin, A M
Mundell, E B M
Munro, C S
Munro, D S
Munro, L M
Muotune, A P
Muotune, H
Murch, C R
Murdoch, D L
Murdoch, D R
Murdoch, F
Murdoch, J R
Murdoch, R M
Murphy, A V
Murphy, D S
Murphy, D J
Murphy, E J
Murphy, G A
Murphy, J B
Murphy, L
Murphy, W J
Murray, C
Murray, C R
Murray, C C
Murray, C D
Murray, F
Murray, F E
Murray, J B
Murray, K J
Murray, L A
Murray, M H
Murray, S B
Murray, T S
Murray, V
Murray, W R
Murty, J G
Murugasu, M D
Mutch, S M
Mutch, W M M
Naftalin, L
Naftalin, L
Nahar, P N
Nairn, L M
Naismith, A J W
Naismith, A J
Naismith, L D
Naismith, W C M K
Nandwani, R
Nanjiani, M
Napier, D E
Napier, E S
Napier, J M
Napier, T G
Nasib, A
Nath, M V
Naysmith, L
Neagle, G M
Neill, H
Neillie, D W R
Neilson, D W
Neilson, R F
Neithercut, M S
Nelson, R R S
Newland, L J M
Newman, B J
Newman, L H
Newman, P M
Newman, W D
Newton, A I
Newton, J
Newton, J M
Newton, W D
Nicoll, A E
Nicoll, J A R
Nicolson, J M
Nightingale, A M
Nijjar, A S
Noble, J S C
Norman, J E
Norris, A
Northcote, R J
Notman, I A
Nzewi, O C
O'Connor, M R
O'Connor, P
O'Donnell, M M
O'Donnell, N G
O'Donoghue, F J M
O'Driscoll, D P
O'Dwyer, P J
O'Hare, K J
O'Hare, R
O'Kane, K P J
O'Leary, C P
O'Neill, A S J
O'Neill, C
O'Neill, G T J
O'Neill, K A
O'Neill, K F
O'Neill, S M
O'Neill, V J
O'Reilly, B F
O'Reilly, C V
O'Reilly, D S J
O'Reilly, P V
O'Rourke, N P
Oates, B D
Oates, J D L
Oates, P D
Oates, V E M
Ockrim, J L
Ockrim, J B
Ockrim, Z K
Ogg, E C
Ogilvie, W A
Oglethorpe, R J L
Ohri, C K
Ohri, K M
Oien, K A
Oldroyd, K G
On, F W
Ong, S M
Oommen, E
Orr, C F
Orr, L A
Orr, R M
Ortega Sipan, A M
Osborne, E A
Osborne, S C
Osborne, S A
Osbourne, G K
Osman, I
Overell, J R
Overton, J G
Owen, P
Pace, N A
Padmanabhan, N
Paice, B J
Pairo Garcia, A
Pandis, V
Panesar, B S
Panesar, S K
Papanastassiou, V
Parbrook, E O
Park, R H R
Parke, T R J
Parker, A N
Parker, B
Parkinson, H S
Pate, E G
Patel, K R
Patel, M
Paterson, A M E
Paterson, A
Paterson, J M
Paterson, J
Paterson, K R
Paterson, P J
Paterson, R E
Paton, I K
Paton, J Y
Patrick, J A
Patrick, W J A
Patterson, J I
Patterson, L M J
Patterson, R
Paul, D L
Pauleau, N F
Peacock, A J
Pearsall, F J B
Pearsall, R W H
Peat, I D
Pell, J P
Pelosi, A J
Pender, J
Penney, S C
Penrice, G M
Percy-Robb, I W
Perera, M J
Periasamy, P
Perry, C G
Perry, S F
Perry, S M B
Peters, A J
Peterson, P L
Petrie, J R
Petrie, M A
Pettigrew, A F
Pettigrew, G
Petty, R K H
Peutrell, J M
Pexton, N F
Pezeshgi, D S
Phillips, G M
Phillips, K
Phillips, S H
Philp, G
Pich Martinez, S
Pickard, M A D
Pickard, W R
Pickering, C P
Pickett, M E J
Piggot, J I
Pirret, M F
Pirwany, I R
Pithie, A D
Pitkeathly, D A
Pitkeathly, I G
Pitt, W H
Platts, M M
Plenderleith, A C H
Plenderleith, J L
Poddar, M L
Pole, I Y
Pollock, J C S
Pollock, J G
Pollock, K M
Pomphrey, E O H
Pont, J M W
Poon, F W
Poon, W S
Porru, D
Porter, D R
Porter, M E
Porter, R J
Pourghazi, S
Povey, W R
Powell, J C
Power, A
Powls, D A
Prabhu-Khanolkar, S D
Prakash, D
Prasad, S
Price, J L
Price, S R
Priddle, D J
Primrose, D A A
Pringle, R M
Pringle, S
Protheroe, K
Pullar, P M
Purdie, A T
Pyone Pyone Myint, Dr
Pyott, A A E
Quasim, I
Quasim, T
Queen, S P
Quigley, A J
Quin, J A
Quin, L M
Quin, R O
Quinn, A C
Quinn, C A
Quinn, E A
Quirk, P A
Rae, A P
Rae, A J
Rae, C A
Rae, C P
Rae, R
Raeburn, R M
Raeburn, S
Raeside, J
Rafferty, C V
Rahman, M Z
Raine, P A M
Raine, W J B
Rajar, R M
Ramage, I J
Ramayya, A
Rampling, R P
Ramsay, C N
Ramsay, I N
Ramsay, J E
Ramsay, L M
Rankin, A C
Rankin, E M
Rankin, M
Rankin, P M
Rankin, W T
Rashid, R
Ratani, T H
Ratzer, M A
Ray, A K
Ray, B C
Ray, K
Raza, A
Rea, M J
Reece, G J
Reekie, R M
Rees, D E
Rees, G L
Reeve, W G
Reeves, I G
Rehana, H A
Reid, A S
Reid, A M
Reid, A W
Reid, A A
Reid, A C
Reid, D G
Reid, D M
Reid, E K
Reid, H C
Reid, I L
Reid, I M
Reid, J P S
Reid, J L
Reid, J M
Reid, J M
Reid, J A
Reid, M J G
Reid, M M W
Reid, M H
Reid, R P
Reid, W
Reid, W
Reid, W H
Reilly, D
Reilly, D J
Reilly, T G
Reinbach, D H
Rejali, S D
Rennie, A L
Rennie, A N
Rennie, A S
Rennie, A C
Reynolds, G M
Reynolds, K N
Riaz, M
Richardson, J P
Richardson, J E
Richardson, M C
Riches, S M-T
Richmond, H A N
Richmond, J R
Richmond, K M
Richmond, M
Richmond, T R A
Riddell, E M
Ridgway, T J
Ripley, P
Ritch, G M
Ritchie, A N
Ritchie, A J
Ritchie, B W
Ritchie, D A W
Ritchie, D M
Ritchie, J
Ritchie, R M
Ritchie, S N
Ritchie, W P
Riyami, B M S
Roan, C A M
Roberts, D T
Roberts, F
Roberts, G B S
Roberts, J C
Roberts, J I
Roberts, J M
Roberts, M A
Robertson, A W
Robertson, A N
Robertson, A G
Robertson, A
Robertson, C J A
Robertson, C J
Robertson, D J
Robertson, D K
Robertson, D A R
Robertson, F E
Robertson, G A
Robertson, H M
Robertson, I W
Robertson, J I S
Robertson, J
Robertson, J L
Robertson, J M
Robertson, K J
Robertson, K W
Robertson, L M
Robertson, M M D
Robertson, N A
Robertson, R A
Robinson, E T
Robinson, G C
Robinson, J F
Robinson, K E
Robinson, P H
Robless, P A
Rodger, A J
Rodger, C J
Rodger, J
Rodger, J C
Rodger, M W
Rodger, R S C
Rodgers, B N
Rodie, V A
Roditi, G H
Roemmele, H A
Rogers, K M
Rogers, P N
Rohatgi, K K
Rollo, A G
Rooney, B P
Rooney, D P
Rooney, K D
Rose, K I
Rosengard, L A
Ross, C M J
Ross, C M
Ross, J S
Ross, L M
Ross, M A
Ross, S K
Rous, S A
Rouse, M E
Roushdy-Gemie, M
Rowan, R M
Rowan, S J
Rowlands, C M
Rowlands, G C
Roxby, E M
Roy, D H
Roy, M S K
Rubin, P
Ruiz, G A
Ruiz, M-C
Rumley, J J
Runcie, C J
Russell, A R
Russell, A J C
Russell, D I
Russell, F M
Russell, F E
Russell, G
Russell, J M
Russell, K A
Russell, L H F
Russell, R I
Russell, S
Russell, S A
Russell, T J
Russell, T S
Russell, W I
Ruthven, S J
Ryan, P F
Saad, B M
Sabharwal, A J R
Sadiq, H A
Salim, R
Salmond, N C N
Salvesen, T M N
Samavedam, S
Sambrook, M G
Sammon, D J
Sanaghan, S A
Sanai, L
Sandford, A E
Sandham, P A
Sands, M G
Sansbury, H M
Sardar, S A
Sarkar, S K
Sattar, N A
Schmulian, L R
Schofield, A D G
Schofield, G E
Schulz, U C
Schuster, H
Schwarz, A A
Scollon, D
Scorgie, I G
Scott, A
Scott, H R
Scott, J L
Scott, J I
Scott, J R
Scott, J W
Scott, K
Scott, M G B
Scott, N B
Scott, P D R
Scott, P J W
Scott, R
Scott, R N
Scott, W S
Scoular, A B
Scullion, H C
Scullion, J C
Scullion, J F
Scullion, R
Seenan, C F
Seltzer, B
Seltzer, B K
Seltzer, M S
Semple, C G
Semple, L C
Semple, P F
Semple, V A
Semple, W G
Sengupta, S
Senthil Kumar, C
Senthilkumar, C
Serpell, M G
Sewell, R A
Sewell, W L
Sewnauth, D K
Sha'Aban, M A J
Shah, I M
Shah, S
Shahriari, S
Shaikh, H
Shaikh, L
Shaker, A G
Shakur, J
Shand, J
Shanmuga Bhaskar, S
Sharif, M M
Sharkey, A
Sharma, P
Sharma, V
Sharp, C
Sharp, G L M
Sharp, J M
Sharp, R A

Glasgow

Sharpe, J E
Shaw Dunn, G
Shaw, A D
Shaw, B G
Shaw, G B
Shaw, J C
Shaw, R W
Shea, J N
Sheard, P M
Shearer, C J
Shearer, H L
Shearer, L M
Sheerin, D F
Sheikh, S H
Sheil, L J
Shemilt, J C
Shenkin, A M
Shepherd, J
Shepherd, K M
Shepherd, M C
Sheridan, J S
Sheridan, M C
Sheridan, P G
Sherry, K L
Shetty, J K
Shetty, M A
Shibib, K J
Shields, S A
Shillito, P C
Shimi, S M
Shinwell, E S
Shoaib, T
Short, A D
Short, J H
Short, L M
Short, W J
Shott, C H
Siann, T L
Sidiki, S S
Silverdale, M A
Sime, R J
Simmons, A L E
Simmons, D A R
Simmons, M
Simmons, W
Simms, C M
Simpson, A M
Simpson, C C
Simpson, D C
Simpson, D D G
Simpson, E M H
Simpson, G C
Simpson, H K L
Simpson, H W
Simpson, I G
Simpson, J
Simpson, J A
Simpson, J C
Simpson, K R
Simpson, L N
Simpson, R G
Sinclair, A
Sinclair, A B
Sinclair, J
Sinclair, J F
Singer, I O
Singh, B J
Singh, I
Singhania, R
Sinha, R N
Skelton, N J
Skeoch, C H
Skeoch, H M
Slane, F
Slater, A C
Slater, P J
Slater, V M A
Slavin, J A
Sleigh, J D
Sloan, J B
Slorach, C C S
Slorach, C A
Sluglett, M
Small, M
Smart, N G
Smellie, F M D M
Smiley, E
Smillie, G D
Smith, A M
Smith, A D
Smith, A C
Smith, C A
Smith, C
Smith, C J
Smith, D M
Smith, D C
Smith, D A
Smith, D
Smith, F M

Smith, G L
Smith, G L F
Smith, G H
Smith, G A
Smith, G Y
Smith, I D
Smith, I S
Smith, J
Smith, J F F
Smith, J S
Smith, J G
Smith, K
Smith, L R N
Smith, M
Smith, M A E
Smith, M B
Smith, M C
Smith, M
Smith, M J
Smith, N M
Smith, N C
Smith, R G
Smith, R K
Smith, R H
Smith, S J
Smith, V
Smith, W A M
Smullen, S
Smyth, M G
Snaith, R J
Snedden, A E
Sneddon, A M
Sneeden, A E T
Snodgrass, M B
Sockalingam, R R
Soler Y Lopez, M D M
Somerville, M J
Sommerville, M J
Sommerville, W T
Sonthalia, V B
Sood, A
Sood, L
Soraghan, P G
Sorensen, S A A
Sorooshian, K
Soukop, M
Soussi, A C
Soutar, D S
Souter, M J
Spence, D F
Spence, G G
Spence, J C
Spencer, M H
Spencer, R M
Spilg, E G
Spilg, S J
Spowart, K J M
Sproule, M W
Sprunt, E M
Sriram, S
Staber, M A
Stack, B H R
Stallard, S
Stanley, A J
Stanton, T
Stark, A D
Stark, I M W
Steen, B M
Steinberg, S V
Steingold, H
Stenhouse, G
Stephen, C M
Stephen, L J
Stephen, M R
Stephens, C S
Stephens, M S
Stephenson, J B P
Steven, A M
Steven, G C
Steven, J M
Steven, K
Steven, R R
Stevenson, A G M
Stevenson, D J
Stevenson, M J
Stevenson, R D
Stewart, A J
Stewart, A I
Stewart, A M
Stewart, A L
Stewart, C J R
Stewart, D A
Stewart, D A
Stewart, E
Stewart, G A
Stewart, I
Stewart, I S
Stewart, J L
Stewart, J F G

Stewart, J T
Stewart, L B
Stewart, M E
Stewart, M
Stewart, P M
Still, R M
Stirling, C A
Stirling, C M
Stirling, J B
Stirling, J L
Stockwell, M C
Stoddart, D G
Stone, D H
Stone, P A
Stones, M M
Stother, I G
Stott, D J
Stott, S M
Strachan, G
Strain, G B
Strang, I W
Strong, A M M
Struthers, I R
Stuart-Smith, D A
Stuart, B S
Stuart, R C
Sturrock, A M
Sturrock, M M
Sturrock, R D
Suckle, N E
Sullivan, F M
Sultan, N
Summers, J
Summers, W B
Sunderland, G T
Susskind, W
Sutherland, A M
Sutherland, C A H
Sutherland, D F
Sutherland, G R
Sutherland, G A
Sutherland, H
Sutton, A M
Swain, E
Swan, F A
Swan, I R C
Swan, L
Swann, U
Sweeney, B
Sweeney, D
Sweeney, K T
Sweenie, A C
Sydney, R
Syme, I G
Symington, I S
Syyed, R
Taggart, C R
Taggart, H F
Taggart, I
Tait, C M
Tait, R C
Tan, K K
Tan, K Y
Tang, B Y W
Tang, T M H
Tankel, H I
Tansey, P J
Tappin, D M
Targosz, S A
Tavadia, S M B
Tay, K Y
Taylor, D A
Taylor, G M
Taylor, J L
Taylor, J R
Taylor, M F
Taylor, M
Taylor, S G
Taylor, Y
Teasdale, G M
Teenan, R P
Teh, L G
Telfer, A B M
Templeton, D J
Tengku Ismail, T S
Teoh, C-M
Teoh, Y Y
Thakker, B
Thampy, R S
Thom, A A
Thomas, A M
Thomas, S R
Thompson, J
Thompson, N F
Thompson, T D B
Thomson, A M
Thomson, A J
Thomson, A J
Thomson, A M P

Thomson, A M W
Thomson, B F M
Thomson, D F
Thomson, E C
Thomson, G L
Thomson, H W
Thomson, J K
Thomson, J
Thomson, J E
Thomson, J
Thomson, J A
Thomson, N C
Thomson, S M
Thomson, T J
Thomson, W B
Thomson, W O
Thomson, W O
Thorburn, D
Thorburn, P J
Thoris, S
Thorp, J M
Tillman, D M
Tindal, M T
Tinto, S A S
Tobias, E S
Tobias, J A
Tobin, R
Todd, A M
Todd, I M
Todd, J K
Todd, M C
Todd, N A
Tolmie, J L
Tomnay, J
Tong, G Y K
Toomey, W F
Torbet, T E
Torley, D F
Torley, D
Toshner, D
Tough, A M
Townsley, A
Townsley, P P
Tran, H N P
Traquair, M R
Travers, J F
Traynor, J P
Treadgold, N J
Trent, R J
Trollen, R M
Tsang, P
Tulhurst, J E
Tullett, W M
Turfrey, D J
Turley, J
Turnbull, A
Turner, J M
Turner, K J
Turner, K L
Turner, M S J
Turner, N R B
Turner, T L
Turner, W J R
Twaddle, J S
Tweddell, G A
Tweedle, J R
Twelves, C J
Ullah, M I
Unkles, R D
Unwin, L G
Ure, D S
Urquhart, C S
Urquhart, K R
Vallance, B D
Vallance, N B
Vallance, R
Van Beinum, M E
Vance, J P
Vanezis, P
Vardy, J M
Vartikovski, R
Vasey, P A
Venner, R M
Vernham, G A
Vernon, D R H
Verrico, J A A
Vickers, L E
Vilaplana Cannon, J P
Villafane Casante, O
Vincent-Smith, L M
Waddell, G A B
Waddell, M M
Wagstaff, A
Walbaum, D W
Wali, R K
Walker, A E
Walker, A P
Walker, A
Walker, A M Z

Walker, A B
Walker, C A
Walker, C R C
Walker, D S
Walker, F C
Walker, G M
Walker, I D
Walker, J W S
Walker, J M
Walker, K G
Walker, M H
Walker, M M
Walker, P I T
Walker, R G
Walker, R S
Wallace, D G
Wallace, I W
Wallace, J B
Wallace, R J C
Wallace, W H
Walsh, B
Walsh, E S
Walters, M R
Walters, R D
Wang, I
Wapshaw, H
Wapshaw, J A
Ward, D M B
Ward, M R
Wardell, A F
Wardhaugh, E J
Warner, C A
Waterson, P G
Watkins, R
Watkinson, G
Watson, D J
Watson, F G
Watson, G C
Watson, H K
Watson, J T
Watson, M J
Watson, M W
Watson, R J
Watt, A J B
Watt, A D
Watt, G C M
Watt, L J
Watt, N
Watt, T A
Waugh, S M L
Weaver, L T
Webb, A F
Webb, A E
Webster, G D
Webster, M H C
Weetch, G A
Weetch, W J
Weiler-Mithoff, E M
Weinhardt, A B
Weir, A I
Weir, J P
Weir, R J
Weir, R
Welch, G H
West, B A K
West, G P
Westerduin, F P
Westwater, J J
Weymes, C
Wheatley, D J
Wheeldon, K
Wheeldon, V C
Wheelwright, E F
Whitby, S
White, A
White, A
White, F J
White, J N
White, M P
White, R J
Whitefield, G A
Whiteford, M L
Whitelaw, A S
Whitelaw, S C
Whitfield, C R
Whitham, G T
Whiting, B
Whitmarsh, T E
Whitty, B L
Whyte, B I
Whyte, K
Whyte, K F
Whyte, L
Whyte, R
Whyte, S J
Whyte, S F
Whyte, W G
Wiggins, P S
Wilcox, A

Wilcox, D E
Wilford, J M
Wilkie, S C
Wilkinson, A E R
Wilkinson, J D
Wilkinson, L M
Will, G
Will, M
Willens, M
Willett, C H
Williams, A M H
Williams, B O
Williams, C J
Williams, L
Williams, L
Williams, P J
Williams, S F
Williamson, D E
Williamson, J M
Williamson, J
Williamson, L M
Williamson, S M
Williamson, S A H
Willis, F R
Willison, H J
Willocks, C M
Willocks, J
Willox, D G A
Willox, J C
Wilmington, S M
Wilson, A J
Wilson, A B
Wilson, B N
Wilson, C I
Wilson, C S
Wilson, C R
Wilson, C A
Wilson, D L
Wilson, E A
Wilson, E S
Wilson, E H C
Wilson, F A
Wilson, F W
Wilson, H E
Wilson, J R M
Wilson, J W
Wilson, L L
Wilson, M E
Wilson, M P
Wilson, N
Wilson, N I L
Wilson, P C
Wilson, P M J
Wilson, R B
Wilson, T S
Wilson, W
Wilson, W D
Winning, J
Winocour, B
Winston, A
Winter, A J
Winter, H L
Winter, J W
Winters, A C E
Wirth, M A
Wise, A
Witkiewicz, T S
Woldman, S J
Wolf, A R
Wolfe, R
Wolff, I
Wolfson, R
Womersley, J
Wong Kim Meng, Dr
Wong, D J
Wong, R A
Wong, S C O
Woo, P N
Woo, Y M
Wood, G A
Wood, S F
Woodburn, K R
Woodger, B A
Woods, J P
Woods, K R
Worrall, E P
Wotherspoon, J M
Wotherspoon, R H
Wray, D M
Wright, C M
Wright, D M
Wright, F
Wright, L
Wright, P M
Wu, W C K
Wykes, W N
Wylie, A S
Wylie, A M
Wynne, A T

Wynne, D M
Yaghan, R J K
Yates, A J
Yates, J A
Yates, R W S
Yellowlees, A J
Yeung Kuate Pin, Y K
Yip, B
Yosef, H M A A
Young, A P
Young, A R
Young, A B
Young, C A
Young, D G
Young, D J R
Young, H W S K
Young, H B
Young, I M
Young, J C
Young, J M
Young, J M
Young, S J
Young, S F
Yusof, A I
Zaireen, W N
Zeki, S M
Zia, M
Zuberi, S M

Glastonbury

Acland-Hood, P L F
Bradshaw, J
Corfield, A R H
Hancock, J M
Helsby, M R
Hughes, R M
Jackson, P A
Jones, D K L
Jones, P A
Kippax, T P
Macdonald, N D
Mason, S A
Massey, R D O
Molina Sanchez, B
Montagnon, S A
Muir, W J
Nicholson-Lailey, P J F
Nompozolo, C N
Openshaw, S E
Openshaw, W A
Sephton, J E
Sharp, H C
Strawford, I D
Welford, R A
Williams, K L
Woolley, A C

Glenrothes

Aitken, C J D
Ball, M E
Ballingall, T A
Bell, J M
Campbell, R G
Carlyle, B E
Carlyle, D L
Carr, W D
Chien, F W
Clayton, M K
Dickson, D
Downie, C H
Dunlop, W B
Dunn, L A
Fawzi, M F M
Fenwick, C D
Galloway, J P
Gergis, E M F
Gordon, G M
Grant, A C
Grant, R M
Hellewell, D R
Howell, R A
Hyndman, N C
Iskander, S Y
Krishnaswamy, B R
McBride, I M
MacDiarmid, N G
Macdonald, C H
Macdonald, W
McElhinney, J H
MacLeod, D S T-Y
Michael, C E
Milne, J A
Paisley, J M
Philipson, G P
Reglinski, F A
Reid, D I
Robertson, R C G
Rothnie, J R
Russell, F E

Smith, J
Stewart, H
Stockwell, W S
Thomson, J B
Wallace, E L
Willdridge, J
Yeates, C L
Yeates, D J

Glossop

Adams, R C
Addy, J A
Ansons, A M
Appaji Gowda, M B G
Banerjee, B
Bennett, T
Bhanumathi, K S
Bhatt, S C
Broome, C J
Broome, J D
Carr, S P
Coburn, S A
Daly, J
Ehlinger, E A
Hanna, W J
Harvey, L E A
Hasnain, N-U
Hui, E H K
Irving, S O
Johnson, A C
Jones, P B B
Kershaw, S W
Lloyd, R G
Metcalfe, H
Morris, A D
Oldham, J
Palmer, L A
Parikh, R V
Purnachandra Rao, V
Roberts, G J
Thorley, N J
Vuyyuru, S
Weller, J M
Westmerland, S P
Woodcock, S A A
Woodyer, A B
Worrall, M A C
Wright, J H

Gloucester

Abaya, V
Adriaans, B M
Aitken, J
Allen, P
Allen, S K
Ambery, P D
Anderson, J R
Angeleri-Rand, E M T
Artamendi Larranaga, P
Atine, G I O
Atubra, D K
Bailey, M A M
Bailey, R G
Bailey, S C
Baker, J G
Baldwin, R N
Bancroft-Livingston, M K
Banks, R A
Barnes, R J
Barr, H
Barrick, V E
Barrow, J M
Barrow, P M
Bell, R W
Bennett, D H
Bennett, E J
Bennett, J W
Bertone, R
Birch, P A
Bos, E G
Bowling, B S
Bradford, D C
Brooke, A E
Brooke, J A
Brown, J L
Buckley, C I W
Buckley, J F
Butland, R J A
Byrne, R J F
Campbell, D J
Canning, T M
Carr, K L
Cartwright, J J
Cartwright, K A V
Cash, T I
Challenor, V F
Chambers, R

Champion, C J
Charles, R
Chaudhuri, A K
Chaudhuri, A K
Chaudhuri, M
Chown, S R
Clift, M R
Coker, W J
Conaty, D J
Cook, T A
Cooke, S G
Cookson, F B
Corrigan, L D
Crabb, I J
Cratchley, M D
Crawshaw, C C V
Croft, G P
Croft, J J
Cronk, P G
Cuthbertson, W A
Dale, C
Dance, J M
Davidson, J C
Davies, R A C
Dawes, R F H
Dew, A B
Dewar, A K
Dicks, A G
Docherty, A D
Dodwell, P J
Donald, I P
Dougherty, S R C
Dowling, S P
Drinkwater, S L
Duffell, E F
Durkin, T E
Dutton, C S
Earnshaw, J J
Ellis, M S
Eltringham, R J
Evans, N J R
Fairbairn, G R H
Fairbairn, M L
Falkus, G K J
Fear, C F
Feilden, E M
Foster, J E
Foster, W H
Fowler, G J
Fuller, G N
Gabbott, D A
Gadsden, P M
Garbutt, N I B
Garstang, C N
Garstang, J E
Gath, A M
Gear, M W L
Gilbert, N J
Gold, C J
Goodwin, F C
Graham-Cumming, A N
Grayling, M
Graystone, S J
Green, C P
Gregson, J S
Griffiths, P F
Harbottle, T G
Hardingham, M
Hardy, P A J
Harney, B A
Harrington, A K
Harrison, K R
Hartrey, R
Hashmat, I
Haynes, W D S
Heather, B P
Hidson, O J
Hill, E E
Hill, M S
Hoare Nairne, J E A
Hodges, P
Hodgson, G I
Hollingworth, M
Holmes, K A
Humphrey, T S
Hunt, D A
Hutchison, J K
Innes, R J
Jadresic, L P
James, A J S
Jarvis, I S
Jatau, J A
Jewell, A P
Jewell, F M A
Johnson, G J
Jones, D J
Jones, S E
Joseph, R H

Kapoor, S
Kazi, B M
Kelsey, I G
Kempson, D A
Khan, M A
Khor, L J H
Knight, D P
Kumar, P
Laite, P A
Lala, A B H
Layzell, J M
Lazar, L K
Lee, J E
Leitch, S P
Lewis, D A
Lindsay, D C
Lister, J H
Livingstone, J A
Logan, M N
Lozsadi, D A
Lucarotti, M E
Lush, P S L
Lynch, A S
McConnell, D L
McCrum, A
McCrum, J C
MacDonald, L J
McDowall, N A
Mackay, R H
McKiddie, M T
Macleod, I N C
Macnair, D R
McNulty, C A
Macpherson, R
Mahendran, D
Majkowski, R S
Marchant, M J
Martin, D R
Mathers, G C
Matthai, M S
Maxted, D F
Medina Galera, J L
Meecham Jones, D J
Meeke, A M
Methven, C T
Millard, F W
Miller, H J
Morphew, J A
Morris, T J
Mulhall, R M
Munir, M
Murphy, J R
Murphy, S D
Murray, W
Nair, H T
Nair, S
Nicol, A
Noonan, W J
Norwich, R P
Odell, M J P
Owen, M E
Pack, S F
Padfield, H J
Parfitt, V J
Parsons, C R
Paterson, R J
Paynter, H E
Pearson, S E
Peniket, J B
Perrin, J E
Petersen, M E V
Pike, W J
Porter, W M
Prior, J G
Pritchard, K
Pryle, B J
Ralph, J K
Read, M D
Reid, A N C
Remfry, C J C
Remfry, R M
Richards, R K
Richards, S E
Ritchie, A W S
Ritchie, B A
Roberts, C J
Roberts, D M
Roberts, L A
Robinson, J M
Rocyn-Jones, J
Ropner, J E
Rouse, M E
Russell, G A
Rutherford, D R
Sammon, A M
Sammon, H M K
Samuel-Gibbon, A G
Sarkar, J
Sarkar, S

Savage, J E
Seacome, M P S
Sell, D M
Seymour, A
Sharples, C J
Sheehan, G E M
Shepherd, N A
Sivananthan, N
Smith, D J
Soundy, V C
Spargo, A E
Spargo, P J R
Spencer, E M
Steinhardt, S I
Stocks, N P
Stretton, C M
Stuart, J M
Sulaiman, M Z C
Swingler, G R
Tasker, T P B
Taylor, L E
Taylor, N H
Temme, C P
Thomas, D M
Thomson, W H F
Thornberry, E A
Thornton, E J
Till, A M
Towle, N D
Uff, J S
Unwin, J
Valori, R M
Vanner, R G
Vassall-Adams, N I
Vipond, M N
Wallace, A R
Wallington, M
Watkins, R M
Watson, K M
Webb, J L
Webb, M S C
Webster, R H
Whitehead, P N
Whittaker, M A
Whittle, R A S
Wilcock, A C
Williams, B A
Williams, K J
Williams, K D N
Williams, L
Williams, N J
Winterbottom, P M
Wintersgill, E M
Youngs, R P
Zaidi, S B A

Godalming

Addis-Jones, C D
Addis-Jones, M E
Anderson, C M
Barnard, R O
Barsham, B
Bigos, J E
Bland, H A
Blowers, J F A
Borthwick, A
Bott, S R J
Bowles, E M
Bray, R L
Brown, M M
Brunet, M D
Bryett, A G
Butler, P R
Caddy, I H
Campbell, P M F
Cauchi, P
Cerullo, A
Childs, A F S
Childs, K J
Clarke, G J R
Cook, A S
Craske, S
Davis, M E L
Dobson, J L C
Dooley, J F
Fleetcroft, C T
Flynn, M J
Garland, J S
Gooddy, E L
Graves, F T
Green, K
Gundry, A C
Hacking, J F
Hampson, S E
Harwood-Yarred, N H
Hassall, D E N
Herring, S A
Higgins, J M
Hill, G W R

Goole

Howe, T V T
Hudson, M G
Hudson, P T P
Hughes, M S
Hughes, R J
Jagger, C R
Jameson, J K
Jenkins, M A
John, M
Jones, S L
Kahlenberg, H G
Kershaw, E J
McCluskie, P J A
Meidlinger, J G
Mitchell, T A
Newman, V R
O'Donnell, M
O'Donnell, P S R
Orwin, J M
Page, R F M
Patel, H
Pooley, S S F
Quiney, N F
Redmen, J E
Riley, S J
Russell-Jones, D L
Savundra, J E
Scott, P H
Sears, A F
Shah, T M
Simons, S E D
Simpson, E K
Sinclair, J A
Slade, V J
Spruell, R I
Teoh, R E
Thomas, K E
Thomas, M
Thorburn, T G
Van Dorp, F A
Van Dorp, M H
Walker, W J
Watling, M I L
Way, G L
Whitaker, J A J
Whitaker, S P
White, D
Wilks, P R
Woodcock, E M
Woolrych, J M
Woolrych, M E
Zylstra, H J

Godstone

Al-Hilaly, N H D
Bale, C G
Egerton, D F
Frost, S M
Gillespie, J A
Glover, M
Howard, C W
Roche, J D

Golspie

Begg, A B
Reid, A R
Ross, L E
Simpson, M M
Thomson, K J

Goodwick

Davies, D E
Van Kempen, C E

Goole

Allen, J P
Booth, F H
Brews, A J
Brown, D A
Clark, D M
Clark, J E
Dangare, N D
Evison, D
Eyre, R M
Gogoi, N K
Greenwood, R
Hardy, D G
Harrison, R W
Harrison, S
Hensby, C
Heptonstall, J
Hewish, P A F
Hulme, J M
Kaiper-Holmes, C
Kumar, B
Kurtis, R E
Mabbott, J L
Maddock, J P
Moghissi, K
Mukherji, S

Gordon

Pinder, J R
Prendergast, B
Price, R B
Rana, A K
Reid, G F
Sarna, N R
Sim, J W
Smith, J L
Sobeih, S E-D R
Varey, N C
Wigglesworth, P
Wignall, J R N
Williamson, A R
Wrightson, L

Gordon
Hollingworth, A V

Gorebridge

Cremona, A
Lee, B C
Lithgow, R S
McKeating, S H
Matear, E A
Murray, E M
Russell, J A
Scales, E A
Stoddart, D
Storrie, M P
Telfer, R C

Gosport

Anderson, J L
Anderson, J H
Anderson, J T H
Andrews, N P
Asbridge, M S
Askew, M G
Aynsworth, S H
Bailey, D J W
Bakhai, J A
Banks, V A
Barker, C P G
Barton, J A
Beasley, P A
Beck, S
Black, D H
Blacklock, N J
Boos, C J
Brand, J J
Brigg, M J
Brook, S J
Brooks, G J
Brooks, S J D
Broome, J R
Brown, D C
Brunning, J
Burge, T S
Burlein, G
Buxton, P J
Cavanagh, M C
Childs, W J
Cockman, N G
Coddington, R
Coggon, S
Collins, B G
Coltman, T P
Connor, M P
Cook, D E
Coonan, B
Cooper, M P
Counter, P R
Crean, D M
Davis, M C
Dean, M R
Edmondstone, W M
Edwards, C J A
Edwards, S A
Erskine, D O
Evans, D A
Evans, G H
Exley, J
Exley, M D
Firth, M
Forster, J E
Fox, D J
Garratt, P P
Golden, F S C
Golding, P L
Goldsworthy, B M
Gray, C P
Green, R J
Gregory, R M
Grocock, J H
Haddon, R W J
Hajiantonis, N C
Hezlett, H A
Horrocks, C L
Houghton, I T
Iddles, A J

Irvine, G S
Jackson, M C H
Jagdish, S
Jarvis, L J
Jones, J
Kershaw, C R
King, L J
Knapman, A C
Lacey, P A
Lenoir, R J
Lindsay, I R
Lloyd, J P
Low, C D T
Loxdale, S J
Luffingham, G H
Lynch, D N
Lynch, S M E
McClintock, C L T
MacLean, A D
Macleod, M A
McNutt, D C
Millar, C W
Millar, S W S
Monnery, P M
Morgan, S R E
Morgans, B T
Morrow, R J
Mugridge, A R
Nelson, I D M
Nicol, P J S
North, D
Nwokora, G E
Okhandiar, A
Palmer, I P
Parrish, M M
Parry, C A
Patrick, K
Pennells, R A
Peters, E J
Peters, N J M
Pick, F W
Pingree, B J W
Pipkin, C
Pitkin, A D
Rampling, A E
Raperport, G
Reston, S C
Rewell, A L
Richardson, J W
Rickard, R F
Rintoul, A J
Risdall, J E
Rose, D J
Scerri, G
Scott-Brown, M M
Sharpley, J G
Shaw, F R
Shawcross, C R
Skinner, T A
Skipper, J J
Streets, C G
Summerton, D J
Sumner, M
Swain, D L
Sykes, E M
Tant, M C O
Traynor, D B
Treharne, P G
Vassallo, D J
Wallis, E M
Watkins, M J G
Webb, W F
Whitbread, T
Whiteoak, R
Whittaker, M A
Williams, M D
World, M J
Wright, B J
Wright, D S
Yeo, H E D
Young, D A
Young, P C

Gourock

Adams, J C
Anthony, G S
Bartholomew, A J
Blair, D
Craig, J D
Gray, R F
Green, D C H
Green, D C
Henderson, J H
Heuchan, A M
Islam, C H
McGarrity, K M
Mackay, W G
McKinnon, S S
McRae, R K

Murray-Lyon, R N
Nelson, E C
Pickett, J A
Robinson, M
Rogers, E
Russell, D D
Russell, M C
Shimmins, C J
Simpson, J M
Sridhar, S
Tyldesley Smith, J T A
Ward, J P

Grange-over-Sands

Adams, J
Allen, J R
Anderson, D W
Anderson, D M M
Arthurton, M W
Atkinson, M
Barton, N V
Birch, A
Birkett, N L
Bowman, I M L
Boyce, A C L
Burrows, G E
Carnachan, G A
Fletcher, D E
Freeman, L J
Hindle, T S
Horrocks, J E
Irwin, J E
Kay, B
Keith, P P
Leslie, J R
Linklater, D M
Lovatt, H M
McGuffie, G M
Mackenzie, K A
Mason, N
Mears, M P
Milligan, S D
Nightingale, J A
Norman, J R
Pearson, D C
Phizacklea, S
Raymond, T M J R
Scarlett, J F
Scarlett, S M
Storey, G O
Swart, C F
Tattersall, J M
Taylor, E R
Ward, J
White, T C

Grangemouth

Allan, W M
Anderson, B G
Ballantine, D I
Bryden, G T
Carlyle, A K
Cruickshank, L J W
Deans, M
Deans, N J
Duggie, J G
Dunsire, M F
Gawn, A V
Hamilton, N
Hegde, B D
Mohan Adyanthaya, K R R
Murdoch, I B
Murray, D R
Selfridge, D I

Grantham

Abdel-Nasser, M R
Akhrass, A
Allison, M F
Allsebrook, I
Andrew, D R
Baker, D J
Bamber, M G
Barker, S J
Baumber, J
Birch, C R
Breckenridge, J L
Brown, E J
Buck, J C
Caley, R
Campbell, G D
Campbell, J H
Campbell, M A
Camphor, S
Cochrane, E M
Coombes, S
Cory, C E
Craig, A J
Crossley, I B

Cruickshank, J A
Cutajar, A P
De Silva, S R
De Silva, S D
Dighe, V C
Dorrington, R E
Doughty, J M
Dunkin, J W
Elder, J B
Fraser-Darling, A
Gallop, A M
Gallop, D M
Garbutt, F E
Garrick, H D O
Gee, R A
Gibb, E F
Gibson, P J
Gillieson, E C
Gilmore, S J B
Gonzalez, O
Goru, S S R
Hale, C
Halliday, A E G
Hammond, E L
Hargreaves, P
Harris, L M
Helmy, E L
Higgins, M T C
Hogg, C L
Holderness, D M
Husemeyer, R P
Ikhena, E I
Jayamaha, A A S
Kathel, B L
Kerr, J S
McIlroy, S S
McKechnie, A
Magbadelo, J A
Manistre, S J
Marshall, S A
Matthews, R A
Mawdesley-Thomas, J
Miles, N A
Mills, S J
Molave, E R
Monteith, H E
Moran, D G M
Mould, G M S
Munday, S A
Murphy, D H
Nicholson, K M
Nicoll, J M V
Nqumayo, C C
O'Riordan, S M
Onugha, C O
Parkin, M G
Patel, M N
Porter, A D
Porter, F N
Potdar, N P
Pugsley, R F
Querejeta, I
Rankin, L C G
Rodrigues, C
Roper, D J
Shaban, M R R
Sharma, J C
Shelbourn, K R
Shrouder, R D
Sie, T H
Singh, A N
Smith, J N
Sneddon, J J
Southall, J G A
Stafford, E J
Stewart, K R
Stutely, J D
Surtees, A
Surtees, R A
Tedbury, M J
Terrill, L M
Townsend, J S
Valerio, D
Van Lany, P
Verel, D
Vogt, S
Walker, I W
Wallace, K R
Watts, A J
Webster, M H
West, E A
Whiteley, E A
Wiggins, B L
Wijayawardhana, U D
Wilson, J A
Zbrzezniak, W S

Grantown-on-Spey

Burns, F W

Glen, T
Grant, P F
Griffiths, G E
Hamilton, S A
Kerr, I H
Lennon, R I
MacBean, L M
Mathers, S B
Peters, S B
Pirie, L K
Smellie, J H
Smellie, W B
Stout, A J
Walters, G E
Watts, R W
Williamson, M E

Gravesend

Ahmad, I
Ali-Khan, G
Bailey, J A
Barker, C E
Bee, A J
Benn, N
Biswas, B K
Board, A P
Bourhili, B D
Boyle, P
Brown, M P
Brown, P E
Carne-Ross, I P
Crawford, H F
Crawford, I
Crick, A F
Davies, J R
Dismorr, H J
Edeleanu, I-D
El-Faramawi, M A A
Fraser, C M
Giles, J H
Glass, J B
Gordon, S E
Gray, H R
Haider, S
Haider, Z J
Hall, J
Hamp, F J
Handy, C F
Harris, A R B
Hobbs, E A
Hopkins, A D
Howie, J H
Jackson-Voyzey, E N
Jenkins, D G
Jenman, J L
Jerreat, P G
Johnson, E P
Keely, V H
Kent, J E
King, S G
Koeller, A W
Kooner, T S
Lakey, P J
Langley, S H
Leung, T Y D
McAlpine, G A
Markwick, C P
Martin, L P
Meakin, L H A
Millar, I S
Mitchell, P J
Moran, S G
Morgan, A H
Mounty, J P
Nada, E M E
Newton, E M
O'Connor, D C
Ozua, C I
Patel, J R A
Patel, M M
Payne, D J
Price, L
Ramsay, W L
Rao, G H
Shanks, R
Shergill, S S
Spurgin, H M K
Stevens, W J
Steward, R E
Stone, P T
Sumner, D J
Sussams, R W
Taruvinga, M
Taylor, H W
Thomson, A J
Todd, R G
Townsend, J C
Vallely, A J B
Vasudaven, B

Vicarage, P H
Ward, J W
Westbrook, M A
White, P R
Woodhead, D M J
Woodhead, N J
Zala, N N

Grays

Abeyewardene, A K
Aggarwal, D R
Baban, S D A
Bansal, A
Boral, S S
Bose, A
Bramwell, R W
Brown, J T
Browning, J W
Byrne, G P
Cameron-Mowat, I C
Catton, M J
Chalkley, B D
Clarke, W H
Colburn, M
Colburn, W F
Conlan, P T M
D'Mello, J M T
Dambawinna, R
Dhillon, G S
Dobson, M H
Dunn, G O
Dutta, B
Fong, G L Y
Gold, D M
Goonewardene, S F
Gunasekara, K V
Gupta, O P
Gupta, S S K
Gurjar, P Y
Headon, O T
Hurter, M D
Jolly, G
Jones, S R
Khan, A A
Khan, K M
Khan, R S
Lake, C G
Martin, P A B
Masson, K K
Matthews, P R
Mitchell, A H
Mohile, R V
Mohile, V V
Moore, J E A
Motashaw, R D
Newell, B A T
Parikh, C
Rahim, M H
Ramachandran, M K
Sandiland, A C E
Shaikh, A
Shergill, S S
Sherrell, H E
Sidana, S S
Sirisena, W G
Smith, D G
Thompson, J A
Welch, C C

Great Missenden

Cairns, D W
Clain, A
Cottam, S-L G
Foote, C K A
Harley, D W
Hopkinson, D A
Hytten, F E
Jenkins, C E
Jenkins, L M
Kadirgamar, A G V
Kennedy, P A
Kirton, V
Laybourn, M L
Llewellyn Smith, M
McLuskie, J
Mair, J H D
Mallard-Smith, R J
Martin, R
Mitchell, M J
Neale, T W
Oliver, L J
Paintin, D B
Pattinson, J K
Peggs, K S
Pool, C J F
Purnell, N
Roberts, A J
Rogers, M H
Silver, J R

Smith, M C
Spencer, A J
Streule, M J
Thomson, H G
Tingey, W R
Trebble, T
Wadge, W J
Wilson, S J P
Withers, J E
Wood, N R
Zachariah, S E

Great Yarmouth

Absalom, S R
Adams, D E
Ahmad, N
Al-Zidgali, F
Allan, A C
Amanat, L A
Anderson, I K
Anverali, J
Ashford-Hodges, W A
Baker, H A
Barakat, A A A
Barco Marcellan, M P
Betts, A F
Black, P D
Blundell, M D
Bonner-Morgan, B M
Bonner-Morgan, R P
Branch, K G
Brown, P E
Burgess, D M
Buysse, S
Cheema, A M
Cliffe, A M
Colvin, A P
Connell, P R
Costley, W B
Cowan, F M
Cowan, J L
Crnades Tudela, E
Crick, M R
Cubie, G M
Dalliwall, K
Dalton, W T G
Dawson, J T
Del Olmo Manosa, J
Delany, O J
Dissanayake, M P
Durance, P G
Eastwood, L H
Eastwood, P R
Edelsten, A D
Ekbery, D J
Ellis, D A
Esser, G
Evans, H A
Fanous, N I
Fleetcroft, R C
Flores, M
Forster, P J G
French, A J
Gay, M P
Gerken, A
Gould, J
Gould, N S
Grabau, W J
Graham, R M
Greenwood, P A
Hamilton-Deane, W H H
Harrison, P R
Harry, T C
Hathaway, C
Hems, R A
Hind, J S
Ibrahim, G M A E-M A
Inyang, V A
Jarvis, R J T
Jesudason, K
Jewell, C
Jeyam, M
Jinadu, F O
Jones, R N
Kher, K K
Kumar, V
Lal, R
Le Jeune, H J
Liddle, A C
Liddle, G C
Livingstone, N M
Loo, W J
McDonald, H A
McIver, N K I
McLean, J G M
McMahon, P J T
Mallion, J A
Mehta, G U

Mercer, R
Miller, I M
Millican, D L
Minns, R T
Mitchell, T R
Nagpal, S
Nagpal, S
Newstead, M R
Notcutt, W G
Novak, A Z S
Oosthuysen, S A V R
Outwin, W R
Oyeleye, A O
Pace, T
Patil, D B
Payne, W S
Penn, A
Pereira, J H
Perkins, D H
Petri, G J
Poole, B J
Premachandra, D J
Rafique, M
Rumble, M
Safwat, S M M
Salvary, I A
Santori, L B
Savage, J S
Shaw, I
Simpson, A D
Singh, S K
Snobl, J
Sood, C K
Srinivasan, V
Statter, N R
Stevens, L F
Stewart, G S J A
Stuart, P J
Stuart, W H
Studley, J G N
Sturzaker, H G
Sudlow, S
Suresh Babu, G
Tadross, A A
Tillu, A B
Tooley, J R
Trigg, S L
Varadarajan, S
Verma, A K
Verma, R
Vining, R M
Watson, D G
Watson, N J
Watts, M R
Wikner, G W
Wilkinson, M J
Willamune, N B
Win, S S
Witana, K Y
Wright, M M
Wright, R M

Greenford

Abdel-Hadi, O B A
Ahmad, J
Ahmed, S
Al Asady, M H S
Alles, R M
Anderman, J E F
Barrington, P
Barton, C M
Barton, J
Choudry, A A
Corn, T H
Doherty, B M
Dollow, S C
Eckland, D J A
Finn, A M
Ganeshalingam, K
Garbett, N D
Gayed, E S
Ghataura, S S
Goraya, B S
Goraya, S S
Guha, S
Gunput, M D
Gurjar, A V
Gurjar, V G
Hanna, D
Heavey, D J
Hernon, J M
Hunjan, M S
Hurton, P B
Issac, N E
Jafree, A J
Jenkins, D A
Jenkins, M M
Jeyasingh, N
Jeyasingh, S

Jurges, E S
Kakar, S
Kapoor, K
Keerthi Kumar, S
Kooner, H S
Lewis, R A
Lones, A R W
Meehan, R A
Miall-Allen, V M
Moore, R C
Munn, S E
Narang, R S
Nasar, R B
Nizam, M
Patel, H
Prakash, S D
Rapeport, W G
Ross, I R
Rut, A R
Salahuddin, M J
Sandhu, I K
Sarantis, N
Sargent, N J
Segal, N H
Segal, S M
Safwat, S M M
Shackell, M M
Shah, R R
Sharma, P
Sharma, S D
Sil, B
Steel, H M
Swords, J
Tak, A M
Thomas, M
Vanderpuije, J A
Vessey, S J R
Wah, T M
Waiter, M R D
Webster, A
Williams, M L
Williams, P
Williams, P M
Winter, C W M
Yogendran, L
Zaki, A

Greenhithe

Bolt, C J
Bright, P E
Gopinathan, M

Greenock

Andrews, G R
Armour, A A
Ayana, A E
Ayana, M S
Barr, P S
Barron, A M K
Biggs, E A C
Blyth, A C
Campbell, D
Campbell, I B
Chan, D S L
Chee Kwan Young, Dr
Clarke, A T
Crawford, G M
Deering, A
Dickson, A R
Dilawari, J B
East, S K
Fisher, S A
Forbes, E A
Foster, D A
Gallagher, J O
Ganai, N K
Goudie, J G
Haggerty, K A
Hamilton, E M
Hannay, W F
Harkins, C M
Harkins, L H
Henderson, W B
Hillman, A
Hlaing, T T
Hulme, A W
Hyett, E L
Jamieson, J A
Jefferies, G D
Jeffery, R
Kapasi, M A
Kelly, F P
Kerr, B A
Kerr, C W
Kerridge, S C E
Khan, I H
Kohlhagen, N
Kurian, O K
Lapsley, S A
Lawrie, J D

Leighton, K M
Lockie, J
Lui, R Y H
Lyon, D
McCallum, H S
McCarey, D W
McCartney, M
McConnell, A A
McDougall, R D
McGarrity, G
McGilp, H C
Maclean, E S
McLellan, J W
Macnab, G M
McNeil, W Y
Majumder, B C
Malloch, A J
Mansfield, D C
Marshall, D A S
Moffat, J
Mohamed, M S
Monedero Isorna, M
Montgomery, J
Morrison, A M
Moultrie, P A
Munro, F J
Murdoch, F A
Murray, M H
Orr, F G G
Petrie, A J
Pettigrew, A M
Porteous, C
Pow, A A
Rainey, M G
Rakhit, D
Reidy, J J
Roach, E
Robins, J B
Roy, J
Rutherford, A
Sardar, J V K
Semple, J M
Semple, P A
Seywright, M M
Sharma, D C
Sim, Y T
Small, H M M
Sykes, R A D
Tam, W K
Tang Ing Ching, J
Taylor, E W
Taylor, J
Thomas, M A
Thompson, J B
Thomson, J E
Travers, J
Travers, K M
Valentine, C B
Vijayakumar, S
Walker, N P
Wallace, J S
Ward, R
Watt, I
Wilson, R
Wright, K C
Wyness, P J
Young, J M

Gretna

Herrick, P R
Kamar, S H
Rigg, A W
Stenhouse, S M

Grimsby

Abourawi, F I
Adhikaree, S N
Adiotomre, J A
Adiotomre, P N A
Aggarwal, N
Ahmad-Salem, M I M A R
Al-Atrakchi, S
Albuquerque, W J
Amin, A A
Amin, H H S
Anderson, J
Ashton, M A
Bagga, P
Bagga, T K
Bain, R J I
Ballantyne, J F
Bandyopadhyay, S
Barton, R O
Bellini, M J
Birch, J S
Bolaji, I I
Bora, J M
Bramwell, R G B

Bristol, K E
Bruning, T J
Buckland, H M
Bwalya, G M
Calthorpe, W R
Campbell, A E R
Carr, J M B
Carter, P A
Chalmers, I D S
Chappel, E C
Chauhan, S
Choudhury, K
Clark, J M
Collett, K A
Crombie, R B
Crowson, J D
Culshaw, T D
Cunningham, J A D J
Davies, J M
Deodhar, B G
Dobson, A H J
Donaldson, L A
East, M R
Elder, D C
Elshazali Osman, G M
Evans, G
Farhan, A-K
Finch, A A
Foulkes, K K
Fulton, G W O
Gardner, G S
Gough, M D
Gough, M B
Gowribalan, R
Gray, P L T
Guest, R
Hallewell, J W
Hanson, J
Harries, R W J
Harris, P
Heath, P
Hobbes, C J C
Holland-Keen, L B
Hopkins, E N
Hopper, D E
Hopper, M S C
Hunter, J L P
Hurst, P
Ingram, I I
James, D W
Jethwa, H
Karim, S S
Kelly, J D C
Kershaw, J B
Khan, K U
Kidson, C J
Knight, S J
Koonar, K S
Kotta, S
Kumar, R
Kweka, E L M
Kyaw Win, Dr
Laver, S R
Law, A L C
Lawless, P
Lee, T
Lopez Sanchez, J E
Luck, D J
Majumder, A K
Massey, B D
Melton, P J
Milne, A N
Mitra, S
Moss, S
Mounfield, P A
Murdoch, W
Myers, R W
Nagi, H M
Nathwani, N
Nicholson, T C
Overton, R C
Packer, P F
Panigrahi, P
Parkes, E C W
Parrish, F J
Peacock, K
Peters, W M
Picton, P
Plotnek, J S
Pool, R W
Potter, J R C
Prior, E M
Rajasekhara, K S
Roberts, J A
Roy, S
Sadiq, P I
Saha, A
Salim, G M
Salisbury, A K

Guernsey

Samy, A K E M
Samy, M A E
Sarkar, S K
Seal, R H
Severin, K M
Sharma, R P
Shaw, N M
Shweikh, A M
Sikka, O P
Sikka, S
Simhachalam, D
Singh, B
Smith, M F
Speed, K R
Stanhope, P B
Stergides, A C
Stinson, S I
Struthers, M W
Sumbwanyambe, N W
Suresh Babu, P
Tait, T J
Tandon, B
Teh, R K K
Tilston, M P
Twomey, C A
Twomey, P A
Varah, S
Vicca, A F
Ward-McQuaid, J M
Wardle, E N
Watkin, J I
Wilkin, J M
Zoon, E

Grouville

Alwitry, A
Birt, S J M C
Blandin, B O
Croft, F F
Finlaison, B H W
Fullerton, D S
Gruchy, R E
Howard, R D
Philips, F K

Guernsey

Adam, A H
Allen, K V
Allen, N H
Alsopp, R H
Andrews, C W
Arduin, M-L
Bacon, H F
Barker, R W F
Bateman, M L T
Bodkin, S E
Bolt, J F
Boyle, A S
Boyle, A G
Brand, D S
Brannan, M A
Brennand Roper, S M
Brereton, M J
Byrom, N P
Chamberlain, M R
Chankun, T S L
Costen, P D M
Creery, R D G
Daff, J A
Degnen, F H
Downing, M P R
Eddie, G
England, R A
Erskine, J
Farmer, C J
Ferguson, J
Fox, V M
Garrett, J N
Gibbs, J R
Gibson, H M
Gill, T R
Gomes, P J
Grant, J M
Grundy, F J
Guy, G W
Hanaghan, J
Haskins, R H
Heyworth, S P
Hollwey, S J
Irvine, R E
Johns, N M
Johnson, A D
King, N C
Kinross, I
Lean, B W
Lee, T R
Lewis-Jones, H J
Longan, J F
McClymont, C

Guildford

Macphail, M M
Monkhouse, C R
Moorshead, J C
Mowbray, M
Mullen, P J P
Nye, C J S
O'Donnell, A J
Oswald, G A
Paluch, N A F
Parkin, B D
Parkin, L
Pearce, J G
Pratt, C I
Pring, D J
Quanten, P P L
Raderschadt, E L
Razzak, J N
Rebstein, J
Reilly, G D
Richards, P W
Richards, S J
Riley, P A F
Robb, R C
Roussel, O N
Salisbury, B J
Seth-Smith, A B
Simpson, P
Sinnerton, T J
Smith, E J
Strickland, J E T
Sutherland, A M
Taberner, C R
Thompson, P J
Tooley, P J H
Toynton, C J
Tucker, V A E
Van Der Hauwaert, N
Warlow, A L
Williams, P G
Wilson, D S M
Wilson, S J V
Wolfe, M J
Wray, S
Yarwood, G D

Guildford

Abood, E A
Ackerley, D
Acton, G
Adams, A E
Adams, N P
Al-Khatib, F A H
Al-Ubaidi, F F
Allam, C L
Allison, H
Allison, M R
Aluwihare, A P R
Arbuckle, J D
Arnold, T D
Avis, R C
Backhouse, C I
Backhouse, O C E V M
Baerselman, G M
Bahmaie, A
Bailey, M E
Bailey, V E
Barbour, L A A
Barnardo, J N
Basarab, A O
Beaumont, J D
Bedson, C R
Behn, A R
Bell, H
Belshaw, C P
Bevington, W P
Bews, S M M
Beynon, P
Blackburn, A R
Blair, E E
Blair, R A
Bland, C J H
Bloomberg, T J
Blundell, R E
Bodgener, S
Bonnici, W
Boodhoo, M G
Booth, A J
Boxer, C M
Breimer, L H
Britton, P
Broadbridge, A T
Brookshaw, J D
Brown, J G
Cane, P J
Carlyon, A M E T
Carpenter, S
Carr-Bains, S
Carr-White, G S
Carroll, J D

Cartwright, R Y
Chambers, S
Chandrasekaran, B
Chapman, P
Chapman, S J
Christopher, A N
Chua, T P
Coates, C J
Coats, P M
Coffey, M T M
Coleman, J M
Collins, K J
Cook, M G
Cooke, J C
Cooke, V A
Cordingley, J J
Cordingley, R A
Couper, D M
Craven, R M
Cross, A P
Crutchley, E
Cummin, A R E
Cunliffe, I F
Curtis, E P P
Daborn, L G
Dalal, A
Dane, D M S
Danford, M H
Das-Gupta, A
Das, S N
Daulton, D P H
Davies, A P
Davies, J H
Davies, J H W
Davis, A K
De Lusignan, S
Dellow, E L
Demetriadi, F E
Dewar, J C
Dewhurst, J K
Domizio, S A G
Douglas, C N
Douglas, I D C
Dowson, A J
Drury, S J M D
Dumbreck, L A
Edkins, C L
Elliott, D R
Englehart, K M
Evans, C M
Evans, C M W
Evans, J
Ewart, I C
Eyre-Brook, A
Eyre-Brook, D G
Fairey, A E
Faller, C
Faulkner, E
Ferns, G A A
Ferreira, I
Field, G E
Fisher, W J
Flannery, M C
Foley, J H
Foley, P W X
Ford, D E
Fowke, R
Franks, O H B
Franks, V E
Fumi, L
Gadd, R L
Gallagher, T M
Game, D M
Garai, J G
Gibbons, J W
Gibbs, N M
Gibson-Smith, S
Gibson, P J
Goddard, P G
Godden, C W
Goodger, J L
Gordon, C J
Gosal, H S
Gray, R E S
Grisewood, H L
Grisewood, M
Groom, F H
Gross, M L P
Guest, C S
Hadwin, R J
Halfpenny, D V A
Hall, J R
Halliwell, I K
Hampson, S W
Han, C F
Harvey, M P
Hatrick, R I
Hayes, M M
Helliwell, C J V

Hepburn, E L
Heslop, I H
Hibbert, J
Hillard, K A
Hillman, H
Hockey, A J
Holliday, M G
Hornett, G A W
Howard, L C
Humphrys, C M
Hunter, M G C A
Hurdle, A D F
Isaac, J
Jackson-Richmond, J
Jackson, E G A
Jackson, P A
James, S E
Jayarajan, V
Jenkins, J G
Jenkins, T P N
Johnson, P A
Jones, A K
Jones, R V
Jordan, M J
Jump, A E
Kalu, G U
Karanjia, C R
Karanjia, N D
Keenan, J M
Kefford, S J E
Kemball, G A
Kemp, F G
Keown, C E
King, M O
Kissin, C M
Kissin, M W
Knight, C A
Laing, R W
Langley, S E M
Laurence, D T
Lawrenson, R A
Leatham, E W
Lee, E
Lee, N J
Leigh, J M
Lennox, H R G
Lockie, A H
Longman, R J
Lopez, A J
Lukaszewicz, C M
McAllister, W A C
Macdonald-Watson, A
McDonald, M
MacGregor, G A
MacMillan, D M
McMullan, C A
Magnussen, P A
Manning, M F
Marks, C G
Marks, V
Marsh, D L
Marsh, J E
Merry, J
Metcalfe, C
Mingo, R M
Morgan, M B F
Morrison, M C
Moss, S M
Neal, A J
Nichols, J A A
Nickells, J S
Nigam, A K
Norris, J S
Notley, R G
O'Connell, M P
Oh, C J E
Osterlund, P J
Oxenbury, J L
Paremain, T J
Parsons, H M
Pash, R
Pike, C P
Piper, S
Powell, J H P
Prakash, R S
Price, J L
Prior, J J
Purkayastha, B B
Qureshi, T I
Rathnavarma, C V R
Rauh, P B
Rawal, K M
Rayner, C M
Read, M T F
Rees, J D G
Reid, K W
Rendall, J
Riaz, N U
Rimmer, A F G

Robbins, G
Roberts, A P
Robertson, N P
Robins, D G
Rossdale-Smith, G J
Rosson, J W
Rowe-Jones, J M
Roy, D K
Rushen, J E
Rushton, K L
Ryalls, M R
Sales, R A
Sarin, U
Saunders, P R
Schweitzer, F A W
Scott, J C R
Sekhawat, B S
Sender, J
Seth, V
Shankland, P M
Sharpe, E L
Shires, P R
Shirley, J A
Shoeb, I H A-H
Sisson, J
Slater, E V
Slater, G H
Slater, I
Sleight, S P
Smith, M R
Smith, M G M
Smith, M J
Sockett, G J P
Solomons, N B
Stebbing, J F
Stiles, P J
Stoner, K B
Sudderick, R M
Sutton, C J G
Sutton, J A
Swindale, F E
Tahir, S S
Tansley, R G
Tarzi, M D
Taylor, J D
Taylor, J S
Taylor, M W
Thomas, B A
Thomson, W G
Tinkler, A M
Titheridge, K L
Tomlinson, M J
Trend, P S J
Trigg, H A
Tutin, A F
Tutin, A M
Tyrrell, G R
Van Every, T H
Wachtel, S L
Walsh, R N
Watson, S J
Weir, N F
West, G M L
West, P
Whitaker, D C
Whitaker, J F
Whitcroft, S I J
White, A J
White, W F
Whitelaw, E A
Whiteley, M S
Wilkinson, A B
Willett, C J
Williams, E S
Williams, J G
Wong, E
Wong, G E
Worthington, S
Wright, D A
Wright, J W
Xavier, S M
Zaidi, S M N

Guisborough

Ashraf, A
Begg, F M
Bell, A J
Bergin, A J
Brownlee, M J
Davis, P A
Dobie, F D
Dobson, L P
Emmerson, W R
Gale, J
Garry, R
Gilliat, J M F
Halloway, A J
Hilton, A
Hobkirk, D W

Irving, S A
Katib, J
Lewis, A M
Marr, D C
Newnam, P T F
Phillips, A G
Smith, A J
Thomas, G L
Williams, S M
Young, M J

Gullane

Auld, J W
Barr, S C G
Berry, J W
Blackett, W L
Brough, C
Cusworth, C J
Durie, A W
Eunson, P D
Hislop, J A
MacLellan, P D
MacLennan, W D
McPhail, P M
McRobbie, I S
Quigley, M G
Robertson, K S
Seymour, I C

Gunnislake

Bowhay, A A
Buxton, N D
Hampton, T R W
Heslop, J V M
Hines, D
Powell, D
Stewart, A P

Haddington

Alexander, G
Alexander, L L
Anderson, M H G
Baptie, J A
Barden, M E
Bethell, J H
Branwood, A W
Brown, J K
Fulton, J F
Glendinning, S M R
Hastings, P D
Henderson, J H
Hogg, V J
Holton, D E
Laidlaw, S C
Langlands, R W D
Lavelle, F M M
Lawson, R J
McInnes, K E
Mercer, G W
Mogey, G A
Preston, T R
Riddle, W J R
Rogers, T D
Sheldon, A J L
Waddell, J L
Wright, H W

Hagley

Heywood, T R

Hailsham

Ahmed, S K
Alston, R H
Appleby, E L
Baker, G R H
Barron, J A
Clarke, N H C
Croucher, M D
Cynk, M S
D'Souza, M A J
Davison, D A
Doraiswamy, W
Dunphy, P W
Elliott, C G
Emslie, M J
Gardner, G A
Griffiths, S S
Hanraty, D A
Haydn Smith, P
Hays, P L
Heap, B J
Holden, J S F
Holmes, P C B
Hope-Gill, M C
Jenkins, A F
Johnson, R
Knight, M B
MacLeod, A
Mason, J
Matravers, P J

Pearce, A J
Riddle, J A
Torkington, J
Tourle, C A
Turner, J A
Turner, J
Wainwright, C J
Williamson, J H
Young, J H

Halesowen

Ajam-Oghli, A R
Akufo-Tetteh, H N
Allen, H C
Ayliffe, G A J
Ball, C J
Bassan, L S
Bathija, A S
Briant, J L
Campbell, D J
Carr, A C
Coates, S J
Constantine, G
Cosslett, N M
Cutler, D H
Daniels, E P
Darby, J H
Dervish, O O
Dervish, S D
Gibbons, A R
Gingell, K H
Gurney, I
Hadden, G C
Hadden, P
Halford, C F
Hall, A D
Hall, J A
Hegarty, D M
Hegarty, K A
Holburn, C J
Holzer, R S
Horsburgh, T B
Hughes, C C M
Hunt, H
Hyne, S J
Jackson, A R
Jenkins, N P
Johnson, B P
Johnson, R A
Khetani, M J
Lai, C W Y
Lee, C
Lennie, J E
Levett, J S
Lewis, R A
Little, R M
Lloyd, H
Love, G M
McCrory, C R L
McNeil, W T
Michell, N P
Mina, A G
Modi, V
Qaiyum, M-U
Saffar, N
Shevket, M
Southam, R J
Spychal, R T
Thorns, R
Thornton, M R
Vamadevan, T

Halesworth

Abbott, A B
Anderson, A J
Baker, S M
Dickson, J M H
Forsythe, D E
Lock, S
Mair, G I
Northover, C S
Peel, D M
Roy, R R
Shapland, J M

Halifax

Ahmed, S R
Aitchison, I
Aiyappa, K S
Akram, A P
Aldabbagh, A
Alderson, C L
Alderson, P J
Anand, V K
Anderson, C M S
Aslam, W
Aspinall, S R
Awan, A W
Bailie, R
Bain, R B

Harrogate

Bamber, P A
Bamforth, M
Banerjee, A K
Banerjee, S
Bangar, V
Barnes, G H
Bartholomew, K M
Bateman, J
Bazaraa, T A S
Binns, H A
Bogoda, D
Bolland, H M
Britto, D J J
Brock, S H
Brown, R T
Bukunola, B
Burley, D
Calvert-Wilson, I
Cameron, W J
Carsley, H A
Carter, P A
Chadwick, C J
Chandratre, P S
Chandratre, S N
Chater, S N
Chatterjee, J H
Chaudhry, Q
Chavda, J L
Chiang, M S
Choucri, M C A
Clay, C B
Clayton-Stead, A J
Clogher, L
Clowes, M A
D'Ambrogio, V J
Davies, M A
Debono, M A
Drucquer, J K
Dunning, T L
Dyson, S J
Edwards, A T
Edwards, R J
El-Bereir, G M A
Ellahi, T
Ellis, G N
Ellwood, D S
Esmond, J R
Evans, A C
Felton, H M
Fernandez, B
Findlay, M J
Flood, B M
Freeman, M N
Galvin, H L
Galvin, T J
Gardiner, S C
Garnett, J E
Garson, R A
Glencross, I H
Goffe, T R P
Goodall, R J R
Goyal, P
Goyal, S K
Grant, S C D
Green, S R
Gunson, E J
Gupta, J
Gupta, P K
Hamilton, S M
Handsley, R D
Hanson, M R
Hardy, R L
Hasnain, R T-U
Hava, M A S
Haynes, V K
Highley, M S
Hosker, K J
Houghton, M W
Howell, J H
Hussain, I
Hussain, I
Hutchinson, C H
Hyland, R K
Johnson, R V
Kanumilli, N
Kazi, A M M A
Killeen, A-M
King, L
Kumar, K V
Lalor, B C
Lesser, P J A
Lord, L
Lumb, K M
McKennell, J
MacKinnon, M W B
McMichael, C M
Maguire, J P
Malenda, A N
Mannall, I G

Manthy, I
Marks, R P M
Mayland, F A
Moncrieff, A B
Mulder, M
Murphy, F A
Muscat-Baron, J
Nortcliffe, S A
Nunn, D
Oade, Y A
Orange, R W
Ormerod, I R
Oyston, J K
Parikh, B K
Parry, C S
Patrick, R K
Pickles, L J
Price, F M
Qureshi, M S A
Ramanathan, C
Robertson, S
Rocheteau, M S
Rogawski, K M
Rosovske, B M
Roulson, J-A
Rust, J H
Saadien-Raad, M
Salt, S D
Sawczyn, P G
Scriven, N A
Sen, B
Shakir, I
Shetty, P R
Shukla, V K
Smith-Moorhouse, G P
Smith, D I H
Smith, P J W
Somerville, I D
Somerville, J J F
Spaine, L A
Spencer, J G
Spencer, S R
Steed, A J
Storah, P K
Strachan, J
Sukumaran, S O
Sutton, L N
Tandon, A P
Taylor, C L
Taylor, D A
Taylor, J V
Taylor, R G
Than Htay, Dr
Thiriloganathan, S
Thomas, G D H
Thomson, J
Thornber, S
Ullah, H
Vaughan, R
Walker, S M
Williams, S
Wyllie, G A M
Wynn, P A
Younis, Y
Zepeda, A R

Sim, C G
Taylor, G S
Thomson, D A

Hamilton

Anderson, A V
Anderson, D N
Baboolal, A W
Barr, D M
Barton, P J M
Birney, S M
Black, K M
Braithwaite, C P
Brown, D R
Brown, F L
Brown, R H
Burleigh, A I
Campbell, M-A
Cromie, D T
Curtis, M
Dawson, C A
Dobbie, D T
Duncan, J
Equi, A C
Findlay, S
Fowler, G E
Gaddis, S
Grant, J M
Hamilton, L M
Hannah, J A M
Herbert, M M
Howie, E M
Howie, R M
Hunter, I P
Ide, C W
Insh, A M
Irvine, K G
Keenan, M C
King, A E
Kohli, H S
Koteswara Rao, M
Lynas, B R
McCorkindale, C M C
McFarlane, M
McLay, R K
Maclean, J
McMenamin, J J
McMurray, P C
Marshall, L J
Mathie, D S
Miller, J M
Moir, D C
Murray, S A
Naismith, D S
Ogilvie, D B
Palmer, D E
Park, H M
Paterson, M E
Russell, S L
Smyth, S C
Stewart, C P
Stewart, M H
Sullivan, A
Tansey, B J
Tansey, M T
Tsang, S W M
Wardle, J C R
Webster, A M
Wedlock, K
White, S M
Wickes, A D
Wilson, A A
Wilson, I D
Young, W C
Young, W M

Hampton

Acharya, B S S
Bal, V S
Baldwin, J M
Bhatia, K S S
Bignall, S
Brenner, E R
Brooks, A A
Butters, J
Carty, P A
Chaku, S K
Clarke, D J A
Cribb, R J
Dave, S D
Davey, A T
Davies, D H
Davies, M R B
Davison, L M
Devaraj, A
Devaraj, S
Dhalla, P
Dighe-Deo, D
Feilerg, K A

Green, R C L
Gupta, S
Halnan, K E
Hinton, R M
Ho, T B L
Howard, N M
Irving, C J
Isaac, R G
Kember, S M
Knights, K V
Kurl, D K
Kurl, L
Lewis, G J
Lynch, D
Lynch, O
Millis, R A
Mitchell-Heggs, C A W
Nielsen, E
O'Donovan, M J
Rieck, J
Subramanyam, P V
Walkden, L
Whyte-Venables, D H
Wile, D B
Williams, R
Woodroffe, D
Wright, A J
Young, J F

Harefield

Lazem, F J

Harlech

Crowe, J B

Harleston

Compton, J
Dinn, A J
Frew, P W
Heath, M J
Kemp, A H
Kemp, P W
Maidment, J C H
Way, B J

Harlow

Abraham, S M
Ackroyd, J S
Al-Samarraie, M T K T
Allen, K H
Allen, P W
Anthony, R Y
Arfman, M H J
Ashar, K N
Bachtalia, P
Bailey, K
Bansal, S
Barber, C J
Barker, K F
Bedford, C A
Bellingham, J M
Beshyah, S A
Bishop, C W
Busby, J C
Campbell, M
Chan, R H
Chhibber, A D
Chhibber, F A
Chowdhury, M H
Chowdhury, N
Compton, C H
Court, M
Crossley, D J
Daniels, S
Daud, S
Davis, J B
Dillon, J A
Dilly, S G
Dixon, G W
Dodd, H
Dunbar, G C
Elamin, M E
Firth, S A
Flaye, D E
French, R C
George, T H G
Gerlis, K L
Gerlis, R D
Green, J
Hamilton, I G
Hemming, C E
Higgens, E W
Hughes, J P
Ingham, E J
Jacobs, M C
Kapasi, F M
Kawa, Z I
Khimji, H M R
Kozdon, A
Lam, T S-T

Lamb, C E M
Leek, C A
Lockwood, J E
Long, M A
Lurkins, M D
Mays, C S
Meehan, D M
Mistry, P
Mitchell, A
Mitchell, K N
Morgan, R F
Nairn, D S
Nash, W N C
Nicholson, P A
O'Riordan, D C
Orrell, M W
Oxley, V E
Pajwani, K S
Paliwala, A H
Peck, R W
Perez-Morales, M M
Phillips, J A J
Phillips, R H
Portelly, J P
Potluri, B S
Presland, A H
Preston, D M
Radhakrishnan, T
Rajani, M H
Richards, C H
Roberts, M J
Roddis, M J
Rogers, S P
Rose, L C
Sharnagiel, Z M
Sharnagiel, Z
Sharpe, P C
Slack, R F Y
Slack, W K
Smalley, C
Smalley, D S
Sreeharan, N
Stoner, S J
Swainsbury, J S
Tasker, T C G
Taylor, A M
Thomas, S E A
Tollinton, H J
Tully, K N
Vanner, A M
Warren, J P
Watson, P H
Weaver, E J M
Williams, M P
Wood, M E
Yogasakaran, N
Zeitlin, H
Zych, Z

Harpenden

Addiscott, C L
Argyle, C M
Bail, H C K K
Balderamos-Price, J M
Barber-Lomax, C A
Barrett, J D
Bayer, C J
Belderbos, S M
Bird, D O
Bolger, J P
Brazier, E A
Cashyap, A
Chafer, A T H
Chandra Raj, I
Chandraraj, R
Chatterjee, D
Christie, J S
Clarke, M D
Cole, A B J
Connolly, C N M
Connolly, H M C
Cook, C J
Cranston, D P
Davies, K S
Davis, N J
Davis, S J
Dudley, B M
Eardley, A J N
Edmundson, P A E
Evans, S R
Evers, A M A
Farrow, C A
Feeney, A J
Feeney, M A
Festenstein, F
Gibbs, R J
Gibson, R B
Goodwin, T G
Habeshaw, J A

Hale, J F
Hall, T
Harris, G E
Hemsi, D N
Henshaw, D J E
Hodgson, R S
Holmes, G W
Holmes, G M
Horwell, D H
Howell, C M
Huck, J D
Hughes, G K
Hyams, G M
Hyman, A O
Impey, J A
Ingram, S D
Jack, M J E S
Jones, R B
Kapadia, R D
Keir, P M
Khwaja, A
Kramer, S L
Lamb, K M
Langdon, J A
Lawson, P J
Le Dune, M A
Logan, R F L
Long, E K
Loweth, S M
Mann, K A
Marsden, H L
Miller, R B
Mills, K E
Mitchell, I C
Morley, D C
Nanayakkara, G
Newbury-Ecob, R A
Nicholson, J P
Norbrook, P J
Ostler, P J
Owen, R
Owens, O J D
Phillips, D G L
Pirie, B G
Pocock, K N J
Quinn, D C
Rajah, A
Ramsay, R
Reid, P C
Robinson, A E
Sanderson, G
Sanderson, R L
Shahrad, P
Smith, S
Stirling, C F M
Stranders, A P O
Tattersfield, J F
Tolia, J J
Walker, R C
Walker, R
Wang, M K
Williams, M F
Wozencroft, E M
Wright, D J
Yellowlees, H

Harrogate

Aldred, J E
Alexander, I B
Amaku, E E
Asaad, I
Asaad, L
Atkinson, F M
Baker, R F
Banks, P C
Bannatyne, D F
Bargh, I A
Barlow, A F
Barrett, L M
Beaini, A Y
Beardsell, I D M
Beer, H L
Beer, M J
Beer, R A
Bennett, R R
Bird, A
Blaydes, K E
Bowker, J R
Boyle, S P
Bradwell, R A
Bray, M K
Bridge, G W K
Brotheridge, S P
Brothwell, J A
Buxton, E J
Bynoe, A G
Calvert, R M
Campbell, A J
Campbell, J R

Halstead

Ambross, A M
Angwin, R A P
Bainbridge, D R
Bainbridge, I M
Beadle, M R
Bristol, M P
Burton, J H
Davis, P S
Duffus, P J
Edwards, N V
Giblin, M E
Gordon, B S
Gordon, R R
Green, R A
Harkness, J
Healy, M J
Jones, S E
Markham, J E
Morgan, K L
Newhouse, S M
Plaut, G S
Salmon, N J
Spencer, B J
Symington, A J F
Train, P
Wright, R

Haltwhistle

Baines, P
Mackie, G E
Ridley, J G
Ridley, P G

Harrow

Carey, M L
Carradine, S
Chan, P S F
Chave-Cox, C
Chave-Cox, R V
Chetcuti, P A J
Conway, K M
Coral, A P
Cornford, S E
Cory, P
Crawfurd-Porter, V E
Creasey, J M
Critchley, I V
Critchley, J M A
Crouch, G A
Cubitt, K A
Cundall, R D
Cutler, P G
Da Costa, A A
Dandie, C E J
Day, M S
Dennis, R W
Dias, B P
Dias, J-P
Dodwell, D J
Dyke, G W
Ellis, M
Emmis, K J
Exley, K A
Fairfield, G E
Falshaw, R L
Fennerty, A G
Foley, S
Fountain, F M
Fowler, O J W
Fraser, I D
Fraser, S E
Frater, R A S
Furniss, D A
Gammack, A J
Gardiner, S
Gasser, A J
Gentle, W A
Gillies, D R N
Gilmore, D A
Givans, R J
Gledhill, A
Gohil, S R
Gold, T
Goldsborough, D
Gordon, G D
Goulding, J A
Goulding, S T
Gray, C
Greenwood, S
Hain, B
Halaka, A N A M
Hall, C J
Hall, R S
Hammond, C M
Hammond, P J
Handley, A K
Hardcastle, J E
Harrison, G L
Harrison, J D
Haves, S E
Heatley, P J
Henderson, J E
Holliday-Rhodes, A D
Holmes, P J L
Houston, M E
Hulse, W
Hutcheon, M H
Ikpeme, J O
Ingles, E M
Ireland, I W
Jackson, R C
James, D G H
Jamieson, A E
Jan, S M
Jessop, S
Jones, P A
Jones, R S
Joyner, S R
Kaye, P D C
Kaza, M
Kaza, R
Kendrew, A
Kidd, L C
King, A M
Kingscote, A D
Kingscote, J M
Knox, R A
Laird, A M
Larkin, H
Law, H
Lawson, A H
Lawson, D G B
Layton, A M

Leach, M A
Leach, S L
Leinhardt, D J
Lewis, I H
London, N J
McClure, L
McEnery, R S K
McEvoy, M W
McIntosh, I M
Mackay, D E
Macklin, J P
MacLeod, D A
McLusky, E G C
McNamara, H P
McPherson, S J
Mahapatra, S B
Malseed, G J
Mann, E T
Mark, J P
Marks, E N
Marshall, P R
Marshall, W
Martin, M F R
Mason, M K
Mather, F M V
Mather, N J V
Metcalfe, T W
Miller, J C
Milne, I S
Milner, J C
Moore, H S C
Moore, M D
Moore, S M L
Morgan, C
Moss, H A
Moss, L H
Mumford, J D
Murray, D K
Nehaul, J J
Newman, R J
O'Neill, M S G
Parkin, G
Penman, R A
Perkins, C A
Platts, S H B
Polito, T C
Polson, G M
Prakash, H C
Quartson, J K
Rawson, I A
Reffitt, D M
Richards, C A L
Richards, I D G
Ricketts, A L
Rider, M A
Rider, S J C
Riley, J M
Rose, J F
Ross, H G
Rowell, E R M
Rugg, A J
Russell, E
Ryan, C M
Saagandi, F W
Sarin, G
Sarma, A
Sarma, J
Sawers, A D I
Scatchard, M A
Scott-Knox-Gore, C L
Scullion, D A
Sharp, R J
Shepherd, G H
Shire, C M E
Short, L C
Shriman Narayan, R
Sinclair, B E
Smith, D E
Smith, M M
Snaith, R P
Spain, J R
Speight, M B
Spencer, R M
Stanworth, A W
Stollard, G E
Stuart, J P
Stuart, N
Suffern, M A
Suffern, W S
Sullivan, C J
Sultan, H Y
Sweeney, R C
Swindells, S R
Symon, T
Tam-Lit, J W-S
Tate, G T
Taylor, D S
Taylor, E
Taylor, N P

Thirlwall, P J
Thompson, A C
Thompson, I D
Thornton, T J
Toop, M J
Town, V J
Travers, C V
Turner, R D
Tyler, G N
Vincenti, G E P
Wadd, N J
Ward-Campbell, G J
Ward, J P
Ward, J L C
Ward, J F C
Warren, J
Waterworth, A M
Watson, A N
Watson, C G
Webster, R A
Weeks, P J
Whitaker, J J
White, D A
Whiteside, O
Wild, S M
Wilken, E H
Wilson, W
Woods, A J
Woods, J C
Wrigley, P F M
Young, J D

Harrow

Abrar, S
Abu Mahfouz, F I S
Adler, L M
Ahluwalia, S
Ahmad, S
Ainley, R M
Ajina, I A A H
Akhtar, N
Akhtar, S
Akinwunmi, J O
Al-Adnani, M
Al-Masri, A A-K
Al-Mousawi, A H F
Al-Mrayat, M A-J K
Allan, L G
Allard, S
Alli, M O
Amin, K M
Andrews, P J
Anstee, Q M
Asante-Siaw, J
Auerbach, R
Bamdad, S
Barnard, M L
Barrington, A J
Bartlett, M J
Bartram, C I
Bates, H
Bentley, P I
Bessant, R
Bethell, H W L
Bhagat, A
Bhandari, J
Bhide, S A
Blair, M E
Blazquez Angulo, J A
Bliss, P W
Bodani, H
Bodani, M
Bodin, M A
Boote, H O
Bounds, G A
Boyle, S
Brady, A F
Brogan, C M O C
Brooker, J C
Budgett, R G M
Burke, M
Carapeti, E A
Carney, M
Carney, M W P
Chadwick, S J D
Chadwick, T S
Chait, I B
Charlton, J S
Chatlani, P T
Chatterji, U
Cherry, P M H
Chidambaram, M
Chowdhury, A S
Chua, E S K
Cliff-Patel, S
Coden, B
Cohen, D L
Cohen, R I
Colbeck, R A

Collins, D R
Costello, M M
Cullen, R M
Cumberworth, V L
Cummins, S M
D'Almada Remedios, D J
Daniels, C C
Das, P K
Dattani, M
Davey, M E
David, P J
Davidson, R N
de Lacey, G J
De Las Heras Garcia, L
De Silva, G U Y
De Silva, R D D
Dean, M R
Denman, A M
Devine, M E
Dhillon, R S
Dhillon, S S
Dobbs, R J
Duggal, V
Eddington, M P
Enoch, M A
Esah, K M
Farooqi, S M A
Feizi, T
Ferguson, H A
Fernandes, C F
Fernandez, S M B
Fisch, L
Forbes, A
Forrest, M R
Forster, S D
Fraenkel, M
Frank, A O
Freedman, L S
Fyfe, I S
Gabe, S M
Gallagher, G M
Garrett, C
George, K
Gill, S K
Gleeson, M J
Golden, G A
Goldfoot, M T
Goldstein, S Y
Goonewardene, T I
Graham, G W S
Grayeff, S B
Green, M C D
Green, R
Greenstein, D
Grigor, C J
Gumpel, J M
Gunasinghe, N U
Gupta, P
Hand, A
Haque, K M
Harbin, L
Harries, M G
Harris, J W
Hassan, N
Haworth, F L M
Hayat, S
Hayward, J A
Hegarty, M K
Herath, S N B
Hershon, H I
Hewlett, A M
Higgens, C S
Hilton, C F
Hinton, J
Horkan, M C
Horwitz, N I
Hughes, M P
Hughes, R T
Hull, J A
Hunjan, A S
Huq, S M
Hussain, F F
Hussain, M
Hwong, M-T
Hyer, W F
Jacobs, B
Jacyna, M R
Jaffe, R
Jaibaji, M M
Janossy, G
Janossy, K M
Jayesinghe, D C R
Jefferys, P M
Jeganathan, S
Jenkins, S E
Jogarajah, T
Justice, J M
Kamlin, C O F

Kamm, M A
Katz, D E
Kausar, M
Kaye, P J
Keat, A C
Kelshiker, A R
Kelshiker, R Y
Kelshiker, S Y
Keshtgar, M R S
Kessling, A M
Khaja, G
Khan, M R H
Khurjekar, S
King, Q G A
Kitchen, P A
Knottenbelt, C M
Knottenbelt, J D
Knottenbelt, R G
Kon, M W S
Kulasekeram, V
Kulkarni, P R
Kulkarni, S P
Kumar, A
Kurzer, A J
Lachman, P I
Lakhanpaul, R S
Lancer, R
Landau, R
Landau, S C
Lazarus, S
Lee Chong, L P F
Lee, J H T
Lee, L C L
Lee, V
Lever, L R
Leverton, T J
Levine, T S
Levy, M L
Lewis, A J
Lixi, G
Lloyd, D J
Loughlin, P J
Loughnan, B A
McCloghry, F J
McCullough, C J
McDonald, A H
McDonald, P J
McIntyre, W
McNally, J D
Malnick, S D H
Malone-Lee, J G
Malone, M J
Manickarajah, P
Mann, S D
Marks, S D
Marshall, S A
Massoud, A F
Mathur, C P
Mee, A D
Mehta, P C
Mehta, S P
Melhuish, H F
Merali, N R
Michaelson, S
Middleton, S B
Missula, A S
Mistry, A D
Mistry, H G
Moore, A F K M
Morgan, D J
Moriarty, M A
Morrell, J M B
Morris, L
Muller, K G
Mullerat, J
Munn, A D
Munshi, F R
Muraleedaran, R
Naik, S
Nathwani, A
Nathwani, D C
Navein, J F
Nayar, A
Newton, M
Nicholl, R M
Nithyanandarajah, G A L
Njoku, L I
Noakes, J E
Northover, J M A
Nurmohamed, A
Ogden, C W
Oyesanya, O A
Paffenholz, M
Paktsun, L W-P
Pallawela, G D S
Pandya, M D
Paraskeva, P A
Parnell, K E

Pasupathy, A
Pasvol, G
Patel, A
Patel, A G
Patel, D K C
Patel, F
Patel, H B
Patel, J R D
Patel, N P
Patel, P C
Patel, S
Patel, S
Patel, T K
Paterson, J S
Paun, S H
Peiris, J G C
Pereira, R S
Persey, M R
Peter, L H
Peters, W
Phillips, R K S
Pitcher, M C L
Poblete Gribbell, M X
Priddy, A R A
Pugh, S J
Qureshi, R
Radhakrishnan, S
Ragbir, R
Rajabali, S
Ralleigh, G
Ramachandra, V
Ranganathan, S
Ravikumar, V
Regunathan, P
Renton, S C
Reuben, J R
Reynolds, P J
Rhodes, M T
Richards, P
Riley, K J
Robinson, A C
Robinson, C G G
Roden, A T
Rogers, L A
Ross, J
Rozewicz, D P
Rutter, M D
Ryan, R M
Sado, G D
Saifuddin, A
Saleh, A
Samadi, N
Saravanamuthu, J
Sargeant, C F
Saunders, B P
Savundra, P A
Scambler, P J
Senanayake, H M
Senathirajah, S S
Senior, R
Seyan, S S A S
Shackleton, G E
Shah, B N
Shah, D
Shah, K P
Shah, N C
Shah, R
Shah, S R
Shah, S K
Shaida, W A
Shaikh, S
Sharma, S M
Sharp, P S
Shaw, A J
Shek, F W-T
Sherif, T
Shukla, R B
Silva, O S G
Sinnatamby, S
Smart, A C
Sodhi, M S
Sodhi, S M
Spencer, J A D
Srikantharajah, I
Stephens, N G
Stephens, R
Subzposh, S Y A
Sufraz, R
Suri, R
Suri, S
Swinburn, J M A
Tadrous, P J
Talbot, I C
Tam, D
Taor, P J
Taylor, P C A
Taylor, V M
Thakrar, J P
Thanabalasingham, Y

Hawick

Thilaganathan, B
Thiruchelvam, T R
Thirunathan, J
Thomas, R M
Thomson, H H
Timlin, M A
Topper, R
Turner-Stokes, L F
Twomey, B P
Vaughan, D J A
Victory, J G G
Vijayanathan, S
Vohra, A D
Vora, M S
Vyas, J
Walsh, W J
Warren, N P
Warren, P J
Wasu, P S
Watkins, S D
Webber, A P
Wee, C E L
Weerasinghe, B P
Weerasinghe, P M
Wells, G J
Whitehead, E M
Wignakumar, V
Wijendra, S D
Wijesurire, J J
Williams, C B
Wilson, J A
Wilson, S Y
Windsor, A C J
Winterborn, C J
Wong, C P
Wong, M C-C
Woyka, W J G
Yahia, B E A A S
Yale, V
Yaqoob, R
Young, N J A
Zuhrie, S R

Hartfield

Caseley, J R
Cochrane, T D
Furneaux, P J S
Gardner, D C
Hancock, P J
Hellmann, K

Hartlepool

Adair, A D
Agarwal, A K
Ahmad, M H-U
Anam, Z
Andelic, S H
Apte, P P
Armstrong, R W W
Awad, A H
Ayre, M A
Bansal, P
Berry, J
Berry, M
Bew, D P
Bowden, W M
Brash, C J H G
Brodie, J E
Brown, W A
Bruce, D W
Burrell, P G
Cacciato, A M
Cooper, A P
Crow, J
Cummins, N L
Daniel, J H D
De Miguel Artal, M
Downs, A P
Dunn, N A
Dunstone, J H
Eaton, A H
El Menahawey,
M A-A A
Emmerson, C M
Faiyaz, F
Fisher, M L
Fortune, L D
Fraser, A
Frater, J K S
Frost, G
Gallagher, J
George, I R
Gibson, R
Hasham, F M R V
Hazle, S K
Heggs, C G
Holmes, A R
Hovenden, J L
Howe, J B

Jani, J
Johnston, F R P
Johnstone, A A
Jwad, A I
Kalmanovitch, D V A
Khan, M C
Kidambi, A V
Kipling, D
Kirby, K M
Kirby, R
Knaggs, T W L
Leigh, J M
Lennox, C M E
Ljunggren, A M O
Lowcock, J
Lowry, W M
McGowan, P F
McGregor, W S P
McKinty, M C
McLatchie, G R
McNaughton, A R
Malone, J P
Martin, A M E
Memon, M A
Milligan, G J
Moncrieff, R
Moody, R G
Murali Krishnan, M
Nagesh-bandi, H A
Nicholson, O P
Oldroyd, D
Oliver, S M
Omer, F
Pagni, P A
Parameswaram, S
Parker, C D
Pickens, P T
Port, A M
Quinn, N D
Reece, D A
Reece, M F
Relton, P G S
Richardson, R W
Roberts, S A M
Robinson, B W
Roy, M K
Russell, F R
Russell, I S
Shaheen, M A E-K
Simpson, A N
Simpson, R L
Singh, A K
Smith, J T
Smith, M J
Smith, M I
Southward, R D
Stoves, C
Strain, E O
Strain, G A
Sutton, P P
Symon, D N K
Tang, S C
Thompson, J
Tildesley, G
Tosson, S R
Trimming, H M
Trory, G H
Tuma, T A-K
Wajid, M A
Watson, J M
Watson, L A
Welch, R G
Whipp, M J
Windram, J D
Wong, J S K
Wood, D
Worthy, J N
Youart, A
Young, A H

Harwich

Alldrick, A R
Balin, G V
Child, S W
Christie, S W
Collins, B B
Ford, G C
Hoskyns, J C
Lovely, B E
Menzies, C J G
Nightingale, P J
Perry, J R
Rankin, J G
Sood, A K
Strachan, J C M
Sullivan, B A
Sullivan, J V
Thompson, R C W

Wilson, R J
Wynne, A T

Haslemere

Ashwood, N
Bawtree, D W
Beatson-Hird, P C
Campbell, C G
Cant, M E
Chapple, D C L
Chapple, S O
Claridge, M W C
Cornish, J W M
Cowan, M M
Davis, J M E
Elliott, D H
Fleming, J W
Forsythe, F M
French, J
Ftyaras, G E
Hampson, E K
Hanly, D J
Houchin, P J
Hunter, A L
Hurst, M
Jones, J T
Low, F M
McKenzie, C G
O'Sullivan, W J
Osborne, P A
Pakenham-Walsh, J T
Panchaud, M L T
Randall, G R
Richards, T M
Ridsdill Smith, P A
Sanways, D M
Senapati, M K
Senapati, R
Sharratt, M
Sherriff, R G
Stoneham, J R
Sutcliffe, P J
Taylor, C P
Tharian, B
Thomas, A A L
Tomes, J S
Townsend, H A
Wathen, S J
Wilks, M
Willson-Pepper, C R

Hassocks

Armitage, E N
Bellamy, J D F
Blair, E J
Christie, T H
Cook, R I
Deering, R B
Farrands, P A
Forsdick, P B
Fraser, A C L
Free, L C
Glasgow, I L
Haigh, A C
Harper, R H
Hawkins, D I
Heeley, P J M
Jeffery, R N
Jenkinson, J L
Juniper, C P
Keat, E C B S
Kemp, R J
Kinane, C F S
Knight, R
MacDermot, V D
Meeks, A C G
Moore, A H
Morris, M T
Murrell, D S
Quibell, E P
Rawlinson, W A L
Reid, H S
Reid, S A
Shearn, C A
Stevens, M
Tombleson, P M J
Tunnadine, C H J
Valentine, W H
Wheeler, R H

Hastings

Bennett, G G
Bradley, R
Bramwell, S O
Bray, L M U
Braybon, E C
Braybon, K W
Chinery, C G
Chisholm-Batten, R E
Cliff, G B

Connor, J A
Cooper, C
Cooper, T F M
Das, P
Davy, P H
Dhalla, P N
Doe, J C
Driver, N P
Dutchman, D A J
Geater, J G
Giles, J A
Haines, A M
Head, A C
Henry, J G
Hicks, I R
Higginson, B M
Hollman, C E
Horsley, I T
Howie, F J T
Hughes, H E
Jadresic, A
Jones, L O
King, D
Kumar, R
Lambie, L
Lee, C G
Meredith, A P E
Metson, M J
Mohan Krishna, N
Nicholson, H P
Paget, S E
Paget, S C
Patel, H C
Prosser, B M
Radia, K
Seal, P L
Sheill, M J
Sinclair, J M
Stewart, S C
Stuart, I M
Waller, C M
Whelan, D E
Whincup, G
Wilcox, G E
Wisby, L R
Wright, A P
Wright, W M A

Hatfield

Ahmed, S A
Brooks, R V
Campbell, I A
Clements, S
Colter, E F
Davies, G S
Davies, I B
Durkin, A
Dymoke, J P
Dytham, N K
Elson, D F
Harvey, P W
Holden, J R
Holt, J A
Jowett, V C
Kann, P E E
Kearns, J R
Kipgen, D
Lewis, G H
Lim, S C
Lloyd, M N H
Lock, J A M
McDowall, G K
Norcross, F H
Oates, A M
Oates, P E
Pullon, H R
Restell, C A
Roe, M F E
Salmon, A H J
Saunders, E M J
Singh, S
Sparrow, A I
Stansfeld, A G
Stansfeld, J M
Steward, M R
Tiwari, N V
Weber, J C P
Wikner, R A
Williams, D J
Willson, T H
Wotton-McTurk, P H

Havant

Allan, T C
Allison, J L
Ayling, P J
Ball, N A
Balthazor, D P J
Barrett, D F

Batty, J A
Bedford, F J
Blatch, J R
Blatch, S M V
Bowley, F C
Capp, S P
Chinn, R H
Cogswell, D F
Cogswell, L K
Cole, C J
Cook, L J
Corbin, M J
Dewar, R
Dilnot, P
Dixon, S J
Earley, M J
Geoghegan, J
Grafen, L
Green, A I
Griffiths, W J H
Hardy, T J
Harper, H R
Hughes, J R
Kennedy-Cooke, C J
McLaren, J M
Maclean, M J
McNeill, A I N
Magee, D B
Manning, G C
Mead, J A
Melville, D H
Morrison, C E
Moss, N H
Naing, S Y
Parkin, R T
Pearson, R N
Phillips, R P
Polak, A
Robinson, B S
Ryle, C A
Sawyer, R A
Sizer, K A
Stainton-Ellis, J A
Summerhays, B G
Sutton, R M
Taylor, B L
Thakrar, P M
Thomas, T R
Torode, N B
Warlow, C N
West, J
Williams, M G
Willicombe, P R
Young, R A B

Haverfordwest

Barnes, A
Bartlett, M
Barton, A D
Barton, B W
Bates, C M
Bell, C J
Bowen, R W
Buntwal, V
Burns, R W
Chandralingham, N K
Clow, W M
Cooke, D A
Cooke, R A
Cross, R
David, D R
David, R E
Davies, D H
Davies, J A K
Early, A E
Edwards, E D
Evans, G W L
Evans, L M
Gammon, R S G
Gibson, A J
Gillam, P G
Grimshaw, R J
Gupta, N D
Hamilton, S A
Hesketh, S J
Howells, M R
Hughes, B J
Jafri, M S
James, C M
Jeyakumar, P
Jones, D J
Jones, G R M
Jones, J N
Jones, R W
Jones, V H
Jowett, N I
Kathirkamasekaran, S
King, A L
Langley, D R

Lewis, R H
Lowman, A J
McEvoy, R C
Maxwell, W A
Meyer, H
Middleton, G W
Milewski, P J
Mohanaruban, K
Neumann, K M
Noott, G G
Nur, O A
Owen, D G
Pandalai, S
Paterson, A M
Perry, C L
Perry, M E R
Polacarz, S V
Premkumar, C S
Price, D R G
Ramaiah, D A
Read, K M
Rees, C M E
Rees, J F
Richards, A D
Robinson, P W H
Saleem, A K N
Saleem, M F
Shahei, E A
Sharma, B R
Sibley, J A
Singh, P D N
Sinha, S
Stamper, P
Thillaiambalam, N
Thomas, D A
Thomas, J E
Thomas, S E
Thompson, R W G
Tucker, B
Vas Falcao, C M G
Vipulendran, S
Vipulendran, V
Vittle, J E
Weaver, A J
Weaver, A L B
Williams, L G
Wilson, P
Wort, M J
Wort, R L
Zakaria, M Y
Zangouras, D T

Haverhill

Baker, R W
Clifton-Brown, A F
Cornish, E
Gardner, E P
Katrak, P M
Lawfield, M F M
Mann, N M
Mohan, H B
Patel, A
Pearson, M D
Selby, J N
Selby, M E
Servant, J B
Smith, S T
Stephenson, P S

Hawes

Hamer, J M
Roche, D C J
West, P K A

Hawick

Bianchi, G
Bishop, J P
Boon, R L
Brogan, E
Bruce, L M
Buchanan, D A
Buchanan, E M
Cameron, D W
Cameron, W R
Clutterbuck, D J
Gill, M M P
Gray, B K
Lockie, P
Macalister, I
Macdonald, J M
Macmaster, H
Macrae, F
Michie, R W
Oliver, C H
Palmer, A A
Paterson-Brown, J
Paterson-Brown, P N
Rolland, D M
Rolland, M B
Ross, G M J

Hayes

Simpson, A R
Wilson, C J F
Woolfenden, E C

Hayes

Ahluwalia, N S
Anand, S
Bakshi, J M
Campbell, H G
Depani, J P
Goud, A B
Grace, D M
Hasan, S A
Iqbal, S
Jenson, C M
Joshi, V P
Kanthan, P R
Khan, F A
Lauwers, A J
Long, C H
Lucas, B B
Lukmany, M F
Madhavan, T
Malik, N S
Michaels, R
Nair, S
Nanavati, M K
Ong, P S
Patel, H A
Prunty, M J
Quadri, S A
Rahim, M S
Rahmaan, A
Raju, T D
Rashid, A Y
Rose, I
Ruparel, Y B
Sembhi, S K
Sethi, K K
Smith, A M J
Thomas, B M
Thurlow, S K
Vyas, K H
Wood, D R
Yianni, J

Hayle

Barrett, N D
Bednarski, T
Blair, B E
Croft, A M
El Gammal, M M Y
Fuller, F M
Gendall, L F
Gibson, N H
Higgs, M J E
Kingshott, B M-M
Knowles, K A B
McQuade, J A
Maskell, A M
Old, F T
Olds, E M
Parasuram, P
Patrudu, M N
Slater, J
Stanley-Jones, D
Stevens, D
Sugrue, D C
Tregenza, N J C

Hayling Island

Chilcott, R C
Coombs, S E
Cumming, F G
D'Alton-Harrison, J J
David, S T
Dawe, J G
Dillner, L M
Dixon, D C
Doherty, D A F
Easthope, M E
Ford, D E
Houghton, L J
Lancaster, T V
McCall, K E
Mossman, A D
Murray, C M M
Prestwood, J M
Stein, D D
Stratford, A J
Tate, J
Turner, C
Walton, J H
Webster, J B L
Williams, R H M
Younghusband, J D

Haywards Heath

Abdel Gawad, A A
Adams, H G

Alden, S R
Allen, J C
Alvarez-Ude, J M
Angel, R J
Arundale, N
Ashkan, K
Barrie, F M M
Barrie, N J
Begg, A H
Bellis, D J
Berresford, P A
Berry, J M
Birch, I D
Blundell, J M
Bratt, C A
Bridger, A D
Chappel, W A
Cheal, H J
Clenshaw, J E E
Conde Fernandez, F
Corbett, C R R
Cox, S R
Crotty, I M
Cutler, B D
Dale, J W
Davies, H T
Dawes, B J
Dawson, P J
Denney, R W
Donaldson, P M W
Durrant, C C J
Eastcott, H R
Edwards, P J
Elkins, A V
Fearn, C B A
Firth, J M
Firth, P S
France, D M
Fulford, W G
Gaete, H P
Ghandi, S
Glenn, R W
Gurner, A C
Harding, A S
Hardingham, J E
Hardwicke, C
Hanker, H A
Hart, P C
Harvey, M R
Harvey, R A H
Herbert, M E
Hill, P R
Hine, K R
Holloway, N J
Holt, S J
Hoyal, R H A
Hughes, P J
Hutchinson, M C E
Irlam, P A
Jannoun, U
Janvrin, S B
Jenkins, E M
Jones, C N O
Jones, I E
Jones, K G
Jones, M A
Jones, R H
Jones, S A M
Kearney, N M P
Kerr, G D
Khine, T T
Kini, M D
Kiss, A
Lafreniere, L M
Lambert, R B H
Lavelle, M A
Lawrence, A J
Lawson, E M
Lawson, K M
Liddell, H W
Liddell, J
Littlejohn, I H
Lynch, M V
McMinn, L
Mair, W S J
Mallender, L J
Marshall, B Y
Masani, K R
Mather, K L
Mather, R J
McKenzie-Gray, B
Mead, J D S
Mehta, T
Metcalfe, J M
Mims, C A
Mitchinson, F J
Morris, R P
Morrish, P K
Mort, L E

Moseling, D M
Nagendra, K H V
Nath, J
Nawrocki, J D
Norris, J S
O'Brien, W
Olney, J S
Parnell, E J
Parrish, F M
Patterson, M H
Pearson, M C
Pyle, E J
Rath, S
Read, D H
Reid, D J
Richardson, D M
Ricketts, D M
Rose, P E
Rouse, J M
Ruotsalainen-Garattoni, T
Sales, D R
Sinclair, D N
Snape, O J
Somerville, P G
St. John-Jones, L S
Stephen, W
Stuart, B M
Sumner, M J
Tahzib, F
Taylor, E P
Taylor, E J
Tildsley, G J
Walter, C M
Walter, J P W
Walter, P H
Ward, P J
Wheatley, T
While, J A
Whitney, D J
Williams, I R
Williams, J T
Wiseman, R A
Woodhams, R W
Woodhams, S D
Young, M P

Headington

Gallen, D D
Licence, K A M
Series, H G
Stirzaker, L
White, P M

Heanor

Ahmed, I
Elliott, C M
Graham, A B
Holland, P A M
Houlton, S C
Lodge, R
Manley, R
Mellor, S
Mukhopadhyaya, P K
Noble, J
Ward, K J

Heathfield

Aldridge, M S
Almeida, J H
Blakey, R T
Cardell, B S
Casares, M E
Chambier, K
Dodge, C J
Dormand, G S
Duncan, N A
Eggleston, A
Farrow, D J D
Gibson, W M
Gray, P F
Griffin, S
Harman, C O D
Jeans, A F
Johnston, M A
Mcconkey, G N
McGowan, J F
Palmer, S
Pendlebury, D G
Place, F C
Redman, D A
Rees, E L
Reid, C H
Robins, S B
Underhill, Y M
Wadman, S M

Hebburn

Brady, M
Burns, M

McIntosh, G D
Nicholls, K-M
Vinayak, I P
Vinayak, V
Withington, B R

Hebden Bridge

Allcock, H
Blomfield, R G
Child, D
Gooch, J A
Grainger, R L
Harris, S R
Hawkes, F A
Lyons, M J
McInnes, S J
Molloy, P C
Taylor, N G
Toms, W H
Unwin, D J
Wadsworth, J A
Wild, D A

Heckmondwike

Findlay, D J
Khan, K
Laher, J P S
Pinder, F A M
Scrivings, B A
Woodhall, A J
Youd, D J
Zaman, K

Helensburgh

Allan, I C
Anderson, J K
Arneil, G C
Baird, G M
Beatton, P O
Brown, A J
Brown, C A R
Brown, W R H
Burgess, J L
Burgess, R C A
Cairns, C S
Calder, B D
Campbell, E B
Campbell, P
Chisholm, C J S
Clark, A S
Clarke, S A
Collins, D W W
Coulter, F
Cox, A L
Crawford, P I
Dewar, W A
Dickson, A S B
Doyle, A C
Duncan, M J P
Dunlop, T D
Falconer, A D
Flatman, G E
Flatman, W L
Gray, A M
Grieve, A R
Harper, J M
Henderson, C M
Hulland, N W
Jamieson, A
Kerr, W J
Kirk, A W
Lamont, W I
Lee, C W
Linzee-Gordon, P A II
Lygo, M H
MacBeath, M C E
McBlane, J H
MacCallum, J R
McCraith, K H
McEwan, I M
McIver, B
McKelvie, J D
McLachlan, B
Macleod, C
MacLeod, R C
McMenemin, I M
Macrae, A R
Mann, K E
Mascarenhas, R A
Morrice, G T
Morrison, M E E
Newberry, J
Ram, A J
Reay, P L
Reitano, T
Robin, J G
Rogerson, J G
Sharara, F
Smith, L S
Smith, M D

Stephen, A J
Storey, N D
Taylor, F G
Thomson, E J
Underwood, E M L
Watkins, R D
Watt, J A G
Wightman, A E
Woodburn, A G
Young, V B

Helmsdale

Singh, D

Helston

Barton, C L
Barton, P A
Chandler, I P
Ching, T V
Coward, N H
Cuff, C M
Davidson, N J
Davies, I A
Davis, P B M
Dorrell, M G
Duckworth, J
Edgerley, R I
Fremantle, J E
Frisken, I K
Gearing, K E
Gifford, L A
Gornall, J B
Harris, P J S
Hawkins, R T J
Herford, M E M
Hosking, R D
Johnston, R P
Kitson, M M
Lansdowne, J D
Lawton, B
Lord, J M
Miller, L F
Oliver, J P
Reckless, H M
Richards, F J A
Sargeant, P W
Shelley, R A
Smith, R S
Smith, S P
Stallbrass, F C
Thomson, M D
Whiter, S A L
Whittingham, D B
Whittle, K G
Wolstencroft, R F
Wood, G H
Wood, M
Wort, I

Hemel Hempstead

Ali, A
Allistone, J C
Antscherl, H E
Bailey, D M
Bairoliya, R P
Bakshi, A
Baron, L A
Barrison, I G
Bayliss, J F J
Benson, G L
Bhamra, R S
Bhatt, S K
Boucher, S L
Bowden, M W
Boyes, G M P
Bradnock, B R D P
Brazier, J C
Bryant, M T T
Bueno Casquero, G
Bulger, G V M
Bull, M J
Burford, T M
Candy, J J
Catnach, S M
Chadwick, S L
Collinson, D J
Cullen, S N
Curry, N J
Darasz, K H
Divers, A R
Drake, M J
Dunphy, K P
Dutta, T
Dyer, M J
Dyson, L
El Naggar, H M A
Falkowski, W A
Farag, R R
Fay, M P

Fernandes, T D
Gallow, R J
Goddard, H C
Gordon, T M
Graham, R S
Gray, P J
Grimer, D P
Guirguis, E G R
Guirguis, S A (
Gunawardena, H
Ha, H C Y
Hackett, D R
Hall, J M
Hallan, R I
Harrison, J F M
Heatley, P T
Hill, S F
Hinsley, D E
Hinsley, S C
Hirji, F M
Hislop, J E
Hobbs, R C
Hodge, K
Hogg, S J
Hulme, H K
Hurst, Z H
James, C
Jameson, V R
Johnston, C L W
Johnston, D F
Kane, J L
Kearney, C E
Kerry, D B
Khatri, H I
Khattak, M A K
King, D S
Lang, J E
Li, L S
Lucas, S O
McFarlane, K J C
Mapara, R
Martlew, K G
Matthews, G A
Mazhar, R
Mishra, K M
Monro, J A
Moring, C F
Mugge, L E A
Nicholls, J C
Nodder, J H
Ormiston, M C E
Pancharatnam, M D
Parry, J I
Phillips, B E
Pigott, T G
Pontefract, C A
Price, R M A
Ratneswaran, D
Raudnitz, L C B
Richardson, A S
Roots, P J
Royston, I M
Royston, N
Rudramoorthy, T
Saunders, A J
Savla, M P
Seetulsingh, P S
Sherwood, H E
Shipley-Rowe, A P
Shrestha, B L
Sleight, V P
Sofat, A
Somerville, N S
Sowa, P K
Stier, S
Thacker, J G M
Thomson, C B
Thomson, C C B
Tipple, B G
Toorawa, D A
White, G Y
Wiener, A J
Wiggins, R J
Wright, J R
Wright, L P
Xavier, S C Y S
Yip, R Y W

Henfield

Bostock, J F
Burdsall, J
Cairns, S R
Crawford Clarke, K E
Gibson, A D
Hardy, H N
Haylett, A C
Hicks, P Y F
Horley, R
McLean, M S

Heywood

Norman, J R
Saxton, R S
Simpson, V M A
Smyth, G V
Squire, J W
White, V L C
Witherspoon, E W
Young, J

Hengoed

Ali, M M
Antao, V R F L F
Ashraf, M T H
Grant, J A
Greville, W D
Griffiths, H M
Henderson, A S
Heneghan, S J
Jones, E
Jones, H O
Jorro, M T C A
Lever, J D
McCann, K M
Rogers, S
Rosser, C A
Scourfield, A J
Thomas, O G
Williams, D T
Williams, M L

Henley-on-Thames

Adnitt, D I
Adnitt, P I
Arthur, E J
Ashby, P A
Bacon, A S
Balme, R H
Barber, A S
Barrass, B J R
Barton, J H
Bentall, J K M C
Bergel, R C
Blagg, S E
Bromilow, J E
Chapman, S C
Clarke, T K
Coldwell, P H
Collett, E
Copeland, J A M R
Craik, M C
Cross, T J
Dixon, A M
Dudeney, T P
Easton, C S
Edgar, W
Elliott, J E
Elliott, M J
Evans, A
Fearnhead, N S
Fenton, J F A
Foster, J C
Friend, K J F
Ganly, N A
Gillespie, E H
Grimshaw, C
Guest, E L H
Hale, A J
Hall, R J
Hall, S L
Holt, C M
Jenkins, J R R
Jones, H G
Laing, A C
Langley, H K
Lukats, V E J
McCarthy, W E
McCullough, S
McEwen, H C
McEwen, L M
MacFarlane, J A
McKendrick, J
McWhirter, J H
McWilliams, D M
Maggs, R F
Milligan, J M
Need, R E
O'Connell, R
O'Gorman, W J
Parton, J
Pigott, P V
Pim, A J
Pitt, N S
Purvis, C R
Rademeyer, I K
Ratcliffe, C G
Robertson, J
Salmon, A J
Silver, L R
Smith, G W

Snell, B J
Snell, N J C
Stallabrass, P
Stephens, V J
Stokes, E J
Stokes, J F
Taylor, M
Terris, A J M
Whitaker, N H G
Willson, W W

Henlow

Batchelor, A J
Broadbridge, R J M
Collins, H E
Cullen, S A
Devnani, K C
Greenish, T S
Hansford, N G
Hill, I R
Matthews, R S J

Hereford

Adams, S J
Allen, C J
Allington, M K E
Allsopp, L E
Armstrong, W B
Ashley, K F
Bainton, D
Baker, W H J
Ballance, J H W
Ballham, A
Barber, M D
Barling, T C
Barnadie, A M
Barnett, P A
Barton, E J
Bathurst, C E
Beach, B
Beach, H I
Beauchamp, M
Beauchamp, P G
Betts, M E
Bhattacharyya, S
Boyce, C J
Bracebridge, M C
Brierley, D S N
Brooks, P E
Brooks, W
Bulmer, R B
Burns, J A S D
Butterfill, A M
Butterfill, J B
Bywater, N J
Caine, D J
Canavan, R E M
Canney, R M L
Canning, C L
Carter, R C
Cartledge, W S
Carton-Kelly, P S
Chandler, D A
Cianchi, F R
Clasper, J C
Cohn, M R
Coleman, T J
Collins, K J
Collins, R J
Conning, D M
Connor, H
Coombs, E
Corder, A P
Corfield, A P
Cottam, R M
Court, S J
Cousens, A R
Crossley, A N
Dallimore, J S
Dalziel, J A
Davies, D M
Davies, J M
Davies, W H
Day, A C
Deakin, M T
Deutsch, J
Devlin, P
Dinneen, J S
Donovan, C F
Donovan, E
Donovan, M J R
Dowling, R M B
Duffett, J M
Edwards, D H
Eggar, R J
England, V M
Epps, M T
Erskine, H R
Evans, J A F

Evans, N-W D
Eyre, A J
Farmer, R E
Ferguson, S
Fleming, J A
Fraser, N C
French, J M
Frith, C W
Galloway, D C
Garlick, P R
Gee, R P
George, L
George, S E
Gibbon, R H
Gill, J M
Gillespie, P N
Glancy, J M
Glen-Bott, A M
Godbett, K
Goodfellow, D P
Goodfellow, J C
Goodwin, J E
Gray, B
Gray, J A
Grech, P
Griffiths, G W
Griffiths, R L
Grigg, J A
Grocott, E C
Gunn, A F
Haggie, M H K
Hall, M J
Hanna, G S S
Harper, P H
Harris, P
Hasan, S
Heal, A J
Hearne, M J
Helme, M M
Helme, V P
Henderson, R J
Hession, M A
Holt, J L
Howard, P A
Hutchinson, J D
Ingham, J E
Iron, J B
Jay, P I
Jenkins, C
Jennings, S F
Johnson, A S
Johnson, A
Johnson, M L
Johnston, J
Jones, A G
Jones, C L
Kaye, P M
Kennedy, F L
King, R A
King, R E
Knight, G D
Kramer, J J
Laird, C J F
Laird, R B
Lattey, N J
Lee, J A
Lewis, A M G
Limond, M G
Llewelyn, R I
Lockwood, J R
Lockwood, W
London, J M
Lowe, C F
McGinty, F
McGinty, M R
McGlashon, D
Mackie, V J
Mahoney, S
Majeed, D
Majeed, L I A
Malins, D M
Marsden, D J
Marsden, S M
Maslen, M J
Matthews, P J
Maxwell, J M
Mears, T P
Medcalf, K R
Menzies, L J
Millard, K
Miller, G A
Miller, R G
Miller, S R
Montgomery, H R
Moore, W J
Morison, C J
Morton, M R
Neubert, S E
Newcombe, G L

Newsholme, G A
Nicholson Roberts, T C
O'Brien, D J
Oakland, D J
Oakland, M H
Orr, A M
Overstall, P W
Parkes, P W J
Penney, O J S J
Penney, R M
Pimblett, J H S
Pitcher, D W
Pollard, N A
Porte, H E
Powell, P D
Press, J D
Price, A C
Ramage, P A J
Ransford, R A J
Reed, A J
Rendall, J R S
Renton, C J C
Renton, M G
Reynolds, I S R
Richardson, B P
Ridgway, S D
Roberts, C C N
Roper, I W M
Rose, N M
Ross, J H
Rothwell Hughes, M E
Rowe, G M
Ryan, P J
Ryding, F N
Salmon, N P
Salter, S H
Scott, K E A
Seal, L A
Seal, P V
Shewell, P C
Shields, D A
Sibly, T F
Sleath, J D
Slee, G C
Smallwood, B H
Smith, B S
Smith, M C F
Smith, R B
Sole, G M
Southall, P H
Spence, A K
Steven, C A
Subak-Sharpe, R J
Sykes, J V
Sykes, R A
Symonds, K E
Thomas, C J
Thomas, G E
Thomas, H R
Thompson, A J
Thomson, C H
Turnbull, M
Wade-Evans, E M
Wade-Evans, T
Wade-Evans, V J
Wagner, N A G
Walsh, P R
Warner, R G
Warsap, A J
Waters, M R
Waters, P
Watt, I D
Watts, A C
Watts, S R
Weavers, B J
Wheeler, H L
Wheeler, J G
While, A C A
Whitby, R M
White, C A
White, J C
Wille, R W
Williams, D H
Williams, R B
Williams, R G
Williams, S
Willoughby, S J B
Wilson, D
Wilson, J M
Wilson, P R
Wilson, S
Yogaratnam, S
Young, P R

Herne Bay

Barton, D G
Boyle, I F D
Brian, C J
Brown, J N

Cleverley, H R
Collier, G M
Conway, E I
Corble, G
Dunn, S J
Gadhia, N
Green, C R
Jackson, R M
Jenkins, R M H
Jones, E M
Lees, P B
Lohrke, B
Manson, H M
Palmer, R H
Parsloe, J B K
Preston, H V
Prince, A W
Read, N P
Ritchie, I W
Samsworth, P R
Senthiraman, V
Steinberg, M
Strutt, M D
Stubgen, S O
Wharfe, S M W
Wheeldon, R
Wilson, R E M
Wright, J D

Hertford

Anderson, D J
Atwill, K N
Bench, J T
Black, G C
Bossley, C J
Bradpiece, H A
Cembala, J A
Chandrasegaram, W
Cheesman, C A
Clifton, M A
Corlett, K J
Cowley, G P
Craighead, S K
Crawley, J E
Crossthwaite, D I
Curtin, B G
Daborn, D K R
Daborn, P G R
Devine, A J P
Eames, J R
Earle, J V
Gibson, K
Grabarska-Kreiss, B K
Griffin, L J
Hamilton, P G
Handysides, J M
Harris, S
Henderson, R
Horsman, A M
Kilkenny, L A
McClure, I R
McLees, D J S
Maiti, H
Mathew, G
Matthews, C J
Mobley, R J
Murray, N H
Newton, J E
O'Reilly, F E
Oates, A P
Pritchard, D S
Ramaswami, U
Rank, T J
Roach, R T
Robinson, W
Sloper, C M L
Sloper, P
Stevens, H P
Steward, R J
Stott, C M
Titcombe, J L M
Watson, L J
White, A W

Hessle

Abraham, T
Adhami, Y
Arnold, A G
Cameron, G I
Crafter, P F
Dore, A M
Haines, D R
Kell, B
Locker, I
Lorences Ruiz, C I
McInnes, A J
Mathur, S
Nicholson, A A
Riddle, M A

Robinson, G
Twinham, D J
Whitty, R T

Hexham

Al-Ali, M S M
Ambrose, J A
Anderson, I
Baillie, M
Blades, D S
Brackenridge, P
Brackenridge, R G
Bradbeer, E G
Bushby, A M
Carner, T A
Chaytor, R G
Chippindale, A J
Coleman, S A
Condie, P W
Cook, D R
Cooper, E A
Crick, J M J
Cuthbertson, J E
Denness, T
Devin, A M
Dryden, F A
Ford, S D
Forsey, J P
Gallagher, E J
Garner, E B
Gatehouse, D
George, M M
Gholkar, J
Gold, J S
Gray, A L
Harrison, V F
Harte, B D
Helliwell, C D
Henderson, M T
Hogarth, M C
Hutchinson, M R
Ismail, H A A R E A
Jeans, J E
Johnson, N G
Keep, N K
Khin Mar Mar, Dr
Longrigg, J N
Lowe, P F
McCollum, J P K
Macklon, A F
Maddick, G
Mathias, I M J
Middleton, C S H
Morrow, G
Murgall, J J
Murray, H N
Myo Nyunt, Dr
Nandy, M K
O'Brien, J M
Papworth, P
Parker, C L
Parry, M R
Patrick, D
Patterson, C A
Powell, F M N
Redpath, A
Renwick, M I
Robinson, S
Rose, K F
Ryder, J B
Sims, P F
Stewart, R H M
Stuart, J M E
Sutton, R A
Taylor, R M R
Thakkar, D H
Thompson, E G E
Thompson, J W
Waddell, M O
Wagg, A
Wagg, M G
Wainwright, C J-P
Walker, M C
Walls, D B
Walls, W A
Walsh, W K
Waring, N A
Weaver, R M
Wells, N J
White, H V
Wildmore, J C
Willis, P
Wilson, T M
Wright, A J
Wright, A E
Wright, H S

Heywood

Adshead, P A

High Peak

Bailey, S
Brady, S D
Bunting, S L
Duffy, C J
Gibson, J A
Hanif, M
Inceman, H
Krysztopik, R J
Mooney, E M
Murray, G
Onon, T
Osborne, E S
Parashchak, M R
Plumb, S
Pokinskyj, S K
Rasheed, S
Russell, J G
Saeed, A
Salkin, C
Saxena, R
Saxena, R
Williams, A
Wood, R A

High Peak

Allardice, J T
Almond, I D
Austin, D J
Bartholomew, A D
Beavis, S E
Boyle, S B
Bullock, R E
Callister, M E J
Caplin, S
Cavill, J D
Chopping, B M
Coleman, C M
Cooper, S P
Creed, F H
Crosby, P
Dobbing, J
Edwards, R N
Edwards, S
Fletcher, G L
Francis, J N
Holderness, J A
Johnson, J S
Jones, R A
Kumar, B
Laughlin, A J
Lord, W D
Losel, T M
McCann, J K
McWilliam, L J
O'Donnchadha, D S
O'Donoghue, J
Parker, R S
Pearson, D
Pote, F W
Potts, W A
Riddell, D J
Storm, M
Williams, D E
Wilson, K L
Wright, J P

High Wycombe

Abaysiriwardena, C H L
Afridi, M V K
Aitchison, R G M
Akbar, F A
Al Hillawi, A H S
Allen, D S
Allim, M
Allim, R M
Amin, S
Anzak, M
Appleyard, M N
Armitage, F H
Armitstead, J G
Aslam, N
Aslam, N
Attar, G S
Atwell, S A
Bacon, N F
Bath, D S G
Bath, E M
Baxter, E N
Bdesha, A S
Bennett, A J M
Bennett, A R
Berry, J F
Binks, A P
Birch, K E
Blair, Z A
Bonney, G L W
Booth, M I
Bopearachchi, T J P

Bose, P P K
Bowker, M H
Branagan, J P
Bray, E C
Buist, R G
Burton, A J
Cadman, P J
Carless, J J
Carter, F C
Channon, G M
Chapman, P J V
Charlesworth, C H
Cheetham, C H
Clark, H E
Clarke, T J
Combe, W A D
Cope, A G
Corless, D J
Cowland, G N D
Cox, G A
Crittenden, G
Crowe, P M
Dahiya, S
Davies, D W
Davis, H M R
Dawson, I M
Delamore, J A
Dexter, T J
Dickinson, B M
Dudley, J
Dutton, J
Duvall-Young, J
Earley, A R C
Eley, N A
Erskine, J A
Evans, R H
Fawcett, V A T
Fender, R G
Fenton, W S R
Ferguson, J E M
Fernandez-Martinez, P
Finch, R
Flint, R P
Foord, C D
Fox, P T
Gallen, I W
Gamell, A P
Garnham, F E
Garnham, J C
Gatzen, C
Gilchrist, N
Glynn, L E
Goldman, J E
Gorard, D A
Graham, D G
Gray, J C
Haffiz, T
Hameed, A
Hammond, D J
Hasan, A K H
Hasnain, Y A
Havelock, P B
Hemsley, D A
Herbert, J J F
Herrero Velasco, L E
Higgs, D R
Hoare, A M
Homer, J R
Horner, J R
Howe, K J
Hussain, I F
Ilyas, S
Jackson, M C
James, H C
Johnson, H C
Kazer, M
Keable-Elliott, R A
Kelleher, J P
Kelly, C M
Kelly, S J
Kennish, N P
Kettle, S J A
Khan, S N
King, M M K
Kirby, A C
Kuhn, K A
Landon, H M
Lethbridge, K G
Lloyd-Jones, R L
Lomax, J A
Lowe, P J
Luzzi, G A
Lyons, J D
Lyons, M M
McCarthy, A L
McCay, D A
McClelland, A J
McDonough, B M
McDonough, S B

McIntyre, A S
Maclaren, R B
McMillan, A H K
Malpass, T S
Man Singh, A
Manchanda, S
Masters, N J
Matthews, M G
Maxmin, J S
Medhurst, A W J
Middleton, S J
Mitchell, J B
Moretto, J C
Morgan, N J
Mughal, N A
Munro, J G
Munro, J H M
Newton, D J
Nice, A M
North, A P
Northeast, A D R
O'Sullivan, M C
Oraedu, O C
Patten, M J
Payne, J M
Payne, M A
Peckham, A V
Phillips, J N
Pincott, J R
Potts, D J
Powell, H D W
Price, D A
Price, S R
Rahman, F
Rajendran, V
Rastogi, G C
Reddy, V
Reggler, J G
Reidy, R N
Roblin, S
Robson, M S
Rogers, S J
Ruberu, T R C
Salmon, R W
Scott, D M
Shakarchi, M A
Shaw, D E
Shroff, N
Silk, R M F
Skinner, C M
Smart, D M
Smith, D G
Spalding, E M
Stapleton, T
Strube, P J
Sumner, D
Tan, K S-W
Taylor, D A
Taylor, E J
Taylor, G J
Theobald, P
Thomas, E G
Thompson, A C
Thompson, F H
Titheridge, R E
Turner, M J
Van Der Watt, M J
Venning, G R
Venning, M R
Waghorn, D J
Wallace, K D
Walter, J A
Walters, E G
Wathen, C G
Watson, P J Q
Wighton, C J
Wills, J
Wilson, A J
Wise, M P
Woolnough, M J
Wright, D D I
Wright, D D
Young, C A
Zaib, S A

Highbridge

Anderson, S J
Barry, P H
Bizon, M J
Clapham, C M
Edwards, M C
Gough, A L
Griffith, R A
James, D M
O'Brien, R A D
Reynolds, C A
Stoddart, P G P
Trowell, G M

Hillsborough

Barron, D W
Bell, D M
Bell, S M
Bill, A
Bingham, J M M
Burns, D M
Chambers, J M J
Coulter, N C
Cupples, S J
Duffin, D
Eames, N W A
Eames, R S
Farrar, M
Ferguson, J I
Field, G G
Fitzpatrick, O J
Fleming, J K
Forde, A
Hewitt, G R
Hicks, N C
Hogan, M M
Hunter, C M
Hunter, I M
Jackson, A C J
Johnston, A J
Kennedy, V R G
Kirkpatrick, M H E
Langlands, J H M
Lappin, J M
Lawther, R E
Lee, C E
McBrien, H S
McCleary, A J
McCreary, R D
McFarland, A R
Morrison, E
Mulholland, M G
Nevin, N C
Orr, P A
Owen, T A
Page, W
Pantridge, J F
Parker, E A
Patton, H H T
Poots, E D M H
Rogers, P P
Shillington, R K A
Smylie, A
Stewart, E C A
Uprichard, A C G
Walker, J
Ware, C F W
White, M A
Wilson, G M
Wilson, J C
Yarr, S N
Young, R A M

Hinckley

Alun-Jones, J E
Barratt, S A
Barrett, D J
Beardsworth, B S
Blackhurst, H R
Bowler, H L
Burton, J D
Choudhary, B P
Cracknell, I D
Field-Lucas, A S
Finnegan, J P
Gilberthorpe, C
Harrison, J
Hewson, B
Howes, H K
Johnson, F C
Johnson, S
McCole, L C
Maity, P B
Marlow, K D M
Mason, P S
Morris, J F
Muthiah, M
O'Malley, A B
Parkinson, A M
Pearson, J R
Riordan, T
Rowe, V L
Ruban, E P
Sacha, B S
Singh, B
Sladden, C S
Steingold, R F
Sutton, F J
Taylor, R S
Warner, R H L
Waterlow, J K
Willmott, N J
Yardley, R A

Hindhead

Baldock, N J D
Bamford, N E C
Cameron, J A P
Carter, F G T
Cavanagh, L C
Colyer, E E S
Dunbar, S J
Ford, J M
Hancock, K G
Jenkinson, P M A
Jobson, P H
Le Coulliard, F J
McNicol, K M
Morris, U V L
Patten, J P
Philpott, B
Sen, B
Sims, R T
Sleator, A M G
Stewart, J W
Tobin, D E
Wise, V A
Woodland, R J T

Hinton St George

Bendall, R
Giles, J A
Wadsworth, B A

Hitchin

Aldeghather, J T
Anklesaria, R P
Baker-Glenn, E J
Bancroft-Livingston, G H
Barasi, F
Barkel, J M
Barwick, A C
Bhatiani, R
Blackman, J M
Carragher, M S
Clarke, M G
Cockbain, R G
Coleman, N J
Cooper, F
Cox, J P H
Coxall, S J
Daniel, K J
Dines, J H
Downey, M F
Duncan, B C O
Edwards, S J E
Fagg, C G
Faiers, M C
Freeman, F E
Gilvarry, M C
Golding, J H
Gradwell, D P
Greenish, K B
Griffiths, S J
Haigh, A B
Hallwood, P M
Hayden, R J
Hillman, R A
Hodgson, M J
Hope, S A
Ingram, G
Ingram, R M
James, N K
Johnstone, R S
Kelly, P D
Kendell, N P
Kennerley, P M
Kenny, C J
King, C M P
King, H A
Lacy, M K
Lawrence, J M
Leaver, A T
Lewis, R S
Lim, M S T
Lincoln, D S
Machen, J
Maclusky, K A
Mallett, B L
Ogilvie, J W
Parker, A
Pedlow, P R B
Peel, M J
Pickett, L C
Ramanathan, R
Rand, J I
Ransom, M J B
Raymond, F D
Richardson, S M
Roberts, C G
Rushton, C A
Ryecart, C N

Seaman, R A J
Shellock, A J
Slattery, M A
Smith, I M
Smith, J W
Smith, R N
Stevenson, J L
Summers, J A
Tadros, A
Tadros, O I
Taylor-Robinson, K
Tidy, G
Tresman, R L
Vergis, M E
Vorster, M A
Wandless, S
Watkins, S M
Williams, D P
Williams, J R B
Withers, K J
Woodman, M J

Hockley

Aukett, M A
Bernardo, M V
Cornes, P S
Donnelly, C A
Galvin, E A S
Kerry, A P
Lacey, P J
Layzell, S
Nicholls, J E
Rees, T P
Taylor, D S
Thomas, P D
Tullett, D C

Hoddesdon

Adlard, R E
Andrews, M
Barclay, A P
Baxter, B
Blankfield, C P
Clayton, F G
Davies, A W
Guptha, S
Hayman, L M
Henderson, F J
Hiscock, I M K
Jolliffe, R J
Knight, J D S
Parkes, G
Patterson, M S
Record, J L
Roberts, J L
Robinson, P J
Robson, J J
Roe, L M
Sandler, M G
Tomiak, R H H
Tyne, H L
Vyas, B S
Waddington, C
Wenley, M R
Willis, D A
Young, J H

Holmrook

Jago, J W
Macfarlane, R C
McKerrow, E
Marsham, S M
Thornton, A

Holsworthy

Barker, I A H
Betts, J B
Betts, N B
Green-Armytage, G K
Hill, J A
Hillebrandt, D K
Human, S J
Kandasamy, R
Page, R J
Pearson, A F
Price-Thomas, S P
Shaw, R F
Wardle, R M

Holt

Appleby, T A
Archer, E G
Arkell, J H
Atiomo, P-L
Birt, A J
Brett, S L
Buckley, A R
Chapman, A C
Cooper, J D
Crawley, H B

Hounslow

Dunnet, W A
Fowle, C S
Franklin, P K
Grove, S J
Harvey, P T
Hill, A N
Jolliffe, M V
Latten, A
Lennane, S B X
Marriott, J M
Moore, E M M
Moss, J W
Paddon, A J
Slator, J
Todd, C
Wellings, P
White, W
Williams, H W G

Holyhead

Bertorelli, S W
Bowen, D J
Burnell, S H
Clyde, R J
Corduff, M B
Davies, R P
English, H L
Evans, E
Evans, I B T
Ford, G
Francis, S B
Griffith, H B
Harrison, M
Ijaz, Q
Jones, E
Leigh, J A
McCoy, B T
Nicholson, B
O'Toole, J G
Parry-Jones, J
Parry-Jones, M
Parry, H
Petty, M G D
Phillips, D E
Phillips, J D
Richardson, J C
Roberts, D M
Roberts, J K
Robson, D J
Stead, A L
Stead, C E C
Thomas, K L
Torbohm, I K-H
Tsang, H F
Tsang, H K
Walker, C F
Williams, D T
Windall, K M

Holywell

Allsopp, L B
Boiston, P A
Chowdhury, S D
Harper, H M
Hughes, R E E
James, A D
Jones, G O
Jones, G M
Jones, N D
Jones, S
Kapur, Y P
Lewis, G R R
McIntyre, O B
Major, R G
O'Keeffe, V M
Roberts, A
Rowlands, M
Williams, P H

Hollywood

Adamson, S I G
Arnold, R G
Bingham, W
Black, D
Black, G W
Blaney, R
Caddy, G R
Clarke, J W
Cleland, J A
Corkey, E P M
Cosgrove, C T
Courtney, J R
Crawford, R M
De Jong, J
Donnan, H L
Dornan, J C
Drain, A J
Eardley, M
Egerton, T J A
Elwood, P E

Fetherston, H S
Foster, G C
Graham, S M
Grieve, P P
Hamilton, K
Hannam, C R
Hawthorne, C T
Hayes, J R
Herriott, T P
Hewitt, R S
Hill, J M
Johnston, J G M
Johnston, L C
Kane, J R B
Lamey, P J
Lawson, G T N
Lawson, R G
Lindsay-Miller, A C M
Lindsay, R T A
Little, B T
McCall, J R
McConnell, D A
McCrea, A P
McCreery, J
McGibben, P D
McGibbon, S P
McGimpsey, J M
McGimpsey, W M M
Martyn, C J
Meehan, L C
Millar, R
Miller, A R
Mollan, R A B
Morrison, G C
Morton, P
O'Neill, B
Orr, L E
Roseveare, H M
Ryan, T G F
Shaw, J
Sheeran, M R M
Shepherd, W H T
Smith, E M
Stevens, R F
Stewart, J L
Stewart, W M
Strong, J E
Wallace, R G H
Watson, R G P
Weir, P E
Williams, M A
Wright, A M
Wright, N D
Wright, O L
Yeates, H A

Honiton

Barber, P C
Betham, V J
Bolt, D E
Courtney, P T
De Sousa, B
Donohoe, M E
Essame, R S K
Forbes, A E
Gibson, J J S
Goulandris, M
Groenendijk, H
Hall, P R
Harvey, N E
Leach, R
Peat, J M
Penwarden, D B
Poels, P J
Roy, A D
Seamark, C J
Seamark, D A
Wallace, O N
Ward, A G
Ward, D G
Ward, J A
Webb, P J

Hook

Barns, H C C
Bradley, M J
Clay, A E
Collins, A J
Davies, A J
Evans, D J
Gilbody, J S
Goncalves-Archer, E B
Goold, I J
Heywood, H C F
Hunter, C J
Kilpatrick, S M
Longstaff, S F
Love, D M
McGinty, H J

MacPhail, I
Malan, D H
Morgan, G N
Morrison, J B
Page, J M
Rees, J
Shand, C R
Weaver, A D
Whittingham, W

Hope Valley

Adler, T J
Beeley, J M
Bell, J H
Brennan, S R
Burton, D J C
Burton, J A
Clancy, A E
Currie, Z I
Dale, S M
Dancocks, A C
De Carteret, A M
Fanning, D M
Farrell, R W R
Fordham, E J
Fox, R M
Glanfield, P A
Goddard, M
Hamilton, R J
Howson, B E
Hutchinson, S P
Jackson, P H
Jenkins, R C
John, R E
Jordan, L K A
Morton, E A
O'Connor, T J
Partington, P E
Read, C A
Robinson, A P
Robinson, J
Ross, J J
Sampson, K
Simpson, J L
Smith, P D
Talbot, C H
Tyson, V C H
Walkden, W J

Horley

Butcher, R M
Chapman, P J C
Conaty, T A
Cook, L A
Courtenay-Evans, P A
Cumming, E M
D'Costa, E F
Daruwalla, N K
Diack, H J
Divers, L S P
Dormer, J K
Dyke, T N
Edgington, K
Gomesz, F A R
Goodwin, S A
Gourlay, N G
Greengrass, A
Harrison, D F N
Hicklin, J A
Hole, S G
House, J H
Jenkins, E M
Keay, D A
Lee-Chong, F L P K
Lightwood, A M
Lightwood, R G
Long, M G
Mander, R S
Middleton, K G
Olliver, R J
Pandita-Gunawardena, V R
Ring, P A
Rolland, P S
Stanley, R S
Tallent, D N
Townsend, P T
Wambeek, N D
Warrington, G
Williamson, C J F L
Williamson, R D C
Wood, D M
Wylie, C M

Horncastle

Bouskill, K C
Burman, L
Dalton, J E
Duckham, C M J
Elliott, E V

Greenwood, T F
Harper-Smith, J R
Owen, Y E M
Read, S M
Watkins, T

Hornchurch

Aggarwal, A
Ahmad, F B S
Ahmad, S
Ahmad, S N
Arasu, P
Asadullah, H
Bhargava, A
Bland, T C
Blewitt, M J
Bowling, J C R
Brodie, K
Caira, J C E
Carruthers, H J
Chandra Mohan, A R
Chopra, B D
Deshpande, A R
Deshpande, S A
Edison, M M
Ellis, P C
Farrow, S J
Gupta, A
Haq, M F
Hilton, C
Hossain, S A
Inglis, S L
Jackson, S L O
Jain, S S
Jaiswal, A L
Johnson, P J
Kalaiya, P B
Kapoor, P D
Kehr, M J
Kendall, K S
Kershaw, P S
Kithulegoda, L M
Kornfeld, A
Kotecha, B
Kundu, T
McComish, P B
Mann, E J
Mannall, J
Mitchell, J B
Moghal, A
Mohan, I C
O'Moore, J C F D
Omoregbee, A I K
Parker, L B
Patel, P M
Rahman, M M
Rawal, J L
Reid, S A
Samanta, N
Sanyal, K P
Sethu, P
Seymour, M W
Sharma, A K
Sharma, P
Sikka, C K
Simpson, E
Sivapathasundaram, P
Sloan, D J
Tilly, A
Tinslay, P I
Tsoi, K C F
Uberoy, V K
Vanniasegaram, I
Walsh, J S
Zaidi, S A R

Hornsea

Collingwood, P I
Deacon, D F C
Hall, J
Morris, S
Quance, I M
Sibley-Calder, I C
Walker, J E S

Horsham

Adcock, H M
Ali, H E A
Allen, P G
Barker, B M
Binns, T B
Bishop, M
Black, T R L
Blackburn, S C F
Bowen, E S
Brookes, J D
Bull, J C
Chubb, E A
Clarke, J E
Clement, J M

Cobb, K B
Darcy, J F
De Bono, J M
Dean, S J
Deere, H M R
Dew, J A
Dewan, S C
Dubrey, S W
Duncan, A C W
Fisher, E M
Fisher, S R
Francis, G M
Gliddon, R P N
Godfree, V A
Grant, C B T
Grant, M E
Gregory, J E J
Hackett, E C
Haimes, G R
Heath, C J
Heatley, J P
Hellier, K D
Hillman, G
Hills, N D
Hodson, A C
Hodson, J M
Holwell, D W
James, C T A
Jarratt, W J
Kewley, G D
Khalafpour, T
Lawson, T K S
Liu, H L
McAvinchey, R P
McDonogh, B A
McGregor, A R
McMahon, J M
McNeil, I D
Marshall, S R
Monro, J B
Morley, S W
Morris, J S
Moult, E M
Mountain, B A
Mulvey, J M
Murray, G H
Neely, J A C
Neville, R
Noel-Paton, M K H
Owen, E R T C
Pal, A
Pallister, D H
Palmer, J C
Parkes, R T
Parr, D J
Peach, A N H
Pearse, S B
Pearson, L S
Penman, H G
Perkins, E L M
Peters, J J
Phillips, M G
Piper, S J
Ramsay, F M
Rathod, N H
Reynolds, R H
Rice, E F
Richardson, D J
Sainsbury, O M
Scanlon, F L
Scott, E B M
Shattles, W G
Shaw, A J
Sheikh, A A
Skipp, D G
Skipp, H J
Smethurst, M E
Smith, K
Smith, P J
Smith, P A J
Sneddon, F E
Stamford, J A
Tallack, F V
Taor, J H
Taylor, F
Thomas, M J G
Thwaites, I G
Topham, C A
Topham, E J
Venables, M T
Vohra, S
Voysey, J R
Wallace, B E
Walton, N P
Watson, R I
Whybrow, A
Williams, G J
Williams, S J
Willis, L K

Woods, P M
Yates, M T
Yates, S C

Houghton-le-Spring

Barker, J M
Bruce, S N
Dingle, P R
Goff, D K
Goudie, R A
Johnson, A G M
Jones, A I
Laws, D
Lilley, R J
Linnett, P J
Locke, F I
McElroy, J H
McElroy, M M P
Mackay, J C S
McKinley, W J
McLaughlin, C
McVie, J L
Marashi, M T
Metcalfe, B
Mishreki, S K
Muthu, B S
Nicholson, J C
Pappachan, V
Pappachan, V J
Pepper, H M
Preston, M S
Prudhoe, R H
Quinn, M G
Roberts, P R G
Sartoris, A
Sekhar, P R
Sharma, S
Shorten, P J
Shrestha, K L
Sinclair, J A
Steele, M C
Thalayasingam, M E L
Thomas, E J
Thornton, H L
Turnbull, D M
Wallace, A S
Walling, A E
Watters, J G
Wilkinson, S E
Wylie, G

Hounslow

Agarwal, R K
Aladerun, S A
Bajoria, R
Bambawale, A K B
Barringer, J
Baum, G
Baum, M R
Bhalla, R K
Bhardwa, J M
Bharti, H K
Bhasin, N
Bhatti, T J N
Birdi, S S
Bogie, W
Chambers, R M
Chitnavis, B P
Chitnavis, S P
Chowdhury, V
Cliffe, D J
Coll, A J
Cooke-Yarborough, C M
Copenhagen, H J
Cresswell, G J
Das, A
Dhadwal, A K
Dhillon, H S
Dunleavy, S J
Dutta, J
Faizan, A
Fayyaz, I
Fernando, S C
Gammie, K M
Garcha, P S
George, B
Gill, K
Gill, P S
Grewal, H S
Grewal, N
Gunjal, D
Hanid, M A
Hanif, R
Husein, Y A
Hyde, C S
Ikram, K
Ikram, S
Irani, B H

Hove

Jarzabek, J B
Jeer, P J S
Jeynes, A M
Jogia, P L
Kaiser, R A
Kalha, I S
Kalsi, J S
Kanagaratnam, C N
Kanani, S
Kanchan, B S
Kanchan, S
Kaur, N
Khan, T I
Khan, Z I
King, W C
Kirk, A E M
Kooner, J S
Kooner, R K
Kullar, H S
Lamont, J E
Loomba, R L
Mangat, S K
Mann, A P S
Mannan, M A
Martin, C B
Masood, S K
Matharu, R S
Mayor, S K
Melichar, K B
Mellors, K D
Mendel, P R
Menon, S
Mody, A
Mohindra, R K
Moran, F M
Mughal, A H
Mukherjee, S
Munro, A J
Murray, N A
Nag, S
Nagra, A
Nanda, D
Nijjar, A S
O'Bryan-Tear, C G
Omayer, A S
Osman, M
Patel, B C
Patel, B
Patel, R M
Patel, V
Prince, C A
Rai, J S
Rajasingam, D
Rajendram, R
Rawll, C C G
Robinson, N D P
Sachar, A
Saini, M
Saini, S R
Sandhu, S S
Sandhu, V
Seddon, L
Sharma, B
Sharma, S
Shenton, P A
Singh, P
Sinha, V N P
Slade, P M
Smith, R H
Sood, S
Tan, K H
Thanabalasingham, S T
Thomas, B
Thomas, B M
Thomas, S
Townsend, J
Tripathi, D P
Turner, M R
Vedi, V
Winayak, K
Zaidi, A Z

Black, C C
Bodkin, N L
Bott, M C
Bound, D S
Briggs, M J
Brown, E A
Brumwell, S E
Buck, T J
Burwood, R J
Cairns, D A O
Cawley, G L
Cayley, F E W
Channing, N A
Chapman, D J
Chauhan, S K
Chittenden, K F
Clark, A W
Condon, N I
Court, C S
Crossman, P T
Daly, P G
Davidson, R A
Deutsch, G P
Dimond, J P
Dobbs, F B
Donaghy, G V
Donaghy, J B
Donnelly, J P P
Donohoe, P T
Dossetor, R S
Doyle, E S P
Emmanuel, S S
Evans, D J E
Evans, P C
Felton, W F
Fergie-Woods, D F
Fielding, M E
Fielding, R E
Fisher, A M H
Fisher, N G S
Fletcher, M S
Flynn, M G
Fox, B
Fox, H G
Gayton, P
Gilsenan, K L
Gimbrett, R C
Godber, G N L
Goddard, F J
Graham, H E
Graham, J R
Greenwood, C E
Hacking, S
Hall-Smith, S P
Haslam, N P
Heal, D S
Hempling, S M
Henderson, E J D
Higson, N
Hindley, R G
Holloway, C M
Holloway, K A
Holmes, N P
Howat, J M
Howat, J M
Hume, D C
Hunt, G B
Hutton, F M
Ingram, S M
Ireland, A
Irwin, M H K
Jackson, R N
Keep, J W
Kelly, M C
Knight, S A
Kocen, J L
Krafft, J M
Krasner, G
Lambe, C J T
Latham, B A
Laurence, W N
Lean Su-Tseng, I S
Levene, M M
Liu, C S C
Lucy, B C
Lyne, P J
MacFaul, P A
McLeish, D G G
McMinn, T G
Mak, V Y Y
Mancey-Barratt, W A
Mankikar, G D
Marron, E M
Melcher, D H
Michaels, S B
Mills, M
Mills, S J
Milroy, S J
Mockett, R J

Morgan, J W
Murdoch, J W
Murray, B R P
Mymin, J S
Nicholls, S W
Nurick, S
O'Doherty, C M
O'Donovan, J T
Oliver, S E K
Osborne, D M
Pash, J D
Pilley, C H F
Polmear, A F
Porritt, S F M
Porter, N H
Porter, W A
Rabbs, J M
Rees, J E
Richards, H H
Richter, G
Risk, A M M
Roberts, C
Royle, M G
Rukmani, K S
Saadah, M A
Sakula, A
Scott-Smith, W
Shamash, K
Sharman, M J
Sharpstone, P
Sless, H
Stearman, A S L
Stewart, A C
Stewart, D B
Stott, W B
Strachan, C J L
Stuart, M H
Tabor, A S
Tate, A R
Tate, R T
Taylor, A D
Taylor, A M C
Taylor, R
Tchamouroff, S E
Thorpe, M O
Tierney, R
Treger, A
Turnbull, T J
Turner, K L
Veale, W F C
Wadsworth, P V
Walker, H J
Wallace, W S
Walley, D R
Walters, B T
Weighill, G E
Wells, R C
West, E A
Williams, J H
Williams, S R
Wren, E M
Wright, C I
Zuha, R

Huddersfield

Adam, M J
Aggarwal, A
Aggarwal, J L
Aggarwal, S
Ah-Fat, L N C
Ahmed, M S N
Ahmed, S
Akam, R M
Al-Badri, A M T
Al-Doori, M I
Al-Egaily, S S
Al-Quisi, N K S
Al-Saigh, G S
Alcide, J M
Anathhanam, J J K
Anderson, D G
Anderson, E J
Anderson, J M
Anderson, M E
Angus, R J
Annan, G
Aparicio Ledesma, J
Atkinson, S M
Bagchi, S K
Bairstow, J A
Balendran, N
Bamford, N J
Banks, J
Barlow, A J E
Barnwell, D
Bashir, S
Beg, G I
Benett, S A
Benson, H A

Benster, B
Berry, P W D
Bhabra, K
Bhandari, H B
Bhasin, B B
Black, H J
Black, S K
Bloomer, T N
Bolance Ruiz, M I
Bose, K
Bottomley, J P
Bourne, S A F
Bower, R L
Bradford, A N
Bradley, G
Bradshaw, W H A
Brennan, S A
Brierly, M C
Brook, M E
Brooks, R J
Bunch, G A
Burnett, I A
Burrows, A W
Butt, M
Butterworth, M J
Buxton, R L
Cameron, A J
Cameron, S
Cannon, P D
Care, A E
Carr, C
Carrigan, T D
Carter, C
Case, W G
Cashin, D A
Cassidy, P P
Chakravorty, N K
Chaudhry, F
Cheema, H S
Cheema, S P S
Cheesbrough, M J
Chowdhury, M R
Clark, A M
Clayden, J R
Clayton, M G G
Cleary, J E
Clogher, C A
Clowes, J R
Coates, E M
Coates, M
Cole, G
Cooling, N J
Cox, H E
Crosse, B A
Curtis, J M
D'Cruz, P A
Darby, M J
Das, A K
Das, P
Davey, K G
Deacon, A R
Deane, M E F
Dempsey, H M
Dewhurst, A
Dey, J M M
Dissanayaka, N
Dransfield, P
Dunne, K M
Dux, M S
Eagland, K G
Eagles, J B
Eales, G
Effa, N N
Eleftheriadis, H
Evans, R P
Exley, A
Farooque, H
Faulkner, P P J
Feeney, A-M R
Feeney, J G
Ferro, M
Findlay, H R
Finney, K
Finney, S M
Fitton, P H
Flaherty, K A
Forrest, K A T
Fox-Hiley, P J
Fox, J E
Gannon, C D
Gehlhaar, E W
Gonzalez Sordo, M D
Gottardo, N G
Gowa, S H N
Graham, A
Grainger, J D
Greenhalgh, N M
Griffiths, H
Groves, J A

Guest, T D
Habib, A
Haigh, S J
Halmshaw, F R
Hameed, F
Hamid, A R A S
Hamilton, A H
Hammond, B O
Hancock, S W
Handa, S M
Hanson, J R
Hargreaves, D C
Hariharan, T
Harrison, M A M
Hasanie, N U H
Hawkswell, J A
Heaton, R W
Higgins, E
Higson, R S
Hill, M A
Hindle, D J
Holdsworth, P J
Hooper, J M
Hooper, M D
Hopkinson, N A
Hughes, D M
Hunt, E T
Hunt, K M
Hussain, A
Ingram, A
Ironside, W M S
Irving, C D
Isaac, C F
Islam, M N
Ives, V J
Jabczynski, M R
Jackson, R M
Jameson, R J
Jenkinson, F T
Jenkinson, R D
Jennings, F O
Jennison, P R
Jindal, B K
Jindal, S
Joffe, J K
Jolly, N C
Jones, S C
Juby, L D
Kaftan, S M H
Kassimos, D
Kathuria, B S
Kay, S
Kaye, N M
Kazemi-Jovestani, A
Kazemi-Jovestani, M
Kerr, A R
Khan, A
Khan, K M
Kiely, M T
Knight, D J W
Knowles, M L
Kucharczyk, W A J
Lacasia Purroy, M D C
Landon, C R
Larkin, E
Lee, R P
Littlewood, J
Littlewood, S R
Lloyd, D R
Lord, J R
Lucas, L E
Lumsden, G V
Lyndon, P J
McCarthy, F J F
McCormack, K G
Macdonald, R C
McGregor, J R
MacIver, N
McKenzie, I P
Mannall, J A M
Manning, J E
Martin, N
Martin, V H
Martland, C P
Miller, M G
Milling, A W F
Mitchell, D E
Mitchell, R D
Moffitt, S J
Mohammed, A
Monkhouse, R
Morgan-Hughes, N J
Murphy, A G
Naik, K S
Naylor, J R
Nazareth, H A A
Newbegin, C J R
Newbegin, H E
Nicholas, P T

Nicholls, P G
Nicholls, S L
Nightingale, J A
Nolan, P J
O'Neil, M J
Oakes, S V
Ong, Y E
Ong, Y G
Orme, L J
Ovens, J E A
Pace, H E
Pacynko, M K
Paes, A R
Parker, C R
Parker, H
Parker, J A
Parmar, P P
Pearson, R N
Priestman, J F W
Ramsden, C S
Rana, P S
Raper, S C
Rawcliffe, D S
Read, S G
Reed, L
Richardson, P
Roberts, C L
Robinson, B
Ross, G
Ross, M H
Rushton, R J
Samanta, K
Samanta, R
Sanderson, A
Sanderson, I A
Savage, V E
Schembri, J A
Scott, D G
Sebastian, T C
Seeley, D
Shamsee, M Y S
Sharaf, L A M
Sharman, R A
Sharman, W E
Shenolikar, A
Short, D C
Shortt, A M
Siddiqui, A A
Siddiqui, S A
Siddiqui, U S
Sills, M A
Smelt, G J C
Smith, A L G
Smith, A J
Smith, G B
Smith, I J
Smith, J M P
Smith, M L
Smith, R E W
Sobala, G M J
Sohail, R
Spencer, H M R S
Spencer, S M
Standring, J N
Stevenson, R N
Steyn, A M
Stiles, M A
Swift, T D
Sykes, D P
Tattersall, A E
Taylor, J
Taylor, M J
Taylor, M A
Taylor, M
Tebbit, A
Thornton, P
Thornton, S J
Thorpe, A W
Tomlinson, J F
Tomlinson, R J
Upsdell, S M
Varma, A
Waddington, D
Wade, K
Walker, D A
Wallwork, M A
Ward, C S
Wardley, A M
Wattis, J P
Watts, C
Welch, M T C
Welsh, C J P
Wilding, P J
Wilkinson, A
Wilkinson, N V
Williams, R E
Wilson, F D
Wilson, W S
Wintersgill, P

Wise, D I
Wood, A B
Wood, R M
Woodhead, R B
Worth, C T
Wright, M J
Wybrew, M E
Wybrew, R W J

Hull

Abd-Mariam, N T
Aber, C P
Ahmed, A E
Ahmed, R E
Alexander, N
Ali, S L
Arowojolu, A O
Ashworth, I A
Atkin, S L
Awan, R K
Ayyub, M
Bajalan, A A A
Balshaw, J
Balshaw, M
Bare, L M J
Barnes, D J
Barraclough, M
Bartlett, R J V
Barwood, A T
Bassi, S
Beddis, I R
Best, J G
Bhaskara, R G
Bickford, J A R
Billings, D
Blackburn, C W
Blackburn, P A
Blake, S R
Blow, J D
Bolton, T
Bott, M H
Brennan, T
Brocklehurst, G
Brophy, C J
Brown, M J
Bruce, J H I
Bunola Cerda, J A
Burgess, P A
Busfield, J D
Cafferty, M D A N
Campbell, A P
Caplin, J L
Carter, J R
Chamberlain, M H
Chan, D W-S
Chandy, J
Chapela, J M
Chauhan, G S
Chipperfield, R S
Clarke, C E
Clarke, G B
Clifford, J M
Colman, A W
Conway, M
Cooksey, G
Costello, D F A
Courtney, E D J
Craig, M O
Crawford, D G
Crick, D L A
Crooks, D A
Crossley, M C
Cruickshank, N R J
Cundill, J G
Curran, G J
Dakkak, M
Dalton, E M
Dalton, M
Daniels, G M
Datta, S K
Datta, S R
Davis, P S J
De Netto, N F O
De, B K
Deacon, G R C
Derham, I A
Doherty, S M
Donaldson, M D J
Dore, P C
Drennan, J D
Driver, R K
Drummond, G B
Dunlop, J M
Dunlop, J L
Dunn, S R
Dyet, J F
Eadington, D W
Early, A S
Earnshaw, J H

Edmiston, D R
Edwards, G M
Ell, S R
Ellwood, R W
Emmott, S M
English, P
Ettles, D F
Fairhurst, C T
Farr, M J
Felgate, M J
Findley, M
Fong, R
Foulds, M
Frearson, R J R
Galea, I A
Gamble, R
Garwood, D J
Gee, D G
Ghosh Ray, G C
Ghosh, P C
Gibson, H G
Giles, T E
Gill, S S
Goebells, P
Gooding, C R
Gooding, M R
Gordon, M L
Goring-Morris, J
Gosnold, J K
Gray, B M
Gray, P A
Green, A M
Green, D A
Green, L C
Greensides, J L
Griffin, R G R
Gurnell, E M
Gurnell, P
Guthrie, K A
Haigh, G G
Haley, P F
Halstead, K A
Hamal, B B
Hammersley, C A
Hammersley, K A
Hanna, C M
Harcus, A W
Hay, D M
Hendow, G T
Henshaw, M E
Hepburn, D A
Hetherington, J W
Heylings, P N K
Hiley, D
Hirst, J M
Holmes, M E
Holmquist, J C
Horton, D
Hovell, B C
Howell, F R
Hunter, A I
Hussain, A W
Hussain, S M
Imrie, A H
Innes, A D
Jackson, T R
Jaffe, L
Jary, C A
Jaworska-Grajek, M
Jefferson, I G
Johnson, B F
Johnson, K
Jones, J J
Jones, P N
Jones, P A H
Jones, T P J
Jorna, F H
Joshi, S U
Kamath, M B
Keczkes, K
Khan, I H
Killick, S R
Kilpatrick, E S
Kings, G L M
Knox, A P
Kundu, P M
Kutte, K J
Lambert, C J
Lawley, D I
Lees, S A
Leng, M D
Levett, I J S
Lewis, J P D
Lightfoot, A
Lind, M J
Lindow, S W
Loose, J H
Lorenz, J R
Lovett, M S

Lowery, S D
Luffingham, R L
Lyons, J M
McAlpin, P G R
McClean, H L
McCollum, P T
McDiarmid, M K
McDonald, N H
McGuinness, J A
McIntyre, G B
McKean, D M
Macphie, S
Maguiness, S D
Mahdi, G E D M
Mallik, M K
Mansoor, M A
Mansoor, M R
Markova, I
Martin-Smith, M H A
Martin Ucar, A
Mason, J I C
Mather, A A
Mawer, S L
Meigh, R E E
Melville, A J
Melville, C R
Miller, J
Mitchell, P C
Mohit Mafi, N
Mohla, D J
Moody, M E A
Morris, K M
Mortimer, A M
Moyes, F W
Musil, J
Nakielny, E A
Nakielny, J M
Nandi, S
Naughton-Doe, P E G
Nayar, J K
Nelson, P
Newman, P F
Nicholas, J L
Nirodi, G N
Noble, S C
Norell, M S
O'Connell, M P
Ogunlesi, T O O
Orr, C W
Pairaudeau, P W
Parker, G T
Parker, J S
Parkin, A E
Patmore, R D
Pattrick, M G
Pearce, I
Pearce, J M S
Peiris, M V S
Pepper, A V N
Percival, R
Pestell, A
Pinney, P D
Platts, C H
Portal, R W
Prasad, N
Pratap Varma, M J
Price, J D
Purdie, D W
Queenan, P J
Rai Choudhury, K
Rangwala, G D
Rasool, H
Rasool, M A
Raut, R
Rawson, M D
Read, J R
Renwick, P M
Richards, K J C
Richardson, J W
Richardson, W T
Riusech Mas, I
Rizk, M S
Robinson, D W
Robinson, J-A P
Rochford, F M M
Rogerson, R
Roper, D J
Rosen, C
Rotherham, J
Rowland Hill, C A
Royston, C M S
Russell, I F
Sabbagh, W
Salvage, D R
Samaan, A
Sande, W G T
Sanders, M S
Sandilands, D G D
Sattari, M

Scarfe, S A
Sedman, P C
Sefton, G K
Sellars, L
Selmi, F
Semeniuk, P
Setiya, M S
Shaikh, M
Sharma, K K Y
Sherman, K P
Shields, R H
Shores, J G
Siddiqui, A S
Singh, M N
Skelton, R E
Smales, C
Smithson, J A J
Snowden, G
Somerville, N A M
Soul, J D
Starr, D G
Steel, N R
Stephenson, J T
Subramaniam, S
Sutton, P R
Tang, K M
Taylor, A D
Taylor, J E
Thackray, P
Thackray, S D R
Thomas, M C
Thomas, R C
Thompson, E C
Thomson, F J
Tommins, K S
Trowell, J E
Turner, W H
Turpin, D F
Tyrrell, S N
Ubhi, S
Umerah, F N
Upadhyay, S K
Van Maarseveen, P L
Venugopal, J
Vollmer, J
Warran, P
Waugh, P N
Webster, J L
Webster, P A C
Wedgwood, K R
Weir, J A D
Whitehead, E
Whitley, I
Wilkinson, A R
Wong, M K
Wright, P J
Wynn, M D
Yagnik, R D
Young, R A
Yousuff, A M
Yu, L F

Hungerford

Baer, G M L
Ballantine, K
Bray, J K
Cane, C S
Colthurst, J R
Dace, H M
Green, H T
Hamilton, R A
Harris, L J M
Hetherington, P I G
Hope, H D A
Johal, N S
Montague, C C
Needham, G D K
Pihlens, H L
Powell, H B
Pullen, M J
Rice, H M
Stewart, M C
Symon, R
Yates, N

Hunstanton

Baluch, M A
Burgess, J E
Calderon, N V S
Charles, I P
Crouch, M
Fellowes, H M
Ford, H K
Le Masurier, R R
Machin, C
Mulligan, R A
Sellick, R J
Tiernan, D G M

Wakes Miller, C H
Yule, I G

Huntingdon

Aggarwal, A K
Aggarwal, R
Al-Kurdi, M
Allan, R B
Amara, S N
Aravindhan, N
Aravindhan, S R
Archer, C C
Babbington, S P
Bacon, N A
Baxter, R
Becker, M G
Benison, P M
Bermingham, D F
Berrington, R M
Bethune, D W
Biram, R W S
Blake, D E
Booth, A J
Booth, J V
Borland, C D R
Bower, P S
Boyle, B E
Boyle, J A
Bray, J D
Brinsden, M D
Brook, J M
Brookes, J M G M
Brooks, A M J H
Brown, R
Brown, S J
Burbidge, E
Caldwell, J
Cameron, B A
Carlyle, R F
Carroll, M J
Caswell, J D
Challener, J
Chan, E W-S
Cheffins, E M
Cheng, K-S
Churms, B K
Collins, E P
Collinson, J E
Connan, D
Cook, S L
Cormack, L E
Cox, A J
Cox, D C A
Cracknell, D D
Crockatt, D R
Culloty, S M
Cuthbert, M F
Cutress, M L
Cutress, R I
Darling, J S
Das, R K
De Cates, C R
Dean, H C
Diamond, J G
Diamond, P A M
Dick, A E
Dickinson, R J
Donnelly, K F
Drabble, E H
Duke, A R
Dumbelton, I B
Fells, J N
Ferreira, F G
Flanagan, D W
Fletcher, P R
Forbes, P B
Forster, S M
Foster, P J
Ghosh, T N
Glover, M W
Goodwin, P R
Granger, A F
Greatrex, A F
Green, A J
Greig, J R
Gryf-Lowczowski, J V D
Gupta, D S
Hackman, M G
Haddock, G D
Haddock, K M
Hage, W K
Haigh, E R
Harper, A D
Harris, M D
Harrower, T P
Hart, J W
Harvey, M S
Haslam, D A

Henderson, R G
Hickey, P L
Hildick-Smith, D J R
Hodson, J
Hoggarth, C E
Holland, H F
Horsnell, J M
Hubbard, C S f
Hunter-Campbell, P
Hunter, D
Irish, N
Irwin, D S S
Jamali, N
Jarvis, E J
Jenaway, A
Jenner, J A
Jennison, K M
Jessop, C H
Jewell, J A
Johnson, A F
Johnson, A T
Johnson, S A
Jones, J A
Jones, S P
Kakani, S R
Kanka, D
King, S M
Krone, S C
Lasman, F C A
Latham, B V
Latimer, R D
Liggins, A J
Lionaki, A
Lund, K A
Lyle, T
Macartney, B W M
McCullough, F W
Mackay, H M
Macleod, C A
MacLeod, K R
Maenpaa, G A
Maister, A R N
Maister, M B
Martin, D J
Mason, N C
Matsiko, K S
Mayhew, S R
Middlemiss, J L
Miles, R N
Millard, P W
Moazzam, A
Monro, P A G
Moor, M J
Mullinger, A V
Nashef, A J
Newby, M R
Ni Bhrolchain, C M
Noel, P R B
Norden, A G W
O'Sullivan, F T
Okagbue, C E
Oubridge, J V
Paraskevaides, E C
Parwaiz, K
Patel, A
Patterson, A
Paul, S C
Pedersen, S W
Perkins, P J
Phillips, N J
Picts, A C
Pike, J M
Pinkerton, G E
Platten, H M J
Pountain, G D
Price, V
Quek, S L G
Quick, C R G
Randhawa, S S
Rawlinson, J
Rea, D P
Reeve, A A
Rej, E
Rene, C
Reynolds, G C S
Richardson, A J
Roberts, D H G
Roberts, D R A
Rodgers, D J
Rutherford, H J
Saban, P A
Sackin, P A
Salman, M N
Schofield, J P
Searle, P J
Sewell, P F T
Sharma, S
Sharp, C
Sibthorpe, J O

Huntly

Slack, M C
Small, G
Smerdon, G R
Smith, R J
Southgate, G W
Stanger, R J R
Stenner, J M C
Sugden, J H
Sweetenham, I A
Swinscoe, A W
Sydenham, J E B
Taggart, S C O
Tak, V M
Taylor, H L
Taylor, N J
Thomas, T M
Thrower, A L
Topham, H W
Tulloch, B C
Turner, J V
Turnill, A
Vaughan-Lane, T
Vickerstaff, K M
Walsh, K J
Walters, S E
Wanendeya, N Y
Warbrick-Smith, D
Watson, B J
Weyell, R S
Whitelock, D E
Whitton, M W
Wilberforce, B D
Wilcock, J M
Williams, I G
Williams, P H
Woodfield, M C
Wrench, R
Wright, A D
Wright, D
Wright, M H G
Zebro, T J
Zulfiker, S O

Huntly

Arthur, A L T
Card, I R
Carter, G
Cosgrove, E E
Cran, J
Easton, D A H
Gatenby, R A B
Gordon, C E T
Harvais, G R
Lockyer, J A
Lyons, K A
Shirreffs, G C
Sinclair, A G
Taylor, J F
Traquair, K E C
Traquair, R N
Troup, J D G
Watt, B

Hyde

Ashworth, W D
Aziz, T Z
Baguneid, M S
Banks, A J
Beenstock, N
Bellhouse, W
Bhatti, Z B
Bradshaw, F R
Carroll, D H
D'Silva, K
Dow, A J
Edmondson, A N
Farrar, S W
Fines, D P
Fitton, R P
Gulati, R K
Gutteridge, L C
Haji-Suhailee, H-A
Hannan, A S
Harvey, J M
Henshall, P
Hillel, M D
Horan, M
Islam, T
Johnston, E M
Joshi Godrez, D M
Kinsey, M A
Lee, S S
Loose, H C
MacGillivray, A
Maclaverty, K G J
Moysey, J O
Napier, I G
Nicholson, G
Patel, R

Peravali, B
Pole, P M
Procter, H M
Proctor, S C
Reynolds, L J
Roberts, M M
Roney, D B
Schofield, P F
Shah, M P
Singh, G P
Tanna, V N M
Thomas, A K
Thornton-Chan, E W C
Wickenden, D H
Williams, J M
Wintle, F C

Hythe

Allen, A P
Bateman, F J A
Besley, C R G
Briggs, R D
Chandrakumaran, K
Cheek, S P
Cochrane, S
De Caestecker, J P
Derry, C D
Diamond, M P
Ford, P G T
Foster, I L
Grainge, S M W
Greaves, F H
Griffiths, N J
Hiscocks, E S
Jones, J S
Kennedy, J F
Kenyon, Z
Klugman, D J
Menin, P T
Mohr, A R
Oakes, J L
Padley, N R
Phillips, C W D
Potter, C J F
Rial, S C
Robertson, A
Torrance, A M
Wells, D G
Wells, M D
Whitby, M E
Wilson, I V

Ibstock

Bridges, J
Cawte, E C
Farley, S E

Ilford

Abdul-Razak, N A J
Abidogun, K A O
Afzal, M
Agu, K C
Ahmad, R
Ahmad, S M A
Ahmed-Shuaib, A
Ahmed, S J
Akhtar, N
Al-Qassab, H K
Ali, M L
Ali, S N
Arawwawala, D P
Ashraf, W
Atalar, A T
Azad, A
Bagg, L R
Bakhai, R P
Bakhsh, N
Balakumar, T
Baloch, A H
Balraj, V
Banerjee, L
Banerjee, N
Banerji, S
Barnardo, A E M
Basra, S S
Bastianpillai, B A
Batheja, M
Beg, M S A
Bell, V A
Bellin, U
Bennett, D L
Bettany, G E A
Bhadra, N B
Bhatt, A N
Bishai, K R T
Boctor, S Z
Born, M S
Briffa, J V
Briggs, J C
Brown, N

Bullon Barrera, F J
Burgess, D
Cameron-Mowat, R J
Chakravorti, S
Chatterjee, H
Choudhury, A K
Chowdhury, R S
Clarke, F A
Clay, R A
Cleary, M P
Cochrane, G W
Colgate, E J
Cooney, V B
Crabbe, I F
Cronin, B
Dabrera, M G A V
Deb, N K
Desai, J D
Deveshwar, S K
Dutta, N N
Edelman, J B
Ehsan, M
El Hussein, N A
Elias, S A
Enver, M K
Fang, C R
Fiberesima, S L
Gautama, P
Ghosh, M
Goel, A
Goel, R
Goyal, M
Grainger, S L
Grant, I R
Green, E M
Greenaway, B J
Gupta, L
Haldar, G
Hanna, N J
Harar, R P S
Hargreaves, C A
Harwood, C A
Hervel, G M
Hobson, J G
Hodges, M J
Hossain, F
Hossain, M
Hossain, M M
Husain, S A
Hussain, K
Hussein, S
Huston, R B
Ip, M
Ishaque, M A
Islam, T M
Iwegbu, C G
Jan, M B
Javed, E B
Javid, S
Jayaraj, S M
Jayaratnam, R
Jayatillake, S M D
Jethwa, S R
Jolaoso, A S
Joshi, N
Kadir, N
Kalebic, B
Kaltsas, D S
Kanagasabai, K
Kanagasundrem, A
Karki, B D
Kashin, M A H
Kerawala, F M
Khan, M Y
Khraishi, D M M S
Knight, C J
Kollipara, P
Krishna Reddy, P
Kulasegaram, Y
Kulendran, S
Kullar, N S
Kumar, R
Kumarakulasingham, R
Lack, S I
Lau, A Y-H
Lester, J F
Levack, B
Levy, R B
Lim, M H
Lin Sin Cho, G L
Littlejohn, R
Lord, M G
McDougall, C M
Mackenzie, G D
McLean, J A F
McMillan, G J S
McNeilly, J C
Mahar, P B
Mahendra-Yogam, P

Mahmood, M
Makar, A S
Mandavia, B J
Margo, A M
Martin, D G
Mayer, T C
Mehta, A
Mendes, R L
Michael, G
Minocha, K
Moss, D
Mughal, R M
Mustfa, G
Naganathar, I
Navaneetharaja, N
Niranjan, K
Nirmalananthan, S
Nischal, V K
Nylander, H H
O'Brien, A E
Osei, E
Padmanathan, C
Pandit, V
Pandya, J
Parmar, H R
Patel, G D
Patel, R B
Patel, R S
Paul, E A A
Pentz, A J L
Pereira, S M
Piyarisi, D L
Purushothman, G
Qayyum, A
Quraishi, M A
Qureshi, M A
Rahim, S
Rainsbury, P A
Rana, D-E-S
Randall, R
Rastogi, R
Ratnakumar, K
Ratnakumar, S
Ray, D
Riordan, D C
Rizvi, S I H
Robin, E C
Robinson, D L
Rodrigues, M J P
Row, K P
Rughani, G
Rughani, V G
Rupal, A
Sadheura, M K
Sadideen, M
Saggu, R S
Saha, A R
Saha, T K
Sahdev, A
Sakthibalan, M
Saleh, F A A
Sanghvi, M V
Sclare, H
Seehra, S S
Segal, I M
Segal, M P L
Selvarajah, K
Sen, D
Sennik, A K
Shah, A K
Shah, S A
Shah, V K
Shaida, A M
Shaikh, A G A
Shan, K
Sharif, S
Sharma, K
Sharma, S
Sharma, V K
Shaw, F J
Shergill, B S
Shillito, M
Shubhaker, U D
Shubhaker, U
Siddique, Y
Singh, H
Sinha, S K
Sinnathamby, S W
Slater, E G W
Smith, S J
Snooks, S J
Soares, P O B
Solebo, J O
Solomon, W C A
Soosay, G N
Spencer, J R
Spiteri, H P
Springer, H W
Srinivasan, S

Steinbergs, G G
Subberwal, K
Suri, A C
Sweeney, M M
Tahir, M
Taslimuddin, A S M
Tek, V
Thomas, J Q
Thurairajah, G
Tsang, D T K
Tse, D T K
Uddin, S
Van Der Putt, R P
Vanstraelen, M
Verma, U K
Vijaya Ganesh, T
Viswanath, I
Wakeel, R A P
Wallach, A L
Webster, E A
Wellings, M J
Wickremasinghe, M I Y
Wickremasinghe, S P
Wickremasinghe, S M
Wijayakoon, A P

Ilfracombe

Bevan, S A
Eames, M R
Eames, R A
Fenner, M T
Freeman, A C
Griffiths, B J
Holmes, E
Hunt, S J
Kilner, G F
Mather, M J C
Richardson, Dr
Wallace, D I R
Warwick, M S
Womersley, J S B

Ilkeston

Adams, R D
Bailey, E W E
Binnie, F J F
Brammer, M A
Bromwich, E J
Brown, B D
Connell, H E
Crowley, G S
Dawson, R D E
Donovan, J A
Downes, N M
Enoch, P J
Finch, G
Futers, G
Gradwell, R Z
Johnson, T M
Ketharthas, R
Ketharthas, S
Kirk, D A
Lalloo, R D
Lund, J N
Miller, S J
Parfitt, C J
Portnoy, A E
Portnoy, D
Purnell, S L
Rogers, R T N
Sinclair, D H
Storey, R F
Thomson, J
Tierney, G M
Tooley, I R
Travell, P D
Turner, D P J
Varnam, R M
Veale, P R
Walton, G M
Webb, C L
Weston Smith, P A

Ilkley

Alexander, C M
Atkins, F E
Atkins, P
Barron, R
Batool, T
Beard, D J
Bearpark, A D
Beaumont, J M
Bingert, T
Boyle, A A
Bramwell, E R
Brand, I R
Brooke, A
Brown, A C
Buller, C H

Burn, G P
Burn, P C
Cape, J
Cavanagh, S P
Church, K E
Clarke, A
Clarke, E M
Clarkson, A D
Cohen, E F
Cowie, J W
Davies, R P
Dawson, W E
Dean, H M
Dickson, P
Dickson, S D
Dixon, J A
Donaldson, R S
Douglas, G K
Drysdale, S H
Duce, G M
Duckworth, G G
Elliott, R W
Ellis, D J P
Evans, V J
Fox, S E
Francis, W H
French, M J R
Frost, J B
Goodwin-Jones, R B
Gore, C P
Hall, G P
Hanson, K E
Hargreaves, R E
Haynes, P A
Hicks, J S
Hoyes, S E
Hughes, T A
Hutchinson, I F
Jadav, M A R
Jewell, B R
Kilburn, P
Laing, M L
Lewis, M A
Macalister, E D
McLellan, A E
Mapstone, N P
Martinez, D
Milnes, J P
Minford, A M B
Moody, E M
Murray, H
Neasham, J P
Nelson, T E
Newby, E A
Newton, E M G
O'Brien, P M J
O'Hara, S D N
Ogilvy, J E
Pacsoo, T C
Patterson, S
Phillips, T J
Plummer, T R
Poulier, R A
Powell, A L
Ragunathan, P
Raubitschek, E
Rawling, A H
Rawling, R G
Roberts, J M
Roberts, S J
Robinson, Q L A
Rolfe, H C
Seidelin, R
Shann, D J
Sheard, C R
Sherwood, G J
Smith, C A
Souyave, J
Srinivasan, T R
Stevenson, D K
Stone, K E
Sugden, M
Tanner, P M
Taylor, H E
Thompson, A J
Tinker, A J
Turner, W
Valentine, J
Van Terheyden, N J E R
Wales, A C
Ward, A J
Warner, D P
Warner, N J
Weatherill, J R
Williams, E A
Willoughby, B J
Woodford, A
Zigmond, A S

Ilminster
Anton, D J
Austin, A D L
Barber, R N
Bond, W M
Boyce, D J
Coleman, J E
Hazlewood, J
Hodges, A E J
Isaac, D H
Outram, M
Patuck, D F
Patuck, J F
Pearce, S N
Perry, A D C
Rahilly, D M
Reeves, W G
Schmidt, K E
Sen Gupta, P
Simpson, R C
Sims, S R
Tipping, J P
Wilson, A G M
Wilson, J E

Immingham
Belcher, P D
Opie, P M
Robertson, J H M
Spalding, A E

Ingatestone
Bolton, M E
Cheung, K-K
Coffin, J P
Emond, R A
Feldman, P M
Hughes, C A
Lacey, A G
Lightowler, C
Lightowler, E
Lightowler, J V J
McKendrick, G D W
Macpherson, T J
Medford, N C
Mellor, E G
Nicol, D J F
O'Reilly, R J
Orford, E D
Pal, S K
Peters, J L
Phillips, D L
Rilstone, F W B
Sudbury, J R
Wallace, A F
Warden, R E

Innerleithen
Cumming, R L
Henderson, I R
Oswald, I
Sanderson, T L
Soutter, F A
Thompson, B A
Watson, E A

Insch
Kay, D M
Mackie, H A
Mitchell, P C
Morrice, G M

Inveraray
Bijral, H S
Bijral, H S
Bijral, K S
Colley, I H
Colley, J K
Craig, L M
Currie, A
Swanson, G H

Invergordon
Barker, P A
Carr, P D
Hutchison, B S
MacLlan, R
Murdoch, J R M

Inverkeithing
Allan, J J
Duguid, I M
Duncan, L E
Eastwood, J
Grant, A R
Jackson, A R
Jalil, M
Jamieson, K A
Paterson, W I
Ritchie, K B
Sanderson, T A

Inverness
Shedden, W I H
Slight, R D
Steele, A H
Taylor, D M

Aitken, A G F
Alexander, E J
Ali, N
Anderson, V
Austin, J B
Baijal, E P
Baikie, M L
Baker, R V V
Ball, J L
Ball, L M
Barker, P M W
Bather, C L
Beasley, R J
Bennet, A J
Blagden, A K
Booth, D H
Boyd, F E
Bramwell, S P
Bratten, M C
Bratten, N T
Briggs, E M G
Brown, C A
Bruce, J
Burton, J A
Butler, D R E
Caddell, R F
Caird, L E
Campbell, A F
Campbell, D
Campbell, H O C
Campbell, M G
Campbell, R J
Campbell, R M
Chalmers, D M
Chancellor, C I
Charters, F K
Chesser, A M S
Christison, J R
Clow, E C M
Collier, M K
Convery, K A
Conway, E M
Cook, C M
Cormack, J G
Cox, Q G N
Currie, J M
Dalmau Carre, J
Davidson, K E
Davidson, W C
Davies, I J T
Deans, J
Deans, M
Dempster, S
Dempster, W H
Dunbar, A C
Duncan, B
Duncan, J L
Edmonstone, Y G
Elia, M H
Ennis, C J
Escott, T E
Farmer, G
Farquharson, G B
Ferguson, I C
Ferguson, M C
Finlayson, D F
Fisher, L R
Forbes, H
Franklin, D H
Fraser, D A S
Fraser, N G
Gajda, A
Galloway, C A S
Gamblin, A J
Gardner, C A
Gillies, N W
Gilmour, R J
Glen, A I M
Godden, D J
Goff, D G
Goodlad, J R
Gordon, P M
Gow, M
Graham, A J
Grant, C E
Grant, J
Gray, S A
Grier, A M
Griffiths, C A
Guy, R D
Hadley, D C G M
Hadley, M W M
Haggerty, S R

Hamilton, A
Harrison, S B
Harvey, R D
Hay, A G
Hay, A J
Hendry, P J
Herd, D J
Higham, L J M H
Ho-Yen, D O
Howie, A F W
Hulks, G
Hulse, M
Humble, R D
Hutchison, S M W
Jack, S A
Jamieson, A D
Jamieson, N F
Jennings, P
Johnston, E A
Johnston, I G
Johnston, J M
Johnston, R
Johnstone, A F
Jones, C J
Kelly, S M
Kelsey, S J E
Kennedy, I
Kerr, F
Khaweri, F A
Kiln, P A
Kirkwood, G A
Laing, M R
Lamont, A M
Leask, J C
Lees, D A R
Logie, J R C
Low, R W D
Lumley, S P
Lush, C J
Maarouf, A S M S
Macaulay, E M
McBride, E
McClure, A
McClure, S
McClymont, L G
MacDonald, C
McDonald, J
McFadden, J A V
MacFadyen, R J
Mcfarlane, A
Macfarlane, E
McFarlane, E A
McGrath Ross, L
MacGregor, A
MacGregor, C M
Machin, J R
McIlwaine, J R
McIntosh, A D
McIntosh, G D
Macintyre, J
McKay, R T
McKenna, J G
McKenzie, E M
Mackenzie, I
Mackenzie, M E F
McKerrow, W S
McKillop, M E
Mackinlay, M G
McKinley, A J
Mackintosh, G J
Mackintosh, L E
Maclaren, M H S
Maclean, B N
Maclean, M L
Maclean, M R
Maclean, M W
MacLellan, L D
Maclennan, A K
MacLeod, A A
MacLeod, A J M
Macleod, A C
Macleod, C L H
Macleod, R S
Macleod, S E
Macleod, S K
McNamara, H I
Macneil, A
McPheat, A S
MacPherson, G R
Macpherson, I
Macpherson, J I
MacPherson, M J P
McPhie, J L
MacRae, J A M
Macrae, M J
MacRury, S M
MacVicar, D
MacVicar, L C
MacVicar, R

Malcolmson, S E
Marshall, S G
Martin, C M
Martin, J A M
Martin, J R
Matheson, M L
May, J R
Mayhew, J A L
Miller, R
Milne, B
Mitchell, J N S
Moore, E J H
Morrison, A
Morrison, A R
Morrison, G H
Muir, J
Munro, A J
Munro, A
Murphy, N M
Murray, R W C
Murray, W
Murray, W D
Nicholls, J
Nichols, D M
Oates, K R
Ong, E K
Palmer, T J
Pearl, S A
Pearson, T N
Philip, D
Potts, L F
Quinn, K S
Ramsay, J W
Rankin, R
Reid, D G
Reid, D W E
Richmond, H G
Robertson, D A
Robertson, P
Ross, J
Ross, W A
Rosser, A K D
Rusk, M
Russell, I C
Scott, I G
Shanks, S D
Sim, A J
Skipsey, I G
Smith, A D
Smith, I R
Smith, S L
Snow, A F
Somerville, D W
Spenceley, J H
Spenceley, J A
Spenceley, N C
Stark, C R
Steven, M M
Stevenson, A W
Stone, G V
Strachan, H M C
Struthers, A D
Sutherland, J
Sutherland, P
Sweenie, J F
Syme, A I C
Taylor, J E
Taylor, T G
Thin, M J
Thomas, R
Tracey, D M
Tracey, S
Traill, E R
Urquhart, C
Urquhart, H M
Vass, L M
Vestey, J P
Walker, A
Walsh, P V
Watt, S M
Waudby, H
Welch, G S
Whillis, D
Whillis, J E
Whitrow, W
Whyte, D K
Whyte, I F
Wilkes, P R
Wilkinson, G W W
Will, S C
Williams, F R
Williams, H
Williams, P
Wilson, J C
Wrench, J G
Wycliffe-Jones, K
Wycliffe-Jones, S C A
Zentler-Munro, P L

Inverurie
Argo, J K
Bainton, R
Beattie, J A G
Black, J E
Brewis, G M
Cannon, A M
Cassidy, K A
Connell, D G
Cooper, D
Downie, A W
Ewen, D M
Flett, A E
Fraser, J H E
Gill, G M
Hamilton, M I K
Harkness, S M
Hawson, D S
Hern, J E C
Hogg, K E
Hood, D B
Humphrey, C A
Ingram, S E
Johnston, V W
Kennedy, B R
McDonald, L
Mack, H N
McKay, F M A
Morrison, K A
Murdoch, J M
Murrison, B L
Oliver, J
Rutledge, D G A
Shepherd, J H
Wallace, R M
Watson, C J
Wilson, T M
Young, G

Ipswich
Adair, H M
Adair, W D
Adapa, U D
Aitken, J
Aldous, I R
Andrews, M J
Ansari, S
Arasaratnam, R B S
Archer, T J
Ashford, P D
Atkinson, E S
Badcock, S
Bailey, D M
Ball, R
Bamford, M F M
Barsoum, M Z
Bawden, S E
Bellhouse, J E
Bhatia, I L
Bisley, G G
Board, J O M
Bowditch, M G
Bradshaw, M F
Brick, T D
Broadway, J W
Brown, C M D
Brown, V J
Browne, G L
Browne, M J
Buckley, R M
Burn, P W
Bush, M F H
Bush, P A
Cameron, A E P
Campbell, J M
Carey, J M
Cavanagh, R A
Chalmers, I M
Chalmers, J A
Chasteney, M L E
Chowdhary, Z A
Chung, N A Y
Clark, C J
Coady, T J
Collins, R J
Cook, C I M
Cook, M H
Coomber, S (E L
Cope, E M
Cox, L E
Craggs, R A
Cruickshank, A N
Cupper, N C
Cushen, M J
Cuthill, J J
Cutler, T P
David, P S
Davies, H T
Davies, R A

Day, J L
Deacon, D J
Dewar, F M M
Digby, I F
Dineen, S J
Dodd, N J
Drinkall, J N
Dubois, S V
Duncan, J N
Edelsten, C
Edwards, M S
El Gaddal, M E H
El Treki, R M H
Evans, W B
Exley, P
Fairhead, M M
Fairweather, J A
Fenton, J C
Flather, J N
Flemming, C J
Flowers, I M
Flynn, T G
Foster, S
Freestone, M D
Fryer, P J
Garber, S J
Garfield, P
Gazeley, S D
Gibbons, N C
Gibbs, A N
Gibbs, S S S
Gill, J B
Glancey, G R
Glason, M S L
Glass, S A
Goddard, R
Goodess, J E
Goodwyn, J R
Gould, G M
Gould, J D M
Goyder, E C
Grierson, C A
Grimmer, S F M
Guirguis, R W
Guirguis, W R
Gunn, A L
Hadden, F M
Hague, J S
Halford, J D
Hall, D R
Hall, S R
Hall, S W
Hallatt, A M
Hallett, J P
Hancock, S P
Harding, K M
Hardman Lea, S J
Harley, S C L
Harper, J W K
Hartfall, W G
Hartley, K E
Head, L
Heley, M M
Helps, C M
Henderson, J C
Henshall, L A H
Hewetson, P R T
Hirst, S G
Hodgkinson, D W
Hodgson, C
Holloway, P
Holt, W J
Hopkinson-Woolley, J A
Howard-Griffin, J R
Howard-Griffin, R M
Howell, P J
Huddy, S P J
Hudson, I
Hutchinson, J R M
Innes, N J
Irvine, N A
Irwin, P T J
Iskander, A Z
Jackson, E P
Jaiswal, B K
James, L M
James, R S
Jansen, M R G
Jarvis, A P
Jeevaratnam, E A J
Jennings, P E
Jesuthasan, A J
Jogeesvaran, S
Johal, B
Johnston, C M
Jones, P H
Jones, S E M
Juby, H B

Irvine

Judd, P A
Jupp, E J
Karia, K R
Keeble, B R
Kent, R J
King, A M
King, D R
King, K A
Kinnear, E
Knight, M A
Kong, A S
Laing, S A
Laking, P J
Laukens, A E P
Lazar, S C
Le Vay, J H
Leather, A T
Lelijveld, H A B M
Lewis, G V
Linsell, W D
Lloyd, M
Lockington, T J
Lockwood, T J
Lord, I J
Lousaing, D E
Lush, A M
McCullagh, M G
McCurdy, D L
McElhinney, D J
MacEwan, H D
McGowan, K T
McKall, K C
McKay, P W
McWilliam, W N
Mamujee, A M
Mamujee, N V
Manji, H
Mansfield, M D
Marcoolyn, G J S
Marsh, R D
Marsh, T D
Marx, C L
Mead, H M B
Mehta, K H
Mercer, R E
Merritt, T J K
Metcalfe, W P
Midforth, J E
Mills, A M
Mills, J W
Mills, M G
Mills, P J
Mindham, M R
Mohamed, M S
Moncrieff, M D S
Mooney, P
Morgan, J S
Moser, E S
Moser, S G
Moser, S
Mott, T J
Mowles, A J
Narayanan, S
Nicholl, A D J
Nightingale, R C
Nourse, C H
O'Neill, K P
Ogden, B E P
Oliver, R M
Orr, J P
Orrell, J M
Palmer, M I
Parry, J R W
Patient, S M
Paulley, J W
Pavitt, J A
Pearce, C J
Pearce, R J
Peecock, F P M
Penkethman, A J
Peyton, H N
Phillips, N E
Phillips, P A
Picken, G
Pitt, J
Powell, J M
Powell, O J
Rauniar, A K
Rayman, G
Reader, C E
Reader, F C
Remeh, B S
Renshaw, N D
Richards, G D H
Ripman, H A
Roberts, E R
Roberts, S J
Roberts, T J H
Robertson, K J

Rowe, R C G
Roy, P K
Royce, S M
Ruddy, M C P
Rush, E M
Salam, M A M E-H
Sarfraz, H S
Schurr, A J V
Scott, I H K
Scott, J R
Seaton, D
Seaton, E D
Shanahan, M D G
Sharman, A
Sharp, D J
Sharpe, C R
Sheehan, J M
Sheehan, L J
Siddique, A Q
Simpson, C N
Skinner, J B
Smith, K S
Smith, S L
Smith, S J
Smithson, N
Sonnex, T S
Souster, H
Squire, C M
Steiner, R R
Stevens, M J
Stock, P M
Strubbe, P A M J
Swinglehurst, D A
Tate, R J
Taylor, S J
Thiruchelvam, N
Thomas, D L C
Thomas, G
Thomas, P D
Thompson, E J
Thomson, L M
Thurairaj, T
Thurtle, O A
Todd, A E
Trowell, J E
Turner, D A
Turner, T E
Vasey, D P
Vickery, H F A
Wadera, S P
Wankowska, H C
Ward, D M
Ward, T
Warren, M D
Watson, M
Watson, R J
Watts, J P
Watts, R A
Webb, F W S
Weir, I K
Wells, F O
Wheatley, D C
Whitear, W P
Wilden, J
Wilkinson, A J
Wilkinson, S L
Williams, B E B
Williams, J R
Williams, P F
Williams, S A
Williams, S G J
Williamson, C C
Wilson, A O
Wilson, J G
Wilson, M E S
Wiltshire, C R
Wiltshire, S J
Wood, P A T
Woodley, J M
Wray, P M
Wright, K J T
Wright, R
Wroe, S J
Wyborn, M V T
Wyke, R J
Wythe, P
Young, K S
Young, T W S
Yuen, K C J
Yung, M W

Irvine

Adamson, A
Barber, J M
Burnett, R R
Campbell, W D
Cunningham, D
David, M C
Doig, M F

Dryden, C M
Frame, W T
Godfrey, J B
Graham, K
Hewitt, A P
Irvine, G A
Kerr, P
Kinmond, S
Luis Ruiz, D
MacDonald, C E
McElhone, J P S
McGlone, P
McGregor, C M
McHugh, C
McKeith, D D
Macleod, I
McMenemin, L S
Macrae, R A
McSherry, G J
Merchant, E S
Miller, A F
Mullin, L
Nixon, A A
Park, L M
Roberts, W
Russell, S G
Sharma, V C
Stewart, B E
Wagner, R M
Wood, I H Y

Isle of Benbecula

Dawson, S K
Neaves, J M
Senior, A J
Tierney, F

Isle of Coll

Carle, G

Isle of Colonsay

Currie, J S

Isle of Eigg

Weldon, R H

Isle of Harris

Finlayson, J A D
Naylor, A I

Isle of Islay

Buchanan, E C
Buller, A J
Perrons, A J
Wood, R J

Isle of Jura

Hawker, D B G

Isle of Lewis

Barker, J A
Belbin, A H
Clark, I
Collacott, R A
Ferguson, M
Gillies, N R
Hamilton, R W
Hay, J C
Jones, A H
Macaulay, J R
Macdonald, C A
Maciver, I
Macleod, M M
Macleod, M
Marshall, L S
Murray, D R
Nichols, D
Ratchford, A
Rigby, D J
Roberts, A M
Smith, G
Vishu (Vishwanath), M C
Watts, M I

Isle of Mull

Charlier, A R
Clegg, W H
Douglas, M
Elder, P M
Ferguson, C E
Garcia Hinarejos, J A
Jack, J A
Jones, T I
Kennedy, S D
Parson, I S R
Sutherland, J D

Isle of Skye

Baker, F M
Ball, A
Ball, J R

Banks, T W F
Cheyne, M F
Donald, A C
Gilbertson, M H M
Hartley, H A
Humphrey, A W
Johnston, H M
Lyon, P R
Maclean, M
Pearce, T
Roberton, N R C
Stuart, A E
Surtees, J K
Tallach, C

Isle of Tiree

Holliday, J D P
Williams, V E

Isle of Wight

Ellis, M R
Ringrose, D W

Isleworth

Abhaya Kumar, S
Adam, B S
Ahmad, S S
Al-Obaidi, M K
Ali, N T
Allard, S A
Alvi, R
Alvi, S A
Anderson, M G
Andrew, R
Antebi, D L
Archibald, C
Ashley, J S A
Banerjee, B
Basu, S
Beckett, M W
Bellringer, J F
Bhattacharyya, B K
Bhave, N A
Bluett, P J
Bonikowski, E J
Carapiet, A M
Cassar, J
Cheetham, D R
Collins, C E
Craig, R G
Dalton, M E
Daniels, D G
Davis, D M
Dawson, P M
Doctor, R S
El Khidir, H H
Ezzat, M H
Forster, P M
Fox, J S
Girling, J C
Greenwood, T W
Guha, I N
Habel, A
Hakeem, V F
Harrison, S J
Heath, D I
Ho, K N V
Hughes, R G
Hussain, H K
Idia, T I J
Jogiya, A
Jones, E C
Kaikini, D W W
Kaikini, D R
Kane, S P
Kangesu, T
Khattar, R S
Koppikar, M G
Kurar, A K
Lau, D P-C
Lett, K S
Macedo, C
Mahendra, M M
Mannan, M A
Massoud, M A K
Matson, A M
Miller, C S
Mitchell, J
Naunton Morgan, T C
Oliver, J R
Owen, E J
Papasiopoulos, S
Parker, S C
Patel, S N
Peters, T M
Platt, J S
Pusavat, L T
Rangasami, J J
Raslan, F
Richmond, C E

Rogers, H S
Sabharwal, T K
Saltissi, S
Sensky, T E
Shah, S
Shah, S M A
Shettar, C K
Sinclair, J C
Slaven, A E
Starr, J M
Thorpe, P A
Venkataraman, G
Walia, S
Warnock, W A
Whiteman, J R
Whitmarsh, S P
Winning, A J
Young, R A L
Zadeh, H G

Iver

Banner, B H
Brooke, S J R
Gibbs, N P H
Gilani, N
Gilani, S M N
Jenkins, L K
Jones, E W
Nowers, C D
Rigby, G V
Roberts, P J
Robinson, V P
Shafi, M A
Trythall, D A H
Webster, P J R

Ivybridge

Anderson, R B
Behennah, L M
Bleasdale, J K
Bleiker, P F
Broadley, A J M
Burnell-Nugent, H M
Campbell-Smith, T A
Campbell, L J F
Churcher, M D
Clark, J T M
Cornock, S J
D'Costa, A A
D'Costa, H F
Day, H C
Dumoulin, J G
Evans, L E
Gregory, G
Griffiths, T N
Hamlyn, E C
Harker, R J
Harris, S J
Holley, P J
Johnson, A L M
Jones, K A
Langsford, M J
Laurens, C
Martin, J R C
Morris, J R
Nicolle, P L
Oakins, M J
Ousey, T J
Pinsent, S E M
Price, J N
Price, M J
Richardson, J B
Russell, A A
Sheppard, S C
Stevens, A G
Waters, R C
West, D
Willcox, J R
Willman, A
Wyatt, R M

Jarrow

Ash, E C
Bedi, A K
Bem, J L
Brewster, N
Cordner, D E S
Davison, M A
Dias, B F
Farrar, D
Farrar, M W
Griffiths, K
Hussain, M S
Lodhi, K A K
Overs, K
Palmer, H M
Simpson, P J
Vis-Nathan, S
Zaidi, S M Z

Jedburgh

Armstrong, J L
Booth, T F
Cook, G A
Dorward, C R
Mitchell, R J
Muir, E S

Jersey

Allardice, J T
Allison, S N
Bailey, D J
Bailhache, N A
Balbes, D I
Barrett, M E
Bellamy, M J
Blackwood, G W
Blampied, A M
Bliss, A K
Bonn, S M J
Borthwick-Clarke, A
Brache, J A
Brown, J R
Brown, R L
Bruce, M P
Buist, W E S
Burke, W M M
Caldwell, I W
Callander, G W R
Cameron, I L
Cameron, Z A
Carpenter, M
Chance, B
Clifford, R P
Clinton, C
Coates, J A
Coleman, P
Comerford, M B
Connor, T P
Conway, J A
Coverley, C T
Cox, M T
Cradock-Watson, J E
Crill, D H
Culsan Lorenzo, J P
Curry, S
Curtis, N R
Dalgleish, D J
Darling, A S
Day, J B
Denny, W R
Dingle, H R
Drew, O E
Dwyer, J
Earley, M A
Ellis, B D
Ellison, A J H
Essex-Cater, A J
Evans, D G
Evans, J E M
Evans, S N
Faiz, G F
Falla, H P L
Farrant, T
Fogarty, J P F
Fortun, P J
Foster, S J
Frank, D C
Franklin, W H
Fullerton, M E N
Gardner, C S
Georgelin, D J
Gibson, H N
Gibson, M
Ginks, S E
Ginks, W R
Gleeson, M H
Glynn, P J H
Goodson, T C
Goulding, H
Gracey, N G A
Grainger, C R
Groom, A M
Guillochon, M A H
Halliwell, A C
Hamilton, D G B
Hamilton, J S H
Harvey, J D
Haydn Taylor, D
Hickson, B
Hickson, R M
Higgins, A
Higgins, P
Himayakanthan, S
Holmes, M B
Howell, J B
Hugh, J E
Hurst, R K
Ilangovan, C K

Kettering

Ince, D A J
Ince, G J
Ingram, N P
Jackson, J D
Joshua, J M
Kauntze, R
Kellett, B C
King, S C
Krohn, P L
Labia, J B
Landor, E C
Lane, J R
Lapasset, MMF
Le Bas, P S
Le Cocq, H D
Le Cornu, J
Le Gresley, J S
Lea, P A W
Leadbeater, N A G
Lewis, J E
Lissenden, J P
Llewellin, G
McBride, M E
MacLachlan, N A
Macmichael, I M
Maine, I H
Marks, M F
Marson-Smith, R A
Mason, C A S
Matthews, P J M
Mattock, C
Maxey, J M
Mickhael, N F
Milner, S M
Minihane, N A
Mirvis, I M
Mitchell, A R J
Mitchell, R J
Mourant, P N
Muhlemann, M F
Muscat, I
Naidu, G C P
Nanson, J K
Newell, J R
Norman, A L S
O'Sullivan, D A
Osmont, J M
Overton, M A
Pai, K P
Parris, R
Peck, T E
Perez Roman, M D
Pope, D G
Porcherot, R C
Preston, S D
Prince, G D
Purcell-Jones, G
Quenault, S L
Raghu, C G
Reid, A C
Reid, J
Richardson, M R
Robertson, B C
Rosser, M J
Russell-Weisz, D J
Santos, S R
Sayers, D E G
Scholefield, I M
Scott Warren, D N M
Selvachandran, P S
Shah, N D
Sheaves, R M
Shenkin, H R
Shenkin, I R
Sinfield, K E
Siodlak, M Z
Slaffer, S N
Slater, E M
Smart, P H
Smith, S G
Smylie, C A
Southall, P J
Sparrow, S A
Spratt, H C
Standring, P
Stevens, N B
Stewart-Jones, J
Swann, J D
Symers, D A
Taylor, J J
Taylor, W D
Thacker, R H
Twiston Davies, C W
Usha, T R
Venn, P M
Vincent, A P
Watson, H P
Watts, N
Webster, N J

Wildy, G S
Williams, A D
Wilson, L
Wilson, M G
Winspear, M
Yates, R W P
Young, M J

Johnstone

Ahmad, R S
Ahmad, S
Alston, A B
Barnes, R E
Baxter, M M
Biggart, B S
Bland, R M
Borthwick, M J
Bradford, C A
Brandon, D J
Burman-Roy, B G
Campbell, A J M
Campbell, A R
Clark, R R
Coats, A E
Conn, I G
Cunning, C A
Dhiya, L H
Dorward, F C
Dunlop, L W
Erwin, L
Fergusson, A J
Fisher, D E
Forrest, G J
Ghaus, P
Gibb, J W
Gibson, J A
Halliday, E C
Harris, G K
Houston, G L
Innes, M R
Jones, C M
Kerr, A M
Khanna, D S
McBryan, D D
McGregor, I
Malcolm, A J H
Matson, I C
Milburn, R A
Mitchell, M M
Muir, J
O'Brien, M T
Ramsay, A L
Raveenthranathan, C
Ross, D S
Russell, A M
Scade, T P
Shadbolt, C J
Simpson, L S
Singh, T N
Smellie, A J
Stewart, L G
Storey, M E
Stromberg, P
Stuart, W E
Todd, J G
Todd, W
Umesh, S
Wallace, J A
Wallace, K A G
Wallace, P G M
Webb, L A
Wills, J F
Wright, A H
Young, K A

Juniper Green

Noble, K W

Keighley

Adley, R
Al-Muhandis, W M
Alim, S A
Allen, D E
Almond, F A
Appleyard, I
Armstrong, R K
Aspin, A J
Baker, D A
Barker, H A
Bell, A E
Belsey, R L
Belton, A
Belton, M E
Blake, J G
Booth, J A
Bostan, A M
Boyle, N A
Bradburn, H
Brash, J H
Britland, A A

Brown, D R
Brown, T S
Brunskill, P J
Burton, J H W
Cadamy, M E
Chambers, C H
Clark, D
Clements, D G
Clements, E J
Collinson, A
Cooper, A M
Cradick, N H
Crawford, S M
Cruikshank, G M
Cryer, P
Cuthbert, A C
Da Costa, P E
Day, C P T
Day, S W
Dev, V J
Dewar, E P
Dickson, M J
Dickson, T
Dinnen, R L
Dudley, M J
Dulson, E V
Dunbar, A M
Duncan, M J
England, J K
England, M A
Ferguson, I G
Fisk, J A
Fontana, J W
Foster, J E
Gill, J C S
Gopal, D T
Griffin, N R
Groves, R
Grunshaw, N D
Hakin, B A
Hakin, R N
Harrington, M G
Harrison, A P
Haworth, M C
Hayes, M L
Haywood, J A
Healey, C J
Helliwell, M F
Hill, R E
Hodgson, J D
Hosker, H S R
Howe, J G
Hoyle, M K
Hudson, R B S
Hughes, M J
Hulands, G H
Huxley, J C
Ilett, S J
Iskander, N Y
Jagger, J H
James, E S
Jepson, D S K
Jones, G M
Kavanagh, M J
Kay, P M
Kehoe, R F
Kennedy, D B J
Khan, P
Kharbanda, Y
Lindsay, K
Maberly, D J
McCulloch, E E
McGill, G M
McGill, R
McKenzie, F R
McLellan, G S M
Middleton, R J
Milbourn, M R
Mohammed, R A
Moore, J A
Mountain, J S
Nagaraja, E G
Nair, R R
Nejim, A N
Nevin, J A
Norton, E R
O'Dowd, J J
Orgles, C S
Parry, J H
Partridge, G W
Phillips, R J M
Pickles, J S
Pope, R M
Porter, G G
Pratt, O W
Preshaw, J M
Price, W J
Pue, P
Purvis, M J

Reisig, V M T
Rhodes, J D
Richardson, S M
Robertson, J A
Saikia, A N
Samtaney, N T
Savage, B F
Savill, G A
Scott, L V A
Severs, P H
Shaikh, N A
Shaw-Smith, C J
Shaw, D A
Shaw, D L
Silverton, N P
Simpson, F M
Sims, C D P
Skarrott, P H
Smith, N A L
Smith, N R
Smith, P A
Solomons, R E B
Sonanis, S V
Stanton, J M
Starkey, C
Sweeting, A E
Sweeting, K W
Sykes, A E
Taylor, P
Thompson, B
Thorburn, W S
Todd, J A
Tones, B J
Towers, S
Tucker, K P
Ullah, S
Wadsworth, D J
Walshaw, C A
Ward, K P
Watson, J P
Webster, P K
Whamond, W N
Whittaker, M W
Whittaker, W M
Wild, R
Wilkinson, K N
Williams, G C
Wilson, H
Wilson, N D
Wood, J M
Wood, R B
Wray, C C
Zaman, S
Zezulka, A V

Keith

Cunningham, D I A
Gould, D C
Harrington, D M
Harrington, J H
Heneghan, T T
Hutchison, K R
Hutchison, R B
Morrison, W M
Sharp, N C
Shaw, S M
Thomason, J

Kelso

Barrie, J D
Bisset, J G
Cameron, C H
Cowe, M E
Cutting, R I
Fingland, I G
Fish, M J
Hood, W G
Johnston, C A
Knox, A M
Knox, W A
Lawley, M A
Lees, L J
Margerison, A C F
Millar, J A
Mooney, G
Morris, A R
Nicol, S A
Nicol, W J
Nisbet, R
Poole, A G B
Potter, S F
Richmond, R
Roberts, R E
Seton, A
Smith, K M
Sutherland, A S
Wickham, M

Kelty

Dougall, T W

Melville, A W T
Sheil, P A
Smart, A G W

Kendal

Aitchison, C I
Breed, J H
Brennan, C
Buckler, J A
Buckler, P W
Burr, S A H
Calvert, F R
Chadwick, I G
Cochrane, S M
Corker, R M
Coulson, R A
Davies, G A M
Dean, G
Dolton, V
Dolton, W D
Duggan, E J
Dunk, R A
Duxbury, S C
Edgell, M S
Elliott, M
Finlay, A M
Foster, H E
Gardner, S J N
Gill, A L A
Green, S A
Hallac, J J
Heaven, W G
Howse, M L P
Howse, M L
Huggett, I M
Ingram, H J
Jackson, R D
Kerigan, P A
McDonald, A M
McGhie, F J
MacKenzie, A G
Melhuish, L M
Meyrick, M R P
Miall, W E
Milnes, R S W
Mitchell, R W
Mukherji, M J
Ostick, S
Payne, J
Pigott, J E
Postius Conde, C
Reeder, S A
Robinson, L A
Sarwar, Q
Scott, R W
Simons, E L
Simons, J E
Simpson, P D
Smith, M G
Spong, A H R
Stokes, C S
Stringer, R M
Thomas, P C
Thornton, S J
Tole, D M
Tower, J E C
Wilding, R P
Wilkinson, H L
Williams, E I
Wilson, A C

Kenilworth

Ahmed, A B
Ahmed, F B
Alexander, D M
Alexander, E A
Allinson, C A
Allsopp, E J
Appleyard, K M
Backhouse, T W
Beckford, L C
Birchall, L A
Boobyer, M D
Botherway, A H
Cable, H R
Clayton, K C
Cremonesini, D P
Curley, M
Curry, A R
Davies, C L
Davies, R N
Dickson, C W
Eaton, T J
Evans, S F
Foster, L M
Geddes, J H
Grogan, R J
Harvey, S G
Jones, D A

Jones, H D
Kander, P L
Lewis, M W D-L-H
Lewis, M A H
McCreadie, M A
Matthews, G A
Miller, P C
Pai, S M
Prosser, S E
Rapley, D M
Riddell, C
Rudd, A G
Scrimshire, J A
Spraggett, D T
Thompson, S M C
Walker, E H
Whelan, R M
Woodward, D A K
Youakim, S S F

Kenley

Collins, F M
Collomosse, J R W
Jones, G N
Joyce, M R L
Qureshi, S
Ray, G
Sivasubramaniam, C
Stanway, P A
Sturgess, M J
Warren, S J P
Weston Underwood, R A

Keston

Child, G V
Child, S C C
Neve, J M
Paddle, J S
Paddle, J J
Scott-Wilson, J H
Scott, J G
Singh, K K
Wright, M J

Keswick

Atack, J A
Blakemore, R
Bulman, J M
Craig, A
Duncan, E M
Eglin, B
Glavina, A H
Graham, J P
Guest, K E
Hadkins, R
Hamilton, M J
Hammond, A
Hooper, T M
Jackson, E S
Keddie, N C
Lacy, W J
Mackay, H J
Moore-Ede, M C
Newton, J V
Ponsonby, W J C
Rae, I F S
Rennie, S M
Turnbull, M R
Tyson, P O M
Watters, B
White, P M
Wise, D
Wood, M E
Woodliff, H J

Kettering

Aaron, J
Abdallah, H M H
Abdel-Latif, M M A
Ablett, J C
Aherne, J J A
Andrews, P S
Antcliffe, R D
Bahall, V
Baines, G F
Balloch, C B
Barclay, P
Barrington, R L
Beckett, N S
Birch, R
Birring, S S
Biswas, S P
Bland, K M
Bland, R M
Blindt, D M
Branford, W A
Braybrooks, L S
Britton, M J
Bromage, J D

Kidderminster

Brown, A R
Bryant, K M
Burke, M
Carr, A S
Carroll, J
Castillo Narvaez, E
Clearkin, R J
Cook, J R
Cope, I J
Corbett, J T
Cotterell, S J
Craven, A F
Datta, A K
Davison, O W
Dempster, R K
Emanuel, W
Fitton, J H K
Fituri, O
Freeman, J
Gainer, N S C
Glover, S J
Goh, G J M
Gonzalez Santos, R
Gostelow, B E
Grabham, A H
Graham, L S
Gunasekera, N P R
Hadaway, E G
Haughney, R V M
Holden, J M
Hunt, J P
Ingram, R M
Ireland, S C
James, M G
Jones, A E
Jones, J R
Kapur, R K
Kelsey, H C
Khan, K M
Khattak, F-I-H
Kiddle, M W
Kimbell, J S
Langendijk, J W G
Lawrence, J H
Lawson-Matthew, J
Lee, R J
Leyden, P V
Loo, P S L
Loveday, N F J
Luthman, J A
McCormick, P A
Macleod, F K
McManus, J B
Matthews, S R
Mattingly, P C
Maye, A J
Maye, M J
Medcalf, P B
Medhurst, G A
Michel, V J-M
Milkins, S R
Minto, S T
Mistry, N H
Mohamedain, H M
Moody, R A
Moore, J S
Morris, J M
Moss, H
Mukhopadhyay, T
Musa, M O H
Nanayakkara, C S
Neill, L G
Nicholas, P O
Nicholas, S P K
O'Malley, B P
Odoi, R E
Ormerod, T E
Osmond, A
Oswell, A D
Padget, K I
Pallewela, C S
Parkinson, M S
Patel, J B
Pease, J J
Penney, T M
Perera, G L S
Perkins, A
Perry, D
Peterson, S
Pettman, J C
Philip-Smith, P B
Piechowski, L
Pinnell, J R
Pollak, T E
Pratt, C A
Prestwich, A
Prince, S E
Radwan, A F M
Rashed, M D
Razak, A A
Reeve, R G
Roberts, F D
Rose, C F
Ross, S M
Russell, A J B
Samtani, B K
Sansome, J D W
Sanyal, B
Scanlon, J J
Scawn, D L
Scott, W E
Shackleton, C D
Shemilt, W P
Sheppard, J
Shields, L A
Sibson, D E
Sibson, K R
Slack, R S
Smith, J S
Smith, R J
Smith, S J
Staff, D M
Stephen, A A
Stocks, P J
Streeter, H L
Sugunakara Rao,
Y V K
Sulch, D A
Taylor, O M
Thamizhavell, R C
Thompson, A J
Tilley, N J
Treharne, L J
Turner, S
Twohey, L C
Vaal, M F
Veasey, K A
Walker, P R
Walters, R L
Walton, C E
Wedatilake, G G D
Wharin, F J
Wharin, P D
Whitby, J D
Whitby, R J
Wigglesworth, R
Wildgoose, A D
Williams, J B
Williams, Dr
Willis, P F
Wood, P L E
Wurm, P

Kidderminster

Adams, J E
Ahmed, N
Allen, T M W
Armitstead, P R
Bakewell, S E
Bassett, W L
Begum, N
Bell, J S P
Bennett, A J
Bielinski, B K
Blanchard, G F
Bolton, C
Booth, S N
Boyle, H C
Budhani, S J R
Burridge, J M
Butcher, L H
Campion, G R C
Campion, T C
Carter, A G
Cawdery, H M
Chaddok, P J
Cockrell, N B
Crnic, V
Cushley, M J
Da Costa, O
Davies, R A
Deshmukh, R G
Eeles, E M P
Eeles, G H
El-Guindi, M E-R M
Farraj, D A A
Fazal, A
Frost, G J
Gajjar, A P
Gerrard, J
Ghobrial, E I
Girgis, M S
Gray, S R
Hayward, C J
Herbert, R E
Hill, B D
Holl, C E
Holzman, R H A
Infeld, D A
Ireland, R W
Irlam, C A
James, J A
Jarve, M C
Jethwa, M L P
Johnstone, R D
Kaushal, C S
Kaushal, P
Kelsey, R J
Killalea, D R
Kondratowicz, G M
Labib, M M
Lalljee, N
Lewis Roberts, G
Lewis, M L
Lindsay, S-A
Lord, M
Malcomson, D H
Malcomson, E J
Mann, P
Marsh, C R
Mendes Da Costa, B
Miller, A R O
Morgan, F B
Mukoyogo, J M
Murray, J F
Murrin, K L
Newrick, P G
Nicol, V S
Nixon, D
Parker, A S
Parker, E J C
Pathirana, C K
Peaston, M J T
Perry, S R
Picton-Robinson, I
Powick, D R
Reid, D V
Sanford, J R A
Sargent, D E
Saverymuttu, T M
Schrieber, V P
Sherwood, B T
Smith, C R
Smith, C M D
Smith, J V
Smith, K L
Smith, S A
Spalding, J P
Stanley, J K
Starkie, C
Starkie, D W
Stephens, J S
Stewart, P A
Summers, A R
Summers, G D
Summers, R O C
Tallents, C J
Taylor, C L
Taylor, M A
Taylor, R T
Tesh, D E
Tewari, S
Thompson, P
Thorley, C H
Thorley, C G
Tooms, D
Trezise, C A
Tudor, J G
Udeshi, U L
Wadsworth, T M
Wetherall, A P
Wilkie, S
Wilkie, V M
Williams, P W
Wilner, J M

Kiddlington

Aitken, A C
Bangham, C R M
Banks, A
Biggs, R C
Birch, W D A
Bridges, W G
Bryceson, W T
Bryson, N H L
Burbidge, H C
Cant, G B
Carr, J M
Crew, J P
Dunnill, M S
Durrant, I J
Ellis, J D
Ellis, M L
Evans, D J
Flynn, J R
Gordon, G
Gough, M H
Gunasekera, K D
Hart, A E T
Heaf, J M
Lee, G J
Lehane, J R
Lister, D M
Lloyd, W A
Louis, E
Marshall, V E
Moncrieff, J M
Newman, W J
Pandher, K S
Parker, I W
Payne, S P K
Pinto, A A
Price, H M R
Ramsell, N J
Roberts, D M H
Rogers, N C
Rogers, P M
Sherwood, W J
Street, S H
Stubbings, M A
Thomas, D P
Tranter, J
Turner, R S L
Wall, I J
Wallace, M J
Watts, A J
Williams, B I
Williams, P O
Young, A C

Kidwelly

Acharya Baskerville, M
Dundrow, J M
Edmunds, E G-H
Hopkins, M P
Kemp, A R
Lyons, R A
Standley, C
Thomas, J

Kilbirnie

Begg, J S
Ferry, D A
Hillman, R G
Kilpatrick, A
MacInnes, P
Smith, R R
Whitelaw, R

Kilgetty

Gillett, J C
Jones, R M
Naik, D R
Williams, O
Williams, S J T

Killin

Blaney, D D
Gordon, G H M
Hope, G M
MacColl, E M
Rough, S A
Syme, D M
Turner, E I
Weaver, H M

Kilmacolm

Adams, K J
Ellis, D L
Fisher, C J
Fraser, K H
Fyfe, T
Hamilton, D N H
Jenkinson, S
Khin May Sein, Dr
Knight, P V
Laurie, H C
Leighton, J L
Little, A S
McGill, A M
McGinn, G H
Mackay, J
McLellan, I S
Marr, A C
Morrice, J J
Morris, G E
Mutch, M W
Mya Thaung, Dr
Newbury, N G
Nicol, M F
Nyunt Tin, Dr
Robertson, J K
Soinne, N
Strathern, H M
Thomas, M C
Weir, J

Winning, T J
Wootton, R P

Kilmarnock

Adams, J N
Adamson, M R
Ahmadouk, N A
Allardyce, J G S
Anderson, K
Aqil, S
Barr, G
Barr, J B
Barr, M E
Beveridge, R D
Black, J P
Boag, D E
Brown, E
Buchanan, I R
Cameron, K J
Carolan, C M
Carruthers, J G
Carton, A T M
Cook, W R
Courtney, J M
Coy, S E
Crawford, H P
Crichton, I S
Crumlish, P
Cunningham, N E
Curran, J D
Currans, J M
Dean, L H
Dean, R T
Dempster, J H
Diament, R H
Drummond, J W
Duke, J D
Duncan, R M
Dunlop, P A
Dunn, F J
Dwyer, C M
Dyson, W H
Elliott, J A
Erskine, J G
Fallows, R
Ferguson, E
Foxworthy, M P
Gaffney, P G
Gardner, F M
Gillespie, J S
Gold, C
Gold, J L
Graham, I
Grant, L
Hambly, K N
Hare, M K B
Henderson, B C
Hills, S
Hislop, W S
Holland, J
Horne, M A M
Howie, P G
Hunter, H S
Illingworth, D M
Inglis, F G
Innes, A
Irvine, K H
Jaap, A J
Johnston, C P
Kalman, C J
Khaliq, K
Kyles, I M
Lang, J A
Lannigan, A M
Lennox, S E
Lipka, A W
Livingston, W S
Lobnitz, O B
Lochrie, A S
Lough, M
Mcadam, J A
McAdam, L A E
Mcadam, S R
McAlpine, W A
McBride, J
McCulloch, T S
MacDiarmid, I R
MacDonald, E T
MacDonald, J B
McDougall, L
McGeechan, P
McGill, R E T
McGregor, E M
McGregor, J R
McHardy, C
McIntyre, L A
McLauchlan, D
McMurtrie, F
MacPherson, J N
McTaggart, A
Magee, J R
Marshall, A H
Martin, C S
Micallef-Eynaud, P D
Mikhail, W M F
Miller, D E
Miller, W
Mills, R D
Morris, A J
Mulugeta, Y
Murphy, J T
Nairn, E R
Nicol, J
Norwell, Z M
Orcharton, A M
Paterson, D H
Paxton, G C
Paxton, J R
Powell, G J
Pugh, R M
Ralston, G J
Ratnasabapathy, U
Rawlings, D
Richards, I M
Richmond, M M
Robertson, W S M
Rodriguez Santos, J
Rubio Gomez, M T
Schwigon, S S
Sengupta, U
Shamlaye, C F
Shaw, D
Shaw, K C
Short, R M
Sirisena, L A P
Smith, M L
Smith, S M
Smyth, M J
Sommerville, J M
Staines, J D
Stewart, W
Sword, D
Sword, L
Syme, B A
Tait, G R
Tellechea Elorriaga, F J
Thompson, B E L
Thompson, H M
Thompson, S E
Timmons, M J
Walker, E
Walker, G W
Wardrop, P J C
Watson, D
Watson, E R
Watt, A G
Watts, J D
White, R J
Williamson, A E
Wilson, G
Wood, M J
Young, D W
Young, R K B
Yu, D Y F
Yusoff, F
Zaidi, S M H

Kilwinning

Allen, D J
Campbell, E M
Forbes, I M B
Gemmell, A C L
Groves, T
Hall, R D
Harper, L
Huggan, D K
Lynch, R
McCreadie, S L
McInroy, B
Macrae, A S
Miller, D J
Paterson, M T
Scollay, G
Sutherland, F T

Kings Langley

Birdwood, G F B
Brownfield, M O N
Cadness-Graves, B H E
Cave, T R C
Cohen, S J
El Borai, C L
Farrow, L J
Griffiths, D L
Kanani, S-A
McLellan, J M
Mann, C F
Perahia, D G S

Kirkcaldy

Percy, C M
Popli, S
Reidy, M J
Rowsell, R B
Tan, W-T
Wallis, E G
West, M F

King's Lynn
Abdel Gadir, M A
Abdy, S
Abukhalil, S H
Aickin, J C
Allen, G B
Anderson, J A R
Applegate, E J
Arafat, Q W
Atkinson, L K
Baldwin, D V T
Bansal, B
Barber, C G
Barber, J C
Barclay, A J
Barter, D A C
Bartlett, D L
Banwood, A J
Bhupathi, V
Biran, R K
Black, D M S
Bolt, G L
Bone, C D M
Brindle, M J
Brown, C S
Burchett, K R
Burgess, A S
Butt, Z A
Byatt, C M
Campbell, I K
Capes, H M
Carlton, J H
Carter, R F
Chakrabarti, A
Chakraborti, D
Chakraborti, S
Chan Seem, C P
Chase, A E
Chowdary, N P
Coates, P B
Collett, A
Connolly, C A
Crosby, G L
Crowe, M T I
Cullen, P T
Cunningham, M D
Cupper, G A
Cushnir, M N
De Silva, K S M
de Whalley, P C S
Denny, N M
Devane, L S
Dhumale, R G
Dootson, G M
Dossetor, J F B
Duncan, B M
Eakins, D
Eakins, P D
Eames, R A
Eaton, A C
Edridge, A W
Edris, M A M
Elston, C C
Fernando, P M P D
Fielding, A P H
Galloway, J M
Gee, C P
George, R
Ghafar, F
Goose, D H
Gray, L J
Greatorex, R A
Haczewski, I
Hambling, C E
Hanley, J M
Hargreaves, R J
Harris, S J
Harrison, E A
Hart, N
Herrod, J J
Hillam, J C
Hobbiger, H E
Hopkin, D J
Hotchin, I K
Howard, S H F
Hubbard, P J E
Hunnam, G R
Isaacs, G
Iyengar, M O P
Iyengar, N
Jacobs, T E

James, M E
Jelfs, B R
Jennings, A M
Karrach, H A
Keidan, A J
Kenny, M T
Kenny, M K
Kenny, T D
King, A D
Knott, S R G
Kumar, E B
Kurma Rao, B
Lacey, A J
Lacey, H P
Laidlaw, E M E
Lake, A K
Lankester, P F R
Lavallee, P J
Lazarus, H I
Li, M N
Luffman, P S
Luxton, D E A
McAdam, A H
Macaskill, S
MacBean, I J
Macdonald, A P
McGowan, R C M
McGourty, J C
Mack, I J
Mackenzie, I A R
Maclean, A R
Maheshwer, C B
Martin, J D
Martin, J S
Munim, F M S A
Neal, B E H
New, N E
Nicholls, E A
Nooh, A M M K
O'Brien, A A
O'Brien, J R
O'Brien, M D
O'Brien, P D
Oakman, N M A
Outred, R
Patel, A R
Pattrick, F G
Pawlowicz, A
Pearce, K A
Philipson, J A M
Phillips, J R N
Plumley, M H
Ponte Tellechea, P
Pryn, R B
Pushpanathan, R J
Redhead, K A
Redman, R C
Redwood, N F W
Richardson, G
Richardson, S J
Rimmer, M J
Robbins, N E
Robinson, A A
Roxburgh, R C
Rubin, S P-A
Russell, J J
Sapey, E
Sasitharan, N
Sconce, F M
Scott, J M
Scully, T L
Shapland, W D
Shaw, N C
Sheppard, L C
Sherwood, A N
Showell, D G L
Singh, S M
Sivakumar, K
Spaight, P Q M
Sparks, M J W
Spink, P
Stabler, R J
Strina, P
Suchak, K K
Summers, S R
Sumpton, J R
Tasker, P R W
Thompson, S G
Thorpe, N C
Tigchelaar, E F
Venning, S L
Waterson, I M
Webber, P A
Welbourne, A S
Weli, G S
Weli, T D
Wells, J M W
Wheater, M
White, N

Whiteman, P D
Wigdahl, J D
Williams, J D
Wilson, A W
Wilson, M G C
Woodsend, R G
Wright, F G L

Kingsbridge
Baldwin, J R
Boughton, B A
Bretherick, P J
Brett, A D
Carter, N W R
Chopin, K T
Clarke, A J
Cole, R J
Cooper, A
Dixon, M D
Eadie, G B
Elliott, D M
Everitt, M T
Everitt, M W
Finzel, H F M
Hall, J H
Hanrott, S F
Hargreaves, S J
Harvey, A J
Hickey, R P
Holcombe, D R
Howells, D B M
Jackson, P N
Kenderdine, A R
London, J A
McIntosh, C G
Mackenzie, F A F
Parry, J H
Reeve, B J
Rose, J D
Scarratt, W L H
Smith, M A
Trounce, C C
Turner, C L
Williams, I A
Williams, S G

Kingston
Richardson, H D
Wong, H J

Kingston upon Thames
Abayasiriwardana, J M
Ahmad, N S
Ahmad, W K
Akbar, S S
Al-Wakeel, B A R
Alhadi, B Z R
Allen, W M C
Ames, D E
Andrew, L J
Aquilina, M
Bak, J E
Ball, C J
Barker, G H
Barrie, M
Beare, J D L
Benz, J K
Berwick, E P
Betts, J
Boos, K P
Bowskill, P A
Bowskill, S J
Boxer, J C
Brown, C L
Brown, M R
Buchan, M C
Bullmore, G H L
Burn, L
Burwell, J M R
Cadman, D M
Cahill, C J
Calder, M H S
Chaliha, C
Choudhury, S S A
Chouhan, M A
Christie, P N
Clements, D M
Cole, S J
Coombs, R R H
Crow, M A B
Culling, W
Curtis, M J
D'Souza, M F
Dalton, R
Daly, K E
Davidson, A
Davies, J R
Davis, P K B
De Launay, L D

Delves, C E
Dick, J A
Dixon, A N
Du Plessis, J M
Duckham, J M
Eardley, G R
Essapen, S
Evans, P A M
Fawcett, A
Fernandez, C
Finn, M
Foddy, S E
Gibbons, C E R
Goel, R N
Gonet, L C L
Grant, E C G
Gregory, S A
Hamdy, A A S A-S
Hawker, D J L
Hetherington, D J
Hickman, N L A
Hilton, S R
Hindmarsh, P C
Hopkins, D M
Howson, A N
Hughes, A R
Jacobs, L R
Jacobs, N A
Jameson, C F
Jawed, S
Jayne, W H W
Jebb, D N
Jeevaratnam, S
Kane, J A
Katay, E I
Kavanagh, R J
Kennagh, A J
Kenney, N C
Kenyon, B K M
King, D W
Knee, G
Knowles, G K
Lee, A K T
Lee, C N
Leonard, H S D
Li, W-Y
Liew, R K C
Lourudusamy, S
McAuliffe, R L
McCall, A W
McCarthy, G A
McCrimmon, F E
Macgibbon, B H
McHugh, P J F
MacKenzie, D L
MacKie, S
McNabb, W R
Maitland, J A
Manche, R
Manning, C L
Marwaha, S
Mason, A M
Mathie, A G
May, D P L
Mitchell, M H
Moalypour, S-M
Morley, R
Morris, O K
Mundy, J D
Mustajab, A
Myers, C A
Nandakumar, K N
Neville, L O
Newman, P J
Norris, P M
O'Connor, K M
Owen, D C
Parekh, V J
Parrish, J R
Patel, K R
Patient, D N
Perera, I M F
Philippas, A
Polanska, A I
Proctor, M T
Rafferty, P G
Railton, G T
Raimondo, C
Ravalia, A
Ray, A
Reed, M G
Reynolds, P R
Rhodes, A I
Richardson, A E
Rigg, C D
Roberts, S H
Robinson, R A
Rodrigues, C A
Rowe, D J

Rowley, M R
Russell, W
Sabih, M R
Sammut Alessi, C W
Sanderson, I B
Sayer, A
Schiess, F J
Scott, R A
Shah, D S
Shallal, S A M A-T
Sheikh, H F
Slee, I P
Smith, A T M
Smith, J M A
Smith, P S
Sommerville, G P
Spiller, R C
Spring, M W
Stacey, R G W
Steel, M R
Steer, C G
Strickland, I D
Strzelecka, M J
Sykes, H
Tang, J G
Thakar, B R
Thakerar, J G
Thayalan, A S
Thonet, R G N
Tillett, D R F
Todd, C E C
Vieten, D
Vines, B H
Wang, M Y E
Ward, C S N
Ward, D A
Ward, M C
Ward, R D
White, M
Whitfield, R L
Whittam, D E
Wijayasinghe, G E S
Willson, P D
Wilson, C L
Wilson, J K
Wimalasiri, R W
Wimalasundera, R C
Winrow, A P
Yadav, H R
Zarnosh, M

Kingswinford
Basheer, M
Bloor, J A
Burrows, A C
Carr, J F
Cripps, D F
Dawes, P
Foster, H M
French, R
Gallimore, D J
Ghali, A A
Hamza, P
Higgins, C M
Kendle, G
Keogh, S P
Kiteley, N A
Mittal, S
Parnell, S J
Pinfold, T J
Plant, N A
Potter, C M
Rathore, J S
Rowlands, J L
Shekhawat, F S
Skilbeck, A B
Swain, C M
Tweddell, W H
Williams, M D

Kington
Cleland, P R
Crawshaw, J M
Hart, S S
Hollingshurst, G G
Jack, W L
Lias, M
Murphy, B J M
Rannie, G H
Terry, R S

Kingussie
Anderson, M E M
Campbell, E D O
Convery, A
Michie, A R
Munro, D G M
Murray, J A

Kinlochleven
Headden, G D

Kinross
Aitken, E
Anderson, D P
Anderson, W M
Campbell, D
Carragher, P J
Cross, A
Currie, J
Farrell, A A
Ferguson, W M
Gardiner, J
Hogg, D H
Khurana, V
Krishnaswamy, D
Lee, M A
McCluskey, C J
Mason, C J
Miller, R S
Robson, P G
Ross, A I
Russell, K J
Silk, F F
Spens, F J
Thornber, M
Wainwright, R I
Wallace, E D

Kirk Michael
Bolton, A M
Naylor, G J
Smith, M E

Kirkby Stephen
Cannon, D S H
Dickinson, K M
Gibb, R
Hallam, C S M
Huck, S
MacDonald, A
Merckel, J C

Kirkby-in-Furness
Clayson, H
Wood, S A

Kirkcaldy
Adam, D J
Adam, M P
Aitken, P
Al-Essa, S E J
Allen, R A
Anderson, S M
Baker, M
Ballantyne, K C
Barker, G G
Barker, J A
Beattie, J A
Bee, D E
Beg, M H A
Begum, F
Black, A G
Blair, A W
Bowie, R A
Boyce, S
Boyd, A T
Brown, G M
Brown, T I S
Buchanan, I J
Buchanan, R C
Buxton, R A
Caldwell, A S
Campbell, I
Chalmers, J
Choo-Kang, Y F J
Clark, C A
Cole, S
Conway, B E
Conway, E J
Cruickshank, G S
Cryer, K J
Dewar, J M
Dumbreck, A
Duncan, A D G
Duncan, C
Ferguson, J M
Ferguson, J D
Ferguson, K D
Ferguson, L A
Flynn, A M
Fraser, D M
Fraser, M S
Galloway, S J
Gardiner, R
Gergis, M I
Ghosh, D
Gourdie, R W
Greig, A I

Kirkcudbright

Greig, G E
Gunn, C
Hakim, S M
Hall, G K M
Hall, W S
Hanafiah, S R
Heap, R E
Hellewell, H E
Humphreys, R A
Hunter, S S
Janczak, J J
Karim, S Z
Kelleher, J J R
Kendall, D J
Lafong, A C
Lamberty, N A
Laurenson, I F
Lees, A P
Lewis, M J
Lindsay, F R
Linnemann, A M
Linnemann, V J
Loudon, M A
McCallum, A E
McCallum, C J
McCallum, S
Macdonald, E A
MacGlone, C M J M
McGourty, L J
McGowan, F J
MacLeod, E H M
McMillan, J F
MacMillan, M G
McTaggart, J
Mahmood, T A
Mair, S J
Mammen, C
Matthews, A R
Meek, J L A
Mitchell, M C
Moonie, L G
Morris, C A
Morris, R L
Mouat, P
Mughrabi, M A M
Murphy, J
Murray, H A
Narayana, S L
Oates, W K
Othman, N
Oudeh, B A R M
Paisley, T A
Pal, S
Petrie, G R
Pinion, S B
Priyadharshan, R
Rahilly, M A
Rahman, M A-U
Rankin, D W
Rebello, G
Redpath, M
Reid, D A
Riad, M M A
Richardson, T J
Robertson, A G
Robertson, J D
Robertson, R
Rogers, S Y
Russell, S C S
Satyanarayana, P
Scott, B A
Scott, R G A
Scragg, S E
Smith, A G
Smith, D H K
Smith, G F N
Smith, R P
Steel, J M
Steer, C R
Stewart, M E
Stobie, F J
Stuart, J C
Sutton, J C
Tevendale, J
Thanoon, M Y
Thrower, M M
Tomlinson, J E M
Urquhart, D R
Wilson, D M
Wilson, D C
Wilson, J S
Wilson, J A
Wishart, H M
Yule, J M

Kirkcudbright

Allison, M M
Ball, N J
Branson, R R
Campbell, K A A
Dow, R C
Duncan, D M
Green, H L
Grieve, R G
Harper, J
Jones, R D
Locke, W J
Mack, R H
Morton, J M
Reid, J P
Rutherfurd, J A F
Shaw, M

Kirkliston

Beedie, R M
Carson, D P
Douglas, E
Milne, R M
Mitchell, J
Simpson, W S

Kirknewton

Bassett, D I
Bassett, W J

Kirkwall

Al-Mukhtar, A A M A
Beaven, S R
Borland, C W
Deans, W J D
Dewar, I G
Fay, E D J
Fay, P J
Groundwater, W
Hamilton, L M
Hamilton, W M
Hepburn, B
Hunter, D A
Konstam, S T
Laird, C
MacInnes, D J
MacInnes, R J N
Nicolson, A L
Van Schayk, M
Walker, J S
Wright, T F

Kirriemuir

Beck, J S
Carlaw, N A
Farquhar, A M
Ferguson, M J
Gilmour, J R
Guthrie, M F
Hunter, M G
Learmonth, J C M
Lendrum, A B G
McAdam, N W
Milne, M J
Mitchell, J A S
Morrison, S L
Ritchie, J M
Weatherhead, A E
Weir, A D
Wilmshurst, A P

Knaresborough

Adamson, P B
Alpin, H R
Arthur, V-M K
Banks, J C D
Bradshaw, J H
Burton, J L
Cameron, S J
Carradine, J S
Corrin, S E
Downes, A J
Hall, J L
Hawe, R
Iddon, J N
Jobling, D I
Keenleside, C L
Keogh, A J
Lee, J N
MacLeod, P A I
Mawhinney, R R
Minty, S J
Murphy, A M
Newman, C P S J
Norton, P M
Oakley, M C
Plowman, M A
Raine, J
Robinson, R M
Roy, S N
Sapherson, D A
Scott, J S
Scott, O
Smith, R B

Tovey, L A D
Wallis, G I
Walsh, C J L
Walton, S F
Ward, J R
Watson, J E
Watson, W F
Yarrow, A D
Young, F M

Knebworth

Bishai, W
Bols, R M-C
Campbell, P J
Cooper, M E
Daniel, R A
Dent, R G
Drake, J
Dugdale, R V
Edmunds, I G
Farey, M B
Faulkner, R E
Forbes, G W
Kalilani, M J M
Kite, S A
Lawson, A
McHugh, L M
Owen, G A
Peters, M A
Salter, J P H
Stanton, J S
Stratford, M
Turner, J E
Wood, D C

Knighton

Cross, P L
Davies, B C
Howcroft, K M
Kiff, M L
Myhill, S B
Pulvertaft, R J V

Knottingley

Atkins, D
Baruah, P C
Berridge, L S
Brahma, P K
Fish, H L
Pal, N R
Parr, M D
Pinder, C A
Pinder, I F
Ward, S G

Knutsford

Airey, G O
Arthur, D K
Ashton, S G
Bates, P R
Bayliss, L A
Berrisford, M H
Billingham, J W
Burrell, C J D
Burslem, R W
Caldwell, J
Clark, S J
Clements, A C
Conroy, J L
Cowling, H E
Davies, J L
Douglas, W K
Eaton, J D
Evans, P J
Fitzgerald, J D
Fleming, H
Gibbons, D R S
Gordon, M W
Harris, S E
Hernon, M
Heseltine, J S
Highcock, M P
Holt, A K I
Howarth, K L
Janus, F
Johnson, S M
Kanjilal, G C
Kearns, P J
Kennon, R W
Khan, A T M M H
La Coste, J J
Lawn, J A
Leicester, G
McHugh, F J
Mallon, T J
Mills, E M
Morgan, J P
Morris, H
Muston, G C
Neale, F R

O'Driscoll, S L
Oldham, B
Powell, K J
Price, H S
Ramsden, A R
Reeves, S M
Robertson, C M
Roy, P J
Shackleton, D A
Smith, M C
Smith, V J
Stephenson, R J
Stones, R N
Taylor, J I
Voight, M
Wardle, T D
Watters, E A
Wright, F B
Youssef, Y Y

Kyle

Hurding, S B
Mackinnon, R E
Macrae, M E S
Morgan, P J P
Tallach, J R
Turville, S A
Zelaya-Mendivil, G F

Lairg

Bruce, V R
Cullen, J R
Dickson, A
Fitzsimons, B J
Hughes, A J
Macdougall, M
Nairn, S A
Pennie, I D
Sutton, G B
Wilkinson, E M

Lampeter

Davies, I N
Howley, H M
Jones, E W
Jones, T M L
Lloyd, A G
Mathew, R
Pyle, D I
Sawyer, M N
Seal, M T

Lanark

Addison, A
Allan, R
Allison, J
Anderson, C M
Barclay, A R
Barclay, R P C
Black, W
Burns, G W
Cassidy, M T
Christie, A J
Clapham, A N
Connaughton, J A
Cooper, J L
Copland, J
Criggie, W R
Dickson, W E
Doherty, E M
Duncan, J M
Fraser, T L
Grant, A M
Hacking, J
Hacking, M W
Hamilton, G S D
Hannay, W T
Hill, J G
Islam, Z U
Kane, I M
Kelly, J C C
Kerr, A T
Kerr, S
McComb, T N
McCorkell, L M
McFadzean, I E
MacGregor, F M
McKnight, F E
McMahon, D J
McQueen, D
MacRitchie, D M
MacRitchie, P A
Martin, J
Murie, J
Nunn, T J
Robb, A G
Scott, W S
Trainer, J F
Ward, N M
Wardrop, N

Watson, D
White, T
Woods, A W
Young, J I

Lancaster

Abraham, J S
Adamson, A R
Agarwal, M
Ahmed, S I
Ainsworth, P
Allen, J W
Anderson, G H
Anderson, V
Anderton, E R G
Ashworth, L J
Austin, K D
Ayres, J F
Bajen, J M
Bali, P L
Balmer, G A
Baraka, M E F M
Bateman, A M
Batty, P D
Beaumont, J M
Bell, L M
Bird, T M
Breckon, K E
Brigg, J K
Brown, A K
Brown, S M
Bulman, C H
Burch, D J
Burr, R H
Burton, V W
Byers, E A
Carling, D
Carvill, P T
Cassar, E
Caun, K
Chandoo, A H
Cochran, D A
Coltman, D B
Cook, N K
Craven, A J
Crawford, A I M
Cunningham, R C
Curzon, I L
Dafforn, E M
Dalziel, M
Davies, J R
Davis, K J
De Bruyne, D M P
Dendy, R A
Dodd, A J
Dodds, W N
Donnelly, J M
Duffy, P M
Duke, B O L
Durham, S T
Dyer, J V
Earnshaw, T G
Eckersley, N G
Edgell, A F
Ellam, M
Elley, C M
Erulkar, J
Feldman, A Y
Finlay, B M
Flanagan, P M H
Fleet, T W
Foster, N J
Foster, S F
Fuller, C
Gallagher, A R
Garcia Garcia, M A
Gaskell, R K
Gibson, P A G
Gill, R W
Gill, V
Gorst, D W
Grealy, S E
Guinan, I
Hacking, J E
Halim, M A
Hallam, D
Halstead, H C
Hamilton, E A G
Hamilton, M
Harding, S A
Harrison, L E
Harrison, P V
Harvey, P W
Healy, E T
Heywood, R J
Hicks, J B
Higham, A D
Hodge, J C
Hong, V T E

Horn, N R
Jackson, G C
Jackson, R G
Jenkinson, T M
Johnstone, N A
Jones, K
Kamal, A K M
Karamura, L N
Kay, J S
Khan, D S A
Kingston, M R
Lavelle, J M
Leese, T
Lomax, R
Longden, D J
Lunt, T J
Lyon, W C
McCafferty, J I
McCaldin, A M
McDonnell, D S
McGlone, R G
McGregor, J C
McIllmurray, M B
McIlmoyle, J
McLellan, I C
MacSharry, C G
Mahendran, S M
Marriott, J D
Marshall, P D
Martlew, R A
Mathen, G
Mechie, D G
Mechie, G L
Milson, A R
Milson, J E
Moffitt, R M
Mom, J S
Morgan, W P
Murgatroyd, A B
Murgatroyd, M J
Ness, L M
Nicholls, G C
Nightingale, P B
North, J K
O'Donnell, M
O'Neill, F C
Oliver, D W
Oliver, K J
Opdebeck, G P E M T
Orrell, D H
Page, I J
Park, J
Paton, A L
Payne, E C
Pearson, J D
Peat, M J
Pilling, G M E
Povedano Canizares, C E
Prasad, B K
Pugh, H
Rabbett, H L
Riley, P M
Roffey, M
Routledge, R
Rucklidge, M A
Rudd, A J
Ruscillo, G A
Seddon, T M
Seville, R H
Shepherd, R J
Shukla, Y P
Sidhu, K
Singh, C A
Smith, A F
Smith, C A
Smith, D J
Smith, M B
Stacey, D J
Staff, W G
Stepanek, P A
Stewart, H D
Stewart, M
Story, C A
Sullivan, R
Swales, C L
Telford, D R
Thomas, J M
Threlfall, J A
Todd, K H L
Toy, A J
Tynan, P F
Van Essen, J C
Vaughan-Jones, N
Vickers, A P
Walker, B H
Walmsley, D
Watts-Tobin, M E A B
Westgarth, T

Leeds

Wetherell, S C
Whittaker, R G
Whitton, A D C
Willey, R F
Williams, A J
Williamson, J T
Williamson, N
Wilson, P
Wong, K E
Wong, M K Y
Wright, S G
Yarnall, D J
Yule, R M
Zeiton, A A

Lancing
Beale, A L
Brummitt, P I
Burton, J P
Campbell, A J
Coyne, L A
Feeney, P J
Ferguson, W R F
Grant, K E
Hindle, W J
Hobson, D G
Ilkiw, P S J
Jewell, J H A
King, H A P
O'Sullivan, P J G
Peskett, D J
Plumb, N J
Robinson, J F
Rowland, P G
Starbuck, D P
Stevenson, A J M
Tierney, P T F
Varty, C P
Woolcock, J A
Young, J M
Young, J H

Langholm
Calder, M A
Kennedy, T M
Phillips, H C
Phillips, M L C
Scott, A
Spencer, G R
Williamson, M B

Langport
Balai, R
Betteridge, T J
Bond, A K
Chubb, S
Fish, S J
Gibson, D W R
Greig, H B W
Henderson, S D
Hussey, O J
Knight, K M
Mallaband, B C
Nightingale, E A E
Nightingale, P J
Pollock, D M
Pollock, L M
Richards, M L
Shrimpton, H D
Strutte, L J F
Talbot, S
Tyler, C L

Larbert
Barron, J
Boyd, J
Brown, S T C
Cole, R A
Duncan, C M
Ellison, D P
Finegan, W C
Fleming, C G
Fletcher, A L
Ghobrial, O S
Gibson, G A
Gibson, L M
Hillan, L R
Leeming, J A
Lynch, P P
McNab, M J W
McNeill, C M
Morrison, S S
Paton, D H
Preshaw, C T
Robinson, J A
Roughead, P
Sharp, J M C
Sinclair, D U
Smith, G
Suresh, T

Thomson, C R
Tuddenham, L M
Wilson, L E

Largs
Auld, A
Brown, H B
Cooper, M I
Ewing, C G
Fitch, M C
Greenfield, M R
Heaney, S J
Howie, S P
Jamieson, I S
Johnstone, M
Keay, K R
Lewis, S G
Lyon, D C
McCarlie, J
McClure, J R
McGurk, D A
MacKeachan, D C
Marshall, C E
Newton, H A
Newton, R A H
Nimmo, D H
Orchardson, R L
Robertson, D A
Shaw, A J
Simpson, J A
Soutter, D A
Templeton, J D
Turner, S L
Walsh, P F
Wilson, J L D

Larkhall
Baird, S H
Cama, E F
Duncan, A C I
Duncan, D
Fattah, H M
Hannah, R
Harvey, G M
Hopkins, D F
Hunter, L C
Kinniburgh, D E
Martin, A R
Mormesh, N M
Morrison, J D R
Noble, P J
Parker, S S I
Rankin, H A
Renfrew, D M
Roy, J P
Russell, C R
Sim, N A
Skehan, P F J
Smart, J F
Spence, E
Telfer, C A L
Thompson, A T
Vyas, R B
Wilson, J R
Zoma, A A

Larne
Bell, J H
Bolton, R H
Bolton, S H
Booth, K
Breen, E P
Bridges, J G M
Campbell, G
Casement, E
Chin, A K L
Craig, A M
Crory, G A C
Cullington, S J
Dornan, J O G
Dunn, J B
Fullerton, J M
Heyburn, G
Hopkins, C
Hopkins, M P
Howie, P K
Johnston, D H
Kitson, J
Knox, S J
Laird, R M
McCloskey, S M
McIlroy, A J
McIlroy, D J
McMinn, D J S
Maguire, K G
Mitchell, W A
Mulligan, R A C
Murphy, E
Nelson, K A
Rutherford, H E

Shanks, B
Steele, C
Todd, G R G
Varghese, M
Wasson, L F
Wilson, J R W
Worthington, J M

Lasswade
Champion, J K
Chapman, K A
Combe, J R
Jones, N C
Macdonald, D J
MacLeod, W A
Pettigrew, N M E
Scott, J N

Lauder
Crombie Smith, H J C
Lowles, J M
Macrae, M C
Megahy, F R C

Launceston
Baker, D M
Baker, P J
Collier, P T
De Glanville, R G
Felton, J R
Fitzgerald, J L
Fitzpatrick, E L
Fletcher, P D
Healey, R J
Houston, W L J
Johnson, A M
Morice, R O
Notley, J W
Ravenscroft, A
Richardson, R
Roberts, J M D
Smith, G T
Wells, M L
Wheal, J D

Laurencekirk
Anderson, M J
Anderson, N J
Box, K M
Lyall, A R
Lyall, F J
Milne, W H
Mulcahy, P D
Pirie, K
Warnock, J M T
Wood, J R

Laxey
Hopkinson, N R
Moran, P J
Mullan, M H
Wilson, K G
Young, D W

Leamington Spa
Ainsworth, P
Allsopp, G M
Allwood, M J
Anderson, J H
Ashley, J
Ashmore, M W
Baker, D S
Begg, R S P
Benning, T B
Bensa, R G R
Bickerton, R C
Blackburn, R A
Blacklay, P F
Bonsall, P A
Boothroyd, C M
Brod, J L
Brown, N E
Buckle, I M
Bull, D
Bull, M D
Cameron, S M
Campbell, F S
Carroll, M P
Carter, J C
Chan, E A
Cheema, J S
Chhina, N
Christopher, P M
Clark, W C
Clowes, C T
Coker, T C
Collins, R J C
Courtenay, R T
Davis, P J M
Dyde, J A
El-Gingihy, A S A

Emery, A J
Emery, J C
Eykyn, M L
Farrall, L A
Fogarty, L M
Forrest, G W
Forsyth, M G
Frampton, J
Freeman, P
Fullbrook, J E
Galbraith, E A
Ghataore, K S
Glass, J M
Godwin, S T
Gough, A
Graveney, M J
Green, M J
Greenwood, C R
Hajarnavis, J
Hall, I A
Hancock, J L
Hancock, M S
Harban, F M J
Harries, S A
Hawkes, G
Healy, P M
Higman, D J
Holley, K J
Holliday, J R
Holloway, V J
Holmes, J E
Hortas, C
Hyland, V M E
Jackson, M
Janda, A
Johnston, A O B
Johnston, N M
Jones, J M R
Jones, M L
Kanta, K
Kennedy, A G
Khan, S Y
Knell, A J
Knell, J E R
Knight, T J
Lamb, J R
Larard, D G
Leigh-Hunt, N J
Lodwick, L M
Lovick, R L J
Lucas, J B
Mactier, F C A
Mann, J
Marsh, J D
Marshall, J R
Martyrossian, J
Matthews, R N
Measey, L G
Moffatt, C D
Morris, C J
Oliver, L
Partridge, J W
Pearson, L C
Pearson, M J
Perks, B M H
Perks, J S
Potts, D A
Privett, J T J
Richards, M V
Rider, J C
Robson, A M
Rohatgi, S
Russell, E H
Saluja, R K
Saluja, S S
Scott, J A
Senior, N E
Shakespeare, D T
Shaw, R E
Shaw, R
Sheldrick, M D
Shenkman, J J
Shipton, P F
Singh, G
Snowdon, C M
Stewart, F E
Stoddart, C A
Strachan, K F
Strudwick, R H
Sumra, R
Supple, N T
Tansey, M A L
Taylor, R A S
Taylor, S
Tranter, S E
Trevelyan, N C
Trye, C J
Vodden, V M
Weinstein, V F

Wilkinson, J J A
Wilmot, J F
Wilne, B D
Wilson, T D P
Yong, C K K

Leatherhead
Anderson, E M
Astley, J
Aumonier, F J
Babajews, A V
Bailey, C S
Balding, J
Banerjee, A K
Barford, M
Barnes, A P
Barr, W S R
Bauer, A G
Belbeck, J S
Bell, J K
Bennett, T J
Benson, R G
Birtwistle, M L
Blow, C M
Bourne, S J
Buchanan, S H J
Cartledge, A G
Chinn, G L
Clark, S J
Close, J B
Creamer, B
Cross, J A
Cross, R A
Davies, J R
Davies, L C
Deane, C J
Degaitas, P
Down, N A C
Draper, R J
Ducker, D M
Evans, A M
Farrow, A K
Finnamore, V P
Fraser, E V
Garnett, R
Gelsthorpe, E
Gilchrist, D T
Glover, R B
Gordon, P A
Gosden, C W
Gray, M S
Harrington, N J
Hibbert, J
Hoole, E M
Jarrett, M E D
Jarrett, P E M
Johnson, P A
Johnston, P M
Jones, G L
Jones, K H
Jones, L J B
Kennedy, J A
Kirkman, D M
Klein, J L
Kooiman, G G
Lawrenson, A L
Lee, J D
Lewis, N R
Littleton, E T
Llewellyn, I V
McKechnie, R N
McLauchlan, S J
McMinn, M E
Manners, J S
Marazzi, P J M
Martin, C
Martinez Del Campo, M
Mead, A J
Meynen, F G C
Millar, D F D
Moore, J R
Morgan, J E
Murray, J B J
New, L C
Nisbet, R J B
O'Connell, M R
Oliver, R M
Parker, B C
Patel, C
Pickin, J H
Pilkington, G A
Powell, S J
Prowse, A D
Prowse, M J
Rose, J A
Rowe, C J
Rubin, I D W
Salmon, C A

Shafik, A M
Speirs, C J
Stephenson, J D
Stewart, J B
Stewart, P J
Thomas, E J
Thomson, R S
Thorley, A S
Torode, S A
Upchurch, F C
Vithayathil, K J
Walter, R M
Watson, J U
Williams, A A
Williams, D O
Wyatt, C M
Zoob, C L

Lechlade
Greenwood, R E
Hancock, F B
O'Reilly, P V
Stephens, D J
Stephens, H M A
Stephens, S J
Thomson, I A
Yapp, J
Yapp, T R

Ledbury
Crook, M C
Davies, S A
Eckersley, J H
Greenall, G
Heath, D F
Hiley, C D
Hunter, W J
Johnson, R
Jones, H B
Moon, R C
Moore, A
Ranasinghe, A M
Ruffell, J
Sandison, R A
Savage, D C L
Scholefield, R D
Scott, B C
Smith, D M A
Smith, E N
Smith, M D
Thorp-Jones, D J
Williams, G R

Lee-on-the-Solent
Ashby, G H
Bassett, J H
Beale, E A
Bell, I S
Butler, R E
Craig, J R
Duff, D R
Duggal, K N
Evans, S D
Head, P W
Jones, M V
Linn, H A
Parsons, M H
Radford, R
Taylor, C A
Whalley, F L

Leeds
Abbas, H
Abbott, C G
Abbott, C R
Achram, M
Adam, J E R
Adams, I D
Adams, J
Adams, J P
Adams, J M
Adams, R J
Adcock, C A
Addlestone, M B
Addlestone, R I
Ade, C P
Adlard, J W
Adshead, D W
Ahmad, N
Ahmad, R
Ahmed, I
Ahmed, Y S
Ainsley, R F D
Aitken, C
Aitken, J
Akagi, H
Akhtar, S
Al-Dabbagh, A K R
Albert, D J
Aldridge, S J

Leeds

Alexander, J M
Alexander, M S
Ali-Naja, S W
Ali, F S
Ali, S A
Alison, D L
Alkatib, M
Allen, A W
Allen, F S
Allen, P
Allibone, E B
Allibone, R O
Allison, E A
Allison, S G
Allman, I G
Alpin, H R
Ambrose, N S
Amery, C M
Ammuri, B J I
Andersen, S Y
Anderson, C K
Andrew, A C
Ang Wan-Ming, C
Anthony, H M
Appleby, M A
Apps, J M
Archer, I A
Arnold, R
Arrowsmith, P
Arthur, R J
Arundel, P
Ash, D V
Ashraf, S S
Asiedu-Ofei, E S
Atherley, C E
Atkinson, H G
Atkinson, J D
Atkinson, J N
Atkinson, K
Atter, M
Aubin, S D
Aumeerally, Z B
Aung, M G
Aviv, R I
Axon, A T R
Aylett, V P
Ayres, J E
Bagnall, W E
Bahrami, J
Baker, S J
Balen, A H
Balfour, L
Ball, R J
Ball, S G
Ball, S A
Balls, M A
Balmford, S E
Bamford, J M
Barber, J M
Barclay, I
Barclay, T L
Barnard, D L
Barnett, D
Barnett, J E
Barodawala, S
Baron, S E
Barraclough, C J
Barry, B N
Barth, J H
Barton, M
Batra, N
Batra, R K
Baxter, A J
Baxter, K F
Beacock, D J
Beck, G N
Beckwith, L
Beecroft, C L
Beh, L K
Belchetz, P E
Belfield, P W
Bell, A P
Bellamy, M C
Bem, C C
Bem, M J
Benech, I
Bennett, C P
Bennett, E K A
Bennett, M I
Bennett, R J
Benson, S E
Benwell, J B
Berkin, K E
Berlet, J K
Berridge, D C
Berridge, J C
Berridge, J M
Berridge, K I
Berridge, M J

Berrill, A J
Berry, G H
Bew, N M
Bew, S A
Bhakta, B
Bhandary, L V
Bhandary, U V
Bhartia, B S K
Bhatia, M S
Bhattacharyya, P K
Billsborough, S H
Bingham, S J
Binnie, J A
Biran, L A
Bird, H A
Birkin, A E
Bishop, N
Bishop, R I
Biwer, J E
Black, D A
Black, H
Black, M A
Black, S J
Blackburn, M E C
Blomfield, I A
Bloomer, M A
Boardman, P
Bobet Reyes, R M
Bodansky, H J
Boddy, J E
Boden, S K
Bolland, H E
Bollard, R C
Bolton, A J
Bong, J J
Bonsoc, G
Bonthron, D T
Boon, A P
Boonin, A S
Bottger, S
Bottomley, D M K
Boulton, M
Bower, S J
Bowie, P C W
Bowman, C E
Boyd, K L
Boylston, A W
Bradbury, K M
Brahma, A K
Branfoot, J T C
Brenchley, J
Brennan, C L
Brennan, T G
Brewin, E G
Bridges, L R
Brill, A M
Brindle, N S
Broch, J I
Brocklebank, J T
Brogden, P R
Brookes, S D
Broom, C
Broughton, D M
Brown, A K
Brown, E
Brown, H
Brown, H B
Brown, J M
Brown, J L
Brown, M A
Brown, S J
Browne, J M
Browning, C A
Browning, F S C
Brownjohn, A M
Brownlee, K G
Buchan, J C
Buckler, J M H
Buckley, J G
Budgen, S A B
Burke, B M
Burke, D
Burkill, A D
Burn, W K
Burns, E
Burr, J M
Burrowes, H P
Burrows, D A
Burton, A J M
Bury, R F
Bush, D J
Bush, S
Butler, G E
Butt, W P
Bynoe, J K
Bywaters, J L
Cade, A
Cahill, B T
Cairncross, R G

Cairns, A
Calder, S J
Caldicott, L D
Calvert, S M
Cameron, A
Cameron, A W
Cameron, I H
Cameron, S J
Campbell, D J
Campbell, D A
Campbell, F M
Campbell, H
Campbell, J A
Campbell, S D
Carder, P J
Carey, B M
Carmichael, D J
Carmody, E A
Carpenter, M J M
Carr, J D
Carrington, N C
Carroll, B N
Carswell, N S
Carter, J
Carter, R F
Cartmill, D J
Cartwright, R A
Cartwright, S C
Cassels-Brown, A
Cassidy, J F
Cassie, J A
Catto, A J
Cave, E M
Challinor, J M
Challinor, P
Chalmers, A G
Chalmers, D M
Chamberlain, M A
Chambers, H H
Chandler, G N
Chang, B
Chapman, A H
Chapman, R A
Chappelow, S
Charley, D J
Charlton, J S
Charlton, P N
Chaudhuri, J K
Chauhan, C
Cheesman, A L
Chennells, P M
Chesser, S G S
Chester, J D
Child, J A
Christian, A S
Christou, T
Christys, A R
Chu, C E
Chu, C H P C
Chua, S E
Chung, A K K
Clappison, D P
Clare, C M
Clare, J
Clare, P A B
Clark, A E
Clark, G W B
Clark, P B
Clark, S M
Clarke, M D
Clarke, P R
Clarkson, K S
Claydon, S M
Clyde, C A
Cohen, A E
Cohen, A P
Cohen, A T
Cohen, A F
Cohen, E M
Cohen, J M
Cohen, M B
Cohen, S A
Cole, P J
Colling, P N
Collinson, M P
Congdon, H M
Conway, S P
Cooke, M L
Cooke, N J
Cooke, S M
Cookson, T W
Cooper, L R
Cooper, N A
Coore, J R
Corrado, O J
Cotterill, J A
Cottrell, D J
Cowan, J C
Cowan, P J

Cowen, P N
Cox, F M
Coyle, C A
Crabbe, D C G
Crawshaw, A L
Creaby, G E
Creighton, J E
Crellin, A M
Crew, A D
Critchley, A T
Crofton-Biwer, C J
Crompton, A C
Crone, A A
Cross, J
Cross, R J
Crossland, G J
Crowson, J B
Cruickshank, J L
Cruickshank, R H
Crystal, B L
Cuckow, P M
Culliney, P
Cundall, D B
Cunliffe, W J
Cunningham, J A
Curgenven, A
Curran, S
Currie, J I
Curtis, N J
Dai, C-C A
Dall, B J G
Danks, J F
Darbyshire, P G
Darigala, S
Darling, J C
Darnborough, A
Darnborough, K
Darnborough, S
Darowski, M J
Davey-Quinn, A P
Davidson, L A
Davies, A-M
Davies, F E
Davies, G R
Davies, J A
Davies, J B
Davies, M H
Davies, R M
Davis, F I
Davis, S M
Davison, A M
Davison, S M
Dawson, J M
Day, A T
De Boer, G M
De Dombal, E
De Graeve, J H
De Haas, L N
de Pauw, K W
De Silva, C
De Silva, N A
Deacon, P
Deacon, V
Dean, S G
Dear, P R F
Dearden, A M
Dearden, N M
Denton, D V
Denton, G C
Denton, M
Denyer, M E
Devaraj, K S
Devaraj, S R
Devaraj, V
Devitt, H J
Dexter, S P L
Dickinson, C J
Dickinson, D F
Dickinson, J R E
Dickson, D E
Dickson, R A
Diekerhof, C
Dilke-Wing, G M
Dintinger, E L
Dix, M
Dixon, J J
Dixon, J A
Dixon, M F
Dobbins, B M
Doig, R L
Dolben, J
Dominguez Alonso, C J
Donaldson-Hugh, M E A
Donnelly, H S
Doore, J R
Doran, R M L
Doughty, C

Douglas, I A C
Dowell, A C
Downing, C
Dowson, D G
Dresner, M R
Drife, D E
Drife, J O
Dryhurst, D J
Duffy, S R
Dunham, R J C
Dunn, E M
Dunphy, R H
Dwyer, A S
Dwyer, N M
Dyson, J B
Eardley, I
Eastham, D G
Easton, A M E
Eastwood, D S
Eastwood, P G
Eccles, J T
Edmondson, R S
Edridge, K A L
Edwards, P A
Edwardson, R S
El-Sayed, M E N M
El-Sherbiny, S M
El-Tigani, M A H
Ellis, F R
Ellison, C
Elmslie, A G M
Elton, S M
Emerton, M E
Emery, C
Emery, P
Entress, A H
Essom, J M
Etherington, C
Evangelou, L
Evans, J
Evans, M A
Evans, N M H
Evennett, H C
Everett, B D
Everett, J E
Everett, M P
Everett, S M
Fairfield, J E
Fairley, I R
Fale, A D
Farbridge, J A
Farrell, P
Fatheazam, S
Fatheazam, S L
Fear, J D
Febbraro, S
Feely, M P
Feeney, M T
Feldman, S M
Fellerman, S M
Fenwick, J D
Ferriman, E L
Field, A M
Finan, P J
Firth, D C G
Fisher, R B
Fisher, S E
Fitzgerald, T A
Fitzpatrick, M M
Flanagan, P
Flannery, D P
Flannigan, C B
Flower, K L
Flowers, M W
Flynn, C M
Foley-Nolan, N D R
Ford, H L
Ford, J A
Ford, P A
Forrester, D W
Forster, S
Foster, C A
Foster, K
Fowler, R C
Fox, T P
Franks, A J
Fraser, K P
Frazer, J B
Freeman, C B
Freeman, L
Freeman, M S
Friend, A R
Frieze, M
Frost, L A
Frost, S F
Gabay, A M
Gajdatsy, A D
Gambles, C S
Gannon, M J

Gardiner, K H
Garrett, C J
Gasson, P M
Gay, A L
Gbolade, B A
George, N D L
Geraghty, P G M
Gerrard, G E
Gerrard, J W
Gesinde, M O
Ghoneim, A T M
Ghoorah, S K B
Giannoudis, P
Gibbs, J L
Gibbs, K
Gibson, J S
Gibson, R M
Gilbey, J E
Gilbey, S G
Gilbody, S M
Gilchrist, C M
Gill, A B
Gilliam, A D
Gilmore, M
Gilmore, R D
Gilson, D
Gimeno Sentamans, C M
Glaser, A W
Glass, M R
Gledhill, J E
Glynn, P M
Goddard, A J P
Godfrey, D J
Godfrey, G
Gokhale, J A
Golding, W R
Gomez Martin, J
Gonzalez Castro, A
Goodman, K M
Goodson, M E
Gooi, H C
Gorman, S R
Gorton, H J
Gough, M J
Gould, M I
Goulden, V
Goulding, P J
Goyder, J F
Goyder, P A
Gozzard, J G
Grant, P J
Green, A L
Green, J B
Greenway, J
Greenwood, J P
Gregory, C A
Greig, C H
Griffith-Jones, M D
Grogan, E
Guckian, D M F
Guillou, P J
Gulliver, S A
Gupta, K K
Gupta, V L
Guthrie, J A
Hackney, R G
Haigh, L I G
Hainsworth, R
Hall, A S
Hall, G D
Hall, G I
Hall, R D
Hall, S K
Halpe, N L
Halsall, P J
Hambling, M H
Hamer, D W
Hamilton, S C C
Hammond, C J
Hammond, S A
Hancock, A K
Hancock, K W
Hanson, D R
Haq, R
Hardo, P
Hargreaves, M D
Harkin, P J R
Harkness, K A C
Haroon, M M
Harries, C J
Harris, A M
Harris, C M
Harris, K A
Harris, K M
Harrison, D F
Harrison, E A
Harrop, G B C
Hashim, N

Leeds

Hassan, T B
Hatcher, S M
Hatfield, A C
Hatton, P
Haward, R A
Hawbrook, G W J
Hawkhead, J L
Hawkings, M D
Hawkins, A
Hayat, M
Hayden, C J
Hayden, J D
Heal, S J V
Hearnshaw, C A S
Heath, C M
Heatley, R V
Heeralall, D
Helliwell, P S
Henderson, D S
Heppell, D
Herrington, R A
Hervey, G R
Hesse, G W A
Heylings, R T
Heywood, P L
Hibble, C J
Hicks, C A
Hicks, F M
Hickson, J R
Higgins, D G
Higgins, J C
Hillman, B
Hillman, J S
Hind, S P
Hipkins, A M
Hirschowitz, P M
Hobbs, C J
Hobman, J W
Hodge, D G
Hodgson, A J
Hodgson, R E
Hogan, S K
Holgate, C S
Holland, P C
Holliday, G M
Hollyoak, V A
Holman, D S
Holmes, C P
Holmes, J D
Hopkins, P M
Horgan, K
Hornbuckle, J
Horner, J L
Horsley, S
Houghton, A M
Houghton, A L
House, A K
House, A O
House, D A
Howden, P
Howdle, P D
Howe, K E M
Hudson, J
Hughes, D
Hughes, P R
Hull, M A
Hume, M J
Humphreys, A C
Humphris, S D
Hunjin, M S
Hunt, D J
Hunt, U M
Hunter, C M
Hurley, M B
Hurwitz, D C
Hurwitz, R
Huston, C
Huston, G J
Hutchinson, K
Hutchinson, S
Hutson, R C
Hutton, W N
Huyton, A J
Hyslop, A R
Igbaseimokumo, U
Iles, P J
Illingworth, K A
Illingworth, R N
Ilsley, D W
Inch, D D
Ingham, J S
Inweregbu, K O
Ionescu, C
Irving, G I
Irving, H C
Isaacs, J D
Islip, M R
Ivbijaro, G O
Iwantschak, A

Jabeen, S
Jack, A S
Jackson, D P
Jackson, K A
Jackson, T L
Jacobs, P
Jain, A
James, J N
James, J J
James, P N E
Jamieson, D R S
Jamieson, M E
Janik, A J
Janulewicz, M A
Januszkiewicz, J S
Jardine, K L
Jarman, R D
Jarrett, S J
Jarvis, E H
Jayasuriya, N L
Jayne, D G
Jenkins, G
Jerram, T C
Johnson, E J
Johnson, G S
Johnson, J
Johnson, M H
Johnson, P A
Johnston, D
Johnston, J
Jones, J M
Jones, M M
Jones, R G
Jones, S K
Jones, W G
Jordan, M N
Jordinson, H
Joyce, A D
Juniper, S E J
Kain, K
Kalia, P
Kaminopetros, P I
Kapur, K C
Kaufmann, S J
Kay, P H
Kay, S P J
Kearney, M T
Kearns, N P
Keeble, R J
Keefe, W J
Keep, M J
Kelly, E J
Kennedy, J E
Kenny, T E
Kerr, K G
Kesavan, S
Kester, R C
Khan, A S N
Khan, A
Khan, O D
Khan, S N
Khan, Y Z A
Kibria, S M G
Kiltie, A E
Kinsey, S E
Kirkham, J
Kirkwood, C J
Kitchen, C A
Kite, S M
Knight, L C
Knight, P R
Knight, S L
Knock, M A R
Kohler, H G
Kolkiewicz, L A
Kolpanowicz, E M
Koslowsky, N
Kotidis, K
Kouli, O
Kouri, A
Kumar, A
Kumar, V S P
Kwok, M C
Lacey, R W
Lacey, V J
Lam, B L
Lam, W
Lamb, J T
Lane, G
Lane, P E
Lane, S A
Lanfear, P C
Langford, R M E
Lannigan, F J
Lansbury, A J
Lansdown, M R J
Lapworth, C
Larvin, M
Last, H A

Lathe, G H
Lavelle, M J
Lawrence, S M
Lawrence, S L
Lawrenson, F J
Lawson, J S
Lawton, J O
Lawton, S L
Laybourn, J K
Laybourn, S M
Leach, A M
Leahy, M G
Leary, E R
Ledger, S J
Lee, A C H
Lee, C E
Lee, P S
Lee, S G
Leech, P A
Leeds, J S
Lees, G A
Lessels, F A
Lestner, R A
Levene, M I
Levin, R I
Levine, D S
Levy, R
Lewis, H N
Lewis, I J
Lewis, M B
Lewis, P D
Li, A G K
Lian, T Y
Liddington, M I
Limb, D L
Linden, R J
Lindsay, H
Lindsay, K A
Lindsay, M A
Lintin, S N
Linton, S
Lipman, G
Liston, J C
Livesey, D J
Livingston, J H
Lloyd, S M
Lobban, M S M
Lockey, A S
Lodge, J P A
Logan, K L
Logan, V S C D
Logarajah, V
Loizou, M
Lok, C
Long, D E
Longbottom, G
Losowsky, M S
Lough, C D
Loukota, R A
Lowe, R A
Lowther, J J H
Lubrano Di
    Scorpaniello, E
Lumb, A B
Lund, J A
Luscombe, H C
Lynagh, J
Lynch, J B
Lynch, L A
Lyons, G R
Lyons, S
McAteer, E M
MacCarthy, J P
McClean, P
McCorry, A
MacDermott, R I J
MacDermott, S J
McDonagh, F M C
Macdonald, D A
Macdonald, H N
MacDonald, R G
McGoldrick, P J
McGonagle, D G
McGowan, A
McGrath, H J
McHale, D P
McHale, M J
McHugh, P J M
McIlroy, J H
McKendrick, F Y
MacKenzie, A C M
McKibbin, M A
McKinlay, J
Mackintosh, A F
McKittrick, M
Maclean, J R
McLenachan, J M
McLennan, A S
Maclennan, K A

MacLennan, S
McMahon, A J
McMahon, M J
McMain, S S
McNeill, E J M
McVerry, B A
McVitie, D R C
McWilliams, D J
Madan, C K
Madan, S
Majid, A
Majumder, S
Mak, E Y-K
Malcolm, N P
Malhotra, A
Malhotra, P K
Mallett, M I
Mancey-Jones, J B
Manning, S I
Manock, K J
Manraj, P R
Mansfield, M W
Manyeula, R T
Markham, A F
Marks, P V
Marsden, J H
Marshall, A M
Marshman, R I
Martins, C A
Marvin, C M
Mary, A S G
Mary, B L
Mascie-Taylor, B H
Mason, E A
Mason, G C
Maston, J
Mateos Duran, L M
Mathialahan, T
Matthews, N R
Matthews, S J E
Mavor, A I D
Mavor, C J
Mayers, J N D
Maz, S S
Mbizeni, J M
Meadow, S R
Meaney, J F M
Mehay, R
Mehrotra, P N
Mellor, D J
Mellor, W E
Melnyk, A P
Menon, R
Mercer, K G
Merchant, W J
Messer, B
Meynell, A
Mezas, L H
Millares Martin, P
Miller, G V
Miller, J E
Miller, K E
Millner, P A
Millner, V A
Mills, C R
Millson, C E
Miloszewski, K J A
Mindham, R H S
Minhas, R B
Minhas, S
Minocha, S
Mitchell, D P
Mohajerin, H
Molto, A
Mooney, A F
Moore, D G
Morgan, A W
Morgan, G J
Morgan, P W
Morrell, A J
Morris, E J
Morris, H
Morris, M
Morris, N A
Morris, W P R
Morrison, J F J
Moss, E
Mossad, M G
Mounsey, N L
Mourmouris, N
Moxon, J W D
Moxon, P
Mueller, R F
Muers, M F
Muir-Cochrane, R R
Muncer, Z K
Munsch, C M
Murdoch Eaton, D G
Murphy, C E

Murphy, S A
Murray, R A
Murty, J A
Myers, C E
Myers, S
Nair, S B
Nair, U R
Najmaldin, A
Nandagopal, N
Narayanan, J
Nawaz, S
Nazir, N
Neal, R D
Nehaul, B B G
Nelson, D
Nelson, J W
Nelson, M A
Nelson, M
Nelson, S
Nensey, M
Neumann, V C M
Neville, P M
Newbound, A D
Newell, D
Newell, S J
Newman, P P
Newstead, C G
Newton Bishop, J A
Ng, K Y
Nic Eoin, M S
Nicholas, A C S
Nicholas, B M
Nicholas, R X
Nielsen, J W
Nix, A L
Nkonde, P M
Noden, J B
Norfolk, D R
Norwood, C
Nunn, G F
O'Brien, T P
O'Connor, J L
O'Connor, P J
O'Donovan, P J
O'Loughlin, B A
O'Mahony, B A
O'Mahony, J G
O'Neill, D P
O'Shea, T S
Ogden, L M
Okereke, R A
Oldroyd, G J
Oliver, S D
Ollerton, S J A
Olsburgh, J D
Onafowokan, J A
Orme, S M
Orton, C J
Osman, C H
Osman, J
Ottman, S C
Owen, R G
Owens, D W
Oxborrow, N J
Page, C E
Page, R L
Pai, H U
Pakrooh, M P
Panezai, A M
Papworth-Smith, J W
Papworth, R D J
Parkin, G J S
Parkin, R D
Parry, D J
Parsloe, M R J
Parsonage, M J
Parsons, M
Parsons, M
Patel, A
Patel, K R
Patel, N K R
Patel, P M
Patel, T B
Paul, A B
Payne, R B
Payne, S M L
Peacock, S G
Pearson, E M
Pearson, L J
Pearson, R E
Pearson, S B
Pearson, S G
Pease, C T
Peckham, D G
Pedder, S J
Pedley, I D
Peel, K R
Penn, N K
Penn, N D

Penny, A E
Pepper, C B
Perez-Carral
    Panchuelo, F J
Perren, T J
Perrins, E J
Petrus, L V
Phelan, F J
Phillip, C E
Phillips, N I
Pickles, V M
Picton, S V
Pierechod, B A
Pieroni, J E
Pinder, A J
Pittard, A J
Plant, P K
Pollard, S G
Pollock, K D
Porter, K G
Potts, E D A
Potts, N J
Potts, R K
Pouya, A
Power, A P
Power, B E
Powersmith, P S M
Prakash-Babu, P C
Prasad, B
Pratt, D
Prentice, C R M
Prescott, S
Preston, S R
Price, P M
Pritlove, J
Puntis, J W L
Pye, D C
Quinn, M A
Quirke, P
Raines, J E
Raistrick, D S
Rait, G
Raja, U
Rajah, C S
Rajkhowa, M
Ralph, S G
Ramsay, J L
Ramsden, W H
Rane, V A
Ranjitkumar, S
Rankine, J J
Raper, J M
Rashid, P A
Ratnalingam, R A
Ravenscroft, A J
Ravenscroft, J C
Ravi, K
Raw, J M
Ray, P J
Raynor, Y M
Razzaq, I
Read, P E
Redman, T F
Reece, A
Rehman, S U
Reid, D H
Reid, J A
Reid, K
Rembacken, B J
Renwick, C A
Renwick, D S
Renwick, S J K
Reynard, K
Reynolds, A
Reynolds, M T
Reynolds, P D
Reynolds, S E
Rhodes, N D
Richards, E M
Richold, J P
Rickards, A F
Rider, I A
Ridout, D M
Roberts, A B
Roberts, F
Roberts, J H
Roberts, J M
Roberts, T E
Robertson, C C
Robertson, I R
Robertson, R J H
Robinson, A S A
Robinson, A
Robinson, J E R
Robinson, M B
Robinson, P F
Robinson, P J A
Robson, D J
Roden, R K

Leek

Roman, V
Roney, G
Rooney, C M
Rooney, C M
Rooney, F J
Rooney, K J
Roots, L M
Rose, D M
Rose, N J
Rothwell, R I
Rowe, C E
Rowell, N R
Rowland, G D
Rowlands, T E
Rudolf, M C J
Russell, J L
Russell, L E
Rutherford, A J
Rutledge, G J
Ryan, B E
Ryan, M J L
Sadaba, J R
Sadiq, F J
Sadler, R S
Saeed, W R
Saffer, C M
Sager, J M
Saha, S C
Sainsbury, P A
Samuel, C A
Sanderson, H
Sandle, G I
Sapier, N V
Sapsford, R J
Sarvananthan, R
Satur, C M R
Saunders, E J
Saunders, E J
Saunders, R N
Saxena, I R
Scallan, B F X
Schallamach, S
Schofield, S F
Schweiger, M S
Scott, B W
Scott, D
Scott, D J
Scott, D J A
Scott, E M
Scott, J N
Scott, N
Seal, A K
Sebag-Montefiore, D J
Sedler, M J
Sefton, J E
Sefton, S
Selby, P J
Sellors, J E
Selsby, D S
Semple, P
Setia, R
Settle, F C
Seyed-Harraf, F
Seymour, M T
Shah, M V
Shah, T H
Shapiro, H
Share, A I S
Sharma, S
Sharpe, D A C
Sharples, D L
Shaw, A B
Shaw, J D
Shaw, N H
Shaw, S A
Shaw, S H
Sheard, T S
Sheehan-Dare, R A
Sheerman-Chase, G L
Shelly, M A
Shenderey, K D
Shepherd, M J
Sheridan, M B
Sheridan, P
Shevlin, P V
Shillito, T J A
Shimmin, H J
Shoesmith, J H
Shooman, H
Short, B
Sibbald, R
Sillender, M
Silman, H
Simm, J M
Simmons, A V
Simmons, M A
Simpson, J C
Simpson, K H
Simpson, N A B

Sims, A C P
Sinclair, G
Sinclair, J M
Sinclair, P D
Singh, G P
Singh, J L
Sinson, J D
Sixsmith, A M
Skinner, J
Slaymaker, A E
Sleightholm, M A
Sloan, J P
Sloan, M C
Smeed, R C K
Smiddy, F G
Smith, D A
Smith, D R
Smith, E S
Smith, G M
Smith, G M
Smith, I
Smith, I M
Smith, I S
Smith, M E
Smith, N A G
Smith, P S
Smith, P H
Smith, R M
Smith, R T
Smith, S A
Smith, W D A
Smith, W E
Smith, W H T
Smithells, R W
Snell, J A
Snell, L R
Somers, S A
Sood, R N
Sood, S
Sooltan, A R
Sooltan, M A
Sorkin, S
Southern, K W
Speakman, M J
Spencer, H A
Spinty, S
Spokes, E G S
Squire, B R
Srivastava, S K
Stahlschmidt, J
Stakes, A F
Staniforth, J L
Stanley, P J
Stanton, J A
Stanton, M
Stark, D P H
Stead, H
Stevens, A M H
Stockton, M R
Stone, M H
Storer, D
Strachan, D B
Straiton, J A
Stringer, M D
Sturdy, J L
Stuttard, S
Sudhakar Krishnan, V
Sue-Ling, H M
Sugden, J C
Sumner, M A E
Sunderland, L A
Sutcliffe, I M
Sutcliffe, R I
Sutherland, J A
Sutton, J B
Sutton, J
Swaby, M J
Swanwick, M V
Sweetnam, A T
Swift, S E
Swinburne,
K A M C O
Swinburne, M L
Swirsky, D M
Sykes, S J
Szulecka, T K
Tagg, G V
Tan, L-B
Tandy, C L
Tannett, P G
Tattersall, J M
Tattersall, R S
Tay, J I-Y
Taylor, C M
Taylor, G B
Taylor, G M
Taylor, J L
Taylor, J M
Taylor, P F

Taylor, P L
Taylor, R M
Taylor, R E
Taylor, S H
Teale, C
Tebay, K E
Templeton, P A
Thakur, M C
Than, N
Thickett, M A
Thistlethwaite, J E
Thomas, A J H
Thomas, D F M
Thomas, H J
Thomas, S J
Thompson, D J
Thompson, J C
Thorburn, J S
Thornton, J G
Thornton, J D
Thorpe, J A C
Thrower, A J
Till, R J A
Timothy, E M
Timothy, J
Timperley, J
Todd, N J
Tolan, D J M
Tolley, J M
Tolman, C J
Tomlinson, F E
Tompkins, D S
Toogood, G J
Tooley, D A
Townley, A
Townsend, P S
Trigwell, P J
Trumper, A L
Tulwa, N
Tummala, V R
Turkington, P M
Turley, J M
Turner, C M I
Turner, G
Turner, J A
Turney, J H
Upadhyaya, G
Uzochukwu, B C
Uzun, O
Valeinis, M
Van De Velde, R I
Van Hille, P T
Vanderwert, R T
Varnavides, C K
Vautrey, R M
Veale, D J
Veiga, M A C
Veldtman, G R
Venters, A D
Vernon, J P
Veysi, V T
Vinall, P S
Vining, D
Wachsmuth, C W
Wachsmuth, R C
Waddelow, J
Waddingham, S E
Waite, A
Walden, F
Walden, H
Waldenberg-Namrow, C
Wales, J K
Walford, L J
Walker, A
Walker, A M
Walker, B E
Walker, D R
Walker, J D
Walker, J J
Walker, J L
Walker, M F
Wall, O R
Wallace, S
Walley, J D
Walls, M J
Walls, W K J
Walsh, G
Walsh, M E
Walters, G
Wanklyn, P D K
Wasawo, S P
Waters, A D
Waterworth, A S
Watkin Jones, A
Watson, C S
Watson, C N
Watson, D L
Watson, J P

Watson, L
Watson, S V J
Watson, T E
Watters, J K
Waugh, M A
Welch, D M
Welch, K A
Welch, M
Welch, R B
Welham, G M
Welsh, M C
Wessell, H N
Weston, A L
Weston, M J
Whelan, P
Whitaker, I A
White, C M
White, M J
Whitelaw, D C
Whiteley, S M
Whitley, A J
Whitmarsh, K A
Whyman, C E
Wickremasinghe, A S
Wilcox, M H
Wilkinson, D
Wilkinson, N B
Wilkinson, S M
Will, E J
Williams, C
Williams, D R R
Williams, E M
Williams, G J
Williams, J G
Williams, L Y
Williams, M A T
Williams, R E D
Williams, S
Williams, S G
Wills, P M
Wilson, A T
Wilson, C L
Wilson, H M
Wilson, I G
Wilson, J D
Wilson, M E
Wilson, R C
Winehouse, J
Winokur, B
Winyard, G P A
Wong, C L
Wong, C I
Wong, J C L
Wong, W Y
Wong, Y F S
Wood, C M
Wood, N W
Wood, P M D
Woodley, H E
Woodrow, G
Woods, D R
Wooler, G H
Wootton, P B
Worrall-Davies, A E
Worthy, T S
Wright, A L
Wright, A L
Wright, D J
Wright, E M
Wright, F J
Wurr, C J
Wyatt, J I
Wyatt, S E
Wynne, C S
Wynne, J M
Yarwood, R
Yates, A P B
Yates, M
Yates, M
Yellin, S D
Yeung Tam Sang, S
Yeung, S R
Young, L F
Zermansky, A J
Zermansky, A G
Zoltie, N
Zoltowski, J A

Leek

Brookes, G S
Carpenter, G R
Clarke, F R
Cox, M L
Elsdon, C J L
Elsdon, S J
Evans, D J
Goodwin, S M
Hall, A G
Harvey, A M

Hughes, D H
Joseph, C P
Kapoor, G K
Lain, D K
Macmillan, J F
Mawby, N C
Norrie, S D
Piggott, R M
Porcheret, M E P
Rees, A F
Scriven, B E
Shiers, C
Shiers, D E
Somerville, S J
Surawy, J
Ward, R A
Watson, H S K
Westaway, C E

Leicester

Abbott, R J
Abbott, S M
Abdul Aziz, F W
Abdul Wahab, M A-R
Ackerley, R G
Adam, S
Adkinson, R K
Agarwal, R
Agarwal, V K
Ageed, A B M A
Aghahoseini, A M R
Agrawal, S
Ahmad, S
Ahmed, M-U-D
Akhtar, R P
Akingba, M A
Akowuah, E F
Al-Azzawi, F A L M
Alexander-Williams, J M
Alexander, C C
Ali, N S
Allen, J C
Allen, J N B
Allen, K M
Allin, S J
Amamani, A
Ambekar, M
Ambelas, A
Ambus, I A
Amin, A J
Amu, S O
Anastasiou, N
Anderson, C S
Anderson, I
Anderson, I G
Anderson, P G
Anderson, S L
Andrade, G G S
Andrew, D C
Andrews, H B
Anwar, M
Anwar, Z R
Appadu, B
Appiah, E K
Aram, G E
Archer, C K
Archer, L N J
Archer, R P
Argiros, G
Ashman, V F
Ashton, L A
Astles, J G
Atcheson, R
Attard, A
Au-Yong, R C L
Austin, D J
Austin, M W E
Austin, R C T
Austin, R T
Baggott, J N
Bahra, R S
Baigent, D F
Bailey, P D
Bailey, S A
Baker, A K
Baker, K
Baker, R H
Baker, R W
Ball, D S
Ball, E L
Ball, K J
Bandesha, G
Banerjee, P J M
Bapodra, S V
Baragwanath, P
Barber, B
Barnes, T W
Barnett, D B

Baron, D E
Barr, M M E
Barrie, L I
Barrie, W W
Barron, J
Barry, P W
Bartlett, J M
Barton, R P E
Batsford, P
Baxendine, C L
Beck, A J
Beck, F
Beddows, M E
Beech, S H
Bell, P R F
Bell, P J R
Benamore, R E
Benghiat, A
Bennetts, R J
Benninger, B L D
Bennison, D P
Bentley, A J J
Berry, D P
Berry, N Y
Best, A J
Bhaduri, S
Bhandal, N K
Bhangoo, P
Bhangoo, R S
Bhangoo, S S
Bharmal, S
Bhate, M S
Bhaumik, S
Bhogadia, H
Bhowal, B
Bhutani, H C
Bibby, K
Bing, R F
Birch, J F
Birchall, H M
Bland, D G
Blanshard, K S
Bloor, A C
Bock, P A
Bodiwala, D
Bodiwala, G G
Bohin, S
Bolia, A A
Bolt, S B
Borley, S R
Borrill, L S
Bouch, D C
Bouch, D C
Bourne, C M
Bourne, T M
Bowry, S
Bradding, P
Bramble, N P
Brammar, T J
Brandon, S
Braybrooke, J R
Brazil, E V
Bretherton, K F
Brett, C T F
Brightling, C E
Brittain, R V
Brocksmith, D
Brombacher, J H-P
Brooke, A M
Brooke, S D
Brooks, H
Brown, A R
Brown, D E
Brown, K F C
Brown, V A
Browne, L E
Browne, R E
Browning, M J
Bruce, D I
Bruce, J M
Brugha, T S
Brundell, S M
Brunskill, J
Bryant, G M C
Bu'Lock, F A
Buck, K S
Buck, R G
Buckler, M E L
Bukhari, S S
Bunn, H J
Buras, J J
Burd, R M
Burden, A C
Burgess, I C
Burke, J G A M
Burnett, M P
Burns, D A
Butt, A
Butterworth, S E

Leicester

Byer, L D
Byrne, E J H
Cairns, R
Calvert, R M
Cameron, D
Camp, R D R
Campbell, S H
Campling, P M
Canorea, F
Cansfield, P J
Cappin, J M
Cappin, S J
Carr, R M
Carr, S J
Carter, E P
Castleden, C M
Chada, N K
Chadwick, C A
Chaloner, D A
Chamberlain, M N
Chan, J C K
Chan, K C
Chan, R N-W
Chapman, C S
Chapple, S-J
Charles, T H S
Chatteris, D J
Chaudhari, I
Chauhan, A
Chauhan, A
Chauhan, B
Chauhan, B
Chauhan, N
Chave, T A
Cheesman, T S
Cheng, K C
Cherryman, G R
Cheung, E S-K
Chillala, S
Chohan, J
Chohan, S S
Chowdhury, F U-H
Church, V A
Churchward, H C V
Clark, C J
Clarke, M
Clarke, R
Clode-Baker, E G
Coakley, F V
Coffey, C J
Coggins, M M
Cole, A G H
Collett, B J
Conboy, P J
Constantinides, S
Cook, A G
Cook, E M
Cook, G D
Cook, J A
Cooke, C M
Cooke, S D S
Cooklin, S
Cookson, A G I
Cookson, J B
Cookson, J F J
Cooper, J G
Corbett, V
Costello, D P
Cottee, C A
Cotton, B R
Craig, D S
Creagh, W J
Cretney, P N
Crighton, J L
Critchley, P H S
Crombie, R D
Crowe, M G F
Crump, B J
Cullen, J H S
Currie, A E
Curwood, V L
Cusack, R J
Dacie, J
Dadge, N G
Daintith, H A M
Dale, A R
Danaher, J G
Danaher, P J
Daniels, D F
Darke, G
Darlington, B G
Das, S
Datta, S
Davda, M
Dave, S
Dave, S K
Davenport, P G
Davies, M J
Davies, M J
Davies, P
Davies, S
Davis, J M
Davis, J L
Davison, H K
Davison, I S
Dayah, D R
de Bono, A M
de Chazal, R C S
Deane, J S
Dennis, M J S
Dennis, M S
Denton, E M C
Desai, B N
Desai, S P
Desor, R
Dey, S K
Dhesi, J K
Di Lustro, M J
Dias, J J
Dickinson, F L
Dickinson, L M
Dickson, K R
Docrat, F
Dogra, N
Donnell, A J H
Doughman Marzouk, T
Downs, P A
Drummond, G A
Drury, J N G
Drybala, G
Dub, I
Duddridge, M
Duggan, F E
Duke, C
Duke, T G
Duncan, C H
Dunkley, C J
Dunkley, M J
Dunn, R A S
Durkan, R M
Duthie, D J R
Dux, A E W
Duxbury, M J
Dyer, M J S
Dziewanowski, R E A
Eaden, J A
Eames, P J V
Earnshaw, D A
Earnshaw, G J
Eastley, R J
Edgar, M A
Edwards, M
Edwards, P J
Edwards, R G
Edwards, V B J
El-Ouzi, E-H B
Elias-Jones, A C
Elliot, C A
Ellis, R
Eltigani, E A H
Elton, C D
Emberton, P
Esler, C N A
Esterlich, R J
Evans, K
Evans, P A
Evans, R A
Evennett, J
Everson, N W
Fahy, G T
Fairfield, M C
Falconer Smith, J F
Fallow, S M
Fancourt, G J
Farhan, M M
Farid, B T
Featherstone, S M
Feehally, J
Fell, D
Finlay, D B L
Finucane, K A
Firek, S C
Firmin, R K
Firth, W R
Fisher, M G
Fisher, M
Fisher, R M
Fishwick, N G
Fisk, P G
Flavell, H L
Fletcher, A
Flint, N J
Flower, A J E
Flynn, C C
Flynn, M J
Ford, S E
Forde, S C O
Forrester, G
Forster, J C
Fotherby, M D
Foulds, G E
Fox, A J
Frain, I K M
Fraser, M
Fraser, R C
Fraser, S M F
Freeman, D
Freeman, R F
Frost, S J
Fry, J M
Fulford, S C V
Fullard, M J
Furlong, C M
Furness, P N
Gadhia, D J
Gaffey, A
Gaili, H E-M E
Gajebasia, S S
Gardi, P D
Gardner, F J E
Gardner, J M
Garlick, A
Garrido Ferrer, A
Gattoni, F E G
Gaunt, M E
Geelan, S D
Geranmayeh, A
Ghanem, H I M
Gharib-Omar, A B
Ghura, H S
Gibbons, C P
Gibbons, G R
Glover, N A J
Godsiff, S P
Goffin, P S
Goh, G T Y
Gohil, V N L
Goldberg, M J
Golshetti, V G
Goodchild, J
Goodier, J C
Gopal, M N
Goraya, P S
Gotla, D W
Gould, M J
Goulstine, D B
Goulstine, M B
Graf, R E
Graham-Brown, R A C
Graham, R G
Graham, R M
Gray, J
Gray, J C
Green, M R
Green, P W
Green, T P
Greenwood, B
Greenwood, R K
Greer, A J
Gregg, A K
Gregory, R
Greiff, J M C
Griffin, B J
Grigg, J M
Grundy, N J
Gundle, V
Guthrie, M J
Habiba, M A H
Hadelmayr-Kuhn, I R
Hainsworth, B H A
Hall, A P
Hall, A W
Hall, A S
Hamer, V A
Hamill, J J
Hampson, E F
Hampson, J M
Hampton, R H
Hanger, S J
Hanly, T P
Hanning, C D
Harris, F
Harris, K P G
Harrison, M J
Harrisson, P A
Harvey, N J
Hassan, W
Hassan, Y
Hastings, A M
Hauck, A
Hawkins, S J
Haworth, C
Hay, A D
Hay, G C
Haykal, N G A
Hayter, J P
Hayward, N S E
Hazeldine, R L
Heer, R
Hellendoorn, J W
Hemingway, D M
Henderson, H P
Hewett, N C
Hewitt, C D
Hickey, F G E
Hickey, M S J
Hickinbotham, P F J
Higgins, H P
Hiley, A L
Hillman, A V
Hinchliffe, A C
Hirani, A
Hirani, N A
Hirani, S
Hird, N E
Hoffler, D E
Hoffman, J
Holbrook, J D
Hollington, A M
Holton, A F
Holton, J L
Honest, Dr
Hopes, D R
Horst, C
Hoskinson, J
Hoskyns, E W
Houghton, A R
Houtman, P N
Howlett, T A
Hsu, R T-H
Hubbard, I M
Hubert, S J
Hubner, P J B
Hubner, R A
Huddy, C L J
Hudson, I
Hudson, N
Hudson, N M
Hugh-Jones, S
Hughes, S D
Hui, Y
Hume Kendall, J A
Humphries, J M
Hung, L C
Hunt, L M
Hunter-Brown, I H
Hunter, A E
Hunter, R J
Hurwood, D S
Hurwood, R S
Hussey, P G
Hutchings, G R
Hutchinson, C V
Hutchinson, R M
Igwe, U C J
Inman, J K
Ireland, D
Isaac, G R
Ives, D R
Jackett, D M R
Jackson, K J
Jagjivan, B
James, D C
Jameson, J S
Jameson, V J
Jarvis, A
Jayakumar, K N
Jefferies-Beckley, A L
Jenkins, G
Jennings, C R
Jennings, T R
Jervis, P N
Jethwa, A A
Jewell, G J
Jeyapalan, I
Jeyapalan, K
Johnson, P N
Johnston, G A
Johnstone, J M S
Jolliffe, D M
Jones, D M
Jones, G W
Jones, I P
Jones, J L
Jones, J M
Jones, M J
Jones, O B
Jones, P A
Jones, S D
Joshi, N H
Joshi, R
Jugessur, D
Julian, S L
Kanabar, R C
Kane, M L
Karim, K A
Karwatowski, W S S
Kaul, A
Kaul, H K
Kaur, S
Kay, D P
Kaye, H J
Kaye, N
Keal, R P
Kehinde, O E
Kelly, M J
Kelvin, N B
Kendall, B R
Kendall, C H
Kennedy, R G
Kenrick, J M T
Kerbel, D G
Kerby, C
Kershaw, C J
Kershaw, I F M
Khalid, A M
Khan, N S
Khan, S L
Khandhadia, S D
Khong, T K
Khoo, E Y H
Khoosal, D I
Khunti, K
Khunti, P
Kiana, S
Kilpatrick, J R B
Kilty, B
Kimber, R M
King, A L
King, N W
Kinsella, B W
Kirwan, P H
Kishore, A
Kishore, K
Knight-Nanan, D M
Knight, A J
Ko, S H
Kockelbergh, R C
Koffman, D
Konje, J C
Kotecha, S H
Kothari, A K
Krarup, K C
Krishnan, H
Krishnan, R
Kuok, S S W
Kweh, M W
Lakhani, D R
Lalji, M K
Lambert, M J
Lampard, R
Langford, K J
Laopodis, V
Larkin, E P
Lauder, I
Laurent, S C
Lawden, M C
Lawrence, I G
Lawrence, N W
Lawrie, I
Lazarus, P A
Leach, R A
Leather, G S J
Lee, A T F
Lee, D J
Lees, B E
Leggat, M
Lennox, A I A
Lenten, P M
Leslie, D R S
Leslie, N A P
Leung, C B
Levene, L S
Leverment, I M G
Lewington, A J P
Lewis, C
Lewis, D G
Lewis, L
Liddicoat, A J
Lightstone, B L
Lightstone, R J
Lim, T W J G
Lim, V R
Lindesay, J E B
Lloyd-Evans, M
Lloyd-Powis, N
Lloyd, S R
Lloyd, T D R
Lo, N M K
Lo, T C N
Lockhat-Clegg, F B
Lodhia, B R
Loftus, I M
Loke, S C
Loke, W I
London, N J M
London, S P
Longworth, S
Lowy, A G J
Lucas, B A C
Lucraft, L
Luyt, D K
Lydford-Davis, H
Macafee, C A J
McAuley, D M
McCarthy, M J
McCaskie, A W
McCullough, J
McDermott, E J
McDonald, H J
McGarrity, C
McGibbon, S
McGrother, C W
McHugh, G
McHugh, G T
Mackay, E H
McKeever, P A
McKinley, R K
McLaren, I M
McLearie, M
McLellan, I
McLoughlin, S J
McMordie, H C
McNally, P G
McParland, P C
MacVicar, D
MacVicar, J
Madden, F J F
Madders, D J
Madira, W M
Maharaj, V
Maini, B
Maini, M
Mandalia, I R
Mansingh, S
Marchant, J
Markham, D H A L
Marshall, S D
Maskell, T W
Matharu, G S
Mathers, A
Maxted, S H
May, A E
May, D W F
Mayberry, J F
Mayne, C J
Mead, M K
Mead, M G
Meagher, T M M
Meakin, C J
Mears, E M L
Mehta, R L
Messios, N
Metcalfe, C A
Millar, J
Milner, A R
Milton, J
Milward, T M
Minhas, H S
Miodrag, A
Mistry, A
Mistry, A K
Mistry, A D
Mistry, B
Mistry, H R
Mistry, S
Mitchell, C J
Mitchell, V E
Mlynik, A
Mobley, K A
Modhwadia, M M
Modi, B V
Mohamed, M
Moloney, J R
Moltu, A P
Moncrieff, C J
Monk, P N
Moody, A R
Moody, T L
Moore, A E J
Moore, G L
Moore, J R
Moran, M F
Morar, K K
Morgan, B
Morgan, M D L
Morgan, S J
Moriarty, R J
Morley, C
Muehlbayer, S
Muir, I F K
Mukadam, H
Mulcahy, K A
Mulla, S C

Leigh

Muller, S
Munro, L M A
Murphy, R M
Mutimer, J E
Myint, S H
Naftalin, N J
Nana, A
Naqvi, S
Narang, R P
Narula, A A P
Nayani, S
Naylor, A R
Neilson, J R
Neuberg, K D
Neuberg, R W
Nevitt, G J
Newland, C J
Newley, K P
Newstead, P
Ng, G A
Ng, L L
Ngwu, U O
Nichani, S H
Nichol, F E
Nicholas, R C
Nicholls-Van Vliet, M A T
Nicholls, S J
Nicholson, M L
Nielsen, F
Nightingale, J M D
Nixon, M C
Noble, M D
Nolan, E M
Nour, S A E-R M
Nydahl, S
O'Brien, R J
O'Callaghan, C L
O'Callaghan, D J
O'Callaghan, M
O'Callaghan, P A
O'Carroll, T M
O'Connell, M A
O'Connor, N C
O'Connor, S R
O'Keeffe, D F
O'Reilly, K M
Offer, G J
Okundi, A J A
Oldham, R
Oldring, J K
Olson, E S
Oni, O O A
Oppenheimer, C A
Ormiston, I W
Osborn, D E
Osborne, J E
Osborne, N W
Osman, A E M
Ottey, D S
Page, J D
Palin, R D
Palmer, R L
Panacer, D S
Pancholi, P
Pandya, R P
Panja, K K
Panton, I R
Papageorgiou, G L
Pararajasingam, R
Parker, J L
Parker, M J
Parker, S G
Parker, S L
Parkin, A
Parmar, H P
Parry, J S
Partridge, F J
Parwaiz, P
Pasi, K J
Patchett, I D
Patel, B P
Patel, B D
Patel, D
Patel, G M
Patel, G D
Patel, I G
Patel, J K V
Patel, K K
Patel, M
Patel, P
Patel, P C
Patel, R
Patel, R N
Patel, R H
Patel, S
Patel, S S
Patel, V R
Pathak, P
Pathak, P L
Pathmanathan, R K
Pathy, H
Pattar, S M
Pavord, I D
Pavord, S R
Peake, M D
Pearson, J E
Peat, I M
Peek, G J
Pepper, M B
Pepperman, M L
Peters, S R
Peterson, M
Pettit, A I
Philpot, K S
Pickering, M A
Pigem Ricart, I
Pinson, K D
Piper, J A
Platts, P
Playford, E D
Playford, R J
Podas, T
Pohl, J E F
Porteous, L D
Poskitt, V J
Potter, J F
Power, C A
Power, R A
Pradhan, T A
Prasad, A
Preston-Whyte, M E
Prettyman, R J
Price, C M
Price, L D
Price, R J
Prideaux, C P
Prowse, G D W
Prydal, J I
Pugh, V W
Pulman, N R
Purdom, D J
Purnell, D
Purohit, S J
Pye, E M
Pye, I F
Quinn, M B
Quinton, D N
Rabbitt, C J
Rabey, P G
Rackham, K T
Rackham, M M
Radula Scott, T
Radvan, J
Raghavjee, I V
Rahman, M
Rai, J
Raitt, D G
Raja, A S
Rajakaruna, C S
Ralli, R A
Ramsay, D W
Range, S P
Ranpura, N
Raper, J A
Rashid, A
Ratan, D A
Rathbone, B J
Rathbone, G V
Rawson, T M S
Raymakers, R L
Rayner, J A
Read, C A
Read, M S
Redding, V J
Reddy, P
Redfern, S J
Redzisz, B
Reek, C
Rees, I W J
Reiman, G
Reuben, M J
Reveley, M A
Rhodes, A J
Richards, C J
Richards, D A
Richardson, S
Rickett, A B
Riedel, J A
Riisnaes, A M
Ring, S J
Ritchie, E C
Robb, A K
Roberts, N D
Robertson, G S M
Robertson, T C
Robinson, L O
Robinson, R J
Robson, F S
Rodgers, M
Rodgers, P M
Roper, P W
Rose, H M
Rosenthal, F D
Roshan, M
Ross, C
Rotchford, A P
Rothwell, K
Rowbotham, D J
Rowe, R E
Rowley, H A T
Roy, G A
Roy, S L
Roy, S
Rudd, G N
Ruddock, C J
Rushman, S C
Russell, I A
Russell, J A
Russell, W C
Russell, W S
Rutty, G N
Ryder, J J
Sabri, K
Saldanha, G S
Salkin, D S
Salt, M J
Samani, N J
Samanta, A K
Sammut, L M
Sandford-Smith, J H
Sandhu, D P S
Sandhu, P
Sansome, D A W
Sarvananthan, N
Saujani, V K T
Sayed, M A
Sayeed, A
Sayers, R D
Scarborough, N P
Schober, P C
Schofield, J
Scott, A D
Scott, K-A
Scott, S A
Scotton, J E
Scriven, J M
Scriven, S D
Self, J B
Sell, P J
Sellen, E M
Selwyn, D A
Senior, N M
Seth, H K
Shaffu, N G
Shafi, S
Shah, A
Shah, B J
Shah, P
Shah, Y B
Shahidullah, H
Shahidullah, M
Shanks, M P
Shannon, R S
Sharma, G K
Sharma, H K
Sharma, N-K
Sharma, R
Sharma, R
Sharma, S K
Sharma, V K O
Sharples, C A
Shaw, S N
Shawket, S A J
Sheehan, J
Sheerin, N S
Sheikh, M N
Sheikh, S A
Sheikh, S B
Sheldon, P J H S
Shepherd, D J
Shepherd, R J
Sher, K S
Sherriff, D
Sherwin, J D
Shikotra, B K
Shikotra, K K
Shinkwin, K R
Sian, S S
Siddiqui, F
Siddons, E M
Sil, S K
Silverman, M
Simpson, K
Simpson, M R
Simpson, N R W
Singh, H
Singh, K
Singh, P J
Singh, R
Singh, V K
Skehan, J D
Skoyles, J R
Sladden, M J
Slesser, B V
Slorach, J
Smart, J G
Smeeton, R J
Smith, G
Smith, G M
Smith, J T
Smith, S H
Solanki, P
Sosnowski, M A
Spaul, K A J
Sperry, T L H
Spooner, S M
Squire, I
Stanley, A G
Stastny, D
Stern, M A
Stern, M C
Stevens, M M
Steward, W P
Stewart, C R
Stewart, J A D
Stewart, K M
Stirton, R F
Stockton, G
Stoddart, P R
Stokes, T N
Stollery, N A
Stotter, A
Stoyle, T F
Stray, C M
Sturmer, H L
Sullivan, G H
Swales, J D
Swann, R A
Swift, P G F
Symonds, R P
Szemis, A H
Tagboto, S K
Tallon, C A
Talwar, S
Tamhne, R C
Tanna, A G
Tanna, R
Tanna, S A
Tansley, P D T
Taylor, D J
Taylor, G A
Taylor, G J S C
Taylor, J A
Taylor, M H
Taylor, R W
Taylor, S
Terry, T R
Thakor, R S
Theophilus, P
Theophilus, S W J
Thomas, A L
Thomas, E E
Thomas, I H
Thomas, M E
Thomas, N E
Thomas, O L
Thomas, P A
Thomas, R G
Thomas, R S A
Thomas, W M
Thompson, B M
Thompson, J P
Thompson, M M
Thomson, J R
Thomson, S
Thul, D M
Thurston, H
Tighe, K E
Tillotson, D M
Timmins, A J
Tomlinson, J D
Toomey, P
Torrance, A H
Trayner, J D
Trayner, J W
Trembath, R C
Triffitt, P D
Trivedi, H V
Trivedi, S H
Trotter, T N
Tsang, B
Tull, D
Tura, J E
Turner, R W
Turner, W D
Tweed, M J
Twigg, L J
Ubhi, S S
Vadgama, B
Vaghela, H K
Valentine, A A
Vallance, T R
Valmiki, V H
Vania, A-K
Varma, S K
Vass, A D
Venkatesh, V
Verma, S S S
Vijayakumar, N
Vindlacheruvu, M
Vlachou, P
Vyas, H D
Vyas, J R
Waldrum, C I
Wales, A T
Wales, J M
Walker, C A
Walker, R A
Walker, S R
Walters, C
Wandless, G M
Wandless, J G
Waraich, M K
Ward-Booth, S
Ward, A
Ward, D J
Ward, G L
Ward, K L
Ward, S C
Warner, R J
Warwick, G L
Waspe, S R
Watkin, E M
Watson, C
Watson, H J
Watson, P
Watt, F E
Webb, J S
Webster, S E
Wells, G R
Wells, J M
Wellstood-Eason, S P
Welsh, K R
West-Jones, J S
West, K P
Weston, P J
Whaley, K
Wheatley Price, N
Wheatley, T J
Wheeler, P C
White, S A
Whiteley, R
Whyte, C R
Whyte, J C
Wicks, A C B
Wildin, C J
Williams, B A
Williams, B
Williams, H D
Williams, M A
Williams, O E
Williams, S T
Williams, S C
Willmott, A M
Wills, A D
Wilson, A D
Wilson, L
Windle, R
Windsor, J
Winston, A P
Wiselka, M J
Witcomb, A H
Wohl, M A
Wolf, P A
Woltmann, G
Wong, J Y W
Wong, L S
Wong, M K Y
Wong, S B-S
Wood, J A
Wood, J K
Wood, K F
Woodbridge, S
Woodings, P L
Woodruff, G H A
Woods, K L
Woolford, M C D
Wordsworth, M T
Worlding, J
Wright, A J
Wright, J M
Wright, M J
Wyatt, R
Wynn-Williams, D L
Yeap, M L
Yong, D E J
Young, C D
Young, I D
Youngman, L M
Younie, M L A
Zickerman, A M
Zillwood, S J
Zirk, M H

Leigh

Babladi, M N
Baldeo, D
Bell, M S
Bottomley, J G H
Chan, C K C
Chau, S K H
Cottrill, M R B
Crompton, J L
Dongre, A S
Doublet-Stewart, M P H
Downes, R M
Fletcher, T S
Fox, S
Fulton, P
Geoghegan, S L
Hardcastle, P F
Hilton, R
Hindle, A T
Holbrook, M C
Horne, R J
Jha, B K
Kohen, D D
Lancaster, P S
Lewis, J L
Malik, A A
Mani, V
Martin, S M
Molajo, A O
Mottram, N P J
Osman, N M O
RamcHandani, M
Rathod, B K
Richardson, P S
Russell, J
Sasse, W M P
Thomas, A
Tomar, S S
Trivedi, D
Wardman, A G
Yan Aung, Dr
Yell, J A
Zadik, E

Leigh-on-Sea

Alawi, M H
Behn, A
Bevan-Jones, A B
Beverton, M J
Bowen, D R V
Bull, L A
Chalmers, J A
Craig, D H
Craig, M F
Craig, P J
Davids, C
Dickens, L A
Doshi, H V
Fasey, C N
Gretton, K L
Halls, G J
Hasan, S Y H
Hassaan, A M H
Hayter, A P
Hayter, N P
Henstridge, V J
Hodge, J-C
Hutson, A M
Idrees, F
Idrees, F
Jayatilaka, G K
Kemmerling, R
Kennedy, H R
Khakhar, A
Kongar, N
Latif-Puri, A A L
Levy, T L
McConnell, J
Malik, S A
Mills, M J
Nagle, L R
Ng, H W K
O'Flynn, D R
O'Neill, K S
O'Riordan, M D J T
Peters, G
Porter, J E
Rough, D P

Lincoln

Sathanandan, S
Singer, L
Sivaji, C
Soman, A
Sudlow, R A
Sutcliffe, N H
Tharmaratnam, J
Watkins, E P H
Williams, L J
Wise, L K
Woods, G T
Zaidi, S
Zaidi, S T A

Leighton Buzzard

Ambiavagar, I N
Bolton, T W
Burge, A J
Butteriss, M
Chapman, R G
Cochrane, T J D
Dry, F J
Dunford, G P
Evershed, E Z G
Ewart, J C
Fothergill, S M
Gibby, M J
Hacking, D F
Harding, R A
Henderson, J L
Hesford, S E
Jones, A M
Keeley, R
Kilpatrick, J W M
King, J M
Lane, T M
Lilley, J A
McHugh, F C
Meade, A M
Minney, P C
Owen, D R
Palmer, R D
Peel, E M
Plumb, M E
Povey, M S
Scudamore, J A
Shafi, M M
Shepherd, M S
Skinner, H L
Srinivasan, R
Stephens, B A F
Stone, M A
Sutton, H B
Taylor, B
Taylor, C L
Thompson, I W
Tunnadine, D E
Wallace, I M
Watkins, R P
Watkins, S E
Watts, E T
Wray, D G
Wright, J I

Leiston

Batson, E L
Doyle, L A
Hopayian, K
Jobson, D H
Mackenzie, M E T
Osler, K
Powell, B W

Leominster

Armitstead, M
Beard, R G
Bishop, E A
Bowen, G J
Boyles, D J
Cathcart, C
Crosland, S M G
Davis, M
Dubberley, J
Dubberley, R V
Fisher, C A H
Gaunt, K J
Gray, J D
James, W A
Jeffery, D G
Jenkins, I
Knight, A L
Knight, C J
McKean, C W F
Marshall, P F
Mathias, T G
Mortimer, J G M
Ovenden, P A
Ovenden, R N
Pritchard, J A
Rees, M P

Rees, R J
Reid, N B
Rerrie, J D
Stokes, J E T
Thompson, R M

Lerwick

Anderson, Y D
Brew, I F
Chalmers, A C
Clarke, G A
Cooper, A B
Coutts, A G
Coutts, E H A
Cox, F C
Farquhar, G
Freshwater, G T
Johnson, F J
McDonald, J
Miller, A R
O'Connor, P J
Porter, D V
Rarity, R A
Rodgers, E
Wilson, P

Letchworth

Adams, R M
Aldridge, F J
Aldridge, R P
Ashwood, C G
Boldy, J A R
Bond, A M
Boomers, G W M
Boomers, O W
Brooks, C A
Brugman, M J J
Celinski, M
Chand, R
Chu, H
Coker, T P
Day, S L
Faulkes, C N
Firth, J C
Forrester, R S
Fruithof, M H
Graham, R J O
Graham, S M
Hall, J D
Hamilton, A L
Hamilton, S A
Heelis, G
Hersey, J A
Irvine, N S
Jarvis, M A
Jaworski, W F
Judd, M B
Kanakaratnam, G
Kirby, M G
Langstaff, R J
Leigh, H A
Leigh, M
Lucas, V C
MacClancy, J R O C
Mason, R J
Nevard, R S C
Rahman, A F M S
Ramsbottom, T J
Rodger, A
Strowger, T B C
Tyler, G J
Walsh, J I
Webb, J B
Whalley, J
Wheatcroft, D J

Leven

Adam, C K
Ashcroft, L P
Barclay, D A
Bayne, S
Bisset, L G M
Bonde, K
Campbell, I W
Chalmers, T S
Christie, L C
Clark, J R
Courtney, H A
Cruickshank, I N
Cruickshank, R
Cumming, I M A
Cumming, R P A
Delaney, E K
Duncan, J A
Dunlop, R A
Dunn, R
Egerton, P J
Elliot, F M
Findlay, M G
Gibson, J H

Gough, A M
Grant, N M
Hay, T K
Hazelton, T L
Heap, A L
Ireland, H C
Keir, R D
Khaled, M A
Kilmurray, E J
Lee, C A
MacCrossan, W R
Macdonald, D
McDonald, M I
MacIntyre, P A
McLaren, G S
MacLean, A C
McLean, D F
McNair, S M D
Martin, L A
Mathewson, A M
Mills, G W
Morgan, J P B
Mukherjee, S
Murdoch, E G
Page, R M
Paterson, W G
Pattison, R B
Pringle, A F
Riddle, H F V
Robertson, A W
Robertson, J A
Rodger, S N G
Ross, J D
Ross, M T
Semple, T
Sinclair, D M
Sinclair, J M
Sinclair, M
Sloan, R L
Sneddon, A J C
Springer, A L C
Stevens, H M
Thomson, W J
Thrower, S M
Wallace, I
Ward, M J
Woolard, F E
Wyse, C T

Lewes

Allaway, A J
Arlett, P R
Ashby, P H
Baker, K F
Barnes, A P
Beasley, M J
Bennett, J
Bickler, G J
Birks, S F
Blake, H V
Blake, K E
Bray, B V H
Bridger, P C
Budleigh, M E
Caldwell, J R
Canavan, A C
Carey, J M
Carter, E J H
Clarkson, P
Claydon, P E
Collins, C A
Crean, E E
Dyson, M P L
Edmands, D F
Estcourt, P G
Evans, J A
Ferns, R A
Fine, E
Forster, E M
Foster, C J
Gillams, C L
Gooding, D J
Gough, K M
Green, E M
Grimston, A J
Gumpert, L C
Hall, R A
Hall, W D
Hargrave, C
Harrison, J R
Hawke, C I
Heanley, C L
Heap, D G
Heath, J A
Heath, M J
Hempshall, I N
Hill, J C
Hindley, J T
Hoque, S N

Horan, F T
Joce, R E
Jones, B E
Khan, Y
Knight, I J
Lamb, E F
Lamberty, J M
Laxton, C E
Lee, A B
Lucas, D J
McCarthy, G T
McGibben, L J
McGrigor, A B
Merritt, C L
Moon, C J
Moore, P N
Nicholson, H
O'Connor, B H
Ponsford, J M
Price, J S
Quin, C E
Ramsay Smith, S R
Randall, J M
Rashbrook, P S
Rees-Jones, A
Revell, E
Rice, M H C
Robinson, E K
Robson, J R
Ross, D
Ross, D W
Ross, R A
Rowland, R G
Ryan, A M
Rydon, A H B
Scanlon, T J P
Shave, P A
Shiel, J I
Simmons, J A
Stewart, L M
Street, M K
Strode, M
Swaine, C A
Swaine, D J
Taylor, P F
Thompson, M A
Thurston, K
Warren, R E
Way, B P J
Welsh, F K S
Williams, O A
Williams, P J

Leyburn

Botheroyd, E M
Brown, J M
Cole, C K
Coltman, K M D
Dawson, A M
Fox, C J
Gardner, R
Gray, M E S
Hall, M
Hoyle, H M
Irvine, A T
MacIntosh, K C
Riley, G A
Sephton, B L
Shuttleworth, H J
Verity, D W
Walker, G R
Wheatley, B
Wheatley, C J
Williamson, W

Leyland

Garg, K K

Lichfield

Allan, A
Baker, H B
Bird, R H
Bligh, A D M
Blundell, S J
Booth, D J
Bretland, C B
Brown, J R D
Brown, M A
Buxton, K M
Carson, A J B
Causer, M S E
Chung-Faye, G A
Cole, N C S
Collier, B R
Cook, A R
Cooper, P H
De, D
De, P P
De, P R
Evans, J

Fayed, G E A R
Fielding, E M P
Fielding, J W L
Game, F L
Gregory, P J
Griffiths, C I
Hackett, G I
Hallifax, L J
Harrington, L T
Harris, A R
Henshaw, R W
Herbert, T J
Huisman, G B
James, J D
Jones, B
Khan, M F
Khan, M T
Kuncewicz, I
Langdown, A J
Le Maistre, S
Lees, A W
Lockwood, C M
Longmore, C H
Lovell, H M
McDonald, R J
Millar, E L
Mohanna, K
Muller, E J
Newson, D C
O'Leary, C L
Pilkington, C J
Plant, I M
Rawle, D
Read, M Y
Rockett, J W
Saleem, M
Saleem, T
Sidaway, S F
Skanderowicz, A G
Southall, G J
Szamocki, J Z M
Tan, W M
Todd, E A
Varadarajan, R
Voice, E A
Webb, D M
Webb, T R
Wells, W D E

Lifton

Dyke, W R
Paterson, W
Sparrow, M A

Lightwater

Barnie-Adshead, R T
McFarlane, S M
Whitfield, A J
Wood, E V
Wood, J V

Limavady

Bicknell, M R
Callaghan, K A
Carson, R L
Day, T K
Devlin, B M
Devlin, D P
Donaldson, D P
England, E G
Farquharson, I K
Finlay, W P
Fulton, R A
Haire, T R
Harkin, D W
Heaney, G L
Henderson, M E
Hutchinson, D R
McCleery, W F
MacFlynn, E J
McIlmoyle, N A
McKenny, N V
McLaughlin, J A
McQuillan, B J
Magee, W H K
Mercer-Smith, N
Misra, B K
Roemmele, P M
Ryan, S S
Spratt, J S
Thompson, T J
White, R J

Lincoln

Abbas, B K
Abbas, E M
Adam, J F
Adelman, M I
Ahmed, I
Ajimoko, B A

Al-Ghonaimi, G S
Al-Kalai, D
Albuquerque, K V P
Ansari, S M
Ash, C E
Asirvatham, R
Asztalos, A L M
Atkins, P F
Atkinson, J M
Atkinson, R J
Attrup, M
Aubrey, S E
Backhouse, C A
Bakar, S J
Baker, M
Bali, B
Bali, H S
Barczak, P J N
Barczak, S M
Barker, S G
Barlow, A P
Barton, R C
Barton, S J
Batty, C J
Beden, R S
Beech, J
Beer, F D
Bell, S J
Bell, W A
Beswick, K C
Beswick, P N
Betts, J W
Bibby, S R
Binks, S E
Birch, E W G
Birch, J-A
Birch, P M
Birch, P S J
Blackbourn, M S
Blackbourn, R J
Bowater, R L
Bramble, D J
Breeson, A J
Brightman, C A J
Broughton, L J
Brown, C A
Burns, P R S
Butcher, H G H
Campbell, J R C
Carmichael, J R
Carty, M H
Carty, S M
Caruana, A
Catterall, E A
Chadderton, S
Chapman, P A
Chaudhary, B A
Chippington, S J
Clark, R
Clarke, H J M
Coffey, J F
Corcoran, J M
Craven, J R
Croft, K F
Curtis, M D
Delaki, E
Devonald, E J
Diffey, R F
Donaldson, A M
Donkin, B
Donnelly, J A
Drummond, P M
Dyer, I R
Edbrooke, J A
El-Hallaq, Y H M
Elgood, F R M
Elwood, P Y
Fallon, A M
Fallon, M E
Fansa, M A C
Fathers, E T
Fernley, C A
Firth, S H
Fisk, G G
Fowles, M W
Fox, E E
Freeman, K
Fussey, C E
Garry, J W
Ghaharian, K
Gibbs, J C
Glencross, J D
Gogan, M P
Golding, M J
Goldstein, H
Gough, G W
Goult, I
Graham, F M
Grant, D I

Lingfield

Greenhalgh, E A
Griffiths, A L
Griffiths, G J
Groggins, R C
Grundy, K N
Gwilliam, N J
Habib, S
Haigh, K M C
Hanson, K B L
Hardy, A
Hargreaves, M
Harkness, D G
Hartley, J L G
Heighway, J D
Hendrie, A
Hepburn, N C
Hinchcliffe, R J
Hindocha, L S
Hindocha, S
Hodge, B D
Hogg, S G
Horton, D
Hughes, G R
Huntley, J N
Hurst, A
Hutton, I M
Hyde, J D
ImmacUlate, M
Inder, G M
Jackson, E
Jakeman, N
Jenkins, K J
Jones, M E
Jones, M W
Kaar, J D W
Kamath, V
Kasi, A G
Kennedy, D H
Kerr, W
Khatib, S N
Kucyi, M D
Kunzemann, M
Kutarski, A A
Lacy, I R
Lamb, M P
Lamerton, A J
Lansdall-Welfare, R W
Latham, M J
Layton, S A
Leach, S
Leeper, K C
Lennon, M M
Lewins, I G
Li Wan Po, G L T N
Locker, M
Logendran, M
Loosmore, S J
Lough, T A M
Lunn, J M
McCafferty, J B
McClemont, E J W
McClemont, J M F
Mcdonald, B J
McFeeters, J I
McGowan, M B
Mack, P
McLoughlin, J G
Maclure, W A
McManners, T
McRae, A R
Magee, M A
Mahalingam, M
Mallett, S A
Mallett, V A
Manandhiar, L D
Morris, S L
Matusiewicz, S P
Maughan, E H
Mehta, T B S
Mendel, L
Millns, C P
Mithal, A
Morris, E W
Moulsdale, P A B
Munro, D E
Murjan, A R
Murjan, S M
Napier, J G
Nattrass, J J
Nicholl, G M J
Nouri-Dariani, E
O'Brien, T M
O'Donoghue, M M
O'Dwyer, C A
O'Grady, T J
O'Kelly, R M
Oakford, A C
Ojo, O E
Owen, G O

Pack, M Y A-M
Parker, J L W
Parkin, J L
Parsons, P A
Paterson, I C
Paxton, A G
Pearson, B J
Perry, C A G
Petherbridge, S P
Phillips, D C
Pillay, J G
Pirzada, B-U-I
Pirzada, O M
Pontin, A J
Porter, M C B
Powles, A B
Protheroe, M C
Protheroe, S A
Pyrgos, N
Pyrgos, V
Qureshi, A H
Qureshi, M Z
Ramon, A J
Rawden, A M
Rea, A J
Reasbeck, P G
Reeves, D M
Reynolds, A D
Richards, A A
Richardson, M
Robbins-Cherry, A M
Roxby, C M
Sadler, A G
Saggiorato, J J
Saleh, F M M
Scammell, A M
Scarisbrick, D A
Scott, B B
Scott, D G
Scott, J A
Scott, R B
Shahrizaila, N
Shanks, W
Shariatmadari, M E
Sharpe, G A
Sheehan, T M
Shewan, D M
Sidahmed, K M
Singh, J
Siriwardena, A N
Smith, B D
Smith, D I A
Smith, R N E
Smith, R P R
Somers, H B A
Sood, V B
Sowerby, R
Standley, D M
Stewart, J O R
Stratton, P
Sturton, P R
Tekriwal, A K
Thava, V R
Thompson, A E
Thompson, M E
Thomson, J D R
Thornton, R J
Thorpe, G W
Thurkettle, A J
Tse, S C Y
Tyler, C K G
Vega, E J
Velaudapillai, C P
Vellacott, I D
Victoria, B A
Wade, J K
Wallace, J G
Waller, D H
Waller, S L
Wallis, T D
Walter, S
Ware, C C
Watson, A T
Watts, T
Webb, A M
Wheatley, M
Whitbread, L
White, D F A
White, J H M
Whitlow, W W
Wilkie, M
Wilkinson, J M
Wilson, J D
Wilson, R J
Wilson, R P
Wood, D A
Wood, M J
Woulds, M
Wright, B E M

Youngs, E R
Zacharia, A Y

Lingfield

Allen, F J
Cliffe, P A H
Francis, I S
Gardner, J E
Harrison, J C
Hills, D G M
Lawson, W L
Magauran, P S
Marshman, L A G
Noble, S I R
Northen, M E
Robertson, A J
Rose, W J M
Stone, B
Whittaker, D J
Wright, H M E

Linlithgow

Ahmed, M
Boyle, M F
Boyle, N J
Brockway, M S
Cawood, T J
Cochran, D F M
Davie, J M
Fitzgerald, A J
Fleming, C J
Fulton, C S
Gray, J K M
McCallum, C A
McGhee, A R
McIntyre, A D
McKechnie, A A
MacKenzie, K W
McLauchlan, G J
McLay, C K A
McMain, T S
McNab, J M
Mickel, D R
Millar, E D
Morley, A D
Orr, T A
Peters, S E
Ramsay, S G
Ratcliffe, H D
Robertson, K J
Scotthorne, A W
Scothorne, R J
Sengupta, F R
Sengupta, T K
Smart, H E
Swinton, S M
Wardall, G J
Wood, S

Liphook

Aylwin, S J B
Barrett, J A
Berry, D J
Bore, J T
Burton, J
Hardwick, J C H
Hardwick, R J
Hayes, S A
Holwill, S D J
Jackson, W F M
Jenkins, D G
Landes, A H L
Neville-Towle, A
O'Reilly, K A
Pullan, C W A
Rice, M
Richardson, J
Rushton, B E A
Van Der Most, R N

Lisburn

Anderson, H M
Anderson, N W
Archbold, J A L
Armstrong, M J
Atkinson, A B
Baird, A E
Balnave, K
Baxter, A E
Beers, H T B
Best, J L
Bolleddula, K P
Boydell, L R
Brown, E F
Bryars, J H
Bryars, N E
Bunn, R T N
Cairns, I R
Calvert, G J
Campbell, C I

Campbell, N S
Campbell, W J
Carlisle, R P
Carragher, A M
Carson, M P
Chadwick, L
Chambers, W E
Chapman, N
Chidrawar, U M
Clenaghan, S D
Close, M E
Collins, J S A
Cormack, E C
Cowan, M G B
Curran, F M
Curry, P M
Daly, O E
Davis, A
Davis, R M W
Deacon, J M M
Dean, B E
Devaney, N M
Doherty, T P
Elder, O P P M
Eyre, E C
Finch, M B
Fleming, B
Gilpin, G N
Gleadhill, I C L
Goodman, A M
Gordon, F C
Graham, L E
Grahame-Smith, H N
Gray, M N
Hamill, D I W
Hare, A C
Harrison, L W
Hegarty, J E
Henderson, H J
Henry, J S R L
Holmes, S M
Hrabovsky, A
Huey, B R T
Humphrey, C A
Huss, B K D
Hutchinson, P D
Ireland, B J
Irwin, A G H
Jefferson, H A
Johnston, S R
Johnston, S E
Jose Thampi, C M
Kirkwood, J A
Knox, S G
Lawton, N R
Lindsay, H S T
Loan, W B
Logan, G
Logan, K R
Love, A M
Lowe, D C
McAlister, J C
McAuley, R T
McBrien, J J S
McClean, H J M
McCloskey, E V
McConnell, E M
McCullough, G W
McCullough, S R
MacDonald, S F
McFarland, D
McIlmoyle, E L
McKeown, A J P
McKeown, M E
McLean, D S
McNeill, A
Malcomson, C I
Martin, G L
Martin, J N
Martin, R E
Mathewson, J S Y
Mawhinney, I N
Mayes, C B D
Meban, C
Milliken, C R
Monaghan, C A
Moore, S
Murray, D
Myles, T J M
Neagle, W B
Nutt, A E C
O'Hanlon, J J
O'Neill, M J
O'Neill, S B
Palmer, R M
Patterson, A H
Patterson, M R
Patterson, S C A
Patterson, W R M

Porter, F J
Pratt, K
Press, J R
Primrose, W J
Quigley, C N
Ramsey, A S
Richardson, R P
Robb, K H
Rodgers, C J
Ruddell, M A
Russell, C M
Sands, S L
Shorten, W W J
Soong, C V
Stanfield, S M
Stanley, J C
Stevenson, J H
Stewart, H J
Turner, L M
Turner, R C
Urey, M R
Wales, I F H
Walker, J M
Walker, T S J
Walmsley, A E
Watson, F L
Weir, J M P
White, A J
White, J B
Wilson, J D
Wilson, R A
Wilson, R R
Wright, S A
Yarr, J E
Young, G I
Zafar, A

Liskeard

Auckland, G D
Cater, E V
Coad, W M
Critchley, J
Eardley, R A A
Eddy, J H
Fagg, C G C
Hainsworth, E
Hargadon, D J
Hart, R D C
Haward, M W A
Holmes, J C S
Jackson, D F
Jefferies, S B
Kneebone, C A
McCartney, M R
Macfarlane, J L
Massey, M R
Milton-Thompson, G J
O'Leary, D R
Paxton, R M
Piper, A R
Ronchetti, M G
Smalley, A D
Smerdon, G H
Sneyd, F M C
Thornton, C M B
Tibbitt, E A
Toms, G R
Tyler, J A
Ussher, J H
Wiseman, H G
Wood, P H N

Liss

Bevan, J R
Cairns, A W
Craig-McFeely, P M
Edwards, C S
Egelstaff, S J
Egerton, D C
Hennelly, M F
Ker, J W
Mackie, A P
O'Leary, C F
Panton, D J
Sedgwick, J R
Selby, L M P
Willatt, I D
Willatt, R A J

Littleborough

Boardman, J
Brazier, D T
Chew, R
Frost, S K
Gordon, D
Hopkinson, M E
Judah, M J
McCarthy, J P
O'Hare, T J
Penrose, A J

Sen, P K
Sidhu, S S
Thakor, S B
Walton, N
Weston, J C

Littlehampton

Anderson, B L
Arthur, G W
Atkinson, T D
Bach, C D
Barrett, J W V
Beeching, Y G H
Bowen, M
Brown, C K
Burch, J E P
Burcombe, D R
Bush, P K D
Butcher, P M
Butt, R P
Byars, G K
Chandrarajan, C S
Coulthard, M
Critchfield, T O
Davies, T A
De Silva, V G
Deans, J S
Denner, J A
Denton, M B
Dey, A C
Diack, J I D
Eastwood, J J H
Farrer-Brown, D
Gerard, S W
Gibbons, L A
Greenwood, J
Handley, D J
Harland, M
Harrison, A J
Hart, G R
Hart, S R
Higgins, P C
Kimber, T J
Kingsbury, A W
Liston, M P
Lovell, P
Lovell, R A
McClean, E G
Mackenzie, D Y
McLeod, D W
Magson, C R
Miller, M R D
Morgan, W
Neild, P J
Oliver, J
Owen, P F B
Pallis, D J
Phillips, T
Plagaro Cowee, S
Rail, J F W
Richards, G
Roberts, R E
Shipsey, M M
Shipsey, M M A
Shore, J H
Stapleton, G A G
Storey, J L
Taylor-Roberts, M G W
Tilley, E J
Walsh, J M M
Walsh, S J M
Warriner, R M
Weinbren, H K
Williams, D G
Williams, S
Wiseman, C E
Wiseman, M
Withers, D J
Wright, S J

Liverpool

Abang Mohammed, D K
Abbott, P M
Abdu, S A M
Abdul Salam, S
Abdulmajid, S A H
Abernethy, L J
Abraham, V V
Acharya, S P
Adab, N
Adisesh, L T
Agarwal, R P
Agius-Fernandez, A
Ah-Fat, F G
Ah-Weng, A
Ahmad, B
Ahmad, R
Ahmado, A R

Liverpool

Ahmed, I
Ahmed, I
Ahmed, N
Ahmed, P R
Ainley, N J
Akhter, H
Al-Janabi, M A M
Alam, M I
Alawattegama, A B
Albert, E G
Albert, P S
Aldridge, S A
Alexander-White, S
Alexander, J L
Ali, S I
Allmand, C A
Allsup, D J
Allwright, G J
Almond, D S
Alty, H M
Alty, M
Amadi, A
Amin, R
Ammir, T F E R
Ananthakrishna Rao, A
Andersen, J A
Anderson, R J
Andrews, M C
Andrews, S J
Angus, R M
Anson, J J
Antal, L C
Anthony, K
Appleton, E J
Appleton, R E
Armstrong, A M
Armstrong, J
Armstrong, K M
Armstrong, R
Arora, P
Arora, R M
Arunachalam, N
Arya, E C
Arya, R P
Asher, R G
Ashok Kumar, J M
Ashton, J R
Ashworth, F L
Askari, S H
Askham, R N H
Aspinall, D J
Atherton, L A
Atkins, P
Atlay, R D
Attwood, M
Au, P W H
Avann, H J
Awi, M M
Aziz, N F
Azurdia, R M
Backhouse, J E
Baderin, A A
Baig, M A A
Bainbridge, E A
Baines, P B
Baird, M A
Bajaj, R K
Bajaj, R K
Bajaj, V
Baker, A
Bakran, A
Ball, A R
Ballantyne, E S
Bamber, M J
Barclay, G A
Barclay, P M
Barker, C
Barlow, C
Barnes, E J L
Barnes, N A
Barnes, R C
Barnes, S N
Barnett, L E
Barnett, R N
Baron, M
Barpujari, V
Barrett, P J
Barry, M G
Barry, P
Barton-Hanson, N G
Barton, P D
Barton, S B
Basu, R
Bate, S L
Bates, C M
Bateson, A
Bateson, P M
Batra, N
Batra, R P

Batterbury, M
Baxter, S T
Bayley, T J
Beacon, S
Beattie, C H
Beattie, J K
Bebb, C E
Beckett, P
Beddow, F H
Beeching, N J
Behbehani, A M
Bell, C H
Bell, G M
Bell, H K
Bennett, A J
Bennett, S P
Bentley, J T
Beresford, M W
Bergel, E
Bevan, G P
Bhushan, V
Bickerstaffe, W E
Billingham, I S
Billingsley, P
Birch, J C
Birch, M
Birchall, E W
Birley, H D L
Bishop, L A
Bishop, S E
Biswas, A
Blackburn, D J
Blackie, D M
Blakeborough, J L
Bligh, J G
Bliss, J L
Bode, D
Boggild, M D
Bolton-Maggs, P H
Bond, C D
Bone, J M
Booker, P D
Boon, R L J
Boothroyd, A E
Bose, S C
Bosma, J
Bowden, A N
Bowers, S G
Bowhay, A R
Bowsher, D R
Box, D E O C
Boyars, L
Boyce, R P
Boyd, I M
Boyle, W J
Brabbins, C J
Brabin, B J
Bracey, A P
Bradley, M G
Bradley, P
Bradshaw, H D
Brady, J A
Brady, O H G
Breakell, A
Brearley, R
Breckenridge, A M
Brennan, J A
Brett, A S
Brewster, J A
Brice, D D
Briggs, M C
Briggs, P E
Brigham, S A
Brindley, A J
Brinksman, H J
Broadbent, D M
Brodbelt, A R
Bromilow, A
Brook, L A
Brookes, M R
Brown, A B
Brown, J S
Brown, J W
Brown, R E
Brown, R
Brownson, P
Bruce, C E
Bruce, L B
Bruce, N G
Brunton, J N
Bryson, J R
Bucknall, R C
Bundred, P E
Bunn, J E G
Burdett-Smith, P
Burke, A G
Burke, U B
Burnham, P R
Burns, J

Burns, L S
Burns, M S
Burra, V S M
Burrow, C T
Burrows, P
Buse, P
Butcher, C K
Butler, I G
Butterell, H C
Byrne, I M
Byrne, M F
Byrne, W
Caldwell, J
Callaghan, J M
Callaghan, M
Callaghan, T A
Callow, D M
Calverley, P M A
Campbell, F
Campbell, J
Campbell, J A
Campion, P D
Cantarini, M V
Canter, A K
Capewell, S J
Carey, P B
Carlton, E A
Carmichael, J H E
Carroll, N S
Carroll, R
Carter, E R
Carter, J M
Carter, N J
Cartwright, J L
Carty, A T
Carty, H M L
Cashen, J A
Cashin, R J
Cassimer, S S
Casson, I F
Caswell, M
Cavadino, A
Cave-Bigley, D J
Cavendish, M E
Cawley, J C
Chadwick, D W
Chakrabarti, B
Chan, A C S
Chan, A T Y
Chan, M C K
Chan, R K-Y
Chandrashekhar, M N
Chapman, L J
Chapman, R
Charles, R G
Charters, P
Chater, N C
Chatterjee, S
Chaudhury, G B
Chaudhury, M
Chawla, N K
Cheesbrough, M F
Cheetham, C
Cheng, K Y M
Cheong, B Y C
Chester, M R
Cheung, W K C
Chisnall, D P
Chitkara, D K
Chiu, Y S
Choudhary, P
Chow, T W P
Choy, L S A
Chu Chi-Mai, P
Chua, H B
Chung, K O
Chung, T T
Church, E N
Clague, J E
Clancy, M J
Claria-Olmedo, M J
Clark, A R
Clark, D I
Clark, D J
Clark, M A
Clark, R E
Clarke, K W
Clarke, M A
Clarke, R W M
Clarkson, J D
Clayton, G S
Clewes, A R
Clifford, J M
Coady, A M
Coady, D A
Cobner, P G
Cockburn, J J
Cohen, A
Cohen, M

Coleman, J M
Coleman, N A
Coleman, N H
Collins, J D
Collinson, I B F
Colville, L J
Comas, A
Condillac, D L
Connelly, D T
Connolly, C M
Connolly, J K
Connolly, M R
Conroy, T A
Conway, A
Conway, M P
Cook, G R
Cook, R C M
Cooke, R W I
Corcoran, G D
Corke, P J
Cornford, P A
Corrigan, G A
Costigan, K J
Coulshed, N
Coulter, J B S
Couriel, J M
Cowan, C M
Cowlard, J D
Craig, S V
Cranney, M
Crawford, L
Crawford, M J
Crawford, N P S
Crawford, V H
Crooke, J W
Crooke, J W
Crosby, S J
Cross, J S
Crowder, S W
Croy, M F
Cruickshank, A H
Cuckson, A C
Cuddihy, P J
Cullen, S P
Cunliffe, M
Cunliffe, N A
Cunningham, N
Curpen, N C
Curran, N C
Currer, M
Currie, S L
Cuthbert, J A
Dainty, C
Dale, R F J
Daley, A J
Dalzell, A M
Damato, B E
Dangerfield, P H
Daniel, J R
Dar, M A
Darabshaw, G S
Darcy, A E
Darcy, C M
Darcy, P F
Darcy, Y A
Darla, S R
Das, A
Das, B
Davenport, S A
Davidson, D C
Davidson, E G
Davidson, N C
Davies, E J
Davies, M W
Davies, P D O
Davis, A J M
Davis, A H
Davis, J
Davis, R J N
De Caluwe, D
De Matas, M
Dempster, I A
Denny, C M
Derringer, E W
Desai, S K
Desmond, A D
Desmond, M J
Devaney, J Y
Devine, A
Devoy, M A B
Dewar, C M
Dhorajiwala, J M
Diab, M A
Diack, A M
Dickinson, P S
Didi, M A
Dihmis, W C
Dilworth, A
Disley, R

Dixon, J L
Dixon, M S
Djabatey, E A
Dobson, C M
Dobson, N U
Dodd, R J
Dodson, M E
Dominic, M A
Donnell, S C
Donnelly, C V
Donnelly, M T
Doran, C L
Doran, M
Dorgan, J C
Dougan, C F
Douglas, J
Dove, W L
Dover, O
Dovey, H
Downie, R J G
Dowrick, C F
Doyle, A M
Drakeley, A J
Drakeley, M J
Drury, P M E
Duckenfield, F M
Duerden, M G
Duffield, D P
Duffy, M F
Dunsby, E
Eardley, N J
Earis, J E
Early, K
Eccles, D R
Edirisinghe, D N
Edwards, P R
Edwards, W M
Edynbry, K D
Egan, G P
El-Jassar, R P
El-Sayed, F E H
Eldridge, J A
Eldridge, P R
Ellershaw, J E
Elliott, M
Ellis, A
Ellis, I H
Ellis, P M
Emmott, M N
Enevoldson, T P
Ensor, J M
Entwistle, A N
Epstein, A C R
Epstein, G A
Ervine, I M
Estlin, E J
Evans, B M
Evans, C C
Evans, E M
Evans, F M
Evans, F I
Evans, I M
Evans, J
Evans, K J
Evans, M D
Evans, R C
Evans, R A
Evans, S
Evans, T R
Exley, D
Fabri, B
Faint, D
Fang, C S J
Farquharson, R G
Farrington, G A
Fazlani, N A
Feld, M S
Fewins, H E
Finch, L D
Finlay, I G
Finn, R
Fish, B M
Fisher, R K
Fiske, A P
Fitzgerald, B
Flanagan, D M
Flattery, P J
Fletcher, L
Fletcher, N A
Flett, H I
Florence, A M
Fook, L J
Forbes, A M W
Ford, C D
Fordham, S E
Forrest, J M
Forshaw, J W B
Forster, A
Forsyth, H G M

Forsyth, L J
Fosdyke, N A
Foster, C S
Foster, J E
Fountain, M A
Fox, M A
Foy, P M
Frais, M M
Francombe, J
Franks, R E
Fraser, B J
Fraser, W D
Freeman, K B N
Frostick, S P
Fryer, A E
Gadhvi, B
Gadhvi, D
Gaier, S
Gallagher, C
Galloway, R W
Galloway, S W
Galtrey, A C
Gama, J G
Garden, A S
Gardner, K A
Garner, P A
Garnett, C A
Garvey, C J
Gauthier, J-B M
Gaze, B I
Gedman, J K
George, A
Gerg, R K
Ghorbal, M M S
Ghose, S L
Gibson, H
Gibson, M G
Gibson, N E
Gibson, P J
Gibson, S P
Gilbertson, A A F
Gilchrist, I R
Giles, A A
Gill, G V
Gill, H
Gilles, H M J
Gillespie, C
Gilling-Smith, G L
Gilmore, I T
Gilmour, J
Gipson, M
Glennon, J E A
Goddard, M L
Godfrey, J J
Goel, Y K
Goenka, G
Goenka, N
Goffman, H L
Gok, M A
Gold, E N
Goldberg, I J L
Goldman, A J
Goldrein, S H J
Goldsmith, D H
Goldsmith, H J
Goldstone, J
Gomes Deraniyagala, G B
Gonsalves, J V
Gonzalez-Martin, J A
Good, A M T
Goodman, B E
Goodman, M
Goonatilleke, M D A P
Gordon, I J
Gore, D M
Gosney, J R
Gosney, M A
Gould, D A
Goulden, M R
Govan, A J
Govardhan Das, K
Gow, J G
Gradden, C W
Graham, I F M
Graham, J C
Gray, I C M
Green, G B
Green, L E
Greenfield, P J
Gregg, J E M
Gregson, J M
Gregson, P N
Grey, P
Griffiths, E M
Griffiths, G E
Griffiths, J M
Griffiths, P M
Griffiths, R D

Liverpool

Grossman, M L
Gunstone, A J
Gupta, P L
Gupta, R L
Gupta, R
Gupta, S K
Guy, J M
Habib, K
Hackett, S J
Hadcroft, J
Haddock, A W
Hadji, F
Haines, J R
Haji Misbak, N
Halabi, S
Haley, C J
Hall, H D
Hallworth, D
Halstead, G M
Hamad, S A K M
Hamilton, E M
Hamilton, J
Hammad, A-E-K S A-E K
Hammond, C
Hanafi, Z
Hankin, T
Hanratty, B
Haqqani, M T
Haque, Q M
Hardie, J E
Hardie, J
Harding, C
Harding, D
Harding, M J
Harding, N
Harding, S P
Hardy, G P S
Hargreaves, F T
Harkins, K J
Harley, A
Harley, J S
Harper, N P A L
Harper, S J
Harrington, Y M
Harris, L
Harris, P C
Harris, P L
Harrison, C B
Hart, C A
Hart, G
Hart, I K
Hartley, J L
Hartley, M N
Harvey, G
Harvey, V A
Harwood, E J
Hasham, F M
Hattaway, B M
Hawkes, D J
Haworth, D E
Haworth, E
Hayes, C F
Hayes, S C
Hayward, M
Hayward, P B
Head-Rapson, A G
Heaf, D P
Healy, B J
Heath, J G
Heatley, M K
Hedge, R N
Hehar, S S
Helliwell, T R
Hennessy, E P
Herrero, J R
Herrington, C S
Hershman, M J
Hewitt, D B D
Hewitt, J
Heyes, J M
Hibbert, W K
Higgie, C B
Higgie, M R
Hill, J W
Hill, S R
Hillman, J
Hillman, S
Hind, C R K
Hirsch, M
Hiscott, P S
Hitch, B M
Ho, V W C
Hobbs, W J C
Hodder, R J
Hoddes, C E
Hoddes, J A
Hoddes, S H
Hodgson, C A

Hogan, J
Holcombe, C
Holemans, J A
Holland, M J
Holland, M A J
Holme, V E
Honey, G E
Hornung, R S
Horton, W A
Hossain, M M
Hough, J A
Houghton, R P
Houghton, T A
Howard, C V
Howard, E C
Howard, H L
Howitt, R J
Hoyen-Chung, E G
Hoyle, H V
Hubbard, A J
Hubbert, C M
Hughes, B
Hughes, D A
Hughes, D M
Hughes, D O
Hughes, D W
Hughes, I W
Hughes, J H
Hughes, M I
Hughes, P J
Humphrey, P R D
Humphriss, B E
Hung, C C
Hunn, M K
Hunt, A L S
Hunukumbure, S B
Hussain, J A
Hussain, S M
Hussain, S
Hussain, T
Hussey, J A
Hussey, R M
Hyde, S W
Ibreck, R F
Inkster, G D G
Innes, C F
Iqbal, D S
Iqbal, J
Irving, I J
Jabeen, Z
Jack, C I A
Jackson, C J
Jackson, C T
Jackson, S R
Jacobs, V J L
Jaffey, L H
James, D
Jameson, F M
Jameson, P P M
Jameson, R M
Jane, M J
Jaques, A E
Jardine, J V
Jayson, S J
Jeanrenaud, P
Jeffreys, R V
Jennings, L
Jesudason, G R R
Johnson, P P
Johnson, S R
Johnston, B M
Johnston, J H
Johnstone, M J
Johnstone, M W
Johnstone, S A
Jones, A G H
Jones, A G
Jones, A S
Jones, A S
Jones, A F
Jones, C A
Jones, C A
Jones, D C
Jones, N E B
Jones, P L
Jones, R G
Jones, T D
Jones, W A
Joseph, J V
Journeaux, S F
Judd, B A
Judge, B P
Judge, G J
Judge, J
Jukka, C M
Kadzombe, E A M
Kalinsky, S
Kan, S M
Kapoor, V

Karmakar, M K
Kehoe, A
Keidan, M
Kelly, J E
Kelly, J M
Kemp, G J
Kennedy, C P
Kent, D L
Kent, M J
Kenyon, R M
Kerr, A R
Kerrigan, D D
Kewley, M
Kewn, D
Keyser, A T
Khan, J A
Khan, S
Khan, Z
Khera, G
Kidd, B C
Kidd, M
Killingley, B M
King, S J
Kingsland, C R
Kingston, R E
Kinloch, L C
Kinloch, P M
Kinloch, T S
Kinn, D R
Kinnersley, A
Kirkland, N B
Kirkman, J L
Kirkpatrick, U J
Kirwan, M
Kishan Rao, V
Knight, M F
Knight, P F
Knowles, I
Koh, C S V
Kong, S-M
Koper, M
Kothari, H P
Krasner, N
Krasner, N I
Kumar, A
Kumar, S
Kumar, S A
Kumar, V
Kuruvilla, G
Kwok Chai Sum, A
Kyle, G M
Lahiri, M
Lakhani, D N
Lalloo, D G
Lamb, G H R
Lamont, G L
Lamplugh, G
Large, C M B
Lau Yee-Lam, E
Lawrence, A
Lawrenz, K
Leach, J P
Lecky, B R F
Ledson, J F
Ledson, M J
Lee, E S-H
Lee, Y C
Lees, H
Lemmens, F M
Lennon, K J
Leonard, D
Lesser, T H J
Levy, E
Levy, F
Levy, M L
Levy, M L
Levy, M
Levy, S B
Lewis-Jones, C M
Lewis-Jones, D I
Lewis-Jones, H G
Lewis, D K
Lewkonia, R M
Leyland, M C
Lezama, M J
Li, D
Libman, M
Lightfoot, I J
Lim, H L
Lim, K C
Lim, K H
Lipkin, N E
Lister, R K
Littlewood, A H M
Littlewood, C M
Lloyd-Jones, G H
Lloyd-Jones, W
Lloyd, D A
Lloyd, E A

Lo, K W
Lock, J D T
Lofthouse, C M
Loftus, T
Lombard, M G
Losty, P D
Loughrey, J D
Lowe, P L
Lubman, D I
Luck, S E
Lund, C E
Lwin, K
Lwin, M K-K
Lye, M D W
Lynch, M C
Lynn, K L
Lythgoe, M W
Maassarani, H A
McBrien, A
McCahy, H J
McCarthy, K
McConnell, R B
McConnell, W
McCormick, M S
McCrossan, L A
McCrossan, P J
McCullagh, W D
McCulloch, P G
McCutcheon, M R
McDonald, P A
McDowell, D K
McDowell, H P M
McElroy, C A
McEvoy, A W
McFadyen, I R
MacFarlane, I A
McFarlane, X A
McGalliard, J N
McGettigan, C P
McGibbon, C
McGowan, P H
Macherianakis, A
Machin, D G
Machin, P L
McKay, J A
McKean, C D
Mackean, J M
Mackean, W M
McKelvie, K P
McKendrick, C S
McKendrick, H M
McKendrick, O M
McKendrick, T
Mackenzie, A J
McKernan, C
Mackie, C R
Mackinnon, A G
Macleod, A I
McLoughlin, G A
McLoughlin, K C
McLoughlin, P L
McLoughlin, R
McMenamin, M
McMinn, M R
McNamara, P S
McNulty, S J
McQuail, P A
McQuillan, S
Macrae, F M H
McVicar, J T
McVicker, J T
Madanayake, S K
Magennis, D A
Magennis, J P M
Maher, B
Maher, S J
Mair, F S
Maitra, S
Majeed, F A A
Malik, D R
Mallaiah, S
Mallucci, C L
Malpas, C E
Mangan, S A
Manley, A F
Manley, S M
Mannar, R
Manning, E M C
Marchant, M K
Marchment, A H C
Marsh, D M
Marsh, I B
Marshall, A G
Marson, A G
Marson, K L
Martin, L
Martin, R M
Martindale, A
Martindale, J H

Martlew, V J
Masip Oliveras, T
Maskrey, N
Massey, R R
Mathie, A G
Matthews, T P
Mattison, H
Maudsley, G
Mawdsley, T
Mawson, S L
May, P L
Mehta, M N
Mehta, R K
Meldrum, D
Melrose, W
Melville, C A S
Mendick, M
Menton, J P
Menzies, D N
Mercer, N P
Messing, Z R
Metcalfe, J W
Metcalfe, K A
Metcalfe, P
Metcalfe, R M
Middleman, M J
Milford, C D
Miller, A S
Miller, B M
Miller, C M
Miller, D H
Mills, K G
Mimnagh, A P
Minn Lwin, Dr
Mintz, B J
Misra, N
Mitchell, S L
Mohamed, A H
Mohammed, A A
Mohanan, K S
Molokhia, M
Moloney, D T
Moloney, D M
Monk, C J E
Monk, D A
Montefiore, M R
Montgomery, S C
Montgomery, S H
Mooney, P J
Moore, A P
Moore, B J
Moore, E W
Moore, K S
Moores, C
Moots, R J
Moran, B P
Moreton, P
Morgan, R
Morris, A I
Morris, A L R
Morris, J
Morrison, C L
Morrison, I M
Morrison, W L
Morriss, R K
Morton, S H
Moss, C I
Mostafa, S M
Mugglestone, S J
Mullen, P F
Mullett, H S
Mullett, S S
Mullin, M S
Mullin, T
Mullins, P A
Mulukutla, R D
Munro, M A
Muogbo, J C
Murphy, J
Murphy, M
Murphy, M E
Murphy, N D
Murphy, P E
Murray, G H
Murray, J J A
Murugananthan, N
Murugananthan, N
Musadiq, M
Muthu, S
Mutton, K J
Myerscough, E G
Nagpal, I S
Naik, J N
Najm-Tehrani, N
Nakhuda, Y E
Nash, J R G
Nash, J A
Nash, T P
Navaneetharajah, N

Nayagam, S
Nayak, G P
Nayak, P R
Naylor, K P
Neal, T J
Needham, A D
Neill, M P
Neilson, J P
Nelki, J S
Nelson, A P
Neoptolemos, J P
Newman, J H
Newsham, J A
Newson, M P
Newstone, J
Nicolaides, P
Nielsen, H J
Nightingale, D A
Niven, S D
Nolan, J
Noland, D J
Noonan, C P
Norman, A E
Nurmikko, T J
Nye, F J
O'Brien, C G
O'Brien, D J
O'Brien, L S
O'Brien, M J
O'Brien, P J
O'Brien, T G
O'Callaghan, C A
O'Connell, N M
O'Connor, A
O'Connor, B D
O'Donnell, J F
O'Donnell, M J
O'Dowd, G M
O'Gorman, M
O'Grady, E A
O'Hanlon, C
O'Hara, D P
O'Leary, M A
O'Malley, A G
O'Neill, J M
O'Neill, M B E
O'Neill, P B
O'Riordan, J E G
O'Shea, P J
O'Sullivan, D G
O'Sullivan, S M
O'Toole, H L
O'Toole, P A
Ochefu, O A
Odogu, K K
Oelbaum, S
Ogden-Forde, F E
Ogden, D J
Ogilvie, C M
Okhah, M
Ooi, K H
Oppenheim, A I
Orlans, D A
Orlans, M
Orme, N J
Oshinowo, O S
Osman, H M
Over, K E
Owen, A W M C
Owen, N C W
Owens, A S
Owens, P M
Page, R D
Pai, V P
Palejwala, A A
Palejwala, R
Palmer, S L
Palwala, A J
Pande, S K
Pande, S K
Pang, L
Panton, R W
Parfrey, H
Parrack, S M
Parry, D M
Parry, E W
Parry, G R
Parslew, R A G
Parsons, K F
Patel, N M
Patsalides, C T
Pearson, M G
Peart, I
Peddi, V
Pellegrini, A V
Pendleton, N
Pennefather, P M
Pennie, B H
Pereira, A C

Llandeilo

Pereira, M C
Perera, H D P W
Perera, J K P
Perrin, P F
Perry, R A
Pettitt, A R
Pfeiffer, U
Pharoah, P O D
Phillips, B M
Phillips, B J
Phillips, G
Phillips, J
Phillips, M F
Philpott, R M
Photiou, S
Pigott, T J D
Pirmohamed, M
Platt, M R
Platt, M J
Playfor, S D
Pollack, J
Pollard, C E
Poole, R G
Poston, G J
Pottinger, K H S
Powell, P M
Powell, W D G
Pownall, D
Pozzi, M
Pramanik, K
Prasad Rao, G
Prasad, N
Prasad, T
Preston, E M
Preston, T R
Prince, G H
Proctor, J L
Proudlove, D A
Pryce, A C W
Pullan, D M
Purewal, T S
Pyatt, J R
Pye, A M
Quigley, C
Rackham, O J
Radha Krishna, L K
Radhakrishna, G
Rai Chowdhury, S L
Rajlawot, G P
Rakowski, J H
Ramadan, M F
Ramamoorthy, S N
Ramsay, E M E
Randev, B
Rao, M S
Rao, P B
Rastogi, S
Rastogi, T K
Ratcliffe, J M
Ratti, N
Ravey, M
Raychowdhuri, R
Razvi, S A H
Reade, D W
Rebmann, C S
Reddington, J A
Reddy, A V G
Redmond, P V S
Redmond, S J
Redmond, T K
Rees, B
Rees, M
Regan, M M C
Reid, M M
Reilly, P C
Reilly, T D
Renton, M C B L
Reynolds, L C
Rhead, E
Rhind, E
Rhodes, J M
Rhodes, L E
Riaz, A
Richards, D E W M
Richardson, D
Richardson, P
Richardson, W R
Richmond, D H
Rickwood, A M K
Rigby, P
Rigg, M
Rimmer, M A
Rintala, R J
Rivlin, J J
Rivlin, M V
Robb, C A
Robb, P M
Roberts, D
Roberts, E

Roberts, J W
Roberts, P J
Roberts, R A
Robertson, J L
Robinson, C J S
Robinson, M L
Robson, W J
Rodgers, I D
Rodrigues, E A
Rodrigues, J
Roe, D A
Roebuck, H
Rogan, A M
Rogers, J H
Rogers, M G H
Rogerson, S R K
Roland, N J
Romer, H C
Rooney, P S
Rosanwo, E O
Rosanwo, M O M
Rose, A P
Rose, H M
Rose, S A
Rosen, M P
Rosenbloom, L
Rosenthal, J M
Rostron, P K M
Rothburn, M M
Roulston, L
Rowlands, J K
Rowlands, M H
Rowlands, P C
Roy, B
Royle, M J
Ruben, S M
Rugen, J
Rushambuza, F G
Russell, G N
Russell, P N
Ryan, D P M
Ryan, M F
Rylands, A J
Saba, G Y S
Sadik, W B
Sadiq, P M
Saha, A K
Saleem, A
Sanderson, C J
Santer, G J
Sapre, S
Sarginson, R E
Sarker, S
Sastrulu, K
Satchithananthan, N
Saunders, P A
Saverimuttu, R K
Scarland, M G
Scawn, N D A
Schlecht, B J M
Schmidt, B E
Scott-Samuel, A J R
Scott, I G
Sekhar, K T
Selby, A M
Sells, R A
Semple, A B
Sen, J
Sendegeya, C
Sephton, V C
Setty, S
Shah, D K
Shamas-Ud-Din, S
Shantha, A L
Sharma, A K
Sharma, A
Sharma, A K
Sharma, N
Sharma, P
Sharma, S P
Sharpe, G R
Shatwell, M A
Shaw, C R
Shaw, M D M
Shaw, S D
Sheard, J D H
Shearer, E S
Shears, P
Sheehan, T J
Sheeran, E
Sheeran, P B M
Shenkin, A
Shepherd, A J N
Shieff, N
Shiffman, E M
Shiffman, I F
Shiffman, K
Shoker, B S
Shokuhi, S

Short, A D
Short, J M
Short, L J
Sidaras, D J G
Sidaras, G A
Siddell, J L
Siddiqi, M A
Sidebottom, A J
Siegler, J
Siller, C S
Sillitoe, A T
Simkin, E P
Simms, A B
Simms, P
Simpson, C K
Singer, R
Singh, B D N
Singh, H K
Singh, N P
Singh, S
Singh, S
Singh, S B P
Singh, S
Singh, S N
Singh, Y
Singhal, A K
Sinha, B K
Sinha, B K
Sinha, S
Sivabalan, P
Sivori, R E
Skaife, P G P
Smart, H L
Smerdon, A W
Smith, D F
Smith, D J
Smith, H M
Smith, I
Smith, J M
Smith, M L
Smith, M R
Smith, M J
Smith, M R
Smith, P J
Smith, P A
Smith, P A
Smith, T K
Smithson, S E
Smyth, M G S
Smyth, R L
Snowdon, R L
Snyder, M
Sobowale, A O
Somauroo, J D
Somjee, S
Soorae, A S
Soulsby, T P
Spofforth, P
Squire, S B
St. Hill, C A
Stables, R H
Stamboultzis, N
Stanaway, S E
Stannard, L
Steiger, C A
Steiger, M J
Stephens, E A
Stevenson, I M
Steyn, R S
Stone, A
Strach, E H
Street, G L
Struik, S S
Suares, M
Subhedar, N V
Sudhakar, K
Sulaiman, H M
Sumner, D J
Sumner, M C
Suri, A K
Sutton, E J
Sutton, R
Sutton, S E
Sweeney, M E
Sweeney, M T
Swift, A C
Taaffe, W G
Taggart, T F O
Tagore, N K
Tamin, J S F
Tatam, M E
Taylor-Robinson, D C
Taylor-Robinson, J W
Taylor, A J N
Taylor, A S
Taylor, J F
Taylor, T H
Taylor, W
Taylor, W H

Taylor, W N
Teebay, P F
Teo, L N
Tewari, V K
Thakur, S C
Theophanous, M
Thom, C M H
Thomas, A G
Thomas, B
Thomas, D A
Thomas, D G
Thomas, E E
Thomas, H O
Thomas, J M
Thomas, K J
Thomas, L S
Thomas, P J
Thomas, P S
Thomas, S D
Thompson, R N
Thompson, R S
Thompson, R E
Thompson, W J
Thomson, J Y
Thong, K F
Thoo, C K
Thornington, R E
Thurnell, C A
Thurston, H A
Tincello, A J
Tincello, D G
Tish, K N
Tobias, M
Todd, R M
Toh, C H
Toke, E
Topping, J
Townley, S A
Tree, A M
Tseung, K W
Tucker, A K
Tulley, P N
Tunn, E J
Turnbull, L S
Turner, G C
Turner, J J
Turnock, R R
Tweedie, I E
Upsdell, M A
Usha-Rani, V
Usher, J L
Van Heyningen, C
Van Saene, H K F
Van Velzen, D
Varma, T R K
Vedavathy, K K
Vella, I
Verbov, J L
Verma, S K
Verstreken, P
Vickers, M J
Vithlani, K P
Vitty, F P
Volk, H M J
Von Bremen, B C
Vora, J P
Waghorn, A J
Wake, P N
Wake, S L
Walczak, P M
Walker, B A
Walker, C R
Walker, P P
Walker, P E
Walker, R J
Walkinshaw, S A
Wallbank, I W
Waller, M
Walley, K
Walley, T J
Wallis, H L
Walls, J A
Walsh, C
Walsh, H P J
Warburton, C J
Ward, J B
Wardle, S P
Warenius, H M
Warner, C W
Watchman, I G
Waters, W H
Watkin, E J
Watkin, F M
Watson, A J M
Wauchob, T D
Webb, A M C
Webster, D
Webster, M
Webster, S W

Weir, W I
Welby, S B
Welch, G P
Welch, J A
Weldon, H J
Wells, J C D
Welsh, C D
Wenstone, R
Weston, P J
Whelan, E
Whelan, M J
Whitby, P J
White, F E
White, N P
Whitehouse, G H
Whitenburgh, M J
Whiteside, C L
Whitfield, C A
Whitley, S
Whitmore, J M
Whittaker, J A
Wild, R E
Wilder-Smith, O H G
Wilding, J P H
Wildsmith, P H
Wilkinson, E A J
Wilkinson, M
Williams, C E
Williams, C
Williams, E
Williams, E M I
Williams, G
Williams, G D
Williams, I R
Williams, S M
Williamson, B H
Williets, T H
Willows, H
Wilson, A D
Wilson, C A
Wilson, E T
Wilson, J A
Wilson, K C M
Wilson, N J E
Wilson, N L
Winchester, S L
Winstanley, P A
Winter, J
Winter, J A C
Winterburn, R
Wishart, P K
Wolf, A
Wolfman, L C
Wolfman, S S
Wolman, D
Wong Ching Hwai, S Y
Wong, A
Wong, K C
Wong, S C P
Wong, V S
Wood, R N A
Woodall, P L
Woodcock, B E
Woods, I M M
Woods, T O
Woodward, J
Woodward, R B
Woolfenden, K A
Woollard, S J
Wooster, J C
Worthington, E F
Wotherspoon, J
Wright, J G
Wright, N B
Wyatt, G B
Wyatt, P H
Wycherley, C R
Yadav, A
Yadav, J K
Yang, Y C
Youell, A
Young, B
Young, C A
Yoxall, C W
Yuen, C H W
Yunus-Khizr, S A A
Zsigmond, A

Liversedge

El Sarraff, M R
Ghafoor, N H
Khan, H
Lee, J H
Pollock, J J
Redshaw, G W
Sarathy, P
Sears, A L
Steward, M A
Thompson, J A

Livingston

Adwani, H P
Ahmad, T
Aspin, J D
Backett, S A
Bailey, P S
Bartholomew, R S
Bateman, M J A
Brown, T M
Buchan, I C
Cook, M K
Cooper, T K
D'Souza, J G
Davie, R M
Dewart, P J
Duncan, L A
Ewing, J C
Farquhar, D L
Ferguson, J B
Finnie, R M
Forbes, J W
Fothergill, N J
Freeland, P
Gardner, K M
Gibson, N M
Gourlay, E J
Grant, A J
Gribben, S C
Haigh, A E J
Hamilton, A S
Handley, J E
Hay, K W
Henderson, D J
Hogg, F J
Hutchinson, A R
Irving, J B
Jacob, A J
Kassam, M L
Lonsdale, M
McCullough, D A
Macdonald, R J M
McEwan, A J
McGowan, N J
McKinnon, M G M
McLauchlan, M A
Macleod, A J
McLeod, I C
MacLeod, L J
Macleod, M F
Martin, E G
Mauchline, R M
Mazza, D J
Mercer, S W
Mitchell, R
Montgomery, B W
Morrison, L M M
O'Donnell, A M
Patel, M S A
Ramesar, K C R B
Raza, Z
Ritchie, J M
Robertson, D A
Robertson, P
Robinson, H J
Roscrow, S E
Shepherd, A
Sim, D W
Simpson, C
Skinner, L P
Sloan, R D
Smart, L M
Smith, P A
Stewart, M L
Teh, H-P
Tripathi, B P
Tripathi, D
Tybulewicz, S M
Ul Haq, I
Van De Meulebroucke, B
Walker, T H
Wallace, J
Watson, J D
Weir, A M
Wild, K A
Williamson, E C M

Llanarth

Bayton, D H
Roberts, N G

Llanbedr

Ledger, P K

Llandeilo

Bassett, D C J
Davies, C M
Davies, I A
Davies, T R
Doey, W D

Llandovery

Evans, R A
George, R I
Goodwin, H A
Leopold, J G
Llewelyn, A D
Nakielny, E A
Sloper-Aitchison, M L
Thomas, C M J
Thomas, D P

Llandovery
Anwyl, W E
Boulter, M J M
Briscoe, C R
Jones, R L
Rees, P J
Richards, J L
Salt, R W

Llandrindod Wells
Arkinstall, G M
Barlow, G
Brown, W M R
Buchan, J
Davies, D
Davies, E
Hetherington, R J
Hilsden, E I
Jenkins, J E
Jones, S A
Lichtenstein, H E
Matson, J S
Ovis, S
Owen, M D
Ruell, S D
Tattersall, T
Warrick, M J S
Warrick, S M

Llandudno
Akasheh, K
Brigg, W M M
Carri, M P
Davey, R J
Davies, A
Davies, P R C
Emmett, P A
Galpin, O P
Green, J J
Gubay, A
Hana, A B
Hay, D J
Hindle, J V
Hotston, S J
Jones, W M
Khattak, A S
King, G D
O'Beirn, D P
Oliver, K R
Roberts-Puw, E H
Roberts, N G
Shaw, R R
Simpson, B
Thomas, E L
Thomas, S K
Williams, S
Wilson, E H

Llandudno Junction
Jayaram, M

Llandysul
Adair, A A
Cule, J H
Evans, M S
Gard, R J
Gordon, K J
Griffiths, D J
Jay, A L
Jefferson, F A
Jeremiah, D S
Jones, D T
Jones, T J
Llewelyn, N
MacBean, S M
Owen-Smith, B
Reiter, M E K
Roberts, D A T
Taylor, N C
Thomas, I M
Thomas, M S

Llanelli
Ahmed, K
Anthony, E L
Aston, A R
Bajoria, S K
Caiach, S M
Cassidy, L J
Daniel, M A M
Davies, A F-D
Davies, B R
Davies, D M
Davies, E L
Davies, H L W
Davies, H E
Davies, M L
Davies, M
Davies, R M
Davies, W F T
Devichand, P
Devonald, R C
Dew, M J
Drummond, R N
Ebden, P
Edmunds, E C H
Edmunds, E
Ellis-Williams, G W
Evans, D W
Evans, H J R
Evans, J V
Evans, T N
Evans, T N W
Evans, T L
Flower, N J
Francis, P W
Gravell, D L
Gravell, E W
Green, M T
Griffiths, A W
Gupta, B
Gwynne, B M
Harries, A I
Harrison, G A J
Hill, A A
Holmes, S C
Holt, S D H
Hopkins, E H B
Howarth, A J
Huws, R G
Jaidev, V C
John, M H
Jones, G L
Jones, G R
Jones, G F
Jones, K E
Jones, M E
Lefebvre, L M
Lewis, J S
Lewis, R W
Llewellyn-Morgan, C A M
Lupini, N J
Mahon, A
Mainwaring, D G
Majer, R V
Meldrum, I M
Morris, G C
Murray, L A
Nigam, A K
Owen, A C
Pease, N J F
Pieper, F A
Prakash, K G
Prigmore, G T
Rees, J E
Richards, A P
Richards, T H
Satarasinghe, K A S
Scourfield, A E
Scourfield, E J
Sharaiha, Y M
Slader, C J
Slader, M I
Stewart, J T B
Thomas, B N
Thomas, D R
Thomas, D B
Thomas, E R
Thomas, G
Thomas, J S I
Thomas, J M
Thomas, R W
Thomas, W C T
Treharne, C J
Treharne, E
Vaughan, M O
Vaziri, M
Waghorne, N J
Walters, P M
Williams, A J
Williams, D D W
Williams, I M
Williams, T D M

Llanerchymedd
Masters, R R
Parry-Jones, C E

Llanfairfechan
Cambridge, I J
Drouet, F H
Ellis, A
Flannery, M D
Hughes, C M
Hughes, S
Hutt, A F
Luithle, E R E
Scott, J M
Summers, D W B
Walker, R M
Williams, N H

Llanfairpwllgwyngyll
Davidsson, G K
Gammon, K
Glyn-Jones, S
Griffiths, J B T
Humphreys Jones, M
Jamison, M H
Jones, D M
Jones, H R
Jones, J
Jones, S G
Jones, T E G
Leyland, M F
McEwan, L M
Owens, D
Pleming, A W
Roberts, G
Roberts, H S
Williams, J G

Llanfyllin
Evans, H C
Griffiths, K R
Hancorn, M K
Jones, L B P
Jones, P N G
Weston, A H S

Llangadog
McVicar, E M

Llangammarch Wells
Hamblett, E P

Llangefni
Edwards, J I
Griffiths, P H
Hughes, B A
Hughes, J H
Hughes, M E
Jones, H I
Jones, R H M
Morgan, G W
Morgan, J P
Morgan, K B
Morgan, L J
Williams, J P

Llangollen
Chalmers, J
Davies, D R W
Davies, J R A
Downes, A J
Edwards, A E
Edwards, C M
Evans, A D
Evans, M
Evans, R M
Gareh, M D
Gemmell, L W
Green, J L
Hughes, H
Jones, E W L
Jones, H L
Kalra, L A
Klenerman, L
Malster, M G
Tanner, R M
Williams, E J
Williams, R E W
Williams, R B

Llanidloes
Collins, S R
Jones, N H
Leslie, S M
Scrase, A M
Scrase, E T
Selly, E W

Llanon
Evans, K P
Griffiths, D B

Llanrwst
Goodwin, G W
Hughes, A J
Johl, S
Kenrick, J E A
Kenrick, R M
Ramsay, R B

Llansantffraid
Barlow, J A

Llantrisant
Abdullah, A N
Davies, C J
Ghufoor, K
Rivron, R P
Sandhu, G S

Llantwit Major
Ashworth, C S L
Bevington, W R P
Crimmins, G J
Foreman, A J
Gronow, T E
Harris, J A
Leuchars, K L
Llewellyn, D J
Morris, J M
Newbold, G F
Richards, B F
Summors, R E
White, J P

Llanwrtyd Wells
Davies, R B

Llanybydder
Davies, A W
Glover, F R
Heneghan, N D H
Rowlands, S G

Llanymynech
Kocheta, A A J
Poole, G G
Thwaite, D S

Llwynypia
Barr, R S G

Loanhead
Dickson, T C
Henderson, I J M
Herbert, G N
Leslie, A
Moonsawmy, S A
Weir, D J G
West, C P

Lochboisdale
MacIntyre, M G
O'Hanlon, A-M
Powell, A P

Lochearnhead
Hulme, A

Lochgelly
Cattanach, S J
Garvey, N
Gordon, H J
Goyal, A K
Khan, F
Khan, M A R
Khan, S
Kidd, C A
Lindsay, S M
MacFarlane, J R
McKean, J R
Mistry, C U
Patel, R V
Rahman, M A

Lochgilphead
Ashton, E J
Brailsford, M M
Corrigan, F M
Davidson, A J W
Fergusson, G M
Gaskell, D F
Guy, P M M
Kidd, J L
Macalister Hall, M S
McCallum, A I
McCulloch, J A T
Mackay, A V P
MacKenzie, S D
Mackie, C S
Macleod, S M
McMinn, M G
McMinn, R M H
Millar, B-A M
Nunn, C M H
Phillips, J K
Provan, A A
Ranger, A F

Simpson, M J
Thompson, P
Thornton, C W
Ward, A D
Weir, R D
Wells, A D

Lochmaddy
Keiller, P W
Macleod, J A J
Pilkington, B S
Wilson, K A

Lochwinnoch
Blair, M M R
Blower, A G
Cohen, M T
Colquhoun, A B
Dalrymple, J G
Grose, R D
Johnson, C P
McCormick, C V
McCusker, C D
McInnes, J C
Waterston, P F

Lockerbie
Armstrong, A
Brown, J T
Cameron, A B
Clayson, C W
Costigan, P S
Crawford, A C
Frost, D
Hill, J J
Longmore, H J A
Ludlam, M
Maclean, N
McQueen, K J
Marr, A W
More, E J
Norris, J F B
Norris, S C
Ogden, A C
Ogden, E C
Palmer, R A
Porteous, G A
Powell, H K R
Rigg, N D
Smith, J D
Taylor, D J
Wilson, J B

Londonderry
Abbott, F A A
Aquino, P J
Ashenhurst, E M
Baird, D S C
Bankhead, K B
Beirne, J A F
Black, E T J
Boyd, L E
Boyle, N B J
Brady, S T
Brennan, M R
Brennan, R J
Brennan, V J
Brown, C M
Brown, D A
Brown, J M
Brown, R M
Burns, J A
Byrne, G A
Cadden, I S H
Campbell, C M A
Canavan, H R
Casey, L J
Cavanagh, V J
Chadwick, M P
Chauhan, N D
Chestnutt, W N
Connolly, D F
Cosgrove, J P
Cosgrove, J M
Cosgrove, J J
Cosgrove, K J
Cosgrove, P J
Cosgrove, P A
Craig, T J M
Crosbie, J J
Curran, M G
Dale, V A
Daly, C A P
Danton, M H D
De Burca, D I
Deacon, T H K
Deane, D M
Deehan, D J
Devlin, E G
Devlin, E M
Devlin, J
Devlin, M M A
Devlin, P B
Devlin, S B
Dickey, W
Doherty, A M
Doherty, J A
Doherty, P J
Dolan, D M
Downey, N J
Duffy, N K
Dunn, H M
Durand, M D M
Elder, F R
Etherson, J
Eyre, D G
Fallon, P T
Fallows, R F
Fallows, S A S
Flanagan, D J
Foster, S E
Frazer, A F
Furness, G
Gamble, W R
Gardiner, P V
Garvey, A J
Gerber, D G
Gilliland, R
Glynn, G M A
Gordon, I R O
Grace, D
Grant, D J
Grant, G A
Gunn, M B
Hamilton, C A
Hamilton, J N
Harper, E J M
Hassett, P D A
Hasson, F P
Healy, M J
Hegarty, J D
Hetherington, C H R
Hill, J M M
Howe, A R
Howie, M B
Hughes, A-M T
Hughes, D F
Hughes, S J
Jadhav, S T
Johnston, F P D
Johnston, H C
Kane, E P
Kasturi, S
Keegan, D A J
Keenan, G F
Keys, R F
Khow, G M
Knowles, E T
Leeson, W P J
Leitch, H C S
Lennon, G M A
Linton, A F
Lynas, A G A
McCabe, T J
McCallion, N E
McCarron, M O
McCartie, B S J
McCauley, D A
McCauley, W J
McClay, M J
McClean, J R
McCloskey, L E
McCloskey, M E
McCloskey, M A
McCord, F B
McCullough, H J
MacDermott, D
McDermott, S M
McEvoy, P J
McGilloway, M M E
McGinley, I G
McIlwaine, J E J
McIvor, P C A
McKelvey, M A
Mackin, J G
McKinney, L A
McLean, R D W
MacMahon, B M
McNeill, A J
McNicholl, F P
Madden, M G
Magee, S E E
Magnier, M R
Manning, R W
Mariswamy, S B
Martin, D H
Millar, J K
Millen, S A
Moles, K W

Luton

Moohan, J M
Moore, T
Morgan, M M
Morrison, A M
Morrison, C M
Morrow, B C
Mulholland, D A
Mullan, C H
Mullan, J R
Munro, C K
Murphy, C A
Murphy, S M
Murray, A P V
Nairn, R M
Nelson, D E
O'Connor, F A
O'Donnell, J J J
O'Flaherty, K A
O'Hara, A G
O'Kane, C M
O'Kane, D P
O'Kane, J G
O'Kane, J J
O'Kane, M J
O'Kane, P J
O'Kelly, J K
O'Neill, R J
O'Sullivan, M J B
Palin, I S
Panesar, K J S
Parker, M J R
Patterson, D R
Patton, N
Phellas, P
Porter, J M
Price, G F W
Purvis, J A
Quinn, M E
Quinn, R J M
Rea, S M
Reidy, J
Reilly, M P
Robertson, I D
Robinson, W L
Ryan, M F
Sadler, E
Samson, J D
Sharma, N K
Sheils, B A
Siddiqui, A M
Simpson, J T
Singh, I P
Sinton, J E
Smith, B T M
Smithson, R D
Smyth, H J
Spence, J E
Stafford, M A
Steele, J A
Stewart, D P E
Stewart, G R
Stone, J C
Taylor, M A
Tedders, B
Thompson, R L E
Toland, M
Toner, J A
Varadarajan, C R
Vazir, M H
Walpole, G A M
Ward, M J
Warne, S A
Warnock, A M M
Watt, L M J
White, C V
White, R G
Wilson, C J
Wray, A R

Longfield
Armstrong, C B
Carter, P M
Cook, S
Davies, P R
Davies, Y M
Dott, A G
Doughty, B J
Faddoul, E
Finnerty, G T
Fraser, M R
Green, A R
Hatrick, J A
Haynes, S J L
Hosny, A A
Hubbard, D J
Kamdar, B A
Luffingham, J N
Moftah, F S
Munasinghe, S B

Patel, H T
Patel, S T
Patel, T D
Puntambekar, S
Ramanathan, N
Ramanathan, S
Rebel, D J
Rosenberg, R H
Selwood, D P
Singh, K H P E
Smith, P K E
Smyth, D A
Thompson, F C
Williams, A A
Williams, E J

Longhope
Billingham, J
Mayer-Jones, L M
Mayer-Jones, R A

Longniddry
Campbell, E M J
Carr, K
Davies, A D
Hally, A D
Hally, M R
Jarvis, I A D
Knight, R S G
Lowe, C H
Lowe, C S
Martin, D L
Reeks, J L
Wood, P

Looe
Aldous, M D E
Brewer, P J J
Canning, B S
Canning, S B
Cheadle, C R
Crosland-Taylor, P J
Davies, G N
Gates, J C
Goss, D R
Grigson, C M B
Horner, J C
Palmer, M J
Roy, I G
Staff, A
Stafford, J B

Lossiemouth
Bishop, L D
Featherstone, C J F
Gormley, G D
McConachie, M
McConachie, J A
Pleasant, E A
Sabiston, N
Smith, M R
Thomson, H N M
White, I H
Williams, D

Lostwithiel
Bowen, H P
Bowen, I R
Denn, P G
Harrison, J M
Howe, R W
McCurdy, R N C
Mackinnon, F M
Woodfield, M

Loughborough
Ahmad, H K
Almassi, M
Atha, P
Aust, W J
Badiani, K N
Bagley, A M
Bailey, J S
Baker, P M
Bal, A S
Barlow, A R
Barlow, C R
Bassi, S K
Benton, J J N
Benton, N D C
Bhatia, G S
Borsada, S C
Brewis, C
Brocklesby, K J
Bromham, J A
Campbell, M A
Campbell, S S
Cannon, P M
Cawdron, B A
Chander, R
Clay, S J C

Coleman, K E
Cornish, D C
Cox, H
Croker, L R
Cullis, S A
Davis, R J
Dean, A D P
Dent, H G R
Dent, M T
Dipple, H C
Drakes, A H
Duffy, S A
Dyson, R P
Earl, A J
Earl, M R
Ellis, C J
Euden, M
Evans, K J
Eveson, S E
Ferguson, M R
Ferris, J M
Fossey, S M
Foulds, R A
French, A J
Frost, M F
Furber, P J
Furlonger, A J
Gerrie, S E
Ghaly, M S
Gill, H K
Gordon, P D
Graham, M M R A
Green, R C
Hale, M C
Hall, E A
Hall, T D
Hall, W B
Hallam, C F
Hanlon, G P
Harding, M L
Harding, P B P
Harding, R J P
Harries, D J
Harries, M J
Harries, S S C
Hawkes, N D
Hay, D P
Haynes, D I
Hazlewood, J H
Heap, B M
Holdich, T A H
Holownia, P J
Holt, P R
Horner, W M L
Hoyle, J T E
Hoyte, D A N
Hughes, H J
Hughes, H P
Hughes, M W
Hunter, M C C
Jasoria, S
Jassal, S S
Jewson, D G
Jivan, S
John, A P K
Jolleys, J C W
Jones, B E
Jones, R T
Kaitiff, N C
Kelly, A T
Kingsley, P J
Kok Shun, M G
Lakhani, M K
Larsen, J E
Leeson, C P M
Lockton, J A
Lott, D J
McDonald, C I
McHale, J F
MacLarnon, K H
McQuade, P R
MacSween, P J
Mak, F
Matthews, K T A
Matthews, P
Matthews, S J
Matts, S J F
Matts, S G F
Mayer, J H
Meadows, I J T
Metcalfe, M S
Middleton, J F
Moir, A A
Moore, A C
Moore, N A
Newbold, K
Newton, A F
Nicholson, K G
O'Toole, S J

Oliver, K J
Ortolani, M L
Parker, S C
Patel, P A
Patel, R S
Patel, R D
Patel, V
Phillipson, E M
Price, C
Price, R J A
Quinn, A G
Read, J D
Redferne, J H
Riley, D O
Riley, V C
Robinson, D B
Ryan, D P
Saund, N S
Schofield, I R
Shahi, M
Shirreffs, E C G
Shortt, S J
Simpson, A J G
Simpson, N H R
Sivaguru, A
Skeoch, A R
Smith, J M-T
Southwell, K F
Spiers, R J
Spiers, S P
Stableford, J S G P
Stafford, P J
Stead, B E
Tandon, S
Tatham, P F
Taylor, R J
Thompson, W M
Ugoji, U U
Unitt, H M
Vadher, S
Vaghela, N N
Veitch, Y
Volpe, N
Wallace, H R
Ward, B J
Ward, J W
West, K J
Wheeley, M S G
Whowell, W B
Whymark, A D
Wilde, S M
Wray, H A
Wynne-Williams, H V

Loughton
Bagguley, K A
Banerjee, B
Barnes, S
Batchelor, C M
Baxter, D
Bhagrath, R A S
Chew, R E
Daniel, C S
De Silva, W M C
Dighton, D H
Dormer, A E
Dubinski, J
Dunn, T B
Frootko, N J
Harrison, T A
Hasan, A
Heathfield, K W G
Herbert, R L
Ide, J E
Kalkat, G S
Kanamia, T
Kari, J A A
Khan, A A
Khan, H U
Lukey, D C
Matthews, S A
Matthews, T H J
Mitchell, F L
Murphy, D S J
Nath, N K
O'Neill, A P
Olliffe, P E
Pang, H T
Pradhan, A M
Prajapati, D
Prashner, P L
Radford, R J E
Ramsey, M C
Ribbens, S C
Roberts, R P L
Runagall, S E
Smith, C J M
Thomas, G P L
Tomlins, F G

Van Der Weyden, B J
Whitaker, J M
Wright, P L
Xavier, R J H

Louth
Ahmed, M
Anderson, I F
Birch, J J
Buch, K A
Clifford, A A R
Crook, D H
Drake, H M
Dwyer, M J A
Edmondson, J S
Firth, R D
Fitzgerald, T B
Foster, A R
Gallagher, A J
Grant, C E P
Humberstone, I P
Jerome, J E
Jones, D A
Khan, M M R
Khan, M U
King, N H T
Knight, P T
Lawless, J M
Maity, S
Mansfield, P J
Morrish, L H B
Mowat, A J
Muldoon, M J
Oke, P T
Parker, G S
Parkes, N R Q
Pike, L C
Qadir, M
Ramkhalawon, M
Ravindra Nath, A
Reynolds, D J
Ross, G
Staunton, D
Stovin, P H
Sykes, P
Taylor, G R
Taylor, O H
Thomas, P J
Topham, S P
Westwood, C A
Whelan, N
Willson, G F
Young, J R

Lowestoft
Atkins, J L
Aylward, M J
Berry, R V
Bigg, A R
Bond, R I
Bouch, K
Butt, M S
Calver, R
Cooper, D I
Cooper, S J
Copithorne, R E C
Cox, S M
Dakin, R
Devereux, B
Drane, N R
Duncan, R W
Ehmann, J F
Goulty, L H
Gunn, K
Halder, D
Hartley, E M
Henderson, D R
James, R G
Johnson-Nurse, C
Johnston, D
Kanjilal, J
Kathuria, R L
Kerry, F M R
Krishnaswamy, S
Krishnaswamy, U
Lall, R S
Lawrence, P W
Lloyd, C N
Lockyer, G J S
McLean, C R
Mann, R A M
Markham, B H
Mawer, B J M
Mohan, G
Moon, E A C
Moorthie, G A
Morrison, J M
Nadarajan, P
O'Driscoll, F A

O'Regan, M H
Periselneris, S R
Prince, S R
Quilliam, P S A
Reidy, A J
Sanger, J L
Scotter, B
Seehra, M S
Stewart, K S
Stocks, R J
Tabberer, H J
Tattersall, L J
Tribe, P H
Turner, D J
Tyson, C J
Vallis, S C
Van Den Broek, A J C M
Van Pelt, H J F

Ludlow
Attlee, W O
Beswick, T S L
Bonner, F E
Brazier, L H
Caldwell, G C F
Capper, E
Collier, C J
Cook, G P
Corfield, P W D
Crawley, P S
Cullen, J D
Currant, P N
Davies, R D
Farnell, B J
Farnell, N J
Fendall, N R E
Foster, S
Gordon, D S
Hall, N R
Heber, J W
Hooker, A G
Horlock, N M
Irani, D A
Kirk, M
Klein, V H
Lane, J W J
Perks, A
Rhodes, P L
Snape, S R
Taylor, M A
Turney, J P
Unsworth, A
Yarham, D D

Lurgan
Chirayath, Dr

Luton
Abuhadra, K S
Acellam-Odong, C C
Adams, M E
Adler, B R
Adler, F P
Agius, M
Ahad, M F R
Ahmad, A
Ahmad, Q
Ahmad, Z
Ahmed, N
Alexander, M S M
Ali-Khan, A
Amin, M R
Ana, J E
Anam, K A K M
Anhal, A L
Ar-Rikaby, H A
Ashford, A C C
Astin, K J
Attais, M
Attias, M
Austwick, D H
Balasubramaniam, K
Barhey, M
Bashir, R
Bath, P S
Bhathal, H S
Bhatnagar, P
Blessing, E
Brewer, A E
Bright, K J
Broomfield, D M
Brosnan, S G
Burrell, S J
Burton, L J
Campbell, J D
Campion, K M E
Chawla, O P
Cheslyn-Curtis, S

Lutterworth

Claramunt Romero, M D C
Clark-Wilson, L J
Clark, E A
Cockerill, K J
Condell, H M
Constable, P J
Craske, E
Dand, P A
Day, J J
Deeley, D P
Denis-Smith, D
Dhabuwala, N D
Dorman, A H
Duffy, U M C
Ebrahim, A-R
Elliott, K E
Ellis, C D W
Erooga, M A
Erotocritou, P P
Farbotko, T A
Fay, D J
Finer, N
Fleming, A E
Francis, H B
Ganju, D
Geraghty, W J A
Griffiths, M
Gupta, M
Gupta, R K
Haider, T
Hall, P L
Hamilton, A J
Harris, C G M
Harris, D J
Harris, F A R
Hey, P A
Hill-Smith, I
Hill, H M
Horak, E
Houghton, D A
Houston, B D
Howard, S V
Hussain, I
Ikeagwu, E O K
Ikeagwu, O K
Iqbal, T
Jabbar, M A
Jackson, N M
Jackson, S J
Jain, V K
Jarvis, M I
Jeffs, N G
Johnson, G M
Jutlla, G S
Kellings, M
Khan, M Y
Khanchandani, H L
Khanchandani, R
Khanu, D D
Kirubakaran, P
Kneebone, J M
Lewis, P A
Lindsay, R S
Lobo, B J
MacBrayne, J T
McGill, H L
Mcloone, M B E
Mahadevan, N
Malik, Z M
Marsden, J K
Martin, S J
Maszadro, Z
Melville, H M
Mirza, I A
Mitchell, A M D
Murray, H M
Mylvaganam, K
Nasim, M
Nesaratnam, S
Nicoll, D M
Norman, M H
Norman, S G
O'Donnell, P M J
O'Dwyer, P
O'Malley, J F
Ozua, P O
Patel, S M
Patroclou, A
Patten, M T
Paul Choudhury, S K
Pellow, R J N
Pereira, E M
Peterson, D B
Pickles, J M
Pinto, R T
Pinto, S C
Pittam, M R
Prakash, O
Prendergast, C H
Rajapakse, Y S
Ramsay, J R
Rasamuthiah, T
Raut, V V
Rieger, C A
Ritchie, H R J
Roberts, M D
Robinson, C A
Roud Mayne, C C A
Russell-Taylor, M A
Safdar, M
Sahdev, A K
Saleh, I
Schembri Wismayer, J
Seery, J A
Semark, D W
Shah, D V
Shah, H M
Shah, K D
Shakoor, A
Sharma, S D
Sherratt, R M
Shokar, N K
Siddiqi, S F
Siegler, D I M
Simmonds, N J
Singer, P A
Sinha, R P
Sivakumar, P
Skyers, P A
Soo, S-C
Spears, F D
Spira, M
Stanton, J R
Stodell, M A
Sule, K K
Swallow, H M
Swan, K M
Tabert, J E K
Talbot, P A J
Talbot, S
Tant, D R
Tew, J H
Thiruchelvam, A
Thit Thit, Dr
Thompson, D S
Thompson, M H
Thomson, M
Towler, G M
Tsahalina, E
Ullah, S
Verghese, A R
Verity, T
Von Arx, D P
Wakefield, P C
Ward, E M C
Warren, M J
Watson, S A
Way, H M M
Williams, H J
Williams, N
Williams, P G
Wykes, K J
Yanny, L B
Yogasakaran, B S

Lutterworth

Adams, R W
Alexander, C A
Allcock, J N
Bartram, D H
Brown, L J R
Coates, A P M
Collinson, J G
Donald, K
Dorok, A J
Dowell, C G
Flaxman, P A
Greaves, J M
Guppy, J M
Jennings, R S
Kendall, H M
Khong, C K
Knights, A C
Masharani, U B
Masharani, V
Orton, D W
Pegg, J G
Reynolds, J C
Robertson, I K
Rowe, M J
Summers, M
Turner, P B
Warburton, D J R
Watson, D M
Wiggins, W J

Lybster

Joiner, P A

Lydbrook

Coates, A J M
Pearce, A F B

Lydbury North

Murphy, C J

Lydney

Bee, A L
Bennett, P J L
Bounds, R J
Cardale, J D
Chambers, J
Christmas, R
Ellis, D L I
Fellows, P R
Henry, W T
Ibbotson, R B
Jones, R B
Miller, M D
Nancollas, C E
Price, E M
Price, J H
Richens, A
Sharma, S R
Swannack, R
Yiend, M E

Lyme Regis

Austin, M A
Bowles, R M L
Cima, P H
Elsom, J F
Eyres, M G
Hamer, N A J
Llewelyn, A H
Noakes, M J
Price, T W
Rajaratnam, D V
Robinson, B J
Ryan, R A

Lymington

Abrams, J W
Arblaster, P G
Arnold, A J
Atkinson, D
Badham, D S
Ball, D H
Bekenn, P J
Birch, S J
Bodley Scott, D D
Bolton, R H
Brooks, E F
Broomhead, I W
Burnham, C R
Carnegie, D M
Carson, M B
Cattanach, A C
Codd, A C M
Collings-Wells, J A
Covell, R G
Cracknell, B D
Davies, J F
Davies, N J H
De Mowbray, J M M
Drew, A J
Eakins, A T
Filose, M A
Fowler, D B
Gaire, C P
Gambier, D M
Gaunt, S P
Graves, J
Greaves, D P
Green, S N
Griffiths, R M
Griffiths, S M
Guy, J
Harcourt-Webster, S
Havers, C I P
Hawthorn, E M
Hempsall, V J
Hobson, A R
Humby, M D
Jackson, D M
Jackson, R K
Johnson, A T
Johnston, I N L
Johnston, S
Keatinge, J M
Langdon, L
Law, C J
Lees, R M
Lemon, P G
Lewis, J W
Lloyd, T W
Lowe, N J
Macalister, A M
McCafferty, J D
Macdonald, D M
McEwen, T H
McNaught, J A
Mason, H K
Maule, L C
Morgan, J M
Mounsey, J A B
Naylor, E G
Odbert, R M
Parry, D N
Rawlings, K O
Rawlinson, Z L
Read, D E
Read, J A J M
Ridout, D L
Rogers, B J
Rogers, J D
Rowe, E
Rowe, P B
Scobie, J D
Seward, C F
Sherwin, S R
Simon, C A E
Smith, S A C
Sommerville, J G
Spencer, D J
Stark, V J M
Steadman, A F
Stewart, J A
Summerhayes, J L V
Swallow, J
Taylor, M C
Thornton, B M
Turner, G F
Tymens, D C
Wagstaff, D P
Walker-Brash, R M T
Walker, C B
Walker, G D
Wilkie, D J K
Williamson, D A J
Williamson, E M
Wood, B S B
Wood, B C
Wood, E C

Lymm

Abbott, J D
Allan, E
Atherton, E A
Bamforth, M A
Barnett, A A
Beattie, E L K-M
Bell, M H
Brooks, N C
Cheetham, E D
Cottrill, P N J
Davies, H W C
Dodd, F M
Gavin, N J
Goodall, J R
Green, P M
Haqqani, M F
Harle, C C
Henderson, S J
Hewitt-Symonds, M W
Hobday, C L
Johnstone, A H
Kelsall, O M
Lynch, M P
McGrath, M B J
Maxton, D G
Millington, G W H
Mirski, E B
Morgan, K P
Morgan, R J
Morton, A K
Murray, C S
Oxynos, C
Parkins, K J
Plunkett, S G
Ramsden, G H
Semple, D M
Shard, H M
White, M M S
Williams, B O
Wise, M S
Witham, E A
Yates, S C
Young, E A

Lympstone

Ross, R A

Lyndhurst

Allin, A C
Aspinal, R J
Atkins, C M
Baldwin, A M J
Balfour, A M
Balfour, D M
Bamber, C C
Birch, S J
Blandy, S E
Chawla, P T
Chinn, S E
Couchman, J M
Crabbe, M G A
Eldon, E A
Griffiths, Y P
Hall, M R P
Hughes, S R
Hyde, I
McAll, F A M
Moynihan, F J
Neil-Dwyer, J S E
Noble, A D
Olliff-Cooper, A K
Randall, C J
Sloley, L J
Smart, J M
Stokes, V V
Struthers, S L
Trickett, J P

Lynton

Ferrar, R J
Frankish, J B
Mold, E T

Lytham St Annes

Acornley, A J
Anderson-Smith, W R
Atherton, M T C
Atkinson, L W
Bamford, C
Barnsley, C J
Bedford, N A
Best, F A
Bilbey, F
Blackburn, M R W
Boardman, A D
Boardman, J
Bound, J P
Brook, M E
Brownlie, S M M
Bucknell, S J
Carrdus, P J
Cashman, M D
Casserley, C A
Cooke, F J
Craw, N I
Curzon, R N
Dale, M J
Dale, T L C
Dempsey, H F M
Dowling, E J
Dowling, E
Duncan, K M
Duncan, P R
Eddie, D A S
Edwards, T B
Edwards, T P
Ellwood, S T
Evans, G L
Farries, J S
Fielding, J D
Fisher, A J
Forrest, L
Foster, K A A
French, P A
Gajawira, N P
Graham, W
Greenwood, K M
Greenwood, S F
Groarke, P
Hall, T M
Hanson, H
Harris, M L
Hartley, M
Hassan, W E
Heaney, H M
Hedley, N G T
Hellier, R J
Hough, D J
Houghton, P D
Irving, A G
Jackson, P J C
Johnson, M C G
Kellett, J K
Khan, J A
Khan, M A R
Khanna, V K
Laundy, N P
Lee, F I
Legg, W J J
Lewis, R N
Lingam, R P
Logan, W F W E
McDonnell, P W
McKenna, M J
Mackey, W T
McLennan, K M
Milner, I G
Moorhouse, P J
Morris, J E
Murray, S M
Newman, M
Nicholson, J A T
Niman, W
Peach, B G S
Peach, R M
Poyner, J G
Priestley, S E
Reed, R W
Reid, C M B
Reid, S P J
Renvoize, E B
Robertson, G S
Rowley, K A
Schofield, C E
Seed, C A
Setna, P H
Shadwick, P
Sloan, M E
Smith, G P
Smith, J K L
Stevens, R
Stewart, A F S
Stewart, I M
Tattersall, C W
Thorpe, R J
Torrance, J D
Tulloh, H P
Wallace, V A
Weinbren, I
Whitson, A
Williams, R W
Wilmington, A M
Woods, C J
Worsley, R
Wright, J M
Wright, J K
Wright, J S

Mablethorpe

Anderson, R
Bagley, J S
Basu, S K
Turner, C G
Wright, S J

Macclesfield

Aglan, M Y A E A
Akerman, N
Allcock, C
Allen, D J
Allerton-Ross, G
Archer, G J
Arnold, B D C
Ashley, D L
Auchincloss, J M
Auty, R M
Baker, P R
Ball, A K
Bamford, F N
Banner, C V
Bardgett, D M M
Barge, A J
Barnes, K A
Baskeyfield, H M
Baxter, A D
Beckett, A K
Beckett, S E
Belliappa, K P
Bennett, M L
Black, D
Black, S M
Blackledge, G R P
Bolton, C E R
Borg, C
Bowie, J S
Bowie, R A
Bradley, W P L
Branson, K
Brimelow, A E
Broughton, N I
Brownhill, A J
Burrows, C J
Calleja, J
Cameron, H A
Carbarns, I R I
Carter, M G
Chasty, R C
Choudhury, G

Maidstone

Clack, G I S
Clandillon, E J
Clark, B M C
Clay, R S
Cochrane, L
Colville, J C
Coope, G A
Coope, J K M
Coope, J R
Coope, M L
Cotton, R C
Cragg, D K
Dale, R H
Daley, G H C
Danziger, A M
Davies, A H
Davies, M
Davison, C E
Day, H J B
Drake, R J
Dunlop, P D M
Earp, A D
Eccleston, G A
Edwards, E C
Entwistle, M P
Fagg, S L
Farrand, D A
Farrington, A
Fawkner-Corbett, D
Fitzsimons, T J
Ford-Young, W P D
Forsythe, B J
Foster, P N
Fowler, P D
Fox, E M
Galloway, J C R
Garcia-Vargas, J E
Gathercole, N J
Gibbs, S A L
Gilbert, J
Graham, R F
Grant, M M
Gray, A J
Gray, H S J
Hales, S A
Handler, K E
Handley, J
Hanson, J R
Harley, D B
Harris, R A
Hastings, S C
Heathcote, J A
Heron, R J L
Heyworth, R C F
Higgins, S A
Hodgson, J M
Holden, D
Holden, H M
Holland, R L
Hopkins, K J
Hughes, A M
Hughes, M S
Huyton, M C
Iqbal, J
Jackson, C
Jones, D
Joseph, S R
Kay, M R
Kelly, D F
Kenworthy, R J
Kerr, D F
Kramer, I M E
Link, C G G
Loughran, C F
Loughran, M T
McLean, A F F
Madden, P L
Marshall, A M
Martin, P J
Massie, J A
Matheson, D M
Maxwell, D A
Meir, A R
Mellor, S
Merry, J R
Milne, L A
Mina, M A Y
Mines, G P
Minton, N A
Monaghan, K N
Morris, C Q
Morris, D R
Morris, L J
Morris, Y S
Murgatroyd, H K
Nagaraj, H N
Nair, R G
Neill, R W K
Nuttall, A M

O'Connor, D O
Olverman, G N
Owens, J R
Partridge, E M
Patterson, E L
Patterson, J S
Patton, J T
Payne, R O
Pears, J S
Perkins, C M
Perry, D A
Phillips, L
Pickles, V A
Plant, G D
Plews, C M
Powell, C V E
Powell, P C
Preece, R M
Quayle, A R
Rajaratnam, A
Rajaratnam, K
Ramsden, V M
Richards, J B
Rimmer, T W
Robinson, C C
Robinson, C R
Robinson, S J
Rodgers, E M
Roskilly, J N
Rothwell, M P
Rowlands, D
Roycroft, R J
Salem, J
Scott, A V
Serafi, S
Shackleton, D B
Shribman, A J
Sinclair, P K
Singer, J A
Smith, L K R
Smith, M P
Smith, R A
Spencer, A C
Spillman, I D
Stead, R J
Steep, E
Stirling, A W
Strutt, K L
Studds, C J
Talbot, M A
Tampi, S C
Taylor, G
Taylor, M A R
Thomas, H J
Thomas, S A
Thomasson, D I
Toman, A
Towers, E A
Tucker, S E
Usher, J R
Van Ross, R T G
Varley, G J
Waheed, M
Waheed, N
Wales, J E J
Walker, D J
Walker, J M
Wallis, N T
Walls, J
Waring, H L
Weaver, A B
White, H L
Whiteman, I A
Wilkinson, F O W
Wilkinson, J L
Willdig, P J
Williams, A R
Williams, A J
Wills, A R
Yates, R A
Young, F R M
Zafar, W U

Struthers, J E
Tedders, R A
Thapa, T B
Thomas, P J
Unsworth, F J
Upadhyay, M
Williams, J I
Witnall, A P

Maesteg

Davies, W A
Ferguson, B J M
Griffiths, H
Jones, D M
Kirsop, B A
Lewis, R J P
Lodwig, G S
Peregrine, A D
Rogers, A
Rogers, M A
Sharma, A
Smith, G L
Stratford, K A
Thomas, K W
Thomas, N B
Walby, C

Maghera

Bryson, M C
Convery, R P
Coskery, G M
Finlay, R J
Harkin, M S
Love, J L
Mullan, B A
Overend, J S
Scullin, P
Stevenson, M M
Young, V K

Magherafelt

Aitken, H C
Bailie, J C T
Barker, D
Barton, C M
Charlton, M A
Chaturvedi, R R
Clark, H S G
Cousley, F M
Doherty, Y E
Donnelly, F M
Donnelly, M R M
Doyle, M B
Forde, J W
Glancy, B P
Gribbin, N M
Harkin, A J
Harkin, C A
Hawe, M J G
Henry, A M
Hernandez-Mansilla Palumbo, J
Heron, M O
Hinds, M C
Hunter, E K
Ingram, E R
Johnston, W R
Keatley, J D
Lambrechts, H A
Lowry, C G
McCloskey, C L
McConnell, A A M
McKee, M J
MacLarnon, P G
McRobert, R
Miller, M F
Mills, H M
Mulholland, B A
Mulholland, J K
Nesbitt, K
Nesbitt, M E
Noble, I S
O'Kane, A G
O'Neill, C O
O'Neill, M P
Phellas, G D
Pyper, P C
Rankin, P V
Scullion, D F
Scullion, U M E
Shastri, K D
Shaw, G M
Sheehan, B E
Thompson, I P C
Tohill, J G
Tohill, M
Walker, L J E
Walls, A T R
Walls, F B
White, C

White, F A
Wilson, C H
Wilson, L L
Wray, R H
Young, M F

Maidenhead

Aldington, D J
Ammar, T
Anderson, F E
Austin, D N
Baillie-Hamilton, A B
Barker, J E
Behrman, R G A
Blackmore, S C
Boyd, J G
Brealey, D A
Brock, P G
Bryett, K A
Burnley, S R
Butler, A H
Butler, A J
Butt, T Y
Coleby, M D
Colyer, P E
Cutting, P A
Davies, D B A L
Dhillon, P T S
Dunning, R G
Dyer, J M A
Easparathasan, V P
Englishby, V L
Fanning, P P
Fletcher, P A
Flew, R
Francis, G C
Ganderton, M A
Gilroy, K J
Grewal, J S
Grewal, N A S
Gutteridge, W H C
Habershon, R J
Hanbury, H I
Harrold, J D
Haslam, D J
Hawkins, F D
Head, C E
Hemmings, P M
Herman, J S
Herrick, E M
Hill, J R
Howitt, J S
Hutchings, C M
Jackson, D A
Jefferson, W L
Jobling, S A
Johnson, E S
Johnson, M V T
Jones, I S
Jones, S C
Joshi, G C
Jowett, C S
Keiller, N P
Khoo, C T-K
Kinder, J A
Kitchin, N R E
Kon, P
Lambton, M
Langdon, C G
Langdon, J A
Larsen, D P F
Laslett, R M
Latchman, P
Lawson, K
Leigh, P S
Line, D H
Lloyd-Williams, D J
Lockhart, J D F
Lockhart, S P
Louth, S
Lytton, J M
McIntosh, E D
Mahmoudi, M
Martin, G G
Maskell, N A
Maudgil, B D
Maudgil, D
Mawson, H N C
Mercer, D R V
Mercer, J C
Mills, K L M
Milne, A D T
Mitchell-Fox, T M
Montague, G R
Moodie, J
Morgan, D R
Mullen, H A
Newman, M
O'Callaghan, C M

Obi, B C
Owens, L A
Parker, J C
Parnell, N D J
Patchett, S E
Pearson, D C
Pillitteri, A J
Pountney, A M
Pratt, S
Ratti, B M
Riley, P J
Roberts, H L
Roberts, J C U
Robertson, A M
Robinson, B L
Rosewall, H L
Rushton, J M
Rutter, P C
Scorer, H J M
Scothorne, C L
Segal, D S
Shaw, P J
Shaw, S L
Shaw, W L
Sidey, E
Sithirapathy, S
Slater, A M
Smith, C F
Smith, R D
Southgate, M J
Sowood, P J
Spann, R G
Sparrow, R W
Spier, S J
Spiers, A E D
Stainton-Ellis, D M
Stallard, P M
Stawarz, M J
Stearnes, G N
Sukhdeo, M K
Symons, K W
Symons, R C F
Tattersall, M L
Thomas, J A
Thomson, W B
Toal, M J
Townsend, C L
Valentine, J L
Watson, M W
Wells, L C
Wheeler, J S
Wickramasinghe, S N
Williams, M K
Williams, S L
Wiltshire, R J
Wright, S

Maidstone

Abson, C A
Adjaye, N T
Akhtar, R
Akram Chaudhry, T M
Alexander, H C
Alkass, W A Y
Anderson, H E
Andrews, S M
Aparicio Knorr, C
Aragones Arroyo, M L
Baldwin, E T
Baluch, N
Baluch, S
Barnett, A M
Barr, G R M
Basma, N
Bearcroft, R I
Beesley, S H
Begg, R A
Belham, M R D
Bentley, A P
Bhaduri, B R
Bingham, J R M
Bird, G L A
Biswas, M
Blight, A R
Bonds, P R
Boyd, C H
Breslin, T J
Brice, C H
Brown, E W J
Brunell, C L
Bulmer, P J
Burland, J G H
Burman, A S
Byrne, B C
Canavan, J S F
Carter, J K
Chamberlin, J E
Christmas, S
Cook, G E

Corfe, J F
Cranston, C J
Cross, G D
Cuddehay, C M
Czaykowski, A A P
Da'Ood, M S
Dawes, L
Dawes, M
De Zoysa, W S L
Dening-Smitherman, P
Dennison, J A
Derry, C P
Dickenson, J E
Dickie, A R
Dolman, L J
Donaldson, J G
Downing, H M
Dunham, A M
Dunkley, B
El-Menshawy, H M M
Ellis, S C
Farmer, A P
Fenn, P J
Fernando, B V E
Fernando, H M T
Fernando, K L
Fernando, R L
Fincham, A C
Frazer, J F D
Gammanpila, S M
Gammanpila, S W
Garcia Abreu, T
Gardner, R F A
Gaston, J C
Gaule, E W
Geadah, M W
George, R L
Gerhards, M
Ghosh, S K
Gibbons, A J
Gilmore, R J
Godsmark, C J
Goodman, J D S
Grant, P A
Gray, A B
Gundry, M F
Hagan, G C
Hammond, A
Hancock, D J
Hanrath, P H J
Haque, F
Haque, S Q
Harland, E C
Harland, T G
Harris, C
Harris, F A S
Harris, S A B
Hart, R
Hay, R L
Head, N E
Henderson, A F
Henry, R C
Hibbert, D J
Hipkins, K C
Hobday, P J
Holt, P M
Houghton, D J
Hulse, J A
Iyer, D
James, G E P
Jenkins, D G
Jessel, C R
Johns, A N
Jones, A M
Jones, C A
Jones, P A
Jones, P V
Jones, S E
Kamalagharan, S C
Kavi, S
Keen, C W
Kemp, L I
Kidd, M N
Lam Shang Leen, E
Laurent, R J
Leech, R C
Lewis, P L
Lilley, J A
Lippold, P F
Little, L
Little, T M
McAllister, R H
McDaniel, W H
MacFarlane, A I
McGavin, D
McIlwraith, G R
McKinna, F E
McLaggan, J G
McLean, I F

Macduff

Brooker, I P

MacDuff

Hoddinott, P M

Macduff

Hossack, W S
Law, E A

Machynlleth

Evans, R
Howkins, J
Hughes, R M
Isles, M G
Kershaw, W W
Morpeth, S J

Maldon

McMillan, P J
McMullen, I D H
Manners, J H E
Mason, A B
Matin, M A
Meech, S H
Mennie, R H
Milroy, A J
Mirza, I H
Mocking, T P D M
Monelle, T J
Mongalee, M-E-R
Montague, J M
Morgan, L V
Mortimer, A R
Moss, M L
Mounter, N A
Munton, C G F
Murray, W G D
Mutimer, J E
Mya Win, Dr
Navaratne, M
Newman, D A
Niall Walker, N M A
Noorani, M A
Oakley, L H
Ormrod, J N
Palmer, D L
Parfitt, M D
Parkes, K N
Parris-Piper, T W
Pentecost, A F
Pickering, D G L
Poggo, C
Pollard, B J
Pollington, B I
Porter, M H
Powell-Jackson, P R
Puffett, A R
Pulham, N L
Rao, A
Rao, I V
Reddy, P J
Reed, A M
Reeves, I A
Reeves, N A
Renkema, S E
Rex, S D
Reynolds, E M R R
Reynolds, M P
Richards, S K
Ring, H P
Ritchie, J P
Roberts, I
Sadler, G M
Sanchez Ballester, J
Schofield, J B
Scott, O J
Shahabdeen, M M
Shahrad, B
Shaikh, T R
Shamim, S U
Shankar, R K
Shanmugalingam, S
Sheth, H
Shrotri, K N
Shrotri, N C
Siggers, G R
Singh, K
Sivakumar, K
Slater, R N S
Slawinska, K M
Soorma, A
Spicer, A J
Sritharan, S
Sterndale Bennett, A
Stevens, A E
Stevenson, P F
Stewart, K R
Storr, B S H
Street, D F
Subash Chandran, S
Sugarman, P A
Taylor, D H
Teed, H
Telfer, T P
Thom, C H
Thom, R B
Thomas, A J
Thomas, J G
Thornburgh, I L
Timms, C M J
Towner, H D
Tudor De Silva, H P B
Unter, C E M
Urquhart, M M
Vaile, M S B
Van Seenus, T E
Van Wyk, G J

Vaux, R H C
Virden, J C
Wahby, C C T
Walker, A E
Walker, C J
Ward, M A G
Waters, T C
Whistler, D M
Widd, S E
Wilford, P J
Williams, R C
Wilson, G
Witt, J M
Worden, R J
Yau, Y Y

Maldon

Booker, P
Bozman, E H
Britten, C S
Brown, L M
Cargill, C L
Carr, M J T
Causton, J A
Chapman, A B C
Cronin, M T
De Souza, R F
Deasy, J M
Elliot, D
Fairhall, D W
Furze, R J
Haeger, M P
Jones, R A
Lim, L
Macdonald, R J M
McDowell, I R
McGeachy, D J
Mann, S G
Morley, S L
O'Connell, M S
Philip, I G
Roper, R M
Shakespear, S
Shirodaria, C V
Smithson, C J
Stylianides, L
Wilkinson, M J

Mallaig

Cameron, J F
Duck, D

Malmesbury

Ansell, S F
Badcock, K
Badenoch, J M
Barron, G J
Charles, D L
Crane, B J
Crawford, C E J
Harrison, J D
Heathcock, J P
Howarth, J A
Neale, J S
Owen, C G
Painter, D J
Pettit, J G
Pettit, P C
Pickering, N J
Pym, J
Roberts, B J
Rycroft, J A
Sturrock, D
Teasdale, K J

Malpas

Clendinnen, B G
Dalzell, A
Dalzell, K
Davies, L M C
Higgie, E J
Howarth, A J
Hulbert, C C
Hulbert, G M
London, A A M
Monck-Mason, J M
Price, M L
Smith, A C

Malton

Balmer, R L
Balmer, S L
Blakeborough, A J
Campbell, L
Carrie, D R
Carrie, M
Diggory, C J
Diggory, T M
Grant, W C
Grove, L

Hobkinson, L M
Jones, C
Lynch, M
Rayne, D
Sleeman, M L
Taylor-Helps, D F
Taylor, H P
Thornton, S M
Umbrich, P
Wilson, D R

Malvern

Adeney, C G
Allbright, M
Allbright, S E
Barnes, R D
Bates, P A S
Birkett, J R
Black, J
Brocklebank, D M
Brown, A L
Buchan, D R
Budd, J M
Busher, G L
Carpenter, L
Colquhoun, M C
Conway, K R
Davies, S J
Draper, M R
Dyer, H E
Dyer, N H
Edwards, J
Fenton, E S N
Fuller, D J
Gilbert, R F
Grant, M I
Gray, J
Hale-Brown, J A
Harcup, D M
Harcup, J W
Herriot, B W A
Herriot, S E
Hinchliffe, M
Hindson, T C
Holland, C R
Holman, R M
Jarrett, K W
Jones, J B
Lambert, R A
Lavin, J B
McCarthy, P H V
McCracken, A L
Mackman, C J
Macleod, I R
Mather, J M
Mayner, P E
Mead, S H
Millard, N R H
O'Flynn, M W
Orgee, J M
Palmer, E N E
Payler, D K
Pearce, J C
Radley, D J
Richards, J A
Richards, M J
Rogers, P J
Rose, P
Sadler, R L
Scott, G S
Sear, A J
Sefton-Fiddian, J
Senior, E L
Shervington, P C
Sinclair, S A
Spanton, D B
Stewart, B R
Tarr, K E
Trueman, T
Tuck, B A
Turner, C E
Vaughan, J A
Vaughan, M M
Walsh, P J F
Ward, B-A
Webster, C D
Wheatstone, S E
Wight, K C
Williams, G M

Manchester

Abbott, M
Abboud, S H
Abu Aisha, B B
Ackrill, P
Adams, J E
Adamski, J K
Addis, V P
Addison, G M

Ag Hj Mohd Hassan, D H
Agarwala, V K
Agius, R M
Ahearne, D A J
Ahluwalia, A
Ahluwalia, A S
Ahluwalia, R S
Ahmad Mohd Zain, Z
Ahmad, M Z
Ahmad, M M
Ahmad, Z H
Ahmed, A R
Ahmed, S N
Ahmed, Z
Ainscow, G
Akbar, A
Akhter, S
Al-Abady, A
Al-Asadi, A D
Al-Gailani, M A-M A-R
Al-Moomen, A H A
Al-Mulla, A
Al-Saffar, Z S A
Alderman, P R
Alderson, D M
Alexander, G S
Ali, A K M
Ali, G
Ali, H H H
Ali, N S
Allan, B K
Allaun, D H
Allcock, D M
Allcock, S
Allen, D L
Allen, G
Allen, N H P
Allkins, J A
Allweis, B
Alnuamaani, T M
Alvi, F-U-H
Amos, H T
Anderson, I M
Ang, C W-M
Anshar, F M
Anwer, K
Appachi, E
Apte, R V
Armstrong, J D
Arnold, F W
Arnold, M M
Arora, S C
Arrowsmith, J M
Arshad, S A
Arya, S
Ashford, P
Ashleigh, R J
Ashworth, H M
Ashworth, H W
Ashworth, J L
Aspinall, G R
Asumu, T O
Atalla, A E
Ataullah, S M
Atrey, A K
Atrey, N
August, P J
Austin, S
Azam, F S
Azam, M
Bahgat, M S
Bahia, S S
Baigel, S
Baildam, A D
Baildam, E M
Bailey, E V
Bailey, N
Bailey, S M
Bainbridge, M A
Baird, R M
Bakhat, A A
Balayogi, K K
Baldwin, R C
Ballardie, F W
Ballin, I A
Ballon, M D
Banerjee, S
Banks, R H
Bannatyne, W
Bannister, C L
Bannister, C M
Bannister, P
Baral, S
Barber, N P
Barber, P V
Barker, H C
Barker, N I
Barman, D N

Barnard, J B
Barnard, R J
Barnard, S J
Barnes, A J
Barnes, D G
Barnes, N L P
Baronos, E
Barooah, K
Barooah, P S
Barr, L
Barrow, J
Barson, A J
Barton, A C
Bass, K
Basu, A M
Basu, P S
Batchelor, J S
Bates, A C
Baxandall, M L
Baxter, D N
Beadsworth, M B J
Beards, S C
Beardwell, C G
Beck, G N
Beetles, U M
Begum, S
Behardien, J Y
Behrana, A J
Bell, M D D
Bellantuono, I
Belli, A
Bellis, A J
Benbow, E W
Benett, I J
Benjamin, S
Bennett, D H
Bentley, A M
Benton, K G F
Berger, S M
Berlyne, N
Bernstein, A A
Bernstein, R M
Bertfield, H
Betts, C D
Bhatia, T
Bhatti, W A
Bhima, G W D
Bianchi, A M
Bianchi, S M
Birchall, W
Birrell, F N
Birtwistle, I H
Birzgalis, A R
Bishop, P N
Bishop, P W
Black, J E B
Blackhall, F H
Blake, I C
Blakey, A F
Blumfield, A
Bodey, S A
Boggis, C R M
Bolton, M J
Bonington, S C
Bonshek, R E
Booton, R
Borg Costanzi, J M
Borrill, J K
Bosson, S
Boulton, A J M
Bourne, D R
Bourne, J
Bourne, M S
Bouskill, J
Bowden, L S
Bowdler, G R
Bowen, J C
Bowley, C A
Boyce, C T
Boyd, M I
Boyd, R
Boylan, C E
Bracegirdle, A P
Bradburn, J W
Bradbury, A J
Bradbury, G A
Bradley, A J
Bradley, D S
Bradley, S M A
Braganza, J M
Braganza, M A
Brahim, K A
Braine, K
Brayshay, M J
Brear, S G
Brennan, B M D
Brew, C J
Brew, S
Bridgewater, B J M

Brien, P F
Briggs, C H
Brim, V D
Broman, S M
Bromley, A B
Brooks, D
Brooks, N H
Brosnan, R D
Brough, P J
Brough, R J
Broughton, J L
Brown, A G
Brown, A L
Brown, A A
Brown, A B
Brown, A P T
Brown, G N
Brown, G C S
Brown, I M
Brown, J R
Brown, S M
Broxton, J S
Bruce, I
Bruce, J
Buchalter, I M
Buchanan, D J
Buckley, C H
Budden, P D
Bundred, N J
Bungay, C J
Burgess, H
Burgess, M I
Burke, P J
Burling, P M
Burman, A
Burnett, H C
Burnie, J P
Burns, A S
Burt, P A
Burton, I D
Burton, I E
Busby, G P
Bussin, J L
Butler, A S
Butler, P A
Butterworth, D M
Byers, R J
Byrne, E J
Byrne, G J
Callander, M J
Camilleri, A E
Campbell, A A
Campbell, C S
Campbell, I T
Campbell, L H
Campbell, M S
Campbell, N J
Campbell, N S
Campbell, R H A
Cant, M M
Canty, D P C
Capek, M E Y
Caplan, G
Caplan, M
Carley, S D
Carlin, J
Carlisle, H R
Carlson, G L
Carnwath, T C M
Carpenter, J E
Carpenter, L J
Carrero Cabo, A C
Carrington, B M
Carter, J B
Cassidy, J M
Cater, E J
Caulfield, H M
Chadwick, I S
Chadwick, P C
Chadwick, T H
Chakravarty, M R
Chalmers, N
Chalmers, R J G
Chan, K P
Chande, C
Chandiok, S
Chandiramani, V A
Chang, J
Chant, H J
Charles-Jones, H D
Charles, S J
Charlesworth, D
Charnley, J
Charters, A J
Chaudhuri, H
Chaudry, I A
Chaudry, N B
Chaudury, F R
Checkley, E J

Manchester

Cheema, R A
Chen, C E
Cheshire, C M
Chetty, M C P
Chew, C A
Chintapatla, S
Chisthi, M K N
Chiswick, M L
Chiu, C T
Chiu, T W
Choi, C F
Choi, D
Choi, P
Chopra, R
Choudhri, A H
Chowdhury, B A
Christmas, R J
Chung, W K
Cinkotai, K I
Clancy, A
Clare, R G
Clark, A F
Clark, A J
Clark, L J
Clarke, A D
Clarke, B
Clarke, C M
Clarke, C P C
Clayson, A D
Clayton-Smith, J
Clayton, A J
Clayton, P E
Cleary, B J
Cleary, M A
Cleator, P J
Clegg, D S
Clough, D L
Clutton, H A
Cockayne, L M
Coe, G J
Coffey, J P
Cohen, S J
Colligan, D
Colville, W C
Conlong, P J M
Connolly, L P
Conroy, J I
Contractor, A S
Conway, M J
Cook, A E
Cooke, C A
Cooke, M J
Coombs, S J
Cooper, A
Cooper, J
Cooper, M
Cooper, P N
Corbett, H J
Cornish, E L
Costello, C B
Couper, D M
Cowie, A G
Cowie, V J
Cox, A E
Coyne, J D
Craig, C V
Crane, M D
Cranston, J
Craufurd, D I O
Crawford, N H B
Creme, I
Cribb, J M
Crocombe, S J
Crook, I
Crook, S A
Cropper, M
Crowther, C H
Crowther, D
Cruickshank, J K
Cryer, L M
Cumming, A M
Cumming, R L
Cunningham, M B
Cunningham, S A
Curran, J N
Curran, J
Currer, B A
Curzen, N P
D'Souza, S W
Dafalla, B E D A
Dainton, M C
Dale, A K
Dalton, S J
Daly, E L
Danczak, A F
Dando, P B
Dar, S A
Das, B C
Das, P K

Dass, L
Dass, S
Datta, P
Davenport, P J
Davenport, R H
Davenport, R
David, T J
Davidson, S E
Davie, H M
Davies, D R A
Davies, H
Davies, R R
Davies, S
Davis, J R E
Davison, M C
Davison, P
Dawes, N J
Dawson, D W
Day, J R
Day, J N
Day, J B
De Silva, H A
De Weever, A C A
De, R N
Deakin, J F W
Deakin, S
Dean, A
Dean, G L
Dean, N
Dearlove, O R
Deas, J
Decalmer, S A
Decatris, M P
Deighton, J G
Delaney, M J
Dellagrammaticas, D
Denning, D W
Densem, C G
Derbyshire, S A
Desmond, J
Dewsnap, C H
Dhadli, M K
Dickson, A P
Dickson, A I
Dickson, J
Din, S A
Dinerstein, I
Dixon, N W
Dixon, P A
Dodd, A S
Dodd, C L
Dodge, O G
Doffman, S R
Dogra, T S
Dolan, L J
Dolan, M C
Dombrowe, A J
Donnai, D
Donnai, P
Donnelly, W J
Doody, P
Doohan, J
Doran, H E
Doran, H M
Dorman, P J
Dornan, C C
Downey, S E
Dowzer, J W
Duane, L P
Dube, P
Dubicka, B W
Ducker, G M
Ducksbury, C F J
Duddy, O M
Duffy, D J
Duncan, J E
Duncan, T
Dunkley, M A
Dunkow, P D
Dunn, K W
Dunningham, T H
Duper, B
Durrington, P N
Dymock, I W
Eastwood, G L
Eccles, N C
Eden, O B
Eden, R I
Eden, S
Edmondson, E D
Edmondson, G M P
Edwards, J D
Eeckelaers, M C W
Egan, J J G F
El Gadi, I A
El-Ghazawy, M A L M A
El-Khashab, T A F
El-Mikatti, N

El Teraifi, H A A
Element, P
Elliot, S D
Ellis, R M
Elsworth, C F
Ementon-Shaw, L A
Eminson, D M
Emmerson, A J B
England, R E
Enoch, B A
Enoch, L C
Ercleve, T N O
Ersfeld, E
Etteh, B E
Evans, B M
Evans, D G R
Evans, J E C
Evans, J H
Everett, J
Ewing, C I
Fajumi, A O
Fallon, J S
Farquhar, A D
Farrington, M R
Farrington, W T
Faza, H N
Fellows, G
Fenerty, C H
Fenton, L M
Ferguson, A M
Ferguson, A P
Ferguson, D A
Fink, P R
Finke, A S
Finn, T J
Firoze, A
Firoze, K V
Fitchet, A
Fitzgerald, Z
Fitzpatrick, H J
Flascher, S M
Flasher, M C
Fleming, D H
Fletcher, C A
Fletcher, K M
Foex, B A
Foley, K N
Ford, J M
Forman, W M
Foster, M E
Fox, D M
Fox, H
Fox, S H
France, M W
Francis, E M
Frank, P I
Frank, P L
Fraser, I S
Fraser, W R
Freed, L
Freedman, F
Freedman, R C
Freeman, A S
Freeman, E
Freeman, S R M
Freemont, A J
Froggatt, P A
Fuller, J E A
Fyans, P G
Fyfe, D W
Gadd, J R
Gage, A J
Gahan, A D
Gale, A C
Gambhir, A K
Gan, Y C
Gandhi, A
Ganvir, P L
Ganvir, S P
Ganvir, U P
Garcia Alen Garcia, L
Gardner, R
Garg, T L
Garland, J B
Garrett, G
Garrett, H M
Garston, J B
Garvey, T P N
Gater, R A
Gatley, M S
Gatoff, H
Gattamaneni, H R
Gerry, B A W
Ghani, R
Ghosh, A K
Gibbs, M G
Gibson, P D
Gilani, S A A
Gilberthorpe, J

Gill, A K
Gill, H M S
Gill, J
Gill, L S
Gill, P
Gill, S
Gillespie, J E
Girolami, A
Gladman, G
Glass, A L
Godfrey, H E
Goel, R P
Gokal, R
Goldberg, H M
Golding, J L
Goldstone, J
Goldwater, D E
Goldwater, H L
Gomm, S A
Goodall, B
Goodall, K L
Goodman, A I
Goodman, M A
Goodman, M J
Goodman, R E
Goodwin, J S
Gordon, D
Gore, D
Gore, H
Gough, D C S
Gough, S G W
Gough, S P
Gough, V M
Gow, D P
Graham, A
Graham, D
Graham, S
Green, J M
Green, K M J
Green, R
Green, S A
Greenaway, T J
Greenbaum, A R
Greene, A
Greenwood, J E
Greig, D G
Griffin, C J
Griffiths, A G
Griffiths, G D
Griffiths, M R
Griffiths, P J
Grinter, K R
Groarke, A W
Grotte, G J
Groves, C J
Gudgeon, E A
Guhathakurta, S
Gulati, R C
Gunda, A F
Gunson, H H
Gupta, N K
Gupta, N K
Guthrie, E A
Guthrie, G E
Guthrie, S K
Guy, R C
Gwinnutt, C L
Hackett, R J
Hadjiloucas, I
Haider, Y
Hair, W M
Haji-Michael, P G
Halder, B
Halder, N
Hall, C M
Halstead, L G
Hamdy, R
Hamilton, A J
Hamilton, R M
Hammer, M R
Hamour, A O A A A
Hampson, F G
Hanley, S P
Hannah, J C
Happold, M E
Haque, I-U
Harake, M D J
Hardinge, K
Hardy, C C
Hardy, L A
Hargreaves, F M
Hargreaves, G K
Harper, N J N
Harrington, R C
Harris, B V
Harris, C P
Harris, H J
Harris, H R
Harris, J

Harris, M A
Harris, M
Harris, P L
Harris, R
Harrison, A M
Harrison, B J
Harrison, C J
Harrison, J A
Hartley, G
Hasan, F
Hasleton, P S
Hasson, A A M
Haughney, S L
Hawes, S J
Hawgood, E A
Hawkesford, L M
Hawkins, K C
Hawnaur, J M
Haworth, D
Haworth, J I
Hay, C R M
Hay, G G
Hayes, M J
Heagerty, A M
Heald, G E
Healey, A E
Healy, T E J
Heathcote, I T
Hellewell, J S E
Helman, S C
Hennessy, D M
Herbert, E A
Hercules, B L
Heron, E C
Hershon, E
Hibbert, D L
Hickling, D J
Higgins, G A
Hill, A S
Hill, J
Hill, J M
Hilton, S R
Hindle, Y A
Hindley, D T
Hira, N
Hirsch, P J
Hoad-Reddick, D A
Hobson, S J
Hodgkinson, J P
Hodgson, E
Hodson, S A
Hogg, M S
Holland-Elliott, K
Holland, J E
Hollingshead, S
Holloway, J
Hollows, P
Holmes, A M
Holmes, R
Holmes, S J
Holt, L P J
Hooper, T L
Hope, B
Hopgood, P
Hopwood, P
Horan, M A
Hore, B D
Horrocks, A W
Horsman, E L
Hosker, H B
Hoskins, A
Hotchkies, I L M
Hotchkies, S A C
Houghton, C M
Houston, E C
Howard, R E
Howat, J M T
Howden, M D
Howe, M C
Howell, A
Howell, S J
Huddy, R B
Hughes, D G
Hughes, J G
Hughes, M I
Hughes, N R
Hughes, P M
Hughes, S M
Hughes, S
Humpherson, J R
Humphreys, J
Huq, H H
Huq, R
Huq, Z
Hurley, E
Hussain, I
Hussain, Z
Hutchinson, C E
Hutchinson, D J

Hutchison, A J
Hutton, A J F
Hyams, N A
Hyde, S M
Hyman, J G
Hynes, J E
Ibrahim, A F
Ibrahim, A M
Iddon, J
Igielman, F I P
Ingram, G
Ioannidou, S S
Isaacs, A B
Isaacson, D M
Isalska, B J
Islam, C O F
Islam, M S
Islam, M S
Issa, B G
Ivinson, M H L
Iyengar, E N
Iyengar, M
Jacks, S P
Jackson, A
Jackson, C W
Jacobs, E M
Jacobs, L G H
Jafaree, S A H
Jafari, B
Jaffe, S M
Jaffe, W
Jain, S K
Jalaluddin, Z
Jamal, W
James, J M
James, P F
James, R D
Jari, S
Jarratt, J W
Jarvis, R R
Javidi, M
Jayachandra Reddy, K
Jayson, D
Jayson, G C
Jeffery, K F K
Jeffries, M
Jeffries, S C
Jenkins, J P R
Jepson, F K
Jha, A N
Jilani, S A
John, A B
Johnson, D S
Johnson, D A W
Johnson, R J
Johnson, R W G
Johnson, R A
Johnston, T A
Jolly, G K
Jolly, S S
Jones, A W
Jones, A C
Jones, A S
Jones, A M
Jones, A C
Jones, B P
Jones, C I
Jones, D J
Jones, D L
Jones, K E
Jones, N P
Jones, S L
Jones, T M
Jones, V L
Joseph, A E
Joseph, C T D
Joseph, S G
Joshi, G D
Joshi, V B
Joyce, P R
Jukes, R A M
Julien, D R
Juma, N M H
Kaczmarski, E B
Kale, M
Kalim, K
Kamaly-Asl, I D
Kaminski, D J
Kanagasegar, S
Kane, K
Kane, S
Karajeh, M A-R
Kauffmann, L A D
Kaur, R
Kaur, S
Kaushal, K
Kaushal, N A
Kaushik, V
Kavanagh, S J G

Manchester

Kawafi, K R
Kawonga, R M P
Kay, C R
Kay, C L
Kay, M J R
Kay, N J
Kay, P R
Kay, R A
Kaye, A H
Kaye, J E
Keaney, M G L
Kearney, G D A
Kebbie, M M
Keenan, D J M
Kelsall, M E
Kennedy, M J
Kenny, N W
Kenrick, D A
Kernohan, P G
Kerns, W
Kerr, E
Kerr, M E
Kerr, S J
Kerrane, J
Kerrin, D P
Kerry, A L
Kershaw, P
Keynes, G R E
Khalid, S
Khan, A A
Khan, A N
Khan, G M
Khan, M A H
Khan, M A
Khan, M A
Khan, M H Z
Khan, N S
Khan, Q A
Khan, S S
Khan, S
Khan, Z A
Khanna, M
Khoo, S H
Khurana, K M
Khurana, M
Kidd, C M
Kiff, E S
King, J E
Kingston, H M
Kingston, P A
Kingston, R D
Kinsella, T J
Kirby, A
Kirk, P R
Kissen, G D N
Kitchener, H C
Kitching, W J
Kiwanuka, A I
Kleinberg, J E
Knox, W F
Kok Shun, J L C S
Kolb, C S
Kondratowicz, T
Koria, K
Kotegaonkar, K S
Kotegaonkar, M K
Krawiecki, J A
Kukula, M S
Kulkarni, J R
Kumar, P
Kumar, S
Kuna, K
Kunwar, A M
Kurdy, N M
Kwartz, J
Kwok, S
Kwong, H T
Kwong, L J
Kyriakides, C A
Ladusans, E J
Laha, S N
Lai, P
Lalloo, F I
Lamond, D N
Lancashire, R W G
Lancashire, S C J
Lang-Sadler, E
Langley, S J
Lansbury, E S
Lascelles, R G
Lashford, L S
Lau, M W-M
Lau, Y N
Lavin, M J
Law, J B
Lawler, W
Lawrence, J A
Lawton, V
Lea, S

Leach, J M
Leahy, B C
Leahy, M D
Leary, T S
Leask, K M
Leatherbarrow, B
Lee, P
Lee, S H
Lee, W R
Leech, A M
Leeming, J T
Leeson, J E
Leitch, D
Lendon, M
Lendrum, J
Lennon, S P
Lennox, B J
Leon, E A
Leschziner, G D
Leveson, C M
Levi, M
Levine, E L
Levy, R D
Levy, R G
Lewis, H M
Lewis, M A
Lewis, M R
Lewis, S W
Liaw, V P
Libbert, D H
Libman, I
Lieberman, B A
Lindsay, S D
Linforth, R A
Lipworth, L
Lissett, C A
Lister, B S
Liu Yin, A
Livingstone, D I
Lloyd, G
Lloyd, H
Lloyd, I C
Lobo, C J
Lockwood, M
Loke, A T-H
Lomas, P A
Lancaster, J A
Longson, D
Lorigan, P C
Louca, L L
Love, E M
Lovell, M E
Lowe, H
Lowe, P J M
Lucas, G S
Ludlow, J P
Lumb, P D
Lydon, B N
Lyons, C A
McArdle, M T
Macbeath, J T
McCann, R A
McCarthy, D K
McCollum, C N
McCorkindale, S
McCracken, J
McCrea, R R
MacDiarmaid-Gordon, A R
McDonagh, C M
MacDonald, H J
MacDowall, J E
Macfarlane, G J
Macfarlane, L
MacFarlane, N D
Macloy, D
McGawley, C M
McGee, M T
McGonigle, T P
McGrath, G J
McGrogan, L P
McGrouther, D A
McIntyre, F J
Mackay, M E
McKechnie, E M
McKenna, F
Mackenzie, F A
Mackenzie, J J
Mackenzie, K R
McKibbin, V P
McKinlay, D M
McKinlay, I A
McKirdy, S W
Mackway-Jones, K C
MacLean, I M
McLean, J M
MacLennan, I
McLeod, D
McMahon, R F T

McMenzie, A J
Macnab, A
McNamara, J F
McNulty, S J
McNulty, S M
McShane, J A
McVey, R J
Madan, Y N
Magee, B J
Mahafza, T A
Mahmood, T
Majid, Z
Makin, D
Makin, G W J
Makin, W P
Malik, R A
Malik, R A
Mallick, N P
Malloy, N P
Maltby, B
Manchester, D J
Mandal, B K
Mangar, S A
Mansfield, J D
Marco Molina, M L
Marcus, R L
Marcuson, R W
Maresh, M J A
Marginson, J E
Margison, F R
Margolis, S
Mark, P E
Marsden, H L
Marsden, H B
Marshall, C F
Marshall, R E
Marsland, A
Marsland, M L
Martin-Hirsch, P L
Martin, C J
Martin, C E G
Martin, D F
Martin, P S
Martin, R B
Martin, S E
Mason, J C
Matthews, R C
Mattison, A F
Maudar, J A
Maurice, S C
Maw, A E
Mawer, G E
Mayall, F G
Mayall, R M
Maynard, S M
Mazhari, H K
Mbaya, P S
Mbonu, G O
Meakin, G H
Meehan, T
Mehraj, Q R
Mehta, S G
Mellor, P J
Mene, R
Merrill, K J
Meshikhes, A-W N
Metzger, R E
Meyer, S
Michael, L A
Middlehurst, R J
Miles, J F
Miller, H E J
Miller, J P
Miller, J S
Miller, L L
Miller, L J
Miller, V
Milligan, H S
Mills, A E
Mills, G F
Mills, K B
Millward, R P
Milton, R S
Mistry, N U
Mitchell, G G
Mitchell, J C
Mitchell, R G
Mitchell, S R
Mo, C-N
Modi, N K
Modi, S P
Mohammad, D
Mohammad, W
Mohr, P D
Mokashi, A V
Molyneaux, B
Momen, A
Monaghan, S J
Montague, L R

Monteiro, B T
Moore, C E G
Moore, M A
Moran, A
Morewood, S A
Morley, J
Moroney, J F
Morris, D P
Morris, E M
Morris, T M
Morton, R J
Moss, D A
Moyo, P K
Mughal, M Z
Mukherjee, D K
Mukherjee, V
Mullins, P D
Munro, K A
Munshi, S B
Murray, S R
Musgrove, B T
Myerscough, A
Naidoo, R K A
Nanavati, B A
Napier-Hemy, R D
Naqui, F A
Nash, J R
Nasim, A
Nauta, M E
Nayar, R
Naylor, K M T
Neary, D
Needham, D J
Neville, T E
Newbould, M J
Newman, W G J
Newton, J S
Newton, J L
Newton, R W
Newton, V E
Nicholsby, D
Nickerson, C B
Nightingale, P
Niven, R M
Nkolokosa, M S
Noble, J L
Noble, J
Nolan, D M
Noone, J F
Noone, M A
Norburn, P S
Norbury, L P
Noronha, E A
Noronha, M J
Nurennabi, A K M
Nussbaum, T
Nylander, D L
Nysenbaum, A M
Nzelu, E N
O'Brien, K
O'Carroll, D J
O'Connor, A M
O'Connor, J M
O'Connor, L M
O'Connor, M B
O'Connor, R D
O'Donnchadha, E P
O'Donnell, A
O'Donoghue, N B
O'Driscoll, K J
O'Driscoll, S C
O'Dwyer, S T P
O'Keeffe, N J
O'Loughlin, C J
O'Malley, P A
O'Reilly, E
Oelbaum, M H
Ogdon, C
Oram, J C
Orr, R J
Orr, W M
Orton, C I
Orton, J K
Osborne, M A
Osu, B A
Owen, K R
Painter, G E
Painter, M J
Pal, B
Panagea, S E
Panikker, S
Pantelides, M L
Parihar, P
Parihar, S S
Parker, G
Parker, S J
Parr, A M
Parrott, N R
Parry, N S

Parsons, H
Parsons, S T
Pasha, M
Patel, D
Patel, L
Patel, M
Patel, R H
Patel, R G
Patel, R R
Pathak, P L
Patrick, M R
Patton, J T
Pattoo, B A
Paul, A S
Payne, S R
Pearson, R C
Pemberton, M N
Pereira, D T M
Pereira, J R
Perera, D M D
Perkins, R J K
Perry, M S
Peters, L A
Petrie, H P
Phillips, K A
Phillips, R S
Phillips, R
Picardo, L
Pickering, C A C
Pickering, G
Pickin, C A
Pickin, J M
Picton, S
Pike, A C
Pilkington, R S
Pitches, D W
Plenderleith, M
Plummer, J R
Pollard, B J
Poller, L
Porczynska, K R
Porritt, A J
Porter, J N
Postlethwaite, R J
Poston, B L
Power, S
Poynton, A M
Prabhakar, D T C
Prabhakar, N
Prendergast, B D
Prescott, M C
Preston, D W
Prestwich, H R
Price, D A
Price, L J
Price, P M
Price, R
Price, R M
Pritchard, D M
Procter, A W
Prodhan, M S
Puddy, V F
Pugh, E W
Puliyel, J M
Pumphrey, R S H
Puri, S
Purohit, N N
Purser, J H
Qasim, F J
Qayyum, N
Quddus, S F
Quinnell, A J
Qureshi, K
Qureshi, M I
Radford, J A
Rahim, O
Rahman, J
Rahman, K M
Rahman, M M
Rahman, T S
Rahuja, S P
Rahuja, S A S
Rajagopal, R
Rakhit, A K
Ralston, A J
Ramesh, C A
Rampling, K
Ramsdale, D R
Ramsden, R T
Rana, S K
Randall, P E
Randhawa, J S
Rankin, W J
Rannan-Eliya, R W D G
Ranote, A S
Ranote, S R
Ranson, M R
Rao, P J

Rasheed, F
Ratcliffe, D S
Ratcliffe, J
Rawson, A
Ray, D W
Ray, S G
Rayner, C R
Razzak, A
Reddy, Dr
Redmond, B
Rees, G A
Reid, H
Renehan, A G
Reynolds, K M M
Rhatigan, M C
Richards, J L
Richardson, J A
Richardson, P L
Richmond, S J
Ridgway, A E A
Rigby, J A
Riley, S F
Rittoo, D B
Rittoo, D
Riza, I M
Rizvi, Q R
Roach, S C
Roberts, D J
Roberts, J
Roberts, M E
Roberts, P-J
Roberts, R E I
Roberts, S P
Roberts, S A
Robertson, J D
Robertson, M A C
Robins, N M
Robinson, A J
Robinson, J M
Robson, G E W
Robson, S A
Roche, M E
Rogers, J E
Rogers, J M
Rojo Llanos, L
Rolan, P E
Roland, M A
Roland, M O
Ronalds, C M
Rose, G K
Rose, K G
Rose, S S
Rosen, E S
Rosenberg, A
Rosenberg, B
Rosenberg, R B
Ross, C E
Ross, K G M
Ross, R S
Rossini, J
Roussak, N J
Rowsell, M A
Roxburgh, R H S R
Royce, S L
Royle, S G
Rozycki, A A
Ruiz De Arcaute, J
Russell, E
Russell, S A
Rutherford, J D
Rutter, R A
Ryan, B P
Ryan, M M
Sabar, M A
Sadiq, M
Sadiq, S A
Sadiq, Z A
Saeed, M
Saeed, N
Saeed, R
Saeed, S R
Sahni, A S
Sahni, V A S
Saidi, S A
Saleem, A
Saleh, S
Salim, R
Salleh, S
Salvi, V G
Samad, A
Samanta, A K
Sambrook, M A
Samuel, M J
Samuels, B T A
Sanchez, E G
Sanders, K J
Sanders, P A
Sandhu, S
Sandle, L N

Margate

Sanehi, O P
Sangha, M S
Sanyal, D
Sarangi, B B
Sarmah, N N
Sastry, S R
Sathi, N
Saunders, M P
Sawyer, R H
Schady, W
Schofield, K P
Scholes, P E Q
Schroeder, U E
Schryer, J
Schwarzer, A
Sclare, P D
Scothern, S R
Seabourne, A E
Seehra, H
Seely, M F
Seex, D M
Segar, S L
Selby, L A
Sell, L A
Sen, D
Sen, S A
Serfaty, M A
Seriki, D M
Seshappa, V
Shafi, R N
Shafiq, M
Shah, D K
Shah, P J
Shah, S M A
Shaikh Konel, S J
Shaikh, N
Shaikh, N
Shakespeare, E J
Shanks, J H
Sharma, M M
Sharma, S K
Sharp, D S
Sharples, A
Shaw, A
Shaw, A L
Shearer, K
Sheikh, M Y
Shelly, M P
Shepard, G J
Sheppard, G E
Sheridan, E G
Sherlock, D J
Sherman, L H
Sherratt, J
Sherry, S J
Shlosberg, D
Shoebridge, P J
Short, C D
Shortall, D A
Shreeve, D R
Shroff, S
Siddiqui, S
Sides, B A
Siew Tu, C-L
Sim, E
Simenoff, C J
Simler, N R
Simon, A S
Simpson, A
Simpson, J C G
Sims, D G
Singh, A
Singh, D P
Singh, H
Singh, K V
Singh, M
Singh, W S G
Singh, Y S
Singleton, N A
Sinha, A
Sinha, S
Siriwardena, A K
Siviter, G
Slack, C B T
Slade, D A J
Slater, C S
Slater, H B
Slater, R M
Slevin, N J
Sloan, G D
Smalldridge, A
Smith, A R B
Smith, E D
Smith, E P
Smith, E J
Smith, G D
Smith, H R
Smith, M G
Smith, N S

Smith, P J
Smith, P H
Smith, P H
Smith, R H
Smith, R A
Smith, S J
Smith, V J
Smyrniou, N N
Snow, P J D
Snowden, H N
Snowden, P R
Sodipo, J A J
Soman, V B
Soni, S G
Soothill, J S
Spooner, S J
Sproston, A R M
Spyrantis, N
Sram, I S
Sreedharan, K
Srivatsa, G
St. John, J M
Stalley, L F
Stanbridge, T N
Statters, D J
Stedman, H G B
Steele, C
Steen, L
Steller, P H
Stevens, E D
Stevens, R F
Stevens, R H
Stewart, A G
Stewart, A R
Stewart, D
Stewart, D J
Stewart, W A
Stone, M J
Stone, P A
Stoner, H B
Stout, R
Strang, F A
Strawford, G R
Sturgess, H
Sugarman, P M
Sulistio, E
Summers, C L
Summers, Y J
Summerton, C B
Sumner, I J
Super, M
Sutcliffe, N
Sutton, E J
Sutton, J F
Swan, J W
Syed, O A
Sykes, A J
Sykes, M G
Symmons, D P M
Szofinska, B
Tahir, T A
Talbot, J S
Talbot, P R
Tamin, S K F
Tamkin, E J
Tamkin, W P
Tan, M M S
Tasker, I T
Tasker, P R S
Tatnall, S K
Taylor, M B
Taylor, M J
Taylor, P A C
Taylor, P M
Taylor, S J
Teale, K F H
Tebbett, J E
Telford, R M
Tench, D W
Tennant, B D
Teo, H-G
Tepper, R
Than Kyaw, Dr
Thapar, A K
Thatcher, N
Theodossiadis, A
Thomas, A G
Thomas, C S
Thomas, N B
Thomas, P W V
Thompson, A R T
Thompson, D
Thompson, H F
Thompson, J C
Thompson, J L
Thorns, G M M
Thurairajasingam, S
Ticehurst, H M
Tighe, B S

Tobias, C M
Todd, I D H
Tolaney, M D
Tolaney, P M
Tomlinson, S
Tong, H N
Tonge, G M
Torr, B
Torr, J B D
Townend, W J K
Towse, M S
Tragen, D J
Trainer, P J
Treacy, F P
Trehan, V K
Tremlett, C H
Trenholm, P W
Trueman, J A
Tsolakis, M G
Tudor, G J
Tuffin, J R
Tullo, A B
Tunbridge, R D G
Turley, I M
Turner, G S
Turner, M A T
Turner, S L
Turner, S J
Turnheim, E
Tyrrell, N M
Unwin, M R
Upadhyay, D R
Upadhyaya, A K
Utting, M R
Valdez, F N
Vallance, H D
Vallance, R L
Valle, J W
Van Den Bos, A
Van Ross, E R E
Vangikar, M B
Varma, B N
Vasanth, E C
Vause, S H
Veitch, I H M
Venning, M C
Verma, S G
Vickers, K
Vites, N P
Vohra, A
Vowles, H A
Vu, T Q
Wacks, H
Waddell, N M R
Wadsworth, R
Waite, I
Waldman, S J
Walker, C E
Walker, H A C
Walker, M G
Walker, R W M
Walker, S
Walker, W D
Walkley, J H C
Waller, C J
Walshe, E A
Walton, J M
Wan Hussein, H Y
Ward, C
Ward, D
Ward, K
Ward, S J
Waring, W B
Warnes, T W
Waterhouse, D G
Webb, F M
Webb, N J A
Webber, M C B
Webster, L
Webster, R C
Weetman, J P
Weighill, F J
Weiner, M
Weinstock, H S
Weir, D C
Weleminsky, A
Wheatly, R S
Wheeldin, W
Whitaker, D K
Whitaker, M R
Whitaker, M J
Whitaker, T
Whitby, D J
White, C E
White, C S
Whitehouse, C R
Whitehouse, R W
Whiteley, J M
Whiting, M R

Whittaker, J
Whitworth, H E
Wijeratne, R K
Wijeyesekera, K G
Wilcock, D J
Wilcock, J
Wiles, P G
Wilkes, J M
Wilkins, E L
Wilkinson, A J
Wilkinson, B A
Williams, B J
Williams, B T J
Williams, M L
Williams, P H
Williams, R T
Williams, Y
Williamson, R
Wilson, A
Wilson, A C
Wilson, F O
Wilson, G E
Wilson, G B
Wilson, J A C
Wilson, M
Wilson, M D
Wimborne, D
Winslow, L
Winstanley, J H R
Winston, M E
Wisely, N A
Witt, J K
Wolman, B
Wong, G A E K-C
Wood, A J
Wood, A M
Wood, D M
Wood, N J
Woodbridge, M
Woodcock, A A
Woodhead, M A
Woodhead, N J
Woodhouse, C J
Woodman, C B J
Woodman, M
Woodwards, R T M
Worden, T W J
Wraith, J E
Wren, A M
Wright, E A
Wright, N J S
Wright, S A
Wroblewska, M H
Wu, F C-W
Wynn, J B
Yap, B K
Yarnell, S
Yates, D W
Yates, M S
Yates, M D
Yates, R W
Yates, W A
Young, A C
Young, H S
Young, I
Young, L B
Young, T M
Younis, N
Yuill, G M
Yuill, G M
Yusuf, S
Zahir, M
Zaidi, A M
Zaidi, N H
Zaidi, S N A
Zakaria, M I
Zaman, M
Zaman, Q
Zarod, A P
Zewawi, A S

Manningtree

Bartley, B J
Hoodbhoy, A P
Kelly, J C
Lhotsky, J
Morris, P M
Morris, R C
Pain, S J
Southgate, C J
Wilkinson, H C
Wilshaw, H A E

Mansfield

Afacan, A S
Ahmad, N
Akbar, A
Allfree, A J
Bakaj, P

Ball, M J
Baranauskas, C V
Barber, J
Baugh, S J
Bilas, Z
Booth, A P
Brauer, S E
Brown, C L
Buck, H A
Butler, E V
Caley, J P
Carlisle, R D
Clarke, J C
Cloughley, E D
Cosgrove, H C
Creedon, J
Cross, B W
Dale, J H
Dalton, M J
Dawson, P P
Day, S P
Dornan, J T
Dubourg, G O
Dutt-Gupta, J
Dutt-Gupta, R K
Faratian, B
Field, H A
Foster, D M C
Frith, P J B
Genever, E E
Genever, R W
Ghosh, B
Glynn, J P
Goulding, N J
Gray, A H
Gray, P M
Hampton, J A L
Haque, M A
Harris, L D
Harrison, E M
Harrison, S H
Hay, E H
Hippisley-Cox, J
Hormis, P
Huggard, S E
Hughes, D W
Hulme, A
Joashi, Y C
Jones, G I
Jones, J A
Joshi, A R
Kaur, M
Koshy, M
Krishna, G
Kulkarni, A S
Kumar, V
Linney, P J
Loker, J E
Lucassen, A E A
McDermott, E M
Macdougall, P W
Macgregor, C J
Maddock, S J R
Masud, H
Maxwell, W G A
Mills, J E
Mokhtar, H H
Mousley, A A
Mulrooney, L
Murphy, J P
Nair, V P R
Nam, R C
Nasser, J
Ockelford, S J
Park, H L
Patel, K R
Peacock, V A
Pearce, V L
Peterson, A C
Pollard, V A
Powell, W M
Quinlan, R M
Rae, D E
Rahman, A B M S
Rahman, A
Rahman, T
Ransford, J
Rasheed, M H
Richards, R G
Roberts, D T
Rose, P S
Sharma, N
Sheikh, R R
Shrestha, S M
Singh Khanna, H D
Singh, V
Smith, A M
Smith, C J
Smith, J M

Smith, M J
Smith, P
Steiner, E S
Stephan, T F
Sudell, C J
Sudell, R P
Syn, T
Tadpatrikar, M H
Temple, D R
Topley, E M
Tut, T T
Ward, S J
Watkins, M D A
Whitaker, A J
Williams, D A
Zdziarska, C A

Marazion

Hamilton, A B
Hancock, C A
Thacker, S J
Walden, N P M
Weber, B E

March

Bhatia, S-S
Cameron, A
Chick, C M
Collings, B R
Goswami, T K
Harrison, W N
Hirson, R B
Ley, C C
Lilley, J
Moore, R S
Sengupta, C
Taylor, M J
Thomas, M G
Walsh, E J
Warrender, T S
Win Maung, Dr
Wordsworth, A D
Wyatt, R D

Margate

Abdel-Hadi,
A H S A Q
Audah, S A
Badkoubei, S
Breytenbach, W J J
Cant, R F
Carrington, B
Carrington, M E
Challiner, Y C M
Chhabra, R K
Ciccone, G K
Cocking, J B
Colin-Jones, D D
Cornell, M S
Davies, E H
Davies, G
Dickin, P D
Diggens, D
Diggens, E F
Fajardo Pando, P
Fajemirokun, E A
Fananas Esteban, A C
Giancola, G L
Greenhalgh, A M
Gunasekera, J B L
Hameed-Ud-Din, S
Hamill, S
Hamour, M A A A
Henry, S I
Jenkinson, M L
Jones, A G
Joy, G J A
Kasiri, F
Kazmie, M
Kelsey, R W
Kerkin, E H
Kha, O S
Laing, E M S
Langworthy, J N D
Lattimer, C R
Leak, A M
Lillicrap, D A
Lillicrap, S H
Lloyd, G L
Lopez Lapena, N
Lown, K R
McCafferty, H
Majeed, S M K
Martin, C M
Morcos, W E
Morgan, A D
Morgan, M G
Mukherjee, S K
Pai, M-C P
Patterson, W M P

Market Drayton

Povedano Canizares, J E
Rahman, M R
Rahman, T A
Ramachandra Raju, K
Raurell Rosique, A
Rfidah, E H I
Rogers, G J
Russell, A I
Ryder, J E
Sagar, C V
Sharp, E J
Shaw, L M A
Sivakumar, M
Smith, C W E
Summerfield, B J
Taha, H M
Tse, N Y
Tumath, D E F

Market Drayton

Ackroyd, C R
Adams, R J
Bates, C G
Bremner, A
Burns, S C E
Burt, S J
Butterworth, J
Butterworth, J R
Byrne, J
Coleman, G P
Corps, B V M
Coventry, S W J
Forrest, J F
Garson, S
Gilbert, E L
Green, C J
Green, M B
Halstead, S
Hares, R A
Haysey, G T
Hindmarsh, E A
Hindmarsh, J C
Hixson, R C
Hobson, J A
Hopkinson, G B
Howell, C J
Hughes, A J
Leno, E M
Lewis, J R
Lyons, R D J
McCulloch, D A
McMinn, J B
Mairs, T D
Mehta, J R
Mehta, R B
Miller, D M
Raichura, N
Ramage, M M
Richards, R W
Rodge, S L
Rowe, S C
Simons, A W
Thain, A
Thorley, H
Tufft, N R
West, D J
Wilkinson, T S
Wilson, A J T
Wood, R G B

Market Harborough

Allen, M J
Aspinall, W P
Ayton, P R S
Bagnall, A J
Ballantyne, M H
Ballantyne, R W
Barouch, C A
Beadsworth, A J
Bennett, A P
Biggin, M F
Bing, A J F
Bird, C R
Bishop, F M
Blake, T M
Bowles, A
Bridger, E M
Briggs, P
Butterworth, P C
Carter, R N
Craven, E R
Crawford, A
Cretney, E J
Crowley, S E
Cumberland, J H
Davidson, A R
Delargy-Aziz, Y K
Delargy, H J

Dell, M E
Eardley, R E
Fydler, T J
Gallant, M J
Hadley, S E
Hartopp, R J
Hastings, E M
Healey, P D
Hearnshaw, J R
Johnson, A T
Jones, A B
Kinmonth, M H
Lancaster, J G
Leach, N T
Lloyd-Davies, S V
Lyttelton, M P A
McGavin, D B
Maxwell, J C
Millac, J M
Mistry, H K
Moss, N A
Moyes, D G
Pink, Q J
Pirie, L E
Sellers, W F S
Shaw, F A
Twidell, S M B
Van Diepen, H R
Voss, H J
Wilkinson, A F R
Williamson, R V
Wilson, J M
Woods, D J

Market Rasen

Bee, D M
Cuff, P
Dipple, R M
Eames, M R
Holford, L C
Lothian, K R
Manners, C E
Maxwell, T M
Meier, V O
Nicol, K
Parry, L G
Rhodes, M J
Shadforth, C
Telfer, J R
Tennant, A W
Vessey, W C
Watson, F J
Weeks, R V
Whitbread, R P
Wood, G C

Markfield

Fernandez, H D
Hailstone, T R
Trzcinski, C J

Marlborough

Ballard, T H
Bishop, D
Black, A W
Black, J S
Butters, P B
Chalkley, F M
Cheshire, A
Cheshire, D G
Chinneck, P J E
Chisholm-Batten, W R
Clapp, B R
Crofts, P K
Cruickshank, E K
Dalziel, N I
Davies, J M
de Vere, R D
Faber, V C
Griffiths, J M
Handford, M H
Hanford, F W
Hanson, S M
Hellier, S C
Huddy, P E
Hyson, G E
James, C C
Johnston, I G
Jones, V D
King, P A
King, T J
Lindsay-Rea, E S
McCleery, W N C
Mackinlay, C I
McQuitty, E L
Manchip, S P
Mapstone, J
Maurice, D P
Maurice, N D
Maurice, T K

Miller, T N
Morris, J
Muller, G S
Owen-Jones, R J F
Papenfus, C B
Parsons, J W
Ramsay, J H
Rayner, J M H
Roberts, J M N
Robinson, R B
Rosalie, R
Rosedale, J O B
Scrivens, J W
Sillett, R E W
Slattery, S A
Stacey, H N
Symon, L
Tiplady, T J
Tulloch, P M B
Underhill, H L
Ward, A
Waters, M A T
Williams, J H
Yearsley, D M
Young, F M

Marlow

Addison, R A
Beresford, A P
Bissell, A E
Black, M J
Burgess, V M
Calwell, H B
Corbridge, L J
Corbridge, R J
Crawford, J A B
Crawford, S P
Davies, G S R
Edwards, S A
Embleton, D C
Fearn, S J
Hartstone, R E
Hayter, J M I
Hobbs, A M B
Kidd, J D
McArthur, K M B
McNally, P J
Mahoney, A
Maxwell, K J
Merritt, J C
Mitchell, G E
Mogg, E J
Morrow, T J
Moston, R H
North, C I
Plater, M E
Quinn, A M
Read, R F
Redgrave, E A
Riyat, M S
Roderick, A H
Sheehan, R T
Sheridan, R P
Smith, F C
Spink, J D
Summers, L W
Swietochowski, J P G
Taylor, I W
Tees, E C
Van Den Berghe, R C
Vincent, E C
Walsh, H M
Watkins, S M
Wheeler, K I
Willsdon, H F

Martock

Bailey, M
Beattie, J K
Bridge, A R
Coates, B M
Eaton, A T
Parker, J H K
Parkes, H G
Quayle, A J M

Maryport

Al-Bassam, A H
Chaudhi, F L
Collins, T M
Havard, B J
Heywood, E A
Kerr, F N
Longstaff, K
Money, B I
Overend, A J
Thornley, S K

Matlock

Bathgate, J T

Bennett, C A C
Burd, D
Cannings, I R
Chamberlain, C A
Clark, D M
Connolly, B P S
Currie, A T
Curtis, R A P
Dawson, J V
Draisey, J H
Edwards, M S D
El-Farhan, N M M
Emmerson, R C
Fray, N F
Grundy, T N
Holden, J S
Holden, P J P
Hyde, J L
Hyde, T W
James, D L
Knifton-Smith, H
Knight, A M
Lindop, A R
Lingard, P S
MacArthur, D G
Macfarlane, C S
MacFarlane, J F
Mayes, N J
Pickworth, D C
Rapoport, J
Ritchie, N J
Rudd, S E
Sinnott, A D
Smallman, R I
Steed, J M
Ter Haar, R G
Twist, J S
Ward, D A
Ward, I J
Ward, M G
Wilderspin, M P

Mauchline

Bhanot, S M
Campbell, W T
Cleland, J R
Cleland, J
Currie, J M
Eveleigh, D J
McCannell, E S
Mackie, H J G
May, J B
Morrison, K M
Philip, J M U
Ramsay, W
Rawson, D A
Scott, A L
Walker, A D W

Maybole

Cochrane, M C
Collie, E
Donaldson, B
Duncan, J A L
Haggarty, E G
Lindsay, M M
Paton, G
Scobie, B
Steele, E S

Mayfield

Bell, D M
Coates, A J
Felton, A E
McAuley, D J
Mathams, A J
Smith, G
Stephen, E D S
Tallett, P R
Williams, R E
Wolstenholme, A G
Youssef, G E-D M

Meifod

Rees, P S C

Melksham

Cardy, G C
Clarke, L W
East, R M
Ellison, D J
Frankland, S M
Gabriel, R J
Harding, C M
Harrison-Smith, M K
Harvey, K E
Howgrave-Graham, T R
Jones, S E O
Kahane, R M

Kingston, P M
Lennon, C H
Phillips, P J
Reid-Brain, H E
Rendall, C M S
Rosser, S A
Simmons, J P
Whatley, R J
Whatley, S A

Melrose

Abdel-All, M A H
Ainslie, D
Amin, A I
Arbuckle, P E M
Barber, I B A
Beighton, R C
Bennett, S A
Braidwood, J M
Broadhurst, P A
Brown, P W
Bryce, J A
Buchan, H
Bunyan, A L
Burley, L E
Burns, J M
Clowes, C B
Cormie, C M
Crichton, J L
Cripps, T P
Cumming, G P
Cumming, H A
Dennyson, W G
Dunbar, J A
Duncan, R A
Dunn, M M
Eade, O E
Ellison, J K
Gordon, A J
Halpin, R M B
Hardwick, D J
Hood, J A
Hosny, M A
Houston, I G
Houston, K E
Humphries, C P
Jones, D M H
King, A
Leary, N P
Leaver, D C
Lennox, M E
Leslie, P J A
Logie, D E
Love, D R
Low, C B
Lowles, I E
McDonagh, N J
McDonald, R D
Mackinnon, D A
McRitchie, H A
Maddox, A J
Magowan, B A
Maguire, P A
McGhee, A-M
Montgomery, C E A
Montgomery, J N
Mordue, A
Murray, R I
O'Neill, J S
Pearson, A J
Pieterse, L R P
Pullen, I M
Reid, J H
Renfrew, S
Richard, C J
Rodgers, J
Sadullah, S
Scott, G A
Sharp, C W
Shepherd, W F I
Simpson, N J
Sloan, M G
Stewart, J H
Stockdill, G
Syme, P D
Watson, A C H
Wilson, G D
Yellowlees, G M
Yellowlees, I H
Young, J

Melton Constable

Bennett, T C R
Burton, D A P
Claridge, A J
Gregory, R J
Meanley, J J
Shaw, G

Melton Mowbray

Ackerley, G C
Adams, M J
Aikman, A N T
Ardron, M E
Barnsdale, E R
Barnsdale, P H
Barrow, D A
Barrow, M
Bolt, C E
Bousfield, J D
Brown, H
Brunskill, N J
Cartwright, J L
Corvin, D J
Davies, S M
Firth, F Y
Gallop, A J
Gosling, O E
Hardcastle, S J
Harvey, D J
Harvey, J M
Hollis, H
Holt, B E
Hooper, G
Howe, P J C
Hykin, J L
Hykin, L R
Johnson, C S
Johnston, P W F
Kirby, H
Kirkup, B
Lamming, C E D
Logan, F A
Lovett, D M
Makwana, N K
Martin, G E
Mawer, S A J
Merrill, J F
Merry, A J
Nassim, M A
O'Shea, R A
Patel, S P
Phillips, K G
Pozuelo Lima, E C
Rees, R G
Reeves, J P
Riley, P
Sidwell, R U
Slevin, P G
Smith, T D W
Thew, R J
Thompson, P A
Webb, J K H
Williamson, B C M
Wooding, S C
Wyatt, T A

Menai Bridge

Batten, S A
Corrado, H A
Davies, M E
Edwards, H A
Farquharson, G C
Gilroy, P L
Griffiths, A G R
Hesketh, G M
Humphreys, W V
Iorwerth, A
Lowes, M E
Maxwell, R T
Maxwell, S E L
Morris, O G
Oliver, R H P
Palin, S J
Palin, S L
Parry, E W
Parry, E
Parry, M
Pearson, N M
Roberts, J G
Robinson, G A
Rolant-Thomas, C M
Shah, K
Speck, E
Thomas, E O
Thomas, M
Tripp, S J
Wadsworth, A M

Menstrie

Todd, C A M

Merriott

Apperly, P R
Randall, S J

Merseyside

Thomson, L E

Milnthorpe

Merthyr Tydfil

Blankson, J M
Cassidy, D M
Chakrabarti, A K
Chandran, V S
Chillal, B
Choudhary, P C
Choudhury, N
Choudhury, S K
Clements, S A C
Cotter, L
Cox, T J
Davies, D B S
Davies, M J
De Silva, M
Drah, M A
Evans, K M
Evans, W V
Ezsias, A
Fleming, J F
Foon, B P
Gabr, S M
Ganesh, S
Gaugain, J V
Gilchrist, H
Gottumukkala, V R
Hourahane, B E
Hussain, A
Hussein, O T M K
Ismaiel, A H M A
Iyer, B R
Jayadev, B U
Jones, H
Karpha, S
Karunakaran, V
Kelly, B V
Kennedy, G P
Khan, M I
Kumar, P D
Lalla, M M
Lewis, A R
Maguire, M J
Mangan, M K
Megharaj, P D M
Menon, L
Murdeshwar, S S
Murphy, L J
Myers, K
O'Dwyer, G A
Okuonghae, H O O
Patel, B T
Pierce, D W
Quirke, R J
Rahim, A
Rangarajan, T
Richards, J P
Saigal, S
Selvananthan, P
Selvananthan, S
Shah, K
Shah, P S
Slyne, D J
Smith, F G M
Srivastava, A K
Steed, E A
Sudhakar, M
Sullivan, G
Tang, S Y
Thomas, D W
Thomas, K R
Vatsala, C N
Williams, D M
Wookey, B

Mexborough

Agrawal, D L
Cooper, D N
Lathia, I
Leach, M C
Lord, C B
Muthulingaswamy, M
Nagpal, I C
Sarkar, S H
Srivastava, A K

Middle Wallop

Austin, G R

Middlesbrough

Acquilla, D B
Ajekigbe, O L
Al-Shukri, S J A
Amann, M E
Anand, R
Anderson, J T
Ankcorn, C T
Artaraz Beobide, J I
Ashley, B D
Ashraf, S
Austin, G L R

Avery, B S
Bailey, S M
Baines, A J
Baptiste, C E
Barclay, P M
Barham, N J
Barsoum, M K
Barton, H R
Beeby, W J
Beere, D M
Bell, J R
Bilous, R W
Blakey, J
Blundell, M D
Boggis, A R J
Bonner, S M
Bowes, C H G
Boxall, M C
Bramble, M G
Broughton, D L
Brown, A E
Brown, A H
Brown, P M
Buckle, S M
Burke, H B
Cann, P A
Canning, J T
Carmichael, A J
Chadwick, D J
Chahal, S S
Chandler, J E
Chappelow, E M
Chaudhry, B S
Cheshire, M E
Chew, K S
Chilton, S A
Choo-Kang, A T W
Clarke, F
Clarke, F L
Clarke, J R
Clarke, M T
Coady, M S E
Compitus, B A
Cooke, W M
Corbett, B P
Corbett, W A
Cornford, C S
Cosbie Ross, J A
Couts, B
Cove-Smith, J R
Cowley, R
Crook, J B
Cruickshank, D J
Cuthbert, A
Dave, S V
Davies, A
Davies, G L
Davies, J L
de Belder, M A
Dellipiani, A W
Desira, W R
Dickinson, G
Dickson, D J
Dickson, J W L
Ditchburn, C
Dixon, E C
Dolan, J C
Donne, C A
Donovan, D T
Doughty, J
Dowd, J C
Drury, J
Duggleby, M R
Duncan, T
Dunlop, P R C
Dunn, L E
Durning, P
Easby, J
Edge, C J
El-Naggar, M H R A
Ellerton, C R
Everett, E F
Farrell, T F
Faulkner, M H
Fazluddin, C R M
Firth, S
Fisher, R R
Flood, L M
Foley, M A
Foster, T A
Franke, B
Fraser, W C
Frood, J D L
Gannon, P F G
Garnett, A R
Gash, A J
Gedge, J
Gedney, J A
Geiser, P

Geldart, J R
Ghosh, S K
Gjertsen, T A
Graham, S G
Grandey, F M
Grant, I H
Green, P A
Greenough, C G
Gutteridge, E
Guy, I T
Halkett, S J
Hall, J A
Hampal, S
Hampton, F J
Hardman, P D J
Hargate, G
Harker, N E M
Harrison, A M
Hartley, R W J
Haslock, D I
Hawthorne, M R
Helbert, D
Herbert, D W
Heywood, P J
Hillebrand, M
Hinman, M M
Hodgson, G
Holtby, I
Horne, H L
Houldsworth, F J
Howard, E G
Howitt, M J
Hudson, N W
Hughes, J H
Hunter, S
Hunton, J
Husain, A
Inch, P J
Iqbal, S
Irvin, P J
Irving, E R
Irwin, A M
Islam, M A
Isserlin, B
Jacott, N J
Jawad, M S M
Johnson, J L W
Johnstone, P W
Jones, R A
Jones, S B
Joshi, N R
Kane, P J
Kanesan, K
Kay, H
Keegan, P E
Kendall, S W H
Kenward, D H
Kerawala, C J
Kerr, D C
Kerr, R
Kessell, G
Khair, A S
Khair, S S
Khondker
Moslehuddin, Dr
Knox, J W S
Koh, J C H
Kokri, M S
Kon, P Y
Kothari, D D
Krishnan, R
Kuan, B H
Kuvelker, G W
Lakeman, J M
Lakin, A R
Lamballe, D P
Lamballe, J
Lamplugh, M
Land, H R
Land, N M
Lassey, A T
Lau, W L M
Lawler, P G P
Leeser, J E
Lehmann, G A
Leigh, H
Leitch, M D
Levie, B B
Lewis, L T
Lewis, W K
Linker, N J
Lone, I A
Lucas, P A
Lyall, M
McCarty, M
McCormack, P
MacDougall, I A
McGuire, D P
McIlhinney, S W

McKeown, C O
McLean, K A
Macleod, A
Maclure, G M
Main, J M
Mair, I M J
Majupuria, A
Malden, M A
Mamujee, S A
Marks, S M
Marshall, M
Martin, F W
Masinghe, N R
Masri, Z
Maximous, J S
McKay-Ferguson, A
Mehta, M
Meikle, R J R
Metcalf, J A S
Mian, M S-N
Middleton, L G
Miller, N B
Miller, R J
Milligan, K A
Milne, S
Mitra, S
Mohammed, H
Montgomery, R J
Morgan, J M
Morgan, T R M
Morpeth, G
Morrison, W J
Morritt, G N
Morritt, J A
Morton, D
Muckle, D S
Muddappa, Y N
Murdoch, R
Murphy, J G
Mutton, A E
Nagarajan, S
Nagendar, K
Nahhas Oubeid, A G
Naisby, G P
Naismith, L J
Newman, P M
Nugent, D
Oatway, H B
Oladipo, J O O
Oo, M
Opaneye, A A
Orlandi, J R
Oswald, N T A
Packer, M E
Pai, B Y
Palczynski, S H
Park, G E
Park, J D
Patience, W A
Perks, G T
Pettit, M
Phellas, A
Phellas, A J
Pinto, T
Prasad, R C
Price, D J A
Puttick, N
Ramwell, J
Rasool, S
Rathmell, A J
Reach, D
Reilly, J G
Ribeiro, A
Riddle, I F
Risebury, M J
Ritchie, C
Roberts, J H
Robertson, J D A
Robson, N L K
Roth, L J
Rowell, N T
Royal, D M S J
Ryan, S M
Saha, R
Sainz Mandiola, A
Sanders, G L
Sandresegaram, K
Santosh, C G
Sarangapani, K
Scoones, D J
Selby, E M
Senor, C B
Seymour, H M
Shaw, S R
Shehade, S
Sherman, J
Shrinath, M
Silcock, J G
Simpson, M D C

Sinclair, C J
Sinclair, D J M
Slade, P H
Smerdon, D L
Smith, A
Smith, R
Srivastava, P K
Stewart, M D
Stewart, M J
Stothard, J
Strachan, R D
Struthers, G D
Sutherland, M S
Symon, M A
Tawse, S B
Taylor, P J
Teece, S C
Thompson, M O
Thompson, S J
Thomson, M F
Tiah, H A
Tilley, J H M
Tilley, P J B
Tolland, J
Tooley, A H
Toop, K M
Townend, A M
Tse, H-W
Turnbull, D H
Ullah, A S
Van Der Voet, J C M
Veitch, D
Vijayakumar, M N
Viva, C
Wakerley, R L
Wallis, J
Walshe, D K
Ward, C R
Wasson, J F M
Waters, H J
Watson, D J
Webster, D D
Webster, E
West, A
Wetherell, H C
Wheatley, P M
Whewell, J
White, C
White, G M J
Whiteway, J E
Wight, R G
Wilkinson, D B
Williams, B R
Williams, H I
Williamson, S F
Willimott, E J
Wilsdon, R B N
Wilson, J K
Winnard, J A
Winter, A
Wood, J
Wood, J R
Wright, R A
Wyatt, G P
Wylie, J M
Wylie, J P
Young, G R
Zabihi, T

Middlesbrugh

Barlow, S S
Barnes, L
Baxter, S M
Thompson, K W
Wheeler, R J
Wood, A C
Young, C F

Middlewich

Atherton, J B
Clarkson, M V
Clifton, M R
Conrad, J J A
Curbishley, P G
Ford, D L
Hyde, N
Jones, C R
Jones, N L
Keen, J H
Ratcliffe, B L
Terry, P M

Midhurst

Allison, S
Andrews, M S
Brownlee, W C
Campbell, M E A
Clarke, S D
Crawford, I P
Davis, E P

Elmslie, I K M
Forshall, S W
Foster, C J
French, B T J
Gabe, I T
Gordon, W I
Guthrie, T
Halfacre, J A
Hart, T B
Hemming, J C
Hill, T J
Hinton, J M
Hopkirk, J A C
Horne, J H M
Hudson, A
Kelly, J B
Laing, S R S
MacCallum, A G
MacCallum, S K
McColl, H
Marien, B J
Martin, H W
Masding, J E
Potter, S J O
Power, N A
Rees, R S O
Saayman, A G
Sherrington, J M
Sim-Davis, D
Skivington, J E
Titley, G J
Warren-Browne, M G
Whitten, C R
Wilkinson, J C

Milford Haven

Chartres, J C
Evans, D L
Evans, P J
Garrett, C A
George, W T
Gunning, M P
Hickson, M J
Jones, T T
Lynch, W M G
Mackintosh, J F
Martin, I R
Meagher, E M
Morgan, J
Sheikh, T B N
Thomas, J M
Warlow, A L
Williams, A D
Wright, C M

Millom

Cook, G
Jackson, A E
Johnson, E A
Matheson, I C C
Patchett, P A
Pogrel, G P
Walker, R C M
Walters, P J

Millport

Bryson, E A
Bryson, J A M
Houston, R A

Milltimber

Al-Sayer, H M
Anderson, S A
Atta, H R
Chabet, C C
Chithila, C J M
Clark, F
Denholm, M J
Downie, A J
Eagles, J I
Engeset, J
Fouin, F L P
Fowlie, M A R
Gibson, J M C
Hogenboom Van Den
Eijnden, M G E
Leng, M E F
McLauchlan, J
Main, R A
Matheson, N A
Morton, M A
Patterson, J E
Wardlaw, D

Milnthorpe

Armitage, E L
Beale, I R
Black, S L
Bonwick, H E
Cleary, P R

Milton Keynes

Darby, C T
Gorrigan, J H
Grocott, M P W
Higginson, D W
Hill, J W
Irving, J A
Jackson, S F
Johnson, B M
Lomax, R J
Orton, C M
Parker, P J
Pearson, E J
Pearson, K M
Perham, E
Robertshaw, N M E
Seddon, N E
Steele, G A
Sutherland, D T
Warren, M R
Wilson, S R
Yates, V M

Milton Keynes

Ahmed, A
Ahmed, J
Ahmed, K A
Allsopp, A
Anaman, S S
Anderson, F M
Anderson, N M
Araez Guarch, R
Assaf, A A-R S
Baker, P D
Barker, G J
Barker, R W
Bates, R A
Bedford, C
Berger, A B
Berkin, P L
Blacklay, O H
Bradley, C J
Bradley, J H
Brandon, E L
Bridgman, K A
Brown, P M
Bunting, N G
Butterworth, R J
Carson, N P S
Carter, R C
Cassidy, M P
Chambers, K H
Chambers, P H
Choudhry, T A
Chowdary, K V
Cianchi, M F
Clements, R D
Clerkin, P M M
Clewett, V
Cowen, M J
Craggs, M E
Crankson, S J
Das Gupta, S
De Gorter, J-J
De Silva, M Q P
De Silva, S J
Dewji, M R M
Dhanoa, S K
Douse, F A
Douse, N A
Dua, J A
Duhra, P
Dun, A F
Dyer, S J
Edwards, S
Evans, D A
Fawdry, A J
Fawdry, R D S
Fernandes, V
Fisher, C W S
Gallagher, K T
Gamlen, T R
Garai, G
Goodman, J C
Gray, S R
Green, A F
Griffiths, J R
Grinyer, S A
Gunn, R S
Hadi, Q M A
Hadida, A
Hanna, G F B
Haq, A-U
Hassan, A O
Havard, A C
Hawkins, J M C
Haynes, J W
Haynes, P J
Herman, C R
Hickman, R J

Hildick-Smith, B A
Hilmy, H H
Hilmy, N M H
Hilton-Jones, D
Ho-Yen, R G
Holford, C P
Holowka, K A
Hopkins, J C
Houston, J D A
Howard, E A
Huish, E F
Huxtable, C A
Jaderberg, E M
Jarvis, P N
Jayaram, P K
Jenkins, E A
Jeyaratnam, D
Jeyaratnam, R
Johannes, S G
Jones, A P
Joss, D V
Kadom, A H M
Kamineni, S
Kansagra, M H
Karia, A V
Katumba-Lunyenya, J N
Kearney, J M
Kelly, H H D
Kempster, A
Kenny, C
Khurana, P
King, B A
Kingston, A H
Kumar, K
Labrum, A S
Lakhani, P K
Lambley, J C G
Lanzon-Miller, S
Latham, P J
Liesching, R A
Logan, C J L
Logsdail, S J
London, P S
Lourie, J A
Lynch, C B
McBride, D D
McCune, G S
McIlwain, L I M C
Mackenzie, L E
McWhinnie, D L
Maddison, B
Mahendran, M
Mallick, D K
Marshall, A J
Mayers, M M
Mead, J L
Mendis, N
Miles, P D
Miller, E J
Miller, G F
Mitchell, A
Mohammed, K I
Moore, P L
Morrison, D J
Moyle, J T B
Muir, J W
Mwansambo, C C V
Mylvaganam, R R X
Nasiri, A Z
Nayani, G R
Neil, V S
Nicolaou, A C
Nicolls, D B
Nott, J G H
O'Malley, S P
Odedra, N
Page, M L
Pai, E S
Patel, B B
Patel, R H
Paterson, R A H
Paton, R C
Petrides, S P
Philbin, J C
Philbin, K H
Platford, J
Porter, J
Prisk, A J
Punch, D M
Reddy, V L N
Rigg, C J
Rivett, J D
Roberts, R R
Roberts, S C
Robertson, A P
Robinson, G B
Rog, D J
Rogers, M J

Rohlfing, R F
Rose, E D
Roy, M
Sadiq, M N M
Sagoe, K B
Satchitananda, M
Schmidt, A C
Scott, S J
Scott, W E
Shah, M R
Sharda, A D
Sharma, A
Shubsachs, A P W
Smith, N L
Smith, R W
Smith, T S
Sorrell, J E
Souter, R G
Staten, P
Steel, M A
Suleman, A
Taylor, A J
Teago, P J
Thakker, Y
Thalakottur, J M
Thompson, A M
Toff, W D
Toomey, H
Travill, C M
Ullah, H
Walker, E M
Walsh, A C
Wanigaratne, D S
Weatherhead, S M
Webb, E J
Wedgbrow, C S
White, A P
Whiteman, S J
Widdas, W F
Williams, R A
Willson, G
Wolfendale, M R
Wright, D R
Wright, M
Wyke, M E
Yahya, A
Yogarajah, S C
Zachariah, J
Zapata-Bravo, E

Minehead

Cooper, P B S
Currie, A L
Currie, M A
Davies, R
Earle, A M
Freeman-Archer, M I
Higgie, J M M
Hunt, C F
Jarman, P D C
Jones, A M M
Jones, T L
Jordan, A R
Kelham, I
Lamacraft, G
Lewis, D E
Lister, K N
Mackie, C M
Milnes, J N
Nelson, A R
Neville, P S
Nicholson, R D
Paine, Dr
Pegg, E M
Platt, K F
Sarsfield, D A
Slade, P J B
Stoner, B A
Thomas, E A
Thomas, H G
Toot, M
Vale, S S
Vint, D G D
Wawman, D M I C
Worssam, A R H

Mirfield

Bedford, M R
Best, M E
Brigg, J M F
Chan, V Y-C
Charles, F W
Clarke, J H
Cowan, D
Davison, M J
Dyson, G D
Eabry, E S
Gooding, J H
Grason, H G

Hall, P J
Hamilton, C M
Holmes, P H
Lukic, M
Meeke, P A E
Moreland, H E
Panter, S J
Parker, R
Ridge, J A F
Roulston, J R
Roulston, R G
Tait, G B
Warner, S T

Mitcham

Adjepong, K
Akinfenwa, O O
Akoo, M S
Annal, D J
Butt, A
Chana, N S
Chandradeva, K
Cochrane, M E M
Cohen, A R
Colborn, R P
De Silva, J V
Dewsnap, P A
Dromgoole, J E
Emmanuel, J J
Foster, H D
Freeman-Wang, T B R
Furey, A H
Ghodse, B
Gunatilleke, A
Hannah, M C
Hill, K P
Hollier, G P
Kirupanantham, P
Lasserson, J A
Mangaleswaran, S
Mansfield, P A
Olorunda, H L O
Otley, A J
Patel, S S
Patel, S J
Rang, E H
Ravetto, S
Rootes, S J
Ross, A E
Saxena, M K
Schapira, H
Shah, M A A
Strangeways, J E M
Thet Tun, Dr
Thomas, A T
Tolufashe, E A
Varagunam, T
Vivekananthan, M
Von Fraunhofer, N A
Whitehead, P J
Yanney, M P

Mitcheldean

Crooks, A J R
Martin, R E
Rodgett, A F
Wakeham, P F
Weiss, P D

Moffat

Baillie, M
Brewster, H
Crosby, R R
Gillies, R
Gillies, S R
Gillies, W J
Graham, J A
Henry, G F J
Jefford, F M
MacEwen, G L
MacLeod, I H
Sharkey, A S
Sloan, L M

Mold

Ali, M A
Banerjee, S
Barnett, E J
Baron, C E
Bartzokas, C A
Beckett, E I
Bevan, C A
Bickerton, D A M
Carri, J P
Crossland, J S
Daley, H M
Davies, A P
Edwards, J W
Egdell, J D
Forbes, J R

Fuld, H
Jones, R A
Lewis, W E
Muckle-Jones, D E
Mwambingu, F A L T
Parry, M E
Payne, S A
Petrovic, M
Roberts, G W
Salib, N R
Salib, Z R
Saunders, F M
Selman, R M
Shillito, R N
Shillito, W E
Thomas, M
Tranter, R
Williams, R D
Woodward, S

Monmouth

Bagwell, A D
Bate, J G
Berger, C P M
Blease, S C
Booker, D F
Brown, I
Calland, A L
Dauncey, T M
Galbraith, J
Griffiths, A R
Griffiths, G E
Hardy, J K
Harries, B D J
Jeans, S L M
Jennings, J P
Jewell, W H M
Jones, A H
Jones, C
Judson, D H
Kelly, M-C M
Kindy, G R
Loffhagen, R J
Matharu, M S
Matharu, N M
Melville Thomas, D G
Messing, H J
Moaby, N M
Old, E G
Payne, J H R
Phillips, A E M
Seymour, J
Shaw, S H D
Sleigh, J
Terry, R W P
Visser, M J

Montgomery

Ashton, P J
Currin, S
Davies, R M
Humphreys, W H
Lindsay, P H
Reid, A
Welton, E J
Wynn-Jones, J

Montrose

Begg, A G
Calder, J G
Carson, W G
Clark, J A L
Clunie, F S
Craig, D L
Diack, P P
Diack, W G H
Drayson, A M
Gammie, S C
Gavin, A J
Goode, H
Griffith, H E
Griffith, J M
Grove-White, I G
Grubb, A B A
Hillyear, M E
Ireland, M
Kroijenga, J
Lewin, C
Logie, S A
Lumsden, W W
Morris, J B
Morris, M G
Mowat, D A E
Noble, J E
Ogilvy, K M
Orr, A W
Piercy, N M
Rice, P M
Smith, J H
Voice, S-A M

Walker, D R
Wilson, P M
Zeylstra, O N

Morden

Ali, S S
Anandarajah, T
Arulrajah, S
Carter, T A
Day, C I
Desai, P M
Downie, R W
Ellerington, M C
Frempong, R Y
Goddard, J D
Hariharan, S
Hartikainen, P H
Hawkins, P
Ho, G S W
Huggins, S T V
Ikomi, A E A
Jephcott, J J
Jethwa, N K
Lafuente Baraza, J
Lawrence, E R
Lee, W P
Madisetti, P
Parameswaran, U
Perera, S T B
Piyasena, C
Rahaman, A E
Shenolikar, B K
Sivagnanavel, S
Smith, A L N
Smith, N J
Soyemi, A O
Sullivan, T J
Wardle, N S
Wyne, K O A

Morecambe

Allinson, A M
Bell, D T S
Brear, S E
Brown, H
Brown, M
Dillon, R
Ellis, J A T
Evans, C D
Forsyth, A S
Gartside, T
Grealy, M G
Greenwood, A M
Herd, G M
Ingham, W G
Ingram, D J
Kapur, H L
Khan, M I
Kilpatrick, A
Knapper, D O
McKinney, N H M
Macleod, A J
Maher, S P
Pidd, S A
Raworth, R E
Ross, E S
Seville, M H
Simm, F
Smith, F
Smith, V H
Sykes, R A
Tattersall, D J
Thomas, H R
Townley, P A
Ward, J L
Whitehorn, S E
Williams, S J
Wilson, S M
Wimborne, J M
Winfield, P J W
Wood, G M

Moreton-in-Marsh

Barling, R G
Birts, R J
Bloxham, R E
Dastgir, M B
Durham, M E
Edwards, D G
Every, M
Kelly, H D B
Lutter, P S
McEvedy, B V
Morton, C C
Pracy, R
Reekie, I
Robinson, D S
Towler, A
Trollope, A A

Turner, A A
Williams, J S

Morpeth

Adam, J I
Anderson, P
Armstrong, H A
Bannerjee, D B
Barker, D C
Barr, A J
Baylis, S M
Bradley, P G
Brown, J M
Brown, T A S
Calder, S C
Cameron, A G
Carmichael, E J
Cash, J W
Cassie, G J
Cavill, G
Colver, A F
Colver, P A
Conn, J S
Craft, I
Craig, D J
Creighton, P A
D'Netto, D C
Day, K A
De, D
Dick, K
Dower, F H
Doyle, G P M
Edmondson, L
Edwards, S B V
Eke, Z S
Elphick, S J
Familton, H
Farndale, J A
Finch, K R
Findlay, A G
Flood-Page, J J
Flood-Page, P T
Fraser, A R
Gordon, S
Grant, W N M
Gray, S P
Greaves, J D
Greenaway, M E
Griffiths, H W
Guest, J
Gunn, A
Gunn, M C
Hankinson, J
Harris, C L
Harrison, J
Hatch, A L
Healicon, J E
Holland, H-C
Hopson, P R
Horner, M S
Howe, J W
Howells, K A
Hughes, A C
Hunt, P G
Jobling, S
Johnstone, H C
Jordon, M
Joyce, J P
Justice, A W
Kaye, M S
Kendall, E P
Kerr, D M
King, J M
Le Gassicke, J
Lilly, J B
Lothian, J L E
MacDonald, A C
McElhinney, I P M
McKay, K
McLaren, A T
McParlin, M J
Macphail, J B
Manners, T
Marr, C
Marshall, S J
Milne, E A
Mitford, P
Morton, S T
Moyle, P N
Myers, J M
O'Driscoll, F H
O'Dwyer, T M
Oliver, S E
Patton, H F
Perini, A F
Pettifer, M W
Phipps, C K L
Pledger, H G
Power, J A S

Proctor, S E
Quigley, B M A
Quinn, J S
Rendell, J A
Reynolds, T
Rich, J A
Ridley, D C
Robson, P C
Ross, E B
Russell, C V
Russell, J K
Sample, S O
Sanderson, J
Savage, R
Scarborough, H
Scott, T B
Seager, M C
Sher, J L
Singleton, S J
Soundararajan, P C
Stark, A M
Steel, C S
Stone, K A
Stonelake, A V
Tait, N P
Tallantyre, H M
Tanner, C P
Thompson, K J
Thomson, G D
Thwaites, B C
Tinegate, H N
Toop, R L
Turnbull, G H
Van Loo, U D
Van Nieuwburg, M A C
Vincent, H R
Wardle, W C
Watkins, G D
Watson-Jones, E M C
Watson, H M S
Wilkes, S
Wilkinson, E C
Wilkinson, F J
Wilkinson, M E
Williams, L S
Winslow, N R
Wubetu, T
Yeoman, C M
Young, E T
Young, N J
Young, S H

Motherwell

Ashraf, M
Bell, G A
Bell, L
Blake, K
Brough, G D
Callaghan, M
Campbell, R J
Child, N J
Clementson, D W
Cross, T W
Culshaw, V
Fleming, M-C
Forrest, E F
Goudie, A W
Hamilton, R M
Hannah, W M
Henderson, J N
Hogan, L A
Hogg, W J
Keegans, P
Keenan, J
Kerr, E C
Lando, J K
Liddle, R D S
Lochhead, J
Logan, A
Logan, G B
Logue, B R
McBride, D F
McGill, B W
McGrane, S
MacInnes, D
MacInnes, D C
McKenzie, H J
Menon, K V K
Mishra, A N
Nor, K B M
Qadir, N
Robertson, J F R
Robison, J M
Rose, G D
Russell, R J
Shah, M
Short, L C
Siddiquie, S

Simpson, J
Sturgeon, J L
Thomas, E M
Thomson, J R
Tilley, M M E

Mountain Ash

Krishnamurthy, R S S
Kulkarni, S R
Manjunath, M
Morgan, D M T
Patel, M R
Putta Gowda, H M
Rajapaksa, R A M
Sanghani, J V
Sanghani, N
Sanghani, R
Skaria, J

Much Hadham

Brookbanks, C F G
Fiddler, G I
French, J L H
Haimes, P F
Keall, G M
Lewthwaite, C J
Mayson, R L
Milne, J R

Much Wenlock

Benbow, R J
Evans, A H
Evans, W M
Gainer, A J
Goodall, R C
Holden, R A
Smith, A G E

Muir of Ord

Bruce, G M
Laing, M
Macdonald, C J
MacDonald, M F U
MacDougall, D A
McKenna, M J
MacLean, I M
Maclean, T
Munro, A H G

Munlochy

Dingwall, D W
Fettes, C D
McNeill, L A
Watson, D A

Musselburgh

Binns, C A
Blaymires, K L
Blyth, A B
Clark, E Y
Clark, I M
Clubb, A S
Cochrane, M A
Doherty, A B
Duncan, S E
Fisken, M N
Frew, J M
George, R E J
Goh, D E
Grubb, D J
Hind, J
Johnston, I S
Jones, M E
MacDonald, H L
Macdonald, P A G G
Maguire, E S
Marshall, I J
Miller, L M
Miller, T M
Munro, J F
Pearson, S L
Philip, M F
Shaw, J
Walker, E C
Watson, A S
Weeple, J A
Westwood, D L
Wilson, J M G

Nairn

Adam, A
Adam, M G
Anderson, A G
Barrington-Ward, B
Barrington-Ward, E W
Bremner, H A
Cox, J B
Henderson, A J
Hogg, J Q G T
Jamieson, M F
Jardine, D E

Leckie, J H
Macaulay, C Z
Macdonald, J D
Mackenzie, G K
MacLennan, A
Main, J M
Main, K H
Noble, A L
Noble, J L
Scott, C H R
Scott, J M
Simpson, K
Stanfield, A C
Stewart, W B
Worthington, J

Nantwich

Alexander, R K
Appleton, R A
Atkinson, A A
Azzam, K
Barron, A A
Basu, R K
Blanchard, H C
Booth, N P
Brady, D W G
Brighten, K A
Butcher, J
Cherry, T
Clowes, N W B
Clulow, G E
Coupe, A S
Cuthill, J
Davenport, G J
Davies, M O
Deans, A J
Dixon, J M
Edgecombe, S J
Ellis, M
Emery, F M
Fitzpatrick, C
Gabbe, D M
Galiot Garcia, F
Hadrill, K C V
Harris, J P
Harrison, M O
Heal, M R
Heppleston, J D
Holdsworth, S
Hollowood, A D
Hulme, S A
Hunter, P A
Jones, D M
Jones, R
Jones, V P
Kerr, D
King, B A
King, N A
Knapman, J H
Leigh, R D
McClelland, P
Mahmoud, A M A
Mamattah, J K-M
Mayor, P E
Monaghan, S D
Moorhouse, P R
Morgan, J M
Murphy, P J
Okell, R W
Palin, R C
Payne, J
Pugh, R E
Rae, F C
Raeburn, A L
Rawsthorne, A M
Rawsthorne, G B
Roberts, K N
Schur, T
Smith, C D
Smith, M S
Spargo, J R
Tellwright, J M
True, R C
Turner, J R T
Walsh, S J
Whiston, R J
Winson, M D
Yousuf, K T

Narberth

Allen, P K
Cadbury, R C
Davies, A R
Edwards, F
Ghosh, A L
Harries, E W
Hyde, J
Jones, D I
Mackintosh, M

McLeod-Baikie, S R
Palit, A
Rees, D G
Rees, J E P
Roberts, M
Thomas, J B
Vasfalcao, I I
Wood, S J

Neath

Agarwal, R C
Alexander, B
Ames, S J
Ayers, R J
Bask, N T
Bell, H H G
Benett, M S
Bennett, A C
Bowen, A C
Cook, B T
Cooze, P H
Copp, L
Davies, A S
Davies, D P
Davies, J P
Devichand, P
Driemel, S J
Dryden, P R
El Shazly, A H A
Elias, J
Elliott, R
Evans, G V
Evans, W E
Griffiths, B L
Gupta, M L
Hammond, T J
Hardie, D M
Harris, A A G
Harry, P I
Herdman, G
Higgs, D S
Howe, A D
James, K E
Jenkins, D M
Jeremiah, G M
John, R B
Jones, A M
Jones, R M
Jones, S L
Kahan, G K S
Kahan, R O
Kelly, D R
Khan, S
Khosa, N S
Langston, A
Langston, L
Lewis, D
Lewis, R
Lewis, R H
Li, M L
Lilley, A J
McMillan, A E
Madhavan, P
Mercurius-Taylor, L A
Morgan, H
Morgan, I B
Morris, H L
Muir, A M
Nabar, B V
Page, G C T
Parfitt, A
Parfitt, J
Pawar, P B
Phillips, S E
Potter, H C
Pradhan, K T
Pusey, C
Rajkumar, V J
Richards, D B
Richardson, J
Roberts-Harry, N G
Roberts, M
Rogers, J H
Roper, B W
Rosser, C A
Rule, J
Schwarz, P A
Scott, D L
Selby, C S
Sheehan, B D
Skidmore, R B D
Sobhi, N H
Southan, A W
Stubbins, J H
Thomas, G R
Thomas, J
Thomas, J N
Thompson, J A
Walters, T J

New Malden

Ware, C-L
Watkins, M W
Westwood, P R
Wilkes, H F
Williams, E M
Yang, D M

Nelson

Ali-Khan, M A
Ashworth, I R
Ashworth, L B
Aziz, S
Baldwin, K A
Banaszkiewicz, P A
Behr, G
Clark, A M
Dodds, A A
Drinkwater, J A
Fleming, D R M
Golding, S K
Greenwood, A P
Gude, S J
Guha, P K
Hall, R G
Hanslip, J M
Haque, F J B
Haque, M A
Haworth, I
Hutchinson, S
Ions, W M
Iwuagwu, C O
Jehangir, Q M
Lewis, D M
Lumb, M A
McDowell, D P
Marsden, N
Marshall, A R
Middleton, C M
Palmowski, B M
Pearson, J M
Pickens, S
Qazi, R A
Qureshi, Z A
Roll, H C C
Sarwar, N
Sarwar, S
Shafar, J
Shafar, S
Summers, J A
Thornton, S J
Webborn, D J

Nethy Bridge

Henderson, J T Y
Henderson, T L

New Malden

Acharya, D D
Acharya, J
Al-Yaqubi, N N
Allison, H J
Arthur, R A
Arulendran, P
Austen, J C
Bailey, P E M
Balendran, R
Barrie, D
Berkinshaw-Smith, E M I
Bhattacharyya, S
Bindi, F
Brown, J K
Brown, S E
Chandola, A
Chang, S L-L
Chapman, C M
Chodera, J D
Choudhury, Z N
Crawford, P
Dale, C P
Denis Le Seve, P T
Dhond, G R
Dhond, M R
Fordham, G T
Forni, L G
Gayed, H W
Ghosh, M
Ghosh, P K
Goel, G S
Goel, M
Grimmett, B M S
Gunasekera, A D
Gupta, B K A
Harris, J N
Harris, S M
Hassanally, D A
Hooker, R C
Huseyin, T S
Insole, J
Iqbal, N

New Milton

Jaitly, S
Jivani, A K
Jivani, N A
Keen, A L
Keohane, S G
Kershaw, M J
Lamb, F J
Levak, V
Lewis, S A
Luckett, J P
McAuley, C
McDonald, A M
Mahadeva, S
Martin, R W
May, J H
Mehrbod, K
Mitchinson, J S
Modarres Sadeghi, H R
Monro, P S
Morgan, H M
Murphy, J B
Nathan, T
Nay Win, Dr
O'Connor, M P
Palmer, S J
Parameswaran, S S
Patel, S N
Phelan, A E
Qureshi, A M
Rahman, M
Rajasingham, P
Reeve, S
Reid, B R
Rooms, M
Ryan, E N M B
Sadiq, S T
Saeed, M
Samarasinghe, I L P
Samarasinghe, N
Samarasinghe, P C
Satkurunathan, S
Seddon, B M
Sharples, P E
Sheldon, N H
Sherski, L A
Sillitoe, K M
Sinton, R I R
Sivakumaran, S
Skinner, G B
South, E A
South, J R
Sperryn, P N
Sternberg, A J
Stevens, G M
Subesinghe, N
Thursby-Pelham, A K
Thursby-Pelham, F W V
Townsend, G E
Wilkins, M
Wilkins, P R

New Milton

Allen, E D B
Bargh, D M
Barker, A S
Blick, P W H
Boucher, C M
Brewer, P
Campbell, P J
Clark, R M
Currie, J L
Dathan, J R E
Davies, G A
Davies, J W H
Edmunds, E M
Hardiman, P M
Huish, R A G
Ives, L A
Jenkins, D
Jenkinson, K A
Josephs, C
Kent, J T
Lam, J Y C
Lambden, P M
McLeod, J B
Martin, P
Parker, D J
Rutherford, A N
Thacker, M P
Thurston, T J
Tonge, J M A
Venables, P
Vivian, P G
Waterman, C E
Watson, N F
Watts, B L
Willard, C J C

New Quay

Bowen, M E V
Evans, S P
Hatcher, L H
Lewis, J A R
O'Connor, L D
Rees, Y
Thomas, T D L
Williams, D

New Romney

Cochrane, P T
Deane, J F
Jarratt, E W
Markland, W E D
Swoffer, S J

New Tredegar

Harris, A R

Newark

Andrews, C A
Andrews, R
Ashton, M B
Ashton, R J A
Attrup, B
Auger, B M
Ayre, A N
Barber, P
Barker, J A
Barnsdale, C A
Baxter, J L
Bennett, J D
Bird, D I
Briggs, G O A
Britt, R G
Britton, D E R
Busson, M
Campbell, L A
Chalmers, R M
Charlesworth, J P
Chong, E M F
Clayton, C P L
Compton, E H
Corlett, D E
Cosslett, A K
Coupland, R E
Crookes, P M B
Dale, L S
Davies, I W
De Gay, A
de Gay, N R
De Silva, P C
Dennis, P J
Donohue, S M
Dyson, A
Fenton, D
Finch, K M
Finch, M E
Gains, J E
Garrow, A D
Garvey, M T
Goodyear, P W A
Hardwick, E
Head, S
Healy, J M
Hiller, E J
Hind, R E
Ho, T H
Hogg, M J
Hull, R E
Hunter, M
Hutton, D A
Ilett, R J
Innes, C G
Jensen, P M
Johnson-Sabine, E C
Johnson, J
Johnson, J M
Johnson, M
Johnston, A J
Jones, P D
Keegan, N J
Kennedy, K
Kerr, D S
Kharkongor, S K
Knight-Jones, D
Lawrence, A C K
Lawrence, L K
Lawrenson, C J
Leach, V
Lendon, D
Lennox, B R
Loudon, M F
McDougald, M
McGill, J G
Machell, R K
Maheson, V S
Makepeace, P A
Maule, E J W

Maung, S W
Mile, D J
Ndukwe, G O
Neil, J F
Nelson, F G
Parkin, A J
Porter, J D
Prangnell, D R
Prasai, J K
Pringle, M A L
Pullinger, S
Ramalingam, Dr
Reeves, P
Reeves, P O
Reid, D A
Ripley, M I
Robertson, P G C
Roffe, T H
Ross, I N
Schlicht, J
Scott, S S
Seivewright, H E
Selwyn, J E
Smith, J M
Spencer-Gregson, R N
Stinchcombe, S J
Sullivan, C J
Sullivan, F D
Tweed, C R
Vohrah, R C
Waller, J M
Ward, H E
Ward, S M
Wathen, D J
West, T P
White, C J
Wright, A C

Newbiggin-by-the-Sea

Imam, S B
Stephenson, T

Newbridge

Pandolfi, A L
Watt, J A

Newbury

Agnew, N M
Anees, W M
Arnold, P D
Baly, P L N
Batagol, D M
Bennett, T A
Beverley, E A
Bingham, E
Bishop, M A
Bishop, T M
Bond, S E L
Bradley-Moore, D M
Britchford, R E
Britz, M
Buckle, D J
Burgert, S
Burman, R E M
Cave, J A H
Chapman, S
Chapman, S J
Choudhuri, S K
Clarke, B B
Cleator, S J
Collins, O D G
Davies, C E
Davies, D J
Donaldson, M J
Dunn, R J
Dyson, M
Ellis, E J
Elvin, B C
Endersby, K
Fisher, H M
Goodyear, K
Goulden, A D
Hall, J M
Harris, P
Harrison, G M
Hazel, S P C
Hughes, G M
Hunter, A E
Hyde, M F
James, S E
John, W R B
Johnson, I C
Jones, J R
Jones, R E
Jones, T J
Leighton, G
Letham, B B
Lloyd, A J
Lovegrove, S C

Lowenthal, L M
McManus, B N
May, R
Millard, P M R
Mitchell, I D
Mitra, S L
Morgan, S L
Muir, A M
Nickson, J
Norman, M G
Norwell, N P
Osmond, T G
Pollard, D J
Powell, J J
Rees, N C
Rendel, S E H
Ribeiro, N M
Richards, R
Robertson, P M
Rudgley, R J
Russell, J A
Sharpe, C M
Shillam, G N
Sievers, P F
Simmons, M G
Smith, C C
Smyth, P J E
Sommerville, D F
Steare, A L
Steare, S E
Stiff, G H
Sullivan, A J
Tapper, R J
Taylor, M J
Tayton, R G
Thirlaway, B M
Thomas, J M
Thomas, K E
Thomas, M L
Thomas, M R M
Thompson, T M
Totten, E
Totten, J W
Treadgold, U A
Tuggey, J M
Vandyk, E
Vevers, G W G
Vooght, M W
Walker, S B
Walsh-Waring, G P
Walter, T N
Watson, R D
Weller, R J G
West, C J
Williams, V N
Willis, C J
Wilson, B E
Wotherspoon, M G
Youdan, M E

Newcastle

Aber, G M
Agarwal, K K
Agarwal, S
Agarwal, S
Ashford, R P
Atkinson, P S
Au, B T
Baker, K
Bale, C J
Bell, G S
Bellingham, K M
Best, J M W
Bhuvanendran, V
Bould, M D
Bowcock, L
Boyd, M W J
Brazenor, E L F
Bready, W D
Brooks, A R
Brown, A J
Butler, M J
Cameron, A J
Campbell, C V
Campbell, E D
Carmichael, I W D
Carson, P H M
Chadalavada, U B
Chadwick, D R
Childs, A J
Chitrapu, R K
Coddington, W G
Cole, R B
Colgan, S J
Common, J D A
Cooper, W J
Cox, G A
Cox, P W
Coxon, F Y

Crome, P
Crymble, B T
Cunningham, J
Dabrowicki, E
Dale, N
Davies, A O
Davies, A R
Denvir, C M O
Devlin, S
Dias, P S
Dick, K S
Dilly, S A
Donnelly, M
Dove, P J
Dudson, C M
Duffy, T J
Dugdale, C J
Dukes, S
Durber, C
Edwards, D H
Elliott, M D
Evans, E F
Farrell, A J
Farrell, S
Fisher, M J Y
Flynn, M E C
Forsyth, I C
Franklin, P J
Fraser, D G W
French, M E
Gallagher, F J
Ganapathy, D H
Gardner, G I
Garnish, R P
Gibson, J C
Goold, M J
Gray, J G
Gray, O M
Green, R J
Griffiths, B
Griffiths, E A
Griffiths, M L
Grindlay, D W S
Grindlay, W
Hall, C
Hamilton, R J
Hanna, G G
Hapuarachchi, J S A
Hatton, W J
Hayward, R A
Heron, A F
Heron, J R
Hollinshead, J F V
Hothersall, T E
Hugh, A E
Hussain, F K
Hussain, L M
Hussain, S K
Hyland, S C
Jeyaratnam, P
Kapur, T R
Keown, A P
Kesava Reddy, M
Khan, M A
Khanam, S
Kirby, R M
Kirk, H H
Kulkarni, B N
Kulkarni, S B
Kyle, J M
Lauckner, M E
Lawson, L J
Lee, K W
Leggett, C D
Levine, A J
Lindup, R
Little, S A
Lloyd, M E
Lynch, S A
Macauley, M R
McBride, D I
McCammon, W J
McCormick, J K
McGowan, S W
McKie, N
McNiff, C G P
MacPherson, E S
McRobie, E R
Malkan, D H
Manudhane, V V
Marshall, T L
Martin, L M
Mellor, S J
Millson, D S
Morgans, G P
Murray, F J
Myers, E D
Naeem, A
Neary, R

Ng, D H L
Nicholas, J C B
O'Connor, N F
O'Donnell, G
Obhrai, M S
Pasi, K C
Patel, K P
Patel, R D
Pugsley, A D
Rafferty, C M
Ramsden, W N
Ravichandran, S S
Ringland, R A
Rogers, W F
Ross, A K
Rotondetto, S
Seddon, S J
Shah, S S
Shapley, M
Sharma, S C
Shaw, P A
Shenton, K C
Sherrard, K E
Shufflebotham, J Q
Sivananthan, U M
Skinner, M D
Smith, A L
Smith, A G
Smith, J M
Smith, K D
Steel, W M
Sterling, V J
Stuart, D W
Thacker, B V
Thorley, K J
Tommey, M F
Torney, J J
Tsang, W C
Tubbs, D B
Tucker, R J
Turner, N B
Tyler, P V
Walker, R A
Wallbank, N J
Walsh, P M
Walsh, S R
Walshe, K G
Walters, F J
Williams, N D
Wilson, H
Withers, P A
Zia-Ul-Hasan, Dr

Newcastle Emlyn

Brook, M T
Cole, D R
Davies, R J
Fitzwilliams, B C A L
Goriah, H
Johnson, R D
Jones, H P
Lindsay, A O
Phillips, E J

Newcastle under Lyme

Acquah, N E
Hollins, M P

Newcastle upon Tyne

Aal, B
Abdelhameed, B E Z
Abdullah, W S
Abeyasinghe, M Y
Adams, B R
Adams, D M
Adams, E M S
Adams, P C
Adamson, F E
Adkin, D E
Advani, A
Agarwal, K
Aggarwal, M L
Ahmad, B
Ahmad, I
Ahmad, M
Ahmad, S
Ahmad, Y A
Ahmed, H S
Airlie, I
Aitchison, J D
Aitchison, W K
Al-Barjas, M
Al-Harbi, O M A M
Al-Otaibi, I M
Alam, S M
Alcorn, A S
Alexander, E M
Ali, A A

Newcastle upon Tyne

Ali, H M M D A
Allcock, L M
Allcock, R J
Anand, Dr
Anand, A
Ancliff, H M
Anderson, C C P
Anderson, M
Anderson, S N
Anderton, J G
Andrews, R M
Ansari, I A
Antoun, P C
Anumba, D O C
Appleby, M A S
Appleton, A L
Archbold, R A
Archer, K
Armstrong, J E
Armstrong, S E
Arya, A
Ashby, C B
Ashcroft, A
Ashley, B K
Ashman, S G
Ashton, C H
Ashton, L C
Atkinson, R S
Awadh, M
Bach, S P
Bachh, Z J
Back, C P N
Badman, M
Bain, H H
Baines, L A
Baker, L C
Baker, M
Baker, S F
Ball, S G
Banerjee, B
Barber, R
Barbour, J A
Barer, M R
Barker, C
Barker, W A
Barlow, T E
Barnaby, C
Barnard, S P
Barnes, M P
Barnes, M P
Barrett, A M
Barrett, K M
Barron, E E
Barron, S L
Barrow, P M
Bartlett, S
Bassendine, M F
Batchelor, A M
Bates, C L
Bates, D
Bates, G H N
Baudouin, C J
Baudouin, S V
Baylis, P H
Bayly, P J M
Beacham, K J
Beesley, J R
Bell, D R
Bell, D J D
Bell, H R
Bell, J F P
Bell, J M
Bell, K R
Bell, R C
Bell, R
Bell, S M
Bell, W J
Benn, D K
Bennett, M K
Bennett, R P
Bennett, S M A
Bernal Canton, M
Bethell, M J
Bethune, C A
Betts, J A
Bevan, J D
Beveridge, C J
Bexon, M F
Bexton, R S
Bhaskaran, A M
Bhate, V S
Bhattacharyya, S
Bhojani, M A
Bhopal, R S
Biggin, C S
Binmore, T K
Bint, A J
Bint, A H
Birch, M K

Bishop, F
Black, D A
Black, F M P
Black, G S
Black, M J M
Black, N M I
Black, S M
Blades, S M
Blain, P G
Blair, A S
Blair, E L
Blakeman, P J
Blessed, G
Bliss, R D
Bolton, D T
Bond, M E
Bone, M
Boobis, L H
Boohene, J A
Bookless, D J
Boonham, J C
Borthwick, M A
Bosanquet, R C
Bourke, J P
Bourke, S C
Bourke, S J
Bower, S
Bowman, M P
Bowmer, R G
Boyce, R C L
Boyd, K
Boyd, K T
Boyle, J G
Boyle, K R
Bozzino, J M
Bradford, C R
Bragg, P M
Brandon, H A
Branson, A N
Brantingham, P
Bratch, J S
Bray, R J
Breakey, F W B
Breakey, R M
Brettell, F R
Briggs, P J
Brittlebank, A D
Broad, A J
Brock, J A
Bromly, J C
Brookes, P H
Brougham, C A
Browell, J A
Brown, A L
Brown, A S
Brown, A G
Brown, B
Brown, G W
Brown, H G
Brown, J E
Brown, K
Bruce, L M
Bryson, M R
Bubb, S C
Buchanan, J M
Buchanan, J
Buchanan, R
Bullock, R E
Bunn, M R
Burden, P L
Burdon, A C J
Burdon, A T
Burn, D J
Burn, J
Burn, M C
Burn, R J
Burnett-Hall, C F
Burns, G P
Burns, K M
Burridge, A
Burt, A D
Burton, C H
Bushby, K M D
Byrne, E J
Bythell, V E
Calder, C E
Callanan, K W R
Caller, P J
Calvert, A H
Cameron, D S
Campbell Hewson, Q D
Campbell, F C
Campbell, R S D
Cant, A J
Carding, K A
Carey, G R
Carmichael, J
Carr, H

Carr, W M
Carrie, S
Carrington, P M
Carrol, E D
Cartlidge, M E
Cartlidge, N E F
Cassidy, T P
Cattell, E L
Catton, B J
Cavet, J
Cawthorne, D J
Chalmers, A J
Chalmers, G
Chamberlain, J
Chamberlain, J I
Chamley, M
Chandler, B J
Channon, C E
Channon, L V
Channon, M E
Chaplin, D A
Chapman, C E
Chappel, D B
Charlewood, A M
Charlewood, J E
Charlton, B G
Charlton, F G
Charlton, J
Charlton, J E
Charnley, R M
Chatterjee, M
Chaudhri, S M B
Chaudhry, T S
Checketts, R G
Cheetham, T D
Chinnery, P F
Chipchase, B B
Chishti, A D
Chishti, S
Chopra, R
Choudhury, N G
Choyce, M Q
Church, C J
Clark, A K
Clark, F
Clark, J S
Clark, J E
Clark, S R
Clark, S C
Clark, S
Clarke, J
Clarke, K
Clarke, L C
Clarke, M J
Clarke, M P
Clarke, T N S
Clasper, S
Cleghorn, N J
Cleland, P G
Clement-Jones, M T
Clements, G C
Clifford-Jones, E
Coapes, C M
Coates, L E
Codd, A A
Cogan, B D M
Cogswell, C C
Coipel, P M
Colback, R J H H
Colbridge, M J
Cole, A J
Collerton, J C
Collier, A D
Collins, A K
Collins, M M
Collins, N S
Collins, R L L
Comaish, B
Comaish, J S
Comiskey, M C
Conlan, B R
Conrad, K W
Constable, F L
Constable, J M
Cook, S
Cooke, M J
Cooke, R J
Cookey, H G
Cooper, E
Cooper, H B
Cooper, J C E
Cooper, K
Cooper, P D
Cooper, P N
Cooper, R G
Cope, M R
Copeland, P F
Corris, P A
Cosgrove, J F

Cottrell, D G
Cottrell, G R
Coulthard, A
Coulthard, D
Coulthard, M G
Court, S
Cowan, W K
Cowell, H
Cowen, D
Cowlam, S R
Cox, D H
Cox, J E
Cox, J E M
Coxon, A
Coyne, H M
Coyne, P M
Craft, A W
Craig, A M S
Crawford, D C
Crawford, P J
Cray, S H
Cree, N V
Cree, R T J
Cresswell, P A
Crisp, A J
Croft, R J
Crombie, A L
Crompton, D E
Crooks, B N
Crossman, J E
Crossman, L C
Cruickshank, S G H
Cumberlidge, D F
Cummings, R A
Cunningham, M T
Currie, A
Curry, K M
Curtis, H J
D'Silva, G C J
Dabner, S
Dahabra, S
Dahl, M G C
Dalal, D K
Dalby, K V
Dalton, S J
Danjoux, G R
Dark, J H
Darling, C H
Datta, H K
Datta, K J
Davenport, R J
Davey, P
Davidson, E M
Davidson, N C
Davies, A J
Davies, J B
Davies, M J
Davis, M
Davison, A M
Davison, E A
Davison, J
Davison, J M
Davison, K
Davison, S
Dawes, P J D K
Dawson, H E
Day, C P
Dayan, M R
De La Hunt, M N
De Soyza, A G
Deane, M
Deegan, J
Deen, C V
Dexter, C S
Dhariwal, M
Dharmapriya, N S K
Diamond, C
Dias, C J
Dickinson, A J
Dickinson, W M
Diddee, R K
Dignum, H M
Dixon, J
Dixon, J H
Dixon, P K
Docton, A J M
Dodds, P A
Doll, N W
Donkin, I
Donne, A J
Dorkin, T J
Douglas, G
Douglas, R
Dowden, N
Drake, G P
Drake, I M
Dresner, S M
Drinkwater, C K
Drought, T K

Dunleavy, D L F
Dunlop, J L
Dunlop, P
Dunlop, W
Dye, R K
Dyer, H E G
Dyer, M P
Earl, C F
Eastham, E J
Eccles, M P
Eccleston, D W
Eccleston, D
Edmondson, R J
Edmunds, R B
Edridge, W W
Edwards, A G K
Edwards, A J
Edwards, J R G
El Badri, S M
El-Harari, M B A
El Mabruk, F M
Elder, M E
Eldridge, M
Elliott, S T
Ellis, E
Ellison, D W
Eltringham, M T
Embleton, N D
Emmerson, C I
Emmerson, K P
Engeset, A-M
Eslah, E
Evans, A J
Evans, J A
Evans, P R
Evans, R G B
Evans, S M
Evemy, K L
Eyre, D H
Eyre, J A
Eyre, K E
Fagan, J M
Fairbairn, A F
Falope, Z F
Fanibunda, H
Farley, A J
Farquharson, R G
Farr, P M
Fawcett, P R W
Fay, A C M
Feathers, L S B
Feggetter, J G W
Fender, D
Fenton, A C
Ferguson, J J
Fernandes, H M
Ferrand, R
Ferrier, V
Field, A B
Findlay, N G
Finklestone, P J
Finn, K L
Finnerty, P A
Fischbacher, C M
Fisher, J C
Fisher, M L
Fisher, S
Fitchett, M J
Fitzgerald, J M
Fletcher, I R
Fletcher, R M
Flint, R A
Flohr, C
Flood, M K
Flynn, P M
Foo, C K
Ford, G A
Forrest, I A
Forster, N D
Forster, T A
Forsyth, R J
Forty, J
Foster, H E
Foster, J A
Foster, J B
Foster, J C
Fowler, C E L
Francis, A J
Francis, R M
Frankenthal, J
Franks, H L
Franks, P
Fraser, C J
Fraser, K A
Fraser, N D
Freake, D
Freedman, G R
Freeman, J G
Frew, I J C

Fulton, B
Furniss, S S
Fyfe, N C M
Gall, S A
Gallagher, B S
Gallagher, H J
Gallagher, P V
Galloway, A
Gardiner, H M
Garner, P J
Garner, R E
Garrood, P V A
Gascoigne, A D
Gascoigne, D
Gaur, A S
Gee, M N
Gelson, J
Gennery, A R
Geoghegan, A T
George, A M
George, M
Gerrand, C H
Gholkar, A R
Ghura, P S
Gibb, R C
Gibbons, C T
Gibson, B M
Gibson, G J
Gibson, M T
Gibson, M J
Gilbert, H
Gilbert, R J
Gilbertson, R J
Gillanders, E M
Gillett, T P
Gillie, R F
Gillis, V E
Gilthorpe, H M
Gilvarry, E
Girling, D K
Gold, R G
Golden, L A M
Golightly, K L
Gomaa, H E S M
Goodacre, J A
Goode, P N
Goodship, J A
Goonetilleke, U K D A
Goorah, S D
Gordon, J E
Gordon, L R
Gould, F K
Gowda, R
Grace, J B
Graham, A L M
Graham, J Y
Graham, J C
Graham, L A
Grainger, A J
Grainger, D N
Grant, A W
Grant, G B
Grant, K
Gray, C
Gray, J E
Gray, R J
Grayson, C
Greaves, S M
Green, J D F
Green, S M
Green, S E
Gregg, P J
Gregory, D A
Gregory, J
Gregory, K M
Gregory, R J H
Greveson, G C
Gribbin, G M
Griffin, S M
Griffith, M J
Griffiths, A B
Griffiths, I D
Griffiths, J
Grime, I D
Groom, P I
Grubin, D H
Guarasci, F
Guellard, P S
Guha, N
Gumbrielle, T P M
Gurney, C
Haines, R M
Hainsworth, P J
Hajioff, D
Hale, J H
Hale, J P
Halford, N W
Hall, A G
Hall, K C

Newcastle upon Tyne

Hall, K
Hall, R R
Hall, V A
Hamdalla, H H M
Hamilton, I J
Hamilton, J R L
Hamilton, P J
Hampton, P J
Han, S W
Hanley, N A
Hanley, S A
Hanratty, C M R
Hanratty, J G
Hanson, J M
Harding, S L
Hargrave, S A
Hargreaves, J N S
Hargreaves, K
Harkis, B A
Harpin, R P
Harris, A M
Harris, F P
Harrison, A T
Harrison, J W K
Harrison, M S
Harvey, J R
Hasan, S T
Haslam, N
Haslam, P J
Hassan, I
Hassan, M S
Hassanyeh, F K
Hawley, V
Hawthorne, G C
Hayes, N
Haynes, S R
Hayward, D
Healicon, R M
Healy, E P
Heap, R
Heaps, E L
Heardman, M J
Hearn, A J
Heaviside, D W
Heaviside, V A
Heidemann, H B
Henderson, I
Henderson, L M
Henderson, S L
Henderson, S C
Hendrick, D J
Henshall, A L
Herbert, O D E
Herrema, I H
Hession, M G
Hewitson, W A
Hewitt, V A
Hey, E N
Heycock, L J
Hide, I G
Hierons, A M
Hierons, C D
Higgins, B G
Higgins, E M
Hilborne, F R
Hill, J
Hill, P M
Hilton, C J
Hilton, P
Hindmarsh, J H
Hingorani, K
Hnyda, B I
Ho, K L
Hodges, S
Hodgkinson, P D
Hodgson, J
Hogg, D W B
Holdsworth, C A
Holland, I S
Holland, J P
Holland, J J
Hollingworth, R
Hollinrake, P U
Holloway, J S
Holmes, R M
Holtham, S J
Holti, G A Z
Holti, G
Home, P D
Horn, J A
Horn, P A
Hornby, R
Hornby, S J
Horne, C H W
Horne, M
Hornung, T S
Howarth, D J
Howat, M E
Hubbard, G H
Hudgson, M J
Hudgson, P
Hudson-Peacock, A S-C
Hudson-Peacock, M J
Hudson, J C
Hudson, M
Hudson, R M
Hudson, W F M
Hughes, A N
Hughes, D G
Hughes, J C
Hughes, J C
Hughes, S C
Hunt, S J
Hunter, A S
Hunter, J D
Hunter, J
Hurford, W E
Hurrell, G D
Hussain, A
Hutchinson, D R
Hutchinson, J E M
Ibrahim, F K
Inkster, J S
Insley, C A
Ireland, M
Irvine, E M
Irvine, S T
Irving, M H
Ismail, M
Jachuck, S J
Jackson, C R
Jackson, E C S
Jackson, G H
Jackson, J M H
Jackson, M J
Jackson, R W
Jackson, R H
Jackson, S E
Jaffray, B
Jaiswal, A
Jalpota, S P
James, H
James, O F W
Jarvis, S N
Jeannon, J P
Jefferson, P D
Jenkins, A J
Jenkins, K S
Jennings, P A
Jessen, E C
Jewitt, C B
Jha, R R
Johnson, H M
Johnson, I J M
Johnson, R E
Johnson, S J
Johnston, I G
Jokelson, D R
Jones-Unwin, C A
Jones, C T A
Jones, D E J
Jones, D W
Jones, E A
Jones, F E
Jones, H E
Jones, K E
Jones, L B K R
Jones, M H
Jones, M S
Jones, N A G
Jones, P M
Jones, R B
Jones, S B
Jones, S C
Joseph, S A
Joughin, B M
Kalbag, R M
Kanagasundaram, N S
Kandasamy, R
Kaplan, C A
Karat, D
Karrar, A A A
Katory, M
Kattash, M M I
Kaura, V
Kay, A J N
Kay, D W K
Kay, L J
Kaye, B
Kearns, P R
Keenlyside, R M
Kelliher, T J
Kelly, C G
Kendal, R Y
Kenna, A P
Kenna, J
Kennair, P
Kennedy, J G
Kenny, M A
Kenny, R A M
Kenny, T
Kent, R M
Kernahan, J
Kerr, C M
Kerry, N A
Khan, A L
Khanum, K
Khattab, A A E N H
Khaw, F M
Khawar, F R
Kheraj, S
Kilburn, J R
Kilner, A J
Kirk, S B
Kirk, S F
Kitching, M D
Kiu, C I
Knight, N F
Knops, M J
Kong, S C
Kor, H S
Kremer, L M
Kumarendran, M
Labadarios, V V G
Ladbrooke, K J
Laidler, C W
Lake, H F
Laker, M F
Lakha, S H
Lamballe, P
Lambert, D
Lambert, H J
Lambert, K E
Lane, A S
Lauckner, H C M
Lavelle, M I
Lawrence, C M
Laws, D P
Lawson, A
Lawson, C N
Lawson, F S
Lawson, J E
Le Couteur, A S
Lee, I C
Lee, K S Y
Lee, M A
Lee, R E J
Lee, Z
Leech, S N
Leeder, A
Lees, T A
Lees, Y C
Legg, J
Leigh, S
Leighton, M
Leitch, D N
Lendrum, R
Lennard, A L
Lennard, T W J
Lenygon, A C
Leonard, H C
Leonard, M A C
Leonard, N
Leontsinis, T G
Lester, S E
Lewis, J
Lewis, R I S
Liddle, A L
Lightfoot, N F
Lim, K L H
Lind, T
Lindley, A M
Lindsey, L A
Linford, D V
Lingam, R Y
Lipman, D T
Liston, A M
Litster, R Y
Livingstone, C
Lloyd-Jones, N D
Lloyd, A J
Lockett, A E
Lombard, L
Lonsdale-Eccles, A A
Loose, H W C
Loraine, C D
Lord, S W
Loughead, J M
Lovedale, C
Lovedale, I L
Lovell, P R
Low, H L
Lowdon, G M M
Lowerson, B
Lowes, S C
Lowry, S C
Lucey, R
Lucraft, H H
Lund, C A
Lunn, B S
Lunney, R W
Lustman, A J
McAllister, V L
McArdle, P A
Macaulay, A
MacAvock, P J
McAvoy, B R
McBride, S R
McCahy, P J
McClelland, H A
McClintock, I R
McClure, D
McClure, S J
McComb, J M
McCombie, C
McConnell, T F
McCormick, K P B
McDonagh, J E
Macdonald, D W R
MacDonald, E M
McDonald, F E
McDowell, G A
Mace, M
McGregor, C S M
McHugh, J P
McInerny, D A
McIntyre, E A
Mackay, D C
Mackay, S G M
McKee, G J
McKeith, I G
MacKenzie, N T
McKenzie, T M
Macklin, H R
McKnight, C K
McLean, L M
McLean, N R
McLelland, J
MacLeod, J M
Macleod, S R
McLoughlin, I J
McMahon, C C
MacMahon, M
McMeekin, K
McMenemie, F M E
McNamara, C M
McNamara, P J G
McNeill, I F
McNulty, J F
Macphail, S
Macritchie, K A N
Magnay, D E
Maguire, A A
Mahmood, A
Malcolm, A J
Malhotra, K
Man, L-K
Mann, J
Mannix, K A
Mansfield, J C
Mansour, D J A
Mansy, H A A
Markham, C R
Marks, J M
Marshall, A H
Marshall, C
Marshall, H F
Marshall, J R
Marshall, S M
Marshall, S I
Martis, P D
Martland, T R
Marwaha, S S
Masel, P J
Mason, D L
Massey, C J
Masson, L J
Masters, J G
Masters, M
Matheson, J G
Matthiensen, U
Mattinson, A B
Mattinson, P J B
May, C D
Mayne, D J
McAllister-Williams, R H
Mears, C
Medhi, A C
Meek, T
Meggitt, S J
Meikle, D
Mellon, J K
Menage, C M
Mendelow, A D
Mensah, E
Menzies, R J
Merson, S R
Metcalfe, S M
Michael, E M
Mickler, G R
Middleton, P M
Midwinter, M J
Millar, M A
Miller, I A
Miller, J S G
Miller, J W
Miller, M R
Milligan, D W A
Milne, D D
Milne, E M G
Milne, J E C
Milne, R K
Milner, R H
Minchin, A H
Misra, U
Mitchell, L E
Mitchell, L
Moate, B J R
Moffett, S P
Mohammad, S
Mohammed, P D
Mohteshamzadeh, M
Monaghan, J M
Moorby, A M
Moore, A R
Moore, P B
Moorghen, M
Moran, G D
Morch-Siddall, J
Morgan, P
Morris, A A M
Morris, D
Morris, D
Morris, P T
Morrison, R P
Morrison, R H
Moss, S
Mounter, P J
Mullin, P
Mulvenna, P M
Munir, A
Murchner, M P
Murdoch, A P
Murgatroyd, J
Murphy, C L
Murphy, O M
Murray, S A
Murrell, H M
Mushet, G L
Musson, J C
Myers, R E
Nagpal, P
Nanson, P
Nargolwala, V S
Nath, S
Neal, D E
Needham, G K
Needham, H J
Nelson, R
Nerurkar, M J
Netts, P H
Newton, J L
Ng, A K M
Nice, C A
Nichol, I E
Nicholson, E
Nielsen, K C
Noble, G M
Noble, J M
Noor, N
Noronha, D T
Nyholm, R E
O'Brien, B S
O'Brien, C J
O'Brien, D F
O'Brien, G
O'Brien, J T
O'Brien, K A
O'Brien, S G
O'Connell, O
O'Hara, L A
O'Neill, K R
O'Reilly, M F
O'Shea, D D P
O'Sullivan, C V
O'Sullivan, C V
O'Sullivan, D C
O'Sullivan, J J
Oglesby, A J
Olley, P W
Ong, L C E
Ong, T K
Oppong, K E N W
Oriolowo, A M
Orr, K E
Orwin, A S
Osei-Bonsu, M A
Owen, T C
Owens, W A
Page, V J
Palmer, J H
Pandit, R J
Panikkar, A
Pape, S A
Parkins, J
Parks, S
Parnell, A P
Parry, G
Parry, S W
Patel, H R H
Paterson, H R
Pattekar, J B
Pattman, M G
Payling, S M
Payne, T C
Peakman, D J
Pearce, S H S
Pearcy, P A M
Pearson, A D J
Pearson, G L
Pearson, T J
Pearston, G J
Peatman, S J
Pedler, S J
Pelham, A
Pennington, S E
Perez Jara, J
Perring, J
Perriss, R W
Perros, P
Perry, R H
Petersen, K S
Pettit, K E O
Petty, A H
Peverley, M C
Phillips, C E
Phillips, E M G
Phillips, J H
Picker, J D
Pickering, F C
Pickering, W G
Piggot, T A
Pilkington, G S
Pinder, I M
Pinnington, S
Plant, N D
Platt, P N
Plummer, C J
Plummer, E R
Plusa, S M
Podd, T J
Podogrocki, A J
Pooley, J
Porter, J R
Porter, R
Posner, B H
Posner, N C
Potkins, D V
Potter, F A
Potter, J
Potterton, A J
Potts, M
Powell, H
Powell, P H
Power, D E
Prasad, M G
Prentice, W M
Preston, M R
Price, A F
Price, S M
Price, T R H
Pridie, A K
Prince, M I
Procter, C N
Proctor, I S
Proctor, S
Proctor, S J
Protheroe, C
Proud, G
Purves, I N
Quader, K
Quasim, M N I
Quigley, M P
Quinby, J M
Quinton, R
Qureshi, K N
Qureshi, M
Raghavan, R
Rahman, S A
Rainey, L
Rainford, P A
Raj, S K

Newport, Gwent

Ramachandrappa, G
Ramesh, V
Ramli, N
Ramsden, A J
Ramsden, P D
Ramshaw, A L
Ranasinghe, H
Rand, W
Rangecroft, L
Rangecroft, M E H
Rannie, I
Rao, P
Record, C O
Redfern, N
Redman, C E
Reece, A T C
Rees, C J
Rees, J L
Rees, R M
Regnard, C F B
Reid Milligan, D A W
Reid, C A
Reid, D S
Reid, L K
Reid, M
Reid, M M
Reynolds, N J
Rich, G F
Richards, C G M
Richards, H C M
Richardson, A
Richardson, A G
Richardson, C A
Richardson, D A
Richardson, D L
Richmond, S W J
Ridley, R E W
Ringrose, T R
Rix, D A
Roberts, D R D
Roberts, J T
Roberts, R G
Robertson, L M
Robinson, C A
Robinson, D P
Robinson, D C
Robinson, D J
Robinson, I S
Robinson, L A
Robinson, S J
Robson, B J
Robson, D J
Robson, P
Robson, P N
Robson, S C
Robson, V-A
Robson, W A
Rodgers, A
Rodgers, H
Rooney, D
Ropner, V A
Rose, J D G
Rose, P G
Ross, D G
Ross, E
Ross, M S
Ross, W E
Routledge, D J
Rowe, L
Rowe, P W
Rowland, D H
Rowntree, P C
Roysam, C S
Rozner, L M
Ruddle, J E
Ruff, S J
Rugg-Gunn, F J
Rutherford, R J
Rutt, G A
Rutter, W
Ryan, D W
Ryan, J D V
Ryder, C
Ryder, W
Rye, G P
Ryman, A E
Saigal, R H
Saint, T M C
Salkeld, D V
Salkeld, J V
Sammut, M S
Sanders, J H L
Sankar, K
Sarang, A
Sarang, K
Saravanamuttu, K M
Sarma, T C
Saul, J L
Saunders, D I

Saunders, P W G
Scarlett, C E
Schapira, K
Schlesinger, A J
Schmid, M L
Schofield, C B S
Schofield, I S
Schofield, P J
Schutte, A
Scott, D J
Scott, H A
Scott, J L
Scott, M E
Scott, S J
Scully, S A
Sein, E P
Self, C H
Sen, A
Sen, B
Shabde, I
Shah, S H
Shah, S G
Shakoor, S
Shamsah, M A
Sharma, P
Sharma, V
Sharp, C
Sharples, P M
Shaw-Binns, S
Shaw, D A
Shaw, J P T
Shaw, P J
Shenfine, J
Shenfine, S D
Sherratt, M T
Shiells, G M
Shinnawi, A K
Shipsey, D
Shuster, S
Siddique, N
Siddiqui, F N
Silva, K G
Silver, A J
Simpson, H
Simpson, K L
Simpson, N
Simpson, N B
Singh, M M
Singh, P
Skinner, J S
Skinner, R
Slatter, M A
Slorach, M
Slowie, D F
Smart, P D
Smith, A J
Smith, A V
Smith, D F
Smith, D F
Smith, D M
Smith, G A
Smith, H C T
Smith, J E
Smith, J E
Smith, J H
Smith, J P
Smith, J D R
Smith, K L
Smith, M J
Smith, M A
Smith, M R
Snodgrass, C A
Snow, M H
Snowden, C P
Sobo, A O
Solomon, S N
Somner, A R
Somner, J
Sooltan, Y
Soward, K M
Sparey, C
Speakman, D W
Speight, E L
Spencer, B T
Spencer, D A
Spencer, I
Spencer, J A
Spickett, G P
Sprake, C M
Spratt, J D
Squires, H G E
Srinivasa Murthy, L N
Stafford, I
Stafford, M A
Stainsby, D
Stainsby, G D
Stamp, P J
Standart, S
Stanley, A J

Stanley, J S
Stannard, K P
Stansfield, R E
Stark, G L
Steckler, T H W
Steel, M
Steel, S
Steiner, H
Stenton, S C
Stephen, D L
Stephenson, P
Stephenson, T
Stevens, I M
Stevenson, C J
Stevenson, G
Stevenson, P S
Stewart, J A
Stewart, M W
Stoddart, J C
Stoddart, M G
Story, D
Strang, C
Stratford, G A
Strick, M J
Strong, N P
Stuart, P R
Stuart, S
Sturgiss, S N
Sudarshan, G
Sudlow, C M
Summers, S P
Sunter, J P
Swann, A G
Swanson, L
Sweeney, J E
Syers, G E
Tacchi, M J
Taggart, S
Tahmassebi, M J
Talbot, D
Tansey, P A H
Tapson, J S
Tay, H L
Taylor, A E M
Taylor, A A
Taylor, P R A
Taylor, P J S
Taylor, R
Taylor, S C
Taylor, W B
Tharakan, P M
Thick, A P
Thomas, D J
Thomas, J L
Thomas, J E
Thomas, P
Thomas, S H L
Thompson, A P
Thompson, J J
Thompson, M D
Thompson, N P
Thompson, R B
Thomson, P J
Thomson, R G
Thong, K J
Thoppil, J P
Thornton, D
Tickle, C
Tiffin, P A
Tissainayagam, M B J
Tocewicz, K
Todd, J P
Todd, K P
Todd, N V
Todd, R M
Tong, P C-Y
Tonge, H W
Tough, S L
Townshend, D N
Trotter, T A
Tsang, R W-K
Turkington, D
Turley, J F
Turley, S A
Turnbull, D M
Turner, A J L
Turner, A J
Turner, A
Turner, H J
Turner, J M
Turner, N M
Turner, S L
Turner, S M
Tweddle, D A
Twelves, N
Tyrer, S P
Tyrie, C M
U-King-Im, J M K S
Underwood, L A

Unwin, N C
Vallis, C J
Van Miert, M M
Van Mourik, W J
Van Zwanenberg, T D
Varma, J S
Vassilikos, P
Veeder, A S
Velangi, M R
Venables, C W
Venkata Rama Sastry, K
Vijayaratnam, D D
Villaquiran Uribe, J A
Vincent, A
Waddington, R J
Wadge, V A
Wagget, J
Wagstaff, T I
Wake, P J
Wakeling, Z C
Walder, D N
Waldron, A C H
Waldron, M N H
Walker, D J
Walker, D R
Walker, J H
Walker, J M
Walker, M
Walker, P A
Walker, R A
Wallis, J P
Walls, M Y
Walls, T J
Walters, F M
Walwyn, J L
Ward Platt, M P
Ward, J C R
Ward, K L
Ward, L E
Ward, M K
Warnell, I H
Warrick, C K
Warrington, J R
Warrington, S
Wastell, H J
Waterman, D
Waterston, A J R
Waterston, E
Watson, B G
Watson, D S
Watson, P G
Watson, S
Watt, J R
Wattsford, R H
Waugh, M
Weaver, J U
Weaver, M K
Weaver, N F
Weeks, P A
Weir, D J
Weithaus, N
Welbury, R R
Welch, A R
Weldon, J R
Weldon, O G W
Weller, C S
Wells, A W
Welsh, J L
Whewell, P J
White, J C
White, M J R
White, R M
Whiteman, H R
Whitfield, K J
Whitford, D L
Whitley, S P
Whitney, P G
Whitty, P M
Wigglesworth, M D
Wild, N J
Wilkes, G
Wilkes, J A
Wilkins, D E M
Wilkinson, B J
Wilkinson, B S
Wilkinson, R
Wilkinson, S A
Williams, C D
Williams, D O
Williams, J R
Williams, N
Williams, T L
Williams, V L
Willis, J M R
Wills, S J
Wilsdon, J B
Wilson, E M J
Wilson, J A

Wilson, K M
Wilson, N J
Wilson, R G
Winburn, P E I
Windebank, K P
Winter, E
Winterton, I S
Winterton, S
Wollaston, J F
Wood, B H
Wood, P C
Woolfall, P
Woolhouse, I S
Woolley, M J
Worthy, S A
Wren, C
Wressell, S E
Wright, A J
Wright, C
Wright, G E
Wright, J
Wright, P D
Wright, P M C
Wright, S E
Wyatt, M G
Wynne, H A
Yates, B H
Yellowley, T W
Yeo, S T
Young Min, S A
Young, A H
Young, C A
Young, J R
Young, S J
Younghusband, A J
Yung, S Y R
Zainuddin, A A
Zaman, S J
Zamiri, M
Zammit-Maempel, I
Zar, N
Zealley, I A
Zimbler, N

Newcastle-under-Lyme

Hill, P
McBride, D J
McIntosh, J W
Male, C G
Panayiotou, B N
Swan, C H J

Newcastleton

Bethune, A D
Blair, J F
Blair, M I
Kennedy, H W
Livingstone, D W

Newent

Anns, J P
Brooks, M E
Brown, J C
Drewett, K A
Holland, S O M
Leigh-Smith, S J
McIlveen, W H
Sillince, D N
Tomlinson, K M
Williams, D G
Wright, P H

Newhaven

Argent, L B
Barker, A M
Bradbury, A
Daintree, R A
Draisey, M H
Edwards, V G
Figgins, R
Jefford, H A
Kavanagh, M J P
Milne, G J
Qazi, H S
Sharp, D J

Newmarket

Abel, M E
Alberts, J C J
Andrews, F
Arthur, N S
Bailey, T R S
Batt, B J
Baxter, L A L
Bodle, J F
Bright, E A
Bright, M V
Calvert, J W
Fawcett, C M

Forsyth, P A
Fowler, A J
Gumpert, E J W
Harper, E F
Kass, T L
Leitch, J A
Lloyd-Jones, K J
Lloyd-Jones, P M
Longman, R J
Macauslan, A D R
McLaren, J A
Mitchell, A C J
Moriarty, A J
Nicholson, J P
Pearce, A J
Polkinhorn, J S
Silverston, P P
Slowe, M R I
Sriskandan, K
Stead, B R
Stephens, N A
Virgo, F E
Wace, M
Wace, R O
Wallace, I R
White, A J S
White, W L
Wiggins, B C

Newmilns

Cameron, R T
Collister, G C
Mackenzie, P M

Newnham

Bhageerutty, R V
Ellwood, N H
Nobbs, W M A
Parsons, C J
Reader, C A
Trapnell, D H

Newport, Dyfed

Ennis, O W
Evans, H I
Evans, S J
Lewis, K E
Lewis, L S
Rees, D A
Revill, S I
Williams, H N

Newport, Gwent

Abbo, S E D M H
Al-Mitwalli, K A H I
Al-Mitwally, Q A H
Al-Shafi, K M K
Alderman, P M
Ambegaokar, S
Anderson, R
Anstey, A V
Arnold, R C
Arsanious, N H N
Ashton, R
Aubrey, N
Baldwin, C J
Bassi, C L
Bassi, R
Basu, U
Bates, C A
Beech, C J
Bernard, M S
Berridge, L
Beswick, N F
Beynon, J H
Bhagwandas, K
Blackmore, M G
Blyth, C P J
Bonn, W A
Bose, M K
Bowen, M E
Bowler, I M
Bowsher, W G
Bright, J C
Bright, M
Brook, F M A
Brown, J W
Brown, J V
Brown, P
Browne, S E M
Burgoyne, S
Burton, A J
Callander, C C
Capper, R H A
Carling, A B
Carr, A W R
Cawdery, J E
Chandrasekaran, T V
Clark, J M
Clark, M B

Newport, Isle of Wight

Clason Thomas, D H
Clements, R
Clubb, A S
Cole-King, A
Cooling, N J
Costello, J P
Cranfield, F R
Cribb, P E
Crocker, P D
Crosbie, J P
Curran, C M
Curtis, J T
Dale, P J
Daniel, D G
Das, R P
Davies, A B
Davies, D
Davies, E A
Davies, E G L
Davies, G J
Davies, G P
Davies, H I
Davies, J
Davies, M E
Davies, R
Davies, R W
Dennis, B D
Diggle, J H
Dodoo, J B
Donaghy, D F
Draper, T J
Dumont, S W
Dye, D J
Edmonds, J E
Edwards, W H
Espitan, H
Evans, D R
Evans, I T G
Evans, V M
Faheem, F G
Farley, C A
Feltham, E R
Ferry, R M
Freeman, E A
Gallagher, T B
Gateley, C A
Gibby, O M
Glynn, R P
Golden, M P
Golding, C L
Golding, R H
Goodman, B
Goodman, K
Gower, R L
Gray, A R
Gray, A E
Greenway, I P C
Griffith, G H
Haigh, P
Hallikeri, C G
Hamilton Kirkwood, L J
Hanna, B W
Hanniford-Youngs, S J
Harding, J R
Hart, J K
Hasan, F
Hawkins, F J
Hayat, M
Hayes, C
Haynes, T K
Hewinson, E E
Hewlett, C F
Hicks, J A
Hickson, V M
Hilliard, T L
Hodkinson, C K
Holgate, N J
Horner, C
Houghton, S J
Hughes, D S
Hughes, J M
Ingrams, D R
Jackson, D M A
James, T E
Jenkins, D A
Jenkins, I R
Jethwa, S K
John, C D
John, D W
John, R A
Johnson, A
Johnson, N
Jones, D G
Jones, D O
Jones, G D
Jones, L
Jones, P A
Jones, P E

Jones, R N
Jones, R H
Jones, R G
Jones, S A
Jordan, S E
Josty, I C
Kaiser, F
Kalidindi, U
Khan-Singh, J
Khonji, N I
Kilsby, A B
Kruger, M
Kubiak, E M
Kuzel, J J
Lalla, O V
Lau, T F W
Lavric, J M
Leitch, L M
Lewis, A J
Lewis, H
Lewis, J C
Lewis, P M
Lewis, W G
Linton, C R
Llewelyn, J
Lloyd Jones, J O
Lloyd, J E
Love, S
Luk, T L
Lyon, T
McCarthy, G J
McCarthy, P M
McGarrigle, A P
McGowan, J J C E
McKenzie, J
Maguire, S A
Magus, S R
Mahapatra, J
Marinakis, I
Martin, R C
Matthias, S
Mehrotra, M
Mian, T M
Michael, R F
Mills, C M
Mintowt-Czyz, W J
Mishra, M D
Misir, A
Moffat, E H
Mohamed, H E A M
Monelle, T J
Moore, R
Morgan, D M
Morgan, E I K
Morgan, W J
Morris, I M
Morrison, M L
Moses, K W
Mulcahy, M P E
Narula, H S
Narula, S K
Nichols, P K T
Osmond, D F
Palmer, B K
Papworth, S E
Pateman, S E
Paul, R G
Peel, M D
Peeling, A M
Petheram, C D
Phillips, A H
Phillips, C W
Phillips, D L
Phillips, G R
Phillips, S E
Poulter, S D
Powell, L J
Price, C J
Price, S D
Rackham, J P
Rampa, B R
Rawlinson, A
Redmore, M J
Reed, M
Rees, S
Rees, W H R
Richards, M B
Richardson, F J
Riley, A J
Roberts, J E
Roblings, G L J
Robson, D A
Rocker, I
Rosehill, S
Rowe, J L
Russell, G K
Ryan, H S S
Saleh, S
Salmon, M M

Salvaji, A
Salvaji, C S
Sanikop, S B
Savage, R
Saxena, R N
Scholey, G M
Scholler, I W
Seaborne, L
Shandall, A A A E F
Shankar, Y P
Sheppard, T J H
Sherif, A S A
Shooter, M S
SimcOck, T A
Sinha, J
Sinnett, K J
Sivagamasundari, U
Small, H J
Smith, T D
Srivastava, E D
Statham, N A
Steiner, J
Stephenson, B M
Stone, A L
Stone, M
Stone, N M
Sturdy, D E
Sullivan, P A
Sweeney, D
Taylor, H M
Taylor, L P G
Taylor, S L
Tejura, H
Telang, S M
Thomas, A E
Thomas, A G
Thomas, D L
Thomas, G D
Thomas, S J
Thomas, S W
Thomas, T E
Thompson, H T
Thompson, P D
Thompson, S D
Toner, J M
Tonkin, L V
Treub, M J
Trivedi, J
Tyers, R N S
Vellacott, K D
Velusami, O
Venkataramanan, P R
Waheed, W
Wake, A M
Warner, N J
Watkins, D W
Webb, W B
Weerakkody, C S
Wiener, J
Williams, D H
Williams, D I
Williams, D J
Williams, E R
Williams, J C
Williams, L M
Williams, P I
Williams, R S
Williamson, I J
Williamson, K
Wilson, G B
Wintle, C J
Wintle, J M
Yule, A G

Newport, Isle of Wight

Alleyne, P J E
Arlt, R
Arshad, S H
Baksi, A K
Barnard, E J W
Basten, J E
Bateman, B J
Beisby, N L
Berrange, E J
Bingham, P
Brooks, M R
Budihal, S S
Cardew, S M
Cashel, M L
Cave, A P D
Chapman, S T
Chulakadabba, A
Close, P J
Cole, J M
Dawes, A J A
Demissie, A
Dick, C A
Elsmore, S

Evans, G
Ewell, E J
Gordon, A R
Gove, A R
Greenwood, N
Grimaldi, P M G B
Guthrie, A
Hakim, E A
Halder, S
Hand, C J
Henderson, M M
Hide, Y H
Hill, M K
Hill, P J
Isaac, D H
James, P
Jilani, M G-U-S
Johnson, I S
Knight, R J
Landon, K
Lindefors-Harris, B-M
Logan, A D
Lynch, S P J
McAlister, H M
McCarthy, I M G
Maclean, H C M
Makunde, J T
Marsh, B A H
Mobbs, C N A
Mucklow, E S
Mudawi, H M Y
Murphy, D
Nasra, S E
Nawari, E O M
Newton-Smith, J G B
O'Grady, M S
Parsons, B E A
Parsons, J A
Premsekar, R
Rahman, M M
Routledge, N G
Russell, H J
Salih, M A
Sandiford, R H
Saxena, S
Sherpa, T P
Shinkfield, M N F
Smith, J
Stutley, J E
Ten Hoeve, W J
Tobey, I
Vairavan, M
Watson, A H
Whelan, T R
Wilks, M
Worby, M E
Yoong, A F-E
Yousif, S T

Newport, Monmouthshire

Sykes, P J

Newport, Shropshire

Allan, T W B
Andrew, R
Bayliss, L
Berrow, P J
Burgess, Y M
Collier, S G
Davies, J
Dennis, J M
Egleston, A A
Fitzgerald Frazer, J S
Handley, D
Henderson, R J
Hopgood, E L
Howdle, S H
James, V U G
Jones, L A
Kitchen, G
Large, J
Lisk, C H
Mercer, D S
Metcalf, J A
Morrhall, G E D
Patterson, R D
Powell, S W
Rosevear, C
Saran, S
Sharan, K
Tindall, N J

Newport Pagnell

Beaver, D J F
Bradlaw, R V
Carter, I S
Greig, A V H
Hickson, C K R

Lees-Millais, J V H
Odeku, K J
Paton, A C
Skinner, P J
Slavin, B M

Newport-on-Tay

Adam, K P
Alexander, V A L
Chalmers, S D
Chisholm, A D
Clark, A D
Cooke, R S
Crawford, P A
Crooks, G W
Curran, J S M
Davidson, A M
Dillon, L
Duncan, H S C
Fleming, C
Gair, M R H
Gallagher, P M
Gray, I G
Hepworth, D M
Hundal, L M
Hunter, I
Ingledew, M E
Johnston, M A
Kenicer, M B
Kilpatrick, A D
Kirk, S E
Lavelle-Jones, M
McKellican, J F
Mackintosh, K D
Mackintosh, N J
McQueen, F
McWhinnie, A J
Maggs, A F P
Merrylees, N
Miller, M C
Morton, H G
Morton, I P B
Nixon, J M
Pink, E J
Ricketts, N E M
Russell, W G
Shepherd, B M
Von Goetz, T C B
Walton, L M

Newquay

Arthur, W R
Blackford, K E M
Boulton, J V W
Buscombe, P
Cornah, L J
Currivan, C W
Davy, B L
Etling, T M
Hunter, C B J
Ingle, J H
Irvine, W N
Jervis, M J
Kersh, L G
Kinder, C
Leslie, R F
Macready, D
Mann, D M
Martin, R D
Olver, R H
Rigby, J M
Sleep, T J
Wooltorton, S J

Newry

Ajam, G S
Allen, J A D
Allen, M T
Allen, T P
Arumugasamy, A
Beattie, G C
Bell, D P
Blaney, C V
Blundell, J
Brown, J R
Brown, R J
Byrne, T P
Campbell, R L
Carroll, A M
Carroll, J
Conlan, E F
Connolly, N B
Corkey, C W B
Craig, J T
Cranley, B
Cunningham, A M
Cunningham, C
Cunningham, M J J
Curran, A M
Daly, C

Deane, M G
Degenaar, G D M
Devlin, B A
Devlin, J E
Digney, J M G
Dillon, B A
Donaldson, G W
Donnelly, K M
Donnelly, P M
Dooley, A P
Farrell, W J A
Fearon, M J
Fearon, P V
Fegan, M
Finnegan, D P
Finnerty, M
Flanagan, M P
Flood, R B
Flood, R D
Flynn, C
Forshaw, S E A
Foster, J H
Gaskin, P M
Gaw, D H
Gilpin, D A
Goss, K C W
Hanna, W J
Haran, M P
Harty, J C
Heaney, H A
Hingorani, T Y
Holland, E L
Holland, I F
Hollywood, M C
Kearney, A B
Kelly, M
Lambe, M B
Lane, P
Larkin, M P
McAlinden, J M F
McAteer, H M
McAteer, J
McBreen, G M M
McCaffrey, P M
McCann, B H G
McCann, G A
McCann, J J
McCann, M C
McCormick, M T
McCrea, R D
McDermott, D J
McDonnell, O L
McDowell, H M
McEvoy, P M
McGivern, A
McGivern, A W
McGivern, J
McGurk, J C
McKeown, R M E
Mackle, M G E
McKnight, M
McLaughlin, A B
McLaughlin, H
McVerry, I T B J
McVerry, M M J
McVerry, M G
McVerry, R G
McWilliams, R
Magee, D J
Maguire, B M
Maguire, P B
Maguire, S M
Mathew, P M
Mercer, J M
Miller, E J
Morgan, L C M
Morris, O D
Mulholland, A O
Mulvaney, D G
Mulvaney, G A
Murphy, M J
Murray, L E
Nash, D T L
O'Brien, C J
O'Donoghue, D B
O'Donoghue, P
O'Hanlon, D T J
O'Hare, A G M
O'Hare, B A M
O'Hare, M
O'Hare, M F
O'Kane, K M
O'Leary, T
O'Loughlin, A M
O'Neill, M M
O'Neill, P M
O'Reilly, D M M
O'Reilly, N
O'Rourke, F M

North Shields

O'Shaughnessy, D M K
O'Tierney, D P
Poots, S A
Quigley, P J G
Quinn, F M
Quinn, M M
Quinn, R P
Radcliffe, J C
Ratnavel, K K
Redman, T M W
Reynolds, J M
Rice, E A
Ryan, P F M
Shannon, E G M
Shannon, J W
Shannon, R I R
Shields, M O
Shortall, M T
Sim, D A J
Sloan, R
Smyth, A
Stokes, M A
Sweeney, C M
Synnott, M E
Treanor, O T
Vettiankal, G G
Walshe-Brennan, K S
Ward, P J
Watters, B V
Woods, W G
Wright, J M
Wright, P J

Hay, D S
Heather, J D
Hemsted, G H M
Henwood, B P
Hickey, S A
Hinde, J M
Hodges, N A
Hoffman, M M D
Hopkins, R J
Houghton, P W J
Howarth, P E H
Howell, J R
Howes, D E L
Hughes, A S
Hunter-Rowe, C K A
Hunter, N O
Kelly, D J
Kennaird, D L
Kennaird, L
Kinsey, V E
Lee, M J C
Leech, K W
Lewtas, D A
Lovell, R A
McDermott, M E
Markham, S
Marsh, S G
Martinus, P M
Melluish, V S-A
Milburn, D
Millar, J P
Minnis, J
Monks, P J W
Morris, T A W
Mules, R J
Munk, M E V
Murphy, C A
Musgrove, J S
Nicholls, J L M
O'Keeffe, C J M
Orton, D A
Parke, R J G
Parker, F A
Parker, P W M
Patey, J
Payne, I W
Phemister, J C
Ranjit, R
Rawlins, J S P
Rhodes, C D P
Richards, M J
Richardson, G A
Richer, L A
Roberts, E L
Robinson, A J
Robinson, G L
Robinson, S T
Rodger, J D
Rushton, S R L
Seale, J R
Sharp, B T
Siddall, W J W
Smith, P S
Smout, S M
Solari, L A
Stackhouse, J R
Stanley, P H
Stevenson, T
Stride, A
Tee, G H
Thomas, A R
Wade, C G B
Wade, R G H
Watkins, N A
Weeden, A C
Weeks, K F
Wildgoose, J L
Wildgoose, N W
Wollaston, S
Wood, P T
Wright, K J
Wright, P
Yeldham, D L

Sheldon, D M
Shenton, A F
Sudarshan, C D
Waterworth, S M
Watson, L J

Charlwood, A P
Chillingworth, T H
Condron, C K
Corrigan, M M
Coyle, P V
Cromey, R S
Crosbie, P J
Curran, C A
Darrah, A J J
Davies, P L
Davies, R C S
Davison, P M
Devine, P M
Diamond, T M P
Doggart, E R
Donaghy, P F
Duke, D F
Dundee, J M
Evans, S A
Ewart, K E
Fair, E A
Farrelly, C P
Flynn, P G
Gamble, J A S
Gibson, J A
Gilmore, J E
Goodwin, D
Gould, C H G
Gray, J G
Harbinson, M E E
Harper, D S
Hart, D J
Hegan, M C
Hendron, M P
Herron, N M
Hill, G
Houston, J R
Huey, T D S
Ingram, P J
Jenkins, L E
Jennings, R K
Kane, R
Kemp, R E
Kennedy, R J
Kyle, C J
Lyons, P
McCloskey, A M
McConkey, K
McCullough, A I
McCusker, T M M
McElderry, R K
McGimpsey, W D
McGowan, C M
McGrath, J J O
McGrath, J S
McKenna, U M
McKenzie, R J
McKeown, D F G
McKimmon, W J
McSorley, F A
Millar, G P
Neary, D M
Neary, J G
Neilly, P J D
O'Connor, B S
O'Hare, J
Oakey, H M
Page, B E
Patterson, A J
Poh, C H
Reid, J M M
Rendall, J C
Seymour, S C
Sloan, S A
Small, L L
Smyth, W R
Spence, C S
Stevenson, A M
Stevenson, R
Stewart, E J
Toland, W J
Whiteside, M L
Wilson, W T C
Wilson, W
Wright, D G

Buchanan, S
Buckley, M R
Bunn, R J
Burnham, J S
Calvert, C H
Campbell, H
Cathcart, J-M B
Charles, C P
Clarke, P
Clements, W I
Cobain, T G
Compton, D M
Coulter, R S
Davidson, K E
Donaghy, U M
Donaldson, D J
Donnelly, M G
Dorman, J K A
Doyle, N J
Duke, F J
Dunlop, J
Elwood, S L
Ferguson, W P
Ferris, J H N
Finlay, S S A
Fitzpatrick, C R
Foster, W F
Gallagher, H W
Gibson, D R
Gilbert, J H
Gilbert, J K
Glasgow, W V
Glennie, A C
Goldring, S D A
Green, J F
Groves, D H M
Hagan, T J
Hall, C E
Harbinson, H J
Henry, I B G
Hicks, E M
Higgins, D A
Hill, P J
Hinds, O
Houston, D G
Hughes, D F
Hughes, P L
Jack, C M
Johnston, N J
Kennedy, G D
Kennedy, R D
Kirk, K T K
Lees, E J
Leonard, E J
Logan, C J H
Lowry, R C
Luney, G M
McAuley, D J
McAuley, R R
McCance, J M
McClements, P G
McCluggage, M J
McClure, P T
McElheron, M L
McGaughey, D G
McIlfatrick, S D
McIlwaine, W J
McIvor, C C M
McKeown, M E
Mageean, R J
Marsh, W G
Martin, P
Mathison, C D
Maxwell, M
Mitchell, O H A
Mitchell, P J
Mitchell, R W
Moffatt, W R
Moffett, G S J
Moles, G
Moles, G I D
Moorehead, R A
Morrow, L A
Newell, K A
Noble, J R
Park, D S
Park, J M W
Patterson, C E
Peacock, D
Perry, E E
Quaite, T J
Reid, G D
Riley, M S
Savage, D M
Scott, A
Scott, L I
Semple, D K
Shanks, N R
Smith, M R

Smyth, R J
Somasundaram, A
Steele, H D
Steele, M A
Stelfox, D E
Stronge, K A
Tolland, J P
Tomb, J J
Trinder, T J
Winter, J K J

Newton Abbot

Adams, L A A
Al-Ashbal, S
Al Fulaij, S
Almond, A J
Arain, A M
Arthur, P J D
Ashworth, R N
Athow-Frost, T A M
Avery, C M
Bamji, J E
Bapty, A A
Barnes, M N
Bates, K J
Batterham, E J
Beabie, R A
Beck, J-K W
Beddoe, V K
Bellamy, P
Bellis, F
Bennett, B L
Bennett, J R
Bloom, V R
Bowen, J M
Branson, H I
Brown, E A
Brown, E J
Brown, K A
Brown, N P R
Bryant, R N
Bumstead, H
Cameron, A
Clarvis, M C
Clegg, A J
Cooksley, R
Coughlan, J B
Crawford, S G W
Crowdy, J P
Curtice, M J R
D'Arcy, N J
Dickinson, N A
Doidge, N H
Dommett, R M
Dudgeon, T A
Dunn, A R
Dunn, J W
Dunn, W
Dunn, W K
Dyer, S J
East, B A
Ellis, D J S
Every, H M
Fairweather, R J
Fergusson, K M
Fry, V
Fyfield, J
Galli, P R
Gardner, A M N
Gordon, C
Greatorex, D G
Hale, A
Hammersley, A G
Harber, M A
Harris, J L
Haskins, H W
Hatton-Ellis, G W

Normanton

Aruna Prasad, G
Bazin, M L F
Clift, J L
Dewhirst, P
Ellis, J
Gallagher, J C
Gupta, R P
Hunter, I A
Robinson, J E
Shaw, C Q
Wunna, R

Newton Aycliffe

Bamford, M R
Chamberlain, W B
Clarke, A S
Cowin, G S
Ferguson, G
Grainger, R H
Jones, J B
Jones, M G
Kerr, W D
Luder, H J
Martin, H
Owen, R I
Pounder, R
Ramsay, P D

North Berwick

Anderson, F M M
Boardman, A E
Boylan, B P
Buchan, A C
Clark, F R
Clark, M
Crawford, M E L
Drillien, C M
Flynn, M W
Jones, N D
McEwan, P N
MacFarlane, R G
Mason Brown, D
Milne, J S
Mulrine, A T
Nicholson, J W
Pretsell, A O
Salucci, G U
Smith, M C
Walinck, J M
Waugh, W N
Williams, W H
Wiseman, R

Newton Stewart

Aitchison, H
Baird, D M
Bremner, B-J
Brewster, M F
Clark, K
Conner, A M
Ducker, C J
Gourlay, D P
Grove, R A E
Hutchinson, J R
Jones, T A
McClintock, C P
Macdonald, J W A
McLean, I C
McNab, D S
Marshall, J G
Marshall, M
Miscampbell, N T
Moffat, P L
Murphie, R W
Robertson, N M
Roe, J
Steven, C M
Sutherland, S J

North Ferriby

Alexander, J G U O
Alexander, P J
Barchard, M C
Beardsworth, S F
Bennett, S R
Carter, D A
Church, I C
Clarke, R G
Davie, J P
Dealey, R A
Fareed, M N
George, P
Gould, L N
Griffith, R J
Grout, P
Holwell, A D
Hood, E A
Hood, W J M
Hunter, P J
Innes, J R
Klakus, J A
Knox, C J
Koul, K K
Maguet, H
Masson, E A
Mitchell, R G
Naylor, U V P
Pande, K
Portal, P
Pratt, A E
Pratt, G E D
Redfern, J N
Robertson, A C
Rogers, M A
Rutherford, S
Saleh, A H S
Seukeran, D C
Sheard, A V
Sheard, L D
Sherman, J M
Siuda, Z E
Speck, E H
Tuck, S P
Walton, C
Ward, A E
Welch, C J

Newton-le-Willows

Arya, R
Bentley, J I
Brierley, J
Connolly, M D
Crotch-Harvey, M A
Foster, R N
James, A
Lim, H H
Lowe, S H
Mahajan, H R
Malham, P A
Pitalia, A K
Pitalia, P L
Raza, M
Russell, A S
Shetty, N V
Smith, C
Smyth, K L
Thompson, C H
Whittaker, J A T
Wynne, I C

North Shields

Aburiziq, I S
Ahmed, B E I

Newtonmore

Fraser, D R M
Henderson, H
Kirk, A M
Martin, E P
Richardson, A I

Newtown

Griffiths, D L
Harries, J D
Hayes, H J
Hughes, G J
James, S P
Jones, R L
Leahy, H
Lewis, K A
McVey, T J
Nevill, C G
O'Brien, M B
O'Neill, E C
Porter, A
Schaefer, W
Swan, A J
Turpin, J
Wielezynski, M
Wilson, M S G K

Newtownabbey

Abdul Rahim, S
Allen, J S D
Archbold, G P R
Armstrong, D J
Bailey, M C
Balmer, G J
Beattie, I J
Bell, R E
Bennett, E V
Boston, B K
Boyd, K
Brolly, T B
Brown, G L
Buchanan, I S
Buchanan, S B
Byrne, E P
Carson, D J L

Newtownards

Adgey, A A J
Anderson, J
Armstrong, M F J
Beare, J M
Beattie, C K
Bissett, J
Bolton, R
Boston, V E
Bradley, M L
Brown, S J
Brown, T A
Bryson, J M

North Tawton

Akak, A M
Alexander, F W
Anderson, J S
Anderson, K N
Baird, M E
Bairstow, P D
Barton, J R
Bates, A M
Benjamin, C M
Bertram, R W
Birch, P J
Black, J E
Bolton, A R
Burgess, B M
Carter, L J
Cashman, D V
Cassidy, J V
Charlton, A E M
Chatterjee, A K
Clark, J A
Cobden, I
Collis, L J
Curless, R H
Derry, J A
Doig, J C
Drury, C A
Durrani, A A
Earl, D S
Emam-Shooshtari, M
Evans, D A
Farrer, V
Ferguson, L P
Firth, R J
Foreman, A G
Forouhi, P
Franz, E C
Freeman, H C
Gandy, A S
Gayner, A D
Ghazal Aswad, S
Greenwell, S K
Griese, K A
Hammouda, M
Harrigan, P
Hodes, P A
Holmes, F J
Houlsby, W T
Hulyer, M C G
Husaini, H M
Hussain, S
Jack, F R
Jackson, J M
Jaiyesimi, R A K
Jelley, D M
John, S
Jones, A I
Kasaraneni, R
Kelly, S B
Kilby, D
Knox, J C
Krueger, J K W
Kumar, A
Lambert, M W
Lawrence, M R
Leon, D
Lewis-Barned, N J
Livingston, M M
Lowry, R J
McCallum, J E
McKenna, P
McManners, M M
Majumdar, A
Malone, M A
Mandal, S K
Megson, K
Menzies, S W S
Moorcroft, A J
O'Hanlon, S
Parkinson, D R
Parkinson, G
Patterson, H
Peel, E T
Pollard, R
Pritchett, C J
Ramachandra, C R S
Reed, J B
Rees, J C
Rees, K S
Rickards, M A
Riordan, D M
Roberts, J B
Roberts, S H
Robertson, J
Rodgers, A D
Rutter, M K
Safe, G
Safe, G A
Sedgwick, P A
Shabde, N

Slater, B J
Smith, S E
Smyth, A G
Spink, C E A
Stainthorp, D H
Tapsfield, W G
Taylor, A J
Tennant, D
Timlin, N A P
Tiwari, R K
Tomson, D P C
Walker, R W
Walker, S E
Welare-Smith, J M
Westgarth, T J
White, L F
Williamson, C J
Wilson, E
Woodhams, A M

North Tawton

Shields, J M
Warre, J H
Webb, H B G

North Walsham

Davidson, S L
Dunn, W T P
England, M H
Everden, P R
Jones, T D
Lloyd, J A
McLeod, H R T A
Pickersgill, D E
Pickersgill, H B
Price, G A R
Robinson, D T
Ryan, C E
Strivens, E
Strivens, T E A
Tyrynis-Thomas, S A
Vavasour, S M A
Whitfield, E
Whitfield, F
Young, R J

Northallerton

Allan, J M
Allen, L-C
Allerton, K E G
Allison, C E
Arthur, R C B
Aszkenasy, O M
Atkins, A F J
Bacon, C J
Barker, F L
Bellas, F J
Benford, S C
Berens, J
Bhatt, B M
Boersma, R
Bosman, D A
Brereton, A G
Browning, M E
Browning, N M
Bryce, F C
Burton, L J
Butterworth, K
Caramello, A J
Colling, W A
Cruickshank, J M
Cummings, T F
Curry, A W
Das, K
Dean, J R
Dias, E M
Eames, A M
Edon, P J
Edwards, M H
Ellis, F
Enevoldson, H J
Erena Minguez, C
Essex-Cater, A
Fisken, R A
Foster, S
Gill, D
Gough, A
Halstead, G D
Hannon, C
Hebblethwaite, N
Henderson, D C
Herbert, A P
Hilborne, J
Holden, E
Holden, F M J
Jackson, D G
James, J R
James, R
Kabuubi, J B L
Leigh-Howarth, M

Lough, M J
Lyth, N A
Mackay, D M
McNeela, B J
McNeela, H E
Mountain, D
Oates, C G
Osterrath, K-W
Preston, C
Puranik, I
Ramsden, P A
Randall, J M
Roberts, A P
Roddie, T W
Samarage, S U
Sarathy, S
Shepherd, A F I
Simpson, C J
Singh, S P
Smith, W M V
Stahlschmidt, J U
Thompson, M C
Todd, C L
Tune, G S
Van Hoogstraten, J W A P
Waise, A A M
Walters, A
Walton, M R
Walton, R S
Ward, D C
Weightman, N C
Wilson, A E
Wolfe, S S
Yoong, S Y
Zelenka, R M

Northampton

Abbatt, R J
Abbott, V J
Abu Kmeil, S S M
Acheson, A G
Ackland, F M
Aitcheson, P E
Al-Hamed, M H
Alment, A
Alston, D J
Anthony, J P
Arnold, P D
Astbury, P
Atkinson, A J
Bailey, R D
Bainton, V C
Bakheit, N Z
Banks, D
Bantock, A M G
Baroni, M L
Barritt, S A
Barrowclough, M D
Bassett, L C
Beeson, M
Berry, A R
Bhattacharyya, A
Birch, N C L
Bird, N J
Birkhead, J S
Birschel, P
Black, R
Blanshard, C G
Bolland, J A
Bond, M L
Bonthala, C M
Boon, J E
Bradley, P M
Bridges, M J
Brown, E M
Brown, H J
Brown, H J
Brunt, N J
Buck, D C
Buckland, C-S
Buckler, D G W
Budge, T S
Bull, D W
Burnett, G B
Burston, D J
Button, M R
Byrne, P K
Cain, P T
Caldwell, N E
Campling, J D
Carroll, C B
Cazes, C I W
Chalmers, I S
Chandarana, V C
Chapman, J
Cherry, J E
Chipchase, J G A
Chmielewski, A T

Ciappara, J
Clark, A R B
Clark, J V
Clark, L A
Clarke, J
Cleal, D J
Clements, S L H A
Coghill, H M
Coghill, S B
Coles, P K L
Collier, J H N
Coneys, T D D
Coombs, M C
Corr, C J
Cotes, S C
Cowper, R A
Cradduck, G W
Crawford, T E
Crawfurd, E J P
Crockett, D J
Crowhurst, E C
Daish, P
Damle, A D
Daniels, M H
Darwood, E M
Dauncey, A C C
Davies, E S
Davies, H H
Davies, J I W
Davies, R E
Davis, T C
Dawson, J W
Dawson, S C
De Brauw, D F R
Dean, A M
Devereux, J G J
Donald, E A
Donald, J F
Duggan, L M
Duncan, A R
Duncan, C F
Dutta, D K
Dwivedi, K N
Eagland, J M
Edwards, A T J
Eliot, B W
Ellam, K S
Ellis, D Y
Elmasry, K M
Fahmy-Gobrial, R N
Fairlie, N C
Fearnley, I R
Fenton, J
Ferguson, G C
Ferguson, H C
Ferguson, J S
Fleming, A C
Fletcher, J K
Fogarty, A C
Fogarty, A W
Fogarty, K W
Fox, C J V
French, C M
Frerk, C M
Gardner, R R
Ghobrial, L A I
Gibbons, K J
Gidden, D J
Gilbody, J
Gill, T J
Gillam, D M
Gillam, M L
Gilmore, A
Gleeson, C M A
Glynn, L J F
Goldsmith, M J
Goodwin, M W P
Gordon, A C H
Gordon, C A
Gordon, J
Gothard, C J
Goulding, S R
Gower, S G
Graham, R D
Gralton, E J F
Greening, S L
Gregory, A L
Gregory, S D
Griffin, J M
Griffin, N K
Grover, D
Gurr, P A
Haczkiewicz, M J
Haines, M E
Hakeem-Habeeb, Q A
Hallas, C L
Halstead, H E
Halstead, P J
Hamer, D B

Hancock, A
Hancock, R J
Hare, J D
Harish Mallya, K
Harper, J R
Harper, R
Harris, M J
Hart, A J
Haw, C M
Heaney, D C
Heaney, P C
Hein, N
Hein, P L R
Hellen, E A
Hewertson, J
Hewitt, C S
Hewitt, N D
Hicks, J L
Hicks, R C J
Hiley, C A S C
Hill, J H W
Hill, K E
Hillier, A R
Hokan, R
Hollway, M C
Hopkisson, J F
Horsnell, S P
Hover, E C
How, N M
Hughes, J W
Hunt, B M A
Hunt, I J
Hunt, J A
Hunt, W J
Hunter, D C
Ireland, J P
Jain, A K
Jayakumar, S
Jayasuriya, H
Jeffrey, A A
Jeffreys, D G F
Jobanputra, R S
Johnson, J M
Johnston, D M
Johnstone, E D
Jordan, A L
Jukes, A M
Kay, N H
Kay, V J
Kaye, P M
Kellett, F R S
Kendrick, R G M
Kennedy, J
Kerr, G R
Kidger, T
Kilvert, J A
King, J E
Kirkbride, D A
Kirresh, Z O I
Kirwan, C C
Kirwan, M
Kneafsey, R W
Krishna Rao, C
Kunkler, R B
Kurpiel, A J
Kyriazis, M
Lad, N
Lakin, K H
Lamba, K S
Lancaster-Smith, J
Lange, B
Leroy, A E
Leydon, K M
Liang, Y F
Lindenbaum, K M
Lindenbaum, R J E
Littlewood, P B
Lloyd, C P
Lloyd, K
Lodge, A B
Lyon, I B
McCracken, M
McCullough, W L
McDonald, J M
McDougall, J L
McFarlane, J O
McGrath, D
MacKay, W P
McKenzie, J
McLain, M W
McLauchlan, I E J
Macmillan, C H
McNicholas, J J K
McQuillan, O M A
McQuillan, W J
Mahfouz, M
Mahood, J M
Makhani, F A
Makwana, N V

Mann, C M
Mapstone, B B
Marsh, R H K
Marshall, C I
Marshall, R D
Mason, F M
Mattingly, S
Meara, J R
Meeking, D R
Mehrez, I A-L
Middleton, J K
Miller, D W J
Miller, M A W
Modi, D
Moffat, B
Molla, A L
Molyneux, A J
Moore, C J F
Moore, F C
Moore, R S
Morgan, P R F
Morgan, R J
Morrant, B L
Moss, C M
Moss, F L S
Mountjoy, C Q
Mudaliar, R K
Mukherji, C S
Nawaz, M
Naylor, J E
Naylor, J P
Nevison-Andrews, D G
Norton, K J
Nottingham, J F
Nuttall, J B
O'Callaghan, D P
O'Connor, M
O'Donnell, J G
Offiah, E C
Ogilvie, A L
Orr, M W
Oswald, T F B
Otto, A D
Oughton, N M
Paine, D L S
Patel, S R
Penfold, H A
Perez, A
Perryer, C J
Phillips, L
Pickering, A J-M C
Platts, D E
Povey, J R
Powis, J A
Poyner, F E
Pratt, D E
Price, S M
Procter, A J M
Pyke, M R
Pyke, R
Quinn, L A
Raggatt, S H
Ramsdale, D
Randell, R A
Raouf, A H
Raphael, J A G
Raphael, J M C
Ratliff, D A
Reeder, J A
Reynolds, T H
Ribbans, W J
Richards, T A
Rickerby, I
Rigden, B R
Roberts, J
Robertson, D W
Robinson, K N
Rogers, P H
Rogers, S M
Rose, M J
Ross, J R Y
Rushton, P D
Saqib, M N-U
Savage, R M
Saynor, C E
Sebugwawo, S
Sefton, D
Seiger, D G
Severn, M
Shapero, J S
Shaxted, E J
Sheppard, L
Sheppard, R F
Sherwood, P V
Shmueli, E
Shribman, J H
Shribman, S J
Smart, D J
Smith, M D

Norwich

Smith, S J E
Smith, W P
Soloff, N
Sood, K K
Southcott, M R
Spencer, H J
Sprigings, D C
Staley, C J
Stevens, G C
Stewart, J A
Stockley, A T
Stubbs, R P
Surendra Kumar, D
Sutcliffe, R L G
Sutton, A
Sutton, T M
Swaroop, M
Swart, S S
Tahghighi, J P
Takla, A F S
Tanqueray, J F
Tapsell, S H J
Tasker, J R
Taylor, C G
Taylor, J B
Thomas, A K
Thomas, D
Thomas, V
Thompson, F J
Thompson, S A
Thompson, S
Thornton, D J
Tickle, S A
Timmins, B C
Tordoff, S G
Toseland, O R
Tough, H G
Trick, K L K
Tringham, J R
Tripney, R E S
Tunnicliff, M
Turk, E P
Twigg, A I
Twigg, S F
Underwood, C J
Van Amerongen, A J
Vann, A M
Vince, A S
Wacogne, I D
Waddy, E H
Waddy, G W
Wade, D C
Wadley, M S
Walker, C A
Walker, G J
Walsma, P
Walton, J L
Ward, A R G
Warnke, N A
Warwick, H M
Webster, R E
West, R C
Wharton, B K
Wharton, R Q
Wheeler, J M D
White, J B
White, R B W
White, R R
White, T J
White, V L
Wilkinson, M B
Williams, A J
Williams, M M
Williams, R F
Willis, A W
Willis, E M
Willows, M A
Willows, R I R
Wilson, B A
Wilson, C R M
Wolfe, K W
Wolverson, K
Wood-Allum, C A
Wood, I R
Wood, P
Woodhams, L J
Yates, S
Yorston, G A
Yule, S F

Northolt

Ali, S O
Aly, S A A F
Azra, S
Balachandran, G
Beirne, A D
Bell, L C
Bhatt, R K
Butt, Z A

Campbell, D J
Evans, D A
Hopkins, C T
Hui, K W
Hundal, K S
Hussain, M
James, A K
Jamil, M N
Jassal, B S
Joshi, B V
Joshi, J P
Kapadia, K B
Kassam, S G
Khanna, M
Knight, D G
Koupparis, L S
Lewis, A D
Mohammad, T S
Nwachuku, O M
Pal, D
Pal, M
Patel, C B
Patel, D
Prashar, S
Quadri, F R
Ramasubramanian, N
Seimon, J W M S C
Seimon, J W M J B
Wogu, G U E

Northwich

Adams, A S
Addagarla-Rao, A
Anthwal, V M
Ashworth, M
Barratt, C J
Bartlett, G V
Beastall, R H
Bill, E J
Brennan, A L
Brettell, A
Brown, S J
Buckley, P W
Bundle, A
Cade, D
Cawthray, P A
Chapman, R O
Chivers, C P
Clegg, J F
Cowpe, O O
Cranmer-Gordon, C R
Cronin, P A C
Daniels, M S
Deakin, F J
Dentschuk, A
Dick, J F
Dickinson, M A J
Dowler, J B
Down, E R
Eastaway, A T
Entwistle, A J
Entwistle, G D
Fisher, P M
Flynn, I M
Forsyth, W J
Fox, E E
Goodall, C M A
Graham, H C
Gurnani, H M
Haeney, L K
Halpin, S P
Hambidge, D M
Hamlett, J W
Hammond, J H
Harding, V
Hazlehurst, D E
Hignett, R
Hill, S E
Hollinrake, M S B
Hughes, A S
Hughes, R J
Hutchinson, D G
Jackson, S R
Jefferson, J M
Jefferson, M F
Jenkins, J E
Jennings, A C M
Kent, D R
Kerslake, J C
Kilby, F K
Langworthy, G W
Laugharne, D M
Lavin, P J
Lewindon, N
Lewindon, P J
Llewellyn, M B
McIlwrick, W M
MacVicker, K M
McGregor-Smith, F A

Morris, C M
Murphy, R J
Norman, A S
O'Byrne, E K
O'Donoghue, A
O'Sullivan, J J M
O'Sullivan, K F
Oldfield, P D
Parker, C C
Parkin, J
Paskin, D G
Patrick, J M
Pickstock, N J
Rickard, S P L
Rossall, A M
Royle, R A
Saunders, G J
Sinclair, B M
Slaney, C J
Strefford, T I
Taberner, D A
Torrance, J M
Westwood, S L
Whittaker, W A
Wilkinson, G M
Winton, M

Northwood

Abdul Wahid, M I
Abrahams, Y
Ahluwalia, N S
Allan, D J
Amos, C F
Ansari, M A
Apthorp, G H
Apthorp, H D
Ashford, R F U
Ataullah, I J
Ayoub, A-W A A
Baddeley, H
Bado, W J F
Barnes, J A
Basden, R D E
Bateman, J G
Bell, G T
Bleehen, I S
Bosmans, L
Brodrick, P M
Brown, M J C
Buckmill, A T
Burcombe, R J
Carnell, D M
Carr, D H
Chalmers, A J
Chatoo, M H B
Cledwyn-Davies, A
Coleman, A J
Coleman, J D
Collins, K M
Cullis, E F
Cussons, P D
Danee, A
Danee, P K
Davenport, H T
Dawrant, M J
Denton, A S
Dhasmana, D
Dhupelia, I R
Dische, S
Dougherty, S T
Douglas-Riley, T R
Douglas, E M
Duncan, M H
England, R M
Eykelbosch, G
Fermont, D C
Fickling, B W
Fine, S R
Fisher, A M
Fletcher, M
Frimpong-Ansah, K N
Gajjar, B
Gandhi, A G
Gardiner, G T
Gault, D T
Geary, P M
Giora, A R
Glover, G W
Glynne-Jones, R G T
Goodman, I L
Goodwin, P R
Goodwin, T J
Goolamali, S K
Green, L M
Greenhow, D S
Grenville-Mathers, A
Grosch, E J
Gura, R J
Haider, S I

Hall, M R
Hamid, S S
Hammond, T M
Haring, S J
Hoskin, P J
James, E B
Jeetle, G S
Jeffery, L A
Johnson, A E
Kang-Budialam, N V
Kant, S R
Karia, K
Khan, J
Khaw, K S
Kingsley, S M
Lab, D M
Lamb, J K
Lawton, P A
Le Fur, R
Lemon, C
Liebeschuetz, S B
Lyn, B E
Machesney, M R
McKeating, J B
MacLeod, T M
Maddison, J S
Maddox, A J
Maher, E J
Majid, A
Makepeace, A R
Makris, A
Melia, H C
Melia, N P
Mellor, S J
Mills, D C
Mitchell, R
Mitchenere, P
Murugesh-Waran, S
Nathoo, Y
Navapurkar, V U
Nawarski, B J
Nicholas, N S
Obadiah, R
Pace, J E
Padhani, A R
Phillips, J B
Pile, A E
Pomerance, A
Potts, J J
Rees, G F M
Reissis, N
Riches, H R C
Rivlin, R S
Rustin, G J S
Sarin, S
Saunders, M I
Sayeed-Uz-Zafar, Dr
Scadding, F H
Scott, F R
Sellaturay, R
Sellaturay, S
Shackman, S G
Shapiro, S M
Sharih, S
Shaw, J P V
Shorey, B A
Smith, P J
Solley, R
Solomon, T A
Stewart, H C
Story, P
Sweatman, M C M
Thakkar, I D
Thakrar, D N
Thomas, P M
Thompson, E A
Thompson, F D
Todd, J J
Veitch, G R
Walford, C S
Waters, C E
Whitehead, M B
Wilson, A R
Wong, S J
Yau, K-M R
Yogeswaran, P
Zuberi, M M

Norwich

Abbott, R T
Abraham, G
Adeney, H W
Ahmed, N
Ainsworth, L F
Albert, J S
Alden, D J
Allan, A
Allanson, N K
Allen, G T

Allen, R W H
Allington-Smith, P F
Ambrose, A
Amies, V M
Anderson, I M
Ansari, N A
Applegate, J M
Arie, M E
Arie, T H D
Armatage, R
Ashbee, C R N
Ashby, L M
Ashford, N P N
Ashken, I C
Ashken, M R H
Astbury, N J
Atkinson, A G
Atkinson, L
Axford, S L
Aylott, C E W
Baako, B N
Bailey, D R
Bailey, H B
Bailey, J R
Ball, H N
Ball, R Y
Bamber, S C
Bangham, C H
Barclay, H
Barclay, R P
Barden, S D
Bardsley, A F
Bardsley, V
Barker, G L
Barker, P
Barker, S S
Barker, T H W
Barkley, A M
Barltrop, I
Barnard, P B
Barnard, P M
Barnard, S L
Barratt, J
Barrie, P M
Barrie, R E
Basketts, A E L
Bass, P G B
Bastable, G J G
Battersby, E F
Battersby, M
Batty Shaw, A
Baxter, L D
Bayliss-Brown, P J
Beach, R C
Beales, I L P
Beales, M S
Beavan, P D
Beeby, M J
Beezhold, J N
Bellamy, J E
Bellamy, L A W
Bennett, C P
Bennett, E R L
Bennett, J C
Berry, P J
Beton McCulloch, M L
Beveridge, J
Beveridge, J M
Bhadrinath, B R
Black, A J
Blackburn, A L
Blundell, C M
Blyth, J A
Bone, J C B
Bookless, D W
Bourne, A J
Bracher, D
Brain, A
Braithwaite, J E G
Brambleby, P J
Brannen, I C
Branson, E
Brantigan, P D
Brazendale, I F
Bremer, C
Briscoe, C E
Brisley, G D
Brito Ramos, J M
Brittain, D R
Brooks, R
Brooksby, I A B
Brown, J A C
Brown, S W
Bryce, D K
Buchan, R D K
Buckton, C
Bulman, A S
Bulto Chirivella, M D M

Burford, R
Burgess, N A
Burns, J D A
Burns, S A
Burrell, M A
Burrows, P J
Bush, A P
Butt, S J
Calder, D A
Cameron, A
Campbell, C R D
Cant, B
Cardoe, N
Carlson, K J V
Carlson, R G C G
Carlyle, D N
Carrington, R W J
Carron-Brown, S L
Carver, P H
Cator, S E
Chapman, P G
Chapman, P C S
Cheatle, T R
Cheesbrough, A J M
Cheetham, A C
Cheuk, M S
Chitale, S V
Christie, A L M
Chua, S C
Chuah, T P
Clark, B E
Clark, G S
Clark, J R
Clark, W A
Clarke, E D
Clarke, J M F
Clarke, T J
Clayton, C L
Clayton, G M
Clayton, P
Clement, M H
Clements, M J
Coathup, P A
Cole, B S
Coleman, C J
Colin, J F
Conway, S
Cooke, L M
Cooper, B A
Copson, S G
Corson, J G
Couch, A H C
Couch, D W
Couldery, A D
Coupland, C R
Coupland, R M
Cowan, J F
Cox, K A
Craig, J C
Craig, K D
Crawford, R J
Crook, W S
Crowle, P M
Crowle, V J
Curtin, J J
Cushing, K E
Dalrymple, J S O
Dalrymple, P A
Davies, P D
Davies, R E
Dawson, B G
Day, A G
Daykin, S M
de Boer, F C
Deane, A M
Del Rio Basterrechea, I
Delvin, D G
Denton, E R E
Devine, E A
Devine, R
Devonshire, R E
Dhesi, A S
Dick, D J
Dods, A S
Donell, S T
Double, D B
Downes, G W
Downs, S M
Dreke, S
Dryhurst, K M
Duckworth, P M
Duncan, I
Dyke, M P
Eason, J D
Echebarrieta, J M
Edmonds, D A
Edmonds, S M
Eke, T
Ellis, M C

Nottingham

Elsby, K P
Elvy, B L
English, J P
Essien, E U
Evans, J K
Evans, P J
Evans, R H
Eve, J R
Evison, P R H
Fairclough, A A
Farman, R D C
Farquharson, S
Fellows, I W
Ferrari, M R
Fielden, A L M
Fincham, C M
Finlayson, B J
Finney, J M
Fisher, J M
Fiske, S J
Fletcher, H C
Fletcher, S J
Fogarty, A J
Forbes, M D
Forsythe-Yorke, W E I
Fox, J J
Fox, S A
Francis, C R T
Francis, R N
Fraser, C S
Fraser, D I
Freeman, L J
Frost, J S
Frost, M W
Fry, T M
Fryers, G R
Fulcher, R A
Furniss, P
Gaffney, J K
Gair, J D
Gall, A R
Gallagher, E G
Garioch, J J
Gaskin, M A
George, A
George, C M
George, J D
Gibson, A G
Gibson, I S
Gilbert, R F T
Gillings, M J
Gilson, J M
Girling, A C
Girling, S D
Glasgow, M M S
Glenn, A M
Glennon, P E
Godfrey, A W H
Goldser, D S
Gordon, M K
Gow, I A
Grantham, K M
Grattan, C E H
Gray, A J G
Gray, I G
Green, C A
Green, M B
Green, N A
Griffiths, S J P
Griffiths, T R L
Grove, A J
Guy, A D
Guy, D J
Hackett, J T A
Hall, P N
Hameed, M B
Hamerton, R A M
Hamilton, D V
Hamilton, G T
Hamlin, P J
Hampsheir, R P
Hancock, G D
Hardy, E G
Harland, R D
Harper, P C W L
Harris-Hall, J J
Harris, J R
Harris, P R
Harris, P R
Harrison, B D W
Harrison, F D
Harrison, K R
Harston, P J R
Hart, A R
Hartley Booth, A C
Harvey, I M
Harwood, J M
Hatoum, A F
Hattersley, T S

Hawthorn, S J
Haydn, K F
Hayward, A P
Head, F A
Headley, M A T
Heaton, A
Heaton, K
Heighton, D R M
Heighton, R W
Henley, P A
Herrero Diaz, M
Heyburn, P J
Hill, D B
Hillen, H A
Hodgkinson, N B
Hodgson, S
Hoey, T E
Holburn, A M
Holland, R C
Holt, S P
Hood, D H J
Househam, E A
Howe, A C
Howe, D C
Howe, R J
Hudspith, M J
Hughes, L O
Hughes, W C
Hunter, A N
Hunter, L C
Hurst, G R
Hutchings, P J G
Hutchinson, C T
Illing, R O
Innes, A J
Innes, H E
Ireland, N J
Iver, E B A
Jackson, A W
James, M R
James, P W
James, P M L
Jathanna, S D
Jenkins, J R
Jenkins, P F
Jewsbury, P
Johnson, P
Jonason, E R
Jonason, P H A
Jones, C N
Jones, D V
Jones, R D
Jones, S M
Joss, G S
Kaszubowski, H A
Keele, G
Keep, P J
Kellet, S H
Kelly, B K
Kendrew, M E
Kennedy, H J
Kerr, L I
Kestin, K J
Kinder, C H
Kirkpatrick, R B J
Kitchener, P G
Kitson, M C
Kluenker, C E M
Knight, J E
Knights, P D
Knights, R C
Knowles, A K
Krichell, A J
Lamb, N J
Lambert, M A
Lane, S E
Latham, J B
Laurence, M D
Lawson, P R
Leach, J M
Leadbeater, M J
Leaman, A M S
Leaney, R M
Ledward, D J
Leeming, D J
Legg, N G M
Leinster, S J
Leney, P M
Lerman, A J
Lesley, C A
Levell, N J
Lewis, J C
Lindsay, A S
Lipp, A C
Lipp, A K
Lister, A J
Lister, G E
Lloyd, A H
Lock, P T

Lockett, S R
Lofting, J A
Logan, A M
Lonsdale, R N
Luck, J D
McAdam, E K
McCann, B G
McCarthy, J J
McCartney, I M
McDonald, N G
McEvett, F C
McEwan, I P
McEwen, M J
McFerran, D H
McGovern, D O
Mackay, J E
McKenzie, A W
McMurdo, L
Macrae, S E
McShane, R
Magrath, A
Main, S J
Maisey, D N
Mallinson, R H
Malpas, C A
Malpas, L C
Mansfield, T G R
Manson-Bahr, P G P
Marshall, A T
Marshall, T J
Martin, R
Martin, S
Martin, W M C
Mason, H C S
Mathur, A B
May, H M
May, S R
Meaden, J D
Merry, P
Meyer, M
Meyerhoff, A
Michel, M-C A
Millar, P M
Miller, J E
Miller, J G
Miller, M P
Millis, J L
Minnaar, G
Mirza, W J
Mitchell, I R
Mitchell, J
Mitchell, W P
Money, T D F
Moreton, C A
Morgan-Hughes, G J
Morgan-Hughes, J O
Morgan, J H
Morgan, W S
Morris, C H
Morris, E P
Morris, M-A C
Morris, N M
Morrow, D R
Morton, I N
Mosedale, B M
Mould, J
Munson, D J
Murphy, H J
Naguib, M F
Nash, C M
Naunton, W J
Neale, A W
Neech, S E K
Nesbitt, W D
Newns, G R
Nicol, A
Nisbet-Smith, C
Noble, M J
Nolan, J E
Nolan, J F
Norman-Taylor, F H
O'Neill, A E
O'Neill, H B
O'Neill, T J
O'Shea, J R
Offer, C M
Ogden, J S M
Okoro, J O
Olive, J E
Oliver, L E
Olney, P J
Ostrowski, M J
Overton, C E
Overy, R D
Pac Soo, C K
Page, A J F
Palframan, A
Pannett, R N
Parachuri, V R

Parikh, A
Park, W D
Parry, G W
Patel, A
Patel, R G
Payne, J F
Pearce, C P
Pearce, K M
Pearce, R D
Pennell, A M
Percival, G O
Perry, G L
Pfang, J A
Phillips, H
Phillips, J E
Phillips, P D
Pickworth, F E
Pilch, D J F
Pilling, J B
Pilling, J R
Pinching, N J
Pinder, N R
Plunkett, T G
Poliakoff, L J
Pope, L E R
Porter, G E
Poulton, B B
Powell, J S
Pratt, N J
Press, A M
Preston, J T
Preston, P G
Preston, W E B
Price-Forbes, A N
Price, C P J
Price, D B
Price, F M
Price, M E
Prinsley, P R
Prior, A
Prosser, D J H
Pugh, C R
Purnell, R J
Pyne, J R
Pyper, A J
Quirke, J J
Raggoo, M D R
Rahman, M
Rahman, N
Raithatha, N
Ralphs, D N L
Ramsay, C F
Ranger, I
Rao, B R S
Rash, G J E
Rattner, G J
Rayner, T W
Reading, R F
Rees, J H
Rees, R T
Reynolds, C M
Rhodes, M
Richards, A E
Richards, J
Richards, M C
Ridley, S A
Rigby, A J
Rippy, E E
Rivett, J F
Rix, T E
Roberts, A J
Roberts, M D
Roberts, P F
Robertson, D A
Robinson, C R
Robinson, G A
Roche, M T
Rolls, N P
Ronaldson, P N
Ross, B A
Ross, C N
Rowan, P A
Rowe, S
Rowe, W L
Rumball, D
Russell-Wells, S J E
Russell, M H
Saada, J
Sabanathan, K
Sale, A C B
Sambandan, S
Sampson, J S
Sampson, M J
Sams, V R
Sansom, J R
Sassoon, E M
Sattar, M
Scherzinger, S H
Schram, J E

Scott-Barrett, S
Scott, D G I
Scott, J D
Scott, S D
Scouller, F E
Senarath, V L
Shaw, C
Shaw, M S
Shaw, T J
Shepherd, P D W
Shinh, N
Shutes, J C B
Sides, J R
Signy, C M
Simmons, H
Simpson, D A
Simpson, R J
Skipper, C
Sladden, D K L
Slocombe, R L
Smith-Howell, M A
Smith, R P P
Smith, S N
Smith, S J
Smyth, E T
Solomka, B T
Souper, D K
Spalding, D R C
Speakman, C T M
Stanley, A K
Stanley, K P
Staples, S A
Steel, N
Steel, S F M
Steele, R G
Stewart, W
Stone, R
Stuttard, C A
Summons, A C
Sutton, I J
Sutton, P H
Taylor, N M
Temple, R C
Tewson, G R
Thirkell, C E
Thomas, A
Thomas, B E
Thomas, C G A
Thomas, G W
Thomas, J M
Thomas, R C
Thomas, T A
Thompson, K O
Thompson, R S
Thorn, D R
Thorpe, R S
Threfall, S J
Thurlow, J
Tighe, M R
Tilford, M P
Tilford, T J
Timms, R F
Tolley, I P
Tomlinson, D
Torrens, J D
Tracey, V V
Tsang, T T M
Tucker, J K
Tucker, S R
Turner, G E
Twentyman, O P
Tyler, X M
Upton, C J
Valentine, J M J
Valentine, L
Varvel, D A
Vaughan, D A
Vaughan, R
Vaughan, S J
Vellacott, C W
Verma, N K
Verma, R
Verpaele, A
Wadge, D A
Wagstaff, M H
Wales, R M
Wallace, M C
Walsh, S J
Walter, S J
Ward, M R
Warminger, M
Warren, J
Warren, R C
Waterhouse, C
Watkin, S W
Watkins, D
Watkins, J
Watkins, R J
Watson, D C T

Watson, M A
Watson, P C
Watt-Smyrk, C W
Watts, Y
Wayman, J
Webb, M C
Welsh, D W
Welton, T
Wenley, W G
Went, E L
White, P M B
Whitehead, T R S W
Wickstead, M
Wilkinson, K A
Wilkinson, L M
Williams, H M S
Williams, J H G
Williamson, K S
Willis, M D F
Willits, D G
Wilson, J R M
Wilson, P A J
Wimperis, J Z
Wisdom, P N
Wong, N C-K
Wood, P M
Woodall, N M
Woodhouse, P R
Woodhouse, S J
Woods, A D
Woollam, C H M
Wright, A
Wright, C J
Wyatt, J D
Yallop, D
Young, K E
Young, P J

Nottingham

Abbott, M D
Abdi, S
Abdul Aziz, A
Abdul-Hamid, S
Abdul, S
Abell, J D
Abercrombie, C A
Abercrombie, J F
Adams, A D
Aderogba, A
Aderogba, K O
Aghel, M M
Agrawal, S K B
Ahluwalia, U
Ahmad, M
Ahmed-Jushuf, I H
Ahmed, F B
Ahmed, S I
Ahrens, C L
Ahsan, A J
Aitkenhead, A R
Al-Hassan, S H
Al-Hilaly, M A L
Al-Sahab, A N A
Alagesan, K
Ali, A R
Ali, S I
Allan, A N
Allen, B R
Allfree, J M
Allison, S P
Amar, S S
Ambler, J J S
Amin, J
Amin, S
Ammar, K M
Amoaku, W M K
Ancliff, N B
Andrew, S L
Ankenbauer, M R
Annesley, S E
Ansell, I D
Arandhara, K K
Arden-Jones, J R
Arey, D K
Arias Abellan, M M
Armitage, F E
Armitage, N C M
Armon, K
Armstrong, J R
Armstrong, R S
Arya, T
Ashpole, E J
Ashpole, R D
Ashworth, A J
Aslam, T M
Aston, I R
Atherley, D B
Atherton, J C
Atkins, R L W

Nottingham

Au, L
Auckland, K M
Auger, M J
Austin, A S
Aveline, A J D
Aveline, M O
Avery, A J
Azar, N E S
Bachra Singh, P
Badrashi, F-V-D
Bain, C N
Bajek, G
Baker, K A
Baker, L
Baker, P N
Baker, T M
Baldwin, D R
Baldwin, P M
Balfour, C E
Balfour, T W
Ballin, N C
Bandyopadhyay, P K
Banks, D C
Banks, J E
Banner, R W
Banton, J G
Barber, D N
Barkataki, H C
Barker, M S A
Barnard, A E
Barrett, P J
Barrett, S M L
Barry, B P
Bashir, M
Bassi, N S
Bassi, S R
Basu, K K
Bates, C P
Bates, J A B
Bath, P M W
Baxendale, B R
Beale, L J
Beatty, J H
Beaver, M W
Bebb, N J M
Beckingham, I J
Bedforth, K J
Bedforth, N M
Bedi, N K
Bekhit, M T M S M
Belk, K M
Bell, C H
Bendall, M J
Beningfield, S A
Bennett, J W
Bennett, J A
Bennett, M W R
Benson, K J
Bentley, S C
Berman, P
Bertenshaw, C J
Bessell, E M
Best, A C
Bhandal, S K
Bhanji, N P
Bhatia, A A
Bhojani, T K
Bhojwani, S C
Bignell, C J
Bignell, J A
Bilkhu, J S
Birch, P C
Birchall, A D
Birchall, J P
Birmingham, A T
Bishop, L J
Bishop, M C
Biswas, A C
Bittiner, P
Black, D G
Bladon, Y M
Blake, M J
Blakeman, J M
Blamey, R W
Blecher, T E
Blumhardt, L D
Blundell, A G
Body, G D
Bogod, D G
Bolarum, S R
Bolis, G U
Bolsher, S J
Bond, S J
Booth, R
Boswell, T C J
Bourke, J B
Bourke, S L
Bowen, L W
Bowering, K

Bowker, R P
Bowler, C
Bowley, C J
Bowman, C A
Boyd, J
Bradbury, N
Bradford, J A
Bradley, P J
Bradley, S J
Braithwaite, B D
Bramley, M D
Bratt, K G
Bratty, J R
Brennan, P
Bridgewater, A L
Brierley, J K
Brittain, A H
Britton, J R
Broadhead, T J
Brockelsby, J C
Broderick, N J
Brook, D R
Brookes, C E
Broughton, A N
Brown, C A
Brown, C M
Brown, K P H
Brown, L M
Brown, M M
Brown, M E
Brown, S F
Brown, T P L H
Browne, N C
Bruce-Lomba, E A
Bruce, B I
Bruce, J E F
Bryan, A G
Buck, B M
Buck, S
Buckell, N A
Buckler, M B
Budge, H J
Buky, A
Bulmer, N J
Bunnage, S J
Bunting, N W
Burden, R P
Burns, R A
Burns, S M
Burr, R W
Burrell, H C
Burton, G A
Burwell, R G
Butcher, C C A
Butler, T K H
Butler, T J
Buxton, N
Byrne, J L
Byrne, P O
Bywater, K H
Caffery, I L
Calder, G R
Calder, J
Caldwell, A J
Campbell, A
Campbell, F A
Campbell, I W
Cantwell, R
Caplin, S A
Capra, M L
Carberry, P J
Carmichael, J
Carolan, B A
Carr, M E
Carruthers, D B
Cartledge, R
Cartmill, M
Cartwright, J E
Cartwright, K E
Cartwright, N P
Cassidy, M J D
Cawthron, P A
Ceurstemont, M A
Chahal, P S
Chalasani, A K
Challen, K B
Chambers, H N
Chan, C Y-Y
Chan, K K K
Chan, Y T S
Chandramohan, S
Chapman, L
Chapman, N D
Charlton, C P J
Chaudhri, Q
Chaudri, M B
Chaudri, M B
Cheeseman, S L
Chell, J

Chester, D L
Chisholm, M
Chu, S Y Y
Chua, W L
Chung, K Y K
Churchill, R D
Clamp, M
Clark, C T
Clark, D H
Clark, E G
Clark, G R
Clarke, J L
Clements, H
Clifford, W A
Cockburn, A P
Cockrill, J
Coffey, F M
Cole, O J
Coleman, T J
Coles, R R A
Colley, M S V
Collinson, B
Colton, C L
Comaish, I F
Connery, T P
Connolly, J A
Conroy, S P
Conway, J F
Cooke, F J
Cooper, J E
Coppens, M
Copping, J R
Corbyn, C N
Corcoran, M E
Corcoran, R
Cornwell, C-A
Cotton, R E
Coultas, A P
Coultas, R J
Cousins, C
Coutts, F
Coutts, S R J
Cox, G M
Cox, G J
Cox, S A
Crawford, K S
Crighton, I M
Crofts, C B
Crosby, V L
Culverwell, N J C
Curnock, D A
Curnock, G H R
Curran, F M
Curran, J P J
Cutajar, P
Cwynar, B U
D'Mello, B J
D'Mello, K A
D'Mello, M T
D'Mello, T A M
Dalton, C M
Daly, J C
Dalziel, K L
Daniels, M P
Darlaston, P J
Darling, W J E
Davidson, I R
Davies, B W
Davies, D
Davies, E
Davies, G J
Davies, G R
Davies, M G
Davies, P
Davis, C J
Davis, G R
Davis, M
Davis, M E
Davis, T R C
Dawson, A
Day, J S
De Silva, E S
De Sousa, C G
De Ville, D C
Deane, M
Deighton, C M
Denley, H E
Denny, P A
Desai, K
Devadason, M J N
Dewar, J C
Dewar, J R
Dexter, P J
Dhar, S
Dickenson, A J
Didcock, E A
Dillon, J B
Dixon, H
Dixon, K

Docherty, B H M
Dodd, S L
Doddy, J A
Doel, V R
Doherty, M
Dolan, G
Donald, F E
Donnan, A B
Donnelly, A
Doran, J
Dornan, J D
Doshi, B
Dove, A F
Dowd, M P
Dowell, J D
Dowell, K
Dowling, F M
Downes, R N
Downing, N D
Drew, J H
Dua, H S
Duffy, A M
Duffy, J P
Duggan, A E
Duggins, R A
Dunderdale, M A
Dunn, G R
Dunn, I A
Dunn, K A
Dunn, M
Dunstan, S P
Durcan, S F
Durrant, J M
Duthie, A
Dutka, D P
Earnshaw, S A
Earwicker, H M
Earwicker, S C
Eaton, M D
Edington, P T
Edwards, J D E
Egginton, M J
Elliott, R H
Elliott, S
Ellis, I O
Ellis, J A
Elston, C W
Emerson, F-M
Emerson, R M
Emery, J G B
Emmerson, A M
Engler, J H W
English, J S C
Esberger, D A
Euinton, L E
Evans, A J
Evans, J H C
Everton, M J
Exley, P M
Eynon, T E P
Fabisch, W
Fagan, D G
Faniyan, A
Farquhar, F J
Farquhar, I K
Farrand, D J E
Fawcett, A N
Felstead, A
Feneley, M R
Fenwick, S W
Ferguson, B G
Ferguson, S H
Fewtrell, M S
Field, M L
Filshie, G M
Filshie, S E
Finch, R G
Finn, D L
Finnegan, G F
Firth, J L
Fish, G H
Fisher, H
Fisher, K M
Fitz-Henry, J K
Fitzgerald, G V
Fitzsimmons, I N
Flambert, H M
Fletcher, A J P
Fletcher, J
Flewitt, A P
Flowerdew, G D
Follows, M C
Foot, V M
Ford, A R
Ford, S A
Forman, K
Forrest, K M
Forster, I W
Foss, A J E

Foulds, A M J
Foweraker, K L
Fowler, R
Fowlie, S M
Fradd, S O
Fraser, J S
Freeman, N J
French, E A
Friedman, T
Fullerton, D G
Gahir, M S
Gale, C P
Gale, R P
Gallagher, C
Galloway, N R
Galloway, S C
Gan, K B
Garcia-Orad Carles, C
Garcia Zarco, M D M
Gard, P D
Garratt, C J
Gauntley, K A
Gavrilovic, A
Geh, E
Geutjens, G
Ghattaora, A S
Ghattaora, R S
Gibbin, K P
Gibbs, E R
Gibson, M I
Gibson, S M
Giddins, J C
Gill, D C
Gill, H K
Gillespie, E M
Gilmore, N M S
Girling, K J
Girling, P A
Gladman, E Y
Gladman, J R F
Glass, K S
Glencross, S J
Glendening, J D
Glynn, A F M
Gnanalingham, G M
Goddard, A F
Goddard, W P
Godfrey, P A L
Godwin-Austen, R B
Godwin, Y
Gokhale, N S
Gokhale, S L
Goldsbrough, J
Gorbutt, N
Gordon, E B
Gordon, J C
Gormley, P D
Gould, N V
Grant De Longueuil, M C
Grant, J
Gray, D
Gray, W M
Greaves, R J
Green, A
Green, D J
Green, R H
Greenbaum, J D
Greenfield, A D M
Gregson, E D
Gregson, R H S
Grevitt, M P
Gribbin, C M
Griffin, N
Griffiths, A L
Griffiths, D E
Griffiths, I L
Griffiths, J P
Griffiths, P G
Guha Ray, P K
Guion, A J
Gulati, R
Guyler, C J L
Guyler, P C
Hage, M D
Hahn, D M
Hall, E J
Hall, I P
Hall, L
Hall, T J
Halstead, P
Hama, T M
Hama, Z A
Hambleton, K L
Hambley, J J
Hamilton, J B
Hammersley, B W
Hammond, R H
Hampson, M E

Hampton, J L
Hampton, J R
Hancock, S M
Hannah, D W
Hanson, M E
Hapgood, D S
Hapgood, R W
Haq, S-U
Hardcastle, J D
Hardman, J G
Hargreaves, E L
Harley, K J
Harris, F G
Harris, J P
Harris, S J
Harrison, A T
Harrison, D J
Harriss, D R
Harte, J H
Hartley, S
Hartman, J A
Harwood, R H
Haskew, E E
Hassan, B S
Hasson, S Y
Hathway, K L
Hatton, M
Hawkey, C J
Haworth, S M
Haycock, J C
Hayes, L J
Haynes, R J
Hayward, A C
Hazlewood, E B
Headley, B M
Heathcote, W
Hebbar, I K
Hedley, R N
Heeps, J M M
Heining, E W
Heining, M P D
Henderson Smith, R
Henderson, L M
Henderson, M J
Henderson, R A
Henfrey, L J
Henley, M
Henley, M J
Henn, M
Henry, D J
Henry, J K
Henry, R I F
Henry, W D
Henshaw, R C
Hepden, M
Heron, J M
Hewitt, M
Hewitt, M J
Hewitt, S M
Hignett, L H
Higton, C R
Hildyard, K J
Hill, S
Hindley, F A
Ho, K J
Hobbs, G J
Hobbs, N J
Hobson, J
Hogarth, P A
Hogarth, T B
Hogg, R A
Holbrook, M R
Holden, N L
Holdsworth, B J
Holdsworth, U J
Holland, I M
Hollingworth, A A
Hollis, C P
Hollis, H R
Holmes, W F
Holt, J C
Holton, B D
Hopkinson, B R
Hopkinson, G R
Hopkinson, H E
Hopton, C
Horn, E H
Horsfield, P W
Horton, J L
Horton, T C
Hosking, D J
Houghton, B L
Howard, J R
Howard, M A
Howarth, E S
Howat, J G M
Howell, C J
Howell, L M
Howell, S J

Nottingham

Howman, E M
Huang, D Y-H
Hubbard, R B
Hubscher, A M
Huggins, D A P
Hughes, S A
Huissoon, A P
Hull, D
Humberstone, M R
Humphrey, E G
Hunt, R J
Hunter, J B
Hunter, R
Hunting, J B
Hussain, F N
Hussain, M
Hussain, S A
Hussain, T
Hutchinson, A
Hutchinson, N J
Hutchinson, R
Hutchon, S P
Hutson, M A
Hutter, C D D
Ibrahim, P
Ilyas, N
Ingram, G R
Ioannou, G R
Ioannou, J M
Irving, W L
Jacklin, P J
Jackson, B R
Jackson, D J
Jackson, R J
Jacobs, B B
Jain, S
Jalloh, I S
James, C A
James, D K
James, L
James, M W
James, P D
James, P J
Jan, I A
Jaram, I
Jardine, A D
Jarosz, K D
Jarratt, G
Jarrett, L N
Jaspani, T
Jayakumar, Y
Jayamaha, J E L
Jeelani, N U O
Jeffcoate, W J
Jelpke, M F D
Jenkins, D
Jenkinson, D
Jessler, H
Jobling, J C
Johnson, C
Johnson, I R
Johnson, J R C J
Johnson, M E
Johnson, P H
Johnson, S R
Johnston, D I
Johnston, I D A
Johnston, M N
Jones, A C
Jones, A M C
Jones, J E
Jones, J A
Jones, K
Jones, M C
Jones, N S
Jones, P A
Jones, P A E
Jones, S A
Jones, T D
Jones, W L
Jowett, A
Junaid, O
Kachroo, M K
Kakaletris, D
Kalsheker, N A
Kandola, L H K
Kapila, L
Kapur, P K
Karim, R S
Karim, R
Karney, V M
Karras, K
Kaur, K
Kayan, A
Kazem, R
Keavney, P J
Kell, S A
Kelly, P
Kendall, D J

Kendrick, D
Kennard, D A
Kennedy, C M
Kenny, L
Kerslake, R W
Kesari, V
Khalid, L J
Khalique, A
Khalique, P
Khan Madni, M M
Khan, A
Khan, M S
Khan, Z
Kime, R
King, R L
Kingdon, S J
Kinnear, W J M
Kinsey, M
Kirwan, M M
Kitchin, S E
Kleimanis-Taylor, N S
Klonin, H
Knapp, D R
Knapp, P
Knight-Jones, E
Knights, D T
Knights, S G
Knott, D K
Knox, A J
Kolinsky, B I
Kolowski, S J
Kong Yao Fah, S-C M-F
Kong, W M
Kramer, A
Kraus, S
Kupfer, R M
Kuruvatti, C C
Kyi, T I
Kyriakides, J P
Kyriakides, K
Lakhani, M
Lakhanpaul, M
Lakshminarayana, C
Lamb, J M
Lambourne, J E
Landman, R S
Lane, P W F
Large, G A
Largey, P M
Lata, A
Latief, K H
Latimer, R K
Lau, Y S
Lavelle, H
Lavelle, P
Lavelle, T
Lawrence, S K
Lawson, P C
Leach, I H
Leadley, J M
Leake, V F
Leask, S J
Ledger, C H
Lee, A S
Lee, M
Leggetter, P P
Leibowitz, R H
Leiper, C A
Leman, P C M
Lemberger, R J
Lennon, K H
Lester, T D
Leuty, G M
Leven-Melzer, H
Levy, D M
Lewis, C
Lewis, M J
Lewis, M
Lewis, S A
Lewthwaite, P
Liau, F O
Lichtarowicz, E J
Lim, A K P
Lim, K K J
Lim, K T C
Lioumi, D
Lipman, A
Lipp, C
Littlewood, S M
Liu Tek-Yung, D
Livesey, O M
Livesey, R M
Lloyd Jones, J K
Lloyd, J A
Lo, S D C
Loch, A B
Logan, R F A
Logan, R P H

Long, R G
Lonsdale, R E
Lott, C M
Low, H L
Low, K-W
Lowe, J S
Lowe, J R
Lowe, S J
Macarthur, D C
MacArthur, M M
McCall, J
McCauley, P M J
McCoach, G N
McConachie, N S
MacCormack, J M
McCracken, F M
McCracken, J S
McCulloch, A E
McCulloch, I W L
McDermott, D M
Macdonald, J A
McDouall, S F
McDowall, K M
Macfarlane, J T
McGlashan, J A
McHale, N P
McHugh, T M A
McKean, M C
McKinlay, R G
McKinney, N M
McLachlan, A N
McLachlan, J I
McLachlan, J K
McLachlan, R E
McLaren, A J
MacLaren, A H
MacLean, J C R
McLean, P C
McLellan, G I M
McLoughlin, E T M
McMaster, J M
McMillan, A K
McMurtry, J L
McNicoll, W D
McNulty, I C
Macpherson, M B A
McVicar, E H
McVicar, I H
Maddock, E F
Madeley, J R
Madeley, R J
Magnago, T S I
Mahajan, J
Mahajan, R P
Mahida, Y R
Maile, L J
Maini, D
Majid, N A
Makhdoom, Z A
Makin, S W
Malik, I A
Manhire, A R
Mann, C E
Mann, G S
Manning, P A
Mansell, P I
Mansfield, R M
Manson, C M
Marder, E
Marenah, C B
Marks, P J
Markus, H S
Marlow, N
Marsden, K J
Marsh, A J
Marsh, L F
Marshall, G B
Marshall, J A
Marshall, R H
Martin, G D R
Martin, P H
Martin, W L
Marval, P D
Mascari, A J
Mascari, R J
Maskery, J J
Mason, P R
Mason, R
Masud, T
Mather, G I
Matthew, J L
Matthews, A J
Matthews, S L B A
Matthews, S M
Mattick, J A
Maxwell-Armstrong, C A
May, T
Mayell, M J

Medley, I R
Mehat, B S
Mehdian, M H
Mellor, D V
Mellor, L J
Mellor, M
Metten, A C
Michel, C A
Middleton, H C
Milburn, J
Miles, H C
Millard, L G
Miller, P J
Milligan, G F
Mills, T A
Milner, S A
Minto, A
Miranda, S M
Mitchell, J A
Mmono, X M K
Moleele, G T
Molyneux, A W P
Montgomery, A R
Moorby, T J
Moorhead, S R J
Moppett, I K
Moran, C G
Morewood, J H M
Morgan, A G
Morgan, C R
Morgan, D A L
Morgan, L J
Morgan, N M J
Morgan, S A
Morgan, W E
Morley, J
Morrant, J D
Morris, G K
Morris, R O
Morton, K M
Moulds, J
Moulton, A
Moxon, J
Mueller, K-M
Mukherjee, S K
Mulholland, K E
Mulholland, R C
Mulholland, S N P
Murad, M J R
Murphy, A
Murphy, C A
Murphy, R E
Murthy, A A
Mussellwhite, A
Mutale, I T R
Myers, B
Myers, D
Myles, D M G
Naidoo, A S
Napthine, E E
Narnor, F W D
Nash, D L
Nathanson, M H
Neal, K R
Neale, R
Nelson, J S
Nessim Morcos, I
Neumann, L
Neville, A J
Newton, R G
Ng, Y K
Nguyen-Van-Tam, J S
Nickalls, R W D
Niezywinski, W A
Nowicki, R W A
O'Donovan, T J
O'Dowd, J K
O'Grady, F W
O'Mahony, J B
O'Neil, H A
O'Neil, M J
O'Shea, R M
O'Sullivan, K T
Oates, M R
Oliver, P A D
Oni, J
Oram, E G
Orr, J T
Ovenden, L A
Ovenstone, I M K
Oza, N
Oza, P
Pabla, H S
Packham, C J
Padfield, C J H
Padmasri, P
Page, K E
Page, N P F
Page, R C L

Page, S R
Pallan, J P
Palmer, N I
Pang, K-K
Panta, R
Park, S B G
Parken, H F
Parken, P N S
Parker, C R
Parker, S J
Parmar, S C
Parry, A W
Parsons, B L
Parsons, S L
Patel, H
Patel, R R
Patel, S R
Paterson, A Z
Pathak, B K
Pathak, C A
Patmore, S J H
Patrick, P R
Patterson, J E
Pavier, P C
Pavis, H M
Payne, S D
Pegg, C A S
Pegge, S M
Pelger, H C
Pemberton, E
Percival, H J
Perez Teruel, M I
Perkins, W
Perks, A G B
Perry, J J
Perry, W R
Persey, A
Persey, D J
Petty, D J
Phelps, T M
Phillips, N N V
Phillips, N V-K
Phipps, K N
Pickering, S A W
Pillai, C N
Pillai, P P C
Pinder, S E
Pinner, G T
Place, G F
Pollard, K J
Pollock, J G
Polnay, J C
Polnay, L
Poole, G H
Porter, D M
Porter, J F H
Powell, M C
Powell, R J
Pradeep Kumar, N
Preston, B J
Prince, H G
Pullan, C R
Punt, J A G
Pye, S M
Queipo De Llano Temboury, A
Queiroz, J E
Quenby, S M
Quraishi, M S
Qureshi, S M
Radford, P J
Raeburn, J A
Raj, D
Rajakaruna, M L
Rajbhandari, S M
Rajendra, B
Rakhit, T
Ramsay, M M
Ramtoola, S
Randall, P J
Randerson, J M
Randhawa, N A
Rands, C E
Rangwani, P M
Raniwalla, J
Rao, A R
Rao, M J
Rao, Y V V S
Raoof, A
Rathbone, P S
Rawcliffe, J A
Rayner, P M C
Redfern, M A
Redmond, I T
Redwood, R
Rees, A M
Rees, J A
Rees, J A
Rees, S

Regan, M M
Rehman, A
Reid, A R
Reid, J A
Reid, M F
Reid, R
Renshaw, S A
Resnick, J V
Reynolds, C W
Reynolds, N J
Rezaul-Karim, S M
Rhoden, F M
Rhodes, J E
Rhodes, K E
Richards, C W
Richards, H J
Richens, D
Ridley, D
Rigg, K M
Riley, B
Riley, S P
Ripley, G S
Rizk, S N M
Roberts, E M
Roberts, L
Robertson, I J A
Robinson, M H E
Robson, D K
Rodgers, H C
Rodrigues, K F
Roe, S D
Roebuck, E J
Rogahn, D
Roith, E
Roper, A F
Roper, P B
Roper, S G
Rose, D H
Rose, J M
Rosser, R L
Rotherham, M J
Rotherham, N E
Rothwell, C I
Roughton, H C
Rowlands, B J
Rowson, J E
Roy, R
Roy, S P
Royle, D J
Rubin, P C
Ruddell, M C
Rudham, S J
Rudin, C S
Rudrashetty, S
Ruse, C E
Russell, A S
Russell, M M
Rutter, N
Rutter, S M
Ruzicka, J M V
Ryan, C J
Ryder, S D
Ryding, A D S
Saad, F
Sabir, S
Sagar, D
Sagar, S D
Saha, A
Sahota, O S
Saihan, Z
Salama, F D
Salisbury, M R
Sama, A
Samuels, L S
Sandher, D S
Sandilands, G A H
Sands, K A
Sanjeev, D
Saunders, A C
Saunders, P
Saunders, P C
Savile, C W
Sawle, G V
Sayers, J D
Scaffardi, R A
Scammell, B E
Scholefield, J H
Scott, A R
Scott, A R
Scott, R A
Scudamore, T O
Sears, R T
Seddon, D J
Seevaratnam, D M
Selwood, A
Sensky, P R
Seth, R N
Sewell, H F
Shackley, T R

Oldbury

Sham, J K W
Shanley, M J
Sharma, K
Sharma, N K
Sharma, O P
Shaw, H M
Shaw, J M
Shaw, R E
Shearstone-Walker, C G
Sheik Hossain, S M
Sheldrake, F E
Shephard, R H
Shepherd, J M
Sherman, R W
Shields, P A
Siddiqi, A G
Silcocks, P B S
Sills, R O
Simmons, P J
Simpson, J D
Singh, J
Singh, P J
Singh, S P
Skelly, R H
Skelton, J B
Skidmore, M J
Skinner, S M
Sklar, I D
Slack, R C B
Small, P G
Smart, P J E
Smeeton, F J
Smereka, A K
Smith, E M
Smith, J G E
Smith, J C
Smith, J D
Smith, N V
Smith, N J
Smith, N K G
Smith, P G
Smith, S J
Smith, S A
Smyth, A R
Soar, J
Soar, N M
Sokal, M P J W
Solomonsz, F A
Somers, J M
Sommers, S M
Soo, S-S
Sood, H C
Sood, N C
Sparrow, I M
Sparrow, M J
Sparrow, N J
Sparrow, R A
Speight, P
Spencer, A F
Spencer, C M
Spencer, J D
Spilsbury, B G
Sprackling, P D
Stack, W A
Staines, J A
Statham, R
Stebbings, N E
Stephen, A B
Stephens, D E F
Stephenson, T J
Stevens, K J
Stevens, M A J
Stewart, D J
Stewart, I D
Stewart, J I M
Stewart, P J
Stewart, R J
Stirling, G A
Stock, A I
Stoddart, N
Story, P A
Strachan, B K
Stryjakiewicz, E G
Stuart, D
Stubington, S R
Sturrock, N D C
Sturrock, S M
Suffield, M J
Sugden, B D
Sullivan, C F
Sully, L
Sun, K F
Sunman, W
Swamy, M S
Swannell, A J
Swinscoe, B D
Symonds, E M
Szabadi, E

Szypryt, E P
Tait, J
Tambyraja, A L
Tan, K C E
Tan, M P
Tan, W-H
Tangri, A K
Tarrant, C J
Tassi, L A
Tattersfield, A E
Tavernor, R M E
Tavernor, S J
Taylor, A J
Taylor, H D
Taylor, H J
Taylor, S M
Teahon, C
Tedstone, I K
Teed, A R
Teh, C P L
Teirney, R
Temple, J D
Tennant, W G
Thelwell, C M
Thew, D C N
Thew, M E
Thomas, A E
Thomas, A R
Thomas, D G
Thomas, H J M
Thomas, M J
Thomas, W A
Thompson, A
Thompson, G M
Thornhill, J D
Thornton, P J
Thornton, S J
Tinsley, M J
Tiong, H Y
Titmuss, J
Tiwari, P P
Tiwari, S R
Toft, K C
Tomlinson, K C
Tomlinson, P A
Toms, D A
Toms, E S
Topham, L A
Tourret, L J
Tredgett, M W
Trescoli Serrano, C T
Trimble, I M G
Trueman, A M
Tse, Y H A
Turnbull, C A
Turner, B P
Turner, P C T
Turner, R J
Turrill, J E
Twining, P
Twomey, J M
Tyers, D J
Ubhi, C S
Uddin, F J
Underwood, F S H
Unitt, E
Upton, M I
Varma, R
Varnam, M A
Venables, T L
Venning, H E
Verma, M S
Verma, S
Vernon, J M
Vernon, S A
Vettraino, M D
Village, A L
Vindla, M
Vindla, S
Vohra, J P S
Vyas, H G
Waite, J
Waldron, B A
Wale, M C J
Wale, P F
Walker, D A
Walker, G
Walker, J D S
Walker, S L
Wallace, W A
Walls, S
Walmsley, J M
Walsh, D A
Walsh, M M T
Walsh, R J
Walters, G D
Walton, S A
Want, E
Ward, B

Ward, J E H
Ward, L M
Warner, J A
Warren, C A
Warsop, A D
Wastie, M L
Watkin, S L
Watson, A R
Watts, S J
Wayman, M J C
Webber, J
Webber, M
Webster, J
Webster, V L
Weir, A
Welch, N T
Weller, D P
Wendelborn, K J
Wenham, P W
Werchola, L O
Weston, V C
Wheatcroft, S B
Whitaker, S C
White, A
White, B D
White, J D
White, K K
White, L R
Whitehouse, A M
Whitehouse, W P A
Whiteley, A M
Whiteley, P
Whitnall, M
Wiecek, M R
Wigfield, A S
Wight, C O
Wilcock, A
Wilcock, D J
Wilcox, R G
Wild, M R
Wilde, S M J J
Wilkins, J L
Wilkinson, E J
Wilkinson, P J
Williams, B T
Williams, C B
Williams, H C
Williams, L
Williamson, K M
Wills, C J
Wills, J S
Wilson, A R M
Wilson, D I
Wilson, D N
Wilson, F
Wilson, R J
Wilson, S H
Wilson, S L
Winter, R J
Winterbottom, K F
Woll, N K
Woll, P J
Wolverson, A S
Wong, C A
Wood, A M
Woods, A H
Woods, L A
Woods, M J
Woodward, E A
Woolrich, L H
Worrall, A-M
Worrall, S M
Worsey, C J
Worth, K V
Worthington, B S
Wright, S R
Wroughton, M A
Wynn, S M H
Wynne, R A
Xenophou, X
Yap, S C
Yassin Kassab, M
Yeoman, P M
Yeung, J M-C
York, S M
Young, A S
Yusuf, S W
Zacharakis, N
Zafar, M R

Nuneaton

Agrawal, V K
Ahmed, N
Al-Sebai, M A H
Allen, S J
Apakama, I G
Arora, M K
Assassa, R P
Bajallan, N M S

Bannister, R V
Barnie-Adshead, A M
Batchelor, Y K
Beadman, A M
Beauchamp, G J P
Beckles, D-E P T
Bee, H W
Benton, P J
Binyon, S E
Bruck, P E
Bullen, A W
Bullen, B R
Burnett, M G
Castells, V
Chapman, P J
Charles, D P J
Charles, E
Chaudhuri, A K
Chhetri, P C K
Clamp, I J
Cossey, A J
Cox, M L
Crosby, P S
Crutchlow, E J
Datta, V
Davies, R H T
Dawson, S L
Dison, G
Drage, M W
Edwards, K J B
El-Sadig, S A
Entwisle, J J
Fagan, J M
Fear, C R
Fitz-Patrick, J D
Gadsby, R
Ganapathi, E N
Garala, K
George, M
Germain, S J
Gill, K
Gill, R S
Godfrey, A J
Gorringe, H R
Gossain, R N
Graham, C N
Grant, H M B
Greenhalgh, S A
Groves, A R
Groves, C F
Guest, M
Gupta, A
Haider, Y
Hajat, C
Handslip, P D J
Haynes, I G
Henderson, B L C
Hickson, P J
Hodges, E J
Howarth, N J
Howl, M
Hutchins, C J
Hyslop, R N
Ingrams, G J
Jacob, J
Johnson, R A
Jones, K L
Jones, S H
Jones, T A
Jordan, J M
Kachbia, B G
Kenyon, V G
Khan, J A
Khan, K
Kisku, W
Law, D G
Lillo Torregrosa, J J
Lim, P V H
Lower, M J
McKeown, C J
Manek, N
Marson, S
Mellor, M J
Mentor, J M
Meystre, C J N
Miller, R I
Morgan, C N
Morrissey, J R
Moshakis, V
Muthiah, C Y T
Nangalia, R
Narayanan, M N
Nasser, Z A-A I
O'Brien, C
Parkianathan, V
Parnaby, R M
Patel, A R
Patel, C R
Patel, R J

Paton, S L
Perera, H M G
Perera, W N R
Phelps, S V
Phipps, J H
Quadri, S A
Quarcoopome, W N S
Qasim, M
Reddy, M A
Reddy, R
Redfern, A C
Reily, C M
Sabih, I
Sayed, S
Schnetler, C
Shenoy, K K
Shirazi, H A
Sidhu, B S
Singh, H
Sinha, S
Smith, A M B
Somasunderam, B
Srivastava, S
Stephenson, S J
Suliman, M T M
Summers, M W
Taggart, P C M
Thankey, K L
Thomas, M P
Thompson, A
Todd, J L
Toone, R P D
Topham, P S
Upponi, S S
Upponi, S K
Vaidya, G A
Vallance, K A
Venkatesh, M N
Walzman, M
Waterer, R M
Whitehouse, A B
Willett, M
Williams, A N
Williams, J G
Wilson, H J A
Woo, M T C
Wood, D W
Wood, G M
Zurub, A A

Oakham

Allanby, K D
Baker, J W
Boston, F K
Cheverton, S G
Clitheroe, E G
Clitheroe, M B
Cowling, R E
Crosthwaite, J D
Dighe, S V
Donnelly, T B
Drye, E R
Eaves, M
Fenby Taylor, J W
Fox, H J
Gaffikin, P E
Gallimore, C H
Gavins, E N
Goraya, J
Guthrie, A E
Henley, A
Inman, G K E
Inman, S M
Jones, E G
Jones, J P
Keating, D C
Ker, D A J
Lawrie, B R
Lennard, N S
McCormack, G E
Martin, M K
Martin, S G
May, D R
May, S A
Milnes, S D
Moore, S J
Newman, M R B
Nolan-Hughes, S A
Nunn, N K
O'Hare, D J
Orrell, M G
Phillimore, C E
Rhodes, P
Richards, C A
Robin, I G
Rodgers, J S
Scotney, A J
Selmes, S E
Seymour, N R

Shewry, S M
Tring, J P
Turner, D P B
Venn, M G P
Westwood, W J A
Wheatley, D A
Whitelaw, J
Woodings, J T
Woolford, D J
Young, S J

Oban

Ambrose, J A E
Ambrose, L J
Armstrong, E M
Armstrong, K M D
Buchanan, S M
Burton, M A F
Cameron, A T
Cameron, M E
Campbell, N M A
Davies, A M
Easton, H G
Forsey, J H
Galloway, J K
Grabbet, G G
Grant, D F
Hadfield, S J
Hannah, G D
Henderson, A F
Henderson, A K
Hill, A G S
Jespersen, E
Lane, P J
Lennox, J B
Loynds, P A
Macdowall, P
McKerrell, W
McLean, J D F
Mair, H E
Milne, E J B
Muir, E A
Murchison, A G
Murray, A M
Robertson, C Y B
Robertson, K M
Robertson, M H
Scobie, D J
Shand, J D
Steiner, E M
Stewart, I D
Taylor, C M
Taylor, S
Walker, J S
Watt, D A L
Wilson, C M
Wilson, E M
Yadav, S N

Okehampton

Bell, T R D
Box, D C
Carter, A P
Cox, A L
Downie, M C
Gandy, P J
Gilpin, T S
Groome, J B A
Gundry, D R T
Hart, H M
Hatcher, R C
Ledger, J A
Macgeon-Morris, R
Macklin, S C
Mellanby, A R
Nielson, P C
Padfield, N N W
Pearson, M
Reeves, J
Ross, J D
Rowe, A
Stainer-Smith, A M
Twomey, J C
Vile, K S M
Watkins, S A
Wawman, R J

Oldbury

Andreou, B A
Blewitt, L A
Chan, J L M
Corbin, D O C
Dau, H S
Demajumdar, R
Finch, J
Garfield, M J
Granville, C M
Griggs, N J
Hanna, H S F
Holtom, K

Oldham

Indwar, A C
Jasim, W A L
Jones, F W
Kamal, L
Kaur, S
Khan, M M
Kharaud, B S
Martin, J R
Naeem, A
Nagra, A S
Patel, B
Rugg-Easey, M L
Springall, C J
Sykes, I R
Tarin, M K
Thacker, A J

Oldham

Aboel Saad, A B
Ahmad, J J
Ahmad, N
Ahmed, Z
Al Saidi, T K J
Alam, S
Alexander, A
Ali, M S
Allen, G
Amin, B C
Anderton, L C
Ashraf, D
Aslam, M
Atherton, D A
Atkinson, M W
Aziz, N L
Badr Eldin, S E A F
Bailey, J S
Baker, R P
Bakht, T
Baldwin, E S
Bandara, D J
Barlow, D J
Barrie, J R
Bayman, R L
Beswick, F B
Bhan, G L
Bhatnagar, D
Boden, M G
Braddock, A
Brady, M C
Brett, I
Brocklehurst, I C
Brown, A I
Brown, C M
Buckley, K G
Byrne, H A
Callow, P J
Capuano, A
Carswell, W
Chadwick, A J
Chadwick, B C
Chakrabarti, A
Clegg, S
Clough, T M
Cogan, F M
Collin, P G
Conroy, D P J
Cook, L B
Cook, P R
Cooper, F
Cope, A
Daud, L R
Davies, T L
Deo, M K
Deo, R S
Devaraja, V C
Dhanawade, S
Dixon, S E
Dockerty, J A
Dodgeon, L M
Dunbar, E M
Duthie, L H
Dyson, K
Ebizie, A O
Edozien, L C
Emslie, B
Faulkner, M A
Ferguson, M E
Fischel, J D
Fleming, D I
Fletcher, G C
Ford, A C
Ford, B D
Foster, M E
Fox, A M
Friedman, E H I
Garside, S H
Ghanim, S N
Gibbons, A M
Gill, B

Gorman, C
Green, J E
Green, N D
Gregory, M A
Grunstein, S
Gupta, M M
Gupta, P
Hackett, L
Hadfield, M B
Hall, S E
Hampson, R M
Heptonstall, J M
Heyes, P
Hodgson, E A
Hollos, R B
Hutton, S J
Imlay, J M
Inston, N G
Isaacs, V R
Jackson, N A
Jain, S R
Jayachandra, C R
Jayakumar, C S
Jayakumar, L
Jeeves, R S
Jethani, P R
Jeyagopal, N
Jojo, K A J
Kamar, Z
Kapur, J K
Keba, S
Kelso, J W
Kenworthy, J W
Kenyon, S J
Kershaw, S A
Khan, M T
Khan, R S H
Khan, S
Khiroya, R
Khurana, A
Khurana, J C
Khurana, R
Khwaja, N
Klimiuk, P S
Knowles, W P
Kobbekaduwe, A E R
Kohli, R
Lawson, J W
Lawson, W R
Lees, B H
Lester-Smith, D
Lewis, B
Lewis, J D
Lighton, L L
Lipton, J R
Logan, S H M
Lynch, B M
McArthur, A
McCoye, A J
McEwan, K L
McGeachie, J F
McGee, H M J
McInnes, R
McIntosh, C A
Mander, A M
Marr, C A H
Martin, A M
Martin, J V
Mehra, S K
Menzies, D A
Middleton, H N
Middleton, K
Mills, M C
Milnes, I
Milton, M H
Mirza, S
Misiry, N T
Mitchell, R
Mkandawire, E A
Mohanty, A
Mokate, T
Moloney, A M
Monks, C J
Mytton, J A
Ncube, W
Northfield, M
Nwokolo, C F
Nye, A D
O'Brien, T D
O'Malley, H A
O'Malley, M
Odeka, B O
Page, F C
Pal, S K
Panigrahi, K
Patel, K R
Patel, R K
Paterson, A
Patrick, J F

Paulley, J S
Poston, M M
Poston, R G M
Prasuna, K
Puddy, B R
Radcliffe, G
Rajasansir, J G S
Ramachandran, K
Randte, S
Ravishankar, R
Reid, P V
Rivera De Zea, A
Robinson, J E
Rothwell, J E
Saha, N K
Salah, M M R M
Samji, F
Saraf, R
Schofield, E C
Schofield, L P
Scott, C G
Shackley, D C
Shah, I K C
Shepheard, B G F
Shipp, P A
Shoaib, A
Sidra, L M
Sikander, N
Sinclair, T
Smith, D E
Solomon, S A
Sood, R P
Spikker, A C W
Starkie, J
Stonehouse, W P B
Suresh, C G K
Suryanarayan Setty, R S
Sydney, J P M
Syed, S H
Taylor, A W
Taylor, M
Thompson, J
Trewinnard, P J
Umeh, C F
Vedi, K K
Walker, C A
Wallace, T J
Walsh, P A
Walton, D A D
Watson, I P M
Watt, T C
Webster, J J
Whitecross, S E S
Whitley, I G
Wilkinson, A
Wilkinson, J
Wilkinson, J
Willan, W K
Wood, E
Wright, J M
Wright, P N

Olney

Bartlett, D R
Beal, S E
Cockings, G F
Cockings, J G L
Curtin, M J
Hall, J P
Law, J C
Partridge, A B
Partridge, B E
Partridge, R E
Paton, C A
Reed, P A
Scott, E A
Short, S D
Snashall, D C

Omagh

Allen, A J
Anand, K
Blair, A L T
Bradley, P B
Brannigan, R
Breen, H A
Brogan, K B M
Cockburn, I R
Connolly, D F
Connolly, T P
Conway, D P
Corry, M J
Courtney, P A
Curran, M P
Davis, W S
Deehan, J A
Deeny, C K M
Dillon, D A

Donnelly, A M
Downey, D G
Fox, D P
Fulton, J K
Gallagher, P M
Garrett, P J
Gervais, T G
Glackin, P
Gormley, D G
Haigney, S A
Hassan, I-U
Hendly, A J
Hicks, K W
Hodkinson, E H
Irwin, J M A
Jackson, H G
Jamison, J P
Jamshidi, R J
Kaluskar, S K
Kelly, B P
Kemp, M T A
Lagan, J A
Lagan, K
Lalsingh, R R
Lalsingh, S L
Law, K P
Loughlin, V
Loughrey, G J
Loughrey, P J
McAleer, A P
McBain, C A
McCallion, W
McCann, J J
McCavert, M
McClean, M
McColgan, B J
McDermott, M A
McDermott, M G
McDonald, B T
McFarland, A J B
McGirr, G P
McGlinchey, P G
McGrath, C
McMullan, E A
McMullan, F H
McSorley, J D
Maghoortaigh, L G M
Maginness, J M F
Maltby, A C V
Manley, P A
Martin, H
Meehan, D D
Miller, G A B
Mitchell, C J H
Monaghan, K F
Morris, P
Muldoon, J G
Nabney, S P W
O'Boyle, C P
O'Connell, G
O'Neill, C A
Pinto, D J D T
Pollock, N C
Quinn, P H M
Robinson, F P
Rodgers, M V
Russell, C J M
Russell, J E
Rutledge, M R
Scully, A G
Scully, P G
Scully, P J
Singh, V
Smith, R A
Stewart, G E
Strain, A G
Sweeney, B E
Sweeney, P L
Thompson, D R P
Toal, P A
Tracey, N G T
Vishweshwar Rao, V
Watson, I R G
Wilmot, T J

Ongar

Dickinson, M C
Ellis, P A
Hatfield, F E S
Hatfield, S A M
Leach, P M
Lloyd, A R N
Menon, N K
Munro, R D
Rix, B D
Rogers, D A
Selway, C A
Taylor, H F

Waters, S D
Winter, C D

Orkney

Broadhurst, R J D
Brooke, J V
Buchan, J
Cant, M E
Cromarty, J I
Cuthbert, O D
Diament, M L
Ellery, A
Gordon, M F
Haunschmidt, S M
Hazlehurst, R V
Johnstone, D D
Kemp, C A
Kemp, H
Kemp, S
Kettle, P R
Le-Mar, C A
Lester, M H
Linklater, M
Logan, E S
Malhotra, V B
Peace, M M
Stuart, E M
Swan, D
Tait, M C
Trevett, A J
Woodbridge, K F

Ormskirk

Abbott, J M
Adam, R F
Al-Aloul, M
Allan, J M
Allan, J M
Anderson, R J L
Ash, G M
Atkinson, R B
Baldwin, A C
Barker, D L C
Bhatti, S S
Bishop-Cornet, H R L
Biswas, S
Boocock, G R
Bradbury, C M
Bradley, J J
Burford, N R
Burford, P A
Canning, W G
Chadwick, L J
Clements, D B
Cook, F
Coppock, L A
Cowin, S W
Crilly, M A
Cunnington, A J
Darley, S N
Devine, W C
Dingsdale, F C
Dobson, S
Edwards, J W L
Edwards, R P
Forrer, J A
Fowler, J
Frampton, S P
Gardiner, A J
Gray, M P
Green, M G
Greenhow, T J
Gupta, J K
Hammond, J S
Hanlon, R
Hargreaves, J B
Harkness, M K
Harper, E M
Hawkes, A C
Hawkes, B L
Hawkes, R A
Hendy-Ibbs, P M
Horsley, J R
Hudson, D C
Hughes, P L
Hurst, P L
Ireland, E A
Johnson, A D
Juste, R N
Kakati, B
Kaye, L C
Kernohan, S M
Kewley, I S
Kingsley, D M
Kippax, A G
Kirby, I J
Knowles, M
Kumar, A S
Kumar, A

Kumar, P
Kumar, V
Law Chin Yung, G L
Law Chin Yung, Y F
Ledson, H
Lee, T G
MacIver, M
McKenzie, M H
Mader, U C
Makepeace, D J
Marshall, S R
Matich, M D
Meehan, S E
Mellor, M S
Mellor, W H
Menon, R J
Menon, T J
Morar, P
Mosscrop, L E
Murphy, J C M
Navan Eetha Rajah, P
Navaneetharajah, B M J
Naylor, G M
O'Brien, B W
O'Brien, D V
Oelbaum, R S
Orrell, J C
Park, P M B
Parker, J C
Parry, H E
Patterson, S A
Patterson, R C
Pollitt, C
Porteous, C R
Porteous, M R H
Price, E
Rae, P G
Rainford, F A
Randall, C
Ratoff, J C
Redfern, L
Reston, P J J
Rosbotham-Williams, G M
Sammon, P M
Saunders, H J
Sechiari, G P
Shawkat, S
Silver, H
Simpson, C H
Simpson, G T
Sinha, G
Smith, D J
Smith, H R
Smith, S R
Smyth, C C A
Smyth, C M
Stanley, J K
Statham, A M
Stubley, M W
Sugden, K J
Suraliwala, K H
Suri, S
Suri, S
Taggart-Jeeva, S
Thomas, C M
Thurlow, B A B
Tong, N A
Travis, C D
Underwood, B
Vaidya, A L
Vian, A S
Walters, C M
Watson, H M
Weerakoon, B S
Weldon, B D
White, K
White, M T
Wickham, T A
Williams, C J
Wright, E J
Wylie, E S
Yusuf, M

Orpington

Abumahlula, M A
Acquaah, V L
Adeoye, O A
Ahmad, A M
Ahmad, S
Al-Salihi, O N
Allan, G D L
Arulambalam, K J
Aung Myint Kyaw, Dr
Bailey, I R
Bailey, J H L
Bain, A H
Baldwin, R W M

Oxford

Barker, G R
Barker, P R
Barnass, S J
Barrett, J F
Bastian, L
Bastian, N
Basu, G
Bates, R E
Begum, M J
Bell, J-A
Berger, K N
Bhan, A
Bicknell, C D
Bindra, A P S
Black, J
Boulis, Z F
Bradley, L
Brennan, J W
Brierley, E-J
Broadbent, J V
Brown, K G E
Brown, R N
Carswell, M J
Carver, R A
Cheung, S T H
Choong, B H
Clement, M I
Comper, J W
Cook, M A
Coonjobeeharry, K R
Coumbe, A
Crosland, S J
Crowell, E M L
Da Costa, N P
Dalal, P U
Daniell, S J N
Darby, C W
Davy, J T
Dawson, E C
De Lord, C F M
De Silva, M
Dennis, K S
Double, G
Dyer, A A
Edmondson, R A
Edwards, A G
Ekpo, E B
Fernando, R A M
Fleming, A
Foo, P S L
Ford-Adams, M E
Forton, J T M
Fraser, C M B
Gancke, A E
Ganeshananthan, V
Gardner, R L
Girija, N
Golding-Wood, D G
Gupta, R M
Hanby, A M
Harris, P W R
Hartung, T K
Hennigan, T W
Hildick-Smith, K W R
Hill, D A
Hobbins, S M
Hones, H J
Hou, D
Jessop, M E
Kensit, J G
Kerecuk, L
Kong, K F
Lamb, J L H
Langford, D T
Lanigan, L P F
Lawes, D E P
Leggett, J C M
Livesley, V A
Llewellyn Smith, S H
Lock, B A
Lokulo-Sodipe, O A
Long, A M
Luckhurst, S P
McAllister, J C R
Mackenzie, C I
Maclay, E
Maheswaran, S
Mansi, A R E
Mansi, J A
Menon, V N
Moir, G C
Morris, G C R
Moss, D B
Motto, J E
Napier, A C
Nawrocka, A S
Neville, L A
Nicholls, M J
Ogunremi, A O

Orphanides, D
Palin, J A
Panesar, R S
Parker, V L
Pasola, M
Patel, M C
Pearce, D A
Perera, A D
Perera, P H M A
Perera, P
Pitt, P I
Potter, A
Purwar, R
Purwar, S R
Purwar, S
Pushparajah, C R
Rajasundaram, S
Ranasinghe, D P
Rand, C
Reid, P J
Rhodes, K M
Riches, M C
Ring, K P
Roberts, H S A
Roberts, M E
Roe, S E
Ross, J A
Rush, J M
Sahi, M K
Sarfraz, M A
Sauve, P S
Sawczenko, A B J
Selvarangan, R
Sharif, J
Sharples, E J
Sharr, M M
Shneerson, G
Singh, R B
Singh, S
Sivarajah, T
Soomro, J A
Steel, G
Steer, C V
Strange, D J
Stutz, J A
Tavabie, A
Tavabie, J A
Terry, R M
Terry, R M S
Thompson, M G
Thompson, R T
Toner, C C
Trew, D R
Tritton, B A
Trotter, G A
Turley, S J
Udoeyop, U W
Vidgeon, S D
Walker, G A
Walton, J C
Waters, M B
Wells, D L
Wharton, C F P
White, J P
Wijayawardhana, P
Wiles, J
Wilkinson, A L
Williams, D L
Williams, J
Wootton, O R
Yousif, N E G
Yu, G K Y

Ossett

Booth, J E
Cane, F L
Cokill, B M
Furness, F
Jones, C S
McCleery, C H
Putman, H R
Ramsay, A M
Reed, S M
Senior, J E
Stoker, J B
Stoker, K E A

Oswestry

Alageli, N A
Alcock, R J
Anderson, G M
Attah, A B
Barling, P S L
Barling, R
Beeston, K M
Braddock, L
Breese, H T R
Brodie-Fraser, F
Bromley, C L G

Butler, R C
Campbell, D L
Cassar-Pullicino, V N
Chantler, I W
Cheetham, M J
Darby, A J
Davie, M W J
Dixey, J
Eardley, H L
Eden, S
Eisenstein, S M
El Deeb, B B E D
El-Masry, W S
Emmett, C P
Evans, G A
Evans, L S
Ford, D J
Gifford, P W W
Glatzel, T G
Greaves, P S
Green, P G
Hamade, P M
Harris, D
Hay, S M
Hodnett, H T
Hogbin, B M
Hogbin, D J
Holian, A C
Hughes, R E M
Hutchison, A G
Jaffray, D C
James, M P
James, M W
Jepson, S R
John, A H
Johnson, M D
Jones, C R
Jones, G
Jones, R S
Jones, S M
Kelly, R J
Kendall, J G
Kuipers, A J
Leather, J
Lewer Allen, C M
Lloyd, C R
Lloyd, E A
Llywarch, B V
Loveday, D J
McCall, I W
Mackereth, A I
McMurray, R G
Madden, D A F
Madden, T B
Makin, M K
Martin, N P
Martin, R F
Middleton, P I
Morgan, B A
Neal, N C
Newey, M L
O'Connor, B T
Osman, A E-T F
Pabbineedi, R
Park, A E
Pfeifer, P M
Pointon, R C S
Prior, K S
Rees, D
Rees, H M
Richardson, J B
Richardson, S M W
Roberts, A P
Roberts, S N J
Rummens, I F
Sankey, K L
Scott-Knight, V C E
Short, D J
Smith, M I A
Symondson, A M
Taylor, A S J
Thomas, A J
Thornley, N
Treasure, R A R
Walker, A N
White, S H
Whittingham, F G

Otley

Allen, N J
Bearpark, A
Brennan, S
Clements, N D
Close, H J
Corrin, C E
Currie, S
Eglesfield, D B M
Gogna, C J
Harrison, R M B

Hide, E M
King, J P
Kirkland, G P
Knott, S
Leung, P M
Lloyd, G M
Lukats, S
Middleton, C H
Middleton, M R
Monte, S L
Montgomery, H D
Morgan, H E G
Nathan, N J
Oldham, K W
Orr, J H
Pieri, S E
Protheroe, A S
Raeburn, H B
Richmond, J B
Robinson, S D
Shea, F W
Spencer, P
Stanley, A M
Stanley, S E A
Stowell, P A
Whitehead, S A
Wilson, G K

Ottery St Mary

Ackroyd, J T
Baker, D M
Brown, J M
Caiger, A C
Cox, T J
Cullen, M
De Sousa, N A
Dilley, C J
Guillem, V L
Gurney, K J
Hatfield, P A
Hodgson, M J
Homewood, L I M
Kerr, S J
King, M R
Lewis, D R H
Macleod, R C
Pegg, J G
Rose, C M
Russell, N L
Steede, F D F
Stone, B C
Tibble, R K
Ward, A H
Ward, G G

Oxford

Aarons, E J
Abell, S A P
Abid, F
Abrahams, A H
Acton, I A
Adams, C B T
Adams, C E
Adams, D H
Adams, R F
Adams, T S T
Addy, E V
Agulnik, P L
Ahmad, T
Ahmed, S
Akinola, M
Akiwumi, B O
Al-Barazi, S A
Alcock, C J
Alderson, P R
Alfaro Adrian, J
Ali, M T
Allanson, J
Allport, T D
Almond, R G P
Alp, N J
Altmann, P N S
Amery, J M
Anderson, K L
Anderson, K J
Andrews, J R
Andrews, T M
Angus, B J
Anscombe, M K
Anslow, P L
Anthony, M Y
Anwar, A J
Armitage, J M
Armstrong, R C
Aronson, J K
Arya, R
Ashworth, G J
Aspel, J L
Atenstaedt, R L

Atkinson, L R N
Atoyebi, O I
Attenburrow, M E J
Awdry, P N
Aziz, G
Babb, A G
Bagnall, M J C
Baigent, C N
Baigrie, C F
Bailey, J
Ball, M J
Banerjee, S R
Banks, E
Banning, A P
Bannister, R
Barlow, D H
Barnes, G M
Barnes, P D
Barnett, R J
Barrett, M S
Barrett, W T
Barter, K L
Bartlett, R A L
Barton, D A
Basheer, T S
Bashir, Y
Bass, C M
Bateman, K L
Bateman, M
Bates, G J E M
Bates, N P
Baxi, A K
Beasley, N J P
Beattie, E H
Beazer, R
Beckett, E A
Bedford, F M
Beer, S
Bell, N J
Bell, R M H
Bender-Bacher, H F F R
Benham, S W
Bennett, C C
Bennett, D H
Benson, A A
Benson, C A
Benson, M K
Benson, M K A
Beral, V
Berendt, A R
Berg, B E M
Berg, S J
Bernau, F L
Bestue, M M
Bethell, D B
Betmouni, S
Bevan, A
Beynon, G W
Binney, L E
Birch, A G
Birdsall, M A
Bissell, I J
Black, J J M
Black, R S
Blakeley, A J
Blazewicz, L W
Blesing, C H
Blogg, C E
Bodmer, H C
Bogdanor, J E
Borley, N R
Bottrill, I D
Bowden, M F
Bowen, M L
Bower, P M C
Bowker, C M
Bowker, L K
Bowler, I C J W
Bowles, M H
Bowness, P
Bowyer, R L
Boyd, C A R
Boyd, P A
Bradley, O P
Brady, S
Brand, J S G
Braybrooke, J P
Brewerton, S A
Brewster, S F
Briggs, M
Briggs, R A
Brink, A K
Britton, B J
Broadbent, C R
Brocklehurst, P
Bron, A J
Brooks, A C
Brown, A J

Brown, D C
Brown, G K
Brown, M A
Brown, M C
Brown, S
Browne, J S
Brownlow, H C
Brownrigg-Gleeson, J A J
Bryan, P L D
Brylewski, J E
Buckley, C D
Buckley, R M
Budden, M L
Buley, I D
Bull, M J V
Bullard, H
Bullock, D B
Bulstrode, C J K
Bunch, C
Burch, M
Burge, P D
Burge, S M
Burgess, S E P
Burgner, D P
Burke, C W
Burke, P D
Burne, S R
Burns, E C
Burrows, N F E
Burt, G
Burtenshaw, F G R
Burton, E A
Burton, M J
Burton, M J
Butcher, C C
Byles, D B
Byren, I V
Byrne, J V
Cadoux-Hudson, H S P
Cadoux-Hudson, T A D
Caird, F I
Callan, M F C
Callender, S T E
Calvert, J K
Campbell, A J
Campbell, F J
Campbell, G S
Campbell, H F
Campbell, L A
Cann, K J
Cantwell, B
Carapiet, D A
Carney, G E
Carr, A J
Carre, E A B
Carrie, L E S
Cartwright, N V
Cassell, O C S
Cerundolo, V
Chadwick, J D H
Chalmers, I G
Chamberlain, P F J
Chan, S M H
Chandler, C C D
Chapel, H M
Chapman-Sheath, P J
Chapman, C J
Chapman, D E
Chapman, G P
Chapman, R W G
Charlton, M
Charnock, F M L
Cheetham, M
Cheng, H
Chew, C K S
Chitnavis, D
Chivers, C A
Chowdhury, S
Christie, H J E
Christopher, A V
Clampitt, L B
Clarke, N R A
Clarke, P J
Clarke, R J
Clemmey, W R L
Clubb, J M
Cocks, T
Cocuzza, C E A
Coffey, P P
Coghlan, M C
Cole, D J
Coleman, D J
Collins, R E
Colman, B H
Conlon, C P
Connolly, D J A
Cook, P J
Cooke, P H

Oxford

Cookson, W O C
Cooper, S M
Cope, E
Corfield, L F
Cornall, R J
Costello, C H
Cowen, P J
Craig, S W
Crampton Smith, A
Cranshaw, J H
Cranston, D W
Crawford, G N C
Craze, J L
Crocket, R W
Crofts, B J
Cronan, W S
Crook, T J
Croom, A J
Crow, G J
Crow, T J
Crowther, R L
Cunliffe, R N
Curtis, S P
Dada, M A
Darby, C R
Davey, A F
David, A F
David, J B
Davidson, L L
Davidson, L E U
Davidson, S I
Davies, D R
Davies, R J O
Dawber, R P R
Dawes, M G
Day, N P J
De Joussineau, S
De Newtown, R K
De Raeve, P A
Dean, G S
Delgado Belloso, E
Dendy, P R
Denman, M S
Dennis, J
Dennis, P D
Dickson, H A
Dike, A E
Dimech, J
Ding, G H Y
Dismorr, A R
Dobson, M B
Dodd, C A F
Doll, R
Donaghy, M J
Dorkins, H R
Dorling, D M
Dorrell, L
Dorrington, K L
Drake, M J
Drury, N
Du Toit, J E
Dubowitz, M N
Dudley, N E
Duley, L M M
Duncan, E L
Dunnill, A
Dunphy, R S
Dunwell, M R
Duong Wust, N T H
Duthie, R B
Duxbury, F R C G
Dyar, O J
Eagleton, H J
Eastwood, I Q
Ebbs, D H G
Edge, J A
Edmonds-Seal, J
Edmonds, S M
Edwards, A
Edwards, C M
Edwards, F C
Edwards, J H
Efthimiou, J
El Abbar, M K
El-Kabir, D R
Elithorn, A
Elkabir, J J
Ellis, F
Emery, J D
English, R E
Entwistle, C C
Epstein, A
Erin, R J
Esiri, F O U
Esiri, M M
Evans, J M
Evans, R D
Fairburn, C J A G
Fairley, A

Fairweather, D S A
Farley, J D
Farmery, A D
Faulkner, J M
Faust, G E S
Fawcett, J
Fazel, S B
Feldman, E J
Fell, P J
Fennell, D A
Fenton, M J
Ferguson, D E J
Fernandez-Bravo Alvarez, J M
Fernandez-Shaw Zulueta, S
Ferris, R J
Fillenz, M
Finnigan, A E
Firoozan, S
Fischer, P E
Fisher, A
Fisher, M M
Fleming, K A
Fleminger, M
Flint, J
Florey, T L
Flower, T D
Foex, P
Foord, T F
Forfar, J C
Forrest, G C
Forsyth, K D
Fowler, G H
Franklin, S L
Frankum, S C
Fraser, G R
Fraser, M
Frayn, E H
Freedman, A
Freeland, A P
Freeman, S D
Friend, P J
Frith, P A
Gaba, M D
Gabriel, S L
Gaffan, J
Galloway, P D
Gancz, G
Ganesan, T S
Gardner, L
Garner, P
Garnett, M R
Gaston, P
Gatter, K C
Geddes, J R
Gelder, M G
Geoghegan, A J
George, H R
Giangrande, P L F
Giatromanolaki, A
Gibbons, C L M H
Gibbons, R J
Gibson, A B F
Gilchrist, J T
Gillmer, M D G
Gilmour, N C
Gisbert Pujals, F
Gleeson, F V
Gleeson, J A
Gleeson, M D
Glynn, C J
Godfrey, A M
Godlee, C J
Godsland, J
Goldacre, M J
Golding, S J
Goldman, D L
Goodacre, T E E
Goodfellow, J W
Gooding, D G
Goodman, T R
Goodwin, G M
Gooptu, C
Goringe, A P
Gould, J E S
Gould, S J
Goulder, P J R
Govier, J L
Gowans, J
Graham-Jones, S
Graham, R D
Grange, C S
Grasby, M P
Gray, D W R
Gray, J A M
Gray, W
Grebenik, C R
Green, J M

Green, L R
Green, R A
Greenall, M J
Greenhall, E A
Greenhall, R C D
Greenwood, C E L
Gregg-Smith, S J
Gregg, I
Gregory, D R
Gribble, F M
Griffiths, S M
Grimley Evans, J
Gundle, R
Haeney, J A
Haggett, P J
Hague, S
Hall, G W
Hall, R M
Halliday, B L
Halliday, D J
Hambleton, S
Hammersley, H N
Hammersley, M S
Hammond, E J
Hammond, N A
Handa, A I
Handley, R C
Hands, L J
Harcourt, W G V
Hardie, I S M
Harding, N G L
Hardinge, F M
Hardingham, C R
Harley, H C
Harnden, A R
Harper, C M
Harries, P G
Harris, A L
Harris, E
Harris, H
Harris, M F
Harris, R L
Harrison, P J
Hassan, A B
Hatton, C S R
Hawton, K E
Hay, J D
Hay, R W
Hayles, S
Haywood, K M
Heaf, M M
Heatley, M I
Hempson Brown, J
Herbert, M A
Herdman, P
Herrin, E J
Hewitt, H R
Hickey, B B
Hicks, L J
Hicks, N R
Higgs, D R
Higham, H E
Hildebrand, G D
Hill, A V S
Hill, P F
Ho, L-P
Hobbs, M J D
Hodge, M G
Hoffenberg, R
Holloway, E A
Holloway, P A H
Holman, R R
Holmes-Siedle, M W
Holmes, A H
Holt, J
Hook, P J
Hope, R A
Hormbrey, E L
Hormbrey, P J
Horne, S T
Houghton-Clemmey, R S A
Hoult, S L
Howarth, L J
Howie, K L
Hrouda, D
Huckstep, M R
Hughes, C M
Hughes, J M
Hughes, J T
Hughes, K A
Huline-Dickens, S J
Hull, J
Hume, A J
Humphreys, D M
Humzah, M D
Hunt, R W
Hurley, P A
Hurst, J A

Huson, S M
Hutchinson, S M
Hyde, B J
Impey, L W M
Ioannides, A
Isaac, P
Ives, N K
Jack, T M
Jackson, A R B
Jacobs, C I
Jacobson, T Z
Jacoby, R J
James, A C D
James, D V
James, E M
Jefferson, T O
Jenkins, E L
Jessop, E
Jewell, D P
Johnson, B W
Johnson, D
Johnson, D J G
Johnson, H J
Johnson, M A
Johnson, P
Johnson, P R V
Jones, A C
Jones, A V
Jones, D P H
Jones, L A
Jones, N
Jones, O M G
Jones, P H
Joshi, R
Julier, D L
Julier, M
Kaklamanis, L
Kanagasabay, T
Karamichalis, I M
Kay, J D S
Kearley, K E
Kearney, S E
Kearns, C F
Keeling, D M
Keenan, J
Kelly, R P F
Kemp, E F
Kennedy, M M
Kennedy, S H
Kennett, R P
Kenworthy-Browne, J M
Kenwright, J
Kenyon, C M
Keoghane, S R
Kerr, E D
Kerr, J H
Kerr, R S C
Khalifeh, H
King, S J A
Kinlen, L J
Klein, R
Klenerman, P
Knight, J C
Knight, M
Knight, T H
Knox, J M
Knox, K A
Koukourakis, M
Kurwa, H A
Kwiatkowski, D P
Lake, S R
Lalvani, A
Lama, M
Lancaster, T R
Lane, D J
Lavery, B A
Law, S
Lawrence, E P
Lawrence, J F
Lawrence, P A
Le Roux, A A
Leach, A
Leaver, L B
Ledingham, E M
Ledingham, J G G
Lee, M B
Lee, M A
Lee, S H
Lessing, M P A
Leszczynski, J
Levitt, N C
Levy, J C
Lewis-Barned, C A
Lewis, P M
Lewis, P J
Lewis, P S
Liebling, R E
Lien Yee Wun, V

Lindsell, D R M
Lintott, P N T
Littlewood, T J
Livesley, B
Livingstone, W N
Llopis Miro, R
Lloyd, D A J
Lloyd, J W
Lloyd, R J S
Lo, Y-M D
Loach, A B
Lockwood, G M
Logan, S
Loh, L
Loke, Y K
Lopez-Bernal, A
Lortan, J E
Lucas, A
Lucassen, A M
Lund, W S
Lusty, T D
Lyn, C W
Maartens, N F
McBeath, H A
McCarthy, S F
McCleery, J M
McCloskey, R M H L
McDonald, B
McDonnell, C T
Macfarlane, J A
McFarlane, M N
McGee, J O D
MacIntosh, C M A
McIntosh, R E
McIntyre, A G
McKenna, C J
Mackenzie, D N
MacKenzie, I Z
McKenzie, P J
MacKinnon, P C B
McLardy Smith, P D
MacLaren, R E
Maclean, A
MacLean, J L
McLellan, J
MacLennan, D N
MacLennan, S A
McManus, E M
McMichael, A J
McNally, E G
McNally, M A
McPherson, A
Macpherson, G G
McQuay, H J
McQuay, T A I
McShane, M A
McShane, R H
McTavish, S F B
Maddison, A D
Magill, P J
Malladi, R K
Mandelbrote, B M
Manek, S
Manji, H H
Mann, M S
Manning, A N
Mant, D C A
Manttan, P L
Marsden, A P
Marsden, R B
Martin, C B
Mason, D G
Mason, D Y
Mather, R A L
Mather, R J
Matkovic, Z
Matthews, D R
Matthews, D S F
Matthews, J M
Matthews, P B C
Matthews, W B
Maynard, N D
Mayon-White, R T
Mayou, R A
Medina Ruiz De Alarcon, R
Mehta, P S
Meisner, S J
Mellanby, H N
Mendes Ribeiro, H K
Merriman, H M
Meston, N
Milford, C A
Millar, D E
Millard, D W
Millard, P R
Miller, D S
Miller, D M
Mills, I W

Milner, A A
Minton, M J
Misbah, S A
Mishra, P
Mitchell, C D
Mitchell, R G
Mitchell, S A
Moher, M G
Mollison, M D
Molyneux, A J
Moncrieff, M W
Mond, N C
Moore, E J
Moore, N R
Moore, P M
Morey, A L
Morgan, B L
Morgan, C E
Morgan, J R
Morgan, M A J
Morgan, N R G
Morgan, N A
Morris, J E
Morris, J F
Morris, M J
Morris, S J
Morrison, J D
Morrison, S D
Mortensen, J A
Mortensen, N J M
Mortimer, C J D
Moser, S C
Moss, K H
Mould, T L
Moxon, E R
Mufti, W-I-S
Mulligan, I P
Murphy, B D D
Murphy, M F
Murray, D W
Murray, J R D
Nadlacan, L M
Naidoo, V V
Nargund, V H
Neale, I A
Neil, H A W
Nemeth, A H
Neubauer, S
Newsom-Davis, J M
Newton, J N
Newton, P N
Newton, R E
Nicholson-Lailey, T J F
Nicholson, R S
Noble, J G
Noman, L
Norris, R J
Nowell, T E
O'Brien, T S
O'Byrne, K J
O'Donoghue, M F
O'Grady, J T
O'Leary, P F G
O'Mahony, D
O'Sullivan, M J
Oben, J A
Odunsi, A O
Ogg, G S
Oppenheimer, C V R P
Oppenheimer, S J
Ormerod, O J M
Ostlere, S J G
Owen, A C
Owen, J E
Oxbury, J M
Pakenham-Walsh, N M
Palace, J A
Paling, J B
Palmer, S H
Pandey, R
Pandit, J J
Parker, C E
Parker, J D
Parkes, M
Parkhouse, J
Parry, A M M
Parry, C M
Parslow, S F
Parsons, D S
Patel, C K
Paterson, G M C M
Paton, A
Patterson, T J S
Pawson, R
Peacock, S J
Pearce, M-J
Pearson, N I C
Pedersen, D L
Peereboom, J M

Peet, K M S
Pendlebury, S T
Percival, H G
Periappuram, M
Perkins, M J
Perry, R J
Perryer, S E
Perumalpillai, R G
Peto, T E A
Phillips-Hughes, J
Phillips, A J
Phillips, C M
Phillips, R E
Phizackerley, P J R
Pike, M G
Piris, J
Pixley, F J
Plint, S J
Pluck, N D
Pointon, A D
Pollard, A J
Pollard, R C
Poole, E W
Porter, B H
Porter, D E
Potter, C P S
Poulton, J
Pover, G M
Powell, A S
Price, A J
Price, E M
Price, E E
Price, J D
Price, J R
Price, N
Price, N
Prysor-Jones, A
Pugh, C W
Punt, L
Puvanendran-Thomas, R
Qizilbash, N
Quaghebeur, G M-M
Quested, D J
Quinlan, M J
Rahemtulla, A
Raine, N M N
Rajagopalan, B
Rajakulendran, T
Raju, S
RamcHaritar, S H
Randall, A A S
Randhawa, B
Randle, P J
Rannan-Eliya, S V
Ratcliffe, P J
Ratnatunga, C P
Rawcliffe, P M
Redman, C W G
Rees, C M P
Reuter, C W
Reynolds, D J M
Reynolds, S M
Richards, A J
Richards, P G
Riddell, A M
Riddell, M A
Riddle, P J
Riefflin, A
Rizza, C R C
Robbins, P A
Roberton, M
Roberts, C
Roberts, D J
Roberts, I S D
Robertson, C M
Robins, D P
Robinson, A J
Robinson, E T
Robinson, J R
Robinson, M
Robinson, S P
Roblin, J
Roblin, P H
Robson, G M W
Robson, M J
Robson, P J
Roddie, A M S
Rogers, R
Rook, C D
Rose, N D B
Rose, S
Rosen, H
Rosen, P H
Rosenberg, W M C
Rosenfeld, P F
Roskell, D E
Ross, B D
Rouse, A K

Rowell, N P
Rowland-Jones, S L
Runciman, D M I
Russell, R M
Rutter, H R
Rutter, L E
Sacks, G E
Sainsbury, M C
Saleem, S
Salisbury, A J
Salisbury, H R
Salmon, J F
Samra, J S
Sanderson, F
Sargent, P A
Sathananthan, M
Satsangi, J
Saunders, P M
Scarfe, D R
Schiller, K F R
Schofield, N M
Screaton, G R
Screaton, N J
Sear, J W
Seaver, R G
Selkon, J B
Sellers, S M
Shakespeare, J M
Shapland, M C
Shawcross, D L
Shefler, A G
Sheldon, P W E
Shelton, M H
Shennan, J C
Shepherd, J E E
Shepstone, B J
Sherrard, J S
Sherrington, L J
Sherry, B J
Shewan, D B
Shlugman, D
Shuker, J P
Sichel, J H S
Sidebottom, E
Sidebottom, P
Silvester, R D
Simmons, J D
Simon, S D
Simpson, A H R W
Sinclair, M E
Singtон, J D
Slack, M P E
Slater, J D E
Slater, J N
Slavotinek, A M
Sleight, G
Sleight, P
Small, D G
Smarason, A K
Smith, B J
Smith, C E
Smith, J C
Smith, K A
Smith, K M
Smith, R
Smith, S C
Solomon, R A
Southgate, J L
Spalding, E C
Spalding, J M K
Speirs, M W
Spilling, R A E
Spivey, R S
Squier, M V
Stanton, A P
Steam, M R
Stedeford, A
Steel, H C
Stein, A L
Stein, J A
Stein, J F
Stein, T R
Steiner, J A
Stephens, J
Stephenson, C J
Stern, D M
Stevens, J E
Stevens, R M
Stewart-Brown, S L
Stewart, A M
Stewart, A
Stewart, J M
Stewart, M R
Stoneham, M D
Stores, G
Storr, C A
Stradling, J R
Strich, S J
Sudlow, C L M

Sugden, E M
Sullivan, P B
Swarup, N
Swift, G R
Taegtmeyer, A B
Taegtmeyer, M
Tagg, C E
Taggart, D P P
Talbot, D C
Talbot, K A
Tasker, C M
Taylor, A
Taylor, K A
Taylor, M J O
Teddy, P J
Teschke, C J
Thakker, R V
Theodoulou, M T
Theologis, T
Thomas, M G
Thomas, S J
Thompson, J L
Thomson, A M
Thomson, A H
Threlfall, A K
Thurston, D W
Tibbs, D J
Tidy, C R
Till, A S
Tilleard-Cole, R R R
Todd, B S
Toff, P R
Townsend, A R M
Traill, Z C
Trowell, J M
Tunbridge, W M G
Turberfield, L M
Turnbull, E P N
Turner, H E
Turner, N C
Turner, R J
Tuson, J R D
Twycross, R G
Tyack, S R
Uden, J A
Ulahannan, T J
Underwood, P M
Unia, C
Ussiskin, S I
Vallis, K A
Van Schaick, S H
Vaughan Williams, E M
Vaux, D J T
Venables, P A
Venning, V A
Vessey, M P
Viale, J P
Vickers, T
Vile, J M
Vincent, A C
Vincent, A L
Viney, D B
Virr, A J
Volmink, J A
Von Eichstorff, P D G
Vyas, P
Wade, D T
Wain, E C E
Wainscoat, J S
Wainwright, A M
Walker, N P J
Wallace, R H
Wallace, T M
Waller, D J
Walton, J N
Walton, R T
Wang Ee Jen, W
Ward, M E
Ware, C J G
Ware, L M
Warner, N J
Warrell, D A
Warrell, M J
Warren, B F
Warwick, J P
Wass, J A H
Watkin, N A
Watkins, H C
Watson, A
Watson, C J E
Watt Smith, S R
Weatherall, D J
Weatherall, J A C
Weatherall, M
Webb, J D
Webster, P N
Weir, A P
Welding, R N

Wells, J C
West, A F
West, J J M
Westaby, S
Westbrook, J L
Weston-Davies, W H
Wheeler, A J
Wheeler, K A H
Whitaker, P J
White, A C
Whiteley, J E
Whitty, M M
Whitworth, F K
Whybrew, K J
Widjaja, A W
Wiesemann, P
Wilde, G P
Wilkie, A O M
Wilkinson, A R
Wilkinson, D A
Wilkinson, M
Wilkinson, P B
Wilkinson, R H
Willcox, H N A
Willett, K M
Williams, C J H
Williams, D L
Williams, E M
Williams, L P
Williams, P R
Williams, S M
Williamson, D
Williamson, K N B
Willison, R G
Wilson-MacDonald, J
Wilson-Smith, E M
Wilson, A S P
Wilson, D J
Wilson, J
Wilson, K R H
Wilson, R P E
Wilson, S J
Wilson, S R
Winner, S J
Winnifrith, T J A
Winters, Z E
Wojnarowska, F T
Wollner, L
Wollner, S H
Wood, A J
Wood, C G A
Wood, M J A
Wood, S
Woodham, C H
Woodman, J R
Woods, C G
Woods, K A
Wordsworth, B P
Worlock, A
Worlock, P H
Wright, E C
Wright, F W
Wright, J A
Wright, P R
Wynne-Davies, R
Young, J D
Zapata, L C

Oxted

Boffa, P S
Burns, D
Campbell, A J
Caplan, B A
Catlin, R J O
Eadie, E C
Everington, T F
Haig, S D
Hill, D J
Hills, S J
Jadalizadeh, N
MacLean, K S
Mills, J D
Morley, P K
Morris, A J
Myers, M J
Namasivayam, K
Nathan, J J
Pinder, C G
Sandler, B M
Skellett, S C C
Spiller, R W
Thomas, D C
Walden, R J
Wartnaby, K M
Williams, J S
Williams, R M J

Padstow

Beattie, B E

Burkinshaw, J H
Chalker, J C
Constance, N D
Ellis, D D
Gay, K H
Grundy, R
Harvey, D
Hellyar, E A

Paignton

Ackers, J W L
Alcroft, J E
Austin, M L
Avery, D A
Ballance, P G
Banks, A A
Batstone, J H
Bishop, H
Bridge, J R
Bullen, J G
Cannizzaro, S
Carr, N
Clunie, J
Cottrell, M A
Coxon, J P
Crowe, S P
Deakin, I P
Deakin, V E
Dibble, L
Dowdell, M P
Eggleton, M L
Elliott, H A
Epstein, M R
Foreman, L P
Green, P A
Hardy, E A
Howitt, W P F
Kennie, A T
Kuur, C R
Landen, J J
Lansdown, S R P
Lowes, A J
MacLoughlin, P J
Masters, R C
Mills, D C
Norley, I
Pappin, C J E
Pletts, R C
Povey, J S
Reade, S K
Richards, G A
Richards, I M
Richardson, A P
Roberts, J D V
Rudland, E N
Slomka, H
Smith, N P
Solomon, L
Somerfield, D J
Southall, E
Spicer, N A J K
Steele, Y E
Stephens, D B
Straiton, N
Strath, D J
Tudor, G P
Walden, A F D
Wander, G C A
Watt, W M
Williams, D L
Wright, M

Paisley

Ahmed, S U
Al-Janabi, S
Anderson, J M
Anderson, M A J
Anderson, W G
Arokianathan, D S
Arokianathan, M C
Arokianathan, T R
Baird, W W
Bannatyne, R A H
Barclay, A A
Barr, W
Basler, M H
Baxter, W P
Blatchford, O M W
Bloomer, J
Boag, J C
Bonham, D A
Brown, C W
Brown, R C
Brown, R
Buchanan, A
Byrne, K E
Campbell, I H
Campbell, S
Candlish, W

Canning, J J
Canning, J C
Chapman, K M
Chaudhri, S
Chawla, J C
Chee, L C
Cheriyan, K E
Chitnis, S L
Clark, K
Coffield, M-J
Crampsey, F M
Cuddihy, A M
Dahill, S W
Dallachy, R
Davidson, D C
Davies, M-L
Dickson, J D
Dickson, J
Dingwall, A M E
Dinnett, E M
Dolan, G P A
Dorward, A J
Downie, A R
Ejaz, S
El-Fallah, M E-M
Elgammal, S
Erskine, R
Evans, C J
Ezebuiro, U I
Feeney, L A
Fitzpatrick, D
Fitzsimons, C P
Frew, W A
Ganguly, D K
Ganly, I
Ghosh, S R M
Gibson, S E G
Gopalan, J
Gravil, J H
Gruer, N E M
Haldane, D A
Hamilton, G J
Hamilton, I J D
Hamilton, S H
Hanlon, L C S
Haran, W J
Hardie, K G
Hardie, L
Hardy, I G
Harkin, H M
Hastings, J L
Hay, R E
Herron, C A
Hislop, J M
Hislop, L J
Hislop, W S
Hodgson, C W L
Holmes, M
Houston, D J K
Innes, C Y
Ireland, T
Jenkins, J T
Johnstone, C J M
Jones, A M
Jones, R W
Khokhar, A A
Kinniburgh, A J
Knox, A D
Leonard, J F
Livingston, H M
Lowe, K
McAlpine, D M
McArthur, D R
McArthur, S M
McCormick, S
McCourtney, J S
McCusker, P
Macdonald Speirs, N A H
McDonald, L A B
McFarlane, P A
McGeoch, K L
McIntyre, M
McKay, P J
MacKenzie, J C
Maclean, M E
McMahon, C P
McMillan, R M
McNaughton, G W
McPeake, J R
Macpherson, T D
Mahmood, A
Manderson, W G
Marr, S T P
Mason, I S
Meehan, C
Miller, S M
Mitchell, K G
Monaghan, S C

Par

Murray, C M
Napier, I R
Negrette, J J
Oliver, J E
Orr, J E
Peden, T C
Pennington, H R
Pennycook, J A
Quinn, A J
Ramsay, A
Reay, L M
Reid, C B
Richmond, R M
Rimmer, E M
Roberts, G C
Robertson, M R I
Robson, B J
Russell, A W B
Scorgie, B M
Scott, B J
Scott, W
Scullion, D M
Selim, A M H
Sengupta, P
Shepherd, R C
Sim, J C
Simpson, G K
Simpson, R B
Slaven, C F
Smith, C M
Smith, L A
Sourindhrin, I
Stephens, I F D
Stewart, G
Stothers, J
Strang, I
Struthers, L J
Sutherland, C G G
Symons, A J C
Thom, D E
Thomson, J E
Thomson, R M
Vinson, M C
Waclawski, E R
Wallace, A D
Walsh, J E
Ward, M
Warnock, P J
Watson, D
Watson, G M
Watson, M A
Watt, J C
Weir, J B V
Weir, W I
Welsh, S L
Wilkie, L M
Wilkieson, C A
Williams, C L C
Williamson, B W A
Winton, D B
Wright, L
Young, J J
Zaher, S A E-A

Par

Gullam, J E
Hannett, B F
Haskins, N
Molyneux, N R
Monk, P E
Nash, S R
Rowe, J G
Tempest, P K
Towell, J D

Pathhead

Dummer, D S
Laurie, A
Sanderson, E P
Wilson, C M

Peacehaven

Barnett, C A
Byrne, L G
Curtis, A J
Etherton, J E
Gill, V S
Gupta, V K
Gurtler, C J
Kumar, A
Leff, S V
Mandal, L B
Mangat, H B S
Patel, B A
Patel, C J
Starling, A J

Peebles

Bacon, M M C
Baird, D
Cameron, H M
Campbell, J A
Cheyne, G Y
Clyde, E M S
Day, F J
Duncan, M E
Harrison, W
Hay, R A
Hegarty, D M
Hunt, K A
Love, D R
McDonald, I A
McEwan, M A
McIntosh, G E
McIver, A
Moore, C S
Morrish, C
Noyes, K J
Paton, A G P
Pyatt, R N
Rait, R B
Ramsay, A
Ross, W A
Simpson, K E
Sparrow, S
Thom, W T
Watt, J V
Young, P T

Peel

Christian, R P
Gray, O S M
Hanks, R J
Hannan, M C
Hudson, A B
Jones, K J
Shaw, D M

Pembroke

Bury, R N
Cox, M O
Cuff, B E
Davies, J V
Dickie, R E
Hannaford, R W
Helliwell, J R
Hudson, D R
Lewis, S J G
Miller, M H
Mules, A B S
Nagaraj, C B
Power, F J
Roberts, J G
Scadden, J E
Thomas, C E A
Thomas, M D
Windsor, A C M
Windsor, P A

Pembroke Dock

Cooper, M M
Evans, A N
Goodson, P
Thomas, J L E W
Tobin, F A

Penarth

Alderson, R A
Alfaham, M
Back, I N
Barnes, P M
Bassett, J I
Bates, J L
Bayer, A J
Baylis, E A H
Bell, S M
Bowler, I
Buchalter, M B
Campbell, I A
Care, E A
Clarke, V
Cobley, M
Copp, S
Cornish, C J
Danielsen, M S
Davies, A J P
Davies, A E J
Davies, A
Davies, B H
Davies, C E
Davies, E J
Davies, G
Davies, H L S
Davies, M C
Davies, R P
Dudley, A E
Edwards, S A
El-Gaylani, N
Elborn, J S
Erin, E M

Evans, A S
Evans, J G
Ferguson, C J
Fiander, A N
Findlay, J A
Finlay, I G
Foster, D L
Frost, P J
Gibbs, A R
Gonzalez, M L R
Gough, J
Grant, A J
Green, J T
Griffith, E F
Griffiths, T L
Hain, R D W
Halpin, S F S
Harrison, J A F
Hasan, M
Hiley, D K
Hubbard, R E
James, M L
Jasper, A L
Jenney, M E M
Jones, J A
Kafetzakis, E
Kemp, A M
Lari, J
Lewis, K E
Lewis, P R W
Lindsay, P C
Lloyd, A
Long, C C
Major, V
Massey, E H
Massey, E J R H
Matthews, S B
Meek, J C
Mehta, A
Morris, J E
Morris, S E L
Morris, S
O'Mahony, M S
Owens, D R
Parker, C R
Parry, D E
Peet, E J R
Pitts, J E
Prickett, F M E
Probert, W E
Quoraishi, A H M A H
Raashed, M
Radcliffe, A G
Raine, P M
Rees, A E J
Roberts, G J
Robinson, T A
Schapel, G J
Seal, R M E
Seaman, A C
Shah, N S
Sibert, J R
Smith, J T L
Stephens, R C M
Stone, M D
Storring, F K
Sutton, D A O
Swift, G L
Taylor, G C B
Thomas, H D
Thomas, J G
Thomas, R H
Tinker, G M
Turton, J
Vafidis, J A
Walker, N A
Warren, C A
Williams, B
Williams, D M
Wilson, E A
Wright, E M

Pencader

Lewis, T
Lucas, N W R
White, M R M

Penicuik

Begg, A D
Begg, D M
Bell, J K
Carluke, I
Collins, R M
Cooney, M K
Craig, R J
Davies, G C
Fraser, I M
Gillespie, D H
Griffin, T M J

Guild, M D
Hider, C F
Johnston, N M
Levstein, C
Livingstone, A G
McDonald, J M
Macdonald, S T
McKay, K M
MacLean, J
McClintock, L A
McRorie, A
Macsween, K F
Marchant, A E
Pollock, M W
Reid, H A H
Rodger, E M E
Smith, C C
Wood, A P

Penmaenmawr

Blake, L-L
Hamelijncк, J A
Rowlands, D E
Williams, C J
Williams, R H L

Penrhyndeudraeth

Daplyn, I R
Endaf, A I
Jones, D P M
Prichard, O M
Thomas, A J

Penrith

Ainscow, D M C
Ashcroft, A E
Barlow, A M
Barr, J E
Barr, R
Blackman, M J
Booth, D
Boulter, P S
Brock, P A C
Bruce, E M
Burch, I M
Cama, L S D
Cameron, J S
Clay, M J
Corner, R W M
Counter, L
Craske, D A
Davidson, F
Dewhirst, K
Dillon, J K S
Dunlop, J
Dunlop, M S
Dunning, H A
Eckersall, A C
Edington, F C
Ellerton, J A
Essenhigh, D M
Frost-Smith, B M
Frost-Smith, M J
Goulding, P G R
Hall, R W
Hanley, M T
Harper, K L
Harrison, R
Hay, C P
Hearsey, J A
Heyworth, J A
Hodkin, J P G
Hutchinson, P M
Jackson, A-M
Johnson, C A
Johnstone, I M
Jones, G A H
Jupp, C M L
Kennedy, D
Kirk, J M
Lewis, G F
Long, H A
MacMillan, C
Mans, M
Matheson, A
Metcalfe, D H H
Miles, J F
Mills, S L
Newton, J
Pearson, D T
Pritchard, I P
Purdy, V L
Redfern, H M
Reed, A
Simpson, L
Smith, M N
Storey, P B
Taylor, A M
Thompson, J A
Tiffin, N J

Unwin, D E J
Uttley, D
Walker, P J R
Wells, C A
Weston, J G
Weston, T P
Whitwham, M
Willcock, G A
Winrow, A M
Young, G L
Young, T S S

Penryn

Beckett, R J
Bintley, T N
Bourne, A J
Brown, I M C
Burns, H
Ellis, M F
Green, B G J
Hartley, C E
James, E P
Katz, J
Paxton, M J
Seddon, A J
Shier, D I
Sutherland, C J
Upton, P M
White, E M
Wood, R M T

Pentraeth

Osborn, M F
Starczewski, A R

Pentre

Bihari, K
Choudhary, B P
Choudhary, H N
Choudhary, M
Gwynne, E I
Lloyd, A M
McCrystal, D J
Morgan, R D
Morley-Davies, R B
Sami, S Z A
Stone, A R
Tomkinson, A

Penzance

Armstrong, W N
Ashby, B S
Bonnar, A J
Breese, D W
Burgess, P A
Campbell, S V
Carruthers, D M
Cormie, P J
Cox, P J
Crosfill, M L
Currie, I D C
Davis, J C
Dunscombe, J L
Dyke, R R
Fletcher, N J
Freeman, M K
Freeman, Z R L
Griffiths, F J
Grigereit, C S
Halls, G A
Hand, M M
Harker, R
Harvey, J R
Hicks, C R
Hicks, P M M
Hunter, C J K
Jago, M E M
Jago, W
Johnson, D G
Jones, M R
Keith, C B
Kiloh, M
Lack, J J
Levine, D F
Long, M H
Mackenzie, M
Macmillan, A L
Manser, R F
Martin, F J
Moore, J Y
Morris, A C
Paterson, A G
Peller, S E
Philip, C J
Pirrie, A L
Pring, J E
Purchas, S F
Robinson, P J
Roxburgh, I O
Rutherfurd, S F

Ryan, J F
Senior, R E
Sproson, J C
Truscott, D E
Tsan, N
Turner, J S
Wearne, S
Williams, S J
Wilson, P P
Wilson, S J S

Perranporth

Evans, J N
Hallworth, N A
Jones, C A
Lenz, R J
Merrin, P K
Murdoch, K A
Partington, S I
Sidebotham, C F
Smith, F H N
Turfitt, M E

Pershore

Alexander, D I A
Alexander, D F
Atkinson, A C
Baldry, P E
Barber, K
Boardman, D
Borchardt, F J
Carter, J J
Cluley, S
Cox, P M
Edwards, K M R
Havard, L K
Hird, J M
Jesson, R E W
Johnstone, G E
Keating, P J S
Kennedy, J M
Knox, E G
Laurie Smith, N
Lloyd, T
McVittie, S G
Milner, C
O'Loghlen, N A
Ooi, Y W
Parsons, J W B
Perks, C E
Pitts-Tucker, T J
Ralphs, G J G
Rankin, J S
Richards, V J
Thomas, K P
Thompson, P J M
Wilson, J M
Wilson, P R
Worlock, F C
Wunsch, C M
Young, C M

Perth

Addison, M L G
Alijani, A
Allan, Y D
Allen, R E
Angus, S L
Archibald, M J D
Balfour, R O
Barclay, L
Barker, K F
Bates, D
Bates, M
Beale, N J
Bell, M
Bisset, R F
Blaikie, A J
Blair, J S G
Boyd, J M
Brennand, E J
Brennand, J K
Brewster, J H
Brown, P H
Brown, P R
Brunton, D P
Buchanan, W E A
Bulcraig, A R
Burnett, L D
Calvert, J E
Cameron, H M
Capper, M E
Carey, D T
Carlin, D D
Carson, P F J
Carter, G E
Cavanagh, E M
Chalmers, A J
Clark, G L
Clark, J E

Petersfield

Clark, R G
Clark, S A
Cockburn, E A
Coe, P A
Coe, S M
Colquhoun, H A
Compson, L J
Connacher, A A
Connelly, P J
Coutts, V C
Cowie, A J H
Currie, F R J
Davidson, A I G
Davidson, G M
Davie, R D M
Dean, B K
Dewhurst, N G
Dolan, L C
Donald, I M
Dowell, J S
Dowie, C R
Dowse, S M
Dutton, A H
Easton, L J C
Eccleston, A D
El-Miligy, M Y M
Elsden, W A
Eriksen, C A
Espley, A J
Falconer, A F
Falconer, T C
Flinn, J
Flint, G D K
Fok, P J
Forbes, D W
Forster, L F
Forster, M R
Forster, R E
Foster, D S
Fowler, K G
Fyfe, J
Gamble, P
Garton, M J
Georgeson, E J
Gordon, G J
Gourley, A A
Gray, E R
Gray, E C
Gray, W
Gregson, E R L
Hadden, C
Hadden, W A
Halliday, P
Hamilton, J R
Hand, J W D
Hewitt, S J
Ho-A-Yun, J E F
Holden, C J
Ince, M M
Islam, H R U
Kastner-Cole, D
Kendell, J
Kennedy, G F
Kerr, J G D
Kirk, J
Kirkwood, D W
Klaassen, B
Kynaston, J H F
Lambie, A M
Lawson, D D A
Leishman, F E A
Lendrum, S
Little, C L
Little, T S
Littlejohn, A I
Lord, S M
Lowdon, N M
Lynch, P T
Lyon, R L
Lyons, E
MacCall, C A
McClatchey, W T
Mcclelland, S M
McClure, I J
MacDonald, E J
MacDonald, M
McFarlane, A G
MacGregor, D F
Macgregor, J D
McGregor, S L
McGuire, B E
McIntyre, P G
MacKay, R M
Maclean, C M
MacLean, J G B
McLeod, N A
McNab, J W
McNeill, R S
Magahy, F D

Majmudar, N G
Marrian, V J
Marson, L P
Mathieson, A M
Meikle, J A K
Mellor, I
Melrose, G A
Melville, R H D.
Menzies, E M
Meyers, R M
Michie, B A
Millar, C G M
Milne, R M
Milne, S J D
Mitchell, R C
Mitra, A D
Morris, A D
Munro, H C
Murdoch, R W G
Murray, D
Murray, W J G
Napper, A J
Norris, A
Page, C S
Pearson, R H
Peebles, M K
Peek, B
Phillips, W D P
Prentice, N P
Pringle, R
Protheroe, D E
Pryde, L A
Pugh, C E
Qureshi, S A
Raschkes, B J
Ratcliff, A J
Reay, B A
Reid, G S
Reid, J H
Reid, R P
Reilly, B M A
Renfrew, M A
Richard, K W
Ripley, C S
Ripley, J S
Ritchie, D A R
Ritchie, E D
Romotowski, L I
Ross, N
Rowland, L J
Roxburgh, C M C
Roxburgh, S T D
Scott, J C
Shackles, D A
Shennan, W J S
Shepherd, A N
Shepherd, N I
Sinclair, J I
Singer, B R
Stalker, H
Stewart, C D
Stewart, J A M
Tait, D H H
Templeton, J S
Thomson, A
Urquhart, A
Walsh, D B
Watson, E T
Watson, J I
Wheatley, S-A
Wilkie, R A
Will, M B
Williams, D T
Williams, S
Winship, S M
Wood, R A
Wood, S M
Wright, D W
Wright, H W
Wylie, T A
Young, D G
Young, J D H

Peterborough

Abdul Karim, A P S S M S
Agbasi, N N
Aladin, A
Amroliwalla, F K
Anand, J K
Anderson, A A
Arnold, S J
Asplin, E J
Bailey, R G
Baker, P M
Banner, A V
Barrett, M
Basi, R S
Beeton, J R

Bellamy, S R J
Berry, E P
Berry, R D
Bhullar, T P S
Bishop, M C
Blackford, H N
Blake, D C S
Blatchford, H L
Blower, A P
Blundell, J W
Bond, A J
Briggs, F A
Brown, C M
Brown, J B
Burley, T K
Cartmel, R M
Caskey, J F
Catnach, T B
Cawood, R H
Chambers, G M
Chopra, N B
Clarke, J W
Clayton, D A
Cole, D R
Coleman, F B
Cooper, A M C
Cope, A R
Cotton, S J
Coxon, T C
Cradwick, J C
Cromie, B W
Dalal, M M
Dalrymple, P M
Damany, D S
Dansie, B
Das, P A
Davies, T M
Dawson, C
Denney, M C
Dennis, B
Dennis, P M
Denton, M J
Devonald, M A J
Dilley, C M
Dodwell, D J F
Dong, Y-S
Doran, J F
Dryburgh, E H
Du Plessis, J V B
Dudgeon, I V
Dugdale, C M
Eades, J B
Edey, M M J
Eldred, K F
Evans, G E
Ewing, A Y
Ewing, G
Famoriyo, A A A
Farrell, M C
Fawcett, S
Feggetter, G S
Fletcher, N J
Flewitt, P C
Flewitt, R M
Flores, F R
Fowler, L
Frow, R W
Fuller, J D
Gall, A J
Gardiner, L J
Gardiner, S E
Gemmell, J H
Gerada, A
Glavina, H M
Glavina, M J
Gleeson, C M
Glover, J R
Gordon, J F
Gordon, R B
Gormly, L M G
Grant, C M
Grant, S J
Grantham, V A
Greaves, I
Griffiths, R
Grimmer, P M
Gunn, A T G
Guttmann, D
Hackman, B W
Hadfield, D A
Hadfield, P B
Hall, D
Ham Kow Boon, Dr
Hammersley, D
Haque, S T A
Hart, C J R
Hartropp, P
Hashemi, M
Hastie, J W

Hegan, T J M
Hemmaway, C J
Henchy, M C N
Heywood, J D
Hipwell, P M
Hobbis, J M
Holmes, J T
Hoole, K
Houghton, R J
Howlin, S G
Hughes-Nurse, J
Hughes, S P
Hunt, E R
Hurst, H B
Hutchings, P T
Iyer, V K S
Jachuck, M S J
Jackson, M A
Jackson, N R
Jacobs, L
Jalili, I K
Johns, D L
Johnston, M E
Johnston, P L
Joshi, K M
Kapila, H
Kauser, A
Kent, J
Kerr, D N S
Kilgallen, C J
Kilgour, H K
Kitson, R M
Klein, J S D
Knights, A J
Kyaw, T
Laundy, T J
Leung, D P Y
Lieber, D E
Little, S
Lucas, A M
Lumb, M R
Lythgoe, S A
McCombe, B H
McKay, R J
McKeown, B J
Maclaine, E
Maddula, M R
Mahmoud, N A H
Malki, D S
Mallett, R B
Mann, S C
Marsh, M H
Marshall, J H
Marshall, N W
Mason, P F
Maxey, A M
Mazumdar, R K
Mbanu, A
Mearns, G S
Mehta, M J
Menzies, S J
Merrill, S B
Mistry, C D
Mistry, H G J
Mitchell, B
Mitchell, C A
Mitchell, D W
Modha, J D
Modha, N J
Morgan, N K
Moshy, R E
Moss, C E
Moulsher, P J
Mulkern, E M
Mungall, I P F
Murthy, V
Myles, J W
Myszka, Z J
Nair, P
Nally, R E
Naunton, A
Navamani, S
Naylor, J R
Nnochiri, C C P
Norman, A W
O'Donnell, P A
O'Reilly, A M
O'Reilly, V H
Okubadejo, A A T
Outar, K P
Pace, J A
Panday, S
Parker, M J
Patel, R C
Paterson, B A
Petangoda, G
Phipps, J S K
Pinder, S P H
Pollard, D E K

Pryor, G A
Purcell, R T
Rajagopalan, N
Rajiv, K
Randall, J M
Rankin, S M
Rao, M S
Rao, T L N
Rawdon Smith, H S
Rawson, W C
Redhead, I H
Reed, P N
Rennie, R A
Richards, S D
Rigg, K S
Rimmer, T J
Rivers, C M
Robertson, J M
Rogers, M
Rogers, S D
Roland, J M
Rowlands, D B
Rytina, E R C
Sadler, M G
Sagovsky, R
Salameh, Y M M H
Sampson, K
Samrai, P S
Sanders, N P
Satya Prasad, K
Sayegh, H F
Scarisbrick, C D
Scott, C G
Scott, R M
Senior, A
Shah, M L
Shaikh, M A
Shair, A B E
Sheehan, N J
Shilliday, P F
Shoban, B K
Simhadri, N
Sivakumaran, M
Smith, D P
Smith, H S
Smith, P J
Smith, T R
Smyth, D G
Squire, J K
Stanton-King, K D
Steel, S A
Stovin, O J
Stuart, G
Takhar, A P S
Thakker, P
Thein, M
Thillaivasan, K
Thomas, D I
Thomas, J A
Thompson, J S
Thompson, M K
Trounce, R F
Tuck, G
Turner, A G
Tweedie, R J
Tyler, M A
Urwin, S C
Van Den Bent, P J
Vardy, S J
Varley, G W
Walker, R T
Walker, S E
Wani, A M
Warren, A Y
Watson, S J
Watts-Russell, J V A
Waugh, J G S
Weeramanthri, S P
Williams, S R R
Wilmot, R A
Wilson-Haffenden, C F
Wilson, N S
Wishart, K C
Withers, R A
Womack, C
Wood, J
Woodcock, M G L
Woolf, D A
Wozencroft, D W
Wright, N S
Youens, J E B
Zerafa, R

Peterculter

Ah-See, M L W
Al-Mohammad, A
Burrows, C J
Harris, D C M
Lawson, C

McHardy, F E
Mahaffy, R G
Millar, D G
Myles, S A R
Phillips, R M
Skerrow, B A
Smith, N C
Stewart, L J

Peterhead

Armstrong, P
Bruce, G M
Campbell, D G D
Cowie, J B
Donaldson, P H
Ferguson, C A
Ferguson, G G
Gauld, A R
Gauld, H M G
Goodbrand, T A
Greeley, N C
Kennedy, D J G
Lacey, E J
Lawrie, D
Lawrie, R F
Leslie, M A
McInnes, R
MacKay, A M G
Mackay, J R
Nicol, D R H
Pollock, M R
Ritchie, L D
Robertson, J B
Sandeman, J M
Small, I R
Smith, S M
Stephen, R S
Stout, J C
Strachan, B T
Strachan, K A B
Tait, J
Taylor, G B
Taylor, J M
Thain, A B
Thompson, N
Watt, G M C
Webster, D

Peterlee

Abbott, R G
Anderson, D G
Barlow, P
Burleigh, A R S
Chandy, J
Choudhary, S R
Gallagher, J B
Gallagher, P G
Hawes, B M
Hays, K J
Houston, W B
Pearson, G
Ramakrishna Gupta, M D
Robertson, J A
Rowlands, P K
Sil, A K
Sukumaran, O
Thomas, A H
Thompson, I

Petersfield

Abercrombie, G F
Andrew, T Y
Angell, M P
Bartlett, C V
Bates, T M
Buckley, S J
Bulmer-Van Vliet, J
Chishick, A R
Christie, C
Christie, J S
Cox, C M
Davenport, T J
De Halpert, P A
Durrant, B W
Ellis, B G
Francis-Lang, A M
Gell, A E
Holden, A F H
Holden, S J
Hopewell, J P
Johns, M
Lamb, S R
Lewis, C E
Lewis, G M
Litchfield, M A
MacDonagh, G R S
MacKeown, I L
Mallows, H R
Mileham, P A

Petworth

Moor, J F
O'Kelly, K F B
Perry, R K K
Rankine, G
Renton, N J
Rogers, B M
Shanks, R O F
Silk, N
Sinclair, C C R
Small, R G D
Smith, G B
Smith, J B
Speed, P J
Stride, J G
Svoboda, V H J
Tyler, A K
Verner, I R
Welch, C B
Whapham, E M
Ziegler, E S M

Petworth

Bonsall, J L
Boothby, H A
Bridger, M G
Clarke, R G
Dally, P J
Godwin, E G
Howard, P
Lyons, G M
Monier-Williams, P L C
Morgan, R
Newberry, R G
Pett, S
Price, D J
Roehr, S P
Smith, R C
Ward, M P
Waugh, P J
Wiltshaw, E

Pevensey

Baig, M I
Bansel, A
Briggs, J A
Carlson, N R
Darwent, A
Darwent, J P
Hewett-Clarke, A H R
Shove, R F
St. Blaize-Molony, R T

Pewsey

Carlisle, J B
Carmichael, I M
Collings, A K
Crabb, H H
Davis, A E
Hewartson, R M
Hunt, H A
Hutson, A J
Jenkins, P D
McGee, P J
Mahroof, M R
Phillips, S W
Ring, J P G
Shirehampton, T A
Vickers, P J

Pickering

Blacklee, M E
Briggs, G H
Capes, D E
Cottingham, D
Duddington, M
Frank, T L
Heap, K I
Lawrence, I H
Thornton, T J
Turner, J R
Woodward, A M

Pinner

Ahmad, N
Baum, A S
Benattar, K D
Biswas, C
Black, B A
Blewden, W E
Byers, A H
Catto, J W F
Catto, J V F
Chang, L P-Y
Chang, S H-P
Collins, M R
Culloty, M
Cumberbatch, G L
Curran, L A
Dastur, N B
Dawood, R B

Dove, N A R
Doyle, M
Edwards, A
Edwards, D M
Fairburn, R A
Farooqui, O A
Fishman, D
Fong, K J
Garlick, N I
Groom, R V
Hammond, S J
Hardman, A
Hazell, N W R
Hegarty, W J
Hoey, R C O N
Holzel, F B
Homapour, B
Hudd, C A M
Hughes, G
Inada-Kim, M
Jayabalan, S N
Jenner, C S
Johnson, E H
Kapembwa, M S
Karim, M Y
Kelshiker, A S
Kirmani, S S
Kodilinye, H C
Kumar, M
Lakhani, S S
Laurence, B E
Lavers, K W
Lawrence, R E
Lewis, B V
Liberman, D
Lister, J
Livingston, E C
Lubel, D D
MacGregor, A J
Majus, R
Markanday, A
Marks, J N
Marks, J E R
Mayer, H M
Mediwake, R G
Medway, D G
Miller, D L
Mistry, K
Nicholls, A J S
O'Callaghan, P
O'Toole, G A
Owen, T E
Parchure, N
Paul, K
Payne, C E
Pollitt, N T
Rajani, K K
Rashbass, B J
Rasooly, R
Reid, C D L
Rizki, S
Rookledge, M A
Rudd, B C
Rudolph, J K
Sahota, A
Saville, S D
Schiller, G I
Shah, S Z
Siddiqui, A R
Sidhu, J S
Smith, S
Sofat, N
Stein, R E
Stevenson, J F
Sundaresan, R
Thakur, M
Tomic, D A
Tonks, C M
Tonks, J M
Tothill, G
Tran, T L
Uszycka, B S A
Vahrman, J
Walport, S
Walton, K R
Waterman, S V
Weller, I V D
Wilson, A R T
Zideman, D A

Pitlochry

Bell, H E
Burns, A S
Caldwell, J D
Campbell, A J
Coope, B M
Cruikshank, D A
Davis, A G
Dreghorn, J

Faulds, M M
Finlay, K C
Forsyth, A
Grant, C W
Grant, I W B
Hull, F M
Kennedy, D S
Leaver, D P
McCrory, G W
McEwen, A J
MacHugh, J I R
Mackenzie, H M
Maisels, C M
Maisels, D O
Robertson, E H L
Robertson, M H
Ross, R T A
Scott, J M
Simmons, R E

Plockton

Knox, K D
Mackenzie, A

Plymouth

Acharya, U R
Ackford, H G
Adams, B M
Adams, J A
Adams, W M
Ahiaku, E K N
Al-Memar, A Y M J
Al-Nahhas, A M M
Al-Qurainy, I A
Alderson, J W
Alexander, I
Alexander, T J D
Allen, S M
Anderson, G H
Anderson, S R
Andrews, C J H
Archer-Koranteng, E
Arkle, J H
Ashley, S
Aughey, T T
Awan, M Y
Baguley, S D K
Bailey, D
Bailey, J V
Bailey, N J
Bakheit, A M O
Balmer, H G R
Basterfield, J E
Baumer, J H
Baxter, L A
Bayliss, S-J
Beasley, A J
Becker, G W
Beckley, S L
Bell, S P
Benjafield, R G
Bennett, M J
Bennett, S G
Benton, J I
Beresford, J K
Bertie, T M
Biggs, J E
Binchy, J M E
Blackstone, H B
Borthwick, M H B
Bouhaimed, M M
Bowler, S K
Boyhan, C R
Boyle, M J
Breddy, P N
Brenton, J E
Bridger, M W M
Brodribb, A J M
Brooks, P R
Brown, C
Brown, E L
Brownlie, G S J
Brumby, J F
Bryson, P J V
Budge, A
Budge, C J
Burdett, N G
Burdon, M S
Burge, A J S
Burgess, A J
Burrell, C J
Burridge, M G
Butcher, J L
Butler, J R
Calder, A D
Calder, E
Campbell, H M
Campbell, J C
Campbell, J K

Campbell, L J
Campbell, P G
Cannon, A M
Carlson, J N R
Carr, A S
Cassidy, S A
Chakraverty, A C
Challenor, R M
Chapman, C W
Chapman, J M
Charnley, G J
Chatfield, T H P
Chiappe, N P
Chowdhury, M S H
Chowdhury, R Y
Churcher, G M
Clapton, K J
Clark, D E
Clark, J D
Coard, K C M
Coates, M B
Coghill, J C
Colby, E M
Cooksley, D E
Copper, J R
Copplestone, J A
Cormack, A J R
Cornish, J F
Cosgrove, H
Couch, J C
Courtney, D J
Coverley, S R
Cox, R R
Cronin, A J
Cronshaw, S J
Crook, P A
Crookall, P R
Croydon, E A P
Cunningham, E B
Cunningham, R
Cunningham, S J
Dalgleish, A T
Dalrymple-Hay, M J R
Dance, D A B
Daniel, F N F
Daniels, J P
Dash, M G
Dashfield, A K
David, H G
Davidson, H E
Davies, P R F
De Mendonca, P M S
Deacon, J F
Dean, J D
Deardon, D J
Defriend, D E
Dickson, S J
Dobbs, F F
Doe, H M
Donaldson, C A
Donovan, R
Downes, C M
Drewer, R W
Drury, R A B
Dryden, P W
Dubbins, P A
Dudleston, K E
Duff, P W
Durman, L R J
Dwyer, D M P
Edwards, B A P
El Reshir, O A
El Shunnar, K S
Ellis, R P
Elphinstone, M G
Embleton, M A
Esson, W R
Etherington, J D
Evans, J
Evans, N M
Evans, P E L
Evans, R E
Farrington, W J
Fearon, J
Feddo, F K
Fell, M B
Ferguson, J B
Ferguson, S S
Fisher, D W
Fletcher, C P
Ford, R A
Ford, R L
Fox, B M T
Franklin, J R
Frappell, J M
Freegard, T J
Freeman, J
Freeman, R M
Freeman, S J

French, A E
Friend, J R
Fulton, J D
Gale, J E S
Galloway, P H
Ganapathy, M
Gardiner, S C
Gasim, A
Gaunt, P N
Geen, I
Gerwat, J
Gibson, J D
Giles, N C L
Gillespie, K
Gilmour, J M
Gordon, D T
Gossman, H H
Grannum, P N
Grant, I C
Grayson, M J
Greene, K R
Greenway, B A
Griffiths, H M
Guly, H R
Gurry, B H
Gutteridge, C M
Habib, N E N
Halawa, M
Hambling, S P
Hambly, J
Hammonds, J C
Hampshire, J E
Hanley, D J
Hardy, P H
Harnett, C L
Harold, R S J
Harold, R S J
Harris, D L
Harry, A J
Harvey, P B
Hasan, S
Haslam, E C
Hateley, S J
Hayfron-Benjamin, T R M
Hayward, C M
Haywood, G A
Heath, R M
Hersey, N G B
Heycock, M H
Hickling, P
Hill, G A
Hill, W T
Hillary, A G
Hilton, D A
Hirst, R S
Hobbs, S J F
Hobson, L J
Hodgins, I R
Hofinger, E
Hopkins, M J L
Hughes, C H
Hughes, D J
Hughes, G W
Hughes, P D
Hunter, K R
Hunter, S
Hurrell, L H
Hutton, C W
Hyland-McGuire, P
Imm, N D H
Inman, M T
Jackson, S A
Jacob, Dr
James, H D
Jenkins, A-L M
Jennings, C L
Johnson, N F
Johnston, C G
Jones, A C
Jones, A M H
Jones, D N
Jones, G M
Jones, P A
Jones, R W A
Jones, R C M
Jones, S J
Kaminski, E R
Kapila, R
Katona, S J
Keddie, F S
Kelly, S A
Keogh, J M E
Kersey, P J W
Khan, N A S
Kinchin, C G J
Kingsnorth, A N
Kingsnorth, J M
Kirby, J

Kirkham, M J
Kitson, M P
Knight, W A
Knights, D L
Kuo, J H U
Labram, E K
Lambert, A W
Lambert, P M
Lambert, S H
Langton, J A
Langton, M J
Lawrence, A J
Lawrence, P K
Leather, H M
Lenden, G J
Lenden, P M
Lewis, C T
Lloyd, C J F
Lloyd, C E F
Lochhead, J
Longhurst, M J
Longworth, J L
Loopstra, E M
Louden, K A
Loughlin, S L
Lovett, J J
Lowe, C H
Loxdale, P H
Lunn, N
Lunn, S M
Luyt, K
Luzietti, R
Lynch, P
Lytle, J
Macartney, J H
Macartney, S I
McBride, K
McCabe, S E T
McCormick, C S F
McCoy, Y
McCullough, S C
McEwing, D J
McGavin, C R
McGill, R M
McGovern, D P B
McInerney, J L
McInerney, P D
Maclennan, I R
Macleod, P M
MacNaughton, P D
Madar, R J
Mahmood, N
Mahony, J
Maitland, R I
Major, G R
Makin, J S
Malaree, S L F
Mann, M J
Mantoura, O A
Marshall, A J
Martin, J P
Mason, R K
Matheson, A J
Melhuish, J E
Mercer, D
Mildmay-White, A A
Millard, S W
Miller, J M
Mitchell, S
Monaghan Addy, D J
Montgomery, J N
Moorcroft, J V
Moore, B W R
Morgan, N V
Morris, A O N
Morris, D J
Morris, J E
Morris, R J
Morrison, G D
Morsman, J M
Motwani, J G
Mulcahy, P D
Murgatroyd, R E
Murphy, F M
Murphy, M
Murphy, W J C
Murray, A E
Murray, S J
Nagabhyru, A
Nagabhyru, A
Natale, S
Neve, H A
Newman, P K
Nichols, E A
Nichols, M E
Nimmo, S B
Norrie, D M
Norrie, M K
Noy Scott, C

Poole

O'Neill, R C O H
Oldman, M J
Oliver, P D
Olsen, N D L
Oppong, F C
Osborn, F A
Overal, S G
Owen, M H
Padley, T J
Page, R M
Pai, R U
Palin, D J
Palmer, J D
Paramsothy, V
Pascall, K G
Patterson, D D L
Pearson, S A
Perham, T G M
Perks, J M
Perry, J N
Pickard, J G
Pobereskin, L H
Pollard, B J
Pollitt, Y
Potter, A B
Prance, S E
Preece, J F
Price, DK
Prior, R C
Protheroe, C K
Quinton, A A G
Rahamim, Y
Rai, K D
Rance, J M
Ransome, C T
Ratcliff, A J
Rawlings, E
Rawlings, I D
Read, A C
Reilly, E P
Reilly, S
Riden, D K
Ring, A E
Ring, N J
Riou, P J
Robbins, J A B
Roberson, F E D
Roberts, S R
Robinson, S J
Rogers, A K J
Rogers, K
Romilly, S A
Roobottom, C A
Ross, J W B
Rossiter, N D
Rowe, P A
Rowlands, T K
Ruddle, A C
Ryan, P D
Sailer, S
Sair, M
Salz, M
Samuel, R A
Savage, T R
Scott, D J
Scott, N W
Seal, K S
Seaton, J A
Seymour, M V W
Shales, C A
Sharples, A
Shaw, J F L
Sherwood, A J
Shewring, P M
Shoheth, J R
Shrestha, B R
Shrestha, R
Sims, D E
Smith, J J
Smith, M E F
Snelson, M G
Sneyd, J R
Soul, A R
Stafford, D M
Stayte, W M
Steeden, A L
Stevens, R J
Stevens, R J
Stewart, A E
Stewart, I P
Stocker, M E
Storrow, K J
Stott, D V
Strachan, J A C
Streets, C A
Suzuki, H
Taams, K O
Tai, G K L
Tatham, R H B

Taylor, P A
Teasdale, C
Thaller, V T
Thom, W F
Thomas, A E
Thomas, A J
Thomas, D I
Thomas, H C
Thomas, H A
Thomas, S
Thornberry, D J
Thorpe, S S
Thrush, D C
Thurstan, N D A
Thurston, B J
Tisdall, J M
Tisdall, M W
Tomlinson, G C
Tooke, J E
Torabi, K
Toynton, N J
Travis, S P L
Turner, D L
Turner, M S
Tutty, M B
Tyrrell, C J
Vital, M F
Vorster, D S
Waddington, D
Waldron, B L G
Walker, A J
Walker, M B
Walker, S
Walsh, G J
Ward, P S
Warlow, P F M
Warrell, R J
Warren, S J
Watkins, R M
Watts, M A
Webb, J K G
Went, J
Westhead, M J
Weston-Baker, E J
Westwood, C N
Wheeldon, F T
Wilkin, T J
Wilkins, D C
Wilkinson, P O
Wilkinson, S P
Williams, M P
Williams, P
Wilson, C E
Wilson, J C
Windle-Taylor, P C
Wood, A C
Woods, J M
Woods, R R
Wrigley, S R
Yarnley, P A
Youell, C D
Zajicek, J P
Zarka, Z A

Plympton
Golding-Cook, A N

Polegate
Abraham, C A C
Adcock, R J
Anderson, J L
Bedford-Turner, C M
Bedford-Turner, E W
Birks, D A
Bramwell, F E
Brown, R D
Cook, W B
De Belder, A J
Desmond, H
Dickson, S R
Felce, J M
Gadd, M C
Guerrier, H P
Hammett, A I
Holme, S B
Johnston, P
Lawrence, E F
Lewis, C J
Lewis, P E
Margetts, B M
Moore, G J D
Narendran, S
Sharp, M P
Simpson, M B
Suleman, M I

Pontefract
Abbott, V P
Abdul-Jalil, D N
Acuyo Pastor, L

Allen, C L O
Babu Rao, E
Bazaz, M L
Beaumont, D G
Belk, W J
Binns, M S
Blackman, M L
Bonney, G
Bowden, D E
Brearley, M M
Brearley, T
Brookes, M J
Brooksby, W P
Broughton, A C
Brown, R B
Buckley, R
Butler, J M
Butler, S E
Butterfield, J K
Caddy, J M
Chakraborty, S K
Chandy, J
Copley, E L
Cording, V L
Crabtree, J
Crawley, L C
Criddle, J W
Darby, D
Davenport, G J
De Mello, W F
Dewes, J M
Diggle, D P
Dodman, B A
Dunphy, R A
Eastwood, J M
Eccles, D
El-Rabaa, S M A
Evans, A E
Farooq Dar, M
Fashakin, E O
Fernandez Gonzalez, F E
Forster, R G
Fox, P A
Galvin, H P
Galvin, M C
Ganorkar, V D
Garland-Collins, J R
Gatecliff, J S
Gatecliff, M
George, E M
Ghosh, A K
Gibson, T C
Gordon, P G
Grove, A M
Gummerson, N W
Hanney, I P G
Harvey, A R
Hashmi, A A
Hassoon, M M
Hawkins, A E
Heller, M H
Helmy, A H I I
Hewitt, A
Horsfall, H O
Hossain, J F M M
Hough, C T
Howe, P D
Huggett, A M
Johnson, A O C
Johnson, M T
Jones, G
Jones, M G
Kamal, L R M
Kanani, R R
Kaul, V
Kupelian, S M
Lannon, M G
Lewis, R V
McClintock, J E
McClintock, J H N
Macdonald Hull, S P
Macdonald, I W C
McGrath, P A
McWilliam, P K A
Magid, Y M A
Marshall, D A
Martin, A M E
Mathews, M
Mayall, K M
Meulendijk, H N
Mistry, D B K
Montgomery, J S
Moulton, E A
Needham, K L
Nicholson, R A
Nugent, A
Okine, E A
Osselton, M

Perkins, A
Playforth, M J
Plowman, R A
Quartley, R G S
Rajgopal, J M
Riley, D
Roberts, D G
Robinson, M R G
Roche, R E
Sahathevarajan, N
Sahgal, S M
Sanderson, K J
Sen, A K
Shahi, A
Shutkever, M P
Singh, R K
Singh, S P
Sinha, S K
Slack, G B
Smith, G D
Stockill, G R
Stockill, R A
Strike, P C
Sweeney, A N
Syam, V
Sykes, A
Tanna, A D
Tanna, D R
Taylor, J M
Terry, D
Thompson, R M
Thorp, J K
Tobin, C P
Troughton, O
Turner, J R B
Uzoigwe, A O
Van Vollevelde, M I
Vaux, A
Viswanathan, P
Wakefield, D A
Ward, G P
Waring, J R
Watson, D B
White, C
Wilkinson, D
Wilson, G S L
Wright, D
Yeung-Wye-Kong, C-K
Zaman, A G
Zaman, A G
Zaman, N Y
Zaw, W

Pontyclun
Anness, V R
Arnold, J M
Barros D'Sa, S H
Bayoumi, M
Benjamin, J A
Bunston, M J
Champ, C S
Collins, I E
Connellan, S-A
Cremin, D D
Crownshaw, T L
Davies, P S
Davies, T D
Davies, W W
De Alwis, C
Dewar, R I
Duffin-Jones, A
Duggan, M A K
Ganguli, P K
Gower-Thomas, K L
Guha, P K
Halford, P D
Hart, A J L
Havard, T J
Hawksworth, N R
Hayes, B R
Hebden, M W
Hopkin, M
Hughes, R J
Hutton, R D
Iles, E A
John, M E
Jones, A S
Jones, J M L
Jones, R M
Jones, S A
Lancaster, J M
Latif, A H A
Lewis, A C W
Lewis, B M
Majumdar, R K
Millar-Jones, L
Mills, L M
Moody-Jones, W D T
Moorcraft, J

Morgan, C J L
Morgan, R J H
Morris, I B
Murray, J M
Parker, V A
Pascual, J A
Pemberton, D J
Perry, H M
Ramanaden, D N
Robinson, D J
Saleem, H
Sami, A S A E H
Singh, K R
Singh, T H
Skeen, E S
Smith, J M
Tanner, J G
Tudbali, P
Wakelin, J H S
Wardhaugh, A D
White, D G
Williams, F G
Williams, H O L
Winter, R K
Woodward, A

Pontypool
Ahmed, N
Aitken, S J
Bevan, R A
Brown, P D
Clewer, G J
Cormack, A S
Cormack, H S
Cottam, D J
Cunningham-Davis, P G
Dare, D R
Davies, I B
Davies, K
Davies, P A
Davies, J P
Devlin, O P
Farr, N J
Graham, G I
Grant, K T
Grantham, C E D
Harries, J M
Hobbs, D J
Hughes, A
Hughes, T M
Jarman, A S
Jeffs, S A
Jilani, M M
Jones, D F
Joshi, H P
Machado, F R D S
Mars, P H
Nathdwarawala, Y R
Nutt, M R
O'Sullivan, D P
Patel, S C
Prabhakaran, U P
Price, E P
Pugh, A C
Rahman, A
Smart, K
Stewart, G E S
Sullivan, P M
Taylor, J
Temple, J M F
Thomas, M P
Tromans, J P
Wardle, A R
Wilkinson, R A
Williams, D G
Wintoniuk, D M

Pontypridd
Ackerman, S
Al-Aslan, S M A K
Al-Hasani, L J
Appanna, A M
Appanna, T C
Bell, D C
Beswal, N L
Billington, K
Blair, A D
Brooks, P T
Brown, M A
Burkhardt, K I
Clarke, J P J
Clee, W B
Darwish, A K
Davies, B R
Davies, D H
Davies, G E
El Naamani, B
Elwood, N F

Evans, G R L
Gammon, V M
Gasson, J N
Griffiths, R H
Harries, O
Harris, W H
Hasan, M
Heatley, M K
Heywood, W
Hodges, I G C
James, D S B
Jerrett, C S
Johnson, R A
Jones, A H
Jones, C D V
Jones, K A
Khalil, D S
Lewis, A S
Lewis, P S
Li, C Y A
Lloyd-Williams, C B A
Menon, R G
Mogford, N J
Morgan, I G
Morris-Stiff, G J
Mukhopadhyay, A K
Myint Myint Mu, Dr
Nagesh Rao, G
Narasimha Murthy, H S
O'Leary, T P
Ozdemir, J
Pascoe, K F
Perry, A
Pierrepoint, S E
Pinkham, K L
Porter, A F
Prabhu, P S A
Purbey, B N
Rajan, K T
Randell, D T H
Rees, D R
Rees, W E L
Richards, J D
Roberts, S A
Robinson, N A
Rowe, S M
Samuel, M J
Sengupta, P S
Sherwood, H
Slade, D E
Smith, S A
Strawbridge, W G C
Taylor, C E
Thomas, J
Thomas, N M
Tipping, T R
Trueman, F A
Varde, K
Vijaya Bhaskar, P
White, D G
Williams, D H
Williams, D
Williams, R J L
Willis, L G F
Wu, K-C

Poole
Adam, R W
Ainley, E J
Al-Khazraji, M R A H
Alam, M A
Alner, M R
Angunawela, R I
Arnold, E J
Arnold, J K
Ashton, W B
Atkinson, P H
Atkinson, S R
Bacon, A P C
Bacon, H A
Bailey, C G
Bailey, P
Ballinger, F C
Barnett, M A
Barron, B M
Battcock, T M
Begic, J
Begley, J P
Bell, A J
Bell, N J V
Black, M M
Blackburn, K F
Blakeway, A C
Boyd, C M
Bracewell, A
Brady, S
Brailsford, J A D
Bray, G M

Port Dinorwic

Brewer, D J
Brown, C A
Brown, K-L
Bruce, D L
Buckmaster, J D
Burn, J P S
Campbell-Ede, S C
Carter, S J
Cheng, K
Cheng, Z
Choudry, N
Clein, G P
Clements, P W
Cogswell, J J
Colbrook, P V
Cole, C C
Cole, M M
Collinson, J D
Cook, A W
Cope, D
Coppen, R J
Coupe, M H
Cousins, C G
Cowley, N
Cox, S N A
Crawford, B
Crawford, C K
Crellin, R P
Crick, A P
Crick, M D P
Crilly, C U
Cuthbert, C J
Dague, J R S
Darke, S G
Davies, J B
Day, R W B
Deacon, R J L
Dean, S E
Dent, P
Dewar, A L
Dickie, A H
Dormon, F M
Doyle, J O
Edwards, J N T
Ellis, K D
Emmanuel, K R
Evershed, M C
Exton, W R
Fairhurst, H E
Falkner-Lee, M J
Fardon, N J M
Farr, C M
Farrier, C D
Fawkner, K J
Fearnley, M E
Fiddian, N J
Fisher, R A
Flanagan, D E H
Flanagan, P G
Flanagan, S-A
Forbes, P J
Ford, M F
Frymann, S J
Fullerton, I S
Gadd, C M
Gallagher, J R
Gankande, A U H
Garland, S J
Garrett, W R
Gatling, W
Gibbs, G W
Glennie-Smith, K
Goode, T D
Goodier, V A
Goodrich, B H
Goodworth, D J
Gordon, I D
Graham, D A
Griffith, A H
Griffiths, S J
Hadden, W E
Hadley, J L
Hanna, A R Y
Hardwick, P J
Harries-Jones, R
Harrington, J G
Harris, N P
Harvey, J E
Hatch, G R
Hattersley, R W
Hayward, M J
Heames, R M
Hendry, A T
Henry, R J W
Herbetko, J
Herodotou, N
Herring, J P
Hext, J E
Hickey, J R
Hill, R A
Hill, R M F
Hill, R D
Hill, S F
Hillard, T C
Hitchings, N B
Hockey, M S
Holford, S A
Holmes, D M
Hosking, S W
Hovell, C J
Howe, A H
Howell, M E
Howell, M-C
Huebner, R
Hussein, K A
Hussey, M H
Hutton, J
Ilankovan, V
Irwin, D B
Jacobs, S A
Jago, R H
Jankelowitz, G S
Jenkins, G J
Jeyes, K B
Jones, C M
Jones, S N
Karlowski, T A
Keane, R
Kelleher, F J
Kelsall, J E
Kidd, K R
Kirkham, S R
Laird, P
Latto, J B
Latto, M G
Laurence, V M
Leatherdale, R A L
Levitt, R J
Lewis, V
Liddiard, G S
Linley-Adams, A C
Litchfield, M
Little, H J
Lockey, B F
Lomax, G P
Lovejoy, J J
Lowe, J J H
Lucas, C
Lyon, J B
Lyons, F M
McArdle, P J
McAulay, A H
McCann, D F
McCutchion, A
McCutchion, R
McDonald, S J
McLeod, A A
Maiden, A
Malik, N A
Marlborough, M
Matthews, D C
May, W
Maycock, R R
Michaels, A A
Middleton, R G
Mikhail, J R
Millar, J W
Miller, J
Milligan, N S
Milligan, N M
Minton, D B
Mitchel, J
Molyneux, H M
Morris, A E
Morris, S
Moy-Thomas, J M
Moyse, G A
Muir, D P R
Mulholland, G V
Murcott, C A
Murray, E
Myatt, J K
Mynors-Wallis, L M
Neave, S M
Nelms, M T
Newman, A J
Newth, J B
Nicholas, A P
Nicholas, D S
O'Connor, J E
O'Connor, J C
O'Keeffe, C J
Ockelford, O K
Osborne, R J
Ould, G A
Packham, R N
Pain, J A
Pandher, G K
Parkin, B T
Pearson, A E G
Playfair, C J
Ponton, A W G
Pouramini, M
Powell, C E
Power, K J
Pratt, E J
Price, G C
Price, S M
Primavesi, J F
Primavesi, S M
Prossor, J E
Purdie, S A
Quinn, G F
Rastogi, S C
Ray, J A
Redpath, S
Reichl, M
Rein, H I
Richards, G E
Richards, S C M
Richardson, D P
Roberts, G W
Robson, N K
Rogers, A M
Rowe-Jones, D C
Rowton-Lee, M A
Rundle, J S H
Rushen, D J
Rutland, A F K
Sakhrani, L
Scott, C M
Scott, J S C
Scott, P M J
Seal, P J
Sepping, P
Sharer, N M
Sharma, R C
Shaw, G L
Shearman, A J
Sheehan, A J
Shelley, F C
Sheridan, E A
Shortland, D B
Simpkiss, M J
Sinha, S K
Smith, G D
Smith, G C
Smith, R N
Smith, T
Snook, J A
Soppitt, A J
Sorapure, J B
Stanley, G E
Stephens, C J M
Stephens, J P
Stevenson, J D
Stevenson, M E
Street, S Q I
Stuart, A L G
Suffling, N J
Surridge, J M
Sutherland, J
Tadros, V R
Talbot, R W
Tarver, D S
Tavakkolizadeh, A
Taylor, G R
Thomas, A M R
Thomas, G E M
Thomas, M
Thomas, S M
Thompson, P W
Tidswell, A T H
Tomkins, S
Tsamis, M
Tuckley, J M
Tufail, S
Upton, C E
Valle Atela, V
Ventham, P A
Villar, M T A
Vine, S M
Vithana, T
Walder, G P
Walkden, S B
Warlow, S
Wayne, H L
Webb, J N
Wee, M Y K
Wegner, M-P
Wells, F R
Wenzerul, A M
Werring, D J
Weston-Smith, P S
Whalen, S H
Wheatcroft, J D
White, E
White, J H
Wilkins, M C
Wilkinson, C P
Willcocks, L C
Williams, D J
Williams, S P
Williams, S R
Williamson, J S
Wise, H J
Wishart, M G
Wood, A D G
Wood, A M
Worsley, A M
Wulff, C H

Port Dinorwic

Roberts, H M
Robinson, M M
White, P W

Port Ellen

Dennis, P J
Knowles, J M

Port Erin

Baker, S B C
Brocklehurst, M Y
Conlon, D E G
Conlon, M B
Davies, D G
Gupta, N
McAndry, S P
McHenry, F A
Mousley, N
Pogue, L J J
Slater, C S
Thomas, L G

Port Glasgow

Cunningham, K J M
Farrell, J P
Holms, L F
Hughes, A M
McKay, D J
Manasses, E
O'Rourke, B
Paton, I C
Ramanathan, R G
Smith, E M S
Smith, M H
Struthers, J O
Wilkie, D J
Wootton, A C

Port Isaac

Baird, A E
Baird, W M
Barker, J M B
Barron, G C
Budd, W E R
Larkin, J M G
Lunny, J J
Partington, E P
Sainsbury, A D
Scovell, E E
Wooder, M L

Port St Mary

Allen, D M
Kelly, A W

Port Talbot

Barnes, J C
Burridge, J W
Clark, S H
Cobbledick, M
Davies, B J
Davies, H J
Davies, J H
Davies, V G
Gibbons, B J
Goodwin, M J
Griffiths, H
Hunt, K P
Isopescu, G A
Jones, A E
Jones, P D
Llewellyn, M H
Lodwig, T S
Mouyen, G J M
Patel, Y A
Penney, R J
Richards, J M
Roach, D L
Roberts, E M
Rohman, S O
Sabir, H M
Stevenson, W
Subbu, V S
Taylor, C F
Townsend, P

Trott, L I
Tyler, R J

Portadown

Hunter, I W E

Porth

Bali, V P
Bali, V
Baron, R T
Benjamin, A
Bishara, S A
Carne, M S
Choudhury, G S
Cronin, H S
Das, S
Doman, L B
Griffiths, A
Kaushal, V L
Lawthom, C
Lloyd, G A
Narayan, R D
Narayan, S
Powar, M R
Saha, T K
Thomas, J P
Williams, H
Williams, K M
Wilton, A

Porthcawl

Alwyn Smith, A H C
Bond, S E
Brown, G
Clark, G W
Cobbledick, C A
Duff, W J P
Dyson, P A
Eales, T D
Evans, J R
Feltham, A M
Ghose, R R
Guest, S
Jenkins, R G
Jones, H D
Khanzada, A M
Kirkby, J A
Landeg, M R
Lewis, W J
Longley, M A
Mackey, P M
Mohajer, C J
Moore, R P
Morgan, C T
Mullens, E L
Overton, M J
Parry, J G
Parry, P A
Prys-Jones, D R V
Rees, G B
Shinkwin, M P
Smith, G S
Thomas, J H
Thomas, K S
Thomas, R J
Thomas, R J
Tinkler, G G
Tracy, P M
Williams, C A
Williams, J S

Porthmadog

Edwards, J M
Niesser, A J
Niesser, A A
Parry, P G
Rogalski, M
Shimmin, C M
Williams, M W

Portland

Adams, T D M
Allsop, E J T
Barnard-Jones, K
Brook, M I
Hargrave, D B
Mason, P J
Ninham, M C
Sami, N
Whisker, R B

Portree

Burge, F N
Crichton, C L
Crichton, C M
Gibson, G E
Gilmour, C A
Henstock-Zapf, C L
McCabe, S D
Macdonald, A N
Macrae, C A

Macrae, C O
Toms, J S M
Wright, G R

Portrush

Anand, K
Bailie, J S
Bresland, M K
Edmundson, H F
Finlay, L
Gardiner, M C
Hill, H E
Hill, W J C
Houston, J C S
Logue, C P
McMillan, R L
Miller, M S
Murphy, E M
Powell, K
Ralhan, R
Rea, O H
Wilson, G S

Portsmouth

Abdul Aziz, L A S
Absolom, M E
Agbaje, I M
Al-Safi, W S A
Allan, A J
Allcock, A C
Arnold, C L C
Ashton, M R
Atchison, D G
Bagshaw, H A
Baldwin, A L
Barker, D P
Baylis, R J H
Bayon, J
Beaumont, J M
Beech, L D
Bevan-Thomas, M-A M
Boase, D L
Boote, D J
Bourne, J P
Bowker, C H
Bradmore, R
Brindle, R J
Brockman, B J
Burby, N G
Burden, R J
Butler, S A
Byrnes, M E S
Cahill, C J
Caldera, S R M K S
Cameron, C
Campkin, N T A
Carss, G A
Castle, N A
Catterall, G A
Chada, K
Charlton, B
Chaudhary, R
Clark, R J
Clarke, H J
Cockcroft, P M
Colin-Jones, D G
Collier, J S
Collins, E
Cox, J S
Cranfield, T G
Cree, I A
Crisp, M D
Croker, G H
Cummings, M H
Curr, R D
Dakin, S M
Daniel, R J E
Dasgupta, A K
Davies, D W
De Vesselitsky
Merriman, G
Devilliers, S H
Dhundee, J
Dickson, R J
Doherty, R P
Dowd, A B
Dubois, J D
Eckersall, S J
Edmondson-Jones, J P
El-Malik, S M O
El-Rabiey, S S M H
Eldridge, A J
Evans, A R
Evans, M
Ewen, S P
Exton, L C
Fairley, I M
Fellows, E J
Flynn, N A K

Preston

Foley, C A
Franklin, L L
Franks, S H
Freeman, A E L
Gabb, J H
Galloway, A M
Ganczakowski, M E
Garstang, J J
Gaught, F J
Ghosh, D S
Giddens, J E
Gill, R J
Gillmore, R J
Glasgow, M C
Glover, M A
Gordon, P A L
Green, B A
Green, P J
Green, W T
Griffiths, K P D
Grindrod, R M
Grover, M L
Grunstein, J A H
Guirgis, R R
Hallett, C L
Hallett, R J
Hardwick, L A
Harindra, V
Harper, G D
Hatfield, A G
Haworth, A E
Haydon, J R
Hedger, N A
Hesketh, J C
Hildebrand, J M
Hirri, H M
Hodkinson, S L
Hogan, J P R
Hogston, P
Holmes, S A V
Holt, H B
Homer-Ward, M D
Howard, J C
Howell, M A
Hughes, B R
Hull, R G
Hutchinson, S G
Isasa Fino, I
Jarrett, D R J
Jeffrey, M J
Jeffrey, M N
Jenkins, I L
Jones, R A
Jorge, E A
Kai, M A
Karkee, N D
Kenyon, A J
Khan, T
Khin, M H
Khoury, G G S
King, F M
Kinirons, B M P
Lalor, A J M
Langham-Brown, J J
Le Masurier, M D
Leach, T D
Ledingham, J M
Lee, A G
Lee, G
Lewis-Russell, J M
Lewis, C H
Lewis, R J
Littledale, E J
Logan, R F
Longbottom, D N
Low, E M
Loxton, J E
McArthur, C J G
MacConnell, L E S
McCormick, D A
McCrae, F C
McCullen, M A
MacGuire, M H
McKenning, S T
McLaughlin, N P
Maclean, A H
McMillan, G H G
McQuillan, P J
Mainwaring, J T
Marley, N J E
Marsh, C S
Mason, J C
Medbak, S H
Mellor, T K
Merton, W L
Mikel, J J
Milligan, W L
Millroy, S J
Mitchell, S W

Moate, R D C
Mooney, S J M
More, R S
Morgan, D L
Mustafa, M S
Nessim, A A
Neville, E
O'Callaghan, A M
O'Connell, F J
O'Rourke, N P
Okonkwo, A C O
Okubadejo, O A
Old, P J
Olford, C A
Oram, D C
Palmer, R J
Partington, F I
Pemberton, R M
Perkins, R J
Perry, P M
Peters, S A
Phillips, S A
Pickford, A M
Pickstock, C C
Plenty, D R
Poller, D N
Poulton, S E
Pringle, M B
Prosser, A S J
Quine, M A
Randall, S
Randall, V R
Randle, M P
Raw, D S
Read, A M
Reid, J M
Reid, R I
Resouly, A
Rich, K M
Richards, R H
Richardson, A M E
Riley, A P
Roberts, E T
Robinson, G J
Rogers, D C
Rogers, P D
Rooke, H W P
Russell, B N
Sadler, P J
Sanderson, R A
Saunders, M L
Schofield, S A
Schroder, F H H J
Scott-Brown, A W
Senapati, A
Serrano Sanchez, S
Severs, M P
Sheehan, J P
Sheen, C L
Shrivastva, D P
Singh, P
Smart, D J G
Smith, G B
Snow, R E
Solomon, L
Somers, S S
Spedding, A V
Speirs, N I
Stevens, J M
Stevenson, K M
Stewart, A D
Stewart, A E
Sutton, W E
Sweatman, C M
Sykes, J J W
Tan, L C
Thomas, R J
Thompson, J A
Thompson, M R
Thornber, D R
Thornton, J N D
Thwaites, R J
Tobin, J M
Tollast, A R
Tompkins, J C R
Toporski, K
Tuckey, J E
Tudor, J C
Turrall, A
Uglow, M G
Underhill, G S
Vardon, V M
Venkat-Raman, G
Vieweg, R
Wace, J R
Walker, J M
Walters, A M
Walters, J D
Ward, S C

Watkins, J
Watson, K J
Watt-Smith, J A
Weaver, P C
Weis, U
Wernick, S P
West, P D B
Wilcockson, A Q
Wilkins, A C
Wilkinson, T J
Williams, A I
Williams, M
Williams, P L
Williamson, K M
Wilson, M S
Wilson, P
Wise, M
Witham, F M
Wong, W M
Wood, M L B
Woolas, K D
Woolas, R P
Wozniak, E R
Yates, A
Yiangou, C
Young, R M
Zaki, G A

Portsmouth Hants

Buchanan, J D

Portstewart

Armour, B M
Boyd, H K
Carlin, P G M
Corrigan, N P
Dick, C R
Donnelly, E E
Dunn, F J
Elliott, N W A
Gilmore, P
Harley, J B
Higgins, P M
Hughes, C M
Jack, H M
Logan, W C
Lynch, B S
McCartney, M D
McGeown, M F J
McLean, J C
McNaul, W D
Magee, S K
Morrison, C C M
O'Loan, P R
Tracey, F
Walsh, D A
Wright, T R

Potters Bar

Abo Abood, N
Airey, M
Almond, D L
Atkins, M C
Ayers, S J
Barnard, M M E
Bevan, A B
Bickerton, M V
Brown, B
Carrington, M
Carter, P J
Ciezak, R F
Clarke, R G B
Crawford, L A
Dain, C J
Davies, R P L
Duncombe, C L
Edwards, S R
Elder, R J
Ferris, A R
Forman, J D
Garrett, J
Grafton, A J
Hadden, N D
Henderson, A
Hyde, S E
Klopper, A D
Knighton, M E
Mizan, J
Montegriffo, V M E
Munro, C M
Nabarro, R M G
Nicol, A E L
Norris, R M
Patel, A
Ramsell, S E
Sadler, C L
Salim, A
Simmons, A J
Somerset, A M
Stansby, G P

Stone, M C
Storring, P L
Tanner, M
Thomson, P J
Traue, D C
Trevor, S
Trowell, J A
Woods, B T
Zalin, H

Poulton-le-Fylde

Atkinson, P A
Au, G T
Bailey, M B
Bailey, S Y
Beswick, S J
Canning, J M
Clark, A
Cook, M C
Cupitt, J M
Dempsey, V J
Didsbury, C L
Eastwood, G
Edge, J D
Evans, M J
Exton, G L
Freeman, P
Haslett, E A
Hutchinson, G
Isherwood, D
Keirby, D P
Lewin, J P
Lockhart, A S
Morrison, W D
Murphy, R
Noblett, A K
O'Donnell, D A
Pilling, A
Pollock, E M T
Prosser, O A
Rayner, T A
Rhodes, R R
Sissons, M C J
Sissons, P J
Smith, P C
Walker, A K
Watt, J N
Whiteley, G L
Wilson, I D
Woods, T L

Prenton

Brace, C A
Cookson, N M P
Eyre, R M
Ferguson, R
Ghosh, A
Jones, M M
Kenyon, C M
Littler, J
Nuttall, P J
Oldham, E P
Patel, R S
Roberts, F J
Roberts, P D

Prescot

Abrams, J
Allen, K D
Amegavie, F L
Anderson, D N
Andrews, F J
Arrazola Berrizbeitia, M T
Atherton, D P L
Atherton, S T
Aung, T M
Baker, B
Ball, J B
Baskett, D W
Bolton-Maggs, B G
Breeze, C
Brindley, L J
Brown, A S
Brown, T D
Buchanan, G K
Buckley, D D
Buckley, R M
Capewell, A E
Cawdell, G M
Chana, L V
Chaudhuri, P S
Cheetham, M E
Choudhury, A
Choudhury, A
Church, S E
Chyc, A D
Clayton, M R
Conway, P G
Corless, J A

Cramp, J C
Crook, V A
Curley, R K
Denton, J S
Desmond, J M A
Di Dario, D
Dissont, A D
Dutta, A
Dutta, A
Edrich, P J
El Badri, A M
El-Sheshtawy Nasr, M H M
Feldberg, L E J
Fildes, N R
Fraser, M D
Gana, H B-Y
Ghosh, J
Giles, V A
Gilligan, R E
Gordon, H L
Graham, C S
Graham, D R
Green, A R
Griffiths, S C
Hancock, K
Hardy, K J
Hargreaves, D B
Hasan, N U
Hasan, Y H
Hedley, D
Hiranandani, M
Hoggarth, C
Howard, R P
Hunter, R W
Ince, C S
James, M I
Jones, E S
Karunaharan, P
Kelly, S A
Kenny, J B
Kirby, A J
Kishore Kumar, R
Kumar, P
Leong, K S
Levy, H S
Mcauley, P A
McGilvray, I
McIlwain, J C
Macmillan, R R
McNeilly, P
Maitra, D
Manning, M P R A
Massey, J A
Meek, D R
Mehra, R K
Mimnagh, C J
Moore, G R
Mukembo, S M
Mulrine, C H
Mylvaganam, A
Nandapalan, V
Nee, P A M
Nelson, V M
Ng, D P-K
Nwosu, E C
O'Donnell, K M
O'Donnell, R
O'Ryan, M F N
Orton, M G
Owen, W M
Poluri, R M
Prabhu, M A
Prabhu, U A
Raftery, S M
Raghupati Raju, A S
Rahman, M K
Rahman, N N
Ramstead, K D
Ray, A
Ridyard, J B
Rifai, R
Sachdev, A P S
Sachdev, R S
Sanderson, C J
Sandland, R M
Sanyal, A
Sarkozy, V E
Scott, M H
Sharma, S
Sharma, V
Silke, C M
Sills, J A
Soni, R K
Soren, D
Stilwell, J H
Teanby, D N
Varma, M R
Vinod Kumar, P A

Watt, S G
Whelan, R J
Wide, J M
Wilson, R N
Woodhall, C R
Wright, N M J

Prestatyn

Aukland, J
Braun, M S
Campbell, F
Davies, D E
Davies, R L
Evans, D G
Faulkner, A J
Gozzard, A
Howes, P T
Hughes-Roberts, H E
Jessup, E D
Jones, C H
Jones, H G
Jones, H
Jones, L M
Kamaluddin, S M
Kerfoot, J A
Lewis, J
MacLeod, A
Macleod, D
Mahad, D J
Mesure, J G
Neville, A E
Neville, W P
Nwabueze, E D
Pal, A K
Phillips, P R
Proctor, T A P
Roberts, S
Row, H G
Scriven, W A
Sixsmith, D J I
Sutherland, D A
Swinburne, A
Tomlinson, B
Wares, A N
Wickramasekera, D
Wright, F K

Presteigne

Goodall-Copestake, J
Humphreys, D R
Humphreys, H C
Martin, J D C
Schofield, W N
Spring, R D L
Watson, W
Whitfield, C T
Williams, W D C
Wilson, D H

Preston

Abou Shanab, K S
Addada, J E
Adhikary, M
Aggett, P J
Ahad, G W
Ahmad, A
Ahmad, Q
Ahmed, N E D A-F
Ali, M M
Allister, A H
Allsup, S J
Almond, S L
Alvarez, E V
Armour, A
Arya, P
Ashcroft, M M
Ashton, K L
Atherton, E N
Atkin, G K
Atkinson, D
Awbery, D E
Bailey, E A
Bale, R S
Balis, N
Ball, D R
Bangash, I H
Banik, J L
Barkby, G D
Barlow, J L
Barnes, C
Barnes, R K
Baroudi, G
Basnyet, D B
Battye, R
Berends-Sheriff, P J
Beswick, D
Beswick, E
Bewlay, M A
Bird, E E
Biswas, A

Prestonpans

Biswas, S
Blackburn, J R
Blades, R A
Blue, A C
Boon, F J
Boothman, B R
Boothman, J
Bourne, M J
Bowker, S G
Bowman, A
Boyle, J J P
Boyle, S
Bradley, J P
Bradley, S M
Bradshaw, F L
Brearley, J M
Brooks, B V
Brooks, D A L
Brooks, G
Brown, C P
Brown, J C M
Brown, P M
Bruce, I A
Buck-Barrett, R
Buckley, E I J
Bunting, A
Bunting, P
Burnett, H L
Burnie, M L
Burton, A L
Cain, A C M
Cairns, A J
Cairns, J P
Cairns, S A
Callaghan, L C
Campbell, A N
Campbell, C J
Caplin, G
Carew-McColl, M
Carter, F
Carter, J H P
Cassels, H T
Cebrian Valencia, L
Chamarette, N P P
Chand, T G
Chatterjee, A K
Chatterjee, N
Chattha, E A
Chattopadhyay, P K
Chaudhri, K
Cheesbrough, J S
Chesworth, R J H
Chikhalikar, G T
Chikhalikar, G
Choudhary, B
Clark, R
Clarke, J
Clarke, J
Clarke, J
Clelland, I A
Coaker, M J
Comer, M B
Connolly, C V
Consiglio, R V
Conway, H P
Cooper, J A L
Cooper, M J
Cooper, W A B
Copplestone-Bruce, J C
Corkill, R G
Cornah, J
Cottam, D C
Cottam, S N
Cottier, F M
Coughlin, P A
Coughlin, S P
Courtney, E
Coutinho, M C A
Coward, R A
Craghill, D M
Craig, M
Crispin, Z L
Croft, J A
Cross, W R
Curley, J W A
Curtis, P R
Daley, A J
Daniels, C J
Das Gupta, R
Das, B T
Davies, D K
Davies, T G
Davis, C H G
Daws, R A
Dawson, T P
Deacon, R H
Deakin, D P W
Dean, S
Deans, R M

Denver, M D
Dickson, C J
Dilliway, G D
Dix, F P
Dixon, N J
Doherty, D J
Donaldson, I C
Doughty, P R
Duff, C G
Duff, D A
Duff, T B
Duncan, P W
Eddy, M J
Eccles, J C
Edge, D M
Edwards, J M
Everiss, J
Eves, M J
Eyre, J A
Fairclough, M
Fairfax, C F W
Fairhurst, R J
Farrier, M P
Farrington, J L
Faruque, S M
Faux, J C
Feaks, R J
Ferrie, R
Fielden, P
Fitzmaurice, D J
Flaherty, T A
Fletcher, D J
Forbes, A S
Forrester, I R
Fowler, S J
Fryer, J M
Gable, I
Garg, A
Gask, L
Gaze, N R
Gee, S D
Ghori, S S
Ghosh, B B
Gibbon, S P
Giencke, K
Giles, E A
Giles, M B
Glenn, M P
Gonzalez, V G
Goodfellow, R C
Graham, F
Graham, W H
Greening, A P
Greenwood, S T
Gregson, J
Grenfell, R C
Griffin, S J
Griffiths, J O
Grimbaldston, A H
Gulati, V
Guly, O C R
Gurusinghe, N T
Hacking, N M
Hafejee, A
Hamad, G M E-S A
Hann, G S
Hann, J C
Hanson, J M
Hardwick, S A
Harrison, B
Harrison, C J
Harrison, G
Harrison, M N
Hart, R J
Hartley, C
Harwood, P J
Hassan, A I
Hatton, D J
Haward, E C
Hawcroft, J
Hayton, M J
Hearn, A R
Heath, S T
Hendy, M S
Hicks, A P
Hicks, A G
Hill, J C
Hindley, A C
Hirst, S N
Hodkinson, R
Hodskinson, R
Holden, C A
Holden, D W
Holt, P G
Horner, J S
Hothersall, E L
Howar, A J
Howcroft, A J
Howell, S A

Howorth, I E
Hudson, D M
Hudson, J M
Hughes, R
Hunt, J L
Hunt, N
Hussain, F I
Huxham, K G
Huyton, C S
Hynes, C J
Irvine, M S
Isherwood, C N
Izzat, M
Jackson, P L
Jamdar, R P
James, M R
Jandu, M S
Jefferies, E M
Jha, J N
Jhooti, T K
John, M E
Johnson, J A
Johnson, T
Jolley, C I
Jones, D S
Jones, G N
Jones, I P
Jones, M J
Kapadia, M
Karri, B
Kelly, A J
Kelly, D R
Kennedy, S
Khan, S
Khanna, A
Kilgour, A J
Kingston, D S R
Kirby, A P
Kitching, G T
Laitung, J G
Lambert, M E
Lancaster, C J
Larsson, S N
Laszlo, T J
Latiff, A
Laurence, A S
Lawson, R C
Leahy, A R
Lee, P F S
Leelakumari, T
Leigh, N F
Letheren, M J R
Lewis, S E
Lim, M S
Linn, P K K
Loh, M Y
Lonie, D S
Lord, B
Loudonsack, J R
Lowe, N C
Lowe, R
Lowrie, A
Lupton, M E
Lusk, J A R
Luthra, R
Lynch, P G
McCann, P
McCraith, N S
McGaahan, C
McGrath, P J
McKenna, J T
Mackenzie, N A
Mackie, J
McKiernan, E P
McKiernan, M V
McLaughlin, J T
McMeekin, B A
McNamara, C
McWilliam, C
McWilliam, J
Mahmood, D A
Majeed, T
Marrott, S
Marshall, A J
Massey, L J
Matanhelia, S S
Matta, A S
Mawson, A C
Mayor, A C
Metzger, S C
Michel, J M
Millns, D
Minshall, C
Mitchell, J D
Moir, C C
Moore, D R
Moss, S D
Mousa, M A A
Moustafa, A A S

Mughal, M T I
Mulla, H M
Muttucumaru, N J
Myo Minn, Dr
Naik, R K
Napier, A M
Nawrooz, N M J
Newton, P J
Nicolson, S J
Nirula, N
Nixon, P
Noble, J G
Noble, W A
Noblett, R W
O'Donnell, E I
Oakley, D P
Orduna Moncusi, M
Ormerod, P S
Owen, I T
Owen, W G
Parker, C S
Parker, J
Parry, H S
Parry, R T
Parson, A M Y
Patel, A N
Patel, D
Patel, H P
Patel, K B
Patel, K
Patel, V H
Pavey, I S J
Pavey, K M F G
Pawar, N M
Perez-Cajaraville, J J
Phillips, A B
Phipps, K
Pidgeon, N D
Pitt, M A
Pollock, J A R
Poulton, M B
Prasad, R K
Pritchett, A H J
Pusey, J M
Qureshi, S A
Radford, R
Rambihar, B V
Ramirez Rodriguez, J M
Rao, C
Read, G
Rebello, A J A
Reddy, G A N
Rees, P
Reid, A D
Rhoden, W E
Riley, A J
Robb, A
Robb, G A
Roberts, J C
Roberts, N
Roberts, R E P
Robertshaw, M F
Robertson, A
Robertson, I G
Robertson, L
Robinson, P W
Robson, A E
Robson, J
Rodriguez, J M
Rossall, C J
Rowlandson, G
Rugman, F P
Ryan, M J R
Saha, N G
Saikia, B
Saikia, N K
Salmon, Z A
Segovia Martin, A
Senathirajah, D
Seth, A
Sethi, R
Shah, J K
Shahid, S Z
Shaw, I J
Shaw, S J
Shaw, S J
Shek, R J
Shorrock, P
Siddiqui, H
Silva, E P C
Simpson, B
Simpson, D
Simpson, J
Singh, A
Singh, B
Singh, B
Singh, H
Singh, J K

Singh, M
Skailes, G E P
Slater, A
Slater, C
Slater, E V
Small, M L
Small, M
Smith, E M
Smith, E G
Smith, R B
Solomon, L R
Southern, L P
Starley, I F
Stevenson, W T J
Stewart, D J
Stringfellow, H F
Stritch, W A
Suddick, E M
Sudell, A J
Sule, H D
Sule, S H
Sullivan, G
Sundaralingam, S
Surtees, K J
Susnerwala, S S
Sutton, D E
Talbot, E M
Tandon, K
Taylor, B E
Taylor, L A
Taylor, M A
Tedd, R J
Tew, E
Tew, J A
Thakur, B
Thomas, P T
Thomasson, R E
Thompson, D F J
Thomson, G J L
Thomson, R G N
Tidswell, P
Tiley, J E
Todman, R H
Tomlin, P I
Tomlinson, R J
Tooher, C J
Townsend, N W H
Tree, D A
Tuck, J J H
Tunstall, S
Turner, M A B
Vakil, S D
Vice, P A
Vijayadurai, P
Wallice, P D B
Walsh, I
Walton, S M
Warburton, R
Ward, S T
Warner, K L
Watkinson, P J
Watson, J B
Watson, M E
Watson, V F
Watt, A
Webster, M
Wharton, L H
Wharton, M R
White, C C
White, H D
White, S R
Whittaker, J D
Wickham, H
Wignall, J B W
Wijethilleke, G G K
Williams, J G
Williams, N
Wilson, C M
Wilson, L J
Wood, G C
Woodroffe, J B
Woollard, A J
Woollard, C M
Wright, D M
Wright, J D
Wright, P A
Yaxley, K M
Yogasundram, Y
Young, D W
Zargar, G A

Prestonpans

Blake, R A
Bremner, D
Brown, D G
McNeill, I S
Menzies, S E
Pollock, W
Scott, G R H

Simmonte, M G
Turvill, J W

Prestwick

Anderson, D G
Anderson, G G J
Barbour, C D
Barbour, W G
Barrie, P J
Boyd, A H
Cattanach, D J
Cornelius, J M
Duthie, W H
Forster, A L
Glen, S B
Hardie, R
Lambert, B A
Leslie, C J
Lindsay, J E
Longman, C A
McCall, J G
Martin, L M
Miller, M M
Nisbet, C
Park, W D
Percival, R
Rae, E R
Roy, D C
Simpson, S A
Smith, A E C
Smollett, M A
Taylor, I N
Walker, A P
Watson, A
White, G J
Wilson, C S
Wilson, P A

Princes Risborough

Adam, E W
Appleton, P N J
Barden, R K
Breese, C W
Campling, C
Cooney, J A
Durban, J
Forbes, A M
Hodder, K M
Hodder, R W
Jones, M H
MacFarlane, A J
McKenzie, R A
Maisey, A R
Parnaby, P B
Partridge, C R-A
Pearson, R
Rainbow, J R
Robertson-MacKay, F C
Robson, A O
Sheerin, S M
Wise, K S H

Prudhoe

Anderson, L M
Bartley, C F M
Berney, T P
Dunstan, J A
Egan, A
Fenwick, M J
Haywood, S C
Jennings, C E
McCarthy, J M
McLain, B I
Prendergast, M
Quilliam, S J
Ryan, M F
Wright, J C

Pudsey

Antrobus, R D
Ball, N S
Belderson, L
Cook, J N
Crane, S D
Daly, R
Darlington, S
Darnborough, D C
Devereux, T A
Dreghorn, C R
Finch, M D
Follows, D M
Follows, G A
Galloway, S J
Groarke, M I
Guerrero, K L
Hall, J F
Hall, M J
Holt, A A
Jarvis, P R E

Redcar

Gunn, A D G
Gupta, S
Hagger, D C
Hague, G F
Haigh, R
Hall, R M
Hamilton, R W
Hamilton, V H
Hampton, J N S
Hardman, S C
Hardwick, C E
Hardy, J E
Harris, P D
Harris, S-A
Harrold, M
Hayes, L J
Haynes, P D
Headon, M P
Hegarty, H M M
Hemsted, E H
Hennessy, A M
Heppell, A C H
Herdman, R C D
Heyworth, T
Hickson, M S
Higgins, C R
Hislop, R M
Hobbs, C G L
Hobbs, J A
Holcombe, E L
Holden, W A
Holloway, S M
Holt, E M
Holtom, N C
Hookway, K M
Horne, D K
Horton, L W L
Houston, J P
Howlett, C R
Hudson, A B
Hudson, G
Hughes, C J
Hunt, W G
Hunter, R C A
Hussain, A
Hussain, S
Hyde, N C
Hyman, N M
Inglis, G S
Iqbal, R K
Irvine, A T
Jackson, E G
Jacobs, I R M
Jacobs, M A
Jago, R H
James, J M
James, M P
Jarman, S J
Jarvis, S J
Jefferson, R J
Johnson, P P
Johnston, E M
Jolly, P N
Kamel, K M
Kapila, A
Kaplan, C
Karim, A H M H
Kaur, S
Kawik, L K
Keith-De Witte-Scott-Spencer, S F
Kemp, I C
Khan, R J K
Kimber, K A
Kinnell, H G
Kitching, M R
Knight, J
Knott, F A
Knowles, I J
Knowlson, P A
Kohli, S C
Kumar, P
La Rosa, C F
Lade, J C
Lambert, N G
Lancaster, J
Lander, D A
Latchford, N C
Latto, C
Lawrance, C A
Lawson, C A
Lee, H A
Lees, W C
Lennox, J S H
Lewis, N J
Lindo, F C
Lisney, F J
Lister, B A
Locham, J
Longfield, J C
Lovett, D L
Luxton, K D
Lyall, J R W
Lynch-Farmery, E M
McCormick, C J
McDonald, B
MacFarlane, A I H
McKinlay, M I
MacLachlan, K G
McMullan, T F W
Macrae, A J
MacWilliam, K M
Madgwick, S A
Magee, T R
Makowska, M T
Malcolm, S J
Malik, A S
Malone, P R
Mann, N P
Mansell, N J
Mansor, F Z L Y
Markham, D C
Markillie, R E D
Marks, A M
Marks, N J
Markwell, D C
Marshall, A M
Marshall, J C W
Marshall, P J
Marshall, R W
Martin-Bates, C R
Martin, T D M
Mary Das, T A
Mascarenhas, R F
Masterman, E B Z
May, A J
Meanock, R I
Mee, A S
Melhuish, A H
Mellors, B E
Michail, M W A
Mikhail, M M S
Millar, J M
Miller, J M
Miller, S M
Milligan, D D
Milne, A B
Milverton, R A
Mittal, R K
Mobey, L J
Modi, K
Modi, S K
Moens, V R T
Moffitt, J A
Mohan, N
Monger, J D
Monk, J F
Moore, J
Moore, J E K
Moore, R M
Morando, S J
Morgan, N J
Morris, S A R
Morris, V C
Moxon, M A
Mullins, M R
Munday, D C
Munday, M J R
Murphy, W A
Murray, N S S
Myszor, M F
Nagaria, A J
Naik, R B
Nainthy, N M
Nairne, A A
Nanu Kandiyil, V
Naran, K B
Narayan, R
Nash, J M
Newman, C I
Newrith, S F
Nichols, R R W
Nirgude, S V
Noone, O P
Nugent, I M
O'Brien, E N
O'Connell, E J
O'Connell, N J
O'Hanlon, S G
Oldershaw, C M
Oppenheimer, M M G
Ord, J J
Ormonde, S E
Orr, W P
Paige, G J
Paige, H
Pailthorpe, C A
Parke, T J
Patel, N G
Patel, S M
Patel, S
Patey, G L T M
Paton, J T
Patterson, M C
Pemberton, D J
Pengelly, A W
Perry, R J
Pethica, B D
Pick, S
Pickup, A J
Pimm, J T
Pizura, V A
Pollitzer, M
Potter, S M
Powell, A R
Powell, H M
Powell, J V
Powell, M P
Price, A J N
Price, D G
Prust, A J
Puddy, M R
Pullinger, R M
Purcell, P F
Quilty, B M
Raban, J S
Rae, S
Rahim, N S
Ralfe, S W
Raman, A
Raman, V
Rankin, J A
Ranson, S A
Razak, Dr
Read, P R
Reece-Smith, H
Reeves, E R J
Reeves, J H K
Requena Duran, M D M
Richards, A B
Richards, D
Richards, J G
Richards, S A
Richardson, T I L
Richmond, H S
Riddell, N J
Riley, D A
Rimmer, M E
Roberts, I J W
Roberts, T E
Roberts, V M
Robertson, R S C
Rock, C L
Rogers, P B
Ronay, S A
Rosam, M J W
Rose, A F
Ross, A E
Ross, H B
Ross, J K
Rosser, D W A
Roth, J A
Rout, J P
Rowe, J A
Roy, R
Ruffle, S P
Rushton, S C
Saad, I E D B
San, S M
Sandercott, A M
Sanders, L R
Scales, J T
Schuller, I
Scott, D M
Selinger, M
Sharma, R P
Sharp, R J
Sharpe, R C
Shaw, M B
Sheppard, E J
Sheppard, H W
Siddal, J N
Sidery, J C
Simmons, P A
Simpson, R I D
Sinclair, M
Six, S
Slater, C B
Smallcombe, G W
Smith, E J
Smith, K S H
Smith, M D
Smith, R B
Smith, R A R
Smith, R A
Smith, S A
Smith, T G C
Soysa, S M
Stacey, A R
Staig, D
Staker, P
Stanbury, P N
Stansfield, J M
Stewart, E H C
Stewart, E J C
Stickland, J K
Stone, D G H
Stone, E J
Strang, C J B
Street, P
Stringer, E C
Stroud, R A
Sumitra, J V
Sutton, L J
Suvarna, J R
Swami, M L
Swami, S
Swan, S E
Taghipour, J
Tait, C R S
Talbot, A J
Talbot, R M
Tang, A L F
Tanner, V
Tarnoky, J M
Taylor, G W
Themen, A E G
Thilo, J B
Thomas, D R T
Thomas, H L
Thomas, P L
Thompson, B C
Thomson, M A
Thurston, J S
Tinto, E I
Titmas, G J
Tomboline, D S
Tomlins, C D C
Tomlinson, I P M
Torrie, E P H
Townsend, R M
Tremlett, J C
Tulley, M M
Turnbull, H E
Underwood, T A
Van Boxel, P J W
Vega Escamilla, I
Verghese, C
Waite, D W
Waldmann, C S
Walker, C P
Walker, J W
Walker, T M
Wallis, S M
Walton, P K H
Warwick, N G
Watson, A M
Watson, M D
Watts, A S
Weeks, R M
Weinstein, C
Welbourn, R B
Welham, R A N
Wells, T A
Westcar, P D
Westermann, W B
Weston, D M
Whalley, M J
Whitehead, C E
Whitwell, D J
Wiesendanger, P H
Wildman, G M
Williams, D L
Williams, F A B
Williams, G W
Williams, H C
Williams, M L L
Williams, R A M
Williams, R M
Williams, S E
Willoughby, R A G E
Wilsey, C M W
Wilson, A R
Wilson, A M
Wilton, A Y
Winchester, J P
Woodrow, D F
Wootton, I D P
Wray, K A A
Yeo, J E
Young, E

Redcar
Ashcroft, D A
Bailey, P
Barker, K M
Barron, R M
Baxter, T W
Bentley, J
Coleclough, G
Conn, W G
Cowser, J
Davidson, R C
Doherty, J C
Dunning, A
Eardley, W G P
Elliott, P A
Fairbairn, I P
Henderson, W A
Jones, C S
Kakkar, A
Kumar, N
Lal, B K
Lal, K R
Lyle, J H
Michie, M H
Moore, D R
Moore, W P F
O'Flanagan, W J D
Oswal, V H
Rudd, C
Smith, F C
Smith, R
Stephen, A K
Stocking, A J H
Summers, E J
Taylor, T C
Thomas, A J
Thomas, A B
Westgate, R
White, J S
Whitehouse, D H
Williamson, M R
Woolder, S I

Redditch

Abdel-Salam, A A
Abu Khalaf, W A I
Ackroyd, D F W
Ahmad, F
Akram, S
Al-Ali, S H A
Ananthram, S
Arafa, M A M
Awaad, M O M A
Bell, K M
Birrell, L N
Boon, H M
Booth, F
Brown, L A
Caranci, G A
Carter, D J
Cassidy, J J
Chandler, S I J
Chiddick, S H
Close, G C
Cochrane, J D
Cohen, J R
Cooper, G R
Cowburn, J E
Da Rocha-Afodu, O
Das, B N
Davenport, R W
Davey, J W
Dawes, N C
Deller, J G
Dior, A R
Doherty, N P
Dow, I C
Dow, J D C
Dow, T C
Echebarria Arteche, J J
Eckersley, P J
El Dosoky, M E
Elias-Jones, J H
Ford, R N
Frame, R J
Franklin, S M
Fraser, B E
Gard, W J
Geddy, P M
Greaves, D N J
Grier, L M
Grieve, A M
Gupta, D R
Hakeem, J A
Hall-Davies, G
Hall, M F R
Hanna, W E M
Haqqani, M R
Haque, S
Hardcastle, P H
Hardwick, C I
Harris, G P M
Hill, C A L
Holland, P
Hopkins, D W J
Houfton, H E
Ip, C B
Jenkins, F H
Jenkins, S J
Jenkinson, S D
Johnstone, C M
Jones, R P
Kai, P
Karagevrekis, C
Katamaneni, R K
Kathuria, V
Keogh, B P
Kerr, K M
King, J R
Kirby, C P
Leach, T A
Lewthwaite, R
Lister, E S
Locke, P R
Lowe, K S
Lowry, P J
McGregor, C H
Macpherson, G H
McPherson, J J
Mann, M C
Matthews, A J
Melley, E T
Millard, R C
Mosieri, C N
Munir, M
Nithianantham, V T
Noreldeen, S A
Obeid, D
Ojukwu, C I
Ounsted, J M
Overton, D J
Parkinson, S J
Peffers, G M
Phillips, C J
Pike, S H
Pitcher, M S
Porter, S M
Price, A J
Pryke, G R
Purser, N J
Rafiqi, M A
Ranganathan, S
Reading, A D
Reavley, C M
Ritchie, A K
Roberts, F P
Robinson, A J
Sankey, R J
Seyler, I B F
Shaw, W J S T
Sidford, K I
Singhal, S N
Sivapragasam, S
Smallman, L A
Smith, B E
Smith, T C
Sutherland, E M
Tha, Z
Tonge, M F R
Tucker, W F G
Vathenen, A S
Velineni, V E
Wells, J J
Williams, A J
Wong, P A
Wosornu Abban, D

Redhill

Abayawickrama, P C K J
Ainley, N C W
Ameen, M
Anderson, D M
Ansell, R W
Arnold, C J
Aslett, D J
Bajorek, P K M
Banky, E J
Barrow, K
Bassily, A A E
Benton, J L
Bhanji, A B
Bray, B M
Bullock, D L E
Butler, J A
Butler, W H
Carson, D G
Carson, R G
Ceccherini, A F A
Chopdar, A
Cole, G

Reading

Kripal, K
Lee, A V
Lee, S M
Lightley, D A
Lindsay, P J
McGechaen, K W
McWilliams, T G
Maddy, P J
Martin, E M
Mason, C M
Mason, J B
Minhas, E-U-M
Minhas, H L
Minhas, H A
Newbould, R A
Peace, S
Ross, R J
Senior, M A
Steward, K A
Tawse, B M
Thrippleton, S A
Walter, D P
Watson, K J
Woodhead, R
Zicchieri, F L

Pulborough

Atkins, P M
Bailey, J E
Bartlett, J S W
Bolton, R
Brooks, A Y
Collyer, T C
Cooper, M
Cooper, M F
Couchman, D R
Diver, J P
Duncan, P A
Eastes, C N E
Ellis, L M
Erskine, J P
Evans, C A
Ferrie, J I
Ferries, J H
Fitzpatrick, S C B
Fooks, T J C
Ford, J H G
Fountain, A B
Gibbon, E A A
Gimson, L V
Hanbury-Aggs, C A
Hard, P L S
Herbertson, R A
Hughes, M
Hutchings, H Q
Jeffery, M P
Jolly, M S
Kalaher, M E
Kilpatrick, F R
King, C P M
King, C J
McBrien, D J
McCann, D G
MacWhirter, G I
Morson, B C
Mulcahy, E F
Newton, J
Parr, G D
Ranken, A M
Rodan, K S
Russell, J G
Sexton, J P
Shillingford, M J
Travers, E H
Tse, B S-W
Turner, Y J
Whitehead, D M
Whittingham, E B
Whyte-Venables, F T
Williams, R
Wrighton, R J

Purley

Bandyopadhyay, U
Barnes, B
Basu, C
Bhalla, A
Blake, H M
Blake, J
Brueton, M J
Carlisle, J M
Chand, M Y
Cohen, H C
Counsell, B R A
Cureton, R J R
Davies, E B
Dhesi, R K
Ferris, M B
Finch, J A L

Gallagher, M H
Gayford, J J
Grasso, P
Griffin, M M
Hawker, H J
Hopkins Jones, K M
Johnson, J M
Jones, C M
Jones, L I
Jones, V E
Karani, J B
Keyes-Evans, O D
Koshy, E S
Lansdown, P F P
Lawrence, R M
Lawther, K M
Lawther, P J
Lees, J A S
Linney, J G
Lloyd, M S
Lobo, M D
McKenzie, C H
McMillan, M
Martin, J C
Milne, P
Mohan, K K
Newlands, P W
Overton, R D C
Pandita-Gunawardena, N D
Peatfield, B J D
Pendower, J E H
Phillips, P C
Platz, C L M
Pollard, C M
Premachandran, S
Rahim, G F
Rogers, D A L
Rose, H K
Rourke, A
Rudolphy, S M
Shore, H R
Shuttleworth, C A R
Sivaloganathan, M
Sivaloganathan, S
Sivaloganathan, S
Stacey, T E
Theva, R
Thin Thin Saing, Dr
Watton, M J
Watton, R W
Wright, E C
Yuce, M

Pwllheli

Bentham, J A
Chapman, J A
Davies, D W
Davies, H L
Davies, H M
Evans, E W
Evans, G W
Griffith, C
Griffith, M M
Grime, R T
Harris, K
Jones-Edwards, G
Jones, B G
Jones, R E
Langley, P R
Lawrence, E
Lawrence, I J
Liddle, D R
McGowan, G K
McInnes, I C
Meyrick, P V
Ogilvie, P J
Ogilvie, P N
Owen, G T
Owen, W L
Parry-Smith, H J
Pritchard, R I
Robinson, A T
Robyns-Owen, D
Terleski, M J
Thomas, D G H
Williams, A F
Williams, A
Williams, D K
Williams, E
Williams, R I

Queenborough

Best, R M

Radlett

Aggarwal, E K L
Allen, L N
Angel, J C
Apthorp, M Q

Arnold, A K
Bartlett, C L R
Bevan, G
Bowen, D A L
Brown, C P T
Carson, A A G
Chavda, D B
Clark, M P A
Cooray, G M
Cooray, S E
Deeny, J E
Donne, R L
Drake, D A
Farewell, J G
FitzGerald, G M
Fitzgerald, S B
Freedman, W
George, M L
Glover, D H
Gold, I D
Griffiths, D C
Handelsman, S M
Herod, J E
Holborow, M
Hurt, R L
Ingram, M J
Jackson, N
Langley, D A
Lawton, G
Leaback, R D
Leung, A W
Lynn, A H
McDermott, P J C
Marriott, S E
Mathew, S
Maxwell, C W
Miller, R M
Mitchell, S E H
Moses, M A
Murray, J M
Ogden, E M
Pegg, M S
Piachaud, M J H
Rasaratnam, R
Ripley, J R
Ruston, J J S
Ruston, M A
Simanowitz, M D
Sims, E C
Swaine, J M
Sweeney, P M
Taylor, F C
Turner, P P
Verdin, S M
Walton, B
Wantman, A C
Watters, P T
Wildman, M A

Raglan

Davies, E
Davies, E J L
Davies, V J
Downing, J A
Farr, J M
Holt-Wilson, A D
Huckle, P L
Lillywhite, A R
Paley, O J
Pantlin, A W
Pook, C W
Sheers, G
Small, G R

Rainham

Adur, R M
Awan, B
Evans, J E
Kemp, P S
Mills, J N
Mushtaq, I
Ogbuehi, N J
Stiff, J H
Subramanian, K A
Sundaralingam, V
Tandon, A
Toni, E E
Wani, M A

Ramsey

Allinson, A J
Armour, J K
Brownsdon, J K
Burrow, G R F
Chan, M S
Clarke, H M
Cowley, L C
De Courcy, D L P
Jones, E J
Kee, J C

Kelsey, A S C
McDonald, A J
McDonald, J R
Maska, M
Munro, L L
Parry, A C
Revill, H
Riley, P J
Seymour-Price, M
Smith, E
Speed, H P
Steer, C
Teare, H C
Walsh, W R
Wilson, G M

Ramsgate

Andrews, R H
Attwood, P R A
Beale, J D
Charley, A R
Crosfield, C E
Gajjar, G S
Hancock, M-C
Hardaker, J M
Harries, D G
Heather, J D
Kelsey, J C
Kitchener, A D
Law, V A
Leeming, C A
Macpherson, A M
Miller, R J
Morcom, R C
Neden, C A
Neden, D A J
Neden, J W D
O'Brien, D A
Peat, C J
Ratnasingham, P
Reeves, M T
Rickenbach, C A M
Sadler, R O
Semple, W J
Stuart, G W
Tigg, A
Timmins, S F
Valentine, P
Ward, A C E
Ward, N C
York, S P

Rastrick

Grant, J P

Ravenglass

Coldrey, R P
Fullagar, I R A

Rayleigh

Anglin, M
Binns, G
Dayson, C C
Glover, P
Kittle, G P
Kulkarni, P
Read, S M
Rigby, D
Soppet, P E R
Swinburne, R M
Thorp, J S
Walton, A W J
Wier, J

Reading

Abdulali, S A
Abdulla, A J
Abid, M
Agathangelou, C O
Ahmad Farouk, A R
Aiono, S
Aitken, F J
Akhtar, J
Al-Shakarchi, B N J
Aldrich, C J
Allen, S C
Allott, H A
Anderson, B E
Anderson, P M D
Anderson, R G W
Andren, S M
Andrews, F M
Andrews, J A B
Astle, L M
Attwood, K
Badie, F Y
Bailey, G M
Baker, J P
Bal, H S
Balkwill, J M

Barker, E A
Barker, L C
Barr, A M
Barrow, I
Battram, J W R
Baxter, S A C
Beacham, W D
Beatty, D C
Bell, J A
Benham, C L
Benham, P
Best, P V
Bhardwaj, V
Billington, B M
Bindra, H S
Bird, C W H
Bird, J E
Bird, S
Birks, M E
Black, D A K
Black, G G
Blackburn, B S
Blackburn, T P D
Blackwell, B
Blomley, D J
Blowers, D A
Bodden, E P
Bohn, G L
Boon, A W
Boon, J E
Booth, C J
Booth, J C L
Borthwick, R M
Boulos, G B
Bowley, C L
Boyle, M D
Bradlow, A
Bradshaw, C J
Brain, A I J
Brand, A D
Brar, S
Bray, I L C
Bray, J E C
Brito-Babapulle, F M C
Brock, N J
Brock, P J M
Brooke, P N R
Brookes, C E
Broome, M
Brown, A L
Brown, C N
Brown, S G E
Brunt, E L
Bucher, J
Buckley, J B
Budd, A K
Burden, P
Burke, J B
Burke, R A
Burnett, G A M
Burnham, D A
Busby, M F
Busfield, G D
Byrne, C V
Bywater, J R
Bywater, J E
Cahill, J
Calvert, H T
Cameron, L A
Campbell, M
Cartwright, F F
Chadha, R K
Chadwick, H N
Chadwick, J M
Chapman, A J
Chapman, J A
Charlton, C D A
Chisholm, J W
Chua, C N
Churchill, D A
Ciecierski, A J K
Clarke, E G W
Clayton, D J
Clayton, J M
Clegg, N G
Clouting, E M
Coe, N L
Colenso, S M
Collett, R W C
Collett, S M
Collin, C F
Connor, J H
Cook, I J
Coomber, A S
Copeland, S A
Corden, D
Corstorphine, W J
Cottrell, J S
Courtney, S P

Coury, J C
Cove-Smith, P A
Cowie, D H G
Cox, E V
Cox, I D
Cracknell, M G
Crawford, J F
Crawley, H S
Creed, M E
Crystal, A M
Cuningham, P M
Curtis, H A
D'Cruz, G L
D'Cruz, J E M
Dadswell, J V
Davidson, A P
Davies, C W H
Davies, J B
Davies, M G
Dawson, W G
De Silva, G E
Dean, L J
Dehn, T C B
Delany, G M
Derbyshire, N D J
Dils, R C
Dixey, J R B
Dixon, J C
Dodds, R D A
Dodson, M J
Dodson, P M
Drake, E J
Dudek, M K
Dziewulski, P G
Edmondson, P W
Edwards-Moss, D J
Edwards, A M
Edwards, A J
Eggleton, S M
Emerson, K M
Evans, D M
Evered, D C
Ewart, M C
Faber, R G
Fane, S K
Farrugia, P D
Faulkner, A-M
Fawcett, D P
Fawcett, H A
Felton, J R
Fennessy, P A
Fergusson, C M
Fielden, J M
Finnigan, D M
Fitzherbert Jones, R C
Fleischer, C C
Flint, S K
Foley, S J
Foskett, D
Foubister, G
Fowler, J M
Franzi, S J
Fraser, D J
Fraser, D M
Fraser, Z M
Freebairn, A J E
French, G S
Frodsham, P F
Froud, E B
Fulford, C J
Galland, R B
Gamba, E
Gargav, A
Gargav, A K
Garside, P J
George, H M S
Ghorashian, S
Ghosh, C
Gibson, M R
Gibson, M
Gilbert, M J
Gildersleve, J Q
Gold, A
Gonzalez Garcia, L V
Goode, A G
Goodwin, D P
Gordon, A F
Goring, J A
Grantham, V A M
Grech, H
Green, C E
Greenhalf, J O
Greenhalgh, L J
Greenland, J H
Gregory, R P
Grice, D M
Grover, N
Groves, R M
Gundur, N S

Collins, N P
Davies, U M
De Zoysa, S
Donnelly, S J
Doyle, J C
Drabu, K J
Ekdawi, M
El-Hariry, A A W M
Ferguson, A E
Ferguson, A J
Fish, D E
Foster, K J
Gaitonde, A M
Gaynor, P A
Gibson, K A A
Gordge, K
Gordon-Wright, A P
Gordon-Wright, H M
Green, M A
Greenwood, J J
Griffith, S M
Guess, H M
Hale, J E
Hieatt, M S
Hildreth, V A
Hill, B M
Hughes, A J
Hughes, C A
Hughes, D J
Jenkins, P
Jennings, M C
Jordan, S J
Kanagarajah, D
Kariyawasam, R A A P
Kelly, K
Kinsella, C M
Lambden, P W
Lewis, E C
Loosemore, T M
Lugg, M A
McDonald, F A
McManners, D L
Matthey, F
Miller, P D
Miller, R G
Momjian, L L B
Moon, P V
Nkanza, K M
O'Sullivan, M F
Onugha, E N
Pangayatselvan, T
Perera, B S F
Phillips, E M
Phongsathorn, V
Pickering, J G
Prajapati, C L
Puzey, S H
Rane, A M
Redd, R A S
Roberts, H L
Rowntree, C A
Sage, F J
Sambrook, J H
Schierenberg, T S F
Sethugavalar, C
Shuja, M A
Skeats, C J
Smith, C D
Sowton, J V
Sowton, T J
Stacey-Clear, A
Stapley, A M
Stern, S C M
Stewart, B A
Tayler, R G O
Tite, L J
Tomei, L D
Tompkin, D M B
Trigg, K H
Twaij, M H A R A
Vejdani, K
Walbrook, E E
Watkins, M E
Wells, A J
Williams, M E M
Wilson, J R
Wilson, R S
Wylie, C E

Redruth

Badve, M I
Baker, T J S
Blake, C E
Blight, S
Carter, A J
Charnaud, A B
Davies, W A
Edmunds, T C
English, C L

English, J D
Evers, J A
Foster, J S
Gethin, I P
Gray, N I D B
Hayes, P M
Hessing, R
Holland, C E
Hollingworth, H C
Hughes, G B
Jones, H M
Jones, P B T
Knowles, S R F
Lindsey, M P
Lusty, W J
McDermott, C A
MacMahon, D G
Naylor, J M
Naylor, S R
O'Carroll, C B
Philpott, D N
Roger, M D
Rogers, T A
Ruscoe, M N J
Smith, J M
Smith, S A
Spittle, M C
Stephens, F G
Swithinbank, I M
Trevail, P R
Weller, E M
Wilkinson, A M
Wilson, C W

Reigate

Andrew, J D
Andrews, H J
Ashby, M A
Basha, M A
Bedford, D F
Bernstein, C A B
Biggart, S A
Bragg, A J D
Casson, A J
Clay, P R
Cory, C C
Curry, P H
Davies, J P H
Dennison, E J
Dunn, N J
Evans, C S
Fahy, H
Fancourt, P
Forsyth, C J
Guinness, E A
Guinness, L F
Haynes, L E R
Hubert, H M
Hunter, S A C
Jackson, P
Jennings, A M
Jennings, D C
Jennings, S
Johnson, I D
Kaiser, T
Kerr, P D
Killick, V
Knight, D
Lambourne, P
Lekh, S K
Lindley, C B
Lyons, J P
McKee, C N
Mackie, G C
Makomaska, A Z S
Makomaska, B M A
Medlock, K E
Middleton, G W
Neeson, L E
Pandya, D J
Pattinson, K T S
Pipe, N G J
Pritchard, J M
Ramanathan, J S
Ramanathan, M
Ramanathan, R S
Reilly, S J
Sharma, R
Shaw, J H W
Solan, M C
Sussman, H S
Taylor, J
Viswapathi, K
Wadzisz, F J
Whitfield, G A
Wittmann, F W

Renfrew

Anderson, A M R

Blackwood, J A
Chan, M W
Davidson, S L
Ellis, E L
Lyons, K G B
McCall, J
McEwan, S C
McQuoney, Q J
Montgomery, A J
Ramage, A E
Seath, G L
Shapiro, B W
Sunderland, A
Ventry, L M

Repton

Evans, G F

Retford

Abdulla, H R
Ainsleigh-Jones, M
Anderson, A R
Atkinson, J F D
Badcock, R J
Baruah, R K
Bendall, P
Blackburn, A
Brodie, V A
Brown, A L
Brown, R L
Cherrill, G
Cochran, D S
Corbett, C L
Cordess, C C
Daniel, A C A
De Silva, G B D N
Dempster, J
Durham, L H
Emmerson, J
Fearn, H M
Foster, P
Garcia-Rodriguez, C R
Gilbert, I J
Hardman, P R J
Herbert, J M
Herbert, P M
Ho, T P
Jiwa, M
Johnston, S J
Keitch, I A P
Langley, R E
Mackrill, M J R
Mundy, E M
Murphy, F B
Nwulu, B N
Parry, W R
Pearson, C H
Perera, V T
Radhakrishnan, G
Rassl, D M
Rennick, M J
Rigby, C C
Roberts, J
Sampson, G A
Sawires, M A A
Scott, H M
Sihra, P K
Sivridis, A
Skeavington, J R
Slingsby, A J
Smith, J G
Speight, H M
Speight, T J
Tonge, J
Travers, R F
Vardy, S B
Verma, S
Waas, M J H B
Walker, J M

Rhayader

Hamer-Davies, E A
Joy, P W
Lee, M
Little, H K
Wynne Evans, B K

Rhosneigr

Luckas, J R A
Thompson, W A L
Whitby, T E

Rhyl

Agell Argiles, I
Alexander, M J
Anderson, S H
Archard, N P
Auf, I A E-H
Balaji, V
Banfield, P J

Bastawros, S S
Beirouti, Z A Y
Bell, C F
Bellamy, C M
Bhowmick, B K
Bickerton, N J
Bracewell, B F
Byrne, R A
Cairn, A M
Cartlidge, D
Champion, A E
Chohan, Z L
Clark, J
Clay, N R
Cochrane, R A
Coulton, E R
Craig, A D A
Dalton, A D A
Daniel, C E
Davies, C J
Davies, G
Davies, N S
Davies, P L
Denman, G
Dobson, S J
Dogra, R S
Edwards, J A
Evans, A C
Evans, C M
Fayaz, M
Finnie, I A
Frost, N
Gollins, S W
Gopashetti, S C
Gozzard, D I
Green, G J
Greenway, M W
Griffiths, M J
Hammad, Z
Harding, E M
Hardway, J M
Hardway, R I
Hardway, R J
Hollingsworth, J D K
Hubbard, M J S
Humphrey Evans, I R
Jones, C
Jones, E G
Jones, J G
Jones, L W
Jones, M O
Khalil, A A
Khalil, K I
Klimach, O E
Knight, A C
Lake, A P J
Lanceley, C P
Landon, R A
Leatt, P B
Looker, D N
Lourens, C P J
Macaulay, M E
McCarthy, D O B
McConnell, C A
Mathur, A C
Murphy, G V
Nethersell, A B W
O'Donnell, M A
Osborne, J E
Padi, R K
Parry, D L
Penfold, C N
Peskett, T R
Phillips, J G
Pickford, L J
Pierce-Williams, G
Pritchard, H M
Rao, B V
Reed, E A
Roberts, E B
Roberts, S E
Rowlands, E
Salahuddin, M
Seager, S J
Shah, M K
Srinivasan, V
Stutchfield, P R
Subramanian, A
Tehan, B E
Thomas, D J
Vedpathak, V S
Veltkamp, U A
Waters, B
Waters, M R
Whyler, D K
Williams, A J
Williams, E G N
Williams, F E

Wood, E H
Yuille, T D

Rhymney

Evans, I L R
Jones, S D
Mwenda, M Y
Potts, T M
Roberts, J D

Richmond, North Yorkshire

Atkinson, P M
Barker, E V
Barrett, J A
Belas, R J
Bond, P R
Bradford, D E
Challis, A L
Clark, J T
Diack, G A M
Dootson, J C
Dunkley, C P
Dykes, L K
Enevoldson, N S P
Fernandes, T J
Gillie, I
Ginns, A D
Goldberg, R S
Hall, M C S
Hamilton, D
Hampson, J
Hansell, R H
Heard, D H
Heaton, N R
Heron, F J
Hodges, C B
Hodgson, M D
Humphrey, A R
Hyde, J
Keavney, M J
Kipling, P T
Lacamp, C J
Lake, B
Lawson, R M
McDonald, J D
Minns, J P
Morrison, J F B
Mowbray, M
Mowbray, M J
Paterson, A G
Pearson, T
Richmond, C S A
Robertson, J D
Smailes, A M
Sutherland, E
Sutherland, E L
Swan, T F
Tregillus, E V
Tregillus, J
Trewby, C S
Troughton, T W E
Watt, S E
Welch, J P L

Richmond, Surrey

Akhtar, S A A
Anderson, L J
Andrews, L J M
Attard, H W
Bainbridge, A D
Barker, S J
Barnard, J A
Bartlett, T P
Bates, F M
Batten, A M M
Batten, J C
Bayne, M C
Bearcroft, J S
Beattie, J C
Bell, L D
Bellamy, M F
Birchwood, E L
Bitensky, L
Black, A S
Blake James, J W
Bocking, L J
Bowen, J S
Bruce-Chwatt, R M
Buchanan-Barrow, S J
Burman, R H
Burrows, R
Burton, J D K
Calder, J D F
Cameron, H C
Carmichael, J O R
Carnegie, C M D
Carter, R T J
Casimir, C L
Chanarin, I
Chapman, M H
Chiesa, M C
Chung, G J-H
Collis, C H
Colvin, D W
Combes, S G
Cornell, M N P
Cox, D R
Cran, E M
Crowley, J M
Crowley, M C R
Cullen, S
D'Netto, P E
Da Costa, L J R
Dangoor, A
Davidson, J M
Davies, H W
Davies, N M
Daya, S
Dick, T S B
Dickinson, J M E
Donaldson, R J
Drew, C D M
Engineer, M P
Ezekiel, G A R
Farmer, R
Feldschreiber, P
Fergusson, I G
Ferris, S T
Flood, J G
Fox, W
Foxworthy, M
Fraser-Moodie, F C
Frater, A J
Fry, M F
Galletly, N P
Garewal, D S
Gaster, R A
Gawlinska, M H
Godbolt, H L
Gore, M E
Gowan, A S O
Greenwood, A J
Griffiths, A P
Griffiths, W E
Hamilton-Bell, P
Hanief, M R
Hargreaves, C
Harrington, A B
Harris, R W
Haslehurst, J M
Healy, K J
Hemphill, B F
Holland, M W
Holman, P L
Hutton-Taylor, S D
Irvine, G
Jackman, N C G
Jacobs, B P
Jayawardene, S A
Jazeel, S N
John, H H
Kelly, B J
Kenn, C W
Kingston, C A
Kirkbride, A V
Knight, R J
Lawrence, J D
Leach, J C D
Levin, J M
Levinson, A M R
Levinson, G A
Levinson, M C
Lewis, K G
Lewis, R O
Lindon, R L
Lorch, C U
McEwan, A S
McQuattie, A
Madgwick, J C A
Maher, J
Mason, J
Montford, H
Morcom, A M
Morgan, J F
Morison, M
Morrell, R A
Morris, E D
Napier, J A
Norton, A M
Norton, M L S
Nunes, M D A
Nunez, V A
O'Donovan, C P
Oddie, S J R
Ooi, M M
Parker, R H
Pasmore, H S
Pattinson, B

Rickmansworth

Pawlowicz, W
Penrose, R J J
Perry, M J A
Philip, V J
Pilkington, P
Pilkington, T R E
Raffle, J A
Redhead, R G
Rosling, L E A
Ryder, T S
Samson, G J
Santos Ramon, A
Savy, L E
Schofield, P B
Sellwood, M W
Sinclair, T A L
Skogstad, W H
Smith, C A
Smith, V C
Solman, N
Sparks, M
Sprackling, M E
Stubbs, P J
Symons, G V
Turner, R M
Urch, C E
Van Lennep, T D
Wakefield, A J
Walker, M J
Ward, C M
Ward, M M
Ward, R V H
Ward, W A
Ward, W D
Watson, H K
Weir, R E P
Weston, S J
Wheatley, C H
White, M E
Wiersema, U F
Witherow, H
Wyatt, J A
York, A H
Yusuf, M N
Zayyan, K S
Zwi, M

Rickmansworth

Amess, J A L
Amess, R M
Angel, J H
Auplish, R N
Bennett, F
Brew, D S J
Broome, P C
Brown, C M L
Cairn, J W N C
Carswell, J W
Cole, C J
Colford, C A
Cooke, G S
Cooke, R T R
Cooper, J R C
Cooper, L C
Corp, N
Cowan, J D
Dale, G C
Dane, V J
Davies, E R
Davies, K D
De Souza, E L
Denham, M J
Diaz-Guijarro Hayes, J
Dominian, J
Dunlop, L S
Evans, P R
Farago, S A S
Fenton, F M
Fernando, A G R
Flude, I D
Foreman, N E
Foster, G R
Fountain, S W
Fox, J P
Fox, R H
Friston, K J
Garrow, J S
Garrow, K J
Godhania, V R
Goh, V J-L
Golin, M R
Goodwin, A T
Goodwin, H A
Greenland, A D
Grundy, E M
Haddad, P F
Hagyard, A H
Hammer, P R C
Harvey, M T

Hatfield, E C I
Hayward, A W
Hernandez, P M
Hilmi, O J
Hodgson, M J
Horsburgh, A G
Horsburgh, A
Hurley, M M
Iacoponi, E
Jenkins, C
Jones, R W
Kemp, D M
King, D J
King, S K F
Lakasing, E
Larkworthy, A J
Lawman, S H A
Macdonald, K M
McKerrow, M B
Maclaurin, R E
Mahmood, B
Mansfield, C P
Mason, M J
Maxwell, P R
Messer, C P
Middleton, F R I
Milledge, J S
Milledge, J T
Miller, D C
Moon, A J
Moon, J V
Nathwani, A C
Owston, E W W
Pavagadhi, B
Pearce, R M
Pollock, B J
Pollock, D J
Rajani, B
Rajani, V
Riddle, P N
Rope, M E
Sandler, L M
Savani, A C K
Savani, N Y
Scorer, M J S
Sharih, G
Shaw, A P L
Shaw, D G
Shaw, K N
Sheikh, I
Shepherd, D A
Sibbald, A R
Sloper, I M S
Topping, A P
Toy, M J
Toy, R
Viira, J A
Visvanathan, S P
Wakefield, M
Yull, D N
Zane, J N

Riding Mill

Harle, J
Lowden, M
Lowden, T G
Sumerling, M D
Wood, N E

Ringwood

Ansell, G L
Belej, J
Boogert, T H W
Bowry, J
Brigstocke, T W O
Caplan, M D
Cary, M T A
Dean, L C
Denman, Y L
Downes, P G C
Elewa, A A-E-H M
Eyles, N
Fautley, M
Francis, M
Gayer, A H
Gemmell, R J
Goodwin, P G
Greatrex, A J
Henshelwood, J A
Hughes, D C C
James, J
James, P A
Kitchin, J C
Kneen, J A
Laband, K M
Langford, D P
Lassetter, J
Lewis, D
Mason, J D

Mathews, C A
Mavor, W O
Nelson, R
North, J
Randall, R J
Robertson, G M
Rouse, E H
Sahlmann, L
Sandeman, J C
Shaw, C H
Shield, N B
Sizmur, F M
Spark, E D
Spencer, A
Taylor, K N
Taylor, S J
Thompson, S P
Trapnell, J E
White, F J
Wilson, E A
Withey, J S
Woodforde, A R
Wormald, P J
Wyse, S D

Ripley

Aspinall, J W
Elliott, L M
Gillatt, D C
Holliday, H
Horsfield, M F A
Jones, M D
Newport, S M
Nightingale, S L
Pett, A N
Tompkinson, J M
Walker, A
Wilkinson, M J
Williams, P A
Wordley, A R

Ripon

Abbott, G R
Akester, H A
Backhouse, P K
Bennett, C J
Bigham, R L O
Bradshaw, E M
Bradshaw, J D
Brown, I G C
Burton, H V
Crawshaw, H M
Davies, W M
Dexter, D
Dickson, P J L
Fletcher, C H
Fletcher, J V
Foggitt, P
France, J K
Gardner, J M
Gregson, J
Grenfell, R C
Harford-Cross, E S
Harford-Cross, M
Hendry, F
Higson, R H
Hill, D R
Holden, L G
Holmes, V A
Holroyd, A
Ingram, A J
Jeary, D
Ledger, J L
Lightowler, C D R
Livingstone, A M
Livingstone, P R
McDowall, M S
McEvoy, C W R
McEvoy, P A E
MacTaggart, M R
Mansfield, R J R
Martindale, A D
Moss, S L
Philip, P F
Prowse, M-J C
Richardson, J O
Robinson, J F
Rowlatt, B
Saunders, I G G
Saunders, M
Thwaites, R
Webb, C B
Whitefield, T D

Robertsbridge

Bel-Eliezer, E J
Clark, J S
Comer, U
Elliot-Pyle, E M
Greenfield, P R

Hooton, N S
Land, R C
Metcalf, Y M
Mills, M
Raven, S C
Shalhoub, J T

Rochdale

Abdelatti, M O
Adler, K M
Alier Laplana, C
Anglin, J T
Ansari, A S
Archibald, L J
Ariyawansa, I
Aslam, R
Ayub, G H
Azam, M U
Babar, I K
Babbs, S L
Barnes, B W
Bauerova, O
Beard, M J
Birkett, J A
Blumenthal, I
Bodner, A
Boldus, M
Bowden, A P
Bowker, D M
Bradgate, M G
Bradley, R S D
Brunt, C V
Budhoo, M R
Caldwell, B M
Cartmill, T D I
Chakrabarti, B
Chatterjea, A
Choudary, V R
Clinton, S T
Cohen, P R
Collighan, S J
Coupe, M O
Crook, A J
D'Vaz, G A
Dalal, V D
Dave, P N
Dawes, S A
Day, A S
De Silva, S
Dhanawade, V
Doshi, M R
Doshi, R M
Doyle, J S
Eastwood, A S
Edmond, N L
El-Sayegh, A Y H
Elliott, J T
Emerson, C E
Etherington, J G
Falk, S
Feeney, E C
Feeney, E C
Firstbrook, K J
Fletcher, M F
Flook, D J
Forman, M L
Forman, P C B
Foster, D N
Fraser, A M A
Gangahar, R
Ghafoor, M B
Ghosh, N
Gibson, A
Gilchrist, J
Gill, N T
Gillighan, J C V
Godbole, M K
Godbole, S
Greenwood, E
Grice, J R G
Guest, K L
Gunn, A C
Haines, L J
Halstead, J C
Hampson, L A
Haq, M I-U
Hargreaves, M R
Harrington, M
Harris, V J
Hartley, R H
Higgs, E L
Hilmi, F G
Horrocks, J E
Horton, J N
Hossack, G F W
Hudson, D J
Humphrey, C S
Ibbotson, G P
Irfan, A

Javid, M A
Jolly, C D
Jones, P E
Kalcev, B
Kasperowicz, R E
Keighley, J
Kelly, J S
Khan, A
Khoo, S M
Kidd, R J G
Knight, M T N
Kourah, M A E A K A
Lacey, H B
Lewis, B
Lomax, P M
McCallum, S J
McFarlane, A R T
McGregor, P A
Mamman, P S
Mani, J
Mansfield, D J
Martin, J E
Mather, J M
Maxwell, S M Y
Mazumder, J K
Meagher, V M C
Miller, P B
Morley, T L
Morris, A P
Morse, J C
Munsadia, I D
Neill, R
Nelson, J J
Nott, M G
Nrialike, P O
O'Byrne, E P M
O'Doherty, M-A
O'Reilly, M A
Osborne, D C
Padwell, A
Paska, L M
Patterson, L J
Platts, H F M
Platts, T S
Porter, R H
Prakash, N G
Purnell, E M
Purnell, L W
Quinn, S J
Rai, S
Raja, R S
Ransome, J A
Rauf, A
Razzaq, A
Razzaq, F
Reynolds, D
Rhodes, S M
Rimmer, D R
Roberts, A P
Roberts, M G
Rose, J A
Rothery, S P
Rowlands, P
Rowlands, P
Sankar, D
Sarginson, J
Sarkar, U
Sermin, N H
Singh, S
Sivakumar, S
Slack, C J
Smith, E E
Smithard, D J
Solomon, P
Speed-Andrews, S C
Stratton, F J
Sundar, M S
Swamy, G N
Taraphdar, S
Taylor, D A
Taylor, G S E
Taylor, J L
Taylor, K J
Thomas, K T
Thomason, F W
Thomson, A A G
Thornton, A J
Threlfall, A E
Tierney, E
Tierney, P B
Travis, S E
Turner, W D W
Tutton, E V M
Verity, L J
Verity, R H
Vidyavathi, M
Vose, M J
Walker, D I
Walton, K

Warrington, S
Winarso, P
Worsell, K E
Zafar, S S
Zaklama, M S
Zeb Khan, A

Rochester

Abbott, M A S
Agarwal, G C
Agarwal, V
Avasthi, A
Baht, H S
Balachander, C S
Bannar-Martin, B R
Beech, N
Bhatia, V K
Birdi, J S
Brophy, J V
Carman, D H
Chakrabarti, B
Clarke, J D
Colbert, T S
De Jong, N S
Dhindsa, A S
Dray, N H
Elman, H A
Etheridge, H E
Farebrother, M J B
Fargher, G
Fisher, J A
Fitzwater, T A
Gandhi, N S
Gandhi, S S
Gee, S
Gilbert, P H
Grace, J F
Grant, N M
Green, P H
Hand, K W
Hart, I J
Harte, M R
Hothi, D K
Hubbard, D C
Hull, S E
Indrasenan, N
James, B J
Jaskmanicki, B Z
Jennings, V M
Johnson, H S
Kunasingam, V
Ladd, H C
Lee, K W
Liem, D B
Lobo, V J E D
Loftus, R C
Lonsdale, J K
MacDonald, R P C
McKeever, G
Mara, H K-M
Martin, G
Minhas, R
Moller, H K
Monsell, R M T
Munasinghe, D W S
Murtagh, F E M
Oliver, D J
Osman, A E A A E M
Parkes, N M
Parnell, C J
Pattanayak, K
Perks, B P W
Phillips, J V
Phillips, L J
Pile, N R
Pimm, J
Pimm, J
Prashad, H H
Premaratne, R V
Rahman, M S
Ralph, M D
Rao, V P
Ray, J N
Redman, J H
Rigby, C H L
Sadik, S R
Sahota, M
Salter, A G
Sastry, M R
Shall, L
Shamshad, S
Shepherd, D C
Shroff, B J
Siddiqi, M A
Spinks, J T W
Stewart, A J
Story, P S
Tanday, J S
Tandon, S L

Rotherham

Thompson, D S
Weeks, J H
Wheeler, A K
Wood, A E
Yeates, F A
Zafar, T

Rochford
Adams, D P
Adams, M S M
Alcock, G S
Birt, R C
Black, A K
Bone, A R
Boylan, M D
Burton, C H
Cobbett, S A
Cordess, W S C
Edwards, A
Fisher, F W
Griffin, G V
Konstantinidou, M
Langan, B C
Nestoridis, G
Puzey, A J
Rothnie, N D
Saville, M J
Shelswell, J H
Singh, B
Tanqueray, A B
Thorne, T C
Timmins, D J G

Romford
Abbas, A M A
Acheson, D C
Adams, G G W
Adhami, Z N
Ahmad, I H
Ahmad, M
Ahmed, S
Akramul Haq, A K M
Al-Okati, D A K A G
Al-Sabti, A H A-R
Al-Saffar, A A
Ali, M M
Ashworth, K L
Aspinall, R W
Aspoas, A R
Baldry, S J
Bampoe, S A
Banan, H
Barua, I
Barua, J M
Bass, D J
Bathool, R
Beddoe, R J
Benjamin, J C
Bhatt, S M
Biassoni, L
Bintcliffe, C J
Bond, S L
Boralessa, H
Boutros, N W M
Brain, A J S
Brownell, A I
Burack, R J
Burke, S J
Burnham, W R
Carabott, F
Chakrabarti, P K
Chakrabarty, B K
Chakravarty, K K
Chawla, J S
Clarke, G R
Coker, A A
Colvin, D A
Coyle, P J
D'Souza, B
D'Souza, J B
Dews, I M
Dinah, A F
Dodd, H J
Dossett, A C
Douglas, M M
Duffy, T M
Duggins, K E
Dungu, R W
Dunnett, S R
El-Hihi, M A
Elian, M
Ellis, N
Ernst, D M
Ernst, M R
Fahal, I H
Falconer, D T
Farrow, R E
Feldman, A
Feldman, M R

Findley, L J
Forster, D M C
Fowler, R W
Fuks, K
Gamble, H P
Garvan, C J
Gbelee, H O
Gershuny, A R
Gibbs, S J
Gilbert, I
Gill, D S
Gill, K S
Goonetilleke, U K D A
Grant, R W
Gupta, N K
Halim, A
Hamilton-Smith, J A
Hamilton, D M
Hampshire, P A
Harris, E
Hartley, S J M
Haskell, K J
Haskell, S J
Hawkes, C H
Hawkes, M
Heylen, V F M
Holden, S T R
Hollanders, F D
Hossain, M N
Hughes, A S B
Irtiza-Ali, A S
Ismail, W W M
Jabbar, A
Jayapal, P
Jeevan, S K
Jibrin, U F
Jones, A C N
Kadr, H H
Kakad, J C
Kapoor, S C
Keefe, J V
Kellerman, A J
Kelsey, C R
Khoo, D E S A
King, A P
King, R J
Knowlson, H A
Kuchhai, N A
Kumar, S
Lakeman, M A
Lang-Stevenson, A I
Lauchlan, M
Leahy, M J
Lecamwasam, D A G
Leigh-Collyer, N
Liu, S H
Lloyd-Thomas, J F
Lord, C J
McDonald, A R
McDonald, H F
MacLellan, G E
Marks, C T C
Marshall, A K
Martin, E E V
Masilamani, N S
Masud, P F
Matthews, R M S
Mazumdar, S
Mehta, K J
Mehta, R M
Mikhael, M S H
Moffat, M
Muir, A
Myers, P C
Nair, I
Namnyak, S S
Nehra, D
Newell, S J
Nigam, S C
O'Doherty, C A
Ola, A O
Oldfield, R H
Palit, S
Patel, A N
Patel, A M
Patel, H D
Patel, L M
Patel, S H
Patel, V J
Patel, V M
Pathak, M L
Pathak, S K
Pemberton, N C
Poologanathan, S
Prasad, J
Prasad, R S
Rabindra-Anandh, K
Rao, N R
Raychaudhuri, D

Roy-Choudhury, D
Roy Chowdhury, S
Roy, K K
Saeed, I T
Saharay, M
Saheecha, B S
Saini, G S
Salisbury, J A
Samaratunga, R D
Sathanandan, M
Satsangi, P N
Saunderson, E M
Schwartz, M
Scowen, B
Selvarajan, M
Shamil, A S A R
Sharma, A
Singh, R R
Sircar, M
Smith, M A
Soneye-Vaughan, F T
Spencer, G M
Srivatsa, S S
Storey, V C
Subramanian, G
Szollar, J
Taghizadeh, A
Tang, C Y K
Tang, K H
Tang, K H
Tanna, K
Tate, P A
Tebbutt, I H
Teckham, P N S
Teotia, N P S
Thompson, R J
To, M S
Toms, G C
Tore, V B
Twardzicki, H M L
Udo, E A
Utidjian, M R A
Viswanath, M
Wajid, A
Wand, L G R
Wareham, D W
Werren, J P
Wickramasinghe, L
Wickramasinghe, L S P
Wyganowska, M E T
Yusuf, H A
Zachariah, S R

Romney Marsh
Bonnard, M A
Bridges, M L M
Codlin, R M S
Cullen, R F
Davies, R B
Downie, P L
Hatcher, A
Kanegaonkar, V G
Mahmood, S
Simpson, R A H

Romsey
Abbott, R M
Abbott, T R
Akerman, F M
Akerman, H F
Allen, S M
Bamford, S L
Barratt, J A
Bland, E P
Bovett, E J
Brennan, P A
Briggs, S W P
Brodie, T R C
Burge, D M
Burn, A J
Burn, P R
Burrows, C J
Burrows, P J
Cecil, T D
Charlton, G A
Chinn, J D
Clunie, R W D
Dale, P G
Davis, A J M
Dawkins, K D
Deane, M H
Dempster, J G
Dempster, W J
Dubras, L A
Duckworth, M J
Edwards, A J
Edwards, J C
Entwisle, I D
Facer, J L

Ferguson, H J
Fitzgerald, J A W
Friedmann, P S
Gillam, P M S
Glanville, J D
Gould, J
Haig, P S
Henderson, E M
Herbertson, M J
Husband, A D
Iles, D J B
Johnson, A D S
Johnson, C E M
Johnson, P G S
Keightley, M A
Keith, I A
Kelly, S R
Kenyon, J B
Kirby, C M
Lalonde, A K
Lambert, E J
Lawrence, M
Leftley, P
Lowndes, K E
Lowndes, S A
McCarthy, A H S
Mitchell, M L
Mooney, A
Neal, J C
Newell Price, R J
Parry-Jones, O J C
Patel, J
Peace, R H
Pearson, C F
Peebles, C R
Platt, M R
Porter, J M
Powell, J A
Prosser, Y I J
Radford, M
Rands, D A
Roberts, L J
Rowe, R G
Royce, C M
Russell-Smith, R
Rutter, D V
Scott, J G
Steer, H W
Still, M A
Summerhayes, M W
Talbutt, A J
Thomas, C P
Tippett, S A
Varney, P R
Veall, R M
Warner, G
Warner, K J
Watson, A J
Wattie, J N
Wedderburn, A W
Wedderburn, C
White, P J
Williams, M T
Winn, C R
Wise, B G
Wright, I C
Yearsley, J K N
Yorston, J C
Yorston, M B
Zeitlin, S R

Roslin
Chambers, M
Guette, J
Hunter, A R A
McIntosh, L G
Pope, J D K

Ross-on-Wye
Brown, R J K
Budd, M
Carruthers, B
Clark, A S G
Clayton, P F
Cochrane, G M
Cook, J M
Cook, R J
Craddock, K H
Crosland, S J
D'Arcy, B L
Davis, E T
Downey, P F
Fletcher, J A
Fletcher, J L M
Fuller, R C
Hartshorn, C R
Hayward, R J
Janis, N B
Jardine, M A

Jones, G A
King, P A
Leeman, A J
McConnell, H D S
Marlowe, G T S
Mellor, R J
Menon, L
Parker, A G
Parker, R H O
Parsons, K C
Parsons, S A
Price, I M S
Richards, J L
Rogers, A J
Sanderson, R M F
Seymour, W R D
Silver, S N
Townsend, A J
Wallace, J R C
Wingate, A P
Wyllie, B W

Rossendale
Ainsworth, C J
Babicki, J W
Berrisford, S B
Bunting, J
Chaudhuri, P
Chauhan, U
Cheesmond, E H D
Choudhry, T W
Coates, M J
Dennison, A R
Doherty, D M
Gill, M S
Grimshaw, M E
Grover, M
Hardie, C J
Hinchliffe, W S
Karoo, R O S
Kermode, A G
King, B
Lamberty, D S
Lee, J B
Lord, J S
Moustafa, A E-F M
Ormrod, J
Pettigrew, R C B
Power, M P
Price, D G
Quero Heredia, F J
Ramsden, A
Reddy, V
Rishton, P
Scott, P D
Sellens, G S
Sibley, A C
Smurthwaite, G J
Wray, M B

Rotherham
Abbas, A M A
Abbey, S J
Abdul, K A C
Abed, R T
Agnew, J F
Ahmed, T M
Ainsworth, G
Akram, A
Al-Jubouri, M A M
Alexander, M C
Allaqaband, G Q
Amos, M W
Anderton, K J
Aravindakshan, K K
Avery, G C
Bader, M S
Baker, J L
Balch, K J
Bardhan, K D
Barker, H F
Barker, W E
Barragry, L F
Basran, G S
Beck-Samuels, P R
Beck, S
Bhamra, M
Bhan, B
Bhimpuria, Y R
Black, J F
Brynes, R M
Bulugahapitiya, D T D
Bulugahapitiya, D S
Burns, S B
Capehorn, M S
Casapieri, M
Chakrabarti, I
Chambers, G
Charity, R M

Chattopadhyay, S
Clark, M C
Clark, T J
Clarke, P J
Coates, J W
Cole, A J
Collinson, P C
Collinson, R C A
Cooper, C A
Cooper, J C
Core, J B
Corrie, G R
Cronly, J P
Crosher, R F
Crowley, G E
Dibb, S
Dudani, P V
Durkan, A M
Dziemidko, H E
Essmaili Shad, J
Everett, B J
Faruq, A
Fawthrop, F W
Fearnside, J E
Fenton, D W
Ford, J B
Forster, M D
Fulbrook, R D
Galvin, J
Ganguli, A
George, W A S
Ghosh, M K
Goel, P K
Goni, A-U-H
Gopinath, M K
Grant, J
Green, N T W
Griffith, P C
Grover, S R L
Haddad, A Q
Hallinan, J A
Hallinan, M J
Hargan, M H
Harkness, P A
Harris, J C
Harrison, C J
Harvey-Dodds, L M
Harvey, L
Haste, A R
Hayes, G D
Hewson, F P B
Hillier, M J
Hinchliffe, R F C
Holt, M E
Hood, H L
Hulley, C M
Husain, M H
Hussain, N
Hutson, C A
Hyndman, N
Islam, M B
Isshak, N S
Jacob, L
Jarjis, H A
Jarvis, H
Jayaswal, B N
Jayaswal, R
Jespersen, S B
Jesson, A J
Jones, B A
Jones, C M
Jones, R B
Jubb, A S
Kamath, M K
Kapur, B
Kapur, R
Kear, C S J
Keith, A J
Kesseler, M E
Khan, Z A
Khonsari, M
Kitlowski, J A
Kitto, W D
Lai, D
Lambertz, M M
Lancer, J M
Latimer, J G
Lavric, J
Lee, J A
Lee, S D
Leese, G J
Levey, C
Littlewood, A J
Livingstone, F D M
Luker, B C H
Lyle, H M
McAndrew, P G
McCrea, P H
MacFarlane, P I

Rothesay

McKessack, J J
McSweeney, E E
McWhinnie, R N
Mahadevan, S
Mahon, D
Majumdar, P
Manson, P R
Martin, P L
Matthews, P J
Mellor, A D
Mendelson, E F
Miller, M
Mirza, B B
Mohammed Ismail Kadar Sha, S H
Mohsini, A A
Mondal, A A
Mondal, B K
Moore, T
Mosharaf, A
Muirhead, R J
Mukhopadhyay, T K
Muthusamy, R
Myers, C P
Neal, F E
Neal, M M
Nemeth, G
Nesha, M
Newby, D M
Norris, E A
Nussbaumer, A
Nussbaumer, M
Ogden, A D
Oji, E O
Oliver, P P
Paes, A
Pal, N K
Parkin, D
Parys, B T
Patel, N A
Peckitt, G B
Phillips, S
Plews, D J
Polkinghorn, D G
Price, R E
Proctor, J C C
Qureshi, H
Rabbani, A A M Z
Raha, H D
Ralph, J F
Reddy, S V
Redgrave, A P
Rees, A J S
Reid, H C
Robson, M J
Rosenberg, B C
Salfield, S A W
Salim, F
Sanders, J A
Sayed, Z
Selson, M G
Sen, S R
Shankar, D
Shorland, J E
Shrivastava, O P
Shrivastava, R
Simpson, E W
Sinha, A K
Smaling, A P
Smith, G
Smith, G W
Spencer, P A S
Spooner, S F
Stacey, R K
Stott, D R
Suckling, R J
Suri, S S
Swallow, M B
Tan Hark Hong, K
Taylor, M A
Taylor, P C
Thakkar, B C
Thambirajah, S
Thomas, P G
Thompson, J S
Thornton, R J
Trend, U
Tucker, D E
Turner, E B
Van Mulders, K
Vatish, M
Velamail, V
Venables, M
Venkatraman, T B
Venkiteswaran, N T
Viney, M J
Viswesvaraiah, M
Wallis, C B
Warren, G C
Wilson, D H
Wood, M L
Zaidi, A A
Zubairu, M B

Rothesay

Berrich, A S
Campbell, R S
Clark, R D
Cunningham, W R
Herriot, D T
Howie, E A
Howie, T J G
Jerome, J M C
Kapoor, B L
Mackenzie, A R
Morton, J S
Morton, T C
Peden, A T
Ritchie, E R J
Robertson, A D
Thomas, M B

Rowlands Castle

Bacon, M T
Bee, B H
Boswell, C M
Collett, P M
Coni, H J A
Francis, J G
Harrison, J R
James, S P
Jones, M P
Neal-Mayall Derks, J A M
Pounder, D
Sissons, J P
Sissons, M P
Williams, M
Wilson, C J
Wren, M W G
Wren, S M E
Young, J R B

Rowlands Gill

Armstrong, P A
Bell, E U
Blair, S
Cassels, A O
Dawson, R T
Dobson, R
Holiday, J E
Imlah, M
Liddle, A B G
Malley, R
Mercer-Jones, M A
Quigley, P J L
Smith, G J
Turner, P

Rowley Regis

Gold, D V
Riley, J P M
Youngson, E M

Roy Bridge

Langan, H A
Macleod, F

Royston

Alderton, D A
Anderson, C R
Bambrick, M
Barnett, S J
Beadsmoore, C J
Brand, A J
Brierley, D M
Brownrigg, M R
Burnford, A M
Cairns, N J W
Clubb, T C
Coladangelo, R C
Connolly, G A
Dancey, F M L
Dancey, G S
Foster, J E
Freedman, D J
Gillespie, J P
Gough, P
Greatrex, S J
Hacon, D S
Handcock, L J
Hay, R N
Hedges, J R
Hedges, S J
Holding, T A
Hone, M P
Hughes Jones, N C
Hughes, E G
Inman, R D
Kothari, M P
Langdale-Brown, M E

Leighton, T J
Lilley, M E
Limbrey, R M
Linnett, P J
Llewellyn, L J
Lobo, A A X
McCormick, A R
MacDonald-Smith, W M G
Maciver, C A
McQuaid, A
Mann, T A N
Mawe, J F
Maxim, R E G
Morris, S J
Polge, C M
Riddell, A J
Rigney, A T
Rodda, L C
Rosser, D M
Stansfield, A J
Taylor, C J A
Taylor, J C
Upward, J W
Van Terheyden, K M R
Walker, W E
Watkins, G D
Wickens, L C
Williams, O A
Wright, J F

Rugby

Abu Samra, M I
Ahluwalia, J S
Al Moudaris, M M A D
Ashby, J M
Atwal, T S
Aulakh, J M S
Balasubramaniam, T S
Barhey, J S
Barhey, N K
Bartram, G F
Bedi, S S
Bemand, B V
Berridge, E M
Biggs, P I
Black, D
Blundstone, D L
Branscombe, F M
Bridgeman, K
Brittain, R D
Brown, S L
Canale-Parola, A
Carne, D R
Carroll, I C
Cartwright, J C
Carvill, S C
Clemons, K R
Cook, N J
Corbey, M T
Cotterill, J W
Cree, S J
Cumming, E J
Czerniewski, I W D
D'Mello, M S
Dahmash, F H
De Veer, G E
Deliyannis, S N
Derrick, J C A
Dhillon, D P
Dinmore, P
Douse, H E
Douse, J E
Draper, I B
Ducharme, A L
Ducharme, W A
Duckitt, K
Edgar, K J
Edmunds, E V
Eedle, E K
Farrington, J
Fielding, W J
Gallagher, B
Gammell, H J B
Gaunt, R M
Goddard, J A
Gostick, N K
Griffiths, R L M
Harvey, A J
Hayward, P W
Henderson, K M
Hodges, L M-C
Holcroft, P J
Holdsworth, R K
Hooke, R L
Houghton, M P
Howell, R S C
Hunter, J A
Illing, R C

Ingram, D A
Jacoby, M N J
Jaron, S J
Jones, J H
Kavuri, S B
Khan, S
Kilvert, P J
Koria, A P
Leach, K J
McDonagh, M J
Margetts, M J
Menon, M R G
Mervin, L A
Miarkowski, R F
Miller, P J
Mistry, D K
Mohamed, W N A E-R
Morris, P
Moule, I
Naidoo, P
Nethisinghe, S
Nethisinghe, S K N
Nigam, B K
O'Hare, J P
Oates, A E
Oláh, K S J
Pannell, B M B
Parker, J R
Parmar, K B
Parsons, A D
Patel, B D
Patel, J N
Porter, D I
Raj, S
Rao, P C
Ray-Chaudhuri, D S
Ray-Chaudhuri, S B
Ray-Chaudhuri, S
Rees, W D
Reynolds, K M
Ribeiro, A A
Richards, S M
Roberts, E J
Rowe, R L
Rye, K A
Saeed, I
Seaman, T F
Shields, G G
Shore, D J
Sinha, R K
Sivapathasuntharam, L
Smith, A J
Tassadaq, T
Thangkhiew, I
Thomas, J D
Twomey, J
Tyagi, D C
Vaile, C L
Veysey, S L
Ward, C
Waterworth, T A
West, C A
Williams, J M
Willis, S A
Wright, M J A
Young, K D

Rugeley

Ansell, G J
Bevan, K W
Boyce, K E
Boyd, N W
Crawford, C D
Davies, N A
Deb, K
Deb, S
Garden, T B
Ibrahim, I H
James, R L
Kyte, D E
Light, L
Longbotham, R C
MacMonagle, P J
Middleton, M A
Mirsadgady, S Y
O'Hara, H
Price, M A B
Rastogi, N C
Sivanesan, V N
Sorrell, J A
Stokes, M J

Ruislip

Abedin, S
Abedin, S S
Ahmed, S
Allen, J A
Andrews, R D
Ansari, R

Aurora, R P
Baines, J D
Berral Redondo, M A
Bhattacharya, M
Brewerton, J M
Brunner, P C
Cain, P A
Chandok, H S
Chandok, R S
Coe, D F
Conn, G E
Connell, S E
Cox, C A
Dangoor, H E L
Duncan, R J
Feast, M J
Feuer, D J
Garg, R
Hobbs, J R
Hobbs, W G R
Howells, B J
Howells, B R
Howells, J B
Jaggi, S K
Jayakumar, R
Joseph, P F
Kaplan, V
Karim, A
King, M N R
Lama, A K
Latif, M A
Laycock, E V
Liberman, M
Livingstone, J A
McDermott, I D
Marriott, A M
Mashru, M K
Morgan-Jones, D V
Nettleton, C L
Newbery, S R
Parsonage, S M
Patel, P B
Pocock, D I G
Price Williams, D A
Price-Williams, R D
Raj, L
Raj, N
Rennie, M
Sharma, A K
Siddiqui, M L R
Sojka, Y J F
Solomon, C M
Solomon, J I
Timmis, C G
Tint Lwin, Dr
Westbury, H
Wilkinson, A E
Williams, A A

Runcorn

Abbott, P M
Allen, C M
Barendt, A B
Bell, B T
Bladen, C
Bohra, P K
Bohra, U
Burns, S J
Canfield, C J
Chapelhow, S J
Colin-Thome, D G
Conway, J D
Corrado, K M
Davies, H M
El-Sergany, A Y
Ewing, R
Fearon, H P
Flanagan, P J
Frith, A G B
Frood, R A W
Gibson, J
Green, B H
Green, M H P
Jenkins, R J
Johnson, J N
Jowett, S L
Kearney, M J
Khaleeli, A A
La Frenais, W S L
McDermott, D
Mallya, R K
Morgan, G J
Mottram, S A
Moulana, N
Munnoch, D A
Munnoch, N A M
Murphy, G J
Murphy, M G
Newey, J A

O'Hara, P J
O'Malley, J E
Orpin, M M
Otiv, S
Perumainar, M
Pollet, J E
Pollet, S M
Richards, C
Rose, E L
Rylance, J M
Saksena, M K
Sandhu, H S
Savin, P T
Sen, R A
Shehu, T
Skinner, J M
Smyth, M D L
Staples, B
Staunton, T
Teebay, L E
Thorpe, M J L
Trevor, A J
Ugwu, C N
Watson, C A
White, C J
Wild, A-M
Williams, J G
Williamson, J C
Wilson, D H
Wreglesworth, J K
Zurek, A A A

Rushden

Appleyard, J H
Barber, V E
Branford, M
Burch, A J
Clarke, H L
Druce, J M
Duncan, A M
Fairweather, N J
Findlay, J B
Hadden, P E
Hanspaul, A S
Hogg, S J
Kelly, J J
Reading, J H
Richards, D J
Ritchie, A F
Simpson, R A
Subramaniam, M K
Thomas, T
Williams, D G

Ruthin

Anderson, J I
Barrie, A R
Barrie, N
Birkin, P J
Carey, G E
Davies, R G
Evans, C E J
Higgitt, A
Humphreys, H I
Jones, C W L
Powell, T P S
Prys-Jones, O E
Roberts, G H
Roberts, L G R
Seddon, J G W
Tudor, N L

Ryde

Arthure, J E
Atine-Okello, M L
Bainbridge, G
Beable, A E
Boyd, N A
Brown, R E
Burton, G E W
Cooney, K D
Craig, A
De Belder, M J K
Denman-Johnson, M
Donaldson, P J
Duncan, G S
Edsall, K C
Foster, R J
Fullerton, J R
Goodwin, P E
Green, A J
Griffin, A J G
Griffiths, S C
Hare, D M
Harrison, W P
Harvey, E L
Hazell, M
Hazell, Y E
Hughes, E J
Jain, B K

Salisbury

Kangatharan, A
Kirk, J A D
Laidlaw, E F
Lammiman, D A
Legg, M D
McKay, D J
Mackett, J
McNeal, A D
Majumdar, B
Majumdar, K
Manning, C J F
Martin, A
Meltzer, J E
Orchard, K H
Osborn-Smith, E H
Osman, B E D I A E M
Perry, D
Porteous, A C
Pradhan, N S
Rees, B S J
Rezk, R N
Ridout, S M
Roberts, J D A
Rogers, J M C
Rudwick, A L
Shah, B K
Sim, D J
Sim, P G
Sutherland, H B
Symes, J M
Taylor, B A
Vijaya Kumar, M N
Walker, V G
Wellington, P E
Williams, R C

Rye

Carroll, J
Chishick, H B J
Craig, C M
Dyson, A J
Ealand, W
Farquharson, A D J
Ferguson, N J
Griffin, A L
Halpin, K D
Harris, G M
James, L P
James, P M
Jeelani, M S W
Jeelani, R A
Lahaise, J E H
Lloyd, M E
Martens, M J
Meares, D E
Neale, D V
Neilson, W R
Pennefather, M E
Pitcher, C S
Rae, S J
Rogers, M C
Stoddart, A P
Ticehurst, R N

Ryton

Bosman, D L
Brown, S J
Carter, L J
Chapman, S W
Doshi, A
Goundry, G G R
Greenough, K R
Hilton, S M
Johnson, M A
Kneale, B N
Moylett, E M
Phillips, M K
Priestley, A C
Purvis, J
Richardson, J

Saffron Walden

Alsos, B
Bassett, J H D
Brand, F J
Brown, C
Brown, J D
Chalmers, R B
Clayton Payne, C D
Cowley, C
De Weerd, J M
Dixon, R M
Eaton, C J
Elliott, P M
Ellis, J C
Evans, D R
Fanning, J K
Fox, T D C
Gande, A R
Gordon, G C

Gourlay, C M
Hill, E B
Hope-Stone, H F
Huey, K A
Humphrey, S M
Jackson, A P
Kendall, W N G
Lort, D J
Lort, E A
Milne, C
O'Donnell, P N S
Pagano, K
Paul, C C
Pegum, J S
Preston, L J
Rockley, P A
Rumsey, S
Shires, S E
Shortt, E
Sills, P R
Smith, A E R
Stephens, C J
Stevens, M N
Stirland, R M
Villar, B L B
Walter, F M
Warner, M W
Weir, J J

Salcombe

Barnicoat, K T N
Hett, W J B
Hummel, J P F
McLarty, E W
McLarty, E
Mallett, J M
Merritt, J K
Rowse, E A
Saxby, N V
Stanley, H W
Twining, D H
Wilks, J M

Sale

Abraham, A P
Al-Hakim, A H A
Ansari, S M M J
Armshaw, K L
Ayuk, T-Y P
Banait, G S
Barlow-Hitchen, S
Berry, J P
Booth, A F
Bradley, B L
Braganza, D M R
Broadfield, E-J C
Broomfield, D J
Brotherton, M J
Buckley, P
Bungay, P M
Burdett-Smith, C B
Burke, Y L
Burley, E R
Burley, R M W
Campbell, N
Carlile, D
Chakrabarty, K H
Chandraker, A K
Chatterjee, A
Chattopadhyay, T K
Cherian, A
Cherian, R
Curtis, M D
Datta, J
Davies, L A
Davis, J D
Davis, N
Denton, P F G
Devine, J C
Dollery, W C
Drake, D J
Driver, C P
Edmondson, D L
Edwards, D L
Ellison, A J
Evans, J D
Frier, S R
Gasiorowski, E R
Gayen, A K
Geggie, D A R
Gilbody, M S
Grace, P M
Gray, P A
Grice, J A
Griffith, J L M
Grubb, F
Gwanmesia, I L
Hall, C N
Hall, P J

Hall, V
Hockenhull, N J
Holloway, M J
Holzel, H S
Jackson, N D
Jackson, P A
Jamal, A F
Jarvis, M A
Johnson, K
Jonas, M P
Jones, J H
Jones, P H
Jones, R G G
Joseph, A
Jowitt, S N
Khan, A Y
Kim, J B
Kirk, S R
Knowlson, G T G
Kocialkowski, A
Labarre, S M
Larkin, B A
Lavin, J M
Lawson, R A M
Leyland, H E
Loftus, N A
Lupton, E W
McBride, T P
MacDermott, N J G
McGarry, M B A
Macheta, M P
McIntyre, I G
McKaigue, O J
McMahon, C
Macmillan, F T
Marchi, C J B
Mazeika, P K
Moley, F M
Moorhead, T
Musgrave, S R
Needham, S B
Ngan, C Y
O'Connor, M M
O'Malley, G
O'Reilly, M H
Olojugba, O H
Platt, G
Pope, V
Porter, S
Ramamurthy, L
Raynor, M K
Regan, D M
Riley, D J
Riley, L
Robertson, E F
Roy Choudhury, S
Royle, J S
Saad, E S M
Sabeti, M
Sarangi, K K
Schofield, R P
Schraibman, I G
Sehat, K R
Shaath, N M
Shackcloth, M J
Shahid, J
Sheikh, J Y
Simpson, P M A
Skrzypiec-Allen, A I
Smith, C J
Smith, R
Smithurst, H J
Stokes, J M
Stone, D R
Sutton, K J
Swain, D R
Taylor, C R
Taylor, N R
Tebb, J B T
Tierney, N M
Todd, D M
Tunney, P J
Vites, C M
Waldman, E I
Wallis, R L
Watson, D A
Welsh, P J
Williams, G
Williams, R F
Wilson, R G
Yates, A J

Salford

Addlestone, L S
Ahmed, S A
Allan, M W B
Allonby-Neve, C L
Amr, M A Y
Anderson, I D

Anderson, M E
Andrew, J G
Andrew, S M
Ardern, K D
Armstrong, G R
Atkins, M R
Attwood, S E A
Austin, M A
Axon, P R
Babbs, C
Bacall, L
Baishnab, R M
Bancewicz, J
Barnes, P C
Beck, M H
Boland, G P
Bowles, B J M
Brooke, R C C
Brookes, M
Broughton, R B
Buckler, H M
Callender, K
Campbell, F N
Carrington, P A
Carroll, C B
Chadwick, P R
Chan, Y-S
Chetty, M S
Chew, L-C
Chisholm, R A
Chowdhury, H R
Citron, L H
Clarke, N W
Clarke, P
Cohen, D L
Collier, P A
Cooper, R G
Crossland, J A
Das, D N
Dass, B K
Davis, W S
De Silva, A O K L
Deacon, R E
Dick, J P R
Dickson, M J
Dieh, A P T
Dornan, T L
Easty, A M
El Mahmoudi, B K A
Ferguson, J E
Ferguson, J W
Finegan, N A
Finlay, M
Fistein, J
Fitzgerald, D A
Forbes, W S C
Formela, L J
Freed, D L J
Galasko, C S B
Garson, M
Geraghty, I F
Ghosh, P R
Girvent Montllor, M
Gonsalkorale, M
Goodman, K L
Goorney, B P
Griffiths, C E M
Haber, S
Haddad, P M
Haeney, M R
Hague, M E
Haigh, C R
Hansen, L J
Harris, L S D
Hasan, A
Hashmi, S S H
Hassan, I
Heald, A H
Heaton, M J
Herrick, A L
Hilton, R C
Horsman, G
Houghton, J B
Hughes, D G
Hurri, H O
Jackson, S J
Jaffe, E
Jayson, M I V
Jeet, I
Jeffree, J S
Jesudason, P J
Jones, A K P
Jones, I H
Jones, S B
Joseph, L A
Kallis, P F
Kalra, P A
Kassam, N N
Kaushal, T S

Kelly, M C J
Kelly, T
Khaled, M A
Kumar, C
Lakshmi, V
Larah, D G
Larsen, J
Lecky, F E
Levenson, S
Levenson, S
Leventhall, P A
Lewis, H J
Lloyd, R E
Lopian, N H
Lowenson, L F C
McElroy, H
McEvoy, A
McHugh, D F
McInerney, J
Mainwaring, A R
Mann, P G
Marsh, M N
Matlin, A J
Maxwell, H A
Million, R
Mitchell, S J
Morgan, R J
Moss, G E
Muir, L T S W
Munjal, R S
Muston, H L
O'Brien, D P
O'Donoghue, D J
O'Driscoll, B R C
O'Driscoll, D L
Owen, W A
Palmer, J H M
Parkar, W
Parsons, V J
Passey, J L
Pira, A
Polson, D W
Powell, D J
Pramanik, A
Protheroe, R T
Quantrill, S J
Quinn, V P
Railton, A
Raj, V B
Ramachandran, S
Randall, S C
Rees, W D W
Reeve, R S
Rehman, S-U
Richards, D M
Robinson, J A
Robinson, J
Robinson, M J
Rodgers, M E
Rogers, C M
Rosenberg, S E
Ross, E R S
Routledge, R C
Royde, C A
Saleh, N
Salim, A
Saxby, K M
Scott, N A
Shaffer, J L
Shaw, E A
Sherrington, C R
Sibley, Y D L
Simon, S
Slade, R J
Soni, S
Spanswick, C C
Spencer, L G
Staniland, J R
Stewart, M F
Stone, C W
Stout, I H
Strickland, P L
Sultan, M
Sussman, J D
Tallis, R C
Tankel, J W
Telfer, N R
Thomas, A N
Thompson, D G
Tingley, P G R
Trimm, A K
Tucker, S C
Turnbull, I W
Tyrrell, P J
Vadgama, P M
Waldek, S
Wallman, P D
Watt, J W G
Weinkove, C

Wilkins, B
Willatt, D J
Williams, C J
Williamson, J B
Wright, J R
Yates, P A
Zotkiewicz, M J

Salisbury

Adams, R A
Adams, R K
Allen, O B
Anderson, J D C
Angell, G R
Annis, J A D
Ansari, S A A H
Armstrong, W L
Atwell, J D
Baker, C C
Barclay, I H
Barnard, N J B
Barnes, L M
Barnsley, R
Barrett, R F
Barrow, G I
Barter, P P
Barton, G M G
Baskerville, R
Baston, J D
Batten, B
Beaumont, A R
Bechter, M W
Bennett, N J
Bentley, B
Bentley, K L
Beswick, F W
Beswick, R E
Beswick, R W
Boddy, N
Bond, H R L
Borrelli, P B
Bottomley, E L
Box, C J
Bradshaw, T C
Brett, M S
Brock, B H
Brockbank, M J
Brooks, T J G
Brown, R M
Buchanan, P
Burrows, L J
Burrows, N C
Butcher, C
Cadier, M A M
Calvert, S L
Carter, L D G
Carty, N J
Carvell, J E
Chave, H S
China, J M
Church, C
Church, J J
Churchill, R S
Clark, K A
Claydon, P J O
Coats, N L B
Cockroft, S
Cole, R P
Collier, J M
Collier, R G
Collings, E M
Collings, F L W
Collyer-Powell, R G
Cook, M J
Cooke, T J C
Corlett, J C R
Crabbe, R W
Crane, R G
Cullis, J O
Culver-James, J W
Cunliffe, P N
Curzen, P
Dalton, B L P
Dalton, J R
Darlow, H M
Davies, C M
Davies, P C
Davies, T G
Dean, I A M
Dirnhuber, M J
Docherty, P W
Donaldson, A K
Downie, I P
Downing, W B L
Drummond, P
Duggal, J A
Eastman, S V
Easton, J A
Egan, S M

Saltash

Ellis, R M
Eminson, P F
English, J M
Evans, S A
Fell, M R
Fenwick, T
Finnegan, T P
Finnis, D
Flood, T R
Fountain, S A
French, R B
Frost, R A
Fuller, C E
Gailey, M D H
Geddes, J D
Gill, R
Glanville, H J
Glaysher, C M R
Gotham, C R
Gray, M I H
Gready, E M
Green, M J
Gregory, R K
Grieve, M G
Griffiths, M A
Grummitt, W M
Grundy, D J
Guy, P J
Haggis, J F
Hall, A
Hamber, R C
Hands, C A H
Harris, Z E
Hartley, D I
Haselden, F G
Healey, F B
Hebbert, F J
Heeley, G M
Helyer, K A-L
Henderson, F B
Hewetson, R P
Higgins, C S
Hobby, J A E
Hoffman, D E H
Holmes, N
Howgrave-Graham, A J
Howson, W J D
Hudson, J D P
Humphry, R C
Hunt, B W
Illingworth, J B
Inman-Meron, D
Jack, I L
Jagger, G M H
James, T M
Janmohamed, S G
Jewson, T E
Johnson, K A
Jonas, D R C
Jones, A L
Jowett, R
Karkera, R
Kerr, J S
Key, I A
Kidman, L V
Kimmance, K J
Kimmance, S N
King, J V
King, R A
Knapton, A
Lacey, O J
Lack, J A
Laidlaw, F C
Lee, B
Lewis, S J
Lie, S E
Lintin, D J
Lynch, M T
Macalister, S M
Macallister, D
McArthur, P
McCallum, M I D
McDowall, R A W
McGee, S G G
McIntosh, G S
McKenna, D M
Mackie, D B
McKinley, N P
McNee, P A J
McNeill, D C
Macready, L
Mann, R G
Marigold, J H
Markey, T E
Martin, H S
Mash, K M
Maslin, P S
Matthies, F A K

Meader, H L
Meers, P D
Mein, D C
Millar, K N A
Miller, G A H
Mitchell, D M
Moore, M V
Morgan, D R
Morgan, M C
Morris, A D P
Morris, M R
Morse, G R
Mrozinski, W J P
Mullan, D P
Myint, C M
Nazeer, A F
Neame, J H
Nettle, C J
Newton Dunn, A R
Nixon, J M G
Nodder, E M L
Norris, J P
O'Connell, N M
O'Connor, K M
O'Keeffe, T S
Oldrey, T B N
Orchard, J A
Parrott, D
Parry, H F
Parry, R M
Patrick, C T
Patrick, S
Peach, F J
Pelly, H J W
Podkolinski, M T
Pope, J B
Powell, F J
Powell, G A
Powell, M J
Ranaboldo, C J
Ray, M
Ray, R J
Rees-Jones, T G
Rees, E G
Reeve, A P M
Reid, R A
Rice, P
Richards, A M
Richardson, A J
Richardson, W W
Ridley, N H L
Roberts, M J
Robertson, J C
Robertson, M E
Rooney, V
Roper, H M
Rose, M A
Ross Russell, F M
Rossi, L F A
Rushforth, G F
Russell, A M
Russell, D H
Rustom, J W
Rutter, D A
Scott-Jupp, R H
Scott, A H C
Scott, C A
Scott, R P F
Seal, S H
Sears, C A N
Sears, E F
Shankar, U
Sharma, S
Shashidharan, M
Shavren, R E
Shaw, E J
Shemilt, P
Short, P A
Simpson, C L
Simpson, J L
Simpson, R W
Smith, D T M
Smithies, A
Soopramanien, A
Soutar, A J
Spedding, S M
Stanger, E
Stanger, N R Y
Stone, J A S
Stratton, D
Strelitz, N S
Swayne, P
Tadros, S S M
Tait, F G
Tanner, E I
Thomas, M A
Thomas, S D
Thompson, P J
Thorne, B M

Tibbitts, A R
Todd, G B
Tomlin, P J
Tromans, A M
Twyman, D G
Tyers, A G
Tyers, R C B
Tyrrell, B M
Tyrrell, D A J
Urmston, J H B
Viney, P L
Vyas, S K
Vyrnwy-Jones, P
Wallace, A S
Walters, C C
Walters, G
Warley, A R H
Wasti, S A
Waters, E A
Weaver, S A
Webb, A J
Webb, E M
West, P S
Whetham, J M
Whittingham, H W
Wilde, J A
Williams, E H
Williams, E M
Willis, R J
Witts, H M
Wood, C D
Wright, G D S
Wright, J V
Yeoh, M J
Zlotnik, J M C

Saltash

Barnicoat, A
Bearblock, C H
Bearblock, P E
Bleksley, M C
Bliss, B P
Booth, C W
Bowes, P J
Bredemeyer, A
Broad, G A
Broadhead, A D
Brown, C
Charlton, S C
Clayton, P B
Cook, R C
Cundy, A L
Davies, P S
Davis, D W
Devonport, N J
Erith, M J
Evans, C W
Farrant, S J
Fisher, N G
Fox, C L
Fullalove, S
Gall, W J
Gegg, J M
Gilmore, J S
Head, C D
Hopper, M A
Hughes, B D
Jackson, S
Jones, P
Kneen, R C B
Kratky, A P
Lewis, T D
MacLeod, M
Mercer, R F
Moore, J R A
Parrish, J
Parrish, R W
Phypers, M G
Randall, C F
Robinson, G A
Smith, D K
Story, T S
Thomas, W G
Walker, B W M
Webster-Harrison, P J
Weiss, A M

Saltburn-by-the-Sea

Armitage, A
Betterton, M J
Boyes, W
Brew, S H
Britton, I
Brownlee, N H
Burrell, P S R
Clements, B W
Connolly, H M F
Costello, B
Cowan, T R

Dall'Ara, R G
Dunn, C M
Earl, U M
Ebeid, S
Etches, F G
Fish, K P F
Glasby, M S
Greaves, S H L
Guyler, R M
Harris, E E
Harvie, A K
Johnson, S A
Lavelle, P H
Lomas, A C
MacAuliffe, R J
Machender, K
Milner, M L
Neville-Smith, R F
Palumbo, L
Parkin, R A
Saxton, J C R
Shepherd, D J
Strang, A K G
Thomson, A P
Todd, R L
Waite, C J
Wiggins, J C
Wood, R H
Yates, R H T

Saltcoats

Briggs, E J
Forsyth, J
Gray, G H
Hales, D S M
McKinlay, J J
Norton, J C G
Robertson, D I S
Thomson, N O
Timmons, J A

Sandbach

Armitage, A J
Armitage, J D
Armitage, J D
Baker, D L
Baxter, R T
Blair, J L
Broadbent, P J
Brown, S R
Clark, J P
Evennett, A J
Friel, J C
Guildford, M A
Hassall, H
Kinder, A J
Mercer, J D
Miller, M W
Olver, M J
Rao, K S
Robinson, M
SimcOck, P D
Tate, M J
Tebby, S J

Sandhurst

Azurdia, M R
Brown, S N
Cornbloom, M L S
Davies, I Z
Halliwell, R P
Jackson, M B A
Kanjaria, N J
Lyne, J A
Newman, B M
Pidgeon, C A
Routledge, H C
Shivayogi, M
Taylor, N M
Thing, J R
Vakil, A
Wagstaff, J

Sandown

Botell, L T
Botell, R E
Brand, J V
Brand, P
Gent, N R E
Griffiths, A
Jones, J C
McMullen, D J
Moore, J S
Randall, P G
Summerhayes, P J
Trowell, H M

Sandwich

Adam, J M
Allen, M J

Atkinson, S N
Berti, C A
Birchall, C E
Blakeley, C R
Bowen-Davies, P E
Browning, R C
Bruce, A T
Bunsell, R P
Butrous, G S
Carnegie, A M
Carnegie, M R
Child, B G
Colquhoun, K B M
Davies, M J
Davis, A E
Duff, C S
Edwards, M R
Ellis, A J
Geewater, D M J
Greaves, J R
Hargreaves, R M
Harris, G
Healy, C J
Hettiarachchi, J
Hughes, J D
Humpston, D J
Layton, M A
Marchant, B G
Milson, J A
Moriarty, K T
Mridha, K A
Nurbhai, S
Osterloh, I H
Power, A C
Pritchard, G
Roblin, D
Uden, S
Whitehead, A M
Wismayer, E C

Sandy

Baker, M R
Baxter, J A
Bourke, B E
Butcher, R A
Coulter, M D
Daunt, F O N
Drake, L K
Gledhill, P D
Green, C A
Greig, M M
Heslop, D A
Howes, P J W
Jones, B M
Kapur, A K
Karamé, M M A
Momen, M
Morris, J R L
Neil, W J
O'Brien, M J
Patel, A M
Reddy, A N
Summers, G D
Taine, D L
Tansey, M J B

Sanquhar

Baker, I R
Burton, C D
Edmund, J V M
Richmond, R
Sloan, K

Saundersfoot

Allan, R C
Canton, D E
Cumpsty, D R
Davies, H E
Fleming, V A
Hurle, D E C
Jones, D S
Jones, M
O'Doherty, K
Ryland, O B
Stather-Dunn, M T
Thomas, G C

Sawbridgeworth

Aldam, C H
Campbell, C E R
Gonzalez Contreras, R B
Hartwell, R
Hempel, A C A
Jones, K A
Kearns, D M
Keller, P H
Miller, C H
Perry, J E
Pontin, A R

Rudra, H D
Taylor, C M
Tennekoon, M S
Weare, R A
Webb, A R
Wilkinson, M I P

Saxmundham

Adams, M G
Backhouse, K M
Banks, J N
Buchanan, J
Dunn, H J
Fagan, N A
Foreman, D W
Foreman, W M
Foster, C A
Graham, H H
Hallam, P J B
Hanson, A
Havard, J S
Henriques, C Q
Lal, M
McKerron, C G
Mair, B U
Mawson, S R
Parks, C J
Phillips, D J
Richardson, J P R
Rutter, L D
Shiells, W A
Stevenson, J A M M
Tesh, A E C

Scarborough

Abrines, M J
Adams, T J
Adamson, J
Adamson, S J
Akar, P E
Allan, B J
Allan, B D S
Ames, D S
Andrews, C M
Arundale, D E
Bacon, P J
Bakeer, G M
Baker, J G D
Barron, L
Bayliss, P F C
Beardsley, F J
Bell, E F H
Boyle, J A
Bradley-Stevenson, C L
Bradley, J G
Brame, K G
Brentnall, A L P
Broadhurst, C
Brown, P M
Buckley, P M
Cappleman, T A
Carnegie-Smith, K
Cheetham, C M
Chow, W M
Christian, M A
Clark, R S
Coles, R W
Coppack, J S
Coppack, J J
Craig, A W
Cull, F E
Davidson, A J
Davies, D R L
Dawes, J A
De Pont, S A M T
Dewar, D H
Dewar, D J
Dewar, J A
Dewar, M E
Drake, J M
Dyer, J D
El Barghouty, N M N
El Tahir, M A
Evans, E
Fettes, I F
Fletcher, C
Ford, D J
Fox, P S
Fraser, N C
Gilfillan, T G
Gill, P M
Glaves, I
Greenan, J
Halloran, K M
Hamp, I R
Hark, A J
Harland, P S E G
Hawkyard, S J
Hayes, G

Shaftesbury

Hollins, B J
Hopkirk, T J
Horn, K W
Humphriss, D B
Jackson, A M
Jackson, M Y
Jacques, A M
Johnson, M J
Jones, D F
Jones, M E
Kaye, H H
Kelly, P A
Kinch, A P J
Knowelden, D J
Kok, R H C
Lahoud, G Y G
Laljee, R M
Laws, M G
Lister, A H
Macfie, J
McGill, D
Mahadeva, S
Marimon Ortiz De Zarate, M
Marshall, N E V
Mason, R A
Matteucci, P L
May, J C
Meiwald, J M
Mensah, J A
Miller, A A M
Missen, M R
Mitchell, C J
Moederle-Lumb, D A
Morgan, D R
Morton, R N
Mumby, P S
Neaves, C H
Nicholl, R S
Nicholson, R D
Noble, E P
Noble, M C B
Normandale, J P
North, A D
O'Sullivan, K M
Oldroyd, D A
Parghi, P D
Penfold, J J
Percival, S P B
Phillips, P D
Pitts, I D
Plant, B
Pollock, A V
Poole, D R
Poppleton, J F
Pretorius, M
Pugh, R J P
Reay, J M R
Redmond, R M
Reeves, A
Reinders, K
Richardson, S
Rickinson, J D
Rigg, P
Roberts, V A B
Robinson, D W
Robinson, P
Robinson, P J
Saffman, C M
Said, W A D K
Saunders, C
Scarborough, M A
Scarborough, S A B
Schaefer, A M
Scott, C J
Sheikh, A A
Shuttleworth, D K
Simpson, F V
Stanley, W E
Stone, P G
Svoboda, D
Taylor, J A
Thompson, B C
Thompson, G L
Thompson, R M
Tring, I C
Turner, M A
Van Zon, G J
Volans, A P
Walker, A
Walker, J M
Walker, L
Ward, R W
Western, J M
Whelan, N H
Whitby, E B
Whitfield, G T
Williams, B J
Williams, R J

Worters, J R
Worthington, E G B

Scourie

Cadamy, A R

Scunthorpe

Ajayi-Obe, O
Akande, O
Al-Adwani, A A
Allardyce, K D
Armstrong, R G
Ayala Ortega, J L
Aye, O
Baker, F G
Balasanthiran, S
Barbier, B F
Barrantes Gallego, R
Basu, D K
Beer, S F
Belda Bilbao, L M
Bernad Gonzalez, M P
Bowler, E R
Bowman, R J
Brown, J A
Bruce, J
Butler, M A
Caley, G L
Chaudhary, A K
Chaudhary, D
Coe, A J
David, N I
Dean, R
Desai, S B R
Devlin, J
Dhawan, J
Drion, M
Dwyer, M J
El Rakshy, M M B E D
Eminson, B I F
Fernando, J A P N
Fraser, A J
Ghosh, A
Ghosh, A
Gibbs, E
Goldthorpe, S B
Gordhandas, A M
Grattage, T J
Hall, C J
Hamad, A A M
Hayes, G J
Heywood, B F
Hockey, M S
Hunt, C M
Hurtado Casanova, A
Hutton, D S
Isaacs, J A
Jackson, J
Jalihal, S S
Jedrzejczyk, A
Jones, G A
Kapil, G P
Kar, A K
Kenny, R H
Kerss, A S
Kulkarni, V A
Kumar, S
Lee, A W
Lees, A M
Leitch, D G
McCormack, P
McGlashan, G
McGuane, K F
McNeil, I A
Maharaj, A K
Maitra, T K
Maitra, T B
Malin, D R
Mallik, T K
Maslin, S C
Mawhinney, E O
Melrose, J R
Millar, J H D
Mitchell, J R
Mohamed, A R A A
Molitor, P J A
Molloy, I
Moore, P J
Mukerjea, S K
Nasr, I S I M
Newman, C G
Oakenfull, I B
Odukoya, A O
Oliver, E M
Pais, V
Pemberton, J M
Penston, J G M
Phillips, E P K
Phillips, R S L

Raha, A K
Rai, N
Rajkumar, S
Ranasinghe, S
Rashid, K
Riley, P B
Riley, P A
Roberts, L J
Ryan, E P M
Sabharwal, S
Saleh, B T
Sanderson, M L
Shafqat, S O
Sharara, K E-S H
Sharkey, D
Shekhar, S
Sinclair, A
Stanford, M F
Stewart, N
Summerton, N
Taylor, A P
Taylor, J W
Terreros Berruete, O
Thant, M
Thompson, J F W
Tindall, S F
Trueman, C J
Velasco Albendea, J M
Vijayakumar, K
Vijayasimhulu, G T
Walshaw, R J
Walter, J C
Walton, T J
Wareing, C R
Webster, P A
Weeks, A D
White, D E
Widders, J
Wilken, B J
Woollands, I G
Worah, R
Wyllie, S M J
Yager, R S
Ying, I A
Young, K R
Zacharias, J

Seaford

Austin, M J
Barnes, M H
Barras, B W
Barton, C S
Bayles, I
Bayles, J M
Bayne, G M
Bird, J M
Blenkarn, R N
Boyd, M M M
Brodribb, J H G
Brown, C S
Cockburn, J M
Day, J C
Dunbar, P A
Foster, S J
Fuller, S
Harvey, C L
Harvey, R W
Imran, S K
Janes, D P
Jeffrey, J C
Jones, J G
Le Brun, H I
Light, D C
Lloyd, M M
McGhee, K J
Macleod, T H R
Mellor, C S
Morris, M J
Mortimer, P M
Pickering, B J
Robinson, H M
Sharman, M A
Sharp, J R
Sutton, P D
Turner, C J
Wallace, M

Seaham

Angus, G
Appanna, B
Barkataki, N
Bresnen, D
Dusad, R K
George, M E
Gustafsson, J V
Kapoor, A L
Kapoor, K R
MacRae, I A
Muscat, S M

Napier, D C
Rawling, K G
Reddy, C N
Reddy, K V
Stancliffe, J B

Seahouses

Charlton, A I A
Simister, J M
Thompson, T R

Seascale

Adkins, G G
Barns, T E C
Carhart, P A
Curry, I P
Jay, S A
Longworth, A E
Lowrey, G E
McAndrew, I W
Macgregor, D H
Maguire, B G
Stevenson, M D
Walker, B
Woffindin, J

Seaton

Bastin, C J
Bramley, R J
Carnaghan, M G
Coop, J A
Farrell, P J S
Gold, J M
Hollick, C L
Hurst, J R
Jones, R V H
Lawrey, K D E
Pitt, G H
Rolls, A
Slater, L K
Stewart, D H
Webb, P S
Wickins, M C

Seaview

Adams, M S
Cahill, A B
Glasgow, T C
Hambly, T
Hounsfield, V
Loach, R S
Payne, M C
Thursfield, W R R

Sedbergh

Alban, M T
Campbell, P L
Falconer, A S
Flindt, M L H
Newson, E R A
Noble, T C
Orr, P A
Orr, W G
Pigott, J B
Sugden, J H
Syred, J R
Thomas, T S

Selby

Bell Syer, E M R
Bilcliffe, E M
Bond, G
Brotherton, B J
Brown, A J
Bruce, J G E
Chau, H N
Dalby, R J
Davis, P R
Docherty, C
Docherty, P F
Edwards, D W
Fox, N J
Haworth, S R
Hepworth, D
Hildore, L M
Hills, R C
House, E V
Jackson, N
Kaufman, R B
Kessel, D O
Lambert, D H
Lewis, I A
Lord, E R
McGrann, P J
Pearson, T E
Reid, J D
Robson, A
Sahay, P
Scott, E J
Shardlow, D L
Stanford, A J

Taylor, A R
Tuck, H A
Wakefield, R J
Williams, M E

Selkirk

Cullen, J G
Davies, S R
Elliot, R
Fiddes, W F G
Gillies, E M
Gillies, J C M
Glen, S E
Lonergan, B A
Pearson, P J M
Ross, C C
Sharpe, C J
Wheelans, J C
Wilson, J F

Settle

Birkett, C I
Brewster, B S
Catherwood, R F
Hall, W W
Huddleston, S
Lewis, J M
Littlejohn, C I
Longhorn, P D
Longhorn, R K
Longton, E B
Moakes, H
Renwick, C J
Renwick, J R
Sandoe, J A T
Ward, E

Sevenoaks

Addison, A K L
Arnott, N D
Ashworth, H L
Baker, A M
Barnaby, J
Barnes, J
Bates, C J
Billinghurst, J R
Botha, M E
Boxall, T A
Brignall, K A
Brook, R
Broomby, R C W
Brown, C M R
Chapman, W A
Clark, F J
Clarke, N A H
Cook, G E
Coole, C W
Cox, J A
Creagh, T M
Creed, H S
Daniel, A C M
Desai, A J
Deshpande, S
Dibble, A M
Dickerson, H E
Dowling, O M T
Dowrick, S E
Draper, C C
Draper, K C
Drysdale, W R
Dunn, P M
Dunn, R P
Edge, M B
Elliott, L M
Evans, D K
Evans, G M
Farraway, N J
Farthing, C P
Finter, A C
Finter, N B
Foley, S E
Forbes, N J
Ford, M A
Fry, L M
Fry, R W
Furness, S J
Giffin, N J
Giorgi, L
Glasspool, M G
Gravatt, D B
Harris, J W S
Harrison, P F
Haworth, G M
Haworth, S C
Headley, P R
Henderson, L
Hewett, B M
Holder, P D
Hosseini, M
House, C V

Hull, K E
Husband, R G
Hyett, A R
Irvine, T E
Jariwalla, A
John, G
Johnson, F R
Johnson, S R
Jones, B C
Keenor, C
Khakoo, S I
Kilbey, J H
King, M
Kotting, S C
Kydd, M V
Landy, P B
Lay, C J
Legg, J R
Lesseps, A
Lindsay, Y
Linnett, D A
Lloyd, J C
Lockhart, N S
Lothian, W
Lynam, A M
McCusker, F E M
MacDonnell, A J R
MacLean, W E
McPherson, J S
Mair, G H M
Martin, M S
Medill, E V
Milton-Thompson, D G
Moosvi, S K
Morgan, S C
Morton, S V
Munro, O I
Murray, R S
Newton, K A
O'Gorman, P
Parker, N J
Parkes, J D
Patel, A C
Paterson, E K J
Pearse, H R
Prout, J W
Prout, M F
Razzell, P J
Rissik, K M
Rodway, A E P
Ross, F A
Rothman, W T
Rowntree, B M
Rowntree, R K
Roxburgh, A C
Shairp, B E
Shannon, S E
Sillitoe, C
Smedley, F H
Smith, J R
Solan, C L
Spencer, R E B
Stow, P J
Stubbs, E J
Taggart, G E
Taggart, M
Taor, L P M
Taylor, A J
Thomas, D G
Thomas, D M
Tonge, A R
Turner, B R
Turner, L M
Tyrell, M S
Unwin, P W
Vadasz, I
Van Zinderen Bakker, R D
Walczak, J P B
Walker, K J
Watson, A J
Watson, C I J
Watson, J N
Whitlock, J A
Williams, O H E
Wilson, J A
Winbow, A J
Wootton, L W
Wright, J J
Wright, M W
Wynter, M J C
Yarrow, D E
Young, W B

Shaftesbury

Appleyard, D S
Brewin, D M C
Brodie, W
Daddy, S

Shanklin

Dodson, J W
Easterbrooke, S J
Emms, R J
Emrys-Roberts, R M
Hewetson, C T
Hinchley, H M
Horner, S S
Jackson, R A
Mainwaring, D
Pyle, P O
Roberts, D M
Tapper, G W
Vere-Hodge, N
Weir, A W
Wynn-MacKenzie, D M

Shanklin

Frame, A G
Gent, G M
Ghurye, R S
Rivers, J W
Stone, B E
Willetts, J M

Sheerness

Armstrong, F J
Betterton, B W
Brew, M D
Clune, F A M
Cook, L
Dhillon, J S
Ellis, D J
Fahmy, M M E-S
Garwood, R E
Jordan, C
Mathews, D D
Morrison, B
Noble, H M S
Noorah, S B
Ramu, V K
Rowe, M P
Tadros-Caudle, M E
Uppal, H K
Youdale, D A

Sheffield

Abbotson, M L
Abell, D J
Abernethy, J S
Ackroyd, R
Adamo, S J
Adams, M
Adams, M G
Adebajo, A O
Adeloye, C K
Admani, A K
Adshead, S-L
Afzal, A
Ahmad, J
Ahmed, J M
Ahmed, R
Ahmedzai, S H
Ainger, M C
Ainscow, C B
Aitken, D A
Aitken, M
Akil, M
Al-Wali, W I A
Alam, A T M S
Alam, R
Alam, S S
Alderson, J D
Aldridge, R E
Alexander, J L S
Alford, A M
Alison, L H
Allan, W
Allen, S T S M
Allsop, S M
Allsopp, E S
Amin, S N
Amos, R S
Anagnostou, E
Anderson, A J
Anderson, J B
Anderson, J E
Anderson, J M
Anderson, P B
Anderton, M
Andrzejowski, A Z
Andrzejowski, A R M
Andrzejowski, J C
Angel, C A
Angier, E A
Ansons, C
Appleton, D F J
Appleyard, T N
Aratari, C
Arcelus Alonso, J
Armstrong, A P
Armstrong, F C
Armstrong, W D
Asghar, R B
Ashby, A F
Ashe, E S A
Ashford, R U
Ashmore, G T
Ashton, A E
Ashton, J G
Askew, L J
Assing, J M G
Aswani, N M
Atkin, C E
Atkin, M
Atkins, C J
Atkinson, A M
Atkinson, E C
Atkinson, J
Atkinson, R E
Atkinson, R M
Atun, A R
Atwell, B M
Atwell, J D
Austin, C A
Ayling, L A
Azmy, I A F
Bacon, M A
Baddoo, M A
Bailey, H
Bainton, R D
Baird, A M
Baker, B R
Baker, E
Baker, R H
Baldwin, M J
Ball, S E
Balsitis, M
Bandekar, M S
Banks, A W
Bant, W P
Barber, C M
Barber, P A
Barclay, C S
Barclay, J H
Barden, A L
Bardsley, P A
Barik, S
Barker, I
Barker, L H
Barley, J A
Barley, S L
Barnes, R J
Barnett, A L
Baron, S
Barrington, N A
Bates, C J
Bates, N A
Bath, A P
Battersby, R D E
Battye, J E
Bax, D E
Bax, N D S
Baxter, A J
Baxter, P S
Beadle, R M
Beard, J D
Beardsworth, T
Beckett, J P
Bedford, M
Beechey, A P G
Beeson, J
Beetham, M D
Belfield, J C
Bell, A D
Bell, M J
Bell, S J
Benjamin, J G
Bennett, A N
Bennett, N R
Bennett, R L
Bennett, V R
Benns, J S
Bentley, C C
Bergvall, U E G
Bernard, J
Berthoud, M C
Bethell, J
Bethell, J N
Bhan, A
Bickerstaff, D R
Birbeck, K F
Bird, S I D
Birkby, E A
Birks, D M P
Birks, R J S
Birtwhistle, M B
Bishop, H E
Bishop, J M
Black, P R M
Blackburn, L M
Blakeborough, A
Blank, C E
Bleakley, C J
Blindt, M
Blockey, P
Blower, S J
Boldy, J A
Bolster, K M
Boston, P F
Bottomley, D R W
Boulton, J
Bowers, J C
Bowes, R J
Bowman, S J
Bowns, C M
Bowry, A
Bowry, V A
Boyd, M D A
Boyd, V
Boyle, M S
Bracewell, M A
Bradbury, C E
Bradbury, P A
Bradford, S L
Bradley, A R
Bradley, H P
Bradley, K E
Bradley, M J
Bradshaw, J P P
Braidley, P C
Bramley, H M
Bramley, P A
Brammar, D K
Brand, A E
Brand, C S
Brar, A S
Brawn, L A
Breakwell, L M
Breen, D P
Bremner, J A G
Brennan, P O B
Bridgewater, C H
Briggs, D M
Brimacombe, L
Brimacombe, M C
Brinkley, A M E
Brinkley, D C
Broadley, P S
Brockbank, J E
Brodie, D B
Bronsdon, C J N
Brook, A M F
Brook, P N
Brookes, L D
Brooks, A J
Brosnahan, D M
Brown, A
Brown, C B
Brown, J D
Brown, J N
Brown, K E
Brown, M J
Brown, M B
Brown, P M
Brown, P G
Brown, P W G
Brown, S R
Brown, V A
Brown, W H
Bruce, A S W
Bryan, B A
Bryant, R C
Bryson, P N
Buchanan, J M
Buckingham, K L
Buffin, J T
Bull, M J
Bull, P D
Bullas, B H
Bundy, J C
Burdett, H J
Burke, J P
Burns, B J
Burton, J
Bush, J M
Bushby, M
Butler, G
Butler, J M
Butler, U G
Byrne, J W
Caddick, S L
Caddy, C M
Caldon, L J M
Caldwell, D L
Caley, M J
Calladine, C
Cameron, I C
Campbell, A M
Campbell, N M
Campbell, P
Campbell, S
Cannon, J S
Cantor, A M
Carey, P E
Carlile, E
Carlile, W W
Carr, A J
Carter, G S
Carter, J
Carter, M J
Carter, N
Caunt, J A
Cautley, W G
Chadha, P
Challands, L
Chalmers, J L
Chambers, G
Chan, D T Y
Chan, K L
Chan, P
Chan, R
Chan, T K J
Chandrasekharan, S
Channer, K S
Chantry, A D
Chantry, J E
Chaplais, J Z
Chapman, C L
Chapman, D F
Chapman, I R
Chapman, J E
Chapple, C R
Charles, B M
Charles, K S
Charlton, H M
Chatterjee, D K
Chauhdry, M S
Chesterman, M S
Chitty, W A
Christie, J P
Chua, I C-I
Chugh, S K
Chung, P-C D
Clark, G P M
Clark, J M
Clark, J C
Clark, J D F
Clark, J R
Clark, P J
Clarke, J J
Clarke, S E
Clement, F M
Cleveland, T J
Clout, C
Clowes, J A
Coad, N R
Coan, A C
Coates, F S
Cobb, J A
Cobb, J J
Cockayne, S E
Coffey, J T
Cohen, G L
Cohen, V M L
Coker, A E O
Cole, A A
Coleman, J P
Coleman, R E
Coley, S C
Colley, P J
Collins, G D
Collins, J S
Collins, M A
Collins, M B
Collins, M C
Collins, R K
Colquitt, H R
Colver, D C B
Colver, S E
Connell, H
Connelly, H R
Connor, M E
Conway, J V
Cook, J A
Cooke, H M G
Cooke, I D
Cooke, S M S
Coombs, R C
Cooper, A E
Cooper, C M S
Cooper, G J
Cooper, J R
Cooper, J E M
Cooper, M W
Cooper, M J
Cooper, M T
Cooper, S M
Cooper, W G
Cork, M J
Cornell, S J
Cort, J M
Cossham, T R
Cotton, D W K
Couldwell, A B C
Cowey, R V
Cox, J R
Cox, R M
Cracknell, P
Craig, J M
Craven, P J
Crawford, B S
Crawford, S E
Creagh, F M
Creasy, J M
Crehan, P
Cressey, D M
Critchlow, J I
Croot, L M
Crosby, A C
Cross, S S
Crossland, D S
Crossman, D C
Crowder, R E
Crowther, A G O
Cullen, D R
Cullen, R J
Cumberland, J E
Cummins, E M
Czauderna, J M
D'Mello, B M T
Da Costa, D F
Da Silva, C K
Dalal, S
Dales, C J
Dallas, F
Daly, R F
Danskin, J M
Darling, S P
Das, A
Dass, M
Datta, D
Davidson, A J
Davidson, I W
Davies-Jones, G A B
Davies, A E
Davies, A C
Davies, A
Davies, A G
Davies, B M
Davies, D P
Davies, G P
Davies, H A
Davies, J G
Davies, J R
Davies, L M
Davies, N P
Davies, P L
Davis, C J
Davis, K J
Dawson, D J
De Mortimer-Griffin, C A E
De Noronha, R J
De Takats, D L P
Deakin, P J
Dennis, A R
Deslandes, R C
Dey, S K
Dibble, T L
Dicks, J R
Doa, J M
Dobbs, P
Dobson, P M S
Doddridge, N J
Dodds, J A
Dolan, S A S
Donnelly, M T
Dorman, T
Dorreen, M S
Douglas, D L
Downes, T W
Downie, W A
Driscoll, P H
Drought, L H
Dube, A K
Duckworth, T
Duff, G W
Duncan, M E
Duncan, S L B
Dunn, K S
Durling, M E
Eapen, S
Eastell, R
Eaton, S E M
Edbrooke, D L
Edenborough, F P
Edeson, J F B
Edhouse, J A
Edney, P
Edwards, M P
Edwards, N D
Edwards, R
Ee, H L
Egner, W
Eilbeck, S C
El-Shazly, M M E-D K
Elliott, S J
Ellis, S J
Elphick, H E
Elphinstone, C D
Emerson, S
Emerson, V J
Eng, J B
Englert, L J
English, B K
Eskin, F
Euinton, H A
Evans, A R
Evans, C A
Evans, H P
Evans, R S
Everard, M L
Everson, G S
Ezzat, V A
Fairbrother, J M
Fairlie, F M
Falder, L S
Farkas, A G
Farmer, R T
Ferguson, A G
Ferguson, C A
Ferguson, C J
Ferguson, D G
Fernandes, N O J
Field, N J
Fieldsend, G A
Fieldsend, R L H
Filby, H J
Finigan, L M
Fisher, J P
Fisher, P C
Fisher, V M
Fishwick, D
Fitch, J A
Fitzgerald, D M
Fitzgerald, G
Flann, P-J A
Fleming, O
Fletcher, A K
Flint, F J
Flowers, M J
Flynn, M E S
Foggitt, C H
Fong, J C W
Foran, B H
Forman, A
Forrest, A R W
Forrester, A M
Forster, D M C
Forster, G
Fothergill, D J
Fowler, I A
Fox, A M
Fox, M
Fox, S
France, M J
Francis, K L
Francis, T A
Franks, S E
Fraser, R B
Freedlander, E
Freeman, C
Freeman, R
French, J J
French, N M
Frymann, R J
Furniss, D L S
Gajjar, P D
Gakhal, R K
Galea, J
Gallagher, D
Gallagher, D F
Gallaher, J M
Galt, O V
Gamsu, M J
Ganapathy, T S
Ganley, P D
Garcia, J A
Gardner, J M
Gaubert, D R
Gaubert, R A P
Gawkrodger, D J
Geh, L C J
Gelipter, D
Gemmell, E

Sheffield

Gent, A M
Georgeou, T
Gerrard, M P
Gerrish, S P
Getty, C J M
Gholkar, S A
Ghosal, S
Gibson, A
Gilchrist, J A
Gildersleve, A A
Giles, J
Gili, N L
Gill, A
Gill, P V
Gillett, M
Gillott, J H
Gillott, T J
Gillow, J L
Gittleson, N L
Gleave, C R
Gleeson, D C
Goddard, J M
Goepel, J R
Gogna, J D
Goh, K K
Goheir, A A
Goldberg, K A
Goldstein, D J
Goodacre, S W
Goodall, H J
Gordon, J E
Gordon, M A
Gordon, R M
Gossiel, R
Gott, E J
Gouta, E A Y
Gow, W M
Gowers, P S D
Gowlett, S J
Grainger, R G
Grant, I C
Grant, Y A M
Gray, C
Gray, T A
Gray, W R
Greaves, C W K H
Greaves, J A H
Greaves, W E
Green, D T
Green, M
Green, M A
Green, N E
Green, S T
Green, T
Greengrass, S R
Greenstreet, D
Greenwell, T J
Greenwood, L J
Gregory, J S
Gregson, A E W
Griffin, J J
Griffiths, P D
Griffiths, R W
Grimshaw, M S
Grimshaw, S L
Grover, A
Groves, E R
Grunewald, R A
Gunn, J P G
Hackney, J S
Hackney, M A
Haddock, R
Hadjivassiliou, M
Hague, R V
Hall, C M
Hall, C
Hall, D M B
Hall, J
Hall, J E
Hall, N A M
Hall, S M
Hallatt, B F
Halle, F M
Halle, H M
Hamdy, F C
Hamdy, N A T C
Hamer, A J
Hamer, D J
Hamilton, D A
Hamilton, M
Hammond, J D S
Hammond, M R
Hampton, K K
Hancock, B W
Hannay, D R
Haq, I U
Harding, M J
Hardisty, C A
Hardy, P J

Hardy, P G
Harker, T G
Harling, D W
Harpin, V A
Harrington, C I
Harrington, D K
Harris, J L
Harris, R M
Harrison, B J
Harrison, D A
Harrison, N
Harvey, P R
Harvey, P J
Harvie, P
Hasan, J R
Hastie, K J
Hastings, J G M
Hatcher, I S
Hatton, C T
Hatton, E R
Hatton, M Q F
Hawkins, K M
Hayes-Allen, M C
Heap, M J
Heathcote, J A
Heathcote, P R M
Heatley, C T
Heller, S R
Hempseed, G D
Hen, B Y
Henderson, F W
Henderson, G M
Hendra, D A
Hendra, T J
Henry, L
Hepple, S
Herdman, C P
Herrera Vega, L
Hettiarachchi, C D
Hettiarachchi, K D M
Hewson, N
Hickman, L
Hicks, D A
Higenbottam, T W
Hill, C
Hill, K S P
Hillam, S J
Hillman, B
Hoare, R J
Hobden, M A
Hobson, N A
Hodgkin, P K
Hodgson, T J
Holden, C R
Holden, V A
Holland, E J
Holland, P A
Hollingworth, K M
Holmes, P C
Holt, G M
Holt, S
Hood, G
Hope, A M
Hopkins, B J
Hopkins, J
Hopkinson, J
Hopper, A D
Hopwood, B
Hornbuckle, J
Horner, O J
Hosie, K B
Hough, R E
Houghton, A M
Howard, A Q
Howard, A C
Howard, K
Howard, P
Howell, S J L
Huck, P
Hudson, A J
Hughes, P
Humphrey, J A
Hunsley, J E
Hunt, R
Hunter, A C
Hunter, J I
Hunter, S J S
Hussain, A
Hutchcroft, B J
Hutchinson, A
Hutchinson, D I
Hutchison, G
Huws, R W
Illingworth, C M
Ince, P G
Inch, H M
Ingram, C E
Ireland, S J
Irons, R P

Irwin, K
Islam, B
Jaafar, A S
Jaafar, F
Jabir, M A
Jackson, B J
Jackson, B C
Jackson, P R
Jacob, G
Jacob, M
Jakeways, M S R
Jakubowski, J
James, A F
James, M D
James, V
Jarratt, J A
Jarvis, C P
Jayasinghe, D S
Jeavons, G H
Jeavons, P
Jeavons, S M
Jellinek, D A
Jenkins, S B
Jenner, F A
Jennings, M
Jepson, M E
Jewes, L A
Jivraj, S S
Joesbury, H E
Johns, R G
Johnson, A G
Johnson, D A N
Johnstone, P S
Jokhi, R P
Jones, D A
Jones, M L
Jones, M A C
Jones, P
Jones, S J
Jones, W M
Jordan, C N
Jordan, N
Kacker, P P
Kacker, S
Kacker, S
Kandler, R H
Kang, S
Kanis, J A
Karim, M S
Kavanagh, J
Kay, A J
Kay, N R M
Kearsley, N J
Keating, D A
Keating, E M
Keegan, S
Keel, J D
Keen, J A
Kell, C
Kelly, C L
Kemeny, A
Kemp, R C
Kemp, R T
Kemplen, A M
Kendall, K M
Kendall, T J G
Kennedy, A
Kennedy, C
Kennedy, R M
Kennedy, R
Kenny, C
Keogh, A K
Kerry, R J
Kerry, R M
Kershaw, J D
Kershaw, L C W
Ketchell, R I
Khan, A M
Khattak, M S K
Kilding, R F
Killey, S H
King, B C A
King, G M
King, H
King, J A
King, K M
King, M
King, P J
Kinghorn, G R
Kinghorn, S A
Kinsey, R M
Kirkbride, V
Kirkpatrick, T
Kirton, C B
Kitching, C M
Kitlowski, A J
Knowles, P R
Krishnan, A T
Kudesia, G

Kugathasan, T
Kumar, A
Kumar, C
Kumar, D
Kwarko, K A
Lane, J W
Lane, V J M
Lang, I M
Lankshear, W M
Latham, C A
Laugharne, J D E
Lavender, A W
Lawson-Matthew, P J
Lawson, C W
Laycock, C L
Lazner, M R
Leach, M T J
Leahy, M
Leddy, C E
Ledger, W L
Ledingham, R G
Ledingham, S N
Lee, C L
Lee, C H
Lee, F K T
Lee, V
Leicester, S
Leigh, F W
Leigh, G
Leigh, V F
Lemon, M J C
Lenthall, J
Leonard, D A
Lethem, K R
Levy, D P
Liddell, A M
Liddle, B J
Lightfoot, D M
Liljendahl, S
Lim, K J H
Lin, K W
Lindley, R M
Lindop, D J
Lindsay, F V
Linnard, G
Lipp, D
Littlewood, C
Livesey, D S J
Lloyd, F E
Lloyd, J M
Lobo, A J
Locke, T J
Lockwood, C S
Lockwood, S E
Loescher, A R
Loh, L C
Loke, D K T
Long, G
Longan, M A
Longfield, S R W
Longshaw, C L
Longshaw, M S
Longstaff, S
Lonsdale, R J
Lord, R C C
Lorenz, E
Loudon, J M
Loughran, A B
Lumb, S E H
Lunn, J E
Lunt, R L
Lupton, S D
Luscombe, M D
Luscombe, N D R
Lyons, V H
McAdam, M S
McAlindon, M E
McAll, G L G
McAllister, D P
MacAskill, N D
McAvoy, J
McBoyle, J R
MacCallum, E A
McCann, C B
MacCarthy, A M
McCarthy, S
McCormack, K
McCormick, S R
McCullough, H C
McDermott, C M
McDonagh, A J G
McDonough, H M
McDonough, J
MacDowell, A D
McElwaine, J G
McFarlane, A
McGorrigan, J L L R
McGrath, L R
McGraw, S J

McGuinness, S P
McIntyre, H
McKendrick, M W
McKenna, J F
McKenna, M M
McKenzie, A I
Mackenzie, C A
Mackenzie, F A
MacKeown, S T
McKevitt, F M
Mackie, A D R
Mackinnon, A E
Macleod, I C
McMillen, G V
McMurray, H R
McNaught, R
McNaughton, F J
MacNeill, A L
McShane, M D
McTague, L
McTavish, K
Maddocks, J L
Magennis, J K
Maheswaran, C M
Maheswaran, R
Mahmood, K
Majeed, A W
Makris, M
Manasse, A P
Mander, D
Manifold, I H
Manley, C A
Mann, M
Manning, L V
Mark, J S
Marples, I L
Marples, M
Marren, D
Marshall, A S
Martin Delgado, R
Marven, S S
Mascott, A
Massey, N
Massey, N J A
Masson, H
Mathers, N J
Mathers, P M A
Mathews, R H
Matta, H
Matthews, S
Maxfield, J B
Mayer, R R
Mehrotra, V B
Mehrotra, V N
Mehta, A B
Mehta, S
Messenger, A G
Metcalf, H M
Metcalfe, B C
Metcalfe, N H
Mezilis, N
Michael, S
Michaels, J A
Miller, J G
Miller, J
Mills, C A
Mills, G H
Milner, G R
Milner, N A
Milroy, C M
Milsom, J W
Minton, E J
Mitchell, C A
Mohammed Fauzi, A R
Moll, J M H
Monaghan, D
Montague, R J
Moody, J E
Mooney, P N
Moore, C A
Moore, D J
Moore, K T H
Moorhead, P J
Moorhead, P J
Moorhead, S P
Moran, D G
Morecroft, J A
Morgan, J E F
Morgan, J P
Morgan, S M
Morley, A F
Moroney, P J
Morris, F P
Morris, H D
Morris, H J
Morton, D E
Morton, L A
Moseley, D J
Moss, G D

Moss, L S
Moss, P J
Moxon, D
Muggleton, R J
Mundy, J V B
Munro, D S
Munro, H R
Munro, J F
Murphy, I J
Murray, P
Murray, R J
Myers, A M
Myers, K
Nabi, D W
Nadkarni, S
Nahami, G R
Naik, D R
Naik, R
Naik, S V I
Nakielny, R A
Nawaz, S
Neal, L M
Neal, M R
Nehring, S J
Nelson, K W
Nelson, M E
Nerurkar, I D J
Newman, C M H
Nicholls, I
Nieder, M
Noble, A D
Noble, D A
Noble, T W
Nohr, K
Norman, P
Norris, M J
Norris, S H
North, G N
North, R A
Norton, P G
Nutt, M N
O'Connell, J P
O'Connor, F P
O'Connor, K R
O'Connor, S P J
O'Dwyer, J M E
O'Rourke, A J
Oakes, S M
Oakley, G D G
Oakley, N
Oates, C S
Oates, D E R
Ogden, J
Okoko, A E J
Okon, M A A
Okorie, N M
Oliver, R
Ong, A C M
Orme, S
Orr, B T
Orth, A
Osborne, M A
Otten, K A
Outtrim, J E N
Ow, K K H
Padfield, A
Page, H
Page, K B
Paget, R J
Palmer, C D
Palmer, C A L
Panarese, A
Pandurangi, V R
Panniker, C B
Panniker, R M
Parker, A J
Parker, D A
Parker, G
Parkes, A M
Parry, M S
Parry, W H
Parsons, H K
Parsons, M A
Pascoe, R J M
Patel, G U
Patel, N H
Patel, P S
Patel, R
Patel, R
Patel, V R
Paterson, I G
Paterson, M M F
Paterson, M E L
Payne, J N
Peace, J M
Peacock, J E
Pearse, R G
Peat, C C
Peat, J

Shefford

Peck, R J
Peel, A J
Peel, N F A
Peet, M
Pereira, N H
Perrett, K
Peters, S
Pettinger, G
Pettinger, R
Phillips, A F
Phillips, J K
Phillips, W S
Phillpots, S
Philp, I
Phythian-Adams, J M
Pickin, D M
Pietersen, S C
Pinches, C E
Pitt, F A
Platt, J
Platts, M M
Pledge, S D
Pollitt, G
Porteous, M
Porter, D W
Porter, W
Portlock, K M
Potter, D
Powell, B P
Powell, G D
Poyser, J
Prakasam, S F R
Pratt, J C
Prenton, M A
Pressley, K J
Preston, F E
Primhak, R A
Procter, A E
Prosser, L J
Purcell, W
Purdy, R H
Pycock, J E
Qamar-Uz-Zaman, S
Quarrell, O W J
Quiyum, S A
Radford, J M C
Radley, H M
Radley, S C
Radstone, D J
Rafferty, R
Raftery, A T
Rahman, S U
Rahman, Z
Rainford, A
Ralston, D R
Ramsay, H M
Ramsay, L E
Ramsay, M H
Rana, H H
Rana, T
Rangi, P S
Rashid, N A
Rashid, S
Ravichandran, G
Rawlin, M E
Rawson, A
Ray, K K
Read, N W
Read, R C
Redding, H L
Reddy, L C S
Redman, K
Redman, P A
Reed, M W R
Reid, J J
Reilly, C S
Reilly, J T
Rennie, E
Rennie, I G
Revill, J
Rhodes, M J
Richards, B W
Richards, J E
Richards, M
Richardson, C D
Rickards, D F
Rickman, M S
Ridgway, B A
Ridgway, E J
Ridsdale, A
Riley, S A
Rimmer, A
Rimmer, C S
Ringrose, C S
Rittey, C D C
Rivett, K A
Rivlin, I
Roberts, A J
Roberts, H E
Roberts, J P
Robertson, B J
Robertson, F C
Robertson, N J
Robinson, C J
Robinson, M H
Robinson, R T C E
Rochester, J R
Roddick, J N
Roden, D
Rogers, M S S
Rogers, N K
Rogstad, K E
Rolan, J M F H
Roman, D E M
Roman, F
Romanowski, C A J
Roper, J N
Rosario, A J
Rosario, D J P
Roscoe, T J
Rose, M W
Ross, B
Ross, R J M
Rosted, P
Rowbotham, C
Rowland, M
Rowland, S J
Rowlands, D A
Rowling, J T
Royston, S L
Ruck, M J Y
Ruck, S E
Rughani, A N
Ruiz, K
Rundle, P A
Russell, M A G
Russell, R G G
Rutter, S
Ryan, C J
Ryan, F P
Ryan, R G
Rybinski, E A
Rybinski, P
Safe, A F
Sagar, H J
Saha, J R
Saleem, M
Saleh, M
Salfield, N J
Salih, A I
Samaniego, N C
Samarage, L H
Samuel, R C
Sanders, A J
Sanders, D S
Sanderson, C A
Sandhu, A S
Sandler, G
Sandys, R M
Sanmuganathan, P S
Sarkar, P N
Sarwar, N
Saunders, N J S G
Saunders, S J
Savage, D A
Savani, R K
Savani, U K
Saxena, S C
Saxena, S
Say, D T
Sayed, Q A
Schatzberger, P M
Scheele, K H
Scholefield, J H
Schrecker, G M K
Schroeder, H G
Scorah, P J
Scott, G R
Scrimgeour, K M A
Seager, C P
Sedler, P A S L
Seeley, D W
Selby, K F
Sercombe, J L
Seth, C
Seth, P C
Seymour, J
Shackley, F M
Shaikh, A M
Sharma, A
Sharma, S S
Sharma, S
Sharp, D J
Sharp, F
Sharpe, M S
Sharrard, M J
Sharrard, W J W
Shaw, A J
Shaw, C H
Shaw, I C
Shaw, J D
Shaw, M
Shaw, T J I
Shaw, T C
Shaw, W A
Shawcross, C J
Shawcross, C S
Shawis, R N S
Sheares, C S K
Shenton, G A
Shepherd, D B
Sherry, K M
Sherry, S
Shibli, K U
Shickle, D A
Shiell, K A
Shirley, R A
Shirt, D J W
Shore, S L
Shorrock, K
Short, J A
Shorthouse, A J
Shum, K W
Shurmer, D M
Siddiqui, S
Simms, R J
Simpson, K L
Singh, A P
Singh, T S
Sinha, A K
Sinuff, S H
Sivapathasundaram, L
Sivarajan, S
Skan, J P
Skerritt, E
Skidmore, D J
Skinner, P P
Skull, J D
Slater, R
Sliwinski, S
Sloan, L M
Sloan, M E
Sloan, S B
Smailes, J
Smallwood, D M
Smethurst, M
Smith, A H L
Smith, B A M
Smith, C M L
Smith, C E
Smith, H N
Smith, H J
Smith, J A
Smith, J A R
Smith, J H F
Smith, K J
Smith, M E
Smith, M F
Smith, N W P
Smith, O O
Smith, R L
Smith, R H
Smith, S N
Smith, T W D
Snaith, M L
Snelson, E J
Sokol, R J
Sorsbie, L
Souper, K
Spear, F G
Spencer, H L
Spinks, M J
Spooner, L
Sprigg, A
Sprigg, N
Sprigg, S J
Spyrlounis, P
Squirrell, D M
St. Leger, S A
Stack, C G
Stamp, R A
Stanley, C K
Stanley, D
Starbuck, M J
Stark, J
Starr, P L
Start, S A
Stefanuti, E
Steiner, G M
Steiner, H R
Stephenson, A J
Stephenson, J A
Stephenson, P M
Stephenson, T J
Stewart, K
Stewart, P
Stierle, C
Stockley, I
Stoddard, C J
Stones, L
Stoodley, K J
Strachan, I M
Strachan, K J
Strode, P A
Strong, E P
Studholme, T J
Sugden, J S
Suhail, M
Suliman, M E G R
Sundar Eswar, Dr
Sutcliffe, M K
Sutherland, J A
Sutton, P M
Suvarna, S K
Sverrisdottir, A
Swales, V S
Swarbrick, M J
Swinden, S J
Swinhoe, A L
Talbot, H
Talbot, J F
Talbot, M D
Tan, S
Tanner, M S
Tantam, D J H
Tattersall, J E
Tatton, P
Taussig, J-A
Tay, P Y S
Tayler, D I
Taylor, A J
Taylor, C J
Taylor, C
Taylor, C J
Taylor, E M
Taylor, M S
Taylor, N M
Taylor, P R P
Taylor, R
Tesfaye, S
Tesfayohannes, B
Thakrar, A
Thevasagayam, M S
Thewles, M J
Thomas, D G
Thomas, S M
Thomas, S N
Thomas, W E G
Thompson, D
Thompson, M C
Thompson, R
Thorman, N A
Thorpe, F G
Tidy, J A
Till, S H
Ting, S C H
Tinker, R M
Tom, P A K
Tooth, D R
Tooth, J A
Tophill, P R
Treacy, P J
Trudgill, N J
Tsintis, P A
Tungland, O P
Tupper, N A
Tupper, R C A
Turk, D C
Turnbull, D K
Turner, B A
Turner, D C
Turner, E C
Tweed, C S
Tweney, J C S H
Udejiofo, S F
Underwood, J C E
Upadhyaya, L M
Usher, A S G
Vaishnav, A A
Valerio, D
Van Geene, P
Vandenberghe, E A M
Variend, S
Varkey, A T
Varkey, S
Vass, H S
Vaughan, J
Veall, G R Q
Venables, G S
Verity, R G
Vlissides, D N
Vohra, S
Von Schreiber, S K
Vora, A J
Waddington, M H G
Wakefield, S E
Wales, J K H
Walewska, R J
Walker, A H
Walker, C J
Walker, D A J
Walker, G T
Walker, J
Wallace, W A H
Wallbridge, C M
Waller, A
Waller, R E
Wallis, E J
Walsh, M P
Walton, C E
Walton, J J
Ward, A M
Ward, C J
Ward, D L
Ward, J D
Ward, S E
Wardrope, J
Wareham, C A
Warner, R W
Warrack, A J N
Warren, C W
Warren, W E
Washington, S E J
Watkinson, P J
Watson, N
Watt, D A L
Watton, R J
Watts, C
Webber, S J
Webster, J
Webster, R E
Weetman, A P
Weir, R D
Welch, I M
Welch, J C
Welch, R A
Welchew, E A
Welchew, K L
Wells, G E
Wells, M
Welsh, C L
Wembridge, K R
Wenham, T N
West, J
West, J N W
West, J A
Wharton, S P
Wheeldon, N M
Whelehan, I M
Whitaker, G R B
White, B M
White, D J K
White, J C
White, M G
White, R W
White, S A
White, T O
Whitehurst, L M
Whiteside, R S
Whiting, P C
Whittaker, S J
Whyte, M K B
Wighton-Benn, W H
Wilbush, J
Wilfin, A H
Wilkie, M E
Wilkie, P
Wilkinson, G A L
Wilkinson, J M
Wilkinson, P A
Williams, A H E
Williams, D G
Williams, J L
Williams, J L
Williams, K
Williams, N H
Williams, R P
Williams, S G
Willoughby, S J
Wilson, A M
Wilson, A G
Wilson, J T
Wilson, L M
Wilson, R M
Winder, S
Winfield, D A
Winfield, J
Withers, M R
Wong, T I
Wood, G E
Wood, J D
Wood, N S
Wood, N I
Wood, R J
Wood, R F M
Woodcock, P J
Woodruff, M J
Woodruff, P W R
Woods, H F
Woodward, D K
Wordsworth, J M
Worthy, E
Wren, M C
Wrench, I J
Wright, C H
Wright, F W
Wright, J E D
Wright, S R
Wyld, L
Wylie, K R
Wyllie, D H
Wyman, A
Yap, B H
Yardley, M P J
Yassa, J G
Yates, R O
Yeo, W W
Yong, S C
Young, C S
Young, N
Zadik, P M
Zadik, S A
Zaman, A C
Zaman, S R

Shefford

Baldock, C A R
Baxter, M J
Bietzk, J E
Bietzk, R G
Black, I E
Bulow, E M
Cakebread, S R
Clough, S C
Cole, M A
Davy, K J
Griffith, S K W
Hooper, B K
Moffitt, S J
Morgan-Gray, K J
Puritz, R
Radford, R
Roscoe, A H
Shipman, A J

Shepperton

Andrews, J D B
Atkin, C M
Bates, C C
Bates, P G
Bellamy, S J
Candappa, N J C
Choat, D J M
Dash, P K
Dowdell, J W
Floyer, C E
Rogers, F A L
Walters, J N
Watson, G C
Wilson, S A

Shepton Mallet

Abel, J C
Balfour, J A
Blandford, A G
Bourke, M P
Cottle, A G
Cotton, J
Cudmore, J K
Horniblow, P J
Howes, C M
King-Holford, C G
Lindsay, J D I
Llewellyn, I E
Neil, C A
Norris, C S
Sharp, G M
Sheldon, J V
Stronkhorst, C H
Swayne, J M D
Walker, T R W
Waters, H M
Watson, D S B

Sherborne

Armstrong, P
Bamber, L H
Bartlett, I A C
Bastin, A C
Beatson, H M
Bishton, R L
Burke, L J
Byfield, D M
Cameron, M D
Cave, S G F

Shrewsbury

Childs, R A
Coast-Smith, R C
Collins, R E
Corfield, R M
Discombe, C J
Ellis, C M
Elsworth, C P
Fazakerley, N W
Forward, R F M
Foster, C A
Gaymer, A R
Gibb, J S
Gledhill, J M
Griffith, R A M
Griffiths, C S
Hargreaves, A J M
Hart, J D
Haynes, A
Heard, J H
Hearnden, A J
Hinton, J M
Jackman, C C
Laing, J D
Leeds, J R
Loud, B W
Lower, E S
Maxted, M J
McKenzie-Newton, E
Miles, G
Morris, S R S
Mottram, S N
Pell-Ilderton, R
Pennycook, C F
Pittman, J A L
Purcell, G R G
Quinn, M
Rasaiah, D
Rhys-Davies, H E
Robinson, M S
Rogers, W
Ross, A M
Royston, N J W
Schofield, L E
Scott Brown, N M
Sherwin, N J P
Smith, F
Stephenson, R V
Stronach-Hardy, S
Thomas, J
Townsend, D W
Tuke, J U

Shere

Taylor-Barnes, K

Sheringham

Colebrook, R D
Diggle, J H
Hurwood, H A
May, R G
Roebuck, P D
Sampson, P W
Smith, I C

Shetland

Aquilina, M P M
Baird, J L
Begg, C M
Bowie, S J
Briscoe, R A
Brown, A E
Cleminson, F B
Clubb, D R
Ditchburn, J S
Ditchburn, R K
Dowle, A K
Hayward, I A
Henry, E B
Howell, J M
Hunter, M D
MacDonald, I A R
McDonnell, M W
MacFarlane, D
Malcolm, D
Marshall, B
Teunisse, F
Vickery, C
Ward, H M

Shifnal

Anderson, E
Bold, L
Brinkley, M A
Dukes, I T
Fitzgerald, R
Hutton, P W
Leigh, P J
MacWhannell, A
Robson, J-A
Serhan, J T

Swarbrick, E T
Underwood-Whitney, A J
Whiting, S W

Shildon

Baliga, S K
Bhagat, A K
Evans, B
Grimes, L K
Velangi, L G
Walton, I T

Shipley

Alexander, S A
Allard, S A
Anderson, E R
Antrum, R M
Baker, A M
Baker, M R
Beauni, Y A
Besrest-Butler, C R
Bibby, J A
Blacker, I
Bradley, M C
Brooke, C M
Carr, M H
Chadwick, S P
Chitsabesan, P
Chitsabesan, P
Clayton, S D
Craig, J G
Crawford, R G
Cuthbert, M M
Dewhirst, C J
Driscoll, P A
Driver, N J
Edwards, P R
Eisner-Kissmann, G
Eisner, M C
Elliott, H
Ellison, J A
Fay, M R
Firth, G V
Gallagher, L B S
Gaunt, M L
Goldman, L H
Gomersall, P M
Halloran, J
Hanson, M
Henderson, M B C
Henderson, P A L
Hickey, K
Hodgson, J D
Hopker, S W
Humphrey, S H
Keating, E F
Kernohan, E E M
Khan, F N
Livingstone, H J
Livingstone, R I
Lynch, C
Marfell, K
Matthews, S
Murdoch, J M
Oldfield, M D
Passant, C C
Pearson, N R
Petty, J
Rajaratnam, G
Renwick, G K
Rewilak, A T
Riley, J L
Roberts, H E
Roberts, J F
Roberts, S E
Ross, R B S
Ruffe, S H
Rutter, I P
Saywell, J H
Sheldon, K M M
Ship, R H
Slinger, B C
Stead, G W
Taylor, M G
Tedd, C B
Thickett, C R
Thornton, D M
Tonks, W S
Towler, J N
Turner, S R
Urwin, S
Van Heel, D A
Waite, I J
Webb, S J
Weber, J S A
Wellsteed, A J
White, E G
Whittaker, M

Wilding, G
Wilson, L G
Yeomans, J D I
Young, L A

Shipston-on-Stour

Bennett, J R
Gilder, J E
Hance, J R
Harris, G
Johnston, I D A
Morgan, D L
Nixon, C M
Race, R L
Schofield, T P C
Smith, M I
Thorogood, C
Twyman, V R
Wemyss-Holden, S A
Whiteley, A M
Williams, G P

Shoreham-by-Sea

Aboutalebi, S
Allenby, M I
Anderson-Upcott, M
Bagley, G
Bagley, G
Banerji, K
Baskar, N
Beardmore, H J
Bellamy, P D
Bisset, A J
Clark, D W
Daneshmand, L
Dias, A M
Dighe, A M
Fellingham, W H
Floyd, M J
Foley, C M
Gordon, D N
Harrison, T H
Howard, S A
James, R W
Jha, P K
Kay, J M
Khalil-Nayer, N
Lal, S A
Lee, J J
Lyons, N S
MacClintock, R M
Melfi, N A
Nayyapam, A T
Nines, R J
O'Dwyer, J P
Prabhaker, S K
Putland, A J
Raiman, A C
Ratnarajah, C R
Redfern, M
Riddle, R W
Sarkar, S K
Selvadurai, V
Shute, P E
Smith, A D
Stafford, J
Stafford, M P C
Stevenson, T R T
Tucker, G P
Turner, P
Walker, T
Watson, A B
White, M-E
Yogalingam, M

Shotts

Galloway, C F
Jaigirdar, S H
Kasem, H
MacFarlane, C P
MacFarlane, V A
Marletta, S A
Milliken, S W G
Myatt, P S
Novosel, S
Walimbe, S

Shrewsbury

Ahmed, M A I
Aldridge, S M
Allen, S
Allsop, C J
Amissah-Arthur, J B
Anderson, P C W
Archer, A D
Arthur, M
Ashton, C A
Atkins, J
Awwad, S T
Baguley, I
Bailey, J J
Baker, S P
Baky, E S
Ballantyne, J H
Barker, A D
Barritt, P W
Bartlett, J I C
Beacock, C J M
Bell, D L
Benady, D R
Bennett, J M
Bennett, P S
Bennetts, K
Beresford, P M
Bevington, D J
Biddulph, J C
Blomfield, P I
Blunt, D J
Blunt, V A W
Boucher, L B
Bouwer, J C
Breese, S J
Bremner, S
Brice, J E H
Briggs, J E
Bright, J
Britton, R J
Brunner, H E
Bryson, J M
Buckett, W M
Bunting, C
Butcher, N B
Cameron, A M
Cameron, E M
Campbell, D C
Campbell, P L
Capps, F P A
Carr, R J
Carter, C B
Carter, E J
Carter, R
Clarke, H M
Clements, G M
Clesham, D J
Clover, A J P
Clowes, P
Cockill, S
Cocks, N M
Cole, G F
Collins, A J
Coppinger, S W V
Corfield, A J
Coventry, P J
Cowie, R S
Craig, E A
Cramp, C E
Cribb, G L
Critchley, M A
Crow, P G
Dapling, R B
Darvell, F J
Das, A K
Davies, G T
Davies, R J
Davis, J A
De Heer, N A
Dean, F K
Dean, M R E
Deshpande, S A
Dickens, D A
Dobrashian, R D
Dobrashian, R M
Dominique, A V
Douglas, C D
Downes, V B
Dunning, M W F
Eden, B W
Edmunds, S J
Edwards, S C
Elliott, A J
English, P J
Evans, C R
Evans, J E
Evans, S J
Everett, P S
Fallon, M J
Farrow, J S
Feather, S D W
Fenton, C J V
Fielding, J A
Fletcher, K D
Foley, S J
Foster, E J H
Foster, J M
Fox, A D
Franklin, G H M
Fraser, R A
Fry, D J
Fryer, M E
Gardner, R D
Geller, R J
Gemmell, H D
Gemmell, P C B
Gerrard, C A
Gill Candon, R
Gill, D B E C
Good, S I
Gould, D A
Gould, T J
Gowans, W J
Grech, W
Green, N J
Griffith, V J
Griffith, W F
Griffiths, T C
Groom, R L
Guarro-Miralles, M
Hallatt, S E
Hardwick, T J
Harnden, C E
Harnett, S J O
Harris, P
Hatts, R
Hawkridge, H
Hay, A M
Heaversedge, J T
Hill, L F
Hill, T R G
Hilton, B A B
Hilton, C M
Hodgson, K G
Hollings, A S J
Hollings, N P
Houghton, A D
Houghton, A L
Hudson, C F E
Hughes, R K G
Hunt, T M
Hurlow, R A
Hussein, R S A
Jenkins, D C R R
Jones, A P
Jones, S G
Joscelyne, J C
Joshi, C M
Kadiani, M R
Katti, S M
Keeling-Roberts, J
Kelly, C P
Kelly, S E
Kendall, C N
Kent, S E
Khan, A R
King, D H
King, N J
King, P
King, R C
Lacey, B W
Lancaster, K L
Lane, J
Latto, D M B
Leaman, C A
Leedham, P W
Lewis, D C
Lewis, D L
Lewis, V J
Linford, S M J
Llewellyn, R E
Lovett, M C
Lowdon, D G R
Lowe, M D
Lowe, P P
Lucas, P L M
Lyle, S A
McCloud, J M
McCloy, J W
McGeoch, C M
Macleod, A F
Matthias, J E
Maurice, C D J
Mike, N N H
Miller, M E
Mitchell, N J
Mollart, J E
Molodecka, J M
Molodeckj, C A
Moore, N A
Moore, P C
Moore, R M A
Morris, C A
Morris, D S
Morris, D F
Morris, J M
Morris, P
Mott, P A E
Muir, D W W
Murphy, C J
Murphy, S M
Myers, D H
Neale, A J
Nehaul, L K
Neil, W F
Nicholls, K R
Nicholls, P E
Nicholson, A B
Nightingale, S R
Norman, W J
O'Connor, N T J
O'Mahony, M F M
O'Neill, P M
O'Shea, M J
O'Sullivan, H L
Oates, S E
Oldroyd, R E
Olley, S F
Orme, R I
Otter, A E
Owen, A E
Owen, E N
Page, M J
Palmer, R M
Park, R
Parry, J M
Patrick, J H
Pattison, A
Penman, E H G
Pepper, J M
Perks, W H
Pickard-Michels, P M H
Pickard, S J
Pollock, D
Povey, J M
Povey, J D
Powell, B J
Prescott, M V
Prichard, A J N
Pringle, R G
Quinton, P J
Rathbone, A R
Redford, D H A
Reeves, S E
Reid, F C
Reid, S C
Roberts, M
Robertson, C
Robinson, D
Rooney, S J
Ross, A
Ross, G B
Rousseau, M J
Russell, K
Russell, N C
Sansom, H E
Sayce, G E
Shaikh, G
Shipstone, D P
Shore, R J
Simmons, M E
Singh, A B
Skinner, D W
Slocombe, G W
Smail, D H
Smail, M V
Smith-Stanleigh, P
Smith, J A
Smith, M S H
Smith, R G M
Smith, R C
Smith, S D
Sobahi, E M
Somervaille, T C P
Somerwell, J I
Sowerbutts, J G
Stapleton, E M
Stringer, J K
Stringer, J R
Symons, M
Tapp, A J S
Taylor, N J
Taylor, W R J
Thevathasan, P A
Thomas, C D
Thompson, A
Thompson, G R
Thompson, J
Thompson, R H
Thorne, A K
Thorne, W I J
Tomlinson, C J
Toms, A D
Treasure, P W
Trethowan, W N
Tully, W M
Tyrrell, C G
Tyrrell, P N M
Ullegaddi, A F

Sidcup

Ullegaddi, R
Waite, A J
Walker, P M
Wallbridge, D R
Walton, W J
Warren, R E
Watson, H R
Watson, T R
Watson, W H
Watson, W M B
Watt, J B
Wedgwood, D L
Welch, R J
West, N E J
West, T E T
Westwood, W D
White, J F
Whittingham, D I
Whittingham, W P
Whitworth, N H
Wilde, A H
Williams, H E
Williams, I
Williamson, J M
Wilmshurst, P T
Wilson, R S E
Wong, W Z
Woodford, C P
Wright, I P
Yeandle, M P
Young, P M

Sidcup

Aboel-Sood, A A M A
Ahluwalia, M S
Amin, R
Bamji, A N
Barker, P G
Barry, W C W
Bhattad, H L
Bhogal, H S
Black, D A
Bokhari, S A J
Bowcock, S J
Chapman, E A
Cheung Chun Wah, N T
Chopra, M
Cooper, J E
Crinall, F J
Currie, P A
Das Gupta, P
Davies, T W
Davis, M I M
Davis, T P
Denton, E P
Donnelly, J E
Donnelly, W J
Durcan, T G
Efthymiou, E
El-Radhi, A S
Elsey, T A
Eustace, D L S
Evans, C D
Farrant, P C
Geraghty, R J
Gibbens, M V
Gillmore, J D
Goligher, J E
Gould, B A
Gutte, H F
Gurruchaga, M
Hall, D S
Harding, D R
Hemlock, A
Hill, M D
Hinds-Howell, C M
Holden, A P
Housley, R C E
Hugkulstone, C E
Isaacs, C J
Ismail, M H M
Jha, A K
Jones, E M
Joyce, J J
Kagalwala, A R
Karunakaran, V
Keshavarz-Kermani, H
Khalid, M A A
Khawaja, H
Khoo, E K
Kingston, J M
Kureya, P
Kwan, W K C
Lam, D G K
Lang, A C
Leary, S M
Lee, D J H
Lynch, S F

Maaita, M E K
McKinnon, J
Martin, G M
Mascarenhas, F J
Medhurst, J
Millard, E M
Milne, D
Money, R P
Neal, C J
Nichols, R W T
Nikolaou, C M
Nosseri, M N A H
O'Gorman, A J
Oliver, B J
Pain, A K
Patel, H
Patel, I S
Patel, N
Pathmanathan, T
Pervaiz, K
Phatak, P S
Quickenden, D R J
Rajayogeswaran, S
Rajvanshi, R
Rana, S
Rao, S G
Rassam, S M B
Reyes, R J
Ritchie, K A
Roberts, E J
Rodricks, N P
Scott, S E
Sharif, A T
Shee, C D
Shepherd, T P
Smart, C C
Smith, R N J
Stellman, R M F
Sutton, P G S
Tanna, V
Taylor, C J
Thilagarajah, K
Ward, S M
Whitefield, L A
Whitmore, D N
Wickramasuriya, B P N
Woodward, J W
Woolfson, J

Sidmouth

Alhadeff, B
Anderson, J C
Anderton, P M
Atkinson, P G
Capper, N D
Carless, C A
Davies, D J
Dervisevic, S
Dillon, B P
Drew, C D
Fison, L G
Gay, M J
Hailey, S R
Hall, D P
Hunt, A C
Kinder, J J
Makinson, D H
Matthews, C E
Meacock, H R
Michelmore, H R A
Morris, E N
Morrison, A B
Moulding, K W
Naylor, P F D
Pepper, G J
Pepper, G J
Rawkins, M D
Read, N J
Ridler, A H
Ruddy, R A
Slot, M J W
Snekal, W
Spence, J S
Thorp, T A J

Sittingbourne

Birch, R G
Brown, C J
Cantor, F M
Clarke, D R
Connellan, E Z
Cotton, J P
Cousins, P
Crawford, I C
Cusworth, R J
Dias, A S
Else, O F
Farquharson, M J
Garlant, A J A
Gray, P

Hall, A P
Hickman, R C
Hickman, S J
Hudsmith, J G
Jones, D G
Kumar, R B
Kyle, D W
Livesey, C A
Marden, J M I
Marsh, C M
Morrish, C H F
Philpott, M J
Puranik, A
Rees, R J
Rishi, N
Russell, J R
Sabaratnam, S
Saha, B K
Selby, K
Sikdar, A N
Singh, P N
Singh, S K
Skudder, J
Taylor, R C
Thompson, I G
Venkatachalam, D N
Wilcox, K E
Witts, S J

Skegness

Almond, I M
Almond, B L
Anderson, J A
Archer, G A
Armstrong, D M
Boulind, P R
Chaggar, J S
Chester, S K
Cotton, P A
Dewar, D D
Fox, M B
Garg, S
Ghani, U
Good, W R
Johnson, R
Jones, J S
Kinnison, R N
Lawson, S A
Loftus, A
Mitchell, P D V
Morris, L G
Najmi, S M A
North, R F
Pendrigh, D C
Pollock, A J E
Rudrappa, C
Seal, R L
Shekhdar, H H
Sykes, S A G
Williams, R J

Skelmersdale

Bhushan, M
Bisarya, A K
Bisarya, A
Brennan, D J M
Chang, D S K
Faza, M K
Flood, G
Gerval, M-O
Gouda, M A-H M
Harrower, J E
Hicks, A J
Hopkins, C
Littler, A D
Mead, G S
Minchom, A M
Modha, J S
Orr, G A
Petermann, A G
Qamruddin, A O
Qamruddin, M
Ryan, D J
Saxena, S
Sharma, A
Shirlaw, H A D
Sibery, A J
Singh, B B
Singh, U
Sur, S K
Tekle, I
Watras, G J
Wilkinson, S L
Williams, L R

Skelmorlie

Balmer, F
Balmer, F J
Balmer, I M
Chassels, M R

Clarke, A
Di Paola, M P
Dunn, H M
Hepburn, J
Lyell, A
McColl, C M
McColl, D J
Seenan, P J
Tam, P G E

Skene

Carleton, R L
Dawson, B M

Skipton

Abelman, W
Allen, J P
Baker, J R
Bostock, E A
Bransfield, J J
Brown, G W
Bundock, A D
Cambeen, L D A F
Churcher, S J
Clarke, J
Cotter, D H G
Crabtree, N A
Craig, C J
Daggett, H R
Davidson, C L
Davies, A
Dudley, B
Egdell, H G
Farrugia, J F P
Fisher, G B R
Gazzard, A M
Goodall, J R
Goodall, J F
Gregory, P A
Hamman, M
Harrison, C R
Hassey, Dr
Hill, R
Holmes, B M
Hunter, M A
Hunter, M
Imrie, J M
Jackson, A J
Keppie, W
Kidd, J L
Kinnish, I K
Kleyn, C E
Lethem, J E
Levy, L J
Love, G P
McAdam, H B
Maddison, J E
Miles, D W
Morgan, A G
Morrison, A
Pearson, D J
Pilkington, C E
Powell, J O J
Pyrah, R D
Robinson, C H
Roper, J P
Smulders, T C
Sumnall, A G
Thomas, J A
Thomas, K E
Tinsley, E G F
Tomlinson, S B
Wagenaar, N
Webber, R J
White, T M
Whitehead, P S
Wilkinson, H S
Wood, J L
Woodhouse, B A
Woods, S M
Wright, C J

Sleaford

Aldaya Lorenzo, J M
Aslam, M
Aslam, N-S
Birrell, A C
Brandreth, T K
Carbonell Casasus, J J
Cartwright, M A
Chambers, H W
Collinge, J D
Denton, G
Dunn, B
Gamble, W G H
Glendinning, D
Hackney, J H
Haigh, R D
Half, A A
Henderson, R W

Hill, K E
Horner, A E
Humphry, N J C
Johnson, R I
Kader, H E H H A
Lorimer, A H
Morris, P A
Morsy, M K
Mukherjee, T
Murphy, D A
Parry, J E
Pinchbeck, F W
Price, P T
Radomski, J W
Sheldon, K J
Swan, A I
Timperley, A C
Varma, A N
Walker, J
Walsham, A C
Webster, J A
Webster, T M
White, P N G
Wiseman, E C

Slough

A-Ali, N
Adam, N S-E
Adcock, K M
Aeberhard, P J
Aggarwal, M
Ahmad, F S
Ahmad, R S
Al-Basi, I A I
Aldren, C P
Ali, R S
Alkateb, K F L
Allen, S M
Allum, R L
Andraka, D
Arora, S K
Asaad, N M
Ashby, M
Badr, A A G M
Bahia, S O
Bain, R
Bambridge, E J C
Banerjee, P
Barakat, K
Barnes, S F
Barrett, A R
Barrett, D
Bartman, M
Benedict, C B
Bhargava, R
Bienz, N
Bird, K J
Biring, M S
Birman, P
Blackwood, R A
Blanshard, G P
Blanshard, M S
Bleach, R N
Botherway, G J D
Bradley, S G
Brockless, J B P
Bukht, M D G
Burden, G J
Burfoot, C
Burkitt, R T
Campbell, E J
Cassell, P G
Charig, M J
Chaudhry, S H
Chawla, K K
Cheese, N E
Chinn, R E
Christian, M S
Christophi, G
Chung, H E
Chung, H M
Clark, R E
Clarke, E D
Clifford, E M
Cockburn, I T R
Coleman, N S
Cook, I S
Coppin, C M S
Cowen, J M
D'Souza, E
Daily, B N J
Daily, S D J
Dalton, A N
Dalton, D
Davies, G R
Davies, S
Davis, N
Dawson, G H

Dawson, S G
Dega, R K
Depani, A J
Dhatt, M S
Diamond, P S
Dickinson, J C
Dimitry, E S
Dogra, V K
Donnison, A B
Draper, P W
Duggal, A
Easton, J A
Edwards, J N
El Zeiny, H M S
Evans, S M
Evans, W M I
Eyers, J G
Fagan, B
Fairbank, J
Farooq, N
Feegrade, M D
Fell, R H
Fernandes, J R
Fernandes, P
Foster, D F
Fryer, H A
Gavin, L D M
Gavin, V J
Gilbert, J M
Gilfeather, L B C
Gordon, N
Green, B J
Green, R W
Green, S J
Grewal, N
Grewal, P D
Gunawardene, K A
Hamid, A W
Harrison, S H
Havelock, C M
Hayward, S A
Hear, G S
Heath, P K
Hemantha Kumar, M L R
Holdstock, G E
Holgate, H
Hussain, M
Irvine, M C G
Jack, R D
Jamal, F
Jamil, M T
Jefferis, A F
Jones, C A
Jones, R A K
Kanski, J J
Kaushal, S
Khan, A
Khan, N
Khan, Q A
King, A
Kochhar, A
Kumar, H
Kumar, S
Kumar, S
Lakhan, A K
Lane, R E
Larcombe, C
Lawn, E M
Levi, S
Lewis, C
Lewis, N L
Lewis, Y K
Litchfield, J C
Llewellyn, M J
Lloyd Parry, J M
Lorch, D M
Loveland, R C
Lunn, J A
Lynch, S M
McCarthy, J
McDonnell, M P
McIlroy, D I
McIntyre, H P J
MacMahon, M T
Maddocks, W T A
Maidment, C G H
Malik, K Z
Malik, Q K
Mann, S S
Marghoob, M A
Marghoob, M S
Martinez Devesa, P
Masood, T
Matheson, A C W
Mickiewcz, A J
Mokete, B
Monro, J A
Moreau, A P M

South Croydon

Mountford, T H
Mudannayaka, T S S
Muneer, A
Murphy, M D
Murrell, H C
Nabi, I M
Neale, R J H
Newson-Smith, G R
Newton, K L
Ng, C Y
O'Dowd, J G M
Ostle, K E
Overton, M R
Parbhoo, P H
Parry-Williams, H W
Paton, D
Peck, B W
Peter, T
Pickering, A H
Posmyk, B M
Purvis, D J
Raj, I
Rajapaksa, T J
Reece, A H M
Reed, J M
Reginald, P W
Rehman, H
Robinson, L
Robinson, M V
Rodgers, D M
Rogers, J E
Rosenberg, R M
Saini, M
Salmon, J G D
Sandhu, G S
Sekhar, R
Sharma, K C
Sharma, U
Shayo, S D
Singh, K M
Skelly, W J
Smith, B L
Sohal, M
Strawford, J
Sudbury, P R
Sulh, J S
Sumanasuriya, R C
Sutlieff, P A
Tansey, S P
Telford, M E
Tewari, R M
Thomas, D J
Thompson, J N
Thomson, H A
Thornton, L S H
Thyveetil, M D
Trivedi, J
Umapathy, A
Vinayak, B C
Walkden, V M
Walker, J A B L
Walters, R J L
Ward, F G
Wardale, D
Watson, L
Watts, M B
West, G P
Westlake, D M
Wiggins, J
Wilkins, M R
Wiseman, D B
Wobi, B
Wood, C B
Wright, K D
Yates, C
Yousif, S Y
Zavody, M

Smethwick

Arrand, R M
Breen, D S T
Chawla, H S
Chawla, S
Clark, D
Dhillon, A S
Etti, O R
Grant, S E A
Grubb, H R
Hale, M C
Hurst, J
Joseph, A P
Kang, L S
Loader, A C
Loader, S M
Mann, M S
Matharu, S S
Middleton, J D
Palmer, A E S
Preston, P R

Rahman, A K M R
Ridley, J
Sam, R C
Sharma, D
Towers, D G
Wanke, M E A
Wong, P T Y
Wright, S L

Snodland

Fahmy, G E I F
Morrissey, T D
Terrell, H M

Solihull

Abdel-Malek, G T
Abdou, M S
Ainsworth, A F C
Ali, N
Anderson, M
Anfilogoff, R
Annetts, S E
Anthony, Y
Arbuthnot, J E
Armond, J R
Aston, W J S
Ball, C M
Ball, E F
Banerjee, A K
Banerjee, S T
Bannourrah, F E A
Barkell, E M
Barraclough, J E
Barsoum, G H G
Baxter, JGB
Bayly, R A
Beale, D J
Beaumont, B
Beaumont, H E
Begum, Z
Benson, M T
Berry, D A
Bhatti, M E
Bieker, M
Bland, K G
Bleby, M J
Botting, T D J
Bower, K L
Bower, R J
Bowie, H I C
Bowser, J
Boyce, A
Bramley, R
Bramley, R H
Bramley, S
Branton, T
Bray, A J
Bridgwater, F A J
Brigstocke, S-J
Brooks, S
Brown, D P
Brown, N S
Browne, A S
Bsat, R A-G
Byrne, P G
Caisley, J
Cameron, P S
Campbell, J B
Canning, W C
Cayton, R M
Challens, A S
Charlton, M H
Cheong, P J H
Chesner, I M
Chillala, J
Chitnis, J-G
Chopra, R
Clapham, M C C
Clarke, J P
Cogbill, P G
Coleman, G A W
Congdon, A M
Congdon, R M
Cooper, R F
Cowles, S M
Cox, J R
Cox, M A
Crean, J P
Cribb, G T
Crichton, B E
Croft, J A
Darling, S G
Davenport, J A
Davies, B Z
Davies, C M
Davies, K P
Davies, P M
Dawson, R G
Dawson, S P

Dean, I M
Dedicoat, M J
Delaney, M P
Dennison, P H
Deval, S
Devarajan, R
Dharmaratnam, R
Dobson, H R
Dobson, S
Ducrow, M
Dunn, K R
Dunn, M J
Dwyer, N S J P
Dwyer, S D N
Dyas, A C
Edwards, C W
Edwards, E
Edwards, S
Ellis, C V
Ellis, M
Evans, A M
Evans, G A
Evans, K R L
Farag, S F S
Faridi, S
Farmer, G S
Farmer, P R
Fear, R C
Feehan, C J
Ferguson, A G A
Finch, T M
Fleming, S K
Fletcher, C J
Flewett, T H
Font Olive, M D M
Forster, E N
Fox, J
Fradd, V J
Francis, A
Fraser Jones, J
Gandhi, B R
Gay, M A
Geddes, A M
Gee, M E
Georgy, M S
Ghannam, I M T
Gibbs, R A
Gill, P S
Grant, A J
Gray, J W
Green, I D
Green, K N
Green, S L
Grewal, G K
Grillage, M G
Grogan, J C
Gupta, V
Habib, N K
Hagon, J A
Hall, S W
Halloran, C M
Hardeman, M E
Harrison, L J
Harrower, R F
Harrower, S I
Harry, J
Hattotuwa, K A G
Hill, E B
Hill, M R
Hobday, D I
Hogan, D J
Hoggart, B
Holland, C J
Holt, J A
Holweger, W I
Homer, J J
Hope, J I
Hopkins, F J
Houghton, A S
Howarth, G F
Hughes, H M
Hukin, A J
Hutton, J F K
Innes, J A
Inwood, J L
Iredale, M J
Jackson, B R
Jacobs, P
Jago, D G T
James, G J
Jarrett, G R
Jenkinson, D M
Jones, E
Jones, M M C
Jones, T G
Joshi, R K
Kadow, K W
Kale, V R
Kale, V

Kalra, N D
Kandula, P
Keenan, R D
Kelly, M M
Kershaw, M J R
Kerton, J E
Khan, I D
King, B A
King, T S
Kinning, E
Knickenberg, C J
Koko, I
Kondratowicz, E A
Kotecha, S B
Lawley, J L
Lee, L K
Leese, J
Leschen, M E
Lewis, C A
Lewis, G A
Leyton, E
Liegeois, H M
Liley, H T
Little, J A
Longson, P J
Love, P S
Lupoli, A
Lynch, W A
McCarthy, B E
McDarmaid, E J
Maceachern, D A
McEvoy, D M
McKenzie, K T C
Mackinnon, J
McNabb, S J
McRoberts, M T
Marson, B W
Marx, H M
Maskill, J M
Mason, E M
McDermott, A-L
Melrose, P A
Ment, J L
Michalos, M
Middleton, M D
Milan, P A
Milligan, W M
Milner, G L
Moore, V J
Moppett, J P
Morgan, I D P
Morgan, R H
Morgan, T A
Moss, S A
Mukherjee, S
Murray, M L
Muthukumar, T
Nagra, I S
Nakhla, V
Naylor, C R
Ndowa, F J
Needham, P G
Nicol, B J
Nicol, R E
Ninan, T K
Nixon, J R
Noel, D J
O'Connor, B B
Orakwe, S I
Oyede, C A
Paget, R I J
Palmer, R G
Parkes, S J
Patel, E D
Patkar, A A
Payne, E G M
Pearson, M J
Perry, D W
Peters, M J
Peters, S E
Phillips, W J
Pickering, A M
Pilling, K J
Playfor, B E
Polson, R J
Portsmouth, O H D
Pottinger, K A
Powis, M D
Price, P H
Priestley, K A
Protheroe, D N
Protheroe, R H B
Putman, J M
Qureshi, S
Raghavan, S
Rahman, S I
Rayner, C R W
Reda, F E
Reddy, V A P

Reuben, A D
Robinson, A W
Robson, J L
Ross, J H
Rowbotham, C J F
Rowe, J L
Rulewski, N J
Ryan, P G
Ryder, I G
Salman, S M
Samworth, L J
Sandhu, J S
Sandler, M
Satchell, S C
Scott, P E
Sengupta, D
Seymour Mead, R
Shackley, E C
Sheikh, A J
Shilling, R S
Shinton, M
Shinton, N K
Shortland-Webb, S C
Shortland-Webb, W R
Simoyi, T
Skinner, G R B
Sloan, P J M
Smethurst, J R
Smith, C A
Smith, C D
Smith, R R
Smyth, A T
Smyth, U R
Sokhi, G S
Soppitt, R W
Stacey, L
Stamp, E J
Stanton, A S
Stenhouse, T
Sterry, M J G
Stevenson, L
Stewart, A M
Stockdale, N A J
Stockdale, R C
Stokes, E L
Stores, O P R
Stuart, I R
Stuart, J
Sturdee, D W
Sutcliffe, A J
Tadros, F F
Tariq, S L
Taverner, J P
Taylor, C M
Taylor, E A
Teare, L J
Terry, S H
Thorpe, G W
Tibbatts, L M
Tincombe, M R
Todman, R C F
Tomkins, M J
Towey, R M
Travis, P J
Tremlett, J E
Upton, W S
Vanhouse, S H
Vijh, M
Waddell, A M
Waddell, J E
Waddell, N J H
Walker, R S
Walker, R A
Walker, W M
Wallis, A J
Ward, E G
Watson, H B
Watts, S G T
Weale, A R
Wears, R
West, C A
Western, P J
Weston, C G
Wijayawickrama, A
Wilkes, D
Willshaw, H E
Wilson, P G
Wilson, R J
Winter, S C A
Wyldes, M P
Xifaras, G P
Younan, F H
Zeitoune, S M

Somerton

Bark, R M
Barnett, J M
Bonnington, S P A
Cruikshank, A

Griffiths, R E
Hill, K S
Short, D H
Skeath, T H
Sleap, P G F
Smith, R A
Steele-Perkins, A P
Taylor, M G
Wolton, A D

South Brent

Adam, P A
Baker, J L
Busfield, A
Dale, B B
Edbrooke, D R
Halliday, J J
Hart, M T W
Hill, J D
Kelly, A S

South Croydon

Ablett, J G
Adams, M B
Adegoke, A O
Ahmed, S
Baverstock, R A
Begum, S
Bookless, A S
Bower, N P
Burrin, E M
Cahill, D J
Cahill, P H M
Campbell, P
Cashman, M E
Chadha, A
Clementson, M R
Cockell, J L B
Danbury, R
Dean, R M
Deane, A M
Dempsey, O P
Ferguson, R
Fisher, B A
Found, S M
Gajjar, S
Gallagher, V A
Garratt, P M
George, M S
Georgekutty, K K A
Gifford, C S E
Gillgrass, J W
Gnani, S
Green, E E
Haq, A I
Heal, K
Hopkin, J A
Jasper, W M
Kanagasundaram, M
Kelleher, D
Khan, M A A
Kumar, A
Kurwa, B R
Larkworthy, J B
Lawlor, K M
Lyell, D A
McEwan, A
McEwan, G J
McEwan, T E
Malik, I S
Matthews, G G
Meeran, M H M
Meese, J D
Mitchiner, M B
Ohuiginn, P
Orchard, A S
Parsons, H M
Patel, N
Perera, P G A A
Phillips, T J G
Rutter, J M
Sachdev, B
Sanderson, R D S
Sathananthan, R
Sathananthan, S
Shaw, C E
Shaw, P C
Smart, L K
Southcott, R D C
Spurring, R D L
Stein, A G
Stiby, E K
Stockley, A G I
Stockwell, J C
Strymowicz, C
Towner, C H
Trompetas, A
Urquhart, J F

South Molton

Walker, A G
Wallace, W J

South Molton
Agnew, S A
Biss, T T
Darling, J C
Doddington, R A
Gibb, C A
Hadfield, C S L
Hawkins, C J
Morris, D
Norris, R L
Shelley, J R
Sherlock, W
Warner, J
Westcott, R H

South Ockendon
Bellworthy, S V
Bulpitt, D C H
Cousins, C H
Davies, A M
Haque, M A
Horgan, J T C
Jayakumar, C S
Lafferty, P M
Leighton, L F A
Okunola, O O
Williams, M
Wright, C E

South Petherton
Barclay, A D M
Bark, O G
Bryant, C J
Buckle, J R
Gaminara, M
Glendinning, N W
Lemon, J H
Lucas, H M
McFadzean, J A
Malins, D F J
Newman, R

South Queensferry
Ashworth, A J
Cackette, C G
Carson, A J
Cormack, A M
Creber, C J
Gilchrist, A M
Hart, W M
Hughes, B M
Hughes, G H
Jack, V J
Kearns, P P
Leckie, G J M
Love, C D B
Macdonald, M J
Osler, D F
Robertson, J F
Stewart, L
Stirrat, F W
Stuart, J D
Williamson, E J

South Shields
Al-Durrah, F M I
Alfakih, K M A
Andrews, J I
Ansari, S H
Armitage, T G
Arthur, J B
Attard, D J
Batchellor, F H
Bennett, R J
Bhalla, R
Bhalla, R
Blair, T T
Bone, M F
Bora, A U
Bradshaw, C
Bryson, L G
Chander, S
Chhabra, S
Cope, L H
Courtenay, H L
Cowley, N
Craig, M S
Cronin, S M
Cummins, K T
Curtis, R J
Davidson, I G
Daya, S G
Dayan, E
Duncan, L E
Eggleston, J M
Evans, M
Fairbairn, D

Gallagher, J E
Gallagher, M
Gandhi, H B
Gooptu, D
Grainger, P G
Haque, M A
Haque, M A
Hargreaves, C S
Hasan, A M
Hendrick, A M
Hill, A M
Holmes, R I
Jackson, A
Jana, K
Jay, R H
Jenkinson, J R
Jones, N K
Joypaul, B V
Karandikar, N
Kulkarni, D J
Lambert, M F
Lishman, A H
McCarthy, J H
McClure, A M
McManus, W H
Macmillan, M
Madhok, R
Malik, B A
Massam, M
Mehta, R
Miller, S G
Minty, I L
Muchall, A J
Mullea, M S
Muncaster, A E
Muncaster, J W
Naroz, N A
Nellist, P J
Nwabineli, N J
O'Donnell, S J
Olajide, V F
Owen, T
Parr, J H
Pattison, I
Perrins, J K
Pervaiz Khan, N
Pollard, K P
Ramli, A S
Reece, V A C
Rogers, I
Roy, S P
Roysam, G S
Sarkar, M
Scott, S
Setty, G R
Seymour, A
Seymour, K
Siepert, M
Simm, A
Spencer, H S
Srivastava, S
Stevens, K M
Swai, E A
Taylor, M
Tose, J
Vadnai, G
Watson, D M
Wilson, C N
Wolferstan, M
Wynne, A
Wynne, K S

South Wirral
Awan, M T S
Barber, N C
Barr, A D B
Birch, A D
Brocki, J L
Burgess, G
Burke, N J
Cassidy, R V
Charlick, B J
Corbett, G F
Cowan, B B
Cunningham, P N
Darling, R A
Dickinson, J E
Dowson, J T
Duckitt, H A
Dupont, M M B
Fawcett, G E
Flattery, H B
Francis, I L
Fraser, F
Graham, P J
Guest, N D
Hackett, R
Haggart, B G
Hales, T B

Harvey, D J
Hayle, G B
Higgins, N L
Jellicoe, P A
Jones, L E
Judge, A P
Kennedy, J A
Kennedy, M R
Kiff, R S
Klafkowski, G
Knowles, K
Knowles, P A
Lockwood, A J
Lockyer, M W
Longstaffe, B C
Macdonald, C J
McGuigan, J R
Martin, H C
Mills, R D
Mills, S J
Mills, T D
Milne, G M
Mitra, S
Mohiuddin, R J
Morrison, I A
Murphy, J
Murphy, P N
Naylor, P
O'Friel, A J
O'Shea, M J
O'Shea, M
O'Shea, S J
Owen, S W
Reilly, E I
Riley, K J
Roberts, J
Roberts, W G
Roohi, S
Searle, T A
Shaw, S A
Smith, N
Snook, R N
Stringer, J
Stuart, R A
Thorneloe, M H
Tolley, P F R
Townson, P J
Troup, D
Van Griethuijsen, H J
Wall, C M
Wallace-Jones, D R
Walsh, J
Warren, F M
Washington, M I
Willan, A L
Willcox, R
Wood, M W W
Wood, N
Woolley, E J

Southall
Aali, S A
Abrahamson, G M
Acland, K M
Aggarwal, A K
Akhtar, A
Akhtar, M S
Alam, F
Amor, T J
Anstiss, T J
Arnold, J D
Ash, S A
Ashraf, M
Aujla, K S
Bagga, A K
Baidwan, M K
Banu, S Z
Baylis, C A
Beverly, M C
Bharal, I
Bimbh, K S
Birring, R K
Botros, A M
Bracey, B J
Bradshaw, E G
Bullock, T
Chatrath, A M
Crouch, G K
Cummins, M C
D'Souza, B
Dabas, V K
Davis, A J
Dent, J A
Dhandee, I S
Dhesi, S S
Eggleston, J
Falzon, M R
Fellow-Smith, E A
Gautam, S K

Gosal, M S
Gowrie Mohan, S
Hayat, F
Hee, C J
Hee, M
Hegde, U M
Hillier, R J
Hinds, N P
Hutchins, K J
Iyer, S K K
Jagdev, S P K
Jhooty, H K
Johal, K K
Johal, S S
Johl, R
Kahtan, N
Karagounis, A
Keany, M
Khin Thet Maw, Dr
Koak, Y P S
Kohli, V K
Korpal, K
Kyaw Htin, M
Lack, S J
Lahon, K
Laishley, R S
Lally, S S
Lambert, M T
Lock, M P A W
McNeil, N I
Malik, A H
Mangat, H K
Mangat, N S
Mann, B S
Martindale, B V
Mather, H M
Mehta, K
Mendel, D
Michie, C A
Nathwani, D K
Naughton, M A
O'Connor, E J M
Papadakis, A
Payne, S D W
Petch, E W A
Philpott, N J
Qadan, H M A
Qureshi, S A
Radhakrishnan, S
Rahman, F K
Rai, J S
Rampes, H
Randhawa, R S
Richman, S
Robertson, J R
Rosenbaum, T P
Rudolf, M
Sadhra, K S
Saluja, R S
Samra, G S
Sandhu, P J S
Sanghera, V
Scott-Coombes, E L
Scott, J C
Sehdev, R S
Seiden, Z A S
Shakir, N A
Sharma, A K
Sharma, K
Sharma, V
Singh, K
Sivanesan, R
Sloper, K S
Soljak, M A
Stanford, M E
Svensson, W E
Taw, H
Taylor, R H
Toor, K S
Treasaden, I H
Verma, S
Walker, A E
Waller, K G
Walsh, P M J
Wesby, R D
Westman, A J
Whitehead, E M
Williams, D O
Wong, A K M W
Woodbridge, K

Southam
Madan, L S
O'Mahony, G A M
Rice, G J

Southampton
Adams, J H
Adcock, S J P

Adey, D F W
Aguilera Roig, X
Ahmed, S
Ajaz, M A
Alemi, Z
Allen, N A
Allen, T E
Alveyn, C G
Anderson, F H
Andrewes, D A
Angus, W H N
Appleton, P J
Arden, N K
Armstrong, R D
Arney, N P
Arthur, M J P
Arulrajan, A E
As, A K
Ashburn, A E A
Ashurst, P M
Asopa, V
Atkinson, A C
Austen, B L
Ayres, C M
Baber, F R
Bailey, I S
Bailey, R L
Bainbridge, B M
Baird, J
Baker, A K
Baker, S S
Bakowski, M T
Baldwin, D S
Balkwill, P H
Bamforth, J
Bamforth, R M W
Bansi, D S
Barber, Z E
Barendt, G H
Barker, C S
Barker, D J P
Barker, R M
Barnard, E E P
Barnes, K
Barnes, R M
Barnfield, M
Barrett, D S
Barros D'Sa, I J
Bartlet, L B
Basarab, A
Bass, P S
Bateman, A C
Batty, V B
Bauchop, A
Baxendine-Jones, J A
Bayley, E K
Bayly, R A
Baynes, S C
Bedford, B
Bennett, M A V
Benning, A S
Bentley, I S
Betts, M T
Betts, P R
Betts, T R
Bevin, S V
Bhatt, H B
Bhatt, S J
Biddle, A
Billington, T R M
Binge, Y
Bingham, M A
Birch, B R P
Birch, S
Blaquière, R M
Blount, A M
Blunden, J
Boddington, H J
Boeree, N R
Bolt, S A
Booth, A D
Bosman, J J
Boulton, F E
Bowyer, G W
Boyd, I E
Boyd, U B
Boyes, S A
Boyle, J R
Bradberry, S W
Bradford, A N B
Brading, L S
Bramley, K W
Brearley, R L
Breen, D J
Brewer, P J
Brewster, A L
Brice, J G
Briggs, R S J
Brighouse, D H

Briley, M
Brock, S J
Brooke, M J
Brown, A S
Brown, E M
Brown, I
Brunton, F J
Buchanan, D R
Buchanan, R B
Buchanan, R
Buckley, H K
Buis, C
Bulleid, J A
Burke, L J
Burns, A C R
Burrows, S
Burton, J
Burwell, J R
Bush, J T
Bute, K J
Butler, D A
Butler, J A
Butler, P J
Byrne, C D T
Callahan, H M
Callinan, L F J
Calver, A L
Cameron, D J S
Campbell, D
Campbell, D R
Campkin, T V
Candy, D R
Candy, J R
Candy, J
Canning, C R
Carey, J A
Carlisle, A J
Carr, N J
Carruth, J A S
Carter, M R
Carter, P P
Casson, I
Cates, C A
Cave, B L D
Chadwick, B D
Chadwick, M
Chaudry, Z R
Chisholm, I H
Choksi, S M D
Choong Kam Chong, L S
Christian, P B
Clancy, M J
Clarke, N M P
Clarke, P J
Clayton, B E
Cleak, V E
Clearkin, P M
Cleave, N J
Clough, J B
Clouter, C A
Clover, J A
Coggon, D N M
Cole, A M
Coleman, G P
Coleman, M A G
Cone, A M
Connett, G J
Constable, G L
Cook, P L
Cookson, S F
Coombs, N J
Cooper, A F A P
Cooper, C
Cooper, E K
Coppin, B D
Coppola, A M T
Corfe, S E
Correa, J B
Corser, R B
Costa, S
Coutts, J F
Crawford, V A
Crook, T L
Crosse, M M
Crossley, R B
Crutchley, D G
Culora, G A
Cumming, J
Cunliffe, J
Cunningham, L M
Curtis, C L
Damms, J C
Darch, M H
Darley, T A
Das, P
Dave, B-R P
Davidson, K W
Davidson, P H

Southampton

Davies, C J
Davies, E M
Davies, K
Davies, M S
Davies, S D T
Davis, D
Dawson, J A
Day, I N M
Day, L R A
Dayson, D F
De Zoysa, N S M
Deane, H J H
Delany, D J
Denham, R A
Dennis, N R
Dennis, S T
Dennison, E M
Dennison, M L
Desai, N K
Detsios, C L
Devane, M J D
Dewbury, K C
Dibben, C R M
Dickson, N K
Dinapala, P L
Diprose, P
Ditchfield, A
Dixon, C J
Dixon, S A
Djukanovic, R V
Donnelly, P X
Doran, D M L
Douglas, M F
Dracass, J F
Draper, E-L
Du Boulay, C E H
Duffill, J
Duncombe, A S
Dunn, N R
Dyer, M J
Eastwood, H D H
Eccles, D M
Eccles, L M
Edwards, J G
Egleston, C V
Elliott, E J
Eni-Olotu, D O
Evans, A J
Evans, B I
Evans, G B
Evans, N A A
Evans, P W G
Faarup, C L
Fairhurst, J J
Fall, C H D
Ffrench-Constant, M C
Field, J
Fine, D R
Fisher, M S
Fitzpatrick, W J
Fleming, W S
Forbes, J A
Foster, C R M
Fowler, A V
Fowler, S P
Frankel, J P
Franks, A C
Fraser, S D S
Freeman, A S J
Frew, A J
Frost, E V
Fuller, A T R
Fung, P J
Gabbay, F J
Gabbay, J
Gage, S
Gallagher, J M
Gallagher, P J
Gandhi, N
Garman, J P
Garman, W M
Gaston, H
Gawne Cain, M L
Geldart, T R
George, S L
Gibb, W R G
Gibbs, A P
Gibbs, P J
Gibson, D J K
Gill, P A
Gill, P S
Gillibrand, A
Gillibrand, P N
Gillibrand, S
Girgis, M M R
Glasspool, J A
Gnanapragasam, J P
Godber, C
Goddard, J M
Godfrey, K M
Godfrey, R C
Godfrey, S J
Godwin, D S
Goodall, H N
Goode, S J
Goodison, S J F
Gordon, A D G
Gorham, C J
Gorrod, W D
Gotzaridis, E
Gove, R I
Gozzard, C
Grabham, J A
Graham, J
Gray, B A
Gray, H H
Gray, P J
Gray, W P
Greaney, M J
Greenberg, N
Gregory, P H
Griffiths, D M
Griffiths, M
Grimble, S A J
Grimshaw, J S
Grosart, A K
Grover, A L
Gulliford, C J
Guly, J K
Gupta, R
Guyer, C H
Habib, M J
Hackett, C L
Hacking, C N
Hadfield, A A
Hadfield, H W
Hadfield, I
Hall, A M
Hall, I S
Hall, M A
Hall, N F
Hamilton, A C E
Hamilton, C R
Hamilton, J C
Harden, S P
Hardie, C J W
Hare, C M B
Harley, J M
Harman, A N
Harries, P G
Harris, C J
Harrison, J
Harvey, J R
Hatchwell, E
Haw, M P
Hawa, L
Hayes, E J
Hayes, N R
Hayes, S E
Hayes, S F
Hayward, H C
Heafield, R J
Heal, S W P
Hemming, C S
Hemming, P A
Henderson, C A
Henderson, J
Hennayake, S P
Hennessy, N L M
Heryet, V E J
Heyes, C B
Heyworth, J R C
Hicks, K A
Hill-Cousins, J L
Hill-Cousins, S P A
Hill, A W
Hill, C M
Hill, M E
Hill, S A
Hillier, E R
Hillier, S J
Hillyard, A C
Hitchcock, A
Hoang, T M
Hoare, G K
Hodgkins, P
Hodgson, A K
Hogg, J I C
Hogg, P S
Hoghton, G B S
Holdsworth, C J S
Holgate, S T
Hollands, M D
Hookway, M O
Hopper, P L
Houghton, C D
Howard, J C
Howarth, P H
Howe, D T
Hudson, S J
Hughes, A H
Hughes, J
Hughes, M D
Hunter, B J
Hunter, S C
Hunter, S L
Hunter, S
Husband, P R
Hutchin, A K M
Hutchings, C J
Hutchinson, D
Ibbitson, D J
Illidge, T M
Ingamells, S
Inman, W H W
Iqbal, Z
Iredale, J P
Ironton, R
Iveson, T J
Jackson, C L
James, C J
James, R
Jameson, T H O
Jariwala, S
Javaid, M K
Jayaprakash, V
Jeffery, I T A
Jellicoe, J A
Johnson, C D
Johnson, P W M
Johnson, W J
Johnston, A
Johnston, S L
Jolly, C B
Jones, A
Jones, D S
Jones, T G
Jordan, T L
Joughin, N A
Judd, M J M
Kadri, A Z
Kakkar, S
Kakkar, V V
Kalra, P R
Karp, K H
Karran, S J
Katifi, H A A
Kause, J B
Keefe, M
Keeton, B R
Kelland, N F
Kelly, J M
Kelly, R W
Kelpie, A G
Kemp, P M
Kendrick, A R
Kennedy, P
Kent-Johnston, C A
Kenwood, C F
Keyworth, M J
King, A T
King, H
Kingdon, D G
Kinsman, F M
Knight, A O C
Knight, J W
Kohler, J A
Kolli, S V
Krentz, A J
Kulkarni, S K
Kumar, S
Kumarajeewa, D I S C
Kurukchi, E F
Lacey, P H
Laing, H C
Lall, D G
Lambert, G L
Lambert, G M
Lambourne, V A
Lanaspre, E
Lang, D A
Lang, I J
Last, A T J
Lau, J H G
Law, C M
Lawes, E G
Lawrence, C
Lawrence, I S
Lawton, A J
Lawton, N F
Laycock, J R D
Le Besque, S E M
Leaper, V A
Lebermann, M E
Ledger, M A
Lee-Elliott, C E
Lee, J A
Lee, M T W
Lee, R D
Lees, P D
Lennon, A J
Lenton, C E
Leonard, E M
Lewington, V J
Lewis, I H
Lewis, M
Lewis, M N
Lewith, G T
Lim, S H B
Linham, S J
Little, P S
Littlejohns, P A
Liu, A C Y
Lowes, J A
Lucas, J S A
Luckens, C J
Lyons, J P
McAndrew, A R
McAndrew, H F
McCaughey, E S
McDermott, R P
McDonald, D S
Macdonald, H
McFarlane, A T
McFarlane, V J
McGill, J I
McGinn, F P
McGrigor, V S
McKay, A
Mackie, E J
McLaren, M I
Maclean, D A
Maclean, J K
McLellan, D L
Macleod, D B
McPherson, J V
McQuitty, A F
Mairs, M L
Malone, P S
Manners, R
Mansbridge, B J
Mansell, A J
Mansfield, J E
Mardel, M J C
Markby, D P
Marshall, B G
Marshall, C A
Marshall, G S
Marshall, M M
Marshall, R P
Martin, I G
Martin, L M
Martin, R M
Martinez Saenz, J A
Martyn, C N
Matthews, H P
Mavroleon, G
May, P G R
Mayers, A J
Mayo, L K
McElwaine-Johnn, H A
Mead, G M
Meadows, A J
Meadows, A E R
Meakins, P G W
Metcalf, K S
Mettam, I M
Michaels, G P
Middleton, J E
Miell, S J
Miles, J C
Miles, R
Miles, S C
Millar, J S
Millar, M B
Miller, J M
Miller, J F
Millman, A M
Milln, J E M
Milln, P T S
Mills, A
Mills, P M
Mills, R G
Millward-Sadler, G H
Millward-Sadler, H
Milne, R I G
Mitchell, S J
Mitchell, T E
Mok Yun Wing, T
Mole, D R
Monkhouse, M
Monro, J L
Moore, T W
Moors, A
Morfey, D H
Morgan, C J
Morgan, J M
Morgan, S
Morrice, K F
Morris, B
Morris, G E
Morris, J C
Morris, P N
Morris, R J
Mortimore, A J
Morton, J A
Mottahedeh, M
Mountfield, S J
Moussa, W A-G M A
Mowbray, A G H
Mowbray, C J
Mufti, S T
Muller, G W
Munro-Davies, L E
Munro, M R
Munro, N P
Munro, W P
Murdoch, S R
Murgatroyd, D
Murphy, C R C
Murphy, E F W
Murphy, F R
Nasr, M S A
Nasrallah, F K S
Naylor, J S
Neil-Dwyer, G
Neil-Dwyer, J G
Nevin, M
Newman, C J
Newman, R M
Nicholas, J J
Nielsen, M S
Nightingale, J H
Nixon, C V C
Nixon, J R
Nolan, C M
Noon, J R
Norman, J
Nugent, K P
Nurse, J M
Nutton, M
O'Callaghan, F J K
O'Connell, B M S
O'Connor, D
O'Leary, A F
O'Sullivan, B M
Obin, O M
Odurny, A
Oeppen, R S
Ogilvie, B C
Ohri, S K
Onslow, J M
Ord-Hume, G C
Osborne, A H
Osgood, V M
Ottensmeier, C H H
Padday, R
Page, A R W
Pal, R
Pal, S P
Pallett, A P
Palmer, E A
Palmer, K T
Palmer, L J
Parker, A J
Parry, K T
Patankar, R S V
Patel, J P
Patel, S
Patel, V S
Patten, T J
Pau, H P H
Paynton, D J
Pearce, C B
Pearce, N W
Pearce, S
Pearson, G C
Peek, W H
Peoples, J A
Pepe, G
Perry, R J
Pettifer, C F
Peveler, R C
Phillips, C P
Phillips, D I W
Phillips, M J
Pierce, J M T
Pierson, J G
Pinder, A
Pinney, D E
Pitman, M C
Pitt, I
Pitts, J E
Pitts, J R
Ponsford, J S
Poole, R B
Pope, A J
Porter, P J
Press, C M
Prevett, M C
Price, N S
Price, S E
Primrose, J N
Pringle, J A
Prinsen, A K E
Pritchard, C N
Putnam, E A
Quiroga Giraldez, I
Rady, A M
Rai, A S
Railton, K L
Rainier-Pope, N D
Rajapaksa, P N
Ram Nath, K
Ramesar, J A S
Randall, J C
Rani, R
Rao, K R
Ratan, H L
Rees-Jones, S V
Reid, C M
Renwick, A C
Rew, D A
Reynolds, K V
Reynolds, R M
Rice, D F
Richards, S T M
Richardson, D S
Ritchie, K H
Roberts, C J
Roberts, H C
Roberts, P R
Roberts, R J
Robertson, J A
Robinson, N A S
Robinson, S J
Roche, J
Roche, W R P
Roderick, P J
Rogers, M L
Rogerson, M E
Rolles, C J
Rolles, T F
Roope, R M
Rosell, P A E
Rosenvinge, H P
Rowden, J D
Royle, F C W
Rubin, C M E
Russell, C
Russell, M M A
Salmon, G L
Salmon, G B
Sampson, M A
Sandeman, D D
Sansome, A J T
Sargeant, R J
Sarsfield, P T L
Saunders, D A
Savill, P J
Savva, N
Schofield, S P
Schofield, T S-W
Scott, R E
Scott, J A
Scott, R J
Sealey, S L
Sedgwick, J E C
Selley, C A
Shand, G
Sharpe, G
Shaw, D A S
Shaw, K J
Shearer, J R
Shearman, C P
Shelly, R W
Shephard, J N
Shepherd, H A
Shepherd, N J
Sheron, N C
Shillinglaw, C L
Shore, D F
Short, G P
Short, P M
Shrub, V A
Shute, S G A
Siddiqui, K A
Simmons, M R L
Simpson, H K
Simpson, I A
Simpson, R L
Simpson, R M
Singh, G K
Singh, J P

Southend-on-Sea

Singha, H S K
Skeates, S J
Skidmore, J R
Sleet, R A
Smalley, C A
Smallwood, J A
Smart, C J
Smedley, J C
Smith, A G
Smith, C L
Smith, D C
Smith, H E
Smith, P J
Smithies, J M A
Solomon, C L
Somerville, J M
Sparrow, O C
Spencer-Smith, M
Spencer, J E
St. George, D P
Stanger, R A
Stanton, M P
Steadman, K E
Steel, M D
Steer, J M
Steinberg, B
Steinbrecher, H A
Stenton, M J
Stephens, C R
Stephenson, J B G
Sterling, G M
Sterling, N
Stevenson, G T
Stevenson, P G
Stobbs, I P
Stokes, P R A
Stones, R W
Stredder, D H
Stringfellow, M J
Stroud, M A
Struthers, J L
Stuart Taylor, M E
Subramanyam, M
Sunak, Y
Sutherland, P D
Sutton, D N
Sutton, G L J
Sutton, M E
Swales, H A
Swann, C M
Swinn, M J
Synek, M
Tabry, H
Tang, A T-M
Tanna, M
Tate, G H A
Tayler, T M
Taylor, A J
Taylor, I R
Taylor, J K E
Taylor, K A
Telfer, P T
Temple, I K
Terry, P M S Q
Thaker, C S
Thomas, A L
Thomas, C A
Thomas, D
Thomas, E O
Thomas, E J
Thomas, M D
Thomas, N H
Thomas, P L
Thomerson, D G
Thomerson, M C R
Thompson, C M
Thompson, C
Thompson, C L
Thompson, E A
Thompson, M J J
Thornett, A M
Thorpe, G J
Threlfall, A L
Thrower, D F
Tice, J W S
Tien, P H S
Tisi, P V
Titcomb, J A
Todd, P G
Toh, S K C
Tolan, M J
Tolcher, R A
Tomson, C M C
Torkington, R M
Townsend, S J
Tran, A D
Trewinnard, B F
Trewinnard, K R
Trotter, C A
Tung, K T
Turner, J J
Turnock, K
Ubhayakar, G N
Ursell, C E
Van Der Star, R J
Van Nunen, A
Vance, G H S
Varney, A D
Varsani, G B
Viggers, J M
Voss, S N
Vulpe, A-M
Vyas, D R
Waddington, G E
Waddington, S J
Wade-West, S C
Wade-West, T
Wainwright, A C
Waite, N R
Wakeling, H G
Walbridge, D G
Waldron, M
Walker-Bone, K E
Walker, F
Walker, V
Walsh, J L
Walsh, S P
Walters, A D
Walton-Smith, P R
Walton, R J
Ward, C P
Ward, I R
Warner, J O
Warwick, D J
Watson, R
Watson, T E
Waugh, N R
Webster, A R
Webster, J H H
Weddell, C R
Wee, B L
Weeden, D F N
Weller, R O
Wellesley, D G
Welzenbach, B J
Westersee, W
Wheeler, R A
Whitaker, S G
White, P J
Whitehead, R H B S
Whitehorn, M
Whitehouse, C
Wield, C E
Wild, S H
Wilkins, B S
Wilkins, D C
Wilkinson, D G
Wilkinson, J A
Williamson, I G
Willmott, F E
Wilson, A W
Wilson, D
Wilson, H N
Wilson, L M
Winder, J H
Wong, Y K
Wood, G J
Wood, R M
Wood, T A
Woodbury-Smith, M R
Woodcock, T E
Woodward, R M
Woolaway, M C
Woolner, C A
Wright, D H
Wrigley, K
Xavier, A B
Yacoub, S
Yardley, D N
Yeomans, N P
Yong, P P L
Zaman, S N
Zardis, M C

Southend-on-Sea

Aggarwal, N K
Aggarwal, V P
Agha, Dr
Back, G W
Bannister, N J
Baqai, A
Bavishi, R K
Beales, S J
Bexfield, S M
Beynon, D G
Boston, D A
Bowring, A R W
Browne, G R
Browne, R D
Buchanan, G
Burges, C R
Clappen, J A
Coull, A B
Davison, A G
Ella, W A
Ellis, I B
Fairbrass, S P
Fearnley, G
Gent, C B
George, V K
Goodchild, C A V
Gould, G T
Grant, D L
Grant, J T
Greenwood, E J
Greig, A J
Gupta, R
Heath, M
Henderson, A L
Hutter, U C
Jack, M E W
Jupp, K
Kent, M B
Khan, F
Kinnear, J A
Kirkpatrick, R A
Kolli, S
Latif, M K
Leonhardt, J H C
Liddell, J K C
Liebeschuetz, H M
Mackay, J
Milligan, J H
Moss, P N B
Mountain, A J C
Naylor, H C
Nicol, M E
O'Sullivan, M G
Odd, D E
Osborne, C E
Pasha, M A
Pearson, R V
Pelta, D E
Pocock, T J
Raza, S A
Roberts, P
Ross, G G
Rushman, G B
Samak, M A R
Seath, K R
Sen, A K
Sen, G
Shah, B D
Shah, M N
Shah, N K
Shanker, J
Shrivastava, A
Sibellas, M
Sills, D W
Singh, D G
Smith, W D
Stuart, M H
Swinburn, H M
Taylor, M G S
Thumpston, M B
Twybte, T S
Vanat, M R
Vanat, T M
Vashisht, S L
Verghese, G S
Ware, C C
Weeks, W T
Weston, M D
Woodham, M J
Yee, A

Southminster

Barclay, A G
Bowton, P A
McGeachy, J E
Montague-Brown, H J
Southey, T J

Southport

Abdul-Jabbar, T V A
Ajayi, J F
Akingbehin, A O
Ali, M A-S
Allan, G M
Amer, K J
Ashton, K L
Bannock, A E A
Beetham, K W
Benjamin, E J S
Bennett, S
Bhatnagar, M
Binnie, A S
Boardman, K
Bolton, C J
Bond, A M
Bond, M D I
Bonnet, S J
Bouton, M J
Bowley, J A
Brown, M A
Burgess, C T A
Burns, S H
Butcher, G P
Butterfield, J S
Cadman, J M
Carden, D G
Charles, I R
Charway, C L
Coackley, A
Coney, S
Cook, R S
Corder, C E
Cornwell, M
Cowling, R J
Currie, F
Dailey, T J
Dalton, J R
Dawson, R E
Dey, N G
Diamond, J
Donnellan, J
Downham, P A
Dundas, S A C
Eccott, J N
Ellis-Jones, W B E
Entwistle, P B
Equizi, F
Evans, A F
Evans, V A
Eyre, O
Farley, T M
Fearns, G M
Firth, G M
Fletcher, G
Foat, G
Ford, F M
Forshaw, M A
Fox, J A
Fox, J P
Freedman, B
Gardner, S E
Garston, B
Garston, H N
Gaughan, A F
Giannelli, P B L
Gibb, A M
Gokul, K
Gould, A D W
Graham, M
Grant, L J
Grenyer, D R
Groves, K E
Gulati, R
Hall, E G
Hancox, D
Hands, A H
Hands, A J
Harris, I
Harrison, I D
Harrison, P A
Hedley, G S
Hewitt, W E
Higgins, M R
Howard, N
Hughes, I M
Humphreys, J
Hussain, E S
Iskander, M N
Islam, S
Izmeth, B
Izmeth, M G A
Janardhanan, K C
Jayson, D W H
Johnson, P
Jolly, I M
Jones, J E
Kilshaw, I M
King, R I
Koram, K O
Lang, P W
Lapsley, P M
Leonard, N J
Levy, A M
Lewinska, H Z
Lewis, C R
Lowe, J
Lynch, M R J
Lynch, P F
McCormack, M L
McCormack, M P
McDicken, I W
MacDonald, J H
McNally, S R
MacSorley, D T
Manning, D P
Mansour, P
Marriott, K N
Memon, A A
Milligan, H P
Mon Mon, G
Moriarty, N
Morrison, A R
Morton, C M
Naidoo, G R
Naidoo, K R
Naidoo, R S
Nanavaty, S
Nelson, C E
Nishith, S
Norman, D
Nugent, C M
O'Donnell, L V
Orford, C E
Osborne, G V
Pactor, R
Parken, D S
Parry, R L
Patel, R R
Pati, U M
Peiris, C S L
Percival, A
Pozzoni, L S
Ramamurthy, A B
Rao, P J
Ratcliffe, C A
Rigby, J C
Rigg, J H
Roberts, E A W
Rodgers, L
Ronson, J A
Rostron, E A
Russell, J
Russell, R M
Ryan, A J
Samuels, B
Scott, C C
Searson, J D
Serlin, M J
Sett, P
Sharma, N K
Sharp, W
Sharpe, G H M
Simmonds, J P
Simmons, S
Singh, G
Slater, L K
Smith, E P
Smith, P
Smith, P S
Smith, S C
Smyth, J H
Soni, B M
Starkey, M R
Stewart, T W
Stubbens, G
Sutcliffe, J R
Swift, E F
Sykes, H R
Szczesniak, L A
Taylor, A V
Thompson, T J
Tobin, S D M
Tomlinson, R J R
Treasure, J
Trivedi, D V
Trivedi, V A
Tun, O
Turner, J G
Turner, P M
Twist, A M
Vaidyanathan, S
Venkateswarlu, V
Vesey, S G
Watson, A P
Watt, J W H
Wesson, M L
Wilkinson, P R
Wilson, C F
Woolfenden, M
Wray, J R E
Zeiderman, M R
Zmyslowski, A J

Southsea

Arnold, T J M
Ashworth, A N
Ayling, C J
Bannell, K J
Barron, G R
Bedford, A D
Bennett, J B
Berney, D M
Bolton, S G
Burnham-Slipper, C N
Caiger, B N
Caiger, M
Cannon, L B
Causer, C A
Clark, J A E
Clarke-Williams, M J
Collins, L S
Cox McNeil Love, R M
Crowley, D J
Dale, B J
Darlow, S J
Dee, G
Edgar, J G
Emerson, A C
Fleming, P M
Foord, R D
Golland, I M
Gorham, D J
Harrison, D T
Hillier, C E M
Hilton, D D
Hodges, M E H
Howlett, N D
Hoyle, A
Jenkins, J E
Keane, F
Lake, R S
Langmaid, J R
Laxton, P D
Lucas, C R
Masheter, S N
Mitchell, B D
Moon, B G
Morgans, C M
Munt, D F
Ostler, K J
Parkin, G T
Pearson, D G R
Peel, S
Pine, I M
Plane, A R
Preston, A P
Price, J P D
Robinson, M
Rollins, J W
Sowden, L M
Sparkes, D J
Spolton, E M
Sprott, V M A
Steger-Lewis, V M
Taylor, A
Trapiella, B
Tutte, K P
Tyrrell, R F
Uppal, M S
Varma, A
Vernon, K G
Vincent, J C
Viner, C R
Wakefield, C J
Wallace, F
Watkins, J
Watkins, S C
White, A J
Williams, C V
Wilson, M R
Winfield, J
Young, E B B

Southwell

Ali, N J
Ashcroft, D G
Atkinson, M J
Buckley, D M G
Byrne, A J
Clark, V J
Collinson, A A R
Cottell, H C
Danby, P R
Duffy, M S
Duffy, M R
Duffy, N C
Durnin, C A
Helmer, M
Hunter, H
James, M K
Layfield, D J
Leach, A J
Macmillan, R D
Markham, S J
Norris, A M
O'Nunain, S S
Platts, B W
Reeves, S D
Savage, J R

St Helens

Sym, R A
Vidhani, K
Ward, K L
Worth, A J J

Southwold
Baylis, J H
Brentnall, G C
Butt, S A
Castle, C R
Church, R E
Clark, P A
Dobney, G H
Eastaugh, A N
Hall, M H
Jackson, I
Morgan, A
Randall, D H
Townsley, G S
Williams, I P

Sowerby Bridge
Acharya, S R
Bradley, C M
Catlow, S I
Gallagher, J
Higham, A
Hinds, R O
Hinton, C A
Hinton, P J
Howson, S D
Kumar, R
Littlewood, C R
Mazey, K A L
Moore, K C
Pickersgill, D E
Pool, R W
Rastall, M P
Reah, G
Rogerson, L J
Sarker, M A K
Veal, H L
Whisker, W B
Whitaker, B
Wyatt, B T

Spalding
Aitken, R M
Bell, A I
Boon, M R
Booth, C C
Brookes, R H
Burgess, D A
Butler, R
Bycroft, J A
Cheshire, D J E
Cole, C R
Corlett, D J
Cowell, J M
Dillon, G
Dillon, H F B
Dutton, A J
Eadie, K M
Gosney, J M
Hamblin, C A
Hamer-Philip, J M
Hewat-Jaboor, D F
Heywood, M F
Jacklin, J B
Jamieson, E C
Lennon, C P B
Low, N J
McCall, A
McCombie, P
Meuwissen, K J A M
Musson, R I
Nathu, A
Owen, C A
Peter, M W
Price, M
Rance, B H
Rayner, S
Richardson, B D
Riley, D J
Rodgers, P F E
Sagar, W
Scott, C A
Shaw, M K
Simpson, J A
Stone, A D R
Sykes, A
Thorpe, R W
Tighe, R J
Walton, A
Whitlock, N J
Wiscombe, K A R

Spean Bridge
Godfrey, J F

Pinney, D C
Tregaskis, M

Spennymoor
Fitt, A W D
Henderson, A J
Hobbs, D D
Ibbott, N E
Kotwall, F B
Long, A J
Patel, S K
Roy, D V
Sanderson, A A F
Sensier, A E
Staines, J E
van den Brul, K A
Wood, M R D

Spilsby
Anderson, A C
Caranza, R A
Cartwright, D E
Haddow, R A
Hovenden, B J
Latto, R J
Morgan, M S
Mowat, A M
Thompson, H M
Wain, M O

St Agnes
Arntsen, K W
Barry, L R
Bradshaw, H J
Fealey, M J L
Fussell, I J
Gill-Carey, M C
Guttridge, B
Harries, C
Henderson, N D
Holloway, K J
Julian, J T
McNeill, E
Richardson, K L
Robertson, J M
Strover, S M
Thorley, J N
Whitworth, C M
Whitworth, H

St Albans
Akoh, J A
Akroyd, I H
Al-Jassim, A H H
Allen, M W
Allistone, A C
Alloway, L J
Amin, M A
Anderson, A L
Aram, J A
Atkinson, A A
Atkinson, C V
Bacchus, R A
Banbery, J K
Bartlett, J A
Beacon, J P
Beare, A S
Beattie, D K
Bentley, G
Bevis, M A
Bishop, J F
Blake, K H
Bonnet, J M
Boodhun, R
Bowman, R M
Bradshaw, D
Brennan, J L
Brennan, J H
Broadwith, E A
Brown, J M
Buckley, B E
Bunyan, P A
Burke, S A
Burnett, F E
Butterworth, P M
Cabot, R
Cahill, D J
Cannell, M C S
Capper, J L H
Carruthers, G J
Chandler, L J
Chiyende, J K
Clark, B J
Clegg, J P
Coombs, G A
Cooper, M B S
Corbett, T J
Corlett, H M
Covell, B R
Davies, A A

Davies, A H
Davies, J L
Day, L M
Dean, B C
Dearing, N C
Democratis, J C
Devonshire, P I
Dexter, K E
Douglas, T J
Dow, I A M
Dowling, S E
Edwards, R J
Elstow, S M
Evans, H
Fairbairn, I M
Fattah, A M N
Ferguson, J W
Fielden, N J S
Findlay, D W
Fitt, I J K
Foss, M V L
Franks, D M
Freedman, J E
Fulford-Kirby, J
Gilham, D
Godlee, J R L
Goodall, I D
Gorton, J D
Green, E A
Griffin, P L
Groves, M C P
Haider, R U
Hamilton, I A
Hammond, A A
Harrison, G D
Hart, G M
Haseler, A R
Hatch, K M S
Heath, J D
Heller, M D A
Henry, S J
Hoole, S M
Hulin, S J
Hussain, S
Hyde, S L
Hynes, M C
Ingram, K L
Irwin, A S
Jaiswal, I
Jaiswal, R C
James, L
Jameson, D M
John, J
Johnson, N S
Jones, J E
Jordache, S M
Jowett, J H G
Karunapala, L G H
Kedia, K
Kedia, P
Kelsall, D J
Kennedy, R C
Khalid, A R
Khan, I H
Kilvington, J M
Kulkarni, S S
Laitner, S M
Lancer, K L
Lee, B K
Lee, C S
Lee, M H M
Lees, M P
Lewis, B
Lister, D S
Livesey, P M
Lofthouse, S
Luke, A J B
McColm, J A
McDonnell, J J
Mainwaring, P J
Margereson, A E
Markar, T N
Martin, H A D
Matthews, G V
Maurice, P D L
Meacher, R L
Miller, J L
Mitchell, J D
Modha, D E
Moore, P R
Mort, D J
Mummery, J
Nathan, J M
Nicholls, H A
O'Mara, V
O'Sullivan, G H
Olin, R H
Pallewela, C C
Papanastassiou, M

Parsons, L M
Paul, P K
Penney, D J
Peters, M J
Phear, D N
Pickering-Pick, M E
Pinkerton, S M
Platts, A J
Postlethwaite, J C
Putterill, J S
Queen, J K
Ramdeo, A
Raymond, S P
Reed, S E
Sabonadiere, P F
Sage, R E M
Sagor, G R
Saleh, M S A D A H
Sasitharan, T
Saunders, S M F
Sawyer, P E L
Schofield, J K
Sebaratnam, N P
Sepai, T M
Shah, M P
Shannon, R W
Sharp, P
Sherif, A H M
Singh, S
Sinha, G
Sivakumar, R
Skelton, P E
Small, C M
Smith, H
Stephens, J
Sterland, J H
Strain, H A
Sullivan, N
Sumners, D G
Sutton, R H
Taylor, R D
Tayob, Y
Tennison, B R
Terry, D A
Thomson, A R
Thurston, A V
Tominey, D P
Vinayagamoorthy, C
Visuvaratnam, M
Visuvaratnam, T
Voyce, C E
Wajed, M A
White, S K
Whitworth, J C
Wickramarathna, L S
Wickramasinghe, K M S S
Wijetunge, U H R
Wilkin, P M R
Williams, R L
Willis, M H G
Woodwark, C
Young, K A

St Andrews, Fife
Backhouse, S S
Ball, A P
Barclay, G A W
Batchelor, I R C
Bell, J R
Bindon, C I
Bowman, A
Brittain, C N
Brown, D G P
Burnett, E M
Caithness, G S
Cameron, E L
Campbell, O C A
Carrick, D
Chapman, J S
Clark, R V
Clark, T J
Cobb, C J
Craik, I F
Cunningham, G L W
Cuschieri, A
Dalziel, A
Davidson, A V M
Davidson, C M
Delaney, J W
Denholm, J L
Dickson, M C
Donald, M J
Duncan, P S
Fairlie, E J
Forrest, K M
Forwell, G D
Frame, J
Freedlander, S C

Gibson, F J
Gifford, J
Graham, G S
Haldane, J D
Hector, M F
Henderson, G
Hill, R A
Hotchkis, B D
Houston, A P
Illingworth, G
Ingram, C G
Johnston, B W
Kerr, Y L
Keymer, M R
Lamb, J F
Lawrie, D M
Lindsay, S F
Linton, M
Lobban, W D
McDonald, J M
McGregor, E M
McKerrow, A H
MacMillan, C S A
McPhate, G F
McTavish, J C
Mathewson, I B
Maxwell, C M
Mills, J H
Mills, J A
Morris, H C T
Murdock, N K
Neil, J M
Olver, W J
Orr, E M
Orr, V A
Outram, D H
Pirie, C A
Pumford, N A
Pumford, S
Qureshi, N R
Randall, E M
Reid, D H S
Reid, M
Robertson-Rintoul, J
Robertson, J C
Rutherford, D
Salamonski, J H
Scott, A J
Seddon, P J
Serjeant, M K
Shaw, C
Sinclair, D W
Sinclair, E M
Sinclair, M A
Smith, M J
Smyth, G P
Sommerville, J A
Sorrie, G S
Stanley-Whyte, E M
Steel, C M
Stewart, J E
Sullivan, D B
Sutherland, A R
Sutherland, J S
Tait, H A
Taylor, W
Thomas, D B
Tweedie-Stodart, N M
Weekes, R D M
Whelan, J A
Whittle, F D
Wigzell, F W

St Andrews, Guernsey
Best, N E G
Dickson, J R
Douglas, H G K
Steel, E J

St Asaph
Abd El-Fattah, A Y M
Arnold, J P
Barnsley, T M
Bhowmick, A K
Cameron, J
Davies, J E
Duffy, J E
Forgan, B J
Hampton, A M
Hurst, L
Lloyd Williams, M A
McConnell, E M
Morton, C E
Nagendran, S
Narain, I
Ng, C S
Osei-Frimpong, S
Owen, B

Puvanachandra, K
Saunders, D C
Taylor, J N
Wainwright, J R
Williams, D

St Austell
Adkins, R B
Atcha, Z
Banerjee, S S
Behennah, M A
Bhonsle, R S
Blackwell-Smyth, P
Burke, F E
Cecil, J R
Chapel, H
Charman, C R
Corbett, E J L
Crawshaw, J A
Davis, A
Dibb, A
Dowling, M F
Forsdick, S J
Foster, P B
Hamersley, H A N
Hargreaves, P N
Hereward, A C
Hotton, T H E
Ife, S P
Iles, R E
Jenkin, D R
Kitson, N I
Leigh, J R O
Mackenzie, I F
Mackrell, D R
Mather, R H
Mather, S H
Miles, D P B
Mitchell, M M
O'Brien, B
Penfold, G K
Phillips, G D
Phillips, P G
Robinson, C D
Robinson, M G
Round, K W
Schenk, P M
Sharp, G T
Travis, P
Wagner, P R
Wakeford, T D
Whitehouse, A R
Williams, J H B

St Bees
Greene, K J
Greene, M K
Yule, D P

St Columb
Emrys-Jones, G J H
Hill, P M
McKelvey, I A
Priest, M S
Turfitt, E N

St Helens
Abernethy, V E
Adams, A J
Atiba, O E
Baig, A
Bainbridge, B A
Baines, J H E
Balachandran, K
Banat, J J
Beeby, K
Birchall, D
Boyd, C E
Chana, S S
Chisnall, J L
Corner, T R J
Cox, S J
Crabtree, C
Cudmore, R E
Cunningham, A S
D'Arcy, J R
Denno, H M
Desmond, M
Dilworth, P A
Dowling, C
Ellison, J
Ferguson, N J
Ferguson, P W
Filletti, P
Finnegan, B C
Finnegan, D M
Finney, S M
Forrest, D R
Gaffney, M P
Ghaffar, A R K

St Ives

Gillanders, V T
Glover, T F
Green, S
Gregan, A C F
Gregan, M J
Gregan, P
Gupta, P
Hanrahan, J M
Hargreaves, S A
Harrison, R J
Hart, N J
Henley, R F
Higgins, J
Hindley, J S
Holden, J D
Houghton, J I
Hugh-Jones, J A
Hughes, J E
Hunt, E J
Johnson, S
Joyce, P W
Junaid, O H
Kilroy, I M
Kurzeja, J A
Lennon, F P
Liptrot, S
Long, A A
McArthur, J B H
McCourt, B A
McGrath, A E
McManus, C J
Macrae, E M R
Macrae, M T
MacRae, R A D
Maini, R
Mansoor, S
Markey, P G
Marsden, A J
Mason, K
Mather, J M
Memon, M S
Mercer, L A
Middleton, J B
Mikhail, K H T
Miles, C M
Miles, L
Mooney, P
Morris, J L
Moss, S
Nasir, A
Naylor, S
O'Brien, M
O'Connell, T J
O'Donnell, J J
O'Donovan, G B
Paul, P J
Pitalia, S
Rahil, H M
Richmond, J P
Rimmer, M G
Roberts, I
Sagar, P
Sathe, S B
Schofield, J
Shah, M
Shaw, G C
Smith, C C
Smith, G L
Smith, P A
Stewart, J M A C
Sutton, J M
Swinhoe, P J
Taylor, M A
Taylor, R B
Thomas, N F
Thomas, R S
Thompson, I
Tolan, S P
Topping, S
Tunstall, P J
Van Dessel, M G
Vaughan, P H
Webb, P
Webster, J
White, G
Whittaker, A
Williams, S E
Wilson, D C
Wilson, P E
Wiratunga, E B P
Woodcock, V E
Wright, R W
Zutshi, R N

St Ives

Campbell, E J
Currie, S
Freegard, S P
Hayes, B J
Hosking, L A
Jewell, W E
Johnson, H D
Joyce, K A
Lakic, J
Machell, R J
Manley, R
Marshall, R J
May, C M I
Moran, S A
Morris, P E
Pardoe, T S
Phillips, M C O
Rostron, K W B
Royston, A M
Sanderson, M R
Sell, J N
Slack, R D
Smith, D W
Weston, M E
White, J R A
Whyte, M B
Wilkins, A N J

St Leonards-on-Sea

Al-Saleem, M A W
Apthorp, L A
Auld, B J
Baer, S T
Banfield, J M
Barker, J P
Barnes, W S F
Beard, J
Board, R H
Boxer, M E
Bruce, S A
Bryden, P J
Buchanan, J A F
Bullen, E K
Butler-Manuel, P A
Cameron, D J
Carr, C M
Clee, M D
Consterdine, E
Cresswell, M A
Cusack, P S Y
Dennison, J
Doig, A S
Eton, B
Evans, P M
Fitzgerald, I M
Fitzgerald, M A
Foord, K D
Freeman, M P
Furley Smith, E A
Gibson-Glubb, S M
Gorsuch, A N
Gregory, P T S
Guy, R L
Hawley, I C
Henderson, E B
Hinves, B L
Ingham, W N
Jones, D E
Kaliniecki, J P J
Khoury, G A
Kinloch, D R
Kwan, S C
Leach, A B
Lee, J V
Lethbridge, J R
Lyttle, J A
M'Munoru, M M
MacCarthy, N E
McIntyre, H F
Mehta, P A
Milton, J C
Motha, S
Moynagh, D K
Mutiboko, I K
Nasar, M A
Ninos, A
Oliver, M C
Parker, L S
Parry, H V
Plail, R O
Plumpton, F S
Rai, S K
Rajbee, F T
Rajbee, T Y
Sapper, M E
Scott, D J
Searson, J W
Segar, E P
Sengupta, G
Serrano Garcia, J A
Shah, C H
Shepherd, M A W
Smith, S G W

Sparkes, R
Steil, H
Stewart, J G
Stock, J G L
Strouthidis, T
Sudhakar Rao, S
Tate, P M
Taubman, R L
Torkington, I M G
Vethanayagam, S V
Walker, D M
Waller, J O D
Ward, T J
Whitehead, S M
Wray, R
Wright, E P
Wylie, F M S
Yedia, S R
Young, A J

St Mary's

Barnes, R
Drake, M R
Gale, J
Gleadle, R I
Watts, P

Stafford

Aggarwal, A K
Aggarwal, S K
Ahmed, S A
Al-Husein, M O M
Alam, M M-U
Albright, E J
Allbeson, M
Allen, D B
Ander, P G M
Armstrong, G C
Baichoo, S
Baig, M F A
Barkley, C
Barnes, C N
Bates, A S
Beal, R M
Bee, E M
Belle, A C
Bhoora, I G
Blanchard, D S
Bland, J M
Brackley, P T H
Bramley, C
Broader, J H
Burra, F F R
Byrne, F
Calhaem, M N
Campbell, T M
Carlin, H W
Carlton, D R
Carr, D M
Carrasco, C D P
Chakraborty, S K
Chambers, R M
Clifford, G N
Coates, G
Coates, P A A
Collier, J D
Connellan, S J
Cooner, B S
Cooper, C J
Cooper, N A
Crisp, J A
Crisp, W J
Daggett, P R
Daniels, E
Daniels, R J
Dapaah, V
Davenport, S M
David, V C
Davies, J A
Davies, S A F
Davies, W A D
de Boer, C H
De Murtinho-Braga
Ossa, J J
Deane, A G
Dillon, S
Dixon, J E
Duggal, H V V P
Dunn, C K
Durrans, D
El-Fakhry, T T
Elizabeth, J E
Elliott, T K
Elsmore, A J
Eqbal, Z S
Eva, L J
Evans, K
Evans, R M
Eyre-Walker, D W

Fairfax, A J
Finn, T L
Foster, D A
Fowler, M
Freschini, A J L
Gallimore, J
Gandham, S R
Ganeri, P
Gee, B C
Gibson, J A
Gillatt, M A M N
Glennon, P
Green, W J
Grero, P S
Grewal, M S
Griffin, N V
Grocott, A E
Gwynn, B R
Haig-Ferguson, D R
Hall, I R
Hannigan, J P
Hardwick, N
Harper, N N
Harris, S C
Hawkins, W J
Haywood, J
Hearn, J S
Hiley, P E
Hiley, S M
Hodgkinson, B R
Holderness, M C
Hollenberg, S
Houlder, A R
Houlder, A-M T
House, M L
Howell, J V
Hoyle, M D
Husselbee, A J
Hutchinson, E C
Hutchinson, R
Iddenden, D A
Iqbal, Z
Iyer, R V
Jani, C M
Jankowski, S L
Johnson, V W
Jones, L M
Jones, M C
Jones, R H V
Joshi, V
Kabbani, M
Kakoullis, T M
Kalra, P L
Kawecki, J Z
Kelly, S E
Ker, W A
Khan, A A
Khan, A
Kluender, O
Knight, S J
Knight, S M
Kumar, A V
Lamb, A S T
Lamb, A B
Lambah, P
Lambah, P A
Leedham, A
Leong, Y H
Liss, M R
Lloyd, R S
Lochee Bayne, E M
Lockhat, M D
Logan, A J
Lotz, J C
Lovett, L M L
Loynes, R D
Loynes, R P
Luck, B M
McCollum, D H
McGeehan, D F
Macleod, A M
Markos, A R M
Martin, H M
Mateu-Lopez, E
Merriott, D E
Miller, C L
Morton, P R
Muir, A
Munslow, D J
Nanavati, B T
Nanavati, C B
Newton, E J
Nock, I D
O'Connell, E P
Oliver, M D
Owen, T R
Palmer, D J L
Palmer, K S
Pancholi, A

Panis, E A H
Patel, P
Paterson, E H
Paterson, P
Paterson, W D
Patterson, J F
Peters, E
Peters, M W
Phaure, T A J
Phillips, S J
Postings, S J
Prasad, N
Price, C I M
Pringle, K
Quader, S E
Raby, M B
Ralphs, A T R
Rawle, M S
Ray, C S
Reddy, T N
Reece, E V
Revell, P G
Richard, H W
Roberts, S F
Roddy, E
Ross, C D
Sage, N J
Salvey, M G
Schofield, S F
Sellwood, W G
Settle, V
Sheeran, T P G
Skilton, G H S
Skilton, J A
Slaski, M C
Smith, P D F
Sofoluwe, G O
Spiers, J M
Steele, N J
Steventon, D M
Stewart, A I
Stott, D B
Styles, H F
Styles, J T
Suarez, V
Summers, B A
Szafranski, J S
Talbot, J L
Taylor, R C H
Thambirajah, M S
Thomas, A
Thomas, E
Thuraisingam, A I
Turner, I M
Turner, P E M
Turner, S A
Uggias, B
Vidyasagar, H N
Villiers, G I L
Villiers, J D
Vishwabhan, S P
Wagner, H
Wakeman, A J
Wall, M K
Walsworth-Bell, J P
Ward, K A
Watts, M
Watwood, K
Wenger, M B
Westwood, T L
Wheeler, D J
Wheeler, M S
Whitehouse, P A
Wilson, I
Woodmansey, P A
Woodyard, J E
Youngman, C A

Staines

Bansal, R
Basra, S K
Blackburn, J R C
Bridger, D H
Cooper, P J F
Curtis Jenkins, G H
Curtis, H S
De Silva, S G
Hughes, P J
Irani, M R
Jurado, R
MacGillivray, R M
Marmion, D V
Martin, J R J
Martin, M E
Mills, C D
Morton, E
Motabhoy, B R
Owen, D A
Pittard, J B

Poots, S J
Quraishy, M M
Rahmati, M A
Richards, W C D
Salahuddin, M
Salaria, D A
Stephens, H E
Tarzi, N
Taylor, J L
Varadi, S
Wallis, M G
Warren, K M
Wells, J M
Williams, M G
Wilson, F M

Stalybridge

Ahmed, S
Al-Turki, W A-H
Ansari, J K
Asthana, J C
Athwal, S S
Barber, N A
Barlow, A B T
Bhattacharyya, S N
Bowers, P J
Clark, R
Cummings, K E
Goel, W P
Hague, R
Haider, M
Hasan, M Q
Herd, J M
Hershon, A L N H
Hinchliffe, J B
Howarth, V S
Howorth, P
Johnson, A E
Kakade, M
McNeil, A F
McNeil, N C H
Matin, M A
Peters, J G
Purcell, M
Rao, J
Rashid, S M
Reeves, S J
Syed, S N
Tapley, M P
Urmila-Rao, N
Walsh, R
Ward, T
Zatman, S T F

Stamford

Ahmed, I
Anandan, N A
Armstrong, V J
Babbs, D J
Barker, M E
Briggs, A C
Brook, S M
Callow, N
Chase, G H G
Crabbe, G G
Davis, L M
Delaney, J A
Donnelly, N P
Doran, P A
Dronfield, M W
Ellor, E M
Fairham, S A
Fawcett, A I
Fields, J R
Gleeson, H K
Glynn, B G
Gobbett, A M
Gregory, G A
Hall, A B
Hall, J H
Hall, S J
Harkness, J N
Harris, T E
Hibble, A G
Holland, J W
Holmes, D A
House, C A
Hudson, P M
Hume, N S
Hunt, P C W
Ingle, H T
Jenkins, T J
Kelly, G E
Kent, S J S
Khan, M A J
Knight, E
Lankester, K J
Lewis, R B
Ley, R J

Stockport

Little, A F M
Little, H M
Livingstone, R K
Lowry, S R
McInerney, L J
Mann, A L
Markey, G S
Marriott, R G
Mason, S A
Mercer, I H
Mitchell, J V
Mowat, I G
Noble, K L
O'Rourke, F L
Parker, V
Pring, C M
Quantrill, J
Reiss, S B
Riley, R E
Robertshaw, R
Sharma, S D
Sibley, E G
Smith, A L
Spencer, S A
Sutcliffe, M L
Tuck, S J
Warner, A A
Watt, M J
Weisz, M T
Wells, A D
Williams, J P
Williams, N E
Young, T W

Stanford-le-Hope

Chatterjee, L M
Craig, I G L
Hanson, K J
Hartree, J F
Holder, E H
Kotecha, M G
Makhdum, R
Mull, P J
O'Doherty, A
Patel, B N
Pattara, A J
Pusey, J M
Shaw, F E
Tresidder, N J
Waraich, M K

Stanley

Astell, S L
Benson, W A
Bhattacharya, K F
Bhattacharya, P K
Bidwell, C M
Birch, G
Clasper, P
Cronin, M S
Dhuny, A R
Douglas, S
Gallwey, B A
Gomathinayagam, A
Graham, P M A
Harbinson, M J
Hijab, A R A
Knowles, G M
Lambert, B
Mackay, J A
Morrison, H H
Nath, P U
Nath, P V
Pandey, S K
Parthasarathy, D
Parthasarathy, M
Rahman, M M
Ramesh, C N
Tyson, A J
Walker, A
Watson, P J

Stanmore

Abood, Y A
Agyare, K
Ardeman, S
Balapaskaran, M
Barcroft, J P
Basu, P
Bayley, I J L
Benn, J M
Berkowitz, J L
Berman, J S
Bhatiani, W
Bhudia, S K
Birch, R
Bodamer, O A
Bray, A P
Brealey, S
Briggs, T W R

Cannon, S R
Colvin, I B
Cowan, J M A
Curry, S H
D'Souza, E R
D'Souza, S A
Dalah, M
De Souza, D S M
Edge, P G
Elwerfalli, M M
Endbinder, H C
Falk, H C
Forty, F
Fox, R S R
Frankel, A H
Friedmann, I
Gadelrab, R R
Gaon, P D
Garcia, S H
Gbegbaje, M E
Gerrard, J
Gould, A M
Gould, L N
Green, R A R
Harrison, D J
Harsiani, S
Hashemi-Nejad, A
Henry, D B
Hetreed, M A
Hicks, F N
Highman, V N
Ismail, F F
Keen, R W
Khanderia, A V
Kotsirakis, A
Lalwani, K
Lam, K H F
Lambert, S M
Lehovsky, J
Lewis, J G
Lipman, R N
Livingston, J A
Lokugamage, A U
Lovett, B E
Malisano, L P
Mandalia, H N
Marks, L J
Maruthappu, J
Michael, G M
Miller, G
Moodaley, V K
Moss, K E
Mownah, A
Nagpaul, C
Nandhabalan, K
O'Sullivan, N N V
Obrecht, K B
Patel, J I
Patel, S
Pearse, D J
Polakoff, S
Prasad, R
Pringle, J A S
Pujara, B K P
Ravikumar, R
Rose, P A
Sassoon, S M H
Seingry, D R J
Shah, D P
Shah, N K
Shukla, C J
Silva, A S C
Silver, G A
Singh, D
Somaratne, D A
Spier, A
Sumners, S M
Suresh, D
Taylor, B A
Thirunavukarasu, R
Tookman, A J
Trickey, E L
Trouli, C
Veldtman, U M
Vijayan, K P
Werb, A
Wieselberg, H M
Wilkes, N
Williams, A M
Wolman, R L
Wood, A J
Yau, K W
Yeap, J S
Zaw Win, Dr

Stansted

Dove, S E
Ferns, M
Griffiths, R C

Hamilton, B A
Hazzard, A J
Jones, P G
Leek, G P
Robinson, R H
Walton, S M

Stevenage

Abbas Ahmed, O
Al-Shihabi, B A
Babinskyj, R M
Baird-Smith, S V
Banerjee, Dr
Barker, J V
Barker, W H
Baxani, R
Beales, J S M
Berry, W H C
Bhardwaj, S K
Bloomer, H J
Borthwick, L J
Brooke, A J
Brooks, P T
Catterall, A P
Chin, S C-P
Coreira, M C
Croft, R D
Dalla Valle, G M
Davies, S A
Dickson, M G
Dorrell, J H
Duggan, M J
Fahmy, S
Farrington, K
Ferrar, J M
Gale, S A
George, D W R
Gilby, E M
Giles, K W
Gillam, S J
Gogbashian, C A
Gooding, I R
Greenwood, R N
Gregory, M M
Grimsell, C H
Hanbury, D C
Hewson, M W
Holme, T C
Hope, P G
Hyde, J C
Irvine, S A-M
Jani, K
Jothilingam, S
Keane, T R
Kelly, S J
Kenyon, A P
Kerr, P S S
Khan, S A
Kirkpatrick, K L
Kostick, A R
Lacey, S J
Lalor, J M
Lambourne, P J
Lee, H M
Leris, A C A
MacDonald, A A
McNicholas, T A
McRitchie, R L
Mahaffey, P J
Meer, J A
Nalini, C S K
Ninan, M
O'Donoghue, P
Ogilvie, D M H
Oo, M M
Osborn, G R
Osindero, A O
Palmer, B V
Palmer, R
Parry, S D
Pickett, T M
Powell, C E
Powles, D P
Prendergast, C M
Rahman, M S
Ramzi, N
Reid, P M
Reiser, J
Richardson, D A
Rickford, W J K
Rollin, S
Rouse, B R
Salter, D H R
Salvesen, D R
San Thein, Dr
Sandhu, A K
Sargeant, I R
Sarkar, J S
Saunders, C J

Savidou, L K
Selvadurai, M A
Selvakumar, S
Sengupta, P
Shareef, S H
Singfield, C J
Singh, M
Sockalingham, I
Sowah, A
Stevenson, J E D
Stimpson, V B
Stratton, J D
Tew, C J
Thompson, H H
Turner, J C S
Uthayakumar, S
Wahab, M A
Wallis, M O
Warner-Smith, J D
Williams, B M
Williams, R D
Wilson, A J
Zaidi, S I A

Stevenston

MacGill, A
McIntosh, R E
Martin, C J

Steyning

Annan, M H
Boger, R F C
Davey, N B
Frank, A J M
Goldsmith, C S
Goodyear, M L
Iversen, S J L
Morrison, E A
Noren, C E
Parr, D C
Pembrey, R L
Schofield, P C H
Shrimpton, G R
Stanwell, P M
Van Ryssen, M E P
Wetson, R E

Stirling

Abel, R A
Alexander, J O D
Allatt, J M
Austin, M S
Baddon, A C J
Balendra, P R
Balnave, S E
Beattie, M T
Bentley, C J M
Berry, P D
Beyer, M S
Bishop-Miller, J
Booth, D B
Boyd, J R
Bramley, P N
Briggs, R D
Brown, R J H
Bryan-Jones, J C
Bryce, R P
Brydie, A D
Campbell, G
Campbell, M B
Cathcart, I R
Cheyne, A I
Clarke, D N
Clayton, D L
Coles, R J
Connor, W C
Conway, S C
Cooper, G L
Coulson, A J
Crawford, G A
Cunningham, C
Cunningham, H E
Dagg, J H
Dahar, N A
Davidson, G G K
De Silva, B Y
Denovan, J
Dick, D C
Doherty, A M
Duncan, E M
Dunsmore, H
El Sapagh, K M A
Evans, T W
Evitt, J A
Fairley, R
Ferguson, E J
Fisher, W G
Forsyth, D E
Foster, G R
Funnekotter, R P

Gallacher, J H
Glen, D A
Green, F C
Haddow, L J
Haig, D C
Hamilton, N W
Hanley, R I
Harrington, D S
Hehir, M
Hendry, W S
Higgins, M T
Hill, D J
Hislop, E M
Holding, D J
Horrobin, D F
Hosking, A G F
Howie, A D
Huggan, J D
Hynd, I M
Innes, A J
Isbister, J F S C
Jabbar, A A
Jack, P W
Johnston, S M E
Jowett, F S
Kasthala, R P
Kelt, C H
Kennedy, B W
Kennedy, S M
Kennie, D C
Kerr, T S
Kilgour, S W L
King, D B M
Kippen, D J
Lenton, R J
Leonard, M L T
Lewis, J S G
Lindsay, A
Lindsay, R S R
Logan, J M
Longmate, A G
Loudon, J B
Lyle, F E
McArthur, J G
McCulloch, G M
McCulloch, J E
MacDonald, J A E
Macdonald, J K
McEwen, J P J
MacFadyen, U M
MacGregor, D B
MacGregor, W
McIlwaine, R J
McIntosh, I B
McKenzie, A K
McKinlay, R G C
Mackintosh, U
McLaren, R
McLeod, M E
McMullen, K W
McNeill, A D
McNeill, J J
MacPhie, J C
McWhirter, M F
Maddox, B R A
Mair, W B
Martin, A
Mehta, S B
Meldrum, R
Morrice, D J
Morrice, G D
Morrison, A B
Morrison, A
Morrison, C A
Morrison, F K
Morton, K D
Muir, A R
Mullen, C C
Munn, E M
Murdoch, G J
Oto Llorens, M
Parker, W A
Paterson, A M
Pearson, S H C
Pettigrew, A M
Pollok, W M
Prabhu, M R
Rankin, J N E
Reith, S B M
Renwick, C J C
Richardson, I R
Riley, A
Ritchie, I K
Ritchie, J M R
Roberts, J J K
Roberts, J L B
Robertson, D H M
Robertson, J U
Romero Portillo, A

Ross, D J
Ross, J R
Ruddell, W S J
Sanderson, C H
Schulga, A
Schulga, J
Scott, J A
Seewald, A
Semple, A J
Sharp, G R
Simpson, C E
Simpson, D S
Simpson, G D
Simpson, W A C
Sinclair, A M R
Smith, A
Smith, J F B
Smith, M W
Smith, M F
Speirs, A L
Sprunt, D C C
Sprunt, T G
Stenhouse, E J
Steven, J D
Stewart, F K
Stewart, K S
Stewart, S L
Stuart, A B
Stuart, C A
Tavadia, H B
Traill, L M
Walford, S A
Ward, S M
Watters, J
Webster, A
Webster, J A
Weir, A W G
Weir, I R J
Weston, P G W
Whiteley, M C W
Wilson, D G
Workman, C L
Worsley, M H
Young, D R
Young, W D

Stockbridge

Adams, M S
Bates, A T
Burnfield, A J
Cross, H A
Duffy, J N
Durnford, S J
Edmonds, R W
Evans, G
Fannon, J K
Ferris, M W
Ferris, R C
Gardiner, H J
Griffiths, T D
Hodgkinson, C R
Johnson, M S
Mackintosh, L A
Mackintosh, N B
Mackintosh, T F P
Manchett, P
Owen-Reece, A R
Parr, R T
Patient, D W
Pickford, L M
Riley, P F B
Rooms, M A
Simpson, D C
Smith, D A
Townsend, A P
Vincent, P J

Stockport

Abadjian, M
Adair, M G M
Adenwala, Y T
Adhya, G
Agarwal, M
Ahluwalia, N K
Ahmed, B A
Akhtar, K
Alam, M
Alexander, D J
Alexandrou, K A
Ali, A A
Ali, J
Alladi, V R
Allan, P J
Allister, J W
Alonso Vicente, M J
Aly, F Z
Amatya, B K
Anderson, C
Anderson, H

Stocksfield

Anderson, M C
Ansell, K S
Appleton, B N
Archer, D S
Archer, R
Arepalli, N
Armstrong, M A
Armstrong, M H
Arora, A
Arora, N
Arrandale, L A
Ash, H C
Ashworth, J
Aswani, D
Atkinson, C J
Ayres, J
Ayub, A
Azeem, T
Azmy, H H
Baillie, N M
Bain, H M
Bakaya, R
Ballin, M S
Bamford, D J
Banerjee, B
Barber, M A
Bardsley, S J
Baron, R L
Bateman, S C
Baxter, S D
Beardsell, R S
Beaumont, G
Bedford, J R D
Bee, D L
Bell, W G T
Belshaw, J
Benjamin, S J
Bennett, J C B
Bennett, P W
Benson, J P
Berry, P M
Bhargava, J S
Bhattacharyya, M N
Bilbey, H
Billington, T N
Bills, G
Binless, J T
Birch, J S
Bircher, J
Bircher, R
Bisatt, J F
Black, G C M
Black, L D
Bolton, B
Booty, J
Bostock, D
Bourne, J A
Boyd, T H
Bradshaw, S J
Briggs, G J F
Briggs, R S
Brindle, T W
Brindley, E
Broadbent, P A
Brochwicz-Lewinski, M J
Brodie, G
Brogan, T D
Brooman, P J C
Brough, W A
Brown, R H L
Brown, S C W
Buchanan, K A
Buckley, A
Buckley, M
Bundred, S M
Burns, H J
Burns, S G
Burrows, G C
Butler, M L
Butterworth, D I
Byrne, J P
Byrne, R L
Canty, S J
Capper, S J
Carmody, M C
Carr, G R
Carr, H M H
Carroll, C D C
Chambers, B J
Chanda, M
Chang, J M
Channing, G M
Cheadle, B
Checkland, K H
Cherry, E M
Chopra, P
Choudhuri, A M
Choudhuri, N J
Chuah, S S
Chui, S H B
Chung, P W-M
Clark, M R S
Clarke, M A
Clarke, S
Cockersole, G M
Cocksedge, S H
Coghlan, B P
Cole, C A
Cole, S J A
Coley, A N
Coley, J C
Collins, G N
Collyer, I T
Cook, G A
Cooper, R A
Copp, E P
Corrigan, N T
Costigan, H M
Cottrell, K A
Court, J E
Cowie, G
Critchlow, B M
Cronin, D P
Crook, G C
Cruickshank, J M
Cryer, R J
Curley, J
Curran, F J M
Curran, N C
Dada, D N
Davies, A B
Davison, D W
Dawson, D L
Dawson, L
Day, C A
De Courcy Grylls, S C
Deans, G T
Derbyshire, N
Devine, N J
Dickie, I W
Dickson, R D
Dillon, J A
Dodd, P D F
Donnan, I G
Dooris, J B
Doran, B R H
Douglas, J K
Downton, J H
Drake, C N
Duckett, G K
Dymock, S M
Ead, R D
Eadsforth, P
Eddleston, B
Edwards, J
Edwards, R
Eeckelaers, E A
El Tayeb, H T
Elbeih, N M K I
Ellis, D J
Ellis, R A
Elmslie, J A G
England, P C
Evans, B K
Eyong, E
Fahmy, N R M
Faith, L
Fallowfield, J M
Farrell, D M
Fawcitt, R A
Fay, H T
Fearn, S J
Feinmann, R
Fidler, H
Fisher, A S
Fletcher, G H
Fountain, A N
Fowler, E
French, J A
Fynn, J A
Gadd, R L
Gadd, V M
Gain, R T G
Gallagher, A C
Gallagher, J M
Gallagher, P
Gandhi, H S
Garner, M R
Geary, C G
Geary, J A
Ghafoor, A
Ghosh, B N
Gill, R S
Gillespie, A
Gillespie, I E
Gilman, A R
Gilmour, S A D
Gilmour, S K
Glass, S E
Goddard, C J R
Gor, M
Gordon, M B
Gradwell, M W
Graham, W B
Greenhough, S G
Gringras, M
Haboubi, N Y
Hale, P J
Hale, R J
Hall, J D
Hall, L M
Hamlet, G
Hammersley, S E
Hanley, M
Haque, M A
Hardie, L
Hardman, R G
Harrison, P L
Harrison, R
Harrison, R K
Harrison, T J R
Hawkes, D J
Hawthorn, T C
Hay, C J
Hayward, L
Heal, C F
Heald, J
Heath, R M
Hedley, P J
Helliwell, W E
Herbert, D L
Herd, J
Hermon, C A
Hesling, C M
Hewett, J
Heyworth, T L
Hick, A G
Hick, P G
Higginbotham-Jones, K J
Higgs, J F
Hill, H F
Hingorani, A D
Hirst, G B
Hollier, P
Hope, S M
Hopkins, P A
Hopkins, S
Hopkinson, J R
Horsfall, A T
Hossain, M A
Housley, L E
Howat, R
Howling, T D
Hughes, N
Hull, C A
Hume, D D
Hunt, C R
Hussain, A
Hussain, N
Huthart, P A
Hutterer, M N
Idoo, J
Ingham, M C
Inkster, C F
Isherwood, I
Jacques, H E
Jain, A K
Jameson, R A
Jawed, F N
Jenkins, S M
Johari, S
Johnson, M E
Jones, B
Jones, D M
Jones, M M
Jones, N F
Jorasz, B M
Kaklugin, V I
Kalra, S K
Katai, F M
Keeling-Roberts, C S
Keen, R I
Keenleyside, G H
Kegg, S J
Kelvin, M
Kennedy Young, A G
Kenyon, N
Khan, A K
Khan, M A
Khan, M Y
Kilmartin, E J
Kirwan, J M J
Knell, P J W
Knowles, D
Kujawa, M L
Kumar, J S
Lalloo, N C
Lane-O'Kelly, A
Lapsia, J
Lapsia, S K
Laughton, J M
Lawton, N M
Lawton, R J
Laxminarasimhaiah, T H
Lee, J W K
Leitch, C R
Lennox, R A
Levy, D W
Levy, S F
Lewis, C J
Lewis, M J
Lewis, P S
Liddle, M W D
Lidstone, P A
Lightowler, B K W
Lindon, E F
Lindsay, R G
Lipshen, G S
Logue, J
Lowe, B A
Lowe, J
Lukka, H R
Lundy, M T
Lunn, E I
Lynch, N F
McCarthy, B P R
McCarthy, J F
McCluskey, A
MacKenzie, S A
MacKinnon, R J
Maclure, I
McMillan, E J
Maguire, A M P
Maher, T V
Mallikarjun, T S
Manton, J R
Markman, P
Marks, J S
Marshall, J S
Marshall, K C
Martin, B W
Martin, C J
Martin, M A
Mason, C J
Mather, M L
Mathewson, R C L
Maxwell, S
Maxwell, W O
McArdle, C-A
Meadows, D P
Meadows, T H
Mehta, R S
Mehta, S C
Mehta, S
Melzer, M
Menzies, D G
Midgley, M
Miller, J E
Miller, P F W
Miller, P I
Milnes, J E
Milson, F E
Milson, J E
Milson, O B
Mishra, A M
Misra, H N
Mitchell, H A
Moola, M I
Moore, A W
Moore, S A L
Morgan, I D F
Morgan, K G
Morgan, L H
Moriarty, A P
Morris, M A
Morrison, J E
Mortimer, J S
Moss, J
Muddu, V
Mukherjee, S K
Munro, T N
Murthy, A P
Murugan, G
Nankhonya, J M
Narrainen, M
Nathoo, V
Natusch, H A
Navarro Serrano, O
Nayar, A
Nazir, T Y
Needham, M J
Nelson, J M
New, F C
New, J P
Nield, F V M
Nowlan, J P
Nugent, J L
Nuttall, I D
Nuttall, N D
O'Driscoll, B J
O'Flynn, K J
O'Hagan, J
O'Kane, R
O'Neill, S S
O'Reilly, P H
Oldham, J R
Oldham, R A
Oulton, R A
Owen, G B
Owen, J R B
Owen, P A
Pal, S
Palmer, J V
Parikh, R A
Parker, G
Parker, L
Parker, T J
Parkinson, C
Parkinson, H M
Parkinson, M J
Patel, L S
Pease, E H E
Peel, S P
Phillips, M E
Pocklington, A G
Pollard, A J
Pontefract, L
Prentice, M H
Quinlan, M H
Quraishy, E
Radcliffe, M H
Raftery, P
Rains, K M
Raju, C S
Rao, S
Rash, A
Rash, R M
Rate, A J
Reeve, H A
Reeve, N L
Reisler, R
Reynolds, C D
Richardson, A M T
Rickards, M
Robertson, A M
Robertson, D M
Rodman, R
Rogers, W A
Roland, J
Roll, M J S
Rooney, M J
Rose, D H
Rowlands, M
Royle, D T
Russell, W F
Saeed, N R
Saeed, N R
Sahal, A K
Samarji, R
Samrah, A
Sayeed, I A
Saynor, G C
Schill, E B
Schnieden, V
Sejrup, O R W
Selby, P L
Semple, I C
Sethi, G
Sharma, A
Sharma, A D
Sharma, P D
Sharma, T
Sharma, Y D
Sharrard, G A W
Shawcross, A W
Shelley, K E
Shepherd, A D
Sim, D M
Simpson, R
Singer, H G
Sinha, V
Sitlani, P K
Smith, J A
Smith, J U A
Smith, M C G
Spence, I P W
Spreckley, D E
Sridharan, G V
Stanley, C H
Stanley, W J
Start, N J
Stewart, A L
Stewart, I D M
Stones, N A
Stratton, F
Strelau-Sowinska, J
Sturgess, D A
Sutherland, S D
Sutton, A G
Sutton, H J
Sykes, R
Tait, A C
Tait, W
Tandon, D K
Taylor, M E
Taylor, S L
Thane, H
Thomas, D R
Thomas, E H
Thomas, W
Thornley, A P
Thorp, M E
Tinsley, H M
Tinston, C
Tipping, K E
Todd, B D
Townsend, M
Travenen, M J
Turner, P G
Tweedie, I S
Tweedy, P S
Uglow, P A
Vasanthi-Sreenivasan, P
Vasey, R O
Vaughan, D H
Vause, M H
Vickers, D M
Vinden, S R
Von Fraunhofer, M A
Walker, E H
Walker, J
Warburton, I R
Ward, S C
Watkins, S J
Watt, C M
Watt, G J
Watt, I A K
Weeks, A K
Wells, K
Wild, A F
Wilde, J M
Wilde, N T
Wilkins, H M
Wilkinson, I E C
Wilkinson, P M
Wilks, D
Williams, G T
Williams, N J
Wilson, M C
Wolfendale, K D
Woodhouse, M N
Wray, D G
Wynne-Jones, M L
Wynroe, J C
Wynroe, S I

Stocksfield

Briel, R C G
Corbett, L
Eastwood, J R
Feeney, D P
Golightly, D L
Graham, R W
Hall, J R
Hawkesford, B
Holt, N D
Johnston, K J A
Kirk, T H
L'Anson, M-J
McKechnie, E P
Madeley, C R
Mansour, M S A
Morrison, A P
Robson, J D
Said, W Q
Sykes, R G

Stockton-on-Tees

Adams, R N
Adamson, K A
Adamson, R M
Ahmad, M A
Anderson, C F
Anderson, D J
Anderson, R L
Andrew, L
Attalla, Y A
Barber, T M
Barlow, A P
Bedi, S S

Stoke-on-Trent

Beveridge, K
Blomley, A J
Bonavia, I C
Boylan, J J B
Brady, A J
Broadway, P J
Brown, K J
Buchan, A
Budge, E M
Burrows, P S
Butler, M
Cameron, M J
Carr, A M
Carr, D
Cattermole, T J
Chadfield, B A
Chalmers, C M
Chalmers, K M
Chaudhry, S
Contractor, B R
Contractor, H B
Cook, A P
Cook, P J
Craven, R M
Critchley, P S
Davidson, G E
Davies, A L
Daynes, G K
De Burca, T T
Devlin, B
Dias, P J
Dias, R C
Dickens, D
Dobson, J A
Douglass, R A
Duckett, S P
Duval, C M
Dwarakanath, A D
Dyson, C
Ellenger, K
Elliot-Smith, A
Ellis, W
Emerton, D G C
English, C J
Entwistle, W
Farooqi, A U
Finney, R D
Fletcher, P
Foley, G P
Frain, A E
Frain, J P J
Fry, E N S
Fuller, I C
Gardner, S
Gaskarth, M T G
Gibbins, F J
Gill, P T
Gilliland, E L
Goodall, M D M
Gordon, R D
Graham, R E
Hall, K G
Hall, R G P
Hannigan, B F
Hardwick, J C
Harley, J J
Harrington, F M
Harrison, M A
Harrison, R N
Haslam, M T
Hatem, M
Hazelton, D C
Hearmon, C J
Hennessy, C
Herd, B M
Hoque, M H
Horne, R A
Horowitz, M
Howorth, P W
Hungin, A S
Jhawar, K
Jones, P R M
Kamlana, S H
Kenyon, S E
Kiberu, S W
Kidd, B
Kirkbride, I R
Kirkpatrick, J R
Krishna Kumar, V
Krishna, M
Kumar, P
Lawson, A J
Layzell, T
Leaper, D J
Leech, D L
Levan, D
Levan, S M
Lewis, K R
Leyshon, R
Lofiego, M C
Macaulay, J H
McCarthy, T J
McGowan, P J
McGuinness, P D
McGuire, J
McInally, J
McKenna, A
Mackenzie, C
Maheshwaran, S S
Makwana, R D
Mann, B M
Margallo Lana, M L
Mathie, I K
Mayes, R W
Mellis, C A
Monkhouse, D
Montgomery, J E
Montrose, M K
Moonie, W C
Naisby, M G
Needham, S J
Nicholas, J R
Noble, S G
Norrie, M S
O'Byrne, K P
O'Donnell, H A
O'Neill, C P
Oliver, G
Parrott, R J
Patel, R B
Peel, A L G
Peters, H J
Phyu Phyu, Dr
Pieri, M
Pocock, S M
Pottage, P
Poyner, T F
Pratt, R K
Rai, S S
Ramaswamy, A
Ramphul, N
Rettman, C
Rigby, C J
Ritchie, A F
Roberts, L H
Roberts, R F
Robinson, N
Roddam, P A
Rosenberg, I L
Royal, V M
Royle, P
Rubin, G P
Russell, B J
Rutter, J
Sandhu, S S
Scaife, B
Scane, A C
Scarth, J C
Scott, B
Shaw, D G M
Shaw, J
Shyam Sundar, A
Sidney, J A
Simmons, S
Sinha, R N
Smith, R H
Stephen, G W
Stephenson, C J
Stockley, S N
Stubbs, L A
Sudhakar, J E
Swords, P J K
Sylvester, S H H
Tanner, A R
Temple, M J
Thompson, A C
Thompson, W D
Thornham, J R
Tunio, F
Turner, A M
Turner, L A
Van Loo, G
Ventress, M A
Verber, I G
Walton, E W
Walton, S M
Webb, L A
White, D H
Wignarajah, N
Wilkinson, J R
Williams, S R
Woodhouse, P
Youssef, M M K I

Stoke-on-Trent

Abdu, T A M
Abraheem, A
Addy, S N
Adjogatse, J K
Ahmad, A
Ahmed, S
Ahuja, M T
Aitken, C M
Akhtar, M
Aldridge, N A
Allen, M B
Alwail, A N
Ananthanarayanan, T S
Angris, S
Ashraf, M
Ashworth, J
Azam, M F
Badcock, L J
Bagchi, D N
Bailey, I S
Bailey, N A
Bajwa, S
Baker, C E
Bamford, W M
Barber, J M
Barker, C L
Barnes, S J
Barnes, S B
Barrett, K
Barrie, B T
Barrow, K E
Bartlam, A S
Bashford, J N R
Bedson, J
Beer, R H
Bennett, A G
Bennett, J D C
Bennett, S B
Bewley, J E
Bloor, R N
Boddie, H G
Bolia, R S
Bolia, S
Bolland, E
Bourne, H C
Bowling, T E
Bradbury, S M
Braithwaite, M
Bridgman, S A
Bridgwood, P S
Brind, A M
Bromley, J S
Brookfield, D S K
Brown, G L
Brown, L S
Brown, M F
Brown, M A I
Brown, R D
Brunt, A M
Burton, K M
Butcher, A B
Campbell, C A
Carlin, N E
Carlin, W V
Carpenter, E H
Carr, D M
Carter, A J
Cartwright, D J
Casement, J R
Chadalavada, V S R
Chakraborty, A
Chamakuri, V
Chan, S C Y
Chand, G T
Chandler, P A
Chatterjee, A
Cheah, K S K
Chehata, J C G
Cheow, H K
Child, H F
Child, P D
Chipping, P M
Chopra, S K
Chopra, U
Clarke, M
Clayton, R N
Cook, A M
Cooper, J C
Cooper, V
Courteney-Harris, R G
Cowan, K A
Cox, J L
Creamer, J E
Croft, P R
Cunningham, N J
Dallow, P C
Davidson, J
Davies, M B
Davies, S J
Davis, J A S
Davis, M J
Davison, P M
Dawes, P T
Deakin, M
Dent, A R
Diamant-Desser, M
Donaldson, A D
Donoghue, C A
Dove, J
Dover, S J
Dowell, I S
Dunn, A T
Dwyer, J S J M
Eardley, R C
Eastwood, N B
Edge, V M
Edgley, J N
Edmends, S
Egginton, J A
Elder, J B
Elliot, I R
Ellis, S J
Evans, D M
Fee, S R
Fernando, L R T A
Fisher, C J
Forrest-Hay, I
Foster, C E
French, D D
French, T A
Garnham, P A R
Garrido, M C
Ghosh, D C
Ghosh, J
Gilby, J A
Godfrey, I C
Gohil, K B
Goldstraw, P W
Golik, P
Goodall, J
Gopalan, V
Graetz, K P
Graetz, P A
Grant, M O
Gray, C A M
Gray, J
Green, J C
Greenslade, A M
Gregson, P A
Griffiths, D
Hancock, M R
Hand, M F
Hares, P S
Harris, A
Harrison, N J
Hartland, A J
Hassan, M K
Hawkins, K A
Hay, E M
Hayter, R C
Heagerty, A H
Heath, P D
Henshaw, C A
Hickson, A F
Hickson, R M
Hill, E W
Hobson, C M
Hodgson, R E
Hoey, A B
Holland, J
Hopcroft, J D
Hopkins, C S
Hopkins, S E
Hopwood, M E F
Howis, A
Hughes, G M
Hully, R
Hurley, D
Hurlstone, D P
Hussain, K
Hutchings, W
Hutchinson, D
Hutchinson, J A
Ishaq, S
Ismail, S
Jafri, A
Jafri, S A
Jafri, S K A
Jain, N K
Jarvis, R J
Jary, M
Jary, S R
Johanson, R B
Johnson, D S
Johnston, B M
Jones, A
Jones, C M
Jones, D H
Jones, R G
Katsimihas, M
Keates, M D
Keating, G W
Kendall, M L
Kerr, C A
Khan, A H
Khunger, A C
Kilding, J-A
King, J M
King, S E
Knapper, S
Knight, C L
Kundu, S
Lam, F Y
Lannigan, A M
Lata, P S
Lawrence, A D M
Lear, G A
Lee, S W
Leese, I D
Lenney, W
Lewis, S E
Lightfoot, P J
Lithgow, P A
Little, J T
Liu, S
Loughney, D G M
Lund, A D
Lyons, E L P
McCarthy, F J
McCarthy, J J
McCarthy, M E F
McCartie, K M
McConnell, J R L
McGowan, J M
McMaster, P D B
McVerry, D N
Magowan, J
Mahmood, Z Z
Malgwa, A
Malgwa, P R
Mali, M
Mallepaddi, N R
Manning, G L
Manudhane, V S
Marathe, R M
Masson, G
Matthews, N C
Mayland, P A
Meaney, T P
Meaton, M L
Mehta, K K
Merali, N A
Merifield, W K
Messiou, C
Mia, M S
Millinship, J
Mirza, S M
Mohajer, M P
Morgan, R H
Morris, P T
Morrison, P J
Mottershead, N J
Mucklow, J C
Mulford, S D
Mustfa, N
Naeem, M
Nayar, M S
Nayar, O K
Nayeemuddin, F A
Neary, R H
Negrycz, R J
O'Brien, A P
O'Brien, P M S
Oakley, P A
Oxtoby, J W
Oxtoby, J D
Page, R J
Pantin, C F A
Parikh, H S
Park, A J
Parkinson, K
Parmar, J M
Parmar, J R
Patel, B D
Patel, C V
Patel, M V
Patel, S V
Patel, V A
Patterson, J A
Pearson, R A
Pedrazzini, A E
Perry, M J
Phillips, C J
Phillips, D W
Phillips, R M
Phillips, R A
Pilpel, J M
Pilpel, P J
Plunkett, M C
Prabhakaran, N
Pratap, B R
Price, D J
Prowse, K
Przyslo, F R
Pullan, A D
Rabie, S M M
Raby, J R
Raffeeq, P M
Rafique, M
Ramachandran, S
Randell, T L
Rao, S Y P C P
Rathi, A K
Reddy, G V
Redman, C W E
Redmond, A D
Reeves, H L
Reynolds, E R
Reynolds, K A
Rice, C P
Richards, P J
Richardson, B
Rickards, N P
Rizvi, F H
Roberts, J O
Roberts, K J
Robinson, I
Rogerson, M E
Rohatgi, M K
Rohatgi, S
Rose, R
Roy, T K
Ruparelia, P
Russell, G I
Ryan, M M B
Saklatvala, J
Salpekar, S D
Salt, M J
Samal, K
Samuels, M P
Sanghera, P
Sankaran, M
Sarwar, H
Scarpello, J H
Schur, P E
Scoble, J E
Scott, A R
Scott, C A
Seth, K N
Sethi, A K
Sethi, K B S
Shadforth, M F
Shah, P H
Shah, S S
Shaikh, M S
Shamsi, S A
Sharaf-Ud-Din, S
Sharaf, A
Shaw, H M A
Shaw, M E L C
Shaw, M W
Shaw, P H
Sheikh-Sajjad, A R
Sheppard, D A
Shevlin, B A
Sieber, F A
Simpkin, N D
Singh, J
Sinha, A K
Sinha, R N
Sissons, A J E
Sivapalan, S
Sivardeen, G M F
Sivardeen, K A Z
Smallpeice, C J
Smith, B A C
Smith, I
Smith, P J
Smith, S D
Soliman, M O A M
Solis Reyes, C
Spencer, S A
Standage, K F
Stephens, M
Stocker, D I
Sugrue, D L
Sule Suso, J
Suxena, S R
Synnott, M B
Talpur, H A
Tattum, C M
Tattum, K T
Taylor, K M
Thackstone, S I
Thomas, G R W
Thomas, H W
Thomas, M P S
Thomas, P B M

Stoke-sub-Hamdon

Till, S J
Tiwari, P
Tomlinson, A A
Tomlinson, I M
Tooth, J S
Topple, N A
Tubbs, H R
Turner, P J
Turner, S E
Turner, W W
Turnidge, J M
Urwin, O M
Vaghmaria, A
Van Der Linden, H H E M
Vaze, B C
Venkateswaran, M
Verborg, S A
Verma, H L
Verma, R K
Verma, R K
Wakley, G M
Walker, A B
Walsh, A K M
Ward, A B
Watson, R A
Watts, D J
Weatherby, S J
Webster, A P
Webster, V G
Weeder, R G
Wells, R D
Welton, M D M
Wilkins, C J
Williams, V
Williamson, A D
Willmer, K A
Willmott, P A
Wilson, P S
Wood, A F
Wood, J H
Woodcock, C J
Worrall, A
Wright, N J
Wu, G Y M
Yadava, R P
Yates, D O
Yates, G
Young, D N
Young, G M
Zafar, F S

Stoke-sub-Hamdon

Bulley, R J
Collins, H F
Hammersley, S G
Parton, J B
Scott, P J
Smith, M J

Stone

Acey, G
Anderson, I V
Atkins, C S
Ballinger, J P
Boyd, A
Boyd, W N
Campbell, C F L
Challiner, R A
Clark, R M
Corbett, M J
Crump, A A S C W
Davis, H
Deaville, A M
Eames, J K
Everall, I P
Farnham, B E
Hamilton, E C
Hamilton, P G
Hand, S E
Hassell, A B
Holden, S W
Ibbotson, R M
Johnson, A M
Kadam, U T
Kimber, V R
Lamb, A J
Letts, K L
McClelland, D
MacKinnon, D L
MacSharry, M J
Malmberg, A K
Markham, R A
Moulson, F J
Murphy, F
Nyamugunduru, G
Ockenden, B G
Sangster, P J
Secker, C J

Skilton, J S
Stafford, A J
Stafford, D M
Taylor, I A
Templeton, J
Warren, J L
Waterhouse, A M
Wooding, D F P
Wooding, S J

Stonehaven

Bowyer, M S
Chan, T T B
Christie, H D
Cordiner, D S
Dossett, A G
Duthie, I M
Fisher, P M
French, W G
Green, E
Herd, J M R
Hopper, N B
Houghton, E J
Howard, D M
Innes, J
Johnson, B
Johnstone, H M G
Jones, A H
MacCuish, A
McIntosh, G H
Mackenzie, I S
Mackenzie, L M
McLay, K A
Maclean, V M
McLeod, I
Milne, A H
Morgan, A H
Morris, V J
N'Dow, K E
O'Hara, A W
Patience, L A
Singer, L J
Stewart, A L
Thomson, J M G
Weir, M J

Stonehouse, Gloucestershire

Anslow, S R F
Cheyne, W G
Esmailji, E A
Fisher, G H
Lake, L A
Latter, M J
O'Dowd, B H
Sivyer, J E
Tasker, L J
Wenham, J A
Woodland, J

Stonehouse, Lanarkshire

Ritchie, E L

Stoneyburn

Stewart, J H

Stornoway

Brydon, S M
Cunningham, G K
Davis, J N
Dickie, A M
Dickie, R J
Gillies, S E
Gray, G L
Hothersall, A P
Maclean, D A
MacLennan, C R
Michie, A B
Murray, D J
Raff, P F
Sarkar, P K
Scott, L
Smith, J
Speirs, W M
Walker, M J
Wouda, M

Stourbridge

Ali, M S
Allen, E K
Allen, S M
Allison, E C
Andrew, T A
Ashton, C T
Bache, J C
Baker, J R
Barrett, E C A
Barrett, S R
Bassett, M R A
Baxter-Smith, D C

Beardsmore, D M
Berwick, S J M
Bloor, M
Booth, J S
Bowers, E F
Bracka, A
Brindley, R J
Browning, D J C
Burbridge, B J
Bury, J P
Butler, A C
Butler, C E
Callender, R
Campbell, G C
Carter, M P
Chaloner, J D
Chandra, E
Charles, A L
Chinnock, J H
Clark, A L
Clymo, A B
Cochrane, J M
Collins, P D
Collins, T M
Cooke, M J
Coope, B J
Cooper, T A
Craggs, A M S
Czapla, K
Davies, S J
Davis, R E
Davis, R C
De Silva, M S
Delamere, J P
Dickinson, K G
Digger, T J
Dingwall, I M
Donovan, R M
Drury, V W M
Dudley, B G
Duncan, J M
Dunn, R M
Dyson, M L
Edwards, T R
Edwin, P J
Evans, G R
Evans, L C
Farley, P S
Feghali, E
Firth, J
Fisher, G C
Flint, E J
Gbinigie, A O
Ghose, A
Gough, N L
Gower, N D
Grainger, M F
Griffiths, C A
Gwynn, C M
Hadlington, K J
Hale, M
Hall, J W
Hanson, C A
Healy, M D
Higgins, R P
Hilton, D D
Hobson, M I
Homer, L M
Humphries, E E
Hunton, M
Hyde, J N
Innes, P A
Iqbal, A
Irfan, F A
Issitt, J S
Jabar, M F
Jenkins, K L
Joy, T K
Kelly, A N
Kelly, S D E
Khalid, N
Killalea, S E
Killin, W P
Krick, R C B
Labib, M H Z
Le Doux, C D G
Lewis, G J
Levland, F C
Lim, S
Louca, O A B
Lovett, J M
McKenzie, M A
McLean, R D
McMinn, D J W
McMinn, M J
Mangat, T S
Mangat, T K
Mann, S J
Mazey, N S

Megyesi-Schwartz, F C
Merotra, S K
Mifsud, R
Mills, S A
Mohite, A S
Moore, E C
Moseley, G E
Mucklow, G K M
Mucklow, J T
Mudgal, R
Murphy, J P
Needoff, J
Nimbkar, V W
O'Meara, K O M B
Oldman, L E
Orange-Lohn, B
Partridge, S J
Patodi, M
Pearce, A J
Pennock, H C
Perry, K A
Phillips, A F
Potter, S J
Powell, D F
Powell, D J S
Raafat, L
Raphael, H M
Raphael, J H
Rees, D A
Renny, F H B
Reshamwala, N K
Richards, D S
Richards, J E H
Riley, K P
Roberts, G A
Rose, M N
Ross, H J T
Sajid, M
Sales, S R
Saraf, T Y
Sarhadi, N S
Shah, N H
Skene-Smith, H S
Smith, R S
Sockalingam, M
Speakman, J K
Spyrou, G
Steven, R E
Tai, Y M A
Tanner, M T
Taylor, V R
Tebbutt, N C
Thomas, S S
Thompson, S D
Thomson, S A
Turner, M H
Turner, N
Tzifa, C
Walker, M A
Walker, R O
Walmsley, R S
Warwick, A P
Watkins, B J
Watson, R S
Watt, A J M
Watton, D
Weyham, C J
Wiesand, M
Wild, A G G
Wilkinson, J L
Wilkinson, S D
Wilson, G R
Wilson, M
Wynne, R A
Yarwood Smith, C H
Zalin, A M

Stourport-on-Severn

Al-Khayat, M A R M
Batty, P F
Black, D K
Brohan, E
Bywater, J W
Chithiramohan, R N
Gait, A J
Gibbins, P M
Goodman, J S
Grice, E G
Griffiths, J M
Hickman, L J
Horton, R J
James, D W
Joanes, K M
Joanes, R F
Kanas, R P
Kingston, W E
Parsons, G J
Priest, M
Rumley, S L P

Tapp, E
Ward Platt, P
Ward, R A

Stowmarket

Campbell, D M T
Cheves, P B
Clapp, R M M
Dean, A F
Egan, D J
Fenning, A H
Fielder, J P S
Franks, P S
Gill, J R
Grundy, R E
Hall, R M
Hayes, P A
Head, P H
Helliwell, M C J
Herman, J M
Hollinrake, A
Jenkins, I A R
Jennings, T B
Kubis, V M
Macpherson, H M
Marlow, H F
Moore-Smith, B
Moore-Smith, J P
Muir, J E
Reti, S R
Rudland, S V
Shenton, M I
Smith, R C
Tuke, J W
Wankowski, A F
Wylde, E M
Yusaf, B

Strabane

Cavanagh, P J
Cooke, C A
Diamond, P M
Donnelly, D M
Duffy, M P
Flanagan, M S
Friel, F C
Fullerton, A T
Gallagher, J
Gillespie, J G
Harron, J C
Harron, M E
Kerr, E G
Leahy, B J P
McCarron, S B
McCluggage, H L
McCrea, K J
McElhinney, B R
McGuinness, A P
McHale, J G A J
O'Donnell, J S
O'Neill, M P O M
O'Reilly, J
Patton, S N
Quigley, B M
Robinson, A
Stewart, S D
Sullivan, C A
Watson, G H V

Stranraer

Baird, W A
Balmer, N W
Black, S M
Calvert, J A
Donnelly, C M
Gall, J F
Gordon, J J
Grieve, R C
Hocken, P B
Lee, J
Lennon, E M
McDougall, F M
McInroy, J
McTaggart, J C
Narain, B
Reid, S C T
Ritchie, I M
Scott, R J
Slater, E A W
Spicer, R J
Vaughan, D A
White, R J
Wooff, D J

Stratford-upon-Avon

Adam, I J
Adam, W J
Adams, L J
Alexander, M K
Alliston, J E
Allwood, I J
Archer, N D
Babu, R
Batt, E M
Bothwell, P W
Box, W J O
Brace, W D
Buckley, D M
Carrington, I M
Carus, A M
Chambers, S J
Clarke, K L
Coigley, M H F
Coulthard, R A
Craddock, D J
Crook, T G
Crowfoot, J
Dalton, J D
Davies, L P
Derbyshire, D R
Dickens, G
Evans, N J B
Ferguson, D
Field, A B
Fitchford, R J
Fitchford, W J
Fletcher, I M
Gabathuler, H
Ganner, A N
Garratt, D M
Gilbert, M P
Gowans, J
Hallworth, S P
Henderson, R M
Hodson, J P A
Jones, J A
Khan, J S
King, K J
Kinoulty, M
Kirkpatrick, P E
Kitchen, H J
Lewis, J V V
Loughridge, M C
McMorran, J P
McMorran, S H
Madagan, N G
Marcus, R T
Mazey, G H
Mitra, S
Morgan, A J A
Nicol, M
Parry, E F H
Peer, R M
Phalp, C G A
Ramesh, G
Redman, V L
Rudge, J W
Schofield, A M
Sykes, G W
Thorne, R J
Vries, L A G
Watkins, E D
Wedderburn, J P
Wells, C A
Wellstood, F G
West, K L
West, M R J
Williams, B D M
Winstanley, A M
Winstanley, C S
Wood, N C
Woodward, M N
Woodward, N A
Wright, A C
Yates, E J

Strathaven

Aitken, R J G
Barbour, M I
Bell, J M
Campbell, C M C
Campbell, W M
Dow, R E
Fulton, J M
Glen, P
Godley, C C
Graham, A
Hackett, J S
Hassall, C M
Hynes, P C
Johnman, L
McEwan, G A
McGowan, J H
Miller, D F
Morris, M
Mosley, A M
Munro, E
Pearce, I

Sunderland

Pepperell, I
Porte, A M
Rankin, J N
Shapiro, F N
Sharma, D
Sharma, S
Sharma, U C
Shearer, J H
Sinclair, W Y
Smith, S M
Sutherland, S S
Watson, M H
Whitelaw, F M

Strathcarron

Cargill, J M
Fisher, C M
Murray, D B
Romanes, G J

Strathdon

Craig, M S
Dudley, H A F
Fitton, J L
Herbert, J P

Strathpeffer

Campbell, C J
Dick, D S
Gate, H B
Macpherson, T S
McWilliam, P J
Murchison, M
Newton, M
Wood, A J

Street

Clark, H M
Elkin, T
Forth, M J
Holland, S J
Last, R D
Lines, J C
Merrick, J
Merry, E J
Monro, A J
Owen, R J
Rushford, C A
Seymour, B J
Singhal, V K
Wolfe, C S

Stromness

Alexander, M
Anderson, D A R
Clark, K H
Hourston, I M
McIntyre, L T
Pyle, W D
Rae, C K
Trickett, A R

Stroud

Abbas, T M
Allan, M
Babor, B E
Baddeley, P G
Barraclough, K
Basker, E L
Bayly, J R
Blatchley, C
Boddam-Whetham, A H C
Booker, N J
Boss, J M N
Bridger, C
Bright, P H
Brown, C M
Brown, P F
Burlingham, A N
Burrows, S K
Bye, I M
Calvert, D G
Campbell, M M F
Chapman, J M
Cobbe, J M
Croser, D H
Crouch, H E
Crouch, T
D'Agapeyeff, K E
Davie, R C
Davies, K
Dickson, A F L W
Doddridge, M C
Dowling, B L
Driscoll, R C
Du Toit, J A
Evans, K L
Evans, M R
Fairgrieve, H
Grace, L M

Graham Munro, F J
Haffenden, D K
Hall, G D
Harlow, J M
Havinga, W H
Hawkins, J P J
Hedley, N E
Holmes, R P H
Horner, G L
Hoyland, H J
Hutter, A
Isaac, D C
Isaac, G J
James, M E
Jansen, C A M
Jarrett, R F
Jones, N D H
Jones, R A
Jorro, B S C
Keating, J
Kelly, P G
Kingston, P J
Lake, I D
Lamb, R W
Lamb, S N
Latham, A M
Lavis, R A
Lees, P F
Lewis, E D
Lewis, J W
Livingstone, D N
Lloyd, G L
Lucas, A J
Mccabe, S E
McCrirrick, A B
McInerney, G M
McKie, N I P
McLaren, M M
Marlow, A-M
Meikle, V M
Merryweather, R
Mills, S J
Mould, J
Pearson, P
Perry-Keene, G H
Poole, R A
Porter, M C M
Pouncey, D A C G
Reed, A
Richards, H
Sackett, K M
Salter, J C
Savage, M J
Shepherd, C B
Shooter, J
Shooter, R A
Simpson, A P F
Slim, J M
Smith, D A
Somervell, D H
Stamforth, C
Stephenson, R H
Stirland, E
Swindell, P J
Tann, O R
Taylor, J H K
Thomas, D M
Thomas, J D
Thomas, S
Thompson, D R
Van Zyl, M E
Vestey, S B
Waldon, R D
Walker, D L
Walters, J C
Weir, S
Whittaker, M D
Witcombe, J B
Womersley, A M E
Wood, R
Woods, C J
Wright, J S
Wright, M P

Studley

Adams, R G
Ash, J V
Buckley, M P
Cartledge, J D
Edwards, D A
Harris, P J
Wade, R J
Walsh, R C

Sturminster Newton

Bolton, J C V
Burton, E C
Casson, E J
Clayton, S J

Cripps, M G
Eslick, M A R
Hopkins, K I
Horler, G D
Huddy, E C H
Hunt, G A L M
Robinson, J P J
Snowden, J
Sparrow, G E A
Stephens, C P
Vardill, D
Watts, P E
Wilson, W G
Wrigley, J H

Sudbury

Adams, E B
Barker, M J M
Benton, M D
Bethell, P A
Bevan, D C P
Bone, A D W
Boyd, T I
Burtenshaw, H M
Carter, J A
Chambers, M E W
Chase, R P
Cope, N M
Coupland, M P M
Crouch, A D K
De Pass, J P C
Deb, A K
Debenham, J A R
Debenham, M R
Dickinson, P J
Donnelly, R
Dunmore, C J
Elson, J G
Enticknap, J B
Feneck, R O
Germaine, D D A
Goodliffe, C D
Grimmett, B M
Hawkins, J A
Hayhow, B
Haythornthwaite, G E
Heller, K B
Hughes, R A
Jetha, S K
Kemp, A R
Kennedy Scott, J P
Kiel, A L M
Langdon, T C
Leeper, A B M
Lesser, G F
Livingstone, I G
McClellan, E
MacDiarmid, F M
McLauchlan, A E
Mason, A J M
Maybury, P L
Moore, T R
Norman, A G
Norris, T C M
Pearce, J F
Penistan, T R
Sarda, K
Sills, S C J
Stewart, A D
Stewart, J A B
Stone, R C
Symes, C
Taylor, D L
Taylor, M E
Trewhella, J D
Welch, C I
Williams, R A J
Williamson, S S
Wood, T C
Wynn, G R

Sunbury on Thames

Hodson, S E

Sunbury-on-Thames

Al-Ani, S-A A
Ali, M
Barnett, R
Bhular, J S
Brackley, K J
Byrne, B
Chapman, G B
Chapman, L
Dix, J H
Dutta, S K
Elvin, V
Inman, N J
Jolly, M M S
Maclaurin, J R C
Martin, A M

Pearce, J J
Pearce, N R
Ranjithakumar, S
Saunders, A P
Van Rhijn, M
Zamenhof-Nietupska, O E

Sunderland

Abu-Harb, M
Adedeji, O A
Ahmed, N
Al-Khalidi, B G O
Al-Omari, A M M
Ali, S S
Allchin, R W
Allen, E D
Anderson, H H D
Anjum, S
Ansell, P J
Arrowsmith, A E
Atchison, R K
Bagchi, S P
Bailey, J L
Banjeree, G
Banks, D C F
Bansal, S K
Barnetson, J K
Barton, J W
Basu, A P
Basu, M B
Baxter, M A
Belger, H S
Bell, G D
Bell, R W D
Bendelow, K
Bernardi, R E
Bhate, S M
Bhatt, N J
Bignardi, G E
Birnie, A J M
Black, W P
Blakey, R E
Bolel, S B
Bose, A A K
Brigham, J D
Brown, A M D
Brown, C J
Brown, M J
Burton, R L
Buswell, W A
Button, C
Cameron, H M
Carey, P J
Carpenter, H C W
Carter, J H
Cervenak, R F E
Chapman, A J
Chapman, F M
Chay, S T S
Chhabra, D R
Chiquito-Lopez, P E
Clague, H W
Clark, L
Cloak, B J
Cochrane, H R
Cohen, C
Cohen, K M
Cohen, S
Connor, J A
Corson, R J
Crighton, I L
Crone, N M
Crone, P B
Cronin, P M
Cross, A T
Crummie, A J M
Dalton, M E
Danjoux, J-P
Datta, P S
Davies, A J
Daymond, T J
Deady, J P
Deshpande, M K
Devapal, D
Dhar, R L
Dhariwal, N K
Dillon, R D S
Donaldson, K I
Donoghue, R E
Dow, A R
Dow, A B
Dulson, K
El-Faki, A E H M A
El Mekkawy, E E D A-K
El Safy, A M I E
Ela, M A A
Featherstone, T

Fernandes, C
Fetherston, T J
Finlay, R
Fletcher, R D M
Ford, R N
Forester, N D
Fraser, E M
Fraser, K M
Fraser, S G
French, N
Furness, J C
Galloway, M J
Gardner, E S
Gautam, S
Gavin, N A
Ghosh, A
Ghosh, P
Gilbert, R K
Gill, P I
Glass, L G
Glatt, D
Glatt, H S
Goldsmith, P V
Golledge, P
Gough, D G
Graham, W
Grant, J A
Gray, C S
Green, J D
Greene, D R J
Gupta, S D
Hall, S J
Hallikeri, S G
Hamad, A H
Hancock, D M
Harvey, G T
Harvey, M C
Hawkins, C
Heard, A M B
Hearne, M J J P
Heaton, J M
Hedge, C V
Henderson, D P
Henderson, M A
Heycock, E G
Heycock, R W
Hickey, P M
Hind, J M
Hinshaw, K
Holland, C D
Hopper, I
Hunsley, D
Hyder, M T
Inglesby, D V
Irwin, L R
Johnson, P A
Johnson, R
Jones, A J
Jones, M I C
Jones, R E
Joshi, N A
Junejo, S
Kachchumarikkar, M S
Karat, S
Karn, K P
Kaul, O
Keaney, N P
Keatings, J
Kelly, J M
Kennedy, R L
Kew, F M
Kilgour, T C
Lahiri, B
Lahiri, S
Langtry, J A A
Lascelles, C F
Lawrie, A W
Lawson, G R
Lee, J
Leeks, A D
Lefley, P J
Leigh, R J
Lennox, J M
Levy, B
Liang Lung Chong, M E K
Lillington, A W
Lobo, F X
Lovell, T W I
Lowry, M F
Lynch, V
Lyndon, S
McBride, G P
McBride, J E
McDonald, J W
Mackay, G
Mackay, L J
McKee, A G
Mackee, I W

Mackenzie, A
Mackrell, J R
MacNab, G
Maidment, G
Mair, J A
Malik, M M A
Maredia, M N
Marsh, R L
Marsh, R J
Martin, A
Martin, A M
Martin, E R
Martin, I C
Mellon, A F
Metcalf, M
Miller, I T
Miller, P D
Milne, D S
Milne, J B B
Mitchison, H C
Mitchison, S
Mittra, B
Moodie, J S
Morgan, S J
Motwani, C A
Mukherjee, S P
Murphy, A-M
Murphy, D A
Murray, B J
Murray, R B
Murtock, T
Nabar, M A
Natarajan, S
Nelson, S
Nepali, P K
Newmark, R W
O'Connell, J E
Oakley, H
Ojo, B A
Orde, S O-U
Owen, N M
Ozuzu, G E
Parker, A J
Parker, C
Partington, J S
Patnaik, S
Patnaik, S N
Pawaroo, L
Phelan, P S
Pickworth, R W
Pilapitiya, R B
Pillai, P M
Pillai, S S
Pinto Wright, R J
Place, M
Powell, S L
Pugh, S E
Purves, G F
Raman, T S
Raphael, G A J
Raphael, M
Rashid, S
Razvi, F M
Reddy, G M
Reid, C J
Richardson, J
Richardson, W A W
Riddle, G D
Robinson, G J
Roy, A I
Runge, A M
Rutherford, R G
Saharia, E
Salkeld, J W
Samuel, P R
Sandbach, C S
Sarma, D I
Sarma, K M
Sarson, D
Sein Win, L C H
Sharma Kavi, K N
Shepherd, R B
Shetty, B K K
Shrestha, T L
Siddiqui, F
Sinclair, P
Singh, H C
Singh, L
Small, P K
Smith, J J
Smithson, S R
Spagnoli, E A
Stassen, L F A
Steel, A M
Steel, D H W
Steele, S C
Stephenson, K
Stirrat, A N
Stone, A W

Surbiton

Sultana, A M U
Tadross, T S F
Tayal, S A
Taylor, I K
Thomas, J B
Thompson, J D
Thorpe, A C
Totts, K S
Tsakos, E
Turpin, J A
Velangi, S S
Waine, C
Walker, M J
Walton, C J
Ward, G C
Watson, A J
Watson, I D
Watters, M M
Weaver, K N J
Welbury, J
Wells, C W
Wetherall, M R B
Whitehead, P T
Whitfield, P H
Whiting, K A
Widdrington, I H
Wilson, I J
Wong, L H
Wong, N C
Wortley, P M
Wright, M E
Wright, W
Young, L J
Young, P F

Surbiton

Agrawal, K
Agrawal, R K
Aldous, C A
Barlin, C A
Bartlett, D
Baruch, A L H
Benney, S A J
Beven, P G H
Boullin, J P
Bowey, O
Byramji, N K
Campbell, N G
Cassell, D M C
Cockburn, J J
Collini, P J
Cotton, M-A
Cotzias, C S
Crawley, S J
D'Souza, J C H
Dalzell, J
Davies, R S
Dhir, K S
Edwards, J M
Gaya, D S
Gentle, S C
Ging, J E
Gonzalez, M A
Gooding, H K
Gordon, D J
Grover, V P B
Hindle, K S
Hinsley, A M
Holden, D P
Holdsworth, W G
Holton, A R
Hulse, M G
Jones, R
Kalsi, M S
Kelly, J
Kodikara, M
Langridge, P
Lark, K A
Law, P K
Lee, R K L
Luke, J J
Majeed, Q
Mansour, N S N
Martin, E C
Menzies, I S I
Milton, R S
Mohan, T C
Moore, P D
Moore, S J
Munby, J S
Munby, J C A
O'Driscoll, M J
Oshea, C P
Pall, A A
Pattison, R M
Peter, J
Phillips, S
Pinkerton, M
Pires, P

Prentice, P A
Pullinger, R H
Punter, J
Rafique, M A
Rajani, R
Rashad, S Y
Rathakrishnan, R
Roberts, D L
Rowland, C J
Saha, B N
Saragoudas, S
Shalom, S D
Shute, C M
Somers, L J
Spotswood, V J
Syed, A A
Syed, J A
Thaman, R
Thapar, V
Thurairaja, R
Topp, J M
Tovey, S J
Turner, C L S
Walsh, B
Waters, M J
Weeks, P H
Wolfson, M S
Wright, L P J

Sutton

Aboud, M A
Akberali, A F
Akram, N S
Ali Khan, M F S
Amin, S M
Arendse, S D
Atra, A A A
Badve, S S
Bailey, J M
Barrett, J J
Barsey, H
Barsey, L
Benyamin, F
Bhattachan, C L
Bhoyrul, S
Bignell, M D
Blackwell, M J
Bloom, H S
Bolodeoku, E O
Bown, P J
Brada, M
Braet, V
Brayden, P C
Brennan, C A M
Bristow, M F
Brown, J H
Bryan-Brown, A B E
Canepa-Anson, A C M
Carter, R L
Carter, T R G
Cauchi, E M
Chan, T M L
Chana, P
Chana, T
Chilvers, A S
Churchill, M A
Clark, D L
Clarke, S J
Coldrey, D A
Cooling, R A
Craig, J O M C
Craig, L B
Croucher, J J
Cunningham, D
Curtis, J R
Dark, G G
Davies, C E
Davies, D M
Davies, D R
Davies, K A
De Silva, P V
Dearnaley, D P
Dearnaley, J M M
Dinnick, S E
Donaldson, J B
Doyle, E X P
Edwards, J M
Eeles, R A
Elliott, C J
Elliott, S D C
Evans, R A
Evans, S A
Falconer, A
Feitelberg, M J
Fernandez, M D
Filshie, J
Fish, D G H
Fleet, H J
Ford, H T

Ford, H E R
Ford, P M
Forrest, A J
Frangoulis, M A
Free, A J
Free, M C
Gardner, M W
Ghosh, M K
Goodliffe, A D R
Gossain, S R
Gough, J S
Gough, P M
Gould, T R
Govender, S
Greer, H S
Grice, J D
Grice, S J
Gunasekera, W S L
Hall, J G
Hardy, J R
Harris, C B
Havelock, J M
Heavey, A P
Henk, J M
Hill, M E
Hji Yiannakis, P
Hogg, H A
Horwich, A
Hossain, S M S
Houlston, R S
Howell, M L
Howell, S E
Huddart, R A
Hudson, B
Husband, J E S
Irvine, R R
James, A H
James, R E
Jefferies, S J
Jelly, L M E
John, A C
Johnstone, D J
Jolley, A W
Jones, A C
Jones, D B D
Jones, V A
Judson, I R
Kalmus, E J
Kanthan, K K
Kar, S V
Kar, S S
Karunasekera, I K
Kathirgamakanthan, S
Kattan, M M
Kay, D M
Kaye, A C
Kaye, S B
Kazi, N M
Kazmi, M S
King, M M
Kothari, J J
Kuppusami, T N
Kurwa, A R
Lall, R P
Lampe, H
Latham, D
Latifi, Q A
Latifi, S Q
Lawson, T D
Lee, M S
Leghari, J A K
Leitch, R J
Likeman, M J
Linnell, A E T
Lodge, J W
Longley, J M
McCready, V R
Macfarlane, D A
McInnes, P B
McIntosh, C S
Macleod, A T
Madan, A
Magauran, D M
Male, A M
Male, D A
Mason, R H
Mathers, C B B
Mehra, M
Meller, S T
Merritt, L G
Middleton, S
Mitchell, E B
Mugglestone, C J
Mullane, M C
Nash, A G
Neville, K M
Neylan, C M M A
Norton, K R W
Nugent, D A W

O'Brien, E A
O'Brien, J T
O'Brien, M E R
O'Donnell, P J
O'Sullivan, C J
Ogeah, Dr
Oshowo, A O
Palmier, B M
Paramothayan, N S
Patroni, B
Paul, S B
Pembrey, J S
Perkin, M R
Perry, A R
Picton-Jones, J
Pinkerton, C R
Popat, S B
Pourgourides, C K
Powles, T J
Pritchard-Jones, K
Prokop, S
Querci Della Rovere, G
Quigley, M M
Rabindra, B
Ramsey, J M
Ramsey, P M
Rathod, R C
Raw, J P
Redwood, D R
Richards, M A
Roberts-Shephard, A
Rodin, M J
Rubio Rodriguez, M D C
Rudin, C E
Ruse, G A
Said, A
Said, A J
Saluja, T R
Sampath, R
Sarin, R
Scully, M A
Seyan, R S A S
Sharma, A
Sharp, M
Shedden, R G
Shepherd, J C
Shiew, C M
Shiew, M M F
Silva, M T
Singhal, S
Smit, I D
Smith, I D
Smith, I E
Smith, J N
Smith, R E
Sohaib, S A A
Soomal, R S
Souberbielle, B E
Spring, L C
Stephenson, W H
Stern, R S
Stinson, D M
Stoddart, F H
Sumpter, K A
Tait, D M
Thethravusamy, J A
Thomas, D V P
Thompson, A M
Thornley, C N
Thorpe, E J
Tinkler, J M
Tompsett, M J
Tonge, A E
Treleaven, J G
Tylee, A T
Tyler, M J
Tyrrell, J M
Ursell, P G
Vernon, J E
Vijayakulasingam, V
Visvanathan, R
Vivekananda, C
Wadhwani, G H
Wannan, G J
Warren, A P
Waterston, A M
Wheate, H W
Whitaker, S J
Whitlow, B J
Whitlow, C M
Williamson, A D B
Wills, G T
Wright, J C
Wurm, R E
Wylie, D W
Wylie, M
Zomas, A

Sutton Coldfield

Abbas, S
Abd-El-Massih, G K
Abdalla, M A-E H M
Abdo, O A
Acland, J D
Al-Salihi, T
Alam, M
Albright, S W
Ali, R
Allan, L M
Allen, K E M
Ananta, M P P
Archer, D F J
Ashwell, S G
Banerjea, B L
Baxter, R J
Beaumont, A L
Benke, E J
Benyon, S L
Bhalla, S K
Bhatt, P I
Bhatt, R I
Bickley, C M
Bishop, N J
Blackburn, M
Blackford, P
Bleasdale, J P
Blight, A P
Bond, A R
Booth, K R
Brake, R C
Brennan, A P
Briscoe, J J D
Broomhead, C R M
Brown, J H
Bullock, J
Burnell, H C
Burnie, S G S
Burton, C C
Burton, P W
Cartmill, R S V
Cassam, S
Chapman, A
Chapman, B M
Chapman, J P O
Charles, S J
Cheyne, C
Chiam, T K
Churchill, D
Clarke, M P
Cole, J G L
Collier, I P
Collier, J B
Constable, T J
Constantine, G
Cooper, N F D
Cope, S J
Coutts, A S
Crawford, W S
Crossley, J M
Cuthbert, A J
Daly, T P
Damerau, N B L E
Darby, S E
Davies, A C
De Wit, A
Deacon, G P
Deshpande, A H
Deshpande, H A
Deshpande, V A
Dippie, T H P
Divall, J M
Dodds, S R
Dolman, M J
Down, S K
Dugas, M J
Duggal, R
Dunbar, M R
East, D M
Eddy, J D
Edwards, J G
Elliot, J M
Ellis, L M
Elmardi, A A A
Farooqi, I S
Finn, C B
Fisken, A G
Flacks, R M
Fletcher, T J
Fookes, B H
Fookes, J R
Forshaw, M L
Fortes Mayer, K D
Foster, J M
Foster, M C
Francis, D A
Frew, I D O
Frost, A R

Gent, R J
Gething, N J
Ghosh, C
Ghosh, K
Gibbins, S J
Goel, V K
Gonzalez Naranjo, D S
Goodwin, I D
Gordon, S A
Gossain, S
Grant, M K
Grant, P H
Grice, E R S
Griffin, M J W
Griffiths, D J
Griffiths, J
Gupta, A D
Gupta, S R
Hamilton, M S
Harris, A W
Hartley, A G J
Hassam, Z
Hayward, P J
Heaney, G A H
Hennessy, J D
Hewspear, D
Hill, S A
Hillenbrand, P
Hodgson, R J
Hooper, E R S
Humpherson, C E
Hunter, M D
Hurst, J
Ingham, B
Ingham, P J
Inglis, J M
Iszatt, M E
Iyer, S J
Jarratt, R M
Jeeva Raj, M V
Jeffery, D M
Jewkes, A J
Johnston, P
Jones, H D
Joseph, R
Kanagaratnam, P
Kapur, P
Kaul, S
Kaul, S
Khaira, G K
Khaira, H S
Khanna, R
Lai, W K
Lambert, L A C
Langley, A M
Laycock, R J
Lee, T J
Lenton, C D
Lesshafft, C S
Lester, H D E
Leung, A Y-T
Leyva-Leon, F A
Lien, W M
Light, A M
Lloyd, N E
Long, S M
Lumley, M A
McCabe, E J
McConachie, J W
McDonald, A J
Mackay, A D
Mah, M S L
Manfield, P A
Martin, S C
Merlin, M J
Messih, M N A E
Metwally, A M
Miller, I M
Mirza, M
Mohler, T
Moloney, M D
Moorjani, N
Moorjani, R
Moreton, E I J
Mundy, P J
Murphy, T J
Murray, P F
Natalwala, S
Nelson, C A
O'Donnell, V A
Oakley, J R
Owens, J
Pai, S H
Pal, B R
Pal, P C
Parkin, J W
Patel, A E
Pennington, J M
Perris, T M

Swansea

Phillips, L A
Pickles, B C B
Platt, R
Plows, C D
Preston, J E
Price, R A
Proctor, H
Rajeshwar, M
Ramanathan, U S
Ramnarine, V D
Rastogi, A
Rawal, P
Ray, L C
Readett, E J
Reddy, E
Rees, T W
Reynolds, J H
Richards, M E
Richardson, D
Ritch, A E S
Roberts, N G
Robinson, W H
Rogers, V J
Rolland, P A
Ruiz Martin, M
Sagoo, V S
Sahota, B S
Sarin, S
Sawar, M O
Seehra, M
Selvadurai, D K
Sen, A
Sethna, E R
Shanker Narayan, P
Shaylor, J L
Shearer, A C I
Shehab, Z H
Sheldrake, J H
Sheldrake, L J
Shepherd, A J
Sherlaw, S R
Simons, M A P
Simons, R M
Simpson, P M
Singh, H B
Singh, S
Slominski, H B
Smith, D M
Smith, R E A
Solari, T J
Soorae, S S
Speak, N J
Spence, J C
Spiers, D P
Spooner, D
Srinivasa, K
Stewart, J
Storer, J I
Strachan, R A
Sullivan, R P
Surendra Kumar, R
Surendrakumar, S M
Tamma, S
Taylor, J G
Teoh, J E
Thirumala Krishna, M
Thomas, C P
Thomas, D I
Thomas, L J
Thompson, A R
Thompson, H
Thompson, R J W
Thrush, S
Tomlinson, D R
Tsagurnis, I
Upthegrove, R A
Upton, A F
Valsalan, V C
Walker, E J
Walker, S A
Wall, D W
Wallis, D E
Walsh, G D
Walsh, L J
Webster, M A
Whitehouse, D R
Whitticase, J E
Wilkes, M M
Willetts, G T S
Willis, A P D
Worden, J A
Wulff, D E
Yousufzai, N M

Sutton-in-Ashfield
Abbott, L P
Ali, S
Alker, M
Allen, S M

Barrett, P
Bishton, I M
Blake, J R S
Bliss, D F
Bull, P T
Chandran, Q
Chandran, T R
Clitheroe, D G
Cooke, G A
Davis, K R
Ewbank, G S A
Fairbrother, B J
Finn, G P
Greasley, L A
Hambidge, J E
Harris, R F
Hastings, A G
Hill, K J
Hook, R A
Hulman, G
Idris, I R
Jenkins, J R F
Kellock, D J
Lacey, A J
Lloyd-Mostyn, R H
Logan, E C M
McInerney, B A
Maddock, C R
Mason, J S
Mathew, T K
Meats, P S
Mowbray, M J
Needoff, M
Nithianandan, P
Nithianandan, S
Noble, V
Pantagani, B S V P
Panto, P N
Pickles, C J
Rahman, M
Robertson, N M
Ross, M T
Rowley, J M
Salter, E J
Sands, K A
Stein, G
Subramaniam, S
Subramanian, T
Taylor, M C
Temple, P I
Thompson, G A
Ulliott, E E J
Ward, M J
Ward, S J
Williamson, J R
Wong, S C K
Woodside, R M
Worsley, A P
Yorke, P H
Young, S M

Swadlincote
Archer, J D
Buckler, E C
Clegg, A
Davidson, A S
Davies, G P
Eaton, D A
Felgate, N G K
Field, M
Follows, R L
Gravestock, N
Hall, M W
Hart, E A
Hignett, A W
Idowu, O A
Jamison, R W
Kenny, T M
Khalid, T
Kirk, J S
Randell, J M
Robinson, J
Sandeman, J G
Sowden, D S
Stack, M M
Taleb, S M
Tellis, M M
Trotter, R F
Vaughan, J M
Von Fragstein, M F F
Walker, J D
Whitehead, I P

Swaffham
Barlow, G E
Barnes, G L
Barton, D I
Dorling, R F
Draper, N E

Hatfield, J M R
Hendrie, O R S
Holmes, M J G
Holmes, N K
McGregor, F M
Rayner, R A
Rosenberg, K
Skinner, J M
Sorensen-Pound, D J
Willy, D M M

Swanage
Aitken, D I
Aitken, D M
Baker, R W
Blair, J N
Caruana, M P
Clark, J C D
Clark, P M R
Clifford-Jones, W E
Cox, A G
Elfes, C J
Freeman Welham, S
Haines, D A
Hatch, J
Heard, W E
Jackson, S
John, E G
Jones, D M M
Knott, D
Lane, H L
Lee-Eldrid, E M
Lees, B A
Leigh, P R
Lodge, J A
Mayr, D C
Milter, M E
Munday, J N R
Murphy, K M
O'Neill, P
Petri, M P
Purser, S H
Rowland, A G
Roxburgh, H B
Woodrow, I H R

Swanley
Ambikapathy, P
Brooman, I C
Burrows, L M
Gregson, S N
King, S J L
Lynch, V J
Muthappan, A K
Pomeroy, W S
Ramphal, P S
Rizwan, M R
Rumfeld, W R
Toothill, S V
Walters, T K

Swanscombe
El-Lakany,
N E-D H A E-H

Swansea
Adams, L J
Adams, R
Adrianvala, F D
Agarwal, N K
Aird, D W
Aird, I A
Al-Ismail, S A D A R
Albuquerque, S R J
Alcolado, R
Allen, H
Anani, A R A
Anderson, M H
Annear, R O D
Antao, A J O
Anten, J L
Apsitis, B
Arthurs, Y M C
Askill, C S
Asscher, A W
Austin, M W
Avery, J G
Avery, P G
Baines, P I B
Baker, R H
Bali, S
Bamber, C S
Banks, J
Barrow, T V
Barton, C R
Baxter, P W
Beardmore, C E
Beddall, A C
Beese, E N A
Bell, J P
Bennett, D G
Bevan, C J
Bevan, J C
Beynon, J
Beynon, P
Biswas, S
Blackford, S L W
Blackwell, A L
Blair, J M
Boladz, W
Boladz, W P
Bourne, S J
Bowen-Simpkins, E J
Bowen-Simpkins, P
Bowen, A
Bowen, H G
Bowen, H J
Bowen, I
Bowen, I E
Bradley, P A
Bradley, S J
Bradley, W A
Bradshaw, D M
Brady, T L
Brennan, E
Brick, S J
Brown, T H
Browne, T F
Browning, H
Browning, S T
Buck, M E
Burgess, H G
Burrow, S
Buxton, T S
Byrne, A J
Calvert, J P
Campbell, A E
Canton, J L
Carr-Hill, S M M
Carr, N D
Cast, I P
Catling, S J
Ch'ng, C L
Chamberlain, G V P
Chamberlain, J O P
Chare, M J B
Cheng, C J C
Clark, G P
Clarke-Smith, E M H
Clement, D A
Clements, D M
Closs, S P
Cobbold, S S
Collinson, M A
Coombs, I P
Cooper, M A C S
Cormack, I S
Cosgrove, C A
Cosgrove, M
Costello, C
Craven, S
Cray, E B
Cribb, C T
Crossland, P E
Cummings, P
Daley, D
Daniel, C J
Danino, C E
Danino, E A
Danino, S M
Davies, A W
Davies, D E
Davies, D H
Davies, D H
Davies, E
Davies, E G
Davies, G R
Davies, H D
Davies, I
Davies, J L
Davies, J M
Davies, J O C
Davies, J S S
Davies, J H
Davies, K I
Davies, L
Davies, M
Davies, M M R
Davies, M J A
Davies, M J
Davies, O M
Davies, P J
Davies, R S
Davies, R N
Davies, S E
Davies, T G
Davies, T M
Davies, V J E
Davies, W B
Davis, P L
Dawkins, C J
Dawson, A
De Arce Seuba, C D
Delahunty, A M
Denholm, S W
Dennis, N J
Devichand, N
Dingley, J
Dinsdale, C L
Dodge, J A
Donnelly, P
Donnelly, P D
Dove, J R
Downes, E M
Downing, H A
Drew, P J
Duane, P D
Durrant, H J
Dyer, D F
Eales, M C
Edwards, P A
Edwards, S M
El-Ghazali, A M S
El Ghazali, K M S
El-Omar, M M A G
El-Sharkawi, A M M
Elkholy, M E S M
Ellis, M M
Emery, S J
Eshun, J A
Evans, A D
Evans, D H
Evans, D R
Evans, H J
Evans, J E
Evans, J E
Evans, J R
Evans, K E
Evans, M L
Evans, M J
Evans, M G
Evans, M J
Evans, R J
Evans, R M
Evans, R M
Evans, R B
Evans, R S
Evans, S L
Evans, S E
Evans, T G
Evans, T I
Factor, D C
Fardy, M J
Fareedi, M A
Fareedi, S
Ferguson, M M
Fielder, C P
Fielder, H M P
Fine, J
Fitton, A R
Fligelstone, L J
Flowers, C I
Forbes, W R
Foulkes, A L
Francis, H C
Gajek, A
Gajek, W R
Gamage, D H
Ganeshanantham, S
Gerson, D A H
Ghosh, S
Ghuman, B S
Gibbons, C P
Gibbs, M D
Gilbey, A G
Giltinan, W M
Goni Sarriguren, A
Gowda, S
Gray, H M
Greenhalgh Lowe, G J
Griffiths, A P
Griffiths, C J M
Griffiths, P D J
Griffiths, R D
Grimes, C J
Gunneberg, A
Gwynne Hughes, L A
Hamon, A M
Hancock, C
Harding, A M
Harkness, J M
Harries, W A
Harrigan, M J
Harris, E E L
Harris, J A
Harris, L A
Harris, P
Harris, R C
Harris, S M
Harrison, N K
Harrop-Griffiths, W
Harry, C R
Harry, L E
Hart, J T
Harvey, D J
Havard-Jones, E L
Hawkins, A K I
Hayes, S L
Helan, S A
Hennessy, A I
Hennessy, M J
Henwood, M
Hickey, B B
Hill, J A
Hill, R J
Hill, W E
Hilliard, J J
Hilliard, J S
Hirst, A E E
Hockridge, K S
Hodder, S C
Hoddinott, H C
Hodges, W G
Hopkin, J M
Hopkins, C L
Hopkins, M K
Hopkins, T P
Horsman, D C
Howell, J F
Howells, G
Howells, M L
Hudson, A J R
Hudson, C N
Hudson, E
Hughes, D M E
Hughes, D P
Hughes, E
Hughes, G W
Hughes, K
Hughes, M P
Hughes, R I
Hutson, H S F
Huws, A M
Hypher, T J
Ingram, W A
Irvine, R J M
Ivey, J R
James-Ellison, M Y
James, E T R
James, N E
Jarvis, S L
Jenkins, A V
Jenkins, C I
Jenkins, C
Jenkins, E B
Jenkins, E S
Jenkins, G H
Jenkins, K L
Jenkins, R I
Jenkins, S P
Jeremiah, G D R
Jerwood, D C
Jimenez Zaratiegui, L F
Joannides, T
John, A
Johns, C J C
Johns, P F
Johns, S R
Jones, A
Jones, A W
Jones, A H
Jones, A
Jones, B G
Jones, C E
Jones, D A
Jones, D M
Jones, D J
Jones, E W L
Jones, E G
Jones, G O
Jones, G M
Jones, G H
Jones, H M
Jones, I T
Jones, J
Jones, J H
Jones, J T
Jones, M
Jones, M B
Jones, M K
Jones, R R
Jones, S R
Jones, T R
Jones, T A
Jones, V L
Jones, W H L
Jones, W I

Swindon

Joynson, D H M
Karney, G R
Kevelighan, E
Khan, M A L
Kingham, J G C
Laing, J H E
Lake, D N W
Lathbridge, A B
Latif, A H A A
Lawrence, M R
Laws, D E
Leary, J A
Legg, J P
Lennox, S D
Leopold, J D
Lervy, B
Lethbridge, J
Lewis, A M
Lewis, C D G
Lewis, H B
Lewis, J M
Lewis, K M M
Lewis, M
Lewis, M S
Leyshon, R L
Lister, J
Littlepage, B N C
Littlewood, R N
Llewellyn-Jones, S A
Llewelyn, R W
Lloyd Jones, F R
Lloyd Jones, P M
Lloyd, A P
Lloyd, B W
Lloyd, D R
Lloyd, M I
Lloyd, R C
Lo, W W C
Long, D H
Long, H R
Lucas, M G
Lyons, R A
McCabe, M J
McCarry, M E
McCarthy, M E
McConnochie, K A
Macdonald, I S
McDonald, J
McFadzean, W A
McGill, F J
McGregor, A D
McKenzie, R J
Maddock, H
Maddocks, J A
Maganas Aguilera, I
Maggs, R G
Mahon, S V
Major, E
Major, H G
Mamiso, J A
Mangat, P S
Mansell-Watkins, T
Manson, E F
Manson, J M
Marshall, P D
Martin, I O
Mason, M C
Mason, R A
Masoud, R
Matthes, J W A
Matthews, J P
Matthews, P C
Matthews, P L
Meecham Jones, S M
Mellor, C H
Mellor, M E
Mellor, P
Mendis, R D
Michail, M I
Midha, R E
Milling, M A P
Millington, I M
Moore, D
Morgan, A G L
Morgan, A R
Morgan, B
Morgan, C R
Morgan, E J R
Morgan, I L
Morgan, J E
Morgan, J E
Morgan, L B
Morgan, L G
Morgan, M
Morgan, P G
Morgan, R N W
Morgan, S M
Morgan, V
Morris, A D

Mortimer, R J
Mundasad, S M
Murison, M S C
Najib, R A M
Nash, P E
Nesling, P M
Newington, D P
Newman, F
Noone, B E M
Norris, P
Norton, A
Nowak, J J R
O'Brien, C J
O'Kane, M J
O'Malley, H F
Oldham, M M
Olliffe, D J
Omoregie, T G
Oppel, A B L G
Owen, J C
Pain, J H
Palmer, A
Parker, R B
Patel, B
Patel, G M
Patel, N
Paulus, J N
Penry, I E W
Phillipps, J J
Phillips, B M
Phillips, G B
Phillips, J
Phillips, J M
Phillips, S J
Pickering, A
Pincott, R G
Piskorowskyj, N
Pogson, D G
Potter, R J
Poulden, M A
Powell, N
Power, A L
Prasad, P M
Price, D E
Pritchard, A
Pritchard, S R
Proud, A M
Provan, D A
Purcell, P M J
Ramadan, A M
Ramsey, M W
Rayani, A P
Rayani, A J
Raynsford, A D
Redfern, R M
Rees-Jones, E C
Rees, A D
Rees, A M
Rees, H A
Rees, H G
Rees, J W
Rees, L J
Rees, O V
Rees, S O
Richards, A M
Richards, D G
Richards, K
Richardson, C E
Richardson, E M
Rickards, C
Ridgewell, M C
Riordan, T P
Roberts, D L L
Roberts, D E
Roberts, S M
Robinson, H C D T
Rogers, D W
Roman, R M
Rose, M B
Rosser, B
Rowley, K H M
Russell, I D
Sadler, M J
Sait, C L
Salter, K E U
Sambrook, D K
Samuel, C
Samuel, T W
Sandifer, Q D
Sansbury, M A
Sartori, J E
Sartori, N
Schreuder, F B
Scott, G
Seager, M J
Sewell, J M A
Sharaf, U I
Sharma, C M P
Shenolikar, V

Silvester, K C
Simpkins, H G
Sinha Roy, S K
Sinha, A K
Sinha, S
Sivakumaran, V
Slowey, H F
Stanton, J A
Staple, G
Statham, B N
Steane, P A
Steene, L
Stefanutto, T B
Stevenson, A D
Stubbs, P G
Sullivan, C L
Sullivan, M J
Summerell, J M
Sweetman, B J
Talbot, J S
Talukder, S B
Tan, G
Tarr, G
Taylor, M A
Thomas, A
Thomas, D W
Thomas, D C
Thomas, E J
Thomas, G
Thomas, I R J
Thomas, J
Thomas, J S
Thomas, K J
Thomas, M A
Thomas, P D
Thomas, P
Thomas, R
Thomas, R E
Thomas, S D
Thomas, W I
Thomas, W R G
Thorpe, C M
Thorpe, M H
Tomos, H W
Treseder, A S
Truman, K H
Tucker, D S
Tudor-Jones, T
Upton, N
Vaughton, K C
Wall, T J
Walters, A S
Wani, M A
Waters, A G
Weatherill, B A
Webster, P P
Weiser, R
Wells, A L
Werner, D J S
West, A P
Westerholm, R
Weston, C F M
Weston, S N
White, C P
White, M
White, N M L
White, P G
Whitehead, M W
Whitehead, M J
Whittet, H B
Whyte, G C
Whyte, U M
Wilkins, E A
Williams, A J
Williams, B
Williams, D D R
Williams, E J
Williams, J G
Williams, J G
Williams, J C
Williams, M E
Williams, M
Williams, N W
Williams, N S
Williams, O G
Williams, P S
Williams, P A M
Williams, R M
Williams, S
Williams, W O
Winsey, A M
Wright, M F L
Yoganathan, K
Yoganathan, M
Yong, C H
York, J R
Youhana, A Y
Zaki, M M R

Swindon

Achar, U
Adams, S
Ager, J A M
Ahilan, R
Ahmad, S L
Amies, P L
Andrews, R M J
Annas, E G
Armstrong, J S
Aslam, H B H
Aslam, M N
Austin-Pugh, C K W
Babington, P C B
Bahia, S S
Baker, A R M
Barnard, H
Barnes, M D
Barnes, P A
Barry, C N
Barthakur, A R
Baxandall, J D C
Beale, A M
Beeby, C P
Belt, J D
Bentley, J
Best, N R
Billingham, G P
Birley, D A H
Blackburn, J C
Blesing, N E
Bliss, W A
Bloomberg, S
Bond, A P
Bowen, J R C
Brading, L C
Brooke, S R M
Buck, J W
Bullock, R A
Burgess, P
Cameron-Street, R W
Campbell, D N C
Campbell, H J
Cannon, C H
Carroll, N J
Carron, R I
Chalstrey, S E
Chandler, H A
Chippendale, S M
Clay, B E M
Clements, P J
Cluett, B E
Cocks, R A
Colley, C M
Collins, C A M
Collins, D A
Cox, N
Crockett, A W B
Crossley, N A
Crouch, P A
Cullimore, J E
Currie, I G
Dale, A
Davies, A G
Day, J R
De Silva, L W
Denton, P H
Deo, S D
Dhanulshan, P
Dippy, J E
Dutta, A
Eastgate, J W
Elliman, J C
Entwistle, M D
Evans, G J
Eyre, R
Fan, S F
Ferguson, D R
Finch, D R A
Finch, D J
Fisher, R
Fletcher, J R
Flew, J P
Fogg, A J B
Foy, M A
Freakley, G C H
Frost, J A
Gale, R S
Galea, M H
Gent, P M
George, A F
Giallombardo, E
Gilbert, C J
Gill, J
Glass, R E
Glover, J R
Godfray, D M
Godwin, J C
Goldstone, J P

Graham, F C
Grain, L A T
Gray, A G
Green, D E
Green, E S
Griffin, L P
Guilding, R C
Gupta, H M
Hall, C A B
Hall, J S
Hanson, P J V
Hardy, R P
Harper, E I
Hassan, S N
Heaton, D C
Hellier, J M
Hellier, M D
Hicks, S C
Hillman, R
Hilton, J W
Hocken, D B
Hocking, E D
Holden, C G
Holden, R E M
Holland, J A
Holliday, E
Holmes, J W L
Holmes, R J L
Howard, D J
Hunt, M N S
Hunt, N G
Huxley, C A
Iacovou, J W
Irby, S J
Ivory, E A
Ivory, J P
Jackson, D M
Jackson, L K
James, B H E
James, C M
Janson, W R
Jeddo, S A
Jefferies, D W
Jephson, C G
Jindal, M M
John, D D
Johnstone, D N
Jones, A M M
Jones, G R
Jones, H E
Jones, R M
Jones, T M
Juniper, M C
Kandiah, A
Kelly, A R M
Kendall, I G
Kidney, E M
Kilaru, N P P
King, J M
Kingston-Shrubb, J M
Kirwin, P A
Klidjian, A
Knight, P N
Kowalczyk, A M
Kumar, R
Lal, A
Lander, J N
Lavelle, S E
Lawrence, R N
Le Coyte, T S J
Lee, M J
Lee, T
Leonard, A J
Leung, A S K
Leung, J O S
Ling, E A
Lister, C O
Lloyd, C R
Lowdon, I M R
McCrea, W A
Maciejewska, E M
Macintyre, A R
Mack, P R
McKemey, M J
Macoustra, S A
Maitland-Ward, K
Mann, R J
Mansour, J T
Marshall, J M H
May, W D
Mayes, P J
Mearns, E A
Mercer, J H
Metcalfe, J A
Mills, H L
Moore, B
Mukherjee, D
Mustafa, Y A
Myatt, I W

Myerson, J S
Narayan, H
Nath, R
Newell, A G
Newton, A S
Newton, H
Nixon, R G
Noble, E P
O'Brien, M K
O'Brien, T P
O'Connell, P J
O'Connor, M
O'Keeffe, P T A
O'Kelly, S W
Oliver, E
Owen-Jones, J M S
Parks, R G
Parsons, C A
Pearce, W B
Phillips, J M
Pickworth, A J
Pierzchniak, P
Pigott, S C
Pihlens, L P
Powley, P H
Price, E J
Price, H L
Printer, K D
Purser, J R
Ramanandan, A
Rawlins, D B
Reynolds, P A
Rhodes, S
Rimmer, C J
Robbins, J C
Roberts, G E
Robertson, M C
Roe, R B
Rooney, G J
Salisbury, A J
Schaps, P
Schlesinger, P E
Scholes, K T
Scott, T E
Scurr, J A
Sewell, S P
Shad, I A
Shimmings, K I
Sleggs, J H
Smith, A M L
Smith, I D
Smith, M B
Smith, P T
Speller, C J
Spray, R J
Stallard, N J
Stean, M L
Steptoe, A M
Strong, A M
Swinyard, P W
Syed, S B
Ta, T C
Tang, C W M
Tattersall, M P
Taylor, E J
Taylor, S J
Tew, D N
Thavaraj, M
Thilakavwardhana,
W D P
Thomas, H G
Thomas, O M
Thomas, P G
Tidbury, P J
To, S S
Turbin, D R
Valentine, M J
Van Hamel, J C M
Vanhegan, R I
Vincent, E J
Vinitharatne, I
Ward, M W
Ward, M
Wharam, P C
White, J H
Whitton, L A
Whitworth, A G
Willan, J C
Williams, P M G
Williamson, D M
Winfield, D
Wittram, C
Wolanczyk, W J
Woodhouse, W J
Woods, D A
Woodworth, A E
Wooller, D M
Wright, F A
Wright, J F

Wright, M E C
Yanez Perez, L M
Yerbury, N O
Young, A M
Young, I W

Tadcaster
Cronin, H F
Dryburgh, W A
Glanville, J N
Hayes, M
Haynes, J C
Inglis, A E
James, D
Lee, T W R
Lewis, J W
Merrifield, S P
Metcalfe, J D
Nicholls, J A J
Parsons, J M
Peel, A J
Reeves, W J
Turton, C L
Turton, E P L
Whittle, D J
Willis, D
Woodhouse, J C

Tadley
Bhanot, S D
Brough, P R
Caren, C A
Castle, S L
Colley, S J
Finch, J M
Griffiths, R L
Hawken, M J
Hawken, R M A
Hollingshead, J F
Hudson, C K
Hudson, E A
Jardine-Brown, C P
Kenshole, D H
Knowles, C
Knowles, M
Perkins, A M Y
Peters, J
Waddingham, R

Tadworth
Acton, J D
Adams, R E
Ahmad, N
Alani, A A
Batchelor, J R
Batchelor, M A
Battinson, A N
Brotherwood, R W
Brown, E A
Burgess, D E
Cantopher, T G A
Carpenter, S F
Cieslicki, S H
Connolly, J
Cooper, J R M
Croft, R S
Day, B P
Dua, L G S
Elsdon-Dew, R W
Fryer, J H
Gerhard, S D
Goodger, N M
Gordon, S J
Graham, A E
Griffith, A H
Harris, S A
Hudson, S L
Jenkins, P A
Juchniewicz, H J
Krapez, J R
Kumar, D
Kumar, K A
Lam, K-P
Malik, A
Moorthy, V
Norman, A E M M
Norman, A P
Orme-Smith, E A
Pashley, C E
Pawulski, Y M
Peel, J S
Pitsiaeli, A P
Rogers, K L
Rowlands, M W D
Singh, S A
Smith, D P Q
Stott, P C
Sutcliffe, M M L
Symes, D M

Verity, H J
Webb, J

Tain
Colvin, I G
Gordon, S R
Graham, P D
Grant, G
Greenwood, J P
Horne, M M
Macdonald, M
Macleod, I C
Runcie, J
Savage, K J
Skinner, J A
Stevenson, B J
Stevenson, J

Talsarnau
Faulkner, R L
Wood, J D

Talybont
Edwards, D L
Lawrence, M H
Parker, M L

Tamworth
Ballard, P
Barker, G M
Beecham, K
Benkert, S T
Bird, C W
Bird, S C
Boss, D P
Boss, V C
Bowen, Y M
Bruce, G J C
Carlisle, T A
Chambers, J S
Choudary, A A
Clamp, H
Clayson, M C
Clegg, D F G
Cooke, L H
Corbett, E A
Crofts, K H M
Cutting, D L
Dabestani, E
Davis, M S K
Deshpande, A A
Edwards, A M
Fitzgerald, H M
Foist, J M E
Gordon, G
Griffiths, H M
Gummery, A R
Halpin, D C
Harrison, P S
Hawkes, R A
Hawkins, J B
Jawed, S H
Johnson, J
Jones, C J
Jones, S P
Khan, L A
Killeen, P D
Kinnis, T D
Lanz, J P
Lawrence, D R
Mair, B M
Mallinson, T J
Martin, C A
Moosa, A S
Moroney, M M
Odber, E A
Pascoe, K L
Patel, R M
Popple, M D
Rajput, R A
Richardson, W L
Samson, H C
Sherlock, J D
Smith, J W
Spenceley, S R
Sreehari Rao, S
Stabler, J M
Tajuddin, M
Tse, C-K V
Turfrey, D M
Vaughan, P J
Wood, P M
Yazdani, Q

Tarbert
Dick, H P
Gourlay, N J
Graham, F M
Howat, I M G
Macdonald, N

Maitland, J
Mayer, A C
Stewart, H V A

Tarporley
Armitt, J M
Aston, P L
Bashford, S E
Black, H E W
Bowman, S N
Caesar, S R
Campbell, P A
Cartwright, A J
Chantler, S
Chappell, G M
Crockford, T K
Durrant, M A
Etherington, R J
Gething, J
Gleek, R N H
Grant, R H E
Griffin, J M
Halstead, N A
Hoy, A N
Hutchinson, K F C
Jones, M B
Lockyer, C R W
Mann, P M
Meekins, J W
Nixon, T E
O'Callaghan, N G
Phillipson, A P
Rowland, K
Stowe, H E
Tate, B S
Taylor, K V
Thomas, S C
Tobias, N F
Vickers, J P

Taunton
Acheson, R R
Adam, R M
Ahmed, W
Allaway, G W
Anderson, E J
Ansell, M J
Ashworth, S L
Atan, D
Austin, G S
Badham, D P
Bakker, A H
Balance, R J
Ball, J E
Barlow, H V L
Barrett, N K
Barrie, R
Barrie, W R I
Barry, M
Barton, J R S
Bates, A K
Beecher, H M
Bell, J M
Benn, P M
Berry, M A
Bett, C J
Bevis, M J
Bhattacherjee, J W
Bhattacherjee, S
Biddell, P B
Biddell, S F
Bidgood, K A
Bilbrough, M
Bird, D F
Bird, R J
Bolt, H L
Bott, E C A
Boyd, D W
Boyle, J
Bradburn, V M
Bray, A J
Brocksom, L A
Brook, R
Brown, T R
Browne, B L
Bryce, G M
Bull, T M
Bulloch, C
Bunting, W
Bunyon, S J
Burbridge, D H D
Burgess, G L
Burton, H L
Butler, R M
Butterfield, F E
Butterworth, H E S
Cadman, D H
Cairns, S R M
Cannon, D J

Canti, G
Carton, R P L
Chadwick, R M
Chalk, E S
Challacombe, D N
Claridge, K G
Clarke, A M
Clarke, H A
Clear, J D
Close, C F
Cockett, A D
Collins, C D
Collins, D M
Collins, S J
Conway, I M
Cooper, S C
Cornes, B
Cornes, M
Cottrell, P W A
Covell, K J
Crabb, K A
Crabtree, B J
Crabtree, R E
Crook, J R
Crowe, R L
Cutting, C J
Dabbous, F M
Danby, G A
Darke, G H
Davidson, J E
Davidson, M J C
Davies, D N I
Davies, J N
Davies, S V
Dayani, A
Daykin, A P
Dean, D C
Desborough, R C
Devine, M D
Downs, D J
Dupuch, L H B
Duthie, Y L
Edmondson, D B
Eggleston, M M
Ellwood, M G
England, K E A
Evans, M
Eve, R C
Eyre-Brook, I A
Fathers, E E
FitzGerald, M R
Fitzpatrick, W O C
Fletcher, M H
Forrester, A J M
Forster, H
Foster, R P
Fox, R
Frazer, S J
Freeburn, E M
French, T J
Galli, E M
Gardner, R J
Gauntlett, I S
Geraghty, E M
Geraghty, J M
Gethen Smith, E B
Gillen, C D
Gorman, M S
Gormley, H K J
Gover, D E
Gover, S M
Gray, R H
Hakin, K N
Halfyard, A E A
Halfyard, I R M
Halliday, N J
Hamilton, S G
Hamlyn, J F
Hanson, S D
Hanspal, R
Harkness, J
Harrington, J C
Harris, N M C
Harris, T
Harrison, R T T
Harrison, S R B
Hart, R J
Harvey, M R
Hayes, J S G
Henderson, A J
Hesford, A C
Hickman, J
Hicks, A A P
Highley, D A
Hinds, P J
Hobbs, R J
Hooper, F D M
Horgan, C H
Howes, T R J

James, M A
Jenkins, C
Jenkins, R
Johnson, C A
Johnson, S A N
Jones, A P
Jones, C
Jones, R W A
Jones, S M
Jowett, A E
Keay, S D
Kelly, A J
Kelly, S E J
Kilbey, R S
Kingsbury, W N
Kinniburgh, D
Klidjian, A M
Lakin, J
Lane, P J
Laurance, J A
Laversuch, C J
Leighton, R E
Lench, T J
Linder, A M
Lucas, J G
Lumb, G N
MacConnell, T J
MacDonagh, R P
MacGregor, R J
MacIver, D H
Mackenzie, N C
Maidlow, W M
Mann, C J
Manning, F J
Manning, H P
Manning, K L
Marsh, H
Martin-Scott, I
May, T F
Meads, J E D
Michaels, M
Moller, C-C B
Moore, J C
Morgan, J M
Moyse, B C
Muggleton, D E M
Murray, S
Nicholls, B J
Nicholls, H J L
O'Boyle, P J
O'Connell, S M
Ogilvie, C
Ohaiseadha, C O
Ostler, E G
Palmer, B M
Partridge, S J
Pascall, C R
Pascall, E J
Pearson, N J
Pearson, V A H
Pendered, L F
Penny, P T
Perry, A J
Pether, J V S
Pfeifer, C Z
Phillips, M J
Phua, V M
Pillman, F R
Pitts, T B
Poole, A J
Prettejohn, E J T
Price, A N C
Probyn, J
Pryce, D W
Pugh, S
Pullin, J A
Radford, A P
Ragheb, S W
Rainey, H A
Ramus, N I
Ravenscroft, P J
Rees, J L
Richardson, J A
Rivett, A
Rivett, R S
Robinson, B F
Roe, P F
Rosser, M A
Rostron, M G
Roy, L C
Ruell, J A
Satchwell, G M
Savage, R H
Scanlon, J G
Scott, G J
Scott, J T
Sells, R W B
Shields, N P
Siddique, M F

Sidwell, I P
Silsby, J F
Skinner, P J
Slack, A J
Sladden, J M
Smith, G D P
Smith, H M
Smith, K
Smith, M P
Smith, M D
Smith, S C
Smith, V P
Smythe, R H
Snaith, A H
Snell, R O L
Snow, A M P
Solanki, T G
Spare, J T
Speakman, M J
Speller, P J
Squire, P L B
Stone, R A
Stradling, P
Swinburn, C R
Symons, L C
Tandy, A D
Thomas, H G
Thomas, P D
Thompson, C C
Thompson, E H
Thompson, P B
Tighe, M
Till, K
Till, M M
Tolliday, J D
Tricks, N C
Trotter, P A
Tucker, R J
Twomey, J M
Upton, J J M
Viner, A S
Vipond, A J
Von Bergen, J E
Von Bergen, S
Wade, C A
Wallace, E
Ward, T M G
Wardle, D P A
Watson, D L
Webb, B W
Webster, M H
Welbourn, C R B
Wells, R
Wells, S K
Wells, S C
White, W J
Whitehead, J P
Whytock, P
Williams, M H
Woodgate-Jones, T
Wright, T
Yardley, M H
Yates, D B
Yates, M W
Yoxall, J H
Zilkha, T R

Tavistock
Allenby, W J
Baker, A B
Barrand, K G
Berry, R H
Bertram, J
Childs, J D M
Clapham, C C
Cox, E
Craig, S M
Cullen, M S
Cummings, G C
Davies, I L
Evans, A J
Evans, J A L
Evans, V L
Farr, A P
Gibbs, D S
Gude, R A
Jayarajah, J M
Kelsey, A M
Kerr, P M
Kersey, J P W
Liggins, S J
Lindsey, B
Lorenzi, A R
MacRostie, J A
Meyrick, R L
Nicholls, C S
Nicol, A P M
Norgren, P M
Norman, P F

Taynuilt

Ostler, A M
Owen, T P
Pascoe, S J
Porterfield, P N
Rea, W E
Ridout, S S
Roberts, M A
Rodgers, P J
Speller, J C
Stokkereit, C
Sweet, R D
Truesdale, P J
Watson, I H
Watt, A M
Watt, P A
Wilson, R J
Winfield, A G

Taynuilt
Galbraith, O
Houston, R M H
Lyon, J M
Macrae, W J
Watson-Jones, A

Tayport
Baxter, A G
Mires, G J
Shaw, J W
Simpson, H A
Torrance, W N

Teddington
Atkinson, C N
Ball, R A
Blake, C H
Bone, S R
Bradley, J A
Brockbank, J
Brougham, P A
Brown, A M
Cobb, J P
De Bruyne, V
Gal, I
Head, C
Hempenstall, K
Hepburn, A L N
Johnson, T W
Kendall, A M
Lamb, S G S
Mawby, I M M
Nicholas, R J
Pace, R F E
Patel, V
Patton, A
Plantevin, O M E P
Porter, F V
Roberts, C M
Ryle, D M
Sandifer, S C
Scott, J A
Scriminger, M W
Sinnott, C R
Stern, D M
Walcot, N R H
Wilson, J E H
Yasin, T
Young, S M

Teignmouth
Best, F W
Billyard, J J C
Butterfield, A R
Clayton-Payne, B J
Cooling, R M
Crow, B M
Crow, R S
Cullen, D
Eldridge, A G
Eldridge, H W
Finneran, N K
Firth, D R
Gale, R N
Gudgeon, D H
Hadfield, G J
Halford, M
Halford, M G
Henley, A J
Hepburn, G E
Hills, K S
Holding, P K
Hudson, K D
Jones, M R R
Karakusevic, C A
King, M H
McCormick, A J A
McGrath, P D P
Melluish, P G
Messent, D O H
Mitford-Barberton, G B

Peirce, C R
Penn, C R H
Porterfield, N N
Powell, E A
Quinnell, G A F
Randalls, P B
Rocyn-Jones, J R
Rowbury, J L
Squires, J P
Thornberry, C J
Thorne, M G
Townsend, E W J
Tuck, M E
Tuck, S C
Venton, T J
Ward, D M
Warland, J C
Whittard, B R
Whittard, S F

Telford
Abbott, G W
Ackroyd, P L
Ahmad, M
Ali, S F N
Awty, M W
Bailey, S K
Balasubramaniam, C
Bandak, R
Bartlett, M H
Barua, A R
Bateman, J M
Beck, G P
Blackmore, J
BrahmacHari, A K
Brown, C I W
Calvert, J
Campbell, R R
Capps, N E
Carley, R H
Cartwright, P D
Cawthorne, B J
Christmas, D
Chuter, P J
Clevenger, E O
Corser, G C
Coventry, C L
Crichlow, T P K R
Dawson, M J
De Klerk, C J
Diggory, R T
Donnellan, I M
Douglas, T A
Duffield, R G M
Elliott, K C
Frain, S P T
Freeman, C J
Ghosh, R K
Goode, T B
Griffiths, H J
Groeneveld, H
Hailey, R W
Hanna, J A R
Hastings, L I
Heber, M E
Herd, E J
Hickmott, K C
Hinde, F R J
Hinton, C E
Hinton, C P
Hinwood, H C R
Hogg, J S
Hollway, J F
Hoque, M S
Hugh, S E J
Hughes, D S
Inglis, A R
Ingram, L C
Innes, M A
Jacobson, G A
Joy, R M
Kallan, B
Keohane, K M
Khin Pyone Yi, Dr
Kirby, P J
Lane, M W
Leaman, A M
Lees, D A
Lewis, C J
Liggett, W G
Lloyd, C
McDonnell, T C
McGavin, J G
Mahmandi, N A K
Manns, R A
Marray, P J
Marshall, A
May, P C
Mell, A K

Metcalfe, E M
Mishra, S K
Mohamed, A O
Moudgil, H
Muris, J E
Newman, P F
Niehues, D M
Nolan, E M
Northern, D G F
Novick, S M
Obonyo, H B
Pandya, L
Parrish, D J
Pearson, C A R
Pelton, C I
Picard, L
Pollock, G
Pooler, A D H
Pooni, J S
Pringle, A J
Pritchard, S J
Quayle, J B
Rathbone, E
Ravikumar, R
Richards, G P
Richards, N C G
Richardson, J P A
Rider, D
Sanghera, M S
Sanghera, S S
Shaw, P Q
Siddiqui, R
Singh, J
Spencer, K P
Summers, B N
Swallow, J W
Taylor, T L O
Thompson, G D
Usman, T
Visick, J
Vrahimis, N
Wainwright, G A
Walsh, M T J
Ward, L S
Welch, C G
Willcock, R D
Williams, M R
Williams, T D
Wright, D J
Wynes, C W
Yates, C J P
Zaki Ahmed, S M
Zaki, I

Templecombe
Beach, F X M
Courtenay, T M A
Pallister, M A
Reid, M J
Speight, J M

Tenbury Wells
Baker, D J M
Brereton, W J
Charles, M D
Chesshire, J S I A
Eames, S M
Foster, N J
Goddard, S
Hardiman, J M A
Hardiman, M C
Hunter, J L
Lear, R J A
Mocroft, A P
Oliver, J H H
Smith, C C
Tinkler, R F W
Watson, B
Wright, A M

Tenby
Bowen, E J
Bowen, J M
Bowen, J R
Coulsting, D R
Coulsting, H S
Griffiths, A J
Hughes, W E
Jenkins, M I
Jenkins, P
Riley, S E
Roberts, H G

Tenterden
Alaily, A B E
Charlesworth, J P
Clothier, J G
Cooling, C I
Cox, S P
Crawfurd, A R

Daddow, J R
Dodds, D H H
Dowling, J M
Harries, D J
Herbert, P M L
Ingle-Finch, F M
Lloyd-Smith, A R
Lloyds, D
Raw, T R F
Rowlands, D M

Tetbury
Andrews, J N H
Austin, L-J S
Huntley, J S
Kirby, A K
Lewsey, D M
Lovatt, G E
Simmons, P T
Ulyatt, F M
Walsh, A
Wardell-Yerburgh, S J
Wood, L

Tewkesbury
Ashbridge, K
Atwick, D L
Buckley, R G
Carver, C H
Chapman, A L
Crossley, I R
Crowther, A N
Crowther, M A A
Cunningham, A C E
Davis, R W
Dore-Green, F
Dunlop, E M
Gormley, K M
Gostling, D P
Hutchison, S R
Lewis, M F
Lewis, M H
Macmorland, L A
Macmorland, T D L
Mahy, D J
Mitchell, M D
Mowbray, I V
Mulrenan, M J
Renfrew, C C
Rigby, A N
Sanders, R K M
Shephard, G D H
Shervey, C S J
Symes, M H
Tuck, A W
Williams, K
Williams, R

Thame
Burch, K W
Chubb, C H T
Farmer, A J
Farmer, M
Fisher, J D
Geaney, D P
Gladwin, B C
Gleadle, J M
Green, S B J
Harrington, R V M
Jackson, T J
Jobson, T M
Keeley, D J
Markus, A C
Markus, P J M
Mitchell, T D
Neal, D A J
Paul, H-J
Skennerton, D E
Taylor, H E A
Turner, S D
Vaughan, M S
Williams, A P
Williams, E E E

Thames Ditton
Barnes, G M
Berry, J B
Bullen, S
Cason, A P E
Curtis, A M
Devine, J
Doughty, A G
Duncan, D A
Gardner, C M
Glasgow, L V M
Griffiths, G I T
Griffiths, P K
Jebb, G A
Keywood, C G A
Killeen, M P

Magrill, L H
Matthews, D J
Miller, A J
Mills, F
Mitchell, T J
Molloy, B
Munn, O M A
Roberts, C A
Simmons, V
Taylor, R D
Teasdale, K
Wilson, R G

Thatcham
Bahia, B S
Hayward, J M
Morgan, M W M
Osborn, M L
Porter, K A
Rixon, R A
Robertson, E A
Robertson, G A

Thetford
Alliott, E S
Alliott, R J
Ball, S M
Belsham, M P
Blaxill, J W
Bryson, J L
Caro, A J
De Bass, F W J
Gibbs, T J
Gray, P S L
Gregson, D J
Hadley Brown, M
Hahn, I R
Hall, S C M
Henderson, W B
Hughes, M J M
Hunter, D M
Leventhorpe, J R B
M'Caw, S A
Mahatme, D A S
Martin, S A
Nisbet, I G
Rabett, R J
Riddell, C W
Sagar, G A
Smith, G R
Taylor, J
Williams, R J
Wilson, D M
Young, A G

Thirsk
Casey, P A
Cawley, L J
Cawley, M E
Cook, E J
Dias, Y M
Donald, J
Frith, M-D S
Garside, J H
Harrison, M T
Hiles, R J
Hodge, C A
Holgate, P F L
Holmes, W
Hull, M R P
Page, R B
Parker, C S
Parker, C M
Parker, D F
Pooley, S F
Potts, M A
Redman, J W
Robinson, P J
Settle, C D
Shaw, C J
Spence, D P S
Stewart, I M
Thomas, P D S
Trzeciak, A W
Wight, G R
Williamson, D K
Wyon, A M

Thornhill
Brodie, R
Brown, I M
Kennedy, J C B S
Kroese, M J D
Park, T
Robertson, E
Russell, M Q
Vernon, F H
White, S C L

Thornton Heath
Adade, K B
Al-Dujaily, S S M
Alexander, G A
Bakare, R O
Chabuk, T M
Dosaj, A K
Gooneratne, H
Guest, M
Gupta, S
Holt, S N
Keet, J P D
Lumley, H S
Mehta, A J
Newland, R A
Patel, C R
Ramsbotham, S E
Reardon, J A
Rodrigues, N F B
Scarisbrick, S A
Tarrant, K N
Whitehead, M A
Wilson, E B

Thornton-Cleveleys
Ahmed, R Y
Azurza Sorrondegui, K M
Boissiere, J A
Boissiere, P F T
Broadley, R M
Brown, H G
Cartmell, N V
Cooper-Smith, J H
Cowpe, J
Ford, W L
Hendrickse, M T
Holgate, R S
Horsfield, P
Johnson, K J
Kitchen, S P
Llewellyn, D J
Macdonald, D W
Muir, A
Naughton, A
Naylor, G
Page, M E
Palin, P H
Pananghat, T P
Pilling, D J
Powell, M F
Qureshi, N S
Raines, K P
Romer, J M
Rowland, B J
Schofield, J
Sundar Rao, P
Sydney, M M
Thiagarajan, M
Turner, B A
Walford, D H H
Walsh, E J
Whitehead, S
Whittle, A D
Zaryckyj, M

Thrybergh
Jacob, L

Thurso
Adam, J A
Birnie, G B
Brooks, A G
Burnett, G R M
Deans, J P
Findlay, S R
Irons, G S
Kelly, D J
Lee, J A W
Lee, R J
Mackay, C
Mackay, N
Macleod, W J J
McNeill, D
McNeill, W
Morris, G J A
Morrison, J D
Ramsay, D
Robertson, A H A

Tidworth
Blackburn, P J
Harley, O J H
Hayes, S C
King, B M
Kuber, A
Piper, M E

Tighnabruaich
Durham, M P

Irvine, J I
Paterson, J G
Sinclair, D M
Thomson, G J

Tilbury
Archer, R
Malvankar, G K J
Saha, P K
Sundaresan, T

Tillicoultry
Basquill, M P
Brodie, J E
Clark, G P
Edmunds, N J
Galloway, L
Harrower, N A
King, J A
Seaman, F M

Tintagel
Jones-Key, W P
Saville, G M

Tipton
Bradley, K M
Bradley, W J
Browne, C J
Dayani, L N
Leadbeater, C M
Loryman, B J L
Patel, H D L
Riley, S G
Robinson, A J
Solomon, G
Swiestowski, I
Walton, I J

Tiverton
Anderson, J P
Backhouse, P J
Baker, A S
Batth, M S
Bloom, J N A
Brannam, H R
Clark, C E
Coffin, C J
Coulter, M E
Davies, J R L
Davies, M C
Frewin, R J
Graham, I C A D P
Graves-Morris, J W
Grieve, D I
Griffiths, M M
Haig, G
Hamer, C E
Hynes, J B P
Johnson-Ferguson, S J
Jones, G D
Kerr, I D
Lambert, D M D
Law, J C
Leach, A L M
Maltby, J W
Maltby, S D
Mew, C J
Miller, A J
Miller, P M
Monahan, J
Mounsey, R M
O'Kelly, F P
Peters, G K
Revolta, A D
Rumble, P B
Rushton, A R A
Savill, G
Savill, H J
Seaton, D N
Seymour, M T J
Seymour, S-J
Sheridan, J H
Snow, L R H
Stevenson, R Y
Whittlesey, R W

Todmorden
Brunt, K E
Clark, R L
Cormack, A S
Davey, N P
Dearden, V A
Dench, D M
Ehrhardt, P O G
Grewal, A P S
Grieve, J M S
Harrison, A J
Lofthouse, R A
Minter, S J
Peck, J E

Ransome, P J
Ryland, D A
Sacco, J
Williams, G

Tonbridge
Anderson, I R M
Anderson, J S N
Baker, J W
Barlas, J A
Bench, P D
Blewett, K A
Bolam, R F
Borley, N C
Bowman, C M
Brennen, R G
Callum, W D
Carpenter, A P
Cheales, N A
Christophers, J
Coles, K R D
Coles, S R D
Cowan, N A
Cowley, E J
Curling, M E
Davies, M C
Dawson, M J
Devenport, C E
Earle, E M
England, J M
Evans, K G C
Evans, N J
Ford, J M T
Forsyth, S G A
Fraser, I M M
Frommer, E A
Furst, H C
Gibbins, N E
Gildeh, P B
Goodridge, D M G
Goozee, P R
Hawkings, J M
Hayden, J T
Hills, A-M E
Howitt, A J
Hunter, M P
Hurter, D G
Ironmonger, M R
Jenner, M J R
Jutting, I G C
Kelynack, J B
Kirby, G
Larchet, P K
Law, E M J
Legg, O C
Lloyd, B A
Love, M E
McCarthy, L S L
McIntyre, C W
Mahadevan, J
Manifold, D K
Manifold, N J
Marshall, M A B
Minett, N P
Moore, J P
Morgan, J E
Morris, M J
Mullins, D F
Nicholls, A P
Nida, A M
O'Carroll, A A
Palmer, T A
Potter, N D M
Potterton, K L
Reynolds, M M
Ripley, L H
Roberts, J M
Robinson, M R
Robinson, T R
Russell, E C
Sanders, F L
Skinner, P V
Skinner, R O
Smale, S J
Smith-Laing, G
Stobart, J A H
Stuart-Buttle, C D G
Sugden, K H
Taylor, T
Thomas, K J
Warner, C M
Watson, J V
Whillier, D E
Whitehead, E J
Woodhouse, P A

Tonypandy
Clifford, W F
Edwards, D A

Jenkins, M A
Jones, D S
Lees, A P
Llewellyn, R
Rahman, M A
Rahman, S
Saunders, D C
Stagles, M J
Tirupathi-Rao, M

Torpoint
Bristow, A H
Crook, J C
Davis, A J
Davis, M P
Franklin, R M
Fraser, V G
Gask, J
Grange, S A W
Gray, J A B
Jolly, R T
Kehoe, J E
Khan, H A
Kirkpatrick, B D
McEleny, P C
Mallett, B L
Mattholie, K M
Moore, D
O'Leary, T D
Pollard, J G
Scaglioni, F G
Sewart, J H
Stewart, M W
Wallace, E N K
Woffenden, L R
Wylie, R D S

Torquay
Ackford, C
Alderson, D J
Allen, K P
Alston, A K
Anderson, L
Ashley, D A
Ashworth, M J
Bailey, N P
Barton, P M B
Bennetto, L P
Birdsall, P D
Bonnin, B L
Bosley, P V
Bradbrook, R A
Broomhall, J
Broughton, W E
Brown, M R
Burke, N J
Cadle, D R
Campbell, N N
Carey, C M U
Carroll, M S A
Chadwick, R G
Copplestone, J F
Crocker, K L
Crook, N J K
Currie, I C
Da Cruz, D J Z
Dales, F A
Dales, H C
Daniels, C H L
Day, D W
De Alwis, E D M K
De Friend, D J
Densham, C A
Densham, L J
Densham, P R
Dickens, J-A
Dickinson, T R
Douglas, P S
Dyer, R G
Edwards, D
Ellis, A W
Fearnley, R H
Fearnley, S-J
Fettes, P D W
Field, K J
Fisher, G W H
Fisher, N
Fitchett, L
Fitter, A C
Fletcher, T G
Folca, P J
Fordyce, A M
Forward, F R
Forward, P J
Foster, R N
Fothergill, G
Foulkes, J E B
Fox, L C
Fox, M

Gardner, G C E
Gardner, G J
Gardner, S J
Ghazi, A
Gillespie, C M
Goldman, J M
Gould, P C E
Gould, S M
Graham, C M
Green, P M
Greenwell, D G
Haas, L
Halkes, M J
Hamad, Z M S
Harris, R E
Harvey, R B
Hearn, M
Hignell, A F
Horner, J E
Horvath, R S
Houghton, K
Huckle, J A
Hughes, R G
Hunt, P G
Hutchinson, P F
Hutchison, J D
Hyde, R F
Irvine, G B
Isaacs, J L
Jackson, A J
James, C R H
Jeffery, D C J
Johnson, M E
Jones, G
Judge, B P P
Kember, P G
Kendall, G P N
Kuyyamudi, C U
Ladwa, V G
Lambourn, J
Law, D J
Lewis, P
Lindsay, J C
Livesey, S J
Lloyd, G H
Lowes, J R
Lyons, J
McCarthy, D A
McCarthy, R J
MacDonnell, P T
Maceachern, A G
McGill, I G
Mackay, N N S
McKay, R E
MacTaggart, D K
MacTaggart, J M
Malherbe, C J
Manley, G W
Marshall, J H
Martin, A C
Mason, M
Mehta, S S
Midgley, R L
Mihssin, N K
Mitchell, A V
Molan, C J
Montgomery, J E
Moore, P L
Morrell, I R
Morris, E
Morris, S C
Murphy, B
Natusch, D I
Nicholson, M A
Nigam, K
Nofal, M A-E M S
Orr, R B F
Osburn Boheimer, N
Paisey, R B
Paley, H
Pappin, J C
Parrott, D R J
Partridge, B W M
Pearce, D N
Perry, J F
Peyser, E E C
Pickering, B N
Poley, B A
Pullan, R D
Razay, G S
Rickett, J W S
Ridge, J M
Robinson, H Y
Rovira, P A
Ryley, N G
Sadler, A P
Sainsbury, C P Q
Scanlan, C M
Scott, C A

Seif Said, V K
Seymour, R
Shaw, M S
Sheppard, S
Shute, P A
Sinclair, D G
Sleight, P J
Smith, K J
Smith, S R
Smith, S J
Snow, D J
Speake, J G
Spear, D W
Stainforth, J N
Stannard, P J
Swart, M L
Tackley, R M
Takyi, A
Taylor, P D
Teague, R H
Thomas, E A
Thorn, V M
Treharne Jones, R
Tresidder, I R
Tucker, A J
Tucker, H S
Tucker, S C
Urquhart, G W
Waldock, A
Watts, E C
Williams, C A K
Williams, D A W
Willmer, J M
Wilson, P G
Womersley, H C
Young, H L
Young, J D

Torrington
Armstrong, B D J
Armstrong, T
Bangay, A P D
Berger, D W
Bremner, A E
Chavasse, S J
Cramp, H E
Lamb, N C
Martineau, J G
Patterson, M D
Searle, G
Searle, J S T
Thomas, R A N
Thompson, A M
Tyler, V J
Wallington, S C H A

Totland Bay
Kingston, R W C

Totnes
Alcroft, P A
Barratt, D K
Benatt, J
Benzies, R A O
Blackshaw, R E
Born, A J
Brunsdon, D F V
Buckingham, S J
Burston, J
Campbell, B M
Cooke, B R B
Cooper, N A
Cosh, J A
Crickmay, J R
Curtin, D M
Dalgliesh, D G
Dixon, J W T
Drysdale, H C
Feloy, J M L
Flear, M E
Frankland, A W
Franklin, J A C
Greene, W J W
Greig, R A
Hall, G F M
Harrison, S L
Hayek, L J H E
Hayne, D
Hendy, S C
Henry, G W
Hubregtse, G
Hunt, M S
Ingham, J N
Ingoldsby, B J
Jacobs, A G
Kent, L J
Leney, B V
Lewendon, G
Lewis, A D
Lewis, N M L

Treharris

Lewis, R J
Loverock, M
Manser, T I
O'Brien, J A
Pettinger, A J
Peyton-Jones, B
Rasaiah, K
Richi, M N M
Robinson, L H
Smyth, B T
Somerville, M
Tatham, P H
Teague, E M
Teague, G
Thompson, E M
Thould, G R
Todd, N B
White, P M

Towcester
Bramley, M J
Cronin, K
Davies, A J
Greenhalgh, J E
Greenhalgh, M G
Gwilt, D J
Hamblin, C G M
Hamer, S A
Hooker, A N
Letts, A
Lewis, M G H
Lopes, O B
Newton, F A
Phillips, T J
Sanger, L V
Sayers, I G
Stoddart, P E B
Sunderland, J R
Supple, M A
Tuck, E A M
Wallace, R B
Ward, N J
Yarrow, S

Tranent
Cameron, C
Crawford, Y E B
Donaldson, I D
Gaskell, P G
Ingham, L J
Irons, A W
Kennedy, G
Kerr, C A
Lange, P J
MacNair, J D
Macrae, A M
Matthews, M B
Morrison, J
Nimmo, W S
Reid, A I
Russell, K J
Salter, D M
Taylor, A W O
Taylor, H S L

Tredegar
Baker, D
Crosbie, S S
Davies, H J
Hla Bu, Dr
Lamerton, R C
Payne, S A
Pritchard, M G
Singh, A
Sinha, S
Wheeler, K M

Tregaron
Gealy, S E
Heneghan, F A
Hockenhull, P D
James, J A
Langley, R C
Thomas, K L

Treharris
Batuwitage, B T
Das, C
Das, D
Dharmasiri, A H C
Emanuel, J A
Griffiths, P
Mahajan, O P
Morgan, N S
Nath, M L
Phadke, A S
Pryce, R A
Rees, J L
Williams, A J

Trimdon Station

Trimdon Station
Carter, J M
Saunders, F C
Srirangalingam, S
Srirangalingam, T S S

Tring
Baxter, R M
Burgess, P L
Calfer, M
Cannon, H L
Frisby, J S
Hall-Jones, A H
Higginson, A G
Higginson, A P
Higginson, I M
Kennedy, C G
Lane, R S
Livingston, G
Livingston, S J M
Ogden, D J
Roberts, R N F
Side, C D
Strong, C K
Swallow, J
Thallon, D F E
Tomlinson, P
Wainwright, A J R
Wolfenden, B A
Woodward, A J

Troon
Auld, C M
Baird, C H
Baird, P J
Beatson, J M
Brown, J
Cameron, J H
Chestnut, R J
Dodds, L M
Douglas, S F
Elliott, M E
Gissen, P
Hamilton, R M
Hildebrand, P J
Hill, A M O
Houston, N M
Joyce, T
King, A G
Krauthamer, I
Lawrie, S C
Livingstone, P D
Lloyd, H J
Logan, W J
MacDougall, J C
McGregor, A J
McGuffie, A C
McHattie, A G
Mackay, D H W
MacNab, G W
Macpherson, J M
Mann, D J
Mann, J G
Matthewson, D J
Melrose, E B
Miller, T D
Mohammed, E P
Morran, C G
Morrison, A D
Murray, E D S
Nixon, L M H
O'Neill, D M
Phillips, T
Pittam, J K
Potts, H E
Roy, W
Ruthven, I S
Scott, M E
Shanks, E M
Smith, D
Smith, J C S
Stewart, J
Sugden, B A
Sweet, E M
Symington, E M
Symington, T
Thomson, P H G
Westbrook, P M
Whitford, P
Whyte, R B
Williams, G R

Trowbridge
Baker, Z C
Blight, J S
Blight, R
Bradbrooke, J G
Bryant, G
Cahill, J P
Clark, S J A

Collins, R A
Cookson, T W S
Davidson, W B
Dawson, S J
Duckworth, M J B
Evans, G M H
Foggett, C
Gracias, S A
Harris, A
Hole, J G
Jay, G E
Jones, R N
Kneebone, R L
Locke, S M
Lodge, L I
McBryde, H M
Mack, H M H
Munro, M E
Nelson, G S
Nye, B M
Parr, L S
Rope, T C
Rowlands, S C
Slack, J E
Smales, K A
Swan, J R
Thompson, L V
Wells, D P

Truro
Adams, E F M
Adcock, S D
Al-Rawi, S J A
Asmussen, T
Asplin, C M
Ball, H J
Ballam, J M D
Barnes, J N
Barton, S J
Barwell, N J
Battle, M O
Bendall, R P
Bensa, R M R
Benson, W G
Bhatti, T S
Biscoe, C A
Bishieri, S Y G
Bishop, J S
Black, M
Boissonade, J
Bolton, J A R
Bowers, P W
Bracey, D J
Bridger, V J
Bridges, V J
Brown, C C
Bryson, P R C
Bulman, G M B
Caldicott, M L
Callen, P J
Campbell, G F
Campbell, S M
Carruthers, W A F
Casey, S F
Chambers, J C
Christensen, D M C L
Ciko, V D
Clare, K A
Coleman, J C
Colson, H W
Conrad, G J
Cook, P G
Cooper, J A
Coutts, I I
Cox, R
Cran, J S
Creagh, M D
Crooks, S
Crouse, M W
Curphey, R N
Dalal, H M
Dale, M H
Dalgleish, A
Dalton, H R
Daltrey, J R
Daniels, M V
Davies, J E
Davies, J N
Davies, M T
Davis, A J G
Davis, E M
Davis, P R
Deodhar, A A
Deodhar, H A
Dingwall, A E
Dodenhoff, R M
Dyson, J L
Evans, A E
Evans, C D

Evers, J-A G
Fairlie, H H
Fairman, H D
Falkner, M J
Farren, J E
Fern, E D
Ffrench-Constant, E P S
Follett, O J
Foote, J W
Friend, P A
Galbraith, D
George, D
Ghey, E M R
Gilbertson, N J
Godbehee, P R
Golding, P J
Goram, J B K
Gould, D J
Gray, J M
Gray, S J
Graymore, R I
Greenhalgh, G P
Griffiths, D P G
Gripper, M B
Gripper, S M
Grundy, G V
Grundy, J R B
Grundy, M F B
Gunn, K L
Hambly, A T
Hancock, J H O
Handfield-Jones, R P C
Harper, J A
Harper, S H
Harris, J
Harrison, R A
Harvey, A J N
Harvey, W R
Hasan, S S
Hawkins, S J
Hayes, D F G
Heron, I D
Hewitt, M
Hey, R S T
Hobbs, A J
Hocking, M A
Hood, D A
Hooker, D
Howarth, P A W
Howarth, S M R B
Hughes, J M
Hussaini, S H
Hutchins, P M
Hyslop, J S
Jackson, W
Jakt, L M
James, K M
Jenkins, B A G
Jenkins, M L
Johnston, P A
Johnston, R T
Jones, C K
Jones, K R
Joseph, E
Julian, C G
Keane, F E A
Kellaway, T D
Lang, D V A
Lansley, C V
Lee, A S
Lester, J E
Lewis, E M
Lichy, R J
Lloyd-Davies, E R V
MacDonald, C M
McIntosh, S P
McKelvey, J A W
McKendrick, M N
McLean, B N
Maling, D J
Maskell, G F
Mathew, J
Maxwell, C M
May, A J
Mills, C H
Mills, J C K
Mitchell, M D
Mitchell, P A
Mohammed, S
Molloy, R E
Moon, C A L
Morgan, G A R
Morgan, J
Morton, E V B
Mourant, A J
Munyard, P F
Murrell, J S
Murrell, S J

Myers, E
Myers, J D
Nixon, J M
Noble, R S
Notman, J A
O'Brien, M M
O'Rourke, J S
Parsons, S W
Peace, P K
Perrett, A D
Perrett, J M
Pettit, B
Phillips, S J
Phippen, A R
Pitcher, R W
Pitman, R H
Poppinghaus, C-M
Portwood, R
Powell, J F
Price, A S
Proctor, M C D
Prout, E J
Radford, I S
Raj, A A
Rayner, N
Redding, G A
Redington, A N
Redpath, D A
Reed, J
Rentoul, J W
Rickford, C R K
Robins, R H C
Rotheray, C F
Rowe, P R
Rozario, J A C
Salfield, D J
Schofield, C M
Scott, T D
Sellwood, R B
Sharp, V A
Shaw, H J
Short, P
Siddig, M A N
Simons, P N
Sinclair, J R
Slade, A K B
Smith, I M
Smith, W H
Stanley-Jones, G H M
Stephens, F R
Stepp-Schuh, K
Stevens, A W
Stevens, P H
Stinson, D J
Stockwell, A J
Sullivan, M
Tadros-Attalla, S G
Taylor, G P
Telfer Brunton, W A
Templeton, A R
Thacker, E J
Theophilus, M N
Thompson, A B
Thorogood, S V
Tisdale, J B
Trotter, J K
Vaidya, D V
Van Der Merwe, W G
Veal, C T
Vickery, C M
Vowles, S C
Voyce, M A
Walker, A K Y
Walker, J B
Wardle, R S
Warner, A P
White, C R
White, R J E
Whitehouse, N J
Whiteley, W N
Widdison, A L
Wilde, A D
Williams, M S
Willis, R G
Wilson, T S
Winterton, E A
Winterton, M C
Wood, K A
Woodward, W M
Woolf, A D
Wragg, S D
Young, D A

Tunbridge Wells
Ahmed, S U
Aron, U
Baillie, E S
Ball, P J
Bamford, P N

Banks, P
Banks, R A
Barnaby, H J
Barnes, D J
Bates, E S
Baylis, E M
Begg, W H B
Bell, J A
Bentley, P G
Bergin, P M D
Boles, P R
Bolger, P G
Bolsover, W J
Bolton, C F
Bolton, J M H
Bolton, V J
Bowden, A S
Bowden, P C
Bowes, R J
Bradshaw, N J M
Bruce, J M
Buchanan, J
Buckland, A G
Bull, A R
Cameron, A J
Chambers, K B
Charlwood, G P
Chase, A J
Chellappah, M
Christopher, J B
Chung, R A
Collins, C M H
Cooke, J B
Cordell, R J
Cottrell, P R
Cripps, J R
Crosby, Z V
Dalton, A J C
Davie, W J A
Day, P
Dean, L J
Delaney, D M
Dismorr, K J
Dodman, S
Doyle, T G
Edwards, A R
Edwards, D M
Ellis, S C
Engleback, M
Everest, M S
Finlay, K D
Firth, D A
Flanagan, J J
Fleming, I M G
Fletcher, F M
Flute, D F
Flynn, G M
Ford, T F
Fordyce, M J F
Gabbott, M C
Galliford, J W
Galliford, T M
Garrett, J P
Garroch, D B
Garthwaite, S E
Gerritsen, E R
Gibb, P A
Gillespie, E J D
Gillett, D S
Gladstone, D I
Goddard, S L
Goodchild, M C
Goorney, A B
Green, D J
Grieve, A J
Hall, S A
Hangartner, J R W
Hardie, T J
Harley, H R S
Harrington, D W M
Harris, A W
Hartnell, H R
Harvatt, C
Hassan, H M G E D
Hedley, K R
Hicks, G E
Hirst, C I
Hoar, F J
Hogben, M M
Hughes, J A
Hurlow, D
Hutchinson, H T
Ignotus, P I
Ironside, J G
Jacques, S L
James, S
Jenner, M R
Johnson, R A A

Jones, A C
Jones, A K
Jones, D I
Jones, M C H
Kilcoyne, M T
Kirwan, M C
Kirwan, S E M
Knight, D M A
Knight, L E
Langrish, C J
Lawes, M R
Lawson, C S
Leeson, P C
Lemerle, M O
Lewis, J L
Lewis, S G
Liebmann, R D
Lloyd Davies, S K
Loke, H T R
Loveday, R
McAllister, T W J
Macdonald-Brown, A J
MacDonald, J C
Mace, P J E
McEvedy, M B
MacFarlane, D G
McLaren, P M
Maling, J A
Mancais, P A
Marshall, J K
Martin, P J
Matthews, M P
Maurice, B A
Maw, D S J
Membrey, A I
Membrey, W L
Mills, P M M
Mills, P
Milton, C M
Mueller, M F F
Murphy, J M
Neville, A M
Nicholl, J E
Orr-Hughes, K
Overy, M K D
Pattison, P R M
Pearson, J M
Pedlow, P L
Phillips, D
Porterfield, A G
Porterfield, A J
Pyne, A
Quarrie, J
Raban-Williams, A
Raju, K S
Reeves, K E G
Reynolds, P J
Robards, M F
Roberts, L A
Robson, E
Rodwell, N A
Roome, J K
Roome, P C
Rorke, S
Rose, C E
Russell, G A
Sachdeva, L
Sachdeva, S K
Sawyer, C J
Schellander, F G
Sergeant, R J
Shakoor, S
Sharma, N
Shields, R P
Short, C
Shotton, J C
Sibthorpe, E M
Sinclair, R M
Sinden, M P
Skerry, C A
Skinner, P W
Smith, D E
Smout, A J R
Somerville, D R
Soon, S Y
Steel, P C
Stone, N
Tanner, N S B
Taylor, A L J
Thomas, G E
Topa, G N F
Trotter, B M
Trounce, D Q
Tuckwell, G D
Turrell, C M
Tuson, K W R
Twydell, H J
Van Grutten, M
Venter, J A

Wakankar, H M
Walker, J M
Walmsley, G L
Warr, O C
Watson, G S
Welch, N M
Weldon, A M
Whichello, K J
Wilcox, M A
Williams, I
Williams, S J
Williams, T G
Williamson, A W R
Wilski-Jaloszynski, A
Winceslaus, S J
Wolfle, A D
Woolgar, M J
Worthley, P
Wykes, C E
Yates, D W
Yates, H A

Turriff

Chapman, A
Duthie, K E S
Eccles, T A
Fraser, K G
Fraser, R B I
Graham, K
Guthrie, P N
Henderson, S C
Joss, N M
Liddell, R W
Milne, M H
Robertson, A G C
Robertson, S B
Smith, A P W
Watson, C

Twickenham

Adams, A M
Alexander, D J
Andrews, J L
Appleton, S G
Badgett, W J L
Barker, G B
Bloom, I T M
Booker, R J
Butt, A M
Cadman, D S
Cash, M E
Cawrse, N H
Chapman, C M
Christie, B A
Coleman, J E
Colquhoun, P S
Cook, V A M
Davey, L F
Dhillon, P J
Dunn, C H
Edmonds, J
Elliott, D S
Gallagher, L M G
Gardner, M L
Gellatly, L A
Ghadiali, P E
Goldwyn, C R L
Gonzalez Carvajal, J R
Goold, M A
Hall, A J M
Hameed, S A
Harper, M N
Harrison, J S
Heads, T C
Higgins, R N T
Holmes, S C
Hotson, P A
Hunter, S R
James, M E M
Johal, B S
Jones, R F N
Kanani, S R
Kar, S C
Kemp, S P T
Kendall, A H
Key, A J
Khan, S
Kumaran, J
Kumaran, V E
Loughridge, L W
Lucas, R A
McCarthy, M R
McCarthy, T
MacIver, D K
Mahmoud, O M M
Maltby, K P
Mathew, M C F
Mehta, M H
Moore, K J

Mullan, E M
Neal-Smith, G A
Ng, W S
Nicholas, R S J
O'Flynn, K G
O'Reilly, U C
Patterson, P M L
Payan, J
Pearson, J G H
Preece, V E J
Pugh, J K
Rees, J P M
Rigby, S P
Roberts, M C
Robertson, A G
Rowlands, G P
Rudman, D J
Salih, A R M M
Sandler, M
Santana, I A
Sardesai, B S
Sardesai, S H
Saunders, P G
Savage, P
Sebaratnam, N R
Sharma, R
Shenton, F G A
Smith, C J
Sobte, U
Soltanpour, A
Somani, R
Sood, A
Sowden, P A
Taylor, N R W
Teodorczuk, A M
Thomas, F M
Thomas, V R
To, T H
Todd, D B
Trayner, I A M
Turvey, J S
Unadkat, M D
Unadkat, M M
Vakil, M A O
Vaziri, K
Walawender, A J
Warren, E S L
Waterfield, N P
Whittingham, C G N
Wild, I C
Williams, G
Wood, E J

Tycroes

Crilly, D D
Williams, O M

Tyn-y-Gongl

Dewar, M E
Jones, C A C
Lewis, J D
Lupton, D J
Williams, D L

Tywyn

Bishton, R B B
Church, D S
Clarke, J H
Coward, J
Farrell, D L
Kitchin, A P
Lycett, N A
Robinson, I F G
Taylor, T A

Uckfield

Argyrou, N A
Barker, D
Baseley, J A
Brown, C L
Bye, P G T
Clare, C A
Coombes, A H R
Ellis, W H B
Fabre, C D
Fincham, E
Fincham, P
Gent, P N C
Giles, J W
Gill, K E
Green, G W
Gurney, M J T
Harborow, P C
Jephcott, C G A
Johnson Smith, E J
Manning, F R C
Mayo, K M
Meikle, C J P
Nocton, J M
Petit, C G C

Phillips, M C R
Price, T M L
Sawcer, D
Sewell, E
Skinner, C P R
Sly, I L C
Wakely, S L
Watson, W F
Wilson, J P
Worlock, M S G
Wright, D S

Ullapool

Dumughn, D B
Hartley, I M
McDougall, C
Peebles, M A C
Poole, H
Smith, G G
Stewart, A
Watmough, G I
Watters, N P

Ulverston

Adams, P J
Bell, S J
Bottrill, D
Brady, D
Brice, J A R
Buckler, K G
Butler, A S
Callingham, R F
Carter, S J
Chojnacki, A
Cooper, M A
Cottam, C G
Daniels, H A
Elliott, S A
Forbes, R D
Gawith, D H
Graham, J P
Green, E W
Horsley, S D
Hubbard, I H
Johnstone, I C
Kaye, S A
Kellgren, J H
Lackey, S A
Liddle, J P
Luksza, A R
Lyness, A L
Maguire, G R
Milne-Redhead, B
Moore, G J
Morris, M B
Murray, G R
Newman, J A
Paterson, D M
Rayner, L
Redman, P J
Riley, R M
Savage, M
Schmidt, J
Sherwin, J R A
Sherwin, K E
Simpson, J M
Smith, I F
Spears, J
Stuart, D W
Sykes, C A
Taylor, J
Taylor, P
Taylor, R J A
Unnikrishnan, M
Waind, A P B
Waind, C M
Watkins, T I
Williams, E J
Wilson, L A

Umberleigh

Hambley, A B
Harper, G D
Keatings, H S
Mair, A
Pattinson, M F
Payne, C E
Payne, M J
Perrett, R G
Preddy, J S

Upminster

Anfilogoff, M E
Anthony, J R
Baig, M M
Baig, S S
Beaton, A
Benjafield, J G
Bingham, N A
Brooks, W V

Chakravarty, P
Chopra, P K
Dahs, C
Daniel, D
Ellis, J F M
Foley, E P
Gouldie, M R
Haider, S S
Haider, S I
Hails, A J
Hanstead, B
Maitra, K
Menon, N P
Rix, R D
Sampson, E L
Sangar, S K
Sudha, I K
Wallace, D
Werry, C A
Wright, C M

Upton

Anderson, J A
Faizallah, R
George, E
Hennessy, M S
Rittoo, D

Usk

Allison, M C
Bodley Scott, R
Botting, J R
Brown, G M
Brown, M J K M
Clayton, M I
Evans, J F
Frampton, C
Goodchild, P A
Hamilton, E M
Horton, G A N
Howells, R J
Hull, L E
Jarrett, A G
Jarrett, S A
King, M R
Leitch, G B
McLoughlin, M K
Nandy, D
Parry, A
Perry, A
Preece, J M
Robinson, D A
Shute, J C
Shute, K
Watkins, J
Zammit, S G

Uttoxeter

Alcock, F
Aldridge, R V H
Barron, O P
Bartlett, P A
Bell, J A
Bennett, J
Brookfield, C D R
Burlinson, A A
Burton, R C
Dalton, T M
Holroyd, B
Johnson, A F
Jones, S G W
Lee, R E
Livingston, E H
McCosh, C
Magapu, V
Pashby, N L
Sicha, M A
Trewin, P J H
Vickers, R J
Wainwright, C T
Webster, N C H

Uxbridge

Abeywardena, B R Y
Ackland, G L
Ahmad, S
Amrani, M
Arthur, I H
Asher, R
Assaf, A K
Atrah, S G K
Bangham, L C
Banner, N R
Barbir, M
Barker, F G
Barnes, P M F
Barrett, S T
Begg, N T
Bhatia, R
Bodey, W N

Boscoe, M J
Bose, A K
Buchdahl, R M
Burke, M M E
Butler, H R
Chan, C M
Charig, E M
Charrett, M A
Chatrath, V K
Chetty, M N
Chui, S L
Chung, G K K
Coghlan, C A
Coleman, D J
Collier, S D
Connell, P A
Conway, A S
Copland, D R
Cortal Pedra, M
Crawford, I B
Daily - Jones, H R
Das, S K
Dewhurst, J
Dodhy, B M A
Doherty, J M
Dovey, P
Edwards, B D
Elmes, E
Etherington, C M
Evans, D A
Faucon, E
Fenton, L M
Fielding, E I
Finlay, M N
Franklin, R C G
Fry, R P W
Fuller, R W
George, S J
Geraint, M
Gill, C P
Gill, R G
Gloster, J
Govan, J R
Grocott-Mason, R M
Hagan, G W E
Hall, A V
Hanspal, R S
Herbert, J R
Higson, D L
Hillson, R M
Hogarth, A M
Hollis, Y
Hunt, J S M
Ilsley, C D J
Jacobs, M F
Jaffe, P
Jaggar, S I
Janmohamed, R M I
Jawad, A N
Jones, C A
Kamaluddin, N A
Kantor, R J
Kerin, P J M
Khaghani, A
Khakoo, G A
Khan, H K
Khan, N A
Kubie, A
Lal, P
Lam-Po-Tang, K L M
Lavis, L S
Lawson, J P
Le Fevre, E J W
Lees, J M
Leong Mook Seng, C C K
Loveless, P M
McBeath, J I
McCarthy, B G
McEwen, M
Machado, F R C
Maclean, A M
Madhok, M
Marshall, M J
Mehta, A
Mehta, A
Millington, M
Mitchell, A G
Mohsen, Y M A
Molloy, C F
Mort, S J A
Muhairez, M A-Q
Murphy, J P
Murray, H G
Musawwir Ali, M
Oliver, A N
Paes, T R F
Palmer, J C
Parry, A C

Virginia Water

Partridge, J B
Patel, K P
Paul, V E
Pope, A J
Price, S H M
Quadri, A F
Rahmaan, G
Rawal, B K
Rigby, J P V
Robbins, P M
Robinson, C A
Rogers, B K
Round, P M
Salmon, H
Sedgwick, J P
Sepsas, E
Serra Mestres, J
Shawe, E A
Shears, D J
Shirley, I M
Siddiqui, A S
Siddiqui, S K
Sims, G M
Singh, I
Singh, K N
Singh, K
Slavik, Z
Stonelake, P A
Stonier, P D
Studdy, P R
Sykes, J A
Takhar, K
Taylor, D E M
Tonge, K A
Turnbull, M J
Usmani, I A
Usmani, M P
Vaughan-Smith, S
Walker, C P R
Watson, N R
Weinbren, J
Williamson, J M S
Wood, J R
Wright, I G
Wylie, G L
Zelisko, R S

Ventnor

Alleyne, H M A
Burndred, E F
Bushe, C J
Byron, A J
Cardew, M P
Champion, A F
Coleman, P A
Doggett, S J
Findley, J R
Gemmeke, M C M
Graham-Stewart, J C
Hammett, P J
Harding, I J
Hayes, A K
Henderson, E E
Hicks, N J
Hooper, P D
Kitt, R
Leigh, H I
Lock, M W
Oakley, E H N
Porter, S M
Sharples, R T E
Smith, M A
Stone, A G H
Swinhoe, P H
Tippett, R J
Turner, D P
Walsh, T H
Wykes, T R

Verwood

Bell, J C G
Brammer, P A
Chamberlain, A S E
Devereux, H J
Khankashi, H A
Layman, P R
Livingstone, C C
Martin, E J
O'Driscoll, M
Polkinghorn, A
Sandy, N K
Segal, J M L

Virginia Water

Adler, A D
Barrett, E L
Carratt, S L
Hargreaves, G F
Kalinkiewicz, M C
Lock, D J

Wadebridge

Loxton, M J
Loxton, P M
Pawsey, S D
Sapsford, I
Shaunak, R
Simmons, S C
Walker, K A
Wilson, J

Wadebridge

Arthur, G D
Baker, J B E
Barker, G K
Barnard, S M
Blatch, M J
Brooke, E M
Davison, S D K
Edwards, G P L
Foster, J A
Geake, M R
Griffiths, F V
Hewitt, C M B
Johnson, P M
Knight, F D W
Price, M G
Rees, W M T
Saitch, C D
Spencer, A G
Spencer, C G C
Venner, E A
Watkins, K P
Yates, D H
Yates, J B A

Wadhurst

Bishop, J M
Blackburn, A M T
Busuttil, W
Collis, A J
Etkin, H
Garland, A P
Goodman, K A
Goulton, J
Green, S M
Harris, R L
Hill, E A
Lewis, W G
Macdonald, A
Macdonald, A
McFarlan, C S
Mills, C S
Mowll, R F
Offord, C M
Pickering, M E A C
Pipe, R A
Roche, D
Ronder, J T
Sewell, A C
Smout, S M
Steinberg, D
Sugg, D J
Thomas, J B
Turnbull, G J
Whitty, H P B

Wakefield

Abbott, C F
Adib, R S
Adler-Tanz, P
Aggarwal, K
Ahmed, K
Ahmed, K
Ahmed, M
Aisbitt, M R
Al Ani, K I J
Alcock, K M
Ali, S
Anand, U
Azmy, M A L
Babiker, M M E D
Baker, E I
Balen, F G
Ballesteros Jimenez, J A
Barker, H E
Barker, P N
Barodawala, K
Basu, H
Basu, S
Bates-Kreuger, J G
Batin, P D
Baverstock, M E
Becker, S J
Belk, D S
Bell, G J
Berry, A D I
Bhattacherjee, S
Bird, G G
Birkinshaw, S E P
Blacker, A J R

Blakemore, L T
Bloomer, P G A
Bloye, D J
Blyth, I H M
Boon, S J
Bottomley, J M
Brain, G A
Braithwaite, P
Brearley, F R
Brown-Doblhoff-Dier, D
Brown, D W
Burns, L J
Burr, W A
Busby, M I
Campbell, H L
Carmichael, R D G
Carpenter, M A
Carpenter, S E
Carroll, A-M
Ch'Ng, K T
Clark, N H
Clarke, J
Clarkson, A G
Collins, P J
Coombs, L M
Cooper, A L
Cooper, J L
Cosimini, A J
Crabbe, S J
Crawford, K P
Cruickshank, C A
Cruickshank, H E
Curley, P J
Daly, D M
Daniel, A C
Darling, C
De Silva, T
De, K R
De, S K
Dean, T A G
Devlin, J A J
Dick, J A
Dick, S M
Donnan, J S
Donner, C M
Dourado, J R
Dublon, G P N
Dublon, V E
Dutton, M
Dunne, C L
Dunwoody, G W
Earnshaw, P
Edmonds, J P F
Edwards, A S
Elasha, H M S
Ellingham, J H M
Elliott, L-A
Elliott, N
Ellis, J R C
Emmott, R A
Evans, A
Farrar, H E
Fenton, O M
Firn, S
Fletcher, S J
Fodden, D I
Foo, R P
Fowler-Dixon, R H
Fuller, R
Fyfe, D R
Gair, T
Gairin Deulofeu, I
Gajjar, J G
Garthwaite, E A
Gaunt, J
Ghali, N N
Gilbert, R J
Gill, S S
Glass, E J D
Gollapudi, S
Gonteb, G
Gray, N R
Green, A
Green, N J
Greenwood, D
Gudgeon, P W
Gupta, R C
Haddad, S J
Hadjichartou, C
Hall, C J
Hall, D J G
Hallott, D E
Hamal, P B
Hancocks, G H J
Hanif, S
Harland, N M
Harrison, S C W
Hart, E M

Harwood, J L
Haskayne, L F
Henderson, R L
Higgins, J A
Hildyard, C L
Hill, B A
Hillmen, P
Hugh, I A
Hughes, P B
Humphry, R J
Hunt, K M
Hutchinson, J W
Ishak, M K
Ismail, A A
Ismail, Y
Issac, J
Jackson, A M
Jackson, K A
Jardine, M Y
Jeffery, D M
Jepson, A M
Johns, H V
Jones, P
Jones, R
Jones, S T
Jordan, J W
Jordan, P
Judkins, K C
Kakroo, S
Kent, J H
Khan, I A
Khan, M A
Khondaker, E H
Kidd, A J
King, L H S
Kirk, G E
Kirkbright, A
Kulanthaivelu, A R S
Kulanthaivelu, M
Lawn, J P J
Leading, A D
Limb, C A
Littlewood, M S
Lowe, J A
Lowe, R
McCormick, I A
McCreery, W C C
MacDonald, A K
McDonald, M
Macfaul, R
McIver, S
McKee, D H
Maclean, A B
Maclean, N
Macrow, P J
Mahanty, S K
Mallick, S N
Mandal, J
Mantell, A J
Mathew, E
Mathew, H
Maxwell, K N
Maynard, D G
Mehta, A K
Mehta, S B
Merrick, R H
Merson, A T
Mieszkowski, J
Millar, E M
Milner, B B
Mitchell, D A
Mitchell, G F B
Mone, A D
Morgan, I
Muller, P W S
Mulroy, J M
Mulroy, R
Munro, D
Murphy, F M
Musa, S A
Mushtaq, N
Myers, C E
Nagar, M P
Nagdee, K A
Naseem, M
Nhemachena, C M
O'Brien, J J
Oo, M K
Oughtibridge, D B
Owen-Smith, R J
Palmer, M A
Patel, D P
Paton, R H
Patrick, J F
Pattison, A C
Phipps, A R
Pinder, G A
Platt, A J
Pollock, C T S

Powell, S M J
Prasad, R
Prasad, S N
Qarshi, A A
Rainey, A E S
Rajan, G
Ram, S
Ramaswami, P K
Ramaswami, R
Ramsden, M J
Ramzan, A Y
Rao, V R
Rashid, S A
Rashid, S T
Rawes, M L
Robertson, C
Robinson, M
Rogers, M J
Runnett, C
Samaranayake, B M
Samaranayake, J J
Schindler, J L
Schofield, P J
Scott, J E
Scott, M C
Scott, M E
Senior, J
Settle, J A D
Sharma, R K
Sharma, S B
Shaw, M B K
Sheppard, A P
Shields, M D
Shinn, C P
Siddiqui, N A
Silva, L F A
Sims, R M
Singh, A
Singh, M
Slater, G D
Slater, P F
Smith, A N
Smith, D A
Smith, H L
Smith, R L
Smith, S N
Sohal, A S
Soulby, G C
Souter, K M
Spencer, M J B
Stanners, A J
Stewart, R G
Stickley, E A
Subramanian, S
Sutherland, T W
Sutton, G C
Switalski, B J
Tabner, J A
Tabner, S A
Tan, K S
Tarrant, D A
Tawfik, R F
Taylor, C M
Taylor, M L
Thomas, K V
Tobin, M V
Tosh, J
Tree-Booker, D A
Turner, P J
Twomey, J A
Ufodiama, B E
Upadhyay, B B
Vaughan, M
Vellenoweth, S M
Walls, J B
Walls, W D
Wass, A R
Watson, H
Weston, P M T
Whitaker, W
White, A J
Wight, J P
Williams, S E
Wilson-Sharp, R C
Wilson, J I
Wilson, S W
Womack, N R
Woodrow, J M
Wroe, S J

Walkerburn

Robertson, D C

Wallasey

Amendy, U
Biezanek, A C
Boggild, M E
Boydell, J S
Bradley, N A

Brown, G B
Caine, J M
Cameron, E F
Cargill, A F
Chadwick, M
Cheridjian, V-E P D C
Cook, J E
Coulson, A
Dunne, W T
Effingham, W H
Falconer, L M
Gallard, S C A
Gardner, D
Gibbons, J J P
Goyal, A L
Green, T H H
Hargreaves, T H
Harris, I J
Hickey, J J M
Hoey, M J
Hollmann, M G
Hopewell, R E
Johnson, P H
Jones, S R
Jordan, C A
Kingsland, J P
Lees, P
Lehane, F M
Lodh, M K
McCormack, P M
Magennis, S P M
Mann, M
Martlew, R H
Moulton, L C
Mukherjee, A
Mukherjee, S K
Nagesh, K
Patel, H R
Patel, R G
Peters, H
Quinn, B N E
Roberts, A
Roberts, G C S
Rudnick, S P
Shah, S C
Shankland, L J
Smye, R A
Stevenson, P A
Swift, N D
Tandon, P K
Tandon, R
Vandeldt, A P
Wainwright, E A
Waldman, J
Wilkes, R G
Wright, L A

Wallingford

Agass, M J B
Allan, A W
Anderson, J A
Archibald, A C I
Bell, J I
Boesen, E A M
Buxton, K L
Christie, A M
Collett, P R G
Cooley, A A
Cornell, J M
Crisp, S R C
Crowe, J N
Da Roza Davis, J M
Dickinson, H A
Duggleby, J E
Emerson, P M
Fadl, O E F M
Fraser, V E N
Geary, K G
Heap, P J D
Heap, R
Helling, J W
Henderson, E J
Hughes, C P
Huins, T J
Hussey, J S
Ingham, F E
Jarman, D M
Jones, A
Jones, C A
Jones, S B
Karunakaran, S
Ledger, S
Leslie, F M
Longhurst, M G
Longhurst, N
Loregnard, A E
Lucas, D R
Millar, A E
Mitchelmore, G E

Mitchelmore, U P
Morgan, J G
Moss, C M
Munn, A
Nehring, J V
Newnham, C T
Parker, D L
Pritchard, P M M
Rafferty, P J
Ramage, V M
Rice, E D
Rogers, G
Rose, P W
Sanders, M N
Sansom, A E A
Sharpe, G C W
Shaw, H E
Short, J A
Simmons, M J
Smith, E B O
Stinchcombe, C E
Thompson, C J
Tilling, K J
Trower, K J
Turberville, S M
Vernon, A R
Vickers, J R
Wilson, D T R
Wintle, T C
Zeckler, S-R

Wallington

Asirwatham, J S
Ayling, J C C
Barnwal, A
Basu, S
Bilston, A E
Boulis-Wassif, S
Cremer, R J
De Monte, J E
Dimmock, D P
Donati, M C
Erskine, M E
Fagbohun, M
Flintan, K
Ghoorbin, V B
Gurner, I E
Halder, T K
Harding, M G B
Henry, J J
Jones, D R E
Joseph, A E A
Kaura, D
Klos, A M
Lal, M M
Lasrado, M F
Lewis, B P
Lings, H R
Lovel, K W
Montgomery, V J
Munden, J E
Obaro, S K
Paget, C J H
Petrie, R A N
Phelan, L K
Pitman, J
Pogson, C J
Radford, N M
Ratcliffe, R M H
Razzaq, Z B
Samarawickrama, P G
Smith, R G
Sucherit-Kaye, R A V
Sutton, S G
Wadud, R
Wells, M P P
Wilson, I M

Wallsend

Abraham, P
Bell, J P
Blair, S E
Cameron, B
Carrie, L A
Coles, J S
Coomber, S J S
Cowper, W B
Dewan, V
Dick, K D
Evans, R L
Fawcett, C E
Fitzgerald, J O
Foxen, P
Griffiths, V A M
Harrison, E M
Jones, S E
Kelly, D M
Kenny, B J
McColl, A W

Warminster

McStay, B
Malik, M N
Mantle, D J
Matthews, J D
Ng, J L
Nicholson, S
Oakley, T N
Page, J M
Potts, L A
Outbell, R M
Riddle, F J
Soulsby, N W
Stoves, J
Sweetman, A C
Thomas, A J
Thomas, S A
Thornton, R D
Tinkler, S D
Vaughan, G J
Westwood, M A
Wright, M

Walsall

Afzal, S
Agrawal, B G
Agrawal, K G
Agrawal, V K
Ahmed, F
Ali-Allaf, A A K
Allen, C A
Alo, G O
Anand, H
Anand, M S
Anderson, J M
Antani, M R
Antani, R D
Arteen, P B
Arumanayagam, J T
Ashraf, A S
Askey, A T
Babatola, F D O
Baig, M M A
Bailey, C
Balachandar, C
Balachandar, K
Balachandran, T
Balagopal, V P
Baldwin, A D
Banerjee, K
Banerjee, S P
Barry, T N
Basu, B J
Basu, D B
Batra, H C
Benjamin, A E
Bevan, W J
Block, U
Bromwich, P D
Brooks, R W S
Browne, M J
Buch, A N
Buch, M H
Buch, M H
Butler, L M
Carter, P F B
Caswell, S J
Chandramani, S
Chattopadhyay, A K
Chhaya, S C
Chivate, J G
Chivate, V J
Coleman, T D
Conod, K C
Cooper, M H
Cotterhill, A T
Crawley, A P
Crowther, M F
Cunnington, A R
Das Gupta, S
Datta Gupta, R
Davies, M K
Davis, B W
De, S
Dean, S
Denihan, C
Dent, T F
Devasia, N D
Dewada, C
Dhaliwal, J S
Din, K M A U
Dolphin, J M
Drew, D
Dugas, M N
Durrell, N G
Edwards, M A
El Shazly, M A E M
Ellis, L
Elves, A W S
Fehilly, B

Ferrie, B G
Fisher, J R H
Galvin, G P
Garratt, F N
Garvie, J M
Gatrad, A H M
Gatrad, A R
Ghaffar, A
Ghatge, R
Ghosh, P
Giles, P D
Goldsmith, A R
Gray, A J
Green, S T
Gunawardana, A A
Hadfield, G T
Haire, A K
Haque, A M Z
Harrison, J M
Harrison, K
Harvey, R A
Head, A C
Hickson, K W
Hock, Y L
Hodgins, P S
Hoskisson, D M
Houlahan, D P J
Hudecek, I P
Hunday, D S
Husain, A
Ismail, S
Jacob, A
Janes, J L
Jarrams, R G
Javeed, M
Johnson, D C
Joseph, C F
Joshi, A A
Katragadda, U
Kaul, P L
Kehler, L M
Kellner, T
Kelly, R N
Khan, R
Khattak, T M
Klair, P S
Kukathasan, G
Kundu, S K
Kushwaha, A P S
Labib, A S
Langton, G M
Latthe, R B
Lavin, I
Lawrence, M R A
Lester, J P
Lloyd, C E
Lochee Bayne, W A
Lodwick, J M
Lodwick, R
McGivern, J
Malik, N J
Mallick, S H
Mallik, S
Manjunatha, S
Masters, K W
Mavi, B S
Maw, K P
Mayne, A J
Mehta, B S
Milne, J M
Milne, M M
Milne, V G
Min, A
Minhas, S S
Misra, G S
Mittal, D
Mo-Szu-Ti, M S Y
Mohammed, M A E-M
Monnington Howe, M-A A
Moore, A J
Moore, P T
Mott, F W M
Muscroft, T J
Nambisan, L S
Neeves, Z W
Newson, C D
Newton, A W
Nicholls, J E
Nixon, K
Norton, M H
Norwood, J M
Nuruzzaman, M
Okubadejo, A A
Paddock, P M
Pansari, N G
Parmar, C S
Patel, A B
Patel, P K

Patel, S
Pathak, N D
Paw, J D
Peacock, K E
Pedder, G H
Phillips, S G
Pitkeathly, W T N
Poxon, I M
Prasad, M
Qureshi, M U
Qureshi, M A
Rajeshwar, K
Rao, V D
Rashid, N Z
Ray, K C
Redlich, L A H
Rietsema, C
Rifat-Ghaffar, Dr
Robertson, D E H
Rolston, E T
Roy, D K
Rozario, E L
Sadique, T
Sahu, S P
Sameja, S
Sarai, R K
Sayaji Rao, K
Seddon, J R M
Sehjpal, A
Sen, S C
Shek, K-C
Siddiq, M A
Siddiqui, M A J
Sikka, G
Sikka, J S
Singal, A K
Singal, A K
Singh, G
Sinha, G P
Sinha, M
St John, H M R
Stanton, R J
Stirling, T B
Sulaiman, S K
Summers, H A H
Suri, A S
Tanner, J W
Tewary, A K
Thiru, N
Thomas, A R
Thomas, R E
Thrush, R
Thuse, M G
Toshniwal, M H
Tozer, A J
Trivedi, M
Turner, J P
Walls, E C
Walls, H E C
Ward, G D
Ward, R M
Washbrook, R A H
Watkins, S L
Webb, A R
Wharton, J G
White, J D
White, N V
Wigmore, J S
Wilson, C J
Wilson, E
Woodhouse, J S
Wootton, R I
Yahia, A O
Yarnall, N J

Walsingham

Dixon, P F
Gorrod, R G
Gorrod, S-J R

Waltham Abbey

Berry, B B
Cromwell, S M
Engineer, S R
Galbraith, S M
Garkal, A
Gervis, J H
Lakha, A G N
Llewelyn, J
Morris, A G
Pearson, J B
Pymont, F E
Richard, D R
Whitmore, I V

Waltham Cross

Baker, A W
Baldas, A
Benjamin, J M
Bhar, G C

Conway, J C
Galaal, K A
Goodwin, A M
Hasan, M
Hodge, R J
King, I J
Misra, K
Nagpal, K K
Naqvi, A T
Neville, W T
Pearce, J A
Raja, A U K
Roberts, N
Sahni, D R
Sengupta, N
Smith, K S B
Southerton, J
Stanton, J C
Stanton, S M
Wakefield, S M
Watson, S C
Weadick, P R
Western, N V B
Whitewright, J R
Wood, D F
Yousef, Z R

Walton on the Naze

Beardmore, C L M
Frost, I
Geldard, J A F
Roper, N D K
Thompson, J H

Walton-on-Thames

Andrews, S J
Arnold, P F
Banham, M J
Barrett, C A M
Bennett, R J J
Blackburn, M N
Blackmore, M J
Britton, G V
Bryan, I R J
Chesover, J
Clark, L A
Cooper, J E S
Econs, A
Edwards, A
Eyre, J
Eyre, P A
Fahmi, F M R
Fisher, F M
Gibson, E O
Gladman, L M
Hancock, N J A
Holdsworth, J A
Kangesu, E
Keane, A B
Lewis, G E
Lippold, O C J
Littlewood, E R
MacVicar, C V
Malde, K
Mant, A K
Meechan, P O
Morgan, D J R
Naylor, P M
Noon, C C
Pirrie, A J
Raptopoulos, P
Ratcliffe, D M
Redfern, R
Reynolds, D A
Ribera Cortada, I
Rice, K M
Salih, J E
Sekhon, S S
Shrimpton, S P
Sillick, J M
Simmonds, M
Warrington, B M V
Warrington, R
Wijnberg, J P
Williams, E C
Woodward, P J
Wyborn, A J N

Wantage

Ambler, P J
Banwell, M E
Baverstock, A M
Blake, E R
Dawe, M S
Dinnis, G A
Drury, V M
Dunning, M T
Fisher, N D
Gillibrand, R
Godlee, R J P

Herd, G J C
Hockaday, J M
Howard, J
Hulse, E V
Jones, B V
Kaye, S M
Kyle, P D
Kyle, S D
Law, L A
Leeming-Latham, L
Lister Cheese, I A F
Livingstone, Q G
Loudon, I S L
McLellan, F M
Masters, H C
Reynolds, J B
Robinson, J C
Shackleton, R F
Shackleton, S C
Sharp, R J
Squires, R C
Teare, C M L
Thrippleton, L K
Triffitt, D J
Uridge, C F
Whipple, S J B
Wise, D G D
Wordsworth, R F

Ware

Barker, V C J
Baverstock, M W J
Bennet, R B
Bridges, I H
Broughton, N B
Davies, M W
Desai, A P
Doherty, M V
Eames, J M
Fish, L J
Gibson, S H
Gilbert, D J
Hans, S F
Harris, S C
Lennox, M S
Lennox, S C
Lockley, D M
McCreadie, J E
Maddams, D J
Martinez Fernandez, I
Merwaha, N
Peters, J L
Preston, P
Rundell, T R
Smith, K R H
Watson, J C
Young, J M S

Wareham

Ashley, E R W
Backhouse, R H
Bennett, C E
Bennett, J R
Booth, A I
Brown, A M
Brown, J M
Brown, T S
Cardew, P N
Collyer, A J
Cox, J S
Gould, A J
Greenfield, R M
Harley, T G
Hetreed, V W J
Hopkins, E A
Irwin, C S
Johnson, M C
Lee-Potter, J P
Lesna, M
Lesny, J
Lyons, C
Lyons, N T
McKinstry, T H
Ormerod, W P
Patten, G D R
Payne, W N
Race, C
Richardson, E A
Ross, P A
Rumbold, C A
Salter, A L
Salter, T C M
Shepherd, R C
Stevenson, C H
Webster, A J
Williams, M G

Warley

Ahuja, D K
Ahuja, J

Warminster

Anwar-Farid, S M
Bathija, S H
Binks, C
Bloxham, S T
Broughton, A J
Collier, D J F
Collier, S J
Cornish, V M
Desai, P M
Dhillon, N S
Forbes, E K
Gibson, P L
Hamilton, D G
Harrington, D A
Harris, E
Iqbal, Y
Jhanjee, V K
Kalsi, G S
Khan, F A
Ladha, K
Loveless, R A
McAndrew, S V
McCathie, N J
McFall, E
Nutbeam, H M
Pall, N K
Pinto, S M
Price, W R
Rahman, K A
Rothwell, B P
Ryan, H T
Sharp, J
Srivastava, K K
Tye, J C
Tyler, J E
Vaughan, K F

Warlingham

Allenby, F
Beckitt, D
Boorman, P A
Bown, M J
Brookes, R C
Brownson, S E
Carpenter, W F
Cruthers, J P
Cruthers, R
Duffell, J C D
Fishman, M
Hinkes, D A
Kelly, E P
Luscombe, B R
Parry, D M
Ramage, P C V
Sewell, R H
Stimmler, L
Turner, M J
Yates, M S

Warminster

Arathoon, D A
Asbridge, G
Bartholomew, N I
Beach, P G
Bell, J M
Bradfield, W J D
Braithwaite, M G
Browne, C H
Church, E
Collyns, T A
Corey, O I M
Crofts, C F
Cupples, S E
Finch, P J C
Fishwick, J
Goedkoop, L C
Greenhalgh, M C S
Greenwood, A
Hammond, V T
Henry, S L
Houghton, S R A
Lawton, G S
Leigh, P R W
Little, D J
Longbourne, D
McBride, E
McBride, K N
Payne, J S
Plaxton, M R K
Price, W J P
Prior, K G
Stevens, V J R
Stilwell, R
Strangeways, P R
Thorpe, M A
Titley, J V
Tomlinson, J
Tremlett, P D

Warrington

Williams, K L
Woolgar, J D

Warrington

Abbott, J B
Abdullah, A
Adair, R J
Adair, T
Agnew, E M
Agnew, M N
Ahmad, M M U
Akasha, K S K
Al-Jafari, M S
Al-Maskari, S M
Al-Shakarchi, B A B
Anderson, J N
Anis, A B
Ansdell-Smith, M
Aromolaran, A A
Asamoah, D K
Aslam, M
Awan, T T
Baines, A G
Baldwin, K J
Bannon, J J E
Bansal, V K
Banyard, P J
Barlow, K M
Barton, P G
Basma, L
Bass, A
Bates, A J
Beare-Winter, A N
Bedford, C D
Bentley, S J
Bishop, P M
Bokhari, A A
Bokhari, S A
Boot, D A
Booth, J A
Boyd, R C
Bradley, G C
Brady, D W J
Brassill, J W
Bree, C G
Brett, M C A
Briggs, J R
Brook, N M
Brook, R
Brooker, G E M
Brown, G J
Brown, Z
Burke, B M
Burke, P L
Burke, S L
Burke, W
Burthem, J
Butler, A J
Cain, S
Caldwell, A J
Cann, P C
Cantrell, P
Caplan, M P
Carmichael, D N
Carr, D J
Cave, D L
Chamberlain, J W
Chetter, I C
Choudhury, A
Clarke, J N
Clayton, W G
Cockburn, K J
Coleman-Smith, I
Collinson, R
Colquhoun, R G
Connell, J E
Coombs, I C
Copeland, G P
Copeman, A J
Coughlin, M
Cox, D A
Cribb, J S
Croton (Mrs Entwishe), J L L
Cunliffe, G
Curran, P
Das, R
Davies, G J
Davis, A M
Davis, P A
Dennis, M W
Desai, M I
Dhir, K
Dickinson, G H J
Dickson, W
Dingle, D G
Dirckze, J M
Dixon, A M
Dixon, S P
Doherty, J A
Doherty, M B
Dolan, K
Douglas, Y J
Downey, P
Durkin, C M
Earlam, L
Edwards, C V S
Edwards, D O
Edwards, D W
Edwards, I G
Elder, W M
Fazackerley, E J
Fearon, J H
Ferguson, J F
Ferran Cabeza, J M
Filobbos, R
Flanagan, S M
Francis, E P
Freeman, C A M
Garvey, R J P
Gerber, S
Ghaffar, A A
Ghazawy, G S
Ghazawy, S
Gleave, D A
Glennon, C M
Gomes, A J
Goodwin, T
Gorman, D F
Graham, M P H
Greene, J F
Hadland, M D
Haigh, P M
Hall, S J
Halliwell, M C
Hannam, D R
Hanumanthu, V R
Harney, J M V
Hartley, M J
Hebbar, G K
Higgs, A G
Hobin, D A
Holland, E F N
Hope, J A
Horgan, D F A
Horton, V M
Howes, A J
Htay Win, Dr
Hughes, T J M
Hunter, J D
Hussain, S A J A-R
Hussein, A M M K
Hutchinson, G H
Hutchinson, P G
Hyland, C
Iceton, N M
Inman, C D C
Ishaque, M
Iskander, L S F
Jacob, T
Jamieson, P A
Jarvis, P D
Jarvis, S J F
John, B
Johnson, E M
Johnson, M
Johnson, R T
Jones, R A
Joshi, H
Kanagavel, N
Karkanevatos, A
Kelleher, P C
Kerr, M A
Khalil, A L
Kieran, J D M
Kishan, B
Knight, S R
Knill, R
Kowalska, K A
Kozman, E L L
Krishna Reddy, T V
Kumaraswamy, S P
Laing, G S
Lal, H
Lawson, W K
Laycock, A N
Leach, J M
Leech, P W
Leech, R S J
Leggat, H M
Leigh, A J
Leneghan, J E
Letchumanan, V
Levy, M
Lewis, S J
Linaker, B D
Lloyd, C C
Loh, Y C
Lord, K M
Lowe, R
Lynch, S C
McCaig, J
McCormack, J R S
McDowell, J D
Mackay, M M
Mackin, E A
McLaren, P J
Malkhandi, A D
Malpica, M G
Manning, G F
Manning, G M
Marcus, P
Martin, B A
Miller, C G
Miller, D G
Miller, W G
Millerchip, R
Mills, G N
Mills, J K
Milroy, P J M
Monks, M
Monteith, P G
Moody, A P
Morton, J D
Moss, L G N
Mott, J H
Mukhopadhyay, P S
Mundell, R H
Myles, J M
Nalla, R R
Napier, J E
Neary, W J
Nixon, S J
O'Brien, P
O'Colmain, B P
O'Connor, A P
O'Flanagan, J O
O'Flanagan, P M
O'Hara, N P
O'Loan, J
O'Malley, M
Obeid, E M H
Oglesby, S D
Oldfield, J A
Orme, M C E
Osborne, A W
Osuna Carrasquilla, F M
Palmer, G R
Paranjothy, C
Park, R
Parkins, A C
Parry, R G
Patel, K
Patel, V
Patiniott, F J
Patterson, J L
Pawley, G R
Pearce, I A
Peckar, C O
Penni, A N
Pepper, J M
Perkins, J
Platts, A S G
Plenderleith, S J
Plumb, E A
Pomfret, S M
Porter, B J
Povey, W P
Priestley, C T
Rahim, M A
Rahman, M B
Rahman, S M S
Ramachandra Rao, V
Ranasinghe, H A N
Rao, S V
Rashid, Z
Ratchford, A M
Rathe, M
Reddy, N S
Redfearn, S W
Rees, M
Reynolds, P A
Rimmer, A J
Ritter, A C
Robertson, D E
Robertson, R M P
Robinson, A E
Robinson, C R
Robinson, K
Ross, S M
Rothwell, D
Rowlands, M
Royle, D A
Ryan, U
Salib, E
Salih, A R M
Sathiyaseelan, S
Sathiyaseelan, S R K
Scott, D L
Scott, G P
Seddon, J A
Shahbazi, S S A H
Shaw, L C
Sheikh, I H
Sherry, P G
Shome, C
Simpson, F A
Skinner, A C
Slovak, A J M
Smith, A T
Smith, C E
Smith, G D
Smith, J M
Smith, S P
Sokhi, J S
Sowinska, E
Spedding, R L
Stanway, T L
Stewart, A M
Stewart, G D
Stockton, P A
Storrar, D A
Stott, J E
Suleman, B A
Tailby, C H
Tandon, H P
Taylor, B A
Thomas, M D
Thompson, H W K
Thorburn, R J
Tourish, P G
Trotter, C
Tunstall, M A
Turner, H J
Tyrer, M
Umnus, L
Veeravahu, R
Vivekanandamurty, K
Wadsworth, M R
Wales, E L
Wales, E K
Walkden, D
Walkden, J A D
Walmsley, R A
Walton, D J
Ward, B
Watson, I N
Webb, C J
Whitcroft, I A
Whitehead, K P
Wild, N J
Williams, A
Williams, N E
Wilson, I S
Winter, S M
Wishart, M S
Wood, R S
Wrather, S E
Yeong, C C
Young, J M M

Warwick

Acharya, A B
Addenbrooke, J C
Allen, A J
Allim, J S S
Anduvan, S
Anthony, A
Antrobus, J H L
Badwan, D A H
Barrowcliff, D F
Bates, J
Bedlow, A J
Begg, H B
Beniston, M A
Bhandal, T S
Bishop, J M
Blacklay, A E
Box, M J
Busby, J W
Byrne, J L
Campbell, C A
Carr, R A
Casey, M D
Chamberlain, S J
Chell, P B
Clark, H L M
Clarke, D P
Clarkson, S G
Clenton, S J
Coleman, H E
Cross, T J
Dallaway, C M
Darby, D O D
Davids, E
Davies, R
Davis, L A
Dawkins, C J
De Villiers, G S
Desai, H
Desborough, S H
Dowell, J R
Dumughn, C
Dunn, R M W
Finney, M E
Fleming, E M
Fraser, I D L
Ghose, A R
Ghose, B
Gopinathan, K P
Gray, D J
Gray, I R
Gray, J A
Greening, J S
Greenway, K J
Grewal, R
Gunton, H J
Hall, L K
Hatton, J A
Haverkorn, C
Hawker, P C
Hayward, C J
Henderson, J M
Hill, L S
Horrocks, P M
Houston, J
Howe, A N C
Hughes, M
Hughes, T B J
Humphreys, F
Inchley, S J
Inman, S M
Jackson, R
Jones, E
Jones, N S C
Kapma, J A A
Khan, A M
Killeen, I P
Laird, S
Le Tocq, M C L
Lewin, S C
Lewis, D C
Leyland, G R
Leyland, M J
Long, T M W
Lord, C F
Lord, M D
McDowall, F J
MacGregor, M E
Mahmood, A
Marguerie, C P
Martin, S J
Mather, S P
Meaden, R W
Meadows, H
Melton, R P
Menage, J L
Millard, F C
Milner, E C R
Milner, M A
Mohamed, H H
Morgan, R N
Morris, I H
Morris, M S
Morrison, R D M
Munday, D F
Murphy, P D
Nancarrow, J
Natin, D J M
Nicholls, M J
Nwagbara, P N
Nwosu, L C
Panting, K
Parker, J E
Parsons, A
Pearce, R H
Penrose, J H
Penter, G
Perthen, K S
Phillips, D E
Pinder, S J
Powell, J G
Reynolds, G E
Rigg, D R
Rivers, D S
Robinson, D A
Rogers, J N
Rose, P E
Rowe, S M
Sansom, D T
Sansome, J F
Schofield, J N M
Schroder, L D
Seymour Mead, A M
Shearman, J D
Silvester, K M
Slowther, C M
Smeyatsky, N R
Smith, F A
Spreadbury, T H
Storrs, C N
Strachan, J R
Struthers, G R
Tait, J S
Tarpey, J J
Templeton, A M
Thorne, D M
Thurley, P A
Tjon Fong Kwie, R T J T
Tweedie, D G
Vaz, F G
Vella, E J
Viswan, A K
Wells, L G
White, H G
Whitehouse, A J
Whitewood, C N
Whitewood, F J
Wilkinson, C E
Wilkinson, J E M
Williams, J H
Williams, P H
Williams, W G
Wilmot, C J M
Wilmot, E F
Wilson, E M
Wilson, R R
Winslow, L J L
Wyatt, S S
Young, H M
Young, S K

Washington

Benn, H M
Berry, R B
Brandes, E A
Burke, M F
Carney, S M
Cowie, S
Dennison, K C
Dixit, C M
Esen, U I
Ganesan, K L
Gollan, J
Goodwin, R
Griffin, J C
Haidar, A
Hassan, E R M
Heaney, R I
Hegde, A K K
Howd, R J
King, J A
Kulkarni, D R
Lawther, I W
McCabe, M M E
McCabe, M G
Mazarelo, J O
Nanavati, N A
Nanda, N
Nanda, U C
Pegman, A J
Prabhu, V R
Ray, N K
Rich, A J
Rigby, R C
Rusman, M
Rutland, R F K
Saravanamattu, K
Shah, T H
Smith, B T
Stafford, F W
Stephenson, G
Thomas, K M
Vakharia, B R
Wong, H S
Yelnoorkar, K

Watchet

Hardman, B M H
Kelly, N J
Lewis, J A
Rush, M
Wilson, M L
Wilson, P A
Woolf, M P S

Waterlooville

Andrews, M I J
Bartlett, D
Bateman, A M S
Batten, S F
Blakeley, S L
Bligh, M D

Welwyn Garden City

Bowerman, R D
Boyle, P D
Brownlie, H A
Burtenshaw, A J
Butler, K J
Churcher-Brown, C J
Clarke-Walker, A R
Clarke-Williams, J E
Cohen, A E
Connor, D J
Cooper, R A
Coppin, A F C
Daley, A C
Gibbons, P M
Gould, R A
Gould, S E
Goulder, T J
Graham, K A
Gregori, M
Griffiths, D G
Hanson, R G
Hargreaves, C M
Hargreaves, M D
Hulme, S-L
Hume, A M
Humphreys-Davies, W P C
Jenkins, S C
Jones, D H
King, A P U
Lennox, I G
Lewis, C J
McErlean, P
Mann, R D
May Mya Nwe, Dr
Millard, M-L
Millard, R V
Millen, N J
Milne, P S
Minay, I F
Morison, S R
Norman, A M
Norman, J R
Penfold, H M
Pompa, P A P
Pringle, J K
Pryce, D P
Reid, H L M
Roberts, N J
Robins, A M
Rowling, A J
Ruthven-Stuart, I A
Ryan, J A
Ryan, P B
Saville, M A
Shaltot, M A A
Shutte, H A N
Spreadbury, P L
Spruell, D A
Stanley, S P
Thomas, L M
van 't Hoff, W
Walters, H M
Warwick-Brown, J M
White, M J

Watford

Ainsley, J
Al-Barazanchi, A J H
Allen, S T
Anthony-Pillai, I
Anthony-Pillai, R D
Apple, M F A
Aron, P M
Aslam, S
Atkin, H S
Awad, R W I
Babu-Narayan, R K
Bancilhon, M L A B
Bani, R H
Bankole, C A
Barham, D H
Bavin, J T R
Bean, B E
Belham, G J
Bintcliffe, B J
Blake, S
Bolitho-Jones, A
Bolitho-Jones, P V
Boret, F A
Borkett-Jones, H J
Borkett-Jones, S E
Boxer, D I
Boyd, T J
Brown, N J
Buist, M
Bulman, W H
Calderwood, E M
Cameron, E A B

Cameron, J D H
Carreras, J C B E
Cates, C J
Chakrabarti, N
Chaudary, M A
Chipperfield, R A
Chowdhury, T
Chung, E M K
Clark, E J
Clements, M R
Coleman, R M
Collas, D M
Connor, A J M
Cooper, R C
Courtney, R M
Cox, M L
Cox, S J
Crisp, J C
Davis, P J
Daya, J
Devine, M A
Dhadwal, K K
Dobney, S
Dodoo, E A
Duckworth, A J
Dullforce, E J
Dyson, A L M B
Ehsanullah, M
Eliad, R A
Essam, M A
Fertleman, M B
Finn, C I
Fuchs-Goldfarb, S
Furbank, I D J
Galan, Y S
Gale, A N
Gallivan, T J
Gavilan, J
Gelister, J S K
Gladstone, G S
Glover, J I
Goolden, A W G
Gordon, A D
Grabczynska, S A
Grice, K
Griffin, D R
Gujral, H K
Gujral, M K
Gunawardana, S S
Hammad, G E-D M
Hart, S M
Hassan-Ali, R
Head, F C
Heckmatt, J Z
Heller, E
Hemmens, S A
Hussain, F M
Hussain, I
Hussain, Z-U
Ineson, N R
Irvine, L M
Isweran, P S
Jackson, A P
Jaffe, M
Jagajeevanram, D
Jankowski, R F
Jessop, J H
Joshi, B P
Kamya, D
Karunasekara, H S
Karunasekara, N R
Kat, H S
Kay, P I
Keen, M J
Khan, P S
King, J A
Kingsley, M
Knight, E J
Kodati, S M R
Lazaro Perlado, F
Lazzerini, V R
Leahy, A J
Lee, T L
Leigh, Y
Levison, W B
Lewis, D M
Leyshon, M W
Lim, S C
Loney, E L
Luck, D J
Lung, C P C
McCann, S J
McCormack, P M
Macfarlane, B J
Mackell, K A
Mackenney, R P
McKitterick, E C
McMurtry, I A
McNally, S A

Markeson, V E
Marshall, C D W
May, A J
Meager, P W D
Mehta, K M
Meyrick Thomas, J
Mir, R S
Mir, S A
Mital, R K
Moore, P F
Morris, H M A
Morris, J
Moss, D P
Moulsdale, M T
Mullan, H M
Munday, P E
Murdoch, M E
Murray, M D
Nair, G V
Nelstrop, G A
Novak, T V
Nyman, L E
O'Connor, P F M
O'Riordan, S P
Oliver, J M
Oren, C L
Owen, L S I
Padwick, M L
Pandit, N A
Paoloni, C C E
Parker, R K H
Parry, H M
Patel, D K K
Patel, S C
Platts, A J
Purbrick, S
Rackham, A J
Rae, H E
Raithatha, M M
Rajasekaran, J
Ramachandran, N
Ramsay, M E B
Ratnavel, T
Raychaudhuri, S
Razzaq, Q M
Reader, P M
Redman, D R O
Renteria, N
Reubin, R D
Richards, B A
Richards, J D M
Richardson, B W T
Rieu, E C
Rizvi, S A H
Robertson, S C
Robinson, E A E
Robson, T W
Rotman, C M H
Rubin, A
Rudran, V
Sa'Adu, A
Sainsbury, W A
Saksena, J
Samra, S E M A
Sarva Isweran, M
Scholes, C F
Scott, J M
Searle, C H
Shanmuganathan, C
Shaw, A D S
Shaw, K J
Shears, D
Sheikh, N F
Shepherd, J S
Sheridan, R J
Sills, D J
Simmons, K L
Singleton, C D
Sinha, J K
Slater, M S
Slessor, I M
Somerville, K W
Somerville, W
Soskin, M A
Starck, G P S C
Starer, F
Steele, C A
Supramaniam, G
Tan, S H
Taylor, G D
Thompson, D T
Tinklin, T S
Tso, M T B Y
Vankelecom, F
Vyramuthu, N
Walker, J A
Wallis, H
Watson, M E J
Webb, R J

Weidmann, S J
Williams, H O
Williams, M J H
Wilson, J N
Wilson, M A
Yadegar, J
Yazdani, M S
Zakani, R

Watlington

Gordon, A C
Gregory, N A P
Hugh-Jones, K
Miller, T R
Rawstron, J R
Smyly, P A J
Stillwell, J M

Wedmore

Clarkson, K S
Counsell, P
Drage, S A C
Goodman, G C
Gover, G
Howard, J C
Malcolm, N
Morrison, C D
Watt, D S
West, A J

Wednesbury

Abedin, M Z
Ahmed, S A
Bhadauria, B S
Bhattacharya, D
Buckley, M P
Carr, V A
Glennie, J A
Huey, D M
Lavender, J P
Morris, C D E
Pearce, G
Rahman, A-U
Rana, S
Saini, A S
Shah, J
Taylor, M B
Tayyebi, G A
Vaid, S J

Welling

Anto, M K
Baruah, A C
Bush, R J
Chahal, J K
Colaco, T D C
Cotter, W A
De Souza, R A
Dhital, A P
Fish, P D
Gupta, C L
Hanner, I E
McEwan, J
Martin, J L
Mascarenhas, N N
Murray, R D
Nwamarah, D E
Oxford, P C J
Patel, M
Raoof, H Y
Ryder, J C
Shah, N
Sylvester, G M
Tayyib, M
Victor-Beza, M
Wijayatilake, N

Wellingborough

Alexander, Z
Barton, L M
Bent, J E
Bevan, J M
Bhala, B B
Booth, A H
Box, W D
Brook, B J
Burton, K L
Byles, L E
Camp, A V
Chung, K Y K
Clifford, P D
Colquhoun, A J
Coulson, W J
Cox, J K
Craig, J H
De, R K
Dent, C C
Dibble, T F C
Dwivedi, A
English, J

Evans, A G
Geeves, N P
Gordon, P J
Goudge, M L
Graves, P B
Hague, J M S
Harry, M L G P
Inns, P
James, J
Jasani, I A M
Johnson, S L
Jollyman, T M
Kapre, M L
King, G R
Kownacki, S
Lambert, A M
Lawrence, D K
McGarity, K L
McGibbon, A F
McInnes, A A
Masih, H
Matheson, I D
Mistry, V K
Nalinasegaren, G
Nandakumar, K
Nicholas, I H
Palfreeman, A J
Pepperman, M A
Perry, R M
Purdy, D R
Reed, N G
Ritchie, J M
Shah, J S
Sharp, R W
Smith, D W
Spencer, M C
Upton, P G
Wainwright, A T
Wall, I F
Whittington, T J
Wingfield, S N

Wellington

Bevan, P W
Bradnock, J P
Bridgman, S J
Cohen, H E
Cole, J H
Fairbairn, S E A
Flowers, J M
Frier, J A
Kenney, J G
Leahy, A C
McCann, D J
Newmarch, B
Peters, H G
Rickard, A M
Thomson, P J
Waterhouse, P
Waterhouse, T D
Wynne, J S

Wells

Ancill, P K
Ashman, R
Barnes, J C
Barnett, A F
Bench, J J
Bridson, C M
Cheriyan, J K
Crawley, H E
Douglass, E J
Fay, R A
Gatrill, R B
Gilks, J M L
Gillen, D P
Goddard, R H
Gould, J C G K
Green, M I
Harrison, F M
Hutchings, D G
Jones, J
Knight, S M
Lopez Leza, P
Marshall, D L
Martin, T J
Matthews, J W
Norman, A S
Pinching, J
Pryer, A A
Stephen, W J
Swale, N F H
Thammanna, Dr
Trafford, P A
Urquhart, A
Woolley, A W
Young, J E

Wells-next-the-Sea

Davenport, J

Ebrill, C S T
Lahbib, F J
Ransom, R M
Watson, P S

Welshpool

Anton-Stephens, D
Blench, P I
Brownbill, C L
Clark, L
Davies, S P
Evans, A V
Hutchinson, E A
Jones, E L
Jones, J M
Jones, M E
Jones, R M
Lambert, S K
Lewis, M R
Milne, L G
Nethercott, A S
O'Dwyer, G M
O'Dwyer, P D
Riley, M
Ryan, T D
Solomon, A L
Townsend, C S
Williams, J A

Welwyn

Abrahams, R C
Almeyda, J S
Almeyda, R V
Aubrey, R J
Bancroft, R M
Chambers, H C
Crane, W P
Cropp, J E
Dansie, C
Dansie, N B
Dansie, O
Dawson, A S
Dawson, M A
Derola, T
Drew, A
Flind, A C
Fowler, L K
Goetz, S C
Gullick, D L
Hammond, T A G
Harrison, S J
Howes, O D
Jory, H I
Lenox-Smith, I
Mackay, E V
McNab, A L
Moore, A R
Moye, A R
Nandy, A M
Napier, H B
Pardoe, C A
Reed, A
Robbins, G M
Roden, M
Ryan, J S
Satchell, R H
Shurz, A M L
Small, B J
Stallard, M C
Stallard, N C
Tobin, M D
Tobin, T A
Tozer, R D C
Trevarthen, F D
Turner, K J
Vaquas, S
Visram, A R
Wilson, H O
Wood, S J

Welwyn Garden City

Al-Izzi, M S S
Aldridge, M C
Angwin, H V
Ashman, A G
Axon, J M C
Bakhru, M N
Barathan, I
Bayoumi, A-H M M
Benbow, A G
Blofeld, A
Boyce, T H
Brewis, R P
Campbell, S H
Charlwood, L M U
Clarke, R
Conroy, S J
Corser, A J
Cranfield, F M

Wembley

Creak, D R
Crilly, D
Dallas, J D A
Dasgupta, J
Davies, R P
Davis, H P
Dobbie, H S
Dobbie, J J D
Dover, C J
Drew, N C
Duggal, S
Dunstan, M E
Dunster, R J
Egbase, P E
Evison, J G
Fineberg, N A
Fox, M H
Gareeboo, M S
Gautam, V
Gleasure, A J
Göhmann, H-D
Goldberg, P L
Goold, J E
Greenfield, S M
Griffin, J P
Hale, G
Hanak, B A
Harding, M J
Haslam, R G E
Hawley, C J
Hayman, M R
Hilditch, R J
Hirst, J R
Holden, A A
Holt, P M
Howell, J D
Hubbard, A P
Husain, H M
Iafelice, E D
Iqbal, Z
Jenkins, C M
Jenkins, J L
Khan, S S
Kingsbury, S J
Kirkpatrick, C T
Kitson, J L
Lamb, Y J
Lauble, S
Lavelle, R C W
Lok, S S
Lund, C D
McCallum, A K
McCue, J L
McGettiga, H
McGhee, A G
McIntyre, P B
McLintock, D G
Mercy, L C
Mithra, S D
Munshi, N I
Newman, M J
Odufuwa-Bolger, T O
Olding, R B
Pallot, D B
Parmar, H
Peachey, J A
Peachey, R S
Perera, S M
Perren, J F
Phiri, D E D
Pugh, G
Quartey, P K
Raffles, A K M
Richardson, E I
Roberts, A G
Robson, R A
Rogerson, R E
Rule, M J
Saetta, J P
Samarasinghe, W
Sandhu, B S
Shah, Z P
Shaw, C A
Sheela Sridhar, K
Sherman, J A
Shrimpton, S B
Stead, J E
Stephens, E W B
Taverner, D M
Turner, S J S
Vaquas, S M
Voke, J M
Waldron, M N
Walker, T J
Waller, S M
Wat, C K Y
Waterfield, A H
Watkins, M E
Whitmore, T K
Wilkins, M H
Wilson, J I
Windsor-Martin, D A
Winocour, P H
Wood, H A

Wembley

Aaronson, R B
Abeysiri, P
Ahmed, A
Al-Hadi, H
Amin, M B
Andrade, E J Y
Apley, M S
Ashour, F A A E-M
Aurora, P
Azzam, Y M A
Bailey, D J O
Bajaj, S
Banerjee, C
Banerjee, S
Bankole, M A
Bayer, M M
Beig, K
Bernstein, J F
Bhardwaj, R
Bhattacharyya, M
Brent, P G
Charles, R H G
Cheung, K-O
Clark, M O
Dabas, R
Drage, S M
Dutton, D
Ellis, P F
Estment, P D
Fergusson, J
Fox, A T
Gandhi, V
Ghawss, M I M
Goodchild, L P
Gor, A S
Gor, M S
Greenham, R M
Griffin, C M
Griffin, R A
Hales, S
Hami, F
Haque, I
Hassabo, M S A-A
Hira, J R
Hunter, C
Hyman, V C
Islamullah, M
Jackson, D A T
Jagadambe, P R
Jegatheesvaran, M
Kaleem, T
Karia, U
Kearns, W E
Khan, A A
Khan, M A A
Kirmani, T H
Kostyn, M
Kotecha, M B
Krotosky, L A
Kumar, A S B
Kunapuli, V S
Kutiyanawala, M
Lamptey, C
Lee, C H
Lewis, C J
Lovett, P C A
McGovern, H
Mahendran, R
Maheswaran, W T
Makhija, S K
Malde, N S
Mamtora, M P
Manocha, K F
Mass, M E
Mathur, R
Mehta, S M
Merchant, R
Milik, N S
Mills, J
Murugiah, S
Nathan, J C D
Naylor, D H R
Negandhi, D B
O'Neill, E M
O'Riordan, D K
Obeng, F
Obeyesekera, S L
Odutola, T A A
Olojohungbe, A B K
Patel, A R
Patel, B B
Patel, B
Patel, H
Patel, J I
Patel, J S
Patel, L V
Patel, M D
Patel, P B
Pradhan, M J
Radia, D H R
Raichura, M M
Rangr, P
Rapp, D A
Rashid, B U
Ross, J
Saad, A
Sabharwal, C K
Sabharwal, N N
Sabharwal, N K
Salame, M Y
Salinsky, J V
Salker, D M
Scrine, M
Selvarajah, K N
Shah, K A
Shah, R S
Shah, S
Shah, S M
Shaikh, A
Shami, S K
Sheikh, S A
Sheth, G P
Shields, J
Singarayer, C
Singh, I
Singh, T G
Strang, R A
Subbiah, S
Syed, S U
Tahir, H I S
Tailor, V G
Tansley, E J
Tayal, N
Taylor-Smith, R G
Teelock, B
Thirumavalavan, V S
Thurairajah, A
Twomey, A F J
Ugboma, K J
Unni, K V S
Venkata Rao, K
Verma, S P S
Vijh, V
Vyas, S
Warner, Z L
Weeks, V C
Wierzbicki, W
Wijayaratna, L O
Wijayatilake, D S
Wijeratne, W K
Wills, C I
Wilson, S R

Wemyss Bay

Gibson, A N
Grabs, A J
McDonald, M R
McKay, L A
McKechnie, S
More, J R S
Shirazi, T

West Bromwich

Agarwal, M D
Agarwal, N K
Agrawal, G K
Ahmed, A H S
Armstrong, J
Bajaj, S
Banerjee, R
Banerjee, S K
Bardha, H S
Bassan, T S
Bellin, J M
Bhatt, R C V
Birch, P C
Bose, R C
Brook, F B
Carter, N P
Cave, K L
Chalkley, M J
Chand, D
Clothier, J C
Cobb, C A
Crampton, G M
Crowther, C A
Crump, M S
Dar, S
Daya, V H
Desai, G
Dexter, B H
Doerry, U G
Edwards, S
El-Gohary, T M T
El-Hilu, S
Ellis, D J
Evans, A R M
Fletcher, J S
Gabbitas, D G
Gilbert, J E
Grindulis, H
Grindulis, K A
Gudi, P V
Hallan, P S
Handa, S I
Harb, M M
Harte, N M
Hughes, E A
Jadhav, S N
Jayatunga, R
Jones, A C V
Jones, MA
Kabukoba, J J
Kaplan, N M F
Karandikar, R V
Kathirgamakarthigeyan, T

Khanna, A
Kranidiotis, L S
Leahy, J F
Macaulay, D D R
McClement, B J
McLeod, D T
Mallya, J U
Mattar, M H
Mehra, R C
Mlele, T J J
Murphy, M
Page, N G
Panikker, N R
Patel, D R
Patel, R M
Pathak, S K
Perera, B L
Prasad, K
Ranga Rao, N
Rao, J N
Rayatt, S S
Robertson, D A
Rose, M
Sajnani, D K
Saunders, D J
Shakeel, M H
Shaw, A S
Singh, C D P
Singh, I
Sreekanta, G
Tahir, M Z
Tutton, G R
Van Den Dwey, K
Verow, P G
Warner, E M
Weissenhorn, G I
Wijewardene, P A
Zulueta Madinabeitia, L

West Byfleet

Barker, E S
Bawtree, H
Bennett, P M J
Blackwell, M J
Cowan, P J
Crossley, J N
Donaldson, J A
Dunstan, C J D
Gilliam, G
Horgan, J L
Hyzler, A H
Karney, P L
Ker, D B
Lech, Y M H
Lynch, M T
McEvoy, H M
Manuel, H
Meechan, H T
Shepheard, A C
Waghorn, D A

West Calder

Barclay, K
Brook, C M
Campbell, A M
Campbell, C M
Gilkison, J N
Haigh, S J
Hewitt, M J
Penny, J M
Pringle, J R
Robertson, J L
Valentine, D E

West Drayton

Abe, P J A
Andrews, L M
Andrews, P
Bowman, A D
Byrne, N J
Chana, G S
Chandra, L
Eraneva, K A
Flower, D J C
Grewal, A
Hikmet, S A
McCulloch, W J
Mian, F U R
Montgomery, J
Norris, V H
Paramanathan, V
Picton, C E
Ponnappa, M A

West Kilbride

Arumugam, C
Caskie, J P
Chisholm, L J
Colburn, D D
Davies, F W
Donald, M R H
Fegan, K G
Graham, H C
Kelly, B M J
Melville, C A
Porteous, E M E
Porteous, G S
Wilson, M T
Young, L M

West Linton

Adamson, P M
Halcrow, J S
Hegarty, B S M
McCann, M A
Philpott, H G
Pollock, A C
Thorp, R H

West Malling

Barnhoorn, A M
Beazleigh, T
Cassim, S D M
Crowther, J W
Crutchfield, L A
Eggleton, S P H
Golebiowski, A
Hirons, R M
Keane, M A
Love, L F C
Musgrave, R J
Newell, R J
Pinder, D K
Rushton, M J
Scott, A J
Tomkins, C M

West Molesey

Bonsu, A K
Mittal, S C

West Wickham

Allen, S D
Amin, S
Arif, M S
Carter, S M
Dilley, R J
Domjan, J M
Dunlop, A J
Gauntlett, S L
Hammill, R M
Holloway, J A C
Jeffs, H G
Jhally, S
Kirby, R N
Langtry, A B
Medlycott, B R
Purwar, V
Ramani, R M
Richards, D P
Robertson, S H
Robson, P
Ross, L V
Sithamparapillai, S
Standfield, N J
Strathdee, G M
Thangarajasingam, V
Van Woerkom, A E
Weber, M E
Whittaker, I D
Willmer, B J
Wills, P C

Young, D C D
Young, M J

Westbury

Ager, P W
Beale, D A
Edwards, R M
Grier, I W
Hibbert, R S
Kostelnik, J R
Moore, K A
Murphy, C F
Powell, D H T
Pullen, P H
Ronn, H H
Salisbury, N S
Siggers, B R C
Siggers, D J

Westcliff on Sea

Abuown, A A
Adey, A J
Adey, C
Aggarwal, R K
Ahlquist, J A O
Al-Shammari, A A
Atkinson, P
Babar, I U
Bain, L A
Ball, A J
Benians, R G
Bowles, J N
Bray, G P
Buckley, J H M
Bullock, A E
Callaghan, S M
Carmichael, D J S
Carr, T W
Chappell, M E
Chaturvedi, K K
Chisnell, P T
Collings, A D
Dasgupta, B
Davies, B S
Diddee, A S
Diddee, S D
Donald, D
Dworkin, M J
Eden, A G Z
Eden, H H A
Eraut, C D
Ewart, I A
Fowler, E F
Franklin, J S
Gabrielczyk, M R
Garofalides, B
Gatland, D J
Ghani, P N
Goldman, L
Gordon, T E
Grover, S P
Gul, J
Halliday, R M
Hamblin, J J
Harter, C
Henderson, S M
Higgins, D J
Hollywood, P G
Hughes, S F
Ibrahim, M N
Kalan, A M H
Kelly, P A
Khan, A
Khan, M R
Lamont, A
Lane, G F
Lewars, M D
Lewis, C P M
Liew, S-H
Lim, K B
Lubel, J S
McKechnie, J
Maher, H A
Majdneya, E
Mellor, J A
Metcalfe, K A
Misbahuddin, A
Mullane, D M
Myers, M
Nicol, S D W
O'Brien, A A J
O'Brien, J D
Obadiah, M
Packer, G J
Park, D M
Pearsons, D E
Perera, S D
Perera, S J
Prejbisz, J W

Whitehaven

Qidwai, A
Ramdin, L S
Rayne-Davis, C W R
Reynolds, D F
Robinson, A C R
Rokan Al-Mallak, H
Roy, S
Rumble, J A
Salter, M C P
Schuster, R
Shah, S S
Shaw, A J
Siani, N M
Siddique, H A
Sinha, A K
Slovick, D I
Sooriakumaran, V
Spitzer, R J
Spivey, C J
Subasinghe, S Z A
Tisi, R B
Tosh, G C
Trask, C W L
Ward, J K
Ward, S
Warwick-Brown, N P
Weller, P J
Whybrow, T R
Willis, A J P
Wisely, C M
Wisely, E H
Wisely, J

Westcliffe on Sea
Gray, A E

Westerham
Bhana, V
Bradley, R D
Brown, K C
Carson, S J
Crosskey, H E
Crosskey, K S M
Dowling, G C V
Gramsma, A
Hatton, M
Higgs, J
Hutchinson, R C
Irving, G A
Ismaili, J A
Ismaili, N
Kapadia, A
Kenwright, K A
Knox, V E
Long, A G G
Lord, J A D
Lyttle, T W
Mackenzie-Ross, C J
Magee, N E
Molyneux, P D
Nicol, R J A
Parker, J R
Pearson, C M G
Peck, S R
Pinchin, R M E
Pullen, M D
Richardson, R G
Sargeant, I D
Singh, K
Singh, S
Skinner, A J
Street, E W

Westgate-on-Sea
Abrokwah, J
Curwen, M
Dean, A J P
Field, G J
Lall, A
Lall, A
Lall, G N
Lewis, M
Mathers, J D
Meakin, D R
Moore, E L
Turtle, J A

Westhill
Alexander, A F
Allan, C G
Brownhill, J E
Brownie, E C
Burnett, J C D
Carter, P E G
Dean, J H S
Ellis, G G
Harris, C C
Hunter, C M
Hutchison, J D
Jibril, J A

MacArthur, M D
Milne, W S
Ritchie, R D
Weir, J

Weston Super Mare
Afifi, R A E M M
Ainsworth, M K
Alam, M M
Armstrong, C P
Bailey, S J
Barff, D M
Bartlett, P G
Bevan, C D
Bhakri, H L
Birkett, J F
Bowering, R J B
Bradley, A
Butchart, J F
Case, R D
Chitty, J R
Clarke, C W
Cockeram, J
Collett, C A
Cooper, E
Corcos, C D
Cossham, P S
Croucher, C L
Danker, K O
Darling, R M
Davies, H C
Day, A P
Devitt, N M
Disley, A
Dixon, J
Easton, P J
England, C M
Evans, D J
Fitzpatrick, R C
Foxton, T M
Foy, G
Frost, C E A
Gallegos, N C
Gamlin, C G
Garvey, G N
Giannoulis, K
Gillis, C V
Gosden, P E
Gould, G A
Grounds, J G
Hartley, D R W
Hasham, N I
Hermaszewska, E J
Hermaszewski, R A
Hinchliffe, A
Hinchliffe, M K
Hugh, D
Johnson, M R
Kelly, J D
Kettle, A B
Krekorian, H A W
Lakin, N P
Langkamer, V G
Latif, M M A
Leonard, M J
Longhorn, I R
Lott, M F
Lumb, P G
Mahajan, A J
Mahajan, T A
MaksimcZyk, P
Milnthorpe, P D
Molesworth, T
Murdin, P G
Mussell, F M R
Newton, A P
Nott-Bower, T M
Osman, M A
Papworth, G W J
Papworth, J E J
Parker, D R
Parsons, J B
Patel, N D
Paterson, D A
Pealing, V M
Pearse-Danker, S C
Petty, W H
Piotrowski, A G
Preston, C W
Preston, R C
Pye, G
Roberts, R D
Saunders, J H
Saw Lwin Aung, Dr
Smith, A J
Smith, P R
Stallworthy, E G
Steggall, E A
Todd, I M

Tomblin, M P M
Umpleby, M H J
Varshney, M P
Vaze, N R
Wakley, E J
Waring, I S
Watkinson, P M
Wilson, E D
Wilson, P B
Woodhead, P J
Wyatt, M T

Wetherby
Atkins, M L
Batchelor, A G G
Beard, A D
Blair, I H
Boyle, P T
Bradley, A M
Brady, M D
Briffa Boothman, J
Brooke, B M
Browning, B S
Browning, S J
Caithness, G S
Childs, A-M
Collier, A M
Crabbe, R M G
Dabbs, T R
Davies, D M
Dillon, S
Drayson, R W
Durham, N P
Edwards, S
Frank, H G
Gibbs, J R
Gilbert, P N
Hall, R
Harriman, B P
Ireland, A P
Jacobs, S I
Jarvis, G J
Jeffery, J R
Knight, J
Lodge, J S H
Lovisetto, S G
McArdle, J M
McIntosh, S J
Marley, J L
Mate, J D
Mawson, A
Morrell, H B
Moxon, J W A
Mulley, G P
Murphy, P G
Norman, A T
O'Meara, M E
Palmer, W C
Pearlman, J A
Preece, J M
Rose, T
Roussounis, S H
Shucksmith, M R
Simpkins, K C
Smith, A
Staples, E J
Stocks, D A
Taylor, J M
Thom, M V
Wain, E A
Walker, A H
Woon, W H
Wynn, P

Weybridge
Abela Hyzler, P
Aylett, M R
Aylett, S E
Bahra, A
Barwell, J G
Bateman, S G
Blackman, J A
Boyle, A M
Brown, I E
Burgess, H K
Burns, A M E
Butler, M
Callow, C G
Cara, D M
Carr, R J
Cocker, D P
Comber, E
Crail, R B
Cusack, N M
Davidson, S M
Dawson, K J P
de Glanville, H
Denning, Z P
Desor, D

Dickson, D G
Dovell, T M
Drake, P H
Fozard, L A
Fraser, J M
Gargan, R E
Gilani, S S M
Glaser, L H
Green, A M
Green, B P
Grob, P R
Hadfield, R N
Hamilton, E M
Harvey, P R
Hinds, R M
Howard, J S
Hughes, J
Jakubowski, K A
Jenner, M W
Jones, B M
Krol, J E
Lawrence, L M
Lee, B T M
Lester, J R
Lewis, A F
Lilliott, M M
McLaren, R D
Marjot, D H
Marshall, J R
Menzies-Gow, L C
Moollan, O C
Moore, M R R
Myles, A B
Offord, G B
Oh, S Y A
Peachey, G R
Pemberton, A J
Plastow, S E
Prince, W T
Raymakers, K L M
Reddy, R
Ross, G I M
Russell, M H
Ryan, N P
Sacoor, M H A
Seiger, C P
Sharma, R
Sharpe, K E
Shefras, J
Sott, A H
Spalding, J A B
Staunton, N J
Stedman, A E
Suryavanshi, V S
Townsend, C R
Vandeberg, C R E
Vincent-Brown, A M B
Volikas, I
Vrionides, Y
Walker, C R
White, E A
Wilson, T A H

Weymouth
Baden Fuller, J J
Barrington, P C
Bendall, A
Bick, S A
Blease, D J
Blunt, A J
Bowditch, W B
Boyd, D C
Buckley, C C
Burgess, D K
Chapman, I
Cheung, S C-K
Chopra, S
Cooke, D L
Cox, J
Coyer, A B
Da Costa, I M V N
Davies, D M
Davies, F M
De Kretser, J
Devey, G F
Dickinson, A G W
Down, P F
Evans, D M
Fernandez, G N
Fowler, N H
Fullerton, A G
Ghazal, M A
Gibbins, P A
Goodman, S
Grogono, G R S
Grogono, K
Haine, G L
Hall, I R
Hancock, R E

Hendricks, M A
Hewett, P J
Hodder, S E
Houston, K C
Hull, P J
Hutchinson, W F
Killoch, M M
Kirkham, K V
Knight, W R
Laird, A J
Laird, G D
Laylee, A M
Llewellyn, H D
Lopez Longas, J F
McEleny, K R
McGregor, W L
McHugh, J G
Man, A
Mann, J H
McGregor-Wood,
P N P
Mitchell, P J
Naylor, K J
Orrell, J M
Orrell, M J
Page, N E
Parkinson, J C E
Porter, P
Pouncey, C M G
Priestley, C J F
Priestley, H S
Rankin, D C T
Roberts, A P
Robinson, G J
Savage, R A
Sengupta, B
Simpson, D S
Slater, D R
Smithson, E F
Stalley, N J
Stewart, J A
Stradling, A J
Talbot, S
Temple, A J
Thacker, C R
Thornton, A
Topp, D O
Townsend, J M
Townsend, M
Turberville Smith, R J
Turberville Smith, R J
Turner, A F
Wagner, M M F
Waldron, R W
Ward, A J
Ward, R D
Warrick, J W
Watson, M
Webb, K I
Wilkinson, R W
Woodall, N A
Wrighton, J D
Young, W H

Whitby
Baird, A M
Bateson, N G R
Bostock, F
Bradford, P
Brewin, P H
Campbell, G B B
Chadwick, W J
Cooper, L D
Croft, G
Cunion, D
Dacre, J A
Davies, W G
De Silva, P N
Emad, F
Fisher, C J
Franklin, R B
Harrison, M M
Holt, T A
Jackson, M
Johnson, P C
Lockstone, D R
McAuley, J J
McCormack, T
Metcalfe, P W
Mian, A H
Moore, N
Newman, R R
Nicol, N T
Pearce, R E
Record, M E
Riddolls, L E
Rippon, D
Smart, A L
Suckling, I G

Thomas, D H
Vasey, D
Ward, N
Ward, P M
Ward, P J
Ward, T A
Wheldon, G R
Williams, B P

Whitchurch, Cardiff
Macbeth, F R

Whitchurch, Hampshire
Boucher, A M G
Card, T R
Chalk, J G
Chalk, P A F
Croft, H D R
Cubbin, S A
Hobbs, J H
Johnson, M H
Styles, R J

Whitchurch, Shropshire
Aikman, A S
Barker, E
Brownlee, T J
Carter, G S E
Clayton, J S
Clayton, R
Flewett, W E
Giles, J P
Giles, S N
Hill, S N
McCarter, J D
Roberts, P J
Rogerson, J P G
Savage, A P
Senior, F L
Shaw, D
Short, W R
Snelling, J P
Teather, S J
Terry, R E
Thompson, R J
Vale, P T
Wilson, P F
Young, P F

Whitehaven
Al-Abdel Rahman,
A M A-N
Allan, S J
Bagshaw, S A
Battistessa, S A
Bober, M J
Bober, S A
Boyle, C E L
Brown, N J W
Burgess, G W S
Campbell, G L
Carter, P E
Christie, M C
Davies, K H
Dhebar, M I
Dickson, J M
Dickson, J G
Dixon, E M
Eldred, J M
Fayeye, M O
Forbat, L N
Godden, M J
Greiss, M E
Griffith, T P
Higgins, B T
Huntley, L S
Iranzo, J
Ironside, F C
Ironside, G J
Jayatilaka, M N D P
Juergens, M
Lamont, D A
Local, F K
McCrea, J D
McMillan, M P
Markandoo, P
Morley, G J E
Moss, B
Murillo, R M
Orugun, E O
Park, P W
Pearson, R H
Precious, S H
Richards, D G
Rocha Janeiro, M M
Rogers, D J
Rudman, J D
Russell, N J

Whitland

Sellar, P W
Sharp, A S
Smith, D
Southward, C G
Stafford, J
Stevenson, N J
Sullivan, S K
Sullivan, V J
Sydney, M A
Timney, A P
Tranter, R
Umar, A
Varghese, S
Verinder, D G R
Walker, M A
Watson, D M
Westhead, J N
Wignall, D C
Williams, M J
Zaheen, M

Whitland

Anthony, C J J D L
Griffiths, A E
Griffiths, I J
Jenkins, H C
Jenkins, R T D
McNeil, B D
Maguire, D M
Penn, G K

Whitley Bay

Barker, J S
Beaumont, D M
Black, D A
Bridgewater, R A M
Buchanan, K J
Burrell, C M
Carlile, A K
Carr, C M E
Carruthers, A
Cockburn, R A
Corbitt, N E
Coundon, H
Craxford, P A
Cresswell, S M
Crilley, P F
Critchlow, B W
Cross, K A
Dale, G
Danskin, M J
Del Estal Huertas, D M
Edirisooriya, A W
Emamy, H F
Falconer, I L
Ferriman, J H
Glaholm, J B
Glass, W J
Glennie, R
Gower, A
Heppell, P S J
Hildreth, K A
Hinds, P R
Huntley, S
Inglis, E
Ingram, A T
Iqbal, A K M
Jackson, A W
Jackson, R G
Joglekar, V M
Johns, G
Kilgour, H A
Lee, C J
Little, E
Lunn, J S
Lunn, T
McDaid, P
MacLennan, D J
McManners, A J
Mayes, D E
Meagher, J C
Mitchell, A P B
Mitchell, J E
Muir, I G
Murray, D
Murray, K S
O'Leary, V G
Oliphant, C J
Olsburgh, B
Piper, M P P
Rae, G
Reay, K A
Richardson, S A
Ridley, A E
Robson, C W
Ross, M J
Sabourn, P W
Sayers, S J
Sendall, K

Shahin, G
Simpson, I R
Srivastava, S P
Steadman, J R
Swann, K J
Taylor, J V
Tose, C B
Tose, J M
Walker, B F
Weatherstone, J M
Welfare, M R
Westgarth, S E
White, A E
White, J H
Wills, J C
Yates, D G

Whitstable

Bexon, A S
Birch, S M
Cuming, T
Hunt, P F
Jardine, M A
Johnson, L F
Kanagasooriam, G M H
Khin Thida, Dr
Lee, H D
Lupton, P M H T
MacDonald-Smith, K A
Macmillan, N C
Mahony, J D H
Mitchell, M P B
Mridha, E U
Pinnock, H J
Puckett, R
Ribchester, J M
Shar, M B
Stefani, T A
Turner, M E C
Turner, R J C
Wain, M L
Witney, R L

Whyteleafe

Collyer, G B
Davies, G R
Roberts, A
Tun, V

Wick

Burns, I J
Cheesman, B P
Cobb, E J
Datta, P K
Farquhar, I H
Finlayson, E A
Fraser, M E
Gordon, A F
Gunn, J
Haughey, F A
Inkster, T J
Johnston, I
Millard, E R
Mitchell, A F
Mowat, J
Pearson, M R
Robertson, P D
Shallcross, T M
Stanley, R A
Sutherland, J

Wickford

Acharyya, S
Agbaje, O A
Aldouri, E A S
Brown, A A
Brown, J C
Chandra Reddy, P
Fattah, S M A A
Fernando, M Y D
French, A H
Harriott, J C
Hepworth, C C
Hunt, M J
Laker, M K
McNamara, P J
Maynard, J R
Moore, T M C
Najim, H A
Persaud, J
Poskitt, M G
Prem, A G
Reddy, S
Richards, P
Seewoonarain, K S K
Stuart, H M
Tanna, S N
Wildin, H M
Yong, A A

Widnes

Biggs, C J
Boggiano, P
Breeden, J S
Brindle, M J
Clarke, H E
Collinson, J A
Crabbe, S A
Creely, S J
Derham, C J
Edwards, S J
Eswarappa, P R
Evans, P J
Fletcher, S N
Gibbons, M
Gyawali, P
Hallam, C P
Holmes, G P
Imison, C L
Jayaram, N
Kumar, S
Kumar, S
Lakshminarayana, M
McLaughlin, A G
McMaster, D S
Manning, D R P
Morris, T
Mottershead, J P
O'Neill, J H
Perritt, S J
Saleemi, M H
Schofield, C I
Simmons, D J
Smith, S
Stanley, B
Tandy, G G
Tierney, C J
Woodforde, C S J

Wigan

Agyeman, A
Ah-Weng, F
Ahuja, A S
Ahuja, R
Ahuja, S K
Alamin, M I
Allan, D J
Anderson, J E
Angior, P G
Arthur, N A
Ashcroft, G S
Ashworth, M R
Atherton, W
Azmi, A H
Baier, S H G
Bajkowski, A
Banerjee, D K
Basu, M K
Bate, C M
Bateman, A P
Benjamin, U B
Best, A G
Bezzina, C L
Bhalerao, V R
Bhavnani, M
Blower, A L
Bolton, J R
Bowyer, K M
Braben, P S
Brodie, D G
Browne, A O J
Burke-Williams, A I
Burke, J J
Burkinshaw, P R
Burnett, N T
Burza, N A
Carey, A S
Chadha, J C
Chambers, F
Chandler, C J
Chattopadhyay, C B
Chattopadhyay, H
Choudhury, R D
Clark, M D A
Clayton, C
Clayton, W M
Clift, D L
Coffey, J
Cooper, C D
Corkan, E J
Coxon, N R
Crook, H E S
Crook, J
Crossan, C B
Curless, E
D'Anfat, P F D
D'Souza, Y B
Dalal, A
Darvill, S P

Davies, J A
Dawson, J K
Dey, N C
Dhesi, I S
Dinnepati, S R
Dittman, R
Doherty, R
Donaldson, K
Donnelly, D
Duffy, M
Earnshaw, S M
El Gawly, R M T
Ellis, A J
Elton, P J
Eshiett, M U-A
Fairhurst-Winstanley, A J
Fairhurst, D A
Fallon, K J
Flatt, N W
Fraser, J M K
Fraser, J A
Frayne, J M
Gandhi, J D
Garner, J P
Ghalayini, M
Ghaly, R G
Ghosh, A K
Gill, K C
Girgis, M H
Godby, C
Gradwell, E
Graham, A R P
Graham, G E L
Graham, R C P
Grant, C A
Greenwood, A P
Grennan, D M
Hacking, N
Haigh, C A A
Hall, J S
Harborne, D J
Harland, R N L
Hart, S A
Hassan, C N
Hathwar, V
Heaton, S G
Herbert, J C
Herod, J J O
Higgins, S P
Hogan, R A J
Holme, A D L
Holme, C A
Holme, J D L
Hopcroft, P W
Hopcroft, R W
Howarth, A F
Howarth, R F B
Hughes, D A
Hughes, J R
Hyde, M T
Ibrahim, T S
Irizar Saborido, C
Ishaque, M
Jacks, R D
Jamdar, S
Jehan, R
Jingree, M
Johnson, D W
Johnson, F
Jones, I W
Jones, R J
Kalougin, A
Kapoor, P D
Kasasian, A H
Kelsall, R A
Khattab, B
Kirk, R S
Knowles, E W
Kofokotsios, A
Koppada, V R
Koussa, F F
Kreppel, P R
Lam, W K
Lane, A D
Ledson, T A
Lee, D
Lees, V T
Levine, H
Livingstone, B N
Lord, C P
Loudon, J R
Lowe, D B
McCarthy, J P
McCarthy, M D W
McCulloch, A B
McDermott, D C P
McDonnell, J G
MacFaul, J P

McGucken, R B
Mann, T J
Marcovic, L
Marples, J
Mars, J S
Marsh, D J
Martin, R H
Marwick, T P
Masterson, G R
Mather, C E
Mellor, S C
Mills, J S
Misra, S N
Moore, V J
Morris, P R
Mughal, S
Mukherjee, A
Mukherjee, S
Mulinga, J D
Mullen, D J
Munro, C J
Murgatroyd, P W
Murnan, A
Murphy, D
Mushahwar, S S S
Nagrani, P
Nandi, S R
Naqvi, N
Natha, S
Nayak, B N
Nsamba, C
O'Connell, I P M
O'Connor, R C
Ollerton, A
Owen, I G
Page, R S
Parr, M A
Patel, M K
Peach, I D
Peck, R M
Pendry, K
Pickersgill, A
Pinto, A L P
Pitalia, S K
Pollard, M
Poon, C L
Porter, M L
Pugh, M D
Queenborough, R
Ratchford, J A
Raut, V V
Ray, A C
Rayner, C A
Rodgers, P
Ross, K
Russell, B S
Rutter, J M
Sanghi, P K
Sathyan, N
Scholes, N E
Seabrook, J D
Seddon, T A
Shackleton, S E
Shaw, S J
Sheals, D G
Siddiqui, S V A
Sillitoe, K
Simpson, P
Sinclair, C M
Smart, S C
Smith, M C
Southern, P J
Speakman, A R
Spence, M T
Spencer, W H
Spittler, I
Stansfield, D A
Stewart, I
Stewart, J S S
Stretch, R F
Suntha, S
Sutton, A N
Sweeney, J N
Swinson, D R
Taylor, A M
Temperley, D E
Thomas, A L
Thomas, B E
Thompson, S W
Thomson, C
Thomson, R M
Thwaite, E L
Titoria, M
Trace, J P I
Trivedi, A D
Turnbull, A D
Twist, W A
Twomey, M J
Tymms, D J

Ugargol, C P
Unwin, H M
Valentine, D T
Van Spelde, J
Vasudeva Kamath, S
Vickers, J E
Wainwright, P A N
Wales, D A
Watson, D A S
Watson, S D
Watters, J
Welding, I J
White, D A
Whittington, M J
Wilson, L
Wolstenholme, R J
Wood, P L R
Wright, C R
Wroblewski, B M
Yashoda, P
Zzaman, K A

Wigston

Buck, P K
Dauncey, S M
Dayah, A R
Mannan, V
Morris, P N
Patel, H
Polak, G J A
Ravat, S
Sharp, A J H
Shaw, J F
Sutton, C D
Taylor, A K S

Wigton

Ajai-Ajagbe, E K O
Anderson, J
Bird, D W K
Brown, G W
Connell, M C
Cox, J
Cox, M I
Elderkin, F M
Elderkin, R A
Hewson, M J
Higgins, D A
Holdsworth, J D
Honeyman, J P
Howe, J L
Johnston, M B
Jones, S
Mackenzie, A G
Rankin, A M
Roderick, E M
Rolland, C F
Russell, C J
Scott, M
Shand, J E G
Spencer, P M
Swan, E A
Swindells, R F C
Townend, M
Turnbull, A T M
Ungar, A

Willenhall

Abdalla, S Z
Badh, C S
Harris, M L
Johal, S S
Lall, G S
Necati, G
Patel, R M
Pendlington, M
Platt, C L
Prasad, A K
Sahota, N S
Shah, A R
Shaw, M J
Shires, K M
Singh-Nijjer, B
Spurlock, C J
Turner, K J
Varkey, T A
Vasudevan Nair, D C
Yacoub, M G
Yusuf, S A J

Wilmslow

Ainsworth, J H
Aldington, S
Allsager, C M
Alun Roberts, G
Anthony, E W
Asbury, M J
Bedi, K S R
Bedi, M S V
Bell, V A

Windlesham

Beton, D C
Bird, J R
Bisset, R A L
Blenkinsopp, J
Boyd, A K
Bray, C L
Brennan, M
Brocklehurst, J C
Burmester, H B C
Caprio, L
Carne, P R
Carter, A C
Case, K M T
Chatterjee, P C
Chatterjee, S S
Chatterjee, T K
Choudhry, H K
Citron, I
Connell, P G
Cooke, S L
Cope, V
Cowan, R A
Cripps, D L
Dalton, G
Damani, Z B
Davies, E T L
Davies, R P
Doran, T N H
Earlam, C M
Feldman, G V
Ford, J M
Ford, R S
Forrester, C
Fouracres, M
Ghosh, A K
Gill, K S
Goodger, A R
Gordon, N S
Gorman, A P
Gregg, A C
Gregg, R C
Hague, J N
Haslam, R J
Hindusa, K
Hirst, P
Hore, I D B
Horton, C A
Huddart, J E
Hussain, Z
Hutchinson, T R
Ismail, A M
Jepsen, F
Johnson, C J
Johnson, R H
Johnston, H A
Jones, A D N
Jones, M H
Jones, S T M
Kettlewell, G
Khafagy, R S
Khafagy, R T
King, J M
Kingston, T P
Lam, A C W
Lane, A J
Lea, R A C
Levy, A H
Levy, L P
Lewis, S E
Longson, D
Longson, J
Luscombe, A H
Luscombe, A C M
McDonald, J P
Mamtora, H
Manning, G A K
Martin, R H
Maxwell, S R
Mecrow, I K
Moss, R M H
Murdoch, A E
Myers, A E
Nash, A F
Neal, B R
Newhouse, R E
Newton, M L
Norris, A J
O'Mahony, B J
O'Sullivan, K A
Patterson, E J
Pichel, A C
Powell, K Y
Price, D T
Ramsay, T M
Rawal, S B
Ring, N M
Rushton, A
Sanville, P R
Savage, H

Schiess, F A
Schuuring, J
Scott, G
Scott, M A
Scott, T S
Silverman, S R
Spencely, M
Stockley, W D
Struthers, J K
Sukumar, P
Titcombe, D H M
Tobias, L
Tooth, J A
Torry, M J W
Unwin, E F
Walker, A M
Walthew, R I
Wasson, C M A
Wasson, S J
Webster, A L
Weir, M W
Welchman, C L
Woo, B-C
Woolley, W

Wimborne
Adlington, P
Adlington, R J
Ahmed, M A
Aquilina, R J
Baldwin, H L
Barron, P J H
Batchelor, S E
Benazon, C M
Beresford, O D
Bradley, E J
Brown, D L
Brown, R C
Carter, P S
Chambers, N
Charleston, M T
Chippindale, P
Clarke, S V
Cooke, B J E
Cooke, J E
Craigmyle, D
Curtis, A R
Davidson, C M
Davies, R K
Dawson, A J
De Freitas, A J S
Deverell, M H
Dickins, P J N
Edwards, T J
Elder, A M
Ferguson, W J
Findlay, G
Francis, J R
Freeman, B S
Garrard, A C
Gee, A A
Gillett, M J
Greenway, N D
Griffin, B P
Guilmant, M V
Hargreaves, D M
Harrocks, D R
Hayden, A
Hirons, M N
Holt, M F
Horgan, J E M
Howard, T R G
Howard, W R G
Howell, D S
Howell, J S
Hutchinson, S E
Lake, R H
Lanham, P R W
Lawrence, S J
Lear, B L
Lee, D G
Leggett, J M
Leschen, A D
Lilley, C W
Linley-Adams, M J
McCall, C J
McDermott, M G
McKevitt, N L
Maiden, L P
Malpas, S M
Mead, B J
Merritt, R A
Moran, C J
Morgan, D F
Nicholas, A S
Nicholson, R G
O'Driscoll, H M C
Ottley, G B
Patten, M G

Pearson, N D
Pharaoh, A M
Pope, D C
Purandare, A S
Rampersad, D S J
Sanders, E M
Sankson, H
Scott, N C
Shakespeare, W M
Shuttleworth, G N
Slade, D E M
Smart, I A
Smyth, P R F
Stephens, J R D
Strauss, J P
Sutton, K H
Sutton, M A W
Swan, M J
Tan, J B L
Taylor, M S
Tulloch, J G
Walden, T A
White, J C
Williams, J P
Wilson-Croome, J W
Woollard, B P
Wright, N R

Wincanton
Elcomb, A M N
Farrant, C F
Fellows, M J
Fewster, H
Gribble, R J N
Hill, L E
Jones, R G
Phillips, I G
Robertson, G D
Sleap, A G

Winchelsea
Alexander, C A
Dewhirst, D
Doherty, W G
Homi, J
McFadyean, K M
McMullin, G P
O'Brien, J E M

Winchester
Abbott, D F
Adams, J P
Adamson, A S
Ahmad, B
Antoniou, A G
Arnold, R C
Ashcroft, M W
Ashcroft, P B
Ashken, J V
Aston, C E
Atchley, J T M
Baker, R A
Bavister, A E
Beasley, R W R
Beaumont, S
Bedford, J
Bell, S J
Benjamin, E
Blair, D G S
Bodington, J R
Bolwell, A G
Bonsall, A M
Bould, E-J
Boyle, D S
Brockway, B D J
Brooke, D J
Brooks, A P
Buchanan, N M M
Buckingham, M S
Buckland, J R
Buckland, R W
Bullock, R G
Burkett, J A
Burlinson, R A
Burrows, F D C
Burrows, J
Burton, P J
Bush, H M
Button, R I
Calogeras, A
Cattermole, G N
Chan-Pensley, E
Chapman, C M
Chapman, S P
Chawner, J M
Cheetham, J E
Coates, D A
Coleman, M G
Conway, M M
Conway, N

Cooke, J T
Corkill, R A
Corlett, R J
Cotton, T G
Cox, N L
Craggs, D A
Crawford, A D
Curson, J A
D'Alfonso, A A L
Davies, J C
Davies, K J
Davies, S L
Davis, A V H
Dawson, J
Deacock, S J C
Dewbury, C E
Diaper, M D
Dickson, F G
Dreaper, R E
Dryden, M S
Du Boulay, P M H
Eddy, T
Edelsten, M A
Elford, J
Ellis, J S
England, P G
Erasmus, T
Evans, M R W
Fairris, G M
Farley, D L B
Faulk, M
Fayers, K E
Firebrace, D A J
Fitzgerald-Barron, A W J
Flower, N G
Fon, P J
Foote, K D
Forsdick, D H
Forster, I D
Foster, B J
Fowler, J L
Fowler, K M A
Fox, H J
Gabb, R J E
Gaffikin, P G M
Gartell, P C
Gavourin, B A
Goldsmith, A L
Gordon, H M
Grant, L J
Grant, S J
Gray, J M
Green, B
Grummitt, C C
Guerrier, T H
Guest, M G
Hall, V L
Hammond, G T
Hanna, H M
Harbott, E J
Harris, N J
Harrison, E M
Harrison, G S M
Haysom, A H
Heard, M J
Hemsley, Z M
Henderson, F H M
Hesketh, K T
Hettiaratchy, P D J
Honeybul, S
Hook, W E
Horn, D N
Howells, C J
Hume-Smith, H V
Hunt, B J
Jaffray, F K
James, C M
Jenkins, C W
Jessop, E G
Jones, D H
Kay, E M
Kelly, J E
Keough, A D
Kerkhoff, R V
Khan-Lim, D H
Khan, H H
King, A W
Kingswell, R S
Klein, D
Knight, H M L
Kurukulaaratchy, R J
Laidlow, J M
Lake, J L
Lale, A M
Lambert, M G B
Lane, R H S
Lee, P J
Lees, B L

Lees, S J
Lewis, A
Lippiett, P V
Lipscomb, N C
Lock, D J
Longworth-Krafft, C V
Longworth-Krafft, G
Loughran, J
McColl, A J
MacDonald, G
McGill, D A F
McGrand, J C
McKee, W J E
McLean, J
Macleod, J D A
MacLeod, M C
MacManus, N L M
Mainwaring, C J M J
Mann, K S
Marquis, A M M
Marsh, D F
Melville, J E M
Michell, R C
Micklem, J N
Miles, A J G
Mitchell, M C
Moore, M E
Moore, M G
Morgan, A T
Morgan, J
Morgan, K
Morley, G E
Morris, K E A
Morton, J R C
Mousley, J S
Mulcock, H
Myers, J H
Nancekievill, M L
Neal, A J D
Nicholson, S M
Nicpon, K J
Norman, L K V
Normand, I C S
Norton, R N
Nott, P N
O'Sullivan, J L
Olliver, M E
Owen, D K
Padgham, M R J C
Page, A C
Paget, T D
Papastathis, D
Paramanathan, N
Parmar, J S
Parmar, M C
Paterson, J A
Pathmadeva, C
Pathmadeva, T W
Patton, W J
Pearson, S
Pell, J B
Percival, I M
Percival, R E
Peyser, P M
Pillow, J R
Plant, I D
Powell-Jackson, J D
Powell-Jackson, M A
Radcliffe, M J
Rains, A J H
Rainsbury, R M
Rall, M H
Read, J A P
Redpath, T H
Roberts, J A
Roberts, J M
Roberts, K E
Rose, J W P
Rowe, K A
Rowland, R G
Ryall, R D H
Ryall, R E
Saffer, G
Samuel, A W
Samuel, M
Sanderson, H F
Saunders, W A
Seeley, C
Selman, J C
Shackleton Bailey, J
Shirley, A D
Shuttleworth, B J
Sinclair, J M A
Slack, M H
Slack, S E
Sladden, R A
Slapak, G I
Slapak, M
Smith-Petersen, V

Smith, D A
Smith, F R
Smith, G I
Smith, H R
Smith, J A E
Smith, L C
Snell, C
Soekarjo, D D
Sparke, P B
Spencer-Silver, P H
Spice, C L
Stannard, T J
Stevens, L C
Steventon, N B
Stewart, A J
Stewart, K O
Stewart, R I
Strange, J W N
Summerfield, R J
Sylvester, N C
Taylor, J
Templeton, L K
Theaker, J M
Thomas, M F
Thomason, A J S
Thompson, J A
Thomson, D J
Thornton, J A
Toff, N J
Tomlinson, J M
Toone, P C
Twist, J R
Van Eyk, J J
Voisey, S C
Watkinson, D J
Watson, B
Watt, P A
Watt, P J
Watts, J A
Weir, J S L
Wethered, O J C
Wheeler, T
White, D
White, L A
White, W D
Wills, D R
Wills, F A
Wilson, A S
Wilson, N M
Woodcock, K R
Woolveridge, A P
Wright, H G
Wright, N
Wright, N J
Yates, S H
Yule, A J

Windermere
Ainley-Walker, J C S
Brockbank, J K
Buchan, A R
Burns, P
Clarke, G M
Cochrane, J H
Edmondson-Jones, G F E
Fogg, M R
Glancy, T T
Gulliford, P
Hawson, J P
Holt, B L
Hynes, J M
Kerr, D G
McGregor, I G
Neville, R C
Oakden, E W R
Pearson, B C
Pearson, P
Pollard, I I
Sloss, J D G G
Smith, A W
Swan, M
Watson, S M
White, G P
Williams, E C
Winter-Barker, J P

Windlesham
Armstrong, K A
Beuzen, J-N
Buxton, F A M
Donnan, F S
Garnett, T J
Handley, S M
Hatty, S R
Hurren, J S
Janes, J M
Keohane, P P
Lim, S M C

Windsor

Lledo Macau, A
Roberts, E W
Simmons, V E
Taylor, J G
Walmsley, A M

Windsor

Atkins, M
Bacon, D H
Barnes, K H
Barrett, G S
Barua, B K
Beatty, R M
Bellon, J S
Beresford, T P
Bradley, R C P
Briscoe, J H D
Brudney, J K
Burn, A J
Butcher, C B
Cheema, S
Cheongvee, E S L
Chukwuemeka, S O
Crossley, R A
Culling, S D
Denny, M R L
Denny, M F
Duncan, D
Eliades, A-M
Evans, D E
Evans, D M
Felstead, M
Fromet De Rosnay, E L P
Gibbings, C R
Goulds, R K
Hales, D A
Hameed, R S A
Harris, D E
Harris, J G
Harvey-Hills, N
Hawk, J L M
Hill, C A
Holliday, J J C
Hope, K M
Horan, S
Houlberg, K A N
Hoy, G A
Hughes, J H
Hussain, S A
Inward, J M
Johnstone, N C
Jones, D R M
Jones, J R
Jordan, L C
Kheterpal, S
Kinnear, F C
Lewis, E S
Lewis, G M
Lewis, M J
Lewis, S I
Liyanage, I S
Liyanage, S P
Lloyd-Broadhurst, A
Luck, R J
Lund, J
McAllister, J A
Macaulay, A J
Mackenzie, J W
Mackie, P H
Maddocks, P D
McKiernan-Krieg, W S
Mills, A P G
Moloney, S J
Morrish, L W
Mower, I M
Mower, M T C
O'Kane, C A J
Packard, R B S
Patterson, J V M
Philpot, J
Pierce, G F M
Power, R J
Rajagopal, R V
Rao, S K
Reed, P I
Roberts, A
Robertshaw, C J
Roddy, R J
Roles, W
Saad, M N
Sawhney, S
Scott, R D M
Sheppard, R G
Shin, C Y-M
Smart, R G
Smith-Walker, M T
Smith, T A
Song, F M

Stewart, D
Stone, J P W
Stoppard, M
Swann, M
Thomas, D K M
Thomas, M
Tillott, R C
Trickey, N R A
Unwin, A J
Van Der Meulen, J J N M
Wallace, M
Walsh, J K
Walter, K H
Wellington, C M
Welsh, R R
Wiggins, G H
Wilkins, A J
Williams, S A

Wingate

Fairlamb, C P
Morle, I J F
Simpson, A M
Sinha, P
Timol, S A
Van Buuren, C M D

Winkleigh

Evans, C P A
Hynes, B

Winscombe

Banister, E H A
Crick, A M A
Crick, M J
Da Cunha, J
Hasham, S
Jackson, J C
John, D H
Laband, J R
Newton, J C
Peebles Brown, D A R
Roberts, J H
Roberts, P H
Ruddell, K B L
Shouls, J C
Smith, I M A
Telford, S B

Winsford

Achurch, S M
Bratt, H J
Fallon, M P M
Gilmour, J E
Green, J H
Hyder, S
Kelly, P D
Llewelyn, J M
Loke, E S I
Mozumdar, S K
Norgate, I F T
Price, J-A
Rasaiah, S
Roy, S K
Shuaib, M
Smith, C G
Talukder, R
Thomas, N R

Wirral

Abbott, G T
Abdulla, U
Agbamu, D A
Agrawal, G S
Ahmed, W
Airey, C L
Aitken, J A
Alawattegama, H D B
Alderman, B
Alderson, M L
Ali, A
Alman, R J
Annis, D
Anthony, K L
Argument, W R
Arroyo Vivar, M A
Ashton, P C B
Atherton, A M J
Atherton, J
Avery, M J
Azurdia, C M
Babla, H J
Ball, A R
Banks, D S
Bansal, O P
Barnard, P D
Barrett, J A
Baruah, A K
Bates, J W

Berstock, D A
Bhati, R
Bibby, J
Bird, H C
Bishop, P R
Bishop, R Y
Blacklin, J
Blair, S D
Blyth, R A
Booth, F J
Booth, J L
Bousfield, P F
Bousfield, S K
Boyd, A H
Brace, J V
Breckenridge, R A
Breen, E M J
Brennan, S M
Brewis, J E
Bricker, S R W
Briggs, J S H
Broadbelt, R P
Brock, J E S
Brown, A G
Bryson, T H L
Burgess, M B
Bush, G H
Bush, K J
Bussey, T J
Byrne, A E
Calderbank, S J
Calow, S A
Campbell, I R
Campbell, M H
Camphor, I A
Carroll, N
Carter, A J
Carter, P B
Causer, J P
Cervetto, P
Chadwick, C
Chadwick, M A
Chalmers, W D
Chambers, J J
Chapman, R J
Charlwood, C A
Cheater, L S
Chesters, S A
Chong, W C C
Clark, A H
Clark, C
Clark, J H
Clark, P I
Clarke, E T
Clarke, S P
Clearkin, L G
Clemenson, C J
Comer, D J
Conway, M
Copeland, J R M
Coppock, P J
Cottier, B
Cowie, F A
Cowper, S G
Coy, A A C
Crosbie, R B
Crosthwaite, O S
Currie, P
Cuthbertson, D J R
Cuthbertson, F M
Cuthbertson, P J R
D'Souza, S P
Dalby, J E
Dalby, M D
Darroch, C J
Darwish, D H
Dasgupta, R K
Davidson, A S
Davies, C S
Davies, J B M
Davies, J M
Davies, S J C
Davis, P R
Dawson, J
Deeble, T J
Deeks, A J
Delaney, H L
Delaney, J C
Dennis, M W
Devlin, J C
Dixon, L A
Dixon, R X
Dolan, S-A
Donnachie, N J
Dorr, A
Downs, H E
Downward, D C
Doyle, P M
Drummond, M H

Drury, J H
Duckworth, M J
Dufton, P A
Dunham, W R
Eastwood, D
Edwards, G M
Edwards, K E
Edwards, K B
Edwardson, K F
El Boghdadly, S A E-K M
Elhibir, E I
Elkington, J S
Elliott, R J
Ellis, A M
England, A G
Enion, D S
Entwistle, I R
Errington, R D
Evans, J C
Evans, M E
Evered, C J
Eyes, B E
Fahy, L T
Fegan, K J
Fletcher, M E
Foggin, W K
Fordham, M V P
Foster, V J
Francis, C Y
Francis, G G
Gannon, J P
Garrett, A M G
Garrett, M
Garrett, M J
Gault, B
Gault, W
Geary, N P J
Gibbs, T J
Gidlow, D A
Gillett, M B
Godfrey, H W
Gokhale, G
Gollins, W J F
Goonesinghe, N S
Grant, K A
Gray, G A
Greaney, M G
Green, A R T
Green, J M
Green, J A
Green, M S
Green, P N
Green, R M
Griffith, C J
Griffith, E B
Guratsky, B P
Haggett, M J
Hamilton, D I
Hamilton, S E
Hanson, H P
Harding, J A
Hardman, G
Hargreaves, S J
Harkins, F
Harrison, J C
Harty, S M
Harvey, R A
Hawe, B J
Hawthornthwaite, E M
Hayes, J C
Hayes, M G
Hayhurst, V
Hazlett, J J
Healy, A P
Healy, C
Heaton, A J
Henderson, A J
Hendrickse, R G
Hennessy, T D
Ho, K W K
Holmes, J J
Holt, E M
Honey, A
Howard, C
Hughes, A P
Hughes, H J
Hughes, J M
Hughes, J D
Hulme, G
Hulme, I S
Hunter, J M
Husband, D J
Hussain, A
Hutchinson, S
Jackson, E J
Jackson, S R
Jackson, S P
Jacobs, E F

Janikiewicz, S M J S
Jayaraman, S
Jefferies, G
Jip, H
Johnson, J W
Johnson, M A
Johnson, R
Johnson, T B W
Johnston, A R
Johnstone, R G
Jones, C M
Jones, D H
Jones, I R
Jones, P O
Jones, R H
Jones, S K
Joynson, C P
Katchburian, M V
Kaye, J C
Keating, R J
Keetarut, S
Kennedy, T D
Kenny, S E
Kerr, A J
Kershaw, D
Khalil, H R
Kidd, G M
Kidd, S A
Kidman, P A
Killeen, D M
King, D
King, S L
Kingston, S P
Klenka, L H
Klenka, Z R
Konig, P C W C
Kutarski, P W
Lacy, A M
Lacy, D E
Lancaster, J L
Lane, C J
Lang, D M
Lannigan, B G
Larkin, P S
Lawrence, D S
Lecky, J M F
Leigh, T J
Leith, S E
Lenfestey, P M
Levycky, H M
Lindop, R
Lipton, M E
Little, A D
Littler, J A H
Littler, T R
Lorains, J W
Lynes, J
McAfee, L A
McAlavey, A J
McCrone, J W
McGee, A M
McGuinness, A J
McIlroy, B S
McKay, J P
McKenzie, A
Mackenzie, C P
McLachlan, H A
Macleod, A J
Macleod, M
McMahon, S M
MacPherson, J J D
McWatt, P J
McWilliams, M J
McWilliams, R G
Madden, M P
Maddock, R A
Magennis, J
Maguire, J
Mahai, A P K
Mahmood, R H
Makin, C A
Malcolm, M T
Mamman, I
Manning, D J
Marrow, J
Marshall, E
Marshall, M A
Martin Hierro, M E
Martin, F E
Matheson, N R
Mawby, N E
Maxwell, M J
Meachim, G
Meachim, R M
Meakin, K A
Meara, R J
Meecham, J
Mellors, A S
Melville, J A

Menon, P K
Merrin, D H
Middlefell, R
Miles, J B
Moloney, A
Moody, D R
Moore, J K
Morris, A D
Morris, D R
Mullin, N H
Murray, A
Murray, A E
Murray, R
Mutch, O R
Neame, K D
Neil, T
Neithercut, W D
Newbury, A L
Nicholas, K S
Nimmo, J P
Noglik, A M
O'Connor, J
O'Hagan, J E
O'Hanlon, D P
O'Neill, M R
O'Reilly, S M M
Oates, J G
Ohiorenoya, B
Ojeda De La Pena, A
Oliver, K
Omari, A A A
Owen, J M
Owens, J L
Oxtoby, A E
Painter, D J
Palmer, M A
Parkinson, R W
Parr, N J
Parry, C R
Parry, D G
Partridge, T M
Paterson, E J
Patrick, D A
Patwala, D Y
Pereira, A A L
Perkins, J A
Phillips, R P
Phipps, M R
Pickin, R B
Pickles, R L
Pierce, A M
Pigott, S J
Pilling, D W
Pillow, S J
Playfer, J R
Pleasance, C M
Porteous, M A
Porter, G C
Potter, F A
Powell, A P
Prashara, K G
Price, A R
Price, D J
Pritchard-Howarth, M R
Prozesky, D R
Pugh, W V N
Quest, L J
Rae, J L
Rafiq, S
Ramdenee, R
Rao, A M
Raraty, C C
Raraty, M G T
Rawal, P
Rawlinson, J K M
Raymond, C J
Razzak, F A
Redmond, E J
Reid, A G
Reilly, D T
Remberg, D C
Reuben, S F
Reynolds, J J
Rhodes, E G H
Rich, P N
Richmond, E E
Richmond, I M
Richmond, M S
Rigby, J G
Roach, S M
Roberton, P A
Roberts, E
Roberts, G S
Roberts, J R
Robertson, S H
Robin, N M
Robinson, J S
Robinson, L Q

Robson, P W
Rodrigues, S M
Roe, D M
Rogerson, K A
Romaniuk, C S
Routh, C P
Rowlands, D J
Ruddy, J P
Rule, E M
Russell, J
Ryan, C R
Ryan, K E
Ryan, S W
Ryan, T D R
Sagar, A
Sagar, S
Sangster, G
Sansom, C D
Scarrow, G D
Scott, A K
Setna, F J
Sewell, E M
Shafiq, A E
Shah, N
Sharma, V
Sharples, R H
Shaw, N J
Sherman, I W
Shiralkar, V M
Sida, E C
Silas, J H
Simison, A J M
Singh, G
Singh, K
Sivasambu, K
Slater, A J
Slavin, J P
Sloka, R A
Smethurst, M E
Smith, A B
Smith, C P
Smith, C S
Smith, D B
Smith, D N
Smith, D A
Smith, M W
Snowden, A E A
Sowden, H
Spencer, B B
Sprigge, J S
Stairmand, R A
Steere, C E
Stevens, R W
Stewart, A B
Stillman, R H
Stokoe, D
Stokoe, D J
Sutherst, J R
Sweeney, E
Syndikus, I M
Tansey, D J
Tansley, A P
Tappin, J A
Tart, T J
Taylor, J C
Thaker, D
Thomas, P C
Thomas, T G
Thompson, J A R
Thompson, S K
Thomson, A J M
Thorp, N J M L
Timmins, D J
Timms, M A J
Todd, P J
Tomlinson, A P
Tomlinson, S D
Townsend, C J
Tracy, H J
Turnbull, C J
Usborne, C M
Vine, D J
Violaris, N S
Wade, R H
Wakely, J H
Waller, D P E
Walsh, C J
Walshaw, M J
Walton, H A S
Warren, V J
Watkins, L M
Watt, F J
Watts, M T
Wauchob, D W
Weaver, A
Weaver, H
Welch, C R
Wells, S M
Welsh, S H

Weston, N C
Where, J L
White, D W
White, P J
White, P C
White, S I
Whiteside, M W
Whitfield, A M
Whitfield, M J
Wight, J A
Wiles, J R
Wilkins, H M
Wilkinson, C E
Wilkinson, H C
Wilkinson, P W
Williams, I A
Williams, P S
Williams, R D
Williams, S H
Williamson, M E R
Williamson, V C
Winston, M P
Winston, S R
Wong, S H D
Wood, J G
Woodcock, B M
Woollons, M J
Wort, S J
Wright, A R
Wright, J E M
Wright, J A
Wright, P K
Wynne, S P M
Young, D J
Zakhour, H

Wisbech

Al-Bitar, M Z
Andrew, C I
Blundell, A C
Chandler, A
Clark, L
Clarke, E J
Doran, K M
Earle, R C
Elliott, E M
Ferriday, C E R
Fester, J S
Forster, D B
Grant, L A
Greer, A W
Hall-Smith, A M
Hall-Smith, H A
Hatcher, G A
Hattersley, D A
Hornett, J
Hudson, B
Karunaratne, W M
Kennedy, G L
Khetani, B N J
Kirkpatrick, C M R
Lees, J M
Lines, J
Mason, I H
Millard, S P
Moffat, G M
Neary, J M
Nelson, S E
Patel, N R
Pryer, M P L
Richardson, M J
Rosier, N C I
Rushmer, C A
Shippey, B J
Somerville, E T
Walker, M P
Webb, R T
Williams, N C
Williams, P R
Wong, Q K K
Wood, C J M

Wishaw

Al-Kureishi, T
Allan, T L
Allen, I C
Begg, L
Clark, C M
Clark, F C E
Connelly, A
Cooper, L A H
Dear, N P M
Dobbie, S
Eatock, C R
Gibb, D B
Helenglass, G
Hotchkiss, C M
Kennedy, J H
Kolhatkar, R K

Lannigan, A K
Lees, C M
Lennox, C E
Logan, A R
Logan, J R
McClung, A R
McCoach, A
McConnell, S M
McCrum, D
Macfarlane, J A
McGuire, L C
McKay, J
McKay, K E H
Macpherson, B C M
MacSween, W A
Majumdar, A A W
Mann, B S
Martin, I C D
Miller, K M
Murphy, E A
Murphy, J W
Naismith, J H
O'Dowd, J J M
Ofili, E A
Parker, I
Paterson, C C C
Reddy, S S
Reid, D B
Reynolds, M F
Stewart, D W
Thom, W R
Thomson, J B
Walsh, J M
Westbrook, F
Wilson, T K

Witham

Ahmed, B S
Baqai, A
Baqai, M A
Beatty, D E
Bridgman, G C
Broadhurst, B W
Carroll, G D
Clarkson Webb, W D
Cohen, R C
Courtman, S P
Craig, I D
Crane, T P
Dattner, R
Davies, D F
Dekker, B J
Fernando, M L P
Flatley, M E
Foster, W
Francis, J K
Gough, B R
Grew, R C
Hawkins, R M
Hopcroft, J P
Hore, A T
Irwin, D J
Karki, C B
Krishnamurthy, K
Krishnamurthy, M R
Kugan, G
Kugan, G
Millership, S E
Murtaza, L N
Netscher, M M
Parry-Jones, N O
Phillips, P K
Shirodaria, C C
Shroff, R
Sizer, B F
Summers, R T
Teverson, E
Wright, C J

Withernsea

Fouracre, A J
Fouracre, R D
French, R S
Heaton, G D
Herbert, P E
Khoury, F

Witney

Ali, A N
Bacon, N C M
Baker, F A
Brylewski, S
Caddick, A N
Chakraverty, R K
Chalmers, C A
Chapman, K
Cruickshank, R J
Davies, J M
Derry, J L
Diacon, M J

Douglas, A
Evans, H W
Grainger, L
Green, B G
Grimwade, P R
Hacking, P M
Hale, D J
Hallett, S
Haslam, L
Herries, J W
Hickman, T M
Jackson, P C
James, M D
Jarvis, J R
Jones, R J
Kay, P G
Kent, R S M
Lawrence, M A
Lole-Harris, C A
Mackenzie, I D
Manning, C J
Maxwell, J M
Morris, C E
Muir, J M
Naidoo, N K
Nelson, G L
Noble, M B
Pearson, J M H
Peterson, D J M
Prosser, P D
Simpson, J R
Sinclair, D I
Sinclair, G W
Smith, S M V
Spence, J R
Stanger, M J
Stephens, A R
Stephens, C A
Stephenson, P B O
Theodorou, S
Thorley, R A
Walton, S E
Watson, P A

Woking

Ambler, L C
Ambrose, G C
Anders, C J
Andrews, G
Armstrong, L J
Atkins, M C
Ayers, A B
Aziz, K A
Aziz, W A
Baker, A W
Barker, N J
Bates, P C
Baughan, C A
Bayley, K L
Beilby, J O W
Bingham, E M
Bird, M M
Bishop, Y M
Blakey, L
Booth, S
Bourke, J J
Bourke, M J
Braithwaite, D W
Branagan, G W
Brockway, C M
Brown, P A
Buchanan, R M
Cameron, E G M
Cane, C E
Carmichael, A R
Chan, S W
Chisholm, E M
Christopherson, T A P
Clark, G R
Clarke, V A
Cleary, C V
Close, A R
Close, L P
Coe, S M
Collins, T M
Collins, Y D
Collister, R M
Condon, R W
Coope, A M
Cruickshank, G W
Cummin, A L
Cummin, O J
Cummin, P J C
Dainow, I I
Darroch, R C
Davies, G
Davies, M P N
Dawkins, J L
De Courcy, S A

Deans, A C
Dear, N J
Dennison, M G
Edmunds, C J
Espitalier-Noel, P J F
Essa, N I S
Evans, B T
Evans, R P
Eyton, S M A
Foote, J A J
Freeman, H G M
Garrett Ryan, F J
Gillham, A B
Glover, J M
Greig, A P M
Grieve, N W T
Grove, C E
Guilder, T F
Ha'Eri Zadeh, H
Hadfield, G
Halepota, M A
Halfhide, A W
Hall, A M
Handa, P
Handousah, S M E
Harding, T M
Harris, A J
Harris, K P
Harwood, A G
Hendry, A E
Hennell, P A
Hindley, D J
Holdstock, D J
Howitt Wilson, M B
Imrie, M M
Johnson, D
Jones, A F
Kelly, C A
Khan, N H Z
Kirthisingha, V A
Knights, H D
Kruchek, D G L
Kuzmin, P J
Lance, N S
Lander, R M
Lawrence, R S
Leach, J R
Leno, S M
Lewis, S E
Lieberman, S
Lindsay, T M C
Lock, K J
Lyle, N J
Lynn, W A
Lytton, G J
McIntosh, S L
McLaughlin, W J
Manners, B T B
Margary, J J
Medd, W E
Mellor, J P
Michelmore, S K
Miller, H B
Miller, J A
Mirza, M R
Morgan, J A
Morgan, J
Morley, N J
Munro, F M E
Nelson, A M
Newbold, S M
Newman, H
Norris, J F
Norris, P R
O'Neill, A-M
O'Neill, V M
Ogden, A B
Oliver, J S
Packe, R I
Panhwar, G-M
Pankhania, B
Parkinson, E L
Parrott, W F
Parveen, S S
Perera, D D T
Pool, R J
Pool, R D
Popham, C M
Prior, T
Ratcliffe, N A
Rauf, K G
Riddle, A F
Roberts, L C
Rogers, B A
Rooney, B A
Rudman, T J
Rumball, B J
Saunders, M I
Scott, J A G

Wokingham

Sellars, N H L
Sellick, B C
Sheikh, A
Shiel, D A
Shotton, M E
Simonis, R B
Slatter, E
Smith, P J R
South, J
Spencer, T S
Sreedaran, E
Steele, K
Sutcliffe, G E
Sweeney, T K
Tappin, A R
Tappin, M J
Tennant, F D
Thomas, D H V
Thompson, J M
Thompson, N J
Tofte, B C
Unwin, T A E
Walker, M C
Wall, A R J
Walsh, M
Ward, P
Warren, N R
Waycott, J A
Wilson Jones, A C R
Wilson Jones, N A H J
Wong, A S-Q
Wright, T G
Yew, B F L
Young, J J
Yusuf, I A
Zaki, M

Wokingham

Allsopp, M R
Arnold, S M
Ball, G V
Barnes, J E
Beard, G A
Beer, P A
Beral, D L
Bhasin, R
Black, A J M
Black, J E B
Brett, D D
Butler, K
Callander, N
Carter, K T
Coghlan, H D
Cooper, C A
Corfield, M H
Cotton, G D
Darlison, M T
Day, A H
Dodd, H S
Doran, J R
Drake-Lee, J W D
Dunnet, S C
Edwards, R C
Emmerson, R W
Evans, R J
Evans, S D
Ferguson, D J
Firth, R A
Gallagher, C J
Goodwin, L G
Goodwin, M D
Griffith, S
Grove, M A
Guyer, B M
Hadfield, G W
Hadfield, K A M
Haslam, M B
Helm, S M
Herman, M J G
Hession, P T
Houghton, D C
Houghton, V P
Hutchison, J B
Kerr, J D
Kitson, G E
Latham, R A
Lee, M C
McAleer, G W
McCall, P D
MacDougall, M E
Maguire, T M
Merrick, H P
Miller, A
Mitra Thakur, G G
Moreno Beteta, A
Morgan, J L
Morton, N B M
Moudiotis, C R
Murphy, A L

Wolverhampton

O'Donnell, C A-M
O'Donnell, D R
Reakes, R E M
Reed, N L
Richards Affonso, N
Ross, P S
Saba, H P
Smith, K G
Sowter, E M
Stangroom, C D
Stewart, A
Thompson, F J
Walker, A
Ward, M L
Wardill, L F
Weeks, N J
Weir, K A J
Williams, M P
Win Hlaing, Dr
Zaheer, S A

Wolverhampton

Adeghe, A J-H
Agrawal, L
Agrawal, S
Agrawal, S R
Aiton-MacBean, D R
Alapont Perez, E
Alexander, J
Allan, E R
Anand, S
Anderson, J M
Anees, N N
Annesley-Williams, D J
Asthana, K
Axon, E J
Babiker, S K
Babu Manohar, M
Bagary, D S
Balaggan, K S
Ball, E S
Barnes, P
Barry, K J
Bastin, M W
Bentley, J M
Bhatia, M M
Bhattacharyya, D P
Bhikha, A
Bienvliet, F P
Bilas, R
Bishop, D G
Black, T J
Blayney, M R
Bose, R K
Bould, M
Bowers, K E J
Bradley, J
Bright, J J
Browning, A J F
Bryan, L H
Bulmer, J H
Bulmer, N J
Burrell, J T
Bush, D M
Canney, J C
Catchpole, C R
Chahal, M S
Chapman, H R
Chohan, M M
Cleeland, J A
Clews, J W
Cockburn, T R
Collins, M A
Cooper, J P
Cooper, M A
Coppolo, M
Corridan, P G J
Corston, R N
Coward, J I G
Cox, C W F M
Creed, T J
Crome, I B
Cross, T J S
Crossley, D R
Crossley, T M
Croudace, J
Cullen, R J
Curran, F T
Currie, S J
D'Costa, D F
Dallal, H J
Darrah, R A
Das Gupta, A
Davies, A
Davies, J E
Davies, M
Dawes, K R
De Rosa, D
De Vivo, L

Deacon, C S
Derso, A
Dexter, E L S
Dey, B N
Dhillon, G S
Dhingra, H S
Diba, V C
Dison, P J
Dix, M R
Dixey, S J
Djati, N
Dobie, D A
Dobie, D K
Domar, A
Dudley, D R
Dukes, A F
Duncan, P J
Dunn, S M
Elcock, M
Evans, D W
Fairlamb, C A W
Fairlamb, D J
Fan, V T W
Fenner, S G
Fletcher, A M
Forrest, G A
Foster, C J
Fotherby, K J
Foulkes, S J
Fowler, J M
Fowler, W
Freeth, M G
Fuggle, W J
Gama, R M
Gardecki, T I M
Ghosh, A
Gill, A S
Glover, H F B
Gnanasegaram, D
Gnanethiran, S
Gogna, S C
Goldie, A M
Gompertz, S M
Gonzalez, E
Goodyear, G M
Gorzenski, M B
Graff, D J C
Grandhi, V
Green, D I
Green, J P
Gregan, A C M
Grew, N R
Grewal, B S
Griffiths, J J
Grinsted, R
Grosvenor, L J
Guest, E H
Gurney, J
Hackett, K
Hadley, C R
Halepota, A A
Hall-Matthews, P N
Hall, H N
Hamad, H A
Handa, S I
Handley, A F
Harrison, A R
Harrison, R J
Hartill, S A
Hassan, H M J
Hearth, M W
Henly, J G
Hester, N W S
Hibbs, H M
Hickman, P
Higgins, J C
Hitchings, G M
Hogg, R A
Hollands, R A
Hommers, C E
Hooper, C R B
Horne, M
Horsley, F
Horton, R C
Houston, J F
Howl, E M C
Hudson, W A
Hughes, H V
Hughes, R C
Hutchison, J T
Ilyas, N
Ingham, M
Inglis, J A
Isbister, E S
Jack, M E
Jackson, M A
Jackson, T N
Jarrams, J W P
Jeewa, M A I

Jenkins, R
Johnson, A
Jolley, D J
Jones, D R
Jones, F C
Jones, K
Jones, L
Jones, P N
Joshi, V S
Joy, H A
Juka, S K
Kainth, M S
Kalra, D S
Kanodia, S K
Kapadia, S A
Kassim, Z
Kaur, H R
Keane, K
Kelleher, H C
Kelly, A D
Kemsley, S
Kew, J M D
Khan, A H
Khan, M I
King, E T
Kissun, D
Konu, G K
Krishan, K S
Kumaratane, B
Lambah, I R
Lantos, H W G
Larkin, E B
Larkin, J M
Lee, E F-Y
Leung, H H
Lewis, M L
Linnemann, M P
Luis, J L C
MacCarthy, B
McCarthy, S W
McCreadie, D W J
Macdonald, D R
McKenzie, J
McLaren, R
McNamee, G G
Mahay, G R
Maidment, P R
Maji, S
Manley, M E P
Mann, J S
Manohar, S
Mantle, M
Marczak, J B
Marker, H R
Martin, J M
Maung, Dr
Mehan, R
Mehta-Nikhar, B R
Meredith, H E
Micklewright, R J
Millar, B G
Mittal, S
Moore, C A
Morgans, J P
Mudie, L L
Murray, G S
Myatt, F C
Myton, T L
Naren, M
Newbold, B
Newton, P
Nguyen, A L
Nightingale, P D
Noble, B S
O'Connell, D M
O'Donovan, N M
O'Donovan, P
O'Dowd, S
Odum, J
Outon Perla, P
Pahwa, M K
Parkes, A J
Parkes, J D
Passi, M M L
Passi, U
Patel, A M
Patel, K A
Paul, M R
Paul, M M
Peacock, S R
Pearson, D J
Perry, M R
Peters, C G
Phillips, A W
Phillips, A J
Phillips, M
Philp, N H
Pickavance, G
Plant, A

Poornan, A M
Porczynska, W I
Prasad, R
Price, N J
Pringle, E
Rahman, M A
Rahman, M H
Rai, J
Ratra, S S
Ravindran, T S
Rayner, R J
Richardson, H B M
Richmond, D J H
Ross, K R
Rowland, R M
Rushton, P J
Russell, I R
Russon, M J
Ryan, G
Rylance, P B
Rylance, W S
Samra, J S
Samra, M K
Sandramouli, S
Sangha, R K
Sarkar, A
Sarkar, P K
Sarkar, P K
Sayers, B F
Scott, K W M
Scotton, S J
Sealey, A R
Seedhouse, J K
Sehdev, G
Serhan, E
Shah, I A
Shah, N K
Shah, S
Shaikh, M G
Shanks, T
Share, A
Sharma, B K
Shortridge, R T J
Shun-Shin, G A
Sidebotham, E L
Sim, I S G
Simon, G R
Simon, R I
Singh, B M
Singh, B B
Singh, M
Smibert, G M
Smith, J K
Smith, J L
Smith, M H
Smith, N I
Smith, S
Solich, F
Staite, M E
Stentiford, N H
Stoves, R
Strain, G J
Swan, M C
Talbot, M S
Tandon, R K
Tandon, S C
Tawiah, A L
Taylor, C
Taylor, D R
Taylor, S A
Tayyab, M
Thet Win, Dr
Thomas, A P
Thomas, R J
Tilsen, E M
Tomlinson, J H
Tovey, G F
Tranter, J V
Turner, A
Turner, R J N
Tyler, L E
Varadharajan, S
Vaughan-Hughes, R G
Vishwanath, L S
Vishwanath, M S
Wagstaff, P J
Wake, M
Walford, S
Walker, C
Walker, H A S
Walker, P J
Walton, R S
Wanas, T M
Warwick, W J G
Watson, A M
Waymont, B
Whale, S A
Whalen, S M
Wheeler, V W

White, J F M
Whitehouse, N J
Wilcox, J
Williams, A
Williams, A E
Williams, C R
Williams, J G
Williams, J T
Willis, M J
Willis, P
Wilson, F
Wilson, H M
Wilson, M
Wiseman, J
Wright, J D
Wrigley, E T
Wulf, R
Yin Yin Win, Dr
Young, R A
Zeya, K

Woodbridge

Alden, A E
Allen, R T
Anderson, J P H
Archer, C A
Baker, H C
Ball, S P
Balme, E J
Banister, A D
Bartlett, K L H
Bartlett, M H
Benton, F M
Bishop, C
Black, D F M
Black, J A
Blaxland, S
Bowles, I M
Boyd, K D
Brierly, E K
Byrne, A J
Byrne, W F
Chester, E M
Craggs, J C
Crowther, K A
Dawnay, P F H
Deliss, L J
Dillon, F C
Driver, I K
Edwards, N J
Elson, C W
Exell, C
Fairweather, D A
Fletcher, A T N
Fletcher, J W
Fletcher, S M E
Gardiner, P A
Glaister, A M
Goble, O A
Gough-Thomas, H
Haigh, J W
Hamilton, T J
Harrison, S G C
Haslam, J S
Hayward, P M
Healey, D G
Huq, A
Johnson, M A
Jolly, C R
Jones, J G
Jones, K M
Keal, E E F
Ker, D S S
Knight, J C
Last, Z A
Leith, I M
Lennard-Jones, J E
Lettin, A W F
Lewis, R E
Lynch, J P W
McCauley, P
McGlennon, M
Mackay, S G
McRae, K A
Millar-Danks, S
Moffatt, R J
Murphy, P M W
Norton, S C
O'Donovan, A L
Odlum, H R
Parkinson, M J
Perkins, S
Phillips, M
Prentice, A I D
Reeve, H S
Rivers, N
Rixon, P E
Rockwell, V E
Rose, M

Rowell, G H R
Rufford, B D
Rufford, C W
Savidge, R S
Schurr, P H
Simmonds, A J
Slater, C J
Smith, M G
Stevens, L A
Tate, A C
Taylor, G H F
Terrell, C
Verrill, R P
Waller, T A N
Waters, J S
Watt, H P
Watts, J C
Wellingham, C B
Wells, G G
Yates, K P
Youngman, P M E

Woodford Green

Ali, N A J
Arora, A K
Barfoot, L C
Basil, E A
Baura, G K
Beavis, A K
Beveridge, B F
Bosch, G
Brauer, E
Brill, G
Brill, S E
Brinckenhoff, W-O
Brohi, A H K
Chatterjee, M
Das, C K
Dasgupta, R
Deo, H D
Deva, S S C
Devereux, E-J
Divakaran, K
Gandhi, M M
Gilani, M S
Graham, J D
Green, B
Gutmann, J H
Guyster, B
Harrison, A P
Harrison, P J
Hathi, M J
Honey, C M
Hughes, M
Hutchinson, F D
Hutchinson, V H
Innes, W G
Ireland, J
Irwin, D H
Jain, V K
Joiner, C E
Jones, R H
Jones, S P
Kunzru, K M N
Lubomirska, K M
Luthra, P N
Lyons, A G
Mohamed, M A M M
Morgan, G
Morris, M D R
Mulligan, M J C
Oates, J K
Okosun, O H
Otto, M J
Palbot, S M
Pippard, J S
Pippard, K M
Price, R V
Raja, F A
Rajakumar, R
Ray, A K
Ray, D
Rubenstein, D I
Sahu, D N
Sahu, U N
Samsami, S M
Sheikh, I S
Sika, M
Smart, J H
Smith, J
Stone, G F
Szanto, S F
Thomas, K M
Tranmer, F M
Webb, A A C
Whitaker, J W
Wright, D E
Wright, E W
Wykes, F C

Worthing

Woodhall Spa
Armour, A J
Butter, K C
Campbell, C S
Ezzat, M A
Malcolm, J M
Murray, M C
Povey, R W
Robertson, J T W
Turpin, M C

Woodstock
Barrington-Ward, D
Billing, J S
Ferrer, H P
Henville, J D
Hope, S L
King, P F
Leck, I M
Leggatt, H D
McNeilly, R H
Martin, A J
Orchard, T R
Pickles, M M
Tasker, G L
Van Oss, H G
Watkins, K
Williams, R A

Woolacombe
Clay, A A
Jones, S J
Wallace, A K

Wooler
Aylett, M J
Carr, F G
Craig, R
Dean, C R
Roy, W N T
Spoor, K M

Woolwich
Carr, J V L
Ketley, N J
Khan, F
Mackay, A D
Robertson, S M
Wright, E S

Worcester
Abudu, T O
Agoston, S A
Aldis, J S
Ali, B
Allen, D J
Allen, P A
Allen, W A B
Armitstead, C P
Ashton, C E
Austin, D I
Ayshford, C A
Back, D L
Barnard, N A
Barnett, G C
Barrell, J P
Battin, D G J
Bellamy, W
Belt, P J
Bennett, S J
Blake, A E
Bond, T P
Bowen, K A C
Bowley, D M G
Braga, A A
Breakwell, J
Breeze-Stringfellow, B
Brookes, P T
Brotherwood, A P
Brown, L M
Brown, M T
Bryant, M G H
Bulman, J N
Burton, J
Butler, J
Bywater, A J
Cairns, D
Calcott, R D
Caldwell, S
Campbell, I M
Castling, D P
Chapman, T W L
Charny, M C
Chen, T F
Chew, T M
Chikwe, J
Childs, F E M
Christys, A G
Clamp, P A
Clark, J M C
Clear, D B
Cockeram-Paranavitana, M N S
Cockeram, S F
Coleman, J I
Collett, L A
Collins, R J
Collis, A T G
Colwill, R C
Constantine, C E
Cook, P J
Cope, P G
Corlett, M P
Cross, S J
Cullen, M G
Cutts, S
Dale, J M
Davie, M J
Davies, H I
Davies, J S
Davies, M C
Davies, T E P
Davis, M J
Davis, P J C
Day, N J
De Cothi, A J
Deighan, M J
Dennis, E A
Dickens, J J
Downing, R
Dunn, P J S
Dye, P C
Earl, P D
England, D W
Everitt, S M A
Ferguson, T A
Flann, G A
Franklin, T S M
Georgiou, A M
Georgiou, G A
Glennie, H R
Goldsmith, C
Gommersall, L M
Gonzalez Elosegui, A M
Goodman, J F M
Griffith, L M V
Griffiths, M J
Griffiths, W D
Hak, C
Hall, R D
Hamilton, M J
Handy, R
Hansell, B
Hardwick, M
Harrison, C
Havercroft, A R
Hewetson, K A
Hickey, N C
Hickling, E J
Higginson, R
Holding, R
Holehouse, G D T
Hosie, C C
Houghton, P W
Huppertz, R C M
Hussain, M A
Hutchinson, M
Jackson, P
Jefferson-Loveday, J W
Jenkins, D
Johnson, P R S
Johnson, R A
Jones, C P
Jones, G L
Jones, I R
Jones, J C
Jones, T J D
Kerton, J J
Khogali, S S
King, S G
Knowles, M
Laidlaw, A J
Laidlaw, K A M
Lake, S P
Langley, A G S
Lavin, S J
Lee, B J
Leng, J D
Lewis, A D
Lewis, A M
Lewis, F M
Lewis, R A
Lord, P W
Lowe, S J
McGrath, B A
Mackichan, R I
Macnamara, O D
Maddison, T J R
Maile, C J D
Marshall, A E
Mason, B
Mennella, M
Mills, A F
Milner, G
Mitchard, K L
Monkley, C R
Morgan, M G G
Morris, J H
Morrison, C A
Morrison, R D
Mulira, A J E L
Munro, A J
Murray, D S
Nazare, J C F
Neil, D
Neillie, J L
New, A C
Newey, S F
Norton, M A
Norton, W D
O'Driscoll, J P
O'Dwyer, K J
O'Hickey, S P
Oeppen, M H
Osborn, J A
Osborn, N A
Osborne, J
Owen, R D
Packer, C N
Parkes, T A W
Parsons, C A
Paton, R S
Pearce, V M
Pedersen, K
Peet, A S
Pennell, I P
Pennock, P F L
Phillips, U N
Phillips, U N
Philpott, R G E
Pickerell, L M W
Pickrell, M D
Pickworth, M J W
Piilberg, O
Pinnock, C A
Pole, J M
Popert, J
Popovic, S
Porter, M J
Pratley, J
Procter, R S
Prosser, E J
Prosser, J A
Pugh, W A
Pycock, C J
Radley, J R
Rai, A
Ratcliffe, P J
Read, P B
Richards, E
Richards, E H
Richardson, A J
Riddick, D G B
Rigby, M C
Roberts, P A
Robertson, C L
Robertson, C S
Robertson, T D
Robinson, D D
Romer, C
Roscoe, B
Roscoe, E J
Roscoe, S A
Rosewarne, H C
Rosewarne, M D
Rouholamin, E
Rowe, I F
Ruparelia, B A
Sandison, A J P
Sawers, A H
Scanlon, J E M
Selvakumar, S P
Sheen, R M
Short, A
Simpson, A N B
Slaney, P L
Smart, P J G
Smart, R A
Smith, D M
Smith, G T
Smith, J E
Smith, R M H
Solesbury, K A
Sorensen, M H
South, D
Spencer, S J W
Stedman, Y F
Steel, R E
Stockley, J M
Tailor, M D
Tarry, J E
Taylor, A J
Teague, I
Tettelaar, M
Thomas, R J
Thompson, J A
Thompson, M A
Timberlake, A H
Timberlake, C M
Toun, A Y
Treadwell, E A
Trevett, M C
Tselentakis, G
Tunnicliffe, W S
Turner, A F
Tweddell, A L
Vella, V M P S
Vickers, A A
Wadge, E J
Walker, S C
Ward, R S
Wardell-Yerburgh, J G O
Watson, S P A
Watterson, G A
Watts, J F
Webberley, M J
Webster, D A
Webster, G M
White, R E B
Whitmore, I R
Wilkes, M C T
Williams, H D
Williams, H T
Wilson, G M
Windsor, C W O
Windsor, M J
Young, M A

Worcester Park
Aerts, S L F
Al-Hasani, H H M A
Al-Khudhairi, M S M
Antonio, S E
Blowers, H V
Bowen-Perkins, H H
Brady, C T M
Clarke, T P A
Coffey, A J D
D'Souza, G R A
Day, B H
De Silva, E B R
Dosani, S
Driscoll, W J
Fatnani, S T
Greene, W J
Ho, C H-K
Hollings, A M
James, W B
Jasani, V
Jones, A S
Kalsi, B S
Mathur, P
Patel, R
Pathmanathan, I K
Suchak, V M
Vara, R
Wallace, W H S

Workington
Bater, E J
Burgul, S D
Butler, A C
Crosby, P
Fleming, H A
Fletcher, P R H
Gibson, R E C
Goodwin, R M
Gourlay, M V
Grant, R N R
Howarth, P
Hull-Davies, J M
Illsley, K M
Jackson, S
Jay, V C B
Jones, C E
Joy, K R
Macbeth, M
McGreevy, N G
McKerrow, N
Morgan, A J
Mort, M J L
Mujahed, M A
Naylor, H A
Palmer, E M
Pavey-Smith, J
Proudfoot, R T
Rao, P B
Rudman, R J
Scott, A V
Slater, C A
Spencer, J V
Steel, G M
Thomas, G M
Ulyett, I
Walker, R D
Ward, A B
Wilmot, J D C

Worksop
Allen, J M
Allen, M J
Alloub, M I A
Anathnanam, A J
Avill, R
Bickerton, G S
Blandford, R L
Bodden, S J
Cashmore, R J
Chambers, C A
Clegg, R T
Collington, A G
Collins, D J
Collins, L A
Corbett, M G
Crate, I D
Crossman, H M
Cyriac, J E A
Davies, I F
Davies, S C
Delaney, W M M
Dixon, A M
Drown, G K M
El Hag, S H
El-Katsha, E W
Elson, P J
Elson, R A
Emery, M C
Emslie, C J
Exposito Coll, P
Finbow, J M
Finbow, J A H
Fulton, J A
Gimenez Burgos, M
Goel, R K
Guirguis, M W
Guirguis, M
Haldar, G
Hall, I M
Harris, R W
Harrow, A
Hashmi, S S J
Heaton, J M
Hepburn, J M
Hobson, P J
Hopkinson, D A W
Howard, J D
Howard, J
Hussain, S M A
Kar-Purkayastha, S K
Khan, I A
Kolar, K M
Lazarowicz, H P
Lee, V F
Lokubalasuriya, D E A
Mammo, M A R
Mannan, M A
Mellows, H J
Merrill, C R
Merriman, L A
Michel, M Z
Millar, L J
Moodie, G R J
Moustafa, W M
Moxon, P J
Muthiah, M M
Omokanye, A M
Patel, S C
Paul, B
Qureshi, N R
Renshaw, A J N
Rice-Oxley, J M
Riddell, W S
Robinson, K R
Rossi, C A M
Rossi, S
Salamani, M M H
Scarrow, P
Sharmacharja, G
Sharmacharja, N R
Shata, M M H
Sinha Roy, A N
Smith, P
Stanley, C P
Stillwell, M D
Stillwell, S
Sturton, E W
Teasdale, D E
Vernon-Parry, J
Vernon-Parry, K C
Warner, S N B
Williams, L H P
Zafar, N

Worthing
Anderson, J G F
Anderson, S K
Appleton, M A C
Arundell, P W
Baillie, A T K
Ball, F I
Bamigbade, T A
Bates, J
Beard, R C
Beney, J R
Bennett, D G
Blows, L J H
Bull, H J M
Bull, J J
Cairns, A J
Caldwell, G
Cameron, E A B
Camp, D F
Campbell, N M
Campbell, P J
Capstick, N S
Carr, P
Carter, D Y
Carter, T J
Chalmers, R M
Chard, M D
Chinoy, V J
Chiu, I H-M
Chouhan, A K
Clarke, D S
Clifford-Jones, R E
Coldwell, S
Collier, J A B
Congdon, R G
Congleton, J E
Cook, B A
Cooper, K V
Corbett, J M E
Corkery, A P
Cox, D T
Craig, D M
Crouch, N S
D'Arcy, S M
Dand, J A
Daniels, D W
Daniels, P S
Das, A N
Dean, P J
Dearing, J
Dickson, G H
Drown, E M
Duckering, J
Duddy, J R
Dyer-Fane, M D
Edge, A J
Edwards, I M E
Edwards, R
English, J D
English, M M
Epsom, M
Escobar Jimenez, A M
Evans, J A
Evans, J D R
Ferguson, I R
Ferguson, K
Fernandez Bonilla, E M
Foley, J
Fowler, D J
Funnell, A R
Gambling, M D
Garcia Ceballos, J I
Garg, A K
Garner, D P
George, M
Giddins, A G
Giddins, E A
Ginn, E A
Gnananandha, C
Gompertz, H R
Graham, J A G
Grant, J J H
Grasset-Molloy, G J M
Grellier, L F L
Grocutt, M P
Gupta, S K
Hadley, D A
Hall, D G

Wotton-under-Edge

Hancock, K J
Hardwick, B R
Hayward, P J
Hiley, N A
Hill, C A M
Hills, R K
Hinchcliffe, M G
Holden, G
Hoile, I S
Holmes, A M W
Hopkins, D R
Howell, M
Hutchings, G M
Imms, J M
Jarvis, A C M
Jenkins, C S
Johnson, C A
Joseph, M S
Juer, L D F
Kelley, S T
Kenny, S
Khin Maung Nyunt, Dr
King, I D H
Kirby, C
Kirkby-Bott, J
Kochhar, P K
Lavies, N G
Leahy, J A
Lermitte, J G C
Lindley, D C
Liston, T G
Lomas, J J P
Longmore, J M
Lyons, M A
MacArthur, J
McCarthy, N R
McCumpha, A I
McCutchan, J D S
McFall, M
Mackinnon, A L
McLean, H
Mannings, D J
Markland, C G
Martin, D M
Martin, P L
Mason, C
Mathew, A
Melton, G
Michaelis, J R
Montgomery, J
Moore, E J
Moriarty, G K
Muir, I W
Murphy, P
Nelson, S A
Newnham, A V
Newnham, J A
Nicholls, F A J
Niyadurupola, T
O'Driscoll, A M
O'Leary, F
Orpin, R P I
Pastor, T
Patel, K E
Pathmanaban, P
Pickworth, S A M
Pike, S C
Pitt, W E R
Plumpton, R J
Potter, J R
Poulsen, H
Powell, A M
Powell, R J
Pullen, D A
Pyper, R J D
Randall, K
Randell, P
Rassam, S M B
Raval, M M
Ravindrane, A
Reardon, M F
Richards, A J
Rist, C L
Riveros Huckstadt, M D P
Roberts, K M
Rockall, L J
Rolph, M J W
Roques, A W W
Roques, C J
Ruddle, A C
Ruoss, C F
Ryan, W J
Rymer, M J
Sanderson, K V
Sandon, P H G
Sargen, F E
Saunders, E S
Sayer, J B

Sayers, R D
Searle-Barnes, P G
Semmens, J M
Sethi, P C
Sharma, K K
Shipsey, M R
Signy, M
Smith, R A
Smith, S M
Smith, T
Smurthwaite, W A
Spargo, J B
Spence, D J
Spence, R N F
Spring, C
Suntharalingam, G
Suntharalingam, M
Sweet, P T
Teimory, M
Thiagarajah, S
Thompson, A M
Thwaites, S M
Topham, J H
Tovey, J E
Tozer, R D
Tree, A L
Trounce, N D
Uncles, D R
Unnithan, S B
Vohra, S L
Von Biel, T A
Wade, A H
Wainstead, H
Waring, E
Warren, J E
Waters, H R
Watton, E
Webb, M A H
Weber, S
Weston, P
Willard, H L
Williams, A C
Williams, B W
Wong, F H
Woods, W G A
Woodward-Court, R I
Woolley, B
Woollons, A
Wormsley, K G
Wrightson, F M
Young, B K
Young, H

Wotton-under-Edge

Angell-James, J
Bailey, A R
Barber, W E
Burns-Cox, N
Burrows, W J
Byles, P B
Easterbrooke, C Z
Fitzgibbon, L P
Green, S M
Hampson, R S
Kabler, J J
MacCarthy, D A
McCarthy, M B
Margerison, J C L
Morrison, W J
Pritchard, P L J
Rowlands, R G
Stokes, M J
Thompson, C L
Twomey, P J
Watt, A J

Wrexham

Ahmad, T
Ahmed, S
Ali, O A
Alltree, M J
Alstead, J A
Alstead, P
Anthonypillai, P
Apthomas, I
Arijon Barazal, M C
Arthurs, G J
Ashworth, I N
Atkin, P D
Baker, A
Baker, J T
Banerjee, S M
Barton, P C
Bates, G J
Bayley, B W
Benjamin, A
Billings, P J
Bolton, V S
Botham, L

Bowman, R W
Braid, N W
Breese, S C
Brock, R S
Burdge, A H
Celal, C
Chaudhry, H M
Child, D F
Chowdhury, E A H
Cliffe, R J
Cluett, D
Collins, M M A
Cook, J P F
Cotter, J A
Coward, A E B
Cowell, R P W
Crumplin, E A
Crumplin, K H
Cummins, M C
Da Silva, A E C F
Dardamissis, E
Davies, D A
Davies, D M
Davies, H R F
Davies, K S
Davies, P I
De Bolla, A R
De Soysa, D L D
Deas, E D
Denkema, J F
Dillon, C G M
Duguid, J K M
Earlam, A D
Edmondson, W C
Edwards, D M
Evans, E J S
Ewah, P O
Fernando, M U
Fleming, J S M
Freudmann, M S
Gibson, T S
Gibson, Y A B
Graham, B
Greaves, R C
Greensmith, M G E
Halpin, K G
Harborne, G C
Harrington, B E J
Harris, S A S
Harvey, J N R
Hill, G M
Horrocks, F A
Hughes, H
Hughes, M R
Husain, A
Hussain, Z
Irvine, C P C
Jackson, S L
Jamieson, A M
Jamieson, J R
Jeffreys, T E
Jones, C C
Jones, D G
Jones, D M
Jones, D
Jones, E T J
Jones, J S
Jones, S W
Kanagaratnam, T
Kapas, K C
Kelly, A M
Kelly, P S
Kendall, N D
Khan, G M
Knight, P R
Laine, C H
Laing, P W
Lancashire, B J
Lee Hai Ean, Dr
Lee, G S
Lee, H S
Leeming, R D
Lim, M-L
Littlejohns, C S
Littler, C
McAndrew, N A
McCaddon, A
McDonald, K A
McGivern, T A
McGrath, D D
McNeill, J M
Mahdi, S
Marchant, J M
Mason, A
Melia, E W
Mercer, J H M
Meulman, J H
Minchom, P E
Minchom, S E

Molloy, J E
Moore, C
Murray, G M
Myres, M P
Nadra, A
Nankani, J N
Nirula, H C
O'Sullivan, M M
Olawo, A O
Oliver, C A V
Otter, M I
Owen, G
Owens, G G
Pack, H M
Parker, D A
Perera, C N
Phillips, E A
Philp, M R
Pickles, R M
Platts, J K
Prathibha, B V
Prendergast, M C
Prussia, C M
Pye, J K
Race, J H
Ratcliffe, S H R
Rawlinson, H R D
Roberts, E G G
Roberts, M J
Roberts, R C
Roberts, T G
Robinson, S H
Roseblade, C K
Rosenberg, M T
Ross, A
Rutherford, P A
Sabri, A M E-S
Salt, E M
Samson, M N
Santhan Gopal, K S
Saul, P D
Scriven, M W
Sen, A
Seward, W P
Shaw, C D
Shields, M A
Siddiqui, S J
Silverstone, E J
Smith, A J
Smith, R M C
Snow, R G
Sowden, J M
Sudworth, H M
Taffinder, A P
Talkhani, I S
Tanti, G J
Tattersall, H J
Tattersall, J
Thomas, A M
Thomas, N E
Tinckler, L F
Toon, P G
Turkie, P V
Underhill, S
Upadhyay, R N
Uppala, R G
Vellacott, M N
Vennam, R B
Vlies, M J
Vlies, P R
Wallice, M R B
Walsh, J E
Walters, P E
Watson, D K
Welham, J
White, A D
Williams, C P
Williams, D G
Williams, O E
Williams, T E J
Wood, H M
Wood, H M
Wood, K M
Wootton, J R
Wright, B K
Wyke, P L

Wylam

Aitchison, E A M
Barer, G R
Bartram, S A
Blain, P A
Brewis, A W
Brough, A K
Brough, W
Donaldson, R W
Fleming, S C
Forsythe, J L R
Harvey, J-A E G

Holden, M P
Knapton, J
Miller, S M
Petrie, A M
Porteous, L A
Power, J S F
Roberts, C J
Scott, J E S
Sprague, D S
Sprague, N B
Swinburn, R T
Vincent, M L
Williams, J

Wymondham

Alexander, J B
Burnell, F B K
Calne, J A
Clark, E M
Cooper, L C G
Cull, M A
Groom, C E
Groom, N H
Groom, T M
Heptinstall, D P
Howell, T J
Kingham, M W
Laurie, W G R M
Lees, N
Seaton, D G F
Smith, P C
Taylor, J G
Thorman, C A L
Thurston, S C

Yarm

Aitken, R H
Bonavia, A
Bradbury, S E
Bryson, D D
Chisholm, A G
Clarke, D
Clarke, J M
Clifford, K M A
Cooper, D W
Crawford, D
Crawshaw, S M
Crews, J R
Curry, R C
Davies, R H
Dodds, C
Dodds, E A
Duncan, T J
Elder, M L
Fleischmann, C W
Gowland, S N
Graham, K A
Grainger, J
Hole, R
Janes, E F
Khan, K J
Kibirige, J I
Kyi Kyi Tin-Myint, Dr
Lack, L J
Mathieson, C B
Merson, R D
Miller, D H T
Moody, T E
Myers, S M
Nath, F P
Neoh, L C
Orr, W S M
Padmore, S J
Paterson, A D
Pollard, S M
Rao, S
Rawlinson, A J
Reynolds, N G
Roberts, N J
Ryall, D M
Stevenson, J S
Stohlner, J
Tahmassebi, A
Targett, K L
Tremlett, M R
Williams, M S
Wilson, R G
Wright, J G
Wright, P J
Wright, S G

Yateley

Allison, J
Aulakh, R
Beamer, J E R
Bird, S M
Bonnevie, J E
Cook, A T
France, R
Guest, R S

Hancock, A L
Hayward, E I
Henley, B
Humphrey, K F
Hunter, R L
Kerslake, D M
Lister, D
McGuire, N G
MacLurg, K M
Palmer, M A
Rogerson, C A
Sant, K E
Teo, A C W
Viner, M A
Walker, N D
Wang, G K P
Wareham, K P
Williams, P G N G

Yelverton

Ames, J A
Baker, J A
Bannon, C F
Barker, D C
Beckly, D E
Beckly, J B
Brindle, J M
Campbell, C J
Chiappe, K N
Choa, R G
Clarance, G A
Cleave, H L
Coats, E H
Cowie, J
Davies, M G
Doyle, H E
Drennan, P C
Evans, D A
Farmer, K D
Farnham, N G J
Finnigan, A G K
Fixsen, J A
Guest, J E
Harmsworth, N J
Hawkins, V J
Hayes, C
Hodgson, R M H
Huggett, R J
Keeling, D H
Langsford, H L
Leather, C M
Leverton, W E J
Longdon, D N
Luscombe, F E
Mallaband, E
Moorby, A L
Murphy, P M
O'Hanlon, J N
Oakes, M
Reece, M W
Rowe, A S S
Rowe, J B
Shephard, J A
Smith, P G D
Smith, W H
Soul, J O
Stocker, C A
Stoecker, H
Stokes, J M
Strelling, M K
Tayler, D J
Taylor, M B
Thomas, M R
Tipple, R W
Wells, I P
Wright, J A M
Young, R C
Youngs, J C

Yeovil

Agnew, I
Allen, A J
Ancill, B R
Ariaratnam, G
Arnot, A M W
Azaz, S Y
Baker, K M
Baldwin, J E
Ball, M J
Bathurst, N C G
Berraondo, L M
Bishop, R P
Bradfield, A M
Brigden, G S
Brooks, S C
Burrell, N L
Camprodon Gazulla, R
Candy, E P
Carr, R G

York

Cawood, J R
Cheale, S M
Cohen, J C
Collins, M J M
Cooper, C A
Cornish, G R L
Cornish, M
Cotterill, S L
Cox, J P
Crowley, G P
Crowther, C A
Daum, R E O
Davey, H M
Davies, A J
Day, C P
Day, H E
Dearlove, J C
Dennis, S E W
Devonshire, H W
Dryden, N K
Duffy, L J
Eaton, M J
Entwistle, M A
Evans, A G R
Faigan, M A
Fawcett, I W
Fisher, C J
Fry, C E
Gajraj, H
Garcia-Ochoa Fernandez, J
Gore, S
Gower, J D G
Gregory, A J
Griffiths, D A
Hacking, J C
Hall, F G
Hart, J F
Hayman, J J
Hepple, J N
Hogben, R M
Holmes, M J
Huins, S J
Hunter, S J
Kemp, S W
Kennedy, R H
Kibblewhite, D G
Kipling, R M
Kirn, G U
Kirn, T E-M
Knight, A C
Kulkarni, R
Latimer, S
McCormick, A G
McCormick, R N
McMaster, A B M
Madden, B K
Majid, M
Maleki-Tabrizi, A
Manser, I N
Minogue, M J O B
Mitchell, J A
Moore, R I
More, R E A
Mortimore, C
Nadin, J C K
Naravi, M K
Nicolson, K T
Nott-Bower, W G
Oberthur, E P A
Omran, H T I
Palferman, T G
Parker, C J
Pattison, G T R
Payne, G S
Perry, J H
Pickles, S T
Priaulx, L-R
Qadiri, M R R
Rashed, K A M
Richards, M J
Royle, C A J P
Saywell, W R
Scott, R W
Scull, J J
Sheffield, J P
Simmonds, A J
Smibert, J G
Smith, L F P
Souster, J L
Summers, A
Summers, S H
Taylor, D R
Tricker, J A
Trower, T P
Umoren, D M
Whelan, A P
Winstone, R

Wootton, M A
Wright, B Y

York

Adams, R D
Alcock, D G
Allenby, C F
Anakwe, G N
Anderson, A W
Anderson, P I
Anderson, S P
Anderton, C J
Aston, C E
Atang, F M
Atkinson, A D
Bagnall, J J
Baines, R J
Baldwin, D W
Ball, R J
Banhatti, R G
Barber, P J
Barnes, M R
Barnet, M C
Barr, C A
Barradell, R
Barritt, J M
Barry, G P
Barry, M R F
Bastable, J R G
Bastable, M J R
Basu, S
Bates, C
Batman, D C
Bavidge, K J N
Beardsworth, S A A
Bearpark, D M
Belbin, D J
Bell-Syer, J W
Bell, D R
Bell, H
Bennett, D A
Berry, C A
Berry, M I
Beverley, D W
Bill, K A
Bingle, J P
Black, J J
Blackburn, D A
Blake James, R B
Blakeborough, J
Blenkiron, P
Blowers, R
Boffa, J A
Bolter, P J
Border, D J
Bottom, S F E
Bowker, A M B
Boyd, L M
Boyle, R M
Bradley, E M
Britton, S A
Brobbel, N J
Bromham, B M
Bromley, B J
Brooke, J P
Brooks, S G
Brown, D P
Brown, H A
Brown, L M
Brown, R F
Bruce, K I
Burgess, P J
Burnett, P R
Bush, J K
Buswell, C K
Caine, J L
Calder, A S C
Campbell, P
Carden, M
Carney, P
Carpenter, M R
Carpenter, R M
Carter, J J
Cass, M A
Chang Kit, H L
Chaplin, J V
Cheng, L H-H
Chesworth, P M
Child, D A
Chubb, S E M
Clarke, A M T
Clarke, P R R
Clarke, S E
Cleary, M M
Coe, K I
Coleman, R L
Collier, S M
Collins, A J
Collinson, D G

Colman, R D
Cook, H L
Coop, D J
Corlett, A J
Coultas, H W H
Cousins, A L
Cox, E M
Craven, J L
Craven, K W E
Crawford, P M
Crockatt, R H I
Crompton, J W
Cross, D A
Curry, S
Daly, D W
Daly, F M
Davies, G A
De Boer, P G
Dell, R E
Delves, G H
Dench, P G R
Dent, A J
Devlin, M
Dickson, J
Dobie, N
Donaldson, T J
Donnellan, C F
Downey, L M
Downing, N P D
Dring, A P M
Dulo, A M N
Duncan, A F
Dunham, J M
Easby, B
Evans, A A
Evans, J C H
Evans, M W
Fair, D S
Faller, P F
Featherstone, J-J
Fenwick, H J
Fernandez Fidalgo, J L
Field, A F
Finan, C M
Fisher, R H
Fleat, G
Forrester, A M
Foster, G P
Foster, K J
Fowler, E V
Galbraith, D J
Gardner, T M
Garry, A C
Garthwaite, E
Gaunt, R M
Geddes, D R
Gibson, G C
Gibson, M F
Gill, N J
Gilleghan, S B
Gillie, A K
Girling, P J E
Glennon, V
Godfrey, J L R
Gold, N G
Gopalaswamy, A K
Grace, A R H
Graham, D
Gray, H
Gray, W C J
Green, A S
Griffith, K E
Griffiths, C J
Grummitt, R M
Guest, P A
Gulya'S, L M
Haddock, G K
Haleem, M A
Hall, R
Hall, W J
Hamilton, J C
Hanson, I M
Hardy, J
Hardy, R G
Harran, M J
Harris, A L
Harrison, P A
Harrison, R E
Harrop, C W
Hartley, D C
Hartley, J E
Hasan, S S
Haselden, J B
Haw, D W M
Haw, M E
Hayes, S J
Haynes, J
Hayward, D M
Hayward, D

Hayward, J M
Heald, A
Heggarty, H J
Helm, W H
Henderson, C A
Heseltine, D
Heslop, A J
Hewitson, J D
Highet, A S
Hildebrand, A E C
Hinton, P H
Hirst, J
Hoddinott, R E
Holman, C J
Honnappa, H
Hopkin, J M
Hopkinson, M C
Hopton, B P
Howard, M R
Hrycaiczuk, W
Hudson, M C
Hughes, T R J
Hunter, A M
Hunter, A J
Hunter, P
Hutchinson, B R G
Hynes, A N
Ibbotson, R N
Idama, T O
Iredale, J L
Isherwood, J
Iveson, J M I
Iveson, R Y
Ivory, C M
Jackson, G B
Jackson, I J B
Jacobs, P M
Jacomb, R G
Jamal, A A
James, D A
Jarman, R A
Jenkins, C N J
Jennings, P E
Johnson, R C
Johnstone, N A
Jones, J M
Jones, M V
Jones, M A
Jones, M H
Jones, P R
Jones, R D
Julian, T R
Kaliszer, O E
Kaye, M G
Kelly, A M
Kelly, S M
Kemp, D S
Kennedy, J M
Kennedy, P F
Kenny, H M
Kerr, M A
Kerr, W S
Ketting, K P
Kimuli, M
King, D G
Kinnell, J D
Kirk, C A
Klar, H-M
Kramer, P B M M
Lacy-Colson, J C H
Laing, J H W
Laing, M B
Lakin, A J
Lakin, H M
Laughey, W F
Lawson, T R
Lazenby, R M
Leathem, W E
Lethem, D G
Lethem, J A
Letty, L J
Leveson, S H
Leyburn, P
Lloyd, J R
Longworth, D
Lonsdale, S
Looker, H C
Love, C A
Lubben-Dinkelaar, M M
Lyall, I M
Lyon, C C
McBride, J M
McBride, P M C
McCahon, I A
McCall, J
MacDermott, K J
McDougle, M D R
Macfie, A J

McHenry, C J
McIntosh, A W
McKenna, J B
Mackenzie, S E
McLaren, A A A
McLaren, C A N
MacLeod, A I
Macleod, J
McPherson, B
Madan, M
Madden, J W C
Madsen, K E
Makepeace, J S
Malik, F
Maloney, J D
Mandour, O E M A
Mannion, R A J
Markham, M V
Markham, R J O S
Marks, R L
Marsden, J D
Marson, J M
Martin, T G H
Matheson, A M
Mattock, E J
Maycock, T P
Meakins, S J
Mechie, K
Megarry, S G
Meldrum, J M
Merritt, S M
Mikhail, T M S
Millman, A G
Milnes, D C
Mitchell, N A
Mitchell, S F
Mizen, K D
Moger, P W
Moncur, P H
Moore, J R
Moore, S R W
Moran, N
Morley, N S
Moroney, J D
Morris, G J
Morris, M
Morris, M D
Morrison, J
Morrison, R E
Mortimer, A H
Moss, P J
Moulson, A M
Muhammed, S
Mujeeb-Ur-Rahman, Dr
Mungall, D F
Munnelly, N
Murdoch, S D
Murphy, K A
Murray, A C
Myers, K W
Newcombe, C P
Newland, T M
Nixon, R J
Noble, T J
Nuttall, J H
O'Brien, A N
Oglesby, A I
Old, S
Oliver, M H
Ormston, B J
Orr, G D
Palmer, J A
Palta, N S
Park, T H
Parker, A F
Parker, D
Parry, C F M
Paterson, J
Pathirana, R S
Pathmanathan, S
Patterson, D H
Patterson, W J
Pearson, A M
Pearson, R E
Peel, R K
Peel, R N
Pegg, D E
Phin, N F
Pierce, A A
Pinder, G W
Pope, S P
Porter, G R
Porter, S M
Potrykus, M
Potterton, O M
Powley, E
Price, E C V
Price, K G
Pring, D W

Procter, D
Pye, M A M
Rea, V
Reaney, S M
Reed, J P
Reeder, M K
Rees, H M
Reid, I N
Reilly, P G
Reilly, S P
Reilly, T M
Richardson, G J R
Rickards, F S
Riley, J E
Rishworth, R H
Ristic, C D
Rix, S M
Roberts, G D D
Roberts, S A
Robertson, N C
Robins, K
Robinson, P M
Roman, M V
Ruston, R
Samuel, M S
Saunders, G P
Saunders, J P
Saunders, P O
Saxty, P
Schofield, S J
Scott, A K
Scott, E A
Scott, J W
Seaton, J M A
Sedano Bocos, A
Sen, S K
Shaw, S P
Sheikh, Z I
Shujia-Ud-Din, O S
Siddique, T B
Sigsworth, E R C
Simon, E L
Simpson, D
Simpson, J O
Simpson, J E
Simpson, R N R
Sinanan, R D K
Smales, J R
Smith, C W
Smith, M
Smith, M R
Smith, P S
Smith, R A
Smith, S M
Smith, W M
Smithson, W H
Smythies, J R
Snape, C J
Spenceley, J E
Stainforth, J M
Stark, R F
Stell, P M
Stephenson, C J
Stewart, O G
Stockdale, W T
Stone, A M
Stone, W D
Stout, E L
Stower, M J
Strang, J R
Summers, A P
Sutton, A G C
Swann, D E
Swanston, J K
Sweeney, A M
Tait, S K
Tams, J
Taylor, J S
Taylor, P J
Taylor, R H
Thompson, R C F
Thomson, H E G
Thomson, I C
Thomson, K F M
Thomson, M J
Thomson, R J
Thomson, S E G
Thorne, P M
Thow, J C
Ticehurst, P R
Tilston, S J
Toomey, P J
Torlesse, R M
Towler, G M
Toynbee, J C
Traynor, C P
Trudgill, M J A
Tuck, C S
Tulloch, J S

Yorkhill

Turnbull, C M
Turner-Parry, A J
Ubhi, B S
Underwood, S A
Urwin, G H
Verow, P W
Vos, H P
Wakerley, M B
Waldron, F M
Walker, J E
Walker, M M
Walker, R G
Wallace, C L M

Walsh, D A
Walsh, J
Walsh, S
Walters, N S
Warnock, N G
Watson, A B
Watson, G D
Watson, S P
Watson, T O
Watt, I S
Wearne, S M
Webb, B J
Webster, A R

Webster, R W
Wedgwood, I M
Wedgwood, J J
Welch, L J
Westerman, R
Wharton, A B
Whicher, J T
Whitaker, I M
Whitcher, D M
White, J E S
White, L A
Wickrema, F R S
Wijesinghe, L D

Wilkinson, B A
Wilkinson, D J
Wilkinson, H
Wilkinson, S M
Williams, C J C
Williams, H R
Williamson, D B
Williamson, J
Willis, F P
Wilson-Sharp, C D
Wilson, J R
Wilson, M A
Wilson, R J T

Wiseman, A M
Wood, S M
Woodford, D
Woodford, H J
Woodrow, S P
Woods, I
Worth, D P
Worth, P J
Wright, H
Wright, J B D
Wylie, C R R
Yates, R C

Yorkston, N J
Young, S

Yorkhill
Ford, J A

Ystrad Meurig
Harrop-Griffiths, H
Rhys-Dillon, C C G
Rhys, W J S E-G

The Medical Directory 2002

Part Two

Healthcare Organisations in the UK

Informa Professional **Medico-Legal Titles**

Do **you** need **regular** medico-legal **updates**? If so then **Informa** has a portfolio of titles to suit **your** needs

Personal and Medical Injuries Law Letter (PMILL)

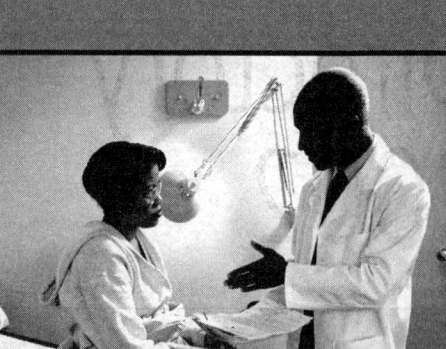

..has been the most highly regarded title within its field for nearly 20 years and is a must for those needing a brief background to current clinical negligence and personal injury cases. In 10 issues a year, you will receive concise and informed updates by a leading consultant editorial team and hear of ground-breaking judgements as soon as they are reached.

10 issues - £294

Medical Law Monitor

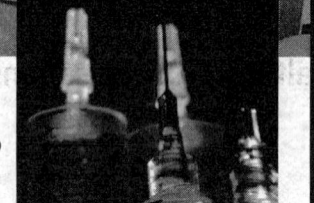

... is essential reading for both medical and legal professionals who need to understand the details and implications of recent developments in medical law. Topics regularly covered include; malpractice, patient confidentiality, clinical negligence, medical ethics, mental health, NHS complaints and professional regulation.

12 issues - £265 – discounts are available to NHS employees

Lloyds Law Reports: Medical

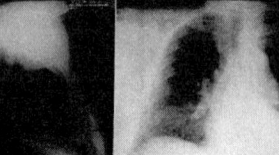

.... provide expert case selection and incisive commentaries from 3 Sergeants' Inn. It aims to provide lawyers and medical experts with authoritative reports of all the major legal cases in this field and includes judgements on clinical negligence litigation, medical ethical cases, mental health, judicial review and doctor's discipline. Bound volumes are available of cases dating back until 1989.

10 issues - £212 – Bound volumes £109 per annum – full set £835

For further information or a **free sample copy** please contact **Emma Cox** on **tel: 020 7017 5441** or **email: emma.cox@informa.com** quoting reference **PPM0005A**

informa
PROFESSIONAL

www.**informabookshop**.com

Orthopaedics I R S Reynolds, P V Seal, P Shewell, T F Sibly, D Williams
Radiology E J Barton, P Grech, G M Rowe, P Wilson

Victoria Eye Hospital
149 -153 Eign Street, Hereford HR4 0AN
Tel: 01432 355444 Fax: 01432 279917
Total Beds: 12

Herefordshire Primary Care Trust

Belmont Abbey, Belmont, Hereford HR2 9RP
Tel: 01432 344344 Fax: 01432 363900
(Coventry, Warwickshire, Herefordshire and Worcestershire Health Authority)

Chair Ted Willmott
Chief Executive Paul Bates

Froome Bank Hospital
Bromyard HR7 4QN
Tel: 01885 488080 Fax: 01885 488675
Total Beds: 24

Psychiatry of Old Age N Wagner

Ledbury Cottage Hospital
The Homend, Ledbury HR8 1BX
Tel: 01531 632488
Total Beds: 15

Leominster Community Hospital
Leominster HR6 8JH
Tel: 01568 614211
Total Beds: 34

Care of the Elderly J A Dalziel, P Overstall
Psychiatry of Old Age N Wagner

Ross Community Hospital
Ross-on-Wye HR9 5LQ
Tel: 01989 562100
Total Beds: 32

Stonebow Unit County Hospital
Hereford HR1 2ER
Tel: 01432 355444
Total Beds: 56

General Psychiatry P Allman, K Godbert, C Thomas
Psychiatry of Old Age V Staples, N Wagner

Victoria Cottage Hospital
Kington HR5 3BX
Tel: 01544 230317
Total Beds: 11

Hertfordshire Partnership NHS Trust

99 Waverley Road, St Albans AL3 5TL
Tel: 01727 811888 Fax: 01727 857900
(Bedfordshire and Hertfordshire Health Authority)

Chair Hattie Llewelyn-Davies

Harpenden Memorial Hospital
Carlton Way, Harpenden AL5 4TA
Tel: 01582 760196 Fax: 01582 767970
Total Beds: 23

Harperbury
Harper Lane, Shenley, Radlett WD7 9HQ
Tel: 01923 854861
Total Beds: 100

General Psychiatry W E J Owino, M J H Piachaud, I Singh, G Stewart

Hertsmere Primary Care Trust

The Elms Clinic, High Street, Potters Bar EN6 5DA
Tel: 01707 647586 Fax: 01707 647594
(Bedfordshire and Hertfordshire Health Authority)

Chair Beth Kelly
Chief Executive Jacqueline Clark

Heywood and Middleton Primary Care Trust

Milton Street, Middleton, Manchester M24 5TU
Tel: 0161 643 6400
(Greater Manchester Health Authority)

Chair David Edwards
Chief Executive Keith Surgeon

High Peak and Dales Primary Care Trust

Newholm Hospital, Baslow Road, Bakewell DE45 1AD
Tel: 01629 814186 Fax: 01629 815589
(Trent Health Authority)

Chief Executive Niel Stanwick

Hillingdon Hospital NHS Trust

Pield Heath Road, Uxbridge UB8 3NN
Tel: 01895 238282 Fax: 01895 811687
(Hillingdon Primary Care Trust)

Chair Steven Coventry

Hillingdon Hospital
Hillingdon, Pield Heath Road, Uxbridge UB8 3NN
Tel: 01895 238282 Fax: 01895 811687
Total Beds: 666

Anaesthetics J Anandanesan, J P Downer, A Knight, C Messer, Dr Smith, A Thorniley, S Vashist, Dr Weinbren
Care of the Elderly S J L Brooy, A Parry, Dr Sweetman, Dr Vowles
Dental Surgery Dr Crow, G T Gardiner
Dermatology Dr Hughes
ENT Dr Mareuis, Dr Ryan
General Medicine Dr Dubney, Dr Grocott-Mason, Dr Hilal, R Hillson, G E Holdstock, C Ilsley, L H Sevitt, D J Thomas, Dr Tonge, Dr Weedham, Dr Wills
General Psychiatry C Coghlan, Dr Conway, Dr Gouhargy, Dr Hadler, Dr Kincher, B Lucas, Dr Nathan, J Palmer, R W Reid
General Surgery Dr Das, P Mitchenere, Dr Mohsen, T Paes, B A Shorey
Genitourinary Medicine Dr Schroeder, S Waldron
Learning Disabilities I Singh
Neurology Dr Malik
Obstetrics and Gynaecology Dr Jackson, N Nicholas, J Price, V P Robinson, N Watson, C S Wright
Ophthalmology P Bloom, Dr Fielder, N Lee
Orthopaedics K M Atrah, W N Bodey, J F Dooley, Dr Kamereri, R Langstaff, Dr Singh
Paediatrics R Buchdahl, M Cruwys, H Hamid, P Jaffe, G Khakoo
Palliative Medicine L Bangham, Dr Lemon, J Maher, G Ruskin

NHS TRUSTS & NHS HOSPITALS

Pathology F Barker, R Jan-Mohamed, R Kaczmarski, D M Rimmer, J Williamson
Plastic Surgery Dr Breech
Psychiatry of Old Age A Conway, J Palmer
Radiology N Chetty, R Devakumar, R J Kantor, Dr Raza, I M Shirley, Dr Whittle
Radiotherapy and Oncology E J Maher
Rheumatology and Rehabilitation R S Hanspal
Thoracic Surgery E R Townsend
Urology Dr Ng, A Pope

Hillingdon Primary Care Trust

Kirk House, 97-109 High Street, Yiewsley, West Drayton UB7 7HJ
Tel: 01895 452000 Fax: 01895 452108
(Hillingdon Primary Care Trust)

Chair Sarah Pond
Chief Executive David Panter

Hinchingbrooke Healthcare NHS Trust

From April 2002 mental health services transferring to Cambridgeshire and Peterborough Mental Health Partnership NHS Trust.

Hinchingbrooke Park, Huntingdon PE18 8NT
Tel: 01480 416416 Fax: 01480 416561
(Norfolk, Suffolk and Cambridgeshire Health Authority)

Chair M Armstrong
Chief Executive Douglas Pattisson

Hinchingbrooke Hospital

Hinchingbrooke Park, Huntingdon PE18 8NT
Tel: 01480 416117 Fax: 01480 416299
Total Beds: 455

Accident and Emergency R K Das, H M Sherriff
Anaesthetics J Aneeshaw, P Benison, A M Brooks, A Fletcher, I Hille, H Holland, N Jamali, B Latham, K R Macleod, V Price, P Roberts, P Roberts, S M Ross
Care of the Elderly C D R Borland, R G Henderson, S Matsiko, K Walsh
Chest Medicine D Bilton, A Promnitz
Child and Adolescent Psychiatry P Millard, S Pedersen
Dermatology C Banfield, P Norris, P Todd
ENT P D M Ellis, R F Gray, P Jani
General Medicine C Borland, R J Dickinson, R G Henderson, S Matsiko, P Roberts, K Walsh
General Psychiatry D F Bermingham, C Corby, R W Latcham, C Royston
General Surgery B Bekdash, J Benson, J Gryf-Lowczowski, C R G Quick, J Reed
Genitourinary Medicine S Forster
Haematology C E Hoggarth, K Rege
Histopathology M Harris
Obstetrics and Gynaecology Dr Alkurdi, P B Forbes, K M Jennison, B Lim
Ophthalmology D W Flanagan, C Rene
Orthopaedics S Amarah, P F T Sewell, G W Southgate, T Vaughan-Lane, A Woojik
Paediatrics B Algawi, M G Becker, J Challener, R N Miles, J Valente
Radiology A Booth, C Clarke, C S F Hubbard, H Taylor, A Warner
Radiotherapy and Oncology D Gilligan, T Li-Tee
Rheumatology and Rehabilitation J R Jenner, G Pountain

Hinckley and Bosworth Primary Care Trust

Health Lane Surgery, Earl Shilton, Leicester LE9 7PB
Tel: 01455 851189 Fax: 01455 846162
(Leicestershire, Northamptonshire and Rutland Health Authority)

Chief Executive Colin Blacker

Homerton University Hospital NHS Trust

Homerton Row, London E9 6SR
Tel: 020 8510 5555 Fax: 020 8510 7608
(North East London Health Authority)

Chair Andrew Windross
Chief Executive N Hallett

Homerton University Hospital

Homerton Row, London E9 6SR
Tel: 020 8510 5555 Fax: 020 8510 7608
Total Beds: 485

Accident and Emergency H Cugnoni, Dr Gant, K Henderson, S Miles
Anaesthetics P Amoroso, M W Ashby, V Carr, J Coakley, L Davis, W Gallagher, Dr Guerin, G H Hackett, Dr Halfpenny, S Harrod, C J Hinds, P R Howell, Dr Okunso, Dr Tham, J D Watson, D J Wilkinson, Dr Wong, G Wray
Cardiology A Kurbaan, D S Tunstall-Pedoe
Care of the Elderly Dr Britton, Dr Cumming, Dr Elegbe, A B Lehmann
Clinical Pharmacology and Therapeutics S M L Abrams
Dermatology R Bull, Dr Goldsmith
Diabetes J V Anderson, Dr Freedman
Gastroenterology C Blanshard, P J Kumar, R Shidrawi
General Medicine S M L Abrams, J V Anderson, Dr Blanstard, G Bothamley, Dr Elegbe, P Freedman, A Lehmann, R Mootoo, R Rajakulasingam, D S Tunstall Pedoe
General Surgery Dr Kadirkamanathan, Dr Mahir, Dr Ravikumac, D Shanahan, Dr Unniss
Genitourinary Medicine J Anderson, S El Gadi, P Mayurahathan
Haematology R J Amos, Dr Evans
Medical Microbiology A Karcher, Dr Macrae
Neurology R J Greenwood, Dr Jarman
Obstetrics and Gynaecology D Akinfenwa, Dr Barnick, E Dorman, K Erskine, K Harrington, R J S Howell, Dr Roberts, C Stacey, N C Wathen, Dr Yoon
Ophthalmology Dr Daniel, R Whitelocke
Oral Surgery I L Hutchison
Orthopaedics K C Kong, D M McCarthy, Dr Mbubaegbu, V Sivagnanavel
Paediatrics J Bucknall, K Costeloe, S Fang, Dr Goddard, D Hodes, S Husain, Dr Maolouf, Dr Sood, A Washington
Palliative Medicine Dr Fever
Radiology S Amin, Dr Brooks, P M Cannon, K Patel, Dr Rockall, Dr Sahdev
Radiotherapy and Oncology M L Slevin, Dr Wells
Rehabilitation Medicine R J Greenwood
Respiratory Medicine G Bothamley, R Rajakulasingam
Rheumatology Dr Bhanj, Dr Mootoo
Urology V Nargund

Horsham and Chanctonbury Primary Care Trust

Park House, North Street, Horsham RM12 1RL
Tel: 01403 215129 Fax: 01403 215128
(Surrey and Sussex Health Authority)

NHS Trusts and NHS Hospitals

England

Addenbrooke's NHS Trust

From April 2002 mental health services transferring to Cambridgeshire and Peterborough Mental Health Partnership NHS Trust.

Hills Road, Cambridge CB2 2QQ
Tel: 01223 245151 Fax: 01223 216520
Email: keith.day@msexc.addenbrookes.anglox.nhs.uk
Website: www.addenbrookes.org.uk
(Norfolk, Suffolk and Cambridgeshire Health Authority)

Chair Tony Deakin
Chief Executive Roy Male

Addenbrooke's Hospital

Hills Road, Cambridge CB2 2QQ
Tel: 01223 245151 Fax: 01223 216520
Email: keith.day@msex.addenbrookes.anglox.nhs.uk
Website: www.addenbrookes.org.uk
Total Beds: 1269

Accident and Emergency G Campbell-Hewson, C Maimaris, S M Robinson

Anaesthetics A Bailey, J Bamber, S P Bass, L J Brennan, R Campbell, C Duffy, W A R Erskine, J Fisher, C W Glazebrook, L S Godsiff, K E J Gunning, A K Gupta, M J Herrick, D R Hughes, R M Jones, D J Kennedy, J R Klinck, R D Latimer, M J Lindop, I M J McKenzie, B F Matta, D K Menon, P J Morris, I T Munday, V U Navapurkar, J P Newell, G R Park, J A Pickett, P G Roe, D J Sapsford, N J Scurrah, HL Smith, A B Swami, D N Tew, J M Turner

Blood Transfusion C Beatty, W H Ouwehande, L M Williamson

Cardiology M R Bennett, D P Dutka, A A Grace, M C Petch, P H Schofield, L H Shapiro, P L Weissberg

Cardiothoracic Surgery S R Large, S S L Tsui, J Wallwork, F C Wells

Chemical Pathology S C Martin, A G W Norton

Clinical Biochemistry L S Culank, C N Hales

Clinical Immunology and Allergy P W Ewan, P W Ewan, M S Nasser, M S Nasser

Clinical Microbiology N Brown, U Desselberger, N Farrington, J E Foweraker, A Gerken, H A Ludlam

Clinical Pharmacology J Brown, M J Brown, S F Haydock, KH O'Shaughnessy, J P Schofield, J W Upward, I B Wilkinson

Dermatology N P Burrows, N Flanagan, P G Norris, R J Pye, J C Sterling, P M Todd

Endocrinology and Diabetes V K Chatterjee, S F Dinneen, O M Edwards, M Evans, S P O'Rahilly

ENT P Axon, P D M Ellis, R F Gray, P Jani, D A Moffat

Gastroenterology M E D Allison, A E S Gimson, J O Hunter, S Middleton, M Parkes

General Medicine J A Benson, A J Carmichael, T M Cox, P B Deegan, D T Fearon, S J Griffin, A-L Kinmouth, P J Lehner, A M L Lever, M J Newport, D Rubenstein, J G P Sissons

Genetics M Bobraw, C K Ffrench-Constant, H V Firth, J Rankin, F L Raymond, D C Rubinsztein, R N Sandford, D Trump, J R U Yates, R L Zimmern

Genitourinary Medicine C A Carne, C Sonnex

Care of the Elderly G A Campbell, D R Forsythe, K-T Khaw, C G Nicholl, E A Warburton, K J Wilson

Haematology T P Baglin, R W Carrell, J I O Craig, A R Green, R E Marcus, S A J Warren

Histopathology M Arends, L G Bobrow, G Callagy, N Coleman, V P Collins, B Cottrell, S E Davies, A F Dean, J W Grant, F A Jessop, A W Marker, R P Moseley, D G O'Donovan, M L O'Donovan, J L Rashbass, E Rytina, V E Save, S Stewart, S Thiru, A Whitehead, D G D Wight, G Williams, A D H Wyllie, J H Xuereb

Immunology D S Kumararatne

Metabolic Bone Medicine J E Compston, J Reeve

Neurology C M C Allen, J M Brown, D A S Compston, R A Barker, J R Hodges, G G Lennox, M R A Manford, P J Martin, P Nestor, J B Pilling, J W Thorpe, S J Wroe

Neurophysiology S J Boniface

Neurosurgery D G Hardy, P J Kirkpatrick, R W Kirollos, R J C Laing, R Macfarlane, J D Pickard, A Waters

Obstetrics and Gynaecology J R Allsop, A I Aziz, K J Dalton, A A El - Kholy, G A Hackett, J A Latimer, C Lees, M J MacDougall, P J D Milton, A Prentice, G C S Smith, S K Smith, J R W Williamson

Occupational Health P J Baxter

Oncology S J Jeffries

Ophthalmology L Allen, Dr Flanagan, J Keast-Butler, M G Kerr-Nuir, P A R Meyer, D K Newman, C Rene, N J C Sarkies, M P Snead

Oral and Maxillofacial Surgery D N Adlam, L Cheng

Orthodontics R J Rimes

Orthopaedic Surgery D P Conlan, C R Constant, D J Dandy, D J Edwards, P R Hamilton, G Keene, N H Matthewson, P J Owen, A M Robinson, N Rushton, R N Villar, A S Wojick

Paediatric Surgery A Aslam, A J L Brain, M P L Williams

Paediatrics J S Ahluwalia, C Acerini, J Challener, D Dunger, I Hughes, R W Iles, A W Kelsall, R J McClure, A L Ogilvy-Stuart, U Ramaswami, R I Ross-Russell, R C Tasker

Palliative Medicine S Booth

Plastic Surgery G C Cormack, P N Hall, M S Irwin, B G H Lamberty, C Malata

Psychiatry G E Berrios, F A M Blake, E Bullmore, S P Calloway, J H Dowson, P C Fletcher, J J Herrod, N J Hunt, N F S Hymas, G Isaacs, P B Jones, M London, P J McKenna, R Ramana, J Shapleske, M Stefan, C Walsh

Public Health Medicine P D P Pharoah, N J Wareham, J Whittaker

Radiology N M Antoun, D S Appleton, P W P Bearcroft, L H Berman, P D Britton, N R Carroll, R A R Coulden, C Cousins, J Cross, A K Dixon, A H Freeman, J H Gillard, J N P Higgins, D J Lomas, T Massoud, C Ng, N Sceaton, P A K Set, R Simmatamby, A Tasker, H L Taylor, R M L Warren

Renal Medicine J R Bradley, M S Ell, J D Firth, D R W Jayne, F E Karet, D K Peters, K G C Smith, P F Williams

Respiratory Medicine E R Chilvers, E R Condliffe, D A Lomas, K D McNeil, R Mahadeva, N W Morreil, R J D Winter

Rheumatology and Rehabilitation A J Crisp, M R Ehrenstein, J S H Gaston, B L Hazleman, J R Jenner, S G B Kirker, C A Speed

Urology K N Bullock, A Doble, W Turner

Fulbourn Hospital

Fulbourn, Cambridge CB1 5EF
Tel: 01223 248074
Email: marian.earle@msexc.addenbrookes.anglox.nhs.uk
Website: www.addenbrookes.org.uk
Total Beds: 340

General Psychiatry S P Calloway, T R Dening, D N Girling, C Gregory, A T Grounds, N J Hunt, N F S Hymas, E C A Lawton, M London, P J McKenna, J Shapleske, A Smith, M Stefan

Psychotherapy F N C Denman

NHS TRUSTS & NHS HOSPITALS

Rosie Hospital

Robinson Way, Cambridge CB2 2SW
Tel: 01223 245151
Email: olive.evans@msexc.addenbrookes.anglox.nhs.uk
Website: www.addenbrookes.org.uk
Total Beds: 122

Anaesthetics A Bailey, C W Glazebrook, D J Kennedy
Obstetrics and Gynaecology R A F Crawford, K J Dalton, G A Hackett, J Latimer, C Lees, M J MacDougall, P J D Milton, A Prentice, S K Smith, J R W Williamson
Paediatrics J S Ahluwalia, I Hughes, R W Iles, A W Kelsall, A L Ogilvy-Stuart, R I R Russell, R C Tasker, D M Williams
Radiology P A K Set

Pathology C T Burrow, M T Haggani, A Khan, A Olujohungbe, J D H Sheard, P A Stevenson, W Taylor, C Van-Heyningen
Radiology A Ap-Thomas, J Curtis, B E Eyes, D S Harty, A H Jones, H Lewis-Jones, E O'Grady, V Pellegrini, F Smethurst, J Tuson, D White
Rheumatology and Rehabilitation R J Moots, H Nirula, R N Thompson, E Williams
Urology D Machin, M Williamson

Walton Hospital

Rice Lane, Liverpool L9 1AE
Tel: 0151 525 5111

Waterloo Day Hospital

Haigh Road, Waterloo, Liverpool L22 3XR
Tel: 0151 928 7243
Total Beds: 40

Adur, Arun and Worthing Primary Care Trust

The Causeway, Goring-by-Sea, Worthing BN12 6BT
Tel: 01903 708400 Fax: 01903 246955
(Surrey and Sussex Health Authority)

Aintree Hospitals NHS Trust

Aintree House, University Hospital Aintree, Longmoor Lane, Liverpool L9 7AL
Tel: 0151 525 5980 Fax: 0151 525 6086
(Cheshire and Merseyside Health Authority)

Chair J Dray
Chief Executive J Birrell

University Hospital Aintree

Longmoor Lane, Liverpool L9 7AL
Tel: 0151 525 5980 Fax: 0151 525 6086
Total Beds: 1139

Accident and Emergency A M Armstrong, E Kadzombe, P Simms
Anaesthetics S P Acharya, M Bamber, D Brice, P Charters, L Colville, M Conway, J R Dalton, M Forrest, I F M Graham, D Gray, J Harrison, C Hodgson, W A Horton, E C Howard, R Kandasamy, E Lacasia-Purroy, D T Maconey, N P Mercer, E M Preston, S A Rogers, S Shaw, E Shearer, G Thind, I Tweedie, B Weldon, J R Wiles, E Wright
Cardiology A Amadi, K Clarke, R Hornung, E Rodrigues
Care of the Elderly J E Clague, I Evans, D McDowell, A K Sharma, M Siddiqi, J Turner
Chest Disease R Angus, P Calverley, R Costello, P D O Davies, J E Earis, C Ford, M Pearson, C Warburton
Endocrinology S B Cohen, G V Gill, I MacFarlane, J Wilding, G Williams
ENT A S David, A Fenton, A S Jones, T Lesser, V Nandapalan, M F Ramadan, N Roland, A C Swift
Gastroenterology N Krasner, P O'Toole, R E Sturgess, R Walker
General Psychiatry M Agarwal, E W Birchall, M Goonatilleke, M Jagannadham, R W Jones, V A Millar, S O'Brien, V Ramamurthy, M Ranatunea, S Simmons
General Surgery D J Cave-Bigley, J M Dhorajiwala, J Joseph, D Kerrigan, P McCulloch, C R Mackie, L Martin, I M Stevenson, R G Ward, A Wu
Infectious Diseases N Beeching, F J Nye
Obstetrics and Gynaecology U Abdulla, P Bousfield, M J Johnstone, M Jones, D Parkinson, G F Rowland, G Shaw
Oncology J Litter, D Smith
Ophthalmology D K Chitkara, D I Clarke, G Kyle, I B Marsh
Oral and Maxillofacial Surgery M Boyle, J S Brown, J C Cooper, D Richardson, S N Rogers, E D Vaughan
Orthodontics T Morris
Orthopaedics N Barton-Hansen, P Brownson, R A Evans, S C Montgomery, B Pennie, M H Thorneloe, H P J Walsh
Palliative Medicine G Corcoran

Airedale NHS Trust

Airedale General Hospital, Skipton Road, Steeton, Keighley BD20 6TD
Tel: 01535 652511 Ext: 4811, 01535 294811, 01535 655570
Fax: 01535 655129
(West Yorkshire Health Authority, North and East Yorkshire and Northern Lincolnshire Health Authority)

Chair Brian R Jewell
Chief Executive Robert E Allen

Airedale General Hospital

Skipton Road, Steeton, Keighley BD20 6TD
Tel: 01535 652511 Fax: 01535 655129
Total Beds: 644

Accident and Emergency P Cryer, M J Dudley
Anaesthetics R Adley, S J Almond, J R Baker, P M Kay, J Scriven, D A Shaw, J M Stanton, C Starkey, K Waite
Cardiology N P Silverton, A V Zezulka
Care of the Elderly D E Allen, M G Harrington, J P Milnes, J A Onafowokan
Dental Surgery S F Worrall
Dermatology A L Wright
ENT C H Raine, C E Vize
Family Planning and Reproductive Health S M Richardson
General Medicine D G Clements, C J Healey, H S R Hosker, C R Parker, R M Pope, M Raashed
General Psychiatry A J Aspin, C H Chambers, G C Finlayson, J A Fisk, J E Foster, R F Kehoe, F R McKenzie, C D P Sims
General Surgery E P Dewar, I F Hutchinson, C R Kapadia, R B N Khan, A H Nejim
Genitourinary Medicine K C Mohanty
Haematology A C Cuthbert
Neurology J G Howe
Obstetrics and Gynaecology J H Brash, P J Brunskill, K M Graham, N Samtaney
Oncology S M Crawford
Ophthalmology A D Atkins, P L Atkinson, J Bradbury, F D Ghanchi, J N James
Orthodontics L Mitchell, C E Young
Orthopaedics D J Beard, A A Faraj, S Ravindran, D T S Tang, C C Wray
Paediatrics A A Britland, S J Ilett, S C Puri, G A Savill, G C Soulby, K P Ward, K N Wilkinson
Palliative Medicine M J Hughes
Pathology N C Bradford, P E d Costa, P G R Godwin, N R Griffin, J J O'Dowd
Plastic Surgery M J Timmons
Radiology S G Blake, I R Brand, N D Grunshaw, K A Lindsay, G G Porter, S E S Whitecross
Radiotherapy and Oncology C J Orton
Rehabilitation Medicine D H G Cotter

Rheumatology A M Cooper
Urology I Appleyard, N A Shaikh

Airedale General Hospital - Day Hospital for Elderly

Skipton Road, Steeton, Keighley BD20 6TD
Tel: 01535 652511 Ext: 2701 Fax: 01535 655129

Bingley Day Hospital for the Elderly

Fernbank Drive, Bingley BD16 4HD
Tel: 01274 563438 Fax: 01274 510565

Bingley Hospital

Fernbank Drive, Bingley BD16 4HD
Tel: 01274 563438 Fax: 01274 510565

Care of the Elderly D E Allen

Castleberg Day Hospital for the Elderly

Raines Road, Giggleswick, Settle BD24 0BN
Tel: 01729 823515 Fax: 01729 823082

Castleberg Hospital

Raines Road, Giggleswick, Settle BD24 0BN
Tel: 01729 823515 Fax: 01729 823082
Total Beds: 21

Care of the Elderly M G Harrington

Ilkley Coronation Day Hospital for the Elderly

Springs Lane, Ilkley LS29 8TG
Tel: 01934 609666 Fax: 01943 816129

Ilkley Coronation Hospital (Outpatient and Minor Injuries)

Springs Lane, Ilkley LS29 8TG
Tel: 01943 609666 Fax: 01943 816129

Skipton General Day Hospital for the Elderly

Keighley Road, Skipton BD23 2RJ
Tel: 01756 792233 Fax: 01756 700485

Skipton General Hospital

Keighley Road, Skipton BD23 2RJ
Tel: 01756 792233 Fax: 01756 700485
Total Beds: 9

Care of the Elderly D E Allen, M G Harrington, J P Milnes, J A Onofowokan
General Medicine H S R Hosker, R M Pope
General Surgery E P Dewar, I F Hutchinson, C R Kapadia, A H Nejim
Neurology J G Howe
Obstetrics and Gynaecology N Samtaney
Ophthalmology J N James
Orthopaedics D J Beard, A A Faraj, D T S Tang, C C Wray
Paediatrics K P Ward
Rheumatology A M Cooper
Urology I Appleyard, N A Shaikh

Airedale Primary Care Trust

Airedale House, 21A Mornington Street, Keighley BD2 2EA
Tel: 01535 690416 Fax: 01535 672639
Website: www.airdale-pct.nhs.uk
(West Yorkshire Health Authority)

Chair Elizabeth Wolstenholme
Chief Executive Kevin Ellis

Amber Valley Primary Care Trust

Babington Hospital, Derby Road, Belper, Derby DE56 1WH
Tel: 01773 827560 Fax: 01773 827360
(Southern Derbyshire Health Authority)

Chair Adrian Evans
Chief Executive Wendy Lawrence

Ashfield Primary Care Trust

The Idlewells, Sutton-in-Ashfield NG17 1BP
Tel: 01623 559568 Fax: 01623 556251
Website: www.ashfield-pcg.nhs.uk
(Trent Health Authority)

Chair Keith Rees
Chief Executive Clive Brookes

Ashford and St Peter's Hospitals NHS Trust

St Peter's Hopital, Guilford Road, Chertsey KT16 0PZ
Tel: 01932 874757, 01932 872000
(Surrey and Sussex Health Authority)

Chair Sian Flynn
Chief Executive Andrew Morris

Ashford Hospital

Ashford TW15 3AA
Tel: 01784 884488 Fax: 01784 884017
Total Beds: 327

Accident and Emergency J S Belstead
Anaesthetics P H Balakrishnan, J C Dawson, D Holden, A Khadiwal, G Vora, J E J Yates
Care of the Elderly H N C Gunther
Chest Disease A J Winning
Dermatology S Parker
ENT V Cumberworth, J Hadley, A Robinson
General Medicine P W Adams, D Newberry, J Thornton, P R Wilkinson
General Surgery W N W Baker, N Browning, J Horner, S Shotria
Neurology R Lane
Obstetrics and Gynaecology A Elias, K Gangar, D W Hyatt
Ophthalmology A Gupta, M Rahman
Oral and Maxillofacial Surgery B M W Bailey, R J Carr
Orthodontics C Hepworth, L Jones
Orthopaedics M Bloomfield, H Roushdi, K A Walker
Paediatrics A Hadad, R C F Newton, S Zoritch
Pathology B Bramble, S Ibrahim, C E S Keenan, N R Kirk, A Laurie
Plastic Surgery D Davies
Radiology E A Bellamy, S M Davidson, R Davies, S R Patel, D Reiff
Radiotherapy and Oncology M Gaze
Rheumatology M S Irani
Thoracic Surgery S W Fountain
Urology B W Ellis, R Kulkarni

St Peter's Hospital

Chertsey KT16 0PZ
Tel: 01932 872000 Fax: 01932 874757
Total Beds: 396

Accident and Emergency V O'Neill, P S J Rana
Anaesthetics J Cooper, G J J Fuzzey, P Houlton, M M Imrie, M Jordan, F Lloyd Jones, J J Margary, M H Russell, B C Sellick
Cardiology D Fluck, M D Joy
Care of the Elderly B A Castleton, C Long, E McInnes
Chemical Pathology H G M Freeman, M Knapp
Chest Disease M G Britton
Child Psychiatry Y Parker, J Sebestik
Dermatology S V Jones, J A Miller, S Neill

NHS TRUSTS & NHS HOSPITALS

Diabetes M A Baxter
ENT P Chapman, N Solomons, P Sudderick
Gastroenterology P Finch
General Medicine M G Britton, P Finch, M D Joy
General Surgery E Chisholm, D R Donaldson, G Layer, H Scott, M Thomas
Genitourinary Medicine J Pritchard
Haematology A L Miller, D O'Shaugnessy
Histopathology M Hall, N A Ratcliffe, T Reagh
Medical Microbiology H C Grundy
Neurology D Barnes
Obstetrics and Gynaecology S Bateman, S Newbold, T Spencer, J T Wright
Ophthalmology M G Boodhoo, R W Condon
Oral and Maxillofacial Surgery R A Peebles
Orthopaedics D Elliott, R P Hollingsworth, K Newman, R D Pool, C Schofield, R B Simonis
Paediatrics J J Bowyer, P Crawshaw, P Martin, W Nackasha, R C F Newton, Z Zersh
Pathology H G M Freeman, H C Grundy, M Hall, M Knapp, A L C Miller, D O'Shaughnessy, D A Ratcliffe
Plastic Surgery R Martin
Radiology C E Bennett, M Creagh, B S Donnellan, J Glover, P P Ho
Rheumatology G Hall, R Hughes
Thoracic Surgery E E J Smith
Urology R Cole, N H Hills
Vascular Surgery K Dawson

Ashford Primary Care Trust

Unit 3, Eurogate Business Park, Thompson Road, Ashford TN24 8XW
Tel: 01233 655800 Fax: 01233 650332
(Kent and Medway Health Authority)

Ashton, Leigh and Wigan Primary Care Trust

Cherrycroft Court, Wigan Lane, Wigan WN1 2JE
Chair Lynne Liptrot
Chief Executive Peter Rowe

Avon Ambulance Service NHS Trust

Marybush Lane, Bristol BS2 0AT
Tel: 01179 277046 Fax: 01179 251419
Email: post@avon ambulance.nhs.uk, post@avonambulance.nhs.uk
Website: www.avonambulance.nhs.uk
(Avon, Gloucestershire and Wiltshire Health Authority)

Chair David Giles
Chief Executive Kevin P Hogarty

Avon and Wiltshire Mental Health Partnership NHS Trust

Bath NHS House, Newbridge Hill, Bath BA1 3QE
Tel: 01225 731731, 01225 731732
(Avon, Gloucestershire and Wiltshire Health Authority)

Chair Christine Reid
Chief Executive Roger Pedley

Barrow Hospital

Barrow Gurney, Bristol BS19 3SG
Tel: 01275 392811 Fax: 01275 394277
Total Beds: 161

Blackberry Hill Hospital

Manor Road, Fishponds, Bristol BS16 2EW
Tel: 0117 965 6061 Fax: 0117 925 4832

Green Lane Hospital

Devizes SN10 5DS
Tel: 01380 731200 Fax: 01380 731308
Total Beds: 60

General Psychiatry J Godfrey, G Lodge, D Stevens, R Thorpe, C Vize

Long Fox Unit

Weston General Hospital, Grange Road, Uphill, Weston Super Mare BS23 4TQ
Tel: 01934 647069 Fax: 01934 643061
Total Beds: 48

Old Manor Hospital

Wilton Road, Salisbury SP2 7EP
Tel: 01722 336262 Fax: 01722 320313
Total Beds: 80

St Martin's Hospital

Midford Road, Bath BA2 5RP
Tel: 01225 832383
Total Beds: 46

Sandalwood Court

Highgrove Road, Swindon SN3 4WF
Tel: 01793 836800 Fax: 01793 836801
Total Beds: 56

Barking and Dagenham Primary Care Trust

The Clock House, East Street, Barking IG11 8EY
Tel: 020 8532 6285 Fax: 020 8532 6371
(North East London Health Authority)

Chair Ray Parkin
Chief Executive Julia Ross

Barking, Havering and Redbridge Hospitals NHS Trust

Harold Wood Hospital, Gubbins Lane, Romford RM3 0BE
Tel: 01708 345533
(North East London Health Authority)

Chair Vijay Vasu
Chief Executive Pete Murphy

Barking Hospital

Upney Lane, Barking IG11 9LX
Tel: 020 8983 8000 Fax: 020 8970 8004
Total Beds: 115

Genitourinary Medicine Y S Hooi

Harold Wood Hospital

Gubbins Lane, Harold Wood, Romford RM3 0BE
Tel: 01708 345533
Total Beds: 405

Anaesthetics R M Mehta, G L Steer, D A Thomas
Care of the Elderly M Smith, L Wicks
Dermatology S Bor, D A Dodd
ENT B Chopra, Dr Chowdhury, D V Furlong, B Kotecha, A Mitra
General Medicine M C P Apps, P Cannon, D J Moul
General Psychiatry D P Cronin, D E S James, S B Mathur, J L Swift

General Surgery T P Brock, B M Handel, M G Prinn
Neurology L J Findley
Obstetrics and Gynaecology P Bolton, V Rao, M Sathanandan, A Tebbit, R Utidjian, A Weekes
Ophthalmology C Clarke, G M B Dawidek, J Pitts, S T Ruben
Orthopaedics R D Kassab, R J J Wenger
Paediatrics G Cheriyan, T H J Matthews
Pathology Z Adhami, R W Dungu, I T Saeed, D P Winstanley
Radiology A S A Karim, D K Saha
Rheumatology G Clarke

King George Hospital
Barley Lane, Goodmayes, Ilford IG3 8YB
Tel: 020 8983 8000 Fax: 020 8970 8001
Total Beds: 542

Accident and Emergency Y Gupta
Anaesthetics P M Bashir
Dermatology R A Wakeel
General Medicine S Grainger, V L Sharman
General Surgery S J Snooks
Haematology I Grant
Medical Microbiology S Lacey
Neurology J Jestico
Obstetrics and Gynaecology S Burgess
Ophthalmology S Bryan
Orthopaedics B Levack
Paediatrics D L Robinson
Radiology C Padmanathan
Urology P Shridharan

Oldchurch Hospital
Oldchurch Road, Romford RM7 0BE
Tel: 01708 345533
Total Beds: 473

Accident and Emergency V E Holkar
Anaesthetics V Badorrey, C Bhah, H Boralessa, G Chitra, D De Villiers, M Gallagher, A Haq, E M Jones, S C Kapoor, R Mehta, M Mikhael, I Nair, M Okoisor, K Raveendran, B Robinson, E Simpson, S M Srivatsa, S M Steer, P Walker, C R Wijesurendra, S Yoganathan
Biochemistry C Corns
Cardiology J D Stephens
Care of the Elderly R Fowler, J Mannakkara, A Sharma, M Smith, R Walker, L S Wicks
Chest Medicine M Apps, R Wetherstone
Dermatology S Bor, H Dodd
Diabetes D Moul, G Toms, J Tremble
ENT B Chopra, A N Mitra
Gastroenterology R W Burnham, D Hollanders, M Newton
General Medicine J R Billinghurst, A J S Brain, W R Burnham, R Fowler, D Hollanders, J A Tallack, R M Weatherstone
General Psychiatry S K Choudhury, N Farnan, C Hewavisenti, E S Meltzer, A C Purches
General Surgery W Ismail, D Johnson, D Khoo, G Ponting, S Shami, A Stuart
Genitourinary Medicine S Ariyanayagam
Haematology A Brownell, D Lewis
Histopathology D Al-Okati
Infectious Diseases M Yong
Medical Microbiology Z H Adhami
Neurology R Capildeo, L J Findley, C N Hawkes, R N Silva
Neuropathology A Marshall
Neurophysiology V Dus, N Muhammed
Neurosurgery A Aspoas, J Benjamin, N Garvan, A J Kellerman
Obstetrics and Gynaecology U Rao, M R A Utidjian, A R L Weekes
Oral and Maxillofacial Surgery D Falconer, S V L Prasad
Orthodontics A Howat
Orthopaedics A Al-Sabti, H Banan, R J King, A I Lang-Stevenson, G E MacLellan, H Plaha, R J J Wenger
Paediatrics T H J Matthews, R Prasad, J Rawal, G Subramanian, J Swift, Dr Szoller, Z H Zaidi
Pathology R Bryan, P A Ellis, N Khan
Pharmacology R Pearson

Plastic Surgery J V H Kemble
Radiology M Alsewan, S K Banyikidde, A Dabbaghian, S R Gademsetty, J Gutman, S R Srivatsa
Radiotherapy and Oncology A R Gershuny, M Quigley, S G Vaidya
Renal Medicine A Brian, I Fahal
Rheumatology and Rehabilitation K Chakravarty, G Clarke, C Kelsey

Barnet and Chase Farm Hospitals NHS Trust

Barnet Hospital, Wellhouse Lane, Barnet EN5 3DJ
Tel: 020 8216 4000 Fax: 020 8216 4954
(North Central London Health Authority)

Chair Jennifer Bowley
Chief Executive Elizabeth Heyer

Barnet General Hospital
Wellhouse Lane, Barnet EN5 3DJ
Tel: 020 8216 4000 Fax: 020 8216 4954
Total Beds: 459

Accident and Emergency B Shravat
Anaesthetics N Fletcher, P McGowan, R Marks, A E Nicol, I E Symons, A Wolff
Care of the Elderly S Arunachalam, M Garland, T Gluck, D Levy, S Vellodi, P Wiseman
Child and Adolescent Psychiatry R Brown
Orthopaedics J C Angel

Chase Farm Hospital
The Ridgeway, Enfield EN2 8JL
Tel: 020 8366 6600 Fax: 020 8366 1361
Total Beds: 469

Accident and Emergency G Hinchley, H Mikhail
Anaesthetics D Harvey, S A I Helwa, K Jash, Y Jayran-Nejad, R Khiroya, N Macartney, R F J Matthews, L Mendonca, B Munro, J Olver, S Pavlou
Dermatology J J R Almeyda
ENT M Z Farag, S Habashi
General Medicine C Baynes, R Davies, A Mier, S Saboor, N Van Someren
General Surgery J Bolton, J R G Gardham, V Jaffe, N Law, M W N Ward
Haematology S M Fairhead, M Treacy
Neurology L Ginsberg
Obstetrics and Gynaecology N R H Boyd, A Jackson, A J Minchin, M Morcos
Oncology S J Karp
Oral and Maxillofacial Surgery M Gaukroger, P McDermott, P S G Perera
Orthopaedics D Archibald, T Bull, D Grace, J Neyt, H Ware
Paediatrics I Pollock, C Rohan, K Withana, B Yuksel
Pathology W Mohamid, R V Mummery, A Norden, H A S Reid
Radiology S Anchor, A Isaacs, G Papas, C Thomas
Rheumatology and Rehabilitation A J Griffin, B Mulcahy
Urology R F P Copland, L Kahn

Cheshunt Community Hospital
King Arthur Court, Crossbrook Street, Cheshunt, Waltham Cross EN8 8XN
Tel: 01992 622157 Fax: 01992 629595

ENT M Z Farag
General Medicine C Baynes, R Davies, S Saboor
General Surgery M Ward
Obstetrics and Gynaecology N Boyd, A Jackson
Paediatrics I Pollock, B Yuksel
Rheumatology A J Griffin
Urology P Copland, L Kahn

NHS TRUSTS & NHS HOSPITALS

Edgware Community Hospital
Edgware HA8 0AD
Tel: 020 8952 2381 Fax: 020 8732 6807

Edgware Day Surgery Unit
Edgware Community Hospital, Edgware HA8 0AD
Tel: 020 8732 6722

Finchley Memorial Hospital
Granville Road, North Finchley, London N12 0JE
Tel: 020 8349 3121 Fax: 020 8346 6043
Total Beds: 76

Care of the Elderly R Breeze, C Vellodi, P Wiseman
Chest Disease J Bradley, R Winter
Diabetes A Barnes
ENT G J Radcliffe
General Medicine K E Gray, A J G Pearson
General Surgery P W Davis, J Postlethwaite
Obstetrics and Gynaecology A Rodin
Orthopaedics S Blackburne, B Ferris
Paediatrics S Laurent
Radiology S Johnson, P Lai
Rheumatology and Rehabilitation J Roseberg, C Smith

Potters Bar Hospital
Mutton Lane, Potters Bar EN6 2PB
Tel: 01707 53286
Total Beds: 51

Care of the Elderly R Breeze
Dermatology H Barnes
ENT G J Radcliffe
General Medicine A J Barnes
General Surgery J S Kenefick, J C Postlethwaite
Obstetrics and Gynaecology H Wagman
Orthopaedics J S Blackburn
Paediatrics S Laurent

Barnet, Enfield and Haringey Mental Health NHS Trust

Avon Villa, Chase Farm Hospital, The Ridgeway, Enfield EN2 8JL
Tel: 020 8366 9167 Fax: 020 8366 1361
Email: firstname.lastname@enfield-tr.nthames.nhs.uk
Website: www.beh.nhs.uk
(North Central London Health Authority)

Chair Brian Gomes da Costa
Chief Executive John Newbury Helps

Chase Farm Hospital Site
The Ridgeway, Enfield EN2 8JL
Tel: 020 8366 6600 Fax: 020 8366 9166
Total Beds: 359

Care of the Elderly R A Jackson, A Mahmood, A Weinstein
Child and Adolescent Psychiatry G Broster, G Broster
Community Child Health R Vijeratnam
Forensic Psychiatry A Akikumni, L Hamilton, D James, Dr Kearns, H Kennedy
General Psychiatry C Capstick, M Cody, M Kember, V Watts
Neurology T Nathan
Orthopaedics S C Chen, D Grace, P D Moynagh, K H Stone
Psychiatry of Old Age J Carrick, J Garner

Colindale Hospital
Colindale Avenue, London NW9 5GH
Tel: 020 8200 1555 Fax: 020 8205 6062
Total Beds: 152

Care of the Elderly S Arunachalam, M H Garland, A Homer, L Wilson

St Ann's Hospital
St. Ann's Road, South Tottenham, London N15 3TH
Tel: 020 8442 6000 Fax: 020 8442 6354
Total Beds: 386

Care of the Elderly R Luder, P Ranmuthu, W Woothipoom
Child and Adolescent Psychiatry T M Naidoo, G Stern
General Psychiatry A Bateman, C Burford, R C S Furlong, A Hoar, G S Ibrahimi, E C Johnson-Sabine, R Lucas, W G Smith, M Weller, A Wijeyekoon
Genitourinary Medicine Dr Nageswaren
Learning Disabilities M Dickenson

Barnet Primary Care Trust

Hyde House, The Hyde, Edgeware Road, London NW9 6QQ
Tel: 020 8201 4800 Fax: 020 8201 4701
(North Central London Health Authority)

Chair Peter Hollins
Chief Executive Averil Dongworth

Finchley Memorial Hospital
Finchley Memorial Day Hospital, Granville Road, North Finchley, London NW9 5HG
Tel: 020 8349 3121 Fax: 020 8346 6043
Total Beds: 76

Barnsley Community and Priority Services NHS Trust

Closure of trust tbc - Services transferring to Barnsley Primary Care Trust.

Kendray Hospital, Doncaster Road, Kendray, Barnsley S70 3RD
Tel: 01226 296782, 01226 777811
(South Yorkshire Health Authority)

Chair Tom Sheard
Chief Executive Ray A Denison

Kendray Hospital
Doncaster Road, Kendray, Barnsley S70 3RD
Tel: 01226 777811 Fax: 01226 296782
Total Beds: 113

Alcohol and Substance Misuse B Mehta
General Psychiatry Dr Addala, T V Mohan

Mount Vernon Hospital
Mount Vernon Road, Barnsley S70 4GP
Tel: 01226 777835 Fax: 01226 283119, 01226 777836
Total Beds: 144

Care of the Elderly Dr Al-Douri, Dr Baruam, Dr Franklin

Barnsley District General Hospital NHS Trust

Gawber Road, Barnsley S75 2EP
Tel: 01226 730000 Fax: 01226 202859
(South Yorkshire Health Authority)

Chair Gordon E Firth
Chief Executive Jan Sobieraj

Barnsley District General Hospital
Gawber Road, Barnsley S75 2EP
Tel: 01226 730000 Fax: 01226 202859
Total Beds: 633

Accident and Emergency D Hughes, S Ramnani, A Smith

BARTS & THE LONDON NHS TRUST

Anaesthetics N Bhaskaran, A Bowry, P Claydon, H Filby, N Gill, M A Longan, V F Metias, Y Myint, R Paton, C Swinhoe
Care of the Elderly M Al-Bazzaz, A El-Trafi, S Gariballa, S Orme, S Parker
Chemical Pathology A Straffen
Dental Surgery J D Price
Dermatology S E Thomas
ENT D Martin-Hirsch, M H Wickham
General Medicine D Bullimore, D Dimov, R V Hague, R V Hague, T Jones, K Kapur, W Rhoden, B Saeed, A Soliman, I Wahedna
General Surgery J J Bannister, J Kenogbon, T Offori, M Shiwani, B G Way
Genitourinary Medicine G M Dilke-Wing, D A Hicks
Histopathology J A Coup
Obstetrics and Gynaecology J D Crosbie, S M Henalla, B F Leabeater, R Watson
Orthodontics J D Holmgren
Orthopaedics A Al-Dada, P A Bryant, M Khan, I H Piper, C Ruddlesdin
Paediatrics L M R Davis-Reynolds, E A Gouta, D Kerrin
Plastic Surgery R Griffiths
Radiology D Darby, J Walls, S Yates, L Yeoman, J Zachary
Rheumatology and Rehabilitation A O Adebajo

Barnsley Primary Care Trust

Hilder House, 49-51 Gawber Road, Barnsley S75 2PY
Tel: 01226 777012 Fax: 01226 208463
(South Yorkshire Health Authority)

Chief Executive Ailsa Claire

Barts and The London NHS Trust

The Royal London Hospital, Whitechapel Road, Whitechapel, London E1 1BB
Tel: 020 7377 7000 Fax: 020 7377 7361
Website: www.bartsandthelondon.org.uk
(North East London Health Authority)

The London Chest Hospital

Bonner Road, London E2 9JX
Tel: 020 7377 7000
Total Beds: 92

Anaesthetics M Messent, S Stacey, K Wark
Cardiology R Balcon, G Clesham, A Deaner, P Kelly, C Knight, P Mills, M Rotham, A Timmis
Cardiothoracic Surgery P Magee, R Uppal, W Weir, K Wong, A Wood
General Medicine and Respiratory Medicine N Barnes
Histopathology I Scheimberg
Respiratory Medicine L Kuitert, S Lozewicz, J Wedicha

The Royal London Hospital

Whitechapel Road, London E1 1BB
Tel: 020 7377 7000 Fax: 020 7377 7401
Total Beds: 698

Accident and Emergency T Coats, H Cugnoni, F Davies, G Davies, K Henderson, S Miles, A Wilson
Anaesthetics J Anderson, C Broomhead, J Challands, C Chin, D Clark, P Colvin, J Cotter, P Flynn, D Goldhill, S Harrod, M Healy, E Mcateer, J McNeil, P Monks, A Mulcahy, M Newton, P O'Shea, H Owen-Reece, M Razzaque, C Sadler, G Samra, R Sashidharan, A Shukla, J Silk, L Struin, A Visram, S Withington, G Wray, P Yate
Dentistry V Booth, M Calvert, M Collins, S Djemal, P Farthing, J Fearne, J Hardie, F Hughes, R Lee, M Thornhill, D Williams, F Wong, P Wright
Dermatology A Quinn (Head), V Bataille, R Cerio, I Leigh, J McGregor
Diabetes S Coppack, G Hitman, P Kopelman
Endocrinology D Wood

Gastroenterology M Glynn, P Kumar, D Rampton, P Swain
General Surgery S Bhattacharya, F Cross, S Dorudi, A W Goode, R Ham, M Sheikh-Sobeh, Dr Siddiqui, M Walsh, N Williams
Genitourinary Medicine G Forster, B T Goh, T McManus, R Shen, C Skinner
Gynaecology P Armstrong, T Beedham, C Davis, G Grudzinskas, V Sivapathasundaram
Haematology B Colvin, F Cotter, C Gutteridge, A Newland, D Proven, P Telfer
Histopathology S Baithun, D Berney, J Martin, M Sheaff
Infection and Immunity G Baily
Medical Microbiology A Mifsud, E Price, A Sefton
Neonatology L De Rooy, M Hird, S Kempley, P Mannix
Nephrology Z Chawdhery, J Conningham, F Marsh, M Raftery, C Rudge, R Thuraisingham, M Yaqoob
Neurology P Bradbury, G Elrington, J Fearnley, J Gawler, D Park, M Swash, R Walker
Neuropathology J Geddes
Neurosurgery F Afshar, P Hamlyn, I Sabin, J Sutcliffe
Nuclear Medicine H Jan
Ophthalmology A Mushin
Oral and Maxillofacial Surgery A Aitken, J Carter, K Coghlan, I Hutchison
Orthopaedics C Natali, M Paterson, G Scott
Paediatrics S Carr, I C Chikanza, C Cord-Udy, V Foster, R Harris, J Kingston, V Larcher, J Lilleyman, S McKenzie, A Martinez, D Misra, D Paige, M Powis, P Rees, V Saha, A Shankar, C Walker
Palliative Medicine D Feuer
Plastic Surgery N Carver, G Moir, M Shibu
Radiology C Blakeney, A Brooks, P Butler, O Chan, M Easty, E Evanson, E Friedman, N Garvie, J Murfitt, A Sharma, C Thakkar
Respiratory Medicine D Empey
Rheumatology and Rehabilitation D Perry (Head), A Jawad, B Kidd, R Stratton
Trauma and Orthopaedic Surgery S Ang, M Barry, T Bucknill, D Goodier, W Grange
Urology C Fowler, A Paris
Virology C Aitken, J Jeffries

St Bartholomew's Hospital

West Smithfield, London EC1A 7BE
Tel: 020 7377 7000
Website: www.bartsandthelondon.org.uk
Total Beds: 290

Anaesthetics P Amoroso, M Ashby, A Bristow, V Carr, J Coakley, C Ferguson, H Hackett, A Hemming, C Hinds, P Howell, N Kellow, J Krapez, R Langford, R Marks, P Saunders, L Tham, B Varley, J Watson, S White, D Wilkinson, L Worthington
Breast Unit R Carpenter
Cardiology A Nathan (Head), S Banim, T Crake, R Dawson, D Dymond, S Gupta, J Hogan, O Kurbaan, J Sayer, R Spurrell, J Stephens, D Tunstall-Pedoe
Cardiothoracic Surgery A Wood (Head), S Edmondson, A Lister, P Peters, A Shipolini
Clinical Neurological Physiology D Ingram
Clinical Oncology C Cottrill, S Gibbs, G Mair, N Plowman, M Powell, P Wells
Clinical Pharmacology and General Medicine S Abrams
Endocrinology S L Chew (Head), J Anderson, A Clark, A Grossman, P Jenkins, J Monson
ENT M Dilkes (Head), M Keene, J Rubin
Gastroenterology P Fairclough (Head), E Alstead, A Ballinger, P Kumar, G Libby
General Surgery J Lumley, S Purkiss
Genitourinary Medicine C Escourt, P Mayura Nathan, R Melville, J Zelin
Gynaecology T Al-Shawaf, O Djahanbakhch, G Grudzinskas, I Jacobs, A Jayarajah, A Lower, D Oram, N Perks
Haematology J Amess, J Cavenagh, P MacCallum, A Rohatiner
Histopathology M Calamanici, P Domizio, D Lowe, A Norton, N Singh, C Wells
Immunology M Murphy, A Pinching
Immunopathology J Parkin

NHS TRUSTS & NHS HOSPITALS

Infection and Immunity J Anderson, M Herlbert
Medical Microbiology S Das, M Prentice
Medical Oncology C Gallagher, T Oliver, D Propper, R Rudd, J Shamash, M Slevin
Metabolism and Diabetes P Freedman, D Galton, D Leslie
Neurological Physiology K Nagendran
Neurosurgery P Hamlyn
Nuclear Medicine K Britton
Obstetrics and Gynaecology J Aquilina
Occupational Health Service D D'Auria
Ophthalmology J Hungerford, R Whitelocke
Paediatric Gastroenterology I Suanderson
Paediatric Medicine N Meadows, M Savage
Pain Clinic J Foster, J Gallagher
Palliative Medicine D Feuer, C Phillips, T Tate
Radiology P Armstrong, P Cannon, A McLean, M Matson, I Nockler, N Perry, R Reznek, S Vinnicombe, J Webb
Respiratory Medicine J Moore-Gillon
Urology Dr Al Sundani, F Chinegwundoh, V Nargund
Virology D Jeffries

Basildon and Thurrock General Hospitals NHS Trust

Basildon Hospital, Nethermayne, Basildon SS16 5NL
Tel: 01268 533911 Fax: 01268 593757
Website: www.basildonandthurrock.org.uk
(Essex Health Authority)

Chair David Hooper

Basildon Hospital

Nether Mayne, Basildon SS16 5NL
Tel: 01268 533911 Fax: 01268 593757
Total Beds: 450

Anaesthetics H Alhameed, A David, M K Gademesetty, L Hoogsteden, R Jones, D M Lowe, M S May, A M Murray, V G Punchihewa, L T Rylah, M Sun Wai, S J Thomson, S F Tinloi, H J W Utting, J P Whitehead, I Youkhana
Cardiology R Aggarwal, S Iyer, W Serino
Cellular Pathology A Abdulla, N Alsanjari, K Osayi, P Ozua
Dermatology M D Catterall, S M Khorshid
Ear, Nose and Throat G Fayad, A Latif, B O'Reilly, A P Su
Elderly Medicine C Chan, R Huwez, G H Jenner, A Jubber, D Mullane
Endocrinology R Khan, M Mulcahy
Gastroenterology D J Gertner, J M Subhani, C P Willoughby
General, Vascular, Breast and Colorectal T Jeddy, F Khan, K Lafferty, I P Linehan, B Lovett, B F Ribeiro, D G St John Collier, H Taylor
Haematology P Cervi, E J Watts
Imaging M Alsewan, T Chan, T Cory, A Hails, A Salahuddin
Internal Medicine E Osman
Microbiology R J Sage
Neurology R Capildeo, A Malaspina
Obstetrics and Gynaecology A R Haloob, A Ikomi, D Ojutiku, R Varma, C C Welch
Oral J McKechnie, D K Madan, P Weller
Orthopaedics R Grewel, N B Ker, I Lennox, T Peckham, R J Pusey, K J Reddy, J Targett, R Wakeman
Paediatrics J Askwith, K Khalefa, R Ramanan, N Sharief, S J Ware
Palliative Care G Tosh
Renal Medicine I Barton, A Lal, S Morgan
Respiratory D K Muckherjee, B Yung
Rheumatology N Gendi, J Palit
Urology P Ewah, D R Osborne

Orsett Hospital

Grays RM16 3EU
Tel: 01268 533911 Fax: 01268 592227
Total Beds: 200

Anaesthetics M K Gademesetty, D M Lowe, A M Murray, V G Punchihewa, L T Rylah, S J Thomson, S F Tinloi, H J W Utting, J P Whitehead
Care of the Elderly C Cook, A J D Farquarson, G H Jenner, A Jubber, D Mullane
Dermatology M D Catterall
ENT D G Fife, A A Latif, B O'Reilly, A P C Su
Gastroenterology D J Gertner, C P Willoughby
General Medicine J F Bridgman, H Y Lee
General Surgery D G S Collier, K Lafferty, I P Linehan, H G Naylor, B F Ribeiro
Haematology P Cervi, E J Watts
Histopathology N Aqel, J Leake, E E Peters, S G Subbuswamy
Medical Microbiology R J Sage
Nephrology S Morgan
Neurology R Capildeo
Obstetrics and Gynaecology A R Haloob, M R Martin, R Varma, C C Welch
Oral Surgery J McKechnie, D K Madan, P Weller
Orthopaedics N B Ker, I Lennox, C D R Lightowler, T Peckham, R J Pusey, J Tagett, R Wakeman
Paediatrics D M Easton, R Ramanan, N Sharief, S J Ware
Pathology P W N Gordon
Radiology T Chan, P Cory, R Hails, A Salahuddin, D T Thompson
Rheumatology and Rehabilitation N Gendi, J Palit
Urology D R Osborne

Basildon Primary Care Trust

The Hatherley, Basildon SS14 2QJ
Tel: 01268 441622 Fax: 01268 441621
Email: basildon.pct@sessex-ha.nthames.nhs.uk
Website: www.basildon-pct.nhs.uk
(Essex Health Authority)

Chair Janet Hawes
Chief Executive Mary-Ann Munford

Bassetlaw Primary Care Trust

Retford Hospital, North Road, Retford DN22 7XF
Tel: 01777 274400 Fax: 01777 710535
Website: www.bassetlawpct.fsnet.co.uk
(Trent Health Authority)

Chair St John Deakin
Chief Executive Louise Newcombe

Bath and North East Somerset Primary Care Trust

St Martins Hospital, Midford Road, Bath BA2 5RP
Tel: 01225 831800 Fax: 01225 840407
Email: info@banes-pct.nhs.uk
Website: www.banes-pct.nhs.uk
(Avon, Gloucestershire and Wiltshire Health Authority)

Chair Malcolm Hanney
Chief Executive Rhona Macdonald

Bebington and West Wirral Primary Care Trust

3rd Floor, Admin Block, St Catherine's Hospital, Church Road, Birkenhead CH42 0LQ
Tel: 0151 651 3979 Fax: 0151 670 9637
Website: www.wirralhealth.org.uk
(Cheshire and Merseyside Health Authority)

Chair Norman Pursglove
Chief Executive Allison Cooke

Bedford Hospitals NHS Trust

Kempton Road, Bedford MK42 9DJ
Tel: 01234 355122 Fax: 01234 218106
Website: www.bedfordhospital.org.uk
(Bedfordshire and Hertfordshire Health Authority)

Chief Executive Andrew Reed

Bedford Hospital

21 Kimbolton Road, Bedford MK40 2AW
Tel: 01234 355122
Total Beds: 475

Accident and Emergency S Shankar, D Small
Anaesthetics M J Burbidge, D A Dutton, B Fahmy, J E Hughes, J Hurst, R Kavan, D Liu, Dr Lucl, J T McNamara, A S Mody, D J Niblett, J Sizer, S L Snape, J U Wilson
Cardiology I C Cooper, J Cooper
Care of the Elderly I Kamal, K L Nandi, N Thangarajah, W N Trounson
Dermatology E Burova, B E Monk
ENT Dr Arasaratnam, M C Frampton, T J Hoare
General Medicine Dr Cahn, R S J Harvey, P A McNamara, N J Morrish, J H B Saunders
General Surgery M J Callam, A Eldin, R J E Foley, I Husain, D C S Parsons, D Skipper, Dr Tisi, N B Waterfall
Genitourinary Medicine K Shanmugaratnam
Haematology D T Howes, V S Neil
Neurology M Manford
Obstetrics and Gynaecology G C Budden, E J Neale, A D R Ogborn, S F Reynolds, R M Wallace
Occupational Health P W Lewthwaite
Oncology R Thomas, J Watson
Ophthalmology F F Fisher, S J P Pieris, A Sharma
Oral and Maxillofacial Surgery Dr Chan, M T Simpson
Orthodontics A B Hewitt
Orthopaedics P A J Edge, C Handley, G Nel, R D Rawlins, T B H Riley
Paediatrics O Kwapong, M Leigh, R D Mehta, M J Pocha, S Rehman
Pathology A J Blackshaw, L Fitch, D T Howes, F Mutch, V S Neil, D B Rimmer, W S Wassif, M J E Wilkins
Plastic Surgery P J Mahaffey
Radiology S J Barter, A M Egan, I P Hicks, R A Moxon, J H Newton, R H Oakley, M I Shaikh
Rheumatology and Rehabilitation S A Rae

Bedford Primary Care Trust

Gilbert Hitchcock House, 21 Kimbolton Road, Bedford MK40 2NW
Tel: 01234 795714 Fax: 01234 342028
(Bedfordshire and Hertfordshire Health Authority)

Chair Alan Loynes
Chief Executive Margaret Stockham

Bedfordshire and Hertfordshire Ambulance and Paramedic Service NHS Trust

Hammond Road, Bedford MK41 0RG
Tel: 01234 408999 Fax: 01234 270480
Email: info@bhamb.nhs.uk
Website: www.bhamb.nhs.uk
(Bedfordshire and Hertfordshire Health Authority)

Chair Maria Ball
Chief Executive Anne Walker

Bedfordshire and Luton Community NHS Trust

Charter House, Alma Street, Luton LU1 2PL
Tel: 01582 700171 Fax: 01582 700151
(Bedfordshire and Hertfordshire Health Authority)

Chair Alison Davis
Chief Executive Ian Hammond

Abbotswood Road Day Hospital

Abbotswood Road, Luton LU2 0LX
Tel: 01582 709162

General Psychiatry G Kanakaratnam, A C Wagle, S A Wagle

Albany Road Day Hospital

1 Albany Road, Bedford
Tel: 01234 346341

Beacon House

5 Regent Street, Dunstable LU6 1LTR
Tel: 01582 709200

Mental Health V Francis

Calnwood Court

Calnwood Road, Luton LU4 0LU
Tel: 01582 538600

General Psychiatry K Bala, J Muthiah, J A Pillai, Y Rao

Crombie House

36 Hockcliffe Street, Leighton Buzzard LU7 8HE
Tel: 01525 751133

Mental Health F H Saleh

Farley Hill Day Hospital

Whipperley Ring, Farley Hill, Luton LU1 5QY
Tel: 01525 708222

Lime Trees EMI Assessment Unit

Calnwood Road, Luton LU4 0FB
Tel: 01582 707538

Elderly Mentally Ill A Evans

Orchard Unit

Calnwood Road, Luton LU4 0DZ
Tel: 01582 657500

General Psychiatry R T Pinto

Weller Wing

Kempston Road, Bedford MK42 9BJ
Tel: 01234 355122 Fax: 01234 340798
Total Beds: 62

General Psychiatry H R Markar, K J Morgan Gray, A Patel, M A Suleiman

Bedfordshire Heartlands Primary Care Trust

1-2 Doolittle Mill, Froghall Road, Ampthill, Bedford MK45 2NX
(Bedfordshire and Hertfordshire Health Authority)

Chair Robin Younger
Chief Executive John Swain

NHS TRUSTS & NHS HOSPITALS

Berkshire Healthcare NHS Trust

Church Hill House Hospital, Crowthorne Road, Bracknell RG12 7EP
Tel: 01344 422722 Fax: 01344 823269
(Thames Valley Health Authority)

Chair Lorna Roberts

Fair Mile Hospital
Reading Road, Cholsey, Wallingford OX10 9HH
Tel: 01491 651281 Fax: 01491 651128
Total Beds: 246

General Psychiatry H Bullard, H A Dickinson, F Fadl, R Ferris, C Haw, J Helling, S B Jones, F Leslie, N Longhurst, J Nehring, D Rice, R Sharma, M Whalley

Heatherwood Hospital (EMI & AMI Units)
London Road, Ascot SL5 8AA
Tel: 01344 623333 Fax: 01344 874340

King Edward VII Hospital (EMI Unit)
St Leonards Road, Windsor
Tel: 01753 860441 Fax: 01753 636107

Newbury Community Hospital (EMI Day Hospital)

St Mark's Hospital (EMI Day Hospital)
St Marks Road, Maidenhead SL6 6DU
Tel: 01628 632012 Fax: 01628 635050

Upton Hospital (EMI Unit)
Albert Street, Slough SL2 4HL
Tel: 01753 821441 Fax: 01753 635050

Wexham Park Hospital (EMI & AMI Units)
Wexham Street, Slough SL2 4HL
Tel: 01753 633000 Fax: 01753 634825

Bexhill and Rother Primary Care Trust

Bexhill Hospital, Holliers, Bexhill on Sea TN40 2DZ
Tel: 01424 735600 Fax: 01424 777026
Website: www.bexhillandrotherpct.nhs.uk
(Surrey and Sussex Health Authority)

Chair John Barnes
Chief Executive Rick Stern

Bexley Primary Care Trust

Marlow House, 109 Station Road, Sidcup DA15 7EU
Tel: 020 8298 6242 Fax: 020 8298 6241
Email: bexley.pct@bexgreen-ha.sthames.nhs.uk
Website: www.bexgreenhealth.nhs.uk
(South East London Health Authority)

Chair Kathy Balcombe
Chief Executive Alwen Williams

Billericay, Brentwood and Wickford Primary Care Trust

Highwood Hospital, Ongar Road, Brentwood CM15 9DY
Tel: 01277 302502 Fax: 01277 302512
(Essex Health Authority)

Chair Angela Bloomfield
Chief Executive Howard Perry

Birkenhead and Wallasey Primary Care Trust

Admin Block, St Catherine's Hospital, Church Road, Birkenhead CH42 0LQ
Tel: 0151 651 0011 Fax: 0151 670 9630
(Cheshire and Merseyside Health Authority)

Chair Muriel Downs
Chief Executive John South

Birmingham Children's Hospital NHS Trust

Diana, Princess of Wales Children's Hospital, Steelhouse Lane, Birmingham B4 6NH
Tel: 0121 333 9999 Fax: 0121 333 9998
(Birmingham and the Black Country Health Authority)

Chair Estella Hindley
Chief Executive J Sandy Bradbrook

Birmingham Children's Hospital
Steelhouse Lane, Birmingham B4 6NH
Tel: 0121 333 9999 Fax: 0121 333 9998
Total Beds: 220

Accident and Emergency K Berry, D Burke
Anaesthetics O Bagshaw, A Cranston, S E F Jones, A Liley, A Moriarty, C R Ralston, N J Robson, M Stokes, A Tatman
Cardiac Surgery D Barron, W J Brawn
Cardiology J de Giovanni, R Dhillon, P Miller, O Stumper, J G C Wright
Clinical Chemistry A Green
Dental Surgery A Shaw, L Shaw
Dermatology C Moss
Endocrinology T Barrett, J Kirk, N Shaw
Gastroenterology I W Booth, S Murphy, S Protheroe
General Psychiatry L Cullen, R El Sharief, F Farook, P Forster, S Handy, D Kat, S Narayan, S Paliwall, D Rothery, D Simmons, L Winkley, F Zaw
Genetics P A Farndon
Haematology P J Darbyshire, F G Hill, S Lawson, M D Williams
Hepatology S Beath, J de Ville de Goyet, D Kelly, P McKiernan, I Van Monrik
Intensive Care K Morris, G Morrison, G Pearson
Medical Microbiology R H George, J Gray
Nephrology S A Hulton, D Milford, C M Taylor
Neurology S H Green
Neurophysiology S Seri
Neurosurgery A D Hockley, S Sgouros, R Walsh
Oncology M English, R Grundy, J R Mann, B Morland
Ophthalmology J R Ainsworth, K Butler, H C Willshaw
Oral and Maxillofacial Surgery A D Hockley, M Wake
Orthopaedics C F Bradish, P Gibbons, P Glithero, D Marks, J O'Hara
Otolaryngology A Drake-Lee, R Irving, J McRac-Moore, K Pearman, D W Proops, A Reid
Paediatric Surgery R Buick, S Donnell, P Gornall, T Lander, K Parashar, D Parikh
Paediatrics G D Belle, A Goldstein, M Hocking, N McLellan, G W Rylance, R Sunderland
Pathology R Brown, F Raafat, P Ramani
Plastic Surgery R Lester, H Nikashaw, R Slater, Y Wilson
Radiology H Alton, S Chapman, F Haigh, P John, K Johnson, L McPherson
Radiotherapy and Oncology D Spooner
Respiratory Medicine J Clarke, P Weller
Rheumatology and Rehabilitation C Ryder, T R Southwood
Thoracic Surgery A Lander, D Parikh

Birmingham Heartlands and Solihull (Teaching) NHS Trust

Birmingham Heartlands Hospital, Bordesley Green East, Birmingham B9 5SS
(Birmingham and the Black Country Health Authority)

Chair Clive Wilkinson
Chief Executive Mark Goldman

Birmingham Heartlands Hospital

Bordesley Green East, Birmingham B9 5SS
Tel: 0121 424 2000 Fax: 0121 424 2200

Accident and Emergency C Park (Head), A Bleetman, E F Jones, A Macnamara, M J Shalley
Anaesthetics J C Carnie (Head), S S Fayek, R I Francis, A L Ganado, F Gao, D J Hawkins, R B Hopkinson, J M James, W A Lynch, T McLeod, B O'Connor, M J Rooney, J Roylance, A H Seymour, M H Taylor, R M Ward
Cardiology R G Murray (Head), J M Beattie, P J Lowry, P Ludman
Care of the Elderly R M Kamalarajan (Head), D Sandler, R A Shinton, D G Swain, P J W Wallis
Dental Surgery B A Hoyle, C J Meryon
Diabetes A H Barnett (Head), S Bain, P M Dodson, S Gough, S Kumar
ENT J B Campbell (Head), Dr Fisher, M Macnamara, D W Morgan, K Pearman
Gastroenterology I M Chesner (Head), R P Walt
General Medicine R Kamalarajan, S Kumar, M J Leyland, H C Rayner
General Surgery R A Cobb, M X Gannon, M D Goldman, D Mosquera, J L Taylor, H J Thomson
Genitourinary Medicine S M Drake, D J White
Haematology D W Milligan (Head), C Fegan
Immunology R A Thompson
Infectious Diseases C J Ellis (Head), A M Geddes, J A Innes, M J Wood
Nephrology H C Rayner, S A Smith, R M Temple
Neurology J M Anderson (Head)
Obstetrics and Gynaecology W E Mackenzie (Head), S W Hall, E Payne, S Sadek, M P Wyldes
Oncology N James
Ophthalmology I Cuncliffe (Head), J R Ainsworth, M T Benson, P Dodson, J M Gibson
Orthopaedics H Rahman, A Sambatakakis, M Shrivastava
Paediatrics S J Rose (Head), H Goodyear, R Mulik, Dr Mupaneamunda, T Ninan, L M Rabb, F A I Riordan, H Roper, M J Tarlow, M Venkataraman, M Watkinson, J Williams
Pathology A F Jones (Head), F B Brook, J Crocker, C W Edwards, I D Farrell, M A Hulten, K A James, J Newman, K J Nye, D Pillay, E G Smith, A Warfield
Radiology J H Reynolds (Head), A K Banerjee, J R Ferrando, M J Henderson, G S Jones, S Sangrasegran, D C Tudway
Respiratory Medicine P S Burge (Head), J G Ayres, R M Cayton, C Skinner, D E Stableforth
Rheumatology S Bowman, Dr Faizal, M Pugh
Thoracic Surgery F J Collins (Head), A G Casson, J Khalil-Marzouk, P Rajesh
Urology B D Sarmah (Head)

Solihull Hospital

Lode Lane, Solihull B91 2JL
Tel: 0121 424 2000 Fax: 0121 424 5496
Total Beds: 400

Accident and Emergency T Bagga
Anaesthetics F E Bannourah, B Hoggart, S Parr, R Shilling, C G Weston
Cardiology R G Murray (Head)
Dermatology A Heaggerty
ENT J Campbell (Head), D Morgan, K Pearman
General Medicine R G Murray, S O'Hickey, R Palmer, R J Polson, K Priestley, M Sandler, S Tan, R Wears, R J Wilson

General Surgery G Barsoum, D Burkitt, A Klidjian, G S Sokhi
Neurology M Anderson (Head)
Obstetrics and Gynaecology P Needham, C J F Rowbotham, R S Settatree, D W Sturdee
Oncology A Stockdale
Ophthalmology G Meeson
Orthodontics B Hoyle
Orthopaedics S Brooks (Head), S Bryan, A Murray
Radiology K B Bhatt, N A Chaudhry, C J Fletcher, G Stewart

Birmingham Specialist Community Health NHS Trust

Trust closure tbc - Part of service transferring to Eastern Birmingham Primary Care Trust, Heart of Birmingham Primary Care Trust, North Birmingham Primary Care Trust and South Birmingham Primary Care Trust.

Mosely Hall Hospital, Alcaster Road, Moseley, Birmingham B13 8JL
Tel: 0121 442 5600
Website: www.bscht.org.uk
(Birmingham and the Black Country Health Authority)

Chair Ahmed Hassam
Chief Executive Cynthia Bower

All Saints' Hospital

Lodge Road, Winson Green, Birmingham B18 5SD
Tel: 0121 623 5500
Total Beds: 72

General Psychiatry P Bracken, C Cavans, A Cobb, M Commander, A Daniels, A Duncan, Q Harris, J Kennedy, A Khan, V Kumar-Singh, J Rayner, I Telfer

Birmingham Dental Hospital

St. Chad's, Queensway, Birmingham B4 6NN
Tel: 0121 236 8611 Fax: 0121 237 2750

Anaesthetics T Bowden, M D Brewin, G Dickson, M Ghoris, R Hibbert, S Hylton, M King, A Malins, J M Watt
Dental Public Health R J Anderson
Oral Medicine J Hamburger
Oral Pathology J W Rippin
Oral Surgery J W Frame, W R Roberts
Orthodontics J W Ferguson, R R Pinson, W P Rock
Paediatric Dentistry L Shaw
Radiology J Rout
Restorative Dentistry I Chapple, J C Davenport, W R E Laird, P J Lumley, E A McLaughlin, M S Saxby, M J Shaw, A C C Shortall, A D Walmsley, K Warren

Highcroft Hospital

Slade Road, Erdington, Birmingham B23 7JA
Tel: 0121 623 5500
Total Beds: 160

General Psychiatry M De-Munshi, C Dean, C M Marengo, A L Mutchell, P M Rauchenberg, R A Wall, R Yuvarajan

Monyhull Hospital

Monyhull Hall Road, Birmingham B30 3QF
Tel: 0121 627 1627 Fax: 0121 627 8217
Total Beds: 212

Consultants D Clarke, V Prasher, K Thinn

Moseley Hall Hospital

Alcester Road, Birmingham B13 8JL
Tel: 0121 442 4321 Fax: 0121 442 3556
Total Beds: 126

Care of the Elderly P P Mayer, J Rowe, A Sinclair

NHS TRUSTS & NHS HOSPITALS

Sutton Cottage Hospital

Birmingham Road, Sutton Coldfield B72 1QH
Tel: 0121 255 4000
Total Beds: 18

West Heath Hospital

Rednal Road, Birmingham B38 8HR
Tel: 0121 627 1627 Fax: 0121 627 8228
Total Beds: 138

Care of the Elderly E J Dunstan, M Goodman, A Main, J Rowe

Birmingham Women's Health Care NHS Trust

Birmingham Women's Hospital, Metchley Park Road, Edgbaston, Birmingham B15 2TG
Tel: 0121 472 1377 Fax: 0121 627 2602
(Birmingham and the Black Country Health Authority)

Chair Christine Kenrick

Birmingham Women's Hospital

Edgbaston, Birmingham B15 2TG
Tel: 0121 472 1377 Fax: 0121 627 2602
Total Beds: 207

Anaesthetics R A Bond, T Bowden, G Cooper, L H Grove, M Lewis, A Malins, P J Millns, A D Wilkey
Clinical Chemistry D Worthington
Cytology A Yoong
Genetics S Bundey, T Cole, P A Farndon, C McKeown, E Maher, J Morton, A Norman
Haematology M Williams
Histopathology S Lee, C Platt, T Rollason
Medical Microbiology J Gray
Obstetrics and Gynaecology M Afnan, S Blunt, K K Chan, J M Emens, H Gee, J A Jordan, M Kilby, J R Newton, H O Nicholson, J Pogmore, R S Sawers, M Shafi, J Weaver, M Whittle
Paediatrics G M Durbin, A Ewer, M Hocking, I Morgan
Pathology S Lee, T P Rollason, D I Rushton
Radiology J M McHugo, J Mould

Black Country Mental Health NHS Trust

48 Lodge Road, West Bromwich B70 8NY
Tel: 0121 553 7676 Fax: 0121 607 3290
(Birmingham and the Black Country Health Authority)

Chair W H Thomas
Chief Executive Karen Dowman

Edward Street Hospital and Day Unit

Edward Street, West Bromwich B70 8NU
Tel: 0121 553 7676 Fax: 0121 607 3576
Total Beds: 96

Psychiatry of Old Age S Edwards, T M T El-Gohary

Blackburn, Hyndburn and Ribble Valley Health Care NHS Trust

From April 2002 mental health services transferring to Lancashire Care NHS Trust.

Queens Park Hospital, Haslingden, Blackburn BB2 3HH
Tel: 01254 263555 Fax: 01254 293803
(Cumbria and Lancashire Health Authority)

Chair Ian Woolley
Chief Executive John Thomas

Blackburn Royal Infirmary

Bolton Road, Blackburn BB2 3LR
Tel: 01254 263555 Fax: 01254 294572
Total Beds: 318

Accident and Emergency H Dardouri, T K George
Anaesthetics P Abbott, M Adhikary, R S Emmott, J A Fenwick, S J Gilligan, A K Grady, W G Hamlin, S Holgate, S Mousdale, D J A Rose, T Sivagnanam, C R Taylor, G Teturswamy, D A Watson
Cardiology D H Roberts
Chest Disease N Horsfield, L P Ormerod
Community Child Health T T Khine, G S Perera
Dental Surgery J C Lowry, M Morton
Dermatology B M Daly
ENT A Abou-El-Farag, J Cherry, P D Gooder, P Morar, M S Timms
General Medicine D S Grimes, G R Jones, D A F Lynch, A Myers, S Ramtoola, R Wilkinson
General Surgery D Chang, C H Davis, A Duncan, D Evans, A E Green, S C Hardy, M R Khan, R W Nicholson, T E B O'Brien, J C Tresadern, R J Watson
Genitourinary Medicine S L Gayed
Neurology E M R Critchley, T Majeed, P Tidswell, P J Tomlin
Ophthalmology A G E Nylander, J P Roper, I Sivayoham, A Vijaykumar
Orthodontics G A Smith
Orthopaedics J L Barrie, I G Lowrie, A P Maskell, R W Paton, V B Shah, M S Srinivasan
Paediatrics G Hambleton, V Miller, I Peart, R Postlethwaite, D A Price, M Super
Pathology A Mene, D A Newsome, R S Prescott, R H Seneviratne, D A Will, D S Wismayer
Plastic Surgery J G Iaitung, R P Jones
Radiology R F Barker, P J Garwood, D R Gavan, E N Kumar, M Rahman, S Susnerwala
Rheumatology P J Smith, L S Teh
Urology D A Jones, D Neilson, G Wymss-Holden

EMI Unit (Hillview) Day Hospital

Day Surgery Unit, Blackburn Royal Infirmary, Bolton Road, Blackburn BB2 3LR
Tel: 01254 263555 Fax: 01254 294572
Total Beds: 16

Queen's Park Hospital

Haslingden Road, Blackburn BB2 3HH
Tel: 01254 263555 Fax: 01254 293803
Total Beds: 502

Care of the Elderly N A Roberts, T Sivagnanam, E S Soliman
Obstetrics and Gynaecology N Ahmed Ebbiary, D Goodall, S R Hill, E A Martindale, S K Najia, P A O'Donovan, C M Schram
Paediatrics J W T Benson, C Fossard, M Lama, K Rakshi, C P Smith

Queen's Park Psychiatric Day Hospital

Queen's Park Hospital, Haslingden Road, Blackburn BB2 3HH
Tel: 01254 293427 Fax: 01254 293406

Blackburn with Darwen Primary Care Trust

Guide Business Centre, School Lane, Guide, Blackburn BB1 2HH
Tel: 01254 267000 Fax: 01254 267009
Website: www.bwdpct.org.uk
(Cumbria and Lancashire Health Authority)

Chair Pauline Walsh
Chief Executive Vivien Aspey

BLACKPOOL, WYRE & FYLDE COMMUNITY HEALTH SERVICES NHS TRUST

Blackpool, Fylde and Wyre Hospitals NHS Trust

Blackpool Victoria Hospital, Whinney Heys Road, Blackpool FY3 8NR
Tel: 01253 300000 Fax: 01253 306873
(Cumbria and Lancashire Health Authority)

Blackpool Primary Care Trust

c/o Blackpool, Wyre and Fylde Community Health Services NHS Trust, Wesham Park Hospital, Wesham, Preston PR4 3AL
Tel: 01253 303158 Fax: 01253 306394
(Cumbria and Lancashire Health Authority)

Chair Tony Shaw
Chief Executive Wendy Potts

Blackpool Victoria Hospital NHS Trust

Closing April 2002 - Services transferring to Blackpool, Fylde and Wyre Hospitals NHS Trust.

Whinney Heys Road, Blackpool FY3 8NR
Tel: 01253 300000 Fax: 01253 306873
Email: David.Gill@exch.bvh-tr.nwest.nhs.uk
(Cumbria and Lancashire Health Authority)

Chair Barry Fothergill
Chief Executive David Gill

Victoria Hospital

Whinney Heys Road, Blackpool FY3 8NR
Tel: 01253 300000 Fax: 01253 306873
Email: David.Gill@exch.bvh-tr.nwest.nhs.uk
Total Beds: 740

Accident and Emergency S N Harrop
Anaesthetics M E Chamberlain, C Clarke, D Counsell, J Cuppitt, C Dunkley, N J Gavin, C Harle, N Harper, M Hartley, C Humphries, G Johnson, D R Kelly, V K Khanna, A S Lockhart, B M Lord, I W McConachie, S Mitchell, R Morgan, P H Palin, N P C Randall, S Vaughan
Cardiology A Chauhan, G Goode, D H Roberts
Child and Adolescent Psychiatry N P Gajawira
Dermatology W Bottomley, J K Kellett
ENT A O Keith, A Nigam
General Medicine A Ahmed, M J Brack, M El-Khateeb, P Flegg, R Gajendragadkar, P J Hayes, M Hendrickse, M S Hendy, S A Husain, P E T Isaacs, T C Li Kam Wa, J D Mackay, M O'Donnell, J F O'Reilly, Y Seth, C Shorrock
General Surgery L Forrest, M Khurshid, M E Lambert, S Pettit, S Ravi, S J Walker
Genitourinary Medicine A M Saeed
Haematology N G Flanagan, P R Kelsey
Neurosurgery B Boothman, N T Gurusinghe
Obstetrics and Gynaecology I Arthur, N A Bedford, S J Duthie, M R Steel, F L Wilcox
Ophthalmology J A Dunne, G Naylor, W Pollock, M Raines
Oral and Maxillofacial Surgery J Cornah
Orthodontics G Bradburn
Orthopaedics K P Boardman, M S Cornah, S D Fewster, C J Hindley, A Javeed, S McLoughlin
Paediatrics P Curtis, M E Johnson, R Roberts, R Stevens
Pathology R Duthie, N I Fernando, J Johnson, B Marshall, M C J Sissons, K S Vasudev
Plastic Surgery R Gaze
Radiology P K Bowyer, R W Bury, L Hacking, G M Hoadley, T P Kane, F Lo Ying Ping, D Montgomery, C Walshaw
Radiotherapy and Oncology A Duncan, N Gupta, G Skailes, S Susnerwala
Rheumatology I Stewart
Thoracic Surgery J Au, R Millner, D Sharpe
Urology C R A Bevis, N R Rothwell

Blackpool, Wyre and Fylde Community Health Services NHS Trust

Closing April 2002 - Mental health services transferring to Lancashire Care NHS Trust; acute services transferring to Blackpool, Fylde and Wyre Hospitals NHS Trust; community services transferring to Blackpool Primary Care Trust, Fylde Primary Care Trust and Wyre Primary Care Trust.

Wesham Park Hospital, Derby Road, Wesham, Preston PR4 3AL
Tel: 01253 303158 Fax: 01253 306394
Email: bev.mcgann@bwfchs-tr.nwest.nhs.uk
(Cumbria and Lancashire Health Authority)

Chair B J Lester

Clifton Hospital

Pershore Road, Off Clifton Drive, Lytham St Annes FY8 1PB
Tel: 01253 306204 Fax: 01253 306214
Total Beds: 133

Care of the Elderly A G Baloch, M J O'Donnell

Devonshire Road Hospital

Devonshire Road, Blackpool FY3 8AZ
Tel: 01253 303364 Fax: 01253 303386
Total Beds: 106

Dermatology W W Bottomley, J K Kellett
General Medicine R J Bibby, M J Brack, P J Hayes, M J Hendrickse, M S Hendy, P E T Isaacs, J D Mackay, J F O'Reilly, C J Shorrock
General Psychiatry C A D Calvert, W J Charles, J A G D'Souza, D S G Kay, C J Molodynski

Fleetwood Hospital

Pharos Street, Fleetwood FY7 6BE
Tel: 01253 306000 Fax: 01253 306029

Colposcopy A Saeed
Dermatology W Bottomeley
General Psychiatry G P Opdebeeck
Rheumatology I Stewart
Urology N Rothwell

Lytham Hospital

Warton Street, Lytham St Annes FY8 5EE
Tel: 01253 303953 Fax: 01253 303972
Total Beds: 123

Dermatology J K Kellett
General Psychiatry C A D Calvert, W J Charles, J A G D'Souza, D S G Kay, C J Molodynski
Orthopaedics M S Cornah, S McLoughlin
Paediatrics S Byrne
Rheumatology S Jones
Urology C R A Bevis, N Rothwell

Parkwood Psychiatric Unit

East Park Drive, Blackpool FY3 8PW
Tel: 01253 306980 Fax: 01253 306961
Total Beds: 118

Elderly Mentally Ill W Charles, M Dale, C Molodynski, G Opdebeeck, E Renvoise
General Psychiatry C A D Calvert, L A Le-Roux, J Mequita, Dr Smith, Dr Tourish
Learning Disabilities J Matthews

NHS TRUSTS & NHS HOSPITALS

Rossall Hospital

Westway, Rossall, Fleetwood FY7 8JH
Tel: 01253 303800 Fax: 01253 303804
Total Beds: 66

Care of the Elderly R S Gulati

South Shore Hospital

Stony Hill Avenue, Blackpool FY4 1HX
Tel: 01253 306106 Fax: 01253 306101
Total Beds: 102

Care of the Elderly R S Gulati
Rheumatology S Jones, I Stewart

Wesham Park Hospital

Derby Road, Wesham, Preston PR4 3AL
Tel: 01253 303280 Fax: 01253 303152
Total Beds: 80

Care of the Elderly A G Baloch, R S Gulati
General Psychiatry C A D Calvert, W J Charles, J A G D'Souza, D S G Kay, C J Molodynski

Blackwater Valley Primary Care Trust

Winchfield Lodge, Old Potbridge Road, Winchfield, Hook RG27 8BT
Tel: 01252 398153 Fax: 01252 398150
(Hampshire and Isle of Wight Health Authority)

Chair Steven Clarke
Chief Executive Phil Chapman

Bolton Hospitals NHS Trust

Royal Bolton Hospital, Minerva Road, Farnworth, Bolton BL4 0JR
Tel: 01204 390426 Fax: 01204 390936
(Greater Manchester Health Authority)

Chair Peter Liptrott
Chief Executive John E Brunt

Belmont Day Hospital

Minverva Road, Farnworth, Bolton BL4 0JR
Tel: 01204 390390

Fall Birch Hospital

Lostock, Bolton BL6 4LQ
Tel: 01204 695714
Total Beds: 35

Hulton Day Hospital

Hulton Lane, Bolton BL3 4JZ

Hulton Hospital

Hulton Lane, Bolton BL3 4JZ
Tel: 01204 390390
Total Beds: 42

Minerva Day Hospital

Minerva Road, Farnworth, Bolton BL4 0JR

Rivington Day Hospital

Minerva Road, Farnworth, Bolton BL4 0JR

Royal Bolton Hospital

Farnworth, Bolton BL4 0JR
Tel: 01204 390390 Fax: 01204 390794
Total Beds: 968

Accident and Emergency J C Adams, C Moulton

Anaesthetics J N Aspbury, J M Chishti, S Deegan, M J Flynn, D P McInerney, N H Naqvi, J P Ryan, R N Shetty, Y Sivalingham, N J Smith
Care of the Elderly K R H Adams, P Baker, A K Banerjee
Dental Surgery D Lewis
Dermatology M H Beck, R J S Chalmers, M Judge
ENT J Mason, L O'Keefe
General Medicine H Bharaj, B J Bradley, J D Dean, K C Hearn, K Moriarty, P J Scott, D Spurr
General Psychiatry M Brownlee, W Dougal, K Mahadeven, M E Taylor
General Surgery G H Ferguson, J H Hobbiss, H Michie, D G Ostick, R J Salem, M J S Wilkinson
Genitourinary Medicine E Curless
Neurology P W Cooper, A C Young
Obstetrics and Gynaecology P Chia, M W Gartside, R E Hopkins, F N Mayers, M Tasker
Ophthalmology S P Kelly, J Kwartz, R F Mehta, A M Morrison, S J Wallis
Oral Surgery J C Lowry, M R Morton
Orthopaedics A J Banks, A A Henderson, J J Henderson, S P Hodgson, W Ryan
Paediatrics F Bowman, J L Burn, J E Ellis, D M Eminson, T H Northover, P Powell, R W Wall
Pathology D L Bisset, R J Farrand, A M Hawks, A J C Hutchesson, J Jip, J M Pearson, S Wells
Radiology M Gowland, I Hassan, P J Lane, A J Maxwell, P Strong, J S Tuck
Rheumatology R C Hilton
Thoracic Surgery N Odom
Urology M E Mobb, M I Pantelides

Bolton Primary Care Trust

3rd Floor, Acresfield House, Crompton Place, Exchange Street, Bolton BL1 1RS
Tel: 01204 547801 Fax: 01204 547830
(Greater Manchester Health Authority)

Chair Pamela Senior
Chief Executive Kevin Snee

Bournemouth Primary Care Trust

The Pokesdown Centre, 11 Shelley Road, Bournemouth BH1 4JQ
Tel: 01202 443700
Email: debbie.fleming@bournemouth-pct.nhs.uk
(Somerset and Dorset Health Authority)

Chair Rex Symons
Chief Executive Debbie Fleming

Bournewood Community and Mental Health Services NHS Trust

Closing April 2002 - Mental health services transferring to North West Surrey Mental Health Parnership NHS Trust.

Bournewood House, Guildford Road, Chertsey KT16 0QA
Tel: 01932 872010 Fax: 01932 875346
(Surrey and Sussex Health Authority)

Chair Douglas Robertson
Chief Executive Carol Pearson
Consultants J J Barry, Charlie Burge, Teresa Carter, Marian De Ruiter, Paola Franciosi, Wellington Hung, Graham Kidd, Ward Lawrence, Caroline Lucas, Philip McCluskie, Dr Manjubhashini, Nathaniel Minton, Nader Mohajer, Wajdi Nackasha, Chris White

Abraham Cowley Unit

Holloway Hill, Lyne, Chertsey KT16 0AE
Tel: 01932 872010 Fax: 01932 875128
Total Beds: 82

Abraham Cowley Unit Day Hospital

Holloway Hill, Lyne, Chertsey KT16 0AE
Tel: 01932 872010
Total Beds: 72

Walton Community Hospital

Rodney Road, Walton-on-Thames KT12 3LB
Tel: 01932 220060 Fax: 01932 253674

Weybridge Hospital

Church Street, Weybridge KT13 8DY
Tel: 01932 852931 Fax: 01932 821966
Total Beds: 30

Care of the Elderly B Castleton
Palliative Medicine C Lucas

Woking Community Hospital

Heathside Road, Woking GU22 7HS
Tel: 01483 715911 Fax: 01483 766195

Care of the Elderly G Kidd, C Long

Bracknell Forest Primary Care Trust

Time Square, Market Street, Bracknell RG12 1JD
(Thames Valley Health Authority)

Bradford City Primary Care Trust

Joseph Brennan House, Sunbridge Road, Bradford BD1 2SY
Tel: 01274 424780 Fax: 01274 424781
Email: citypct@bradford-ha.nhs.uk
Website: www.bradfordcity-pcg.nhs.uk
(West Yorkshire Health Authority)

Chair Mohammed Ajeeb
Chief Executive Lynnette Throp

Bradford Community Health NHS Trust

Leeds Road Hospital, Maudsley Street, Bradford BD3 9LH
Tel: 01274 363504 Fax: 01274 363516
(West Yorkshire Health Authority)

Chair John Watson
Chief Executive Con Egan

Daisy Bank

109 Duckworth Lane, Bradford BD9 6RL
Tel: 01274 494194
Total Beds: 18

General Psychiatry J Throssell

Daisy Hill House

Heights Lane, Bradford BD9 6DP
Tel: 01274 363839 Fax: 01274 363827
Total Beds: 68

Psychiatry of Old Age K Bhatnagar, M Cohen

Leeds Road Hospital

Maudsley Street, Bradford BD3 9LH
Tel: 01274 494194 Fax: 01274 725652
Total Beds: 18

Lynfield Mount Hospital

Heights Lane, Bradford BD9 6DP
Tel: 01274 494194 Fax: 01274 483494
Total Beds: 210

General Psychiatry S J Baugh, K Bhatnager, P Bracken, L Cann, M Cohen, H Daudjee, M Ellis, M Hamilton, L Harrop, L Hewson, S Hopker, D James, P Thomas, J Throssell, A Venables, J C T Webster

Rosebery House

40 Rosebery Road, Bradford BD9 7QB
Tel: 01274 547518
Total Beds: 10

General Psychiatry J Throssell

St Catherine's Hospital

St. Mary's Road, Bradford BD8 7QG
Tel: 01274 543371 Fax: 01274 772433
Total Beds: 34

Care of the Elderly J Tucker, J Young

Shipley Hospital

98 Kirkgate, Shipley BD18 3LT
Tel: 01274 773390 Fax: 01274 773392
Total Beds: 18

Rehabilitation Medicine E White, J Young

Stoney Ridge Hospital

Stoney Ridge Road, Cottingley, Bingley BD16 1UL
Tel: 01274 495737 Fax: 01274 227923
Total Beds: 18

Westwood House

Cooper Lane, Bradford BD6 3NL
Tel: 01274 882001 Fax: 01274 883469
Total Beds: 26

Learning Disabilities T U K Nasir

Bradford Hospitals NHS Trust

Bradford Royal Infirmary, Duckworth Lane, Bradford BD9 6RJ
Tel: 01274 364788 Fax: 01274 364786
Email: Sedgwicm@brihosp.mhs.compuserve.com
Website: www.bradfordhospitals.nhs.uk
(West Yorkshire Health Authority)

Chair John Ryan
Chief Executive David Jackson

Bradford Royal Infirmary

Duckworth Lane, Bradford BD9 6RJ
Tel: 01274 542200 Fax: 01274 364026
Email: Sedgwicm@brihosp.mhs.compuserve.com
Website: www.bradford-tr.northy.nhs.uk
Total Beds: 925

Accident and Emergency A F Shenton (Head)
Anaesthetics P G W Cramp (Head), J Bembridge, P J Bickford-Smith, I Blacker, P M Brown, K Budd, A D G Dawson, C S Evans, M Fairbrass, L B S Gallagher, P A L Henderson, J Keeler, P A Knappett, W J Price, J Richardson, C A Sides, M J Wade
Care of the Elderly J S Tucker, J B Young
Dermatology D J Barker, A J G McDonagh, A L Wright
ENT C Vize (Head)
General Medicine C Bradley, J M Findlay, P J Hollins, A P Manning, G W Morrison, D Parker, A B Shaw, R L Woodhead

NHS TRUSTS & NHS HOSPITALS

General Surgery R M Antrum, J R Ausobsky, J J Price, M Whittaker
Laryngology D G Comerford, C H Raine, A G Tucker, C E Vize
Neurology R N Hakin
Neurosurgery G M Towns
Obstetrics and Gynaecology J K Clayton (Head), I Beck, S E Jones, P J O'Donovan, R J Rand
Ophthalmology A D Atkins, J Bradbury, D J Hopkins, J R Weatherill
Oral and Maxillofacial Surgery M J Carroll (Head)
Orthopaedics S R Bollen (Head), J B Hamilton, W Holms, K Jepson
Paediatrics S Chatfield, D Haig, G T Lealman, A M B Minford, M L Smith
Pathology P A Batman, D R Gouldesbrough, S N Hanna, J W Lowe, B Naylor, L A Parapia, A T Williams
Radiology R A Lowe (Head), A W Atukorala, T S Brown, O J Follows, M L Gaunt, T D Gopichandran, D A Sapherson, R N Setia, R A Smith
Radiotherapy and Oncology G H Berry, D W Jones, R E Taylor
Rheumatology W N Dodds, R D Melsom
Thoracic Surgery A J Mearns, S Sabanathan
Urology G M Flannigan, P A Hamilton Stewart
Vascular Surgery P Vowden

St Luke's Hospital

Little Horton Lane, Bradford BD5 0NA
Tel: 01274 734744
Email: Sedgwicm@brihosp.mhs.compuserve.com
Website: www.bradford-tr.northy.nhs.uk
Total Beds: 367

Anaesthetics P G W Cramp (Head), D R Ball, P J Bickford-Smith, I Blacker, A D G Dawson, C S Evans, M Fairbrass, L B S Gallagher, J Keeler, P A Knappett, E M Modgill, W J Price, J Richardson, M J Wade
Care of the Elderly E G White (Head), G B Smith, E A Tamlyn, J S Tucker, J B Young
Community Child Health P C Corry, D Subesinghe
Dental Surgery M J Carroll (Head), D A Mason
General Medicine C Bradley, A P Manning, C A Morley, D A G Newton, D Parker, A B Shaw, A T Williams, R L Woodhead
General Surgery R M Antrum, J R Ausobsky, D L Froggatt, J J Price, M Whittaker
Genitourinary Medicine C J N Lacey, K C Mohanty, E T Morgan
Histopathology J W Lowe
Neurology R N Hakin
Neurophysiology J A Twomey
Obstetrics and Gynaecology J K Clayton (Head), I Beck, S E Jones, P J O'Donovan, R J Rand
Oral and Maxillofacial Surgery V Joshi, D A Mason
Orthodontics A K Tipnis, C E Young
Orthopaedics S R Bollen (Head), J B Hamilton, W Holms, K Jepson
Paediatrics S Chatfield, D Haig, G T Lealman, A M B Minford, M L Smith
Pathology B Naylor (Head), P A Batman, A R B Feeney
Plastic Surgery D T Sharpe, M J Timmons
Radiology R A Lowe (Head), T S Brown, O J Follows, M L Gaunt, T D Gopichandran, R N Setia, R A Smith
Rheumatology W N Dodds, R D Melsom
Urology P A H Stewart
Vascular Surgery P Vowden

Bradford South and West Primary Care Trust

Queensbury Health Centre, Russell Road, Queensbury, Bradford BD13 2AG
Tel: 01274 321800 Fax: 01274 321805
(West Yorkshire Health Authority)

Chair Barbara Hakin
Chief Executive Sarah Warner

Brent, Kensington, Chelsea and Westminster Mental Health NHS Trust

30 Eastbourne Terrace, London W2 6LA
Tel: 020 8237 2000 Fax: 020 8746 8978
(North West London Health Authority)

Chair Ruth Runciman
Chief Executive Peter Carter

Collingham Gardens

4-5 Collingham Gardens, London SW5 0HR
Tel: 020 8846 6644 Fax: 020 8846 6641
Total Beds: 12

Gordon Hospital

Bloomburg Street, London SW1V 2RH
Tel: 020 8746 5505 Fax: 020 8746 8711
Total Beds: 90

General Psychiatry C Flannigan, O S Frank, A Parshall
Psychiatry of Old Age R Menon
Psychotherapy A Etchegoyen

Brent Primary Care Trust

Willesden Community Hospital, Harlesden Road, London NW10 3RY
(North West London Health Authority)

Chair Jean Gaffin
Chief Executive Lise Llewellyn

Brighton and Hove City Primary Care Trust

6th Floor, Vantage Point, New England Road, Brighton BN1 4GW
Tel: 01273 295490 Fax: 01273 295461
(Surrey and Sussex Health Authority)

Chair Jean Spray
Chief Executive Gary Needle

Brighton and Sussex University Hospitals NHS Trust

Royal Sussex County Hospital, Easter Road, Brighton BN2 5BE
(Surrey and Sussex Health Authority)

Chair Michael Whiting
Chief Executive Stuart Welling

Princess Royal Hospital (East Wing)

Lewes Road, Haywards Heath RH16 4EX
Tel: 01444 441881 Fax: 01444 414174
Total Beds: 286

Accident and Emergency D J Harborne
Anaesthetics H Adams, D Bellis, R H A Hoyal, W A L Rawlinson, D H Read, J M Rouse, P B Wemyss-Gorman
Care of the Elderly S P Cheek
Dermatology D M France
ENT H W Elcock, R Tranter
General Medicine K R Hine, J Metcalfe, J R R Spurrell, T Wheatley
General Psychiatry A Abraham
General Surgery C R R Corbett, M A Lavelle, D J Reid
Haematology P R Hill
Histopathology P A Berresford
Medical Microbiology E A Harper
Neurology J E Rees

Neurosurgery P H Walter, P Ward
Obstetrics and Gynaecology T Bashir, G D Kerr, B McKenzie-Gray
Orthopaedics C B d Fearn, E Parnell, M H Patterson
Radiology J M Berry, I J Runcie
Rheumatology and Rehabilitation H I Keith

Royal Alexandra Hospital for Sick Children

Dyke Road, Brighton BN1 3JN
Tel: 01273 28145
Total Beds: 65

Community Child Health E A Livesay
General Medicine N Alton, N Evans, P Hildick-Smith, P Seddon, J Trounce, F Weir
Neurosurgery P Ward
Oncology A Davidson
Orthodontics I G Crossman
Paediatric Surgery A Allaway, V Kalidasan, A Van Der Avoirt

Royal Sussex County Hospital

Eastern Road, Brighton BN2 5BE
Tel: 01273 696955
Total Beds: 414

Accident and Emergency G Bryant, C Perez-Avila, J Ryan
Anaesthetics E N Armitage, C S B Child, A J Davey, H F Drake, N G S Fisher, A C L Fraser, J M Lamberty, B R P Murray, M K Street, C N Swaine, D Taylor, M Twohig, J H Williams, P A D Williams
Breast Care R Gumpert, G Rubin, A Yelland
Cardiac Surgery A Forsyth, W Pugsley, U Trivedi
Cardiology C Davidson, A De Belder, S Holmberg, S O'Dunain, R Vincent
Clinical Haematology J Duncan, M Kenny
Endocrinology J Quin, N Vaughan
Gastroenterology S Cairns, A Ireland
Genitourinary Medicine M Fisher, S Panja, D Williams
Intensive Care O Boyd, M Street
Medical Physics J Lutkin
Neonatology N Alton, F Weir
Neurology (Outpatients) P Hughes, P Morrish, A Nisbet
Neurosurgery C Hardwidge, P Walter, P Ward
Nuclear Medicine R Burwood, P Robinson
Oncology D Bloomfield, G Deutsch, D Geoff, N Hudson, J Simpson, M Wilkins
Oral and Maxillofacial Surgery K Altman, J Herold
Orthodontics I Crossman
Private Patients P Austin, D Brett
Public Health Medicine M Cubbon, J Paul
Renal Medicine M Bewick, L Goldberg, N Iggo, C Kingswood, A MacDiarmid-Gordon, P Sharpstone
Thoracic Surgery (Outpatients) J Dussek

Brighton Health Care NHS Trust

Closing April 2002 - Services transferring to Brighton and Sussex University Hospitals NHS Trust.

Royal Sussex County Hospital, Eastern Road, Brighton BN2 5BE
Tel: 01273 696955 Fax: 01273 626653
Website: www.brighton-healthcare.nhs.uk
(Surrey and Sussex Health Authority)

Chair Michael Whiting
Chief Executive Stuart Welling

Sussex Eye Hospital

Eastern Road, Brighton BN2 5BE
Tel: 01273 606126
Total Beds: 22

Ophthalmology P Brittain, A J Casswell, S Vickers

Bristol North Primary Care Trust

King's Square House, 26-27 King Square, Bristol BS2 8EE
Tel: 0117 900 2400 Fax: 0117 900 2677
(Avon, Gloucestershire and Wiltshire Health Authority)

Bristol South and West Primary Care Trust

King Square House, King House, Bristol BS2 8EE
Tel: 0117 976 6600 Fax: 0117 900 2548
Website: www.avon.nhs.uk/bsawpcg
(Avon, Gloucestershire and Wiltshire Health Authority)

Chair Tom Dowell
Chief Executive Deborah Evans

Broadland Primary Care Trust

The Octagon, St. Michael's Hospital, Cawston Road, Aylsham, Norwich NR11 6NA
Tel: 01263 738600 Fax: 01263 735086
(Norfolk, Suffolk and Cambridgeshire Health Authority)

Bromley Hospitals NHS Trust

Farnborough Hospital, Farnborough Common, Orpington BR6 8ND
Tel: 01689 814000 Fax: 01689 862423
Email: generalenquiry@bromleyhospitals.nhs.uk
Website: www.bromleyhospitals.nhs.uk
(South East London Health Authority)

Chair Bryan Collins
Chief Executive Mark D Rees

Beckenham Hospital

379 Croydon Road, Beckenham BR3 3QL
Tel: 020 8289 6600 Fax: 020 8289 6627

ENT R M Terry, Dr Thomas
General Medicine J Hunt
Obstetrics and Gynaecology J McQueen
Radiology Z F Boulis, S J N Daniell, C Fraser, A M K Thomas
Rheumatology C C Erhardt, P Pitt

Bromley Hospital

Cromwell Avenue, Bromley BR2 9AJ
Tel: 020 8289 7000 Fax: 020 8289 7127
Total Beds: 215

Accident and Emergency G Evans, S Nash
Anaesthetics R Hedley, N Jones, P King, K McCarthy, B H D Magrath, A Martin, R Morey, D J Peebles, J Perera, R M E Pinchin, J C Scott, P R Vine
Cardiology Dr Akhras, E Langford
Chest Disease B Richards, E Sawicka
Dental Surgery M Hosseini
ENT R M Terry
General Medicine S Gibbs, J Hunt, A P Jenkins, M Sawicka
General Surgery T Hennigan, C Midwood, F Smedley
Neurology C G Clough
Obstetrics and Gynaecology N C W Hill
Orthopaedics P Allen, A Franklin, P C Shaw, H D Smith, D Yanni
Plastic Surgery Dr Mercer
Radiology Z F Boulis, S J Daniell, C Fraser, A M K Thomas

Farnborough Hospital

Farnborough Common, Orpington BR6 8ND
Tel: 01689 814000 Fax: 01689 814127
Total Beds: 379

NHS TRUSTS & NHS HOSPITALS

Diabetes K G E Brown
ENT D Golding-Wood, R M Terry, J N Thomas
General Medicine K G E Brown, C F P Wharton
General Psychiatry M W Bernadt, J Bird, Dr Cook, Dr Harvey-Smith, Dr Sivaloganathan, G Stein, Dr Whaby, D R Wood
Obstetrics and Gynaecology J Erian, R Gardner, N Hill, J McQueen
Ophthalmology D Trew
Orthopaedics P C Shaw, H D Smith
Paediatrics C W Darby, M De Silva, S Hobbins, A Long, S H Ng
Pathology K Arulambalam, I Bailey, S Barnass, M H Elmahallawy, A K Lakhani, T Perera, H A Roberts, I Samaratunga
Radiology Z F Boulis, R A Carver, S J N Daniell, C Fraser, A M K Thomas
Radiotherapy and Oncology J Dobbs, D Tong
Rheumatology K Erhardt, P Pitt
Urology M R L Joyce, D Nurse

Orpington Hospital

Sevenoaks Road, Orpington BR6 9JU
Tel: 01689 815000 Fax: 01689 815018
Total Beds: 75

Care of the Elderly K W R Hildick-Smith, L Kalra, B Lock, D Lyons, G Yu
Dental Surgery P S Ellisdon, M Hosseini
Dermatology M Clement, A C Pembroke
ENT D Golding-Wood, P Ratnesar
General Medicine B Richards, C F P Wharton
General Psychiatry F Ghali
General Surgery F Smedley
Neurology W F Michael
Obstetrics and Gynaecology C Steer
Radiology R A Carver, C Fraser, A Thomas

Bromley Primary Care Trust

Global House, Station Approach, Hayes BR2 7EH
Tel: 020 8315 8315 Fax: 020 8426 6767
(South East London Health Authority)

Chair Adrian Eddleston
Chief Executive Bridget Riches

Broxtowe and Hucknall Primary Care Trust

The Health Centre, 1 Curtis Street, Hucknall, Nottingham NG15 7JE
Tel: 0115 859 0224 Fax: 0115 859 0229
(Trent Health Authority)

Chair Melanie Hatto
Chief Executive Elizabeth McGuirk

Buckinghamshire Mental Health NHS Trust

Manor House, Bierton Road, Aylesbury HP20 1EG
Tel: 01296 393363 Fax: 01296 504603
(Thames Valley Health Authority)

Chair Shirley Williams
Chief Executive Keith Nieland

Buckingham Hospital

High Street, Buckingham MK18 1NU
Tel: 01280 813243 Fax: 01280 824966
Total Beds: 17

Harlow House

Harlow Road, High Wycombe HP13 6AA
Tel: 01494 436393
Total Beds: 40

General Psychiatry J Ferguson

Manor House

Bierton Road, Aylesbury HP20 1EG
Tel: 01296 393363
Total Beds: 187

General Psychiatry J Baruch
Learning Disabilities G Barton
Paediatrics M Wakefield

Burnley Health Care NHS Trust

From April 2002 mental health services transferring to Lancashire Care NHS Trust.

Burnley General Hospital, Casterton Avenue, Burnley BB10 2PQ
Tel: 01282 425071 Fax: 01282 474444
(Cumbria and Lancashire Health Authority)

Chair A Ali
Chief Executive D J Chew
Assistant Chief Executive D Meakin

Burnley General Hospital

Casterton Avenue, Burnley BB10 2PQ
Tel: 01282 425071 Fax: 01282 474444
Total Beds: 591

Accident and Emergency E Bayton, S Bhattacharyya, M Tan
Anaesthetics and Chronic Pain T Calow, U Damerow, N Graveston, C M Middleton, S Price, J Richardson, A M Sabri, R K Shah, R K Shah, A Shakir, A Swanepoel, E Van Der Heiden, J C Watts
Cardiology R A Best, G Gladman, A Chauhan
Cardiothoracic Surgery D A C Sharpe
Child and Adolescent Psychiatry S Ahmad, T Morris
Dermatology I H Coulson, B M Daly, N M Craven
Elderly Mentally Ill I Chaudry, J Darlington, J Ngowi, K Yasin
ENT J R Cherry, A Farag, P D Gooder, P Morar, M S Timms
General Medicine I Hafeez, A T Green, C E F Grimley, M D Littley, F M Zaman, S Pickens
General Psychiatry S Bobmanuel, M Javed, M A Launer, S Quraishi, P Riordan
General Surgery H Al-Khaffaf, T R Dilrajgopal, M N Goorah, E Gross, R H Hyatt, L J Patterson, A Rahi, D G D Sandilands, P D Scott, S C Sharma
Genetics B Kerr, K Metcalfe, M Super
Genitourinary Medicine S L Gayed
Nephrology M Bradbury, J G Anderton
Neurology S Shaunak, J D Mitchell, R W Newton
Neurosurgery G Roberts
Obstetrics and Gynaecology J M Cruickshank, F C Hamer, K S Haworth, T C M Inglis, I W Mahady, F R Clarke, H M Ribbans
Ophthalmology M J Abdul-Nabi, M Mohan, A G E Nylander, J P Roper, A Vijaykumar
Oral Surgery G C S Cousin, A E Green, S Langton
Orthodontics P A Banks
Orthopaedics S R D'Souza, L Markovic, H A J Marynissen, A N Saikai, R Sarin
Paediatric Surgery J Bruce, J Bowen
Paediatrics I H Brown, P Ehrhardt, J Iqbal, I L Swann
Pathology A A Al-Dawoud, S F Dealler, G Horsman, J R Kendra, W D Salman, Z Twaij
Plastic Surgery J G Laitung
Radiology Y Nakhuda, N S Malik, S S Panditaratne, P M Woodhead
Radiotherapy and Oncology A N Abbasi, T Mughal, G Read
Rheumatology and Rehabilitation R Ariyaratna, M J Burke
Urology A Yakubu, A McGeorge, M Pillai

Pendle Community Hospital

Leeds Road, Nelson BB9 9SZ
Tel: 01282 474900 Fax: 01282 474980
Total Beds: 72

Care of the Elderly Dr Deldeniya, Dr Hyatt, L J Patterson, Dr Sharma, R P Singh

Rossendale General Hospital

Haslingden Road, Rawtenstall, Rossendale BB4 6NE
Tel: 01706 215151 Fax: 01706 233210
Total Beds: 80

Burnley, Pendle and Rossendale Primary Care Trust

31-33 Kenyon Road, Lomeshaye Estate, Briefield, Nelson BB9 5SZ
(Cumbria and Lancashire Health Authority)

Chair James Heyes
Chief Executive David Peat

Burntwood Lichfield and Tamworth Primary Care Trust

The Coach House, St Michaels Hospital, Trent Valley Road, Lichfield WS13 6EF
Tel: 01543 442011 Fax: 01543 442024
(Shropshire and Staffordshire Health Authority)

Chair Susan Durrant
Chief Executive Alan Snuggs

Burton Hospitals NHS Trust

Queen's Hospital, Belvedere Road, Burton-on-Trent DE13 0RB
Tel: 01283 566333 Fax: 01283 593032
Website: www.burtonhosp.com
(Shropshire and Staffordshire Health Authority)

Chair Terry Tricker
Chief Executive David Anderson

Queen's Hospital

Belvedere Road, Burton-on-Trent DE13 0RB
Tel: 01283 566333 ext: 5557 Fax: 01283 593032
Website: www.burtonhosp.com
Total Beds: 459

Accident and Emergency F O'Dwyer
Anaesthetics P Allsop, J D Anderson, M J W Eason, C M Heal, R T Hedge, P Holgate, U Kamath, J W Martin, S W Millar, R M G Pearson, I Roberts, C Stenhouse, C Webb
Care of the Elderly G S Matharu, C Reisner, W Sawiers
Chemical Pathology T M Reynolds
Dermatology P Cartwright, H Nelson
ENT P R De, J Oates, T J Rockley, A C Thompson
General Medicine J J Benn, J D Hill, J W S Sheldon, D Watmough, H Why
General Surgery T E Bucknall, R J K Gompertz, R Lee, C A Rogers
Genitourinary Medicine C A Murray
Haematology N L Rymes, A G Smith
Histopathology D M Green, N Kasthuri, P Ong
Medical Microbiology J H Paton
Obstetrics and Gynaecology J K Artley, B Ginz, J Hollingworth, Y G Ibrahim, W Oakley, A D G Roberts
Ophthalmology S Chawdhary, R Harrison, A Rauf, T Worstmann
Oral and Maxillofacial Surgery P Doyle, D J Spary
Orthodontics D J Spary
Orthopaedics M R Hamlet, A M Johns, S Khemka, M Wallace
Paediatrics A Choules, T Jacob-Samuel, A Manzoor, M M B Mirfattahi

Radiology M Adas, N Barraclough, K Nanda, J Singanayagam, A Zafar
Rheumatology M Nisar
Urology R A Corfield, D M Thomas

Bury Health Care NHS Trust

Closing April 2002 - Mental health services transferred to Penine Care NHS Trust; acute services transferring to Pennine Acute Hospitals NHS Trust; community services transferring to Bury Primary Care Trust.

Fairfield General Hospital, Rochdale Old Road, Bury BL9 7TD
Tel: 0161 778 3827 Fax: 0161 778 3602
(Greater Manchester Health Authority)

Chief Executive Jude Kay

Bealey Community Hospital

Dumers Lane, Radcliffe, Manchester M26 9QD
Tel: 0161 723 2371
Total Beds: 16

Bury General Hospital

Walmersley Road, Bury BL9 6PG
Tel: 0161 764 6081 Fax: 0161 705 3249
Total Beds: 206

Chemical Pathology F J Stratton
Haematology Dr Brammer, Dr Grey
Histopathology Dr Bhatnagar, M Herd
Microbiology Dr Burman

Fairfield General Hospital

Rochdale Old Road, Jericho, Bury BL9 7TD
Tel: 0161 764 6081 Fax: 0161 705 3656
Total Beds: 577

Anaesthetics Dr Gadiyar, K Kataria, P Kotak, Dr Madhavan, Dr Marthi, A H M Mollah, Dr Pandya, N M Tierney
Cardiothoracic Surgery Dr Jones
Care of the Elderly Dr Bowden, Dr Finnegan, Dr Goodman, Dr Haslam, Dr Kouta, Dr Mushahwar, A Narayan, Dr Prudham, Dr Savage, P Sethi, Dr Sinniah, Dr Smith, Dr Smithurst, U N Wadhwa
Dental Surgery A E Green, S G Langton
Dermatology Dr Fitzgerald, Dr Judge
ENT Dr Bhatnagar, J T Brandrick, D Gordon, Dr Sheppard
General Psychiatry Dr Paul, Dr Prasad, Dr Sagar, K T Thomas, Dr Vaidya
General Surgery Dr deSouza, Dr Kutiyanawala, Dr Pearson, Dr Sharif
Genitourinary Medicine Dr Lacey
Neurology Dr Mohr
Obstetrics and Gynaecology K S Haworth, Dr Hayden, A J Russell, C R Wake
Ophthalmology Dr Hashmi, Dr Jacobs, Dr Khan, Dr Qureshi
Orthodontics P A Banks
Orthopaedics A F M Brewood, J Doyle, A I Hegab, Dr Ilango, R McGivney
Paediatrics Dr Bose-Haider, D T Hindley, Dr Prabhakar, P U Prabhu, V S Sankar
Radiology S Augustine, D Brigg, S Garewal, S Singanayagam
Radiotherapy and Oncology Dr Slevin

Pennine House

Rochdale Old Road, Bury BL9 7TD

Ramsbottom Cottage Hospital

Nuttall Lane, Ramsbottom, Bury BL0 9JZ
Tel: 01706 823123
Total Beds: 16

Consultants A Narayan, P Sethi, U N Wadhwa
General Psychiatry Dr Paul, Dr Prasad, Dr Sagar, Dr Thomas, Dr Vaidya

NHS TRUSTS & NHS HOSPITALS

Roch House Day Hospital

Rochdale Old Road, Bury BL9 7TD

Bury Primary Care Trust

21 Silver Street, Bury BL9 0LN
(Greater Manchester Health Authority)

Chair Hilda Harvey
Chief Executive Evan Boucher

Calderdale and Huddersfield NHS Trust

From April 2002 mental health services transferring to South West Yorkshire Mental Health Trust.

Trust HQ, The Royal Infirmary, Acre Street, Lindley HD3 3EA
Tel: 01484 34 20 00 Fax: 01484 34 22 53
(West Yorkshire Health Authority)

Abraham Ormerod Day Hospital

Burnley Road, Todmorden OL14 7BY
Tel: 01706 817911

Foster Day Hospital

Northowram Hospital, Northowram, Halifax HX3 7SW
Tel: 01422 201011 Fax: 01422 206056

Halifax General Hospital

Salterhebble, Halifax HX3 0PW
Tel: 01422 357171 Fax: 01422 380357
Total Beds: 375

Anaesthetics R Bailie, P A Bamber, S N Chater, P J Lesser, S A Siddiqui, I D Somerville, J Thomson
Care of the Elderly Dr Chandratre, P Rajjayabun, J L Sarin, I Shakir
Child and Adolescent Psychiatry P M Chapman
Dental Surgery J Jones
Dermatology M J Cheesebrough, E D A Potts
General Medicine P M Humberstone, B C Lalor, M S A Qureshi, A P Tandon, R G Taylor
General Surgery A K Banerjee, R J R Goodall, V K Modgill, P Surtees
Obstetrics and Gynaecology M D Bono, C Choy, S Hamilton, D Jones
Orthodontics R Y Shuff
Paediatrics L J Clogher, V Kumar, A Muhammed, Y Oade
Radiology N K Jain, H D Montgomery, T J C Price, L N Sutton
Urology K Rogawski, J J F Somerville

Holme Valley Memorial Hospital

Holmfirth, Huddersfield HD7 2TS
Tel: 01484 681711 Fax: 01484 482357
Total Beds: 44

Huddersfield Royal Infirmary

Lindley, Huddersfield HD3 3EA
Tel: 01484 422191 Fax: 01484 482888
Total Beds: 438

Accident and Emergency R Birkenshaw, M G G Clayton
Anaesthetics N K S Al-Quisi, J J K Anathhanam, R J Brooks, J Esmond, L Fahy, R M Jackson, F O Jennings, D R Lloyd, A Mallick, C G Nandakumar, J Nunez, M J O'Neil, J O'Riordan, R K Vadhera
Cardiology R Stevenson, C P Welsh
Care of the Elderly R Angus, J R Naylor, P Rana, E Silwo
Child and Adolescent Psychiatry I McKenzie
Dermatology M J Cheesbrough, D Cowan
ENT D Boyd, C J R Newbegin, G J C Smelt
Forensic Psychiatry S Bhattacherjee, D Hargreaves

General Medicine A W Burrows, A Graham, R W Heaton, G Sobala
General Surgery M I Aldoori, P J Holdsworth, M K Jovestani, R C Macdonald, I Morris, J R Sainsbury
Genitourinary Medicine S S Al-Egaily, A Kazi, C Knowles
Haematology C Carter
Immunology D Misbah
Neurology B E D Dafalla, B E D Dafalla
Neurophysiology K Spillane
Obstetrics and Gynaecology K Bharbra, J M Campbell, J G Feeney, P Jackson, M Prafullatha
Old Age Psychiatry O Burma Wilson, N Greenhalgh
Oncology B Crosse, J K Joffe, M Snee
Ophthalmology J L Aggarwal, K E Davey, A G Murphy
Oral and Maxillofacial Surgery P D Cannon
Orthodontics R Y Shuff
Orthopaedics J E Cleary, A W F Milling, R K Sharma, A Shenolikar, H M Williams, D I Wise
Paediatrics C Clogher, A Exley, A H Hamilton, M G Miller, G Parry, A Short, M A Sills
Pathology A M T al-Badri, H H Ali, M Aslam, D Birkenhead, C Carter, G J Coast, A M Feeney, J P Fitzmaurice, H Griffiths, M A Khan
Plastic Surgery M Ang, D J Britto, P Fox-Hiley, E Gehlhaar, J Gooding, S M Hassan, D T Sharp, D Waddington
Radiology J P Bottomley, S Gurney, B O Hammond, K Naik, A R Paes, K Roberts
Rheumatology R Reece
Urology M A Ferro, S M Upsdell, M A Ferro, M A Khan, S M Upsdell

Northowram Hospital

Northowram, Halifax HX3 7SQ
Tel: 01422 201101 Fax: 01422 206056
Total Beds: 224

Care of the Elderly Dr Chandatre, P Rajjayabun, J L Sarin, I Shakir
Psychiatry of Old Age S Thiriloganathan

Royal Halifax Infirmary

Free School Lane, Halifax HX1 2YP
Tel: 01422 357222 Fax: 01422 342581
Total Beds: 185

Accident and Emergency M Mahmoud, B K Parikh
Anaesthetics R Bailie, P A Bamber, S N Chater, P J A Lesser, S A Siddiqui, I D Somerville, J Thomson
Cardiology A P Tandon
ENT D A Boyd, G Smelt
General Medicine P M Humberstone, B C Lalor, M S A Qureshi, A P Tandon, R G Taylor
General Surgery A K Banerjee, R J R Goodall, V K Modgill, P Surtees
Genitourinary Medicine S S Al-Egaily
Neurology S M Omer
Ophthalmology C Hutchinson, T James, S R Spencer
Orthopaedics C J Chadwick, J A Chapman, B M Flood
Pathology I Burnett, R P M Marks, K Shorrock, A J Steed, G D H Thomas
Plastic Surgery I T S Foo
Radiology N K Jain, H D Montgomery, T J C Price, L N Sutton
Radiotherapy and Oncology H J Close

St Luke's Hospital

Blackmoorfoot Road, Crosland Moor, Huddersfield HD4 5RQ
Tel: 01484 654711 Fax: 01484 482409
Total Beds: 195

General Psychiatry H Sayer
Radiology C Clout, P F Evans, B O Hammond

Shaw Day Hospital

Northowram Hospital, Northowram, Halifax HX3 7SW
Tel: 01422 201101 Fax: 01422 206056

Travelling Day Hospital

Northowram Hospital, Northowram, Halifax HX3 7SW
Tel: 01422 201101 Fax: 01422 206056

Calderdale Primary Care Trust

School House, 56 Hopwood Lane, Halifax HX1 5ER
Tel: 01422 397300 Fax: 01422 397301
Website: www.calderdale-pcg.nhs.uk
(West Yorkshire Health Authority)

Chair Joyce Catterick
Chief Executive Martyn Pritchard

Calderstones NHS Trust

Mitton Road, Whalley, Clitheroe BB7 9PE
Tel: 01254 822121 Fax: 01254 823023
(Cumbria and Lancashire Health Authority)

Chair Christine Kirk
Chief Executive Russ Pearce

Calderstones

Mitton Road, Whalley, Clitheroe BB7 9PE
Tel: 01254 822121
Total Beds: 230

Psychiatry of Learning Disability and Forensic Psychiatry of Learning Disabilities A Adewunmi, B Brown, M Ferguson, S Ghosh, A Kumar, M A Razzaque

Cambridge City Primary Care Trust

Heron Court, Ida Darwin, Fulbourn, Cambridge CB1 5ee
Tel: 01223 885700 Fax: 01223 885728
Website: www.cambcity-pcg.nhs.uk/
(Norfolk, Suffolk and Cambridgeshire Health Authority)

Cambridgeshire and Peterborough Mental Health Partnership NHS Trust

Kingfisher House, Kingfisher Way, Hinchingbrook Business Park, Huntingdon PE29 6FH
(Norfolk, Suffolk and Cambridgeshire Health Authority)

Chair Owen Ingram
Chief Executive Richard Taylor

Camden and Islington Community Health Services NHS Trust

Trust closure tbc - Part of service transferring to Camden Primary Care Trust and Islington Primary Care Trust.

St Pancras Hospital, 4 St Pancras Way, London NW1 0PE
Tel: 020 7530 3000 Fax: 020 7530 3104
(North Central London Health Authority)

Chair Usman Khan

Hornsey Central Hospital

Park Road, Crouch End, London N8 8JL
Tel: 020 8219 1700 Fax: 020 8219 1701
Total Beds: 45

Care of the Elderly C Bielawska, S Mitchell, G S Rai

Jules Thorn Day Hospital

4 St Pancras Way, London NW1 0PE
Tel: 020 7530 3390 Fax: 020 7530 3391

The London Foot Hospital and School of Podiatric Medicine

33 Fitzroy Square, London W1P 6AY
Tel: 020 7530 4500 Fax: 020 7530 4540

St Luke's Hospital

Woodside Avenue, Muswell Hill, London N10 3HU
Tel: 020 8219 1800 Fax: 020 8219 1801
Total Beds: 72

General Psychiatry E Chesser, I Collis, O Hill, S Stansfield

St Pancras Hospital

4 St. Pancras Way, London NW1 0PE
Tel: 020 7530 3500 Fax: 020 7530 3510
Total Beds: 213

Care of the Elderly K Arnold, J Croker, J Malone-Lee
Psychiatry of Old Age T Katz

Southwood Hospital

Southwood Lane, London N6 5SP
Tel: 020 8340 8778 Fax: 020 8340 8776
Total Beds: 22

Camden and Islington Mental Health NHS Trust

2nd Floor East Wing, St Pancreas Hospital, 4 St Pancras Way, London NW1 0PE
Tel: 020 7530 3094 Fax: 020 7530 3083
(North Central London Health Authority)

Chair David Taylor
Chief Executive Erville Millar

Camden Primary Care Trust

110 Hampstead Road, London NW1 2LJ
Tel: 020 7853 5310, 020 7853 5487 Fax: 020 7853 5549
(North Central London Health Authority)

Chair John Carrier
Chief Executive Rob Larkman

Cannock Chase Primary Care Trust

1811 Coppice Ward, Cannock Chase Hospital, Brunswick Road, Cannock WS11 2XY
(Shropshire and Staffordshire Health Authority)

Canterbury and Coastal Primary Care Trust

Chestfield Medical Centre, Reeves Way, Chestfield, Whitstable CT5 3QU
Tel: 01227 794777 Fax: 01227 794973
Email: canterbury&coastal.pcg@ccmail.ekent-ha.sthames.nhs.uk
Website: www.ekent-ha.sthames.nhs.uk
(Kent and Medway Health Authority)

NHS TRUSTS & NHS HOSPITALS

Cardiothoracic Centre Liverpool NHS Trust

Thomas Drive, Liverpool L14 3PE
Tel: 0151 228 1616 Fax: 0151 220 8573
(Cheshire and Merseyside Health Authority)

Chief Executive Michael Bone

Carlisle and District Primary Care Trust

The Coppice, Cumwhinton Drive, Carlisle CA1 3SX
Tel: 01228 603500 Fax: 01228 603612
(Cumbria and Lancashire Health Authority)

Chair Ruth Copple
Chief Executive Graham Ogden

Castle Point and Rochford Primary Care Trust

12 Castle Road, Rayleigh SS6 7QF
(Essex Health Authority)

Central Cheshire Primary Care Trust

Barony Hospital, Barony Road, Nantwich CW5 5QU
Tel: 01270 628823, 01270 415391
Chair Pauline Ong
Chief Executive Mike Pryah

Central Cornwall Primary Care Trust

John Keay House, Tregonissey Road, St Austell PL25 4NQ
(South West Peninsula Health Authority)

Central Derby Primary Care Trust

118 Osmaston Road, Derby DE1 2RD
Tel: 01332 203102 Fax: 01332 203206
(Southern Derbyshire Health Authority)

Chair Stuart Fletcher
Chief Executive Graham English

Central Liverpool Primary Care Trust

Hartington Road Family Health Centre, Hartington Road, Lesseps Road, Liverpool L8 0SQ
Tel: 0151 734 5090 Fax: 0151 735 0891
(Cheshire and Merseyside Health Authority)

Chair Gideon Ben-Tovim
Chief Executive Derek Campbell

Central Manchester and Manchester Children's University Hospitals NHS Trust

Manchester Royal Infirmary, Cobbett House, Oxford Road, Manchester M13 9WL
Tel: 0161 276 1234 Fax: 0161 273 6211
(Greater Manchester Health Authority)

Chair Peter Mount
Chief Executive John Scampion

Booth Hall Children's Hospital

Charlestown Road, Blackley, Manchester M9 7AA
Tel: 0161 727 2363, 0161 795 7000 Fax: 0161 220 5387, 0161 727 2370

Accident and Emergency S Derbyshire, L Duane
Anaesthetics P Ashford, H L Goldwater, A Griffiths, W D Lord, T Montague, R Perkins, A Razak, Y Y Youssef
Child and Adolescent Psychiatry D Firth, J M Green, A L Trumper
Dermatology T J David, C Ewing, L Patel
ENT Dr Jaffari, A P Zarod
Gastroenterology S Davidson, V Miller, A Thomas
General Medicine M Bone, T J David, G Hambleton, D A Price, E Wraith
General Surgery J Bowen, A P Dickson, C M Doig
Intensive Care K Hawkins, S Kerr, D Stewart, R Yates
Nephrology M Lewis, N Webb
Neurology M A Clarke, I Hughes, T Martland, R W Newton
Ophthalmology J L Noble
Oral and Maxillofacial Surgery P R White
Orthodontics D Beam, D Heggarty
Orthopaedics J B Day, P R Kay, T Meadows
Paediatrics E Baildam, M Bone, J M Couriel, T J David, S Davidson, C Ewing, H Jacques, V Miller, L Patel, A Thomas, E M Baildam, M Bone, S Davidson, C I Ewing, H Jacques
Pathology G Addison, C Cullinane, A Kelsey, A Milford, M Newbould, R Sanyal, R F Stevens, A Will
Plastic Surgery P J Davenport, K Dunn, D J Whitby
Radiology B Barry, C Broome, U Hughes, B P M Wilson
Rheumatology E Baildam, P J L Holt

Manchester Royal Eye Hospital

Oxford Road, Manchester M13 9WH
Tel: 0161 276 5526 Fax: 0161 273 2028
Total Beds: 35

Anaesthetics D Barman, A J Charlton, D G D Davidson, E L Horsman, P W Jackson, A A Khan, I C Lloyd, A K Morton, J Shaw, M E Simpson, R M Slater
Ophthalmology A M Ansons, C L Dodd, N P Jones, M J Lavin, B Leatherbarrow, C Lloyd, D McLeod, K B Mills, J L Noble, E O'Donoghue, A E A Ridgway, A Tullo, G S Turner

Manchester Royal Infirmary

Corbbett House, Oxford Road, Manchester M13 9WL
Tel: 0161 276 1234 Fax: 0161 273 6211
Website: www.cmmc.nhs.uk
Total Beds: 519

Accident and Emergency K Mackway-Jones, R Morton, B Phillips
Anaesthetics J M Anderton, D Barman, R A Bowman, I T Campbell, A K Charlton, D G D Davidson, B R H Doran, L Doyle, J M Eddleston, R Fletcher, S Greenhough, N J N Harper, E J Healey, E L Horsman, A A Khan, A K Morton, N O'Keefe, B J Pollard, J Shaw, M E Simpson, R Slater, T Strang, S Varley, A Vohra, D Whitaker
Audiological Medicine V K Das, V Newton
Cardiology B Clarke, L Cotter, A Fitzpatrick, D J Rowlands
Cardiothoracic Surgery G J Grotte, R Hasen, D J M Keenan, N Odom
Care of the Elderly P Bannister, C M Cheshire, M J Connolly
Chemical Pathology M France

Dermatology R J G Chalmers, H Muston
Diabetes A J M Boulton, R Davies, S Tomlinson
Endocrinology J R E Davies, F Wu
Gastroenterology J M Braganza, T W Warnes
General Medicine M Davies, P Durrington, C C Hardy, A M Heagerty, P Selby, R D G Tunbridge, M A Woodhead
General Psychiatry I Anderson, R C Baldwin, S M Benbow, S Benjamin, D Crauford, F H Creed, J F W Deakin, E Dyer, E Guthrie, J Harrison, D Hughes, G McGrath, F R Margison, A Poynton, A Proctor, N J Simpson, P R Snowden, A G Sutton, L Webster
General Surgery J Hill, R W G Johnson, R F McCloy, I MacLennan, N R Parrott, R C Pearson
Genitourinary Medicine M N Bhattacharyya, T K Chatterjee, B Goorney
Haematology J G Chang, C R M Hay, E M Love, G Lucas, C Shiech, S Shwe, J A L Yin
Immunology J P Burnie, R C Matthews, R S H Pumphrey, J K Struthers
Infectious Diseases B K Mandal
Intensive Care B Doran
Medical Microbiology J P Burnie, R C Mathews, J K Struthers
Nephrology F W Ballardie, R Gokal, A Hutchinson, R W G Johnson, N P Mallick, N R Parrott, R C Pearson, H Riad, L D Short
Neurology J Dick, N McDermott, G Mawer, D Neary, W Schady, P Talbot
Neurosurgery R H Lye, P L Richardson, F A Strang
Nuclear Medicine M C Prescott, H J Testa
Orthopaedics P Hirst, N Kenny, B Maltby, A Paul
Otolaryngology A Birzgalis, P Canty, W T Farrington, R T Ramsden
Pathology A J Barson, E W Benbow, R E Bonshek, C H Buckley, A J Freemont, S Lee, J McClure, R F T McMahon, L Moore, R V Persad, H Reid, C Stanbridge
Plastic Surgery A Brain
Radiology J E Adams, N Chalmers, R A Fawcitt, J E Gillespie, A Jackson, J P R Jenkins, S Lee, S Rimmer, S A Russell, P M Taylor, N A Watson, R W Whitehouse
Rheumatology and Rehabilitation R M Bernstein, P J L Holt, J Keenan, E R E Ross, A Silman
Urology R N P Carroll, J Harney, S Payne
Vascular Surgery R Marcuson, M Walker
Virology G Corbitt

Royal Manchester Children's Hospital

Hospital Road, Pendlebury, Manchester M27 4HA
Tel: 0161 794 4696 Fax: 0161 727 2364
Total Beds: 182

Anaesthetics O R Dearlove, T Howell, G Meakin, D Patel, D N Robinson, R Walker
Cardiac Surgery G Gladman, E J Ladusans, R G Patel
Chemical Pathology G M Addison
Child and Adolescent Psychiatry R Harrington, M Kelsall, L Kroll, H Lloyd
Clinical Genetics B Kerr, M Super
Developmental Medicine I McKinlay
Endocrinology P E Clayton, D A Price
ENT M P Rothera, D J Willatt
Haematology R F Stevens, A Will, R Wynn
Intensive Care K Hawkins, D Stewart, R Yates
Nephrology M Bradbury, M Lewis, R Postlethwaite, N Webb
Neurology M Clarke, I Hughes, T Martland, R Newton
Neurosurgery C Bannister, R A Cowie, J R S Leggate, A Sofat, G Victoratos, C G H West
Oncology B Brennan, T Eden, L Lashford
Oral Surgery I Campbell, R Lloyd
Orthopaedics C S B Galasko, A Henry, E Ross, J Spilsbury, B Williamson
Paediatric Surgery A Bianchi, J Bowen, J Bruce
Paediatrics P Clayton, M Cleary, G Hambleton, D A Price, H C Smith, A Thomas, J Walter, J E Wraith
Pathology C Cullinane, A M Kelsey, M Newbould, R Sanyal
Radiology B Barry, B P M Wilson
Respiratory Medicine G Hambleton

Rheumatology E Baildam, A Herrick
Thoracic Surgery R A M Lawson
Transplant Surgery R Stevens, A Will
Urology J Bruce, D C S Gough, U Hughes, K O'Flynn

St Mary's Hospital for Women and Children

Whitworth Park, Manchester M13 0JH
Tel: 0161 276 1234 Fax: 0161 276 6107
Total Beds: 200

Anaesthetics J M Anderton, A J Charlton, D G D Davidson, S Greenhough, N J N Harper, E L Horsman, A A Khan, A K Morton, B J Pollard, J Shaw, M E Simpson, W D Smith, D Whittaker
Cardiology G Gladman, E Ladusans
Genetics J Clayton-Smith, D I O Crawford, D Donnai, G Evans, R Harris, H Kingston
Immunology R S H Pumphrey
Obstetrics and Gynaecology P Buck, P Donnai, T Johnston, H Kitchener, B A Lieberman, M J A Maresh, K Reynolds, M Seif, A R B Smith
Paediatric Surgery A Bianchi, A P Dickson, C M Doig
Paediatrics M L Chiswick, I Doughty, S W D'Souza, A Emmerson, M Z Mughal, D G Sims
Pathology A J Barson, C H Buckley, S Lee, L Moore, C M Stanbridge
Radiology S Rimmer, S A Russell

University Dental Hospital of Manchester

Higher Cambridge Street, Manchester M15 6FH
Tel: 0161 275 6666 Fax: 0161 275 6776
Total Beds: 14

Dentistry A Mellor, A Shearer
Oral and Maxillofacial Surgery R Middlehurst, B Musgrove
Radiology K Horner
Restorative Dentistry D J Eldridge, J R Heath, P S Hull, J D Lilley, J F McCord, G A Smith, M Wilson, N H F Wilson

Central Manchester Primary Care Trust

Oak House, 47 Graham Street, Manchester M11 3BB
Tel: 0161 958 4000 Fax: 0161 861 7191
Website: www.centralmanchesterpct.co.uk
(Greater Manchester Health Authority)

Chair E Asante-Mensah
Chief Executive S Assar

Central Suffolk Primary Care Trust

Stow Lodge Centre, Chilton Way, Stowmarket IP14 1SZ
Tel: 01449 616346 Fax: 01449 616340
Website: www.centralsuffolk-pcg.nhs.uk
(Norfolk, Suffolk and Cambridgeshire Health Authority)

Chair Brain Parrott
Chief Executive Harper Brown

Charnwood and North West Leicestershire Primary Care Trust

53 Baxter Gate, Loughborough LE11 1TH
Tel: 01509 838696 Fax: 01509 038694
(Leicestershire, Northamptonshire and Rutland Health Authority)

Chief Executive Andrew Clarke

NHS TRUSTS & NHS HOSPITALS

Chelmsford Primary Care Trust

Wood House, St John's Hospital, Wood Street, Chelmsford CM2 9BG
Tel: 01245 456033 Fax: 01245 465868
Email: office@chelmsford-pcg.nhs.uk
(Essex Health Authority)

Chelsea and Westminster Healthcare NHS Trust

Chelsea and Westminster Hospital, 369 Fulham Road, Chelsea, London SW10 9NH
Tel: 020 8746 8000 Fax: 020 8746 8111
Website: www.chelseawestminster.co.uk
(North West London Health Authority)

Chair Juggy Pandit
Chief Executive Heather Lawrence

Chelsea and Westminster Hospital

369 Fulham Road, Chelsea, London SW10 9NH
Tel: 020 8746 8000 Fax: 020 8846 6539
Total Beds: 497

Accident and Emergency J Booth, P Longstaff
Anaesthetics P K Barnes, M Bloch, J Chandy, M Cox, S Cox, D Dob, J Durbridge, N Fauvel, K Haire, M Hayes, A Holdcroft, T Kirwan, A Lawson, M Naze, A Rice, J Robotham, N C Soni, V J E Thomas, G Towlerton, M Weston, S Yentis
Cardiology S Kaddoura (Head), I Belfour-Lynn, P Daubeney, S Davies, R Sutton
Care of the Elderly H Gillespie, P Kroker, D J Morgan, M D Pelly
Chest Medicine J Collins, T Evans
Clinical Pharmacology and Therapeutics M Feher
Cytology N Livni
Dental Surgery K Barnard, J Smallridge
Dermatology T Basarab, C Bunker, J Cream, S C Mayou, N Roberts, R C D Staughton
Diabetes C McIntosh
ENT P Clarke (Head), J Harcourt, I Mackay
Gastroenterology M Anderson, J Andreyev, J Andreyev, B Gazzard, I Murray-Lyon, D Westaby, R Zeegen
General Surgery T Allen-Mersh, N Cheshire, M Henry, D Nott, J Snellie, J Thompson
Genitourinary Medicine D Asboe, S Barton, F Boag, D Hawkins, S McCormack, K Mclean, A McOwan, S Mitchell, M Nelson, A Posniak, N Smith
Haematology C Costello, E Kanfer
Medical Microbiology B Azadian, D J M Wright
Neurology R Guiloff, A Kennedy, I Mak
Obstetrics and Gynaecology S Abdullah, G Ayida, A Bispham, J Bridges, C Gilling-Smith, M Johnson, E Jones, R Marwood, M E Pawson, Z Penn, R Richardson, C D Sims, R Smith, M Stafford, P Steer, J Studd, C Sutton, G Thorpe-Beeston, N Wales, M Williams
Ophthalmology N Joshi, P Kinnear, R P Knowlden, T Leonard, M B E Mathalone, S Mitchell
Oral and Maxillofacial Surgery J Clarke, B Coghlan, D Evans, D Martin, J Nanchanal, N Perceval, N Waterhouse, G Wilson
Orthopaedics P R E Baird, S Evans, A Hulme, V Lavelle, W Radford
Paediatrics E Abramson, D Acolet, I Balfour-Lynne, K Bernard, S Biswas, N Bridges, M Brueton, N Cavanagh, B Cooper, M Elsawi, J Fell, M Haddad, M Johnson, E Jones, I Kovar, K Lakhoo, N Madden, M Markiewicz, B Miller, J Nanchanal, P O'Driscoll, E Ogundipe, J Penrice, N Percival, M Rigby, G Sleigh, J Smallridge
Radiology Z Amin, R Chinn, J Healy, D M King, J McCall, J Newton, S Padley, M Phelan
Rheumatology S Kaye, C Mackworth Young
Urology T Christmas, M Dineen, J Ramsay, I Zegbu

Cheltenham and Tewkesbury Primary Care Trust

C/o The Chapel, St Paul's Medical Centre, 121 Swindon Road, Cheltenham GL50 4DP
Tel: 01242 707664 Fax: 01242 707826
Chair Ruth Fitzjohn

Cherwell Vale Primary Care Trust

Bodicote House, Bodicote, Banbury OX15 4AA
Tel: 01295 221746 Fax: 01295 221747
Website: www.cherwellvale-pct.nhs.uk
(Thames Valley Health Authority)

Chair Anita Higham
Chief Executive Barry Thomas

Cheshire and Wirral Partnership NHS Trust

Formed April 2002 by merger of the mental health and learning disability services of Cheshire Community Healthcare NHS Trust, Countess of Chester Hospital NHS Trust, East Cheshire NHS Trust, Mid Cheshire Hospitals NHS Trust and Wirral and West Cheshire Community NHS Trust; no contact details available at time of going to press.

Cheshire Community Healthcare NHS Trust

Closing April 2002 - Mental health and learning disability services transferring to Cheshire and Wirral Partnership NHS Trust; part of service transferring to Central Cheshire Primary Care Trust.

Headquarters, Barony Road, Nantwich CW5 5QU
Tel: 01270 415300 Fax: 01270 627469
(Cheshire and Merseyside Health Authority)

Chair Don Hammond

Cheshire West Primary Care Trust

21A Garden Lane, Chester CH1 4EU
Tel: 01244 400966 Fax: 01244 401351
(Cheshire and Merseyside Health Authority)

Chair Robert Hodwson
Chief Executive Ged Taylor

Chester and Halton Community NHS Trust

Closing April 2002 - Specialist services transferring to 5 Borough Partnership NHS Trust; part of service transferring to Cheshire West Primary Care Trust, Ellesmere Port and Neston Primary Care Trust and Halton Primary Care Trust.

Victoria House, Holloway, Runcorn WA7 4TH
Tel: 01928 790404 Fax: 01928 590594
Email: chalton@ccfh.demon.co.uk
Website: www.ccfh.demon.co.uk
(Cheshire and Merseyside Health Authority)

Chair Bob Hodson
Chief Executive Chris S Griffiths

Chesterfield and North Derbyshire Royal Hospital NHS Trust

Calow, Chesterfield S44 5BL
Tel: 01246 277271 Fax: 01246 276955
Email: name@cndrh-tr.trent.nhs.uk
Website: www.cndrh-tr.trent.nhs.uk
(Trent Health Authority)

Chair Michael Wall
Chief Executive Avril Johns

Chesterfield and North Derbyshire Royal Hospital

Calow, Chesterfield S44 5BL
Tel: 01246 277271 Fax: 01246 276955
Total Beds: 619

Accident and Emergency M M Alam, N H Aziz, R C Bailey, K Lendrum
Anaesthetics I R Gell (Head), C M S Cooper, J M Cort, S J Dale, I M Dods, R W Eustace, D Farquharson, J B Groves, E S Howell, G Hutchinson, I Makkison, J S Mark, R J Murray, P R Rayner, T J I Shaw, C S N Spittle, J D Stevens, R P Wroth
Child and Adolescent Psychiatry S Blomfield, J de Cartaret, J Edmondson, E Girgis, J Wilkinson
Dermatology G B Colver, R Murphy
General Medicine J W Hadfield (Head), A G Archer, M G Ashton, J T Bourne, D J Brooks, S W Crooks, K L E Dear, K Fairburn, M J Grundman, S M Parnacott, D A Sandler
General Surgery J M Simms (Head), D Bardsley, N R Boucher, D R Chadwick, N J Everitt, J Hall, S Holt, M J James, P K Kumar, W G Lambert
Genitourinary Medicine P A Fraser, K Rogstad
Haematology R C Colin, R M Stewart
Health Care of the Elderly D Chew, M W Cooper, P Iqbal, P Medcalf, M Reza
Histopathology D Hughes, D Mckenna, K Ramsden, R D Start
Microbiology K Thomas
Obstetrics and Gynaecology J M McDonnell (Head), J L Cresswell, D P Hey, S C Smith, P M Tromans, S Vindla
Ophthalmology C Brand, D Chand, K K F Mohamad, S Stafanous
Oral and Maxillofacial Surgery S J Davies, P T Doyle, P McCloughlin, P J Sandler
Orthopaedics S M As'ad, C G Beauchamp, M J Bryant, G Davies, M S d Edwards, K A Ennis, I R Scott, S Shahane, P M Williams
Otorhinolaryngology F M Nofal, V R Talati
Paediatrics G Collins, K Holt, P M Preece, M Reynolds, I F Roberts, R M Tyler
Radiology A Cohen (Head), P de vos Meiring, J Glaves, K V Nair, M Shaw, P W Sheppard, S Singh

Chesterfield Primary Care Trust

Walton Hospital, Whitecotes Lane, Chesterfield S40 3HW
Website: www.northderbyshirehealth.nhs.uk
(Trent Health Authority)

Chair Tricia Foster
Chief Executive Prem Singh

Chiltern and South Bucks Primary Care Trust

Chiltern District Council Offices, King George V Road, Amersham HP6 5AW
Tel: 01494 732020 Fax: 01494 732021
(Thames Valley Health Authority)

Chair Richard Worrell
Chief Executive Steve Young

Chingford, Wanstead and Woodford Primary Care Trust

Becketts House, 2-14 Ilford Hill, Ilford IG1 2QX
Tel: 020 8926 5262 Fax: 020 8926 5009
(North East London Health Authority)

Chair David Kelly
Chief Executive Angela McNab

Chorley and South Ribble NHS Trust

From April 2002 mental health services transferring to Lancashire Care NHS Trust; acute services transferring to a new acute trust (name tbc).

Chorley District Hospital, Preston Road, Chorley PR7 1PP
Tel: 01257 261222 Fax: 01257 245309
(Cumbria and Lancashire Health Authority)

Chair Dennis Benson

Chorley and South Ribble District General Hospital

Preston Road, Chorley PR7 1PP
Tel: 01257 261222 Fax: 01257 245309
Total Beds: 400

Accident and Emergency R J Fairhurst
Anaesthetics O E Akinpelu, M A Calleja, J Jayasuriya, C F Loyden
Chest Disease B E Taylor
Dermatology N K Saikia
ENT J Curley, T B Duff, M Small
General Medicine R A Coward, I Drake, R C Gupta, S Madi, S N H Naqvi, S C Wallis, D A L Watt
General Psychiatry M F Burrell, T G Chand, J M T Damas-Mora, I J Leonard, B Miller
General Surgery M M Mughal
Neurology P Tomlin
Obstetrics and Gynaecology J F B Clarke, I G Robertson, S K Shah, J D Wright
Oncology R A Cowan
Ophthalmology H P Adhikary, E M Talbot
Oral and Maxillofacial Surgery J Cornah, J Trenouth
Orthopaedics S Ehrendorfer, A I Hassan, A Mohammed, M J Shaw, R B Smith
Paediatrics A N Campbell, S A Clark, D A Mahmood, J R Owen
Pathology P Wright
Radiology S C Galletly, B C Spinks, R Stockwell
Urology S S Matanhelia, R G N Thomson

Royal Preston Hospital

Sharoe Green Lane North, Fulwood, Preston PR2 4QF
Tel: 01772 716565 Fax: 01772 710162
Total Beds: 608

Accident and Emergency J M Hanson, M James, M C McColl
Anaesthetics P Bunting, F DeSilva, P W Duncan, J M Fryer, A J Gosling, J O Griffiths, C Isherwood, G N Jones, S J Keens, A S Lawrence, P F S Lee, A Lowrie, E P McKiernan, R A Martlew, W A Noble, I Selby, A Seth, G K Vanner, J G Williams
Care of the Elderly J McCann, P McDonald, M Waqar Uddin
Dermatology A Butt, J K Kellet, N K Saikia
ENT J d Carpentier, J W A Curley, B Jafari, M Small
General Medicine A L Burton, S A Cairns, R A Coward, A Lakhdar, L Solomon, B E Taylor, J M Temperley, P A Vice
General Surgery A R Hearn, R Hughes, D J Stewart, G Thomson
Genitourinary Medicine A Saeed
Neurology I Bangash, B Boothman, T Majeed, J D Mitchell, P Tidswell, S D Vakil
Neurosurgery C H Davis, N S Gurusinghe, A J Keogh

NHS TRUSTS & NHS HOSPITALS

Oncology A Biswas, A Hindley, T Mughal, G Read, G Skailes, S Susnerwala
Ophthalmology H P Adhikary, A T Ekdawy, G Griffith, E M Talbot
Oral and Maxillofacial Surgery J Cornah
Orthodontics M J Trenouth
Orthopaedics R S Bale, J C Faux, V Shah, S J Shaw, R M Smith, M R Wharton
Paediatrics A N Campbell, S A Clark, D Mahmood, J R Owen, P I Tomlin
Pathology A Armour, T A Flaherty, A J Howat, P G Lynch, C M Nicholson, M A Pitt, F Rugman, N Williamson, P Wright
Plastic Surgery N R Gaze, A J Howcroft, R P Jones, J G Laitung
Radiology J P Bradley, J M Brown, C Coutinho, M Dobson, S D'Souza, W J Gunawardena, I Harris, J C Hill
Thoracic Medicine R W J Millner
Urology B Elem, S Matanhelia, M E Watson

Sharoe Green Hospital

Sharoe Green Lane South, Fulwood, Preston PR2 4DU
Tel: 01772 716565 Fax: 01772 710622
Total Beds: 263

Care of the Elderly J McCann, P McDonald, M Waqar-Uddin
General Medicine A L Burton, B E Taylor, P A Vice
Obstetrics and Gynaecology J F B Clarke, S Hughes, I G Robertson, S K Shah, J D Wright
Orthopaedics R S Bale, J C Faux, V Shah, S J Shaw, R M Smith, M R Wharton
Paediatrics A N Campbell, S A Clark, D Mahmood, J R Owen, P A Tomlin

Chorley and South Ribble Primary Care Trust

Dob Bridge Cottage, Twin Lakes Park, Bretherton Road, Croston, Preston PR5 7RF
Tel: 01772 602800 Fax: 01772 601519
(Cumbria and Lancashire Health Authority)

Chair Dennis Benson
Chief Executive Judith Faux

Christie Hospital NHS Trust

Wilmslow Road, Withington, Manchester M20 4BX
Tel: 0161 446 3000 Fax: 0161 446 3977
Website: www.christie.man.ac.uk
(Greater Manchester Health Authority)

Chair Arthur Sandford
Chief Executive Joanna Wallace

Christie Hospital

Wilmslow Road, Withington, Manchester M20 4BX
Tel: 0161 446 3000 Fax: 0161 446 3977
Total Beds: 320

Chest Medicine P V Barber
Clinical Oncology E Allan, P Burt, R Cowan, S E Davidson, D P Deakin, C Faivre-Finn, R D Hunter, E Levine, J Logue, B Magee, M Saunders, N Slevin, A L Stewart, R Stout, A J Sykes, R Welch, J Wylie
Clinical Pharmacology P M Wilkinson
Cytology M Desai, H A El Teraifi, D Perera
Endocrinology S M Shalet, P Trainer
ENT A Birzgalis, W Farrington
Epidemiology A Moran, C Woodham
Haematological Oncology R Chopra
Haematology J Chang, G Morgenstern
Histopathology S Banerjee, Dr Menasce, J Shanks
Medical Genetics G Evans
Medical Oncology H Anderson, R Hawkins, A Howell, G Jayson, J A Radford, M Ranson, N Thatcher, J Valle, Dr Wardley, C Williams

Microbiology B Oppenheim
Obstetrics and Gynaecology M Kitchener, K Reynolds, R J Slade
Occupational Health Dr Persad
Oral Surgery W Simpson
Paediatric Oncology B Brennan, O B Eden, H R Gattamaneni
Paediatrics Histopathology A Kelsey
Palliative Care and Clinical Oncology W P Makin
Plastic Surgery A Brain
Psychological Medicine P Hopwood, P M Maguire
Radiology R Bramley, B Carrington, P Hulse, R J Johnson, J Lawrance, B Taylor
Surgery A Baildam, N Bundred, S O'Dwyer, D Tweedle
Urology N Clarke, M Wilson

City and Hackney Primary Care Trust

St Leonard's, Nuttall Street, London N1 5LZ
Tel: 020 7301 3000 Fax: 020 7739 8455
(North East London Health Authority)

Chair Jane Winder
Chief Executive Laura Sharpe

City Hospital NHS Trust

Closing April 2002 - Services transferring to Sandwell and West Birmingham Hospitals NHS Trust.

Headquarters, Dudley Road, Birmingham B18 7QH
Tel: 0121 554 3801 Fax: 0121 551 5569
(Birmingham and the Black Country Health Authority)

Chair Richard Steer

City Hospitals Sunderland NHS Trust

Kayll Road, Sunderland SR4 7TP
Tel: 0191 565 6256 Fax: 0191 514 0220
Website: www.sunderland.nhs.uk
(Northumberland, Tyne and Wear Health Authority)

Chair David Graham
Chief Executive Andrew F Gibson

Ryhope General Hospital

Ryhope, Sunderland SR2 OLY
Tel: 0191 585 6256
Total Beds: 306

Care of the Elderly S K Bansal, S K Basu, S Ghosh, S D Gupta, A R Mandal

Sunderland Eye Infirmary

Queen Alexandra Road, Sunderland SR2 9HP
Tel: 0191 528 3616
Total Beds: 60

Ophthalmology R W Allchin, E D Allen, D Chitkara, J P Deady, D V Inglesby, C N J McGhee, S J Morgan, P S Phelan, J Richardson, C M Wood

Sunderland Royal Hospital

Kayll Road, Sunderland SR4 7TP
Tel: 0191 565 6256 Fax: 0191 514 0220
Total Beds: 947

Accident and Emergency R K Banerjee, C L Muwanga
Anaesthetics J I Andrews, A E Arrowsmith, P M Baker, J Baldasera, C M E Carr, A K Choudhry, N Ghosh, J Halshaw, I Herrema, M K Johnson, L J Mackay, A R Mahroo, K A Price, R V Samak, N Smith

Care of the Elderly S K Bansal, S K Basu, S Ghosh, S D Gupta, A R Mandal
General Medicine B I Chazan, G R Harlow, D S Pugh
General Psychiatry P G Baines, M Place
General Surgery L Boobis, J Rich, A J Warrington
Genitourinary Medicine S Rashid, K M Saravanamuttu
Neurology P G Cleland, R E Jones
Obstetrics and Gynaecology H Cameron, M E Dalton, M J Goakes, K Godfrey, G Macnab, B J Murray
Oral and Maxillofacial Surgery I Martin, L Stasson
Orthodontics I A Shaw, D J Vase
Orthopaedics J M Buchanan, R G Checketts, A T Cross, P Gill, A Stirrat
Otolaryngology P J D Dawes, I Hopper, I W Mackee, P R Samuel, F Stafford
Paediatrics G Lawson, M F Lowry, M Massam, S W J Richmond, M Taylor
Plastic Surgery R B Berry, K M R Chrystal, J H James
Radiology J Connor, S England, M S K Marikkar, R L Marsh, P W Sheppard
Radiotherapy and Oncology V Mallick, J T Roberts
Rheumatology and Rehabilitation A J Chuck, T J Daymond, C Holland
Thoracic Medicine Dr Hylton

Clatterbridge Centre for Oncology NHS Trust

Clatterbridge Road, Bebington, Wirral CH63 4JY
Tel: 0151 334 1155
(Cheshire and Merseyside Health Authority)

Consultants J E S Brock, Dr Clark, Mr Cottier, R D Errington, A Flavin, Keith A Grant, J A Green, K Hayat, B Haylock, Dave J Husband, J A H Littler, J Maguire, E Marshall, S Myint, S O'Reilly, C Romaniuk, Dr Shenoh, A J Slater, David B Smith, I Syndikus, Dr Thorpe

Colchester Primary Care Trust

Health Offices, Turner Road, Colchester CO4 5JR
Tel: 01206 288500 Fax: 01206 288501
Website: www.colchester-pct.nhs.uk
(Essex Health Authority)

Chair Maggie Shackell
Chief Executive Brendan Osborne

CommuniCare NHS Trust

Closing April 2002 - Psychology and drug services transferring to Lancashire Care NHS Trust; remainder of services transferring to Hyndburn and Ribble Valley Primary Care Trust.

Headquarters, 33 Eagle Street, Accrington BB5 1LN
Tel: 01254 356800 Fax: 01254 356837
Website: www.communicare.24.freeserve.co.uk
(Cumbria and Lancashire Health Authority)

Chair Sheila Maw
Chief Executive Ken Johnson

Accrington Victoria Community Hospital

Haywood Road, Accrington BB5 6AS
Tel: 01254 263555 Fax: 01254 687367
Total Beds: 20

Clitheroe Community Hospital

Chatburn Road, Clitheroe BB7 4JX
Tel: 01200 427311 Fax: 01200 442966
Total Beds: 63

Ribchester Community Hospital

Ribchester, Preston PR3 3XD
Tel: 01772 782216
Total Beds: 15

Community Health Sheffield NHS Trust

Fulwood House, Old Fulwood Road, Sheffield S10 3TH
Tel: 0114 271 6600 Fax: 0114 271 6712
(South Yorkshire Health Authority)

Chair Alan C Walker
Chief Executive Barbara A Walsh

Beighton Hospital

Sevenaires Road, Beighton, Sheffield S19 6NZ
Tel: 0114 271 6572

Forest Lodge

5 Forest Lodge Close, Sheffield S30 3JW
Tel: 0114 271 6081

Grenoside Grange

Saltbox Lane, Sheffield S30 3QS
Tel: 0114 271 6131
Total Beds: 10

Nether Edge Hospital

Cavendish Ward 1, Osbourne Road, Sheffield S11 9EL
Tel: 0114 271 6787
Total Beds: 25

Shirle Hill Day Hospital

St Andrews Road, Nether Edge, Sheffield S11 9AA
Tel: 0114 271 6383 Fax: 0114 271 6382

Shirle Hill Hospital

Cherry Tree Road, Sheffield S11 9AA
Tel: 0114 271 6863
Total Beds: 6

Community Health South London NHS Trust

Trust closure tbc - Part of service transferring to Lambeth Primary Care Trust, Lewisham Primary Care Trust and Southwark Primary Care Trust.

Elizabeth Blackwell House, Wardalls Grove, Avonley Road, London SE14 5ER
Tel: 020 7635 5555 Fax: 020 7771 5115
Email: firstname.lastname@chsltr.sthames.nhs.uk
(South East London Health Authority)

Chair Ansel Wong
Chief Executive Annie Brough
Consultants Lesley Bacon, Helen Massil

Community Healthcare Bolton NHS Trust

Closing April 2002 - Wigan element of specialist services transferring to 5 Borough Partnership NHS Trust; community services and remaining specialist services transferring to Bolton Primary Care Trust.

St Peter's House, Silverwell Street, Bolton BL1 1PP
Tel: 01204 377000 Fax: 01204 377004
(Greater Manchester Health Authority)

NHS TRUSTS & NHS HOSPITALS

Cornwall Healthcare NHS Trust

Porthpean Road, St Austell PL26 6AD
Tel: 01726 291000 Fax: 01726 291080
Email: enquiries@cht.swest.nhs.uk
(South West Peninsula Health Authority)

Chair Sandra Benjamin
Chief Executive Tony Gardner

East Cornwall Hospital
Total Beds: 25

Fowey and District Hospital
Green Lane, Fowey PL23 1EE
Tel: 01726 832241 Fax: 01726 832775
Total Beds: 14

Lamellion Hospital
Station Road, Liskeard PL14 4DG
Tel: 01579 335300 Fax: 01579 335319
Total Beds: 55

Launceston General Hospital
Link Road, Launceston PL15 9JD
Tel: 01566 765650 Fax: 01566 765680
Total Beds: 20

Newquay and District Hospital
St. Thomas' Road, Newquay TR7 1RQ
Tel: 01637 893600 Fax: 01637 893659
Total Beds: 22

Passmore Edwards Hospital
Barras Place, Liskeard PL14 6AY
Tel: 01579 335277 Fax: 01579 335290
Total Beds: 19

St Austell Community Hospital
Porthpean Road, St Austell PL26 6AA
Tel: 01726 291100 Fax: 01726 291140
Total Beds: 66

St Barnabas' Hospital
Higher Porth View, Saltash PL12 4BU
Tel: 01752 857400 Fax: 01752 857429
Total Beds: 17

St Lawrence's Hospital
Westheath Avenue, Bodmin PL31 2QT
Tel: 01208 251301 Fax: 01208 251512
Total Beds: 122

Selwood House
60 Alexandra Road, St Austell PL25 4QN
Tel: 01726 291250 Fax: 01726 291251
Total Beds: 10

Stratton Hospital
Hospital Road, Stratton, Bude EX23 9BP
Tel: 01288 287700 Fax: 01288 287729
Total Beds: 17

Cotswold and Vale Primary Care Trust

C/o Coronium House, Cirencester Hospital, Tetbury Road, Cirencester GL7 1UY
Tel: 01285 884694 Fax: 01285 884652
(Avon, Gloucestershire and Wiltshire Health Authority)

Chair Elizabeth Law
Chief Executive Richard James

Countess of Chester Hospital NHS Trust

From April 2002 mental health and learning disability services transferring to Cheshire and Wirral Partnership NHS Trust.

Countess of Chester Health Park, Liverpool Road, Chester CH2 1UL
Tel: 01244 365000 Fax: 01244 365292
Website: www.coch.org
(Cheshire and Merseyside Health Authority)

Chair Susan Sellers
Chief Executive Peter Herring

Countess of Chester Hospital
Liverpool Road, Chester CH2 1UL
Tel: 01244 365000 Fax: 01244 365292
Total Beds: 600

Accident and Emergency Dr Makower, M Waters
Anaesthetics Dr Bricker, Dr Childs, Dr Fergusson, Dr Forrest, Dr Hill, Dr Jameson, Dr Logan, Dr Nelson, Dr Robin, Dr Setty, S Singh, Dr Skues, Dr Tighe
Child Health L G Evans-Jones, S Gentle, J Gibbs, S Littlewood, N P Murphy, E Ngwane, D Rogahn, L Thornton
Elderly Medicine Dr Choudhury, Dr Fitzroy Smith, Dr Spencer
ENT, Oral and Maxillofacial Dr Cawood, Dr Chadwick, Dr MacKinnon, Dr Melrose, Dr Richardson, Dr Spencer
General Medicine Dr Boggild, Dr Bowden, Dr Drakeley, Dr Ewins, Dr Finnerty, Dr Fletcher, R Harris, Dr Keeping, P G Reid, Dr Sedgwick, Dr Somauroo, Dr Varma, Dr Wardle, R C Worth
General Surgery L de Cossart, Dr Edwards, Dr Foster, Dr Harding Mackean, D N Monk, Dr Redmond
Obstetrics and Gynaecology J Davies-Humphreys, N Haddad, Dr Hawe, J McCormack, A Peattie, J Williams
Ophthalmology Dr Armstrong, Dr Butcher, Dr Tutton
Orthopaedics Dr Anderton, Dr Braithwaite, Dr Campbell, Dr Harvey, Dr Phillipson
Pathology S Bowles, V Clough, B Hamid, P Hunter, W E Kenyon, P Mannion, M W Myskow, E Rhodes, P R M Steele
Plastic Surgery Dr Dhital, Dr Fahmy, D McGeorge
Radiology G T Abbot, G Doyle, R Etherington, J E Houghton, W J Pilbrow, G R J Sissons, R A Sloka, A Wright
Sub-Specialities D Bulgen, J V Clough, A V Crowe, A Franks, S Mendelsohn, C O'Mahony, K Over, E Rhodes
Urology Dr Pettersson, Dr Powell

County Durham and Darlington Priority Services NHS Trust

Earls House, Lanchester Road, Durham DH1 5RD
Tel: 0191 333 6262 Fax: 0191 333 6363
(County Durham and Tees Valley Health Authority)

Chief Executive Sandy Taylor

Bowes Lyon Unit
Lanchester Road, Durham DH1 5RD
Total Beds: 30

County Hospital, Durham
North Road, Durham DH1 4ST
Tel: 0191 333 6262 Fax: 0191 333 3400
Total Beds: 58

General Psychiatry M Appleton, E Jones, K Linsley, S Martin, J Tomkinson

Derwent Clinic

Shotley Bridge Hospital, Shotley Bridge, Consett DH8 0NB
Tel: 01207 583583 Fax: 01207 586049
Total Beds: 40

Earls House

Lanchester Road, Durham DH1 5RD
Total Beds: 93

The Gables

Sedgefield, Stockton-on-Tees TS21 3EJ
Tel: 01740 620521 Fax: 01740 624288
Total Beds: 36

The Goodall Centre

The Goodall Centre, Bishop Auckland DL14 6QW
Tel: 01388 603161
Total Beds: 11

Pierremont Unit and Beaumont

Hollyhurst Road, Darlington
Tel: 01325 743564 Fax: 01325 743588
Total Beds: 95

Sedgefield Community Hospital

Sedgefield, Stockton-on-Tees TS21 3EJ
Tel: 01740 626600 Fax: 01740 626689
Total Beds: 16

Coventry Healthcare NHS Trust

Trust closure tbc - Part of service transferring to Coventry Primary Care Trust.

Parkside House, Quinton Road, Coventry CV1 2NJ
Tel: 024 7655 3344 Fax: 024 7652 6800
(Coventry, Warwickshire, Herefordshire and Worcestershire Health Authority)

Chair C W Goody
Chief Executive P Boileau

River House Day Centre

Gulson Road, Coventry CV1 2HR
Tel: 024 76 553344

Tamar Day Unit

Walsgrave Campus, Clifford Bridge Road, Coventry CV2 2TE
Tel: 024 76 602020 Fax: 024 76 538920

Coventry Primary Care Trust

Christchurch House, Greyfriars Lane, Coventry CV1 2GQ
Tel: 024 7624 6016 Fax: 024 7622 2687
(Coventry, Warwickshire, Herefordshire and Worcestershire Health Authority)

Craven, Harrogate and Rural District Primary Care Trust

Sovereign House, Kettlestring Lane, York YO30 4GQ
(North and East Yorkshire and Northern Lincolnshire Health Authority)

Crawley Primary Care Trust

Crawley Hospital, West Green Drive, Crawley RH11 7DH
(Surrey and Sussex Health Authority)

Chair Malcolm Liles
Chief Executive Lynne Regent

Croydon Primary Care Trust

Knollys House, 17 Addiscombe Road, Croydon CR0 6SR
Tel: 020 8401 3971 Fax: 020 8680 2418
Website: www.croyden.nhs.uk
Chair Toni Letts
Chief Executive Caroline Taylor

Croydon and Surrey Downs Community NHS Trust

Trust closure tbc - Part of service transferring to Croydon Primary Care Trust.

12-18 Lennard Road, Croydon CR9 2RS
Tel: 020 8680 2008 (Information Point: Ext: 282)
Fax: 020 8666 0495
Email: steve.hunt@csdct.nhs.uk, steve.hunt@crdct.nhs.uk
Website: www.csdct.nhs.uk
(South West London Health Authority)

Chair Valerie Vaughan-Dick
Consultants Shade Alu, Faiza Davids, Pappu Goberdhan, Sluiman Jawad, Joy Okpala

Cumbria Ambulance Service NHS Trust

Ambulance Headquarters, Salkeld Hall, Infirmary Street, Carlisle CA2 7AN
Tel: 01228 596909 Fax: 01228 520382
(Cumbria and Lancashire Health Authority)

Chair Brian Clayton
Chief Executive Alan Donkersley

Dacorum Primary Care Trust

Isbisher Centre, Chaulden House Gardens, Off Chaulden Lane, Hemel Hempstead HP1 2BW
Tel: 01442 840950 Fax: 01442 840951
Email: general@dacorum-pct.nhs.uk
Website: www.dacorum-pct.nhs.uk
(Bedfordshire and Hertfordshire Health Authority)

Chair Mary Pedlow
Chief Executive Toni Horn

Darlington Primary Care Trust

Appleton House, Lanchester Road, Durham DH1 5XZ
Tel: 0191 333 3232 Fax: 0191 333 3233
(County Durham and Tees Valley Health Authority)

Chair Sandra Pollard
Chief Executive Colin Morries

Dartford and Gravesham NHS Trust

Darent Valley Hospital, Darenth Wood Road, Dartford DA2 8DA
Tel: 01322 428100 Fax: 01322 428259
(Kent and Medway Health Authority)

Chair Sarah Dunnett
Chief Executive Sue Jennings

NHS TRUSTS & NHS HOSPITALS

Darent Valley Hospital

Darenth Wood Road, Dartford DA2 8DA

Accident and Emergency J Thurston (Head), G R Kerur
Anaesthetics R J C Evans (Head), M A S Abbott, G Disanayake, E P Kelly, R Madan, B Lobo, H T Patel, M Protopapas, J Smith
Care of the Elderly W J Fitzpatrick, S Hussein, W Jayawardena
Dental/Maxillofacial Dr Lavery, P Scanlon
Dermatology C Grech
General Medicine V Andrews, D Brennand-Roper, H Alban Davies, R Ede, M Kazmi, W Melia, M Mushtaq, A Tavakkoli, I Vadasz, I Zoukos
General Surgery A J McIrvine (Head), M C Parker, G Thomas, M Stewart, P Strauss
Genitourinary Medicine P Key
Nephrology I McDonald
Obstetrics and Gynaecology A Lesseps (Head), M Jones, R MacDermott, A Schreiner
Oncology M Leslie, M O'Connell, J Prendiville, A Visioli
Ophthalmology M Gibbens, R Goel, L Whitefield
Paediatrics H R Patel (Head), M D'Costa, D Leung
Pathology C Farquhar (Head), V E Andrews, M Kasmi, M Z Khan, A T Rashid, A Shaw, P Thebe
Plastic Surgery R W Smith
Radiology B Al-Murrani, D Allen, J Kirk, C K Koo, N Sathananthan
Respiratory Medicine M Mushtaq, A Tavakkoli
Rheumatology I Vadasz
Trauma and Orthopaedics A K Addison (Head), B A Kamdar, A Leyshon, F Moftah, S Sait
Urology J K Dickinson, R Ravi

Gravesend and North Kent Hospital

Bath Street, Gravesend DA11 0DG
Tel: 01474 564333 Fax: 01474 574018
Total Beds: 104

Dartford, Gravesham and Swanley Primary Care Trust

Livingstone Hospital, 1st Floor, East Hill, Dartford DA1 1SA
Tel: 01322 622369 Fax: 01322 622384
(Kent and Medway Health Authority)

Chair Martin Henwood
Chief Executive Stephanie Stanwick

Daventry and South Northamptonshire Primary Care Trust

Danetre Hospital, London Road, Daventry NN11 4DY
Tel: 01327 705610 Fax: 01327 877058
Email: enquiries@thepct.co.uk
Website: www.thepct.co.uk
(Leicestershire, Northamptonshire and Rutland Health Authority)

Chair Simon Schanschieff
Chief Executive Julia Squire

Danetre Hospital

London Road, Daventry NN11 4DY
Tel: 01327 702113 Fax: 01327 300509
Total Beds: 37

Derbyshire Dales and South Derbyshire Primary Care Trust

Derwent Court, 1 Stuart Street, Derby DE1 2FZ
Tel: 01332 626300 Fax: 01332 626350
(Southern Derbyshire Health Authority)

Chief Executive Mike Goodwin

Derwentside Primary Care Trust

Appleton House, Lanchester Road, Durham DH1 5XZ
Tel: 0191 333 3232 Fax: 0191 333 3233
(County Durham and Tees Valley Health Authority)

Chair Keith Murrey-Hetherington

Devon Partnership NHS Trust

Wonford House Hospital, Dryden Road, Exeter EX2 5AF
Tel: 01392 208657 Fax: 01392 208663
(South West Peninsula Health Authority)

Chair Keith Portlock
Chief Executive Valerie Howell

Dewsbury Health Care NHS Trust

Closing April 2002 - Mental health services transferring to South West Yorkshire Mental Health Trust; acute services transferring to Mid Yorkshire Hospitals NHS Trust.

Dewsbury and District Hospital, Halifax Road, Dewsbury WF13 4HS
Tel: 01924 816116, 01924 512000 Fax: 01924 816192, 01924 816192
Email: emma.newsome@dhc-tr.northy.nhs.uk
(West Yorkshire Health Authority)

Chair John Hemingway
Chief Executive Roger French

Dewsbury and District Hospital

Halifax Road, Dewsbury WF13 4HS
Tel: 01924 512000, 01924 816116 Fax: 01924 816192
Email: emma.newsome@dhc-tr.northy.nhs.uk
Total Beds: 529

Accident and Emergency P K Ancill, S M Barnes, Dr Kerner, Dr Okereke
Anaesthetics S A Brayshaw, J Brook, N Dwyer, P Goulden, K Ismail, O A Maher, J Perfettini, Dr Queneshi, S A Quereshi, Dr Reddy, Dr Riad, P Smith, M A Thickett, Dr Wilson
Cardiology Dr Smyllie
Care of the Elderly C K Biswas, Dr Cox, I Craig
Child and Adolescent Psychiatry Dr Edwards
Dental Surgery Dr Mitchell
Dermatology G Ford, M Shah, G Taylor
Elderly Psychiatry Dr Booya
ENT Dr Hassan, L C Knight, Dr London, C J Woodhead
General Medicine Dr Chidambra, D C Currie, Dr Fitzpatrick, T M Kemp, B Sivaramakrishnan, Dr Sutcliffe
General Psychiatry H Mathew, Dr Mathur
General Surgery W Case, J Lovegrove, P J Lyndon, C M White
Genitourinary Medicine P A D Silva
Learning Disabilities Dr Galaprathie
Obstetrics and Gynaecology T Aslam-Tariq, K Fishwick, A Trehan
Oncology M Bond, C Coyle, Dr Orton
Ophthalmology A Cassells-Brown, N George, D O'Neill
Orthodontics R Y Shuff
Orthopaedics P D Angus, A Maroof, J Ridge, J G Shea
Paediatrics Dr Allaboa, P Gorham, P MacKay, A M A Soulioti, G M Wilson
Palliative Medicine R Lane
Pathology Dr Cadman, M R Chappell, P W Gudgeon, A Jackson, M M Raj
Plastic Surgery Dr Fenton, Dr Southern
Radiology P L N Ah-Fat, Dr Altikaiti, E Cave, P James, M Vaidya
Rheumatology L Hordon, S Miles

Doncaster and Bassetlaw Hospitals NHS Trust

Doncaster Royal Infirmary, Armthorpe Road, Doncaster DN2 5LT
Tel: 01302 366666 Fax: 01302 320098
Website: www.dbh.nhs.uk
(South Yorkshire Health Authority)

Chair Margaret Cox
Chief Executive Nigel Clifton

Bassetlaw District General Hospital

Blyth Road, Worksop S81 0BD
Tel: 01909 500990 Fax: 01909 502246
Total Beds: 300

Accident and Emergency M El-Salamani
Anaesthetics S Aquim, A M Dixon, R W Harris, A J N Renshaw, P Smith
Dermatology SB Bittner
ENT P Chui, M Watson
General Medicine M Al-Khoffash, A Alwail, R L Blandford, C L Corbett, S Kar-Purkayastha, M M Muthiah
General Psychiatry M Bates, S Bloomberg, C A Chambers, M Eid, H Inch, C L Narayana, S Peters, J Schlicht
General Surgery R Avill, C Caddy, I Crate, K M Kolar, J Muen, S Singh, P Tan
Haematology J Joseph, B Paul
Obstetrics and Gynaecology M Alloub, M Mammo, H J Mellows, M Michel
Ophthalmology A Mishra, L R Kolli
Orthopaedics S Ali, R Bajekal, M J Farhan, A Mubashir, K Shahi, M Zeraati
Paediatrics S J Bodden, H S Mulenga, R Shawis, L H P Williams
Pathology A Anathhanam, A J D Aveline, A Moffatt, P Parsons, B Paul
Radiology R K Goel, J Howard, C R Merrill
Rheumatology R Amos

Doncaster Royal Infirmary

Armthorpe Road, Doncaster DN2 5LT
Tel: 01302 366666 Fax: 01302 320098
Total Beds: 800

Accident and Emergency C G A Chikhani, J R Paskins, A Wright
Anaesthetics P W Bailey, A G Chaffe, D Grahams, M C Hudson, T J Hughes, J Jessop, G Kesseler, T Kirkpatrick, P E Mann, B R Milne, D Northwood, D Raithatha, I H Taylor, J Train
Chemical Pathology C E Wilde
Dermatology S B Bittner, H C McGrath
ENT P Chui, K B Hughes, U Masieh, M Watson
General Medicine M W Baig, R P Bolton, D Chadha, J Hosker, G James, E W Jones, S Kang, R J E Leggett, A Oates, G Payne, A Rajathurai, T Rogers
General Surgery J Baggley, J Coker, G B Coombes, R J Cuschieri, G Jacob, N Kazzazi, K Khamis, J V Psaila, S Singh
Genitourinary Medicine T Moss
Haematology G Majumdar
Histopathology S Beck, S Rogers, L Sheehan
Medical Microbiology P A Fenton, L A Jewes
Obstetrics and Gynaecology G P Chandler, M Alloub, M R Heslip, W K Moores
Ophthalmology S P Desai, G Jayamanne, V Kayarkar, L R Kolli, P J Noble
Oral and Maxillofacial Surgery N Peckitt
Orthodontics A Holmes, J P Simpson
Orthopaedics P S Fagg, R Helm, J G Matthews, M Pickin, J F Redden
Paediatrics S Ahmad, W A Arrowsmith, J Inglis, D Keene, M Madlom
Radiology J Y Mackinlay, P C Martin, D Monaghan, P Stannard, D A Ward
Rheumatology and Rehabilitation J Lambert
Urology J Leveckis, K Siddiqui, I Townend

Montagu Hospital

Adwick Road, Mexborough S64 0AZ
Tel: 01709 585171 Fax: 01709 571689
Total Beds: 115

Accident and Emergency C J A Chikhani
Anaesthetics A G Chaffe, M C Hudson, T Kirkpatrick, D Northwood, H H Raithatha
ENT M Watson
General Medicine D N Cooper, E W Jones, R J Leigh
General Surgery R J Cuschieri, J V Psaila
Obstetrics and Gynaecology W K Moores
Ophthalmology P J Noble
Orthopaedics P S Fagg, R Helm
Paediatrics W A Arrowsmith, J Inglis, D Keene
Pathology S Beck, L A Jewes
Radiology J Y Mackinlay, P C Martin, D Monaghan, U Patel, P Stannard, D A Ward

Retford Hospital

North Road, Retford DN22 7XF
Tel: 01777 705261 Fax: 01777 710535

Paediatrics S J Bodden, H S Mulenga, L H P Williams
Pathology A J D Aveline, P A Parsons, B Paul
Radiology Dr Goel, J Howard, C R Merrill

Doncaster and South Humber Healthcare NHS Trust

Closing April 2002 - Services transferring to Doncaster, South Humber and Rotherham NHS Trust (name tbc).

St Catherine's House, St Catherine's Hospital, Tickhill Road, Balby, Doncaster DN4 8QN
Tel: 01302 796000 Fax: 01302 796161
Website: www.dsh-nhs.co.uk
(North and East Yorkshire and Northern Lincolnshire Health Authority)

Chair David Bertram
Chief Executive Liam Hayes

Diana Princess of Wales Hospital, Grimsby

Scartho Road and Dudley Street, Grimsby DN33 2BA
Tel: 01472 874111
Total Beds: 58

Doncaster Royal Infirmary

Armthorpe Road, Doncaster DN2 5LT
Tel: 01302 366666
Total Beds: 82

Loversall Hospital

Weston Road, Balby, Doncaster DN4 8NX
Tel: 01302 796000 Fax: 01302 796066
Total Beds: 127

Rehabilitation Medicine M O'Leary

St Catherine's Hospital

Tickhill Road, Doncaster DN4 8QN
Tel: 01302 796000 Fax: 01302 796066
Total Beds: 87

General Psychiatry J Roberts, N W H Silvester

St. John's Hospice

Weston Road, Doncaster DN4 8QL
Tel: 01302 311611 Fax: 01302 796660

Scunthorpe General Hospital (Ward 18)

Cliff Gardens, Scunthorpe DN15 7BH
Tel: 01724 282282 Ext: 2651

NHS TRUSTS & NHS HOSPITALS

Total Beds: 29

General Psychiatry A Chaudhary, B Saleh

Tickhill Road Hospital

Doncaster DN4 8QL
Tel: 01302 796000 Fax: 01302 796066
Total Beds: 229

Care of the Elderly D K Chadha, A J Oates, A Rajathurai
Elderly Mental Health M Broughton, K Wildgoose

Doncaster Central Primary Care Trust

Central House, St Catherine's Hospital, Tickhill Road, Doncaster DN4 8QN
Tel: 01302 796800 Fax: 01302 796799
Email: enquiries@doncastercentralpct.nhs.uk
Website: www.doncastercentralpct.nhs.uk
(South Yorkshire Health Authority)

Chair David Kitson
Chief Executive Simon Morritt

Doncaster East Primary Care Trust

Barclay Court, Heavens Walk, Doncaster DN4 5HZ
Tel: 01302 381940 Fax: 01302 381925
(South Yorkshire Health Authority)

Chair Roger Greenwood
Chief Executive Jayne Brown

Doncaster, South Humber and Rotherham NHS Trust

Formed April 2002 by merger of the mental health services of Rotherham Priority Health Services NHS Trust and Doncaster and South Humber Healthcare NHS Trust; trust name to be confirmed; no contact details available at time of going to press.

Doncaster West Primary Care Trust

West Lodge, St Catherine's Hospital, Tickhill Road, Doncaster DN4 8QN
Tel: 01302 796828
(South Yorkshire Health Authority)

Chair Ian Olsson
Chief Executive Mike Potts

Dorset Ambulance NHS Trust

Ringwood Road, St Leonards, Ringwood BH24 2SP
Tel: 01202 896111 Fax: 01202 891978
Email: chief.exec@ms.dorsetamb-tr.swest.nhs.uk
(Somerset and Dorset Health Authority)

Chair Trevor Jones
Chief Executive John Cape

Dorset Health Care NHS Trust

11 Shelley Road, Boscombe, Bournemouth BH1 4JQ
Tel: 01202 303400 Fax: 01202 301798
Email: enquiries@dorsethc-tr.swest.nhs.uk
Website: www.dorsethealthcare.org
(Somerset and Dorset Health Authority)

Chair Michael Parkinson
Chief Executive Roger Browning

Alderney Hospital

Ringwood Road, Poole BH12 4NB
Tel: 01202 735537 Fax: 01202 730657
Total Beds: 109

Care of the Elderly M Thomas
Elderly Mental Health D Cope, J Smithies
Mental Health M Ford, Dr Mynors-Wallis, S Pearson, A Wenzerul

Flaghead Unit

Fairmile House, Tasman Close, Jumpers Road, Christchurch BH23 2JT
Tel: 01202 484250 Fax: 01202 496117
Total Beds: 10

Rehabilitation N Choudry

Herbert Hospital

Alumhurst Road, Westbourne, Bournemouth BH4 8EW
Tel: 01202 584300 Fax: 01202 584311
Total Beds: 15

Rehabilitation S Rastogi

Kings Park Hospital

Gloucester Road, Boscombe, Bournemouth BH7 6JE
Tel: 01202 303757 Fax: 01202 395738
Total Beds: 58

Elderly Mental Health G Brown, J Hewitt, N Pearson
Learning Disabilities S Ghosh, D Scull

The Mallards

59 Stour Road, Bournemouth BH8 8SY
Tel: 01202 476313 Fax: 01202 479408
Total Beds: 6

Learning Disabilities S Ghosh, D Scull

Oakley House

15 Oakley Lane, Canford Magna, Wimborne BH21 1SF
Tel: 01202 849031 Fax: 01202 849031
Total Beds: 20

Elderly Mental Health M Milad

St Ann's Hospital

69 Haven Road, Canford Cliffs, Poole BH13 7LN
Tel: 01202 708881 Fax: 01202 707628
Total Beds: 147

Alcohol and Substance Misuse N Choudry
Elderly Mental Health G Brown, D Cope, J Hewitt, M Milad, N Pearson, J Smithies
Forensic Psychiatry S Beer
General Psychiatry J Bonello, J Bray, M Ford, L Mynors-Wallis, S Pearson, S Rastogi, G Searle, A Wenzerul

St Leonard's Hospital

241 Ringwood Road, Ringwood BH24 2RR
Tel: 01202 871165 Fax: 01202 895945
Total Beds: 52

Dermatology N Jensen, C Stephens
General Medicine S C Allen, T Batcock, R Day, R Haigh, R Harris-Jones
Rheumatology N Hopkinson

Springbourne House

22 Tower Road, Boscombe, Bournemouth BH1 4LB
Tel: 01202 300024 Fax: 01202 396844
Total Beds: 22

Elderly Mental Health J Smithies

Swanage Hospital

Queen's Road, Swanage BH19 2ES
Tel: 01929 422282 Fax: 01929 423872
Total Beds: 15

Care of the Elderly R Harries-Jones, S Miller
ENT D G John
General Medicine G P Clein
General Surgery D C Rowe-Jones
Obstetrics and Gynaecology J Scott
Ophthalmology D Etchells
Oral Surgery A Marcus
Orthopaedics P Conning, G Hall
Paediatrics P Johnston
Radiotherapy and Oncology S Dean
Rheumatology and Rehabilitation P Thompson

Wareham Hospital

Streche Road, Wareham BH20 4QQ
Tel: 01929 552433 Fax: 01929 550170
Total Beds: 32

Care of the Elderly Dr Cope, R Harries-Jones

Wimborne Hospital

Victoria Road, Wimborne BH21 1ER
Tel: 01202 841101 Fax: 01202 849516
Total Beds: 42

ENT P Addington
General Surgery J Pain, D Pope, J Rundle
Obstetrics and Gynaecology J Edwards
Oral Surgery A Markus
Orthopaedics M Hussain, R L Jowett, P Salter
Radiology R A Hill, S N Jones, W C Scott
Rheumatology C Moran

Dudley Beacon and Castle Primary Care Trust

Cross Street Health Centre, Cross Street, Dudley DY1 1RN
Tel: 01384 366217 Fax: 01384 457361
(Birmingham and the Black Country Health Authority)

Dudley Group of Hospitals NHS Trust

Wordsley Hospital, Wordsley, Stourbridge DY8 5QX
Tel: 01384 456111 Fax: 01384 244395
(Birmingham and the Black Country Health Authority)

Chair Alfred Edwards
Chief Executive Paul Farenden

Corbett Hospital

Stourbridge DY8 4JB
Tel: 01384 456111
Total Beds: 150

Anaesthetics K Arunsalam, T V Gnanadurai, P M Scriven
Cardiology C Barr, E J Flint, P Forsey
Care of the Elderly A K Banerjee, W A Saunders
Chest Disease M J Cushley, M Doherty
Dermatology Dr Basheer
Gastroenterology A N Hamlyn, B Jones
General Medicine R S Smith, A M Zalin
General Surgery R P Grimley, A P Jayatunga
Neurology R N Corston
Orthodontics M Hammond
Orthopaedics M S Ali, M Butt, R Mifsud
Radiology L Arkell, F H B Renny, A P Wolinski
Urology A D Rowse

Guest Hospital

Tipton Road, Dudley DY1 4SE
Tel: 01384 456111

Anaesthetics T V Gnanadurai
Care of the Elderly W A Saunders
Dermatology Dr Basheer
Genitourinary Medicine Dr El-Dalil, S Oojoo, M Stevenson
Immunology V Nagendran
Ophthalmology S V Aggarwal, J Al-Ibrahim, S Thompson
Rheumatology J P Delamere

Russells Hall Hospital

Dudley DY1 2HQ
Tel: 01384 456111 Fax: 01384 244051
Total Beds: 435

Accident and Emergency I K Dukes, R Blayney, C Read
Anaesthetics P Whitehurst
Cardiology C Barr, E J Flint, P Forsey
Dermatology A Basheer
General Medicine C Czapia, T El-Hadd, A M Zalin, J Stellmjan, R S Smith, S Sivakumar
General Surgery R Blunt, R P Grimley, A P Jayatunga, H C Norcott, R Patel, A P Savage, J T Williams, K F Yoong
Obstetrics and Gynaecology R Callender, N Fiz-Gibbons, G J Lewis, L Meer, E Watson
Orthodontics M Hammond
Paediatrics Z Ibrahim, R Mudgal, Dr Mohite, A Sharma, P Thaker
Plastic Surgery M Ali, A Bracka, S Sarhadi
Radiology L Arkell, J El-Ibrahim, F H B Renny, A P Wolinski
Rheumatology J P Delamere, G Kitas, A Whallett
Urology L Emtage, A D Rowse

Wordsley Hospital

Stourbridge DY8 5QX
Tel: 01384 456111 Fax: 01384 244395
Total Beds: 368

Anaesthetics E Acquah, K Arunsalam, L Burke, J Danks, H Funkel, T J Digger, T V Gnanadurai, A Moors, P Scriven, J Tye, P Whitehurst
Cardiology C Barr, E Flint, P Forsey
Care of the Elderly A Banerjee, W A Saunders, J Stellerman
Dental Surgery B G Millar, N Whear
ENT R J Cullen, L P Glossop, N C Molony, R T J Shortridge, F Wilson
General Medicine M J Cushley, M Doherty, A N Hamlyn, M Healey, B Jones, N Fisher, T Fiad
General Surgery R Blunt, H C Norcott, R Patel, A P Savage, J T Williams
Neurology R N Corston, R Etti
Ophthalmology S P Aggarwal, J Al-Ibrahim, M Quinian, S Shafquat, S Thompson
Oral and Maxilofacial Surgery N M Whear
Orthopaedics M Ahmed, M S Ali, R Mifsud, Dr Qadri, S Roy, Dr Subzposh, K Sulaiman
Pathology J L Christie, S Ghosh, P Harrison, M Labib, J Neilson, E Rees, S G N Richardson, J M Symonds, Dr Wasfi
Radiology L Arkell, R Shave, A Gregan, P Oliver, F H B Renny, A P Wolinski
Radiotherapy and Oncology R Allerton

Dudley Priority Health NHS Trust

Closure of trust tbc - Services transferring to Dudley South Primary Care Trust and Dudley Beacon and Castle Primary Care Trust.

Ridge Hill, Brierley Hill Road, Stourbridge DY8 5ST
Tel: 01384 457373 Fax: 01384 400217
(Birmingham and the Black Country Health Authority)

Chair Margaret Bamford
Chief Executive Robert Bacon

NHS TRUSTS & NHS HOSPITALS

Bushey Fields Hospital
Russells Hall, Dudley DY1 2LZ
Tel: 01384 457373
Total Beds: 168

Ridge Hill Mental Handicap Unit
Stourbridge DY8 5ST
Tel: 01384 457373
Total Beds: 71

General Psychiatry A C Butler
Paediatrics A Sharma

Dudley South Primary Care Trust

Paytons House, Ridgehill, Brierley Hill Road, Stourbridge SY8 5ST
Tel: 01384 78053, 01384 244470 Fax: 01384 77609
(Birmingham and the Black Country Health Authority)

Durham and Chester-le-Street Primary Care Trust

Appleton House, Lanchester Road, Durham DH1 5HZ
Tel: 0191 333 3232 Fax: 0191 383 3233
(County Durham and Tees Valley Health Authority)

Chair Ann Calman
Chief Executive Andrew Young

Durham Dales Primary Care Trust

Appleton House, Lanchester Road, Durham DH1 5XZ
Tel: 0191 333 3232 Fax: 0191 333 3233
(County Durham and Tees Valley Health Authority)

Chair Anne Beeton
Chief Executive Andrew Kenworthy

Ealing Hospital NHS Trust

Ealing Hospital, Uxbridge Road, Southall UB1 3HW
Tel: 020 8967 5000 Fax: 020 8967 5630
(North West London Health Authority)

Chief Executive Lorraine Clifton

Ealing Hospital
Uxbridge Road, Southall UB1 3HW
Tel: 020 8967 5000 Fax: 020 8967 5630
Total Beds: 353

Accident and Emergency S Payne, J Redhead
Anaesthetics B J Bracey, E Bradshaw, R Laishley, M Meurer-Laban, M Renna, C Schmulian, R Skinner, E Whitehead
Care of the Elderly P Evans
Chest Disease R Mathur, M Rudolf
Dental Surgery G F Goubran
Dermatology K Acland, A Chu, R D Russell-Jones
ENT K Patel, N Tolley
General Medicine J D Arnold, J Kooner, N I McNeil, H M Mather, S Rosen
General Surgery P Abel, P Forouhi, G Geroulakis, A Isla, T Rosenbaum, D Sellu
Haematology G Abrahamson, H M Hegde, N Phillpott
Histology I A Lampert
Infectious Diseases S Ash, W Lynn
Medical Microbiology F J Ahmad
Neurology H Jenkins
Obstetrics and Gynaecology Y Abrahams, L Fusi, A Gordon, A D Haeri, N Mahadevan

Orthopaedics M Beverley, R Coombes, P England, M J Evans, J Hollingdale, J Hucker, S Hughes, R Strachan, R Thomas
Paediatrics M Cummins, N Hasson, C Michie, K Sloper
Radiology Dr Lavender, P R Patel, Dr Stroudley, W Svensson, T Tran
Radiotherapy and Oncology P Price, S Stewart
Rheumatology and Rehabilitation M Naughton

Ealing Primary Care Trust

West Ealing House, 2 St James Avenue, London W13 9DJ
Tel: 020 8326 3572 Fax: 020 8579 6511
(North West London Health Authority)

Chair Marion Saunders
Chief Executive Robert Creighton

Easington Primary Care Trust

Appleton House, Lanchester Road, Durham DH1 5XZ
Tel: 0191 333 3232 Fax: 0191 333 3233
Chair Penelope Young
Chief Executive Roger Bolas

East and North Hertfordshire NHS Trust

Lister Hospital, Coleys Mill Lane, Stevenage SG1 4AB
Tel: 01438 314333
(Bedfordshire and Hertfordshire Health Authority)

Chair Roy Swanston
Chief Executive Maggie Donovan

Ascots Day Hospital
Howlands, Welwyn Garden City AL7 4HQ

Danesbury
Welwyn AL6 9PW
Tel: 01438 840692
Total Beds: 30

Elderly Care Day Hospital, Lister Hospital
Strathmore Wing, Lister Hospital, Stevenage SG1 4AB
Tel: 01438 314333 Fax: 01438 781449

Hitchin Hospital
Oughtonhead Way, Hitchin SG5 2LH
Tel: 01462 422444
Total Beds: 44

Lister Hospital
East & North Herts NHS Trust, Coreys Mill Lane, Stevenage SG1 4AB
Tel: 01438 781076 Fax: 01438 781442
Total Beds: 630

Accident and Emergency P D Kelly, P M Reid
Anaesthetics O W Boomers, M R Chilvers, S J Eckersall, G Gowrie-Mohan, K Jani, S Jothilingam, J M Lalor, P Patel, W J K Rickford, P Sengupta, I Sockalingham, J Thiagarajan, L Wickremasinghe
Audiological Medicine B Al-Shihabi
Cardiology C D J Illesley, M Lynch, V Paul
Cardiothoracic Surgery A Rees
Care of the Elderly M Ehsanullah, P Ghosh, S Khan
Chest Disease N N Stanley
Dermatology C A Green
ENT A Frosh, G Mochloulis, S J Quinn
Gastroenterology A Catterall, S Greenfield, I Sargeant
General Medicine L J Borthwick

General Surgery T C Holme, A Mahomed, B V Palmer, S Selvakumar, H H Thompson
Genitourinary Medicine H Maiti, S Uthayakumar
Nephrology K Farrington, R N Greenwood, P Warwicker
Neurology J M Gibbs, T T Warner
Obstetrics and Gynaecology Dr Banerjee, D R Salvesen, R S Sattin, W Tenuwara, J B Webb
Oral and Maxillofacial Surgery A D Giles, M T Simpson
Orthodontics A B Hewitt
Orthopaedics J H Dorrell, P G Hope, P S Kerr, D P Powles, S Wickremsinghe
Paediatrics O A Ahmed, R D Croft, S A Davies, J C Hyde, J Reiser
Pathology A MacDonald, D J Madders, A Rainey, C J Tew, L L Yong
Plastic Surgery M G Dickson, N K James, P J Mahaffey
Radiology N D Amerasekera, J S M Beales, P T Brooks, C M P King, H M Lee, C M Prendergast
Radiotherapy and Oncology B E Lyn, A R Makepeace
Restorative Dentistry A J McCullock
Rheumatology and Rehabilitation A I Binder
Urology G Boustead, D Hanbury, T A McNicholas

Queen Elizabeth II Hospital

Howlands, Welwyn Garden City AL7 4HQ
Tel: 01707 328111
Total Beds: 550

Accident and Emergency V Gautam, Y Saetta
Anaesthetics S Bates, M Fox, P Goldberg, A Maye, M A Moxon, Z P Shah, S Susay, T Walker
Care of the Elderly O Feizi, M Seeveratnam
Dermatology A H Bayoumi, C J O'Doherty
General Medicine A Catterall, R G Dent, S Greenfield, P M Keir, P McIntyre, P Winocour
General Surgery M Aldridge, P Crane, M Dickson, M S Lennox, S Lok, J L McCue
Genitourinary Medicine H Maiti
Neurology D Kidd, R W Orrell
Obstetrics and Gynaecology R Atalla, N C Drew, M Hemaya, D G McLintock, M H Wilkins
Oncology C Coulter, B E Lynn, A Makepeace
Ophthalmology S Campbell, T Coker, B S Sandhu, M Toma
Orthopaedics T Kitson, H V Parmar, M C Stallard, A Waterfield, D J Williams
Paediatrics J Chiyende, A K M Raffles, S Shukia, A M L Shurz
Pathology M Al-Izzi, H P Davis, A Fattah, N Fernando, M Fyffe, J Voke
Radiology B E Hartley, H I Jory, S Khan, A H Lynn, C Ropel
Rheumatology J Axon
Urology J Vanwaevenbergh

Queen Victoria Memorial Hospital

Welwyn AL6 9PW
Tel: 01438 714488
Total Beds: 40

Care of the Elderly M Seevaratnam

Royston and District Hospital

London Road, Royston SG8 9EN
Tel: 01763 242134
Total Beds: 24

Western House Hospital

Collett Road, Ware SG12 7LZ
Tel: 01920 68954
Total Beds: 30

Care of the Elderly O Feizi, M Seeveratnam

East Anglian Ambulance NHS Trust

Hospital Lane, Hellesdon, Norwich NR6 5NA
Tel: 01603 424255 Fax: 01603 418667
Email: david.hewer@eaamb.anglox.nhs.uk
(Norfolk, Suffolk and Cambridgeshire Health Authority)

Chair A Egerton-Smith
Chief Executive Chris Carney

East Berkshire Community Health NHS Trust

Closure of trust tbc - Services transferring to Bracknell Forest Primary Care Trust and Windsor, Ascot and Maidenhead Primary Care Trust.

King Edward VII Hospital, St. Leonards Road, Windsor SL4 3DP
Tel: 01753 860441 Fax: 01753 636107
(Thames Valley Health Authority)

Chair Geoffrey Blacker, Mary Spinks
Chief Executive P Burgess, Margaret Stockham

King Edward VII Hospital (Windsor)

Windsor SL4 3DP
Tel: 01753 860441 Fax: 01753 636107
Total Beds: 20

Care of the Elderly J Harding, S K Rao
Dermatology A Roberts, V Walkden
Diabetes R D M Scott
ENT N Bleach, A F Jefferis
Gastroenterology S Levi
General Psychiatry G Gall, L D Silva
General Surgery G S Barrett
Neurology D J Thomas
Obstetrics and Gynaecology P Reginald, J Spring
Ophthalmology J J Kanski, J A McAllister, R B S Packard
Oral Surgery C Yates
Orthodontics D Slattery
Orthopaedics G Deane, J Jones, M Swann
Paediatrics J Cowan
Plastic Surgery D Crawford
Radiology S Colenso, S Ghiacy
Radiotherapy H Thomas
Rheumatology S P Liyanage
Thoracic Surgery E R Townsend
Urology C Hudd, O Karim
Vascular Medicine P Rutter

St Mark's Hospital

St. Mark's Road, Maidenhead SL6 6DU
Tel: 01628 632012 Fax: 01753 638569
Total Beds: 106

Care of the Elderly R Behrman, J Harding
Dermatology A Roberts, J Wilkinson
ENT M Wallace
Gastroenterology M MacMahon
General Medicine R Blackwood
General Psychiatry M Atkins, P D Maddocks
General Surgery P G Cassell, A Gordon, P Rutter
Neurology D J Thomas
Obstetrics and Gynaecology S Dinitry, P Reginald
Ophthalmology R Packard
Oral Surgery M Issa
Orthopaedics R Allum, M Swann, M Thomas, A Unwin
Paediatrics J Connell, J L Pearce
Plastic Surgery C Khoo
Rheumatology S P Liyanage
Urology D Fawcett, C Hudd, O Karim

NHS TRUSTS & NHS HOSPITALS

Upton Hospital

Slough SL1 2BJ
Tel: 01753 821441 Fax: 01753 635050
Total Beds: 105

Care of the Elderly R Behrman, R Chauhan, A Darowski, S K Rao
Chest Medicine M Smith, J Wiggins
Child and Adolescent Psychiatry J Brockless, K Friend, M Kingswood
Genitourinary Medicine S Dawson
Paediatrics M Colbey
Psychiatry of Old Age G Dawson

East Birmingham Primary Care Trust

Birmingham Children's Hospital, 2nd Floor, J Block, Whittall Street, Birmingham B4 6NH
Tel: 0121 236 4221 Fax: 0121 236 6364
(Birmingham and the Black Country Health Authority)

Chair J Aldred, M Ford
Chief Executive M Sharon

East Cambridgeshire and Fenland Primary Care Trust

Exchange Tower, Alexandra Road, Wisbech PE13 1HQ
Tel: 01945 469400 Fax: 01945 469401
Website: www.eastcambsandfenland-pct.nhs.uk
(Norfolk, Suffolk and Cambridgeshire Health Authority)

East Cheshire NHS Trust

From April 2002 mental health and learning disability services transferring to Cheshire and Wirral Partnership NHS Trust.

Macclesfield District General Hospital, Victoria Road, Macclesfield SK10 3BL
Tel: 01625 421000 Fax: 01625 661644
(Cheshire and Merseyside Health Authority)

Chair Kathy Cowell

Congleton and District War Memorial Hospital

Canal Road, Congleton CW12 3AR
Tel: 01260 272227 Fax: 01260 294827
Total Beds: 28

Cardiology A Cubukcu
Dermatology Dr Griffiths, T Kingston
ENT J Deans
General Medicine C Davison, P N Foster, M A R Taylor
General Psychiatry H Waring
General Surgery W A Brough, D M Matheson, D M Neill
Learning Disabilities L Jenkins
Minor Operations N J Gathercole
Obstetrics and Gynaecology P Dunlop
Ophthalmology L B Freeman
Orthopaedics G W Keys, M G Norris
Paediatrics I E Losa
Radiology C Loughran
Rheumatology S Knight, Dr Symmons
Urology D Holden

Ingersley and Millbrook Unit Psychiatric Day Hospital

West Park, Macclesfield District General Hospital, Victoria Road, Macclesfield SK10 3BL
Tel: 01625 663403 Fax: 01625 661118
Total Beds: 127

Psychiatry D Black, A Blakey, J Bowie, W Braude, J Galloway, L Jenkins, H Waring, J Weetman

Knutsford and District Community Hospital

Bexton Road, Knutsford WA16 0ED
Tel: 01565 632112 Fax: 01565 632544
Total Beds: 18

Cardiology Dr Egdell
Chest Disease R J Stead
Dermatology T Kingston
Diabetes Dr Taylor
ENT J E Davies
General Medicine R J Stead
General Psychiatry Dr Galloway
General Surgery D M Matheson
Learning Disabilities Dr Jenkins
Medicine D J Walker
Obstetrics and Gynaecology Dr Hall
Orthopaedics G W Keys
Paediatrics Dr Marinaki
Rheumatology S Knight
Urology D Holden

Macclesfield District General Hospital

Victoria Road, Macclesfield SK10 3BL
Tel: 01625 663306 Fax: 01625 663963
Total Beds: 365

Accident and Emergency N J Gathercole
Anaesthetics M Y Aglan, P B Backx, Dr Gorman, Dr Hunter, S B Rawal, M Rothwell, A J Shribman
Child and Adolescent Psychiatry R McGowan, Dr Weaver
Community Paediatrics (Audiology) Dr Batchelor
Dental Surgery D Eldridge, M Patel
Dermatology Dr Griffiths, T Kingston
ENT J E Davies, J A Deans
General Medicine P N Foster, R J Stead, M A R Taylor, D J Walker
General Surgery Dr Brough, D M Matheson, A R Quayle
Genitourinary Medicine M H Khan, Dr Morgan
Learning Disabilities L Jenkins
Nephrology Dr Venning
Neurology Dr MacDermott
Neurosurgery Dr Richardson
Obstetrics and Gynaecology P Dunlop, Dr Hall, Dr Lether, S Mellor
Oncology Dr Davidson
Ophthalmology R Gupta, Dr Hubbard, M A Neugebauer
Orthodontics R Thompson
Orthopaedics J M Auchincloss, K Barnes, G W Keys, M G Norris
Paediatrics J Gilbert, Dr Losia, K Marinaki, J R Owens, Dr Spillman, A Y C Wilton
Pain Control Dr Aglan
Palliative Medicine R T
Pathology C Burrows, S A Hales, Dr Robins, A R Williams, A Wills
Radiology A D Baxter, J Coffey, Dr Crotch-Harvey, C F Loughran, E Partridge
Rheumatology S Knight, D Symmons
Urology Dr Holden, Dr Namasivayam

Rosemount Day Care Services

Chester Road, Macclesfield SK11 8QA
Tel: 01625 421000 Fax: 01625 663581

East Devon Primary Care Trust

Dean Clarke House, Southenhay East, Exeter EX1 1PQ
Tel: 01392 207521 Fax: 01392 270910
(South West Peninsula Health Authority)

Chair Lynda Price
Chief Executive Iain Tulley

East Elmbridge and Mid Surrey Primary Care Trust

Cedar Court, Guilford Road, Fetcham, Leatherhead KT22 9RX
Tel: 01372 227300
(Surrey and Sussex Health Authority)

Chair Jackie Bell

East Gloucestershire NHS Trust

Closing April 2002 - Mental health and learning disability services transferring to Gloucestershire Partnership NHS Trust; acute services transferring to Gloucestershire Hospitals NHS Trust; community services transferring to Cheltenham and Tewkesbury Primary Care Trust, Cotswold and Vale Primary Care Trust and West Gloucestershire Primary Care Trust.

Trust Headquaters, 1 College Lawn, Cheltenham GL53 7AG
Tel: 01242 222222 Fax: 01242 221214
(Avon, Gloucestershire and Wiltshire Health Authority)

Chair Penny A Bennett
Chief Executive Paul Lilley

Charlton Lane Unit

Charlton Lane, Leckhampton, Cheltenham GL53 9DZ
Tel: 01242 527784 Fax: 01242 527784
Total Beds: 88

Cheltenham General Hospital

Sandford Road, Cheltenham GL53 7AN
Tel: 01242 222222 Fax: 01242 273516
Total Beds: 482

Accident and Emergency P Davies, P Wilson
Anaesthetics W J Brampton, A N Burlingham, M Copp, J G d Courcy, J Francis, D T Goodrum, S Karadia, M McSwiney, C Mather, M Parmar, S Rees, M J Richards, P A Ritchie, G S Routh, S Smith, S West, P N Young
Cardiology V Challenor, R Chamberlain-Webber, D Lindsay, M Peterson
Chest Disease A Penketh
Dermatology B Adriaans, T J Delaney
ENT J Hamilton, M Hardingham, D Thomas, S Wood
General Medicine S Al-Ahbar, M Bialas, V Challener, I Crossley, A Deering, P Fletcher, I Mortimore, A Penketh, P Roscoe, H Sawyers, S Sawyers
General Psychiatry M Alexander, M Cooper, M Dharmendra, H Forsyth, J Laidlaw, M Mitcheson, Dr Moliver, C Robson, R Ropner
General Surgery N Borlay, J Bristol, H Chan, D Clarke, A Goodman, S Haynes, R Kinder, K Poskitt, M Whyman
Nephrology A Williams
Neurology G Fuller, R Martin, M Silua
Obstetrics and Gynaecology Dr Holmes, R H J Kerr-Wilson, A McCrum, M Pilllai, M Sutton
Ophthalmology J Ferris, R Johnston, J Kirkpatrick, G Macintosh, A McNaught, N C Price
Oral and Maxillofacial Surgery J Harrison, C Perkins
Orthodontics J Dickson
Orthopaedics D A P Ainscow, J G McKinnon, G Rooker, J S Wand
Paediatrics S Ackroyd, E Crowne, A Day, J Frank, M Hamilton-Ayres, L Huskinson, S Kinder, M McGraw, R Martin, R Sacer
Palliative Medicine D Jeffrey
Pathology E Blundell, R G Dalton, S G Edmondson, N Gubbay, P A Laite
Radiology P J Briers, M Brock, P F Brown, M Gibson, C P Robinson
Radiotherapy and Oncology K Benstead, R Counsell, S Elyan, D Farruga, R Owen, S Shepherd
Rheumatology D Collins, E Price
Urology H Gilbert, R Kinder

Cirencester Hospital

The Querns, Tetbury Road, Cirencester GL7 1UY
Tel: 01285 655711 Fax: 01285 640456
Total Beds: 127

Accident and Emergency P Wilson
Anaesthetics W Brampton, J Francis, D Goodrum, C Mather, P Richie
Cardiology V Challenor
Care of the Elderly M Bialas, A Derring, P Fletcher
Dermatology J P Ellis, R J Mann, D Milne, I Porter, L Whittam
ENT J Hamilton, M Hardingham
General Medicine J Anderson, M Bralas, V Challenger, I R Crossley, I Mortimore, A Penketh, H Sawers
General Psychiatry E Ronson, K Williams
General Surgery A J Goodman, K R Poskitt
Nephrology A Williams
Obstetrics and Gynaecology D Holmes, R Kerr-Wilson, M Pillai, M Sutton
Ophthalmology N Kirkpatrick, N C Price
Oral and Maxillofacial Surgery J M Harrison, C Perkins
Orthopaedics J Field, G Holt, G D Rooker, J Wand, P Wilson
Paediatrics R S Ackroyd, A Day, S Kinder
Plastic Surgery I Whitworth
Radiology M Brock, P Brown, P Robinson
Radiotherapy and Oncology K Benstead
Urology H Gilbert, R Kinder

Delancey Hospital

Charlton Lane, Leckhampton, Cheltenham GL53 9DU
Tel: 01242 222222 Fax: 01242 272105
Total Beds: 86

Care of the Elderly M Bialas, A Deering, P Fletcher

Fairford Cottage Hospital

Fairford GL7 4BB
Tel: 01285 712212
Total Beds: 15

Moore Cottage Hospital

Bourton-on-the-Water, Cheltenham GL54 2AZ
Tel: 01451 820228 Fax: 01451 810817
Total Beds: 34

General Medicine J Anderson, V Challenor, I Crossley, A Deering, I Mortimore
General Surgery K Poskitt
Obstetrics and Gynaecology R Kerr-Wilson
Ophthalmology N Kirkpatrick, A McNaught
Orthopaedics G Holt, J G MacKinnon
Paediatrics R S Ackroyd
Psychiatry of Old Age I Porter
Rheumatology D Collins

Moreton District Hospital

Moreton-in-Marsh GL56 0BS
Tel: 01608 650456 Fax: 01608 651599
Total Beds: 30

Cardiology V Challenor
Care of the Elderly I Porter
ENT C Milford, D Thomas
General Medicine M Benson, A Deering, J M Holt
General Psychiatry M Dharmendra
General Surgery K Poskitt
Obstetrics and Gynaecology M Sutton
Ophthalmology A McNaught, N Price
Orthopaedics D A P Ainscow, J Fairbank, J McKinnon
Paediatrics R S Ackroyd
Psychiatry of Old Age D Martin, A Moliver
Rheumatology A G Mowat

NHS TRUSTS & NHS HOSPITALS

Tewkesbury Hospital

Barton Road, Tewkesbury GL20 5QN
Tel: 01684 293303 Fax: 01684 285887
Total Beds: 5

Cardiology V Challenor
Care of the Elderly P Fletcher
Chest Disease I Mortimore
ENT D Thomas
General Medicine V Challenor, P Fletcher, S Sawyers
General Psychiatry M Clarke, M Whyman
General Surgery S Haynes
Obstetrics and Gynaecology D Holmes
Ophthalmology A McNaught
Orthopaedics D A P Ainscow, J Field, J G Mackinnon
Paediatrics R S Ackroyd, A Day, M Hamilton-Ayres, S Kinder
Rheumatology J Woodland
Urology R Kinder

Winchcombe District Hospital

Winchcombe, Cheltenham GL54 5NQ
Tel: 01242 602341 Fax: 01242 604024
Total Beds: 22

General Medicine J Anderson, I Crossley, P Fletcher
General Surgery S Haynes
Obstetrics and Gynaecology M Sutton
Orthopaedics D Ainscow
Paediatrics M Hamilton-Ayres
Urology R Kinder

East Hampshire Primary Care Trust

Raeburn House, Hulbert Road, Waterlooville PO7 7GP
Tel: 023 9224 8800 Fax: 023 9224 8810
(Hampshire and Isle of Wight Health Authority)

Chair Margaret Scott
Chief Executive Tony Horne

East Kent Coastal Primary Care Trust

42 High Street, Broadstairs CT10 1JT
Tel: 01843 608500 Fax: 01843 608501
(Kent and Medway Health Authority)

East Kent Community NHS Trust

Trust Headquarters, Littlebourne Road, Canterbury CT1 1AZ
Tel: 01227 459371 Fax: 01227 812268
(Kent and Medway Health Authority)

Chair G Medd, Mary Crittenden
Chief Executive David Parr

St Martin's Hospital

Littlebourne Road, Canterbury CT1 1TD
Tel: 01227 459584 Fax: 01227 812268
Total Beds: 120

General Psychiatry S Anathakopan, B Beats, C Cook, S Wood
Psychology S Hewson

Thanet Mental Health Unit

164 Ramsgate Road, Margate
Tel: 01843 225544
Total Beds: 60

General Psychiatry M Hamour, T Helm, J Kaladini, G Rehling

Western Avenue Day Hospital

Ashford Hospital, Western Avenue, Ashford TN23 1LX
Tel: 01233 623321

East Kent Hospitals NHS Trust

Buckland Hospital, Coombe Valley Road, Dover CT17 0HD
Tel: 01304 201624 Fax: 01304 208189
Website: www.eastkentnhs.org
(Kent and Medway Health Authority)

Chair Peter Hermitage
Chief Executive David Astley

Buckland Hospital

Coombe Valley Road, Buckland, Dover CT14 0HD
Tel: 01304 201624 Fax: 01304 214371
Total Beds: 240

Anaesthetics H G C Bradfield, J N Bulmer, J E Morris, C J F Potter
Care of the Elderly K G E Frohnsdorff, N A Sheikh, M A Vella
Dental Surgery N Bradley
Dermatology V Neild
ENT M D Wells
General Medicine G W Bradley, S Kenwright, A J R Morris, A D C Norris, P G Wheeler
General Psychiatry M F S Abdurahman, R Shiwach
General Surgery T Bates, A M Deane, C D Derry, N J Griffiths, D Keown, J F McPartlin
Haematology D G Wells
Neurology A C F Colchester
Obstetrics and Gynaecology C M Stewart, W Ursell
Ophthalmology R S Edwards, J McConnell
Orthodontics W G Webb
Orthopaedics M Lock, R Wetherell
Paediatrics C A Porter, S Williamson
Pathology C W Lawson, N R Padley
Radiology D Nadarajah, P Paciorek, A Santhakumaran, R H F Waitt, W H Webb
Radiotherapy and Oncology R Coltart, H M Smedley
Rheumatology and Rehabilitation P W Bull, J R Sewell

Kent and Canterbury Hospital

Ethelbert Road, Canterbury CT1 3NG
Tel: 01227 766877 Fax: 01227 864120
Website: www.ekh.tr-s.thames.nhs.uk
Total Beds: 368

Accident and Emergency S C Brooks, J A Maryosh
Anaesthetics A C Beaumont, B G Bradburn, J Broadley, H Dent, G R Hollister, C J Lamb, C G M Lynch, J MacKinnon, P Moskovits
Care of the Elderly Dr Carpenter, A J Heller, A Owen, J M Potter, I Sturgess
Chest Disease A J Johnson
Dental Surgery E G Asquith, N Bradley, C Hendy, T J Storrs, W G Webb
Dermatology D Goldin
ENT J S R Baxter, D Mitchell, N Padgham
General Medicine D I Prosser, M O Rake, C I Roberts
General Surgery R E C Collins, R M Heddle, D B Jackson, N Wilson
Nephrology D I Prosser, P Stevens
Neurology L Nashaf, S Pollock
Neurophysiology J D P Bland
Nuclear Medicine A J Coakley, M J O'Doherty
Obstetrics and Gynaecology M P Milligan, K Neales, N M Rafla, L M Shaw
Ophthalmology N C Andrew, R D Cock, R H J Darvell, R S Edwards
Orthodontics W G Webb
Orthopaedics N Blackburn, M E Conybeare, P Housden, D J Klugman, R Wetherall
Paediatrics W J Appleyard, D M Cook, D Long, N D T Martin, C A Porter

Pathology P K Buamah, E Lamb, C Lawson, M Leahy, B Maguire, E M Ndawula, Y F Williams, J B M Winter
Radiology A R Carter, M O Downes, P G Elton, K Entnistle, S Field, I Morrison
Radiotherapy and Oncology W A H Bodger, R S Coltart, N Mithal, H M Smedley
Rheumatology and Rehabilitation R H Withrington
Urology H Evans, K H A Murray

Queen Elizabeth the Queen Mother Hospital

Ramsgate Road, Margate CT9 4AN
Tel: 01843 225544 Fax: 01843 220048
Total Beds: 388

Anaesthetics E Davies, A Ferguson, N Kulasinghe, W E Morcos, E A Proctor, Y M A Tai, B C Tofte, H J Wilton
Care of the Elderly Y Challiner, M L Jenkinson, S K Mukherjee
Chest Disease A J Johnson
Dental Surgery E G Asquith, T J Storrs
Dermatology D Goldin, M Hudson-Peacock
General Medicine J B Cocking, A Marshall, A D Morgan
General Surgery G Davies, P J Pheils
Genitourinary Medicine C S Wijesurendra
Neurology W F Michael
Obstetrics and Gynaecology P V Belgaumkar, J K Robertshaw, L M A Shaw
Orthopaedics M E Conybeare, D Saran, I B M Stephen
Paediatrics D M Cook, E Ikhena, E Rfidah, A Sarmah
Pathology P K Buamah, M L Evans, E M Ndawula
Radiology A H Abdel-Hadi, P G Barker, M Farrar, G Giancola, A M Greenhalgh
Rheumatology and Rehabilitation A Leak, R H Withrington
Thoracic Surgery O J Lau
Urology J H Evans, K H A Murray

Royal Victoria Hospital

Radnor Park Avenue, Folkestone CT19 5BN
Tel: 01303 850202 Fax: 01303 854433
Total Beds: 92

Anaesthetics A S Gardiner, C M H Miller-Jones, J E Morris
Care of the Elderly S P Bhatia, K G E Frohnsdorff, N A Sheikh, M Vella
Dermatology V Neild
ENT G S Kanegaonkar
General Medicine G W Bradley, S Kenwright, A J R Morris, A D C Norris, P Wheeler, I V Wilson
General Psychiatry G H Rehling
General Surgery T Bates, A M Deane, C D Derry, N J Griffiths, D Keown, J F McPartlin
Haematology D G Wells
Obstetrics and Gynaecology J O Davies, W Ursell
Ophthalmology R S Edwards, J McConnell, E Simpson, J T Snow
Orthopaedics E R Jones, D J Klugman
Paediatrics C A Porter, S Williamson
Pathology C W Lawson, N R Padley
Radiology D Nadarajah, P Paciorek, A Santhakumaran, R H F Waitt, W M Webb
Radiotherapy and Oncology R S Coltart
Rheumatology and Rehabilitation P W Bull, J R Sewell

William Harvey Hospital

Kennington Road, Willesborough, Ashford TN24 0LZ
Tel: 01233 633331 Fax: 01233 616008
Total Beds: 449

Anaesthetics H G C Bradfield, J N Bulmer, A S Gardiner, C M H Jones, J E Morris, C J F Potter, A J Rampton, R J Thompson
Care of the Elderly S P Bhatia, R G E Frohnsdorff
Dermatology V S Neild, C M E Rowland-Payne
ENT G S Kanegaonkar, M D Wells
General Medicine G W Bradley, S Kenwright, A J R Morris, A D C Norris, P G Wheeler, I V Wilson
General Psychiatry A Cameron, J P Ryley, S Shere

General Surgery T Bates, A M Deane, C D Derry, N J Griffiths, J F McPartlin
Haematology D G Wells
Medical Microbiology J Q Nash
Neurology A C F Colchester, W F Michael
Obstetrics and Gynaecology J O Davies, C M Stewart, W Ursell
Ophthalmology J McConnell, E Simpson
Oral Surgery N Bradley, T J Storrs
Orthodontics W G Webb
Orthopaedics E R L Jones, D J Klugman, M Lock
Paediatrics C A Porter, S Williamson
Pathology C W Lawson, N R Padley
Radiology D Nadarajah, P M Paciorek, A Santhakumaran, R H F Waitt, W M Webb
Radiotherapy and Oncology R S Coltart
Rheumatology and Rehabilitation P W Bull, J R Sewell

East Leeds Primary Care Trust

Nurses Home, Seacroft Hospital, York Road, Leeds LS14 6UH
(West Yorkshire Health Authority)

Chair Linda Phipps
Chief Executive Laim Hughes

East Lincolnshire Primary Care Trust

C/o Louth County Hospital, High Holme Road, North Somercotes, Louth LN11 0EU
Tel: 01507 608342 Fax: 01507 354957
(Trent Health Authority)

East London and The City Mental Health NHS Trust

St Clements Hospital, 2A Bow Road, London E3 4LL
Tel: 020 8880 6296 Fax: 020 8880 6250
Website: www.elcmht.nhs.uk
(North East London Health Authority)

Chair Geraldine Huka
Chief Executive Peter Horn

East Midlands Ambulance Service NHS Trust

Trust Headquarters, Beechdale Road, Nottingham NG8 3LL
Tel: 0115 929 6151 Fax: 0115 962 7727
(Trent Health Authority)

Chief Executive Adrian Chubb

East Somerset NHS Trust

Yeovil District Hospital, Higher Kingston, Yeovil BA21 4AT
Tel: 01935 475122 Fax: 01935 426850
(Somerset and Dorset Health Authority)

Chair A J Dupont
Chief Executive James Scott

Crewkerne Hospital

Middle Path, Crewkerne TA18 8BG
Tel: 01460 72491 Fax: 01460 75423
Total Beds: 20

ENT G Ford

NHS TRUSTS & NHS HOSPITALS

General Medicine I W Fawcett, T G Palferman
General Surgery C Royle

South Petherton Hospital

South Petherton TA13 5AR
Tel: 01460 241106 Fax: 01460 242292
Total Beds: 44

Orthopaedics M J Maxted, J A Tricker

Verrington Hospital

Verrington Knap, Wincanton BA9 9DQ
Tel: 01963 32006 Fax: 01963 31898
Total Beds: 44

Care of the Elderly K A Rashed
General Medicine F X M Beach, T G Palferman
General Surgery C Royle
Orthopaedics M J Maxted

Yeovil District Hospital

Higher Kingston, Yeovil BA21 4AT
Tel: 01935 475122 Fax: 01935 426850
Total Beds: 253

Accident and Emergency Dr Brooks
Anaesthetics R Daum, C P Elsworth, R M Forward, S J Hunter, Dr Kerr, R M Kipling, G R G Purcell, Dr Wootton
Dermatology J Boyle, Dr Downs, D Pryce
ENT G Ford, N B Hopkin
General Medicine F X M Beach, G Brigden, I W Fawcett, S Gore, T Palferman, M Qadiri, K A Rashed, Dr Walker
General Surgery H Gajraj, R Kennedy, C Parker, C Royle
Genitourinary Medicine M Fitzgerald
Haematology Dr Bolam, S Davies, S A N Johnson
Medical Microbiology S Cotterill
Neurology Dr Farthers, P Heywood, Dr Smith
Obstetrics and Gynaecology A J Davies, J Giles, Dr Osoba, M Zakaria
Ophthalmology Dr Bray, Dr Pathmanathan, Dr Tadros
Oral and Maxillofacial Surgery M Davidson, J Hamlyn
Orthodontics Dr Atack, Dr Mitchell
Orthopaedics M J Maxted, Dr Shardlow, G Smibert, J A Tricker
Paediatrics J C Dearlove, M Eaton, Dr Heaton, M J Smith
Pathology C Fisher, J Sheffield
Plastic Surgery Dr Orlando, Dr Tiernan
Radiology J Baldwin, N C G Bathurst, J Hacking, W Saywell
Radiotherapy and Oncology S Falk, S Goodman

East Staffordshire Primary Care Trust

Outwoode Site, Belvedere Road, Burton-on-Trent DE13 0QL
Tel: 01283 593151 Fax: 01283 593162
(Shropshire and Staffordshire Health Authority)

East Surrey Primary Care Trust

St John's Court, 51 St John's Road, Redhill RH1 6DS
Tel: 01737 780209 Fax: 01737 787373
(Surrey and Sussex Health Authority)

Chair Martin Kitchen

East Sussex County Healthcare NHS Trust

Bowhill, Management HQ, The Drive, Hellingly, Hailsham BN27 4EP

East Sussex Hospitals NHS Trust

Eastbourne District General Hospital, Eastbourne District General Hospital, King's Drive, Eastbourne BN21 2UD
Tel: 01323 417400 Fax: 01323 417966
Website: www.esh.nhs.uk
Chair John Lewis
Chief Executive Annette Sergeant

East Yorkshire Primary Care Trust

33 Lairgate, Beverley HU17 8ET
Tel: 01482 862832 Fax: 01482 860176
(North and East Yorkshire and Northern Lincolnshire Health Authority)

Chair Helen Varey
Chief Executive Andrew Williams

Eastbourne and County Healthcare NHS Trust

Closing April 2002 - Mental health and learning disability services transferring to East Sussex County Healthcare NHS Trust.

Bowhill, The Drive, Hellingly, Hailsham BN27 4EP
Tel: 01323 440022 Fax: 01323 842868
(Surrey and Sussex Health Authority)

Chair Geoffrey Williams
Chief Executive Stephanie Parkes-Crick
Consultants S K Ahmed, P Argiriu, R Bowskill, R Canagaratnan, J Hargreaves, A N Naliyawala

Amberstone Mental Health Unit

Carters Corner, Hailsham BN27 4HG
Fax: 01323 844676
Total Beds: 24

Ashen Hill, Forensic Psychiatry Unit

The Drive, Hellingly, Hailsham BN27 4ER
Total Beds: 15

Crowborough War Memorial Hospital

South View Road, Crowborough TN6 1HB
Tel: 01892 652284 Fax: 01892 668877
Total Beds: 32

Roborough Day Hospital

Princess Alice Hospital, Carew Road, Eastbourne BN21 2AX
Tel: 01323 638972

Seaford Day Hospital

Sutton Road, Seaford BN25 2AX
Tel: 01323 490989

Southview Challenging Behaviour Unit

The Drive, Hellingly, Hailsham BN27 4ER
Tel: 01323 440022
Total Beds: 20

Uckfield Community Hospital

Framfield Road, Uckfield TN22 5SW
Tel: 01825 769999
Total Beds: 47

Eastbourne Downs Primary Care Trust

6th Floor, Greencoat House, 32 St. Leonards Road, Eastbourne BN21 3UT
Tel: 01323 417714 Fax: 01323 416161
(Surrey and Sussex Health Authority)

Chair Mary Colato
Chief Executive John Vesely

Eastbourne Hospitals NHS Trust

Closing April 2002 - Services transferring to East Sussex Hospitals NHS Trust.

Eastbourne District General Hospital, Kings Drive, Eastbourne BN21 2UD
Tel: 01323 417400 Fax: 01323 414966
(Surrey and Sussex Health Authority)

Chair Anne Bolter

All Saints' Hospital, Eastbourne

King Edward's Parade, Eastbourne BN20 7XA
Tel: 01323 417400
Total Beds: 105

Care of the Elderly C Athulathmudali, A Karunanayake

Eastbourne District General Hospital

King's Drive, Eastbourne BN21 2UD
Tel: 01323 417400 Fax: 01323 414930
Total Beds: 559

Accident and Emergency R Cottingham (Head), A R Durrani
Anaesthetics J B Hester (Head), G Bloor, S K N Chung, J H Cook, T King, R McGregor, K Myerson, P J Nash, S Nicoll, B Steer, A J Walmsley, N Watson
Dermatology K Liddell (Head)
ENT N Violaris (Head), G Manjaly
General Medicine J J Bending, A A Dunk, T Higgins, A Macleod, D Maxwell, N Patel, A Pool, A Smith, N Sulke, J Wilkinson
General Surgery S Allan, G Evans, P H Rowe, M Saunders, B J Stoodley
Neurology W N Macleod (Head)
Obstetrics and Gynaecology V Argent, M Malak, M Milligan
Ophthalmology A P Plumb (Head), D J Garlick, D T H Tarbuck, I Wearne
Oral Surgery K Altman (Head), P J Bathard-Smith
Orthodontics J Herold (Head)
Orthopaedics K R Ross (Head), A Bonnici, J C D'Arcy, S E James
Paediatrics Dr El-Abiary (Head), J Kinder, M Liebenberg, Dr Mitchell, G Wearmouth
Pathology S K Bangert, R P Cooke, A M Gilmour, P A Gover, R Grace, C H Mason, J Mercer, S Umasankar
Radiology H Anderson, D Howlett, D V Hughes, N Marchbank, E Ruffell, D Sallani
Radiotherapy and Oncology N J Hodson
Rheumatology J A Wojtulewski (Head)
Urology W T Lawrence (Head), A Cowie, G Watson

Eastern Cheshire Primary Care Trust

Toft Road Surgery, Toft Road, Knutsford WA16 9DX
Tel: 01565 621071 Fax: 01565 633298
(Cheshire and Merseyside Health Authority)

Chair Christine Greenhalgh
Chief Executive Peter Cubbon

Eastern Hull Primary Care Trust

Netherhall, Wawne Road, Hull HU7 4YG
(North and East Yorkshire and Northern Lincolnshire Health Authority)

Chair Maureen Foers
Chief Executive Iain McInnes

Eastern Leicester Primary Care Trust

3 De Montford Mews, Leicester LE1 7FW
(Leicestershire, Northamptonshire and Rutland Health Authority)

Chair Philip Parkinson
Chief Executive Carolyn A Clifton

Eastern Wakefield Primary Care Trust

Friarwood House, Friarwood Lane WF8 1UA
Tel: 01977 602000 Fax: 01977 606050
(West Yorkshire Health Authority)

Chair Roy Widdowson
Chief Executive Mike Grady

Eastleigh and Test Valley South Primary Care Trust

The Mount Hospital, Church Road, Bishopstoke, Eastleigh SO50 6ZB
Tel: 023 8065 2375 Fax: 023 8065 2568
(Hampshire and Isle of Wight Health Authority)

Eden Valley Primary Care Trust

8 Tynefield Drive, Penrith CA11 8JA
Tel: 01768 245317 Fax: 01768 245318
(Cumbria and Lancashire Health Authority)

Chair Beth Furneaux
Chief Executive Peter Kohn

Ellesmere Port and Neston Primary Care Trust

5 Civic Way, Ellesmere Port CH65 0AX
Tel: 0151 373 4900 Fax: 0151 356 7403
(Cheshire and Merseyside Health Authority)

Chair Michael Darby
Chief Executive Jacqui Harvey

Enfield Primary Care Trust

Avon Villa, Chase Farm Hospital Site, The Ridgeway, Enfield EN2 8JL
Tel: 020 8366 6600 Fax: 020 8366 1361
(North Central London Health Authority)

Chair Caroline Berkeley
Chief Executive Sally Johnson

NHS TRUSTS & NHS HOSPITALS

Epping Forest Primary Care Trust

Birchwood House, St Margaret's Hospital, The Plain, Epping CM16 6TN
Tel: 01902 902010 Fax: 01902 902012
(Essex Health Authority)

Chair Susan Leggate
Chief Executive Aidan Thomas

Epsom and St Helier NHS Trust

Epsom General Hospital, Dorking Road, Epsom KT18 7EG
Tel: 01372 735735 Fax: 01372 735310
(South West London Health Authority, Surrey and Sussex Health Authority)

Chair J Denning
Chief Executive Jim Stephenson
Consultants Felicity Anderson, Pete Andrews, Mike Bailey, Serge Bajada, Amolak Bansal, Jeffrey Barron, Sachu Battacharya, Judith Behrens, J Keith Bell, Justin Bendig, Mike R Bending, Marina P Benedict, Martin Benson, Nick Bett, Peter T Blenkinsopp, Sandra Blewitt, John Boyd, Ronald Brandt, Stephen Breathnach, Stephen J D Brecker, Christine Burren, Paul Byrne, Steve Capps, Joy S Catling, Clive Charig, Ruth Charlton, Muhammed Chawdhery, Philip Cheong-Leen, Sonny Chong, Mark Churchill, Neil Citron, A Clarke, Mary F Clarke, Sandeep Cliff, Val Cook, Nigel T Cooke, Angela Cunningham, David Cunningham, L G Darlington, Joan Desborough, Tony Eisinger, Cheryl Ellis, Steve Estreich, Bernadette Ewah, Richard E Field, Meda A Frangoulis, Julian A Gaer, Martin Gardner, David Gateley, Chris George, H Jane Gilford, Brian M Gompels, M Gore, Peter Gough, Stuart Gould, Andrew Gregory, Alison Halliday, Khalid N Haque, Chris C Harland, Simon S Hawkins, M Henk, Dr Hindmarsh, S J Keith Holmes, Philip J Howard, Anwar Hussein, Stanislaw Jankowski, A Chris John, Chris R Jones, Lydia Jones, Viji Kakumani, Mike Katesmark, Manil Katugampola, T Gerry Kavanagh, Michael Keane, Jan Klosok, Jonathan Kwan, Gabrielle Lamb, Bill Landells, John Langdon, Michael Lapsley, Bosena Laskiewicz, R Jane Leitch, Guam Lim, Will A Lindsay, Stanley Ling, Anne Linnell, Bob McFarland, Marion McGowan, C John MacKay, David Male, Janet Mantell, Tina Matthews, Simon T Meller, Jane Mercieca, Daniel Mok, Deborah Moncrieff, Dr Murday, Tony Nash, Dhiren Nehra, E Nicholls, Elizabeth A North, John O'Connell, Sola Odemuyiwa, Benedicta Ogeah, David Ogilvie, Robin T Orchard, Sharon Orton-Gibbs, Ellie M O'Sullivan, Winston Pais, Mike K Palmer, Maxine Partridge, Sanjeev Patel, Leonie Penna, Chris M Perry, Charles W Pumphrey, Patrick Radford, Kingsley W Ranasinha, Don C Rangedera, Geoffrey Robb, Peter Robb, Andrew Rodin, A Maria Rollin, Mark Rosenthal, Leslie D Ross, Samad Samadian, Stephen Sampson, Margaret Semple, Sanjay Shah, Elizabeth Sherriff, Linda N Singh, Ian Smith, Susan Snashell, Paula Sneath, Sugi Somanathan, Jim Stephenson, Andrew Stewart, Martin A Stockwell, Kathy Stoner, Shamshudin Suleman, Rene Tayar, L Temple, A Thayalan, Paul Thomas, A Thurston, Paul Toomey, Roy Twyman, Veronica Varney, Nestor Velasco, Michael C Ward, Mary Warren, Margaret H Whieldon, A Hervey Wilcox, Clare R Williams, Peter Williamson, Geoff Wilson, Stephen Wilson, Richard Worth, Robin L Yeoh, Kirsten Younger

Cobham Cottage Hospital

Portsmouth Road, Cobham KT11 1HT
Tel: 01932 584200 Fax: 01932 584201
Total Beds: 20

Epsom General Hospital

Dorking Road, Epsom KT18 7EG
Tel: 01372 735735 Fax: 01372 735310
Total Beds: 418

Accident and Emergency Dr Massoud, Dr Suleman
Anaesthetics J K Bell, S Bhattacharya, Dr Desborough, B Ewah, C J Mackay, W A Pais, Dr Pathmabaskaran, A M Rollin
Cardiology S Odemuyiwa

Chemical Pathology Dr Lapsley
Dermatology S Breathnach
ENT B M Laskiewicz, P Robb
General Medicine L G Darlington, S R Gould, Dr Lim, P F Mitchell-Heggs, Dr Rahman, K W Ranasinha, D C Rangedera, G H Robb
General Surgery W Allum, Dr Almusawi, A Halliday, R McFarland, Dr Raj, Dr Toomey
Haematology L Jones, M Semple
Histopathology T Matthews, L Temple
Medical Microbiology J Bendig, S Chambers
Neurology S G Wilson
Obstetrics and Gynaecology C Ellis, V Kakumani, M Katesmark, R W Worth
Occupational Health A Thayalan
Oncology D Cunningham, M Gore, M Henk, I Smith
Ophthalmology P Fison, M Frangoulis, Dr Leitch, A Linnell, Dr Shah
Oral Surgery J Langdon, M Partridge
Orthopaedics Dr Cobb (Head), P Cheong-Leen, Dr Chockalingam, D Mok, R Twyman
Paediatrics Dr Nicholls (Head), Dr Charlton, Dr Garcia, M Katugampola, J O'Connell, P Sneath
Radiology C George, B M Gompels, A M Gregory, Dr Lamb, K Stoner, K A Younger
Urology M J Bailey, C Charig, Dr Walker

Leatherhead Hospital

Poplar Road, Leatherhead KT22 8SD
Tel: 01372 384384 Fax: 01372 384360
Total Beds: 30

Nelson Hospital

Kingston Road, Merton, London SW20 8DB
Tel: 020 8296 2000
Total Beds: 10

New Epsom and Ewell Cottage Hospital

c/o West Park Hospital site, Horton Lane, Epsom KT19 8PB
Tel: 01372 734734 Fax: 01372 729641
Total Beds: 20

Queen Mary's Hospital for Children

St. Helier Hospital, Carshalton SM5 1AA
Tel: 020 8296 2000
Total Beds: 36

St Helier Hospital

Wrythe Lane, Carshalton SM5 1AA
Total Beds: 600

Accident and Emergency L Stevens (Head), S Pappasauvas
Anaesthetics M Gardner, S Hawkins, Dr Hussein, S Ling, D Male, P Radford, S Renwick, Dr Said, S Somanathan, C M Steven, M Stockwell, Dr Turner, C Williams
Audiological Medicine Dr Snashall, R Yeoh
Cardiology Dr Brecker, Dr Pumphrey
Care of the Elderly S Samadian, M Ward
Dental Surgery P Blenkinsopp, Dr Brandt, Dr Jones, Dr Orton-Gibbs, Dr Stewart
Dermatology Dr Harland, C A Holden
ENT A C John, Dr Laskiewicz, Dr Williamson
General Medicine M R Bending, Dr Benson, N T Cooke, Dr Duke, P Howard, R Orchard, Dr Rodin, Dr Varney
General Surgery N J Bett, A Chilvers, Dr Nehru, Dr Raja, Dr Thomas, Dr Zaidi
Genitourinary Medicine S Estreich, J Mantell
Nephrology Dr Eisinger (Head), Dr Andrews, M Bending, Dr Kwan, Dr Makanjoula, Dr Velasco
Neurology R O McKeran
Obstetrics and Gynaecology N A McWhinney (Head), Dr Croucher, P Gough, D Moncrieff, Dr Penru, Dr Perry, L D Ross, Dr Shehata, Dr Sherriff

Orthopaedics Dr Chockalingam, M Churchill, N Citron, Dr Field, T G Kavanagh, J Klosok, Dr Patel

Paediatrics Dr Blewitt, Dr Burren, Dr Chong, K Haque, Dr Holmes, Dr McGowan, Dr Ogeah, D Ogilvie, Dr Rosenthal, Dr Shepherd

Pathology J R Stephenson (Head), Dr Anderson, Dr Bansal, J L Barron, J Behrens, M Clarke, W Landells, Dr Lapsley, Dr Mercleca, L N Singh, A H Wilcox

Radiology A R Cunningham (Head), P Byrne, Dr Cook, J Gilford, Dr Keane, E A North, E M O'Sullivan, M K Palmer, R Tayar, Dr Warren

Rheumatology and Rehabilitation O Duke

Urology Dr Boyd (Head), Dr Jones, Dr Walker, Dr Watkin

Sutton Hospital

Cotswold Road, Sutton SM2 5NF
Tel: 020 8296 2000
Total Beds: 32

Erewash Primary Care Trust

Ilkeston Health Centre, South Street, Ilkeston DE7 5PZ
Tel: 0115 951 2300 Fax: 0115 951 2350
(Southern Derbyshire Health Authority)

Chair Anthea Thompson
Chief Executive Paula Clark

Essex Ambulance Service NHS Trust

Broomfield, Chelmsford CM1 7WS
Tel: 01245 443344 Fax: 01245 442920
Website: www.essamb.co.uk
(Essex Health Authority)

Chair Brian Goodwin
Chief Executive Gron Roberts

Essex Rivers Healthcare NHS Trust

Trust Headquarters, Colchester General Hospital, Turner Road, Colchester CO4 5JL
Tel: 01206 747474 Fax: 01206 854877
(Essex Health Authority)

Chair Michael Salmon
Chief Executive Michael Pollard

Colchester General Hospital

Turner Road, Colchester CO4 5JL
Total Beds: 582

Essex County Hospital

Lexden Road, Colchester CO3 3NB
Tel: 01206 747474 Fax: 01206 744512
Total Beds: 56

Halstead Hospital

Hedingham Road, Halstead CO9 2DL
Tel: 01787 291010 Fax: 01787 291023
Total Beds: 20

Exeter Primary Care Trust

Dean Clarke House, Southernhay East, Exeter EX1 1PQ
Tel: 01392 207513 Fax: 01392 494726
(South West Peninsula Health Authority)

Chair Mary Nisbet
Chief Executive Jill Ashton

Fareham and Gosport Primary Care Trust

Unit 18, 166 Fareham Road, Gosport PO13 0FW
Tel: 01329 233447 Fax: 01329 234984
Chair Lucy Doherty
Chief Executive Ian Piper

5 Borough Partnership NHS Trust

Trust Headquaters, Hollins House, Hollins Park, Hollins Lane, Winwick, Warrington WA2 8WA
(Cheshire and Merseyside Health Authority)

Frimley Park Hospital NHS Trust

Portsmouth Road, Frimley, Camberley GU16 7UJ
Tel: 01276 604604, 44 01276 604100 Fax: 01276 604148
(Surrey and Sussex Health Authority)

Chair Jane Cooke
Chief Executive Andrew V Morris

Frimley Park Hospital

Portsmouth Road, Frimley, Camberley GU16 5UJ
Tel: 01276 604604
Total Beds: 700

Accident and Emergency R Partridge

Anaesthetics Dr Bernardo, Dr Carroll, M H Davies, G F Goddard, Dr Gudgeon, P Joshi, Dr Keeling, S M Kilpatrick, K Markham, Dr Pepall, P Rawle, Dr Shaikh, Dr Slade, Dr Taylor, Dr Walsh, D G White

Care of the Elderly Dr Debrah, I K Ibrahim, K I Mundy

Dermatology Dr Boxer, R H Felix

ENT Dr Hosni, D Jonathan, R Kumar, Dr McCombe

General Medicine R L Bown, M J Boyd, R J Frankel

General Surgery Dr Daoud, Dr Gerrard, M Gudgeon, I Laidlaw, P Leopold, Dr Mellor, I Paterson, Dr Singh

Neurology D Wren

Obstetrics and Gynaecology Dr Bartells, Dr Beynon, J Cockburn, Dr Deans, A Riddle, P J Toplis

Ophthalmology A Elliott, J A Govan, C M Griffiths, M K Tandon

Oral and Maxillofacial Surgery Dr Danford, P Johnson

Orthopaedics A Ashbrooke, Dr Chissell, S Davies, D Dempster, D Harrison, Dr Hull, Dr Pike, Dr Quaile, Dr Sakellariou

Paediatrics F M Howard, P E Walker

Pathology Dr Alton, N Cumberland, P Denham, Dr Elmahallany, J E W Pette, C E T Smith, Dr Wang, M Williams

Plastic Surgery D Martin

Radiology Dr Ahmad, J Hall, Dr Hatrick, F J Hearn, A Keightley, H Massouh

Radiotherapy R Laing

Rheumatology and Rehabilitation Dr Lloyd, P Reilly

Thoracic Medicine R K Knight

Urology B Montgomery, Dr Naeger, E Palfrey

Fylde Primary Care Trust

Ground Floor Office, 16-18 St George's Road, Lytham St Annes FY8 2AE
Tel: 01258 789170 Fax: 01253 789695
(Cumbria and Lancashire Health Authority)

Chair Herbert Waddington
Chief Executive Julie Goulding

NHS TRUSTS & NHS HOSPITALS

Gateshead Health NHS Trust

From April 2002 mental health services transferring to South of Tyne and Wearside Mental Health NHS Trust.

Queen Elizabeth Hospital, Sheriff Hill, Gateshead NE9 6SX
Tel: 0191 482 0000 Fax: 0191 482 6001
(Northumberland, Tyne and Wear Health Authority)

Chair Peter John Smith
Chief Executive Karen Straughair

Bensham Hospital

Saltwell Road, Gateshead NE8 4YL
Tel: 0191 482 0000 Fax: 0191 478 3357
Total Beds: 151

Care of the Elderly D Barer, D M Beaumont, M Davies
Radiology J Hall, P Lord, J Rawlinson, R Uberoi
Rheumatology C Heycock, C Kelly

Dryden Road Day Hospital

134 Dryden Road, Gateshead NE9 5BY
Tel: 0191 403 6600 Fax: 0191 403 6601

Dunston Hill Day Unit

Whickham Highway, Dunston, Gateshead NE11 9QT
Tel: 0191 403 6474 Fax: 0191 403 6505

Dunston Hill Hospital

Gateshead NE11 9QT
Tel: 0191 482 0000 Fax: 0191 403 6408
Total Beds: 70

Queen Elizabeth Hospital

Sheriff Hill, Gateshead NE9 6SX
Tel: 0191 482 0000 Fax: 0191 491 1823
Total Beds: 537

Accident and Emergency B Dorani
Anaesthetics R M Freeman, A McHutchon, I M J Mathias, P Matthew, H May, M Weaver
Child and Adolescent Psychiatry L Barrett, D Bone, J McDonald
Dermatology M C G Dahl
General Medicine N Bailey, D Barer, J Barker, D M Beaumont, M Davies, C T A Jones, C Kelly, L G Lunt, J Mansfield, D J Peakman, T Petterson, C Scott, P Turner, J U Weaver, L A Webb, J R Young
General Surgery D A Browell, S M Chandhry, W J Cunliffe, M J Higgs
Obstetrics and Gynaecology A Beeby, M Das, S M Field
Oncology N Bailey, T d Lopes, J M Monaghan, D P Sinha
Orthopaedics J A Antrobus, J Pooley
Otology D B Mathias, A R Welch, J Wilson
Paediatrics J R Beesley, S Hoare, S Hodges, A Steele
Pathology M Abela, P Cross, M J Egan, S Hudson, J P Sunter
Radiology J Hall, P Lord, J Rawlinson, R Uberoi
Rheumatology and Rehabilitation C Heycock, C Kelly
Urology H A Ashour, A M M Mudawi

Tranwell Unit

Windy Nook Road, Gateshead NE10 9RW
Tel: 0191 482 0000 Fax: 0191 402 6221
Total Beds: 127

Gateshead Primary Care Trust

Horsley Hill Road, South Shields NE33 3DP
(Northumberland, Tyne and Wear Health Authority)

Gedling Primary Care Trust

Carlton Health Clinic, 61 Burton Road, Carlton, Nottingham NG4 3DQ
Tel: 0115 840 5921 Fax: 0115 840 5925
(Trent Health Authority)

Chair Derek Stewart

George Eliot Hospital NHS Trust

Lewes House, College Street, Nuneaton CV10 7DJ
Tel: 024 7635 1351 Fax: 024 7686 5175
(Coventry, Warwickshire, Herefordshire and Worcestershire Health Authority)

Chair Cllr F McCarney
Chief Executive John G Tounsend

George Eliot Hospital

College Street, Nuneaton CV10 7DJ
Tel: 024 7635 1351 Fax: 024 7686 5175
Total Beds: 404

Accident and Emergency G Gordon
Anaesthetics J A Dako, D G Heap, N S Kaduskar, R I Miller, S Nithianandan, S Shawket, P C M Taggart
Cardiology M Bean, Y Haider, A Venkataraman
Cardiothoracic Medicine R Norton
Care of the Elderly A W Bullen, A B Whitehouse
Child and Adolescent Psychiatry S Thavasothy
Dermatology J Berth-Jones, S Charles-Holmes
ENT P Patel, J M Stansbie
General Medicine P D J Handslip, V Patel, G Wood
General Psychiatry M Quasim
General Surgery H Bishop, B R Bullen, I Haynes, V Moshakis
Genitourinary Medicine L M David, M Walzman
Haematology M Narayanan
Histopathology N Bajallan, J Mercer, J Nottingham
Nephrology M Edmunds
Neurology J R Ponsford
Obstetrics and Gynaecology C J Hutchins, V G Kenyon, J Phipps
Ophthalmology R D Kumar
Orthopaedics A Aboel-Salam, D T Sharif, R Steingold
Paediatrics R C Boer, V Datta, M Venkataraman
Plastic Surgery A Groves, R N Matthews, S Srivastava
Radiology S Bera, A Gupta, R Patel, S P Sinha, K Vallance
Radiotherapy and Oncology R N Das
Rheumatology J Coppock, G C Zaphiropoulos
Urology I J Apakama, K K Prasad

Gloucestershire Ambulance Services NHS Trust

Horton Road, Gloucester GL1 3PX
Tel: 01452 395050 Fax: 01452 383331
(Avon, Gloucestershire and Wiltshire Health Authority)

Chair Carolyn Elwes
Chief Executive Richard Davis

Gloucestershire Hospitals NHS Trust

1 College Lawn, Cheltenham GL53 7AG
(Avon, Gloucestershire and Wiltshire Health Authority)

Chair Dame Janet Trotter
Chief Executive Paul Lilley

Gloucestershire Partnership NHS Trust

Rikonel, Montpellier, Gloucester GL1 1LY
(Avon, Gloucestershire and Wiltshire Health Authority)

Chair Robert Maxwell
Chief Executive Jeff James

Gloucestershire Royal NHS Trust

Closing April 2002 - Acute services transferring to Gloucestershire Hospitals NHS Trust.

Gloucestershire Royal Hospital, Great Western Road, Gloucester GL1 3NN
Tel: 01452 528555 Fax: 01452 394737
(Avon, Gloucestershire and Wiltshire Health Authority)

Chair Margaret Greenwood
Chief Executive Paul Lilley

Gloucestershire Royal Hospital

Great Western Road, Gloucester GL1 3NN
Tel: 01452 528555 Fax: 01452 310737
Total Beds: 583

Accident and Emergency S McCabe, Dr Vickery
Anaesthetics Dr Bakewell, J Brown, Dr Clarke, Dr Cooper, Dr Crabb, Dr Duncan, M A Durkin, R J Eltringham, D Gabbott, Dr Garcia-Rodriguez, W Grayling, C Green, P Hardy, Dr Jeffrey, Dr Khor, A McCrirrick, Dr Pryle, C Roberts, Dr Savidge, E Spencer, A S Thornberry, R Vanner, J Waters, P N Young
Care of the Elderly Dr Asghar, M Bannerjee, I Donald
Dermatology Dr Adriaans, Dr Milne, Dr Parker
ENT K Evans, Dr Hamilton, M Hardingham, Dr Thomas, Dr Youngs
General Medicine R Banks, Dr Brown, R Butland, D Lindsay, Dr Meecham-Jones, M Peterson, Dr Pickett, J Prior, Dr Ulahannan, R Valori, A J Williams, J Woodland
General Surgery H Barr, Dr Cook, J Earnshaw, Dr Gilbert, B P Heather, D Jones, M Lucarotti, A Ritchie, Dr Sammon, W H F Thomson, M Vipond
Genitourinary Medicine D Sulaiman
Neurology G Fuller, Dr Martin, Dr Silva
Obstetrics and Gynaecology Dr James, Dr Mahendran, Dr Pike, M D Read, E Smith, G Swingler, Dr Whittaker
Ophthalmology B Harney, G Mackintosh, J Nairne
Oral Surgery Dr Godden, J M Harrison, C Perkins
Orthodontics J Dickson, Dr Macey-Dave
Orthopaedics D Asante, Dr Close, Dr Craig, C C Crawshaw, C Curwen, C Knudsen, R Majkowski, B D Morris, T B Tasker
Paediatrics L Jadresic, Dr Matthai, Dr Pandya, Dr Rushforth, D W Stevens, M S C Webb
Pathology Dr Chown, Dr Christie-Brown, P A Laite, M Logan, Dr McCarthy, K McCarthy, J E Ropner, N Shepherd, J S Uff
Radiology P Birch, E F Brown, S Cooke, Dr Jelly, F Jewell, S E Jones, A Tottle, Dr Wallace, J B Witcombe
Rheumatology Dr Coombes, J Woodland

Standish Hospital

Stonehouse GL10 3DB
Tel: 01453 822481
Total Beds: 119

Chest Disease R Butland, J Prior
Orthopaedics D Asante, C C Crawshaw, R A C Davies, C Knudsen, B D A Morris, T P B Tasker
Rheumatology J Woodland

Good Hope Hospital NHS Trust

Rectory Road, Sutton Coldfield B75 7RR
Tel: 0121 378 2211 Fax: 0121 311 1074
Website: www.goodhope.org.uk
(Birmingham and the Black Country Health Authority)

Chair Bernard Zissman
Chief Executive Jeff Chandra
Consultants I S Foulds, M Hope-Ross, J J Milles, Mr Moloney, OG Titley, J Tucker

Good Hope Hospital

Rectory Road, Sutton Coldfield B75 7RR
Tel: 0121 378 2211 Fax: 0121 311 1074
Total Beds: 550

Accident and Emergency K Gupta, A Tabani
Anaesthetics J Elliott, J Hull, P Johnston, M N A Messih, F Murray, J H Sheldrake, D Siggins, D Thomas
Biochemistry R A Hall
Care of the Elderly J Atiea, A A Farooqi, L Lambert, M P Skander
Child and Adolescent Psychiatry A A E Sorour-El Sharief
Dermatology I S Foulds
ENT E Fisher, A Johnson, D Morgan
General Medicine J Atiea, T Fletcher, P Hillenbrand, L Lambert, A Mackay, J J Milles, M V J Raj, S Singh, M P Skander, R Smith
General Surgery A Allan, P Bearn, M Crowson, M Foster, A Jewkes, B Jones, D R Thomas
Haematology M S Hamilton, J Tucker
Neurology D J Jamieson
Obstetrics and Gynaecology R Cartmill, D Churchill, G Constantine, C Finn, M D Moloney
Oncology T N Latief
Ophthalmology P Lin Lip, M H Ross, P Shah, G A Sutton
Orthodontics S Weerakone
Orthopaedics B Banerjee, G J Benke, G Krishnamusthy, I M Miller, K Wahab
Paediatrics A Baxi, S Bennett Britton, T J Lee, J Meran
Pathology N Aluwihare, A M Light, D Mortiboy, J Tucker, R S Whittaker
Plastic Surgery J H Goldin
Radiology C Bickley, E Millar, C Nelson, A Parnell
Rheumatology T Price, T Sheeran
Urology M C Foster, D R Thomas

Great Ormond Street Hospital for Children NHS Trust

Great Ormond Street, London WC1N 3JH
Tel: 020 7405 9200 Fax: 020 7829 8643
(North Central London Health Authority)

Chair Gyril Chantler
Chief Executive Roger Harris

The Hospital for Children

Great Ormond Street, London WC1N 3JH
Tel: 020 7405 9200 Fax: 020 7829 8643
Total Beds: 327

Anaesthetics R M Bingham, A Black, J Delima, E K Facer, D Hatch, R Howard, E Jackson, I G James, A Lloyd-Thomas, J Lockie, A McEwan, A Mackersie, E Sumner, M Sury, I Walker
Audiological Medicine S C Bellman, C O'Mahoney, K Sirimanna
Cardiology C Bull, J Deanfield, S Haworth, P Rees, I Sullivan, J Taylor
Clinical Pathology R Jones
Consultants J Payan, M Preece
Dental Surgery M Calvert, R Evans, D R James, M Mars
Dermatology D J Atherton, J I Harper
ENT D Albert, C M Bailey, J N G Evans, S E J Leighton

NHS TRUSTS & NHS HOSPITALS

General Medicine A Aynsley-Green, C Brook, P Clayton, M Dillon, R Dinwiddie, S Hill, J Leonard, P J Milla, I Smith, P Sonksen, R Stanhope, C Wallis

General Surgery B D Drake, E G S Kiely, A Pierro, L Spitz

Genetics M Baraitser, L Chitty, M Pembrey, P Scambler, R Winter

Haematology J Chessells, J Evans, A Goldman, I Hann, A Michalski, J Pritchard, P Veys

Histopathology P Ramani, R A Risdon

Immunology D Goldblatt, A Jones, R J Levinsky, G Morgan, S Strobel, P Veys

Infectious Diseases D Gibb, V Novelli

Medical Microbiology H Holzel, E Price

Nephrology T M Barratt, M Dillon, O N Fernando, L Rees, R Trompeter, A Woolf

Neurology S Boyd, F Kirkman, B Neville, M Pitt, J Wilson

Neuropathology B N Harding

Neuroradiology B Kendall, R D Kingsley

Neurosurgery W Harkness, R Hayward

Occupational Health A Haines

Ophthalmology J Russell-Eggitt, D Taylor

Orthopaedics J A Fixsen, R Hill, H Noordeen

Plastic Surgery R B M Jones, P Smith, B Sommerlad

Psychology D Glaser, R V Howarth, B Lask, M Prendergast, D Skuse

Radiology R d Bruyn, W Chong, C M F Dicks-Mireaux, I Gordon, C M Hall, D Kingsley, D G Shaw

Radiotherapy and Oncology P N Plowman, J Pritchard

Rheumatology N Hasson, M Rooney, P Woo

Thoracic Surgery M J Elliott, M D Leval, J Stark

Urology P G Duffy, P Moriquand, P G Ransley

Great Yarmouth Primary Care Trust

Astley Cooper House, Estcourt Road, Great Yarmouth NR30 4JH Tel: 01493 856156 Fax: 01493 856005 (Norfolk, Suffolk and Cambridgeshire Health Authority)

Chair Bernard Williamson **Chief Executive** Michael Stonard

Greater Derby Primary Care Trust

5 Stuart Street, Derby DE1 2EQ Tel: 01332 298700 Fax: 01332 342881 (Southern Derbyshire Health Authority)

Chair Ali Naqwi **Chief Executive** Veronica Marsden

Greater Manchester Ambulance Service NHS Trust

Bury Old Road, Whitefield, Manchester M45 6AQ Tel: 0161 796 7222 Fax: 0161 796 0435 (Greater Manchester Health Authority)

Chair Alan Stephenson **Chief Executive** John Burnside

Greenwich Primary Care Trust

1 Hyde Vale, London SE10 6QG Tel: 020 8694 7300 Fax: 020 8694 6994 (South East London Health Authority)

Chair Ken May **Chief Executive** Jane Schofield

Guild Community Healthcare NHS Trust

Closing April 2002 - Services transferring to Lancashire Care NHS Trust.

Moor Park House, 1 Moor Park Avenue, Preston PR1 6AS Tel: 01772 401000 Fax: 01772 401001 (Cumbria and Lancashire Health Authority)

Chair Pradeep Passi **Chief Executive** Finlay Robertson

Avondale Unit

Royal Preston Hospital, Sharoe Green Lane North, Fulwood, Preston PR2 9HT Tel: 01772 710639, 01772 710668, 01772 710709 Fax: 01772 710195 Total Beds: 56

Ribbleton Hospital

Miller Road, Preston PR2 6LS Tel: 01772 401300 Fax: 01772 651091

Guildford and Waverly Primary Care Trust

Sheppey Community Hospital, Wards Hill Road, Minster On Sea, Sheerness ME12 2LN Tel: 01483 783116 Fax: 01483 783179 Website: www.guilford.nhs.uk (Surrey and Sussex Health Authority)

Chief Executive Lis Slinn

Guy's and St Thomas' NHS Trust

Guy's Hospital, St. Thomas Street, London SE1 9RT Tel: 020 7955 5000 Fax: 020 7955 8803 Website: www.hospital.org.uk (South East London Health Authority)

Chair Patricia Moberly **Chief Executive** Jonathan Michael

Grove Park Hospital

Marvels Lane, London SE12 9PD Tel: 020 8857 1191 Total Beds: 168

General Psychiatry R E Bates, N Bouras

Guy's Hospital

St. Thomas Street, London SE1 9RT Tel: 020 7955 5000 Fax: 020 7955 8803 Website: www.hospital.org.uk Total Beds: 553

Accident and Emergency L Stimmler, D Watson

Alcohol and Substance Misuse M Allen

Anaesthetics A P Adams, M B Barnett, W Coutinho, H D Dervos, J G Diamond, J Hellewell, P B Hewitt, N Newton, J S Paddle, R S Parsons, A Pearce, M Thompson, R Towey, J R Wedley, C Wood

Biochemistry R Swaminathan

Cardiology C Bucknall, J Chambers, P V L Curry, G Jackson, G E Sowton

Cardiothoracic Medicine D Anderson, C Blauth, P D Deverall, J Dussek

Care of the Elderly R Lewis, W McNabb

Child and Adolescent Psychiatry A Cox, H Davies, D R Glaser, R J Jezzard, T Moran, M Wiseman

Cytology N Fagg, I Filipe, B Hartley, D Levison, R Millis, P Wilson

HAMBLETON & RICHMONDSHIRE PRIMARY CARE TRUST

Dental Surgery F P Ashley, A Banner, S J Challacombe, R Edler, S Farrant, N Fisher, T P Ford, D H Gibb, R Haskell, E Kidd, T Lehner, P Likeman, P Longhurst, M McGurk, M Meikle, J Metclaf, P Morgan, R I Nairn, R Palmer, D Pool, D J Ramsay, G J Roberts, P Robinson, R Savavanamuttu, A M Skelly, B G N Smith, B J Smith, A Thom, L A Usiskin, J D Walter, T L P Watts, E Whaites

Dermatology J N W Baker, R J Hay, D M MacDonald

Diabetes S A Amiel, N Finer, G C Viberti

Endocrinology S A Amiel, S Clarke, I Fogelman, B Hicks, M Maisey, P Winter

ENT E Chevretton, E Douek, M Gleeson, J Hibbert

Forensic Medicine Dr Shepherd, I E West

Gastroenterology R H Dowling, G E Sladen, M Wilkinson

General Medicine G M Cochrane, A W Frankland, T Gibson, J Henry, B H Hicks, R K Knight, T Lee, R R Lewis, R McNabb, P J Rees, J Ritter, G Volans, L J F Youlten

General Psychiatry P Bridges, P Davenport, M Dunn, E Hendry, J L Herzberg, M Lipsedge, A McCarthy, D Master, D Morgan, A Pynton, M Rafferty, A J Ramierez, B Rosen, J P Watson

General Surgery M Jourdan, T L McColl, R Mason, W J Owen, P Taylor

Genetics A C Berry, M Bobrow, S V Hodgson

Genitourinary Medicine S Tovey

Haematology K G A Clark, S Schey, G Smith

Histopathology L Bobrow

Intensive Care M Smithies

Medical Microbiology G French, N Simmons

Neurology A Colchester, R A C Hughes, B Moffat, M D O'Brien

Neurophysiology J Payan

Neurosurgery C Polkey, A J Strong

Nuclear Medicine S Clarke, I Fogelman, P M N Maisey

Obstetrics and Gynaecology M Chapman, T M Coltart, R Forman, C Lloyd, D Maxwell, E D Morris, J Rymer, M Thom

Ophthalmology D Calver, R Daniels, D M Watson

Oral and Maxillofacial Surgery P M O'Driscoll

Orthopaedics P Allen, M Laurence, D Nunn, J Spencer, M S Watson

Paediatrics M Agrawal, L Allen, G Baird, E Baker, M Borzykowski, D M Calver, C Chantler, A G B Clarke, P Evans, G Haycock, M Joyce, M Lynch, I Murdoch, S Qureshi, S Rigden, S Robb, R Robinson, L Stimmler, M Tynan

Palliative Medicine T Bozek

Periodontology M N Naylor, D J Neill, H W Preiskel

Radiology A Adam, J Bingham, T Cox, S Rankin, J Reidy, M R Salari, A J S Saunders

Radiotherapy and Oncology M Chaudary, P Harper, E Macdonald, A Raminez, M A Richards, R D Rubens, S A Schey, D Tong

Renal Medicine J S Cameron, G Koffman, C Ogg, S Sacks, D G Williams

Rheumatology T J Gibson, R Grahame, G S Panayi

Toxicology Dr Edwards, J A Henry, V Murray, G N Volans, B Widdop

Urology J F Flannery, M L Joyce, A R Mundy

St Thomas's Hospital

Lambeth Palace Road, London SE1 7EH
Tel: 020 7928 9292 Fax: 020 7633 9292
Website: www.hospital.org.uk
Total Beds: 813

Accident and Emergency D J Williams

Alcohol and Substance Misuse T S Onen

Anaesthetics C Aps, A J Clement, T Hunt, D M Justins, M Lim, R A F Linton, J A Mathias, G H O'Sullivan, C E Pither, F Reynolds, G T Spencer, K Williams, R P Wise

Cardiology D J Coltart, B S Jenkins, M M Webb-Peploe

Cardiothoracic Surgery J Dussek, G E Venn, C P Young

Care of the Elderly A H Hopper, F Martin, A Rudd

Chemical Pathology I S Menzies, B Slavin

Child and Adolescent Psychiatry P Loader, H F Roberts, H Swadi

Clinical Physiology R D Bradley, D F Treacher

Cytology N W Derias

Dermatology D J Atherton, A K Black, M M Black, B M Breathnach, A D M Bryceson, R O R Camp, R A J Eady, M W Greaves, W A D Griffiths, J L M Hawk, R J Hay, R R Jones, G M Levene, P McGibbon, R J G Rycroft, N P Smith, M F Spittle, N P J Walker, I White

Endocrinology R H Jones, C Low, I S Menzies, B Slavin, P H Sonksen, A E Young

ENT E B Chevreton, J N G Evans, A F F O'Connor

Forensic Psychiatry D Murphy

Gastroenterology P J Ciclitера, R J Ede, R P H Thompson

General Medicine N T Bateman, I R Cameron, D J Coltart, D N Croft, P J Hilton, B S Jenkins, F C Martin, O Nunan, R P H Thompson, C H C Twort, M M Webb-Peploe, A J Wing

General Practice F Gelder, M Goyal, G Hillman, R Jones, W S Marson, B Olding, D J Sharp, L I Zander

General Psychiatry Dr Craig, M Samuel

General Surgery N L Browse, K J Burnand, B T Jackson, C W Jamieson, M Jourdan, A E Young

Genitourinary Medicine D Barlow, J S Bingham, C Bradbeer, E M Graham, R N Thin

Haematology R Carr, B Hunt, T C Pearson, G F Savidge, N P Slater

Histopathology C P M Fletcher, P H McKee, H Pambakian

Immunology D C Dumonde, A S Hamblin, J C Taylor

Medical Microbiology S J Eykyn, I Phillips

Medical Oncology M A Richards

Neonatology A M Kaiser, A D Milner

Nephrology P Hilton, A J Wing

Neurology R Howard, I C E Ormerod, R W R Russell

Neurophysiology C Panayiotopoulos

Nuclear Medicine D N Croft, T Nunan, H J O'Doherty

Obstetrics and Gynaecology P Braudie, I L C Fergusson, R X Goswamy, A Kenney, A Kubba, S Raju, E Versi

Occupational Health C Dow, D Snashall

Ophthalmology A H Chignell, M J Falcon, T J ffytche, E Graham, M K Muir, G T Plant, R W Ross-Russell, J S Shilling, D J Spalton

Orthopaedics R N Brueton, F W Heatley, D A Reynolds, M A Smith

Paediatric Surgery H Ward

Paediatrics G S Clayden, G Dumont, G D Haycock, A J Hulse, M L R Lima, C M M Stern

Palliative Medicine D Justins, C Pither

Plastic Surgery P K B Davis, B J Mayou, D Mercer

Proctology B T Jackson, R J Nicholls

Psychiatry of Old Age E Fottrell

Psychology Z Atakan, J A G Besson, H D Kopelman, H F Oakeley, D Roy, J P R Young

Psychotherapy K Dustan

Public Health Medicine W W Holland, R J Rona

Radiology A B Ayers, L M MacDonald, J Pemberton, K A Tonge

Radiotherapy and Oncology T D Bates, R P Beaney, F Calman, H J Dobbs, M F Spittle, A R Timothy

Rheumatology G R V Hughes, J A Mathews, D A H Yates

Thoracic Medicine N T Bateman, I R Cameron, M J B Farebrother, I M O'Brien, D F Treacher, C H C Twort

Thoracic Surgery J E Dussek

Urology M I Bultitude, R W L Davies, R Tiptaft

Vascular Surgery N L Browse, K G Burnand, C W Jamieson

Virology J E Banatvala

Halton Primary Care Trust

Unit G11, Waterloo Centre, Waterloo Road, Widnes WA8 0PR
Tel: 0151 495 3293 Fax: 0151 420 6788
(Cheshire and Merseyside Health Authority)

Hambleton and Richmondshire Primary Care Trust

Sovereign House, Kettlestring Lane, York YO30 4GQ

NHS TRUSTS & NHS HOSPITALS

(North and East Yorkshire and Northern Lincolnshire Health Authority)

Hammersmith and Fulham Primary Care Trust

The Brook Green Medical Centre, Bute Gardens, London W6 7EG
Tel: 020 8237 2805 Fax: 020 8237 2804
(North West London Health Authority)

Chair Lucinda Bolton
Chief Executive Sally Hargreaves

Hammersmith Hospitals NHS Trust

Hammersmith Hospital, Du Cane Road, London W12 0HS
Tel: 020 8383 2030
(North West London Health Authority)

Chair Murray Stuart
Chief Executive John Cooper

Hammersmith Hospital

Du Cane Road, London W12 0HS
Tel: 020 8383 1000 Fax: 020 8383 3169
Total Beds: 450

Anaesthetics G Baldock, D Harris, A Holdcroft, R D Jack, G G Lockwood, J Lumley, M Morgan, D A Zideman
Anatomy and Physiology P J Bourdillon
Bacteriology J Cohen
Cardiology A Benetar, P Camigi, G Davies, H Gardiner, J Gibbs, R Hall, J Koonar, P Nihoyannopyoulos
Cardiothoracic Surgery B Keogh, R N Sapsford, P L C Smith, K M Taylor
Care of the Elderly C Bulpitt, P Elliott, P J Evans, M G Impallomeni, C Nicholl
Chemical Pathology S Girgis
Chest Disease J M B Hughes, P W Ind, N B Pride
Clinical Oncology A G Dalgleish, A A Epentos, H E Lambert, C G McKenzie, P Price, K Sikora, S J Stewart, C C Vernon, J Waxman
Dermatology A C Chu, R Russell-Jones
Endocrinology S R Bloom, E M Kohner, J A Lynn, H M Mather, K Meeron, L M Sandler, R V Thakker
Gastroenterology J Calam, H J F Hodgson, J Walters
General Medicine S Blunt, P Hawkins, G Howitt, M Lab, J S Savil, J Scott, G R Thompson
General Surgery J H Baron, P Grace, N Habib, W A Kmiot, J Lynn, D P Sellu, J Spencer, N J Stanfield, R K Strachan, J N Thompson, R C N Williamson
Haematology J F Apperley, J M Goldman, M Laffan, E T Letsky, I Roberts, P O Skacel, D Swirsky, E G V Tuddenham
Histopathology H Cook, P Cox, D J Evans, P Hall, T Krausz, I A Lampert, N R Lemdine, D V Parvms, M N Pignatelli, J M Polak, G Stamp, J S Wigglesworth, N A Wright
Imaging D O'Shea
Immunology R I Lechler, M B Pepys
Infectious Diseases J Cohen, R G Feldman, S Shaunak
Nephrology E Clutterbuck, D N S Kerr, C D Pusey, C Savage
Neurology D J Brooks, R S Frackowiak, N J Legg, A Monzur
Obstetrics and Gynaecology M G Elder, L Fusi, D Hawkins, R A Margara, U Nicolini, W P Soutter, R M L Winston
Ophthalmology E M Kohner, W E Schulenburg
Oral Surgery H S Coonar
Paediatrics B Dubowitz, A D Edwards, J Heckmatt, K Lakoo, A Whitelaw
Pathology T Evans
Pharmacology J Brown, P J Lewis, J MacDermot, M Wilkins
Radiology A Adam, D J Allison, G M Bydder, C Cousins, W Curati, P Dawson, J E Jackson, A M Peters, M J Raphael
Renal Medicine A Warrens
Respiratory Medicine P Ind

Rheumatology K A Davies, D O Haskard, M J Walport
Urology P Abel, E Kiely, G Williams
Vascular Medicine A O Mansfield, J Pflug, J H N Wolff
Virology K Ward

Queen Charlotte's and Chelsea Hospital

Goldhawk Road, London W6 0XG
Tel: 020 8383 1111
Website: www.hhnt.org
Total Beds: 120

Anaesthetics M Barton, B M Morgan, G W Stephen
General Medicine M d Swiet
Haematology E A Letsky
Medical Microbiology L E T Houang, R Hurley
Obstetrics and Gynaecology E Bryan, T M Coltart, D K Edmonds, N M Fisk, F Loefler, J Malvern, J L Osborne, C D Sims
Paediatrics D R Harvey, N Modi
Radiology J C Hollway

Hampshire Ambulance Service NHS Trust

Highcroft, Romsey Road, Winchester SO22 5DH
Tel: 01962 863511 Fax: 01962 842156
Website: www.hantsam.org.uk
(Hampshire and Isle of Wight Health Authority)

Chair Sarah Murray
Chief Executive Richard A Mawson

Haringey Primary Care Trust

St Ann's Hospital, St Ann's Road, London N15 3TH
Tel: 020 8442 6000 Fax: 020 8442 6567
(North Central London Health Authority)

Chair Richard Sumray
Chief Executive David Sloman

Harlow Primary Care Trust

Level 16, Terminus House, Terminus Street, Harlow CM20 1XE
Tel: 01279 694747 Fax: 01279 694740
(Essex Health Authority)

Chair Tom Farr
Chief Executive Pam Court

Harrogate Health Care NHS Trust

Strayside Wing, Harrogate District Hospital, Lancaster Park Road, Harrogate HG2 7SX
Tel: 01423 554423, 01423 885959 Fax: 01423 555806, 01423 555791
Email: graham.g.saunders@hhc-tr.northy.nhs.uk
(North and East Yorkshire and Northern Lincolnshire Health Authority)

Chief Executive Graham Eric Saunders

Harrogate District Hospital

Lancaster Park Road, Harrogate HG2 7SX
Tel: 01423 885959 Fax: 01423 555353
Total Beds: 379

Accident and Emergency W Hulse
Anaesthetics J Campbell, P G Cutler, R A S Frater, J Gasser, I S Milne, P M Norton, G Parkin
Care of the Elderly A J Bennett, S Brotheridge, J J Whitaker
Dermatology A Layton
ENT M Benamer, A Nicolaides, P G Reilly

General Medicine G Davies, A Fennert, R Hammmond, H Larkin
General Psychiatry J Brothewell, K Jones, H Loizou, A J Rugg, D Ryan
General Surgery R A Knox, A H Lawson, D J Leinhardt
Ophthalmology D I Bowen, T W Metcalfe
Oral and Maxillofacial Surgery M Telfer, P Whitfield
Orthodontics J Kindelan
Orthopaedics N J London, R J Newman, G K Sefton, G E Stollard
Radiology S Carradine, A Coral, R Mawhinney, D Sapherson, D Scullion
Rheumatology and Rehabilitation A Gough
Urology A H Lawson, P Singh

Ripon Community Hospital

Firby Lane, Ripon HG4 2PR
Tel: 01765 602546 Fax: 01765 606628
Total Beds: 21

Care of the Elderly A J Bennett, S Brotheridge, J J Whitaker

Harrow and Hillingdon Healthcare NHS Trust

Trust closure tbc - Services transferring to Harrow Primary Care Trust.

Malt House, Field End Road, Eastcote, Ruislip HA4 9NJ
Tel: 020 8956 3200 Fax: 020 8426 1191
(North West London Health Authority)

Chair Anthony Woodbridge

Northwood and Pinner Cottage Hospital

Pinner Road, Northwood HA6 1DE
Tel: 01923 824182
Total Beds: 31

Harrow Primary Care Trust

Kenmore Clinic, Kenmore Road, Harrow HA3 9EN
Tel: 020 8204 9083 Fax: 020 8204 9084
(North West London Health Authority)

Chair Geoffrey Rose
Chief Executive Sue McLellen

Hartlepool Primary Care Trust

3rd Floor, Mandale House, Harbour Walk, The Marina, Hartlepool TS24 0UX
Tel: 01429 285079 Fax: 01429 286944
(Tees Health Authority)

Chair Gerald Wistow
Chief Executive Graeme K Oram

Hastings and Rother NHS Trust

Closing April 2002 - Mental health and learning disability services transferring to East Sussex County Healthcare NHS Trust; acute services transferring to East Sussex Hospitals NHS Trust.

St. Anne's House, 729 The Ridge, St Leonards-on-Sea TN37 7PT
Tel: 01424 755255 Fax: 01424 758052
Website: www.harnlst.org.uk
(Surrey and Sussex Health Authority)

Chair Margaret Brett
Chief Executive Geoffrey Haynes

Bexhill Hospital

Holliers Hill, Bexhill-on-Sea TN40 2DZ
Tel: 01424 755255 Fax: 01424 213250
Total Beds: 50

Anaesthetics C A Alexander, Dr Arnold, W G Doherty, I Hicks, A B Leach, J R Lethbridge, Dr Parsloe, I Reeve, A Slater, J Stock, A Stoddart, A R Thompson
Cardiology D Walker, R Wray
Care of the Elderly S A Bruce, J Dennison
Chest Disease A J Dyson
Dermatology K Liddell
ENT S Baer, A Meredith
General Medicine K Ahmed, A Gorsuch, J Rademaker, M Whtehead
General Surgery P Callaghan, G A Khoury, J A Lyttle, R Plail, A Sandison, S Whitehead
Mental Health G Smith
Neurology M Chowdhurry
Obstetrics and Gynaecology A Alaily, B Auld
Ophthalmology P T S Gregory, D Lloyd-Jones, C D Merrick
Orthopaedics H Apthorp, D Buchanan, P A Butler-Manuel, B Hinves, J A N Shepperd
Paediatrics L Bray, M Nasar, D J Scott, T Ward, G Whincup
Radiology L Apthorp, K D Foord, J A Giles, R Guy, V B Vaidya
Rheumatology E Henderson

Conquest Hospital

The Ridge, St Leonards-on-Sea TN37 7RD
Tel: 01424 755255 Fax: 01424 758025
Total Beds: 521

Accident and Emergency P Comelius, T Underhill
Anaesthetics C Alexander, Dr Arnold, W Doherty, I Hicks, A Leach, J Lethbridge, Dr Parsloe, I Reeve, A Slater, J Stock, A Stoddart, A R Thompson
Cardiology D Walker, R Wray
Care of the Elderly S A Bruce, J Dennison, M McIntyre, Dr Rahmani
Chest Disease M Clee, A J Dyson
ENT S Baer, A Meredith
General Medicine K Ahmed, A Gorsuch, E Henderson, J Rademaker, P Stafford, Dr Whitehead
General Surgery P Callaghan, G Khoury, J Lyttle, R Plail, A Sandison, S Whitehead
Neurology Dr Chowdhury
Obstetrics and Gynaecology P Sinha, J Zaidi
Oncology G Sadler
Ophthalmology P Gregory, D Lloyd-Jones, C Merrick
Orthopaedics H Apthorp, J Buchanan, A Butler-Manuel, B Hinves, J Shepperd
Paediatrics L Bray, M Nasar, D Scott, T Ward, G Whincup
Pathology W Barnes, J Beard, M Boxer, I Hawley, S Weston-Smith, P Wright
Plastic Surgery M Pickford
Radiology L Apthorp, K Foord, J Giles, R Guy, R Joarder

Irvine Unit, Bexhill Hospital

Holliers Hill, Bexhill-on-Sea TN40 2DZ

Hastings and St Leonards Primary Care Trust

PO Box 124, St Leonards-on-Sea TN38 9WH
Tel: 01424 457100 Fax: 01424 204145
Website: www.hastingsandstleonardspct.nhs.uk
(Surrey and Sussex Health Authority)

Chair Marie Casey
Chief Executive Toni Wilkinson

NHS TRUSTS & NHS HOSPITALS

Havering Primary Care Trust

St George's Hospital, 117 Suttons Lane, Hornchurch RM12 6RS
Tel: 01708 465000 Fax: 01708 465300
Email: ralph.mccormack@bhbchc-tr.nthames.nhs.uk
(North East London Health Authority)

Heart of Birmingham Teaching Primary Care Trust

Carnegie Institute, Hunters Road, Hockley, Birmingham B19 1DR
Tel: 0121 255 7695 Fax: 0121 255 7699
(Birmingham and the Black Country Health Authority)

Heatherwood and Wexham Park Hospitals NHS Trust

Wexham Park Hospital, Wexham, Slough SL2 4HL
Tel: 01753 63300 4824 Fax: 01753 634848
(Thames Valley Health Authority)

Chair Ruth Watts Davies
Chief Executive Andrew Way

Heatherwood Hospital

Ascot SL5 8AA
Tel: 01344 23333 Fax: 01344 874340
Total Beds: 274

Anaesthetics J Restall, K Spelina, W J Wraight
Cardiology R A Blackwood
Dermatology A Roberts
ENT A F Jefferis
General Medicine R Blackwood, L Hart, R D M Scott, M Smith
General Psychiatry M S L de Silva, R G Gall, W Lang, A J Wilkins
General Surgery G S Barrett, C Desai
Medicine for the Elderly R G A Behrman, S K Rao
Neurology M Johnson
Obstetrics and Gynaecology J Fairbank, J Spring
Oral and Maxillofacial Surgery C Yates
Orthodontics D Slattery
Orthopaedics R Allum, G Deane, J Jones, G Singer, M Thomas, A Unwin
Paediatrics J Pearce
Plastic Surgery J Dickinson, C T Khoo
Radiology I Liyanage, C Luck, C Rodgers
Rheumatology and Rehabilitation S P Liyanage
Urology C Hudd, O Karim, H Mottiwala

Wexham Park Hospital

Slough SL2 4HL
Tel: 01753 633000 Fax: 01753 684825
Total Beds: 542

Accident and Emergency J C Litchfield, A C W Matheson
Anaesthetics M D G Bukht, S Davies, R Fernandes, R D Jack, L Leibler, R C Loveland, A May, J Pattison, J Rangasami, T S Silva, B Smallman, B L Smith, K Spelina, E Umerah, R Woolf
Dermatology V Walkden
ENT C Aldren, N Bleach, A F Jefferis
General Medicine R A Blackwood, D Dove, S Levi, G Maidment, C Missouris, J Wiggins
General Psychiatry J Brockless, R E Chinn, E Clifford, G Dawson, E D'Souza, J W Harding, W Lang, A McCauley, S Parameswaran, P Sudbury
General Surgery A Desai, J Gilbert, A Gordon, S E Knight, P Rutter
Genetics J Hurst
Medicine for the Elderly D Chauhan
Neurology J Wade
Obstetrics and Gynaecology S Dimitri, P Reginald

Ophthalmology Dr Kanski, Dr Packard
Oral Surgery and Orthodontics M Issa, Dr Slattery, C Yates
Orthopaedics R Allum, G Deane, R Dega, J Jones, G Singer, M Swann, M Thomas
Paediatrics J A Connell, J Cowen, Z Huma, R Jones, J L Pearce, P Sebire
Pathology M Ali, N Bienz, H Chapel, C Havelock, A Lessing, M MacIntyre, P H Mackie, Dr Sharif, I Walker
Plastic Surgery Dr Armstrong, Dr Crawford, J Dickinson, C T K Khoo
Radiology Dr Charig, S Colenso, D K Grieve, M Moreland, R Stewart
Radiotherapy and Oncology R Ashford
Rheumatology and Rehabilitation A Hall, Dr Steuer
Urology C Hudd, O Karim, H Mottiwala

Hereford and Worcester Ambulance Service NHS Trust

Bransford, Worcester WR6 5JD
Tel: 01886 834200 Fax: 01886 834210
(Coventry, Warwickshire, Herefordshire and Worcestershire Health Authority)

Chair Paul Leopold
Chief Executive Cliff F Orme

Hereford Hospitals NHS Trust

County Hospital, Union Walk, Hereford HR1 2ER
Tel: 01434 355444 Fax: 01434 354310
(Coventry, Warwickshire, Herefordshire and Worcestershire Health Authority)

Chair G Brian Nelson
Chief Executive Jeremy W Millar

Hereford County Hospital

Hereford HR1 2ER
Tel: 01432 355444 Fax: 01432 354310
Total Beds: 340

Anaesthetics J H W Ballance, C A Day, R M B Dowling, I P Hine, J D Hutchinson, W Moore, N P Salmon, W Williams
Care of the Elderly J A Dalziel, C Jenkins, P Overstall
Dental Surgery K Ashley, D Evans
Dermatology J R S Rendall
ENT G Hanna, M Porter
General Medicine A Blake, H Connor, J Glancy, M Hall, D W Pitcher, P Ryan, J A Spillane
General Surgery A P Corder, A P Corfield, E Grocott, P H Harper, G Sole
Obstetrics and Gynaecology M Cohn, R B Smith, R Subak-Sharpe
Paediatrics R Adelman, A M Butterfill, N C Fraser
Palliative Medicine J Sykes
Pathology T J Coleman, J S Dinnen, M Hayes, F McGinty
Plastic Surgery D S Murray
Radiology E J Barton, P Grech, G M Rowe, P Wilson
Radiotherapy and Oncology Dr Elyan, C Roch-Berry
Rheumatology D Rees, R B Williams

Hereford General Hospital

Nelson Street, Hereford HR1 2PA
Tel: 01432 355444 Fax: 01432 340425
Total Beds: 106

Accident and Emergency A Ballham
Anaesthetics J H W Ballance, C Day, R M B Dowling, I P Hine, J D Hutchinson, W Moore, N P Salmon, W Williams
Care of the Elderly J A Dalziel, C Jenkins, P W Overstall

Chair Leonard Crosbie
Chief Executive Angela Ugur

Hounslow and Spelthorne Community and Mental Health NHS Trust

Trust closure tbc - Part of mental health services transferring to North West Surrey Mental Health Partnership NHS Trust; part of service transferring to Ealing Primary Care Trust and Houslow Primary Care Trust.

Trust Headquarters, Phoenix Court, 531 Staines Road, Hounslow TW4 5DP
Tel: 020 8321 2017 Fax: 020 8321 2490
Email: john.hutchings@hscmh-tr.nthames.nhs.uk
(North West London Health Authority)

Chair Thelma Golding
Chief Executive Rosalynde Lowe

Clayponds Hospital

Occupation Lane, South Ealing, London W5 4RN
Tel: 020 8560 4011 Fax: 020 8568 7341
Total Beds: 66

Care of the Elderly J Arnold, P Evans
Psychiatry of Old Age G O'Oommen

Ealing Day Treatment Centre

Britton Drive, Southall UB1 2SH
Tel: 020 8571 1143 Fax: 020 8574 6510

Hounslow Primary Care Trust

92 Bath Road, Hounslow TW3 3LN
Tel: 020 8321 2310 Fax: 020 8321 2347
(North West London Health Authority)

Chair Christine Hay
Chief Executive John James

Huddersfield Central Primary Care Trust

Princess Royal Community Health Centre, Greenhead Road, Huddersfield HD1 4EW
Tel: 01484 344211 Fax: 01484 344211
(West Yorkshire Health Authority)

Hull and East Riding Community Health NHS Trust

West House, Westwood Hospital, Beverley HU17 8BU
Tel: 01482 886600 Fax: 01482 886541
(North and East Yorkshire and Northern Lincolnshire Health Authority)

Chair Ros Taylor
Chief Executive Linda Glasby

Alfred Bean Hospital

Bridlington Road, Driffield YO25 7JR
Tel: 01377 241124 Fax: 01262 607237
Total Beds: 20

Care of the Elderly M A Nasar
Dermatology Dr Stainforth
ENT Dr Baker, S L Smith
General Medicine P M Brown, Dr Pond

General Psychiatry D Armstrong, A Talbot
General Surgery Dr Duthie, J N Fox, K Wedgewood
Obstetrics and Gynaecology R Yeo
Ophthalmology S K Datta, B K De, S Setty
Orthopaedics Dr Bryant, A D North
Paediatrics J L Nicholas, Dr Skelton, Dr Venkatesh
Radiotherapy and Oncology M Holmes
Rheumatology W Tomlinson
Urology K Brame

Coltman Street Day Hospital and Community Support Teams

Coltman Street, Hull HU3 2SG
Tel: 01482 328807 Fax: 01482 223643

Hornsea Cottage Hospital

Eastgate, Hornsea HU18 1PL
Tel: 01964 533146, 01964 535563 Fax: 01964 534273
Total Beds: 22

Psychiatric Residential Unit

Hawthorne Court, Manor Road, Beverley
Tel: 01482 880011

Withernsea Community Hospital

Queen's Street, Withernsea HU19 2PZ
Tel: 01964 614666 Fax: 01964 615238
Total Beds: 22

Hull and East Yorkshire Hospitals NHS Trust

Anlaby Road, Hull HU3 2JZ
Tel: 01482 328541 Fax: 01482 674196
(North and East Yorkshire and Northern Lincolnshire Health Authority)

Chair Ian Blakey
Chief Executive Chris Appleby

Castle Hill Hospital

Castle Road, Cottingham HU16 5JQ
Tel: 01482 875875 Fax: 01482 623209
Total Beds: 413

Anaesthetics S Bennett, S Dunn, P Evans, Dr Pollock, A H S Saleh, R T Whitty
Cardiology G C Kaye
Cardiothoracic Medicine M E Cowen, S Griffin, L Guvendik
Care of the Elderly S F Beardsworth, A Farnsworth, E Haworth
General Medicine A G Arnold, M A Greenstone, D V McGivern, B Nanda
General Surgery G Duthie, J Fox, P Lee, J R T Monson, K R Wedgwood
Genitourinary Medicine U Joshi
Infectious Diseases B S Nanda
Obstetrics and Gynaecology G M Fawcett, K Phillips, G H Randle, R Yeo
Occupational Health A N Kazem
Orthopaedics M Bryant, M R Korab-Karpinski
Radiology G R Avery, V P L Hornsby, S L Mann, A Pratt
Rheumatology and Rehabilitation B N M Jayawardhana, J W Tomlinson
Thoracic Medicine A G Arnold, M A Greenstone, D V McGivern

Hull Maternity Hospital

Hedon Road, Hull HU9 5LX
Tel: 01482 376215 Fax: 01482 374542
Total Beds: 143

Obstetrics and Gynaecology D M Hay, A H Imrie, S R Killick, S W Lindow, A Palmer, D W Purdie, F H Speck, S N Tyrrell

NHS TRUSTS & NHS HOSPITALS

Hull Royal Infirmary

Anlaby Road, Hull HU3 2JZ
Tel: 01482 328541 Fax: 01482 674196
Total Beds: 680

Accident and Emergency J K Gosnold, P Grout
Anaesthetics P Cain, J G Cundill, J P Davie, S R Dunn, P S Eccersley, P Evans, B M Gray, P A Gray, D R Haines, B C Hovell, M R Kamath, I Locker, C G Pollock, G M Purdy, I F Russell, C Smales, J Waterland, J L Webster, R T Whitty, T I R Williams, D P Winder
Cardiology J L Caplin, M S Norell
Care of the Elderly S R Datta, E Haworth, J Knox, P H Neligan, N R Steel, F Thomson
Dental Surgery C W Blackburn, G M Edwards
Dermatology K Keczkes, J P Vestey
ENT S L Smith, C L Wengraf, E Whitehead
Gastroenterology J R Bennett, D R Sutton
General Medicine E Baguley, J R Bennett, S M Doherty, E A Massan, L Sellars, Dr Sutton, C Walton, M C White
General Surgery P J Carleton, J N Fox, J M D Galloway, P W R Lee, C M S Royston, A R Wilkinson
Genitourinary Medicine R Fong
Nephrology M J Farr, L Sellars
Neurology C E Clarke, M D Rawson
Neurophysiology A A A Bajalan
Neurosurgery G Brocklehurst, M R Gooding, B G Mathew
Ophthalmology S K Datta, U K Goddard, J R Innes, A K Mathur, A K Singh
Orthodontics J W Coope, J J D Neal
Orthopaedics T J Cain, F R Howell, G V Johnson, M R K Karpinski, G L M Kings, K D Sargison, K P Sherman
Paediatric Surgery J L Nicholas
Paediatrics M Baxter, I R Beddis, I G Jefferson, M J Lewins, R F Massey, P W Pairaudeau
Pathology G P R Boran, P A Burgess, H P R Bury, I Chorlton, A W Macdonald, S L Mawer, J Meigh, R E E Meigh, D M Piercy, J R Read, J A Wilson
Radiology R J V Bartlett, J A Clarke, A M Cook, J F Dyet, A S Early, C R Hill, M J Imrie, A L Laubscher, A A Nicholson, A D Taylor, L W Turnbull
Rheumatology E Baguley, S M Doherty

Kingston General Hospital

Beverley Road, Hull HU3 1UR
Tel: 01482 28631 Fax: 01482 589002
Total Beds: 168

Care of the Elderly S R Datta, E Haworth, J Knox, P H Neligan, N R Steel, F Thomson
Pathology P C Dore, D A Montgomery, C G L Raper
Plastic Surgery N B Hart, P M O'Hare, Dr Ramakrishnan

Princess Royal Hospital

Saltshouse Road, Hull HU8 9HE
Tel: 01482 701151 Fax: 01482 676737
Total Beds: 188

Obstetrics and Gynaecology D M Hay, A H Imrie, S R Killick, S W Lindow, A Palmer, D W Purdie, E H Speck, S N Tyrrell
Radiotherapy and Oncology A Dealey, M E Holmes, C I Preston
Urology D J Almond, G Cooksey, J Hetherington

Huntingdonshire Primary Care Trust

The Priory, Priory Road, St Ives, Huntingdon PE27 5BB
Tel: 01480 308222 Fax: 01480 308234
Website: www.hunts-pct.nhs.uk
(Norfolk, Suffolk and Cambridgeshire Health Authority)

Chair Michael Lynch
Chief Executive Karen Bell

Hyndburn and Ribble Valley Primary Care Trust

Old Town Hall Building, Great Harwood, Blackburn BB6 7DA
Tel: 01254 880000 Fax: 01254 392585
Chair Martin Hill
Chief Executive Leigh Griffin

Invicta Community Care NHS Trust

Closing April 2002 - Services transferring to West Kent NHS and Social Care Trust.

35 Kings Hill Avenue, West Malling ME19 4AX
Tel: 01732 520400 Fax: 01732 520401
(Kent and Medway Health Authority)

Chair Kate Lampard
Chief Executive Jon Wilkes

Edenbridge and District War Memorial Hospital

Edenbridge TN8 5DA
Tel: 01732 862137
Total Beds: 23

Hawkhurst Cottage Hospital

High Street, Hawkhurst, Cranbrook TN18 4PU
Tel: 01580 753345
Total Beds: 15

Highlands House

10 Calverley Park Gardens, Tunbridge Wells TN2 2JN
Tel: 01732 455155
Total Beds: 35

Pembury Hospital (Psychiatric Services)

Pembury, Tunbridge Wells TN2 4QJ
Tel: 01892 823535 Fax: 01892 823545

Priority House

Hermitage Lane, Maidstone ME16 9PH
Tel: 01662 725000 Fax: 01662 723200
Total Beds: 57

Sevenoaks Hospital

Hospital Road, Sevenoaks TN13 3PG
Tel: 01732 455155 Fax: 01732 465544
Total Beds: 47

Tonbridge Cottage Hospital

Vauxhall Lane, Tonbridge TN11 0NE
Tel: 01732 353653 Fax: 01732 368000
Total Beds: 27

Ipswich Hospital NHS Trust

Heath Road, Ipswich IP4 5PD
Tel: 01473 712233 Fax: 01473 703400
Website: www.ipswichhospital.org.uk
(Norfolk, Suffolk and Cambridgeshire Health Authority)

Chair Peter Bye
Chief Executive Peter Morris

Ipswich Hospital

Heath Road, Ipswich IP4 5PD
Tel: 01473 712233 Fax: 01473 703400
Website: www.ipswichhospital.org.uk
Total Beds: 795

Accident and Emergency D Hodgkinson

Anaesthetics D M Bailey, J Broadway, W F Byrne, M Dixon, I K Driver, D J Elliott, M Garfield, R M Howard-Griffin, P Howell, A P Jarvis, A Kong, M D Mansfield, P J Mills, A D J Nicholl, E M Rush, J B Skinner, M G Smith, J Stevens, S J Wiltshire
Cardiology N A Irvine, R Oliver
Cardiothoracic Surgery D Watson
Care of the Elderly S F M Grimmer, T J Lockington, P A Phillips, L J Sheehan, N Trepte
Chemical Pathology C J Pearce
Clinical Psychologist V Potter
Dermatology T P Cutler, S Gibbs
ENT Dr Arasaratum, A Hilger, M Salam, M W Yung
General Medicine R Chatoor, J L Day, D R Hall, N Innes, N A Irvine, Y Miao, R M Oliver, R G Rayman, D Seaton, S G W Williams, R J Wyke
General Surgery H M Adair, T J Archer, A E P Cameron, S P J Huddy, C Mortimer, I Osman, J Pitt, I H K Scott
Haematology J A Ademokun, I Chalmers, N J Dodd
Histopathology E M Carlsen, P A Judd, J Orrell, R C G Rowe, J E Trowell
Nephrology G R Glancey, P F Williams
Neurology H Manji, S V Tan, S J Wroe
Obstetrics and Gynaecology R M Eltreki, B Johal, A T Leather, P Mooney, T Omara-Boto, F Reader, C Spencer, G Thomas, D P Vasey
Occupational Health S Coomber
Oncology J S Morgan, T Podd, C Scrase, J H L Vay
Ophthalmology C Edlesten, R Goble, S Hardman-Lea, R E Lewis
Oral and Maxillofacial Surgery H T Davies, T I Davies, R J Tate
Orthopaedics R Baxandall, M A Bowditch, J P Hallett, J Hopkinson-Wooley, I Hudson, C Marx, J M Powell, D G Shanahan, D J Sharp
Paediatrics M F M Bamford, J D M Gould, M James, K Murtagh, K P O'Neill, C Yale
Pathology P Jones
Plastic Surgery A F Bardsley, A M Logan, T J O'Neill
Radiology S Garber, P Jennings, K R Karia, R C Nightingale, D A O'Driscoll, G Picken, A d C Tate, W P Whitear
Rheumatology and Rehabilitation G Clunie, R A Watts
Sexual Health F Reader, H Wankowska
Thoracic Surgery D Watson, G Wyn Parry
Urology P Donaldson, M Habib, S Irving, J Parry

Ipswich Primary Care Trust

Allington House, 427 Woodbridge Road, Ipswich IP4 4ER
Tel: 01473 275260 Fax: 02473 275270
(Norfolk, Suffolk and Cambridgeshire Health Authority)

Isle of Wight Healthcare NHS Trust

St. Mary's Hospital, Newport PO30 5TG
Tel: 01983 524081 Fax: 01983 822569
Website: www.iowht.org.uk
(Hampshire and Isle of Wight Health Authority)

Chair Allan Munds
Chief Executive Graham Elderfield

Frank James Community Hospital

Adelaide Grove, East Cowes PO32 6BZ
Tel: 01983 280700 Fax: 01983 280757
Total Beds: 24

Laidlaw Day Hospital

St Mary's Hospital, Newport
Tel: 01983 524081

St Mary's Hospital

Parkhurst Road, Newport PO30 5TG
Tel: 01983 524081 Fax: 01983 822569
Total Beds: 413

JAMES PAGET HEALTHCARE NHS TRUST

Accident and Emergency P Wellington
Adult Psychiatry A Guthrie, J Newson Smith
Anaesthetics P E Goodwin, H Hay, K Landon, A Hof, A McEwan, H Noble, G Taylor, C Wareham
Child and Adolescent Pyschiatry S Parslow
Dermatology M Hazell
ENT P M G Grimaldi
General Medicine H Arshad, A K Baksi, M Connaughton, A Demissie, A Hossenbocus, D Murphy, E A Hakim
General Surgery S Elsmore, V Mehmet, M Shinkfield, J M Symes, T H Walsh
Haematology R Joshi
Histopathology N Greenwood, J Mikel
Metabolic Medicine J Smith
Microbiology S T Chapman
Obstetrics and Gynaecology A F E Yoong, A D McNeal, D Ridley
Old Age Psychiatry D Harwood
Ophthalmology D Dhingra, M Rhatigan
Oral and Maxillofacial Surgery M C Hetherington, T Mellor
Orthodontics S Robinson
Orthopaedics N Hobbs, S Nagra, J Gardiner, K Rahall
Paediatrics P R Cooke, P H Rowlandson, A H Watson
Palliative Care I Johnson
Pathology S Chapman, N Greenwood, R Joshi, J Smith
Radiology S Voigt, P Close, APD Cave
Rheumatology and Rehabilitation J A Parsons
Urology J Makunde

Staplers Road Assessment and Treatment Unit

52 & 52A Staplers Road, Newport PO30 2DE
Tel: 01983 524805
Total Beds: 10

Isle of Wight Primary Care Trust

Whitecroft, Sandy Lane, Newport PO30 3ED
Tel: 01983 535455 Fax: 01983 822142
(Hampshire and Isle of Wight Health Authority)

Chair Valerie Anderson
Chief Executive David Crawley

Islington Primary Care Trust

110 Hampstead Road, London SN8 4AS
Tel: 020 7853 5353 Fax: 020 7853 5353
(North Central London Health Authority)

Chair Rachel Tyndall
Chief Executive Paula Kahn

James Paget Healthcare NHS Trust

Lowestoft Road, Gorleston, Great Yarmouth NR31 6LA
Tel: 01493 452452 Fax: 01493 452078
(Norfolk, Suffolk and Cambridgeshire Health Authority)

Chair John Wells
Chief Executive David Hill

James Paget Hospital

Lowestoft Road, Gorleston, Great Yarmouth NR31 6LA
Tel: 01493 452452 Fax: 01493 452078
Total Beds: 564

Accident and Emergency R Franklin
Anaesthetics Dr Blossfeldt, R E Davies, S Ganepola, M Gay, J R Jenkins, Dr Koessler, R A M Mann, D Millican, W G Notcutt, S Oosthuysen, H Stuart, D Tupper-Carey, M Wright
Care of the Elderly Dr Brett, T Cotter, D A Ellis, P J G Forster, W J Grabau, P Harrison, Dr Huston, C Jamieson, K Jesudason
Chemical Pathology S Absalom
Dermatology R M Graham, Dr Salvary

NHS TRUSTS & NHS HOSPITALS

ENT D J Premachandra, P Prinsley
General Medicine Dr Brett, T Cotter, D A Ellis, P J G Forster, W J Grabau, P Harrison, N Huston, C Jamieson, K Jesudason
General Surgery J Pereira, J R Sansom, Dr Schneider, J G N Studley, H G Sturzaker
Genitourinary Medicine T C Harry
Haematology Dr Barkhuizen, T Jeha, Dr Sadullah
Histopathology W Kinsey, M Wilkinson
Medical Microbiology Dr Elumogo
Nephrology Dr Ross
Neurology D J Dick, J B Pilling, Dr Woodward
Obstetrics and Gynaecology Dr Ekanayke, P Greenwood, J G M Mclean, Dr Oligbo, T A Pozyczka, J Preston, A Simons
Ophthalmology L A Amanat, Dr Belfer, P D Black, N Watson
Oral and Maxillofacial Surgery Dr Hadinnapola, Dr Prince
Orthodontics Dr Tewson
Orthopaedics C Johnson-Nurse, R Jones, P Nadarajan, J Petri, Dr Venalainen
Paediatrics J Chapman, A D Edelsten, R J Stocks, A Verma
Radiology Dr Hamid, F Holly-Archer, V Kumar, A L Laubsher, P W Lawrence, E Thomas, M Webber
Radiotherapy and Oncology A Bulman, C Martin, M J Ostrowski
Urology Dr Simpson, G Suresh

Lowestoft Hospital

Tennyson Road, Lowestoft NR32 1PT
Tel: 01502 587311 Fax: 01502 589510
Total Beds: 62

Child and Adolescent Psychiatry O J Delany
Dermatology R M Graham
General Medicine P Harrison
General Surgery Dr Schneider
Paediatrics B J Mawer

Northgate Hospital

Northgate Street, Great Yarmouth NR30 1BU
Tel: 01493 337600 Fax: 01493 852753
Total Beds: 36

Care of the Elderly P Harrison
Child and Adolescent Psychiatry O J Delany
Dermatology Dr Salvary
General Medicine Dr Cotter, Dr Forster, W J Grabau
General Psychiatry E Gallagher, F McEvett, P McMahon, I Shaw
Paediatrics A D Edelsten, R J Stocks

Northgate Therapy Centre

Nothgate Hospital, Northgate Street, Great Yarmouth NR30 1BU
Tel: 01493 337600 Fax: 01493 852753

Kennet and North Wiltshire Primary Care Trust

C/o Postern House, Cherry Orchard, Marlborough SN8 4AS
Tel: 01672 517643 Fax: 01672 515346
(Avon, Gloucestershire and Wiltshire Health Authority)

Chair Tim Boucher
Chief Executive Barbara Smith

Kensington and Chelsea Primary Care Trust

125 Old Brampton Road, London SW7 3RP
Tel: 020 8237 2520 Fax: 020 8237 2522
Chair Terry Banford
Chief Executive Paul Haigh

Kent Ambulance NHS Trust

Headquarters, Heath Road, Coxheath, Maidstone ME17 4BG
Tel: 01622 747010 Fax: 01622 743565
Email: jill.good@kentamb.nhs.uk
(Kent and Medway Health Authority)

Chair Tim Davis
Chief Executive K Smith

Kettering General Hospital NHS Trust

Kettering General Hospital, Rothwell Road, Kettering NN16 8UZ
Tel: 01536 492000 Fax: 01536 492599, 01536 492295
(Leicestershire, Northamptonshire and Rutland Health Authority)

Chair B R Silk
Chief Executive Geraint Martin

Kettering General Hospital

Rothwell Road, Kettering NN16 8UZ
Tel: 01536 492000 Fax: 01536 492599, 01536 493767
Total Beds: 523

Accident and Emergency A Dancocks, R Thamizhavell
Anaesthetics J C Burnell, R Dravid, R N Enraght-Moony, D Findlow, J Freeman, E G Hadaway, L Hollos, J Luthman, R Moody, R N Moony, M Sebastian, W Sellers, J Szafranski, J Snape, L Twohey, A Bilolikar
Dermatology W A Branford, A Vorster
ENT M A Latif, R J Lee
General Medicine G Clifford, J Cullen, A R Davidson, N Gunasekera, I Hubbard, A Hussain, S P O'Malley, N Shaukat, A Steel, R L Walters, T J Williams
General Surgery V Bahal, S Al-hamali, R E Jenner, S El-Rabaa, R D Stewart, M Taylor
Obstetrics and Gynaecology R Haughney, M R B Newman, R J Smith, D J W Wilkin, P L Wood
Ophthalmology D Banarjee, P Baranyovits, T Blamires, K El-ghazali
Oral Surgery C Harrod, W Smith
Orthodontics J R S O'Neill
Paediatrics T Biswas, A I Mukhtar, C Nanayakkara, P Rao, Dr Bilolikar
Pathology B E Gostelow, H Kelsey, M Lyttleton, G McCreanor, A Manjula, S R Milkins, J Uraiby
Plastic Surgery D Ward
Radiology G Goh, S Peterson, R G Reeve, A J Thompson, D Walter, D J Woods
Radiotherapy and Oncology C MacMillan
Rheumatology and Rehabilitation P C Mattingly, I M Morris
Trauma and Orthopaedics G Allardice, R L Barrington, S P Biswas, J D Bromage, P Latham, S Naima, B Shah
Urology M Al Sudeni, O W Davison, M Lynch

King's College Hospital NHS Trust

King's College Hospital, Denmark Hill, London SE5 9RS
Tel: 020 7734 4000 Fax: 020 7346 3445
Email: info@kingsch.nhs.uk
Website: www.kingshealth.com
(South East London Health Authority)

Chair Michael Doherty
Chief Executive Ron De Witt
Consultants T Peters, C Roberts

King's College Hospital

Denmark Hill, London SE5 9RS
Tel: 020 7737 4000 Fax: 020 7346 3445
Total Beds: 712

KING'S LYNN & WISBECH HOSPITALS NHS TRUST

Accident and Emergency R Brown, E E Glucksman, G Little
Anaesthetics J B Broadfield, I M Corall, S Cottam, T D W Davies, F D'Costa, A P Fisher, M F Fisher, T Ginsberg, D Green, M Hanna, C W Howell, P I E Jones, S Peat, J C Ponte, D Potter, R J Ware
Audiological Medicine J V R Sastry
Biochemistry W Marshall, T J Peters
Cardiology D E Jewitt, P Richardson, R Wainwright
Cardiothoracic Surgery J Desai, A T Forsyth, Dr Marrrinan
Care of the Elderly A Blackburn, J Close, D J Evans, S Jackson, K Pettingale, C Swift
Chemical Pathology W Marshall, C Moniz, Dr Peters
Child and Adolescent Psychiatry J Dare, F Nikapoka, F Subotsky, L Wheelan
Dental Surgery M Alcalay, S N Bhatia, B M Eley, P S Ellisdon, G H Forman, I D Gainsford, J R Garrett, J.D Harrison, R D Howard, A T Inglis, M G D Kelleher, J D Langdon, K Marshall, B H Miller, B C O'Riordan, G Parker, C K Schrieber, N J D Smith, P B Smith, G F Tinsley, R M Watson, S M Wright
Dermatology C Fuller, A C Pembroke, A W P Vivier
Diabetes S Amiel, M Edmunds, S Thomas
ENT W G Edwards, H Ludman, J N Thomas
Forensic Medicine I West
General Medicine J F Costello, A L W Eddleston, I Forgacs, W Gardner, A M McGregor, J Moxham, K W Pettingale, P J Watkins
General Psychiatry L Campbell, G Davies, F Holloway, A D Isaacs, E G Lucas, D McLean, J R Morgan, P Robinson, M Silverman, K Sivakumar, D Somekh, N O T Temple, B K Toone
General Surgery P A Baskerville, I V Benjamin, J Rennie
Genitourinary Medicine A Brooke, P East, T J McManus, C Taylor, J Welch
Haematology D Devereaux, D M Layton, G Mufti, A Pagliuca
Histopathology S Humphreys, B C Portmann
Immunology D E H Tee, D Vergani
Medical Microbiology J N Philpott-Howard, J Wade
Nephrology H Cairns, B Hendry
Neurology P N Leigh, J D Parkes, J Payan, E H Reynolds, D N Rushton, M P Sheehy, K J Zilkha
Neurosurgery P Bullock, C Chandler, R Gullen, J McCabe, C E Polkey, M Sharp, A Strong
Nuclear Medicine M Buxton-Thomas
Obstetrics and Gynaecology S Campbell, L Cardozo, W Collins, D Gibb, F Lawton, J M McEwan, K Nicolaides, J Parsons, M Whitehead
Ophthalmology W A I Aclimandos, R Coakes, P A Hunter
Orthopaedics G Groom, S Phillips, J Sixla
Paediatrics A Baker, C Ball, D Candy, M Crouchman, J Dare, S Devane, H R Gamsu, A Greenough, G Mieli-Vergani, A P Mowat, J F Price, P Robson, E M Ross, K C Tan
Pathology F E Dische, M Driver, S Humphreys, P J O'Donnell, B Portmann, J Salisbury, I E West, W F Whimster
Public Health Medicine G Bickler, Y Doyle, N Noah
Radiology P Gishen, J Karani, H B Meire, M Michell, N J D Smith, H Walters
Radiotherapy and Oncology F Calman, H Dobbs, A W B Nethersell
Rheumatology and Rehabilitation H Berry, D Choy, C J Goodwill, R Luff, D Scott
Urology J P Pryor, P Thompson
Virology S Sutherland, A H C Uttley

King's Lynn and Wisbech Hospitals NHS Trust

From April 2002 the Cambridgeshire element of mental health services transferring to Cambridgeshire and Peterborough Mental Health Partnership NHS Trust.

Queen Elizabeth Hospital, Gayton Road, King's Lynn PE30 4ET
Tel: 01533 613613 Fax: 01533 613700
(Norfolk, Suffolk and Cambridgeshire Health Authority)

Chatterton House

Goodwins Road, King's Lynn PE30 5PD
Tel: 01553 613613 Fax: 01553 613703
Total Beds: 48

Psychiatry of Old Age Dr Hillam, K Rao

North Cambridgeshire Hospital

The Park, Wisbech PE13 3AB
Tel: 01945 585781 Fax: 01945 584316

Anaesthetics K R Burchett, R N Francis, M Plumley
Care of the Elderly M S Ell, J C McGourty, D Turfer
Dermatology J A R Anderson
ENT B P Cvijetic, P A Webber
General Medicine A M Jennings, R C McGouran
General Surgery P T Cullen, R A Greatorex, S M Singh
Haematology P B Coates
Obstetrics and Gynaecology S H Abukhalil, C D M Bone, S Monaghan, H M A Taher, A B W Taylor
Ophthalmology C Jakeman, N A Johnson
Oral and Maxillofacial Surgery E A Flower
Orthopaedics N Coleman, N P Packer
Paediatrics D A C Barter, J F B Dossetor
Radiology Q Arafat, M Crowe, G R Hunnam, M J Rimmer, M J Sparks, J Stabler, M Sultan
Radiotherapy and Oncology Dr Ahmad, M Daly
Rheumatology J D Williams
Urology A C Eaton

Parkside Day Hospital

North Cambridgeshire Hospital, Wisbech PE13 3AB
Tel: 01553 613613

Queen Elizabeth Hospital

Gayton Road, King's Lynn PE30 4ET
Tel: 01553 613613 Fax: 01553 613700
Total Beds: 627

Accident and Emergency N Burchett, R Florance
Anaesthetics J G Allen, A J Barclay, M Blunt, K R Burchett, N M Denny, N H Duncan, R N Francis, S J Harris, Dr Hobbiger, M Miller, M Plumley, B Watson
Care of the Elderly M S Ell, J C McGourty, J Phillips
Chemical Pathology C P C Seem
Dermatology J A R Anderson, G Dootson
ENT B P Cvijetic, P A Webber
General Medicine A Douds, E George, A M Jennings, E Kumar, K Lingam, R C McGouran, A Pawlowicz
General Psychiatry L Ho, G Isaacs, A Ogilvie, A Wagle
General Surgery P T Cullen, P Gough, R A Greatorex, N Redwood, S M Singh, H Warren
Genitourinary Medicine K Sivakumar
Haematology P B Coates, J Keidan
Histopathology R A Eames, N E New, E Rytina
Medical Microbiology M A Hegarty
Neurology J Brown
Obstetrics and Gynaecology S H Abukhalil, C D M Bone, S Monaghan, H M A Taher, A B W Taylor
Ophthalmology Z Butt, C Jakeman, N A Johnson, P J Pushpanathan
Oral and Maxillofacial Surgery E A Flower
Orthodontics J Bottomley
Orthopaedics N Coleman, M Gadir, J Jeffrey, A Murray, N P Packer
Paediatrics D A C Barter, J F B Dossetor, S P Rubin, M Wheatley
Radiology Q Arafat, M Crowe, G R Hunnam, M J Rimmer, M J Sparks, J Stabler, M Sultan
Radiotherapy and Oncology A Ahmad, M Daly
Rheumatology J D Williams
Urology A C Eaton

NHS TRUSTS & NHS HOSPITALS

Kingston Hospital NHS Trust

Galsworthy Road, Kingston Upon thames KT2 7QB
Tel: 020 8546 7711 Fax: 020 8547 2182
(South West London Health Authority)

Chair C Swabey
Chief Executive John Langan

Kingston Hospital NHS Trust Hospital

Galsworthy Road, Kingston upon Thames KT2 7QB
Tel: 020 8546 7711 ext: 2814 Fax: 020 8547 2182
Total Beds: 555

Accident and Emergency B Al-Wakeel, D Goel, S M Moalypour
Anaesthetics L Andrew, F L Barton, A Blythe, G Brindle Smith, B Buxton, J Fennel, R Graham, S Howsam, A Landes, J P Maynard, J Ratnayake, A Ravalia, G Samsoon, I Sinton, C Stableforth, R Stacey, A Volger, J Zwaal
Care of the Elderly C Lee, H Lo, W McNabb, A Neil, C Rodrigues
Dermatology K J Misch, L Ostlere
ENT A E Hinton, D Mendonca, T Mugliston, S Saunders
General Medicine W Culling, T Heymann, G K Knowles, R Roberts, K Shotliff, M Spring, I D Strickland
General Surgery I T Bloom, J Cahill, R Cummins, P E M Jarrett, R D Leach, S Ray, P Willson
Genitourinary Medicine G McCarthy
Neurology A Al-Memar, Y Hart
Obstetrics and Gynaecology H Anderson, R Ballard, R Bevan, A Clement, K Danter, M Davis, J McGrath, D May, O Morris, A Pooley, R Thonet, J Wilson
Ophthalmology J Beare, I Gillespie, S Horgan
Oral and Maxillofacial Surgery P Blenkinsop
Orthopaedics R Chapman, M Curtis, K Daly, B C Parker, G Railton
Paediatrics S Al-Jawad, W I Anshasi, E Jurges, R G Wilson, A Winrow
Pathology Z Abboufi, S Gothraie, C Jameson, G Knee, A Kothari, J B Leach, P McHugh, S Martin, L Neville, M Rowley, D Simms, H V Sykes, S Wong
Plastic Surgery P K B Davis
Radiology S A Evans, P Frank, A Mathie, B C O'Dwyer, M O'Reilly, R Pearson, G Picken, H Richardson, P Scott-Mackie, A Thornton, C Todd, C Ward, M M White
Rheumatology and Rehabilitation S Jawad, H Jones
Urology J A Dick, R Morley

Kingston Primary Care Trust

Woodroffe House, Tolworth Hospital, Red Lion Road, Surbiton KT6 7QU
Tel: 020 8390 0102 Fax: 020 8390 1236
(South West London Health Authority)

Chair Neslyn Watson-Druée
Chief Executive Janet Kells

Knowsley Primary Care Trust

Moorgate Road, Knowsley Industrial Park, Liverpool L33 7XW
Tel: 0151 477 4700 Fax: 0151 477 4705
Chair Rosemary Hawley
Chief Executive Ian Davies

Lambeth Primary Care Trust

Lambeth Walk, London SE11 6SP
(South East London Health Authority)

Chief Executive Kevin Barton

Lancashire Ambulance Service NHS Trust

Broughton House, 449-451 Garstang Road, Preston PR3 5LN
Tel: 01772 862666, 01772 773005 Fax: 01772 773098
Email: johncalderbank@las-tr.nwest.nhs.uk, john.calderbank@las-tr.nwest.nhs.uk
Website: www.lancashireambulance.com
(Cumbria and Lancashire Health Authority)

Chair Ruth R Winterbottom
Chief Executive David W Hill

Lancashire Care NHS Trust

Moor Park House, 1 Moor Park Avenue, Preston PR1 6AS
(Cumbria and Lancashire Health Authority)

Langbaurgh Primary Care Trust

13 Park Avenue, Redcar TS10 3LA
Tel: 01642 480935 Fax: 01642 516300
(Tees Health Authority)

Leeds Community and Mental Health Services Teaching NHS Trust

Meanwood Park, Tongue Lane, Leeds LS6 4QB
Tel: 0113 295 2800 Fax: 0113 274 5172
(West Yorkshire Health Authority)

Chair Ian Hughes
Chief Executive Mike Atkin

Aire Court Community Unit

Aire Court, Lingwell Grove, Leeds LS10 4RE
Tel: 0113 277 4861 Fax: 0113 277 4895

Aire Court Hospital

Lingwell Grove, Middleton, Leeds LS10 3RE
Tel: 0113 277 4861 Fax: 0113 277 4895
Total Beds: 30

Asket Croft Day Hospital

2 Asket Place, Seacroft, Leeds LS14 1PP
Tel: 0113 305 7000

Crooked Acres

Spen Lane, Leeds LS5 3SJ
Tel: 0113 295 3590 Fax: 0113 295 3288

Learning Disabilities B Easby, S G Read

Hawthorn Day Hospital

St Mary's Hospital, Greenhill Road, Leeds LS13
Tel: 0113 279 0121 ext: 4315

High Royds Hospital

Menston, Ilkley LS29 6AG
Tel: 01943 876151 Fax: 01943 870471
Total Beds: 375

Anaesthetics Q L A Robinson
General Medicine K E Berkin
General Psychiatry M S Alexander, I S Berg, P C W Bowie, A M Dearden, D P Flannery, S J Harris, D S Holman, T C Jerram, J K Laybourn, R H Mindham, D Newby, D S Raistrick, D Tamlyn, D J Thompson, D R D Wallace, J P Wattis, A S Zigmond

Linden Day Hospital
St Mary's Hospital, Greenhill Road, Leeds LS13
Tel: 0113 279 0121 Ext: 4321

Malham House Day Hospital
25 Hyde Terrace, Leeds LS2 9ON
Tel: 0113 292 6716 Fax: 0113 292 6718

Millfield House
Kirk Lane, Yeadon, Leeds LS19 7LX
Tel: 0113 250 7117 Fax: 0113 250 6751

Oak Day Hospital
St Mary's Hospital, Greenhill Road, Leeds LS13
Tel: 0113 279 0121 Ext: 4213

St Mary's Hospital
Greenhill Road, Leeds LS12 3QE
Tel: 0113 279 0121 Fax: 0113 231 0185
Total Beds: 63

General Psychiatry Dr Tarnley, Dr Zigmond
Psychiatry of Old Age P Bowie, D Deardon

Towngate House Day Hospital
Towngate House, 1 Towngate Close, Guiseley LS20 9LA
Tel: 01943 472000 Fax: 01943 472001

Tuke House
60 Sholebrook Avenue, Leeds LS7 3HB
Tel: 0113 295 2790 Fax: 0113 295 2791

Leeds North East Primary Care Trust

St. Mary's House (South Wing), St. Mary's Road, Leeds LS7 3JX
Tel: 0113 295 2436 Fax: 0113 295 2436
(West Yorkshire Health Authority)

Chair Brian Stein
Chief Executive Thea Marsden

Leeds North West Primary Care Trust

Wharfedale General Hospital, Administration Building, Newell Carr Road, Otley, Leeds LS21 2LY
Tel: 0113 392 7010 Fax: 0113 392 7011
(West Yorkshire Health Authority)

Chair Martin Drury
Chief Executive Lesley Smith

Leeds Teaching Hospitals NHS Trust

St. James' University Hospital, Beckett Street, Leeds LS9 7TF
Tel: 0113 231 6446 Fax: 0113 231 6336
Website: www.leedsteachinghospitals.com
(West Yorkshire Health Authority)

Chair Bill Kilgallon
Chief Executive Neil McKay

Chapel Allerton Hospital
Harehills Lane, Leeds LS7 4SA
Tel: 0113 262 3404
Total Beds: 259

Breast Services Dr Horgan

LEEDS TEACHING HOSPITALS NHS TRUST

Care of the Elderly P W Belfield, Dr Burns, A Cameron, Dr Catto, O J Corrado, Dr Wanklyn
Gastro-intestinal Medicine Dr Chalmers
Gastro-intestinal Surgery Dr Finan
Haematology D R Norfolk
Pain Management Dr Bush, Dr Dickson, Dr Simpson
Radiology Dr Chennells, Dr Parkin
Rehabilitation Dr Chamberlain, Dr Neuman
Rheumatology Dr Bird, Dr Chamberlain, Dr Emery, Dr Pease
Vascular Surgery Dr Gough

Cookridge Hospital
Hospital Lane, Cookridge, Leeds LS16 6QB
Tel: 0113 267 3411
Total Beds: 96

Clinical and Medical Oncology Dr Ash, Dr Bond, Dr Bottomley, Dr Close, Dr Coyle, Dr Crelin, Dr Dodwell, Dr Gerrard, Dr Gilson, Dr Jones, Dr Orton, Dr Roberts, Dr Rothwell, Dr Sebag-Montefiore, Dr Seymour, Dr Snee, Dr Taylor
Clinical Haematology Dr Barnard, Dr Morgan
Pain Management Dr Dickson
Radiology B Carey

Leeds Dental Institute
The Worsley Building, Clarendon Way, Leeds LS2 9LU
Tel: 0113 244 0111

Dental and Orthodontics Dr Basker, Dr Chan, Dr Cook, Dr Curzon, Dr Duggal, Dr Dyson, Dr Fayle, Dr Fortune, Dr Glyn Jones, Dr High, Dr Hirschmann, Dr Hume, Dr Kellett, Dr Luther, Dr Martin, Dr Meredith, Dr Morris, Dr Nattress, Dr O'Sullivan, Dr Patterson, Dr Ralph, Dr Roberts-Harry, Dr Speirs, Dr Watson, Dr Youngson
Oral and Maxillofacial Surgery Dr Loukota, Dr Pedlar, Dr Russell
Radiology Dr Carmichael

Leeds General Infirmary
Great George Street, Leeds LS1 3EX
Tel: 0113 243 2799
Total Beds: 1345

Accident and Emergency Dr Hamer, Dr Hardern, Dr Hassan, Dr Sloan, Dr Walsh, Dr Zoltie
Breast Services Dr Bello, Dr Horgan
Cardiology J C Cowan, J M McLenachan, Dr Perrins, E J Perrins, Dr Sivanathan, Dr Tan, Dr Williams
Care of the Elderly P W Belfield, E Burns, A Cameron, Dr Catto, O J Corrado, Dr Wanklyn
Chemical Pathology and Metabolic Medicine Dr Barth
Clinical and Medical Oncology Dr Gilson, Dr Rothwell, Dr Snee, Dr Taylor
Community Paediatrics Dr Cundall, Dr Lee, Dr Murdoch-Eaton, Dr Rudolf, Dr Skelton, Dr Wyatt
Dermatology M J D Goodfield, Dr Goulden, Dr Sheehan-Dare, Dr Wilkinson
Diabetes and Endocrinology Dr Belchetz, Dr Bodansky, Dr Grant, Dr Orme, Dr Wales
ENT J D Fenwick, Dr Fraser, D R Hanson, Dr Knight, Dr London, Dr Woodhead
Gastro-intestinal Surgery Dr Axon, Dr Burke, Dr Chalmers, Dr Dexter, Dr Finan, Dr Larvin, Dr McMahon, Dr Sagar, Dr Sue-Ling
General Medicine Dr Amery, Dr Feely, Dr Hardern, C T Pease, C R M Prentice, Dr Roberts, Dr Turney, J K Wales, Dr Woodrow
General Surgery E A Benson, R L Doig, P J Finan, M J Gough, D Johnston, M J McMahon
Genitourinary Medicine J Clarke, E F Monteiro, M A Waugh, J D Wilson
Haematology J A Child, Dr Morgan, D R Norfolk, Dr Smith, Dr Swirsky
Histopathology J E Boddy, P N Cowen, C Gray, P Harnden, A S Jack, C M Quinn, P Quirke, W A Reid, J Sutton, M Wells
Liaison Psychiatry Dr Kumar, Dr Protheroe, Dr Trigwell
Neonatal Medicine Dr Gill, Dr Puntis
Nephrology A M Brownjohn, J H Turney
Neurology Dr Jamieson, E G S Spokes

NHS TRUSTS & NHS HOSPITALS

Neurophysiology I S Smith
Neuroradiology Dr Bonsor, Dr Nelson, Dr Straiton
Neurosurgery Dr Chumas, P T v Hille, P V Marks, Dr Phillips, Dr Ross, Dr Towns
Obstetrics and Gynaecology J O Drife, Dr Ferriman, M R Glass, Dr Landon, G Mason, Dr Simpson, Dr Sparey, Dr Thein, Dr Thornton, P S Vinall
Ophthalmology Dr Cassells-Brown, R M L Doran, Dr George, Dr Menage, B A Noble, Dr O'Neill, Dr Simmons, Dr Woon
Oral and Maxillofacial Surgery Dr Loukota, Dr Pedlar, Dr Russell
Orthopaedics Dr Calder, Dr Cruickshank, Dr Emerton, Dr Hackney, Dr Harris, J O Lawton, Dr Scott, M H Stone, Dr Templeton
Paediatric Cardiology Dr Blackburn, Dr Dickinson, Dr Gibbs, Dr Parsons
Paediatric Cystic Fibrosis and Respiratory Medicine Dr Chetcuti
Paediatric Dermatology Dr Clark
Paediatric Endocrinology Dr Butler
Paediatric Neurology Dr Ferrie, Dr Livingstone
Paediatric Neurosurgery Dr Tiagi
Paediatric Surgery Dr Sugarman
Paediatrics Dr Cleary, P C Holland, Dr Williams
Pain Management Dr Dickson
Palliative Medicine Dr Kite
Pathology C R Abbott, C K Anderson, G Batcup, L Bridges, A G Bynoe, P N Cowen, C Gray, C J O'Brien, W A Reid, J Sutton, M Wells
Plastic Surgery Dr Batchelor
Radiology R J Arthur, G Bonsor, R F Bury, A G Chalmers, P M Chennells, Dr Dall, Dr Dunham, R C Fowler, Dr Gibbon, Dr Harris, Dr Macpherson, Dr Martinez, Dr Moss, Dr O'Connor, G J S Parkin, Dr Robertson, Dr Straiton, J A Straiton
Radiotherapy and Oncology D V Ash, G H Berry, H J Close, A M Crellin, C A Joslin, J Stone
Rehabilitation Dr Chamberlain
Renal Services Dr Brownjohn
Reproductive Medicine Dr Rutherford
Respiratory Medicine Dr Henry, Dr Muers, Dr Pearson, Dr Watson
Rheumatology H A Bird, M A Chamberlain, Dr Emery, Dr Isaacs, C Pease
Thoracic Surgery Dr Papagiannopoulos, Dr Thorpe
Urology Dr Cartledge, I Eardley, A D Joyce, Dr Paul, Dr Prescott
Vascular Surgery Dr Doig, Dr Gough, Dr Homer-Vanniasikham, Dr Mavor

St James's University Hospital

Beckett Street, Leeds LS9 7TF
Tel: 0113 243 3144 Fax: 0113 242 6496
Total Beds: 1166

Accident and Emergency Dr Gray, R N Illingworth, Dr Johnson, A McGowan, R K Roden
Adult Cystic Fibrosis Dr Conway
Cardiology Dr Berkin, Dr Tan
Care of the Elderly J Dolben, Dr Dudley, J T Eccles, Dr Mcintosh, G P Mulley, N Penn
Child Development Dr Darling
Community Paediatrics Dr Thomas, Dr Topley
Dermatology Dr Newton-Bishop, Dr Wilson
Diabetes Dr Mansfield
ENT I D Fraser, Dr Knight, Dr London, Dr Woodhead
General Medicine Dr Berkin, Dr Denyer, Dr Elliott, Dr Gilbey, R V Heatley, P D Howdle, Dr Mackintosh, Dr Peckham, Dr Stoker
General Surgery N S Ambrose, T G Brennan, P Guillou, M R J Lansdown, J P A Lodge, Dr Sandle, Dr Toogood
GI Medicine Dr Hull
Haematology Dr Barnard, S E Kinsey, B A McVerry
Histopathology A P Boon, Dr Carder, Dr Harnden, K A MacLellan, Dr Roy, Dr Verbeke, Dr Wilkinson, J I Wyatt
Immunology H C Gooi
Liver Services Dr Davies, Dr Millson, Dr Pollard, Dr Prasad
Medical Microbiology N Todd
Neonatal Medicine Dr Dear, Dr Newell, Dr Thomas

Neuro Rehabilitation Dr Bhakta
Neurology J M Bamford, Dr Ford, P J Goulding, M H Johnson
Neurophysiology A A D Costa
Obstetrics and Gynaecology Dr Buxton, D J Campbell, S Duffy, Dr Gbolade, M Griffith-Jones, Dr Hutson, G J Jarvis, G Lane, Dr Thein, J J Walker
Oncology D Alison, Dr Jones, Dr Leahy, Dr Patel, T Perren, Dr Roberts, P J Selby, Dr Taylor, J T Whicher
Ophthalmology T R Dabbs, J S Hillman, Dr McKibbin, A J Morrell, Dr Simmons
Oral and Maxillofacial Surgery A M Corrigan, D P Dyson
Orthodontics P A Cook, Dr Dyson, Dr Morris, Dr Roberts-Harry
Orthopaedics I A Archer, Dr Campbell, R A Dickson, Dr Limb, D Macdonald, Dr Matthews, Dr Millner, Dr Scott, Dr Templeton
Paediatric Cystic Fibrosis and Respiratory Medicine Dr Brownlee, Dr Conway
Paediatric Surgery Dr Crabbe, A Najmaldin, B R Squire, M D Stringer, D F M Thomas
Paediatrics Dr Brocklebank, Dr Campbell, Dr Davison, Dr Fitzpatrick, Dr Glaser, Dr Hobbs, C J Hobbs, Dr Lewis, Dr McClean, Dr Picton, Dr Richards
Pain Management Dr Bush, Dr Simpson
Palliative Care Dr Alison, Dr Hicks
Pathology Dr Hartley
Plastic Surgery A G G Batchelor, S P J Kay, S L Knight, Dr Liddington, Dr Saeed
Radiology W P Butt, A H Chapman, Dr Gibbon, Dr Guthrie, L I G Haigh, H C Irving, D Kessel, J C Liston, Dr Moss, Dr Nelson, Dr O'Connor, Dr Patel, W H Ramsden, Dr Rankine, Dr Robertson, I R Robertson, R J H Robertson, M B Sheridan, J A Spencer, Dr Swift, M J Weston, Dr Woodley
Radiotherapy W G Jones, F Roberts
Renal Services Dr Davison, Dr Mooney, Dr Newstead, Dr Will
Respiratory Medicine Dr Page, Dr Plant
Rheumatology Dr Isaacs, M F Martin
Urology Dr Cartledge, I Eardley, A Joyce, S N Lloyd, Dr Paul, Dr Prescott, P Whelan
Vascular Surgery Dr Berridge, Dr Kent, Dr Kester, Dr Scott

Seacroft Hospital

York Road, Leeds LS14 6UH
Tel: 0113 264 8164 Fax: 0113 260 2528
Total Beds: 256

Adult Cystic Fibrosis Dr Conway
Cardiology Dr Berkin, G J Williams
Dermatology Dr Newton-Bishop, Dr Wilson
Elderly Medicine Dr Dolben, Dr Eccles, Dr Mcintosh, Dr Mulley, Dr Penn
ENT J D Fenwick, I D Fraser, A G Ghandhi, D R Hanson
General Medicine Dr Berkin, M Denyer, G J Huston, Dr Peckham, P Sheridan, M Sleightholm, Dr Teale
General Surgery Dr Ambrose, T Brennan, Dr Lansdown
Haematology Dr Barnard
Infectious Diseases Dr Minton, P J Stanley
Radiology Dr Haigh, Dr Liston
Respiratory Medicine Dr Plant
Urology Dr Lloyd
Vascular Surgery Dr Berridge, Dr Kester

Wharfedale General Hospital

Newall Carr Road, Otley LS21 2LY
Tel: 01943 465522
Total Beds: 95

Care of the Elderly Dr Bradley, Dr Thompson
Clinical and Medical Oncology Dr Jones
Clinical Haematology Dr Smith
Dermatology Dr Sheehan-Dare
Diabetes and Endocrinology Dr Orme
ENT J D Fenwick, D R Hanson
General Medicine Dr Amery
General Surgery Dr Larvin, Dr McMahon McMahon, A W M Owen, Dr Sagar, Dr Sue-Ling
Neurology Dr Jamieson

Obstetrics and Gynaecology M R Glass, Dr Vinall
Ophthalmology Dr Menage, Dr Woon
Orthopaedics Dr Calder, J O Lawton
Radiology R F Bury, B Carey, G J S Parkin
Respiratory Medicine Dr Henry
Urology Dr Whelan
Vascular Surgery Dr Mavor

Leeds West Primary Care Trust

Army Park Court, Stanningley Road, Leeds LS12 2AE
(West Yorkshire Health Authority)

Chair Kuldip Bharj
Chief Executive Chris Reid

Leicester City West Primary Care Trust

16 Foss Road South, Leicester LE3 0QD
Tel: 0116 255 2042 Fax: 0116 255 2017
(Leicestershire, Northamptonshire and Rutland Health Authority)

Chair Bernard Greaves
Chief Executive Rob McMahon

Leicestershire and Rutland Healthcare NHS Trust

George Hine House, Gipsy Lane, Leicester LE5 0TD
Tel: 0116 225 6000 Fax: 0116 225 3684
Website: www.lrh-tr.org.uk
(Leicestershire, Northamptonshire and Rutland Health Authority)

Chair Wendy Hickling
Chief Executive Maggie Cork

Ashby-de-la-Zouch and District Hospital

Leicester Road, Ashby-de-la-Zouch LE65 1DG
Tel: 01530 414222 Fax: 01530 563036
Total Beds: 16

Dermatology R Graham-Brown
ENT T Alun-Jones
General Medicine G Fancourt
General Surgery Dr Bucknall, Dr Hall
Obstetrics and Gynaecology H M Bushfield
Orthopaedics G Taylor, H Thomas
Paediatrics J R Moore

Coalville Community Hospital

Broom Leys Road, Coalville, Leicester LE67 4DE
Tel: 01530 510510
Total Beds: 96

Dermatology R Graham-Brown
ENT T Alun-Jones
General Medicine R F Bing, J d Caestecker, Dr Gregory
General Psychiatry D I Khoosal, S Nayani
General Surgery A W Hall, Dr Rew, Dr Scott
Haematology C S Chapman
Integrated Medicine M Ardron, Dr Fotherby
Obstetrics and Gynaecology R C S Chazal
Oncology Dr Vasanthan
Ophthalmology J H Sandford-Smith
Orthopaedics J J Dias
Paediatrics J R Moore
Plastic Surgery D J Ward
Radiology S Campbell, A Crozier
Radiotherapy and Oncology S Khanna, I M Peat
Rheumatology A Samanta
Urology Dr Kockleburg, D P S Sandhu

Feilding Palmer Cottage Hospital

Gilmorton Road, Lutterworth LE17 4DZ
Tel: 01455 552150 Fax: 01455 558083
Total Beds: 15

Cardiology Dr Skehan
General Surgery Dr Lloyd
Obstetrics and Gynaecology Dr Neuberg
Orthopaedics Dr Margetts
Paediatrics Dr Tamhne

Gorse Hill Hospital

Anstey Lane, Leicester LE7 7GX
Tel: 0116 225 5200 Fax: 0116 225 5202
Total Beds: 82

Hinckley and District Hospital

Mount Road, Hinckley LE10 1AG
Tel: 01455 451800 Fax: 01455 451888
Total Beds: 36

Anaesthetics M Eason
Cardiology P Hubner
Care of the Elderly A Miodrag
Dermatology R Graham-Brown
ENT R S Thomas
Gastroenterology B J Rathbone
General Medicine P G McNally
General Surgery N W Everson, D P Fossard, N London
Haematology P E Hutchinson
Obstetrics and Gynaecology A Davidson, J Phipps
Ophthalmology D J Austin
Orthopaedics O O A Oni, R Power
Paediatrics T G Green, U M MacFadyen, J Moore
Plastic Surgery H P Henderson, J Ward
Radiotherapy I M Peat
Respiratory Medicine I Pavord
Rheumatology S Roy
Urology T R Terry

Hinckley Sunnyside Hospital

Ashby Road, Hinckley LE10 3DA
Tel: 01455 451800 Fax: 01455 619936
Total Beds: 18

Integrated Medicine Dr Ives, A Miodrag

Leicester General Hospital Brandon Unit

Gwendolen Road, Leicester LE5 4PW
Tel: 0116 225 6200 Fax: 0116 225 6228
Total Beds: 174

General Psychiatry J Bruce, T S Brugha, B Dalton, M S Dennis, G Drybala, T Friedman, S J Frost, J M T Kenrick, D I Khoosal, A L King, J Lindesay, R L Palmer, R Shinkwin, C Walker, J S Warrington, S P Wellstood-Eason

Loughborough General Hospital

Baxter Gate, Loughborough LE11 1TT
Tel: 01509 611600
Total Beds: 25

Anaesthetics A J Earl, D Fell
Cardiology Dr Gershlick
Care of the Elderly G J Fancourt, R J Shepherd
Chiropody and Podiatry R Jogia
Dermatology P E Hutchinson
Endocrinology Dr Burden, Dr Swift
ENT Dr Murty, A Narula
General Medicine R F Bing, J Ward, Dr Wicks
General Psychiatry W R Firth, J M T Kenrick
General Surgery Dr Dennison, M J Kelly, Dr Macpherson, Dr Rew, S Veitch
Genitourinary Medicine P C Schober
Neurology P H S Critchley

NHS TRUSTS & NHS HOSPITALS

Obstetrics and Gynaecology J Emembolv, Dr Kirwan, C A J Macafee, C J Mayne, N J Naftalin, Dr Oppenheimer
Ophthalmology Dr Amoaku, Dr Goulstine, Dr Gregson, Dr Raychaudhuri
Oral Surgery Dr Hayter
Orthopaedics T G Green, J Hoskinson, Dr Kershaw, Dr Sell
Paediatrics A Elias-Jones, S Nour, M Wailoo
Plastic Surgery T Milward
Radiology K C Krarup
Radiotherapy and Oncology S K Khanna
Respiratory Medicine D Pavord
Rheumatology A K Samanta
Urology D E Osborn

Loughborough Hospital
Epinal Way, Loughborough LE11 0JY
Tel: 01509 611600
Total Beds: 96

Care of the Elderly G F Fancourt, R J Shepherd
Psychiatry of Old Age J E B Lindesay

Woodlands Unit
Forest Road, Narborough, Leicester LE9 5E3
Tel: 0116 225 5850
Total Beds: 20

The Lewisham Hospital NHS Trust

University Hospital Lewisham, High Street, Lewisham, London SE13 6LH
Tel: 020 8333 3000 Fax: 020 8333 3333
Email: enquiries@uhl.nhs.uk
Website: www.uhl.ac.uk
(South East London Health Authority)

Chair Steve Bullock
Chief Executive Vivien Rhodes

The Lewisham Hospital
University Hospital Lewisham, High Street, Lewisham, London SE13 6LH
Tel: 020 8333 3000 Fax: 020 8333 3333
Email: enquiries@uhl.nhs.uk
Website: www.uhl.ac.uk
Total Beds: 600

Accident and Emergency N Nayeem, W Smallman
Anaesthetics M Albin, R Arnold, N Dasey, P Di-Vadi, W Hamann, M Heath, N V Heerden, C Lanigan, A Marsh, J Pook, C Roulson
Biochemistry P Eldridge
Cardiology J Gill, P G Jackson, S Lewis
Care of the Elderly P Gunawardena, P Luce, I Starke
Chest Disease N M Eiser, P Luce, L Youlten
Cytology C Keen, G Phillip
Dental Surgery S Bhinda
Dermatology H du P-Menarge, J J Ross, C Smith
Diabetes A Worsley
Endocrinology J Miell
ENT D A Bowdler, T Harris, J Rubin, N Salama
General Medicine N Eiser, P G Jackson, P Luce, J Miell, G Sladen, I Starke, R Stott, A Worsley
General Surgery B Edmondson, A Gotlieb, H Hamed, J Linsell, W Owen, N Slater, A Steger, P Taylor
Genitourinary Medicine J Bingham
Haematology Dr Nahheed-Mir, L Tillyer
Histopathology C Keen, C Philip
Medical Microbiology G Rao
Neurology R Chaudhuri
Nuclear Medicine S Clarke
Obstetrics and Gynaecology V G Harris, P Knott, M Savas
Ophthalmology W Acclimandos, D McHugh
Oral Surgery V Rajayogeswaran, P Robinson
Orthodontics D Ramsay

Orthopaedics P Earnshaw, R Gore, B Povlsen
Paediatrics M Agrawal, C Daman-Willems, E Dykes, R Evans, D Garvie, A Lorek, M McCullagh, J Maynard, J Stroobant, H Ward
Palliative Medicine D Bozek
Pathology G Smith
Radiology C Bradshaw, J Jacomb-Hood, C Kennedy, D McIver, M R Salari, R Toye
Radiotherapy A Timothy
Rheumatology G Kingsley, G Yanni
Thoracic Medicine N Eiser, P Luce, D Shelton
Urology J Buckley, R Popert

Lewisham Primary Care Trust

5th Floor Leegate House, Burnt Ash Road, London SE12 8RG
Tel: 020 8297 0707 Fax: 020 8297 8285
(South East London Health Authority)

Lifespan Healthcare NHS Trust

Closing April 2002 - Services transferring to Cambridgeshire and Peterborough Mental Health Partnership NHS Trust.

Ida Darwin Hospital, Fulbourn, Cambridge CB1 5EE
Tel: 01223 884008 Fax: 01223 884038
(Norfolk, Suffolk and Cambridgeshire Health Authority)

Chair Diana Abbott
Chief Executive Richard Taylor

Brookfields Hospital
Mill Road, Cambridge CB1 3DF
Tel: 01223 723001 Fax: 01223 723002
Total Beds: 70

Care of the Elderly G Campbell, D R Forsyth, S Webster

Chesterton Hospital
Union Lane, Cambridge CB4 1PT
Tel: 01223 363415 Fax: 01223 357673
Total Beds: 53

Care of the Elderly G Campbell, D R Forsyth, S Webster

The Croft Children's Unit
28-30 Long Road, Cambridge CB2 2PZ
Tel: 01223 210314
Total Beds: 8

Child and Adolescent Psychiatry P Boulton, A Dezery, I Goodyear, M Murphy

Ida Darwin
Fulbourn, Cambridge CB1 5EE
Tel: 01223 884314 Fax: 01223 884313
Total Beds: 10

Ida Darwin Hospital
Fulbourn, Cambridge CB1 5EE
Tel: 01223 884022 Fax: 01223 884038
Total Beds: 6

Learning Disabilities M Bambrick, T Holland, E Vithayathil

The Princess of Wales Hospital
Lynn Road, Ely CB6 1DN
Tel: 01353 652000 Fax: 01353 652003
Total Beds: 34

Lincolnshire Ambulance and Health Transport Service NHS Trust

Cross O'Cliff Court, Bracebridge Heath, Lincoln LN4 2HL Tel: 01522 545171 Fax: 01522 534611 Email: enquiries@lincsambulance.nhs.uk (Trent Health Authority)

Chair Linda Honey **Chief Executive** Margaret Sema

Lincolnshire Healthcare NHS Trust

Orchard House, South Rauceby, Sleaford NG34 8PP Tel: 01529 416000 Fax: 01529 416092 (Trent Health Authority)

Chair Elizabeth A Allison **Chief Executive** Chris Slavin **Consultants** Dr Khan

Ash Villa

Willoughby Road, South Rauceby, Sleaford NG34 8QA Tel: 01529 416047 Fax: 01529 488239 Total Beds: 16

Ashley House

Beaconfield Site, Sandon Road, Grantham NG31 9DR Tel: 01476 573986 Total Beds: 10

Beech House

Toot Lane, Fishtoft, Boston PE21 0AX Tel: 01205 354988 Fax: 01205 354837 Total Beds: 10

Elm Lodge

Beaconfield Site, Sandon Road, Grantham NG31 9DR Tel: 01476 573752 Fax: 01476 578210 Total Beds: 10

Maple Lodge

Toot Lane, Fishtoft, Boston PE21 0AX Tel: 01205 354900 Fax: 01205 354837 Total Beds: 10

Mayflower Day Unit

Department of Psychiatry, Pilgrim Hospital, Sibsey Road, Boston PE21 9QS Tel: 01205 36480 ext: 3517 Total Beds: 20

Mental Health Day Unit

17 Lumley Avenue, Skegness PE25 2AP Tel: 01754 610509 Fax: 01754 769434 Total Beds: 12

Sycamore Assessment Unit

Beaconfield Site, Sandon Road, Grantham NG31 9DF Tel: 01476 579707 Fax: 01476 579799 Total Beds: 24

Wilson House

64 St Thomas' Road, Spalding PE11 2XT Tel: 01775 760525 Fax: 01775 761807 Total Beds: 16

Lincolnshire South West Primary Care Trust

Annex C, Council Offices, Eastgate, Sleaford NG34 7EP Tel: 01529 304438 (Trent Health Authority)

Chair Michael Boddy **Chief Executive** Derek Bray

Liverpool Women's Hospital NHS Trust

Crown Street, Liverpool L8 7SS Tel: 0151 708 9988 Fax: 0151 702 4028 Website: www.lwh.org.uk (Cheshire and Merseyside Health Authority)

Chair Rosemary Cooper **Chief Executive** Ann Marr

Liverpool Women's Hospital

Crown Street, Liverpool L8 7SS Tel: 0151 708 9988 Fax: 0151 702 4028 Website: www.lwh.org.uk Total Beds: 271

Anaesthetics S Malliah, G Meadows, B Phillips, T D R Ryan, T Wauchob, R G Wilkes **Genitourinary Medicine** I A Tait **Obstetrics and Gynaecology** Z Alfirevic, R D Atlay, R G Farquharson, A S Garden, J Hewitt, G M Kidd, C Kingsland, R E Kingston, J Neilson, D Richmond, C M Thom, S Walkinshaw **Paediatrics** R W I Cooke, B Shaw, A M Weindling **Radiology** S King, D W Pilling, F E White

Local Health Partnerships NHS Trust

The Lodge, Castleton Way, Eye IP23 7BH Tel: 01379 873095 Fax: 01379 873096 Email: janet.young@lhp.nhs.uk, janet.younh@ihp.nhs.uk (Norfolk, Suffolk and Cambridgeshire Health Authority)

Chair Sandra Walmsley **Chief Executive** Antek Lejk

Aldeburgh and District Community Hospital

Park Road, Aldeburgh IP15 3ES Tel: 01728 452778 Fax: 01728 454056 Total Beds: 35

Bartlet Hospital

Undercliff Road East, Felixstowe IP11 7LT Tel: 01394 284292 Fax: 01394 671384 Total Beds: 56

Beccles and District War Memorial Hospital

St. Mary's Road, Beccles NR34 9NQ Tel: 01502 712164 Fax: 01502 714696 Total Beds: 48

ENT K Mangat **General Psychiatry** P R Eastwood **General Surgery** P Aukland **Oncology** J Ostrowski **Orthopaedics** G H Moore

Felixstowe General Hospital

Constable Road, Felixstowe IP11 7HJ Tel: 01394 282214 Fax: 01394 671384 Total Beds: 28

NHS TRUSTS & NHS HOSPITALS

Hartismere Hospital

Eye IP23 7BH
Tel: 01379 870543 Fax: 01379 870340
Total Beds: 86

Care of the Elderly P Philips, L J Sheehan

Hillcrest and Phoenix Day Hospital

Hospital Road, Bury St Edmunds IP33 3NR
Tel: 01284 725333 ext: 2384

Minsmere House

Heath Road, Ipswich IP4 5PD
Tel: 01473 704200 Fax: 01473 704227
Total Beds: 35

General Psychiatry M Barsoum, L Head, A Siddique

Patrick Stead Hospital

Bungay Road, Halesworth IP19 8HP
Tel: 01986 872124 Fax: 01986 874838
Total Beds: 20

General Medicine D Seaton
General Psychiatry P R Eastwood
Orthopaedics R Jones, P Nadarajan

St Clements Hospital

Foxhall Road, Ipswich IP3 8LS
Tel: 01473 715111 Fax: 01473 276558
Total Beds: 231

General Psychiatry M Barsoum, A J Byrne, R Caracciolo, D Dodwell, M Gaddal, R Goddard, Dr Siddique, M J Stevens

Southwold and District Hospital

Field Stile Road, Southwold IP18 6LD
Tel: 01502 723333 Fax: 01502 782 4216
Total Beds: 17

ENT D J Premachandra
General Surgery P Aukland
Ophthalmology P Black
Orthopaedics R Jones, P Nadarajan

Stow Lodge Day Hospital

Chilton Way, Stowmarket IP14 1DF
Tel: 01449 614024 Fax: 01449 615829

Violet Hill Day Hospital

Violet Hill Road, Stowmarket IP14 1JS
Tel: 01449 673872 Fax: 01449 673872

Whitwell House Day Hospital

Saxon Road, Saxmundham IP17 1EE
Tel: 01728 605652

London Ambulance Service NHS Trust

220 Waterloo Road, London SE1 8SD
Tel: 020 7921 5100 Fax: 020 7921 5129
Website: www.londonambulance.nhs.uk
(North West London Health Authority)

Chair Sigurd Reinton

Luton and Dunstable Hospital NHS Trust

Lewsey Road, Luton LU4 0DZ
Tel: 01582 491122 Fax: 01582 598990
(Bedfordshire and Hertfordshire Health Authority)

Chair Eric Fountain
Chief Executive Anna Anderson, Stephen Ramsden

Luton and Dunstable Hospital

Lewsey Road, Luton LU4 0DZ
Tel: 01582 491122 Fax: 01582 598990
Total Beds: 556

Accident and Emergency M B Kotecha, M A Nafis
Anaesthetics M A Alexander, S G Brosnan, M I Carter, H M Hill, T V Isitt, N G Jeffs, E M Lang, S Logarajah, M T Patten, CC A Roud Mayne, F D Spears, I D Srikantharajah, A J Twigley, B S Yogasakaran
Cardiology P G Rees, C M Travill
Cardiothoracic Surgery M O Maiwand
Chemical Pathology D B Freedman, D B Freedman
Clinical Oncology K Goodchild, A Makris, M I Saunders
Dermatology A F Swain
Endocrinology R G Stanhope
ENT O P Chawla, M C Frampton, T J Hoare, D F Johnston, J M Pickles
General Medicine N Finer, A E Griffiths, S R Jain, D B Peterson, D I M Siegler, N J Simmonds, S C Soo, M A Stodell
General Surgery S Cheslyn-Curtis, V K Jain, J R Novell, M R Pittam, J M Towler
Genitourinary Medicine T Balachandran
Haematology H Flora, D C Linch, D S Thompson, J Voke
Histopathology J W Dove, D A S Lawrence, Y Maria-Nayagam, P O Ozua
Medical Microbiology M C Faiers, R J Mulla
Medicine for the Elderly J J Day, K Mandaleson, K Mylvaganam, S Puthrasingam
Neurology A N Gale
Neurophysiology R M Sherratt
Neurosurgery R S Maurice-Williams
Obstetrics and Gynaecology S J Burrell, M Griffiths, D H Horwell, M O Lobb, O J D Owens, P C Reid
Occupational Health N Plunkett, F D Trevarthen
Oncology A Makris
Ophthalmology N Anand, J D Heath, S J P Pieris, M P Snead, J J Tolia
Oral and Maxillo-Facial Surgery M T Simpson
Oral Surgery A D Giles, M G Gilhooly, M T Simpson, C M Wesson
Orthodontics L R O Hale
Paediatrics B R Adler, M J Chapple, D B Houston, P Sivakumar, M H Thompson
Plastic Surgery A O Grobbelaar, R Sanders
Radiology M S M Alexander, S A Allen, S J Barter, J S M Beales, B E Hartley, I P Hicks, G S Jutlla, M J Warren, R J Warwick, D J Wright
Radiotherapy and Oncology P J Hoskin, M I Saunders
Rehabilitation Medicine S Mullick
Rheumatology D Fishman
Thoracic Surgery M O Maiwand
Trauma and Orthopaedics D H Austwick, P H P Dyson, P A J Edge, R Pandit, C J Read, J S Sarkar, J M Scott
Urology A M Alam

St Mary's Day Hospital

Dunstable Road, Luton
Tel: 01582 721621

Luton Primary Care Trust

Nightingale House, 94 Inkerman Street, Luton LU1 1JD
Tel: 01582 528840 Fax: 01585 528841
(Bedfordshire and Hertfordshire Health Authority)

Chair Gurche Randawa
Chief Executive Regina Shakespeare

Maidstone and Tunbridge Wells NHS Trust

Pembury Hospital, Beech House, Pembury, Tunbridge Wells TN2 4QJ
Tel: 01892 823535 Fax: 01892 825468
Website: www.nhskent.org.uk
(Kent and Medway Health Authority)

Chair Mary Symes
Chief Executive Stephen Collinson, Annette Sergeant

Kent and Sussex Hospital

Mount Ephraim, Tunbridge Wells TN4 8AT
Tel: 01892 526111 Fax: 01892 528381
Total Beds: 226

Accident and Emergency J M Walker
Anaesthetics J Appleby, L Baldwin, R Chung, H T Hutchinson, R Loveday, T Ludgrove, A J Porterfield, A Pyne, D W Yates
Child and Adolescent Psychiatry R I Bearcroft
Dermatology A Macdonald
ENT C M Milton, R J Sergeant, J Shotton
General Medicine R A Banks, D Barnes, A Harris, J A Hughes, C S Lawson
General Surgery P G Bentley, A J Cook, T F Ford, J L Lewis, M R Tyrrell, T G Williams
Genitourinary Medicine S Winceslaus
Medical Microbiology D I Gladstone
Neurology T J Fowler
Ophthalmology J A Bell, N Rowson
Oral and Maxillofacial Surgery P Banks
Orthodontics N Hunt, A R Thom
Orthopaedics N J Fordyce, P A Gibb, P W Skinner, K W R Tuson
Paediatrics W J Bolsover, P Day, M F Robards
Radiology B G Conry, J J Flanagan, P Garrett, P R Tallett, C W Whetton
Radiotherapy and Oncology D M Barrett

Kent County Ophthalmic and Aural Hospital

Church Street, Maidstone ME14 1DT
Tel: 01622 673444 Fax: 01622 679979
Total Beds: 27

Anaesthetics S W Gammanpila
Ophthalmology C D Jenkins

Maidstone Hospital

Hermitage Lane, Maidstone ME16 9QQ
Tel: 01622 729000 Fax: 01622 224124
Total Beds: 381

Accident and Emergency G Cook, A Soorma
Anaesthetics M Biswas, J Dickenson, S W Gammanpila, D Iyer, A Jappie, S Sritharan, W S L Zoysa
General Medicine G Bird, A Hammond, D J Hibbert, P Holt, G R McIlwraith, P R Powell-Jackson, C Thom
General Surgery P A Jones, L M South, G Trotter
Haematology H J H Williams
Obstetrics and Gynaecology A Dunham, J D S Goodman, R H Kefford
Orthopaedics S Ellis, R N S Slater, C A Stossel, C J Walker
Paediatrics B Badhuri, J A Hulse, C E M Unter
Radiology J Donaldson, P McMillan
Radiotherapy and Oncology F McKenna, M O'Brien, D Pickering, G M Sadler, J Summers
Thoracic Surgery O J Lau
Urology P Reddy

Pembury Hospital

Pembury, Tunbridge Wells TN2 4QJ
Tel: 01892 823535 Fax: 01892 824267
Total Beds: 206

Anaesthetics J Appleby, L Baldwin, R Chung, H T Hutchinson, R Loveday, T Ludgrove, A J Porterfield, A Pyne, D W Yates

Care of the Elderly M Chellappah, P Reynolds, P Tsang
Dermatology A Macdonald
General Medicine R A Banks, A Harris, J A Hughes, C S Lawson
General Surgery P G Bentley, A J Cook, T F Ford, J L Lewis, M R Tyrrell, T G Williams
Haematology D S Gillett, C G Taylor
Histopathology R N Basu
Neurology T J Fowler
Obstetrics and Gynaecology P N Bamford, O Chappatte, D B Garrioch
Paediatrics W Bolsover, P Day, M F Robards
Radiology B G Conry, J J Flanagan, P Garrett, P R Tallett, C W Whetton

Maidstone Weald Primary Care Trust

Preston Hall, Royal British Legion Village, Aylesford ME20 7NJ
Tel: 01622 225750 Fax: 01622 255770
Website: www.nhskent.org.uk/maidstone_malling
(Kent and Medway Health Authority)

Maldon and South Chelmsford Primary Care Trust

Administration Block, St Peter's Hospital, 32A Spital Road, Maldon CM9 6EG
Tel: 01621 727300 Fax: 01621 727301
(Essex Health Authority)

Chair Tony Plumridge
Chief Executive Mike Harrison

Mansfield District Primary Care Trust

Chadburn House, Weighbridge Road, Littleworth, Mansfield NG18 1AH
Tel: 01623 473200 Fax: 01623 473230
Website: www.mansfielddistpct.org.uk
(Trent Health Authority)

Chair Tony Hughes
Chief Executive Eleri de Gilbert

Mayday Healthcare NHS Trust

530 London Road, Croydon CR7 7YE
Tel: 020 8401 3000 Fax: 020 8665 1974
(South West London Health Authority)

Chair Sue Eardley
Chief Executive Keith Ford
Assistant Chief Executive F McGirrin

Mayday Hospital

London Road, Croydon CR7 7YE
Tel: 020 8401 3000 Fax: 020 8665 1974
Total Beds: 670

Accident and Emergency C Blakeley, RH Courtney-Evans, K Hashemi
Anaesthetics K Amir-awsari, M Baruya, N Chitkara, D G Cohen, J Collyer, K Hughes, A Knibb, G Menon, V Muralitharan, J Heriot, M Navaratnarajah, A Peebles-Brown, T Waddell, D Walton
Cardiology R Canepa-Anson, S P Joseph, P Stubbs
Care of the Elderly P O'Mahoney, P Diggory, D Griffiths, V Jones, E Lawrence, A Mehta
Chemical Pathology A Tarn
Dermatology E Mallon

NHS TRUSTS & NHS HOSPITALS

ENT J R Knight, S Mady
General Medicine P Johnson, N L Essex, A C Miller, N Velasco, M Mendall, A Theodossi
General Surgery S Ebbs, P Hurley, M Abulafi, I Swift
Genitourinary Medicine T Newell, M Rodgers
Haematology H Lumley, J Martland, C Pollard
Histopathology A Arnaout, M Coppen, E Rawelly, S Thomas, S Thomas, A Zaitoun
Neurology F Schon
Neurophysiology H Modarres-Sadeghi
Obstetrics and Gynaecology M Booker, R Hamid, P Clarkson, P Shah, G Ward, A Sultan
Ophthalmology W Ayliffe, D DeAlwiss, H Seward
Oral and Maxillofacial Surgery M Manisali
Orthodontics A J Banner
Orthopaedics G Marsh, A J Miller, M A S Mowbray, A Iossifidis
Paediatrics J Chang, K Cottrall, T Fenton, S Hart, A Kumar, H Underhill
Palliative Care L Gibbs, S Popert
Pathology P Riley, M Sahathevan
Radiology H N Blake, A Newman-Sanders, R Evans, M Hoskins, S Lowe, N Bees, S Maheshwaren
Restorative Dentistry A G Gilmour
Rheumatology and Rehabilitation J A Reardon, R Sathananthan
Urology G Das, p Shamugaraju
Vascular Surgery J Derodra, M Williams

Purley and District War Memorial Hospital

856 Brighton Road, Purley CR2 2YL
Tel: 020 8401 3000
Total Beds: 42

Care of the Elderly D Griffith

Medway NHS Trust

Medway Hospital, Windmill Road, Gillingham ME7 5NY
Tel: 01634 830000 Fax: 01634 825290
(Kent and Medway Health Authority)

Chair Janardan Sofat
Chief Executive Jan Filochowski

Medway Maritime Hospital

Windmill Road, Gillingham ME7 5NY
Tel: 01634 830000 Fax: 01634 815811
Total Beds: 633

Accident and Emergency M A Mason, A Morrice, V M Sethkumar
Anaesthetics R Buist, G Cross, S Day, C J Parnell, M Pick, D A Simpson, N Venkat, T J Wilson
ENT J Davis, P Gluckman, R C Henry, A Hosny, A Johns, V Lobo
General Medicine R C Day, R Jones, I M O'Brien, I Scobie, G Smith-Laing, A G Stewart, A J Stewart, D S Thompson
General Surgery D I Beeby, C Butler, R W Hoile, O Khan, P J Webb
Neurology S Chong, G Hardwood
Nuclear Medicine P Ryan
Occupational Health J Wood
Ophthalmology M N Kidd, A I MacFarlane, C G F Munton
Orthopaedics J P Fleetcroft, B Gopalgi, A Hammer
Paediatrics T M Little, P D Manuel, P Williams
Pathology A Azzopardi, R P Lindley, A K Missan, B J Randall
Plastic Surgery H Belcher
Radiology H Belcher, P Mills, K Reddy, S Sivathasan, P Varda, M D Velamati
Rheumatology and Rehabilitation B K Sharma, P L Williams
Urology G R Mufti, J H Palmer

Medway Primary Care Trust

Admiral's Office, Church Lane, The Historic Dockyard, Chatham ME4 4TE
Tel: 01634 810812 Fax: 01634 810817
(Kent and Medway Health Authority)

Melton, Rutland and Harborough Primary Care Trust

St Mary's Hospital, Thorpe Road, Melton Mowbray, Leicester LE13 1SJ
Tel: 01664 855000 Fax: 01664 855001
(Leicestershire, Northamptonshire and Rutland Health Authority)

Chair Ann G Harding
Chief Executive Wendy Saviour

Mendip Primary Care Trust

St Adhelm's Hospital, Green Lane, Frome BA11 4JW
Tel: 01373 468010 Fax: 01373 468019
Website: www.somerset-health.org.uk
(Somerset and Dorset Health Authority)

Chair Ron Ballantine
Chief Executive Robin Smith

Mental Health Services of Salford NHS Trust

Bury New Road, Prestwich, Manchester M25 3BL
Tel: 0161 773 4121 Fax: 0161 772 4639, 0161 772 4444
(Greater Manchester Health Authority)

Prestwich Site

Bury New Road, Prestwich, Manchester M25 3BL
Tel: 0161 773 9121
Total Beds: 349

General Psychiatry P Ainsworth, S M Bailey, D Black, A A Campbell, S Colgan, S A Davenport, D M Eminson, G I Gowers, D James, H B Kelly, K J Merrill, E P Owens, N A Seivewright, E D Smith, P R Snowden, S D Soni, C W Stone, L Thornton
Haematology J B Houghton, R C Routledge
Histopathology R S Reeve
Medical Microbiology L A Ganguli, M G L Keaney
Psychiatry of Old Age G E Moss, I H Stout
Psychotherapy T J Black, K Hyde

Mersey Care NHS Trust

Rathbone Hospital, Mill Lane, Liverpool L9 7JP
Tel: 0151 250 3000
(Cumbria and Lancashire Health Authority)

Chair Stephen Hawkins
Chief Executive Alan Yates

Ashworth Hospital

Parkbourn, Maghull, Liverpool L31 1HW
Tel: 0151 473 0303 Fax: 0151 526 6603
Total Beds: 572

Broadoak Mental Health Unit

Thomas Drive, Liverpool L14 3PJ
Tel: 0151 250 3000 Fax: 0151 252 0091
Total Beds: 88

Consultants R Higgo, R McCutcheon, M Munro, C O'Brien, G Segarjasingham, E Windgassen

Mossley Hill Hospital
Park Avenue, Liverpool L18 8BU
Tel: 0151 250 3000 Fax: 0151 729 0227
Total Beds: 65

Consultants D Anderson, P Metcalf, R Philpott, D Selverajah

Rathbone Hospital
Mill Lane, Liverpool L13 4AW
Tel: 0151 250 3000 Fax: 0151 220 4291
Total Beds: 88

Wavertree Lodge/Wavertree Bungalow
Old Mill Lane, Wavertree, Liverpool L15 8LW
Tel: 0151 250 3000
Total Beds: 12

Windsor House
40 Upper Parliament Street, Liverpool L8 7LF
Tel: 0151 250 3000 Fax: 0151 709 7608
Total Beds: 24

Mersey Regional Ambulance Service NHS Trust

Elm House, Belmont Grove, Liverpool L6 4EG
Tel: 0151 260 5220 Fax: 0151 260 7441
(Cheshire and Merseyside Health Authority)

Chair Basil Jeuda
Chief Executive Janet Davies

Mid Cheshire Hospitals NHS Trust

From April 2002 mental health and learning disability services transferring to Cheshire and Wirral Partnership NHS Trust.

Leighton Hospital, Middlewich Road, Crewe CW1 4QJ
Tel: 01270 255141 Fax: 01270 587696
(Cheshire and Merseyside Health Authority)

Chair Robin L Farmer
Chief Executive Simon Yates

Leighton Hospital
Middlewich Road, Crewe CW1 4QJ
Tel: 01270 255141 Fax: 01270 587696
Total Beds: 700

Accident and Emergency J B Bache
Anaesthetics M Brown, F M Emery, C S Hopkins, K E Jones, P Lewis, A Martin, R W Okell
Care of the Elderly H W Jones, D P Walters
Dental Surgery J T Cawood, E C H Huddy
Dermatology P J August
ENT J E Davies, J Deans
General Medicine R R Davies, P Dodds, J S McKay, M D Winson
General Psychiatry D Hambidge, L Lovett, R G Millward, K Rao, Dr Segarajasingham
General Surgery D Cade, J F Clegg, A Guy, G B Rawsthorne
Genitourinary Medicine M H Khan
Obstetrics and Gynaecology J E Felmingham, P J Murphy, G Scott
Ophthalmology L B Freeman, B Moriarty, M A Neugebauer
Orthodontics J H Martin
Orthopaedics R Gillies, M O'Driscoll, T R Redfern, D Rees
Paediatrics T K R Chandran, R E Pugh, A P J Thomson
Pathology S Al-Azzawi, H Allison, S Mallya, J M Morgan, A Nicol, M O'Donoghue

Radiology P Mayor, P R Moorhouse, E D O'Doherty, J Scally, L R N Selvadurai
Rheumatology R C Butler
Thoracic Surgery A N A Rahman
Urology S Brough, C S Powell

Victoria Infirmary
Northwich CW8 1AW
Tel: 01606 74331 Fax: 01606 74331 ext: 4020
Total Beds: 34

Accident and Emergency J B Bache
Care of the Elderly H W Jones, P Walters
Dermatology P J August
ENT J E Davies
General Medicine R Davies, J S McKay, M D Winson
General Surgery J F Clegg, A Guy, G B Rawsthorne
Obstetrics and Gynaecology J E Felmingham, P J Murphy, G Scott
Ophthalmology L B Freeman
Orthopaedics M O'Driscoll, T R Redfern, D Rees
Paediatrics T K R Chandran, R Pugh
Radiology E D O'Doherty
Urology S Brough, C Powell

Mid Devon Primary Care Trust

Newcourt House, Old Rydon Lane, Exeter EX2 7JU
Tel: 01392 449700
(South West Peninsula Health Authority)

Chair Bud Wendover
Chief Executive Lesley Dunaway

Mid Essex Hospital Services NHS Trust

Broomfield Court, Pudding Wood Lane, Broomfield, Chelmsford CM1 7WE
Tel: 01245 440761 Fax: 01245 514675
(Essex Health Authority)

Chair D Bullock
Chief Executive A Pike

Broomfield Hospital
Court Road, Broomfield, Chelmsford CM1 7ET
Tel: 01245 440761 Fax: 01245 514166
Total Beds: 560

Accident and Emergency A Mariathas, R Zwink
Anaesthetics J Alexander-Collins, M Alexander-Williams, J Carter, M Davis, J J Durcan, B Emerson, A Hassani, N Huddy, D Kelly, K Kiff, J Lloyd, C McCartney, C McCartney, L Ooi, S Pal, D Peck, G Philpott, I Seggie, D J M Williams
Burns/Plastic Surgery P Dziewulski, D Elliott, A F S Flemming, T Loshan Kangesu, N Niranjan
Care of the Elderly R K Puri, A Qureshi, V Umachandran
Chest Disease A Blainey, J A Utting
Dermatology A Harrison, M R Klaber
General Medicine G Clesham, D Cunnah, J Fletcher, C Khin, S H Saverymuttu, D R Turner, M J Weston
General Surgery T Browne, M Harvey, Y Panayiotdpoulos, N Richardson, A H M Ross, P Sauven
Neurology P G Bradbury
Ophthalmology T A G Bell, A Sinha, M T Thoung
Orthopaedics J K Dowell, H Lyall, M Pereira, M Taylor, J Tuite, W Williams
Paediatrics A Agrawal, A P Lipscomb
Pathology M A Ahmed, K J Al Janabi, S Al-Sam, O H A Baugh, V Chowdhury, Y Thway
Radiology G Harverson, P H Lee, P G Pratt, H D Punnyadasa, K S Rao, R Whitney, P Wou

NHS TRUSTS & NHS HOSPITALS

Radiotherapy and Oncology N Davidson, T A Lister, S Tahir
Rheumatology and Rehabilitation P G Davies, A Srinivasan
Urology H J E Lewi, T Tassadq

Courtauld (W. J.) Hospital

London Road, Braintree CM7 2LJ
Tel: 01245 440761 Fax: 01376 552531
Total Beds: 38

Obstetrics and Gynaecology C Goodfellow, J Onwude, C Partington, P J Robarts

St John's Hospital

Wood Street, Chelmsford CM2 9BG
Tel: 01245 440761 Fax: 01245 513671
Total Beds: 172

Anaesthetics J Carter, M Davis, J J Durcan, J L Handy, A Hassani, N Huddy, D Kelly, C McCartney
Care of the Elderly R K Puri, V Umachandran
ENT D G Fife, A Pace-Balzan, C B Singh
Obstetrics and Gynaecology C F Goodfellow, C J Partington, D J Robarts
Orthodontics G Howe
Paediatrics A Agrawal, G Bridgman, G Kugan, A P Lipscomb, R N Mahesh Babu, L Murtaza
Pathology M A Ahmed, K J Al Janabai, A Al-Sam, O H A Baugh, V Chowdhury, Y Thway
Radiology G Harverson, P H Lee, P G Pratt, H D Punnyadasa, K S Rao, R Whitney, P Wou

St Michael's Hospital

142 Rayne Road, Braintree CM7 2QJ
Tel: 01245 440761 Fax: 01376 558538

Care of the Elderly A Qureshi, V Umachandran
Dermatology A Harrison
ENT C B Singh
General Medicine A Blainey, D Cunnah, S H Saverymuttu
General Surgery Y Panayiotopoulos
Ophthalmology M T Thoung
Paediatrics A Agrawal, G C Bridgman, A P Lipscomb, R N Mahesh Babu
Rheumatology and Rehabilitation P G Davies

St Peter's Hospital

Spital Road, Maldon CM9 6EG
Tel: 01376 551221
Total Beds: 75

Care of the Elderly R K Puri, V Umachandran
Dermatology M R Klaber
General Medicine J Utting, M J Weston
General Surgery P Sauven
Obstetrics and Gynaecology C K Partington
Ophthalmology T A G Bell, A Sinha, M T Thoung
Orthopaedics K Cheah
Paediatrics A P Lipscomb
Pathology M A Ahmed, S Al-Sam, O H A Baugh, Y Thway
Rheumatology and Rehabilitation A Srinivasan

Mid-Hampshire Primary Care Trust

Friarsgate Medical Centre, Winchester SO23 8EF
Tel: 01962 85 200 Fax: 01962 850577
(Hampshire and Isle of Wight Health Authority)

Chair Barbara North
Chief Executive Chris Evennett

Mid Staffordshire General Hospitals NHS Trust

Staffordshire General Hospital, Weston Road, Stafford ST16 3SA
Tel: 01785 257731 Fax: 01785 245211
(Shropshire and Staffordshire Health Authority)

Chair J Jessel
Chief Executive David O'Neill

Cannock Chase Hospital

Brunswick Road, Cannock WS11 2XY
Tel: 01543 572757, 01785 257888
Total Beds: 142

Staffordshire General Hospital

Weston Road, Stafford ST16 3SA
Tel: 01785 257731 Fax: 01785 245211
Total Beds: 400

Accident and Emergency D F McGeehan
Anaesthetics G Earnshaw, M Grewal, W J Hawkins, R W G Johns, A S T Lamb, D A McCulloch, Y M Salib, C Secker, W G Sellwood, A Taylor
Care of the Elderly M Casey, J Elizabeth, A Oke
Dermatology N Hardwick, A G Smith, K A Ward
ENT V C David, T N Reddy
General Medicine P Coates, P R Daggett, Dr Dickenson, A J Fairfax, J A Gibson, P Singh, P Woodmansey, J Yeoh
General Surgery W Crisp, D Durrans, R Gendy, B Gwynn, R Hutchinson, J C Lotz
Genitourinary Medicine A R Markos
Haematology Dr Amos, P G Revell
Histopathology S C Harris, Dr Platt, V Suarez
Medical Microbiology E Olson, M L Yee
Neurology B Summers
Obstetrics and Gynaecology K Chin, V Dapaah, J Dixon, K Powell
Ophthalmology M P Headon, J Price
Oral and Maxillofacial Surgery T Malins
Orthodontics A M Bond, J D Muir
Orthopaedics I Bhoora, T El-Fakhri, M Hoyle, V Kathuria, R D Loynes, J Travlos
Paediatrics D R Carlton, D C Gordon-Nesbitt, C Melville, S K Sethi
Radiology P G Ander, R P Loynes, A M MacLeod, D Steventon, R Suarez, Dr Willard
Radiotherapy and Oncology A M Brunt, J E Scoble
Rheumatology D Mulherin, T Price, T Sheeran

Mid Sussex NHS Trust

Closing April 2002 - Mental health and learning disability services transferring to West Sussex Health and Social Care NHS Trust; acute services transferring to Brighton and Sussex University Hospitals NHS Trust.

Downsmere, The Princes Royal Hospital, Lewes Road, Haywards Heath RH16 4EX
Tel: 01444 441881, 01444 441528
(Surrey and Sussex Health Authority)

Chair Christine Field
Chief Executive Stefan Cantore

Colwood Hospital

Haywards Heath RH16 4EZ
Tel: 01444 441881
Total Beds: 18

Larchwood Hospital

Haywards Heath RH16 4EZ
Tel: 01444 441881

Mid-Sussex Primary Care Trust

Downsmere, Princess Royal Hospital, Lewes Road, Haywards Heath RH16 4EX
Tel: 01444 440331 Fax: 01444 440390
(Surrey and Sussex Health Authority)

Chair Christine Barwell
Chief Executive Mike Wood

Mid Yorkshire Hospitals NHS Trust

Formed April 2002 by merger of the acute services of Dewsbury Health Care NHS Trust and Pinderfields and Pontefract Hospitals NHS Trust.

Rowan House, Aberford Road, Wakefield WF1 4EE
Tel: 01924 213850 Fax: 01924 814929

Middlesbrough Primary Care Trust

Poole House, Stokesley Road, Nuneaton, Middlesbrough TS7 0NJ
Tel: 01642 320000 Fax: 01642 304023
(Tees Health Authority)

Milton Keynes General Hospital NHS Trust

Standing Way, Eaglestone, Milton Keynes MK6 5LD
Tel: 01908 660033 Fax: 01908 669348
(Thames Valley Health Authority)

Chair Margaret Hales, Mike Rowlands
Chief Executive Jill Rodney

Milton Keynes General Hospital

Standing Way, Eaglestone, Milton Keynes MK6 5LD
Tel: 01908 660033 Fax: 01908 669348
Total Beds: 410

Accident and Emergency K Kumar, P Thomas
Anaesthetics P H Chambers, J Cooney, M J Cowen, F E Evans, J P Hall, H Howells, V Jeevananthan, H Mangi, J T B Moyle, J Porter, P A Reed, B Slavin, A P White
Dermatology P Duhra
ENT P Brown, P Gurr, S T O'Malley
Gastroenterology S Lanzon-Miller, R Madhotra
General Medicine C W S Fisher, D Gwilt, V Kumar, P Medhi, I Mulligan, R C Paton
General Surgery P C Holford, D Mcwhinnie, K Mainprize, A Mitchell, R G Souter, E M Walker
Neurology R Butterworth, D Hilton-Jones
Obstetrics and Gynaecology R D Fawdry, P Haynes, C B Lynch, G S McCune, A Stock
Ophthalmology A Assaf, R Bates, A Kadom, B Kumar
Orthodontics D G M Greig
Orthopaedics A Floyd, R S Gunn, G F Miller, D Wallace, M Wetherill
Paediatrics V Joss, P K Lakhani, P Latham, E Moya
Pathology B C Das, T R Gamlen, S S Jalloh, K Y Lwin, E Miller, D J Moir, D White
Radiology Dr Choji, P Evans, O P Fitzgerald-Finch, N Graham, C Hardingham, A Havard, Y Manu, A Ul Haq, S Yogarajah
Urology I Anjum, E Walker

Milton Keynes Primary Care Trust

Hospital Campus, Standing Way, Eaglestone, Milton Keynes MK6 5NG

Tel: 01908 660033 Fax: 01908 694919
Website: www.mkpct.org.uk
(Thames Valley Health Authority)

Chair Jackie Swift
Chief Executive Barbara Kennedy

Moorfields Eye Hospital NHS Trust

City Road, London EC1V 2PD
Tel: 020 7253 3411 Fax: 020 7253 4696
Email: info@moorfields.org.uk
Website: www.moorfields.org.uk
(North Central London Health Authority)

Chair Thomas Boyd - Carpenter
Chief Executive Ian Balmer

Moorfields Eye Hospital

City Road, London EC1V 2PD
Tel: 020 7253 3411 Fax: 020 7253 4696
Total Beds: 80

Anaesthetics C A Carr (Head), S Bailey, A J Budd, N Catteruccia, A Coren, M Kadim, B Logan, R L McAuliffe, C Mathur, C M Moore, S Powrie
General Medicine D J Galton, B T Goh, G Plant
Ophthalmology G W Adams, B Allen, G W Aylward, K Barton, M Beaconsfield, A C Bird, R J Buckley, D Charteris, E Ezra, D F Garway-Heath, C Cunningham, R D Daniel, J K Dart, J Dowler, T J ffytche, L Ficker, W Franks, D S Gartry, Z Gregor, A Ionides, R A Hitchings, J Hungerford, V Maurino, P T Khaw, F Larkin, A Webster, J P Lee, P Desai, S Lightman, M H Miller, A T Moore, I Murdoch, C Pavesio, G E Rose, J J Sloper, J Stevens, P Sullivan, S Tuft, R Wormald
Radiology I F Moseley (Head)

Morecambe Bay Hospitals NHS Trust

Westmorland General Hospital, Burton Road, Kendal LA9 7RG
Tel: 01539 795366 Fax: 01539 795313
(Cumbria and Lancashire Health Authority)

Chair E Idris Williams
Chief Executive Ian R Cumming

Furness General Hospital

Dalton Lane, Barrow-in-Furness LA14 4LF
Tel: 01229 870870 Fax: 01229 871182
Total Beds: 400

Accident and Emergency S N Mardel
Anaesthetics S N Costigan, V Govenden, A D Haughton, J N Hodkinson, V Renshaw, L J Williams
Dental Surgery R A Dendy
Dermatology P V Harrison, V M Yates
ENT P J Stoney, B C S Whitfield
General Medicine M M El-Nazar, P C Gautum, J Keating, A R Luksza, F Medici, W S Mitchell, C A Sykes
General Surgery D Allan, C S Ball, D G Nasmyth
Nephrology S Gibson
Neurology J D Mitchell
Obstetrics and Gynaecology I Y Hussein, P K Misra, D E P Shapland
Oncology A Hindley
Ophthalmology I H Hubbard, E Khadem, A L Lyness
Oral Surgery P V Dyer
Orthodontics J G McCracken
Orthopaedics A N Baqai, N H Courtman, R J Michaud, A Smith
Paediatrics A Olabi, R M Rifkin, P T Ward
Palliative Medicine N J Sayer
Pathology W Blundell, V M Joglekar, A T Macheta, A Taylor
Radiology P J S Crawshaw, P Farndell, S Jagath, N Morar

NHS TRUSTS & NHS HOSPITALS

Rheumatology W S Mitchell
Urology K Madhra, R Y Wilson

Queen Victoria Hospital

Thornton Road, Morecambe LA4 5NN
Tel: 01524 411661
Total Beds: 48

Dermatology P V Harrison

Royal Lancaster Infirmary

Ashton Road, Lancaster LA1 4RP
Tel: 01524 65944 Fax: 01524 846346
Total Beds: 437

Accident and Emergency S T Durham, R G McGlone, A Sinha
Anaesthetics T M Bird, J R Davies, S Harding, A W McEwan, W G Park, A M Severn, M B Smith, B G Swales, C B Till, A P Vickers
Dental Surgery R A Dendy
ENT M E M Baraka, C H Bulman
General Medicine A R Adamson, A K Brown, C M Brown, I Huggett, M B McIllmurray, A B Murgatroyd, J D Pearson, D Walmsley, R F Willey
General Surgery J S Abraham, J K Brigg, J F Kelly, T Leese, W P Morgan
Immunology N Williamson
Medical Oncology M B McIllmurray
Neurology S D Vakil
Obstetrics and Gynaecology D J Burch, K Jones, I J Page, R J Shepherd
Ophthalmology R K Khanna, J Milson
Oral and Maxillofacial Surgery R A Dendy
Orthodontics J G McCracken
Orthopaedics V W Burton, D W Higginson, P Marshall, A Sinha, H D Stewart
Paediatrics P A G Gibson, M M Placzek, C A Ramesh
Pathology R W Blewitt, D W Gorst, C L Kozlowski, J A Morris, D H Orrell, M Stewart, D R Telford, N Williamson
Plastic Surgery A Howcroft
Radiology M Dalziel, P M Flanagan, J M Lavelle, L M Ness, W H J Wall
Radiotherapy and Oncology B Magee
Rheumatology W N Dodds, J P Halsey
Thoracic Surgery M A R Khan
Urology G Carswell, A K M Kamal, W G Staff

Ulverston Hospital

Stanley Street, Ulverston LA12 7BT
Tel: 01229 583635 Fax: 01229 580803
Total Beds: 46

General Medicine J Keating, M Krishnan, A R Luksza, W S Mitchell, H M Palmer, C A Sykes

Westmorland General Hospital

Burton Road, Kendal LA9 7RG
Tel: 01539 732288 Fax: 01539 740852
Total Beds: 234

Accident and Emergency R McGlone
Anaesthetics T M Bird, J R Davies, A McKewan, W Park, M Smith, B G Swales, A Vickers
Care of the Elderly I M Huggett
Dental Surgery R A Dendy
Dermatology D B Brookes, P V Harrison
ENT S Banerjee, C H Bulman, P Stoney, B Whitfield
General Medicine A R Adamson, A K Brown, C Brown, D Walmsley, R F Willey
General Surgery J Abraham, J A Brigg, J F Kelly, W P Morgan
Obstetrics and Gynaecology K Jones, I J Page, R J Shepherd
Oncology M B McIllmurray
Ophthalmology I H Hubbard, E Khadem, R K Khanna, A L Lyness, J E Milson
Orthodontics J G McCracken

Orthopaedics V W Burton, D W Higginson, P Marshall, H D Stewart
Paediatrics P A G Gibson, D MacGregor, M M Placzek
Pathology R W Blewitt, D Gorst, L Griffith, J A Morris, D H Orrell, D R Telford
Radiology M Dalziel, P M Flanagan, J M Lavelle, L M Ness, W H J Wall
Radiotherapy and Oncology S Davidson
Rheumatology and Rehabilitation W Dodds, J P Halsey
Urology W G Staff, R Y Wilson

Morecambe Bay Primary Care Trust

Tenterfield, Brigsteer Road, Kendal LA9 5EA
Tel: 01539 797800
(Cumbria and Lancashire Health Authority)

Chair Robin Talbot
Chief Executive David Jordison

New Forest Primary Care Trust

8 Sterne Road, Tatchbury Mount, Calmore, Southampton SO40 2RZ
Tel: 023 8087 4270 Fax: 023 8087 4275
(Hampshire and Isle of Wight Health Authority)

Chair Kay Sonneborn
Chief Executive Ian Ayres

New Possibilities NHS Trust

Turner Village, Turner Road, Colchester CO4 5PJ
Tel: 01206 844840 Fax: 01206 842301
(Essex Health Authority)

Chair Janet Fulford
Chief Executive Mark Halladay, Chris Jarvis

Newark and Sherwood Primary Care Trust

65 North Gate, Newark NG24 1HD
(Trent Health Authority)

Chair Bonnie Jones
Chief Executive Charles Allen

Newbury and Community Primary Care Trust

Andover Road, Newbury RG14 6LS
Tel: 01635 230107 Fax: 01635 31459
(Thames Valley Health Authority)

Chair Bruce Laurie
Chief Executive Graham Slater

Newcastle, North Tyneside and Northumberland Mental Health NHS Trust

St Georges Hospital, Morpeth NE61 2NU
Tel: 01670 512121 Fax: 01670 511637
(Northumberland, Tyne and Wear Health Authority)

Chair Sue Whittaker
Chief Executive Steve Shrub

St George's Hospital

Morpeth NE61 2NU
Tel: 01670 512121 Fax: 01670 511637
Email: carol.banks@nmht.org.uk
Total Beds: 302

General Psychiatry D Benn, A Brittlebank, L C Brown, W Grant, H Griffiths, C Luke, D L P Marshall, T O'Dwyer, M Parry, S E Proctor, E Sein, A M Walsh, P Yappa

St Nicholas Hospital

Gosforth, Newcastle upon Tyne NE3 3XT
Tel: 0191 213 0151 Fax: 0191 213 0821
Total Beds: 501

General Psychiatry B R Adams, W Barker, S Bhate, M Campbell, R Cawthra, A Cole, D Dunleavy, A F Fairbairn, R G Farquharson, I N Ferrier, E Gilvarry, H Griffiths, F Hassanyeh, S Joseph, T A Kerr, C A Lund, I McKeith, J L Scott, P Tayler, D Turkington, P Whewell

Sanderson Hospital

Salters Road, Gosforth, Newcastle upon Tyne NE3 4DT
Tel: 0191 285 0171

Newcastle Primary Care Trust

Benfield Road, Walkergate, Newcastle upon Tyne NE6 4PF
Tel: 0191 219 6000
(Northumberland, Tyne and Wear Health Authority)

Chair Gina Tiller
Chief Executive Bob Smith

Newcastle-under-Lyme Primary Care Trust

Brandwell Hospital, Talke Road, Chesterton, Newcastle ST5 7NJ
Tel: 01782 425440 Fax: 01782 425445
(Shropshire and Staffordshire Health Authority)

Newcastle upon Tyne Hospitals NHS Trust

Freeman Hospital, High Heaton, Newcastle upon Tyne NE7 7DN
Tel: 0191 284 3111 Fax: 0191 213 1968
(Northumberland, Tyne and Wear Health Authority)

Chair S Leonard Barron
Chief Executive Leonard R Fenwick

Freeman Hospital

Freeman Road, High Heaton, Newcastle upon Tyne NE7 7DN
Tel: 0191 284 3111 Fax: 0191 213 1968
Total Beds: 810

Anaesthetics P J M Bayly, D T Bolton, M C Burn, R F Carter, S A Coleman, I D Conacher, P D Cooper, P F Copeland, D K Girling, S R Haynes, D W Heaviside, N M Heggie, C K McKnight, M L Paes, H Powell, A K Pridie, D R D Roberts, D W Ryan, B G Watson, O G W Weldon

Anatomy and Physiology D W Ryan

Cardiology P C Adams, H H Bain, R S Bexton, J Bourke, K L Evemy, J S Furniss, A S Hunter, A Kerry, J M McComb, G Parry, D S Reid, D O Williams, C Wren

Cardiothoracic Surgery J R L Hamilton, A Hasun, C J Hilton, M P Holden, S Ledingham

Chest Medicine P A Corris, G J Gibson, B G Higgins

ENT J Hill, J Wilson

General Medicine K G M Alberti, M F Bassendine, D N Bateman, F Clark, I Cobden, R G Cooper, G A Fari, R M Francis, P D Home, O F W James, R A Kenny, R Lendrum, M D Rawlins, C O Record, M Walker

General Psychiatry M T Campbell, C Cole, D Turkington

General Surgery J Chamberlain, R M Charnely, N A G Jones, M Thick, P D Wright, M G Wyatt

Haematology P J Kesteven, J P Wallis

Histopathology T Ashcroft, M K Bennett, A D Burt, A J Malcolm, A R Morley, M C Robinson, J Soumes

Medical Microbiology F K Gould, K E Orr

Nephrology A Brown, T H J Goodship, J S Tapson, M K Ward, R Wilkinson

Orthopaedics J J Briggs, M J Gibson, P J Gregg, R Hornby, I M Pinder, J Pooley, J Quinby, P Sanderson, P R Stuart

Otolaryngology D S Cameron, D Kilby, H F Marshall, D B Mathias, D Meikle, A R Welch

Paediatric Surgery M N D Hunt

Radiology C J Baudouin, S T Elliott, H W C Loose, M M P McElroy, L Mitchell, L N S Murthy, J D G Rose, J R Young, I Zammit-Maempel

Rehabilitation Medicine N C M Fyfe

Rheumatology and Rehabilitation P R Crook, J A Goodacre, I D Griffiths, P N Platt, D J Walker

Urology D M Essenhigh, J G W Feggetter, F C Hamdy, D E Neal, P H Powell, P D Ramsden

Newcastle General Hospital

Westgate Road, Newcastle upon Tyne NE4 6BE
Tel: 0191 273 8811 Fax: 0191 272 2641
Total Beds: 467

Accident and Emergency D D Milne

Anaesthetics R E Bullock, T N S Clarke, R J H Colback, D C Crawford, S G H Cruickshank, B Fulton, M Hudgson, D G Hughes, H James, A E I Marshall, S P Moffett, A W Murray, N Redfern, I H Shaw, C W Thomson, I H Warnell, J A Wilkes

Biochemistry G Dale, M F Laker

Care of the Elderly R M Francis, P Harrigan

Child and Adolescent Psychiatry S Bhate, P J Tayler

General Medicine S Bourke, K L Evemy, D J Hendrick, Dr Ong, M H Snow, W M C Tunbridge

General Psychiatry W Barker, D L F Dunleavy, D Eccleston, R G Farquharson, S A Joseph, C A Lund, J C O'Grady, P C Soundararajan

General Surgery M B Clague, M S Griffin, C D M Griffith, R G Wilson

Genitourinary Medicine R S Pattman, K Sankar, P G Watson

Haematology P W G Saunders

Immunology A C Fay, G V Spickett

Medical Microbiology A A Codd, H R Ingham, I M Lightfoot, M S Sprott

Neurology D D Barwick, P G Cleland, P R W Fawcett, D Gardner-Medwin, J B Harris, P Hudgson, A J Jenkins, R E Jones, I S Schofield, T J Walls

Neuropathology P G Ince, R H Perry

Neuroradiology A R Gholkar, K Hall, V L McAllister

Neurosurgery P J Crawford, A Jenkins, A D Mendelow, R P Sengupta, M V Todd

Obstetrics and Gynaecology A S McIntosh, E M Michael, P F Simms, M M Singh, C A Snodgrass, T I Wagstaff

Occupational Health J Harrison

Ophthalmology D G Cottrell, R F Gillie, P G Griffiths, R Porter, R E W Ridley

Oral and Maxillofacial Surgery J E Hawkesford, C V Lansley, K L Posthlewaite

Orthopaedics M J Gibson, I M Pinder, S R Smith

Paediatrics F W Alexander, A J Cant, R J Cooke, J A Eyre, A P Kenna, D W A Milligan, A D J Pearson, M W Platt, H Steiner

Pathology J D Hemming, D J Scott, J J Shrimankar, V Wadehra

Plastic Surgery N R McLean, R H Milner, T A Piggot

Psychiatry of Old Age A F Fairbairn, I G McKeith

Radiology A J Chippendale, B Kaye, M M P McElroy, L M McLean, J D G Rose, W Simpson, J B Wilsdon

NHS TRUSTS & NHS HOSPITALS

Radiotherapy and Oncology R S Atkinson, J M Bozzino, A N Branson, M Brewis, A H Calvert, B M J Cantwell, P J D Dawes, R G B Evans, N J Lind, H H Lucraft, U K Mallick, J T Roberts

Newcastle upon Tyne Dental Hospital

Richardson Road, Newcastle upon Tyne NE2 4AZ
Tel: 0191 232 5131

Dental Surgery I E Barnes, I Geffner, A J Rugg-Gunn, R A Seymour, D G Smith

Oral and Maxillofacial Surgery G S Blair, K B Fanibunda, J E Hawkesford, D J Lovelock

Orthodontics T G Bennett, N E Carter, P H Gordon, J J Murray

Pathology J V Soames

Periodontology B H Smith

Royal Victoria Infirmary

Queen Victoria Road, Newcastle upon Tyne NE1 4LP
Tel: 0191 232 5131 Fax: 0191 201 0155
Total Beds: 806

Accident and Emergency N J Fox, P Goode, A K Maitra, B Sen

Anaesthetics I Anderson, P M Barrow, R J Bray, M R Bryson, R E Bullock, V E Bythell, J E Charlton, T N S Clarke, S A Coleman, S Cook, D C Crawford, S G H Cruickshank, G R Enever, I R Fletcher, B Fulton, N G Girdler, J D Greaves, J Halshaw, S A Hargrave, R P Harpin, I H Herrema, D G Hughes, C J Hull, J D M Jeffrey, D A Laffey, K A Price, N Redfern, A Redpath, I H Shaw, M A Stafford, C J Vallis, I H Warnell, B E Welsh, J A Wilkes

Biochemistry K H Dale, M F Laker, C H Self

Cardiology P C Adams, K L Evemy

Care of the Elderly R Kenny, V M Vardon

Cytology J D Hemming, S J Johnson, V Wadehra

Dental Conservation D J Jacobs, A S McMillan, A W G Walls, R W Wassell

Dentistry P H Gordon, J H Nunn, A J Rugg-Gunn, R R Welbury

Dermatology M C Dahl, P M Farr, C M Lawrence, J McLelland, J L Rees, N J Reynold, N B Simpson

Endocrinology T Cheetham

Forensic Medicine P N Cooper

General Medicine D N Bateman, S V Baudouin, P H Baylis, P G Blain, S J Bourke, R A L Brewis, R G Dyer, G Greveson, D J Hendrick, P D Home, G H Jackson, R A James, P Kendall-Taylor, R A Kenny, S M Marshall, K Matthewson, P G O'Mahony, E L C Ong, S J Proctor, C O Record, M H Snow, S C Stenton, M W Stewart, M Walker, R Wilkinson, A J Wright, H A Wynne

General Surgery R J Bentley, F C Campbell, D Gatehouse, S M Griffin, C D M Griffith, A B Griffiths, N Hayes, T W J Lennard, J G Meechan, G Proud, R M Weaver

Genetics J Burn, S A Lynch

Haematology P W Condie, P J Hamilton, G H Jackson, S J Proctor, M M Reid, P W G Saunders

Histopathology M K Bennett, A D Burt, C H W Horne, A J Malcolm, A R Morley, D J Scott, J Shrimankar

Immunology A Fay, G P Spickett

Medical Microbiology M R Barer, A J Bint, A Galloway, S J Pedler

Neonatology R J Cooke, A C Fenton, D W A Milligan, S N Sturgiss, M P Ward-Platt

Nephrology E J Eastham, T H J Goodship, H J Lambert, M K Ward

Neurology D Bates, D Burns, N E F Cartlidge, P G Cleland, P R W Fawcett, R J Forsyth, P Hudgson, M J Jackson, R E Jones, V Ramesh, P J Shaw, D M Turnbull, T J Walls

Neuropathology P Ince, R H Perry

Neurophysiology P R W Fawcett, I S Schofield

Neuroradiology A R Gholkar, K Hall, V L McAllister

Obstetrics and Gynaecology J M Davison, W Dunlop, J P Forsey, P Hilton, T Lind, A S McIntosh, S McPhail, S Macphail, M S A Mansour, E M Michael, S C Robson, P F Sims, M M Singh, T I Wagstaff

Ophthalmology M K Birch, R C Bosanquet, M P Clarke, D G Cottrell, A J Dickinson, F C Figueiredo, R F Gillie, P G Griffiths, J W Howe, R Porter, R E W Ridley, K P Stannard, N Strong

Oral and Maxillofacial Surgery K Fanibunda, J E Hawkesford, K Postlethwaite, P J Thomson

Oral Medicine A Nolan

Oral Pathology J V Soames

Orthodontics T G Bennett, N E Carter

Orthopaedics P J Briggs, M J Gibson, J Holland, R Hornby, J Quinby, P L Sanderson, P R Stuart, R A Sutton, W K Walsh, D J Weir

Paediatric Surgery A M Barrett, M N d Hunt, L Rangecroft, J Wagget

Paediatrics M Abinum, F W Alexander, A J Cant, M G Coulthard, A W Craft, E J Eastham, J A Eyre, T J Flood, M T Gibson, E N Hey, S Hodges, J Kernahan, R Nelson, A D J Pearson, U K Wariyar, K P Windebank, M Yung

Pathology A D Burt, C H W Horne, A J Malcolm, A R Morley, H Ranasinghe, H Wastell, A J Watson, C Wright

Periodontology I D M Macgregor, D G Smith

Pharmacology C H Ashton, D N Bateman, M D Rawlins, J W Thompson

Plastic Surgery M J M Black, P D Hodgkinson, N R McLean, R H Milner, S A Pape, C A Reid

Psychology D L F Dunleavy, D Eccleston, I N Ferrier, F Hassanyeh, C A Lund, J L Scott, S P Tyrer

Radiology A Burridge, A J Chippendale, A D M Coulthard, A Crisp, E Garner, J Gholkar, K Hall, B Kaye, R E J Lee, D J Lovelock, M M P McElroy, L M McLean, J P Owen, A J Potterton, D L Richardson, W Simpson, J B Wilsdon, S Worthy

Radiotherapy and Oncology P J D Dawes, R G B Evans, J P Hale, R Skinner

Rheumatology and Rehabilitation M Anderson, P R Crook, W C Dick, I D Griffiths, P N Platt, D J Walker

Virology C R Madeley

Walkergate Hospital

Benfield Road, Newcastle upon Tyne NE6 4GD
Tel: 0191 265 4521 Fax: 0191 224 0358
Total Beds: 325

Care of the Elderly R G Cooper, G A Ford, R M Francis, P Harrigan, O F W James

Newham Healthcare NHS Trust

Newham General Hospital Academic Centre, Glen Road, Plaistow, London E13 8SL
Tel: 020 7476 4000 Fax: 020 7363 8181
(North East London Health Authority)

Chair Stuart Innes
Chief Executive Kathy Watkins

Newham General Hospital

Glen Road, Plaistow, London E13 8SL
Tel: 020 7476 4000
Total Beds: 344

Accident and Emergency J Myers, J Oliver

Anaesthetics V Manam, G Russell

Cardiology K Ranjadayalan, A D Timmis

Care of the Elderly M Gill, S Lightowler, C Pratt

Chest Disease J V Meadway, T O'Shaghnessy, G Packe, R M Rudd

Dermatology D Fenton, M Glover, F Lawlor

ENT J O'Flynn

Gastroenterology C Ainley, V Kulhalli

General Medicine S Gelding, D Littlejohns, S Vijayaraghavan

General Surgery N R Fieldman, A A Hooper, M G Lord, M Mahir, B J Pardy

Obstetrics and Gynaecology J Boulton, R Chenoy, O Djahanbakhch, A A Naftalin, P Roberts

Oncology C Gallagher

Ophthalmology N Kayali

Orthopaedics T Dolan, M El-Zebdeh, R Gad El Rab

Palliative Medicine C Phillips

Pathology S I Baithun, S Bulusu, S Dodo, C Gutteridge, P Wilson

Radiology F Durrani, K M Mourad

Radiotherapy G Mair

Rheumatology and Rehabilitation I Chikanza, A Jawad, M G Wright

Urology F Chinegwundoh, C Fowler

St Andrew's Hospital

Devons Road, Bow, London E3 3NT
Tel: 020 7476 4000
Total Beds: 71

Newham Primary Care Trust

Plaistow Hospital, Samson Street, London E13 9EH
Tel: 020 8548 3700 Fax: 020 8552 3732
(North East London Health Authority)

Chair Stephen Jacobs
Chief Executive David Stoute

East Ham Memorial Hospital

Shrewsbury Road, Forest Gate, London E7 8QR
Tel: 020 8586 5000 Fax: 020 8586 5099
Total Beds: 83

Margaret Scott Day Hospital

63 Appleby Road, London E16 1LQ
Tel: 020 7474 5666 Fax: 020 7445 7008

General Psychiatry D Abrahamson, J Feldman, D Lefevre, R Zimmer

Plaistow Day Hospital

Plaistow Hospital, Samson Street, Plaistow, London E13 9EH
Tel: 020 8586 6225 Fax: 020 8586 6204

Plaistow Hospital

Samson Street, London E13 9EH
Tel: 020 7472 7001 Fax: 020 8586 6204
Total Beds: 90

Sally Sherman Nursing Home

Albert Dock Hospital Site, Alnwick Road, London E16 3EZ
Tel: 020 7473 4386
Total Beds: 28

Norfolk and Norwich University Hospital NHS Trust

Norfolk and Norwich Hospital, Colney Lane, Norwich NR4 7UY
Tel: 01603 286286 Fax: 01603 287211
(Norfolk, Suffolk and Cambridgeshire Health Authority)

Chair Tony Holden
Chief Executive Malcolm Stamp

Cromer Hospital

Mill Road, Cromer NR27 0BQ
Tel: 01263 513571 Fax: 01263 514764
Total Beds: 37

Norfolk and Norwich University Hospital

Colney Lane, Norwich NR4 7UY
Tel: 01603 286286 Fax: 01603 287547
Total Beds: 955

Accident and Emergency T J Daynes, B Finlayson, M A Lambert, K Walters

Anaesthetics G L Barker, P Barker, A M Duthie, S Farquharson, B Fleming, S J Fletcher, P Furniss, A J G Gray, R Harwood, P E Hodgson, P J G Hutchings, P J Keep, L I Kerr, M J Leadbeater, K C MacIntosh, J F Payne, P D Phillips, G E Porter, R J Purnell, S P Rhodes, S A Ridley, W L Rowe, J M J Valentine, K A Wilkinson, N M Woodall, C H M Woollam

Cardiology I A B Brooksby, L Hughes, A J F Page, T Whistow

Care of the Elderly R A Fulcher

Chemical Pathology T Tickner

Diabetes R H Greenwood, P J Heyburn, M J Sampson, R Temple

ENT A J Innes, K S Mangat, P Montgomery, P Prinsley, M Wickstead

General Surgery T R Cheatle, J M F Clarke, J F Colin, D N L Ralphs, M Rhodes, S Scott, C T M Speakman, W S L Stebbings

Genitourinary Medicine J K Evans, J D Meaden

Haematology M Deane, G E Turner, J Wimperis

Histopathology R Y Ball, T H W Barker, A Girling, R Lonsdale, B G McCann, P F Roberts, V R Sams, X Tyler

Nephrology A Heaton

Neurology Dr Cochious, D J Dick, J B Pilling

Obstetrics and Gynaecology F d Boer, S G Crocker, D I Fraser, R Martin, K P Stanley, M F d Vere, R C Warren

Oncology H Baillie-Johnson, A Bulman, C Martin, M J Ostrowski

Orthopaedics J S Albert, P G Chapman, R J Crawford, S Donell, P Gallagher, M M S Glasgow, J F Nolan, A Patel, H Phillips, J K Tucker

Paediatric Surgery A B Mathur, T T M Tsang

Paediatrics P Aggett, R C Beach, P M Crowle, M Dyke, R Proops, R G Reading, C J Upton

Radiology J J Curtin, S D Girling, G R Hurst, P G Kitchener, J B Latham, P E Pickworth, J R Pilling, P G Preston, S Scott-Barrett, J H Visick, P A J Wilson

Radiotherapy H Baillie-Johnson, A Bulman, C Martin, M J Ostrowski

Respiratory Medicine B D W Harrison, J M Shaylor, O P Twentyman, S Watkin

Rheumatology J K Gaffney, P Merry, D G I Scott

Thoracic Surgery R Vaughan, D Watson

Urology N A Burgess, C G C Gaches, K K Sethia, R J Webb

Norfolk Mental Health Care NHS Trust

Drayton Old Lodge, 146 Drayton High Road, Drayton, Norwich NR8 6AN
Tel: 01603 421421 Fax: 01603 421118
Website: www.nmhct.nhs.uk
(Norfolk, Suffolk and Cambridgeshire Health Authority)

Chair Lesley Kant
Chief Executive Pat Holman

Bethel Child and Adolescent Directorate

Mary Chapman House, Hotblack Road, Norwich NR2 4HN
Tel: 01603 421421

General Psychiatry L Ashby, B R Badrinath, D Kinnaird, E McAdam

Hellesdon Hospital

Drayton High Road, Norwich NR6 5BE
Tel: 01603 421421
Total Beds: 220

General Psychiatry S Barker, L Callinan, K Craig, W Crook, D Double, Dr Hughes, M Kitson, A Nicol, C Reynolds, D Rumball, N Willamune

The Julian Hospital

Bowthorpe Road, Norwich NR2 3TD
Tel: 01603 421421 Fax: 01603 421831
Total Beds: 97

Elderly Mentally Ill C Morris, I Shaw, A Tarbuck, N Viale, R Wesby

Northgate Hospital

Northgate Street, Great Yarmouth NR30 1BU
Tel: 01493 330054 Fax: 01493 852753
Total Beds: 107

NHS TRUSTS & NHS HOSPITALS

North and East Cornwall Primary Care Trust

John Keay House, Tregonissey Road, St Austell PL25 4NQ
(South West Peninsula Health Authority)

North Birmingham Primary Care Trust

Ley Hill Surgey, 228 Lichfield Road, Sutton Coldfield B74 2UE
Tel: 0121 323 4648 Fax: 0121 323 2682
(Birmingham and the Black Country Health Authority)

North Bradford Primary Care Trust

Eccleshill Clinic, Rillington Mead, Bradford BD10 0ED
Tel: 01274 322190
(West Yorkshire Health Authority)

Chair Norman Roper
Chief Executive Ian Rutter

North Bristol NHS Trust

Executive Base, Frenchay Hospital, Beckspool Road Frenchay, Bristol BS16 1SE
Tel: 0117 975 3802 Fax: 0117 975 3806
(Avon, Gloucestershire and Wiltshire Health Authority)

Chair Phylida Parsloe
Chief Executive Anthony Woolgar

Blackberry Hill Hospital

Manor Road, Fishponds, Bristol BS16 2EW
Tel: 0117 965 6061 Fax: 0117 975 4832
Total Beds: 356

Forensic Psychiatry A Lillywhite, J E Smith, A Tomison

Burden Neurological Hospital

Stoke Lane, Stapleton, Bristol BS16 1QT
Tel: 0117 956 7444 Fax: 0117 965 4141
Total Beds: 25

General Psychiatry J M Bird, D G C Rogers

Clevedon Hospital

Old Street, Clevedon
Tel: 0117 987 2212
Total Beds: 21

General Medicine J E Harvey

Cossham Memorial Hospital

Lodge Road, Kingswood, Bristol BS15 1LF
Tel: 0117 967 1661 Fax: 0117 961 8421
Total Beds: 28

Donal Early House

Southmead Hospital, Westbury on Trym, Bristol BS10 5NB
Tel: 0117 959 5821 Fax: 0117 959 5804

Frenchay Hospital

Frenchay Park Road, Bristol BS16 1LE
Tel: 0117 970 1212 Fax: 0117 956 3880
Total Beds: 537

Accident and Emergency K Jones, C Oakland
Anaesthetics W Blancke, J A Carter, D F Cochrane, S Coniam, A W Diamond, J Dunnet, J Eaton, J Eaton, G L Greenslade, M Gregory, D Harris, C Jewkes, D Lockley, A R Manara, J Mendham, M Milne, D Ouer, S Plastow, J Rogers, S Shinde, P J Simpson, C Stannard, C Stannard, C Stapleton, F J M Walters, R M Weller, G Wrathall, P Younge
Cardiology M Papouchado
Care of the Elderly R Barber, L Dow, J Pounsford, Dr Wilcock
Chemical Pathology C E Dawkins
Child and Adolescent Psychiatry D L Bazeley-White, J Crooks, I Skeldon
Dermatology R D G Peachey
ENT D L Baldwin, M A Birchall
Gastroenterology R F Harvey
General Medicine C J Burns-Cox, L Dow, R F Harvey, V Kyle, R J White
General Psychiatry A R Tomison, S H West
General Surgery C P Armstrong, A Baker, S J Cawthorn, A Dixon, R E May
Haematology P J Whitehead
Histopathology N B N Ibrahim, H S Rigby
Medical Microbiology E M Brown
Neurology J Bird, N Kane, D Rogers
Neuropathology S Love, T H Moss
Neurophysiology M H Morgan
Neurosurgery C Bolger, H B Coakham, B H Cummins, S S Gill, R Nelson, I Pople, D R Sandeman
Obstetrics and Gynaecology F N McLeod, P Savage
Orthodontics I S Hathorn
Orthopaedics N Blewitt, I Nelson, A J Ward
Paediatrics H Hargreaves, G Roberts, J Schulte
Plastic Surgery D A Burd, J M Kenealy, N S Mercer, C Reid, L Sacks, D Sammut, P L G Townsend
Radiology J R Bradshaw, M J Cobby, T T Lewis, A J Longstaff, M H Morse, N Slack, R Watura
Rheumatology and Rehabilitation V Kyle

Ham Green Hospital

Pill, Bristol BS20 0HW
Tel: 01179 812661
Total Beds: 21

Care of the Elderly G R Burston
General Medicine S C Glover, J Harvey
General Psychiatry I D Chisholm, R M Hawley, I H Mian, F D Whitwell
Genitourinary Medicine M W Price
Neurology I T Ferguson
Pathology P A Burton, H White
Radiology J M Haworth, A B C Johnson, J B Penry
Radiotherapy and Oncology V L Barley, S E Goodman, B T Hale
Rheumatology P Hollingworth
Urology P Abrams, R C L Feneley, J C Gingell

Southmead Hospital

Westbury-on-Trym, Bristol BS10 5NB
Tel: 0117 950 5050 Fax: 0117 959 0902
Total Beds: 975

Accident and Emergency A Montague
Anaesthetics M Dirnhuber, F Donald, I A Dunnett, N Goodman, N Griffiths, C R Hall, K Holder, D H Holland, C Johnson, N Koehli, S K Lahiri, J Leigh, F McVey, A P Madden, G Morris, S Robinson, S Robinson, J Soar, E M Walsh
Care of the Elderly C Chan, M G Cheesman, L Potts
Clinical Chemistry D J Goldie
Clinical Pathology P A Burton
Community Child Health S Clements, A Elmond, H Hargreaves, J Price, G Roberts, J Schulte, O H Stanley
Dermatology C T C Kennedy
ENT D Baldwin, M Birchall, P Robinson
General Medicine J Dwight, E A M Gale, S C Glover, M Hartog, J Harvey, S Hughes, A Johnson, P R Walker
General Psychiatry I E Babiker, J A Culling, R M Hawley, R C Meller, R H C Meller, I H Mian, F E Newbery, J Truscott, F D Whitwell
General Surgery P A Lear, D Mitchell, B D Pentlow, A Roe, M H Thomson

Genitourinary Medicine M W Price
Haematology R Evely, R R Slade
Immunology T B Wallington
Medical Microbiology A P MacGowan, D S Reeves
Nephrology C Dudley, T Feest, S Harper, C R V Tomson
Neurology I T Ferguson
Obstetrics and Gynaecology D Bisson, D Joyce, F N McLeod, J Murdoch, P E Savage, P A Smith, S Vyas
Ophthalmology J C Dean-Hart, R H C Markham
Oral and Maxillofacial Surgery H G Irvine
Orthopaedics C Ackroyd, G C Bannister, E J Smith, I G Winson
Paediatrics T L Chambers, A A Leaf, M E McGraw, B D Speidel, H M Thomas
Pathology P J Berry, P A Burton, J D Davies, I D Fraser, D J Goldie, A McIver, E MacKenzie, D S Reeves, H White
Radiology D Breen, M Darby
Radiotherapy and Oncology E J Chambers
Rheumatology P Hollingworth
Urology P Abrams, R C L Feneley, D Gillatt, J C Gingell, A G Timoney

Thornbury Hospital

Thornbury, Bristol BS12 1DN
Tel: 01454 412636 Fax: 01454 281364
Total Beds: 38

Care of the Elderly G R Burston
General Psychiatry S L W Jayewardene, I H Mian

North Cheshire Hospitals NHS Trust

From April 2002 specialist services transferring to 5 Borough Partnership NHS Trust.

Hospital Way, Runcorn WA7 2DA
Tel: 01928 714567 Fax: 01928 753104
(Cheshire and Merseyside Health Authority)

Chair John Beecham
Chief Executive Mike Deegan

Halton General Hospital

Hospital Way, Runcorn WA7 2DA
Tel: 01928 714567 Fax: 01928 753104
Total Beds: 300

Anaesthetics M G D Salem, R K Strahan
Care of the Elderly A Moloney
Dental Surgery S Rudge
Dermatology M M Molokhia
ENT S Kent, K Reddy
Gastroenterology B D Linaker
General Medicine S Church, A Khaleeli, B D Linaker, R Mallya, E Rose, C N Ugwu, J Williams
General Psychiatry M Bamforth, P Decalmer, B Green, M Green, J A Marks, S Pollet
General Surgery G H Hutchinson, J N Johnson, J E Pollet
Genitourinary Medicine M Veeravahu
Haematology K Dhir
Neurology Dr Enevoldson
Obstetrics and Gynaecology J Davies-Humphreys, J Langton
Oncology D Errington
Ophthalmology Dr Matthew
Oral Surgery D Richardson
Orthodontics S J Rudge
Orthopaedics D A Boot, P Sherry, G J Stewart
Paediatrics C Bedford, J R Briggs, Dr Mir, N Wild
Radiology J D Conway, F Fraser, T Houghton, G Murphy
Urology R Ewing, S Gupta

Warrington Hospital

Lovely Lane, Warrington WA5 1QG
Tel: 01925 635911 Fax: 01925 662099

Total Beds: 632

Accident and Emergency A Robinson, A J Saleh
Anaesthetics M G Abdel-Salam, P J Barrett, S W Crowder, E J Fazakerley, S V Jagadesh, P Jarvis, A K Malaiya, A Morrison, D K Mwanje, R E Park, C E Smith, J A Tytler
Care of the Elderly G Barton, A A Ghaffir
Dermatology M M Molokhia, M Molokjia
ENT S E Kent, K T V Reddy
General Medicine S J Bentley, J M Jefferson, B D Linaker, S Owen, D Pearson, S J S Virk
General Psychiatry S A Bokhari, N M Brooks, B Soma
General Surgery M Brett, G C Copeland, A P Moody, B A Taylor, P N Wake
Genitourinary Medicine M Veeravahu
Neurology A M Dean, T P Easvoldson
Obstetrics and Gynaecology G D Entwistle, H B Griffiths, E F N Holland, E L Kozman, G Ramsden
Ophthalmology M I Fraser, P Palimar, C O Peckar, M S Wishart
Oral Surgery J Brown
Orthodontics J W Jones
Orthopaedics D Boot, H Casserley, M B Jones, I Shackleford, P G Sherry, G Stewart
Paediatric Cardiology K P Walsh
Paediatrics C D Bedford, J R Briggs, N A Mir, N J Wild
Pathology M S Al-Jafari, A Davis, K Dhir, R J P Garvey, N Hasan, D S Shareef
Plastic Surgery P V Kumar
Radiology D K Asamoah, P Cantrell, M P Caplan, J M Desmond, A J Sheridan, R E Wild, C C Yeong
Radiotherapy and Oncology P Clark, B Cottier
Rheumatology A Salih
Thoracic Surgery R Page
Urology L Q Robinson

North Cumbria Acute Hospitals NHS Trust

West Cumberland Hospital, Hensingham, Whitehaven CA28 8JG
Tel: 01946 693181
Website: www.northcumbriahealth.nhs.uk/acute
(Cumbria and Lancashire Health Authority)

Chair Barbara Cannon
Chief Executive Nick Wood

Cumberland Infirmary

Newtown Road, Carlisle CA2 7HY
Tel: 01228 523444 Fax: 01228 591889
Total Beds: 442

Accident and Emergency J V Foxworthy
Anaesthetics J Harrison, D F Jones, S Kennedy, A Linsley, M R Payne, R C Rodgers, A Shanks, P C Stride, M D Tidmarsh, Y H Tzabar, M White
Bacteriology M A Knowles
Biochemistry C Lord
Care of the Elderly J S Billett, D P Davies, J George, J M Orgee
Chemical Pathology C Lord
Clinical Genetics J Goodship
Dermatology N H Cox, W D Paterson
General Medicine D Burke, M L Cowley, D M Large, C E McDonald, C P Mustchin, R H Robson
General Surgery F L Hinson, J D Holdsworth, J G Palmer, S Raimes, J E G Shand, M R Williams
Genitourinary Medicine B Stanley
Haematology H A W O'Brien
Histopathology A W Popple, F I Young
Medical Immunology G Spickett, A Todd
Medical Physics W I Keyes
Nephrology D N Bennett-Jones, P Mead
Neurology D Bates, M Jackson
Neurosurgery P Crawford, N Todd
Obstetrics and Gynaecology R Lawley, S E Pearson, W Reid

NHS TRUSTS & NHS HOSPITALS

Ophthalmology M Bearn, D N Depla, M Hasan, R P S Smith
Oral and Maxillofacial Surgery A W Patterson, G D Putnam
Orthodontics R Tyrrell
Orthopaedics C G Brignall, G H Broome, A N Edwards, G Ferrier, G K Ions, M Orr
Otolaryngology D R Clark, N J Murrant, A K Robson
Paediatric Oncology A Craft
Paediatrics O Sabir, J M P Storr, C A Stuart, P Whitehead
Palliative Medicine G Dunkley
Plastic Surgery P Hodgkinson, N R McLean, A C Reid
Radiology G N Athey, J Deeble, J Edge, J Jackson, P Jennings, R McNeill
Radiotherapy and Oncology P Dyson, J Nicoll
Rehabilitation Medicine M H W Roberts
Rheumatology and Rehabilitation I D L Brewis, C E Kidd
Thoracic Medicine M H Holden, G M Moritt
Urology J A Cumming, R G Willis

West Cumberland Hospital

Hensingham, Whitehaven CA28 8JG
Tel: 01946 693181 Fax: 01946 523513
Total Beds: 447

Accident and Emergency M K Greene (Head), C Brett
Anaesthetics S Frazer (Head), F Graham, M Hodson, Q Kingsbury, M Saudi, I Ulyett, G A Van Mourik, D M Watson
Care of the Elderly F K Local (Head), E Haworth, E O Orugun, N J Russell
General Medicine W T Berrill (Head), L Forbat, J D McCrea, K Willmer
General Psychiatry C Scholefield (Head), A Lamont, G Morley
General Surgery M Walker (Head), S El Rabaa, N Nik Abdulla, D G Richards, A Sowinski
Learning Disabilities A Bassam
Obstetrics and Gynaecology S A Bober (Head), J Eldred, M Jayatilika, M Matar, J Stafford
Ophthalmology P Sellar (Head), S Verghese, M Zaheen
Orthopaedics M I Dhebar (Head), M Greiss, N S Rao, D Verinder
Paediatrics P Carter (Head), M Ben-Hamida, I Boles, D Lee, S Precious
Palliative Medicine E Palmer (Head)
Pathology N C West (Head), S Mathews, C Ozo, S Richards
Psychiatry of Old Age M Bober (Head), P D Benjamin
Radiology T A Eyre (Head), N Huntley, B G Maguire, B Mucci
Rehabilitation Medicine M Roberts

North Cumbria Mental Health and Learning Disabilities NHS Trust

The Coppice, The Carleton Clinic, Carlisle CA1 3SX
Tel: 01228 602000
(Cumbria and Lancashire Health Authority)

Chief Executive Nigel Woodcock

Arnwood House

148 Blackwell Road, Carlisle CA2 4DL
Total Beds: 8

Brampton War Memorial Hospital

Brampton CA8 1TX
Tel: 016977 2534 Fax: 016977 41607
Total Beds: 15

Care of the Elderly J S Billett

The Carleton Clinic

Cumwhinton Drive, Carlisle CA1 3SX
Tel: 01228 602000
Total Beds: 142

Garlands Hospital

Carlisle CA1 3SX
Tel: 01228 602000 Fax: 01228 602550
Total Beds: 142

General Psychiatry V Y Allison-Bolger, C Hallewell, A J Macdonald, K Porter, D Prosser, C Tyrie
Psychotherapy D Prosser

Mary Hewetson Cottage Hospital (Elderly and Mental Health)

Keswick CA12 5PH
Tel: 017687 72012 Fax: 017687 75881
Total Beds: 32

General Practice J Atack, M J Hamilton, J D Mitchell, P H White
Ophthalmology M Bearn
Orthopaedics H M Barber
Rheumatology I D L Brewis
Urology J A Cumming

Orton Lea

Orton Road, Carlisle CA9 3QX
Total Beds: 6

Penrith Hospital

Bridge Lane, Penrith CA11 8HX
Tel: 01768 245300 Fax: 01768 245302
Total Beds: 89

Care of the Elderly J S Billett, P L Chin
Dermatology N H Cox, W D Patterson
General Medicine P Mustchin
General Psychiatry C Tyrie
General Surgery J G Palmer
Obstetrics and Gynaecology A A Brown, R G Rangecroft, W Reid
Ophthalmology M Hasan
Orthopaedics C G Brignall, G H H Broome, A N Edwards
Paediatrics J M P Storr
Rheumatology and Rehabilitation I Brewis
Urology R G Willis

Ruth Lancaster James Cottage Hospital

Alston CA9 3QX
Tel: 01434 381218 Fax: 01434 381 2134
Total Beds: 13

General Practice M T Hanley, S L Mills

Wigton Hospital

Wigton CA7 9DD
Tel: 016973 43121 Fax: 016973 45766
Total Beds: 35

Care of the Elderly J George
General Practice G Brown, J Honeyman, C Russell, R Swindells

Windermere Day Hospital (EMI)

West Cumberland Hospital, Whitehaven CA28 8JG
Tel: 01946 693181 Fax: 01946 523513
Total Beds: 22

North Derbyshire Community Health Care Service NHS Trust

Closing April 2002 - Mental health services transferring to Derbyshire Mental Health Services NHS Trust.

Trust HQ, Walton Hospital, Whitecotes Lane, Chesterfield S40 3HW
Tel: 01246 551785 Fax: 01246 206162
(Trent Health Authority)

Chair Dianne M Jeffrey
Chief Executive Maggie Cork

Ash Green Learning Disabilities Centre

Ashgate Road, Ashgate, Chesterfield S42 7JE
Tel: 01246 565000 Fax: 01246 565014
Total Beds: 40

Bolsover Day Hospital

Welbeck Road, Bolsover, Chesterfield S44 7DG
Tel: 01246 827901 ext: 156 Fax: 01246 240373

Bolsover Local Hospital

Welbeck Road, Bolsover, Chesterfield S44 6DH
Tel: 01246 827901 Fax: 01246 240373
Total Beds: 72

Care of the Elderly P K Sinha
Psychiatry of Old Age J R Sykes

Buxton Hospital

London Road, Buxton SK17 9NJ
Tel: 01298 22293 Fax: 01298 71702
Total Beds: 30

Anaesthetics K O Sullivan
Chest Disease B Chargee
Child Health M R Reynolds
Chiropody and Podiatry B T Brown
Dermatology J B O'Driscoll
ENT N J Kay
General Medicine P Hale
General Surgery W Brough, M Davies, P C England, P Gallagher
Obstetrics and Gynaecology C Candelier, D Swinhoe
Paediatrics K Lacey, M A A Siddiqi
Radiology J Glaves, M R P Shaw
Urology P J C Brooman

Cavendish Day Hospital

Manchester Road, Buxton SK17 6TE

Cavendish Hospital

Manchester Road, Buxton SK17 6TE
Tel: 01298 79236 Fax: 01298 72054
Total Beds: 51

Care of the Elderly J Catania
Psychiatry of Old Age J Galloway

Clay Cross Hospital

Market Street, Clay Cross, Chesterfield S45 9NZ
Tel: 01246 863031 Fax: 01246 861602
Total Beds: 35

Care of the Elderly P Iqbal
Psychiatry of Old Age J R Sykes

Elderly Rehabilitation Unit

Whitecotes Lane, Chesterfield S40 3HW

Care of the Elderly D Chew, P Iqbal, P Metcalf, M Reza, P K Sinha

Newholme Hospital

Bakewell DE45 1AD
Tel: 01629 812525 Fax: 01629 813479
Total Beds: 48

Walton Hospital

Whitecotes Lane, Chesterfield S40 3HW
Tel: 01246 277271 Fax: 01246 558747
Total Beds: 200

Care of the Elderly D Chew, P Iqbal, P Medcalf, M Reza, P K Sinha
Dermatology G B Colver
Orthopaedics T R Allen, C G Beauchamp, A G Davies, K A Ennis, I R Scott
Psychiatry of Old Age J R Sykes, V M Whittingham

Whitworth Hospital

330 Bakewell Road, Matlock DE4 2JD
Tel: 01629 580211 Fax: 01629 583037
Total Beds: 47

Care of the Elderly D Chew
Dermatology G B Colver
ENT F M Nofal
General Medicine D G Ashton, J W Hadfield
General Surgery D Bardsley, S Holt, W Lambert, J M Sims
Learning Disabilities R Madina
Obstetrics and Gynaecology D Fothergill, J M McDonnell
Ophthalmology K Mohamad
Paediatrics M R Reynolds
Rheumatology J Bourne

North Devon Primary Care Trust

12 Bouport Street, Barnstaple EX31 1RW
Tel: 01271 327779
(South West Peninsula Health Authority)

Chair Dennis Osbourne
Chief Executive Kate Tomkins

North Dorset Primary Care Trust

Forston Clinic, Herrison Centre, Dorchester DT2 9TB
Tel: 01305 361300 Fax: 01305 361330
(Somerset and Dorset Health Authority)

Chair Mary Penfold
Chief Executive Paul Turner

North Durham Health Care NHS Trust

Dryburn Hospital, North Road, Durham DH1 5TW
Tel: 0191 333 2150 Fax: 0191 333 2699
(County Durham and Tees Valley Health Authority)

Chair Angela Ballatt
Chief Executive Steven Mason
Consultants J Banks, W Ellis, S Green

Dryburn Hospital

North Road, Durham DH1 5TW
Tel: 0191 333 2333 Fax: 0191 333 2685
Total Beds: 427

Accident and Emergency J G Banks, C E Phillips
Anaesthetics W G M Bremner, G W Brown, S C Craddock, S Dowson, C R D Laird, M Lothian, P A McBride, R W D Mitchell, A W Murray, I Spencer, D G Thomas, S Tomlinson, D Weatherill, R Will, D W Wood, P J Wood
Care of the Elderly H A Brown, P M Earnshaw, S G Hutchinson, P Robson, I Wandless
Chest Disease P Cook, N C Munro, S J Pearce
Dermatology M M Carr, J Langtry, S Natarajan, S Sinclair, S Velangi
ENT T G Leontsinis, L Lindsey, P R Samuel, F W Stafford
General Medicine M H Cave, W R Ellis, M I McHugh, A F Macklon, A M Martin, E Sanders, J Y Yiannakou
General Surgery I Bain, K R Clark, A I M Cook, P J Cullen, P J English, S Green, I E Hawthorn, D W Herring
Genitourinary Medicine A G Wardropper, C White
Haematology A Iqbal, F M Keenan
Neurology D J Burn
Obstetrics and Gynaecology D Irons, F H Lloyd, J D Lorimer, P Marsden, G E Morgan, B S Sengupta, S Shanmugalingham, D R White
Ophthalmology J P Deady, S J Morgan, P Tiffin
Oral and Maxillofacial Surgery I C Martin

NHS TRUSTS & NHS HOSPITALS

Orthodontics I Shaw
Orthopaedics H P Epstein, R J H Gregory, D V Heath, A Jennings, K U Wright
Paediatrics T G Omoregie, D R S Smith, A N P Speight, H V Stewart
Pathology D Allison, P D Barrett, G Horne, D J L Maloney, R D G Neely, J A Zuk
Plastic Surgery M Erdmann, R B Perry
Radiology P Cadigan, S M Desai, S N E Marsden, I Minty, S K Young
Radiotherapy and Oncology C G Kelly, W B Taylor
Rheumatology A J Chuck, S Hailwood, P Mangion
Urology P Richmond, C Roberts

Earls House Hospital

Lanchester Road, Durham DH1 5RE
Tel: 0191 333 6262 Fax: 0191 333 6363
Total Beds: 100

Nuffield Day Hospital

Dryburn Hospital, North Road, Durham DH1 5TW
Tel: 0191 332666

Shotley Bridge Hospital

Shotley Bridge Hospital, Consett DH8 0NB
Tel: 01207 583583 Fax: 01207 586003
Total Beds: 336

Anaesthetics D I MacNair, M Sekar
Cardiothoracic Medicine G N Morritt
Community Child Health S K Pandey
Dermatology F A Ive
ENT D S Cameron
General Medicine A P Mukherjee, P Robson
General Psychiatry J M Brockington, K B Gururaj-Prasad, K Hurren, P E Watson
General Surgery D Gatehouse, J R Mason
Haematology D Stainsby
Obstetrics and Gynaecology B Johnston
Ophthalmology R C Bosanquet, R F Gillie
Oral and Maxillofacial Surgery J M Ryan
Orthodontics I A Shaw
Orthopaedics V S Nargolwala
Paediatrics B Thalayasingam
Pathology D Allison, C M Dobson, J A Zuk
Plastic Surgery R B Berry, J H James, G S Rao
Radiology J Gholkar, R A Robson, G Timmons
Radiotherapy and Oncology R C B Evans

South Moor Hospital

South Moor, Stanley DH9 6DS
Tel: 0191 333 6262
Total Beds: 20

North East Ambulance Service NHS Trust

Scotswood House, Amethyst Road, Newcastle Business Park, Newcastle upon Tyne NE4 7YL
Tel: 0191 273 1212 Fax: 0191 273 7070
(Northumberland, Tyne and Wear Health Authority)

Chair Peter Innes
Chief Executive Simon Featherstone

North East Lincolnshire Primary Care Trust

Scartho Hall, Scartho Road, Grimsby DN33 2BA
Tel: 01472 875621 Fax: 01472 503257

(North and East Yorkshire and Northern Lincolnshire Health Authority)

Chair Valerie Waterhouse
Chief Executive Jane Lewington

North East London Mental Health NHS Trust

Trust Head Office, Tantallon House, Goodmayes Hospital Campus, Barley Lane, Ilford IG3 8YB
Tel: 020 8590 6060 Fax: 020 8970 8424
Website: www.nelmht.nhs.uk
(North East London Health Authority)

Chapters House

Goodmayes Hospital Campus, Barley Lane, Goodmayes, Ilford IG3 8XJ
Tel: 0208 590 6060 Fax: 020 8970 8170
Total Beds: 70

General Psychiatry S Pereira, P Caveston, M Cleany, R Duffett, A El-Hadi, L Feldman, M Jones, A Lau, R Littlejohn, M Magner, A M Margo

Mascalls Park

Mascalls Lane, Warley, Brentwood CM14 5HQ
Tel: 01277 302600 Fax: 01277 302602

General Psychiatry M Frampton, J Chaloner, F Dunne, A Majid, S Mathur, S Srikumour, A C Purches, J Taylor

Nasebury Court

2 Merrien Close, London E4 9JQ

Stonlea

Langthorne Road, London E11 4HJ

Woodbury Unit

Whipps Cross Hospital, Samuel Boyce Lodge, 178 James Lane, London E11 1NU

North East Oxfordshire Primary Care Trust

Montgomery House Surgery, Piggy Lane, Bicester OX6 7HT
Tel: 01869 876540 Fax: 01869 876544
(Thames Valley Health Authority)

Chair Ian Inshaw
Chief Executive Geraint Griffiths

North East Warwickshire Primary Care Trust

Westgate House, 21 Market Street, Warwick CV34 4DE
(Coventry, Warwickshire, Herefordshire and Worcestershire Health Authority)

North Eastern Derbyshire Primary Care Trust

St Mary's Court, St Mary's Gate, Chesterfield S41 7TD
Tel: 01246 551158 Fax: 01246 544620
(Trent Health Authority)

Chief Executive Kevin Holder

North Essex Mental Health Partnership NHS Trust

Cuton Hall, Cuton Hall Lane, Springfield, Chelmsford CM2 5PX
Tel: 01245 318400 Fax: 01245 318401
(Essex Health Authority)

Chair Mary St Aubyn
Chief Executive Richard Coleman

Chelmsford and Essex Day Unit
New London Road, Chelmsford CM2 9QU
Tel: 01245 318600 Fax: 01245 318601

Ferguson Close
Radwinter Road, Saffron Walden CB11 3HY
Tel: 01799 528088
Total Beds: 24

The Gables Day Hospital
17 Bocking End, Braintree CM7 9AE
Tel: 01376 555700 Fax: 01376 555705

Harwich Day Hospital
419 Main Road, Dovercourt, Harwich CO12 4EX
Tel: 01255 207400 Fax: 01255 207417

Herts and Essex General Hospital
Haymeads Lane, Bishop's Stortford CM23 5JH
Tel: 01279 655191
Total Beds: 115

Care of the Elderly A Dain, R Morgan, R Whale
Genitourinary Medicine M A E Symonds

Longview Adolescent Unit
216 Turner Road, Colchester CO4 5JR
Tel: 01206 228745
Total Beds: 10

Martello Court Day Hospital
Clacton Hospital, Tower Road, Clacton-on-Sea CO15 1LH
Tel: 01255 253540 Fax: 01255 222352

Mayfield Centre (Day Hospital)
93 Station Road, Clacton-on-Sea CO15 1TX
Tel: 01255 207040 Fax: 01255 207044

Ongar War Memorial Hospital
Fyfield Road, Shelley, Ongar CM5 0AL
Tel: 01277 362629
Total Beds: 13

Rannoch Lodge
146 Broomfield Road, Chelmsford CM1 1RN
Tel: 01245 544869 Fax: 01245 544888

Saffron Walden Community Hospital
Radwinter Road, Saffron Walden CB11 3HY
Tel: 01799 522464
Total Beds: 56

St Margaret's Hospital
The Plain, Epping CM16 6TN
Tel: 01992 561666
Total Beds: 62

Care of the Elderly G Ambepitiya
General Psychiatry S El-Fadl, W Lang, P Robotis, Z Walker

Severalls House
2 Boxted Road, Colchester CO4 4HG
Tel: 01206 228630 Fax: 01206 228660
Total Beds: 21

Spencer Close
The Plain, Epping CM16 6TU
Tel: 01992 578755
Total Beds: 26

Stanwell House
Stanwell Street, Colchester CO2 7DL
Tel: 01206 287321 Fax: 01206 287320

White Lodge Day Unit
21 Coggeshall Road, Braintree CM7 6DB
Tel: 01376 308250 Fax: 01376 308251

Willow House
2 Boxted Road, Colchester CO4 5HG
Tel: 01206 228691

Wych Elm House
Hamstel Road, Harlow CM20 1QR
Tel: 01279 692300 Fax: 01279 692323

North Hampshire Hospitals NHS Trust

Aldermaston Road, Basingstoke RG24 9NA
Tel: 01256 473202 Fax: 01256 313098
Email: Laura.Cullum@bas.swest.nhs.uk
(Hampshire and Isle of Wight Health Authority)

Chair Colin Davies
Chief Executive Mark Davies

North Hampshire Hospital
Basingstoke RG24 9NA
Tel: 01256 473302 Fax: 01256 313098
Total Beds: 450

Accident and Emergency B C Elvin, J Kitching, H Simpson
Anaesthetics S Ali, P J C Baxter, P Creagh-Barry, A C Haigh, J E Hurley, D W Robins, M A Rose, K Thomas, J K G Wells, P Wilson
Care of the Elderly S Arianaliagam, J Bernstein, J Mallya
Dermatology M Crone, H A Fawcett, Dr Powell
ENT J Blanshard, P Spraggs
General Medicine A Bishop, C Brookes, R J C Guy, K McKinlay, J Ramage, T Yek
General Surgery C Eden, D Gold, T John, B Moran, M Rees, A B Richards, A S Ward
Genitourinary Medicine D H Jackson
Neurology N Lawton, M Prevett
Obstetrics and Gynaecology R Bates, T Sayer, B O'Sullivan
Ophthalmology S Keightley, D Morseman, C Sandy
Oral and Maxillofacial Surgery C Kerawala
Orthodontics R T Reed
Orthopaedics J Benfield, J Britton, J Hobby, G Stranks, N P Thomas
Paediatrics P Llangoyan, A Mitchell, J Pleydon-Pearle, R O Walters, R Wigfield
Pathology D L Aston, J M Finch, E M Husband, A Milne, H S Platt
Radiology I Green, H O'Neill, J C Parker, G R T Plant, D F Shelley
Radiotherapy and Oncology G Sharpe, S Tinkler
Rheumatology C Batten, P Prouse, D Shane

NHS TRUSTS & NHS HOSPITALS

North Hampshire Primary Care Trust

Parklands Hospital, Executive Suite, Aldermaston Road, Basingstoke RG24 9RH
Tel: 01256 376391 Fax: 01256 376330
(Hampshire and Isle of Wight Health Authority)

Chair Tony Ludlow
Chief Executive Gill Duncan

North Hertfordshire and Stevenage Primary Care Trust

Solutions House, Dunhams Lane, Letchworth SG6 1BE
Tel: 01462 708470
(Bedfordshire and Hertfordshire Health Authority)

Chair Rachel Fox
Chief Executive Jill Peters

North Kirklees Primary Care Trust

12 Central Arcade, Cleckheaton BD19 5DN
Tel: 01924 359359 Fax: 01924 359935
(West Yorkshire Health Authority)

North Lincolnshire Primary Care Trust

Health Place, Wrawby Road, Brigg DN20 8GS
Tel: 01652 601233 Fax: 01652 601160
Email: cathy.waters@shumber-ha.trent.nhs.uk
Website: www.nlincspcg.org
(North and East Yorkshire and Northern Lincolnshire Health Authority)

Chair John Mason
Chief Executive Cathy Waters

North Liverpool Primary Care Trust

Cottage No 7, Newhall Campus, Longmoor Lane, Liverpool L10 1LD
Tel: 0151 239 1900 Fax: 0151 284 7517
Chair Lilly Hopkins
Chief Executive Joanne Forrest

North Manchester Healthcare NHS Trust

Closing April 2002 - Services transferring to Pennine Acute Hospitals NHS Trust.

North Manchester General Hospital, Crumpsall, Manchester M8 5RL
Tel: 0161 795 4567 Fax: 0161 740 4450
(Greater Manchester Health Authority)

Chair William Egerton
Chief Executive Elaine Leaver

North Manchester General Hospital

Crumpsall, Manchester M8 6RL
Tel: 0161 795 4567 Fax: 0161 720 2705
Total Beds: 898

Accident and Emergency Dr Derbyshire, L Duane, P E Randall, M J Stuart

Anaesthetics R Bhishma, G S C Brown, I S Chadwick, I K Hartopp, Dr Jones, V Kapoor, P Kirk, I D Macartney, R Mayall, H V Petts, G E W Robson, P H Steller, H D Vallance, H A C Walker, Y Y Youssef
Cardiology P Atkinson, J Swan
Care of the Elderly Dr Ahmed, P Gibson, V Khanna, M Yates
ENT Dr Murphy, Z P Shehab, A P Zarod
General Medicine S P Hanley, H J Klass, Dr Mcfarlane, M G Pattrick, D C Weir
General Psychiatry N R Bishay, D J Marshall, A Theodossiadis, B T Williams, E Wyn-Pugh
General Surgery J M T Howat, M Madan, D J Sherlock, W F Tait, Dr Vadeyar, Dr Walls, G T Williams, R J Williams
Genitourinary Medicine S P Higgins
Haematology Dr Robertson, M Rowlands
Histopathology D M Butterworth, D M H De Kretser
Infectious Diseases Dr Bonington, E M Dunbar, E G L Wilkins
Neurophysiology I H Bangash
Obstetrics and Gynaecology A M Ferguson, A S Jones, D Macfoy, C F Rice
Occupational Medicine T Persad
Ophthalmology S J Charles
Oral and Maxillofacial Surgery A G Addy, Dr Bhatti, Dr Boyd, M E Foster, P R White, R T M Wodwards
Orthopaedics A D Clayson, T M Meadows, P Rae, D Sochart, B S Sylvester
Pathology Dr Butterworth, Dr de Kretser, M Hammer, H Panigrahi, Dr Robertson, Dr Rowlands
Radiology M R C Aird, Y S Al-Khattab, R A L Bissett, C Jones, A N Khan, N B Thomas, I W Turnbull, Dr Walker
Restorative Dentistry T Boyd
Rheumatology and Rehabilitation Dr Harrison, N Snowden
Urology D Barnes, W M Chow, C B Costello

North Manchester Primary Care Trust

Victoria Mill, off Varley Street, Lower Vickers St, Miles Platting, Manchester M40 7LG
Tel: 0161 205 4796 Fax: 0161 205 5961
Email: mnpct@manchester.nwest.nhs.uk
Website: www.manchesterhealth.co.uk
(Greater Manchester Health Authority)

Chair Winfred Dignan
Chief Executive Laura Roberts

North Mersey Community NHS Trust

Rathbone Hospital (HQ), Mill Lane, Liverpool L9 7JP
Tel: 0151 250 3000 Fax: 0151 228 0486
(Cheshire and Merseyside Health Authority)

Chair Rosemary Hawley
Chief Executive Alan Yates

Sir Alfred Jones Memorial Hospital

Church Road, Garston, Liverpool L19 2LP
Tel: 0151 250 3000 Fax: 0151 494 0163
Total Beds: 28

North Middlesex University Hospital NHS Trust

Sterling Way, London N18 1QX
Tel: 020 8887 2000 Fax: 020 8887 4219
(North Central London Health Authority)

Chair Jane Kelly
Chief Executive Rosie Gibb

North Middlesex Hospital

Sterling Way, Edmonton, London N18 1QX
Tel: 020 8887 2000 Fax: 020 8887 4219
Total Beds: 400

Accident and Emergency E Weithers (Head), A E Rajarajan
Anaesthetics I N Rao (Head), A Chan, M Jesuthasan, P Patel, N Poobalasingam, A Ramachandran, D Shah, S Siriwardhana
Cardiology S O Banim (Head), T Crake
Chemical Pathology P West
Chest Disease S Lozewicz (Head), H Makker
Clinical Oncology N Davidson (Head), S A Davies, S J Karp, P Leone, F F Neave
Dermatology J J R Almeyda (Head), T A Mann
Diabetes H Tindall
ENT D I Choa, H Grant, T Joseph
General Medicine J Ainsworth, A Millar, J Onwubalili, M Vanderpump
General Surgery R J Croft, D M Melville, D L Stoker, J J Wood
Haematology T O Kumaran, J K Luckit, D A Yardumian
Histopathology K J Jarvis, M Sundaresan
Infectious Diseases Y M Yong
Medical Microbiology Y N Drabu, P Lee
Neurology J Gawler
Obstetrics and Gynaecology F Evans, P Hardiman, S Okolo
Ophthalmology G Palexus, R M Phillips, S Shah, E Taylor, K A Thiagarajah
Orthodontics P S G Perera
Orthopaedics J H Challis, M Kurer, Dr Trakru, V Woolf
Paediatrics L Alsford, M Meates, M A Rossiter, A R Shah
Radiology R L Borgstein, A Dinath-Seedat, A Husien, S Pathmanandam, M R Sebastianpillai, J Stroudley
Radiotherapy and Oncology N Davidson, S A Davies, S J Karp, F F Neave
Rheumatology and Rehabilitation M F Grayson, H D Sinclair
Urology G Fowlis, J A McDonald

North Norfolk Primary Care Trust

Kelling Hospital, Cromer Road, Holt NR25 6QA
Tel: 01263 710611 Fax: 01263 710645
Email: office@nnpcg.org
Website: www.nnpcg.org
(Norfolk, Suffolk and Cambridgeshire Health Authority)

Chair Lee Muston
Chief Executive Diana Clarke

North Peterborough Primary Care Trust

St John's, Thorpe Road, Peterborough PE3 6JG
Tel: 01733 882288 Fax: 01733 882293
(Norfolk, Suffolk and Cambridgeshire Health Authority)

Chair Mohammad Choudhary
Chief Executive Chris Town

North Sefton and West Lancashire Community NHS Trust

Closing April 2002 - Services transferring to Lancashire Care NHS Trust.

Ormskirk and District General Hospital, Wigan Road, Ormskirk L39 2JW
Tel: 01695 598000 Fax: 01695 598104
(Cumbria and Lancashire Health Authority)

Chair Sylvia McGeachie
Chief Executive Geoff Hammond

Bickerstaffe House
Ormskirk & District General Hospital, Wigan Road, Ormskirk L39 2JW
Total Beds: 54

Adult Mental Health G Ash, P Mason, M McKenzie
Elderly Mentally Ill C Broadhurst

North Sheffield Primary Care Trust

Welfare House, North Quadrant, Firth Park, Sheffield S5 6NU
Tel: 0114 226 4031 Fax: 0114 226 4030
Website: www.sheffield-ha.nhs.uk
(South Yorkshire Health Authority)

Chair Robert Bailey

North Somerset Primary Care Trust

1st Floor The Courthouse, 25-27 Old Weston Road, Flax Bourton, Bristol BS48 1UL
Tel: 01275 465200 Fax: 01275 464995
Website: www.avon.nhs.uk/nsomerset/
(Avon, Gloucestershire and Wiltshire Health Authority)

Chair Jane Corke

North Staffordshire Combined Healthcare NHS Trust

Bucknall Hospital, Eaves Lane, Bucknall, Stoke-on-Trent ST2 8LD
Tel: 01782 273510 Fax: 01782 275116
Website: www.nsch-tr.wmids.nhs.uk
(Shropshire and Staffordshire Health Authority)

Chief Executive Christopher Buttanshaw

Boulton Ward, Haywood Hospital
High Lane, Burslem, Stoke-on-Trent ST6 7AQ
Tel: 01782 425795
Total Beds: 25

General Medicine R C Hayter

Bradwell Hospital
Talke Road, Chesterton, Stoke-on-Trent
Tel: 01782 425400 Fax: 01782 425408
Total Beds: 74

General Medicine P Crome
General Psychiatry M Davies

Bucknall Hospital
Eaves Lane, Bucknall, Stoke-on-Trent ST2 8LD
Tel: 01782 273510 Fax: 01782 275116
Total Beds: 123

General Medicine M Browne, R C Hayter, K P Patel, S Sangeelee

Cheadle Hospital
Royal Walk, Cheadle, Stoke-on-Trent ST10 1NS
Tel: 01538 487500 Fax: 01538 487538
Total Beds: 81

General Medicine M Browne

City General Hospital
Elderly Care Unit, 578 Newcastle Road, Stoke-on-Trent ST4 6QG
Total Beds: 84

General Medicine M Browne, P Crome, R C Hayter, K P Patel, C Roffe

NHS TRUSTS & NHS HOSPITALS

Greenfield Centre
Mental Resource Centre, Furlong Road (behind Furlong Medical Centre), Tunstall, Stoke-on-Trent ST6 5UD
Tel: 01782 425740 Fax: 01782 425741
Total Beds: 8

Leek Moorlands Hospital
Ashbourne Road, Leek ST13 5BQ
Tel: 01538 487100 Fax: 01538 487138
Total Beds: 66

General Medicine Dr Paul

Longton Cottage Hospital
Upper Belgrave Road, Longton, Stoke-on-Trent ST3 4QX
Tel: 01782 425600 Fax: 01782 425656
Total Beds: 43

Elderly Care Dr Patel

Roundwell Place Day Hospital
Roundwell Street, Tunstall, Stoke-on-Trent ST6 5JJ
Tel: 01782 425732

Westcliffe Hospital
Turnhurst Road, Chell, Stoke-on-Trent ST6 6LA
Tel: 01782 425860 Fax: 91782 425878
Total Beds: 68

Care of the Elderly Dr Patel

North Staffordshire Hospital NHS Trust

Trust Headquarters, North Staffordshire Royal Infirmary, Princes Road, Stoke-on-Trent ST4 7LN
Tel: 01782 715444 Fax: 01782 555202
(Shropshire and Staffordshire Health Authority)

Chair Calum Paton
Chief Executive Stephen Eames

North Staffordshire Hospital
Trust Headquarters, North Staffordshire Royal Infirmary, Princes Road, Stoke-on-Trent ST4 7LN
Tel: 01782 715444 Fax: 01782 555202
Total Beds: 1386

Anaesthetics Dr Akhtar, S A Araffin, J Ashworth, Dr Baker, B Carr, A J Carter, N W B Clowes, N A Coleman, N Eastwood, S Edmends, S J Foster, D Frechini, J C Hindmarsh, C Howell, P Jeyaratam, C L Knight, F Y Lamm, M E Lauckner, Dr Lennon, C G Male, N C Matthews, Dr Mills, P Morrison, P Oakley, Dr Payne, C P Rice, S J Seddon, B Smith, I Smith, A I Stewart, A A Tomlinson, J Wilkins, V Williams

Cardiology M Clarke, J Creamer, J A S Davis, J Nolan, P O'Gorman

Cardiothoracic Surgery A J Levine, J Nolan, J M Parmar, P Ridley

Clinical Pharmacology and Therapeutics J C Mucklow

Community Medicine J Davidson, P Lithgow, K Reynolds, S Williams

Dermatology J P H Byrne, A G Smith, B B Tan

E.N.T. Surgery M V Carlin, Dr Courteney-Harris, J T Little, P Wilson

Emergency Medicine C Gray, I Phair

Endocrinology R Clayton, J H B Scarpello, A Walker

General Surgery Dr Adjogatse, M Deakin, T J Duffy, J B Elder, J F Forrest, C Hall, G Hopkinson, R Kirby, R Morgan, A Walsh

Genitourinary Medicine G Singh, S Sivapalan

Infectious Diseases H Tubbs

Nephrology S Davies, P N Harden, P Naish, G I Russell

Neurology H G Boddie, S J Ellis, C Hawkins

Neurophysiology P Heath

Neurosurgery H Brydon, P Dias, J Singh

Obstetrics and Gynaecology J Cooper, J D Gough, R Johanson, G Masson, V Menon, M Obhrai, P O'Brien, C Redman

Oncology F A Adab, A M Brunt, A Cook, J E Scobie

Ophthalmology R D Brown, J D A Common, T Gillow, P A Shaw

Oral Surgery Dr Grime, T Mallins, Dr Perry

Orthodontics J D Muir

Orthopaedics E N Ahmed, M Brown, I Dos Remedios, J Dove, J Dwyer, D Griffiths, D McBride, N Neale, J Templeton, P Thomas, C H Wynn Jones

Paediatrics D Brookfield, C Campbell, W Lenney, B Ley, A Magnay, A A Melville, K Palmer, P M Rafeeq, M Samuels, P Smith, D Southall, S A Spencer

Pathology R C Chasty, P M Chipping, G Douce, M C Garrido, J Gray, R M Ibbotson, C Musgrove, R H Neary, M Rogerson, V Smith, M Stephens, N D Williams

Plastic Surgery P Davison, Dr Prinsloo, J O Roberts

Radiology S Bajwa, D Bakalinova, M Braithwaite, N Haq, J Oxtoby, P Richards, J Saklatvala, M D Skinner, S Tebby, N A Watson, D West, D Wilcock

Rehabilitation Medicine A B Ward

Respiratory Medicine M Allen, C F A Pantin, K Prowse, M A Spiteri

Rheumatology P T Dawes, A B Hassell, E Hay, T E Hothersall, M F Shadforth

Urology M French, S Liu, M Saxby

North Stoke Primary Care Trust

Haywood Hospital, High Lane, Burslem, Stoke-on-Trent ST6 7AG
Tel: 01782 817428 Fax: 01782 817712
Website: www.northstokepcg.com
(Shropshire and Staffordshire Health Authority)

Chair Brenda McGough
Chief Executive Peter Hammersley

North Surrey Primary Care Trust

Bournewood House, St Peter's Hospital, Guildford Road, Chertsey KT16 0QA
Tel: 01932 723577 Fax: 01932 877680
Website: www.surreythames.nhs.uk

North Tees and Hartlepool NHS Trust

University Hospital of Hartlepool, Holdforth Road, Hartlepool TS24 9AH
Tel: 01429 266654 Fax: 01429 235389
(Tees Health Authority)

Chair Bryan Hanson
Chief Executive Joan E Rogers

Peterlee Community Hospital
O'Neill Drive, North Blunts, Peterlee SR8 5TZ
Tel: 0191 586 3474 Fax: 0191 586 6562

University Hospital of Hartlepool
Holdforth Road, Hartlepool TS24 9AH
Tel: 01429 266654 Fax: 01429 235389
Email: comms@hed.br.northy
Total Beds: 334

Accident and Emergency J Clancy, A Simpson, D Southward

Anaesthetics V L Gupta, H Mohan, D Morle, J J Rao, M K Roy, K Uddin, G Vadnai

Community Health K N Agrawal

Dermatologist S Shehade

ENT M Hawthorne

Genitourinary Medicine S Tayal

Medicine D W Bruce, B K Chaudhury, B F Hannigan, A Khan, P P Sutton, C R Ward
Obstetrics and Gynaecology M A El-Menabawey, A A Robertson, S R Tosson
Occupational Health C J English
Oral Surgery B Avery
Orthodontist N A Fox
Orthopaedics C M E Lennox, A Rangan, M A Shaheen, A Shetty, S C Tang
Paediatrics S Gupta, J C Jani, D N Symon
Pathology J K S Frater, M O Mohamdee, S Pollard, A Youart
Radiology D Hide, A A Jwad, A V Kidambi, H Kidambi
Surgery H Bandi, R Kirby, G McLatchie, R Thomson, C P L Wood

University Hospital of North Tees

Hardwick, Stockton-on-Tees TS19 8PE
Tel: 01642 617617
Total Beds: 446

Accident and Emergency D Emerton, P Stamp, S Wadhwani
Anaesthetics P Broadway, H Contractor, S Gooneratne, J E Hall, G Harris, S Jurgens, P Ritchie, P Royle, V Sarma
Dermatology A Carmichael, A Milligan, W Taylor
Medicine D Carr, A W Dellipiani, D Dwarakanath, R Harrison, B Herd, A Shyam-Sundar, R Smith, P Snashall, D Spence, A Tanner, D Wright
Obstetrics and Gynaecology E V Gouk, H M Hatem, J Macaulay, I C Macleod, E A Ryall, S Walton
Occupational Health C J English
Orthopaedics N Bayliss, M Krishna, S Maheswaran, D Miller, C Tulloch
Paediatrics R Dias, C I Harikumar, C McCowen, B McLain, M Oo, I Verber, K A Whiting
Pathology R Finney, J Hoffman, Z T Maung, M Noone, C Rettman
Radiology P Gill, T Hughes, J Latimer, P Tait, W Thompson, M J Trewhella
Radiology and Oncology S L Chawla
Surgery L Gillland, C Hennessy, A Peel, D Rosenberg, L Rosenberg, M A Tabaqchali, - Yassin

North Tees Primary Care Trust

Tower House, Teesdale South, Thornaby Place, Thornaby TS17 6SE
Tel: 01642 352297 Fax: 01642 351644
Website: www.northteespcg.co.uk
(Tees Health Authority)

Chair Richard Nicholson
Chief Executive Christine Willis

North Tyneside Primary Care Trust

Benfield Road, Walkergate, Newcastle upon Tyne NE6 4PF
Tel: 0191 219 6000 Fax: 0191 219 6066
(Northumberland, Tyne and Wear Health Authority)

Chair David Luke
Chief Executive Pam McDougall

North Warwickshire NHS Trust

Trust closure tbc - Part of service transferring to North East Warwickshire Primary Care Trust and Rugby Primary Care Trust.

139 Earls Road, Nuneaton CV11 5HP
Tel: 024 7664 2200 Fax: 024 7635 1434
(Coventry, Warwickshire, Herefordshire and Worcestershire Health Authority)

Chair Cynthia Banning
Chief Executive Anne Heckles

Bramcote Hospital

Lutterworth Road, Nuneaton CV11 6QL
Tel: 024 7638 8200 Fax: 024 7635 0616
Total Beds: 44

Care of the Elderly A W Bullen, A B Whitehouse
Child and Adolescent Psychiatry S Thavasothy

Brooklands Hospital

Coleshill Road, Marston Green, Birmingham B37 7HL
Tel: 0121 779 6981 Fax: 0121 779 4695
Total Beds: 129

General Psychiatry M Baxter, A Roy, C Sansom, N Suleman

Hospital of St Cross

Barby Road, Rugby CV22 5PX
Total Beds: 36

Lea Castle Hospital

Wolverley, Kidderminster DY10 3PP
Tel: 01562 850461
Total Beds: 79

Learning Disabilities J A Corbett, A J Martin, D E Tesh
Ophthalmology C J Tallents
Orthopaedics D K Cleak
Paediatrics P S Crawley

Manor Hospital

Manor Court Avenue, Nuneaton CV11 5SP
Tel: 024 7635 1351
Total Beds: 30

North West Anglia Health Care NHS Trust

Closing April 2002 - Mental health services transferring to Cambridgeshire and Peterborough Mental Health Partnership NHS Trust.

53 Thorpe Road, Peterborough PE3 6AN
Tel: 01733 318108 Fax: 01733 318139
Email: laschetting@nwahc-tr.anglox.nhs.uk
(Norfolk, Suffolk and Cambridgeshire Health Authority)

Chair D Lanicester
Chief Executive S Hatton

Stamford and Rutland Hospital

Ryhall Road, Stamford PE9 1UA
Tel: 01780 764151 Fax: 01780 763385

Swaffham Hospital

Swaffham PE37 7HL
Tel: 01760 21363

North West London Hospitals NHS Trust

Northwick Park and St. Mark's Hospital, Watford Road, Harrow HA1 3UJ
Tel: 020 8864 3232 Fax: 020 8869 2009
(North West London Health Authority)

Chair Alastair McDonald
Chief Executive John Pope

Central Middlesex Hospital

Acton Lane, Park Royal, London NW10 7NS
Tel: 020 8965 5733 Fax: 020 8961 0012
Total Beds: 240

NHS TRUSTS & NHS HOSPITALS

Accident and Emergency J Hayes, A Sivakumar, S S Tachakra
Anaesthetics G Abbondati, M A Ali, I F Collier, D Davies, R Griffin, K Kurer, P L Pantin, S Wijegitilleka, M Wrigley
Audiological Medicine D A Bumby
Cardiology T Bowker, C M Dancy, D W Davies
Cardiothoracic Surgery R d L Stanbridge
Care of the Elderly C Cayley, B Kaufman, D McCrea
Chemical Pathology P Frost
Dermatology A Powles
ENT S Abramovich, R Ryan, P C A Taylor
Gastroenterology A Raimundo, D Sherman, D B A Silk
General Medicine D Brown, A Grenfell, A Palmer, S Mc Hardy Young
General Surgery M Ghilchick, W Kmiot, N Menzies-Gow
Genitourinary Medicine G Brook, S Murphy
Haematology Z Abboudi, S Davies, K Ryan
Histopathology M Al-Adnani, C N Amerasinghe
Medical Microbiology Dr Rahman, M S Shafi
Neurology R Shakir
Neurophysiology M Elian, N Khalil
Obstetrics and Gynaecology N Armar, S Kerslake, E Manning, N Morris
Occupational Health S Miller
Ophthalmology T Fallon, J Joseph, C Nimalasena, G Vafidis
Oral and Maxillofacial Surgery D J Archer, H Thuau
Orthodontics T Davies
Orthopaedics A Forester, J Goodall, J Hollingdale, M Pearse
Paediatrics H Davies, B Edwards, R Franklin, J Loftus, R Radley-Smith, R H Schwartz, M Scrine, A Sharma
Plastic Surgery J Nanchahal
Radiology C Allen, D Dutton, A Hine, I Nochler, P Shorvon
Radiotherapy C Vernon
Rehabilitation Medicine K Williams
Rheumatology B Colaco, Dr Yuksel
Thoracic Medicine V Graham, V Mak, F Moss, D Ornadel
Urology M Gleeson, E Rogers, H Whitfield

Northwick Park Hospital

Watford Road, Harrow HA1 3UJ
Tel: 020 8864 3232 Fax: 020 8869 2014
Total Beds: 800

Cardiology H Bethell, N Stevens
Endocrinology P Sharp
Gastroenterology M Pitcher
General Medicine D Cohen
General Surgery M Burke, D Greenstein, R Philips, S Renton
Genetics C Garrett, J Patterson
Genitourinary Medicine A Shaw
Immunology A Denman
Infectious Diseases R Davidson
Obstetrics and Gynaecology A Priddy, J Spencer
Paediatrics A Massoud, R Thomas
Rheumatology C Higgens

St Mark's Hospital

Watford Road, Harrow HA1 3UJ
Tel: 020 7601 7792 Fax: 020 7601 7973
Total Beds: 74

Epidemiology W Atkin
Gastroenterology A Emmanuel, A Forbes, S Gabe, M A Kamm, B Saunders, H Thomas, C B Williams
General Psychiatry J Stern
General Surgery S J D Chadwick, C R G Cohen, P McDonald, R J Nicholls, J M A Northover, R K S Phillips, A C J Windsor
Nuclear Medicine K E Britton, M Granowska
Pathology A Price, I C Talbot
Radiology C I Bartram, S Halligan

Wembley Hospital

Fairview Avenue, Wembley HA0 4UH
Tel: 020 8903 1323 Fax: 020 8903 8365
Total Beds: 53

General Medicine S M Young
General Surgery M Menzies-Gow
Obstetrics and Gynaecology E Manning
Orthopaedics J Hollingdale
Pathology C N Amerasinghe
Radiology D Dutton
Radiotherapy and Oncology C Vernon

Willesden Hospital

Harlesden Road, London NW10 3RY
Tel: 020 8459 1292
Total Beds: 76

Care of the Elderly B Kaufman
Chest Disease V A L Graham, V Mak
Oral and Maxillofacial Surgery D J Archer
Pathology C N Amerasinghe
Radiology D Dutton
Rheumatology B Colaco
Thoracic Medicine V Graham, V Mak

North West Surrey Mental Health Partnership NHS Trust

Abraham Cowley Unit, Holloway Hill, Lyne, Chertsey KT16 0AE
Tel: 01932 872010 Fax: 01932 875128

Northallerton Health Services NHS Trust

Closing April 2002 - Acute services transferring to South Tees Hospitals NHS Trust.

Friarage Hospital, Northallerton DL6 1JG
Tel: 01609 779911 Fax: 01609 777144
(North and East Yorkshire and Northern Lincolnshire Health Authority)

Chair Johnny Wardle
Chief Executive Tony Bruce

Friarage Hospital

Northallerton DL6 1JG
Tel: 01609 779911 Fax: 01609 777144
Total Beds: 284

Anaesthetics J Berens, D G Jackson, M Thompson, M Walton
Dermatology A Senkeran, S Shehade
ENT J Carlin, R W Ruckley, S P Singh
General Medicine M Connolly, R Fisken, U Somasundram, D Spence
General Surgery R Bryan, M H Edwards, D C Ward
Neurology D Jay
Obstetrics and Gynaecology F Bryce, N Hebblethwaite, Kumarendram
Ophthalmology H S Dang, J D Haslam, G S Willets
Oral and Maxillofacial Surgery A Smyth
Orthodontics E May
Orthopaedics K Allerton, L Van Vumren, A C Weeber
Paediatrics D Dammann, A Essex-Cater, J James
Pathology N M Browning, D C Henderson, K V Prasad, A Waise, N Weightman
Plastic Surgery M Coady, C Vivakanathan
Radiology J Murray, J Van Hoogstraten
Radiotherapy and Oncology V Der Voet
Rheumatology A Isdale

Lambert Memorial Hospital

Chapel Street, Thirsk YO7 1LU
Tel: 01845 22292
Total Beds: 22

Richmond Victoria Hospital

Queens Road, Richmond DL10 4AJ
Tel: 01748 822109
Total Beds: 12

Rutson Hospital Rehabilitation Unit

Northallerton DL7 8EN
Tel: 01609 779911

Northampton General Hospital NHS Trust

Cliftonville, Northampton NN1 5BD
Tel: 01604 634700 Fax: 01604 545786
Website: www.northamptonshire.nhs.uk
(Leicestershire, Northamptonshire and Rutland Health Authority)

Chair Bronwen Curtis
Chief Executive David Wilson

Northampton General Hospital

Cliftonville, Northampton NN1 5BD
Tel: 01604 634700 Fax: 01604 545786
Total Beds: 700

Accident and Emergency A Dancocks, S Moore
Anaesthetics A Chmielewski, A Dash, C Frerk, C P O Garrett, N H Kay, R H K Marsh, K Robinson, S Tordoff, G Walker, R Webster, J B White
Biochemistry J O'Donnell
Care of the Elderly L Brawn, B Morgan, R Morgan
Dermatology J Clarke, J Mahood
ENT R Pyke, A K Thomas
General Medicine J S Birkhead, G C Ferguson, C J Fox, A Gordon, A Jeffrey, A Kilvert, A Ogilvie, E Shmueli, D Sprigings
General Surgery A Berry, J Dawson, D Hamer, D C Hunter, S J A Powis, D Ratliff
Genitourinary Medicine R A Cowper
Haematology M E Haines, J R Y Ross, S Swart
Histopathology J V Clark, S B Coghill, A J Molyneux
Medical Microbiology M Severn
Neurology P Davies, C J F Pursdon-Davis
Neurophysiology I Bissessar
Obstetrics and Gynaecology J Anthony, J G Bibby, W A R Davies, A R Duncan, E Shaxted
Ophthalmology A Atkinson, I Fearnley, P L R Hein
Oral and Maxillofacial Surgery M J Dean, D G H Grieg, W Smith
Orthodontics D G M Greig
Orthopaedics A Baker, N Birch, E Crawford, G Kerr, W J Ribbans
Paediatrics F M Ackland, P Daish, N K Griffin, J Hewertson, S Shribman, F Thompson
Plastic Surgery P J Regan, A H N Roberts
Radiology A M Dean, N Fairlie, A K Jain, V Kay, R G M Kendrick, K H Lakin, F L S Moss
Radiotherapy and Oncology A L Houghton, C Macmillan, J Stewart
Rheumatology and Rehabilitation T C Beer, P C Mattingly, I Morris
Urology J Chapman, J Fergus

Northampton Primary Care Trust

Highfield, Cliftonville Road, Northampton NN1 5DN
Tel: 01604 615000 Fax: 01604 615010
(Leicestershire, Northamptonshire and Rutland Health Authority)

Chair John Toby
Chief Executive Mary Burrows

Northamptonshire Healthcare NHS Trust

York House, Isebrook Hospital, Irthlingborough Road, Wellingborough NN8 1LP
Tel: 01993 44 00 99 Fax: 01536 49 31 47
(Leicestershire, Northamptonshire and Rutland Health Authority)

Chair Andrew Scarborough
Chief Executive John Rom

Adams Day Hospital

Weedon Road, Upton, Northampton NN5 6UH
Tel: 01604 752323

Psychiatry of Old Age M Bonthala, R Mudalier

Corby Community Hospital

Cottingham Road, Corby NN17 2UN
Tel: 01536 400070
Total Beds: 19

General Medicine N P R Gunasekera, A Steel, R L Walters

Haddon House Day Hospital

Danetre Hospital, Daventry NN11 4DY
Tel: 01327 72610

General Psychiatry C M Bonthala, A O'Neill-Kerr

Isebrook Hospital

Irthlingborough Road, Wellingborough NN8 1LP
Tel: 01933 440099
Total Beds: 49

Adult Rehabilitation V Comp, Dr Matthews
Care of the Elderly N P R Gunasekera, A Hussein, A Steel

Kettering General Hospital

Rothwell Road, Kettering NN16 8UZ
Tel: 01536 492000 Ext: 2037
Total Beds: 26

General Psychiatry A Blewett, M Chawla, D V Jones

Mayfair Day Hospital

The Headlands, Kettering NN15 7HP
Tel: 01536 410365
Total Beds: 10

Oundle Community Care Unit

Glapthorn Road, Oundle, Peterborough PE8 4JA
Tel: 01832 274255
Total Beds: 6

General Psychiatry M Branford

Princess Marina Hospital

Weedon Road, Upton, Northampton NN5 6UH
Tel: 01604 752323 Fax: 01604 592880
Total Beds: 249

General Psychiatry C M Bonthala, H Masih, R K Mudaliar

Rushden Hospital

Wymington Road, Rushden NN10 9JS
Tel: 01933 440666 Fax: 01933 410754
Total Beds: 42

Psychiatry of Old Age M Branford

St Mary's Hospital

London Road, Kettering NN15 7PW
Tel: 01536 410141 Fax: 01536 493242
Total Beds: 112

Care of the Elderly N P R Gunasekera, R L Walters

NHS TRUSTS & NHS HOSPITALS

General Psychiatry S Mitchell
Palliative Medicine J S Smith
Psychiatry of Old Age M Branford, M T A Christian

Upton House Day Hospital

31 Billing Road, Northampton NN1 5DQ
Tel: 01604 32958

Northamptonshire Heartlands Primary Care Trust

Nene House, Isebrook Hospital, Irthlingborough Road, Wellingborough NN8 1LP
Tel: 01536 494134 Fax: 01536 494431
(Leicestershire, Northamptonshire and Rutland Health Authority)

Northern Birmingham Mental Health NHS Trust

71 Fentham Road, Erdington, Birmingham B23 6AL
Tel: 0121 623 5500 Fax: 0121 623 5770
(Birmingham and the Black Country Health Authority)

Chair Judith Mackay
Chief Executive John Mahoney

Northern Devon Healthcare NHS Trust

North Devon District Hospital, Raleigh Park, Barnstaple EX31 3JB
Tel: 01271 322577 Fax: 01271 325564
(South West Peninsula Health Authority)

Chair Alan Eastwood
Chief Executive Shaw Edwards

Bideford and Torridgeside Hospital

Bideford EX39 3AG
Tel: 01237 472692 Fax: 01237 471408
Total Beds: 68

Care of the Elderly M Dent, G Harper
General Medicine I Lewin, A Moran, M H Oliver, T Roberts
General Psychiatry M V Buren
General Surgery J R Barker, D R Harvey
Learning Disabilities A Boucherat
Obstetrics and Gynaecology A H L Boyle, S Eckford
Ophthalmology R A Gibson
Oral and Maxillofacial Surgery I Buchanan
Orthopaedics V Giles, C Mills, V Treble, P Van Der Wal
Paediatrics A Arend, A J Bosley
Rheumatology H Averns
Urology S Agrawal

Holsworthy Community Hospital

Dobles Lane, Holsworthy EX22 6JG
Tel: 01409 253424 Fax: 01409 254963
Total Beds: 28

Care of the Elderly M Dent
General Medicine A Marshall
General Psychiatry M V Buren
General Surgery M Markham
Orthopaedics M Halawa
Paediatrics A Bosley, M Hughes
Rheumatology Dr Hutton
Urology S Agrawala

Ilfracombe and District Tyrrell Hospital

St Brannock's Park Road, Ilfracombe EX34 8JP
Tel: 01271 863448 Fax: 01271 867813
Total Beds: 14

Care of the Elderly G Harper
ENT J Riddington-Young
General Medicine T Roberts
General Surgery R Bourne
Obstetrics and Gynaecology S Bennett, N Giles
Orthopaedics C Mills, N Treble, P Van Der Wall
Paediatrics M Hughes
Psychiatry Dr Sewell
Rheumatology H Ferris
Urology S Agrawal

North Devon District General Hospital

Raleigh Park, Barnstaple EX31 4JB
Tel: 01271 322577 Fax: 01271 311541
Total Beds: 354

Accident and Emergency H Shenavar
Anaesthetics E Barron, H R Bastiaenen, T Cobby, S Forster, D Hurrell, A Laycock, B Loader, N P O'Donovan, G R Sowden, A Walder, H Williams
Cardiothoracic Surgery - Berrisford
Care of the Elderly M Dent, G Harper
Dermatology M Boss
Endoscopy A Latham
ENT J Riddington-Young
Family Planning V Nyman
General Medicine I Lewin, A Moran, M H Oliver, T Roberts
General Psychiatry M V Buren, J Holmes, G Roberts, M Sewell
General Surgery J R Barker, R Bourne, D R Harvey, N Markham
Haematology B Attock
Histopathology A Bull, J Davies
Learning Disabilities A Boucherat
Medical Microbiology G Speirs
Medical Oncology M Napier, Dr Sheehan
Nephrology - D'Souza
Neurology D Footit, W Honan
Obstetrics and Gynaecology S Bennett, A H L Boyle, S Eckford, A M Wheble
Ophthalmology B E Enoch, R A Gibson
Oral and Maxillofacial Surgery I Buchanan, A McLennan, M Moore
Orthopaedics C Mills, N Treble, P Van Der Walt
Paediatrics A Arend, A J Bosley, J Cox, M Hughes
Plastic Surgery - Inglefield
Radiology H Bradley, J Rhymer, A Sanderson, P Treweeke
Rheumatology H Averns
Thoracic Medicine M H Oliver
Urology S Agrawal, M Crundwell, H Syed

Riverside Day Unit

Litchdon Street, Barnstaple EX32 8ND
Tel: 01271 378781 Fax: 01271 325991

South Molton Community Hospital

Widgery Drive, South Molton EX36 4DP
Tel: 01769 572164 Fax: 01769 574271
Total Beds: 28

Children J Cox
Elderly Mentally Ill S Barber
General Psychiatry M Sewell
Obstetrics and Gynaecology S Eckford
Orthopaedics N Giles, C Mills, N Treble, P Van der Watt
Rheumatology H Averns

Torrington Cottage Hospital

Calf Street, Great Torrington, Torrington EX38 7BJ
Tel: 01805 622208 Fax: 01805 625108
Total Beds: 14

Care of the Elderly S Barber
ENT J Riddington-Young
General Surgery D R Harvey
Obstetrics and Gynaecology S Bennett

Northern Lincolnshire and Goole Hospitals NHS Trust

Diana Princess of Wales Hospital, Scartho Road, Grimsby DN33 2BA
Tel: 01472 874111 Fax: 01472 875357
Email: enquires@nlg.nhs.uk
Website: www.nlg.nhs.uk
(North and East Yorkshire and Northern Lincolnshire Health Authority)

Chair Ade Brooks
Chief Executive Andrew North

Diana Princess of Wales Hospital

Scartho Road, Grimsby DN33 2BA
Tel: 01472 874111 Fax: 01472 875392
Email: simon.rigg@ne.lincs-trent.nhs
Total Beds: 650

Accident and Emergency A Shweikh
Anaesthetics A Asumang, R Bramwell, F M Ghandour, M B Gough, R Khan, H Nagi, A A Samaan, B Tandon, J M C Ward-McQuaid
Care of the Elderly S N Adhikaree, J Adiotomre, L Woosnam
ENT H Amin, H Bellini, B Singh
General Medicine R J I Bain, D A Jones, S Moss, A Nadvi, M Walters
General Psychiatry Dr Konar, T V Mohan, L K Roy
General Surgery L A Donaldson, H J Pearson, A Sahy, H Souka, M Tilston, C A Westwood
Genitourinary Medicine P C Gupta
Obstetrics and Gynaecology I Bolaji, W Mueller, A Saha
Ophthalmology P Bagga, K Bhattacharya, S Kotta
Orthodontics B Holmes
Orthopaedics T K Bagga, C Grant, J A Roberts, D Stoffelen
Paediatrics P Adiotomre, J M Davies, A Fan, S M Herber, B M Reynolds
Pathology M Ashton, A Borggrech, A Hepppleston, D D Kennedy, J B Kershaw, P Parsons, W M Peters, K R Speed, A Vicca
Radiology R W T Harries, E Kweka, P F Packer, I Rizui, N W Sumbwanyambe
Radiotherapy and Oncology P Mack
Rheumatology and Rehabilitation T Gillott, D W James, T Tait

Goole and District Hospital

Woodland Avenue, Goole DN14 6RX
Tel: 01405 720720 Fax: 01405 768993
Total Beds: 82

Care of the Elderly P K Dasgupta, A Roy
Dermatology S Walton
ENT P K Bose
General Medicine S Beer, J Dhawan, D G Leitch, J R A Perumal, S Reynolds
General Surgery A Kar, P J Moore
Haematology S Jalihal
Obstetrics and Gynaecology K Young
Ophthalmology Y R Mankad, M D Parekh
Oral and Maxillofacial Surgery A O M Perriman
Orthopaedics P Molitor
Paediatrics J Devlin, I Evans, M E M Wing
Pathology D Kennedy
Radiology M C Fernando, S Maslin, T N Mehrotra, G T Vijay
Radiotherapy and Oncology T Sreeni
Urology M R G Robinson

Scunthorpe General Hospital

Cliff Gardens, Scunthorpe DN15 7BH
Tel: 01724 282282
Total Beds: 504

Accident and Emergency M Hockey
Anaesthetics A Coe, H El-Rakshy, S Goulding, J Jayamaha, C Moore, R Sharawi, J F W Thompson
Cardiothoracic Surgery M Cowen, K K Nair
Care of the Elderly P K D Gupta, A Roy
Chemical Pathology D D Kennedy
Dermatology S Walton
ENT P N Agarwal, P K Bose
General Medicine S Beer, J Dhawan, D G Leitch, J R A Perumal, S Reynolds
General Surgery A Kar, P J Moore, S F Tindall, B J Wilken
Genitourinary Medicine P C Gupta
Haematology S Jalihal
Neurology M D Rawson
Obstetrics and Gynaecology B F Heywood, L Roberts, S Sabharwal, K Young
Ophthalmology Y R Mankad, M D Parekh
Oral Surgery A Perriman
Orthodontics D M Penketh
Orthopaedics P Molitor, S Shafqat, K Sharara, A P Walker
Paediatrics J Devlin, I Evans, Dr Shekhar, M E M Wing
Pathology C Hunt, D Kennedy
Radiology M C Fernando, S Maslin, T N Mehrotra, G T Vijay
Radiotherapy and Oncology T Sreeni

Northgate and Prudhoe NHS Trust

Northgate Hospital, Morpeth NE61 3BP
Tel: 01670 394000 Fax: 01670 394002
(Northumberland, Tyne and Wear Health Authority)

Chief Executive Linda Ions

Northgate Hospital

Morpeth NE61 3BP
Tel: 01670 394000 Fax: 01670 394002
Total Beds: 294

General Psychiatry J Joyce, E Milne, G O'Brien, A F Perini, J Radley, P C Rajan

Prudhoe Hospital

Prudhoe NE42 5NT
Tel: 01670 394000 Fax: 01661 514590
Total Beds: 192

General Psychiatry T Berney, M Bhate, J McCarthy, M Prendergast, S P Tyrer

Northumbria Health Care NHS Trust

North Tyneside General Hospital, Rake Lane, North Shields NE29 8NH
Tel: 0191 259 6660 Fax: 0191 293 2745
(Northumberland, Tyne and Wear Health Authority)

Chair J Caullay, Brian Flood, D Laffey
Chief Executive Sue Page

Alnwick Infirmary

Alnwick NE66 2NS
Tel: 01665 626700 Fax: 01665 626761
Total Beds: 60

Chest Disease P J E Brown
Dermatology N Simpson
ENT A Welch
General Medicine J C G Cox, E T Young

NHS TRUSTS & NHS HOSPITALS

General Psychiatry S E Proctor
General Surgery M Griffin
Obstetrics and Gynaecology T A Lavin
Ophthalmology N P Strong
Orthopaedics A Innes, J L Sher
Radiology K Howells
Rheumatology and Rehabilitation P R Crook
Urology J G W Feggetter

Ashington Hospital
West View, Ashington NE63 0SA
Tel: 01670 521212
Total Beds: 79

Berwick Infirmary
Berwick upon Tweed TD15 1LT
Tel: 01289 356600 Fax: 01289 355665
Total Beds: 74

Chest Disease P J E Brown
Dermatology N Simpson
General Psychiatry S E Proctor
General Surgery M Bradburn, A B Griffiths, R F Mather, G R Proud
Obstetrics and Gynaecology P Franks
Orthodontics T G Bennett
Orthopaedics J M Leitch
Radiology K Howells
Rheumatology and Rehabilitation P R Crook
Urology J G W Feggetter

Blyth Community Hospital
Thoroton Street, Blyth NE24 1DX
Tel: 01670 396400 Fax: 01670 396492
Total Beds: 78

General Medicine R S S Yapa

Coquetdale Cottage Hospital
Rothbury, Morpeth NE65 7TT
Tel: 01669 620555 Fax: 01669 621527
Total Beds: 17

Orthopaedics Dr Partington

Haltwhistle War Memorial Hospital
Westgate, Haltwhistle NE49 9AJ
Tel: 01434 320225
Total Beds: 19

Hexham General Hospital
Corbridge Road, Hexham NE46 1QJ
Tel: 01434 655655 Fax: 01434 607920

Anaesthetics I Anderson, D Laffey, A Redpath
Dermatology P Farr
General Medicine K Matthewson, A J Wright
General Surgery R M Weaver
Obstetrics and Gynaecology J P Forsey, P F Sims
Ophthalmology R E W Ridley, Dr Strong
Oral and Maxillofacial Surgery J E Hawkesford
Orthopaedics R Sutton, W K Walsh
Otolaryngology C Diamond
Paediatrics A P Kenna
Pathology P W Condie
Radiology J B Douglas, E B Garner
Radiotherapy and Oncology H H Lucraft

Morpeth Cottage Hospital
South Road, Morpeth NE61 8UW
Tel: 01670 395600 Fax: 01670 395657
Total Beds: 86

General Medicine R S Yeppa

North Tyneside General Hospital
Rake Lane, North Shields NE29 8NH
Tel: 0191 259 6660 Fax: 0191 293 2745
Total Beds: 546

Accident and Emergency C C Goring
Anaesthetics P Cooper
Chemical Pathology P McKenna
General Medicine O A Afolabi, I Cobden, C Doig, E T Peel
General Surgery Dr Goulbourne, F J Holmes, S Kelly, R Pollard
Haematology H Tinegate
Histopathology P Birch, S Johri, A D Rodgers
Medical Microbiology R Stansfield
Obstetrics and Gynaecology D A Evans
Orthopaedics S Asaad, J M Caullay, A D Gaynor, D Kramer
Paediatrics W T Houlsby
Psychiatry of Old Age R Adams, M Livingston, G Ramsey
Radiology D Tennant

Sir G B Hunter Memorial Hospital
The Green, Wallsend NE28 7PB
Tel: 0191 262 4403

Wansbeck General Hospital
Woodhorn Lane, Ashington NE63 9JJ
Tel: 01670 521212 Fax: 01670 529047
Total Beds: 309

Norwich Primary Care Trust
Little Plumstead Hospital, Hospital Road, Little Plumstead, Norwich NR13 5EW
Tel: 01603 307334 Fax: 01603 307421
(Norfolk, Suffolk and Cambridgeshire Health Authority)

Chair Susan Gale
Chief Executive Chris Price

Nottingham City Hospital NHS Trust
Nottingham City Hospital, Hucknall Road, Nottingham NG5 1PB
Tel: 0115 969 1169 ext: 45662 Fax: 0115 962 7788
Website: www.ncht.org.uk
(Trent Health Authority)

Chair Christine Bowering
Chief Executive Gerry McSorley

Nottingham City Hospital
Hucknall Road, Nottingham NG5 1PB
Tel: 0115 969 1169 Fax: 0115 962 7788
Website: www.ncht.org.uk
Total Beds: 1116

Anaesthetics C Abercrombie, A Aitkenhead, K Alagesan, A Biswas, D G Bogod, C J Bowley, A Byrne, J P J Curran, J Fitzhenry, A J P Fletcher, G D Flowerdew, D E Griffiths, M P D Heining, V Hodgkinson, S Hussain, S Z Hussain, C Hutter, A Jardine, J E L Jayamaha, D T Knights, M J Levitt, R P Mahajan, A Matthews, J Nicholl, R W D Nickalls, N A Okonkwo, A Ravenscroft, M S Shajar, H J Skinner, J R Skoyles, P E Tatham, P Tomlinson, J M Vernon, J A Warner, L A Woods
Breast and General Surgery R W Blamey, K L Cheung, D Macmillan, J F R Robertson
Cardiology A J Ahsan, M Baig, R A Henderson, G K Morris, A J Ahsan, M Baig, R A Henderson, G K Morris
Clinical Chemistry C Marenah
Clinical Genetics T Parkin, J A Raeburn, M Suri, C Gardiner
Gastroenterology C M Teahon
General Medicine P Berman, D L Cohen, A W G English, P H Fentem, S M Fowlie, N P Kumar, T Masud, S K Mukherjee, A M Trueman

General Surgery K Rigg, Dr Ubhi, N T Welch
General Surgery/Breast R Blamey, K Cheung, D MacMillan, J Roberstson
Haematology J L Byrne, S Donohue, A Hayes, P A E Jones, A K McMillan, N H Russell
Histopathology I D Ansell, Z Chaudry, H Denley, I O Ellis, C W Elston, J Johnson, A H S Lee, T A McCulloch, S R O'Connor, Dr Pinder, I N Soomro
Infectious Diseases R G Finch, B J Thomson, P Venkatesan
Integrated Medicine P Berman, S Fowlie, FL Game, W Goddard, DJ Hosking, R Hubbard, WJ Jeffcoate, R Long, T Masud, R O Morris, R C L Page, N Smith, N K G Smith, N D C Sturrock, W Sunman, A Tattersfield, A M Trueman
Microbiology T Boswell, F Donald, S Pugh, S Soo, V Weston
Neurology PMW Bath, D H Mellor, A M Whiteley
Obstetrics and Gynaecology C N Bain, J E F Bruce, T N Fay, I R Johnson, L H Kean, D T Y Liu, S Watkin, K Williamson
Oncology E Bessell, J Carmichael, S Chan, D Fyfe, D Morgan, S Morgan, M Sokal, P Woll
Oral/Maxillofacial Surgery J Rowson
Orthopaedics A P Broodryk, S Dhar, M Hatton, C J Howell, L Neumann, B E Scammell, P D Triffitt, W A Wallace
Paediatrics G Croaker, D Curnock, J Evans, R Gregson, E B Knight-Jones, R Leanage, N Marlow, D Mellor, C Rance, N Rutter, C Smith, A R Smyth, A Watson
Palliative Medicine R Corcoran, V L Crosby, A Wilcock
Plastic Surgery J C Daly, M Henley, A G B Perks, I F Starley, D I Wilson
Radiology N J Broderick, H C Burrell, E J Cornford, A J Evans, K J Fairbairn, D J Green, J James, J C Jobling, J C Jobling, K H Latief, A R Manhire, K S Pointon, D H Rose, J M Somers, A R M Wilson
Renal Medicine R P Burden, M J D Cassidy, S D Roe, M Shehata
Respiratory Medicine D R Baldwin, J R Britton, T Harrison, A J Knox
Rheumatology C M Deighton, M Doherty, A C Jones, J F Mchale, I R A Pande, D Walsh
Sexual Health I Ahmed, C J Bignell, C A Bowman, E M Carlin
Thoracic/Cardiac Surgery F D Beggs, J P Duffy, I Mitchell, W E Morgan, S Nalk, D Richens
Transplantation K M Rigg, M Shehata
Urology M Bishop, M C Bishop, M Dunn, D R Harriss, R J Lemberger, M Taylor

Nottingham City Primary Care Trust

Linden House, 261 Beechdale Road, Aspley, Nottingham NG8 3EY
Tel: 0115 942 8961 Fax: 0115 840 8693
(Trent Health Authority)

Chair David Atkinson
Chief Executive Samantha Milbank

Nottinghamshire Healthcare NHS Trust

Sycamore House, Southwell Road, Mansfield NG18 4HH
Tel: 01623 784821 Fax: 01623 784819
Website: www.nottinghamshirehealthcare.nhs.uk
(Trent Health Authority)

Chair Brian Edwards
Chief Executive Jeremy Taylor

Rampton Hospital

Retford DN22 0PD
Tel: 01777 248321 Fax: 01777 248442
Total Beds: 490

General Psychiatry D V Atapattu, B C S Gunawardene, D S Hamilton, S Jegadason, I A P Keitch, E P Larkin, F B Murphy, A F

Perini, B Razdan, G S Sarna, A P W Shubsachs, I D Wilson, S M Wood, N A Zaki

Wathwood Hospital

Gypsey Green Lane, Wath-upon-Dearne, Rotherham S63 6HJ
Tel: 01709 873106 Fax: 01709 879976
Total Beds: 60

Forensic Psychiatry G Hayes, Dr Tombs

Nuffield Orthopaedic Centre NHS Trust

Windmill Road, Headington, Oxford OX3 7LD
Tel: 01865 741155 Fax: 01865 742348
Website: www.noc.org.uk
(Thames Valley Health Authority)

Chair Joanna Foster
Chief Executive Jan Fowler
Consultants Joel David, John Kenwright, Ian McNab, James The

The Oldbury and Smethwick Primary Care Trust

Kingston House, 438-450 High Street, West Bromwich B70 9LD
Tel: 0121 500 1500 Fax: 0121 500 1501
(Birmingham and the Black Country Health Authority)

Chief Executive Richard Nugent

Oldham NHS Trust

Closing April 2002 - Mental health services transferring to Penine Care NHS Trust; acute services transferring to Pennine Acute Hospitals NHS Trust; community services transferring to Oldham Primary Care Trust.

Headquarters, Westhulme Avenue, Oldham OL1 2PN
Tel: 0161 624 0420 Fax: 0161 627 3130
(Greater Manchester Health Authority)

Chair Mary F M Firth
Chief Executive Alan Moran
Consultants D Curtis

Orchard House Day Hospital

Milton Street, Royton, Oldham OL2 6QX
Tel: 0161 633 6219

The Royal Oldham Hospital

Rochdale Road, Oldham OL1 2JH
Tel: 0161 624 0420 Fax: 0161 627 8119
Total Beds: 835

Accident and Emergency P S Kumar, P K Luthra, R Sohaie, M Zahir
Anaesthetics J Barrie, M Boyd, L B Cook, P R Cook, M A Gregory, J Kenworthy, A Krishnan, J F McGeachie, J K Orton, B R Puddy, A L Richards, D B Rittoo, H Stewart, T C Watt
Audiology I J MacKenzie
Cardiothoracic Surgery T Hooper
Chemical Pathology D Bhatnaghar
Child and Adolescent Psychiatry L R Daud
Dental Surgery A G Addy, M E Foster
Dermatology R D Ead
ENT N K Saha, V L Sharma
General Medicine B Bajaj, J Barclay, G L Bhan, D Conlong, M O Coupe, P Haynes, P S Klimiuk, B Rameh, A Robinson, S A Solomon, G V Sridharan, W Thomas, J Vassallo, K K Vedi
General Psychiatry A Hardman, G P Rajagopal, A Stewart

NHS TRUSTS & NHS HOSPITALS

General Surgery D Flook, M Hadfield, N R Hulton, I H McIntosh, T Oshodi, A Rahe, D Richards
Genetics H M Kingston
Haematology V Sen
Histopathology A Padwell
Liaison Psychiatry S Burlinson
Medical Microbiology B S Perera
Nephrology P A Kalra
Neurology O Ismayl, L E L Sayed
Neurosurgery G Victoratos
Obstetrics and Gynaecology S W Ali, O Amu, N L Aziz, A Boulos, L Edozien, J F Patrick
Occupational Therapy N Clayton, S Logan, F Page, S Turner
Ophthalmology J B Garston, K Goodall, J Lipton, J Suharwardy
Orthopaedics T Asumu, K A Buch, C F Elsworth, L G H Jacobs, M S Sundar
Paediatrics I Blumenthal, C Howard, R Levy, E B Odeka, B Padmakumar, N G Prakash
Plastic Surgery V Rees
Psychiatry of Old Age A Dey, D W Tench
Radiology N Jeyagopal, M Kumar, L K L Lee Cheong, M Nadarajah, P Solomon, C Swainson
Radiotherapy and Oncology C F Finn, R Stout, R Welch
Rehabilitation Medicine K Walton
Restorative Dentistry S Bhatti, T Boyd
Urology S D Chowdhury, N Sharma

Sycamores Day Hospital

Rochdale Road, Oldham OL1 2JH
Tel: 0161 627 8101

Oldham Primary Care Trust

1 Southlink Business Park, Southlink, Oldham OL4 1DE
Tel: 0161 652 0827 Fax: 0161 626 7681
Chair Riaz Ahmad

Oxford City Primary Care Trust

The Farmhouse, Warneford Hospital, Headington, Oxford OX3 7JX
Tel: 01865 226236 Fax: 01865 226424
(Thames Valley Health Authority)

Chair Malcom Fearn
Chief Executive Andrea Young

Oxford Radcliffe Hospital NHS Trust

John Radcliffe, Headley Way, Headington, Oxford OX3 9DU
Tel: 01865 741166 Fax: 01865 741408
(Thames Valley Health Authority)

Chair Peter Bagnall
Chief Executive John MacDonald

The Churchill

Old Road, Headington, Oxford OX3 7LJ
Tel: 01865 741841 Fax: 01865 225011
Total Beds: 350

Anaesthetics C J A Glynn, T M Jack, H J McQuay, P C Young
Clinical Genetics E M Blair, G K Brown, C J Chapman, J A Hurst, S M Huson, H S Stewart, I P M Tomlinson, A O M Wilkie
Clinical Oncology C J Alcock, N P Bates, C H Blesing, D J Cole, A C Jones, B A Lavery, A J Salisbury, E M Sugden, N J Warner, A Weaver
Dermatology S M Burge, R P R Dawber, S A George, H A Kurwa, J J Powell, S M Powell, R C Ratnavel, R J Turner, V A Venning, F T Wojnarowska
General Surgery C R Darby, D J Deardon, P J Friend, D W R Gray
Haematology P L F Giangrande, D M Keeling, S N Wickramsinghe

Immuno-pathology H M Chapel, S E F Marshall, S A Misbah
Infectious Diseases A R Berendt, C P Conlon, P Klenerman, S J McConkey, K Marsh, T E A Peto, S L Rowland-Jones, J A Scott
Medical Oncology T S Ganesan, A L Harris, A Hassan, M R Middleton, A Protheroe, D C Talbot, C J H Williams
Mental Illness A K Malmberg
Nephrology P Altman, P D Mason, C G Winearls
Paediatrics E C Burns, C M Robertson, J A Shaw
Palliative Medicine J Chamberlain, J C Chambers, M G Miller, M J Minton, R G Twycross
Radiology R F Adams, N C Cowan, R E English, F V Gleeson
Rheumatology K R Mackay
Thoracic Medicine L S Bennett, M K Benson, R J O Davies, F Hardinge, M G Slade, J R Stradling
Urology S F Brewster, D W Cranston, J P Crew, J G Noble, J M Reynard

Horton Hospital

Banbury OX16 9AL
Tel: 01295 275500 Fax: 01295 229055
Total Beds: 192

Accident and Emergency G C George
Anaesthetics J E R Beamer, S K Chamberlain, J Everatt, P S Laurie, A E Richards, M A Sicinski, B A Thornley, C M Wait, D G Willatts
General Medicine I R Arnold, A J Ellis, T M Pathrose, S R (R Smith, A V G Taylor
General Surgery G V N Appleton, M N (N Dehalvi, C L Griffiths, R E K Marshall
Haematology O I Atoyebi
Histopathology G I N Greywoode, N J Mahy
Medical Microbiology C J Hall
Obstetrics and Gynaecology S H Canty, E R Laird, H G Naoum, J S Nicholls
Paediatrics R I Ahmed, R A F Bell, M F Hunter, E E Matthews, B J A Stewart
Radiology B P Barry, M D Bindal, H F D'Costa, P J Haggett, F K Macleod
Trauma and Orthopaedics N R Gillham, A Hughes, J P Pollard, B Shafighian

The John Radcliffe

Headley Way, Oxford OX3 9DU
Tel: 01865 741166 Fax: 01865 741408
Total Beds: 650

Accident and Emergency J J M Black, P J Hormbrey, R A Pullinger, D V Skinner
Anaesthetics E V Addy, Q P Ainsworth, M T Ali, S J Berg, H S Bridge, G Burt, M B Dobson, K L Dorrington, O J Dyar, J M Evans, R D Evans, A D Farmery, P J A Foex, F A M Gibson, C S Grange, C R Grebenik, P R Hambly, J D Henville, H E Higham, C F Kearns, J R Lehane, A B Loach, L Loh, C McGuinness, P J McKenzie, M S Mann, D G Mason, J M Millar, C J Nagle, J J Pandit, T M Parry, D W Pigott, R C Pollard, M T Popat, M J Quinlan, F M Ratcliffe, R Rogers, R M Russell, S V Rutter, Y Ryckwaert, M C Sainsbury, N M Schofield, J W Sear, D Shlugman, M E Sinclair, J E Stevens, M D Stoneham, M E Ward, O J Warner, J P Warwick, J L Westbrook, S A Wheatley, D A Wilkinson, E M Williams, J D Young
Blood Transfusion M F Murphy
Cardiology A P Banning, Y Bashir, H H H Becher, S Bhattacharya, B Casadei, K M Channon, J C Forfar, D C Lindsay, I P Mulligan, S Neubauer, O J M Ormerod, H Watkins
Cardiothoracic Surgery S H Armistead, R G Perumal Pillai, C P Ratnatunga, D P Taggart, S Westaby
Chemical Pathology A K Abraha, P A H Holloway, J D S Kay, J Keenan, B S F Shine
Clinical Genetics S M Price
Clinical Immunology J E Lortan
Clinical Pharmacology and Therapeutics J K Aronson
Clinical Physiology B Rajagopolan
Gastroenterology R Aga, R W G Chapman, D P Jewell, S P L Travis, J M Trowell

OXLEAS NHS TRUST

General Medicine M P ?, B J Angus, J I Bell, C Bunch, V Cerundolo, J D Collier, J S J Dwight, R J Gibbons, M S Hammersley, A Lalvani, A J McMichael, R E Phillips, C W Pugh, P J Ratcliffe, D J M Reynolds, G R Screaton, P Sleight, R V Thakker, A R M Townsend, D A Warrell, N J White, P Zimbwa

General Surgery B J Britton, P J Clarke, J Collin, C Cunningham, B D George, M J Greenall, A I Handa, L J Hands, N D Maynard, P J Morris, N J M Mortensen, J M T Perkins, G P Sadler

Haematology G W Hall, C R S Hatton, D R Higgs, J Jones, S J Kelly, T J Littlewood, D Y Mason, R Pawson, S L Thein, P Vyas, J S Wainscoat

Histopathology I D Buley, C A Clelland, D R Davies, K A Fleming, S B Fox, K C Gatter, W Gray, K Hollowood, M Ilyas, S Manek, P R Millard, F Pezzella, J Piris, I S D Roberts, D E Roskell, K A Shah, B F Warren

Immunopathology A C Vincent, H Waldmann

Infectious Diseases N P J Day, A V S Hill, T G Tudor-Williams

Intensive Therapy S W Benham, J Chantler, C S Garrard, N M McGuire

Medical Microbiology B L Atkins, I C J Bowler, K J Cann, D W M Crook, S J Peacock, M P E Slack

Nephrology R J Cornall

Oral Surgery F R Carls, D R Cunliffe, M G Hodge, S R Watt-Smith

Orthodontics G Kidner, M M McKnight, F G Nixon

Paediatric Cardiology S S Adwani, L N J Archer, I Ostman Smith, R C Radley-Smith, D M I Runciman

Paediatric Neurology M A McShane, M G Pike

Paediatric Surgery H W Grant, R J I Hitchcock, P R V Johnson, K K Lakhoo

Paediatrics F M Ackland, S J Allen, J L Craze, D B Dunger, J A Edge, M C English, P J R Goulder, J Hull, Z Huma, M A Johnson, C J Killick, D P Kwiatkowski, C D Mitchell, E R Moxon, J Panisello, A J Pollard, J Poulton, A G Shefler, P B Sullivan, A H Thomson, W G Van't Hoff, J T Warner, K A H Wheeler, T N Williams

Radiology P Boardman, S J Golding, T R Goodman, D R M Lindsell, E McNally, H K Mendes Riberio, N R Moore, S J G Ostlere, J Phillips-Hughes, B J Shepstone, Z C Traill, D J Wilson, C H Woodham

Rheumatology P Bowness, M A Brown, M F C Callan, M A Hall, B P Wordsworth

Trauma and Orthopaedics W G Bowden, C J Bulstrode, P D Burge, A J Carr, J C T Fairbank, D R Griffin, R C Handley, G Kambouroglou, R I Keyes, I S H McNab, M A McNally, T N Theologis, G P Wilde, K M Willett, J Wilson-MacDonald, P H Worlock

Virology C Roberts

Women's Centre M Y Anthony, D H Barlow, C M Bowker, P G Chamberlain, J E Cullimore, M D G Gilmer, S J Gould, P A Hurley, L W M Impey, N K Ives, N V Jackson, S R Jackson, P Johnson, S H Kennedy, P M Lewis, I Z MacKenzie, J E McVeigh, P J Magill, E A Opute, Dr Redman, J M Thomas, M Usherwood, A R Wilkinson

Radcliffe Infirmary

Oxford OX2 6HE
Tel: 01865 311188 Fax: 01865 224566
Total Beds: 250

Chemical Pathology K Evans

Clinical Neurology E A Bissessar, R P Kennett, A Virgincar, Z Zaiwalla

Diabetes A J Farmer, R R Holman, P F Karpe, J C Levy, D R Matthews, H A W Neil, W M G Tunbridge, H E Turner, J A H Wass

Gastroenterology R P Anderson

Genitourinary Medicine I D V Byren, A Edwards, G A Luzzi, G Rooney, J S Sherrard

Geriatric Medicine P J Cook, A Darowski, J G Evans, D S Fairweather, H W Jones, N A R Stewart, S J Winner

Medical Oncology D J Kerr

Neurology J E Adcock, D Briley, C J F Davis, M J Donaghy, G Ebers, P B C Fenwick, P T Grant-Davies, R C D Greenhall, R P Gregory, Y Hart, D Hilton-Jones, N M Hyman, M C Jackson, P M Matthews, P J M Newsom-Davis, J M Oxbury, J A Palace, P M Rothwell, K A Talbot

Neuropathology M M Esiri, B McDonald, J H Morris, M V Squier

Neurosurgery C B T Adams, J Akinwunmi, T Z Aziz, R S C Kerr, P G Richards, R J Stacey, P J Teddy

Ophthalmology A J Bron, H Cheng, S M Downes, J S Elston, P A Frith, S Hague, P J McCormack, C K (C Patel, P H Rosen, J F Salmon, K G Schmidt

Otolaryngology G J E Bates, I Bottrill, M J Burton, R J Corbridge, G Cox, A P Freeland, C A Milford

Plastic Surgery O C S Cassell, C R Charles, D J Coleman, H Giele, T E E Goodacre, M D Humzah, C J Inglefield, A Platt, S A Wall

Radiology P L Anslow, J V Byrne, A J Molyneux, G M Quaghebeur

Oxfordshire Ambulance NHS Trust

Churchill Drive, Old Road, Headington, Oxford OX3 7LH
Tel: 01865 740100 Fax: 01865 741974
(Thames Valley Health Authority)

Chief Executive John Nichols

Oxfordshire Learning Disability NHS Trust

Slade House, Horspath Driftway, Headington, Oxford OX3 7JH
Tel: 01865 747455 Fax: 01865 228182
(Thames Valley Health Authority)

Chair Helen Baker
Chief Executive Yvonne Cox

Oxfordshire Mental Healthcare NHS Trust

Littlemore Hospital, 33 Sandford Road, Littlemore, Oxford OX4 4XN
Tel: 01865 778911 Fax: 01865 226507
Email: enquiries@oxmhc-tr.anglox.nhs.uk
(Thames Valley Health Authority)

Chair Anthony Purkis
Chief Executive Julie Waldron

Park Hospital for Children

Old Road, Headington, Oxford OX3 7LQ
Tel: 01865 226213 Fax: 01865 226355
Total Beds: 18

Child and Adolescent Psychiatry G C Forrest, D P H Jones, M Purkis, A L Stein, G Stores, E Walters

Neurology Z Zaiwalla

Warneford Hospital

Warneford Lane, Headington, Oxford OX3 7JX
Tel: 01865 778911 Fax: 01865 226507
Total Beds: 81

Child and Adolescent Psychiatry A C D James

General Psychiatry D Chalmers, C Davison, M Elphick, C J A Fairburn, D P Geaney, S Hampson, K E Hawton, R A Hope, R A Mayou, D O'Leary, C Oppenheimer, N Rose

Psychotherapy M J D Hobbs, A S Powell

Oxleas NHS Trust

Pinewood House, Pinewood Place, Dartford DA2 7WG
Tel: 01322 625700 Fax: 01322 555491
(South East London Health Authority)

Chair Dave Mellish
Chief Executive Andrew Casey

NHS TRUSTS & NHS HOSPITALS

Bracton Centre

Medium Secure Unit, Forensic Mental Health, Bracton Lane, off Leyton Cross Road, Dartford DA2 7AP
Tel: 01322 294300 Fax: 01322 293595
Total Beds: 80

Green Parks House

Green Parks House, Farnborough Hospital, Farnborough Common, London BR6 8NY
Tel: 01689 880000 Fax: 01689 851211
Total Beds: 88

Woodlands

Woodlands, Queen Mary's Hospital, Frognal Avenue, Sidcup
Tel: 0208 308 3100
Total Beds: 66

Papworth Hospital NHS Trust

Specialist Acute

Papworth Everard, Cambridge CB3 8RE
Tel: 01480 830541 Fax: 01480 831315
Website: www.papworth.hospital.org.uk
(Norfolk, Suffolk and Cambridgeshire Health Authority)

Chair Audrey Stenner
Chief Executive Stephen Bridge

Papworth Hospital

Papworth Everard, Cambridge CB3 8RE
Tel: 01480 830541 Fax: 01480 831315
Total Beds: 200

Anaesthetics D W Bethune, S Ghosh, I Hardy, J D Kneeshaw, R D Latimer, J Mackay, A Oduro
Cardiology M C Petch, P Schofield, L M Shapiro, D L Stone
Cardiothoracic Surgery J Dunning, S R Large, S A M Nashef, A Ritchie, J Wallwork, F C Wells
Chemical Pathology J Foote
Haematology C E Hoggarth
Histopathology N R B Cary, S Stewart
Medical Microbiology J Foweraker
Oncology D Gilligan
Palliative Medicine M Saunders
Radiology D S Appleton, R Coulden, C D R Flower, M Skading
Thoracic Medicine D Bilton, C Laroche, D Lomas, J N Shneerson, I Smith

Parkside Health NHS Trust

Closure of trust tbc - part of service transferring to Brent Primary Care Trust, Kensington and Chelsea Primary Care Trust and Westminster Primary Care Trust.

Courtfield House, St Charles Hospital, Exmoor, London W10 6DZ

The Pennine Acute Hospitals NHS Trust

Westhulme, Oldham OL1 2PL
(Greater Manchester Health Authority)

Pennine Care NHS Trust

Tameside General Hospital, Fountain Street, Ashton-under-Lyne OL6 9RW
Tel: 0161 331 5151 Fax: 0161 331 5007
(Greater Manchester Health Authority)

Hyde Hospital

Grange Road South, Hyde SK14 5NY
Tel: 0161 366 8833 Fax: 0161 368 2834
Total Beds: 32

General Psychiatry F Oliver

Shire Hill Hospital

Bute Street, Glossop SK13 9PZ
Tel: 01457 866021 Fax: 01457 857519
Total Beds: 54

Care of the Elderly O M P Jolobe, H H Wan

Wood's Hospital

Glossop SK13 9BQ
Tel: 01457 860783 Fax: 01457 868704
Total Beds: 24

General Psychiatry F Oliver

Peterborough Hospitals NHS Trust

Edith Cavell Hospital, Bretton Gate, Peterborough PE3 9GZ
Tel: 01733 874000 Fax: 01733 874001
(Norfolk, Suffolk and Cambridgeshire Health Authority)

Chair Clive Morton
Chief Executive Malcolm Lowe-Lauri

Edith Cavell Hospital

Bretton Gate, Peterborough PE3 9GZ
Tel: 01733 874000 Fax: 01733 875001
Total Beds: 250

Anaesthetics B Appadu, P Baker, D Blake, A M Cooper, P Das, M Farrell, M Glavina, R Griffiths, S G Howlin, P C Hunt, R F Jeevaratnam, P L Johnston, S B Merrill, A Naunton, P Reed, R Robertshaw, M Saleh, S Short, H Smith, D Smyth, M Weisz
Care of the Elderly H Kapila, R Mittra, D Okubadejo, P Owusu-Aguei
ENT N Bhatt, P Leong, A G Pfleiderer, A Varma
General Medicine C Mistry, J M Roland, D B Rowlands, S Sahi
General Surgery F Bajwa, E Duggan, J T Holmes, S J Kent
Neurology C M Allen, J Thorpe
Orthopaedics T Bhullar, G M Chambers, A Doran, B K Dutta, S Lewis, G Pryor, I Sargent, M L Sutcliffe, G Varley
Radiology C M Brown, B McKeown, B F Millet, R E Moshy
Rheumatology and Rehabilitation N J Sheehan, N Williams
Urology H N Blackford, C Dawson, S Sharma, A G Turner

Peterborough District Hospital

Thorpe Road, Peterborough PE3 6DA
Tel: 01733 874000 Fax: 01733 874001
Total Beds: 500

Accident and Emergency I Adams, A Cope, I Greaves, B Roy
Anaesthetics B Appadu, P Baker, A M C Cooper, P Das, M C Farrell, M J Glavina, S Howlin, P C W Hunt, R Jeevaratham, P Johnston, S Merrill, A Naunton, P N Reed, R Robertshaw, S Short, H S Smith, D Smyth
Care of the Elderly H Kapila, K M Myint, D Okubadejo, P Owusu-Agyei
Chemical Pathology J F Doran
Dermatology P M Hudson, R Mallett
General Medicine A Batchelor, M W Dronfield, C Hunter, T Laundy, C Mistry, I P F Mungall, P Nair, J Roland, D B Rowlands, S Sahi
General Surgery J H Hall, J T Holmes, S J S Kent, P P Mason, R T Walker, A Wells
Genitourinary Medicine A Palfreeman
Haematology S A Fairham, M Sivakumaran
Histopathology P M Dennis, M Gertenbach, A Y Warren, C Womack
Medical Microbiology A Hellyar, A J Mifsud

Obstetrics and Gynaecology I Jelen, M Lumb, B Ramsay, J Randall, M Slack, A Sriemevan, S Steel
Ophthalmology A Hashim, T Rimmer, S Vardy
Oral and Maxillofacial Surgery W T Lamb, J M Robertson, R Shepherd
Orthopaedics T Bhullar, G M Chambers, A Doran, B K Dutta, S Lewis, G Pryor, M L Sutcliffe, G Varley
Paediatrics S Babike, V Reddy, M Richardson, A Sumner, S J Tuck, D Woolf, D Yong
Plastic Surgery P Hall
Radiology C M Brown, J C Cradwick, R Dharmeratnam, A E W Dux, B Jones, B McKeown, J H Marshall, T Maskell, B F Millet, R E Moshy
Radiotherapy and Oncology R Benson, K Fife, K McAdam, - Tan
Thoracic Surgery J Dunning, F Wells

Pinderfields and Pontefract Hospitals NHS Trust

Closing April 2002 - Services transferring to Mid Yorkshire Hospitals NHS Trust.

Trust Headquarters, Pinderfields General Hospital, Rowan House, Aberford Road, Wakefield WF1 4EE
Tel: 01924 213850 Fax: 01924 814929
(West Yorkshire Health Authority)

Chair Bob Kirk
Chief Executive Keith Salsbury

Pinderfields General Hospital

Rowan House, Aberford Road, Wakefield WF1 4EE
Tel: 01924 213850 Fax: 01924 814929
Total Beds: 608

Anatomy and Physiology J A D Settle
Cardiology J I Wilson (Head)
General Medicine W A Burr, N J Dudley, W D Walls, S E Williams
Medical Microbiology A S Sohal
Neurology A S N Al-Din, L A Loizou
Neurophysiology J A Twomey
Neuroradiology G Bonsor, M Nelson, J Straiton
Neurosurgery D J Price, G Towns
Ophthalmology S K Sharma, K S Toor
Oral Surgery D Hutchinson, R Loukota
Orthodontics J K Williams
Orthopaedics P Deacon, N N Ghali, A E S Rainey
Paediatrics E Glass, S T Jones, R MacFaul, P Tawfik
Palliative Medicine P Gajjar
Pathology M C Galvin, P B Hamal, M A Khan
Plastic Surgery K Judkins, A Phipps, O M Fenton, L Fourie, A Phipps
Radiology S K Jain, J B Walls, C Wilson-Sharp
Restorative Dentistry V K Joshi
Rheumatology R G Cooper
Urology S Harrsion, P Weston

Pontefract General Infirmary

Pontefract
Tel: 01977 600600 Fax: 01977 606852
Total Beds: 540

Accident and Emergency M J Playforth (Head)
Anaesthetics A S Christian (Head)
Dental Surgery D Hutchinson
General Medicine A K Ghosh, M Gundroo, R V Lewis, M D Peake, M V Tobin, C White
Genitourinary Medicine J Clarke, P A D Silva
Neurology A Burt, L A Loizou
Obstetrics and Gynaecology A Forbes, P D Howe, G Hunter
Ophthalmology S K Sharma, K S Toor
Orthopaedics M S Binns, S M Gollapudi, R A Nicholson, D Riley
Paediatrics J M T Alexander, M M Hasson, D Rutter
Pathology M M Aslam, J Haynes, I W C Macdonald, R Sibbald

Plastic Surgery L Fouri
Radiology J H M Ellingham, V D Ganorkar, G S Jutlla
Radiotherapy and Oncology A Crellin, R I Rothwell
Urology M R G Robinson, P G Shanmugaraju

Plymouth Hospitals NHS Trust

Derriford Hospital, Derriford Road, Plymouth PL6 8DH
Tel: 01752 777111 Fax: 01752 768976
Email: contact@phnt.swest.nhs.uk
Website: www.phnt.swest.nhs.uk
(South West Peninsula Health Authority)

Chair Russell Mitchell
Chief Executive Paul Roberts

Mount Gould Hospital

Mount Gould Road, Plymouth PL4 7QD
Tel: 01752 268011 Fax: 01752 672971
Total Beds: 5

Child and Adolescent Psychiatry S Walker

Royal Eye Infirmary

Apsley Road, Plymouth PL4 6PL
Tel: 01752 662078
Total Beds: 27

General Surgery N M Evans, T Freegard, M Ganapathy, N Habib, V T Thaller
Ophthalmology N Evans, T Freegard, N Habib, V Thaller

Scott Hospital

Beacon Park Road, North Prospect, Plymouth PL2 2PQ
Tel: 01752 550741 Fax: 01752 606958

Paediatrics A J Cronin, R Evans

Plymouth Primary Care Trust

Derriford Business Park, Building 1, Brest Road, Derriford, Plymouth PL6 5QZ
Tel: 01752 769092 Fax: 01752 766832
(South West Peninsula Health Authority)

Chair David Connelly
Chief Executive Ann James

Poole Hospitals NHS Trust

Poole Hospital, Longfleet Road, Poole BH15 2JB
Tel: 01202 665511 Fax: 01202 442562
Email: selkin@poole-tr.swest.nhs.uk
Website: www.poolehar.org
(Somerset and Dorset Health Authority)

Chair Peter Harvey
Chief Executive Lloyd Adams

Poole General Hospital

Longfleet Road, Poole BH15 2JB
Tel: 01202 665511
Total Beds: 800

Accident and Emergency G Cumberbatch, M Reichl
Anaesthetics R Aquilina, W Ashton, F Dorman, J Holloway, P R W Lanham, A McCormick, B Newman, R N Packham, K Power, B P Sweeney, G M L Van Hasselt, P Ventham, M Wee
Care of the Elderly T Battcock, R Day, R Harries-Jones, M Thomas, T Villar
Dermatology M Hazell, C J M Stephens
ENT D G John, P Scott, S R Williams
General Medicine D Bruce, G P Clein, D Coppini, S Crowther, W Gatling, A McLeod, J W Millar, N Sharer, J Snook

NHS TRUSTS & NHS HOSPITALS

General Surgery N Bell, S W Hosking, J Pain, R Talbot
Neurology J P S Burn, J Cole, C J K Ellis, N M Milligan, C H Wulff
Obstetrics and Gynaecology J N T Edwards, R Henry, T Hillard, J W Scott
Oral Surgery V Ilankovan, A F Markus, W J Peters
Orthopaedics M Farrar, N J Fiddian, D O'Connor
Paediatrics M M Black, R Coppen, J Kelsal, A H McAuley, R Rao, D B Shortland
Palliative Medicine S Kirkham
Pathology J Alexander, J Begley, A J Bell, C M Boyd, K Hussein, F Jack, D Nicholas, A Worsley
Radiology M R Andress, J A D Brailsford, P Burn, M Creagh-Barry, J Herbetko, M Ismail, N K Robson, J Stutley, D Tarver, S B Walkden, A Wood
Radiotherapy N Cowley, P Crellin, S Dean, T D Goode, T Hickish, V Lawrence
Rheumatology and Rehabilitation P Thompson

Poole Primary Care Trust

Parkstone Health Centre, Mansfield Road, Poole BH14 0DJ
Tel: 01202 710100 Fax: 01202 710109
(Somerset and Dorset Health Authority)

Portsmouth City Primary Care Trust

Finchdean House, Milton, Portsmouth PO34 6DP
Tel: 023 9283 5020 Fax: 023 9283 5030
Website: www.portsmouthpcg.org.uk
(Hampshire and Isle of Wight Health Authority)

Chair Zenna Atkins
Chief Executive Sheila Clarke

Portsmouth Health Care NHS Trust

Closure tbc - Part of service transferring to Fareham and Gosport Primary Care Trust.

Trust Central Office, St James Hospital, Locksway Road, Portsmouth PO4 8LD
Tel: 023 9282 2444 Fax: 023 9229 3437
Website: www.portsmouth-healthcare.org
(Hampshire and Isle of Wight Health Authority)

Chair Anne Monk
Chief Executive Max Millett

Gosport War Memorial Hospital

Bury Road, Gosport PO12 3PW
Tel: 023 9252 4611 Fax: 023 9258 0360

Havant War Memorial Hospital

59 Crossway, Havant PO9 1NG
Tel: 023 9248 4256
Total Beds: 23

Queen Alexandra Hospital

Department of Medicine for Elderly People, Southwick Hill Road, Cosham, Portsmouth PO6 3LY
Tel: 023 9228 6941 Fax: 023 9220 0381

Care of the Elderly A B Dowd, J A H Grunstein, D R Jarrett, R F Logan, A Lord, I Reid, M P Severs, J C Tandy

St Christopher's Hospital

Wickham Road, Fareham PO16 7DJ
Tel: 01329 286321 Fax: 01329 281173
Total Beds: 73

St James' Hospital

Locksway Road, Milton, Portsmouth PO4 8LD
Tel: 023 9282 2444 Fax: 023 9229 3437
Total Beds: 244

General Psychiatry R N Bale, P M Fleming, L A Hardwick, N Renton, V P Samaratunga, J Sinclair, C A Trotter, A Wear

St Mary's Hospital

Department of Medicine for Elderly People, Milton Road, Portsmouth PO3 6AD
Tel: 023 9228 6892 Fax: 023 9220 0381

Care of the Elderly A B Dowd, J A H Grunstein, D R Jarrett, R F Logan, A Lord, M P Severs, J C Tandy

Portsmouth Hospitals NHS Trust

De La Court House, Queen Alexandra Hospital, Southwick Hill Road, Cosham, Portsmouth PO 6 3LY
Tel: 023 9228 6000 Fax: 023 9228 6073
Website: www.portshosp.org.uk
(Hampshire and Isle of Wight Health Authority)

Chair Michael Waterland
Chief Executive Mark Smith

Blackbrook House Maternity Home

Blackbrook Drive, Fareham PO14 1PA
Tel: 01329 232275
Total Beds: 12

Obstetrics and Gynaecology I M Golland

Gosport War Memorial Hospital

Bury Road, Gosport PO12 3PW
Tel: 023 9252 4611
Total Beds: 180

Obstetrics and Gynaecology J G Francis, P Hogston

Queen Alexandra Hospital

Southwick Hill Road, Cosham, Portsmouth PO6 3LY
Tel: 023 9228 6000 Fax: 023 9228 6012
Total Beds: 595

Accident and Emergency C J Cahill, G A Carss, S Mullett
Anaesthetics N Barnes, R Burden, N Campkin, N Chaderton, G Craig, A J Davies, D A Desgrand, J Eldridge, S Elliott, M Ghurye, G Graig, J Harrison, P Heath, P Jeyabalam, F King, D H MacDougall, R McMurragh, P McQuillan, D Marsh, Q Miller, J R A Moon, J Nightingale, R Palmer, S Pilkington, D Pounder, A S J Prosser, P Rogers, C J Shannon, G B Smith, P L Spreadbury, B Taylor, K Torlot, A Turrell, J Vincent, J Wace, J Watt-Smith, A Wilkins, M Wood, A Yates, J R B Young
Audiological Medicine P West
Dental Surgery J D W Barnard, H Beckett, G Zaki
Dermatology L J Cook, A Haworth, B Hughes, S Keohane
ENT W S Al Safi, A E Davis, C I Johnstone, G Madden, E Nilssen, M Pringle, A Resouly, D Robinson, P West
General Medicine R J Clark, D C Colin-Jones, M Cummins, H Duncan, R Ellis, P M Goggin, N Hedger, A W Matthews, K M Shaw
General Surgery K Abusin, N Digard, J M Kelly, S Payne, M Pemberton, P M Perry, W G Prout, S A Sadek, A Sanapati, S Somers, G L Sutton, M R Thompson, S Toh, A Walters, P C Weaver, M Wise, C Yiangou
Genitourinary Medicine V Harindra, J M Tobin
Intensive Care G Craig, J Knighton, P McQuillan, G B Smith, B L Taylor, G Tweeddale
Microbiology R J Brindle, P M Crockcroft, G S Underhill
Occupational Health Medicine D Shand
Ophthalmology D L Boase, R E Butler, A R Evans, D Farnworth, W Green, M N Jeffrey, H Maclean, S Millroy, A J Pechel, J C Tudor
Orthodontics D Barnard, H Beckett, D J Birnie, H Hilling, S N Robinson, G Zaki

Orthopaedics H J Clarke, N A Flynn, M Grover, S Hodkinson, J G Hussell, I T Jeffery, D M Longbottom, M McLaren, A S Mansour, R H Richards

Palliative Medicine H Jones

Pathology M I J Andrews, J Conroy, T Cranfield, J Dhundee, S Di Palma, M Ganczakowski, H Hirri, M J Jeffrey, L Kissan, D A McCormick, N J E Marley, D Poller, A Spedding, R M Young

Radiology J Atchley, J Domjan, M N H Gonem, P Gordon, R Harrison, R G Hull, A R Jackson, J J Langham-Brown, E A Tilley, S P Ward, F Witham

Rheumatology R G Hull, J Ledingham, F McCrae, R Shaban, A L Thomas

Royal Hospital Haslar

Gosport PO12 2AA
Tel: 023 9258 4255
Total Beds: 210

St Mary's Hospital

Milton Road, Portsmouth PO3 6AD
Tel: 023 9228 6000 Fax: 023 9286 6413
Total Beds: 551

Care of the Elderly A D Dowd, J A H Grunstein, D R Jarrett, R F Logan, A Lord, M P Severs, J C Tandy

Dermatology D F Barrett, L J Cook, B Hughes

General Medicine S Evans, T G Farrell, R J Lewis, J G B Millar, E Neville, J Stevens, J Watkins

Genitourinary Medicine V Harindra, J M Tobin

Nephrology R Lewis, J C Mason, S A Sadek, J Stevens, G Venkat Venkat-Raman, A Walters, M Wise

Neurology W Gibb, A M Turner

Neurophysiology W L Merton

Obstetrics and Gynaecology J R Bevan, A D Clark, D W Davies, J G Francis, I Golland, R R Guirgis, P Hogston, V Osgood

Paediatrics M Ashton, M J Hardman, S Peters, R Thwaites, J M Walker, E R Wozniak

Pathology R Brindle, R Buchanan, P M Cockroft, J Dhundee, P J Green, N J Marley, J Mikes, G Underhill

Radiology I M Fairley, T V Lancaster, M H MacGuire, M A A Shaltot

Radiotherapy and Oncology D J Boote, J D Dubois, P F Golding, G G Khoury, E M Low

Rehabilitation Medicine M Homer-Ward

Urology S J Chiverton, S Holmes, B H Walmsley

Preston Acute Hospitals NHS Trust

From April 2002 merging with the acute service of Chorley and South Ribble NHS Trust to form a new acute trust (name tbc).

Royal Preston Hospital, Sharoe Green Lane, Fulwood, Preston PR2 9HT
Tel: 01772 716565 Fax: 01772 710162
(Cumbria and Lancashire Health Authority)

Chief Executive Peter Morgan Capner

Preston Primary Care Trust

Sharoe Green Hospital, Sharoe Green Lane, Fulwood, Preston PR2 8DU
Tel: 01772 711774
Chair Wendy Hogg
Chief Executive Jan Hewitt

The Princess Alexandra Hospital NHS Trust

Princess Alexandra Hospital, Hamstel Road, Harlow CM20 1QX
Tel: 01279 444455 Fax: 01279 429371
(Essex Health Authority)

Chair Martin Lawn
Chief Executive Gary Belfield

Princess Alexandra Hospital

Hamstel Road, Harlow CM20 1QX
Tel: 01279 444455
Total Beds: 451

Anaesthetics R Cattermole, P Dodd, L N Iskander, D Lightman, R Rajendram, Z Zych

Chest Disease J R Milne, J Waller, J Warren

Dermatology H Dodd

ENT A A A Amen, C E M Lamb

General Medicine J R Milne, D Preston, J F Waller, J P Warren

General Surgery J Ackroyd, M A Clifton, M W E Morgan, J Peters

Neurology M A Barrie, R Walker

Obstetrics and Gynaecology R Hartwell, P Kumaranagkan, M E Samarren

Ophthalmology I Fawcett, D Flaye

Oral and Maxillofacial Surgery J Carter, K Coghlan, F J Evans, B Littler

Orthopaedics C H Aldam, P Allen, D S Nairn, L K H Therkildsen

Pathology K Agarwal, R G M Letcher, J Mackenzie, V Oxley, S Thands, S Vilevaratham

Radiology C Barber, A Chanha, S Dimmock, J Lockwood, Y Steele, R M L Warren

Rheumatology and Rehabilitation J Currie

Urology J S Virdi

Princess Royal Hospital NHS Trust

Apley Castle, Telford TF6 6TF
Tel: 01952 641222 Fax: 01952 242817
(Shropshire and Staffordshire Health Authority)

Chair Phil Homer
Chief Executive Neil Taylor

Princess Royal Hospital

Apley Castle, Telford TF6 6TF
Tel: 01952 641222 Fax: 01952 242817
Total Beds: 344

Accident and Emergency P Alfonsi, A Leaman

Anaesthetics R H Carley, P D Cartwright, D Christmas, G C Corser, K C Hickmott, G H Phillips, S Sanghera, N Tufft

Chemical Pathology N E Capps

Dermatology S Kelly

General Medicine J Bateman, R R Campbell, M Heber, M E Heber, R Jones, N Mike, H Mollogil, D O'Gorman, G Townson, T E T West

General Surgery R G M Duffield, C P Hinton, J B Quayle

Genitourinary Medicine S V Devendra

Haematology G W Slocombe

Histopathology J M Grainger

Medical Microbiology P O'Neil

Neurology P Newman

Orthodontics D C Tidy

Orthopaedics T P K Crichlow, R Dodenhoff, P May, R D Perkins, B Summers

Paediatrics S Abdu, F Hinde, L Ingram, N Vrahimis

Radiology P Lowe, R A Manns, M T J Walsh

Urology C J M Beacock, S Coppinger, A Hay

Priority Healthcare Wearside NHS Trust

Closing April 2002 - Services transferring to South of Tyne and Wearside Mental Health NHS Trust.

Wellfield Mews, Cherry Knowle Hospital, Ryhope, Sunderland SR2 0NB
Tel: 0191 565 6256 Fax: 0191 569 9455

NHS TRUSTS & NHS HOSPITALS

(Northumberland, Tyne and Wear Health Authority)

Chair Cynthia Rickitt
Chief Executive A Hall

Brooke House

Hetton Road, Houghton-le-Spring
Tel: 0191 584 2717
Total Beds: 10

Cherry Knowle Hospital

Ryhope, Sunderland SR2 0NB
Tel: 0191 565 6256 Fax: 0191 569 9455
Total Beds: 329

General Psychiatry H R Board, I Cameron, A Lawrie, P O Miller, S Mitchison, J L C Perera, S Rastogi, K L Shrestha
Psychiatry of Old Age A Cooper, P Cronin, G Harvey, D Hunsley

Monkwearmouth Hospital

Newcastle Road, Sunderland SR5 1NB
Tel: 0191 565 6256 Fax: 0191 569 9248
Total Beds: 80

Queen Elizabeth Hospital NHS Trust

Queen Elizabeth Hospital, Stadium Road, London SE18 4QH
Tel: 020 8836 6000
Website: www.qehospital.com
(South East London Health Authority)

Chair Colin Campbell
Chief Executive Alan Perkins

Memorial Hospital

Shooters Hill, Woolwich, London SE18 3RZ
Tel: 020 8856 5511

Queen Elizabeth Hospital

Stadium Road, Woolwich, London SE18 4QH
Tel: 020 8836 6000

Accident and Emergency A-M Huggon, S Metcalf
Anaesthetics RG H Baxter, H Bretschneider, F Moulla, M Pannell, D Markovic, S J Power, P Ravindran, S M Robertson, Dr Shariff, V Vijayakulasin, E Wright
Cardiology L Corr, D Robson, C Shakespeare
Care of the Elderly S Ali, E Ekpo, K Le Ball
Dermatology B deSilva, A Harris, D McGibbons
General Medicine P Marsden, W Seymour, T Stokes, J Webb
General Surgery M Al-Hilaly, N Aston, A Harrison, A Montgomery, G Rather, TA M Stoker, P Sutaria, C Y Yiu, K F Yoong
Neurology M Rose, E Silber
Obstetrics and Gynaecology JV L Carr, J A Elias, Dr Leitch, N Perks, C J Young
Paediatrics B Al-Rubeyi, A Evans, T Fenton, H Issler, G Young

Queen Mary's Sidcup NHS Trust

Queen Mary's Hospital, Frognal Avenue, Sidcup DA14 6LT
Tel: 020 8302 2678 Fax: 020 8308 3052
(South East London Health Authority)

Chair Colin Campbell
Chief Executive Helen Moffatt

Erith and District Hospital

Park Crescent, Erith DA8 3EE
Tel: 020 8302 2678 Fax: 020 8308 3052

Greenwich District Hospital

Vanbrugh Hill, Greenwich, London SE10 9HE
Tel: 020 8858 8141
Total Beds: 583

Queen Mary's Hospital

Frognal Avenue, Sidcup DA14 6LT
Tel: 020 8302 2678 Fax: 020 8308 3052
Total Beds: 430

Accident and Emergency C Taylor
Anaesthetics T M Akhtar, M Bassilious, T P Davis, T Durcan, M Fisher, O Hifzi, W S Rao, E Roberts
Care of the Elderly R Geraghty, J Kelleher, S Roe
Dental Surgery P S Ellison
Dermatology A Kagawala
ENT - Beg, D Golding-Wood, T M Harris
General Medicine D Black, I Cranston, B A Gould, M J Lancaster-Smith, W N Seymour, C D Shee
General Psychiatry A Ansari, Dr Browning, C Goddard, J M Hirons
General Surgery T Davies, J Ellul, H Khawaja, J G Payne, T Walters
Haematology S Bowcock, S Rassam, S Ward
Medical Microbiology J Kensit
Neurology T Britton, W F Michael
Obstetrics and Gynaecology L S Hanna, S Morcos, R Smith, J Woolfson
Ophthalmology J R Chesterton, M Gibbens, Dr Goel, C Hugkulstone, H C Laganowski, L Lanigan, Dr Pillai, J S Shilling, K Stevenson, D Trew
Oral Surgery D H Gibb, K Hussain
Orthodontics Dr Metcalf, D Young
Orthopaedics T Mani, A J L Percy, M Rowntree, C Schizas
Paediatrics W Barry, S A Bokhari, A S El-Radhi, J Hood
Pathology E J A Aps, S Bowcock, J Cooper, J G Kensit, M K Khan, S Rassam
Radiology I Abdelhadi, A U Ahmed, J E Goligher, M Gotlieb, C G Pinder
Rheumatology and Rehabilitation A N Bamji, T F W Dilke

Queen's Medical Centre, Nottingham University Hospital NHS Trust

Derby Road, Nottingham NG7 2UH
Tel: 0115 924 9924 Fax: 0115 970 9196
Website: www.qmc.nhs.uk
(Trent Health Authority)

Chair E F Cantle
Chief Executive John MacDonald

University Hospital

Queen's Medical Centre, Nottingham NG7 2UH
Tel: 0115 924 9924 Fax: 0115 970 9196
Total Beds: 1366

Accident and Emergency A F Dove, D A Esberger, L N Jarrett, L Williams
Anaesthetics C A Abercrombie, A R Aitkenhead, K Alagesan, J R Armstrong, B Baxendale, M Bennet, D G Bogod, J D Bousfield, C J Bowley, M Brown, A J Byrne, F A Campbell, J P J Curran, I K Farquhar, G D Flowerdew, J C Haycock, M P D Heining, G Hobbs, S Z Hussain, A Hutchinson, C D D Hutter, A D Jardine, J M Lamb, D J Layfield, D Levy, M C Luxton, S Markham, P Martin, A J Matthews, M H Nathanson, R W D Nickalls, J M Nicoll, A Norris, N I Palmer, M F Reid, B Riley, D A Selwyn, P Singh, J Stewart, P F Tatham, P A Tomlinson, B A Waldron, R J Winter, P M Yeoman
Care of the Elderly M J Bendall, C Donegan, J R F Gladman, R Harwood, R M Kupfer, J D Morrant, D Seddon
Child Health N Marlow, L Polnay, J Punt, N Rutter, T J Stephenson, M Vloeberghs

Dermatology B R Allen, K L Dalziel, J S C English, L G Millard, W Perkins, E M Saihan, H C Williams
ENT J P Birchall, P J Bradley, K P Gibbin, N S Jones, J A McGlashan, G M O'Donoghue
General Medicine S P Allison, A J Cowley, D Gray, I P Hall, J R Hampton, C J Hawkey, R Henderson, I D A Johnston, W J M Kinnear, R F A Logan, Y R Mahida, S R Page, P Rubin, R C Spiller, R G Wilcox
General Surgery J F Abercrombie, N C M Armitage, T W Balfour, J B Bourke, J Doran, B R Hopkinson, M S T MacSweeney, B J Rowlands, J D Hardcastle, W G Tennant, C S Ubhi, N T Welch, P W Wenham
Haematology J M Davies, G Dolan, K Forman, E L Horn
Histopathology M C Anderson, D G Fagan, N R Griffin, P D James, D Jenkins, C J H Padfield, A Stevens, D R Turner
Immunology R J Powell, H F Sewell
Medical Microbiology F Donald, A M Emmerson, R G Finch, H Grundman, W Irving, M J Lewis, S F Pugh, R C B Slack, B Thompson
Neurology R B Godwin-Austen, D Jefferson, A M Whiteley
Neuropathology J S Lowe, K Robson
Neurophysiology L M Henderson, N J Smith
Neurosurgery R Ashpole, P O Byrne, J L Firth, D T Hope, J A G Punt, I J A Robertson, M Vloeberghs, B D White
Obstetrics and Gynaecology P T Edington, G M Filshie, R H Hammond, D K James, I R Johnson, M B A Macpherson, L Mascarenhas, M C Powell, M Ramsay
Occupational Health I A Aston, J D Dornan
Ophthalmology W M K Amoaku, R N Downes, H S Dua, A J Foss, N R Galloway, R M Gregson, S M Haworth, D Knight-Jones, G M Orr, S A Vernon
Oral and Maxillofacial Surgery S E Fisher, S Harris, M McGurk, I McVicar
Orthodontics R R Nashed
Orthopaedics T R C Davis, S Dhar, I W Forster, M Grevitt, D Hahn, B J Holdsworth, C J Howell, J B Hunter, S M H Mehdian, C G Moran, R C Mulholland, P J Radford, E P Szypryt, W A Wallace, J K Webb
Paediatric Surgery L Kapila, R J Stewart
Paediatrics C P J Charlton, J Grant, M Hewitt, D I Johnson, D Mellor, D Thomas, H Vyas
Pathology N Kalsheker, L Morgan
Radiology S S Amar, N Broderick, S Dawson, W Dunn, R H S Gregson, K Halliday, I M Holland, T Jaspan, Dr Kersake, Dr Ludman, Dr McConachie, A Moody, B J Preston, J Somers, P Twining, M L Wastie, Dr Whitaker

Ophthalmology S Daya (Head), M Mulhearn
Oral and Maxillofacial Surgery A E Brown (Head), K Lavery, K Sneddon, P Ward-Booth
Orthodontics A R Thom, L Winchester
Orthopaedics E J Parnell
Paediatrics K Greenaway
Plastic Surgery P Arnstein, H R Belcher, J G Boorman, K W Cullen, P Gilbert, N Parkhouse, M Pickford, R Smith, T C Teo
Radiology N B Bowley

Reading Primary Care Trust

57-59 Bath Road, Reading RG30 2BA
Tel: 0118 982 2882 Fax: 0118 982 2914
Website: www.berkshire.nhs.uk/reading
(Thames Valley Health Authority)

Chair Penny Henrion
Chief Executive Janet Fitzgerald

Redbridge Primary Care Trust

Beckett House, 2-14 Ilford Hill, Ilford IG1 2QX
Tel: 020 8478 5151
(North East London Health Authority)

Chair Clive Myers
Chief Executive Tom Easterling

Redditch and Bromsgrove Primary Care Trust

Crossgate House, Crossgate Road, Park Farm Industrial Estate, Redditch B98 7SN
(Coventry, Warwickshire, Herefordshire and Worcestershire Health Authority)

Chief Executive Graham Vickery

Richmond and Twickenham Primary Care Trust

Teddington Memorial Hospital, Hampton Road, Teddington TW11 0JL
Tel: 020 8408 8245 Fax: 020 8408 8292
(South West London Health Authority)

Riverside Community Healthcare NHS Trust

Closing April 2002 - Services transferring to Hammersmith and Fulham Primary Care Trust.

Parsons Green Centre, 5-7 Parsons Green, London SW6 4UL
Tel: 020 8846 7954 Fax: 020 8846 7654
(North West London Health Authority)

Chair Lucinda Bolton
Chief Executive Pearl Brown

Robert Jones and Agnes Hunt Orthopaedic and District Hospital NHS Trust

Gobowen, Oswestry SY10 7AG
Tel: 01691 404000 Fax: 01691 404066
Website: www.rjah.nhs.uk

Queen Victoria Hospital NHS Trust

Holtye Road, East Grinstead RH19 3DZ
Tel: 01342 410210 Fax: 01342 317907
Email: queenvic@queenvic.demon.co.uk., queenvic@queenvic.demon.co.uk
Website: www.queenvic.demon.co.uk
(Kent and Medway Health Authority, Surrey and Sussex Health Authority)

Chair Garry Martin
Chief Executive Jan Bergman

Queen Victoria Hospital

Holtye Road, East Grinstead RH19 3DZ
Tel: 01342 410210 Fax: 01342 317907
Email: queenvic@queenvic.demon.co.uk
Website: www.queenvic@demon.co.uk
Total Beds: 140

Anaesthetics P Jones (Head), C J Barham, J Curran, A Diba, S Fenlon, S Krone, J Sanders, K Sim, S J Squires, P Venn, N Vorster
Care of the Elderly T Martin (Head)
ENT R J Sergeant
General Medicine D Jewitt, W Shattles
General Surgery A Stacey-Cear, T Williams
Obstetrics and Gynaecology M Long

NHS TRUSTS & NHS HOSPITALS

(Shropshire and Staffordshire Health Authority)

Chair Michael Bolderston
Chief Executive Jo Cubbon

Robert Jones and Agnes Hunt Orthopaedic Hospital

Oswestry SY10 7AG
Tel: 01691 404000 Fax: 01691 404050
Total Beds: 227

Anaesthetics R Alcock (Head), C Emmett, B Morgan, P M Pfeifer, S Ray
Care of the Elderly S Shulto
General Medicine M Davie, L Hill, S Hill
General Surgery A Fox, A Schofield
Gynaecology D Redford, S Robinson, A Tapp
Histopathology A J Darby (Head)
Neurology G Cole, S Ellis, C Hawkins
Orthopaedics P Cool, S Eisenstein, W El Masry, G A Evans, D Ford, P Gregson, S Hay, M J S Hubbard, D C Jaffray, A Jamieson, C Kelly, P Laing, K Lewis, C M McGeoch, N Makwena, J H Patrick, D Rees, J Richardson, A Roberts, S Roberts, D Short, R Spencer-Jones, S White, D H Williams
Paediatrics G Evans, J Patrick, R Quinlivan, A Roberts
Plastic Surgery J Roberts
Radiology I W McCall, V Pullicino, P Tyrell
Respiratory Medicine R Wilson
Rheumatology R G Butler, J J Dixey

Rochdale Healthcare NHS Trust

Closing April 2002 - Mental health services transferring to Pennine Care NHS Trust; acute services transferring to Pennine Acute Hospitals NHS Trust; community services transferring to Rochdale Primary Care Trust.

Trust Headquarters, Birch Hill Hospital, Rochdale OL12 9QB
Tel: 01706 377777 Fax: 01706 754108
(Greater Manchester Health Authority)

Chair Steven Price
Chief Executive Robert Clegg

Birch Hill Hospital

Rochdale OL12 9QB
Tel: 01706 377777 Fax: 01706 754108
Total Beds: 293

Anaesthetics O Abdelatti, S Drake, A Eskander, J Kini, R Shaikh, A Swayampraksam
Care of the Elderly M Finlay (Head), R Namushi, R K Sharma
Child and Adolescent Psychiatry A M Fraser
ENT J T Brandrick, D Gordon, D Sheppard
General Medicine T Akintewe, M F Fletcher, D N Foster, R George, M Hargreaves, S Jegarajah, D J Smithard
General Psychiatry D M Bowker, L J Haines, T J O'Hare, R Porter
Neurosurgery Dr King
Ophthalmology N Jacobs, S Kafle, K N Khan, I H Qureshi
Paediatrics S DeSilva
Pathology M G Bradgate, Dr Brammer, R Fitzmaurice, Dr Grey
Radiology J Mather, Dr Shah, D P Winarso
Rheumatology and Rehabilitation A Bowden, E E Smith, K Walton

Rochdale Infirmary

Whitehall Street, Rochdale OL12 0NB
Tel: 01706 377777 Fax: 01706 655474
Total Beds: 272

Anaesthetics O Abdelatti, R Drake, A Eskander, I Kini, R Shaikh, A Swayampraksam
Cardiology M Hargreaves
Cardiothoracic Medicine J G Grotte
Care of the Elderly M Finlay, R Namushi, R K Sharma

Dermatology R D Ead
General Medicine T Akintewe, M F Fletcher, D N Foster, R George, S Jegarajah, D J Smithard
General Surgery S Afify, K Akhtar, C S Humphrey
Genitourinary Medicine H Lacey
Neurophysiology J C Smaje
Obstetrics and Gynaecology A Atalla, M Dickson, S A F Ghobrial, M S Zaklama
Oral Surgery P R White, R I Woodwards
Orthopaedics S Alcock, M A Ali, V Devadoss, E R Jago
Paediatrics M A Ariyawansa, R Smith
Pathology M G Bradgate, D T I Cartmill, R Fitzmaurice, F J Stratton
Plastic Surgery D J Whitby
Radiology J Mather, R S Raja, K Shah, D P Winarso
Radiotherapy and Oncology Dr Wylie
Rheumatology and Rehabilitation A Bowden, E E Smith
Urology M Kourah

Rochdale Primary Care Trust

Unit 1, St James Place, 164 Yorkshire Place, Rochdale OL16 2DL
Tel: 01706 516900 Fax: 01706 632153

Rotherham General Hospitals NHS Trust

Rotherham District General Hospital, Moorgate Road, Oakwood, Rotherham S60 2UD
Tel: 01709 820000 Fax: 01709 824200
(South Yorkshire Health Authority)

Chair Alan Hartley
Chief Executive Paul Nesbitt

District General Hospital

Moorgate Road, Rotherham S60 2UD
Tel: 01709 820000 Fax: 01709 304303
Total Beds: 860

Accident and Emergency F L P Heyes, H Qureshi
Anaesthetics A Blackburn, V Boyd, A E Cooper, I C Grant, P J Matthews, P J Mawson, M Miller, D M Newby, N A Okonkwo, K Ruiz, H Shah, R K Stacey, E Taylor
Care of the Elderly M K Ghosh, B K Mondal, J M Nankhonya
Dermatology M E Kessler, M L Wood
ENT L Durham, J M Lancer
General Medicine K D Bardhan, P A Bardsley, G S Basran, F Creagh, A R Haste, R Muthusamy
General Surgery J C Cooper, S J Haggie, R B Jones, C C Rigby
Genitourinary Medicine E B Turner
Obstetrics and Gynaecology K J Anderton, D W Fenton, C Ramsden, B C Rosenberg, S F Spooner
Occupational Health A Rimmer
Ophthalmology V A Burton, A K Maudal, E Oji, A A Zaidi
Oral and Maxillofacial Surgery P G McAndrew
Orthodontics W L Yap
Orthopaedics M Bhamra, A J S Rees, M J Robson, M M Zaman
Paediatrics D T D Bulugahapitiya, C Harrison, P I MacFarlane, S A W Salfield, J E Shorland
Pathology A M A Abbas, H E Barlow, L Harvey, D Slater, G Smith, P C Taylor
Radiology J L Alexander, M J Bradley, K F Lan, D Skidmore, P Spencer
Radiotherapy and Oncology D A Champion
Rheumatology and Rehabilitation M Dabrera, M E Holt
Thoracic Surgery J A C Thorpe
Urology J Levechis, B T Pays

Rotherham General Hospital Day Surgery Centre

Moorgate Road, Rotherham S60 3AJ
Tel: 01709 820000 ext: 4560/4565/5906 Fax: 01709 304563

Rotherham Primary Care Trust

Office 1 Nine Trees Trading Estate, Morthen Road, Thurcroft, Rotherham S66 9JG
Tel: 01709 302630
(South Yorkshire Health Authority)

Chair A Tolhurst
Chief Executive John McIvor

Rotherham Priority Health Services NHS Trust

Closing April 2002 - Mental health services transferring to Doncaster, South Humber and Rotherham NHS Trust (name tbc); part of service transferring to Rotherham Primary Care Trust.

Doncaster Gate Hospital, Doncaster Gate, Rotherham S65 1DW
Tel: 01709 304892 Fax: 01709 304890
(South Yorkshire Health Authority)

Chair Tony Palmer
Chief Executive Kath Atkinson

Beechcroft Unit

Moorgate Road, Rotherham S60 2UD
Tel: 01709 820000 ext: 5657 Fax: 01709 304740
Total Beds: 40

Learning Disabilities E DeSaram

Doncaster Gate Hospital

Doncaster Gate, Rotherham S65 1DW
Tel: 01709 820000 ext: 3320 Fax: 01709 304890

Child and Adolescent Psychiatry I Cariapa, M G Thomas

Hawthorn Day Hospital

Doncaster Gate Hospital, Doncaster Gate, Rotherham S65 1DW
Tel: 01709 304805

General Psychiatry D Nabi

Rowley, Regis and Tipton Primary Care Trust

Kingstone House, 438-450 High Street, West Bromwich B70 9LD
Tel: 0121 500 1590 Fax: 0121 500 1604
(Birmingham and the Black Country Health Authority)

Chief Executive Doug Round

Royal Berkshire Ambulance Service NHS Trust

44 Finchampstead Road, Wokingham RG40 2NN
Tel: 0118 936 5500 Fax: 0118 977 3923
(Thames Valley Health Authority)

Chair Keith Kerr
Chief Executive Keith Nuttall

Royal Berkshire and Battle Hospitals NHS Trust

Royal Berkshire Hospital, London Road, Reading, RG1 5AN
Tel: 0118 987 5111 Fax: 0118 987 8042
(Thames Valley Health Authority)

Chair Colin Maclean
Chief Executive Mark Gritten
Assistant Chief Executive Anne Sheen

Battle Hospital

Oxford Road, Reading RG3 1AG
Tel: 0118 987 5111
Total Beds: 274

Care of the Elderly M W Pearson, A Van Wyk
General Medicine J A Bell, N Spyrou
Neurology R Gregory, N Hyman
Paediatrics H A Curtis, S M Wallis
Rehabilitation Medicine C Collin
Respiratory Medicine C Davies, J Thomas
Rheumatology A Bradlow, J D McNally
Urology D Fawcett, P Malone, H N Whitfield

Royal Berkshire Hospital

London Road, Reading RG1 5AN
Tel: 0118 987 5111
Total Beds: 508

Accident and Emergency M Dudek, P Farrugia, S Soysa
Anaesthetics S C Allen, K J Bird, J Collie, P C Dill-Russel, M C Ewart, J Fielden, R M Hall, F Idrees, R H Jago, R Jones, A Kapila, A J Kitching, K E Krzeminska, K Machlachlan, J W MacKenzie, T Parke, M Rimmer, C M Danbury, C Verghese, C S Waldmann, L Worthington
Biochemistry G Challand, G Lester, D Williams
Chemical Pathology D L Williams
Clinical Oncology J M Barrett, C D C Charlton, A Freehairn, J Q Gildersleve, P Rogers
Dermatology C Higgins, J Holder, M P James
ENT W Colquhoun-Flannery, R Herdman, N J Mansell, N J Marks
General Medicine J Booth, M F El Shieikh, A S Mee, M Myszor, R B Naik, J D Simmons, H C R Simpson
General Surgery S Courtney, T C B Dehn, R G Faber, R Farouk, R B Galland, T R Magee, S B Middleton, H Reece-Smith, H N Umeh
Genitourinary Medicine S Rajamanoharan, A Tang
Haematology F Brito-Babapulle, H Grech, G R Morganstern
Histopathology L W L Horton, C J McCormick, R A Menai Williams, T Saleem
Obstetrics and Gynaecology H A Allott, A M Crystal, J O Greenhalf, E M Holt, M Selinger, J Siddall-Allum, K M Smith, P Street, R M Williams
Occupational Health A Ross
Ophthalmology A S Bacon, B M Billington, M Leyland, P Constable, V Tanner, A R Pearson
Oral Surgery M F Patel, C D C Tomlins
Orthodontics D Bryan, C R Harper
Orthopaedics S A Copeland, R D A Dodds, C M Fergusson, O Levy, R W Marshall, I M Nugent, S T O'Leary, C A Pailthorpe, S Tavares, A E G Themen
Paediatrics A W Boon, S Edees, A Gordon, A J Macrae, N P Mann, C L Newman, M J Clements
Radiology A Brown, N D J Derbyshire, E Elson, M Gibson, C I Meanock, N S Rahim, R S C Robertson, E P H Torrie, T M Walker

Royal Bournemouth and Christchurch Hospitals NHS Trust

Royal Bournemouth Hospital, Castle Lane East, Bournemouth BH7 7DW
Tel: 01202 303626 Fax: 01202 704077
Website: www.rbh.org.uk

NHS TRUSTS & NHS HOSPITALS

(Somerset and Dorset Health Authority)

Chair S Collins
Chief Executive T Spotswood

Christchurch Hospital

Christchurch BH23 2JX
Tel: 01202 486361 Fax: 01202 705225
Total Beds: 210

Care of the Elderly S C Allen, K Amar, D Jenkinson, Z Raza, M Vassallo
Palliative Medicine F Randall
Radiology M Andreas, R Bull, T S Creasy, B Donnellan, A Drury, S N Jones, D F C Shepherd, J Sheridan, J Small, J D Stevenson, D J Tawn
Rheumatology and Rehabilitation C Dunne, N D Hopkinson, K Mounce, B Quilty

Royal Bournemouth Hospital

Castle Lane East, Bournemouth BH7 7DW
Tel: 01202 303626 Fax: 01202 704077
Total Beds: 694

Accident and Emergency G Cumberbatch, K Hassan
Anaesthetics D M Dickson, R P H Dunnill, D M Hargreaves, M Michel, N S Milligan, J K Myatt, B Newman, M P Rafferty, M Schuster-Bruce, A Scott, B Sweeney, G Van Hasselt, P A Ventham, M Wee, M J Whittle
Dermatology P G Goodwin, M Hazel
General Medicine M Armitage, D Cavan, D Kerr, D Laws, T Levy, M McCallum, J Radvan, A Rozkovec, J Turner, A J Williams, P Winwood
General Surgery D Bennett, S G Darke, N Davies, J B J Fozard, R J Lawrance, S Parvin, A I Skene, L Wijesinghe
Genitourinary Medicine A H de Silva, M J Hayward
Obstetrics and Gynaecology A J Evans, J S Pampiglione
Ophthalmology M D P Crick, C Davison, A Denning, E D Dorrell, D E Etchells, H J Franks
Oral and Maxillofacial Surgery A F Markus, W J Peters
Orthodontics J F W Hodgkins, M Short
Pathology T J Hamblin, M Lesna, D G Oscier, D M C Parham
Radiology M Andress, R Bull, T S Creasey, B Donnellan, A Drury, S N Jones, D F C Shepherd, J Sheridan, J Small, J D Stevenson, D J Tawn
Urology F J Bramble, C Carter, J S Rundle, A Wedderburn

Royal Brompton and Harefield NHS Trust

Sydney Street, London SW3 6NP
Tel: 020 7352 8121 Fax: 020 7351 8473
Website: www.rbh.nthames.nhs.uk
(North West London Health Authority)

Chair Lord Newton
Chief Executive Mark Taylor

Harefield Hospital

Harefield, Uxbridge UB9 6JH
Tel: 01895 823737 Fax: 01895 822870
Total Beds: 184

Anaesthetics M J Boscoe, J Farrimond, S Kamath, B Riedal, D Royston, R E McLaurin, A P Triscott, C Wall, G Wright
Cardiology R Greenbaum, C Ilsley, P Keir, E J Knight, A Mitchell, V Paul, C Travill, P Wilkinson
Cardiothoracic Surgery G Dreyfus, W Fountain, J Gaer, A Khaghani, U Maiwand, M Amrani, A Rees, S Tadjkarimi, E Townend
Chest Medicine J R Govan, A Nath, P Studdy
General Surgery T Paes
Nephrology F D Thompson
Paediatrics R D G Franklin, P Jaffe, R C Radley-Smith
Palliative Medicine L Bangham

Pathology D J Allan, S Amin, M Burke, D Cummins, L S Nakhla
Radiology J Partridge
Thoracic Surgery S W Fountain, O Maiwand, A Rees, E R Townsend

Royal Brompton Hospital

Sydney Street, London SW3 6NP
Tel: 020 7352 8121 Fax: 020 7351 8473
Total Beds: 300

Anaesthetics T Evans, C Gillbe, J W W Gothard, B Keogh, C J Morgan, M J Scallan
Cardiology J Clague, A Coats, P Collins, S Davies, K M Fox, L Gerlis, D G Gibson, M Henein, S Kaddoura, M Mallen, P J Oldershaw, P Poole-Wilson, A F Rickards, R Sutton, D Wood
Cardiothoracic Surgery P Goldstraw, J C R Lincoln, N Moat, J R Pepper, D Shore
ENT I S Mackay
Paediatrics I Balfour-Lynn, A Bush, J Carvalho, H Gardiner, L Gerlis, J Larovere, D Macrae, A Magee, M L Rigby, M Rosenthal, Z Salvik, B Setnia, E A Shinebourne, J Till
Pathology J Burman, B Corrin, H Gaya, R J L Hooper, M Sheppard
Radiology D Carr, D Firmin, D M Hansell, D Pennell, M B Rubens, S R Underwood
Respiratory Medicine P Barnes, R D Bois, K F Chung, J V Collins, S Durham, T Evans, D M Geddes, M Green, M Hodson, A B Kay, D N Mitchell, A Simonds, A J N Taylor, R Wilson

Royal Cornwall Hospitals NHS Trust

Royal Cornwall Hospital (Treliske), Truro TR1 3LJ
Tel: 01872 250000 Fax: 01872 252708
(South West Peninsula Health Authority)

Chair Angela Alderman
Chief Executive Brian J Milstead

Royal Cornwall Hospital

Truro TR1 3LJ
Tel: 01872 250000 Fax: 01872 252708
Total Beds: 900

St Michael's Hospital

Haye TR27 4JA
Tel: 01736 753234 Fax: 01736 753344
Total Beds: 56

West Cornwall Hospital

Clare Street, Penzance TR18 2PF
Tel: 01736 874000 Fax: 01736 874081
Total Beds: 74

General Medicine C M Asplin, D O Gibbons, D Levine
General Surgery P J Cox, M MacKenzie, A G Paterson

Royal Devon and Exeter Healthcare NHS Trust

Barrack Road, Exeter EX2 5DW
Tel: 01392 411611 Fax: 01392 402067
(South West Peninsula Health Authority)

Chair Ruth Hawker
Chief Executive Angela Pedder
Assistant Chief Executive Steve Astbury

Royal Devon and Exeter Hospital

Barrack Road, Exeter EX2 5DW
Tel: 01392 411611 Fax: 01392 402067
Total Beds: 850

Accident and Emergency A R Harris, C McLauchlan

Anaesthetics P K Ballard, C Berry, R W Boaden, C Collins, D Conn, M Dougherty, A Dow, E Hammond, E Hartsilver, C Day, F P F Marshall, J Munn, B W Perriss, J Purday, F L Roberts, J M Saddler, D Sanders, B K Sandhar, P MacIntyre, A Teasdale, R J Telford, I H Wilson, K Allman
Cardiology J Dean, M Gandhi, L D Smith
Care of the Elderly M James, M Jeffries, V R Pearce, S Harris
Chemical Pathology M Salzman
Clinical Genetics C Brewer
Clinical Oncology P Bliss, A Goodman, A Hong, D Sheehan, E Toy, C G Rowland
Dermatology C Bower, A P Warin
Emergency Medicine A Harris, C McLauchan
General Medicine R Ayres, M Beaman, T K Daneshmend, R D'Souza, A Hattersley, K Macleod, A J Nicholls, J Christie, M Daly
General Surgery W B Campbell, M J Cooper, A Cowan, J Dunn, A Gee, T T Irvin, A J S Knox, J F Thompson
Genitourinary Medicine I Alexander, G D Morrison
Haematology M V Joyner, R Lee, M Pocock, C Rudin
Medical Microbiology A Colville, M Morgan, T Riordan
Neurological Rehabilitation D Footitt
Neurology C Gardner-Thorpe, N Gutowski, M Honan
Neurophysiology E Ragi
Obstetrics and Gynaecology N Colley, N Liversedge, J Renninson, R Sturley, J West
Occupational Medicine A Rossiter
Ophthalmology J S H Jacob, A Quinn, T Simcock, D Byles, J Thomsitt
Oral Surgery A V Babajews, A McLennan
Orthodontics M Moore, K M Postlewaite
Orthopaedics T D Bunker, D Chan, P Cox, K Eyres, G A Gie, N Giles, M Hubble, C D Jefferiss, P Schranz, J Timperley, C R Weatherley
Otolaryngology G Werier, A Brightwell, R Garth
Paediatrics C Hayes, C Holme, S Imong, D L Kennaird, A McNinch, P Oades, M W Quinn, R Smith, J H Tripp
Palliative Medicine J F Gilbert, M Ryan
Pathology C Keen, T Clarke, N Cope, D Day, P Sarsfield, C Mason, P MuCullagh, R H W Simpson
Plastic Surgery V Devaraj, C J Palmer, P J Saxby, C Stone
Radiology C R B Bayliss, C Prider, J Coote, C Hamilton-Wood, J Harington, S Harris, D C Kinsella, M D McLean, D Silver, A Spiers
Respiratory Medicine D Halpin, C Sheldon, N Withers
Rheumatology R Haigh, R Jacoby
Thoracic Surgery R Berrisford
Urology M Crundwell, R D Pocock, M A Stott

Royal Free Hampstead NHS Trust

Pond St, London NW3 2QG
Tel: 020 7794 0500 Fax: 020 7830 2468
(North Central London Health Authority)

Chair Pamela J Chesters
Chief Executive Martin Else
Assistant Chief Executive Mark Easton

Queen Mary's House

124 Heath Street, Hampstead, London NW3 1DU
Tel: 020 7431 4111 Fax: 020 7830 2020
Total Beds: 101

Royal Free Hospital

Pond Street, London NW3 2QG
Tel: 020 7794 0500 Fax: 020 7830 2468
Total Beds: 950

Accident and Emergency P Belsham, A Fogarty
Anaesthetics B Astley, C Beard, I Calder, S Charlton, G Collee, D England, A Evans, R Fernando, T Gruning, B D Higgs, J Howard, D Jackson, T Khanam, S Mallett, B O'Donoghue, A Ordman, A Patel, T Peachey, M S Pegg, S Renwick, J Ruddock, J Ruston, S Shaw, R Simons, L Vella, J Watts
Audiology B Cadge, K Harrop-Griffiths, D Lim, D Lucas, B McCardle, R Roshini
Cardiology G Coghlan, T R Evans, D Lipkin
Cardiothoracic Surgery R Walesby
Child and Adolescent Psychiatry M Berelowitz
Child and Family Development A Stein
Cytology A Deery
Dermatology C Orteu, B Phillips, M Rustin, S Whittaker
Endocrinology S Al-Damluji, P Bouloux, M Press, M Vanderpump
ENT H Caulfield, R Quiney, G Radcliffe, M Stearns
Gastroenterology O Epstein, M Hamilton
General Medicine A K Burroughs, M Caplin, J S Dooley, G Dusheiko, O Epstein, L Fine, P Hawkins, P Hodgson, I James, N McIntyre, K Moore, M Y Morgan, M Pepys, M Vanderpump
General Psychiatry A S Bird, M Blanchard, L Caparroita, S Jeffreys, M King, G Lloyd, A McNaught, P Raven, P Robinson, S Weich
General Surgery D Baker, B Davidson, G Hamilton, A A M Lewis, R Lord, G Ogunbiyi, S P Parbhoo, K Rolles, D Wheeler
Genetics K Macdermot
Genitourinary Medicine G Gabriel, D Ivans, A Nageswaran, M Weir
Haematology S Brown, C Lee, A B Mehta, D Perry, M Potter, H G Prentice, C Taylor
Health Services for Elderly People A Davies, D Lee, J Morris, S Stone, A Wu
Histopathology J Crow, S Davies, A P Dhillon, M Jarmukowicz, T Levine, N McDermott, J E McLaughlin, P Revell
Immunology P Amlot, G Janossy, L Poulter
Infectious Diseases B Bannister, W Weir
Medical Microbiology S H Gillespie, N Hutchinson, C Kibbler, A Simpson, J Steer
Medical Physics J Agnew
Nephrology A Burns, A Davenport, H S Powis, P Sweny
Neurology H Angus-Leppan, J Bowler, R Brenner, C Davie, A Gale, J Gibbs, L Ginsberg, D Kidd, R Orrell, L Parsons, A Schapira, R Sherratt, L A Wilson
Neurophysiology R Hallin
Neurosurgery R Bradford, N Dorward, R S Maurice-Williams, C Shieff
Nuclear Medicine J Buscombe
Obstetrics and Gynaecology J Barter, D Economides, A Magos, T Mould, W Reid, E Scott, S M Tuck, P Walker
Occupational Medicine S Williams
Oncology R Begent, D Hochhauser, A Jones, K Pigott
Ophthalmology J Brazier, C C Davey, J Forbes, M Harris, J D Jagger, J Lawson, B Little
Orthopaedics G Dowd, D Eastwood, N Garlick, N Goddard
Paediatrics D M Flynn, B Lloyd, A Lloyd-Evans, C Morgan, S Murch, B Taylor, M Thomson, V van Someren
Palliative Medicine A Tookman
Pathology D Mikhailidis, M Thomas
Plastic Surgery M D Brough, P Butler, G McGrouther, P Malucci
Postgraduate Training J Dooley
Primary Care M Lloyd, P Wallace
Psychological Medicine S Davies
Psychotherapy S Davies
Radiology L A Berger, S Edwards, J Hinton, B Holloway, C E Mackintosh, A D Platts, L Savy, A R Valentine, A Watkinson
Radiotherapy and Oncology C Collis
Rheumatology H Beynon, C Black, C Denton, A G White
Thoracic Medicine P Dilworth
Thoracic Surgery R K Walesby
Urology M Al-Akraa, A V Kaisary, R T Morgan
Virology B Bannister, P D Griffiths, C Loveday, W Weir

Royal National Throat, Nose and Ear Hospital

Gray's Inn Road, London WC1X 8DA
Tel: 020 7915 1300 Fax: 020 7833 5518
Total Beds: 51

Anaesthetics B Astley, P Bailey, D H Enderby, A Evans, B O'Donoghue, A Patel, J Ruddock

NHS TRUSTS & NHS HOSPITALS

Audiological Medicine R Alles, B Cadge, K Harrop-Griffiths, D Lim, D Lucas, B MacArdle, R Palanniapan
Clinical Immunology G Scadding
ENT G B Brookes, J Lary, D Choa, C B Croft, C East, L Badia, J Graham, H Grant, D Howard, T Joseph, B Kotecha, V Lund, P O'Flynn, J Rubin, A Wright
General Psychiatry M Greenberg
Paediatrics M Bellman
Radiology T Beale, L Savy

Royal Liverpool and Broadgreen Hospitals University NHS Trust

Prescot Street, Liverpool L7 8XP
Tel: 0151 706 2000 Fax: 0151 706 5806
(Cheshire and Merseyside Health Authority)

Chair Roger L James
Chief Executive Pearse Butler, David Cain

Broadgreen Hospital

Thomas Drive, Liverpool L14 3LB
Tel: 0151 282 6292 Fax: 0151 282 6988
Total Beds: 382

Accident and Emergency L Jaffey
Anaesthetics D D Brice, A M Florence, D M Gabbe, S Malliah, P L Misra
Biochemistry A Stott
Care of the Elderly D Barer, N Carroll, D P Choudhury, M Lye, M G Malster, G Phillips, J R Playfer
Dermatology S Evans, C King, M M Molokhia, J L Verbov
Gastroenterology A Ellis, H Smart
General Medicine T J Bayley, R C Bucknall, I Casson, P D Davies, D Glynne-Thomas, C R K Hind, B A Walker, M Walshaw
General Surgery J M Dhorajiwala, A N Kingsnorth, W Lloyd-Jones, R Shields, B A Taylor, J H W Winstanley
Ophthalmology S P Harding
Orthopaedics J Campbell, W A Jones, M C Lynch, H P J Walsh
Pathology P Chu, W E Kenyon, M W Myskow, T H Williets
Plastic Surgery M Gipson
Radiology D A Gould, C Ryall, E Thomas
Urology A D Desmond, M Fordham

Royal Liverpool University Dental Hospital

Pembroke Place, Liverpool L3 5PS
Tel: 0151 706 2000

Anaesthetics D D Brice, M Cohen, P Jarvis, G Lamplugh
Medical Microbiology M V Martin
Oral and Maxillofacial Surgery P Hardy, E D Vaughan
Oral Medicine E A Field
Oral Pathology J Scott, J Woolgar
Oral Surgery J S Brown, G T R Lee, D R Llewelyn, O A Pospisil, D Richardson, J Scott
Orthodontics N Pender, S J Rudge, J Warren-Jones
Plastic Surgery M Gipson, A R Green, L A Holbrook
Radiology J B Hutton
Restorative Dentistry D Adams, J Cunningham, T G Heaney, D G Hillam, R A Howell, K S Last, M Lennon, L P Longman, T Nisbet, A Watts

Royal Liverpool University Hospital

Prescot Street, Liverpool L7 8XP
Tel: 0151 706 2000
Website: www.rlbuh-tr.nwest.nhs.uk
Total Beds: 903

Accident and Emergency P Burdett-Smith, A Good, L H Jaffey, L C Luke
Anaesthetics R S Ahearn, E J T Allsop, L Bardosi, M Cohen, M W Davies, A Devine, A M Florence, S J Harper, J M Hunter, A G Jones, A Leach, S Mallaiah, G J Masterson, P L Misra, S M Mostafa, P M Mullen, B V S Murthy, C Parker, B J Phillips, T D R Ryan, T Sajjad, J M Scott, R Wenstone, R G Wilkes
Care of the Elderly N Carroll, M A Gosney, C I A Jack, M D W Lye, M G Malster, G Phillips, J R Playfer
Chemical Pathology W D Frazer, G J Kemp, E M C Manning, A Shenkin
Dermatology S Evans, D A Gunarwardena, C M King, L Rhodes, G R Sharpe, J L Verbov
Endocrinology J P Vora
General Medicine M G Barry, T J Bayley, G M Bell, J M Bone, A M Breckenridge, R C Bucknall, I F Casson, T A Dixon, J E Ellershaw, A J Ellis, I H Ellis, C C Evans, A Fryer, C F Gilks, I T Gilmore, C R K Hind, M Hommel, M G Lombard, M Molyneux, A I Morris, P A Mullins, M C L Orme, M Pirmohamed, T S Purewal, J Rhodes, S S Saltissi, J M Skinner, H L Smart, D H Smith, S B Squire, E J Tunn, B A Walker, M J Walshaw, H M Warenius, T Whalley, E Williams, P S Williams, P A Winstanley
General Surgery P Atkins, A Bakran, J A Brennan, G L Gilling-Smith, P L Harris, M N Hartley, M J Hershman, C Holcombe, W Lloyd-Jones, J P Neoptolemos, G J Poston, P S Rooney, R A Sells, J P Slavin, R Sutton, J H R Winstanley
Genitourinary Medicine A B Alawattegama, H D L Birley, P B Carey, A K Ghosh, T F Schulz, I A Tait, D J Timmins
Haematology J C Cawley, P Chu, R E Clark, V J Martlew, C H T Toh
Histopathology P A Smith
Immunology R M R Barnes
Medical Microbiology C A Hart, A Percival, P Shears, G W Smith, C Y W Tong, D Van Saene, T H Williets
Nephrology R Ahmed, G M Bell, J M Bone, P S Williams
Neurophysiology K A Pang
Nuclear Medicine M Critchley, M L Smith
Orthopaedics V Bobic, S P Frostick, I C M Gray, M J Jane, W A Jones, S F Journeaux, M C Lynch, S Nayagam, D S O'Donoghue, S K Thompson, C R Walker
Otolaryngology A Jones, M S McCormick
Pathology F Campbell, C S Foster, J R Gosney, D M Guerin, T R Helliwell, C S Herrington, C P Johnson, I W McDicken, J R G Nash, J P Sloane, L S Turnbull
Plastic Surgery J R Bryson, A R Green
Radiology A T Carty, C J Garvey, D A Gould, J A Holemans, E Hurley, G H R Lamb, R G McWilliams, K A Meakin, D A Ritchie, P Rowlands, C J Ryall, C Sampson, M Sperber, F E White, G H Whitehouse
Radiotherapy and Oncology J E S Brock, R D Errington, S Myint, A J Slater, I Syndikus
Transplant Surgery A Bakran, M W Brown, R A Sells
Urology A D Desmond, M V Fordham, K F Parsons, K A Woolfenden

Royal Liverpool Children's NHS Trust

Eaton Road, Liverpool L12 2AP
Tel: 0151 228 4811 Fax: 0151 252 5846
(Cheshire and Merseyside Health Authority)

Chair F W Taylor
Chief Executive Tony Bell

Alder Hey Children's Hospital

Eaton Road, West Derby, Liverpool L12 2AP
Tel: 0151 228 4811
Total Beds: 330

Accident and Emergency R Massey, W J Robson
Anaesthetics I S Billingham, P D Booker, A Bowhay, I M Boyd, M Cunliffe, R E Sarginson, R E Thornington
Child and Adolescent Psychiatry J Hill
Dental Surgery J C Cooper, D R Llewelyn, B B J Lovius
Dermatology P Friedman, J L Verbov
ENT J H Rogers, S D Singh
General Psychiatry J S Nelki, A Oppenheim, F E Stewart

General Surgery G Lamont, D A Lloyd, P L May, R Rintala, R Turnock
Immunology T A Dixon, J A Wilson
Neuroradiology N R Clitherow, E T S Smith
Ophthalmology A Chanda, S Kaye
Orthopaedics J C Dorgan, J F Taylor, J Walsh
Paediatrics R Arnold, I A Choonara, R W I Cooke, D C Davidson, D P Heaf, J Martin, L Rosenbloom, J A Sills, C S Smith, A Thomson
Pathology P Bolton-Maggs, D Isherwood, G Kokai, H K F Saene
Plastic Surgery J R Bryson, M Gipson, A R Green, G Hancock, J H Stilwell
Radiology L J Abernethy, A E Boothroyd, H M L Carty, D W Pilling, A Sprigg
Radiotherapy and Oncology H M L Carty, D W Pilling, A Sprigg
Tropical Medicine J B S Coulter
Urology A M K Rickwood

The Royal Marsden Hospital NHS Trust

Fulham Road, London SW3 6JJ
Tel: 020 7352 8171 Fax: 020 7376 4809
Email: chief.executive@rmh.nthames.nhs.uk
Website: www.royalmarsden.org.uk
(North West London Health Authority)

Chair T Green
Chief Executive Cally Palmer

Royal Marsden Hospital (Chelsea)

Fulham Road, London SW3 6JJ
Tel: 020 7352 8171 Fax: 020 7376 4809
Website: www.royalmarsden.org.uk
Total Beds: 152

Royal Marsden Hospital (Sutton)

Downs Road, Sutton
Tel: 020 8642 6011 Fax: 020 8770 9297
Email: chief.executive@rmh.nthames.uk
Website: www.royalmarsden.org.uk
Total Beds: 168

Anaesthetics J M Edwards, J Filshie, J J Kothari, D Skewes
Chemical Pathology C R Tillyer
Dermatology P S Mortimer
General Surgery A Nash, P Rhys-Evans, J Shepherd, J M Thomas
Haematology D Catovsky, M J S Dyer
Histopathology C Fisher, P A Trott
Medical Oncology D Cunningham, M Gore, I Judson, R L Powles, T J Powles, I E Smith
Microbiology N Mackenzie
Nuclear Medicine V R McCready
Ophthalmology P J Holmes-Sellors, R Whitelocke
Oral and Maxillofacial Surgery D J Archer
Paediatrics S Meller, R Pinkerton
Radiology J C Husband, D M King, D MacVicar, E C Moskovic
Radiotherapy P R Blake, M Brada, D Dearnaley, H T Ford, J P Glees, C L Harmer, J M Henk, A Horwich, D Tait, J R Yarnold

Royal National Hospital for Rheumatic Diseases NHS Trust

Upper Borough Walls, Bath BA1 1RL
Tel: 01225 465941 Fax: 01225 421202
(Avon, Gloucestershire and Wiltshire Health Authority)

Chair Kate Lyon
Chief Executive Nicola Carmichael

Royal National Hospital for Rheumatic Diseases

Upper Borough Walls, Bath BA1 1RL

Tel: 01225 465941 Fax: 01225 421202
Total Beds: 85

Rheumatology and Rehabilitation A K Bhalla, D Blake, A Calin, A K Clarke, J Davies, T Jenkinson, N McHugh

Royal National Orthopaedic Hospital NHS Trust

Brockley Hill, Stanmore HA7 4LP
Tel: 020 8954 2300 Fax: 020 8954 6933
(North West London Health Authority)

Chair Peter Mansell
Chief Executive Jacky Sherman

Royal National Orthopaedic Hospital

Brockley Hill, Stanmore HA7 4LP
Tel: 020 8954 2300 Fax: 020 8954 6933
Total Beds: 239

Anaesthetics J P Barcroft, J Berman, G Edge, M Fennelly, R Fox, R Gad-el Rab, M Hetreed, A P Rubin, D R J Seingry, V Taylor, K Yau
Consultants G Blunn, E Hanspal, L Marks
Dental Surgery B C O'Riordan, D Williams
General Medicine F R I Middleton
General Psychiatry L Weiselburg
Medical Microbiology P J Sanderson
Neurology M Powell, G D Schott
Orthodontics D W Williams
Orthopaedics J C Angel, J I L Bayley, G Bentley, R Birch, T Briggs, P Calvert, S Cannon, T Carlstedt, J Johnson, S Lambert, T R Morley, W Muirhead-Allwood, D Singh, J Skinner, M F Sullivan, B Taylor
Paediatrics D Eastwood, A Hashemi-Nejad, S Herman, F Monsell
Plastic Surgery R Sanders
Radiology R Green, N Mitchell, P Renton, A Saifuddin
Rehabilitation Medicine J Cowan, F R I Middleton
Rheumatology R Sturge., R Wolman
Urology J Shah

Royal Orthopaedic Hospital NHS Trust

Bristol Road South, Northfield, Birmingham B31 2AP
Tel: 0121 685 4000, 0121 686 4007 Fax: 0121 685 4111, 0121 685 4222
Email: christine.miles@ro-tr.wmids.nhs.uk
(Birmingham and the Black Country Health Authority)

Chair Les Lawrence
Chief Executive Christine Miles

Royal Orthopaedic Hospital

Bristol Road South, Northfield, Birmingham B31 2AP
Tel: 0121 685 4000 Fax: 0121 627 8211
Website: www.royalortho.org.uk
Total Beds: 126

Anaesthetics C Bhimarasetty, V Girgis, D Hawes, B Kumar, T Neal, O Owen-Smith, P Riddell, G Shinner, J Watt
Orthopaedics A Abudu, K Baloch, C F Bradish, S R Carter, G Chana, M Craigen, D Dunlop, P Gibbons, P Glithero, M Green, R J Grimer, A Jackowski, P Jobanputra, D J A Learmonth, D McMinn, D S Marks, P J Mulligan, J O'Hara, J L Plewes, A J Stirling, A M C Thomas, A G Thompson, R M Tillman, R B C Treacy, M A Waldram
Radiology G Allen, A M Davies, N S Evans

Royal Shrewsbury Hospitals NHS Trust

Royal Shrewsbury Hospital, Mytton Oak Road, Shrewsbury SY3 8XQ

NHS TRUSTS & NHS HOSPITALS

Tel: 01743 261000 Ext: 1001 Fax: 01743 261489
Website: www.rsh.org.uk
(Shropshire and Staffordshire Health Authority)

Chair Tom Caulcott

Royal Shrewsbury Hospital

Mytton Oak Road, Shrewsbury SY3 8XQ
Tel: 01743 261000 Fax: 01743 261006
Total Beds: 520

Anaesthetics I Baguley, H Brunner, M E Fryer, R Hatts, D H King, C T Major, J E Marshall, M Mehta, G R Thompson, I Williams
Bacteriology N J Mitchell, P M O'Neill, R E Warren
Care of the Elderly S N Agnihotri, J E Briggs, S N Hill
Dental Surgery S F Olley, D Wedgwood
Dermatology S Kelly
General Medicine R C Butler, S P Davies, L F Hill, A F Macleod, D Maxton, W H Perks, M E Simmons, M S H Smith, P T Wilmshurst, R S E Wilson
General Surgery A Houghton, T Hunt, R A Hurlow, A Schofield
Genitourinary Medicine S U Devendra
Neurology S Nightingale
Neurosurgery J A Elexpuru Camiruaga, J A MacIntosh
Obstetrics and Gynaecology B B Bentick, J Lane, M Mohajer, S Oates, D H A Redford, N N Reed, A S J Tapp
Orthodontics J C Chadwick
Orthopaedics D J Ford, S Hay, C Kelly, C M McGeoch, J Patrick, R Spencer-Jones, S White
Paediatrics J E H Brice, S Deshpande, R C M Quinlivan, J Watt, R Welch
Pathology R A Fraser, J M Grainger, N Green, C E Hinton, T J Jones, P D Leedham, P Murphy, P E Nicholls, N O'Connor, G W Slocombe
Plastic Surgery P Davison
Radiology S M Aldridge, M R E Dean, J A Fielding, W J Norman, R I Orme, H R Watson
Radiotherapy and Oncology A Agrawal, S Awwad
Urology C Beacock, S V Coppinger, A M Hay

Royal Surrey County Hospital NHS Trust

Royal Surrey County Hospital, Egerton Road, Guildford GU2 7XX
Tel: 01483 571122 Fax: 01483 464160, 01483 537747
(Surrey and Sussex Health Authority)

Chair Chris Coates, Colston Herbert
Chief Executive Jeff Faulkner

Royal Surrey County Hospital

Egerton Road, Guildford GU2 7XX
Tel: 01483 571122
Total Beds: 520

Accident and Emergency B Brooks, A Wan
Anaesthetics G Dhond, W Fawcett, J R Fozard, T M Gallagher, H B A Griffiths, J G Jenkins, E J Kershaw, J M Leigh, M Payne, N F Quiney, P R Saunders, M Scott, J R Stoneham
Audiological Medicine V Jayarajam
Cardiology T P Chua, E Leatham
Cardiothoracic Surgery R E Sayer, E E J Smith
Care of the Elderly A Blight, H Khoshnaw, H Powell, V Seth
Dermatology E Wong
ENT P Chapman, J Rowe-Jones, N Solomons, R Sudderick, N F Weir
General Medicine R Jones, W A C McAllister, M G M Smith
General Surgery M E Bailey, M Karanjia, M W Kissin, C G Marks, J Stebbing, M Whiteley
Neurology P S Trend
Neurophysiology M Sheehy
Obstetrics and Gynaecology E P Curtis, R Hutt, A Kent, K E Morton, C J G Sutton, S Whitcroft
Ophthalmology G Boodhoo, R Condon, A Gilvarry, J Keenan, C McClean

Oral and Maxillofacial Surgery M Damford, P Haers, P Johnson
Orthodontics N Taylor
Orthopaedics C Coates, M Flannery, M Helliwell, P Magnussen, G Paremain, J W Rossen
Paediatrics S Chapman, M Evans, J H Foley, C Godden, M Ryalls
Pathology R L Carter, M G Cook, L Daborn, S De Sanctis, S Deacock, I D C Douglas, G Ferns, P Jackson, E Mannion, G Robbins
Radiology C J Bland, T J Bloomberg, J C Cooke, A Lopez, W J Walker
Radiotherapy and Oncology S Houston, M Illsley, R Laing, G Middleton, A Neal, H Thomas, C Topham, S Whittaker
Rheumatology and Rehabilitation A R Behn, R E J Gray
Urology J Davies, S Langley, A Nigam

Royal United Hospital Bath NHS Trust

Royal United Hospital, Combe Park, Bath BA1 3NG
Tel: 01225 428331 Fax: 01225 824304
Website: www.ruh-bah.swest.nhs.uk
(Avon, Gloucestershire and Wiltshire Health Authority)

Chair Gerald Chown
Chief Executive Richard Gleave

Royal United Hospital

Combe Park, Bath BA1 3NG
Tel: 01225 428331 Fax: 01225 824395
Email: info@ruh-bath.swest.nhs.uk
Total Beds: 566

Accident and Emergency D Watson (Head), S Meek
Anaesthetics T M Craft (Head), A F Avery, M Baird, T Cook, A P L Goodwin, K Gupta, J M Handel, P Hersch, S L Hill, L Jordan, P McAteer, P Magee, R Marjot, V C Martin, A H Mayor, J Nolan, A Padkin, C Peden, R Seagger, T Simpson, A Souter, J Tuckey
Biochemistry A Taylor
Cardiology W N Hubbard (Head), R D Thomas
Chest Disease N Foley (Head), A Alexander
Clinical Genetics R Newbury-Ecob
Dermatology C R Lovell (Head)
Diabetes J P Reckless (Head), E L Higgs, T Robinson
ENT J Waldron (Head), R J Canter, A Jardine, R Slack
Gastroenterology D A Robertson (Head), M Davis, M Farrant
General Medicine D E Bateman, T Bennett, M Davis, K Dawson, C L Hall, W N Hubbard, P Lyons, J P D Reckless, D A F Robertson, R D Thomas, R Young
General Surgery D C Britton, J S Budd, M Horrocks, P Maddox, J J Tate, H C Umpleby, M Williamson
Gynaecology D Walker (Head), G D Dunster, N Johnson, R J Porter, N C Sharp, T M Tonge
Haematology C Singer, J G Smith
Neurology D E Bateman, K Dawson, P Lyons
Obstetrics and Gynaecology G Dunster, R Holmes, N Johnson, R Porter, N Sharp, M Tonge, D Walker
Occupational Health C Payton (Head)
Ophthalmology J Luck (Head), R Antcliff, R Baer, J Boulton, S Webber
Oral and Maxillofacial Surgery M J Lutterloch (Head), J Schnetler
Oral Surgery M Lutterloch, J Schnetler
Orthodontics A Ireland, H Knight
Orthopaedics C B Jones (Head), M Bishay, N Bradbury, M Burwell, G Giddins, S Gregg-Smith, M Paterson, S Pope, J L Pozo, A C Ross
Paediatrics P T Rudd (Head), A Billson, S Jones, J P Osborne, J Tyrrell
Pathology A Taylor (Head), L Biddlestone, L Hirschowitz, P Kitching, C Meehan, N Rooney, S Rose
Pharmacology P N Bennett
Radiology S J Hayward (Head), A H Chalmers, D A B Dunlop, D Glew, D Goddard, J Hardman, S Malthouse, M J Noakes, M O'Driscoll, A Phillips, L Robinson, A Sandeman

Radiotherapy and Oncology E D Gilby (Head), C Knechtli, H F V Newman, G J G Rees

Respiratory Medicine A Alexander, N Foley, A Malin

Urology C U Moisey (Head), T Bates, C Gallegos, G Howell

The Royal West Sussex NHS Trust

St. Richard's Hospital, Spitalfield Lane, Chichester PO19 4SE
Tel: 01243 788122 Fax: 01243 531269
Website: www.rwst.org.uk
(Surrey and Sussex Health Authority)

Chair Lis Spence
Chief Executive Robert Lapraik

St Richard's Hospital

Spitalfield Lane, Chichester PO19 4SE
Tel: 01243 788122 Fax: 01243 531269
Total Beds: 405

Anaesthetics A S Carter, A B Conyers, J G Dalgleish, A Kendall, P McDonald, S P McHale, M R Nott, C Smith, G A Turner

Audiological Medicine P D West

Chemical Pathology J R Quiney

Dermatology P R Coburn, A V Levantine

ENT A E Davis, C I Johnstone

General Medicine A G Dewhurst, R A Haigh, R A E Holman, G B Lee, I M Morrison, C J Reid, R D Simpson

General Surgery D R Allen, R C Bowyer, R A P Scott, J N L Simson

Genitourinary Medicine M P G Gomez

Haematology P C Bevan, W P Stross

Histopathology B Conroy, J Conroy, B French, J P O'Sullivan

Medical Microbiology M Greig

Neurology S R Hammans

Neurophysiology R J van der Star

Obstetrics and Gynaecology J L Beynon, J G Hooker, Z H Z Ibrahim

Ophthalmology P Fox, T Niyadurupola, M Teimory

Oral and Maxillofacial Surgery D W MacPherson, C J Poate, J R L Townend, J L Williams

Orthodontics A M Hall

Orthopaedics S P Cavanagh, B Elliott, M C Moss, L J Taylor

Paediatrics M A Bracewell, D Cardy, L S Lamont, T M Taylor, A C M Wallace

Palliative Medicine S J Dolin

Plastic Surgery B Coglan

Radiology N Ashford, A M Guilding, D N Kay

Radiotherapy and Oncology G G S Khoury

Restorative Dentistry P D Cheshire

Rheumatology and Rehabilitation M G Ridley

Urology J P Britton, P G Carter

Royal Wolverhampton Hospitals NHS Trust

Trust Management Offices, Holly Bush House, New Cross Hospital, Wolverhampton WV10 0QP
Tel: 01902 307999 Fax: 01902 642810
(Birmingham and the Black Country Health Authority)

Chair Mel Chevannes
Chief Executive Mark Hackett

New Cross Hospital

Wednesfield Road, Wolverhampton WV10 0QP
Tel: 01902 307999 Fax: 01902 642810

Accident and Emergency D W J McCreadie, I Robertson-Steel, M Zahir

Anaesthetics G P Beck, A G Bryan, S G Fenner, G M Hitchings, R Micklewright, L L Mudie, K Nandi, R Patel, C G Peters, A J Phillips, D J H Richmond, J T Styles, J H Tomlinson, R J N Turner

Care of the Elderly K J Fotherby, R Lodwick

Chemical Pathology A G Jacobs

Dermatology S Oliwieki, D R Taylor

ENT R Cullen, L P Glossop, R T J Shortridge, M Wake, F Wilson

General Medicine S J Connellan, R Horton, M A Jackson, S Kapadia, J S Mann, J Odum, J W Pidgeon, P B Rylance, B M Singh, E T Swarbrick, G S Walford, R M Williams

General Surgery L Coen, F T Curran, T I M Gardecki, R H Grace, B Isgar, J B Marczak, S A Taylor, C R Williams, J G Williams

Haematology A MacWhannel, A M Patel

Medical Microbiology C R Catchpole

Neurology R N Corston, R C Hughes

Neurophysiology A K Gupta

Obstetrics and Gynaecology A J F Browning, C Cox, D Little, D J Murphy, J S Samra

Oral and Maxillofacial Surgery E B Larkin, B G Millar, N Whear

Orthodontics R I W Evans

Orthopaedics A M Fraser, E S Isbister, A P Thomas, R J Thomas, A Turner

Paediatrics J M Anderson, P J Dison, D S Kalra, B Kumararatne, R J Rayner, K R Ross

Pathology J E Bridger, M G Freeth, J S Haldane, K W M Scott

Radiology M Collins, C S Deacon, R Fitzgerald, M Hale, S A Hill, G Mackie, Y Osafo-Agyare

Radiotherapy and Oncology R Allerton, D J Fairlamb, R C Mehra, T J Priestman

Rheumatology H A Ali, P Netwon

Urology J A Inglis, N H Philp, B Waymont

Wolverhampton Eye Infirmary

Compton Road, Wolverhampton WV3 9QR
Tel: 01902 26731 Fax: 01902 645019
Total Beds: 25

Ophthalmology C K S Chew, P G J Corridan, M P Headon, N J Price, S Sandamouli, G A Shun-Shin

Royston, Buntingford and Bishop's Stortford Primary Care Trust

Herts & Essex Hospital, Haymeads Lane, Bishop's Stortford CM23 5JH
Tel: 01279 651277 Fax: 01279 651278
(Bedfordshire and Hertfordshire Health Authority)

Chair Mavis Garner
Chief Executive Gareth Jones

Rugby Primary Care Trust

Westgate House, 21 Market Street, Warwick CV34 4DE
Tel: 01926 493491 Fax: 01926 495074
(Coventry, Warwickshire, Herefordshire and Worcestershire Health Authority)

Chair Edward Pallot
Chief Executive Peter Maddock

Rushcliffe Primary Care Trust

6 Bridgford Road, West Bridgford, Nottingham NG2 6AB
Tel: 0115 914 3225 Fax: 0115 914 3229
(Trent Health Authority)

Chair John Tarrant
Chief Executive Mark Morgan

St Albans and Harpenden Primary Care Trust

99 Waverley Road, St Albans AL3 5TL

NHS TRUSTS & NHS HOSPITALS

Tel: 01727 831219 Fax: 01727 812686
(Bedfordshire and Hertfordshire Health Authority)

Chair John Bennett
Chief Executive Steve Knighton

St George's Healthcare NHS Trust

Blackshaw Road, Tooting, London SW17 0QT
Tel: 020 8672 1255 Fax: 020 8672 5304
Website: www.st-georges.org.uk
(South West London Health Authority)

Chair Catherine McLoughlin
Chief Executive Ian Hamilton

Atkinson Morley's Hospital

31 Copse Hill, Wimbledon, London SW20
Tel: 020 8946 7711 Fax: 020 8725 4140
Total Beds: 67

Anaesthetics G Hall, T E Hollway, M A Kraayenbrink, P Razis, A C Thurlow

Neurology D M Barnes, O J F Foster, Y M Hart, H R Modarres-Sadeghi, F Schon, M Schwartz, S G Wilson, D Wren

Neuroradiology J Britton, A Clifton

Neurosurgery B A Bell, F G Johnston, H T Marsh, A Moore, S R Stapleton, P E Wilkins

Bolingbroke Hospital

Wandsworth Common, London SW11 6HN
Tel: 020 7223 7411 Fax: 020 7223 5865
Total Beds: 89

Care of the Elderly J Coles, M A Cottee, I Hastie, J J Oram, S Samadian

St George's Hospital

Blackshaw Road, London SW17 0QT
Tel: 020 8672 1255 Fax: 020 8672 5304
Total Beds: 930

Accident and Emergency M Lynch, D Wallis, D Wijetunge

Anaesthetics J Allt-Graham, J D Boyd, R W Brown, J N Cashman, J T Clarke, G Farnsworth, I L Findley, R M Grounds, M G Hulse, S E Hutchinson, M Kraayenbrink, J B Liban, L J Murdoch, P J Newman, J A O'Riordan, P A Razis, P A Rich, B J Stanford, B A Sutton, A C Thurlow, J P Van Besouw

Audiological Medicine E M Raglan, S E Snashall

Cardiology S J D Brecker, A J Camm, W McKenna, C W Pumphrey, D E Ward

Cardiothoracic Surgery A J Murday, R E Sayer, E J Smith, T Treasure

Care of the Elderly J A Coles, M A Cottee, I R Hastie, J J Oram, S Samadian

Chemical Pathology P Collinson, G E Levin

Clinical Genetics V A Murday, M A Patton

Dermatology R A Marsden, P S Mortimer, L S Ostlere

General Medicine J Eastwood, P W Jones, J D Maxwell, C R Newton, S S Nussey, A Panahloo, C F J Rayner

General Surgery J A Dormandy, A Fiennes, A Halliday, M J Knight, D Kumar, R J Leicester, T Loosemore, R McFarland, D Melville, A Sharma

Genitourinary Medicine E A F Davidson, P E Hay, R Lau, J Mantell

Haematology S E Ball, D H Bevan, E Gordon-Smith, J C W Marsh

Histopathology J Chow, C M Corbishley, T Creagh, C J Finlayson, I J M Jeffrey, V A Thomas, P Wilson, M P A Young

Infectious Diseases G E Griffin, M H Wansbrough-Jones

Medical Microbiology A Breathnach

Nephrology M Bewick, R W S Chang, J B J Eastwood, S R Nelson, D Oliveira, C Streather

Nuclear Medicine A E A Joseph

Obstetrics and Gynaecology D Barton, T H Bourne, S Campbell, P Carter, I T Manyonda, G Nargund, S L Stanton, B Thilaganathan, T R Varma

Occupational Health N A Mitchell-Heggs

Ophthalmology W Aylward, C K Rostron, G M Thompson

Oral and Maxillofacial Surgery M Danford, M Manisali

Orthodontics S J Powell

Orthopaedics M D Bircher, S H Bridle, P T Calvert, A Day, A C Fairbank, A M Jackson, R H Vickers

Otolaryngology A E Hinton, V L Moore Gillon

Paediatrics M D Bain, A R Bedford-Russell, S M Boddy, C Brain, S A Calvert, S N J Capps, J A Christopher, E G Davies, D A C Elliman, S J Fonseca, P A Hamilton, J E Hammond, S J K Holmes, S Mitton, P J Rye, M Sharland, T T N Sim, S M Thurlbeck

Plastic Surgery D Gateley, A L H Moss, J O'Donoghue, B W Powell

Radiology E J Adam, R A Allan, A M Belli, T M Buckenham, D D Dundas, R M Given-Wilson, A Grundy, H L Hale, C W Heron, A E Joseph, K T Khaw, U Patel, A G Wilson

Radiotherapy and Oncology A Dalgleish, J P Glees, C L Harmer, F Lofts, J L Mansi, R Pettengell

Rehabilitation Medicine B E Bourke, F E Bruckner, P Kiely

Restorative Dentistry P F A Briggs

Rheumatology J Axford, B E Bourke, F E Bruckner, P Kiely

Urology K Anson, M Bailey, R S Kirby

St Helens and Knowsley Community Health NHS Trust

Closing April 2002 - Specialty services transferring to 5 Borough Partnership NHS Trust; community services transferring to Knowsley Primary Care Trust and St Helens Primary Care Trust.

The Hollies, Cowley Hill Lane, St Helens WA10 2AP
Tel: 01744 697200 Fax: 01744 453405
(Cheshire and Merseyside Health Authority)

Chief Executive Daniel K McCaul

Consultants K Balachandran, J Ellison, J Gauthier, Carol Harvey, H Joshi, A Kirby, C Nkonde, P O'Grady

St Helens and Knowsley Hospitals NHS Trust

From April 2002 specialist services transferring to 5 Borough Partnership NHS Trust.

Whiston Hospital, Warrington Road, Prescot L35 5DR
Tel: 0151 426 1600 Fax: 0151 430 1425
(Cheshire and Merseyside Health Authority)

Chair Mavis Wareham
Chief Executive Kenneth J Sanderson

Newton Community Hospital

Bradlegh Road, Newton-le-Willows WA12 8RB
Tel: 01925 222731
Total Beds: 30

Care of the Elderly J Abrams

Dermatology R K Curley

ENT J C McIlwain

General Medicine A M G Cochrane

General Psychiatry B John

General Surgery M Scott

Obstetrics and Gynaecology G Buchanan, M Hamed

Ophthalmology J Villada

Orthopaedics M E Cavendish, I M Shackleferd

Paediatrics L Amegavie, E L Badri, C R Woodhall

St Bartholomew's Day Hospital

Station Road, Roby, Liverpool L36 4HU
Tel: 0151 489 6241

St Helens Hospital

Marshalls Cross Road, St Helens WA9 3EA
Tel: 01744 26633 Fax: 01744 451321
Total Beds: 211

Accident and Emergency G Inkster
Anaesthetics P Atherton, H Davies, G M Edwards, H L Gordon, T Hankin, K Levshankov, J Nash, G Saba
Care of the Elderly J Abrams, D K Banerjee
Child and Adolescent Psychiatry J Ellison
Dermatology R K Curley, S Evans
ENT S Jackson, J C McIlwain
General Medicine S T Atherton, A M G Cochrane, J Cunningham, R Faizallah, D Graham, M P Lynch, M H Scott
General Psychiatry A Dutta, M Murugananthan, V Sharma
General Surgery M R Colmer, R H Johnson, C J Sanderson
Genitourinary Medicine M Veerahavu
Ophthalmology J Ghosh, P Joyce
Oral and Maxillofacial Surgery J C Cooper
Orthopaedics B Bolton-Maggs, M E Cavendish, J S Denton, M P Manning, D Teanby
Paediatrics M Amegavie, C E Cramp, A El-Badari, C R Woodhall
Pathology K D Allen, C J Coast, E Gradwell, G Satchithananthan, J A Tappin
Radiology A F Evans, S Evans, J C Herbert, J Kenny, G C Markham, C R Thind, R E Wild
Radiotherapy and Oncology J E S Brock
Urology H Gana, J A Massey

Stewart Day Hospital

Peasley Cross Wing, St Helens Hospital, Marshall Cross Road, St Helens WA9 8DA
Tel: 01744 458380 Fax: 01744 458461

Whiston Hospital

Whiston, Prescot L35 5DR
Tel: 0151 426 1600 Fax: 0151 430 1425
Total Beds: 795

Accident and Emergency T Brown, C S Graham, G Inkster, P A M Nee, E Worthington
Anaesthetics P Atherton, C Breeze, H Davies, G M Edwards, H L Gordon, T Hankin, C Harris, R P Howard, C S Ince, K Levshankov, R R Macmillan, J Nash, V Nelson, S Raftery, G Saba, A Skinner, E Whelan
Care of the Elderly J Abrams, D K Banerjee, A Capewell, D N Carmichael, T Smith
Child and Adolescent Psychiatry J M Gauthier-Le-Tendre
Dental Surgery J C Cooper, J Hussain
ENT S Banerjee, A Daud, V Nandapalan
General Medicine S T Atherton, J Ball, S Church, C Francis, R Griffiths, J Hendry, S Leong, M P Lynch, J McLindon, J Morris, D Padmakumar, J B Ridyard
General Psychiatry D Arya, M Conway, A Dutta, D Ibitoye, D Johnson, A Oxtoby
General Surgery R Audisio, L Chagla, R Kiff, D Maitra, C J Sanderson, M H Scott
Microbiology M A Al-Jouburi
Neurology M G Steiger, B M Tedman
Obstetrics and Gynaecology G M Cawdell, Dr Hamed, T Idama, J Langton, P Morgan, C Nwosu
Ophthalmology J Ghosh, P Joyce
Orthodontics S Husain
Orthopaedics B Bolton-Maggs, J S Denton, M P Manning, D N Teanby
Paediatrics M Alwaidh, L Amegavie, A El-Badri, J A Sills, C R Woodhall
Pathology K D Allen, E Gradwell, N U Hasan, S A Kelly, M J R Pinto
Plastic Surgery J R Bryson, L Feldberg, K Graham, A R Green, K Hancock, M I James, V Kumar
Radiology S Desmond, A F Evans, S Evans, O Harris, J C Herbert, G C Markham, D Meek, C R Thind

Radiotherapy and Oncology J E S Brock, A Flavin, D Husband, E Marshall

St Helens Primary Care Trust

Cowley Hill Lane, St Helens WA10 2AP
Tel: 01744 457333 Fax: 01744 736827
Chair Nora Giubertoni
Chief Executive Morag Day

St Mary's NHS Trust

Praed Street, London W2 1NY
Tel: 020 7886 666 Fax: 0207 886 6314
Email: brown.gillian@st-marys.nhs.uk
(North West London Health Authority)

St Mary's Hospital

Praed Street, London W2 1NY
Tel: 020 7725 6666 Fax: 020 7886 1017
Total Beds: 700

Accident and Emergency N J Fothergill, R Touquet
Anaesthetics J A Gil-Rodriguez, A W Harrop-Griffiths, J A Jones, R M Jones, P F Knight, K P Kyriakou, K G A Macleod, M Platt, M Price, J C Roberts, D J C Robinson, J E Shepherd, J B Smith, G V Symons
Biochemistry R Williamson
Cardiology M Dancy, D W Davies, R A Foale, D Hackett, C Handler, D Sheridan
Cardiothoracic Surgery B Glenville, R Sapsford, R d L Stanbridge
Care of the Elderly A M Middleton, S Roche, S C Webb
Chemical Pathology A Fairney
Chest Disease D M Mitchell, P Openshaw, R Shaw
Cytology E M Bates, D V Coleman
Dermatology L Fry, J Leonard, A V Powles
Diabetes R S Elkeles, D G Johnston, M McCarthy
Endocrinology R S Elkeles, D G Johnston, M McCarthy
ENT S Abramovich, S Soucek, N Stafford, N Tolley, G P Walsh-Waring, J L W Wright
Gastroenterology J H Baron, J S Summerfield, H Thomas, H C Thomas
General Medicine D Gordon, R Lancaster, P Richards
General Surgery M W Ghilchik, G Glazer, B Glenville, D M Hunt, J R Johnson, A O Mansfield, R D Rosin, A Spigelman, R d L Stanbridge, G Stansby
Genetics L Brueton
Genitourinary Medicine M Byrne, D Cheetham, E Claydon, R J Coker, D Goldmeier, J R W Harris, V Kitchen, J Main, P Munday, S Murphy, D Taylor-Robinson, D R Tomlinson, J Weber
Haematology S H Abdalla, B J Bain, H Cohen, S M Wickramasinghe
Histopathology V Cattell, T Cook, D Evans, A M Flanagan, R D Goldin, M M Walker
Immunology J Lamb, J Lorton, J Mowbray, R O'Hehir
Medical Microbiology S Barrett, Q N Karim
Nephrology B Hulme, L C K Lin, A Palmer, D Taube
Neurology J Ball, M N Rossor, S Smith, D J Thomas
Neurosurgery D Thomas
Obstetrics and Gynaecology R W Beard, S Franks, A Fraser, F E Loeffler, W P Mason, K W Murphy, C M Paterson, L Regan, J Rizvi, J Smith
Oncology C A Coulter, P Price, J Stewart
Ophthalmology J F Acheson, R J Marsh, C Migdal, M J Olver, W E Schulenburg, C Townsend, P L Wormald
Orthopaedics J R T Eckersley, R Emery, D Hunt, J Johnson
Paediatric Surgery N Madden
Paediatrics S Bignall, H T F Davies, J E Deal, P Habibi, S Kroll, M Levin, T Lissauer, M Miles, R A P Rivers, R Schwartz, D Smyth, G Supramanian, G Tudor-Williams, D Walters
Pharmacology A Gorchein, C J Mathias, N Poulter, P S Sever, S Thom

NHS TRUSTS & NHS HOSPITALS

Plastic Surgery N Waterhouse
Radiology S Ahuja, M A O Al-Kutoubi, S Burnett, M E Crofton, D A Cunningham, W Gedroyc, C Owens, J M Stevens
Rheumatology R G Rees, M H Seifert
Urology M E Snell, J A Vale, R O Witherow
Vascular Medicine A O Mansfield, A N Nicolaides, G Stansby, J H N Wolfe
Virology P Watkins

Western Eye Hospital

Marylebone Road, London NW1
Tel: 020 7402 4211
Total Beds: 20

Salford Primary Care Trust

Suite 21-23, 5th Floor, St James' House, Pendleton Way M6 5FW
Tel: 0161 212 4821 Fax: 0161 212 4801
(Greater Manchester Health Authority)

Chair Eileen Fairhurst
Chief Executive Edna Robinson

Salford Royal Hospitals NHS Trust

Hope Hospital, Stott Lane, Salford M6 8HD
Tel: 0161 789 7373 Fax: 0161 787 5974
Email: enquires@hope.srht.nwest.nhs.uk
Website: www.srht.nwest.nhs.uk
(Greater Manchester Health Authority)

Chair Jim Potter
Chief Executive Dr [New Person], William H Sang

Hope Hospital

Stott Lane, Salford M6 8WH
Tel: 0161 789 7373 Fax: 0161 787 5974
Total Beds: 800

Accident and Emergency P A Driscoll, I Sammy, D W Yates
Anaesthetics M W B Allan, S M Berger, B J M Bowles, J J Brown, C Earlam, I Geraghty, C L Gwinnutt, T W Johnson, R Kishen, C M Rogers, C Spanswick, M D Trask
Care of the Elderly M Gonsalkorale, A K M Karim, R C Tallis
Chemical Pathology M F Stewart, C Weinkove
Dental Surgery I D Campbell, R E Lloyd
Dermatology C Griffiths
ENT M P Rothera, D J Willatt
General Medicine P C Barnes, H Buckler, T L Dornan, R O'Donoghue, R O'Driscoll, W D Rees, Dr Sandle, J Shaffer, D G Thompson, S Waldek, R J Young
General Surgery J Bancewicz, N Scott
Genitourinary Medicine B P Goorney
Haematology P Carrington, J B Houghton, R C Routledge
Histopathology G R Armstrong, R H McDonald, R S Reeve
Immunology M R Haeney
Medical Microbiology L A Joseph, M G L Keaney
Nephrology D O'Donoghue, S Waldek
Neurology P D Mohr, A C Young
Neurosurgery R A Cowie, R A C Jones, G G H West
Obstetrics and Gynaecology G F Falconer, G G Mitchell, D Poulson, A Railton
Oncology D Crowther, J H Scarffe
Oral and Maxillofacial Surgery I D Campbell, R E Lloyd
Orthodontics J Brady
Orthopaedics G Andrew, C S B Galasko, J Noble, E R S Ross, J B Williamson
Paediatrics G Hambleton, M J Robinson
Plastic Surgery C I Orton, J S Watson
Radiology J D K Brown, R A Chisholm, W S C Forbes, S G Gupta, D Hughes, H Mamtora, D Nicholson

Rheumatology and Rehabilitation A Herrick, R C Hilton, A K P Jones
Urology N Clarke

Ladywell Hospital

Eccles New Road, Salford M5 2AA
Tel: 0161 789 7373
Total Beds: 246

Care of the Elderly M Gonsalkorale, A K M Karim, A Scott, R C Tallis, G E Whittingham
Haematology J B Houghton, R C Routledge
Medical Microbiology L A Joseph, M G L Keaney
Neurology P D Mohr, A C Young
Radiology J D K Brown, S Thurairajasingam
Rheumatology and Rehabilitation R C Hilton, M I V Jayson, A K P Jones

Salisbury Healthcare NHS Trust

Salisbury District Hospital, Salisbury SP2 8BJ
Tel: 01722 336262 Fax: 01722 330221
Website: www.salisburyhealthcare.org
(Avon, Gloucestershire and Wiltshire Health Authority)

Chair David Noble
Chief Executive Frank Harsent

Fordingbridge Hospital

Bartons Road, Fordingbridge SP6 1JD
Tel: 01425 652255 Fax: 01425 654705
Total Beds: 40

General Medicine J H Marigold

The Old Manor

Wilton Road, Salisbury SP2 7EP
Tel: 01722 336262 Fax: 01722 331879
Total Beds: 156

General Psychiatry T G Davies, A Gregoire, J F Haggis, M F Humphreys, R King, D J S West

Salisbury District Hospital

Salisbury SP2 8BJ
Tel: 01722 336262 Fax: 01722 330221
Total Beds: 535

Accident and Emergency N C Burrows
Anaesthetics S Abbas, R F Barrett, S L Calvert, J J Church, S Cockroft, C Cox, K N Duggal, J A Lack, D J Lintin, M I D McCallum, D P Murray, R J Ray, R P F Scott, P Swayne
Burns E Tiernan
Care of the Elderly J H Marigold
Child and Adolescent Psychiatry M A Griffiths, M I Vereker
Dermatology R H Meyrick-Thomas, D Mitchell
ENT M J Brockbank, G B Todd
General Medicine S Biggart, S Janmohamed, J H Marigold, S Vyas, A R H Warley
General Surgery N J Carty, H Chave, T J C Cooke, D Finnis, P J Guy, G S McIntosh, C Ranaboldo
Genitourinary Medicine M S A Nasr
Obstetrics and Gynaecology P W Docherty, S A Fountain, D M McKenna, J A Wilde
Oncology K Gregory, T Iveson
Ophthalmology R G Collyer-Powell, R C Humphry, A G Tyers
Oral and Maxillofacial Surgery T R Flood, D L Shinn
Orthopaedics A R Beaumont, N Chappell, D R Cox, G F Rushforth, G Shergill
Paediatrics M M Lwin, R H Scott-Jupp, D Stratton
Palliative Medicine J Olberton, C D Wood
Pathology S Burroughs, J Cullis, C E Fuller-Watson, H F Parry, C A Scott
Plastic Surgery M Cadier, R P Cole, J A E Hobby, R A W McDowall, L F A Rossi, I Whitworth

Radiology J A D Annis, B Bentley, R A Frost, S Hegarty, K Johnson, S G McGee, A D P Morris
Rheumatology and Rehabilitation R M Ellis, J C Robertson
Spinal Injuries F Jamil, A Soopramanian, A M Tromans

Westminster Memorial Hospital

Abbey Walk, Shaftesbury SP7 8BD
Tel: 01747 851535 Fax: 01747 850152
Total Beds: 38

Sandwell and West Birmingham Hospitals NHS Trust

City Hospital, Dudley Road, Birmingham B18 7QH
Tel: 0121 554 3801
Website: www.swbh.nhs.uk
Chair Najma Hafeez
Chief Executive John Adler

City Hospital

Dudley Road, Birmingham B18 7QH
Tel: 0121 554 3801 Fax: 0121 523 0951
Total Beds: 737

Accident and Emergency P Ahee, M Ansar, D Moore
Anaesthetics J Bleasdale, R A Botha, V V Chhaya, J Clift, K K Dutt, A Hahn, A Kabear, Dr Khan, K L Kong, G A Lewis, A A McKenzie, J Macleod, S Mittal, A Mosquera, J F O'Dea, Dr Pooni, R Rasanayagam, J Shah, N Sherwood, A Vella, A M Veness, S B Vohra, G P Xifaras
Cardiology G Lip, T Millane, N Prasad, R D S Watson
Care of the Elderly S Ballantyne, M Ehtisham, A Ritch, M A P Simons
Chemical Pathology A Bignell
Clinical Chemistry A Bignell
Dermatology I S Foulds, C J Paul, K S Ryatt, C Y Tan
Endocrinology S L Jones, R E Ryder, K G Taylor
ENT A Batch, P Dekker, J O'Connell, A L Pahor, P E Robin
Gastroenterology B T Cooper, T Iqbal, P Wilson
General Medicine R E Ferner, D W Young
General Surgery J Dmitrewski, I A Donovan, M J R Lee, M L Obeid, S H Silverman, R Spychal, P Stonelake, R L Wolverson
Haematology D Bareford, J Wright
Histopathology S Y Chan, P Colloby, R Ganesan, J C Gearty
Immunology J North
Medical Microbiology A Fraise, M Gill, T Weller, R Wise
Neurology C Clarke, D G Jamieson, S G Sturman
Neurophysiology A K Gupta
Nuclear Medicine L K Harding, A Notghi, W Thomson
Obstetrics and Gynaecology N Bhatti, R G Condie, G Downey, L Dwarakanath, I Etherington, M Luckas, D Luesley
Ophthalmology Dr Ainsworth, M Benson, Dr Burdon, Dr Cunliffe, E M Eagling, J M Gibson, M Hope-Ross, G R Kirkby, Dr Larkin, P McDonnell, P I Murray, E O'Neill, T Reuser, P Shah, P Stavrou, G A Sutton, Dr Tsaloumas, H E Willshaw
Oral and Maxillofacial Surgery B Speculand
Orthodontics B Speculand
Orthopaedics S Deshmukh, Dr Lin, B K Singh, M S Vishwanath
Paediatrics A Akbar, A Aukett, J G Bissenden, S Lalonde, J Nycyk, H Robertson, Dr Shaw, Dr Simkiss, A Skinner, P H Weller
Plastic Surgery M S Fatah
Radiology F A Aitchison, S Bodicoat, S V Chadva, J Clarke, D M Dawkins, S R Hesslewood, K Lee, M J McMinn, M Moss, S L Walker, J P Wingate
Radiotherapy and Oncology Dr Poole, D Spooner
Renal Medicine D C Wheeler
Respiratory Medicine P B Iles, Dr Khair
Rheumatology and Rehabilitation R D Situnayake
Toxicology A Jones, J A Vale
Urology D G Arkell, P G Ryan

Rowley Regis Hospital

Moor Lane, Rowley Regis, Warley B65 8DA
Tel: 0121 607 3465
Total Beds: 76

Sandwell District General Hospital

Lyndon, West Bromwich B71 4HJ
Tel: 0121 553 1831 Fax: 0121 607 3117
Total Beds: 562

Accident and Emergency C J Holburn, J Rizkalla
Anaesthetics J M Bellin, D Bhar, N P Carter, H Daya, D H Dubash, I F Duncan, S Kanari, E Leno, D D R Macaulay, A Patel, D Poole, M C Suchak, J Van Vuren
Biochemistry E Hughes
General Medicine R Ahmad, I Ahmed, G V H Bradby, P J Cadigan, C Cobb, D Connolly, C Crowther, P Davies, K A Grindulis, M Hussain, F Khattak, D T McLeod, N Page, J Paul, T K Ray, D A Robertson, H Shakeel, E Smith, N Trudgill
General Surgery A Aukland, E T Bainbridge, D J Ellis, D Gourevitch, M Vairavan, K Wheatley
Haematology S Handa, P Stableforth, Y Zaidi
Histopathology S Banerjee, F Brook, U Pandey, J Simon
Microbiology A Davies, N Williams
Obstetrics and Gynaecology I Abukhalil, J Kabukoba, M Mattar, R K Smith
Occupational Medicine P Verow
Ophthalmology S P Aggarwal, J Al-Ibrahim, M Quinlan, S M Thompson, A Tyagi
Orthopaedics J C Clothier, M M El-Safty, S S Geeranavar, P Shaylor, M Taylor
Paediatrics C Agwu, H Grindulis, R Jayatunga, D C Low, A J Mayne, H Nachi, J Nycyk
Plastic Surgery A Khanna, J M Porter
Radiology A H S Ahmed, R C Bhatt, D Chand, R M Donovan, A R M Evans, J F Leahy
Urology M A Jones, K Kadow

Sandwell Healthcare NHS Trust

Closing April 2002 - Services transferring to Sandwell and West Birmingham Hospitals NHS Trust; community services transferring to Rowley, Regis and Tipton Primary Care Trust, The Olbury and Smethwick Primary Care Trust and Wednesbury and West Bromwich Primary Care Trust.

Sandwell District General Hospital, Lyndon, West Bromwich B71 4HJ
Tel: 0121 553 1831 Fax: 0121 607 3177
(Birmingham and the Black Country Health Authority)

Chair Bryan Knight
Chief Executive David W Lingwood

Heath Lane Hospital

Health Lane, West Bromwich B71 2BQ
Tel: 0121 553 7676 Fax: 0121 607 3070

Learning Disabilities Dr Mlele

Scarborough and North East Yorkshire Health Care NHS Trust

Scarborough Hospital, Woodlands Drive, Scarborough YO12 6QL
Tel: 01723 368111 Fax: 01723 377223
(North and East Yorkshire and Northern Lincolnshire Health Authority)

Chair John Allen
Chief Executive Robert Crawford

NHS TRUSTS & NHS HOSPITALS

Bridlington and District Hospital
Bessingby Road, Bridlington YO16 4QP
Tel: 01262 606666 Fax: 01262 400583
Total Beds: 150

Haworth Unit
Scarborough Hospital, Woodlands Drive, Scarborough YO12 6QL

Malton, Norton and District Hospital
Middlecave Road, Malton YO17 7NG
Tel: 01653 693041 Fax: 01653 600589
Total Beds: 70

Anaesthetics D F Jones
Dermatology A S Highet
ENT E B Whitby
General Medicine R S Clark, D Humphriss, C J Mitchell
General Surgery E P Perry
Obstetrics and Gynaecology D W Robinson
Ophthalmology P J Bacon
Orthopaedics J G Bradley
Paediatrics A R Falconer
Radiology I Glaves

Scarborough Hospital
Woodlands Drive, Scarborough YO12 6QL
Tel: 01723 368111 Fax: 01723 377223
Total Beds: 398

Accident and Emergency P E Akar, A P Volans
Anaesthetics P M Buckley, D F Jones, J P Normandale, I C Tring, M A Turner
Cardiothoracic Medicine M Cowen, K K Nair
Care of the Elderly S K Chatterjee, R Perara
Chest Disease D Ford
Dental Surgery G D D Roberts, M R Telfer
Dermatology C A Henderson, A S Highet
ENT J G D Baker, E B Whitby
General Medicine P Brown, R S Clark, D Ford, D Humphriss, C J Mitchell
General Surgery N El-Bargouti, J MacFie, K Mannur, E P Perry
Neurology A Ming
Obstetrics and Gynaecology A D Booth, M C B Noble, D R Poole, D W Robinson
Ophthalmology P Bacon, S P B Percival, R Redmond
Orthodontics J J Crabb, P Jenkins
Orthopaedics J G Bradley, A G Donovan, A Hazemi, A North
Paediatrics A Falconer, T Lwin, I Rawashdeh, A N Stanton, V R Ventakesh
Pathology A M Jackson, D J Johnstone, D R Morgan
Radiology J A Boyle, J Dyer, I Glaves, I Renwick, D Y II Wai
Radiotherapy and Oncology M Holmes
Rehabilitation Medicine J Paterson
Restorative Dentistry J Ralph
Rheumatology Z Al Safar
Urology K G Brame, S Hawkyard

Whitby Hospital
Spring Hill, Whitby YO21 1EE
Tel: 01947 604851 Fax: 01947 820568
Total Beds: 96

Care of the Elderly S K Chatterjee
Dermatology A S Highet
ENT E B Whitby
General Medicine R S Clark, D Humphriss
Obstetrics and Gynaecology J Patterson
Ophthalmology S P B Percival
Orthopaedics J G Bradley
Radiology J A Boyle, D Wai

Scarborough, Whitby and Ryedale Primary Care Trust
Severeign House, Kettlestring Lane, York YO30 4GQ
Tel: 01904 825110 Fax: 01904 825125
(North and East Yorkshire and Northern Lincolnshire Health Authority)

Sedgefield Primary Care Trust
Appleton House, Lanchester Road, Durham DH1 5XZ
Tel: 0191 333 3232 Fax: 0191 333 3233
(County Durham and Tees Valley Health Authority)

Chair Alan Gray
Chief Executive Nigel Porter

Selby and York Primary Care Trust
37 Monkgate, York YO31 7PB
Tel: 01904 632142 Fax: 01904 627839
(North and East Yorkshire and Northern Lincolnshire Health Authority)

Chair Janet Looker
Chief Executive Sue Ross

Severn NHS Trust
Closing April 2002 - Mental health and learning disability services transferring to Gloucestershire Partnership NHS Trust; community services transferring to Cheltenham and Tewkesbury Primary Care Trust, Cotswold and Vale Primary Care Trust and West Gloucestershire Primary Care Trust.

Rikenel, Montpellier, Gloucester GL1 1LY
Tel: 01452 891000 Fax: 01452 891001
(Avon, Gloucestershire and Wiltshire Health Authority)

Chair Christopher Weaver
Chief Executive Richard James

Berkeley Hospital
Berkeley GL13 9AB
Tel: 01453 562000 Fax: 01453 562001
Total Beds: 20

Care of the Elderly N Baldwin (Head)
ENT A R Maw (Head)
Gastroenterology R Valori (Head)
General Medicine J Prior (Head)
General Surgery H Barr (Head), M Vipond (Head)
Obstetrics and Gynaecology G R Swingler (Head)
Orthopaedics D K Asante
Psychiatry M Barber, K Sackett
Urology A R Ritchie

Denmark Road Day Hospital
18 Denmark Road, Gloucester GL1 3HZ
Tel: 01452 891220 Fax: 01452 891221

Dilke Memorial Hospital
Cinderford GL14 3HX
Tel: 01594 598100 Fax: 01594 598101
Total Beds: 36

Cardiology D C Lindsay (Head)
Care of the Elderly I Donald (Head)
ENT K L Evans (Head)
Gastroenterology R M Valori (Head)
General Psychiatry K Williams (Head)
General Surgery H Barr, J J Earnshaw, B P Heather

Nephrology R A Banks (Head)
Obstetrics and Gynaecology M D Read
Orthopaedics R S Majkowski (Head)
Paediatrics A Rushforth
Radiology S Jones (Head)
Rheumatology Dr Mack
Thoracic Medicine M Jones, D M Meecham-Jones
Urology A W S Ritchie

Holly House Day Hospital

West Lodge Drive, Coney Hill, Gloucester
Tel: 01452 891380 Fax: 01452 891381
Total Beds: 25

Lydney and District Hospital

Lydney GL15 5JF
Tel: 01594 598220 Fax: 01594 598221
Total Beds: 27

Cardiology M Peterson (Head)
Dermatology J M Boss
ENT K L Evans (Head)
General Psychiatry G Hodgson
General Surgery J J Earnshaw, B P Heather, M Lucorrotti
Obstetrics and Gynaecology M D Read
Ophthalmology J Hoare-Nairn (Head)
Orthopaedics Dr Asante, R S Majkowski, B D Morris
Paediatrics M S Webb (Head)
Rheumatology G Coombs
Urology H Gilbert, A W S Ritchie

Stonebury Day Hospital

22 Grove Road, Lydney GL15 2JE
Tel: 01594 598260 Fax: 01594 598261

Stroud General Hospital

Stroud GL5 2HY
Tel: 01453 562200 Fax: 01453 562201
Total Beds: 61

Cardiology D C Lindsay, M Peterson
Care of the Elderly M Bannerjee (Head)
Dermatology J M Boss
ENT M Hardingham
Gastroenterology R M Valori
General Medicine R Banks (Head)
General Surgery J Bristol, J J Earnshaw, W H Thomson, M Vipond
Nephrology R A Banks
Obstetrics and Gynaecology G Swingler
Ophthalmology M Joyce, G Mackintosh
Orthopaedics C C Crawshaw, C J Knudsen, T P Tasker
Paediatrics M S Webb
Radiology P Birch, S Jones, J B Witcombe
Radiotherapy and Oncology K Benstead (Head)
Rheumatology J Woodland (Head)
Urology D J Jones (Head)

Stroud Maternity Hospital

Stroud GL5 2JB
Tel: 01453 562140 Fax: 01453 562141
Total Beds: 10

Obstetrics and Gynaecology M Read

Stroud Road Unit

136 Stroud Road, Stroud
Tel: 01452 891200 Fax: 01452 891201

Tyndale Centre Day Hospital

The Slade, Dursley GL11 4JX
Tel: 01453 562390

Wotton Lawn Hospital

Wotton Lawn, Gloucester GL1 3PX
Tel: 01452 891500 Fax: 01452 891501
Total Beds: 74

General Psychiatry N J R Evans, C Fear, G Hodgson, G L Lloyd, R McPherson, I Pennell, K Sackett, K Williams
Learning Disabilities P Winterbottom (Head)
Psychiatry of Old Age J Lugg

Sheffield Children's Hospital NHS Trust

Western Bank, Sheffield S10 2TH
Tel: 0114 271 7000 Fax: 0114 272 3418
(South Yorkshire Health Authority)

Chair Lynn Hagger
Chief Executive John Adler

Sheffield Children's Hospital

Western Bank, Sheffield S10 2TH
Tel: 0114 271 7000 Fax: 0114 272 3418
Total Beds: 159

Accident and Emergency P O B Brennan, D Burke, B Tesfayohannes, J Yassa
Anaesthetics I Barker, N R Bennett, T Dorman, J M Goddard, R John, C Kirton, N H Pereira, C Stack
Audiological Medicine O P Tungland
Cardiology D Dickenson, J Gibbs, J Parsons
Chemical Pathology J Bohnam
Dental Surgery L Davidson
Dermatology M J Cork, A G Messenger
ENT P D Bull, D F Chapman
General Psychiatry S Hughes, R Waller
Genetics J Cook, O Quarrell
Haematology E A M Vandenberghe, A Vora
Medical Education H Davies
Medical Microbiology D Harris, L Ridgeway
Ophthalmology D Brosnahan, J Burke
Oral and Maxillofacial Surgery P P Robinson, S E Ward
Orthopaedics M J Bell, A G Davis, D L Douglas, M J Flowers, A C Howard, M Saleh, T W D Smith
Paediatric Surgery A E Mackinnon, J Roberts, R Shawis, J Walker
Paediatrics L H Allison, J dez Chaplais, M Everard, A H R Finn, M P Gerrard, C A MacKenzie, G Moss, K Price, R Primhak, S Tanner, C J Taylor, J K H Wales
Pathology S Variend
Plastic Surgery T M Brotherston, E Freedlander, R W Griffiths, J G Miller, R E Page
Radiology P S Broadley, P Griffiths, I Lang, G Long, A Sprigg
Rheumatology R Amos

Sheffield South West Primary Care Trust

Station Yard, Archer Road, Milhouses, Sheffield S8 0LA
Tel: 0114 226 4020 Fax: 0114 226 4026
(South Yorkshire Health Authority)

Chair Ann Le Sage
Chief Executive Judy Jones

Sheffield Teaching Hospitals NHS Trust

8 Beech Hill Road, Royal Hallamshire Hospital, Sheffield S10 2SB
Tel: 0114 226 1000 Fax: 0114 226 1001
Website: www.sth.nhs.uk
(South Yorkshire Health Authority)

NHS TRUSTS & NHS HOSPITALS

Chair David Stone
Chief Executive Andrew Cash

Charles Clifford Dental Hospital
Wellesley Road, Sheffield S10 2SZ
Tel: 0114 271 7800 Fax: 0114 271 7836

Child Dental Health P Benson, A H Brook, L E Davidson, M Stern, D R Willmot
Oral and Maxillofacial Surgery I M Brook, A R Loescher, P P Robinson, A T Smith, S Ward, C M Yeoman
Oral Pathology G T Craig, C D Franklin, C J Smith
Restorative Dentistry I R Harris, R I Joshi, D J Lamb, A Rawlinson, T F Walsh, R B Winstanley, P F Wragg

Jessop Wing Women's Hospital
Tree Root Walk, Sheffield S10 2SF
Tel: 0114 271 1900 Fax: 0114 271 1901
Total Beds: 119

Northern General Hospital
Herries Road, Sheffield S5 7AU
Tel: 0114 243 4343 Fax: 0114 256 0472
Total Beds: 1200

Royal Hallamshire Hospital
Glossop Road, Sheffield S10 2JF
Tel: 0114 271 1900 Fax: 0114 271 1901
Total Beds: 750

Anaesthetics S Ahmedzai, J C Andrzejowski, D F Appleton, R E Atkinson, M Berthoud, R J Birks, D P Breen, A J Davidson, D F Doyle, D L Edbrooke, G A Francis, R Freeman, S P Gerrish, E Groves, J V B Mundy, P Murray, J E Peacock, M Pullman, M N Richmond, D B Shepherd, G R Veall, P A Wilkinson, I J Wrench
Cardiology K S Channer, D Oakley, J N West
Dermatology M J Cork, D J Gawkrodger, C I Harrington, N C Hepburn, A J McDonagh, A G Messenger
Diabetes S L Caddick, M W Savage, S Tesfaye
Endocrinology D R Cullen, G T Gillett, T H Jones, R Ross, J Webster
ENT P D Bull, D F Chapman, A J Parker, O P Tungland, T J Woolford, M P Yardley
Gastroenterology D C Gleeson, A Lobo, M E McAlindon
General Surgery A G Johnson, S R Kohlhardt, A W Majeed, M W R Reed, A J Shorthouse, C J Stoddard, W E G Thomas
Genitourinary Medicine G M Dilke-Wing, P A Fraser, D A Hicks, G R Kinghorn, K E Rogstad, M D Talbot, A M Wright
Haematology K K Hampton, M Makris, F E Preston, D C Rees, J T Reilly, E A M Vandenberghe, D A Winfield
Infection and Tropical Medicine S T Green, M W McKendrick, R C Read
Metabolic Medicine J A Kanis
Ophthalmology J Burke, J Chan, S Longstaff, M Nelson, I Rennie, P Rundle, J Talbot, J West, S Winder
Pathology C A Angel, S S Cross, A K Dube, J R Goepel, P G Ince, J A Lee, M A Parsons, A Sherif, D N Slater, J H F Smith, T J Stephenson, W R Timperley, J C E Underwood, C W Warren, M Wells
Pharmacology N D S Bax, P R Jackson, L E Ramsay, H F Woods, W W Yeo
Respiratory Medicine D Fishwick, T W Higenbottam, R Lawson, M K Whyte
Rheumatology M A Akil, R S Amos, D E Bax, C J M Getty, J G Miller, M L Snaith, D Stanley, S H Till, A G Wilson, J Winfield
Stroke Medicine A J Anderson, T J Hendra
Urology J Anderson, C Chapple, F C Hamdy, K Hastie, N Oakley, D Smith, P Tophill, K Wylie

Weston Park Hospital
Whitham Road, Sheffield S10 2SJ
Tel: 0114 226 5000 Fax: 0114 226 5555
Total Beds: 109

Oncology K S Dunn, P Fisher, B W Hancock, M Q Hatton, P Kirkbride, D P Levy, P C Lorigan, I H Manifold, B Orr, S D Pledge, O P Purohit, D J Radstone, S Ramakrishnan, M H Robinson

Sheffield West Primary Care Trust

4 Dragoon Court, Hillsborough Barracks, Penistone Road, Sheffield S6 2GZ
Tel: 0114 285 6920 Fax: 0114 285 6921
(South Yorkshire Health Authority)

Chair Dorothy Dixon-Barrow
Chief Executive Simon Gilby

Shepway Primary Care Trust

8 Radnor Park Avenue, Folkestone CT19 5BN
Tel: 01303 222481, 01303 222487
(Kent and Medway Health Authority)

Sherwood Forest Hospitals NHS Trust

Mansfield Road, Sutton-in-Ashfield NG17 4JL
Tel: 01623 622515 Fax: 01623 621770
(Trent Health Authority)

Chair Brian Meakin
Chief Executive Jeffrey Worrall

Ashfield Community Hospital
Portland Street, Kirkby-in-Ashfield, Nottingham NG17 7AE
Tel: 01623 785050
Total Beds: 80

King's Mill Centre for Healthcare Services
Mansfield Road, Sutton-in-Ashfield NG17 4JL
Tel: 01623 622515 Fax: 01683 621770
Total Beds: 635

Anaesthetics J A Anderson, P Barrett, I Bishton, P T Bull, A Dyson, T Keane, J S Mason, M Mowbray, D Naylor, A Rahman, P J Randall, M T Ross, R Vindlacheruvu, A Voice, A J Whitaker
Dermatology S M Littlewood, E M Saihan
ENT S Ali, W D McNicoll, - Osiname
General Medicine N Ali, M Mahmoud, R H Lloyd Mostyn, S O'Nunain, J Rowley, K A Sands, J Snape, M Vassallo, M Ward
General Surgery J R S Blake, B J Fairbrother, G H Greatrex, F R Jackaman, D Reid
Haematology M Auger, E C Logan
Medical Microbiology M Rahman
Obstetrics and Gynaecology R Dixon, C A Gie, P Makepeace, C J Pickles, G Shrestha
Occupational Health B W Platts
Ophthalmology T Arulampalam, P Nithianandan, A S Rubasingham
Oral and Maxillofacial Surgery P G Watts
Orthodontics D G Nashed
Orthopaedics J Hambidge, P J Livesley, A Moulton, M Needoff, H G Prince, V M Srivastava
Paediatrics S A Beningfield, R F Harris, D I Johnston, V Noble, A P Worsley
Pathology F M Dowling, G Hulman, P J Stocks
Plastic Surgery F B Baillie, M Deane
Radiology S E Brauer, C C A Butcher, H K Chow, E J Cornford, P Ghosh, P N Panto, S Stinchcombe
Radiotherapy E M Bessell
Rheumatology and Rehabilitation K Lim
Urology R J Lemberger, M C Taylor

Mansfield Community Hospital

Stockwell Gate, Mansfield NG18 5QJ
Tel: 01623 785050 Fax: 01623 635357
Total Beds: 112

Care of the Elderly A Akbar, A B M Rahman, J Snape
Radiology S E Brauer, C Butcher, P N Panto, D Svenne

Newark Hospital

Boundary Road, Newark NG24 4DE
Tel: 01636 681681 Fax: 01636 610177
Total Beds: 101

Anaesthetics F D Sullivan
Chest Disease J MacFarlane
Dermatology S M Littlewood
ENT K P Gibbin
General Medicine C R Birch, R S Chowhan, I N Ross
General Psychiatry D A James
General Surgery V S Maheson, C Ubhi, J L Wilkins
Obstetrics and Gynaecology C Gie, R P Husemeyer, R Spencer-Gregson
Ophthalmology T Arulampalam, D Knight-Jones, A S Rubasingham
Orthopaedics J S Hopkins
Paediatrics C S Nanyakkara
Pathology A Lawrence
Radiology S J Bradley
Radiotherapy and Oncology S Chan
Urology J Dunn

Shropshire County Primary Care Trust

William Farr House, Mytton Oak Road, Shrewsbury SY3 8XL
Tel: 01743 261300 Fax: 01743 261362
(Shropshire and Staffordshire Health Authority)

Shropshire's Community and Mental Health Services NHS Trust

Trust closure tbc - part of service transferring to Shropshire County Primary Care Trust and Telford and Wrekin Primary Care Trust.

Shelton Hospital, Bicton Heath, Shrewsbury SY3 8DN
Tel: 01743 261000 Fax: 01743 261279
(Shropshire and Staffordshire Health Authority)

Chair John Oldham-Malcolm
Chief Executive Simon Conolly

Bishops Castle Community Hospital

Bishops Castle SY9 5AJ
Tel: 01588 638220 Fax: 01588 638756
Total Beds: 24

Bridgnorth Hospital

Bridgnorth WV16 4EU
Tel: 01746 762641 Fax: 01746 766172
Total Beds: 30

Ludlow Hospital

Gravel Hill, Ludlow SY8 1QX
Tel: 01584 872201 Fax: 01584 877908
Total Beds: 63

The Mount

Wellington, Telford TF1 1QX
Tel: 01743 232228
Total Beds: 15

Royal Shrewsbury Hospital (Shelton)

Bicton Heath, Shrewsbury SY3 8DN
Tel: 01743 261000 Fax: 01743 261279
Total Beds: 238

West Bank Hospital

300 Holyhead Road, Wellington, Telford TF1 2FF
Tel: 01952 243482 Fax: 01952 641953
Total Beds: 12

Whitchurch Hospital

Whitchurch SY13 1QS
Tel: 01948 666292
Total Beds: 56

Slough Primary Care Trust

1st Floor, Walk in Centre, Upton Hospital, Albert Street, Slough SL1 2BJ
Tel: 01753 635018 Fax: 01753 635047
(Thames Valley Health Authority)

Chair Geoff Cutting
Chief Executive Mike Attwood

Solihull Primary Care Trust

20 Union Road, Solihull B91 3EF
Tel: 0121 711 7171 Fax: 0121 711 7212
(Birmingham and the Black Country Health Authority)

Chair A Dorrow
Chief Executive Carol Clarke

Somerset Coast Primary Care Trust

Bridgwater Community Hospital, Salmon Parade, Bridgwater TA6 5AH
Tel: 01278 436746 Fax: 01278 436785
Website: www.somerset-health.org.uk
(Somerset and Dorset Health Authority)

Chair Christine Dore
Chief Executive Alan Carpenter

Bridgwater Community Hospital

Salmon Parade, Bridgwater TA6 5AH
Tel: 01278 451501 Fax: 01278 444896
Total Beds: 66

Accident and Emergency G Bryce, C J Cutting
Care of the Elderly M Evans
Dermatology J Boyle, C J W Guerrier, D Pryce
ENT J J M Upton, S C Wells
General Medicine M Barry, M G Ellwood, M James, C Swinburn, D B Yates
General Psychiatry P V Hunt
General Surgery J F Chester, C D Collins, I A Eyre-Brook, S M Jones, I N Ramus
Neurology N K Banerji
Neurophysiology E Ragi
Obstetrics and Gynaecology K Bidgood, H Marsh, J A Richardson, H M Smith
Ophthalmology R R Acheson, K Bates, A Stockwell, J R Twomey
Oral and Maxillofacial Surgery M Davidson, J Hamlyn
Orthopaedics R P Foster, C H Marsh, C Ogilvie, H A Rainey
Paediatrics D N Challacombe, T French, A Tandy, M Webster
Radiology J Bell, T Brown, P Cavanagh, D Cooke, H Thomas, S Wells, S Willson
Urology P O'Boyle, M Speakman

NHS TRUSTS & NHS HOSPITALS

Burnham-on-Sea War Memorial Hospital

Love Lane, Burnham-on-Sea TA8 1ED
Tel: 01934 78226 Fax: 01278 793367
Total Beds: 23

Dermatology Dr Archer
ENT Dr Mal, Dr Tomlin
General Medicine Dr Bhakri, Dr Bowman, Dr Malcolm, Dr Wakely
General Surgery Dr Flew, Dr Gough
Haematology Dr Scott
Obstetrics and Gynaecology Dr Afifi, Dr Hounton, Dr Smith
Ophthalmology Dr Turner
Orthopaedics Dr Abdel-All, Dr Dixon, Dr Ogilvie
Urology Dr Hinchliffe

Minehead and West Somerset Hospital

The Avenue, Minehead TA24 5LY
Tel: 01643 707251 Fax: 01643 707251
Total Beds: 34

Accident and Emergency G Bryce, C J Cutting
Chest Disease C R Swinburn
Dermatology C J Guerrier
General Medicine C McDonald, D B Yates
General Psychiatry W Ahmed
General Surgery C D Collins, I A Eyre-Brook
Obstetrics and Gynaecology H Marsh
Ophthalmology A Stockwell, J M Twomey
Oral and Maxillofacial Surgery J F Hamlyn
Orthopaedics R P Foster, C Ogilvie
Radiology J M Bell, S K Wells
Radiotherapy and Oncology J Bullimore
Urology P O'Boyle

Williton and District Hospital

Williton, Taunton TA4 4RA
Tel: 01984 32422 Fax: 01984 633026
Total Beds: 45

Care of the Elderly P F Roe

Somerset Partnership NHS and Social Care Trust

Broadway House, Broadway Park, Barclay Street, Bridgwater TA6 5YA
Tel: 01278 446151 Fax: 01278 446147
(Somerset and Dorset Health Authority)

Chair Christina Baron
Chief Executive Paddy Cooney

Barnfield House

Selbourne Place, Minehead TA24 5TY
Tel: 01643 706999 Fax: 01643 707291
Total Beds: 16

Beech Court

Southgate Park, Taunton Road, Bridgwater TA6 3LS
Tel: 01278 444737 Fax: 01278 446717
Total Beds: 23

Cedar House

Cedar Lodge, Holly Court, Summerlands, Yeovil BA20 2BN
Tel: 01935 428420 Fax: 01935 411612

College House

Broadway Park, Barclay Street, Bridgwater TA6 5YA
Tel: 01278 446149

Cranleigh House

Broadway Park, Barclay Street, Bridgwater TA6 5YA
Tel: 01278 446165 Fax: 01278 446154
Total Beds: 18

Hadspen Wood and Ridley Day Hospital

Verrington Hospital, Dancing Lane, Wincanton BA9 9DQ
Tel: 01963 32006 Fax: 01963 34708
Total Beds: 6

Little Court

2 Pinnockscroft, Burnham-on-Sea TA8 2NF
Tel: 01278 786876 Fax: 01278 795290
Total Beds: 16

Orchard Lodge Young People's Unit

Cotford St Luke, Taunton TA4 1DB
Tel: 01823 432211 Fax: 01823 432541
Total Beds: 14

General Psychiatry A D Cockett

Ridley Day Hospital at Verrington Hospital

Dancing Lane, Wincanton BA9 9DQ
Tel: 01963 32006 Fax: 01963 34708

Rosebank - Wells

Priory Park, Glastonbury Road, Wells BA5 1TH
Tel: 01749 683320 Fax: 01749 683380
Total Beds: 18

Rydon House

Cheddon Road, Taunton TA2 7AZ
Tel: 01823 333438 Fax: 01823 333287
Total Beds: 32

South and East Dorset Primary Care Trust

Wimborne Clinic, Rowlands Hill, Wimborne BH21 1AR
Tel: 01258 458580 Fax: 01258 458583
(Somerset and Dorset Health Authority)

Chair Ruth Bussey
Chief Executive Andrew Cawthron

South Birmingham Mental Health NHS Trust

Trust Headquarters, Vincent Drive, Edgbaston, Birmingham B15 2TZ
Tel: 0121 678 2400 Fax: 0121 678 2401
(Birmingham and the Black Country Health Authority)

Chair Jean Trainor
Chief Executive Sue Turner

Queen Elizabeth Psychiatric Hospital

Mindlesohn Way, Edgbaston, Birmingham B15 2TZ
Tel: 0121 678 2000 Fax: 0121 678 2036
Total Beds: 195

General Psychiatry M Beedie, P Bentham, J Birtle, I Brockington, S Choong, B Coope, B Dalal, A J Farmer, M George, E Gregg, R Z Ismail, P O'Brien, F Oyebode, A Patel, M Radford, D Robertson, S Singhal, A P Taylor, A Van Woeerkom, C Vassilas, G Wainscott, A White

South Birmingham Primary Care Trust

Windsor House, 11A High Street, Kings Heath, Birmingham B14 6BB
Tel: 0121 687 4600 Fax: 0121 687 4650
(Birmingham and the Black Country Health Authority)

Chief Executive David Cox

South Buckinghamshire NHS Trust

Trust Offices, Amersham Hospital, Whielden Street, Amersham HP7 0JD
Tel: 01494 526161 Fax: 01494 734753
(Thames Valley Health Authority)

Chair Bryan Long
Chief Executive Roy Darby

Amersham Hospital

Whielden Street, Amersham HP7 0JD
Tel: 01494 526161 Fax: 01494 734753
Total Beds: 57

Anaesthetics R Allim, N Allison, J Anderson, G Biswas, A Dark, T Dexter, L Graham, A Mahoney, D Overton, C Pal-Soo, P J Strube, E Taylor, J Watson
Care of the Elderly H Al Hillawi
Dental Surgery D Cunliffe, M McKnight
Dermatology P Budney, S George, J Hughes, D Orton, R Ratnavel, J Wilkinson, E Young
ENT J W R Capper, H Thompson
General Medicine I Gallen, D Gorard, M Jackson, B Lavery, A McIntyre, L Sandler, C G Wathen, A Weaver
General Surgery A Bdesha, C Gatzen, J Greenland, J L Grogono, G A D McPherson, A Northeast
Obstetrics and Gynaecology Y Akinsola, D Eustace, M Robson, D Sumner, C Wayne
Ophthalmology N Cox, J Duvall-Young, R Khooshabeh
Orthopaedics G M Channon, A Fernandes, G Matthews, G Taylor, K S H Wise
Pathology R Aitchison, D Bailey, Y Chia, S J Kelly, M Lyons, J Pattinson, S Price, M Turner, D Waghorn
Radiology P Cadman, C Charlesworth, K Hasan, R Horwitz, G Hussain, M Musaji
Rheumatology A Kirk, R Stevens
Urology J P Kelleher

Chalfonts and Gerrards Cross Hospital

Hampden Road, Chalfont St Peter, Gerrards Cross SL9 9DR
Tel: 01753 883821 Fax: 01753 891958
Total Beds: 30

Dermatology J Wilkinson
ENT J W R Capper, H Thompson
General Surgery G A D McPherson
Ophthalmology N Cox, J Duvall-Young
Orthopaedics A Fernandez, G Matthews, M Swann, K Wise
Plastic Surgery M Saad
Radiology G Hussain
Rheumatology R Stevens

Hayward House

Queens Road, High Wycombe HP13 6AQ
Tel: 01494 425306
Total Beds: 30

Marlow Community Hospital

Victoria Road, off Glade Road, Marlow SL7 1DJ
Tel: 01628 471348
Total Beds: 14

Wycombe Hospital

High Wycombe HP11 2TT
Tel: 01494 526161 ext: 6377 Fax: 01494 426387
Total Beds: 438

Accident and Emergency T S Malpass, D Potts, G Thirumanivannan
Anaesthetics J Anderson, G Biswas, A Dark, T Dexter, C Graham, A Mahoney, D Overton, C Pac-Soo, P Strube, E Taylor, J Watson
Dental Surgery D Cunliffe, M McKnight
Dermatology S George, J Hughes, D Orton, R Ratnaval, J D Wilkinson, E Young
ENT J Capper, H Thomson
General Medicine I Gallen, D Gorard, W G Hendry, A McIntyre, L Sandler, C G Wathen
General Surgery A Bdesha, C Gatzen, J Greenland, J L Grogono, G A D McPherson, A Northeast
Genitourinary Medicine G Luzzi
Neurology M Jackson
Obstetrics and Gynaecology Y Akinsola, D Eustace, M Robson, D Sumner, C Wayne
Ophthalmology N Cox, J Duvall-Young, R Khooshabeh
Orthopaedics G M Channon, A Fernandes, G Matthews, G Taylor, K S Wise
Paediatrics C H Cheetham, A Earley, R Finch, G Rastogi, K K Sawhney
Pathology R Aitchison, D Bailey, Y Chia, S Kelly, M Lyons, J Pattinson, S Price, M Turner, D Waghorn
Plastic Surgery P Budney, R Ratnaval
Radiology P J Cadman, C Charlesworth, K Hasan, R Horwitz, G Hussain, M Musaji
Urology A Bdesha, J P Kelleher

South Cambridgeshire Primary Care Trust

Heron Court, Block 23, Ida Darwin, Fulbourn, Cambridge CB1 5EE
Tel: 01223 885700 Fax: 01223 855705
(Norfolk, Suffolk and Cambridgeshire Health Authority)

Chair Ruth Rogers
Chief Executive Sally Hind

South Devon Health Care NHS Trust

South Devon Healthcare NHS Trust, Hengrave House, Torbay Hospital, Lawes Bridge, Torquay TQ2 7AA
Tel: 01803 614567 Fax: 01803 616334
(South West Peninsula Health Authority)

Ashburton and Buckfastleigh Hospital

Ashburton, Newton Abbot TQ13 7AP
Tel: 01364 652203 Fax: 01364 653676
Total Beds: 14

Bovey Tracey Hospital

Furzeleigh Lane, Bovey Tracey, Newton Abbot TQ13 9HJ
Tel: 01626 832279 Fax: 01626 835818
Total Beds: 16

Brixham Hospital

Greenswood Road, Brixham TQ5 9HW
Tel: 01803 882153 Fax: 01803 856099
Total Beds: 19

Dawlish Hospital

Barton Terrace, Dawlish EX7 9DH
Tel: 01626 868500 Fax: 01626 868543
Total Beds: 18

NHS TRUSTS & NHS HOSPITALS

Newton Abbot Hospital
50 East Street, Newton Abbot TQ12 4PT
Tel: 01626 354321 Fax: 01626 332105
Total Beds: 63

Paignton Hospital
Church Street, Paignton TQ3 3AG
Tel: 01803 557425 Fax: 01803 665245
Total Beds: 68

Teignmouth Hospital
Mill Lane, Teignmouth TQ14 9BQ
Tel: 01626 772161 Fax: 01626 771121
Total Beds: 34

Torbay Hospital
Lawes Bridge, Torquay TQ2 7AA
Tel: 01803 614567 Fax: 01803 616334
Total Beds: 610

Accident and Emergency H Cosgrove, J N T Egan, G Gardner, J Horner

Anaesthetics J Ackers, A Bainton, P G Ballance, N Boheimer, N Campbell, S J Fearnley, M Hearn, K Houghton, A Magides, D Natusch, I Norley, J Norman, J C Pappin, B Randall, M Swart, R Tackley, J L Thorn

Care of the Elderly E Hawarth, G P Kendall, P J Sleight

Child and Adolescent Psychiatry I MacLeod, M Roberts

Dermatology J Adams, M Shaw

ENT D Alderson, S A Hickey, F P Houlihan, J D Hutchison

General Medicine C Carey, R G Chadwick, R Dyer, K George, J Goldman, P Keeling, G P Kendall, J Lowes, I Mahy, R B Paisey, D Sinclair, P Sleight, R H Teague

General Surgery R A Bradbrook, P Donnelly, D D Friend, P Houghton, R G Hughes, P Lewis, S MacDermott, R Pullan

Genitourinary Medicine J R Willcox

Haematology F Booth, N Rymes, S Smith

Learning Disabilities S Manawadu

Microbiology T Maggs

Neurology J D Gibson, D C Thrush, J Zajicek

Obstetrics and Gynaecology J Barrington, J E B Foulkes, A Sadler, P J Stannard

Old Age Psychiatry J Dunn, D Somerfield, N Todd

Oncology D Bailey

Ophthalmology M Cole, C M Graham, C R H James, S J Livesey

Oral and Maxillofacial Surgery P Douglas, A Fordyce

Orthodontics C Dysdale, R Robinson, A J Smith

Orthopaedics M Ashworth, P Birdsall, V Conboy, J Davis, G B Irvine, A G MacEachern

Paediatrics J Broomhall, L Dibble, S Imong, D L Kennaird, C P Sainsbury, B Singh

Palliative Medicine J Sykes

Pathology D W Day, D Farrell, N Ryley

Plastic Surgery P Saxby

Radiology R Bolton, D Buckley, R Heafield, S Horbon, J Isaacs, P Kember, E Morris, R Seymour, G W Urquhart

Radiotherapy and Oncology P Bliss, A Goodman, A Hong, A Lydon

Restorative Dentistry C Drysdale

Rheumatology N Viner

South Downs Health NHS Trust

From April 2002 mental health and learning disability services transferring to East Sussex County Healthcare NHS Trust.

Brighton General Hospital, Elm Grove, Brighton BN2 3EW
Tel: 01273 696011 Fax: 01273 698312
(Surrey and Sussex Health Authority)

Chair Quintin Barry
Chief Executive Andrew Horne

Brighton General Hospital
Elm Grove, Brighton BN2 3EW
Tel: 01273 696011
Total Beds: 465

Anaesthetics E N Armitage, A J Davey, H Drake, M E Fielding, A C L Frazer, J M Lamberty, M Twohig, P A D Williams

Care of the Elderly G D Mankikar, H O'Neal

Dermatology C Darley, M Price

General Medicine S R Cairns, C Kingswood, J R R Spurrell

General Psychiatry C Aldridge, W Assin, P Bermingham, N Farhoumand, K Shamash

General Surgery A Clark, P A Farrands, B M Hogbin, P Hurst, C J L Strachan

Obstetrics and Gynaecology R J Beard, J F Bostock, R Bradley, B Measday

Orthopaedics I W Bintcliffe

Pathology D H Melcher

Plastic Surgery N S B Tanner

Radiology T Doyle, P Gordon, J Jeyakumar, G J Price

Rehabilitation Medicine S Novak, E Saadah

Rheumatology L Fernandes, B Latham, M T Walters

Chailey Heritage
Clinical Services, Beggars Wood Road, North Chailey, Lewes BN8 4EF
Tel: 01825 722112 Fax: 01825 723544
Total Beds: 60

Paediatrics E Green, G McCarthy

Newhaven Downs
Church Hill, Newhaven BN9 9WH
Tel: 01273 513441
Total Beds: 40

Care of the Elderly G D Mankikar, H O'Neal

Victoria Hospital
Nevill Road, Lewes BN7 1PF
Tel: 01273 474153 Fax: 01273 473362
Total Beds: 39

Cardiology C Davidson

Chest Disease M B Jackson, C W Turton

Dermatology C Darley

Gastroenterology S Cairns, A Ireland

General Psychiatry C Aldridge

General Surgery M Brooks, R Gumpert, P Hale, P Hurst

Obstetrics and Gynaecology K Boos, D Holden

Orthopaedics R Turner, C Williams

Radiology C Sonksen

Rheumatology B Stuart

Urology N Harrison, P Thomas

Victoria Hospital Day Surgery Unit
Nevill Road, Lewes BN7 1PF
Tel: 01273 474153 Fax: 01273 473362
Total Beds: 38

South Durham Health Care NHS Trust

Darlington Memorial Hospital, Hollyhurst Road, Darlington DL3 6HX
Tel: 01325 380100 Fax: 01325 743622
(County Durham and Tees Valley Health Authority)

Chair Paul Trippett
Chief Executive John Saxby

Bishop Auckland General Hospital
Cockton Hill Road, Bishop Auckland DL14 6AD
Tel: 01388 454000 Fax: 01388 454127
Total Beds: 340

Darlington Memorial Hospital

Hollyhurst Road, Darlington DL3 6HX
Tel: 01325 380100 Fax: 01325 743622
Total Beds: 450

Accident and Emergency A West
Anaesthetics C Beeton, J Brooker, R S Drummond, R Hargreaves, H Khalil, C Kotur, M A Quader, D Saha, P d Silva
Care of the Elderly G V Williams
Dermatology W D Taylor
ENT J Carlin, R W Ruckley, S P Singh, C Watson
General Medicine E W Barnes, P H Carr, C K Connolly, J J Murphy, P N Trewby
General Surgery P M Atkinson, R Brookstein, N Corner, M G Whittaker
Genitourinary Medicine P A Rajah
Neurology P J B Tilley
Obstetrics and Gynaecology R H Aitken, M Ali, D J R Hutchon, J H Macdonald
Ophthalmology M S Dang, J D Haslam, P Koay, L Singh
Oral and Maxillofacial Surgery C Edge
Orthodontics J Coote
Orthopaedics A Bawarish, T J Fernandes, J H Rutherford, T J Stahl
Paediatrics R Ahmed, D Bosman, R Carpenter, I M Thakur
Pathology U Earl, J Hodge, F S Pagan, C Williams, P Williamson
Plastic Surgery C Viva
Radiology E Dillon, T Featherstone, G Heath, R Henderson
Rheumatology and Rehabilitation M A Sattar
Urology P M Atkinson

Homelands Hospital

Helmington Row, Crook DL15 0SD
Tel: 01388 762339
Total Beds: 37

Hornhall Hospital

Stanhope DL13 2JR
Tel: 01388 528233 Fax: 01388 528213
Total Beds: 20

Tindale Crescent Hospital

Tindale Crescent, Bishop Auckland DL14 9TE
Tel: 01388 602080
Total Beds: 72

South East Hertfordshire Primary Care Trust

1-4 Limes Court, Conduit Lane, Hoddesdon EN11 8EP
Tel: 01992 706120 Fax: 01992 706121
(Bedfordshire and Hertfordshire Health Authority)

Chair Ian White
Chief Executive Vince McCabe

South East Oxfordshire Primary Care Trust

Wallingford Community Hospital, PO Box 194, Wallingford OX10 9DU
Tel: 01491 208570 Fax: 01491 208580
Email: anne.kirkpatrick@seoxon-pct.nhs.uk
Website: www.seoxon-pct.nhs.uk
(Thames Valley Health Authority)

Chair Cedric Scroggs
Chief Executive Anne Kirkpatrick

South East Sheffield Primary Care Trust

9 Orgreave Road, Handsworth, Sheffield S13 9LQ
Tel: 0114 226 4050 Fax: 0114 226 4051
Website: www.sheffield-ha.nhs.uk
(South Yorkshire Health Authority)

Chair Adebola Fatogun
Chief Executive Helen Sentimen

South Essex Mental Health and Community Care NHS Trust

Head Office, Dunton Court, Aston Road, Laindon SS15 6NX
Tel: 01375 364650 Fax: 01268 492856
(Essex Health Authority)

Chair J Tout
Chief Executive P Geoghegan
Consultants A Canagasabey, P Conlan, I El, C Faey, L Fernando, M Laker, L Lawson, K Lehner, M Murphy, D Palazzi, K Porodie, Dr Puvanendran, P Roberts, M Shaikh, R Shen, S Sooria, D Tullett, Dr Vanstreaton

John Tallack Day Hospital, Thurrock Community Hospital

Long Lane, Grays RM16 2PX
Tel: 01375 364576 Fax: 01375 394970

Mayflower House

Blunts Wall Road, Billericay
Tel: 01277 634236
Total Beds: 40

Mental Health Unit

Basildon Hospital, Nethermayne, Basildon SS16 5NL
Tel: 01268 533911

Mountnessing Court

240 Mountnessing Road, Billericay CM12 0EH
Tel: 01268 366054, 01277 634711
Total Beds: 30

Rochford Hospital

Union Lane, Rochford SS4 1RB
Tel: 01702 578000 Fax: 01702 549542
Total Beds: 75

Runwell Hospital

Runwell Hospital, Runwell Chase, Wickford SS11 7XX
Tel: 01268 366054 Fax: 01268 366076
Email: teresa.compton@southessex-trust.nhs.uk
Total Beds: 13

Consultants B Canagasabey

Thurrock Community Hospital

Thurrock Community Hospital, Long Lane, Grays RM16 2PX

South Gloucestershire Primary Care Trust

King Square House, King Square, Bristol BS2 8EE
Tel: 0117 900 2633 Fax: 0117 900 2668
Website: www.sglos-pct.nhs.uk
(Avon, Gloucestershire and Wiltshire Health Authority)

Chair Brian Goodson
Chief Executive Jo Whitehead

NHS TRUSTS & NHS HOSPITALS

South Hams and West Devon Primary Care Trust

The Lescaze Offices, Shinners Bridge, Dartington, Totnes TQ9 6JE
Tel: 01803 866665 Fax: 01803 867679
Website: www.shandwd-pct.nhs.uk
(South West Peninsula Health Authority)

Chair Sally Foxhall
Chief Executive Alan Tibbenham

South Huddersfield Primary Care Trust

Ward 6, St. Luke's Hospital, Blackmoorfoot, Huddersfield HD4 5RQ
Tel: 01484 343460 Fax: 01484 343414
(West Yorkshire Health Authority)

South Leeds Primary Care Trust

Fountain Medical Centre, Little Fountain Lane, Morley, Leeds LS27 9EN
Tel: 0113 295 1678 Fax: 0113 295 1677
(West Yorkshire Health Authority)

South Leicestershire Primary Care Trust

48 Leicester Road, Wigston LE18 1DR
Tel: 0116 278 8723
(Leicestershire, Northamptonshire and Rutland Health Authority)

Chief Executive Julie Wood

South Liverpool Primary Care Trust

The Surgery, 1 Childwall Park Avenue, Liverpool L16 0JE
Tel: 0151 291 7359 Fax: 0151 291 7360
Chair Beatrice Fraenkel
Chief Executive Christine Wall

South London and Maudsley NHS Trust

Trust HQ, 9th Floor, The Tower Building, 11 York Road, London SE1 7NX
(South East London Health Authority)

Chair Madeliene Long
Chief Executive Stuart Bell

Adult Mental Health Unit

108 Landor Road, London SW9 9NT
Tel: 020 7346 5400
Total Beds: 137

Maudsley Hospital

Denmark Hill, London SE5 8AZ
Tel: 020 7703 6333
Total Beds: 165

South Manchester Primary Care Trust

1st Floor, Home 4, Withington Hospital, Nell Lane, West Didsbury, Manchester M20 2LR
Tel: 0161 438 8600 Fax: 0161 434 1521
Website: www.smanpct.com
(Greater Manchester Health Authority)

Chair Mike Green
Chief Executive Adrian Mercer

South Manchester University Hospitals NHS Trust

First Floor, Tower Block, Wythenshawe Hospital, Southmoor Road, Manchester M23 9LT
Tel: 0161 998 7070 Fax: 0161 291 2603
(Greater Manchester Health Authority)

Chair D Harnden
Chief Executive E J Herbert

Adult Psychiatry Day Hospital

Withington Hospital, Nell Lane, West Didsbury, Manchester M20 8LR
Tel: 0161 447 4367 Fax: 0161 447 4441
Total Beds: 151

Atu Day Hospital

Nell Lane, West Didsbury, Manchester M20 8LR
Tel: 0161 447 4312 Fax: 0161 447 4441

Burton House Day Hospital

Nell Lane, West Didsbury, Manchester M20 8LR
Tel: 0161 447 4509 Fax: 0161 447 3785

Duchess of York Children's Hospital

Withington Hospital, Nell Lane, West Didsbury, Manchester M20 8LE
Tel: 0161 291 4620 Fax: 0161 291 3056
Total Beds: 33

Anaesthetics R Lawton
Cardiology R Patel
Neurology I Hughes
Orthopaedics J G Lemon, F J Weighill
Paediatrics A J Bradbury, A Dickson, D C S Gough, S A Roberts, A Robinson
Plastic Surgery C I Orton
Radiology I Lang

Old Age Psychiatry Day Hospital

Withington Hospital, Nell Lane, West Didsbury, Manchester M20 8LR
Tel: 0161 447 4910

Withington Hospital

Nell Lane, West Didsbury, Manchester M20 8LR
Tel: 0161 445 8111 Fax: 0161 445 5631
Total Beds: 675

Accident and Emergency S Hawes
Anaesthetics S Beards, M Bellman, I T Campbell, M Columb, N El-Mikatti, D Greig, J Hargreaves, A Luthra, M McKavney, H Michael, A J Mortimer, P Nightingale, D M Nolan, M Osbourne, S P Roberts, M P Shelly, C L Tolhurst-Cleaver
Care of the Elderly A K Bancrjee, N J Linker, P A O'Neill, J M Robinson, V Srinivas
Chest Disease A M Hilton
Dermatology J Ashworth, P J August, J Ferguson
ENT A E Camilleri, P H Jones

General Medicine C M Beardwell, J D Edwards, A M Heagerty, J P Miller, T Roberts, S M Shalet, P J Whorwell

General Psychiatry J L J Appleby, A Burns, J Byrne, Dr Garrett, R A Gater, B D Hore, C Hyde, S Lennon, S Lewis, C Thomas, L Webster, A Wieck, A J Wood

General Surgery A D Baildam, L Barr, N J Bundred, D Charlesworth, E S Kiff, C N McCollum, S T O'Dwyer, D E F Tweedle

Genitourinary Medicine S Chandiok, P D Woolley

Medical Oncology A Howells

Nephrology P Ackrill, M C Venning

Neurology J Dick

Obstetrics and Gynaecology D J Hickling, P J Hirsch, R Kirkman

Oral and Maxillofacial Surgery J E Curphey, D J Eldridge, C B Tattersall, J R Tuffin

Orthodontics R P J Thompson

Orthopaedics E M Holt, D M Lang, J G Lemon, F J Weighill

Paediatrics A J Bradbury, A P Dickson, D C S Gough, S A Roberts, A Robinson

Pathology I Burton, J Coyne, J Craske, N Y Haboubi, E B Kaczmarski, A M Kelly, W F Knox, L McWilliam, B Oppenheim, D A Taberner

Plastic Surgery A N Brain, P J Davenport, K W Dunn, V Lees, C Orton, J S Watson, D J Whitby

Radiology D L Asbury, R J Ashleigh, C R M Boggis, R England, D Martin, S Reaney, S Sukumar, M Wilson

Rheumatology and Rehabilitation J R Kulkarni, B Pal, E R E Ross, P A Sanders

Urology R J Barnard, N J R George, E W Lupton, P N Rao

Wythenshawe Hospital

Southmoor Road, Wythenshawe, Manchester M23 9LT Tel: 0161 998 7070 Fax: 0161 291 2037 Total Beds: 539

Accident and Emergency B Ryan

Anaesthetics N Braude, P T Conroy, F Dodd, K Grady, D Greenhalgh, H S J Grey, P J Hall, K G Lee, M R Patrick, G Phillips, W A Thomas, M A Tobias, S Wheatly, W Wooldridge

Cardiology D Bennett, C L Bray, N Brooks, R D Levy, R G Patel, S G Ray, C Ward

Chest Disease P V Barber, K B Carroll, J J Egan, A M Hilton, C A C Pickering, A K Webb, A Woodcock

Dental Surgery M Patel, K Sanders

Dermatology H L Muston

ENT A R Birzgalis, A E Camilleri, P H Jones

General Medicine S G Brear, J R Crampton, P E Jones, J J Manns

General Psychiatry P Mbaya

General Surgery C N Hall, B D Hancock, D Jones

Medical Oncology H Anderson, N Thatcher

Nephrology P Ackrill

Neurology J Dick

Obstetrics and Gynaecology M Fouracres, D J Hickling, P J Hirsch, G A Morewood, J S Wynn

Ophthalmology G S Turner

Oral and Maxillofacial Surgery M Patel, K Sanders, W Simpson

Orthodontics R P J Thompson

Paediatrics A J Bradbury, R G Patel, S A Roberts, A Robinson

Pathology P Bishop, H Doran, P S Hasleton, T N Stanbridge

Radiology R Ashley, G Economou, R England, A W Horrocks, I Lang, A E Mattison, R Sawyer

Rheumatology H N Misra, B Pal

Thoracic Surgery B J Bridgewater, C S Campbell, H K Deiraniya, T L Hooper, M T Jones, R A M Lawson, A Rahman

South of Tyne and Wearside Mental Health NHS Trust

Cherry Knowle Hospital, Ryhope, Sunderland SR2 0NB

South Peterborough Primary Care Trust

St John's, Thorpe Road, Peterborough PE3 6JG Tel: 01733 882288 Fax: 01733 882299 (Norfolk, Suffolk and Cambridgeshire Health Authority)

Chair Marco Cereste Chief Executive Lise Llewellyn

South Sefton Primary Care Trust

First Floor, Merton House, Stanley Road, Bootle L20 3DL Tel: 0151 288 5300 (Cheshire and Merseyside Health Authority)

South Somerset Primary Care Trust

South Petherton Hospital, Hospital Lane, South Petherton TA13 5AR Tel: 01460 243011 Fax: 01460 243010 (Somerset and Dorset Health Authority)

Chair Keith Pearson Chief Executive Virginia Pearson

Chard and District Hospital

Crewkerne Road, Chard TA20 1NF Tel: 01460 63175 Fax: 01460 68172 Total Beds: 35

Care of the Elderly M Evans

Dermatology C J W Guerrier

ENT S C Wells

General Medicine M G Ellwood

General Psychiatry A Poole

General Surgery S M Jones

Obstetrics and Gynaecology K Bidgood

Ophthalmology K Bates

Orthopaedics H A Rainey

Urology M J Speakman

South Staffordshire Healthcare NHS Trust

Corporation Street, Stafford ST16 3AG Tel: 01785 782715 Fax: 01785 372722 (Shropshire and Staffordshire Health Authority)

Chair Julia Jessel Chief Executive David O'Neill

Barton-under-Needwood Cottage Hospital

Barton-under-Needwood, Burton-on-Trent DE13 8LB Tel: 01283 712323 Total Beds: 14

The Foundation NHS Trust Hospital (Stafford)

Corporation Street, Stafford ST16 3AG Tel: 01785 257888 Fax: 01785 258969 Total Beds: 144

Child and Adolescent Psychiatry C Dunn (Head), M S Thambirajah

Forensic Psychiatry N V Griffin (Head), C Barkley

General Psychiatry C J Cooper, A A Khan, L Lovett, A Muir, D P Srinivasan

Psychiatry of Old Age G Acey, A G Deane

Rehabilitation Medicine E Mateu, S E Quader

NHS TRUSTS & NHS HOSPITALS

Hammerwich Hospital

Hospital Road, Burntwood, Walsall WS7 0EH
Tel: 01543 686224
Total Beds: 20

Dermatology P Cartwright
ENT D East, J Oates
General Medicine J Attiea
General Psychiatry A Mishra, D Mitra, J Ornoigiu
General Surgery R Lee, I Patterson
Obstetrics and Gynaecology G Constantine
Orthopaedics A Banerjee, G Benke
Paediatrics S Bennett-Britton, T J Lee
Urology D Foster

Kingswood Day Hospital

Cannock Chase Hospital, Brunswick Road, Cannock WS11 2XY
Tel: 01785 257888 ext: 6103 Fax: 01785 258969
Total Beds: 6

Sir Robert Peel Hospital

Plantation Lane, Mile Oak, Tamworth B78 3NG
Tel: 01827 263800 Fax: 01827 263803

Dermatology P Cartwright, H Nelson
ENT E Fisher, D Morgan, J Oates, T Rockley, A Thompson
General Medicine J Eddy, P P Hillengrand, R Raj, J Sheldon, R Smith
General Surgery P Bearn, S Salman
Obstetrics and Gynaecology G Constantine, Y Ibrahim, M Maloney
Ophthalmology S Chawdhary, R Harrison, T Worstmann
Oral Surgery A Stevenson
Orthodontics S Weerakone
Orthopaedics G Krisnamurthy, I Miller, K Wahab
Paediatrics S Bennett-Britton, T Lee
Rheumatology T Sheeran
Urology D Thomas

Spring Meadow Day Hospital

Cannock Chase Hospital, Brunswick Road, Cannock WS11 2XY
Tel: 01785 257888 ext: 6170 Fax: 01785 258969

Victoria Hospital

Friary Road, Lichfield WS13 6QN
Tel: 01543 414555
Total Beds: 30

Cytology A Roberts
Dermatology H Nelson, Dr Oliviecki
ENT P De, D East, J Oates, T Rockley, A Thompson
General Medicine J D Eddy, J D Hill, P Hillenbrand, J Milles, R Smith, Dr Why
General Surgery A Allan, S Glick, I Paterson
Obstetrics and Gynaecology J Artley, Dr Churchill, G Constantine
Oncology T Latief
Ophthalmology S Chawdhary
Orthopaedics A Banerjee, G Benke, G Green, A Johns, S Khemka, I M Miller, A Thomas, Dr Wahab, M Wallace
Paediatrics S Bennett-Britton, T J Lee, L Light, J Meran
Rheumatology and Rehabilitation Dr Aung, T Price
Urology Dr Corfield, D Foster

South Stoke Primary Care Trust

278 Duke Street, Fenton, Stoke-on-Trent ST4 3NT
Tel: 01782 326708 Fax: 01782 328965
(Shropshire and Staffordshire Health Authority)

Chair Michael Tappin
Chief Executive Tony McGovern

South Tees Hospitals NHS Trust

From April 2002 the trust will incorporate the acute services of Northallerton Health Services NHS Trust.

Middlesbrough General Hospital, Ayresome Green Lane, Middlesbrough TS5 5AZ
Tel: 01642 854153, 01642 850850 Fax: 01642 854136, 01642 828095
(Tees Health Authority)

Chair J Foster
Chief Executive Bill Murray

Guisborough General Hospital (Maternity Services)

Guisborough TS14 6HZ
Tel: 01287 633542

The James Cook University Hospital

Marton Road, Middlesbrough TS4 3BW
Tel: 01642 850850 Fax: 01642 854636
Total Beds: 664

Cardiology A Davies, M A De-Belder, J A Hall
Cardiothoracic Surgery G Morritt, J Wallis
Care of the Elderly A Ashraf, A Bergin, D L Broughton, R Murdoch
General Medicine M G Bramble, P A Cann, J R Cove-Smith, H R Gribbin, J Main, R Murdoch, A D Paterson, D J M Sinclair
General Surgery J R Bell, D Clarke, I A E Clason, W M Cooke, W A Corbett, P Durning, A H Tooley, R G Wilson
Haematology J E Chandler, G P Sommerfield
Nephrology J R Cove-Smith, J Main, A D Paterson, D Reaich
Obstetrics and Gynaecology A F J Atkins, S Bailey, J A Cosbie-Ross, D J Cruickshank, R Garry, R S Hutchison, P J Taylor, K M Toop
Occupational Health D P McGuire
Paediatrics R C Dias, M S Kibirige, P Morrell, S Sinha, G P Wyatt, J Wyllie
Radiology A S S Ahmed, R S C Campbell, K M A Clifford, R W J Hartley, G L S Leen, M McCarty, G Naisby
Radiotherapy and Oncology S L Chawla, P R C Dunlop, P D J Hardman, A J Rathmell
Rheumatology J N Fordham, I Haslock
Thoracic Medicine H R Gribbin, D J M Sinclair
Urology D Chadwick, J R Hindmarsh, J E Whiteway

Middlesbrough General Hospital

Ayresome Green Lane, Middlesbrough TS5 5AZ
Tel: 01642 850850 Fax: 01642 854136
Total Beds: 334

Accident and Emergency K H Han
Diabetes R Bilous, W F Kelly
Endocrinology R W Bilous, W F Kelly
Gastroenterology M G Bramble, P A Cann
General Medicine R N Bilous, S K Ghosh, W F Kelly, D P McCormack
Genitourinary Medicine A A Opaneye
Histology R A Jones
Histopathology C Ritchie
Infectious Diseases S K Ghosh
Neurology P K Newman, R Shaki, P J B Tilley
Neuropathology M A Nurbhai
Neuroradiology N Bradey, R Parameswaren, C Santosh
Neurosurgery P Kane, S M Marks, F Nath, E J Sinar, R Strachan
Oral Surgery B S Avery, C J Edge, R J Pratt
Orthodontics J D Coote, N Fox, E J May
Orthopaedics J T Anderson, C G Greenough, R J Montgomery, D S Muckle, B Y Pai, J Stothard, I W Wallace
Plastic Surgery K Sarang, C Viva
Radiology M S Jawad
Rehabilitation Medicine M K Barsoum

North Riding Infirmary

Eye, Ear, Nose & Throat Centre, Newport Road, Middlesbrough TS1 5JE
Tel: 01642 850850 Fax: 01642 854064
Total Beds: 73

ENT D Bosman, L M Flood, M R Hawthorne, F W Martin, R G Wight
Ophthalmology J R Clarke, T C Dowd, J M Hudson, B J McNeela, D Smerdon

West Lane Hospital (Neuro Rehabilitation Services)

West Lane, Middlesbrough TS5 4EE
Tel: 01642 813144 Fax: 01642 822717
Total Beds: 21

South Tyneside Healthcare NHS Trust

From April 2002 mental health services transferring to South of Tyne and Wearside Mental Health NHS Trust.

Harton Wing, South Tyneside District Hospital, Harton Lane, South Shields NE34 0PL
Tel: 0191 454 8888 Ext: 2773 Fax: 0191 427 9908
Email: lorraine.lambert@eem.sthct.northy.nhs.uk
(Northumberland, Tyne and Wear Health Authority)

Chair Peter Davidson
Chief Executive Lorraine Lambert

Charles Palmer Day Hospital

Palmer Community Hospital, Wear Street, Jarrow NE32 3UX
Tel: 0191 489 7777 Fax: 0191 428 1072

Monkton Hall Hospital

Jarrow NE32 5HN
Tel: 0191 489 4111
Total Beds: 56

Moorlands Day Hospital

South Tyneside District Hospital, Harton Lane, South Shields NE34 0PL
Tel: 0191 454 8888

Palmer Community Hospital

Wear Street, Jarrow NE32 3UX
Tel: 0191 489 7777 Fax: 0191 428 1072
Total Beds: 82

Primrose Hill Hospital

Jarrow NE32 5HA
Tel: 0191 489 7766 Fax: 0191 428 4839
Total Beds: 16

South Tyneside District Hospital

Harton Lane, South Shields NE34 0PL
Tel: 0191 454 8888 Fax: 0191 427 9908
Total Beds: 538

Accident and Emergency A Reece
Anaesthetics I Kruepe
Care of the Elderly A Rodgers
Child and Adolescent Psychiatry A McClure
Dermatology J McLelland
General Medicine M Bone, L G Bryson, A Lishman, J H Parr, C Rees
General Psychiatry M Akhtar, M Akhtar
General Surgery V Joypaul, C Pritchett, I M Rogers, K Wynne
Genitourinary Medicine S Rashid, K M Saravanamuttu
Haematology A Hendrick
Medical Microbiology R Ellis

Obstetrics and Gynaecology V Esen, N Fawzi, A J Jones, N J Nwabineli, S Orife
Ophthalmology E D Allen, P J O'Rourke
Oral and Maxillofacial Surgery L Stassen
Orthodontics D Vasey
Orthopaedics I Hugh
Otolaryngology I Hopper, I W Mackee, S S Pillai, P Samuel
Paediatrics N Brewster, S Cronin, M Massam, H Palmer
Pathology K Pollard
Psychiatry of Old Age M J Akhtar
Radiology R Cooper, L H Cope, H S Spencer
Radiotherapy and Oncology J M Bozzino
Urology T Armitage

South Tyneside Primary Care Trust

Horsley Hill Road, South Shields NE33 3DP
(Northumberland, Tyne and Wear Health Authority)

South Warwickshire Combined Care NHS Trust

Trust closure tbc - part of service transferring to South Warwickshire Primary Care Trust.

Head QuartersGovenors House, 153 Cape Road, Warwick W34 5DJ
Tel: 01926 403403 Fax: 01926 409122
(Coventry, Warwickshire, Herefordshire and Worcestershire Health Authority)

Chair Bransby Thomas
Chief Executive Catherine Griffiths

Alcester Hospital

Kinwarton Road, Alcester
Tel: 01789 762470 Fax: 01789 764363
Total Beds: 22

Ellen Badger Hospital

Shipston-on-Stour CV36 4AX
Tel: 01608 661410 Fax: 01608 663373
Total Beds: 35

Royal Leamington Spa Rehabilitation Hospital

Heathcote Lane, Heathcote, Warwick
Tel: 01926 317700 Fax: 01926 317710
Total Beds: 112

St Michael's Hospital

St Michael's Road, Warwick CV34 5QW
Tel: 01926 406789, 01926 496241 Fax: 01926 406700
Total Beds: 90

South Warwickshire General Hospitals NHS Trust

Warwick Hospital, Lakin Road, Warwick CV34 5BW
Tel: 01926 495321 Fax: 01926 482603
(Coventry, Warwickshire, Herefordshire and Worcestershire Health Authority)

Chair David Evans
Chief Executive Paul Farenden, Andrew Riley

Stratford-upon-Avon Hospital

Arden Street, Stratford-upon-Avon CV37 6NX
Tel: 01926 495321 Fax: 01789 414915
Total Beds: 28

Care of the Elderly H N Desai, F G Vaz, A K Viswan

NHS TRUSTS & NHS HOSPITALS

Warwick Hospital

Lakin Road, Warwick CV34 5BW
Tel: 01926 495321 Fax: 01926 482603
Total Beds: 446

Anaesthetics J M L Antrobus, J M S Aulakh, D Derbyshire, S P Mather, J Richardson, D A Robinson, D G Tweedie
Cardiology N Qureshi, M F Shiu, H Singh
Care of the Elderly H Desai, F G Vaz, A K Viswan
Dental Surgery D R Purnell
Dermatology R Charles-Holmes, F Humphreys
ENT R C Bickerton, H R Cable, D Phillips
General Medicine P C Hawker, L S Hill, P M Horrocks, K D Lee, C Marguerie
General Psychiatry C Campbell, T D E Richardson, N Smeyatsky
General Surgery P F Blacklay, I Fraser, A O B Johnston, P D Murphy
Genitourinary Medicine D J Natin
Neurology D Riddoch
Neurosurgery M Choksey, P Stanworth
Obstetrics and Gynaecology T B J Hughes, R Jackson, K S J Olah, M J Pearson
Ophthalmology N G Brown, G Misson
Orthodontics P J Turner
Orthopaedics P Binfield, D T Shakespeare, M A L Tansey, S Young
Paediatrics K Nathavitharana, C N Storrs
Pathology A R Ghose, K J Holley, M S Khan, K Newbold, P E Rose, E J Vella, F Wells
Plastic Surgery A R Groves
Radiology D Clarke, M Hughes, F Millard, G Penter, G D Stewart, P Williams
Urology D C Lewis, J Strachan

South Warwickshire Primary Care Trust

Westgate House, 21 Market Street, Warwick CV34 4DE
Tel: 01926 493491 Fax: 01926 495074
(Coventry, Warwickshire, Herefordshire and Worcestershire Health Authority)

South West Dorset Primary Care Trust

1A Acland Road, Dorchester BH1 1JW
Tel: 01305 259366 Fax: 01305 259275
(Somerset and Dorset Health Authority)

Chair Anne Thomas
Chief Executive Peter Mankin

South West Kent Primary Care Trust

Sevenoaks Hospital, Hospital Lane, Sevenoaks TN13 3PQ
Tel: 01732 464813 Fax: 01732 455155
(Kent and Medway Health Authority)

Chair Malcolm Forsyth
Chief Executive Steve Ford

South West London and St George's Mental Health NHS Trust

Springfield University Hospital, 61 Glenburnie Road, London SW17 7DJ
Tel: 020 8672 9911 Fax: 020 8682 6703
Website: www.swlstg-tr.org.uk
(South West London Health Authority)

Chair Jan Hildreth
Chief Executive Duncan Selbie

Henderson Hospital

2 Homeland Drive, Sutton SM2 5LT
Tel: 020 8661 1611 Fax: 020 8770 3676

Springfield University Hospital

61 Glenburnie Road, London SW17 7DJ
Tel: 020 8672 9911 Fax: 020 8682 6703
Total Beds: 449

General Psychiatry J S Bolton, T P Burns, R Chaplin, J Colgan, L Drummond, N L G Eastman, W Falkowski, N Fisher, H Ghodse, P Hughes, R Jacobson, C M B Jarman, J Kellett, B Matthews, G Mezey, P Moodley, D Oyebode, M Potter, S J Robertson, R S Stern, G Zolese

South West London Community NHS Trust

Trust closure tbc - part of service transferring to Richmond and Twickenham Primary Care Trust, Sutton and Merton Primary Care Trust and Wandsworth Primary Care Trust.

Queen Mary's Hospital, Roehampton House, Roehampton Lane, London SW15 5PN
Tel: 020 8789 6611 Fax: 020 8780 1089
(South West London Health Authority)

Chair Elizabeth Nelson

Putney Hospital

Commondale, Lower Richmond Road, Putney, London SW15 1HW
Tel: 020 8789 6633 Fax: 020 8788 2839
Total Beds: 78

Consultants M Al-Yassiri, A F Neil, G Wright

Queen Mary's Hospital

Roehampton Lane, Roehampton, London SW15 5PN
Tel: 020 8789 6611 Fax: 020 8780 1089
Total Beds: 417

Anaesthetics R Graham
Cardiology R Roberts, E Shinebourne
Care of the Elderly H Lo, A Neil
Dermatology T Basarab, S Mayou, N Roberts
Developmental Medicine D Keen
Gastroenterology S Mitton, C Tibbs
General Medicine J Foley, R Roberts, C Tibbs
General Surgery I Bloom, R A D Booth, R Cummins, N Madden, P Willson
Genitourinary Medicine P Lister
Haematology M Rowley
Medical Genetics M Patton
Neurology A Al-Memar
Obstetrics and Gynaecology R Ballard, A Clement
Oncology I Hanham
Ophthalmology J Beare, D Spalton
Orthopaedics J Bell, M Curtis, K Daly, M Proctor, D Ward
Paediatric Surgery N Madden
Paediatrics T Ayeni, M Bommen, C Brook, M Hubbard, E Jurges, D Lindo, C Newman, D Wilson
Pathology H J Wong
Physician I Balfour-Lynn, K Shotliff
Plastic Surgery J A Clarke, A Moss, B Powell
Renal Medicine A Eisenger
Rheumatology and Rehabilitation J Foley, S Jawad, H Jones, S Sooriakumaran
Urology K Anson, J A Dick, R Morley

SOUTHAMPTON COMMUNITY HEALTH SERVICES NHS TRUST

Richmond Royal Hospital

Community Hospital, Kew Foot Road, Richmond TW9 2TG
Tel: 020 8940 3331

Springfield Hospital

Joan Bicknell Centre, Burntwood Lane, Springfield Hospital, London SW17 7DJ
Tel: 020 8700 0450 Fax: 020 8700 0480

General Psychiatry J Bernal
Learning Disabilities I Forshaw
Occupational Therapy M Lewis
Physiotherapy A Avis

South West Oxfordshire Primary Care Trust

Wantage Health Centre, Garston Lane, Wantage OX12 7AY
(Thames Valley Health Authority)

Chair Martin Avis
Chief Executive Mary Wicks

South West Yorkshire Mental Health NHS Trust

Fieldhead, Ouchthorpe Lane, Wakefield WS1 3SP
Tel: 01924 327000
Website: www.southwestyorkshire.nhs.uk
(West Yorkshire Health Authority)

Chair Sukhdev Sharma
Chief Executive Judith Young

South Western Staffordshire Primary Care Trust

Council Offices, Wolverhampton, Codsall, Wolverhampton WV8 1PX
Tel: 01902 696402 Fax: 01902 696111

South Wiltshire Primary Care Trust

42-44 Chipper Lane, Salisbury SP1 1BG
Tel: 01722 341319 Fax: 01722 326768
Website: www.healthywiltshire.org.uk
(Avon, Gloucestershire and Wiltshire Health Authority)

Chair Ken Clark
Chief Executive John Nicholas

South Worcestershire Primary Care Trust

Unit 19, Isaac Meddox House, Shrub Hill Industrial Estate, Worcester WR4 9RW
Tel: 01905 760000
(Coventry, Warwickshire, Herefordshire and Worcestershire Health Authority)

Chair David Barlow

Evesham Community Hospital

Waterside, Evesham WR11 4JH
Tel: 01386 502345 Fax: 01386 502344
Total Beds: 132

Anaesthetics J J Lee, D M Phillips
Care of the Elderly C Ashton, H R Glennie, C Pycock
Dermatology W Tucker

ENT H Cable
General Medicine R Lewis
General Surgery P Blackley, M Corlett, S Lake
Obstetrics and Gynaecology W D Griffiths, M D Pickrell, Y Stedman
Ophthalmology N Price
Oral and Maxillofacial Surgery N Barnard
Orthopaedics K O'Dwyer, P Ratcliffe, E Rouholamin, A Salam, M Trevitt
Paediatrics A P Cole, M Hanlon, A Mills, J Scanlon
Urology T F Chen, C Lewis, J Strachan

Malvern Community Hospital

Lansdowne Crescent, Malvern WR14 2AW
Tel: 01684 612600
Total Beds: 18

Care of the Elderly H R Glennie
General Medicine C Pycock
General Surgery N C Hickey, C Robertson
Obstetrics and Gynaecology B A Ruparelia, P C Shervington
Orthopaedics J S Davies, M Trevitt
Paediatrics Dr Childs, A Cole, B Mason

Pershore Cottage Hospital

Defford Road, Pershore WR10 1HZ
Tel: 01386 502070 Fax: 01386 502082
Total Beds: 18

South Yorkshire Metropolitan Ambulance and Paramedic Services NHS Trust

Ambulance Service HQ, Fairfield, Moorgate Road, Rotherham S60 2BQ
Tel: 01709 820520 Fax: 01709 827839
Email: info@symaps.com
(South Yorkshire Health Authority)

Chair Stephen Hunter
Chief Executive Ray Shannon

Southampton City Primary Care Trust

Central Office, Moorgreen Hospital,, Botley Road, West End, Southampton SO30 3JB
Tel: 023 8047 6484 Fax: 023 8047 3484
(Hampshire and Isle of Wight Health Authority)

Chair Pauline Qwan-Arrow
Chief Executive Brian Skinner

Southampton Community Health Services NHS Trust

Central Health Clinic, East Park Terrace, Southampton SO14 0YL
Tel: 023 8090 2500 Fax: 023 8090 2600
(Hampshire and Isle of Wight Health Authority)

Chair Jonathon Montgomery
Chief Executive Mike R Lager
Consultants Moira Ledger, Helen Matthews, Denis O'Leary

Fenwick Day Hospital

Pikes Hill, Lyndhurst, Southampton SO43 7NG
Tel: 023 8028 2782 Fax: 023 8028 2161
Total Beds: 22

NHS TRUSTS & NHS HOSPITALS

Fenwick Hospital
Pikes Hill, Lyndhurst, Southampton
Tel: 023 8028 2782 Fax: 023 8028 2161
Total Beds: 22

Harefield Day Hospital
Moorgreen Hospital, Southampton

Hythe Day Hospital
Beaulieu Road, Hythe, Southampton SO45 7NG
Tel: 023 8084 6046

Hythe Hospital
Beaulieu Road, Dibden Purlieu Hythe, Southampton SO45 5ZB
Tel: 023 8084 6046 Fax: 023 8020 7285
Total Beds: 24

Inroads Day Hospital
Western Community Hospital, Walnut Grove, Millbrook, Southampton SO16 4XE
Tel: 023 8047 5401 Fax: 023 8047 5402

Lymington Day Hospital
East Hill, Lymington SO41 9ZJ
Tel: 01590 676085 Fax: 01590 670749

Lymington Hospital
Southampton Road, Lymington SO41 9ZH
Tel: 01590 677011 Fax: 01590 671787
Total Beds: 84

Lymington Infirmary
East Hill, Lymington SO41 9ZJ
Tel: 01590 676081 Fax: 01590 670749
Total Beds: 37

Milford-on-Sea Day Hospital
Sea Road, Milford on Sea, Lymington SO41 0PG
Tel: 023 8064 3016

Milford-on-Sea War Memorial Hospital
Sea Road, Milford-on-Sea, Lymington SO41 0PG
Tel: 01590 643016 Fax: 01590 645939
Total Beds: 19

Moorgreen Day Hospital
Botley Road, West End, Southampton SO30 3JB
Tel: 023 8047 6233 Fax: 023 8046 3176

Moorgreen Hospital
Botley Road, West End, Southampton SO30 3JB
Tel: 023 8047 5400 Fax: 023 8046 5385
Total Beds: 190

Ravenswood House
Medium Secure Unit, Knowle, Fareham PO17 5NA
Tel: 01329 836000
Total Beds: 58

Romsey Hospital
Mile Hill, Winchester Road, Romsey SO51 8ZA
Tel: 01794 512343 Fax: 01794 524465
Total Beds: 24

Western Community Hospital
Walnut Grove, Millbrook, Southampton SO16 4XE
Tel: 023 8047 5401

Southampton University Hospitals NHS Trust

Trust Management Offices, Southampton General Hospital, Tremona Road, Southampton SO16 6YD
Tel: 023 8079 6172 Fax: 023 8079 4153
Website: www.suht.nhs.uk
(Hampshire and Isle of Wight Health Authority)

Countess Mountbatten House
Moorgreen Hospital, Botley Road, West End, Southampton SO30 3JB
Tel: 023 8047 7414 Fax: 023 8047 3501
Total Beds: 25

Princess Anne Hospital
Coxford Road, Southampton SO16 5YA
Tel: 023 8077 7222 Fax: 023 8079 4143
Total Beds: 183

Royal South Hants Hospital
Graham Road, Southampton SO14 0YG
Tel: 023 8063 4288 Fax: 023 8082 5206
Total Beds: 138

Southampton General Hospital
Tremona Road, Southampton SO16 6YD
Tel: 023 8077 7222 Fax: 023 8079 4153
Total Beds: 1065

Southend Hospital NHS Trust

Southend Hospital, Prittlewell Chase, Westcliff on Sea SS0 0RY
Tel: 01702 435555 Fax: 01702 221300
Website: www.southend-hospital.co.uk
(Essex Health Authority)

Chair John Bruce
Chief Executive David Brackenbury
Assistant Chief Executive Chris Humbles

Southend Hospital
Prittlewell Chase, Westcliff on Sea SS0 0RY
Tel: 01702 435555 Fax: 01792 221300
Total Beds: 800

Accident and Emergency A Kumar, H Rokan
Anaesthetics R C Birt, B Boira, C H W Browne, C Buckore, N Cocker, D Barwell, M Gabrielczyk, D Higgins, P G Hollywood, J Kinnear, H C Naylor, M Nicol, D Ringrose, S J Ward, M J Woodham
Cardiology P Kelly
ENT D J Gatland, A Su, N P Warwick-Brown, G Watters
General Psychiatry A B Jack, N Killala
General Surgery M Dworkin, E Gray, F Hughes, M Jakeaways, N Rothnie, M C P Salter
Genitourinary Medicine D Evans
Nephrology M Almond, D Carmichael, S H Morgan, J F Moro-Azuela
Neuro-Surgeons J Benjamin, J Kellerman
Neurology H Hewazy, D M Park, G Warner
Obstetrics and Gynaecology V Aggarwai, P Hagan, D Jennings, C Lee, K B Lim, T J Pocock, J Ward
Ophthalmology R Aggarwal, W L Alexander, S Kasaby, R Pearson, Z Subasinghe
Oral and Maxillofacial Surgery D Madan, J Makechnie, P Weller
Orthodontics S Nute
Orthopaedics D A Boston, R Kazim, G Packer, S Raza, S Sarkar, R A Sudlow, A White
Paediatrics F Awadalla, M El Habbal, I Hadi, A Khan, I Margarson, V Nerminathan, A Shrivastava, S Sriskandan
Palliative Medicine G Tosh
Pathology M Chappell, D Donald, E F Fowler, M J Mills

Plastic Surgery D Elliott, L Kangesu
Radiology M Aslam, M N Ibrahim, M Lewars, S D Perera, B D Shah, A B Tanqueray, T Toma
Radiotherapy and Oncology A Jamshed, A Lamont, A Robinson, C Trask, J Whelan
Rheumatology and Rehabilitation B Dasgupta, T Gordon, W Main Wong
Thoracic Surgery R Walesby
Urology A Ball, T Carr, R Lodge

Southend-on-Sea Primary Care Trust

Harcourt House, Harcourt Avenue, Southend-on-Sea SS2 6HE
Tel: 01702 224600 Fax: 01702 224601
Email: southend.pct@sessex-ha.nthames.nhs.uk
Website: www.southend-pct.nhs.uk
(Essex Health Authority)

Chair Katherine Kirk
Chief Executive Julie Garbutt

Southern Derbyshire Acute Hospitals NHS Trust

Derby City General Hospital, London Road, Derby DE1 2QY
Tel: 01332 340131 Fax: 01332 625566
Website: www.sdah-tr.trent.nhs.uk
(Southern Derbyshire Health Authority)

Chair Peter Brewin
Chief Executive Julie Acred

Derby City Hospital

Uttoxeter Road, Derby DE22 3NE
Tel: 01332 340131 Fax: 01332 290559
Total Beds: 475

Anaesthetics A H Boyd, D P Cartwright, A Crossley, W L Dann, S Kethar-Thas, G F McLeod, D Patel, S Piggott, D Rogerson, M Vater, R Verma
Care of the Elderly J Birtwell, K A Muhiddin, N Mylvahan
General Medicine J R M Bateman, A Cole, J G Freeman, P R Golding, A McCance
General Surgery C P Chilton, R I Hall, H W Holliday, A Locker, K W Munson, J Reynolds, M Sibbering, J H Williams
Obstetrics and Gynaecology H M B Busfield, R L K Chapman, M Cust, J F Darne, A Fowlie, J Hodgkins, H M L Jenkins, I V Scott
Paediatrics J H M Axton, I Choonara, K L Dodd, R E Morton, C S Nelson, N Ruggins
Radiology D Clarke, M E L Cohen, J Minford, J G Pallan, A Turnbull, G M Turner
Rehabilitation Medicine C D Wood

Derbyshire Children's Hospital

North Street, Derby DE1 3BA
Tel: 01332 340131 Fax: 01332 200857
Total Beds: 71

Anaesthetics D P Cartwright, A W A Crossley, W L Dann, S Kethar-Thas, G F Macleod, S Piggott, D Rogerson, M Vater, R Verma
Care of the Elderly A J Birtwell, K A Muhiddin, N Mylvahan
General Medicine J R M Bateman, A J Birtwell, J G Freeman, P R Golding, A J McCane
General Surgery C P Chilton, R I Hall, H W Holliday, A P Locker, K W Munson, J Reynolds, J H Williams
Obstetrics and Gynaecology H M Busfield, R L K Chapman, M P Cust, J F Darne, A Fowlie, J Hodgkins, H M L Jenkins, I V Scott
Paediatrics J H M Axton, K L Dodd, R E Morton, C S Nelson, N Ruggins
Radiology M E L Cohen, J E Minford, J G Pallan, A E Turnbull, G M Turner

Derbyshire Royal Infirmary

London Road, Derby DE1 2QY
Tel: 01332 347141 Fax: 01332 295652
Total Beds: 610

Accident and Emergency A Fraser-Moodie, S M Hewitt, P E Pritty
Anaesthetics M M Ankutse, P H Bavister, A H Boyd, D P Cartwright, D H Chapman, A W A Crossley, W L Dann, R Dua, R H Elliott, R J Erskin, P H P Harris, R B S Hudson, S Kethar-Thas, B T Langham, G F MacLeod, D A Mulvey, D Patel, S Piggott, S Ralph, D Rogerson, A E Searle, M Vater, R Verma
Cardiology S Burne, A McCance, M W Millar-Craig
Care of the Elderly W P Gorman, C MacLean, R M Mishra
Chemical Pathology J S Harrop, P G Hill
Dermatology J M Gartside
ENT B Majumdar, D A Parker, J Sharp
General Medicine W P Gorman, G K T Holmes, M W Millar-Craig, B Norton, I Peacock, A Scott, W J Windebank
General Surgery K G Callum, A M Gudgeon, S Y Ifiikhar, J R Nash, J R Reynolds
Genitourinary Medicine R Rajakumar
Haematology A McKernan, S Mayne, D C Mitchell
Histopathology C S Holgate, I P Hopper, I Robinson, D Semeraro
Medical Microbiology D W Bullock, A R Mellersh
Neurology R B Godwin-Austen, D Jefferson
Neurophysiology N J Smith
Neurosurgery P O Byrne, T Hope
Ophthalmology P T C Docherty, I D Gardner, R Holden, H A M Salem
Oral and Maxillofacial Surgery K Jones, P Korczak
Orthodontics A Murray, O O'Keefe
Orthopaedics L C Bainbridge, F Burke, D Calthorpe, A O Cargill, S Chamberlain, A J P Henry, P Howard, P Lunn, R C Quinnell, J W Rowles, T Wilton
Palliative Medicine J M L Hocknell, V L Keeley
Plastic Surgery F B Baillie, M Henley, M L Sully
Radiology M E L Cohen, N Cozens, N Dann, M De Nunzio, S Elliott, D Hinwood, G Narborough, J P Pallam, A L M Piotrowicz, F D Smith, A Turnbull
Radiotherapy and Oncology P Chakraborti, D Guthrie, G Thomas
Rehabilitation Medicine C F Murray-Leslie
Rheumatology and Rehabilitation M Regan, G D Summers, R A Williams

Nightingale Macmillan Continuing Care Unit

117A London Road, Derby DE1 2RA
Tel: 01332 254900
Total Beds: 15

Southern Derbyshire Community and Mental Health Services NHS Trust

Kingsway Hospital, Kingsway, Derby DE22 3LZ
Tel: 01332 36 22 21
(Southern Derbyshire Health Authority)

Chair Judith Frost
Chief Executive Mike Shewan

Babington Hospital

Chevin Ward, Derby Road, Belper DE56 1WH
Tel: 01773 824171 Fax: 01773 824155
Total Beds: 10

Derbyshire Royal Infirmary (Mental Health)

London Road, Derby DE1 2QY
Tel: 01332 347141 Fax: 01332 295652
Total Beds: 33

Psychiatry of Old Age P Balakrishnan, J Hartman, E Komocki, S Pore, S Thacker

NHS TRUSTS & NHS HOSPITALS

Dovedale Day Hospital (Elderly Services)

London Road, Derby DE1 2XX
Tel: 01332 254886

The Grove

London Road, Shardlow, Derby DE7 2GT
Tel: 01332 792210 Fax: 01332 799036
Total Beds: 60

Ilkeston Community Hospital

Woodside Ward, Heanor Road, Ilkeston DE7 8LN
Tel: 0115 930 5522 Fax: 01159 441800
Total Beds: 15

Psychiatry of Old Age Dr Komocki

Kingsway Hospital

Kingsway, Derby DE22 3LZ
Tel: 01332 362221 Fax: 01332 331254
Total Beds: 217

General Psychiatry M A Bhuiyan, A Clayton, C Clulow, A Cook, R Denny, M Duggan, D Fowler, J M Hay, S McCance, R T Owen, K P Rao, M Sherman, N Sisodia, R Stocking-Korzen
Psychiatry of Old Age Dr Balakrishnan, J Hartman, E Komocki, S Pore, S Thacker

Derby City General Hospital (Mental Health)

Uttoxeter Road, Derby DE22 3NE
Tel: 01332 340131 Fax: 01332 624587
Total Beds: 173

General Psychiatry M A Bihiliyn, A Clayton, C Clulow, A Cook, R S H Denny, M T Duggan, B Fowler, J Hay, S McCane, R T Owen, K P Rao, M A Sherman, N Sisodia, R Stocking-Korzen
Psychiatry of Old Age P Balakrishnan, J A Hartman, E Komocki, S Pore, S Thacker

Resource Centre Day Hospital

Mental Health Resource Centre, London Road, Derby DE1 2QY
Tel: 01332 254818 Fax: 01332 254936

St Oswald's Hospital

Belle Vue Road, Ashbourne DE6 1AU
Tel: 01335 342121 Fax: 01335 300599
Total Beds: 40

Care of the Elderly R M Mishra
Dermatology M Shahidullah
ENT Dr Parker
General Medicine A Cole
General Surgery Dr Reynolds
Orthopaedics R C Quinnell
Rheumatology and Rehabilitation R Williams
Ultrasound G Turner

Southern Norfolk Primary Care Trust

St. Andrew's House, Northside, St. Andrew's Business Park, Thorpe St Andrew, Norwich NR7 0HT
Tel: 01603 300600 Fax: 01603 307387
(Norfolk, Suffolk and Cambridgeshire Health Authority)

Chair Helen Wilson

Southport and Formby Primary Care Trust

The Hesketh Centre, 51-55 Albert Road, Southport PR4 0RT
Tel: 01704 530940 Fax: 01704 536072
Website: www.southportandformbypct.nhs.uk

(Cheshire and Merseyside Health Authority)

Chair Mark Winstanley
Chief Executive Jane Beenstock

Southport and Ormskirk Hospital NHS Trust

Southport & Formby District General Hospital, Town Lane, Kew, Southport PR8 6PN
Tel: 01704 547471 Fax: 01704 704541
Website: www.sohnet.co.uk
(Cheshire and Merseyside Health Authority)

Chair Andrew Johnson
Chief Executive Jonathan Parry

Christiana Hartley Maternity Unit

Town Lane, Kew, Southport PR8 6PN
Tel: 01704 547471
Total Beds: 35

Obstetrics and Gynaecology G Foat, M N Iskander, S Sharma

Ormskirk and District General Hospital

Wigan Road, Ormskirk L39 2AZ
Tel: 01695 577111 Fax: 01695 583028

Accident and Emergency C C Scott
Anaesthetics C L Charway, D Jayson, J Jones, A P Kent, J Kirby, J W H Watt
Care of the Elderly M Ahmed, N G Dey
Chemical Pathology C V Heyningen
Chest Disease M J Serlin
Dermatology T W Stewart
General Medicine J P Simmonds
General Surgery I D Harrison, D Jones, S Vesey, M R Zeiderman
Medical Microbiology J A Bowley
Ophthalmology A Ekdawy, A Watson
Oral and Maxillofacial Surgery T Morris, O A Pospisil
Orthopaedics M Ali, D E.Carden, A G Hayes
Paediatrics A Al-Kharusi, M Zbaeda
Pathology B E Woodcock
Plastic Surgery A R Green
Radiology A Brown, P Hughes, R Subramaniam
Rheumatology and Rehabilitation H Sykes, E Williams
Spinal Injuries B Sett, P Sett
Thoracic Surgery J Mercer
Urology S Vesey

Ruffwood House

Ormskirk & District Hospital, Wigan Road, Ormskirk L39 2AZ

Southport and Formby District General Hospital

Town Lane, Kew, Southport PR8 6PN
Tel: 01704 547471 Fax: 01704 548229

Southport General Infirmary

Scarisbrick New Road, Southport PR8 6PN
Tel: 01704 547471

Care of the Elderly M Ahmed, N G Dey
ENT T Lesser, A Swift
Obstetrics and Gynaecology G Foat, M N Iskandar, S Sharma
Pathology D Dundas

Southwark Primary Care Trust

East Dulwich Grove, London SE22 8PT
Tel: 020 7346 6444 Fax: 020 7346 6445
(South East London Health Authority)

Chief Executive Chrise Bull

Staffordshire Ambulance Service NHS Trust

70 Stone Road, Stafford ST16 2TQ
Tel: 01785 253521 Fax: 01785 246238
(Shropshire and Staffordshire Health Authority)

Chair William H Gourlay
Chief Executive Roger C Thayne

Staffordshire Moorlands Primary Care Trust

Leek Moorlands Hospital, Ashbourne Road, Leek ST13 5BQ
Tel: 01538 487141 Fax: 01538 487146
(Shropshire and Staffordshire Health Authority)

Stockport NHS Trust

Stepping Hill Hospital, Poplar Grove, Stockport SK2 7JE
Tel: 0161 419 5001 Fax: 0161 419 5003
Website: www.stockport.nhs.uk
(Greater Manchester Health Authority)

Chair Nuala Swords-Isherwood
Chief Executive C Burke

Stepping Hill Hospital

Poplar Grove, Stockport SK2 7JE
Tel: 0161 483 1010 Fax: 0161 419 5003
Total Beds: 750

Anaesthetics J A Bourne, J W Dowdall, M Liddle, R G Lindsay, A McCluskey, C Mason, D Meadows, R G Mitchell, K O'Sullivan, C J Pemberton, S Remington, J Rigg, T Tramsey
Care of the Elderly G P Choudary, M L Dattachoudary, J Downton, G K Duckett
Dental Surgery R P J Thompson
Dermatology Dr Ashworth, Dr O'Driscoll
General Medicine N Ahluwalia, G J Archer, R J Cryer, I W Dymock, R Feinmann, P J Hale, P S Lewis, M A Martin
General Surgery W Brough, M Davies, G Deans, P E England, P Gallagher
Obstetrics and Gynaecology J C Depares, E Eyong, T McFarlane, I D Nuttall
Ophthalmology R Brown, B L Hercules, L M Morgan
Orthopaedics D Bamford, N Fahmy, J M Laughton, M Morris, B Todd, P G Turner
Pathology R Hale, P J Martin, S Maxwell, K Morgan, N L Reeve, D M Vickers
Radiology R D Dickson, W T Easson, T L Heyworth, C S Keeling-Roberts, N Lynch, S Mehta, A J Pollard, P Sanville
Thoracic Surgery A K Deiraniya
Urology P J Brooman, S Brown, G Collins, P H O'Reilly

Stockport Primary Care Trust

Springwood House, Poplar Grove, Hazel Grove, Stockport SK7 5BY
Tel: 0161 419 4706 Fax: 0161 419 4603
Email: enquiries@stockport-pct.nhs.uk
Website: www.stockporthealth.nwest.nhs.uk
(Greater Manchester Health Authority)

Chair Sam Moore
Chief Executive Richard Popplewell

Stoke Mandeville Hospital NHS Trust

Mandeville Road, Aylesbury HP21 8AL
Tel: 01296 315000 Fax: 01296 316604
(Thames Valley Health Authority)

Chair Anthony Woodbridge
Chief Executive Fiona Wise

Stoke Mandeville Hospital

Mandeville Road, Aylesbury HP21 8AL
Tel: 01296 315000 Fax: 01296 316604
Total Beds: 520

Accident and Emergency K Bizos, A Gammon
Dermatology S Burge
ENT I Bottrill, G Cox, R Ratnavel
General Medicine J Blackwell, P Collins, C J Durkin, A L Hillawi, A H Knight, M J Weldon, S J Williams
General Surgery P McArthur, A Mogg, A R Taylor, J H Tweedie
Genitourinary Medicine A Boakes
Neurology D Bridley, R C D Greenhall
Neurosurgery P Teddy
Obstetrics and Gynaecology F Ashworth, I Currie, B Reid, M M Usherwood
Ophthalmology A Assaf, R A Bates, L Benjamin, N Cox, B James, R G Smith
Oral Surgery M C Mace
Orthodontics F B Christie
Orthopaedics M E Guindi, H Henderson, D Johnston, B McElroy
Paediatrics P Adlard, R S Brown, C Noone
Pathology A P Gillett, J O'Driscoll, M O'Hea, A F Padel, M Reid, S Sheerin, B S F Shine, A J C Tudway, A Watson
Plastic Surgery P Budny, T Hyewood, A H N Roberts, M Scott
Radiology R N Bodley, A Booth, T Meagher, K Melvin, C Record, P Savage
Radiotherapy and Oncology C Alcock
Rheumatology and Rehabilitation S Edmonds, M Webley
Spinal Injuries H L Frankel, B P Gardner, I Nuseibeh
Urology G J Fellows

Suffolk Coastal Primary Care Trust

Bartlet Hospital Annexe, Undercliff Road East, Felixstowe IP11 7LT
(Norfolk, Suffolk and Cambridgeshire Health Authority)

Suffolk West Primary Care Trust

Thingoe House, Cotton Lane, Bury St Edmunds IP22 1YJ
(Norfolk, Suffolk and Cambridgeshire Health Authority)

Sunderland Teaching Primary Care Trust

Durham Road, Sunderland SR3 4AF
Tel: 0191 565 6256 Fax: 0191 528 3455
Website: www.sunderland.nhs.uk/teachingpct
(Northumberland, Tyne and Wear Health Authority)

Surrey Ambulance Service NHS Trust

The Horseshoe, Bolters Lane, Banstead SM7 2AS
Tel: 01737 353333 Fax: 01737 370868
Email: iac@surram.org.uk
Website: www.surram.org.uk

NHS TRUSTS & NHS HOSPITALS

(Surrey and Sussex Health Authority)

Chair Helen Gardiner

Surrey and Sussex Healthcare NHS Trust

East Surrey Hospital, Canada Avenue, Redhill RH1 5RH
Tel: 01737 768511 Fax: 01737 231769
Website: www.eastsurreyhealth.nhs.uk
(Surrey and Sussex Health Authority)

Chair Vivien Hepworth
Chief Executive Ken Cunningham

Caterham Dene Hospital

Church Road, Caterham CR3 5RA
Tel: 01883 349324 Fax: 01883 346978
Total Beds: 20

Care of the Elderly V Phongsathorn
ENT G Warrington
General Medicine K J Foster
Obstetrics and Gynaecology P Townsend
Ophthalmology S Chatterjee
Orthopaedics H Maurice
Paediatrics M Jawad
Urology P Miller

Crawley Hospital

West Green Drive, Crawley RH11 7DH
Tel: 01293 600300 Fax: 01293 600341
Total Beds: 254

Accident and Emergency A Mabrook
Anaesthetics W Chappell, L S J Jones, D J R Lyle, J Manjiani, C J Moon, V Newman
Cardiothoracic Medicine P Jenkins
Care of the Elderly R J Bailey, F Ramsay, A G Vallon
Child Psychiatry M N Cheng
Dermatology E Derrick, D M France, E Lenton
ENT K Bevan, J D Brookes, A Sha'aban, G Warrington
General Medicine A Gossage, W Shattles, J Sneddon, J L Thirkettle
General Psychiatry J Edeh, T Onen, G Spoto, M Veerabangsa, M Warsi
General Surgery A Ball, J C Bull, N F Gowland-Hopkins, E R T Owen
Haematology A C Nandi
Learning Disabilities I Ishkhans
Microbiology J Child
Neurology P Hughes
Obstetrics and Gynaecology D M Abayomi, D Booth, P Jackson, G D Kerr, S Vethanayagam
Occupational Health M Webb
Oncology C Topham
Ophthalmology B McLeod, M Spolton
Oral and Maxillofacial Surgery J R L Vincent-Townend
Orthopaedics A J Campbell, K Ratnakumar, C D P Stone
Paediatrics P I Atkinson, A Bonavia, C Greenaway, G D Kewley, I G Lewis
Pathology D Donaldson, E Harper, C Hunter-Craig, W Ramanathan, J Weston
Radiology J M C Davies, A B Hawrych, Dr Pascaline, J Vive

East Surrey Hospital

Canada Avenue, Redhill RH1 5RH
Tel: 01737 768511
Total Beds: 389

Accident and Emergency S Akbar, A Mabrook, A Lelo
Anaesthetics P Bajorek, B M Bray, A Gaynor, M Green, G Kar, F Lamb, F Sage, S.M. Ali, P Williams, S Kotting
Care of the Elderly T A Jesudason, V Phongasthorn, C Prajapati

Dermatology S Cliff, N Cowley
Family Planning T Peers
General Medicine U Davies, Dr Eisenger, K J Foster, F Guiness, P Jenkins, J P Lyons, E M Phillips
General Surgery M.A. Dissanayake, J Grabham, Dr Jennings, R G Lightwood, T Loosemore, P Miller, Dr Sayer, R.D. Southcott, A Stacey-Clear
Genitourinary Medicine P Deheragoda
Haematology S Stern
Microbiology B Stewart
Neurology J Kimber, M Mavra, J Thompson
Obstetrics and Gynaecology A Gordon-Wright, M Long, J Penny, J Pipe, P Townsend
Ophthalmology A Chopdar, F O'Sullivan, M Spolton, R S Wilson
Oral and Maxillofacial Surgery R Siva, P Ward-Booth
Orthodontics A Banner
Orthopaedics A Bassily, A J Campbell, K Drabu, H D Maurice, T J Selvan, G Selentakis
Paediatrics S Dotse, F Awadallah, M Jawad, A Kari, N Thalange, M Williams
Pathology M Ameen, D Fish, B M Hill, R Jackson, F Matthey
Radiology B Anastasi, A Ceccherini, C N O Digges, S Gwyther, R McAvinchey, D Mukasa, N Sellars
Radiotherapy and Oncology M Illsley, J Money-Kirle
Reproductive Health Dr Shinewi
Rheumatology S Griffiths
Thoracic Surgery R E Sayer
Urology M Jennings, P Miller, Dr Rane

Horsham Hospital

Hurst Road, Horsham RH12 2DR
Tel: 01403 227000 Fax: 01403 227030
Total Beds: 86

Care of the Elderly R J Bailey, F Ramsay, A G Vallon

Surrey Hampshire Borders NHS Trust

Farnham Hospital, Hale Road, Farnham GU9 9QL
Tel: 01483 782000 Fax: 01483 782299
(Surrey and Sussex Health Authority)

Chair Mary Sennett MBE
Chief Executive Fiona Green

Acorn Drug and Alcohol Services

Firth Cottage, Church Road, Frimley, Camberley GU16 5AD
Tel: 01276 670883 Fax: 01276 679474

Beech House Mental Health Service Day Centre

Church road, Frimley, Camberley GU16 5AD
Tel: 01276 670911 Fax: 01276 691428

Briarwood Rehabilitation Unit (Mental Health)

Sorrel Close, Cove, Farnborough GU14 9XW
Tel: 01252 378264 Fax: 01252 378255

Cranleigh Village Community Hospital

6 High Street, Cranleigh GU6 8AE
Tel: 01483 782400 Fax: 01483 782499
Total Beds: 14

Care of the Elderly H Powell, V Seth
ENT N W Weir
General Medicine T H Foley
General Surgery A E Giddings, N D Karanjia, M W Kissin, C G Marks
Obstetrics and Gynaecology P M Coats, K Morton
Paediatrics P J Gibson

Farnham Community Hospital

Hale Road, Farnham GU9 9QL
Tel: 01483 782000 Fax: 01483 782015
Total Beds: 73

Care of the Elderly K Debrait, I Ibrahim, K Mundy
Dermatology Dr Crone, R H Felix, Dr Woollam
ENT Dr Jonathon, R Kumar, A McCombe, Dr Sudderick
General Medicine Dr Amery, R L Bown, M J Boyd, R J Frankel, Dr Laidlaw, Dr Leopold, Dr Paterson, Dr Rutter
General Psychiatry Dr Hassan
General Surgery M Laidlan, M Leopold, M Singh
Haematology Dr Shirley, J E W Van de Pette
Neurology Dr Trend
Obstetrics and Gynaecology Dr Coates, S E Inman, Dr Riddle, P J Toplis
Oncology Dr Laing
Ophthalmology Dr Elliott, J A Govan, Dr Hashim, M K Tandon
Orthopaedics Dr Ashbrooke, S Davies, D Dempster, Dr Harrison, Dr Magnussen, Dr Pike, Dr Syed
Paediatrics Dr Howard, Dr Maltby, C Sena
Rheumatology and Rehabilitation J H P Cuddigan, Dr Reilly
Thoracic Medicine R K Knight
Urology Dr Kutarski, Dr Notley, Dr Palfrey

Farnham Road Mental Health & Community Hospital Health Services

Farnham Road, Guildford GU2 5LX
Tel: 01483 443535 Fax: 01483 443502
Total Beds: 32

General Psychiatry S Ahmad, G Andrews, J Mugisha, I H Shoeb, S J Watson, S M N Zaidi

Fleet Community Hospital

Church Road, Fleet GU13 8LB
Tel: 01483 782700 Fax: 01483 782799
Total Beds: 31

Florence Desmond Day Hospital

Royal Surrey County Hospital, Egerton Road, Guildford GU2 7XX
Tel: 01483 464001
Total Beds: 20

Haslemere and Community Hospital

Church Lane, Haslemere GU27 2BJ
Tel: 01483 782300 Fax: 01483 782398
Total Beds: 31

Audiological Medicine V Jayarajan, S E Snashall
Care of the Elderly H J Powell, V Seth
Chest Medicine W A C McAllister
Dermatology E Wong
ENT D McMillan, D Wright
General Medicine T H Foley, M G M Smith, M J Smith
General Psychiatry H Boothby
General Surgery M E Bailey, A E B Giddings, N D Karanjia, M Kissin, C Marks
Neurology P S Trend
Obstetrics and Gynaecology E P Curtis, K Morton, C J G Sutton
Ophthalmology A Gilvarry, S W Hampson
Orthopaedics C J Coates, M C Flannery
Paediatrics P J Gibson, M Ryalls
Plastic Surgery B Powell
Radiology B J Loveday
Rheumatology A R Behn, R E S Gray
Urology J H Davis, F A W Schweitzer

Milford Rehabilitation Hospital

Tuesley Lane, Godalming GU7 1UF
Tel: 01483 782000 Fax: 01483 782699

Odiham Cottage Hospital

Buryfields, Odiham
Tel: 01256 393600 Fax: 01256 393610

Parklands Hospital

Aldermaston Road, Basingstoke
Tel: 01256 817718 Fax: 01256 376315

Ridgewood Centre

Old Bisley Road, Frimley, Camberley GU16 5QE
Tel: 01276 692919 Fax: 01276 605360
Total Beds: 64

General Psychiatry G Andrews, A Chakrabarti, M Hawthorne, H Jameel, S Khalaf, S Lieberman, J Rutherford

Royal Surrey County Hospital Hindhead Ward

Egerton Road, Guildford GU2 7XX
Tel: 01483 443535
Total Beds: 24

Surrey Oaklands NHS Trust

Oaklands House, Coulsdon Road, Caterham CR3 5YA
Tel: 01883 388300, 01883 383838 Fax: 01883 383522
(Surrey and Sussex Health Authority)

Chair Brian Perkins
Chief Executive Gill Galliano, Gill Galliano
Consultants R Alloway, M T Attard, C De Alwis, S De Zoysa, Dr Manalagedeka, V R Pandita-Gunhwardenn, R Peernahcmed, M Prunty, S Santana, M Sevitt, J Stevens, K Vejdani, H Wienardena, J Wilson, F Yousaf

Sussex Ambulance Service NHS Trust

Ambulance Headquarters, 40-42 Friars Walk, Lewes BN7 2XW
Tel: 01273 489444 Fax: 01273 489445
Email: scalvert@sussamb.nhs.uk, info@sussamb.nhs.uk
(Surrey and Sussex Health Authority)

Chair Patrick Herbert
Chief Executive David Griffiths

Sussex Downs and Weald Primary Care Trust

Rother House, The Office Village, River Way, Uckfield TN22 1SL
Tel: 01825 768688 Fax: 01825 768689
(Surrey and Sussex Health Authority)

Chair Beryl Hubson
Chief Executive Fiona Henniker

Sussex Weald and Downs NHS Trust

Closing April 2002 - Mental health and learning disability services transferring to West Sussex Health and Social Care NHS Trust.

9 College Lane, Chichester PO19 4FX
Tel: 01243 787970 Fax: 01243 530767
(Surrey and Sussex Health Authority)

Chair Susan Pyper
Chief Executive Frances Russell

NHS TRUSTS & NHS HOSPITALS

Arundel and District Hospital
Chichester Road, Arundel BN18 0AB
Tel: 01903 882543
Total Beds: 20

Bognor Regis War Memorial Hospital
Shripney Road, Bognor Regis PO22 9PP
Tel: 01243 865418 Fax: 01243 827125
Total Beds: 61

Graylingwell Hospital
College Lane, Chichester PO19 4PQ
Tel: 01243 787970 Fax: 01243 783965
Total Beds: 245

Child and Adolescent Psychiatry Q Spender
Forensic Psychiatry M B Matthews (Head)
General Psychiatry R A Jackson, N Joughin, J C Wilkinson
Psychiatry of Old Age H Leegood (Head), T D Coates
Psychotherapy S J Hartland (Head)

Horsham Hospital
Hurst Road, Horsham RH12 2DR
Tel: 01403 227000 Fax: 01403 227018
Total Beds: 80

Midhurst, Easebourne and District Cottage Hospital
Dodsley Lane, Easebourne, Midhurst GU29 9AW
Tel: 01730 813105 Fax: 01730 812424
Total Beds: 12

Sutton and Merton Primary Care Trust

Morden Road Clinic, 254 Morden Road, London SW19 3DA
Tel: 020 8251 1111 Fax: 020 8251 1122
(South West London Health Authority)

Swale Primary Care Trust

Sheppey Community Hospital, Wards Hill Road, Minster on Sea, Sheerness ME12 2LN
(Kent and Medway Health Authority)

Chair John McCrae
Chief Executive John Mangan Medlock

Swindon and Marlborough NHS Trust

Princess Margaret Hospital, Okus Road, Swindon SN1 4JU
Tel: 01793 536231 Fax: 01793 480817
Website: www.swindon-marlborough.nhs.uk
(Avon, Gloucestershire and Wiltshire Health Authority)

Chair Nicholas Godden
Chief Executive Sonia Mills

Princess Margaret Hospital
Okus Road, Swindon SN1 4JU
Tel: 01793 536231 Fax: 01793 480817
Total Beds: 625

Accident and Emergency B Aslam, I Kendall
Anaesthetics C P Beeby, D N Campbell, R Craig, A Dale, M D Entwistle, J Griffiths, J W L Holmes, D M Jackson, H E Jones, B Maxwell, M O'Connor, S O'Kelly, A J Pickworth, I Smith, M P Tattersall, C Van Hamel, M Watters
Cardiology W McCrea

Care of the Elderly E Giallombardo, D J Howard, D Mukherjee, H Newton
Child and Adolescent Psychiatry J W Eastgate, R Eyre, W Woodhouse
Dermatology D Buckley, R J Mann, L Whittam
ENT S Chalstrey, J P Donnelly, M T Higazi, S S To
Gastroenterology P J V Hanson
General Medicine S Ahmed, M J Hayes, M D Hellier, E Higgs, M Juniper, A Leonard, P A Price
General Surgery P Burgess, D R A Finch, M Galea, R E Glass, D Hocken, R N Lawrence
Genitourinary Medicine G Rooney
Neurology S Wimalaratna
Obstetrics and Gynaecology A P Bond, J E Cullimore, P A Forbes-Smith, D N Majumdar, H Narayan
Ophthalmology S E P Burgess, P McCormack, J H Ramsay
Oral Surgery C R Charles, J Fieldhouse
Orthopaedics A Brooks, S Deo, A J B Fogg, M A Foy, J Ivory, I M R Lowdon, D M Williamson, D Woods
Paediatrics R Chinthapalli, L Grain, J M King, P T O'Keefe, H Price, S T Zengeya
Pathology J Armstrong, N Blesing, C M Colley, A G Gray, E S Green, B Kirkpatrick, W C Ng, U Ni Riain, J A Scurr, P Tidbury, R I Vanhegan
Plastic Surgery D J Coleman
Radiology A Beale, J Cook, J Henson, L K Jackson, A Jones, N Ridley, S J Taylor, A Troughton
Radiotherapy D J Cole
Rheumatology and Rehabilitation D A Collins, E Price, L Williamson
Urology J W Iacovou

Savernake Hospital
Marlborough SN8 3HL
Tel: 01672 514571 Fax: 01672 514021
Total Beds: 36

Swindon Primary Care Trust

Frankland Road, Blagrove, Swindon SN5 8YF
Tel: 01793 425265 Fax: 01793 425245
(Avon, Gloucestershire and Wiltshire Health Authority)

Chair David Wright
Chief Executive Jan Stubbings

Tameside and Glossop Acute Services NHS Trust

Tameside General Hospital, Fountain Street, Ashton-under-Lyne OL6 9RW
Tel: 0161 331 6000 Fax: 0161 331 6026
(Greater Manchester Health Authority)

Chief Executive Christine Green
Consultants B Banerjee, W Hood, A I Kiwanuka, A Saleh, A Woodyer

Tameside General Hospital
Fountain Street, Ashton-under-Lyne OL6 9RW
Tel: 0161 331 5151 Fax: 0161 331 5007
Total Beds: 664

Accident and Emergency A Saleh, Y Sharma
Anaesthetics V D Brim, U Deulkar, N Jena, A Kulkarni, J K Mazumder, H Rehman, K Sultan
Dental Surgery A G Addy, M E Foster
Dermatology E Parry
ENT A E R Kobbe, Dr Saha, P D Sharma
General Medicine B E Boyes, M P Chopra, S Horner, N M O'Mullane, C R Payne, S Puri, G Whatley
General Surgery I Benhamida, P Clothier, M Cooper-Wilson, Dr Ellenbogen, K H Siddiqui, Dr Welch, A B Woodyer

Genitourinary Medicine M R Girgis
Neurology C Sherrington
Neurosurgery A Sofat
Obstetrics and Gynaecology S Ali, J Foden-Schroff, A I Kiwanuka, K Rahman, A Watson
Ophthalmology Dr Jojo, J Lipton
Orthodontics W H J Bogues
Orthopaedics R Creedon, T H Dunningham, A O Ebizie, B N Muddu, E M H Obeid, M Pena
Pathology W Hood, A Joseph, P F Unsworth, A Yates
Radiology B Bannerjee, I Brett
Radiotherapy and Oncology Dr Sykes
Rheumatology T Brammah
Urology S Brown

Tameside and Glossop Community and Priority Services NHS Trust

Closing April 2002 - Services transferring to Penine Care NHS Trust.

Tameside General Hospital, Fountain Street, Ashton-under-Lyne OL6 9RW
Tel: 0161 331 5151 Fax: 0161 331 5007
(Greater Manchester Health Authority)

Chair Maurice Travers
Chief Executive J R Davenport

Hyde Hospital

Grange Road South, Hyde SK14 5NY
Tel: 0161 366 8833 Fax: 0161 368 2834
Total Beds: 16

Old Age Psychiatry Dr Baynes, Dr Jagus, Dr Watson

Shire Hill Hospital

Bute Street, Glossop SK13 9PZ
Tel: 01457 866021 Fax: 01457 857519
Total Beds: 54

Medical Services for Older People Dr Hameed, O Jalobe, H Rakicka

Tameside General Hospital

Fountain Street, Ashton-under-Lyne OL6 9RW
Tel: 0161 331 5151 Fax: 0161 331 5007
Total Beds: 128

Mental Health and Old Age Psychiatry B Baynes, P Bowers, F Creighton, S Darvill, Dr Gonrisvnkar, C E Jagus, A Kushlick, Dr McDade, Dr Shaw, Dr Tait, I Telfer, Dr Theofilepoulos, C Watson

Wood's Hospital

Glossop SK13 9BQ
Tel: 01457 860783 Fax: 01457 868704
Total Beds: 22

Old Age Psychiatry Dr Baynes, Dr Jagus, Dr Watson

Tameside and Glossop Primary Care Trust

Country House, 107-109 Market Street, Hyde SK11 1HL
Tel: 0161 873 9535 Fax: 0161 873 9501
Chair Ian McCrae
Chief Executive Mike Ditchfield

Taunton and Somerset NHS Trust

Taunton and Somerset Hospital, Musgrove Park, Taunton TA1 5DA
Tel: 01823 333444 Fax: 01823 336877
Website: www.somerset-health.org.uk

(Somerset and Dorset Health Authority)

Chair Brian Tanner
Chief Executive Anne Cooley

Taunton and Somerset Hospital

Musgrove Park, Taunton TA1 5DA
Tel: 01823 333444 Fax: 01823 336877
Website: www.somerset-health.org.uk
Total Beds: 800

Accident and Emergency G Bryce, D Mann
Anaesthetics C Blumgart, B Browne, T M Bull, A Daykin, R C Desborough, I Gauntlett, J Lucas, B Nichols, V J Prior, P J Ravenscroft
Cardiology M James, D MacIver
Care of the Elderly S Cooper, M Evans, P Kist, T Solanki
Chest Disease C R Swinburn
Dermatology J Boyle, C J W Guerrier, D Pryce
ENT J J Upton, S C Wells
General Medicine M Barry, M G Ellwood, D MacIver, C Swinburn, D B Yates
General Psychiatry W Ahmed, P Hunt, A Poole
General Surgery J F Chester, C D Collins, I A Eyre-Brook, S M Jones, I N Ramus
Genitourinary Medicine M Fitzgerald
Haematology S A N Johnson, M J Phillips
Infectious Diseases C R Swinburn
Medical Microbiology J W Jones, M Smith
Neurology N K Banerji
Obstetrics and Gynaecology K Bidgood, H Marsh, J A Richardson, H M Smith
Occupational Health P T Penny
Ophthalmology R R Acheson, K Bates, A Stockwell, J M Twomey
Oral and Maxillofacial Surgery M Davidson, J F Hamlyn
Orthodontics M Brenchley, D J McConnell
Orthopaedics A Clarke, R P Foster, C M Marsh, C Ogilvie, H A Rainey, P Webb
Paediatrics D Challacombe, T J French, R Mann, A Tandy, M Webster
Pathology A E Adam, S A N Johnson, M J Phillips, S C Smith
Plastic Surgery R W Piggott, P L Townsend
Radiology J M Bell, T R Brown, P M Cavanagh, D Cooke, H Thomas, S K Wells, S A Willson
Radiotherapy and Oncology J Bullimore, E C Whipp
Urology P O'Boyle, M J Speakman
Vascular Surgery J F Chester, S M Jones

Taunton Deane Primary Care Trust

Health Authority Building, Wells Spring Road, Taunton TA2 7PQ
Tel: 01823 344401 Fax: 01823 344406
(Somerset and Dorset Health Authority)

Chair Alan Hopper
Chief Executive Edward Colgan

Taunton Community Hospital

Musgrove Park, Taunton TA1 5DA
Tel: 01823 343756

Wellington and District Cottage Hospital

South Street, Wellington TA21 8QQ
Tel: 01823 662663
Total Beds: 11

Care of the Elderly M Evans
General Psychiatry D W Ahmed
General Surgery N I Ramus
Obstetrics and Gynaecology J A Richardson
Orthopaedics C H Marsh
Urology P J O'Boyle

NHS TRUSTS & NHS HOSPITALS

Tavistock and Portman NHS Trust

Tavistock Centre, 120 Belsize Lane, London NW3 5BA
Tel: 020 7435 7111 Fax: 020 7447 3709
Website: www.tavi-port.org
(North Central London Health Authority)

Chief Executive N Temple

Portman Clinic

89 Fitzjohn's Avenue, London Nw3 5NA
Tel: 020 794 8262

The Tavistock Mulberry Bush Day Unit

33 Daleham Gardens, London NW3 5BU
Tel: 020 7794 3553
Total Beds: 27

Tees and North East Yorkshire NHS Trust

Flatts Lane Centre, Flatts Lane, Normanby, Middlesbrough TS4 0SZ
Tel: 01642 288288 Fax: 01642 516470
Email: margaret.harvey@stcmh-tr.northy.nhs.uk
(Tees Health Authority)

Chair Eileen Grace
Chief Executive Moira Britton

Carter Bequest Hospital

Cambridge Road, Middlesbrough TS5 5NH
Tel: 01642 850911 Fax: 01642 816140
Total Beds: 44

East Cleveland Hospital

Alford Road, Brotton, Saltburn-by-the-Sea TS12 2FF
Tel: 01287 676205 ext: 2211

Guisborough General Hospital

Northgate, Guisborough TS14 6HZ
Tel: 01287 633542 ext: 4032 Fax: 01287 610508
Total Beds: 36

St Luke's Hospital

Marton Road, Middlesbrough TS4 3AF
Tel: 01642 850850 Fax: 01642 821810
Total Beds: 226

St Mary's Hospital

Dean Road, Scarborough YO12 7SN
Tel: 01723 376111 Fax: 01723 342857
Total Beds: 26

Care of the Elderly S K Chatterjee
General Psychiatry N K Chawla, R D Nicholson, M R Timperley

Stead Memorial Hospital

Kirkleatham Street, Redcar TS10 1QR
Tel: 01642 483251 Fax: 01642 477521
Total Beds: 36

Tees East and North Yorkshire Ambulance Service NHS Trust

Fairfields, Shipton Road YO30 1XW
Tel: 01904 666000 Fax: 01904 666050
Email: nyas999@aol.com
(North and East Yorkshire and Northern Lincolnshire Health Authority)

Chair John Nelson
Chief Executive David Craig

Teignbridge Primary Care Trust

Seminar Room Offices, Newton Abbot Hospital, 64 East Street, Newton Abbot TQ12 4PT
Tel: 01626 357384 Fax: 01626 357214
(South West Peninsula Health Authority)

Chair Christine Cribb
Chief Executive Pam Smith

Telford and Wrekin Primary Care Trust

Wellington Health Centre, Chapel Lane, Wellington, Telford TF1 1PZ
Tel: 01952 226013 Fax: 01952 226020
(Shropshire and Staffordshire Health Authority)

Tendring Primary Care Trust

Carnarvon House, Carnarvon Road, Clacton-on-Sea CO15 6QD
Tel: 01255 206060 Fax: 01255 206061
(Essex Health Authority)

Chair David Rex
Chief Executive Paul Unsworth

Thames Gateway NHS Trust

Closing April 2002 - Services transferring to West Kent NHS and Social Care Trust.

Trust HQ, 7-8 Ambley Green, Bailey Drive, Gillingham ME8 0NJ
Tel: 01634 382777 Fax: 01634 382700
(Kent and Medway Health Authority)

Chair Brigita Amey
Chief Executive John Mangan

Archery House

Bow Arrow Lane, Dartford DA2 6PB
Tel: 01322 227211
Total Beds: 59

General Psychiatry E Clarke, V Gunasingham, Dr Sadik

Little Brook Hospital

Bow Arrow Lane, Dartford
Tel: 01322 622222
Total Beds: 52

Sheppey Community Hospital

Wards Hill Road, Minster, Sheerness ME12 2LN
Tel: 01795 872116
Total Beds: 39

Sittingbourne Memorial Hospital

Bell Road, Sittingbourne ME10 4DT
Tel: 01795 418300 Fax: 01795 418301
Total Beds: 48

General Psychiatry S Feeney

Stone House

Dartford DA2 6AU
Tel: 01322 622222
Total Beds: 104

General Psychiatry V Matthew, Dr Osmay, R R Sharma

Thurrock Primary Care Trust

PO Box 83, Civic Offices, New Road, Grays RM17 6FD
Tel: 01375 406400 Fax: 01375 406401
(Essex Health Authority)

Chair Valerie Liddiard
Chief Executive Vi Wagner

Torbay Primary Care Trust

Rainbow House, Avenue Road, Torquay TQ2 5LS
Tel: 01803 210910 Fax: 01803 292975
Website: www.torbay-pct.nhs.uk
(South West Peninsula Health Authority)

Chair Mike Wickens
Chief Executive Simon Worswick

Tower Hamlets Primary Care Trust

Block One, Mile End Hospital, Bancroft Road, London
Tel: 020 8709 5000 Fax: 020 8709 5010
Website: www.thpct.nhs.uk
(North East London Health Authority)

Chair Richard Gee
Chief Executive Chris Carter

Mile End Hospital

Bancroft Road, London E1 4DG
Tel: 020 7377 7920 Fax: 020 7377 7931
Total Beds: 200

Royal London Hospital

Bancroft Road, Mile End, London E1 4DG
Tel: 020 7377 7000 Fax: 020 7377 7401
Total Beds: 48

St Clement's Hospital

2A Bow Road, London E3 4LL
Tel: 020 7377 7953 Fax: 020 7377 7963
Total Beds: 91

Trafford Healthcare NHS Trust

Trafford General Hospital, Moorside Road, Urmston, Manchester M41 5SL
Tel: 0161 748 4022 Fax: 0161 746 7214
(Greater Manchester Health Authority)

Chair Helen Busteed
Chief Executive David Cain

Altrincham General Hospital

Market Street, Altrincham WA14 1PE
Tel: 0161 928 6111 Fax: 0161 928 5657
Total Beds: 41

Anaesthetics B K Greenwood
Care of the Elderly J A Anandadas, T Kondratowicz, S N Laha, S R Musgrave
Child Health H M Lewis
Dermatology H L Muston
General Medicine B C Leahy, F McKenna, S R Musgrove, W P Stephens, C B Summerton, J M Trelawny
General Psychiatry J S Bamrah
General Surgery I M Aldean, E M Hoare, P A Sykes
Obstetrics and Gynaecology K M Graham, A M Nysenbaum
Ophthalmology M J Lavin, G S Turner
Orthopaedics M Ismail, S G Royle, M C B Webber
Paediatrics R H A Campbell, H M Lewis

Pathology D M Alderson, L N Sandle
Psychiatry J S Bamrah
Radiology U M Beetles, A E Mattison, P S Norburn
Urology P N Rao

St Anne's Hospital

Woodville Road, Bowdon, Altrincham WA14 2AQ
Tel: 0161 928 5851
Total Beds: 20

Care of the Elderly J A Anandadas, S N Laha
ENT A El-Kholy, E Jaffari
General Medicine F McKenna
General Psychiatry J S Bamrah

Stretford Memorial Hospital

226 Seymour Grove, Stretford, Manchester M16 0DE
Tel: 0161 881 5353
Total Beds: 12

Anaesthetics T J Kinsella
Care of the Elderly T Kondratowicz, S R Musgrave
ENT A El-Kholy, E Jaffari
General Medicine B C Leahy, W P Stephens, C B Summerton, J M Trelawny
General Surgery F X Marazerlo
Obstetrics and Gynaecology G Ainscow, K M Graham, R J Howell
Ophthalmology M J Lavin, G S Turner
Orthopaedics M C B Webber

Trafford General Hospital

Moorside Road, Davyhulme, Urmston, Manchester M41 5SL
Tel: 0161 748 4022 Fax: 0161 746 8556
Total Beds: 537

Accident and Emergency C Libetta, C L Summers
Anaesthetics G Beck, M Eltoft, B K Greenwood, T J Kinsella, R T Longbottom, A G Pocklington, A Shaw, C Van Oldenbeek
Audiological Medicine P Kuna
Cardiology J Trelawney
Care of the Elderly J A Anandadas, T Kondratowicz, S N Laha, S R Musgrave
Child Health A A A Bagadi, R H A Campbell, D Jayson, A B John, P Kuna, H M Lewis, E B Turya
Dermatology H L Muston
ENT A El-Kholy, E Jaffari
Gastroenterology C Summerton
General Medicine B Leahy, F McKenna, F Radwan, W P Stephens, C B Summerton, S C O Taggart, J M Trelawny
General Psychiatry S Amin, J S Bamrah, T Carnwath, J S E Hellewell, L R Montague, P O'Malley
General Surgery I M Aldean, E M Hoare, F Mazarelo, P A Sykes
Genitourinary Medicine E Curless
Neurology W Schady
Obstetrics and Gynaecology G Ainscow, K M Graham, R J Howell, A M Nysenbaum
Occupational Health A Stewart
Ophthalmology M Lavin, G S Turner
Oral and Maxillofacial Surgery T Boyd, S Caldwell, R E Lloyd
Orthopaedics R P Goel, M Ismail, S Royle, M C B Webber
Paediatrics R H A Campbell, A B John, H Lewis, E B Turya
Pathology D M Alderson, P A Carrington, J Croall, F Hilmi, L N Sandle, M Y Sheikh
Radiology U M Beetles, A H Choudhuri, M D Howden, A Mortimer, P S Norburn
Restorative Dentistry T Boyd
Thoracic Surgery R A M Lawson
Urology P Downey, P N Rao

Trafford North Primary Care Trust

Peel House, 4th Floor, Albert Street, Eccles M30 0NJ
Tel: 0161 787 0248 Fax: 0161 787 0308

NHS TRUSTS & NHS HOSPITALS

(Greater Manchester Health Authority)

Chair Fae Selvin
Chief Executive Tim Riley

Trafford South Primary Care Trust

Peel House, Albert Street, Eccles, Manchester M30 0NJ
Tel: 0161 787 0131 Fax: 0161 787 0290
(Greater Manchester Health Authority)

Chair Norma Raynes, L Robinson
Chief Executive Peter Cubbon

Two Shires - Northampton and Bucks Ambulance NHS Trust

The Hunters, Buckingham Road, Deanshanger, Milton Keynes MK19 6HL
Tel: 01908 262422 Fax: 01908 265014
(Thames Valley Health Authority)

Chair Ken Cooper
Chief Executive Paul Martin

United Bristol Healthcare NHS Trust

Trust Headquarters, Marlborough Street, Bristol BS1 3NU
Tel: 0117 929 0666 Fax: 0117 925 6588
Email: ubht@ubht.swest.nhs.uk
Website: www.ubht.nhs.uk
(Avon, Gloucestershire and Wiltshire Health Authority)

Chair Philip Gregory
Chief Executive Hugh Ross

Bristol Eye Hospital

Lower Maudlin Street, Bristol BS1 2LX
Tel: 0117 923 0060 Fax: 0117 928 4686
Total Beds: 46

Ophthalmology S Cook, D L Easty, R H B Grey, R Harrad, J C D Hart, R H Markham, M Potts, J Sparrow

Bristol General Hospital

Guinea Street, Bristol BS1 6SY
Tel: 0117 926 5001 Fax: 0117 928 6245
Total Beds: 164

Care of the Elderly S Croxson, M MacMahon, P Murphy, G W Tobin

Bristol Homoeopathic Hospital

Cotham Hill, Cotham, Bristol BS6 6JU
Tel: 0117 973 1231 Fax: 0117 923 8759

Homoeopathic Medicine D S Spence

Bristol Royal Hospital for Children

Upper Maudlin St, Bristol BS2 8BJ
Tel: 0117 921 5411 Fax: 0117 928 5820
Total Beds: 456

Cardiac Surgery A Pawade
Child and Adolescent Psychiatry H E Barnes, J Culling, C Lewin, R J W Williams
Clinical Genetics P Lunt, R Newbury-Ecob, E Sheridan
Orthopaedics M Gargan, P J Witherow
Paediatric Surgery E Cusick, J D Frank, L Huskisson, R Spicer
Paediatrics J D Baum, E C Crowne, A Emond, P J Fleming, A B M Foot, L Goldsworthy, A M Hayes, J Henderson, P Jardine, H S Joffe,

S P Lowis, D Marks, R Martin, M G Mott, A Oakhill, G A B Russell, B Sandhu, P M Sharples, M Thoresen, A Whitelaw
Pathology M T Ashworth, P J Berry, H J Porter

Bristol Royal Infirmary

Marlborough Street, Bristol BS2 8HW
Tel: 0117 923 0000 Fax: 0117 928 3413
Total Beds: 456

Accident and Emergency I O'Sullivan, N Rawlinson, A H Swain
Anaesthetics J I Alexander, A M S Black, D Coates, A H Cohen, I M Davies, F C Forrest, T H Gould, S J Howell, D G Hughes, I Jenkins, R W Johnson, S Kinsella, S G Lauder, S P K Linter, S Masey, S J Mather, C Monk, P J Murphy, M Nevin, V Penning-Rowsell, S J Pryn, C Prys-Roberts, I G Ryder, L E Shutt, P A Stoddart, D Terry, T A Thomas, P G N Thornton, S Underwood, P M Weir, S Willatts, N B Williams, A R Wolf
Cardiology T Cripps, J V Jones, J C Pitts-Crick
Cardiothoracic Surgery G D Angelini, A J Bryan, J Dhasmana, J Hutter
Care of the Elderly S Croxson, M MacMahon, P Murphy, G Tobin
Chemical Pathology A P Day, C A Pennock, D Stansbie
Clinical Pharmacology and Therapeutics C J C Roberts
Dermatology C B Archer, D d Berker, G Dunnill, C T C Kennedy, J Sansom
Endocrinology R Corrall, C Dayan
Gastroenterology D Alderson, P Barham, R E Barry, P Durdey, K W Heaton, R A Mountford, C J Probert, M Thomas
General Medicine R E Barry, J Catterall, K W Heaton, A Levy, S L Lightman, R A Mountford, C J Probert, C J C Roberts, D Wynick
General Psychiatry D A G Cook, S O'Connor, J Parker
Genitourinary Medicine P J Horner, A J Scott
Histopathology C J Calder, A Charles, C M P Collins, N Moorghan, J Pawade, E A Sheffield
Immunology M O Symes
Medical Microbiology M R Miller, R C Spencer
Nephrology J C Mackenzie
Neurology I E C Ormerod
Neuropathology T H Moss
Neurosurgery H Coakham
Occupational Health C C Harling, R Phillip
Orthopaedics R M Atkins, P G Eames, M Gargan, M Jackson, I Learmouth, I J Leslie, J H Newman, P Sarangi
Pathology M T Ashworth, P J Berry, C M P Collins, C A Pennock, H J Porter, D Stansbie
Pharmacology C J C Roberts
Plastic Surgery A Bird, N Mercer
Radiology H Andrews, A M Baird, J E Basten, D J Crier, A Duncan, P Goddard, A J Jones, J Kabala, E Kutt, P Murphy, M Rees, J Virjee, C J Wakeley, I Watt, R P Wilde
Respiratory Medicine J R Catterall, M R Hetzel, G Laszlo
Rheumatology M Byron, P A Dieppe, J R Kirwan, J Tobias
Thoracic Medicine J R Catterall, M R Hetzel, G Laszlo
Urology M Persad, G Sibley, P J B Smith

Keynsham Hospital

Keynsham, Bristol BS18 1AG
Tel: 0117 986 2356 Fax: 0117 986 2356 ext: 256

Care of the Elderly F Bigwood, M Cameron, R G Davidson, N R Nutt

St Michael's Hospital

Southwell Street, Bristol BS2 8EG
Tel: 0117 921 5411 Fax: 0117 928 5842
Total Beds: 270

ENT P G Bicknell, M Birchell, M V Griffiths, A R Maw
Obstetrics and Gynaecology R S Anderson, D Cahill, S Glew, U Gordon, M G R Hull, J Jenkins, P Kyle, M S Mills, J B Murdoch, P A R Niven, P Soothill, G M Stirrat, P G Wardle

University of Bristol Dental Hospital and School

Lower Maudlin Street, Bristol BS1 2LY

Tel: 0117 923 0050 Fax: 0117 928 4443

Consultants M Addy, J G Cowpe, P Crawford, J Eveson, M J Griffiths, P Guest, N W Harradine, A Harrison, I S Hathorn, A Ireland, G Irvine, P King, H Knight, N Meredith, J Moran, G Pell, S Prime, J Rees, J Sandy, C D Stephens, C M Woodhead

United Lincolnshire Hospitals NHS Trust

Grantham and District Hospital, 101 Manthorpe Road, Grantham NG31 8DG
Tel: 01476 565232 Fax: 01476 567358
Email: connie.galati@ulh.nhs.uk
(Trent Health Authority)

Chair Jenny Green
Chief Executive David Loasby

County Hospital

High Holme Road, Louth LN11 0EU
Tel: 01507 600100
Total Beds: 128

Anaesthetics H Myint, M Serajuddin
Diabetes and Endocrinology M Rehman
General Medicine C Cook, M Teli
General Surgery P Reasbeck
Orthopaedics R Nayak

Grantham and District Hospital

101 Manthorpe Road, Grantham NG31 8DG
Tel: 01476 565232
Total Beds: 148

Accident and Emergency H D Garrick
Anaesthetics J L Breckenridge, C E Cory, S Jayamaha, C Onugha, N Platt, T P Shepherd, Dr Tore, Dr Udom
General Medicine C R Birch, J H Campbell, P S Jayaratne, U D Wijayawardhana
General Surgery D R Andrew, J G McAdam, D Mathur, D Valerio
Haematology V M Tringham
Histopathology D M Clark
Microbiology J Francis
Obstetrics and Gynaecology R P Husemeyer, S Vogt
Orthodontics J Kotyla
Orthopaedics A E Halliday, W A Niezywinski, S M O'Riordan, Dr Singhavia
Radiology S J Bradley, P J Gibson

Johnson Hospital

Priory Road, Spalding PE11 2XD
Tel: 01775 722386
Total Beds: 28

Lincoln County Hospital

Greetwell Road, Lincoln LN2 5QY
Tel: 01522 512512 Fax: 01522 573419
Total Beds: 653

Accident and Emergency J G Pillay, N Pyrgos
Anaesthetics S Cole, J Craggs, J Donnelly, A E Feerick, R Francis, A Kutarski, A M Liddle, L Mendal, C A O'Dwyer, D C Phillips, A B Powles, A D Reynolds, R B Scott, D M Shewan, J Stonham, R J Thornton, C K G Tyler, A B Victoria, A Webb, N Williams, A S Wolverson
Care of the Elderly A Kamal, S Leach, M Rizeq, D M Stokoe
Dental Surgery M A Coupland, S A Layton, A G Sadler
ENT A Connolly, A R McRae, G Owen
General Medicine S Ahmed, R Andrews, Dr Ashtan, Dr Davies-Jones, Dr Duffy, N C Hepburn, Dr Hubner, Dr Jan Von Der Werth, S Kelly, E J W McClemont, B MacDonald, S P Matusiewicz, D Ng, J L W Parker, I C Paterson, A J Rea, B B Scott, B Sharrack, I D Woodlands

UNITED LINCOLNSHIRE HOSPITALS NHS TRUST

General Surgery A P Barlow, P K Basu, N P Buchholz, P Dunning, O Eremin, H Henderson, I M Hutton, J A Jibril, A J Lamerton, I Mark, T Milward, S K Varma, D J Ward
Haematology M I Adelman, A Hepplestone, A Hunter, D R Prangnell
Medical Microbiology C A J Brightman, E R Youngs
Nephrology Dr Warwick
Obstetrics and Gynaecology A J Breeson, G W Gough, R Husemeyer, M P Lamb, I D Vellacott, S Vogt
Ophthalmology A A Castillo, P M Drummond, E G Hale, B Redmill
Orthodontics M A Coupland
Orthopaedics R Asirvatham, M Feeney, D Gale, I D Hyde, E W Morris, S M O'Riordan, J M Wilkinson
Paediatrics R C Groggins, M J Lewins, C P Millns, A Scammell, Dr Suresh Babu
Pathology G Cowley, G J Griffiths, J A Harvey, J M F McClemont
Radiology A L Griffiths, S G Hogg, M Kamel, J B McCafferty, C I Rothwell, S Stinchcombe, V Thava, G W Thorpe, G Vijayashimhulu, D Wheatley
Radiotherapy and Oncology J M Eremin, P Mack, E C Murray, T M Sheehan, T Sreenivasan
Rheumatology J E Carty, I C Gaywood, B P Hunt

Pilgrim Hospital

Sibsey Road, Boston PE21 9QS
Tel: 01205 364801 Fax: 01205 354395
Total Beds: 526

Anaesthetics G Batchelor, M D R Bexton, E P D Chalmers, E Dichmont, J M Massey, A C Norton, D A Sagar, A Syed, H M Thompson
Care of the Elderly D Mangion, D J Meacock
Dental Surgery D E H Glendinning
ENT R N Joshi, G A Westmore
General Medicine D A R Boldy, M J Fairman, C R Nyman, S A Olczak
General Surgery M A Al-Fallouji, N J Andrews, C I Massey
Genitourinary Medicine J Clay
Haematology S Sobolewski, V M Tringham
Nephrology J Feehally
Neurology R A Godwin-Austen
Obstetrics and Gynaecology D A Adeyemi, A S Binks, G B Leckie, E D Pereira, A Shaheen
Ophthalmology M N Abdel-Khalek, A Rahman
Orthodontics F J Calvert
Orthopaedics D Achary, - Bismil, R J Latto, T H Minhas, J A S Watson
Paediatrics M J Crawford, S K Hanumara, M J Vaizey
Pathology D C S Durrant, K Loudon, S M Shah
Plastic Surgery T M Milward, D Ward
Radiology M Aslam, K P Gill, R Jones, P T King, G M McGann
Rheumatology and Rehabilitation J E Carty, B P Hunt
Urology N Dahar, D T L Turner

St George's Hospital

Long Leys Road, Lincoln LN1 1EJ
Tel: 01522 512512 Fax: 01522 573 2019
Total Beds: 46

Dermatology N C Hepburn
Oncology K Baria, J Eremin, E C Murray, T M Sheehan, T Sreenivasan
Plastic Surgery H Henderson, T Milward, D J Ward

Skegness and District Hospital

Dorothy Avenue, Skegness PE25 2BS
Tel: 01754 762401 Fax: 01754 760132
Total Beds: 39

Welland Hospital

Roman Bank, Spalding PE11 2HW
Tel: 01775 766800

NHS TRUSTS & NHS HOSPITALS

Total Beds: 28

Care of the Elderly D J Meacock

University College London Hospitals NHS Trust

Trust Headquarters, Vezey Strong Wing, 112 Hampstead Road, London NW1 2LT
Tel: 020 7387 9300 Fax: 020 7380 9963
Website: www.uclh.org
(North Central London Health Authority)

Chair Ronald Mason
Chief Executive Robert Naylor

The Eastman Dental Hospital

256 Gray's Inn Road, London WC1X 8LD
Tel: 020 7915 1000 Fax: 020 7915 1012
Total Beds: 12

The Elizabeth Garrett Anderson Hospital and Obstetric Hospital

Huntley Street, London WC1E 6DH
Tel: 020 7380 3501 Fax: 020 7383 3415
Total Beds: 20

Anaesthetics B Astley, E M Grundy, A McCara, W O'Brien, P Painter, P Stracey
Consultants L Morrison
Dermatology P Dowd
General Surgery M W Ghilchick
Obstetrics and Gynaecology J Guillebaud, G C L Lachellin, C Lucas, A Mills, J Osborne, M A Pugh, N C Siddle, A C Silverstone, J A Spencer, S J Steele
Radiology A Schneidau

The Heart Hospital

Westmoreland Street, London W1G 8PH

The Hospital for Tropical Diseases

Mortimer Market, Capper Street, Tottenham Court Road, London WC1E 6AU
Tel: 020 7387 4411 Fax: 020 7388 7645
Website: www.uclh.org
Total Beds: 22

General Medicine R H Behrens, A D M Bryceson, P L Chiodini, G C Cook, A d L Costello, A P Hall, D C W Mabey, K McAdam, A M Tomkins, M F R Waters, S G Wright
General Surgery A G A Cowie
Ophthalmology T Ffytche
Pathology P L Chiodini

The Middlesex Hospital

Mortimer Street, London W1T 3AA
Tel: 020 7636 8333
Total Beds: 454

Anaesthetics B Astley, P J Bennett, R M Bowen-Wright, E M Grundy, J A Hulf, W J O'Brien, W K Pallister, I R Verner
Bacteriology J M Holton, J Pattinson, G A W Rook, J L Stanford
Cardiology R H Swanton, J M Walker
Cardiothoracic Surgery P Goldstraw, M F Sturridge, T Treasure
Care of the Elderly G P J Beynon, J R Croker
Chemical Pathology M D Buckley-Sharp, A L Miller
Consultants F T C Harris, G B Newman
Dermatology P Dowd, J J H Gilkes, G M Levene, T W E Robinson
ENT D G Davies, R A Williams
General Medicine A Hatfield, H S Jacobs, N M Johnson, A B Kurtz, J L H O'Riordan, P Salmon, S J G Semple, J D H Slater, T C B Stamp
General Psychiatry O W Hill, C R Pugh, R Rosser, H M Wieselberg

General Surgery M Adiseshiah, M Hobsley, J A P Marston, R C G Russell, J H Scurr, W W Slack
Genitourinary Medicine M Adler, J S Bingham, A Mindell
Haematology D C Linch, S J Machin
Immunology J Brostoff
Neurology M J Harrison, A J Lees, P M L Quesne, G M Stern
Nuclear Medicine P J Ell, E S Williams
Obstetrics and Gynaecology J L Guillebaud, R Lloyd-Jones, J L Osborne, S J Steele
Oral and Maxillofacial Surgery H P Cook, D Winstock
Orthopaedics M A Edgar, D R Sweetnam
Paediatrics C G D Brook, A M Kilby
Pathology D S J Brew, M H Griffiths, W Highman, D R Katz, G Koojan, A Nisbett-Smith, M C Parkinson, J Rode, N Woolf
Public Health Medicine J H Fuller
Radiology M Chapman, B E Kendall, W Lees, R R Mason, M J Raphael, D Rickards
Radiotherapy and Oncology A Cassone, C A E Coulter, G Duchesne, R L Souhami, M F Spittle
Rheumatology and Rehabilitation M Corbett, J C W Edwards, D A Isenburg, F Middleton, M Shipley, M L Snaith, R A Sturge
Urology A G A Cowie, E J G Milroy, R W Turner-Warwick, P H L Worth
Virology R S Tedder

The National Hospital for Neurology and Neurosurgery

Queen Square, London WC1N 3BG
Tel: 020 7837 3611 Fax: 020 7829 8720
Total Beds: 244

Anaesthetics I Calder, N P Hirsch, G S Ingram, P R Nandi, M Smith, S R Wilson
Chemical Pathology J M Land, E J Thompson
ENT G B Brookes, H Ludman
General Psychiatry R J Dolan, K J Friston, M M Robertson, M A Ron, M R Trimble
Haematology P M Norman
Medical Microbiology P M Norman
Neurology J A Ball, D J Brooks, P Brown, L R A Clarke, J S Duncan, S Farmer, R S Frackowiak, P J Goadsby, R J Greenwood, A E Harding, M J G Harrison, R S Howard, R Kapoor, R S Kocen, A J Lees, W I McDonald, C D Marsden, C J Mathias, D H Miller, J A Morgan-Hughes, G T Plant, N P Quinn, M N Rossor, P Rudge, J W A Sander, J W Scadding, A H V Shapira, S P Shorvon, G M Stern, R A H Surtees, R J S Wise, N W Wood
Neuropathology D N Landon, T Revesz, F Scaravilli, M Thom
Neurophysiology D R Fish, N M F Murray, S J M Smith, B D Youl
Neurosurgery H A Crockard, W F J Harkness, R D Hayward, N D Kitchen, M P Powell, L Symon, D G T Thomas
Ophthalmology J F Acheson, E M Graham, P Riordan-Eva, M D Sanders
Otology G B Brookes, R A Davies, H Ludman, L M Luxon
Radiology D P E Kingsley, I F Moseley, J M Stevens, W J Taylor
Rehabilitation Medicine A J Thompson
Urology C J Fowler

Royal London Homoeopathic Hospital

66 Great Ormond Street, London WC1N 3HR
Tel: 020 7837 8833 Fax: 020 7833 7229
Total Beds: 6

University College Hospital

Grafton Way, London WC1E 3BG
Tel: 020 7387 9300
Website: www.uclh.org.
Total Beds: 63

Accident and Emergency H Baderman
Anaesthetics R F Armstrong, B A Astley, R Greenbaum, E M Grundy, G A Ingram, L Kaufman, S L Lincoln, J Ormrod, J S Secker-Walker, P J Verrill, S D Woods
Bacteriology R N Gruneberg, G L Ridgway, G Scott
Biochemistry D J Betteridge, D P Brenton

UNIVERSITY HOSPITALS COVENTRY & WARWICKSHIRE NHS TRUST

Cardiology J M Walker
Care of the Elderly K Arnold, J R Croker, G S Malone-Lee
Chemical Pathology F V Flynn, D A Gardner
Dermatology J J H Gilkes, T W E Robinson
Endocrinology M Katz, P J A Moult
Gastroenterology S G Bown, M Sarner, R Valori
General Medicine D J Betteridge, D P Brenton, S L Cohen, J R Croker, P Pacy, B N C Prichard, M Sarner, A W Segal, S G Spiro, R Valori, J M Walker
General Psychiatry B G Adams, H L Caplan, R M Fraser, P J Shoenberg, D A Sturgeon
General Surgery M Adiseshiah, C C R Bishop, P B Boulos, M Hobsley, A Marston, R C G Russell, J H Scurr
Genitourinary Medicine E Allason-Jones, A Robinson
Haematology A H Goldstone, J D M Richards
Neurology A J Lees, G M Stern
Obstetrics and Gynaecology H A Brant, G C L Lachelin, C H Rodeck, N Siddle, A C Silverstone, J A D Spencer, S J Steele, R H T Ward
Ophthalmology D J Brazier, J H Kelsey
Orthopaedics J P Cobb, M A Edgar, A O Ransford
Paediatric Surgery V M Wright
Paediatrics A M Kilby, E O R Reynolds, J C L Shaw, A Stewart, D Walters, J S Wyatt
Pathology M H Griffiths, P G Isaacson
Pharmacology C W I Owens, B N C Prichard
Plastic Surgery M D Brough, B Jones, D A McGrowther, B D G Morgan
Radiology M Chapman, P Renton, P J Shaw, B M Thomas, K M Walmsley
Radiotherapy and Oncology J N Godlee, R L Souhami, J S Tobias
Rheumatology and Rehabilitation D A Isenberg, F Middleton, M L Snaith
Thoracic Medicine M R Hetzel, S Semple, S G Spiro
Vascular Surgery M Adiseshiah, A G A Cowie, E J G Milroy, P H L Worth

University Hospital Birmingham NHS Trust

Trust Headquarters, PO Box 9551, Main Drive, Queen Elizabeth Medical Centre, Edgbaston, Birmingham B15 2PR
Tel: 0121 432 3232 Fax: 0121 627 8201
(Birmingham and the Black Country Health Authority)

Chair John Charlton
Chief Executive Mark Britnell

Queen Elizabeth Hospital

Queen Elizabeth Medical Centre, Birmingham B15 2TH
Tel: 0121 472 1311, 0121 627 2202
Total Beds: 550

Anaesthetics J F Bion, L Blaney, M I Bowden, M D Brewin, M Clapmam, T H Clutton-Bruck, G M Cooper, I F Duncan, M H Farooqui, J Freeman, T Gallagher, G Geskins, G R Harrison, A C Hill, N Huggins, P Hutton, J Isaac, A P F Jackson, M Knowles, M Lewis, J P Lilley, A D Malins, P Moor, J Moysey, N Murphy, M Nicholas, A Patel, R Riddle, S Riddlington, M Rosser, S H Russel, J L Shah, M Suchak, A J Sutcliffe, D Turfrey, S Walia, J M Watt, M Wilkes, A D Wilkey, M Wilson, J Xifaris
Bacteriology I Das, T J Elliott, J G M Hastings
Cardiology R A Bonser, N Buller, M Davies, M D Gammage, T Graham, M Griffiths, W Littler, H Marshall, S Thorne, J N Townend, J C Wilson
Cardiothoracic Surgery R S Bonser, D Pagano, S Rooney, B E Keogh
Care of the Elderly E Dunstan, A Main, P Mayer, P P Mayer
Consultants R Cramb
Dental Surgery H D Edmondson, J W Frame, M J C Wake

General Medicine R N Allan, A J Franklyn, A Franklyn, D A Heath, M Kendall, M Nattress, M C Sheppard, P Stewart, R A Stockley, M A Waite
General Surgery A D Barnes, J A C Buckels, L J Buist, N J Dorricott, D England, J R F Fielding, M Hallisey, M Keighley, D Kumar, A D Mayer, P Stewart, J G Temple
Genitourinary Medicine M Hrensberg, J Ross, M Shahmanesh
Haematology R Chakraverty, C Craddock, H Doughty, I R Franklin, F G H Hill, P Mahendra, P Moss, J Stuart, J Wilde
Immunology I C M McLennon
Neurology J M Anderson, P C Barber, C Barraclough, R N Corston, D A Francis, T Heaffield, D J Jamieson, P J McDonnell, R Mitchell, A P Mocroft, K Morrison, S Nightingale, H Pall, J A Spillar, E Stusman, A Williams, J Winer
Neurophysiology J E Fox, D E Rao
Neurosurgery G S Cruickshank, G Flint, S Harland, A D Hockley, C Meyer, S Sgouros, A R Walsh, J Wasserberg
Occupational Health A Robertson
Otolaryngology A B Drake-Lee, A D Gupta, A Johnson, D W Proops
Pathology P Barber, A R Bradwell, R Harrison, A J Howie, S G Hubscher, E L Jones, D I Rushton, H Thompson, J Young
Plastic Surgery C Kat, N Moleman, R Papini, J Peart, G Titley
Radiology G M Allen, N C Chokshi, J R Lee, I McCafferty, J Ollif, S Ollif, P I Riley, E B Rolfe, H Skene Smith, J R West, D A Yates
Radiotherapy and Oncology V R Archer, A J Banks, A Chetiywardana, S Darby, I Fernando, D Ferry, C Foule, I Geh, J Glaholm, P Guest, N James, D Kerr, T N Latief, J J Mould, Dr Pearce, D Spooner, A Stevens, D J Tattersall
Rheumatology P Bacon
Urology A J Arnold, D J Fariar, M A Hughes, A J Manning, D M A Wallace

Selly Oak Hospital

Raddlebarn Road, Birmingham B29 6JD
Tel: 0121 627 1627 Fax: 0121 627 8214
Total Beds: 450

Anaesthetics M Arif, C V Bonnici, S Burnley, P J M Clifton, G Dickson, M Ghoris, A Jackson, M King, F Levins, D Malins, M Manji, T Millins, P L Riddell, J Shal, J E M Smith, H Wilkey, P Wood
Cardiology R E Nagle
Care of the Elderly E J Dunstan, A N H Main, P P Mayer
Dental Surgery P Pracey
Dermatology C Hodgson, H Lewis, J Marsden, D Stewart
General Medicine M H B Carmalt, R Cockel, F Dunne, K Kane, U Martin, P Mayer, M Miller, H Morrison, M M Page
General Psychiatry A H Ogden
General Surgery D Campbell, N Dorricott, T Ismail, M H Simms, S Smith
Haematology J A Murray
Neurology H Pall, A C Williams, J B Winer
Neurophysiology J A Finnegan
Occupational Health A Robertson
Ophthalmology M Burdon, G Kirby, T Matthews, P J McDonald, R Scott, M Tsaloumus
Orthopaedics E Alpour, J P Cooper, M Craigen, M Green, D Learmouth, J Plewes, K M Porter, R S Sneath, A Thomas, O Tubbs, M Waldram
Otolaryngology I Donaldson, P Johnson, J R M Moore, P Pracey, A P Reid, P Talati
Plastic Surgery D Murray, J D Nancarrow, R Waters
Radiology M Alner, S Bradley, N C Chokshi, M J Duddy, V R Kale, C Walker
Rheumatology P A Bacon, P Jobanputra, R W Jubb, E Rankin, D S, T R Southwood
Urology D J Farrar

University Hospitals Coventry and Warwickshire NHS Trust

Clifford Bridge Road, Walsgrave, Coventry CV2 2DX
Tel: 024 7660 2020 Fax: 024 7662 2197

NHS TRUSTS & NHS HOSPITALS

(Coventry, Warwickshire, Herefordshire and Worcestershire Health Authority)

Chair Gary Reay
Chief Executive David Loughton

Coventry and Warwickshire Hospital

Stoney Stanton Road, Coventry CV1 4FH
Tel: 024 7622 4055 Fax: 024 7622 1655
Total Beds: 250

Accident and Emergency A Alchalabi, S Vlachtsis
Biochemistry H Griffiths
Chest Disease C V P Lawford
Genitourinary Medicine A A H Wade
Haematology R I Harris, M J Strevens
Medical Microbiology R M Hutton, P R Mortimer
Neurosurgery P Stanworth, W Whatmore
Ophthalmology N E Brown, L Butler, I G Calder, A J Chadwick, T J Fetherston, M Handscombe, R D Kumar, T Vythilingham
Oral and Maxillofacial Surgery J Burland, J M Fagan, I Moule
Orthodontics C P Briggs, N A E Robertson
Orthopaedics M J Aldridge, M E Blakemore, J Clegg, W F Merriam, P Roberts, S Turner, P Wade, P E H Wilson
Plastic Surgery A R Groves, R N Matthews

Coventry Maternity Hospital

Walsgrave, Coventry CV2 2DX
Tel: 024 7660 2020
Total Beds: 231

Obstetrics and Gynaecology L J S Cassia, K A Cietak, C R Kennedy, M F Reed
Paediatrics S M Brown, J G Davies, E E Jones, S McNamara

Hospital of St Cross

Adrivals Court, 37 Nelson Way, Bilton, Rugby CV22 7LW
Tel: 01788 572831 Fax: 01788 545151
Total Beds: 180

Anaesthetics P Kai, S Nethisinghe, J R Parker, A Singh
Cardiology M Been
Cardiothoracic Surgery R Norton
Dental Surgery I Moule
Dermatology D I Porter
ENT A Curry, P L Kander
General Medicine A K Basu, P I Biggs, R F Gunstone, D Loft
General Psychiatry S Thavasothy
General Surgery A A J D'Sa, G A G Mogg, T A Waterworth
Genitourinary Medicine Dr Walzman
Haematology A Abdul-Cader
Neurology J R Ponsford
Obstetrics and Gynaecology L P Harvey, A D Parsons
Ophthalmology A J Chadwick
Orthodontics N A Robertson
Orthopaedics S N Deliyannis, A W Hughes
Plastic Surgery A Groves, R N Matthews
Radiology J Aaron, D M Alexander, J Chandy, N Hadid
Radiotherapy and Oncology R J Grieve
Rheumatology G R Struthers

Walsgrave Hospital

Clifford Bridge Road, Walsgrave, Coventry CV2 2DX
Tel: 024 7660 2020 Fax: 024 7662 2197
Total Beds: 1015

Anaesthetics N Bhasin, T Bhatti, M D Boobyer, E Borman, F Choksey, K C Clayton, R Elton, G Evans, K Evans, A Frost, M Holt, R S C Howell, R A Johnson, C J Knickenberg, W McCulloch, M Mead, C Mendonca, P Mulrooney, J S Perks, A Phillips, S Radhakrisna, A Scase, J Sherwin, A Singh, E A Taylor, A Thacker, M Wyse
Breast Surgery B Ackroyd, A Al-Dabbagh, S Habib, T A Waterworth
Cardiology M Been, R K Mattu, M F Shiu, H Singh

Cardiothoracic Surgery N Briffa, W R Dimitri, R Norton, R Patel, M D Rosin
Chest Disease R Bell
Colorectal Surgery N Williams
Dermatology J Berth-Jones, B Dharmagunawarden, A Ilchyshyn
ENT A P Bath, P Kander, P Patel
Gastroenterology M Aldersley, D Loft, C Nwokolo
General Medicine N R Balcombe, R Bell, P I Biggs, L J Booth, A Chaudhry, D P Dhillon, E Hillhouse, I D Khan, M Khan, P Lawford, J R Lismore, A J Sinclair, F P Vince
General Surgery A J Barros D'Sa, A R E Blacklock, K Desai, I Fraser, D Higman, C Imray, S H Kashi, F T Lam, R W Parker, A Rhodes, P N Roberts, M Wills
Haematology R I Harris, N Jackson, M J Strevens
Histopathology K Chen, S Ferryman, T Guha, J Macartney, P Matthews, M Newbold, T Rollason, J Snead
Intensive Care S Evans, S Jayaratnasingam, B Murphy, I Tsagurnis, D Watson
Medical Microbiology M Weinbren
Nephrology D C Dukes, M Edmunds, R Higgins, S Kashi
Neurology A Grubneac, J R Ponsford, A Shehu
Neurophysiology R Paul
Neurosurgery M Choksey, M Christie, P Stanworth
Obstetrics and Gynaecology A Anyanwu, K A Cietak, L Farrall, K Goswami, S Keay, C Kennedy, S Thornton, P Vanderkerckhove, L J Wood
Oncology I Bown, R Das, R Grieve, M Hocking, C Irwin, D Jones, S Sothi, A Stockdale
Orthopaedics I Dunn
Paediatrics M Al-Moudaris, K Blake, N G Coad, A Coe, E Simmonds, H Stirling
Palliative Medicine M Barnett, A Franks, R Walker
Pathology T Ashworth, K Chen, T Guha
Radiology T T Aye, D J Beale, S K Bera, J Chandy, A Duncan, D Durrani, T Goodfellow, C Oliver, M P Patel, P D Phelps, R Rattenhali, W Shatwell, K Sherlala, A Vohrah, R Wellings
Radiotherapy and Oncology R N Das, R J Grieve, D A Jones, A Stockdale
Rehabilitation Medicine N Brain
Renal Medicine D Dukes, M Edmunds, S Fletcher, R Higgins, A Stein
Rheumatology and Rehabilitation M Allen, J S Coppock, P Perkins, G R Struthers
Urology A R E Blacklock, K M Desai, K Prasad, M Wills

University Hospitals of Leicester NHS Trust

Glenfield Hospital, Groby Road, Leicester LE3 9QP
Tel: 0116 287 1471 Fax: 0116 258 3950
Website: www.uhl-tr.nhs.uk
(Leicestershire, Northamptonshire and Rutland Health Authority)

Chair Phillip Hammersley
Chief Executive Peter Reading

Glenfield Hospital

Groby Road, Leicester LE3 9QP
Tel: 0116 287 1471 Fax: 0116 258 3950
Total Beds: 520

Anaesthetics M E Bone, A G H Cole, B Collett, D J R Duthie, M Jones, D G Lewis, E S Lin, I McLellan, K Mobley, N Moore, R Rousseau, J Swanevelder, S Taylor, T Trotter, K West, R Wyatt
Cardiology D d Bono, C J Garratt, A H Gershlick, P J Hubner, N J Samani, D J Skehan
Cardiothoracic Surgery R K Firmin, M S J Hickey, J N Leverment, A Sosnowski, T J Spyt
Care of the Elderly R F Bing, J S deCaestecker, G Fancourt, M D Fotherby, J Potter, J Ward
General Surgery A W Hall, D Rew, A D N Scott, A Stotter, R Windle

Integrated Medicine R F Bing, J De Caestecker, G J Fancourt, M D Fotherby, J F Potter, J W Ward
Orthodontics R F Deans, T G Leggatt, F A Mackay, R Samuels
Orthopaedics J J Dias, W M Harper, O Oni, R A Power, G Taylor, H Thomas, P Triffitt
Paediatric Cardiology K C Chan, R Leanage
Paediatrics Z Slavik
Radiology A Crozier, H Daintith, N Hudson, K Jeyapalan, R Keal, C Reek
Respiratory Medicine J B Cookson, M D Morgan, J M Wales, A J Wardlaw
Restorative Dentistry R F Deans, T G Leggat, F A Mackay, R H A Samuels

Leicester General Hospital

Gwendolen Road, Leicester LE5 4PW
Tel: 0116 249 0490 Fax: 0116 258 4666
Total Beds: 680

Anaesthetics S Coley, J M Hampson, C D Hanning, D E Hoffler, I Jeyapalan, N King, D G Lewis, P Rabey, D G Raitt, P Spiers, C M Stray, O Williams
Care of the Elderly C M Castleden, D M R Jackett, N Lo, S Parker, R J Shepherd, T R Vallance
General Medicine A C Burden, P Critchley, R Gregory, J F Mayberry, R Oldham, J E F Pohl, A Scriven, M A Stern, A C B Wicks
General Surgery W W Barrie, M Dennis, A Dennison, M J Kelly, S Macpherson, M Nicholson, P S Veitch
Immunology M A Stern
Nephrology S Carr, J Feehally, K Harris, J Walls, G Warwick
Obstetrics and Gynaecology R M Graham, P Kirwan, C Mayne, H Narayan, G M Smith, C R Stewart
Orthopaedics M Allen, R N Chan, Q Cox, T Green, M L Harding, J Hoskinson, J M Jones, C Kershaw, R A Richardson, P Sell
Paediatrics A Elias-Jones, E W Hoskyns
Pathology P Furness, R Iqbal, E H Mackay, K O'Reilly
Radiology D Bruce, P Emberton, K A Mulcahy, C Newland, Y Rees, E M Watkins
Rehabilitation Medicine P Critchley
Rheumatology R Oldham
Urology J T Flynn, D E Osborn, D Sandhu, T R Terry

The Leicester Royal Infirmary

Infirmary Square, Leicester LE1 5WW
Tel: 0116 254 1414 Fax: 0116 258 5631
Total Beds: 1107

Accident and Emergency G G Bodiwala, P Evans, D Quinton
Anaesthetics R Atcheson, D F Baigent, B J Collett, B R Cotton, A E De Melo, R J Eastley, D Fell, M R Ferguson, J Grief, R H James, G W Jones, R L J Kohn, I McLaren, A E May, M Mushambi, T M O'Carroll, M L Pepperman, D J Rowbotham, W Russell, T A Samuels, G Smith, S W J Theophilus, J Thompson, K Tighe, D A B Turner, J G Wandless, M Wellstood-Eason
Audiological Medicine J R Moloney
Care of the Elderly M Ardron, J Davis, D R Ives, A Miodrag
Chemical Pathology S J Iqbal, J Lunec, W M Madira, F Smith
Clinical Pharmacology and Therapeutics D B Barnett, S R J Maxwell, L L Ng
Dermatology D A Burns, R D R Camp, R A C Graham-Brown, P E Hutchinson
ENT J Cook, T A Jones, A A Moir, G Murty, A A Narula, R S A Thomas
Gastroenterology J Nightingale, B J Rathbone
General Medicine M Davies, T A Howlett, P McNally, H Thurston, B Williams
General Surgery P R F Bell, N W Everson, D P Fossard, D Hemmingway, J M S Johnstone, D Lloyd, N London, R Naylor, S Nour, D F L Watkin
Genetics M Barrow, R C Trembath
Genitourinary Medicine P G Fisk, V C Riley, P C Schober
Haematology C S Chapman, R M Hutchinson, V E Mitchell, J K Wood

Histopathology D C Bouch, L J Brown, A Fletcher, C Kendall, I Lauder, P A McKeever, C Moffat, S Muller, P A V Shaw, R A Walker, K P West
Immunology M Browning, K Whaley
Infectious Diseases K G Nicolson, K Wiselka
Medical Microbiology C Morris, S H Myint, R A Swann
Neurology R J Abbott, M Lawden, I F Pye
Obstetrics and Gynaecology A Azzawi, R C S Chazal, A Davidson, A Halligan, D Ireland, N J Naftalin, R W Neuberg, C Oppenhiemer, Dr Taylor
Ophthalmology D J Austin, K Bibby, J M Cappin, G Fahy, D B Goustine, W Karwatowski, P P Ray-Chaudhuri, J H Sandford-Smith, G H A Woodruff
Oral Surgery J Hayter
Orthopaedics C Kershaw
Paediatrics S Bohin, E Carter, D P Field, M Green, F Harris, A Holton, P Houtman, C Howarth, D K Luyt, S Nichani, C O'Callaghan, R S Shannon, M Silverman, P G F Swift
Plastic Surgery H P Henderson, T Milward, S K Varma, D Ward
Radiology A A Bolia, G R Cherryman, D B L Finlay, K C Krarup, A Liddicoat, N Messios, A Rickett, L Robinson, P M Rodgers, D J Wilcock
Radiotherapy S Khanna, F J F Madden, J K O'Byrne, I M Peat, N Rudd, W Steward, S Vasanthan
Rheumatology and Rehabilitation F E Nichol, S Roy, A Samanta, P Sheldon

Uttlesford Primary Care Trust

John Tasker House, 56 New Street, Great Dunmow CM6 1BH
Tel: 01371 878295 Fax: 01371 875070
(Essex Health Authority)

Chair David Barron
Chief Executive Peta Wilkinson

Vale of Aylesbury Primary Care Trust

Manor House, Bierton Road, Aylesbury HP20 1RG
Tel: 01296 504200 Fax: 01296 504642
(Thames Valley Health Authority)

Chair Avril Davies
Chief Executive Shaun Brogan

Wakefield and Pontefract Community Health NHS Trust

Closing April 2002 - Services transferring to South West Yorkshire Mental Health NHS Trust.

Trust HQ, Fieldhead, Ouchthorpe Lane, Wakefield WF1 3SP
Tel: 01924 327000 Fax: 01924 327021
(West Yorkshire Health Authority)

Chair Roy Widdowson
Chief Executive Ray A Wilk

Aberford Centre for Psychiatry

Ouchthorpe Lane, Wakefield WF1 3SP
Total Beds: 82

General Psychiatry C A Cruickshank

Castleford, Normanton and District Hospital

Castleford WF10 5LT
Tel: 01977 605500 Fax: 01977 605501
Total Beds: 24

Child and Adolescent Psychiatry M Kay
Psychiatry of Old Age I Hammad
Public Health Medicine R S Thiagarajah

NHS TRUSTS & NHS HOSPITALS

Fieldhead Hospital
Ouchthorpe Lane, Wakefield WF1 3SP
Tel: 01924 327000 Fax: 01924 327021
Total Beds: 199

Learning Disabilities L F A Silva

Pontefract General Infirmary
Friarwood Lane, Pontefract WF8 1PL
Tel: 01977 600600

Southmoor Hospital
Southmoor Road, Hemsworth, Pontefract WF9 4LU
Tel: 01977 610661
Total Beds: 15

Stanley Royd Hospital
Aberford Road, Wakefield WF1 4DQ
Tel: 01924 201688
Total Beds: 353

Wakefield West Primary Care Trust
Thornhill Street, Wakefield WF1 1NL
Tel: 01924 213010 Fax: 01924 213157
(West Yorkshire Health Authority)

Chair William Barker
Chief Executive Alastair Geldhart

Walsall Community Health NHS Trust

Trust closure tbc - Part of service transferring to Walsall Primary Care Trust.

Upland House, 5 Lichfield Road, Walsall WS4 2HT
Tel: 01922 858000 Fax: 01922 858477
(Birmingham and the Black Country Health Authority)

Chair Elisabeth Buggins
Chief Executive Alistair Howie

Bloxwich Hospital
Reeves Street, Bloxwich, Walsall WS3 3JJ
Tel: 01922 858600 Fax: 01922 858639
Total Beds: 40

Dorothy Pattison Hospital
Alumwell Close, Walsall WS2 9XH
Tel: 01922 858000 Fax: 01922 858085

Kings Hill Day Hospital
School Street, Wednesbury WS10 9JB
Tel: 0121 526 4405

Mossley Day Hospital
Sneyd Lane, Bloxwich, Walsall WS3 2LW
Tel: 01922 858680

Walsall Hospitals NHS Trust
Manor Hospital, Moat Road, Walsall WS2 9PS
Tel: 01922 721172 Fax: 01922 656621
(Birmingham and the Black Country Health Authority)

Chair B Blower
Chief Executive John Rostill

Goscote Hospital
Goscote Lane, Walsall WS3 1SJ
Tel: 01922 710710 Fax: 01922 712195

Total Beds: 131

Care of the Elderly R W S Brookes, S Panayiotou, S K Sinha, M N Zaman

Manor Hospital
Walsall WS2 9PS
Tel: 01922 721172 Fax: 01922 656621
Total Beds: 641

Anaesthetics F D Babatula, K Balachander, I P Hudecek, H Ianny, M A Kettern, C Newson, H Sinha, M S Youssef
Care of the Elderly R W S Brookes, B Panayiotou, S K Sinha, M Zaman
Dental Surgery Dr Larkin
Dermatology K S Ryatt
ENT D M East, N Turner
General Medicine I Ahmad, A Alalaf, V P Balagopal, T J Constable, M Cox, A R Cunnington, S Dean, T C Harvey, R C Joshi, A Palejwala, M Payne, M Payne, D B Trash, A Wright
General Surgery A Khan, G Little, K D F Mayer, T J Muscroft, J Stewart
Genitourinary Medicine Dr Joseph
Haematology G Galvin
Neurology D A Francis
Obstetrics and Gynaecology C Balachandar, M J Browne, A C Head, S Panda, J Pepper, R Reddy
Ophthalmology P G J Corridan, Dr Sandromouli, S Shin, Dr Yang
Orthodontics J W Ferguson
Orthopaedics G Alo, M A A Khan, T Sadique, Dr Shoaib
Paediatrics U M Chidrawar, D Drew, A R Gatrad, B J Muhammad, G P Sinha
Pathology C Allen, G P Galvin, P D Giles, Z A Hassam, Y L Hock
Radiology E R Allan, C L Holland, H Rai, M G Thuse
Radiotherapy and Oncology A D Chetiyawardana

Walsall Primary Care Trust
Kingfisher Medical Centre, 65 Fisher Street, Willenhall WV13 2HT
Tel: 01902 606303 Fax: 01902 606333
Website: www.walsall.wmids.nhs.uk/pct/
(Birmingham and the Black Country Health Authority)

Chair Dennis Ray
Chief Executive A Howie

Walthamstow, Leyton and Leytonstone Primary Care Trust
Beckett House, 12-14 Ilford Hill, Ilford IG1 2QX
Tel: 020 8926 5236 Fax: 020 8926 5204
Website: www.walthamstow-pct.nhs.uk
(North East London Health Authority)

Chair Joan Saddler
Chief Executive Sally Gorham

Walton Centre for Neurology and Neurosurgery NHS Trust
Lower Lane, Fazakerley, Liverpool L9 7LJ
Tel: 0151 525 3611 Fax: 0151 529 5500
(Cheshire and Merseyside Health Authority)

Chair Joyce Brittain
Chief Executive Kate Abendstern

Wandsworth Primary Care Trust
1 Belleville Road SW11 6QS
Tel: 020 7585 2302 Fax: 020 7585 2358

(South West London Health Authority)

Chair Melba Wilson
Chief Executive Helen Walley

Warrington Community Health Care NHS Trust

Clsoing April 2002 - Specialist services transferring to 5 Borough Partnership NHS Trust; part of service transferring to Warrington Primary Care Trust.

Hollins Park House, Hollins Lane, Winwick, Warrington WA2 8WA
Tel: 01925 664000 Fax: 01925 664052
Email: hq@warrington-health.co.uk
(Cheshire and Merseyside Health Authority)

Chair John Gartside
Chief Executive Laura McMurtrie

Hollins Park

Hollins Park House, Hollins Lane, Winwick, Warrington WA2 8WA
Tel: 01925 664000 Fax: 01925 664052
Email: hq@warrington.health.co.uk
Total Beds: 196

General Psychiatry M N Agnew, M Al-Asady, M Al-Bachari, B C Bende, S A Bokhari, N Brook, H Ranasinghe, E A Salib, E A Sunderashain

Warrington Primary Care Trust

Woolston Clinic, Holes Lane, Woolston, Warrington WA1 4NE
Tel: 01925 811058 Fax: 01925 813986
Chair Robin Brown
Chief Executive Tim Deeprose

Warwickshire Ambulance Service NHS Trust

Dale Street, Leamington Spa CV32 5HH
Tel: 01926 881331 Fax: 01926 488409
(Coventry, Warwickshire, Herefordshire and Worcestershire Health Authority)

Chair Michael Langman
Chief Executive Malcolm J Hazell

Watford and Three Rivers Primary Care Trust

1A High Street, Rickmansworth WD3 1ET
Tel: 01923 713050 Fax: 01923 718921
Website: www.watford3r-pct.nhs.uk
(Bedfordshire and Hertfordshire Health Authority)

Chair Pam Handley
Chief Executive Felicity Cox

Waveney Primary Care Trust

Beccles Hospital, St Mary's Road, Beccles NR34 9NQ
Website: www.lowestoft-pct.nhs.uk
(Norfolk, Suffolk and Cambridgeshire Health Authority)

Chair Carol Sherriff
Chief Executive Peter Horbury

Wednesbury and West Bromwich Primary Care Trust

Kingston House, 438-450 High Street, West Bromwich B70 9LD
Tel: 0121 500 1593 Fax: 0121 500 1604
(Birmingham and the Black Country Health Authority)

Welwyn Hatfield Primary Care Trust

Charter House, Parkway, Welwyn Garden City
Tel: 01707 361217 Fax: 01707 361286
Website: www.welwyn-hatfield-pct.nhs.uk
(Bedfordshire and Hertfordshire Health Authority)

Chair Carol Sherriff
Chief Executive Peter Horbury

West Cumbria Primary Care Trust

Staff Hostel, West Cumberland Hospital, Hensingham, Whitehaven CA28 8JG
Tel: 01946 523806 Fax: 01946 523803
(Cumbria and Lancashire Health Authority)

Chair Patrick Everingham
Chief Executive Veronica Marsden

West Dorset General Hospitals NHS Trust

Dorset County Hospital, Williams Avenue, Dorchester DT1 2JY
Tel: 01305 251150 Fax: 01305 254155
Email: (name)@dorch.wdgh-tr.swest.nhs.uk
Website: www.dch.org.uk
(Somerset and Dorset Health Authority)

Chief Executive Nicholas Chapman
Consultants R Clifford, G Gallimore, R Purvis, S Stanley, W Ward, Dr Wylie

Dorset County Hospital

Williams Avenue, Dorchester DT1 2JY
Tel: 01305 251150 Fax: 01305 254155
Total Beds: 563

Accident And Emergency D Cain
Anaesthesia (ICU) D S Andrew, Dr Ball, T Doyle, R Foxell, K J Gill, R Hebblethwaite, M Hitchcock, N Hollis, M Hough, J Wilson
Cardiology T Edwards, S Winterton
Care of the Elderly A Blake, Dr Bruce-Jones, A Webb, R Williams
Clinical Chemist K Wakelin
Clinical Neurophysiology C Wulff
Dermatology S Tucker
ENT H Cox, G Ford, N Hopkin
General Medicine Dr Cove, P Down, C Hovell, A Macklin, G Philips
Genitourinary Medicine C Priestly
Haematology M Al-Hilali, Dr Moosa
Histopathology A M Anscombe, D Parums
Microbiology S Crook, S Groom
Nephrology N Hateboer, C Weston
Obstetrics and Gynaecology B Ahmed, M Dooley, M Iftikhar
Ophthalmology L Bray, T Pathmanathan, G Porter, A Reck, A Tadros
Oral Surgery V Ilankovan
Orthodontics H Bellis, D Shinn, M Short
Orthopaedics/Trauma I Barlow, N Fernandez, G Hall, C Thacker
Paediatrics J Doherty

NHS TRUSTS & NHS HOSPITALS

Radiology P Camm, A Johnson, J Lesny, C Orgles, S Scott, N Smith, P N Taylor
Renal Medicine J Taylor
Rheumatology M Helliwell
Surgery A Flowerdew, C Gosling, M Graham, P Jeffery, N Lagatolla
Urology A Cornaby

West Gloucestershire Primary Care Trust

Units 14-15, Highnam Business Park, Newent Road, Highnam, Gloucester GL2 8DN
Tel: 01452 389400 Fax: 01452 389429
(Avon, Gloucestershire and Wiltshire Health Authority)

Chair Liz Boait
Chief Executive Stephen Golledge

West Hampshire NHS Trust

Maples Building, Horseshoe Drive, Tatchbury Mount, Calmore, Southampton SO40 2RZ
Tel: 023 8087 4300 Fax: 023 8087 4301
Chair Jonathan Montgomery
Chief Executive Martin Barkley

Alcohol Advisory Day Hospital

63 Romsey Road, Winchester SO22 5DG
Tel: 01962 825071 Fax: 01962 824247

The Beacon Centre

The Fairway, Barton On Sea, New Milton BH25 7AE
Tel: 01425 623802 Fax: 01425 627803

Community Mental Health Team and Day Hospital

Connaught House, 63B Romsey Road, Winchester SO22 5DE
Tel: 01962 825128 Fax: 01962 825280

Crane Ward

Old Manor Hospital, Wilton Road, Salisbury SP2 7EP
Tel: 01722 336262 Ext: 3143 Fax: 01722 425165

The Croft

Badger Farm Road, Winchester SO22 4JG
Tel: 01962 863511 Ext: 404
Total Beds: 8

Department of Psychiatry

Royal South Hants Hospital, Brintons Terrace, Off St Mary's Road, Southampton SO14 0YG
Tel: 023 8063 4288 Fax: 023 8023 3189

Leigh House Hospital

Cuckoo Bushes Lane, Chandlers Ford, Eastleigh SO53 1JY
Tel: 023 8025 2418 Fax: 023 8027 0733
Total Beds: 15

Melbury Lodge

Royal Hampshire County Hospital, Romsey Road, Winchester SO22 5DG
Tel: 01962 825507 Fax: 01962 825512

Ravenswood House

Medium Secure Unit, Fareham PO17 5NA
Tel: 01329 836000 Fax: 01329 834780

St Waleric (Psychogeriatric Day Hospital)

Park Road, Winchester SO23 7BE
Tel: 01962 841941 Fax: 01962 841590

War Memorial Community Hospital, Day Hospital and Day Surgery Unit

Charlton Road, Andover SP10 3LB
Tel: 01264 835273 Fax: 01264 351424
Total Beds: 10

Weyhill Road Mental Handicap Unit

4 Weyhill Road, Andover SP10 3AA
Tel: 01264 53433
Total Beds: 8

Wolversdene Road

8 Wolversdene Road, Andover SP10 2AX
Tel: 01264 58631
Total Beds: 8

West Hertfordshire Hospitals NHS Trust

Watford General Hospital, 60 Vicarage Road, Watford WD1 8HB
Fax: 01923 217908
(Bedfordshire and Hertfordshire Health Authority)

Chair Rosie Sanderson
Chief Executive Stephen Eames

Hemel Hempstead General Hospital

Hillfield Road, Hemel Hempstead HP2 4AD
Tel: 01442 213141
Total Beds: 387

Accident and Emergency A Marchon
Anaesthetics M T T Bryant, F J Griffiths, M E Pickering-Pick, W Yanny
Care of the Elderly R R Farag
Dermatology P D L Maurice
ENT H K K Bail, J A Harding
General Medicine I G Barrison, J F J Bayliss, C Johnston
General Surgery J C Nicholls, M Ormiston
Neurology J Gibbs
Obstetrics and Gynaecology J L Kane, D A Rosenberg, Y Tayob
Ophthalmology R N Auplish
Orthodontics L R O Hale
Orthopaedics J P Beacon, G M Hart, D Hirschowitz
Paediatrics B K Lee, H e Naggar
Pathology Dr Gaminara, A P O'Reilly
Radiology B V Clegg, D P Grimer, D S Shetty
Radiotherapy and Oncology E J Grosch
Rheumatology and Rehabilitation M A Wajed
Thoracic Medicine A R Nath

Mount Vernon Hospital

Rickmansworth Road, Northwood HA6 2RN
Tel: 01923 826111 Fax: 01923 844460
Total Beds: 144

Anaesthetics A Arnold, J Binns, P M Brodrick, K Collins, A Hayward, D Mills, D K Patel, E Stielow
Care of the Elderly Dr Al-Douri, Dr Baruam, Dr Franklin
ENT R England, G W Glover
General Medicine T J Goodwin, R Hillson, G E Holdstock, J Pace, D W B Thomas, D Thomson
General Surgery P Mitchenere, T Paes, J E L Sales
Neurology R Peatfield
Obstetrics and Gynaecology V P Robinson
Oral and Maxillofacial Surgery G Bounds, G T Gardiner, M Issa
Orthodontics J Noar
Orthopaedics G Belham, W N Bodey, J Dooley, N Reissis
Palliative Medicine L Bangham, I Trotman
Pathology D J Allan, S Amin, W K Blenkinsopp, A Coady, D Cummins, P Mahendra, P I Richman, R Smith
Plastic Surgery P Cussons, D Gault, A Grobelaar, D H Harrison, B D G Morgan, R Sanders, P J Smith

Radiology A W Ayoub, H Baddeley, N Damani, P Dovey, M Rassa, W Wong

Radiotherapy and Oncology R F U Ashford, D C Fermont, R Glynne-Jones, E J Grosch, P Hoskin, P Lawton, B E Lyn, J Maher, A Makepeace, G Rustin, M Saunders

Urology M A Ruston

St Albans City Hospital

Normandy Road, St Albans AL3 5PN
Tel: 01727 866122
Total Beds: 187

Anaesthetics M T T Bryant, D U S Pathirana, W A Yanny

Care of the Elderly Dr Farag

Dental Surgery B C O'Riordan

Dermatology P D L Maurice

ENT H K K Bail

General Medicine I G Barrison, J F J Bayliss, C Johnston, I P Williams

General Surgery M C Ormiston, G R Sagor

Genitourinary Medicine J John

Neurology J M Gibbs

Obstetrics and Gynaecology J L Kane, D A Rosenberg, Y Tayob

Ophthalmology J F Tattersfield, M K Wang

Orthodontics A B Hewitt

Orthopaedics J P Beacon, D Hirschowitz

Paediatrics C M Gabriel

Pathology R L Abeyesundere, E J Gaminara, S F Hill

Plastic Surgery P J Smith

Radiology B V Clegg, D P Grimer, B E Hartley, D S Shetty, E Sheville

Radiotherapy and Oncology E Grosch

Rheumatology and Rehabilitation M A Wajed, K A Young

Watford General Hospital

Vicarage Road, Watford WD1 8HB
Tel: 01923 244366 Fax: 01923 217440
Total Beds: 383

Accident and Emergency H J Borkett-Jones, J Oliver

Anaesthetics G Baker, C P Lung, V Page, H M Parry, D R O Redman

Care of the Elderly M L Cox, A Sa'Adu, W Somerville

Dermatology M E Murdoch, F Tatnall

ENT R Auerbach, R Dhillon, R England

General Medicine M R Clements, E J Knight, B Macfarlane, G A Nelstrop, P R Studdy

General Surgery R W Awad, J I Livingstone, S Sarin, J M Thomas

Genitourinary Medicine P E Munday

Neurology G D Schott

Obstetrics and Gynaecology B E Bean, D R Griffin, L Irvine, B V Lewis, M Padwick, R Sheridan

Ophthalmology S Kodati, D Owen, R M Pearce, N Young

Oral and Maxillofacial Surgery G Bounds

Orthopaedics J Jessop, R P Mackenney

Paediatrics E Douek, G Supramaniam, M J H Williams

Pathology A McMillan, M T Moulsdale, A Rubin

Radiology D Boxer, B Gajjar, S Pathmanathan, T F E Sayed

Radiotherapy and Oncology R F U Ashford

Rheumatology and Rehabilitation N A Pandit

Urology J C Crisp

West Hull Primary Care Trust

Brunswick House, Strand Close, Beverley Road, Hull HU2 9DB
Tel: 01482 606644 Fax: 01482 606627
(North and East Yorkshire and Northern Lincolnshire Health Authority)

Chief Executive Graham Rich

West Kent NHS and Social Care Trust

Unit 7/8, Ambley Green, Gillingham Business Park, Gillingham ME8 0NJ
(Kent and Medway Health Authority)

West Lancashire Primary Care Trust

Ormskirk and District General Hospital, Wigan Road, Ormskirk L39 2JW
Tel: 01695 598084 Fax: 01695 598104
Website: www.westlancspct.nhs.uk
(Cumbria and Lancashire Health Authority)

Chair James Barton

Chief Executive Jane Thompson

West Lincolnshire Primary Care Trust

Cross O'Cliff, Bracebridge Heath, Lincoln LN4 2HN
Tel: 01522 513355 Fax: 01522 540706
(Trent Health Authority)

Chair Stanley Keyte

Chief Executive Vanessa Coomber

West London Mental Health NHS Trust

St Bernard's Hospital, Uxbridge Road, Southall UB1 3EU

Broadmoor Hospital

Broadmoor Hospital, Crowthorne RG45 7EG
Tel: 01344 773111 Fax: 01334 754388, 01334 773327
Total Beds: 483

West Middlesex University Hospital NHS Trust

Twickenham Road, Isleworth TW7 6AF
Tel: 020 8560 2121
(South West London Health Authority)

Chief Executive Gail Wannell

West Middlesex University Hospital

Twickenham Road, Isleworth TW7 6AF
Tel: 020 8560 2121
Total Beds: 427

Accident and Emergency M W Beckett, Z Mirza

Cardiology T Greenwood

Care of the Elderly B K Bhattacharyya, J Platt

Chest Disease A Winning

Dermatology Dr Michael, S Parker

ENT V Cumberworth, N Daly, A Robinson

General Medicine S Allard, M Anderson, J Cassar, C Collins, T W Greenwood, S P Kane, A Winning

General Surgery P Dawson, J Ramsay, H Rogers, R Vashist, R A L Young

Genitourinary Medicine D Asboe, D Daniels

Nephrology M Anderson, E Brown, C Collins, S Kane

Neurology R Pearce

Obstetrics and Gynaecology J M Baldwin, J S Fox, J Girling, E Owen

NHS TRUSTS & NHS HOSPITALS

Oral Surgery R G D Burr, R J Carr
Orthopaedics K Desai, N Nathan, F W N Paterson, H Zadeh
Paediatrics D Hafiz, V Hakeem, J Rangasami, D Ratnasinghe
Pathology R S Fink, R G Hughes, S Karim, M Kyi, M Sekhar, P A Thorpe
Radiology F Aref-Adib, C Miller, T Naunton-Morga, M Owen, C Ramsay, M Watson
Radiotherapy and Oncology M Spittle
Rheumatology S A Allard
Thoracic Surgery W J Fountain
Urology J Bellringer, J Ramsay

West Midlands Metropolitan Ambulance Service NHS Trust

4th Floor, Falcon House, 6 The Minories, Dudley DY2 8PN
Tel: 01384 215555 Fax: 01384 215559
Email: kay.cullen@wmas-tr.wmids.nhs.uk, emquiries@wmas-tr.wmids.nhs.uk
Website: www.wmas.org
(Birmingham and the Black Country Health Authority)

Chair Doug H Jinks
Chief Executive Barry M Johns

West Norfolk Primary Care Trust

St James', Exton's Road, King's Lynn PE30 5NU
Tel: 01553 816200 Fax: 01553 761104
Email: enquiries@westnorfolk-pct.nhs.uk
Website: www.westnorfolk-pct.nhs.uk
(Norfolk, Suffolk and Cambridgeshire Health Authority)

Chair Sheila Childerhouse
Chief Executive Hilary Daniels

West of Cornwall Primary Care Trust

Josiah Thomas Memorial Hall, Trevithick Road, Camborne TR14 8LQ
Tel: 01209 886533 Fax: 01209 886572
Website: www.cornwallhealth.org.uk
(South West Peninsula Health Authority)

Chair Ed Ferrett
Chief Executive Gina Brocklehurst

Camborne/Redruth Community Hospital

Barncoose Terrace, Redruth TR15 3ER
Tel: 01209 881688 Fax: 01209 881713
Total Beds: 72

Edward Hain Memorial Hospital

Albany Terrace, St Ives TR26 2BS
Tel: 01736 576100 Fax: 01736 576118
Total Beds: 14

Falmouth Hospital

Trescobeas Road, Falmouth TR11 2JA
Tel: 01326 434700 Fax: 01326 434769
Total Beds: 34

Helston Community Hospital

Meneage Road, Helston TR13 8DR
Tel: 01326 435800 Fax: 01326 435859
Total Beds: 34

Poltair Hospital

Heamoor, Penzance TR20 8SR
Tel: 01736 575570 Fax: 01736 575580
Total Beds: 26

St Mary's Hospital

Hugh Town, St Mary's
Tel: 01720 422392 Fax: 01720 423134
Total Beds: 14

West Suffolk Hospitals NHS Trust

Hardwick Lane, Bury St Edmunds IP33 2QZ
Tel: 01284 713000 Fax: 01284 701993
Website: www.wsufftrust.org.uk
(Norfolk, Suffolk and Cambridgeshire Health Authority)

Chair Veronica Worrall
Chief Executive John Parkes

Elderly Day Hospital

Walnuttree Hospital, Walnuttree Lane, Sudbury CO10 6BE
Tel: 01787 371404 Fax: 01787 371339

Care of the Elderly J Fasler, J S Greener, M G F Troup
Dermatology S J Handfield Jones
General Surgery T Justin, N Keeling, D O'Riordan
Ophthalmology K Jordan
Paediatrics D Mabin, H M Scott
Rheumatology D O'Reilly

Joyce Cockram Day Hospital

West Suffolk Hospital, Hardwick Lane, Bury St Edmunds IP33 2QZ
Tel: 01284 713560 Fax: 01284 701993

Newmarket Community Hospital

Exning Road, Newmarket CB8 7JG
Tel: 01638 564000 Fax: 01638 564068

Care of the Elderly A Nicholson, M G F Troup
Diabetes A N Wijineike
General Medicine G N W Kerrigan, J Majeed, D O'Reilly
General Surgery M Gaunt, D Lawrence
Obstetrics and Gynaecology M Judd, K Mattotuwa
Ophthalmology R J Lamb
Orthopaedics A August, W Schenk
Thoracic Medicine J M Schneerson
Urology C Kennedy

St Leonard's Hospital

Newton Road, Sudbury CO10 6RQ
Tel: 01787 371341 Fax: 01787 313977

Diabetes A N Wijineike
ENT P Axon
Obstetrics and Gynaecology R Giles, M Judd
Orthopaedics A Bedford, M Porteous, S Sjolin, M Wood

Thetford Cottage Hospital

Earls Road, Thetford IP24 2AD
Tel: 01842 752499 Fax: 01842 762035

Care of the Elderly M Troup
Dermatology S J Handfield-Jones
Diabetes A N Wijineike
ENT R Skibsted
General Medicine P Siklos
General Surgery T Justin, N Keeling
Obstetrics and Gynaecology R Giles, P Spencer
Ophthalmology A Ramsay
Orthopaedics A Bedford, M Porteous, S Sjolin, M Wood
Paediatrics Dr Evans, D Mabin
Rheumatology Dr Johansen
Urology J McLoughlin

West Suffolk Hospital

Hardwick Lane, Bury St Edmunds IP33 2QZ
Tel: 01284 71300
Total Beds: 650

Accident and Emergency M Sach, A Sauvage
Anaesthetics C N Adams, J E Boys, A Burns, A E Chow, P Chrispin, J Field, J Hall, Z Jafri, S S Lowe, K H Matheson, J Mauger, R Munglani, M Palmer, N Penfold, J Slade, J Urquhart
Cardiology E M Lee, D L Stone
Care of the Elderly J Fasler, J S Greener, A Nicholson, M G F Troup
Dermatology S J Handfield-Jones, R Jenkins
Diabetes J Clark, A N Wijineike
General Medicine I Aziz, J M Clarke, G N W Kerrigan, C Laroche, J Majeed, D O'Reilly, D Sharpstone, J M Shneerson, P W L Siklos
General Surgery T Justin, N Keeling, D Lawrence
Genitourinary Medicine S Edwards
Haematology P K Mehrotra, I Singer
Histopathology Dr Kamlesh, Dr Munthali
Neurology E Harper, E Harper
Obstetrics and Gynaecology R Giles, S Gull, K Hattotuwe, M Judd, P J Spencer
Ophthalmology K Jordan, R J Lamb, A Ramsay, A Vivian
Oral Surgery R Davies, R J Tate
Orthodontics R Davies
Orthopaedics A C August, A F Bedford, M Porteous, W Schenk, S Sjolin, M Wood
Paediatrics G L Briars, D Mabin, C M Noble-Jamieson, H M Scott, S Thompson
Radiology R Bannon, J S Cantlay, R Darrah, R J Godwin, J Guy, M MacFarlane, L Watson
Radiotherapy and Oncology D H Jones, M Moody, H Patterson
Rheumatology Dr Johansen
Thoracic Medicine C Laroche, J M Shneerson
Urology C L Kennedy, J McLoughlin

West Sussex Health and Social Care NHS Trust

Arundel Road, Worthing BN13 3EP

West Wiltshire Primary Care Trust

Unit B, Valentines, Epsom Square, White Horse Business Park, Trowbridge BA14 0XG
Tel: 01225 754453 Fax: 01225 754648
Website: www.westwiltshire-pcg.org.uk
(Avon, Gloucestershire and Wiltshire Health Authority)

Chair Angie Barker
Chief Executive Donna Stiles

Bradford-on-Avon Community Hospital

Berryfields, Bradford-on-Avon BA15 1TA
Tel: 01225 862975 Fax: 01225 867488
Total Beds: 15

Melksham Community Hospital

Spa Road, Melksham SN15 3AL
Tel: 01225 703088 Fax: 01225 708301, 01225 764334
Total Beds: 24

Trowbridge Community Hospital

Adcroft Road, Trowbridge BA14 8PH
Tel: 01225 752558 Fax: 01225 764334
Total Beds: 45

Warminster Community Hospital

The Close, Warminster BA12 8QS
Tel: 01985 212076 Fax: 01985 846286
Total Beds: 24

Westbury Community Hospital

Hospital Road, The Butts, Westbury BA13 3EL
Tel: 01373 823616 Fax: 01373 827414
Total Beds: 24

Westbury Hospital

Westbury BA13 3EL
Tel: 01373 823616

West Yorkshire Metropolitan Ambulance Service NHS Trust

Threelands, Bradford Road, Birkenshaw, Bradford BD11 2AH
Tel: 01274 707070 Fax: 01274 707071
(West Yorkshire Health Authority)

Chair Shirley Tate
Chief Executive Trevor Molton

Westcountry Ambulance Services NHS Trust

Trust HQ, Abbey Court, Eagle Way, Exeter EX2 7HY
Tel: 01392 261501 Fax: 01392 261510
Website: www.was.co.uk/was
(South West Peninsula Health Authority)

Chair Samuel Jones
Chief Executive Michael Willis

Western Sussex Primary Care Trust

1st Floor, Women and Children's Block, St Richard's Hospital, Spitalfield Lane, Chichester PO19 4SE
Tel: 01243 770770 Fax: 01243 770799
(Surrey and Sussex Health Authority)

Westminster Primary Care Trust

The Medical Centre, Woodfield Road, London W9 3XZ
Tel: 020 8451 8074 Fax: 020 8451 8162
(North West London Health Authority)

Chair Diana Scott
Chief Executive Lynda Hamlyn

Weston Area Health NHS Trust

Weston General Hospital, Grange Road, Uphill, Weston Super Mare BS23 4TQ
Tel: 01934 636363 Fax: 01934 647176
(Avon, Gloucestershire and Wiltshire Health Authority)

Chair John Post
Chief Executive Roger Moyse

Weston General Hospital

Grange Road, Uphill, Weston Super Mare BS23 4TQ
Tel: 01934 636363 Fax: 01934 647029
Total Beds: 252

Accident and Emergency A Swain
Anaesthetics P Cossham, J Dixon, J Friend, G Jephcott, M A Walker
Dental Surgery J W Ross
Dermatology C Archer
ENT R K Mal
General Medicine H Bhakri, C Bowman, Dr Dyan, G Gould, Dr Parker, E J Wakley

NHS TRUSTS & NHS HOSPITALS

General Psychiatry S Britten, M K Hinchliffe, H Krekorian
General Surgery Dr Dickerson, Dr Gallegos, Dr Gillatt, A L Gough, Dr Hinchliffe, G Pye
Histopathology M Lott, D Paterson
Neurology I Ormerod
Obstetrics and Gynaecology R Afifi, C Bowman, N Dwyer
Ophthalmology S Cook, C Dean-Hart, R H B Grey, I Harrod
Orthodontics N Harradine, I Hathorn
Orthopaedics J Dixon, V G Langkamer, R F Spencer
Paediatrics Barff
Pathology G L Scott, D Stansbie
Radiology V Barley, E Kutt, P G P Stoddart, P Woodhead
Radiotherapy and Oncology V Barley
Rheumatology P A Dieppe
Urology Dr Dickerson, D Gillatt, A Hinchliffe

Whipps Cross University Hospital NHS Trust

Trust Head Quarters, Whipps Cross Hospital, Whipps Cross Road, Leytonstone, London E11 1NR
Tel: 020 8535 6800 Fax: 020 8535 6439
(North East London Health Authority)

Chair Michael Haines
Chief Executive Peter Coles, Dr [New Person]

Whipps Cross University Hospital

Whipps Cross Road, Leytonstone, London E111NR
Tel: 020 8539 5522 Fax: 020 8558 8115
Total Beds: 750

Accident and Emergency M Hunt, A Sadana
Anaesthetics W D J Cantrell, E A F Clements, D C Erwin, C Gauci, M Hamilton-Farrell, D G Rees, J Windsor, J Youssef
Cardiology S Gupta, J Hogan
Care of the Elderly K Kafetz, G McElligot, J O'Farrell, B Rossiter
Chest Disease M Roberts, R Taylor
Dermatology S Salisbury
Diabetes D Levy
ENT R S Dawkins, N Frootko, D M Mackinnon
General Medicine A Alstead, I Barton, D V Doyle, J Lanham, M Roberts, A Sawyer, R Taylor, P L Wright
General Psychiatry A A Khan, N Savla
General Surgery S Brearley, P Thomas, J M Wellwood
Genitourinary Medicine T Philp
Histopathology R Owen, K M Thomas
Medical Microbiology B Chattopadhyay, C Goodbourne
Neurology C R Clarke
Obstetrics and Gynaecology H Annan, R W M Baldwin, T Hollingsworth, S Hussain, D Viniker
Ophthalmology S Bryan, C Claoue, H Towler, N Kayali, R Ohri
Oral and Maxillofacial Surgery F J Evans, B Littler
Orthodontics S Ash
Orthopaedics B Goldie, K M N Kunzru, T McAuliffe, A G Zahir
Paediatrics A Duthie, S Fang, G McEnery, M O'Callagan, J Raine
Pathology C Anderson, P E Foley, C W M Silva
Plastic Surgery C C Walker
Radiology J Frank, I Mootoosamy, J Namasivayam, N Reading, P Thurley
Radiotherapy and Oncology A Munro
Rheumatology S Donelly, J Lanham

Whittington Hospital NHS Trust

Highgate Hill, London N19 5NF
Tel: 020 7272 3070 Fax: 020 7288 5550
(North Central London Health Authority)

Chair Michael Abrams
Chief Executive Trevor Campbell Davis

Whittington Hospital

Highgate Hill, London N19 5NF
Tel: 020 7272 3070 Fax: 020 7288 5550
Total Beds: 470

Accident and Emergency A Banerjee, G M A Heaton, R Landau
Anaesthetics B El-Behesy, C Hargreaves, S Ishaq, R L A Jayaweera, S Kanagasundram, P Lee, G H Lim, D Makinde, G Panch, J Powney
Care of the Elderly C Bielawska, R Gray, S Mitchell, G S Rai
Chest Disease N M Johnson, S Lock, L Restrick
Child and Adolescent Psychiatry S W S Kraemer, J Roberts
Dermatology D Harris, T Lambiris
ENT D I Choa, T Joseph
General Medicine J R Davies, K Earle, S Hardman, P J A Moult, D L H Patterson, F R Vicary, J S Yudkin
General Surgery C Bishop, M D Brough, J P S Cochrane, M Hashemc, C Ingham Clark, H Mukhtar, A J Wilson
Haematology N E Parker, B Wonke
Histopathology D C Brown, S Desai, S Ramachandra
Medical Microbiology M C Kelsey
Neurology J W Scadding, A Thompson
Obstetrics and Gynaecology T P Dutt, F Eben, G L Henson, A Kyer-Mensah, M E Mansell, C Mellon, H Morgan, C Paul, M Setchell, A Singer, C Spence-Jones
Ophthalmology C Davey, B Little
Oral and Maxillofacial Surgery N D Evans, P S G Perera
Orthopaedics I Bacarese-Hamilton, S Muirhead-Allwood, P Thomas, L Wilson
Paediatrics H Bantock, E Broadhurst, M Jaswon, H S Mackinnon, A Robins
Palliative Medicine A Kurowska
Radiology J C Davis, D S Grant, D Hakhamaneshi, J B Timmis, J M Young
Rheumatology and Rehabilitation J Dacre, J Worrall
Urology R A Miller, D Ralph

Wiltshire Ambulance Service NHS Trust

Dorman House, Malmesbury Road, Chippenham SN15 5LN
Tel: 01249 443939 Fax: 01249 443217
(Avon, Gloucestershire and Wiltshire Health Authority)

Chair Kevin Small
Chief Executive Dennis Lauder

Wiltshire and Swindon Health Care NHS Trust

Trust closure tbc - Part of service transferring to Swindon Primary Care Trust.

Trust Headquarters, Southgate House, Pans Lane, Devizes SN1 5EQ
Tel: 01380 736000 Fax: 01380 736049
(Avon, Gloucestershire and Wiltshire Health Authority)

Chair Sue Bates
Chief Executive Tim Skelton

Chippenham Community Hospital

Rowden Hill, Chippenham SN15 2AJ
Tel: 01249 447100 Fax: 01249 444511
Total Beds: 131

Devizes Community Hospital

Devizes SN10 1EF
Tel: 01380 723511 Fax: 01380 726456
Total Beds: 46

Learning Disabilities Service
147-150 Beaver Road, Victoria Road, Swindon SN1 3BU
Total Beds: 55

Malmesbury Community Hospital

Burton Hill, Malmesbury SN16 0EQ
Tel: 01666 823358 Fax: 01666 825026
Total Beds: 27

Victoria Hospital

Okus Road, Swindon SN1 4HZ
Tel: 01793 481182 Fax: 01793 437636
Total Beds: 46

Winchester and Eastleigh Healthcare NHS Trust

Royal Hampshire Hospital, Romsey Road, Winchester SO22 5DG
Tel: 01962 863535 Fax: 01962 825190
(Hampshire and Isle of Wight Health Authority)

Chief Executive R. Halls
Consultants A P Brooks, N Buchanan, D Butler, A Calver, J Chong, N Cox, J Duffy, G M Fairris, C Gordon, H Gordon, A Grove, H Jones, J D Powell-Jackson, J A Roberts, H A Shepherd, K Stewart

Andover War Memorial Community Hospital

Charlton Road, Andover SP10 3LB
Tel: 01264 835226 Fax: 01264 351424
Total Beds: 100

Mount Day Hospital

Bishopstoke, Eastleigh SO50 6ZB
Tel: 023 8061 2335 Fax: 023 8065 0954

Royal Hampshire County Hospital

Romsey Road, Winchester SO22 5DG
Tel: 01962 863535 Fax: 01962 824826
Total Beds: 530

Accident and Emergency J McKeever, S Singh
Anaesthetics R W Buckland, J C Criswell, K J Davies, S J Deacock, P M du Boulay, C Fairley, A Goldsmith, R Hutchinson, K Morris, M L Nancekievill, R J Summerfield, G Watson, W D White
Care of the Elderly C J Gordon, K O Stewart
Dental Surgery T H Redpath
Dermatology G M Fairris, D H Jones
ENT P B Ashcroft, T H Guerrier
General Medicine A P Brooks, M S Hammersley, J D Powell-Jackson, J A Roberts, H A Shepherd
General Psychiatry C Bellenis, E Chan-Pensley, P Courtney, P D Hettiaratchy, S Olivieri, I Plant, C Platz, R I Stewart, P Courtney
General Surgery P C Gartell, R H S Lane, A Miles, R M Rainsbury, N M Wilson
Genitourinary Medicine K Woodcock
Learning Disabilities A Hobbs
Medical Microbiology M Dryden
Neurology P Kennedy
Obstetrics and Gynaecology M S Buckingham, M J Heard, K A Louden, A D Noble
Ophthalmology A Macleod, R J Morris, J Watts
Oral and Maxillofacial Surgery N Baker
Orthodontics S C Cole
Orthopaedics J L Fowler, H Fox, W E Hook, A W Samuel, N P Trimmings
Paediatrics A G Antoniou, K D Foote, T F Mackintosh, D Schapiro
Pathology R K Al-Talib, B Green, C James, W O Mavor, M J Sworn
Radiology J Cheetham, J Hogg, J M Laidlow, A C Page, O J C Wethered
Rheumatology and Rehabilitation N Buchanan, N L Cox
Urology A Adamson, G S Harrison

Winchester Day Hospital

Royal Hampshire County Hospital, 8 St Paul's Hill, Winchester SO22 5DG
Tel: 01962 863535 Fax: 01962 824826

Windsor, Ascot and Maidenhead Primary Care Trust

St Leonard's Road, Windsor SL4 3DP
Tel: 01753 621435 Fax: 01753 621445
(Thames Valley Health Authority)

Wirral and West Cheshire Community NHS Trust

Closing April 2002 - Services transferring to Cheshire and Wirral Partnership NHS Trust.

St Catherine's Hospital, Church Road, Birkenhead CH42 0LQ
Tel: 0151 678 7272 Fax: 0151 652 8764
(Cheshire and Merseyside Health Authority)

Chair David Eva
Chief Executive Stephen Dalton

Ashton House

26 Village Road, Oxton, Birkenhead CH43 5SR
Tel: 0151 653 9660 Fax: 0151 670 9772
Total Beds: 18

Learning Disabilities M T Hand, S Singhal

Ellesmere Port Hospital

Whitby Road, Ellesmere Port CH65 6FQ
Tel: 01244 365000 Fax: 01244 362922
Total Beds: 92

Rehabilitation Medicine S Choudhury

St Catherine's Hospital

Church Road, Tranmere, Birkenhead CH42 0LQ
Tel: 0151 678 7272 Fax: 0151 652 8764
Total Beds: 42

Alcohol and Substance Misuse T Garney, S Janckiewicz
Elderly Mentally Ill K Wilson
Learning Disabilities M Hand, S Singhal
Women's and Sexual Health Services K Widd

Victoria Central Hospital

Mill Lane, Wallasey CH44 5UF
Tel: 0151 678 5111 Fax: 0151 639 2478

General Psychiatry V Shanma, M Wilkinson

West Cheshire

Liverpool Road, Chester CH2 1UL
Tel: 01244 365000 Fax: 01244 364194

Elderly Mentally Ill C Gilmore, A Siuanantuan
General Psychiatry R Chitty, S Crabbe, I Davidson, N Halstead
Learning Disabilities M Hand

Wirral Hospital NHS Trust

Arrowe Park Road, Upton, Wirral CH49 5PE
Tel: 0151 678 5111 Fax: 0151 604 7148
Email: wirral.enq@ccmail.wirralh-tr.nwest.nhs.uk
Website: www.wirralhealth.org.uk
(Cheshire and Merseyside Health Authority)

Chief Executive Frank Gordon Burns

NHS TRUSTS & NHS HOSPITALS

Arrowe Park Hospital

Arrowe Park Road, Upton, Wirral L49 5PE
Tel: 0151 678 5111
Total Beds: 918

Accident and Emergency C Doherty, J Marrow, B Ohiorenoya, A G Pennycook

Anaesthetics A Atherton, B Bapat, J J Chambers, J C Devlin, D Eastwood, J P Gannon, B P Guratsky, B Hedayati, G Jefferies, S Leith, J K Moore, S Ralston, A Rao, N Scawn, M W Smith, J S Sprigge, K Stevens, R W Stevens, J E Sweeney, T J Tarr, M Van Miert, P Williams

Care of the Elderly J A Barrett, D King, J W Lorains, R Morgan, J Russell, G Sangster, A Scott, C J Turnbull

Chemical Pathology W D Neithercut

Dermatology S K Jones, S S Mendolsohn, S I White

ENT D G O'Sullivan, I W Sherman, V Srinovasan

General Medicine P Currie, J Dawson, J C Delaney, R Faizallah, R Ferguson, D B Jones, I R Jones, D S Lawrence, D Rittou, J H Silas

General Surgery D Berstock, S D Blair, M G Greaney, C A Makin, A Masters, D T Reilly, S Sagar, C Walsh

Genitourinary Medicine A K Ghosh

Haematology T J Deeble, D Galvani

Histopathology D Agbamu, A H Clark, J Elder, M B Gillett, A R T Green, R Seneviratne, K C Sidky, H D Zakhour

Medical Microbiology J Cunniffe, A E Murray

Nephrology A Crowe, P McClelland

Obstetrics and Gynaecology B Alderman, P M Doyle, N Gul, A D Murray, D J Rowlands, C R Welch, I A Williams

Ophthalmology L G Clearkin, P Pennefather, M Watts

Oral Surgery D Jones, G D Wood

Orthodontics G R P Barry

Orthopaedics N Donnachie, N P J Geary, R A Harvey, M Hennesey, J C Kaye, R W Parkinson, A J M Simison, D N Smith

Paediatrics E Bentsi-Enchill, J Fellick, A Hughes, D E Lacy, D J Manning, J Seager, P J Todd

Palliative Medicine C M Lewis-Jones

Radiology P J Evans, A M Garrett, D H Green, D M Killeen, Z R Klenka, M E Lipton, J Magennis, V C Williamson

Rheumatology and Rehabilitation E George, S Keetarut, T D Kennedy, C Pinder

Urology P Kutarski, N J Parr, R N Stephenson

Clatterbridge Hospital

Bebington, Wirral L63 4JY
Tel: 0151 334 4000
Total Beds: 252

Anaesthetics J J Chambers, J C Devlin, D Eastwood, J P Gannon, B P Guratsky, G Jefferies, S Leith, J K Moore, S Ralston, M W Smith, J S Sprigge, R W Stevens, J E Sweeney, T J Tarr, M Van Miert

Care of the Elderly J A Barrett, D King, J W Lorains, R Morgan, J Russell, G Sangster, C J Turnbull

Chemical Pathology W D Neithercut

Dermatology S K Jones, S S Mendelsohn, S I White

General Surgery D A Berstock, S D Blair, M G Greaney, C A Makin, D T Reilly, S Sagar, C Walsh

Haematology T J Deeble, D Galvani

Histopathology D Agbamu, A H Clark, M B Gillett, A R T Green, K C Sidky, H D Zakhour

Medical Microbiology A E Murray

Orthopaedics N Donnachie, N P J Geary, R A Harvey, J C Kaye, R W Parkinson, A J M Simison, D N Smith

Palliative Medicine C M Lewis-Jones

Radiology A M Garrett, D H Green, D M Killeen, Z Klenka, M E Lipton, J Magennis, V C Williamson

Rheumatology and Rehabilitation E George, S Keetarut, T D Kennedy, C Pinder

Urology P Kutarski, N J Parr, R N Stephenson

Woking Primary Care Trust

Woking Community Hospital, Heathside Road, Woking GU22 7HS
Tel: 01483 715911 Fax: 01483 757308
(Surrey and Sussex Health Authority)

Wokingham Primary Care Trust

Wokingham Hospital, Barkham Road, Wokingham RG41 2RE
Tel: 0118 949 5000 Fax: 0118 977 5880
(Thames Valley Health Authority)

Chair Alan Penn
Chief Executive Sue Heatherington

Wolverhampton City Primary Care Trust

Coniston House, Chapel Ash, Wolverhampton WV3 0XE
(Birmingham and the Black Country Health Authority)

Wolverhampton Health Care NHS Trust

Clevelands House, 10/12 Tettenhall Road, Wolverhampton WV1 4SA
Tel: 01902 444000 Fax: 01902 444446
(Birmingham and the Black Country Health Authority)

Chair M Benton
Chief Executive M Pyrah

Groves Day Hospital

Penn Hospital, Penn Road, Wolverhampton WV4 5HN
Tel: 01902 444130
Total Beds: 22

Learning Disability Service

44 Pond Lane, Wolverhampton WV2 1HG
Tel: 01902 444002
Email: annette.shakespeare@whc-tr.nhs.uk
Total Beds: 19

General Psychiatry Dr Coley

Penn Hospital

Penn Road, Wolverhampton WV4 5HN
Tel: 01902 444141
Total Beds: 40

Elderly Mentally Ill S Benbow, S Dixey, R Jenkins, D Jolley

West Park Rehabilitation Hospital

Park Road West, Wolverhampton WV1 4PW
Tel: 01902 444000 Fax: 01902 444085
Total Beds: 109

Care of the Elderly F O Nehikhare, S N Verma
Consultants T Aung

Worcestershire Acute Hospitals NHS Trust

Worcester Royal Infirmary, Ronkswood, Newtown Road, Worcester WR5 1HN
Tel: 01905 763333 Fax: 01905 760555
(Coventry, Warwickshire, Herefordshire and Worcestershire Health Authority)

Chair Harold Musgrove
Chief Executive Ruth Harrison

Alexandra Hospital

Woodrow Drive, Redditch B98 7UB
Tel: 01527 503030 Fax: 01527 517432
Total Beds: 340

Accident and Emergency M A Ansari
Anaesthetics H A Aitken, H B J Fischer, R M Haden, B G Head, J McPherson, C Mosieri, C A Pinnock, P V Scott, Dr Smith
Care of the Elderly S N Singhal
Dental Surgery A W Harris
Dermatology W F G Tucker
ENT P J E Johnson, J R M Moore
General Medicine D J Carter, L J Libman, P J Lowry, S Singhal, G D Summers, A Vathenen
General Surgery R Brown, J H Burman, Dr Jenkes, C D Rennie, R G Tudor
Haematology D Obeid
Histopathology L Brown, G M Kondratowicz, J Stone
Medical Microbiology H M Cawdery
Neurology C R Barraclough
Obstetrics and Gynaecology J H Elias-Jones, S D Jenkinson, G H Macpherson
Ophthalmology B Das, M J Freeman, S M D Porter, P A Thomas
Orthodontics C Gait
Orthopaedics M A M Arafa, J Bell, O S J Costa, A J Price, L Read
Paediatrics G C Close, C I Fraser, R J Sankey
Pathology P P Brown
Radiology C Dale, J M Elliott, P Holland, F H Jenkins, J L Morgan, C Phillips, S R J Reddy
Radiotherapy A D Stockdale

Kidderminster General Hospital

Bewdley Road, Kidderminster DY11 6RJ
Tel: 01562 823424 Fax: 01562 67412
Total Beds: 301

Dermatology F Lewis

Tenbury District Hospital

Tenbury Wells WR15 8AT
Tel: 01584 810643 Fax: 01584 829987
Total Beds: 16

Worcester Royal Hospital

Newtown Road, Worcester WR5 1HN
Tel: 01905 763333
Total Beds: 483

Accident and Emergency R Johnson, A J E Mulira
Anaesthetics I Davis, M Hardwick, N Jones, J Lee, P W Lord, C Maile, D M Philips, J A Prosser, B Roscoe, N M Rose, C Studd, H Williams
Cardiology W A Littler
Care of the Elderly C Ashton, R Glennie, C Pycock
Chemical Pathology A J Munro
Chest Disease R A Lewis
Child Psychiatry G Knowles
Dermatology F Lewis
ENT J E D MacLaren, M Porter
General Medicine N H Dyer, D Jenkins, R A Lewis, S Spencer, S Spencer, M J Webberley
General Psychiatry D Battin, J Doran, G Knowles, I Pennell, E H Richards, J Tarry, J Vaughan, R White
General Surgery J Black, M Corlett, R Downing, N Hickey, S Lake, C Robertson, H T Williams
Genitourinary Medicine A J R Crooks
Haematology A H Sawers, R J Stockley
Medical Microbiology C Constantine, J Webberley
Neurology J A Spillane
Neurophysiology A E Blake, A Munro
Obstetrics and Gynaecology B Ruparelia
Ophthalmology R Hall

Oral Surgery N A Barnard, P Earl
Orthodontics D Evans
Orthopaedics J S Davies, K O'Dwyer, P Ratcliffe, D Robinson, E Rouholamin, M Trevett
Paediatrics A P Cole, M Hanlon, B Mason, A S Mills, J E Scanlon
Pathology P J S Dunn, L Smallman, G Smith
Plastic Surgery D S Murray
Psychiatry of Old Age D G J Battin, J E Tarry
Radiology S Bailey, M Brown, J Mould, D Rosewarne, D South, R S Ward
Radiotherapy and Oncology J J Mould
Rheumatology A Rai, I F Rowe
Thoracic Surgery F J Collins
Urology T Chen

Worcester Royal Infirmary

Newtown Hospital, Newtown Road, Worcester WR5 1JG
Tel: 01905 763333 Fax: 01905 760494
Total Beds: 88

Worcestershire Community and Mental Health NHS Trust

Isaac Maddox House, Shrub Hill Road, Worcester WR4 9RW
Tel: 01905 681511 Fax: 01905 681515
(Coventry, Warwickshire, Herefordshire and Worcestershire Health Authority)

Chair John Calvert
Chief Executive Sue Hunt
Consultants Jane Abbey, Andrew Mills

Brook Haven Mental Health Unit

Stourbridge Road, Bromsgrove B61 0BB
Tel: 01527 488279
Total Beds: 18

Hill Crest

Quinneys Lane, Redditch B98 7WG
Tel: 01527 500575 Fax: 01527 500519
Total Beds: 25

Princess of Wales Community Hospital

Stourbridge Road, Bromsgrove B61 0BB
Tel: 01527 488027 Fax: 01527 574857
Total Beds: 20

Rowan Day Hospital

Smallwood House, Church Green West, Redditch B97 4BD
Tel: 01527 488620

Worthing and Southlands Hospitals NHS Trust

Worthing Hospital, Lyndhurst Road, Worthing BN11 2DH
Tel: 01903 205111 Fax: 01903 285045
Website: www.worthinghospital.nhs.uk
(Hampshire and Isle of Wight Health Authority)

Chief Executive Roger Greene

Southlands Hospital

Upper Shoreham Road, Shoreham-by-Sea BN43 6TQ
Tel: 01273 455622 Fax: 01273 446042

Genitourinary Medicine A T Nayagam
Oral and Maxillofacial Surgery D W Macpherson, J R L Vincent-Townend, J L Williams
Orthopaedics D Clark, D Craig, A J Edge, A C Jarvis, J D S McCutchan
Pathology J Bates, K Blessing, J Grant, C L Rist, K M Roberts, A A Roques, H Southgate, C D Wright

NHS TRUSTS & NHS HOSPITALS

Radiology D G Hall, M Hinchcliffe, A E Hubbard, A McKinnon, L J Rockall, D Withers

Rheumatology and Rehabilitation M D Chard, M Rice-Oxley, A J Richards

Worthing Hospital

Lyndhurst Road, Worthing BN11 2DH
Tel: 01903 205111 Fax: 01903 285045
Total Beds: 460

Accident and Emergency M Grocutt, M Jackson, B Wynn-Davies
Anaesthetics S Ahmed, S Anderson, R Edwards, N Lavies, J O'Dwyer, M V Ryssen, P T Sweet, D Uncles, H R Waters, A C Williams
Care of the Elderly M Reardon, M Suntharalingam, R Tozer, A White
Dermatology P R Coburn, A V Levantine
ENT M Harries, J H Topham, J Weighill
General Medicine H J M Bull, G Caldwell, P Carr, J A Evans, M Signy
General Surgery R C Beard, G H Dickson, T Liston, A Miles, D C Parr, A Salman, W Woods
Neurology R E Clifford-Jones
Neurophysiology C P Chandrasekera
Obstetrics and Gynaecology R Pyper, C F Ruoss, M Rymer
Ophthalmology P D Fox, R T Niyadurupola, S Rassan, M Teimory
Orthodontics A M Hall
Paediatrics A Garg, S Nicholls
Pathology J Bates, K Blessing, J Grant, C L Rist, K M Roberts, A W W Roques, H Southgate, E D Wright
Radiology D G Hall, M Hinchcliffe, A E Hubbard, A McKinnon, L J Rockall, D Withers
Radiotherapy and Oncology G P Deutsch, C Newman
Rheumatology and Rehabilitation M D Chard, H Rice-Oxley, A J Richards
Thoracic Surgery R E Sayer

Worthing Priority Care Services NHS Trust

Closing April 2002 - Mental health and learning disability services transferring to West Sussex Health and Social Care NHS Trust.

Trust HQ, Arundel Road, Worthing BN13 3EP
Tel: 01903 843000 Fax: 01903 843001
(Surrey and Sussex Health Authority)

Chair John Hooper
Chief Executive Richard Congdon

Acre Day Hospital

29 Wordsworth Road, Worthing BN11 3NJ
Tel: 01903 216807 Fax: 01903 212511

Crescent House

Glenville Road, Rustington, Littlehampton BN16 2EA
Tel: 01903 858150 Fax: 01903 858151
Total Beds: 18

Littlehampton Hospital

Fitzalan Road, Littlehampton BN17 5EU
Tel: 01903 717101 Fax: 01903 732981
Total Beds: 15

Meadowfield

Arundel Road, Worthing BN13 3EF
Tel: 01903 843200 Fax: 01903 843201
Total Beds: 48

Ridings Southlands Hospital

Shoreham-by-Sea BN43 6TQ
Tel: 01273 455622 Fax: 01273 446042
Total Beds: 23

Salvington Lodge

Salvington Hill, Off Arundel Road, Worthing BN13 3EP
Tel: 01903 266399 Fax: 01903 266388
Total Beds: 66

Travelling Day Hospital (Mental Health over 65s)

Pepperville House, Littlehampton BN17 7QU
Tel: 01903 735960 Fax: 01903 735961

Travelling Day Hospital (Mental Health under 65s)

Glebelands, Middle Road, Shoreham-by-Sea BN43 6LL
Tel: 01273 441586 Fax: 01273 441586

Zachary Merton Hospital

Glenville Road, Rustington, Littlehampton BN16 2EB
Tel: 01903 858100 Fax: 01903 858101
Total Beds: 29

Wrightington, Wigan and Leigh NHS Trust

From April 2002 specialist services transferring to 5 Borough Partnership NHS Trust.

The Elms, Royal Albert Edward Infirmary, Wigan Lane, Wigan WN1 2NN
Tel: 01942 882159
(Cumbria and Lancashire Health Authority, Greater Manchester Health Authority)

Chief Executive Sheena Cumiskey

Avenue Day Hospital

Leigh Infirmary, The Avenue, Leigh WN7 1HS

Billinge Hospital

Upholland Road, Billinge, Wigan WN5 7ET
Tel: 01942 244000 Fax: 01695 626113
Total Beds: 250

Anaesthetics D J Allan, G Field, P Ford, P J Galea, R G Ghaly, I W Jones, F Koussa, K A Phillips, P Venkataraman
Obstetrics and Gynaecology A Bells, C J Chandler, J Davies, R M El Gawley, C P Harris, P A Lewis, R H M Martin
Paediatrics Dr Bhadoria, Dr Cooper, Dr Farrier, Dr Heal, Dr Robinson
Pathology M Bhavnani
Radiology E J Corkan, S Mukherjee, P Rodgers, D G Sheals

Hanover Assesment and Treatment Centre

Leigh Infirmary, The Avenue, Leigh WN7 1HS

Leigh Infirmary

The Avenue, Leigh WN7 1HS
Tel: 01942 672333 Fax: 01942 264388
Total Beds: 298

Anaesthetics D J Allan, J Aslam, P G Coloner, G Field, N W Flatt, P Ford, R Foster, V Jaitly, R G Ghaly, I W Jones, F Koussa, R Saad, P Venkataraman
Care of the Elderly A N Khan, S R Nandi, A Kumar
Dental Surgery I D Campbell, R E Lloyd
Dermatology E Stewart, J Yell
ENT S K Banerjee, D Murphy, C Nsamba
General Medicine D Lewis, V Mani, A O Molajo, N Naqvi, A G Wardman
General Surgery M C Holbrook, J Mosley, W D Richmond
Neurology S Duncan
Obstetrics and Gynaecology C J Chandler, R M El Gawley, C P Harris, R H Martin
Ophthalmology D Banerjee, J S Chawla, S Mars

Orthopaedics M S Bell, A O Browne, P W Hopcroft, B Livingstone
Paediatrics A S Ahuja, R Downes, R B McGucken
Pathology M Bhavnani, A Chaudhuri, I Gupta, J Marples, K Schwe, J M Torry
Psychiatry N Bano, M Chowdhury, D Kohen, A A Malik, B P Maragakis, B K Rathod, D Sena, J G Thomas, S Malik
Radiology E J Corkan, S Desai, S Mehta, S Mukherjee, C L Poon, P Rodgers, D G Sheals, D Temperley, A C Troop, S D Watson
Radiotherapy and Oncology R D James
Rheumatology D R Swinson
Urology W D Richmond

Royal Albert Edward Infirmary

Wigan Lane, Wigan WN1 2NN
Tel: 01942 244000 Fax: 01942 822042
Total Beds: 480

Accident and Emergency D Harbourne, A Pinto
Anaesthetics D J Allan, J Alsam, G Field, P G Coloner, NW Flatt, P J Galea, R G Ghaly, V Jaitty, I W Jones, F Koussa, R Foster, R Saad, P Venkataraman
Dental Surgery I D Campbell
Dermatology E Stewart, J Yell
ENT M S Izzat, B N Kumar, V B Pothula
General Medicine C M Bate, D Lewis, V Mani, A Molajo, N Naqvi, D J Tymms, A G Wardman, R J Wolstenholme
General Psychiatry P A Cook, A Kushlick, A A Malik, S Malik, B P Maragakis, B K Rathod, G Thomas, K Yasin
General Surgery A Blower, C Campbell, R N Harland, M C Holbrook, N McKenzie, R Gupta, J Mosley, M Jamel
Genitourinary Medicine J A Forrer
Neurology J Susman
Neurosurgery R A Cowie, J Leggate, C West
Obstetrics and Gynaecology A Bellis, C J Chandler, R M El Gawley, C P Harris, P A Lewis, R H Martin
Occupational Health S Kumar
Ophthalmology D Banerjee, C Heaven, S Mars, S Natha, A Siddiqui
Oral Surgery I D Campbell, R Middlehurst
Orthodontics J Brady
Orthopaedics M S Bell, A O Browne, P W Hopcroft, B Livingstone
Paediatrics A S Ahuja, R S Bhadoria, R Downes, J A Fraser, R Greenham, R B McGucken, P Simpson
Pathology M Bhavnani, A K Chaudhuri, I Dhesi, I Gupta, J Marples, K H Schwe, J M Torry
Radiology E J Corkan, S Desai, S Mukherjee, C L Poon, P Rodgers, D G Sheals, D Temperley, A C Troop, S D Watson
Radiotherapy E Allen
Rheumatology D R Swinson

Whelley Hospital

Bradshaw Street, Whelley, Wigan WN1 3XD
Tel: 01942 244000 Fax: 01942 822630
Total Beds: 89

Care of the Elderly S Nandi
Occupational Health S Kumar
Rehabilitation Medicine M Eshiett

Wrightington Hospital

Hall Lane, Appley Bridge, Wigan WN6 9EP
Tel: 01257 252211 Fax: 01257 253809
Total Beds: 147

Anaesthetics U Benjamin, B Frayne, V Koppada, M Jingree, C Martin, M Tittota
Orthopaedics A Browne, J Haines, P Burbacks, A Mohammed, M L Porter, V Raut, J K Stanley, J H Stilwell, I A Trail, P L R Wood, B M Wroblewski
Pathology A Browne, R Murali, J Hodgkinson
Radiology J Corkan, D Shiels, D Temperley
Rheumatology C Chattopadhyay, D M Grennan, D R Swinson, J Davies

Wycombe Primary Care Trust

Carrington House Surgery, 19 Priory Road, High Wycombe HP13 6SL
Tel: 01494 524761 Fax: 01494 522046
Website: www.buckshealth.com
(Thames Valley Health Authority)

Chief Executive Tracey Baldwin

Wyre Forest Primary Care Trust

7th Floor, Brook House, Kidderminster Hospital, Bewdley Road, Kidderminster DY11 6RJ
Tel: 01562 863694 Fax: 01562 862767
(Coventry, Warwickshire, Herefordshire and Worcestershire Health Authority)

Chair David Priestnall
Chief Executive Peter Forrester

Wyre Primary Care Trust

Furness Drive, Poulton-le-Fylde FY6 8JT.
(Cumbria and Lancashire Health Authority)

York Health Services NHS Trust

Bootham Park, York YO30 7BY
Tel: 01904 454066 Fax: 01904 454439
Website: www.yorkhealthservices.org
(North and East Yorkshire and Northern Lincolnshire Health Authority)

Chair Alan K Maynard
Chief Executive Simon Pleydell, George T Wood

Bootham Park Hospital

Bootham, York YO30 7BY
Tel: 01904 610777 Fax: 01904 454439
Total Beds: 120

General Psychiatry R D Adams, L M Brown, A J Gopalaswamy, C Henderson, C A Kirk, S P Reilly, S P Shaw

York District Hospital

Wigginton Road, York YO31 8HE
Tel: 01904 631313
Total Beds: 818

Accident and Emergency M F Gibson, M J Williams
Anaesthetics D A Child, G Cundill, R M Grummitt, P Hall, I J B Jackson, T H Madej, P J Moss, M K Reeder, P Toomey, R G Wheatley, J Wilson, I Woods
Care of the Elderly A Corlett, J Coyle, D Heseltine, A McEvoy
Dermatology C Henderson, A S Highet, A Myatt, J M Stainforth
ENT A R Grace, A Nicolaides, P G Reilly
General Medicine R M Boyle, A M Hunter, P Jennings, S Kelly, M Pye, J C Thow, A J Turnbull, J E White, D P Worth
General Surgery D Alexander, S G Brooks, R Hall, S H Leveson, S Nicholson
Genitourinary Medicine I Fairley
Neurology P M Crawford, A Heald
Neurophysiology H K C Laljee
Obstetrics and Gynaecology R W Hunter, E J Mattock, S Mitchell, D W Pring, C S Tuck
Ophthalmology J M Hayward, P J Jacobs, R Taylor
Oral and Maxillofacial Surgery P Cove, G D D Roberts, M Telfer
Orthodontics P M Jenkins
Orthopaedics P G d Boer, P Campbell, A J Gibbon, C A N McLaren, I A Whitaker
Otolaryngology A R Grace

NHS TRUSTS & NHS HOSPITALS

Paediatrics R Ball, D W Beverley, M J Harran, R A Smith
Pathology A W Anderson, C Bates, L R Bond, M R Howard, I N Reid, H Wilkinson
Radiology C M Ivory, R Mannion, A M Murphy, M E Porte
Rheumatology and Rehabilitation J M I Iveson
Urology K Seenivasgam, M J Stower, G H Urwin

Yorkshire Wolds and Coast Primary Care Trust

1st Floor, Westwood Hospital, Woods Lane, Beverley HU17 9BU
Tel: 01482 886679 Fax: 01482 886516
(North and East Yorkshire and Northern Lincolnshire Health Authority)

Chair Scilla Smith
Chief Executive Adrian Smith

Scotland

Argyll and Clyde Acute Hospitals NHS Trust

Vale of Leven District General Hospital, Main Street, Alexandria G83 0UA
Tel: 01389 754121 Fax: 01389 755948
(Argyll and Clyde NHS Board)

Chair George M Gibb
Chief Executive David A Sillito

Inverclyde Royal Hospital

Larkfield Road, Greenock PA16 0XN
Tel: 01475 633777 Fax: 01475 636753
Total Beds: 368

Anaesthetics A Ahmed, O P Maini, F Munro, M Simmons, M C Thomas, D Thomson, T J Winning
Biochemistry A McConnell
Dermatology C Fitzsimons, M Young
ENT R J McGuinness, I C Paton
General Medicine G Curry, J B Dilawari, A Mackay, D A S Marshall, H Papaconstaninou, P Semple, J E Thomson
General Surgery G Bell, J J Morrice, G Orr, J Reidy, I Watt
Genitourinary Medicine R Nandwani
Haematology D L Ellis, G Rainey
Medical Microbiology A E Biggs
Neurology R Petty
Obstetrics and Gynaecology G S Anthony, L Cassidy, J Robins
Ophthalmology S R Gupta, D Mansfield
Orthodontics B D Collin
Orthopaedics S Barnes, M Di Paola, T K Ghosh, G McGarrity, R Venner
Paediatrics G Hunt, O Kurian, R C Shepherd
Pathology M Seywright, M A Thomas
Plastic Surgery M Webster
Radiology F P Kelly, A Ramsay, R Shaw, P F Walsh

Lorn and Islands District General Hospital

Glengallan Road, Oban PA34 4HH
Tel: 01631 567500 Fax: 01631 567134
Total Beds: 138

Anaesthetics A Murchison, J Walker, C Wilson
Care of the Elderly G G Garabet
General Medicine A F Henderson, A K Henderson
General Surgery D Scobie, S N Yadav

Royal Alexandra Hospital

Corsebar Road, Paisley PA2 9PN
Tel: 0141 887 9111 Fax: 0141 887 6701
Email: Karen.Murray@rah.scot.nhs.uk
Total Beds: 596

Accident and Emergency C Allister, L Hislop, G McNaughton, R Marshall, F Russell
Adult Medicine A Dorward, I Findlay, J Gravil, J Hinnie, W Hislop, S Hood, P Macintyre
Anaesthetics H Aitken, J J Canning, S Chaudhri, F Davies, J Dickson, G Fletcher, T Goudie, T Ireland, E James, R L McDevitt, S Madsen, J E Orr, B M Scorgie, R Simpson, M Smith
Biochemistry P Stromberg
Care of the Elderly C Leslie, D Mack, G Simpson, A Uni, C Wilkieson
Dermatology C P Fitzsimons, I Hay, M J Young
ENT R J McGuinness, C Murray, I C Paton, A White
General Medicine A J Dorward, I Findlay, B M Fisher, J Gravil, W S Hislop, P McIntyre, J McPeake
General Surgery J McCourtney, A J McEwan, M McKirdy, K G Mitchell, C Porteous, B W A Williamson
Haematology P McKay, M Robertson
Medical Microbiology A Eastaway
Obstetrics and Gynaecology J A Gemmell, K C Muir, A Quinn, G Sarkar, A Thomson
Ophthalmology H Bennett, L Esakowitz, S B Murray, L Webb
Orthodontics K H Moore
Orthopaedics D A R Aaron, I J Cartlidge, S Chitnis, C Kumar, N Kumar, S Smith
Paediatrics G Hunt, L Nairn, M Ray, R C Shepherd, G Stewart
Pathology W Candlish, S Dahill, C Sutherland
Radiology C Adams, C Alexander, L P Cram, M L Davies, J Negrette, L Semple, M Stevenson, A Wallace
Urology L Morton

Vale of Leven Hospital

Main Street, Alexandria G83 0UA
Tel: 01389 754121 Fax: 01389 755948
Total Beds: 255

Anaesthetics T Barber, A E Cameron, G Douglas, W R Easy, A M Tully
Cardiology M N Al-Khafaji
Care of the Elderly N T Manning
Clinical Biochemistry J Series
Cytopathology H Scullion
Dermatology J Thomson
ENT L Cooke, D G Garrick
General Medicine M Al-Khafaji, H Al-Shamma, H A Carmichael, D McCruden
General Psychiatry M Al-Mousawi, F Coulter, I McClure, I McIvor, K Towlson
General Surgery M Al-Nassar, P Finn, J R MacCallum, E W Taylor
Haematology P Clarke
Medical Microbiology S Dancer
Obstetrics and Gynaecology A S Clark, M J Haxton, N Kenyon
Paediatrics M Ray, G Stewart
Pathology F Forbes, E L Murray, M Reid
Radiology J McGlinchey

Ayrshire and Arran Acute Hospitals NHS Trust

Crosshouse Hospital, Kilmarnock KA2 0BE
Tel: 01563 521133 Fax: 01563 572431
Website: www.show.scot.nhs.uk/aaaht
(Ayrshire and Arran NHS Board)

Chair Gordon Wilson
Chief Executive Stephen Greep, J Young

AYRSHIRE & ARRAN PRIMARY CARE NHS TRUST

Ayr Hospital

Dalmellington Road, Ayr KA6 6DX
Tel: 01292 610555 Fax: 01292 288952
Total Beds: 348

Anaesthetics K Mackenzie, R McMahon, B H Meiklejohn, I N Taylor
Biochemistry M Lough
Care of the Elderly J M Blair
Dermatology R A Hardie
General Medicine S Bicknell, J A Collier, J A Elliott, J D Gemmill, P M G Reynolds, J D R Rose
General Surgery A L Forster, I McMillan, C J Simpson, G Stewart, C Wilson
Haematology C Nisbet, P Vosylius
Ophthalmology A Gaskell, I T Hanna, B Hutchison, A Singh
Oral Surgery A Carton, S Hislop
Orthodontics J R Pilley
Orthopaedics D Large, A Muirhead, H E Potts, P S Rae
Paediatrics M Blair, S Kinmond, J P McClure, I S Ruthven
Radiology K N A Osborne
Urology G S Meddings, G S Watson

Ayrshire Central Hospital

Kilwinning Road, Irvine KA12 8SS
Tel: 01294 274191 Fax: 01294 278680
Total Beds: 252

Care of the Elderly G Duncan, J B W Godfrey, F Inglis, H McMillan
Obstetrics and Gynaecology C H Baird, H G Dobbie, D H Gibson, G Irvine, D H W MacKay, E B Melrose, S M M Prigg, T V N Russell, E M Walker
Paediatrics S Kinmond, I S Ruthven, J Staines
Rehabilitation Medicine P Mattison

Biggart Hospital

Biggart Road, Prestwick KA9 2HQ
Tel: 01292 470611 Fax: 01292 614546
Total Beds: 165

Care of the Elderly J M Blair, S Ghosh

Crosshouse Hospital

Crosshouse, Kilmarnock KA2 0BE
Tel: 01563 521133 Fax: 01563 572496
Total Beds: 540

Accident and Emergency A Lannigan, J Stevenson, S M H Zaidi
Anaesthetics J Chestnut, P J Hildebrand, S Lawrie, C Martin, A R Michie, T D Miller, A J Morris, H Neill, M K Shaw, C Thompson, R J White, P A Wilson, R K B Young, S Zimmer
Biochemistry D Boag, M Lough
Care of the Elderly G Duncan, J B W Godfrey, F Inglis, H McMillan
Dermatology J A Craig, C Dwyer, R A Hardie
ENT J H Dempster, E M Shanks, P Wardrop
General Medicine A Innes, A Jaap, J B Macdonald, I G Mackay, J N MacPherson, D O'Neill, G R Williams
General Surgery R H Diament, J R McGregor, C G Morran, A Newland, B A Sugden, P Whitford
Haematology J G Erskine, M McColl, P Vosylius
Medical Microbiology G W Downie, L Gorman, R Hardie
Oral Surgery A Carton, W S Hislop
Orthodontics D Morrant, J R Pilley
Orthopaedics B FitzGerald, M I Foxworthy, I Mackay, G R Tait
Paediatrics M Blair, J P McClure, I S Ruthven
Pathology M R Adamson, N E Cunningham, I Graham, J Lang, A Milne, E R Nairn, E Walker
Radiology N Corrigan, P Crumlish, W M F Dean, E Lindsay, G McLaughlan, M A H McMillan, D Rawlings

Ayrshire and Arran Primary Care NHS Trust

1A Hunters Avenue, Ayr KA8 9DW
Tel: 01292 513600 Fax: 01292 513665
Email: enquiries@aapct.scot.nhs.uk
(Ayrshire and Arran NHS Board)

Chair Aileen Bates
Chief Executive Allan Gunning

Ailsa Hospital

Ailsa Hopital, Dalmellington Road, Ayr KA6 6AB
Tel: 01292 610556 Fax: 01292 513027
Total Beds: 283

General Psychiatry C Aryiku, W Creaney, J A Flowerdew, C Lind, B Martin, J Stewart

Arran War Memorial Hospital

Lamlash, Brodick KA27 8LE
Tel: 01770 600777 Fax: 01770 600445
Total Beds: 22

Ayrshire Central Hospital (Psychiatric Unit)

Ayrshire Central Hospital, (Psychiatric Unit), Irvine KA12 8SS
Tel: 01294 274191 Fax: 01294 278680
Total Beds: 42

General Psychiatry A K Bodane

Brooksby House Hospital

Greenock Road, Largs KA30 8NE
Tel: 01475 672285 Fax: 01475 672439
Total Beds: 18

Davidson Cottage Hospital

Girvan KA26 9DS
Tel: 01465 712571 Fax: 01465 714382
Total Beds: 28

Garnock Day Hospital

Ayrshire Central Hospital, Irvine KA12 8SS
Tel: 01294 323050 Fax: 01294 311747

Holmhead Hospital

Cumnock KA18 1RR
Tel: 01290 422220 Fax: 01290 423589
Total Beds: 56

Kirklandside Hospital

Kilmarnock KA1 5LH
Tel: 01563 525172 Fax: 01563 575408
Total Beds: 89

Lady Margaret Hospital

College Street, Millport KA28 0HF
Tel: 01475 530307 Fax: 01475 530117
Total Beds: 14

Maybole Day Hospital

Maybole KA19 7BY
Tel: 01655 882211 Fax: 01655 889698

Roseburn Day Hospital

Holmhead Hospital, Cumnock KA18 1RR
Tel: 01290 422220 Fax: 01290 423589

NHS TRUSTS & NHS HOSPITALS

Borders General Hospital NHS Trust

Borders General Hospital, Melrose TD6 9BS
Tel: 01896 826702 Fax: 01896 526040
Website: www.show.scot.nhs.uk/bgh
(Borders NHS Board)

Chair John Smithson
Chief Executive John Glennie

Borders General Hospital

Melrose TD6 9BD
Tel: 01896 826000 Fax: 01896 823476
Website: www.show.scot.nhs.uk/bgh
Total Beds: 321

Accident and Emergency J E Phillips
Anaesthetics R C Beighton, J M Braidwood, T C Cripps, N P Leary, J N Montgomery, I Yellowlees
Cardiology P Broadhurst
Care of the Elderly P A Maguire, C A Norris, P D Syme
Child and Adolescent Psychiatry S Davies, S Glen
Dermatology C Benton, D Kemmet
ENT M Armstrong, S Moralee
General Medicine F Bollert, M I Brown, O E Eade, J Fletcher, J Gaddie, P J Leslie, P Syme, D Usher
General Surgery J M Gollock, R Halpin, J S O'Neill
Haematologist A Hung, J Tucker
Obstetrics and Gynaecology A J Gordon, I E Lowles, B Magowan
Ophthalmology R I Murray, W F I Shepherd
Oral Surgery R Mitchell
Orthodontics J Fish
Orthopaedics C B Clowes, W G Dennyson, J E Phillips, G H Tiemessen
Paediatrics E D Daniels, A Duncan, A C F Margerison, J C Stephens
Palliative Medicine J Rodgers
Pathology M I Brown, S Sadullah
Radiology D Hardwick, H McRitchie, A J Pearson, J Reid, H Shannon

Borders Geriatric Day Hospital

Borders General Hospital, Melrose TD6 9BS
Tel: 01896 754333 ext: 1222 Fax: 01896 823476
Website: www.show.scot.nhs.uk/bgh

Borders Primary Care NHS Trust

Newstead, Melrose TD6 9DB
Tel: 01896 828282 Fax: 01896 828298
Website: www.show.scot.nhs.uk/bpct
(Borders NHS Board)

Chair Barbara Wright
Chief Executive John Turner

Coldstream Cottage Hospital

Kelso Road, Coldstream TD12 4LQ
Tel: 01890 882417 Fax: 01890 883954
Total Beds: 14

Eyemouth Day Hospital (Geriatric)

Houndlaw Park, Eyemouth TD14 5DA
Tel: 01890 751101

Firholm Day Unit (Elderly with Dementia)

Innerleithen Road, Peebles EH45 8BD
Tel: 01721 720544 Fax: 01721 724063

Gala Day Unit (Elderly with Dementia)

10 Sime Place, Galashiels TD1 1ST
Tel: 01896 754669 Fax: 01896 754669

Hawick Cottage Hospital

Buccleuch Road, Hawick TD9 0EJ
Tel: 01450 372162 Fax: 01450 373935
Total Beds: 24

Hawick Day Hospital (Geriatric)

Buccleuch Road, Hawick TD9 0EJ
Tel: 01450 370000

Haylodge Day Hospital (Geriatric)

Neidpath Road, Peebles EH45 8JG
Tel: 01721 722080

Haylodge Hospital

Neidpath Road, Peebles EH45 8JG
Tel: 01721 722080
Total Beds: 46

Kelso Day Hospital (Geriatric)

Inch Road, Kelso TD5 7JP
Tel: 01573 225779

Kelso Hospital

Inch Road, Kelso TD5 7JP
Tel: 01573 223441 Fax: 01573 225321
Total Beds: 35

Knoll Day Hospital (Geriatric)

Station Road, Duns TD11 3EL
Tel: 01361 883373

Knoll Hospital

Station Road, Duns TD11 3EL
Tel: 01361 883373 Fax: 01361 882186
Total Beds: 27

Princes Street Day Unit (Adult Mental Illness)

Princes Street, Hawick TD9 7EJ
Tel: 01450 377515 Fax: 01450 373425

Priorsford Day Unit (Adult Mental Illness)

Tweed Green, Peebles EH45 8AR
Tel: 01721 723701 Fax: 01721 724052

Sister Margaret Cottage Hospital

Castlegate, Jedburgh TD8 6QD
Tel: 01835 863212 Fax: 01835 864917
Total Beds: 9

West Port Day Unit (Elderly with Dementia)

Drumlanrig Square, Hawick TD9 0BG
Tel: 01450 378028 Fax: 01450 373482

Dumfries and Galloway Acute and Maternity Hospitals NHS Trust

Dumfries and Galloway Royal Infirmary, Bankend Road, Dumfries DG1 4AP
Tel: 01387 246246 Fax: 01387 241639
(Dumfries and Galloway NHS Board)

Chair Hilary L Grieve
Chief Executive John Burns

Dumfries and Galloway Royal Infirmary

Bankend Road, Dumfries DG1 4AP
Tel: 01387 246246 Fax: 01387 241639

Total Beds: 386

Accident and Emergency J W Burton
Anaesthetics D R Ball, D B Bennie, H A Brewster, R Meek, J Palmer, V Perkins, J Rutherford, N T B Watson, D Williams
Bacteriology F J Bone, B S Dale
Biochemistry J R Paterson
Care of the Elderly I Hay, G Rhind
Dental Surgery M Clark
Dermatology J F B Norris
ENT E Flint, B Joshi, S Metcalfe
General Medicine S Cross, C G Isles, G Jones, H A Sawers, M McMahon, P Rafferty, J S A Sawers, G W Tait
General Surgery C Auld, I M Muir, A D F Walls
Haematology A Stark, F Toolis
Obstetrics and Gynaecology H Currie, M F Geals, A Patterson, A McCullough, P K A Mensah, S J Wisdom
Ophthalmology G J Bedford, B J Power
Orthodontics J C Aird
Orthopaedics G Nimon, P Costigan, I McLean, A C Ogden, A Ratnam, K Saad
Paediatrics A Chapman, M Higgs, R M Simpson, R B Thomson
Palliative Medicine L Martin
Pathology W Candlish, I Gibson, A M Lutfy
Radiology D Hill, D N Jones, P Kelly, P Law, D G Watson
Radiotherapy and Oncology I H Kunkler
Rehabilitation Medicine R Holden
Rheumatology M J McMahon
Urology M Shearer

Dumfries and Galloway Primary Care NHS Trust

Crichton Hall, Crichton Royal Hospital, Bankend Road, Dumfries DG1 4TG
Tel: 01387 244000 Fax: 01387 247706
(Dumfries and Galloway NHS Board)

Chief Executive David Fraser

Annan Day Hospital

Stapleton Road, Annan
Tel: 01461 202017 Fax: 01461 201581
Total Beds: 34

Annan Hospital

Stapleton Road, Annan DG12 6NQ
Tel: 01461 203425 Fax: 01461 201581
Total Beds: 34

Castle Douglas Day Hospital

Academy Street, Castle Douglas
Tel: 01556 502333 Fax: 01556 502370
Total Beds: 26

Castle Douglas Hospital

Castle Douglas DG7 1EF
Tel: 01556 502333 Fax: 01556 502370
Total Beds: 34

Crichton Royal Hospital

Crichton Hall, Bankend Road, Dumfries DG1 4TG
Tel: 01387 244000 Fax: 01381 247706
Website: www.show.scot.nhs.uk/dgpct
Total Beds: 371

General Psychiatry J Graham, D Hall, J Leuvenninic, R McCreadie, A McFadyen, J Mackie, G Morrison, E Powell, R Slinn, J Waterhouse, E R M Wood

Dalrymple Day Hospital

Dalrymple Street, Stranraer
Tel: 01776 706900 Fax: 01776 706918
Total Beds: 10

Dalrymple Hospital

Stranraer DG9 7DQ
Tel: 01776 702323 Fax: 01776 706918
Total Beds: 44

Kirkcudbright Hospital

Kirkcudbright DG6 4BE
Tel: 01557 330549 Fax: 01557 331825
Total Beds: 14

Lochmaben Day Hospital

Lochmaben, Lockerbie
Tel: 01387 810255 Fax: 01387 810613
Total Beds: 10

Lochmaben Hospital

Lochmaben, Lockerbie DG11 1RQ
Tel: 01387 810255 Fax: 01387 810613
Total Beds: 18

Care of the Elderly I Hay, J B Wilson

Moffat Day Hospital

Moffat
Tel: 01683 220031 Fax: 01683 220539
Total Beds: 6

Moffat Hospital

Moffat DG10 9JY
Tel: 01683 220031 Fax: 1683 220539
Total Beds: 15

Newton Stewart Day Hospital

Newton Stewart
Tel: 01671 402015 Fax: 01671 402855
Total Beds: 10

Newton Stewart Hospital

Newton Stewart DG8 6LZ
Tel: 01671 402015 Fax: 01671 402855
Total Beds: 25

Nithbank Day Hospital

Dumfries
Tel: 01387 244455
Total Beds: 15

Thomas Hope Day Hospital

Market Square, Langholm
Tel: 01387 380417 Fax: 01387 381428
Total Beds: 8

Thornhill Day Hospital

Thornhill
Tel: 01848 302505
Total Beds: 12

Thornhill Hospital

Thornhill DG3 5AA
Tel: 01848 330205
Total Beds: 15

Fife Acute Hospitals NHS Trust

Hayfield House, Hayfield Road, Kirkcaldy, Fife KY2 5AH
Tel: 01592 643355 Fax: 01592 648060
Website: www.faht.scot.nhs.uk

NHS TRUSTS & NHS HOSPITALS

(Fife NHS Board)

Chair D Stobie
Chief Executive JG Connaghan

Forth Park Maternity Hospital

30 Bennochy Road, Kirkcaldy KY2 5RA
Tel: 01592 643355 Fax: 01592 642376
Total Beds: 106

Queen Margaret Hospital

Whitefield Road, Dunfermline KY12 0SU
Tel: 01383 623623 Fax: 01383 624156
Total Beds: 401

Victoria Hospital

Hayfield Road, Kirkcaldy KY2 5AH
Tel: 01592 643355 Fax: 01592 643355
Total Beds: 366

Fife Primary Care NHS Trust

Cameron House, Cameron Bridge, Leven KY8 5RG
Tel: 01592 712812 Fax: 01592 712762
(Fife NHS Board)

Chair J Gallacher
Chief Executive G J Brechin

Adamson Hospital

Bank Street, Cupar KY15 4JG
Tel: 01334 652901
Total Beds: 39

Care of the Elderly D Ghosh
General Surgery K Ballantyne
Obstetrics and Gynaecology D Urquhart
Orthopaedics T Brown
Urology C McCreadie

Cameron Hospital

Cameron Bridge, Windygates, Leven KY8 5RR
Tel: 01592 712472 Fax: 01592 716442
Total Beds: 130

Care of the Elderly A K Datta, D Ghosh, R Shenoy
Rehabilitation Medicine L Sloan
Rheumatology J Gibson

Forth Park Hospital

30 Bennochy Road, Kirkcaldy KY2 5RA

Glenrothes Day Hospital

1 Lodge Rise, Forresters Lodge, Glenrothes KY7 5QT
Tel: 01592 743505 Fax: 01592 753655
Total Beds: 20

Glenrothes Hospital

Lodge Rise, Glenrothes KY7 5TG
Tel: 01592 743505 Fax: 01592 743655
Total Beds: 62

Care of the Elderly R Shenoy
Rehabilitation Medicine L Sloan

Lynebank Hospital

Halbeath Road, Dunfermline KY11 4UW
Tel: 01383 623623 Fax: 01383 621955
Total Beds: 178

Learning Disabilities K King, R Logan

Netherlea Hospital

65 West Road, Newport-on-Tay DD6 8HR
Tel: 01382 543233

Total Beds: 10

Care of the Elderly D Ghosh

Randolph Wemyss Day Hospital

Wellesley Road, Donbeath, Buckhaven, Leven
Tel: 01592 712427 Fax: 01592 716267
Total Beds: 20

Randolph Wemyss Memorial Hospital

Wellesley Road, Buckhaven, Leven KY8 1HU
Tel: 01592 712427 Fax: 01592 716267
Total Beds: 54

Care of the Elderly A K Datta
General Medicine I Campbell, D Lawrie, J Wilson

St Andrews Memorial Hospital

Abbey Walk, St Andrews KY16 9LG
Tel: 01334 472327
Total Beds: 34

General Surgery R Diggory
Orthopaedics R Buxton
Urology J McFarlane

Stratheden Hospital

Cupar KY15 5RR
Tel: 01334 652611 Fax: 01334 656560
Total Beds: 311

Child and Adolescent Psychiatry V Davidson, R Sime, D L Taylor
General Psychiatry D Neilson, G Stevenson, G S Winslow

Townhill Day Hospital

Total Beds: 20

Weston Day Hospital

West Port, Cupar KY15
Tel: 01334 652163
Total Beds: 30

Whyteman's Brae Day Hospital

Whyteman's Brae, Kirkcaldy KY1 2ND
Tel: 01592 643355 Fax: 01592 640159
Total Beds: 80

Whyteman's Brae Hospital

Whyteman's Brae, Kirkcaldy KY1 2LA
Tel: 01592 643355 Fax: 01592 640159
Total Beds: 108

General Medicine S Clark, M Falzon, J Murphy, D Reid, M Roll, M Stewart

Forth Valley Acute Hospitals NHS Trust

Trust Headquarters, Westburn Avenue, Falkirk FK1 5ST
Tel: 01324 678502 Fax: 01324 678523
(Forth Valley NHS Board)

Chair Ian Mullen
Chief Executive Jim Currie

Falkirk and District Royal Infirmary

Major's Loan, Falkirk FK1 5QE
Tel: 01324 624000 Fax: 01324 616068
Total Beds: 379

Anaesthetics I Broom, R G Law, A McDonald, J C Murray, H Robb, A J Semple, D S Simpson, W J Thomson
Care of the Elderly R J Lenton, P Murdoch, I Scolgall, J Taylor
Chemical Pathology M Holliday
Dermatology D C Dick, C Morton

ENT D G Keay, D A L McCallum, J McGarva, A M Pettigrew
General Medicine L Buchanan, D Doig, A Hargreaves, P D McSorley, D Morrison, N R Peden, W S J Ruddell, S C Wright
General Surgery A Al-Asadi, D R Harper, N W S Harris, J A E McDonald, R C Smith
Genitourinary Medicine J N Harvey
Geriatric Medicine A Grant, R J Lenton, E Millar, P S Murdoch, I Scougal
Haematology A D J Birch
Medical Microbiology I King, J McGavigan
Obstetrics and Gynaecology R A Cole, F Crichton, K A Grant, D McQueen
Ophthalmology J D Huggan, L S Jackson, G D Morrice, W A C Simpson
Oral and Maxillofacial Surgery J McManners
Orthodontics C M Wood
Orthopaedics K Buring, J De Leeuw, J R Lindsay, M Vishwanath
Paediatrics I Abu-Arafeh
Pathology D C Carfrae, K D Morton, H B Tavadia
Radiology J Barry, A J Byrne, D Roxburgh, L Stewart
Radiotherapy and Oncology J Cassidy, L MacMillan, J M Russell
Rheumatology and Rehabilitation M Brzeski
Urology M Hehir, A C N Rogers, M Smith

Stirling Royal Infirmary

Livilands, Stirling FK8 2AU
Tel: 01786 434000 Fax: 01786 450588
Total Beds: 469

Anaesthetics C R G Crawford, H M M Finlay, W Mair, C R G Reid, W Richards, D H Robertson, A J Trench
Care of the Elderly D C Kennie, C H McAlpine, J Reid
Chemical Pathology G F Follett
Child and Adolescent Psychiatry C Greenshaw, B Norten, M E N O'Gorman
Cytology D Sprunt
Dermatology D C Dick
ENT D G Keay, D A McCallum, D B MacGregor, A M Pettigrew
General Medicine D N Clarke, A D Howie, S B M Reith, J F B Smith
General Psychiatry R J McIlwaine, D A Pemberton
General Surgery D B Booth, W H S Henry, A D McNeill, A Smith
Genitourinary Medicine J N Harvey
Haematology A D J Birch, D H Ramsey
Medical Microbiology J McGavigan
Obstetrics and Gynaecology M Sathanandan, J D Steven, K S Stewart
Ophthalmology J D Huggan, L S Jackson, G D Morrice, W A C Simpson
Orthodontics C M Wood
Orthopaedics R D Briggs, J F S Isbister, T S Kerr, A A Robertson, D J Ross
Paediatrics J O Beattie, J H Higgins, J A Inall, R C McWilliam
Pathology D C Carfrae, K D Morton, H B Tavadia
Radiology H E Cunningham, P McDermot
Radiotherapy and Oncology N S Reed, A G Robertson
Urology M Hehir, G B McKelvie, A C N Rogers

Forth Valley Primary Care NHS Trust

Royal Scottish National Hospital, Old Denny Road, Larbert FK5 4DS
Tel: 01324 570700 Fax: 01324 562367
Website: www.fvpc.scot.nhs.uk/nhsfv/index.html
(Forth Valley NHS Board)

Chair Doris Littlejohn
Chief Executive Anne Hawkins

Bannockburn Hospital

Bannockburn, Stirling FK7 8AH
Tel: 01786 813016 Fax: 01786 812071
Total Beds: 114

Care of the Elderly D C Kennie
Old Age Psychiatry R J Coles, Dr Kidd

Bellsdyke Hospital

Bellsdyke Road, Larbert FK5 4SF
Tel: 01324 570700 Fax: 01324 562367
Total Beds: 102

General Psychiatry Dr Brown, Dr McFlynn, Dr Morrison

Bo'ness Hospital

Dean Road, Bo'ness EH51 0DH
Tel: 01506 823032 Fax: 01506 822680
Total Beds: 40

Care of the Elderly R Lenton, Dr McKean

Bonnybridge Hospital

Falkirk Road, Bonnybridge FK4 1BD
Tel: 01324 814685 Fax: 01324 815652
Total Beds: 90

General Medicine P Murdoch, Dr Scougall
Psychiatry of Old Age G McLean, Dr Woolf

Clackmannan County Day Hospital

Clackmannan County Hospital, Ashley Terrace, Alloa FK10 2BE
Tel: 01259 723840
Total Beds: 20

Clackmannan County Hospital

Ashley Terrace, Alloa FK10 2BE
Tel: 01259 723840 Fax: 01259 724740
Total Beds: 32

General Psychiatry Dr Collins, C Crawford
Psychiatry of Old Age D R Coles

Dunrowan Day Hospital

Maggie Woods Loan, Falkirk
Tel: 01324 639009
Total Beds: 20

Kildean Day Hospital

Drip Road, Stirling FK8 1RW
Tel: 01786 446114
Total Beds: 20

Kildean Hospital

Drip Road, Stirling FK8 1RW
Tel: 01786 446114 Fax: 01786 458605
Total Beds: 30

Care of the Elderly A Mackenie
Psychiatry of Old Age R J Coles

Orchard House Day Hospital

Union Street, Stirling FK8 1PA
Tel: 01786 474161 Fax: 01786 447430
Total Beds: 25

Princes Street Day Hospital

5 Princes Street, Stirling FK8 1HQ
Tel: 01786 474230
Total Beds: 20

Royal Scottish National Hospital

Old Denny Road, Larbert FK5 4EH
Tel: 01324 570700 Fax: 01324 558382
Total Beds: 140

General Psychiatry Dr McVicker

NHS TRUSTS & NHS HOSPITALS

Sauchie Hospital
Sunnyside, Alloa FK10 3BW
Tel: 01259 722060 Fax: 01259 720474
Total Beds: 30

Care of the Elderly J Bishop-Miller

Westbank Day Hospital
West Bridge Street, Falkirk FK1 5RT
Tel: 01324 624111
Total Beds: 20

Grampian Primary Care NHS Trust
Bennagate, Royal Cornhill Hospital, Aberdeen AB25 2ZH
Tel: 01224 663123 Fax: 01224 403602
Website: www.gpct.org.uk
(Grampian NHS Board)

Chair J Royan
Chief Executive Ewan Robertson, Jeremy Taylor

Aberdeen City Hospital
Urquhart Road, Aberdeen AB24 5AN
Tel: 01224 663131
Total Beds: 115

Care of the Elderly P C Gautam, D Newnham, J Scott
General Psychiatry M Shanks

Aboyne Hospital
Aboyne AB34 5HQ
Tel: 01339 886433 Fax: 01339 885373
Total Beds: 48

Campbell Hospital
Park Crescent, Portsoy, Banff AB45 2TR
Tel: 01261 842202 ext: 201 Fax: 01261 843971
Total Beds: 26

Chalmers Hospital
Clunie Street, Banff AB45 1JA
Tel: 01261 812567 ext: 71168 Fax: 01261 818074
Total Beds: 58

General Psychiatry D Fowlik

Dr Gray's Hospital (Mental and Community)
Elgin IV30 1SN
Tel: 01343 543131 Fax: 01343 558504

Fleming Hospital
Aberlour AB38 9PR
Tel: 01340 871464 Fax: 01340 871814
Total Beds: 15

Fraserburgh Hospital
Lochpots Road, Fraserburgh AB43 5NF
Tel: 01346 513151 Fax: 01346 514548
Total Beds: 66

General Psychiatry D Fowlik

Glen O'Dee Hospital
Banchory AB31 3SA
Tel: 01330 822233 Fax: 01330 825718
Total Beds: 60

Insch and District War Memorial Hospital
Rannes Street, Insch AB52 6JJ
Tel: 01464 820213 Fax: 01464 820233
Total Beds: 15

Inverurie Hospital
Upperboat Road, Inverurie AB51 3UL
Tel: 01224 663131, 01467 620454 ext: 51723 Fax: 01467 624023
Total Beds: 69

General Psychiatry E Alexander

Jubilee Hospital
Bleachfield Street, Huntly AB54 5EX
Tel: 01224 663131, 01466 792114 ext: 51302 Fax: 01466 794544
Total Beds: 51

Kincardine Community Hospital
Stonehaven AB39 2NH
Tel: 01569 792020
Total Beds: 49

General Psychiatry P Olley

Kincardine O'Neil War Memorial Hospital
St Marnan Road, Torphins, Banchory AB31 7JQ
Tel: 01339 882302 Fax: 01339 882580
Total Beds: 11

Ladysbridge Hospital
Whitehills, Banff AB45 2JS
Tel: 01261 861361 Fax: 01261 861779
Total Beds: 165

General Psychiatry R D Drummond, K McKay, J Oliver

Leanchoil Hospital
Forres IV36 0RF
Tel: 01309 672284 Fax: 01309 673935
Total Beds: 35

Maud Hospital
Maud Hospital, Bank Road, Maud AB42 5NR
Tel: 01771 604236
Total Beds: 50

General Psychiatry D Fowlik

Peterhead Community Hospital
21 Links Terrace, Peterhead AB42 6XB
Tel: 01779 478234 Fax: 01779 478111
Total Beds: 35

General Psychiatry D Fowlik

Royal Cornhill Hospital
26 Cornhill Road, Aberdeen AB25 2ZH
Tel: 01224 557433 Fax: 01224 403407
Total Beds: 505

General Psychiatry E R Alexander, M Bremner, S Calder, J S Callender, J M Eagles, L M Emslie, D G Fowlie, S Gilfillan, R Hamilton, D LePoidevin, J Lolley, L A McCrone, I McIlwain, H Millar, M Muir, P Ollem, A G Oswald, A Palin, A D T Robinson, P D Sclare, M Shanks, D St. Clair, L Sweeney, P Trotter, J Warrington, A Wells, L Whalley, G E Wilson, Dr Wischik

Seafield Hospital
Buckie AB56 1EJ
Tel: 01542 832081 Fax: 01542 834254
Total Beds: 66

Spynie Hospital
Elgin IV30 2PW
Tel: 01343 53131 Fax: 01343 552185
Total Beds: 66

Stephen Hospital

Dufftown, Keith AB55 4BH
Tel: 01340 820215 Fax: 01340 820593
Total Beds: 21

Turner Memorial Hospital

Turner Street, Keith AB55 5DJ
Tel: 01542 882526 Fax: 01542 882317
Total Beds: 27

Turriff Community Hospital

Balmellie Road, Turriff AB53 4SR
Tel: 01888 563293 Fax: 01888 562431
Total Beds: 19

Ugie Hospital

Ugie Road, Peterhead AB42 6LZ
Tel: 01779 72011 Fax: 01779 471109
Total Beds: 44

General Psychiatry D Fowlik

Woodlands Hospital

Craigton Road, Cults, Aberdeen AB15 9PR
Tel: 01224 663131 Fax: 01224 404018
Total Beds: 64

Learning Disabilities R D Drummond, K McKay

Grampian University Hospitals NHS Trust

Foresthil House, Ashgrove Road West, Aberdeen AB25 2ZB
Tel: 01224 681818 Fax: 01224 685307
Website: www.show.scot.nhs.uk/guh
(Grampian NHS Board)

Chair Hance Fullerton
Chief Executive Alec Cumming

Aberdeen Maternity Hospital

Cornhill Road, Aberdeen AB25 2ZL
Tel: 01224 681818 Fax: 01224 684880
Total Beds: 144

Anaesthetics A Campbell, F M Knox, A W Sheikh
Neonatal P Booth, P Duffty, D J Lloyd
Obstetrics D R Abramovich, P M Fisher, M H Hall, G D Lang, D E Parkin, N C Smith, H W Sutherland, A A Templeton, P B Terry

Aberdeen Royal Infirmary

Foresterhill, Aberdeen AB25 2ZN
Tel: 01224 681818
Total Beds: 1100

Accident and Emergency Dr Cooper, Dr Ferguson, Dr Hiscox, J G Page
Anaesthetics G D Adey, J S Blaiklock, G Byers, A Campbell, W R Casson, W Chambers, R W Davidson-Lamb, K Ferguson, J M Imray, G M Johnston, B R Kennedy, F M Knox, H J McFarlane, J D Mckenzie, D M Macleod, M S P Macnab, D Noble, R Patey, G Ramayya, E A Robertson, G S Robertson, D G Ross, A W Sheikh, G Smith, I Smith
Cardiology K Jennings
Dermatology A D Ormerod, L Stankler, M I White
ENT K A McLay, W J Newlands, D J Veitch, L C Wills, H A Young
General Medicine N B Bennett, J S Bevan, P W Brunt, A A Dawson, A S Douglas, N Edward, N B Haites, D J King, K C McHardy, A W McKinley, A M MacLeod, N A G Mowat, D Ogston, D W M Pearson, J C Petrie, S Ralston, J M Rowless, T S Sinclair, A H Watt, S J Watt, M J Williams
General Surgery A K Ah-See, G Cooper, A I Davidson, J Engeset, O Eremin, S Heys, R A Keenan, P King, N M Koruth, Z H Krukowski, S S Miller, G G Youngson

Genitourinary Medicine A J Downie
Haematology A A Dawson, R R Khaund, P J King
Neurology R J Coleman
Neurosurgery D G Currie, G Kaar
Ophthalmology H R Atta, W H Church, W B M Donaldson, J V Forrester, F D Green, C H Hutchinson, A G R Rennie
Oral and Maxillofacial Surgery N Renny
Orthopaedics J McLauchlan, T R Scotland, J M Scott, P A Slater, D Wardlaw
Plastic Surgery Dr Davies, J D Holmes, P S Kolhe
Thoracic Surgery J S Cockburn, R Jeffrey, S Prasad
Urology S McClinton, L E F Moffat

Dr Gray's Hospital (Acute)

Elgin IV30 1SN
Tel: 01343 543131 Fax: 01343 558504
Website: www.show.scot.nhs.uk/guh
Total Beds: 190

Anaesthetics A Bruce, G M Duthie, C McFarlane
General Medicine R Harvey, R D M MacLeod, D Williams
General Surgery I G Gunn, R McIntyre, J D B Miller
Medical Paediatrics A Attenburrow, H Stander
Obstetrics and Gynaecology Dr Evans, B Lim, S Navani
Ophthalmology J Wallace
Orthopaedics D Anderson, G Kilian, M Roos

Foresterhill Hospital

Foresterhill, Aberdeen AB9 8AQ
Tel: 01224 681818 Fax: 01224 840597
Total Beds: 1093

Royal Aberdeen Children's Hospital

Cornhill Road, Aberdeen AB25 2ZG
Tel: 01224 681818 Fax: 01224 840704
Website: www.show.scot.nhs.uk/guh
Total Beds: 113

Anaesthetics G Byers, A Campbell, J M Imray, G Johnstone, G S Robertson, A Sheikh, G Smith
Dermatology A D Ormerod, L Stankler, M I White
ENT K A McLay, W J Newlands, D Veitch, L C Wills, H A Young
General Medicine I A Auchterlonie, P Booth, G F Cole, P Duffty, A D Kindley, D J Lloyd, G Russell, P J Smail
General Psychiatry M Brown, D D Chisholm, C Reed
General Surgery G Ninan, G G Youngson
Neurosurgery C T Blaiklock, D G Currie
Ophthalmology H R Atta, W H Church, W B M Donaldson, J V Forrester, F D Green, C H Hutchinson, A G R Rennie
Oral and Maxillofacial Surgery N W Kerr
Orthodontics S Hewage, G Wright
Orthopaedics P H Gibson, J McLauchlan, T R Scotland
Plastic Surgery J Holmes, P Kohle

Tor-Na-Dee Hospital

Milltimber, Aberdeen
Tel: 01224 867307 Fax: 01224 840771
Website: www.show.scot.nhs.uk/guh
Total Beds: 71

Woodend Hospital

Eday Road, Woodend, Aberdeen AB15 6XS
Tel: 01224 663131 Fax: 01224 404179
Website: www.show.scot.nhs.uk/gov
Total Beds: 332

Anaesthetics G R Dundas
Care of the Elderly P C Gautam, S J C Hamilton, M D MacArthur, D Newnham, W R Primrose, C J Scott, G Seymour, S Wilkinson
Orthopaedics G P Ashcroft, R Battacharya, R B Chesney, P H Gibson, J Hutchison, D Knight, W Ledingham, J McLauchlan, N Maffulli, T Scotland, D Wardlaw
Rehabilitation Medicine J A Cozens, S J C Hamilton, R E Scorgie, C J Scott, R Seymour

NHS TRUSTS & NHS HOSPITALS

Greater Glasgow Primary Care NHS Trust

Gartnavel Royal Hospital, 1055 Great Western Road, Glasgow G12 0XH
Tel: 0141 211 3600 Fax: 0141 211 0307
Website: www.show.scot.nhs.uk/ggpct
(Greater Glasgow NHS Board)

Chair Andrew Robertson
Chief Executive Tim Davison

Acorn Street Day Hospital

23 Acorn Street, Glasgow G40
Tel: 0141 556 4789
Total Beds: 30

General Psychiatry G T Crockett, D I Melville, P C Misra

Gartnavel Royal Hospital

1055 Great Western Road, Glasgow G12 0XH
Tel: 0141 211 3600
Total Beds: 210

Leverndale Hospital

510 Crookston Road, Glasgow G53 7TU
Tel: 0141 211 6400 Fax: 0141 211 6421
Total Beds: 397

General Psychiatry S Alfred, J Baird, D A Coia, C Flanigan, A Fraser, J Gray, T Henderson, A V M Hughson, G Jackson, D Lyons, J P McKane, A Mitchell, D Palmer, G Shaw-Dunn, J Summers, J Taylor, S Whyte

MacKinnon House

Stobhill Hospital, 133 Balornock Road, Glasgow G21 3UZ
Tel: 0141 531 3100 Fax: 0141 531 3236

The Orchards

153 Panmure Street, Glasgow G20
Tel: 0141 531 5900 Fax: 0141 945 3851

Parkhead Hospital

81 Salamanca Street, Glasgow G31 5ES
Tel: 0141 211 8300 Fax: 0141 211 8312

General Psychiatry E H Bennie, D Brodie, C Flanigan, P Jauhar, Dr Mason, P C Misra, Dr Moore, M M Walker, Dr White, Dr Williams

Shettleston Day Hospital

150 Wellshot Street, Glasgow G32
Tel: 0141 778 8381

General Psychiatry J G Knill-Jones

Woodilee Hospital

Lenzie, Glasgow G66 3UG
Tel: 0141 777 8000 Fax: 0141 776 2532
Total Beds: 265

General Psychiatry D Ball, J G Campbell, M M Kemp, A Kerr, G McGovern, D McInroy, M Z Rahman, J B Riddell, A Sim, Dr Todd
Psychiatry of Old Age A H Frame, J McKnight, M Smith

Highland Acute Hospitals NHS Trust

Raigmore Hospital, Old Perth Road, Inverness IV2 3UJ
Tel: 01463 704000 Fax: 01463 711322
(Highland NHS Board)

Chair Stuart Whiteford

Chief Executive Richard Carey
Consultants S Macleod, L Smith

Belford Hospital, Fort William

Belford Road, Fort William
Tel: 01397 702481 Fax: 01397 792772
Total Beds: 43

Raigmore Hospital

Perth Road, Inverness IV2 3UJ

Highland Primary Care NHS Trust

Royal Northern Infirmary, Inverness IV3 5SF
Tel: 01463 242860 Fax: 01463 713844
(Highland NHS Board)

Chair Heather Sheerin
Chief Executive Helen Master

Belford Hospital (Midwifery)

Belford Road, Fort William PH33 6BS
Tel: 01397 702481 Fax: 01397 702772
Total Beds: 6

Belhaven Ward, Belford Hospital

Fort William
Tel: 01397 702481 Fax: 01397 702772
Total Beds: 23

County Hospital, Invergordon

Invergordon IV18 0JR
Tel: 01349 852496 Fax: 01349 854328
Total Beds: 44

Dr Mackinnon Memorial Hospital

Broadford, Isle of Skye
Tel: 01471 822491 Fax: 01471 822298
Total Beds: 25

General Surgery J R Ball

Dunbar Hospital

Thurso KW14 7XE
Tel: 01847 893263 Fax: 01847 892263
Total Beds: 16

Gesto Hospital

Edinbane, Portree, Isle of Skye
Tel: 01470 582262 Fax: 01470 582360
Total Beds: 16

Glencoe Hospital

Glencoe, Ballachulish
Tel: 01855 811254
Total Beds: 25

Ian Charles Hospital

Grantown-on-Spey
Tel: 01479 872528
Total Beds: 18

Invergordon County Hospital

Invergordon IV18 0JR
Tel: 01349 852496 Fax: 01349 852328
Total Beds: 44

Care of the Elderly P K Srivastava

Lawson Memorial Hospital

Station Road, Golspie KW10 6SS
Tel: 01408 633157 Fax: 01408 633947
Total Beds: 15

Anaesthetics K A Abraham, V Gadiyar, R Nanda Kumar
General Surgery P Fisher, W G Johnston

Lawson Memorial Hospital (Surgical Services) (Cambusavie)

Station Road, Golspie KW10 6SS
Tel: 01408 633157 Fax: 01408 633947
Total Beds: 30

Migdale Hospital

Bonar Bridge, Ardgay IV24 3AP
Tel: 01863 766211 Fax: 01863 766623
Total Beds: 34

Nairn Town and County Hospital

Cawdor Road, Nairn IV12 5EE
Tel: 01667 452101
Total Beds: 19

New Craigs

Inverness IV3 6JU
Tel: 01463 242860 Fax: 01463 236154
Total Beds: 223

General Psychiatry Dr Baeker, K Blagden, J Deans, Y Edmonstone, D Gordon, A Hay, G Jones, A MacGregor

Portree Hospital

Portree, Isle of Skye
Tel: 01478 613200 Fax: 01478 613526
Total Beds: 13

Ross House Day Hospital

Inverness
Tel: 01463 718302 Fax: 01463 718303

Ross Memorial Hospital

Ferry Road, Dingwall IV15 9QT
Tel: 01349 863313 Fax: 01349 865852
Total Beds: 31

Royal Northern Infirmary

Inverness IV3 5SS
Tel: 01463 242860 Fax: 01463 713884
Total Beds: 30

Care of the Elderly V P Sood, P K Srivastava

St Vincent's Hospital

Kingussie
Tel: 01540 661219 Fax: 01540 661035
Total Beds: 39

Town and County Hospital

Wick KW1 5NQ
Tel: 01955 604025 Fax: 01955 604606
Total Beds: 20

York Day Hospital

Ness Walk, Royal Northern Infirmary, Inverness IV3 5SF
Tel: 01463 242860 Fax: 01463 713884

Lanarkshire Acute Hospitals NHS Trust

Centrum Park, Hagmill Road, Coatbridge ML5 4TD
Tel: 01236 438100 Fax: 01236 438111
Website: www.show.scor.nhs.uk/laht
(Lanarkshire NHS Board)

Chair James Dunbar

Chief Executive Joe Owens
Consultants R Wright

Hairmyres Hospital

Eaglesham Road, East Kilbride G75 8RG
Tel: 01355 585000 Fax: 01355 584473
Total Beds: 446

Accident and Emergency P O'Connor
Anaesthetics J W Burns, G W Davidson, J M Glasser, J V Lees, W A McCulloch, F C McGroarty, G A Weetch
Biochemistry K Cunningham
Care of the Elderly G Cunning, B Martin, M E Stewart, B Yip
Chest Disease C J Clark, M D Clee
Dermatology F Campbell, C Evans, S O Neil, A Strong
ENT J L Handa, G L Picozzi, P S White
General Medicine C J Clark, H N Cohen, K Oldroyd, B D Vallance
General Surgery J R Goldring, D Knight, D F Miller, J R Richards, W O Thomson
Haematology A Roetaf, S Shahriari
Medical Microbiology D Baird
Obstetrics and Gynaecology H Gordon, J M Grant, G K Osbourne, K Spowart
Ophthalmology I Syme
Orthopaedics A Goresori, P J John, W D Newton, J T Watson
Pathology H Kamel, A McLay
Radiology R Connor, R H Corbett, A McCallum, S Millar, F Mohsen, R Weir
Rheumatology A A Zoma
Thoracic Surgery A N Al-Jilaihawi, D Prakash
Urology P S Orr, B S Satye Vedanan, L Walker

Monklands Hospital

Monkscourt Avenue, Airdrie ML6 0JS
Tel: 01236 748748 Fax: 01236 760015
Total Beds: 498

Accident and Emergency M T Brookes, I McLaren, M Watt
Anaesthetics M S Brink, D Clough, T Dunn, M D Inglis, R Mackenzie, S MacVicar, S Marshall, V Muir, A J W Naismith, P Paterson, V Reid, J M Thorp
Bacteriology M Morgan
Biochemistry K J M Cunningham
Care of the Elderly L R Schmulian
Cytology S Gardiner, J E A Imrie
Dermatology W S Douglas, C D Evans, A M M Strong, N Wainwright
ENT N Balagji, J Handa, A Johnston, G Picozzi, E Stewart
General Medicine J Bath, A Gardiner, T Gilbert, M Hand, A D B Harrower, R J Holden, N Kennedy, L McAlpine, D Mathews, A Pell, A Prach, A Raeside, J C Rodger, W J G Smith, W T A Todd
General Surgery Dr Brookes, A McDonald, Dr Mackenzie, Dr Mackenzie, D Murphy, Dr Scott
Gynaecology R Cassie, D Conway, T G B Dow, V Harper
Haematology G Cook, J Murphy, W H Watson
Histopathology R T Zuk
Infectious Diseases N Kennedy, W T A Todd
Maxillofacial Surgery N Hammersley
Neurology D Grosset, R Petty
Ophthalmology A Wylie
Orthodontics M C Easton
Orthopaedics Dr Braidwood, D Bramley, A Campbell, Dr Singh
Paediatrics M Loudon, J Whyte
Radiology J Guse, R M Holden, K Hughes, J A Johnstone, W Mowat, R Railton, K J Wallers
Urology P S Orr, L Walker

Wishaw General Hospital

50 Netherton Street, Wishaw ML2 0DP
Tel: 01698 361100 Fax: 01698 376671
Total Beds: 633

NHS TRUSTS & NHS HOSPITALS

Lanarkshire Primary Care NHS Trust

Trust Headquarters, Strathclyde Hospital, Airbles Road, Motherwell ML1 3BW
Tel: 01698 245000 Fax: 01698 245009
Email: enquiries@lanpct.scot.nhs.uk
Website: www.show.scot.nhs.uk/lanpct/
(Lanarkshire NHS Board)

Chair Iain Laidlaw
Chief Executive Martin Hill

Alexander Hospital
Blair Road, Coatbridge ML5 2EP
Tel: 01698 422661
Total Beds: 20

Birkwood Hospital
Lesmahagow, Lanark ML11 1JP
Tel: 01555 892382 Fax: 01555 894860
Total Beds: 168

General Practice Dr Christie

Caird House
Caird Street, Hamilton ML3 0AL
Tel: 01698 540182
Total Beds: 10

Cleland Hospital
Bellside Road, Cleland, Motherwell ML1 5MR
Tel: 01698 860293 Fax: 01698 862453
Total Beds: 172

Care of the Elderly J McCallion, R W Pettersson
General Practice Dr McInnes
General Psychiatry A Sinclair

Coathill Hospital
Hospital Street, Coatbridge ML5 4DN
Tel: 01236 421266 Fax: 01236 431252
Total Beds: 146

Care of the Elderly G P Canning, L R Schmulian
Pathology S R Howatson

Hartwood Hospital
Hartwood, Shotts ML7 4LA
Tel: 01501 23286

Kello Hospital
Biggar ML12 6AF
Tel: 01899 220077
Total Beds: 22

General Medicine R H Baxter
General Practice Dr Bewsher
General Surgery J Cannon

Kirklands Hospital
Fallside Road, Bothwell, Glasgow G71 8BB
Tel: 01698 245000 Fax: 01698 852340
Total Beds: 226

General Psychiatry C Mani, H Masih

Lady Home Hospital
Douglas, Lanark ML11 0RE
Tel: 01555 851210
Total Beds: 22

General Medicine M Drah
General Practice Dr Scott
General Surgery J Cannon

Red Deer Day Hospital
Alberta Avenue, Westwood, East Kilbride, Glasgow G74 8N8
Tel: 01355 244254

Roadmeetings Hospital
Goremire Road, Carluke ML8 4PS
Tel: 01555 752242 Fax: 01555 752328
Total Beds: 81

Care of the Elderly J McCallion, R W Pettersson

Strathclyde Hospital
Airbles Road, Motherwell ML1 3BW
Tel: 01698 258800
Total Beds: 76

Udston Hospital
Farm Road, Burnbank, Hamilton ML3 9LA
Tel: 01698 723200 Fax: 01698 710700
Total Beds: 140

Care of the Elderly B Mishra, Dr Semple, Dr Sim, M E Stewart

Victoria Cottage Hospital
Glasgow Road, Kilsyth, Glasgow G65 9AG
Tel: 01236 822172
Total Beds: 17

General Practice Dr Walker

Wester Moffat Hospital
Towers Road, Airdrie ML6 8LW
Tel: 01236 763377 Fax: 01236 759913
Total Beds: 60

Lomond and Argyll Primary Care NHS Trust

Trust Headquarters, Aros, Lochgilphead PA31 8LB
Tel: 01546 602323 Fax: 01546 606568
Website: www.abaro.demon.co.uk
(Argyll and Clyde NHS Board)

Chair Vivien Dance
Chief Executive Michael J Bews

Argyll and Bute Hospital
Blarbuie Road, Lochgilphead PA31 8LD
Tel: 01546 602323
Total Beds: 181

General Psychiatry F M Corrigan, G M Fergusson, A V P Mackay, R Sandler, P Thompson

Campbeltown Hospital
Ralston Road, Campbeltown PA28 6LE
Tel: 01586 552224 Fax: 01586 554966
Total Beds: 62

Dumbarton Cottage Hospital
Towned Road, Dumbarton G82
Tel: 01389 763151

Dumbarton Joint Hospital
Cardross Road, Dumbarton G82 5JA
Tel: 01389 762317 Fax: 01389 764677
Total Beds: 42

Dunaros Hospital
Salen, Isle Of Mull PA72 6JF
Tel: 01680 300392

Dunoon General Hospital

Sandbank Road, Dunoon PA23 7RL
Tel: 01369 704341 Fax: 01369 702192
Total Beds: 84

Islay Hospital

Gortonvoggie Road, Bowmore PA43 7JD
Tel: 01496 810219 Fax: 01496 810754
Total Beds: 26

Lorn and Islands District General Hospital

Glengallen Road, Oban PA34 4HH
Tel: 01631 567500

Mid-Argyll Hospital

Blarbuie Road, Lochgilphead PA31 8JZ
Tel: 01546 602952 Fax: 01546 606500
Total Beds: 47

Vale of Leven District General Hospital

Main Street, Alexandria G83 0UA

Victoria Hospital Annexe

High Street, Rothesay PA20 9JH
Tel: 01700 502943 Fax: 01700 505147
Total Beds: 31

Care of the Elderly P Lawson

Victoria Hospital, Isle of Bute

High Street, Rothesay PA20 9JJ
Tel: 01700 503938 Fax: 01700 502865
Total Beds: 24

Victoria Infirmary

93 East King Street, Helensburgh G84 7BU
Tel: 01436 672158 Fax: 01436 672159
Total Beds: 36

Care of the Elderly N T Manning

Lothian Primary Care NHS Trust

St Roque, Astley Ainslie Hospital, 133 Grange Loan, Edinburgh EH9 2HL
Tel: 0131 537 9532 Fax: 0131 537 9500
Email: firstname.surname@lpct.scot.nhs.uk
(Lothian NHS Board)

Chair Garth Morrison
Chief Executive Murray Duncanson

Astley Ainslie Hospital

133 Grange Loan, Edinburgh EH9 2HL
Tel: 0131 537 9000 Fax: 0131 537 9500
Total Beds: 246

Care of the Elderly C T Currie
Rehabilitation Medicine J D Hunter, B Pentland, I Todd

Belhaven Hospital

Beveridge Row, Dunbar EH42 1TR
Tel: 01368 862246
Total Beds: 40

Care of the Elderly L Morrison

Corstorphine Hospital

136 Corstorphine Road, Edinburgh EH12 6TT
Tel: 0131 332 2566
Total Beds: 68

Eastern General Hospital

Seafield Street, Edinburgh EH6 7LN
Tel: 0131 536 7000 Fax: 0131 536 7474
Total Beds: 30

Edenhall Hospital

Pinkieburn, Musselburgh EH21 7TZ
Tel: 0131 536 8000 Fax: 0131 536 8152, 0131 536 8153
Total Beds: 60

Elderly Mentally Ill C Rodgers

Edington Cottage Hospital

54 St. Baldred's Road, North Berwick EH39 4PU
Tel: 01620 892878
Total Beds: 9

Herdmanflat Hospital

Haddington EH41 3BU
Tel: 0131 536 8300 Fax: 0131 536 8500
Total Beds: 97

General Psychiatry G Mercer, W Riddle, C R Rodger, T D Rogers

Loanhead Hospital

Hunter Avenue, Loanhead EH20 9SW
Tel: 0131 440 0174
Total Beds: 42

Roodlands Hospital

Hospital Road, Haddington EH41 3PF
Tel: 0131 536 8300 Fax: 0131 536 8399, 0131 536 8400
Total Beds: 64

Care of the Elderly A Jamieson, L Morrison

Rosslynlee Hospital

Roslin EH25 9QE
Tel: 0131 536 7600 Fax: 0131 536 7637
Total Beds: 120

Consultants J Craig, D Garbutt, A P R Moffoot

Royal Edinburgh Hospital

Morningside Terrace, Edinburgh EH9 1RJ
Tel: 0131 537 6000 Fax: 0131 537 6109
Total Beds: 628

Child and Adolescent Psychiatry R Glaze, R M Wrate
Consultants D Blackwood, A Carson, J Crichton, T Dalkin, K Ebmeier, P Hoare, E Johnston, P Lefevre, D Owens
General Psychiatry J Chick, D Chiswick, J Christie, C P Freeman, A M Lodge, J B Loudon, R Lyall, P McConville, S MacDonald, D Morrison, P A Morrison, T Murphy, N Nuttall, P O'Farrell, A L Phanjoo, E B Ritson, A Scott, K Slatford, J G Strachan, A Wells

Lothian University Hospitals NHS Trust

Royal Infirmary of Edinburgh, 1, Lauriston Place, Edinburgh EH3 9YW
Tel: 0131 536 1000 Fax: 0131 536 1001
(Lothian NHS Board)

Chair Barry Sealey
Chief Executive Allister Stewart

City Hospital

51 Greenbank Drive, Edinburgh EH10 5SB
Tel: 0131 536 1000 Fax: 0131 536 6001
Total Beds: 81

Anaesthetics G M R Bowler, C Morton, G C Pugh, G Sharwood-Smith

NHS TRUSTS & NHS HOSPITALS

ENT D L Cowan, W E Grant, A I G Kerr, G MacDougall, A G D Maran, R Mills
Medical Microbiology F X S Emanuel
Radiology A J A Wightman
Virology S Burns, N Hallam

Edinburgh Dental Institute

Lauriston Place, Edinburgh EH3 9YW
Tel: 0131 536 4900 Fax: 0131 536 4901

Anaesthetics G Keenan
Oral Medicine R I MacLeod
Oral Surgery R Brown, R Mitchell
Orthodontics W J Barrie, J Hammond, J P McDonald
Paediatric Dentistry M Dunn
Pathology G H Moody
Restorative Dentistry P D Callis, N J A Grey

Royal Hospital for Sick Children

9 Sciennes Road, Edinburgh EH9 1LF
Tel: 0131 536 0000 Fax: 0131 536 0001
Total Beds: 151

Accident and Emergency T Beattie
Anaesthetics L Aldridge, E Doyle, J Freeman, I Hudson, M Rose, D Simpson, C Young
Audiological Medicine D L Cowan, A I G Kerr
Biochemistry J Kirk
General Psychiatry F Forbes, P Hoare, B Norton, S Valentine
Haematology A E Thomas, H Wallace
Orthopaedics M McNicol
Paediatric Surgery G MacKinlay, F Munro, J Orr, D Wilson-Storey
Paediatrics D G D Barr, D Brown, J K Brown, J E Burns, J Burt, W A M Cutting, A T Edmunds, P Evenson, M Godman, C Kelnar, N Macintosh, T Marshall, R A Minns, G Stark, W S Uttley, H Wallace, D C Wilson
Pathology J Keeling, K MacKenzie
Plastic Surgery J D Watson
Radiology G M A Hendry, S MacKenzie, M McPhillips, A Wilkinson

Royal Infirmary of Edinburgh

Lauriston Place, Edinburgh EH3 9YW
Tel: 0131 536 1000 Fax: 0131 536 1001
Total Beds: 904

Accident and Emergency C Robertson, D Steedman
Anaesthetics R P Alston, I Armstrong, F Arnstein, D Beamish, G Bowler, D T Brown, A S Buchan, V Clark, I A Davidson, A Delvaux, M Dickson, J Donnelly, G B Drummond, J Jenkins, G Keenan, A Lee, D G Littlewood, M R Logan, J H McClure, A Mackenzie, S MacKenzie, D W McKeown, A Macrae, N A Malcolm-Smith, N Maran, J Milne, C Moores, C Morton, A Nimmo, S Nimmo, R Park, A T Pollock, G Pugh, D Ray, D H T Scott, D Semple, G H Sharwood-Smith, E Simon, C J Sinclair, A A Spence, H Spens, D Swann, T Walsh, J Wang, D Watson, D Weir
Biochemistry S W Walker
Cardiac Surgery E Brackenbury, E W J Cameron, C Campanella, P S Mankad, S Prasad, W S Walker
Cardiology P Bloomfield, N Boon, A Flapan, K A A Fox, H C Miller, N Uran
Care of the Elderly B J Chapman, N Colledge, C T Currie, D Grant, C Stewart, J Whitwell
Dermatology R D Aldridge, E Benton, D K Buxton, G M Cavanagh, V Doherty, J A A Hunter, G Kavanash, D Kemmett, J Rees, J A Savin, O M Schofield, M J Tidman
ENT D Cowan, W E Grant, A I G Kerr, G Macdougall, R Mills
Gastroenterology N D C Findlayson, P Hayes, R C Heading, A J McGilchrist, J Plevris, K Simpson
General Medicine D Bell, B Chapman, B Frier, R C Heading, E Housley, C Kelly, T Mackay, A Patrick, C Stewart, A Toft, M Uren, J Walker, M L Watson, C Whitworth, M Young
General Surgery D C C Bartolo, T J Crofts, A de Beaux, K C H Fearon, J L Forsythe, S Fraser, O J Garden, D Lee, A B MacGregor, K K Madhaven, S Paterson-Brown
Genitourinary Medicine A McMillan, G R Scott, C Thomson

Medical Microbiology S Burns, D H Crawford, F Emmanuel, N Hallam, R S Miles, M M Ogilvie, P Simmons, S Sutherland, D M Weir
Metabolic Disease B Frier, A Patrick, A Toft, J Walker, M Young
Nephrology A D Cumming, R G Phelps, C P Swainson, N Turner, C Whitworth, R J Winney
Neurology C Leueck, C Mumford
Obstetrics and Gynaecology R Anderson, D T Baird, K Boddy, A Brown, A D G Brown, C Busby-Earle, A A Calder, E S Cooper, H O D Critchley, K Dundas, D I M Farquharson, R Hughes, D S Irvine, F D Johnstone, S Lawson, M M Lees, W A Liston, H McPherson, J A Milne, G E Smart, C Tay, C P West
Orthopaedics J Christie, C M Court-Brown, J F Keating, M M M McQueen, C W Oliver, C M Robinson, A Simpson
Paediatrics I Laing, A Lyon, G Menon, B Stenson
Pathology A I Al-Nafussi, T J Anderson, J Bell, A Busuttil, E Cowan, E Duvall, P Fineron, S Fleming, H M Gilmour, K M Grigor, D J Harrison, H Kamel, D Lamb, A Lammie, E McGoogan, K M McLaren, M O'Sullivan, J Piris, B Purdue, W A Reid, D M Salter, A R W Williams, A H Wyllie
Psychology S Machale, G Masterton, S G Potts
Radiology P L Allan, I Beggs, S E Chambers, I N Gillespie, S Ingram, K McBride, G McKillop, S Monssa, S Moussa, J Murchison, D Patel, I M Prossor, D N Redhead, R Sellar, J Walker, J Walsh, A J A Wightman
Respiratory Medicine S Donnelly, N Douglas, C Haslet, A Hill, W MacNee, T Makay, T J Sethi, J Simpson
Thoracic Surgery E W J Cameron, W Walker
Vascular Surgery A Bradbury, R Chalmers, A M Jenkins, D Kitts, J A Murie
Virology M M Ogilvie, S Sutherland

Royal Infirmary of Edinburgh (Little France)

Old Dalkeith Road, Edinburgh EH16 4SU
Tel: 0131 536 1000 Fax: 0131 536 1001
Total Beds: 201

Anaesthetics M Logan, D McKeown, N A Malcolm-Smith, D Weir
Orthopaedics I H Annan, J Campbell, J N A Gibson, C Howie, G Keenan, G Lawson, J McBirnie, M McMaster, M F Macnicol, L Martin, R Nutton, J Robb
Radiology I Beggs
Rheumatology J Campbell

Royal Victoria Hospital

Craigleith Road, Edinburgh EH4 2DN
Tel: 0131 537 5000 Fax: 0131 537 5140
Total Beds: 200

General Medicine R Lindley, E MacDonald, R G Smith, J Starr
General Psychiatry E McLennan, A Stewart

Western General Hospital

Crew Road South, Edinburgh EH4 2XU
Tel: 0131 537 1000 Fax: 0131 537 1001
Total Beds: 604

Anaesthetics A Ahmed, P Andrews, T Aziz, C Brookman, G L M Carmichael, B Cook, M Cullen, J Fitzgerald, I Foo, J Freshwater, I S Grant, G Jones, K P Kelly, E Lloyd, S Mackenzie, S Midgley, M Rutledge, B Slawson, A Stewart, R B Sutherland, C B Wallis, J J Wedgewood, D J Wright
Bacteriology J E Coia, M F Hanson, R G Masterton
Biochemistry J P Ashby, P Rae, P R Wenham
Cardiology M Denvir, D B Northridge, T R D Shaw, I R Starkey, G R Sutherland
Chest Disease A P Greening, J A Innes
Endocrinology R Brown, R L Kennedy, J McKnight, P L Padfield, J S Seckl, B Walker, D J Webb
ENT D L Cowan, W Singh
Gastroenterology S Ghosh, K P Palmer
General Medicine M S Dennis, P L Padfield, W H Price, J S Seckl, D J Webb
General Psychiatry K Slatford, W A Tait

NORTH GLASGOW UNIVERSITY HOSPITALS NHS TRUST

General Surgery E Anderson, U Chetty, M Dixon, M Dunlop, D W H Hodges, C McArdle, I M C McIntyre, S J Nixon, R G Wilson
Genetics D Brock, D Fitzpatrick, M Porteus, A Wright
Haematology J Davies, M J Mackie
Neurology M Dennis, R Grant, C Lueck, T Russell, P Sandercock, R Sellars, P Statham, A J W Steers, C Warlow, I R Whittle
Neuropathology J E Bell, J Ironside, G A Lammie, R Will
Neurophysiology R Cull
Neurosurgery P Andrews, G L M Carmichael, D Child, J L Jenkinson
Oncology D Jodrell, J F Smyth
Pathology T J Anderson, J Bell, K M Grigor, J Ironside, J Lamb, G Lammie, A M Lessells, M A McIntyre, P Rae, J S J Thomas, J N Webb
Radiology J P Brush, M Chapman, D Collie, R J Gibson, D C Grieve, R J Sellar, A J Stevenson, C M Turnbull, J Wardlaw, A R Wright, W Young
Radiotherapy and Oncology V Cowie, A Gregor, G W Howard, L H Kunkler, R H MacDougall, P Syme
Rheumatology N Hurst, R Luqmani, G Nuki
Urology P Boilina, T B Hargreaves, A McNeill, S Moussa, G Smith, L H Stewart, D Tolley, D Tulloch

North Glasgow University Hospitals NHS Trust

Trust HQ, 300 Balgrayhill Road, Glasgow G31 2UR
Tel: 0141 211 4200 Fax: 0141 211 4202
(Greater Glasgow NHS Board)

Chair Ronnie Cleland
Chief Executive Maggie Boyle

Blawarthill Hospital

129 Holehouse Drive, Blawarthill, Glasgow G13 3TG
Tel: 0141 211 9000 Fax: 0141 211 9007
Total Beds: 120

Canniesburn Hospital

Switchback Road, Bearsden, Glasgow G61 1QL
Tel: 0141 211 5600 Fax: 0141 211 5651
Total Beds: 190

Plastic Surgery Dr McKay, R Ratcliffe, A Ray, D S Soutar, I Taggart, S Watson, M H C Webster

Drumchapel Hospital

Drum Chapel Road, Glasgow G15 6PX
Tel: 0141 211 6000
Total Beds: 120

Care of the Elderly W J Gilchrist, J MacDonald

Gartnavel General Hospital

1053 Great Western Road, Glasgow G12 0NY
Tel: 0141 211 3000 Fax: 0141 211 3466
Total Beds: 512

Anaesthetics T Algie, A J Asbury, A Binning, J H Brown, C Brydon, K M S Dewar, J R I Dougall, J J Henderson, A Hope, H Howie, I Keston, T B McCubbin, A Macfie, A D McLaren, A M McLeod, I McMenemin, N O'Donnell, N Pace, J L Plenderleith, D W Proctor, J A Reid, K M Rogers, C Runcie, M Serpell, P Stone, J G Todd, P G M Wallace
Biochemistry M H Dominiczak, I W Percy-Robb
Care of the Elderly W J Gilchrist, A Hendry, J McDonald, B O Williams
General Medicine J G Allan, S Dover, J Hunter, K E L McColl, P R Mills, D Porter, M Small, B H R Stack, R J Weir
General Surgery D Byrne, G Fullarton, D J Galloway, A J McKay, R Molloy, R O Quin, P Rogers
Haematology I L Evans, E Fitzsimmons, N P Lucie
Infectious Diseases R Fox, D Kennedy, A Pithie, E Walker
Ophthalmology T Barrie, H M Hammer, D J Holding, R McFadzean
Orthopaedics J F Crossan, U Fazzi, A Gray, P Grigoris, D L Hamblen, W Leach, J S Moir, A Reece
Otolaryngology G Browning, D Carrick, L Cooke, N K Geddes, G McGarry, F MacGregor, K MacKenzie, M Morrissey, I R C Swan
Radiology R Edwards, N C McMillan, J G Moss, R Vallance, L Wilkinson
Respiratory Medicine K R Patel, A Peacock, B H R Stack, N Thomson
Rheumatology J Hunter, D Porter
Urology M Aitchison, R F Deane, D Kirk, M Palmer
Virology G Clements

Glasgow Dental Hospital and School

378 Sauchiehall Street, Glasgow G2 3JZ
Tel: 0141 211 9600 Fax: 0141 211 9800

Anaesthetics A J Asbury, J R I Dougall, T D McCubbin, A McFie, A M McLeod, D Proctor, J A Reid, P Stone, J G Todd
Oral and Maxillofacial Surgery L Brocklebank, H A Critchlow, D A McGowan, K F Moos, D I Russell, D Stenhouse, G A Wood
Oral Medicine D H Felix, D Wray
Orthodontics D B Forsyth, D E Fung, W S J Kerr, J G McLennan, D T Millett, J S Reid, G S Taylor
Pathology J Bagg, D G MacDonald
Periodontology W M M Jenkins, D F Kinane, K W Stephen
Restorative Dentistry K J Jennings, A B Lamb, M F Lyons, J McCrossan, W P Saunders, S W Sharkey, I B Watson

Glasgow Eye Infirmary

3 Sandyford Place, Glasgow G3 7NB
Tel: 0141 211 3000

Ophthalmology T Barrie, H Hammer, D J Holding, J L Jay, C Kirkness, R McFadzean

Glasgow Homoeopathic Hospital

1053 Great Western Road, Glasgow G12 0XG
Tel: 0141 211 1600 Fax: 0141 211 1610
Total Beds: 20

General Medicine D T Reilly, T Whitmarsh

Glasgow Royal Infirmary

84 Castle Street, Glasgow G4 0SF
Tel: 0141 211 4000 Fax: 0141 211 7185
Total Beds: 751

Oncology D R M Soukop, D Dunlop
Respiratory Medicine S Banham, M Cotton, R Stevenson
Accident and Emergency R Crawford, A Ireland, I J Swann
Anaesthetics Dr Booth, Dr Church, Dr Colquhoun, M Daniel, W Fitch, W T Frame, Dr Geddes, Dr Greenhalgh, Dr Hamid, Dr Hickey, M Higgins, K James, J N C Kenny, Dr Kilpatrick, Dr Kinsella, Dr McGrady, T T McLintock, M McNeil, B H Maule, R Parris, Dr Patrick, Dr Paul, Dr Pearshall, Dr Reeve, K Simpson, Dr Smart, M C Stockwell, G A Sutherland, Dr Tan
Bacteriology J Hood, Dr Jones, B Thakker
Biochemistry F Dryburgh, Dr O'Reilly, J Shepherd
Cardiothoracic Surgery V Pathi, U Nkere, P Belcher, Dr Colquhoun, K G Davidson, A Murray, J C S Pollock, D J Wheatley
Care of the Elderly J Burns, B L Devine, P V Knight, P Longhorne, D Stott
Cytology F Mutch, Dr Stewart
Dermatology A A Forsyth, J Thomson
ENT G G Browning, K McKenzie, I R C Swan
General Medicine M Cotton, S Banham, J M Boulton-Jones, G Boyd, I T Boyle, Dr Brady, S Cobbe, D Dunlop, Dr Dunnigan, Dr Eteiba, H W Gray, I Hutton, D H Lawson, M Lean, A R Lorimer, G Lowe, A C McCuish, J F Mackenzie, J H McKillop, Dr Morris, Dr Neilly, K Paterson, Dr Rae, Dr Rankin, R I Russell, K Simpson, M Soukop, R Stevenson, J A Thomson
General Surgery Dr Anderson, Dr Carter, T G Cooke, I G Finlay, Dr Horgan, C W Imrie, R Mckee, W R Murray, Dr Stanton, Dr Stuart

NHS TRUSTS & NHS HOSPITALS

Genitourinary Medicine Dr Hillman, Dr Nandwani, J Roberts, Dr Scoular, G Sharp
Haematology G McQuaker, A Parker, Dr Franklin, I D Walker
Neurology W F Durward
Obstetrics and Gynaecology H Lyall, H Mactier, I Grier, R Howat, J H Kennedy, C B Lunan, H P McEwan, A Mathers, Dr Norman, R W S Yates
Ophthalmology B Browne, Dr Grierson, Dr Montgomery
Orthopaedics R Ingram, P James, I Kelly, R Simpson, I G Stother
Pathology A Foulis, Dr Going, F D Lee, Dr McNicol, Dr McPhader
Plastic Surgery D S Soutar, I Taggart, S Watson, M Webster
Radiology Dr Howie, Dr Lean, Dr Litherland, Dr McCarter, Dr Wilson, D E Anderson, A F Forrester, F W Poon, A W Reid, I Stewart
Rheumatology H Capell, M Field, R Madhok, R D Sturrock
Urology C Buck, P Paterson
Vascular Surgery D G Gilmour, D P Lieberman, J G Pollock

Princess Royal Maternity Unit

Glasgow Royal Infirmary, Alexander Parade, Glasgow G31 2ER
Tel: 0141 211 5400
Total Beds: 109

Anaesthetics W Frame, M McNeill
Biochemistry F Dryburgh
General Medicine A C MacCuish
Haematology I Walker
Obstetrics and Gynaecology I Grier, M Hepburn, R L Howat, J Kennedy, C B Lunan, H P McEwan, A Mathers, Dr Norman, R W S Yates
Paediatrics L Alroomi, P Galea, C Skeoch
Radiology J R McKenzie

Lightburn Hospital

966 Carntyne Road, Glasgow G32 6ND
Tel: 0141 211 1500 Fax: 0141 211 1521
Total Beds: 120

Care of the Elderly J Burns, B L Devine, P V Knight, P Longhorne, D Stott, J Taylor

Stobhill Hospital

Balgrayhill Road, Glasgow G21 3UR
Tel: 0141 201 3907 Fax: 0141 558 1575
Total Beds: 650

Anaesthetics R L Hughes, K Lamb, S D Macdonald, A H McKee, J B M McKellar, C D Miller, R K Parikh, D K Sewnauth, P J Slater
Bacteriology C Edwards, R W A Girdwood
Biochemistry B F Allam
Cardiology F G Dunn, N Goodfield, K J Hogg
Care of the Elderly J W Davie, L Erwin, F A Johnston, P J W Scott
Dental Surgery H A Critchlow
Dermatology R S Chapman, D C Dick, R E I Kerr
ENT B W H Irvine, B F O'Reilly, D Simpson
General Medicine B Z Danesh, J A H Forrest, P E McGill, E H McLaren
General Surgery M H Calvert, R Dalling, D T Hansell, A McMahon, J S Smith
Haematology R L C Cumming, R B Hogg
Nephrology J Fox, R MacTier
Obstetrics and Gynaecology J A Davis, M Deeny, C A Forrest, R A L Low
Ophthalmology H H Fawzi, J Murdoch
Orthopaedics G C Bennet, A W E Kinninmonth, L Rymaszewski, E F Wheelwright
Pathology D Millan, G D Smith
Radiology F Bryden, S Ingram, I A Macleod, J Shand
Radiotherapy and Oncology P Symonds
Respiratory Medicine G Boyd, R Milroy
Urology J Crooks, I S McLaughlin, A J Yates

Western Infirmary

Dumbarton Road, Glasgow G11 6NT
Tel: 0141 211 2000 Fax: 0141 211 1920
Total Beds: 527

Accident and Emergency P T Grant, W M Tullett
Anaesthetics T Algie, A J Asbury, A Binning, J H Brown, C Brydon, K M S Dewar, J R I Dougall, J J Henderson, A Hope, H Howie, I Kestin, T D McCubbin, A Macfie, A D McLaren, A M McLeod, I McMenemin, N O'Donnell, N Pace, J L Plenderleith, D W Proctor, J A Reid, K M Rogers, C Runcie, M Serpell, P Stone, J G Todd, P G M Wallace
Bacteriology S R Alcock, G P Corcoran
Cardiology H J Dargie, W S Hillis, J A Kennedy, J D McArthur, J McMurray
Cardiothoracic Surgery G Berg, A Faichney, M P G Jamieson, A Kirk, K McArthur
Chest Disease K R Patel, A Peacock, B H R Stack, N C Thomson
Dermatology M Fallowfield, R Lever, P McHenry, R MacKie, D Tillman
General Medicine M J Brodie, J M C Connell, D L Davies, A Dominiczak, H L Elliott, W S Hillis, A Jardine, K R Lees, K E L McColl, G T McInnes, A D McLellan, J Reid, P Semple, B Whiting
General Surgery W D George, D Hamilton, S G Macpherson, P J O'Dwyer, A D Purushstham
Genitourinary Medicine J Roberts
Haematology I L Evans, E Fitzsimmons, N P Lucie
Immunology A Farrell, E M Kirkwood, F Y Liew, A Mowat
Nephrology J D Briggs, B J R Junor, M McMillan, R S C Rogers
Neurology I Bone, P G Kennedy
Obstetrics and Gynaecology A Cameron, I Cameron, W R Chatfield, J W Cordiner, K Hanretty, M Lumsden
Ophthalmology J Dudgeon, G N Dutton, H Hammer, J L Jay, E Kemp, C Kirkness, W R Lee, D Seal
Orthopaedics J F Crossan, U Fazzi, A Gray, P Grigoris, D L Hamblen, W Leach, J S Moir, A Reece
Pathology W M H Behan, I L Brown, R A Burnett, A Cromie, M Fallowfield, W R Lee, G B M Lindop, T MacLeod, R N M MacSween, E Mallon, I A R More, R Reid, R Soutar
Public Health Medicine A Bryson
Radiology F G Adams, G Baxter, M D Cowan, R Edwards, W Kincaid, N C McMillan, J Moss, N Raby, G Stenhouse, R Vallance
Radiotherapy and Oncology P Canney, D Dodds, T Evans, R Jones, E Junor, J Cassidy, N O'Rourke, R P Rampling, N S Reed, D Ritchie, A G Robertson, J M Russell, D Dunlop, R P Symonds, C Twelves, P Vasey, J Welsh, H M A Yosef
Vascular Medicine A J McKay, R O Quin
Virology W Carman, E McCruden

Renfrewshire and Inverclyde Primary Care NHS Trust

Trust HQ, Merchiston Hospital, Brookfield by Johnstone, Paisley PA2 7DE
Tel: 01505 384000 Fax: 01505 384001
(Argyll and Clyde NHS Board)

Chair Graham Harells
Chief Executive George Buchanan

Dykebar Hospital

Grahamston Road, Paisley PA2 7DE
Tel: 0141 884 5122 Fax: 0141 884 5425
Total Beds: 332

General Psychiatry D A Bonham, J M Dingwall, J Gallacher, A Jones, S Miller, A J Naismith, M Smith, J Thompson
Psychiatry of Old Age A Hughes, H Livingston, K Philips

Hawkhead Hospital

Hawkhead Road, Paisley PA2 7BL
Tel: 0141 889 8151 Fax: 0141 848 7372
Total Beds: 96

Child and Adolescent Psychiatry N Speirs
General Psychiatry A Hughes

Johnstone Hospital
Bridge of Weir Road, Johnstone PA5 8YX
Tel: 01505 331471 Fax: 01505 336497
Total Beds: 104

Care of the Elderly D Mack, G K Simpson, C Wilkieson
General Psychiatry A Hughes

Merchiston Hospital
Brookfield, Johnstone PA5 8TY
Tel: 01505 328261 Fax: 01505 335803
Total Beds: 176

General Psychiatry M Ayana, T V S Chanrasekhar, A Deering, S Groves, H Small, R A D Sykes

Ravenscraig Hospital
Inverkip Road, Greenock PA16 9HA
Tel: 01475 733777 Fax: 01475 721547
Total Beds: 230

Care of the Elderly P Lawson, R E Young

Royal Alexandra Hospital (Care of the Elderly)
Corsebar Road, Paisley PA2 9PN
Tel: 0141 887 9111 Fax: 0141 887 6701
Total Beds: 130

General Psychiatry M Ayana, T V S Chanrasekhar, A Deering, S Groves, H Small, R A D Sykes

South Glasgow University Hospitals NHS Trust

Management Office, 1345 Govan Road, Glasgow G51 4TF
Tel: 0141 201 1100 Fax: 0141 201 2999
Website: www.show.scot.nhs.uk/sguht
(Greater Glasgow NHS Board)

Chair Elinor Smith
Chief Executive Robert Calderwood

Cowglen Hospital
10 Boydstone Road, Glasgow G53 6XJ
Tel: 0141 211 9200 Fax: 0141 636 6088
Total Beds: 148

Care of the Elderly S A Fraser, G J A McPhee, W Reid, J C Young

Mansionhouse Unit
100 Mansion House Road, Langside, Glasgow G41 3DX
Tel: 0141 201 6161 Fax: 0141 201 6159
Total Beds: 252

Care of the Elderly K Beard, I Lennox, J Potter, M A Roberts, D Stewart

Mearnskirk House
Newton Mearns, Glasgow G77 5RZ
Tel: 0141 616 3742
Total Beds: 72

Care of the Elderly K Beard, I M Lennox, J Potter, M Roberts, D Stewart

Rutherglen Maternity Hospital
Stonelaw Road, Rutherglen, Glasgow G73 2PG
Tel: 0141 201 6060 Fax: 0141 201 6423
Total Beds: 57

Anaesthetics J Purdie, B S Stuart
Bacteriology P J Redding

Biochemistry A Glen
Haematology P Tansey
Obstetrics and Gynaecology S Bjornsson, A Kraszewski, A N McDougall, D S Mack
Paediatrics J A Ford, P Galea
Radiology M A Millar

Southern General Hospital
1345 Govan Road, Glasgow G51 4TF
Tel: 0141 201 1100 Fax: 0141 201 2999
Total Beds: 854

Neurology J P Ballantyne, I Bone, A Chaudhuri, R Duncan, W F Durward, J Greene, D Grosset, P G E Kennedy, A C Mann, R Metcalfe, A Myfanwy Thomas, C O'Leary, R K H Petty, A J Russell, A I Weir, H J Wilson

Victoria Infirmary
Langside, Glasgow G42 9TT
Tel: 0141 201 6000 Fax: 0141 201 5206
Total Beds: 485

Accident and Emergency I W R Anderson, D Ritchie
Anaesthetics A Brown, B Cowan, J A Davidson, A Dell, J A Gillespie, G W A Gillies, R Glavin, G Gordon, J C Howie, R L Marshall, J H Maule, J Oates, J Purdie, D Singh, B S Stuart, D F Thomson
Bacteriology R M F Lewis, P Redding
Biochemistry A Glen
Cardiology D Ballantyne, H McAlpine, R Northcote
Care of the Elderly K Beard, I Lennox, J Potter, M A Roberts, D Stewart
Chest Disease D McIntyre, D R H Vernon
Dental Surgery D I Russell
Dermatology D Bilsland, C Munro, D Roberts
ENT B Bingham, J Crowther, R A Kell, E A Osborne
General Medicine D Ballantyne, K M Cochran, C M Kesson, J Larkin, H MacAlpine, D MacIntyre, R Northcote, D Rooney, S D Slater, D R H Vernon
General Surgery J Drury, G Gillespie, G R Gray, I Pickford, D C Smith, I S Smith
Haematology P J Tansey
Obstetrics and Gynaecology S Bjornsson, A Kraszewski, A N McDougall, D S Mack
Ophthalmology W M Doig, P Kyle, J Williamson, W N Wykes
Orthopaedics D Allan, E R Gardner, T Hems, C Mainds, P D R Scott
Pathology I Gibson, D R MacLellan, E A Mallon, W G S Spilg
Radiology J Calder, S E G Goudie, J Lauder, G McInnes, G McKillop, M A Millar, W R Pickard
Urology B J Abel, I G Conn

Tayside Primary Care Trust

Ashlundie Hospital, Monifieth DD5 4HQ
Tel: 01382 423000 Fax: 01382 527891
(Tayside NHS Board)

Chair Murray Petrie
Chief Executive Tony Wells

Aberfeldy Cottage Hospital
Aberfeldy PH15 2DH
Tel: 01887 820314 Fax: 01887 829604, 01887 829664
Total Beds: 25

Care of the Elderly I M Lightbody
General Medicine A N Shepherd
General Surgery P J Fok

Arbroath Infirmary
Arbroath DD11 2AT
Tel: 01241 872584 Fax: 01241 872584
Total Beds: 55

NHS TRUSTS & NHS HOSPITALS

Child and Adolescent Psychiatry I C Menzies
Dermatology J G Lowe
ENT B C Davis
General Medicine T S Callaghan, K D Morley, J S A Sawers
General Psychiatry K M G Keddie
Obstetrics and Gynaecology G B James, A A Thomson
Ophthalmology C McEwen
Orthopaedics J E Scullion
Paediatrics J S Forsyth, S A Greene
Radiology W J A Gibson, J A Tainsh

Ashludie Day Hospital
Ashludie Hospital, Monifieth, Dundee DD5 4HQ
Tel: 01382 527830

Ashludie Hospital
Monifieth, Dundee DD5 4HQ
Tel: 01382 423000 Fax: 01382 527849
Total Beds: 215

Care of the Elderly M McMurdo, R S McWalter, W J Mutch, J M Watson
General Psychiatry D J Findlay, A McHarg, A H Reid

Birch Avenue Day Hospital
55 Birch Aveune, Scone, Perth PH2 6LE
Tel: 01738 553920

Learning Disabilities C B Ballinger

Blairgowrie Cottage Hospital
Blairgowrie PH10 6EE
Tel: 01250 874466 Fax: 01250 876194
Total Beds: 62

Care of the Elderly I M Lightbody

Brechin Infirmary
Infirmary Street, Brechin DD9 7AW
Tel: 01356 622291 Fax: 01356 666075
Total Beds: 54

Care of the Elderly J D Fulton
Consultants J Mills
ENT B C Davis
General Medicine T S Callaghan
General Psychiatry A M Drayson
General Surgery A D Irving, N H Townell
Orthopaedics R Buckley

Crieff Hospital
King Street, Crieff PH7 3HR
Tel: 01764 653173 Fax: 01764 654051
Total Beds: 60

Care of the Elderly I M Lightbody
General Medicine N Dewhurst, M Garton
General Surgery R W G Murdoch
Obstetrics and Gynaecology R Allen

Forfar Infirmary
Forfar DD8 2HS
Tel: 01307 464551 Fax: 01307 465129
Total Beds: 50

Consultants R Smith
ENT R P Mills
General Medicine T S Callaghan
General Psychiatry A M Drayson
General Surgery A D Irving
Orthopaedics J E Scullion
Radiology W J A Gibson, J A Tainsh

Glaxo Day Hospital
Ashludie Hospital, Victoria Street, Monifieth, Dundee DD5 4HQ
Tel: 01382 423000 Fax: 01382 527852

Hawkhill Day Hospital
Peddie Street, Dundee DD1 5LB
Tel: 01382 423000

Irvine Memorial Hospital
Pitlochry PH16 5HP
Tel: 01796 472052 Fax: 01796 474279
Total Beds: 27

Care of the Elderly I M Lightbody
General Medicine P Brown, A Connacher
General Surgery P J Fok

Little Cairnie Hospital
Cairnie Road, Arbroath DD11 3RA
Tel: 01241 872584 Fax: 01241 872584
Total Beds: 57

Care of the Elderly J D Fulton, I Gillanders

Meigle Community Day Hospital
Meigle, Blairgowrie PH12 8SE
Tel: 01828 640211 Fax: 01828 640714

Montrose Royal Infirmary
Montrose DD10 8AJ
Tel: 01674 830361 Fax: 01674 830361
Total Beds: 44

Care of the Elderly J D Fulton
ENT R P Mills
General Psychiatry K M G Keddie
General Surgery A D Irving, N H Townell
Obstetrics and Gynaecology P W Howie, D J Taylor
Ophthalmology P S Baines
Orthopaedics R Buckley

Murray Royal Hospital
Perth PH2 7BH
Tel: 01738 621151, 01738 621158 Fax: 01738 442630
Total Beds: 340

General Psychiatry S Clark, P J Connelly, M A Field, H E Kirk, D Mowat, K Richard, D H Tait

Orleans Day Hospital
Orleans Place, Menzieshill, Dundee DD2 4BH
Tel: 01382 667322

General Psychiatry A H Ried, M M Semple

Roseangle Day Hospital
23 Roseangle, Dundee DD1 4LS
Tel: 01382 423000 Fax: 01382 204070

General Psychiatry L R Treliving, C D B White

Rosemount Day Hospital
Rosemount Road, Arbroath DD11 2AY
Tel: 01241 72584, 01241 872584

General Psychiatry K M G Keddie

Royal Dundee Liff Hospital
Liff, Dundee DD2 5NF
Tel: 01382 423000 Fax: 01382 423055
Total Beds: 337

General Psychiatry C B Ballinger, P H Dick, J L Fellows, D J Findlay, B B Johnston, A M McHarg, A H Reid, I C Reid, M M Semple, B M Shepherd, A H W Smith, L R Treliving, C D B White

Royal Victoria Day Hospital
Jedburgh Road, Dundee DD2 1SP
Tel: 01382 423000 Fax: 01382 423122

Royal Victoria Hospital

Jedburgh Road, Dundee DD2 1SP
Tel: 01382 423000 Fax: 01382 423122
Total Beds: 180

Care of the Elderly M McMurdo, R S McWalter, W J Mutch, J M Watson
General Medicine D Gentleman
Palliative Medicine M Leiper

St Margaret's Hospital

Auchterarder PH3 1JH
Tel: 01764 662246 Fax: 01764 664084
Total Beds: 16

General Medicine P Brown, A Connacher
General Surgery P J Fok
Orthopaedics W Hadden

Strathmartine Hospital

Dundee DD3 0PG
Tel: 01382 423000 Fax: 01382 528027

Consultants C B Ballinger, A H Reid, A H W Smith, P J Walker

Sunnyside Royal Hospital

Montrose DD10 9JP
Tel: 01674 830361 Fax: 01674 830361
Total Beds: 195

General Psychiatry A M Drayson, K M G Keddie, S Logie, P Rice

Threshold Day Hospital

2-3 Dudhope Terrace, Dundee DD3 6HG
Tel: 01382 423000 Fax: 01382 202585

General Psychiatry P H Dick

Whitehills Hospital

Forfar DD8 3DY
Tel: 01307 464551 Fax: 01307 465129
Total Beds: 38

Care of the Elderly J D Fulton, I Gillanders

Tayside University Hospitals NHS Trust

Ninewells Hospital, Medical School, Dundee DD1 9SY
Tel: 01382 660111 Fax: 01382 660445
Website: www.show.scot.nhs.uk/tuht
(Tayside NHS Board)

Chair James McGoldrick
Chief Executive Paul White

Dundee Dental Hospital and School

2 Park Place, Dundee DD1 4HR
Tel: 01382 660111 Fax: 01382 635998
Total Beds: 96

Oral and Maxillofacial Surgery P R H Brown, G R Ogden
Oral Medicine C J Allan, D M Chisholm, A R Grieve, N B Pitts, J R Radford, R Yemm
Oral Radiology E Connor
Orthodontics R B Erskine, D Evans, D Stirrups

Ninewells Hospital

Dundee DD1 9SY
Tel: 01382 660111 Fax: 01382 660445
Total Beds: 703

Anaesthetics C W Allison, R H Allison, J Bannister, J R Colvin, D Coventry, S A Crofts, I G Gray, W F D Hamilton, T Houston, G L Hutchison, W McClymont, N Mackenzie, G A McLeod, W Macrae, P R Manthri, F A Millar, M K Milne, G Rodney, A J Shearer, A C Staziker, P B Taylor, M F Thomson, J A W Wildsmith, E Wilson
Biochemistry E Dow, C R Patterson
Cardiology B K W Green, G P McNeill, S Pringle, T H Pringle
Dermatology J Ferguson, C A Green, K J A Kenicer, J G Lowe, S M Morley
ENT R L Blair, J K Brennand, B C Davis, J Irwin, R P Mills, R E Mountain, P S White
Epidemiology C Florey, H Tunstall-Pedoe
General Medicine J Belch, J B C Dick, J Dillon, C D Forbes, D A Johnston, R T Jung, G P Leese, D G McDevitt, T McDonald, R S McWater, K D Morley, A D Morris, R W Newton, C R Pennington, T Pullar, A D Struthers
General Psychiatry I Reid
General Surgery A Cuschieri, J C Forrester, M Lavelle-Jones, M H Lyall, P E Preece, S Shimi, D M Smith, R J Steele, P Stonebridge, A M Thompson, R A B Wood
Haematology D T Bowen, P Cachia, G Galea, A Heppleston, M J Pippard
Medical Microbiology J Kavi, P G McIntyre, G Orange, D Parratt, G M A Phillips
Nephrology I Henderson, M Jones, E A McGregor
Obstetrics and Gynaecology P Agustsson, F W Chien, I D Duncan, J Gupta, A J Harrold, P W Howie, J A Mills, G Mires, N Patel, R S Smith, M A R Thomson
Ophthalmology P S Baines, J A Coleiro, C J MacEwen, C N J McGhee, S T D Roxburgh, J D H Young
Paediatrics J S Forsyth, S A Greene, R Hume, M Kirkpatrick, A Mehta, S Mukhopadhyay, R E Olver, W O Tarnow-Mordi, R A Wilkie
Pathology N Alsanjari, F A Carey, A Evans, D Goudie, D Hopwood, J Lang, S Lang, D A Levison, J B McCullough, B A Michie, S Nicoll, C A Purdie, A J Robertson
Radiology J D Begg, R C P Cameron, R I Doull, J G Houston, A S McCulloch, D F McLean, G Main, M Nimmo, J W Shaw, T Taylor
Radiotherapy and Oncology S Das, J A Dewar, A J Munro, E M Rankin, P M Windsor

Perth Royal Infirmary

Jeanfield Road, Perth PH1 1NX
Tel: 01738 623311 Fax: 01738 473206
Total Beds: 335

Anaesthetics M Bell, P Coe, W A Elsdon, D W Forbes, D Kapur, A Kutarski, F Magahy
Biochemistry D Walsh
Care of the Elderly I M Lightbody, P J Stephen
Chest Disease A Shepherd
Dental Surgery I McClure
Dermatology J Ferguson
ENT L Blair, J Irwin
General Medicine P Brown, A Connacher, N Dewhurst, A N Shepherd
General Surgery C Erikson, P J Fok, R W G Murdoch, W J G Murray
Genitourinary Medicine A Ghaly
Haematology A Heppleston
Histopathology B Michie
Medical Microbiology G Orange
Obstetrics and Gynaecology R Allen, P Lynch, W D P Phillips
Ophthalmology S T D Roxburgh, J D H Young
Oral Surgery I McClure
Orthodontics J D Clark
Orthopaedics A J Espley, W A Hadden, J G B MacLean, G G McLeod
Paediatrics D MacGregor, V J Marrian, R Wilkie
Plastic Surgery A M Morris, A Nasaan, J H Stevenson, Dr Wilmshurt
Radiology J Flinn, K Fowler, P Gamble, R H S Murray
Radiotherapy and Oncology D P Quilty
Rheumatology M Garton

Stracathro Hospital

Brechin DD9 7QA
Tel: 01356 647291 Fax: 01356 648163

NHS TRUSTS & NHS HOSPITALS

Total Beds: 241

Anaesthetics C W Allison, I G Grove-White, A Houghton
Care of the Elderly J D Fulton, I Gillanders
Consultants J Mills, D J Taylor
Dermatology J G Lowe
General Medicine T S Callaghan, J S A Sawers
General Surgery P J Fok, A D Irving, N H Townell
Neurosurgery D Gentleman
Ophthalmology J Coleiro
Orthopaedics R Buckley, J E Scullion, N W Valentine
Paediatrics J I Cater
Pathology P E G Mitchell
Radiology W J A Gibson, J A Tainsh

West Lothian Healthcare NHS Trust

St John's Hospital at Howden, Howden Road West, Livingston EH54 6PP
Tel: 01506 419666 Fax: 01506 416484
Website: www.show.scot.nhs.uk/wlt
(Lothian NHS Board)

Chair James Findlay
Chief Executive Peter Gabbitas

Bangour Village Hospital

Broxburn EH52 6LW
Tel: 01506 419666 Fax: 01506 811727
Total Beds: 90

General Psychiatry I Coffey, J D Hendry

St John's Hospital at Howden

Howden, Livingston EH54 6PP
Tel: 01506 419666 Fax: 01506 416484
Total Beds: 545

Accident and Emergency J Fothergill, P Freeland
Anaesthetics P Armstrong, M S Brockway, D Burke, M Fried, D Galloway, M Lonsdale, E Martin, L M M Morison, S Rowbottom, K G Stewart, K Watson
Care of the Elderly D Farquhar, S Ramsay, J A Wilson
Clinical Chemistry D A McCullough
Dermatology O Schofield
ENT R J Sanderson, D W Sim
General Medicine R S Gray, J B Irving, A J Jacob, W G Middleton
General Psychiatry S A Backett, T M Brown, I Coffey, J D Hendry, M Mcleod, S Roscrow
General Surgery D Anderson, G G P Browning, J B Rainey, I W J Wallace
Haematology M K Cook
Hand Surgery G Hooper
Neurology A Zeman
Obstetrics and Gynaecology G Beattie, T K Cooper, P Dewart, P G Thomson
Oral and Maxillofacial Surgery R Koay
Orthopaedics R Burnett, A Gibson, G Keenan, G Lawson, R J M Macdonald
Paediatrics A J Burt, H F Hammond, D Theodosiou, D Valentine
Palliative Care D Oxenham
Pathology R M Davie, K Ramesar
Plastic Surgery M Butterworth, J C McGregor, A A Quaba, J D Watson
Radiology P Bailey, C Beveridge, T Fitzgerald, I Parker, L M Smart
Radiotherapy G Howard
Rheumatology V B Dhillon

St Michael's Hospital

Linlithgow EH49 6QS
Tel: 01506 842053
Total Beds: 30

Care of the Elderly D Farquhar, J A Wilson

Tippethill Hospital

Bathgate EH48 3BQ
Tel: 01501 740342
Total Beds: 46

Care of the Elderly D Farquhar, J A Wilson

Whitburn Day Hospital

1 Weavers Lane, Whitburn, Bathgate EH47 0QU
Tel: 01501 742637

The Yorkhill NHS Trust

Yorkhill, Glasgow G3 8SJ
Tel: 0141 201 0000 Fax: 0141 201 0836
Website: www.show.scot.nhs.uk/yorkhill/
(Greater Glasgow NHS Board)

Chair Sally Kuenssberg
Chief Executive Jonathan Best

The Queen Mother's Hospital

Yorkhill, Glasgow G3 8SH
Tel: 0141 201 0550 Fax: 0141 201 0836
Total Beds: 78

Anaesthetics C S Cairns, J Reid, J Thorburn
Obstetrics and Gynaecology A D Cameron, W R Chatfield, J W Cordiner, K Hanretty, M A Lumsden, L Macara
Paediatrics J Coutts, B Holland, T L Turner

Royal Hospital for Sick Children

Yorkhill, Glasgow G3 8SJ
Tel: 0141 201 0000 Fax: 0141 201 0836
Total Beds: 306

Accident and Emergency J O Beattie, N V Doraiswamy
Anaesthetics G Bell, C Best, P Cullen, P Copples, D Hallworth, R A Lawson, L R McNicol, P Bolton, N S Morton, J Peutrell, J F Sinclair
Biochemistry J M Connor
Cardiology J M McLeod, A B Houston, N Wilson
Cardiothoracic Surgery K McArthur, J Pollock
Child Psychiatry J Barton, R Lindsay, M Morton, J C Shemilt, A Sneddon
Community Child Health S Evans, J Herbison, K Leyland, K McKay, D Stone, A Sutton, D Tappin
Dental Surgery A Wray, H A Critchlow, D Fung
Dermatology D Burden, R Lever, P McHendry
ENT N K Geddes, F McGregor, S Morrisey, H Sadiq
Genetics J M Conner, H R Davidson, J Tolmie, M Whiteford, P Wilcox
Haematology E Chalmers, B S Gibson
Neurology R McWilliam, M O Regan, S Zobari
Obstetrics and Gynaecology A Cameron, R Chatfield, J Cordiner, K Hanretty, M Lumsden, L Macara
Ophthalmology J Dudgeon, G T Dutton
Oral and Maxillofacial Surgery J G McLennan
Orthopaedics G C Bennett, R Duncan, D Sammon, D S Sherlock, N H Wilson
Paediatric Surgery A A F Azmy, R Carachi, C Davis, A H B Fyfe, G Haddock, S O'Toole, P A M Raine, C Hajioassiliou
Paediatrics F Ahmed, L Alroomi, J Beattie, D Cochran, J Coutts, M Donaldson, J A Ford, P Galea, N Gibson, R Hague, B Holland, H Maxwell, A V Murphy, J Y Paton, K J Robertson, P H Robinson, C H Skeoch, T L Turner, L T Weaver, M P White
Pathology A G Howatson
Radiology A Watt, S Maroo, A MacLennan, A G Wilkinson

Orkney Islands

(Orkney NHS Board)

Balfour Hospital

Kirkwall KW15 1BX
Tel: 01856 885400 Fax: 01856 885411
Total Beds: 99

General Surgery W Groundwater

Shetland Islands

(Shetland NHS Board)

Gilbert Bain Hospital

Lerwick ZE1 0RB
Tel: 01595 743000 Fax: 01595 696608
Total Beds: 70

Anaesthetics A B Cooper, G T Freshwater, N D R Laidley
Gastroenterology Z Jussa
General Medicine F Johnson, N D R Laidlay
General Psychiatry D Senior
General Surgery A G Coutts, M Hosny

Montfield Hospital

Lerwick ZE1 0LA
Tel: 01595 743000
Total Beds: 20

Western Isles

(Western Isles NHS Board)

Daliburgh Hospital

Daliburgh, Lochboisdale
Tel: 01878 700311
Total Beds: 21

General Surgery D Chatterjee

Lochmaddy Hospital

Lochmaddy
Tel: 01876 500325
Total Beds: 25

St Brendans

Castlebay
Tel: 01871 810465
Total Beds: 5

Western Isles Hospital

MacAulay Road, Stornoway
Tel: 01851 704704
Total Beds: 212

Anaesthetics A P Hothersall
General Medicine J A D Goodall
General Psychiatry I Clark
General Surgery D A MacLean
Obstetrics and Gynaecology D J Herd
Radiology I C F Riach

Wales

Bro Morgannwg NHS Trust

Trust Headquarters, 71 Quarella Road, Bridgend CF31 1YE
Tel: 01656 752752 Fax: 01656 752570
Website: www.bromor-tr.wales.nhs.uk
(Iechyd Morgannwg Health Authority)

Chair Russell Hopkins
Chief Executive Paul Williams

Cimla Hospital

Cymla, Neath SA11 3SU
Tel: 01639 641161
Total Beds: 58

Care of the Elderly A B Davies, - El Khatieb

Glanrhyd Hospital

Tondu Road, Bridgend CF31 4LN
Tel: 01656 752752
Total Beds: 170

General Psychiatry R Colgate, R H Davies, P Huckle, C Hunter, A T Lloyd, S S Palia, T Williams

Groeswen Hospital

Margam Road, Port Talbot SA13 2LA
Tel: 01639 641161
Total Beds: 50

Care of the Elderly A B Davies, - El Khatieb

Hensol Hospital

Pontyclun CF7 8YS
Tel: 01656 752752
Total Beds: 225

Learning Disabilities V Anness, T H Singh

Llwyneryr Hospital

151 Clasemont Road, Morriston, Swansea SA6 6AH
Tel: 01792 771262
Total Beds: 46

General Psychiatry D Ganeshananthan

Maesteg Community Hospital

Neath Road, Maesteg, Bridgend CF34 9PW
Tel: 01656 732732
Total Beds: 47

Anaesthetics H F Davies, D H C Evans, B J M Ferguson, P S Gataure, M T Jones, R W Morris, D G Thomas
ENT S Brodie, R Evans, C Roberts
General Medicine D J Beale, C J H Jones, J S Morris, D Parry, D Webb, W E Wilkins
General Surgery A G Evans, R Hedges, J Higgs, J Stamatakis
Obstetrics and Gynaecology A Allman, R P Balfour, P G Morris
Paediatrics P D L Edwards, A Goodwin, R H T Jones
Radiology N Al-Mokhtar, F M Bowyer, D R Foster, J H Williams, T Young

Neath General Hospital

Brian Ferry Road, Neath SA11 2LQ
Tel: 01639 641161 Fax: 01639 641286
Total Beds: 262

Anaesthetics B Basu, A Driemel, S Driemel, R Emmanuel, B Green, H Hassan
Care of the Elderly A B Davies, - El Khatieb
Child and Adolescent Psychiatry J S Talbot
Dental Surgery C W Rowse
Dermatology B N Statham

NHS TRUSTS & NHS HOSPITALS

ENT D W Aird, J J Phillips
General Medicine G M Jeremiah, R O Kahan, S Lennox, R K Sinha, J G Williams
General Psychiatry R Anneas, S R John, J Rule
General Surgery R Baker, P J Coyle, J Elias, L A M Taylor
Haematology A C Beddall
Histopathology C O'Brien
Medical Microbiology P Thomas
Neurology R Weiser
Obstetrics and Gynaecology M Dossa, M Freites, R Llewellyn
Ophthalmology J E A Hoare-Nairne, R G Powell
Orthodontics J Crooks
Orthopaedics A Clements, R M Davies, D N W Lake
Paediatrics M Ellison, M O'Hagan
Psychiatry of Old Age J Rule
Radiology R Evans, S E Evans, C Flowers, D G Richards, B W Roper
Radiotherapy W R Gajek
Rheumatology D Smith, B J Sweetman

Port Talbot Hospital
Hospital Road, Port Talbot SA12 6PD
Tel: 01639 641161
Total Beds: 25

Anaesthetics I M Evans
Care of the Elderly P B Pawar
Dermatology B N Statham
ENT D W Aird, C F Fielder, J J Phillips
General Medicine G M Jeremiah, J P White
General Psychiatry R O Annear
General Surgery M J B Chare, P J Coyle, A G Radcliffe, R H P Williams
Genitourinary Medicine A L Blackwell
Obstetrics and Gynaecology M T Al-Samarrai, M S Benett, M Dossa
Ophthalmology A Pickering
Orthopaedics D N W Lake, J P Matthews
Paediatrics B L Griffiths
Radiology B W Roper

Princess of Wales Hospital
Coity Road, Bridgend CF31 1RQ
Total Beds: 529

Anaesthetics H F Davies, D H C Evans, B J M Ferguson, P S Gataure, M Jones, R W Morris, D G Thomas
Dermatology S W Lanigan, R A Logan
ENT S Brodie, R Evans
General Medicine D J Beale, C J H Jones, J S Morris, R Owen, D Parry, D Webb, W E Wilkins
General Psychiatry R H Davies, A T Lloyd, S S Palia
General Surgery A G Evans, R Hedges, J M Higgs, J Stamatakis
Haematology V Davalia
Neurology I N F McQueen
Obstetrics and Gynaecology C Allman, R P Balfour, P G Morris
Ophthalmology M T Baynham, M S Hashmi, H Khatib
Oral and Maxillofacial Surgery A Ezsias, C S Holland, E S Nash
Orthodontics P T Nicholson
Orthopaedics J D M Blayney, D Gilmartin, K Singhal, J P R Williams
Paediatrics J Crockett, P D L Edwards, A Goodwin, R H T Jones
Pathology C Banerji, V Devalia, D Pace, A M Rees, E J Williams
Radiology N Al-Mokhtar, F M Bowyer, D R Foster, J H Williams, T Young
Radiotherapy and Oncology M Adams, B K James
Rheumatology and Rehabilitation F M Khan

Tonna Hospital
Tonna, Neath SA11 3LX
Tel: 01639 635404 Fax: 01639 641312
Total Beds: 80

Consultants S R Johns, J Rule

Cardiff and Vale NHS Trust
Heath Park, Cardiff CF14 4XW
Tel: 02920 747747 Fax: 02920 743838
Email: enquiries@cardiffandvale.wales.nhs.uk
Website: www.cardiffandvale.wales.nhs.uk
(Bro Taf Health Authority)

Chair David Durham
Chief Executive David Edwards

The Barry Hospital
Colcot Road, Barry CF62 8HE
Tel: 01446 704000 Fax: 01446 704103
Total Beds: 81

Cardiff Royal Infirmary - West Wing
Newport Road, Cardiff CF24 0SZ
Tel: 029 2049 2233 Fax: 029 2048 39683
Total Beds: 79

Genitourinary Medicine A R G Manuel, R A Sparks
Geriatric Medicine J E Grey

John Pathy Day Hospital
Rookwood Hospital, Fairwater Road, Llandaff, Cardiff CF5 3YN
Tel: 029 2056 6281

Lansdowne Hospital
Sanitorium Road, Canton, Cardiff CF11 8PL
Tel: 029 2023 3651, 029 2023 7378 Fax: 029 2023 7378
Total Beds: 110

Community Paediatrics P M Davis, A M Mott, E P Penny, E V J Webb
Obstetrics and Gynaecology C Kerby

Llandough Geriatric Day Hospital
Llandough, Penarth CF64 2XX
Tel: 029 2070 5411

Care of the Elderly D A O Sutton, G M Tinker

Llandough Hospital
Llandough Hospital, Penlan Road, Llandough, Penarth CF64 2XX
Tel: 029 2071 1711 Fax: 029 2070 8973
Total Beds: 514

Anaesthetics I Bowler, N D Groves, J E Hall, M W Hebden, A Mehta, S Morris, M R W Stacey, C Taylor, A Turley, E M Wright
Chemical Pathology S B Matthews
Community Paediatrics A M Kemp, J M R Morgan, J R Sibert
Dermatology C C Long
General Medicine P Beck, B H Davies, J T Green, J H Lazarus, D R Owens, P A Routledge, G L Swift, J P Thompson
General Paediatrics and Neonatology M A Alfaham, D P Tuthill, H Williams
General Surgery J S Harvey, I J Monypenny, A G Radcliffe, D J T Webster, R J Whiston
Geriatric Medicine M S O'Mahony, M F V Sim, M D Stone, G M Tinker, K W Woodhouse
Haematology A I M Al-Sabah, D P Bentley
Histopathology R L Attanoos, N S Dallimore, A R Gibbs, R Olafsdottir
Medical Microbiology A H Quoraishi
Obstetrics and Gynaecology J Evans, P C Lindsay, A E J Rees, A Roberts
Paediatric Oncology R D W Hain, M E M Jenney
Radiology H Adams, R E Bleehen, A J Blethyn, M D Crane
Respiratory Medicine I A Campbell, T L Griffiths, D J Shale, A P Smith
Trauma and Orthopaedics P R Davies, C M Dent, J A Fairclough, G P Graham, S S Hemmadi, J P Howes, A W John, M V S Maheson, R L Morgan-Jones, D P W O'Doherty, D J Shewring, D P Thomas, S S Upadhyay, R L Williams, C A Wilson

Rookwood Hospital

Fairwater Road, Llandaff, Cardiff CF5 2YN
Tel: 029 2041 5415 Fax: 029 2056 4065
Total Beds: 49

Rehabilitation - Spinal Injuries T A T Hughes, C G Inman

Royal Hamadryad Hospital

Royal Hamadryad Hospital, Hamadryad Road, Cardiff CF1 6UQ
Tel: 029 2048 0895 Fax: 029 2046 5530
Total Beds: 34

General Psychiatry M D Aldrick, D Ridley-Siegert

Tegfan Day Hospital

Whitchurch Hospital, Whitchurch, Cardiff CF4 7XB
Tel: 029 2069 3191 Fax: 029 2061 4799

Ty Hafan Day Hospital

Whitchurch Hospital, Whitchurch, Cardiff CF4 7XB
Tel: 029 2069 3191 Fax: 029 2061 4799

University Dental Hospital and School

University Dental Hospital, Heath Park, Cardiff CF14 4XY
Tel: 029 2074 7747 Fax: 029 2074 2421

Dentistry I Chestnutt, S J Crean, M L Hunter, J Knox, E T Treasure, D K Whittaker
Oral Surgery E G Absi, M J Fardy, C M Hill, J P Shepherd, D W Thomas
Orthodontics P Durning, M L Jones, R G Oliver, S Richmond
Paediatric Dentistry B L Chadwick, B Hunter
Pathology M A O Lewis, A J C Potts
Restorative Dentistry P M H Dummer, D H Edmunds, A S M Gilmour, P H Jacobsen, R G Jagger, R McAndrew, W S McLaughlin, J M A Wilton

University Hospital of Wales

Heath Park, Cardiff CF4 4XW
Tel: 029 2074 7747 Fax: 020 2074 3838
Total Beds: 944

Accident and Emergency R C Evans, R J Evans, P W Richmond
Anaesthetics R J Abel, I M Aguilera, I R Appadurai, T S H Armstrong, J Azami, J E S Barry, P A Clyburn, M Cobley, R E Collis, T S Dhallu, M P Drage, J A Dunne, D E N Evans, J M Foy, C D Gildersleve, S Grundler, M Harmer, R C Hughes, R M Jones, I P Latto, S W Logan, C McBeth, N McCann, P Morgan, K R Murrin, D G Place, S J Plummer, S C Pugh, M S Read, N J Stallard, C N H Tan, G A Wenham, L J Wheeler, M P Whitten, P C Wiener, B A Willis
Cardio-Thoracic Surgery A A Azzu, E G Butchart, E N P Kulatilake, P A O'Keefe, U O Von Oppell
Cardiology M B Buchalter, J R Cockroft, A G Fraser, M P Frenneaux, P H Groves, N D Masani, P A O'Callaghan, W J Penny, A M Shah, M R Stephens
Chemical Pathology M N Badminton, I F W McDowell, B P Morgan, P E Williams
Clinical Genetics A J Clarke, S J Davies, J R Gray, P S Harper, H E Hughes, D T Pilz, F M Pope, D Ravine, M T Rogers, J R Sampson
Dermatology M M U Chowdhury, A M Farrell, A Y Finlay, P J A Holt, R J Motley
ENT R G S Mills, G R Shone, S D G Stephens, A Tomkinson, R G Williams
General Medicine J S Davies, A R Freedman, C M Gelder, A J Godkin, A B Hawthorne, M J Lewis, M B Llewellyn, J R Peters, J A E Rees, M F Scanlon, G A O Thomas
General Paediatrics and Neonatology P H T Cartlidge, D P Davies, C B Doherty, I J M Doull, M R Drayton, H R Jenkins, C V E Powell, G J Shortland
General Surgery A Asderakis, W J Byrne, R E Chavez Cartaya, G W B Clark, W T Davies, K G Harding, I F Lane, R E Mansel, M C A Puntis, B I Rees, H M Sweetland, H L Young
Geriatric Medicine A M Johansen, R E Morse, J A Pascual, B S D Sastry, H G M Shetty

Haematology A K Burnett, P W Collins, A P Goringe, C H Poynton, J A Whittaker, K M O Wilson
Histopathology A M Davison, S Dojcinov, A G Douglas-Jones, D F R Griffiths, S M Ismail, D S James, B Jasani, P Laidler, E J Lazda, S Leadbetter, M Varma, G M Vujanic, G T Williams, D Wynford-Thomas
Intensive Care G P Findlay, M N Smithies
Medical Microbiology R A Barnes, B I Duerden, K A N Hosein, A J Howard, J A Munro, C D Ribeiro, D Westmoreland
Nephrology K Baboolal, K L Donovan, R H Moore, D M Thomas, J D Williams
Neurology J P Heath, I N F McQueen, N P Robertson, A E Rosser, P E M Smith, C M Wiles
Neuropathology G A Lammie, J W Neal
Neurosurgery R H Hatfield, B A Simpson, G C Stephenson, J A Vafidis
Obstetrics and Gynaecology N N Amso, R B Beattie, N J Davies, A S Evans, L D Klentzeris, R J A Penketh
Ophthalmology M Beck, R A Cheema, C Gorman, C M Lane, K J Lowe, R J E McPherson, J E Morgan, K N Rajkumar, R F Walters, P O Watts
Paediatric Cardiology O Onuzo, O Uzun, D G Wilson
Paediatric Intensive Care R H Al-Samsam, C H Fardy, M Gajraj, A D Pryor
Paediatric Nephrology G C Smith, K Verrier-Jones
Paediatric Neurology F M Gibbon, S S Jayawant
Paediatric Surgery S N Huddart, K A R Hutton, R H Surana
Radiology M W Bourne, D L Cochlin, C Evans, A C Gordon, T M Griffith, S F S Halpin, K Hammer, S K Harrison, M D Hourihan, A Jones, B W Lawrie, D C F Lloyd, K Lyons, S J Morris, J I S Rees, S A Roberts, N G Stoodley, A M Wood
Rheumatology J P Camilleri, S M Jones, M P Pritchard, B D Williams
Transplant Surgery A Asderakis, R E Chavez Cartaya, W A Jurewicz
Trauma and Orthopaedics P R Davies, J A Fairclough, G P Graham, S S Hemmadi, J P Howes, A W John, M V S Maheson, R L Morgan-Jones, D P W O'Doherty, D J Shewring, D P Thomas, S S Upadhyay, R L Williams, C A Wilson
Urology S N Datta, B J Jenkins, H G Kynaston, P N Matthews, T P Stephenson

Whitchurch Hospital

Whitchurch Hospital, Park Poad, Whitchurch, Cardiff CF4 7XB
Tel: 029 2069 3191 Fax: 029 2033 6339
Total Beds: 329

General Psychiatry M D Alldrick, R I Araya, J I Bisson, H L Chubb, M M Creaby, G Davies, W I Fraser, P D Halford, J Hillier, H P Holmes, S S M Jawad, G H Jones, R G Jones, A M P Kellam, A Korszun, J E Lewis, A J McBride, G Martinez, J Morgan, M J Owen, D A Ridley-Siegert, A T Sabir, R C Scorer, S J Smith, A Thapar, A J Williams, P A Williams

Carmarthenshire NHS Trust

Mynydd Mawr Hospital, Llannon Road, Upper Tumble, Llanelli SA14 6BU
Tel: 01269 841343 Fax: 01269 832913
Website: www.carmarthen.wales.nhs.uk
(Dyfed Powys Health Authority)

Chair Margaret Price
Chief Executive M Jones
Consultants P Thomas

Amman Valley Hospital

Glanamman, Ammanford SA18 2BQ
Tel: 01269 822226 Fax: 01269 826953
Total Beds: 28

Care of the Elderly G C Morris
General Surgery H J R Evans, M Taube
Haematology R V Major

NHS TRUSTS & NHS HOSPITALS

Obstetrics and Gynaecology J M Blair, T H Bloomfield
Ophthalmology D Jones, T J Roberts-Harry

Bryntirion Hospital

Llanelli SA15 3DX
Tel: 01554 756567
Total Beds: 59

Care of the Elderly T P L Thomas
General Psychiatry A C Owen

Llandovery Hospital

Llandovery SA20 0LA
Tel: 01550 720322 Fax: 01550 721270
Total Beds: 18

Mynydd Mawr Hospital

Tumble, Llanelli SA14 6BU
Tel: 01269 841343 Fax: 01269 832681
Total Beds: 38

Care of the Elderly G C Morris
Haematology R V Majer

Prince Philip Hospital

Bryngwynmawr, Dafen, Llanelli SA14 8QF
Tel: 01554 756567 Fax: 01554 749853
Total Beds: 239

Accident and Emergency M Vaziri
Anaesthetics V C Jaidev, A K Nigam, D C Richards
Chemical Pathology N A A Haboubi
Dermatology S L W Blackford
ENT S Browning, B R Davis, H B Whittet
General Medicine P Avery, M J Dew, P Ebden, E C Morris, T P L Thomas, T D M Williams
General Surgery H J R Evans, S D Holt, S Rowley
Haematology R V Majers
Medical Microbiology G Harrison
Obstetrics and Gynaecology J M Blair, T H Bloomfield, L Joels, N Piskorowski
Ophthalmology D Jones, T J Roberts-Harry
Oral and Maxillofacial Surgery K C Sylvester
Orthodontics D J Howells
Orthopaedics J Adams, S Caiach, R S Johnson, H Richards
Paediatrics M Cosgrove, G Owen, C Sullivan, S Warren, C White
Pathology L A Murray
Radiology T N W Evans, A Richards
Radiotherapy and Oncology C S Askill, T Joannides
Rheumatology D H Smith, B J Sweetman

Priory Day Hospital

West Wales General Hospital, Carmarthen SA31 2AF
Tel: 01267 227384 Fax: 01267 237662

West Wales General Hospital

Carmarthen SA31 2AF
Tel: 01267 235151 Fax: 01267 227715
Total Beds: 388

Accident and Emergency J H Williams
Anaesthetics A G P Laxton, C F Loyden, R O'Donohoe, R Prasad, P J Rimell, W Thompson, M J Turtle, B H Yate
Dermatology V Vgoji
ENT B R Davis, N J Morgan, M A Thomas
General Medicine S K Gupta, C G Llewellyn-Jones, I Salam, N C Taylor
General Surgery A Locker, B M O'Riordan, W G Sheridan, W R G Thomas
Genitourinary Medicine V R Battu
Haematology V R Cumber
Neurology C Rickards
Obstetrics and Gynaecology T H Bloomfield, K G P McSweeney, N Piskorowskyj
Oncology M Wilkins

Ophthalmology P M Brown, D Jones, J Roberts-Harry
Oral and Maxillofacial Surgery S Hodder, K C Silvester
Orthodontics S J James
Orthopaedics R J Black, S Chatterji, S R Johnson, H Richards
Paediatrics G Owen, V R Saxena, S Warren
Palliative Medicine P M Purcell
Pathology R B Denholm, N A A Haboubi, J Murphy
Plastic Surgery M A C Cooper
Public Health Medicine G A J Harrison
Radiology G M Allen, C G Bartlett, M A H El-Heis, C C Ngoma
Radiotherapy A M M El-Sharkawi
Sexual Health A Cattell
Urology J L Edwards, M Taube

Ceredigion and Mid Wales NHS Trust

Bronglais General Hospital, Aberystwyth SY23 1ER
Tel: 01970 623131 Fax: 01970 635923
Email: paul.barnett@ceredigion-tr.wales.nhs.uk
(Dyfed Powys Health Authority)

Chair Eleri Ebenezer
Chief Executive Paul Michael Barnett

Aberaeron Cottage Hospital

Aberaeron SA46 0JJ
Tel: 01545 570225
Total Beds: 14

Bronglais General Hospital

Aberystwyth SY23 1ER
Tel: 01970 623131 Fax: 01970 635923
Total Beds: 146

Anaesthetics G Bonsu, B Campbell, M Collingborne, R M Henderson, K P Mishra, K Phillips
Care of the Elderly G V Boswell, P Jones
General Medicine A T Axford, A G Davies
General Surgery J L Edwards, D Jackson, R Visvanathan
Haematology H I Atrah
Medical Microbiology L McFarlane
Obstetrics and Gynaecology S A Awad, R W Myles
Ophthalmology K Sahni
Orthopaedics A D Meredith, W Spaeth
Paediatrics D D Walters, J Williams
Pathology C G B Simpson
Radiology P Cornah

Cardigan and District Memorial Hospital

Cardigan SA43 1DP
Tel: 01239 612214 Fax: 01239 621394
Total Beds: 25

Tregaron Hospital

Tregaron SY25 6JP
Tel: 01974 298203 Fax: 01974 298024
Total Beds: 29

Conwy and Denbighshire NHS Trust

Glan Clwyd Hospital, Rhyl LL18 5UJ
Tel: 01745 583910 Fax: 01745 583143
Email: mail@cd-tr.wales.nhs.uk
Website: www.conwy-denbighshire-nhs.org.uk
(North Wales Health Authority)

Chair Hilary Stevens
Chief Executive Gren R D Kershaw

Abergele Hospital

Abergele LL22
Tel: 01745 832295
Total Beds: 71

Chest Disease T J Charles, K Taylor
Orthopaedics S Bastawrous, N R Clay, A O'Kelly, A Sinna
Rheumatology W R Williams

Colwyn Bay Community Hospital

Hesketh Road, Colwyn Bay LL29 8AY
Tel: 01492 515218 Fax: 01492 518103
Total Beds: 42

Conwy Hospital

Bangor Road, Conwy LL32 8EB
Tel: 01492 592333 Fax: 01492 572903
Total Beds: 59

Care of the Elderly J V Hindle, D P O'Beirn

Denbigh Community Hospital

Ruthin Road, Denbigh LL16 3ES
Tel: 01745 812624 Fax: 01745 815851
Total Beds: 49

General Medicine C Madoc Jones

Glan Clwyd District General Hospital

Bodelwyddan, Rhyl LL18 5UJ
Tel: 01745 583910
Total Beds: 683

Accident and Emergency D Cartlidge, S Gandham
Anaesthetics C F Bell, G Davies, A J P Lake, S J Seager, B Tehan, B Waters, T B Webb, E G N Williams
Care of the Elderly B K Bhowmick, M W Greenway, R J Meara, J D D Wood
Dermatology R E A Williams
ENT Z Hammad, J E Osborne
General Medicine T J Charles, G J Green, R Sheers
General Surgery J Clark, C J Davies, C M Evans, D J Hay, O E Klimach, V Srinivasan
Genitourinary Medicine O E Williams
Neurosurgery R V Jeffreys, M T M Shaw
Obstetrics and Gynaecology P Banfield, N Bickerton, J A Edwards, D J Thomas
Oral Surgery C N Penfold, J G Phillips
Orthodontics R C Parkhouse
Orthopaedics N R Clay, M J S Hubbard, J Lewis, A L N Tilikawardane
Paediatrics P D Cameron, P R Stutchfield, A J Williams, T D Yuille
Pathology A D A Dalton, D R Edwards, D I Gozzard, D N Looker, M E McCaulay, B Rodgers
Radiology N P Archard, R A Byrne, S J Hotson, C A McConnell, E Moss, H G Row, D J Widdowson, J Williams, C H Wright
Rheumatology W R Williams

HM Stanley Hospital

St Asaph LL17 0RS
Tel: 01745 583275
Total Beds: 16

Ophthalmology D Saunders

Llangollen Community Hospital

Abby Road, Llangollen LL20 8SP
Tel: 01978 860226 Fax: 01978 861047
Total Beds: 18

General Medicine M D Gareh

Prestatyn Community Hospital

49 The Avenue, Woodlands Park, Prestatyn LL19 9RD
Tel: 01745 853487 Fax: 01745 887479
Total Beds: 12

Royal Alexandra Hospital

Marine Drive, Rhyl LL18 3AS
Tel: 01745 343188 Fax: 01745 344574
Total Beds: 54

Care of the Elderly B K Bhowmick
General Medicine H Jones

Ruthin Hospital

Llanrhydd Street, Ruthin LL15 1PS
Tel: 01824 702692 Fax: 01824 704719
Total Beds: 48

General Medicine J D G Williams

Gwent Healthcare NHS Trust

Grange House, Llanfrechfa Grange, Cwmbran NP44 8YN
Tel: 01633 623623 Fax: 01633 623836
Website: www.gwent-tr
(Gwent Health Authority)

Chair Dennis Jessopp
Chief Executive Martin Turner

Aberbargoed and District Hospital

Aberbargoed, Bargoed CF8 9BU
Tel: 01443 821621 Fax: 01443 820587
Total Beds: 28

Abertillery and District Hospital

Pendarren Road, Aberbeeg, Abertillery NP3 2XA
Tel: 01495 214123
Total Beds: 52

Consultants M Edwards, N Y Haboubi, P B Khanna

Blaina and District Hospital

Hospital Road, Nantyglo, Ebbw Vale NP23 4LY
Tel: 01495 293250 Fax: 01495 291091
Total Beds: 47

Consultants M Edwards, N Y Haboubi, P B Khanna

Caerphilly And District Miners' Hospital

St. Martins Road, Caerphilly CF8 2WW
Tel: 029 2085 1811
Total Beds: 139

Anaesthetics M Kant, W S Ng, M P Whitten
Care of the Elderly M Hasan, M Joglekar, J Thomas
Chest Disease B H Davies
General Medicine M Hall, J R Peters, L D K Premawardhana, A Rees
Obstetrics and Gynaecology N Jayawickrama, C J Richards, T V Stout
Orthopaedics P M Alderman, A J Grant, K Hariharan
Pathology A H M Quoraishi
Radiology H Adams

Chepstow Community Hospital

Tempest Way Road, Chepstow NP16 5YX
Tel: 01291 636636
Total Beds: 84

Care of the Elderly S E M Browne
General Medicine I S Petheram

County Hospital

Pontypool NP4 5YA
Tel: 01495 768768 Fax: 01495 768707
Total Beds: 97

Care of the Elderly E A Freeman, J M Toner
Learning Disabilities P V Ramachandran

NHS TRUSTS & NHS HOSPITALS

Obstetrics and Gynaecology D G Daniel, R H Golding, M Stone, A N A Weerakkody, J J Wiener
Radiology F Brook, N Kennan, B Sullivan, B A R Williams

Ebbw Vale Hospital
Hillside, Ebbw Vale NP3 5YA
Tel: 01495 356900
Total Beds: 23

Consultants M Edwards, N Y Haboubi, P B Khanna

Llanfrechfa Grange Hospital
Llanfrechfa, Cwmbran NP44 8YN
Tel: 01633 623623
Total Beds: 79

Learning Disabilities P V Ramachandran, U Suvagamasundari

Maindiff Court Hospital
Ross Road, Abergavenny NP7 8NF
Tel: 01873 735500
Total Beds: 74

Alcohol and Substance Misuse M Rowlands
Child and Adolescent Psychiatry E Kapp, K Moses, M Shooter
General Psychiatry J A Davies, V M Evans, S Hunter, R Huws, P L Jenkins, M M Jilani, I Jones, P H Mars, K Rice
Psychiatry of Old Age R M L Lewis, V B Rao, P Ruth, N J Warner, K Williamson

Monmouth Hospital
15 Hereford Road, Monmouth NP5 3HG
Tel: 01600 713522
Total Beds: 25

Nevill Hall Hospital
Beacon Road, Abergavenny NP7 7EG
Tel: 01873 732732
Total Beds: 107

Accident and Emergency N H Jenkins
Anaesthetics W P Cave, D I Fry, C Harrison, D J Hoad, T F Parker, D Ryan, P R Sengupta
Care of the Elderly M Edwards, N Y Haboubi, P B Khanna
Dermatology C N A Matthews
ENT M J K Brown, M I Clayton, I T G Evans
General Medicine E Boyd, S Hutchison, J Saunders, G O Thomas
General Psychiatry M M Jilani, R M L Lewis
General Surgery R L Blackett, C J Bransom, D R B Jones, R F Rintoul
Medical Microbiology N Carbarns
Obstetrics and Gynaecology A Dawson, W D Jackson, I M Stokes
Ophthalmology A D Holt-Wilson, A G Karseras, M Y Khan, N W D Walshaw
Oral and Maxillofacial Surgery J Llewellyn
Orthodontics H Taylor
Orthopaedics H Davies, P W Edwards, I Mackie
Paediatrics A D Griffiths, T H C Williams
Pathology R J Kellett, P W B Scott
Plastic Surgery M A P Milling
Radiology S Bleese, R B Pickford, D H Reed, D A Robinson, F Williams
Rheumatology A Borg, T Jenkinson
Urology R L Gower

Oakdale Hospital
Blackwood NP2 0JH
Tel: 01495 225207 Fax: 01495 230072
Total Beds: 20

Care of the Elderly M Toglekar

Redwood Memorial Hospital
Rhymney NP2 5XB
Tel: 01685 840314 Fax: 01685 844928
Total Beds: 21

Royal Gwent Hospital
Cardiff Road, Newport NP20 2UB
Tel: 01633 234234 Fax: 01663 221217
Total Beds: 731

Accident and Emergency G McCarthy, W J Morgan, F Richardson
Anaesthetics J Butler, C Callander, G S Clark, S W Dumont, H O Dwyer, D J Dye, J Gough, I P C Greenway, T Haynes, D I Jones, H M Jones, T Mian, P Nicholls, M Sage, D L Thomas, G D Thomas, A B Williams
Child and Adolescent Psychiatry E Kapp
Clinical Oncology A Brewster
Dermatology A V Anstey, C N A Matthews, C Mills
ENT M J K Brown, M I Clayton, I T G Evans, J M Preece
General Medicine M Allison, E G Anderson, S E M Browne, S G Cotton, J Davies, E A Freeman, O M Gibby, S Ikram, H J Lloyd, I S Petheram, E D Srivastava, D A Sykes, J Toner, I Williamson
General Psychiatry J A Davies, V M Evans, S Hunter, R Huws, P L Jenkins, P M Ruth, N J Warner
General Surgery C A Gateley, G H Griffith, W G Lewis, A A Shandall, K Shute, B M Stephenson, K Vellacott
Genitourinary Medicine R Das
Learning Disabilities U S Sondari
Neurology J G Llewelyn
Obstetrics and Gynaecology D G Daniel, R H Golding, M Stone, A N A Weerakkody, J J Wiener
Oral and Maxillofacial Surgery M Gregory, J Llewelyn
Orthodontics S Wigglesworth
Orthopaedics P M Alderman, W J M Czyz, A Grant, K Hariharen, D G Jones, P Roberts, R Savage, K J J Tayton
Paediatrics J Barton, I Bowler, P Buss, S D Ferguson, S Maguire
Palliative Medicine P Grzybowska, H Taylor
Pathology K M Al Shafit, R W Fortt, C Hewlett, E Kubiak, E Moffatt, E W Owen, M D Penney, A M Rashid, I W Thompson
Plastic Surgery M A P Milling
Radiology M Bernard, F Brook, R Clements, J Harding, D Jackson, A Jones, M Kennan, B Sullivan, G Thomas, A Wake, B A R Williams
Rheumatology A Borg, T Jenkinson, P I Williams
Urology W Bowsher, R L Gower

St Cadoc's Hospital
Caerleon, Newport NP6 1XQ
Tel: 01633 436700 Fax: 01633 436734
Total Beds: 112

Child and Adolescent Psychiatry E Kapp, K Moses, M Shooter
General Psychiatry J A Davies, V M Evans, P Hullis, S Hunter, P L Jenkins
Psychiatry of Old Age R M L Lewis, P Ruth

St Woolos Hospital
131 Stow Hill, Newport NP9 4SZ
Tel: 01633 234231 Fax: 01622 221774
Total Beds: 191

Anaesthetics J Butler, G S Clark, S Dumont, I Greenway, H M Jones, T M Mian, G D Thomas
Care of the Elderly S E M Browne, E A Freeman, D A Sykes, J M Toner
Occupational Health A Misir
Ophthalmology A D Holt-Wilson, A G Karseras, M Y Khan, N W D Walshaw
Psychiatry of Old Age V M Evans, N J Warner
Radiology J R Harding

Tredegar General Hospital
Park Row, Tredegar NP2 3XP
Tel: 01495 722271

Total Beds: 58

Care of the Elderly M Edwards, N Y Haboubi, P B Khanna

Ystrad Mynach Hospital

Caerphilly Road, Ystrad Mynach, Hengoed CF82 7XU
Tel: 01443 811411
Total Beds: 84

Care of the Elderly M Hasan, M Joglekar, J Thomas
Learning Disabilities J M Rao
Psychiatry of Old Age D Aldrich

North East Wales NHS Trust

Wrexham Maelor Hospital, Croesnewydd Road, Wrexham LL13 7TD
Tel: 01978 291100
(North Wales Health Authority)

Chair Lloyd FitzHugh
Chief Executive Hilary Pepler

Chirk Community Hospital

Off St. John's Street, Chirk, Wrexham LL14 5LN
Tel: 01691 772430 Fax: 01691 772342
Total Beds: 31

General Medicine W P Seward

Deeside Community Hospital

Plough Lane, Higher Shotton, Deeside CH5 1XS
Tel: 01244 830461 Fax: 01244 836323
Total Beds: 31

General Medicine W Jolly

Dobshill Hospital

Chester Road, Buckley, Deeside CH5 3LZ
Tel: 01244 550233 Fax: 01244 547872
Total Beds: 46

Medicine for the Elderly M U Fernandon

Flint Community Hospital

Cornist Road, Flint CH6 5HG
Tel: 01352 732215 Fax: 01352 730494
Total Beds: 18

General Medicine E Matthews

Holywell Community Hospital

Pen-y Maes Road, Holywell CH8 7UH
Tel: 01352 713003 Fax: 01352 715395
Total Beds: 18

General Medicine Dr Kapur

Lluesty Hospital

Old Chester Road, Holywell CH8 7SA
Tel: 01352 710581
Total Beds: 30

Meadowslea Hospital

Vounog Hill, Penyffordd, Chester CH4 0EA
Tel: 01978 760412 Fax: 01978 762871
Total Beds: 43

General Medicine Dr Botham, I U Shah

Mold Community Hospital

Ash Grove, Mold CH7 1XG
Tel: 01352 758744 Fax: 01352 750469
Total Beds: 40

Penley Hospital

Whitchurch Road, Penley, Wrexham LL14 0LH
Tel: 01948 830341 Fax: 01948 830765
Total Beds: 12

General Medicine J D McCarter

Trevalyn Hospital

Chester Road, Rossett, Wrexham LL12 0HL
Tel: 01244 570446 Fax: 01244 571481
Total Beds: 32

Medicine for the Elderly A White

Wrexham Maelor Hospital

Croesnewydd Road, Wrexham LL13 7TD
Tel: 01978 291100 Fax: 01978 290951
Total Beds: 588

Accident and Emergency M A T Cook, A Sen
Anaesthetics G J Arthurs, S Coughlan, C Dowling, C Edmundson, A E Edwards, L W Gemmell, J R Jamieson, R A Jones, C Littler, V Scott-Knight, D A Southern, S Underhill
Cardiology R Cowell, R J Trent
Care of the Elderly M U Fernando, I U Shah, A White
Dermatology R Lister, J Sowden
ENT A R Chandra-Mohan, J F Coakley, D G Snow
General Medicine J T Baker, D F Child, P J T Drew, J Harvey, N McAndrew, M O'Sullivan, A Ross, P Rutherford, O Williams
General Surgery Dr Billings, Dr Cochrane, A E da Silva, P Marsh, J K Pye, M Scriven
Obstetrics and Gynaecology C Rosenblade, W Taylor, P G Toon, P R Vlies
Occupational Health P Zacharias
Ophthalmology K S Chawla, N C Kaushik
Oral and Maxillofacial Surgery C Penfold
Orthodontics J G Heyes
Orthopaedics G Evans, Dr Graham, P Laing, K Lewis, S Roberts, J Wootton
Paediatrics B Harrington, P Minchom, G G Owens
Pathology A H Burdge, C Cefai, J Duguid, M Otter, D K Watson, C P Williams, R B Williams
Radiology J Green, M G E Greensmith, V W Jones, C H Laine, S Meecham-Jones, G M Murray, D Parker
Restorative Dentistry T Nisbet
Urology P S Anandaram, A R d Bolla

North Glamorgan NHS Trust

Prince Charles Hospital, Merthyr Tydfil CF47 9DT
Tel: 01685 721721 Fax: 01865 388001
(Bro Taf Health Authority)

Chair Jill Penn
Chief Executive Robert B Lewis

Aberdare Hospital

Aberdare CF44 0RF
Tel: 01685 872411 Fax: 01685 882741
Total Beds: 89

Care of the Elderly I B Davies
General Medicine Rehab Dr Davies, Dr Drah, B E Griffiths, Dr Hand, Dr Hanna, T J Morris
General Surgery P A Braithwaite, C Fontaine, M I Khan, W H Thomas
Ophthalmology Dr Chaudrey
Orthopaedics Surgical Rehab Dr Braithwaite, Dr Harey, Dr Hussein, Dr Izzidien, Dr Jones, Dr Khalifeh, Dr Massoud, Dr Zaphiropoulos
Out Patients Dr Azzuz, Dr Blankson, Dr Cassidy, Dr Davies, Dr De Silva, Dr Drah, Dr Evans, Dr Evans, Dr Geibally, Dr Griffiths, Dr Hand, Dr Hanna, Dr Haray, Dr Hawkes, Dr Hussain, Dr Ismael, Dr Izzidien, Dr Jones, Dr Kahsey, Dr Khaled, Dr McQueen, Dr Maguire,

NHS TRUSTS & NHS HOSPITALS

Dr Marks, Dr Masoud, Dr Maulik, Dr Myers, Dr O'Brien, Dr Pearce, Dr Singh, Dr Singh, Dr Zaifiropoulos

Paediatrics J M Blankson, R W Evans, M J Maguire

Radiology R A Davies, R M Ginwalla, D W Gregory, R J Parker, A M Wake

Visiting Consultants Dr Cassidy, Dr Gregory, Dr Inwood, Dr Jayawant, Dr Jenkins

Mountain Ash Hospital

Mountain Ash CF45 4DE
Tel: 01685 872411 Fax: 01685 882741
Total Beds: 35

General Medicine B E Griffiths, T J Morris

Out Patient Dr Asaad, Dr Desilva, Dr Hussain, Dr Izzidien, Dr Johnson, Dr Morris, Dr Myers, Dr O'Brien, Dr Sullivan, Dr Zafiroppoulos

Prince Charles Hospital

Merthyr Tydfil CF47 9DT
Tel: 01685 721721 Fax: 01685 388001
Total Beds: 442

Accident and Emergency Dr Reece, Dr Tovey

Anaesthetics Dr Hukasa, J Manser, Dr Muthuswamy, J Pickford, Dr Sanikop, Dr Scott

Care of the Elderly I B Davies, M Direkze

ENT Dr Shah

General Medicine W V Evans, B E Griffiths, Dr Hand, T J Morris

General Psychiatry P C Choudhury

General Surgery P A Braithwaite, Dr Masoud

Neurology I N F McQueen

Obstetrics and Gynaecology H R Elliott, T G Maulik

Oral and Maxillofacial Surgery A Ezsias, C S Holland, E S Nash

Orthodontics P T Nicholson

Orthopaedics Dr Ismaiel

Paediatrics J M Blankson, R W Evans, M J Maguire, Dr Rangarajan

Pathology K Myers, Dr Sweerts

Radiology R A Davies, R M Ginwalla, D W Gregory, Dr Hussein, Dr Valli

Rheumatology and Rehabilitation M D Silva

St Tydfil's Day Hospital (Medicine)

Upper Thomas Street, Merthyr Tydfil CF47 0SJ
Tel: 01685 723244 Fax: 01685 385171

St Tydfil's Hospital (Mental health)

Merthyr Tydfil CF47 0SJ
Tel: 01685 723244 Fax: 01685 385171
Total Beds: 162

Care of the Elderly I B Davies, M Direkze

General Psychiatry P C Choudhury

Seymour Berry Community Mental Health Team

Victoria Street, Dowlais, Merthyr Tydfil
Tel: 01685 721671

North West Wales NHS Trust

Ysbyty Gwynedd, Penrhosgarnedd, Bangor LL57 2PW
Tel: 01248 384486, 01248 384384 Fax: 01248 370629
Email: christine.jones@www.tr.wales.nhs.uk
Website: www.northwestwales.org
(North Wales Health Authority)

Chair R Hefin Davies MBE

Chief Executive Keith Thomson

Consultants N Abdullah, C Adams, E Ahiaku, W Ahmed, K D Algawi, S Amjad, U Andrady, G A Attara, C Baldwin, G S Barr, P Barry, N C Barwick, A Bates, G F A Benfield, P Birch, L L O Bloodworth, L M Bolton, P Carson, A W Caslin, D C Crawford, R C Crawford, M J Cronin, N Curzen, P Cutting, R H Davies, M Devakumar, F H Drouet, C Eickmann, A El-Sheikha, B Elnazir, G Evans, E M Farley-Hills, A Fitzpatrick, A Fowell, S B Francis, A Gash, H Godfrey, K Griffiths, T J B Harris, D Healy, J V Hindle, N G Hodges, J Horn, W V Humphreys, S G Hunter, Q Ijaz, W James, M Jamison, L L R Jenkinson, M M Jibani, I Johnson, J Jones, M W Jones, R Y Jones, G Jones-Edwards, R Kanvinde, L Kaye-Wilson, H A Khan, N Khan, P J M Kinahan, B Kumar, S Leeson, R Lewis, K Lynch, A W MacFarlane, L McSweeney, P J Maddison, B Madkour, H S Mohammed, K J Mottart, D O'Beirn, D J Oberholzer, B C Owen, D Owens, D H Parry, W J Parry, J G Phillips, T G Powell, D Prichard, A P Roberts, H Roberts, W O Roberts, G A Robinson, J R C Seale, A Shambrook, S Smith, A R Starczewski, N S A Stuart, S Talwar, K J Thomas, C M Thorpe, P Tivy Jones, A Valijan, A L Vaterlaws, L Vati, A M Walker, G T Watkin, D M Wayte, S Wenham, G S W Whiteley, J G Williams, A Wilton, S Zeki

Bron y Garth Hospital

Penrhyndeudraeth LL48 6HE
Tel: 01766 770310 Fax: 01766 772142
Total Beds: 31

Bryn Beryl Hospital

Pwllheli LL53 6TT
Tel: 01758 701122 Fax: 01758 701295
Total Beds: 39

Care of the Elderly P N Ohri, D R Prichard

General Medicine D R Prichard

Bryn Seiont Hospital

Caernarfon LL55 2YU
Tel: 01286 673371 Fax: 01286 678228
Total Beds: 33

Bryn-Y-Neuadd Hospital

Llanfairfechan LL33 0HH
Tel: 01248 682682 Fax: 01248 681832
Total Beds: 113

General Psychiatry F Drouet, L Vati

Psychiatry of Old Age M Devakumar

Carreg Fawr Bed Support Unit at Bryn y Neuadd Hospital

Llanfairfechan LL33 0HH
Tel: 01248 682304
Total Beds: 8

Cefni Hospital

Llangefni LL77 7PP
Tel: 01248 753124 Fax: 01248 753124
Total Beds: 35

Care of the Elderly A B Bates, A R Starczewski

Coed Lys

Llangefni
Tel: 01248 724318
Total Beds: 8

Deiniol Day Hospital

Ysbyty Gwynedd, Penrhosgarnedd, Bangor LL57 2PW
Tel: 01248 384068 Fax: 01248 370629

Dolgellau and Barmouth District Hospital

Dolgellau LL40 1NP
Tel: 01341 422479 Fax: 01341 423684
Total Beds: 40

Care of the Elderly J V Hindle, D P O'Beirn

Dryll y Carr Unit

Llanaber, Barmouth LL42 1YY
Tel: 01341 281049 Fax: 01341 281049
Total Beds: 8

Eryri Hospital

The Park, Caernarfon LL55 2YE
Tel: 01268 672481 Fax: 01286 674380
Total Beds: 36

Care of the Elderly P N Ohri, D R Prichard, A R Starczewski, R Subashchandran

Ffestiniog Memorial Hospital

Blaenau Ffestiniog LL41 3DW
Tel: 01766 831281 Fax: 01766 830584
Total Beds: 17

Llandudno General Hospital

Llandudno LL30 1LB
Tel: 01492 860066 Fax: 01492 871668
Total Beds: 112

Care of the Elderly J V Hindle, D P O'Beirn
General Medicine J Cunningham, A L Vaterlaws
General Surgery E K N Ahiaku, D J Crawford, L R Jenkinson, G T Watkin, G Whiteley

Mental Health Acute Unit

Hergest Unit, Ysbyty Gwynedd, Penrhosgarnedd Road, Bangor LL57 2PW
Tel: 01248 384384
Total Beds: 60

Minffordd Hospital

Bangor LL57 4DR
Tel: 01248 352308 Fax: 01248 371005
Total Beds: 16

Elderly Mentally Ill M Devakumar

Ty Llywelyn (Medium Secure Unit) at Bryn y Neuadd Hospital

[New Address], Llanfairfechan LL33 0HH
Tel: 01248 682132
Total Beds: 25

Tywyn and District War Memorial Hospital

Tywyn LL36 9HH
Tel: 01654 710411 Fax: 01654 712206
Total Beds: 24

Ysbyty Gwynedd

Penrhosgarnedd, Bangor LL57 2PW
Tel: 01248 384384 Fax: 01248 370629
Total Beds: 508

Accident and Emergency P Cutting
Anaesthetics P Barry, C Eickmann, E M Farley-Hills, T J B Harris, W James, I Johnson, R P Lewis, K Mottart, W O Roberts, A Shambrook, S Smith, C H Thorpe, A Valijan
Cardiology P Carson, S Talwar
Care of the Elderly A B Bates, J V Hindle, D P O'Beirn, D R Prichard, A R Starczewski
Clinical Oncology N S A Stuart
Dermatology A W MacFarlane
ENT G S Barr, M B Madkour, A Sheka
General Medicine W Ahmed, G F A Benfield, L L O Bloodworth, N G Hodges, M Jibani, N Khan, H S Mohammed, D Owens, A Wilton
General Surgery N Abdullah, D J Crawford, W V Humphreys, M H Jamison, L Jenkinson, G T Watkin, G Whiteley
Genitourinary Medicine U Andrady
Haematology D H Parry, J R C Seale
Neurology N Fletcher, B R F Lecky

Neurosurgery P R Eldridge
Obstetrics and Gynaecology L Bolton, B Kumar, S C Leeson, P Tivy-Jones
Occupational Health B C Owen
Oncology N S A Stuart
Ophthalmology K D Al-Gawi, S Amjad, L Kaye-Wilson, P J Kinahan, G Robinson, S Zeki
Oral and Maxillofacial Surgery J G Phillips
Orthodontics W J Parry
Orthopaedics G A Attara, S G Hunter, M Jones, R Kanvinde, L McSweeney
Paediatrics M J Cronin, R H Davies, B Elnazir, J S M Horn, T G Powell, H Roberts
Palliative Medicine A Fowell
Pathology A W Caslin, K D Griffiths, A M Walker, D M Wayte
Radiology C Adams, N C Barwick, P D Birch, R C Crawford, A J Gash, H Godfrey, J Jones, R Y Jones, S Wenham, J G Williams
Rheumatology P J Maddison
Urology E K N Ahiaku, K Thomas

Ysbyty Penrhos Stanley

Holyhead LL65 2PR
Tel: 01407 766000 Fax: 01407 766091
Total Beds: 50

Care of the Elderly A B Bates
Psychiatry of Old Age M Devakumar

Pembrokeshire and Derwen NHS Trust

Withybush General Hospital, Fishguard Road, Haverfordwest SA61 2PZ
Tel: 01437 764545 Fax: 01437 773353
Email: admin@pdt-tr.wales.nhs.uk
Website: www.pdt-tr.wales.nhs.uk
(Dyfed Powys Health Authority)

Chair Lynette George
Chief Executive Stuart Fletcher

Bro Cerwyn Psychiatric Day Hospital

Fishguard Road, Haverfordwest SA61 2PZ
Tel: 01437 773157 Fax: 01437 773057

Brynhaul Day Hospital

Bryntirion Hospital, Swansea Road, Llanelli SA15 3DX
Tel: 01554 756567 Fax: 01554 753519

Brynmair Day Hospital

Brynmair Clinic, 11 Goring Road, Llanelli SA15 3HH
Tel: 01554 772768

Bryntirion Hospital

Swansea Road, Llanelli SA15 2DX
Tel: 01554 756567
Total Beds: 20

Cleddau Rehabilitation Unit

Fort Road, Pembroke Dock SA72 6SX

St Brynach's Day Hospital

Fishguard Road, Haverfordwest SA61 2PZ
Tel: 01437 764545

St David's Hospital

Carmarthen SA31 3HB
Tel: 01267 237481 Fax: 01267 221895
Total Beds: 154

General Psychiatry R Atkinson, M S Elameer, N Evans, S Gurucharanam, C A Hooper, T Magee, H Matthews, C Moyle, E Richardson, M P Sargeant, B Thompson, R Wilson

NHS TRUSTS & NHS HOSPITALS

South Pembrokeshire Hospital
Fort Road, Pembroke Dock SA72 6SX
Tel: 01646 682114 Fax: 01646 774114
Total Beds: 35

Swn-Y-Gwynt Day Hospital
Tir-Y-Dail Lane, Glanamman, Ammanford SA18 3AS
Tel: 01269 595473 Fax: 01269 597518

Tenby Cottage Hospital
Trafalgar Road, Tenby SA70 7EE
Tel: 01834 842040 Fax: 01834 844097
Total Beds: 13

Withybush General Hospital
Fishguard Road, Haverfordwest SA61 2PZ
Tel: 01437 764545 Fax: 01437 773353
Total Beds: 332

Accident and Emergency G Evans
Anaesthetics D Bryant, R A Cooke, R Cross, R B Griffiths, D A Thomas, M J Wort
General Surgery K M C Abrew, W Maxwell, P J Milewski
Haematology H Grubb, A N Saleem
Integrated Medicine and Rehabilitation C M James, D J Jones, N I Jowett, K Mohanaruban, A Vaishnavi
Microbiology M Sheppard
Obstetrics and Gynaecology W M Clow, M R Howells, C Overton
Occupational Health R Wort
Oncology P Purcell
Paediatrics A Palit, G Vas Falcao, V Vipulendran
Pathology G R Melville-Jones, S Polacarz
Radiology K Bradshaw, I Martin
Trauma and Orthopaedics P Kanse, G Phillips

Withybush Rehabilitation Day Hospital
Fishguard Road, Haverfordwest

Withybush Surgical Day Hospital
Fishguard Road, Haverfordwest

Y Delyn Day Hospital
Canolfan Gwenog, West Wales General Hospital, Carmarthen SA31 2AF
Tel: 01267 235151 Fax: 01267 237662

General Medicine S M A Aslan, P S Davies, R Dewer, J R Dowdle, R T M Edwards, M D Page, A Pandit
General Psychiatry S Jawad
General Surgery M E Foster, M H Lewis, R J L Williams
Obstetrics and Gynaecology J M Arnold, D H O Pugh
Oncology I Kerby
Ophthalmology N Hawksworth, R Raghu-Ram, S C Sullivan
Orthopaedics J M Murray, D Pemberton
Paediatrics I C G Hodges, R J H Morgan
Pathology C DeAlwis, D Stock
Radiology C J Davies, S G Davies, E Hicks, R Winter
Rheumatology J Martin
Urology A J L Hart

Royal Glamorgan General Hospital
Ynys Maerdy, Llantrisant CF72 8XR
Tel: 01443 443443 Fax: 01443 217213
Total Beds: 509

Accident and Emergency W D T Moody Jones
Anaesthetics S Ackerman, M Bayoumi, R Davies, T R Tipping, T G L Watkins, P V Woodsford
Dermatology R A Logan, C Long
ENT A H Jones, R Rivron, H Williams
General Medicine S M A Aslan, P S Davies, R I Dewar, J R Dowdle, R M T Edwards, G Ellis, M D Page, A Pandit, J White
General Surgery M E Foster, T Havard, M H Lewis, R J Williams, A Woodward
Genitourinary Medicine A N Abdullah, A R G Manuel
Neurology I N F McQueen
Obstetrics and Gynaecology J M Arnold, D H O Pugh, S Vine
Ophthalmology N Hawkesworth, A R RaghuRam, S C Sullivan
Orthopaedics P Evans, A Jenkins, J M Murray, T Owen, D Pemberton
Paediatrics I C G Hodges, L Miller-Jones, J Moorcraft, R J H Morgan
Pathology C D Alwis, C Champ, D Stock, A Verghasa, D White
Radiology C J Davies, S G Davies, K L Gower-Thomas, E Hicks, R Rhys, R Winter
Rheumatology and Rehabilitation J Martin
Urology A J L Hart, D Jones

Ysbyty George Thomas
Mattie Collins Way, Treorchy CF42 6YG
Tel: 01443 440440 Fax: 01443 775042
Total Beds: 100

Pontypridd and Rhondda NHS Trust

Trust Management Offices, Dewi Sant Hospital, Albert Road, Pontypridd CF37 1LB
Tel: 01443 486222 Fax: 01443 443842
(Bro Taf Health Authority)

Chair Ian Kelsall
Chief Executive Margaret Foster

Dewi Sant Hospital
Albert Road, Pontypridd CF37 1LB
Tel: 01443 486222 Fax: 01443 403268
Total Beds: 100

General Medicine S M A Aslan, P S Davies, R Dewer, J R Dowdle, R T M Edwards, M D Page, P Valabhji

Llwynypia Hospital
Llwynypia, Tonypandy CF40 2LX
Tel: 01443 440440 Fax: 01443 431611
Total Beds: 143

Accident and Emergency W D T Moody-Jones
ENT A H Jones, R P Rivron

Powys Health Care NHS Trust

Bronllys Hospital, Bronllys, Brecon LD3 0LS
Tel: 01874 711661 Fax: 01874 711828
Website: www.powys-tr.wales.nhs.uk
(Dyfed Powys Health Authority)

Chair Antony Lewis
Chief Executive Martin Woodford

Brecon War Memorial Hospital
Cerrigcochion Road, Brecon LD3 7NS
Tel: 01874 622443 Fax: 01874 625752
Total Beds: 76

Care of the Elderly A Pinhorn
General Medicine Dr Boyd
Obstetrics and Gynaecology Dr Dawson, Dr Jackson, Dr Stokes

Bro Ddyfi Community Hospital
Newtown Road, Machynlleth SY20 8AD
Tel: 01654 702266 Fax: 01654 703795
Total Beds: 43

Care of the Elderly G Boswell
General Medicine A T Axford, Dr Davies, Dr Singh
Obstetrics and Gynaecology Dr Myles

Bronllys Hospital

Bronllys, Brecon LD3 0LS
Tel: 01874 711255 Fax: 01874 712447
Total Beds: 93

Care of the Elderly A M Dunn
Haematology Dr Haboush
Rheumatology Dr Williams

Builth Wells Cottage Hospital

Hospital Road, Builth Wells LD2 3HE
Tel: 01982 552221 Fax: 01982 554353
Total Beds: 23

Care of the Elderly A Dunn
General Medicine J Saunders
Obstetrics and Gynaecology E Barton, P Grech, G Rowe, R Rubak-Sharpe, P Wilson

Knighton Hospital

Ffrydd Road, Knighton LD7 1DF
Tel: 01547 528633 Fax: 01547 520522
Total Beds: 5

Care of the Elderly A M Dunn

Llandrindod Wells County War Memorial Hospital

Temple Street, Llandrindod Wells LD1 5HF
Tel: 01597 822951 Fax: 01597 828764
Total Beds: 70

Llanidloes and District War Memorial Hospital

Eastgate Street, Llanidloes SY18 6HF
Tel: 01686 412121 Fax: 01686 412999
Total Beds: 36

Care of the Elderly G Boswell

Montgomery County Infirmary

Llanfair Road, Newtown SY16 2DW
Tel: 01686 617200 Fax: 01686 617249
Total Beds: 48

Care of the Elderly G Boswell

Victoria Memorial Hospital

Salop Road, Welshpool SY21 7DU
Tel: 01938 553133 Fax: 01938 558093
Total Beds: 45

Ystradgynlais Community Hospital

Glanrhyd Road, Ystradgynlais, Swansea SA9 1AE
Tel: 01639 844777 Fax: 01639 846479
Total Beds: 52

Care of the Elderly A Pinhorn

Swansea NHS Trust

Central Clinic, Trinity Buildings, 21 Orchard Street, Swansea SA1 5AT
Tel: 01792 651501 Fax: 01792 517018
Website: www.swansea-tr.wales.nhs.uk
(Iechyd Morgannwg Health Authority)

Chair D Hugh Thomas
Chief Executive David M Williams

Cefn Coed Hospital

Waunarlwydd Road, Cockett, Swansea SA2 0GH
Tel: 01792 561155 Fax: 01792 580740
Total Beds: 255

Child and Adolescent Psychiatry S Ames, G Salmon, J S Talbot

General Psychiatry S Davies, P Donnelly, M D Gibbs, A Wooding
Old Age Psychiatry S Albuquerque, M Ellis, D D R William

Clydach War Memorial Hospital

Clydach, Swansea SA6 5DT
Tel: 01792 842260
Total Beds: 20

Fairwood Hospital

Total Beds: 28

Garngoch Hospital

Gorseinon, Swansea
Tel: 01792 892921 Fax: 01792 899127
Total Beds: 40

General Psychiatry M Ellis, D D R Williams

Gellinudd Hospital

Total Beds: 30

Consultants A Treseder

Gorseinon Hospital

Total Beds: 66

Consultants D J Leopold

Hill House Hospital

Swansea SA2 0FB
Tel: 01792 203551
Total Beds: 86

Morriston Hospital

Morriston, Swansea SA6 6NL
Tel: 01792 702222 Fax: 01792 703499
Total Beds: 747

Accident and Emergency H Allen, M McCabe
Anaesthetics Dr Beese, E P Bennett, J Bowes, A J Byrne, M Davies, J Dingley, S D N Dwyer, M L Evans, P J Hilton, D Hope, J A Hughes, L A G Hughes, D C Jerwood, R C King, J Leary, D H Long, W A McFadzean, H W Maddock, S Mahon, E Major, P S Mangat, P C Matthews, J R Morgan, W A Rogers, P A Schwartz, H Speedy, D W Thomas, T J Wall
Cardio-Thoracic Surgery V Argano, S Ashraf, A Y Youhana
Cardiology M Anderson, K E Evans, G H Jenkins, M N Ramsey, P Thomas
Care of the Elderly D J Leopold, A S Treseder, M Wani
Chemical Pathology A Gunneberg
Chest Medicine K Harrison
Diabetes D E Price
Gastroenterology P Duane, J G Williams
General Surgery J Baxter, T Brown, M Chare, C Ferguson, L Fligelstone, C P Gibbons
Haematology S Al-Ismail, A C Beddall
Histopathology A Dawson, P Griffiths, C J O'Brien, N Toffazzal
Medical Microbiology A Lewis, P D Thomas
Neurology C Rickards, I Sawhney, R Weiser
Neurosurgery J Buxton, J Martin, R Redfern
Occupational Health D Bell
Oral and Maxillofacial Surgery K Bishop, S Hodder, D J Howells, J Knox, D N Patton, K Silvester, A W Sugar
Orthopaedics D A Clement, E M Downes, H C Hoddinott, M Holt, E T R James, R L Leyshon, D Newington, N Price, D J Woodnutt
Palliative Medicine S Closs, H Taylor
Plastic Surgery M A C Cooper, W A Dickson, P S Drew, J H Laing, A D McGregor, M A P Milling, M S C Murison
Radiology A J Davies, J H Davies, R S Davies, R M Evans, S E Evans, C I Flowers, E W Jones, L G McKnight, D Markham, N Powell, D G Richards, D E Roberts, P G White
Renal Medicine A J Antao
Rheumatology and Rehabilitation A I Hennessy, D H Smith, B J Sweetman
Urology P Bose, N J Fenn, M G Lucas, K C Vaughton

NHS TRUSTS & NHS HOSPITALS

Singleton Hospital

Sketty, Swansea SA2 8QA
Tel: 01792 205666 Fax: 01792 208647
Total Beds: 539

Anaesthetics S J Catling, J S S Davies, M Evans, R Falconer, R A Mason, R N W Morgan, A L Murphy, P Nesling, H Slowey, P A Steane, J S Thomas, M J Whitehead, A R Williams
Community Paediatrics S Jones, A Maddox
Dermatology S Blackford, D L L Roberts, B Statham
ENT D W Aird, S Browning, C P Fielder, J J Phillips, H B Whittet
General Medicine J Banks, W Harris, J Hopkin, C Hudson, M K Jones, J G C Kingham, L Thomas, C Weston
General Surgery J Beynon, N D Carr, J Manson, M C Mason, A R Morgan
Genitourinary Medicine V Battue, A L Blackwell, K Yoganathan
Haematology S Al-Ismail, A Beddall, M S Lewis
Obstetrics and Gynaecology M Bonduelle, P B Bowen-Simpkins, J P Calvert, M Dossa, S Emery, O Freites, J Gasson, E Kevelighan, R Llewellyn, M Morgan
Ophthalmology M W Austin, E G Davies, R J Hill, D E Laws, A Pickering, G Shuttleworth
Paediatrics M Cosgrove, D R Evans, M James-Ellison, G Morris, M O'Hagan, C L Sullivan, C White
Pathology D H M Joynson, V Shah, P D Thomas, N Tofazzal, D W Williams, N Williams, S Williams
Psychiatry G Salmon, J Talbot
Radiology D Harvey, B Patel, A L Power, M White
Radiotherapy C S Askill, A M M El-Sharkawi, W R Gajek, T Joannides, R Leonard, K H M Rowley, P Savage

Ty-Einon Day Hospital

Princess Street, Gorseinon, Swansea SA4 2US
Tel: 01792 898078

Velindre NHS Trust

Velindre Hospital, Velindre Road, Whitchurch, Cardiff CF14 2TL
Tel: 029 2061 5888 Fax: 029 2052 2694
Website: www.velindre-tr.wales.nhs.uk
(Bro Taf Health Authority)

Chair Tony Hazell
Chief Executive John Richards

Velindre Hospital

Whitchurch, Cardiff CF4 2TL
Tel: 029 2061 5888 Fax: 029 2052 2694
Total Beds: 69

Radiology M Bourne, L B Williams
Radiotherapy P Pimm

Welsh Ambulance Services NHS Trust

HM Stanley Hospital, Upper Denbigh Road, St Asaph LL17 0WA
Tel: 01745 585106 Fax: 01745 584101
Email: eleri.jones@ambulance.wales.nhs.uk
Website: www.was-tr.wales.nhs.uk
(North Wales Health Authority)

Chief Executive Don Page, E Pritchard

Northern Ireland

Altnagelvin Hospitals HSS Trust

Altnagelvin Area Hospital, Glenshane Road, Londonderry BT47 6SB
Tel: 028 7134 5171 Fax: 028 7161 1222

(Western Health and Social Services Board)

Chair Denis F Desmond
Chief Executive Stella Burnside, S O'Kane
Consultants L A McKinney, J Steele

Altnagelvin Area Hospital

Glenshane Road, Londonderry BT47 6SB
Tel: 028 7134 5171 Fax: 028 7161 1222
Total Beds: 504

Accident and Emergency L A McKinney, J Steele
Anaesthetics W N Chestnutt, E G Devlin, G Di Mascio, G Furness, P Glover, D Grace, J N Hamilton, A P Jain, B C Morrow, G A Nesbitt, C O'Hare
Care of the Elderly J A F Beirne, J G McElroy
Dermatology R A Fulton, P Podmore
ENT J R Cullen, W E Harris, G McBride
General Medicine J A F Beirne, J G Daly, W Dickey, H M Dunn, P V Gardiner, A Garvey, D A J Keegan, J G McElroy, A J McNeil, K W Moles, F A O'Connor, J A Purvis, R Sharkey
General Surgery P G Bateson, R J Gilliland, P Neilly, K J S Panesar, R L E Thompson
Genitourinary Medicine W W Dinsmore
Obstetrics and Gynaecology Dr Fallows, S E E Magee, D H Martin, J Moohan, M J Parker
Ophthalmology M E A Hanna, P Hassett, D Mulholland, N K Sharma, J Sinton
Oral Surgery R C Boyd, M Ryan
Orthodontics R McMullan
Orthopaedics M J McCormack, H McGee, N S Simpson, J Wong, A R Wray
Otolaryngology J R Cullen, W E Harris, G McBride
Paediatrics D A Brown, C Imrie, F B McCord, N P Corrigan, R J M Quinn
Pathology J J Crosbie, G M Glynn, D F Hughes, M Madden, M J O'Kane, M H Vazir
Radiology P B Devlin, C S Elliott, P R Jackson, C C Morrison, M P Reilly, N A Sharkey
Urology G Lennon, C K Mulholland

Armagh and Dungannon HSS Trust

St. Lukes Hospital, Armagh BT61 7NG
Tel: 028 3752 2381 Fax: 028 3752 6302
(Southern Health and Social Services Board)

Chair James D Shaw
Chief Executive P Stanley

Armagh Community Hospital

Tower Hill, Armagh BT61 9DR
Tel: 028 3752 2381

Audiological Medicine S Hall (Head), M McGee
Dermatology K W Scott
ENT R K Hingorani
General Medicine T J Baird, K Balnave
General Psychiatry M McCourt
General Surgery R Campbell, J J O'Neill, J W R Peyton
Obstetrics and Gynaecology R N Heasley, J C R MacHenry
Ophthalmology D G Fraser, C Ware
Orthopaedics J R M Elliot
Paediatrics C Shepherd
Radiology S Hall, R A J Todd

Longstone Hospital

Loughall Road, Armagh BT61 7PR
Tel: 028 3752 2381
Total Beds: 155

General Psychiatry N Keenan, J F McGuinness

Mullinure Hospital

Loughgall Road, Armagh
Tel: 028 3752 2381
Total Beds: 36

Care of the Elderly P McCaffery

St Luke's Hospital

Loughgall Road, Armagh BT61 7NQ
Tel: 028 3752 2381 Fax: 02837 414548
Email: Bmaben@adhsst.n-i.nhs.uk
Total Beds: 148

Anaesthetics I Samuels
General Psychiatry S Best, C Cassidy, N Chada, M McCourt, C Monaghan, E Saddler

Belfast City Hospital HSS Trust

Belfast City Hospital, Lisburn Road, Belfast BT9 7AB
Tel: 028 9032 9241 Fax: 028 9032 6614
(Eastern Health and Social Services Board)

Chair J Ruddock
Chief Executive J Quentin Coey

Belfast City Hospital

Lisburn Road, Belfast BT9 7AB
Tel: 028 9032 9241 Fax: 028 9032 6614
Total Beds: 708

Accident and Emergency K E Dowey, R B Fisher
Anaesthetics R W Allen, P F Bell, M Brady, G A Browne, J D R Connolly, P Convery, K T J Fitzpatrick, J A S Gamble, K A George, I A Gillespie, J E Hegarty, J P Howe, D S Hurwitz, M C Kelly, N T Kenny, C Kerr, G J McCarthy, J S C McCollum, A C McKay, C C McLoughlin, K R Milligan, O T Muldoon, J E Strong, G Turner, P S Weir, C S Wilson
Anatomy and Physiology J A Allen, W F M Wallace
Bacteriology C Goldsmith, P Rooney
Cardiology E W Chew, N Herity, J G Murtagh, D B O'Keeffe, S G Richardson, M E Scott
Cardiothoracic Surgery J Cleland, D J Gladstone, H O J O'Kane
Care of the Elderly C Foy, K J Fullerton, A P Passmore, I M Rea, R W Stout, H M Taggart
Chemical Pathology G P R Archbold, C Loughrey
Clinical Genetics P J Morrison, F J Stewart
Cystic Fibrosis J S Elborn
Cytology H Elliott
Dental Surgery N Cambell
Dermatology J R Corbett, J F Dawson, J Handley, J C McKenna, J C McMillan
ENT M J Cinnamond, S Hampton, T J Stewart, J G Toner, A P Walby
General Medicine J R Hayes, R W Henry, G D Johnson, S D Johnston, J I Logan, G E McVeigh, K G Porter, J G Riddell
General Psychiatry S J Cooper, M Doherty, C B Kelly, R J McClelland, R Ingram, J N Scott
General Surgery P D Carey, A Carragher, A Carragher, R J Hannon, K Khan, B Lee, K G McManus, M J G O'Reilly, S Refsum, S Refsum, C V Soong, R A J Spence, R A J Spence, A J Wilkinson, A J Wilkinson
Haematology H D Alexander, R Cuthbert, P Kettle, G M Markey, T C M Morris
Histopathology D C Allen, H Elliot, T F Lioe, R W Lyness, P D McGibben, D T McManus, D M O'Rourke, M Y Walsh
Nephrology C C Doherty, J F Douglas, P T McNamee, A P Maxwell, W E Nelson, J D Woods
Neurology Dr Droogan, T Esmonde, J M Gibson, S Hawkins, J I Morrow, K A Pang, V H Patterson, B Sawhney, M Watt
Obstetrics and Gynaecology M Casement, S Dobbs, H R McClelland, P McFaul, J H Price, S Tharma
Occupational Medicine L Rodgers

Oncology W P Abram, R J Atkinson, J Clarke, B Corcoran, R Davidson, R L Eatkin, M Eatock, R J A Harte, P G Henry, R F Houston, P G Johnston, S Kelly, C M J Loughrey, JJ A McAleer, K P Moore, A J Patterson, D Stewart, S Stranex, R H Wilson
Ophthalmology P M Harte, SJ A Rankin, J A Sharkey
Organophosphate G Johnston
Osteoporosis H Taggart
Pathology N Anderson, L Caughley
Pharmacology G D Johnston, J G Riddell
Plastic Surgery K Khan
Psychology R Davidson
Radiology J G Crothers, L C Johnston, J T Lawson, W Loan, J P Lowry, J McAllister, C Boyd, A M Shiels, N G Tracey, S R Vallely
Radiotherapy and Oncology RJ Atkinson, PG Johnston
Restorative Dentistry J G Kennedy
Rheumatology A L Bell, A J Taggart
Transplant Surgery J K Connelly, J Connolly
Urology R A Donaldson, S R Johnston, P F Keane, R M Kernohan, W G G Loughridge, T H Lynch, I K Walsh

Belvoir Park Hospital

Hospital Road, Belfast BT8 8JR
Tel: 028 9069 9069
Total Beds: 208

Causeway HSS Trust

Causeway Trust Headquarters, 8E Coleraine Road, Ballymoney BT53 6BP
Tel: 028 2766 6600 Fax: 028 2766 1200
Email: bill.tweed@chsst.n-i.nhs.uk, Bill.Tweed@chsst.n-1.nhs.uk
(Northern Health and Social Services Board)

Chair Margaret Craig
Chief Executive W S Tweed

Causeway Hospital

4 Newbridge Road, Coleraine BT52 1HS
Tel: 028 7032 7032
Total Beds: 240

Accident and Emergency M Bell
Anaesthetics A R Cooper, W A W McGowan, K Pillow, M J Symington, C Watters, D G Wright
Chemical Pathology M Ryan
ENT C Scally
General Medicine O C Finnegan, P Gilmore, D G Sinnamon, F Tracey, A Varghese
General Psychiatry M E C Donnelly, S Kirk, T Leeman, M F Walsh
General Surgery M G Brown, J G W Matthews, F Mullan
Genitourinary Medicine W Dinsmore
Haematology P Burnside
Medical Microbiology E A Davies
Neurology S Hawkins
Obstetrics and Gynaecology W R Harvey, B M S Marshall, J A Wallace
Ophthalmology Dr Hanna
Oral and Maxillofacial Surgery R C Boyd
Orthodontics R McMullan
Orthopaedics A Yeates
Paediatric Cardiology B Craig
Paediatric Neurology E M Hicks
Paediatrics M V Ledwith, M D Rollins, D A Walsh
Radiology M de Jode, P M Higgins, D H Kirkpatrick
Rheumatology E M Whitehead
Urology R Kernohan

Dalriada Hospital

Coleraine Road, Ballycastle BT54 6BA
Tel: 028 2076 2666
Total Beds: 28

NHS TRUSTS & NHS HOSPITALS

Robinson Memorial Hospital

Ballymoney BT53 6HH
Tel: 028 2766 0322
Total Beds: 24

Ross Thomson Unit

Causeway Hospital, 4 Newbridge Road, Coleraine BT52 1TP
Tel: 028 7032 7032
Total Beds: 34

Craigavon and Banbridge Community HSS Trust

Bannvale House, Moyallan Road, Gilford, Craigavon BT63 5JX
Tel: 028 3883 1983 Fax: 028 3883 1993
(Northern Health and Social Services Board, Southern Health and Social Services Board)

Chair Michael Morrow
Chief Executive W Denis Preston

Craigavon Psychiatric Unit

68 Lurgan Road, Portadown, Craigavon BT63 5QQ
Tel: 028 3833 4444
Total Beds: 80

Craigavon Area Hospital Group HSS Trust

68 Lurgan Road, Portadown, Craigavon BT63 5QQ
Tel: 028 3833 4444 Fax: 028 3835 0068
(Southern Health and Social Services Board)

Chair Elizabeth McClurg
Chief Executive John Templeton
Consultants D K B Armstrong, T J Baird, B A Bell, B A Bell, Mr Bhatti, H K Boyd, H E Bunting, R Campbell, R Campbell, C A Carson, C R Clarke, M R Clarke, I H Connolly, R P Convery, C Corkey, N Damani, D J Eedy, D J Eedy, C R A Fee, R N Heasley, G Hewitt, M M Hogan, D Hull, C A Humphrey, I Hunter, A Jones, P P Kerr, P Leyden, N Liggett, M H S Love, D Lowry, D Lowry, D S Lowry, C McAllister, C McAllister, E J McAteer, J A McAteer, P M McCaffrey, W McCaughey, M McClure, P M McConaghy, G J McCusker, G J M McCusker, D Mceneaney, B J McGrady, C MacHenry, E Mackie, E Mackle, E McNaboe, O Morris, M Morrow, P Murphy, S A O' Reilly, A O'Brien, A O'Brien, D A Orr, I A Orr, R Peyton, C M Ritchie, T J Robinson, D Scullion, P C Sharpe, C W Shepherd, K P Singh, K P Singh, M Smith, J E Sommerville, D Streathorn, S Thompson, J Walker, R J Wallace, C Weir, M Young

Craigavon Area Hospital

68 Lurgan Road, Portadown, Craigavon BT63 5QQ
Tel: 028 3833 4444 Fax: 028 3835 0068
Total Beds: 414

Accident and Emergency C Fee, P P Kerr, S O'Reilly
Anaesthetics H E Bunting, C Clarke, D Lowry, J McAteer, W McCaughey, M Morrow, A C Gallagher, D Hughes, D Orr, I Orr, S Oyindon, D Scullion, D Streahoew
Cardiology D Mceneaney
Care of the Elderly P McCafferey
Dental Surgery R Kendrick, D Kernohan, I Saunders, J Sutcliffe
Dermatology D K B Armstrong, D J Eedy
ENT S Hall, P Leyden, E McNaboe, K P Singh
General Medicine J Baird, R Lee, B McNamee, P Murphy, C M Ritchie, N Liggett
General Surgery I Stirling, J Campbell, R Campbell, G Hewitt, E Mackle, R Peyton, C Weir
Laboratory and Pathology Services M A R Clarke, N Damani, C A Humphrey, G J M McCusker, B J McGrady, P C Sharpe, J E Sommerville

Obstetrics and Gynaecology H Sidhu, R N Heasley, I Hunter, C MacHenry, R J Wallace
Ophthalmology R Best
Orthodontics I Connolly
Orthopaedics Dr Beverland, Dr Elliot, R Wallace, Dr Yeats
Paediatrics B A Bell, C Corkey, M M Hogan, D R C Shepherd, M Smith, Dr Thompson
Palliative Care, Cancer Services C Humphries, K Boyd
Radio-Diagnosis and Imaging C A Carson, S Hall, M H S Love, E McAteer, M McClure, J Walker
Urology A O'Brien, M Young

Lurgan Hospital

Sloan Street, Lurgan, Craigavon BT66 8NX
Tel: 028 3832 3262 Fax: 028 3832 9483
Total Beds: 113

Dermatology D J Eedy (Head)

Down Lisburn HSS Trust

Lisburn Health Centre, 25 Linenhall Street, Lisburn BT28 1BH
Tel: 028 9266 5181 Fax: 028 9266 5179
(Eastern Health and Social Services Board)

Chair Denise Fitzsimons
Chief Executive John Compton

Downe Hospital

9A Pound Lane, Downpatrick BT30 6JA
Tel: 028 4461 3311 Fax: 028 4461 5699
Total Beds: 94

Anaesthetics Dr Kerr, P Convey, C Hawthorne, M Milhench
Care of the Elderly C M Jack
Dermatology J Handley
ENT S Hampton, T J Stewart
General Medicine G Jacob, H Whitehead
General Surgery M Ismail, J A A Archbold, J C Bell
Obstetrics and Gynaecology R L A Erskine, R G N Storey
Ophthalmology Dr Early
Orthopaedics A McAlinden, R A B Mullan
Paediatrics P Jackson, L Martel
Radiology A M Thompson

Downpatrick Maternity Hospital

Struell Road, Downpatrick BT30 6JR
Tel: 028 4461 3311
Total Beds: 20

Obstetrics R L A Erskine, R G N Storey

Downshire Hospital

Ardglass Road, Downpatrick BT30 6RA
Tel: 028 4461 3311 Fax: 028 4461 2444
Total Beds: 232

Anaesthetics C B Girvan, C Hawthorne, M Milhench, L Wilson-Davis
General Psychiatry R McCleary, M Moynihan, Dr Watts

Lagan Valley Hospital

39 Hillsborough Road, Lisburn BT28 1JP
Tel: 028 9266 5141 Fax: 028 9266 6100
Total Beds: 169

Anaesthetics G McClean, H T B Beers, L Harrison, B K D Huss, A Kursurkar, G Thompson
Care of the Elderly R Kelly, S P Gawley
Dermatology J F Dawson
General Medicine I Gleadhill, T Harding, K R Logan
General Psychiatry O Daly, N Devanney, B Fleming, N Quigley, D Shields
General Surgery A Carragher, A Kennedy, V Loughlin

Obstetrics and Gynaecology M L W Crooks, M Joyce, A Love, S Shahid
Ophthalmology S Rankin
Orthopaedics G R Dilworth, J A Halliday
Otolaryngology G McKee, W J Primrose
Paediatrics M M Reid
Radiology J E McNulty, S Ogbobi, W Page

Slievegrane/ Inch/ Downshire Hospital

Ardglass Road, Downpatrick BT30 6RA
Tel: 028 4461 3311
Total Beds: 10

Thompson House Hospital

19/21 Magherlave Road, Lisburn BT28 3BJ
Tel: 028 9266 5646 Fax: 028 9266 7681
Total Beds: 42

Neurology J Morrow

Foyle Health and Social Services Trust

Riverview House, Abercorn Road, Londonderry BT48 6SB
Tel: 028 7126 6111 Fax: 028 7126 0806
Email: mmcgingley@foylehq.n-i.nhs.uk
Website: www.foyletrust.org
(Western Health and Social Services Board)

Chair Anthony Jackson
Chief Executive Elaine Way
Consultants Anne-Marie Holmes, Artie O'Hara

Gransha Hospital

Clooney Road, Londonderry BT47 1TF
Tel: 028 7186 0261
Total Beds: 138

General Psychiatry M Kee, C McDonnell, D McGlearon, A Murray, A O'Hara, S M Rea, I Robertson

Stradreagh Hospital

Gransha Park, Clooney Road, Londonderry BT47 1TF
Tel: 028 7186 0261
Total Beds: 68

General Psychiatry M G Curran, D G Eyre

Waterside Hospital

16 Gransha Park, Londonderry
Tel: 028 7145 171
Total Beds: 55

Care of the Elderly J A F Beirne, J G McElroy

Green Park Healthcare HSS Trust

Musgrave Park Hospital, 20 Stockman's Lane, Belfast BT9 7JB
Tel: 028 9066 9501 Fax: 028 9038 2008
(Eastern Health and Social Services Board)

Chair Norman Shaw
Chief Executive Hilary Boyd

Forster Green Hospital

110 Saintfield Road, Belfast BT8 4HD
Tel: 028 9079 3681 Fax: 028 9040 1830
Total Beds: 83

Care of the Elderly T O Beringer, J G McConnell, I Taylor
Child Psychiatry L Cassidy, A Haller
Neurology J McCann, V H Patterson

Musgrave Park Hospital

Stockmans Lane, Belfast BT9 7JB
Tel: 028 9066 9501 Fax: 028 9038 2008
Total Beds: 348

Anaesthetics R Allen, P Bell, J P H Fee, J A S Gamble, I Gillespie, J E Hegarthy, D S Hurwitz, N T Kenny, J S C McCollum, A C McKay, C McLoughlin, R Martin, K R Milligan, Dr Muldoon, E Stiby, J E Strong, Dr Turner, Dr Weir, Dr Wilson
Care of the Elderly T R O Beringer, S P Gawley, D Gilmore, A Gilmore, I Steele, I Wiggan
Orthopaedics I V Adair, Dr Andrews, Dr Barr, D E Beverland, J G Brown, J W Calderwood, J Corry, Dr Cosgrove, G H Cowie, G R Dilworth, J R M Elliott, A Hamilton, S Henderson, H Laverick, C J McClelland, G F McCoy, Dr Maginn, Dr Marsh, H J D Mawhinney, Dr Mobbs, R A B Mollan, R Nicholas, J R Nixon, Dr Nolan, Dr Swain, T C Taylor, R G Wallace, H A Yeates
Radiology M D Crone, Dr Grey, H B Murtagh
Rehabilitation Medicine J P McCann
Rheumatology A Bell, M Finch, Dr Rooney, A J Taggart, Dr Wright
Sports Medicine M Cullen

Homefirst Community HSS Trust

The Cottage, 5 Greenmount Avenue, Ballymena BT43 6DA
Tel: 028 2563 3700 Fax: 028 2563 3733
Website: www.n-i.nhs.uk/homefirst
(Northern Health and Social Services Board)

Chair Billy Boyd
Chief Executive Christie Colhoun

Holywell Hospital

60 Steeple Road, Antrim BT41 2RJ
Tel: 028 9446 5211 Fax: 028 9446 1803
Total Beds: 367

Anaesthetics A C Scott
General Psychiatry S A Compton, M E C Donnelly, F Duke, T P Elliott, G Henry, C B Kelly, D J King, S Kirk, G Lynch, G M MacFlynn, P E Potter, M R Watson

Mater Infirmorum Hospital HSS Trust

45-51 Crumlin Road, Belfast BT14 6AB
Tel: 028 9074 1211 Fax: 028 9074 1342
Website: www.n-i.nhs.uk/mater
(Eastern Health and Social Services Board)

Chair L McCollum
Chief Executive Patricia Gordon

Alexandra Gardens Day Hospital

Old See House, 603 Antrim Road, Belfast BT15 3LJ
Tel: 028 9077 3311 Fax: 028 9077 3311

Mater Infirmorum Hospital

47-51 Crumlin Road, Belfast BT14 6AB
Tel: 028 9074 1211 Fax: 028 9074 1342
Total Beds: 216

Accident and Emergency G Lane
Anaesthetics H Matthews (Head), P Gormlay, J O'Hanlon, E Thompson
Cardiology B McClements (Head)
Chest Disease S Guy (Head)
ENT F G D'Arcy (Head)
General Medicine M J J Gormley (Head), S Guy, B McClements, J C McLoughlin
General Psychiatry A O'Neill (Head), D M Brennan, P S Curran, E A Montgomery
General Surgery B Wilson (Head), T Diamond, C F Harvey

NHS TRUSTS & NHS HOSPITALS

Genitourinary Surgery B Wilson (Head)
Neonatology R Tubman (Head)
Obstetrics and Gynaecology P Weir (Head), R White
Ophthalmology G Kervick (Head), O Earley
Radiology J S McLoughlin (Head), V Bhandari, A Norris

Newry and Mourne HSS Trust

5 Downshire Place, Downshire Road, Newry BT34 1DZ
Tel: 028 3026 0505 Fax: 028 3026 9064
Email: orla.maverly@ohn.n-i.nhs.uk
(Eastern Health and Social Services Board)

Chair J McEvoy
Chief Executive E Bowyer

Daisy Hill Hospital

5 Hospital Road, Newry BT35 8DR
Tel: 028 3083 5000 Fax: 028 3025 0624
Total Beds: 265

Anaesthetics R J Carlisle, P G Loughran, Dr Wright, P Wright
Dermatology D J Eedy
ENT P Leyden, E McNaboe
General Medicine J E Devlin, H M McDowell, C J O'Brien
General Psychiatry C Campbell, J Cotter, E Sadler, J Simpson
General Surgery G Blake, R J Brown, B Cranley
Obstetrics and Gynaecology R De Courcy-Wheeler, Dr Mckinney, K McKinney, M O'Hare, D Sim
Ophthalmology Y Canavan, A Page
Oral Surgery Dr Ramsey-Baggs
Orthopaedics Dr Barr, Dr Beveraland
Paediatrics B Aljarad, Dr Corkey, Dr Hughes
Plastic Surgery Dr Leonard
Radiology Dr Thornbury, R A J Todd
Thoracic Surgery K McManus

Mourne Hospital

Kilkeel, Newry BT34 4DP
Tel: 028 7963 1031 Fax: 028 7963 3050

General Medicine H McDowell, C J O'Brien
General Surgery R J Brown, B Cranley
Obstetrics and Gynaecology R De Courcy-Wheeler, K McKinney, D Sim

North and West Belfast HSS Trust

Glendinning House, 6 Murray Street, Belfast BT1 6DP
Tel: 028 9032 7156 Fax: 028 9082 1285
(Eastern Health and Social Services Board)

Chair Gordon Burnison
Chief Executive Richard G Black

Muckamore Abbey Hospital

1 Abbey Road, Muckamore, Antrim BT41 4FH
Tel: 028 9446 3333 Fax: 028 9446 7730
Total Beds: 497

Anaesthetics J S C McCollum
General Psychiatry G J Calvert, D D M Collins, J Galway, M G McGinnity, C M Marriott, O E P Shanks

Northern Ireland Ambulance Service HSS Trust

Ambulance Headquarters, Site 30, Knockbrachen Healthcare Park, Saintfield Road, Belfast BT8 8SG
Tel: 028 400999 Fax: 028 400901
(Eastern Health and Social Services Board)

Chair Douglas Smyth
Chief Executive Paul McCormick

Royal Group of Hospitals and Dental Hospital HSS Trust

Royal Victoria Hospital, Grosvenor Road, Belfast BT12 6BA
Tel: 028 9024 0503 Fax: 028 9024 0899
Website: www.royalhospitals.ac.uk
(Eastern Health and Social Services Board)

Chair Paul McWilliams
Chief Executive William S McKee

Royal Belfast Hospital for Sick Children

180 Falls Road, Belfast BT12 6BE
Tel: 028 9024 0503 Fax: 028 9023 5340
Total Beds: 129

Anaesthetics P M Crean, T M Gallagher, S R Keilty, G McCarthy, R H Taylor
Cardiac Surgery J Cleland, D J Gladstone
Cardiology B G Craig, H C Mulholland
Child and Adolescent Psychiatry M T Kennedy, R R McAuley
Dental Surgery I D F Saunders
Dermatology E A Bingham, D Burrows, J R Corbett
Genetics N C Nevin
Haematology S I Dempsey
Orthopaedics T C Taylor
Otolaryngology D A Adams, M J Cinnamond, R Gibson, A P Walby
Paediatric Surgery V E Boston, S Brown, S R Potts
Paediatrics D J Carson, J A Dodge, J F T Glasgow, H L Halliday, E M Hicks, A E Hill, P Jackson, B G McClure, A O B Redmond, M M Reid, J M Savage, M D Shields
Plastic Surgery M D Brennan, A G Leonard, R Millar
Radiology L E Sweeney, P S Thomas

Royal Maternity Hospital

Grosvenor Road, Belfast BT12 6BB
Tel: 028 9089 4656 Fax: 028 9023 6203
Total Beds: 79

Anaesthetics S Atkinson, W Carabine, M A Lewis, K McGrath, D B Wilson
Cardiology B G Craig, H C Mulholland
Genetics N C Nevin
Obstetrics and Gynaecology D D Boyle, J C Dornan, M A Harper, H Lamki, P McFaul, M Reid, W Thompson, A I Traub
Paediatrics H L Halliday, B G McClure, M M Reid
Radiology L E Sweeney, P S Thomas

Royal Victoria Hospital

Grosvenor Road, Belfast BT12 6BA
Tel: 028 9024 0503 Fax: 028 9024 0899
Total Beds: 750

Accident and Emergency C H Dearden, J Martin, L Rocke
Anaesthetics S Atkinson, K M Bill, I W Carson, D L Coppel, H J L Craig, P Elliott, P A Farling, J P H Fee, F M Gibson, K W Harper, H M L Johnston, J R Johnston, G G Lavery, M A Lewis, W B Loan, K G Lowry, S M Lyons, R J McBride, G McCarthy, T J McMurray, R K Mirakhur, T D E Sharpe, J C Stanley, R H Taylor, V K N Unni, D B Wilson
Bacteriology K M Bamford, J G Barr, E T M Smyth, C H Webb
Cardiac Surgery G Campalani, J Cleland, D J Gladstone, H O J O'Kane, M Sarsam
Cardiology J Adgey, N P S Campbell, B G Craig, G W W Dalzell, M M Khan, D MacBoyle, H C Mulholland, S W Webb, C M Wilson
Care of the Elderly T R O Beringer, D H Gilmore
Cytology J Willis
Dental Surgery I C Benington, T Clifford, C G Cowan, D L Hussey, R W Kendrick, D C Kernohan, M J Kinirons, P J Lamey, G J Linden,

J G McGimpsey, P Ramsay-Beggs, I D F Saunders, J M Sheridan, T W Swinson

Dermatology G E Allen, E A Bingham, D Burrows, J R Corbett

ENT D A Adams, D S Brooker, J E T Byrne, M J Cinnamond, F G D'Arcy, R Gibson, A G Kerr, W J Primrose, A P Walby

General Medicine A B Atkinson, P M Bell, K D Buchanan, M E Callender, J S A Collins, D R Hadden, A H G Love, D R McCance, D P Nicholls, S D Roberts, C F Stanford, R G P Watson

General Psychiatry A Kerr, G McDonald, P McGarry, W A Norris

General Surgery A A B D'Sa, J M Hood, G W Johnston, R J Maxwell, G W Odling-Smee, B J Rowlands, C J F Russell, A J Wilkinson

Genetics N C Nevin

Genitourinary Medicine W W Dinsmore, D M McBride, R D Maw

Haematology J M Bridges, S I Dempsey, F G C Jones, W M McClelland, E E Mayne

Histopathology H Bharucha, L M Caughley, M Mirakhur, M D O'Hara, M Y Walsh

Immunology D R McCluskey, T A McNeill

Medical Microbiology T A McNeill, D I H Simpson

Nephrology C C Doherty, J F Douglas, P T McNamee, W E Nelson

Neurology J M Gibson, S A Hawkins, J A Lyttle, J I Morrow, V H Patterson

Neuropathology I V Allen, M Mirakhur

Neurophysiology B B Sawhney

Neurosurgery I C Bailey, D P Byrnes, T F Fannin, W J Gray

Obstetrics and Gynaecology D D Boyle, J C Dornan, H Lamki, W Thompson, A I Traub

Ophthalmology D B Archer, J H Bryars, T A S Buchanan, Y M Canavan, O E Early, D G Frazer, P B Johnston, G McGinnity, C J F Maguire, A B Page

Orthodontics A Richardson

Orthopaedics I V Adair, J Brown, J W Calderwood, C J McClelland, G F McCoy, H J D Mawhinney, R A B Mollan

Paediatrics V Boston

Pathology C M Hill, C Meban, P D A Owens, J M Sloan, P G Toner, E R Trimble

Periodontology G J Linden

Pharmacology G D Johnston, J G Riddell

Plastic Surgery G Ashall, M D Brennen, A G Leonard, R Millar, J O Small

Public Health Medicine P M Darragh, A E Evans, M J Scott

Radiology K E Bell, M D Crone, J G Crothers, J D Laird, M McGovern, E M McIlrath, C S McKinstry, A McNeill, J E McNulty, J O M Mills, A J O'Doherty, L E Sweeney, P S Thomas, A M Thompson

Radiotherapy and Oncology W P Abram, B D Burrows, W S B Lowry

Rheumatology A L Bell, M B Finch, J P McCann

Thoracic Surgery J M McGuigan, K McManus

Urology S R Johnston, J A Kennedy

Virology P V Coyle

South and East Belfast HSS Trust

Knockbracken Healthcare Park, Saintfield Road, Belfast BT8 8BH
Tel: 028 9056 5555 Fax: 028 9056 5813
(Eastern Health and Social Services Board)

Chief Executive Robert Ferguson

Albertbridge Road Day Hospital

225 Albertbridge Road, Belfast BT5 4PX

Sperrin Lakeland Health and Social Care Trust

Strathdene House, Tyrone & Fermanagh Hospital, Omagh BT79 0NS
Tel: 028 8224 4127 Fax: 028 8224 4570
Website: www.sperrin-lakeland.org
(Western Health and Social Services Board)

ULSTER COMMUNITY & HOSPITALS TRUST

Chair Richard Scott
Chief Executive Hugh Mills

Erne Day Hospital

Cornagrade Road, Enniskillen BT74 6AY
Tel: 028 6632 4711 Fax: 028 6632 6131

Care of the Elderly J F Kelly

Erne Hospital

Cornagrade Road, Enniskillen BT74 6AY
Tel: 028 6632 4711
Total Beds: 232

Anaesthetics C A Armstrong, T Auterson, M W Cody, W Holmes

Care of the Elderly J F Kelly

Dental Surgery R Parfitt

Dermatology P Podmore

ENT S K Kaluskar, K P Law

General Medicine M P S Varma, J R Williams

General Surgery A Kibbin, Dr Marshall, J Strahan

Haematology Dr Cutheburt

Neurology V Patterson

Obstetrics and Gynaecology S Cheah, R Jamshidi, J E T Mulholland, W E Stewart

Oncology J Clarke

Ophthalmology D Mulholland

Orthodontics R McMillan

Orthopaedics D Beverland, H Cowie, G McCoy

Paediatrics W C Halahakoon, M O'Donahoe

Radiology G Loughey, J C McGregor

Rheumatology Dr Gardiner

Tyrone and Fermanagh Hospital

1 Donaghanie Road, Omagh BT79 0NS
Tel: 028 8224 5211
Total Beds: 182

Forensic Psychiatry I T Bownes

General Psychiatry K K Bindal, D D Cody, T Foster, M A McDermott, P J Mannion

Tyrone County Hospital

Hospital Road, Omagh BT79 0AP
Tel: 028 8224 5211 Fax: 028 8224 6293
Total Beds: 161

Anaesthetics K Anand, R R Lalsingh, J M F Maginness, F P Robinson

Care of the Elderly E Hodkinson

Dermatology R A Fulton, P Podmore

ENT S K Kaluskar, N B Kouyalamudi, K P Law

General Medicine E Bergin, A L T Blair, P Garrett, C J Russell

General Psychiatry P J Mannion

General Surgery G A B Miller, D J D Pinto, M Sulaiman

Nephrology E Bergin, P Garrett

Neurology V Patterson

Obstetrics and Gynaecology M Anderson, M Cheah, J E T Mulholland

Ophthalmology P Hassett

Oral Surgery Dr El-Atter

Orthodontics R McMullan

Orthopaedics G F W Price, A R Wray

Paediatrics D Halakoohoon, D O'Donahoe, S Simpson

Radiology M C Gregor, G J Loughrey

Radiotherapy R F Houston

Rheumatology P V Gardiner

Ulster Community and Hospitals Trust

Health & Care Centre, 39 Regent Street, Newtownards BT23 4AD
Tel: 028 9181 6666 Fax: 028 9182 0140
(Eastern Health and Social Services Board)

NHS TRUSTS & NHS HOSPITALS

Chair Jim Shields
Chief Executive J McCall

Ards Community Hospital

Church Street, Newtownards BT23 4AS
Tel: 028 9101 2661 Fax: 028 9151 0111
Total Beds: 20

Anaesthetics T H Boyd, D Carson, D Coyle, C Hickey, J K Lilburn, K Lindsay, D M McAuley, C M Wilson
Cardiology J D S Higginson, S R McMechan
Care of the Elderly J Mathai
Day Procedure Unit M J Allen, B G Best, W Calvert, W J Campbell, S J Dolan, S J Kirk, R J Moorehead
Dermatology J F Dawson
ENT T J Stewart
General Medicine R Harper, W J McIlwaine, B MacLennon, T Trinick
General Psychiatry J Anderson, J K Gilbert, J Green, H Harbinson, D J MacFarlane, A Scott
General Surgery M J Allen, B G Best, S Dolan
Haematology M R EL-AGNAF
Obstetrics and Gynaecology J M W Park
Ophthalmology T A S Buchanan
Orthopaedics G R Dilworth
Pathology M Agnaff, J Hunter, T Trinick
Radiology W F Foster, P D Hanley

Bangor Community Hospital

Castle Street, Bangor BT20 4TA
Tel: 028 9147 5120, 028 9147 5140 Fax: 028 9147 5153
Total Beds: 40

Cardiology D Cochrane
Care of the Elderly J Mathai
Dermatology J Handley
ENT J Toner
General Medicine W J McIlwaine, T Trinick
General Surgery M J Allen, C H Calvert, R J Moorehead
Haematology K Bailie
Obstetrics and Gynaecology P Fogarty, J M W Park
Ophthalmology T A S Buchanan
Radiology R E Wright

Mental Health Day Hospital

Mental Health Directorate, Ards Community Hospital, Newtownards BT23 4AS
Tel: 028 9181 2661 Fax: 028 9151 0111

The Ulster Hospital

Upper Newtownards Road, Dundonald, Belfast BT16 1RH
Tel: 028 9048 4511 Fax: 028 9048 1753
Total Beds: 576

Accident and Emergency S McGovern, J B Martin, C J Martyn
Anaesthetics P Bell, T Boyd, W I Campbell, D Carson, J R Darling, A M Hainsworth, W H K Haslett, D A Hill, C Hinkley, D Hugh, K Lilburn, K G Lindsay, D M McAuley, M S McKenney, N McLeord, M V S Rao, M Reid, C Renfrew, J T Trinder, C M Wilson
Biochemistry T R Trinick
Cardiology D Cochrane, J D S Higginson, S R McMechan
Care of the Elderly J G McConnell, J Mathai, M J P Power, I C Taylor
Child and Adolescent Psychiatry G Walford
Dermatology J F Dawson, J Handley, K McKenna
ENT T J Stewart, J G Toner
General Medicine D M Boyle, B G Craig, R Harder, D Higginson, R J McFarland, W J McIlwaine, W R McKane, B MacLennan, C Mulholand, J K Nelson, Dr Salathia, T Tham
General Psychiatry J Anderson, J K Gilbert, J Green, H Harbinson, D McFarlane, A Scott
General Surgery M J Allen, B G Best, C H Calvert, W J Campbell, S Dolan, S J Kirk, R J Moorehead
Genitourinary Medicine R D Maw
Medical Microbiology A Loughrey

Obstetrics and Gynaecology E B Bond, J M Dunlop, P Fogarty, J M W Park, R N Roberts
Ophthalmology D B Archer, P B Johnston
Oral and Maxillofacial Surgery T A Gregg, R W Kendrick, P Ramsay-Baggs, S M Sheridan
Orthopaedics J G Brown, G R Dilworth, J A Halliday, G McAlinden, P Maginn, R G H Wallace, A Yeates
Paediatric Surgery V E Boston, S Brown, W McCallion, S R Potts
Paediatrics A Bell, E A Black, T Brown, C Gaston, V Gleadhill, J Major, L Martell, D Primrose
Pathology K Bailie, M El-Agnaff, J Hunter, A Moore, T R Trinick
Plastic Surgery M D Brennan, D J Gordon, K J Herbert, A G Leonard, J S Sinclair
Radiology P D Hanley, M Hyland, C Loughrey, J M McAllister, J R A McNally, C W Majury, N R Pathirana, H K Wilson, R E R Wright
Radiotherapy and Oncology W P Abram, J Clarke

United Hospitals HSS Trust

Bush House, Antrim BT41 2RL
Tel: 028 9442 4655 Fax: 028 9442 4654
(Northern Health and Social Services Board)

Chair R H McGuigan
Chief Executive J Bernard Mitchell

Antrim Hospital

Antrim BT41 2RL
Tel: 028 9442 4000 Fax: 028 9442 4293
Total Beds: 370

Accident and Emergency D N S Gleadhill
Anaesthetics I M Bali, I H C Black, R Ghosh, D J Grainger, P Leyden, H N McLeod
Cardiology T Trouton, C Wilson
Care of the Elderly P G Flanagan, A K Sarkar, M Varghese
ENT R P Agarwala, J H A Black, G Gallagher, C Scally
General Medicine J B McConnell, B A Sims, G R G Todd, M Varghese
General Surgery W I H Garstin, W G Humphreys, A H McMurray, D G Mudd
Obstetrics and Gynaecology R G Ashe, R M McMillen, W A H Ritchie, P Smith
Orthodontics N M Stratford
Orthopaedics W I H Garstin, D N S Gleadhill, W G Humphreys, A H McMurray, D G Mudd
Paediatrics J Jenkins, J H K Lim, J McAloon, C MacLeod, J Nicholson
Pathology J M Alderdice, P Burnside, J G Carson, E A Davies, M P Kearney, B D Kenny, A Kyle, P D McGibben, M Ryan
Radiology S T Brady, J C Clarke, P M Higgins, D H Hill, J P Lowry, C J Sinclair
Renal Medicine H Brown
Rheumatology E M Whitehead

Braid Valley Hospital

Cushendall Road, Ballymena BT43 6HH
Tel: 028 2565 5200 Fax: 028 2563 5385
Total Beds: 75

Care of the Elderly P G Flanagan, A K Sarkar

Mid-Ulster Hospital

59 Hospital Road, Magherafelt BT45 5EX
Tel: 028 7963 1031 Fax: 028 7963 4078
Total Beds: 191

Anaesthetics M O'Neill, A C Scott
Dental Surgery R W Kendrick
Dermatology R S Matthews
General Medicine N C Chatervedi, E K Hunter, L J E Walker
General Surgery M J G Hawe, P Pyper
Haematology P Burnside
Obstetrics and Gynaecology H C Aitken, H Clarke

Ophthalmology M Sharma
Orthodontics J A Scott, N Stratford
Orthopaedics P Dolan
Paediatrics J H K Lim, C MacLeod
Radiology C J Sinclair

Moyle Hospital

Gloucester Avenue, Larne BT40 1RP
Tel: 028 2827 5431 Fax: 028 2827 5346
Total Beds: 45

Dermatology H A Jenkinson
ENT R P Agarwala
General Medicine G R G Todd, M Varghese
General Psychiatry G Henry
General Surgery I Garston, A H McMurray
Neurology J Morrow
Obstetrics and Gynaecology R McMillen
Ophthalmology J H Bryars
Orthopaedics J R Nixon
Radiology S T Brady

Whiteabbey Hospital

Doagh Road, Newtownabbey BT37 9RH
Tel: 028 9086 5181 Fax: 028 9036 5083
Total Beds: 171

Accident and Emergency R Wylie
Anaesthetics C J Ferres, K Seetha
Cardiology P Crowe
Care of the Elderly E Byrne, J E Gilmore
Chest Disease G Todd
Dermatology H A Jenkinson, R W D Ross
ENT G Gallagher
General Medicine W J Andrews, P F Crowe, J E Gilmore
General Psychiatry J R Noble, P E Potter
General Surgery D Gilroy, D C McCrory, M Shahidullah
Haematology A Kyle
Obstetrics and Gynaecology R M McMillen, P Smith
Radiology A Hrabovsky, N Pathnana

Channel Islands

Castel Hospital

Neuve Rue, Castel, Guernsey GY5 7NJ
Tel: 01481 725241 Fax: 01481 252099
Total Beds: 100

General Hospital St Helier

Gloucester Street, St Helier JE2 3QS
Tel: 01534 59000
Total Beds: 302

Accident and Emergency C Clinton
Anaesthetics P Coleman, J R Lane, G D Prince, G Purcell-Jones
Dental Surgery J D Fleet
Dermatology M F Muhlemann
ENT N Shah, M Siodlak
General Medicine H Gibson, W R Ginks, M Gleeson, M Richardson, R Sheaves
General Psychiatry G W Blackwood, C Coverley, D G Evans, G F Faiz, L Wilson
General Surgery J Allardice, N Ingram
Haematology C Mattock
Histopathology H Goulding, P Southall
Medical Microbiology I Muscat
Obstetrics and Gynaecology J B Day, N Maclachlan
Ophthalmology M Alwitry, I M Macmichael
Orthopaedics R P Clifford, C Twiston-Davies
Paediatrics J Eason, H C Spratt
Radiology A Borthwick-Clarke, J Cockburn, A P Nisbet
Urology N P Ingram

King Edward VII Hospital Guernsey

Sanitarium Lane, Castel, Guernsey GY5 7NU
Tel: 01481 725241 Fax: 01481 253135
Total Beds: 100

Mignot Memorial Hospital

Crabby, Alderney, Guernsey
Tel: 01481 822822 Fax: 01481 823087
Total Beds: 24

Overdale Hospital

Westmount, St Helier
Tel: 01534 59000
Total Beds: 125

General Medicine M Richardson

Princess Elizabeth Hospital

Le Vauquiedor, Guernsey GY4 6UU
Tel: 01481 725241 Fax: 01481 35905
Total Beds: 200

Care of the Elderly M Green
ENT P J P Mullen, C J Toynton
General Medicine N P Byrom, F Degren, G Oswald, P A F Riley
General Practice R Barker, P Biggins, S E Bodkin, D S Brand, S M Brennand Roper, M Brereton, M Chamberlain, T L S Chankun, J G Curran, M P Downing, J Erskine, J R Gibbs, T R Gill, R G J Hanna, S P Heyworth, S Hollwey, N C King, T R Lee, J F Longan, B G Mackay, D S McKerrell, C Monkhouse, M Mowbray, A J O'Donnell, N Paluch, B D Parkin, J G Pearce, G D Reilly, P W Richards, P Simpson, T J Sinnerton, E J Smith, D G Swainston, S C M Sweet, D S M Wilson, S Wray
General Psychiatry R Browne, T Byrne, C J Farmer, P J Thompson
General Surgery N Allen, R H Allsopp, J Ferguson, N V D Hauwaert, T N D Peet, D Pring
Obstetrics and Gynaecology A H Adam, M A Brannan, R H Haskins
Ophthalmology H Bacon, R M P Reynolds
Paediatrics B W Lean
Pathology J D Buchanan, B Gunton-Bunn
Radiology S N Allison, M L Gaunt, J Hanaghan

St Saviour's Hospital

Princes Tower Road, St Saviour JE2 7UW
Tel: 01534 856777
Total Beds: 210

Isle of Man

Ballamona Hospital

Braddan, Douglas
Tel: 01624 642642
Total Beds: 188

General Psychiatry D Balakrishna, E Chinn, M N Elias, D N O'Malley, M O'Sullivan

Noble's Isle of Man Hospital

Westmoreland Road, Douglas
Tel: 01624 642642
Total Beds: 250

Anaesthetics M J Biggart, P Kelsall, J W McCrory, K Wilkinson
Dental Surgery R M Godfrey
ENT S L Manuja
General Medicine R B Clague, N F Hockings, G S Khuraijam, C R H Murray
General Surgery N R Batey, J O Lee
Obstetrics and Gynaecology J Brooks, M J Divers, R J Fayle
Ophthalmology J P Travers
Orthodontics J H Martin

NHS TRUSTS & NHS HOSPITALS

Orthopaedics A D L Green
Paediatrics N J Birkin, J Martin
Pathology B T French, J K Wardle
Radiology D B Stevens, E W Williams
Radiotherapy and Oncology A Slater
Thoracic Surgery R J Donnelly

Ramsey and District Cottage Hospital

Cumberland Road, Ramsey
Tel: 01624 811811 Fax: 01624 811818
Total Beds: 77

General Medicine J K Armour, J K Brownsdon, M S Chan, A S C Kelsey, A J Lamming, J R McDonald, M Maska, G M Wilson

Health Authorities and Boards

England

Directorate of Health and Social Care London

Department of Health, 40 Eastbourne Terrace, London W2 3QR

Director of Health and Social Care John Bacon

North Central London Health Authority

Victory House, 170 Tottenham Court Road, London W1P 0HA

Chair Marcia Saunders
Chief Executive Christine Outram

North East London Health Authority

Aneurin Bevan House, 81 Commercial Road, London E1 1RD
Tel: 020 7655 6601 Fax: 020 7655 6621
Email: carolyn.regan@elcha.nhs.uk

Chair Elaine Murphy
Chief Executive Carolyn Regan

North West London Health Authority

Victory House, 170 Tottenham Court Road, London W1P 0HA
Email: firstname.lastname@nwlondon-stha.nhs.uk

Chair Jane Kelly
Chief Executive Ron De Witt

South East London Health Authority

1 Lower Marsh, London SE1 7NT
Email: duncan.selbie@lslha.sthames.nhs.uk

Chair Linda Smith
Chief Executive Duncan Selbie

South West London Health Authority

The Wilson, Cranmer Road, Mitcham CR4 4TP
Tel: 020 8648 3021 Fax: 020 8646 6240

Chair James Cochrane
Chief Executive Julie Dent

Directorate of Health and Social Care Midlands and East

Department of Health, Quarry House, Quarry Hill, Leeds LS2 7UE

Director of Health and Social Care David Nicholson

Bedfordshire and Hertfordshire Health Authority

c/o Hertfordshire Health Authority, Tonman House, 63-77 Victoria Street, St Albans AL1 3ER
Tel: 01727 812929
Email: jane.herbert@herts-ha.nhs.uk

Chair Ian White
Chief Executive Jane Herbert

Birmingham and the Black Country Health Authority

St Chad's Court, 213 Hagley Road, Birmingham B16 9RG
Tel: 0121 695 2445
Email: Geoff.scaife@bbcha.nhs.uk

Chair Elisabeth Buggins
Chief Executive Geoff Scaife

Coventry, Warwickshire, Herefordshire and Worcestershire Health Authority

Coventry Healthcare NHS Trust, Parkside House, Quinton Road, Coventry CV1 2NJ
Tel: 024 7652 6802

Chair Charles Goody
Chief Executive Mike Marchment

Essex Health Authority

c/o South Essex Health Authority, Arcadia House, Warley Hill Business Park, The Drive, Great Warley, Brentwood CM13 3BE
Tel: 01277 755200

Chair Michael Brookes
Chief Executive Terry Hanafin

Leicestershire, Northamptonshire and Rutland Health Authority

Gwendolen Road, Leicester LE5 4QF

Chair Richard Tilt
Chief Executive David Sissling

Norfolk, Suffolk and Cambridgeshire Health Authority

c/o Eastern Regional Office, Capital Park, Fulbourn, Cambridge CB1 5XB
Tel: 01223 597529 Fax: 01223 597529
Email: peter.houghton@doh.gsi.gov.uk

Chair Stewart Francis
Chief Executive Peter Houghton

Shropshire and Staffordshire Health Authority

Mellor House, Corporation Street, Stafford ST16 3BR
Tel: 01785 252233

Chair Michael Brereton
Chief Executive Bernard Crump

Trent Health Authority

c/o Nothingham Health Authority, 1 Standard Court, Park Row, Nottingham NG1 5DN
Tel: 0115 912 3344
Email: alan.burns@trent-sha.nhs.uk

Chair Arthur Sandford
Chief Executive Alan Burns

Directorate of Health and Social Care North

Department of Health, Quarry House, Quarry Hill, Leeds LS2 7UE

Director of Health and Social Care Peter Garland

Cheshire and Merseyside Health Authority

c/o NHS North West Regional Office, 930-932 Birchwood Boulevard, Warrington WA3 7QN
Tel: 01925 704250

Chair Judith Greensmith
Chief Executive Christine Hannah

HEALTH AUTHORITIES & BOARDS

County Durham and Tees Valley Health Authority

c/o County Durham and Darlington Health Authority, Appleton House, Lanchester Road, Durham DH1 5XZ
Tel: 0191 333 3205

Chair Tony Waites
Chief Executive Ken Jarrold

Cumbria and Lancashire Health Authority

c/o Chorley and South Ribble Primary Care Trust, Grove House, Langton Brow, The Green, Eccleston PR7 5PD
Tel: 01257 495100
Email: pearse.butler@lsca2.nwlancs-ha.nwest.nhs.uk

Chair Kath Reade
Chief Executive James Pearse Butler

Greater Manchester Health Authority

c/o Manchester Health Authority, Gateway House, Piccadilly South, Manchester M60 7LP
Tel: 0161 237 2011 Fax: 0161 237 2264
Email: downeyj@manchesterhealth.co.uk/gmha/
Website: www.manchesterhealth.co.uk/gmha/

Chair Philip Smith
Chief Executive Neil Goodwin

North and East Yorkshire and Northern Lincolnshire Health Authority

Suite 1.32, The Innovation Centre, York Science Park, Innovation Way, Heslington, York YO10 5DG
Tel: 01904 435331

Chair David Johns
Chief Executive David Johnson

Northumberland, Tyne and Wear Health Authority

c/o Newcastle and North Tyneside Health Authority, Newcastle General Hospital, Westgate Road, Newcastle upon Tyne NE4 6BE
Tel: 0191 256 3347
Email: david.flory@nant-ha.northy.nhs.uk

Chair Peter Carr
Chief Executive David Flory

South Yorkshire Health Authority

c/o Sheffield Health Authority, 5 Old Fulwood Road, Sheffield S10 3TG
Tel: 0114 271 1132 Fax: 0114 230 3745
Email: mike.farrar@sheffield-ha.nhs.uk

Chair Kathryn Riddle
Chief Executive Mike Farmer

West Yorkshire Health Authority

c/o Leeds Health Authority, Blenheim House, West One, Duncombe Street, Leeds LS1 4PL
Tel: 0113 295 2114 Fax: 0113 295 2126
Email: sue.wilson@lh.leeds-ha.northy.nhs.uk

Chair Alistair Graham
Chief Executive Richard Jeavons

Directorate of Health and Social Care South

Department of Health, 79 Whitehall, London SW1A 2NL

Director of Health and Social Care Ruth Carnell

Avon, Gloucestershire and Wiltshire Health Authority

c/o Sue Cook, Wiltshire Health Authority, Southgate House, Pans Lane, Devizes SN10 5EQ
Tel: 01380 728899
Email: mark.outhwaite@ekentha.nhs.uk

Chair Anthea Millett
Chief Executive Mark Outhwaite

Hampshire and Isle of Wight Health Authority

Oakley Road, Aldermaston Road, Southampton SO16 4GX
Tel: 023 8072 5400 Fax: 023 8072 5457

Chair Peter Bingham
Chief Executive Gareth Cruddace

Kent and Medway Health Authority

Preston Hall, Aylesford ME20 7NJ
Tel: 01622 713107 Fax: 01622 713129
Email: candy.morris@wkent-ha.sthames.nhs.uk

Chair Kate Lampard
Chief Executive Candy Morris

Somerset and Dorset Health Authority

Charter House, Bartec 4, Watercombe Lane, Lynx West Trading Estate, Yeovil BA20 2SU
Tel: 01935 384000 Fax: 01935 384079

Chair Jane Barrie
Chief Executive Ian Carruthers

South West Peninsula Health Authority

Cornwall and Isles of Scilly Health Authority, John Keay House, Tregonissey, St Austell PL25 4NQ
Tel: 01726 627900
Email: thelma.holland@ciosha.nhs.uk

Chair Judith Leverton
Chief Executive Thelma Holland

Surrey and Sussex Health Authority

c/o East Sussex, Brighton and Hove Health Authority, 36-38 Friar's Walk, Lewes
Tel: 01273 403504

Chair Terese Hawksworth
Chief Executive Simon Robbins

Thames Valley Health Authority

c/o Berkshire Health Authority, 57-59 Bath Road, Reading RG30 2BA
Tel: 0118 982 2703 Fax: 0118 982 2704
Email: nick.relph@berkshire.nhs.uk

Chair Jane Betts
Chief Executive Nick Relph

Scotland

Argyll and Clyde NHS Board

Ross House, Hawkhead Road, Paisley PA2 7BN
Tel: 0141 842 7200 Fax: 0141 848 1414
Website: www.show.scot.nhs.uk/achb

Chair John Mullin
Chief Executive Neil A McConachie

Ayrshire and Arran NHS Board

Boswell House, 10 Arthur Street, Ayr KA7 1QJ
Tel: 01292 611040 Fax: 01292 610636
Website: www.show.scot.nhs.uk/aahb

Chair J Morrow
Chief Executive Wai-Yin Hatton

Borders NHS Board

Newstead, Melrose TD6 9DB
Tel: 01896 825500 Fax: 01896 825580
Email: bordershb@borders.scot.nhs.uk
Website: www.show.scot.nhs.uk/bhb

Chair D A G Kilshaw
Chief Executive Lindsay Burley

Dumfries and Galloway NHS Board

Grierson House, The Crichton, Bankend Road, Dumfries DG1 4ZG
Tel: 01387 272700 Fax: 01387 252375
Website: www.show.scot.nhs.uk/dghb

Chair John Ross
Chief Executive Malcolm R Wright

Fife NHS Board

Springfield House, Cupar KY15 5UP
Tel: 01334 656200 Fax: 01334 652210
Website: www.show.scot.nhs.uk/fhb

Chair Esther Roberton
Chief Executive Tony Ranzetta

Forth Valley NHS Board

33 Spittal Street, Stirling FK8 1DX
Tel: 01786 463031 Fax: 01786 471337
Email: email@fvhb.scot.nhs.uk
Website: www.show.scot.nhs.uk/nhsfv

Chair Frank Clark
Chief Executive Fiona Mackenzie

Grampian NHS Board

Summerfield House, 2 Eday Road, Aberdeen AB9 6RE
Tel: 01224 663456 Fax: 01224 558609
Website: www.show.scot.nhs.uk/ghb

Chair C A MacLeod
Chief Executive Neil Campbell, Frank E L Hartnett

Greater Glasgow NHS Board

Dalian House, 350 St Vincent Street, Glasgow G3 8YZ
Tel: 0141 201 4444 Fax: 0141 201 4401
Website: www.show.scot.nhs.uk/gghb

Chair David Hamblen
Chief Executive Chris Spry

Highland NHS Board

Assynt House, Beechwood Park, Inverness IV2 3HG
Tel: 01463 717123 Fax: 01463 235189
Email: reception@ms.highland.hb.scot.nhs.uk
Website: www.highlandhealth.org.uk

Chair Caroline Thomson
Chief Executive G V Stone

Lanarkshire NHS Board

14 Beckford Street, Hamilton ML3 0TA
Tel: 01698 281313 Fax: 01698 423134
Website: www.scot.nhs.uk/lhb

Chair Ian Livingstone
Chief Executive David Pigott

Lothian NHS Board

Deaconess House, 148 Pleasance, Edinburgh EH8 9RS
Tel: 0131 536 9000 Fax: 0131 536 9009
Website: www.nhslothian.scot.nhs.uk

Chair Brian Cavanagh
Chief Executive James Barbour

Orkney NHS Board

Garden House, New Scapa Road, Kirkwall KW15 1BQ
Tel: 01856 885400 Fax: 01856 885411
Email: orkney.health.board@orkney.com
Website: www.show.scot.nhs.uk/ohb

Chair J Leslie
Chief Executive Judi Wellden

Scottish Ambulance Service

National Headquarters, Tipperlinn Road, Edinburgh EH10 5UU
Tel: 0131 446 7000 Fax: 0131 446 7001

Chair Owen Clarke
Chief Executive Adrian Lucas

Shetland NHS Board

Brevik House, South Road, Lerwick ZE1 0TG
Tel: 01595 696767 Fax: 01595 696727

Chair Betty Fullerton
Chief Executive Sandra Laurenson

Tayside NHS Board

King's Cross, Clepington Road, Dundee DD3 8EA
Tel: 01382 818479 Fax: 01382 424003
Website: www.show.scot.nhs.uk/thb

Chair Peter Bates

Western Isles NHS Board

37 South Beach Street, Stornoway PA87 2BN
Tel: 01851 702997 Fax: 01851 704405

Chair Alexander Matheson
Chief Executive Murdo Maclennan

Wales

Bro Taf Health Authority

Churchill House, Churchill Way, Cardiff CF1 4TW
Tel: 029 2040 2402 Fax: 029 2040 2403
Website: www.bro-taf-ha.wales.nhs.uk

Chair Simon Jones
Chief Executive Jan Williams

Dyfed Powys Health Authority

c/o St Davidss Hospital, Jobswell Road, Carmarthen SA31 3YH
Tel: 01267 225225 Fax: 01267 232179
Email: enquiries@dyfpws-ha.wales.nhs.uk
Website: www.dyfpws-ha.wales.nhs.uk

Chair Ainsley Reid
Chief Executive Stuart Gray

Gwent Health Authority

Mamhilad House, Mamhilad Park Estate, Pontypool NP4 0YP
Tel: 01495 765065 Fax: 01495 750985
Website: www.gwent-ha.wales.nhs.uk

Chair Fiona Peel
Chief Executive Bob Hudson

Iechyd Morgannwg Health Authority

41 High Street, Swansea SA1 1LT
Tel: 01792 458066 Fax: 01792 607533
Website: www.morgannwg-ha.org.uk

Chair Robert Davies
Chief Executive Jane Perrin

HEALTH AUTHORITIES & BOARDS

North Wales Health Authority

Preswylfa, Hendy Road, Mold CH7 1PZ
Tel: 01352 700227 Fax: 01352 754649
Website: www.nwales-ha.wales.nhs.uk

Chair Pauline Wood
Chief Executive David Hands

Western Health and Social Services Board

15 Gransha Park, Clooney Road, Londonderry BT47 6FN
Tel: 028 7186 0086 Fax: 028 7186 0311
Website: www.whssb.org

Chair John Bradley
Chief Executive Steven Lindsay

Northern Ireland

Eastern Health and Social Services Board

Champion House, 12-22 Linenhall Street, Belfast BT2 8BS
Tel: 028 9032 1313 Fax: 028 9055 3681
Email: enquiry@ehssb.n_i.nhs.uk
Website: www.n_inhsuk/boards/boards.html

Chair David Russell
Chief Executive Paula Kilbane

Northern Health and Social Services Board

County Hall, 182 Galgorm Road, Ballymena BT42 1RF
Tel: 028 2565 3333 Fax: 028 2566 2311
Website: www.nhssb.n-i.nhs.uk

Chair Michael Wood
Chief Executive Stuart MacDonnell

Southern Health and Social Services Board

Tower Hill, Armagh BT61 9DR

Chair William F Gillespie
Chief Executive Brendan P Cunningham

Channel Islands

States of Guernsey Board of Health

John Henry House, Le Vauquiedor, St. Martin's, Guernsey GY4 6UU
Tel: 01481 725241 Fax: 01481 235341

Chief Executive D Hughes

States of Jersey Health and Social Services

4th Floor, Peter Crill House, Gloucester Street, St Helier, Jersey JE2 3QS
Tel: 01534 622291 Fax: 01534 622887
Email: l.wilson@gov.je

Chief Executive Graham Jennings

Isle of Man

Isle of Man Department of Health and Social Security

Markwell House, Market Street, Douglas IM1 2RZ
Tel: 01624 685028 Fax: 01624 685130
Email: ceo@dhss.gov.im
Website: www.gov.im/dhss

Chief Executive Ken Tomlinson

Independent Hospitals

England

Abbey Caldew Hospital

64 Dalston Road, Carlisle CA2 5NW
Tel: 01253 531713 Fax: 01228 590158
Email: caldew@abbeyhospitals.co.uk
Website: www.abbeyhospitals.co.uk
Owners: Abbey Hospitals Ltd
Total Beds: 14

Abbey Gisburne Park Hospital

Gisburn, Clitheroe BB7 4HX
Tel: 01200 445693 Fax: 01200 445688
Email: gisburne@abbeyhospitals.co.uk
Website: www.abbeyhospitals.co.uk
Owners: Abbey Hospitals Ltd
Total Beds: 35

Abbey Park Hospital

Dalton Lane, Barrow-in-Furness LA14 4TP
Tel: 01229 813388 Fax: 01229 813366
Email: barrowabbeypark@lineone.net
Website: www.abbeyhospitals.co.uk
Owners: Abbey Hospitals Ltd
Total Beds: 10

Abbey Sefton Hospital

Park Road, Waterloo, Liverpool L22 3XE
Tel: 0151 257 6700 Fax: 0151 928 7477
Email: sefton@abbeyhospitals.co.uk
Website: www.abbeyhospitals.co.uk
Owners: Abbey Hospitals Ltd
Total Beds: 40

Acland Nuffield Hospital

Banbury Road, Oxford OX2 6PD
Tel: 01865 404142 Fax: 01865 556303
Website: www.nuffieldhospitals.org.uk
Owners: Nuffield Hospitals
Total Beds: 37

All Hallows Hospital

Station Road, Ditchingham, Bungay NR35 2QL
Tel: 01986 892728 Fax: 01986 895063
Email: admin@all-hallows.org.uk
Owners: The Hospital Management Trust
Total Beds: 30

The Ashdown Nuffield Hospital

Burrell Road, Haywards Heath RH16 1UD
Tel: 01444 456999 Fax: 01444 454111
Owners: Independent Care Management and Independent Surgery Centre Ltd
Total Beds: 42

Ashtead Hospital

The Warren, Ashtead KT21 2SB
Tel: 01372 221400 Fax: 01322 221445
Email: enquiries@ashtead-hospital.co.uk
Owners: Community Hospitals Group plc
Total Beds: 67

Belvedere Private Clinic

Off Knee Hill, Abbey Wood, London SE2 0GD
Tel: 020 8310 8866, 020 8311 4464 Fax: 020 8311 8249
Email: belvedere@btconnect.co
Website: www.cosmeticsurgerybelvedere.co.uk
Owners: Privately Owned
Total Beds: 8

Benenden Hospital

Goddards Green Road, Benenden, Cranbrook TN17 4AX
Tel: 01580 240333 Fax: 01580 241877
Owners: Benenden Healthcare Society Ltd
Total Beds: 145

Berkshire Independent Hospital

Wensley Road, Coley Park, Reading RG1 6UZ
Tel: 0118 956 0056 Fax: 0118 902 8125
Owners: Community Hospitals Group plc
Total Beds: 71

Birkdale Clinic (Rotherham) Ltd

Clifton Lane, Rotherham S65 2AJ
Tel: 01709 828928 Fax: 01709 828372
Owners: Privately Owned
Total Beds: 16

Birmingham Nuffield Hospital

22 Somerset Road, Edgbaston, Birmingham B15 2QQ
Tel: 0121 456 2000 Fax: 0121 454 5293
Owners: Nuffield Hospitals
Total Beds: 50

Blackdown Clinic

Old Milverton Lane, Blackdown, Leamington Spa CV32 6RW
Tel: 01926 334664 Fax: 01926 425291
Website: www.bpas.org
Owners: British Pregnancy Advisory Service
Total Beds: 10

BMI The Alexandra Hospital

Mill Lane, Cheadle SK8 2PX
Tel: 0161 428 3656 Fax: 0161 491 3867
Email: alexandrahospital@bmialex.demon.co.uk
Owners: BMI Healthcare
Total Beds: 165

BMI Bath Clinic

Claverton Down Road, Combe Down, Bath BA2 7BR
Tel: 01225 835555 Fax: 01225 835900
Owners: BMI Healthcare
Total Beds: 75

BMI The Beardwood Hospital

Preston New Road, Blackburn BB2 7AE
Tel: 01254 507607 Fax: 01254 507608
Website: www.bmihealthcare.co.uk
Owners: BMI Healthcare
Total Beds: 31

BMI The Beaumont Hospital

Old Hall Clough, Chorley New Road, Lostock, Bolton BL6 4LA
Tel: 01204 404404 Fax: 01204 404488
Owners: BMI Healthcare
Total Beds: 34

INDEPENDENT HOSPITALS

BMI Bishops Wood Hospital
Rickmansworth Road, Northwood HA6 2JW
Tel: 01923 835814 Fax: 01923 835181
Email: arobertson@bmihealthcare.co.uk
Owners: BMI Healthcare
Total Beds: 47

BMI The Blackheath Hospital
40-42 Lee Terrace, Blackheath, London SE3 9UD
Tel: 020 8318 7722 Fax: 020 8318 2542
Website: www.bmihealthcare.co.uk
Owners: BMI Healthcare
Total Beds: 58

BMI Chatsworth Suite
Chesterfield Royal Hospital, Calow, Chesterfield S44 5BL
Tel: 01246 544400 Fax: 01246 205703
Website: www.bmihealthcare.co.uk
Owners: BMI Healthcare
Total Beds: 16

BMI The Chaucer Hospital
Nackington Road, Canterbury CT4 7AR
Tel: 01227 825100 Fax: 01227 762733
Owners: BMI Healthcare
Total Beds: 60

BMI Chelsfield Park Hospital
Bucks Cross Road, Chelsfield, Orpington BR6 7RG
Tel: 01689 877855 Fax: 01689 837439
Email: chelsfield@bmihealthcare.co.uk
Owners: BMI Healthcare
Total Beds: 46

BMI The Chiltern Hospital
London Road, Great Missenden HP16 0EN
Tel: 01494 890890 Fax: 01494 890250
Website: www.bmihealthcare.co.uk
Owners: BMI Healthcare
Total Beds: 69

BMI The Clementine Churchill Hospital
Sudbury Hill, Harrow HA1 3RX
Tel: 020 8872 3872 Fax: 020 8872 3871
Email: cch@bmihealthcare.co.uk
Owners: BMI Healthcare
Total Beds: 120

BMI The Droitwich Spa Hospital
St Andrew's Road, Droitwich Spa WR9 8DN
Tel: 01905 794793 Fax: 01905 779095
Owners: BMI Healthcare
Total Beds: 43

BMI The Esperance Hospital
Hartington Place, Eastbourne BN21 3BG
Tel: 01323 411188 Fax: 01323 410626
Owners: BMI Healthcare
Total Beds: 50

BMI Fawkham Manor Hospital
Manor Lane, Fawkham, Longfield DA3 8ND
Tel: 01474 879900 Fax: 01474 879827
Website: www.bmihealthcare.co.uk
Owners: BMI Healthcare
Total Beds: 36

BMI The Garden Hospital
46-50 Sunny Gardens Road, Hendon, London NW4 1RX
Tel: 020 8457 4500 Fax: 020 8457 4567
Email: garden@bmihealthcare.co.uk
Owners: BMI Healthcare
Total Beds: 30

BMI Goring Hall Hospital
Bodiam Avenue, Goring-by-Sea, Worthing BN12 5AT
Tel: 01903 506699 Fax: 01903 242348
Website: www.bmihealthcare.co.uk
Owners: BMI Healthcare
Total Beds: 52

BMI The Hampshire Clinic
Basing Road, Old Basing, Basingstoke RG24 7AL
Tel: 01256 357111 Fax: 01256 329986
Email: hampshire@bmihealthcare.co.uk
Owners: BMI Healthcare
Total Beds: 52

BMI The Harbour Hospital
St Mary's Road, Poole BH15 2BH
Tel: 01202 244200 Fax: 01202 244201
Owners: BMI Healthcare
Total Beds: 40

BMI The Highfield Hospital
Manchester Road, Rochdale OL11 4LZ
Tel: 01706 655121 Fax: 01706 860719
Email: highfield@bmihealthcare.co.uk
Website: www.bmihealthcare.co.uk/highfield
Owners: BMI Healthcare
Total Beds: 57

BMI The Kings Oak Hospital
Chase Farm (North Side), The Ridgeway, Enfield EN2 8SD
Tel: 020 8370 9500 Fax: 020 8370 9501
Website: www.bmihealthcare.co.uk
Owners: BMI Healthcare
Total Beds: 54

BMI The London Independent Hospital
1 Beaumont Square, Stepney Green, London E1 4NL
Tel: 020 7780 2400 Fax: 020 7780 2401
Website: www.bmihealthcare.co.uk
Owners: BMI Healthcare
Total Beds: 102

BMI The Manor Hospital
Church End, Biddenham, Bedford MK40 4AW
Tel: 01234 364252 Fax: 01234 325001
Website: www.bmihealthcare.co.uk
Owners: BMI Healthcare
Total Beds: 25

BMI Meriden Wing
Walsgrave Hospital NHS Trust, Clifford Bridge Road, Coventry CV2 2DX
Tel: 024 7660 2772 Fax: 024 7660 2329
Website: www.bmihealth.co.uk/meriden
Owners: BMI Healthcare

BMI The Nuneaton Private Hospital
132 Coventry Road, Nuneaton CV10 7AD
Tel: 0247 635 7500 Fax: 0247 635 7520
Owners: BMI Healthcare
Total Beds: 24

BMI The Paddocks Hospital
Aylesbury Road, Princes Risborough HP27 0JS
Tel: 01844 346951 Fax: 01844 344521
Owners: BMI Healthcare
Total Beds: 34

BRITISH HOME & HOSPITAL FOR INCURABLES

BMI The Park Hospital
Sherwood Lodge Drive, Burntstump Country Park, Arnold, Nottingham NG5 8RX
Tel: 0115 967 0670 Fax: 0115 967 0381
Owners: BMI Healthcare
Total Beds: 92

BMI The Princess Margaret Hospital
Osborne Road, Windsor SL4 3SJ
Tel: 01753 743434 Fax: 01753 743435
Email: pmh@bmihealthcare.co.uk
Website: www.bmihealthcare.co.uk
Owners: BMI Healthcare
Total Beds: 80

BMI The Priory Hospital
Priory Road, Edgbaston, Birmingham B5 7UG
Tel: 0121 440 2323 Fax: 0121 440 0804
Email: priory@bmihealthcare.co.uk
Website: www.bmihealthcare.co.uk/priory
Owners: BMI Healthcare
Total Beds: 120

BMI The Ridgeway Hospital
Moormead Road, Wroughton, Swindon SN4 9DD
Tel: 01793 814848 Fax: 01793 814852
Owners: BMI Healthcare
Total Beds: 40

BMI The Runnymede Hospital
Guildford Road, Ottershaw, Chertsey KT16 0RQ
Tel: 01932 877800 Fax: 01932 875433
Owners: BMI Healthcare
Total Beds: 60

BMI The Sandringham Hospital
Gayton Road, King's Lynn PE30 4HJ
Tel: 01553 769770 Fax: 01553 767573
Owners: BMI Healthcare
Total Beds: 35

BMI Sarum Road Hospital
Sarum Road, Winchester SO22 5HA
Tel: 01962 844555 Fax: 01962 842620
Owners: BMI Healthcare
Total Beds: 44

BMI The Shelbourne Hospital
Queen Alexandra Road, High Wycombe HP11 2TR
Tel: 01494 888700 Fax: 01494 888701
Total Beds: 30

BMI Shirley Oaks Hospital
Poppy Lane, Shirley Oaks Village, Croydon CR9 8AB
Tel: 020 8655 5500 Fax: 020 8655 5555
Email: shirleyoaks@bmihealthcare.co.uk
Website: www.bmihealthcare.co.uk
Owners: BMI Healthcare
Total Beds: 50

BMI The Sloane Hospital
125 Albemarle Road, Beckenham BR3 5HS
Tel: 020 8466 6911 Fax: 020 8464 1443
Owners: BMI Healthcare
Total Beds: 57

BMI The Somerfield Hospital
63-77 London Road, Maidstone ME16 0DU
Tel: 01622 208000 Fax: 01622 674706
Website: www.bmihealthcare.co.uk
Owners: BMI Healthcare
Total Beds: 48

BMI The South Cheshire Private Hospital
Leighton, Crewe CW1 4QP
Tel: 01270 500411 Fax: 01270 583297
Owners: BMI Healthcare
Total Beds: 32

BMI Thornbury Hospital
312 Fulwood Road, Sheffield S10 3BR
Tel: 0114 266 1133 Fax: 0114 268 6913
Owners: BMI Healthcare
Total Beds: 60

BMI Three Shires Hospital
The Avenue, Cliftonville, Northampton NN1 5DR
Tel: 01604 620311 Fax: 01604 629066
Website: www.bmihealthcare.co.uk
Owners: BMI Healthcare
Total Beds: 50

BMI The Winterbourne Hospital
Herringston Road, Dorchester DT1 2DR
Tel: 01305 263252 Fax: 01305 265424
Website: www.bmihealthcare.co.uk
Owners: BMI Healthcare
Total Beds: 38

Bournemouth Nuffield Hospital
The Derwent Suite, Castle Lane East, Bournemouth BH7 7DR
Email: margaret.turner@nuffieldhospitals.org.uk
Website: www.nuffieldhospitals.org.uk
Owners: Nuffield Hospitals
Total Beds: 99

Brain Injury Services - Community Rehabilitation and Supported Living
Kelpie, 63 Park Avenue South, Abington, Northampton NN3 3AB
Tel: 01604 604310 Fax: 01604 38176
Email: info@partnershipsincare.co.uk
Owners: Partnerships in Care Ltd
Total Beds: 10

Brain Injury Services Elm Park
Elm Park, Station Road, Ardleigh, Colchester CO7 7RT
Tel: 01206 231055 Fax: 01206 231596
Email: info@partnershipsincare.co.uk
Owners: Partnerships in Care Ltd

Brain Injury Services Grafton Manor
Grafton Manor, Grafton Regis, Towcester NN12 7SS
Tel: 01908 543131 Fax: 01908 542644
Email: info@partnershipsincare.co.uk
Owners: Partnerships in Care Ltd

The Bristol Nuffield Hospital at Chesterfield
3 Clifton Hill, Clifton, Bristol BS8 1BP
Website: www.nuffieldhospitals.org.uk
Owners: Nuffield Hospitals
Total Beds: 63

The Bristol Nuffield Hospital at St Mary's
Upper Byron Place, Clifton, Bristol BS8 1JU
Tel: 0117 987 2727 Fax: 0117 925 4909
Website: www.nuffieldhospitals.org.uk
Owners: BUPA Hospitals Ltd
Total Beds: 43

British Home and Hospital for Incurables
Crown Lane, Streatham, London SW16 3JB
Tel: 020 8670 8261 Fax: 020 8766 6084
Owners: Charity/Association
Total Beds: 125

INDEPENDENT HOSPITALS

Broadway Lodge

Oldmixon Road, Weston Super Mare BS24 9NN
Tel: 01934 812319 Fax: 01934 815381
Email: mailbox@broadwaylodge.org.uk
Website: www.broadwaylodge.org.uk
Owners: Charity/Association
Total Beds: 39

Bromhead Hospital

Nettleham Road, Lincoln LN2 1QU
Tel: 01522 578000 Fax: 01522 514021
Email: enquiries@bromheadhospital.co.uk
Website: www.bromheadhospital.co.uk
Owners: Charity/Association
Total Beds: 40

BUPA Alexandra Hospital

Impton Lane, Walderslade, Chatham ME5 9PG
Tel: 01634 662810 Fax: 01634 686162
Owners: BUPA Hospitals Ltd
Total Beds: 42

BUPA Belvedere Hospital

Belvedere Road, Scarborough YO11 2UT
Tel: 01723 365363 Fax: 01723 377513
Email: cservice-bl@bupa.com
Owners: BUPA Hospitals Ltd
Total Beds: 37

BUPA Cambridge Lea Hospital

30 New Road, Impington, Cambridge CB4 9EL
Tel: 01223 266900 Fax: 01223 233421
Email: cservice-ce@bupa.com
Website: www.bupahospitals.co.uk/cambridgelea
Owners: BUPA Hospitals Ltd
Total Beds: 60

BUPA Chalybeate Hospital

Chalybeate Close, Tremona Road, Southampton SO16 6UY
Tel: 023 8077 5544 Fax: 023 8070 1160
Owners: BUPA Hospitals Ltd
Total Beds: 78

BUPA Dunedin Hospital

16 Bath Road, Reading RG1 6NB
Tel: 01189 587676 Fax: 01189 503847
Website: www.bupahospitals.co.uk/dunedin
Owners: BUPA Hospitals Ltd
Total Beds: 53

BUPA Fylde Coast Hospital

St Walburgas Road, Blackpool FY3 8BP
Tel: 01253 394188 Fax: 01253 397946
Owners: BUPA Hospitals Ltd
Total Beds: 38

BUPA Gatwick Park Hospital

Povey Cross Road, Horley RH6 0BB
Tel: 01293 785511 Fax: 01293 774883
Website: www.bupa.co.uk
Owners: BUPA Hospitals Ltd
Total Beds: 85

BUPA Hartswood Hospital

Eagle Way, Brentwood CM13 3LE
Tel: 01277 232525 Fax: 01277 200128
Website: www.bupahospitals.co.uk/hartswood
Owners: BUPA Hospitals Ltd
Total Beds: 58

BUPA Hospital Bristol

The Glen, Redland Hill, Durdham Down, Bristol BS6 6UT
Tel: 0117 973 2562 Fax: 0117 974 3203
Owners: BUPA Hospitals Ltd
Total Beds: 64

BUPA Hospital Bushey

Heathbourne Road, Bushey, Watford WD2 1RD
Tel: 020 8950 9090 Fax: 020 8950 7556
Owners: BUPA Hospitals Ltd
Total Beds: 80

BUPA Hospital Clare Park

Clare Park, Crondall Lane, Crondall, Farnham GU10 5XX
Tel: 01252 850216 Fax: 01252 850228
Owners: BUPA Hospitals Ltd
Total Beds: 34

BUPA Hospital Elland

Elland Lane, Elland HX5 9EB
Tel: 01422 324000 Fax: 01422 377501
Owners: BUPA Hospitals Ltd
Total Beds: 47

BUPA Hospital Harpenden

Ambrose Lane, Harpenden AL5 4BP
Tel: 01582 763191 Fax: 01582 712312
Website: www.bupahospitals.co.uk/harpenden
Owners: BUPA Hospitals Ltd
Total Beds: 62

BUPA Hospital Hastings

The Ridge, St Leonards-on-Sea TN37 7RE
Tel: 01424 757400 Fax: 01424 757424
Email: clinical-hs@bupa.com
Owners: BUPA Hospitals Ltd
Total Beds: 29

BUPA Hospital Hull and East Riding

Lowfield Road, Anlaby, Hull HU10 7AZ
Tel: 01482 659471 Fax: 01482 654033
Email: cservice-hl@bupa.com
Owners: BUPA Hospitals Ltd
Total Beds: 40

BUPA Hospital Leeds

Jackson Avenue, Roundhay, Leeds LS8 1NT
Tel: 0113 269 3939 Fax: 0113 268 1340
Owners: BUPA Hospitals Ltd
Total Beds: 78

BUPA Hospital Leicester

Gartree Road, Oadby, Leicester LE2 2FF
Tel: 0116 272 0888 Fax: 0116 272 0666
Owners: BUPA Hospitals Ltd
Total Beds: 76

BUPA Hospital Little Aston

Little Aston Hall Drive, Little Aston, Sutton Coldfield B74 3UP
Tel: 0121 353 2444 Fax: 0121 353 1592
Owners: BUPA Hospitals Ltd
Total Beds: 67

BUPA Hospital Manchester

Russell Road, Whalley Range, Manchester M16 8AJ
Tel: 0161 226 0112 Fax: 0161 227 9405
Owners: BUPA Hospitals Ltd
Total Beds: 86

BUPA Hospital Norwich

Old Watton Road, Colney, Norwich NR4 7TD
Tel: 01603 456181 Fax: 01603 250968

Owners: BUPA Hospitals Ltd
Total Beds: 67

BUPA Hospital Portsmouth

Bartons Road, Havant PO9 5NP
Tel: 023 9245 6000 Fax: 023 9245 6100
Owners: BUPA Hospitals Ltd
Total Beds: 49

BUPA Hospital Tunbridge Wells

Fordcombe Road, Fordcombe, Tunbridge Wells TN3 0RD
Tel: 01892 740047 Fax: 01892 740046
Owners: BUPA Hospitals Ltd
Total Beds: 40

BUPA Hospital Washington

Picktree Lane, Rickleton, Washington NE38 9JZ
Tel: 0191 415 1272 Fax: 0191 415 5541
Owners: BUPA Hospitals Ltd
Total Beds: 54

BUPA Methley Park Hospital

Methley Lane, Methley, Leeds LS26 9HG
Tel: 01977 518518 Fax: 01977 519014
Owners: BUPA Hospitals Ltd
Total Beds: 29

BUPA North Cheshire Hospital

Fir Tree Close, Stretton, Warrington WA4 4LU
Tel: 01925 265000 Fax: 01925 215098
Owners: BUPA Hospitals Ltd
Total Beds: 40

BUPA Parkway Hospital

1 Damson Parkway, Solihull B91 2PP
Tel: 0121 704 1451 Fax: 0121 711 3436, 0121 711 7483
Website: www.bupa.co.uk
Owners: BUPA Hospitals Ltd
Total Beds: 51

BUPA Redwood Hospital

Canada Drive, Redhill
Tel: 01737 277277 Fax: 01737 277288
Website: www.bupa.co.uk
Owners: BUPA Hospitals Ltd
Total Beds: 36

BUPA Regency Hospital

West Street, Macclesfield SK11 8DW
Tel: 01625 501150 Fax: 01625 501800
Owners: BUPA Hospitals Ltd
Total Beds: 33

BUPA Roding Hospital

Roding Lane South, Ilford IG4 5PZ
Tel: 020 8551 1100 Fax: 020 8709 7804
Website: www.bupahospitals.co.uk/roding
Owners: BUPA Hospitals Ltd
Total Beds: 65

BUPA St Saviour's Hospital

73 Seabrook Road, Hythe CT21 5QW
Tel: 01303 265581 Fax: 01303 261441
Email: cumminsc-hs@bupa.com
Website: www.bupa.co.uk
Owners: BUPA Hospitals Ltd
Total Beds: 38

BUPA South Bank Hospital

139 Bath Road, Worcester WR5 3YB
Tel: 01905 350003 Fax: 01905 357765

Owners: BUPA Hospitals Ltd
Total Beds: 41

BUPA Wellesley Hospital

Eastern Avenue, Southend-on-Sea SS2 4XH
Tel: 01702 462944 Fax: 01702 600160
Owners: BUPA Hospitals Ltd
Total Beds: 51

The Bury St Edmunds Nuffield Hospital

St Mary's Square, Bury St Edmunds IP33 2AA
Tel: 01284 701371 Fax: 01284 769998
Website: www.nuffieldhospitals.org.uk
Owners: Nuffield Hospitals
Total Beds: 40

Care Perspectives

St John's House Hospital, Lion Road, Palgrave, Diss IP22 1BA
Tel: 01379 643334 Fax: 01379 641455
Email: cp@careperspectives.demon.co.uk
Website: www.partnershipsincare.co.uk
Owners: Partnerships in Care Ltd
Total Beds: 88

Cheadle Royal Hospital

100 Wilmslow Road, Cheadle SK8 3DG
Tel: 0161 428 9511 Fax: 0161 428 1870
Website: www.cheadleroyal.co.uk
Total Beds: 212

The Cheltenham and Gloucester Nuffield Hospitals

Hatherley Lane, Cheltenham GL51 6SY
Tel: 01242 246500 Fax: 01242 246501
Email: Cheryl.Ewing@nuffieldhospitals.org.uk
Website: www.nuffieldhospitals.org.uk
Owners: Nuffield Hospitals
Total Beds: 38

The Children's Trust

Tadworth Court, Tadworth KT20 5RU
Tel: 01737 365000 Fax: 01737 365084
Owners: The Children's Trust
Total Beds: 44

Claremont Hospital

401 Sandygate Road, Sheffield S10 5UB
Tel: 0114 263 0330 Fax: 0114 230 9388
Owners: The Hospital Management Trust
Total Beds: 40

Cleveland Nuffield Hospital

Junction Road, Norton, Stockton-on-Tees TS20 1PX
Tel: 01642 360100 Fax: 01642 556535
Email: lesleygalloway@nuffieldhospitals.org.uk
Owners: Nuffield Hospitals
Total Beds: 31

The Coach House

25 Brighton Road, Salfords, Redhill RH1 6PP
Tel: 01293 783004 Fax: 01293 771170
Owners: Priory Hospitals Limited

Cromwell Clinic

Cromwell House, 82 High Street, Huntingdon PE29 3DP
Tel: 01480 411411 Fax: 01480 411411
Email: info@cromwellclinic.co.uk
Owners: Privately Owned
Total Beds: 52

INDEPENDENT HOSPITALS

Cromwell Hospital
Cromwell Road, London SW5 0TU
Tel: 020 7460 2000 Fax: 020 7460 5555
Email: info@cromwell_hospital.co.uk
Website: www.cromwell_hospital.co.uk
Owners: Medical Services International
Total Beds: 150

Cygnet Hospital Ealing
22 Crofton Road, Ealing, London W5 2HT
Tel: 020 8991 6699
Owners: Cygnet Healthcare plc
Total Beds: 29

Danum Lodge Clinic
123 Thorne Road, Doncaster DN2 5BQ
Tel: 01302 325508 Fax: 01302 768206
Owners: British Pregnancy Advisory Service
Total Beds: 11

Dean Park Clinic
Austy Manor, Wootten Wawed, Solihull B95 6BX
Tel: 01564 795225 Fax: 01564 744935
Website: www.bpas.org
Owners: British Pregnancy Advisory Service
Total Beds: 11

The Dene
Gatehouse Lane, Goddards Green, Hassocks BN6 9LE
Tel: 01444 231000 Fax: 01444 231086
Owners: Partnerships in Care Ltd
Total Beds: 48

The Diving Diseases Research Centre
The Hyperbaric Medical Centre, Tamar Science Park, Derriford Road, Plymouth PL6 8BQ
Tel: 01752 209999 Fax: 01752 209115
Email: enquires@ddrc.org, enquiries@ddrc.org
Website: www.ddrc.org
Owners: Charity/Association
Total Beds: 4

Droitwich Knee Clinic
St Andrews Road, Droitwich Spa WR9 8YX
Tel: 01905 794858 Fax: 01905 795916
Email: enquiries@kneeclinics.co.uk

Duchy Hospital
Penventinnie Lane, Treliske, Truro TR1 3UP
Tel: 01872 226100 Fax: 01872 226124
Owners: Community Hospitals Group plc
Total Beds: 35

Duchy Nuffield Hospital
Queens Road, Harrogate HG2 0HF
Tel: 01423 567136 Fax: 01423 524381
Owners: Nuffield Hospitals
Total Beds: 26

East Midlands Nuffield Hospital
Rykneld Road, Littleover, Derby DE23 7SN
Tel: 01332 517891 Fax: 01332 512481
Owners: Nuffield Hospitals
Total Beds: 32

Essex Nuffield Hospital
Shenfield Road, Brentwood CM15 8EH
Tel: 01277 695695 Fax: 01277 201158
Website: www.nuffieldhospitals.org.uk
Owners: Nuffield Hospitals
Total Beds: 48

Euxton Hall Hospital
Wigan Road, Euxton, Chorley PR7 6DY
Tel: 01257 276261 Fax: 01257 261882
Owners: Community Hospitals Group plc
Total Beds: 24

The Evelyn Hospital
4 Trumpington Road, Cambridge CB2 2AF
Tel: 01223 303336 Fax: 01223 316068
Owners: Charity/Association, The Hospital Management Trust
Total Beds: 57

Exeter Nuffield Hospital
Wonford Road, Exeter EX2 4UG
Tel: 01392 276591 Fax: 01392 425147
Website: www.nuffieldhospitals.org.uk
Owners: Nuffield Hospitals
Total Beds: 46

Farm Place
Stane Street, Ockley, Dorking RH5 5NG
Tel: 01306 627742 Fax: 01306 627756
Email: farmplace@whc.co.uk
Owners: Westminster Health Care Ltd
Total Beds: 25

Fitzwilliam Hospital
Milton Way, South Bretton, Peterborough PE3 9AQ
Tel: 01733 261717 Fax: 01733 332561
Owners: Community Hospitals Group plc
Total Beds: 59

Florence Nightingale Clinic Chelsea
1-5 Radnor Walk, London SW3 4PB
Tel: 020 7349 3900 Fax: 020 7351 7098
Website: www.florencenightingalehospitals.co.uk
Owners: Florence Nightingale Hospitals
Total Beds: 40

Florence Nightingale Hospital
11-19 Lisson Grove, London NW1 6SH
Tel: 020 7535 7700 Fax: 020 7724 9440
Website: www.florencenightingalehospitals.co.uk
Owners: Florence Nightingale Hospitals
Total Beds: 73

Florence Nightingale Hospital Liverpool
Park Road, Waterloo, Liverpool L22 3XE
Tel: 0151 257 6200
Owners: Florence Nightingale Hospitals
Total Beds: 22

Florence Nightingale Psychological Medicine Centre
Cromwell Hospital, Cromwell Road, London SW5 0TU
Tel: 020 7460 5672 Fax: 020 7460 5671
Website: www.florencenightingalehospitals.co.uk
Owners: Florence Nightingale Hospitals
Total Beds: 14

Fulwood Hall Hospital
Midgery Lane, Fulwood, Preston PR2 9SZ
Tel: 01772 704111 Fax: 01772 795131
Owners: Community Hospitals Group plc
Total Beds: 31

The Gainsborough Clinic and Nursing Home
22 Barkham Terrace, Lambeth Road, London SE1 7PW
Tel: 020 7716 1500, 020 7928 5633 Fax: 020 7928 1702
Owners: The Hospital Management Trust
Total Beds: 87

Grosvenor Nuffield Hospital

Wrexham Road, Chester CH4 7QP
Tel: 01244 680444 Fax: 01244 680812
Website: www.nuffieldhospitals.org.uk
Owners: Nuffield Hospitals
Total Beds: 34

The Guildford Nuffield Hospital

Stirling Road, Guildford GU2 7RF
Tel: 01483 555800 Fax: 01483 555888
Website: www.gnhnuffieldhospitals.org.uk
Owners: Nuffield Hospitals
Total Beds: 54

Guy's Nuffield House

(Guy's & St Thomas's Hospital Trust), Newcomen Street, London SE1 1YR
Tel: 020 7955 4953 Fax: 020 7955 4476
Owners: Guy's and St Thomas' NHS Trust
Total Beds: 44

The Harley Street Clinic

35 Weymouth Street., London W1N 4BJ
Tel: 020 7935 7700 Fax: 020 7487 4415
Email: info@harleystreetonline.hcahealthcare.co.uk
Website: www.columbiahealthcare.co.uk/hsc
Owners: PPP/Columbia Healthcare Ltd
Total Beds: 101

Harrogate Clinic

23 Ripon Road, Harrogate HG1 2JL
Tel: 01423 500599 Fax: 01423 531074
Owners: Cygnet Healthcare plc
Total Beds: 34

The Heath Clinic

58 West Heath Drive, London NW11 7QH
Tel: 020 8458 4416 Fax: 020 8905 5274
Owners: Privately Owned
Total Beds: 10

Highbank

Walmersley House, Walmersley Road, Bury BL9 5LX
Tel: 01706 829540 Fax: 01706 829534
Owners: Westminster Health Care Ltd
Total Beds: 65

Highgate Private Hospital Ltd

17-19 View Road, Highgate, London N6 4DJ
Tel: 020 8341 4182 Fax: 020 8342 8347
Email: highgate.privatehospital@lineone.net
Website: www.highgatehospital.co.uk
Owners: Privately Owned
Total Beds: 30

Holly House Hospital

High Road, Buckhurst Hill IG9 5HX
Tel: 020 8505 3311 Fax: 020 8506 1013
Owners: Aspen Healthcare Ltd
Total Beds: 59

Holy Cross Hospital

Hindhead Road, Haslemere GU27 1NQ
Tel: 01428 643311 Fax: 01428 644007
Email: info@holycross.org.uk
Website: www.holycross.org.uk
Owners: Charity/Association
Total Beds: 54

The Horder Centre for Arthritis

St John's Road, Crowborough TN6 1XP
Tel: 01892 665577 Fax: 01892 662142
Email: arthritis@horder.co.uk
Owners: Charity/Association
Total Beds: 59

Hospital of St John and St Elizabeth

60 Grove End Road, St Johns Wood, London NW8 9NH
Tel: 020 7286 5126 Fax: 020 7268 4813
Email: info@hje.org.uk
Website: www.hje.org.uk
Owners: Charity/Association
Total Beds: 110

Hove Nuffield Hospital

55 New Church Road, Hove BN3 4BG
Tel: 01273 779471 Fax: 01273 220919
Owners: Nuffield Hospitals
Total Beds: 9

HRH Princess Christian's Hospital

12 Clarence Road, Windsor SL4 5AG
Tel: 01753 853121 Fax: 01753 831185
Website: www.nuffieldhospitals.org.uk
Owners: Nuffield Hospitals
Total Beds: 24

Huddersfield Nuffield Hospital

Birkby Hall Road, Huddersfield HD2 2BL
Tel: 01484 533131 Fax: 01484 428396
Website: www.nuffieldhospitals.org.uk
Owners: Nuffield Hospitals
Total Beds: 29

Hull Nuffield Hospital

Entrance 3, Castle Hill Hospital, Castle Road, Hull NU16 5FQ
Owners: Nuffield Hospitals
Total Beds: 38

Kemple View

Longsight Road, Langho, Blackburn BB6 8AD
Tel: 01254 248021 Fax: 01254 248023
Email: Info@partnershipsincare.co.uk
Website: www.partnershipsincare.co.uk
Owners: Partnerships in Care Ltd
Total Beds: 64

King Edward VII Hospital

Midhurst GU29 0BL
Tel: 01730 812341 Fax: 01730 816333
Total Beds: 174

King Edward VII's Hospital for Officers

Beaumont Street, London W1N 2AA
Tel: 020 7486 4411 Fax: 020 7467 4303
Email: info@kingedwardvii.bdx.co.uk
Website: www.kingedwardvii.bdx.co.uk
Owners: Charity/Association
Total Beds: 69

Kneesworth House Hospital

Bassingbourn-cum-Kneesworth, Royston SG8 5JP
Tel: 01763 255700 Fax: 01763 255718
Website: www.partnershipsincare.co.uk
Owners: Partnerships in Care Ltd
Total Beds: 145

Lancaster and Lakeland Nuffield Hospital

Meadowside, Lancaster LA1 3RH
Tel: 01524 62345 Fax: 01524 844725
Email: steve.broomhall@nuffieldhospitals.org.uk

INDEPENDENT HOSPITALS

Owners: Nuffield Hospitals
Total Beds: 29

The Leeds Private Hospital

The Fallodon Private Surgical Hospital, 4 Allerton Park, Leeds LS7 4ND
Tel: 0113 269 2231
Total Beds: 21

The Leicester Nuffield Hospital

Scraptoft Lane, Leicester LE5 1HY
Tel: 0116 276 9401 Fax: 0116 246 1076
Owners: Nuffield Hospitals
Total Beds: 46

Leigham Clinic

76 Leigham Court Road, Streatham, London SW16 2QA
Tel: 020 8677 5522 Fax: 020 8769 8578
Owners: British Pregnancy Advisory Service

The Lister Hospital

Chelsea Bridge Road, London SW1W 8RH
Tel: 020 7730 3417 Fax: 020 7824 8867
Email: info@lister.hcahealthcare.co.uk
Website: www.thelisterhospital.com
Total Beds: 70

London Bridge Hospital

27 Tooley Street, London SE1 2PR
Tel: 020 7407 3100 Fax: 020 7407 3162
Email: info@lbh.hcahealthcare.co.uk
Website: www.londonbridgehospital.co.uk
Total Beds: 119

The London Clinic

20 Devonshire Place, London W1G 6BW
Tel: 020 7935 4444 Fax: 020 7486 3782
Email: info@thelondonclinic.co.uk
Website: www.thelondonclinic.co.uk
Owners: Privately Owned
Total Beds: 190

Lourdes Hospital

57 Greenbank Road, Liverpool L18 1HQ
Tel: 0151 733 7123 Fax: 0151 735 0446
Total Beds: 58

Lynden Hill Clinic

Linden Hill Lane, Kiln Green, near Twyford, Reading RG10 9XP
Tel: 0118 940 1234 Fax: 0118 940 1424
Email: enquiries@lynden-hill-clinic.co.uk
Website: www.lynden-hill-clinic.co.uk
Total Beds: 30

Marie Curie Centre, Ardenlea

Queen's Drive, Ilkley LS29 9QR
Tel: 01943 607505 Fax: 01943 816469
Email: info@mariecurie.org.uk
Owners: Marie Curie Cancer Care
Total Beds: 20

Marie Curie Centre, Caterham

Harestone Drive, Caterham CR3 6YQ
Tel: 01883 342226 Fax: 01883 341992
Email: info@mariecurie.org.uk
Website: www.mariecurie.org.uk
Owners: Marie Curie Cancer Care
Total Beds: 18

Marie Curie Centre, Edenhall

11 Lyndhurst Gardens, London NW3 5NS
Tel: 020 7853 3400 Fax: 020 7853 3437
Email: info@mariecurie.org.uk
Website: www.mariecurie.org.uk
Owners: Marie Curie Cancer Care
Total Beds: 32

Marie Curie Centre, Liverpool

Speke Road, Woolton, Liverpool L25 8QA
Tel: 0151 801 1400 Fax: 0151 801 1458
Email: info@mariecurie.org.uk
Website: www.mariecurie.org.uk
Owners: Marie Curie Cancer Care
Total Beds: 30

Marie Curie Centre, Newcastle

Marie Curie Drive, Newcastle upon Tyne NE4 6SS
Tel: 0191 219 5560 Fax: 0191 272 3067
Email: info@mariecurie.org.uk
Website: www.mariecurie.org.uk
Owners: Marie Curie Cancer Care
Total Beds: 22

Marie Curie Centre, Warren Pearl

911-913 Warwick Road, Solihull B91 3ER
Tel: 0121 254 7800 Fax: 0121 254 7840
Email: info@mariecurie.org.uk
Website: www.mariecurie.org.uk
Owners: Marie Curie Cancer Care
Total Beds: 21

Marie Stopes Bristol

3 Great George Street, Clifton, Bristol BS1 5RR
Owners: Marie Stopes International

Marie Stopes Ealing

87 Mattock Lane, Ealing, London W5 5BJ
Tel: 020 8567 0102 Fax: 020 8567 3636
Email: services@stopes.org.uk
Website: www.mariestopes.org.uk
Owners: Marie Stopes International
Total Beds: 18

Marie Stopes Essex

88 Russell Road, Buckhurst Hill IG9 5QB
Tel: 020 8505 6358 Fax: 020 8498 9637
Owners: Marie Stopes International
Total Beds: 28

Marie Stopes House

108 Whitfield Street, London W1P 6BE
Owners: Marie Stopes International

Marie Stopes Leeds

10 Queen Square, Leeds LS2 8AJ
Tel: 0113 244 0685 Fax: 0113 244 8865
Owners: Marie Stopes International

Marie Stopes Maidstone

10 Brewer Street, Maidstone ME14 1RU
Owners: Marie Stopes International

Marie Stopes Manchester

2 St John Street, Manchester M3 4DB
Tel: 0161 832 4260 Fax: 0161 834 4872
Owners: Marie Stopes International

Marie Stopes South London

1A Raleigh Gardens, Brixton Hill, London SW2 6AB
Tel: 020 8671 1542 Fax: 020 8674 3173
Email: services@stopes.org.uk
Website: www.mariestopes.org.uk
Owners: Marie Stopes International
Total Beds: 16

Merseyside Clinic

32 Parkfield Road, Liverpool L17 8UJ
Tel: 0151 727 1851 Fax: 0151 726950
Owners: BUPA Hospitals Ltd
Total Beds: 30

Mid Yorkshire Nuffield Hospital

Outwood Lane, Horsforth, Leeds LS18 4HP
Tel: 0113 258 8756 Fax: 0113 258 3108
Owners: Nuffield Hospitals
Total Beds: 30

Mount Alvernia Hospital

Harvey Road, Guildford GU1 3LX
Tel: 01483 570122 Fax: 01483 532554
Email: admin@mount-alvernia.co.uk
Owners: Charity/Association
Total Beds: 90

Mount Stuart Hospital

St Vincents Road, Torquay TQ1 4UP
Tel: 01803 313881 Fax: 01803 311185
Owners: Community Hospitals Group plc
Total Beds: 35

New Hall Hospital

Bodenham, Salisbury SP5 4EY
Tel: 01722 422333 Fax: 01722 435158
Owners: Community Hospitals Group plc
Total Beds: 34

The Newcastle Nuffield Hospital

Clayton Road, Jesmond, Newcastle upon Tyne NE2 1JP
Tel: 0191 281 6131 Fax: 0191 212 0163
Email: joanne.hansom@nuffieldhospitals.org.uk
Website: www.nuffieldhospitals.org.uk
Owners: Nuffield Hospitals
Total Beds: 53

North Downs Hospital

46 Tupwood Lane, Caterham CR3 6DP
Tel: 01883 348981 Fax: 01883 341163
Email: enquiries@north-downs-hospital.co.uk
Owners: Community Hospitals Group plc
Total Beds: 24

North London Nuffield Hospital

Cavell Drive, Uplands Park Road, Enfield EN2 7PR
Tel: 020 8366 2122 Fax: 020 8367 8032
Website: www.nuffieldhospitals.org.uk
Owners: Nuffield Hospitals
Total Beds: 45

North Staffordshire Nuffield Hospital

Clayton Road, Newcastle ST5 4DB
Tel: 01782 625431 Fax: 01782 712748
Owners: Nuffield Hospitals
Total Beds: 32

The Nottingham Nuffield Hospital

748 Mansfield Road, Woodthorpe, Nottingham NG5 3FZ
Tel: 0115 920 9209 Fax: 0115 967 3005
Website: www.nuffieldhospitals.org.uk
Owners: Nuffield Hospitals
Total Beds: 60

Oaklands Hospital

19 Lancaster Road, Salford M6 8AQ
Tel: 0161 787 7700 Fax: 0161 787 8097
Email: enquiries@oaklands-hospitals.co.uk
Website: www.capio.co.uk
Owners: Community Hospitals Group plc
Total Beds: 28

The Oaks Hospital

Oaks Place, Mile End Road, Colchester CO4 5XR
Tel: 01206 752121 Fax: 01206 852701
Owners: Community Hospitals Group plc
Total Beds: 57

Old Court Hospital

19 Montpelier Road, London W5 2QT
Tel: 020 8998 2848 Fax: 020 8997 5561
Total Beds: 49

Olivet

17 Sherbourne Road, Acocks Green, Birmingham B27 6AD
Tel: 0121 683 8700
Owners: Charity/Association
Total Beds: 60

The Orchard Hospital

189 Fairlee Road, Newport PO30 2EP
Tel: 01983 520022 Fax: 01983 528788
Total Beds: 30

Park Hill Hospital

Thorne Road, Doncaster DN2 5TH
Tel: 01302 730300 Fax: 01302 322499, 01302 738614
Owners: Community Hospitals Group plc
Total Beds: 21

Parkside Hospital

53 Parkside, Wimbledon, London SW19 5NX
Tel: 020 8971 8000 Fax: 020 8971 8002
Owners: Aspen Healthcare Ltd
Total Beds: 71

Pinehill Hospital

Benslow Lane, Hitchin SG4 9QZ
Tel: 01462 422822 Fax: 01462 421968
Email: Kerry.Elliot@community-hospitals.co.uk
Website: www.community-hospitals.co.uk
Owners: Community Hospitals Group plc
Total Beds: 34

The Plymouth Nuffield Hospital

Derriford Road, Plymouth PL6 8BG
Tel: 01752 775861 Fax: 01752 768969
Owners: Nuffield Hospitals
Total Beds: 41

The Portland Hospital for Women and Children

205-209 Great Portland Street, London W1W 5AH
Tel: 020 7580 4400 Fax: 020 7390 8012
Email: info@portland.hcahealthcare.co.uk
Website: www.theportlandhospital.com
Total Beds: 106

The Princess Grace Hospital

42-52 Nottingham Place, London W1U 5NY
Tel: 020 7486 1234 Fax: 020 7908 2492
Email: info@dghcmc.demon.co.uk

INDEPENDENT HOSPITALS

Owners: PPP/Columbia Healthcare Ltd
Total Beds: 103

The Priory Clinic Cantebury

92B Broad Street, Canterbury CT1 2LU
Tel: 01227 452171 Fax: 01227 452823
Owners: Priory Hospitals Limited

The Priory Clinic Keats House

24/26 St Thomas Street, London SE1 9RS
Tel: 0207 955 4290 Fax: 0207 407 2915
Owners: Priory Hospitals Limited

The Priory Clinic Nottingham

Ransom Road, Nottingham NG3 5GS
Tel: 0115 969 3388 Fax: 0115 969 3388
Owners: Priory Hospitals Limited

Priory Grange

Micklefield Lane, Rawdon, Leeds LS19 6BA
Tel: 0113 239 1999
Total Beds: 22

The Priory Grange

Tottingworth Park, Heathfield TN21 8UN
Tel: 01435 864545 Fax: 01435 865084
Owners: Priory Hospitals Limited

The Priory Hospital Altrincham

Rappax Road, Hale, Altrincham WA15 0NX
Tel: 0161 904 0050 Fax: 0161 980 4322
Owners: Priory Hospitals Limited
Total Beds: 47

The Priory Hospital Bristol

Heath House Lane, off Bell Hill, Stapleton, Bristol BS16 1EQ
Tel: 0117 952 5255 Fax: 0117 952 5552
Website: www.prioryhealthcare.co.uk/heathhouse
Owners: Priory Hospitals Limited
Total Beds: 37

The Priory Hospital Chelmsford

Stumps Lane, Springfield Green, Springfield, Chelmsford CM1 7SJ
Tel: 01245 345345 Fax: 01245 346177
Owners: Priory Hospitals Limited
Total Beds: 42

The Priory Hospital Hayes Grove

Prestons Road, Hayes, Bromley BR2 7AS
Tel: 020 8462 7722 Fax: 020 8462 5028
Website: www.prioryhealthcare.co.uk
Owners: Westminster Health Care Ltd
Total Beds: 50

The Priory Hospital Lancashire

The Priory Manor, Rosemary Lane, Bartle, Preston PR4 0HB
Tel: 01772 691122 Fax: 01772 691246
Website: www.prioryhealthcare.co.uk
Owners: Westminster Health Care Ltd
Total Beds: 24

The Priory Hospital Marchwood

Hythe Road, Marchwood, Southampton SO40 4WU
Tel: 023 8084 0044 Fax: 023 8020 7554
Email: enquiries@prioryhealthcare.co.uk
Website: www.prioryhealthcare.co.uk
Owners: Westminster Health Care Ltd
Total Beds: 47

The Priory Hospital North London

Grovelands House, The Bourne, Southgate, London N14 6RA
Tel: 020 8882 8191 Fax: 020 8447 8138
Email: nlondon@prioryhealthcare.co.uk
Website: www.prioryhealthcare.co.uk
Owners: Westminster Health Care Ltd
Total Beds: 58

The Priory Hospital Roehampton

Priory Lane, Roehampton, London SW15 5JJ
Tel: 020 8876 8261 Fax: 020 8392 2632
Website: www.prioryhealthcare.co.uk/roehampton
Owners: Westminster Health Care Ltd
Total Beds: 103

The Priory Hospital Sturt

Sturts Lane, Walton-on-the-Hill, Tadworth KT20 7RQ
Tel: 01737 814488 Fax: 01737 813926
Email: alisonpleszak@PrioryHealthcare.co.uk
Owners: Westminster Health Care Ltd
Total Beds: 24

The Priory Hospital Woking

Chobham Road, Knaphill, Woking GU21 2QF
Tel: 01483 489211 Fax: 01483 797053
Website: www.prioryhealthcare.co.uk/woking
Owners: Westminster Health Care Ltd
Total Beds: 26

The Priory Ticehurst House

Ticehurst, Wadhurst TN5 7HU
Tel: 01580 200391 Fax: 01580 201006
Email: Ticehurst@whc.co.uk
Website: www.prioryhealthcare.co.uk
Owners: Westminster Health Care Ltd
Total Beds: 95

Purey Cust Nuffield Hospital

Precentors Court, York YO1 7EL
Tel: 01904 641571 Fax: 01904 643115
Website: www.nuffieldhospitals.org.uk
Owners: Nuffield Hospitals
Total Beds: 34

Redford Lodge Hospital

15 Church Street, Edmonton, London N9 9DY
Tel: 020 8956 1234 Fax: 020 8956 1233
Website: www.partnershipsincare.co.uk
Owners: Partnerships in Care Ltd
Total Beds: 61

Renacres Hall Hospital

Renacres Lane, Halsall, Ormskirk L39 8SE
Tel: 01704 841133 Fax: 01704 842030
Owners: Community Hospitals Group plc
Total Beds: 30

The Retreat

107 Heslington Road, York YO10 5BN
Tel: 01904 412551 Fax: 01904 430828
Email: info@retreat-hospital.org
Website: www.retreat-hospital.org
Owners: Charity/Association
Total Beds: 160

The Rivers Hospital

High Wych Road, Sawbridgeworth CM21 0HH
Tel: 01279 600282 Fax: 01279 600212
Owners: Community Hospitals Group plc
Total Beds: 69

Robert Clinic

162 Station Road, Kings Norton, Birmingham B30 1DB
Tel: 0121 458 1483 Fax: 0121 458 4320
Owners: British Pregnancy Advisory Service
Total Beds: 14

Rosslyn Clinic

15-17 Rosslyn Road, East Twickenham, Twickenham TW1 2AR
Tel: 020 8891 3173 Fax: 020 8892 2633
Owners: British Pregnancy Advisory Service
Total Beds: 16

Rowley Hall Hospital

Rowley Park, Stafford ST17 9AQ
Tel: 01785 223203 Fax: 01785 249532
Owners: Community Hospitals Group plc
Total Beds: 15

Royal Hospital for Neuro-disability

West Hill, Putney, London SW15 3SW
Tel: 020 8780 4501 Fax: 020 8780 4500
Email: info@neuro-disability.org.uk
Website: www.neuro-disability.org.uk
Owners: Charity/Association
Total Beds: 273

St Andrew's at Harrow (Bowden House Clinic)

London Road, Harrow-on-the-Hill, Harrow HA1 3JL
Tel: 020 8966 7000 Fax: 020 8864 6092
Owners: Cygnet Healthcare plc
Total Beds: 49

St Andrew's Group of Hospitals

Billing Road, Northampton NN1 5DG
Tel: 01604 616000 Fax: 01604 232325
Email: Admin@standrew.co.uk
Website: www.stah.org.uk
Owners: Charity/Association
Total Beds: 574

St Anthony's Hospital

London Road, North Cheam, Sutton SM3 9DW
Tel: 020 8337 6691 Fax: 020 8335 3325
Email: info@stanthonys.org.uk
Website: www.stanthonys.org.uk
Owners: Privately Owned
Total Beds: 92

St Hugh's Hospital

Peaks Lane, Grimsby DN32 9RP
Tel: 01472 251100 Fax: 01472 251130
Email: admin@hmt-st-hughs.demon.co.uk
Owners: The Hospital Management Trust
Total Beds: 31

St John of God Hospital

Scorton, Richmond DL10 6EB
Tel: 01748 811535 Fax: 01748 812345
Owners: Privately Owned
Total Beds: 92

St John's House

Care Perspectives, Lion Road, Palgrave, Diss IP22 1BA
Tel: 01379 643334 Fax: 01379 641455
Website: www.partnershipsincare.co.uk
Owners: Partnerships in Care Ltd
Total Beds: 55

St Luke's Hospital for the Clergy

14 Fitzroy Square, London W1T 6AH
Tel: 020 7388 4954 Fax: 020 7383 4812
Email: stluke@stlukeshospital.org.uk
Website: www.stlukeshospital.org.uk
Owners: Charity/Association
Total Beds: 22

St Matthew's Private Hospital

St Matthew's Parade, Northampton NN2 7EZ
Tel: 01604 711222 Fax: 01604 711222
Owners: Abbey Hospitals Ltd
Total Beds: 26

St Michael's Hospital

4 Trelissick Road, Hayle TR27 4JA
Tel: 01736 753234 Fax: 01736 753344
Owners: Privately Owned
Total Beds: 91

Shropshire Nuffield Hospital

Longden Road, Shrewsbury SY3 9DP
Tel: 01743 282500 Fax: 01743 247575
Owners: Nuffield Hospitals
Total Beds: 34

Sketchley Hall

Manor Way, Burbage, Hinckley LE10 3HT
Tel: 01455 890023 Fax: 01455 636282
Owners: Westminster Health Care Ltd
Total Beds: 123

Somerset Nuffield Hospital

Staplegrove Elm, Taunton TA2 6AN
Tel: 01823 286991 Fax: 01823 338951
Owners: Nuffield Hospitals
Total Beds: 44

The Springfield Hospital

Lawn Lane, Springfield, Chelmsford CM1 7GU
Tel: 01245 234000 Fax: 01245 234001
Email: enquiries@springfield-hospital.co.uk
Website: www.community-hospitals.co.uk
Owners: Community Hospitals Group plc
Total Beds: 69

Stockton Hall Hospital

The Village, Stockton-on-the-Forest, York YO3 9UN
Tel: 01904 400500 Fax: 01904 400354
Email: info@partnershipsincare.co.uk
Website: www.partnershipsincare.co.uk
Owners: Partnerships in Care Ltd
Total Beds: 106

The Suffolk Nuffield Hospital

Foxhall Road, Ipswich IP4 5SW
Tel: 01473 279100 Fax: 01473 279101
Email: sue.verow@nuffieldhospitals.org.uk
Owners: Nuffield Hospitals
Total Beds: 30

Sussex Nuffield Hospital

Warren Road, Woodingdean, Brighton BN2 6DX
Tel: 01273 624488 Fax: 01273 620101
Owners: Nuffield Hospitals
Total Beds: 56

The Thames Valley Nuffield Hospital

Wexham Street, Wexham, Slough SL3 6NH
Tel: 01753 662241 Fax: 01753 662129
Website: www.nuffieldhospitals.org.uk

INDEPENDENT HOSPITALS

Owners: Nuffield Hospitals
Total Beds: 50

Tunbridge Wells Nuffield Hospital

Kingswood Road, Tunbridge Wells TN2 4UL
Tel: 01892 531111 Fax: 01892 515689
Website: www.nuffieldhospitals.org.uk
Owners: Nuffield Hospitals
Total Beds: 48

Unsted Park Hospital

Munstead Heath, Godalming GU7 1UW
Tel: 01483 892061 Fax: 01483 898858

Warwickshire Nuffield Hospital

The Chase, Old Milverton Lane, Leamington Spa CV32 6RW
Tel: 01926 427971 Fax: 01926 428791
Owners: Nuffield Hospitals
Total Beds: 46

Warwickshire Orthopaedic Hospital

St Gerard's, Coventry Road, Coleshill, Birmingham B46 3EB
Tel: 01675 463242 Fax: 01675 467191
Total Beds: 49

The Wellington Hospital

(Wellington South), 8A Wellington Place, London NW8 9LE
Tel: 020 7586 5959 Fax: 020 7586 1960
Owners: PPP/Columbia Healthcare Ltd
Total Beds: 266

Wessex Nuffield Hospital

Winchester Road, Chandlers Ford, Eastleigh SO53 2DW
Tel: 023 8026 6377 Fax: 023 8025 1525
Owners: Nuffield Hospitals
Total Beds: 42

West Midlands Hospital

Colman Hill, Halesowen B63 2AH
Tel: 01384 560123 Fax: 01384 411103
Owners: Community Hospitals Group plc
Total Beds: 34

Winfield Hospital

Tewkesbury Road, Longford, Gloucester GL2 9WH
Tel: 01452 331111 Fax: 01452 331200
Owners: Community Hospitals Group plc
Total Beds: 47

Wistons Clinic

138 Dyke Road, Brighton BN1 5PA
Tel: 01273 506263 Fax: 01273 562337
Owners: British Pregnancy Advisory Service
Total Beds: 51

Woking Nuffield Hospital

Shores Road, Woking GU21 4BY
Tel: 01483 227800 Fax: 01483 227810
Owners: Nuffield Hospitals
Total Beds: 47

Wolverhampton Nuffield Hospital

Wood Road, Tettenhall, Wolverhampton WV6 8LE
Tel: 01902 754177 Fax: 01902 793292
Owners: Nuffield Hospitals
Total Beds: 41

Women's Secure Services

Annesley House, Mansfield Road, Annesley NG15 0AR
Tel: 01623 727901 Fax: 01623 727911
Email: info@partnershipsincare.co.uk
Owners: Partnerships in Care Ltd

The Woodbourne Priory Hospital

21 Woodbourne Road, Edgbaston, Birmingham B17 8BY
Tel: 0121 434 4343 Fax: 0121 434 3270
Email: woodbourne@prioryhealthcare.co.uk
Owners: Priory Hospitals Limited
Total Beds: 42

Woodland Hospital

Rothwell Road, Kettering NN16 8XF
Tel: 01536 414515 Fax: 01536 412155
Owners: Community Hospitals Group plc
Total Beds: 39

Wye Valley Nuffield Hospital

Venns Lane, Hereford HR1 1DF
Tel: 01432 355131 Fax: 01432 274979
Owners: Nuffield Hospitals
Total Beds: 23

The Yorkshire Clinic

Bradford Road, Bingley BD16 1TW
Tel: 01274 560311 Fax: 01274 551247
Owners: PPP/Columbia Healthcare Ltd
Total Beds: 72

Scotland

Abbey Carrick Glen Hospital

Dallmellington Road, Ayr KA6 6PG
Tel: 01292 288882 Fax: 01292 283315
Email: carrickglen@abbeyhospitals.co.uk
Website: www.abbeyhospitals.co.uk
Owners: Abbey Hospitals Ltd
Total Beds: 22

Abbey Kings Park Hospital

Polmaise Road, Stirling FK7 9PU
Tel: 01786 451669 Fax: 01786 465296
Email: kingspark@abbeyhospitals.co.uk
Website: www.abbeyhospitals.co.uk
Owners: Abbey Hospitals Ltd
Total Beds: 19

Albyn Hospital

21-24 Albyn Place, Aberdeen AB10 1RW
Tel: 01224 595993 Fax: 01224 589869
Total Beds: 44

BMI Ross Hall Hospital

221 Crookston Road, Glasgow G52 3NQ
Tel: 0141 810 3151 Fax: 0141 882 7439
Email: enquiry@rosshall.com
Website: www.rosshalll.com
Owners: BMI Healthcare
Total Beds: 101

Bon Secours Hospital

36 Mansionhouse Road, Langside, Glasgow G41 3DW
Tel: 0141 632 9231 Fax: 0141 636 5066
Owners: Bon Secours Health System
Total Beds: 57

BUPA Murrayfield Hospital - Edinburgh

122 Corstorphine Road, Edinburgh EH12 6UD
Tel: 0131 334 0363 Fax: 0131 334 7338
Email: cserice-ed@bupa.com
Website: www.bupahospitals.co.uk/edinburgh
Owners: BUPA Hospitals Ltd
Total Beds: 65

Erskine Hospital

Bishopton PA7 5PU
Tel: 0141 812 1100 Fax: 0141 812 3733
Owners: Charity/Association
Total Beds: 219

Fernbrae Hospital

329 Perth Road, Dundee DD2 1LJ
Tel: 01382 667203 Fax: 01382 660155
Email: enquires@fernbraehospital.co.uk
Owners: Privately Owned
Total Beds: 26

Glasgow Nuffield Hospital

Beaconsfield Road, Glasgow G12 0PJ
Tel: 0141 334 9441 Fax: 0141 339 1352
Website: www.nuffieldhospitals.org.uk
Owners: Nuffield Hospitals
Total Beds: 48

Marie Curie Centre, Fairmile

Frogston Road West, Edinburgh EH10 7DR
Tel: 0131 445 2141, 0131 445 2142 Fax: 0131 445 5845
Email: med@mcccfairmile.u-net.com
Website: www.mariecurie.org.uk
Owners: Marie Curie Cancer Care
Total Beds: 37

Marie Curie Centre, Hunters Hill

Belmont Road, Springburn, Glasgow G21 3AY
Tel: 0141 558 2555 Fax: 0141 558 0336
Email: info@mariecurie.org.uk
Website: www.mariecurie.org.uk
Owners: Marie Curie Cancer Care
Total Beds: 41

The Priory Hospital Glasgow

38 Mansionhouse Road, Langside, Glasgow G41 3DW
Tel: 0141 636 6116 Fax: 0141 636 5151
Owners: Westminster Health Care Ltd
Total Beds: 32

St Joseph's Service

72 Carnethie Street, Rosewell, Edinburgh EH24 9AR
Tel: 0131 440 7200 Fax: 0131 440 4556
Owners: Privately Owned
Total Beds: 120

Wales

BMI Werndale Hospital

Bancyfelin, Carmarthen SA33 5NE
Tel: 01267 211500 Fax: 01267 211511
Website: www.werndale@bmihealthcare.co.uk
Owners: BMI Healthcare
Total Beds: 28

Brain Injury Services Beechwood House

Beechwood House, Penperlleni, Pontypool NP4 0AH
Tel: 01873 881200 Fax: 01873 881201
Owners: Partnerships in Care Ltd
Total Beds: 18

BUPA Hospital Cardiff

Croescadarn Road, Pentwyn, Cardiff CF2 7XL
Tel: 029 2073 5515 Fax: 029 2073 5821
Owners: BUPA Hospitals Ltd
Total Beds: 66

BUPA Yale Hospital

Wrexham Technology Park, Croesnewydd Road, Wrexham LL13 7YP
Tel: 01978 291306 Fax: 01978 291397
Owners: BUPA Hospitals Ltd
Total Beds: 27

Llanarth Court Hospital

Llanarth, Raglan NP15 2YD
Tel: 01873 840555 Fax: 01873 840591
Email: info@partnershipsincare.co.uk
Website: www.partnershipsincare.co.uk
Owners: Partnerships in Care Ltd
Total Beds: 65

Marie Curie Centre, Holme Tower

Bridgeman Road, Penarth CF64 3YR
Tel: 029 2070 0924 Fax: 029 2071 1070
Email: info@mariecurie.org.uk
Website: www.mariecurie.org.uk
Owners: Marie Curie Cancer Care
Total Beds: 30

North Wales Medical Centre

Queen's Road, Craig-y-Don, Llandudno LL30 1UD
Tel: 01492 879031 Fax: 01492 876754
Owners: Bettercare Group
Total Beds: 32

The Priory Clinic

45 The Parade, Roath, Cardiff
Tel: 029 2049 7123 Fax: 029 2049 7020
Owners: Priory Hospitals Limited

St Joseph's Private Hospital

Harding Avenue, Malpas, Newport NP9 6ZE
Tel: 01633 820300 Fax: 01633 858164
Email: saintjoseph@btclick.com
Owners: Privately Owned
Total Beds: 53

Sancta Maria Hospital

Ffynone Road, Swansea SA1 6DF
Tel: 01792 479040 Fax: 01792 641452
Email: admin@hmt-sancta-maria.demon.co.uk
Owners: The Hospital Management Trust
Total Beds: 33

Northern Ireland

Marie Curie Centre, Belfast

Kensington Road, Belfast BT5 6NF
Tel: 028 9079 4200 Fax: 028 9040 1962
Email: info@mariecurie.org.uk
Website: www.mariecurie.org.uk
Owners: Marie Curie Cancer Care
Total Beds: 19

St John's House and Southern Area Hospice Services

Courtney Hill, Newry BT34 2EB
Tel: 028 3767 711 Fax: 028 3768 492
Owners: Privately Owned
Total Beds: 25

Ulster Independent Clinic

Stranmillis Road, Belfast BT9 5JH
Tel: 028 9066 1212
Owners: Privately Owned
Total Beds: 48

Educational Institutions

Universities and Medical Schools

England

Great Ormond Street Hospital Medical School

30 Guilford Street, London WC1N 1EH
Tel: 020 7242 9789 Fax: 020 7831 0488

Dean R J Levinsky
Secretary I R Middleton

Institute of Child Health

Biochemistry
Lecturer G M Taylor
Reader D P R Muller, B Winchester
Senior Lecturer A W Johnson

Biophysics
Lecturer M King
Professor D G Gadian
Reader S R Williams
Senior Lecturer A Connelly

Cell and Molecular Biology
Lecturer Rosiemarie Dalchau
Professor J W Fabre, R J Levinsky, P Thorogood, M W Turner
Reader R E Callard, A J Copp, S Strobel
Senior Lecturer Patrizia Ferretti, D Goldblatt, K Gustafsson, Christine T Kinnon, N Klein

Child Health and Growth
Lecturer I Dattani, W Van'T Hoff
Professor A Aynsley-Green, J V Leonard, M A Preece
Reader P J Milla
Senior Lecturer P T Clayton, R G Stanhope

Child Psychiatry
Professor D H Skuse

Clinical Biochemistry
Senior Lecturer R W Jones

Dermatology
Senior Lecturer D J Atherton

Developmental Paediatrics
Senior Lecturer Patricia M Sonksen

Haematology and Oncology
Lecturer P Collins, Ruth Leisner
Professor Judith M Chessells
Senior Lecturer F E Cotter

Histochemistry
Professor B D Lake

Histopathology
Lecturer Irene B Scheimberg

International Child Health
Dean C D Marsden
Clinical Sub-Dean N P Quinn
Lecturer Marie-Claude Foster, Susan F Murray
Professor A M Tomkins
Secretary R P Walker
Senior Lecturer A Costello, S MacGregor, Sheila Wirz

Neurology
Professor B G Neville
Senior Lecturer G Jackson, Fennella Kirkham, R A H Surtees

Ophthalmology
Senior Lecturer C Harris

Paediatric Anaesthesia
Professor D J Hatch

Paediatric Cardiology
Professor Glennys Haworth
Senior Lecturer Catharine Bull, J Deanfield

Paediatric Epidemiology
Professor Catherine S Peckham
Senior Lecturer Carol Dezateux, Diane M Gibb, Ruth Gilbert, G S Logan, Marie-Louise Newell, Christine Power, I Roberts

Paediatric Genetics
Professor M E Pembrey, R M Winter
Reader Susan Malcolm, P Scambler
Senior Lecturer Elizabeth Anionwu, Lynn Chitty

Paediatric Nephrology
Professor T M Barratt
Senior Lecturer M J Dillon, A S Woolf

Paediatric Surgery
Professor L Spitz
Senior Lecturer A Pierro

Paediatric Urology
Senior Lecturer P G Ransley

Physiology
Lecturer Susan Hall, R Lane
Senior Lecturer Alison Hislop, Janet Stock

Psychology
Senior Lecturer R Hastings, Farinah V Khadem, Helen R McConachie

Speech Pathology
Lecturer Debbie Sell

Statistics
Lecturer D Dunn, Angela Wade
Reader A E Ades
Senior Lecturer K R Sullivan

Imperial College Faculty of Medicine

Sir Alexander Fleming Building, Imperial College Road, London SW7 2AZ

IMPERIAL COLLEGE FACULTY OF MEDICINE

Tel: 020 7589 5111
Website: www.med.ic.ac.uk

Principal Leszek Borysiewicz
Assistant Secretary, Faculty of Medicine Susan Hartmen
Secretary John T Green

Biomedical Sciences Division (South Kensington Campus)

Biological Chemistry/Molecular Toxicology
Lecturer Elaine Holmes
Professor John Caldwell, Jeremy Nicholson
Reader Nigel J Gooderham
Senior Lecturer Paul L Carmichael, Stephen C Mitchell

Biological Structure and Function
Lecturer Jonathan Bennett
Professor Michael Ferenczi, John Squire
Reader Nancy Curtin
Research Lecturer Pradeep Luther
Senior Lecturer Maggie Lowrie

Cell and Molecular Biology
Professional Research Fellow Charles Coutelle
Professor Leonard Archard, John Couchman, Tony Magee, Roger Mason, Miguel Seabra
Reader Nancy Curtin, Clare Huxley
Research Lecturer Nadia Wahab
Senior Lecturer Angela Clerk, Cheryl Gregory-Evans

Leukocyte Biology
Hon. Senior Lecturer Ian Sabroe
Lecturer Peter Clark, Adele Hartnell, James Pease
Professor Anthony Firth, Tim Williams
Reader Mick Bakhle
Research Lecturer Dolores Conroy
Senior Lecturer Peter Jose, Sara Rankin

Charing Cross Campus

Fulham Palace Road, London W6 8RF
Tel: 020 8383 0000

Cardiology
Head of Section Desmond Sheridan
Clinical Senior Lecturer Nicholas Peters
Lecturer Nicholas Flores

Cardiovascular Medicine
Head of Section Mark Noble
Professor Max Lab
Senior Lecturer Angela Drake-Holland

Clinical Pharmacology
Head of Section Peter Sever
Clinical Lecturer Ben Ariff
Clinical Professor Neil Poulter
Clinical Senior Lecturer Abel Gorchein, Michael Schacter, Simon Thom
Reader Alun Hughes

Haematology
Lecturer S C M Stern, Anna Wood
Professor D A Lane
Senior Lecturer M D Foadi, E J Kanfer, D MacDonald, Diana Samson

Immunology
Hon. Lecturer Nesrina Imami
Hon. Senior Lecturer Donald C Henderson
Lecturer R Aspinall, Jill Gilmour
Professor Frances Gotch
Senior Lecturer E I Larsson-Sciard, R S Pereira

Medical Microbiology
Lecturer K Haynes
Reader D J M Wright
Senior Lecturer A P Roberts

Respiratory Medicine
Head of Section William Seed, S Semple
Clinical Senior Lecturer Christopher Corrigan, Andrew Cummin
Lecturer Susan Smith

Respiratory Physiology
Head of Section Lewis Adams
Clinical Professor A Guz
Lecturer Douglas Corfield

Division of Investigative Science

Professor John Goldman, Myrtle Y A Gordon, David Lane
Reader S M Lewis

Haematology
Lecturer Helga Schneider, Tom Vulliamy
Professor Sally Davies, Junia Vaz de Melo, John Goldman, Myrtle Y A Gordon, David Lane, Irene Roberts, Chris Rudd, Edward Tuddenham, Winifred Watkins, Sunitha Wickramasinge
Reader Jane F Apperley, Barbara Bain, Inderjit Dokal, Mark Layton, S M Lewis, Philip Mason
Senior Lecturer Saad H Abdulla, C M Casimir, Mahes de Silva, Diana Samson, Minou Foadi, Edward Kanfer, Michael Laffan, Donald MacDondald, Amin Rahemtulla, Fiona Regan, Cecil Reid, Nina Salooja, Mallika Sekhar, Abdul Shlebak, Edith Weiner

Histochemistry
Professor Julia Polak
Senior Lecturer A E Bishop, M V Hakkanen

Histopathology
Lecturer Michael Barrett
Professor Malcolm Allison, Dulcie Colman, H Terence Cook, El-Nasir Lalani, Ashley Price, Gordon Stamp
Senior Lecturer Robert D Goldin, P Richman, M Sami Shousha, Marjorie M Walker

Immunology
Lecturer Martin Goodyear, K G Gould
Professor Charles Bangham, Frances Gotch, Stella Knight
Senior Lecturer W Peter Kelleher, Sarah Marshall, Ingrid Muller

Infectious Diseases and Microbiology
Lecturer Michael Jones
Professor Herbert Arst, David W Holden, Thomas Rodgers, Douglas Young
Reader Thomas Evans, Jonathan Friedland, Sunil Shaunak, Christopher Tang
Senior Lecturer Danny Altmann, Kathleen Bamford, I N Brown, Kenneth Haynes, Alison Holmes, Catherine A Ison, Quazi Karim, Shiranee Sriskandan

Metabolic Medicine
Lecturer James Gardiner, Caroline Small, Sarah Stanley
Professor Stephen Bloom
Reader Jamshid Alaghband-Zadeh, Dominic Withers
Senior Lecturer Stephen M Dilworth, Mohammed Ghatei, Samia Girgis, M Karim Meeran, Jeannie Todd

Tissue Engineering
Lecturer Lee Buttery
Professor Julia Polak
Senior Lecturer Anne E Bishop

Virology
Lecturer Richard Greaves
Professor Martin Allday, Paul Farrell, Geoff Smith

UNIVERSITIES & MEDICAL SCHOOLS

Division of Medicine

Cancer Medicine
Lecturer Andrew Chantry
Professor R Charles Coombes, Nicholas Lemoine, Edward Newlands, Jonathan Waxman
Reader B Jones, Michael J Seckl
Senior Lecturer David Kim, John S Stewart, D Vigushin, H Wasan

Care of the Elderly
Professor Christopher Bulpitt
Senior Lecturer Frank Miskelly, C Rajkumar

Clinical Pharmacology
Professor Alan Boobis, Donald Dugin, John MacDermott, Martin R Wilkins
Senior Lecturer H J N Andreyev, G W Taylor

Dermatology
Professor Richard Groves
Senior Lecturer A C Chu

Endocrinology and Metabolic Medicine
Lecturer M Schrey
Professor Desmond Johnston, Mark McCarthy, M J Reed
Reader J C Stevenson, G R Williams
Senior Lecturer A Fairney, D C Parrish

Gastroenterology
Professor R J Playford
Reader J R Walters
Senior Lecturer B P Saunders

Glycobiology
Professor John A Summerfield

Hepatology
Professor Howard C Thomas
Senior Lecturer Graham R Foster, P Karayiannis, Michael McGarvey, Janice Main, S D Taylor-Robinson, Mark R Thursz

Immunology
Professor Robert Lechler, Mary Ritter
Senior Lecturer Andrew J T George, G Lombardi, Hans Stauss, J Wharton

Infectious Diseases
Professor Paul Farrell, G Pasvol, Jonathon Weber
Senior Lecturer I F Godsland, C J N Lacey, Graham P Taylor

Prosthodontics
Professor Darryl Pappin

Renal Medicine
Professor Charles D Pusey
Senior Lecturer E J Clutterbuck, Gillian Gaskin, Elizabeth B Lightstone, A N Warrens

Rheumatology
Professor Mark Walport
Reader Kevin A A Davies
Senior Lecturer M Botto, Robina Coker, R J Festenstein, Bernard Morley, Timothy J Vyse

Division of Neuroscience and Psychological Medicine

Cognitive Neuroscience and Behaviour
Lecturer J Kidd, Deborah Nestel
Professor John Gruzelier
Senior Lecturer Adrian Burgess

Molecular and Integrative Neuroscience
Lecturer M J Hankins, Robert Lucas

Professor Russell Foster

Neuro-Otology
Professor Adolfo Bronstein
Visiting Professor Michael Gresty

Neuroendocrinology
Lecturer Pamela Houston
Professor Julia Buckingham, Christopher Mathias
Reader Glenda Gillies, John Laycock
Senior Lecturer Nigel J Legg

Neurogenetics
Professor John Collinge, Martin Rossor
Senior Lecturer Simon Hawke

Neuroinflammation
Professor Richard Reynolds
Senior Lecturer Martin Croucher, Steven Gentleman, Dr Ling Sun Jen

Neuromuscular Diseases
Professor Jacqueline de Belleroche
Reader Diana J Watt, Dominic J Wells
Senior Lecturer Robert Navarrete

Neuropathology
Clinical Research Fellow Richard Banati
Professor Manuel Graeber

Ophthalmology
Professor Alistair Fielder
Reader Kevin Grebory-Evans
Senior Lecturer Merrick Moseley

Psychiatry
Professor Thomas Barnes, Elena Garralda, Paul Grasby, Steven Hirsch
Professor (Emeritus) R G Priest
Senior Lecturer Christopher Bench, Michael Maier
Senior Research Investigator Isaac Marks

Public Mental Health
Professor Peter Tyrer
Professor (Forensic, St Bernards) Anthony Maden
Reader Thomas Sensky
Senior Lecturer Michael Crawford, James Warner
Senior Lecturer (Child and Adolescent) Elena Garralda

Sensorimotor Systems
Professor Praveen Anand, David Brooks, Peter Ellaway, Christopher Kennard, Richard Wise
Senior Lecturer Peter Bain, Masud Husain

Division of Paediatrics, Obstetrics and Gynaecology

Institute of Reproductive and Developmental Biology
Professor/Director Malcolm Parker

Maternal and Fetal Medicine
Lecturer Nick J Dibb
Professor Philip Bennett, Nicholas Fisk, Philip Steer
Reader John D White
Senior Lecturer Hazem El-rafaey, Allison Elliman, Helena Gardiner, Katherine Hardy, Mark Johnson, Gundrun Moore, P Stanier, Mark H Sullivan, David Williams

Paediatrics
Professor David Edwards, David Harvey, Simon Kroll, Mike Levine, Francisco Muntoni
Reader Martin Brueton, Rodney P A Rivers
Senior Lecturer S Bignall, Mitchell Blair, Frances Cowan, Parviz Habibi, Martin L Hibberd, Gideon Lack, Paul R Langford, H Mehmet,

IMPERIAL COLLEGE FACULTY OF MEDICINE

Neena Modi, Neil Murray, Steve Obaro, M D G Walters, Gareth Tudor Williams

Reproductive Science and Medicine
Professor Stephen Franks, Lesley Regan, Lord Winston
Reader R Margara, William P Souter, J White
Senior Lecturer Jennifer Higham, Vikram Khullar

Division of Primary Care and Population Health Sciences

Epidemiology and Public Health
Lecturer Mark Little, Clare Marshall
Professor David Balding, David Briggs, N Chaturvedi, Paul Elliott, Sylvia Richardson
Reader Michael Joffe, Jon Wakefield
Senior Lecturer Paul Aylin, Nicky Best, Lars Jarup, Marjo-Riitta Jarvelin, Helen Ward

Infectious Disease Epidemiology
Professor Roy Anderson, Neil Ferguson, Brian Spratt
Reader Christl Donnelly, Geoff Garnett
Senior Lecturer Maria-Gloria Basanez, Simon Gregson, Edwin Michael

Medical and Community Genetics
Lecturer Alex Blakemore, Michelle Penny
Professor Anna Kessling
Senior Lecturer Gail Davies

Primary Health Care and General Practice
Lecturer Piers Benn, Elizabeth Muir
Lecturer (Medical Ethics) Richard Ashcroft
Professor Nicholas Bosanquet, George Freeman, Konrad Jamrozik, Brian Jarman
Professor (Medical Ethics) Raanan Gillon
Senior Lecturer Jonathan Fuller

Social Science and Medicine
Lecturer Linda Cusick
Professor Gerry Stimson
Reader David Blane, Adrian Renton
Senior Lecturer Matthew Hickman, Tim Rhodes

Division of Surgery, Anaesthetics and Intensive Care

Anaesthetics and Intensive Care
Professor Mervyn Maze
Reader John A Crowhurst, Anita I Holdcroft
Senior Lecturer Mas Fujinaga, Andrew Rice, Masao Takata
Senior Lecturer (Northwick Park) Douglas Newton

Musculoskeletal Surgery
Professor Andrew Amis, Sean Hughes
Professor (A&E) John A Henry
Senior Lecturer Srinath Kamenini, Jagdeep Nanchahal, Michael Pearse, Rhidian Thomas, Andrew Wallace

Surgical Oncology and Technology
Professor Timothy Allen-Mersh, Ara Darzi, John Northover
Reader (Urology) Paul Abel
Senior Lecturer Stuart Gould, Nagy Habib, Ajay K Kakkar, Timothy Rockall
Senior Lecturer (St Marks) Anton Emmanuel, Simon Gabe

Vascular Surgery
Professor Rodger Greenhalgh
Reader Alun H Davies
Senior Lecturer George Geroulakos

Hammersmith Campus

Du Cane Road, London W12 0NN
Tel: 020 8383 1000

Head of Section Kenneth Taylor
Clinical Senior Lecturer Chandana Ratnatunga, Peter Smith

Cardiovascular Medicine
Head of Section Dorian Haskard
Lecturer Clive Landis
Senior Lecturer John Gibbs, Susanne Nourshargh

Clinical Cardiology
Head of Section Roger Hall
Clinical Senior Lecturer Graham Davies, Peter Nihoyannpopoyulos, Stuart Rosen

Haematology
Lecturer A Shleback
Professor J M Goldman
Reader M Y A Gordon, S M Lewis
Senior Lecturer J F Apperley, N Cross, I Dokal, E Kanfer, M Laffan, P J Mason, I A G Roberts, P Skacel, D Swirsky

Histopathology
Lecturer C E Sarraf
Professor T Krausz, Gordon W H Stamp, J S Wigglesworth
Reader M R Alison, T Cook
Senior Lecturer P D Byers, P Cox, R Goodlad, A Hanby, R Hasserjian, E-N Lacani, I A Lampert, P D Lewis, M N Pignatelli, P Richman, D T Towsley-Hughes

Molecular Medicine
Head of Section James Scott

Respiratory Medicine
Head of Section Philip Ind
Clinical Professor Rory Shaw

Institute of Obstetrics and Gynaecology

Queen Charlotte's Hospital for Women, Goldhawk Road, London W6 0XG
Tel: 020 8383 3922 Fax: 020 8383 1838

Lecturer M de Swiet
Professor Lord Winston

Hammersmith Hospital
Lecturer N Dibb, K Hardy, M H S Sullivan
Professor P Bennett, M G Elder, R M L Winston
Reader W P Soutter, J White
Senior Lecturer L Fusi, R Margara

Obstetrics and Gynaecology
Lecturer C Gilling-Smith, F M E Wadsworth
Professor R W Beard, S Franks
Senior Lecturer L Regan

Queen Charlotte's and Chelsea Hospital
Hon. Senior Lecturer Moyna Barton, T Coltart, D K Edmonds, Vivette Glover, Elizabeth Letsky, J Malvern, J Osborne, C Sims, G W Stephen
Professor P R Bennett, N M Fisk, D R Harvey
Senior Lecturer M de Swiet, Alison M Elliman, D T Hughes, P Johnson, G Moore, P Stanier, J D G Talbert

Kennedy Institute of Rheumatology

Lecturer Andrew Clark
Professor Marc Feldmann, Brian Foxwell, Marco Londei, Ravinder N Maini, Hidiake Nagase, Jeremy Saklatvala, Patrick Venables
Senior Lecturer Fionulla Brennan, Andrew Cope, Yoshifumi Itoh, Peter Taylor

UNIVERSITIES & MEDICAL SCHOOLS

Medical Departments

Head of Department Howard Thomas

Anaesthetics
Lecturer G Lees, R S Sharpe
Professor R M Jones
Senior Lecturer D E F Newton, M W Platt, A Rice

Anatomy and Cell Biology
Lecturer J P Bennett, P Clark, E J Robins
Professor J A Firth
Senior Lecturer M B Lowrie, C Stolinski

Biochemistry
Lecturer R Cotter, E M C Fisher, C M P Huxley
Professional Fellow C Coutelle
Professor J Collinge
Senior Lecturer P C Hirom, P Millburn

Cardiovascular Medicine
Lecturer J R E Kimber, R S More
Professor C J Mathias, D J Sheridan
Senior Lecturer N Peters

Cellular and Integrative Biology
Lecturer S D Head, O M Rutherford, M S Szatkowski, M Whittington
Professor C C Michel
Reader M W Rampling
Senior Lecturer S P Canfield

Clinical Pharmacology
Professor P S Sever
Senior Lecturer A Gorchein, S A M Thom

Epidemiology and Public Health
Professor P Elliott
Senior Lecturer M Boulton, M Joffe, A M Renton, M J A Wadsworth

General Medicine
Lecturer P Karayiannis, M J McGarvey, M C Poznansky, M R Thursz
Professor G Pasvol, P Richards, J A Summerfield, D Taylor-Robinson, H C Thomas, J Weber
Reader J P Monjardino
Senior Lecturer R N Davidson, G R Foster, M S Kapembwa, V S Kitchen, J Main, R J Shaw

General Practice
Lecturer M Wallace
Professor N Bosanquet, B Jarman
Senior Lecturer A Berlin, B Hurwitz, C Salisbury

General Surgery
Hon. Lecturer N J Cheshire, M Gilchick, G Glazer, D J Hadjiminas, R D Rosin
Professor A Darzi, A O Mansfield, A Nicolaides
Senior Lecturer G Stansby

Haematology
Professor S N Wickramasinghe
Senior Lecturer S H Abdalla, B J Bain, H Cohen, E Wiener

Histochemistry
Lecturer A E Bishop
Professor Julia Margaret Polak
Senior Lecturer J Wharton

Histopathology
Professor D V Coleman, D J Evans
Senior Lecturer V Cattell, H T Cook, A M Flanagan, R D Goldin, M M Walker

Immunology
Lecturer C M Hawrylowicz, M R Salaman
Professor C Bangham
Senior Lecturer J Lortan

Medical Microbiology
Lecturer J E R Thole, B M G Wilson
Professor D B Young
Senior Lecturer S P Barrett, I N Brown, C A Ison, Q N Karim, R P F Watkins, J D Williamson

Medicine and Community Genetics
Professor A Kessling

Metabolic Medicine
Lecturer D S Parish, M P Schrey
Professor D G Johnston, M J Reed
Reader G H Tait
Senior Lecturer A Fairney

Molecular Pathology Group
Lecturer A Clerk, G R Coulton, H Y Zhang
Professor L C Archard, R M Mason
Senior Lecturer A K Allen

Neuroscience and Psychological Medicine
Divisional Head C Kennard
Chief of Neurosciences, Chief of Service C Kennard
Consultant T Aziz, A T H Casey, R J Guiloff, A Kennedy, R J M Lane, N Mendoza, R Peatfield, G D Perkin, D Peterson, J M Rice Edwards, R Shaker, J P H Wade
Lecturer J V Bowler
Reader T J Steiner
Senior Lecturer P C Bain, S Hawke

Paediatrics
Lecturer R Booy, J Evans, P Langford
Professor J S Kroll, M Levin
Reader R P A Rivers
Senior Lecturer S Bignall, P Habibi, G Tudor-Williams, M D S Walters

Pharmacology
Lecturer P Carmichael, J Mills
Professor J Caldwell, R L Smith
Senior Lecturer N Goodenham, S Hotchkiss, S C Mitchell

Psychiatry
Lecturer J Kidd
Professor E M Garralda, I C McManus, S A Montgomery, R G Priest, P J Tyrer
Senior Lecturer S Eagger, M Hodes, P L A Joseph

Radiotherapy and Oncology
Professor K Sikora

Statistics
Head S G Thompson
Lecturer R Omar
Professor P Royston
Senior Lecturer B Lausen

Surgery
Director R C N Williamson
Professor S P F Hughes, K Taylor
Reader J Spencer
Senior Lecturer P Abel, M C Beverly, R H H Coombs, H C Crock, J P S England, M J Evans, A J Forester, N Habib, J A Lynn, I McCarthy, R T Mathie, C P Ratanunga, W E Schulenburg, D P Sellu, P L C Smith, N J Standfield, R Strachan, G Williams

Virology and Infectious Disease
Lecturer M D Jones, J Ryan

Professor H Arst, J M Cohen, B E Griffin, D W Holden, T R F Rogers

Senior Lecturer R G Feldman, J S Friedland, K A Haynes, R Koshy, S Shaunak, K N Ward, N Wedderburn

MRC Clinical Sciences Centre

Professor Paolo Camici, Terry Partridge, Elizabeth Simpson
Professor/Director Christopher Higgins

Academic Imaging
Professor David Cosgrove, Richard Underwood
Reader David Firmin
Senior Lecturer Martin Blomley, Walter Curati-Alasonatti, Nandita Desouza, James Jackson, Paola Piccini, Nicola Strickland

National Heart and Lung Institute

Allergy and Clinical Immunology
Lecturer Mark Larche, Sun Ying
Professor A Barry Kay
Senior Lecturer Douglas Robinson

Cardiac Electrophysiology
Professor Nicholas Peters, Nicholas Severs

Cardiology
Lecturer Nicholas Flores
Professor Andrew Coats, Martin R W Cowie, Roger Hall, Steven Marsten, Dudley Pennell, Philip Poole-Wilson, Desmond J Sheridan, Peter Sugden, S R Underwood, Alan Williams, D A Wood
Reader Peter Collins, Sian Harding, Peter Nihoyannopoulos, Peter Nihoyannopoulos
Senior Lecturer J P Bagger, J R Clague, Graham Davies, Stephen Fuller, J S Gibbs, Michael Y Henein, J S Kooner, Nicholas Lefroy, Kenneth Macleod, Stuart Rosen, Rebecca Sitsapesan, George C Sutton

Cardiothoracic Surgery
Lecturer Nigel J Brand, Adrian Chester, Patricia M Taylor, Colin H Wheeler
Professor John Pepper, Kenneth Taylor
Reader P J R Barton, M J Dunn, Marlene Rose
Senior Lecturer Cahdana Ratnatunga, Peter Smith

Cardiovascular Medicine
Professor Paolo G Camici, Dorian Haskard, Max Lab
Senior Lecturer John Gibbs, R Landis, Justin C Mason, Sussan Nourshargh

Clinical Epidemiology
Professor David Wood

Clinical Pharmacology and Therapeutics
Lecturer Joanne Lymn
Professor Alun Hughes, Neil R Poulter, Peter Sever
Reader Simon Thom
Senior Lecturer Abel Gorchein, Michael Schachter

Gene Therapy
Professor Eric Alton
Senior Lecturer John C Davis, Myra Stern

Heart Science (Harefield Hospital)
Professor Magdi Yacoub
Senior Lecturer M Amrani, A Khaghani, Nandor Marczin

Molecular Medicine
Professor James Scott

Occupational and Cardiology
Senior Lecturer T P Cullinan

Paediatric Cardiology
Reader A Bush

Senior Lecturer E Shinebourne

Respiratory Medicine
Lecturer Ian M Adcock, Douglas Corfield, M Giembycz, Susan Gordon, Justin C W Mak, Jane A Mitchell, Susan Smith
Professor Sebastian Johnston, Peter Openshaw, Rory J Shaw
Professor (Upper Respiratory) Stephen Durham
Reader Peter K Jeffery
Senior Lecturer Andrew Cummin, Philip Ind, Meinin Jones, Richard A Knight, Duncan F Rogers, Claire Shovlin

Thoracic Medicine
Professor Peter J Barnes, Kian Fan Chung, T Evans, J Moxham
Professor (Cystic Fibrosis) Margaret Hodson
Senior Lecturer Trevor T Hansel

Recognised Clinical Institutions
Ashford and St Peter's Hospitals NHS Trust, Brent, Kensington, Chelsea and Westminster Mental Health NHS Trust, Central Middlesex Hospital, Charing Cross Hospital, Chelsea and Westminster Hospital, Ealing Hospital, Hammersmith Hospital, Hillingdon Hospital, North West London Hospitals NHS Trust, Royal Brompton Hospital, St Mary's Hospital, West London Mental Health NHS Trust, Westminster Primary Care Trust

King's College London

James Clerk Maxwell Building, 57 Waterloo Road, London SE1 8WA
Tel: 020 7836 5454
Website: www.kcl.ac.uk

Principal A Lucas
Vice-Principal and Dean G Catto
College Secretary and Registrar H T Musselwhite
Assistant College Secretary Jeremy Williams

Guy's, King's and St Thomas' Dental Institute

Medical School Building, Guy's Hospital, London Bridge, London SE1 9RT

Dean N H F Wilson

Community Dentistry, Sedation and Special Care Dentistry
Deputy Head L Zoitopoulos
Head A M Skelly

Conservative Dentistry, Polyclinics and General Practice
Head B G N Smith

Craniofacial Development, Biomaterials
Deputy Head J Nicholson
Head P Sharpe

Dental Public Health and Oral Health Services Research, School of Dental Nursing
Head D Gibbons

Department of Team Care Dentistry
Deputy Head M Woolford
Head S Dunne

Oral and Maxillofacial Surgery, Dental Radiology, Dental Accident and Emergency
Deputy Head M McGurk
Head J D Langdon

Oral Medicine and Pathology, Microbiology and Immunology
Deputy Head D Beighton
Head S J Challacombe

Orthodontics and Paediatric Dentistry
Deputy Head P B Smith
Head M Meikle

UNIVERSITIES & MEDICAL SCHOOLS

Periodontology and Preventive Dentistry, Hygiene School
Deputy Head B M Eley
Head R M Palmer

Prosthetic Dentistry, Technical Schools
Deputy Head D M Davis
Head J D Walter

Guy's, King's and St Thomas' School of Medicine

Dean D Gwyn Williams
Vice-Dean John Moxham
Postgraduate Dean Charles Twort, Jan Welch
Director of Research Alan McGregor
Deputy Director of Research Adrian Hayday

Clinical Laboratory Sciences
Deputy Head Pat Doherty
Head and Head of Haematological Medicine Ghulam Mufti
Clinical Chemistry (Guy's and St Thomas') Ramasamyiyer Swaminathan
Clinical Chemistry (King's) Timothy Peters
Experimental Pathology Pat Doherty
Histopathology Sebastian Lucas, Jonathan Salisbury
Immunobiology Adrian Hayday
Infection Gary French, John Philpott-Howard
Molecular Medicine Farzin Farzaneh

Clinical Neurosciences
Chair of Neuroinflammation Research Group Kenneth Smith
Deputy Head and Head of Neuroimmunology Richard Hughes
Head Nigel Leigh
Clinical Neurophysiology Colin Binnie

Dermatology
Deputy Head (tbc) Antony Young
Head and Head of Inflammation and Therapeutics Jonathan Barker
Cell and Molecular Pathology Robin Eady, John McGrath
Dermatological Immunopathology Martin Black, Eduardo Calonje
Infection and Immunity Rod Hay
Photobiology and Environmental Dermatology John Hawk

General Medicine
Lecturer A G Demaine, J Erusalimsky, R E A Smith
Professor B Hendry, A M McGregor, J F Martin
Senior Lecturer J P Banga, D E H Llewelyn, K W Pettingale, A L Pozniak, D L Scott

Medical and Molecular Genetics
Deputy Head Chris Mathew
Head Ellen Solomon

Medicine
Head Alan McGregor
Cardiology Michael Marber, Ajay Shah
Clinical Sciences John Fabre
Diabetes, Endocrinology and Internal Medicine Bruce Hendry, Steven Sonksen
Healthcare of the Elderly Tony Rudd, Cameron Swift
Hepatology Adrian Bomford
HIV/GUM Philippa Easterbrook, Barry Peters
Oncology (Temp.) Ian Hart
Paliative Care and Policy Irene Higginson
Palliative Care and Policy Julia Addington Hall
Renal Medicine Steven Sacks
Respiratory Medicine and Allergy John Costello, Professor Tak Lee
Rheumatology Gabriel Panayi, David Scott

Primary Care and Public Health Sciences
General Practice and Primary Care Roger Higgs, Roger Jones

Medical and Dental Education Paul Booton, John Rees
Ocupational Medicine David Snashall
Public Health Sciences Peter Burney, Roberto Rona

Psychological Medicine
Deputy Head Thomas Craig
Head Robin Murray

Radiological Sciences and Medical Engineering
Medical Engineering and Physics Colin Roberts, Alan Turner-Smith
Radiological Science Michael Maisey
Radiological Sciences Graeme Taylor

Surgery and Anaesthesia
Head Irving Benjamin
Anaesthesia Orthopaedics Wolfgang Hamann
ENT Michael Gleeson
General Surgery Kevin Burnand

Women's and Children's Health
Child Health Anne Greenough
Obstetrics and Gynaecology Peter Braude

Leicester Warwick Medical School

University of Leicester, School of Medicine, Maurice Shock Medical Sciences Building, PO Box 138, University Road, Leicester LE1 9HN
Tel: 0116 252 2522 Fax: 0116 252 3013
Email: pkj3@leicester.ac.uk
Website: www.lwms.ac.uk

Vice-Chancellor R G Burgess, D Van de Linde
Dean of LWMS I Lauder
Postgraduate Dean P N Johnson
Clinical Vice-Dean D J Taylor
Sub-Dean L Howard
Registrar K J Julian, J Nicholls
Secretary to the Facility N P Siesage
Senior Assistant Registrar C Lindsay

Medicine

Cardiac Surgery
Clinical Lecturer G J Peek
Clinical Professor M Galifianes
Clinical Research Fellow N C Jones, H Vohra
Clinical Senior Lecturer L Hadjinikolaou
Hon. Lecturer S Ghosh
Hon. Senior Lecturer T J Spyt

Cardiology
Clinical Research Fellow R K Singh
Clinical Senior Lecturer G A Ng, P J Stafford, W M Toff
Hon. Senior Lecturer A H Gershlick
Lecturer N Chong
Professor N J Samani

Centre for Studies in Community Health Care
Director A Lennox

Chemical Biochemistry
Professor and Head of Department J Lunec
Lecturer M S Cooke, J V Hunt
Senior Lecturer A Goodall

Child and Adolescent Psychiatry
Clinical Lecturer S K Ganghadaran, K Karim
Clinical Professor P Vostanis
Clinical Senior Lecturer N Dogra, A Parkin

Child Health
Head M Silverman
Clinical Lecturer P Bustani, J P Roper, P Sender

LEICESTER WARWICK MEDICAL SCHOOL

Clinical Professor D J Field
Clinical Research Fellow I M Brookes, A Oommen
Clinical Senior Research Fellow J M Grigg
Hon. Senior Lecturer P W Barry, A Brooke
Lecturer C S Beardsmore, T Ehtezazi
Professor C L P O'Callaghan
Research Fellow W A Stannard
Senior Lecturer S Kotecha, M P Wailoo
Visiting Professor S H Myint

Dermatology

Clinical Professor R D R Camp
Hon. Senior Lecturer R A C Graham-Brown, P E Hutchinson
Lecturer J M Hales

Epidemiology and Public Health

Professor & Head of Department D R Jones
Clinical Lecturer R T H Hsu
Clinical Professor P Burton
Clinical Research Fellow G S Matharu, T D W Smith
Clinical Senior Lecturer J Kurinczuk
Hon. Lecturer M A Eager
Hon. Senior Lecturer R P Assassa, J Barrett, J L Botha
Lecturer M M Dixon-Woods, C E Exley, P C Lambert, A Sutton, N Taub
Professor M Clarke, C Jagger, G Parker
Reader K Abrams
Research Fellow B Shepperdson, M Tobin
Senior Lecturer C W McGrother
Visiting Professor B Crump, L J Donaldson, D Field, J A Lewis, D Machin, I D Young

Forensic Mental Health

Clinical Lecturer J Milton
Clinical Professor C F Duggan
Clinical Senior Lecturer S Davies

Forensic Pathology

Clinical Professor G N Rutty

General Practice and Primary Health Care

Head R C Fraser
Clinical Lecturer G E Aram, C J Barlow, A Enriquez-Puga, A M Hastings, M K Lakhani, P A Lazarus, A K Sood, F J Sutton, J Turner
Clinical Research Fellow A Farooqui
Clinical Senior Lecturer K Khunti, T N Stokes
Hon. Lecturer N Robertson
Hon. Professor J Dale
Hon. Senior Lecturer C McCargow
Lecturer K Stevenson
Professor & Director of CRDU R H Baker
Senior Lecturer R K McKinley, M E Preston-Whyte, S A Redsell, A D Wilson

Haematology

Clinical Professor M Dyer, K J Pasi
Clinical Senior Lecturer S Pavord
Lecturer E L Karran

Histopathology

Clinical Professor and Head of Department R A Walker
Clinical Professor I Lauder
Clinical Senior Lecturer P N Furness, J L Jones, G Saldanha
Lecturer J A Shaw, B Yang
Reader J H Pringle
Senior Lecturer K E Herbert

Medical Education

Professor & Head of Division S A Petersen
Clinical Senior Lecturer in Basic Medical Education D Heney, S Pavord
Clinical Senior Lecturer (Warwick) M J Tweed
Hon. Professor J B Cookson
Hon. Senior Lecturer T Alun-Jones, A Hastings

Lecturer in Anatomy (Warwick) A Stansbie
NHS Community Co-ordinator (Warwick) A Jackson
Senior Lecturer (Leicester) E S Anderson
Senior Lecturer (Warwick) L Maxwell

Medical Genetics

Clinical Professor R C Trembath
Clinical Research Fellow R Harrison
Hon. Lecturer M Barrow, D Duckett
Lecturer C J Talbot

Medical Physics

Professor & Head of Division David H Evans
Hon. Lecturer C Deehan, K Martin
Professor Ronney B Panerai
Reader Mark A Horsfield

Medicine and Therapeutics

Professor & Head of Department H Thurston
Clinical Lecturer A G Stanley
Clinical Professor L L Ng
Clinical Research Fellow I M Loke, R J Westacott, R K M Wong
Clinical Senior Lecturer I B Squire
Hon. Lecturer S Carr, D Ketley, J M Qualie
Hon. Professor E W Hillhouse
Hon. Reader A C Burden
Hon. Senior Lecturer R Bing, J E Davies, M J Davies, J S de Caestecker, T A Howlett, J F Mayberry, M Peake
Lecturer D Lodwick
Professor D B Barnett, B Williams, K L Woods
Senior Lecturer R I Norman

Medicine for the Elderly

Clinical Professor J F Potter
Clinical Research Fellow P Eames, D J Eveson
Clinical Senior Lecturer M D Fotherby, T G Robinson

Microbiology and Immunology

Professor & Head of Department P H Williams
Clinical Professor M Barer, K G Nicholson, H W L Zeigler-Heitbrock
Clinical Senior Lecturer K Rajakumar
Hon. Lecturer S Kilvington, C Stover, A Swann
Hon. Professor M McCrae
Hon. Senior Lecturer M Wiselka
Lecturer A J Cann, P Freestone, S Heaphy
Professor P W Andrew, W D Grant
Reader W Schwaeble
Senior Lecturer M J Browning, P J H Sheldon
University Fellow D Jones
Visiting Professor G J Boulnois, B E Jones

Nephrology

Clinical Lecturer J Barratt, A J P Lewington
Clinical Reader K P G Harris
Clinical Senior Lecturer N J Brunskill
Clinical Senior Research Fellow P Topham
Hon. Professor J Feehally
Hon. Senior Lecturer S J Carr
Lecturer A C Allen, A Bevington

Non-Clinical Appointments (Warwick)

Lecturer H Bradby, C Davis, A Dolan, G Grimshaw, M Hodgkin, C Meyer, R Newton, P Squires, A Withnail
Professor G Hundt, R Stanfield
Senior Lecturer R Blackburn, J Hutton, K Lee, D Spanswick

Obstetrics and Gynaecology

Professor & Head of Department D J Taylor
Clinical Lecturer A Akkad, P C McParland
Clinical Research Fellow A A A Ewies, J P Hodson, F Lockhat
Hon. Lecturer J J S Waugh, I White
Hon. Senior Lecturer Q Davis, C Mayne
Lecturer A H Taylor

UNIVERSITIES & MEDICAL SCHOOLS

Professor S C Bell, A W F Halligan
Senior Lecturer F Al-Azzawi, M A Habiba, J C Konje

Oncology
Professor and Head of Department William P Steward
Hon. Lecturer N Rudd
Hon. Professor A Gescher, L Marshall
Hon. Reader M Manson
Hon. Senior Lecturer A Benghiat, J Botha, M-L Willams
Lecturer G D D Jones, M L Williams
Reader R P Symonds
Senior Lecturer D Heney, K O'Byrne

Ophthalmology
Professor & Head of Department I Gottlob
Clinical Lecturer C M Knapp
Hon. Senior Lecturer J I Prydal, J R Thompson
Lecturer F A L Proudlock
Senior Lecturer G H A Woodruff

Orthopaedic Surgery
Professor & Head of Department W M Harper
Clinical Lecturer R Sharma, A Ullah, S Williams
Clinical Research Fellow M R Acharya
Senior Lecturer C A N Esler, P D Triffit

Pathology
Hon. Senior Lecturer L J R Brown, E C Conley, A Flectcher, P Greaves, K P West, J K Wood

Pre-Clinical Sciences
Director of Human Morphology & Head of Department A P Gulamhusein
Hon. Lecturer D Dinsdale, K Fananapazir
Lecturer H Crick, R Donga, I Fussey, D J Pallot, J Wakely
Professor S A Petersen
Senior Lecturer L Howard, T S Law, W Montague, C D Ockleford, J J A Scott

Psychiatry
Clinical Lecturer M Al-Uzri
Hon. Lecturer J Burke, W Firth
Hon. Senior Lecturer H B Andrews, S Bhaumik, E J Button, M A Nasser
Professor T L Brugha, M A Reveley
Senior Lecturer R L Palmer
Visiting Professor T Fryers, H I Meltzer

Psychiatry for the Elderly
Clinical Professor and Head of Department J E B Lindesay
Clinical Lecturer S Suribhatla
Clinical Senior Lecturer M S Dennis, R J Prettyman

Radiology
Professor & Head of Department G R Cherryman
Hon. Senior Lecturer A Bolia
Senior Lecturer B Morgan

Respiratory Medicine
Clinical Professor A J Wardlaw
Clinical Research Fellow C E Brightling, R Green, R Thomas
Clinical Senior Research Fellow P Bradding
Hon. Lecturer S J Singh
Hon. Senior Lecturer P T C Harrison, M D L Morgan, I D Pavord

Surgery
Professor and Head of Department P R F Bell
Clinical Lecturer D J Adam, P Hayes, I Loftus, M J McCarthy
Clinical Research Fellow A J P Clover, K J Molloy, A Tadros, S Webster
Hon. Lecturer T Horsburgh
Hon. Senior Lecturer J A Cook, P A Evans, A R Naylor, R Sayers, M M Thompson, P S Veitch
Professor N J M London

Reader R F L James
Research Fellow J Evans, K A Gill, N C Jones
Senior Lecturer N P J Brindle

Transplant Surgery
Clinical Lecturer S White
Clinical Professor M L Nicholson
Clinical Research Fellow N R Brook, R M Kimber, D M Ridgway, J Waller

Urology
Clinical Professor J K Mellon
Clinical Research Fellow A J Colquhoun
Lecturer E Tulchinsky

Degrees and diplomas
BMedSci, BSc, MBChB, MSc, Postgrade Certificate/Diploma

Recognised Clinical Institutions
Burton Hospitals NHS Trust, Coventry Health Authority, George Eliot Hospital, Kettering General Hospital NHS Trust, Leicestershire, Rutland and North Leicestershire District, North Warwickshire NHS Trust, Peterborough Hospitals NHS Trust, South Warwickshire Combined Care NHS Trust, South Warwickshire General Hospitals NHS Trust, United Lincolnshire Hospitals NHS Trust, University Hospitals Coventry and Warwickshire NHS Trust, University Hospitals of Leicester NHS Trust

London School of Hygiene and Tropical Medicine

Keppel Street, London WC1E 7HT
Tel: 020 7636 8636 Fax: 020 7436 5389
Website: www.lshtm.ac.uk

Dean A P Haines
Distance Learning Co-ordinator J P Ackers
Research Degrees Programme Director G Walt
Secretary and Registrar W Surridge
Teaching Programme Director S R A Huttly

Epidemiology and Population Health

Head of Department Charles Normand
Departmental Research Degrees Director M G Kenward
Taught Course Director L Clarke

Cancer and Public Health Unit
Head of Unit M P Coleman
Teaching Staff Member I Dos Santos Silva, O Fletcher, C Higgins, G Leydon, H Meller, J Peto

Centre for Population Studies
Head of Unit E Grundy
Teaching Staff Member L Clarke, J Cleland, A B Sloggett, I M Timaeus, B W Zaba

Epidemiology Unit
Head of Unit A E Fletcher
Teaching Staff Member P E Doyle, D Leon, P M Mckeigue, N E S Maconochie, M J Prince

Medical Statistics Unit
Head of Unit D R Elbourne
Teaching Staff Member M I Abdalla, C D Frost, M Kenward, S J Pocock

Public Health Intervention Research Unit
Head of Unit B R Kirkwood
Senior Lecturer T Marshall, I Roberts
Teaching Staff Member S Cousens, C Forst, S Huttly, S Morris

ROYAL FREE & UNIVERSITY COLLEGE MEDICAL SCHOOL OF UNIVERSITY COLLEGE LONDON

Public Health Nutrition Unit
Head of Unit A Ashworth-Hill
Teaching Staff Member S Morris, A Prentice, R Uauy

Infectious and Tropical Diseases

Head of Department H M Dockrell
Departmental Research Degrees Director J A Thomas
Taught Course Director Q D Bickle, L C Rodrigues

Clinical Research Unit
Head of Department D C W Mabey
Teaching Staff Member R Bailey, P Godfrey-Faussett, P Mayaud, J D H Porter

Disease Control and Vector Biology Unit
Head of Unit C R Davies
Teaching Staff Member A M Cairncross, C Curtis, B Greenwood, J Lines, M Rowland, C Shulman, G A T Targett

Immunology Unit
Head of Unit E M Riley
Teaching Staff Member G J Bancroft, Q D Bickle, S L Croft, H M Dockrell, P Kaye, M G Taylor, J A Thomas

Infectious Disease Epidemiology Unit
Head of Unit S N Cousens
Teaching Staff Member U Blumenthal, O Campbell, J Glynn, A Hall, R Hayes, S Jaffar, T Marshall, N Noah, J Whitworth

Pathology Molecular Biology and Biochemistry Unit
Head of Unit M Miles
Teaching Staff Member C Clark, U Gompels, J M Kelly, P Roy, D C Warhurst

Public Health and Policy

Head of Department Nick Black
Departmental Research Degrees Director M Thorogood
Taught Course Director N Thorogood

Environmental Epidemiology Unit
Head of Unit J A Dowie
Teaching Staff Member B G Armstrong, A C Fletcher, P Wilkinson

Health Policy Unit
Head of Unit B I McPake
Teaching Staff Member D C Arhin, R Brugha, J A Fox-Rushby, L J Gilson, D K Lee-Gilmore, A J Mills, G A Walt, C H Watts

Health Promotion Research Unit
Head of Unit S Hagard
Teaching Staff Member V Berridge, M Hillson, A Kessel, W McDowell, M Thorogood, N Thorogood, K Wellings

Health Services Research Unit
Head of Unit A M Rafferty
Reader J A Roberts
Teaching Staff Member N A Black, A E Clarke, R Danziger, J M Green, D L Lamping, C M McKee, I G Reeves, C F B Sanderson, M G Traynor

Royal Free and University College Medical School of University College London

Gower Street, London WC1E 6BT
Tel: 020 7679 2000 Fax: 020 7383 2462
Website: www.ucl.ac.uk

Dean of the Faculty of Life Sciences A R Lieberman
Dean of the Medical School and Faculty of Clinical Sciences K M Spyer

Vice-Dean and Campus Director D I Patterson
Vice-Dean and Campus Director (RF) H Hodgson
Faculty Sub-Dean R Armstrong, D A Bender, M Berelowitz, C Bielawska, D Brenton, B Cross, G Hamilton, D Jordan, M Lloyd, R Noble, F D Thompson
Faculty Graduate Tutor V Emery
Faculty Tutor B Cross, N Woolf

Bloomsbury Campus

Gower Street, London WC1E 6BT
Tel: 020 7679 2000

CRC and UCL Cancer Trials Centre
Senior Lecturer J Houghton

Epidemiology and Public Health
Lecturer J Adda, A R Britton, Y J Kelly, P Primatesta, G Tsakos
Professor M Bartley, J H Fuller, M J Jarvis, M McCarthy, M G Marmot, M A Russell, S J Senn, A P A Steptoe, S R Sutton, F J Wardle
Reader D J L Kuh, J Y Nazroo
Senior Lecturer P A Batchelor, M Bobak, E J Brunner, H M Colhoun, J A Head, W S Marcenes, M J Shipley, R G Watt

Haematology
Lecturer M Nash
Professor A H Goldstone, D C Linch, S J Machin, J B Porter
Reader S Mackinnon
Senior Lecturer S D'Sa, R E Gale, A Khwaja, I J Mackie, S Mackinnon, A Nathwani, K L Yong

Histopathology
Lecturer A A Freeman
Professor P G Isaacson
Reader M Q Du, A M Flanagan
Senior Lecturer E Benjamin, A Dogan, M H Griffiths, G Kocjan, P P Osin, R J Scott

Immunology and Molecular Pathology
Lecturer S Chowdhury, R S Coffin, S J Dawson, L T C Ho
Professor B M Chain, M K L Collins, D R Katz, P M Lydyard, T W Rademacher, R A Weiss, P M M Woo
Reader P J Delves, W D C Lawson, T Lund, N J Marshall

Institute of Laryngology and Otology
Professor A Forge, D T Kemp, V J Lund, D K Prasher, A Wright
Senior Lecturer H C Dodson, D J Howard

Institute of Nuclear Medicine
Lecturer S Gacinovic
Professor P J Ell
Reader D C Campos Costa
Senior Lecturer I D Cullum, G Davies

Institute of Orthopaedics and Musculoskeletal Science
Lecturer M J K Bankes, H L Birch, M J Coathup, L Di-Silvio, J Hua, V Mudera
Professor G W Blunn, M W Ferguson-Pell, A E Goodship
Senior Lecturer R W Keen, J A M Skinner

Leopold Muller Centre for Child and Family Psychiatry
Lecturer C Hoyos
Senior Lecturer J Barnes, R Senior

Medical Microbiology
Professor G A W Rook, J L Stanford
Reader J M Holton
Senior Lecturer H D Donoghue

Medicine
Lecturer J C Achermann, R A Breckenridge, B Clapp, S L Cohen, N A Davies, D M Flavell, P A Glynne, S Hodges, S Kinloch
Professor D J Betteridge, P M Dowd, J C W Edwards, L G Fine, J Godovac-Zimmermann, M A Horton, S E Humphries, D A Isenberg,

UNIVERSITIES & MEDICAL SCHOOLS

G J Laurent, W R Lees, J F Martin, A W Segal, M Singer, S G Spiro, R J Unwin, P J T Vallance, D Vergani, R S Williams, D M Yellon, A Zumla

Reader A A Bertoletti, P C Hindmarsh, M Kitamura, R J McAnulty, J R McEwan, R F Miller, N V Naoumov, P Talmud, A Tinker, I C Zachary

Senior Lecturer H F Baxter, G J Bellingan, M R Ehrenstein, J D Erusalimsky, A R Gillams, R W Groves, A D Hingorani, R Jalan, R J MacAllister, R A K Mageed, H E Montgomery, J T Norman, C W I Owens, G Prelevic, M A A Rahman, C C T Smith, G W Stewart, A Wagg

MRC Clinical Trials Unit

Reader D M Gibb

Senior Lecturer M H Hooker

Obstetrics and Gynaecology

Lecturer J A Hyett, F Shenfield

Professor J D A Delhanty, J Guillebaud, C H Rodeck

Reader E R M Jauniaux

Senior Lecturer J Harper, M Katz, R Noble, D M Peebles, G Raivich

Oncology

Professor P C L Beverley, C H Boshoff, J A Hartley, M I Saunders

Reader P J Hoskin, J A Ledermann

Senior Lecturer J A Bridgewater

Paediatrics and Child Health

Lecturer T Austin, R Chodhari, C R Fertleman

Professor R M Gardiner, J S Wyatt

Senior Lecturer H M E Bantock, E M K Chung, H M Mitchison, S E Mole, M Rees, S C Roth

Psychiatry and Behavioural Sciences

Lecturer L B Myers, L M M Noble, A L Sandor, T G Stevens, A Strydom

Professor P E Bebbington, H M Gurling, R P Hobson, C L E Katona, R M Littlewood, S P Newman, M M Robertson, G N Scambler

Reader C Feinmann, G A Livingston, M W Orrell

Senior Lecturer L C Bailly, P T Byrne, J E Carter, S L Dein, A Hassiotis, P F Higgs, S S Jadhav, I S Johnson, J M Moncrieff, J A Thompson, Z Walker

Reta Lila Weston Institute of Neurological Studies

Professor A J Lees

Senior Lecturer D S Holder

School of Podiatry

Lecturer J Mooney, B Nolan, M T Sullivan, M Wood

Senior Lecturer A S H Wilson, A R Wood

Sexually Transmitted Diseases

Lecturer A J Copas, P J Newton, J E Richens

Professor M W Adler, A G Babiker, J H Darbyshire, A M Johnson, I V D Weller

Senior Lecturer F M Cowan, K A Fenton, R J C Gilson, A C Hayward, M K Maini, D E Mercey, R M Power, J M Stephenson, I G Williams

Surgery

Lecturer M Douek, M V Dwek, S J Hollingsworth, F J Savage, J S Vaidya

Professor P B Boulos, S G Bowen, C J Green, M J O'Hare, J M Ryan, I Taylor

Reader R A Brown, P D Coleridge-Smith, M A Edgar, B J Fuller

Senior Lecturer S G E Barker, L M Bromley, E J Chaloner, J T Chowaniec, J A Hulf, M R Keshtgar, A J Leathem, M C Loizidou, A J MacRobert, J R C Sainsbury, J H Scurr, A M Seifalian

Urology and Nephrology

Professor J R W Masters, A R Mundy, G H Neild

Reader C R J Woodhouse

Senior Lecturer M Emberton, S J Harland, M C Parkinson, P J R Shah

Virology

Lecturer D Hudson, J W T Tang

Professor M D Craggs, C H Fry, R S Tedder

Senior Lecturer P J D Foxall, J A Garson

Eastman Dental Institute for Oral Health Care Science

256 Gray's Inn Road, London WC1X 8LD
Tel: 020 7915 1000
Website: www.eastman.ucl.ac.uk

Dean and Director of Studies and Research C Scully

Sub-Dean G A Dunk, P N Holliday

Biostatistics

Lecturer D R Moles

Senior Lecturer A Petrie

Conservation

Lecturer J Mount, Y L Ng, S Rahbaran, D A Spratt

Senior Lecturer K Gulabivala, D J Setchell

Continuing Dental Education

Lecturer G E Evans, G R Finn, K P Hoffernan, B Mizrahi

Senior Lecturer A H Croysdill, R K Raja Rayan, A N S Stokes

Dental and Medical Informatics

Professor P Hammond

Dental Materials

Lecturer F H Jones, S N Nazhat, A M Young

Reader J C Knowles

Senior Lecturer J A Williams

Implantology

Lecturer D P Atel, M C Haswell, C G P Manhem

Professor S Sindet-Pedersen

Microbiology

Lecturer R McNab

Professor M Wilson

Senior Lecturer P Mullany

Oral and Maxillofacial Surgery

Lecturer B Aghabeigi, M A Bamber, C Hopper, S P Nair

Professor B Henderson

Reader S Meghji

Senior Lecturer A W Evans, C Feinmann

Oral Medicine

Lecturer R G Hadland, R G Madland

Professor S R Porter, C M Scully

Oral Pathology

Lecturer J H Bennett, S A Whawell

Professor P M Speight

Senior Lecturer A W Barrett

Orthodontics

Lecturer M P Lewis, H L Tippett

Professor N P Hunt

Senior Lecturer S J Cunningham

Paediatric Dentistry

Lecturer P F Ashley, M J Golbier

Professor G J Roberts

Senior Lecturer A M Bloch-Zupan

Periodontology

Lecturer P M Brett, N Donos, I G Needleman

Professor I Olsen, M Tonetti

ROYAL FREE & UNIVERSITY COLLEGE MEDICAL SCHOOL OF UNIVERSITY COLLEGE LONDON

Senior Lecturer G S Griffiths, L F H Laurell

Prosthetics

Professor J A Hobkirk
Senior Lecturer P G T Howell, J A Howlett

Radiology

Lecturer J E Brown

Transcultural Oral Health

Lecturer E L Dini
Professor R Bedi
Senior Lecturer N Gulsati

Faculty of Life Sciences

Anatomy and Development Biology

Lecturer D Becker, S Bhattacharya, K P Giese, V Lo, K Nobes, J P Simons, D Whitmore
Professor P N Anderson, G G Burnstock, L W F Bynum, H Cook, S W Davis, M C Dean, M Fitzgerald, G Gabella, G Goldspink, S Hunt, K Jessen, C J Lawrence, A R Lieberman, R Mirsky, V Nutton, P O'Higgins, J O'Keefe, J G Parnavelas, C D Stern, A E Warner, L Wolpert, S M Zeki
Reader T Arnett, J Browne, N Burgess, L Conrad, T Cowan, L Dale, S E Evans, A Hardy, P Martin, F Spoor, K Swan, E M Tansey, S Wilson, C H Yeo
Senior Lecturer J D W Clarke, J E Cook, T Cowan, B P Fulton, I Johnson, M Neve, M Rosendaal, J Scholes, J P Simmons, A Wear

Biochemistry

Lecturer E M Chance, R K Cramer, A Dingley, S Djordjevic, R E Drew, I T Gout, S Naaby-Hansen, A Townsend-Nicholson, D J Williams, M Zvelebil
Professor J P Brockes, K R Bruckdorfer, A L Burlinghame, A Hall, C A Orengo, L H Pearl, S J Perkins, P W Piper, E D Saggerson, E A Shephard, P F Swann, J M Thornton, M D Waterfield
Reader M D Crompton, P Jat, J Mowbray, A Ridley
Senior Lecturer D A Bender, P C Driscoll, A E Michael, P R Shepherd, S K S Srai, J M Ward, H A White, D J Williams

Biology

Lecturer H J P Richards, A Ruiz-Linares, H Smith
Professor C Danpure, M C Evans, D B Goldstein, J S Hyams, J S Jones, J Mallet, J H A Nugent, L Partridge, A Pomiankowski, M S Povey, M Raff, P R Rich, W D Richardson, R J Rowbury, J N Wood, Z Yang
Reader A M Lister, S Purton, J Wolfe
Senior Lecturer J P Field, K Fowler, S E Mole, A P Mudge, C W Mullineaux, J Pearson, T M Preston, R N Strange, M Thomas, J B Wood, R S Wotton

Gatsby Computational Neuroscience Unit

Lecturer Z Ghahramani
Reader P Dayan, Z Li

Human Communication Science

Lecturer C J Bruce, L J Cavelli, A L Constable, J Donkovicova, A S Edmundson, S Martin, L Nathan, R I Rees, C Smith, M A Vance
Professor R Campbell, H Van der Lely
Reader S Chiat
Senior Lecturer W Best, M Black, C Donlan, A Goulandris, M Kersner, M Mahon, J Maxim, A Parker, J Swettenham, R Wilkinson, J Wright

Pharmacology

Lecturer T D Carter, M Farrant, N Millar, S Nurrish, J Pitcher, M Stocker, D Willis
Professor D A Brown, D Colquhoun, S G Cull-Candy, A H Dickenson, A C Dolphin, J C Foreman, J Garthwaite, S J Moss, T Smart
Reader A J Gibb, A G Ramage, R Schoepfer, S C Stanford
Senior Lecturer D G Haylett, I Marshall, G W J Moss, T Sihra

Physiology

Lecturer J Carroll, S Casalotti, D McAlpine, P Milner, P Pedarzoni, R E A Tunwell
Professor J F Ashmore, D I Attwell, S Bolsover, S Cockcroft, M R Duchen, C H Fry, D Jordan, P G Mobbs, C D Richards, K M Spyer, J A Stephens, A M Thomson, R J Unwin, R C Woledge, D M Yellon
Reader L J Bindman, E S Debnam, F A Edwards, A R Gardner-Medwin, M P Gilbey, J V Halliwell, B Lynn, P E R Tatham
Senior Lecturer K W T Caddy, B A Cross, J P Fry, L M Harrison, P J Harrison, B F King, A Koffer, R Noble, P M I Sutton

Psychology

Lecturer R R Benedyk, R J R Blair, P Cairns, L Clare, K Jeffery, H Joffe, K Langley, K Scior, M L Solms, M Steele, P Stenner, G Vigliocco, J Ward
Professor J Atkinson, C Brewin, B L Butterworth, H V Curran, J S Driver, P Fonagy, U Frith, A F Furnham, N J W Harvey, C Heyes, P Howell, A Johnston, I C McManus, H C Plotkin, M Rugg, T Shallice, D R Shanks, H Thimbleby, C Vincent
Reader P Burgess, S Channon, N Lavie
Senior Lecturer C B Barker, S Butler, D F Einon, M Ennis, N Frederickson, D W Green, P Haggard, P K Lunt, A G R McClelland, D A Oakley, N E Pistrang, R E Rawles, A Schlottmann, H Steele, M Target

Institute of Child Health

30 Guilford Street, London WC1N 1EH
Tel: 020 7242 9789 Fax: 020 7831 0488
Website: www.ich.ucl.ac.uk

Dean D S Latchman
Vice-Dean for Clinical Research and Development A Aynsley-Green
Vice-Dean for Education and Training S Strobel

Behavioural and Brain Sciences (Neurosciences and Mental Health Theme)

Professor U Goswami, D H Skuse
Senior Lecturer T Charman

Biochemistry, Endocrinology and Metabolism (Biochemical and Nutritional Sciences Theme)

Professor (Head of Unit) B Winchester
Lecturer J Achermann, S Eaton, K Hussain, S Rahman, O Williams
Professor A Aynsley-Green, P Clayton, J Leonard, M Preece, J Wyatt
Reader P Hindmarsh, D Muller
Senior Lecturer M Dattani

Cardiac (Cardiorespiratory Sciences Theme)

Professor J Deanfield
Senior Lecturer C Bull

Children's Nursing and Allied Health Professional Research (Cardiorespiratory Sciences Theme)

Lecturer F Gibson, E Main
Professor L Franck

Clinical and Molecular Genetics (Genes, Development and Disease Theme)

Lecturer S Feather, K Woodward
Professor S Malcolm, M E Pembrey, R Winter
Senior Lecturer M Bitner-Glindzicz, L Chitty, I Hopkinson

Developmental Biology (Neurosciences and Mental Health Theme)

Lecturer S J Chan, J Sowden
Reader P Ferretti

Developmental Cognitive Neuroscience (Neurosciences and Mental Health Theme)

Lecturer M de Hann
Professor F Vargha-Khadem
Senior Lecturer T Baldeweg

UNIVERSITIES & MEDICAL SCHOOLS

Developmental Vascular Biology and Pharmacology (Cardiorespiratory Sciences Theme)
Lecturer P Boels, S M Hall
Professor G Howarth
Reader A A Hislop

Immunobiology (Infection and Immunity Theme)
Professor R Callard, J Harper, S Strobel, M W Turner
Reader D Goldblatt, N Klein

Infectious Diseases and HIV (Infection and Immunity Theme)
Reader N Klein

International Child Health (Population Health Sciences Theme)
Lecturer S Filteau, M-C Foster, S Murray
Professor A Costello, S McGregor, A Tomkins
Senior Lecturer K Sullivan, S Wirz

International Prenatal Care (Population Health Sciences Theme)
Lecturer S Murray
Professor A Costello

Medical Molecular Biology (Genes, Development and Disease Theme)
Lecturer V Budhram-Mahadeo, M Payne-Smith, A Stephanou
Professor D Latchman
Senior Lecturer A Matilla

Molecular Embryology (Genes, Development and Disease Theme)
Professor M Monk

Molecular Haematology and Cancer Biology (Cancer Theme)
Lecturer J Anderson, M Hubank, O Williams
Professor J M Chessells
Reader H Brady, P Brickell
Senior Lecturer J Ham, Dr Price, A Sala

Molecular Immunology (Infection and Immunity Theme)
Lecturer R Ali, B Gaspar, H White
Professor C Kinnon, R Levinsky
Reader K Gustafsson, A Thrasher
Senior Lecturer S Hart

Molecular Medicine (Genes, Development and Disease Theme)
Lecturer P Beales, F Goodman, P Riley
Professor P Scambler

Nephro-Urology (Genes, Development and Disease Theme)
Lecturer S A Feather, H T Yuan
Professor M J Dhillon, A S Woolf
Senior Lecturer P G Ransley, P J D Winyard

Neural Development (Neurosciences and Mental Health Theme)
Lecturer N Greene
Professor A Copp
Senior Lecturer A Burns, A Stoker

Neurocognitive Development (Neurosciences and Mental Health Theme)
Professor A Karmiloff-Smith

Neurosciences (Neurosciences and Mental Health Theme)
Lecturer V Ganesan, I Newsom-Davis
Professor R Guerrini, L M Luxon, B G R Neville
Reader R A H Surtees
Senior Lecturer J H Cross, F J Kirkham

Nutrition (Biochemical and Nutritional Sciences Theme)
Lecturer J Wells
Professor A Lucas
Reader D Muller
Senior Lecturer V Carnielli, M Lawson, A Sunghal

Paediatric Epidemiology and Biostatistics (Population Health Sciences Theme)
Lecturer J Rahi
Professor T Cole, M L Newell, C Peckham, C Power
Reader C Dezateux
Senior Lecturer M C Borja, R Gilbert, S Logan, A Wade

Portex Anaesthesia, Intensive Therapy and Respiratory Medicine (Cardiorespiratory Sciences Theme)
Professor D Harch, J Stocks
Senior Lecturer C Dezateux

Radiology and Physics (Neurosciences and Mental Health Theme)
Lecturer F Clamante, V Ganesan, M King, M Lythgoe, R Scott
Professor D Gadian, I Gordon, A Todd-Pokropek
Reader A Connelly

Rheumatology (Infection and Immunity Theme)
Lecturer Bin Gao
Professor P Woo
Senior Lecturer Lucy Wedderburn

Surgery (Biochemical and Nutritional Sciences Theme)
Lecturer D M Albert, C M Bailey, M Calvert, D Drake, S Eaton, R D Evans, R Hill, S Hill, D James, B M Jones, D H Jones, E Kiely, S Leighton, K Lindley, M Mars, F Monsell, L Newman, M Noordeen, P Smith, B Sommerlad
Professor P Milla, A Pierro, G Roberts, L Spitz
Senior Lecturer D Sell

Visual Sciences (Neurosciences and Mental Health Theme)
Lecturer J Rahi
Senior Lecturer D Taylor

Institute of Neurology

Queen Square, London WC1N 3BG
Tel: 020 7837 3611
Website: www.ion.ucl.ac.uk

Dean R S J Frackowiak
Clinical Sub-Dean N P Quinn
Secretary R P Walker

Clinical Neurology
Lecturer H Cock, C Good
Professor M M Brown, J Collinge, J S Duncan, D R Fish, C J Fowler, R S J Frackowiak, P J Goadsby, M Koltzenburg, D M Kullmann, C J Mathias, D H Miller, N P Quinn, M N Rossor, J W A Sander, A H V Schapira, S D Shorvon, A J Thompson, N W Wood
Reader P Brown
Senior Lecturer K Bhatia, G Giovannoni, M Hanna, H Kaube, M Koepp, P D Limousin, P N Patsalos, E D Playford, J Rees, M Reilly, S M Sisodiya, D J Thomas

Miriam Marks Division of Neurochemistry
Professor B Clark, M L Cuzner, E Fisher, L Lim, E J Thompson
Reader C Hall, J M Land
Senior Lecturer J M Pocock

Neuropathology
Lecturer M Groves
Professor F Scaravilli
Reader T Revesz
Senior Lecturer J Holton, M Thom

Neuropsychiatry and Neuropsychology
Lecturer A Schrag

ROYAL FREE & UNIVERSITY COLLEGE MEDICAL SCHOOL OF UNIVERSITY COLLEGE LONDON

Professor R Dolan, K J Friston, C D Frith, M Ron, M R Trimble
Reader C J Price

Neuroradiology and Neurophysics

Lecturer S Free
Professor P S Tofts, R Turner, T Yousry
Reader H-R Jaeger, L Lemieux

Neurosurgery

Lecturer T J Warr
Professor D G T Thomas
Senior Lecturer L D Watkins

Sobell Division of Neurophysiology

Lecturer L Greensmith
Professor H Bostock, R N Lemon, J Rothwell
Reader P A Kirkwood, D Wolpert
Senior Lecturer A H Pullen

Institute of Ophthalmology

11-43 Bath Street, London EC1V 9EL
Tel: 020 7608 6800
Website: www.ucl.ac.uk/ioo/

Director A M Silito

Cell Biology

Lecturer M Bailly, M S Balda, C E Futter, T P Levine
Professor J Greenwood, S E Moss
Reader P Adamson, K Matter

Clinical Ophthalmology

Lecturer V Calder
Professor A C Bird, S L Lightman

Epidemiology and International Child Health

Lecturer J S Rahi
Professor G J Johnson
Reader P Minassian
Senior Lecturer C Gilbert

Inherited Eye Disease

Professor A T Moore

Molecular Genetics

Lecturer L Erskine, A J Hardcastle
Professor S S Bhattacharya, D M Hunt
Reader A P Ali
Senior Lecturer M Meyer

Ocular Immunology

Lecturer K-Y Chau
Professor S J Ono

Pathology

Lecturer M E Cheetham
Professor P T Khaw, P J Luthert

Rehabilitation

Lecturer P Bex
Professor G Rubin

Visual Science

Lecturer S C Dakin, R B Lotto, S L Macknik, S Martinez-Conde
Professor J K Bowmaker, F Fitzke, T E Salt, A M Sillito, A Stockman
Senior Lecturer G Jeffery

Royal Free Campus

Royal Free and University College Medical School, Rowland Hill Street, London
Tel: 020 7794 0500

Vice-Dean and Campus Director H Hodgson

Clinical Neurosciences

Lecturer J W Taanman, P A Wilkinson
Professor A H V Schapira
Senior Lecturer J M Cooper, C A Davie, R W Orrell, T T Warner

Haematology

Lecturer R J Anderson
Professor H G Prentice
Reader L Foroni, P J Travers
Senior Lecturer T R Jackson, M W Lowdell, D J Perry, M N Potter, R G Wickremasinghe

Histopathology

Lecturer N Al-Saffar, N Prasad, A F G Quaglia, H Wang
Professor A P Dhillon, P A Revell
Senior Lecturer A Anthony, J C Crow

Immunology and Molecular Pathology

Lecturer I Vorechovsky
Professor A N Akbar, G Janossy, L W Poulter
Reader D P Mikhailidis
Senior Lecturer P L Amlot, M R Dashwood

Medical Microbiology

Lecturer I Balakrishnan, B M Charalambous, T D McHugh
Professor S H Gillespie, J M T Hamilton-Miller
Senior Lecturer J N Zuckerman

Medicine

Lecturer S Behboudi, P Collins, A A O Fagbemi, H J Latchmann, X Z Ruan, A C Selden, G A Tennent
Professor G M Dusheiko, P N Hawkins, H J F Hodgson, R E Pounder, S H Powis
Reader D J Abraham, P M G Boulox, J S Dooley, T J Harrison, M Y Morgan
Senior Lecturer S Al-Damluji, C P Denton, S Keshav, K P Moore, J S Owen, A P Walker, D Wheeler

Obstetrics and Gynaecology

Lecturer W U Atiomo, C W Perrett, K Singh
Professor A B Maclean
Senior Lecturer P J J Hardiman

Oncology

Professor R H J Begent
Senior Lecturer K A Chester, D Hochhauser, S M Wilkinson

Paediatrics and Child Health

Lecturer K L Moshal
Professor B W Taylor
Senior Lecturer C Morgan, S H Murch, A G Sutcliffe

Primary Care and Population Science

Lecturer S J Conaty, D Gill, M M Jones, D L Kirklin, F C Lampe, A J Mocroft, A Selwyn, S Singh, F A Stevenson
Professor A N Phillips, P G Wallace
Reader M H Lloyd, C A Sabin
Senior Lecturer M H Leighton, R P Meakin, R W Morris, J J Rosenthal, N B D Towson, M K Walker

Psychiatry and Behavioural Sciences

Lecturer J Pimm, C W Ritchie
Professor M B King
Senior Lecturer M R Blanchard, J Dunn, D V James, K J Mckenzie, P W Raven, M A Serfaty, S R Weich

Surgery

Lecturer S Wajed
Professor B R Davidson, M C Winslet
Senior Lecturer O A Ogunbiyi

Virology

Lecturer P Balfe, D A Clark
Professor V C Emery, P D Griffiths, C Loveday

UNIVERSITIES & MEDICAL SCHOOLS

Whittington Campus

Royal Free and University College Medical School, Highgate Hill, London N19 5NF
Tel: 020 7272 3070

Vice-Dean and Campus Director D Patterson

CHIME

Lecturer J Durbridge, J E Richardson, P M Taylor
Professor S P Bate, J E Dacre, D Ingram, I C McManus, L J Southgate
Reader J Radcliffe Richards
Senior Lecturer J D Cartledge, J Murphy

Medicine

Lecturer R Gray, V Mohamed Ali
Professor J G Malone-Lee, J S Yudkin
Senior Lecturer C Wu

Obstetrics and Gynaecology

Professor A Singer
Senior Lecturer H Morgan

Primary Care and Population Science

Lecturer J Barber, D J Bavin, J Biddulph, M M Bond, P A Bryant, W G T Coppola, M A S Griffin, D Jones, P Lenihan, J S Marshall, J Martin, B Peter, J Russell, J E Sackville-West, P S Salomon, S Saxena, A J Schamroth, G R Wong
Professor C L R Bartlett, A Bowling, L Elton, P M Greenhalgh, M Modell
Reader S R Iliffe
Senior Lecturer M J Buszewicz, V M Drennan, C Goodman, C G Helman, I Hopkinson, D Kalra, E Murray, I D Nazareth, S Rogers, P D Toon

Surgery

Senior Lecturer M Hashemi, A Wilson

Wolfson Institute for Biomedical Research

University College London, Gower Street, London WC1E 6BT
Tel: 020 7679 2000

Lecturer K P Giese, H K Smith
Professor I G Charles, J Garthwaite, S Moncada, W D Richardson
Senior Lecturer G Garthwaite, G Koentges

Recognised Clinical Institutions

Barnet, Enfield and Haringey Mental Health NHS Trust, Barnet and Chase Farm Postgraduate Medical Centre, Camden and Islington Community Health Services NHS Trust Postgraduate Centre, Eastman Dental Institute for Oral Health Care Science, Great Ormond Street Hospital for Children NHS Trust, Moorfields Eye Hospital, North East Essex Mental Health NHS Trust, North East London Mental Health NHS Trust, North Middlesex Hospital, Royal Free Hospital, Royal National Orthopaedic Hospital, Tavistock and Portman NHS Trust, Whittington Hospital

St Bartholomew's and The Royal London School of Medicine and Dentistry

Turner Street, London E1 2AD
Tel: 020 7377 7603 Fax: 020 7377 7612
Website: www.mds.qmw.ac.uk

Assistant Warden (Education) C G Fowler
Assistant Warden (Research) I M Leigh
Assistant Warden (Student Affairs) B Colvin
Deputy Warden P G Kopelman
Warden N A Wright

Clinical Dentistry

Comprehensive Dental Care

Senior Lecturer S Morganstein

Conservative Dentistry

Head D Y D Samarawickrama
Lecturer V J Kingsmill, C E Mercer, K G Seymour
Reader W M Tay
Senior Lecturer A R Leon, E J R Lynch

Dental Auxiliary School

Principal Dental Nurse Tutor J Jackson
Principal Dental Therapy/Hygiene Tutor S Murray
Director E S Davenport

Dental Biophysics

Head J C Elliott
Lecturer G R Davis
Senior Lecturer P Anderson

Dental Public Health

Head R Croucher
Lecturer W Marcenes

Oral and Maxillofacial Surgery

Professor P F Bradley
Reader H Cannell
Senior Lecturer A Aiken, P Flynn, J M Richards

Oral Biomaterials

Professor M R Anseau

Oral Medicine

Head J M Zakrzewska
Lecturer J A G Buchanan

Oral Microbiology

Professor J M Hardie

Oral Pathology

Head David M Williams
Lecturer Alan Cruchley, Supriya Kapas, Margaret Scragg
Senior Lecturer Paula M Farthing, Gareth Howells

Orthodontics

Professor J P Moss
Senior Clinical Lecturer R Kirschen, D Lawton, B Selwyn-Barnett
Senior Lecturer J M Battagel, M L Calvert

Paediatric Dentistry

Head M Hector
Consultant Janice Fearne
Lecturer H Liversidge
Senior Lecturer E S Davenport, F Wong

Periodontology

Head F J Hughes

Prosthetic Dentistry

Head M R Heath
Senior Lecturer M J Barsby, P S Wright

Clinical Medicine

Anaesthetics

Professor L Strunin
Senior Lecturer D E R Burt, P J Flynn, D Goldhill, C J Hinds, R M Langford, J A Stamford, J D Watson, P S Withington

Biochemical Pharmacology

Professor R J Flower
Senior Lecturer B Whittle

ST BARTHOLOMEW'S & THE ROYAL LONDON SCHOOL OF MEDICINE & DENTISTRY

Bone and Joint Research Unit (supported by ARC)
Professor D R Blake
Reader C J Morris
Senior Lecturer J R Archer, M Grootveld, B L Kidd, P G Winyard

Cardiology
Senior Lecturer D S Dymond, A H McDonald, P G Mills, A W Nathan, D S Tunstall Pedoe

Cardiovascular Biochemistry
Professor N Miller

Centre for Medical and Dental Education
Director of Clinical Skills D M Chaput de Saintonge
Head P McCrorie
Lecturer S R Collinson, A Hall
Senior Lecturer H Fry

Chemical Endocrinology
Professor Lesley Rees
Reader A J Clark
Senior Lecturer S H Medbak

Child Health
Professor C B S Wood
Reader Kathleen Costeloe
Senior Lecturer R J Harris, S Husain, Janice Roper, G J A I Snodgrass

Clinical Biochemistry
Professor C P Price
Reader J M Burrin
Senior Lecturer Anne Dawnay, H L J Makin

Clinical Haematology
Professor A C Newland
Reader C A Facer
Senior Lecturer R Amos, J P Cavenagh, B T Colvin, C N Gutteridge, S M Kelsey

Clinical Pharmacology
Head N Benjamin
Senior Lecturer S M Abrams, M Caulfield, R M Pearson

Dermatology
Professor I M Leigh
Senior Lecturer Veronique Bataille, C M Proby
Senior Lecturer (Non-Clinical) I McKay

Diabetes
Professor E A Gale
Reader R D Leslie
Senior Lecturer P Bingley

Diagnostic Radiology
Head P Armstrong
Professor R Reznek
Senior Lecturer A P Brooks, A R Gillams

Environmental and Preventive Medicine
Head N J Wald
Professor T W Meade
Reader M R Law

Gastroenterology/GI Science
Head D Wingate
Professor M J G Farthing
Reader Parveen J Kumar, C P Swain
Senior Lecturer Elspeth Alstead, D F Evans, P Fairclough, S Patchett

General Practice and Primary Care
Professor Yvonne Carter

Senior Lecturer G Feder, C J Griffiths, A Jamieson, P A Julian, Jeanette Naish, J Raiman, Wendy Savage, M G Sheldon

Health Care of the Elderly
Reader G Bennett
Senior Lecturer K Somerville

Histopathology and Morbid Anatomy
Head Colin Berry
Reader D G Lowe
Senior Lecturer S Baithun, C L Brown, A Coumbe, S M Dodd, P Domizio, J Geddes, S E Greenwald, J Martin, A J Norton, J Van der Walt

Human Metabolism and Molecular Genetics
Professor D Galton

Human Nutrition
Head J Powell-Tuck

Human Science and Medical Ethics
Professor L Doyal, Sheila Hillier
Senior Lecturer Ann Cushing, P Hajek

Immunology
Professor G F Bottazzo, A J Pinching
Reader J A Sachs
Senior Lecturer P A Biro, A Matossian-Rogers, G L Schwarz
Senior Lecturer (Non Clinical) W J W Morrow

Intensive Care
Senior Lecturer C Hinds

Medical Electronics
Reader D P Jones
Senior Lecturer J R Roberts

Medical Microbiology
Head Soad Tabaqchali
Professor J D Williams
Reader E J Shaw, B W Wren
Senior Lecturer J Breuer, L Hall, D M Livermore, Louise Neville, M B Prentice, A M Sefton, P Wilson

Medical Oncology
Head T A Lister
Professor R T D Oliver, B D Young
Reader A Z S Rohatiner
Senior Lecturer C J Gallagher, R K Gupta

Medical Unit/Diabetes and Metabolism
Head R D Cohen
Professor G A Hitman, R A Iles
Senior Lecturer B J Boucher, P G Kopelman, D F Wood

Medical Unit/Endocrinology (Adult and Paediatrics)
Head G M Besser
Professor A Grossman, D Perrett
Reader J Monson
Senior Lecturer A Tate, P Trainer, D F Wood

Nephrology
Senior Lecturer F P Marsh

Neurology
Professor M Swash
Senior Lecturer P Anand

Neurosurgery
Senior Lecturer T H Koeze

Nuclear Medicine
Professor K E Britton
Reader Maria Granowska

UNIVERSITIES & MEDICAL SCHOOLS

Obstetrics and Gynaecology
Professor J G Grudzinskas
Reader O Djahanbakhch
Senior Lecturer N P I Armstrong, E Silman

Orthopaedics
Senior Lecturer J B King

Paediatric Endocrinology
Reader M O Savage
Senior Lecturer A M Cotterill

Paediatric Gastroenterology
Professor T T MacDonald

Paediatric Oncology
Professor J Lilleyman
Senior Lecturer J E Kingston, V Saha

Psychological Medicine
Head T G Dinan
Professor J Coid
Senior Lecturer E O Akuffo, M P Deahl, Sandra Evans, S Fleminger, C A Kelly, J V Lucey, Sheila A Mann, Siobhan Murphy, Parvathy Nayer, D Ndegwa, D K B Nias, H A Ring, P D White

Radiation Biology
Head K R Trott
Reader J E Coggle
Senior Lecturer C Bowlt, B E Lambert

Rehabilitation
Professor D Rushton

Respiratory Medicine
Professor R J Davies

Rheumatology
Professor D R Blake
Senior Lecturer D P D'Cruz

School of Occupational Therapy
Senior Lecturer K Gannon, G Roberts, L Summerfield-Mann

Sports Medicine
Head J B King
Course Administrator Fiona Barrington
Research Physiotherapist & Lecturer Ioe Hudson
Senior Lecturer Roslyn Carbon, A J H Wade

Surgery
Head N S Williams
Professor A W Goode, J S Lumley
Senior Lecturer L Chalstrey, L Meleagros, J Northover, S Purkiss, D J Shanahan

Toxicology
Head A D Dayan
Professor A J Paine
Senior Lecturer C J Powell

Virology
Head D J Jeffries
Professor (Non-Clinical) J Oxford
Senior Lecturer Woon Ling Chan

Wolfson Institute of Environmental and Preventative Medicine
Professor R A Feldman

Degrees and diplomas
MB BS, MSc, Dip MB BS

Recognised Clinical Institutions
Basildon Hospital, Broomfield Hospital, Eastbourne District General Hospital, Epsom General Hospital, Frimley Park Hospital, Homerton University Hospital, Hurstwood Park Neurological Centre, King George Hospital, Newham General Hospital, North Middlesex Hospital, Oldchurch Hospital, Princess Alexandra Hospital, Southend Hospital, St Bartholomew's Hospital, St Richard's Hospital, The London Chest Hospital Education Centre, Wellcome Trust, Whipps Cross University Hospital

St George's Hospital Medical School

Cranmer Terrace, Tooting, London SW17 0RE
Tel: 020 8672 9944 Fax: 020 8767 4696
Website: www.sghms.ac.uk

Principal Robert Boyd
Secretary R B Hill

Medical Departments

Anaesthesia
Professor G M Hall
Senior Lecturer G Nicholson

Anatomy
Lecturer C C Chumbley, J Pocock, M K Richardson
Professor P N Dilly, D G Whittingham
Reader D E Ashhurst, D C Bennett
Senior Lecturer D C Davies

Biochemistry
Professor M J Clemens, L M Fisher, J R Griffiths
Reader C L Bashford
Senior Lecturer U-A Bommer, S E Y Goodbourn, G S J Whitley

Cardiology
Professor A J Camm, W J McKenna, C A Seymour
Senior Lecturer J C C Kaski Fullone, G J Leech, E Rowland

Child Health
Lecturer D Jellinek
Professor N D Carter, D V Walters
Reader M A Patton
Senior Lecturer M D Bain, S A Calvert, R A Chalmers, E G Davies, P A Hamilton, D K Haque, S Jeffery, S Mitton, C M de Sousa, A F Williams

Clinical Biochemistry
SDU Leader J A Nisbet
Senior Lecturer K W Colston, G E Levin

Clinical Neuroscience
Professor B A Bell
Senior Lecturer M M Brown

Communicable Diseases
Professor G E Griffin
Senior Lecturer D J M Lewis, M H Wansbrough-Jones

Forensic Medicine Unit
Hon. Senior Lecturer P Dean, D Rogers, M Stark
Senior Lecturer R Chapman, R Shepherd

General Practice
Lecturer T Harris, P Oakeshott, S Patel, J S Shindler
Professor S R Hilton, F M Ross
Senior Lecturer A R Kendrick, A T Tylee
Senior Tutor A C Cohen, C Sudhakar

Geriatrics
Consultant M C Ward
Lecturer J M Simpson

Professor P H Millard
Senior Lecturer J Colgan, I R Hastie, J M Kellett

Haematology
Lecturer L C Dunlop
Professor E C Gordon-Smith
Senior Lecturer S E Ball, D H Bevan, E J Parker-Williams, T R Rutherford

Histopathology
Lecturer S Deen, J M Mann
Professor T J Chambers, M J Davies
Senior Lecturer J W M Chow, C M Corbishley, S A Dilly, C J Finlayson, M J Warburton

Immunology
Professor F C Hay, A P Johnstone, P Riches
Senior Lecturer J S Axford, T A Poulton

Medical Microbiology
Professor A R M Coates
Reader D K Banerjee
Senior Lecturer J C Booth, P D Butcher, M M Roberts

Medicine
Lecturer T L Griffiths, M A Mendall, D A Rodin
Professor G A MacGregor, T C Northfield
Reader E D Bennett, K W Colston, P W Jones, J D Maxwell, S S Nussey
Senior Lecturer M M Brown, J B Eastwood, C C Harland, P J Howard, G E Levin, P S Mortimer

Obstetrics and Gynaecology
Lecturer J E Cockburn, P V Johnson
Professor S Campbell, C A J Wilson
Senior Lecturer T H Bourne, P E Hay, F C Reader, T R Varma, Y Ville

Oncology
Professor A G Dalgleish
Senior Lecturer Ruth Pettengell

Pharmacology and Clinical Pharmacology
Professor T B Bolton, W A Large
Reader J G Collier, R W Horton
Senior Clinical Lecturer D R J Singer
Senior Lecturer C Robinson

Physiology
Lecturer P C Murphy
Professor J R Levick, M J Stock, B J Whipp
Reader P L R Andrews, P S Richardson, T L Williams
Senior Lecturer S A Whitehead

Psychiatry
Lecturer C D H Evans, G H Rassool
Professor T P Burns, A H Ghodse, P D Hill, S C Hollins, J H Lacey
Senior Lecturer S J Bernal, M F Bristow, A W Burke, K M Checinski, C R Drummond, D C Drummond, L M Drummond, N L G Eastman, J C Edeh, R Farmer, P A Hindley, P M Hughes, R R Jacobson, A J Kent, O A Oyefesu, A J Riley, J Turk, H M C Warwick

Psychology
Professor A D Pickering, A P A Steptoe, R J West

Public Health Sciences
Lecturer B K Nicholas, J L Peacock
Professor H R Anderson, J M Bland
Senior Lecturer D G Cook, P Littlejohns, L B D MacDonald, A M Pollock, D P Strachan, C Victor

Radiology
Senior Lecturer A Grundy

Surgery
Head J Hermon-Taylor
Professor B M Austen
Senior Lecturer A G Twistleton-Wykeham-Fienn, D J Winterbourne

Recognised Clinical Institutions
Springfield Hospital, St George's Hospital, St Helier Hospital

University of Birmingham

Faculty of Medicine and Dentistry, Edgbaston, Birmingham B15 2TT
Tel: 0121 414 3858 Fax: 0121 414 4036
Website: www.bham.ac.uk

Vice-Chancellor & Principal M Stirling
Dean of Medicine, Dentistry & Health Sciences W F Doe
Registrar & Secretary D J Allen
Director and Head of School of Dentistry R J Marquis
Head of the School of Health Sciences P Wrightson

School of Dentistry

St Chad's Queensway, Birmingham B4 6NN

Director and Head of School P M Marquis
Professor F J T Burke, W R E Laird, A J Smith, A D Walmsley

School of Health Science

Head of School P A Wrighton
Professor C Clifford, C M Hicks, P Nolan
Senior Lecturer J E Broadfield, J E Clark, V E Cross, A Hewison

School of Medicine

Cancer Studies
Deputy Head of Division E L Jones
Head of Division L S Young

Cardiovascular Surgery
Professor W A Littler

Clinical Trials Unit
Professor R Gray

General Practice
Professor F D R Hobbs, D B Morton

Geriatric Medicine
Professor A Sinclair

Health Sciences
Professor C Clifford, P Wrightson

Immunology
Deputy Head of Division I C M MacLennan
Head of Division E J Jenkinson

Infectious Disease
Professor A M Geddes, R Wise

Medical Sciences
Deputy Head of Division J M Marshall
Head of Division M C Sheppard

Medicine
Professor A H Barnett, D G Beevers, J Franklyn, M J S Langman, M C Sheppard, P M Stewart

Neurosciences
Head of Division S Cumella
Professor A C Williams

Obstetrics and Gynaecology
Head M J Whittle
Professor D M Luesley, J R Newton

UNIVERSITIES & MEDICAL SCHOOLS

Occupational Health
Professor J M Harrington

Paediatrics and Child Health
Professor I W Booth, S E Bundey, P A Farndon, M A Hulten, E R Maher

Pathology
Professor E L Jones

Pharmacology
Professor N G Bowery

Physiology
Vice-Principal D R Westbury
Head J H Coote
Professor J A Jefferys, E J Johns, J Marshall, R Traub

Primary Care, Public and Occupational Health
Head of Division F D R Hobbs

Psychiatry
Head I F Brockington
Lecturer D J Clarke
Professor J A Corbett, N J Craddock, S P Sashidharan
Senior Lecturer T A Betts
Senior Research Fellow S Cumella

Public Health and Epidemiology
Professor P Boyle, K K Cheng, R K Griffiths, R J Lilford, A Stevens, A M Stewart

Reproductive and Child Health
Head of Division M J Whittle

Rheumatology
Clinical Lecturer C Buckley, D Carruthers, N Erb, J Gardner-Medwin
Hon. Clinical Lecturer A Exley, M Farr
Hon. Senior Clinical Lecturer P Jobanputra, R Jubb, G Kitas, R Palmer, M Pugh, L Rankin, R Situnayake
Lecturer H Bhayani
Locum Clinical Lecturer J McDonagh
Professor P A Bacon
Reader M Salmon
Senior Clinical Lecturer S Bowman, C Gordon, T Southwood
Senior Lecturer S Young

Surgery
Professor M R B Keighley, P McMaster, J G Temple
Senior Lecturer E K Alpar, D G Morton, S M A Phillips

Degrees and diplomas
MBChB, BDS, BMedSc, BNurs, BSc Physiotherapy, PhD, MD, DDS, MPhil, MSc, MPH

Recognised Clinical Institutions
Birmingham Children's Hospital NHS Trust, Birmingham Heartlands and Solihull (Teaching) NHS Trust, Birmingham Heartlands Hospital, Birmingham Specialist Community Health NHS Trust, Birmingham Women's Health Care NHS Trust, Black Country Mental Health NHS Trust, Burton Hospitals NHS Trust, City Hospital NHS Trust, Coventry Healthcare NHS Trust, Dudley Group of Hospitals NHS Trust, Dudley Priority Health NHS Trust, Foundation NHS Trust, Good Hope Hospital, Hereford Hospitals NHS Trust Postgraduate Medical Centre, North Staffordshire Hospital NHS Trust Postgraduate Medical Centre, North Warwickshire NHS Trust, Northampton General Hospital, Northampton General Hospital NHS Trust, Northern Birmingham Mental Health NHS Trust, Royal Orthopaedic Hospital NHS Trust, Royal Shrewsbury Hospitals NHS Trust Postgraduate Medical Centre, Royal Wolverhampton Hospitals NHS Trust, Sandwell Healthcare NHS Trust, Shropshire's Community and Mental Health Services NHS Trust, South Birmingham Mental Health NHS Trust, University Hospital Birmingham NHS Trust, Walsall Community

Health NHS Trust, Walsall Hospitals NHS Trust Postgraduate Medical Centre, Wolverhampton Health Care NHS Trust, Worcestershire Acute Hospitals NHS Trust, Worcestershire Community and Mental Health NHS Trust

University of Bristol

Faculty of Medicine, Senate House, Tyndall Avenue, Bristol BS8 1TH
Tel: 0117 928 8333 Fax: 0117 934 9854
Email: Anne.Keane@bristol.ac.uk

Faculty of Medicine

Vice-Chancellor Eric Thomas
Dean of Clinical Medicine & Dentistry David J Nutt
Dean of Faculty Stephen J W Lisney
Faculty Administrator Alison R Bryson
Faculty Secretary Anne Keane, Stephen Brooke
Professor of Physics and Engineering in Medicine P N T Wells

Anatomy
Demonstrator M R E Harris, I G Sergides, C A Wong
Lecturer Z I Bashir, J F Burn, C J Fuller, M J Perry, A Sengupta, D J Tortonese
Lecturer in Equine Studies G R Colborne
Lecturer in Neuroscience E Molnar
Professor D S McNally
Professor of Anatomy and Cognitive Neuroscience M W Brown
Professor of Molecular Neuroscience J M Henley
Professor of Neuroscience J M Muller
Professor of Neuroscience in Anatomy G L Collingridge
Reader J B Wakerley
Research Associate in Anatomy A J Doherty
Research Fellow W W Anderson, J W Crabtree, A Terashima
Senior Lecturer M A Adams, P Dolan, J R T Greene, G K Wakley
Senior Lecturer in Anatomy G Clarke
Senior Lecturer in Anatomy (Oral Biology) J R Musgrave
Senior Research Fellow Z A Bortolotto
Teaching Fellow A M Roberts, J Townsend
Temporary Lecturer E C Warburton
Travelling Research Fellow S E Lauri

Biochemistry
Beit Memorial Research Fellow P J Lockyer
Lecturer M B Avison, P J Booth, S G Burston, C E Dempsey, J Frayne, K L Gaston, E J Griffiths, A T Hadfield, L M Henderson, M R Jones, D Meredith, S K Moule, N J Savery
Professor A R Clarke, R M Denton, A P Halestrap, S E Halford, J J Holbrook, M J A Tanner, J M Tavare
Professor of Molecular Genetics L Hall
Project Manager A Cameron
Reader G S Banting, R L Brady, P J Cullen, J D McGivan, A J Rivett, G A Rutter
Research Fellow G B Bloomberg, N A Gormley, P S Jayaraman, A Jepson, W J Mawby, A H Mellor, R B Sessions, M D Sherzelkun, A Varadi
Senior Lecturer P M Wood
Wellcome Trust International Prize Travelling Fellow M J Parker

Cardiac, Anaesthetic and Radiological Sciences
BHF Professor of Clinical Surgery & Director, Bristol Heart Institute G D Angelini
BHF Professor of Vascular Cell Biology A C Newby
Consultant Senior Lecturer R P Casula, A T Lovell, M A Oberhoff, M J Underwood
Consultant Senior Lecturer in Anaesthesia A M S Black, S J Howell
Lecturer, Vascular Cell Biology S J George
Lecturer in Cardiac Surgery C L Jackson
Professor of Cardiology K R Karsch
Professor of Clinical Radiology M R Rees

UNIVERSITY OF BRISTOL

Reader in Cardiac Cellular Physiology M S Suleiman
Reader in Cardiology A Baumbach
Research Fellow in Cardiac Surgery R C Bush, G Sala-Newby
Senior Research Fellow J Y Jeremy

Care of the Elderly
Professor G K Wilcock
Research Associate in Medicine S H MacGowan

Centre for Ethics in Medicine
Lecturer S J L Edwards
Professor A V Campbell

Child Dental Health
Senior Research Fellow A J Sprod

Child Health
Head of Biological Collections R W Jones
Consultant Senior Lecturer J P Hamilton-Shield, A J W Henderson, M Saleem, O H Stanley
Lecturer in Neonatal Medicine D Harding
Medical Statistician in Child Health P S P Blair
Professor A G L Whitelaw
Professor of Infant Health and Developmental Physiology P J Fleming
Professor of Paediatric and Prenatal Epidemiology M J Golding
Research Assistant K North
Research Associate I S Cowan
Research Fellow J C Ingram
Senior Audiologist A J Hall
Senior Lecturer M Thoresen
Senior Lecturer in Medical Statistics L P Hunt
Senior Ophthalmologist C E M Williams
Senior Research Nutritionist P M Emmett

Clinical Medicine and Dentistry
Dean of Clinical Medicine & Dentistry David Nutt
Senior Teaching Associate M A Byron

Dental Postgraduate Unit
Regional Adviser in General Dental Practice M E Green
Vocational Training Adviser M D Bruce, I Holloway

Department of Social Medicine
Consultant Senior Lecturer Y Ben-Shlomo, M Egger, D J Gunnell, A Ness
Lecturer J Coast, Elise Whitley
Professor S B J Ebrahim, S J Frankel, G Davey Smith
Reader J L Donovan, T J Peters
Senior Lecturer J A C Sterne

In-Vitro Centre for Reproductive Medicine
Clinical Co-ordinator in Reproductive Medicine C Kallasam

Laryngology, Rhinology and Otology
Clinical Lecturer C Dunning, M Hilton, K V Ravi, M Sauders, A Toma
Senior Clinical Lecturer D Baldwin, P G Bicknell, M V Griffiths, R K Mal, A R Maw, P J Robinson

Medical Postgraduate Division
Adviser D Kenny
GP Education Adviser P F Godfrey
Regional Adviser in General Practice R C W Hughes, A P Lewis

Medicine
Consultant Senior Lecturer R E Barry, A L Malizia, R M Smith
Consultant Senior Lecturer in Care of the Elderly and General Internal Manager L Dow
Consultant Senior Lecturer in Diabetic Medicine P J Bingley
Consultant Senior Lecturer in Medicine C S J Probert
Consultant Senior Lecturer in Neurology M E Hill

Consultant Senior Lecturer in Respiratory Medicine A B Millar
Lecturer K M Gillespie, S D Hearing
Lecturer in Medicine C H Bolton
Professor N J Scolding
Professor of Diabetic Medicine E A M Gale
Professor of Renal Medicine P W Mathieson
Research Fellow L Armstrong, A J Swan
Research Fellow in Medicine E C Smith
Senior Research Fellow in Medicine A P Corfield

Neuroendocrinology
Consultant Senior Lecturer C M Dayan, D Wynick
Professor S L Lightman, D Murphy
Reader in Medicine D Dawbarn, N C H Kerr, A Levy, C A McArdle, G G F Mason, J B Uney
Research Associate F M De Bree
Senior Lecturer in Medicine M S Harbuz, M R Norman
Senior Research Fellow D S Jessop
Sigmund Gestetner Research Fellow in Medicine S J Allen

Norah Fry Research Centre
Joseph Rowntree Research Fellow R J Townsley
Professor M Ward
Reader C E Robinson
Reader in Mental Health J A O Russell
Research Fellow J Rodgers
Senior Research Fellow K R Simons

Obstetrics and Gynaecology
Consultant Senior Clinical Lecturer in Reproductive Medicine and Surgery J M Jenkins
Consultant Senior Lecturer D J Cahill, D J Murphy
Consultant Senior Lecturer in Obstetrics and Gynaecology S S Glew
Consultant Senior Lecturer in Reproductive Medicine U D Gordon
Lecturer A J Hunter, L A Joels
Lecturer in Reproductive Immunology Beverley J Randle
Professor of Maternal and Foetal Medicine P W Soothill
Senior Lecturer A T A Thein
Senior Lecturer in Obstetrics and Gynaecology C H Holmes

Oncology
McAlpine Macmillan Consultant Senior Clinical Lecturer in Palliative Medicine A N T Davies
Professor of Palliative Medicine G W C Hanks
Research Fellow P Grainger

Ophthalmology
Consultant Senior Lecturer A J Churchill
Lecturer S Banerjee
Professor A D Dick
Research Fellow M S Berry, S M Nicholls, C Shimeld, V A Smith
Senior Research Fellow W J Armitage

Oral and Dental Science
Clinical Lecturer in Restorative Dentistry L M McNally, D J O'Sullivan
Clinical Research Fellow in Prosthodontics & Periodontology N C A Claydon
Clinical Research Lecturer S R Sheen
Consultant Senior Lecturer in Child Dental Health P J M Crawford
Consultant Senior Lecturer in Periodontology J M Moran
Consultant Senior Lecturer in Restorative Dentistry J S Rees
Lecturer Y E Y Aboush, H A Pontefract, S J Thavaraj
Lecturer in Cancer Studies A Hague, I C Paterson
Lecturer in Child Dental Health J P Mansell
Lecturer in Conservative Dentistry Susan M Hooper, K J Marshall
Lecturer in Dental Education S R Greenwood
Lecturer in Oral Microbiology D Dymock
Lecturer in Oral Pathology C M Robinson

UNIVERSITIES & MEDICAL SCHOOLS

Lecturer in Paediatric Dentistry K Duncan
Lecturer in Prosthetic Dentistry D R Williams
Lecturer in Restorative Dentistry G B Gray, N X West, R Yates
Locum Lecturer in Restorative Dentistry G M Boswell
Professor in Orthodontics C D Stephens
Professor in Periodontology M Addy
Professor of Dental Care of the Elderly Alan Harrison
Professor of Experimental Pathology S S Prime
Professor of Oral Microbiology H F Jenkinson
Professor of Oral Surgery J G Cowpe
Professor of Orthodontics J R Sandy
Reader in Oral Pathology J W Eveson
Senior Lecturer S J Thomas
Senior Lecturer in Dental Materials Science and Biomaterials K D Jandt
Senior Lecturer in Restorative Dentistry D C Jagger

Orthopaedic Surgery
Consultant Senior Lecturer in Orthopaedic Surgery J R W Hardy
Consultant Senior Lecturer in Orthopaedic Surgery and Pathology C P Case
Lecturer M J W Hubble
Professor of Orthopaedic Surgery I D Learmonth

Pathology and Microbiology
Clinical Fellow J M Bradshaw
Consultant Senior Lecturer C M P Collins, N J Goulden, R S Heyderman, M Moorghen, H J Porter, E A Sheffield, G R Standen, C G Steward, P C Turner
Lecturer P J Brown, A Herman, L J Moore, D J Morgan
Professor P J Berry, C J Elson, T R Hirst, C Paraskeva, M Pignatelli, M Virji, D C Wraith
Reader P M Bennett, W D Billington, F Carswell, M J Day, T J Hill, A J Morgan, G R Pearson
Research Assistant C I Westacott
Research Associate C M Richards
Research Fellow R J Birtles, D J E Elder, B Kenny, N M McKechnie, K T A Malik, G Mazza, S L Parry, A W Rowbottom, A D Wilson, N A P Wood
Senior Lecturer K W Brown, A M Pullen, N A Williams
Wellcome Senior Research Fellow in Clinical Science F S Wong

Pharmacology
Consultant Senior Lecturer C J C Roberts
Lecturer A W Poole, E S J Robinson
Professor G Henderson, P J Roberts
Reader R Z Kozlowski, N V Marrion
Research Assistant S J Culliford
Research Fellow D Shepherd
Senior Lecturer E P Kelly, P V Taberner, M M Usocwicz

Physiology
Professor D M Armstrong, P M Headley, S J W Lisney, B Matthews
Reader J C Hancox, M C Holley, R S G Jones, S N Lawson, R W Meech, K W Ranatunga
Research Associate D Davies, L Djouhri, G M Mutungi
Research Career Development Fellow H J Kennedy
Research Fellow D O Bates, C M N Rivolta
Senior Lecturer J R Harris, R M A P Ridge, D M Woolley
Senior Research Fellow R Apps, N Cooper, J F R Paton

Primary Care
Consultant Senior Lecturer C J Salisbury
Professor D J Sharp
Research Fellow C R Baxter
Senior Lecturer T P Fahey
Special Lecturer in Medical Educational K A Feest

Psychiatry
Consultant Senior Lecturer J Evans, A R Lingford-Hughes
Lecturer S Argyropoulos
Lecutrer A Sipos

Locum Consultant Senior Lecturer J P Potokar
Norah Cooke Hurle Professor of Mental Health G L Harrison
Reader in Cross-cultural Psychiatry D B Mumford

Psycho-Pharmacology Unit
Professor D J Nutt
Research Fellow S J Wilson
Team Leader A L Hudson

Rheumatology Unit
Consultant Senior Lecturer J H Tobias
Professor A P Hollander
Reader J R Kirwan
Senior Research Fellow M E J Billingham, J M Rodgers

Surgery
Consultant Senior Lecturer J M Blazeby, M Jackson, P A Lear, F C T Smith, M G Thomas
Professor D Alderson, J R Farndon, J M P Holly
Reader M A Birchall
Senior Clinical Lecturer R M Atkins, Z E Winters

Transplantation Sciences
Director B A Bradley
Professor J M Hows
Research Fellow P A Denning-Kendall, C Donaldson

Degrees and diplomas
BSc, MB ChB, PhD, MD, ChM, MSc, BDS, MCD, DDS

Recognised Clinical Institutions
Bristol Eye Hospital, Bristol General Hospital, Bristol Royal Hospital for Children, Bristol Royal Infirmary, Frenchay Hospital, Southmead Hospital, St Michael's Hospital, University of Bristol Dental Hospital and School, Weston General Hospital

University of Cambridge

The Old Schools, Cambridge CB2 1TN
Tel: 01223 337733
Website: www.cam.ac.uk

Vice-Chancellor A N Broers
Registrar T J Mead
Secretary General of the Faculties D A Livesey

Biology

Anatomy
Director of Research W A Harris
Head M H Johnson
Associate Lecturer G M W Cook
Clinical Anatomist F G Parkin
Lecturer J H Brackenbury, S J Bray, D J Burton, D J Chivers, R E J Dyball, S A Edgley, A C Ferguson-Smith, R C Hardie, M H Hastings, C E Holt, R J Keynes, V Navaratnam, A C Roberts, P N Schofield, R A H White
Reader J Herbert, M V Sofroniew
STO, Prosector B M Hogan
Technical Director of the Multi-Imaging Centre, Safety J N Skepper
Veterinary Clinical Anatomist J B Grandage

Biochemistry
Lecturer D S Bendall, K M Brindle, D M Carrington, P Dupree, P A Evans, T R Hesketh, C J Howe, A P Jackson, D Kerridge, E D Laue, B R Martin, P E Reynolds, P H Rubery, C W J Smith, N M Standart, C J R Thorne, A M Tolkovsky
Professor T L Blundell, J C Metcalfe, R N Perham, G P C Salmond, J O Thomas
Reader M D Brand, D J Ellar, R J Jackson, P F Leadlay

Experimental Psychology
Head N J Mackintosh

Lecturer B P Bradley, M Eimer, D R J Laming, R A McCarthy, I P L McLaren, S Monsell, J Russell, P Whittle
Professor B J Everitt, B C J Moore, T W Robbins
Reader A Dickinson, S B Dunnett, J D Mollon

Pathology

Head M A Ferguson-Smith
Associate Lecturer J R Anderson, D C Barker, D F J Brown, D L Brown, N R B Cary, U Desselberger, M Farrington, J W Grant, H A Ludlam, S G Stewart, D G D Wight, T G Wreghitt
Clinical Lecturer T A McKee
Lecturer N A Affara, J W Ajioka, J Arno, D E Bowyer, I Brierley, T D K Brown, M R Clark, N Coleman, D W Dunne, P A W Edwards, S Efstathiou, N J Holmes, I B Kingston, V Koronakis, M J Mitchinson, R W F Le Page, S Thirunavukkarasu, J H Xuerub, J R W Yates
Professor J M Blackwell, V P Collins, A C Minson, J Trowsdale
Reader A Cooke, C Hughes, Y W Loke, M A Stanley

Pharmacology

Lecturer B A Callingham, J M Edwardson, T-P D Fan, D R Ferguson, R M Henderson, C R Hiley, S B Hladky, A J Morton, R D Murrell-Lagnado, P J Richardson, P Thorn, J M Young
Professor A W Cuthbert, R F Irvine
Reader E K Matthews, C W Taylor, M J Waring

Physiology

Lecturer R J Barnes, J Brown, R H S Carpenter, W H Colledge, S L Dickson, J W Fawcett, A L R Findlay, D A Giussani, J C D Hickson, A E Hill, A P Hillier, H R Matthews, H P C Robinson, J H Rogers, S O Sage, C J Schwiening, R L Tapp, D J Tolhurst, T M Winter, R I Woods
Professor A C Crawford, T D Lamb, M A H Surani, R C Thomas
Reader A V Edwards, A L Fowden, C L-H Huang

Clinical Medicine

The Clinical School, Addenbrooke's Hospital, Hills Road, Cambridge CB2 2QQ
Tel: 01223 336700 Fax: 01223 336709

Clinical Dean C M C Allen
Associate Dean P F Jenkins, P W L Sikles, J E Stark
Assistant Directors of Studies in General Practice D Cox, A G Males, J R Perry, A J S White
Professor L D Hall, K-T Khaw
Regional Postgraduate Dean J S G Biggs
Regius Professor of Physic Keith Peters
Secretary of the Clinical School S M Pinnock

Clinical Biochemistry

Lecturer G T E Kealey, J P Luzio
Professor C N Hales, K Siddle
Reader J P Luzio

Community Medicine

Consultant P J Baxter
Lecturer C E G Brayne, B D Cox, T W Davies, D F Easton, R Hanka, N T A Oswald, J W Powles
Professor N E Day, R L Himsworth, A L Kinmonth
Reader A W F Edwards

Haematology

Lecturer C R Barker, W H Ouwehand, J K H Rees, L M Williamson
Professor J P Allain, R W Carrell
Reader H H Lee

Medical Genetics

Clinical Lecturer E A L Reid
Lecturer A J Green
Professor M Bobrow, C ffrench-Constant

Medicine

Clinical Lecturer I L P Beales, S F Haydock, M J Hudspith, N P Robertson

Lecturer G J M Alexander, J R Hodges, S J Kenwrick, S M Lachmann, A M L Lever, C M Lockwood, D A Lomas, J H Sinclair, K G C Smith, M G Spillantini, J Sterling
Professor M J Brown, D A S Compston, T M Cox, J S H Gaston, P J Lachmann, D K Menon, S O'Rahilly, J G P Sissons, P L Weissberg
Reader C M Lockwood
Regius Professor of Physic Keith Peters

Obstetrics and Gynaecology

Clinical Lecturer N H Morris
Lecturer K J Dalton, A Prentice, S Thornton
Professor S K Smith

Oncology

Lecturer N G Burnet, C Caldas, H M Earl, E Gherardi, J Mackay
Professor B A J Ponder

Paediatrics

Clinical Lecturer S F Ahmed, I V Cheema
Lecturer J R Hawkins, C J Morley, A D Tait
Professor I A Hughes

Psychiatry

Clinical Lecturer R Kelvin, A D Ogilvie
Lecturer S Baron-Cohen, G E Berrios, P F Bolton, J H Dowson, A J Holland, F A Huppert, B J Sahakian
Professor I M Goodyer, E S Paykel

Public Health Institute

Director N E Day

Radiology

Clinical Lecturer P W P Bearcroft
Lecturer L H Berman, D J Lomas
Professor A K Dixon

Surgery

Clinical Lecturer S P Harland
Lecturer P J Friend, N V Jamieson, P J Kirkpatrick, N Rushton, D J G White
Professor Roy Y Calne, J D Pickard

Degrees and diplomas

BA, MB, BChir, MChir, MSc, MEng, MBA, MD, MPhil, PhD, ScD

Recognised Clinical Institutions

Addenbrooke's Hospital

University of East Anglia, School of Medicine

University of East Anglia, Norwich NR4 7TJ
Tel: 01603 456161
Website: www.med.uea.ac.uk

Dean Sam Leinster
Health Protection Paul Hunter
Primary Care Amanda Howe

University of Exeter

Barrack Road, Exeter EX2 5DW
Tel: 01392 54631
Website: www.ex.ac.uk

Director D J Pereira Gray
Deputy Director B J Kirby

School of Postgraduate Medicine and Health Sciences

Director J E Tooke

UNIVERSITIES & MEDICAL SCHOOLS

Biological Sciences
Hon. Senior Lecturer J M Garland

Child Health
Research Fellow Monica Cockett
Senior Lecturer M Quinn, R C Smith, J H Tripp

Complementary Medicine
Fellow J Rand
Professor E Ernst
Research Fellow N Abbott, J Barnes, A White

Geriatric Medicine
Senior Lecturer V R Pearce

Health Services Research
Lecturer M Greco, R Powell, K Sweeney

Histopathology
Senior Lecturer R H W Simpson

Institute of General Practice
Fellow M T Claridge, E Hopkins, C Owens
Hon. Senior Lecturer R Goble
Lecturer P Evans, S Pocklington, D A Seamark, R Steele, M Watt
Professor D J Pereira Gray
Research Fellow J Allen, M Anderson, R Ayres, D Bickerton, N Bradley, A Clark, C Clark, M Dixon, A Freeman, A Jacobs, D Kessler, M P Lewis, D Russell, B Sawyer, J P Scott, Clare Seamark, K Sheehy, J W Stead, C Thorne, C Turner, R Westcott
Senior Lecturer A P Lewis

Medicine
Hon. Research Fellow Ann Homer
Hon. Senior Lecturer D B Shaw
Professor B J Kirby
Senior Lecturer K McLeod

Mental Health
Hon. Senior Lecturer R Blacker, J Holmes
Lecturer J Davies

Nursing
Lecturer S Openshaw

Oncology
Senior Lecturer C Rowland

Palliative Medicine
Hon. Lecturer J Gilbert

Public Health
Hon. Senior Lecturer P Gentle
Senior Lecturer M Owen

Vascular Medicine
Professor Angela Shore, J E Tooke

University of Keele

Thornburrow Drive, Hartshill, Stoke-on-Trent ST4 7QB
Tel: 01782 621111
Website: www.keele.ac.uk

Vice Chancellor Janet Finch

School of Postgraduate Medicine

Dean of Postgraduate Medicine R N Clayton

Anaesthetics
Senior Lecturer I Smith

Biomedical Engineering and Medical Physics
Reader P Mountford
Senior Lecturer A El-Lat

Clinical Biochemistry
Professor R C Strange

Clinical Pharmacology
Senior Lecturer J C Mucklow

Clinical Training
Senior Clinical Lecturer J R B Green

Dermatology
Senior Clinical Lecturer A G Smith

Epidemiology
Professor P Croft

General Surgery
Professor J B Elder
Senior Clinical Lecturer R Kirby
Senior Lecturer M Deakin, C Hall, R Morgan, A Walsh

Geriatric Medicine
Professor P Crome
Senior Clinical Lecturer K P Patel
Senior Lecturer R W S Brookes, S Hill, B Panayiotou, C Ruffe, S K Sinha

Infectious Disease
Senior Clinical Lecturer H R Tubb

Maxillofacial Surgery
Senior Research Fellow P J Leopard

Medicine
Professor R N Clayton

Neurology
Senior Clinical Lecturer S Ellis
Senior Lecturer C Hawkins

Obstetrics and Gynaecology
Professor P M S O'Brien
Senior Clinical Lecturer A Clubb, A B Duke, J Felmingham, M Grant, M S Obhrai, O H A Redford, A Roberts
Senior Lecturer R Johanson, C W E Redman

Occupational Medicine
Hon. Senior Research Fellow C A Veys

Ophthalmological Surgery
Senior Clinical Lecturer R Brown

Oral and Maxillofacial Surgery
Senior Lecturer S Worrall

Orthopaedic Surgery
Professor A Redmond, J Templeton
Senior Clinical Lecturer B Ashton, J B Bach, M Davie, D H Edwards, S Eisenstein, W El-Masry, G Evans, T E Hothersall, D C Jaffray, D Jones, D J McBride, M Nortmore-Ball, J Patrick, I Phair, M Prescott, C Pyllilino, S Roberts, A A Tomlinson, M E Wallace, A B Ward, C H Wynn Jones
Senior Lecturer P J Leopard, N Neal, A D Redmond, A Roberts, P B M Thomas, J Travlus
Senior Research Fellow J Dove, P Oakley
Zimmer Chair of Orthopaedics J Richardson

Paediatrics
Professor P Southall
Senior Lecturer M Samuels, S A Spencer
Senior Research Fellow E Heycock

Primary Health Care
Senior Clinical Lecturer M J Y Fisher
Senior Lecturer R Charlton, E Hay, P F Nash

Psychiatry
Professor J L Cox
Senior Clinical Lecturer K Barrett, R Bloor, S W Brown, I Crome, S Elliott, R Hudgson, M S Jursh, F McMillan, D M Scheepers, K Standage
Senior Lecturer W Acuda, S Dover, D Foreman, C Henshaw

Public Health Medicine
Senior Lecturer S Bridgeman, G Rajaratnam

Radiological Sciences
Professor I McCall

Renal Medicine
Senior Clinical Lecturer P Rylance
Senior Lecturer S Davies, G I Russell

Respiratory Medicine
Senior Clinical Lecturer K Prowse
Senior Lecturer C F A Pantin, M Spiteri

Rheumatology
Research Fellow D L Mattey
Senior Clinical Lecturer P Dawes

University of Leeds

Leeds LS2 9JT
Tel: 0113 243 1751
Website: www.leeds.ac.uk

Vice-Chancellor A G Wilson
Secretary R Gair

Medicine, Dentistry, Psychology and Health

Dean of Postgraduate Dental Education J P Ralph
Dean of Postgraduate Medical Education Rosemary G Macdonald
Research Dean M Smith
Teaching and Learning Dean P McWilliam

Research School of Medicine

St. James's University Hospital, Beckett Street, Leeds LS9 7TF

Director M A Smith

Bone and Body Composition Research Group
Chairman M A Smith
Steering Group J O Drife, A Hay, R G Jones, M S Losowsky

Centre for Research into Primary Care
Assistant Director P Heywood
Lecturer Helen Moore, Richard Neal, Alison Wilson

Clinical Information Science Unit
Director Susan Clamp
Research Assistant A Softley

Clinical Pharmacology Unit (Rheumatology Research)
Director H A Bird
Research Registrar Ann Morgan

Diabetes and Thrombosis Research Group
Chairman P J Grant
Steering Committee J Andrew Davies, C R M Prentice, J K Wales

Epidemiology and Health Services Research
Professor H Cuckle, R J Lilford, Mary Renfrew
Senior Lecturer A J Franks, J G Thornton

Foetal and Neonatal Research Group
Chairman M I Levene
Steering Committee H Cuckle, P R F Dear, P C Holland, G Mason, J W L Puntis, S W Smye, J Thornton

ICRF Cancer Medicine Research Unit
Director P J Selby
Professor Margaret Knowles, K Maclennan
Senior Lecturer Rosamunde E Banks, M Leahy, T J Perren, A Protheroe, M Seymour, L Tredjdosiewicz

Institute for Cardiovascular Research
Lecturer A J Balmforth, A Hall, G W Reynolds
Professor S G Ball, D F Goldspink, R Hainsworth
Senior Lecturer T F C Batten, P N McWilliam, D A S G Mary, Lip-Bun Tan, P F T Vaughan

Leukaemia Research Fund Centre for Clinical Epidemiology
Director R A Cartwright

Paediatric Epidemiology Group
Director Patricia A McKinney

Prescribing Research Unit
Director C M Harris
Associate Director A D Clayden

Rheumatology and Rehabilitation Research Unit
Principal Research Fellow Alan Tennant
Professor M Anne Chamberlain
Reader B B Seedhom
Senior Lecturer Bipin Bhakta, Vera Neumann

West Riding Medical Research Trust Molecular Medicine Unit
Lecturer Patricia L Coletta
Professor A W Boylston, A F Markham, M Wells
Senior Lecturer D E Meredith, J F J Morrison
Senior Research Fellow Patricia M Clissold

School of Biological Sciences

Director J B C Findlay
Head of School M A Orchard
Secretary E S Gray

Biochemistry and Molecular Biology
Head Edward J Wood
Associate Lecturer W A Bonass, Jennifer Kirkham, C Robinson, P G Stockley
Lecturer A Baker, A Berry, J Colyer, P Gilmartin, A K H Holzenburg, N M Hooper, Jennifer D Houghton, J A Illingworth, J P Knox, S E Radford, S C Wright
Professor S B Brown, J B C Findlay, P J F Henderson, A C T North, S E V Phillips, A J Turner
Reader S A Baldwin, B D Hames, P F Knowles, E J Wood
Research Fellow A Aruna, G Bentley, M Bonade, B E Causier, M C Clarke, Caroline Connolly, Marie Ann Convery, A Corner, A Cox, K N Degtyarenko, D Donnelly, G M Drago, Fiona Gibbs, T D Gibson, M Griffiths, E E T Hansen, G Hughes, C Hurrell, R Hyde, N Ito, Y Kamisughi, Y Knight, R Leach, Yi Li, Wei-Jun Liang, Catherine J Lilley, T P Macdonald, G E M Martin, Sara Movahedi, M Newman, Catherine A O'Neill, E Parkin, M Parsons, Margarita Perez-Casal, J P Porter, R A Preston, Joanne Proffitt, G J Reynolds, N G Rutherford, Clare E Sansom, C P Scutt, M W Smith, S Stoiloua, G Teakle, G Thompson, J -F Valdor, C A Watkins, Carrie M Wilmot, S R Wood, J C Yang, E A Yates
Senior Lecturer G Eric Blair, A G Booth, A J Geddes, D G Herries, S J Higgins, J E Lydon, W Mackie, M J McPherson, P A Millner, N M Packter, J Howard Parish, J H Walker
Senior Research Fellow Kathleen Barnes, J N Keen, Margaret dos Santos Medeiros, D I Vernon
Senior Teaching Fellow Linda B Bonnett, M Orchard
Teaching Fellow Isobel M Halliburton, Janet Higgins

UNIVERSITIES & MEDICAL SCHOOLS

Visiting Research Fellow A L Kruckeberg
Wellcome Fellow M A Harrison, C Thomas

Microbiology
Principal Research Fellow E Anne Eady
Head K Holland
Hon. Lecturer J N Kearney
Hon. Research Fellow Deborah Gascoyne-Binzi
Hon. Senior Clinical Lecturer A T M Ghoneim
Lecturer M P G Harris, J Heritage, M K Phillips-Jones, J A T Sandoe
Professor I Chopra, E G V Evans, R W Lacey, D J Rowlands
Reader I W Halliburton
Research Fellow H R Ashbee, H M Doherty, J I Ross, Anna M Snelling, J L Tipper
Senior Lecturer D G Adams, D J Adams, J H Cove, Eileen Ingham, K G Kerr, R A Killington, J S Knapp, M H Wilcox
Senior Research Fellow R A Bojar

Pharmacology
Head D A Wray
Lecturer D J Beech, D Donnelly, D Gawler, H Pearson, A Sivaprasadarao
Research Fellow N Hodson
Senior Lecturer C J Bowmer, J P Gent, I E Hughes, M S Yates
Visiting Professor D A Brown, N Shepperson, D J Triggle

Physiology
Principal Research Fellow T G Dobie
Head of Department Kathleen M Rayfield
Hon. Lecturer R G Cooper, D Cotterrell, Surg Rear Admiral Frank St C Golden, H M Snow, M J Tipton
Lecturer S M Harrison, Z Henderson, A J Hulley, Anne E King, N Messenger, D L Turner, E White
Reader A V Holden, M Hunter, F Karim, W Winlow
Research Director C H Orchard
Research Fellow Aziz Asqhar, Sunil Bhandari, V N Biktashev, Yu Dong Bo, Sarah Calaghan, Amar Chiter, Guido Drago, S J Harris, S S Hasan, Christopher Howarth, M Hussain, Makoto Kawai, Iftikhar Khan, Sergei Khasabov, Zuzana Knudsen, Shuhua Liv, Ruth McDonald, David Marples, Z Shui, H Zhang, Du Zhi
Senior Lecturer D J Potts, Kathleen M Rayfield, Elaine M Whitaker, Deborah J Withington
Senior Teaching Fellow M S Hetherington, Anne C Robinson

School of Dentistry

Clarendon Way, Leeds LS2 9LU
Tel: 0113 233 6173 Fax: 0113 233 6278

Dean W J Hume
Institute Director and Dean of the School W J Hume

Child Dental Health
Lecturer A Beese, M S Duggal, Friederike Luther, K J Toumba
Professor M E J Curzon, Sonia A Williams
Research Fellow E A O'Sullivan
Teaching Fellow I Ahmed, Rebecca V Todd

Dental Surgery
Head of Division M Corrigan
Hon. Senior Lecturer R Loukota, J Russell
Research Fellow P Hart
Senior Lecturer A S High, D Main, J Pedlar

Oral Biology
Head C Robinson
Lecturer W A Bonass, S J Brookes
Professor J Kirkham, P Marsh
Senior Lecturer D Devine, R C Shore

Restorative Dental Medicine
Head J C Glyn Jones

Lecturer Kathryn Fox, D Lynn Gutteridge, Dominic Hassall, M Manogue, B R Nattress, C J W Patterson, Kathleen Powell, D Tinsley, Aru Tugnait, C C Youngson
Professor R M Basker
Senior Lecturer D Valerie Clerehugh, D M Martin, C J Watson

School of Medicine

Dean of Postgraduate Dental Education J Ralph
Dean of Postgraduate Medical Education R MacDonald
Dean of School of Medicine P Guillou
Director of Learning and Teaching D Cottrell
Department Chair & Professor P J McMahon
Learning and Teaching Dean M Manogue
Lecturer S Habib Kashi
Professor R A Dickson, D Johnston, M Lavin, W G Lewis, I G Martin, S S Somers
Research Dean M Smith
Senior Lecturer P A Lodge, P A Millner, J V, Reynolds, S A Sadek, H M Sue-Ling

Cardiovascular Medicine
Professor S Ball, R Hainsworth, A Hall
Senior Lecturer A Balmforth, T Batten, D Mary, G Reynolds, L -B Tan

General Surgery, Medicine and Anaesthesia
Lecturer J Britton, P Clark, S Dexter, K Dolan, S Everett, H Gorton, P Hamlin, D Jayne, S Preston, A Sarela, D Tooley
Professor F R Ellis, P Guillou, P Howdle, M McMahon
Senior Lecturer D Burke, G Clark, R Heatley, P Hopkins, M Hull, P Moayyedi, D O'Riordain, M Vucevic

Medical Physics
Lecturer S Clamp
Professor M Smith
Research Fellow A Fitzgerald, S Kelly, E Pittard, S Tanner, M Westwood
Senior Lecturer M Barker, A Cowen, J Evans
Senior Research Fellow B Oldroyd, M Stringer

Molecular Epidemiology Unit
Lecturer M Routledge
Professor C Wild
Reader A Hay
Research Fellow J Allan, Y Gong, L Hardie, P Turner, K White
Senior Fellow C Schorah

Molecular Medicine
Lecturer P Coletta
Professor D Bonthron, A Boyleston, A Markham, R Mueller, G Sandle
Senior Lecturer M Hull, C Inglehearn, J Isaacs, D Meredith, A Mighell

Musculoskeletal and Rehabilitation Medicine
Lecturer P Giannoudis, B Griffiths, R Hall
Nurse Lecturer J Hill
Professor H Bird, M Chamberlain, R Dickson, P Emery, A Tennant
Reader B Seedhom
Senior Lecturer B Bhakta, P Helliwell, J Isaacs, R Kent, D Limb, P Milner, V Neumann, D Veale

Obstetrics and Gynaecology
Lecturer E.G.R. Downes
Professor H Cuckle, J O Drife, R Gosden, J Walker
Reader J Thornton
Senior Lecturer S Duffy, C Landon, D Miller, H Picton, N Simpson, Pamela Taylor

Paediatrics and Child Health
Chair and Professor M I Levene
Deputy Chair & Senior Lecturer P.R.F. Dear

Lecturer M G Bradbury, F Campbell, C J Darling, P Kapila, D C Murdoch-Eaton, C M Wood
Professor S. Roy Meadow

Pathology
Lecturer A Cairns, J Stahlschmidt
Professor M Dixon, A Hanby, R Mueller, P Quirke
Senior Lecturer L Bridges, P Burns, A Franks, R Jones, N Mapstone

Primary Care
Lecturer H Moore
Professor W Ahmad, P Heywood
Senior Lecturer S Ali, A Evans, R Sutcliffe, J Thistlethwaite

Psychiatry and Behavioural Sciences
Head D J Cotterell
Lecturer S Barton, S Curran, T Hughes, S P J Lynch, S Smart, C T Williams
Professor R H S Mindham, S Morley, A C P Simms
Senior Lecturer Jan Aldridge, A Beese, Jan H Burns, A W J Butler, A R Dabbs, S J Harris, A J Hill, T Jerram, D Owens, L Pieri, S G Read, A Worrall-Davies

Vascular Medicine
Professor J Davies, P Grant, T Roberts
Senior Lecturer A Catto, M Feely, J Wales

University of Liverpool

Liverpool L69 3BX
Tel: 0151 794 2000
Website: www.liv.ac.uk

Vice-Chancellor P N Love
Dean of the Faculty of Medicine M J Johnson
Postgraduate Dean D R Graham
Admissions Sub-Dean R C Richards
Registrar M D Carr
Academic Sub-Dean S Kaney, D I Lewis-Jones, J R G Nash
Administrative Sub-Dean G A Bridgett

School of Dentistry

Administrator M Wainwright

Clinical Dental Sciences
Dean of Dental Studies G Embery
Head L H Mair
Hon. Lecturer D E J Bowden, J S Brown, J I Cawood, J C Cooper, M Davies, P Hardy, R A Howell, G M Humphris, A M Jenner, J W Jones, B K Klaus, D R Llewelyn, K M Milson, T Nisbet, S J Rudge
Hon. Tutor C Arnold, F M Daley, K J Davis, H A Dreaves, L Gough, J Husain, R S Moore, T A Morris, S Mysorekar, S M O'Brien, A J P Riley, J C Riley, S M Stewart, M C Williams, S M Woodward, J M Wyatt
Lecturer N Cooper, Carol E Dewhurst, P J Farrelly, Judith M Fletcher, M P Forde, M J Gregory, S A Hibbert, D J Holt, N M Jedynakiewicz, N Kemp, D K Lithgow-Smith, Lesley P Longman, L H Mair, N Martin, A Milosevic, G Peers, S E Rimmer, J W Smalley, P M Smith, Eileen M Theil, A Triantafyllou, E Varga, J S T Willasey
Professor G Embery, J K Field, J Scott, A Watts
Senior Lecturer D Adams, J Appleton, E A Field, K S Last, G T R Lee, M V Martin, C Parnell, G West, M J Williams

School of Health Science

Director of Health and Community Care Research Unit E Perkins
Lecturer M S Ling

School of Medicine

Lecturer S L Fowell
Professor J G Bligh

Senior Lecturer P Bradley

Anaesthetics
Professor R Jones, M Leuwer
Senior Lecturer P D Booker

Child Health
Director of Studies (Child Development & Handicap) L Rosenbloom
Hon. Lecturer J B S Coulter, Anne S Garden, P J Howard, D J Kitchiner
Hon. Senior Lecturer S Ryan
Lecturer S P Wardle
Professor Richard W I Cooke, D A Lloyd
Reader A M Weindling
Senior Lecturer H I Ellis, P D Losty, C S Smith, R L Smyth

Clinical Chemistry
Professor A Shenkin
Reader W D Fraser
Senior Lecturer M J Diver

Clinical Engineering
Hon. Lecturer A Bakran, M C Brown, A C Fisher, G R Lightfoot
Lecturer R A Black, P J Doherty, J A Hunt, N Martin, R L Williams
Professor D F Williams
Senior Lecturer T V How

Clinical Psychology
Hon. Lecturer J C Butler, D G Heywood, J D McGinley, M A Potier de la Morandiere
Lecturer J Bogg, S Kaney, A E O'Kane
Professor P Salmon
Senior Lecturer J McGuire, T Mason

Geriatric Medicine
Hon. Lecturer S J Benbow
Lecturer D N Carmichael, Vanita Jassel
Professor M D W Lye
Senior Lecturer M A Gosney

Haematology
Hon. Lecturer Jennifer K M Duguid, Vanessa J Martlew, P D Sherrington, J A Tappin, B E Woodcock
Lecturer S D Griffiths, A R Pettitt
Professor J C Cawley
Reader R E Clark, R E Clark
Senior Lecturer C H Toh

Human Anatomy and Cell Biology
Hon. Lecturer I J Mackenzie, P K Ray
Lecturer Yvonne S Allen, P H Dangerfield, M M Gunther, J C Jarvis, Rhian V Lynch, G Macho, D J Moss, S R Pennington, A W M Simpson
Professor P Cobbold, J A Gallagher
Reader R H Crompton, R H Crompton
Senior Lecturer M R Chester, R C Connolly, D H Edgar, C V Howard, S Marshall-Clarke, R C Richards
Teacher L Thomson

Immunology
Lecturer B F Flanagan, P J McLaughlin, G S Vince, D C West
Professor P M Johnson
Senior Lecturer S E Christmas

Institute of Human Ageing
Hon. Lecturer A M Holehan
Lecturer A J Sixsmith
Senior Lecturer B J Merry

Medical Imaging
Lecturer J C Akehurst, E T Henshaw, V J Moscrip, J M Walton
Professor G H Whitehouse
Senior Lecturer N D Scutt, Vanessa A Sluming

UNIVERSITIES & MEDICAL SCHOOLS

Medical Microbiology and Genitourinary Medicine
Hon. Lecturer U L Andrady, N A Cunliffe, V Damjanovic, J J Neal, C M Parry, C Winstanley
Professor C A Hart
Reader H K F Van Saene
Senior Lecturer D Baxby, D H L Birley, P Shears, G W Smith, C-y W Tong

Medicine
Director of Studies (Ophthalmology) M Batterbury
Hon. Lecturer C Bing, I E Buchan, L G Clearkin, S Dryden, H Gibson, N M Lowe, B J Moriarty, R P Phillips, J Phoenix, M T Watts
Lecturer F J Andrews, T J Bayley, K Bodger, B J Campbell, R Campbell, L Davies, O Gerasimenko, M Hussain, D Hutchinson, J Jenkins, K S Leong, I J London, F McArdle, J D Milton, A Palejwala, L Pazmany, M F Phillips, H J Power, D M Pritchard, J N Roberts, A G M Scholes, D M Tidd, R L Williams, C E Willoughby
Professor P M Calverley, I Grierson, G Hart, M J Jackson, J M Rhodes, H M Warenius, A J M Watson, D G Wilkinson, G Williams
Reader G V Gill
Senior Lecturer M R Chester, D T Connelly, R W K Costello, J A Green, R D Griffiths, P S Hiscott, Rustom Knox, M G Lombard, R J Moots, G R Sharpe, P S Widdowson, J P H Wilding

Musculoskeletal Science
Hon. Lecturer D A Broclie, P H Dangerfield, E M Holt
Lecturer Q Yin
Professor S P Frostick, J A Gallagher
Senior Lecturer G Kemp

Neurological Science
Lecturer A Marson, T Solomon
Professor D W Chadwick, P C Warnke
Senior Lecturer G A Baker, I Hart, A P Moore

Nursing
Hon. Lecturer H M Davies, P Dylak, R A Heath, K James, Susan M Wilkinson
Lecturer P Alexander, J Billington, C Booth, A L Caress, M Farrell, M Kenrick, M J McKeown, S Meah, D Mercer, C L Watkins, E Whitehead, L Woods
Professor Caroline Carlisle
Senior Lecturer M Flynn, T Mason
Tutor Angela Hogg, R Whittington

Obstetrics and Gynaecology
Hon. Lecturer N Van den Brock
Lecturer M J M Luckas, Devender Roberts, D Tincello
Professor C M Gosden, J P Neilson
Senior Lecturer Z Alfirevic, Anne S Garden, D I Lewis-Jones

Occupational Therapy
Lecturer M Anderson, A Armfield, R F Couch, J Donaldson, B Tyldesley, M A Willis
Senior Lecturer J M Martin

Orthotics
Hon. Lecturer M Batterbury, A Chandna, I B Marsh
Lecturer Sarah J P Lewin, D Newsham, H P Orton, P D Ridges, F J A Rowe
Reader M Gail Stephenson

Otorhinolaryngology
Hon. Lecturer G R Lightfoot, P E Young
Lecturer P D Morar
Professor A S Jones

Pathology
Hon. Lecturer K D Murray, P A Smith, Lesley S Turnbull
Lecturer Y Ke
Professor C S Foster
Reader J R Gosney, T R Helliwell
Senior Lecturer C S Herrington, P S Hiscott, G K Kokai, I W McDicken, J R G Nash, P H Smith

Pharmacology and Therapeutics
Hon. Lecturer C Jackson, G O Kokwaro, P Morgan, W M Watkins
Lecturer Bridget Maher, P M O'Neill, N E Williams
Professor D J Back, A M Breckenridge, M Orme, B K Park, M Pirmohamed, T J Walley, S A Ward, P A Winstanley
Reader J W Coleman, W G McLean
Senior Lecturer S J Coker, I G Edwards, N R Kitteringham, W E Lindup

Physiology
Lecturer T Burelyga, M J Clague, G Erdemli, R J Gayton, A Morgan, M J Taggart, D C M Taylor
Professor R D Burgoyne, R Dimaline, G J Dockray, O H Petersen, Susan C Wray
Reader D V Gallagher, A Varro
Senior Lecturer A V Tepiken

Physiotherapy
Lecturer J M Finlayson, A Gilbert, C E Kitteringham, H M Lean, J Sharp, J P Simpson, M T Swinfield, S Tittle
Senior Lecturer Eileen Thornton

Primary Care
Community Clinical Teacher A Barker, R Bonsor, P Burns, S Magennis, P Owens, J Quinn, C Thomas
Lecturer F M Ford, L J Frith, A Hak, J Henry, Margaret S Ling, A C Litva, A Sixsmith, S P Smith
Professor C F Dowrick, A Jacoby
Reader P E Bundred
Senior Lecturer M B Gabbay, F S Mair

Psychiatry
Hon. Lecturer J Higgins
Lecturer R Davis, C F M McCracken, J H Payne, C P Routh
Professor S G Gowers, J W Hill, S G Hill, R K Morriss, D G Wilkinson, K C Wilson
Senior Lecturer V K Sharma, M Swinton

Public Health
Hon. Lecturer K D Ardern, I R Cumming, P Grey, B Hanratly, G K Hayhurst, A Hoskins, J Hotchkiss, M A O'Dwyer, C Quigley, C M Regan, J A Reid, D Sen, K L Smith, I Sram, Q Syed
Lecturer L Kennedy, S Sheard, D L Stanistreet, R Tudor Edwards, C R West
Professor S Capewell, M M Whitehead
Senior Lecturer N G Bruce, G Maudsley, M J Platt, A J R Scott-Samuel, Evelyn M I Williams
Visiting Professor J Ashton, R Hussey

School of Tropical Medicine

Pembroke Place, Liverpool L3 5QA
Tel: 0151 708 9393 Fax: 0151 708 8733

Professor J Hemingway

International Health Division
Lecturer A Brown, K de Koning, T Martineau, J Martinez, P J Nickson, E Potts, M L Vasquez
Middlemass Hunt Professor of International Community Health A Kroeger
Senior Lecturer P Garner, D Haran, P Nickson, P Sandiford, A W Smith

Molecular Biology and Immunology Division
Lecturer P A Bates
Professor A E Bianco, J M Crampton, M Hommel, R D G Theakston
Reader G V Gill
Senior Lecturer A G Craig

Parasite and Vector Biology
Lecturer D Williams
Professor R W Ashford, M W Service, H Townson, A J, Trees

Senior Lecturer G Barnish, M Birley, M L Chance, I G Edwards, I Marshall

Tropical Medicine Division
Lecturer L Cuevas, K Floyd, N French, Y Ganley, J Hill, C Piper, M J Samuel, B Schlecht, D Wilkinson
Professor C Gilks, M E Molyneux
Senior Lecturer N Beeching, B J Brabin, L Brabin, J B S Coulter, K A Fletcher, S Graham, S Macfarlane, P Shears, D H Smith, S B Squire, G B Wyatt

Degrees and diplomas
MBChB, BN, MD, ChM, MSc, MPhil, PhD, BSc, MChOrth, MCommH, MPH, MPsychMEd, DClinPsychol., MTropPaeds, MTropMed., MRad, BDS, MDS, MPhil (in Dentistry), MDentSci & PhD, DTM & H, DTCH, DMRD, MSc/Pg Dip/Pg Cert

Recognised Clinical Institutions
Aintree Hospitals NHS Trust, Ashworth Hospital, Cardiothoracic Centre Liverpool NHS Trust, Clatterbridge Hospital, Countess of Chester Hospital, Glan Clwyd District General Hospital, Greaves Hall, Halton General Hospital, Leighton Hospital, Liverpool Women's Hospital, Macclesfield Hospital, Ormskirk and District General Hospital, Royal Liverpool and Broadgreen Hospitals University NHS Trust, Royal Liverpool Children's NHS Trust, Royal Liverpool University Dental Hospital, Sefton General Hospital, Southport District General Hospital, University Hospital Aintree, Walton Centre for Neurology and Neurosurgery NHS Trust, Walton Hospital, West Cheshire NHS Trust, Whiston Hospital, Winwick Hospital, Wrexham Maelor Hospital

University of London

Senate House, London WC1E 7HU
Tel: 020 7862 8051 Fax: 020 7862 8052
Email: medinfo@medfac.lon.ac.uk
Website: www.lon.ac.uk

Vice-Chancellor Graham Zellick
Pro Vice-Chancellor for Medicine & Dentistry Robert Boyd
Academic Registrar Gillian Roberts
Secretary & Registrar for Medicine David Eames

Degrees and diplomas
MB, BS, MD, MS, DSc, BMedSci, BDS, MClinDent, MDS, MSc

Schools of the University
Imperial College Faculty of Medicine, Imperial College of Science, Technology and Medicine, King's College London, London School of Hygiene and Tropical Medicine, Queen Mary and Westfield College, School of Pharmacy, Royal Free and University College Medical School of University College London, St Bartholomew's and The Royal London School of Medicine and Dentistry

Recognised Clinical Institutions
Barts and The London NHS Trust

University of Manchester

Oxford Road, Manchester M13 9PL
Tel: 0161 275 2000
Website: www.man.ac.uk

Vice-Chancellor M B Harris
Registrar & Secretary E Newcomb
Secretary to the Faculty G A Evans

Dental School

Higher Cambridge Street, Manchester M15 6FH
Tel: 0161 275 6602

Dean A S Blinkhorn, J F McCord

Bacteriology
Reader D B Drucker

Basic Dental Science
Head of Department and Professor M W J Ferguson

Biomaterials Science
Professor D C Watts

Dental Public Health
Hon. Clinical Lecturer Jacqueline Duxbury, Sabrina Fuller, Madeline Harding, Anthony Jenner, Geoffrey O Taylor, J Gory Whittle
Hon. Clinical Senior Lecturer Roger Elwood
Lecturer Rebecca C Craven, Michelle Crossley, Tatiana McFarlane
Professor R M Davies, Elizabeth J Kay
Reader Helen V Worthington
Senior Lecturer Martin Tickle

Operative Dentistry and Endodontology
Clinical Lecturer P A Brunton, L A Morrow
Consultant Alison J E Qualtrough
Hon. Clinical Senior Lecturer Margaret A Wilson

Oral and Diagnostic Medical Sciences
Hon. Clinical Lecturer Martin Patrick, M Pemberton, William Tait, Robert Woodwards
Lecturer D H Carter, Jacqueline James, Vivien E Rushton, Elizabeth D Theaker, Catherine M Waters
Professor K Horner, P Sloan
Senior Lecturer A J Duxbury, N S Thakkar

Oral and Maxillofacial Surgery
Hon. Clinical Lecturer R J Middlehurst, B T Musgrove
Lecturer R Oliver
Senior Lecturer P Coulthard, Ameeta Joshi

Orthodontics
Hon. Clinical Lecturer D H Lewis, M J F Read
Lecturer D R Bearn, Anne-Marie Glenny, Nicola Mandall, Urike Mayer
Professor M J Dixon, K D O'Brien, W C Shaw
Senior Lecturer Gunvor Semb

Paediatric Dentistry
Hon. Clinical Lecturer Fiona A Blinkhorn, Collette Bridgman, A N Crawford, Felicity Murray
Hon. Clinical Senior Lecturer F J Hill
Professor A S Blinkhorn
Senior Lecturer I C Mackie

Periodontology
Hon. Clinical Lecturer David Aldridge
Senior Lecturer Peter S Hull

Primary Dental Care
Consultant A C Mellor

Prosthodontology
Head of Department J F McCord
Lecturer D C Attrill, S J Davies, P W Smith
Senior Lecturer in Dental Education Gillian Hoad-Reddick
Senior Lecturer in Restorative Dentistry H Devlin

Medicine, Dentistry, Nursing and Pharmacy

Cancer Studies
Professor of Cancer Epidemiology Pat Price, C B Woodman
Professor of Cancer Studies R J Hawkins, A Howell
Professor of Medical Oncology J T Gallagher, N Thatcher
Professor of Radiological Physics P C Williams

UNIVERSITIES & MEDICAL SCHOOLS

Child Health, Obstetrics and Gynaecology, Child Health, Medical Genetics

Professor of Child Health P E Clayton
Professor of Child Health and Paediatrics T J David
Professor of Child Health and Physiology C P Sibley
Professor of Gynaecological Oncology H C, Kitchener
Professor of Human Genetics A Read
Professor of Maternal and Foetal Health P N Baker
Professor of Medical Genetics D Donnai
Professor of Paediatric Oncology O B Eden
Professorial Research Fellow Jillian M Birch

Epidemiology and Health Sciences

ARC Professor of Rheumatic Disease Epidemiology A J Silman
Professor of Biomedical Statistics G Dunn
Professor of Epidemiological and Social Sciences A R Pickles
Professor of Epidemiology G F Macfarlane
Professor of Immunogenetics W E R Ollier
Professor of Occupational and Environmental Medicine R Agius, N M Cherry
Professor of Public Health R F Heller
Professor of Rheumatology and Musculoskeletal Engineering D P M Symmons

Hope Hospital

Professor of Dermatology C Griffiths
Professor of Emergency Medicine D W Yates
Professor of Endocrine Science A White
Professor of Gastroenterology D G Thompson
Professor of Geriatric Medicine M A Horan, R C Tallis
Professor of Hand Surgery J K Stanley
Professor of Orthopaedic Surgery C S B Galasko

Imaging Science and Biomedical Engineering

Professor Emeritus I Isherwood
Professor of Diagnostic Radiology J E Adams, A Jackson
Professor of Medical Biophysics C Taylor, S R Williams
Professor of Molecular Imaging T Jones

Laboratory Medicine

Professor of Infectious Diseases R C Matthews
Professor of Medical Microbiology J P Burnie
Professor of Neuropathology D M A Mann
Professor of Pathological Science A J Freemont, J McClure

Medicine and Surgery Central

Professor of Medical Biochemistry C M Kielty
Professor of Medicine J R E Davis, P N Durrington, A M Heagerty
Professor of Anaesthesia B J Pollard
Professor of Cardiac Physiology D Eisner
Professor of Cardiology C J Garratt
Professor of Medicine A J M Boulton
Professor of Medicine (Cardiology) L Neyses
Professor of Ophthalmology D McLeod

Primary Care

Professor of General Practice M Marshall, M O Roland
Professor of Health Services Research B Sibbald, D Wilkin
Professor of Social Policy C Glendinning
Professor of Teaching Medicine in the Community C R Whitehouse
Professor of the Sociology of Health Care A Rogers
Professorial Fellow J Hayden

Psychiatry and Behavioural Sciences

Professor of Adult Psychiatry S W Lewis
Professor of Child & Adolescent Psychiatry R C Harrington
Professor of Clinical Psychology N Tarrier
Professor of Community Psychiatry F H Creed
Professor of Personal Social Services Research Unit D Challis
Professor of Psychiatric Social Work M J Kerfoot
Professor of Psychiatry L Appleby, J F W Deakin

Professor of Psychological Medicine G P Maguire
Professor of Psychological Medicine & Medical Psychotherapy E A Guthrie
Professor of the Psychiatry of Old Age A S Burns

South Manchester

Professor of Medical Education P A O'Neill
Professor of Plastic and Reconstructive Surgery D A McGrouther
Professor of Respiratory Medicine A Woodcock
Professor of Surgery C McCollum
Professor of Thoracic Medicine A K Webb

School of Biological Sciences

Professor Richard Balment, Neil Bulleid, Maynard Chase, Alan Crossman, Michael Dixon, Michael Emes, Mark Ferguson, David Garrod, Michael Grant, Roger Green, Keith Gull, Tim Hardingham, Stephen High, Martin Humphries, Ian Hutchinson, Karl Kadler, Andrew Loudon, Steve Oliver, Frank Owen, Leon Poller, Ian Roberts, Nancy Rothwell, Colin Sibley, Colin Stirling, David Tomlinson, Anthony Trinci, Arthur Weston, Anne White

Reader Eric Bell, Jayne Brookman, David Drucker, Malcolm Jones, David Moore, Ian Morris, John Sheehan, Adrian Shuttleworth, Paul Slater, Rodger Small, Rodger Wood

Degrees and diplomas
MB, ChB, BSc, BNurs,MD, ChM, MSc BDS, MDS, DDS, PhD, DMR (T), FRC, MRCPsych.

Recognised Clinical Institutions
South Manchester University Hospitals NHS Trust

University of Newcastle upon Tyne

Faculty of Medicine, Medical School/Dental School, Framlington Place, Newcastle upon Tyne NE2 4HH
Tel: 0191 222 6000, 0191 222 7007 Fax: 0191 222 6137, 0191 222 6521
Website: www.ncl.ac.uk

Dean of Dentistry J J Murray
Dean of Medicine P H Baylis
Postgraduate Dean P Hill
Postgraduate Sub-Dean A D J Pearson
Associate Clinical Sub-Dean for Durham & Teesside R W Bilous
Associate Clinical Sub-Dean for Northumbria J R Barton
Associate Clinical Sub-Dean for Tyne & Wear MP Clarke
Clinical Sub-Dean S Macphail
Sub-Dean of Biomedical Studies E Williams
Director of Biomedical Sciences A Allen
Director of Medical Studies & Deputy Dean of Medicine R K Jordan
Director of Research D E Neal
Academic Sub-Dean S Cholerton
Medical School Administrator Michelle Parker
Postgraduate Tutor J A Kirby
Senior Tutor A F Fairbairn, J A Spencer
Senior Tutor for Admissions J W Soames

Child and Adolescent Psychiatry

Professor A S Le Couteur
Senior Lecturer S R Bhate, C A Kaplan, P McArdle, H R McConachie

Child Health

Head of Department A W Craft
Lecturer S C Clifford, G J Clowry, M Pourfarzam
Professor of Community Child Health S N Jarvis
Professor of Paediatric Biochemistry K Bartlett
Professor of Paediatric Neuroscience J A Eyre
Professor of Paediatric Oncology A D J Pearson

UNIVERSITY OF NEWCASTLE UPON TYNE

Reader in Experimental Paediatric Oncology A G Hall
Reader in Neuro-Oncological Pathology D Ellison
Reader in Paediatric Epidemiology L Parker
Senior Lecturer T D Cheetham, R J Forsyth, H Foster, B Jaffray, R Skinner, J Thomas
Senior Lecturer in Community Child Health A F Colver, E M L Towner
Senior Lecturer in Forensic Paediatrics C M De San Lazaro
Senior Lecturer in Paediatric Oncology K P Windebank

Child and Adolescent Psychiatry
Professor A S Le Couteur
Senior Lecturer S R Bhate, C A Kaplan, P McArdle, H R McConachie

Institute of Human Genetics

Lecturer R C Davies, D J Elliott, D Henderson
Medical Director J Burn
Professor K M D Bushby, J A Goodship, A Schedl
Reader H Peters
Scientific Director T Strachan
Senior Lecturer S G Ball, M S Jackson, B D Keavney, S J Lindsay, S Pearce, A Trainer

School of Biochemistry and Genetics

Head of School M A Hughes
Lecturer C St-J Butler, T Jowett, W M MacFarlane, N J Morris, I C West, SK Whitehall
MRC Fellows J D Brown, J Quinn
Professor S J Yeaman, B A Connolly, P T Emmerson, A R Hawkins, J H Lakey, N J Robinson
Reader B A Morgan
Senior Lecturer C A Austin, M P Rogers, R Virden

School of Clinical and Laboratory Sciences

Head of School S J Proctor

Cancer Research Unit
Director (Cancer Research Unit) A H Calvert
Lecturer N J Curtin, J M Lunn, M J Tilby
Professor R J Griffin, D R Newell
Reader B W Durkacz, A G Hall, J Lunec
Senior Lecturer A V Boddy

Centre for Liver Research
Director A D Burt

Clinical Biochemistry
Head of Department C H Self
Lecturer D B Cook
Professor K Bartlett, C J McNeil
Reader M F Laker
Senior Lecturer H K Datta, A W Skillen, G A Turner

Haematology
Head of Department S J Proctor
Lecturer P G Middleton
Senior Lecturer A M Dickinson, A L Lennard, S G O'Brien

Medical Physics
Head of Department B L Diffey
Professor A Murray

Oncology
Head of Department A H Calvert
Lecturer S C Clifford, I. Hardcastle
Reader D. Ellison
Senior Lecturer G G Dark, M W Verrill

Pathology
Head of Department A D Burt
Lecturer J J Anderson, F G Charlton, M G Thompson

Professor B R Westley
Senior Lecturer B Angus, J N Bulmer, P N Cooper, N Leonard, F E B May, C Wright

Radiology
Head of Department and Senior Lecturer J P Owen
Senior Lecturer A Coulthard

School of Clinical Medical Sciences

Head of School O F W James

Cardiology
Head of Department B Keavney
Senior Lecturer J P Bourke

Diabetes and Metabolism
Head of Department S M Marshall
Professor K G M M Alberti, R W Bilous, P D Home, R Taylor
Reader L Agius, M Walker
Senior Lecturer N C Unwin, J U Weaver

Endocrinology
Lecturer S H S Pearce
Professor P H Baylis, P A Kendall-Taylor
Senior Lecturer S G Ball, R A James, R Quinton, C P F Redfern

Gastroenterology and Hepatology
Head of Department M F Bassendine
Fellow D E J Jones
Lecturer M G Bramble, I Cobden, P T Donaldson, W R Ellis, K Matthewson, K E N W Oppong, N P Thompson
Professor J R Barton, C P Day
Senior Lecturer R Lendrum, J C Mansfield, C O Record, M Welfare

Geriatric Medicine
Head of Department R A Kenny
Professor D H Barer, G A Ford, C S Gray, O F W James
Reader R M Francis
Senior Lecturer Michele Davis, J E O'Connell, H Rodgers, H A Wynne

Gerontology
Professor T B L Kirkwood
Senior Lecturer A A Burkle, T von Zglinicki

Infection and Tropical Medicine
Head of Department E L C Ong
Senior Lecturer M H Snow

Medical Cell Biology
Head of Department A Geerts

Nephrology
Head of Department R Wilkinson
Lecturer N A Hoenich
Senior Lecturer T H J Goodship, T H Thomas, M K Ward

Respiratory Medicine
Head of Department Professor Gibson
Professor P A Corris, P D Snashall
Senior Lecturer S Bourke, P J Cook, D J Hendrick, S C Stenton

Rheumatology
Head of Department T E Cawston
Lecturer A D Rowan
Reader N McKie

School of Dentistry

Faculty of Medicine, Dental School, Framlington Place, Newcastle upon Tyne NE2 4HH
Tel: 0191 222 6000 ext: 8347 Fax: 0191 222 6137

Head of School J J Murray

UNIVERSITIES & MEDICAL SCHOOLS

Child Dental Health
Lecturer A Maguire, P J Moynihan, N A Niven, P J Waterhouse
Professor J J Murray
Senior Lecturer P H Gordon, R S Hobson, R S Lowry

Dental Radiology
Lecturer A M Adams

Oral and Maxillofacial Surgery
Head of Department P J Thomson
Lecturer M Greenwood, U J Moore
Senior Lecturer K Fanibunda, I C Martin, J G Meechan

Oral Biology
Head of Department R R B Russell
Lecturer D S Brown, S D Hogg, P J Moynihan, J J Taylor

Oral Pathology
Head of Department J V Soames
Lecturer M F Reed
Senior Lecturer A Nolan

Restorative Dentistry
Head of Department R A Seymour
Lecturer P M Preshaw, S K Sidhu, E R Smart
Professor J F McCabe, A W G Walls
Senior Lecturer N M Girdler, P A Heasman, N J A Jepson, J G Steele, J M Thomason, R W Wassell, J M Whitworth

School of Health Sciences

Head of School S Bond
Professor M P Eccles

Centre for Health Services Research
Head of Department S Bond
Professor J Bond, C May

Department of Microbiology and Immunology
Professor & Head of Department C E Hormaeche
Lecturer E G Routledge, J S Turner-Cavet
Professor M A Kehoe, G S Besra
Reader C R Harwood, J H Robinson
Senior Lecturer C M Anjam Khan, C G Brooks, J E Calvert, R Demarco de Hormaeche, A G Diamond, A C Fay, R. Frederick, I C Hancock, R Scott, G P Spickett, G L Toms, E Williams

Epidemiology and Public Health
Lecturer R Bell, P R Edwards, C M Fischbacher, P McNamee, S Moffatt, T Pless-Mulloli, D Walker
Professor R G Thomson
Senior Lecturer D M Howel, H Rodgers, N C Unwin, M White, P M Whitty

Primary Health Care
Senior Lecturer and Head of Department P H Pearson
Lecturer J Deckers, J O E Harland, P Jones, J P K McCollum, T R H Price, S Purdy, J H Roberts, J. A. N. Slade, D Slowie, B G Vernon
Professor M Eccles, N T A Oswald, J A Spencer
Senior Lecturer K P Jones, A L Robinson, C R Stacy

Sowerby Centre for Health Informatics
Professor I N Purves

School of Neurosciences and Psychiatry

Head of School J B Harris
Senior Lecturer T P Kelly

Department of Neurosciences
Senior Lecturer and Head of Department S McHanwell
Professor M P Barnes, J B Harris, R N Lightowlers, C R Slater, D M Turnbull

Senior Lecturer D Bates, P M Bradley, D J Burn, N E F Cartlidge, M P Clarke, A Goonetilleke, P G Griffiths, G R Hammond, P R Murphy, E Sernagor, A C Webb

MRC Newcastle Centre Development for Clinical Brain Aging
Director J A Edwardson

Psychiatry
Lecturer S E Gartside, B Gillmer, D A Huey, S R J Moorhead, S Parsons, C Stevenson, A J Thomas
Professor I N Ferrier, P J Barker, D Grubin, C D Ingram, I G McKeith, J T O'Brien, R H Perry, A H Young
Professorial Research Fellow R N Kalaria
Senior Lecturer P L Cornwall, P G Ince, B Lunn, J M McCarthy, P B Moore, G P O'Brien, P M Shajahan

School of Pharmacological, Environmental and Dermatological Sciences

Head of School M D Rawlins

Dermatology
Head of Department N J Reynolds
Lecturer M A Birch-Machin

Environmental and Occupational Medicine
Head of Department P G Blain
Lecturer O Sepai
Reader F M Williams
Senior Lecturer J Harrison

Pharmacological Sciences
Head of Department M D Rawlins
Lecturer F Kamali, R McQuade
Professor G A Ford
Senior Lecturer S Cholerton, A Daly, S H L Thomas

Physiological Sciences
Head of Department M J Whitaker
Head of Department (Acting) B E Argent
Lecturer K T Jones, A D McDougall
Professor A Allen, B H Hirst, N L Simmons
Reader G G R Green, A C Hurlbert, J P Pearson, D T Thwaites, A Werner
Senior Lecturer C D A Brown, T R Cheek, M A Gray, J W Reed, A Rees, D J Sanders

Psychology
Head of Department M P Young
Lecturer G Balfour, B G Charlton, P L Cornelissen, I Croft, A C Downing, G Erdos, G M Harris, G Jordan, J G Roberts, Y Tadmor, A Thiele
Professor L M Gosling, L T Sharpe
Reader J Lazarus, M Petrie, M J Tovee
Senior Lecturer K H Nott

School of Surgical and Reproductive Sciences

Head of School D E Neal

Anaesthetics
Head of Department P M C Wright
Lecturer S Bower
Senior Lecturer S V Baudouin

Cardiothoracic Surgery
Professor J H Dark

Neurosurgery
Professor A D Mendelow

Obstetrics and Gynaecology
Head of Department S C Robson

Lecturer G N Europe-Finner
Professor J M Davison, W Dunlop
Senior Lecturer S Macphail, E M Michael

Otolaryngology
Professor J A Wilson
Senior Lecturer P N Carding, B Jaffray, I J M Johnson, R H Milner

Surgery
Head T W J Lennard
Lecturer S Ali, B R Davies
Professor J I Gillespie, S M Griffin, D J Leaper, D E Neal, G Stansby
Senior Lecturer S B Kelly, J S Varma, R G Wilson, P D Wright

Transplantation Surgery
Reader J A Kirby

Trauma and Orthopaedic Surgery
Lecturer M A Birch, F-M. Khaw
Professor A W McCaskie
Senior Lecturer J R Williams

Urological Surgery
Lecturer M J Drake
Professor D E Neal
Senior Lecturer J D Kelly, H Y Leung, C N Robson

Recognised Clinical Institutions
Newcastle and North Tyneside Health Authority, Newcastle upon Tyne Dental Hospital, Tees Health Authority

University of Nottingham

Medical School B Floor, Queen's Medical Centre, Nottingham NG7 2UH
Tel: 0115 970 9381 Fax: 0115 970 9922
Website: www.nottingham.ac.uk

Vice-Chancellor Colin M Campbell
Dean of the Faculty of Medicine & Health Sciences P C Rubin
Vice-Dean for Postgraduate Studies Ian Todd
Vice-Dean for Undergraduate Studies Stuart Brown
Postgraduate Dean G Batstone
Clinical Sub-Dean P T Edington
Sub-Dean for Admissions David James
Registrar D J Allen
Adviser in General Practice R N Hedley
Faculty Secretary Chris Farrell
Secretary to the Medical School C J Farrell

Medicine and Health Sciences

Anaesthetics
Lecturer B R Bazendale, K J Girling, J G Hardman
Professor A R Aitkenhead
Senior Lecturer A W A Crossley, G J Hobbs, R P Mahajan

Biochemistry
Lecturer A J Bennett, M A Billett, S Brown, F J Doherty, P Jones, P J Scotting
Professor R E Glass, Dr Gregory, R J Mayer, P E Shaw
Reader M Landon
Senior Lecturer B Middleton, D A White

Child Health
Lecturer Jain Anoopam, Helen Budge, Michael L Capra, Helen Heussler, Catherine Rands, Michael Symonds
Professor Jnete Choomara, Neil Marlow, Nick Rutter, Terence J Stephenson
Reader Leon Polnay
Senior Lecturer Mitch E Blair, Jonathan Punt, Michael H J Vloeberghs, David A Walker

Clinical Laboratory Sciences
Lecturer D Ala'aldeen, J L Byrne, A Cockayne, H Denley, R Edwards, H Grundmann, A P Haynes, K Morgan, F Shakib, M J Thomas, P J Tighe
Professor A M Emmerson, R G Finch, D Greenwood, N Kalsheker, J Lowe, H F Sewell, P Williams
Reader M C Anderson, I Ellis, W L Irving, D Jenkins, A R Robins, N H Russell
Senior Lecturer G Couley, D G Fagan, P D James, L Morgan, S Pinder, R J Powell, G Robinson, R C B Slack, A Stevens, B Thomson, I Todd

General Practice
Lecturer C M Anderson, M Baker, A R Barlow, D G Black, A L Bridgewater, K P H Brown, R D Carlisle, R D Churchill, M F T von Fragstein, A J Hampshire, J Hippisley Cox, C Johnson, K Kaur, P A D Oliver, R P Petchey, N Qureshi, K E Rhodes, N Sparrow, J D Temple
Professor M A L Pringle
Senior Lecturer A J Avery, J A Jones, D Kendrick

Health Care of the Elderly
Lecturer J M Lilley, G T Pinner, O S Sahota
Research Officer A E R Drummond
Senior Lecturer J R F Gladman, R G Jones

Human Anatomy and Cell Biology
Lecturer C Kent, L Leach, C N Ludman, T L Parker, P M C Wigmore
Professor S Downes, T M Mayhew, B S Worthington
Reader R H Clothier
Senior Lecturer A Moody, M K Pratten, R A Sparrow

Learning Disability
Senior Lecturer J A Clegg, A Craft, P J Standen, D N Wilson

Medicine
Lecturer J M Brown, M D Hoherward, J Hughes, R E Langley, L L Pinnington, D Playford, E Stylianou
Professor L Blumhardt, J Carmichael, M Doherty, C J Hawkey, P C Rubin, J S Savill, A E Tattersfield, C D Ward
Reader J R Britton, J C Murray
Senior Lecturer J R Cockroft, D Gray, I P Hall, E H Horn, A J Knox, G G Lennox, Y R Mamida, G V Sawle, A Wilcock, H C Williams, P J Woll

Nursing Studies
Lecturer N J Allcock, M A Avis, M Chapple, L A East, C P Glazebrook, E A Hart, J L Maxwell, A G Meal, S Owen, A M Rafferty, J M Repper, S M Sparrow, H J Wharrad, D M Williams
Professor V C James
Senior Lecturer J Fletcher

Obstetrics and Gynaecology
Lecturer P N Baker, I M Symonds, W Van Wijngaard
Professor S Arulkumaran, J D Brook, I Choonara, S B Fishel, D K James, I R Johnson, F Broughton Pipkin, J A Raeburn, E M Symonds
Reader G M Filshie, A C Perkins
Senior Lecturer K Dowell, J O Gardosi, P V Maynard

Orthopaedic and Accident Surgery
Lecturer Dr Kemp, A R Lyons
Professor W A Wallace
Senior Lecturer M E Batt, B E Scammell

Physiology and Pharmacology
Lecturer S P H Alexander, W R Dunn, P L Greenhaff, D M Randall
Professor T Bennett, S M Gardiner, S J Hill, I A Macdonald, C A Marsden
Reader G W Bennett, D A Kendall
Senior Lecturer K C F Fone, J R Fry, R Mason, A H Short, V Wilson

UNIVERSITIES & MEDICAL SCHOOLS

Physiotherapy
Head of Division I C Rutherford
Clinical Tutor M J Liley
Lecturer J P Fessey, K I W Hyndes, J A Lockwood, S P Mockett, J C L Pitt-Brooke, G Pope, J C Spedding, A I Thomas
Senior Lecturer K Kerr

Psychiatry
Lecturer J S Brewin, R Cantwell, D Clark, J Collier, T J Croudace, C P Glazebrook, S B G Park, S Roberts, S P Singh
Professor C M Bradshaw, P Jones, J B Pearce, E Szabadi
Senior Lecturer C Duggan, E J Feldman, P Garrud, H C Middleton, M R Oates

Public Health Medicine and Epidemiology
Lecturer C A Coupland, D Kendrick, K R Muir, J S Nguyen-van-Tam
Professor C E D Chilvers, P A Gillies, R F A Logan, R J Madeley, B T Williams
Senior Lecturer M E Dewey, K Neal, J C G Pearson, L Rushton, J A White

Surgery
Lecturer P D Gormley, R J Haynes, M H E Robinson, P S Rooney, D M Sibbering, A F Spencer, P J Tighe, N Washington
Professor J P Birchall, R W Blamey, H S Dua, J D Hardcastle, B Rowlands
Senior Lecturer W M K Amoaku, T W Balfour, L G Durrant, G M O'Donoghue, J F R Robertson, J F R Robinson, J H Scholefield

Recognised Clinical Institutions
City Hospital NHS Trust, Derby City Hospital, Derbyshire Children's Hospital, Derbyshire Royal Infirmary, King's Mill Centre for Healthcare Services, Lincoln County Hospital, Mapperley Hospital, Queen's Medical Centre, Nottingham University Hospital NHS Trust

University of Oxford

The Medical School Office, John Radcliffe Hospital, Headington, Oxford OX3 9DU
Tel: 01865 221689 Fax: 01865 750750
Email: enquiries@medschool.ox.ac.uk
Website: www.medicine.ox.ac.uk/medsch/

Director of Clinical Studies S M Burge
Director of Clinical Studies (Deputy) P A Frith
Director of Postgraduate Medical and Dental Education W M G Tunbridge
Director of Pre-Clinical Studies S J Goss
Registrar D R Holmes
Head of Division of Medical Sciences K A Fleming
Secretary of Faculties and Academic Registrar A P Weale
Secretary of the Medical School D E H Bryan

Clinical Medicine

Anaesthetics
Head of Department P Foex
Clinical Lecturer M J Bennett
Clinical Reader J W Sear, J D Young
Professor C E W Hahn, H J MacQuay

Cardiovascular Medicine
Head of Department H C Watkins
Clinical Lecturer R Choudury, S G Myerson
Clinical Reader K M Channon, S Neubauer
Lecturer M Farroll

Clinical Laboratory Sciences
Head of Department K C Gatter
Clinical Lecturer F J Leong, N Meston, A Nemeth, A J Peniket, G J Pillai, G Turner, D H Wyllie
Clinical Reader K A Fleming
Clinical Tutor J E Lortan

Locum S B Fox
Professor D Y Mason, B C Sykes
Reader S J H Ashcroft
University Lecturer R Callaghan, R J Gibbons, S J Peacock, M P E Slack

Clinical Medicine
Head of Department J I Bell
Clinical Lecturer J M Gleadle, A Lalvani
Clinical Tutor B J Angus
Lecturer P H Maxwell, A J Pollard
Professor C I Newbold, R Peto, R E Phillips, P J Ratcliffe, R V Thakker, A R M Townsend, D A Warrell

Clinical Neurology
Head of Department G C Ebers
Clinical Lecturer E A Burton
Clinical Reader M J Donaghy
Professor M M Esiri, A C Vincent

Clinical Pharmacology
Head of Department and Professor D J Kerr
Clinical Lecturer Y K Loke, D B Richards
Clinical Reader J K Aronson

Geriatric Medicine
Lecturer D S Fairweather
Professor John Grimley Evans

Medical Oncology
Head of Department A L Harris

Molecular Medicine
Professor A J McMichael

Obstetrics and Gynaecology
Head of Department D H Barlow
Clinical Lecturer P T-Y Ayuk, K Duckitt
Clinical Reader S H Kennedy, I Z Mackenzie
Lecturer P F Chamberlain, H J Mardon, I L Sargent
Professor C W G Redman

Ophthalmology
Clinical Lecturer P G Ursell
Professor N N Osborne
University Lecturer J M Tiffany

Orthopaedic Surgery
Head of Department A J Carr
Clinical Lecturer H C Brownlow, C F Kellett, D E Porter
Clinical Reader D R Griffin
Lecturer M J O Francis
Professor C J K Bulstrode, R G G Russell

Paediatrics
Head of Department E R Moxon
Clinical Lecturer J P Buttery, M A Herbert, G L Nicolin
Lecturer P B Sullivan
Professor A Harris, A R Wilkinson
University Lecturer J Hull

Palliative Medicine
Clinical Reader R G Twycross

Psychiatry
Head of Department G M Goodwin
Clinical Lecturer J M McCleery, J M B Morrell, B D Sheehan
Clinical Tutor J Price
Professor P J Harrison, R Jacoby, R A Mayou, G Stores
University Lecturer R D Rogers

Public Health and Primary Health Care
Head of Department D Mant
Clinical Lecturer J Patterson

UNIVERSITY OF SHEFFIELD

Clinical Reader T R Lancaster
Lecturer T P C Schofield
Professor R M Fitzpatrick, R A Hope
University Lecturer L M Carpenter, S Graham-Jones, H A W Neil, M Parker, K M Venables, P L N Yudkin

Radiology

Head of Department B J Shepstone
Lecturer N R Moore
University Lecturer S J Golding

Rheumatology

Clinical Lecturer S O Donnelly
Professor B P Wordsworth

Surgery

Clinical Reader and Acting Head of Department L J Hands
Clinical Lecturer P J Horton, G G Libertiny, D J Phillips, N B Steventon
Clinical Reader P R V Johnson
Clinical Tutor A I Handa
Professor K J Wood
Reader J M Austyn
University Lecturer D W R Gray

Physiological Sciences

Human Anatomy and Genetics

Head of Department K E Davies
Professor J F Morris, G M Morriss-Kay
Reader H M Charlton
University Lecturer C A R Boyd, H C Christians, T J Horder, Z Molnar, J S H Taylor, I M G Tracey, C Wilson, M J A Wood

Pathology

Head of Department H Waldman
Professor G G Brownlee, P R Cook, J Errington, S Gordon, N J Proudfoot
Reader G G MacPherson
University Lecturer S J Goss, S V Hunt, D J T Vaux

Pharmacology

Head of Department A D Smith
Professor A F Brading, E Sim
Reader D A Terrar
University Lecturer T C Cunnane, N J Emptage, A Galione

Physiology

Head of Department J C Ellory
Professor C C Ashley, C B Blakemore, J J B Jack, D Noble, A J Parker, T Powell, P A Robbins, J F Stein, R D Vaughan-Jones
Reader D J Paterson
University Lecturer K L Dorrington, S J Judge, C Korbmacher, P C G Nye, O Paulsen, I D Thompson

Degrees and diplomas

BM, BCh, DM, MCh

Recognised Clinical Institutions

Nuffield Orthopaedic Centre NHS Trust, Park Hospital for Children, Radcliffe Infirmary, The Churchill, The John Radcliffe, Warneford Hospital

University of Sheffield

Beech Hill Road, Sheffield S10 2RX
Tel: 0114 271 3413 Fax: 0114 271 3960
Email: k.dewsnap@sheffield.ac.uk
Website: www.shef.ac.uk

Chancellor Peter Middleton

Dental School

Dean C J Smith
Deputy Dean P P Robinson

Child Dental Health

Head of Department A H Brook
Hon. Clinical Lecturer L E Davidson, J D Holmgren, P J Sandler, J P Simpson, D R Willmot, Y L Yap
Hon. Clinical Teacher R Blankenstein, P J B Hill
Hon. Teacher J M Jones
Lecturer S A H Craig, D Regan, H Rodd, G R Wilkinson
Senior Lecturer C J Minors

Dental Services

Head P S Rothwell
Hon. Clinical Lecturer R A Heesterman, H D Lunn, N M Thomas
Hon. Clinical Teacher N Andrews, P M Bateman, J M Bullen, C R J Dinsdale, E I Frazer, E I Grossman, V H Letch, J B R Matthews, R K Mehta, B M Moroney, M E Pendlebury, R E Taylor, L S Worthington
Hon. Lecturer G H D Walker
Lecturer D J Chesham

Oral and Maxillofacial Surgery

Head I M Brook
Hon. Clinical Lecturer M R Bromige, S J Davies, M H Holden, P G McAndrew, M Payne, J D Price, S E Ward
Hon. Clinical Teacher C W Blackburn, G Cheney, K H Figures, J N James, P Leopard, A O M Perriman, J M Robertson, D Simons, B Speculand, P G Watts, H Yusuf
Hon. Research Fellow R C W Dinsdale
Lecturer F M Boissonade, A R Loescher, C M Yeoman
Professor P P Robinson
Senior Lecturer K G Smith

Oral Pathology

Head C J Smith
Lecturer B M J Stringer
Reader G T Craig
Senior Lecturer C W I Douglas, C D Franklin

Restorative Dentistry

Head T F Walsh
Dental Instructor A Johnson, D G Wildgoose
Hon. Clinical Lecturer R I Joshi, P F Wragg
Hon. Clinical Teacher M Bishop, A Buddle, P Diss, C O Freeman, J Hinchliffe, D Hughes, C Kilvington, K Lamb, V Letch, D McDonald, M Masood, J Meyer, D Minors, G Morris, M Parsons, R Sheehan, M Thomas, K Tomlinson, K Wilson
Hon. Tutor P Little, C Pollock
Lecturer G Cannavina, L G Davis, A L Fairclough, P V Hatton, D C McDonald, C A McQuaid, S E Northeast, J M Walsh
Reader R van Noort
Senior Lecturer D J Lamb, A Rawlinson, G E White, R B Winstanley

Medical School

Dean of the Medical School P M Enderby
Deputy Dean C S Reilly
Sub-Dean M D Talbot
Associate Postgraduate Dean S E Thomas, G S Venables
Regional Postgraduate Dean C L Welsh
Undergraduate Dean R E Page

Biomedical Sciences

Arthur Jackson Professor of Biomedical Science & Head of Department P W Andrews
Hon. Lecturer J H Egan, D J Goldstein, M C Hayes-Allen, G Wiseman
Lecturer M A Cambray-Deakin, K A Clarke, A K Jowett, R D E Rumsey, S White
Professor A Angel, R C A Pearson, G P Reynolds
Reader M J Dunne, R J Levin

UNIVERSITIES & MEDICAL SCHOOLS

Senior Lecturer M E Atkinson, R G Chess-Williams, G H Cope, D Grundy, J Hardcastle, P T Hardcastle, S Jacob, N T James, M A Warren

Cancer Studies
Professor B W Hancock
Reader R E Coleman, R C Rees
Research Fellow P M Ingleton, J Lawtry, R M Sharrard
Senior Lecturer R E Coleman, P R M Dobson, P Lorigan, M H Robinson
Senior Research Scientist A Murray
Sir George Martin Professor of Virology & Director C W Potter

Cardiology
Hon. Clinical Lecturer R J Bowes, S Campbell, G D G Oakley

Chest Diseases
Hon. Clinical Lecturer P B Anderson, S R Brennan, B J Hutchcroft

Clinical Neurology
Clinical Lecturer J D Sussman
Frank Moody Professor of Clinical Neurology H J Sagar
Hon. Clinical Lecturer A K Chattopadyhay, G A B Davies-Jones, A Gibson, R A Grunewald, S J L Howell, J A Jarratt, N Jordan, R Kandler, G S Venables
Lecturer (Non-Clinical) N M Hunkin
Professor A R Mayes

Clinical Oncology
Head B W Hancock
Clinical Research Assistant M B Birtwhistle, J M Danskin
Clinical Research Fellow A M Gillespie, J Vinholes
Hon. Clinical Lecturer J J Bolger, A E Champion, K S Dunn, I H Manifold, O P Purohit, D J Radstone, S Ramakrishman, M J Whipp
Hon. Lecturer J Roch
Reader R E Coleman
Senior Lecturer P C Lorigan, M H Robinson

Communicable Diseases
Hon. Clinical Lecturer M W McKendrick

Diseases of the Ear, Nose and Throat and Medical Audiology
Hon. Clinical Lecturer J T Buffin, P D Bull, D F Chapman, R T Clegg, J D Shaw

Forensic Pathology
Head M A Green
Hon. Lecturer C P Dorries, G S Everson, A R W Forrest, S Silvaloganathan
Lecturer G N Rutty
Senior Lecturer N Carter, J C Clark, C M Milroy

Genitourinary Medicine
Hon. Clinical Lecturer D A Hicks, G R Kinghorn, M D Talbot

Human Communication Sciences
Head J L Locke
Clinical Tutor C Gray
Lecturer S M Brumfitt, P E Cowell, M Freeman, J Hartley, S J Howard, A Locke, I S Peers, M R Perkins, D Syder, D A Treharne, R Varley, S Whiteside
Professor Associate J M Boucher

Human Metabolism and Clinical Biochemistry
Head R G G Russell
Clinical Research Fellow G M Coombes, A M Cooper, S Khan, E V McCloskey, J M Orgee, N F A Peel
Hon. Clinical Lecturer P R Beck, A R W Forrest, T A Gray, M A Prenton, E Worthy
Hon. Demonstrator I D Marsh

Hon. Lecturer R A D Bunning, P R M Dobson, D Guilland-Cummings, P M Ingleton, S Mac Neil, A M Parfitt, D J Watts, C E Wilde, N J Y Woodhouse
Lecturer A P Hollander, N McKie
Professor B L Brown, R Eastall, J A Kanis
Research Fellow S J Hodges, H Hughes
Senior Lecturer D J Buttle, E E Qwarnstrom

Medical Gastroenterology
Hon. Clinical Lecturer D J Dawson, D C Gleeson, C D Holdsworth, F P Ryan
Hon. Lecturer N W Reed

Medical Microbiology
Head R Jennings
Hon. Clinical Lecturer P A Fenton, S Green, G Kudesia, M W McKendrick, P Norman, M S Osman, E Ridgway, P M Zadik
Hon. Teacher K W Bennett
Lecturer A W Heath, M S Thomas
Research Associate P Dullforce, J Shaw
Senior Clinical Lecturer R C Read
Senior Lecturer A R Eley

Medical Physics and Clinical Engineering
Associate Professor D C Barber, B H Brown
Emeritus Professor M M Black
Hon. Lecturer A T Barker, R P Betts, C K Bomford, J Conway, C I Franks, C Griffiths, P A Griffiths, M W Harper, N D Harris, B W Heller, A M Holroyd, R D Moore, D S Ottewell, W I J Pryce, A Robinson, S B Sherrif, J M Stamp, J C Stevens, W D Tindale, A C Underwood, J Unsworth, A J Wilson
Lecturer J W Fenner, D R Hose, P V Lawford
Professor R H Smallwood
Reader E A Trowbridge

Medicine
Sir Arthur Hall Professor of Medicine and Head A P Weetman
Emeritus Professor D S Munro
Hon. Clinical Lecturer P B Anderson, R J Bowes, S R Brennan, C B Brown, M J Brown, S Campbell, D Datta, D Dawson, C A Hardisty, S R Heller, B J Hutchcroft, P J Moorhead, G D G Oakley, K V Phadke, J T Reilly, S A Riley
Hon. Lecturer J Watkins
Lecturer M E Barker, J Earland, A K Fletcher, S E Francis, S French, J Gunn, P F Watson
Professor D C Crossman, A M El-Nahas, N W Read
Reader S Mac Neil, A M Ward
Senior Lecturer J Haylor, C H Newman, R J M Ross

Medicine and Pharmacology
Sir George Franklin Professor of Medicine and Head H F Woods
Hon. Clinical Lecturer A J Anderson, M J Brown, K S Channer, D R Cullen, K Foreman, D A Gawkrodger, M L Ghosh, C I Harrington, V James, M E Kessler, A G Messenger, O W J Quarrell, J T Reilly, R J Sokol, C A Sudstin, S E Thomas, W Wagstaff, D A Winfield, M L Wood
Hon. Lecturer J M Clifford, A Goodeve, R G Malia, A M Potter
Hon. Teacher C J Emery, G R Weeks
Lecturer M E M Daly, S B Gordon, F A Guesdon, S Keohane, M Nicklin, P T Peachell, J Sayers, P R Winship
Lord Florey Professor of Molecular Medicine G W Duff
Professor S K Dower, T W Higenbottam, L E Ramsay, G T Tucker, J D Ward, M K Whyte
Professor Associate F E Preston
Reader G C S Collins, M S Lennard, J L Maddocks
Research Fellow M A Akil, S W Ellis, I U Haq, S Jones, R Murphy, D T Pilz
Senior Lecturer N D S Bax, M Cork, F S di Giovine, P R Jackson, M Makris, M Makris, A H Morice, M L Snaith, R M Wilson
Sir Edward Mellanby Professor of Molecular Medicine I R Peake

UNIVERSITY OF SHEFFIELD

Molecular Biology and Biotechnology

Head E Bailey
Demonstrator A D Bailey, A Treffry
Hon. Lecturer D Curtis, D Mangnall
Lecturer R W Anderson, P A Bullough, D J Gilmour, J Gray, B A Helm, C J McDonald, J W B Moir, I A Murray, L J Partridge, T E Treffry, G S Warren, D J Watts
Professor J R Guest, P Horton, C N Hunter, P W Ingham, H D M Moore, R K Poole, D W Rice, G Turner
Reader P J Artymiuk, G C Ford, J A Higgins, M P Williamson
Senior Lecturer M M Attwood, E M Carey, M Grindle, D P Hornby, D J Kelly, S L Kelly, J Kinderlerer, A Moir, P E Sudbery, M Wainwright, J P Waltho

Neurological Surgery

Hon. Clinical Lecturer R D E Battersby, D M C Forster, J Jakubowski
Hon. Instructor A A Kemeny

Obstetrics and Gynaecology

Head R B Fraser
Hon. Clinical Lecturer M Connor, M E L Paterson, W Porter, P Stewart
Lecturer A D Blackett, P Sarhanis
Professor F Sharp
Senior Lecturer D Patel, J A Tidy

Ophthalmology and Orthoptics

Head I G Rennie
Hon. Clinical Lecturer J Burke, S Longstaff, M E Nelson, I M Strachan, J F Talbot
Lecturer L Baker, A Y Firth, H Griffiths, C M Leach, P S R Richardson, J Whittle
Senior Lecturer H Davis

Paediatric Surgery

Hon. Clinical Lecturer A E MacKinnon, J P Roberts, R N Shawis, J Walker

Paediatrics

Head M S Tanner
Clinical Research Associate H Elphick
Clinical Research Fellow F G Bell, S Choo, P M Field, S Ghosal, S M Marven, O Pirzada, J C Welch
Fellow M Sharrard
Hon. Clinical Lecturer L H Alison, P O Brennan, J A Cook, R C Coombs, H A Davies, J De Z Chaplais, M L Everard, M P Gerrard, A T Gibson, S M Hall, V A Harpin, G Long, P I Macfarlane, C A MacKenzie, A E MacKinnon, G D Moss, R G Pearse, K J Price, M Richards, C D C Rittey, J P Roberts, S A W Salfield, R N Shawis, M F Smith, A Sprigg, S Variend, A J Vora, J Walker, R E Waller, J G Yassa
Hon. Lecturer J R Bonham, N J Manning, S E Olpin, R J Pollitt
Hon. Teacher V A Binney, E Fitzpatrick
Lecturer G S Evans, S Gibb, C V E Powell, N Wright
Professor D M B Hall, M Saleh, C J Taylor
Senior Lecturer A H R Finn, H J Powers, R A Primhak, A S Rigby, J K H Wales

Pathology

Joseph Hunter Professor & Head J C E Underwood
Hon. Clinical Lecturer A J Coup, L Harvey, A Kennedy, D M McKenna, J R Shortland, D N Slater, C M L Smith, J H F Smith, T J Stephenson, S K Survana, W R Timperley, S Variend
Hon. Teacher G Anderson
Lecturer M D Barker, D E Hughes, R J Landers, J A Royds
Professor M Wells
Senior Lecturer C A Angel, S S Cross, J R Goepel, J A Lee, C E Lewis, M A Parsons

Psychiatry

Director of Centre for Psychotherapeutic Studies T J G Kendall
Head A S Hale

Hon. Clinical Lecturer R T Abed, J K Amin, W P Bant, I Capriapa, C A Chambers, A K Chaudhary, J V Conway, D M Dickens, S E Eacott, P V Gill, R Haddock, J M Ludlow, N D Macaskill, A J Mackie, A L MacNeil, K M Malcolm, B M Mehta, B N Nwulu, G A Sampson, A K Sinha, A Soliman, J D Stirland, T K Szulecka, M G Thomas, C M Wallbridge, R E Waller, M N Zaman
Lecturer N Crossley, D G Edwards, M Heap, J L Henzell, J Laugharne, A Lidmila, M W Lock, D Maclagan, D S Marks, J Monach, B Murphy, S Peters, G C Warren, W H Wighton-Benn, S R Wright
Professor D J H Tantam, R M Young
Senior Clinical Lecturer M Peet
Senior Lecturer G G Kent, P Nicolson, J O'Dwyer

Radiodiagnosis

Hon. Clinical Lecturer N A Barrington, M J Bradley, M C Collins, C H Davies, H A Euinton, P A Gaines, D J Moore, S K Morcos, D R Naik, R A Nakielny, R J Peck, T Powell, A E Procter, B Ross, P A Spencer
Senior Lecturer T J Cleveland

Rheumatology

Clinical Lecturer M Atril
Hon. Clinical Lecturer R S Amos, D E Bax, J Winfield
Senior Lecturer M Snaith

Sheffield Institute of Sports Medicine and Exercise Science

Chairman T Duckworth
Academic Director T Cochrane
Lecturer J M Saxton
Professor M Saleh
Research Fellow R C Davey

Surgical and Anaesthetic Sciences

Clinical Lecturer N Bhaskaran, D Brooks, S M Hay, G M Holt, J B Luntley, A W Majeed, C F Swinhoe, S Wakefield
Hon. Clinical Lecturer J D Alderton, D F J Appleton, T N Appleyard, R E Atkinson, R H Baker, I Barker, J D Beard, A Beechey, M J Bell, N R Bennett, M C Berthoud, D R Bickerstaff, R J S Birks, D P Breen, J A Caunt, G P M Clark, N Coad, J R Cole, A C Crosby, G K Davies, P M S Dobson, T Dorman, D L Douglas, D L Edbrooke, D G Ferguson, G A Francis, S P Gerrish, J M Goddard, D A Harrison, K M Harrison, S K Hawley, D G Hood, J E Hunsley, R E John, N J Kehoe, N J A Massey, S Michael, W Morris-Jones, J V B Mundy, A Padfield, J E Peacock, N H Pereira, D R Powell, M W R Reed, M N Richmond, T C Shaw, K M Sherry, A J Shorthouse, C Stack, C J Stoddard, W E G Thomas, E A Welchew, G A Weston, D J K White, P A Wilkinson, A M Wilson
Hon. Clinical Teacher A B Mehta
Lecturer (Non-Clinical) N C Bird, N J Brown
Professor S Ahmedzai, D Clark, T Duckworth, A G Johnson, C S Reilly
Senior Lecturer N D Edwards, D M C Forster, K T H Moore, W Noble, P J Treacy, M Yardley

Surgical Sciences

Head R F M Wood
Clinical Lecturer S Nayagam, I Reid
Clinical Research Fellow N Malik
Hon. Clinical Lecturer J M Ahmed, G L Cohen, R A Elson, E Freelander, C J M Getty, J J Goiti, R W Griffiths, B J Harrison, T J Locke, M R McClelland, F P Morris, S H Norris, R E Page, A T Rafferty, G Ravichandran, J A R Smith, T W D Smith, D G Thomas, J A C Thorpe, J Wardrope, C L Welsh, G A L Wilkinson
Hon. Research Fellow E Anagnostau
Lecturer C Eaton, C M Holt, D Mangnall, A G Pockley, L Yang
Professor D C Cumberland, M Saleh
Research Fellow J A Mitchell
Senior Lecturer P Chan, M El Shazly, K B Hosie

Urological Surgery

Hon. Clinical Lecturer J B Anderson, C R Chapple, K J Hastie, K T H Moore, D G Thomas

UNIVERSITIES & MEDICAL SCHOOLS

University of Southampton

The University, Southampton SO9 5NH
Tel: 023 8059 5000 (Switchboard) Fax: 023 8059 4159
Website: www.soton.ac.uk

Vice-Chancellor H Newby

Medicine, Health and Biological Sciences

Level C South Academic Block, Mailpoint 801, Southampton General Hospital, Southampton SO16 6YD
Tel: 023 8079 6581 Fax: 023 8079 4760

Dean of Medicine, Health and Biological Studies R S Briggs
Postgraduate Dean (Medicine) G Winyard
Clinical Sub-Dean (Medicine) J Jellicoe
Associate Dean (Medicine - Portsmouth) J G B Millar, S A Evans
Director of Education (Medicine) C R Stephens
Director of Research (Medicine) M J Arthur
Head of School of Biological Science A Lee
Head of School of Medicine E J Thompson
Head of School of Nursing and Midwifery Jill Macleod Clark
Head of School of Professions and Rehabilitation Sciences R F Barnitt
School Administrator J E Morris
Senior Assistant Registrar R Tank

Biochemistry and Molecular Biology

Lecturer C H Barton, J B Cooper, K A Lillycrop
Professor M Akhtar, C Anthony, A G Lee, P M Shoolingin-Jordan
Reader K R Fox, D C Wilton, S P Wood
Senior Lecturer W T Drabble, J M East, I G Giles, M G Gore, C D O'Connor, P C Poat, G J Sale

Clinical Neurological Sciences

Lecturer A K Pringle, L E Sundstrom
Professor J A R Nicoll, R O Weller
Senior Lecturer C Holmes, P D Lees

Medical Education Division

Lecturer D Patten, R P Sharma
Senior Lecture B L Wee
Senior Lecturer F J Hill, E R Hillier, S A Evans, B S Mitchell, C R Stephens

MRC Environmental Epidemiology Unit

Director D J P Barker
Reader D N M Coggon, C Cooper

Scotland

University of Aberdeen

University Office, Regent Walk, Aberdeen AB24 3UX
Tel: 01224 681818
Website: www.abdn.ac.uk

Medical School Postgraduate Studies

Postgraduate Studies, Foresterhill, Aberdeen AB9 2ZD

Chairman G G Youngson
Postgraduate Dean R A Wood
Adviser for Women Doctors Alison Douglas
Adviser in General Dental Practice M Steed
Adviser in General Practice W Reith
Postgraduate Tutor R A Wood
Specialty Adviser W Chambers, P Duffty, D G Fowlie, F Green, K M Kerr, M D MacArthur, G Needham, D Parkin, N M C Rennie, C C Smith, W C S Smith, G G Youngson

Medicine and Medical Sciences

Dean of the Faculty of Medicine & Medical Sciences G R D Catto
Postgraduate Dean R A Wood

Biomedical Physics and Bioengineering

Emeritus Professor J R Mallard
Hon. Lecturer A Fairhead, M J Nieman, G Robertson, R D Selbie, P Wade, R White
Hon. Senior Lecturer H G Gemmell
Lecturer K Lockie, A Welch
Professor D Hukins, P F Sharp
Reader J M S Hutchison, M Hutchison
Senior Lecturer A R Allen, A R Allen, B Heaton, D J Lurie, P E Undrill

Biomedical Sciences

Emeritus Professor E J Clegg
Hon. Lecturer J H Beattie
Hon. Professor P Trayhurn
Hon. Reader G M Lees, H J McArdle
Hon. Senior Lecturer N W Kerr, I Kimber, E A Lock, D A Smith, K W J Wahle
Lecturer G S Bewick, F Bowser-Riley, A M Lawrie, D J MacEwan, G T A McEwen, G F Nixon, R Payne, B Platt, D C Spanswick
Professor M J Ashford, G M Hawksworth, C Kidd, S D Logan, R J Maughan
Reader A G Macdonald, R G Pertwee
Senior Lecturer N E Cameron, M A Cotter, S N Davies, P W Johnston, C D McCaig, K R Page, R D Scott, H M Wallace
Teaching Fellow M J Moore

Child Health

Hon. Lecturer A Devlin
Hon. Senior Lecturer E Ashcroft, I Auchterlonie, W M Bisset, P Booth, G F Cole, J Crum, s Davd, P Duffy, D Kindley, D J King, D J Lloyd, P Smail
Lecturer R Brooker
Professor P J B Helms
Reader G Russell
Senior Lecturer B E Golden

Clinical Biochemistry

Clinical Senior Lecturer J Broom, I S Ross
Senior Lecturer P H Whiting

Environmental and Occupational Medicine

Hon. Senior Lecturer D Godden
Lecturer F Dick, M Watt, M E Wright
Professor A Seaton
Research Fellow C A Soutar
Senior Lecturer J W Cherrie, R J Graves, J A S Ross, S J Watt

General Practice

Hon. Lecturer J N Wyness
Hon. Senior Lecturer M McFadyen, W Reith
Lecturer C Bond, G Deans, I Duthie, K Lawton, A J W McLauchlan, F Richardson, J S Shand, G G Shirreffs, B H Smith
Professor J N Norman, L D Ritchie, D G Seymour
Senior Lecturer J A Brebner, L McKie, M W Taylor, R J Taylor

Medical Illustration, Computer Assisted Learning Unit (CAL)

Director K P Duguid
Head of CAL Unit N Hamilton

Medical Microbiology

Hon. Senior Lecturer I M Gould, P J Molyneux, T S Reid
Lecturer P Carter, K Forbes
Professor T H Pennington
Senior Lecturer P Cash, H McKenzie

Medicine and Therapeutics

Hon. Reader S Urbaniak

Lecturer H Cameron, H Galley, D J Godden, R D Harvey, I H Khan, A Kumar, G McNeill, H Peace, R G Phelps, L Sharp
Professor J Cassidy, G R D Catto, M H N Golden, G M Hawksworth, J Little, J N Norman, D Ogston, J C Petrie, D G Seymour, N R Webster
Reader N B Bennett, N E Haites, S H Ralston
Regius Professor A Rees
Senior Lecturer E R Kaminski, J McLay, A M McLeod, H L McLeod, A N Turner, H M Wallace, A H Watt

Mental Health
Professor D A Alexander, L J Whalley, C Wischik
Senior Lecturer D St. Clair, L G Walker

Molecular and Cell Biology
Lecturer A M Cumming, K Shennan
Professor I R Booth, K Docherty, J E Fothergill, G W Gooday, N A R Gow, N E Haites, W J Harris, J Jeffery, J I Prosser, D J Shaw
Reader A J P Brown
Senior Lecturer N A Booth, L A Glover, W F Long, W T Melvin, C K Pearson, S B Wilson

Obstetrics and Gynaecology
Consultant U Acharya
Hon. Senior Lecturer M Hall, H Kitchener
Lecturer A MacLeod
Professor A A Templeton
Reader D R Abramovich
Senior Lecturer D M Campbell, M P R Hamilton

Ophthalmology
Lecturer J M Liversidge
Professor J V Forrester
Senior Lecturer A D Dick

Pathology
Professor F Walker
Reader J G Simpson, D N Wheatley
Senior Clinical Lecturer K M Kerr, Mary E McKean, J M Mackenzie, J L McPhie, I D Miller, Margaret M Sheekan, Louise M Smart
Senior Lecturer S W B Ewen, E S Gray, J H K Grieve, P W Johnston, G I Murray, G B Scott, W D Thompson

Public Health
Director of Health Services Research Unit A Grant
Head of Department W C S Smith
Information Services Manager D O Phillips
Lecturer D Bennett, J Mollison, E van Teijlingen, M S Watson, B J Wilson
Professor E M Russell

Surgery
Professor J D Hutchison
Regius Professor O Eremin
Senior Registrar R Murali
Senior Lecturer A K Ah-See, N R Binnie, D B Gough, S B Heys

University of Dundee

Faculty of Medicine, Dentistry & Nursing, Level 10, Ninewells Hospital & Medical School, Dundee DD1 9SY
Tel: 01382 632763 Fax: 01382 644267
Email: medschoff@dundee.ac.uk
Website: www.dundee.ac.uk

Principal & Vice-Chancellor Alan Langlands
Faculty Secretary W M Williamson

Biomedical Research Centre

Director C R Wolf
Lecturer D J Jamieson, B M McStay

Reader J D Hayes
Senior Lecturer T H Friedburg

Centre for Medical Education

Tay Park House, 484 Perth Road, Dundee DD2 1LR
Tel: 01382 631972 Fax: 01382 645748

Director R M Harden
Hon. Lecturer R Neil, R H Richardson
Lecturer Pauline Horton, Margaret Kindlen, J McAleer
Senior Lecturer M Davis, E C B Rogerson

Clinical Skills Centre

Director Jean Ker

Dental School and Hospital

Park Place, Dundee DD1 4HN

Hon. Lecturer A J Crighton, J Levitt, S Manton, A Neilson, C J Tilley
Hon. Senior Lecturer C J Allan, J D Clark, E Connor, C M Jones, I J McClure, M C W Merrett, A Shearer
Lecturer G Bateman, K Davey, J Foley, A Forgie, R V Hunter, P McGoldrick, M Macluskey, P Maillou, A G Mason, D N J Ricketts, S N Scrimgeour, F M J Stewart, C Tait
Professor D M Chisholm, G R Ogden, C Pine, N B Pitts, W P Saunders, S L Schor, D R Stirrups
Reader C H Lloyd, P A Mossey, N M Nuttall, A M Schor
Secretary to Dental School J D M Gray
Senior Lecturer S W Cadden, R G Chadwick, J E Clarkson, J R Drummond, R Duguid, D J P Evans, A D Gilbert, C Longbottom, J P Newton, J R Radford, E M Saunders, B J J Scott

Faculty of Medicine, Dentistry and Nursing

Level 10, Ninewells Hospital & Medical School, Dundee DD1 9SY
Tel: 01382 660111 ext: 2763 Fax: 01382 644267

Dean of Dentistry W P Saunders
Dean of Faculty D A Levison
Postgraduate Dean R Newton
Faculty Secretary W M Williamson

Anaesthesia
Hon. Senior Lecturer C W Allison, R H Allison, J Bannister, P A Coe, J Colvin, D M Coventry, S A Crofts, L Duncan, I G Gray, I G Grove-White, W F D Hamilton, A Houghton, T Houston, G L Hutchinson, W McClymont, N Mackenzie, W A Macrae, P R Manthri, M K Milne, A Ratcliff, A J Shearer, M F Thomson, E Wilson
Lecturer M R Checketts
Professor J A W Wildsmith
Senior Lecturer G A McLeod, F A Millar

Anatomy and Physiology
Lecturer K N Christie, J R Elliott, A A Harper, J M Lucocq, P M Taylor, P W Watt
Professor E B Lane, C G Proud, M J Rennie, R R Sturrock, C A Tickle, J G Williams
Senior Lecturer A R Chipperfield, D L Dawson, G C Leslie, N J Part, C J Weiser
Senior Manager M R Ward

Biochemical Medicine
Hon. Assistant W A Bartlett, H G Clark, J Scott
Hon. Lecturer J B C Dick, J Evans, I Hanning, J P Moody, L M Nelson, K Tebbutt
Hon. Senior Lecturer C G Fraser, R Hume
Lecturer I J Holt
Professor B Burchell
Senior Lecturer J D Baty, M Cougtrie, C R Paterson

Biochemistry
Hon. Lecturer Elizabeth Carey, C Higgins, M A Kerr, M Lewis, G Warren

UNIVERSITIES & MEDICAL SCHOOLS

Lecturer G C Barr, M Ferguson, A J Flavell, S Homans, R Quinlan, M Stark, C Watts
Professor D H Boxer, P Cohen, C Downes, D Glover, D Lane, D Lilley, D Nicholls
Reader D Hardie
Senior Lecturer R Booth, P Cohen, J C Kernohan, D A Stansfield

Cardiovascular Epidemiology Unit
Director H Tunstall Pedoe
Hon. Lecturer S Somerville

Child Health
Hon. Lecturer S Dewar, P Fowlie, A Kurian, A McKinnon, J Mires, R A Wilkie
Hon. Senior Lecturer J S Forsyth, S A Greene, Valerie J Marrian, D C S Theodosiou, J A Young
Lecturer S Mukhopadhyay
Professor R Hume, R E Olver
Senior Lecturer J I Cater, H J McArdle, A Mehta

Dermatology
Hon. Senior Lecturer J Ferguson, C M Green, K J A Kenicer, J G Lowe, S Morley

Diagnostic Radiology
Hon. Lecturer N McConachie
Hon. Senior Lecturer J D Begg, W J A Gibson, K Hasan, A S McCulloch, J W McNab, R H S Murray, M Nimmo, J W Shaw, J Tainsh, A Thompson, C M Walker

Epidemiology and Public Health
Health Services Research Co-ordinator B Williams
Hon. Senior Lecturer K Adam, D Coid, M Kenicer, Z Mathewson, A J Tannahill
Lecturer S Ogston, F L R Williams
Professor I Crombie
Senior Lecturer P James

Forensic Medicine
Hon. Lecturer J A Dunbar, J A S Mitchell
Hon. Senior Lecturer D Marshall
Professor D J Pounder
Senior Lecturer D W Sadler

General Practice
Hon. Lecturer D Blaney, J Grant, R A Hendry, A D McKendrick, D H R Mowat, A Ramsay, A D Shaw
Hon. Senior Lecturer R F Scott
Professor D J G Bain, F Sullivan
Senior Lecturer D Snadden

Haematology
Hon. Senior Lecturer P G Cachia, A Heppleston
Professor M J Pippard
Senior Lecturer D T Bowen

Medical Microbiology
Hon. Sen. Clinical Teacher Paul G McIntyre
Hon. Senior Lecturer Gillian Valerie Orange, Gabby Phillips
Lecturer Bernard W Senior
Senior Registrar David A Hill
Senior Clinical Lecturer Jay Kavi

Medical Physics
Hon. Lecturer D K Harrison, N S J Kennedy, B W Millar, W W Stewart, D Sutton, F M Tulley
Hon. Senior Lecturer R A Lerski

Medicine
Hon. Assistant A Munishankarappa
Hon. Lecturer J Blair, B Dymock, U K Ghosh, M S R MacEwan, R J Swingler, C J A Thompson
Hon. Professor R T Jung, R W Newton, C R Pennington

Hon. Senior Lecturer T S Callaghan, R A Clark, A A Connacher, D L W Davidson, D P Dhillon, A Forster, A J France, J D Fulton, W Gray, J L Hanslip, I S Henderson, J M Leiper, I M Lightbody, G P McNeill, R S McWalter, K D Morley, W J Mutch, D Nathwani, T H Pringle, T Pullar, D Shaw, A N Shepherd, P J Stephen, Joyce M Watson, J H Winter
Lecturer F G Inglis, M McLaren
Professor J J Belch, C D Forbes
Senior Lecturer M McMurdo, R C Roberts, P E Ross, H Tunstall-Pedoe

Molecular and Cellular Pathology
Hon. Senior Lecturer P G Cachia, A Heppleston
Senior Lecturer D T Bowen
Senior Manager Martin J Pippard

Neurosurgery
Hon. Senior Lecturer M S Eljamel, Peter Mathew, T R K Varma

Obstetrics and Gynaecology
Hon. Lecturer J K Gupta, G J Mires
Hon. Senior Lecturer P Agustsson, R Allen, J A Mills, N K B Patel, W D P Phillips, R Smith, M A R Thomson
Lecturer C H Brierley
Professor A Burchell
Reader I D Duncan

Ophthalmology
Head C MacEwan
Clinical Research Fellow A D Brown
Hon. Senior Lecturer P S Baines, J A Coleiro, S T D Roxburgh, K H Weed, J D H Young
Lecturer J P Craig

Orthopaedics and Traumatic Surgery
Emeritus Professor G Murdoch
Hon. Lecturer G I Bardsley, C A Kirkwood, J R Linskell, C P U Stewart, D E Young
Hon. Senior Lecturer J R Buckley, D N Condie, A J Espley, W A Hadden, A S Jain, J E Scullion, M M Sharma, A J G Swanson, N W Valentine
Lecturer M J Dolan, G G McLeod
Professor D I Rowley
Senior Lecturer J Dent

Otolaryngology
Hon. Senior Lecturer R L Blair, J K Brennand, B C Davis, J Irwin, R P Mills, R Mountain, P S White

Pathology
Hon. Lecturer A Baird, M Boxer, K T Evans, B A Spruce, W W Stewart
Hon. Senior Lecturer D R Goudie, K Hussein, J Lang, S Lang, J B McCullough, B A Michie, S M Nicoll, A J Robertson
Lecturer J Woof
Professor S Fleming, D Levison
Reader D Hopwood, M A Kerr
Senior Lecturer M J W Faed, R A Kay

Pharmacology and Clinical Pharmacology
Hon. Lecturer G R Barclay, T R P Dodd, D A Johnston, A M MacConnachie, T A Moreland
Hon. Professor C Pennington
Hon. Senior Lecturer D MacLean, F E Murray
Hon. Tutor D M Shepherd
Lecturer K C Breen, B Lipworth, R J McFadyen, N M Wheeldon
Professor J Lambert, D G McDevitt, J McEwen, D G Nicholls, I H Stevenson, A D Struthers
Reader D J K Balfour, P Davey
Senior Lecturer G Lyles, T M McDonald, J Peters

Psychiatry
Emeritus Professor G W Fenton

Hon. Lecturer Joan Clark, M Guthrie, S E Hopwood, M M Semple, P Walker

Hon. Senior Lecturer Constance B Ballinger, S E Bonnar, I Clark, S Clark, P Connelly, P H Dick, M A Field, D J Findlay, B B Johnston, K M G Keddie, Anne M McHarg, A H Reid, P Rice, B M Shepherd, Anne H W Smith, C Smith, D Tait, L Treliving, P J Walker, A J Yellowlees

Lecturer D A Reid

Professor K Matthews, Ian C Reid

Senior Lecturer David Coghill, R C Durham, D R May, C de B White

Radiotherapy and Oncology

Hon. Senior Lecturer S Das, J A Dewar, P M Windsor

Surgery

Hon. Senior Lecturer K Baxby, D J Byrne, A I G Davidson, J C Forrester, A D Irving, M Lavelle-Jones, M H Lyall, P T McCollum, A M Morris, W J G Murray, J H Stevenson, P A Stonebridge, W H Townell, R A B Wood

Lecturer T G Frank, E L Newman

Professor A Cuschieri, D Lane, R J C Steele

Senior Lecturer S M Shimi, A M Thomson

Recognised Clinical Institutions

Monklands Hospital, Murray Royal Hospital, Ninewells Hospital, Perth Royal Infirmary, Queen Margaret Hospital, Raigmore Hospital, Royal Dundee Liff Hospital, St John's Hospital, St Luke's Hospital, Stirling Royal Infirmary, Stracathro Hospital, Stratheden Hospital, Sunnyside Royal Hospital, The James Cook University Hospital, West Cumberland Hospital

University of Edinburgh

The Medical School, Teviot Place, Edinburgh EH8 9AG Tel: 0131 650 3192 Fax: 0131 650 6525 Website: www.med.ed.ac.uk

Principal & Vice-Chancellor Stewart Sutherland **Secretary to the University** M D Cornish

Division of Biomedical and Clinical Laboratory Sciences

Biomedical Sciences Section

Hon. Professor V van Heyningen

Hon. Senior Lecturer P R Mitchell

Professor A Aitken, M H Kaufman, G Leng, J A Russell

Reader D K Apps, J B L Bard, G W Pettigrew, D J Price, N R Spears

Senior Lecturer R H Ashley, A Boyd, J P Bradshaw, J A Davies, M B Dutia, D Ellis, G S Findlater, P W Flatman, G Gray, A C Hall, N K MacLeod, R R Meeman, I A Nimmo, N L Poyser, J P Shaw, M J Shipston, S van Heyningen, N H Wilson

Department of Neuroscience

Head of Department R G M Morris, R G M Morris

Professor I M L Donaldson, S.G.N. Grant, A J Harmar, J S Kelly, D S McQueen

Reader R R Ribchester

Senior Lecturer G W Arbuthnott, F Kristmundsdottir, H J Olverman

Medical Microbiology Section

Head S G B Amyes

Clinical Teacher J E Coia, M F Hanson, R C Masterton

Hon. Senior Lecturer G R Barclay, M I Brown, S M Burns, H A Cubie, W Donachie, F X S Emmanuel, A P Gibb, I F Laurenson, J Petrik, E Williamson

Lecturer T Haque, S J Talbot, H Young

Professor S G B Amyes, D H Crawford, P Ghazal, J R W Govan, M Norval, I R Poxton, P Simmonds

Senior Lecturer R S Miles, M M Ogilvie, J Stewart

Division of Clinical Sciences and Community Health

Head of Division (Respiratory Medicine Section) Chris Haslett

Department of Clinical and Surgical Sciences, Accident and Emergency Medicine

Clinical Tutor P Freeland

Hon. Senior Lecturer A J Gray, K Little, C Robertson, D J Steedman

Department of Clinical and Surgical Sciences, Anaesthetics

Clinical Teacher L M Alridge, I R Armstrong, F E Arnstein, D Beamish, G M R Bowler, D T Brown, A S Buchan, D Burke, G L M Carmichael, V A Clark, T P Cripps, M J Cullen, J A Freeman, I S Grant, D J Henderson, I N Hudson, J Jenkins, G Jones, G M A Keenan, D G Littlewood, E L Lloyd, M R Logan, A F McCrae, T N Montgomery, C P J Morton, S M Nimmo, A J Pollock, G C Pugh, M L C Rutledge, D H T Scott, G H Sharwood-Smith, E J Simon, D L Simpson, C J Sinclair, D Watson, K J Watson, D Weir, D J Wright, C H Young

Hon. Senior Lecturer P J Armstrong, E Doyle, I T Foo, K P Kelly, A Lee, J H McClure, S J Mackenzie, D W McKeown, S Midgley, A F Nimmo, D C Ray, D Semple, C J Sinclair, A V G Stewart

Professor I Power

Reader P J D Andrews

Senior Lecturer R P Alston, L A Collvin, N J Maran, C Moores, D Swann, T S Walsh

Department of Clinical and Surgical Sciences, Cardiac Surgery

Clinical Tutor E W J Cameron, C Campanella

Hon. Senior Lecturer W S Walker

Senior Lecturer P Mankad

Department of Clinical and Surgical Sciences, Geriatric Medicine

Clinical Teacher P J Beaugang, J Bishop-Miller, N C Chapman, A K Datta, D Ghosh, J B Godfrey, A C Grant, D Grant, I F C Hay, A D Jamieson, S B Kulkarni, R J Lenton, H MacMillan, P A Maguire, E Millar, E Millar, P S Murdoch, C A Norris, S E Pound, G B Rhind, I J D Scougal, S J Smith, I C Stewart, J A Wilson

Hon. Senior Lecturer B J Chapman, N R Colledge, A T Elder, D L Farquhar, D C Kennie, E MacDonald, L G Morrison, S G Ramsay, R G Smith

Professor A Young

Senior Lecturer C T Currie

Senior lecturer G Mead

Senior Lecturer J M Starr, P D Syme

Department of Clinical and Surgical Sciences, Heptology/Gastroenterology/Renal

Clinical Teacher D A S Jenkins, W S J Ruddell, J Wilson

Clinical Teacher Hep/Gas O E Eade

Hon. Professor B M Frier

Hon. Senior Lecturer R W Crofton, N D C Finlayson, A J MacGilchrist, J N Plevris, C P Swainson, K C Trimble, M L Watson, C E Whitworth, R Winney

Lecturer T E S Delahooke, S M Wood

Professor C D Gregory, P C Hayes, J S Savill, A N Turner

Reader R C Heading

Senior Lecturer D B L McClelland, R G Phelps, K J Simpson, P L Yap

Senior Lecturer, Renal A D Cumming

Department of Clinical and Surgical Sciences, Ophthalmology

Clinical Teacher A H Adams, G G McIlwaine

Hon. Senior Lecturer A Azuara-Blanco, B J Dhillon, B W Fleck, D W Sim, J Singh, M R Wright

UNIVERSITIES & MEDICAL SCHOOLS

Department of Clinical and Surgical Sciences, Orthopaedic Surgery
Clinical Teacher I H Annan, I C Brenkel, T I S Brown, R Burnett, R A Buxton, T W Dougall, G M Lawson, R J M MacDonald, J C McGregor, I G C Weir
Hon. Senior Lecturer J Christie, G Hooper, C R Howie, M J McMaster, R W Nutton, J Robb
Professor C M Court-Brown, W J Gillespie, A H R Simpson
Senior Lecturer J N A Gibson, J F Keating, M F MacNicol, M M McQueen, C W Oliver, D E Porter, C M Robinson

Department of Clinical and Surgical Sciences, Otolaryngology
Hon. Senior Lecturer David L Cowan, W E Grant, A I G Kerr, R J Sanderson
Senior Lecturer R P Mills

Department of Clinical and Surgical Sciences, Rehabilitation Medicine
Hon. Senior Lecturer J Hunter
Senior Lecturer B Pentland, I C Todd

Department of Clinical and Surgical Sciences, Surgery
Clinical Teacher K C Ballantyne, A T Boyd, G G P Browning, T Daniel, R Diggory, J M Gollock, R Halpin, M Hehir, M A Hosny, C A B Johnston, D Lee, J A E MacDonald, A B MacGregor, J S O'Neill, A A Quaba, R C Smith, I W J Wallace
Hon. Senior Lecturer M Akyol, E D C Anderson, D C C Bartolo, T J Crofts, A C Debeaux, J L R Forsythe, A Howd, K Madhaven, S Paterson-Brown, H.C.C. Pleass, J B Rainey, A R Turner, J D Watson
Lecturer C H Wakefield, S J Wigmore
Professor David Carter, K C H Fearon, O J Garden, O J Garden, W R Miller
Senior Lecturer R W Parks, J A Ross

Department of Clinical and Surgical Sciences, Vascular Surgery
Clinical Teacher W A Abdel-Razik, A D Al-Asadi, A A Milne
Hon. Senior Lecturer R T A Chalmers, S C A Fraser, A McL Jenkins, J A Murie

Department of Community Health Sciences, General Practice Section
Clinical Teacher D Andrews, R Balfour, C B Bickler, C N Black, E Brogan, C Brook, A L M Currie, A Curtis, D W Ewart, P A Gaskell, D H Gillespie, A R B Hutchison, S C M Illingworth, B Innes, I S Johnston, G Leckie, F H Lossock, D Macaulay, I M McCulloch, P P McGavigan, L G McIntosh, I McKay, J A McLaren, A P W McNutt, H Merriless, C H Oliver, A G Reid, H J Rodgers, R Scott, I S M Smart, D Taylor, S A Tothill, W Treasure, M W Wilson, A P Wood
Hon. Senior Lecturer K J Boyd, C J Boyle, C J Boyle, A Brimelow, A K Cullen, R I Dickson, J L Dunn, M J Ferguson, F O George, M A Grubb, A H McIntosh, G M McPartlin, F J Macpherson, L M Myskow, S M O'Neil, H E Ross, E A Stewart, C J Sykes, L J Tulloch, W F Wallace, R J Williams
Lecturer K Fairhurst
Professor D Weller
Senior Lecturer S A Murray, A M D Porter, A A Sinclair, D McD Thomson

Department of Community Health Sciences, Public Health Sciences Section
Clinical Teacher E Baijal, A M A Bisset, T Cattermole, D R Gornon, S Payne, P Upton, A M Wallace
Clinical Tutor M J Douglas, L J C Graham
Hon. Senior Lecturer M Bain, D M Brewster, L Burley, L E Burley, R V Carlson, J W T Chalmers, G M Fletcher, A Mordue, H J T Ward, J G Wrench
Lecturer P E Warner
Professor F E Alexander, R Bhopal, F G R Fowkes, G D Murray
Reader C Campbell, S Cunningham-Burley
Senior Lecturer A Amos, J F Forbes, I D McGruther, R J Prescott, J R Stirling

Department of Medical and Radiological Sciences, Cardiovascular Research
Head of Department K A A Fox
Hon. Senior Lecturer P Bloomfield, N Boon, A D Flapan, M Galea, N Grubb, E H Horn, R J Kellett, D Northridge, T.R.D. Shaw, I R Starkey
Professor K A A Fox, C A Ludlam, J J Mullins
Senior Lecturer M A Denvir, D E Newby, R A Riemersma, N G Uren

Department of Medical and Radiology Sciences, Dermatology
Clinical Teacher R D Aldridge, P K Buxton, G M Kavanagh, M Schofield
Hon. Senior Lecturer E C Benton
Professor J L Rees
Senior Lecturer R C MacKenzie, M J Tidman, R P Weller

Department of Medical and Radiology Sciences, Medical Physics Section
Clinical Teacher V Doherty
Hon. Senior Lecturer W J Hannan
Lecturer M E Bastin
Professor W Norman McDicken
Senior Lecturer H M Brash, I Marshall

Department of Medical and Radiology Sciences, Medical Radiology
Clinical Teacher R D Adam, P S Bailey, I Beggs, S E Chambers, M E Chapman, M S Fleet, R J Gibson, D C Grieve, G M A Hendry, A E Kirkpatrick, H L MacDonald, S Mackenzie, M McPhillips, H A McRitchie, S A Moussa, B Muir, I Parker, J H Reid, L M Smart, A J M Stevenson, J S J Walsh, S R Wild
Hon. Senior Lecturer I N Gillespie, S Ingram, K.D.P. McBride, G McInnes, G McKillop, J T Murchison, D Patel, I Prossor, D Redhead, C M Turnbull, J Walker, A J A Wightman
Professor J J K Best
Senior Lecturer P L Allan, D A Collie, R J Sellar, A R Wright

Department of Medical and Radiology Sciences, Respiratory Medicine
Clinical Teacher J C J Bath, J Gaddie, D Gordon, R S Gray, D A Johnstone, W G Middleton, J S Millar, D B Morrison, E A Murphy
Hon. Senior Lecturer D Bell, P J Leslie, T Mackay, A W Patrick, M F Sudlow, A D Toft, J D Walker, S.C Wright, M J Young
Professor N J Douglas, C Haslett, J R Lamb, W MacNee, J Mullins
Reader I B Dransfield, T J Sethi
Senior Lecturer A J B Simpson, P M Warren

Reproductive and Developmental Sciences, Child Life and Health
Clinical Teacher I A Abu-Arafeh, M Aldoori, R P C Barclay, S Bloomfield, J W Cresswell, E D Daniels, D E Goh, A M Grant, J Grigor, M Higgs, E E Hollingdale, S E Ibhanesebhor, P D Jackson, M Loudon, U M Macfadyen, M M McGregor-Schuerman, M G MacMillan, A C F Margerison, F D Munro, B Norton, J M Ritchie, C R Steer, D C S Theodosiou, R B Thomson, D E Valentine
Hon. Senior Lecturer T F Beattie, A W Blair, D C Brown, J K Brown, J Burns, A J Burt, Z M Dunhill, A T Edmunds, P Eunson, F C M Forbes, H F Hammond, D A Johnson, D N Manders, T G Marshall, J D Orr, R M Simpson, A Thomas
Lecturer L E Bath
Reader C J H Kelnar
Senior Lecturer P Hoare, G A Mackinley, P Midgley, R A Minns, D C Wilson

Reproductive and Developmental Sciences, Clinical Biochemistry
Clinical Teacher A C Don-Wauchupe
Hon. Senior Lecturer J P Ashby, P W H Rae, J Seth, P R Wenham
Lecturer S D Morley, J E Roulston
Professor J I Mason
Reader G J Beckett
Senior Lecturer S W Walker

Reproductive and Developmental Sciences, Genitourinary Medicine
Clinical Tutor D Clutterbuck
Hon. Senior Lecturer G R Scott
Senior Lecturer A McMillan

Reproductive and Developmental Sciences, Neonatology Section
Professor N McIntosh
Senior Lecturer I A Laing, A Lyon, G Menon, P Midgley, B Stenson

Reproductive and Developmental Sciences, Obstetrics and Gynaecology
Clinical Teacher T Cooper, M F Geals, M G Hill, I E Lowles, A M McCulloch, C K Tay, D R Urquhart
Hon. Professor R W Kelly, A S McNeilly, R P Millar
Hon. Senior Lecturer R A Anderson, G J Beattie, A D G Brown, P J Dewart, D I M Farquharson, A J Gordon, R G Hughes, D S Irvine, W A Liston, T A Mahmood, J A Milne, P G Thomson
Lecturer S Cameron, W C Duncan, S C Riley
Professor A A Calder, H O D Critchley, S G Hillier
Senior Lecturer T A Bramley, A F Glasier, F D Johnstone, S C Riley, K J Thong, C P West, J D West

Division of Molecular and Clinical Medicine

Head of Division, (Oncology) J F Smyth

Clinical Neurosciences
Clinical Tutor T Russell
Hon. Senior Lecturer R E Cull, R Davenport, G L Hall, G D Moran, C Mumford, A J W Steers
Professor P A G Sandercock, J M Wardlaw, Charles Warlow, I R Whittle, R G Will
Reader M S Dennis, M A Glasby, P A T Kelly
Senior Lecturer R Grant, R S G Knight, R Lindley, C Lueck, C Mumford, B Pentland, P F X Statham, A Zeman

Medical Sciences
Clinical Teacher T F Benton, P D McSorley, K R Palmer, N R Peden, D Wilks
Hon. Professor H Cooke, V Van Heyningen, A F Wright
Hon. Senior Lecturer I W Campbell, V B Dhillon, R J Fergusson, M J Ford, L J Kenyon, C M Lambert, C M Lambert, C L S Leen, J A McKnight, E R Mcrurie, G R Nimmo, J Nimmo, D Northridge, P T Reid, T R D Shaw, J R Starkey, P S Welsby
Lecturer C Abbot, R Andrew, G Blackhurst, M R Gillett, Y Kutelevtsev, J J Oliver, W G Waring, W S Waring
Professor G Nuki, G Nuki, D Porteous, J Satsangi, J R Seckl, D J Wabb, D J Webb
Reader D N Bateman, R P Brettle, A P Greening, P L Padfield
Senior Lecturer R W Brown, A E Capewell, K E Chapman, M A Denvir, N P Hurst, J A Innes, C L S Leen, R Luqmani, S Maxwell, I D Penman, M E M Porteous

Oncology
Clinical Teacher M K Cook, V J Cowie, L M Matheson
Clinical Tutor P W Kutarski, F Little, L M Stewart, G Stockdill
Hon. Senior Lecturer U Chetty, A M Cull, H Gabra, P S Ganly, J Gillon, A Gregor, J M T Griffiths, G C W Howard, P R E Johnson, J S Keen, R H Macdougall, I.M.C. Macintyre, M McKean, M J Mackie, D Mclaren, C M McLean, A McNeill, A T Redpath, S Rodgers, D I Thwaites
Lecturer D R Camidge, F Nussey
Professor J D Ansell, M G Dunlop, W R Miller, A Price, J F Smyth
Reader F K Habib, D J Jodrell
Senior Lecturer E D C Anderson, D A Cameron, J M Dison, M T Fallon, L Forrester, T B Hargreave, I H Kunkler, S J Nixon, M L Turner

Pathology
Clinical Teacher C Anderson, B Beenadevi, R M Davie, K Kurian,

A McGregor, M A McIntyre, K J Mckenzie, N Mayer, H Monaghan, K Murray
Hon. Senior Lecturer H M Kamel, J W Keeling, A M Lessells, J St J Thomas
Professor T J Anderson, J E Bell, C C Bird, A Busuttil, D J Harrison, M L Hooper, J W Ironside, D W Melton
Reader S E M Howie
Senior Lecturer A Al-Nafussi, C Bellamy, E Duvall, H M Gilmour, K M Grigor, E McGoogan, K M McLaren, M L O'Sullivan, W A Reid, D M Salter, C Smith, A R W Williams

Psychiatry
Clinical Teacher J Aspin, S A Backett, A Beveridge, T M Brown, M S Bruce, I W Coffey, R J Craig, D Garbutt, S M Gilfillan, D J Hall, J D Hendry, R G McCreadie, S McHale, A R P Moffoot, W J R Riddle, C R Rodger, T D Rogers, S Roscrow, M Stewart, W A Tait, F E Watson
Hon. Senior Lecturer A K Carson, D Chiswick, C Freeman, F H Lang, A M Lodge, J B Loudon, P McConville, G Masterton, D Morrison, P A Morrison, T J C Murphy, A L Phanjoo, S Potts, E B Ritson, A I F Scott, P Shah, N J Simpson, K Slatford, J G Strachan, K J Woodburn, R M Wrate
Lecturer R Darjee, K Laidlaw, A M McIntosh, S O'Rouke, M Schwannauer, D M Semple, R M Steel, J D Steele, R Thomson
Professor JJK Best, D H Blackwood, K Ebmeier, E Johnstone, D G C Owens, M J Power
Senior Lecturer J D Chick, P Hoare, W J Muir, M C Sharpe, L D G Thomson

Faculty of Medicine General

Lister Postgraduate Institute
Professor and Head of Department S G Macpherson
Clinical Tutor I H Annan, T M Brown, N Hallam, K R Palmer, C Stewart
Hon. Senior Lecturer D N Anderson, T F Beattie, A W Blair, D Blaney, N R Colledge, F X S Emmanual, D I M Farquharson, B W Fleck, J L R Forsythe, I N Gillespie, P J Leslie, J H McClure, M B MacKean, J A McKnight, C Mumford, M B O'Regan, A W Patrick, H C C Pleass, G R Scott, T R D Shaw, A Thomas, J D Watson, M L Watson, R J Winney
Professor P C Hayes, S G Macpherson, G Nuki, A Price, J L R Rees, D J Webb, I R Whittle
Senior Lecturer H M Gilmour, J A Innes, I Kunkler, C L S Leen, G A MacKinlay, P S Mankad, R P Mills, B Pentland, M Porteous, M Turner, S W Walker

Postgraduate Dental Institute
Professor and Head of Department R J Ibbetson
Hon. Senior Lecturer G E Ball, J Barrie, R D Brown, P G Callis, C H Derry, M F Dunn, N J A Grey, J J Hammond, K E Harley, J P McDonald, I Mcleod, R Mitchell, G H Moody, M B O'Regan
Senior Lecturer G Lello

Medical Teaching Division

Senior Lecturer S van Heyningen

Centre for Medical Education
Hon. Senior Lecturer D L Farquhar, D A D MacLeod, F Nicol
Professor A L Muir
Senior Lecturer M O Wright

Learning Technology
Senior Lecturer D G Dewhurst

Medical Teaching Organisation
Senior Lecturer K M Boyd, A D Cumming

University of Glasgow

Glasgow G12 8QQ
Tel: 0141 339 8855 Fax: 0141 330 4808
Website: www.gla.ac.uk

UNIVERSITIES & MEDICAL SCHOOLS

Hon. Clinical Sub-Dean K Anderson, F M M Bryden, A Collier, R Scott

Professor A F Huntingford, G W Kirby, J G Lindsay, S McLean, R H Trainor, N C Wright

Vocational Studies Tutor A Allister, M Watson

Dental School

378 Sauchiehall Street, Glasgow G2 3JZ

Dean of Dental Education T W MacFarlane

Hon. Clinical Lecturer C Anderson, F F H Andrews, D Attwood, L M H Barbanel, P Benington, P O Black, R A Black, A K Brewer, R Broadfoot, D Brunton, M Carruthers, R H Chandrachud, D Collington, D J Crawford, D N Crighton, R M Day, J C Devennie, R Edwards, P M Finlay, J M Flynn, I E Grant, F F Hannah, M L Hendry, J Hinshalwood, B A Hogan, M Jamieson, A I Johnson, C R Keith, D Koppel, E M Leggate, D J Logan, T S MacAdam, G McKirdy, D G Morrant, A Ross, M S Simpson, J Southcott, P C Sweeney, G K Taylor, A Walker, S H Winning, H P Wright, R Young

Hon. Lecturer A W Baker, M R Cope, D C Devennie, A Haleem, M G J Haughney, S J Liggins, G A R Meek, H Milne, A J Paterson, F Paterson

Hon. Professor K F Moos

Hon. Research Fellow R M Ross

Hon. Senior Clinical Lecturer I Buchanan, B D Collin, H A Critchlow, M C Easton, D H Felix, D Forsyth, D Fung, N Hammersley, W M M Jenkins, D P McCall, J G McLennan, J McManners, K Moore, D I Russell, G S Taylor, M M Taylor, J Gordon Todd, T R Watkins, I B Watson, G A Wood

Hon. Senior Lecturer I G Chestnutt, R Strang

Hon. Senior Research Fellow D A M Geddes, D A Lunt, David K Mason

Lecturer A F Ayoub, D C A Bain, V Binnie, L Cross, J Gibson, A B Gillies, A F Hall, M Kjeldsen, M A McCann, J McCrosson, S Miller, M Riggio, M Russell, A J Smith, A G Stevenson, D M Still, J Taylor, M E Watt, A P M Wray

Personal Professor D F Kinane, D G MacDonald, T W MacFarlane, W P Saunders, K W Stephen

Professor F J T Burke, W J Kerr, D A McGowan, D Wray

Senior Lecturer J Bagg, J Beeley, L M Brocklebank, A B Lamb, M F Lyons, M D Macpherson, D Millett, L Sander, S W Sharkey, D Stenhouse

Department of Postgraduate Medicine

124 Observatory Road, Glasgow G12 8QQ
Tel: 0141 954 9324

Dean of Postgraduate Medicine (Ext. 5273) N MacKay

Adviser for Women Doctors Eve Kirkwood

Adviser in General Practice (Ext. 5276) T S Murray

Assistant Regional Adviser (Assessment) (Ext. 5279) L M Campbell

Associate Adviser M Kelly

Associate Adviser Medical Audit M Lough

Deputy Adviser in General Practice (Ext. 6097) G S Dyker

Postgraduate Tutor R H Baxter, A Cameron, C J Clark, J W Davie, I K Drainer, W S Hislop, D Kennie, T McCubbin, J F MacKenzie, E Melrose, R D H Monie, J J Morrice, N Peden, M Roberts, W T A Todd, A Walls

Specialty Adviser C Allister, A Baxter, D M Campbell, W R Chatfield, K M Cochran, J Dudgeon, D Felix, R B Hogg, A Kerr, A McKay, N C McMillan, B Maule, R Rampling, H Thomson, T L Turner, D Watt, B O Williams

Institute of Biomedical and Life Sciences

Adviser of Studies J A T Dow

Associate Lecturer C A Growney, R Locke, V Penpraze, M R Prach, P M Rea, C E Ross, C M Spooner, A M Tierney, A A Watt, S A White

Associate Lecturer and Adviser of Studies A C D Brown, B Cogdell, I Coombs, M R Griffiths, M E Jackson, R Sutherland, M F Tatner

Hon. Lecturer R L P Adams, Sohail Tahir Ali, Gordon Allan, Robert James Armer Atkinson, Jean M Banks, Michael C Barber, Colin W Bean, James Beattie, Mark Bolton, Martin Boocock, Patricia Bradley, Martin Delisle Burns, David G Chamberlain, Henrikka Clarkeburn, Roger A Clegg, Vaughan Cleghorn, Sean David Colloms, Andrew John Davison, Cameron Easton, Roger David Everett, David J Flint, John Patrick Goddard, Iain F Gow, Jason Hall-Spencer, Ian D Hamilton, Edward Geoff Hancock, Fiona Hannah, Carl Holt, David S Horne, Andrew Charles Kitchener, Christopher H Knight, Andreas Kolb, Jeffrey Leaver, Christine Leggate, Ann Lewendon, Howard Sinkinson Marsden, George Marshall, Paul Matthews, Azra Meadows, Peter S Meadows, Donald D Muir, Gillian Ann Nimmo, Andrew Pitt, Linda Pooley, Christopher Maurice Preston, Valerie Grace Preston, Nigel Price, William Ure Primrose, Howard Brittain Roberts, Graham E Rotheray, David B Shennan, Huw V Smith, Peter Spencer-Davies, Maureen T Travers, Richard G Vernon, Dale R Walters, Sarah Wanless, Keith Watson, Colin J Wilde, Mark Wilkinson, Victor A Zammit

Hon. Professor James W Black, Henry J Dargie, Robert Fraser, Patrick A Humphrey, Duncan J McGeoch, Charles Ian Ragan

Hon. Research Fellow John Joseph Barker, Joanna Bottomley, Richard Francis Burton, Don D Clarke, Bernard Lewis Cohen, Derrick James Dargan, John H Freer, Sibte Hadi, Oliver Holmes, Max Huxham, Sunil Kadri, Brian John McGinn, John McLauchlan, John F MacLean, Fiona Anne McPhie, Arvind Hirabhai Patel, David Pollock, Frazer John Rixon, Nigel Dennis Stow, Richard J Sugrue, Suzanne L Ullmann, Scott Peter Webster, Robert Paul Yeo

Hon. Senior Lecturer William Frederick Carman

Hon. Senior Research Fellow Stuart Charles Clarke, David W T Crompton, Lynda Gail Darlington, Charles A Fewson, Richard William Horobin, Otto F Hutter, David McEwan Jenkinson, Sheila M Jennett, John T Knowler, Anthony J Lawrence, John A S McGuigan, David Frederick Mitchell, Thomas C Muir, Judith Pratt, Jay Rosenberg, Neil Connell Spurway, Duncan Stewart-Tull, Keith Vickerman, Alaistair C Wardlaw, Malcolm B Wilkins

Lecturer R Aitken, A Amtmann, M E S Bailey, J G Beeley, D J Blackbourn, O Byron, R L Davies, P J Dominy, G R Douce, S F Goodwin, S V Graham, J V Gray, R Griffiths, L Keller, J E Lindstrom, M Lucas, S W McDonald, K MacEachern, N G MacFarlane, C J McInerny, A R MacLean, J L Matthews, G H May, R G Nager, T M Palmer, Y Pitsiladis, L C Ranford-Cartwright, J S Riddell, M O Riehle, P F Shelbourne, J M Wastling, W S Wilson, S Winder, S J Yarwood

Lecturer and Adviser of Studies L M Fixter, J D Morrison, J M Morrison, R H Wilson

Personal Professor H G Nimmo, A P Payne

Professor M R Blatt, J B Clements, R J Cogdell, J R Coggins, G H Coombs, A Crozier, A S G Curtis, R W Davies, J H Dickson, R M Elliott, M C Frame, R W Furness, D A F Gillespie, G W Gould, P Hagan, M D Houslay, D C Houston, F A Huntingford, G I Jenkins, K J Johnson, K Kaiser, M W Kennedy, W Kolch, J R Kusel, N B La Thangue, J G Lindsay, J C McGrath, M R MacLean, W Martin, N B Metcalfe, G Milligan, T J Mitchell, P Monaghan, B J Morris, N Mutrie, R S Phillips, N C Price, G L Smith, T W Stone, A J Todd, S A Ward, R J White

Professor and Adviser of Studies A M Campbell

Reader M P Barrett, T H Birkbeck, J G Coote, W Cushley, D J Evans, W R Ferrell, M H Gladden, D J Miller, E J Milner-White, D G Monckton, R D M Page, G D Ruxton, W M Stark, A C Taylor, C M R Turner, A R Walmsley

Research Fellow B H Al-Adhami, S Bearhop, A Bridgen, G J R Brock, M C Bruce, L H Chamberlain, D Chen, S R Cobb, S A Davies, H P de Koning, N Fraser, F R Härdling, J Hartwell, S Humphries, A K Kennedy, H M Kokko, F R Quinn, T F Rayner, I P Salt, P H Scott, R C Spike, D A Vouuuyiouklis, G M Walker, B J Whipp

Research Technologist L Tetley

Senior Lecturer C E Adams, W J P Barnes, A J Clutterbuck, J W Dow, J R Downie, J G Edwards, D P Leader, J G McCarron, E A B McCruden, W L Maxwell, K J Murphy, D M Neil, R Orchardson, J Shaw Dunn, R H C Strang, R G Sutcliffe, J B Wilson

Senior Lecturer and Adviser of Studies R H Baxendale, C T Brett, L J Douglas, D P Gilmore, S J Grant, M H Hansell, S MacKay, J J Milner, G R Moores, K M C O'Dell, R Parton, R Thompson

Senior Lecturer and Advisor of Studies P G Skett, R A Smith

Senior Research Fellow K R Ayscough, S C Colloms

UNIVERSITY OF GLASGOW

Visiting Professor Stephen Blackmore, Graham John Boulnois, Robert Duncan Campbell, Michael P Harris, John R Hillman, David S Ingram, L L Iversen, John T Knowler, Peter Salisbury Maitland, David G Mann, P Geoffrey Moore, Rupert Ormond, William V Shaw, John J Skehel, Christopher C R Somerville, John E Thorpe, Arno N Vermeulen, Brian Whipp

Medicine

Dean B Whiting
Dean of Postgraduate Medicine N Mackay

Anaesthetics

Clinical Lecturer R R J Gajraj, S A Grant, J A C Murdoch, D J Turfrey
Clinical Professor G Kenny
Hon. Clinical Lecturer C C Hawksworth, K S James, J H Maule, Fiona Pearsall
Hon. Senior Clinical Lecturer T Algie, W G Anderson, D S Arthur, W L M Baird, D B Bennie, J M Borthwick, H A Brewster, J H Brown, A H Burke, A E Cameron, A D Colquhoun, D F Cossar, B Cowan, Kirsteen M S Dewar, J R Dougall, G A Douglas, W R Easy, W T Frame, R J Glavin, T Goudie, J J Henderson, J C Howie, R L Hughes, J Kinsella, J C Lees, T D McCubbin, A G Macdonald, J C McDonald, E M McGrady, A H McKee, A D McLaren, T T C McLintock, R McNicol, W B Mair, D R G Marsh, R L Marshall, B Maule, C D Miller, D C Miller, N S Morton, J A Patrick, J L Plenderleith, D W Proctor, K M Rogers, D K Sewnauth, N G Smart, D F Steel, P A Stone, B Stuart, G A Sutherland, J B Thomson, J Thorburn, J M Thorp, J G Todd, A M Tully, J P Vance, P G M Wallace, P A Wilson, M Worsley
Professor W Fitch
Reader A J Asbury
Research Fellow K James, A Millar, Marie Pollock
Senior Lecturer G N C Kenny

Bacteriology

Clinical Lecturer K M Hadley
Hon. Clinical Lecturer J A G Bremner, L Gorman
Hon. Lecturer Shelia Cameron
Hon. Senior Clinical Lecturer D Baird, G B Clements, G D Corcoran, G F S Edwards, Grace Gallacher, R W A Girdwood, J Hood, G Lindsay, M G Morgan, Penelope Redding
Lecturer G R Jones
Reader C G Gemmell
Research Assistant J Cameron, T M Good, Carron Nairn
Senior Lecturer D J Platt

Behavioural Sciences Group

Hon. Research Fellow F Finnigan, M Reid
Lecturer K Mullen
Professor K Millar
Senior Lecturer R H Hammersley

Cardiac Surgery

Professor D J Wheatley
Research Assistant G Bernacca, T G Mackay

Child and Adolescent Psychiatry

Clinical Director Valerie Sellars
Hon. Clinical Lecturer Heather Gardiner, A McGrath, Helen Mann
Hon. Lecturer Eleanor E Kerr
Hon. Research Fellow H J Minnis
Hon. Senior Clinical Lecturer Robert J R McCabe, John C Powell, John C Shemilt, Michael E Van Beinum
Hon. Senior Research Fellow B Parry-Jones, C Puckering
Senior Lecturer Joanne Barton

Child Health (Medicine)

Hon. Clinical Lecturer R M Bland, N M Croft, A Ferguson, S C Ling, L Nairn, M Ray, A C Rennie, L Ross, J Schulga, F R Willis, S Zuberi
Hon. Clinical Senior Lecturer J Beattie
Hon. Clinical Teacher J D Wilkinson

Hon. Lecturer P L K Mackie, H MacTier
Hon. Professor J B P Stephenson
Hon. Research Fellow M B McFadyen
Hon. Senior Clinical Lecturer L Alroomi, T J Beattie, Katherine E Byrne, K E Cheriyan, J A P Coutts, N A Coutts, Ruth E Day, W B Doig, B Donaldson, T J Evans, B J Fredericks, P Galea, Brenda Gibson, N Gibson, K M Goel, R A Hague, J Herbison, B M Holland, A Hollman, A B Houston, S Kinmond, J P McClure, P D MacDonald, J R MacKenzie, A V Murphy, J E Richardson, K J Robertson, P H Robinson, C M J Ross, R C Shepherd, E Simpson, A Sutton, T L Turner, M P White, N Wilson
Hon. Senior Research Fellow F Cockburn
Professor L T Weaver

Clinical Medicine Planning Unit

Clinical Senior Lecturer J M Morrison
Computer Cluster Manager T M Muir
Lecturer L J Schwartz
Senior Research Fellow P M J Wilson

Clinical Physics and Bioengineering

Head A T Elliott
Hon. Lecturer T E Wheldon
Hon. Research Fellow M S Bradnam, W T Millar, J Patterson, M J Sik
Hon. Senior Clinical Lecturer G Gillen, R C Lawson, C J Martin, J O Rowan, R Strang
Hon. Senior Research Fellow T E Hilditch, J R O Owens, L Wilson
Professor D J Wyper

Dermatology

Clinical Lecturer S Holmes
Hon. Clinical Lecturer C P Fitzsimon
Hon. Lecturer G S Shankland
Hon. Senior Clinical Lecturer D J Bilsland, R S Chapman, D C Dick, M Fallowfield, A Forsyth, D Kemmett, R E I Kerr, P McHenry, C S Munro, M Richardson, D T Roberts, J Thomson, M J Young
Lecturer J L Godden
Professor R M MacKie
Research Assistant R Choudhry
Senior Lecturer M Edward, M B Hodgins

Forensic Medicine and Science

Clinical Lecturer A M Davison
Hon. Research Fellow S M Black, G Fernie
Hon. Senior Clinical Lecturer W D S McLay
Personal Professor H Smith
Professor P Vanezis
Research Assistant W H Goodwin, G McCombe, C M Morrison
Senior Lecturer R A Anderson, J S Oliver

General Practice

Clinical Lecturer P Cotton, U MacLeod, J MacNaughton, K J Moffat, H M Richards, M N Upton
Hon. Clinical Teacher M F L Barnes, D J Esler, K Fellows, J Graham, E Guthrie, M Sutherland, M A Wirth
Hon. Senior Clinical Lecturer D Baillie, M E Blatchford, E A Caven, M S Cowan, J Herron, E A Johnson, C J M Johnstone, L J Jordan, I McCarlie, A McDevitt, D McGhee, J A MacKenzie, A Potter, B Thomson, J A Tobias
Hon. Senior Research Fellow J T Hart
Lecturer S J Ross
Professor T S Murray
Research Assistant L Carroll, M Colledge, I M Gemmell, A McConnachie, E D Mitchell, H J Thomson

Geriatric Medicine

Hon. Clinical Sub-Dean S A Fraser
Hon. Clinical Lecturer A M Campbell, C Leslie, A K McKenzie, E G Spilg
Hon. Senior Clinical Lecturer K Beard, J M A Burns, G Canning, B L Devine, L Erwin, A Hendry, F Johnston, P V Knight, I M Lennox, J B MacDonald, D J Mack, G J A MacPhee, N T Manning, B J

UNIVERSITIES & MEDICAL SCHOOLS

Martin, W Reid, M A Roberts, P J W Scott, D A Stewart, M E Stewart, C Wilkieson, B O Williams, J C Young, R E Young
Professor D J Stott
Senior Lecturer P Langhorne

Human Nutrition

Clinical Lecturer S Campbell
Hon. Professor J C Seidell
Hon. Senior Research Fellow M G Dunnigan
Lecturer C A Edwards, J J Reilly
Professor M E J Lean
Research Assistant A S Anderson, Susan Eley, M K Khan, M McDonald, M Martin, J M Ralston

Immunology

Hon. Lecturer E Holme, C McSharry, A B J Speekembrink
Hon. Senior Research Fellow P C Wilkinson
Lecturer P Garside, I C McKay
Professor F Y Liew
Reader J H Brock
Research Assistant C Guillen, F P Huang, K J MacLeod, W Niedbala, D M Piedrafita, W A Sands, R E Smith, X Wei, D Xu
Senior Lecturer D I Stott

Medical Cardiology

Head S M Cobbe
Clinical Lecturer M Denvir
Hon. Professor A R Lorimer
Hon. Senior Clinical Lecturer F G Dunn, A Rae
Lecturer F L Burton, M N Hicks
Personal Professor P W Macfarlane
Research Assistant J M Bradley, B Devine, A M Howarth, S Latif, A J Workman

Medical Genetics

Clinical Director J M Connor
Clinical Senior Lecturer D E Wilcox
Hon. Lecturer J M Colgan, A Cooke, J A Crossley
Hon. Senior Clinical Lecturer D A Aitken, E Boyd, H R Davidson, W G Lanyon, G W Lowther, J Tolmie
Senior Lecturer Fiona Lyall

Medical Oncology

Hon. Professor J A Wyke
Hon. Senior Clinical Lecturer J S Adam, M Soukop
Lecturer W N Keith
Professor A Barrett, S B Kaye
Research Assistant R Brown, R Mairs, J A Plumb, J Zhao
Senior Clinical Lecturer A B Simpson
Senior Lecturer R I Freshney

Medicine

Clinical Lecturer J Hinnie
Clinical Senior Lecturer P Langhorne
Hon. Clinical Sub-Dean K M Cochran
Hon. Clinical Lecturer J M Boulton-Jones, A P Gallagher, R Neilson, D B D Vallance
Hon. Lecturer S E G Goudie
Hon. Professor D H Lawson
Hon. Senior Clinical Lecturer D E Anderson, D Ballantyne, S W Banham, J C J L Bath, G Boyd, A Bridges, R C Brown, F M Bryden, J F Calder, H A Capell, H N Cohen, R W Crofton, R L C Cumming, I Findlay, A W Forrester, J G Fox, A J S Gardiner, D Gordon, H W Gray, A D B Harrower, J M Harvey, R Hillman, K J Hogg, R B Hogg, R J Holden, D Kennedy, C M Kesson, J Larkin, J C Lauder, E Leen, H M McAlpine, A MacCuish, P McGill, G McInnes, D McIntyre, J F MacKenzie, E H McLaren, I A MacLeod, M A McMillan, R MacTier, D A S Marshall, M A Millar, R Milroy, A J Morris, E A Murphy, J J Negrette, J B Neilly, R J Northcote, I O'Brien, K R Paterson, W R Pickard, A D Pithie, F W Poon, D Reilly, J Roberts, J C Rodger, R I Russell, A Scoular, S Shahriari, J Shand, K Simpson, S D Slater, J F B Smith, W G J Smith, R D Stevenson, C Thompson, D R H Vernon, E Walker, W H Watson, A Zoma
Hon. Senior Research Fellow R M Wilson

Professor D J Stott
Research Assistant M M Dunbar, J A Gracie, A Rumley, F B Smith, I A Tulloch

Medicine and Therapeutics

Clinical Lecturer E M El-Omar, A G Jardine, P Neary, J R Petrie, D Thorburn
Hon. Clinical Lecturer J G Allan, K O'Kane
Hon. Lecturer E Davies, M McIntyre
Hon. Professor M J Brodie, H J Dargie, R Fraser, J McMurray, N C Thomson
Hon. Research Fellow J L Curzio
Hon. Senior Clinical Lecturer F G Adams, M N Al-Khafaji, M R Al-Shamma, A D Beattie, J D Briggs, J E Bunney, C Campbell, H A Carmichael, M D Cowan, B J Danesh, A J Dorward, S Dover, J G Erskine, A G Fennerty, J C Ferguson, B M Fisher, J A H Forrest, S M Frasor, T Fyfe, S Gallacher, D Grosset, W S Hislop, J A Hunter, B J R Junor, A W Kelman, J R Lawrence, J D McArthur, G T McCreath, D C McCruden, J B MacDonald, I G Mackay, T W MacKay, A R McLellan, N C McMillan, I R R McNeil, P R Mills, R D H Monie, J J Morton, R Park, K R Patel, A Peacock, D Porter, P M G Reynolds, R S C Rodger, C G Semple, P J A Semple, M Small, B H R Stack, G Stenhouse, A H Thomson, J E Thomson, R Vallance, R J Weir, T E Whitmarsh
Hon. Senior Research Fellow J H Dagg, A F Lever, D J Sumner
Lecturer N H Anderson, M J Brosnan
Professor J M Allen, J Connell, J L Reid, B Whiting
Research Assistant E C Beattie, G Blackhurst, C Clark, J S Clark, E Davies, J Fenton, D Gillooly, W K Lee, B Melville, S K Miller, N Padmanabhan, R Reid, G J Sills, I Sim, M Tree
Senior Lecturer C A Hamilton, P A Meredith, L S Murray

Neurology

Burtonl Professor P G E Kennedy
Clinical Senior Lecturer A Chaudhuri
Hon. Clinical Teacher M McCarron, Aileen McGonigal, K W Muir
Hon. Professor I Bone
Hon. Research Felloww Uma Shahani
Hon. Senior Clinical Lecturer J P Ballantyne, R Duncan, W F Durward, J Greene, D. Grosset, G A Jamal, A C Mann, R Metcalfe, A Myfanwy Thomas, C O'Leary, R K H Petty, Aline J C Russell, A I Weir
Hon. Senior Research Fellow Peter O'Behan
Professor S Moira Brown
Reader H J Willison
Research Assistant Claire L Alexander, Judith M Boffey, P Dunn, Una Fitzgerald, Esther Grinfeld, June Harland, S D Keir, G M O'Hanlon, Kathleen Simpson
Senior Lecturer Susan C Barnett, J Gow

Neuropathology

Hon. Senior Clinical Lecturer D Doyle
Professor D Graham
Research Assistant K Sturrock
Senior Lecturer J A R Nicoll

Neurosurgery

Hon. Clinical Lecturer P Barlow
Hon. Senior Clinical Lecturer R A Johnston, K W Lindsay, E Teasdale
Hon. Senior Research Fellow S Galbraith, C W Roy
Professor G M Teasdale
Research Assistant R Cruickshank, M K G Fiddes, E Stewart, S Thornhill

Nursing and Midwifery Studies

Hon. Lecturer B Johnston, F J Phillips, A M Rice
Hon. Senior Clinical Lecturer J J Dunne
Lecturer O Brittian, R Hoskins, J P Joy, M E Lait, G Lindsay, J R McDowell, M M McGuire, G A McPhail, E Rankin, A J Robb, F Whyte, S Wright
Professor L N Smith
Research Assistant L Reid
Research Fellow S Kerr

UNIVERSITY OF GLASGOW

Senior Lecturer D E Carter, E M Hillan, T Ibbotson

Obstetrics and Gynaecology, Medicine

Clinical Lecturer I R Pirwany, P Rekha, M R Thomas
Clinical Senior Lecturer U Acharya
Hon. Clinical Lecturer M Deeny, J A Gemmell, F Mackenzie, D McQueen, K Phillips, A Quinn, R N Roberts, M W Rodger, G C Sarkar
Hon. Clinical Teacher L Macara
Hon. Lecturer T A Johnston, H Lyall, N Siddiqui
Hon. Senior Clinical Lecturer A Bidrigg, S Bjornsson, L C Burnett, A D, Cameron, M J Carty, W R Chatfield, A S Clark, J W Cordiner, C A Forrest, J Gibbon, D H Gilmore, K P Hanretty, R J S Hawthorn, V D Hood, R C L Howat, J H Kennedy, A Kraszewski, R A L Low, A N McDougall, H P McEwan, D S Mack, A M Mathers, A W F Miller, J Mowat, K C Muir, W C M Naismith, I N Ramsay, R W S Yates
Hon. Senior Research Fellow R Fleming, D M Hart
Lecturer S Campbell, M A George, F Lyall
Professor I T Cameron, I A Greer
Research Assistant J Fleming, G C Smith, J Telfer
Senior Lecturer J R T Coutts

Ophthalmology

Hon. Clinical Lecturer M P Gavin, M J Houliston, B M Hutchison, D M Montgomery
Hon. Senior Clinical Lecturer T Barrie, B H Brown, J Chawla, W M Doig, J Dudgeon, G N Dutton, L Esakowitz, H Fawzi, A Fern, H M Hammer, D J Holding, P M Kyle, P M Kyle, R M McFadzean, S Murray, M Nanjiani, J Williamson, W N Wykes
Professor C M Kirkness, W R Lee
Research Fellow M Bradnam, Frances Kinnear, R Stevenson
Senior Research Fellow J Hay

Orthopaedics

Clinical Lecturer G MacKay
Hon. Clinical Teacher R M Venner
Hon. Senior Clinical Lecturer D Aaron, D B Allan, C Allister, E G Anderson, D W Bell, M Bransby-Zachary, I Cartlidge, R Crawford, J F Crossan, E R Gardner, M W G Gordon, P T Grant, M G Hullin, R Ingram, I G Kelly, A Kinninmonth, S W McCreath, G McGarrity, C Mainds, L Rymaszewski, P D R Scott, I G Stother, W M Tullett, J T Watson
Professor D L Hamblen

Paediatric Surgery

Clinical Lecturer C Hajivassiliou
Hon. Senior Clinical Lecturer A Azmy, G C Bennet, C Davis, N V Doraiswamy, I K Drainer, A H B Fyfe, G Haddock, M P G Jamieson, P A M Raine, D A Sherlock
Professor D G Young

Pathology Biochemistry

Clinical Lecturer A Gaw
Hon. Clinical Lecturer J Hinnie, J Hinnie, M Murphy, M Murphy
Hon. Clinical Teacher P J Galloway, J H McIlroy, N Sattar
Hon. Lecturer W W Borland, E Farish, D Gaffney, M H Miller, R D Paton, R Spooner, A M Wallace
Hon. Professor C J Packard
Hon. Senior Clinical Lecturer B F Allam, F C Ballantyne, G H Beastall, D E Boag, A M Cruikshank, M H Dominczak, F J Dryburgh, A C A Glen, I R Gunn, A S Hutchison, A M Kelly, M Lough, A A McConnell, D St J O'Reilly, M D Rae, J Series, P Stromberg
Hon. Teacher J Knepil, D Shapiro
Lecturer R A Cowan
Professor G S Fell, I W Percy-Robb, J Shepherd
Research Assistant E W Crawford, S Shaw
Senior Lecturer B Clark, B Cook

Pathology (including Haematology)

Hon. Clinical Lecturer D Barker, B J Clark, I W Gibson, S N Karim, D W Millan, C L Nandini, F Roberts
Hon. Lecturer M A Farquharson, M Stephen
Hon. Professor F D Lee

Hon. Senior Clinical Lecturer M Burgoyne, R A Burnett, J F Davidson, I L Evans, A K Foulis, R H A Green, A G Howatson, S R Howatson, R Jackson, N P Lucie, P McKay, D McLellan, E A Mallon, J R Michie, R Morton, E L Murray, F Mutch, J R O'Donnell, W J A Patrick, M A Peterkin, M M Rahilly, M R I Robertson, G P Sandilands, R A Sharp, G D Smith, W G S Spilg, C J R Stewart, R C Tait, P Tansey, I D Walker, R Watkins
Lecturer K Oien, A J Russell
Professor W R Lee, R N MacSween
Reader G B M Lindop, A M McNicol
Senior Lecturer W M H Behan, I L Brown, E J Fitzsimons, J J Going, A R McPhaden, I A R More, R P Reid, R Souter

Psychological Medicine

Clinical Lecturer S A Beesley, K Bowden, R C Kelly
Hon. Clinical Lecturer J M Barber, D H Brown, M Connolly, T Henderson, A Hillman, E C McCue, K Phillips, G E Ralston
Hon. Lecturer A Carpenter, G Hampson, C Kyle, A S Pashley
Hon. Research Associate A Paul
Hon. Research Fellow S Cheseldine, J White
Hon. Senior Clinical Lecturer C A Allan, H M Anderson, J A Baird, D Ball, T S Bedi, E H Bennie, D Bonham, D J Brodie, R Cantwell, R Caplan, D V Carpy, N Clark, D A Coia, D J Cooke, A F Cooper, K M Davidson, M J Dingwall, A R Douglas, C J Downie, A A Fraser, J Gallagher, R Gillham, R Gray, J G Greene, A M Hughes, A V M Hughson, R Hunter, P Jauhar, A M Jones, M M Kemp, E A Kerr, J G Knill-Jones, C K Li, R Lindsay, H Livingston, D Lyons, R G McCreadie, J P McKane, A V P MacKay, J McKnight, S A McLaren, M R Malcolm, I C Matson, S M Miller, P C Misra, F Munro, D M Murray, A J Naismith, A Nightingale, D E Palmer, M Z Rahman, J Reid, J B Riddell, A M Scott, G Shaw-Dunn, I D Smith, M Smith, J A Taylor, M S Turner, M M Walker, L J Watt, R Whyte, S F Whyte, J P Woods, E P Worrall
Hon. Senior Lecturer K G Bonham
Lecturer F Finnigan, A V P Mackay, K Mullen, Christine Puckering, A Stallard
Professor M R Bond, C A Espie, K Millar
Research Assistant J S Clark, J Evans
Senior Clinical Lecturer E Campbell
Senior Lecturer J Atkinson, M Livingston

Public Health

Clinical Lecturer A Carnon
Hon. Clinical Lecturer J H Cossar, P McCarron
Hon. Lecturer L E Calvert, K Fleming, D S Gordon, F J Raeside, C Tannahill, S Twaddle, A Walker
Hon. Professor S McIntyre, D Reid
Hon. Research Associate G P Ashe
Hon. Research Fellow D Coia, G D Smith
Hon. Senior Clinical Lecturer S Ahmed, C A Birt, D A Breen, B Brown, A Bryson, H J G Burns, D M Campbell, J M Cowden, L De Caestecker, A Downie, A G Elder, M R Gardee, C R Gillis, D Goldberg, L Gruer, D J Hole, C W Ide, C J Kalman, A C K Lockie, G McIlwane, M McWhirter, D C Moir, G P Morris, A T B Muir, S J O'Brien, A J Pelosi, L M Reay, W J Reilly, S N Scott, C Stark, K M Stewart, I S Symington, E R Waclawski, A D Watt, L M Wilkie, J Womersley
Hon. Senior Research Fellow M Kelly, O L Lloyd, M B Tannahill
Lecturer N Craig, L J Curtice, P H Evans
Professor J McEwen, A Petch
Research Assistant J Bicanic, H Davison, M A De-Ridder, G Dewsbury, N Drummond, R Ghafoor, C A H Hart, C L Hart, M A Khan, A Knill-Jones, B Laffey, A H Leyland, S G MacAskill, C S McCulloch, J S McGregor, A McLeod, P McLoone, K J Murray, L M Naven, C A O'Donnell, J Pearson, K A Ritchie, E E Semple, W Wright
Senior Lecturer J M Atkinson, R B Jones, M E Reid

Radiation Oncology

Hon. Senior Clinical Lecturer P A Canney, T Habeshaw, A N Harnett, R D Jones, E Junor, N Reed, A G Robertson, R P Symonds, H M A Yosef
Professor J Welsh
Senior Lecturer Roy Rampling

UNIVERSITIES & MEDICAL SCHOOLS

Surgery
President I W R Anderson
Clinical Lecturer J C Doughty, C J McKay, M Oko, A D Purushotham, D A Stell, M Ward
Hon. Clinical Sub-Dean G Bell, R Dalling, A Smith
Hon. Clinical Lecturer C Morran, B Sugden, B W A Williamson
Hon. Clinical Teacher W O Thomson
Hon. Lecturer A Johnston, D C McMillan
Hon. Professor S Gatehouse, C W Imrie, D Kirk
Hon. Research Associate S A Ballantyne, D Chong, C P Kalogeropoulou, H Kasem
Hon. Research Fellow A J Beveridge, A D Clarke, J D Howell, C K MacKay
Hon. Senior Clinical Lecturer B J Abel, M Aitchison, M Akyol, J R Anderson, B J G Bingham, R W Brookes, A C Buck, M H Calvert, H R Chandrachud, I G Conn, L D Cooke, J A Crowther, R F Deane, J K Drury, A Faichney, J C Ferguson, I G Finlay, G M Fullarton, D J Galloway, N Geddes, G Gillespie, D G Gilmour, E S Glen, J A Goldberg, J R Goldring, G R Gray, R O Gun, W S Hendry, B W H Irvine, A Johnston, R A Kell, D Lanigan, G C MacBain, J R MacCallum, A J McEwan, G W McGarry, J R McGregor, A J McKay, C Mackay, R F McKee, I S McLaughlin, A J McMahon, D F Miller, K G Mitchell, J J Morrice, A L Morton, W R Murray, B F O'Reilly, G Orr, E A Osborne, P J Paterson, J G Pollock, J J Reidy, J R Richards, P N Rogers, R Scott, P J Shouler, D C Simpson, J Sinclair, D C Smith, I S Smith, D S Soutar, G T Sunderland, I J Swann, E W Taylor, R P Teenan, M H C Webster, G H Welch, A White
Hon. Senior Research Fellow H Simpson
Hon. Teacher G A Day
Lecturer J M S Bartlett, E M Bolton, S Jamieson, J R McGregor
Professor J A Bradley, G G Browning, T Cooke, W D George
Research Assistant J Gallagher, H E Marshall, S E Middleton, A Millar, J R Reeves, C Sharples, A M Wood
Research Fellow D MacMillan, A L Morton, D Murphy, K Robertson, E M M El Tahir, J R Tweedle, K Walker, G Wishart
Senior Lecturer W J Angerson, G Gallagher

Systems
Lecturer M R McLean
Personal Professor W Martin, N Spurway
Senior Lecturer R Orchardson, D Pollock

Virology
Lecturer A R MacLean

Wellcome History of Medicine Unit
Research Assistant J T A Bradley, M W Dupree, A J Hull, F A MacDonald, M A M Nicolson, I H Spencer
Senior Lecturer J Geyer-Kordesch

Wellcome Surgical Institute
Lecturer D Dewar, I M MacRae
Professor A M Harper, J McCulloch
Research Assistant H Carswell, K Horsburgh, D G MacGregor, O Touzani

Degrees and diplomas
MB, ChB, BDS, BN, BSc, PhD, D.Clin.Psy, MScMed.Sci, MN, MPH, MD, DDS

University of St Andrews

St Andrews KY16 9AJ
Tel: 01334 476161
Website: www.st-and.ac.uk

Principal & Vice-Chancellor B Lang
Pro Dean Medical Science D W Sinclair
Secretary D J Corner

Science

Biomedical Sciences
Head of School/Professor K T Sillar

Lecturer M G Burdon, S Guild, D Jackson, M J Milner, C J M Nicol
Professor R T Hay, R E Randall, C M Steel, J B Tucker
Reader P E Bryant, W J Heitler, R R Ramsay
Senior Lecturer J F Aiton, G Cramb, M R Farrally, F W Flitney, R Griffiths, W J Ingledew, G D Kemp, G F McPhate, R M Pitman, A C Riches, M D Ryan, D W Sinclair, J Sommerville, S C Whiten

Chemistry
Professor P G Bruce
Reader A R Butler

Psychology
Head of School V J Brown
Professor D W Johnston, M Johnston, R E O'Carroll

Degrees and diplomas
BScMed.Sci, MSc, PhD

Wales

University of Wales, Aberystwyth

PO Box 2, King Street, Aberystwyth SY23 2AX
Tel: 01970 62311 Fax: 01970 611446
Website: www.aber.ac.uk

Vice-Chancellor & Principal D Llwyd Morgan
Registrar & Secretary D Gruffydd Jones
Student Health Officer, University Psychiatrist Ann Rhys

Institute of Biological Sciences

Lecturer A J Bond, D R Causton, P Darcy, P M Evans, J W Forster, J H R Gee, I Ap Gwynn, M L R Johnston, A K Jones, M G Jones, M A Kaderbhai, D M Lewis, J R Ling, L N Manchester, D P Russell, S C Russell, J P Savidge, I Scott, J Scullion, R J Simmonds, A R Smith, R J Turner
Professor J Barrett, R N Beechy, M A Hall, J R Hinchliffe, D G Jones, R N Jones, D B Kell, J G Morris, L J Rogers, P Wathern
Reader W A Adams, R B Kemp, P W Trudgill, M Young
Senior Lecturer B H Davies, G H M Evans, J D Fish, D J Hopper, M P Ireland, E I Mercer, A J Smith, R J Wootton
Senior Research Associate G Jenkins, R K Narayan

Physics

Lecturer P Cadman, D F Falla, M J Mitchell, I L Morris, S E Pryse, G O Thomas, W P Wilkinson
Professor L Kersley, L Thomas, P J S Williams
Reader K Birkinshaw
Senior Lecturer T E Jenkins, G Vaughan

University of Wales, Cardiff

PO Box 920, Cardiff CF1 3XP
Tel: 029 2087 4000 Fax: 029 2037 1921
Website: www.cardiff.ac.uk

Vice-Chancellor David Grant

Cardiff School of Biosciences

Professor Clarke Alan, Moxham Bernard, Caterson Bruce, Archer Charlie, Lloyd David, Bowen Ifor, Harwood John, Kay John, Wimpenny Julian, Fox Kevin, Evans Martin, Ehrmann Michael, Bruford Mike, John Rob, Eccles Ronald, Richards Roy, Dunnett Steve, Hacob Tim, Duance Victor, Crunelli Vincenzo

Molecular and Medical Biosciences

University of Wales, Cardiff, Museum Avenue, PO Box 911, Cardiff CF1 3US
Tel: 029 2087 4829 Fax: 029 2087 4116

Experimental Officer J E Liddell

Fellow K Berube, S Marshall
Lecturer S Barasi, J M Basford, J R Bedwani, R C Caswell, Alison Davies, D J R Evans, E J Evans, R C Hall, S K Hall, P Kille, A P L Kwan, D J Mason, A P Morby, D P Ramji, R M Rose, G E Sweeney
Professor C W Archer, B Caterson, V Crunelli, A Cryer, R Eccles, J L Harwood, T J C Jacob, R A John, J Kay, B J Moxham, R J Richards, M H T Roberts, D I Wallis
Reader V C Duance, G A Foster
Royal Society Fellow C Berry
School Administrator John Robertson
School Fellow T Wells, R D Young
Senior Lecturer M Benjamin, D A Carter, P F J Chapman, K D Fox, J G Jones, A H Olavesen, J R Presley, J R Ralphs, R M Santer, A H D Watson, G F White, P J Winterburn, F S Wusteman

Optometry

Lecturer Julie Albon, Richard Earlam, Jon Erichsen, Jeremy Guggenheim, Pia Makela, Tom Margrain, Kola Oduwaiye, Andrew Quantock, Outi Ukkonen
Professor Neville Drasdo, Gerald Elliott, Stuart Hodson, Keith Meek, Jyrki Rovamo, John Wild
Senior Lecturer Paul Murphy, Rachel North, J M Woodhouse

Pharmacy

King Edward VII Avenue, Cathays Park, Cardiff CF1 3XF
Tel: 029 2087 4000 Fax: 029 2087 4149

Director - WCPPE D J Temple
Deputy Head of School P J Nicholls
Head Welsh School of Pharmacy D K Luscombe
Lecturer A S Cotterill, J R Furr, I H Gilbert, C Grout, M Gumbleton, D N John, J Y Maillard, W J Pugh, R G Stevens
Professor K J Broadley, J Hadgraft, I W Kellaway, C McGuigan, A D Russell, P S J Spencer, R D Walker
Senior Lecturer N A Armstrong, K R Brain, S Daniels, R D E Sewell, M S Shayegan-Salek, G Taylor
Senior Research Fellow K Wann

Psychology

Lecturer J H Adam, C Barry, J L Boivin, K B C Carnelley, M A Good, K A F Greenland, G T Harold, K W Hirsh, A Howes, W J M Macken, G R Maio, R P Martin, C Miles, Michelle J Morgan, C M Morrison, J L Muir, A J Tattersall
Professor J P Aggleton, D E Blackman, H D Ellis, F D Fincham, M R C Hewstone, D M Jones, M R Oaksford, S J Payne, J M Pearce
Reader R J Snowden
Senior Lecturer N J Frude, T M Honess, J Patrick, J O Robinson, P A White

Pure and Applied Biology

University of Wales College of Cardiff, PO Box 915, Cardiff CF1 3TL
Tel: 029 2087 4000 Fax: 029 2087 4190

Director of Teaching D R Lees
Lecturer M J Bosley, J H Bourne, D W Bowker, R J Cowie, P J Evans, J D Hardege, A J Morgan, P F Randerson, H J Rogers, A J Weightman, T Wigham, J E Young
Professor L Boddy, I D Bowen, W T Coakley, J C Fry, T M G Gabriel, J Hemingway, D Lloyd, J H Slater, J W T Wimpenny
Reader M J Day, D Francis, N A C Kidd
Senior Lecturer B N Dancer, M S Davies, J R Dickinson, P N Ferns, M A Jervis, C J Mettam, S J Ormerod, D Pascoe, D J Stickler, D H Thomas, W A Venables

School of Psychology

Emeritus Professor D E Blackman, K D Duncan
Hon. Associate Professional Tutor C Alders, D G Allen, A Brooks, S A Ellis, P D G Harris, J Hill-Tout, R Jenkins, T Kidd, J Reed, J Rees, M Thomson, S E Vivian-Byrne
Hon. Lecturer S V Austin, P D Bennett, A L Brazier, J McBride, N Mills, J L Moses, J Onyett, F R Young
Hon. Professor E W Farmer, R D P Griffiths, R D Hare, C M Judd, M E P Seligman

Hon. Research Fellow E A Gaffan, J E J Gallacher, S L Grand, E Griffiths, D R Laws, P K H McKenna, T Mason, D S Owen, R F Westbrook
Lecturer John P Aggleton, Todd Bailey, Simon Banbury, Jacky Boivin, H C M Carroll, John Culling, Hadyn D Ellis, Tom Freeman, Mark A Good, Nicola Gray, Geoffrey Haddock, Ulrike Hahn, Gordon Harold, Dale Hay, Rob Honey, Andrew Howes, Dylan M Jones, Michael Lewis, Bill Macken, Gregory Maio, Chris Miles, Catriona Morrison, Janice L Muir, Mike Oaksford, John Patrick, Stephen J Payne, John Pearce, Andy Smith, Robert J Snowden, Geoff Thomas, Peter White, Ed Wilding, Patricia Wright
Professorial Research Fellow Peter Halligan
Research Assistant Melissa Allman, Afia Begum, Vaughan Bell, Steve Belt, Andrea Chadwick, Rachel Dowling, Andrew Edmonds, Neil Ellis, Mark Haselgrove, Kathryn Hodder, Sophie MacCulloch, Vanessa Marshall, Kerry Rees, Nic Row, Jennifer Smith, Michael Zorawski
Research Associate Joanne Beale, Gary Christopher, Bryany Cusens, James Futter, David George, Kyla Honey, Robert Houghton, Anthony McGregor, Rachel Mcnamara, Susanna Moss, Alastair Nicholls, Will Reader, Helen Sharpe, Christine Shaw, Sharon Simpson, Jane Sumnall, David Sutherland, Seralynne Vann, Jasper Ward-Robinson, Fei Zhao
Research Fellow Vincent Casteras, Ana da Costa, Etienne Coutureau, Trisha Jenkins, Marie Thomas
Research Technician Eman Amin, Moira Davies, Diane Ellis, John Gameson, Heather Phillips, Gill Rhydderch
Senior Research Fellow Mary McMurran

Degrees and diplomas

BA, BSC, MA, MSC, BSCECON, MSCECON, MBA, DPHIL, MPHIL, PHD, MENG, BENG

University of Wales College of Medicine

Heath Park, Cardiff CF14 4XN
Tel: 029 2074 2072 Fax: 029 2074 2914
Email: turnercb@cardiff.ac.uk
Website: www.uwcm.ac.uk

Vice-Chancellor S Tomlinson
Pro Vice-Chancellor & Dean of School of Healthcare Studies N Palastanga
Dean and Director of Postgraduate Medical and Dental Education T M Hayes
Dean of Dental School M L Jones
Dean of School of Medicine K Woodhouse
Dean of School of Nursing Studies & Midwifery Studies Ann M. Tucker
Registrar L F J Rees
Secretary C B Turner

Dental School

Dean M L Jones
Vice-Dean D H Edmunds
Adult Dental Health P M H Drummer
Basic Dental Science D K Whittaker
Dental Health & Development S Richmond
Oral Surgery J P Sheperd

Adult Dental Health
Clinical Teacher Carolanne B Beck, Isobel Cummingham, C H Dalton, R A Fuge, Barbara A Geddes, J S Gerrish, Janet Griffiths, D Howells, P Jones, W S McLaughlin, T J O'Donovan, Josephine Prior, J R S Roll, R W Seaman, A W Sugar, Patricia A Thompson, Shelagh A Thompson, M Townson, M Wills-Wood
Lecturer P J Ash, J J Evans, D M W Goodwin, N Hall, S J Hayes, R Hicks, Susan M Jenkins, S Lewis, J H Llewellyn, J S Owens, R B Smith, J Sweet, D K Wills, J Wilson
Professor P M H Dumme, I C MacKenzie, J M A Wilton
Reader D H Edmunds, P H Jacobsen
Senior Lecturer A S M Gilmaur, R G Jagger, N D Robb

The Medical Directory © Informa Professional 2002

UNIVERSITIES & MEDICAL SCHOOLS

Basic Dental Science
Professor & Head of Department D K Whittaker
Lecturer P Rooney, M G J Waters
Reader J Middleton, K R Williams
Senior Lecturer R C Hall, Rachel J Waddington

Child Dental Health and Development
Clinical Teacher J Beechey, J Collier, Eliyabeth M. Davies, K Davies, S Edmunds, C Fawcett, C Hoddell, J Jobbins, E Jones, J Jones, R Jones, P Leech, C Payner, J Simove
Hon. Clinical Teacher P T Nicholson, P Stephenson, H Taylor, S Wigglesworth
Lecturer Claudia Blakytny, C Daniels, Jennifer J Gyton, L Hunter, Gillian M Jones, M Z Morgan, Kate Robson, Celia Topping
Professor S Richmond, Elizabeth T Treasure
Professor & Dean of Dental School M L Jones
Senior Lecturer Barbara L Chadwick, I G Chestnutt, B Hunter, J Knox, R G Oliver

Oral Surgery, Medicine and Pathology
Professor & Head of Department J P Shepherd
Clinical Teacher J Bisson, M J Fardy, C S Holland, J Llewelyn, E S Nash, D Patton, A W Sugar
Hon. Instructor M E J Craddock
Lecturer M R Brickley, S J Oliver, V Sivarajasingam, M J Wilson
Professor M A O Lewis
Senior Lecturer E G Absi, C M Hill, A J C Potts, D W Thomas

School of Healthcare Studies

Pro Vice-Chancellor and Dean N Palastanga
Occupational Therapy, Vice-Dean M Booy

School of Medicine

Dean K Woodhouse
Vice-Dean I G Finlay

Anaesthetics and Intensive Care Medicine
Head M Harmer
Head of Department M Harmer
Clinical Teacher J E Barry, P A Clyburn, M Cobley, J S Davies, J A Dunne, N M Dunne, D E N Evans, Judith M Foy, C D Gildersleve, N D Groves, M W Hebden, P L Jones, I P Latto, N McCann, S Morris, K R Murrin, W S Ng, S C Pugh, M S Read, M N Smithies, M R W Stacy, A Turley, R S Vaughan, G A Wenham, M P Whitten, P C Wiener, B A Willis
Lecturer I Bowler, M P Gilbert
Senior Lecturer J E Hall, I Hodzovic, B J Jenkins, J S Mecklenburgh

Child Health
Head D P Davies
Clinical Teacher M Alfaham, Annette Davies, P M Davies, I Doull, M R Drayton, M W English, H Farley, T G Ferguson, F Gibbon, S N Huddart, K Hutton, H R Jenkins, M Jenny, Fiona Jewkes, C R Kirk, A M Mott, E P Penny, G J Shortland, G C Smith, E Street, R Surana, D Tuthill, H Williams
Hon. Teacher R Lloyd-Richards
Lecturer R Brooks, B Evans, G Morris
Professor J R Sibert
Reader Kate Verrier-Jones
Senior Lecturer P H T Cartlidge, J W Gregory, R.D.W. Hain, Alison Kemp, H Payne, Elspeth Webb

Dermatology
Head of Department A J Finlay
Clinical Teacher P Holt, A G Knight, C C Long, R Motley
Hon. Lecturer P Dykes
Lecturer C Edwards, M Gonzalez, H Judodiharjo
Professor R Marks
Senior Research Fellow P E Bowden

Diabetes Research Unit
Professor Professor Owens

Diagnostic Radiology
Professor & Head of Department G M Roberts
Clinical Teacher H Adams, J Blethyn, M W Bourne, D Ll Cochlin, M D Crane, C Evans, S F S Halpin, S Harrison, Margaret D Hourihan, A Jones, Margaret R Jones, B W L Lawrie, D C F Lloyd, Kathleen A Lyons, Susan Morris, J I S Rees, N G Stoodley, L B Williams, A M Wood
Lecturer David H Edwards, D Parthimos
Professor T M Griffith

Epidemiology, Statistics and Public Health
Professor & Head of Department Mansel Talbot
Reader I P Matthews, N J Vetter
Senior Lecturer S R Palmer, C C Potter, A Round, A.A.R. Rushdy, J Watkins

Forensic Pathology
Lecturer L D M Nokes
Senior Lecturer A M Davison, D S James, S Leadbeatter

General Practice
Professor & Head of Department Helen Houston
Clinical Teacher K S Dayananda
Hon. Professor Ilora G Finlay
Lecturer K Hood
Professor Roisin Pill, Clare Wilkinson
Senior Lecturer P Bennett, G Butler, A Edwards, A Jones, E Jones, P Kinnersley, S Rollnick, Lorna Tapper-Jones

Geriatric Medicine
Clinical Teacher J S Chadha, B S D Sastry, M D Stone, G M Tinker
Professor, Dean of Medicine K W Woodhouse
Senior Lecturer M Hasan, R J Meara, Sinead O'Mahony

History of Medicine
Hon. Curator E E Payne
Lecturer J H Cule

Medical Biochemistry
Head G H Elder
Clinical Teacher S B Matthews, P E Williams
Hon. Tutor R John
Lecturer P Gasque, N K Rushmere
MRC External Scientific Staff W H Evans
Professor A K Campbell
Reader R L Dormer
Senior Lecturer M N Badminton, D H Llewellyn, I F W McDowell, M A McPherson
Wellcome Senior Clinical Research Fellow B P Morgan

Medical Computing and Statistics
Deputy Director of Medical Computing Unit V C McBroom
Head E C Coles
Computer Officer M J Evans, D A Myles, T D Ruckinski
Lecturer A K Allen
Network Officer F D J Dunstan
Senior Lecturer R G Newcombe, A.B.J. Nix

Medical Genetics
Professor & Head of Department J R Sampson
Clinical Lecturer J Gray
Clinical Teacher M Creasy, S Davies, D Ravine
Hon. Professor F M Pope
Hon. Senior Lecturer H E Hughes
Lecturer J P Cheadle, D S Millar, D S Owens
Professor D N Cooper, P S Harper, M J Owen
Reader A Clarke

Medical Microbiology
Head B I Duerden
Clinical Teacher K Al-Shafi, I Hosein, A Quoraishi, C D Ribeiro, Diana Westmoreland
Hon. Lecturer A J Howard

UNIVERSITY OF WALES COLLEGE OF MEDICINE

Lecturer H C Ryley
Senior Lecturer Rosemary A Barnes, P G Flanagan, J D Fox, S K Jackson

Medical Microscopy Sciences Unit
Research Fellow J A Hobot
Senior Lecturer and Director G R Newman

Medical Physics and Bioengineering
Professor H Griffiths, J P Woodcock
Radiation Protection Adviser A R Richards
Research Fellow R Morris

Medical Resources Centre
Director R A Morton
Deputy Director K Bellamy
Learning Resource Centre Manager I Thompson
Learning Technology I A Nicholls
Senior Lecturer S Young

Medicine
Head C M Wiles
Professor & Head of Department M Davies
Arthritis & Rheumatism Council Fellow S M Linton
Clinical Teacher M H Pritchard
Glaxo Wellcome Fellow A O Phillips
Hon. Lecturer K Baboolal, J Furmaniak
Hon. Professor G A Coles, J Rhodes
Hon. Senior Lecturer T Maughan, B Rees Smith
Lecturer T M Lawson, E.C.Y. Wang, O M Williams
Leukaemia Research Fund Lecturer P Brennan
Professor M Mason, J Rhodes, M Rowe, M F Scanlon, D J Shale, S.D.G. Stephens, B D Williams, J D Williams
Reader J H Lazarus
Royal Society Fellow S.T.K. Man
Senior Lecturer J Alcolado, A R Freedman, T L Griffiths, J N Harvey, M O Labeta, R J Matthews, M A Mir, J E Morgan, N P Robertson, P A Rutherford, R Steadman, N Topley, G W G Wilkinson
Wellcome Trust Fellow T. Bowen, C M Geldiet

Obstetrics and Gynaecology
Clinical Teacher B Beattie, N Davies, A S Evans, Janet Evans, A Fiander, L D Klentzeris, P C Lindsay, R Penketh, A E J Rees, A Roberts
Lecturer S Bell-Thomas, P S Bhal, Shanon Paynter
Professor R W Shaw
Senior Lecturer N N Amso, O A Ladipo

Pathology
Head D Wynford Thomas
Clinical Teacher M M Cotter, N S Dallimore, A R Gibbs, R Olafsdottir
Lecturer C J Jones, P Matthews
Professor P J Smith, G T Williams
Senior Lecturer R Attanoos, A G Douglas-Jones, D F R Griffiths, S M Ismail, B Jasani, D G Kipling, P Laidler, A Lammie, E J Lazda, J W Neal, G M Vujanic

Pharmacology, Therapeutics and Toxicology
Hon. Lecturer M G Spencer
Lecturer V B O'Donnell, J Williams
Professor M J Lewis, P A Routledge
Senior Lecturer J A Davies, R W Marshall, H G Rees, J F Wilson

Psychological Medicine
Head P McGuffin
Professor & Head of Department M J Owen
Clinical Teacher M D Alldrick, J Bisson, N Davies, G Harborne, J Hillier, Helen Holmes, G Howells, C Hunter, R Jacques, M Jenkins, G H Jones, M R Keen, A M P Kellam, J Lewis, A McBride, D Ridley-Segart, R C Scorer, M S Shooter, D R Thomas, Sarah E Watkins, A J Williams, P A Williams, Tegwyn Williams
Hon. Lecturer D G Allen

Hon. Teacher A A-B Badawy
Lecturer Z Ahmed, A L Jones, A Thapar, H V Thomas, A A Watt
Professor D Felce, W I Fraser, G H Lewis, M J MacCulloch, M C O'Donovan
Reader P Buckland, D T Healy, Julie Williams
Senior Lecturer R I Araya, A Cardno, S Deb, P L Jenkins, M P Kerr, A Korzun, M Liddell
Wellcome Trust Advanced Fellow G Kirov

Surgery
Head R E Mansel
Clinical Teacher M Beck, I M Breckenridge, E G Butchart, W T Davies, J S Harvey, R Hatfield, S N Huddart, J W Hunter, B J Jenkins, E N P Kulatilake, H Kynaston, C M Lane, I F Lane, K Lowe, P Matthews, I J Monypenny, A Radcliffe, G Shone, T Stephenson, J A Vafidis, R F Walters, H L Young
Hon. Professor M H Wheeler
Lecturer P Drew
Senior Lecturer M Hallett, R Hardwick, W G Jiang, R G S Mills, M C A Puntis, Helen Sweetland, D J T Webster

Trauma and Orthopaedic Surgery
Clinical Teacher J Fairclough, G P Graham, M Maheson, D O'Doherty, C Wilson
Senior Lecturer C M Dent

Welsh Combined Centre for Public Health
Director S R Palmer
Administrator A Midha
Hon. Professor I T Russell
Hon. Senior Research Fellow R Henry, R L Salmon, R M Smith, D R Thomas
Lecturer S Hayes, C Hillier
Senior Lecturer Dr Evans, H.M.P. Fielder, A I Jader, R A Lyons

Wound Healing Research Unit
Director K Moore, P Price
Clinical Research Fellow L Krishnamoorthy, H Morris, S Natarajan
Hon. Senior Research Officer M Clark
Professor and Director K G Harding
Senior Lecturer V Jones

School of Nursing and Midwifery Studies

Nursing Studies
Dean Ann Tucker
Vice-Dean Llynos M Lloyd
Lecturer Peter Akinwunmi, Erica S Alabaster, Sandra J Arthur, Rhian Barnes, H C Beckett, Elaine S Beer, Judith Benbow, Susan K Bennett, Jagdish Bheenuck, Jeremy D Bray, Carol Britton, Lynne R Broome, Janice Campsie, Christine A Casey, Paul Challinor, Paul F Coe, Ronald D Constant, Linda H Cooper, J Corbett, David Coyle, Joanna Davies, Ruth E Davies, M Anne Edwards, Nazmabai S Esufali, N Evans, Patricia Farr, Anne Fothergill, Margaretta Furness, Timothy S Gibson, Dianne W Griffiths, D Gukhool, Lynne Gunter, Christine Hanks, B Hannigan, Suzanne F Hazell, Una Hebden, Grace M Henshall, Peter M Hirstyj, Janice Hoover, Georgina Hourahane, Linda Houston, John Howe, Jadwiga B Howell, Ian Hulatt, Maureen F Humphreys, Helen Husband, Susanne M Hutchings, Janet A Israel, Margaret B John, Angela Johnson, Elizabeth M Jones, Keith Jones, Michael J Jones, Patricia Jones, Ootra Jugessur, C Laugharne, Maureen Lewis, Chong H Lim, Christine Luke, Gwyneth C Luke, P McKnee, George A McWhirter, Ruth J Marshall, Andrew R Matthews, B J Millar, Cynthia Moore, Jane Moore, Jennifer E G Morris, Leonard V Moss, Janet Olsen, Els Ooijen van, David R Powell, Morag Prowse, Colin Rees, Sally E Rees, Gerard M Roche, Nichola B Rowlands, Harry D Ruck, Cathryn S Russell, J L Ryan, Sandra M Samuel, C Searle, Mary Semper, Julia Styles, Chai T Tang, Margaret L Taylor, Eiddwen M Thomas, Jane V Treharne-Davies, Mary J Tully, Linda Walker, Rose Waring, Dianne Watkins, Francesca A Webber, Irene J Webber, Keith W Weeks, Zoe Whale, Gail Williams, Grant Williams, R W Williams, Anthony J Willis, Vivienne F Winspear

UNIVERSITIES & MEDICAL SCHOOLS

Professor Philip Burnard, Patricia A Lyne
Reader Evelyn Parsons
Senior Lecturer Francis C Biley

University of Wales, Swansea

Singleton Park, Swansea SA2 8PP
Tel: 01792 205678 Fax: 01792 295618
Website: www.swansea.ac.uk

Vice-Chancellor R H Williams
Pro Vice-Chancellor P Townsend

Biological Sciences

Professor and Head of School R Waters
Hon. Professor J Ashby, J N Baxter, B L Bayne, D Tweats
Lecturer T Butt, R S Conlan, E A Dyrynda, P L M Lee, C J Mayfield
Professor P F Brain, J R Gallon, R P Newton, J M Parry, N A Ratcliffe, A F Rowley, J S Ryland, D Skibinski
Reader K J Flynn
Research Fellow E M Parry, S H Reed
Senior Lecturer M S Berry, P J Dyson, G Hays, P J Hayward, C R Mayfield, D H Jones, Susan E Shackley, C J Smith, S J Wainwright, T J Walton

Chemistry

Head of Department & Professor K Smith
Hon. Professor/Fellow John I G Cadogan, D Evans
Lecturer P Douglas, A E Graham, J M Maud, C P Morley
Professor J H Beynon, A G Brenton, D E Games, J O Morley
Reader T W Bentley, R S Ward
Senior Lecturer J S Davies, R S Mason

Physics

Head of Department M Charlton
Lecturer P R Dunstan, H Fretwell, W B Perkins
Professor A J Davies, D I Olive, G M Shore, H H Telle
Reader N Dorey, D C Dunbar, S J Hands, T Hollowood
Senior Lecturer C R Allton

School of Health Science

Director of Health Informatics B A Goldberg
Assistant Director J Evans, A Hopkins
Head of School B Green
Hon. Professor C W Delaney, K Freeman, V M Lawton
Hon. Senior Lecturer H Allen, A R Griew, A Maddocks, R G Royce, R L Scheid, J H Williams
Professor D J Hughes
Professor in Nursing A M Williams
Professor of Community Nursing M J Clark
Senior Lecturer N M Eaton, S D Edwards, C J Evans, H M Evans, L J Griffiths, B Hunter, J A Merrell, C P Phillips, M I Tait, P J Wainwright, J C White

Swansea Clinical School

Director J M Hopkin
Hon. Lecturer V S Menon
Hon. Professor J A Dodge, T Shirakawa
Hon. Research Fellow R Y Mann, K Ragunath
Hon. Research Officer D L James
Hon. Senior Lecturer J Beynon, M Cosgrove, P Ebden, S A Jenkins, J G C Kingham
Lecturer B G A Thomas, W Walker
Professor of Cancer Studies R C F Leonard
Professor of Plastic Surgery A D Mcgregor
Professor/General Surgery J N Baxter
Research Fellow D Durai
Research Officer F L Maggs-Rapport
Secretarial Assistant C Jones, M Jones
Senior Lecturer B Lervy
Senior Lecturer (Palliative Medicine) H M Taylor

Northern Ireland

Queen's University of Belfast

Whitla Medical Building, 97 Lisburn Road, Belfast BT9 7BL
Tel: 028 9024 5133, 028 9027 2010, 028 9027 2196
Fax: 028 9033 0571
Email: k.copeland@qub.ac.uk
Website: www.qub.ac.uk

Head of Administration Karen Copeland

College of Medicine and Health Services

University Road, Belfast BT7 1NN
Tel: 028 9024 5133 ext: 3477 Fax: 028 9033 0571

Dean of Faculty R W Stout

Anaesthetics

Lecturer J M Murray
Professor J P H Fee, R Mirakhur

Anatomy

Professor G R Dickson, Ruth StC Gilmore, D J Heylings, C B O'Reilly, P D A Owens, D J Wilson

Child Health

Professor D J Carson, J Jenkins, B G McClure, J M Savage, M D Shields, Moira C Stewart

Clinical Biochemistry

Lecturer W E Allen, G Skibinski
Professor Elisabeth R Trimble
Senior Lecturer Madeline Ennis

Dental Education

Professor E O'Neill

Dental Radiology

Professor A D Gough

Dental Surgery

Lecturer F T Lundy, B M Murray
Professor G C Cowan, P J Lamey, J G McGimpsey, J J Marley
Senior Lecturer W A Coulter, C G Cowan

Epidemiology and Public Health

Lecturer M R Stevenson
Professor A E Evans, A Gavin, F E Kee, C C Patterson, J W G Yarnell
Senior Lecturer G W Cran, L J Murray

General Practice

Professor M E Cupples, A E W Gilliland, G N Johnson, K J McGlade, P M Reilly, W K Steele

Geriatric Medicine

Lecturer D Craig, Vivienne L S Crawford, S P McIlroy
Professor R W Stout
Senior Lecturer I Maeve Rea, A P Passmore

Haematology

Professor T Lappin, Mary F McMullin

Institute of Telemedicine and Telecare

Professor R Wootton

Medical Education

Director J M Savage
Assistant Director K J McGlade
Senior Lecturer M I Boohan

QUEEN'S UNIVERSITY OF BELFAST

Medical Genetics
Head D A Savage
Reader Anne E Hughes, A P Maxwell

Medicine
Head of Department D R McCluskey
Lecturer U Bayraktutan, MMT O'Hare, J V Woodside
Professor I S Young
Reader S A Hawkins, C F Johnston
Senior Lecturer A L Bell, L G Heaney, PP Mckeown, M E Rooney, R G P Watson

Mental Health
Professor S J Cooper, M T Kennedy, R J McClelland
Senior Lecturer C C Mulholland, F A O'Neill

Microbiology and Immunology
Lecturer I R Henderson
Professor J A Johnson, M J Pallen
Senior Lecturer M A Armstrong, S Patrick

Nursing Studies
Professor A M Begley, B Blackwood, A Lazenbatt, Caroline Mason, Jean A Orr, Eileen J Pollock, S Porter, Kathy Rowe, Marlene Sinclair

Obstetrics and Gynaecology
Professor M A Harper, S E M Lewis, N McClure

Oncology
Head P G Johnston
Lecturer D P Harkin, A Ouhtit, D J Waugh
Professor R J Atkinson, J J A McAleer
Reader D McCormick, H van den Berg
Senior Lecturer S E H Russell

Ophthalmology
Head D B Archer
Lecturer T A Gardiner
Professor Usha Chakravarthy, Giuiliana Silvestri, A W Stitt
Senior Lecturer D A Adams, W J Curry

Orthodontics
Professor D J Burden, C D Johnson

Orthopaedic Surgery
Head D R Marsh
Lecturer G Li
Senior Lecturer P C Nolan

Otorhinolaryngology
Professor D A Adams

Paediatrics and Preventive Dentistry
Professor R E Freeman, M J Kinirons

Pathology
Lecturer J Diamond, K M Williamson

Professor H Bharucha, C H S Cameron, S Louise Cosby, P Hall, P W Hamilton, Claire M Hill, J Kirk, M D O'Hara

Physiology
Head J A Allen
Professor Judith A Allen, M A Hollywood, J P Jamison, C Johnson, J G McGeown, N G McHale, C N Scholfield, K D Thornbury

Radiology
Professor L C Johnston

Restorative Dentistry
Professor I C Benington, C A Burnett, T J Clifford, D L Hussey, C R Irwin, J G Kennedy, G J Linden, E Lynch, C A Mitchell
Senior Lecturer B H Mullally

Surgery
Lecturer A McGinty
Professor F C Campbell
Senior Lecturer M C Reagan

Therapeutics and Pharmacology
Head G D Johnston
Lecturer D Bell, D Bell
Professor D J King, D J King, R G Shanks
Reader B J McDermott, J G Riddell, J G Riddell, B Silke, B Silke, H W Van den Berg
Research Fellow C G Hanratty
Senior Lecturer Barbara J McDermott, G E McVeigh

Degrees and diplomas
MB, BCh, BAO, BMedSc, MD, MCh, MMedSc, BDS, BSc, MSc, MA

Recognised Clinical Institutions
Altnagelvin Area Hospital, Altnagelvin Hospitals HSS Trust, Antrim Hospital, Arden Centre, Ards Community Hospital, Armagh and Dungannon HSS Trust, Belfast City Hospital, Belfast City Hospital HSS Trust, Braid Valley Hospital, Causeway Hospital, Causeway HSS Trust, Craigavon and Banbridge Community HSS Trust, Craigavon Area Hospital, Craigavon Psychiatric Unit, Daisy Hill Hospital, Down Lisburn HSS Trust, Downe Hospital, Downshire Hospital, Erne Hospital, Foyle Health and Social Services Trust, Gransha Hospital, Green Park Healthcare HSS Trust, Holywell Hospital, Homefirst Community HSS Trust, Knockbracken Mental Health Services, Lagan Valley Hospital, Longstone Hospital, Lurgan Hospital, Massereene Hospital, Mater Infirmorum Hospital, Mater Infirmorum Hospital HSS Trust, Mid-Ulster Hospital, Muckamore Abbey Hospital, Musgrave Park Hospital, Newry and Mourne HSS Trust, North and West Belfast HSS Trust, Royal Belfast Hospital for Sick Children, Royal Group of Hospitals and Dental Hospital HSS Trust, Royal Maternity Hospital, Royal Shrewsbury Hospitals NHS Trust Postgraduate Medical Centre, Royal Victoria Hospital, South and East Belfast HSS Trust, Sperrin Lakeland Health and Social Care Trust, St Luke's Hospital, Stradreagh Hospital, The Ulster Hospital, Tyrone and Fermanagh Hospital, Tyrone County Hospital, Ulster Community and Hospitals Trust, United Hospitals HSS Trust, University Dental Hospital and School, Whiteabbey Hospital

Postgraduate Medical Centres

England

Airedale NHS Trust, Department of Medical Education

Steeton, Keighley BD20 6TD
Tel: 01535 294410 Fax: 01535 292196

Clinical Tutor P Dickson
Clinical Tutor (VTSO) S G T Holmes, D Pearson, B Tones
Director Medical Education M Harrington
Education Centre Manager Ann Troth

The Avery Jones Postgraduate Medical Centre

Central Middlesex Hospital NHS Trust, Park Royal, London NW10 7NS
Tel: 020 8453 2500 Fax: 020 8453 2659

Centre Manager I McSherry
Clinical Tutor D McCrea

Barnet and Chase Farm Postgraduate Medical Centre

Barnet General Hospital, Wellhouse Lane, Barnet EN5 3DJ
Tel: 020 8216 4514, 020 8216 4833 Fax: 020 8216 4678

Postgraduate Education Manager Margaret Beedie

Barnsley Education Centre

Barnsley District Hospital NHS Trust, Gawber Road, Barnsley S75 2EP
Tel: 01226 730000 Ext: 2637 Fax: 01226 779319

Clinical Tutor J D Price
CollegeTutor W Rhoden, D Smith
Course Organiser Dr Lane, Dr Rose, J Walker
Course Organiser (CME) L Sykes
Obstetrics & Gynaecology Tutor S Whittaker
Postgraduate Manager G Hatton
Specialty Tutor Y Myint

Barrow Postgraduate Medical Centre

Furness General Hospital, Dalton Lane, Barrow-in-Furness LA14 4LE
Tel: 01229 491292

Clinical Tutor D E P Shapland
Specialty Tutor P K Misra, G Murray, L J Williams, R Y Wilson

Barts and The London NHS Trust

Royal London Hospital, 48 Ashfield Street, Whitechapel, London E1 2AJ
Tel: 020 7377 7760 Fax: 020 7377 7187

Assistant Director MDE Anita Kapoor
Director of Medical Education John Krapez

The Bateman Centre for Postgraduate Studies

Birch Hill Hospital, Rochdale OL12 9QB
Tel: 01706 370403, 01706 517061 Fax: 01706 370403

Centre Manager Eileen Molyneux
Clinical Tutor M Zaklama
Specialty Tutor S Afify, C Datta, V Devadoss, M Dickson, A Hussain, S Jegarajah, D Mackechnie, R Porter, I H Qureshi, R Smith

Bedford Medical Institute

Bedford Hospital NHS Trust, South Wing, Ampthill Road, Bedford MK42 9DJ
Tel: 01234 792267 Fax: 01234 792127
Email: asa.mann@bedhos.anglox.nhs.uk
Website: www.bedfordhospital.org.uk

Clinical Tutor E J Neale
Director of Clinical Studies N B Waterfall

GP Tutor D J Howard
Postgraduate Centre Manager Åsa Mann
Specialty Tutor G C Budden, A B Hewitt, M Leigh, D Liu, D Parsons, A G Patel

Belmont Postgraduate Psychiatric Centre

Chiltern Wing, Sutton Hospital, Cotswold Road, Sutton SM2 5NF
Email: bpgpc@swlstg-tr.nhs.uk

Centre Manager Margaret O'Leary
College Tutor C Mathers

Blackburn Postgraduate Medical Centre

Royal Infirmary, Blackburn BB2 3LR
Tel: 01254 687242

Clinical Tutor T K George
Clinical Tutor - Surgery D Chang
Dental Tutor N Taylor
Director of Medical Education C M H Schram
GP Tutor S Gunn
Royal College Tutor J W Benson, G W Hamlin, E Martindale, A G E Nylander, R Prescott, M Rahman, N A Roberts, S N Waghray

Blackpool Health Professional Education Centre

Victoria Hospital, Whinney Heys Road, Blackpool FY3 8NR
Tel: 01253 303566

Clinical Tutor P E T Isaacs
GP Tutor H Preslley
Specialty Tutor G Dunkley, P Flegg, L Hacking, C Hindley, G Naylor, S Ravi, R Roberts, G Smith, K S Vasudev, F L Wilcox

Booth Hall Postgraduate Medical Centre

Booth Hall Children's Hospital, Charlestown Road, Blackley, Manchester M9 7AA
Tel: 0161 220 5018 Fax: 0161 220 5579

Clinical Tutor Adrian Thomas
Postgraduate Centre Manager Lynne Leacock, Maria Pak

Boston-Pilgrim Hospital Postgraduate Centre for Medical and Dental Education

United Lincolnshire Hospitals NHS Trust, Pilgrim Hospital, Sibsey Road, Boston PE21 9QS
Tel: 01205 364801 Fax: 01205 442150

Director of Medical Education D A Sagar
Manager L K Davis
Specialty Tutor M Aslam, D A R Boldy, D E H Glendinning, S K Hanumara, C Kelly, M Khalek, A C Norton, E D Pereira, P J Woods

Bournemouth Postgraduate Medical Centre

Royal Bournemouth Hospital, Castle Lane East, Bournemouth BH7 7DW
Tel: 01202 704268 Fax: 01202 704489

Clinical Tutor J McN Turner
Dental Tutor S Doman
GP Tutor P Blick
Postgraduate and Medical Personnel Manager C Hardwick
Undergraduate Tutor P Winwood

Bradbury Postgraduate Medical Centre

Epsom General Hospital, Dorking Road, Epsom KT18 7EG
Tel: 01372 735172/5/6 Fax: 01372 749502
Email: epsompgmc@aol.com
Website: epsompgmc.co.uk

Clinical Tutor Christopher George
District GP Tutor Nicky Payne
PGMC Manager, Epsom Vivien Martin
Specialty Tutor Richard Cowlard, Joan Desborough, Alison Halliday, Michael Katesmark, Manil Katugampola, Guan Lim, Jane Moore, Roy Twyman, Jim Wilson

POSTGRADUATE MEDICAL CENTRES

Broadgreen Postgraduate Medical Centre

Broadgreen Hospital, Thomas Drive, Liverpool L14 3LB
Tel: 0151 706 2000 Fax: 0151 282 6988

Director of Postgraduate Medical Education P Chu
Postgraduate Manager S Bynne

Brook Hospital Postgraduate Medical Centre

Brook General Hospital, Shooters Hill Road, Woolwich, London SE18 4LW
Tel: 020 8312 6269

Clinical Tutor B Bryant
Specialty Tutor E P Butler, J Metcalf, A C V Montgomery, R Price

Broomfield Hospital Medical Academic Unit

Broomfield Hospital, Broomfield, Chelmsford CM1 7ET
Tel: 01245 514731 Fax: 01245 514667

Clinical Tutor A D Blainey
PGCM Kate Vann
Specialty Tutor A Agrawal, D Cunnah, J Durcan, N Richardson, P Robarts, W Williams

Burnley Mackenzie Medical Centre

The Mackenzie Medical Centre, Casterton Avenue, Burnley BB10 2PQ
Tel: 01282 474723 Fax: 01282 474254

Clinical Tutor S Bhattacharyya, R H Hyatt
Specialty Tutor A A Al-Dawoud, H Al-Khaffaf, F Clarke, A T Green, S E T Holmes, J Iqbal, C M Middleton, A G E Nylander, N H Taylor, G Wright, K Yasin, F M Zaman

Burton Graduate Medical Centre

Queen's Hospital, Burton Hospitals NHS Trust, Belvedere Road, Burton-on-Trent DE13 0RB
Tel: 01283 566333 Fax: 01283 510347

Clinical Tutor A Manzoor

Bury Postgraduate Centre

Bury General Hospital, Walmersley Road, Bury BL9 6PG
Tel: 0161 705 3258

Clinical Tutor A Narayan
Postgraduate Centre Manager Jean France
Specialty Tutor B Bose-Haider, V Gadiyar, D Gordon, K Haworth, K S Kotegaonkar
Undergraduate Tutor M Saab

Bury St Edmunds District Postgraduate Medical Centre

Bedford Hospital NHS Trust, South Wing, Ampthill Road, Bedford MK42 9DJ
Tel: 01234 762267 Fax: 01243 792127

Clinical Tutor R J Godwin
PGMC Speciality Tutor N Adams, A C August, B Boothby, J Calvert, E Cockayne, R Giles, J Hare, M Hone, C Ingram, K Jordan, M P McBrien, D Polkinhorn, R Rutherford, P W Siklos, R Youngs

Cambridge District Postgraduate Medical and Dental Education Centre

Addenbrooke's Hospital, Hills Road, Cambridge CB2 2QQ
Email: ma10001@medsch.cam.ac.uk

Clinical Tutor A Gupta, Jane MacDougall
Manager Mary Archibald
Specialty Tutor Simon Brown, Sarah Rann, S I M Robinson, Paul Sackin

Camden and Islington Community Health Services NHS Trust Postgraduate Centre

Education and Training Centre, St. Pancras Conference Centre, St. Pancras Hospital, 4 St. Pancras Way, London NW1 0PE

Tel: 020 7530 3575

Clinical Tutor M Greenberg
Medical Education Manager Caroline Lough-White

Central Manchester Postgraduate Health Sciences Centre

Manchester Royal Infirmary, Oxford Road, Manchester M13 9WL
Tel: 0161 276 4169 Fax: 0161 276 8012

Clinical Tutor P Bannister
Course Manager K Stuart
Director of Postgraduate Medical Education M Cheshire
GP Tutor J Sandars
Specialty Tutor D Barman, P Donnai, A Emmerson, D Longson, A Makin, A Siriwardena, F Spencer

Centre for Medical and Dental Education Pilgrim Hospital United Lincolnshire Hospitals NHS Trust

Pilgrim Hospital, Sibsey Road, Boston PE21 9QS
Tel: 01205 364801 Fax: 01205 357494 (Centre Manager), 01205 442150 (Departmental)

Centre Manager L K Davis
Clinical Tutor Dr Sagar
Dental Tutor D E H Glendenning
GP Tutor Dr Woods
GPVTS Course Organiser/GP Advisor Dr Kelly
Specialty Tutor N J Andrews, M Aslam, S K Hanumara, S Ikhena, M Khalek, A C Norton, M Perry

Charing Cross Hospital Postgraduate Medical Centre

Fulham Palace Road, London W6 8RF
Tel: 020 8846 7196 Fax: 020 8846 7704

Clinical Tutor H Millington
Postgraduate Centre Manager Sue Evans
Postgraduate Manager Sue Evans

Charles Hasting Postgraduate Medical Centre

Worcestershire Acute Hospitals NHS Trust, Newton Road, Worcester WR5 1HW
Tel: 01905 760600 Fax: 01905 767834

Clinical Tutor C Pycock

Chase Postgraduate Medical Centre

Chase Farm Hospital, The Ridgeway, Enfield EN2 8JL
Tel: 0181 366 9121 Fax: 020 8363 4662, 020 8366 9121

Clinical Tutor P Copland
Dental Tutor T Payne
GP Tutor R Hume
Postgraduate Centre Manager Z Khan
Postgraudate Education Manager Z Khan
Undergraduate Tutor B Yuksel

Chelsea and Westminster Hospital Postgraduate Centre

369 Fulham Road, London SW10 9NH
Tel: 020 8746 5590, 020 8746 8310 Fax: 020 8746 8248
Email: s.price@chelwest.nhs.uk

Director of Medical Education Alastair Scotland
Postgraduate Centre Manager Sylvia Price

Cheltenham Postgraduate Medical Centre

2 College Lawn, Cheltenham GL53 7AG
Fax: 01242 273242
Email: William.Brampton@egnhst.org.uk

Centre Manager Kate Bartlett
Clinical Tutor W J Brampton, N Morrison

POSTGRADUATE MEDICAL CENTRES

Specialty Tutor J Anderson, K Benstead, C C Burgess, J Ferris, W Foster, M Gibson, A J Goodman, M Hamilton-Ayres, M Hardingham, R Hensher, E Kerr-Wilson, K McCarthy, R Mackay, D R Martin, A Pascall, M Richards, S Silver, J Wand, P Wilson

Chesterfield Education Centre

Chesterfield and North Derbyshire Royal Hospital NHS Trust, Chesterfield S44 5BL
Tel: 01246 552057 Fax: 01246 552685
Email: val.johnson@cndrh-tr.trent.nhs.uk

Clinical Tutor K Fairburn
Education Centre Manager V Johnson
Specialty Tutor G Collins, J Cunnane, J Glaves, S Holt, G Hutchinson, P Metcalf, S Smith

Chichester Medical Education Centre

St Richards Hospital, Chichester PO19 4SE
Tel: 01243 788122 Fax: 01243 532576
Website: cmecinfo.co.uk

Dental Tutor D MacPherson
GP Education Manager B Smithers
GP Tutor A Copsey, J Price
Postgraduate Manager Bebba Smithers
Specialty Tutor D R Allen, F Barrett, A Carter, Dr Conroy, Dr Haigh, Mr Moss, Mr Simons, Dr Taylor
Undergraduate Tutor P Britton, G Dewhurst

Chiltern Medical Education Centre

Level 1 Phase 4, Wycombe Hospital, High Wycombe HP11 2TT
Tel: 01494 426382 Fax: 01494 426387

CDP Tutor (GP) B Neal
Clinical Tutor Go A Luzzi
Education Centre Manager Sandra Harding
Specialty Tutor A Bdesha, S Cox, D Eustace, A Fernandes, C Graham, A McIntyre, J Margo, J Maxmin, D Orton, D Potts, K Sawhney, R Stevens, H Thomson, M Turner

Chorley and Ribble Postgraduate Education Centre

Preston Road, Chorley PR7 1PP
Tel: 01257 245600

Clinical Tutor S Wallis
Specialty Tutor B Rambihar, I G Robertson, S Wallis

City Hospital NHS Trust Postgraduate Medical Centre

Dudley Road, Birmingham B18 7QH
Tel: 0121 507 4980 Fax: 0121 523 4562

Centre Manager Jo Collins
Clinical Tutor D Dawkins
Manager J Collins

City Hospitals Sunderland, Postgraduate Medical Centre

Sunderland Royal Hospital, Kayll Road, Sunderland SR4 7TP
Tel: 0191 569 9634 Fax: 0191 569 9246
Email: pgmc@chs.northy.nhs.uk

Centre Manager Ruth Turner
Clinical Tutor N P Keaney
Postgraduate Centre Manager Ruth Turner
Specialty Tutor J Carter, J Chapman, H Cochrane, P Cronin, A Cross, S England, S Fraser, K Hinshaw, I MacKee, A Mellon, N Place, J Ryan

The Clinical Education Centre

Southport and Ormskirk NHS Trust, Southport and Formby District General Hospital, Town Lane, Southport PR8 6PN
Tel: 01704 704377 Fax: 01704 704452
Email: heather.ainscough@mail.soh-tr.nwest.nhs.uk

Director of Medical Education Dr Serlin
GP Tutor R Patel
Manager of Medical Education Miss Ainscough
Specialty Tutor Jonathan Fox, Charles Scott, Pradip Sett, Sanjeev Sharma, Ian Wallbank, Matouk Zbaeda, Mike Zeiderman

Coastal Postgraduate Medical Centre

James Paget Hospital, Lowestoft Road, Gorleston, Great Yarmouth NR31 6LA
Tel: 01493 452466 Fax: 01493 452182
Email: cmec@jpaget.nhs.uk

Clinical Tutor R E Davies
Postgraduate Centre Manager I Walker
Specialty Tutor A Amant, Dr Ashford, A Bigg, T Cotter, A Eastaugh, R Fleetcroft, J Lindsay, A Millican, P Nadarajan, J H Pereira, J Preston, P Prinsley, P Quilliam, N Statter, R Stocks, A Walker

Colchester and North-East Essex Postgraduate Medical Centre

Colchester General Hospital, Turner Road, Colchester CO4 5JL
Tel: 01206 742149 Fax: 01206 851231
Email: pwest.colpgmc@virgin.net
Website: www.cghpgmc.calroom.co.uk

Assistant Manager Cara Gosbell
Centre Manager P West
Clinical Tutor R A Elston
PGMC Kate Felstead

Cornwall Postgraduate Medical Centre

Royal Cornwall Hospital, (Treliske), Truro TR1 3LJ

Clinical Tutor S S Hasan, D Levine, A Simcock, S J O Watkins, A D Woolf
Specialty Tutor C V R Blacker, P Cook, P Cox, G Edwards, D Gould, W F Haines, R Jones, M Mitchell, A S Price, A B Roberts, M N J Ruscoe, Y Sivathondan, J Weld

Crawley and Horsham Postgraduate Centre

Crawley Hospital, West Green Drive, Crawley RH11 7DH
Tel: 01293 600316 Fax: 01293 600387

Centre Manager Eve Savage
Clinical Tutor Alan Vallon
GP Tutor J E Oliver
Postgraduate Centre Manager Eve Savage
Specialty Tutor D Acharya, I Lewis, D J Lyle, E Owen, G Spoto, S Vethanayagam
VTS Course Organiser P Stillman

Cripps Postgraduate Medical Centre

Northampton General Hospital, Northampton NN1 5BD
Tel: 01604 545448 Fax: 01604 545590
Email: pat.hawkins@ngh-tr.anglox.nhs.uk

Associate Clinical Tutor G French
District Clinical Tutor A Jeffrey
GP Course Organiser S Greening, S Gregory
Postgraduate Centre Manager Pat Hawkins
Specialty Tutor J Anthony, I Fearnley, J Hewertson, D C Hunter, G Kerr, J O'Donnell, A Ogilvie, C Pratt, F Thompson, M Wilkinson
VTS Course Organiser P Halstead, R Willows

Darlington Postgraduate Medical Centre

Darlington Memorial Hospital, Hollyhurst Road, Darlington DL3 6HX
Tel: 01325 743232 Fax: 01325 743222

Clinical Tutor U Earl
Education Support Officer Mandy Maddison
Librarian C Houghton, C Masterman
Specialty Tutor A S M Ali, A Bawarish, L Burton, J Carlin, M S Dang, H Dixon, W Elliot, E Evans, R Hargreaves, D J R Hutchon, I M Thakur, A West, C Williams

POSTGRADUATE MEDICAL CENTRES

Dartford Postgraduate Medical Centre
Joyce Green Hospital, Dartford DA1 5PL

Clinical Tutor M Stewart
Specialty Tutor A Addison, M Hamer, A Lessops, W I Mikhail, M Parker, A T M F Rashid, J Rush

Department for NHS Postgraduate Medical and Dental Education (Yorkshire Deanery)
University of Leeds, Willow Terrace Road, Leeds LS2 9JT
Tel: 0113 233 1506 Fax: 0113 233 1530

Adviser on Overseas Doctors P Neligan
Assistant Director to Postgraduate Dean J Stoker
Assistant for the PRHO Year Alistair McGowan
Careers and Personal Development Adviser R Roden
Dean of Postgraduate Medical Education Rosemary MacDonald
Director of Postgraduate General Practice Education J Bahrami
Manager P Kentley

Derby City General Hospital Medical Education Centre
Uttoxeter Road, Derby DE22 3NE
Tel: 01332 625580

Clinical Tutor D Clarke
Specialty Tutor M Denunzio

Derbyshire Royal Infirmary Postgraduate Medical Education Centre
Derbyshire Royal Infirmary NHS Trust, London Road, Derby DE1 2QY

Clinical Tutor S Y Iftikhar
Specialty Tutor C R Chilton, W P Gorman, A R Lindop, G F MacLeod, J Noble, D J Poll, D Young

Doncaster Postgraduate Medical Teaching Centre
Doncaster Royal Infirmary and Montagu Hospital NHS Trust, Armthorpe Road, Doncaster DN2 5LT
Tel: 01302 366666 Ext: 3583 Fax: 01302 320098

Clinical Tutor R Cushieri
Postgraduate Administrator Wendy Jones
Specialty Tutor S J Ahmad, M Broughton, D K Chadha, G P Chandler, C G A Chikhani, D Graham, P Harkeness, P J Helm, A Holmes, D R Malin, P J Noble, J P Simpson, S Singh
VTS Course Organiser M F Hasenfuss, N M Sinclair

Douglas Pickup Postgraduate Medical Centre
Pontefract General Infirmary, Friarwood Lane, Pontefract WF8 1PL
Tel: 01977 600600 ext: 6361 Fax: 01977 606361
Email: christine.sanderson@panp-tr.northy.nhs.uk

Director Postgraduate Medical Education A R Harvey
Medical Education Service Manager C Sanderson
Postgraduate Centre Manager C Sanderson

Dover Postgraduate Medical Centre
Buckland Hospital, Buckland, Dover CT17 0HD
Tel: 01304 201624 Fax: 01304 205834

Clinical Tutor M A Vella
Specialty Tutor M Collins

Durham Postgraduate Medical Centre and Dryburn Education Centre
Dryburn Hospital, North Road, Durham DH1 5TW
Tel: 0191 333 2333, 0191 333 2485 Fax: 0191 333 2088
Website: www.numedsun.ncl.ac.uk/~npd/PIMD/text/durham.html

Clinical Tutor David Laird
Education Centre Manager Anne Sewell

Hon. Science Lecturer Sarah Pearce
Senior Lecturer Peter Cook

Ealing Hospital NHS Trust Postgraduate Centre
Uxbridge Road, Southall UB1 3HW
Tel: 020 8967 5202 Fax: 020 8967 5008

Clinical Tutor Jay Arnold
Education Services Manager Anne Wakenell
Postgraduate Education Manager Anne Wakenell

East Cheshire Association for Medical Education
Macclesfield Hospital, West Park Branch, Prestbury Road, Macclesfield SK10 3BL

Clinical Tutor R J Stead
Clinical Tutor (VTSO) M Coope
Director of Medical Education N R Calver

East Cumbria Postgraduate Medical Centre
Cumberland Infirmary, Carlisle CA2 7HY
Tel: 01228 814883 Fax: 01228 814822

Centre Manager Margaret Tait
Clinical Tutor R H Robson
GP Tutor C P Mitchell
Specialty Tutor M Bearn, P Blakeman, C Lord, C E MacDonald, D Prosser, Y H Tzabar, P Whitehead, M R Williams

East Hertfordshire Postgraduate Centre
Queen Elizabeth II Hospital, Howlands, Welwyn Garden City AL7 4HQ
Tel: 01707 365418 Fax: 01707 365421
Email: postgrad@geii.enherts-tr.nhs.uk, postgrad@qeii.enherts-tr.nhs.uk

Postgraduate Centre Manager Christine Crick
Specialty Tutor S Greatrex, J Young

East Riding Medical Education Centre
Hull Royal Infirmary, Anlaby Road, Hull HU3 2JZ
Tel: 01482 604313 Fax: 01482 586587
Email: joanne.clemenson@hey.nhs.uk

Administrator Joanne Clemenson
Associate Royal College Tutor - (Surgery) G V Johnson, P Renwick
Course Organiser for General Practice P Davis, D Roper, S Towers
Dental CME Tutor J Holguin
Dental VTS Advisor T Kilcoyne
Director Brian Johnson
General Practice CME Tutor S Kapur, A Parkin
GP VTS Course Organiser P Davis, D Roper, S Towers
Manager Sue Hubbard
Royal College Tutor J Bestley, P Clarke, M Cope, M Donaldson, P Grout, G Harkness, B N M Jayanardhana, S Lindow, A W MacDonald, E A Masson, P W Pairaudeau, K Phillips, V Ramakrishan, D Salvage, A Samaan, P Sedman
Specialty Tutor G Cooksey, M R Cope, S Griffin, P Grout, G V Johnson, G O'Reilly, J Smithson, N Stafford, P Stanley, Delyth Wynne-Jones

East Surrey Hospital Postgraduate Medical Centre
Canada Avenue, Three Arch Road, Redhill RH1 5RH

Associate Director of Medical Education Bruce Stewart
GP Tutor Elizabeth Hornung
Library and Information Manager Sheila Marsh
Postgraduate Centre Manager Tamsin Hoare
Psychiatric Training Co-Ordinator Christine Denda
RCP Tutor Simon Stern

POSTGRADUATE MEDICAL CENTRES

Specialty Tutor M Jawad, M Long, F O'Sullivan, T Selvan, J Stephens, Philip Williams
VTS Organiser Hillary Diack, Paul Stillman

Eastbourne Postgraduate Medical and Psychiatry Centre

District General Hospital, King's Drive, Eastbourne BN21 2UD
Tel: 01323 414967 Fax: 01323 414932
Email: liz.oliver-taylor@ed.obh-tr.sthames.nhs.uk

Clinical Tutor Jeremy J Bending
Manager Postgraduate Centre Liz Oliver-Taylor
Specialty Tutor V P Argent, P Argiriu, W El-Abiam, M Saunders, D Tarbuck, H Walmsley, J Wilkinson

Eastern Deanery

Postgraduate Medical & Dental Education, Block 3, Ida Darwin Site, Fulbourn, Cambridge CB1 5EE
Tel: 01223 884848 Fax: 01223 884849
Website: www.easternregion.org.uk

Associate Dean (Flexible Training) C A Lawton
Associate Dean (Hospital Education) C A Lawton
Associate Dean (Pre-Registration) A J Crisp, D L Stone
Director of Hospital Education & Deputy Postgraduate Dean D H Jones
Director of Postgraduate Dental Education J M Heath
Director of Postgraduate General Practice A G Hibble
Postgraduate Dean R W Shaw
Receptionist Lynsey Sennitt

Edgware Postgraduate Centre

Edgware Community Hospital, Burnt Oak Broadway, Edgware HA8 0AD
Tel: 020 8952 9924 Fax: 020 8732 6626

Clinical Tutor George Ikkos
Postgraduate Centre Manager Judy Maisner

The Education Centre

Tower Hamlets Primary Care Trust, Mile End Hospital, Bancroft Road, London E1 4DG
Tel: 020 7377 7000 Ext: 4436 Fax: 020 7377 7944
Email: ruth.caudwell@thpct.nhs.uk

Lead Clinician Ruth Caudwell

Edward Jenner Teaching Centre

Bristol Royal Infirmary, Bristol BS2 8HW

Clinical Tutor R A Mountford, P J B Smith, T Smyth
Specialty Tutor R Anderson, J Catterall, D R Coles, M V Griffiths, I S Hathorn, G Hughes, M Lemon, I J Leslie, R Martin, S Mather, P Murphy, G Rees, B Robinson, J Sparrow

Epsom and St Helier NHS Trust

St Helier Hospital, Wrythe Lane, Carshalton SM5 1AA
Tel: 020 8296 2605 Fax: 020 8296 3219
Email: sthhpgmcgp@aol.com

Clinical Tutor N T Cooke
District GP Tutor R Seyan
GP Administrator M Smithers
Specialty Tutor P Byrne, M Churchill, O Duke, B Ghoorbin, K Haque, S Hawkins, J Merceica, J Moore, L Ross, S Shah

Exeter Postgraduate Medical Centre

Royal Devon and Exeter Healthcare NHS Trust, Barrack Road, Exeter EX2 5DW
Tel: 01392 403006 Fax: 01392 403007

Clinical Tutor Richard D'Souza, David Leeder, Marina Morgan
College Tutor Colin Berry, Tim Bunker, Julie Dunn, Charles Holme, John Jacob, Richard Lee, Nick Withers
Director of Medical Education Iain Wilson

Medical Education Manager Rosemary Ash
Obstetrics and Gynaecology Rachel Sturley

Farnborough Education Centre

Farnborough Hospital, Farnborough Common, Orpington BR6 8ND
Tel: 01689 814300 Fax: 01689 861218
Email: lynne.archer@bromleyhospitals.nhs.uk
Website: www.bromleyhospitals.nhs.uk

Centre Manager Lynne Archer
Clinical Tutor Andrew Long
GP Tutor D Barker
Specialty Tutor A Combe, M De Silva, G Ghosh, N Hill, E Langford, A Martin, A Thomas
VTS Course Organiser M Collins, J Tavabie

Fieldhouse Teaching Centre

Bradford Royal Infirmary, Duckworth Lane, Bradford BD9 6RJ

Clinical Tutor J A Bibby, P J O'Donovan
Clinical Tutor (VTSO) R N Ashworth, A P Kenny, M Purvis

The Frank Refkin Postgraduate Centre

Hope Hospital, Stott Lane, Salford M6 8HD

Clinical Tutor A N Thomas
GP Tutor W M Forman
Specialty Tutor N Clarke, I Geraghty, A Jones, P Kalra, D Nicholson, A Railton, I H Stout

Freeman Hospital Education Centre

Freeman Hospital, Newcastle upon Tyne NE7 7DN
Tel: 0191 223 1284 Fax: 0191 223 1247

Centre Manager A Williamson
Clinical Tutor S Murray
Specialty Tutor C Baudouin, K Beacham, C Hilton, R Pickard, V A Wadge

Frenchay Postgraduate Centre.

Frenchay Hospital, Bristol BS16 1LE
Tel: 0117 975 3704 Fax: 0117 970 1691
Email: Linda.Bruce-Smith@north-bristol.swest.nhs.uk
Website: www.orthbristol.nhs.uk

Clinical Tutor C Jewkes, P Younge
Clinical Tutor (GP) C Miras
Deputy Director of Medical Education C Dawkins
Medical Education Centre Administrator Linda Bruce-Smith
Specialty Tutor A Dixon, L Dow, J Goodrick, M Gregory, F McLeod, J Pounsford, N Slack

Frimley Park Hospital Postgraduate Medical Centre

Portsmouth Road, Frimley, Camberley GU16 5UJ

Administrator Tracey Wilson
GP Tutor R Blackman, R Knight
Specialty Tutor P Alton, Miss Deans, K Debrah, J R W Hall, F Howard, P Keeling, P Leopold, Mr Montgomery, J Oxenbury, T Pepall, P A Reilly, A Riddle, A Sakellariou, M Tandon

Frognal Centre for Medical Studies

Queen Mary's Hospital, Sidcup DA14 6LT
Tel: 020 8308 3030 Fax: 020 8308 3058

Clinical Tutor K Kelleher
Medical Education Manager V Greenwood
Specialty Tutor A Abbas, T Davis, T Duncan, M Gotleib, K Hussain, N Joyner, D Milne, K Pervaiz, S Roe, M Rowntree, I Schuller, H Stoate, L Whitefield, G Yu
Specialty Tutor - Pathology M Khan

Gateshead Postgraduate Medical Centre

Queen Elizabeth Hospital, Gateshead NE9 6SX
Tel: 0191 482 0000 ext: 2107 Fax: 0191 482 3341

POSTGRADUATE MEDICAL CENTRES

Clinical Tutor S Hudson
Education Centre Manager L Heppenstall
Specialty Tutor Mr Antrobus, P Cross, M Das, G Enever, M J Higgs, Dr Hodges, D Peakman, M Suchdev, P Thompson, G V Williams

The George Pickering Postgraduate Centre

John Radcliffe Hospital, Headington, Oxford OX3 9DU

Associate Clinical Tutor C Conlon, H Jones, H Simpson
Associate GP Tutor H Merriman
Clinical Tutor M Burch
District Dental Tutor P Lawson
Specialty Tutor C Chubb, A P Freeland, M Gilmer, J Humphreys, J D Kay, N Mortensen, O O'Dayar, C Oppenheimer, S Ostlere, J Roblin, J Shakespeare, P Watts-Smith, P R Williams

Giving for Living Research and Postgraduate Centre

Royal Manchester Children's Hospital, Pendlebury, Manchester M27 4HA
Tel: 0161 727 2155

Clinical Tutor C Gladman
Specialty Tutor C Doig, C Gladman, A Kelsey, H Lloyd, D Lord, D Nicholson

Gloucester Postgraduate Medical Centre

Gloucestershire Royal Hospital, Great Western Road, Gloucester GL1 3NN
Tel: 01452 394727 Fax: 01452 394734
Email: pgmec@gloucs-tr.swest.nhs.uk

Clinical Tutor R Valori
Critical Tutor E Spencer
Office Manager Rebecca Brown
Specialty Tutor B Adrianns, P A Birch, A McCrinrick, A Pike, M D Read, N A Shepherd, M Vipond
Sub-Specialty Tutor I Donald, G Fuller, S McCabe, R Majkowski, C Perkins, A Ritchie, J Ropner, E Spencer, M Thomas

Good Hope Education Centre and Library

Good Hope Hospital NHS Trust, Rectory Road, Sutton Coldfield B75 7RR
Tel: 0121 378 6038 Fax: 0121 378 6039
Email: sheila.hannington@goodhot.wmids.nhs.uk

Centre Manager S Hannington, Sheila Hannington
Clinical Tutor RSV Cartmill
GP Tutor A McDonald
Specialty Tutor R Cartmill, M Elliott, K Gupta, P Houlston, B Jones, T Lee, S Singh, A Tabani, K Wahab

Grantham and District Hospital Postgraduate Medical Centre

United Lincolnshire Hospitals NHS Trust, Grantham & District Hospital, Manthorpe Road, Grantham NG31 8DG
Tel: 01476 565232

Clinical Tutor J L Breckenridge
Postgraduate Administrator S Barnston
Specialty Tutor J H Campbell, N D Platt, D Valerio

Great Ormond Street Hospital for Children NHS Trust

Great Ormond Street, London WC1N 3JH
Tel: 020 7405 9200 Fax: 020 7813 8227

Director of Medical Education and Clinical Tutor H Cass
Medical Director J Collins
PGME Manager Rachel Moreton
Vice-Dean for Training S Strobel

Greenwich District Hospital Postgraduate Centre

Vanbrugh Hill, London SE10 9HE
Tel: 020 8312 6191 Fax: 020 8858 5717

Clinical Tutor J Carr
Specialty Tutor E P Butler, J Carr, A Montgomery, S Power, T R Price

Grimsby Postgraduate Medical Centre

Northern Lincolnshire & Goole Hospitals NHS Trust, Diana Princess of Wales Hospital, Grimsby DN33 2BA
Tel: 01472 875275 Fax: 01472 875329

Clinical Tutor S Moss
GP Tutor K Collett
PGME Senior Manager L Young
Pre-Registration House Officer Co-Ordinator A Naqvi
Specialty Tutor S Dixon, S Herber, I Kehman, S Kotta, A Saha, K Speed
Tutor H Nagi, J Roberts
VTS Course Organiser J Potter

Guildford Postgraduate Medical Centre

Royal Surrey County Hospital, Guildford GU2 7XX
Tel: 01483 571122 ext: 4244 Fax: 01483 303691

Medical and Dental Education Manager Sue Cranham
Specialty Tutor S Chapman, P Curtis, S Deacock, A Gilvarry, H Griffiths, M Kissin, A Neal, H Powell, W Walker, M Whiteley

Gurney Postgraduate Centre

Hemel Hempstead General Hospital (Acute), Hillfield Road, Hemel Hempstead HP2 4AD
Tel: 01442 287666 Fax: 01442 287670

Deputy Clinical Tutor S Hill
Director of Education I Barrison
GP VTS Course Organiser B Covell, P Heatley
Postgraduate Education Manager David Goodier
Specialty Tutor I Barrison, S Catnach, R Gallow, R Griffin, R Hallan, S Hill, Y Tayob, A Young

Guy's Department of Postgraduate Studies

Sherman Education Centre, Guy's Hospital, London SE1 9RT
Tel: 020 7955 4300 Fax: 020 7955 4913

Postgraduate Co-ordinator Vanessa Gray
Postgraduate Dean Charles Twort
Specialty Tutor Clare Gerada

Halton Education Centre

Halton General Hospital NHS Trust, Hospital Way, Runcorn WA7 2DA
Tel: 01928 753318 Fax: 01928 753268

Centre Manager D I Palmer
Clinical Sub-Dean A Muloney
Clinical Tutor J N Johnson
GP Tutor P Johnson
Librarian L Chapellion

Hammersmith Hospital Postgraduate Centre

Hammersmith Hospital, Du Cane Road, London W12 0HS
Tel: 020 8383 3462 Fax: 020 8383 3464
Email: mmcnamara@hhnt.org

Director of Medical Education Gill Gaskin
Postgraduate Centre Administrator Maggie McNamara

Harefield Hospital Postgraduate Centre

Harefield Hospital, Hill End Road, Harefield UB9 6JU
Tel: 01895 828735 Fax: 01895 828735

Clinical Tutor D Cummins
Postgraduate Centre Manager Lesley Barker

POSTGRADUATE MEDICAL CENTRES

Harold Wood Hospital Postgraduate Academic Centre

Gubbins Lane, Harold Wood, Romford RM3 0BE
Tel: 01708 345156 (Direct Line) Fax: 01708 345156

Associate Tutor A Aspoas
Centre Administrator Lynne Trew
Contact Manager L Freegard
Director of Medical Education R Weatherstone
Specialty Tutor S Gibbs, H Haddock, M Saphandan, S Shami, M Smith, W White

Harperbury Horizon

Harperbury Hospital, Harperbury Lane, Shenley, Radlett WD7 9HQ
Tel: 01923 854861 Fax: 01923 859148

Clinical Tutor Iqbal Singh

Harrogate Postgraduate Medical Centre

Strayside Education Centre, Harrogate District Hospital, Lancaster Park Road, Harrogate HG2 7SX
Tel: 01423 553092 Fax: 01423 553094
Email: Strayside.Education@hhc-tr.northy.nhs.uk

Education Centre Manager Liz Watson
Specialty Tutor G Dyke, J Gasser, A Gough, C Gray, W Hulse, L Kidd, S Rahman, D Ryan, J Warren

Hartlepool Postgraduate Medical Centre

University Hospital of Hartlepool, Holdford Road, Hartlepool TS24 9AH
Tel: 01429 522343 Fax: 01429 522739

Clinical Tutor D Bruce, D W Bruce
Specialty Tutor B K Chaudhury, Mrs Emerson, J Frater, Dr Jani, A V Kidambi, Dr Mohan, C P L Wood

Hastings Postgraduate Medical Education Centre

The Education Centre, Conquest Hospital, The Ridge, St Leonards-on-Sea TN37 7RD
Tel: 01424 755255 Fax: 01424 758097
Website: harnst.org.uk

Clinical Tutor S A Bruce
GP Tutor J Dinwiddie
Postgraduate Medical Centre Manager Gill McGovern
Specialty Tutor S Baer, M Boxer, D Fitzpatrick, M Nasar, A Stoddart, S Weston-Smith

Hereford Hospitals NHS Trust Postgraduate Medical Centre

Union Walk, Hereford HR1 2ER
Tel: 01432 364025 Fax: 01432 355265
Email: pat.rossi@dial.pipex.com

Centre Manager Pat Rossi
GP Training Course Organiser P Clayton, S Hasan
GP Tutor J Barnes
Postgraduate Clinical Tutor D W Pitcher
Royal College Tutor C Byatt, T Coleman, D Williams, W Williams
Tutor R Subak-Sharpe

The Hertfordshire Partnership NHS Trust Postgraduate Centre

Harperbury Hospital, Harper Lane, Shenley, Radlett WD7 9QH
Tel: 01923 427216 Fax: 01923 427370

Postgraduate Manager Anne Lund

Hexham Postgraduate Medical Centre

General Hospital, Hexham NE46 1QJ
Tel: 01434 655655 ext: 5046 Fax: 01434 655048

Clinical Tutor P Sims
Librarian S Ellingham

Postgraduate Centre Coordinator K Mitchell
Specialty Tutor M Mansour, W K Walsh, A Wright

Hillingdon Hospital Postgraduate Centre

Pield Heath Road, Hillingdon, Uxbridge UB8 3NN
Tel: 01895 279799 Fax: 01895 234150
Email: christine.massey@thh.nhs.uk

Deputy Clinical Tutor Robin Kantor, Anthea Parry
Medical Education Manager Christine Massey

Hinchingbrooke Postgraduate Medical and Dental Education Centre

Hinchingbrooke Hospital, Hinchingbrooke Park, Huntingdon PE18 8NT
Tel: 01480 416117 Fax: 01480 416299

Clinical Tutor S M Forster
Director of Clinical Studies Basam Bekdash
GP Tutor Ian Sweettenham
Medical Director D Flanagan
Postgraduate Centre Manager Joyce Murphy
Royal College Tutor Kathleen Jennison, Cornelius Rene, Phil Roberts, George Southgate, K. Walsh
Specialty Tutor S N Amarah, Martin Becker, Donald Bermingham, R K Das
Vocational Training Scheme Organiser Malcolm Wright

Homerton University Hospital Postgraduate Education Centre

Homerton Hospital, Homerton Row, London E9 6SR
Tel: 020 8510 7747 Fax: 020 8510 7314

Clinical Tutor D Shanahan
Postgraduate Centre and Medical Personnel Manager Nic Nicolaou

Horton Hospital Postgraduate Centre

Horton Hospital, Long Grove Road, Epsom KT19 8PZ
Tel: 020 8237 2000

Tutor J R Robertston

Huddersfield Medical Centre

Huddersfield Royal Infirmary, Lindley, Huddersfield HD3 3EA
Tel: 01484 482655 Fax: 01484 347052
Email: chrisane.scaife@hudderd-tr.northy.nhs.uk

Clinical Tutor H Griffiths, J Lord
Clinical Tutor (VTSO) T D Swift

Huntingdon District Postgraduate Medical Education Centre

Hinchingbrooke Hospital, Hinchingbrooke Park, Huntingdon PE18 8NT

Director Clinical Studies Kevin Walsh
Specialty Tutor S N Amarah, M G Becker, C Borland, R Das, S Forster, B Greenway, D S Hughes, R Latcham, D A Morris, J Oubridge, P Roberts, M Slack, I A Sweettenham, M Wright

Institute of Orthopaedics Postgraduate Medical Centre

Robert Jones & Agnes Hunt Orthopaedic and District Hospital NHS Trust, Oswestry SY10 7AG
Tel: 01691 404391 Fax: 01691 404071
Email: judy.harris@rjahoh-tr.wmids.nhs.uk
Website: www.keele.ac.uk/depts/rjah/rjah.htm

Course Organiser Erica Wilkinson
Postgraduate Clinical Tutor D J Ford
Senior Clinical Lecturer B Ashton, M W J Davies, S M Eisenstein, W El Masri, G Evans, D C Jaffray, J Middleton, J H Patrick, V C Pullicino, J Richardson, A Roberts, S Roberts

POSTGRADUATE MEDICAL CENTRES

Ipswich Hospital NHS Trust Postgraduate Centre

Ipswich Hospital, Heath Road, Ipswich IP4 5PD
Tel: 01473 702561 Fax: 01473 702503
Email: mary.bartlett@ipsh-tr.anglox.nhs.uk
Website: www.ipswichhospital.org.uk

Clinical Tutor R Howard-Griffin
Dental Tutor I Davies
Dental VTS Course Organiser J Stokes
GP VTS Course Organiser J Jesuthasan, G Jones, M Ward
Postgraduate Medical Centre Manager M Bartlett
Specialty Tutor M Bowditch, H Davies, I Driver, C Edelsten, D Hodgkinson, S Irving, B Johal, K O'Neill, I Osman, G Rayman, M Salam, D Sharp

James Fawcett Education Centre

Barley Lane, Goodmayes, Ilford IG3 8YB
Tel: 020 8970 8017 Fax: 020 8970 8269
Email: james.fawcett@rbhc-tr.nthames.nhs.uk

Centre Manager B Hutton
Director Postgraduate Education G Cochrane

The John Fawcett Postgraduate Medical and Dental Education Centre

Peterborough District Hospital, Thorpe Road, Peterborough PE3 6DA
Tel: 01733 874660 Fax: 01733 347142

Centre Manager B Petrie
Clinical Sub-Dean J Porter
Clinical Tutor A Palfreeman
Director of Clinical Studies & Medicine Tutor P Nair
Specialty Tutor S Babiker, R Griffiths, S Lewis, H Mistry, C Nnochiri, A G Pfleiderer, B Ramsay, R Rimes, T Rimmer, D Wozencroft
VTS Course Organiser A Bond, T Davies

John Lister Postgraduate Centre

Wexham Park Hospital, Slough SL2 4HL

Associate Clinical Tutor P Sebire
Clinical Tutor Carole Luck, G Maidment
Dental Tutor R Walters
Hospital Specialty Tutor S Dimitry, D Dove, Z Huma, R Loveland, S Para-Meswaran, J Wilkins
Medical Education & Centre Manager Maura Stock
Primary Care CPD Tutor B Sainsbury
Specialty Tutor C Aldren, M Ali, N Desmond, A Gordon, G C Kassianos, S Kheterpal, C Khoo, C Litchfield, C Maloney, H Motiwala, J Pearce, J Restall, H Sharif, P Shaw, G Singer, M Thomas, C Yates
VTS Course Organiser P Aeberhard

Kendal Education Centre

Westmorland General Hospital, Burton Road, Kendal LA9 7RG
Tel: 01539 795230 Fax: 01539 795308

Associate Clinical Tutor Ian Chadwick
Education Centre Manager Chris Newsham
GP Tutor E Williams
Specialty Tutor I M Huggett

Kent Postgraduate Medical Centre

Kent & Canterbury Hospital, Ethelbert Road, Canterbury CT1 3NG
Tel: 01227 766877 Ext: 4034/4367/4361, 01227 783108
Fax: 01227 864155
Website: www.ekh.org.uk

Clinical Tutor Dr Carter, A J Johnson, C Lamb, M Leahy, D Long, N Rafla, N Wilson
College Tutor K Stillman, H Winstone
Dental Tutor G Manley
GP Tutor P Biggs
GP Vocational Training P Livesey
Medical Education Manager Trish Jordan

Kidderminster Postgraduate Medical Centre

Worcestershire Acute Hospitals NHS Trust, Bewdley Road, Kidderminster DY11 6RJ

Clinical Tutor P Newrick
GP Tutor C Prince
GP VTS Organiser C Wilkinson
Postgraduate Centre Manager S Gallagher

King's Healthcare NHS Trust Postgraduate Medical Centre

Postgraduate Medical & Dental Education, Weston Education Centre, Cutcombe Road, London SE5 9RS
Tel: 0207 848 5525

Assistant Postgraduate Dean / Deputy Director Andy Leather
Director Postgraduate Medical Education / Postgraduate Dean Jan Welch
GP Tutor David Tovey, Kishor Vasant
Librarian Jean Yeoh
PGMDE Advisor/ Manager Joanne Hiley
Postgraduate Dental Tutor Martin Kelleher
Senior Educational Administrator Lenka Hooper

King's Lynn Postgraduate Medical and Dental Education Centre

Queen Elizabeth Hospital, Gayton Road, King's Lynn PE30 4ET
Tel: 01553 613791 Fax: 01553 613903
Email: jane.dearling@klshosp.nhs.uk

Clinical Tutor H AL Taher
GP Tutor B McGuiness, K Redhead
GP VTS Course Organiser J Dearling
Medical Education Centre Manager J Dearling
Specialty Tutor S Abukhalil, J Bottomley, A Chakrabarti, S Ell, S Hillam, H Hobbiger, N Johnson, John Keidan, S Singh, M Sparks, I Waterson, M Wheater

The Kings Mill Education Centre

Sherwood Forest Hospitals NHS Trust, Kings Mill Hospital, Sutton-in-Ashfield NG17 4JL
Fax: 01623 672374
Email: Margaret.Murray@kmc-tr.nhs.uk

Course Organiser P Bakaj, Mr Robertson, P Smith
Director of Postgraduate Education Mr Livesley
Education Centre Manager Mrs Murray
Specialty Tutor R Weston-Price

Kingston Postgraduate Medical Centre

1 Galsworthy Road, Kingston upon Thames KT2 7QB
Tel: 020 8546 7711 Ext: 2579, 020 8934 2579
Fax: 020 8547 3960

Anaesthetics R Stacey
Centre Manager Jeanne Browne
Clinical Tutor A Winrow
Dental Tutor M Preiss
GP Tutor M F D'Souza
GP VTS Joint Course Organiser I Johnson
Paediatrics & Child Health Tutor E Jurges
Pathologists Tutor P McHugh
Physicians Tutor M Spring
Specialty Tutor K Daly, R Pearson, A Pooley
Surgery Tutor J Cahill

Kingsway Hospital Postgraduate Centre

Southern Derby Mental Health NHS Trust, Kingsway, Derby DE22 3LZ

Clinical Tutor J Tombs

Lancaster Postgraduate Medical Centre

Royal Lancaster Infirmary, Ashton Road, Lancaster LA1 4RR
Tel: 01524 583950 Fax: 01524 848289
Email: Sue.Newall@l.bay-tr.nwest.nhs.uk

POSTGRADUATE MEDICAL CENTRES

Centre Manager Sue Newall
Clinical Tutor and Specialty Tutor S Durham
Dental Tutor C Hoyle
GP Tutor S Brear
Specialty Tutor Linda Ashworth, R W Blewitt, D Burch, Dr Ramesh, C Till, Debbie Wales, P Wilson

Learning and Development Centre

Calderdale Royal Hospital, Salterhebble, Halifax HX3 0PW
Tel: 01422 224385 Fax: 01422 224185
Email: Angela.Bottomley@calderdale.nhs.uk

Centre Manager Angela Bottomley
Clinical Tutor (VTSO) T Swift
Director Postgraduate Education S N Chater
Librarian H Curtis, C Jackson
Manager A Bottomley

Leeds Infirmary Postgraduate Medical Centre

The General Infirmary, Great George Street, Leeds LS1 3EX
Tel: 0113 392 3327 Fax: 0113 392 3965
Email: mavisprice@leedsth-nhs.uk
Website: www.leedsteachinghospitals.com

Postgraduate Centre Manager M Price

Leicester Clinical Education Centre

University Hospitals of Leicester NHS Trust, Leicester Royal Infirmary, Leicester LE1 5WW
Tel: 0116 254 1414, 0116 258 6381 Fax: 0116 258 5679
Email: rachael@webleicester.co.uk

Centre Administrator Tracey Smith
Clinical Tutor R J Abbott
Specialty Tutor M E Ardron, K Bibby, D Fell, J Konje, K C Krarup, D Lloyd, D K Luyt, D Quinton, S Vasanthan, D Ward, K P West

Lewisham Education Centre

Lewisham Hospital, High Street, London SE13 6LH
Tel: 020 8333 3000 Fax: 020 8333 3079

Clinical Tutor John Stroobant
Education Centre Manager Anne Ellis
Specialty Tutor Sarah Flint, F Majid, John Miell, D Misselbrook, John Pook, Gopal Rao, Richard Simo, Elizabeth Sleight, A Steger, H Tegner

Lincoln County Hospital Postgraduate Medical Centre

Lincoln & Louth NHS Trust, Sewell Road, Lincoln LN2 5QY
Tel: 01522 573866

Clinical Tutor D Stokoe
CME Organiser P Fairchild
Director of Postgraduate Medical Education M Lewins
Postgraduate Centre Manager J Evans
Undergraduate Tutor M A Coupland
VTS Course Organiser C Campbell, J Coffey, M Magee, R P Whitbread

Lister Hospital Postgraduate Centre

East & North Herts NHS Trust, Coreys Mill Lane, Stevenage SG1 4AB
Tel: 01438 781076 Fax: 01438 781442
Email: sgoring@bmihs.co.uk

Clinical Tutor C A Green
Dental Tutor J Chico
Deputy Clinical Tutor J Thiagarajan
Deputy VTS Course Organiser Keith Cockburn
GP Tutor R A S Christie, J Machen
Postgraduate Centre Manager J Costigan
Specialty Tutor S A Davies, M Ehsanullah, K Farrington, D Hanbury, T C Holme, N K James, P D Kelly, P S Kerr, R Patel, C Prendergast, S J Quinn, I Sargeant, R Sattin, I Sockalingham
VTS Course Organiser/GP Tutor M Hodgson

The London Chest Hospital Education Centre

Bonner Road, London E2 9JX
Tel: 020 8983 2342 Fax: 020 8983 2202

London Postgraduate Medical and Dental Education

20 Guilford Street, London WC1N 1DZ
Tel: 020 7692 3232 Fax: 020 7692 3396

Dean Director Elisabeth Paice
Dean of Postgraduate Medical Education Shelley Heard
Dental Dean Ian Waite
Director of Operations Alan Waller
GP Dean Neil Jackson

Luton and Dunstable Hospital NHS Trust Medical Centre

Lewsey Road, Luton LU4 0DZ
Tel: 01582 497200 Fax: 01582 497389
Email: diana.hardy@ldh-tr.anglox.nhs.uk
Website: www.ldmedics.nhs.uk

Career & Counselling Tutor B Adler
Clinical Tutor J Day
Dental Tutor L Hale
Deputy Clinical Tutor T Isitt
GP Tutor A Sahdev
Medical Centre Manager D J Hardy
Medical Librarian D Johnson
Medical Tutor D Peterson
Obstetrics & Gynaecology Tutor D H Horwell
Ophthalmology Tutor D Heath
Orthopaedics Tutor J Scott
Paediatrics Tutor P Sivakumar
Pathology Tutor D Freedman
Psychiatry Tutor J Pillai
Surgery Tutor R Novell
Tutor J Pickles, A Twigley
VTS Course Organiser R Khanchandani, J Marsden

Marsh-Jackson Postgraduate Medical Centre

Yeovil District Hospital, Higher Kingston, Yeovil BA21 4AT
Tel: 01935 384476 Fax: 01935 384670
Email: moonh@est.nhs.uk

Centre Manager Hazel Moon
Director of Medical Education/Clinical Tutor S Hunter
Specialty Tutor N C G Bathurst, S Brooks, J Dearlove, C Elsworth, T G Palferman, C Parker, M Quadiri, C Royle, J Tricker, M Zakaria
Undergraduate Teaching Co-ordinator M Eaton
VTS Course Organiser M J O Minogue

Medway Postgraduate Medical Centre

Medway Hospital, Windmill Road, Gillingham ME7 5NY
Tel: 01634 830000 Fax: 01634 819425

Clinical Tutor I M O'Brien
Specialty Tutor R J Buist, C M Butler, J S Tanday

Mersey Deanery

NHS Executive (North West) & The University of Liverpool, Hamilton House, 1st Floor, 24 Pall Mall, Liverpool L3 6AL
Tel: 0151 285 2021 Fax: 0151 236 5264

Associate Postgraduate Dean L de Cossart, J Higgins, G Lamont, H D Zakhour
Business Manager (PGME) D M Hart
Postgraduate Medical Dean D R Graham
Regional Adviser for Postgraduate Medical & Dental Education D Bridgen

Mid Staffordshire Postgraduate Medical Centre

Staffordshire General Hospital, Weston Road, Stafford ST16 3SA

Tel: 01785 230634 Fax: 01785 230639
Email: pgmc@msgh-tr.wmids.nhs.uk
Website: www.postgrad.free-online.co.uk

Course Organiser I C Greaves, J Hall, A Logan
Director of Medical Education B R Gwynn
Manager (Postgraduate Services) Ann Whiteman
Specialty Tutor P Coates, V C David, J Dixon, C K Dunn, G Earnshaw, C Gibson, C Greaves, S J Hands, S C Harris, R S Lloyd, C Melville, D Mulherin, D Palmer, E Paterson, S Suleman, A Taylor

Mid-Sussex Postgraduate Medical Centre

Princess Royal Hospital, Lewes Road, Haywards Heath RH16 4EX
Tel: 01444 441881 Ext: 4459 Fax: 01444 451576
Email: judy.keys@mid-sussex.stnames.nhs.uk

Clinical Tutor A Begg, J Rouse
Library Services Manager J Thorpe
Postgraduate Centre Manager Judy Keys
Specialty Tutor A Berresford, J Berry, Cathy Gleeson, Peter Harberow, J Herold, P Hughes, Martin Jones, I Littlejohn, B McKenzie-Gray, William Mair, J Nawrocki, John Norris, E Parnell, Gautam Ray

Milton Keynes Postgraduate Education Centre

Milton Keynes General NHS Trust, Standing Way, Eaglestone, Milton Keynes MK6 5LD
Tel: 01908 243178 Fax: 01908 234642

Associate District Clinical Tutor P Lakhani
Centre Manager Marilyn Hopkins
District Clinical Tutor N Graham
GP Tutor B Patel, A Prisk
PGEC Manager Marilyn Hopkins
Specialty Tutor A Assaf, Dr Fawdry, A Floyd, D G M Greig, D Merchevsky, E Miller, D Moir, Dr Moya, S P O'Malley, A Razzak, G J Smart, P Thomas
Tutor J Hall
VTS Course Organiser Dr Austin, A Watson

Moorfields Hospital Postgraduate Centre

City Road, London EC1V 2PD

Director of Medical Education John Lee
Postgraduate Centre Manager Susan McEever

Mount Vernon Postgraduate Medical Centre

Mount Vernon Hospital, Rickmansworth Road, Northwood HA6 2RN
Tel: 01923 844237 Fax: 01923 827216

Clinical Tutor M Saunders
GP Tutor Di Monaco
Postgraduate Centre Manager Audrey Mullet
Specialty Tutor G Bounds, J Livingstone, A Makris, N Reissis, P J Smith

Newcastle General Hospital Postgraduate Medical Centre

Tomlinson Medical Centre, Department of Medical Education, NNN, Mental Health Trust, Westgate Road, Newcastle upon Tyne NE4 6BE
Tel: 0191 256 3804 Fax: 0191 256 3804

Centre Manager Dee Smith
Director of Medical Education Suresh Joseph
Specialty Tutor Bob Barber, Dr Brittlebank, Dr Dunleavy, Professor Ferrier, Professor McKeith, Dr Mushet, Dr Turkington, Jean Wilkinson

Newham General Hospital Postgraduate Centre

Glen Road, Plaistow, London E13 8RU
Tel: 020 7363 8144 Fax: 020 7363 8090

Clinical Tutor A Naftalin
Postgraduate Centre Manager Lesley Elias

Norfolk and Norwich Institute of Medical Education

Norfolk & Norwich University Hospital, Colney Lane, Norwich NR4 7UY
Tel: 01603 286286 Ext: 2880 Fax: 01603 286779

Clinical Tutor K Gaffney, J Richards
Manager Madeleine Kent
Specialty Tutor Dr Ball, Dr Daynes, Dr Fleming, Dr Holton, Mr Meyer, Mr Morris, Mr Patel, Dr Ramakrishna, Mr Speakman, Miss Stanley, Dr Tarbuck, Mr Tewson, Dr Upton, Mr Walters, Dr Watkin

North Devon Postgraduate Medical Centre

North Devon District Hospital, Barnstaple EX31 4JB
Tel: 01271 322373 Fax: 01271 322374

Centre Manager Sarita Warmington
Clinical Tutor Dr Cox, Dr Wilson
Specialty Tutor Brian Attock, Dr Eckford, Dr Enoch, Dr Hughes, Dr Loader, Dr Markham, J Moore, Dr Moran, Dr van Buren
VTS Tutor Dr Bigge, Dr Brown, Dr York-Moore

North Hampshire Hospitals NHS Trust Postgraduate Medical Centre

North Hampshire Hospitals NHS Trust, Aldermanston Road, Basingstoke RG24 9NA
Tel: 01256 313380 Fax: 01256 313385
Email: Laura.Cullum@bas.swest.nhs.uk

Associate Clinical Sub-Dean H Simpson
Clinical Tutor C Jardine-Brown
Dental Tutor C Kerawala
GP Tutor R Lorge
Postgraduate Administrator Laura Cullum
Specialty Tutor C Batten, J Benfield, A Haigh, C Iffland, T John, J Kitching, G Plant, J Pleydell-Pearce, J Rees, C Sandy, P Spraggs

North Hertfordshire Postgraduate Centre

Corey's Mill Lane, Stevenage SG1 4AB
Tel: 01438 781076 Fax: 01438 781442

Clinical Tutor C A Green
Deputy Clinical Tutor J Thiagarajan
GP Tutor R A S Christie, J Machen
Postgraduate Education Manager Jean Costigan
VTS Course Organiser M Hodgson

North London Staff Development and Education Centre

St. Ann's Hospital, Tottenham, London N15 3TH
Tel: 020 8442 6000 Ext: 6492 Fax: 020 8442 6726

Clinical Tutor Dr Bateman
Education Centre Administrator Jhansi Ramful
Medical Director Dr Johnson-Sabine
Specialty Tutor Dr Heiw, Dr Shaw

North Manchester Postgraduate Medical Centre

North Manchester General Hospital, Crumpsall, Manchester M8 5RN
Tel: 0161 720 2720 Fax: 0161 720 2721

Clinical Tutor W F Tait
GP Tutor G O'Shea
Specialty Tutor D MacFoy, J Miles, W Potts, G T Williams, L Wyn-Pugh

North Middlesex Hospital Academic Centre

Sterling Way, Edmonton, London N18 1QX
Tel: 020 8887 2481 Fax: 020 8345 6809

Postgraduate Education Manager Jocelyn D'Albret

POSTGRADUATE MEDICAL CENTRES

North Staffordshire Combined Health Care NHS Trust Postgraduate Medical Centre

Ashlands Mental Health Resource Centre, 35 North Street, Newcastle-under-Lyme ST5 1AZ

Tutor H Thorley

North Staffordshire Hospital NHS Trust Postgraduate Medical Centre

Hartshill, Stoke-on-Trent ST4 7LN

Postgraduate Clinical Tutor C A Campbell

North Tees Postgraduate Medical Centre

Hardwick, Stockton-on-Tees TS19 8PE

Clinical Tutor E L Gilliland
Specialty Tutor N Bayliss, H M Hatem, G O'Leary, V Sarma, A Scane

North Tyneside HA Postgraduate Department

Education Centre, North Tyneside General Hospital, Rake Lane, North Shields NE29 8NH
Tel: 0191 293 2741 Fax: 0191 293 2762
Email: c.e.brown@ncl.ac.uk

Clinical Tutor Dr Welfare
Postgraduate Manager Caroline Brown
Specialty Tutor Dr Colver, Dr Doig, D Evans, Dr Goulbourne, S Johri, Dr Milner

North West Durham Postgraduate Medical Centre

General Hospital, Shotley Bridge, Consett DH8 0NB

Clinical Tutor S Dowson
Specialty Tutor D Gatehouse, P Robson, M Sekar, B S Sengupta, B Thalayasingham, P Watson

North Western (North) Postgraduate Medical Centres

Department of Postgraduate Medicine and Dentistry, University of Manchester, Gateway House, Piccadilly South, Manchester M60 7LP
Tel: 0161 237 2189

Associate Dean J Adams, C Ewing, R Feinmann
Dean of Postgraduate Medical Studies Jacky Hayden
Director of Postgraduate General Practice Education David McKinlay

Northallerton Postgraduate Medical Education Centre

Study Centre, Friarage Hospital, Northallerton DL6 1JG
Tel: 01609 764619 Fax: 01609 761126
Email: sfraser@nahs-tr.northy.nhs.uk

Course Organiser (VTSO) B H Davies, Roger Higson
Director Postgraduate Education Dr Ahmed
Medical Education Tutor Cath Snape Waise
PGCM Sue Fraser

Northwick Park Hospital, Medawar Postgraduate Department

Watford Road, Harrow HA1 3UJ
Tel: 020 8869 2251 Fax: 020 8869 2250

Director of Medical Education Michael Bannon
Medical Education Manager Ann Pyatt

Nottingham City Postgraduate Education Centre

Nottingham City Hospital NHS Trust, Hucknall Road, Nottingham NG5 1PB
Tel: 0115 962 7758, 0115 969 1169 Fax: 0115 962 7937
Website: www.ncht.org.uk

Director of Postgraduate Education Christine Bowman
Manager of Postgraduate Medical Education Alison Lawley
Specialty Tutor Dr Baldwin, Dr Burrell, Mr Dhar, T Fay, Mr Henley, A E Jones, Dr McLachlan, Dr Marenah, S A Morgan, Dr Patel, Dr Pinder, Dr Skoyles, Dr Watkin

Oakwell Centre for Learning and Development

Dewsbury District Hospital, Halifax Road, Dewsbury WF13 4HS
Tel: 01924 816246 Fax: 01924 816081
Email: medical.education@dhc-tr.northy.nhs.uk

Clinical Tutor (VTSO) R J Adams
Director Postgraduate Medical Education P Ah-Fat, J Brook, A Jackson

Oldham Medical and Dental Education Department

Royal Oldham Hospital, The Education Centre, Rochdale Road, Oldham OL1 2JH
Tel: 0161 627 8461 Fax: 0161 778 5628

Clinical Tutor Dr Cook
Medical and Dental Education Manager M Kenway
Royal College Tutor Dr Munro
Specialty Tutor I Brocklehurst, A Dey, L Edozien, C Elsworth, N Jeyagopal, Dr Prakash, S Solomon, J Suharwardy

Oliver Plunkett Postgraduate Centre

St. Peters Hospital, Chertsey KT16 0PZ
Email: marian.kerr@asph.nhs.uk

Associate Clinical Tutor P Martin
College Tutor T Balakumar, M Knapp, R Kulkarni, C Long, S Newbold, D Robinson
Director of Medical Education C Bennett
GP Tutor J Weston
Librarian Sylvia Stafford
Senior Centre Manager and Business Manager Medical Education Marian Kerr

Ormskirk Postgraduate Medical Education Centre

Ormskirk & District General Hospital, Wigan Road, Ormskirk L39 2AZ
Tel: 01695 656800 Fax: 01695 656704
Email: ormpgmec@hotmail.com

Accident and Emergency Tutor Dr Odedun
Clinical Tutor Susan O'Halloran
Director of Medical Education M J Serlin
GP Tutor Dr Mullen
Medical Education Manager Heather Ainscough
Medicine Tutor M MacIver
Obstetrics & Gynaecology Tutor Mr Davies
PGMEC Administrator Odette Bell
Psychiatry Tutor M McKenzie
Surgical Tutor Dr Menon
Trust Library Services Manager M Mason
Undergraduate Tutor Dr Anderson

Oxford Regional Postgraduate Medical

Oxford Postgraduate Medical and Dental Education Training, The Triangle, Roosevelt Drive, Headington, Oxford OX3 7XP
Tel: 01865 740600 Fax: 01865 740699
Email: pgdean@oxford-pgmde.co.uk

Associate Director Education and Training A Jefferies
Associate Director Flexible Training B Thornley
Associate Director Overseas Doctors S Laurie
Director of Postgraduate Medical and Dental Education W M G Tunbridge
Medical Personnel Manager Pauline Swann

POSTGRADUATE MEDICAL CENTRES

Peter Hodgkinson Centre

Lincoln District Healthcare NHS Trust, Posgraduate Centre, Greetwell Road, Lincoln LN2 5QY
Fax: 01522 525327

Clinical Tutor K Sidahmed
Postgraduate Administrator M Blavesley

Peterborough District Postgraduate Medical and Dental Education Centre

Peterborough District Hospital, Thorpe Road, Peterborough PE3 6DA

Clinical Tutor N J Sheehan
PGMC Speciality Tutor H Fernando, C Grant, P Johnston, S Kent, H Mistry, C Nnochiri, A G Pfleiderer, J Randall, T Rimmer, J Robertson, J M Roland, C Scarisbrick, M Sutcliffe, S J Tuck

Plymouth Medical Centre

Derriford Hospital, Plymouth PL6 8DH

Clinical Tutor J D Dean, H R Guly, R C B Neve, Surg Comm W Smith, M Williams
Consultant C Hutton
Specialty Tutor A Beasley, J D Dean, R Donovan, A D Falconer, I Kestin, W E J Leverton, P MacLeod, R Parrish, A G Prentice, C F Randall, A Read, R Robinson, J Shaw, R J I Sibbald

Poole Postgraduate Medical Centre

Poole General Hospital, Longfleet Road, Poole BH15 2JB

Clinical Tutor T Battcock
Postgraduate Centre Manager Gill Sibthorp
Specialty Tutor N Bell, S Doman, M Ford, I Mynors-Wallis

Portsmouth Hospitals NHS Trust

Department Postgraduate Medical & Dental Education, Cosham, Portsmouth PO6 3LY
Tel: 023 9228 6000 Fax: 023 9228 6024

Associate Director of Postgraduate General Practice Education Julia Oxonbury
Clinical Tutor Simon Toh
Director Postgraduate Medical & Dental Education Vicky Osgood
Postgraduate Administrator M Smale
RCP Tutor R Clark, D Meeking

Postgraduate Institute for Medicine and Dentistry

10-12 Framlington Place, The University, Newcastle upon Tyne NE2 4AB
Tel: 0191 227041

Postgraduate Dean Peter Hill

Postgraduate Medical Education Centre

St Mary's Hospital, Newport PO30 5TG
Tel: 01983 534231 Fax: 01983 521963
Website: www.iwhealthcare.org.uk

Clinical Tutor Dr Walsh
Dental Tutor J Wickens
GP Tutor L Botell
Medical Tutor D Murphy
PGMC Manager Zorina Walsh
Specialty Tutor R Ridley
Surgical Tutor M Shinkfield

Preston Postgraduate Medical Centre

Watling Street Road West, Fulwood, Preston PR2 8DY
Tel: 01772 711234 Fax: 01772 774741

Clinical Tutor L R Solomon
Specialty Tutor P Bunting, A Davis, T A Flaherty, W J Gunawardena, M James, P McDonald, J McKenna, D A Mahmood, A Robb, R B Smith

Prince William Postgraduate Medical Education Centre

Kettering General Hospital, Kettering NN16 8UZ
Tel: 01536 492853 Fax: 01536 492856

Associate Tutor J O'Neill
Centre Manager A Gaunt
Clinical Tutor A Steel
Specialty Tutor V Bahal, T Blamires, M Chawla, J Hart, R Latham, M A Latif, D Lawrence, S Mehra, C Nanayakkara, J Szafranski, R Thamizhavell, J Uraiby, R Walters, P Wood

Princess Alexandra Hospital Postgraduate Medical Centre

Parndon Hall, Hamstel Road, Harlow CM20 1QX
Tel: 01279 827020 Fax: 01279 451263

Clinical Director K Harvey
Postgraduate Centre Manager Jennifer A Bixby

Queen Elizabeth II Hospital Postgraduate Centre

Howlands, Welwyn Garden City AL7 4HQ
Tel: 01707 364518 Fax: 01707 365421
Email: postgrad@geji.enherts-tr.nhs.uk

Clinical Tutor J Saetta
Deputy Clinical Tutor M Al-Izzi
Postgraduate Centre Manager Christine Crick
Specialty Tutor J Chiyende, E Hemaya, D Jain, K Jones, H Parmar, A Roberts, C Shaw, P Shilliday, T Walker

Queen Mary's University Hospital Postgraduate Medical Centre

Roehampton Lane, London SW15 5PN

Clinical Tutor A F Neil
Specialty Tutor P T Blenkinsopp, C Higgens, P Hutton, J M Page, R Thonet

Queen's Centre for Clinical Studies

East Kent Hospital NHS Trust, Queen Elizabeth the Queen Mother Hospital, St Peters Road, Margate CT9 4AN
Tel: 01843 225544 Fax: 01843 296082

Clinical Tutor A M Leak
Medical Education Manager J Galbraith

Queen's Medical Centre

Nottingham University Hospital NHS Trust, Nottingham NG7 2UH

Clinical Tutor R Stewart
Specialty Tutor L Kapila, S Karim, R Kupfer, A Lee, R Seth, M Varnam

The Robert Hardwick Postgraduate Centre

Maidstone Hospital, Hermitage Lane, Barming, Maidstone ME16 9QQ
Tel: 01622 729000 Fax: 01622 224141
Email: diane.pgcmaidstone@lineone.net

Clinical Tutor G Bird
Manager Dr Vander
Specialty Tutor F Ahfat, S Andrews, B Bhaduri, A Henderson, T Jones, R Leech

Romford Medical Academic Centre

Oldchurch Hospital, Romford RM7 0BE
Tel: 01708 746090

Clinical Tutor R M Weatherstone
Specialty Tutor R J Burack, H J Carruthers, T K Gosh, E M Jones, P C Myres, G A Ponting, M R A Utidjian

POSTGRADUATE MEDICAL CENTRES

Rotherham General Hospitals NHS Trust Postgraduate Centre
Moorgate Road, Oakwood, Rotherham S60 2UD

Clinical Tutor P Taylor
Director of Public Health T Patterson
Medical Education Manager E Webster
Specialty Tutor H Barker, A Cooper, J Mahajan, C Myers, C Ramsden, MG Thomas

The Royal Bolton Hospital Postgraduate Medical Education Centre
Bolton Royal Infirmary, Bolton BL4 0JR
Tel: 01204 390426 Fax: 01204 527001

Clinical Tutor P Baker
GP Tutor M C Brown
Postgraduate Centre Manager C Paisley
Specialty Tutor W Dougal, R E Hopkins, H Michie, H Northover, J M Pearson, W G Ryan, N Smith, G Yeung

Royal National Orthopaedic Hospital Trust Postgraduate Centre
45-51 Bolsover Street, London W1 8AQ
Tel: 020 8909 5326 Fax: 020 8954 6933

Clinical Tutor T W R Briggs
Postgraduate Education Manager Carol Winston

Royal National Throat, Nose and Ear Hospital Postgraduate Centre
330 Gray's Inn Road, London WC1X 8EE
Tel: 020 7915 1514 Fax: 020 7837 9279

Clinical Tutor A Wright
Postgraduate Education Administrator C Overington

Royal Orthopaedic Hospital Research and Teaching Centre
The Woodlands, Northfield, Birmingham B31 2AP
Tel: 0121 685 4027 Fax: 0121 685 4030
Email: postgrad@roh.mdirect.co.uk, roh-postgrad@bham.ac.uk

Clinical Tutor J Plewes
Director Research & Teaching Centre P Pynsent
Manager Research & Teaching Centre A Weaver

Royal Shrewsbury Hospitals NHS Trust Postgraduate Medical Centre
Mytton Oak Road, Shrewsbury SY3 8XF
Tel: 01743 261079 Fax: 01743 261169
Email: violet@smirsh.demon.co.uk

Centre Manager V Redmond
Clinical Tutor D W Skinner
Librarian C Carr, Z Debenham

Royal Victoria Infirmary Postgraduate Medical Education Centre
Queen Victoria Road, Newcastle upon Tyne NE1 4LP
Tel: 0191 282 4710 Fax: 0191 227 5154
Email: pgcm.rvi@ncl.ac.uk

Centre Manager Mrs Smith
Clinical Tutor N J Fox
Dental Clinical Tutor Mr Jacobs
Postgraduate Centre Manager J Brown
Specialty Tutor T G Bennett, A J Bint, S Bourke, W Bythell, M P Clarke, A Coulthard, E Curtis, J J Murray, S Plusa, D G Smith, S Sturgiss

St Albans City Hospital Postgraduate Centre
Floor 2 Moynihan Block, Waverley Road, St Albans AL3 5PN
Tel: 01727 897683 Fax: 01727 897246

Administrator C Roberts

Clinical Tutor I Barrison
Postgraduate Centre Administrator C Roberts
Specialty Tutor B Cavell, J Ferguson

St Charles' Medical Centre
Exmoor Street, London W10 6DZ
Tel: 020 8969 2488

St Helens and Knowsley Postgraduate Medical Centre
Whiston Hospital, Prescot L35 5DR
Website: www.merseyworld.com/skhealth

Clinical Tutor C I Littlewood
Clinical Tutor (VTSO) AC Skinner
Medical Education Administrator C C Foster
Specialty Tutor TD Brown

St James's Hospital Postgraduate Department
2nd Floor Ashley Wing, St James's University Hospital, Leeds LS9 7TF
Tel: 0113 206 4825 Fax: 0113 244 8575
Email: Jackie.Burrows@gw.sjjsum.northy.nhs.uk

Postgraduate Centre Manager J Burrows
Postgraduate Director S G Gilbey
Trust Medical Education Manager M M Ward

St Martin's Education Centre
St Martin's Hospital, Littlebourne Road, Canterbury CT1 1TD
Tel: 01227 812017 Fax: 01227 812005
Email: brigette.frost@ekentc-tr.sthames.nhs.uk, education.centre@ekentc-tr.sthames.nhs.uk

CPD Co-ordinator R Harte
Education Centre Administrator Maureen Bryant
Education Centre Manager Brigitte Frost

St Mary's NHS Trust Postgraduate Centre
Postgraduate Centre, St Mary's Hospital, Praed Street, London W2 1NY
Tel: 020 7725 6151 Fax: 020 7725 6314

Centre Manager Gillian Brown
Clinical Tutor J Jones, J Leonard
General Manager, PGME and R&D R Abbot
GP VTS Organiser P Kiernan
Specialist Medical Courses Organiser N Ognejenovic
Specialty Tutor Wyn Davies, Robert Goldin, J Johnson, Andrew Palmer, John Smith, Julian Teare, Sam Walters

St Matthew's Hospital Postgraduate Medical Centre (Psychiatric Centre)
St Matthew's Hospital, Burntwood WS7 9ES

Postgraduate Teacher P Zikis

St Thomas' Postgraduate Department
Ground Floor, Gassiot House, St Thomas' Hospital, Lambeth Palace Road, London SE1 7EH
Tel: 020 7928 9292 Fax: 020 7401 8591
Email: gloria.barrow@kcl.ac.uk, kim.latimer@kcl.ac.uk
Website: www.kcl.ac.uk

Postgraduate Dean C H C Twort
Postgraduate Manager K Latimer
Postgraduate Secretary G Barrow
Postgraduate Sub-Dean D Hamilton-Fairley, S Mowle
Specialty Tutor D Goldsmith, A Williams

Salisbury Postgraduate Education Centre
Salisbury District Hospital, Salisbury SP2 8BJ
Tel: 01722 336262 ext 4492/4493 Fax: 01722 410940

Clinical Tutor H Parry
Dental Tutor V Reese

Department Manager Lady Granville-Chapman
GP Tutor P D Jenkins
GP VTS Course Organiser A Armstrong
Undergraduate Tutor R Scott-Jupp

Sandwell Health Care NHS Trust Medical Education Centre

Lyndon Street, West Bromwich B71 4HG
Tel: 0121 607 3436 Fax: 0121 607 3397

Centre Manager Jane Davies
Clinical Sub-Dean E T Bainbridge
Clinical Tutor E Hughes
Specialty Tutor I Abukhahl, A Ahmed, J Berlin, P Davies, D G Hamilton, R Jayatunga, P Shaylor, Dr Staldeforth
VTS Course Organiser Dr Ball

Scarborough Postgraduate Medical Centre

Scarborough Hospital, Woodlands Drive, Scarborough YO12 6QL
Tel: 01723 342077 Fax: 01723 501594
Email: postgrad.scarborough@talk21.com

GP Tutor P Metcale
Postgraduate Centre Manager M J Dixon
Postgraduate Clinical Tutor D Brown
VTS Course Organiser Dr Chadwick, Dr Davies, Dr Dowley

Scunthorpe Postgraduate Medical Centre

Scunthorpe General Hospital, Cliff Gardens, Scunthorpe DN15 7BH
Tel: 01724 290177 Fax: 01724 290090

Postgraduate Centre Manager Rachel Key
Tutor O A Odukoya
VTS Course Organiser A S Kerss

Selly Oak Hospital Education Centre

Selly Oak Hospital, Birmingham B29 6JD
Tel: 0121 627 8748 Fax: 0121 627 8581
Email: christine.yates@university-b.wmids.nhs.uk

Centre Manager Christine Yates
Clinical Tutor M Alner

Sheffield Teaching Hospitals NHS Trust Medical Education Centre

Northern General Hospital Campus, Herries Road, Sheffield S5 7AU

Clinical Tutor Dr Levy
Medical Education Manager Mrs Foers
Specialty Tutor J Buchanan, G Hood, Dr Howard, Dr Lawson, H McCullough

Sheila Sherlock Postgraduate Centre

Royal Free Hospital, Rowland Hill Street, London NW3 2PF
Tel: 020 7830 2182 Fax: 020 7830 2167
Email: Ann.Pyatt@rfh.nthames.nhs.uk

Director of Postgraduate Medical Education J S Dooley
Postgraduate Education Services Manager Ann Pyatt

Somerset Postgraduate Centre

Taunton and Somerset Hospital, Musgrove Park, Taunton TA1 5DA
Tel: 01823 342430 Fax: 01823 342432
Email: Postgrad.Centre@tst.nhs.uk

Clinical Tutor G Bryce, D Pryce
GP Course Organiser D N H Greig
GP Tutor R Crabtree, A Wright
Postgraduate Centre Manager Nancy Beveridge
Specialty Tutor Dr Bryce, J Chester, Dr Collins, D Cooke, S Cooper, M Davidson, R Fox, S Johnson, R Mann, C Ogilvie, J Twomey
VTS Course Organiser Dr Hansford, Dr Kelham

South Cheshire Postgraduate Medical Centre

Leighton Hospital, Middlewich Road, Crewe CW1 4QJ
Tel: 01270 612015 Fax: 01270 250484

Associate Postgraduate Clinical Tutor C Henshaw
Dental Tutor T Thayer
Dental VTSO N Cooper
GP Tutor J Howard
Postgraduate Centre Manager Gill Newall
Postgraduate Clinical Tutor A P J Thomson
VTSO N G M Wilson

South Essex Postgraduate Medical Centre

Basildon Hospital, Nether Mayne, Basildon SS16 5NL
Tel: 01268 593360 Fax: 01268 598280

General Manager Jill Sharley
Specialty Tutor I Barton, R Haloob, J Mckenzie, D Mulllane, B O'Reilly, N Shareif, H Taylor, D Tullett, R Wakeman, J Whitehead
Training Director M Imana

South Tees Postgraduate Medical Centre

Education Centre, The James Cook University Hospital, Marton Road, Middlesbrough TS4 3BW
Tel: 01642 854809 Fax: 01642 825331
Email: m.d.bruce@ncl.ac.uk
Website: www.southteespostgrad.org.uk

Clinical Tutor S Sinha
Postgraduate Medical Education Manager Mandy Bruce
Specialty Tutor D Bosman, R Cawthra, Mr Cruickshank, N Fox, J Hall, P D J Hardman, R Jones, B McNeela, P Morrell, M Tremlett, I Wallace, J Wallis, G Young

South Thames Department of Postgraduate Medical and Dental Education

33 Millman Street, London WC1 3EJ
Tel: 020 7692 3142 Fax: 020 7692 3101
Website: ww.tpmde.ac.uk

Dean Director Brendan Hicks
Dean of Postgraduate GP Education Abdol Tavabie
Dean of Postgraduate Medicine Hugh Seeley
Executive Assistant Christine Turner
Office Manager/Executive Assistant Alan Ip

South Tyneside Postgraduate Medical Centre

South Shields General Hospital, Harton Lane, South Shields NE34 0PL
Tel: 0191 454 8888 Fax: 0191 427 0096

Clinical Tutor M J Akhtar
PGMC Manager Nicola Whitelock
Specialty Tutor M Bone, A Muchall, N J N Nwabineli, G Okugberi, K Pollard, C Pritchett, A Reece, G S Roysam, H Spencer, S Stein

South West Durham Postgraduate Medical Centre

General Hospital, Bishop Auckland DL14 6AD
Tel: 01388 454000 Ext: 2266 Fax: 01388 454194
Email: lawrence@smtp.sdhc-tr.northy.nhs.uk

Centre Manager Ena Lawrence
Clinical Tutor R W G Prescott
Medical Staffing Manager Dr Stainthorpe
Specialty Tutor R Abbasi, T Layzell, C Lim, G Nyamugunduru, B Saleh

South Western Regional Postgraduate Medical Centres

The University, Medical Postgraduate Department, Academic Centre, Frenchay Hospital, Bristol BS16 1LE
Tel: 0117 975 7050 Fax: 0117 975 7060

POSTGRADUATE MEDICAL CENTRES

Course Organiser Philip Pemberton
Dean of Postgraduate Medical Education R J West

Southampton Postgraduate Medical Centre

South Academic Block, Mailpoint 10, General Hospital, Southampton SO16 6YD
Tel: 023 8079 4098 Fax: 023 8079 6816
Email: meded@sotonpgc.demon.co.uk

PGC Manager Kathryne Viuesid

Southend-on-Sea Medical Education Centre

Education Centre, Southend Hospital, Prittlewell Chase, Westcliff on Sea SS0 0RY
Tel: 01702 221070 Fax: 01702 221406
Email: education.centre@hospital.southend.nhs.uk, jsharpe@southend.nhs.uk

Clinical Tutor M Almond, A A Brown
Education Centre Manager Judi Sharpe

Southmead Centre for Medical Education

Southmead Hospital, Westbury-on-Trym, Bristol BS10 5NB
Tel: 0117 959 5331 Fax: 0117 959 5332

Centre Administrator S Nutland
Clinical Tutor J Chambers, H Morgan, J Unsworth
Medical Education Centre Administrator Pat Hinton, S Nuttand
Specialty Tutor D Bisson, M Brett, J Hardy, P Jardine, A Johnson, N Khoehli, E Loveday, R Newbery, B Pentlow

Stockport Postgraduate Medical Education Centre

Pinewood House Education Centre, Stepping Hill Hospital, Poplar Grove, Stockport SK2 7JE
Tel: 0161 419 4684, 0161 419 4685 Fax: 0161 419 4686

Postgraduate Medical Education Centre Manager P Sykes
Specialty Tutor R Brown, C Candelier, R Cruckshank, G Deans, A J Gray, R Hale, R Jameson, N Kay, C Keeling-Roberts, B Larkin, D Meadows, D Menzies, T Ramsay, J Simpson

Stoke Mandeville Hospital Postgraduate Medical Centre

Mandeville Road, Aylesbury HP21 8AL

Clinical Tutor R Smith
Specialty Tutor F Ashworth, G Barton, R Bodley, P Cohen, S Edmonds, A Graham, M J Knightley, A M O'Hea, M Paul, D Stott, A Tudway, J Tweedie, I Wallace

Sussex Postgraduate Medical Centre

Brighton General Hospital, Elm Grove, Brighton BN2 3EW
Tel: 01273 696011 Fax: 01273 690032
Email: sue.hayes@brighton-healthcare.nhs.uk

Dental Tutor J Herold
Dental Vocational Training Adviser T Fallowfield
Director of Medical Education Dr Hartley
GP Tutor L Argent
GP Vocational Training Adviser R McLintock
Postgraduate Centre Manager Sue Hayes
Psychiatric Clinical Tutor N Farhoumand
Specialty Tutor D Bloomfield, P Brittain, N Brooks, N Gainsborough, V Kalidasan, N Kirkham, J Montgomery, M Parry, C Perez-Avila, C Sonksen, M Street, P Thomas, T Turnbull, J Weighill

Swindon Postgraduate Medical Centre

Princess Margaret Hospital, Okus Road, Swindon SN1 4JU
Tel: 01793 426581 Fax: 01793 426712
Email: swindon.pgmc@sunlist.swest.nhs.uk

Clinical Tutor M O'Connor
Postgraduate Centre Manager (GP & Dental) E O'Flynn
Postgraduate Centre Manager (Hospital) Siobhan Timms

Specialty Tutor A Beale, R Beck, P Burgess, M Colley, J Fieldhouse, S Green, T Higazi, I Kendall, P McCormack, D Majumdar, Dr Manchip, P O'Keeffe, S O'Kelly, S Wimalaratna

Tameside Postgraduate Medical Centre

Tameside General Hospital, Ashton-under-Lyme OL6 9RW
Tel: 0161 331 6344 Fax: 0161 331 6345

Clinical Tutor I Brett
Specialty Tutor R Arya, A Haheed, B N Muddu, R H Rehman, C Shaw, V N H Tanna, P Unsworth, A Watson

Terence Mortimer Postgraduate Education Centre

Horton Hospital, Banbury OX16 9AL
Tel: 01295 229314 Fax: 01295 254437
Email: meded@pgec-horton.demon.co.uk
Website: www.pgec-horton.demon.co.uk

Clinical Tutor E Laird
Postgraduate Centre Manager L Clarke
Specialty Tutor J Everatt, A Hughes, R Marshall, E Matthews, J Nicholls, A Taylor, N Thompson, C Thorogood

Thomas Sydenham Educational Centre

Dorset County Hospital, Williams Avenue, Dorchester DT1 2JY
Tel: 01305 255258 Fax: 01305 255359

Clinical Tutor A Blaine
Course Organiser Tanya Murray
Dental Tutor H Bellis
Specialty Tutor N Lyons

Torbay Hospital Postgraduate Education Department

Lawes Bridge, Torquay TQ2 7AA

Clinical Tutor N Cooper, J Lowes
Specialty Tutor N Campbell, C M Carey, J E B Foulkes, C M Gillespie, C R H James, A G MacEachern, P Moore, R G H Wade

Trafford Education Centre

Trafford General Hospital, Moorside Road, Davyhulme, Manchester M41 5SL
Tel: 0161 746 2036

Clinical Tutor S A Bennett
Specialty Tutor P A Carrington, M E Eltott, W Fraser, K M Graham, J F Haines, H M Lewis, L Montague, S R Musgrave

Trent Regional Postgraduate Medical Centres

NHS Executive Trent, Fulwood House, Old Fulwood Road, Sheffield S10 3TH
Tel: 0114 263 0300

Director Postgraduate General Practice Education R N Hedley, P W F Lane, D Sowden
Postgraduate Dean (Leicester) J Walls
Postgraduate Dean (Nottingham) G Batstone
Regional Adviser in Clinical Community Dentistry N Thomas
Regional Adviser in General Dental Practice M E L Pendlebury
Regional Postgraduate Dean (Sheffield) C L Welsh
Regional Postgraduate Dental Dean P S Rothwell

Tunbridge Wells Postgraduate Medical Centre

The Kent & Sussex Hospital, Mount Ephraim, Tunbridge Wells TN4 8AT
Tel: 01892 534477 Fax: 01892 517692
Email: pip.twpgc@ukgateway.net
Website: www.twpgc.com

Centre Manager Phillippa Cook
Clinical Tutor D Yates
Course Organiser K Finlay, A Howitt, K Lay
Dental Tutor K Sneddon
GP Tutor C Dewing

Specialty Tutor L Baldwin, R Banks, P Day, D Edwards, J Flanagan, P Gibb, L Roberts, N Rowson, R Sergeant

UCL Hospitals Postgraduate Office

48 Riding House Street, London W1W 7EY
Tel: 020 7679 9370 Fax: 020 7679 9248
Website: www.uclh.org

Director Medical Education Lesley Bromley
Manager Susan Harper
Primary Care Tutor S Nazeer

University Hospital NHS Trust Postgraduate Medical Centre

Queen Elizabeth Hospital, Metchley Park Road, Edgbaston, Birmingham B15 2TQ
Tel: 0121 627 2860 Fax: 0121 414 0211

Clinical Tutor M Clapham
Director Robert Allen
Manager Louise Atkins

University Hospitals Coventry and Warwickshire NHS Trust

Postgraduate Medical Centre, Clifford Bridge Road, Walsgrave, Coventry CV2 2DX

Clinical Tutor I Fraser

Wakefield Postgraduate Medical Centre

Pinderfields & Pontefract Hospitals NHS Trust, Aberford Road, Wakefield WF1 4DG
Tel: 01924 212622 Fax: 01924 814546

Associate Director PGMDE D Nagi
Dental VTS Course Organiser G Baggaley
Director Postgraduate Education A Harvey
Medical Education Service Manager C Sanderson
VTS Course Organiser S Bullimore, T Gair

Walsall Hospitals NHS Trust Postgraduate Medical Centre

Manor Hospital, Moat Road, Walsall WS2 9PS

Clinical Tutor A Cunningham

Wansbeck Postgraduate Medical Centre

Woodhorn Lane, Ashington NE63 9JJ

Clinical Tutor P R Crook
Specialty Tutor P R Crook, L Edmondson, J L Sher, P R Sill

Wessex Deanery

Highcroft, Romsey Road, Winchester SO22 5DH
Tel: 01962 863511

Director of Postgraduate General Practice Education F Smith
Operations Manager Jan Zietara
Postgraduate Dental Dean R T Reed
Postgraduate Medical Dean G Winyard

West Berkshire Postgraduate Medical Education Centre

Royal Berkshire Hospital, Reading RG1 5AN
Tel: 0118 987 7831 Fax: 0118 987 7837

Associate Clinical Tutor A Bradlow
District Clinical Tutor T Parke
Regional Dental Tutor J Dejai
Specialty Tutor H Allott, A Bacon, P Burden, R Collett, R Dodds, S Edees, P Farrugia, J Gildersleve, Diana Grice, M James, S Jones, A Kaplin, T Magee, C Meanock, R J Parker, C Tomlins, A Tony, P Van Boxall, A Watson

West Cheshire Postgraduate Medical Centre

Countess of Chester Hospital NHS Trust, Liverpool Road, Chester CH2 1UL
Tel: 01244 383676 Fax: 01244 364722
Email: barbara.kirkham@cogh-tr.nwest.nhs.uk

Clinical Tutor S Bowles, Dr Finnerty
GP Tutor R Gleek

West Cumberland Postgraduate Medical Centre

West Cumberland Hospital, Hensingham, Whitehaven CA28 8JG
Tel: 01946 693181 Ext: 2538 Fax: 01946 591772
Email: westcumbriavtspostgrad@compuserve.com
Website: www.northcumbriahealth.nhs

Clinical Tutor F J Local
College Tutor J Eldred, S Javaid, D Prosser, N S Rao
Postgraduate Centre Manager B Husgrave

West Hertfordshire and Watford Postgraduate Medical Centre

Watford General Hospital, Shrodells Wing, Vicarage Road, Watford WD1 8HB
Tel: 01923 217436 Fax: 01923 217910

Director of Medical Education M R Clements
GP Tutor N Small
Postgraduate Manager S Watkins
Specialty Tutor D R Griffin, J Livingstone, H Parry, A Sa'adu, G Supramaniam

West Hertfordshire Hospitals NHS Trust Postgraduate Medical Centre

Hemel Hempstead Hospital, Hillfield Road, Hemel Hempstead HP2 4AD
Tel: 01442 287666 Fax: 01442 287670
Email: hhghpostgrad@hotmail.com

Deputy Clinical Tutor Sarah Hill
Joint Associate Medical Director for Education & Training Ian Barrison
Postgraduate Education Manager David Goodier

West Midlands Board of Postgraduate Medical and Dental Education

The Medical School, The University of Birmingham, Edgbaston, Birmingham B15 2TT
Tel: 0121 414 6892 Fax: 0121 414 3155

Consultant V Y Subhedar, A Whitehouse
Dean P Scriven
Deputy Postgraduate Dean D W Wall
Regional Postgraduate Dean J G Temple

West Suffolk Postgraduate Medical Centre

West Suffolk Hospital, Hardwick Lane, Bury St Edmunds IP33 2QZ
Tel: 01284 713284 Fax: 01284 712598
Email: lynn@ljones.demon.co.uk

Clinical Sub-Dean M Wood
Clinical Tutor S Robling
Dental Tutor Dr Hare
Director of Postgraduate Medical Education S Edwards
GP Tutor J Webb
Medical Director/Director of Education K H Matheson
Postgraduate Medical Centre Manager Lynn Jones
Royal College Tutor A August, A Burns, M Judd, R Lamb, D Mabin, J Majeed, I Singer, L Watson
VTS Course Organiser J Calvert, J Masters, D Pearson

Weston General Hospital Postgraduate Medical Centre

Grange Road, Uphill, Weston Super Mare BS23 4TQ

Clinical Tutor M Lewis, P G P Stoddart

POSTGRADUATE MEDICAL CENTRES

Specialty Tutor J Dixon, J H Dixon, A Gough, A Hinchliffe, M Lewis, E J Wakley

Wharfedale Medical Centre Department of Medical Education Postgraduate Centre

Wharfedale General Hospital, Newall Carr Road, Otley LS21 2LY
Tel: 0113 392 3010, 0113 392 6072 Fax: 01943 468314
Email: PatD.Clark@leedsth.nhs.uk

Secretary Pat Clark

Whipps Cross Hospital Medical Education Centre

Whipps Cross Hospital, London E11 1NR
Tel: 020 8539 5522 ext: 5789
Email: admin@meoffice.demon.co.uk
Website: www.nthames.tprnde.ac.uk/ntrl/mec/index.htm

Centre Manager S Bumfrey
Clinical Tutor C M Roberts
GP Tutor G Ivbijaro
Head & Neck/Dental Clinical Tutor S Ash
Medicine Tutor S Donnolly
Obstetrics & Gynaecology Tutor A Hollingworth
Paediatrics Tutor J Raine
Specialty Tutor R A Atun, S Brearley, D Erwin, N Frootko, D L McMillan, M O'Callaghan, P L Wright
Surgery Tutor S Begarley
VTS Tutor A Khan

Whittington Hospital Postgraduate Centre

Holborn Union Building, Archway Campus, Highgate Hill, London N19 3UE
Tel: 020 7288 5185 Fax: 020 7288 5625

Bloomsbury RGM VTS A Dicker
Clinical Tutor C Ingham Clark
Course Organiser J Conway, L Speight
Specialty Tutor J Salinsky, S Wiseman
VTS Course Organiser J Salinsky

Wigan and Leigh Medical Institute

Thomas Linacre House, Royal Albert Edward Infirmary, Wigan WN1 2NN
Tel: 01924 248208, 01942 822507 Fax: 01942 822355

Clinical Tutor J Marples
DRHO Tutor S Arya
Postgraduate Medical Education Manager Carol Hitchmough
Specialty Tutor A Bellis, P Bliss, C Cooper, S Desai, I Dhesi, B Duper, F F Koussa, S Malik, J Mosley

William Harvey Postgraduate Medical Centre

William Harvey Hospital, Kennigton Road, Willesborough, Ashford TN24 0LZ
Tel: 01233 616055 Fax: 01233 613597

Clinical Tutor B Al-Shaikh
GP Tutor G Del Bianco
Specialty Tutor M Heravi, J Hossain, R Insall, R Lapworth, M Miller-Jones, M Milligan, M Rahman
VTS Course Organiser T Lister, A Lloyd-Smith

Wirral Postgraduate Medical Centre

Clatterbridge Hospital, Bebington, Wirral CH63 4JY
Tel: 0151 482 7848 Fax: 0151 334 6379

Clinical Tutor D W Galvani, J S Sprigge
Dental Course Organiser/IT Tutor M J R Williams
Dental Tutor M Horrocks
Director of Medical Education H D F Zakhour
GP Tutor G G Francis
Manager B L Rice
VT Course Organiser A S Mellors

Withington Department of Postgraduate Medical Studies

Research and Teaching Block, Withington Hospital, Nell Lane, Manchester M20 8LR

Clinical Tutor M J Whitaker
GP Tutor M J Whitaker
Specialty Tutor R Ashleigh, A Baildam, A Bradley, P Hirsch, B Mbaya, B Oppenheim, T E Roberts, C Tolhurst-Cleaver

Worthing Postgraduate Medical Centre

Park Avenue, Worthing BN11 2HR
Tel: 01903 285024 Fax: 01903 285125
Website: www.worthinghospital.org.uk

Associate Clinical Tutor Andrew White
Centre Manager Brenda Davies
Clinical Tutor Elizabeth Wright
Undergraduate Sub-Dean John Southgate

The Wynne Davies Postgraduate Medical Centre

Worcestershire Acute Hospitals NHS Trust, Alexandra Hospital, Woodrow Drive, Redditch B98 7UB
Tel: 01527 518490
Email: pgmc@ahc-tr.wmids.nhs.uk, pgmc@worcsacute.wmids.nhs.uk

Clinical Tutor P Holland
PGMC Administrator A Preston
PGMC Manager P Smith
Royal College Tutor M Arafa, V Asokan, J Kwias Jones
Tutor K Nathavitharara

Wythenshawe Hospital Postgraduate Medical Centre

Wythenshawe Hospital, Southmoor Road, Manchester M23 9LT
Tel: 0161 291 2345 Fax: 0161 291 2345
Email: postgrad@fsl.with.man.ac.uk

Manager T Gough
Specialty Tutor A K Deiraniya, D Greenhalgh, S Hawes, D Hickling, D Jones, R D Levy, S Reaney, S A Roberts, B Ryan, K Shearer, T N Stanbridge

York Postgraduate Medical Centre

District Hospital, Wigginton Road, York YO31 8HE
Tel: 01904 454325 Fax: 01904 632811
Email: york.postgrad@clara.co.uk
Website: www.york.postgrad.clara.net

GP Tutor Dr Moroney
Postgraduate Centre Manager Ruth Bycroft
Postgraduate Medical Director J C Thow
VTS Course Organiser Dr Calder, J R Lloyd

Scotland

Lister Postgraduate Institute

11 Hill Square, Edinburgh EH8 9DR
Tel: 0131 650 2609 Fax: 0131 662 0580
Website: www.lister-institute.ed.ac.uk

Adviser to Women Doctors Margaret Chambers
Associate Postgraduate Dean D A A MacLeod, M F Sudlow
Associate Postgraduate Dean (Flexible Training) M Chambers
Associate Postgraduate Dean (General Practice) D Blaney
Associate Postgraduate Dean (Medicine) K R Palmer
Dean of Postgraduate Medicine A L Muir
Dental Co-ordinator P Sutcliffe
Postgraduate Dean S G Macpherson
Postgraduate Dental Adviser H B Mathewson
Postgraduate Tutor D Anderson, A W Blair, P Bloomfield, D Farquhar, P Leslie, J Mcknight, B O'Regan, S Paterson-Brown, H Pleass, G Rhind, C Stewart, G Stockdill, A Thomas

North of Scotland Deanery

North of Scotland Institute of Postgraduate Medical Education, Raigmore Hospital, Inverness IV2 3UJ
Tel: 01463 704347, 01463 704348
Email: elaine.hodgson@scpmde.scot.nhs.uk, helen.whyte@scpmde.scot.nhs.uk, jane.jack@scpmde.scot.nhs.uk, roslyn.munro@scpmde.scot.nhs.uk, shirley.sturrock@scpmde.scot.nhs.uk, tina.bassindale@scpmde.scot.nhs.uk
Website: www.inverness-pgmc.demon.co.uk

Associate Adviser in General Practice N Davis, R Dickie, C Higgott, I Johnston, M Mack, J Nicholls, J O'Rourke, D Pinney, J Ramsey, A Smith, R Spencer-Jones, J Tittmar
Associate Director of Postgraduate Medical Education R Rankin, P K Srivastava
Centre Manager T Bassindale
Clinical Tutor R Collacott, I J T Davies, H M Fattah, B Tregaskis
Director of Postgraduate General Practice Education H I McNamara
Director of Postgraduate Medical Education I J T Davies
GP Training Administrator Jane Jack

Scottish Council for Postgraduate Medical and Dental Education

2nd Floor, Hanover Buildings, 66 Rose Street, Edinburgh EH2 2NN
Tel: 0131 225 4365 Fax: 0131 225 5891
Email: enquiries@scpmde.scot.nhs.uk

Chair P W Howie
Chief Executive Dr Buckley
Dean, East Region R Newton
Dean, North/North East Region Professor Needham
Dean, South East Region S Macpherson
Dean, West Region K Cochran
Education Development Unit R M Harden

University of Glasgow, Department of Postgraduate Medical Education/West of Scotland Deanery

124 Observatory Road, Glasgow G12 8UZ
Tel: 0141 330 6283 Fax: 0141 339 8819
Website: www.show.scot.nhs.uk/scpmde

Administrative Officer E Watt
Assistant Director A Short
Assistant Director (Accreditation & VT) M Kelly
Assistant Director (Audit) M Lough
Assistant Director (CPD) D Kelly
Associate Postgraduate Dean G Orr
Associate Postgraduate Dean (Flexible Training) S F Whyte
Associate Postgraduate Dean (Management Education) Dr Williams
Business Manager F Miller
CPD Officer E Duncan
Director of Postgraduate General Practice Education T S Murray
Finance Officer M Paul
Head of Hospital Training J Allan
Officer Manager (GP) I Robertson
PA to PG Dean/Management Education Co-ordinator L A Pearson
Postgraduate Dean K M Cochran
Postgraduate Tutor S Benbow, R Carachi, D Felix, S K Ghosh, I Gunn, A Henderson, S W Hislop, J M McGregor, D McIntyre, D McQueen, B Maule, R Milroy, G Orr, W Reid, I Ritchie, J Series
SHO Development Team Leader F Dorrian
Specialty Tutor M Aitchison, D B Allan, J G Allan, T J Beattie, F Bryden, R Crawford, D H Gilmore, R A Kell, J Kinsella, C Kirkness, J McHardy, E Melrose, S Miller, C Morran, D O'Reilly, R Rampling, M Roberts, I R C Swan, E Waclawski

Wales

Bridgend Postgraduate Centre

Princess of Wales Hospital, Coity Road, Bridgend CF31 1RQ
Tel: 01656 752081 Fax: 01656 752086
Email: jackiejones@bromer-tr.nhs.uk
Website: bromer-tr.wales.uk

Centre Manager J A Jones
Medicine Tutor D Webb
Postgraduate Organiser M Jones
Specialty Tutor I Ali, A Goodwin, R Hadley, R Hedges, G Thomas

Bronglais Hospital Postgraduate Medical Centre

Bronglais General Hospital, Aberystwyth SY23 1ER
Tel: 01970 635806 Fax: 01970 635806

Postgraduate Organiser D S Jackson
Specialty Tutor H I Atrah, G Boswell, A G Davies, D R Evans, F Gerrard, A D Meredith, R Myles, R Visvanathan, D Walters

Cardiff Postgraduate Medical Centre

University Hospital of Wales, Heath Park, Cardiff CF4 4XW
Tel: 029 2074 2474 Fax: 029 2074 6239

Paediatrics G Smith
PGCM L Coe
Postgraduate Organiser S Davies, P Smith
Specialty Tutor M Hourihan, R Penketh, C Poynton, H Shetty, A Turley, D Webster
VTS Organiser G Morgan
VTSO A Cooper

Clwyd North Postgraduate Medical Centre

Glan Clwyd Hospital, Bodelwyddan, Rhyl LL18 5UJ

CME Tutor R Barrie
PA to Trust Chief Executive Joanne Wood
Specialty Tutor P Elliott, G J Green, D Hay, A P Lake, J G Thomas

Glantawe Postgraduate Medical Centre

Morriston Hospital, Morriston, Swansea SA6 6NL.

Postgraduate Organiser D Price
Specialty Tutor Mr Ali, M Buck, C P Gibbons, D Anthony Jones, B Lervy, A Maddocks, D Thomas, R Westerholme, A J Williams
VTSO M Lewis, P Matthews, S Watts

Gwent Postgraduate Medical and Dental Centre

The Friars, Friars Road, Newport NP20 4EZ
Tel: 01633 238143 Fax: 01633 238123

Assistant Postgraduate Organiser K Alshafi
Dental Adviser A Griffiths
Dental Postgraduate Organiser N Claydon
Postgraduate Centre Manager Sandra Workman
Postgraduate Organiser F J Richardson
Specialty Tutor M Bernard, A Carling, P Dales, M Gregory, W Lewis, M Penney, M Preece, K Tayton, S Webber, A Weerakkody, I Williamson
Sub-Dean and Assistant Medical Director H Jones
VTCO D Dare

Gwynedd Centre for Postgraduate Medical and Dental Education

Gwynedd Hospital, Penrhosgarnedd, Bangor LL57 2PW.
Tel: 01248 384621 Fax: 01248 355819

Centre Manager Maddy Chester
Events Co-ordinator D Lewis
Specialty Tutor D Crawford, J Horn, S Hunter, T Jones, A Roberts, A R Starczewski, C Tilson, P Tivy-Jones, A Valijan, C Walker

POSTGRADUATE MEDICAL CENTRES

Haverfordwest Postgraduate Medical Centre

Withybush General Hospital, Haverfordwest SA61 2PZ
Tel: 01437 773726 Fax: 01437 773736
Email: pgrad@wbush.demon.co.uk
Website: www.wbush.demon.co.uk

Dental Tutor T Griffiths
Manager J Noble
Postgraduate Organiser I Martin, A K N Saleem
Royal College Tutor R Cross, R Howells, P Milewski, V Pulendzan, A Vaishnawi
Specialty Tutor N Jowett, W A Maxwell
Undergraduate Organiser C James
VTSO R W Burns

Llanelli Postgraduate Medical Centre

Prince Philip Hospital, Llanelli SA14 8QF
Tel: 01554 783249 Fax: 01554 749962
Email: alison@llanpgmc.demon.co.uk

CME Associate N Flower
CPD Co-ordinator Carmarthenshire C Jones
Medical Tutor P Avery
Postgraduate Manager A Chapman
Postgraduate Organiser J Jaidev

Merthyr and Cynon Valley Postgraduate Centre

Prince Charles Hospital, Merthyr Tydfil CF47 9DT
Tel: 01685 721721 Ext: 8175, 01685 721721 Ext: 8412
Fax: 01685 721240

Specialty Tutor P Baynham, I B Davies, M De Silva, A Y Izzidien, M A Khaled, M J Maguire, M Winstone

Neath General Hospital Postgraduate Centre

Neath General Hospital, Neath SA11 2LQ

Postgraduate Organiser Dr Mercurius-Taylor
Specialty Tutor Dr Dossa, Dr Pathy, Dr Sinha, Dr Williams

Nevill Hall Postgraduate Centre

Nevill Hall Hospital, Abergavenny NP7 7EG
Tel: 01873 732660 Fax: 01873 732662
Email: r.bentham@virgin.net

Centre Manager Mrs Thompson
Deputy Manager A Jones
GP Tutor D Dare, H P Joshi, J Keely
Librarian Liz Lewis
Postgraduate Centre Manager Mrs Thompson
Postgraduate Organiser P B Khanna, B V Prathibha
Specialty Tutor R L Blackett, H Habboush, N Jenkins, M Kocan, R Pickford, I M Stokes, T H C Williams

Royal Glamorgan Postgraduate Medical Centre

Royal Glamorgan Hospital, Ynysmaerdy, Llantrisant CF72 8XR
Tel: 01443 443571 Fax: 01443 443405
Email: Postgrad@Pr-tr.Wales.nhs.uk

Postgraduate Centre Manager Anne Cowell
Postgraduate Organiser M Foster
Specialty Tutor S Davies, P Fitzgerald, I Hodges, M Hopkin, M Page, S S Palia, A R Ragu Ram, S Vine, D H Williams, R Williams, J Wynne Jones

University of Wales College of Medicine School of Postgraduate Medical and Dental Education

Heath Park, Cardiff CF4 4XN
Tel: 029 2074 7747 Ext: 3927 Fax: 029 2075 4966

Dean T M Hayes
Deputy Director Postgraduate Dental Education Ann M Rockey

Director Postgraduate Dental Education E S Nash
Hon. Senior Lecturer J G Williams
Lecturer J C Bird, S J Brigley, J K Campbell, F C Johnson, Stephanie Williams
Professor Anne Farmer
Senior Lecturer Lynne A Allery, G Parry-Jones, K Richards, A Rogers, D G E Wood
Sub-Dean S A Smail

University of Wales Swansea Postgraduate Medical School

Singleton Park, Swansea SA2 8PP

Lecturer W Y Cheung, R. Roberts
Professor (Cancer Studies) R Leonard
Professor (Experimental Medicine) J M Hopkin
Professor (General Surgery) J N Baxter
Professor (Health Services Research) J G Williams
Professor (Plastic & Reconstructive Surgery) A D McGregor
Senior Lecturer B Lervy, H A Snooks
Visiting Professor (Experimental Medicine) T Shirakawa

Welsh Postgraduate Medical Centre

University of Wales College of Medicine, Heath Park, Cardiff CF4 4XN
Tel: 029 2074 3927

Director and Dean of Postgraduate Studies/Professor of Medical Education T M Hayes

West Wales General Hospital Postgraduate Medical Centre

Francis Well, West Wales General Hospital, Carmarthen SA31 2AF
Tel: 01267 227505 Fax: 01267 223480
Email: sian@carmpostgrad.org.uk
Website: www.carmpostgrad.org.uk

CPD Co-ordinator Dr Jones
Manager's Assistant S Harrison
Postgraduate Centre Manager S Morris
Postgraduate Organiser P Cumber, C Llewellyn-Jones
VTS Course Organiser Dr Lewis

Wrexham Medical Institute

Technology Park Centre, Croesnewydd Road, Wrexham LL13 7YP
Tel: 01978 727451 Fax: 01978 290346
Email: Yvonne.Smith@new-tr.wales.nhs.uk

Postgraduate Centre Manager Yvonne Smith
Postgraduate Organiser D A Parker
Specialty Tutor S Botham, C Cefai, K C Park, P Saul

Northern Ireland

Altnagelvin Hospital Postgraduate Medical Centre

Clinical Education Centre, Altnagelvin Hospitals HSS Trust, Altnagelvin Area Hospital, Londonderry BT47 6SB
Tel: 028 7134 5171

Clinical Tutor P B Devlin, P V Gardiner
Consultant J Beirne, N Corrigan, W Dickey, R Gilliland, D Grace, D Hughes, P Jackson, A McKinney, S Magee, K Moles, M O'Kane, R Thompson, A Wray
Postgraduate Clinical Tutor Dr Gardiner
VTSO P J McEvoy

Antrim Hospital Postgraduate Medical Centre

Antrim Hospital, 45 Bush Road, Antrim BT41 2RL
Tel: 028 9442 4275 Fax: 028 9442 4127

Course Organiser (GP Registrars) Brian Bonnar
Course Organiser (GP SHOs) Jean McCaughern, Michelle Stone

Medical Education Service Manager Beth McAllister
Trust Clinical Tutor Philip Burnside

Belfast Postgraduate Medical Centre

Belfast City Hospital, Lisburn Road, Belfast BT9 7AB

Clinical Tutor P F Keane, Patrick Morrison
VTSO J G Clements

Craigavon Area Hospital Postgraduate Medical Centre

Craigavon Area Hospital Group HSS Trust, 68 Lurgan Road, Craigavon BT63 5QQ
Tel: 028 3861 2399 Fax: 028 3861 2884
Email: pgc@cahgt.n-i.nhs.uk

Clinical Tutor C M Ritchie
Postgraduate Secretary Kelly Jones
VTSO Margaret Chambers

Northern Ireland Council for Postgraduate Medical and Dental Education

5 Annadale Avenue, Belfast BT7 3JH

Tel: 028 9049 2731 Fax: 028 9064 2279
Email: nicpmde@nicpmde.gov.uk
Website: www.nicpmde.com

Administrative Director Ms Roberts
Chair Dr Keegan
Chief Executive/Postgraduate Medical Dean Dr McCluggage
Director of Postgraduate General Practice Education Agnes McKnight
Postgraduate Dental Dean Mr Saunders
Vice-Chairman Dr Jenkins

Isle of Man

Isle of Man Postgraduate Medical Centre

Noble's Hospital, Douglas
Tel: 01624 625516 Fax: 01624 611922
Email: katethatcher@manx.net

Centre Administrator K P Thatcher
Clinical Tutor M J Divers

ROYAL COLLEGES & FACULTIES

Royal Colleges and Faculties

Faculty of Accident and Emergency Medicine (FAEM)

35-43 Lincoln's Inn Fields, London WC2A 3PE
Tel: 020 7405 0318, 020 7405 7071
Email: faem@compuserve.com
Website: www.faem.org.uk

President I W R Anderson
President Elect A McGowan
Dean D Skinner
Registrar Ed Glucksman
RC Anaesthetist J Nolan
RCP Edinburgh P Freeland
Treasurer J Wardrope

Faculty of Pharmaceutical Medicine of the Royal Colleges of Physicians of the United Kingdom

1 St. Andrew's Place, Regent's Park, London NW1 4LB
Tel: 020 7224 0343 Fax: 020 7224 5381
Email: fpm@f-pharm-med-org.uk
Website: www.fpm.org.uk

President Peter Stonier
Registrar C R Franks
Academic Registrar M Page
Administrator K Swanson
Treasurer V Phillips

Faculty of Public Health Medicine of the Royal Colleges of Physicians of the United Kingdom

4 St Andrew's Place, Regent's Park, London NW1 4LB
Tel: 020 7935 0243 Fax: 020 7224 6973
Email: enquiries@fphm.org.uk
Website: www.fphm.org.uk

President Sian Griffiths
Vice-President Stephen Horsley
Registrar Keith Williams
Academic Registrar Ian Harvey
Treasurer Peter Donnelly

Royal College of Anaesthetists

48-49 Russell Square, London WC1B 4JY
Tel: 020 7908 7300 Fax: 020 7813 1876
Email: info@rcoa.ac.uk
Website: www.rcoa.ac.uk

President P Hutton
Vice-President P J Simpson, G Smith
Personal Assistant to President P Bernays
Council Members P Cartwright, G M Cooper, J P T Curran, O R Dearlove, J M Fielden, P Foex, CSB Galasko, MJ Garfield, S Harries, C P H Heneghan, G S Ingram, R M Jones, D M Justins, G N C Kenny, J A Lack, P Lawler, A McGowan, M Morgan, A J Mortimer, AM Rollin, D A Saunders, L Strunin, V Webster, J A W Wildsmith, C Williamson

Royal College of General Practitioners (RCGP)

14 Princes Gate, Hyde Park, London SW7 1PU
Tel: 020 7581 3232 Fax: 020 7225 3047
Email: info@rcgp.org.uk
Website: www.rcgp.org.uk

President Lesley Southgate
Chairman Davide Haslam
Chairman of Scottish Council William Reith
Hon. Secretary Maureen Baker
Council Members Dr Allen, G Archard, K Aswani, D Bailey, C Barber-Lomax, S Bhanot, M Boland, S Brown, Y Carter, J Cox, R Dickie, K Donaldson, A Downes, J Dracass, G S Dyker, P R E Evans, R Fieldhouse, J Foster, A Freeman, D Gardner, C Gerada, J Hayden, P Hewish, C Hughes, M G Jeffries, B Keighley, R Kirk, M Knapton, G Mackinnon, C Martin, G F Morgan, R Mortimer, C Moss, C Nagpaul, S O'Connell, M Pringle, K Prudhoe, J Repper, L Ridsdale, J Rodger, T Scholfield, N Sparrow, A Spooner, C Thomas, J Toby, P Watson, D Whillier, M Wilkinson, S Wright

Royal College of Midwives

15 Mansfield Street, London W1G 9NH
Tel: 020 7312 3535 Fax: 020 7312 3536
Email: info@rcm.org.uk
Website: www.rcm.org.uk

Deputy General Secretary Louise Silverton
General Secretary Karlene Davies

Royal College of Nursing

20 Cavendish Square, London W1G 0RN
Tel: 020 7409 3333 Fax: 020 7355 1379
Website: www.rcn.org.uk

General Secretary Beverly Malone

Royal College of Obstetricians and Gynaecologists (RCOG)

27 Sussex Place, Regent's Park, London NW1 4RG
Tel: 020 7772 6200 Fax: 020 7723 0575
Website: www.rcog.org.uk

President William Dunlop
Vice-President Matthew John Carty, Heather Jean Mellows
Hon. Secretary Allan Templeton
Hon. Treasurer Peter Bowen-Simpkins
Council Members David Hearnshaw Barlow, Alison Bigrigg, Pamela Buck, Andrew Alexander Calder, John Philip Calvert, Alan Dougal Cameron, Linda Dolores Cardozo, Melanie Clare Davies, James Connor Dornan, Andrew John Drakeley, Anthony Dale falconer, Pauline Anne Hurley, Mark David Kilby, Justine Chi Konje, Mylvaganam Kumar Kumarendran, Henry Raymond McClelland, Lorna Muirhead, John Francis Murphy, Patrick Michael (Shaughn) O'Brien, Timothy Graeme Overton, Charles Henry Rodeck, Janice Rymer, Mourad Wahby Seif, John Studd, Sanjay Kumar Vyas, James Johnston Walker, Richard Charles Warren, Martin John Whittle, Charles Stewart Weatherly Wright

Faculty of Family Planning and Reproductive Health Care

19 Cornwall Terrace, Regent's Park, London NW1 4QP
Tel: 020 7935 7149, 020 7935 7196 Fax: 020 7935 8613
Email: mail@ffprhc.org.uk
Website: www.ffprhc.org.uk

President A Bigrigg
Vice-President M Kishen
Hon. Secretary H Massil
Hon. Treasurer C Wilkinson

Royal College of Ophthalmologists

17 Cornwall Terrace, London NW1 4QW
Tel: 020 7935 0702 Fax: 020 7935 9838
Website: www.rcophth.ac.uk

President Paul Hunter
Senior Vice-President Ian Rennie
Vice-President Nicholas Astbury, Stuart Cook, Stuart Roxburgh
Hon. Secretary Brenda Billington
Hon. Treasurer David Ingram

Royal College of Paediatrics and Child Health

50 Hallam Street, London W1W 6DE
Tel: 020 7307 5600 Fax: 020 7307 5601
Email: enquiries@rcpch.ac.uk
Website: www.rcpch.ac.uk

President David Hall
Vice-President Richard Cooke, Alan Craft
Chairman Academic Board Ian Booth
Hon. Secretary Patricia Hamilton
Hon. Treasurer Alun Elias Jones

Royal College of Pathologists

2 Carlton House Terrace, London SW1Y 5AF
Tel: 020 7451 6700 Fax: 020 7451 6701
Email: info@rcpath.org
Website: www.rcpath.org

President John Lilleyman
Vice-President Mansel Haeney, Don Jeffries, James Underwood
Chief Executive Daniel Ross
Registrar Helen Williams
Assistant Registrar Paola Domizio
Treasurer William Marshall
Council Members Berge Azadian, Graham Beastall, Jem Berry, Adrian Bint, Paul Cockroft, Marcela Contreras, Elisabeth Logan, James Lowe, Archie Malcolm, Peter Morgan-Capner, Treen Morris, Adrian Newland, John Old, Michael Penney, Marilyn Pocock, Phillip Quirke, Geoff Ridgway, Grace Smith, Jeremy Thomas, Stephen Wells, Christopher Womack

Royal College of Physicians

11 St. Andrews Place, Regent's Park, London NW1 4LE
Tel: 020 7935 1174 Fax: 020 7487 5218
Email: info@rcplondon.ac.uk
Website: www.rcplondon.ac.uk

Academic Vice-President Chris Evans
Chairman of MRCP(UK) Part 1 Examining Board J A Vale
Chief Executive P Masterton-Smith
Director Clinical Effectiveness and Evaluation Unit Michael Pearson
Director Continuing Professional Development Paveen J Kumar
Director Education L H Rees
Director General Professional Training Ed Neville
Director International Office Keith Prowse
Director Medical Workforce Unit W Rodney Burnham
Registrar Ian T Gilmore
Academic Registrar Charles Plisey
Censor N T Bateman, J A Bell, R Lendrum, GP Mulley
Clinical Vice-President John Wells
Flexible Working Officer Catherine Nelson-Piercy
Harveian Librarian W Ian McDonald
Joint Committee on Higher Medical Training Alexander L Muir
Journal Editor Peter J Watkins
Treasurer John R Bennett

Council Members M W Adler, M Armitage, L R I Baker, B K Bhowmick, C Bunch, M I D Cawley, L Cotter, R H Dowling, L S Elkeles, H C Mitchison, P A Poole-Wilson, R E Pounder

Faculty of Occupational Medicine of the Royal College of Physicians

6 St. Andrews Place, Regent's Park, London NW1 4LB
Tel: 020 7317 5890 Fax: 020 7317 5899
Email: fom@facoccmed.ac.uk
Website: www.facoccmed.ac.uk

President J J W Sykes
Registrar Alex Grieve
Assistant Registrar Ursual Ferriday
Academic Dean John Harrison
Board Member K G M M Alberti, M G Braithwaite, P S Burge, S E L Coomber, N K Cooper, N F Davies, W W Davies, T P Finnegan, E B Macdonald, J Mackie, A J Scott, D I M Skan, D C Snashall
CME Director Keith Palmer
Conference Secretary R Thornton
Training Dean Gordon Parker
Treasurer P Litchfield

Royal College of Physicians and Surgeons of Glasgow

232-242 St Vincent Street, Glasgow G2 5RJ
Tel: 0141 221 6072 Fax: 0141 221 1804
Email: registrar@rcpsglasg.ac.uk

President A R Lorimer
Vice-President A Beattie, D C Smith
Dean of Dental Faculty R T Reed
Registrar R Littlejohn
Treasurer D J Galloway
Council Members J A Burton, H Capell, R Dalling, B Danesh, C R Gillis, G R Gray, J R Hayes, G T McInnes, A E MacKinnon, K J Mitchell, K R Pateson, P A M Raine, A A Renwick, P d'A Semple, J Taylor, J Wurie, A Zoma

Royal College of Physicians of Edinburgh

9 Queen Street, Edinburgh EH2 1JQ
Tel: 0131 225 7324 Fax: 0131 220 3939
Website: www.rcpe.ac.uk

President N D C Finlayson
Vice-President N J Douglas
Dean M L Watson
Registrar N G Dewhurst
Assessor G D O Lowe
Deputy Editor I Bouchier
Editor A Busuttil
Hon. Librarian I M L Donaldson
Representative on General Medical Council A D Toft
Social Convener M M Lees
Treasurer R A Wood
Council Members C A Birt, I W Campbell, C T Currie, P Freeland, D R Hadden, R L Kennedy, I A Laing, J S Legge, T M MacDonald, D Maclean, W MacNee, D M Matthews, D C Moir, R H Smith, A E Thomas, P L Zentler-Munro

Royal College of Psychiatrists

17 Belgrave Square, London SW1X 8PG
Tel: 020 7235 2351 Fax: 020 7245 1231
Email: rcpsych@rcpsych.ac.uk
Website: www.rcpsych.ac.uk

President John Cox
Vice-President A H Ghodse, R G McCreadie
Dean C L E Katona

ROYAL COLLEGES & FACULTIES

Sub-Dean D Bhugra, J S Bolton, M M Robertson, S F Whyte
Registrar M S Shooter
Deputy Registrar S M Bailey, R K Baruah, S A Pidd
Editor D G Wilkinson
Treasurer F E Subotsky
Council Members I D Cormac, F M C Denman, J C Gunn, R Haigh, S Hunter, R Jenkins, R G Jones, I F MacIlwain, R M Murray, R Ramsay, M M Robertson, A C P Sims

Royal College of Radiologists

38 Portland Place, London W1N 4JQ
Tel: 020 7636 4432 Fax: 020 7323 3100
Email: enquiries@rcr.ac.uk
Website: www.rcr.ac.uk

President D Ash
Dean Faculty of Clinical Oncology Dr Buchanan
Registrar A Barrett
Consultant P J Hoskin
Faculty Board Member H J Dobbs, J T Roberts
Treasurer H C Irving
Warden A Horwich
Council Members Professor Adam, P L P Allan, V L Barley, J A Fielding, C J Garvey, C L Harmer, Professor Husband, J R Owen, G J G Rees, M F Spittle

Royal College of Speech and Language Therapists

2-3 White Hart Lane, London SE1 1NX
Tel: 020 7378 1200 Fax: 020 7403 7254
Email: info@rcslt.org

Vice-President Simon Hughes
Chair F Parsons

Editor Jenny Sheridan
Professional Director Kaamini Gadhok

Royal College of Surgeons of Edinburgh

Nicolson Street, Edinburgh EH8 9DW
Tel: 0131 527 1600 Fax: 0131 557 6406
Email: mail@rcsed.ac.uk
Website: www.rcsed.ac.uk

President J G Temple
Vice-President J St C McCormick, Mr Macleod
Chief Executive J R C Foster
Dean and Convener of the Dental Council M C Meikle
Dean Faculty of Dental Surgery J P McDonald
Hon. Secretary I M C Macintyre
Hon. Treasurer A B MacGregor
Council Members C J K Bulstrode, U Chetty, P K Datta, O Eremin, C M Evans, W S Hendry, M Khan, Professor Learmonth, D Lee, J R C Logie, J D Orr, I K Ritchie, J A R Smith, Professor Wheatley

Royal College of Surgeons of England

35-43 Lincoln's Inn Fields, London WC2A 3PE
Tel: 020 7405 3474 Fax: 020 7831 9438
Website: www.rcseng.ac.uk

President Peter Morris
Vice-President Peter R F Bell, George Bentley
Council Members David Barnard, Michael Bishop, Charles D Collins, David J Dandy, Thomas Duckworth, Michael A Edgar, Charles Galasko, Leela Kapila, Peter J Leopard, John Lowry, John S P Lumley, Valerie J Lund, Averil Mansfield, Peter C May, Anne Moore, Anthony R Mundy, Hugh Phillips, Andrew T Raftery, Bernard Ribeiro, R David Rosin, Mr Russell, Tom Treasure

Research Institutions

Bath Institute for Rheumatic Diseases

Trim Bridge, Bath BA1 1HD
Tel: 01225 448444 Fax: 01225 336809

Chair N D Hall

Blond McIndoe Centre

Queen Victoria Hospital, East Grinstead RH19 3DZ
Tel: 01342 313088 Fax: 01342 301701
Email: enquiries@blondmcindoe.com,
enquiriesips@blondmcindoe.com
Website: www.blondmcindoe.com

Chairman Simone Prendergast
Deputy Director Giorgio Terenghi
Appeals Director Caroline Leet
Research Group Leader Robin Martin

British Paediatric Surveillance Unit of the Royal College of Paediatrics and Child Health

50 Hallam Street, London W1W 6DE
Tel: 020 7307 5680 Fax: 020 7307 5690
Email: bpsu@rcpch.ac.uk
Website: www.bpsu.inopsu.com

Chairman of Executive Committee M Preece
Medical Adviser H Kirkbride, J Rahi
Scientific Co-ordinator R Lynn, R Lynn

Cancer Research UK

61 Lincoln's Inn Fields, London WC2A 3PX
Tel: 020 7269 3602 Fax: 020 7269 3644
Website: www.cancerresearchuk.org

Chair Baroness Hayman
Director General Paul Nurse (Head), Gordon McVie
Director of Communications Susan Osborne
Interim CEO Andrew Miller

Cancer Epidemiology Unit: Oxford

The Gibson Building, The Radcliffe Infirmary, Oxford OX2 6HE
Tel: 01865 311933 Fax: 01865 310545
Director V Beral

Clinical Oncology Unit: Churchill Hospital and Institute of Molecular Medicine, Oxford

Blenham Ward, The Churchill Hospital, Oxford Radcliffe Hospital,
Headington OX3 7LJ
Tel: 01865 225310
Hon. Director A Harris

Colorectal Cancer Unit: St Mark's Hospital

St Mark's Hospital, Northwick Park, Watford Road, Harrow HA1 3UJ
Tel: 020 8235 4250 Fax: 020 8235 4277
Hon. Director J Northover

General Practice Research Group: Oxford

Institute of Health Sciences, Old Road, Headington, Oxford OX3 7LF
Tel: 01865 227062 Fax: 01865 227137
Hon. Director M Murphy

Health Behaviour Unit: UCL

University College London Brook House, Dept of Epid & Public
Health, 2-16 Torrington Place, London WC1E 6BT
Tel: 020 6796 642 Fax: 020 7813 2848
Director J Wardle

ICRF Biology of Metastasis Richard Dimbleby Laboratory: St Thomas' Hospital

Cancer Research, Lambeth Palace Road, London SE1 7EH
Tel: 020 7928 9292 Fax: 020 7922 8216
Hon. Head I R Hart

ICRF Breast Cancer Laboratory: Edinburgh

Head W Miller

ICRF Breast Cancer Research Groups, Kings and Guys and St Thomas'

Guy's Hospital, 3rd Floor, Thomas Guy Street, London SE1 9RT
Tel: 020 7955 5000 ext: 4542 Fax: 020 7378 6662
Hon. Director M Richards

ICRF Cancer Medicine Research Unit: Leeds

St James University Hospital, Beckett Street, Leeds LS9 7TF
Tel: 0113 243 3144
Hon. Director P Selby

ICRF Genetic Epidemiology Laboratory: Leeds

Cancer Genetics Building, St James University Hospital, Leeds
LS9 7TF
Tel: 0113 206 9002 Fax: 0113 234 0183
Head D T Bishop

ICRF Laboratories: Institute of Molecular Medicine, Oxford

John Radcliffe Hospital, Headington, Oxford OX3 9DU
Tel: 01865 741166 Fax: 01865 222431
Deputy Director I Hickson
Hon. Director D Weatherall

ICRF Medical Statistics Group: Churchill Hospital, Oxford

Centre for Statistics in Medicine, Institute of Health Sciences, Old
Road Headington, Oxford OX3 7LF
Tel: 01865 226996 Fax: 01865 226962
Head D G Altman

ICRF Molecular Oncology Unit: Imperial College

Hammersmith Hospital, Imperial College School of Medicine, Du
Cane Road, London W12 0MS
Tel: 020 8383 3257
Acting Director N Lemoine

ICRF Molecular Pharmacology Unit: Dundee

Ninewells Hospital, Biomedical Research Centre, Dundee DD1 9SY
Tel: 01382 660111
Hon. Director C R Wolf

ICRF Skin Tumour Laboratory: Royal London Hospital

The London Hospital, 2 Newark Street, London E1 2AT
Tel: 020 7377 7000 Fax: 020 7295 7171
Hon. Head I M Leigh

ICRF/MRC/BHF Clinical Trials and Epidemiological Studies: Oxford

The Harkness Building, Radcliffe Infirmary, Oxford OX2 6HZ
Tel: 01865 557241 Fax: 01865 558817
Hon. Co-Director R Collins, R Peto

RESEARCH INSTITUTIONS

Medical Oncology Unit: Edinburgh

The Western General Hospital, ICRF Medical Oncology Unit, Crewe Road, Edinburgh EH4 2XU
Tel: 020 7537 1000 Fax: 0131 332 8494
Hon. **Director** J F Smyth

Medical Oncology Unit: St Bartholomew's Hospital

45 Little Britain, London EC1A 7BE
Tel: 020 7601 8888 Fax: 020 7796 8979
Hon. **Director** T A Lister

Nuclear Medicine Group: St Bartholomew's and St Mark's Hospitals

Dominion House, 59 Bartholomew Close, London EC1A 9BE
Tel: 020 7601 7153 Fax: 020 7796 3907
Hon. **Director** K E Britton

Institute for the Health of the Elderly

Newcastle General Hospital, Westgate Road, Newcastle upon Tyne NE4 6BE
Tel: 0191 256 3322 Fax: 0191 256 3011
Email: ihe@ncl.ac.uk, L.patterson@ncl.ac.uk

Director J A Edwardson

Institute of Cancer Research, Royal Cancer Hospital

123 Old Brompton Road, London SW7 3RP
Tel: 020 7352 8133
Email: s.neidle@icr.ac.uk
Website: www.icr.ac.uk

Chief Executive P W J Rigby
Dean S Neidle
Director of Research & Head Laboratories (Chelsea) K R Willison
Head of Clinical Laboratories A Horwich
Head of Laboratories at Sutton C S Cooper
Biochemistry M Dowsett
Breakthrough Toby Robins Breast Cancer Research Centre A Ashworth
Cancer Genetics M Stratton
Cell and Molecular Biology C J Marshall
Centre for Cancer and Palliative Care J Corner
CRC Centre for Cancer Therapeutics P Workman
Epidemiology J Peto
Gene Function and Regulation T Enver
Haematology D Catovsky
Leukemia Medicine Research Fund Centre M Greaves
Molecular Carcinogenesis C S Cooper
Paediatric Oncology R Pinkerton
Physics S Webb
Radiotherapy A Horwich
Structural Biology D Barford

Institute of Occupational Medicine

8 Roxburgh Place, Edinburgh EH8 9SU
Tel: 0131 667 5131 Fax: 0131 667 0136

Chief Executive Colin A Soutar

Ludwig Institute for Cancer Research

6th Floor, Glen House, Stag Place, London SW1E 5AG

Tel: 020 7828 0202 Fax: 020 7828 5427

Associate Director A Munro Neville

Marie Curie Research Institute

The Chart, Oxted RH8 0TL
Tel: 01883 722306 Fax: 01883 714375
Website: www.mcri.ac.uk

Chair Nicholas Fenn
Chief Executive, Marie Curie Cancer Care Tom Hughes-Hallett
Hon. **Treasurer** David Gibson

Medical Research Council

20 Park Crescent, London W1B 1AL
Tel: 020 7636 5422 Fax: 020 7436 2665
Email: firstname.surname@headoffice.mrc.ac.uk
Website: www.mrc.ac.uk

Chairman Anthony Cleaver
Chief Executive G K Radda
Member E M Armstrong, J I Bell, William Castell, R M Denton, P Fellner, R Fitzpatrick, D Flint, Chris Henshall, E Johnstone, I MacLennan, Ruth Hall, Alan North, J Pattison, G Richardson, N Rothwell

Glasgow MRC Institute of Hearing Research

Queen Elizabeth Building, Glasgow Royal Infirmary, 16 Alexandra Parade, Glasgow G31 2ER
Tel: 0141 211 4695 Fax: 0141 552 8411

Health Services and Public Health Research Board

Website: www.mrc.ac.uk
Chairman R Fitzpatrick

MRC Anatomical Neuropharmacology Unit

Mansfield Road, Oxford OX1 3TH
Tel: 01865 271865 Fax: 01865 271647
Website: www.mrcanu.pharm.ox.ac.uk
Director P Somogyi

MRC Biochemical and Clinical Magnetic Resonance Unit

John Radcliffe Hospital, Headington, Oxford OX3 9DU
Tel: 01865 221868 Fax: 01865 221112
Website: www.bioch.ox.ac.uk

MRC Biostatistics Unit

Institute of Public Health, University Forvie Site, Robinson Way, Cambridge CB2 2SR
Tel: 01223 330366 Fax: 01223 330388
Website: www.mrc-bsu.cam.ac.uk
Director Nicholas Day

MRC Cambridge Centre for Brain Repair

ED Adrian Building, University Forvie Site, University Way, Cambridge CB2 2PY
Tel: 01223 331160 Fax: 01223 331174
Website: www.brc.cam.ac.uk

MRC Cell Mutation Unit

University of Sussex, Falmer, Brighton BN1 9RR
Tel: 01273 678123 Fax: 01273 678121
Website: www.biols.susx.ac.uk/mrc
Director Bryn Bridges

MRC Centre for Synaptic Plasticity

Department of Anatomy, University of Bristol, School of Medical Sciences, University Walk BS8 1TD

MEDICAL RESEARCH COUNCIL

Tel: 0117 928 7420 Fax: 0117 929 1687
Website: www.bris.ac.uk/depts/synaptic/res2.html
Director G L Collingridge

MRC Child Psychiatry Unit

Institute of Psychiatry, De Crespigny Park, Denmark Hill, London SE5 8AF
Tel: 020 7703 5411 Fax: 020 7708 6800
Acting Director E Taylor

MRC Clinical Sciences Centre

Imperial College School of Medicine, Hammersmith Hospital, Du Cane Road, London W12 0NN
Tel: 020 8383 8250 Fax: 020 8383 8337
Website: www.csc.mrc.ac.uk
Director Chris Higgins

MRC Clinical Trials Unit

222 Euston Road, London NW1 2DA
Tel: 020 7670 4700 Fax: 020 7670 4818
Email: contact@ctu.mrc.ac.uk
Website: www.ctu.mrc.ac.uk
Director J H Darbyshire

MRC Cognition and Brain Sciences Unit

15 Chaucer Road, Cambridge CB2 2EF
Tel: 01223 355294 Fax: 01223 359062
Website: www.mrc-cbu.cam.ac.uk
Director W Marslen-Wilson

MRC Collaborative Centre

1-3 Burtonhole Lane, Mill Hill, London NW7 1AD
Tel: 020 8906 3811 Fax: 020 8906 1395
Head of Antibody Engineering Group S Tarran Jones
Head of Virology Group A Stanley Tyms
Business Development Executive Catherine Kettleborough
Commercial Director David Copsey

MRC Dunn Human Nutrition Unit

Dunn Clinical Nutrition Centre, Hills Road, Cambridge CB2 2DH
Tel: 01223 252700 Fax: 01223 252715
Website: www.mrc-dunn.cam.ac.uk
Director John Walker
Deputy Director Sheila Bingham

MRC Environmental Epidemiology Unit

Southampton General Hospital, Southampton SO16 6YD
Tel: 023 8077 7624 Fax: 023 8070 4021
Director David Barker

MRC Epidemiology and Medical Care Unit

Wolfson Institute of Preventative Medicine, St Bartholomew's & the Royal London School of Med & Dent, Charterhouse Square, London EC1M 6BQ
Tel: 020 7982 6251 Fax: 020 7982 6253
Email: t.w.meade@mds.qmw.ac.uk

MRC Harwell; Radiation and Genome Stability Unit; Mammalian Genetics Unit and UK Mouse Genome Centre

Chilton, Didcot OX11 0RD
Tel: 01235 834393 Fax: 01235 834776
Website: www.har.mrc.ac.uk
Director of Mammalian Genetics Unit and UK Mouse Genome Centre Steve Brown
Director of Radiation and Genome Stability Unit Dudley Goodhead

MRC Health Services Research Collaboration

University of Bristol, Canynge Hall, Whiteladies Road, Bristol BS8 2PR

Tel: 0117 928 7343 Fax: 0117 928 7236
Website: www.epi.bristol.ac.uk/hsrc
Director P A Dieppe

MRC Human Genetics Unit

Western General Hospital, Crewe Road, Edinburgh EH4 2XU
Tel: 0131 322 2471 Fax: 0131 343 2620
Website: www.hgu.mrc.ac.uk
Director Nick Hastie

MRC Human Immunology Unit

Institute of Molecular Medicine, John Radcliffe Hospital, Headington, Oxford OX3 9DU
Tel: 01865 222679 Fax: 01865 222502
Director A McMichael

MRC Human Movement and Balance Unit

Institute of Neurology, National Hospital for Neurology and Neurosurgery, Queen Square, London WC1N 3BG
Tel: 020 7837 3611 Fax: 020 7837 7281
Website: www.ion.ucl.ac.uk/~dizzymrc/hmbu.html
Director J C Rothwell

MRC Human Reproductive Sciences Unit

Centre for Reproductive Biology, 37 Chalmers Street, Edinburgh EH3 9EW
Tel: 0131 229 2575 Fax: 0131 228 5571
Director R P Millar

MRC Immunochemistry Unit

University Department of Biochemistry, South Parks Road, Oxford OX1 3QU
Tel: 01865 275354 Fax: 01865 275729
Website: www.bioch.ox.ac.uk/immunoch
Director K B M Reid

MRC Institute for Environment and Health

University of Leicester, 94 Regent Road, Leicester LE1 7DD
Tel: 0116 223 1600 Fax: 0116 223 1601
Website: www.le.ac.uk/ieh
Acting Director Paul Harrison

MRC Institute of Hearing Research

Unipark, University of Nottingham, Nottingham NG7 2RD
Tel: 0115 922 3431 Fax: 0115 951 8503
Website: www.ihr.mrc.ac.uk
Director Mark Haggard

MRC Laboratory for Molecular Cell Biology

University College London, Gower Street, London WC1E 6BT
Tel: 020 7380 7806 Fax: 020 7380 7805
Website: www.ucl.ac.uk/lmcb

MRC Laboratory of Molecular Biology

Hills Road, Cambridge CB2 2QH
Tel: 01223 248011/402215
Website: www.mrc-lmb.cam.ac.uk
Director Richard Henderson

MRC Molecular Haematology Unit

Institute of Molecular Medicine, John Radcliffe Hospital, Headington, Oxford OX3 9DU
Tel: 01865 222359
Senior Manager David Weatherall

MRC Muscle and Cell Motility Unit

New Hunts House, GKT School of Biomedical Sciences, London Bridge, London SE1 1UL
Tel: 020 7848 6434 Fax: 020 7848 6435
Website: www.kcl.ac.uk
Director R Simmons

RESEARCH INSTITUTIONS

MRC Neurochemical Pathology Unit

Newcastle General Hospital, Westgate Road, Newcastle upon Tyne NE4 6BE
Tel: 0191 273 5251 Fax: 0191 272 5291
Director James Edwardson

MRC Prion Unit

Imperial College School of Medicine at St Mary's, Norfolk Place, London W2 1PG
Tel: 020 7594 3792 Fax: 020 7706 7094
Director J Collinge

MRC Protein Function and Design Unit

Department of Chemistry, University of Cambridge, Lensfield Road, Cambridge CB2 1EW
Tel: 01223 336341
Director Alan Fersht

MRC Protein Phosphorylation Unit

Department of Biochemistry, Medical Sciences Institute, University of Dundee, Dundee DD1 4HN
Tel: 01382 344241 Fax: 01382 223778
Website: www.dundee.ac.uk/biochemistry/mrcppu
Director Philip Cohen

MRC Resource Centre for Human Nutrition Research

Downhams Lane, Milton Road, Cambridge CB4 1XJ
Tel: 01223 426356 Fax: 01223 426617
Website: www.mrc-hnr.cam.ac.uk
Director A Prentice

MRC Social and Public Health Sciences Unit

6 Lilybank Gardens, Glasgow G12 8QQ
Tel: 0141 357 3949 Fax: 0141 337 2389
Website: www.msoc-mrc.gla.ac.uk
Director Sally Macintyre

MRC Social, Genetic and Developmental Psychiatry Centre

Institute of Psychiatry, De Crespigny Park, Denmark Hill, London SE5 8AF
Tel: 020 7740 5121 Fax: 020 7740 5123
Director Peter McGuffin

MRC Toxicology Unit

Hodgkin Building, University of Leicester, PO Box 138 Lancaster Road, Leicester LE1 9HN
Tel: 0116 252 6000 Fax: 0116 252 5616
Acting Director F Cohen

MRC Virology Unit

Institute of Virology, Church Street, Glasgow G11 5JR
Tel: 0141 330 4017 Fax: 0141 337 2236
Website: www.vir.gla.ac.uk
Director D J McGeoch

National Institute for Medical Research

The Ridgeway, Mill Hill, London NW7 1AA
Tel: 020 8959 3666 Fax: 020 8906 4477
Website: www.nimr.mrc.ac.uk
Director John Skehel

Nottingham MRC Institute of Hearing Research

Ropewalk House, 113 The Ropewalk, Nottingham NG1 6HA
Tel: 0115 948 5537 Fax: 0115 948 5568

Physiological Medicine and Infections Board

Website: www.mrc.ac.uk
Chair A M McGregor

Research Management Group

20 Park Crescent, London W1N 4AL
Tel: 020 7636 5422 ext 6227 Fax: 020 7436 6179
Website: www.mrc.ac.uk

Southampton MRC Institute of Hearing Research

Department of Otolaryngology, Royal South Hampshire Hospital, Southampton SO9 4PE
Tel: 02380 637946 Fax: 02380 825611

UK Human Genome Mapping Project Resource Centre

Wellcome Trust Genome Campus, Hinxton Hall, Hinxton, Cambridge CB10 1RQ
Tel: 01223 494500 Fax: 01223 494512
Website: www.hgmp.mrc.ac.uk
Group Leader (Research), Unit Safety Coordinator Ramnath Elaswarapu

Novartis Foundation

41 Portland Place, London W1B 1BN
Tel: 020 7636 9456 Fax: 020 7436 2840
Website: www.novartisfound.org.uk
Director & Secretary to the Executive Council D J Chadwick

Research Institute for the Care of the Elderly

St Martin's Hospital, Combe Down, Bath BA2 5RP
Tel: 01225 835866 Fax: 01225 840395
Website: www.rice.org.uk
President John Grimley Evans
Chairman M Rowe
Director R W Jones

Royal College of Physicians, Clinical Effectiveness and Evaluation Unit

11 St Andrew's Place, Regent's Park, London NW1 4LE
Tel: 020 7935 1174 Ext: 247 Fax: 020 7487 3988
Email: ceeu@rcplondon.ac.uk
Director Michael Pearson (Head)
Manager Jane Ingham

Tavistock Institute of Medical Psychology

Tavistock Centre, 120 Belsize Lane, London NW3 5BA
Tel: 020 7435 7111 Fax: 020 7435 1080
Email: timp@tmsi.org.uk, tmsi@tmsi.org.uk
Website: www.tmsi.org.uk
Company Secretary D Obadina

Wellcome Trust

183 Euston Road, London NW1 2BE
Tel: 020 7611 8888 Fax: 020 7611 8545
Email: infoserve@wellcome.ac.uk
Website: www.wellcome.ac.uk
Chairman Dominic Cadbury
Director Mike Dexter

Government and Statutory Bodies

England

Charity Commission (for England and Wales)

Harmsworth House, 13-15 Bouverie Street, London EC4Y 8DP
Tel: 0870 333 0123 Fax: 020 7974 2300
Email: feedback@charity-commisssion.gov.uk
Website: www.charity-commission.gov.uk

Executive Director Lynne Berry
Public Relations Manager S Amar

Charity Commission - Liverpool

20 Kings Parade, Queens Dock, Liverpool L3 4DQ
Tel: 0870 333 0123 Fax: 0151 703 1555

Charity Commission - Taunton

Woodfield House, Tangier, Taunton TA1 4BL
Tel: 0870 333 0123 Fax: 01823 345003

Commission for Health Improvement

Finsbury Tower, 103-105 Bunhill Row, London EC1Y 8TG
Tel: 020 7448 9200 Fax: 020 7448 9222
Email: information@chi.nhs.uk
Website: www.chi.nhs.uk

Chair of Commission Board Deirdre Hine
Director Peter Homa
Director of Communications Matt Tee
Director of Human Resources Harry Hayer
Director of Nursing Elizabeth Fradd
Director of Operations Steve Graham O B E
Director of Policy and Development Jocelyn Cornwell
Director of Research and Information Bevan Gwyn
Deputy Director of Communications Rebecca Gray
Medical Director Linda Patterson

Committee on Safety of Medicines

Market Towers, 1 Nine Elms Lane, London SW8 5NQ
Tel: 020 7273 0451 Fax: 020 7273 0493

Chairman Alasdair Muir Breckenridge (Head)
Chairman of the Chemistry, Standards and Pharmacy Subcommittee J Midgley
Chairman of the Biological Committee G Duff
Chairman Pharmacovigilance Subcommittee M Kendall
Principal Assessor (Abridged) J A Nicholson
Principal Assessor Chemistry, Pharmacy and Standards Subcommittee L Anderson
Principal Assessor (New Drugs) J A Nicholson
Principal Assessor of Biologicals Subcommittee L Tsang
Principal Assessor (Pharmacovigilance) S Wark
Member of the Chemistry, Standards and Pharmacy Subcommittee R Calvert
Secretary Leslie R Whitbread
Secretary to Pharmacovigilance Subcommittee S Morris

Council for Professions Supplementary to Medicine

Park House, 184 Kennington Park Road, London SE11 4BU
Tel: 020 7582 0866 Fax: 020 7820 9684
Website: www.cpsm.org.uk

Chairman Brian Edwards (Head)
Registrar Michael D Hall
PA to Registrar J Tuxford

Department for Education and Skills

Sanctuary Buildings, Great Smith Street, London SW1P 3BT
Tel: 0870 00 12345 (Switchboard),
0870 000 2288 (Public Enquiry Unit) Fax: 01928 794248
Email: info@dfes.gov.uk, info@dfes.gsi.gov.uk
Website: www.dfes.gov.uk

Minister of State for Lifelong Learning & Higher Education Margaret Hodge MP
Minister of State for School Standards Stephen Timms MP
Parliamentary Under Secretary for Early Years and School Standards Cathy Ashton of Upholland
Parliamentary Under Secretary for Young People and Learning Ivan Lewis MP
Parliamentary Under Secretary of State for Adult Skills John Healey MP
Secretary of State for Education and Skills Estelle Morris MP

Department of Health

Richmond House, 79 Whitehall, London SW1A 2NS
Tel: 020 7210 4850 Fax: 020 7210 5661
Email: dhmail@doh.gsi.gov.uk
Website: www.doh.gov.uk

Chief Dental Officer Margaret Seward
Chief Medical Officer for England Liam Donaldson
Chief Medical Officer for Northern Ireland Henrietta Campbell
Chief Medical Officer for Scotland Mac Armstrong
Chief Medical Officer for Wales Ruth Hall
Chief Nursing Officer Sarah Mullally
Chief Pharmaceutical Officer Jim Smith
Minister of State John Denham MP, John Hutton MP
NHS Chief Executive and Permanent Secretary Nigel Crisp
Parliamentary Under Secretary of State Hazel Blears MP
Parliamentary Under Secretary of State for Public Health Yvette Cooper MP
Parliamentary Under Secretary of State (Lords) Lord Hunt of King's Heath
Secretary of State Alan Milburn MP, Jacqui Smith MP

Departmental Resources and Services Group

Richmond House, 79 Whitehall, London SW1A 2NS
Tel: 020 7210 3000

NHS Executive

Quarry House, Quarry Hill, Leeds LS2 7UE
Tel: 0113 254 5000

Public Health Group

Quarry House, Quarry Hill, Leeds LS2 7UE
Tel: 0113 254 5000

GOVERNMENT & STATUTORY BODIES

Social Care Group

Richmond House, 79 Whitehall, London SW1A 2NS
Tel: 020 7210 3000

National Director for Mental Health Louis Appleby

Department of Social Security (Corporate Medical Group)

Office of the Chief Medical Adviser, Department of Social Security, The Adelphi, 1-11 John Adam Street, London WC2N 6HT
Tel: 020 7962 8702 ext: 28702 Fax: 020 7712 2330
Email: m.aylward@ms41.dss.gsi.gov.uk

Chief Medical Adviser and Director of Medical Policy & Research Mansel Aylward (Head)
Medical Director, War Pensions Medical Services Paul Kitchen
Medical Policy Adviser Mark Allerton, Nick Niven-Jenkins, Susan Reed, Roger Thomas, Peter Wright
Medical Policy Manager Anne Braidwood, Moira Henderson, Philip Sawney, Paul Stidolph
PES to Chief Medical Adviser Tracy Straker

English National Board for Nursing, Midwifery and Health Visiting

Victory House, 170 Tottenham Court Road, London W1T 7HA
Tel: 020 7388 3131 Fax: 020 7383 4031
Website: www.enb.org.uk

Chair Ron De Witt (Head)
Chief Executive Anthony Smith, CBE
Director, Educational Policy/Assistant Chief Executive Rita Le Var
Director Adult & Children's Nursing Jane Marr
Director Human Resources Pauline McEvoy-Williams
Director Mental Health & Learning Difficulties Geoff Bourne
Director Midwifery, Education & Practice Meryl Thomas
Director of Finance & Administration Sam Koroma
Director Primary Health Care Education Tom Langlands

Bristol Office

1st Floor, Goldsmith's House, Broad Plain, Bristol BS2 0JP
Tel: 01179 259143 Fax: 01179 251800

Director of Midwifery Education and Practice M Thomas

Chester Office

BSP House, Station Road, Chester CH1 3DR
Tel: 01244 311393 Fax: 01244 321140

Director of Primary Health Care T Langlands

York Office

East Villa, 109 Heslington Road, York YO10 5ZH
Tel: 01904 430505 Fax: 01904 430309

Director of Adult and Childrens Nursing Jane Marr

General Dental Council

37 Wimpole Street, London W1G 8DQ
Tel: 020 7887 3800 Fax: 020 7224 3294
Email: information@gdc-uk.org
Website: www.gdc-uk.org

President Nairn Wilson
Chief Executive Antony Townsend

General Medical Council

178 Great Portland Street, London W1W 5JE
Tel: 020 7580 7642 Fax: 020 7915 3641
Email: gmc@gmc-uk.org
Website: www.gmc-uk.org

President Graeme Catto
Chief Executive and Registrar of the Council Finlay Scott (Head)
Council Secretariat Lazaros Foukas
GMC Director Dennis Cantwell, Andrew Ketteringham, Isabel Nisbet, Paul Philip, Amanda Watson
Treasurer Shiv Kumar Pande, Denis McDevitt

Appointing Bodies not otherwise represented on Council

Peter Hutton, Deborah Sharp

Members of Council appointed by Universities and Royal Colleges

Faculties of Occupational Health and Public Health Medicine David C Snashall
Queen's University of Belfast Robert W Stout
Royal College of Anaesthetists David J Hatch
Royal College of General Practitioners Mike Pringle
Royal College of Obstetricians and Gynaecologists Naren Patel
Royal College of Ophthalmologists Jeffrey L Jay
Royal College of Psychiatrists Sheila A Mann
Royal College of Radiologists and Pathologists Roderick N MacSween
The Five Colleges of Surgeons and Physicians of England and Scotland Neil J Douglas, Norman MacKay, Averil O Mansfield
Universities of Aberdeen, Dundee, Edinburgh and Glasgow Michael J G Farthing, Denis G McDevitt
Universities of Birmingham, Leicester, Nottingham and Sheffield Peter C Rubin, Hubert F Woods
Universities of Bristol and Southampton Chris Thompson
Universities of Leeds and Newcastle Robert Dickson
Universities of Manchester and Liverpool Roger Green
Universities of Oxford and Cambridge Joan M Trowell
University of London Graeme Catto
University of London and Society of Apothecaries Colin Berry, Robert D H Boyd, Graeme R D Catto
University of Wales Stephen Tomlinson

Members of Council Elected for the Constituency of England, the Channel Islands and the Isle of Man

Karim Admani, Munther Al-Doori, George Alberti, Rachel Angus, James Appleyard, Kumbakonam Bhanumathi, Elizabeth Bingham, Edwin Borman, Cecilia Bottomley, Stephen Brearley, Fiona Caldicott, Sir Cyril Chantler, John Chisholm, Naginah Choudhuri, Jennifer Colman, Caroline Doig, James Drife, David Fergusson, Simon Fradd, Alexandra Freeman, Brian Goss, Pearl Hettiaratchy, Barry Jackson, Alam Khan, Krishna Korlipara, Surendra Kumar, Alexander Macara, Olusola Oni, Shiv Pande, Denis Pereira Gray, Rosalind Ranson, Peter Richards, Wendy Savage, Abulfatah Sayeed, Robert Slack, Andrew Stewart, Hilary Thomas, Nichola Toynton, Fay Wilson, Michael Wilson, Ronald Zeegen

Members of Council Elected for the Constituency of Scotland

Douglas Gentleman, Brian Keighley, Richard Kennedy, Arnold Maran, Fiona Pearsall, Jean Rennie, Anthony Toft

Members of Council Elected for the Constituency of Wales

Malcolm Lewis, Nigel Stott, Jane Wood

Members of the Council Elected for the Constituency of Northern Ireland

Chitra Bharucha, John McCluggage

Nominated by Her Majesty on the advice of Her Privy Council

Arun D Midha, Ijaz Ashraf, Rani Atma, K Barron MP, C Breed MP, M Clark-Glass, Manny Devaux, R Doven, R Evans, Graham Forbes, Sue Leggate, L Macdonald, Angela Macpherson, H Malins MP, Campbell Morton, R Nicholls, Chris Robinson, John Shaw, D Smyth, Winifred Tumim, Eileen Walker, Gareth Wardell MP, Bob Winter, Rodney Yates

General Optical Council

41 Harley Street, London W1G 8DJ
Tel: 020 7580 3898 Fax: 020 7436 3525
Email: goc@optical.org
Website: www.optical.org

Chairman of the Council R Varley
Registrar & Chief Executive Peter Coe
Deputy Chairman and Adviser on Educational Matters E S Page
Hon. Treasurer D T Boyd
PA to Chief Executive M Smith

Health Development Agency

Trevelyan House, 30 Great Peter Street, London SW1P 2HW
Tel: 020 7222 5300 Fax: 020 7413 8900
Email: hda.enquirydesk@hda-online.org.uk
Website: www.hda-online.org.uk

Chair Yve Buckland
Chief Executive Richard Parish
Corporate Resources Carolyn Hughes
Health Improvement Viv Speller
Planning, Partnerships and Communication Jeff French
Research and Information Mike Kelly

Health Service Commissioner (Ombudsman) for England, Scotland and Wales

Millbank Tower, Millbank, London SW1P 4QP
Tel: 020 217 4163, 0845 015 4033 Fax: 020 7217 4000
Email: OPCA.Enquiries@ombudsman.gsi.gov.uk

Director Hilary Bainbridge, Linda Charlton, Nicholas Jordan, David Pinchin
Director of Clinical Advice Carole Seymour
Health Service Commissioner Michael Buckley
Health Service Commissioner (Deputy) Hilary Scott
Information Manager Suzanne Burge

Health Service Commissioner's Office - Scotland

28 Thistle Street, Edinburgh EH2 1EN
Tel: 0131 225 7465, 0845 601 0456 Fax: 0131 226 4447

Investigations Manager George Keil

Health Service Commissioner's Office - Wales

5th Floor, Capital Tower, Greyfriars Road, Cardiff CF10 3AG
Tel: 029 2039 4621, 0845 601 0987 Fax: 029 2022 6909

Investigations Manager Stan Drummond

Human Fertilisation and Embryology Authority

Paxton House, 30 Artillery Lane, London E1 7LS
Tel: 020 7377 5077 Fax: 020 7377 1871
Website: www.hfea.gov.uk

Chairman Suzi Leather (Head)
Acting Chief Executive Hugh Whittall
Authority Member B Almond, S Avery, D Barlow, P Braude, M Coath, C Gosden, A Grubb, H Leese, S Lewis, A McLaren, S Muhammed, S Nathan, M Nazir-Ali, S Nebhrajani, F Shenfield, J Smith, A Templeton, J Tugendhat, L Woods
Deputy Chairman Jane Denton
IT Manager Allan Wright
Personnel & Resources Manager Derek Hodge

Medical Practices Committee

1st Floor, Eileen House, 80-94 Newington Causeway, London SE1 6EF
Tel: 020 7972 2930 Fax: 020 7972 2985
Website: www.open.gov.uk/doh/mpc/mpch.htm

Chairman Ro Day
Committee Member Sadiq Ali, Sarah Jarvis, Michael Jeffries, Bob Jewitt, Linda Pollard, Andrew Procter, Michael Sheldon, Fedelma Winkler
Deputy Committee Secretary & Case Manager Paul Barnett

Medicines Commission

Market Towers, 1 Nine Elms Lane, London SW8 5NQ
Tel: 020 7273 0652 Fax: 020 7273 0121
Email: sue.jones@mca.gsi.gov.uk

Chair Parveen Kumar
Secretary Sue Jones

Medicines Control Agency

Market Towers, 1 Nine Elms Lane, London SW8 5NQ
Tel: 020 7273 0000 Fax: 020 7273 0353
Email: info@mca.gov.uk
Website: www.open.gov.uk/mca/mcahome.htm

Chief Executive (Chair) Keith Jones

Mental Health Act Commission

Maid Marian House, 56 Houndsgate, Nottingham NG1 6BG
Tel: 0115 943 7100 Fax: 0115 943 7101
Email: chiefexec@mhac.trent.nhs.uk
Website: www.mhac.trent.nhs.uk

Chairman Margaret Clayton
Vice-Chair Kamlesh Patel

National Blood Authority

Oak House, Reeds Crescent, Watford WD1 1QH
Tel: 01923 486800 Fax: 01923 486801
Email: submissions@nbs.nhs.uk
Website: www.blooddonor.org.uk

Chairman Mike Fogden (Head)
Chief Executive Martin Gorham
Director of Finance and Administration Barry Savery
Medical Director Angela Robinson
National PR & Donor Services Manager Sue Cunningham

GOVERNMENT & STATUTORY BODIES

Bio Products Laboratory
Dagger Lane, Elstree, Borehamwood WD6 3BX
Tel: 020 8905 1818 Fax: 020 8258 2601

Chief Executive Richard Walker

International Blood Group Reference Laboratory
Southmead Road, Bristol BS10 5ND
Tel: 0117 991 2100 Fax: 0117 991 2002

Director David Anstee

National Blood Service - Birmingham Blood Centre
Vincent Drive, Edgbaston, Birmingham B15 2SG
Tel: 0121 253 4000 Fax: 0121 253 4003

Lead Medical Consultant G S Gabra

National Blood Service - Brentwood Blood Centre
Crescent Drive, Brentwood CM15 8DP
Tel: 01277 306000 Fax: 01277 306132

National Blood Service - Bristol Blood Centre
Southmead Road, Bristol BS10 5ND
Tel: 0117 991 2000 Fax: 0117 001 2002

National Blood Service - East Anglia Centre
University of Cambridge, Long Road, Cambridge CB2 2PT
Tel: 01223 548000 Fax: 01223 458114

National Blood Service - Lancaster Blood Centre
Ashton Road, Royal Lancaster Infirmary, Lancaster LA1 3JP
Tel: 01524 306200 Fax: 01524 306273

National Blood Service - Leeds Blood Service
Bridle Path, Leeds LS15 7TW
Tel: 0113 214 8600 Fax: 0113 214 8737

National Blood Service - Manchester Blood Centre
Plymouth Grove, Manchester M13 9LL
Tel: 0161 251 4200 Fax: 0161 251 4331

National Blood Service - Mersey and North Wales Blood Centre
West Derby Street, Liverpool L7 8TW
Tel: 0151 551 8800 Fax: 0151 551 8896

Consultant Jennifer K M Duguid, A J N Shepherd

National Blood Service - Newcastle Blood Centre
Holland Drive, Barrack Road, Newcastle upon Tyne NE2 4NQ
Tel: 0191 219 4400 Fax: 0191 219 4505

Operations Manager M E Ashford

National Blood Service - North London Blood Centre
Colindale Avenue, Colindale, London NW9 5BG
Tel: 020 8258 2700 Fax: 020 8258 2970

National Blood Service - Oxford Blood Centre
John Radcliffe Hospital, Headington, Oxford OX3 9DU
Tel: 01865 447900 Fax: 01865 447915

National Blood Service - Plymouth Blood Centre
Derriford Hospital, Derriford Road, Plymouth PL6 8DH
Tel: 01752 763870 Fax: 01752 617806

National Blood Service - South Thames Blood Centre
75 Cranmer Terrace, Tooting, London SW17 0RB
Tel: 020 8258 8300 Fax: 020 8258 8453

National Blood Service - Southampton Blood Centre
Coxford Road, Southampton SO16 5AF
Tel: 023 8029 6700 Fax: 023 8029 6760

Head of Production Mike Northcott

National Blood Service - Trent Blood Centre
Longley Lane, Sheffield S5 7JN
Tel: 0114 203 4800 Fax: 0114 203 4911

Operations Manager B Jestico

National Health Service Litigation Authority

Napier House, 24 High Holborn, London WC1V 6AZ
Tel: 020 7430 8700

Medical Director Robert Cocks

National Institute for Biological Standards and Control

Blanche Lane, South Mimms, Potters Bar EN6 3QG
Tel: 01707 654753 Fax: 01707 646854
Email: enquiries@nibsc.ac.uk
Website: www.nibsc.ac.uk

Director G C Schild (Head)
Assistant Director (Administration) R Stewart
Assistant Director (Scientific) Monica Jordan
Bacteriology Division M Corbel
Cell Biology and Imaging Division G Stacey
Endocrinology Division A Bristow
Haematology Division T Barrowcliffe
Immunobiology Division R C Thorpe
Molecular Structure Laboratory C Jones
Retrovirology Divison N Almond
Virology Division P D Minor

National Institute for Clinical Excellence

11 The Strand, London WC2N 5HR
Tel: 020 7766 9191 Fax: 020 7766 9123
Email: nice@nice.nhs.uk
Website: www.nice.org.uk

Chair Michael Rawlins
Chair, Appraisals Committee David Barnett
Chair, Guidelines Committee Martin Eccles
Chief Executive Andrew Dillon
Clinical Director Peter Littlejohns
Communications Director Anne-Toni Rodgers
Communications Assistant Luisa Gill
Planning Resource Director Andrea Sutcliffe

Office for National Statistics

1 Drummond Gate, London SW1V 2QQ
Tel: 08456013034

Director of Business Change Judith Walton
Director of Economic Statistics John Kidgell
Director of Finance & Property Peter Murphy
Director of Human Resources Eryl Williams
Director of Information Age Access Programme John Pullinger
Director of Information Management & Technology Dayantha Joshua
Director of Methodology & Statistical Development Susan Linacre
Director of National Statistics & Policy Division Stephen Penneck
Director of Registration Division Isobel Macdonald-Davies
Director of Social Statistics Karen Dunnell
Economic Secretary to HM Treasury Ruth Kelly
National Statistician Len Cook

Pharmaceutical Services Negotiating Committee

59 Buckingham Street, Aylesbury HP20 2PJ
Tel: 01296 432823 Fax: 01296 392181

Chairman Barry Andrews
Chief Executive Sue Sharpe
Member Gerald Alexander, Noel Baumber, Paul Bennett, Dhiran Bhatt, Roy Carrington, Wally Dove, Steve Duncan, Digby Emson, Michael Grossman, R Hazelhurst, Dilip Joshi, Lisa Martin, Neil Maxwell, Andrew Murdock, Rakesh Panesar, Phil Parry, Hemant Patel, Indrajit Patel, Kirit Patel, Raj patel, Umesh Patel, Chris Paxman, Allen Tweedie, Steven Williams

Public Health Laboratory Service

Headquarters Office, 61 Colindale Avenue, London NW9 5DF
Tel: 020 8200 1295 Fax: 020 8200 7868
Email: bduerden@phls.nhs.uk
Website: www.phls.co.uk

Chair L Turnberg (Head)
Director of the Service Diana Walford
Deputy Director of the Service/Board Secretary Keith M Saunders
Deputy Director of the Service/Medical Director Brian I Duerden
Head of Corporate Affairs Valerie Cain
Head of External Communications Simon Gregor
Head of Finance Larry Harris
Head of Human Resources John H Phipps
Head of Marketing and Commercial Management Robert Chester-Smith
Head of Scientific Development Paul Boseley
Deputy Chair Roger Tabor
Medical and Scientific Postgraduate Dean Stephen Rousseau

Antibiotic Resistance Monitoring and Reference Laboratory

CPHL, 61 Colindale Avenue, London
Email: dlivermore@phls.nhs.uk
Website: www.phls.co.uk

Director David M Livermore

Central Public Health Laboratory

61 Colindale Avenue, London NW9 5HT
Tel: 020 8200 4400 Fax: 020 8200 7874
Email: pborriello@phls.nhs.uk
Website: www.phls.co.uk

Director S P Borriello (Head)
Deputy Director A Christine McCartney

Enteric, Respiratory and Neurological Virus Laboratory

CPHL, 61 Colindale Avenue, London NW9 5HT
Email: dbrown@phls.nhs.uk
Website: www.phls.co.uk

Director David W G Brown

Food Safety Microbiology Laboratory

Headquaters Office, 61 Colindale Avenue, London NW9 5DF
Tel: 020 8200 1295
Email: fbolton@phls.nhs.uk
Website: www.phls.co.uk

Director Eric Bolton

Laboratory of Enteric Pathogens

CPHL, 61 Colindale Avenue, London NW9 5HT
Email: hsmith@phls.nhs.uk
Website: www.phls.co.uk

Acting Director Henry Smith

Laboratory of Hospital Infection

CPHL, 61 Colindale Avenue, London NW9 5HT
Tel: 020 8200 4400 Ext: 4289 Fax: 020 8200 7449
Email: bcookson@phls.nhs.uk
Website: www.phls.co.uk

Director Barry D Cookson

PHLS Communicable Disease Surveillance Centre

Colindale, London NW9 5EQ
Tel: 020 8200 6868

Director Angus Nicoll (Head)
Deputy Director Michael Catchpole
Head of Department Andre Charlett, Barry Evans, Hilary Heine, Elizabeth Miller, Bob Mitchell, Sarah O'Brien, Roland Salmon, John Watson

PHLS Laboratory Group East

Institute of Food Research, Norwich Research Park, Colney Lane, Norwich NR4 7UA
Tel: 01603 506900 Fax: 01603 501188

Head of Department Ulrich Desselberger, Philip Jones, Peder Nielsen, Judith Richards, E Louise Teare
Group Director Philippa White (Head)

PHLS Laboratory Group London and South East

40 Eastbourne Terrace, London W2 3QR
Tel: 020 7725 2757 Fax: 020 7725 2597
Email: r.gross@phls.nhs.uk

Group Director Roger Gross (Head)
Laboratory Director Paul Cockroft, Andrew Lowes, James Q Nash, John Paul, M Shuja Shafi, Jim Wade

PHLS Laboratory Group Midlands

Group Directorate Office, Public Health Laboratory, The Royal Shrewsbury Hospital, Mytton Oak Road, Shrewsbury SY3 8QX
Tel: 01743 261336 Fax: 01743 261292

Head of Department John Gray, Beryl Oppenheim, Keith Struthers, Roderic E Warren
Group Director Roderic E Warren (Head)
Group Business Manager Paul Goble

PHLS Laboratory Group North

Milburn House, E Floor (North Corridor), Dean Street, Newcastle upon Tyne NE1 1LF
Tel: 0191 271 2577 Fax: 0191 261 2578
Email: grpuligh@north.phls.nhs.uk

GOVERNMENT & STATUTORY BODIES

Group Director Nigel F Lightfoot
Laboratory Director Carlisle PHL Margaret A Knowles
Laboratory Director Hull PHL Stewart L Mawer
Laboratory Director Leeds PHL D S Tompkins
Laboratory Director Middlesbrough PHL G Tebbutt
Laboratory Director Newcastle PHL Roger Freeman

PHLS Laboratory Group North West

University Hospital Aintree, Lower Lane, Liverpool L9 7AL
Tel: 0151 529 4900 Fax: 0151 529 4918

Group Director & Laboratory Director Ian D Farrell (Head)
Laboratory Director Eric Bolton, Phil Mannion, Peter A Wright

PHLS Laboratory Group South West

Group Directorate Office, Gloucester Royal Hospital, Great Western Road, Gloucester GL1 3NN

Group Director & Laboratory Director Keith A V Cartwright (Head)
Laboratory Director Owen Carl, Tom Coleman, David A B Dance, Simon Hill, M Jones, Margaret Logan, Sharon Patrick, Terry Riordan, W Andrew Telfer-Brunton

PHLS Laboratory Group Trent

Group Directorate Office, 29 Bridgford Road, West Bridgford, Nottingham NG2 6AU
Tel: 0115 981 5544 Fax: 0115 981 5500
Email: pjwilkinson@trent.phls.nhs.uk

Group Director Peter J Wilkinson (Head)
Laboratory Director Paul Norman, Simon F Pugh, R Andrew Swann, Elizabeth R Youngs

PHLS Laboratory Group Wales

Group Directorate Office, Department of Medical Microbiology and Public Health Laboratory, Heath Park, Cardiff CF14 4XW
Tel: 029 2074 4515 Fax: 029 2074 6403

Acting Laboratory Director Carmarthen Graham Harrison
Group Director & Laboratory Director Tony Howard (Head)
Laboratory Director Aberystwyth Lorna MacFarlane
Laboratory Director Bangor Mark Walker
Laboratory Director Cardiff Tony Howard
Laboratory Director CDSC Roland Salmon
Laboratory Director RHLY D Nicholas Looker
Laboratory Director Swansea Philip Thomas

Quality Assurance Laboratory

Central Public Health Laboratory, 61 Colindale Avenue, London NW9 5HT
Email: organiser@ukneqasmic.win.uk.net
Website: www.phls.co.uk

Director Jerry Snell

Respiratory and Systematic Infection Laboratory

CPHL, 61 Colindale Avenue, London NW9 5HT
Email: rgeorge@phls.nhs.uk
Website: www.phls.co.uk

Director Robert C George

Sexually Transmitted and Blood-Borne Virus Laboratory

CPHL, 61 Colindale Avenue, London NW9 5HT
Email: pmortimer@phls.nhs.uk
Website: www.phls.co.uk
Director Philip P Mortimer

United Kingdom Central Council for Nursing, Midwifery and Health Visiting

23 Portland Place, London W1N 4JT
Tel: 020 7637 7181 Fax: 020 7436 2924
Email: communications@ukcc.org.uk
Website: www.ukcc.org.uk

President A Norman (Head)
Chief Executive/Registrar S Norman
Head of Communications S Skyte
Acting Registrar and Chief Executive Catherine McLaughlin

United Kingdom Transplant

Fox Den Road, Stoke Gifford, Bristol BS34 8RR
Tel: 0117 975 7575 Fax: 0117 975 7577
Email: info@uktransplant.org
Website: www.uktransplant.org.uk

Chair Gwynneth Flower
Chief Executive S J Sutherland
Director of Communications Penny Hallett
Director of Finance Martin Davis
Director of Information and Technology Management David Shute
Head of Corporate Administration Katharyn Burdon
Head of Statistical and Audit Services Mark Belger
Medical Director C J Rudge
Scientific Services Adviser Sue Fuggle

Unrelated Live Transplant Regulatory Authority (ULTRA)

Room 420, Wellington House, 133-155 Waterloo Road, London SE1 8UG
Tel: 020 7972 4812 Fax: 020 7972 4852

Chair Roddy MacSween
Ultra Secretariat Jennie Mullins

Scotland

Blood Transfusion Service Scotland

Ellen's Glen Road, Edinburgh EH17 7QT
Tel: 0131 536 5700 Fax: 0131 536 5701

Acting Director of Finance Anne Maria Hamilton
National Director Angus Macmillan Douglas
National Medical & Scientific Director Ian M Franklin
Personal Assistant Yvonne Todd
Quality Director George Inglis
Supply Chain Director Martin Bruce

Aberdeen and North East of Scotland Blood Transfusion Service

Regional Transfusion Centre, Foresterhill Road, Foresterhill, Aberdeen AB9 2ZW
Tel: 01224 685685 Fax: 01224 695351

Director Henry Hambley

Diagnostics Scotland

21 Ellen's Glen Road, Edinburgh EH17 7QT
Tel: 0131 536 5700 Fax: 0131 536 5701

Director John Allan

NATIONAL BOARD FOR NURSING, MIDWIFERY & HEALTH VISITING FOR SCOTLAND (NBS)

East of Scotland Blood Transfusion Service

Ninewells Hospital, Dundee DD1 9SY
Tel: 01382 645166 Fax: 01382 642551

Director Sam Rawlinson

Edinburgh and South East Scotland Regional Blood Transfusion Service

41 Lauriston Place, Edinburgh EH3 9HB
Tel: 0131 536 5360 Fax: 0131 536 5301

Director Marc Turner

National Science Laboratory

21 Ellen's Glen Road, Edinburgh EH17 7QT
Tel: 0131 536 5700 Fax: 0131 536 5701

Director Chris Prowse

North of Scotland Blood Transfusion Service

Raigmore Hospital, Inverness IV2 3UJ
Tel: 01463 704212 Fax: 01463 237020

Director Peter Forsythe

Protein Fractionation Centre

21 Ellen's Glen Road, Edinburgh EH17 7QT
Tel: 0131 536 5700 Fax: 0131 658 1624

Director Bob Perry

West of Scotland Blood Transfusion Centre

Gartnavel General Hospital, 25 Shelley Road, Glasgow G12 0XB
Tel: 0141 357 7700 Fax: 0141 357 7701

Director Rachel Green

Common Services Agency for the National Health Service in Scotland

Trinity Park House, South Trinity Road, Edinburgh EH5 3SE
Tel: 0131 551 8631, 0131 552 6255 Fax: 0131 552 8651
Website: www.show.scot.nhs.uk/csa

Chair Graeme Millar (Head)
Vice-Chair Fiona Stephenson
Director of Finance Eric Harper Gow
Director of Human Resources Janine Emerson
Head of Public Affairs & Communications Fiona Stewart
Executive Co-ordinator Ruth Wallace
General Manager Francis Gibb
Member Janine Emerson, Francis Gibb, Eric Harper Gow, Jane Jolly, Christine Lenihan, Gordon Lounsbach, Jim McNeillage, Linda McPherson, Fiona Stephenson

Central Legal Office

Trinity Park House, South Trinity Road, Edinburgh EH5 3SE
Tel: 0131 552 6255 Fax: 0131 551 3957

Legal Adviser Ranald Macdonald

Information and Statistics Division

Trinity Park House, South Trinity Road, Edinburgh EH5 3SQ
Tel: 0131 551 8899 Fax: 0131 552 1392

Director Richard Copland

National Services Division

Trinity Park House, South Trinity Road, Edinburgh EH5 3SE
Tel: 0131 551 8136, 0131 552 6255 Fax: 0131 551 2855
Email: deidre@nsd.csa.scot.nhs.uk, deirdre@nsd.csa.scot.nhs.uk

Director Deirdre Evans

Practitioner Services Division

Trinity Park House, South Trinity Road, Edinburgh EH5 3SE
Tel: 0131 551 8106 Fax: 0131 552 0742

Assistant Director Bob Anderson
Acting Director Richard Copland

Scottish Centre for Infection and Environmental Health

Clifton House, Clifton Place, Glasgow G3 7LN
Tel: 0141 300 1100 Fax: 0141 300 1170

Director Ian Jones

Scottish Health Service Centre

Crewe Road South, Edinburgh EH2 2LF
Tel: 0131 623 2500 Fax: 0131 315 2369

Director J Lyelle

Scottish Healthcare Supplies

Trinity Park House, South Trinity Road, Edinburgh EH5 3SE
Tel: 0131 552 6255 Fax: 0131 552 6536

Director Steve Atherton

Health Education Board for Scotland

Woodburn House, Canaan Lane, Edinburgh EH10 4SG
Tel: 0131 536 5500 Fax: 0131 536 5501
Website: www.hebs.com

Chair Lesley Hinds (Head)
Director of Education and Training Peter Gumbrell
Director of Finance and Support Services Alan H Crawford
Director of Health Information James Inglis
Director of Programmes and Communications Lindsay MacHardy
Acting Director of Research and Evaluation Erica Wimbush

Mental Welfare Commission for Scotland

K Floor, Argyle House, 3 Lady Lawson Street, Edinburgh EH3 9SH
Tel: 0131 222 6111 Fax: 0131 222 6112, 0131 222 6113
Email: support@mwcscot.co.uk
Website: www.mwcscot.org.uk

Director J A T Dyer (Head)
Medical Commissioner A Lodge, M Osborn
Secretary Alison McRae

MRC Technology Scotland

Crewe Road South, Edinburgh EH4 2LF
Tel: 0131 623 2559 Fax: 0131 623 2555

Director M Dalrymple

National Board for Nursing, Midwifery and Health Visiting for Scotland (NBS)

22 Queen Street, Edinburgh EH2 1NT
Tel: 0131 226 7371 Fax: 0131 225 9970
Email: margaret.alexander@nbs.org.uk
Website: www.nbs.org.uk

Chair Margaret Alexander
Chief Executive David Benton
Board Secretary David Ferguson
Deputy Chair Linda Sydie

GOVERNMENT & STATUTORY BODIES

National Health Service Tribunal

40 Craiglockhart Road North, Edinburgh E14 1BT
Tel: 0131 443 2575 Fax: 0131 443 2575

Chairman Malcolm G Thomson
Clerk to the NHS Tribunal W Bryden

Scottish Executive Health Department

St Andrews House, Regent Road, Edinburgh EH1 3DG
Tel: 0131 244 2410 Fax: 0131 244 2162
Email: ceu@scotland.gov.uk

Chief Executive Trevor Jones

Chief Scientist's Office

Scottish Executive Health Department, St Andrews House, Edinburgh EH1 3DG
Tel: 0131 244 2248 Fax: 0131 244 2285

Director Alison M Svaull (Head)
Chief Scientist Graham R D Calto

Scottish Medical Practices Committee

Scottish Health Service Centre, Crewe Road South, Edinburgh EH4 2LF
Tel: 0131 623 2540 Fax: 0131 623 2518
Email: committee@shsc.csa.scot.nhs.uk

Chairman G McIntosh (Head)
Committee Secretary Elsie Horobin

Wales

NHS Directorate

National Assembly for Wales, Cathys Park, Cardiff CF10 3NQ

Director, NHS Wales Ann Lloyd
Chief Medical Officer Ruth Hall
Health and Social Services Minister Jane Hutt

Welsh Blood Service

Ely Valley Road, Talbot Green, Pontyclun CF72 9WB
Tel: 01443 622088 Fax: 01443 622199

Donor Recruitment Officer Trudi Evans

Welsh National Board for Nursing, Midwifery and Health Visiting

2nd Floor, Golate House, 101 St. Mary Street, Cardiff CF10 1DX
Tel: 029 2026 1400 Fax: 029 2026 1499
Email: info@wnb.org.uk
Website: www.wnb.org.uk

Chief Executive David A Ravey
Director of Business Services Wendy Fawcus
Director of Quality and Standards Thomas J Moore

Northern Ireland

Department of Health, Social Services and Public Safety

Castle Buildings, Stormont, Belfast BT4 3PP

Tel: 028 9052 0500
Website: dhsspsni.gov.uk

Chief Executive C Thompson
Permanent Secretary Mr Gowdy

Dental Services

Castle Buildings, Stormont, Belfast BT4 3PP
Tel: 028 9052 0500

Chief Dental Officer D Wilson

Health and Personal Social Services Management Group

Dundonald House, Upper Newtownards, Belfast BT4 3SF
Tel: 028 9052 0500

Chief Executive of Health Estates Agency R H Browne
Director Modernisation Unit D A Baker
Director of Child and Community Care L Frew
Director of Human Resources D Bingham
Director of Planning and Performance Management J McGrath
Director of Secondary Care B Grzymek
Acting Director J Thompson
Deputy Secretary P Simpson

Medical and Allied Services

Castle Buildings, Stormont, Belfast BT4 3PP
Tel: 028 9052 0500

Chief Medical Officer H Campbell
Chief Nursing Officer J E Hill

Pharmaceutical Advice and Services

Castle Buildings, Stormont, Belfast BT4 3PP
Tel: 028 9052 0500

Chief Pharmaceutical Officer N Morrow
Director Finance A Hamilton
Director of Information Systems G Williams
Director Personnel & Corporate Services P A Conliffe
Director Public Safety, Strategic Planning & Information & Analysis Unit D McMahon
Deputy Secretary D Hill

Social Services Inspectorate

Castle Buildings, Stormont, Belfast BT4 3PP
Tel: 028 9052 0500

Chief Inspector Paul Martin

National Board for Nursing, Midwifery and Health Visiting for Northern Ireland (NBNI)

Centre House, 79 Chichester Street, Belfast BT1 4JE
Tel: 028 9023 8152 Fax: 028 9033 3298
Email: enquiries@nbni.n-i.nhs.uk, enquiries@nbni.n.i.nhs.uk
Website: www.n-i.nhs.uk/NBNI/index.htm

Chief Executive O D'A Slevin
Director of Finance and Administration E N Thom

Northern Ireland Blood Transfusion Service

Belfast City Hospital Complex, Lisburn Road, Belfast BT9 7TS
Tel: 028 9032 1414 Fax: 028 9043 9001

Donor Administration Manager Penny Toal
Donor Services Manager Charles Kinney
Nurse Manager Shelagh Reilly
Recruitment and Organisation Manager Paull McElkerney

NORTHERN IRELAND CENTRAL SERVICES AGENCY FOR THE HEALTH & SOCIAL SERVICES

Northern Ireland Central Services Agency for the Health and Social Services

25-27 Adelaide Street, Belfast BT2 8FH
Tel: 028 9032 4431 Fax: 028 9023 2304
Website: www.csa.n-i.nhs.uk

Chair Brian Carlin (Head)
Chairman Dental Statutory Committee W K Graham
Chairman Medical Statutory Committee J E Donnelly
Chairman Ophthalmic Statutory Committee B Mooney
Chairman Pharmaceutical Statutory Committee T Hannawin
Chief Executive Stephen Hodkinson
Director of Family Practitioner Services Paula Sheils

Director of Finance Paul Gick
Director of General Dental Services Ivan McCappin
Director of Human Resources Hugh McPoland
Director of Legal Services Alfy Maginness
Director of NICARE Colin Sullivan
Head of Pharmacy Services Katheryn Turner
Operational Director of Research and Development Michael Neely
Regional Supplies Director Teresa Molloy

NIHPSS Supplies Service

Supplies Distribution Centre, Boucher Crescent, Belfast BT12 6HU
Tel: 028 9066 7799 Fax: 028 9066 8989

Director Teresa Molloy
PA to Chief Executive Amanda Mills

Coroners

England

The Queen's Household

7 Orchard Rise, Richmond TW10 5BX
Tel: 020 8876 5386

Coroner J D K Burton

Bath and North East Somerset, Bristol City, North Somerset and South Gloucestershire

Coroner's Court, Backfields, Off Upper York Street, Bristol BS2 8QP
Tel: 01272 428322 Fax: 01272 445492

Coroner Dr Forrest

Bedfordshire and Luton

Coroner's Office, Greyfriars Police Station, Bedford MK40 1HR
Tel: 01234 275263 Fax: 01234 275266

Coroner David S Morris

Berkshire, East District

Messrs Coleman, 27 Marlow Road, Maidenhead SL6 7AE
Tel: 01628 631051 Fax: 01628 622106
Email: coroner@colemans.co.uk

Coroner Peter Bedford

Berkshire, Reading District

Vane House, Nuffield, Henley-on-Thames RG9 5RT
Tel: 01491 641444
Email: coroner@reading.gov.uk

Coroner A J Pim

Berkshire, West District

The Old Rectory, Church Road, Shaw, Newbury RG14 2DR
Tel: 01635 40181

Coroner C Hoile

Blackburn, Hyndburn and Ribble Valley

7 Richmond Terrace, Blackburn BB1 7BB
Tel: 01254 263091 Fax: 01254 681442

Coroner Michael Singleton

Bournemouth, Poole and Eastern District

The Coronor's Court, Stafford Road, Bournemouth BH1 IPA
Tel: 01202 310049 Fax: 01202 780423
Email: sheriff@bournemouth.gov.uk

Coroner S S Payne

Brighton and Hove District

Coroner's Office, Woodvale, Lewes Road, Brighton BN2 3QB
Tel: 01273 292046

Coroner Miss Hamilton Deeley

Buckinghamshire District

Courtyard Offices, 3 High Street, Marlow SL7 1AU
Tel: 01438 757000, 01628 476988 Fax: 01628 890857

Coroner R A Hulett

Cambridgeshire, North and East District

Messrs. Dawbarns, 1 York Row, Wisbech PE13 1EA
Tel: 01945 461456 Fax: 01945 461364

Coroner W R Morris

Cambridgeshire, South and West District

11-13 Ferrars Road, Huntingdon PE18 6DQ
Tel: 01480 456110 Fax: 01296 67543

Coroner David Morris

Cheshire, Halton and Warrington

57 Winmarleigh Street, Warrington WA1 1LE
Tel: 01925 444216 Fax: 01925 444219

Coroner Nicholas Rheinberg

City of London District

Coroner's Court, Milton Court, 2nd Floor, Moor Lane, London EC2Y 2BJ
Tel: 020 7601 2714 Fax: 020 7332 1559

Coroner Paul Matthews

Cornwall, East District

14 Barrack Lane, Truro TR1 2DW
Tel: 01872 261612 Fax: 01872 262738

Coroner Emma Carlyon

Cornwall, Western District

14 Barrack Lane, Truro TR1 2DW
Tel: 01872 261612 Fax: 01872 262738

Coroner Edward Carlyon

County of Herefordshire

36-37 Bridge Street, Hereford HR4 9DJ
Tel: 01432 355301 Fax: 01432 356619
Email: herefordcoroner@lambecorner.co.uk

Coroner D Halpern

Cumbria, Furness District

Central Police Station, Market Street, Barrow-in-Furness LA14 2LE
Tel: 01229 848966 Fax: 01229 824705

Coroner I Smith

Cumbria, North Eastern District

19 Castle Street, Carlisle CA3 8SY
Tel: 01228 525195 Fax: 01228 511051

Coroner I H Morton

Cumbria, Southern District

116 Stricklandgate, Kendal LA9 4QA
Tel: 01539 721945 Fax: 01539 740640

Coroner T C Prickett

Cumbria, Western District

38/42 Lowther Street, Whitehaven CA28 7JU
Tel: 01946 692461 Fax: 01946 692015

Coroner J A H Walker

Darlington and South Durham

5 Market Place, Bishop Auckland DL14 7NW
Tel: 01388 762466 Fax: 01388 607899

Coroner C E Penna

Derbyshire, Derby and South Derbyshire District

St. Katherine's House, 18 St. Mary's Wharf, Mansfield Road, Derby DE1 1TQ
Tel: 01332 613104 Fax: 01332 294942

Coroner P G Ashworth

CORONERS

Derbyshire, High Peak District
10 Buxton Road, Hazel Grove, Stockport SK7 6AD
Tel: 0161 419 9626 Fax: 0161 419 9604

Coroner C G Rushton

Derbyshire, Scarsdale District
71 Saltergate, Chesterfield S40 1JS
Tel: 01246 201391 Fax: 01246 221081

Coroner T Kelly

Devon, Plymouth and South West Devon District
3 The Crescent, Plymouth PL1 3AB
Tel: 01752 204636 Fax: 01752 203503
Email: nigel.meadows@plymouth.gov.uk

Coroner Dr Meadows

Devon, South Devon and Torbay District
Messrs. Kitsons, 2 Vaughan Parade, Torquay TQ2 5EF
Tel: 01803 296221 Fax: 01803 296823

Coroner H M Turner

Dorset, Western District
Outhays House, 2 The Plocks, Blandford Forum DT11 7QB
Tel: 01258 453733/5 Fax: 01258 455747

Coroner M C Johnston

Durham, Northern District
Post Office House, Elliott Street, Crook DH15 8QH
Tel: 01388 767770

Coroner Mr Tweddle

East Sussex District
28/29 Grande Parade, St Leonards on Sea TN37 6DR
Tel: 01424 200144 Fax: 01424 200145

Coroner A Craze

Essex, No.1 District
The Old Manse, 3 Roxwell Road, Chelmsford CM1 2LY
Tel: 01245 347016 Fax: 01245 267742

Coroner Mrs Beasley-Murray

Essex, No. 2 District
2 Little Haylands, 99 High Road, Chigwell IG7 6QQ
Tel: 020 8502 6337 Fax: 020 8502 6337

Coroner P J Dean

Exeter and Greater Devon District
Raleigh Hall, Fore Street, Topsham, Exeter EX3 0HY
Tel: 01392 876575 Fax: 01392 876574

Coroner R J Van Oppen

Gloucestershire, Cheltenham District
109 Promenade, Cheltenham GL50 1NW
Tel: 01242 221064 Fax: 01242 226575

Coroner A L Maddrell

Gloucestershire, Gloucester District
Wellingtons, Solicitors, 57 Westgate Street, Gloucester GL1 1JS
Tel: 01452 525164 Fax: 01452 307935

Coroner D M Gibbons

Greater London, Eastern District
Coroner's Court, Queen's Road, London E17 8QP
Tel: 020 8520 7246 Fax: 020 8521 0096

Coroner E Stearns

Greater London, Inner North London District
St. Pancras Coroner's Court, Camley Street, London NW1 0PP
Tel: 020 7387 4882, 020 7987 3614

Coroner Dr Hungerford

Greater London, Inner South London District
HM Coroner's Court, 1 Tennis Street, London SE1 1YD
Tel: 020 7407 5611, 020 8691 8832 (Greenwich office)
Fax: 020 7378 8401

Coroner Selena Lynch

Greater London, Inner West London District
Coroner's Court, 65 Horseferry Road, London SW1P 2ED
Tel: 020 7228 6044 (Merton & Wandsworth Office),
020 7828 0041, 020 7834 6515 Fax: 020 7828 2837

Coroner P A Knapman

Greater London, Northern District
Coroner's Court, Myddelton Road, Hornsey, London N8 7PY
Tel: 020 8348 4411 Fax: 020 8347 5229
Email: hmcwd@freenet.co.uk

Coroner W F G Dolman

Greater London, Southern District
Croydon Coroner's Court, Barclay Road, Croydon CR9 3NE
Tel: 020 8681 5019 Fax: 020 8686 3491

Coroner Roy N Palmer

Greater London, Western District
Coroner's Court, 25 Bagley's Lane, London SW6 2QA
Tel: 020 7371 9935 Fax: 020 7384 2762

Coroner Alison Thompson

Greater Manchester, Manchester District
Fifth Floor, City Magistrate's Court, Crown Square, Manchester M60 1RP
Tel: 0161 819 5666

Coroner L N Gorodkin

Greater Manchester, North District
Fourth Floor, Telegraph House, Baillie Street, Rochdale OL16 1QY
Tel: 0161 624 4971, 01706 49922 Fax: 01706 40720

Coroner B Williams

Greater Manchester, South District
10 Greek Street, Stockport SK3 8AB
Tel: 0161 476 0971 Fax: 0161 476 0972
Email: john.pollard@stockport.gov.uk

Coroner J S Pollard

Greater Manchester, West District
Paderborn House, Civic Centre, Howell Croft North, Bolton BL1 1JW
Tel: 01204 527322 Fax: 01204 387674

Coroner A Cotter

Hampshire, Central District
19 St. Peter Street, Winchester SO23 8BU
Tel: 01962 84388 Fax: 01962 842300

Coroner G A Short

Hampshire, North East District
76 Bounty Road, Basingstoke RG21 1BZ
Tel: 01256 22911 Fax: 01256 27811

Coroner A M Bradley

CORONERS

Hampshire, Portsmouth and South East District
15 Landport Terrace, Portsmouth PO1 2QS
Tel: 023 9282 2311 Fax: 023 9275 3611

Coroner J R Kenroy

Hampshire, Southampton and New Forest District
Woodford & Ackroyd, Solicitors, The Director General's House, Rockstone Place, Southampton SO1 2EP
Tel: 023 8032 1000 Fax: 023 8032 1001

Coroner Dr Wiseman

Hartlepool District
155 York Road, Hartlepool TS26 9EQ
Tel: 01429 274732 Fax: 01429 260199

Coroner C W M Donnelly

Hertfordshire, Hertford District
Room 18, County Hall, Hertford SG13 8DE
Tel: 01992 555545 Fax: 01992 555495

Coroner A Lawson

Hertfordshire, Hitchin District
The Coroner's Unit, Leahoe House, County Hall, Hereford SG13 8DE
Tel: 01992 556608 Fax: 01992 556602
Email: john.viek@virgin.net

Coroner J A S Vick

Hertfordshire, West District
West Hertforshire Coroner's Unit, Leahoe House, County Hall, Hertford SG13 8EH
Tel: 01992 556608 Fax: 01992 556602

Coroner E G Thomas

Isle of Wight District
The Coroner's Office, 3-9 Quay Street, Newport PO30 5BB
Tel: 01983 520697 Fax: 01983 520697

Coroner Dr Mathews

Isles of Scilly District
20 Lelant Meadows, Lelant, St. Ives TR26 3JS
Tel: 01736 756287

Coroner D W Pepperell

Kent, Ashford and Shepway District
Elphicks Farmhouse, Hunton, Maidstone ME15 0SB
Tel: 01622 820412 Fax: 01622 820412

Coroner Rachel Redman

Kent, North West District
The White House, 1 Hook Lane, Welling DA16 2DJ
Tel: 020 8306 2222 Fax: 020 8306 2221

Coroner R L Hatch

Kent, Thanet District
5 Lloyds Road, Broadstairs CT10 1HX
Tel: 01843 863260 Fax: 01843 603927

Coroner R M Cobb

Kingston upon Hull and East Riding of Yorkshire District
Coroner's Court, Essex House, Manor Street HU1 1YU
Tel: 01482 613009, 01482 613011 Fax: 01482 613020

Coroner G M Saul

Lancashire, Blackpool and Fylde District
283 Church Street, Blackpool FY1 3PG
Fax: 01253 751055

Coroner S G Lee

Lancashire, East District
6a Hargreaves Street, Burnley BB11 1ES
Tel: 01282 438446 Fax: 01282 446525

Coroner Dr Taylor

Lancashire, North District
2 Castle Hill, Lancaster LA1 1YR
Tel: 01524 32484 Fax: 01524 35945

Coroner G C Howson

Lancashire, Preston and South-West Lancashire District
Coroner's Court, Lawson Street, Preston PR1 2QT
Tel: 01772 821788 Fax: 01772 828755

Coroner M H McCann

Leicestershire, Leicester City and South Leicestershire District
Room 6, Town Hall, Town Hall Square, Leicester LE1 9BG
Tel: 0116 225 2534/5 Fax: 0116 225 2537
Email: jms@freeboustell.co.uk

Coroner J M Symington

Leicestershire, Rutland and North Leicestershire District
39 Granby Street, Loughborough LE11 3DU
Tel: 01509 238 8222

Coroner T Kirkman

Lincolnshire, Boston and Spalding District
c/o County Hall, Boston PE21 6LX
Tel: 01205 351114 Fax: 01205 311234

Coroner M Taylor

Lincolnshire, Grantham District
94 West Parade, Lincoln LN1 1JZ
Tel: 01522 560055 Fax: 01522 560055

Coroner R Atkinson

Lincolnshire, Lincoln District
94 West Parade, Lincoln LN1 1JZ
Tel: 01522 530055 Fax: 01522 530055

Coroner R Atkinson

Lincolnshire, North Lincolnshire and Grimsby District
Cleethorpes Town Hall, Knoll Street, Cleethorpes DN35 8LN
Tel: 01472 324005 Fax: 01472 324007

Coroner J S Atkinson

Lincolnshire, Sleaford District
27-31 Northgate, Sleaford NG34 7BW
Tel: 01529 302800 Fax: 01529 413703

Coroner Dr Warnes

Lincolnshire, Spilsby District
Thimbleby Fisher Solicitors, Lindum House, 10 Queen Street, Spilsby PE23 5JE
Tel: 01790 752219 Fax: 01790 752427
Email: ThimblebyFisher@yahoo.co.uk

Coroner S P G Fisher

CORONERS

Lincolnshire, Stamford District
10 Briggate Quay, Whittlessy, Peterborough PE7 1DH
Tel: 01733 351010 Fax: 01733 351141

Coroner G S Ryall

Merseyside, Knowsley, St. Helens and Sefton District
County Coroners Court, Gordon House, 3/5 Leicester Street, Southport PR9 0ER
Tel: 01704 531643 Fax: 01704 534321

Coroner C Sumner

Merseyside, Liverpool District
H M Coroners Court, The Cotton Exchange, Old Hall Street, Liverpool L3 9UF
Tel: 0151 233 4700 Fax: 0151 233 4710

Coroner Andre J A Rebello

Merseyside, Wirral District
Midland Bank Buildings, Grange Road, West Kirby, Wirral CH48 4EB
Tel: 0151 625 6538 Fax: 0151 625 7727

Coroner C W Johnson

Mid Kent and Medway
Whitehead, Monckton & Co., Solicitors, 72 King Street, Maidstone ME14 1BL
Tel: 01622 698033
Email: rogersykes@whitehead-monkton.co.uk

Coroner R J Sykes

Milton Keynes
10 Market Square, Buckingham MK18 1NJ
Tel: 01280 822217 Fax: 01280 813269

Coroner R H G Corner

Newbury District
The Old Rectory, Church Road, Shaw, Newbury RG12 2DR
Tel: 01635 40181 Fax: 01635 521964

Coroner C Hoile

Norfolk, Great Yarmouth District
6 South Quay, Great Yarmouth NR30 2QJ
Tel: 01493 855555 Fax: 01493 330055

Coroner K M Dowding

Norfolk, King's Lynn District
Messrs. Dawbarns, 1 York Row, Wisbech PE13 1EA
Tel: 01945 461456 Fax: 01945 461364

Coroner W R Knowles

North Yorkshire, Eastern District
4 Old Malton Gate, Malton YO17 0EQ
Tel: 01653 600070 Fax: 01653 600049

Coroner M D Oakley

North Yorkshire, Western District
Bilton House, 31 Park Parade, Harrogate YO7 1ET
Tel: 01423 705587 Fax: 01423 705587

Coroner J D Cave

Northamptonshire District
300 Wellingborough Road, Northampton NN1 4EP
Tel: 01604 624732 Fax: 01604 232282

Coroner A Pember

Northumberland, North District
4 Quay Walls, Berwick-upon-Tweed TD15 1HD
Tel: 01289 304318, 01289 306724 Fax: 01289 330323

Coroner I G McCreath

Northumberland, South District
1 Stanley Street, Blyth NE24 2BS
Tel: 01670 354777 Fax: 01670 355951

Coroner C B Gallon

Norwich, Diss and Dereham District
William House, 19 Bank Street, Norwich NR2 4FS
Tel: 01603 666588 Fax: 01603 666588

Coroner W J Armstrong

Nottinghamshire District
50 Carrington Street, Nottingham NG1 7FG
Tel: 0115 941 2332 Fax: 0115 950 0141

Coroner Nigel D Chapman

Oxfordshire District
Southern House, 1 Cambridge Terrace, Oxford OX1 1RR
Tel: 01865 721451 Fax: 01865 251804

Coroner Dr Gardiner

Peterborough District
10 Briggate Quay, Whittlesey, Peterborough PE7 1DH
Tel: 01733 203418 Fax: 01733 351141

Coroner G S Ryall

Shropshire, Mid and North West District
Lythwood House, Lyth Hill Road, Bayston Hill, Shrewsbury SY3 0AU
Tel: 01743 874300 Fax: 01743 874300

Coroner Dr Crawford-Clarke

Shropshire, South District
18 Broad Street, Ludlow SY8 1NG
Tel: 01584 873918/9 Fax: 01584 876787

Coroner A F T Sibcy

Somerset, Eastern District
Faulkners Solicitors, Argyll House, Bath Street, Frome BA11 1DP
Tel: 01761 411030 Fax: 01761 416272
Email: hmcoroner@faulkners.co.uk

Coroner T Williams

Somerset, Western District
6 Hammet Street, Taunton TA1 1RG
Tel: 01823 337474 Fax: 01823 259643

Coroner M R Rose

South Yorkshire, East District
5 Union St. off St. Sepulchre Gate West, Doncaster DN1 3AE
Tel: 01302 320844 Fax: 01302 364833

Coroner E S Hooper

South Yorkshire, West District
Medico-Legal Centre, Watery Street, Sheffield S3 7ET
Tel: 0114 273 8721 Fax: 0114 278 4909

Coroner C P Dorries

Staffordshire, South District
15 Martin Street, Stafford ST16 2LX
Tel: 01785 276127 Fax: 01785 276128
Email: andrew.haigh@staffordshire.gov.uk

Coroner Mr Haigh

CORONERS

Stoke-on-Trent and North Staffordshire
Coroner's Chambers, 547 Hartshill Road, Stoke-on-Trent ST4 6HF
Tel: 01782 234777 Fax: 01782 234783

Coroner E J Wain

Suffolk, Ipswich District
2 Little Haylands, 99 High Road, Chigwell IG7 6QQ
Tel: 020 8502 6337 Fax: 020 8502 6337

Coroner P J Dean

Suffolk, Lowestoft District
4 Halesworth Road, Reydon, Southwold IP18 6NH
Tel: 01502 726017 Fax: 01502 726048

Coroner A G L de Lacroix

Suffolk, West District
Partridge & Wilson, 88 Guildhall Street, Bury St Edmunds IP33 1PT
Tel: 01284 762281 Fax: 01284 761214

Coroner H B Walrond

Surrey District
44 Ormond Avenue, Hampton TW12 2RX
Tel: 020 8979 6805 Fax: 020 8979 6805

Coroner Dr Burgess

Teesside District
The Register Office, Corporation Road, Middlesbrough TS1 2DA
Tel: 01642 262065 Fax: 01642 262083

Coroner Dr Sheffield

Telford and Wrekin District
Edgbaston House, Walker Street, Wellington, Telford TF1 1HF
Tel: 01952 641651 Fax: 01952 247441
Email: info@gwynnes.com

Coroner M T Gwynne

Tyne and Wear, Gateshead and South Tyneside District
Law Court Chambers, 2 Coronation Street, South Shields NE33 1AP
Tel: 0191 456 3201 Fax: 0191 454 4761

Coroner W Duffy

Tyne and Wear, Newcastle upon Tyne District
Coroners Court, Bolbec Hall, Westgate Road, Newcastle upon Tyne NE1 1SE
Tel: 0191 261 2845 Fax: 0191 261 2952

Coroner D Mitford

Tyne and Wear, North Tyneside District
1 Stanley Street, Blyth NE24 2BS
Tel: 01670 354777 Fax: 01670 355951

Coroner C B Gallon

Tyne and Wear, Sunderland District
57 John Street, Sunderland SR1 1QP
Tel: 0191 567 1851 Fax: 0191 567 6728

Coroner M C Shaw

Warwickshire District
Field Overall, Solicitors, 42 Warwick Street, Leamington Spa CV32 5JS
Tel: 01926 422101 Fax: 01926 450568

Coroner M Coker

West Midlands, Birmingham District
Coroner's Court, 50 Newton Street, Birmingham B4 6NE
Tel: 0121 303 3920/3228 Fax: 0121 233 4841

Coroner Aidan Cotter

West Midlands, Coventry District
10 The Quadrant, Coventry CV1 1EQ
Tel: 024 7655 3181 Fax: 024 7625 8573

Coroner D R Sarginson

West Midlands, Dudley District
21 Dingle Road, Pedmore, Stourbridge DY9 0RS
Tel: 0121 626 8018 Fax: 01384 354477

Coroner V F Bond

West Midlands, Sandwell District
Guardian House, Cronehills Linkway, West Bromwich B70 8SW
Tel: 0121 553 2945 Fax: 0121 553 2079

Coroner R Balmain

West Midlands, Walsall District
Addison, Cooper, Jesson & Co Solicitors, Kelvin House, 23 Lichfield Street, Walsall WS1 1UL
Tel: 01922 725515 Fax: 01922 643403

Coroner J Leeming

West Midlands, Wolverhampton District
7 Waterloo Road, Wolverhampton WV1 1BY
Tel: 01902 420261 Fax: 01902 426091

Coroner Dr Allen

West Sussex District
50 Westgate, Chichester PO19 3HE
Tel: 01243 530388 Fax: 01243 530389

Coroner Mr Stone

West Yorkshire, Eastern District
71 Northgate, Wakefield WF1 3BS
Tel: 01924 302180 Fax: 01924 291603

Coroner D Hinchliff

West Yorkshire, Western District
Coroner's Court, The City Courts, The Tyrls, Bradford BD1 1LA
Tel: 01274 391362 Fax: 01274 721794

Coroner R L Whittaker

Wiltshire and Swindon District
Lloyds Bank Chambers, 6 Castle Street, Salisbury SP1 1BB
Tel: 01722 326870, 01722 337591 Fax: 01722 332223

Coroner D Masters

Worcester District
21 Dingle Road, Pedmore, Stourbridge DY9 0RS
Tel: 01905 759831

Coroner V F Round

York District
Sentinel House, Peasholme Green, York YO1 7PP
Tel: 01904 716000 Fax: 01904 716000

Coroner W D F Coverdale

Wales

Bridgend and Glamorgan Valleys

3 Victoria Square, Aberdare CF44 7LA
Tel: 01685 881122, 01685 884477 Fax: 01685 870322

Coroner P M Walters

Cardiff and Vale of Glamorgan

Coroner's Court, New Police Headquarters, Cathays Park, Cardiff CF1 3NN
Tel: 029 2023 3886 Fax: 02920 2202 0638
Email: L.S.A@btinternet.com

Coroner Dr Addicott

Carmarthenshire District

Solicitors, Corner House, Llandeilo SA19 6SG
Tel: 01558 822215 Fax: 01558 822933

Coroner W J Owen

Central North Wales District

Marble House, Overton Arcade, High Street, Wrexham LL13 8LL
Tel: 01978 357775 Fax: 01978 358000

Coroner J B Hughes

Ceredigion District

Brunton & Co, 6 Upper Portland Street, Aberystwyth
Tel: 01970 612567, 01970 617931 Fax: 01970 615572

Coroner P L Brunton

Gwent District

Victoria Chambers, 11 Clytha Park Road, Newport NP20 4PB
Tel: 01633 264194 Fax: 01633 841146

Coroner D T Bowen

Neath and Port Talbot District

The Health Centre, Sybil Street, Clydach, Swansea SA6 5EU
Tel: 01792 845058/843821 Fax: 01792 844902

Coroner Dr Osborne

North East Wales District

69 King Street, Wrexham LL11 1HR
Tel: 01978 357775 Fax: 01978 358000

Coroner J B Hughes

North West Wales District

Evans Lane, Maes glas 37 y Maes, Caernarfon LL55 2NN
Tel: 01286 673387 Fax: 01286 672804

Coroner D Pritchard Jones

Powys District

Garth, Llanidloes SY18 6NN
Tel: 01686 411184 Fax: 01686 412948

Coroner J Hollis

Swansea District

Calvert House, Calvert Terrace, Swansea SA1 6AP
Tel: 01792 655215 Fax: 01792 467002

Coroner J R Morgan

Wales, Pembrokeshire District

25 Hamilton Terrace, Milford Haven SA73 3JJ
Tel: 01646 698129 Fax: 01646 690607

Coroner M S Howells

Medical Associations and Societies

Action for Sick Children (National Association for the Welfare of Children in Hospital)
National Children's Bureau, 8 Wakley Street, London EC1V 7QE
Tel: 020 7843 6016
Email: action_for_sick_children_edu@msn.com
Website: www.actionforsickchildren.org

Information Manager Pamela Barnes

Action for Victims of Medical Accidents
44 High Street, Croydon CR0 1YB
Tel: 020 8686 8333 Fax: 020 8667 9065
Email: admin@avma.org.uk
Website: www.avma.org.uk

Action on Smoking and Health (ASH)
102 Clifton Street, London EC2A 4HW
Tel: 020 7739 5902 Fax: 020 7613 0531
Email: action.smoking.health@dial.pipex.com
Website: www.ash.org.uk

Action Research
Vincent House, North Parade, Horsham RH12 2DP
Tel: 01403 210406 Fax: 01403 210541
Email: info@actionrsearch.co.uk
Website: www.actionresearch.co.uk

Chief Executive Simon Moore
Research Administrator Tracey Swinfield

Age Concern England (The National Council on Ageing)
Astral House, 1268 London Road, London SW16 4ER
Tel: 020 8765 7200 Fax: 020 8679 6069, 020 8765 7211
Email: ace@ace.org.uk, infodep@ageconcern.org.uk
Website: www.ace.org.uk

Director General Gordon Lishman

Alcohol Concern
Waterbridge House, 32-36 Loman Street, London SE1 0EE
Tel: 020 7928 7377 Fax: 020 7928 4644
Email: contact@alcoholconcern.org.uk
Website: www.alcoholconcern.org.uk

Director E Appleby

Alzheimer's Society
Gordon House, 10 Greencoat Place, London SW1P 1PH
Tel: 020 7306 0606, 0845 300 0336 (helpline)
Fax: 020 7306 0808
Email: info@alzheimers.org.uk
Website: www.alzheimers.org.uk

Director of Fundraising Stephanie Smith
Executive Director H Cayton
Finance Director Lindsay Sartori
Information & Education Director C Evers
Press Officer Catherine Griffiths
Regional Development Director Peter Ackland

Ambless - Accident, Loneliness and Bereavement Support
Shalom House, Lower Celtic Park, Enniskillen BT74 6HP
Tel: 028 6632 0320 Fax: 028 6632 0320

Chief Executive John Wood

Anaesthetic Research Society
Academic Unit of Anaesthesia, St. James's University Hospital, Leeds LS9 7TF
Tel: 0113 206 5274 Fax: 0113 206 4140
Email: p.m.hopkins@leeds.ac.uk
Website: www.ars.ac.uk

Hon. Secretary P M Hopkins
Hon. Treasurer D G Lambert
President G Smith

Anatomical Society of Great Britain and Ireland
Department of Anatomy, Biosciences Institute, University College, Cork
Tel: 21 490 2115, 21 490 2246 Fax: 21 427 3518
Email: j.fraher@ucc.ie, morrissk@ermine.ox.ac.uk
Website: www.anatsoc.org.uk

Assistant Secretary D Watt
Hon. Secretary J P Fraher
President J F Morriss
Treasurer B J Moxham

Arthritis Research Campaign
Copeman House, St. Mary's Court, St. Mary's Gate, Chesterfield S41 7TD
Tel: 01246 558033 Fax: 01246 558007
Email: info@arc.org.uk
Website: www.arc.org.uk

Chief Executive Fergus Logan
Press Officer Jane Tadman

Arts for Health
The Manchester Metropolitan University, All Saints, Oxford Road, Manchester M15 6BY
Tel: 0161 236 8916, 0161 247 1091 Fax: 0161 247 6390
Email: p.senior@mmu.ac.uk
Website: www.artdes.mmu.ac.uk

Director Peter Senior

Association for Child Psychology and Psychiatry
St. Saviour's House, 39/41 Union Street, London SE1 1SD
Tel: 020 7403 7458 Fax: 020 7403 7081
Email: acpp@acpp.co uk

Acting Manager L Curtis

Association for Improvements in the Maternity Services
10 Porthall Street, Brighton BN1 5PJ
Tel: 020 8960 5585 Fax: 01753 654142
Website: www.aims.org.uk

Hon. Secretary S Warshal

Association for Residential Care
ARC House, Marsden Street, Chesterfield S40 1JY
Tel: 01246 555043 Fax: 01246 555045
Email: contact.us@arcuk.org.uk
Website: www.arc.org.uk

Chief Executive James Churchill
National Branch Manager Yvonne Furze
National Projects and Services Manager Jane Livingstone

National Training Manager Alan Rhodes
NVQ Consortium Manager Julie Crowther

Association for Spina Bifida and Hydrocephalus

National Centre, 42 Park Road, Peterborough PE1 2UQ
Tel: 01733 555988 Fax: 01733 555985
Email: postmaster@asbah.org
Website: www.asbah.org

Executive Director A Russell

Association for the Study of Medical Education

ASME Office, 12 Queen Street, Edinburgh EH12 1JE
Tel: 0131 225 9111 Fax: 0131 225 9444
Email: info@asme.org.uk
Website: www.asme.org.uk

Chairman S J Leinster
Journal Editor J Bligh
President J S G Biggs
Secretary F R Smith
Treasurer J L Herzberg

Association of Anaesthetists of Great Britain and Ireland

9 Bedford Square, London WC1B 3RE
Tel: 020 7631 1650 Fax: 020 7631 4352
Email: info@aagbi.org
Website: www.aagbi.org

Hon. Secretary B Buckland
President L Strunin
President Elect P G M Wallace

Association of British Dispensing Opticians

ABDO College of Education, Godmersham Park, Godmersham CT4 7DT
Tel: 01227 738829 Fax: 01227 733900
Email: education@abdo.org.uk
Website: www.abdo.org.uk

General Secretary Anthony Garrett
Registrar D G Baker

Association of British Neurologists

Ormond House, 4th Floor, 27 Boswell Street, London WC1N 3JZ
Tel: 020 7405 4060 Fax: 020 7405 4070
Email: abn@abnoffice.demon.co.uk
Website: www.theabn.org

Administrator S C Tann
Hon. Secretary D H Miller

Association of British Paediatric Nurses

Greenfield House, 9 Church Lane, South Gosland, Huddersfield HD4 7DB
Website: www.abpn.org.uk

General Secretary Chris Hall

Association of Clinical Biochemists

130-132 Tooley Street, London SE1 2TU
Tel: 020 7403 8001 Fax: 020 7403 8006
Email: admin@acb.org.uk
Website: www.acb.org.uk

Chair M J Hallworth
President A Shenkin
Secretary P J Wood

Association of Clinical Pathologists

189 Dyke Road, Hove BN3 1TL
Tel: 01273 775700 Fax: 01273 773303
Email: info@pathologists.org.uk
Website: www.pathologists.org.uk

Chairman Russell M Young
Hon. Secretary W A Telfer Brunton

Association of Medical Microbiologists

Department of Microbiology, Conquest Hospital, The Ridge, St Leonards-on-Sea TN37 7RD
Tel: 01424 755255 ext: 8333 Fax: 01424 758022
Email: ep.wright@virgin.net
Website: www.amm.co.uk

Hon. Secretary B A Oppenheim
Hon. Treasurer S T Chapman
President R C B Slack
Publications Secretary E P Wright

Association of Medical Research Charities

61 Grays Inn Road, London WC1X 8TL
Tel: 020 7269 8820 Fax: 020 7242 2484
Email: amrc@mailbox.ulcc.ac.uk

Chairman Leslie Busk
Chief Executive Diana Garnham

Association of Operating Department Practitioners (AODP)

Lewes Enterprise Centre, 112 Malling Street, Lewes BN7 2PE
Tel: 0870 746 0984 Fax: 0870 746 0985
Email: office@aodp.org
Website: www.aodp.org

Association of Optometrists

61 Southwark Street, London SE1 0HL
Tel: 020 7261 9661 Fax: 020 7261 0228
Email: postbox@assoc-optometrists.org
Website: www.assoc-optometrists.org

Head of Communications David Craig
Chief Executive Ian Hunter

Association of Police Surgeons

Clarke House, 18A Mount Parade, Harrogate HG1 1BX
Tel: 01423 509727 Fax: 01423 566391
Email: chris@forensic-science-society.org.uk, chris@fscisoc.demon.co.uk

Hon. Secretary M Knight

Association of Surgeons of Great Britain and Ireland

The Royal College of Surgeons, 35-43 Lincoln's Inn Fields, London WC2A 3PE
Tel: 020 7973 0300 Fax: 020 7430 9235
Website: www.asgbi.org.uk

Executive Officer Nechama Lewis
Hon. Secretary G T Layer

Assurance Medical Society, Lettsom House

11 Chandos Street, London W1H 0EB
Tel: 020 7636 6308 Fax: 020 7580 5793

Hon. Secretary Ian Croxson

Ataxia-UK

10 Winchester, Kennington Park, Cranmer Road, London SW9 6EJ
Tel: 020 7582 1444 Fax: 020 7582 9444
Email: office@ataxia.org.uk

Administrator Julia Willmott
Director Judith Kidd

MEDICAL ASSOCIATIONS & SOCIETIES

Backcare

16 Elmtree Road, Teddington TW11 8ST
Tel: 020 8977 5474 Fax: 020 8943 5318
Email: back_pain@compuserve.com
Website: www.backpain.org

Chairman Frank Davies
Company Secretary Alistair Mackechnie

Bardhan Research and Education Trust of Rotherham Ltd

Modern House, Summer Lane, Barnsley S70 2NP
Tel: 01226 771226

Executive Administrator E A Green

Barnardo's

Tanners Lane, Barkingside, Ilford IG6 1QG
Tel: 020 8550 8822 Fax: 020 8551 6870
Website: www.barnardos.org.uk

Chief Executive Roger Singleton

Beit Memorial Fellowships for Medical Research

c/o Institute of Molecular Medicine, John Radcliffe Hospital, Headington, Oxford OX3 9DS
Tel: 01865 222679 Fax: 01865 222600

Administration Secretary M Goble

Biochemical Society

59 Portland Place, London W1B 1QW
Tel: 020 7580 5530 Fax: 020 7637 3626
Email: genadmin@biochemsoc.org

Chairman C Peter Downes

Brain Research Trust

Bloomsbury House, 74-77 Great Russell Street, London WC1B 3DA
Tel: 020 7636 3440 Fax: 020 7636 3445
Email: thebrt@aol.com

Breakthrough Breast Cancer

6th Floor, Kingsway House, 103 Kingsway, London WC2B 6QX
Tel: 020 7405 5111 Fax: 020 7831 3873
Email: info@breakthrough.org.uk
Website: www.breakthrough.org.uk

Chief Executive Delyth Morgan

British Academy of Forensic Sciences

Anaesthetic Unit, The Royal London Hospital, Whitechapel, London E1 1BB
Tel: 020 7377 9201 Fax: 020 7377 7126

Secretary General P J Flynn

British Association for Accident and Emergency Medicine

The Royal College of Surgeons of England, 35-43 Lincoln's Inn Fields, London WC2A 3PN
Tel: 020 7831 9405 Fax: 020 7405 0318
Email: baem1@compuserve.com
Website: www.baem.org.uk

Hon. Secretary S McCabe
Hon. Treasurer P Burdett-Smith
President R C Evans
President Elect J R C Heyworth

British Association for Paediatric Nephrology

Great Ormond Street Hospital, Great Ormond Street, London WC1N 3JH
Tel: 020 7405 9200 Fax: 020 7829 8841

Hon. Secretary Lesley Rees

British Association for Parenteral and Enteral Nutrition

BAPEN Office, Secure Hold Bussiness Centre, Studley Road, Redditch BN98 7LG
Tel: 01527 457850 Fax: 01527 458718

Chairman C R Pennington
Hon. Secretary Ann Micklewright
Hon. Treasurer T K Cottam

British Association for Psychopharmacology

Mrs S. Chandler, 6 Regent Terrace, Cambridge CB2 1AA
Tel: 01223 358395 Fax: 01223 321268
Email: susan@bap.org.uk
Website: www.bap.org.uk

General Secretary Ian Anderson

British Association for Service to the Elderly

119 Hassell Street, Newcastle-under-Lyme ST5 1AX
Tel: 01782 661033 Fax: 01782 661033
Email: base@intonet.co.uk
Website: www.base.org.uk

Business Manager Linda Hayler
Chief Executive Christopher Joyce
Director, Wales Betty Wackerbarth

British Association for Tissue Banking

20-22 Queensbury Place, London SW7 2DZ
Tel: 020 7351 8460 Fax: 020 7351 8461
Email: r.parker@rbh.nthames.nhs.uk
Website: www.batb.org.uk

General Secretary Joan Power
President Robert Parker

British Association of Day Surgery

The Royal College of Surgeons, 35-43 Lincoln's Inn Fields, London WC2A 3PN
Tel: 020 7973 0308 Fax: 020 7973 0314
Email: bads@bads.co.uk
Website: www.bads.co.uk

President Paul Baskerville
Secretary Joe Cahill

British Association of Dermatologists

19 Fitzroy Square, London W1T 6EH
Tel: 020 7383 0266 Fax: 020 7388 5263
Email: admin@bad.org.uk

Executive Officer Marilyn Benham
Hon. Secretary Katherine Dalziel
President R Hay

British Association of Health Services in Higher Education (BAHSHE)

Cripps Health Centre, University Park, University of Nottingham, Nottingham NG7 2QW
Tel: 0115 950 1654 Fax: 0115 948 0347

Hon. Secretary Carrie Ellison

British Association of Occupational Therapists and College of Occupational Therapists

The College of Occupational Therapists, 106-114 Borough High Street, London SE1 1LB
Tel: 020 7357 6480 Fax: 020 7450 2299
Email: cot@cot.co.uk
Website: www.cot.co.uk, www.baot.co.uk

Chairman Helena Culshaw

British Association of Oral and Maxillofacial Surgeons

Royal College of Surgeons, 35-43 Lincolns Inn Fields, London WC2A 3PN
Tel: 020 7405 8074 Fax: 020 7430 9997
Email: baoms@netcom.uk.co.uk
Website: www.baoms.org.uk

Hon. Secretary M Corrigan
President E D Vaughan
President Elect J D Langdon

British Association of Otorhinolaryngologists-Head and Neck Surgeons

The Royal College of Surgeons, 35-43 Lincoln's Inn Fields, London WC2A 3PE
Tel: 020 7404 8373 Fax: 020 7404 4200
Email: orl@bao-hns.demon.co.uk
Website: www.orl-baohns.org

Hon. Secretary Alan P Johnson
President Ian S Mackay

British Association of Paediatric Surgeons

Royal College of Surgeons of England, 35-43 Lincoln's Inn Fields, London WC2A 3PN
Tel: 020 7869 6915 Fax: 020 7869 6919
Email: honsec@baps.org.uk
Website: www.baps.org.uk

Hon. Secretary & Treasurer Elect Lawrence Rangecroft
President D Lloyd
President Elect Peter Raine

British Association of Perinatal Medicine

50 Hallam Street, London W1W 6DE
Tel: 020 7307 5682 Fax: 020 7307 5601
Email: bapm@rcpch.ac.uk
Website: www.bapm-london.org

Hon. Secretary David Field
Hon. Treasurer David Lloyd
President Andrew Wilkinson

British Association of Plastic Surgeons

The Royal College of Surgeons, 35-43 Lincoln's Inn Fields, London WC2A 3PN
Tel: 020 7831 5161 Fax: 020 7831 4041
Email: secretariat@baps.co.uk
Website: wwwbaps.co.uk

Hon. Secretary C M Paddy
Senior Administrator H C Roberts

British Association of Psychotherapists

37 Mapesbury Road, London NW2 4HJ
Tel: 020 8452 9823 Fax: 020 8452 5182
Email: mail@bap-psychotherapy.org
Website: www.bap-psychotherapy.org

Chairperson Faith Miles

British Association of Surgical Oncology

c/o Royal College of Surgeons of England, 35-43 Lincoln's Inn Fields, London WC2A 3PN
Tel: 020 7405 5612 Fax: 020 7404 6574

Hon. Secretary D A Rew

British Association of Urological Surgeons

35-43 Lincoln's Inn Fields, London WC2A 3PE
Tel: 020 7405 1390 Fax: 020 7404 5048
Email: admin@baus.org.uk
Website: www.baus.org.uk

Chief Executive P M Neville

British Cardiac Society

9 Fitzroy Square, London W1P 5AH
Tel: 020 7383 3887 Fax: 020 7388 0903
Email: enquiries@bcs.com
Website: www.bcs.com

Hon. Secretary P M Schofield
Hon. Treasurer D W Davies
President A J Camm
President Elect H H Gray

British Colostomy Association

15 Station Road, Reading RG1 1LG
Tel: 0118 939 1537, 0800 328 4257 Fax: 0118 956 9095
Email: sue@bcass.org.uk
Website: www.bcass.org.uk

Association Secretary Olivia Reed
Director of Field Operations Margaret Reid

British Council

Bridgewater House, 58 Whitworth Street, Manchester M1 6BB
Tel: 0161 957 7474 Fax: 0161 957 7029
Email: douglas.buchanan@britishcouncil.org
Website: www.britcoun.org/health/index.htm

Director Health Douglas Buchanan

British Council for the Prevention of Blindness

12 Harcourt Street, London W1H 1DS
Tel: 020 7724 3716 Fax: 020 7262 6199
Email: bcpb@globalnet.co.uk

Chairman Andrew Elkington

British Dental Association

64 Wimpole Street, London W1G 8YS
Tel: 020 7563 4563 Fax: 020 7487 5232
Email: enquiries@bda-dentistry.org.uk
Website: www.bda-dentistry.org.uk

Chair J Renshaw
Chief Executive and Secretary I Wylie
President P Swiss

British Dietetic Association

5th Floor, Charles House, 148-149 Great Charles Street, Queensway, Birmingham B3 3HT
Tel: 0121 200 8080 Fax: 0121 200 8081
Email: info@bda.uk.com
Website: www.bda.uk.com

Hon. Chairman Loretta Cox
Secretary John Grigg

British Epilepsy Association

New Anstey House, Gate Way Drive, Yeadon, Leeds LS19 7XY
Tel: 0113 210 8800, 0808 800 5050 Fax: 0113 391 0300, 0808 8005 5559
Email: epilepsy@bea.org.uk
Website: www.epilepsy.org.uk

Chief Executive Philip Lee
Public Relations Officer Sharon Hudson

British Geriatrics Society

Marjory Warren House, 31 St John's Square, London EC1M 4DN
Tel: 020 7608 1369 Fax: 020 7608 1041
Email: info@bgs.org.uk
Website: www.bgs.org.uk

Administrative Director R G Lynham
Hon. Secretary C Vellodi

MEDICAL ASSOCIATIONS & SOCIETIES

British Heart Foundation

14 Fitzhardinge Street, London W1H 6DH
Tel: 020 7935 0185 Fax: 020 7486 5820
Website: www.bhf.org.uk

Chairman of the Council Keith Peters
Director General Maj General L F H Busk
Medical Director Charles George

British Homeopathic Association

15 Clerkenwell Close, London EC1R 0AA
Tel: 020 7566 7800 Fax: 020 7566 7815
Email: info@trusthomeopathy.org
Website: www.trusthomeopathy.org

Chief Executive Sally Penrose

British Hypertension Society

Information Service, The Blood Pressure Unit, St George's Hospital Medical School, Cranmer Terrace, London SW17 0RE
Tel: 020 8725 3412 Fax: 020 8725 2959
Email: bhsis@sghms.ac.uk
Website: www.hyp.ac.uk/bhs/

President E A MacGregor
Secretary N R Poulter
Treasurer G Russell

British Infection Society

Nuffield Department of Medicine, John Radcliffe Hospital, Oxford OX3 9DU
Tel: 01865 220154 Fax: 01865 222962
Email: chris.conlon@ndm.ox.ac.uk

Hon. President R Finch
Hon. Secretary C Conlon
Hon. Treasurer I M Gould
Membership Secretary D Dance

British Institute of Dental and Surgical Technologists

Department of Chemistry & Materials, Faculty of Science & Engineering, Manchester Metropolitan University, Chester Street, Manchester M1 5GD
Tel: 0161 247 1418
Email: j.west@mmu.ac.uk
Website: www.bidst.mmu.ac.uk

Chair M Gilbert
CPD S Taylor
President A C Roberts
Secretary Janet West
Treasurer C Dean
Vice-Chair S Wood

British Institute of Industrial Therapy

63 South Street, Bishop's Stortford CM23 3AL
Tel: 01279 465075 Fax: 01279 758143

General Secretary Michael Tarling

British Institute of Learning Disabilities

Campion House, Green Street, Kidderminster DY10 1JL
Tel: 01562 723010 Fax: 01562 723029
Email: enquiries@bild.org.uk
Website: www.bild.org.uk

British Institute of Musculoskeletal Medicine

34 The Avenue, Watford WD17 3AH
Tel: 01923 220999 Fax: 01923 249037
Email: bimm@compuserve.com
Website: www.bimm.org.uk

Administrator D Harris
General Manager Deena Harris

Hon. Secretary M Grayson
President P Skew

British Institute of Radiology

36 Portland Place, London W1B 1AT
Tel: 020 7307 1400 Fax: 020 7307 1414
Email: admin@bir.org.uk
Website: www.bir.org.uk

General Secretary Tony Hudson
Hon. Secretary A Budge, A M Thomas
Hon. Treasurer D S McIntosh
President P Sharpe

British Leprosy Relief Association

Fairfax House, Causton Road, Colchester CO1 1PU
Tel: 01206 562286 Fax: 01206 762151
Email: lepra@lepra.org.uk
Website: www.lepra.org.uk

Director Terry Vasey
Programme Assistant Debbie Sharp

British Lung Foundation

78 Hatton Garden, London EC1N 8LD
Tel: 020 7831 5831 Fax: 020 7831 5832
Email: blf@britishlungfoundation.com
Website: www.lunguk.org

British Medical Acupuncture Society

12 Marbury Lane, Higher Whitley, Warrington WA4 4QW
Tel: 01925 730727 Fax: 01925 730492
Email: admin@medical-acupuncture.org.uk
Website: www.medical-acupuncture.co.uk

British Medical Association

BMA House, Tavistock Square, London WC1H 9JP
Tel: 020 7387 4499 Fax: 020 7383 6400
Website: www.bma.org.uk

Chair I G Bogle
President David Carter

British Medical Ultrasound Society

36 Portland Place, London W1B 1LS
Tel: 020 7636 3714 Fax: 020 7323 2175
Email: b_m_u_s@compuserve.com, secretariat@bmus.org
Website: www.bmus.org

General Secretary E Brown
Hon. Secretary K Martin
Hon. Treasurer G M Baxter
President D W Pilling
President Elect Jane Bates

British Menopause Society

36 West Street, Marlow SL7 2NB
Tel: 06128 890199 Fax: 01628 474042

Chairman L Cardozo
Deputy Director M A Upsdell
Executive Director F A Patterson
Hon. Treasurer J Pitkin

British Nuclear Medicine Society

1 Wimpole Street, London W1G 0AE
Tel: 020 8291 7800 Fax: 020 8699 2227
Email: bnmsl@pavilion.co.uk

Secretary Susan Hatchard

British Nutrition Foundation

High Holborn House, 52-54 High Holborn, London WC1V 6RQ
Tel: 020 7404 6504 Fax: 020 7404 6747
Email: postbox@nutrition.org.uk
Website: www.nutrition.org.uk

Director General Robert Pickard
Education Director Stephanie Valentine
Science Director Judith Buttriss
Secretary N Porter

British Occupational Hygiene Society

Suite 2, Georgian House, Great Northern Road, Derby DE1 1LT
Tel: 01332 298101 Fax: 01332 298099
Website: www.bohs.org

Hon. Secretary C P Beach
Hon. Treasurer L S Waterman
President K Gardiner
President Elect B Holyoak

British Orthodontic Society

291 Gray's Inn Road, London WC1X 8QJ
Tel: 020 7837 2193 Fax: 020 7837 2193
Email: awrightbos@msn.com
Website: awrightbos@msn.com

Hon. Secretary David Tidy
Society Administrator Ann Wright

British Orthopaedic Association

Royal College of Surgeons, 35-43 Lincoln's Inn Fields, London WC2A 3PN
Tel: 020 7405 6507 Fax: 020 7831 2676
Email: ceo@boa.ac.uk
Website: www.boa.ac.uk

Chief Executive D C Adams
Hon. Secretary N J Fiddian

British Orthoptic Society

Tavistock House North, Tavistock Square, London WC1H 9HX
Tel: 020 7387 7992 Fax: 020 7383 2584
Email: bos@orthoptics.org.uk
Website: www.orthoptics.org.uk

Chairman June Carpenter
Hon. Secretary Rosie Auld
Hon. Treasurer Jacky Nolan

British Performing Arts Medicine Trust

196 Shaftesbury Avenue, London WC2H 8JL
Tel: 020 7240 4500, 0845 602 0235 Fax: 020 7240 3335
Email: bpamt@dial.pipex.com

British Pharmacological Society

16 Angel Gate, City Road, London EC1V 2SG
Tel: 020 7417 0113 Fax: 020 7417 0114
Email: sjs@bps.ac.uk
Website: www.bps.ac.uk

Executive Officer Sarah-Jane Stagg

British Pharmacopoeia Commission

Market Towers, 1 Nine Elms Lane, London SW8 5NQ
Tel: 020 7273 0559 Fax: 020 7273 0566
Email: bpcom@mca.gov.uk
Website: www.pharmacopoeia.org.uk

Scientific Director Robin Hutton
Secretary Robin Hutton

British Polio Fellowship

Ground Floor, Unit A, Eagle Office Centre, The Runway, Ruislip HA4 6SE
Tel: 0800 018 0586 Fax: 020 8842 0555
Email: info@britishpolio.org

Chief Executive Andrew Kemp
National Welfare Officer Dorothy Maltrass

British Pregnancy Advisory Service

Austy Manor, Wootton Wawen, Solihull B95 6BX
Tel: 01564 793225 Fax: 01564 794935
Email: info@bpas.org
Website: www.bpas.org

Chief Executive Ann Furedi

British Psycho-Analytical Society

114 Shirland Road, London W9 2EQ
Tel: 020 7563 5000 Fax: 020 7563 5001
Email: 113367.3577@compuserve.com, editors@psychoanalysis.org.uk
Website: www.psychoanalysis.org.uk

President D Campbell

British Psychological Society

St Andrews House, 48 Princess Road East, Leicester LE1 7DR
Tel: 0116 252 9539 Fax: 0116 247 0787
Email: mail@bps.org.uk, stewhi@bps.org.uk
Website: www.bps.org.uk

Directorate Manager Stephen White
Executive Secretary Barry Brooking
Hon. General Secretary Ingrid Lunt

British Red Cross Society

9 Grosvenor Crescent, London SW1X 7EJ
Tel: 020 7235 5454 Fax: 020 7245 6315
Email: information@redcross.org.uk
Website: www.redcross.org.uk

Director General Nicholas Young

British Retinitis Pigmentosa Society

PO Box 350, Buckingham MK18 1GZ
Tel: 01280 821334 (office), 01280 860363 (helpline)
Fax: 01280 815900
Email: lynda@brps.demon.co.uk
Website: www.brps.demon.co.uk

British Society for Haematology

2 Carlton House Terrace, London SW1Y 5AF
Tel: 020 8643 7305 Fax: 020 8770 0933
Email: janice@bshhya.demon.co.uk
Website: www.blackwell-science.com/uk/society/bsh/default.htm

Administrator Janice O'Donnell
President M Greaves
Secretary John T Reilly
Vice-President A G Prentice

British Society for Human Genetics

Clinical Genetics Unit Admin. Office, Birmingham Women's Hospital, Edgbaston, Birmingham B15 2TG
Tel: 0121 627 2634 Fax: 0121 627 2634
Email: bshg@bshg.org.uk
Website: www.bshg.org.uk

General Secretary Rob Elles

British Society for Immunology

Triangle House, Broomhill Road, London SW18 4HX
Tel: 020 8875 2406
Email: allison@immunology.org, bsi@immunology.org
Website: www.immunology.org

General Secretary P Riches
Managing Editor Allison Lang

British Society for Music Therapy

25 Rosslyn Avenue, East Barnet, Barnet EN4 8DH
Tel: 020 8368 8879 Fax: 020 8368 8879
Email: info@bsmt.org
Website: www.bsmt.org

MEDICAL ASSOCIATIONS & SOCIETIES

Administrator Denize Christophers
Chairperson Nigel Hartley

British Society for Oral Medicine

Glasgow Dental Hospital and School, 378 Sauchiehall Street, Glasgow G2 3JZ
Tel: 0141 211 9600 Fax: 0141 353 2899
Email: secretary@oralmedicine.uk.com
Website: www.oralmedicine.uk.com

President Joanna M Zakrzewska
Secretary D H Felix

British Society for Parasitology

BSP Secretariat, Triangle House, Broomfield Road, London SW18 4HX
Tel: 020 8875 2433 Fax: 020 8875 2424
Email: bsp@parasitology.org.uk
Website: www.abdn.ac.uk/bsp/

Hon. General Secretary R C Tinsley
Hon. Meetings Secretary K Matthews
Hon. Treasurer Susan Welburn
President G Targett
Vice-President D Rollinson

British Society for Rheumatology

41 Eagle Street, London WC1R 4AR
Tel: 020 7242 3313 Fax: 020 7242 3277
Email: bsr@rheumatology.org.uk
Website: www.rheumatology.org.uk

Chief Executive Samantha Peters
Hon. Secretary R Butler
Hon. Treasurer R Jubb
President G Panay

British Society for Surgery of the Hand

The Royal College of Surgeons, 35-43 Lincoln's Inn Fields, London WC2A 3PN
Tel: 020 7831 5162 Fax: 020 7831 4041
Email: secretariat@bssh.ac.uk
Website: www.bssh.ac.uk

Hon. Secretary J Dias
Senior Administrator H C Roberts

British Society of Applied Social Science

Department of Applied Social Science, Stirling FK9 4LA
Tel: 01786 467701 Fax: 01786 467689
Email: k.davidson@surrey.ac.uk, susan.tester@stir.ac.uk

Secretary Susan Tester

British Society of Gastroenterology

3 St. Andrews Place, Regent's Park, London NW1 4LB
Tel: 020 7387 3534 Fax: 020 7487 3734
Email: bsg@mailbox.ulcc.ac.uk
Website: www.bsg.org.uk

Executive Secretary Di Tolfree
Hon. Secretary D Loft, J Sandersen
President D P Jewell

British Society of Medical and Dental Hypnosis

17 Keppel View Road, Kimberworth, Rotherham S61 2AR
Tel: 07000 560309 Fax: 07000 560309
Email: nat.office@bsmdh.org
Website: www.bsmdh.org

National Office Secretary R Jackson

British Society of Rehabilitation Medicine

c/o Royal College of Physicians, 11 St. Andrews Place, London NW1 4LE

Tel: 01992 638865 Fax: 01992 638865
Email: admin@bsrm.co.uk
Website: www.bsrm.co.uk

Executive Secretary Sandy Weatherhead
Hon. Secretary Roop Hanspal
President A O Frank

British Thoracic Society

6th Floor, North Wing, New Garden House, 78 Hatton Garden, London EC1N 8LD
Tel: 020 7831 8778 Fax: 020 7831 8766
Email: admin@brit-thoraic.org.uk, admin1@brit-thoracic,org.uk

Chief Executive S Edwards

Cancer and Leukaemia in Childhood

Abbey Wood, Bristol BS34 7JU
Tel: 0117 311 2600, 0117 311 2610 (Retail), 0117 311 2622 (Services), 0117 311 2630 (Fundraising)
Fax: 0117 311 2649

Chief Executive David Ellis
Development & Operations Patrick Holmes
Services Director Susan George

CancerBacup

3 Bath Place, Rivington Streen, London EC2A 3JR
Tel: 020 7696 9003, 0808 800 1234 Freephone
Fax: 020 7696 9002
Website: www.cancerbacup.org.uk

Cancer Information Service Manager Judith Brodie
Chairman Mavice L Slevin
Chief Executive Joanne Rule
Finance Manager D Fallon
Fundraising Manager Rebecca Porta
Publications Manager Sarah Vicory

Cancerlink

11-21 Northdown Street, London N1 9BR
Tel: 020 7833 2818 Fax: 020 7833 4963
Email: cancerlink@cancerlink.org.uk

Central Council of Physical Recreation

Francis House, Francis Street, London SW1P 1DE
Tel: 020 7854 8500 Fax: 020 7630 8820, 020 7854 8501
Email: admin@ccpr.org.uk
Website: www.ccpr.org.uk

Chief Executive Malcolm Denton

Centre for Policy on Ageing

19-23 Ironmonger Row, London EC1V 3QP
Tel: 020 7553 6500 Fax: 020 7553 6501
Email: cpa@cpa.org.uk
Website: www.cpa.org.uk

Chartered Society of Physiotherapy

14 Bedford Row, London WC1R 4ED
Tel: 020 7306 6666 Fax: 020 7306 6611
Email: csp@csphysio.org.uk
Website: www.csp.org.uk

Co-Director of Industrial Relations Richard Griffin
Director of Communications Neil Tesver
Director of Education Alan Walker
Director of Professional Affairs Penelope Robinson

Chest Heart and Stroke Scotland

65 North Castle Street, Edinburgh EH2 3LT
Tel: 0131 225 6963, 0845 077 6000 Fax: 0131 220 6313
Email: admin@chss.org.uk
Website: www.chss.org.uk

Chief Executive D H Clark

Child Accident Prevention Trust

4th Floor, Clerks Court, 18/20 Farringdon Lane, London EC1R 3HA
Tel: 020 7608 3828 Fax: 020 7608 3674
Email: safe@capt.org.uk
Website: www.capt.org.uk

Director Katrina Phillips
Projects Director M Hayes

Child Growth Foundation

2 Mayfair Avenue, Chiswick, London W4 1PW
Tel: 020 8994 7625, 020 8995 0257 Fax: 020 8995 9075
Email: cgflondon@aol.com

Hon. Chairman Tam Fry

The Children's Trust

Tadworth Court, Tadworth KT20 5RU
Tel: 01737 365000 Fax: 01737 365084
Email: c-trust@netcomuk.co.uk
Website: www.the childrenstrust.org.uk

Business Development Manager Sally Jenkinson
Chief Executive Andrew Ross
Director of Children's Services Pauline Stow
Financial Director Andrew Dick

Children's Liver Disease Foundation

36 Great Charles Street, Queensway, Birmingham B3 3JY
Tel: 0121 212 3839 Fax: 0121 212 4300
Email: cld@childliverdisease.org
Website: www.childliverdisease.org

Chief Executive Catherine Arkley
Children and Adolescents Support Officer Karen Jones
Family Support Officer Susan Davis

College of Health

St Margaret's House, 21 Old Ford Road, London E2 9PL
Tel: 020 8983 1225 Fax: 020 8983 1553
Email: info@collegeofhealth.org.uk
Website: www.collegeofhealth.org.uk

Business Manager Ian Flack
Director Marianne Rigge
Senior Research Fellow Marcia Kelson
Training and Marketing Manager Jessica Bush

The College of Optometrists

42 Craven Street, London WC2N 5NG
Tel: 020 7839 6000 Fax: 020 7839 6800
Email: optometry@college-optometrists.org
Website: www.college-optometrists.org

Secretary Peter Leigh

College of Pharmacy Practice

University of Warwick, Science Park, Barclays Venture Centre, Sir William Lyons Road, Coventry CV4 7EZ
Tel: 024 7669 2400 Fax: 024 7669 3069
Email: cpp@collpharm.org.uk
Website: www.collpharm.org.uk

Chief Executive Ian Simpson

The Commonwealth Nurses Federation

c/o Royal College of Nursing, 20 Cavendish Square, London W1G 0RN
Tel: 020 7647 3593 Fax: 020 7647 3593
Email: cnf@rcn.org.uk

Executive Secretary Michael Stubbings

Community and District Nursing Association

Westel House, 32-38 Uxbridge Road, Ealing, London W5 2BS
Tel: 020 8280 5342 Fax: 020 8280 5341
Email: cdna@tvu.ac.uk
Website: www.cdna.org.uk

Chair Anne Duffy

Company Chemists' Association Ltd

1 Thane Road, Nottingham NG2 3AA
Tel: 0115 959 3432 Fax: 0115 959 3314
Email: lisa.henshaw@boots-plc.com

Administration Priscilla Dawson
Chairman Digby Emson
Secretary Lindsey Popplewell

Conservative Medical Society

32 Smith Square, Westminster, London SW1P 3HH
Tel: 01737 243926 Fax: 01737 240486
Email: conmedsoc@cs.com, consmedsoc@cs.com

Chairman Anthony Clarke

Continuing Care at Home Association (CONCAH)

54 Glasshouse Street, Countess Wear, Exeter EX2 7BU

Coronary Prevention Group

2 Taviton Street, London WC1H 0BT
Tel: 020 7927 2125 Fax: 020 7927 2127
Email: cpg@ishtm.ac.uk

President P James
Secretary A Dave
Treasurer T Mukherjee
Vice-President H Spencer

Council for Awards in Children's Care and Education (incorporating CEYA and NNEB)

8 Chequer Street, St Albans AL1 3XZ
Tel: 01727 847636 Fax: 01727 867609
Email: info@cache.org.uk
Website: www.cache.org.uk

Chief Executive Richard Dorrance
Marketing Manager Beth Bachelor

Council for Music in Hospitals

74 Queens Road, Hersham, Walton-on-Thames KT12 5LW
Tel: 01932 252809, 01932 252811 Fax: 01932 252966
Email: info@music-in-hospitals.org.uk

Director (England, Wales and Northern Ireland) Diana Greenman
Director (Scotland) Alison Frazer

Counsel and Care-Advice and help for older people

Twyman House, 16 Bonny Street, London NW1 9PG
Tel: 0845 300 7585 Fax: 020 7267 6877
Email: advice@counselandcare.org.uk
Website: www.counselandcare.org.uk

Chief Executive Martin Green

Cystic Fibrosis Trust

11 London Road, Bromley BR1 1BY
Tel: 020 8464 7211 Fax: 020 8313 0472
Email: enquiries@cftrust.org.uk
Website: www.cftrust.org.uk

Chairman D Bluck
Chief Executive R Barnes
Life President R Luff

MEDICAL ASSOCIATIONS & SOCIETIES

Defeating Deafness (The Hearing Research Trust)
330-332 Gray's Inn Road, London WC1X 8EE
Tel: 020 7833 1733, 0808 808 2222 Fax: 020 7278 0404
Email: ddeafness.info@ucl.ac.uk
Website: www.defeatingdeafness.org

Diabetes UK
10 Queen Anne Street, London W1G 9LH
Tel: 020 7323 1531 Fax: 020 7637 3644
Email: info@diabetes.org.uk
Website: www.diabetes.org.uk

Chairman Board of Trustees British Diabetic Association M Hall
Chief Executive Paul R Streets
Director of Research Moira Murphy

Digestive Disorders Foundation
3 St. Andrews Place, London NW1 4LB
Tel: 020 7486 0341 Fax: 020 7224 2012
Email: ddf@digestivedisorders.org.uk
Website: www.digestivedisorders.org.uk

Director Geraldine Oliver
President Hermon Dowling

Disabled Drivers Association
National Headquarters, Ashwellthorpe, Norwich NR16 1EX
Tel: 0870 770 3333 Fax: 01508 488173
Email: ddahq@aol.com
Website: www.dda.org.uk

Executive Director Douglas Campbell
Information Officer Janet Johnson

Disabled Living Foundation
380-384 Harrow Road, London W9 2HU
Tel: 020 7289 6111 Fax: 020 7266 2922
Email: dlf@dlf.org.uk, info@dlf.org.uk
Website: www.dlf.org.uk

DrugScope
32-36 Loman Street, London SE1 0EE
Tel: 020 7928 1211 Fax: 020 7928 1771, 020 7928 3343
Email: services@drugscope.org.uk
Website: www.drugscope.org.uk

Chief Executive Roger Howard

Dystrophic Epidermolysis Bullosa Research Association (DEBRA)
DEBRA House, 13 Wellington Business Park, Dukes Ride, Crowthorne RG45 6LS
Tel: 01344 771961 Fax: 01344 762661
Email: debra.uk@btinternet.com, john.dart@btinternet.com
Website: www.debra.org.uk

Adult Nurse Specialist (North) Jacqueline Hitchin
Adult Nurse Specialist (South) Liz Pallay
Clinical Nurse Specialist (Paediatrics) Jacqueline Denyer
Corporate Appeals Director J Taylorson
Support Worker for Scotland Denise Mackenzie

Emergency Bed Service
Fielden House, 28 London Bridge Street, London SE1 9SG
Tel: 020 7407 7181 Fax: 020 7357 6705

Manager Graham Hayter
Operations Manager Barry Khodabukus, Alison Oakes

Encephalitis Support Group
44A Market Place, Malton YO17 7LW
Tel: 01653 699599 Fax: 01653 692583
Email: info@esg.org.uk
Website: www.esg.org.uk

Project Manager Keith M Steven

Epilepsy Action Scotland
48 Govan Road, Glasgow G51 1JL
Tel: 0141 427 4911 Fax: 0141 419 1709
Email: enquiries@epilepsyscotland.org
Website: www.epilepsyscotland.org.uk

Chief Executive Hilary Mounfield
PR Officer Allana Parker

Family Welfare Association
501-505 Kingsland Road, Dalston, London E8 4AU
Tel: 020 7254 6251 Fax: 020 7249 5443

Federation of Independent Practitioner Organisations
14 Queen Anne's Gate, London SW1H 9AA
Email: info@fipo.org

Federation of Ophthalmic and Dispensing Opticians
113 Eastbourne Mews, London W2 6LQ
Tel: 020 7258 0240 Fax: 020 7724 1175
Email: info@fodo.com
Website: www.fodo.com

Chairman Brian Carroll

Fellowship of Postgraduate Medicine
12 Chandos Street, London W1G 9DR
Tel: 020 7636 6334 Fax: 020 7436 2535
Website: www.fpmpmj.demon.co.uk

Forensic Science Society
Clarke House, 18A Mount Parade, Harrogate HG1 1BX
Tel: 01423 506068 Fax: 01423 566391
Email: president@forensic-science-society.org.uk

Assistant Editor Jane Cross
Hon. Secretary P Lamb
Office Manager Christine Houseman

Foundation for Liver Research (formerly Liver Research Trust)
Institute of Heptology, 69-75 Chenies Mews, London WC1E 6HX
Tel: 020 7679 6510, 020 7679 6511 Fax: 020 7380 0405
Email: roger.williams@ucl.ac.uk

Director R Williams

Foundation for the Study of Infant Deaths
Artillery House, 11-19 Artillery Row, London SW1P 1RT
Tel: 020 7222 8001, 020 7233 2090 (24 Hours Helpline)
Fax: 020 7222 8002
Email: fsid@sids.org.uk
Website: www.sids.org.uk/fsid

Chairman Colin Baker
Director Joyce Epstein
Fundraising Manager Joanna Christophi
Information and Media Manager Sarah Kenyon
National Co-ordinator Ann Deri-Brown

FPA
2-12 Pentonville Road, London N1 9FP
Tel: 020 7837 5432 Fax: 020 7837 3042
Website: www.fpa.org.uk

Chief Executive Anne Weyman

Gay and Lesbian Association of Doctors and Dentists (GLADD)

PO Box 5606, London W4 1WY
Tel: 0870 765 5606
Email: secretary@gladd.org.uk
Website: www.gladd.org.uk

Hon. Co-Chairperson David Harvey
Hon. Secretary Daniel Saunders
Hon. Treasurer Jolyon Oxley

Greater London Fund for the Blind

12 Whitehorse Mews, 37 Westminster Bridge Road, London SE1 7QD
Tel: 020 7620 2066
Email: glfb@glfb.org.uk
Website: www.glfb.org.uk

Chair David Hawkins

The Guide Dogs for the Blind Association

Hillfields, Burghfield Common, Reading RG7 3YG
Tel: 0118 983 5555 Fax: 0118 983 5433, 0118 983 5477
Email: guidedogs@gdba.org.uk
Website: www.gdba.org.uk

Chief Executive Geraldine Peacock

Guild of Catholic Doctors

Brampton House, Hospital of St John and St Elizabeth, 60 Grove End Road, London NW8 9NH
Tel: 020 7266 4246 Fax: 020 7266 4813
Email: enquiries@catholicdoctors.org.uk
Website: www.catholicdoctors.org.uk

Hon. Secretary J Morewood
Master M Jarmulowicz

The Haemophilia Society

Chesterfield House, 385 Euston Road, London NW1 3AU
Tel: 020 7380 0600, 0800 018 6068 (Helpline)
Fax: 020 7387 8220
Email: info@haemophilia.org.uk
Website: www.haemophilia.org.uk

Chief Executive Karin Pappenheim

Harveian Society of London

11 Chandos Street, Cavendish Square, London W1M 0EB
Tel: 020 7580 1043 Fax: 020 7580 5793

Executive Secretary Richard Kinsella-Bevan

Headway - The Brain Injury Association

4 King Edward Court, King Edward Street, Nottingham NG1 1EW
Tel: 0115 924 0800 Fax: 0115 958 4446
Email: enquiries@headway.org.uk
Website: www.headway.org.uk

Chief Executive Peter McCabe
Information Services Manager Marian Carey

Help the Hospices

34-44 Britannia Street, London WC1X 9JG
Tel: 020 7520 8200 Fax: 020 7278 1021
Email: info@helpthehospices.org.uk
Website: www.helpthehospices.org.uk

Chairman Lord Newton of Braintree

History of Anaesthesia Society

118 Appledown Drive, Bury St Edmunds IP32 7HQ
Tel: 01223 713330 Fax: 01223 701993
Email: adams118@keme.co.uk

Hospital Chaplaincies Council (Church of England)

Church House, Great Smith Street, Westminster, London SW1P 3NZ
Tel: 020 7898 1894 Fax: 020 7898 1891

Chief Executive and Director of Training Edward Lewis
Training and Development Officer Tim Battle

Hunterian Society

Lettsom House, 11 Chandos Street, Cavendish Square, London W1M 0EB
Email: mailbox@hunteriansociety.org.uk
Website: www.hunteriansociety.org.uk

Hon. Senior Secretary David Hunter

The Ileostomy and Internal Pouch Support Group (IA)

PO Box 132, Scunthorpe DN15 9YW
Tel: 0800 018 4724 Fax: 01724 721601
Email: ia@ileostomypouch.demon.co.uk
Website: www.ileostomypouch.demon.co.uk

National Secretary J B McKenzie

Independent Healthcare Association

22 Little Russell Street, London WC1A 2HT
Tel: 020 7430 0537 Fax: 020 7242 2681

Chairman David T Ervine
Chief Executive Barry Hassell
Executive Director Tim Evans, Ann Mackay

Institute of Biomedical Science

12 Coldbath Square, London EC1R 5HL
Tel: 020 7713 0214 Fax: 020 7436 4946
Email: mail@ibms.org
Website: www.ibms.org

Chief Executive Alan Potter

Institute of Chiropodists and Podiatrists

27 Wright Street, Southport PR9 0TL
Tel: 01704 546141 Fax: 01704 500477
Email: secretary@inst-chiropodist.org.uk
Website: www.inst-chiropodist.org.uk

Assistant Secretary - Advertising Manager Jill Burnett-Hurst
Secretary Susan Kirkham

Institute of Health Studies

School of Community and Health Studies, Faculty of Health, University of Hull, Hull HU6 7RX
Tel: 01482 465811 Fax: 01482 466402
Email: a.m.alaszewski@comhealth.hull.ac.uk, j.m.wilson@comhealth.hull.ac.uk

Deputy Director Lynda Buckingham
Director Greta Bradley
Lecturer Penny Grubb

Institute of Physics and Engineering in Medicine

Fairmount House, 230 Tadcaster Road, York YO24 1ES
Tel: 01904 610821 Fax: 01904 612279
Email: office@ipem.org.uk
Website: www.ipem.org.uk

Finance Ian Wolstencroft
General Secretary Robert W Neilson
Meetings and Exhibitions Eva Elsner

Institute of Psychosexual Medicine

12 Chandos Street, Cavendish Square, London W1G 9DR
Tel: 020 7580 0631 Fax: 020 7580 0631

Administrative Secretary Susan Beck

MEDICAL ASSOCIATIONS & SOCIETIES

Director of Training Anne V Smith
Scientific Adviser Prudence Tunnadine

Institute of Sports Medicine

The Royal Free and University College Medical School, Charles Bell House, 67-73 Riding House Street, London W1W 7EJ
Tel: 020 7813 2832 Fax: 020 7813 2832
Email: m.hobsley@ucl.ac.uk

Chairman David Money-Coutts
Hon. Secretary W T Orton

International Glaucoma Association

108C Warner Road, London SE5 9HQ
Tel: 020 7737 3265 Fax: 020 7346 5929
Email: info@iga.org.uk
Website: www.iga.org.uk/iga

Chief Executive D Wright
General Manager J Eastick
President R Pitts Crick

International Spinal Research Trust

Bramley Business Centre, Station Road, Bramley, Guildford GU5 0AZ
Tel: 01483 898786 Fax: 01483 898763
Email: info@spinal-research.org, isrt@isrthq.demon.co.uk
Website: www.spinal-research.org

Head of Communications Simon Barnes
Chairman of Trustees Paul Sharpe
Chief Executive Peter Banyard

The Iris Fund for Prevention of Blindness

2nd Floor York House, 199 Westminster Bridge Road, London SE1 7UT
Tel: 020 7928 7743 Fax: 020 7928 7919
Email: info@irisfund.org.uk

Chairman C J Prideaux
Executive Director Michael Roberts
Treasurer G M Powell

King's Fund

11/13 Cavendish Square, London W1G 0AN
Tel: 020 7307 2400 Fax: 020 7307 2801
Email: a.bell@kingsfund.org.uk
Website: www.kingsfund.org.uk

Chief Executive Julia Neuberger
Director of Resources Frank Jackson

Leonard Cheshire Foundation

30 Millbank, London SW1P 4QD
Tel: 020 7802 8200 Fax: 020 7802 8250
Email: info@london.leonard.cheshire.org.uk
Website: www.leonard.cheshire.org.uk

Chair Charles Morland
Director of Public Affairs Peter Maple

Leukaemia Research Fund

43 Great Ormond Street, London WC1N 3JJ
Tel: 020 7405 0101 Fax: 020 7405 3139
Email: info@lrf.org.uk
Website: www.lrf.org.uk

Chief Executive Douglas Osborne
Scientific Director David Grant

Limbless Association

Rehabilitation Centre, Roehampton Lane, London SW15 5PR
Tel: 020 8788 1777 Fax: 020 8788 3444
Website: www.limbless-association.org

Chairman Sam Gallop

Lincoln Clinic and Centre for Psychotherapy

19 Abbeville Mews, 88 Clapham Park Road, London SW4 7BX
Tel: 020 7978 1545 Fax: 020 7720 4721
Email: info@lincoln-psychotherapy.org.uk
Website: www.lincoln-psychotherapy.org.uk

Director and Board Chair Michael Heavens
Professional Committee Chair Duncan McLean

Listening Books

12 Lant Street, London SE1 1QH
Tel: 020 7407 9417 Fax: 020 7403 1377
Email: info@listening-books.org.uk
Website: www.listening-books.org.uk

Lister Institute of Preventive Medicine

The White House, 70 High Road, Bushey Heath, Watford WD23 1GG
Tel: 020 8421 8808 Fax: 020 8421 8818
Email: secretary@lister-institute.org.uk
Website: www.lister-institute.org.uk

Chairperson Dame Anne McLaren
Hon. Treasurer P W Allen
Secretary F K Cowey

The Little Foundation

c/o Mac Keith Press, High Holborn House, 52-54 High Holborn, London WC1V 6RL
Tel: 020 7831 4918 ext: 267 Fax: 020 7405 5365

Chairman A C Robinson

MACA (Mental After Care Association)

25 Bedford Square, London WC1B 3HW
Tel: 020 7436 6194 Fax: 020 7680 1970
Email: maca-bs@maca.org.uk
Website: www.maca.org uk

Chief Executive Gil Hitchon

Macmillan Cancer Relief

89 Albert Embankment, London SE1 7UQ
Tel: 020 7840 7840 Fax: 020 7840 7841
Email: information_line@macmillan.org.uk
Website: www.macmillan.org.uk

Chief Executive Peter Cardy

Marie Curie Cancer Care

89 Albert Embankment, London SW1 7TP
Tel: 020 7599 7777 Fax: 020 7599 7788
Email: info@mariecurie.org.uk
Website: www.mariecurie.org.uk

Acting Research Director Peter O'Hare
Caring Services Director Gail Sharp
Chief Executive Thomas Hughes-Hallett
Finance Director Claire Newton
Human Resources Director Caroline Hamblett
Medical Adviser Teresa Tate
P R & Marketing Director Chris Dainty

Mason Medical Research Foundation

c/o BDO Stoy Hayward, Nile House, PO Box 1034, Nile Street, Brighton BN1 1JB
Tel: 01273 324411 Fax: 01273 779172

Secretary A W Schofield

The Medical Commission on Accident Prevention

35-43 Lincoln's Inn Fields, London WC2A 3PN
Tel: 020 7242 3176 Fax: 020 7242 3176

Chairman K Hashemi

President H R H Prince Michael of Kent
Secretary P C McCausland

The Medical Council on Alcoholism

3 St. Andrew's Place, Regent's Park, London NW1 4LB
Tel: 020 7487 4445 Fax: 020 7935 4479
Email: mca@medicouncilalcol.demon.co.uk
Website: www.medicouncilalcol.demon.co.uk

Chair B Ritson
Executive Director G E Ratcliffe

Medical Missionary Association

First Floor, 106-110 Watney Street, London E1W 2QE
Tel: 020 7790 1336 Fax: 020 7790 1384
Email: info@healthserve.org

Administrator Abraham Ajay
Director Steven Fouch
Fund Raiser Rachel East
Medical Director Peter Armon

Medical Protection Society

Granary Wharf House, Leeds LS11 5PY
Tel: 0113 243 6436 Fax: 0113 241 0500
Email: info@mps.org.uk
Website: www.mps.org.uk

Chairman J P Miller
Chief Executive J Youngman
Communications Manager Liz Peck
Company Secretary Simon Kayll
Marketing Manager John Lamb
Medical Director J Hickey

Medical Research Society

Renal Unit, L Block, Imperial College, Du Cane Road, London W12 0NN
Tel: 020 8383 3152 Fax: 020 8383 2062
Email: a.chaudhry@ic.ac.uk

Chair C Haslett
Hon. Secretary Afzal Chaudhry
Membership Secretary Corinne Wade
Treasurer R D Cohen

Medical Society for the Study of Venereal Diseases

c/o 1 Wimpole Street, London W1G 0AE
Tel: 020 7290 2968 Fax: 020 7290 2989
Email: mssvd@rsm.ac.uk
Website: www.mssvd.org.uk

Hon. Secretary K W Radcliffe
Hon. Treasurer S E Barton
President A J Robinson

The Medical Society of London

Lettsom House, 11 Chandos Street, London W1M 0EB
Tel: 020 7580 1043 Fax: 020 7580 5793

Deputy Registrar B A Smallwood
Registrar Richard Kinsella-Bevan

Medical Women's Federation

Tavistock House North, Tavistock Square, London WC1H 9HX
Tel: 020 7387 7765 Fax: 020 7388 9216
Email: MWF@m-w-f.demon.co.uk
Website: www.mwfonline.org.uk

Hon. Secretary Helen Goodyear
Hon. Treasurer Selena Gray
MWF Office Manager Doreen Desa
President Kate Ward
Vice-President Pauline Brumblecombe

Medico-Legal Society

c/o Hempsons Solicitors, 20 Embankment Place, London WC2N 6NN
Website: www.medico-legalsociety.org.uk

Hon. Legal Secretary Jill Crombie

MENCAP

National Centre, 123 Golden Lane, London EC1Y 0RT
Tel: 020 7454 0454, 020 7608 3254
Email: information@mencap.org.uk
Website: www.mencap.org.uk

Chairman Brian Baldock
Chief Executive Fred Heddell
Director of Communications and Fundraising David Scott-Ralphs
Director of Finance David Lawrence
Director of Operations Martin artin Gallagher
Director of Public Affairs David Congdon

Meningitis Trust

Fern House, Bath Road, Stroud GL5 3TJ
Tel: 01453 768000 Fax: 01453 768001
Email: info@meningitis-trust.org.uk
Website: www.meningitis-trust.org.uk

Deputy Chief Executive Angela Dudley

Mental Health Foundation

UK Office, 20-21 Cornwall Terrace, London NW1 4QL
Tel: 020 7535 7400 Fax: 020 7535 7474
Email: mhf@mhf.org.uk
Website: www.mentalhealth.org.uk

Director Ruth Lesirge

Mental Health Matters

9-10 Enterprise House, Kingsway, Team Valley Trading Estate, Gateshead NE11 0SR
Tel: 0191 497 1600 Fax: 0191 487 7945

Chief Executive Ian Grant

Mental Health Media

356 Holloway Road, London N7 6PA
Tel: 020 7700 8171 Fax: 020 7686 0959
Email: info@mhmedia.com
Website: www.mhmedia.com

Deputy Director David Crepaz-Keay
Director Karen Mattison

Migraine Action Association

Unit 6, Oakley Hay Lodge Business Park, Great Folds Road, Great Oakley NN18 9AS
Tel: 01932 352468 Fax: 01932 351257
Email: info@migraine.org.uk
Website: www.migraine.org.uk

Director Ann Turner

Migraine Trust

45 Great Ormond Street, London WC1N 3HZ
Tel: 020 7831 4818 Fax: 020 7831 5174
Website: www.migrainetrust.org

Head of Fundraising and PR Rebecca Porta
Director Ann Rush
Education Officer Cathy Fernandes
Support Services Manager Pauline Sythoff

MIND (National Association for Mental Health)

15-19 Broadway, London E15 4BQ
Tel: 020 8519 2122, 0845 7 660163 (Infoline)
Fax: 020 8522 1725
Email: a.hendra@mind.org.uk

MEDICAL ASSOCIATIONS & SOCIETIES

Chief Executive Richard Brook
Finance & Resources Director Katherine Gardiner

Motor Neurone Disease Association

PO Box 246, Northampton NN1 2PR
Tel: 08457 626262 Fax: 01604 624726
Email: enquiries@mndassociation.org
Website: www.mndassociation.org

Chairman Paul Spencer
Chief Executive G Levy
Treasurer Alistair Johnston

Multiple Sclerosis Society of Great Britain and N. Ireland

MS National Centre, 372 Edware Road, London NW2 6ND
Tel: 020 8438 0700, 0808 800 8000 (Helpline)
Fax: 020 8438 0701
Email: info@mssociety.org.uk
Website: www.mssociety.org.uk

Chief Executive Ken Walker

Muscular Dystrophy Campaign

7-11 Prescott Place, London SW4 6BS
Tel: 020 7720 8055 Fax: 020 7498 0670

Chairman Martin Bobrow
Executive Director Christine Cryne
President Lord Attenborough of Richmond

Myasthenia Gravis Association

Keynes House, Chester Park, Alfreton Road, Derby DE21 4AS
Tel: 01332 290219 Fax: 01332 293641
Email: mg@mgaderby.fsnet.co.uk

Patron The Duchess of Devonshire

National Association for Medical Education Management (incorporating NAPMECA)

Education Centre, Southend Hospital, Westcliff on Sea, Essex SS0 0RY
Tel: 01702 221083 Fax: 01702 221406
Email: jsharpe@southend.nhs.uk
Website: www.namem.org.uk

Chairman Jenny Murray
Executive Secretary Judy Sharpe
Vice Chairman Allysen Williamson

National Association for the Education of Sick Children

18 Victoria Park Square, Bethnal Green, London E2 9PF
Tel: 020 8980 8523 Fax: 020 8980 3447
Email: naesc@ednsick.demon.co.uk
Website: www.sickchildren.org.uk / www.satelliteschool.org.uk

Director Carolyn E Skilling

National Association of Clinical Tutors

1 Wimpole Street, London W1G 0AE
Tel: 020 7629 4000 Fax: 020 7629 4000
Email: office@nact.org.uk

Chairman Alistair Thomson

National Association of GP Co-operatives

Regency House, 90-92 Otley Road, Leeds LS6 4BA
Tel: 0113 278381 Fax: 0113 278 3674
Email: manager@nagpc.org.uk
Website: www.nagpc.org.uk

Chair Mark Reynolds

The National Association of Primary Care

Lettsom House, 11 Chandos Street, Cavendish Square, London W1G 9DP
Tel: 020 7636 7228 Fax: 020 7636 1601
Email: napc@primarycare.co.uk
Website: www.primarycare.co.uk

Chairman Peter Smith
Chief Executive Eric McCullough
Hon. Secretary Roger O'Brian-Hill
President Rod Smith
Treasurer James Carne

National Asthma Campaign

Providence House, Providence Place, London N1 0NT
Tel: 020 7226 2260, 0845 701 0203 (Asthma Helpline)
Fax: 020 7704 0740
Website: www.asthma.org.uk

Chief Executive Donna Covey
Hon. Treasurer A Gairdner

National Autistic Society

393 City Road, London EC1V 1NG
Tel: 020 7833 2299 Fax: 020 7833 9666
Email: nas@nas.org.uk
Website: www.nas.org.uk

Chief Executive Vernon Beauchamp
Director of Services Richard Mills

National Birthday Trust Fund

27 Sussex Place, Regent's Park, London NW1 4SP
Tel: 020 7772 6400 Fax: 020 7724 7725
Email: wellbeing@rcog.org.uk
Website: www.wellbeing.org.uk

Secretary Peter Wiard

National Cancer Alliance

PO Box 579, Oxford OX4 1LB
Tel: 01865 251050, 01865 793566
Email: nationalcanceralliance@btinternet.com
Website: www.nationalcanceralliance.co.uk

Director Rebecca Miles

The National Childbirth Trust

Alexandra House, Oldham Terrace, Acton, London W3 6NH
Tel: 0870 444 8707 (Enquiries),
0870 444 8708 (Breastfeeding Helpline),
0870 770 3236 (Administration), 0870 770 3238 (Press Office),
0870 990 8040 (Membership Hotline) Fax: 0870 770 3237
Email: enquiries@national-childbirth-trust.co.uk
Website: www.nctpregnancyandbabycare.com / www.nct-online.org

Head of Policy Research Mary Newburn
Chairman of Trustees Council Bernadette Matus

National Children's Bureau

8 Wakley Street, London EC1V 7QE
Tel: 020 7843 6000 Fax: 020 7278 9512
Email: membership@ncb.org.uk
Website: www.ncb.org.uk

Chief Executive Paul Ennals

National Council for Hospice and Specialist Palliative Care Services

7th Floor, 1 Great Cumberland Place, London W1H 7AL
Tel: 020 7723 1639 Fax: 020 7723 5380
Email: enquiries@hospice-spc-council.org.uk
Website: www.hospice-spc-council.org.uk

Executive Director Eve Sara Richardson

National Counselling Service for Sick Doctors

1 Park Square West, London NW1 4LJ
Tel: 020 7306 3272 Fax: 020 7306 3271

The National Deaf Children's Society

National Office, 15 Dufferin Street, London EC1Y 8UR
Tel: 020 7250 0123 Helpline, 020 7490 8656
Fax: 020 7251 5020
Email: ndcs@ndcs.org.uk

National Eczema Society

Hill House, Highgate Hill, London N19 5NA
Tel: 020 7281 3553 Fax: 020 7281 6395
Website: www.eczema.org

The National Kidney Research Fund

Kings Chambers, Priestgate, Peterborough PE1 1FG
Tel: 01733 704650 Fax: 01733 704699
Email: enquiries@nkrf.org.uk
Website: www.nkrf.org.uk

Head of Charity Affairs N Turkentine
Chief Executive A A Pinchera
Director of Finance C D Thomas
Director of Fundraising M Nation

The National League of the Blind and Disabled

2 Tenterden Road, Tottenham, London N17 8BE
Tel: 020 8808 6030 Fax: 020 8885 3235

General Secretary J P B Mann

National Library for the Blind

Far Cromwell Road, Bredbury, Stockport SK6 2SG
Tel: 0161 355 2000, 0161 355 2043 Minicom Fax: 0161 355 2098
Email: enquiries@nlbuk.org
Website: www.nlbuk.org

Acting Chief Executive Helen Brazier

National Meningitis Trust

Fern House, Bath Road, Stroud GL5 3TJ
Email: support@meningitis-trust.org.uk
Website: www.meningitis-trust.org.uk

Chair Geoff Shaw
Chief Executive Philip Kirby
President Andrew Harvey

National Osteoporosis Society

Camerton, Bath BA2 0PJ
Tel: 01761 471771 Fax: 01761 471104
Email: info@nos.org.uk
Website: www.nos.org.uk

Director Linda Edwards

National Pharmaceutical Association

Mallinson House, 40-42 St Peter's Street, St Albans AL1 3NP
Tel: 01727 840858 Fax: 01727 810252
Email: npa@npa.co.uk
Website: www.npa.co.uk

Chief Executive John D'Arcy

National Schizophrenia Fellowship

28 Castle Street, Kingston upon Thames KT1 1SS
Tel: 020 8547 3937 Fax: 020 8547 3862
Email: info@nsf.org.uk
Website: www.nsf.org.uk

Head of Fundraising Louise Farnell
Head of Policy & Campaigning Gary Hogman
Chair Jenny Fisher
Chief Executive Cliff Prior
Deputy Chief Executive Liz Felton

Director of Human Resources Chris Bolton
Director of Membership Terry Hammond
Director of NSF N. Ireland Michael Woodhall
Director of NSF Wales Bill Walden Jones
Director of Operations Willi Butler, Eddie Greenwood
Director of Public Affairs Paul Farmer
Director of Service Development Erica Lewis
Finance Director Noel Flannery
President J K Wing

National Society for Epilepsy

Chesham Lane, Chalfont St Peter SL9 0RJ
Tel: 01494 601300, 01494 601400 Helpline Fax: 01494 871927
Website: www.epilepsynse.org.uk

Chief Executive Graham Faulkner
Director of Finance and Facilities Michael De Vol
Director of Nursing and Care Colin Bradbury
Director of Personnel and Training Carol Macham
Medical Director John Duncan
PA to Chief Executive Liz Ward

National Society for the Prevention of Cruelty to Children (NSPCC)

NSPCC National Centre, 42 Curtain Road, London EC2A 3NH
Tel: 020 7825 2500 Fax: 020 7825 2525

NCH Action for Children

85 Highbury Park, London N5 1UD
Tel: 020 7704 7000 Fax: 020 7226 2537
Website: www.nchafc.org.uk

Chief Executive Deryk Mead

The Neuro-Disability Research Trust

Royal Hospital for Neuro-disability, West Hill, London SW15 3SW
Tel: 020 8780 4568 Fax: 020 8789 3098
Email: pkennerley@rhn.org.uk
Website: www.rhn.org.uk/nrt

Chairman P Crossland

NHS Confederation

1 Warwick Row, London SW1E 5ER
Tel: 020 7959 7239, 020 7959 7275
Email: enquiries@nhsconfed.co.uk
Website: www.nhsconfed.net

Chief Executive Gillian Morgan

NHS Retirement Fellowship

Central Office, Stoke Mandeville Hospital, Mandeville Road, Aylesbury HP21 8AL
Tel: 01296 330471 Fax: 01296 330471

Fellowship Director Roger Titley

NHS Support Federation

37-39 Great Guildford Street, London SE1 0ES
Tel: 020 7633 0801 Fax: 020 7633 0343
Email: website@nhscampaign.org
Website: www.nhscampaign.org

Assistant Director Paul Evans
Director Michael Walker
President Harry Keen

NHS Training and Conference Centre

The White Hart, Cold Bath Road, Harrogate HG2 0NF
Tel: 01423 505681

General Manager Andrew Sillars

MEDICAL ASSOCIATIONS & SOCIETIES

Nuffield Institute for Health

The University of Leeds, 71-75 Clarendon Road, Leeds LS2 9PL
Tel: 0113 233 6942 Fax: 0113 246 0899
Email: nuffield@leeds.ac.uk
Website: www.leeds.ac.uk/nuffield/home.html

Information and Admissions Co-ordinator Zeba Ahmed
Senior Administrator Vivienne Sercombe

Nuffield Trust

59 New Cavendish Street, London W1G 7RD
Tel: 020 7631 8450 Fax: 020 7631 8451
Email: mail@nuffieldtrust.org.uk
Website: www.nuffieldtrust.org.uk

Secretary John Wyn Owen

Nutrition Society

10 Cambridge Court, 210 Shepherds Bush Road, London W6 7NJ
Tel: 020 7602 0228 Fax: 020 7602 1756
Email: office@nutsoc.org.uk
Website: www.nutsoc.org.uk

Hon. Secretary Judith Buttris
President John Mathers

Obstetric Anaesthetists' Association

PO Box 3219, Barnes, London SW13 9XR
Tel: 020 8741 1311 Fax: 020 8741 0611
Email: secretariat@oaa-anaes.ac.uk
Website: www.oaa-anaes.ac.uk

Hon. Secretary Mike Wee
Hon. Treasurer Roshan Fernando
President Anne May

Office of Health Economics

12 Whitehall, London SW1A 2DY
Tel: 020 7930 9203 Fax: 020 7747 1419
Website: www.ohe.org

Associate Director Jon Sussex
Director Adrian Towse

One Parent Families (National Council for One Parent Families)

255 Kentish Town Road, London NW5 2LX
Tel: 020 7428 5400, 0800 018 5026 Fax: 020 7482 4851
Email: info@oneparentfamilies.org.uk
Website: www.oneparentfamilies.org.uk

The Pain Society

9 Bedford Square, London WC1B 3RE
Tel: 020 7636 2750 Fax: 020 7323 2015
Email: painsoc@compuserve.com

Hon. Secretary Chris Wells

Parkinson's Disease Society of the United Kingdom

215 Vauxhall Bridge Road, London SW1V 1EJ
Tel: 020 7931 8080, 0808 800 0303 Helpline (Freephone)
Fax: 020 7233 9908
Email: enquiries@parkinsons.org.uk

Chief Executive Linda Kelly
President Richard Briers

Pathological Society of Great Britain and Ireland

2 Carlton House Terrace, London SW1Y 5AF
Tel: 020 7976 1260 Fax: 020 7976 1267
Email: administrator@pathsoc.org.uk
Website: www.pathsoc.org.uk

Administrator R A Pitts

General Secretary M Wells
Meetings Secretary C S Herrington
President N A Wright
Treasurer D A Levison

The Patients Association

PO Box 935, Harrow HA1 3YJ
Tel: 020 8423 9111, 0845 608 4455 (Helpline)
Fax: 020 8423 9119
Email: mailbox@patients-association.com

Chairman Vanessa Bourne

The Pituitary Foundation

PO Box 1944, Bristol BS99 2UB
Tel: 0870 774 3355 Fax: 0870 774 3355
Email: helpline@pitpat.demon.co.uk
Website: www.pituitary.org.uk

Director Tim Wheadon
Patient Support Manager Theresa O'Neill

Primary Immunodeficiency Association

Alliance House, 12 Caxton Street, London SW1H 0QS
Tel: 020 7976 7640 Fax: 020 7976 7641
Email: pimmune@dial.pipex.com
Website: www.pia.org.uk

General Secretary David G Watters

Psoriasis Association

7 Milton Street, Northampton NN2 7JG
Tel: 01604 711129 Fax: 01604 792894
Email: mail@psoriasis.demon.co.uk

Chief Executive Gladys Edwards

Queen's Nursing Institute

3 Albemarle Way, Clerkenwell, London EC1V 4RQ
Tel: 020 7490 4227 Fax: 020 7490 1296
Email: info@qni.org.uk
Website: www.qni.org.uk

QUIT

Victory House, 170 Tottenham Court Road, London W1T 7NR
Tel: 020 7388 5775 Fax: 020 7388 5995
Email: PeterJ-McCabe@compuserve.com
Website: www.quit.org.uk

Director Peter McCabe

Rainbow Trust

Claire House, Bridge Street, Leatherhead KT22 8BZ
Tel: 01372 363438 Fax: 01372 363101
Email: enquiries@rainbowtrust.org.uk
Website: www.rainbowtrust.org.uk

Chief Executive Heather Wood

REMEDI For Relief of Disability

The Old Rectory, Stanton Prior, Bath BA2 9HT
Tel: 01761 472662 Fax: 01761 470662
Email: g.coles_remedi@btinternet.com
Website: www.remedi.org.uk

Chairman A K Clarke
Director P D Mesquita
Treasurer A H M Heagerty

Research into Ageing

PO Box 32833, London N1 9ZQ
Tel: 020 7843 1114 Fax: 020 7843 1559
Email: ria@ageing.org

Chairman Jack Mather
Director Michael Lake
Research Manager Susanne Sorensen

The Restoration of Appearance and Function Trust

Leopold Muller Building, Mount Vernon Hospital, Northwood HA6 2RN
Tel: 01923 835815 Fax: 01923 844031
Email: charity@raft.ac.uk
Website: www.raft.ac.uk

Accountant John Shepherd
Board of Trustees Chairman David C T Pollock
Director (Admin and Appeals) Hilary Bailey
Director of Research Roy Sanders

Restricted Growth Association

PO Box 4744, Dorchester DT2 9FA
Tel: 01308 898445 Fax: 01308 898445
Email: RGA1@talk21.com
Website: www.ragonline.org.uk

Association Manager Sandy Marshall

Richmond Fellowship

80 Holloway Road, London N7 8JG
Tel: 020 7697 3300 Fax: 020 7697 3301
Website: www.richmondfellowship.org.uk

Royal Association for Deaf People

RAD Head Office, Walsingham Road, Colchester CO2 7BP
Tel: 01206 509509, 01206 577090 (Text),
01206 710064 (Videophone) Fax: 01206 769755
Email: info@royaldeaf.org.uk
Website: www.royaldeaf.org.uk

Chief Executive Tom Fenton

Royal Association for Disability and Rehabilitation

12 City Forum, 250 City Road, London EC1V 8AF
Tel: 020 7250 3222 Fax: 020 7250 0212
Email: radar@radar.org.uk
Website: www.radar.org.uk

Director Michael Smith

The Royal British Legion

48 Pall Mall, London SW1Y 5JY
Tel: 020 7973 7200 Fax: 020 7973 7399
Email: info@britishlegion.org.uk
Website: www.britishlegion.org.uk

Secretary General I G Townsend

Royal British Nurses Association

Duke of York's Headquarters, 424 Left Wing, Turks Road, Chelsea, London SW3 4RY
Tel: 020 7730 0624

Chairperson and Vice-President H M Campbell

Royal Institute of Public Health

28 Portland Place, London W1B 1DE
Tel: 020 7580 2731 Fax: 020 7580 6157
Email: info@riph.org.uk
Website: www.riph.org.uk

Communications Officer Julie Knope

Royal Medical Benevolent Fund

24 King's Road, Wimbledon, London SW19 8QN
Tel: 020 8540 9194 Fax: 020 8542 0494
Email: info@rmbf.org
Website: www.rmbf.org.uk

Chief Executive Officer Michael Baber

The Royal Medical Foundation

Epsom College, Epsom KT17 4JQ
Tel: 01372 821010, 01372 821011 Fax: 01372 821013
Email: rmf@epsomcollege.org.uk
Website: www.epsomcollege.org.uk/rmt

Administrator John H Higgs

Royal Medical Society

Student Centre, 5/5 Bristo Square, Edinburgh EH8 9AL
Tel: 0131 650 2672 Fax: 0131 650 2672
Email: enquiries@royalmedical.co.uk
Website: www.royalmedical.co.uk

President Tim Andrews, Kirsty Moreland
Senior President Katherine Paramore
Senior Secretary Joanne Sells

Royal National Institute for Deaf People

19-23 Featherstone Street, London EC1Y 8SL
Tel: 0808 808 0123, 0808 808 9000 Fax: 020 7296 8199
Website: www.rnid.org.uk

Chairman David Livermore
Chief Executive James Strachan

Royal National Institute for the Blind

105 Judd Street, London WC1H 9NE
Tel: 020 7388 1266, 0845 766 9999 Fax: 020 7388 3160
Email: helpline@rnib.org.uk
Website: www.rnib.org.uk

Director General I Bruce
Hon. Treasurer David Gadbury

Royal Pharmaceutical Society of Great Britain

1 Lambeth High Street, London SE1 7JN
Tel: 020 7735 9141 Fax: 020 7735 7629
Email: enquiries@rpsgb.org.uk
Website: www.rpsgb.org.uk

President Christine Glover

The Royal Society

6 Carlton House Terrace, London SW1Y 5AG
Tel: 020 7839 5561 Fax: 020 7930 2170
Email: info@royalsoc.ac.uk
Website: www.royalsoc.ac.uk

Executive Secretary Stephen Cox

Royal Society for the Prevention of Accidents

Royal Society for the Prevention of Accidents (RoSPA), Edgbaston Park, 353 Bristol Road, Birmingham B5 7ST
Tel: 0121 248 2000 Fax: 0121 248 2001
Email: help@rospa.co.uk
Website: www.rospa.co.uk

Chief Executive John D Hooper

The Royal Society for the Promotion of Health

38A St George's Drive, London SW1V 4BH
Tel: 020 7630 0121 Fax: 020 7976 6847
Email: nkendall@rshealth.org.uk, rshealth@rshealth.org.uk
Website: www.rsph.org

Chief Executive Hugh A Lowson

The Royal Society of Medicine

1 Wimpole Street, London W1G 0AE
Tel: 020 7290 2900 Fax: 020 7290 2992
Email: membership@rsm.ac.uk
Website: www.rsm.ac.uk

Director of Finance David Laughton
Director of Information Services Ian Snowley
Director of Publications Peter Richardson

MEDICAL ASSOCIATIONS & SOCIETIES

Director of Support Services John Tyrrell
Executive Director Anne Grocock
Membership Director Stephen Barton

Royal Society of Tropical Medicine and Hygiene

Manson House, 26 Portland Place, London W1B 1EY
Tel: 020 7580 2127 Fax: 020 7436 1389
Email: mail@rstmh.org
Website: www.rstmh.org

Administrator Caryl R Guest

RSAS Agecare (Royal Surgical Aid Society)

47 Great Russell Street, London WC1B 3PA
Tel: 020 7637 4577 Fax: 020 7323 6878
Email: enquiries@agecare.org.uk
Website: www.agecare.org.uk

Chairman J Wedgwood
Chief Executive Michael Corp

The Sainsbury Centre for Mental Health

134 Borough High Street, London SE1 1LB
Tel: 020 7827 8300 Fax: 020 7403 9482
Website: www.scmh.org.uk

Director Matt Muijen

St Andrew's Ambulance Association

St Andrew's House, 48 Milton Street, Glasgow G4 0HR
Tel: 0141 332 4031 Fax: 0141 332 6582
Email: firstaid@staaa.demon.co.uk
Website: www.firstaid.org.uk

Chief Executive Brendan Healy
Training Manager Jim Dorman

St Dunstan's (Caring for Blind Ex-Service Men and Women)

12-14 Harcourt Street, London W1H 4HD
Tel: 020 7723 5021 Fax: 020 7262 6199

Chief Executive Robert Leader
Director of Admissions & Grant Making Services Jeremy Hinton

St John Ambulance

1 Grosvenor Crescent, London SW1X 7EF
Tel: 020 7235 5231 Fax: 020 7235 0796

Chief Executive Lewis Martin

St John and Red Cross Joint Committee

5 Grosvenor Crescent, London SW1X 7EH
Tel: 020 7201 5131 Fax: 020 7235 9350

St John's Hospital Dermatological Society

St John's Institute of Dermatology, St Thomas' Hospital, London SE1 7EH
Tel: 020 7928 9292 Ext: 1334 Fax: 020 7922 8346

Hon. Secretary Piu Banerjee

Stillbirth and Neonatal Death Society

SANDS - Stillbirth and Neonatal Death Society, 28 Portland Place, London W1B 1LY
Tel: 020 7436 5881 (Helpline), 020 7436 7940 (Office)
Fax: 020 7436 3715
Email: support@uk-sands.org
Website: www.uk-sands.org

Chair Hélène Currie

SANE/SANELINE

1st Floor, Cityside House, 40 Adler Street, London E1 1EE
Tel: 020 7375 1002, 0845 767 8000 (Helpline)
Fax: 020 7375 2162
Email: info@sane.org.uk
Website: www.sane.org.uk

Save the Children

17 Grove Lane, London SE5 8RD
Tel: 020 7703 5400 Fax: 020 7703 2278
Website: www.savethechildren.org.uk

Director General Michael Aaronson
UK Director Judy Lister

Scope

Cerebral Palsy Helpline, PO Box 833, Milton Keynes MK12 5NY
Tel: 01908 321051, 0808 800 3333
Email: cphelpline@scope.org.uk
Website: www.scope.org.uk

Chairman Gerald McCarthy
Chief Executive Richard Brewster
Executive Director, Contract Services John Adams
Helpline Manager Veronica Lynch

Scottish Association for Mental Health

Cumbrae House, 15 Carlton Court, Glasgow G5 9JP
Tel: 0141 568 7000 Fax: 0141 568 7001
Email: enquire@samh.org.uk
Website: www.samh.org.uk

Scottish Committee of Optometrists

7 Queens Buildings, Queensferry Road, Rosyth, Dunfermline KY11 2RA
Tel: 01383 419444 Fax: 01383 416778

Chairman Frank A Munro
Secretary & Treasurer David S Hutton

Scottish Health Visitors' Association

Douglas House, 60 Belford Road, Edinburgh EH4 3UQ
Tel: 0131 226 2662 Fax: 0131 220 6389

General Administration Officer David F Forbes

Scottish Hospital Endowments Research Trust

Princes Exchange, 1 Earl Grey Street, Edinburgh EH3 9EE
Tel: 0131 659 8800 Fax: 0131 228 8118

Chairman Roland Jung

The Scottish National Federation for the Welfare of the Blind

5 Balmashanner Rise, Forfar DD8 1PD
Tel: 01307 460359 Fax: 01307 460359
Email: snfwb@care4free.net

Hon. Treasurer John Duncan

Scottish Pharmaceutical General Council

42 Queen Street, Edinburgh EH2 3NH
Tel: 0131 467 7766 Fax: 0131 467 7767
Website: www.spgc.org.uk

Secretary Colin Virden

Sesame Institute (UK)

Christchurch, 27 Blackfriars Road, London SE1 8NY
Tel: 020 7633 9690
Email: sesameinstituteuk@btinternet.com

Chair Susan Bulmer
Hon. Secretary Sarah Hall-Matthews

Shaftesbury Society

16 Kingston Road, London SW19 1JZ
Tel: 020 8239 5555 Fax: 020 8239 5580
Email: info@shaftesburysoc.org.uk
Website: www.shaftesburysoc.org.uk

Chief Executive Fran Beckett

Shape London

LVS Resource Centre, 356 Holloway Road, London N7 6PA
Tel: 020 7700 8139 Fax: 020 7700 8143

Chief Executive Steve Mannix

The Sigma Centre

29A Netherhall Gardens, London NW3 5RL
Tel: 020 7794 2445 Fax: 020 7431 3726
Email: info@thesigmacentre.com
Website: www.thesigmacentre.com

Chairman Warren Kinston
Managing Partner Verity Goitein

The Sir Jules Thorn Charitable Trust

24 Manchester Square, London W1U 3TH
Tel: 020 7487 5851 Fax: 020 7224 3976
Email: julesthorntrust@compuserve.com
Website: www.julesthorntrust.org.uk

Chairman Ann J Rylands
Director David H Richings
Trust Secretary Marcia Howard

Smith and Nephew Foundation

Heron House, 15 Adam Street, London WC2N 6LA
Tel: 020 7960 2276 Fax: 020 7960 2298
Email: barbara.foster@smith-nephew.com
Website: www.snfoundation.org.uk

Executive Secretary Davis Hawkins

The Society and the College of Radiographers

207 Providence Square, Mill Street, London SE1 2EW
Tel: 020 7740 7200 Fax: 020 7740 7204
Email: info@sor.org
Website: www.sor.org

Director of Finance Neil Williams
Director of Industrial Relations Warren Town
Director of Professional Development Caroline Wright

Society for Endocrinology

17-18 The Courtyard, Woodlands, Bradley Stoke, Bristol BS12 4NQ
Tel: 01454 642200 Fax: 01454 642222
Email: info@endocrinology.org
Website: www.endocrinology.org

Executive Director S Franks, Sue Thorn
General Secretary S R Bloom

Society of Academic and Research Surgery

SARS Secretariat, Academic Surgical Unit, University of Hull, Castle Hill Hospital, Castle Road, Cottingham HU16 5JQ
Tel: 01482 623225 Fax: 01482 623274
Email: J.R.Monson@medschool.hull.ac.uk
Website: www.surgicalresearch.org.uk

Hon. Secretary J R T Monson
President D Bouchier-Hayes

Society of British Neurological Surgeons

University Department of Neurosurgery, Royal College of Surgeons, 35-43 Lincoln's Inn Fields, London WC2 3PN
Tel: 020 7869 6892 Fax: 020 7869 6890
Email: admin@sbns.freeserve.co.uk

President G M Teasdale

Treasurer R S Maurice-Williams
Vice-President G Neil-Dwyer

Society of Cardiothoracic Surgeons of Great Britain and Ireland

Royal College of Surgeons of England, 35-43 Lincoln's Inn Fields, London W2A 3PN
Tel: 020 8696 893
Email: sctsadmin@scts.org
Website: www.scts.org

Hon. Secretary B Keogh
President J Monro

The Society of Chiropodists and Podiatrists

1 Fellmongers Path, Tower Bridge Road, London SE1 3LY
Tel: 020 7234 8620 Fax: 020 7234 8621
Email: enq@scpod.org
Website: www.feetforlife.org

Director of External Relations Nita Parmar

Society of Occupational Medicine

6 St Andrew's Place, Regent's Park, London NW1 4LB
Tel: 020 7486 2641 Fax: 020 7486 0028
Email: som@sococcmed.demon.co.uk
Website: www.som.org.uk

Hon. Secretary D H Wright

Society of Public Health

28 Portland Place, London W1N 4DE
Tel: 020 7580 2731, 020 7636 1208 Fax: 020 7580 6157

The Stroke Association

Stroke House, 123 Whitecross Street, London EC1Y 8JJ
Tel: 020 7566 0300 Fax: 020 7490 2686
Email: stroke@stroke.org.uk
Website: www.stroke.org.uk

Chief Executive Margaret Goose
Secretary Richard Polson

Tavistock Institute

30 Tabernacle Street, London EC2A 4UE
Tel: 020 7417 0407 Fax: 020 7417 0567

Tenovus

43 The Parade, Cardiff CF24 3AB
Tel: 029 2048 2000 Fax: 029 2048 4199
Email: post@tenovus.com
Website: www.tenovus.com

Chief Executive Marc Phillips

Terrence Higgins Trust Lighthouse

52-54 Gray's Inn Road, London WC1X 8JU
Tel: 020 7831 0330 Fax: 020 7242 0121
Email: info@tht.org.uk
Website: www.tht.org.uk

Chief Executive Nick Partridge

TFC Frost Charitable Trust

Holmes & Co., 10 Torrington Road, Claygate, Esher KT10 0SA
Tel: 01372 465378 Fax: 01372 464539

Secretary J Holmes

Tuberous Sclerosis Association

PO Box 9644, Bromsgrove B61 0FP
Tel: 01527 871898 Fax: 01527 579452
Email: support@tuberous-sclerosis.org
Website: www.tuberous-sclerosis.org

MEDICAL ASSOCIATIONS & SOCIETIES

Head of Appeals and Publicity Officer Anne Carter
Head of Support Services Janet Medcalf

UK Centre for the Advancement of Interprofessional Education (CAIPE)

344-354 Gray's Inn Road, London WC1X 8BP
Tel: 020 7278 1083 Fax: 020 7278 6604
Website: admin@caipe.org.uk

Chief Executive Barbara Clague

UK Public Health Association (UKPHA)

Trevelyan House, 30 Great Peter Street, London SW1P 2HW
Email: info@ukpha.org.uk
Website: www.ukpha.org.uk

Chair Geof Rayner

WellBeing

27 Sussex Place, Regent's Park, London NW1 4SP
Tel: 020 7772 6400
Email: Wellbeing@rcog.org.uk
Website: www.wellbeing.org.uk

Director Jane Arnell

Wessex Medical Trust (Hope)

Allport House, Prince's Street, Southampton SO14 5RP
Tel: 023 8033 3366 Fax: 023 8033 3377
Email: info@hope.org.uk

West Midlands Health Research Unit

Room 133, Gazette Buildings, 168 Corporation Street, Birmingham B4 6TF
Tel: 0121 236 0483 Fax: 0121 200 8336
Email: research@wmhru.u.net.com

Co-Director Louise Kilbride, Paula Smith

William Harvey Research Institute

St. Bartholomew's Hospital Medical College, Charterhouse Square, London EC1M 6BQ

Tel: 020 7982 6119 Fax: 020 7251 1685

Chairman Sir John Vane

The Wishbone Trust

35-43 Lincoln's Inn Fields, London WC2A 3PE
Tel: 020 7869 6930 Fax: 020 7869 6940
Email: info@wishbone.org.uk
Website: www.wishbone.org.uk

Executive Director S V M Clark

Women's Nationwide Cancer Control Campaign

1st Floor, Charity House, 14-15 Perseverance Works, London E2 8DD
Tel: 020 7729 4688 Fax: 020 7613 0771
Email: admin@wncc.org.uk
Website: www.wnccc.org.uk

Administrator Judy Harding
Chairman Mary Buchanan
Information Officer Mary Button

The Worshipful Society of Apothecaries of London

Apothecaries Hall, Black Friars Lane, London EC4V 6EJ
Tel: 020 7236 1180 Fax: 020 7329 3177
Email: examoffice@apothecaries.org
Website: www.apothecaries.org

Clerk R J Stringer

Yorkshire Cancer Research

39 East Parade, Harrogate HG1 5LQ
Tel: 01423 501269 Fax: 01423 527929
Website: www.ycr.org.uk

Chairman B P Jackson
Chief Executive Elaine King
Consultant M R Harrison
Scientific Advisory Committee Chair E A Dawes
Secretary Elaine King

Index by Organisation Name

Abbey Caldew Hospital 4557
Abbey Carrick Glen Hospital 4568
Abbey Gisburne Park Hospital 4557
Abbey Kings Park Hospital 4568
Abbey Park Hospital 4557
Abbey Sefton Hospital 4557
Abbotswood Road Day Hospital 4371
Aberaeron Cottage Hospital 4536
Aberbargoed and District Hospital 4537
Aberdare Hospital 4539
Aberdeen City Hospital 4520
Aberdeen Maternity Hospital 4521
Aberdeen Royal Infirmary 4521
Aberfeldy Cottage Hospital 4529
Aberford Centre for Psychiatry 4501
Abergele Hospital 4537
Abertillery and District Hospital 4537
Aboyne Hospital 4520
Abraham Cowley Unit 4377
Abraham Cowley Unit Day Hospital 4377
Abraham Ormerod Day Hospital 4382
Accrington Victoria Community Hospital 4389
Acland Nuffield Hospital 4557
Acorn Drug and Alcohol Services 4490
Acorn Street Day Hospital 4522
Acre Day Hospital 4512
Action for Sick Children (National Association for the Welfare of Children in Hospital) 4664
Action for Victims of Medical Accidents 4664
Action on Smoking and Health (ASH) 4664
Action Research 4664
Adams Day Hospital 4447
Adamson Hospital 4518
Addenbrooke's Hospital 4363
Addenbrooke's NHS Trust 4363
Adult Mental Health Unit 4480
Adult Psychiatry Day Hospital 4480
Adur, Arun and Worthing Primary Care Trust 4364
Age Concern England (The National Council on Ageing) 4664
Ailsa Hospital 4515
Aintree Hospitals NHS Trust 4364
Aire Court Community Unit 4420
Aire Court Hospital 4420
Airedale General Hospital 4364
Airedale General Hospital - Day Hospital for Elderly 4365
Airedale NHS Trust 4364
Airedale NHS Trust, Department of Medical Education 4622
Airedale Primary Care Trust 4365
Albany Road Day Hospital 4371
Albertbridge Road Day Hospital 4549
Albyn Hospital 4568
Alcester Hospital 4483
Alcohol Advisory Day Hospital 4504
Alcohol Concern 4664
Aldeburgh and District Community Hospital 4425
Alder Hey Children's Hospital 4464
Alderney Hospital 4394
Alexander Hospital 4524
Alexandra Gardens Day Hospital 4547
Alexandra Hospital 4511
Alfred Bean Hospital 4415
All Hallows Hospital 4557
All Saints' Hospital 4373
All Saints' Hospital, Eastbourne 4403
Alnwick Infirmary 4449
Altnagelvin Area Hospital 4544
Altnagelvin Hospital Postgraduate Medical Centre 4640
Altnagelvin Hospitals HSS Trust 4544
Altrincham General Hospital 4495
Alzheimer's Society 4664
Amber Valley Primary Care Trust 4365
Amberstone Mental Health Unit 4402
Ambless - Accident, Loneliness and Bereavement Support 4664
Amersham Hospital 4477
Amman Valley Hospital 4535
Anaesthetic Research Society 4664
Anatomical Society of Great Britain and Ireland 4664
Andover War Memorial Community Hospital 4509
Annan Day Hospital 4517
Annan Hospital 4517
Antrim Hospital 4550
Antrim Hospital Postgraduate Medical Centre 4640
Arbroath Infirmary 4529
Archery House 4494
Ards Community Hospital 4550
Argyll and Bute Hospital 4524
Argyll and Clyde Acute Hospitals NHS Trust 4514
Argyll and Clyde NHS Board 4554
Armagh and Dungannon HSS Trust 4544
Armagh Community Hospital 4544
Arnwood House 4438
Arran War Memorial Hospital 4515
Arrowe Park Hospital 4510
Arthritis Research Campaign 4664
Arts for Health 4664
Arundel and District Hospital 4492
Ascots Day Hospital 4396
Ash Green Learning Disabilities Centre 4439
Ash Villa 4425
Ashburton and Buckfastleigh Hospital 4477
Ashby-de-la-Zouch and District Hospital 4423
The Ashdown Nuffield Hospital 4557
Ashen Hill, Forensic Psychiatry Unit 4402
Ashfield Community Hospital 4474
Ashfield Primary Care Trust 4365
Ashford and St Peter's Hospitals NHS Trust 4365
Ashford Hospital 4365
Ashford Primary Care Trust 4366
Ashington Hospital 4450
Ashley House 4425
Ashludie Day Hospital 4530
Ashludie Hospital 4530
Ashtead Hospital 4557
Ashton House 4509
Ashton, Leigh and Wigan Primary Care Trust 4366
Ashworth Hospital 4428
Asket Croft Day Hospital 4420
Association for Child Psychology and Psychiatry 4664
Association for Improvements in the Maternity Services 4664
Association for Residential Care 4664
Association for Spina Bifida and Hydrocephalus 4665
Association for the Study of Medical Education 4665
Association of Anaesthetists of Great Britain and Ireland . . . 4665
Association of British Dispensing Opticians 4665
Association of British Neurologists 4665
Association of British Paediatric Nurses 4665
Association of Clinical Biochemists 4665
Association of Clinical Pathologists 4665
Association of Medical Microbiologists 4665
Association of Medical Research Charities 4665
Association of Operating Department Practitioners (AODP) . . . 4665
Association of Optometrists 4665

INDEX BY ORGANISATION NAME

Association of Police Surgeons 4665
Association of Surgeons of Great Britain and Ireland 4665
Assurance Medical Society, Lettsom House 4665
Astley Ainslie Hospital 4525
Ataxia-UK 4665
Atkinson Morley's Hospital 4468
Atu Day Hospital 4480
Avenue Day Hospital 4512
The Avery Jones Postgraduate Medical Centre 4622
Avon Ambulance Service NHS Trust 4366
Avon and Wiltshire Mental Health Partnership NHS Trust . . 4366
Avon, Gloucestershire and Wiltshire Health Authority 4554
Avondale Unit 4408
Ayr Hospital 4515
Ayrshire and Arran Acute Hospitals NHS Trust 4514
Ayrshire and Arran NHS Board 4554
Ayrshire and Arran Primary Care NHS Trust 4515
Ayrshire Central Hospital 4515
Ayrshire Central Hospital (Psychiatric Unit) 4515

Babington Hospital 4487
Backcare 4666
Balfour Hospital 4533
Ballamona Hospital 4551
Bangor Community Hospital 4550
Bangour Village Hospital 4532
Bannockburn Hospital 4519
Bardhan Research and Education Trust of Rotherham Ltd . . 4666
Barking and Dagenham Primary Care Trust 4366
Barking, Havering and Redbridge Hospitals NHS Trust 4366
Barking Hospital 4366
Barnardo's 4666
Barnet and Chase Farm Hospitals NHS Trust 4367
Barnet and Chase Farm Postgraduate Medical Centre 4622
Barnet, Enfield and Haringey Mental Health NHS Trust . . . 4368
Barnet General Hospital 4367
Barnet Primary Care Trust 4368
Barnfield House 4476
Barnsley Community and Priority Services NHS Trust 4368
Barnsley District General Hospital 4368
Barnsley District General Hospital NHS Trust 4368
Barnsley Education Centre 4622
Barnsley Primary Care Trust 4369
Barrow Hospital 4366
Barrow Postgraduate Medical Centre 4622
The Barry Hospital 4534
Bartlet Hospital 4425
Barton-under-Needwood Cottage Hospital 4481
Barts and The London NHS Trust 4369, 4622
Basildon and Thurrock General Hospitals NHS Trust 4370
Basildon Hospital 4370
Basildon Primary Care Trust 4370
Bassetlaw District General Hospital 4393
Bassetlaw Primary Care Trust 4370
The Bateman Centre for Postgraduate Studies 4622
Bath and North East Somerset, Bristol City, North Somerset and
South Gloucestershire 4658
Bath and North East Somerset Primary Care Trust 4370
Bath Institute for Rheumatic Diseases 4645
Battle Hospital 4461
The Beacon Centre 4504
Beacon House 4371
Bealey Community Hospital 4381
Bebington and West Wirral Primary Care Trust 4370
Beccles and District War Memorial Hospital 4425
Beckenham Hospital 4379
Bedford Hospital 4371
Bedford Hospitals NHS Trust 4371
Bedford Medical Institute 4622
Bedford Primary Care Trust 4371
Bedfordshire and Hertfordshire Ambulance and Paramedic Service
NHS Trust 4371
Bedfordshire and Hertfordshire Health Authority 4553
Bedfordshire and Luton 4658
Bedfordshire and Luton Community NHS Trust 4371
Bedfordshire Heartlands Primary Care Trust 4371
Beech Court 4476
Beech House 4425
Beech House Mental Health Service Day Centre 4490
Beechcroft Unit 4461
Beighton Hospital 4389
Beit Memorial Fellowships for Medical Research 4666
Belfast City Hospital 4545
Belfast City Hospital HSS Trust 4545
Belfast Postgraduate Medical Centre 4641
Belford Hospital, Fort William 4522
Belford Hospital (Midwifery) 4522
Belhaven Hospital 4525
Belhaven Ward, Belford Hospital 4522
Bellsdyke Hospital 4519
Belmont Day Hospital 4376
Belmont Postgraduate Psychiatric Centre 4622
Belvedere Private Clinic 4557
Belvoir Park Hospital 4545
Benenden Hospital 4557
Bensham Hospital 4406
Berkeley Hospital 4472
Berkshire, East District 4658
Berkshire Healthcare NHS Trust 4372
Berkshire Independent Hospital 4557
Berkshire, Reading District 4658
Berkshire, West District 4658
Berwick Infirmary 4450
Bethel Child and Adolescent Directorate 4435
Bexhill and Rother Primary Care Trust 4372
Bexhill Hospital 4411
Bexley Primary Care Trust 4372
Bickerstaffe House 4443
Bideford and Torridgeside Hospital 4448
Biggart Hospital 4515
Billericay, Brentwood and Wickford Primary Care Trust . . . 4372
Billinge Hospital 4512
Bingley Day Hospital for the Elderly 4365
Bingley Hospital 4365
Biochemical Society 4666
Birch Avenue Day Hospital 4530
Birch Hill Hospital 4460
Birkdale Clinic (Rotherham) Ltd 4557
Birkenhead and Wallasey Primary Care Trust 4372
Birkwood Hospital 4524
Birmingham and the Black Country Health Authority 4553
Birmingham Children's Hospital 4372
Birmingham Children's Hospital NHS Trust 4372
Birmingham Dental Hospital 4373
Birmingham Heartlands and Solihull (Teaching) NHS Trust . . 4373
Birmingham Heartlands Hospital 4373
Birmingham Nuffield Hospital 4557
Birmingham Specialist Community Health NHS Trust 4373
Birmingham Women's Health Care NHS Trust 4374
Birmingham Women's Hospital 4374
Bishop Auckland General Hospital 4478
Bishops Castle Community Hospital 4475
Black Country Mental Health NHS Trust 4374
Blackberry Hill Hospital 4366, 4436
Blackbrook House Maternity Home 4456
Blackburn, Hyndburn and Ribble Valley 4658
Blackburn, Hyndburn and Ribble Valley Health Care NHS
Trust 4374
Blackburn Postgraduate Medical Centre 4622
Blackburn Royal Infirmary 4374
Blackburn with Darwen Primary Care Trust 4374
Blackdown Clinic 4557
Blackpool, Fylde and Wyre Hospitals NHS Trust 4375
Blackpool Health Professional Education Centre 4622
Blackpool Primary Care Trust 4375
Blackpool Victoria Hospital NHS Trust 4375

INDEX BY ORGANISATION NAME

Blackpool, Wyre and Fylde Community Health Services NHS Trust 4375
Blackwater Valley Primary Care Trust 4376
Blaina and District Hospital 4537
Blairgowrie Cottage Hospital 4530
Blawarthill Hospital 4527
Blond McIndoe Centre 4645
Blood Transfusion Service Scotland 4654
Bloxwich Hospital 4502
Blyth Community Hospital 4450
BMI The Alexandra Hospital 4557
BMI Bath Clinic 4557
BMI The Beardwood Hospital 4557
BMI The Beaumont Hospital 4557
BMI Bishops Wood Hospital 4558
BMI The Blackheath Hospital 4558
BMI Chatsworth Suite 4558
BMI The Chaucer Hospital 4558
BMI Chelsfield Park Hospital 4558
BMI The Chiltern Hospital 4558
BMI The Clementine Churchill Hospital 4558
BMI The Droitwich Spa Hospital 4558
BMI The Esperance Hospital 4558
BMI Fawkham Manor Hospital 4558
BMI The Garden Hospital 4558
BMI Goring Hall Hospital 4558
BMI The Hampshire Clinic 4558
BMI The Harbour Hospital 4558
BMI The Highfield Hospital 4558
BMI The Kings Oak Hospital 4558
BMI The London Independent Hospital 4558
BMI The Manor Hospital 4558
BMI Meriden Wing 4558
BMI The Nuneaton Private Hospital 4558
BMI The Paddocks Hospital 4558
BMI The Park Hospital 4559
BMI The Princess Margaret Hospital 4559
BMI The Priory Hospital 4559
BMI The Ridgeway Hospital 4559
BMI Ross Hall Hospital 4568
BMI The Runnymede Hospital 4559
BMI The Sandringham Hospital 4559
BMI Sarum Road Hospital 4559
BMI The Shelbourne Hospital 4559
BMI Shirley Oaks Hospital 4559
BMI The Sloane Hospital 4559
BMI The Somerfield Hospital 4559
BMI The South Cheshire Private Hospital 4559
BMI Thornbury Hospital 4559
BMI Three Shires Hospital 4559
BMI Werndale Hospital 4569
BMI The Winterbourne Hospital 4559
Bognor Regis War Memorial Hospital 4492
Bolingbroke Hospital 4468
Bolsover Day Hospital 4439
Bolsover Local Hospital 4439
Bolton Hospitals NHS Trust 4376
Bolton Primary Care Trust 4376
Bon Secours Hospital 4568
Bo'ness Hospital 4519
Bonnybridge Hospital 4519
Booth Hall Children's Hospital 4384
Booth Hall Postgraduate Medical Centre 4622
Bootham Park Hospital 4513
Borders General Hospital 4516
Borders General Hospital NHS Trust 4516
Borders Geriatric Day Hospital 4516
Borders NHS Board 4555
Borders Primary Care NHS Trust 4516
Boston-Pilgrim Hospital Postgraduate Centre for Medical and Dental Education 4622
Boulton Ward, Haywood Hospital 4443
Bournemouth Nuffield Hospital 4559
Bournemouth, Poole and Eastern District 4658
Bournemouth Postgraduate Medical Centre 4622
Bournemouth Primary Care Trust 4376
Bournewood Community and Mental Health Services NHS Trust 4376
Bovey Tracey Hospital 4477
Bowes Lyon Unit 4390
Bracknell Forest Primary Care Trust 4377
Bracton Centre 4454
Bradbury Postgraduate Medical Centre 4622
Bradford City Primary Care Trust 4377
Bradford Community Health NHS Trust 4377
Bradford Hospitals NHS Trust 4377
Bradford-on-Avon Community Hospital 4507
Bradford Royal Infirmary 4377
Bradford South and West Primary Care Trust 4378
Bradwell Hospital 4443
Braid Valley Hospital 4550
Brain Injury Services Beechwood House 4569
Brain Injury Services - Community Rehabilitation and Supported Living 4559
Brain Injury Services Elm Park 4559
Brain Injury Services Grafton Manor 4559
Brain Research Trust 4666
Bramcote Hospital 4445
Brampton War Memorial Hospital 4438
Breakthrough Breast Cancer 4666
Brechin Infirmary 4530
Brecon War Memorial Hospital 4542
Brent, Kensington, Chelsea and Westminster Mental Health NHS Trust 4378
Brent Primary Care Trust 4378
Briarwood Rehabilitation Unit (Mental Health) 4490
Bridgend and Glamorgan Valleys 4663
Bridgend Postgraduate Centre 4639
Bridgnorth Hospital 4475
Bridgwater Community Hospital 4475
Bridlington and District Hospital 4472
Brighton and Hove City Primary Care Trust 4378
Brighton and Hove District 4658
Brighton and Sussex University Hospitals NHS Trust 4378
Brighton General Hospital 4478
Brighton Health Care NHS Trust 4379
Bristol Eye Hospital 4496
Bristol General Hospital 4496
Bristol Homoeopathic Hospital 4496
Bristol North Primary Care Trust 4379
The Bristol Nuffield Hospital at Chesterfield 4559
The Bristol Nuffield Hospital at St Mary's 4559
Bristol Royal Hospital for Children 4496
Bristol Royal Infirmary 4496
Bristol South and West Primary Care Trust 4379
British Academy of Forensic Sciences 4666
British Association for Accident and Emergency Medicine . . . 4666
British Association for Paediatric Nephrology 4666
British Association for Parenteral and Enteral Nutrition . . . 4666
British Association for Psychopharmacology 4666
British Association for Service to the Elderly 4666
British Association for Tissue Banking 4666
British Association of Day Surgery 4666
British Association of Dermatologists 4666
British Association of Health Services in Higher Education (BAHSHE) 4666
British Association of Occupational Therapists and College of Occupational Therapists 4666
British Association of Oral and Maxillofacial Surgeons 4667
British Association of Otorhinolaryngologists-Head and Neck Surgeons 4667
British Association of Paediatric Surgeons 4667
British Association of Perinatal Medicine 4667
British Association of Plastic Surgeons 4667
British Association of Psychotherapists 4667
British Association of Surgical Oncology 4667
British Association of Urological Surgeons 4667
British Cardiac Society 4667

INDEX BY ORGANISATION NAME

British Colostomy Association 4667
British Council 4667
British Council for the Prevention of Blindness 4667
British Dental Association 4667
British Dietetic Association 4667
British Epilepsy Association 4667
British Geriatrics Society 4667
British Heart Foundation 4668
British Home and Hospital for Incurables 4559
British Homeopathic Association 4668
British Hypertension Society 4668
British Infection Society 4668
British Institute of Dental and Surgical Technologists 4668
British Institute of Industrial Therapy 4668
British Institute of Learning Disabilities 4668
British Institute of Musculoskeletal Medicine 4668
British Institute of Radiology 4668
British Leprosy Relief Association 4668
British Lung Foundation 4668
British Medical Acupuncture Society 4668
British Medical Association 4668
British Medical Ultrasound Society 4668
British Menopause Society 4668
British Nuclear Medicine Society 4668
British Nutrition Foundation 4668
British Occupational Hygiene Society 4669
British Orthodontic Society 4669
British Orthopaedic Association 4669
British Orthoptic Society 4669
British Paediatric Surveillance Unit of the Royal College of Paediatrics and Child Health 4645
British Performing Arts Medicine Trust 4669
British Pharmacological Society 4669
British Pharmacopoeia Commission 4669
British Polio Fellowship 4669
British Pregnancy Advisory Service 4669
British Psycho-Analytical Society 4669
British Psychological Society 4669
British Red Cross Society 4669
British Retinitis Pigmentosa Society 4669
British Society for Haematology 4669
British Society for Human Genetics 4669
British Society for Immunology 4669
British Society for Music Therapy 4669
British Society for Oral Medicine 4670
British Society for Parasitology 4670
British Society for Rheumatology 4670
British Society for Surgery of the Hand 4670
British Society of Applied Social Science 4670
British Society of Gastroenterology 4670
British Society of Medical and Dental Hypnosis 4670
British Society of Rehabilitation Medicine 4670
British Thoracic Society 4670
Brixham Hospital 4477
Bro Cerwyn Psychiatric Day Hospital 4541
Bro Ddyfi Community Hospital 4542
Bro Morgannwg NHS Trust 4533
Bro Taf Health Authority 4555
Broadgreen Hospital 4464
Broadgreen Postgraduate Medical Centre 4623
Broadland Primary Care Trust 4379
Broadmoor Hospital 4505
Broadoak Mental Health Unit 4428
Broadway Lodge 4560
Bromhead Hospital 4560
Bromley Hospital 4379
Bromley Hospitals NHS Trust 4379
Bromley Primary Care Trust 4380
Bron y Garth Hospital 4540
Bronglais General Hospital 4536
Bronglais Hospital Postgraduate Medical Centre 4639
Bronllys Hospital 4543
Brook Haven Mental Health Unit 4511
Brook Hospital Postgraduate Medical Centre 4623
Brooke House 4458
Brookfields Hospital 4424
Brooklands Hospital 4445
Brooksby House Hospital 4515
Broomfield Hospital 4429
Broomfield Hospital Medical Academic Unit 4623
Broxtowe and Hucknall Primary Care Trust 4380
Bryn Beryl Hospital 4540
Bryn Seiont Hospital 4540
Bryn-Y-Neuadd Hospital 4540
Brynhaul Day Hospital 4541
Brynmair Day Hospital 4541
Bryntirion Hospital 4536, 4541
Buckingham Hospital 4380
Buckinghamshire District 4658
Buckinghamshire Mental Health NHS Trust 4380
Buckland Hospital 4400
Bucknall Hospital 4443
Builth Wells Cottage Hospital 4543
BUPA Alexandra Hospital 4560
BUPA Belvedere Hospital 4560
BUPA Cambridge Lea Hospital 4560
BUPA Chalybeate Hospital 4560
BUPA Dunedin Hospital 4560
BUPA Fylde Coast Hospital 4560
BUPA Gatwick Park Hospital 4560
BUPA Hartswood Hospital 4560
BUPA Hospital Bristol 4560
BUPA Hospital Bushey 4560
BUPA Hospital Cardiff 4569
BUPA Hospital Clare Park 4560
BUPA Hospital Elland 4560
BUPA Hospital Harpenden 4560
BUPA Hospital Hastings 4560
BUPA Hospital Hull and East Riding 4560
BUPA Hospital Leeds 4560
BUPA Hospital Leicester 4560
BUPA Hospital Little Aston 4560
BUPA Hospital Manchester 4560
BUPA Hospital Norwich 4560
BUPA Hospital Portsmouth 4561
BUPA Hospital Tunbridge Wells 4561
BUPA Hospital Washington 4561
BUPA Methley Park Hospital 4561
BUPA Murrayfield Hospital - Edinburgh 4568
BUPA North Cheshire Hospital 4561
BUPA Parkway Hospital 4561
BUPA Redwood Hospital 4561
BUPA Regency Hospital 4561
BUPA Roding Hospital 4561
BUPA St Saviour's Hospital 4561
BUPA South Bank Hospital 4561
BUPA Wellesley Hospital 4561
BUPA Yale Hospital 4569
Burden Neurological Hospital 4436
Burnham-on-Sea War Memorial Hospital 4476
Burnley General Hospital 4380
Burnley Health Care NHS Trust 4380
Burnley Mackenzie Medical Centre 4623
Burnley, Pendle and Rossendale Primary Care Trust 4381
Burntwood Lichfield and Tamworth Primary Care Trust 4381
Burton Graduate Medical Centre 4623
Burton Hospitals NHS Trust 4381
Burton House Day Hospital 4480
Bury General Hospital 4381
Bury Health Care NHS Trust 4381
Bury Postgraduate Centre 4623
Bury Primary Care Trust 4382
Bury St Edmunds District Postgraduate Medical Centre 4623
The Bury St Edmunds Nuffield Hospital 4561
Bushey Fields Hospital 4396
Buxton Hospital 4439

INDEX BY ORGANISATION NAME

Caerphilly And District Miners' Hospital 4537
Caird House 4524
Calderdale and Huddersfield NHS Trust 4382
Calderdale Primary Care Trust 4383
Calderstones 4383
Calderstones NHS Trust 4383
Calnwood Court 4371
Camborne/Redruth Community Hospital 4506
Cambridge City Primary Care Trust 4383
Cambridge District Postgraduate Medical and Dental Education Centre 4623
Cambridgeshire and Peterborough Mental Health Partnership NHS Trust 4383
Cambridgeshire, North and East District 4658
Cambridgeshire, South and West District 4658
Camden and Islington Community Health Services NHS Trust 4383
Camden and Islington Community Health Services NHS Trust Postgraduate Centre 4623
Camden and Islington Mental Health NHS Trust 4383
Camden Primary Care Trust 4383
Cameron Hospital 4518
Campbell Hospital 4520
Campbeltown Hospital 4524
Cancer and Leukaemia in Childhood 4670
Cancer Research UK 4645
CancerBacup 4670
Cancerlink 4670
Canniesburn Hospital 4527
Cannock Chase Hospital 4430
Cannock Chase Primary Care Trust 4383
Canterbury and Coastal Primary Care Trust 4383
Cardiff and Vale NHS Trust 4534
Cardiff and Vale of Glamorgan 4663
Cardiff Postgraduate Medical Centre 4639
Cardiff Royal Infirmary - West Wing 4534
Cardigan and District Memorial Hospital 4536
Cardiothoracic Centre Liverpool NHS Trust 4384
Care Perspectives 4561
The Carleton Clinic 4438
Carlisle and District Primary Care Trust 4384
Carmarthenshire District 4663
Carmarthenshire NHS Trust 4535
Carreg Fawr Bed Support Unit at Bryn y Neuadd Hospital . . 4540
Carter Bequest Hospital 4494
Castel Hospital 4551
Castle Douglas Day Hospital 4517
Castle Douglas Hospital 4517
Castle Hill Hospital 4415
Castle Point and Rochford Primary Care Trust 4384
Castleberg Day Hospital for the Elderly 4365
Castleberg Hospital 4365
Castleford, Normanton and District Hospital 4501
Caterham Dene Hospital 4490
Causeway Hospital 4545
Causeway HSS Trust 4545
Cavendish Day Hospital 4439
Cavendish Hospital 4439
Cedar House 4476
Cefn Coed Hospital 4543
Cefni Hospital 4540
Central Cheshire Primary Care Trust 4384
Central Cornwall Primary Care Trust 4384
Central Council of Physical Recreation 4670
Central Derby Primary Care Trust 4384
Central Liverpool Primary Care Trust 4384
Central Manchester and Manchester Children's University Hospitals NHS Trust 4384
Central Manchester Postgraduate Health Sciences Centre . . 4623
Central Manchester Primary Care Trust 4385
Central Middlesex Hospital 4445
Central North Wales District 4663
Central Suffolk Primary Care Trust 4385
Centre for Medical and Dental Education Pilgrim Hospital United Lincolnshire Hospitals NHS Trust 4623
Centre for Policy on Ageing 4670
Ceredigion and Mid Wales NHS Trust 4536
Ceredigion District 4663
Chailey Heritage 4478
Chalfonts and Gerrards Cross Hospital 4477
Chalmers Hospital 4520
Chapel Allerton Hospital 4421
Chapters House 4440
Chard and District Hospital 4481
Charing Cross Hospital Postgraduate Medical Centre 4623
Charity Commission (for England and Wales) 4649
Charles Clifford Dental Hospital 4474
Charles Hasting Postgraduate Medical Centre 4623
Charles Palmer Day Hospital 4483
Charlton Lane Unit 4399
Charnwood and North West Leicestershire Primary Care Trust 4385
Chartered Society of Physiotherapy 4670
Chase Farm Hospital 4367
Chase Farm Hospital Site 4368
Chase Postgraduate Medical Centre 4623
Chatterton House 4419
Cheadle Hospital 4443
Cheadle Royal Hospital 4561
Chelmsford and Essex Day Unit 4441
Chelmsford Primary Care Trust 4386
Chelsea and Westminster Healthcare NHS Trust 4386
Chelsea and Westminster Hospital 4386
Chelsea and Westminster Hospital Postgraduate Centre . . . 4623
The Cheltenham and Gloucester Nuffield Hospitals 4561
Cheltenham and Tewkesbury Primary Care Trust 4386
Cheltenham General Hospital 4399
Cheltenham Postgraduate Medical Centre 4623
Chepstow Community Hospital 4537
Cherry Knowle Hospital 4458
Cherwell Vale Primary Care Trust 4386
Cheshire and Merseyside Health Authority 4553
Cheshire and Wirral Partnership NHS Trust 4386
Cheshire Community Healthcare NHS Trust 4386
Cheshire, Halton and Warrington 4658
Cheshire West Primary Care Trust 4386
Cheshunt Community Hospital 4367
Chest Heart and Stroke Scotland 4670
Chester and Halton Community NHS Trust 4386
Chesterfield and North Derbyshire Royal Hospital 4387
Chesterfield and North Derbyshire Royal Hospital NHS Trust . 4387
Chesterfield Education Centre 4624
Chesterfield Primary Care Trust 4387
Chesterton Hospital 4424
Chichester Medical Education Centre 4624
Child Accident Prevention Trust 4671
Child Growth Foundation 4671
The Children's Trust 4561, 4671
Children's Liver Disease Foundation 4671
Chiltern and South Bucks Primary Care Trust 4387
Chiltern Medical Education Centre 4624
Chingford, Wanstead and Woodford Primary Care Trust . . . 4387
Chippenham Community Hospital 4508
Chirk Community Hospital 4539
Chorley and Ribble Postgraduate Education Centre 4624
Chorley and South Ribble District General Hospital 4387
Chorley and South Ribble NHS Trust 4387
Chorley and South Ribble Primary Care Trust 4388
Christchurch Hospital 4462
Christiana Hartley Maternity Unit 4488
Christie Hospital 4388
Christie Hospital NHS Trust 4388
The Churchill 4452
Cimla Hospital 4533
Cirencester Hospital 4399
City and Hackney Primary Care Trust 4388
City General Hospital 4443
City Hospital 4471, 4525
City Hospital NHS Trust 4388

INDEX BY ORGANISATION NAME

City Hospital NHS Trust Postgraduate Medical Centre 4624
City Hospitals Sunderland NHS Trust 4388
City Hospitals Sunderland, Postgraduate Medical Centre . . . 4624
City of London District 4658
Clackmannan County Day Hospital 5519
Clackmannan County Hospital 4519
Claremont Hospital 4561
Clatterbridge Centre for Oncology NHS Trust 3389
Clatterbridge Hospital 4510
Clay Cross Hospital 4439
Clayponds Hospital 4415
Cleddau Rehabilitation Unit 4541
Cleland Hospital 4524
Clevedon Hospital 4436
Cleveland Nuffield Hospital 4561
Clifton Hospital 4375
The Clinical Education Centre 4624
Clitheroe Community Hospital 4389
Clwyd North Postgraduate Medical Centre 4639
Clydach War Memorial Hospital 4543
The Coach House 4561
Coalville Community Hospital 4423
Coastal Postgraduate Medical Centre 4624
Coathill Hospital 4524
Cobham Cottage Hospital 4404
Coed Lys 4540
Colchester and North-East Essex Postgraduate Medical
Centre 4624
Colchester General Hospital 4405
Colchester Primary Care Trust 4389
Coldstream Cottage Hospital 4516
Colindale Hospital 4368
College House 4476
College of Health 4671
The College of Optometrists 4671
College of Pharmacy Practice 4671
Collingham Gardens 4378
Coltman Street Day Hospital and Community Support Teams 4415
Colwood Hospital 4430
Colwyn Bay Community Hospital 4537
Commission for Health Improvement 4649
Committee on Safety of Medicines 4649
Common Services Agency for the National Health Service in
Scotland 4655
The Commonwealth Nurses Federation 4671
CommuniCare NHS Trust 4389
Community and District Nursing Association 4671
Community Health Sheffield NHS Trust 4389
Community Health South London NHS Trust 4389
Community Healthcare Bolton NHS Trust 4389
Community Mental Health Team and Day Hospital 4504
Company Chemists' Association Ltd 4671
Congleton and District War Memorial Hospital 4398
Conquest Hospital 4411
Conservative Medical Society 4671
Continuing Care at Home Association (CONCAH) 4671
Conwy and Denbighshire NHS Trust 4536
Conwy Hospital 4537
Cookridge Hospital 4421
Coquetdale Cottage Hospital 4450
Corbett Hospital 4395
Corby Community Hospital 4447
Cornwall, East District 4658
Cornwall Healthcare NHS Trust 4390
Cornwall Postgraduate Medical Centre 4624
Cornwall, Western District 4658
Coronary Prevention Group 4671
Corstorphine Hospital 4525
Cossham Memorial Hospital 4436
Cotswold and Vale Primary Care Trust 4390
Council for Awards in Children's Care and Education (incorporating
CEYA and NNEB) 4671
Council for Music in Hospitals 4671
Council for Professions Supplementary to Medicine 4649

Counsel and Care-Advice and help for older people 4671
Countess Mountbatten House 4486
Countess of Chester Hospital 4390
Countess of Chester Hospital NHS Trust 4390
County Durham and Darlington Priority Services NHS Trust . 4390
County Durham and Tees Valley Health Authority 4554
County Hospital 4497, 4537
County Hospital, Durham 4390
County Hospital, Invergordon 4522
County of Herefordshire 4658
Courtauld (W. J.) Hospital 4430
Coventry and Warwickshire Hospital 4500
Coventry Healthcare NHS Trust 4391
Coventry Maternity Hospital 4500
Coventry Primary Care Trust 4391
Coventry, Warwickshire, Herefordshire and Worcestershire Health
Authority 4553
Cowglen Hospital 4529
Craigavon and Banbridge Community HSS Trust 4546
Craigavon Area Hospital 4546
Craigavon Area Hospital Group HSS Trust 4546
Craigavon Area Hospital Postgraduate Medical Centre 4641
Craigavon Psychiatric Unit 4546
Crane Ward 4504
Cranleigh House 4476
Cranleigh Village Community Hospital 4490
Craven, Harrogate and Rural District Primary Care Trust . . 4391
Crawley and Horsham Postgraduate Centre 4624
Crawley Hospital 4490
Crawley Primary Care Trust 4391
Crescent House 4512
Crewkerne Hospital 4401
Crichton Royal Hospital 4517
Crieff Hospital 4530
Cripps Postgraduate Medical Centre 4624
The Croft 4504
The Croft Children's Unit 4424
Crombie House 4371
Cromer Hospital 4435
Cromwell Clinic 4561
Cromwell Hospital 4562
Crooked Acres 4420
Crosshouse Hospital 4515
Crowborough War Memorial Hospital 4402
Croyden Primary Care Trust 4391
Croydon and Surrey Downs Community NHS Trust 4391
Cumberland Infirmary 4437
Cumbria Ambulance Service NHS Trust 4391
Cumbria and Lancashire Health Authority 4554
Cumbria, Furness District 4658
Cumbria, North Eastern District 4658
Cumbria, Southern District 4658
Cumbria, Western District 4658
Cygnet Hospital Ealing 4562
Cystic Fibrosis Trust 4671

Dacorum Primary Care Trust 4391
Daisy Bank 4377
Daisy Hill Hospital 4548
Daisy Hill House 4377
Daliburgh Hospital 4533
Dalriada Hospital 4545
Dalrymple Day Hospital 4517
Dalrymple Hospital 4517
Danesbury 4396
Danetre Hospital 4392
Danum Lodge Clinic 4562
Darent Valley Hospital 4392
Darlington and South Durham 4658
Darlington Memorial Hospital 4479
Darlington Postgraduate Medical Centre 4624
Darlington Primary Care Trust 4391
Dartford and Gravesham NHS Trust 4391

INDEX BY ORGANISATION NAME

Dartford, Gravesham and Swanley Primary Care Trust 4392
Dartford Postgraduate Medical Centre 4625
Daventry and South Northamptonshire Primary Care Trust . . 4392
Davidson Cottage Hospital 4515
Dawlish Hospital 4477
Dean Park Clinic 4562
Deeside Community Hospital 4539
Defeating Deafness (The Hearing Research Trust) 4672
Deiniol Day Hospital 4540
Delancey Hospital 4399
Denbigh Community Hospital 4537
The Dene 4562
Denmark Road Day Hospital 4472
Department for Education and Skills 4649
Department for NHS Postgraduate Medical and Dental Education (Yorkshire Deanery) 4625
Department of Health 4649
Department of Health, Social Services and Public Safety . . . 4656
Department of Psychiatry 4504
Department of Social Security (Corporate Medical Group) . . 4650
Derby City General Hospital Medical Education Centre 4625
Derby City Hospital 4487
Derbyshire Children's Hospital 4487
Derbyshire Dales and South Derbyshire Primary Care Trust . 4392
Derbyshire, Derby and South Derbyshire District 4658
Derbyshire, High Peak District 4659
Derbyshire Royal Infirmary 4487
Derbyshire Royal Infirmary (Mental Health) 4487
Derbyshire Royal Infirmary Postgraduate Medical Education Centre 4625
Derbyshire, Scarsdale District 4659
Derwent Clinic 4391
Derwentside Primary Care Trust 4392
Devizes Community Hospital 4508
Devon Partnership NHS Trust 4392
Devon, Plymouth and South West Devon District 4659
Devon, South Devon and Torbay District 4659
Devonshire Road Hospital 4375
Dewi Sant Hospital 4542
Dewsbury and District Hospital 4392
Dewsbury Health Care NHS Trust 4392
Diabetes UK 4672
Diana Princess of Wales Hospital 4449
Diana Princess of Wales Hospital, Grimsby 4393
Digestive Disorders Foundation 4672
Dilke Memorial Hospital 4472
Directorate of Health and Social Care London 4553
Directorate of Health and Social Care Midlands and East . . 4553
Directorate of Health and Social Care North 4553
Directorate of Health and Social Care South 4554
Disabled Drivers Association 4672
Disabled Living Foundation 4672
District General Hospital 4460
The Diving Diseases Research Centre 4562
Dobshill Hospital 4539
Dolgellau and Barmouth District Hospital 4540
Donal Early House 4436
Doncaster and Bassetlaw Hospitals NHS Trust 4393
Doncaster and South Humber Healthcare NHS Trust 4393
Doncaster Central Primary Care Trust 4394
Doncaster East Primary Care Trust 4394
Doncaster Gate Hospital 4461
Doncaster Postgraduate Medical Teaching Centre 4625
Doncaster Royal Infirmary 4393
Doncaster, South Humber and Rotherham NHS Trust 4394
Doncaster West Primary Care Trust 4394
Dorothy Pattison Hospital 4502
Dorset Ambulance NHS Trust 4394
Dorset County Hospital 4503
Dorset Health Care NHS Trust 4394
Dorset, Western District 4659
Douglas Pickup Postgraduate Medical Centre 4625
Dovedale Day Hospital (Elderly Services) 4488
Dover Postgraduate Medical Centre 4625

Down Lisburn HSS Trust 4546
Downe Hospital 4546
Downpatrick Maternity Hospital 4546
Downshire Hospital 4546
Dr Gray's Hospital (Acute) 4521
Dr Gray's Hospital (Mental and Community) 4520
Dr Mackinnon Memorial Hospital 4522
Droitwich Knee Clinic 4562
DrugScope 4672
Drumchapel Hospital 4527
Dryburn Hospital 4439
Dryden Road Day Hospital 4406
Dryll y Carr Unit 4541
Duchess of York Children's Hospital 4480
Duchy Hospital 4562
Duchy Nuffield Hospital 4562
Dudley Beacon and Castle Primary Care Trust 4395
Dudley Group of Hospitals NHS Trust 4395
Dudley Priority Health NHS Trust 4395
Dudley South Primary Care Trust 4396
Dumbarton Cottage Hospital 4524
Dumbarton Joint Hospital 4524
Dumfries and Galloway Acute and Maternity Hospitals NHS Trust 4516
Dumfries and Galloway NHS Board 4555
Dumfries and Galloway Primary Care NHS Trust 4517
Dumfries and Galloway Royal Infirmary 4516
Dunaros Hospital 4524
Dunbar Hospital 4522
Dundee Dental Hospital and School 4531
Dunoon General Hospital 4525
Dunrowan Day Hospital 4519
Dunston Hill Day Unit 4406
Dunston Hill Hospital 4406
Durham and Chester-le-Street Primary Care Trust 4396
Durham Dales Primary Care Trust 4396
Durham, Northern District 4659
Durham Postgraduate Medical Centre and Dryburn Education Centre 4625
Dyfed Powys Health Authority 4555
Dykebar Hospital 4528
Dystrophic Epidermolysis Bullosa Research Association (DEBRA) 4672

Ealing Day Treatment Centre 4415
Ealing Hospital 4396
Ealing Hospital NHS Trust 4396
Ealing Hospital NHS Trust Postgraduate Centre 4625
Ealing Primary Care Trust 4396
Earls House 4391
Earls House Hospital 4440
Easington Primary Care Trust 4396
East and North Hertfordshire NHS Trust 4396
East Anglian Ambulance NHS Trust 4397
East Berkshire Community Health NHS Trust 4397
East Birmingham Primary Care Trust 4398
East Cambridgeshire and Fenland Primary Care Trust 4398
East Cheshire Association for Medical Education 4625
East Cheshire NHS Trust 4398
East Cleveland Hospital 4494
East Cornwall Hospital 4390
East Cumbria Postgraduate Medical Centre 4625
East Devon Primary Care Trust 4398
East Elmbridge and Mid Surrey Primary Care Trust 4399
East Gloucestershire NHS Trust 4399
East Ham Memorial Hospital 4435
East Hampshire Primary Care Trust 4400
East Hertfordshire Postgraduate Centre 4625
East Kent Coastal Primary Care Trust 4400
East Kent Community NHS Trust 4400
East Kent Hospitals NHS Trust 4400
East Leeds Primary Care Trust 4401
East Lincolnshire Primary Care Trust 4401

INDEX BY ORGANISATION NAME

East London and The City Mental Health NHS Trust 4401
East Midlands Ambulance Service NHS Trust 4401
East Midlands Nuffield Hospital 5562
East Riding Medical Education Centre 4625
East Somerset NHS Trust 4401
East Staffordshire Primary Care Trust 4402
East Surrey Hospital 4490
East Surrey Hospital Postgraduate Medical Centre 4625
East Surrey Primary Care Trust 4402
East Sussex County Healthcare NHS Trust 4402
East Sussex District 4659
East Sussex Hospitals NHS Trust 4402
East Yorkshire Primary Care Trust 4402
Eastbourne and County Healthcare NHS Trust 4402
Eastbourne District General Hospital 4403
Eastbourne Downs Primary Care Trust 4403
Eastbourne Hospitals NHS Trust 4403
Eastbourne Postgraduate Medical and Psychiatry Centre . . . 4626
Eastern Cheshire Primary Care Trust 4403
Eastern Deanery 4626
Eastern General Hospital 4525
Eastern Health and Social Services Board 4556
Eastern Hull Primary Care Trust 4403
Eastern Leicester Primary Care Trust 4403
Eastern Wakefield Primary Care Trust 4403
Eastleigh and Test Valley South Primary Care Trust 4403
The Eastman Dental Hospital 4498
Ebbw Vale Hospital 4538
Eden Valley Primary Care Trust 4403
Edenbridge and District War Memorial Hospital 4416
Edenhall Hospital 4525
Edgware Community Hospital 4368
Edgware Day Surgery Unit 4368
Edgware Postgraduate Centre 4626
Edinburgh Dental Institute 4526
Edington Cottage Hospital 4525
Edith Cavell Hospital 4454
The Education Centre 4626
Edward Hain Memorial Hospital 4506
Edward Jenner Teaching Centre 4626
Edward Street Hospital and Day Unit 4374
Elderly Care Day Hospital, Lister Hospital 4396
Elderly Day Hospital 4506
Elderly Rehabilitation Unit 4439
The Elizabeth Garrett Anderson Hospital and Obstetric
Hospital 4498
Ellen Badger Hospital 4483
Ellesmere Port and Neston Primary Care Trust 4403
Ellesmere Port Hospital 4509
Elm Lodge 4425
Emergency Bed Service 4672
EMI Unit (Hillview) Day Hospital 4374
Encephalitis Support Group 4672
Enfield Primary Care Trust 4403
English National Board for Nursing, Midwifery and Health
Visiting 4650
Epilepsy Action Scotland 4672
Epping Forest Primary Care Trust 4404
Epsom and St Helier NHS Trust 4404, 4626
Epsom General Hospital 4404
Erewash Primary Care Trust 4405
Erith and District Hospital 4458
Erne Day Hospital 4549
Erne Hospital 4549
Erskine Hospital 4569
Eryri Hospital 4541
Essex Ambulance Service NHS Trust 4405
Essex County Hospital 4405
Essex Health Authority 4553
Essex, No.1 District 4659
Essex, No. 2 District 4659
Essex Nuffield Hospital 4562
Essex Rivers Healthcare NHS Trust 4405
Euxton Hall Hospital 4562

The Evelyn Hospital 4562
Evesham Community Hospital 4485
Exeter and Greater Devon District 4659
Exeter Nuffield Hospital 4562
Exeter Postgraduate Medical Centre 4626
Exeter Primary Care Trust 4405
Eyemouth Day Hospital (Geriatric) 4516

Faculty of Accident and Emergency Medicine (FAEM) 4642
Faculty of Pharmaceutical Medicine of the Royal Colleges of
Physicians of the United Kingdom 4642
Faculty of Public Health Medicine of the Royal Colleges of
Physicians of the United Kingdom 4642
Fair Mile Hospital 4372
Fairfield General Hospital 4381
Fairford Cottage Hospital 4399
Fairwood Hospital 4543
Falkirk and District Royal Infirmary 4518
Fall Birch Hospital 4376
Falmouth Hospital 4506
Family Welfare Association 4672
Fareham and Gosport Primary Care Trust 4405
Farley Hill Day Hospital 4371
Farm Place 4562
Farnborough Education Centre 4626
Farnborough Hospital 4379
Farnham Community Hospital 4491
Farnham Road Mental Health & Community Hospital Health
Services 4491
Federation of Independent Practitioner Organisations . . . 4672
Federation of Ophthalmic and Dispensing Opticians 4672
Feilding Palmer Cottage Hospital 4423
Felixstowe General Hospital 4425
Fellowship of Postgraduate Medicine 4672
Fenwick Day Hospital 4485
Fenwick Hospital 4486
Ferguson Close 4441
Fernbrae Hospital 4569
Ffestiniog Memorial Hospital 4541
Fieldhead Hospital 4502
Fieldhouse Teaching Centre 4626
Fife Acute Hospitals NHS Trust 4517
Fife NHS Board 4555
Fife Primary Care NHS Trust 4518
Finchley Memorial Hospital 4368
Firholm Day Unit (Elderly with Dementia) 4516
Fitzwilliam Hospital 4562
5 Borough Partnership NHS Trust 4405
Flaghead Unit 4394
Fleet Community Hospital 4491
Fleetwood Hospital 4375
Fleming Hospital 4520
Flint Community Hospital 4539
Florence Desmond Day Hospital 4491
Florence Nightingale Clinic Chelsea 4562
Florence Nightingale Hospital 4562
Florence Nightingale Hospital Liverpool 4562
Florence Nightingale Psychological Medicine Centre 4562
Fordingbridge Hospital 4470
Forensic Science Society 4672
Forest Lodge 4389
Foresterhill Hospital 4521
Forfar Infirmary 4530
Forster Green Hospital 4547
Forth Park Hospital 4518
Forth Park Maternity Hospital 4518
Forth Valley Acute Hospitals NHS Trust 4518
Forth Valley NHS Board 4555
Forth Valley Primary Care NHS Trust 4519
Foster Day Hospital 4382
Foundation for Liver Research (formerly Liver Research Trust) 4672
Foundation for the Study of Infant Deaths 4672
The Foundation NHS Trust Hospital (Stafford) 4481

INDEX BY ORGANISATION NAME

Fowey and District Hospital 4390
Foyle Health and Social Services Trust 4547
FPA 4672
Frank James Community Hospital 4417
The Frank Refkin Postgraduate Centre 4626
Fraserburgh Hospital 4520
Freeman Hospital 4433
Freeman Hospital Education Centre 4626
Frenchay Hospital 4436
Frenchay Postgraduate Centre. 4626
Friarage Hospital 4446
Frimley Park Hospital 4405
Frimley Park Hospital NHS Trust 4405
Frimley Park Hospital Postgraduate Medical Centre 4626
Frognal Centre for Medical Studies 4626
Froome Bank Hospital 4413
Fulbourn Hospital 4363
Fulwood Hall Hospital 4562
Furness General Hospital 4431
Fylde Primary Care Trust 4405

The Gables 4391
The Gables Day Hospital 4441
The Gainsborough Clinic and Nursing Home 4562
Gala Day Unit (Elderly with Dementia) 4516
Garlands Hospital 4438
Garngoch Hospital 4543
Garnock Day Hospital 4515
Gartnavel General Hospital 4527
Gartnavel Royal Hospital 4522
Gateshead Health NHS Trust 4406
Gateshead Postgraduate Medical Centre 4626
Gateshead Primary Care Trust 4406
Gay and Lesbian Association of Doctors and Dentists
(GLADD) 4673
Gedling Primary Care Trust 4406
Gellinudd Hospital 4543
General Dental Council 4650
General Hospital St Helier 4551
General Medical Council 4650
General Optical Council 4651
George Eliot Hospital 4406
George Eliot Hospital NHS Trust 4406
The George Pickering Postgraduate Centre 4627
Gesto Hospital 4522
Gilbert Bain Hospital 4533
Giving for Living Research and Postgraduate Centre 4627
Glan Clwyd District General Hospital 4537
Glanrhyd Hospital 4533
Glantawe Postgraduate Medical Centre 4639
Glasgow Dental Hospital and School 4527
Glasgow Eye Infirmary 4527
Glasgow Homoeopathic Hospital 4527
Glasgow Nuffield Hospital 4569
Glasgow Royal Infirmary 4527
Princess Royal Maternity Unit 4528
Glaxo Day Hospital 4530
Glen O'Dee Hospital 4520
Glencoe Hospital 4522
Glenfield Hospital 4500
Glenrothes Day Hospital 4518
Glenrothes Hospital 4518
Gloucester Postgraduate Medical Centre 4627
Gloucestershire Ambulance Services NHS Trust 4406
Gloucestershire, Cheltenham District 4659
Gloucestershire, Gloucester District 4659
Gloucestershire Hospitals NHS Trust 4406
Gloucestershire Partnership NHS Trust 4407
Gloucestershire Royal Hospital 4407
Gloucestershire Royal NHS Trust 4407
Good Hope Education Centre and Library 4627
Good Hope Hospital 4407
Good Hope Hospital NHS Trust 4407

The Goodall Centre 4391
Goole and District Hospital 4449
Gordon Hospital 4378
Gorse Hill Hospital 4423
Gorseinon Hospital 4543
Goscote Hospital 4502
Gosport War Memorial Hospital 4456
Grampian NHS Board 4555
Grampian Primary Care NHS Trust 4520
Grampian University Hospitals NHS Trust 4521
Gransha Hospital 4547
Grantham and District Hospital 4497
Grantham and District Hospital Postgraduate Medical Centre 4627
Gravesend and North Kent Hospital 4392
Graylingwell Hospital 4492
Great Ormond Street Hospital for Children NHS Trust 4407, 4627
Great Ormond Street Hospital Medical School 4570
Great Yarmouth Primary Care Trust 4408
Greater Derby Primary Care Trust 4408
Greater Glasgow NHS Board 4555
Greater Glasgow Primary Care NHS Trust 4522
Greater London, Eastern District 4659
Greater London Fund for the Blind 4673
Greater London, Inner North London District 4659
Greater London, Inner South London District 4659
Greater London, Inner West London District 4659
Greater London, Northern District 4659
Greater London, Southern District 4659
Greater London, Western District 4659
Greater Manchester Ambulance Service NHS Trust 4408
Greater Manchester Health Authority 4554
Greater Manchester, Manchester District 4659
Greater Manchester, North District 4659
Greater Manchester, South District 4659
Greater Manchester, West District 4659
Green Lane Hospital 4366
Green Park Healthcare HSS Trust 4547
Green Parks House 4454
Greenfield Centre 4444
Greenwich District Hospital 4458
Greenwich District Hospital Postgraduate Centre 4627
Greenwich Primary Care Trust 4408
Grenoside Grange 4389
Grimsby Postgraduate Medical Centre 4627
Groeswen Hospital 4533
Grosvenor Nuffield Hospital 4563
The Grove 4488
Grove Park Hospital 4408
Groves Day Hospital 4510
Guest Hospital 4395
The Guide Dogs for the Blind Association 4673
Guild Community Healthcare NHS Trust 4408
Guild of Catholic Doctors 4673
The Guildford Nuffield Hospital 4563
Guildford Postgraduate Medical Centre 4627
Guildford and Waverly Primary Care Trust 4408
Guisborough General Hospital 4494
Guisborough General Hospital (Maternity Services) 4482
Gurney Postgraduate Centre 4627
Guy's and St Thomas' NHS Trust 4408
Guy's Department of Postgraduate Studies 4627
Guy's Hospital 4408
Guy's Nuffield House 4563
Gwent District 4663
Gwent Health Authority 4555
Gwent Healthcare NHS Trust 4537
Gwent Postgraduate Medical and Dental Centre 4639
Gwynedd Centre for Postgraduate Medical and Dental
Education 4639

Haddon House Day Hospital 4447
Hadspen Wood and Ridley Day Hospital 4476
The Haemophilia Society 4673

INDEX BY ORGANISATION NAME

Hairmyres Hospital 4523
Halifax General Hospital 4382
Halstead Hospital 4405
Halton Education Centre 4627
Halton General Hospital 4437
Halton Primary Care Trust 4409
Haltwhistle War Memorial Hospital 4450
Ham Green Hospital 4436
Hambleton and Richmondshire Primary Care Trust 4409
Hammersmith and Fulham Primary Care Trust 4410
Hammersmith Hospital 4410
Hammersmith Hospital Postgraduate Centre 4627
Hammersmith Hospitals NHS Trust 4410
Hammerwich Hospital 4482
Hampshire Ambulance Service NHS Trust 4410
Hampshire and Isle of Wight Health Authority 4554
Hampshire, Central District 4659
Hampshire, North East District 4659
Hampshire, Portsmouth and South East District 4660
Hampshire, Southampton and New Forest District 4660
Hanover Assesment and Treatment Centre 4512
Harefield Day Hospital 4486
Harefield Hospital 4462
Harefield Hospital Postgraduate Centre 4627
Haringey Primary Care Trust 4410
The Harley Street Clinic 4563
Harlow House 4380
Harlow Primary Care Trust 4410
Harold Wood Hospital 4366
Harold Wood Hospital Postgraduate Academic Centre 4628
Harpenden Memorial Hospital 4413
Harperbury 4413
Harperbury Horizon 4628
Harrogate Clinic 4563
Harrogate District Hospital 4410
Harrogate Health Care NHS Trust 4410
Harrogate Postgraduate Medical Centre 4628
Harrow and Hillingdon Healthcare NHS Trust 4411
Harrow Primary Care Trust 4411
Hartismere Hospital 4426
Hartlepool District 4660
Hartlepool Postgraduate Medical Centre 4628
Hartlepool Primary Care Trust 4411
Hartwood Hospital 4524
Harveian Society of London 4673
Harwich Day Hospital 4441
Haslemere and Community Hospital 4491
Hastings and Rother NHS Trust 4411
Hastings and St Leonards Primary Care Trust 4411
Hastings Postgraduate Medical Education Centre 4628
Havant War Memorial Hospital 4456
Haverfordwest Postgraduate Medical Centre 4640
Havering Primary Care Trust 4412
Hawick Cottage Hospital 4516
Hawick Day Hospital (Geriatric) 4516
Hawkhead Hospital 4528
Hawkhill Day Hospital 4530
Hawkhurst Cottage Hospital 4416
Haworth Unit 4472
Hawthorn Day Hospital 4420, 4461
Haylodge Day Hospital (Geriatric) 4516
Haylodge Hospital 4516
Hayward House 4477
Headway - The Brain Injury Association 4673
Health Development Agency 4651
Health Education Board for Scotland 4655
Health Service Commissioner (Ombudsman) for England, Scotland
and Wales 4651
The Heart Hospital 4498
Heart of Birmingham Teaching Primary Care Trust 4412
The Heath Clinic 4563
Heath Lane Hospital 4471
Heatherwood and Wexham Park Hospitals NHS Trust 4412
Heatherwood Hospital 4412
Heatherwood Hospital (EMI & AMI Units) 4372
Hellesdon Hospital 4435
Help the Hospices 4673
Helston Community Hospital 4506
Hemel Hempstead General Hospital 4504
Henderson Hospital 4484
Hensol Hospital 4533
Herbert Hospital 4394
Herdmanflat Hospital 4525
Hereford and Worcester Ambulance Service NHS Trust 4412
Hereford County Hospital 4412
Hereford General Hospital 4412
Hereford Hospitals NHS Trust 4412
Hereford Hospitals NHS Trust Postgraduate Medical Centre . . 4628
Herefordshire Primary Care Trust 4413
Hertfordshire, Hertford District 4660
Hertfordshire, Hitchin District 4660
Hertfordshire Partnership NHS Trust 4413
The Hertfordshire Partnership NHS Trust Postgraduate
Centre 4628
Hertfordshire, West District 4660
Herts and Essex General Hospital 4441
Hertsmere Primary Care Trust 4413
Hexham General Hospital 4450
Hexham Postgraduate Medical Centre 4628
Heywood and Middleton Primary Care Trust 4413
High Peak and Dales Primary Care Trust 4413
High Royds Hospital 4420
Highbank 4563
Highcroft Hospital 4373
Highgate Private Hospital Ltd 4563
Highland Acute Hospitals NHS Trust 4522
Highland NHS Board 4555
Highland Primary Care NHS Trust 4522
Highlands House 4416
Hill Crest 4511
Hill House Hospital 4543
Hillcrest and Phoenix Day Hospital 4426
Hillingdon Hospital 4413
Hillingdon Hospital NHS Trust 4413
Hillingdon Hospital Postgraduate Centre 4628
Hillingdon Primary Care Trust 4414
Hinchingbrooke Healthcare NHS Trust 4414
Hinchingbrooke Hospital 4414
Hinchingbrooke Postgraduate Medical and Dental Education
Centre 4628
Hinckley and Bosworth Primary Care Trust 4414
Hinckley and District Hospital 4423
Hinckley Sunnyside Hospital 4423
History of Anaesthesia Society 4673
Hitchin Hospital 4396
HM Stanley Hospital 4537
Hollins Park 4503
Holly House Day Hospital 4473
Holly House Hospital 4563
Holme Valley Memorial Hospital 4382
Holmhead Hospital 4515
Holsworthy Community Hospital 4448
Holy Cross Hospital 4563
Holywell Community Hospital 4539
Holywell Hospital 4547
Homefirst Community HSS Trust 4547
Homelands Hospital 4479
Homerton University Hospital 4414
Homerton University Hospital NHS Trust 4414
Homerton University Hospital Postgraduate Education Centre 4628
Hope Hospital 4470
The Horder Centre for Arthritis 4563
Hornhall Hospital 4479
Hornsea Cottage Hospital 4415
Hornsey Central Hospital 4383
Horsham and Chanctonbury Primary Care Trust 4414
Horsham Hospital 4490, 4492
Horton Hospital 4452

INDEX BY ORGANISATION NAME

Horton Hospital Postgraduate Centre 4628
Hospital Chaplaincies Council (Church of England) 4673
The Hospital for Children 4407
The Hospital for Tropical Diseases 4498
Hospital of St Cross 4445, 4500
Hospital of St John and St Elizabeth 4563
Hounslow and Spelthorne Community and Mental Health NHS
Trust 4415
Hounslow Primary Care Trust 4415
Hove Nuffield Hospital 4563
HRH Princess Christian's Hospital 4563
Huddersfield Central Primary Care Trust 4415
Huddersfield Medical Centre 4628
Huddersfield Nuffield Hospital 4563
Huddersfield Royal Infirmary 4382
Hull and East Riding Community Health NHS Trust 4415
Hull and East Yorkshire Hospitals NHS Trust 4415
Hull Maternity Hospital 4415
Hull Nuffield Hospital 4563
Hull Royal Infirmary 4416
Hulton Day Hospital 4376
Hulton Hospital 4376
Human Fertilisation and Embryology Authority 4651
Hunterian Society 4673
Huntingdon District Postgraduate Medical Education Centre . 4628
Huntingdonshire Primary Care Trust 4416
Hyde Hospital 4454, 4493
Hyndburn and Ribble Valley Primary Care Trust 4416
Hythe Day Hospital 4486
Hythe Hospital 4486

Ian Charles Hospital 4522
Ida Darwin 4424
Ida Darwin Hospital 4424
Iechyd Morgannwg Health Authority 4555
The Ileostomy and Internal Pouch Support Group (IA) 4673
Ilfracombe and District Tyrrell Hospital 4448
Ilkeston Community Hospital 4488
Ilkley Coronation Day Hospital for the Elderly 4365
Ilkley Coronation Hospital (Outpatient and Minor Injuries) . . 4365
Imperial College Faculty of Medicine 4570
Independent Healthcare Association 4673
Ingersley and Millbrook Unit Psychiatric Day Hospital 4398
Inroads Day Hospital 4486
Insch and District War Memorial Hospital 4520
Institute for the Health of the Elderly 4646
Institute of Biomedical Science 4673
Institute of Cancer Research, Royal Cancer Hospital 4646
Institute of Chiropodists and Podiatrists 4673
Institute of Health Studies 4673
Institute of Occupational Medicine 4646
Institute of Orthopaedics Postgraduate Medical Centre 4628
Institute of Physics and Engineering in Medicine 4673
Institute of Psychosexual Medicine 4673
Institute of Sports Medicine 4674
International Glaucoma Association 4674
International Spinal Research Trust 4674
Inverclyde Royal Hospital 4514
Invergordon County Hospital 4522
Inverurie Hospital 4520
Invicta Community Care NHS Trust 4416
Ipswich Hospital 4416
Ipswich Hospital NHS Trust 4416
Ipswich Hospital NHS Trust Postgraduate Centre 4629
Ipswich Primary Care Trust 4417
The Iris Fund for Prevention of Blindness 4674
Irvine Memorial Hospital 4530
Irvine Unit, Bexhill Hospital 4411
Isebrook Hospital 4447
Islay Hospital 4525
Isle of Man Department of Health and Social Security 4556
Isle of Man Postgraduate Medical Centre 4641
Isle of Wight District 4660

Isle of Wight Healthcare NHS Trust 4417
Isle of Wight Primary Care Trust 4417
Isles of Scilly District 4660
Islington Primary Care Trust 4417

The James Cook University Hospital 4482
James Fawcett Education Centre 4629
James Paget Healthcare NHS Trust 4417
James Paget Hospital 4417
Jessop Wing Women's Hospital 4474
The John Fawcett Postgraduate Medical and Dental Education
Centre 4629
John Lister Postgraduate Centre 4629
John Pathy Day Hospital 4534
The John Radcliffe 4452
John Tallack Day Hospital, Thurrock Community Hospital . . 4479
Johnson Hospital 4497
Johnstone Hospital 4529
Joyce Cockram Day Hospital 4506
Jubilee Hospital 4520
Jules Thorn Day Hospital 4383
The Julian Hospital 4435

Kello Hospital 4524
Kelso Day Hospital (Geriatric) 4516
Kelso Hospital 4516
Kemple View 4563
Kendal Education Centre 4629
Kendray Hospital 4368
Kennet and North Wiltshire Primary Care Trust 4418
Kensington and Chelsea Primary Care Trust 4418
Kent Ambulance NHS Trust 4418
Kent and Canterbury Hospital 4400
Kent and Medway Health Authority 4554
Kent and Sussex Hospital 4427
Kent, Ashford and Shepway District 4660
Kent County Ophthalmic and Aural Hospital 4427
Kent, North West District 4660
Kent Postgraduate Medical Centre 4629
Kent, Thanet District 4660
Kettering General Hospital 4418, 4447
Kettering General Hospital NHS Trust 4418
Keynsham Hospital 4496
Kidderminster General Hospital 4511
Kidderminster Postgraduate Medical Centre 4629
Kildean Day Hospital 4519
Kildean Hospital 4519
Kincardine Community Hospital 4520
Kincardine O'Neil War Memorial Hospital 4520
King Edward VII Hospital 4563
King Edward VII Hospital (EMI Unit) 4372
King Edward VII Hospital Guernsey 4551
King Edward VII Hospital (Windsor) 4397
King Edward VII's Hospital for Officers 4563
King George Hospital 4367
King's College Hospital 4418
King's College Hospital NHS Trust 4418
King's College London 4575
King's Fund 4674
King's Healthcare NHS Trust Postgraduate Medical Centre . . 4629
Kings Hill Day Hospital 4502
King's Lynn and Wisbech Hospitals NHS Trust 4419
King's Lynn Postgraduate Medical and Dental Education
Centre 4629
King's Mill Centre for Healthcare Services 4474
The Kings Mill Education Centre 4629
Kings Park Hospital 4394
Kingston General Hospital 4416
Kingston Hospital NHS Trust 4420
Kingston Hospital NHS Trust Hospital 4420
Kingston Postgraduate Medical Centre 4629
Kingston Primary Care Trust 4420
Kingston upon Hull and East Riding of Yorkshire District . . . 4660

INDEX BY ORGANISATION NAME

Kingsway Hospital 4488
Kingsway Hospital Postgraduate Centre 4629
Kingswood Day Hospital 4482
Kirkcudbright Hospital 4517
Kirklands Hospital 4524
Kirklandside Hospital 4515
Kneesworth House Hospital 4563
Knighton Hospital 4543
Knoll Day Hospital (Geriatric) 4516
Knoll Hospital 4516
Knowsley Primary Care Trust 4420
Knutsford and District Community Hospital 4398

Lady Home Hospital 4524
Lady Margaret Hospital 4515
Ladysbridge Hospital 4520
Ladywell Hospital 4470
Lagan Valley Hospital 4546
Laidlaw Day Hospital 4417
Lambert Memorial Hospital 4446
Lambeth Primary Care Trust 4420
Lamellion Hospital 4390
Lanarkshire Acute Hospitals NHS Trust 4523
Lanarkshire NHS Board 4555
Lanarkshire Primary Care NHS Trust 4524
Lancashire Ambulance Service NHS Trust 4420
Lancashire, Blackpool and Fylde District 4660
Lancashire Care NHS Trust 4420
Lancashire, East District 4660
Lancashire, North District 4660
Lancashire, Preston and South-West Lancashire District . . 4660
Lancaster and Lakeland Nuffield Hospital 4563
Lancaster Postgraduate Medical Centre 4629
Langbaurgh Primary Care Trust 4420
Lansdowne Hospital 4534
Larchwood Hospital 4430
Launceston General Hospital 4390
Lawson Memorial Hospital 4522
Lawson Memorial Hospital (Surgical Services) (Cambusavie) . 4523
Lea Castle Hospital 4445
Leanchoil Hospital 4520
Learning and Development Centre 4630
Learning Disabilities Service 4509
Learning Disability Service 4510
Leatherhead Hospital 4404
Ledbury Cottage Hospital 4413
Leeds Community and Mental Health Services Teaching NHS Trust 4420
Leeds Dental Institute 4421
Leeds General Infirmary 4421
Leeds Infirmary Postgraduate Medical Centre 4630
Leeds North East Primary Care Trust 4421
Leeds North West Primary Care Trust 4421
The Leeds Private Hospital 4564
Leeds Road Hospital 4377
Leeds Teaching Hospitals NHS Trust 4421
Leeds West Primary Care Trust 4423
Leek Moorlands Hospital 4444
Leicester City West Primary Care Trust 4423
Leicester Clinical Education Centre 4630
Leicester General Hospital 4501
Leicester General Hospital Brandon Unit 4423
The Leicester Nuffield Hospital 4564
The Leicester Royal Infirmary 4501
Leicester Warwick Medical School 4576
Leicestershire and Rutland Healthcare NHS Trust 4423
Leicestershire, Leicester City and South Leicestershire District 4660
Leicestershire, Northamptonshire and Rutland Health Authority 4553
Leicestershire, Rutland and North Leicestershire District . . . 4660
Leigh House Hospital 4504
Leigh Infirmary 4512
Leigham Clinic 4564

Leighton Hospital 4429
Leominster Community Hospital 4413
Leonard Cheshire Foundation 4674
Leukaemia Research Fund 4674
Leverndale Hospital 4522
Lewisham Education Centre 4630
The Lewisham Hospital 4424
The Lewisham Hospital NHS Trust 4424
Lewisham Primary Care Trust 4424
Lifespan Healthcare NHS Trust 4424
Lightburn Hospital 4528
Limbless Association 4674
Lime Trees EMI Assessment Unit 4371
Lincoln Clinic and Centre for Psychotherapy 4674
Lincoln County Hospital 4497
Lincoln County Hospital Postgraduate Medical Centre 4630
Lincolnshire Ambulance and Health Transport Service NHS Trust 4425
Lincolnshire, Boston and Spalding District 4660
Lincolnshire, Grantham District 4660
Lincolnshire Healthcare NHS Trust 4425
Lincolnshire, Lincoln District 4660
Lincolnshire, North Lincolnshire and Grimsby District . . . 4660
Lincolnshire, Sleaford District 4660
Lincolnshire South West Primary Care Trust 4425
Lincolnshire, Spilsby District 4660
Lincolnshire, Stamford District 4661
Linden Day Hospital 4421
Listening Books 4674
Lister Hospital 4396
The Lister Hospital 4564
Lister Hospital Postgraduate Centre 4630
Lister Institute of Preventive Medicine 4674
Lister Postgraduate Institute 4638
Little Brook Hospital 4494
Little Cairnie Hospital 4530
Little Court 4476
The Little Foundation 4674
Littlehampton Hospital 4512
Liverpool Women's Hospital 4425
Liverpool Women's Hospital NHS Trust 4425
Llanarth Court Hospital 4569
Llandough Geriatric Day Hospital 4534
Llandough Hospital 4534
Llandovery Hospital 4536
Llandrindod Wells County War Memorial Hospital 4543
Llandudno General Hospital 4541
Llanelli Postgraduate Medical Centre 4640
Llanfrechfa Grange Hospital 4538
Llangollen Community Hospital 4537
Llanidloes and District War Memorial Hospital 4543
Lluesty Hospital 4539
Llwyneryr Hospital 4533
Llwynypia Hospital 4542
Loanhead Hospital 4525
Local Health Partnerships NHS Trust 4425
Lochmaben Day Hospital 4517
Lochmaben Hospital 4517
Lochmaddy Hospital 4533
Lomond and Argyll Primary Care NHS Trust 4524
London Ambulance Service NHS Trust 4426
London Bridge Hospital 4564
The London Chest Hospital 4369
The London Chest Hospital Education Centre 4630
The London Clinic 4564
The London Foot Hospital and School of Podiatric Medicine . 4383
London Postgraduate Medical and Dental Education 4630
London School of Hygiene and Tropical Medicine 4578
Long Fox Unit 4366
Longstone Hospital 4544
Longton Cottage Hospital 4444
Longview Adolescent Unit 4441
Lorn and Islands District General Hospital 4525, 4514
Lothian NHS Board 4555

INDEX BY ORGANISATION NAME

Lothian Primary Care NHS Trust 4525
Lothian University Hospitals NHS Trust 4525
Loughborough General Hospital 4423
Loughborough Hospital 4424
Lourdes Hospital 4564
Loversall Hospital 4393
Lowestoft Hospital 4418
Ludlow Hospital 4475
Ludwig Institute for Cancer Research 4646
Lurgan Hospital 4546
Luton and Dunstable Hospital 4426
Luton and Dunstable Hospital NHS Trust 4426
Luton and Dunstable Hospital NHS Trust Medical Centre . . 4630
Luton Primary Care Trust 4426
Lydney and District Hospital 4473
Lymington Day Hospital 4486
Lymington Hospital 4486
Lymington Infirmary 4486
Lynden Hill Clinic 4564
Lynebank Hospital 4518
Lynfield Mount Hospital 4377
Lytham Hospital 4375

MACA (Mental After Care Association) 4674
Macclesfield District General Hospital 4398
MacKinnon House 4522
Macmillan Cancer Relief 4674
Maesteg Community Hospital 4533
Maidstone and Tunbridge Wells NHS Trust 4427
Maidstone Hospital 4427
Maidstone Weald Primary Care Trust 4427
Maindiff Court Hospital 4538
Maldon and South Chelmsford Primary Care Trust 4427
Malham House Day Hospital 4421
The Mallards 4394
Malmesbury Community Hospital 4509
Malton, Norton and District Hospital 4472
Malvern Community Hospital 4485
Manchester Royal Eye Hospital 4384
Manchester Royal Infirmary 4384
Manor Hospital 4445, 4502
Manor House 4380
Mansfield Community Hospital 4475
Mansfield District Primary Care Trust 4427
Mansionhouse Unit 4529
Maple Lodge 4425
Derby City General Hospital (Mental Health) 4488
Margaret Scott Day Hospital 4435
Marie Curie Cancer Care 4674
Marie Curie Centre, Ardenlea 4564
Marie Curie Centre, Belfast 4569
Marie Curie Centre, Caterham 4564
Marie Curie Centre, Edenhall 4564
Marie Curie Centre, Fairmile 4569
Marie Curie Centre, Holme Tower 4569
Marie Curie Centre, Hunters Hill 4569
Marie Curie Centre, Liverpool 4564
Marie Curie Centre, Newcastle 4564
Marie Curie Centre, Warren Pearl 4564
Marie Curie Research Institute 4646
Marie Stopes Bristol 4564
Marie Stopes Ealing 4564
Marie Stopes Essex 4564
Marie Stopes House 4564
Marie Stopes Leeds 4564
Marie Stopes Maidstone 4564
Marie Stopes Manchester 4564
Marie Stopes South London 4565
Marlow Community Hospital 4477
Marsh-Jackson Postgraduate Medical Centre 4630
Martello Court Day Hospital 4441
Mary Hewetson Cottage Hospital (Elderly and Mental Health) 4438

Mascalls Park 4440
Mason Medical Research Foundation 4674
Mater Infirmorum Hospital 4547
Mater Infirmorum Hospital HSS Trust 4547
Maud Hospital 4520
Maudsley Hospital 4480
Maybole Day Hospital 4515
Mayday Healthcare NHS Trust 4427
Mayday Hospital 4427
Mayfair Day Hospital 4447
Mayfield Centre (Day Hospital) 4441
Mayflower Day Unit 4425
Mayflower House 4479
Meadowfield 4512
Meadowslea Hospital 4539
Mearnskirk House 4529
The Medical Commission on Accident Prevention 4674
The Medical Council on Alcoholism 4675
Medical Missionary Association 4675
Medical Practices Committee 4651
Medical Protection Society 4675
Medical Research Council 4646
Medical Research Society 4675
Medical Society for the Study of Venereal Diseases 4675
The Medical Society of London 4675
Medical Women's Federation 4675
Medicines Commission 4651
Medicines Control Agency 4651
Medico-Legal Society 4675
Medway Maritime Hospital 4428
Medway NHS Trust 4428
Medway Postgraduate Medical Centre 4630
Medway Primary Care Trust 4428
Meigle Community Day Hospital 4530
Melbury Lodge 4504
Melksham Community Hospital 4507
Melton, Rutland and Harborough Primary Care Trust 4428
Memorial Hospital 4458
MENCAP 4675
Mendip Primary Care Trust 4428
Meningitis Trust 4675
Mental Health Act Commission 4651
Mental Health Acute Unit 4541
Mental Health Day Hospital 4550
Mental Health Day Unit 4425
Mental Health Foundation 4675
Mental Health Matters 4675
Mental Health Media 4675
Mental Health Services of Salford NHS Trust 4428
Mental Health Unit 4479
Mental Welfare Commission for Scotland 4655
Merchiston Hospital 4529
Mersey Care NHS Trust 4428
Mersey Deanery 4630
Mersey Regional Ambulance Service NHS Trust 4429
Merseyside Clinic 4565
Merseyside, Knowsley, St. Helens and Sefton District 4661
Merseyside, Liverpool District 4661
Merseyside, Wirral District 4661
Merthyr and Cynon Valley Postgraduate Centre 4640
Mid-Argyll Hospital 4525
Mid Cheshire Hospitals NHS Trust 4429
Mid Devon Primary Care Trust 4429
Mid Essex Hospital Services NHS Trust 4429
Mid-Hampshire Primary Care Trust 4430
Mid Kent and Medway 4661
Mid Staffordshire General Hospitals NHS Trust 4430
Mid Staffordshire Postgraduate Medical Centre 4630
Mid Sussex NHS Trust 4430
Mid-Sussex Postgraduate Medical Centre 4631
Mid-Sussex Primary Care Trust 4431
Mid-Ulster Hospital 4550
Mid Yorkshire Hospitals NHS Trust 4431
Mid Yorkshire Nuffield Hospital 4565

INDEX BY ORGANISATION NAME

Middlesbrough General Hospital 4482
Middlesbrough Primary Care Trust 4431
The Middlesex Hospital 4498
Midhurst, Easebourne and District Cottage Hospital 4492
Migdale Hospital 4523
Mignot Memorial Hospital 4551
Migraine Action Association 4675
Migraine Trust 4675
Mile End Hospital 4495
Milford-on-Sea Day Hospital 4486
Milford-on-Sea War Memorial Hospital 4486
Milford Rehabilitation Hospital 4491
Millfield House 4421
Milton Keynes 4661
Milton Keynes General Hospital 4431
Milton Keynes General Hospital NHS Trust 4431
Milton Keynes Postgraduate Education Centre 4631
Milton Keynes Primary Care Trust 4431
MIND (National Association for Mental Health) 4675
Minehead and West Somerset Hospital 4476
Minerva Day Hospital 4376
Minffordd Hospital 4541
Minsmere House 4426
Moffat Day Hospital 4517
Moffat Hospital 4517
Mold Community Hospital 4539
Monklands Hospital 4523
Monkton Hall Hospital 4483
Monkwearmouth Hospital 4458
Monmouth Hospital 4538
Montagu Hospital 4393
Montfield Hospital 4533
Montgomery County Infirmary 4543
Montrose Royal Infirmary 4530
Monyhull Hospital 4373
Moore Cottage Hospital 4399
Moorfields Eye Hospital 4431
Moorfields Eye Hospital NHS Trust 4431
Moorfields Hospital Postgraduate Centre 4631
Moorgreen Day Hospital 4486
Moorgreen Hospital 4486
Moorlands Day Hospital 4483
Morecambe Bay Hospitals NHS Trust 4431
Morecambe Bay Primary Care Trust 4432
Moreton District Hospital 4399
Morpeth Cottage Hospital 4450
Morriston Hospital 4543
Moseley Hall Hospital 4373
Mossley Day Hospital 4502
Mossley Hill Hospital 4429
Motor Neurone Disease Association 4676
The Mount 4475
Mount Alvernia Hospital 4565
Mount Day Hospital 4509
Mount Gould Hospital 4455
Mount Stuart Hospital 4565
Mount Vernon Hospital 4368, 4504
Mount Vernon Postgraduate Medical Centre 4631
Mountain Ash Hospital 4540
Mountnessing Court 4479
Mourne Hospital 4548
Moyle Hospital 4551
MRC Technology Scotland 4655
Muckamore Abbey Hospital 4548
Mullinure Hospital 4545
Multiple Sclerosis Society of Great Britain and N. Ireland . . 4676
Murray Royal Hospital 4530
Muscular Dystrophy Campaign 4676
Musgrave Park Hospital 4547
Myasthenia Gravis Association 4676
Mynydd Mawr Hospital 4536

Nairn Town and County Hospital 4523

Nasebury Court 4440
National Association for Medical Education Management (incorporating NAPMECA) 4676
National Association for the Education of Sick Children . . . 4676
National Association of Clinical Tutors 4676
National Association of GP Co-operatives 4676
The National Association of Primary Care 4676
National Asthma Campaign 4676
National Autistic Society 4676
National Birthday Trust Fund 4676
National Blood Authority 4651
National Board for Nursing, Midwifery and Health Visiting for Northern Ireland (NBNI) 4656
National Board for Nursing, Midwifery and Health Visiting for Scotland (NBS) 4655
National Cancer Alliance 4676
The National Childbirth Trust 4676
National Children's Bureau 4676
National Council for Hospice and Specialist Palliative Care Services 4676
National Counselling Service for Sick Doctors 4677
The National Deaf Children's Society 4677
National Eczema Society 4677
National Health Service Litigation Authority 4652
National Health Service Tribunal 4656
The National Hospital for Neurology and Neurosurgery . . . 4498
National Institute for Biological Standards and Control . . . 4652
National Institute for Clinical Excellence 4652
The National Kidney Research Fund 4677
The National League of the Blind and Disabled 4677
National Library for the Blind 4677
National Meningitis Trust 4677
National Osteoporosis Society 4677
National Pharmaceutical Association 4677
National Schizophrenia Fellowship 4677
National Society for Epilepsy 4677
National Society for the Prevention of Cruelty to Children (NSPCC) 4677
NCH Action for Children 4677
Neath and Port Talbot District 4663
Neath General Hospital 4533
Neath General Hospital Postgraduate Centre 4640
Nelson Hospital 4404
Nether Edge Hospital 4389
Netherlea Hospital 4518
The Neuro-Disability Research Trust 4677
Nevill Hall Hospital 4538
Nevill Hall Postgraduate Centre 4640
New Craigs 4523
New Cross Hospital 4467
New Epsom and Ewell Cottage Hospital 4404
New Forest Primary Care Trust 4432
New Hall Hospital 4565
New Possibilities NHS Trust 4432
Newark and Sherwood Primary Care Trust 4432
Newark Hospital 4475
Newbury and Community Primary Care Trust 4432
Newbury Community Hospital (EMI Day Hospital) 4372
Newbury District 4661
Newcastle General Hospital 4433
Newcastle General Hospital Postgraduate Medical Centre . . 4631
Newcastle, North Tyneside and Northumberland Mental Health NHS Trust 4432
The Newcastle Nuffield Hospital 4565
Newcastle Primary Care Trust 4433
Newcastle-under-Lyme Primary Care Trust 4433
Newcastle upon Tyne Dental Hospital 4434
Newcastle upon Tyne Hospitals NHS Trust 4433
Newham General Hospital 4434
Newham General Hospital Postgraduate Centre 4631
Newham Healthcare NHS Trust 4434
Newham Primary Care Trust 4435
Newhaven Downs 4478
Newholme Hospital 4439

INDEX BY ORGANISATION NAME

Newmarket Community Hospital 4506
Newquay and District Hospital 4390
Newry and Mourne HSS Trust 4548
Newton Abbot Hospital 4478
Newton Community Hospital 4468
Newton Stewart Day Hospital 4517
Newton Stewart Hospital 4517
NHS Confederation 4677
NHS Directorate 4656
NHS Retirement Fellowship 4677
NHS Support Federation 4677
NHS Training and Conference Centre 4677
Nightingale Macmillan Continuing Care Unit 4487
Ninewells Hospital 4531
Nithbank Day Hospital 4517
Noble's Isle of Man Hospital 4551
Norfolk and Norwich Institute of Medical Education 4631
Norfolk and Norwich University Hospital 4435
Norfolk and Norwich University Hospital NHS Trust 4435
Norfolk, Great Yarmouth District 4661
Norfolk, King's Lynn District 4661
Norfolk Mental Health Care NHS Trust 4435
Norfolk, Suffolk and Cambridgeshire Health Authority 4553
North and East Cornwall Primary Care Trust 4436
North and East Yorkshire and Northern Lincolnshire Health Authority 4554
North and West Belfast HSS Trust 4548
North Birmingham Primary Care Trust 4436
North Bradford Primary Care Trust 4436
North Bristol NHS Trust 4436
North Cambridgeshire Hospital 4419
North Central London Health Authority 4553
North Cheshire Hospitals NHS Trust 4437
North Cumbria Acute Hospitals NHS Trust 4437
North Cumbria Mental Health and Learning Disabilities NHS Trust 4438
North Derbyshire Community Health Care Service NHS Trust . . 4438
North Devon District General Hospital 4448
North Devon Postgraduate Medical Centre 4631
North Devon Primary Care Trust 4439
North Dorset Primary Care Trust 4439
North Downs Hospital 4565
North Durham Health Care NHS Trust 4439
North East Ambulance Service NHS Trust 4440
North East Lincolnshire Primary Care Trust 4440
North East London Health Authority 4553
North East London Mental Health NHS Trust 4440
North East Oxfordshire Primary Care Trust 4440
North East Wales District 4663
North East Wales NHS Trust 4539
North East Warwickshire Primary Care Trust 4440
North Eastern Derbyshire Primary Care Trust 4440
North Essex Mental Health Partnership NHS Trust 4441
North Glamorgan NHS Trust 4539
North Glasgow University Hospitals NHS Trust 4527
North Hampshire Hospital 4441
North Hampshire Hospitals NHS Trust 4441
North Hampshire Hospitals NHS Trust Postgraduate Medical Centre 4631
North Hampshire Primary Care Trust 4442
North Hertfordshire and Stevenage Primary Care Trust 4442
North Hertfordshire Postgraduate Centre 4631
North Kirklees Primary Care Trust 4442
North Lincolnshire Primary Care Trust 4442
North Liverpool Primary Care Trust 4442
North London Nuffield Hospital 4565
North London Staff Development and Education Centre 4631
North Manchester General Hospital 4442
North Manchester Healthcare NHS Trust 4442
North Manchester Postgraduate Medical Centre 4631
North Manchester Primary Care Trust 4442
North Mersey Community NHS Trust 4442
North Middlesex Hospital 4443
North Middlesex Hospital Academic Centre 4631
North Middlesex University Hospital NHS Trust 4442
North Norfolk Primary Care Trust 4443
North of Scotland Deanery 4639
North Peterborough Primary Care Trust 4443
North Riding Infirmary 4483
North Sefton and West Lancashire Community NHS Trust 4443
North Sheffield Primary Care Trust 4443
North Somerset Primary Care Trust 4443
North Staffordshire Combined Health Care NHS Trust Postgraduate Medical Centre 4632
North Staffordshire Combined Healthcare NHS Trust 4443
North Staffordshire Hospital 4444
North Staffordshire Hospital NHS Trust 4444
North Staffordshire Hospital NHS Trust Postgraduate Medical Centre 4632
North Staffordshire Nuffield Hospital 4565
North Stoke Primary Care Trust 4444
North Surrey Primary Care Trust 4444
North Tees and Hartlepool NHS Trust 4444
North Tees Postgraduate Medical Centre 4632
North Tees Primary Care Trust 4445
North Tyneside General Hospital 4450
North Tyneside HA Postgraduate Department 4632
North Tyneside Primary Care Trust 4445
North Wales Health Authority 4556
North Wales Medical Centre 4569
North Warwickshire NHS Trust 4445
North West Anglia Health Care NHS Trust 4445
North West Durham Postgraduate Medical Centre 4632
North West London Health Authority 4553
North West London Hospitals NHS Trust 4445
North West Surrey Mental Health Partnership NHS Trust . . . 4446
North West Wales District 4663
North West Wales NHS Trust 4540
North Western (North) Postgraduate Medical Centres 4632
North Yorkshire, Eastern District 4661
North Yorkshire, Western District 4661
Northallerton Health Services NHS Trust 4446
Northallerton Postgraduate Medical Education Centre 4632
Northampton General Hospital 4447
Northampton General Hospital NHS Trust 4447
Northampton Primary Care Trust 4447
Northamptonshire District 4661
Northamptonshire Healthcare NHS Trust 4447
Northamptonshire Heartlands Primary Care Trust 4448
Northern Birmingham Mental Health NHS Trust 4448
Northern Devon Healthcare NHS Trust 4448
Northern General Hospital 4474
Northern Health and Social Services Board 4556
Northern Ireland Ambulance Service HSS Trust 4548
Northern Ireland Blood Transfusion Service 4656
Northern Ireland Central Services Agency for the Health and Social Services 4657
Northern Ireland Council for Postgraduate Medical and Dental Education 4641
Northern Lincolnshire and Goole Hospitals NHS Trust 4449
Northgate and Prudhoe NHS Trust 4449
Northgate Hospital 4418, 4435, 4449
Northgate Therapy Centre 4418
Northowram Hospital 4382
Northumberland, North District 4661
Northumberland, South District 4661
Northumberland, Tyne and Wear Health Authority 4554
Northumbria Health Care NHS Trust 4449
Northwick Park Hospital 4446
Northwick Park Hospital, Medawar Postgraduate Department 4632
Northwood and Pinner Cottage Hospital 4411
Norwich, Diss and Dereham District 4661
Norwich Primary Care Trust 4450
Nottingham City Hospital 4450
Nottingham City Hospital NHS Trust 4450
Nottingham City Postgraduate Education Centre 4632
Nottingham City Primary Care Trust 4451

INDEX BY ORGANISATION NAME

The Nottingham Nuffield Hospital 4565
Nottinghamshire District 4661
Nottinghamshire Healthcare NHS Trust 4451
Novartis Foundation 4648
Nuffield Day Hospital 4440
Nuffield Institute for Health 4678
Nuffield Orthopaedic Centre NHS Trust 4451
Nuffield Trust 4678
Nutrition Society 4678

Oak Day Hospital 4421
Oakdale Hospital 4538
Oaklands Hospital 4565
Oakley House 4394
The Oaks Hospital 4565
Oakwell Centre for Learning and Development 4632
Obstetric Anaesthetists' Association 4678
Odiham Cottage Hospital 4491
Office for National Statistics 4652
Office of Health Economics 4678
Old Age Psychiatry Day Hospital 4480
Old Court Hospital 4565
The Old Manor 4470
Old Manor Hospital 3366
The Oldbury and Smethwick Primary Care Trust 4451
Oldchurch Hospital 4367
Oldham Medical and Dental Education Department 4632
Oldham NHS Trust 4451
Oldham Primary Care Trust 4452
Oliver Plunkett Postgraduate Centre 4632
Olivet 4565
One Parent Families (National Council for One Parent Families) 4678
Ongar War Memorial Hospital 4441
The Orchard Hospital 4565
Orchard House Day Hospital 4451, 4519
Orchard Lodge Young People's Unit 4476
Orchard Unit 4371
The Orchards 4522
Orkney Islands 4533
Orkney NHS Board 4555
Orleans Day Hospital 4530
Ormskirk and District General Hospital 4488
Ormskirk Postgraduate Medical Education Centre 4632
Orpington Hospital 4380
Orsett Hospital 4370
Orton Lea 4438
Oundle Community Care Unit 4447
Overdale Hospital 4551
Oxford City Primary Care Trust 4452
Oxford Radcliffe Hospital NHS Trust 4452
Oxford Regional Postgraduate Medical 4632
Oxfordshire Ambulance NHS Trust 4453
Oxfordshire District 4661
Oxfordshire Learning Disability NHS Trust 4453
Oxfordshire Mental Healthcare NHS Trust 4453
Oxleas NHS Trust 4453

Paignton Hospital 4478
The Pain Society 4678
Palmer Community Hospital 4483
Papworth Hospital 4454
Papworth Hospital NHS Trust 4454
Park Hill Hospital 4565
Park Hospital for Children 4453
Parkhead Hospital 4522
Parkinson's Disease Society of the United Kingdom 4678
Parklands Hospital 4491
Parkside Day Hospital 4419
Parkside Health NHS Trust 4454
Parkside Hospital 4565
Parkwood Psychiatric Unit 4375
Passmore Edwards Hospital 4390

Pathological Society of Great Britain and Ireland 4678
The Patients Association 4678
Patrick Stead Hospital 4426
Pembrokeshire and Derwen NHS Trust 4541
Pembury Hospital 4427
Pembury Hospital (Psychiatric Services) 4416
Pendle Community Hospital 4381
Penley Hospital 4539
Penn Hospital 4510
The Pennine Acute Hospitals NHS Trust 4454
Pennine Care NHS Trust 4454
Pennine House 4381
Penrith Hospital 4438
Pershore Cottage Hospital 4485
Perth Royal Infirmary 4531
Peter Hodgkinson Centre 4633
Peterborough District 4661
Peterborough District Hospital 4454
Peterborough District Postgraduate Medical and Dental Education Centre 4633
Peterborough Hospitals NHS Trust 4454
Peterhead Community Hospital 4520
Peterlee Community Hospital 4444
Pharmaceutical Services Negotiating Committee 4653
Pierremont Unit and Beaumont 4391
Pilgrim Hospital 4497
Pinderfields and Pontefract Hospitals NHS Trust 4455
Pinderfields General Hospital 4455
Pinehill Hospital 4565
The Pituitary Foundation 4678
Plaistow Day Hospital 4435
Plaistow Hospital 4435
Plymouth Hospitals NHS Trust 4455
Plymouth Medical Centre 4633
The Plymouth Nuffield Hospital 4565
Plymouth Primary Care Trust 4455
Poltair Hospital 4506
Pontefract General Infirmary 4455, 4502
Pontypridd and Rhondda NHS Trust 4542
Poole General Hospital 4455
Poole Hospitals NHS Trust 4455
Poole Postgraduate Medical Centre 4633
Poole Primary Care Trust 4456
Port Talbot Hospital 4534
The Portland Hospital for Women and Children 4565
Portman Clinic 4494
Portree Hospital 4523
Portsmouth City Primary Care Trust 4456
Portsmouth Health Care NHS Trust 4456
Portsmouth Hospitals NHS Trust 4456, 4633
Postgraduate Institute for Medicine and Dentistry 4633
Postgraduate Medical Education Centre 4633
Potters Bar Hospital 4368
Powys District 4663
Powys Health Care NHS Trust 4542
Prestatyn Community Hospital 4537
Preston Acute Hospitals NHS Trust 4457
Preston Postgraduate Medical Centre 4633
Preston Primary Care Trust 4457
Prestwich Site 4428
Primary Immunodeficiency Association 4678
Primrose Hill Hospital 4483
Prince Charles Hospital 4540
Prince Philip Hospital 4536
Prince William Postgraduate Medical Education Centre . . . 4633
Princes Street Day Hospital 4519
Princes Street Day Unit (Adult Mental Illness) 4516
Princess Alexandra Hospital 4457
The Princess Alexandra Hospital NHS Trust 4457
Princess Alexandra Hospital Postgraduate Medical Centre . . 4633
Princess Anne Hospital 4486
Princess Elizabeth Hospital 4551
The Princess Grace Hospital 4565
Princess Margaret Hospital 4492

INDEX BY ORGANISATION NAME

Princess Marina Hospital 4447
Princess of Wales Community Hospital 4511
Princess of Wales Hospital 4534
The Princess of Wales Hospital 4424
Princess Royal Hospital 4416, 4457
Princess Royal Hospital (East Wing) 4378
Princess Royal Hospital NHS Trust 4457
Priority Healthcare Wearside NHS Trust 4457
Priority House 4416
Priorsford Day Unit (Adult Mental Illness) 4516
The Priory Clinic 4569
The Priory Clinic Cantebury 4566
The Priory Clinic Keats House 4566
The Priory Clinic Nottingham 4566
Priory Day Hospital 4536
Priory Grange 4566
The Priory Grange 4566
The Priory Hospital Altrincham 4566
The Priory Hospital Bristol 4566
The Priory Hospital Chelmsford 4566
The Priory Hospital Glasgow 4569
The Priory Hospital Hayes Grove 4566
The Priory Hospital Lancashire 4566
The Priory Hospital Marchwood 4566
The Priory Hospital North London 4566
The Priory Hospital Roehampton 4566
The Priory Hospital Sturt 4566
The Priory Hospital Woking 4566
The Priory Ticehurst House 4566
Prudhoe Hospital 4449
Psoriasis Association 4678
Psychiatric Residential Unit 4415
Public Health Laboratory Service 4653
Purey Cust Nuffield Hospital 4566
Purley and District War Memorial Hospital 4428
Putney Hospital 4484

Queen Alexandra Hospital 4456
Queen Charlotte's and Chelsea Hospital 4410
Queen Elizabeth Hospital 4406, 4419, 4458, 4499
Queen Elizabeth Hospital NHS Trust 4458
Queen Elizabeth II Hospital 4397
Queen Elizabeth II Hospital Postgraduate Centre 4633
Queen Elizabeth Psychiatric Hospital 4476
Queen Elizabeth the Queen Mother Hospital 4401
Queen Margaret Hospital 4518
Queen Mary's Hospital 4458, 4484
Queen Mary's Hospital for Children 4404
Queen Mary's House 4463
Queen Mary's Sidcup NHS Trust 4458
Queen Mary's University Hospital Postgraduate Medical
Centre 4633
The Queen Mother's Hospital 4532
The Queen's Household 4658
Queen's Medical Centre, Nottingham University Hospital NHS
Trust 4458
Queen Victoria Hospital 4432, 4459
Queen Victoria Hospital NHS Trust 4459
Queen Victoria Memorial Hospital 4397
Queen's Centre for Clinical Studies 4633
Queen's Hospital 3381
Queen's Medical Centre 4633
Queen's Nursing Institute 4678
Queen's Park Hospital 4374
Queen's Park Psychiatric Day Hospital 4374
Queen's University of Belfast 4620
QUIT 4678

Radcliffe Infirmary 4453
Raigmore Hospital 4522
Rainbow Trust 4678
Rampton Hospital 4451
Ramsbottom Cottage Hospital 4381

Ramsey and District Cottage Hospital 4552
Randolph Wemyss Day Hospital 4518
Randolph Wemyss Memorial Hospital 4518
Rannoch Lodge 4441
Rathbone Hospital 4429
Ravenscraig Hospital 4529
Ravenswood House 4486, 4504
Reading Primary Care Trust 4459
Red Deer Day Hospital 4524
Redbridge Primary Care Trust 4459
Redditch and Bromsgrove Primary Care Trust 4459
Redford Lodge Hospital 4566
Redwood Memorial Hospital 4538
REMEDI For Relief of Disability 4678
Renacres Hall Hospital 4566
Renfrewshire and Inverclyde Primary Care NHS Trust . . . 4528
Research Institute for the Care of the Elderly 4648
Research into Ageing 4678
Resource Centre Day Hospital 4488
The Restoration of Appearance and Function Trust 4679
Restricted Growth Association 4679
Retford Hospital 4393
The Retreat 4566
Ribbleton Hospital 4408
Ribchester Community Hospital 4389
Richmond and Twickenham Primary Care Trust 4459
Richmond Fellowship 4679
Richmond Royal Hospital 4485
Richmond Victoria Hospital 4447
Ridge Hill Mental Handicap Unit 4396
Ridgewood Centre 4491
Ridings Southlands Hospital 4512
Ridley Day Hospital at Verrington Hospital 4476
Ripon Community Hospital 4411
River House Day Centre 4391
The Rivers Hospital 4566
Riverside Community Healthcare NHS Trust 4459
Riverside Day Unit 4448
Rivington Day Hospital 4376
Roadmeetings Hospital 4524
Robert Clinic 4567
The Robert Hardwick Postgraduate Centre 4633
Robert Jones and Agnes Hunt Orthopaedic and District Hospital NHS
Trust 4459
Robert Jones and Agnes Hunt Orthopaedic Hospital . . . 4460
Robinson Memorial Hospital 4546
Roborough Day Hospital 4402
Roch House Day Hospital 4382
Rochdale Healthcare NHS Trust 4460
Rochdale Infirmary 4460
Rochdale Primary Care Trust 4460
Rochford Hospital 4479
Romford Medical Academic Centre 4633
Romsey Hospital 4486
Roodlands Hospital 4525
Rookwood Hospital 4535
Roseangle Day Hospital 4530
Rosebank - Wells 4476
Rosebery House 4377
Roseburn Day Hospital 4515
Rosemount Day Care Services 4398
Rosemount Day Hospital 4530
Rosie Hospital 4364
Ross Community Hospital 4413
Ross House Day Hospital 4523
Ross Memorial Hospital 4523
Ross Thomson Unit 4546
Rossall Hospital 4376
Rossendale General Hospital 4381
Rosslyn Clinic 4567
Rosslynlee Hospital 4525
Rotherham General Hospital Day Surgery Centre 4461
Rotherham General Hospitals NHS Trust 4460

INDEX BY ORGANISATION NAME

Rotherham General Hospitals NHS Trust Postgraduate Centre 4634
Rotherham Primary Care Trust 4461
Rotherham Priority Health Services NHS Trust 4461
Roundwell Place Day Hospital 4444
Rowan Day Hospital 4511
Rowley Hall Hospital 4567
Rowley, Regis and Tipton Primary Care Trust 4461
Rowley Regis Hospital 4471
Royal Aberdeen Children's Hospital 4521
Royal Albert Edward Infirmary 4513
Royal Alexandra Hospital 4514, 4537
Royal Alexandra Hospital (Care of the Elderly) 4529
Royal Alexandra Hospital for Sick Children 4379
Royal Association for Deaf People 4679
Royal Association for Disability and Rehabilitation 4679
Royal Belfast Hospital for Sick Children 4548
Royal Berkshire Ambulance Service NHS Trust 4461
Royal Berkshire and Battle Hospitals NHS Trust 4461
Royal Berkshire Hospital 4461
Royal Bolton Hospital 4376
The Royal Bolton Hospital Postgraduate Medical Education Centre 4634
Royal Bournemouth and Christchurch Hospitals NHS Trust . . 4461
Royal Bournemouth Hospital 4462
The Royal British Legion 4679
Royal British Nurses Association 4679
Royal Brompton and Harefield NHS Trust 4462
Royal Brompton Hospital 4462
Royal College of Anaesthetists 4642
Royal College of General Practitioners (RCGP) 4642
Royal College of Midwives 4642
Royal College of Nursing 4642
Royal College of Obstetricians and Gynaecologists (RCOG) . . 4642
Royal College of Ophthalmologists 4643
Royal College of Paediatrics and Child Health 4643
Royal College of Pathologists 4643
Royal College of Physicians 4643
Royal College of Physicians and Surgeons of Glasgow 4643
Royal College of Physicians, Clinical Effectiveness and Evaluation Unit 4648
Royal College of Physicians of Edinburgh 4643
Royal College of Psychiatrists 4643
Royal College of Radiologists 4644
Royal College of Speech and Language Therapists 4644
Royal College of Surgeons of Edinburgh 4644
Royal College of Surgeons of England 4644
Royal Cornhill Hospital 4520
Royal Cornwall Hospital 4462
Royal Cornwall Hospitals NHS Trust 4462
Royal Devon and Exeter Healthcare NHS Trust 4462
Royal Devon and Exeter Hospital 4462
Royal Dundee Liff Hospital 4530
Royal Edinburgh Hospital 4525
Royal Eye Infirmary 4455
Royal Free and University College Medical School of University College London 4579
Royal Free Hampstead NHS Trust 4463
Royal Free Hospital 4463
Royal Glamorgan General Hospital 4542
Royal Glamorgan Postgraduate Medical Centre 4640
Royal Group of Hospitals and Dental Hospital HSS Trust . . . 4548
Royal Gwent Hospital 4538
Royal Halifax Infirmary 4382
Royal Hallamshire Hospital 4474
Royal Hamadryad Hospital 4535
Royal Hampshire County Hospital 4509
Royal Hospital for Neuro-disability 4567
Royal Hospital for Sick Children 4526, 4532
Royal Hospital Haslar 4457
Royal Infirmary of Edinburgh 4526
Royal Infirmary of Edinburgh (Little France) 4526
Royal Institute of Public Health 4679
Royal Lancaster Infirmary 4432
Royal Leamington Spa Rehabilitation Hospital 4483
Royal Liverpool and Broadgreen Hospitals University NHS Trust 4464
Royal Liverpool Children's NHS Trust 4464
Royal Liverpool University Dental Hospital 4464
Royal Liverpool University Hospital 4464
Royal London Homoeopathic Hospital 4498
Royal London Hospital 4495
The Royal London Hospital 4369
Royal Manchester Children's Hospital 4385
Royal Marsden Hospital (Chelsea) 4465
The Royal Marsden Hospital NHS Trust 4465
Royal Marsden Hospital (Sutton) 4465
Royal Maternity Hospital 4548
Royal Medical Benevolent Fund 4679
The Royal Medical Foundation 4679
Royal Medical Society 4679
Royal National Hospital for Rheumatic Diseases 4465
Royal National Hospital for Rheumatic Diseases NHS Trust . . 4465
Royal National Institute for Deaf People 4679
Royal National Institute for the Blind 4679
Royal National Orthopaedic Hospital 4465
Royal National Orthopaedic Hospital NHS Trust 4465
Royal National Orthopaedic Hospital Trust Postgraduate Centre 4634
Royal National Throat, Nose and Ear Hospital 4463
Royal National Throat, Nose and Ear Hospital Postgraduate Centre 4634
Royal Northern Infirmary 4523
The Royal Oldham Hospital 4451
Royal Orthopaedic Hospital 4465
Royal Orthopaedic Hospital NHS Trust 4465
Royal Orthopaedic Hospital Research and Teaching Centre . . 4634
Royal Pharmaceutical Society of Great Britain 4679
Royal Preston Hospital 4387
Royal Scottish National Hospital 4519
Royal Shrewsbury Hospital 4466
Royal Shrewsbury Hospital (Shelton) 4475
Royal Shrewsbury Hospitals NHS Trust 4465
Royal Shrewsbury Hospitals NHS Trust Postgraduate Medical Centre 4634
The Royal Society 4679
Royal Society for the Prevention of Accidents 4679
The Royal Society for the Promotion of Health 4679
The Royal Society of Medicine 4679
Royal Society of Tropical Medicine and Hygiene 4680
Royal South Hants Hospital 4486
Royal Surrey County Hospital 4466
Royal Surrey County Hospital Hindhead Ward 4491
Royal Surrey County Hospital NHS Trust 4466
Royal Sussex County Hospital 4379
Royal United Hospital 4466
Royal United Hospital Bath NHS Trust 4466
Royal Victoria Day Hospital 4530
Royal Victoria Hospital 4401, 4526, 4531, 4548
Royal Victoria Infirmary 4434
Royal Victoria Infirmary Postgraduate Medical Education Centre 4634
The Royal West Sussex NHS Trust 4467
Royal Wolverhampton Hospitals NHS Trust 4467
Royston and District Hospital 4397
Royston, Buntingford and Bishop's Stortford Primary Care Trust 4467
RSAS Agecare (Royal Surgical Aid Society) 4680
Ruffwood House 4488
Rugby Primary Care Trust 4467
Runwell Hospital 4479
Rushcliffe Primary Care Trust 4467
Rushden Hospital 4447
Russells Hall Hospital 4395
Ruth Lancaster James Cottage Hospital 4438
Rutherglen Maternity Hospital 4529
Ruthin Hospital 4537
Rutson Hospital Rehabilitation Unit 4447

INDEX BY ORGANISATION NAME

Rydon House 4476
Ryhope General Hospital 4388

Saffron Walden Community Hospital 4441
The Sainsbury Centre for Mental Health 4680
St Albans and Harpenden Primary Care Trust 4467
St Albans City Hospital 4505
St Albans City Hospital Postgraduate Centre 4634
St Andrew's Ambulance Association 4680
St Andrew's at Harrow (Bowden House Clinic) 4567
St Andrew's Group of Hospitals 4567
St Andrew's Hospital 4435
St Andrews Memorial Hospital 4518
St Anne's Hospital 4495
St Ann's Hospital 4368, 4394
St Anthony's Hospital 4567
St Austell Community Hospital 4390
St Barnabas' Hospital 4390
St Bartholomew's and The Royal London School of Medicine and Dentistry 4584
St Bartholomew's Day Hospital 4468
St Bartholomew's Hospital 4369
St Brendans 4533
St Brynach's Day Hospital 4541
St Cadoc's Hospital 4538
St Catherine's Hospital 4377, 4393, 4509
St Charles' Medical Centre 4634
St Christopher's Hospital 4456
St Clements Hospital 4426
St Clement's Hospital 4495
St David's Hospital 4541
St Dunstan's (Caring for Blind Ex-Service Men and Women) . 4680
St George's Healthcare NHS Trust 4468
St George's Hospital 4433, 4468, 4497
St George's Hospital Medical School 4586
St Helens and Knowsley Community Health NHS Trust 4468
St Helens and Knowsley Hospitals NHS Trust 4468
St Helens and Knowsley Postgraduate Medical Centre 4634
St Helens Hospital 4469
St Helens Primary Care Trust 4469
St Helier Hospital 4404
St Hugh's Hospital 4567
St James' Hospital 4456
St James's Hospital Postgraduate Department 4634
St James's University Hospital 4422
St John Ambulance 4680
St John and Red Cross Joint Committee 4680
St John of God Hospital 4567
St. John's Hospice 4393
St John's Hospital 4430
St John's Hospital at Howden 4532
St John's Hospital Dermatological Society 4680
St John's House 4567
St John's House and Southern Area Hospice Services 4569
St Joseph's Private Hospital 4569
St Joseph's Service 4569
St Lawrence's Hospital 4390
St Leonard's Hospital 4394, 4506
St Luke's Hospital 4378, 4382, 4383, 4494, 4545
St Luke's Hospital for the Clergy 4567
St Margaret's Hospital 4441, 4531
St Mark's Hospital 4397, 4446
St Mark's Hospital (EMI Day Hospital) 4372
St Martin's Education Centre 4634
St Martin's Hospital 4366, 4400
St Mary's Day Hospital 4426
St Mary's Hospital . . 4417, 4421, 4447, 4456, 4457, 4469, 4494, 4506
St Mary's Hospital for Women and Children 4385
St Mary's NHS Trust 4469
St Mary's NHS Trust Postgraduate Centre 4634
St Matthew's Hospital Postgraduate Medical Centre (Psychiatric Centre) 4634
St Matthew's Private Hospital 4567
St Michael's Hospital 4430, 4462, 4483, 4496, 4532, 4567
St Nicholas Hospital 4433
St Oswald's Hospital 4488
St Pancras Hospital 4383
St Peter's Hospital 4365, 4430
St Richard's Hospital 4467
St Saviour's Hospital 4551
St Thomas' Postgraduate Department 4634
St Thomas's Hospital 4409
St Tydfil's Day Hospital (Medicine) 4540
St Tydfil's Hospital (Mental health) 4540
St Vincent's Hospital 4523
St Waleric (Psychogeriatric Day Hospital) 4504
St Woolos Hospital 4538
Salford Primary Care Trust 4470
Salford Royal Hospitals NHS Trust 4470
Salisbury District Hospital 4470
Salisbury Healthcare NHS Trust 4470
Salisbury Postgraduate Education Centre 4634
Sally Sherman Nursing Home 4435
Salvington Lodge 4512
Sancta Maria Hospital 4569
Sandalwood Court 4366
Sanderson Hospital 4433
Stillbirth and Neonatal Death Society 4680
Sandwell and West Birmingham Hospitals NHS Trust 4471
Sandwell District General Hospital 4471
Sandwell Health Care NHS Trust Medical Education Centre . 4635
Sandwell Healthcare NHS Trust 4471
SANE/SANELINE 4680
Sauchie Hospital 4520
Save the Children 4680
Savernake Hospital 4492
Scarborough and North East Yorkshire Health Care NHS Trust 4471
Scarborough Hospital 4472
Scarborough Postgraduate Medical Centre 4635
Scarborough, Whitby and Ryedale Primary Care Trust 4472
Scope 4680
Scott Hospital 4455
Scottish Ambulance Service 4555
Scottish Association for Mental Health 4680
Scottish Committee of Optometrists 4680
Scottish Council for Postgraduate Medical and Dental Education 4639
Scottish Executive Health Department 4656
Scottish Health Visitors' Association 4680
Scottish Hospital Endowments Research Trust 4680
Scottish Medical Practices Committee 4656
The Scottish National Federation for the Welfare of the Blind 4680
Scottish Pharmaceutical General Council 4680
Scunthorpe General Hospital 4449
Scunthorpe General Hospital (Ward 18) 4393
Scunthorpe Postgraduate Medical Centre 4635
Seacroft Hospital 4422
Seafield Hospital 4520
Seaford Day Hospital 4402
Sedgefield Community Hospital 4391
Sedgefield Primary Care Trust 4472
Selby and York Primary Care Trust 4472
Selly Oak Hospital 4499
Selly Oak Hospital Education Centre 4635
Selwood House 4390
Sesame Institute (UK) 4680
Sevenoaks Hospital 4416
Severalls House 4441
Severn NHS Trust 4472
Seymour Berry Community Mental Health Team 4540
Shaftesbury Society 4681
Shape London 4681
Sharoe Green Hospital 4388
Shaw Day Hospital 4382

INDEX BY ORGANISATION NAME

Sheffield Children's Hospital 4473
Sheffield Children's Hospital NHS Trust 4473
Sheffield South West Primary Care Trust 4473
Sheffield Teaching Hospitals NHS Trust 4473
Sheffield Teaching Hospitals NHS Trust Medical Education Centre 4635
Sheffield West Primary Care Trust 4474
Sheila Sherlock Postgraduate Centre 4635
Sheppey Community Hospital 4494
Shepway Primary Care Trust 4474
Sherwood Forest Hospitals NHS Trust 4474
Shetland Islands 4533
Shetland NHS Board 4555
Shettleston Day Hospital 4522
Shipley Hospital 4377
Shire Hill Hospital 4454, 4493
Shirle Hill Day Hospital 4389
Shirle Hill Hospital 4389
Shotley Bridge Hospital 4440
Shropshire and Staffordshire Health Authority 4553
Shropshire County Primary Care Trust 4475
Shropshire, Mid and North West District 4661
Shropshire Nuffield Hospital 4567
Shropshire, South District 4661
Shropshire's Community and Mental Health Services NHS Trust 4475
The Sigma Centre 4681
Singleton Hospital 4544
Sir Alfred Jones Memorial Hospital 4442
Sir G B Hunter Memorial Hospital 4450
The Sir Jules Thorn Charitable Trust 4681
Sir Robert Peel Hospital 4482
Sister Margaret Cottage Hospital 4516
Sittingbourne Memorial Hospital 4494
Skegness and District Hospital 4497
Sketchley Hall 4567
Skipton General Day Hospital for the Elderly 4365
Skipton General Hospital 4365
Slievegrane/ Inch/ Downshire Hospital 4547
Slough Primary Care Trust 4475
Smith and Nephew Foundation 4681
The Society and the College of Radiographers 4681
Society for Endocrinology 4681
Society of Academic and Research Surgery 4681
Society of British Neurological Surgeons 4681
Society of Cardiothoracic Surgeons of Great Britain and Ireland 4681
The Society of Chiropodists and Podiatrists 4681
Society of Occupational Medicine 4681
Society of Public Health 4681
Solihull Hospital 4373
Solihull Primary Care Trust 4475
Somerset and Dorset Health Authority 4554
Somerset Coast Primary Care Trust 4475
Somerset, Eastern District 4661
Somerset Nuffield Hospital 4567
Somerset Partnership NHS and Social Care Trust 4476
Somerset Postgraduate Centre 4635
Somerset, Western District 4661
South and East Belfast HSS Trust 4549
South and East Dorset Primary Care Trust 4476
South Birmingham Mental Health NHS Trust 4476
South Birmingham Primary Care Trust 4477
South Buckinghamshire NHS Trust 4477
South Cambridgeshire Primary Care Trust 4477
South Cheshire Postgraduate Medical Centre 4635
South Devon Health Care NHS Trust 4477
South Downs Health NHS Trust 4478
South Durham Health Care NHS Trust 4478
South East Hertfordshire Primary Care Trust 4479
South East London Health Authority 4553
South East Oxfordshire Primary Care Trust 4479
South East Sheffield Primary Care Trust 4479
South Essex Mental Health and Community Care NHS Trust . 4479
South Essex Postgraduate Medical Centre 4635
South Glasgow University Hospitals NHS Trust 4529
South Gloucestershire Primary Care Trust 4479
South Hams and West Devon Primary Care Trust 4480
South Huddersfield Primary Care Trust 4480
South Leeds Primary Care Trust 4480
South Leicestershire Primary Care Trust 4480
South Liverpool Primary Care Trust 4480
South London and Maudsley NHS Trust 4480
South Manchester Primary Care Trust 4480
South Manchester University Hospitals NHS Trust 4480
South Molton Community Hospital 4448
South Moor Hospital 4440
South of Tyne and Wearside Mental Health NHS Trust 4481
South Pembrokeshire Hospital 4542
South Peterborough Primary Care Trust 4481
South Petherton Hospital 4402
South Sefton Primary Care Trust 4481
South Shore Hospital 4376
South Somerset Primary Care Trust 4481
South Staffordshire Healthcare NHS Trust 4481
South Stoke Primary Care Trust 4482
South Tees Hospitals NHS Trust 4482
South Tees Postgraduate Medical Centre 4635
South Thames Department of Postgraduate Medical and Dental Education 4635
South Tyneside District Hospital 4483
South Tyneside Healthcare NHS Trust 4483
South Tyneside Postgraduate Medical Centre 4635
South Tyneside Primary Care Trust 4483
South Warwickshire Combined Care NHS Trust 4483
South Warwickshire General Hospitals NHS Trust 4483
South Warwickshire Primary Care Trust 4484
South West Dorset Primary Care Trust 4484
South West Durham Postgraduate Medical Centre 4635
South West Kent Primary Care Trust 4484
South West London and St George's Mental Health NHS Trust 4484
South West London Community NHS Trust 4484
South West London Health Authority 4553
South West Oxfordshire Primary Care Trust 4485
South West Peninsula Health Authority 4554
South West Yorkshire Mental Health NHS Trust 4485
South Western Regional Postgraduate Medical Centres 4635
South Western Staffordshire Primary Care Trust 4485
South Wiltshire Primary Care Trust 4485
South Worcestershire Primary Care Trust 4485
South Yorkshire, East District 4661
South Yorkshire Health Authority 4554
South Yorkshire Metropolitan Ambulance and Paramedic Services NHS Trust 4485
South Yorkshire, West District 4661
Southampton City Primary Care Trust 4485
Southampton Community Health Services NHS Trust 4185
Southampton General Hospital 4486
Southampton Postgraduate Medical Centre 4636
Southampton University Hospitals NHS Trust 4486
Southend Hospital 4486
Southend Hospital NHS Trust 4486
Southend-on-Sea Medical Education Centre 4636
Southend-on-Sea Primary Care Trust 4487
Southern Derbyshire Acute Hospitals NHS Trust 4487
Southern Derbyshire Community and Mental Health Services NHS Trust 4487
Southern General Hospital 4529
Southern Health and Social Services Board 4556
Southern Norfolk Primary Care Trust 4488
Southlands Hospital 4511
Southmead Centre for Medical Education 4636
Southmead Hospital 4436
Southmoor Hospital 4502
Southport and Formby District General Hospital 4488
Southport and Formby Primary Care Trust 4488
Southport and Ormskirk Hospital NHS Trust 4488

INDEX BY ORGANISATION NAME

Southport General Infirmary 4488
Southview Challenging Behaviour Unit 4402
Southwark Primary Care Trust 4488
Southwold and District Hospital 4426
Southwood Hospital 4383
Spencer Close 4441
Sperrin Lakeland Health and Social Care Trust 4549
Spring Meadow Day Hospital 4482
Springbourne House 4394
Springfield Hospital 4485
The Springfield Hospital 4567
Springfield University Hospital 4484
Spynie Hospital 4520
Staffordshire Ambulance Service NHS Trust 4489
Staffordshire General Hospital 4430
Staffordshire Moorlands Primary Care Trust 4489
Staffordshire, South District 4661
Stamford and Rutland Hospital 4445
Standish Hospital 4407
Stanley Royd Hospital 4502
Stanwell House 4441
Staplers Road Assessment and Treatment Unit 4417
States of Guernsey Board of Health 4556
States of Jersey Health and Social Services 4556
Stead Memorial Hospital 4494
Stephen Hospital 4521
Stepping Hill Hospital 4489
Stewart Day Hospital 4469
Stirling Royal Infirmary 4519
Stobhill Hospital 4528
Stockport NHS Trust 4489
Stockport Postgraduate Medical Education Centre 4636
Stockport Primary Care Trust 4489
Stockton Hall Hospital 4567
Stoke Mandeville Hospital 4489
Stoke Mandeville Hospital NHS Trust 4489
Stoke Mandeville Hospital Postgraduate Medical Centre . . . 4636
Stoke-on-Trent and North Staffordshire 4662
Stone House 4494
Stonebow Unit County Hospital 4413
Stonebury Day Hospital 4473
Stoney Ridge Hospital 4377
Stonlea 4440
Stow Lodge Day Hospital 4426
Stracathro Hospital 4531
Stradreagh Hospital 4547
Stratford-upon-Avon Hospital 4483
Strathclyde Hospital 4524
Stratheden Hospital 4518
Strathmartine Hospital 4531
Stratton Hospital 4390
Stretford Memorial Hospital 4495
The Stroke Association 4681
Stroud General Hospital 4473
Stroud Maternity Hospital 4473
Stroud Road Unit 4473
Suffolk Coastal Primary Care Trust 4489
Suffolk, Ipswich District 4662
Suffolk, Lowestoft District 4662
The Suffolk Nuffield Hospital 4567
Suffolk, West District 4662
Suffolk West Primary Care Trust 4489
Sunderland Eye Infirmary 4388
Sunderland Royal Hospital 4388
Sunderland Teaching Primary Care Trust 4489
Sunnyside Royal Hospital 4531
Surrey Ambulance Service NHS Trust 4489
Surrey and Sussex Health Authority 4554
Surrey and Sussex Healthcare NHS Trust 4490
Surrey District 4662
Surrey Hampshire Borders NHS Trust 4490
Surrey Oaklands NHS Trust 4491
Sussex Ambulance Service NHS Trust 4491
Sussex Downs and Weald Primary Care Trust 4491
Sussex Eye Hospital 4379
Sussex Nuffield Hospital 4567
Sussex Postgraduate Medical Centre 4636
Sussex Weald and Downs NHS Trust 4491
Sutton and Merton Primary Care Trust 4492
Sutton Cottage Hospital 4374
Sutton Hospital 4405
Swaffham Hospital 4445
Swale Primary Care Trust 4492
Swanage Hospital 4395
Swansea District 4663
Swansea NHS Trust 4543
Swindon and Marlborough NHS Trust 4492
Swindon Postgraduate Medical Centre 4636
Swindon Primary Care Trust 4492
Swn-Y-Gwynt Day Hospital 4542
Sycamore Assessment Unit 4425
Sycamores Day Hospital 4452

Tamar Day Unit 4391
Tameside and Glossop Acute Services NHS Trust 4492
Tameside and Glossop Community and Priority Services NHS
Trust 4493
Tameside and Glossop Primary Care Trust 4493
Tameside General Hospital 4492, 4493
Tameside Postgraduate Medical Centre 4636
Taunton and Somerset Hospital 4493
Taunton and Somerset NHS Trust 4493
Taunton Community Hospital 4493
Taunton Deane Primary Care Trust 4493
Tavistock and Portman NHS Trust 4494
Tavistock Institute 4681
Tavistock Institute of Medical Psychology 4648
The Tavistock Mulberry Bush Day Unit 4494
Tayside NHS Board 4555
Tayside Primary Care Trust 4529
Tayside University Hospitals NHS Trust 4531
Tees and North East Yorkshire NHS Trust 4494
Tees East and North Yorkshire Ambulance Service NHS Trust 4494
Teesside District 4662
Tegfan Day Hospital 4535
Teignbridge Primary Care Trust 4494
Teignmouth Hospital 4478
Telford and Wrekin District 4662
Telford and Wrekin Primary Care Trust 4494
Tenbury District Hospital 4511
Tenby Cottage Hospital 4542
Tendring Primary Care Trust 4494
Tenovus 4681
Terence Mortimer Postgraduate Education Centre 4636
Terrence Higgins Trust Lighthouse 4681
Tewkesbury Hospital 4400
TFC Frost Charitable Trust 4681
Thames Gateway NHS Trust 4494
Thames Valley Health Authority 4554
The Thames Valley Nuffield Hospital 4567
Thanet Mental Health Unit 4400
Thetford Cottage Hospital 4506
Thomas Hope Day Hospital 4517
Thomas Sydenham Educational Centre 4636
Thompson House Hospital 4547
Thornbury Hospital 4437
Thornhill Day Hospital 4517
Thornhill Hospital 4517
Threshold Day Hospital 4531
Thurrock Community Hospital 4479
Thurrock Primary Care Trust 4495
Tickhill Road Hospital 4394
Tindale Crescent Hospital 4479
Tippethill Hospital 4532
Tonbridge Cottage Hospital 4416
Tonna Hospital 4534
Tor-Na-Dee Hospital 4521

The Medical Directory © Informa Professional 2002

INDEX BY ORGANISATION NAME

Torbay Hospital 4478
Torbay Hospital Postgraduate Education Department 4636
Torbay Primary Care Trust 4495
Torrington Cottage Hospital 4448
Tower Hamlets Primary Care Trust 4495
Town and County Hospital 4523
Towngate House Day Hospital 4421
Townhill Day Hospital 4518
Trafford Education Centre 4636
Trafford General Hospital 4495
Trafford Healthcare NHS Trust 4495
Trafford North Primary Care Trust 4495
Trafford South Primary Care Trust 4496
Tranwell Unit 4406
Travelling Day Hospital 4383
Travelling Day Hospital (Mental Health over 65s) 4512
Travelling Day Hospital (Mental Health under 65s) 4512
Tredegar General Hospital 4538
Tregaron Hospital 4536
Trent Health Authority 4553
Trent Regional Postgraduate Medical Centres 4636
Trevalyn Hospital 4539
Trowbridge Community Hospital 4507
Tuberous Sclerosis Association 4681
Tuke House 4421
Tunbridge Wells Nuffield Hospital 4568
Tunbridge Wells Postgraduate Medical Centre 4636
Turner Memorial Hospital 4521
Turriff Community Hospital 4521
Two Shires - Northampton and Bucks Ambulance NHS Trust 4496
Ty-Einon Day Hospital 4544
Ty Hafan Day Hospital 4535
Ty Llywelyn (Medium Secure Unit) at Bryn y Neuadd
Hospital 4541
Tyndale Centre Day Hospital 4473
Tyne and Wear, Gateshead and South Tyneside District . . . 4662
Tyne and Wear, Newcastle upon Tyne District 4662
Tyne and Wear, North Tyneside District 4662
Tyne and Wear, Sunderland District 4662
Tyrone and Fermanagh Hospital 4549
Tyrone County Hospital 4549
Tywyn and District War Memorial Hospital 4541

Uckfield Community Hospital 4402
UCL Hospitals Postgraduate Office 4637
Udston Hospital 4524
Ugie Hospital 4521
UK Centre for the Advancement of Interprofessional Education
(CAIPE) 4682
UK Public Health Association (UKPHA) 4682
Ulster Community and Hospitals Trust 4549
The Ulster Hospital 4550
Ulster Independent Clinic 4569
Ulverston Hospital 4432
United Bristol Healthcare NHS Trust 4496
United Hospitals HSS Trust 4550
United Kingdom Central Council for Nursing, Midwifery and Health
Visiting 4654
United Kingdom Transplant 4654
United Lincolnshire Hospitals NHS Trust 4497
University College Hospital 4498
University College London Hospitals NHS Trust 4498
University of Wales, Aberystwyth 4616
University Dental Hospital and School 4535
University Dental Hospital of Manchester 4385
University Hospital 4458
University Hospital Aintree 4364
University Hospital Birmingham NHS Trust 4499
University Hospital NHS Trust Postgraduate Medical Centre . . 4637
University Hospital of Hartlepool 4444
University Hospital of North Tees 4445
University Hospital of Wales 4535

University Hospitals Coventry and Warwickshire NHS
Trust 4499, 4637
University Hospitals of Leicester NHS Trust 4500
University of Aberdeen 4606
University of Birmingham 4587
University of Bristol 4588
University of Bristol Dental Hospital and School 4496
University of Cambridge 4590
University of Dundee 4607
University of East Anglia, School of Medicine 4591
University of Edinburgh 4609
University of Exeter 4591
University of Glasgow 4611
University of Glasgow, Department of Postgraduate Medical
Education/West of Scotland Deanery 4639
University of Keele 4592
University of Leeds 4593
University of Liverpool 4595
University of London 4597
University of Manchester 4597
University of Newcastle upon Tyne 4598
University of Nottingham 4601
University of Oxford 4602
University of St Andrews 4616
University of Sheffield 4603
University of Southampton 4606
University of Wales, Cardiff 4616
University of Wales College of Medicine 4617
University of Wales College of Medicine School of Postgraduate
Medical and Dental Education 4640
University of Wales, Swansea 4620
University of Wales Swansea Postgraduate Medical School . . 4640
Unrelated Live Transplant Regulatory Authority (ULTRA) . . . 4654
Unsted Park Hospital 4568
Upton Hospital 4398
Upton Hospital (EMI Unit) 4372
Upton House Day Hospital 4448
Uttlesford Primary Care Trust 4501

Vale of Aylesbury Primary Care Trust 4501
Vale of Leven District General Hospital 4525
Vale of Leven Hospital 4514
Velindre Hospital 4544
Velindre NHS Trust 4544
Verrington Hospital 4402
Victoria Central Hospital 4509
Victoria Cottage Hospital 4413, 4524
Victoria Eye Hospital 4413
Victoria Hospital 4375, 4478, 4482, 4509, 4518
Victoria Hospital Annexe 4525
Victoria Hospital Day Surgery Unit 4478
Victoria Hospital, Isle of Bute 4525
Victoria Infirmary 4429, 4525, 4529
Victoria Memorial Hospital 4543
Violet Hill Day Hospital 4426

Wakefield and Pontefract Community Health NHS Trust . . . 4501
Wakefield Postgraduate Medical Centre 4637
Wakefield West Primary Care Trust 4502
Wales, Pembrokeshire District 4663
Walkergate Hospital 4434
Walsall Community Health NHS Trust 4502
Walsall Hospitals NHS Trust 4502
Walsall Hospitals NHS Trust Postgraduate Medical Centre . . 4637
Walsall Primary Care Trust 4502
Walsgrave Hospital 4500
Walthamstow, Leyton and Leytonstone Primary Care Trust . 4502
Walton Centre for Neurology and Neurosurgery NHS Trust . . 4502
Walton Community Hospital 4377
Walton Hospital 4364, 4439
Wandsworth Primary Care Trust 4502
Wansbeck General Hospital 4450
Wansbeck Postgraduate Medical Centre 4637

INDEX BY ORGANISATION NAME

War Memorial Community Hospital, Day Hospital and Day Surgery Unit 4504
Wareham Hospital 3395
Warminster Community Hospital 4507
Wameford Hospital 4453
Warrington Community Health Care NHS Trust 4503
Warrington Hospital 4437
Warrington Primary Care Trust 4503
Warwick Hospital 4484
Warwickshire Ambulance Service NHS Trust 4503
Warwickshire District 4662
Warwickshire Nuffield Hospital 4568
Warwickshire Orthopaedic Hospital 4568
Waterloo Day Hospital 4364
Waterside Hospital 4547
Watford and Three Rivers Primary Care Trust 4503
Watford General Hospital 4505
Wathwood Hospital 4451
Waveney Primary Care Trust 4503
Wavertree Lodge/Wavertree Bungalow 4429
Wednesbury and West Bromwich Primary Care Trust 4503
Welland Hospital 4497
WellBeing 4682
Wellcome Trust 4648
Weller Wing 4371
Wellington and District Cottage Hospital 4493
The Wellington Hospital 4568
Welsh Ambulance Services NHS Trust 4544
Welsh National Board for Nursing, Midwifery and Health Visiting 4656
Welsh Postgraduate Medical Centre 4640
Welwyn Hatfield Primary Care Trust 4503
Wembley Hospital 4446
Wesham Park Hospital 4376
Wessex Deanery 4637
Wessex Medical Trust (Hope) 4682
Wessex Nuffield Hospital 4568
West Bank Hospital 4475
West Berkshire Postgraduate Medical Education Centre . . . 4637
West Cheshire 4509
West Cheshire Postgraduate Medical Centre 4637
West Cornwall Hospital 4462
West Cumberland Hospital 4438
West Cumberland Postgraduate Medical Centre 4637
West Cumbria Primary Care Trust 4503
West Dorset General Hospitals NHS Trust 4503
West Gloucestershire Primary Care Trust 4504
West Hampshire NHS Trust 4504
West Heath Hospital 4374
West Hertfordshire and Watford Postgraduate Medical Centre 4637
West Hertfordshire Hospitals NHS Trust 4504
West Hertfordshire Hospitals NHS Trust Postgraduate Medical Centre 4637
West Hull Primary Care Trust 4505
West Kent NHS and Social Care Trust 4505
West Lancashire Primary Care Trust 4505
West Lane Hospital (Neuro Rehabilitation Services) 4483
West Lincolnshire Primary Care Trust 4505
West London Mental Health NHS Trust 4505
West Lothian Healthcare NHS Trust 4532
West Middlesex University Hospital 4505
West Middlesex University Hospital NHS Trust 4505
West Midlands, Birmingham District 4662
West Midlands Board of Postgraduate Medical and Dental Education 4637
West Midlands, Coventry District 4662
West Midlands, Dudley District 4662
West Midlands Health Research Unit 4682
West Midlands Hospital 4568
West Midlands Metropolitan Ambulance Service NHS Trust . 4506
West Midlands, Sandwell District 4662
West Midlands, Walsall District 4662
West Midlands, Wolverhampton District 4662
West Norfolk Primary Care Trust 4506
West of Cornwall Primary Care Trust 4506
West Park Rehabilitation Hospital 4510
West Port Day Unit (Elderly with Dementia) 4516
West Suffolk Hospital 4506
West Suffolk Hospitals NHS Trust 4506
West Suffolk Postgraduate Medical Centre 4637
West Sussex District 4662
West Sussex Health and Social Care NHS Trust 4507
West Wales General Hospital 4536
West Wales General Hospital Postgraduate Medical Centre . 4640
West Wiltshire Primary Care Trust 4507
West Yorkshire, Eastern District 4662
West Yorkshire Health Authority 4554
West Yorkshire Metropolitan Ambulance Service NHS Trust . 4507
West Yorkshire, Western District 4662
Westbank Day Hospital 4520
Westbury Community Hospital 4507
Westbury Hospital 4507
Westcliffe Hospital 4444
Westcountry Ambulance Services NHS Trust 4507
Wester Moffat Hospital 4524
Western Avenue Day Hospital 4400
Western Community Hospital 4486
Western Eye Hospital 4470
Western General Hospital 4526
Western Health and Social Services Board 4556
Western House Hospital 4397
Western Infirmary 4528
Western Isles 4533
Western Isles NHS Board 4555
Western Isles Hospital 4533
Western Sussex Primary Care Trust 4507
Westminster Memorial Hospital 4471
Westminster Primary Care Trust 4507
Westmorland General Hospital 4432
Weston Area Health NHS Trust 4507
Weston Day Hospital 4518
Weston General Hospital 4507
Weston General Hospital Postgraduate Medical Centre . . . 4637
Weston Park Hospital 4474
Westwood House 4377
Wexham Park Hospital 4412
Wexham Park Hospital (EMI & AMI Units) 4372
Weybridge Hospital 4377
Weyhill Road Mental Handicap Unit 4504
Wharfedale General Hospital 4422
Wharfedale Medical Centre Department of Medical Education Postgraduate Centre 4638
Whelley Hospital 4513
Whipps Cross Hospital Medical Education Centre 4638
Whipps Cross University Hospital 4508
Whipps Cross University Hospital NHS Trust 4508
Whiston Hospital 4469
Whitburn Day Hospital 4532
Whitby Hospital 4472
Whitchurch Hospital 4475, 4535
White Lodge Day Unit 4441
Whiteabbey Hospital 4551
Whitehills Hospital 4531
Whittington Hospital 4508
Whittington Hospital NHS Trust 4508
Whittington Hospital Postgraduate Centre 4638
Whitwell House Day Hospital 4426
Whitworth Hospital 4439
Whyteman's Brae Day Hospital 4518
Whyteman's Brae Hospital 4518
Wigan and Leigh Medical Institute 4638
Wigton Hospital 4438
Willesden Hospital 4446
William Harvey Hospital 4401
William Harvey Postgraduate Medical Centre 4638
William Harvey Research Institute 4682
Williton and District Hospital 4476

INDEX BY ORGANISATION NAME

Willow House 4441
Wilson House 4425
Wiltshire Ambulance Service NHS Trust 4508
Wiltshire and Swindon District 4662
Wiltshire and Swindon Health Care NHS Trust 4508
Wimborne Hospital 4395
Winchcombe District Hospital 4400
Winchester and Eastleigh Healthcare NHS Trust 4509
Winchester Day Hospital 4509
Windermere Day Hospital (EMI) 4438
Windsor, Ascot and Maidenhead Primary Care Trust 4509
Windsor House 4429
Winfield Hospital 4568
Wirral and West Cheshire Community NHS Trust 4509
Wirral Hospital NHS Trust 4509
Wirral Postgraduate Medical Centre 4638
Wishaw General Hospital 4523
The Wishbone Trust 4682
Wistons Clinic 4568
Withernsea Community Hospital 4415
Withington Department of Postgraduate Medical Studies . . 4638
Withington Hospital 4480
Withybush General Hospital 4542
Withybush Rehabilitation Day Hospital 4542
Withybush Surgical Day Hospital 4542
Woking Community Hospital 4377
Woking Nuffield Hospital 4568
Woking Primary Care Trust 4510
Wokingham Primary Care Trust 4510
Wolverhampton City Primary Care Trust 4510
Wolverhampton Eye Infirmary 4467
Wolverhampton Health Care NHS Trust 4510
Wolverhampton Nuffield Hospital 4568
Wolversdene Road 4504
Women's Nationwide Cancer Control Campaign 4682
Women's Secure Services 4568
The Woodbourne Priory Hospital 4568
Woodbury Unit 4440
Woodend Hospital 4521
Woodilee Hospital 4522
Woodland Hospital 4568
Woodlands 4454
Woodlands Hospital 4521
Woodlands Unit 4424
Wood's Hospital 4454, 4493

Worcester District 4662
Worcester Royal Hospital 4511
Worcester Royal Infirmary 4511
Worcestershire Acute Hospitals NHS Trust 4510
Worcestershire Community and Mental Health NHS Trust . . 4511
Wordsley Hospital 4395
The Worshipful Society of Apothecaries of London 4682
Worthing and Southlands Hospitals NHS Trust 4511
Worthing Hospital 4512
Worthing Postgraduate Medical Centre 4638
Worthing Priority Care Services NHS Trust 4512
Wotton Lawn Hospital 4473
Wrexham Maelor Hospital 4539
Wrexham Medical Institute 4640
Wrightington Hospital 4513
Wrightington, Wigan and Leigh NHS Trust 4512
Wych Elm House 4441
Wycombe Hospital 4477
Wycombe Primary Care Trust 4513
Wye Valley Nuffield Hospital 4568
The Wynne Davies Postgraduate Medical Centre 4638
Wyre Forest Primary Care Trust 4513
Wyre Primary Care Trust 4513
Wythenshawe Hospital 4481
Wythenshawe Hospital Postgraduate Medical Centre 4638

Y Delyn Day Hospital 4542
Yeovil District Hospital 4402
York Day Hospital 4523
York District 4662
York District Hospital 4513
York Health Services NHS Trust 4513
York Postgraduate Medical Centre 4638
The Yorkhill NHS Trust 4532
Yorkshire Cancer Research 4682
The Yorkshire Clinic 4568
Yorkshire Wolds and Coast Primary Care Trust 4514
Ysbyty George Thomas 4542
Ysbyty Gwynedd 4541
Ysbyty Penrhos Stanley 4541
Ystrad Mynach Hospital 4539
Ystradgynlais Community Hospital 4543

Zachary Merton Hospital 4512

Index of Hospitals by Town

Aberaeron
Aberaeron Cottage Hospital 4536

Aberdare
Aberdare Hospital 4539

Aberdeen
Aberdeen City Hospital 4520
Aberdeen Maternity Hospital 4521
Aberdeen Royal Infirmary 4521
Albyn Hospital 4568
Foresterhill Hospital 4521
Royal Aberdeen Children's Hospital 4521
Royal Cornhill Hospital 4520
Tor-Na-Dee Hospital 4521
Woodend Hospital 4521
Woodlands Hospital 4521

Aberfeldy
Aberfeldy Cottage Hospital 4529

Abergavenny
Maindiff Court Hospital 4538
Nevill Hall Hospital 4538

Abergele
Abergele Hospital 4537

Aberlour
Fleming Hospital 4520

Abertillery
Abertillery and District Hospital 4537

Aberystwyth
Bronglais General Hospital 4536

Aboyne
Aboyne Hospital 4520

Accrington
Accrington Victoria Community Hospital 4389

Airdrie
Monklands Hospital 4523
Wester Moffat Hospital 4524

Alcester
Alcester Hospital 4483

Aldeburgh
Aldeburgh and District Community Hospital 4425

Alexandria
Vale of Leven Hospital 4514

Alloa
Clackmannan County Day Hospital 4519
Clackmannan County Hospital 4519
Sauchie Hospital 4520

Alnwick
Alnwick Infirmary 4449

Alston
Ruth Lancaster James Cottage Hospital 4438

Altrincham
Altrincham General Hospital 4495
The Priory Hospital Altrincham 4566
St Anne's Hospital 4495

Amersham
Amersham Hospital 4477

Ammanford
Amman Valley Hospital 4535
Swn-Y-Gwynt Day Hospital 4542

Andover
Andover War Memorial Community Hospital 4509
War Memorial Community Hospital, Day Hospital and Day Surgery
Unit 4504
Weyhill Road Mental Handicap Unit 4504
Wolversdene Road 4504

Annan
Annan Day Hospital 4517
Annan Hospital 4517

Annesley
Women's Secure Services 4568

Antrim
Antrim Hospital 4550
Holywell Hospital 4547
Muckamore Abbey Hospital 4548

Arbroath
Arbroath Infirmary 4529
Little Cairnie Hospital 4530
Rosemount Day Hospital 4530

Ardgay
Migdale Hospital 4523

Armagh
Armagh Community Hospital 4544
Longstone Hospital 4544
Mullinure Hospital 4545
St Luke's Hospital 4545

Arundel
Arundel and District Hospital 4492

Ascot
Heatherwood Hospital 4412
Heatherwood Hospital (EMI & AMI Units) 4372

Ashbourne
St Oswald's Hospital 4488

Ashby-de-la-Zouch
Ashby-de-la-Zouch and District Hospital 4423

Ashford, Kent
Western Avenue Day Hospital 4400
William Harvey Hospital 4401

Ashford, Middlesex
Ashford Hospital 4365

INDEX OF HOSPITALS BY TOWN

Ashington
Ashington Hospital 4450
Wansbeck General Hospital 4450

Ashtead
Ashtead Hospital 4557

Ashton-under-Lyne
Tameside General Hospital 4492, 4493

Auchterarder
St Margaret's Hospital 4531

Aylesbury
Manor House 4380
Stoke Mandeville Hospital 4489

Ayr
Abbey Carrick Glen Hospital 4568
Ailsa Hospital 4515
Ayr Hospital 4515

Bakewell
Newholme Hospital 4439

Ballachulish
Glencoe Hospital 4522

Ballycastle
Dalriada Hospital 4545

Ballymena
Braid Valley Hospital 4550

Ballymoney
Robinson Memorial Hospital 4546

Banbury
Horton Hospital 4452

Banchory
Glen O'Dee Hospital 4520
Kincardine O'Neil War Memorial Hospital 4520

Banff
Campbell Hospital 4520
Chalmers Hospital 4520
Ladysbridge Hospital 4520

Bangor, County Down
Bangor Community Hospital 4550

Bangor, Gwynedd
Deiniol Day Hospital 4540
Mental Health Acute Unit 4541
Minffordd Hospital 4541
Ysbyty Gwynedd 4541

Bargoed
Aberbargoed and District Hospital 4537

Barking
Barking Hospital 4366

Barmouth
Dryll y Carr Unit 4541

Barnet
Barnet General Hospital 4367

Barnsley
Barnsley District General Hospital 4368
Kendray Hospital 4368
Mount Vernon Hospital 4368

Barnstaple
North Devon District General Hospital 4448
Riverside Day Unit 4448

Barrow-in-Furness
Abbey Park Hospital 4557
Furness General Hospital 4431

Barry
The Barry Hospital 4534

Basildon
Basildon Hospital 4370
Mental Health Unit 4479

Basingstoke
BMI The Hampshire Clinic 4558
North Hampshire Hospital 4441
Parklands Hospital 4491

Bath
BMI Bath Clinic 4557
Royal National Hospital for Rheumatic Diseases 4465
Royal United Hospital 4466
St Martin's Hospital 4366

Bathgate
Tippethill Hospital 4532
Whitburn Day Hospital 4532

Beccles
Beccles and District War Memorial Hospital 4425

Beckenham
Beckenham Hospital 4379
BMI The Sloane Hospital 4559

Bedford
Albany Road Day Hospital 4371
Bedford Hospital 4371
BMI The Manor Hospital 4558
Weller Wing 4371

Belfast
Albertbridge Road Day Hospital 4549
Alexandra Gardens Day Hospital 4547
Belfast City Hospital 4545
Belvoir Park Hospital 4545
Forster Green Hospital 4547
Marie Curie Centre, Belfast 4569
Mater Infirmorum Hospital 4547
Musgrave Park Hospital 4547
Royal Belfast Hospital for Sick Children 4548
Royal Maternity Hospital 4548
Royal Victoria Hospital 4548
The Ulster Hospital 4550
Ulster Independent Clinic 4569

Belper
Babington Hospital 4487

Berkeley
Berkeley Hospital 4472

Berwick upon Tweed
Berwick Infirmary 4450

Beverley
Psychiatric Residential Unit 4415

Bexhill-on-Sea
Bexhill Hospital 4411
Irvine Unit, Bexhill Hospital 4411

INDEX OF HOSPITALS BY TOWN

Bideford
Bideford and Torridgeside Hospital 4448

Biggar
Kello Hospital 4524

Billericay
Mayflower House 4479
Mountnessing Court 4479

Bingley
Bingley Day Hospital for the Elderly 4365
Bingley Hospital 4365
Stoney Ridge Hospital 4377
The Yorkshire Clinic 4568

Birkenhead
Ashton House 4509
St Catherine's Hospital 4509

Birmingham
All Saints' Hospital 4373
Birmingham Children's Hospital 4372
Birmingham Dental Hospital 4373
Birmingham Heartlands Hospital 4373
Birmingham Nuffield Hospital 4557
Birmingham Women's Hospital 4374
BMI The Priory Hospital 4559
Brooklands Hospital 4445
City Hospital 4471
Highcroft Hospital 4373
Monyhull Hospital 4373
Moseley Hall Hospital 4373
Olivet 4565
Queen Elizabeth Hospital 4499
Queen Elizabeth Psychiatric Hospital 4476
Robert Clinic 4567
Royal Orthopaedic Hospital 4465
Selly Oak Hospital 4499
Warwickshire Orthopaedic Hospital 4568
West Heath Hospital 4374
The Woodbourne Priory Hospital 4568

Bishop Auckland
Bishop Auckland General Hospital 4478
The Goodall Centre 4391
Tindale Crescent Hospital 4479

Bishops Castle
Bishops Castle Community Hospital 4475

Bishop's Stortford
Herts and Essex General Hospital 4441

Bishopton
Erskine Hospital 4569

Blackburn
Blackburn Royal Infirmary 4374
BMI The Beardwood Hospital 4557
EMI Unit (Hillview) Day Hospital 4374
Kemple View 4563
Queen's Park Hospital 4374
Queen's Park Psychiatric Day Hospital 4374

Blackpool
BUPA Fylde Coast Hospital 4560
Devonshire Road Hospital 4375
Parkwood Psychiatric Unit 4375
South Shore Hospital 4376
Victoria Hospital 4375

Blackwood
Oakdale Hospital 4538

Blaenau Ffestiniog
Ffestiniog Memorial Hospital 4541

Blairgowrie
Blairgowrie Cottage Hospital 4530
Meigle Community Day Hospital 4530

Blyth
Blyth Community Hospital 4450

Bodmin
St Lawrence's Hospital 4390

Bognor Regis
Bognor Regis War Memorial Hospital 4492

Bolton
Belmont Day Hospital 4376
BMI The Beaumont Hospital 4557
Fall Birch Hospital 4376
Hulton Day Hospital 4376
Hulton Hospital 4376
Minerva Day Hospital 4376
Rivington Day Hospital 4376
Royal Bolton Hospital 4376

Bo'ness
Bo'ness Hospital 4519

Bonnybridge
Bonnybridge Hospital 4519

Boston
Beech House 4425
Maple Lodge 4425
Mayflower Day Unit 4425
Pilgrim Hospital 4497

Bournemouth
Bournemouth Nuffield Hospital 4559
Herbert Hospital 4394
Kings Park Hospital 4394
The Mallards 4394
Royal Bournemouth Hospital 4462
Springbourne House 4394

Bowmore
Islay Hospital 4525

Bradford
Bradford Royal Infirmary 4377
Daisy Bank 4377
Daisy Hill House 4377
Leeds Road Hospital 4377
Lynfield Mount Hospital 4377
Rosebery House 4377
St Catherine's Hospital 4377
St Luke's Hospital 4378
Westwood House 4377

Bradford-on-Avon
Bradford-on-Avon Community Hospital 4507

Braintree
Courtauld (W. J.) Hospital 4430
The Gables Day Hospital 4441
St Michael's Hospital 4430
White Lodge Day Unit 4441

Brampton
Brampton War Memorial Hospital 4438

Brechin
Brechin Infirmary 4530

INDEX OF HOSPITALS BY TOWN

Stracathro Hospital 4531

Brecon
Brecon War Memorial Hospital 4542
Bronllys Hospital 4543

Brentwood
BUPA Hartswood Hospital 4560
Essex Nuffield Hospital 4562
Mascalls Park 4440

Bridgend
Glanrhyd Hospital 4533
Maesteg Community Hospital 4533
Princess of Wales Hospital 4534

Bridgnorth
Bridgnorth Hospital 4475

Bridgwater
Beech Court 4476
Bridgwater Community Hospital 4475
College House 4476
Cranleigh House 4476

Bridlington
Bridlington and District Hospital 4472

Brighton
Brighton General Hospital 4478
Royal Alexandra Hospital for Sick Children 4379
Royal Sussex County Hospital 4379
Sussex Eye Hospital 4379
Sussex Nuffield Hospital 4567
Wistons Clinic 4568

Bristol
Barrow Hospital 4366
Blackberry Hill Hospital 4366, 4436
Bristol Eye Hospital 4496
Bristol General Hospital 4496
Bristol Homoeopathic Hospital 4496
The Bristol Nuffield Hospital at Chesterfield 4559
The Bristol Nuffield Hospital at St Mary's 4559
Bristol Royal Hospital for Children 4496
Bristol Royal Infirmary 4496
BUPA Hospital Bristol 4560
Burden Neurological Hospital 4436
Cossham Memorial Hospital 4436
Donal Early House 4436
Frenchay Hospital 4436
Ham Green Hospital 4436
Keynsham Hospital 4496
Marie Stopes Bristol 4564
The Priory Hospital Bristol 4566
St Michael's Hospital 4496
Southmead Hospital 4436
Thornbury Hospital 4437
University of Bristol Dental Hospital and School 4496

Brixham
Brixham Hospital 4477

Brodick
Arran War Memorial Hospital 4515

Bromley
Bromley Hospital 4379
The Priory Hospital Hayes Grove 4566

Bromsgrove
Brook Haven Mental Health Unit 4511
Princess of Wales Community Hospital 4511

Bromyard
Froome Bank Hospital 4413

Broxburn
Bangour Village Hospital 4532

Buckhurst Hill
Holly House Hospital 4563
Marie Stopes Essex 4564

Buckie
Seafield Hospital 4520

Buckingham
Buckingham Hospital 4380

Bude
Stratton Hospital 4390

Builth Wells
Builth Wells Cottage Hospital 4543

Bungay
All Hallows Hospital 4557

Burnham-on-Sea
Burnham-on-Sea War Memorial Hospital 4476
Little Court 4476

Burnley
Burnley General Hospital 4380

Burton-on-Trent
Barton-under-Needwood Cottage Hospital 4481
Queen's Hospital 4381

Bury
Bury General Hospital 4381
Fairfield General Hospital 4381
Highbank 4563
Pennine House 4381
Ramsbottom Cottage Hospital 4381
Roch House Day Hospital 4382

Bury St Edmunds
The Bury St Edmunds Nuffield Hospital 4561
Hillcrest and Phoenix Day Hospital 4426
Joyce Cockram Day Hospital 4506
West Suffolk Hospital 4506

Buxton
Buxton Hospital 4439
Cavendish Day Hospital 4439
Cavendish Hospital 4439

Caernarfon
Bryn Seiont Hospital 4540
Eryri Hospital 4541

Caerphilly
Caerphilly And District Miners' Hospital 4537

Camberley
Acorn Drug and Alcohol Services 4490
Beech House Mental Health Service Day Centre 4490
Frimley Park Hospital 4405
Ridgewood Centre 4491

Cambridge
Addenbrooke's Hospital 4363
Brookfields Hospital 4424
BUPA Cambridge Lea Hospital 4560
Chesterton Hospital 4424
The Croft Children's Unit 4424

INDEX OF HOSPITALS BY TOWN

The Evelyn Hospital 4562
Fulbourn Hospital 4363
Ida Darwin 4424
Ida Darwin Hospital 4424
Papworth Hospital 4454
Rosie Hospital 4364

Campbeltown
Campbeltown Hospital 4524

Cannock
Cannock Chase Hospital 4430
Kingswood Day Hospital 4482
Spring Meadow Day Hospital 4482

Canterbury
BMI The Chaucer Hospital 4558
Kent and Canterbury Hospital 4400
The Priory Clinic Cantebury 4566
St Martin's Hospital 4400

Cardiff
BUPA Hospital Cardiff 4569
Cardiff Royal Infirmary - West Wing 4534
John Pathy Day Hospital 4534
Lansdowne Hospital 4534
The Priory Clinic 4569
Rookwood Hospital 4535
Royal Hamadryad Hospital 4535
Tegfan Day Hospital 4535
Ty Hafan Day Hospital 4535
University Dental Hospital and School 4535
University Hospital of Wales 4535
Velindre Hospital 4544
Whitchurch Hospital 4535

Cardigan
Cardigan and District Memorial Hospital 4536

Carlisle
Abbey Caldew Hospital 4557
Arnwood House 4438
The Carleton Clinic 4438
Cumberland Infirmary 4437
Garlands Hospital 4438
Orton Lea 4438

Carluke
Roadmeetings Hospital 4524

Carmarthen
BMI Werndale Hospital 4569
Priory Day Hospital 4536
St David's Hospital 4541
West Wales General Hospital 4536
Y Delyn Day Hospital 4542

Carshalton
Queen Mary's Hospital for Children 4404
St Helier Hospital 4404

Castle Douglas
Castle Douglas Day Hospital 4517
Castle Douglas Hospital 4517

Castlebay
St Brendans 4533

Castleford
Castleford, Normanton and District Hospital 4501

Caterham
Caterham Dene Hospital 4490
Marie Curie Centre, Caterham 4564

North Downs Hospital 4565

Chard
Chard and District Hospital 4481

Chatham
BUPA Alexandra Hospital 4560

Cheadle
BMI The Alexandra Hospital 4557
Cheadle Royal Hospital 4561

Chelmsford
Broomfield Hospital 4429
Chelmsford and Essex Day Unit 4441
The Priory Hospital Chelmsford 4566
Rannoch Lodge 4441
St John's Hospital 4430
The Springfield Hospital 4567

Cheltenham
Charlton Lane Unit 4399
The Cheltenham and Gloucester Nuffield Hospitals 4561
Cheltenham General Hospital 4399
Delancey Hospital 4399
Moore Cottage Hospital 4399
Winchcombe District Hospital 4400

Chepstow
Chepstow Community Hospital 4537

Chertsey
Abraham Cowley Unit 4377
Abraham Cowley Unit Day Hospital 4377
BMI The Runnymede Hospital 4559
St Peter's Hospital 4365

Chester
Countess of Chester Hospital 4390
Grosvenor Nuffield Hospital 4563
Meadowslea Hospital 4539
West Cheshire 4509

Chesterfield
Ash Green Learning Disabilities Centre 4439
BMI Chatsworth Suite 4558
Bolsover Day Hospital 4439
Bolsover Local Hospital 4439
Chesterfield and North Derbyshire Royal Hospital 4387
Clay Cross Hospital 4439
Elderly Rehabilitation Unit 4439
Walton Hospital 4439

Chichester
Graylingwell Hospital 4492
St Richard's Hospital 4467

Chippenham
Chippenham Community Hospital 4508

Chorley
Chorley and South Ribble District General Hospital 4387
Euxton Hall Hospital 4562

Christchurch
Christchurch Hospital 4462
Flaghead Unit 4394

Cinderford
Dilke Memorial Hospital 4472

Cirencester
Cirencester Hospital 4399

INDEX OF HOSPITALS BY TOWN

Clacton-on-Sea
Martello Court Day Hospital 4441
Mayfield Centre (Day Hospital) 4441

Clevedon
Clevedon Hospital 4436

Clitheroe
Abbey Gisburne Park Hospital 4557
Calderstones 4383
Clitheroe Community Hospital 4389

Coatbridge
Alexander Hospital 4524
Coathill Hospital 4524

Cobham
Cobham Cottage Hospital 4404

Colchester
Brain Injury Services Elm Park 4559
Colchester General Hospital 4405
Essex County Hospital 4405
Longview Adolescent Unit 4441
The Oaks Hospital 4565
Severalls House 4441
Stanwell House 4441
Willow House 4441

Coldstream
Coldstream Cottage Hospital 4516

Coleraine
Causeway Hospital 4545
Ross Thomson Unit 4546

Colwyn Bay
Colwyn Bay Community Hospital 4537

Congleton
Congleton and District War Memorial Hospital 4398

Consett
Derwent Clinic 4391
Shotley Bridge Hospital 4440

Conwy
Conwy Hospital 4537

Corby
Corby Community Hospital 4447

Cottingham
Castle Hill Hospital 4415

Coventry
BMI Meriden Wing 4558
Coventry and Warwickshire Hospital 4500
Coventry Maternity Hospital 4500
River House Day Centre 4391
Tamar Day Unit 4391
Walsgrave Hospital 4500

Craigavon
Craigavon Area Hospital 4546
Craigavon Psychiatric Unit 4546
Lurgan Hospital 4546

Cranbrook
Benenden Hospital 4557
Hawkhurst Cottage Hospital 4416

Cranleigh
Cranleigh Village Community Hospital 4490

Crawley
Crawley Hospital 4490

Crewe
BMI The South Cheshire Private Hospital 4559
Leighton Hospital 4429

Crewkerne
Crewkerne Hospital 4401

Crieff
Crieff Hospital 4530

Cromer
Cromer Hospital 4435

Crook
Homelands Hospital 4479

Crowborough
Crowborough War Memorial Hospital 4402
The Horder Centre for Arthritis 4563

Crowthorne
Broadmoor Hospital 4505

Croydon
BMI Shirley Oaks Hospital 4559
Mayday Hospital 4427

Cumnock
Holmhead Hospital 4515
Roseburn Day Hospital 4515

Cupar
Adamson Hospital 4518
Stratheden Hospital 4518
Weston Day Hospital 4518

Cwmbran
Llanfrechfa Grange Hospital 4538

Darlington
Darlington Memorial Hospital 4479
Pierremont Unit and Beaumont 4391

Dartford
Archery House 4494
Bracton Centre 4454
Darent Valley Hospital 4392
Little Brook Hospital 4494
Stone House 4494

Daventry
Danetre Hospital 4392
Haddon House Day Hospital 4447

Dawlish
Dawlish Hospital 4477

Deeside
Deeside Community Hospital 4539
Dobshill Hospital 4539

Denbigh
Denbigh Community Hospital 4537

Derby
Derby City Hospital 4487
Derbyshire Children's Hospital 4487
Derbyshire Royal Infirmary 4487
Derbyshire Royal Infirmary (Mental Health) 4487
Dovedale Day Hospital (Elderly Services) 4488
East Midlands Nuffield Hospital 4562

The Grove 4488
Kingsway Hospital 4488
Derby City General Hospital (Mental Health) 4488
Nightingale Macmillan Continuing Care Unit 4487
Resource Centre Day Hospital 4488

Devizes
Devizes Community Hospital 4508
Green Lane Hospital 4366

Dewsbury
Dewsbury and District Hospital 4392

Dingwall
Ross Memorial Hospital 4523

Diss
Care Perspectives 4561
St John's House 4567

Dolgellau
Dolgellau and Barmouth District Hospital 4540

Doncaster
Danum Lodge Clinic 4562
Doncaster Royal Infirmary 4393
Loversall Hospital 4393
Park Hill Hospital 4565
St Catherine's Hospital 4393
St. John's Hospice 4393
Tickhill Road Hospital 4394

Dorchester
BMI The Winterbourne Hospital 4559
Dorset County Hospital 4503

Dorking
Farm Place 4562

Douglas
Ballamona Hospital 4551
Noble's Isle of Man Hospital 4551

Dover
Buckland Hospital 4400

Downpatrick
Downe Hospital 4546
Downpatrick Maternity Hospital 4546
Downshire Hospital 4546
Slievegrane/ Inch/ Downshire Hospital 4547

Driffield
Alfred Bean Hospital 4415

Droitwich Spa
BMI The Droitwich Spa Hospital 4558
Droitwich Knee Clinic 4562

Dudley
Bushey Fields Hospital 4396
Guest Hospital 4395
Russells Hall Hospital 4395

Dumbarton
Dumbarton Joint Hospital 4524

Dumfries
Crichton Royal Hospital 4517
Dumfries and Galloway Royal Infirmary 4516
Nithbank Day Hospital 4517

Dunbar
Belhaven Hospital 4525

Dundee
Ashludie Day Hospital 4530
Ashludie Hospital 4530
Dundee Dental Hospital and School 4531
Fernbrae Hospital 4569
Glaxo Day Hospital 4530
Hawkhill Day Hospital 4530
Ninewells Hospital 4531
Orleans Day Hospital 4530
Roseangle Day Hospital 4530
Royal Dundee Liff Hospital 4530
Royal Victoria Day Hospital 4530
Royal Victoria Hospital 4530
Strathmartine Hospital 4531
Threshold Day Hospital 4531

Dunfermline
Lynebank Hospital 4518
Queen Margaret Hospital 4518

Dunoon
Dunoon General Hospital 4525

Duns
Knoll Day Hospital (Geriatric) 4516
Knoll Hospital 4516

Dunstable
Beacon House 4371

Durham
Bowes Lyon Unit 4390
County Hospital, Durham 4390
Dryburn Hospital 4439
Earls House 4391
Earls House Hospital 4440
Nuffield Day Hospital 4440

Dursley
Tyndale Centre Day Hospital 4473

East Cowes
Frank James Community Hospital 4417

East Grinstead
Queen Victoria Hospital 4459

East Kilbride
Hairmyres Hospital 4523

Eastbourne
All Saints' Hospital, Eastbourne 4403
BMI The Esperance Hospital 4558
Eastbourne District General Hospital 4403
Roborough Day Hospital 4402

Eastleigh
Leigh House Hospital 4504
Mount Day Hospital 4509
Wessex Nuffield Hospital 4568

Ebbw Vale
Blaina and District Hospital 4537
Ebbw Vale Hospital 4538

Edenbridge
Edenbridge and District War Memorial Hospital 4416

Edgware
Edgware Community Hospital 4368
Edgware Day Surgery Unit 4368

Edinburgh
Astley Ainslie Hospital 4525

INDEX OF HOSPITALS BY TOWN

BUPA Murrayfield Hospital - Edinburgh 4568
City Hospital 4525
Corstorphine Hospital 4525
Eastern General Hospital 4525
Edinburgh Dental Institute 4526
Marie Curie Centre, Fairmile 4569
Royal Edinburgh Hospital 4525
Royal Hospital for Sick Children 4526
Royal Infirmary of Edinburgh 4526
Royal Infirmary of Edinburgh (Little France) 4526
Royal Victoria Hospital 4526
St Joseph's Service 4569
Western General Hospital 4526

Elgin
Dr Gray's Hospital (Acute) 4521
Dr Gray's Hospital (Mental and Community) 4520
Spynie Hospital 4520

Elland
BUPA Hospital Elland 4560

Ellesmere Port
Ellesmere Port Hospital 4509

Ely
The Princess of Wales Hospital 4424

Enfield
BMI The Kings Oak Hospital 4558
Chase Farm Hospital 4367
Chase Farm Hospital Site 4368
North London Nuffield Hospital 4565

Enniskillen
Erne Day Hospital 4549
Erne Hospital 4549

Epping
St Margaret's Hospital 4441
Spencer Close 4441

Epsom
Epsom General Hospital 4404
New Epsom and Ewell Cottage Hospital 4404

Erith
Erith and District Hospital 4458

Evesham
Evesham Community Hospital 4485

Exeter
Exeter Nuffield Hospital 4562
Royal Devon and Exeter Hospital 4462

Eye
Hartismere Hospital 4426

Eyemouth
Eyemouth Day Hospital (Geriatric) 4516

Fairford
Fairford Cottage Hospital 4399

Falkirk
Dunrowan Day Hospital 4519
Falkirk and District Royal Infirmary 4518
Westbank Day Hospital 4520

Falmouth
Falmouth Hospital 4506

Fareham
Blackbrook House Maternity Home 4456
Ravenswood House 4486
St Christopher's Hospital 4456

Farnborough
Briarwood Rehabilitation Unit (Mental Health) 4490

Farnham
BUPA Hospital Clare Park 4560
Farnham Community Hospital 4491

Felixstowe
Bartlet Hospital 4425
Felixstowe General Hospital 4425

Fleet
Fleet Community Hospital 4491

Fleetwood
Fleetwood Hospital 4375
Rossall Hospital 4376

Flint
Flint Community Hospital 4539

Folkestone
Royal Victoria Hospital 4401

Fordingbridge
Fordingbridge Hospital 4470

Forfar
Forfar Infirmary 4530
Whitehills Hospital 4531

Forres
Leanchoil Hospital 4520

Fort William
Belford Hospital, Fort William 4522
Belford Hospital (Midwifery) 4522
Belhaven Ward, Belford Hospital 4522

Fowey
Fowey and District Hospital 4390

Fraserburgh
Fraserburgh Hospital 4520

Galashiels
Gala Day Unit (Elderly with Dementia) 4516

Gateshead
Bensham Hospital 4406
Dryden Road Day Hospital 4406
Dunston Hill Day Unit 4406
Dunston Hill Hospital 4406
Queen Elizabeth Hospital 4406
Tranwell Unit 4406

Gerrards Cross
Chalfonts and Gerrards Cross Hospital 4477

Gillingham
Medway Maritime Hospital 4428

Girvan
Davidson Cottage Hospital 4515

Glasgow
Acorn Street Day Hospital 4522
Blawarthill Hospital 4527
BMI Ross Hall Hospital 4568

INDEX OF HOSPITALS BY TOWN

Bon Secours Hospital 4568
Canniesburn Hospital 4527
Cowglen Hospital 4529
Drumchapel Hospital 4527
Gartnavel General Hospital 4527
Gartnavel Royal Hospital 4522
Glasgow Dental Hospital and School 4527
Glasgow Eye Infirmary 4527
Glasgow Homoeopathic Hospital 4527
Glasgow Nuffield Hospital 4569
Glasgow Royal Infirmary 4527
Princess Royal Maternity Unit 4528
Kirklands Hospital 4524
Leverndale Hospital 4522
Lightburn Hospital 4528
MacKinnon House 4522
Mansionhouse Unit 4529
Marie Curie Centre, Hunters Hill 4569
Mearnskirk House 4529
The Orchards 4522
Parkhead Hospital 4522
The Priory Hospital Glasgow 4569
The Queen Mother's Hospital 4532
Red Deer Day Hospital 4524
Royal Hospital for Sick Children 4532
Rutherglen Maternity Hospital 4529
Shettleston Day Hospital 4522
Southern General Hospital 4529
Stobhill Hospital 4528
Victoria Cottage Hospital 4524
Victoria Infirmary 4529
Western Infirmary 4528
Woodilee Hospital 4522

Glenrothes
Glenrothes Day Hospital 4518
Glenrothes Hospital 4518

Glossop
Shire Hill Hospital 4454, 4493
Wood's Hospital 4454, 4493

Gloucester
Denmark Road Day Hospital 4472
Gloucestershire Royal Hospital 4407
Holly House Day Hospital 4473
Winfield Hospital 4568
Wotton Lawn Hospital 4473

Godalming
Milford Rehabilitation Hospital 4491
Unsted Park Hospital 4568

Golspie
Lawson Memorial Hospital 4522
Lawson Memorial Hospital (Surgical Services) (Cambusavie) . . 4523

Goole
Goole and District Hospital 4449

Gosport
Gosport War Memorial Hospital 4456
Royal Hospital Haslar 4457

Grantham
Ashley House 4425
Elm Lodge 4425
Grantham and District Hospital 4497
Sycamore Assessment Unit 4425

Grantown-on-Spey
Ian Charles Hospital 4522

Gravesend
Gravesend and North Kent Hospital 4392

Grays
John Tallack Day Hospital, Thurrock Community Hospital . . . 4479
Orsett Hospital 4370
Thurrock Community Hospital 4479

Great Missenden
BMI The Chiltern Hospital 4558

Great Yarmouth
James Paget Hospital 4417
Northgate Hospital 4418, 4435
Northgate Therapy Centre 4418

Greenock
Inverclyde Royal Hospital 4514
Ravenscraig Hospital 4529

Grimsby
Diana Princess of Wales Hospital 4449
Diana Princess of Wales Hospital, Grimsby 4393
St Hugh's Hospital 4567

Guernsey
Castel Hospital 4551
King Edward VII Hospital Guernsey 4551
Mignot Memorial Hospital 4551
Princess Elizabeth Hospital 4551

Guildford
Farnham Road Mental Health & Community Hospital Health Services 4491
Florence Desmond Day Hospital 4491
The Guildford Nuffield Hospital 4563
Mount Alvernia Hospital 4565
Royal Surrey County Hospital 4466
Royal Surrey County Hospital Hindhead Ward 4491

Guisborough
Guisborough General Hospital 4494
Guisborough General Hospital (Maternity Services) 4482

Guiseley
Towngate House Day Hospital 4421

Haddington
Herdmanflat Hospital 4525
Roodlands Hospital 4525

Hailsham
Amberstone Mental Health Unit 4402
Ashen Hill, Forensic Psychiatry Unit 4402
Southview Challenging Behaviour Unit 4402

Halesowen
West Midlands Hospital 4568

Halesworth
Patrick Stead Hospital 4426

Halifax
Foster Day Hospital 4382
Halifax General Hospital 4382
Northowram Hospital 4382
Royal Halifax Infirmary 4382
Shaw Day Hospital 4382
Travelling Day Hospital 4383

Halstead
Halstead Hospital 4405

INDEX OF HOSPITALS BY TOWN

Haltwhistle
Haltwhistle War Memorial Hospital 4450

Hamilton
Caird House 4524
Udston Hospital 4524

Harlow
Princess Alexandra Hospital 4457
Wych Elm House 4441

Harpenden
BUPA Hospital Harpenden 4560
Harpenden Memorial Hospital 4413

Harrogate
Duchy Nuffield Hospital 4562
Harrogate Clinic 4563
Harrogate District Hospital 4410

Harrow
BMI The Clementine Churchill Hospital 4558
Northwick Park Hospital 4446
St Andrew's at Harrow (Bowden House Clinic) 4567
St Mark's Hospital 4446

Hartlepool
University Hospital of Hartlepool 4444

Harwich
Harwich Day Hospital 4441

Haslemere
Haslemere and Community Hospital 4491
Holy Cross Hospital 4563

Hassocks
The Dene 4562

Havant
BUPA Hospital Portsmouth 4561
Havant War Memorial Hospital 4456

Haverfordwest
Bro Cerwyn Psychiatric Day Hospital 4541
St Brynach's Day Hospital 4541
Withybush General Hospital 4542
Withybush Rehabilitation Day Hospital 4542
Withybush Surgical Day Hospital 4542

Hawick
Hawick Cottage Hospital 4516
Hawick Day Hospital (Geriatric) 4516
Princes Street Day Unit (Adult Mental Illness) 4516
West Port Day Unit (Elderly with Dementia) 4516

Haye
St Michael's Hospital 4462

Hayle
St Michael's Hospital 4567

Haywards Heath
The Ashdown Nuffield Hospital 4557
Colwood Hospital 4430
Larchwood Hospital 4430
Princess Royal Hospital (East Wing) 4378

Heathfield
The Priory Grange 4566

Helensburgh
Victoria Infirmary 4525

Helston
Helston Community Hospital 4506

Hemel Hempstead
Hemel Hempstead General Hospital 4504

Hengoed
Ystrad Mynach Hospital 4539

Hereford
Hereford County Hospital 4412
Hereford General Hospital 4412
Stonebow Unit County Hospital 4413
Victoria Eye Hospital 4413
Wye Valley Nuffield Hospital 4568

Hexham
Hexham General Hospital 4450

High Wycombe
BMI The Shelbourne Hospital 4559
Harlow House 4380
Hayward House 4477
Wycombe Hospital 4477

Hinckley
Hinckley and District Hospital 4423
Hinckley Sunnyside Hospital 4423
Sketchley Hall 4567

Hitchin
Hitchin Hospital 4396
Pinehill Hospital 4565

Holsworthy
Holsworthy Community Hospital 4448

Holyhead
Ysbyty Penrhos Stanley 4541

Holywell
Holywell Community Hospital 4539
Lluesty Hospital 4539

Horley
BUPA Gatwick Park Hospital 4560

Hornsea
Hornsea Cottage Hospital 4415

Horsham
Horsham Hospital 4490, 4492

Houghton-le-Spring
Brooke House 4458

Hove
Hove Nuffield Hospital 4563

Huddersfield
Holme Valley Memorial Hospital 4382
Huddersfield Nuffield Hospital 4563
Huddersfield Royal Infirmary 4382
St Luke's Hospital 4382

Hull
BUPA Hospital Hull and East Riding 4560
Coltman Street Day Hospital and Community Support Teams 4415
Hull Maternity Hospital 4415
Hull Nuffield Hospital 4563
Hull Royal Infirmary 4416
Kingston General Hospital 4416
Princess Royal Hospital 4416

INDEX OF HOSPITALS BY TOWN

Huntingdon
Cromwell Clinic 4561
Hinchingbrooke Hospital 4414

Huntly
Jubilee Hospital 4520

Hyde
Hyde Hospital 4454, 4493

Hythe
BUPA St Saviour's Hospital 4561

Ilford
BUPA Roding Hospital 4561
Chapters House 4440
King George Hospital 4367

Ilfracombe
Ilfracombe and District Tyrrell Hospital 4448

Ilkeston
Ilkeston Community Hospital 4488

Ilkley
High Royds Hospital 4420
Ilkley Coronation Day Hospital for the Elderly 4365
Ilkley Coronation Hospital (Outpatient and Minor Injuries) . . 4365
Marie Curie Centre, Ardenlea 4564

Insch
Insch and District War Memorial Hospital 4520

Invergordon
County Hospital, Invergordon 4522
Invergordon County Hospital 4522

Inverness
New Craigs 4523
Raigmore Hospital 4522
Ross House Day Hospital 4523
Royal Northern Infirmary 4523
York Day Hospital 4523

Inverurie
Inverurie Hospital 4520

Ipswich
Ipswich Hospital 4416
Minsmere House 4426
St Clements Hospital 4426
The Suffolk Nuffield Hospital 4567

Irvine
Ayrshire Central Hospital 4515
Ayrshire Central Hospital (Psychiatric Unit) 4515
Garnock Day Hospital 4515

Isle of Skye
Dr Mackinnon Memorial Hospital 4522
Gesto Hospital 4522
Portree Hospital 4523

Isleworth
West Middlesex University Hospital 4505

Jarrow
Charles Palmer Day Hospital 4483
Monkton Hall Hospital 4483
Palmer Community Hospital 4483
Primrose Hill Hospital 4483

Jedburgh
Sister Margaret Cottage Hospital 4516

Johnstone
Johnstone Hospital 4529
Merchiston Hospital 4529

Keighley
Airedale General Hospital 4364
Airedale General Hospital - Day Hospital for Elderly 4365

Keith
Stephen Hospital 4521
Turner Memorial Hospital 4521

Kelso
Kelso Day Hospital (Geriatric) 4516
Kelso Hospital 4516

Kendal
Westmorland General Hospital 4432

Keswick
Mary Hewetson Cottage Hospital (Elderly and Mental Health) 4438

Kettering
Kettering General Hospital 4418, 4447
Mayfair Day Hospital 4447
St Mary's Hospital 4447
Woodland Hospital 4568

Kidderminster
Kidderminster General Hospital 4511
Lea Castle Hospital 4445

Kilmarnock
Crosshouse Hospital 4515
Kirklandside Hospital 4515

King's Lynn
BMI The Sandringham Hospital 4559
Chatterton House 4419
Queen Elizabeth Hospital 4419

Kingston upon Thames
Kingston Hospital NHS Trust Hospital 4420

Kington
Victoria Cottage Hospital 4413

Kingussie
St Vincent's Hospital 4523

Kirkcaldy
Forth Park Hospital 4518
Forth Park Maternity Hospital 4518
Victoria Hospital 4518
Whyteman's Brae Day Hospital 4518
Whyteman's Brae Hospital 4518

Kirkcudbright
Kirkcudbright Hospital 4517

Kirkwall
Balfour Hospital 4533

Knighton
Knighton Hospital 4543

Knutsford
Knutsford and District Community Hospital 4398

Lanark
Birkwood Hospital 4524
Lady Home Hospital 4524

INDEX OF HOSPITALS BY TOWN

Lancaster
Lancaster and Lakeland Nuffield Hospital 4563
Royal Lancaster Infirmary 4432

Langholm
Thomas Hope Day Hospital 4517

Larbert
Bellsdyke Hospital 4519
Royal Scottish National Hospital 4519

Largs
Brooksby House Hospital 4515

Larne
Moyle Hospital 4551

Launceston
Launceston General Hospital 4390

Leamington Spa
Blackdown Clinic 4557
Warwickshire Nuffield Hospital 4568

Leatherhead
Leatherhead Hospital 4404

Ledbury
Ledbury Cottage Hospital 4413

Leeds
Aire Court Community Unit 4420
Aire Court Hospital 4420
Asket Croft Day Hospital 4420
BUPA Hospital Leeds 4560
BUPA Methley Park Hospital 4561
Chapel Allerton Hospital 4421
Cookridge Hospital 4421
Crooked Acres 4420
Hawthorn Day Hospital 4420
Leeds Dental Institute 4421
Leeds General Infirmary 4421
The Leeds Private Hospital 4564
Linden Day Hospital 4421
Malham House Day Hospital 4421
Marie Stopes Leeds 4564
Mid Yorkshire Nuffield Hospital 4565
Millfield House 4421
Oak Day Hospital 4421
Priory Grange 4566
St James's University Hospital 4422
St Mary's Hospital 4421
Seacroft Hospital 4422
Tuke House 4421

Leek
Leek Moorlands Hospital 4444

Leicester
BUPA Hospital Leicester 4560
Coalville Community Hospital 4423
Glenfield Hospital 4500
Gorse Hill Hospital 4423
Leicester General Hospital 4501
Leicester General Hospital Brandon Unit 4423
The Leicester Nuffield Hospital 4564
The Leicester Royal Infirmary 4501
Woodlands Unit 4424

Leigh
Avenue Day Hospital 4512
Hanover Assesment and Treatment Centre 4512
Leigh Infirmary 4512

Leighton Buzzard
Crombie House 4371

Leominster
Leominster Community Hospital 4413

Lerwick
Gilbert Bain Hospital 4533
Montfield Hospital 4533

Leven
Cameron Hospital 4518
Randolph Wemyss Day Hospital 4518
Randolph Wemyss Memorial Hospital 4518

Lewes
Chailey Heritage 4478
Victoria Hospital 4478
Victoria Hospital Day Surgery Unit 4478

Lichfield
Victoria Hospital 4482

Lincoln
Bromhead Hospital 4560
Lincoln County Hospital 4497
St George's Hospital 4497

Linlithgow
St Michael's Hospital 4532

Lisburn
Lagan Valley Hospital 4546
Thompson House Hospital 4547

Liskeard
Lamellion Hospital 4390
Passmore Edwards Hospital 4390

Littlehampton
Crescent House 4512
Littlehampton Hospital 4512
Travelling Day Hospital (Mental Health over 65s) 4512
Zachary Merton Hospital 4512

Liverpool
Abbey Sefton Hospital 4557
Alder Hey Children's Hospital 4464
Ashworth Hospital 4428
Broadgreen Hospital 4464
Broadoak Mental Health Unit 4428
Florence Nightingale Hospital Liverpool 4562
Liverpool Women's Hospital 4425
Lourdes Hospital 4564
Marie Curie Centre, Liverpool 4564
Merseyside Clinic 4565
Mossley Hill Hospital 4429
Rathbone Hospital 4429
Royal Liverpool University Dental Hospital 4464
Royal Liverpool University Hospital 4464
St Bartholomew's Day Hospital 4468
Sir Alfred Jones Memorial Hospital 4442
University Hospital Aintree 4364
Walton Hospital 4364
Waterloo Day Hospital 4364
Wavertree Lodge/Wavertree Bungalow 4429
Windsor House 4429

Livingston
St John's Hospital at Howden 4532

Llandovery
Llandovery Hospital 4536

INDEX OF HOSPITALS BY TOWN

Llandrindod Wells
Llandrindod Wells County War Memorial Hospital 4543

Llandudno
Llandudno General Hospital 4541
North Wales Medical Centre 4569

Llanelli
Brynhaul Day Hospital 4541
Brynmair Day Hospital 4541
Bryntirion Hospital 4536, 4541
Mynydd Mawr Hospital 4536
Prince Philip Hospital 4536

Llanfairfechan
Bryn-Y-Neuadd Hospital 4540
Carreg Fawr Bed Support Unit at Bryn y Neuadd Hospital . . 4540
Ty Llywelyn (Medium Secure Unit) at Bryn y Neuadd
Hospital 4541

Llangefni
Cefni Hospital 4540
Coed Lys 4540

Llangollen
Llangollen Community Hospital 4537

Llanidloes
Llanidloes and District War Memorial Hospital 4543

Llantrisant
Royal Glamorgan General Hospital 4542

Loanhead
Loanhead Hospital 4525

Lochboisdale
Daliburgh Hospital 4533

Lochgilphead
Argyll and Bute Hospital 4524
Mid-Argyll Hospital 4525

Lochmaddy
Lochmaddy Hospital 4533

Lockerbie
Lochmaben Day Hospital 4517
Lochmaben Hospital 4517

London
Adult Mental Health Unit 4480
Atkinson Morley's Hospital 4468
Belvedere Private Clinic 4557
BMI The Blackheath Hospital 4558
BMI The Garden Hospital 4558
BMI The London Independent Hospital 4558
Bolingbroke Hospital 4468
British Home and Hospital for Incurables 4559
Central Middlesex Hospital 4445
Chelsea and Westminster Hospital 4386
Clayponds Hospital 4415
Colindale Hospital 4368
Collingham Gardens 4378
Cromwell Hospital 4562
Cygnet Hospital Ealing 4562
East Ham Memorial Hospital 4435
The Eastman Dental Hospital 4498
The Elizabeth Garrett Anderson Hospital and Obstetric
Hospital 4498
Finchley Memorial Hospital 4368
Florence Nightingale Clinic Chelsea 4562
Florence Nightingale Hospital 4562
Florence Nightingale Psychological Medicine Centre 4562
The Gainsborough Clinic and Nursing Home 4562
Gordon Hospital 4378
Green Parks House 4454
Greenwich District Hospital 4458
Grove Park Hospital 4408
Guy's Hospital 4408
Guy's Nuffield House 4563
Hammersmith Hospital 4410
The Harley Street Clinic 4563
The Heart Hospital 4498
The Heath Clinic 4563
Highgate Private Hospital Ltd 4563
Homerton University Hospital 4414
Hornsey Central Hospital 4383
The Hospital for Children 4407
The Hospital for Tropical Diseases 4498
Hospital of St John and St Elizabeth 4563
Jules Thorn Day Hospital 4383
King Edward VII's Hospital for Officers 4563
King's College Hospital 4418
Leigham Clinic 4564
The Lewisham Hospital 4424
The Lister Hospital 4564
London Bridge Hospital 4564
The London Chest Hospital 4369
The London Clinic 4564
The London Foot Hospital and School of Podiatric Medicine . 4383
Margaret Scott Day Hospital 4435
Marie Curie Centre, Edenhall 4564
Marie Stopes Ealing 4564
Marie Stopes House 4564
Marie Stopes South London 4565
Maudsley Hospital 4480
Memorial Hospital 4458
The Middlesex Hospital 4498
Mile End Hospital 4495
Moorfields Eye Hospital 4431
Nasebury Court 4440
The National Hospital for Neurology and Neurosurgery . . . 4498
Nelson Hospital 4404
Newham General Hospital 4434
North Middlesex Hospital 4443
Old Court Hospital 4565
Parkside Hospital 4565
Plaistow Day Hospital 4435
Plaistow Hospital 4435
The Portland Hospital for Women and Children 4565
Portman Clinic 4494
The Princess Grace Hospital 4565
The Priory Clinic Keats House 4566
The Priory Hospital North London 4566
The Priory Hospital Roehampton 4566
Putney Hospital 4484
Queen Charlotte's and Chelsea Hospital 4410
Queen Elizabeth Hospital 4458
Queen Mary's Hospital 4484
Queen Mary's House 4463
Redford Lodge Hospital 4566
Royal Brompton Hospital 4462
Royal Free Hospital 4463
Royal Hospital for Neuro-disability 4567
Royal London Homoeopathic Hospital 4498
Royal London Hospital 4495
The Royal London Hospital 4369
Royal Marsden Hospital (Chelsea) 4465
Royal National Throat, Nose and Ear Hospital 4463
St Andrew's Hospital 4435
St Ann's Hospital 4368
St Bartholomew's Hospital 4369
St Clement's Hospital 4495
St George's Hospital 4468
St Luke's Hospital 4383
St Luke's Hospital for the Clergy 4567
St Mary's Hospital 4469

INDEX OF HOSPITALS BY TOWN

St Pancras Hospital 4383
St Thomas's Hospital 4409
Sally Sherman Nursing Home 4435
Southwood Hospital 4383
Springfield Hospital 4485
Springfield University Hospital 4484
Stonlea 4440
The Tavistock Mulberry Bush Day Unit 4494
University College Hospital 4498
The Wellington Hospital 4568
Western Eye Hospital 4470
Whipps Cross University Hospital 4508
Whittington Hospital 4508
Willesden Hospital 4446
Woodbury Unit 4440

Londonderry
Altnagelvin Area Hospital 4544
Gransha Hospital 4547
Stradreagh Hospital 4547
Waterside Hospital 4547

Longfield
BMI Fawkham Manor Hospital 4558

Loughborough
Loughborough General Hospital 4423
Loughborough Hospital 4424

Louth
County Hospital 4497

Lowestoft
Lowestoft Hospital 4418

Ludlow
Ludlow Hospital 4475

Luton
Abbotswood Road Day Hospital 4371
Calnwood Court 4371
Farley Hill Day Hospital 4371
Lime Trees EMI Assessment Unit 4371
Luton and Dunstable Hospital 4426
Orchard Unit 4371
St Mary's Day Hospital 4426

Lutterworth
Feilding Palmer Cottage Hospital 4423

Lydney
Lydney and District Hospital 4473
Stonebury Day Hospital 4473

Lymington
Lymington Day Hospital 4486
Lymington Hospital 4486
Lymington Infirmary 4486
Milford-on-Sea Day Hospital 4486
Milford-on-Sea War Memorial Hospital 4486

Lytham St Annes
Clifton Hospital 4375
Lytham Hospital 4375

Macclesfield
BUPA Regency Hospital 4561
Ingersley and Millbrook Unit Psychiatric Day Hospital 4398
Macclesfield District General Hospital 4398
Rosemount Day Care Services 4398

Machynlleth
Bro Ddyfi Community Hospital 4542

Magherafelt
Mid-Ulster Hospital 4550

Maidenhead
St Mark's Hospital 4397
St Mark's Hospital (EMI Day Hospital) 4372

Maidstone
BMI The Somerfield Hospital 4559
Kent County Ophthalmic and Aural Hospital 4427
Maidstone Hospital 4427
Marie Stopes Maidstone 4564
Priority House 4416

Maldon
St Peter's Hospital 4430

Malmesbury
Malmesbury Community Hospital 4509

Malton
Malton, Norton and District Hospital 4472

Malvern
Malvern Community Hospital 4485

Manchester
Adult Psychiatry Day Hospital 4480
Atu Day Hospital 4480
Bealey Community Hospital 4381
Booth Hall Children's Hospital 4384
BUPA Hospital Manchester 4560
Burton House Day Hospital 4480
Christie Hospital 4388
Duchess of York Children's Hospital 4480
Manchester Royal Eye Hospital 4384
Manchester Royal Infirmary 4384
Marie Stopes Manchester 4564
North Manchester General Hospital 4442
Old Age Psychiatry Day Hospital 4480
Prestwich Site 4428
Royal Manchester Children's Hospital 4385
St Mary's Hospital for Women and Children 4385
Stretford Memorial Hospital 4495
Trafford General Hospital 4495
University Dental Hospital of Manchester 4385
Withington Hospital 4480
Wythenshawe Hospital 4481

Mansfield
Mansfield Community Hospital 4475

Margate
Queen Elizabeth the Queen Mother Hospital 4401
Thanet Mental Health Unit 4400

Marlborough
Savernake Hospital 4492

Marlow
Marlow Community Hospital 4477

Matlock
Whitworth Hospital 4439

Maud
Maud Hospital 4520

Maybole
Maybole Day Hospital 4515

Melksham
Melksham Community Hospital 4507

INDEX OF HOSPITALS BY TOWN

Melrose
Borders General Hospital 4516
Borders Geriatric Day Hospital 4516

Merthyr Tydfil
Prince Charles Hospital 4540
St Tydfil's Day Hospital (Medicine) 4540
St Tydfil's Hospital (Mental health) 4540
Seymour Berry Community Mental Health Team 4540

Mexborough
Montagu Hospital 4393

Middlesbrough
Carter Bequest Hospital 4494
The James Cook University Hospital 4482
Middlesbrough General Hospital 4482
North Riding Infirmary 4483
St Luke's Hospital 4494
West Lane Hospital (Neuro Rehabilitation Services) 4483

Midhurst
King Edward VII Hospital 4563
Midhurst, Easebourne and District Cottage Hospital 4492

Millport
Lady Margaret Hospital 4515

Milton Keynes
Milton Keynes General Hospital 4431

Minehead
Barnfield House 4476
Minehead and West Somerset Hospital 4476

Moffat
Moffat Day Hospital 4517
Moffat Hospital 4517

Mold
Mold Community Hospital 4539

Monmouth
Monmouth Hospital 4538

Montrose
Montrose Royal Infirmary 4530
Sunnyside Royal Hospital 4531

Morecambe
Queen Victoria Hospital 4432

Moreton-in-Marsh
Moreton District Hospital 4399

Morpeth
Coquetdale Cottage Hospital 4450
Morpeth Cottage Hospital 4450
Northgate Hospital 4449
St George's Hospital 4433

Motherwell
Cleland Hospital 4524
Strathclyde Hospital 4524

Mountain Ash
Mountain Ash Hospital 4540

Musselburgh
Edenhall Hospital 4525

Nairn
Nairn Town and County Hospital 4523

Neath
Cimla Hospital 4533
Neath General Hospital 4533
Tonna Hospital 4534

Nelson
Pendle Community Hospital 4381

New Milton
The Beacon Centre 4504

Newark
Newark Hospital 4475

Newcastle
North Staffordshire Nuffield Hospital 4565

Newcastle upon Tyne
Freeman Hospital 4433
Marie Curie Centre, Newcastle 4564
Newcastle General Hospital 4433
The Newcastle Nuffield Hospital 4565
Newcastle upon Tyne Dental Hospital 4434
Royal Victoria Infirmary 4434
St Nicholas Hospital 4433
Sanderson Hospital 4433
Walkergate Hospital 4434

Newhaven
Newhaven Downs 4478

Newmarket
Newmarket Community Hospital 4506

Newport, Gwent
Royal Gwent Hospital 4538
St Cadoc's Hospital 4538
St Joseph's Private Hospital 4569
St Woolos Hospital 4538

Newport, Isle of Wight
Laidlaw Day Hospital 4417
The Orchard Hospital 4565
St Mary's Hospital 4417
Staplers Road Assessment and Treatment Unit 4417

Newport-on-Tay
Netherlea Hospital 4518

Newquay
Newquay and District Hospital 4390

Newry
Daisy Hill Hospital 4548
Mourne Hospital 4548
St John's House and Southern Area Hospice Services 4569

Newton-le-Willows
Newton Community Hospital 4468

Newton Abbot
Ashburton and Buckfastleigh Hospital 4477
Bovey Tracey Hospital 4477
Newton Abbot Hospital 4478

Newton Stewart
Newton Stewart Day Hospital 4517
Newton Stewart Hospital 4517

Newtown
Montgomery County Infirmary 4543

Newtownabbey
Whiteabbey Hospital 4551

INDEX OF HOSPITALS BY TOWN

Newtownards
Ards Community Hospital 4550
Mental Health Day Hospital 4550

North Berwick
Edington Cottage Hospital 4525

North Shields
North Tyneside General Hospital 4450

Northallerton
Friarage Hospital 4446
Rutson Hospital Rehabilitation Unit 4447

Northampton
Adams Day Hospital 4447
BMI Three Shires Hospital 4559
Brain Injury Services - Community Rehabilitation and Supported
Living 4559
Northampton General Hospital 4447
Princess Marina Hospital 4447
St Andrew's Group of Hospitals 4567
St Matthew's Private Hospital 4567
Upton House Day Hospital 4448

Northwich
Victoria Infirmary 4429

Northwood
BMI Bishops Wood Hospital 4558
Mount Vernon Hospital 4504
Northwood and Pinner Cottage Hospital 4411

Norwich
Bethel Child and Adolescent Directorate 4435
BUPA Hospital Norwich 4560
Hellesdon Hospital 4435
The Julian Hospital 4435
Norfolk and Norwich University Hospital 4435

Nottingham
Ashfield Community Hospital 4474
BMI The Park Hospital 4559
Nottingham City Hospital 4450
The Nottingham Nuffield Hospital 4565
The Priory Clinic Nottingham 4566
University Hospital 4458

Nuneaton
BMI The Nuneaton Private Hospital 4558
Bramcote Hospital 4445
George Eliot Hospital 4406
Manor Hospital 4445

Oban
Lorn and Islands District General Hospital 4525, 4514

Oldham
Orchard House Day Hospital 4451
The Royal Oldham Hospital 4451
Sycamores Day Hospital 4452

Omagh
Tyrone and Fermanagh Hospital 4549
Tyrone County Hospital 4549

Ongar
Ongar War Memorial Hospital 4441

Ormskirk
Bickerstaffe House 4443
Ormskirk and District General Hospital 4488
Renacres Hall Hospital 4566
Ruffwood House 4488

Orpington
BMI Chelsfield Park Hospital 4558
Farnborough Hospital 4379
Orpington Hospital 4380

Oswestry
Robert Jones and Agnes Hunt Orthopaedic Hospital 4460

Otley
Wharfedale General Hospital 4422

Oxford
Acland Nuffield Hospital 4557
The Churchill 4452
The John Radcliffe 4452
Park Hospital for Children 4453
Radcliffe Infirmary 4453
Warneford Hospital 4453

Paignton
Paignton Hospital 4478

Paisley
Dykebar Hospital 4528
Hawkhead Hospital 4528
Royal Alexandra Hospital 4514
Royal Alexandra Hospital (Care of the Elderly) 4529

Peebles
Firholm Day Unit (Elderly with Dementia) 4516
Haylodge Day Hospital (Geriatric) 4516
Haylodge Hospital 4516
Priorsford Day Unit (Adult Mental Illness) 4516

Pembroke Dock
Cleddau Rehabilitation Unit 4541
South Pembrokeshire Hospital 4542

Penarth
Llandough Geriatric Day Hospital 4534
Llandough Hospital 4534
Marie Curie Centre, Holme Tower 4569

Penrhyndeudraeth
Bron y Garth Hospital 4540

Penrith
Penrith Hospital 4438

Penzance
Poltair Hospital 4506
West Cornwall Hospital 4462

Pershore
Pershore Cottage Hospital 4485

Perth
Birch Avenue Day Hospital 4530
Murray Royal Hospital 4530
Perth Royal Infirmary 4531

Peterborough
Edith Cavell Hospital 4454
Fitzwilliam Hospital 4562
Oundle Community Care Unit 4447
Peterborough District Hospital 4454

Peterhead
Peterhead Community Hospital 4520
Ugie Hospital 4521

Peterlee
Peterlee Community Hospital 4444

INDEX OF HOSPITALS BY TOWN

Pitlochry
Irvine Memorial Hospital 4530

Plymouth
The Diving Diseases Research Centre 4562
Mount Gould Hospital 4455
The Plymouth Nuffield Hospital 4565
Royal Eye Infirmary 4455
Scott Hospital 4455

Pontefract
Pontefract General Infirmary 4455, 4502
Southmoor Hospital 4502

Pontyclun
Hensol Hospital 4533

Pontypool
Brain Injury Services Beechwood House 4569
County Hospital 4537

Pontypridd
Dewi Sant Hospital 4542

Poole
Alderney Hospital 4394
BMI The Harbour Hospital 4558
Poole General Hospital 4455
St Ann's Hospital 4394

Port Talbot
Groeswen Hospital 4533
Port Talbot Hospital 4534

Portsmouth
Queen Alexandra Hospital 4456
St James' Hospital 4456
St Mary's Hospital 4456, 4457

Potters Bar
Potters Bar Hospital 4368

Prescot
Whiston Hospital 4469

Prestatyn
Prestatyn Community Hospital 4537

Preston
Avondale Unit 4408
Fulwood Hall Hospital 4562
The Priory Hospital Lancashire 4566
Ribbleton Hospital 4408
Ribchester Community Hospital 4389
Royal Preston Hospital 4387
Sharoe Green Hospital 4388
Wesham Park Hospital 4376

Prestwick
Biggart Hospital 4515

Princes Risborough
BMI The Paddocks Hospital 4558

Prudhoe
Prudhoe Hospital 4449

Purley
Purley and District War Memorial Hospital 4428

Pwllheli
Bryn Beryl Hospital 4540

Radlett
Harperbury 4413

Raglan
Llanarth Court Hospital 4569

Ramsey
Ramsey and District Cottage Hospital 4552

Reading
Battle Hospital 4461
Berkshire Independent Hospital 4557
BUPA Dunedin Hospital 4560
Lynden Hill Clinic 4564
Royal Berkshire Hospital 4461

Redcar
Stead Memorial Hospital 4494

Redditch
Alexandra Hospital 4511
Hill Crest 4511
Rowan Day Hospital 4511

Redhill
BUPA Redwood Hospital 4561
The Coach House 4561
East Surrey Hospital 4490

Redruth
Camborne/Redruth Community Hospital 4506

Retford
Rampton Hospital 4451
Retford Hospital 4393

Rhyl
Glan Clwyd District General Hospital 4537
Royal Alexandra Hospital 4537

Rhymney
Redwood Memorial Hospital 4538

Richmond, North Yorkshire
Richmond Victoria Hospital 4447
St John of God Hospital 4567

Richmond, Surrey
Richmond Royal Hospital 4485

Ringwood
St Leonard's Hospital 4394

Ripon
Ripon Community Hospital 4411

Rochdale
Birch Hill Hospital 4460
BMI The Highfield Hospital 4558
Rochdale Infirmary 4460

Rochford
Rochford Hospital 4479

Romford
Harold Wood Hospital 4366
Oldchurch Hospital 4367

Romsey
Romsey Hospital 4486

Roslin
Rosslynlee Hospital 4525

INDEX OF HOSPITALS BY TOWN

Ross-on-Wye
Ross Community Hospital 4413

Rossendale
Rossendale General Hospital 4381

Rotherham
Beechcroft Unit 4461
Birkdale Clinic (Rotherham) Ltd 4557
District General Hospital 4460
Doncaster Gate Hospital 4461
Hawthorn Day Hospital 4461
Rotherham General Hospital Day Surgery Centre 4461
Wathwood Hospital 4451

Rothesay
Victoria Hospital Annexe 4525
Victoria Hospital, Isle of Bute 4525

Royston
Kneesworth House Hospital 4563
Royston and District Hospital 4397

Rugby
Hospital of St Cross 4445, 4500

Runcorn
Halton General Hospital 4437

Rushden
Rushden Hospital 4447

Ruthin
Ruthin Hospital 4537

Saffron Walden
Ferguson Close 4441
Saffron Walden Community Hospital 4441

Salford
Hope Hospital 4470
Ladywell Hospital 4470
Oaklands Hospital 4565

Salisbury
Crane Ward 4504
New Hall Hospital 4565
The Old Manor 4470
Old Manor Hospital 4366
Salisbury District Hospital 4470

Saltash
St Barnabas' Hospital 4390

Saltburn-by-the-Sea
East Cleveland Hospital 4494

Sawbridgeworth
The Rivers Hospital 4566

Saxmundham
Whitwell House Day Hospital 4426

Scarborough
BUPA Belvedere Hospital 4560
Haworth Unit 4472
St Mary's Hospital 4494
Scarborough Hospital 4472

Scunthorpe
Scunthorpe General Hospital 4449
Scunthorpe General Hospital (Ward 18) 4393

Seaford
Seaford Day Hospital 4402

Settle
Castleberg Day Hospital for the Elderly 4365
Castleberg Hospital 4365

Sevenoaks
Sevenoaks Hospital 4416

Shaftesbury
Westminster Memorial Hospital 4471

Sheerness
Sheppey Community Hospital 4494

Sheffield
Beighton Hospital 4389
BMI Thornbury Hospital 4559
Charles Clifford Dental Hospital 4474
Claremont Hospital 4561
Forest Lodge 4389
Grenoside Grange 4389
Jessop Wing Women's Hospital 4474
Nether Edge Hospital 4389
Northern General Hospital 4474
Royal Hallamshire Hospital 4474
Sheffield Children's Hospital 4473
Shirle Hill Day Hospital 4389
Shirle Hill Hospital 4389
Weston Park Hospital 4474

Shipley
Shipley Hospital 4377

Shipston-on-Stour
Ellen Badger Hospital 4483

Shoreham-by-Sea
Ridings Southlands Hospital 4512
Southlands Hospital 4511
Travelling Day Hospital (Mental Health under 65s) 4512

Shotts
Hartwood Hospital 4524

Shrewsbury
Royal Shrewsbury Hospital 4466
Royal Shrewsbury Hospital (Shelton) 4475
Shropshire Nuffield Hospital 4567

Sidcup
Queen Mary's Hospital 4458
Woodlands 4454

Sittingbourne
Sittingbourne Memorial Hospital 4494

Skegness
Mental Health Day Unit 4425
Skegness and District Hospital 4497

Skipton
Skipton General Day Hospital for the Elderly 4365
Skipton General Hospital 4365

Sleaford
Ash Villa 4425

Slough
The Thames Valley Nuffield Hospital 4567
Upton Hospital 4398
Upton Hospital (EMI Unit) 4372
Wexham Park Hospital 4412

INDEX OF HOSPITALS BY TOWN

Wexham Park Hospital (EMI & AMI Units) 4372

Solihull
BUPA Parkway Hospital 4561
Dean Park Clinic 4562
Marie Curie Centre, Warren Pearl 4564
Solihull Hospital 4373

South Molton
South Molton Community Hospital 4448

South Petherton
South Petherton Hospital 4402

South Shields
Moorlands Day Hospital 4483
South Tyneside District Hospital 4483

Southall
Ealing Day Treatment Centre 4415
Ealing Hospital 4396

Southampton
BUPA Chalybeate Hospital 4560
Countess Mountbatten House 4486
Department of Psychiatry 4504
Fenwick Day Hospital 4485
Fenwick Hospital 4486
Harefield Day Hospital 4486
Hythe Day Hospital 4486
Hythe Hospital 4486
Inroads Day Hospital 4486
Moorgreen Day Hospital 4486
Moorgreen Hospital 4486
Princess Anne Hospital 4486
The Priory Hospital Marchwood 4566
Royal South Hants Hospital 4486
Southampton General Hospital 4486
Western Community Hospital 4486

Southend-on-Sea
BUPA Wellesley Hospital 4561

Southport
Christiana Hartley Maternity Unit 4488
Southport and Formby District General Hospital 4488
Southport General Infirmary 4488

Southwold
Southwold and District Hospital 4426

Spalding
Johnson Hospital 4497
Welland Hospital 4497
Wilson House 4425

St Albans
St Albans City Hospital 4505

St Andrews
St Andrews Memorial Hospital 4518

St Asaph
HM Stanley Hospital 4537

St Austell
St Austell Community Hospital 4390
Selwood House 4390

St Helens
St Helens Hospital 4469
Stewart Day Hospital 4469

St Helier
General Hospital St Helier 4551
Overdale Hospital 4551

St Ives
Edward Hain Memorial Hospital 4506

St Leonards-on-Sea
BUPA Hospital Hastings 4560
Conquest Hospital 4411

St Mary's
St Mary's Hospital 4506

St Saviour
St Saviour's Hospital 4551

Stafford
The Foundation NHS Trust Hospital (Stafford) 4481
Rowley Hall Hospital 4567
Staffordshire General Hospital 4430

Stamford
Stamford and Rutland Hospital 4445

Stanhope
Hornhall Hospital 4479

Stanley
South Moor Hospital 4440

Stanmore
Royal National Orthopaedic Hospital 4465

Stevenage
Elderly Care Day Hospital, Lister Hospital 4396
Lister Hospital 4396

Stirling
Abbey Kings Park Hospital 4568
Bannockburn Hospital 4519
Kildean Day Hospital 4519
Kildean Hospital 4519
Orchard House Day Hospital 4519
Princes Street Day Hospital 4519
Stirling Royal Infirmary 4519

Stockport
Stepping Hill Hospital 4489

Stockton-on-Tees
Cleveland Nuffield Hospital 4561
The Gables 4391
Sedgefield Community Hospital 4391
University Hospital of North Tees 4445

Stoke-on-Trent
Boulton Ward, Haywood Hospital 4443
Bradwell Hospital 4443
Bucknall Hospital 4443
Cheadle Hospital 4443
City General Hospital 4443
Greenfield Centre 4444
Longton Cottage Hospital 4444
North Staffordshire Hospital 4444
Roundwell Place Day Hospital 4444
Westcliffe Hospital 4444

Stonehaven
Kincardine Community Hospital 4520

Stonehouse
Standish Hospital 4407

INDEX OF HOSPITALS BY TOWN

Stornoway
Western Isles Hospital 4533

Stourbridge
Corbett Hospital 4395
Ridge Hill Mental Handicap Unit 4396
Wordsley Hospital 4395

Stowmarket
Stow Lodge Day Hospital 4426
Violet Hill Day Hospital 4426

Stranraer
Dalrymple Day Hospital 4517
Dalrymple Hospital 4517

Stratford-upon-Avon
Stratford-upon-Avon Hospital 4483

Stroud
Stroud General Hospital 4473
Stroud Maternity Hospital 4473
Stroud Road Unit 4473

Sudbury
Elderly Day Hospital 4506
St Leonard's Hospital 4506

Sunderland
Cherry Knowle Hospital 4458
Monkwearmouth Hospital 4458
Ryhope General Hospital 4388
Sunderland Eye Infirmary 4388
Sunderland Royal Hospital 4388

Sutton
Henderson Hospital 4484
Royal Marsden Hospital (Sutton) 4465
St Anthony's Hospital 4567
Sutton Hospital 4405

Sutton-in-Ashfield
King's Mill Centre for Healthcare Services 4474

Sutton Coldfield
BUPA Hospital Little Aston 4560
Good Hope Hospital 4407
Sutton Cottage Hospital 4374

Swaffham
Swaffham Hospital 4445

Swanage
Swanage Hospital 4395

Swansea
Cefn Coed Hospital 4543
Clydach War Memorial Hospital 4543
Garngoch Hospital 4543
Hill House Hospital 4543
Llwyneryr Hospital 4533
Morriston Hospital 4543
Sancta Maria Hospital 4569
Singleton Hospital 4544
Ty-Einon Day Hospital 4544
Ystradgynlais Community Hospital 4543

Swindon
BMI The Ridgeway Hospital 4559
Learning Disabilities Service 4509
Princess Margaret Hospital 4492
Sandalwood Court 4366
Victoria Hospital 4509

Tadworth
The Children's Trust 4561
The Priory Hospital Sturt 4566

Tamworth
Sir Robert Peel Hospital 4482

Taunton
Orchard Lodge Young People's Unit 4476
Rydon House 4476
Somerset Nuffield Hospital 4567
Taunton and Somerset Hospital 4493
Taunton Community Hospital 4493
Williton and District Hospital 4476

Teignmouth
Teignmouth Hospital 4478

Telford
The Mount 4475
Princess Royal Hospital 4457
West Bank Hospital 4475

Tenbury Wells
Tenbury District Hospital 4511

Tenby
Tenby Cottage Hospital 4542

Tewkesbury
Tewkesbury Hospital 4400

Thetford
Thetford Cottage Hospital 4506

Thirsk
Lambert Memorial Hospital 4446

Thornhill
Thornhill Day Hospital 4517
Thornhill Hospital 4517

Thurso
Dunbar Hospital 4522

Todmorden
Abraham Ormerod Day Hospital 4382

Tonbridge
Tonbridge Cottage Hospital 4416

Tonypandy
Llwynypia Hospital 4542

Torquay
Mount Stuart Hospital 4565
Torbay Hospital 4478

Torrington
Torrington Cottage Hospital 4448

Towcester
Brain Injury Services Grafton Manor 4559

Tredegar
Tredegar General Hospital 4538

Tregaron
Tregaron Hospital 4536

Treorchy
Ysbyty George Thomas 4542

INDEX OF HOSPITALS BY TOWN

Trowbridge
Trowbridge Community Hospital 4507

Truro
Duchy Hospital 4562
Royal Cornwall Hospital 4462

Tunbridge Wells
BUPA Hospital Tunbridge Wells 4561
Highlands House 4416
Kent and Sussex Hospital 4427
Pembury Hospital 4427
Pembury Hospital (Psychiatric Services) 4416
Tunbridge Wells Nuffield Hospital 4568

Turriff
Turriff Community Hospital 4521

Twickenham
Rosslyn Clinic 4567

Tywyn
Tywyn and District War Memorial Hospital 4541

Uckfield
Uckfield Community Hospital 4402

Ulverston
Ulverston Hospital 4432

Uxbridge
Harefield Hospital 4462
Hillingdon Hospital 4413

Wadhurst
The Priory Ticehurst House 4566

Wakefield
Aberford Centre for Psychiatry 4501
Fieldhead Hospital 4502
Pinderfields General Hospital 4455
Stanley Royd Hospital 4502

Wallasey
Victoria Central Hospital 4509

Wallingford
Fair Mile Hospital 4372

Wallsend
Sir G B Hunter Memorial Hospital 4450

Walsall
Bloxwich Hospital 4502
Dorothy Pattison Hospital 4502
Goscote Hospital 4502
Hammerwich Hospital 4482
Manor Hospital 4502
Mossley Day Hospital 4502

Waltham Cross
Cheshunt Community Hospital 4367

Walton-on-Thames
Walton Community Hospital 4377

Ware
Western House Hospital 4397

Wareham
Wareham Hospital 4395

Warley
Rowley Regis Hospital 4471

Warminster
Warminster Community Hospital 4507

Warrington
BUPA North Cheshire Hospital 4561
Hollins Park 4503
Warrington Hospital 4437

Warwick
Royal Leamington Spa Rehabilitation Hospital 4483
St Michael's Hospital 4483
Warwick Hospital 4484

Washington
BUPA Hospital Washington 4561

Watford
BUPA Hospital Bushey 4560
Watford General Hospital 4505

Wednesbury
Kings Hill Day Hospital 4502

Wellingborough
Isebrook Hospital 4447

Wellington
Wellington and District Cottage Hospital 4493

Wells
Rosebank - Wells 4476

Welshpool
Victoria Memorial Hospital 4543

Welwyn
Danesbury 4396
Queen Victoria Memorial Hospital 4397

Welwyn Garden City
Ascots Day Hospital 4396
Queen Elizabeth II Hospital 4397

Wembley
Wembley Hospital 4446

West Bromwich
Edward Street Hospital and Day Unit 4374
Heath Lane Hospital 4471
Sandwell District General Hospital 4471

Westbury
Westbury Community Hospital 4507
Westbury Hospital 4507

Westcliff on Sea
Southend Hospital 4486

Weston Super Mare
Broadway Lodge 4560
Long Fox Unit 4366
Weston General Hospital 4507

Weybridge
Weybridge Hospital 4377

Whitby
Whitby Hospital 4472

Whitchurch
Whitchurch Hospital 4475

Whitehaven
West Cumberland Hospital 4438

INDEX OF HOSPITALS BY TOWN

Windermere Day Hospital (EMI) 4438

Wick
Town and County Hospital 4523

Wickford
Runwell Hospital 4479

Wigan
Billinge Hospital 4512
Royal Albert Edward Infirmary 4513
Whelley Hospital 4513
Wrightington Hospital 4513

Wigton
Wigton Hospital 4438

Wimborne
Oakley House 4394
Wimborne Hospital 4395

Wincanton
Hadspen Wood and Ridley Day Hospital 4476
Ridley Day Hospital at Verrington Hospital 4476
Verrington Hospital 4402

Winchester
Alcohol Advisory Day Hospital 4504
BMI Sarum Road Hospital 4559
Community Mental Health Team and Day Hospital 4504
The Croft 4504
Melbury Lodge 4504
Royal Hampshire County Hospital 4509
St Waleric (Psychogeriatric Day Hospital) 4504
Winchester Day Hospital 4509

Windsor
BMI The Princess Margaret Hospital 4559
HRH Princess Christian's Hospital 4563
King Edward VII Hospital (EMI Unit) 4372
King Edward VII Hospital (Windsor) 4397

Wirral
Arrowe Park Hospital 4510
Clatterbridge Hospital 4510

Wisbech
North Cambridgeshire Hospital 4419
Parkside Day Hospital 4419

Wishaw
Wishaw General Hospital 4523

Withernsea
Withernsea Community Hospital 4415

Woking
The Priory Hospital Woking 4566
Woking Community Hospital 4377
Woking Nuffield Hospital 4568

Wolverhampton
Groves Day Hospital 4510
Learning Disability Service 4510
New Cross Hospital 4467
Penn Hospital 4510
West Park Rehabilitation Hospital 4510
Wolverhampton Eye Infirmary 4467
Wolverhampton Nuffield Hospital 4568

Worcester
BUPA South Bank Hospital 4561
Worcester Royal Hospital 4511
Worcester Royal Infirmary 4511

Worksop
Bassetlaw District General Hospital 4393

Worthing
Acre Day Hospital 4512
BMI Goring Hall Hospital 4558
Meadowfield 4512
Salvington Lodge 4512
Worthing Hospital 4512

Wrexham
BUPA Yale Hospital 4569
Chirk Community Hospital 4539
Penley Hospital 4539
Trevalyn Hospital 4539
Wrexham Maelor Hospital 4539

Yeovil
Cedar House 4476
Yeovil District Hospital 4402

York
Bootham Park Hospital 4513
Purey Cust Nuffield Hospital 4566
The Retreat 4566
Stockton Hall Hospital 4567
York District Hospital 4513